C000144581

Crockford's

Clerical
Directory

2004/2005

Crockford's

Clerical
Directory | 2004/2005

Ninety-eighth edition
First issue 1858

A Directory of the Clergy
of the Church of England
the Church of Wales
the Scottish Episcopal Church
the Church of Ireland

CHURCH HOUSE
PUBLISHING

Crockford's Clerical Directory published December 2003 for The Archbishops' Council by:

Church House Publishing
Church House
Great Smith Street
London SW1P 3NZ

98th edition (2004/2005) © The Archbishops' Council 2003.

Please send any corrections to the Compiler, Crockford (address as above), Tel (020) 7898 1012 Fax (020) 7898 1769 E-mail crockford@c-of-e.org.uk

ISBN 0 7151 8128 9 (hardback)
       0 7151 8129 7 (paperback)

Jacket and cover design by Visible Edge Ltd

Typeset by
RefineCatch Ltd,
Bungay, Suffolk

Printed by
Clays Ltd,
Bungay, Suffolk

CONTENTS

INDEX TO ADVERTISEMENTS

Advertisements can be found on the following pages:

The inclusion of advertisements is for purposes of information and is not to be taken as implying acceptance of the objects of the advertiser by the publishers or proprietors.

Founded A.D. 1655

Corporation of the Sons of the Clergy

(Trustee for the Clergy Orphan Corporation)
Founded 1655   Incorporated by Royal Charter 1678
Charity registration number 207736

For assisting clergy of the Anglican Church and their
widows/widowers and dependants, and for providing grants for
education and maintenance of children of the clergy of the
dioceses of the United Kingdom, Ireland and the mission field.

Corporation of the Sons of the Clergy
1 Dean Trench Street
Westminster
London
SW1P 3HB

Telephone: 020 7799 3696
Fax: 020 7222 3468
E-mail: registrar@sonsoftheclergy.org.uk

The Corporation distributed some £1.4m in 2002 by way of grants

The annual Festival Service in St.Paul's Cathedral is held in May
and applications for tickets should be sent to the Registrar
at the above address.

Regular payments, donations, church and school collections and
legacies to provide funds to support our work are appreciated
and will be gratefully acknowledged.

Further information on our grants and how you can help us is
available on request from the Registrar.

The Friends of the Clergy Corporation

continues to help clergy and their dependants, carrying on a tradition of giving to the clergy and their families which started over 150 years ago.

In 2001/2002, the Corporation made grants of £992,400 to nearly one thousand clergy and their dependants in need.

These grants have provided help towards:
◆ holiday breaks ◆ school clothing ◆ funeral expenses
◆ help during the trauma of marriage breakdown
◆ resettlement and retirement
◆ undergraduate maintenance ◆ relief from debt

To maintain this tradition, it relies on **your** continued generosity.

You can help us by making a donation – or by remembering the Corporation in your Will. Parish donations are equally gratefully received.

For further information on how you can help, or if you know someone who needs our help, please contact the Secretary:

The Friends of the Clergy Corporation
27 Medway Street, Westminster, London SW1P 2BD
Telephone: 020 7222 2288 Email: focc@btinternet.com
or visit our website: www.friendsoftheclergy.co.uk
Regd. Charity No. 264724

Sunday Services

0800   Holy Communion

1015   Sung Mattins

1130   Sung Eucharist

1515   Sung Evensong

1800   Evening Service

*On other days of the week
Evensong is usually sung at 1700*

*For the latest information on services,
please visit our web site: www.stpauls.co.uk*
or telephone 020 7236 4128

St Paul's Cathedral

On Feast Days and at other times, service times may be subject to change

The Mission to Seafarers

A world mission agency of the Church of England

Earning a living at sea, bringing food to our tables and resources for our industry, is one of the most dangerous jobs in the world. On average 10 ships and 25 seafarers are lost at sea every month. Pirate attacks on merchant ships are on the increase with hundreds of assaults each year – sometimes resulting in loss of life.

Through a network of chaplains, lay staff and volunteers, the Mission has a presence in some 300 ports around the world, caring for the spiritual and practical welfare of seafarers and their families.

If you would like to become part of this important ministry by either joining our worldwide team of chaplains or our voluntary service scheme for young people, or if you would like more information about other ways in which to share in God's work among seafarers, please contact:

The Revd Tom Heffer
The Mission to Seafarers
St Michael Paternoster Royal
College Hill, London EC4R 2RL
Tel: 020 7248 5202
Fax: 020 7248 4761
Email: ministry@missiontoseafarers.org
Registered charity no: 212432

Caring for seafarers around the world

INTRODUCTION

This, the ninety-eighth edition of *Crockford's Clerical Directory*, provides details as at 4 August 2003 of more than 25,000 clergy and deaconesses in the Church of England (including the Diocese in Europe), the Church in Wales, the Scottish Episcopal Church, and the Church of Ireland. It also includes in the main biographical section those Michaelmas ordinands of whom we were notified in advance.

First published in 1858, the publication of *Crockford* now spans almost one and a half centuries. The Oxford University Press purchased the copyright for *Crockford* in 1921, publishing thirty-six editions before transferring ownership to the Church Commissioners and the Central Board of Finance, on economic grounds, sixty years later. This is the second edition under the sole ownership of the Archbishops' Council.

The publishing, design, advertising, selling and distribution of the directory are carried out by Church House Publishing in partnership with the *Crockford* Department, who are responsible for the actual compilation of the text. The information that generates the biographical entries is stored on a database, which is updated daily. Much of this information is obtained from the direct link with the Church Commissioners' central clergy pay-roll. Any alterations to this pay-roll (for example, changes of address or appointment) are automatically reflected on the *Crockford* database. However, approximately 7,000 (nearly 30 per cent) of the clergy are not on the central pay-roll. These are principally non-stipendiary ministers, those engaged in some form of ministry outside the parochial system (such as hospital, university, prison or service chaplains) and those serving in Wales, Scotland and Ireland. In maintaining the records of these clergy, we continue to rely greatly on the assistance of bishops' secretaries and diocesan offices, and information contained in diocesan directories, year books and the Church Press. We are also grateful for the help provided by the central authorities of the Church in Wales, the Scottish Episcopal Church, the Church of Ireland, the Ministry of Defence, the Hospital Chaplaincies Council, and our various overseas contacts.

A tremendous amount of help has come from the clergy themselves. We are enormously grateful to all those who have provided us with information, and have helped to minimize omissions and errors. For reasons of time, space and consistency, we are unable to include all the information clergy request us to publish, and we apologise that it has not been possible to respond to each letter individually. We are also grateful to Richard Christmas, Ruth Shobande and Angela Cann, who have been responsible for most of the work in compiling the directory, and have coped with a rush of last-minute correspondence.

We are always glad to be informed of amendments to entries, and we particularly appreciate any information about clergy whose addresses are not currently known to us (see list on p. 1212). Information relating to omissions or amendments should be sent to the *Crockford* Department; requests for archival information from earlier editions should be addressed in writing to Lambeth Palace Library; and requests for other information should be addressed to the Church of England Enquiry Centre.

Crockford Department	*The Librarian*	*Church of England Enquiry Centre*
Church House	*Lambeth Palace Library*	*Church House*
Great Smith Street	*Lambeth Palace*	*Great Smith Street*
London SW1P 3NZ	*London SE1 7JU*	*London SW1P 3NZ*
Tel (020) 7898 1012	Fax (020) 7928 7932	Tel (020) 7898 1445
E-mail crockford@c-of-e.org.uk		E-mail feedback@c-of-e.org.uk

JOHN CROCKFORD

John Crockford, publisher (?1823–1865) is best remembered for his association with the clerical directory that bears his name. He was the eldest child of a Somerset schoolmaster and his wife, John and Hannah Crockford; and by 1841 he was working as an attorney's clerk in Taunton, Somerset. John Crockford Sr was described in 1869 as Gentleman, of Rowbarton near Taunton. By his early twenties he was in business as a printer and publisher at 29 Essex Street, Strand; and it was from that address that *Crockford* was first published in 1858. On 6 December of the same year, John Crockford moved to new business premises at 346 Strand and 19 Wellington Street North.

His private address at that time was 16 Oakley Square, Hampstead Road; though by 1865 he had moved to 10 Park Road, Haverstock Hill.

Crockford's business association of more than two decades with Edward William Cox (1809–1879) had begun in 1843, when the *Law Times* first appeared. Both men are claimed as publisher – Crockford by Boase in *Modern English Biography*; Cox by the *Athenaeum* and by *Notes and Queries*. There is similar lack of agreement over other publications, such as the ill-fated *Critic*. "[Crockford] tried to establish a literary paper, the *Critic*. To this he brought all his great ability, but after fifteen years he gave it up in despair" (*Notes and Queries*): whereas the *Dictionary of National Biography* has it that Cox became "proprietor of . . . two other papers called respectively 'The Critic' and 'The Royal Exchange'."

The truth appears to be that the two men, who shared the same business address in Essex Street, were joint founders of a number of projects. Cox – the elder, more established and richer man – was often the financier and named publisher, with Crockford as the manager of the undertaking. Each had his own specialities: Cox, called to the bar in 1843, and successively Recorder of Helston & Falmouth (1857–1868) and of Portsmouth (1868–1879), was no doubt the leader in the establishment of the *Law Times*, to which, in *DNB*'s words, he "thenceforth devoted . . . the larger portion of his time and attention." But the legend which has arisen that Cox, restrained by professional ethics from using his own name, chose, almost at random, the name of one of his clerks to bear the title of his new clerical directory in 1858 – thus, in the words of the first postwar editor (probably Newman) bestowing "a more than tomb-stone meed of remembrance" – cannot be substantiated. As the jubilee account of the *Field* notes, Crockford was an equal partner in the success of the joint enterprises: "It was John Crockford who purchased the paper for Mr Cox. He obtained it from Mr Benjamin Webster for a trifling sum . . . In a short time the net profits amounted to 20,000*l*. a year. The management was placed under Crockford's control. He was a splendid man of business" (*Notes and Queries*).

The first *Clerical Directory* (1858), "A Biographical and Statistical Book of Reference for facts relating to the clergy and the Church", seems to have been assembled in a very haphazard fashion, with names added "as fast as they could be obtained", out of alphabetical order and with an unreliable index. By 1860 the *Directory* had become a very much more useful work of reference; and by 1917, with the absorption of its only serious rival, the *Clergy List*, reigned supreme.

No more than glimpses survive of Crockford's personality, and those mostly from the account of him given by John C. Francis, in the *Field* jubilee article already referred to. "I had occasion to call upon him a short time before his death, when we joined in a hearty laugh over his former furious attacks upon the *Athenaeum*. 'Dilke's Drag' he used to call it, and would accuse it of 'vulgar insolence and coxcombry' and 'the coarsest vulgarity'. As we parted he said, 'You have the *Athenaeum* to be proud of, and we have the *Field*.'"

John Crockford died suddenly at his home on 13 January 1865, at the age of 41. He left a widow, Annie (née Ellam) whom he married on 24 December 1847 at St Pancras Old Church. A daughter, Florence Annie, was born in St Pancras in 1852. (Florence married Arthur Brownlow in 1875 and had a son called Frederick.) His very brief will, proved 6 February 1865 at the Principal Probate Registry, left everything to his widow. His personal effects were valued at less than £1,000, but the family must have lived in some style, since one of the witnesses to the will was the resident coachman. Crockford's widow moved to 4 Upper Eton Place, Tavistock Hill, and died there on 26 July 1868.

BRENDA HOUGH

A request from the *Dictionary of National Biography* for a notice of the life of John Crockford led to the preparation of this article, a shorter version of which appeared in *The Dictionary of National Biography: Missing Persons*, 1993. For the information from the 1841 Census, and the record of Crockford's daughter Florence, we are indebted to Mr Ken Rhoades, of Kent.

A USER'S GUIDE TO *CROCKFORD*

Who is included in Crockford?
Crockford includes details of over 25,000 clergy and deaconesses of the Church of England, the Church in Wales, the Scottish Episcopal Church and the Church of Ireland. Clergy currently serving overseas qualify for inclusion if they have trained or have been licensed in this country (see **Overseas clergy**). Clergy who have died since the last edition are listed on p. 1214. Generally, clergy who have resigned their offices (but not their orders) are included unless they are known to have been received into another Church. A small number of clergy are excluded at their own request.

Readers and lay workers are not included: please consult diocesan directories. The *Who's Who* section of *The Church of England Year Book* (published annually by Church House Publishing and covering most aspects of the life and institutions of the Church of England) lists members of General Synod and principal members of staff of the Church's central organizations.

Addresses and telephone numbers
Where more than one telephone number is given, the first will normally relate to the address shown.

Addressing the clergy
See p. *31*.

Appointment details in the *Biographies* section
These reflect the legal pastoral situation prevailing at 4 August 2003, the date of the compilation of this edition of *Crockford*. Conventional districts, proprietary chapels and local ecumenical projects are also recorded. Benefice names are only recorded once in a biographical entry when they apply to successive appointments.

Crockford does not record group ministries, informal local arrangements, areas of special responsibility, emeritus appointments (except as reflected in the style of address), licence or permission to officiate when held in conjunction with another appointment from the same diocese, commissary appointments, examining chaplaincies, or secular appointments (except for educational or charitable posts).

Appointments held before ordination are not included (apart from service as a deaconess) unless they straddle the date of ordination.

Archbishops overseas
The presiding (arch-)bishop or metropolitan of each of the provinces of the Anglican Communion is listed in the main *Biographies* section, cross-referenced as appropriate, together with the Moderator of each of the united churches.

Archdeaconries
See *Archdeaconries, deaneries and rural deans* on p. 945.

Archdeacons
Look up the place name in *Biographies*: this is cross-referenced to a personal name.

Bishops (diocesan, area, suffragan, and provincial episcopal visitors)
Look up the place name in *Biographies*: this is cross-referenced to a personal name. See also p. 899, which lists the diocesan, area, suffragan and assistant bishops by diocese, as well as provincial episcopal visitors.

Bishops (assistant)
See *Bishops in England, Wales, Scotland and Ireland* on p. 899.

Bishops in the House of Lords
See p. 902.

Bishops overseas
See *Bishops of Anglican dioceses overseas* on p. 1186, and *Bishops of united churches* on p. 1207. Further information about the Anglican Communion can be found in *The Church of England Year Book.*

Bishops and archbishops, former
A list of former archbishops and bishops (diocesan and suffragan) will be found on p. 903.

Boundaries, provincial and diocesan
Maps of England and Wales, Scotland and Ireland, showing provincial and diocesan boundaries and cathedral cities, will be found on p. 1218.

Cathedral clergy
See *Cathedrals* on p. 938 for full-time cathedral clergy. The list does not include honorary appointments.

Chapel Royal
See *Royal Peculiars* on p. 940.

Christian names
The name by which a person prefers to be known, if not the first Christian name, is underlined (for example, SMITH, David John prefers to be called John). Names 'in religion' or names not part of a person's legal name are shown in parentheses.

Church: how to find the names of clergy responsible for a particular church
Look up the place name in the appropriate *Benefices and churches* section, see pp. 953–1163: if the entry is in bold type, the names of all clergy are listed and can be cross-referenced in the *Biographies* section; if the place name is not in bold type, the name of the benefice is given where the names of all clergy will be found.

Church: how to find the names of clergy responsible for a particular church when there is a vacancy
If the benefice is vacant, the telephone number of the clergy house is usually given in the appropriate *Benefices and churches* section to enable contact to be made with a new incumbent or priest-in-charge. The deanery reference (e.g. *Guildf 2*) following the benefice name cross-refers to *Archdeaconries, deaneries and rural deans* on p. 945 by means of which the name of the rural dean responsible for the vacant benefice can be found.

College chaplains
See p. 1180 for chaplains at universities, colleges of further education, colleges of higher education, sixth-form colleges, and schools.

Corrections
Please send notice of any corrections to: *Crockford Compiler, Church House, Great Smith Street, London SW1P 3NZ* Tel (020) 7898 1012 Fax (020) 7898 1769 E-mail crockford@c-of-e.org.uk

Crockford
The full title is *Crockford's Clerical Directory. Crockford* (not *Crockford's*) is an accepted abbreviation. See also the biography of John Crockford on p. *23.*

Deaconesses
See separate section on p. 897.

Deacons
See *Biographies* section.

Deaneries
See rural or area deans below.

Deans
Look up the place name in *Biographies*: this is cross-referenced to a personal name. See also *Cathedrals* on p. 938, and *Royal Peculiars* on p. 940.

Diocesan offices
Details of the diocesan offices in England, Wales, Scotland and Ireland can be found on p. 941.

E-mail addresses
These are provided where known. See after the telephone and/or fax number.

Europe, chaplains in
See *Chaplains of the Diocese of Gibraltar in Europe* on p. 1164.

Fax numbers
The exchange number is only given if different from that of the preceding telephone number.

Hospital chaplains
Whole-time and part-time hospital chaplains are listed under their NHS trusts on p. 1171. Cross-references have been inserted for individual hospitals.

Lay workers
Lay workers are not included in *Crockford*: please consult diocesan directories.

London churches
See *English benefices and churches* on p. 953. City and Guild churches are listed under LONDON CITY CHURCHES and LONDON GUILD CHURCHES. In other cases, see under church name (e.g. LANGHAM PLACE (All Souls), WESTMINSTER (St Matthew)).

Married or single?
Crockford does not provide information on marital status. However, we have included the form of address Miss, Mrs or Ms where requested. Where there has been a change of surname, a cross-reference may be found from the previous name.

Non-stipendiary clergy
Non-stipendiary clergy are listed in the main *Biographies* section.

Ordination courses
See *Theological colleges and courses* on p. 1184.

Overseas clergy
Clergy who are on the *Crockford* database and who are currently serving overseas qualify for inclusion. Service overseas has in the past been recorded simply by country, though higher office (e.g. as bishop or archdeacon) has also been noted. Other eligible appointments are now being added on request.

Overseas addresses and telephone numbers are given as required by a user in the UK, and include the international access and country codes, as well as the area code. If dialling from within the country concerned, the user will need to omit the international access and country codes, and dial zero immediately before the area code.

Patronage
The patron of each benefice is listed under the benefice name in *English benefices and churches* on p. 953.

Prison chaplains
See p. 1169.

Proprietary chapels
See *English benefices and churches* on p. 953.

Provincial episcopal visitors
Look up the place name in *Biographies*: this is cross-referenced to a personal name. See also p. 899, which lists the diocesan, area, suffragan and assistant bishops and provincial episcopal visitors.

Provosts
Look up the place name in *Biographies*: this is cross-referenced to a personal name. See also *Cathedrals* on p. 938.

Queen's Chaplains
See *Royal Peculiars* on p. 940.

Readers
Readers are not included in *Crockford*: please consult diocesan directories.

Religious orders
For members of religious orders where the Christian name alone is commonly used (e.g. Brother Aidan) a cross-reference is provided to the surname. Names 'in religion' not forming part of a person's legal name will be shown in parentheses. Details of religious communities are provided in *The Church of England Year Book*.

Retired clergy
The description 'rtd' does not imply that ministry has ceased, only that clergy so described are now in receipt of a pension. All eligible appointments are now recorded.

Rural or area deans
See *Archdeaconries, deaneries and rural deans* on p. 945. To find who is the rural dean of a particular church, look up the place or benefice name in the appropriate *Benefices* section: the deanery reference (e.g. *Guildf 2*) following the benefice name cross-refers to *Archdeaconries, deaneries and rural deans* on p. 945 where the name of the rural dean responsible can be found.

School chaplains
See p. 1182 for chaplains in schools.

Service chaplains
See p. 1167.

Sixth-form colleges
See p. 1181.

Theological colleges and courses
See p. 1184.

University chaplains
See p. 1180.

HOW TO ADDRESS THE CLERGY

In offering the advice below, we do not intend to imply that other practices are necessarily to be discouraged (for example, the use of Father as in 'Father Smith'). A good deal depends on circumstances, and, where a personal preference is known, it is usually good practice to follow it.

The following notes show acceptable current usage

(a) on an envelope or formal listing
(b) in starting a social letter or in speech, and
(c) when referring to a member of the clergy

Category (a) is not open to much variation, owing to the formality of the context, but categories (b) and (c) will often vary according to circumstances. It is always acceptable to use the appropriate Christian name in place of initials (for example, the Revd Alice Smith). In the absence of any style or title conferred by a post, all deacons and priests are styled 'The Reverend', and all who have been consecrated bishop are styled 'The Right Reverend'.

For abbreviations, see paragraph 13 below.

1 Deacons and Priests

(a) The Reverend A B Smith
(b) Mr/Mrs/Miss/Ms Smith (unless it is known that some other style is preferred – the title Vicar or Rector is acceptable only if the person so addressed really is the incumbent of the parish where you live or worship)
(c) The Reverend A B Smith at the first mention, and Mr/Mrs/Miss/Ms Smith thereafter

Notes 1 The form 'Reverend Smith' or 'The Reverend Smith' should *never* be used this side of the Atlantic. If the Christian name or initials are not known, the correct forms are
(a) The Reverend—Smith, *or* The Reverend Mr/Mrs/Miss/Ms Smith
(b) Mr/Mrs/Miss/Ms Smith
(c) The Reverend Mr/Mrs/Miss/Ms Smith at the first mention, and Mr/Mrs/Miss/Ms Smith thereafter

2 There is no universally accepted way of addressing an envelope to a married couple of whom both are in holy orders. We recommend the style 'The Reverend A B and the Reverend C D Smith'.

2 Prebendaries

(a) The Reverend Prebendary A B Smith
(b) Prebendary Smith
(c) Prebendary Smith

3 Canons (both Residentiary and Honorary)

(a) The Reverend Canon A B Smith
(b) Canon Smith
(c) Canon Smith

4 Archdeacons

(a) The Venerable the Archdeacon of X
(b) Archdeacon, *or more formally* Mr Archdeacon
(c) The Archdeacon of X at the first mention, and the Archdeacon thereafter

Notes 1 In the case of an archdeacon (or dean/provost, bishop, or archbishop) in office, the style above is to be preferred. The personal name should be used only for the purpose of identification.

2 For an archdeacon emeritus, the correct forms are
(a) The Venerable A B Smith
(b) Archdeacon
(c) Archdeacon Smith

5 Deans and Provosts
  (a) The Very Reverend the Dean/Provost of X
  (b) Dean/Provost, *or more formally* Mr Dean/Provost
  (c) The Dean/Provost of X at the first mention, and the Dean thereafter (see also note 1 to paragraph 4 above)

6 Bishops, Diocesan and Suffragan
  (a) The Right Reverend the Bishop of X, *or* The Right Reverend the Lord Bishop of X
  (b) Bishop, *or more formally* My Lord
  (c) The Bishop of X at the first mention, and the Bishop thereafter (see also note 1 to paragraph 4 above)

  Notes 1 The use of 'Lord' before 'Bishop' is diminishing. It is a matter of individual preference whether it should be used.
       2 The Bishop of London is a Privy Councillor, and has the style 'The Right Reverend and Right Honourable the Lord Bishop of London'.
       3 The Bishop of Meath and Kildare is styled 'The Most Reverend'.

7 Assistant and Retired Bishops
  (a) The Right Reverend A B Smith
  (b) Bishop
  (c) Bishop Smith

8 Archbishops
  (a) The Most Reverend the Lord Archbishop of X
  (b) Archbishop, *or more formally* Your Grace
  (c) The Archbishop of X at the first mention, and the Archbishop thereafter (see also note 1 to paragraph 4 above)

  Notes 1 The Archbishops of Canterbury and York, being Privy Councillors, also have 'Right Honourable' included in their style (for example, The Most Reverend and Right Honourable the Lord Archbishop of Canterbury).
       2 The presiding bishop of the Scottish Episcopal Church is the Primus, and the correct forms are
         (a) The Most Reverend the Primus
         (b) Primus
         (c) Primus
       3 A retired archbishop properly reverts to the status of bishop, but may be given as a courtesy the style of an archbishop.

9 Chaplains to the Armed Services
  (a) The Reverend A B Smith RN (*or* CF *or* RAF)
  (b) Padre, *or* Padre Smith
  (c) The Padre, *or* Padre Smith

10 Titled Clerics
  Where a member of the clergy also holds a temporal title, this is always preceded in writing by the ecclesiastical one.

  Barons (other than retired archbishops)
  (a) The Reverend the Lord Smith of Y
  (b) Lord Smith
  (c) The Reverend the Lord Smith at the first mention, and Lord Smith thereafter

  Baronets
  (a) The Reverend Sir Alan Smith Bt
  (b) Sir Alan Smith or Sir Alan
  (c) The Reverend Sir Alan Smith at the first mention, and Sir Alan Smith thereafter

  Knights
  An ordained priest may be appointed to an order of knighthood, but will not normally receive the accolade or title. The appropriate designation will follow the name or

ecclesiastical title (for example, The Right Reverend the Bishop of X, KCVO). If he was knighted *before* he was ordained, he will retain his title.

11 Ordained Members of Religious Orders

(a) The Reverend Alan/Alice Smith XYZ; The Reverend Brother Alan/Sister Alice XYZ
(b) Father, Father Smith, *or* Father Alan; Brother Alan/Sister Alice
(c) The Reverend Alan/Alice Smith; Father Alan Smith; Father Smith; Brother Alan/ Sister Alice

Notes 1 A name 'in religion', shown in parentheses in the biographical entry, should be used in preference to the baptismal name or initials. Sometimes the surname is not used. In this Directory, however, the entry will be found under the surname, whether it is normally used or not, and, if appropriate, a cross-reference is given under the Christian name.

2 Some orders use 'Brother' and 'Sister' for lay and ordained members without distinction, along with Christian names.

3 It is customary to specify the religious order by giving the appropriate letters after the name.

12 Academics

When a member of the clergy holds more than one title, the ecclesiastical one is normally used.

Professor   (a) The Reverend Canon A B Smith
also Canon   (b) Canon Smith, *or* Professor Smith, according to context
                 (c) Canon Smith, *or* Professor Smith, according to context
Canon   (a) The Reverend Canon A B Smith (degree)
also Doctor   (b) Canon Smith, *or* Dr Smith, according to context
                 (c) Canon Smith, *or* Dr Smith, according to context

13 Abbreviations

The following abbreviations are in common use

Reverend: Revd *or* Rev
Father: Fr
Right Reverend: Rt Revd *or* Rt Rev
Prebendary: Preb
Venerable: Ven

Reverend, Right Reverend, Very Reverend, Most Reverend and Venerable, whether abbreviated or not, should always be preceded by the definite article.

ABBREVIATIONS USED IN CROCKFORD'S CLERICAL DIRECTORY

A

AAAI .... Associate, Institute of Administrative Accountants

AACCA .... Associate, Association of Certified and Corporate Accountants (see ACCA)

AB .... Bachelor of Arts (USA)

ABEng............. Associate Member of the Association of Building Engineers

ABIA............... Associate, Bankers' Institute of Australasia

ABIPP .... Associate, British Institute of Professional Photography

ABIST .... Associate, British Institute of Surgical Technology

ABM .... Advisory Board of Ministry (now Ministry Division)

ABPsS .... Associate, British Psychological Society (now see AFBPsS)

ABSM .... Associate, Birmingham and Midland Institute School of Music

ACA .... Associate, Institute of Chartered Accountants

ACC .... Anglican Consultative Council

ACCA .... Associate, Chartered Association of Certified Accountants (formerly AACCA)

ACCM............. Advisory Council for the Church's Ministry (now Ministry Division)

ACCS .... Associate, Corporation of Secretaries

ACCTS........... Association for Christian Conferences, Teaching, and Service

ACE................. Associateship of the College of Education

.... Member, Association of Conference Executives

ACF................. Army Cadet Force

ACGI............... Associate, City and Guilds of London Institute

ACIArb .... Associate, Chartered Institute of Arbitrators

ACIB .... Associate, Chartered Institute of Bankers (formerly AIB)

ACIBS .... Associate, Chartered Institute of Bankers in Scotland

ACII .... Associate, Chartered Insurance Institute

ACIOB .... Associate, Chartered Institute of Building

ACIPA............. Associate, Chartered Institute of Patent Agents

ACIPD .... Associate, Chartered Institute of Personnel and Development

ACIS................ Associate, Institute of Chartered Secretaries and Administrators

ACIT .... Associate, Chartered Institute of Transport

ACMA .... Associate, Chartered Institute of Management Accountants (formerly ACWA)

ACMI.............. Associate, Chartered Management Institute (formerly AIMgt)

ACORA .... Archbishops' Commission on Rural Areas

ACP................. Associate, College of Preceptors

ACS .... Additional Curates Society

ACSM .... Associate, Camborne School of Mines

ACT................. Australian Capital Territory

.... Australian College of Theology

ACTVR .... Advanced Certificate in Television and Radio

ACUPA .... Archbishops' Commission on Urban Priority Areas

ACWA.............. Associate, Institute of Cost and Works Accountants (now see ACMA)

ACertC .... Advanced Certificate in Counselling

ACertCM .... Archbishop of Canterbury's Certificate in Church Music

AD.................... Area Dean

ADC................. Advanced Diploma in Counselling

ADCM .... Archbishop of Canterbury's Diploma in Church Music

ADEDC .... Advanced Diploma in Education of the Deaf and Partially Hearing Children

ADFM .... Advanced Diploma in Farm Management

ADMT .... Advanced Diploma in Ministerial Theology

ADPS .... Advanced Diploma in Pastoral Studies

ADTPS............. Advanced Diploma in Theology and Pastoral Studies

ADUT............... Advanced Diploma in Urban Theology

ADipR.............. Archbishop's Diploma for Readers

AEdRD............ Associateship in Educational Research and Development

AFAIM .... Associate Fellow, Australian Institute of Management

AFBPsS............ Associate Fellow, British Psychological Society (formerly ABPsS)

AFC .... Air Force Cross

AFIMA .... Associate Fellow, Institute of Mathematics and its Applications

AGSM .... Associate, Guildhall School of Music and Drama

AHSM *or* AHA Associate, Institute of Health Service Management (formerly Administrators)

AIA .... Associate, Institute of Actuaries

AIAS .... Associate, Incorporated Association of Architects and Surveyors

AIAT .... Associate, Institute of Animal Technicians

AIB................... Associate, Institute of Bankers (now see ACIB)

AIDS .... Acquired Immunity Deficiency Syndrome

AIFST .... Associate, Institute of Food Science and Technology

AIGCM............ Associate, Incorporated Guild of Church Musicians

AIIM .... Associate, Institute of Investment Management

AIL................... Associate, Institute of Linguists

AIMLS............. Associate, Institute of Medical Laboratory Sciences

AIMSW........... Associate, Institute of Medical Social Work

AIMarE........... Associate, Institute of Marine Engineering

AIMgt .... Associate, Institute of Management (now see ACMI)

AIPM .... Associate, Institute of Personnel Management (now see ACIPD)

AIQS .... Associate, Institute of Quantity Surveyors (now see ARICS)

AITI .... Associate, Institute of Taxation in Ireland

AKC .... Associate, King's College London

ALA .... Associate, Library Association

ALAM .... Associate, London Academy of Music

ALBC............... Associate, London Bible College

ALCD .... Associate, London College of Divinity

ALCM.............. Associate, London College of Music

ALSM .... Associate, Lancashire School of Music

AM .... Albert Medal

.... Master of Arts (USA)

AMA .... Associate, Museums Association

AMASI .... Associate Member of the Architects and Surveyors Institute

AMBIM .... Associate Member, British Institute of Management (later MBIM; now see FBIM)

AMCST............ Associate, Manchester College of Science and Technology

AMCT............. Associate, Manchester College of Technology

AMIBF .... Associate Member, Institute of British Foundrymen

AMIC............... Associate Member, Institute of Counselling

AMICE .... Associate Member, Institution of Civil Engineers (now see MICE)

AMICME .... Associate Member, Institute of Cast Metal Engineers

AMIDHE......... Associate Member, Institute of Domestic Heating Engineers

AMIEE .... Associate Member, Institution of Electrical Engineers (now see MIEE)

AMIEHO......... Associate Member, Institution of Environmental Health Officers

AMIM.............. Associate Member, Institute of Metals

AMIMMM .... Associate Member, Institute of Materials, Minerals and Mining

AMIMechE....... Associate, Institution of Mechanical Engineers (now see MIMechE)

AMIMinE......... Associate Member, Institute of Mining Engineers

AMITD............ Associate Member, Institute of Training and Development (now see ACIPD)

AMIW.............. Associate Member, Institute of Welfare (formerly AMIWO)

AMInstT .... Associate Member, Institute of Transport

AMInstTA .... Associate Member, Institute of Transport Administration

AMRSH............ Associate Member, Royal Society of Health

AMSIA .... Associate Member, Society of Investment Analysts

AMusLCM .... Associate in Music, London College of Music

AMusTCL........ Associate in Music, Trinity College of Music London

ANC................. African National Congress

ANCA............... Advanced National Certificate in Agriculture

AO .... Officer, Order of Australia

APhS .... Associate, Philosophical Society of England

ARAM .... Associate, Royal Academy of Music

ARCA .... Associate, Royal College of Art

ARCIC .... Anglican-Roman Catholic International Commission

ARCM.............. Associate, Royal College of Music

ARCO.............. Associate, Royal College of Organists

ARCO(CHM) ... Associate, Royal College of Organists with Diploma in Choir Training

ARCS .... Associate, Royal College of Science

ARCST............. Associate, Royal College of Science and Technology (Glasgow)

ARCT	Associate, Royal Conservatory of Music Toronto
ARCUK	Architects' Registration Council of the United Kingdom
ARHistS	Associate, Royal Historical Society
ARIAM	Associate, Royal Irish Academy of Music
ARIBA	Associate, Royal Institute of British Architects (now see RIBA)
ARIC	Associate, Royal Institute of Chemistry (later MRIC; now see MRSC)
ARICS	Associate, Royal Institution of Chartered Surveyors
ARMCM	Associate, Royal Manchester College of Music
ARPS	Associate, Royal Photographic Society
ARSM	Associate, Royal School of Mines
AS	Associate in Science (USA)
ASCA	Associate, Society of Company and Commercial Accountants
ASSP	Society of All Saints Sisters of the Poor
ASVA	Associate, Incorporated Society of Valuers and Auctioneers
ATC	Air Training Corps
ATCL	Associate, Trinity College of Music London
ATD	Art Teacher's Diploma
ATI	Associate, Textile Institute
ATII	Associate Member, Institute of Taxation
ATL	Association of Teachers and Lecturers
ATPL	Airline Transport Pilot's Licence
ATV	Associated Television
ATh(SA)	Associate in Theology (South Africa)
AVCM	Associate, Victoria College of Music
Ab	(Diocese of) Aberdeen and Orkney
Aber	Aberdeen
Abp	Archbishop
Abth	Aberystwyth
AcDipEd	Academic Diploma in Education
Ad	Advanced
AdCertEd	Advanced Certificate of Education
AdDipCrim	Advanced Diploma in Criminology
AdDipEd	Advanced Diploma in Education
AdDipPTS	Advanced Diploma Pastoral and Theological Studies
AdDipTh	Advanced Diploma in Theology
Admin	Administration
	Administrative
	Administrator
Adn	Archdeacon
Adnry	Archdeaconry
Adv	Adviser
	Advisory
Agric	Agricultural
	Agriculture
Aid	Aidan
	Aidan's
alt	alternate
Andr	Andrew
	Andrew's
	Andrews
Angl	Anglican
	Anglicans
Ant	Anthony
	Anthony's
Appt	Appointment
Arg	(Diocese of) Argyll and The Isles
Arm	(Diocese of) Armagh
Assn	Association
Assoc	Associate
Asst	Assistant
Aug	Augustine
	Augustine's
Aus	Australian

Aux	Auxiliaries
	Auxiliary

B

b	Born
B & W	(Diocese of) Bath and Wells
B or Bapt	Baptist
	Baptist's
BA	Bachelor of Arts
BA(Econ)	Bachelor of Arts in Economics
BA(Ed)	Bachelor of Arts in Education
BA(QTS)	Bachelor of Arts (Qualified Teacher Status)
BA(Theol)	Bachelor of Arts in Theology
BAC Acc	Accredited Counsellor (British Association for Counselling)
BAI	Bachelor of Engineering (also see BE and BEng)
BAO	Bachelor of Obstetrics
BASc	Bachelor of Applied Science
BAdmin	Bachelor of Administration
BAgr	Bachelor of Agriculture
BAppSc(OT)	Bachelor of Applied Science (Occupational Therapy)
BArch	Bachelor of Architecture
BBA	Bachelor of Business Administration
BBC	British Broadcasting Corporation
BBS	Bachelor of Business Studies
BC	British Columbia (Canada)
BCA	Bachelor of Commerce and Administration
BCC	British Council of Churches (now CTBI)
BCL	Bachelor of Civil Law
BCMS	Bible Churchmen's Missionary Society (now Crosslinks)
BCh or BChir	Bachelor of Surgery (also see BS and ChB)
BCom or BComm	Bachelor of Commerce
BCombStuds	Bachelor of Combined Studies
BD	Bachelor of Divinity
BDA	Bachelor of Dramatic Art
BDQ	Bachelor of Divinity Qualifying Examination
BDS	Bachelor of Dental Surgery
BDSc	Bachelor of Dental Science
BE	Bachelor of Engineering (also see BAI and BEng)
BEM	British Empire Medal
BEcon	Bachelor of Economics (USA)
BEd	Bachelor of Education
BEdSt	Bachelor of Educational Studies
BEng	Bachelor of Engineering (also see BAI and BE)
BFA	Bachelor of Fine Arts
BFBS	British and Foreign Bible Society
BIE	Bachelor of Industrial Engineering (USA)
BL	Bachelor of Law
BLib	Bachelor of Librarianship
BLitt	Bachelor of Letters
BM	Bachelor of Medicine (also see MB)
BM, BCh	Conjoint degree of Bachelor of Medicine, Bachelor of Surgery
BMMF	Bible and Medical Missionary Fellowship (now Interserve)
BMU	Board for Mission and Unity
BMedSci	Bachelor of Medical Science
BMet	Bachelor of Metallurgy
BMin	Bachelor of Ministry
BMus	Bachelor of Music (also see MusB or MusBac)
BMusEd	Bachelor of Music Education
BN	Bachelor of Nursing
BNC	Brasenose College
BPaed	Bachelor of Paediatrics
BPh or BPhil	Bachelor of Philosophy
BPharm	Bachelor of Pharmacy
BPhil(Ed)	Bachelor of Philosophy (Education)

BRE	Bachelor of Religious Education (USA)
BRF	Bible Reading Fellowship
BS	Bachelor of Science (also see BSc)
	Bachelor of Surgery (also see BCh, BChir and ChB)
BSB	Brotherhood of St Barnabas
BSE	Bachelor of Science in Engineering (also see BScEng)
BSEd	Bachelor of Science in Education (USA)
BSP	Brotherhood of St Paul
BSS	Bachelor of Social Studies
BSSc	Bachelor of Social Science (also see BSocSc)
BSW	Bachelor of Social Work
BSc	Bachelor of Science (also see BS)
BSc(Econ)	Bachelor of Science in Economics
BSc(Soc)	Bachelor of Science (Sociology)
BScAgr	Bachelor of Science in Agriculture
BScEcon	Bachelor of Science in Economics
BScEng	Bachelor of Science in Engineering (also see BSE)
BScFor	Bachelor of Science in Forestry
BScTech	Bachelor of Technical Science
BSocAdmin	Bachelor of Social Administration
BSocSc	Bachelor of Social Science (also see BSSc)
BT	Bachelor of Teaching
BTEC HNC	Business and Technician Education Council Higher National Certificate
BTEC NC	Business and Technician Education Council National Certificate
BTEC ND	Business and Technician Education Council National Diploma
BTS	Bachelor of Theological Studies
BTech	Bachelor of Technology
BTh or BTheol	Bachelor of Theology (also see STB)
BVM&S	Bachelor of Veterinary Medicine and Surgery
BVSc	Bachelor of Veterinary Science
BVetMed	Bachelor of Veterinary Medicine (also see VetMB)
Ball	Balliol
Ban	(Diocese of) Bangor
Barn	Barnabas
	Barnabas's
Bart	Bartholomew
	Bartholomew's
Bd	Board
Bedf	Bedford
Belf	Belfast
BesL	Bachelier es Lettres
Bibl	Biblical
Birm	(Diocese of) Birmingham
Blackb	(Diocese of) Blackburn
Bp	Bishop
Br	British
Bradf	(Diocese of) Bradford
Bre	(Diocese of) Brechin
Brig	Brigadier
Bris	(Diocese of) Bristol
Bt	Baronet

C

C	Curate
c	Consecrated
C & O	(Diocese of) Cashel and Ossory (united dioceses of Cashel, Waterford, Lismore, Ossory, Ferns and Leighlin)
C of E	Church of England
C of S	Church of Scotland
C&G	City and Guilds
C, C & R	(Diocese of) Cork, Cloyne and Ross
C-in-c	Curate-in-charge
c/o	Care of

CA .... Church Army
.... Member, Institute of Chartered Accountants of Scotland
CA(Z) .... Member, Institute of Chartered Accountants of Zimbabwe
CACP .... Certificate in Advanced Counselling Practice
CACTM .... Central Advisory Council for the Ministry (now Ministry Division)
CANDL .... Church and Neighbourhood Development in London
CANP .... Certificate in Advanced Nursery Practices
CAP .... Certificat d'aptitude de la Prêtrise
CARA .... Care and Resources for people affected by AIDS/HIV
CARE .... Christian Action Research and Education
CASA .... Anglican Church of the Southern Cone of America
CASS .... Certificate in Applied Social Studies
CB .... Companion, Order of the Bath
CBE .... Commander, Order of the British Empire
CBIM .... Companion, British Institute of Management
CBTS .... Certificate in Biblical and Theological Studies
CBiol .... Chartered Biologist
CCBI .... Council of Churches for Britain and Ireland (now see CTBI)
CCC .... Corpus Christi College
.... Council for the Care of Churches
CCCS .... Commonwealth and Continental Church Society
CCSk .... Certificate in Counselling Skills
CCT .... Certificate in Clinical Teaching
CCWA .... Churches Community Work Alliance
CChem .... Chartered Chemist
CD .... Canadian Forces Decoration
.... Conventional District (also see ED)
CDipAF .... Certified Diploma in Accounting and Finance
CECD .... Church of England Council for the Deaf
CECM .... Certificate of Education for the Church's Ministry
CECS .... Church of England Children's Society (now known as the Children's Society)
CEIR .... Certificate in Economics and Industrial Relations
CEMS .... Church of England Men's Society
CETD .... Certificate in the Education of the Deaf
CEng .... Chartered Engineer
CF .... Chaplain to the Forces
CFTV .... Certificate in Film and Television
CGA .... Community of the Glorious Ascension
CGLI .... City and Guilds of London Institute
CGeol .... Chartered Geologist
CH .... Companion, Order of Honour
CIO .... Church Information Office
CIPFA .... Chartered Institute of Public Finance and Accountancy
CITC .... Church of Ireland Theological College
CJGS .... Community of the Companions of Jesus the Good Shepherd
CLCE .... Certificate for Leadership in Christian Education
CLJ .... Commander, Order of St Lazarus of Jerusalem
CM .... Carnegie Medal

CMBHI .... Craft Member, British Horological Institute
CMC .... Community Mission Chaplaincy
CMD .... Cambridge Mission to Delhi (now see USPG)
CME .... Continuing Ministerial Education
CMG .... Companion, Order of St Michael and St George
CMIWSc .... Certificate, Institute of Wood Science
CMJ .... Church's Ministry among Jewish People
CMS .... Church Mission Society (formerly Church Missionary Society)
CMath .... Chartered Mathematician
CNAA .... Council for National Academic Awards
CNI .... Companion, Nautical Institute
COPEC .... Conference on Politics, Economics and Community
CORAT .... Christian Organizations Research and Advisory Trust
CORE .... City Outreach through Renewal Evangelism
CP .... Community Priest
CPA .... Chartered Patent Agent (formerly FCIPA)
CPAS .... Church Pastoral Aid Society
CPC .... Certificate of Professional Competence (Road Transport)
CPES .... Certificate in Post Excavation Studies
CPEng .... Chartered Professional Engineer (of Institution of Engineers of Australia)
CPFA .... Member Chartered Institute of Public Finance and Accountancy (formerly IPFA)
CPM .... Colonial Police Medal
CPPS .... Certificate of Proficiency in Pastoral Studies
CPS .... Certificate in Pastoral Studies
CPSS .... Certificate in Pastoral and Social Studies
CPTS .... Certificate in Pastoral and Theological Studies
CPhys .... Chartered Physicist of the Institute of Physics
CPsychol .... Chartered Member, British Psychological Society
CQSW .... Certificate of Qualification in Social Work
CR .... Community of the Resurrection (Mirfield)
CSA .... Community of St Andrew
CSD .... Co-operative Secretaries Diploma
.... Community of St Denys
CSF .... Community of St Francis
CSG .... Company of the Servants of God
CSMV .... Community of St Mary the Virgin
CSP .... Community of St Peter
CSS .... Certificate in Social Service
CSSM .... Children's Special Service Mission
CSWG .... Community of the Servants of the Will of God
CSocSc .... Certificate in Social Science
CStJ .... Commander, the Most Venerable Order of the Hospital of St John of Jerusalem
CTBI .... Churches Together in Britain and Ireland (formerly CCBI)
CTBS .... Certificate of Theology and Biblical Studies
CTM .... Certificate in Theology for Ministry
CUF .... Church Urban Fund
CVO .... Commander, Royal Victorian Order
CWME .... Commission on World Mission and Evangelism
CWWCh .... Certificate of Women's Work in the Church
CY .... Church and Youth
CYCW .... Certificate in Youth and Community Work

CYFA .... Church Youth Fellowships Association
Cam .... Cambridge
Can .... Canon
Cand .... Candidate
.... Candidate's
.... Candidates'
Cant .... (Diocese of) Canterbury
Capt .... Captain
Carl .... (Diocese of) Carlisle
Cath .... Catharine/Catherine
.... Catharine's/Catherine's
Cathl .... Cathedral
Cdre .... Commodore
Cen .... Centre
.... Center
.... Central
Cert .... Certificat(e)
CertBibKnowl ... Certificate of Bible Knowledge
CertCS .... Certificate in Christian Studies
CertCT .... Certificate in Ceramic Technology
CertCYW .... Certificate in Community and Youth Work
CertEd .... Certificate of Education
CertFAI .... Certificate in French, Arabic and Islamic Studies
CertFE .... Certificate of Further Education
CertFT .... Certificate in Family Therapy
CertHE .... Certificate in Higher Education
CertHist .... Certificate in History
CertMBiol .... Certificate of Microbiology
CertMS .... Certificate in Management Studies
CertMan .... Certificate in Management
CertMin .... Certificate in Ministry
CertPSC .... Certificate in Professional Studies in Counselling
CertRE .... Certificate in Religious Education
CertRK .... Certificate in Religious Knowledge
CertRS .... Certificate in Religious Studies
CertSS .... Certificate in Social Studies
CertTESLA .... Certificate as a Teaching English as a Second Language to Adults
CertTESOL .... Certificate in Teaching English to Speakers of Other Languages
CertTS .... Certificate in Timber Surveying
CertYS .... Certificate in Youth Service
Ch .... Christ
.... Christ's
.... Church
Ch Ch .... Christ Church
ChB .... Bachelor of Surgery (also see BCh, BChir and BS)
ChLJ .... Chaplain, Order of St Lazarus of Jerusalem
ChStJ .... Chaplain, the Most Venerable Order of the Hospital of St John of Jerusalem
Chan .... Chancellor
Chapl .... Chaplain
.... Chaplaincies
.... Chaplaincy
.... Chaplains
Chas .... Charles
.... Charles's
Chelmsf .... (Diocese of) Chelmsford
Chelt .... Cheltenham
Ches .... (Diocese of) Chester
Chich .... (Diocese of) Chichester
Chmn .... Chairman
.... Chairwoman
Chpl .... Chapel
Chr .... Christian
.... Christians
Chris .... Christopher
.... Christopher's
Chrys .... Chrysostom
.... Chrysostom's
Chu .... Churchill
Cl-in-c .... Cleric-in-charge
Clem .... Clement
.... Clement's
Cllr .... Councillor/Counsellor

Clogh................	(Diocese of) Clogher
Co......................	Company
....	County
....	Counties
Co-ord..............	Co-ordinator
	Co-ordinating
Col....................	Colonel
Coll..................	College
Colleg	Collegiate
Comdr..............	Commander
Comdr OM	Commander, Order of Merit
(Italy)................	of the Italian Republic
Commn	Commission
Commr..............	Commissioner
Comp................	Comprehensive
Conf	Confederation
....	Conference
Conn.................	(Diocese of) Connor
Corp.................	Corporation
Coun.................	Council
Cov	(Diocese of) Coventry
Cttee................	Committee
Cust	Custodian
	Custody
Cuth	Cuthbert
	Cuthbert's
Cypr	Cyprian
....	Cyprian's

D

d.........................	Ordained Deacon
D & D	(Diocese of) Down and Dromore
D & G	(Diocese of) Dublin and Glendalough
D & R................	(Diocese of) Derry and Raphoe
D&C..................	Dean and Chapter
DA.....................	Diploma in Anaesthetics (England)
....	Diploma in Art (Scotland)
DAA..................	Diploma in Archive Administration
DAC	Diploma in Adult Counselling
DACE................	Diploma in Adult and Continuing Education
DAES	Diploma in Advanced Educational Studies
DAM	Diploma in Archives Management
DAPC................	Diploma in Advanced Psychological Counselling
DASAE	Diploma of Advanced Study in Adult Education
DASE	Diploma in the Advanced Study of Education
DASHE	Diploma in Advanced Studies in Higher Education
DASS................	Diploma in Applied Social Studies
DASSc..............	Diploma in Applied Social Science
DATh	Diploma of the Arts in Theology
DArch...............	Doctor of Architecture
DB.....................	Bachelor of Divinity (USA)
DBF	Diocesan Board of Finance
DBMS	Diploma in Biblical and Mission Studies
DBO	Diploma of the British Orthoptic Society
DBP..................	Diocesan Board of Patronage
DBRS................	Diploma in Biblical and Religious Studies
DBS.................	Diploma in Biblical Studies
DBTS	Diploma in Biblical and Theological Studies
DC.....................	District of Columbia (USA)
DCAe	Diploma of the College of Aeronautics
DCC..................	Diploma in Crisis Counselling of the Institute of Counselling
DCCD...............	Diploma in Church and Community Development
DCE	Diploma in Careers Education
DCEG...............	Diploma in Careers Education and Guidance
DCG.................	Diploma in Careers Guidance
DCH..................	Diploma in Child Health

DCHC...............	Diploma in Counselling and Hospital Chaplaincy
DCL	Doctor of Civil Law
DCM	Diploma in Christian Ministry
DCMus.............	Diploma in Church Music
DCR	Diploma of the College of Radiographers
DCR, MU..........	Diploma of the College of Radiographers in Medical Ultra Sound
DCYW	Diploma in Community and Youth Work
DChemEng	Diploma in Chemical Engineering
DClinPsych	Diploma in Clinical Psychology
DCnL................	Doctor of Canon Law
DD	Doctor of Divinity
DDPH...............	Diploma in Dental Public Health
DEHC...............	Diploma in the Education of Handicapped Children
DEd...................	Doctor of Education (also see EdD)
DEng................	Doctor of Engineering
DFC..................	Distinguished Flying Cross
DFM	Distinguished Flying Medal (Canada)
DGA	Diploma in Government Administration
DGM................	Diploma in Geriatric Medicine
DHA	District Health Authority
DHL..................	Doctor of Humane Letters
DHRK	Diploma in Humanities and Religious Knowledge
DHSA	Diploma in Health Services Administration
DHistA	Diploma in the History of Art
DIC	Diploma of Membership of Imperial College London
DIH	Diploma in Industrial Health
DIL...................	Diploma of the Institute of Linguists
DIS	Diploma in Industrial Studies
DIT...................	Diploma in Interpreting and Translating
DL	Deputy Lieutenant
DLA	Diploma in Liturgy and Architecture
DLC	Diploma of Loughborough College
DLIS	Diploma in Library and Information Studies
DLLP...............	Diploma in Law and Legal Practice
DLO	Diploma in Laryngology and Otology
DLSc................	Doctor of Legal Science
DLitt	Doctor of Letters (also see LittD)
DLitt et Phil	Doctor of Letters and Philosophy
DMA................	Diploma in Municipal Administration
DMEd..............	Diploma of Management in Education
DMS.................	Diploma in Management Studies
DMS(Ed)	Diploma in Management Studies (Education)
DMin................	Doctor of Ministry
DMinTh	Doctor of Ministry and Theology
DMusEd............	Diploma in Music Education
DN	Diploma in Nursing
DNM................	Diploma in Nuclear Medicine
DOE	Department of the Environment
DOMS...............	Diploma in Ophthalmic Medicine and Surgery
DON	Diploma in Ophthalmic Nursing
DPA..................	Diploma in Public Administration
DPH..................	Diploma in Public Health
DPM	Diploma in Psychological Medicine
DPMSA	Diploma in Philosophy of Medicine, Society of Apothecaries
DPS	Diploma in Pastoral Studies

DPSA	Diploma in Public and Social Administration
DPSE	Diploma in Professional Studies in Education
DPSN	Diploma in Professional Studies in Nursing
DPST................	Diploma in Pastoral and Social Theology
DPhil	Doctor of Philosophy (also see PhD)
DProf...............	Doctor in Professional Studies
DRBS...............	Diploma in Religious and Biblical Studies
DRCOG	Diploma of the Royal College of Obstetricians and Gynaecologists
DRI	Diploma in Radionuclide Imaging
DRSAMD........	Diploma of the Royal Scottish Academy of Music and Drama
DRSS	Diploma in Religious and Social Studies
DSC..................	Distinguished Service Cross
DSCE	Diploma in Social and Community Education
DSM.................	Distinguished Service Medal
DSO	Companion, Distinguished Service Order
DSPT................	Diploma in Social and Pastoral Theology
DSRS	Diploma in Social and Religious Studies
DSS	Diploma in Social Studies
DST..................	Doctor of Sacred Theology (also see STD)
DSc..................	Doctor of Science (also see ScD)
DSc(Eng)..........	Doctor of Science in Engineering
DSocSc............	Doctor of Social Science
DTI...................	Department of Trade and Industry
DTM	Diploma in Tropical Medicine
DTM&H	Diploma in Tropical Medicine and Hygiene
DTPH...............	Diploma in Tropical Public Health
DTPS................	Diploma in Theological and Pastoral Studies
DTech	Doctor of Technology
DTh..................	Doctor of Theology (also see ThD)
DUP..................	Docteur de l'Université de Paris
DUniv	Doctor of the University
Darw	Darwin
Dav	David
....	David's
DeS...................	Docteur es sciences
Dep...................	Deputy
Dept..................	Department
DesL.................	Docteur es Lettres
Det....................	Detention
Dio	Diocese
Dioc..................	Diocesan
Dip	Diploma
DipAD	Diploma in Art and Design
DipADO	Diploma of the Association of Dispensing Opticians
DipAE..............	Diploma in Adult Education
DipAI	Diploma in Artificial Insemination
DipAdEd..........	Diploma in Advanced Education
DipAgr	Diploma in Agriculture
DipApTh..........	Diploma in Applied Theology
DipArch	Diploma in Architecture
DipBA..............	Diploma in Business Administration
DipBBSS	Diploma in Bilingual Business and Secretarial Studies
DipBS...............	Diploma in Business Studies
DipC&G...........	Diploma in Counselling and Guidance
DipC&S............	Diploma in Counselling and Supervision
DipCACP.........	Diploma in Cognitive Approaches to Counselling and Psychotherapy
DipCOT	Diploma of the College of Occupational Therapists

DipCSM............ Diploma of the Cork School of Music
DipCart .... Diploma in Cartography
DipCombStuds . Diploma in Combined Studies
DipDA............... Diploma in Dramatic Art
DipEE .... Diploma in Electrical Engineering
DipEED .... Diploma in Environmental Engineering and Design
DipEH............... Diploma in Environmental Health
DipEd................ Diploma in Education
DipEdAdmin .... Diploma in Educational Administration
DipEurHum...... Diploma in European Humanities
DipFD............... Diploma in Funeral Directing
DipFE .... Diploma in Further Education
DipFL .... Diploma in Foreign Languages
DipG&C........... Diploma in Guidance and Counselling
DipGD .... Diploma in Graphic Design
DipGL.............. Diploma in German Language
DipHCM........... Diploma in Hotel and Catering Management
DipHE............... Diploma in Higher Education
DipHSM .... Diploma in Health Services Management
DipHSW .... Diploma in Health and Social Welfare
DipHV.............. Diploma in Health Visiting
DipInfSc........... Diploma in Information Science
DipInstAM .... Diploma of the Institute of Administrative Management
DipInstBM........ Diploma of the Institution of Merchanting (Builders)
DipInstHSM ..... Diploma of the Institute of Health Service Management
DipInstM .... Diploma of the Institute of Marketing
DipLaw .... Diploma in Law
DipM................ Diploma in Marketing
DipMM............. Diploma in Mission and Ministry
DipMMin.......... Diploma in Management for Ministry
DipMaths .... Postgraduate Diploma in Mathematics
DipMechE........ Diploma in Mechanical Engineering
DipMgt .... Diploma in Management
DipMin............. Diploma in Ministry
DipN .... Diploma in Nursing
DipNCTD........ Diploma of the National College of Teachers of the Deaf
DipOAS............ Diploma in Oriental and African Studies
DipOHS .... Diploma in Occupational Health and Safety
DipOT .... Diploma in Occupational Therapy
DipP&C .... Diploma in Psychology and Counselling
DipPE............... Diploma in Physical Education
DipPS .... Diploma in Pastoral Studies
DipPSA .... Diploma in Public and Social Administration
DipPSE .... Diploma in Personal and Social Education
DipPhil............ Diploma in Philosophy
DipPsychP&C ... Diploma in Psychodynamic Psychotherapy and Counselling
DipRAM .... Diploma of the Royal Academy of Music
DipRCM .... Diploma of the Royal College of Music
DipRD .... Diploma in Reading Development
DipRE.............. Diploma in Religious Education
DipREBT......... Diploma in Rational Emotive Behaviour Therapy and Counselling
DipREM .... Diploma in Rural Estate Management

DipRIPH&H .... Diploma of the Royal Institute of Public Health and Hygiene
DipRK .... Diploma in Religious Knowledge
DipRS .... Diploma in Religious Studies
DipRSAMDA... Diploma of the Royal Scottish Academy of Music and Dramatic Art
DipSC.............. Diploma in Student Counselling
DipSM.............. Diploma in Sales Marketing of the Managing and Marketing Sales Association
DipSS .... Diploma in Social Studies
DipSocSc.......... Diploma in Social Sciences
DipTE .... Diploma in Transportation Engineering
DipTLSA .... Diploma in Teaching Literacy Skills to Adults
DipTM .... Diploma in Training Management
DipTS .... Diploma in Transport Studies
DipTSM .... Diploma in the Techniques of Safety Management
DipTT .... Diploma in Travel and Tourism
DipTh.............. Diploma in Theology
DipVG.............. Diploma in Vocational Guidance
DipYESTB....... Diploma of the Youth Employment Service Training Board
DipYL.............. Diploma in Youth Leadership
DipYS.............. Diploma in Youth Service
Dip Psych .... Diploma in Psychology
Dipl-Reg........... Diplom-Regisseur für Musiktheater
Dir................... Director
Distr .... District
Div................... Divinity
Div Test .... Divinity Testimonium
DivCert............. Divinity Certificate
Dn-in-c .... Deacon-in-charge
Dom .... Domestic
Down................ Downing
Dr..................... Doctor
DrTheol............ Doctor of Theology (Germany)
Dss................... Deaconess
dss................... Admitted Deaconess
Dub .... Dublin
Dur.................. (Diocese of) Durham

E

E .... East
.... Eastern
EAMTC........... East Anglian Ministerial Training Course
EC .... Emergency Commission
ED .... Ecclesiastical District (also see CD)
.... Efficiency Decoration
EMMTC .... East Midlands Ministry Training Course
EN(G) .... Enrolled Nurse (General)
EN(M)............. Enrolled Nurse (Mental)
ERD .... Emergency Reserve Decoration
ESC .... Ecole Superieure de Commerce
ESMI............... Elderly, Sick and Mentally Infirm
Ecum .... Ecumenical
.... Ecumenics
.... Ecumenism
Ed .... Editor
.... Editorial
EdD.................. Doctor of Education (also see DEd)
EdM .... Master of Education (USA) (also see MEd)
Edin................. (Diocese of) Edinburgh
Edm................. Edmund
.... Edmund's
Educn .... Education
.... Educational
Edw .... Edward
.... Edward's
Eliz .... Elizabeth
.... Elizabeth's
Em.................... Emmanuel

Emb.................. Embassy
EngD................ Doctor of Engineering
EngTech .... Engineering Technician
Episc................ Episcopal
.... Episcopalian
Eur................... (Diocese of) Gibraltar in Europe
.... Europe
.... European
EurIng.............. European Engineer
Ev..................... Evangelist
.... Evangelist's
.... Evangelists
Evang .... Evangelical
.... Evangelism
Ex .... (Diocese of) Exeter
Ex Dioc Cert ..... Exeter Diocesan Certificate
Exam .... Examining
Exec.................. Executive
Exor.................. Executor
Ext.................... Extension

F

F&HE .... Further and Higher Education
FAA.................. Fellow, Institution of Administrative Accountants
FACC .... Fellow, American College of Cardiology
FACCA .... Fellow, Association of Certified and Corporate Accountants (now see FCCA)
FACOG .... Fellow, American College of Obstetricians and Gynaecologists
FADO .... Fellow, Association of Dispensing Opticians
FAEB .... Fellow, Academy of Environmental Biology (India)
FAHA .... Fellow, Australian Academy of the Humanities
FAIM .... Fellow, Australian Institute of Management
FAIWCW .... Fellow, Australian Institute of Welfare and Community Workers
FASI .... Fellow, Architects' and Surveyors' Institute
FBA.................. Fellow, British Academy
FBCO............... Fellow, British College of Ophthalmic Opticians (Optometrists)
FBCS .... Fellow, British Computer Society
FBCartS .... Fellow, British Cartographic Society
FBDO .... Fellow, Association of British Dispensing Opticians
FBEng.............. Fellow, Association of Building Engineers
FBIM................ Fellow, British Institute of Management (formerly MBIM)
FBIS .... Fellow, British Interplanetary Society
FBIST .... Fellow, British Institute of Surgical Technologists
FBOA............... Fellow, British Optical Association
FBPICS............ Fellow, British Production and Inventory Control Society
FBPsS............... Fellow, British Psychological Society
FBS .... Fellow, Burgon Society
FCA .... Fellow, Institute of Chartered Accountants
FCCA............... Fellow, Chartered Association of Certified Accountants (formerly FACCA)
FCFI .... Fellow, Clothing and Footwear Institute
FCIArb .... Fellow, Chartered Institute of Arbitrators
FCIB .... Fellow, Chartered Institute of Bankers
.... Fellow, Corporation of Insurance Brokers
FCII .... Fellow, Chartered Insurance Institute
FCILA .... Fellow, Chartered Institute of Loss Adjusters

FCIM .... Fellow, Chartered Institute of Marketing (formerly FInstM)

FCIOB .... Fellow, Chartered Institute of Building

FCIPA .... Fellow, Chartered Institute of Patent Agents (now see CPA)

FCIPD .... Fellow, Chartered Institute of Personnel and Development

FCIS .... Fellow, Institute of Chartered Secretaries and Administrators

FCIT .... Fellow, Chartered Institute of Transport

FCMA .... Fellow, Institute of Cost and Management Accountants

FCMI .... Fellow, Chartered Management Institute (formerly FIMgt)

FCO .... Foreign and Commonwealth Office

FCOptom .... Fellow, College of Optometrists

FCP .... Fellow, College of Preceptors

FCollP .... Ordinary Fellow, College of Preceptors

FDS .... Fellow in Dental Surgery

FDSRCPSGlas .. Fellow in Dental Surgery, Royal College of Physicians and Surgeons of Glasgow

FE .... Further Education

FEPA .... Fellow, Evangelical Preachers' Association

FEng .... Fellow, Royal Academy (formerly Fellowship) of Engineering

FFA .... Fellow, Institute of Financial Accountants

FFAEM .... Fellow, Faculty of Accident and Emergency Medicine

FFARCS .... Fellow, Faculty of Anaesthetists, Royal College of Surgeons of England

FFChM .... Fellow, Faculty of Church Music

FFDRCSI .... Fellow, Faculty of Dentistry, Royal College of Surgeons in Ireland

FFHom .... Fellow, the Faculty of Homoeopathy

FFPHM .... Fellow, Faculty of Public Health Medicine

FGA .... Fellow, Gemmalogical Association

FGCM .... Fellow, Guild of Church Musicians

FGMS .... Fellow, Guild of Musicians and Singers

FGS .... Fellow, Geological Society of London

FHCIMA .... Fellow, Hotel Catering and Institutional Management Association

FHSM .... Fellow, Institute of Health Services Management

FHSM or FHA . Fellow, Institute of Health Service Management (formerly Administrators)

FIA .... Fellow, Institute of Actuaries

FIBD .... Fellow, Institute of British Decorators

FIBMS .... Fellow, Institute of Bio-Medial Sciences

FIBiol .... Fellow, Institute of Biology

FICE .... Fellow, Institution of Civil Engineers

FICM .... Fellow, Institution of Commercial Managers

FIChemE .... Fellow, Institution of Chemical Engineers

FIDiagE .... Fellow, Institution of Diagnostic Engineers

FIED .... Fellow, Institution of Engineering Designers

FIEE .... Fellow, Institution of Electrical Engineers (formerly FIERE)

FIEEE .... Fellow, Institution of Electrical and Electronics Engineers (NY)

FIERE .... Fellow, Institution of Electronic and Radio Engineers (now see FIEE)

FIFF .... Fellow, Institute of Freight Forwarders

FIFireE .... Fellow, Institution of Fire Engineers

FIHT .... Fellow of the Institution of Highways and Transportation

FIHospE .... Fellow, Institute of Hospital Engineering

FIIM .... Fellow, Institution of Industrial Managers (formerly FIPlantE)

FIL .... Fellow, Institute of Linguists

FILEx .... Fellow, Institute of Legal Executives

FIMA .... Fellow, Institute of Mathematics and its Applications

FIMEMME ...... Fellow, Institution of Mining Electrical and Mining Mechanical Engineers

FIMI .... Fellow, Institute of the Motor Industry

FIMLS .... Fellow, Institute of Medical Laboratory Sciences

FIMM .... Fellow, Institution of Mining and Metallurgy (now see FIMMM)

FIMMM .... Fellow, Institute of Materials, Minerals and Mining

FIMS .... Fellow, Institute of Management Specialists

FIMSSA .... Fellow, Institute of Mine Surveyors of South Africa

FIMarE .... Fellow, Institute of Marine Engineers

FIMechE .... Fellow, Institution of Mechanical Engineers

FIMgt .... Fellow, Institute of Management (now see FCMI)

FINucE .... Fellow, Institution of Nuclear Engineers

FIOSH .... Fellow, Institute of Occupational Safety and Health

FIPD .... Fellow, Institute of Personnel Development

.... Fellow, Institute of Personnel and Development (now see FCIPD)

FIPEM .... Fellow, Institute of Physics and Engineering in Medicine

FIPM .... Fellow, Institute of Personnel Management (now see FCIPD)

FIPlantE .... Fellow, Institution of Plant Engineers (now see FIIM)

FIQA .... Fellow, Institute of Quality Assurance

FISM .... Fellow, Institute of Supervisory Management

FIST .... Fellow, Institute of Science and Technology

FIStructE .... Fellow, Institution of Structural Engineers

FITD .... Fellow, Institute of Training and Development (now see FCIPD)

FIWSc .... Fellow, Institute of Wood Science

FInstAM .... Fellow, Institute of Administrative Management

FInstE .... Fellow, Institute of Energy

FInstFF .... Fellow, Institute of Freight Forwarders (now see FIFF)

FInstM .... Fellow, Institute of Marketing (now see FCIM)

FInstMC .... Fellow, Institute of Measurement and Control

FInstP .... Fellow, Institute of Physics

FInstSMM .... Fellow, Institute of Sales and Marketing Management

FInstTT .... Fellow, Institute of Travel and Tourism

FKC .... Fellow, King's College London

FLA .... Fellow, Library Association

FLAME .... Family Life and Marriage Education

FLAS .... Fellow, Chartered Land Agents' Society (now see FRICS)

FLCM .... Fellow, London College of Music

FLIA .... Fellow, Life Insurance Association

FLS .... Fellow, Linnean Society

FMA .... Fellow, Museums Association

FNI .... Fellow, Nautical Institute

FPS .... Fellow, Pharmaceutical Society of Great Britain

FPhS .... Fellow, Philosophical Society of England

FRACI .... Fellow, Royal Australian Chemical Institute

FRAI .... Fellow, Royal Anthropological Institute

FRAM .... Fellow, Royal Academy of Music

FRAS .... Fellow, Royal Asiatic Society

.... Fellow, Royal Astronomical Society

FRAeS .... Fellow, Royal Aeronautical Society

FRCA .... Fellow, Royal College of Anaesthetists

FRCGP .... Fellow, Royal College of General Practitioners

FRCM .... Fellow, Royal College of Music

FRCO .... Fellow, Royal College of Organists

FRCOG .... Fellow, Royal College of Obstetricians and Gynaecologists

FRCOphth .... Fellow, Royal College of Ophthalmologists

FRCP .... Fellow, Royal College of Physicians

FRCP(C) .... Fellow, Royal College of Physicians of Canada

FRCPEd .... Fellow, Royal College of Physicians Edinburgh

FRCPGlas .... Fellow, Royal College of Physicians and Surgeons, Glasgow (also see FRCSGlas)

FRCPath .... Fellow, Royal College of Pathologists

FRCPsych .... Fellow, Royal College of Psychiatrists

FRCR .... Fellow, Royal College of Radiologists

FRCS .... Fellow, Royal College of Physicians and Surgeons of England

FRCSE or .... Fellow, Royal College of
FRCSEd .... Surgeons of Edinburgh

FRCSGlas .... Fellow, Royal College of Physicians and Surgeons, Glasgow (also see FRCPGlas)

FRCSI .... Fellow, Royal College of Surgeons in Ireland

FRCVS .... Fellow, Royal College of Veterinary Surgeons

FRGS .... Fellow, Royal Geographical Society

FRHS .... Fellow, Royal Horticultural Society

FRHistS .... Fellow, Royal Historical Society

FRIAS .... Fellow, Royal Incorporation of Architects of Scotland

FRIBA .... Fellow, Royal Institute of British Architects

FRIC .... Fellow, Royal Institute of Chemistry (now see FRSC)

FRICS .... Fellow, Royal Institution of Chartered Surveyors (formerly FLAS and FSI)

FRIN .... Fellow, Royal Institution of Navigation

FRINA .... Fellow, Royal Institution of Naval Architects

FRIPHH .... Fellow, Royal Institute of Public Health and Hygiene

FRMetS .... Fellow, Royal Meteorological Society

FRS .... Fellow, Royal Society

FRSA .... Fellow, Royal Society of Arts

FRSAI .... Fellow, Royal Society of Antiquaries of Ireland

FRSC .... Fellow, Royal Society of Canada

.... Fellow, Royal Society of Chemistry (formerly FRIC)

FRSCM .... Hon Fellow, Royal School of Church Music

FRSE	Fellow, Royal Society of Edinburgh
FRSH	Fellow, Royal Society for the Promotion of Health
FRSL	Fellow, Royal Society of Literature
FRSM	Fellow, Royal Society of Medicine
FRTPI	Fellow, Royal Town Planning Institute
FSA	Fellow, Society of Antiquaries
FSAScot	Fellow, Royal Society of Antiquaries of Scotland
FSCA	Fellow, Royal Society of Company and Commercial Accountants
FSI	Fellow, Chartered Surveyors' Institution (now see FRICS)
FSJ	Fellowship of St John the Evangelist
FSR	Fellowship Diploma of the Society of Radiographers
FSS	Fellow, Royal Statistical Society
FTC	Flying Training Command
	Full Technological Certificate, City and Guilds of the London Institute
FTCD	Fellow, Trinity College Dublin
FTCL	Fellow, Trinity College of Music London
FTII	Fellow, Institute of Taxation
FVCM	Fellow, Victoria College of Music
FWeldI	Fellow, Institute of Welding
Fell	Fellow
Fitzw	Fitzwilliam
Foundn	Foundation
Fran	Francis
	Francis's

G

G&C	Gonville and Caius
GB	Great Britain
GBSM	Graduate of the Birmingham School of Music
GCMG	Knight Grand Cross, Order of St Michael and St George
GCVO	Knight Grand Cross, Royal Victorian Order
GDipGP	Graduate Diploma in Gestalt Psychotherapy
GFS	Girls' Friendly Society
GGSM	Graduate Diploma of the Guildhall School of Music and Drama
GIBiol	Graduate of the Institute of Biology
GIFireE	Graduate of the Institute of Fire Engineers
GIMechE	Graduate of the Institution of Mechanical Engineers
GIPE	Graduate of the Institution of Production Engineers
GInstP	Graduate of the Institute of Physics
GLCM	Graduate Diploma of the London College of Music
GM	George Medal
GNSM	Graduate of the Northern School of Music
GRIC	Graduate Membership, Royal Institute of Chemistry
GRNCM	Graduate of the Royal Northern College of Music
GRSC	Graduate of the Royal School of Chemistry
GRSM	Graduate of the Royal Schools of Music
GSM	(Member of) Guildhall School of Music and Drama
GTCL	Graduate Diploma of Trinity College of Music, London
Gabr	Gabriel
	Gabriel's
Gd	Good
Gen	General
Geo	George
	George's
Gib	Gibraltar
Glam	Glamorgan
Glas	(Diocese of) Glasgow and Galloway

Glas	Glasgow
Glos	Gloucestershire
Glouc	(Diocese of) Gloucester
Gov	Governor
Gp	Group
Gr	Grammar
Grad LI	Graduate of the Landscape Institute
GradCertEd(FE)	Graduate Certificate in Education (Further Education)
GradDipEd	Postgraduate Diploma of Education (Australia)
GradDipPhys	Graduate Diploma in Physiotherapy
GradDipRE	Postgraduate Diploma in Religious Education (Australia)
GradIEE	Graduate of the Institution of Electrical Engineers
GradIMI	Graduate of the Institute of the Motor Industry
GradIPM	Graduate of the Institute of Personnel Management
GradInstT	Graduate of the Institute of Transport
Greg	Gregory
	Gregory's
Gt	Great
Gtr	Greater
Guildf	(Diocese of) Guildford

H

H	Holy
H&FE	Higher and Further Education
HA	Health Authority
HDipEd	Higher Diploma in Education
HDipHV	Higher Diploma in Health Visit Studies
HDipRE	Higher Diploma in Religious Education
HE	Higher Education
HIV	Human Immunodeficiency Virus
HM	Her (or His) Majesty
HMI	Her (or His) Majesty's Inspector (or Inspectorate)
HMS	Her (or His) Majesty's Ship
HNC	Higher National Certificate
HND	Higher National Diploma
HND(IMechE)	Higher National Diploma, Institution of Mechanical Engineers
HQ	Headquarters
HTC	Higher Technical Certificate
HTV	Harlech Television
HVCert	Health Visitor's Certificate
Hatf	Hatfield
Hd	Head
Heref	(Diocese of) Hereford
Hertf	Hertford
Hist	Historic
	Historical
	History
Ho	House
Hon	Honorary
	Honourable
HonDLaws	Honorary Doctor of Laws
HonFChS	Honorary Fellow, Society of Chiropodists
HonLMStJ	Honorary Life Member, St John's Ambulance Association
HonRCM	Honorary Member, Royal College of Music
Hosp	Hospital

I

I	Incumbent
IAAP	International Association for Analytical Psychology
IBA	Independent Broadcasting Authority
ICF	Industry Churches Forum (formerly Industrial Christian Fellowship)
ICM	Irish Church Missions
ICS	Intercontinental Church Society
IDC	Inter-Diocesan Certificate
IDWAL	Inter-Diocesan West Africa Link

IEAB	Igreja Episcopal Anglicana do Brasil
IEng	Incorporated Engineer
	Incorporated Engineer (formerly TEng(CEI))
IFES	International Fellowship of Evangelical Students
ILEA	Inner London Education Authority
IMinE	Institution of Mining Engineers
IPFA	Member, Chartered Institute of Public Finance and Accountancy
ISO	Imperial Service Order
IT	Information Technology
ITV	Independent Television
IVF	Inter-Varsity Fellowship of Evangelical Unions (now see UCCF)
IVS	International Voluntary Service
Imp	Imperial
Inc	Incorporated
Ind	Industrial
	Industry
Info	Information
Insp	Inspector
Inst	Institut
	Institute
	Institution
Intercon	Intercontinental
Internat	International
Interpr	Interpretation
Is	Island
	Islands
	Isle
	Isles

J

JCD	Doctor of Canon Law
JCL	Licentiate in Canon Law
JD	Doctor of Jurisprudence
JEM	Jerusalem and the East Mission (now see JMECA)
JMECA	Jerusalem and Middle East Church Association (formerly JEM)
JP	Justice of the Peace
Jas	James
	James's
Jes	Jesus
Jo	John
	John's
Jos	Joseph
	Joseph's
Jt	Joint
Jun	Junior

K

K	King
	King's
K, E & A	(Diocese of) Kilmore, Elphin and Ardagh
KA	Knight of St Andrew, Order of Barbados
KBE	Knight Commander, Order of the British Empire
KCB	Knight Commander, Order of the Bath
KCMG	Knight Commander, Order of St Michael and St George
KCVO	Knight Commander, Royal Victorian Order
KLJ	Knight, Order of St Lazarus of Jerusalem
KPM	King's Police Medal
KStJ	Knight, Most Venerable Order of the Hospital of St John of Jerusalem
Kath	Katharine/Katherine
	Katharine's/Katherine's
Kt	Knight

L

L & K	(Diocese of) Limerick and Killaloe (united dioceses of Limerick, Ardfert, Aghadoe, Killaloe, Kilfenora, Clonfert, Kilmacduagh and Emly)
LASI	Licentiate, Ambulance Service Institute

LBIPP	Licentiate, British Institute of Professional Photography
LCC	London County Council
LCL	Licentiate in Canon Law
LCP	Licentiate, College of Preceptors
LCST	Licentiate, College of Speech Therapists
LDS	Licentiate in Dental Surgery
LDSRCSEng	Licentiate in Dental Surgery of the Royal College of Surgeons of England
LDiv	Licentiate in Divinity
LEA	Local Education Authority
LEP	Local Ecumenical Project
LGCM	Lesbian and Gay Christian Movement
LGSM	Licentiate, Guildhall School of Music and Drama
LHSM	Licentiate, Institute of Health Services Management
LICeram	Licentiate, Institute of Ceramics
LIMA	Licentiate, Institute of Mathematics and its Applications
LLA	Lady Literate in Arts
LLAM	Licentiate, London Academy of Music and Dramatic Art
LLB	Bachelor of Laws
LLCM	Licentiate, London College of Music
LLD	Doctor of Laws
LLM	Master of Laws
LMH	Lady Margaret Hall
LMPA	Licentiate Master, Photographers' Association
LNSM	Local Non-stipendiary Minister (or Ministry)
LOROS	Leicestershire Organization for the Relief of Suffering
LRAM	Licentiate, Royal Academy of Music
LRCP	Licentiate, Royal College of Physicians
LRCPI	Licentiate, Royal College of Physicians of Ireland
LRCSEng	Licentiate of the Royal College of Surgeons in England
LRIC	Licenciate, Royal Institute of Chemistry
LRPS	Licentiate, Royal Photographic Society
LRSC	Licentiate, Royal Society of Chemistry
LRSM	Licentiate Diploma of the Royal Schools of Music
LSE	London School of Economics and Political Science
LSHTM	London School of Hygiene and Tropical Medicine
LSIAD	Licentiate, Society of Industrial Artists and Designers
LSMF	Licentiate, State Medical Faculty
LST	Licentiate in Theology (also see LTh)
LSocEth	Licence en Sociologie-Ethnologie
LTCL	Licentiate, Trinity College of Music London
LTh	Licentiate in Theology (also see LST)
LVCM	Licentiate, Victoria College of Music
LVO	Lieutenant, Royal Victorian Order
LWCMD	Licentiate, Welsh College of Music and Drama
Lamp	Lampeter
Lanc	Lancaster
Laur	Laurence
	Laurence's
Lawr	Lawrence
	Lawrence's
Ld	Lord
Ldr	Leader
Lect	Lecturer
Leic	(Diocese of) Leicester
Leon	Leonard
	Leonard's
Lib	Librarian

Lib	Library
Lic	Licence
	Licensed
	Licentiate
LicIM&C	Licentiate, Institute of Measurement and Control
LicTh	Licence in Theology
Lich	(Diocese of) Lichfield
Linc	(Diocese of) Lincoln
Lit	Literature
LittD	Doctor of Letters (also see DLitt)
Liturg	Liturgical
Liv	(Diocese of) Liverpool
Llan	(Diocese of) Llandaff
Lon	(Diocese of) London
Loughb	Loughborough
Lt	Lieutenant
	Little
Ltd	Limited
LèsL	Licencié ès Lettres

M

M & K	(Diocese of) Meath and Kildare
MA	Master of Arts
MA(Ed)	Master of Arts in Education
MA(MM)	Master of Arts in Mission and Ministry
MA(TS)	Master of Arts in Theological Studies
MA(Theol)	Master of Arts in Theology
MAAIS	Member, Association of Archaeological Illustrators and Surveyors
MAAR	Member, American Academy of Religion
MAAT	Member, Association of Accounting Technicians
MACC	Member, Australian College of Chaplains
MACE	Member, Australian College of Education
MACT	Member, Association of Corporate Treasurers
MAE	Member, Academy of Experts
MAJA	Member, Association of Jungian Analysts
MAMIT	Member, Associate of Meat Inspectors Trust
MAOT	Member, Association of Occupational Therapists (now see MBAOT)
MAPsS	Member, Australian Psychological Society
MASCH	Member, Australian Society of Clinical Hypnotherapists
MASI	Member, Architects and Surveyors Institute
MATA	Member, Animal Technicians' Association
MATCA	Member, Air Traffic Control Association
MArch	Master of Architecture
MB	Bachelor of Medicine (also see BM)
MB,BS *or* MB,ChB	Conjoint degree of Bachelor of Medicine, Bachelor of Surgery
MBA	Master of Business Administration
MBAC	Member, British Association for Counselling
MBAOT	Member, British Association of Occupational Therapists (formerly MAOT)
MBAP	Member, British Association of Psychotherapists
MBASW	Member, British Association of Social Workers
MBATOD	Member, British Association of Teachers of the Deaf
MBC	Metropolitan (or Municipal) Borough Council
MBCO	Member, British College of Optometrists
MBCS	Member, British Computer Society
MBChA	Member, British Chiropody Association
MBE	Member, Order of the British Empire
MBEng	Member, Association of Building Engineers

MBHI	Member, British Horological Institute
MBIM	Member, British Institute of Management (formerly AMBIM; now see FBIM)
MBKSTS	Member, British Kinematograph, Sound and Television Society
MBPsS	Member, British Psychological Society
MC	Military Cross
MCA	Member, Institute of Chartered Accountants
MCB	Master in Clinical Biochemistry
MCCDRCS	Member in Clinical Community Dentistry, Royal College of Surgeons
MCD	Master of Civic Design
MCE	Master of Civil Engineering
MCIArb	Member, Chartered Institute of Arbitrators
MCIBS	Member, Chartered Institute of Bankers in Scotland
MCIBSE	Member, Chartered Institute of Building Service Engineers
MCIEH	Member, Chartered Institute of Enviromental Health (formerly MIEH)
MCIH	Corporate Member, Chartered Institute of Housing
MCIJ	Member, Chartered Institute of Journalists
MCIM	Member, Chartered Institute of Marketing (formerly MInstM)
MCIMA	Member, Chartered Institute of Management Accountants
MCIOB	Member, Chartered Institute of Building
MCIPD	Member, Chartered Institute of Personnel and Development
MCIPS	Member, Chartered Institute of Purchasing and Supply
MCIT	Member, Chartered Institute of Transport
MCIWEM	Member, Chartered Institution of Water and Enviromental Management
MCL	Master of Canon Law
MCMI	Member, Chartered Management Institute (formerly MIMgt)
MCS	Master of Christian Studies
MCSD	Member, Chartered Society of Designers
MCSP	Member, Chartered Society of Physiotherapy
MCST	Member, College of Speech Therapists
MCT	Member, Association of Corporate Treasurers
MCThA	Member, Clinical Theology Association
MChOrth	Master of Orthopaedic Surgery
MChS	Member, Society of Chiropodists
MChemA	Master in Chemical Analysis
MCollP	Member, College of Preceptors
MCom	Master of Commerce
MD	Doctor of Medicine
MDiv	Master of Divinity
MEHS	Member, Ecclesiastical History Society
MEd	Master of Education
MEng	Master of Engineering
MFA	Master of Fine Art
MFBA	Member, Freshwater Biological Association
MFCM	Member, Faculty of Community Medicine
MGDSRCSEng	Membership in General Dental Surgery, Royal College of Surgeons of England
MHCIMA	Member, Hotel Catering and Institutional Management Association
MHSA	Member, Hymn Society of America

MHSGBI	Member, Hymn Society of Great Britain and Ireland
MHSM	Member, Institute of Health Services Management
MHort (RHS)	Master of Horticulture, Royal Horticultural Society
MHums	Master of Humanities
MIA	Malawi Institute of Architects
MIAAP	Member, International Association for Analytical Psychology
MIAAS	Member, Incorporated Association of Architects and Surveyors
MIAM	Member, Institute of Administrative Management
MIAP	Member, Institution of Analysts and Programmers
MIAT	Member, Institute of Asphalt Technology
MIBC	Member, Institute of Business Counsellors
MIBCO	Member, Institution of Building Control Officers
MIBF	Member, Institute of British Foundrymen
MIBiol	Member, Institute of Biology
MICA	Member, International Cartographic Association
MICAS	Member, Institute of Chartered Accountants of Scotland
MICE	Member, Institution of Civil Engineers (formerly AMICE)
MICFM	Member, Institute of Charity Fundraising Managers
MICFor	Member, Institute of Chartered Foresters
MICS	Member, Institute of Chartered Shipbrokers
MIChemE	Member, Institution of Chemical Engineers
MICorrST	Member, Institution of Corrosion Science and Technology
MIDPM	Member, Institute of Data Processing Management
MIE	Member, Institute of Engineers and Technicians
MIEAust	Member, Institute of Engineers and Technicians Australia
MIED	Member, Institute of Engineering Designers
MIEE	Member, Institution of Electrical Engineers (formerly AMIEE & MIERE)
MIEEE	Member, Institute of Electrical and Electronics Engineers (NY)
MIEEM	Member, Institute of Ecology and Environmental Management
MIEH	Member, Institute of Environmental Health (now see MCIEH)
MIERE	Member, Institution of Electronic and Radio Engineers (now see MIEE)
MIEleclE	Corporate Member, Institution of Electrical and Electronics
	Incorporated Engineers
MIEx	Member, Institute of Export
MIFA	Member, Institute of Field Archaeologists
MIGasE	Member, Institution of Gas Engineers
MIH	Member, Institute of Housing
MIHE	Member, Institute of Health Education
MIHEEM	Member, Institute of Healthcare Engineering and Estate Management
MIHT	Member, Institution of Highways and Transportation
MIHospE	Member, Institute of Hospital Engineers
MIIExE	Member, Institute of Incorporated Executive Engineers
MIIM	Member, Institution of Industrial Managers
MIInfSc	Member, Institute of Information Scientists
MIL	Member, Institute of Linguists
MILT	Member, Institute of Logistics and Transport
MIM	Member, Institute of Metals (formerly Institution of Metallurgists)
MIMA	Member, Institute of Management Accountants
	Member, Institute of Mathematics and its Applications
MIMC	Member, Institute of Management Consultants
MIMI	Member, Institute of the Motor Industry
MIMM	Member, Institution of Mining and Metallurgy (now see MIMMM)
MIMMM	Member, Institute of Materials, Minerals and Mining
MIMarE	Member, Institute of Marine Engineers
MIMechE	Member, Institution of Mechanical Engineers (formerly AMIMechE)
MIMfgE	Member, Institute of Manufacturing Engineers
MIMgt	Member, Institute of Management (now see MCMI)
MIMunE	Member, Institution of Municipal Engineers
MINucE	Member, Institute of Nuclear Engineers
MIOSH	Member, Institution of Occupational Safety and Health
MIOT	Member, Institute of Operating Theatre Technicians
MIPD	Member, Institute of Personnel and Development (now see MCIPD)
MIPI	Member, Institute of Private Investigators
MIPM	Member, Institute of Personnel Management (now see MCIPD)
MIPR	Member, Institute of Public Relations
MIProdE	Member, Institution of Production Engineers
MIQA	Member, Institute of Quality Assurance
MISE	Member, Institute of Sales Engineers
MISM	Member, Institute of Supervisory Management
MISW	Member, Institute of Social Welfare
MIStructE	Member, Institute of Structural Engineers
MITD	Member, Institute of Training and Development (now see MCIPD)
MITE	Member, Institution of Electrical and Electronics Technician Engineers
MITMA	Member, Institute of Trade Mark Agents
MITPA	Member, International Tax Planning Association
MITSA	Member, Institute of Trading Standards Administration
MITT	Member, Institute of Travel and Tourism
MIW	Member, Institute of Welfare (formerly MIWO)
MInstAM	Member, Institute of Administrative Management
MInstC(Glas)	Member, Institute of Counselling (Glasgow)
MInstD	Member, Institute of Directors
MInstE	Member, Institute of Energy
MInstGA	Member, Institute of Group Analysis
MInstM	Member, Institute of Marketing (now see MCIM)
MInstP	Member, Institute of Physics
MInstPC	Member, Institute of Psychotherapy and Counselling
MInstPI	Member, Institute of Patentees and Inventors
MInstPS	Corporate Member, Institute of Purchasing and Supply
MInstPkg	Member, Institute of Packaging
MInstTA	Member, Institute of Transport Administration
MLL	Master of Laws
MLS	Master of Library Studies
MLitt	Master of Letters
MM	Military Medal
MMCET	Martyrs' Memorial and Church of England Trust
MMS	Member, Institute of Management Services
MMedSc	Master of Medical Science
MMet	Master of Metallurgy
MMin	Master of Ministry
MMinTheol	Master in Ministry and Theology
MMus	Master of Music (also see MusM)
MNAAL	Member, North American Academy of Liturgy
MNFSH	Member, National Federation of Spiritual Healers
MOD	Ministry of Defence
MPH	Master of Public Health
MPS	Master of Professional Studies
	Member, Pharmaceutical Society (now see MRPharmS)
MPhil	Master of Philosophy
MPhys	Master of Physics
MPsychSc	Master of Psychological Science
MRAC	Member, Royal Agricultural College
MRAeS	Member, Royal Aeronautical Society
MRCGP	Member, Royal College of General Practitioners
MRCO	Member, Royal College of Organists
MRCOG	Member, Royal College of Obstetricians and Gynaecologists
MRCP	Member, Royal College of Physicians
MRCPath	Member, Royal College of Pathologists
MRCPsych	Member, Royal College of Psychiatrists
MRCS	Member, Royal College of Surgeons
MRCSE	Member, Royal College of Surgeons of Edinburgh
MRCVS	Member, Royal College of Veterinary Surgeons
MRHS	Member, Royal Horticultural Society
MRIA	Member, Royal Irish Academy
MRIC	Member, Royal Institute of Chemistry (formerly ARIC; now see MRSC)
MRICS	Member, Royal Institution of Chartered Surveyors
MRIN	Member, Royal Institute of Navigation
MRINA	Member, Royal Institution of Naval Architects
MRIPHH	Member, Royal Institute of Public Health and Hygiene
MRPharmS	Member, Royal Pharmaceutical Society (formerly MPS)
MRSC	Member, Royal Society of Chemistry (formerly MRIC)
MRSH	Member, Royal Society for the Promotion of Health
MRSL	Member, Order of the Republic of Sierra Leone
MRST	Member, Royal Society of Teachers
MRTPI	Member, Royal Town Planning Institute
MRTvS	Member, Royal Television Society

MRelSc	Master of Religious Science
MS	Master of Science (USA)
	Master of Surgery
MSAICE	Member, South African Institution of Civil Engineers
MSAPP	Member, Society of Advanced Psychotherapy Practitioners
MSE	Master of Science in Engineering (USA)
	Minister (or Ministers) in Secular Employment
MSERT	Member, Society of Electronic and Radio Technicians
MSGT	Associate Member, Society of Glass Technology
MSHAA	Member, Society of Hearing Aid Audiologists
MSI	Member, Securities Institute
MSIAD	Member, Society of Industrial Artists and Designers
MSOSc	Member, Society of Ordained Scientists
MSOTS	Member, Society for Old Testament Study
MSR	Member, Society of Radiographers
MSSCLE	Member, Society for the Study of the Crusades and the Latin East
MSSCh	Member, School of Surgical Chiropody
MSSTh	Member, Society for the Study of Theology
MSSc	Master of Social Science (also see MSocSc)
MSTSD	Member, Society of Teachers of Speech and Drama
MSW	Master of Social Work
MSacMus	Master of Sacred Music
MSc	Master of Science
MSc(Econ)	Master of Science in Economics
MScRel	Maitrise es Sciences Religieuses
MSoc	Maitrise en Sociologie
MSocSc	Master of Social Sciences (also see MSSc)
MSocWork	Master of Social Work (USA)
MSt	Master of Studies
MTD	Master of Transport Design
MTS	Master of Theological Studies
MTech	Master of Technology
MTh *or* MTheol	Master of Theology (also see STM and ThM)
MU	Mothers' Union
MVI	Member, Victoria Institute
MVO	Member, Royal Victorian Order
Magd	Magdalen/Magdalene
	Magdalen's/Magdalene's
Man	(Diocese of) Manchester
Man Dir	Managing Director
Mansf	Mansfield
Marg	Margaret
	Margaret's
Matt	Matthew
	Matthew's
Mert	Merton
MesL	Lettres Modernes
Metrop	Metropolitan
Mgt	Management
Mich	Michael
	Michael's
	Michael and All Angels
Midl	Midlands
Mil	Military
Min	Minister
	Ministries
	Ministry
	Minor
Minl	Ministerial
Miss	Mission
	Missions
	Missionary
Missr	Missioner
Mon	(Diocese of) Monmouth
Mor	(Diocese of) Moray, Ross and Caithness
Mt	Mount
MusB *or*	Bachelor of Music (also see
MusBac	BMus)

MusD *or*	Doctor of Music
MusDoc	
MusM	Master of Music (also see MMus)

N

N	North
	Northern
NACRO	National Association for the Care and Rehabilitation of Offenders
NASA	National Aeronautics and Space Administration (USA)
NC(BS)	National Certificate in Business Studies (Irish Republic)
NCA	National Certificate in Agriculture
NCEC	National Christian Education Council
NCTJ	National Certificate for the Training of Journalists
NDA	National Diploma in Agriculture
NDAD	National Diploma in Art and Design
NDD	National Diploma in Design
NDFOM	National Diploma in Farm Organisation and Management
NDH	National Diploma in Horticulture
NDN	National District Nurse Certificate
NDTJ	National Diploma in the Training of Journalists
NE	North East
NEBSS	National Examinations Board for Supervisory Studies
NEOC	North East Oecumenical Course (formerly North East Ordination Course)
NHS	National Health Service
NIDA	National Institute of Dramatic Art
NJ	New Jersey
NNEB	National Nursery Examination Board
NS	Nova Scotia (Canada)
NSM	Non-stipendiary Minister (or Ministry)
NSPCC	National Society for the Prevention of Cruelty to Children
NSW	New South Wales (Australia)
NT	New Testament
NTMTC	North Thames Ministerial Training Course
NUI	National University of Ireland
NUU	New University of Ulster
NW	North West/Northwestern
NWT	North West Territories (Canada)
NY	New York (USA)
NZ	New Zealand
Nat	National
Nath	Nathanael/Nathaniel
	Nathanael's/Nathaniel's
Newc	(Diocese of) Newcastle
Nic	Nicholas/Nicolas
	Nicholas's/Nicolas's
Nor	(Diocese of) Norwich
Northn	Northampton
Nottm	Nottingham
Nuff	Nuffield

O

OAM	Medal of the Order of Australia
OBE	Officer, Order of the British Empire
OBI	Order of British India
OCF	Officiating Chaplain to the Forces
OGS	Oratory of the Good Shepherd
OH	Ohio
OHP	Order of the Holy Paraclete
OLM	Ordained Local Minister (or Ministry)
OM	Order of Merit
OM(Ger)	Order of Merit of Germany
OMF	Overseas Missionary Fellowship

ONC	Ordinary National Certificate
OND	Ordinary National Diploma
OSB	Order of St Benedict
OSJM	Prelate, Order of St John of Malta
OSP	Order of St Paul
OStJ	Officer, Most Venerable Order of the Hospital of St John of Jerusalem
OT	Old Testament
Offg	Officiating
Offic	Officiate
Ord	Ordained
	Ordinands
	Ordination
Org	Organizer
	Organizing
Ox	(Diocese of) Oxford

P

P	Patron(s)
	Priest
p	Ordained Priest
P in O	Priest in Ordinary
P-in-c	Priest-in-charge
PACTA	Professional Associate, Clinical Theology Association
PBS	Pengeran Bintang Sarawak (Companion of the Order of the Star, Sarawak)
PC	Perpetual Curate
	Privy Counsellor
PCC	Parochial Church Council
PCVG	Postgraduate Certificate of Vocational Guidance
PDATS	Postgraduate Diploma in Applied Theological Studies
PEV	Provincial Episcopal Visitor
PGCE	Postgraduate Certificate in Education
PGCPT	Postgraduate Certificate in Pastoral Theology
PGCTh	Postgraduate Certificate in Theology
PGCertEBD	Postgraduate Certificate in Emotional and Behavioural Disorders
PGD	Postgraduate Diploma
PGDE	Postgraduate Diploma in Education
PGDHE	Postgraduate Diploma in Healthcare Ethics
PGDPT	Postgraduate Diploma in Pastoral Theology
PGDTMM	Postgraduate Diploma in the Theology of Mission and Ministry
PGDTheol	Postgraduate Diploma in Theology
PGDipESL	Postgraduate Diploma in English as a Second Language
PM	Priest Missioner
PO	Post Office
PPAC	Post Professional Award in Counselling
PQCSW	Post-Qualifying Certificate in Social Work
PV	Priest Vicar
Par	Parish
	Parishes
Paroch	Parochial
Past	Pastoral
Patr	Patrick
	Patrick's
	Patronage
Pemb	Pembroke
Penn	Pennsylvania (USA)
Perm	Permission
Pet	(Diocese of) Peterborough
	Peter
	Peter's
Peterho	Peterhouse
PhB	Bachelor of Philosophy
PhC	Pharmaceutical Chemist
PhD	Doctor of Philosophy (also see DPhil)
PhD(Educ)	Doctor of Philosophy in Education
PhL	Licentiate of Philosophy
Phil	Philip
	Philip's
plc	public limited company

Poly	Polytechnic
Portsm	(Diocese of) Portsmouth
Pre-Th	Pre-Theological
Preb	Prebendary
Prec	Precentor
Prep	Preparatory
Pres	President
Prin	Principal
Pris	Prison
	Prisons
Prof	Professor
	Professorial
Progr	Program
	Programme
	Programmes
Prop	Proprietary
Prov	Province
	Provincial
Pt	Point

Q

QC	Queen's Counsel
QCVS	Queen's Commendation for Valuable Service
QFSM	Queen's Fire Service Medal for Distinguished Service
QGM	Queen's Gallantry Medal
QHC	Queen's Honorary Chaplain
QN	Queen's Nurse
QPM	Queen's Police Medal
QSM	Queen's Service Medal
QSO	Queen's Service Order of New Zealand
QUB	The Queen's University of Belfast
QVRM	Queen's Volunteer Reserve Medal
Qld	Queensland
Qu	Queen
	Queen's
	Queens'

R

R	Rector
	Royal
R and D	Research and Development
R of O	Reserve of Officers
R&SChTrust	Rochester and Southwark Church Trust
RAAF	Royal Australian Air Force
RAChD	Royal Army Chaplains' Department
RAD or RADD	Royal Association in Aid of Deaf People (formerly Deaf and Dumb)
RADICLE	Residential and Drop-in Centre London Enterprises
RAEC	Royal Army Educational Corps
RAF	Royal Air Force
RAFVR	Royal Air Force Volunteer Reserve
RAM	(Member) Royal Academy of Music
RAN	Royal Australian Navy
RANSR	Royal Australian Naval Strategic Reserve
RC	Roman Catholic
RCA	Royal College of Art
RCAF	Royal Canadian Air Force
RCM	Royal College of Music
RCN	Royal Canadian Navy
	Royal College of Nursing
RCNT	Registered Clinical Nurse Teacher
RCPS	Royal College of Physicians and Surgeons
RCS	Royal College of Surgeons of England
RCSE	Royal College of Surgeons of Edinburgh
RD	Royal Navy Reserve Decoration
	Rural Dean
RE	Religious Education
RFN	Registered Fever Nurse
RGN	Registered General Nurse
RHV	Registered Health Visitor
RIA	Royal Irish Academy
RIBA	(Member) Royal Institute of British Architects (formerly ARIBA)
RLSMD	Royal London School of Medicine and Dentistry
RM	Registered Midwife

RMA or RMC	Royal Military Academy (formerly College), Sandhurst
RMCM	Royal Manchester College of Music
RMCS	Royal Military College of Science, Shrivenham
RMN	Registered Mental Nurse
RN	Registered Nurse (Canada)
	Royal Navy
RN(MH)	Registered Nurse (for the mentally handicapped)
RNIB	Royal National Institute for the Blind
RNLI	Royal National Lifeboat Institution
RNMH	Registered Nurse for the Mentally Handicapped
RNR	Royal Naval Reserve
RNT	Registered Nurse Tutor
RNVR	Royal Naval Volunteer Reserve
RNZN	Royal New Zealand Navy
RS	Religious Studies
RSCM	(Member) Royal School of Church Music
RSCN	Registered Sick Children's Nurse
RTCert	Certified Reality Therapist
RTE	Radio Telefis Eireann
RVC	Royal Veterinary College
RVO	Royal Victorian Order
Reg	Registered
Relig	Religion
	Religious
Relns	Relations
Rem	Remand
Rep	Representative
Res	Residence
	Resident
	Residential
	Residentiary
Resp	Responsibility
Resurr	Resurrection
Revd	Reverend
Rich	Richard
	Richard's
Ripon	Ripon and Leeds
Rob	Robinson
Roch	(Diocese of) Rochester
Rt	Right
Rtd or rtd	Retired

S

S	South
	Southern
S & B	(Diocese of) Swansea and Brecon
S & M	(Diocese of) Sodor and Man
S'wark	(Diocese of) Southwark
S'well	(Diocese of) Southwell
SA	Salvation Army
SAMS	South American Mission Society
SAP	(Member) Society of Analytical Psychologists
SBStJ	Serving Brother, Most Ven Order of the Hospital of St John of Jerusalem
SCM	State Certified Midwife
	Student Christian Movement
SE	South East
SEITE	South East Institute for Theological Education
SEN	State Enrolled Nurse
SHARE	Shelter Housing and Renewal Experiment
SMF	Society for the Maintenance of the Faith
SNTS	Society for New Testament Studies
SOAS	School of Oriental and African Studies
SOMA	Sharing of Ministries Abroad
SOSc	Society of Ordained Scientists
SPCK	Society for Promoting Christian Knowledge
SPG	Society for the Propagation of the Gospel (now see USPG)
SRCh	State Registered Chiropodist
SRD	State Registered Dietician
SRN	State Registered Nurse

SROT	State Registered Occupational Therapist
SRP	State Registered Physiotherapist
SS	Saints
	Saints'
	Sidney Sussex
SSB	Society of the Sisters of Bethany
SSC	Secretarial Studies Certificate
	Societas Sanctae Crucis (Society of the Holy Cross)
	Solicitor before the Supreme Court (Scotland)
SSEES	School of Slavonic and East European Studies
SSF	Society of St Francis
SSJ	Society of St John of Jerusalem
SSJE	Society of St John the Evangelist
SSM	Society of the Sacred Mission
STB	Bachelor of Theology (also see BTh)
STD	Doctor of Sacred Theology (also see DST)
STETS	Southern Theological Education and Training Scheme
STL	Reader (or Professor) of Sacred Theology
STM	Master of Theology (also see MTh or MTheol and ThM)
STV	Scottish Television
STh	Scholar in Theology (also see ThSchol)
	Student in Theology
SW	South West
SWJ	Servants with Jesus
Sacr	Sacrist
	Sacristan
Sarum	(Diocese of) Salisbury
Sav	Saviour
	Saviour's
ScD	Doctor of Science (also see DSc)
Sch	School
Sec	Secretary
Selw	Selwyn
Sem	Seminary
Sen	Senior
Sheff	(Diocese of) Sheffield
Shep	Shepherd
So	Souls
	Souls'
Soc	Social
	Society
Southn	Southampton
Sqn Ldr	Squadron Leader
St	Saint
St Alb	(Diocese of) St Albans
	St Alban
	St Alban's
St And	(Diocese of) St Andrews, Dunkeld and Dunblane
St As	(Diocese of) St Asaph
St D	(Diocese of) St Davids
St E	(Diocese of) St Edmundsbury and Ipswich
Ste	Sainte
Steph	Stephen
	Stephen's
Sub	Substitute
Succ	Succentor
Suff	Suffragan
Supt	Superintendent
Syn	Synod

T

T, K & A	(Diocese of) Tuam, Killala and Achonry
TA	Territorial Army
TAVR	Territorial and Army Volunteer Reserve
TC	Technician Certificate
TCD	Trinity College, Dublin
TCert	Teacher's Certificate
TD	Team Deacon
	Territorial Efficiency Decoration
TDip	Teacher's Diploma
TEAR	The Evangelical Alliance Relief
TEM	Territorial Efficiency Medal

TEng................	Senior Technician Engineer
TEng(CEI)	Technician Engineer (now see IEng)
TISEC	Theological Institute of the Scottish Episcopal Church
TM	Team Minister (or Ministry)
TP......................	Team Priest
TR	Team Rector
TS	Training Ship
TSB	Trustee Savings Bank
TV	Team Vicar
....	Television
TVS	Television South
Tas	Tasmania
Tech	Technical
....	Technology
temp...................	temporarily
Th	Theologian
....	Theological
....	Theology
ThA	Associate of Theology
ThB	Bachelor of Theology (USA)
ThD...................	Doctorate in Theology (also see DTh)
ThDip...............	Theology Diploma (Australia)
ThL	Theological Licentiate
ThM	Master of Theology (also see MTh or MTheol and STM)
ThSchol	Scholar in Theology (also see STh)
Thos	Thomas
....	Thomas's
Tim.....................	Timothy
....	Timothy's
Tr	Trainer
....	Training
Treas..................	Treasurer
....	Treasurer's
Trin....................	Trinity

U

UAE	United Arab Emirates
UCCF	Universities and Colleges Christian Fellowship of Evangelical Unions (formerly IVF)
UCD..................	University College, Dublin
UEA	University of East Anglia
UED..................	University Education Diploma
UK	United Kingdom
UKRC...............	United Kingdom Register of Counsellors
UMCA	Universities' Mission to Central Africa (now see USPG)
UMIST.............	University of Manchester Institute of Science and Technology
UNISA..............	University of South Africa
UPA...................	Urban Priority Area (or Areas)
URC...................	United Reformed Church
US *or* USA	United States (of America)
USCL	United Society for Christian Literature
USPG................	United Society for the Propagation of the Gospel (formerly SPG, UMCA, and CMD)
UWE	University of the West of England
UWIST.............	University of Wales Institute of Science and Technology
Univ...................	University

V

V	Vicar
....	Virgin
....	Virgin's

VRD	Royal Naval Volunteer Reserve Officers' Decoration
Ven	Venerable
VetMB...............	Bachelor of Veterinary Medicine (also see BVetMed)
Vic	Victoria (Australia)
Vin.....................	Vincent
....	Vincent's
Voc....................	Vocational
....	Vocations

W

W	West
....	Western
w........................	with
W/Cdr................	Wing Commander
WCC..................	World Council of Churches
WEC..................	Worldwide Evangelism Crusade
WEMTC	West of England Ministerial Training Course
WMMTC.........	West Midlands Ministerial Training Course
WRAF	Women's Royal Air Force
Wadh	Wadham
Wakef	(Diocese of) Wakefield
Westf.................	Westfield
Westmr	Westminster
Wilts	Wiltshire
Win	(Diocese of) Winchester
Wm.....................	William
Wolfs.................	Wolfson
Wolv	Wolverhampton
Worc	(Diocese of) Worcester

Y

YMCA	Young Men's Christian Association
YOI...................	Young Offender Institution

A

AAGAARD, Angus Robert. b 64. Moray Ho Coll of Educn CQSW86. Ripon Coll Cuddesdon BTh93. **d** 93 **p** 94. C Taunton St Andr *B & W* 93-97; TV Southampton (City Cen) *Win* 97-01; TR N Lambeth *S'wark* from 01. *St Anselm's Vicarage, 286 Kennington Road, London SE11 5DU* Tel (020) 7735 3415 *or* 7735 3403 Mobile 07810-646644
E-mail angus.aagaard@virgin.net

ABAYOMI-COLE, Bimbisara Alfred (Bimbi). b 58. CCC Ox BA80 MA85. Trin Coll Bris BA94. **d** 94 **p** 95. C Deptford St Pet *S'wark* 94-98; V Crofton St Paul *Roch* from 98. *St Paul's Vicarage, 2 Oakwood Road, Orpington BR6 8JH* Tel and fax (01689) 852939 E-mail bimbi@anthea1.freeserve.co.uk

ABBEY, Canon Anthony James. b 36. Selw Coll Cam BA59 MA63 ARCO61. Ely Th Coll 59. **d** 61 **p** 62. C Wanstead St Mary *Chelmsf* 61-63; C Laindon w Basildon 63-67; R Sandon 67-76; V Epping St Jo 76-92; Hon Can Chelmsf Cathl 85-01; P-in-c Doddinghurst and Mountnessing 92-01; rtd 01. *Canons Piece, 2 The Squires, Blackminster, Evesham WR11 7XN* Tel (01386) 834119

ABBOTT, Barry Joseph. b 59. Sunderland Univ BA98 Newc Coll of Arts DipEH81 DipOHS83 DipTSM83 MIEH. NEOC DipHE92. **d** 92 **p** 93. NSM Bishopwearmouth Ch Ch *Dur* 92-98; NSM Silksworth 98-00; P-in-c Lumley from 00; AD Chester-le-Street from 02. *Christ Church Vicarage, Great Lumley, Chester le Street DH3 4ER* Tel 0191-388 2228 Mobile 07801-074909

ABBOTT, Charles Peter. b 25. Maryland Univ 60. Pecusa Ord Course. **d** 62 **p** 62. USA 62-66; C Oxhey St Matt *St Alb* 66-70; Asst Chapl Alleyn's Foundn Dulwich 70-72; C Dulwich St Barn *S'wark* 70-72; V Southway *Ex* 72-78; V Whitgift w Adlingfleet and Eastoft *Sheff* 78-79; rtd 86. *1 St Augustine's Close, Cooden Drive, Bexhill-on-Sea TN39 3AZ*

ABBOTT, Christopher Ralph. b 38. Univ of Wales (Lamp) BA59. Wells Th Coll 59. **d** 61 **p** 62. C Camberwell St Giles *S'wark* 61-67; C Portsea St Mary *Portsm* 67-70; V Portsea St Cuth 70-87; P-in-c Gt Milton *Ox* 87-88; P-in-c Lt Milton 87-88; R Gt w Lt Milton and Gt Haseley 88-93; R Chailey *Chich* 93-00; Chapl Chailey Heritage Hosp Lewes 95-00; rtd 00; Perm to Offic *Chich* from 01; Chapl SSB from 02. *6 Winchfield Crescent, Havant PO9 3SP* Tel (023) 9247 7376

ABBOTT, David John. b 52. CertEd. St Jo Coll Nottm LTh. **d** 87 **p** 88. C Biddulph *Lich* 87-90; C Tunbridge Wells St Jas *Roch* 90-92; TV Tunbridge Wells St Jas w St Phil 92-98; V Sunnyside w Bourne End *St Alb* from 98. *The Vicarage, Ivy House Lane, Berkhamsted HP4 2PP* Tel (01442) 865100
E-mail ssvicarage@yahoo.co.uk

ABBOTT, David Robert. b 49. Edin Univ BD72 Birm Univ DipTh73. Qu Coll Birm 72. **d** 74 **p** 75. C Kirkby *Liv* 74-78; C Ditton St Mich 78-80; R Ashton-in-Makerfield H Trin from 80. *The Rectory, North Ashton, Wigan WN4 0QF* Tel (01942) 727241

ABBOTT, Miss Geraldine Mary. b 33. SRN55 SCM58 Open Univ BA77 Lon Univ MTh85. Oak Hill Th Coll BA82. **dss** 86 **d** 87 **p** 94. Tutor Oak Hill Th Coll 86-96; St Alb St Paul *St Alb* 86-87; Hon Par Dn 87-94; Hon C from 94. *2 Wheatleys, St Albans AL4 9UE* Tel (01727) 860869

ABBOTT, Mrs Kathleen Frances. b 60. STETS 96. **d** 99 **p** 00. NSM St Helens *Portsm* 99-02; P-in-c Wootton from 02. *The Rectory, 32 Church Road, Wootton Bridge, Ryde PO33 4PX* Tel (01983) 882213 Fax as telephone
E-mail kath.abbott@btinternet.com

ABBOTT, Canon Nigel Douglas Blayney. b 37. Open Univ BA87. Bps' Coll Cheshunt 58. **d** 61 **p** 62. C Northampton St Mich *Pet* 61-64; C Wanstead St Mary *Chelmsf* 64-66; Chapl St Jo Sch Tiffield 66-69; V Earls Barton *Pet* 69-73; V Cov H Trin *Cov* 73-80; Provost St Jo Cathl Oban *Arg* 80-86; R Oban St Jo 80-86; TR Hemel Hempstead *St Alb* 86-96; RD Hemel Hempstead 94-96; Chmn BSR 94-00; R Much Hadham 96-02; Hon Can St Alb 90-02; rtd 02. *1 Cambridge Road, Ely CB7 4HJ* Tel (01353) 662256 E-mail ndbabbot@waitrose.com

ABBOTT, Peter John. b 48. S Glam Inst HE CQSW86. St Mich Coll Llan 94. **d** 96 **p** 97. C Neath w Llantwit *Llan* 96-98; C Merthyr Tydfil Ch Ch 98-00; P-in-c Llangeinor w Nantymoel and Wyndham 00-02; V Cwmogwr from 02. *The Vicarage, Coronation Street, Ogmore Vale, Bridgend CF32 7HE* Tel (01656) 840248

ABBOTT, Stephen Anthony. b 43. K Coll Cam BA65 MA69 Edin Univ BD68 Harvard Univ ThM69. Edin Th Coll 66. **d** 69 **p** 70. C Deal St Leon *Cant* 69-72; Chapl K Coll Cam 72-75; C Cambridge St Matt *Ely* 75-76; Asst Chapl Bris Univ *Bris* 77-80; Hon C Clifton St Paul 77-80; Perm to Offic from 81. *29 Withleigh Road, Bristol BS4 2LG* Tel 0117-977 9270
E-mail stephen.abbott@withleigh.freeserve.co.uk

ABBOTT, Stephen John. b 62. Qu Mary Coll Lon LLB83. Linc Th Coll BTh92. **d** 92 **p** 93. C E Dereham and Scarning *Nor* 92-95; TV Penistone and Thurlstone *Wakef* 95-97; R Brandon and Santon Downham w Elveden *St E* 97-00; P-in-c Gt Barton from 00. *The Vicarage, Church Road, Great Barton, Bury St Edmunds IP31 2QR* Tel (01284) 787274
E-mail sj.abbott@lineone.net

ABBOTT, Mrs Valerie Ann. b 45. Keele Univ BA68 Bris Univ DipTh69 MLitt00. Dalton Ho Bris 68 Trin Coll Bris 98. **d** 00 **p** 01. NSM Knowle St Martin *Bris* 00-01; NSM Brislington St Chris and St Cuth from 01. *29 Withleigh Road, Bristol BS4 2LG* Tel and fax 0117-977 9270 Mobile 07979-997968
E-mail val.abbott@btinternet.com

ABDY, John Channing. b 38. Nottm Univ BA63. Cuddesdon Coll 63. **d** 65 **p** 66. C Leagrave *St Alb* 65-69; C N Mymms 69-72; V Kings Walden 72-79; V S Woodham Ferrers *Chelmsf* 79-85; V Walthamstow St Pet 85-91; V Burrington and Churchill *B & W* from 91. *The Parsonage, Bristol Road, Langford, Bristol BS40 5JE* Tel (01934) 852295

ABECASSIS, Mrs Joanna Margaret. b 54. Girton Coll Cam BA75 MA79 PhD81. WEMTC 99. **d** 02 **p** 03. C Tavistock and Gulworthy *Ex* from 02. *32 Plym Crescent, Tavistock PL19 9HX* Tel (01822) 615501 E-mail joanna@abecassis.freeserve.co.uk

ABEL, David John. b 31. S'wark Ord Course 71. **d** 74 **p** 75. NSM Crowhurst *S'wark* 74-85; NSM Lingfield and Crowhurst 85-92; Perm to Offic 92-98; Perm to Offic *Chich* from 98. *Balcombe Mill, Mill Lane, Balcombe, Haywards Heath RH17 6QT* Tel (01444) 811121

ABELL, Canon Brian. b 37. Nottm Univ BA61 DipEd Leeds Univ MA95. Cuddesdon Coll 61. **d** 63 **p** 64. C Lightcliffe *Wakef* 63-66; C-in-c Mixenden CD 66-68; Lect Linc Coll of Tech 68-69; Chapl Trent Coll Nottm 70-74; V Thorner *Ripon* 74-82; V Far Headingley St Chad 82-86; Deputation Appeals Org CECS 86-89; V Masham and Healey *Ripon* 89-00; Hon Can Ripon Cathl 99-00; rtd 00; Perm to Offic *Ripon* from 00. *Manor Garth, 1 Manor Road, Harrogate HG2 0HP* Tel (01423) 526112 Fax as telephone E-mail brian.abell@virgin.net

ABELL, George Derek. b 31. Selw Coll Cam BA54 MA68. Qu Coll Birm 54. **d** 56 **p** 57. C Stoke upon Trent *Lich* 56-60; C Wolverhampton 60-64; R Bridgnorth St Mary *Heref* 64-70; P-in-c Oldbury 64-70; Australia 70-73; R Withington w Westhide and Weston Beggard *Heref* 73-81; R Withington w Westhide 81-83; P-in-c Sutton St Nicholas w Sutton St Michael 76-81; R 81-83; Preb Heref Cathl 82-83; V Basing *Win* 83-88; rtd 88; Perm to Offic *Heref* from 88. *51 Buckfield Road, Leominster HR6 8SF* Tel (01568) 614564

ABELL, Peter John. b 45. Chich Th Coll 67. **d** 70 **p** 71. C Churchdown St Jo *Glouc* 70-74; Chapl RAF 74-98; R Kilkhampton w Morwenstow *Truro* from 98. *The Rectory, East Road, Kilkhampton, Bude EX23 9QS* Tel (01288) 321314 Fax as telephone E-mail rectorkilkstow@aol.com

ABERDEEN AND ORKNEY, Bishop of. See CAMERON, The Most Revd Andrew Bruce

ABERDEEN AND ORKNEY, Dean of. See STRANRAER-MULL, The Very Revd Gerald Hugh

ABERDEEN, Provost of. See KILGOUR, The Very Revd Richard Eifl

ABERNETHY, Canon Alan Francis. b 57. QUB BA78 BD89 TCD DipTh81. CITC 81. **d** 81 **p** 82. C Dundonald *D & D* 81-84; C Lecale Gp 84-86; I Helen's Bay 86-90; I Ballyholme from 90; Preb Down Cathl from 00. *Ballyholme Rectory, 3 Ward Avenue, Bangor BT20 5JW* Tel (028) 9146 6357 Fax as telephone E-mail ballyholme@btinternet.com

ABERNETHY, David Terence Phillips (Terry). b 42. St D Coll Lamp 64. **d** 65 **p** 66. C Abergele *St As* 65-72; Bermuda 72-84; V Beaulieu and Exbury and E Boldre *Win* from 84. *The Vicarage, Palace Lane, Beaulieu SO42 7YG* Tel (01590) 612242 Fax as telephone
E-mail t.abernethy@beaulieu-rectory.org.uk

ABINGTON, David John Barringer. b 48. EAMTC 91. **d** 94 **p** 95. C Newport w Longford and Chetwynd *Lich* 94-96; C Newport w Longford, Chetwynd and Forton 96-98; R Adderley, Ash, Calverhall, Ightfield etc 98-02; R Brading w Yaverland *Portsm* from 02. *The Vicarage, Mall Road, Brading, Sandown PO36 0DE* Tel (01983) 407262 Mobile 07855-086978

ABLETT, Edwin John. b 37. Clifton Th Coll 64. **d** 67 **p** 68. C Sneinton St Chris w St Phil *S'well* 67-70; R High and Gd Easter w Margaret Roding *Chelmsf* 70-73; Chile 73-75; SAMS 73-75; C Gt Baddow *Chelmsf* 75-78; V Newchapel *Lich* 78-82; V S Westoe *Dur* 82-86; V Tibshelf *Derby* 86-00; rtd 00; Perm to Offic *St D* from 00. *22 Dolaufan, Burry Port SA16 0RD* Tel (01554) 834709 Fax as telephone E-mail john.ablett@tinyworld.co.uk

ABLETT, Mrs Jennifer Vera. b 46. Dioc OLM tr scheme 97. **d** 00 **p** 01. OLM Henley, Claydon and Barham *St E* from 00. *10 Phillipps Road, Barham, Ipswich IP6 0AZ* Tel (01473) 830205

ABLEWHITE, Stanley Edward. b 30. Birm Univ BSocSc59 LSE CASS60. Tyndale Hall Bris 64 Wycliffe Hall Ox 73. **d** 73 **p** 74. C Much Woolton *Liv* 73-77; V Brough w Stainmore *Carl* 77-84; Min Aldridge *Lich* 84-90; P-in-c Swindon 90-96; P-in-c Himley 90-96; rtd 96. *33 Paddock Lane, Aldridge, Walsall WS9 0BP* Tel (01922) 658710

ABRAHAM, Brian. b 42. Dioc OLM tr scheme 97. **d** 00 **p** 01. OLM Burscough Bridge *Liv* from 00. *31 Pardoe Court, Junction Lane, Burscough, Ormskirk L40 5XH* Tel (01704) 892547

ABRAHAM, Canon David Alexander. b 37. AKC61. **d** 62 **p** 63. C Oswestry St Oswald *Lich* 62-63; C Gt Wyrley 63-65; C Sprowston *Nor* 65-67; V Ormesby w Scratby 67-81; R Oxborough w Foulden and Caldecote 81-87; R Cockley Cley w Gooderstone 81-87; V Didlington 81-87; R Gt and Lt Cressingham w Threxton 81-87; R Hilborough w Bodney 81-87; P-in-c Nor St Giles 87-96; Chapl Asst Norfolk and Nor Hosp 87-91; V Thorpe St Matt *Nor* 96-00; Hon Can Nor Cathl 95-00; rtd 00; Perm to Offic *Nor* from 00. *170 Desmond Drive, Old Catton, Norwich NR6 7JW* Tel (01603) 402797

ABRAHAM, Canon John Callis Harford. b 31. Univ of W Aus BA52. Westcott Ho Cam 53. **d** 55 **p** 56. C Wigan St Anne *Liv* 55-57; Australia 57-67 and from 68; C Northam Perth 57-60; R Wongan Hills 60-62; Vice-Warden Wollaston Th Coll and R Graylands 63-67; P-in-c City Beach 66-67; Lic to Offic *Birm* 67-68; R Applecross Perth 68-76; Can Perth 71-84; R Leeming 76-79; Chapl Home Miss 79-81; R Wembley 81-89; R Albany 90-94; Can Bunbury 92-94; rtd 94. *10 Royston Park, Pioneer Street, Albany, W Australia 6330* Tel (0061) (8) 9841 1809

ABRAHAM, Richard James. b 42. Liv Univ BA63. Ridley Hall Cam 64. **d** 66 **p** 67. C Warrington St Ann *Liv* 66-70; C Golborne 70-73; V Bickershaw 73-78; V Ewerby w Evedon *Linc* 78-82; R Kirkby Laythorpe w Asgarby 78-82; R Kirkby Laythorpe from 82. *The Rectory, Kirkby Laythorpe, Sleaford NG34 9NY* Tel (01529) 304804

ABRAHAMS, Peter William. b 42. Southn Univ BA77. Sarum Th Coll 77. **d** 78 **p** 79. C Bitterne Park *Win* 78-82; C Old Brumby *Linc* 82-84; V Mitcham Ascension *S'wark* 84-91; TV Riverside *Ox* from 91. *The Vicarage, Mill Street, Colnbrook, Slough SL3 0JJ* Tel and fax (01753) 682156 *or* tel 687654 E-mail frapeter@aol.com

ABRAM, Paul Robert Carrington. b 36. Keble Coll Ox BA62 MA65. Chich Th Coll 60. **d** 62 **p** 63. C Redcar *York* 62-65; CF 65-89; V Salcombe *Ex* 89-96; Miss to Seafarers from 89; rtd 96; Chapl to The Queen from 96; Chapl St Pet-ad-Vincula at HM Tower of Lon from 96; Dep P in O from 96. *1 The Green, HM Tower of London, London EC3N 4AB* Tel (020) 7488 5689 Fax 7702 2214

ABRAM, Steven James. b 50. Lon Univ DipTh74 BD76. Oak Hill Th Coll 71. **d** 76 **p** 77. C Biddulph *Lich* 76-79; C Heatherlands St Jo *Sarum* 79-83; Libya 83-84; C Stratford-on-Avon w Bishopton *Cov* 84; V Alderholt *Sarum* 84-90; V Daubhill *Man* from 90. *St George's Vicarage, Roseberry Street, Bolton BL3 4AR* Tel (01204) 61067 E-mail sj@abram.org.uk

ABREY, Mark Evans John. b 66. Ripon Coll Cuddesdon BTh93. **d** 93 **p** 94. C W Derby St Mary *Liv* 93-97; P-in-c Anfield St Marg 97-01; Chapl Royal Liverpool Children's NHS Trust 97-99; R Chase *Ox* from 01; P-in-c Ascott under Wychwood from 01. *The Vicarage, Church Road, Chadlington, Chipping Norton OX7 3LY* Tel (01608) 676572 E-mail mark@abreys.com

ABREY, Philip James. b 51. N Ord Course 82. **d** 85 **p** 86. NSM Hindley All SS *Liv* 85-90; C Caversham St Pet and Mapledurham etc *Ox* 90-00; Min Caversham Park LEP 90-00; Co Ecum Officer (Berks) 96-00; Perm to Offic *Cov* from 01; Chapl HM Pris The Mount from 02. *HM Prison, The Mount, Molyneux Avenue, Bovingdon, Hemel Hempstead HP3 0NZ* Tel (01442) 834363

ABSALOM, Alexander James David Edward. b 69. St Jo Coll Dur BA91. Cranmer Hall Dur Dip Minl Studies 94. **d** 94 **p** 95. C Cranham *Chelmsf* 94-98; Perm to Offic *Sheff* from 98. *The King's Centre, Union Road, Sheffield S11 9EH* Tel 0114-250 7277 E-mail kcoffice@jubilee.net

ABSALOM, Hugh Pryse. b 10. Fitzw Ho Cam BA31 MA36 Lon Univ BD56. **d** 36 **p** 37. C Abergavenny H Trin *Mon* 36-39; C Torquay St Luke *Ex* 39-43; Chapl RAFVR 43-49; Canada 49-52; C Brixham *Ex* 52-53; V Friday Bridge *Ely* 53-57; V Coldham 53-57; V Lucton w Eyton *Heref* 57-61; C-in-c Croft w Yarpole 57-61; Chapl and Master Lucton Sch 57-61; Chapl St Hild Coll Dur 61-73; Chapl and Sen Lect St Hild's Tr Coll Dur 61-73; R Walton W w Talbenny and Haroldston W *St D* 73-77; rtd 77. *43 Pine Walk, Carshalton SM5 4ES*

ABSOLON, Michael John. b 33. St Jo Coll Cam BA54 MA59 Lon Hosp BChir57 MB57 FRCS FRCOPhth. Wycliffe Hall Ox 95. **d** 96 **p** 97. NSM Micheldever and E Stratton, Woodmancote etc *Win* 96-98; NSM Chipping Campden w Ebrington *Glouc* 98-99 and from 00; Perm to Offic 99-00. *Oakham House, Ebrington, Chipping Campden GL55 6NL* Tel (01386) 593123

ABUJA, Bishop of. See AKINOLA, The Most Revd Peter Jasper

ABULEMOI, Joseph Oriho. See CHOUFAR, Joseph Oriho Abulemoi

ACARNLEY, Rita Kay. b 57. Girton Coll Cam BA79 MA83 Newc Univ MA94 St Jo Coll Dur BA98 DMS99. Cranmer Hall Dur 96. **d** 99 **p** 00. NSM Humshaugh w Simonburn and Wark *Newc* 99-00; Tutor TISEC from 00; Prov Local Collaborative Min Officer Scotland from 00; Perm to Offic *Newc* from 01. *Heron House, Wark, Hexham NE48 3HF* Tel (01434) 230224

ACHESON, James Malcolm. b 48. BNC Ox BA70 MA73. Sarum & Wells Th Coll 83. **d** 85 **p** 86. C Highgate St Mich *Lon* 85-88; TV Tisbury *Sarum* 88-94; Offg Chapl RAF 88-94; R Storrington *Chich* from 94. *The Rectory, Rectory Road, Storrington, Pulborough RH20 4EF* Tel (01903) 742888

ACHESON, Canon Russell Robert. b 16. Univ Coll Ox BA39 MA45 DipTh47. Wells Th Coll 45. **d** 47 **p** 48. C Bedminster Down *Bris* 47-49; Youth Chapl 49-54; Chapl Bris Univ 55-66; V Clifton St Paul 57-66; Hon Can Bris Cathl 64-66; V Much Wenlock w Bourton *Heref* 66-79; P-in-c Hughley w Church Preen 69-79; RD Condover 72-78; P-in-c Harley w Kenley 73-75; Preb Heref Cathl 74-79; P-in-c Shipton 76-79; P-in-c Easthope w Long Stanton 76-79; Warden of Readers 78-83; Can Res Heref Cathl 79-83; rtd 83; Perm to Offic *Heref* from 83; Perm to Offic *Ban* from 97. *1 Penras Terrace, Newborough, Llanfairpwll-gwyngyll LL61 6RS* Tel (01248) 440325

ACHONRY, Dean of. *Vacant*

ACHURCH, Peter William Hammond. b 37. ACT DipTh87 Tabor Coll (Australia) DipC&G98. Ridley Coll Melbourne 82 St Barn Coll Adelaide 85. **d** 82 **p** 84. Australia 82-00; C Port Lincoln 82-84; P-in-c Elliston w Lock and Wuddina 86; R 87-89; Par P Leigh Creek 89-93; TV Madeley *Heref* from 00. *Sutton Hill Vicarage, 1 Spencer Drive, Sutton Hill, Telford TF7 4JY* Tel (01952) 680004

ACKERLEY, Glyn James. b 57. HNC83. Cranmer Hall Dur 84. **d** 87 **p** 88. C Tonbridge SS Pet and Paul *Roch* 87-90; R Willingham *Ely* 90-94; R Rampton 90-94; V Chatham St Phil and St Jas *Roch* from 94. *The Vicarage, 139 Sussex Drive, Walderslade, Chatham ME5 0NR* Tel (01634) 861108 *or* 862498 E-mail glynackerley@lineone.net

ACKERLEY, Herbert. b 20. St Deiniol's Hawarden 60. **d** 61 **p** 62. C Atherton *Man* 61-64; R Ardwick St Matt 64-68; P-in-c Longsight St Clem 67-68; R Longsight St Matt w St Clem 68-71; R Longsight St Luke 71-85; rtd 85; Perm to Offic *Man* from 85. *Ches* from 86. *c/o Mrs D A Warren, 46 Clumber Road, Manchester M18 7LZ* Tel 0161-320 3709 *or* 0845 878 3310

ACKLAM, Leslie Charles. b 46. Birm Univ BEd71. Ripon Coll Cuddesdon 78. **d** 80 **p** 81. C Chingford St Anne *Chelmsf* 80-83; C Spalding *Linc* 83-85; V Spalding St Paul 85-93; P-in-c Linc St Faith and St Martin w St Pet from 93; Chapl Linc Univ from 96. *165C Carholme Road, Lincoln LN1 1RU* Tel (01522) 887827 E-mail leslie.acklam@ntlworld.com

ACKLAND, John Robert Warwick. b 47. **d** 82 **p** 83. Lic to Offic *S'wark* 82-88; Hon C Shooters Hill Ch Ch 82-88; Hon C Mottingham St Andr 82-94; Hon C Woolwich St Thos 94-96; Hon C Bellingham St Dunstan 96-03; Hon Chapl S'wark Cathl 98-03; P-in-c Forest Hill from 03; P-in-c Perry Hill St Geo from 03. *Priory Cottage, 39 Upton Road, Bexleyheath DA6 8LW* Tel (020) 8301 0718 E-mail johnackland1@compuserve.com

ACKROYD, David Andrew. b 66. Coll of Ripon & York St Jo BA90 St Jo Coll Dur BA97. Cranmer Hall Dur 94. **d** 97 **p** 98. C Lilleshall and Sheriffhales *Lich* 97-01; Asst Chapl R Wolv Hosps NHS Trust 01-02; C Ogley Hay *Lich* from 02. *25 Snowdrop Close, Clayhanger, Walsall WS8 7RN* Tel (01543) 454816 E-mail revandy@tinyworld.co.uk

ACKROYD, Dennis. b 36. Cranmer Hall Dur 67. **d** 70 **p** 71. C Newcastle w Butterton *Lich* 70-73; C Horsell *Guildf* 73-77; P-in-c Moreton and Woodsford w Tincleton *Sarum* 77-82; R 82-86; RD Dorchester 79-85; R Ewhurst *Guildf* 86-94; V Cleckheaton St Luke and Whitechapel *Wakef* 94-02; rtd 02. *17 Charles Street, Weymouth DT4 7JE* Tel (01305) 7781221

ACKROYD, Eric. b 29. Leeds Univ BA51 Liv Univ MA71 Leic Univ MA(Ed)86. St Jo Coll Dur DipTh54. **d** 55 **p** 56. C Newland St Jo *York* 55-58; Succ Birm Cathl *Birm* 58-60; Chapl K Sch Bruton 61-66; Lect Kirkby Fields Coll of Educn *Liv* 67-72; Sen Lect Nene Coll of HE Northn 72-85; rtd 85. *40 Lumbertubs Lane, Northampton NN3 6AH* Tel (01604) 717848

ACKROYD, John Michael. b 32. Lon Univ BSc53. Ripon Hall Ox 71. **d** 73 **p** 74. C Keighley *Bradf* 73-76; TV 76-81; V Keighley All SS 81; V Whalley *Blackb* 81-97; Chapl Calderstones Hosp Clitheroe 81-93; Chapl Calderstones NHS Trust 93-97; rtd 97; Perm to Offic *Blackb* from 97. *1 Calder Vale, Whalley, Clitheroe BB7 9SR* Tel (01254) 823943

ACKROYD, Peter Michael. b 60. Jes Coll Cam BA82 MA86 Fontainebleau MBA87 Edin Univ PhD02. Wycliffe Hall Ox BA93 DipTh94 MA00. **d** 94 **p** 95. C Denton Holme *Carl* 94-97; Sec Proclamation Trust 97-00; V Wootton *St Alb* from 02. *The Vicarage, Church Road, Wootton, Bedford MK43 9HF* Tel (01234) 768391 E-mail ackroyds@lineone.net

ACKROYD, Prof Peter Runham. b 17. Down Coll Cam BA38 Trin Coll Cam MA42 PhD45 Lon Univ MTh42 DD70 FKC69 St Andr Univ Hon DD70. Westcott Ho Cam 57. **d** 57 **p** 58. Lect Div Cam Univ 52-61; Hon C Cambridge H Trin *Ely* 57-61; Select Preacher Cam Univ 58; Prof OT Studies Lon Univ 61-82; Select Preacher Ox Univ 62 and 81; rtd 82. *155 Northumberland Road, Harrow HA2 7RB* Tel (020) 8429 0396

ACKROYD, William Lancelot. b 1900. Egerton Hall Man 31. **d** 33 **p** 34. C Salford Ch Ch *Man* 33-35; C Pendlebury St Jo 35-37; R Ardwick St Thos 37-42; V Bolton SS Simon and Jude 42-45; Gen Sec BFBS 45-47; R Old Trafford St Jo *Man* 47-53; V S Petherwin w Trewen *Truro* 53-60; V St Germans 60-64; V Eastleach w Southrop *Glouc* 64-68; rtd 68; C Stokenham w Sherford *Ex* 69-71; Perm to Offic *Truro* 72-03. *Elysian, Linden Avenue, Port St Mary, Isle of Man IM9 5ER*

ACLAND, Simon Henry Harper. b 41. Westcott Ho Cam 65. **d** 67 **p** 68. C Prestwich St Marg *Man* 67-69; New Zealand 69-71 and 75-85; Singapore 71-74; C Kensington St Mary Abbots w St Geo *Lon* 85-87; C Chelsea Ch Ch 87; C Chelsea St Luke and Ch Ch 87-93; Dir Post-Ord Tr 87-94; C Kensington St Mary Abbots w St Geo 93-94; Perm to Offic from 99; rtd 01. *87 Kennington Park Road, London SE11 4JJ* Tel (020) 7735 5898

ACONLEY, Carole Ann. b 51. Hull Univ BTh01. NEOC 99. **d** 02 **p** 03. NSM Langtoft w Foxholes, Butterwick, Cottam etc *York* from 02. *Hawthorn Farm, Sledmere Road, Langtoft, Driffield YO25 3BT* Tel (01377) 267219 E-mail caroleaconley1@tinyworld.com

ACREMAN, John. b 53. Oak Hill Th Coll 86. **d** 88 **p** 89. C Iver *Ox* 88-92; R Hook Norton w Gt Rollright, Swerford etc from 92. *The Rectory, Hook Norton, Banbury OX15 5QQ* Tel (01608) 737223 E-mail acreman@xalt.co.uk

ACWORTH, The Ven Richard Foote. b 36. SS Coll Cam BA62 MA65. Cuddesdon Coll 61. **d** 63 **p** 64. C Fulham St Etheldreda *Lon* 63-64; C Langley All SS and Martyrs *Man* 64-66; C Bridgwater St Mary w Chilton Trinity *B & W* 66-69; V Yatton 69-81; V Yatton Moor 81-90; P-in-c Taunton St Jo 81-84; P-in-c Taunton St Mary 81-85; V 85-93; Preb Wells Cathl 87-93; Adn Wells, Can Res and Preb Wells Cathl from 93. *The Old Rectory, The Crescent, Croscombe, Wells BA5 3QN* Tel (01749) 342242 Fax 330060 E-mail adwells@bathwells.anglican.org

ACWORTH, William Richard Philip. b 30. Ch Ch Ox BA52 MA56 Paris Univ DèsL70. **d** 63 **p** 63. In RC Ch 63-67; C Walthamstow St Mary w St Steph *Chelmsf* 68-70; P-in-c Lt Sampford 70-76; P-in-c Gt Sampford 74-76; Lect Bath Coll of HE 76-77; Lect Th Derby Lonsdale Coll *Derby* 77-83; Derbyshire Coll of HE 83-88; P-in-c Newton Tracey, Alverdiscott, Huntshaw etc *Ex* 88-96; TR Newton Tracey, Horwood, Alverdiscott etc 96-98; RD Torrington 94-97; rtd 98; Perm to Offic *Portsm* from 98. *91 Oaklands Road, Havant PO9 2RL* Tel (023) 9245 0567

ADAIR, Raymond. b 33. Ripon Hall 66. **d** 72 **p** 73. C Knottingley *Wakef* 72-75; C Sandal St Helen 75-77; V Sandal St Cath 77-87; V Brownhill 87-97; rtd 97. *15 Chestnut Fold, Upper Lane, Netherton, Wakefield WF4 4HW* Tel (01924) 274640

ADAIR, William Matthew. b 52. Open Univ BA. CITC 77. **d** 77 **p** 78. C Portadown St Mark *Arm* 77-78; Asst Chapl Miss to Seamen 78-80; C Lisburn Ch Ch Cathl *Conn* 80-84; I Kildress w Altedesert *Arm* 84-92; I Portadown St Columba from 92; Dioc Sec Min of Healing 95-99. *St Columba's Rectory, 81 Loughgall Road, Portadown, Craigavon BT62 4EG* Tel (028) 3833 2746

ADAM, Canon David. b 36. Kelham Th Coll 54. **d** 59 **p** 60. C Auckland St Helen *Dur* 59-63; C Owton Manor CD 63-67; V Danby *York* 67-90; Can and Preb York Minster 89-90; V Holy Is *Newc* 90-03; rtd 03. *The Old Granary, Warren Mill, Belford NE70 7EE* Tel (01668) 214770

ADAM, Gordon Angus James. b 62. SSC. SEITE 97. **d** 00 **p** 01. NSM Kentish Town St Silas and H Trin w St Barn *Lon* 00-03; NSM Boxmoor St Jo *St Alb* from 03. *167 Long Chaulden, Hemel Hempstead HP1 2JH* Tel and fax (01442) 246538 Mobile 07721-020334 E-mail gaja1962@aol.com

ADAM, Canon John Marshall William. b 09. Oriel Coll Ox BA31 MA36. Wycliffe Hall Ox 31. **d** 33 **p** 34. C Endcliffe *Sheff* 33-35; Chapl Sheff Cathl 35-36; India 36-39; Chapl Sheff Cathl *Sheff* 39-42; V Paddock *Wakef* 42-46; Home Sec Miss Coun of Ch Assembly 46-55; R Friern Barnet St Jas *Lon* 55-63; V Preston St Jo *Blackb* 63-69; Hon Can Blackb Cathl 64-74; RD Preston 67-70; V Broughton 69-74; rtd 74; Perm to Offic *Blackb* from 74.

7 Caton Green Road, Brookhouse, Lancaster LA2 9JL Tel (01524) 770030

ADAM, Lawrence. b 38. N Ord Course 82. **d** 82 **p** 83. C Thornton-le-Fylde *Blackb* 82-86; Dioc Video Production Co-ord 85-97; P-in-c Scorton 86-91; C W Burnley 91-97; P-in-c Ashton St Jas *Man* 97-99; TV Ashton 00-03; rtd 03. *23 Dryden Avenue, Cheadle SK8 2AW*

ADAM (née YATES), Mrs Lindsay Anne. b 69. Selw Coll Cam BA91 MA95 Barrister 92 K Coll Lon DipTh96. Ripon Coll Cuddesdon BTh99. **d** 99 **p** 00. C Bampton w Clanfield Ox 99-02; Chapl Pemb Coll Cam from 02. *The Rectory, 40 Church Lane, Girton, Cambridge CB3 0JP* Tel and fax (01223) 276235 *or* tel 338100 E-mail cha@pem.cam.ac.uk *or* laa@luxmundi.org

ADAM, Michael MacIntosh. b 48. Sarum & Wells Th Coll. **d** 84 **p** 85. C Stamford Hill St Thos *Lon* 84-87; rtd 88; Perm to Offic *Lon* from 88. *Flat 1, 112 Millfields Road, London E5 0AP*

ADAM, Canon Peter James Hedderwick. b 46. Lon Univ BD73 MTh76 Dur Univ PhD81. Ridley Coll Melbourne ThL69. **d** 70 **p** 71. Australia 70-72, 73-74 and from 82; C Ivanhoe St Jas 70-72; C Rosanna 72; Hon C Holborn St Geo w H Trin and St Bart *Lon* 72-73; C Essendon St Thos and Tutor Ridley Coll 73-74; Tutor St Jo Coll Dur 75-82; Hon C Dur St Cuth *Dur* 75-82; P-in-c Carlton St Jude 82-88; V 88-01; Adn Melbourne 88-91; Chapl Melbourne Univ 95-01; Can Melbourne from 96; Prin Ridley Coll from 01. *160 The Avenue, Parkville, Vic, Australia 3053* Tel (0061) (3) 9207 4800 Fax 9387 5099 E-mail principal@ridley.unimelb.edu.au

ADAM, William Jonathan. b 69. Man Univ BA91 Univ of Wales (Cardiff) LLM03. Westcott Ho Cam 92 Bossey Ecum Inst Geneva Cert Ecum Studies 94. **d** 94 **p** 95. C Beaconsfield *Ox* 94-97; C Witney 97-98; TV 98-02; P-in-c Girton *Ely* from 02; Dioc Ecum Officer from 02. *The Rectory, 40 Church Lane, Girton, Cambridge CB3 0JP* Tel (01223) 276235 Fax as telephone E-mail wja@luxmundi.org

ADAMS, Mrs Alison Mary. b 51. Girton Coll Cam MA73 Birm Univ BMus76 CertEd77 Sheff Univ MPhil93. EAMTC 94. **d** 97 **p** 98. NSM Burbage w Aston Flamville *Leic* 97-00; Dir Bloxham Project from 00. *29 Leicester Lane, Desford, Leicester LE9 9JJ* Tel (01455) 823674 E-mail alisonadams@leicester.anglican.org

ADAMS, Anthony John. b 42. St Jo Coll Nottm 83. **d** 85 **p** 86. C Wellesbourne *Cov* 85-89; R Weddington and Caldecote 89-01; P-in-c Butlers Marston and the Pillertons w Ettington from 01; P-in-c Alderminster and Halford from 01. *The Vicarage, Warwick Road, Ettington, Stratford-upon-Avon CV37 7SH* Tel (01789) 748137 E-mail stour.dene5@btinternet.com

ADAMS, Anthony Paul. b 41. St Alb and Ox Min Course 95. **d** 98 **p** 99. NSM Banbury St Hugh *Ox* 98-01; P-in-c Wootton w Glympton and Kiddington from 01. *The Vicarage, Castle Road, Wootton, Woodstock OX20 1EG* Tel (01993) 812543 E-mail adamsfamily1@supanet.com

ADAMS, Brian Hugh. b 32. Pemb Coll Ox BA54 MA57 Lon Univ DipTh56. Sarum & Wells Th Coll 77. **d** 79 **p** 80. Hon C Crediton *Ex* 79-81; Chapl St Brandon's Sch Clevedon 81-85; C Street w Walton *B & W* 86-88; RD Glastonbury 86-92 and 93-97; V Baltonsborough w Butleigh and W Bradley 88-97; rtd 97; Perm to Offic *B & W* from 97. *Manor Cottage, Weir Lane, Yeovilton, Yeovil BA22 8EU* Tel (01935) 840462 E-mail adamsbj@eurobell.co.uk

ADAMS, Brian Peter. b 47. FInstD FRSA Avery Hill Coll CertEd70 Lon Univ CertRS92 DiprRS93. S'wark Ord Course 90. **d** 93 **p** 94. NSM Tonbridge SS Pet and Paul *Roch* 93-99; P-in-c Chatham St Mary w St Jo from 99. *The Rectory, 65 Maidstone Road, Chatham ME4 6DP* Tel (01634) 843632 Mobile 07778-777824 E-mail b.adams@cableinet.co.uk

ADAMS, Mrs Celia. b 39. R Holloway Coll Lon BSc60 Cam Univ CertEd61. Sarum & Wells Th Coll 86. **d** 88 **p** 94. NSM Canley *Cov* 88-91; NSM Cov N Deanery 91-92; C Coventry Caludon 92-97; Asst to Dioc Dir of Educn 92-93; Asst Chapl Geo Eliot Hosp NHS Trust Nuneaton 97-01; rtd 01; Perm to Offic *Ban* and *Cov* from 01. *22 Frankwell Street, Tywyn LL36 9EW* Tel (01654) 711604

ADAMS, The Ven Charles Alexander. b 29. MBE73 CBE82 JP. AKC59. **d** 60 **p** 61. C Bishopwearmouth St Mich w St Hilda *Dur* 60-63; C Ox SS Phil and Jas *Ox* 63-66; C Tunbridge Wells St Barn *Roch* 66-68; St Vincent from 68; Miss to Seafarers from 68; Can Kingstown Cathl from 73; Adn St Vincent & The Grenadines 76-98; rtd 98. *St Mary's Rectory, Bequia, Northern Grenadines, Windward Islands* Tel (001784) 458 3234 Fax 457 3532 E-mail caadams@caribsurf.com

ADAMS, Capt Christopher John. b 40. **d** 98 **p** 99. C Luton St Fran *St Alb* from 98. *91 Byron Road, Lewsey, Luton LU4 0HX* Tel (01582) 529373

ADAMS, David. See ADAMS, John David Andrew

ADAMS, David James. b 58. Trin Coll Bris 95. **d** 97 **p** 98. C Wirksworth *Derby* 97-00; P-in-c Seale and Lullington 00-02; R Seale and Lullington w Coton in the Elms from 02. *The Rectory, Church Street, Netherseal, Swadlincote DE12 9AF* Tel (01283) 761179

3

ADAMS, David John Anthony. b 46. QUB BSc70 DipArch72. Bris Sch of Min 81. **d** 84 **p** 85. NSM Sea Mills *Bris* 84-97; C Henbury 97-00; V Longwell Green from 00. *The Vicarage, 85 Bath Road, Longwell Green, Bristol BS30 9DF* Tel 0117-983 3373 Mobile 07803-330727 E-mail djaadams@surfaid.org

ADAMS, Denis Leslie. b 23. Ox NSM Course 78. **d** 81 **p** 82. NSM Reading All SS *Ox* 81-82; C Wargrave 82-83; C Skegness and Winthorpe *Linc* 83-85; V Gainsborough St Jo 85-89; rtd 89; Perm to Offic *Linc* 89-01. *4 Collum Gardens, Ashby, Scunthorpe DN16 2SY* Tel (01724) 842554

ADAMS, Donald John. b 46. St Jo Coll Nottm 86. **d** 88 **p** 89. C Byfleet *Guildf* 88-93; P-in-c E Molesey St Mary from 93; Perm to Offic *S'wark* from 96. *The Vicarage, St Mary's Road, East Molesey KT8 0ST* Tel (020) 8979 1441 Fax as telephone E-mail cada@ukgateway.net

ADAMS, Douglas George. b 39. ALBC65 St Luke's Coll Ex CertEd69 MEd87. SW Minl Tr Course 86. **d** 89 **p** 90. NSM Bude Haven and Marhamchurch *Truro* 89-93; P-in-c St Mewan from 93; P-in-c Mevagissey and St Ewe from 00; Chapl Mt Edgcumbe Hospice 93-96. *The Rectory, St Mewan, St Austell PL26 7DP* Tel (01726) 72679 Fax 63264 E-mail dougstmewan@tinyworld.co.uk

ADAMS, George Ernest. b 12. Sarum Th Coll 37. **d** 39 **p** 40. C Fordington *Sarum* 39-42; P-in-c Stevenage H Trin *St Alb* 42-43; R Belchamp Otten *Chelmsf* 45-56; R Bulmer w Belchamp Walter 45-56; Chapl RAF 56-59; R Wrestlingworth *St Alb* 60-66; V Dunton 60-66; V Arlesey w Astwick 66-70; R Gillingham w Geldeston and Stockton *Nor* 70-80; rtd 80; Perm to Offic *Nor* from 82; Perm to Offic *St E* from 87. *4 Malthouse Court, London Road, Harleston IP20 9BU* Tel (01379) 853604

ADAMS, Gillian. *See* WILTON, Mrs Gillian Linda

ADAMS, Godfrey Bernard. b 47. Local Minl Tr Course. **d** 93 **p** 94. OLM Saddleworth *Man* from 93. *11 Springmeadow Lane, Uppermill, Oldham OL3 6EP* Tel (01457) 875126 E-mail godfreyadams@compuserve.com

ADAMS, Hubert Theodore. b 28. FCA. OLM course 96. **d** 98 **p** 99. OLM Blurton *Lich* from 98. *12 Earls Road, Trentham, Stoke-on-Trent ST4 8DG* Tel (01782) 641383

ADAMS, Ian Robert. b 57. R Holloway Coll Lon BA79. Ridley Hall Cam 95. **d** 97 **p** 98. C Thame w Towersey *Ox* 97-98; C Thame from 98. *8 Victoria Mead, Thame OX9 3HY* Tel (01844) 218832 E-mail gailian@waitrose.com

ADAMS, James Michael. b 49. Man Univ LLB71 Lon Univ PGCE79. St Jo Coll Nottm DipTh. **d** 82 **p** 83. C Luton St Mary *St Alb* 82-85; TV Cove St Jo *Guildf* 85-92; V Chislehurst Ch Ch *Roch* from 92. *Christ Church Vicarage, 62 Lubbock Road, Chislehurst BR7 5JX* Tel (020) 8467 3185 *or* tel and fax 8325 3557 E-mail michaeladams@fish.co.uk

ADAMS, Mrs Jayne Maxine. b 57. Westhill Coll Birm CertEd78. WMMTC 94. **d** 97 **p** 98. NSM Cotteridge *Birm* 97-99; NSM Nechells from 99. *6A Kings Gardens, Birmingham B30 1DX* Tel 0121-451 1961

ADAMS, John. b 38. Lon Univ DipEd66 Open Univ BA79. Linc Th Coll 68. **d** 70 **p** 71. C Skipton H Trin *Bradf* 70-72; C Bassingham *Linc* 72-73; Chapl St Piers Hosp Sch Lingfield 73-74; Hon C Keighley *Bradf* 76-79; P-in-c Bredenbury and Wacton w Grendon Bishop *Heref* 79-84; P-in-c Edwyn Ralph and Collington w Thornbury 79-84; P-in-c Pencombe w Marston Stannett and Lt Cowarne 79-84; V Macclesfield St Jo *Ches* 84-87; R Wimblington *Ely* 87-90; V Manea 87-90; R Hallaton w Horninghold, Allexton, Tugby etc *Leic* 90-96; P-in-c Moulton *Linc* 96-97; V 97-03; rtd 03. *17 Linden Drive, Burgh le Marsh, Skegness PE24 5BP* Tel (01754) 810366

ADAMS, Canon John Christopher Ronald. b 29. St Paul's Coll Grahamstown LTh55. **d** 55 **p** 56. Rhodesia 55-66; C Northolt Park St Barn *Lon* 67-68; C W Brompton St Mary 68-69; Zimbabwe 69-98; rtd 98; Perm to Offic *S'wark* from 01. *The College of St Barnabas, Blackberry Lane, Lingfield RH7 6NJ* Tel (01342) 870544

ADAMS, John David Andrew. b 37. TCD BA60 MA64 BD69 Div Test61 Reading Univ MEd74. **d** 62 **p** 63. C Belfast St Steph *Conn* 62-65; Asst Master Lacunza Academy Spain 65-67; Asst Master Tower Ramparts Sch Ipswich 67-70; Asst Master Robert Haining Sch Surrey 70-74; Hd Master St Paul's Secondary Sch Addlestone 74-82; Hd Master Weydon Secondary Sch Farnham 82-98; NSM Bourne *Guildf* 80-99; NSM The Bourne and Tilford from 99; Chapl to The Queen from 94; Consultant to Secondary Schs from 98. *Brookside Farm, Oast House Crescent, Farnham GU9 0NP* Tel (01252) 652737 E-mail j.david_adams@ntworld.com

ADAMS, John Mark Arthur. b 67. Reading Univ BSc89. St Jo Coll Nottm MA98. **d** 99 **p** 00. C Skegby *S'well* 99-02; C Bletchley *Ox* from 02. *14 Hamilton Lane, Bletchley, Milton Keynes MK3 5LU* Tel (01908) 366083 Mobile 07712-674824 E-mail rev-mark@ntlworld.com

ADAMS, John Peter. b 42. Lon Univ BD69. Oak Hill Th Coll 65. **d** 70 **p** 71. C Whitnash *Cov* 70-73; Hon Asst Chapl Basle *Eur* 73-74; Chapl Davos 74-75; Chapl Düsseldorf 75-76; C Gt Baddow *Chelmsf* 77-80; Miss Eur Chr Miss 80-91; Perm to Offic

Chelmsf 80-91; Hon Asst Chapl Vienna *Eur* 90-91; Asst Chapl Zürich 91-95; P-in-c Harmondsworth *Lon* 95-99; TV Shebbear, Buckland Filleigh, Sheepwash etc *Ex* 99-02; rtd 02. *The Leas, Kingscott, Torrington EX38 7JW* Tel (01805) 622161 E-mail john@adams1100.freeserve.co.uk

ADAMS, John Richard. b 38. St D Coll Lamp BA62 Lich Th Coll 62. **d** 64 **p** 65. C Falmouth K Chas *Truro* 64-68; C Bath Twerton-on-Avon *B & W* 68-72; C Milton *Win* 72-79; P-in-c Weymouth St Edm *Sarum* 79-90; V 90-95; Chapl Westhaven Hosp Weymouth 79-94; P-in-c The Winterbournes and Compton Valence from 95. *The Rectory, Martinstown, Dorchester DT2 9JZ* Tel (01305) 588241

ADAMS, Jonathan Henry. b 48. St Andr Univ MA73. Cranmer Hall Dur 73. **d** 76 **p** 77. C Upperby St Jo *Carl* 76-78; C Sunderland St Chad *Dur* 78-82; Soc Resp Officer 83-91; TV Willington Team *Newc* 91-96; Local Min Development Officer 91-96; P-in-c Byker St Silas 96-01; Perm to Offic from 01. *5A Tunstall Vale, Sunderland SR2 7HP* Tel 0191-525 1881 E-mail jonathan@openroad.fsnet.co.uk

ADAMS, Margaret Anne. *See* FREEMAN, Mrs Margaret Anne

ADAMS, Martin Philip. b 57. BA. Sarum & Wells Th Coll 88. **d** 90 **p** 91. C Sandringham w W Newton *Nor* 90-93; P-in-c Docking w The Birchams and Stanhoe w Barwick 93-95; V Docking, the Birchams, Stanhoe and Sedgeford 95-97; V Orrell *Liv* 97-03; R Aughton St Mich from 03. *The Rectory, 10 Church Lane, Ormskirk L39 6SB* Tel (01695) 423204 E-mail mpadams@cix.co.uk

ADAMS, Michael. *See* ADAMS, James Michael

ADAMS, Canon Michael John. b 48. St Jo Coll Dur BA77. Ripon Coll Cuddesdon 77. **d** 79 **p** 80. C Falmouth K Chas *Truro* 79-81; C St Buryan, St Levan and Sennen 81-83; P-in-c Lanlivery w Luxulyan 83-84; V 84-88; V St Agnes 88-99; V Newquay from 99; RD Powder 90-96; Hon Can Truro Cathl from 03; Perm to Offic *Ex* from 94. *20 St Michael's Road, Newquay TR7 1RA* Tel (01637) 872096 Fax as telephone E-mail vicar@st-michaels-newquay.org.uk

ADAMS, Nigel David. b 40. Sarum & Wells Th Coll 86. **d** 88 **p** 89. C Tile Hill *Cov* 88-91; C Coventry Caludon 91-92; TV 92-97; Asst Chapl HM YOI Onley 92-95; Sub Chapl HM Pris Birm 95-01; P-in-c Nuneaton St Mary *Cov* 97-01; rtd 01; Perm to Offic *Ban* and *Cov* from 01. *22 Frankwell Street, Tywyn LL36 9EW* Tel (01654) 711604

ADAMS, Olugboyega Adeoye. b 55. Illinois Univ BSc81 Univ of Kansas MSc82 Lon Univ PhD93. EMMTC 99. **d** 02 **p** 03. C Glenfield *Leic* from 02. *8 Lynmouth Close, Glenfield, Leicester LE3 8RW* Tel 0116-287 8224

ADAMS, Peter. Bris Univ CertEd52 Lon Univ AdDipEd72. Oak Hill Th Coll 91. **d** 91 **p** 92. NSM Towcester w Easton Neston *Pet* 91-95; Perm to Offic *Ex* from 94. *3 Copperwood Close, Ashburton, Newton Abbot TQ13 7JQ* Tel (01364) 654261

ADAMS, Canon Peter. b 37. K Coll Lon AKC65 Trin Coll Cam MA70. St Boniface Warminster 65. **d** 66 **p** 67. C Clapham H Trin *S'wark* 66-70; Chapl Trin Coll Cam 70-75; Warden Trin Coll Cen Camberwell 75-83; V Camberwell St Geo *S'wark* 75-83; RD Camberwell 80-83; P-in-c W Dulwich All SS and Em 83-85; V 85-92; V Addington 92-02; Hon Can S'wark Cathl 99-02; rtd 02. *26 Mansfield Road, South Croydon CR2 6HN* Tel (020) 8680 3191 E-mail canon.adams@talk21.com

ADAMS, Peter Anthony. b 48. K Coll Lon BD70 AKC70 MTh72. **d** 72 **p** 74. Lic to Offic *Eur* 72-73; C Ashford *Cant* 73-79; P-in-c Ramsgate H Trin 79-86; P-in-c Ramsgate St Geo 84-86; R Ramsgate H Trin and St Geo from 86. *Holy Trinity Rectory, Winterstoke Way, Ramsgate CT11 8AG* Tel (01843) 593593

ADAMS, Peter Harrison. b 41. Tyndale Hall Bris 63. **d** 68 **p** 69. C Kendal St Thos *Carl* 68-71; C W Bromwich Gd Shep w St Jo *Lich* 71-75; R Aldham *Chelmsf* 76-81; R Marks Tey 76-81; R Marks Tey w Aldham and Lt Tey 81-85; NSM Colchester St Jo from 85; Dioc Missr from 85. *4 St Jude's Gardens, St John's Estate, Colchester CO4 4PP* Tel (01206) 854041

ADAMS, Raymond William. b 58. Reading Univ BA79. Oak Hill Th Coll BA85. **d** 85 **p** 86. C Blackpool St Thos *Blackb* 85-88; C Padiham 88-90; TV Rodbourne Cheney *Bris* 90-92; RD Cricklade 97-99; V Haydon Wick from 02. *The Vicarage, 54 Furlong Close, Swindon SN25 1QP* Tel (01793) 634258

ADAMS, Richard. *See* ADAMS, John Richard

ADAMS, Richard John. b 48. Leeds Univ BA70. St Alb and Ox Min Course 94. **d** 97 **p** 98. C N Hinksey and Wytham *Ox* 97-01; V Fence-in-Pendle and Higham *Blackb* from 01. *The Vicarage, 12 Wheatcroft Avenue, Fence, Burnley BB12 9QL* Tel (01282) 617316 E-mail richard@gwyneth.net

ADAMS, Robin Thomas. b 49. QUB BSc76. Oak Hill Th Coll BA79. **d** 79 **p** 80. C Magheralin *D & D* 79-82; C Coleraine *Conn* 82-86; I Belfast St Aid 86-89; USA from 89; I Tecumseh St Pet 89-97; V Ch of the Word from 98. *14215 Lee Highway, Gainsville, VA 20155, USA* Tel (001) (703) 754 9673 E-mail theword@erols.com

ADAMS, Roger Charles. b 36. Em Coll Cam BA60 MA64. Tyndale Hall Bris 60. **d** 62 **p** 63. C Longfleet *Sarum* 62-65; C Uphill *B & W* 66-71; R Ramsden Crays w Ramsden Bellhouse

Chelmsf 71-78; SW Area Sec BFBS 78-84; P-in-c Plymouth St Aug *Ex* 84-85; TV Plymouth Em w Efford 85-90; V Paignton Ch Ch 90-01; rtd 01. *171 Elburton Road, Plymouth PL9 8HY* Tel (01752) 407287

ADAMS, Ms Ruth Helen. b 73. St Jo Coll Dur BA94 CITC BTh97. **d** 97 **p** 98. C Drumragh w Mountfield *D & R* 97-99; Chapl Trin Coll Cam from 00. *Trinity College, Cambridge CB2 1TQ* Tel (01223) 338472 E-mail rha20@cam.ac.uk

ADAMS, Stephen Paul. b 56. Ex Univ BSc78. Sarum & Wells Th Coll 85. **d** 87 **p** 88. C Swansea St Nic *S & B* 87-88; C Llwynderw 88-91; R Badby w Newham and Charwelton w Fawsley etc *Pet* 91-97; R Abington from 97; RD Northn from 01. *The Rectory, 5 Abington Park Crescent, Northampton NN3 3AD* Tel (01604) 631041 Fax as telephone
E-mail stephen@abingtonrectory.fsnet.co.uk

ADAMS (née DABIN), Susan. b 51. NTMTC 96. **d** 00 **p** 01. NSM Hullbridge *Chelmsf* from 00. *49 Crouch Avenue, Hullbridge, Hockley SS5 6BS* Tel (01702) 231825

ADAMS, Theo. *See* ADAMS, Hubert Theodore

ADAMS, William Thomas. b 47. Chester Coll of HE CertEd69 Open Univ BA74 Leic Univ MA91. EAMTC 97. **d** 00 **p** 01. NSM Helmdon w Stuchbury and Radstone etc *Pet* from 00. *Brookdale, Mill Road, Whitfield, Brackley NN13 5TQ* Tel (01280) 850683 E-mail will.adams@tesco.net

ADAMSON, Anthony Scott. b 49. Newc Univ BA70. St Jo Coll Dur 75. **d** 78 **p** 79. C High Elswick St Paul *Newc* 78-86; C Benwell Team 86-92; V Tweedmouth from 92; P-in-c Scremerston from 02; P-in-c Spittal from 02; AD Norham from 00. *The Vicarage, Main Street, Tweedmouth, Berwick-upon-Tweed TD15 2AW* Tel (01289) 306409

ADAMSON, Arthur John. b 38. Keble Coll Ox BA61 MA65. Tyndale Hall Bris 61. **d** 63 **p** 64. C Redhill H Trin *S'wark* 63-66; Chapl Trent Park Coll of Educn 66-69; C Enfield Ch Ch Trent Park *Lon* 66-70; Ind Chapl *S'wark* 70-74; V Battersea St Geo w St Andr 70-74; R Reedham *Nor* 74-80; Min Beighton and Moulton 75-80; P-in-c Cantley w Limpenhoe and Southwood 77-80; R Oulton St Mich 80-90; Chapl Lothingland Hosp 80-90; R Laceby *Linc* 90-98; R Laceby and Ravendale Gp 98-03; rtd 03. *24 Mill Lane, Cottesmore, Oakham LE15 7DL* Tel (01572) 812816 E-mail ajaca@compuserve.com *or* ajohnadamson@aol.com

ADAMSON, Paul. b 35. Leeds Univ BA58. Coll of Resurr Mirfield. **d** 60 **p** 61. C Southwick St Columba *Dur* 60-63; Br Guiana 63-66; Guyana 66-75; C Benwell St Jas *Newc* 75-77; V Cowgate 77-83; V Prudhoe 83-93; TV N Tyne and Redesdale Team 93-98; TR 98-00; RD Bellingham 98-00; rtd 00; Perm to Offic *Newc* from 01. *11 Carham Close, Corbridge NE45 5NA* Tel (01434) 633274

ADAMSON, Richard Edwin Aidan. b 56. Pepperdine Univ BA76 Hamburg Univ Dipl-Reg86. Coll of Resurr Mirfield 89 Sarum & Wells Th Coll 90. **d** 91 **p** 92. C Reddish *Man* 91-93; Chapl Bryanston Sch 93-94; USA from 94; P-in-c Lindsay St Jas 94-99; Chapl St Matt Episc Day Sch San Mateo from 99. *Charles House, 15 2nd Avenue, San Mateo, CA 94401, USA* Tel (001) (650) 347 2484 E-mail padrerick@aol.com

ADAN, Howard Keith. b 62. **d** 01 **p** 02. C Amsterdam w Den Helder and Heiloo *Eur* from 01. *Korvet 14, 1186 WE Amstelveen, The Netherlands* Tel (0031) (20) 453 9085 Fax 453 9086
E-mail howie@christchurch.nl

ADDENBROOKE, Peter Homfray. b 38. Trin Coll Cam BA59 MA68 Ex Univ PGCE60. Lich Th Coll 61. **d** 63 **p** 64. C Bakewell *Derby* 63-67; C Horsham *Chich* 67-73; P-in-c Colgate 73-98; Adv for Past Care and Counselling 73-93; rtd 98; Perm to Offic *Chich* from 99. *Oaks, Forest Road, Colgate, Horsham RH12 4SZ* Tel (01293) 851362

ADDIS, Arthur Lewis. b 11. TD. Worc Ord Coll 62. **d** 64 **p** 65. C Highcliffe w Hinton Admiral *Win* 64-66; R W Dean w E Grimstead *Sarum* 66-70; V Stratford sub Castle 70-79; rtd 79; Perm to Offic *Sarum* from 79. *78 Park Street, Salisbury SP1 3AU* Tel (01722) 500328

ADDISON, David John Frederick. b 37. Museums Assn Dip 73 K Coll Dur BA60 DipEd62 Birm Univ MA79 Bris Univ MLitt93. Wells Th Coll 64. **d** 66 **p** 71. C Rastrick St Matt *Wakef* 66-67; Perm to Offic *Bradf* 67-71; Hon C Manningham St Luke 71-73; Perm to Offic *Glouc* 77-79; Hon C Bisley w Oakridge 79-81; V Newland and Redbrook w Clearwell 81-02; Chapl R Forest of Dean Coll 89-02; rtd 02; Perm to Offic *Glouc* from 02. *28 Patterson Way, Monmouth NP25 5BS* Tel (01600) 719530

ADDISON, Philip Ives. b 29. K Coll Dur 49. Ely Th Coll 59. **d** 61 **p** 62. C Waltham Cross *St Alb* 61-64; C Bedford St Paul 64-66;

Chapl Bedford N Wing Hosp 64-66; Chapl R N 66-70; V Foleshill St Laur *Cov* 70-74; C-in-c Halsham *York* 74-78; V Owthorne and Rimswell w Withernsea 74-99; Chapl Withernsea Hosp 74-99; rtd 99; Perm to Offic *York* from 99. *10 Park Avenue, Beverley HU17 7AT* Tel (01482) 872714

ADDISON SMITH, Canon Anthony Cecil. b 18. Keble Coll Ox BA48 MA53. Linc Th Coll 48. **d** 49 **p** 50. C Berwick H Trin *Newc* 49-52; V Middlesbrough St Chad *York* 52-58; V Saltburn-by-the-Sea 58-64; R Long Marston 64-66; V Easingwold w Raskelfe 66-78; RD Easingwold 70-77; Can and Preb York Minster 76-83; V Selby Abbey 78-83; rtd 83; Perm to Offic *Ox* 83-85 and from 87; C Cookham 85-86; C Hambleden Valley 87. *5 Tierney Court, Marlow SL7 2BL* Tel (01628) 483288

ADDLEY, David Bernard. b 41. St Paul's Cheltenham CertEd64 Leic Univ DipEd69 Bradf Univ MSc73. Ox Min Course 91. **d** 92 **p** 93. NSM Claydon w Mollington *Ox* 92-94; NSM Ironstone 94-03; P-in-c Aston Cantlow and Wilmcote w Billesley *Cov* 03; Perm to Offic *Pet* from 95. *The Vicarage, Church Road, Wilmcote, Stratford-upon-Avon CV37 9XD* Tel 07941-728652 (mobile) Fax (01789) 292376

ADEKANYE, Joseph (Kehinde). b 47. Lon Bible Coll DipRS82 Liv Inst of Educn MA98. Immanuel Coll Ibadan DipTh72 Oak Hill Th Coll BA84. **d** 72 **p** 73. Nigeria 72-80 and from 84; Lect Abp Vining Coll of Th Akure from 94; Perm to Offic *Liv* 97-00. *Archbishop Vining College, PO Box 3, Akure, Nigeria* Tel (00234) (34) 233031

ADEMOLA, Canon Ade. b 62. Goldsmiths' Coll Lon BA91 N Lon Univ MA94. NTMTC 95. **d** 98 **p** 99. NSM Lt Ilford St Barn *Chelmsf* 98-02; V Leyton Em from 02; Can Ibadan from 03. *Emmanuel Vicarage, 149 Hitcham Road, London E17 8HL* Tel (020) 8539 2200 Mobile 07941-029084
E-mail orison@ntlworld.com

ADENEY, Harold Walter. b 14. OBE76. Qu Coll Cam BA35 MB BChir38 MA53. Trin Coll Bris. **d** 75 **p** 76. Burundi 75-82; Perm to Offic *St Alb* 83-98; Perm to Offic *Nor* from 92. *5 Coles Way, Reepham, Norwich NR10 4LW* Tel (01603) 871932

ADEY, John Douglas. b 33. Man Univ BSc54. Coll of Resurr Mirfield 56. **d** 58 **p** 59. C Forton *Portsm* 58-64; C Northolt St Mary *Lon* 64-67; V Snibston *Leic* 67-72; V Outwood *Wakef* 72-78; V Clifton 78; V Upton Priory *Ches* 79-81; V Hyde St Thos 81-82; V Newton in Mottram 82-89; R Roos and Garton in Holderness w Tunstall etc *York* 89-92; C Woodchurch *Ches* 92-95; C Coppenhall 95-98; rtd 98; Perm to Offic *Portsm* from 98. *90A Winter Road, Southsea PO4 9BX* Tel (023) 9273 4116

ADFIELD, Richard Ernest. b 31. Oak Hill Th Coll 62. **d** 64 **p** 65. C Bedworth *Cov* 64-67; V Whitehall Park St Andr Hornsey Lane *Lon* 67-77; V Kensington St Helen w H Trin 77-86; V Turnham Green Ch Ch 86-92; rtd 92; Perm to Offic *Chich* from 92; Chapl Brighton Health Care NHS Trust from 02; Man Chapl S Downs Health NHS Trust from 02. *363 Hangleton Road, Hove BN3 7LQ* Tel (01273) 732538

✠**ADIE, The Rt Revd Michael Edgar.** b 29. CBE94. St Jo Coll Ox BA52 MA56 Surrey Univ DUniv95. Westcott Ho Cam 52. **d** 54 **p** 55 **c** 83. C Pallion *Dur* 54-57; Abp's Dom Chapl Cant 57-60; V Sheff St Mark Broomhall *Sheff* 60-69; RD Hallam 66-69; R Louth w Welton-le-Wold *Linc* 69-75; P-in-c N w S Elkington 69-75; TR Louth 75-76; V Morton w Hacconby 76-83; Adn Linc 77-83; Can and Preb Linc Cathl 77-83; Bp Guildf 83-94; rtd 95; Perm to Offic *Portsm* from 95; Hon Asst Bp Portsm from 95; Hon Asst Bp Chich from 96. *Greenslade, Froxfield, Petersfield GU32 1EB* Tel (01730) 827266

ADKINS, Peter Vincent Alexander (Alex). b 44. Lon Univ DipTh68 Lanc Univ BA71 Lon Inst of Educn CertEd78. Kelham Th Coll 63. **d** 69 **p** 70. SSM 67-73; Tutor Kelham Th Coll 71-73; Jerusalem 73-75; Hon C Cambridge St Giles w St Pet *Ely* 76-78; Hon C Northolt St Mary *Lon* 81-83; P-in-c Hanworth St Geo 83-86; R 86-88; Adult Educn Officer 83-86; Burford Priory 89-93; Warden Edw King Ho *Linc* from 93; Gen Preacher from 93; Hon Succ Linc Cathl from 99. *Edward King House, The Old Palace, Lincoln LN2 1PU* Tel (01522) 528778 Fax 527308
E-mail enjoy@ekhs.org.uk

ADLAM, Keith Richard. b 44. STETS 00. **d** 03. NSM Binstead *Portsm* from 03; NSM Havenstreet St Pet from 03. *23 Queen's Road, Ryde PO33 3BG* Tel (01983) 616903 Fax 810270
E-mail kejo@jakaranda75.freeserve.co.uk

ADLEY, Ernest George. b 38. Leeds Univ BA61. Wells Th Coll 62. **d** 64 **p** 65. C Bideford *Ex* 64-67; C Yeovil St Mich *B & W* 67-70; V Taunton Lyngford 70-79; V Skegness and Winthorpe *Linc* 79-91; R Wantage Downs *Ox* from 91. *The Rectory, Church Street, East Hendred, Wantage OX12 8LA* Tel (01235) 833235

ADLINGTON, David John. b 51. AKC73. K Coll Lon 70 St Aug Coll Cant 73. **d** 74 **p** 75. C Clapham St Paul *S'wark* 74-77; C Bethnal Green St Matt *Lon* 77-80; P-in-c Stepney St Pet w St Benet 80-84; PV and Succ *S'wark* Cathl *S'wark* 84-87; PV and Succ Llan Cathl *Llan* 88-91; Dioc Dir of Educn 91-00; V St Hilary 91-94; TV Cowbridge 94-95; C Whitchurch 95-00; P-in-c Folkestone St Mary and St Eanswythe *Cant* 00-02; V from 02; Hon Min Can Cant Cathl from 01. *The Vicarage, Priory Gardens, Folkestone CT20 1SW* Tel (01303) 252947

ADNETT, Roy Gumley. b 14. Tyndale Hall Bris 39. **d** 42 **p** 43. C Blackb Ch Ch *Blackb* 42-44; C Denton Holme *Carl* 44-46; V Constable Lee *Man* 46-49; R Peldon w Gt and Lt Wigborough *Chelmsf* 49-55; V Chilcompton *B & W* 55-80; RD Midsomer Norton 78-81; R Chilcompton w Downside and Stratton on the Fosse 80-81; rtd 81; Perm to Offic *Leic* 81-96. *Bosbury, St James Close, Pangbourne, Reading RG8 7AP* Tel 0118-984 3781

ADOYO, Miss Eugeniah Ombwayo. b 54. Lon Bible Coll 84 Westmr Coll Ox BA86 MPhil90. **dss** 82 **d** 91 **p** 91. Kenya 82-94; Internat Sec Crosslinks 94-97; Hon C Hatcham St Jas *S'wark* 94-97; C S'wark Ch Ch and Chapl S Lon Ind Miss 97-02; TV Plaistow and N Canning Town *Chelmsf* from 02. *St Philip's Vicarage, 19 Abbey Street, London E13 8DT* Tel (020) 7474 4596

ADSETTS, Ms Marilyn Ann. b 47. St Jo Coll York CertEd69 Leeds Univ BEd70 Spurgeon's Coll Lon MTh00. EAMTC 98. **d** 00 **p** 01. C Rushmere St E from 00; V Rhymney *Mon* from 03. *The Vicarage, Lawn Terrace, Rhymney NP22 5LL* Tel (01685) 840500 E-mail mbygrace@aol.com

ADU-BOACHIE, Francis. b 60. Oak Hill Th Coll DipTh95. **d** 95 **p** 96. C Stonebridge St Mich *Lon* 95-01; V Wembley St Jo from 01. *The Vicarage, 3 Crawford Avenue, Wembley HA0 2HX* Tel (020) 8902 0273

ADYERI, James Joloba. b 58. Redcliffe Coll 96 Chelt & Glouc Coll of HE BA99. United Th Coll Bangalore 91. **d** 84 **p** 85. Uganda 85-88, 89-91, 92-96 and from 99; India 88-89 and 91-92; Perm to Offic *Glouc* 96-99. *PO Box 84, Mityana, Uganda* Tel (00256) (46) 23 36

AFFLECK, John. b 20. Liv Univ LLB48. K Coll Lon 68 St Aug Coll Cant 71. **d** 71 **p** 72. C Hutton *Chelmsf* 71-74; P-in-c Hawkchurch, Fishpond, Bettiscombe, Marshwood etc *Sarum* 74-80; R Marshwood Vale 80-86; rtd 86; Perm to Offic *Sarum* from 86. *23 St Nicholas Hospital, St Nicholas Road, Salisbury SP1 2SW* Tel (01722) 334659

AFFLECK, Stuart John. b 47. AKC69. St Aug Coll Cant. **d** 70 **p** 71. C Prittlewell St Mary *Chelmsf* 70-75; Asst Chapl Charterhouse Sch Godalming 75-78; Chapl 78-80; Warden Pilsdon Community 80-94. *3 Chislehurst Road, Richmond TW10 6PW*

AGAR, George. b 40. Edin Univ BSc63 Ox Univ PGCE64. N Ord Course 92. **d** 94 **p** 95. Hd Biddulph High Sch Stoke-on-Trent 94-96; NSM Sandbach *Ches* 94-99; NSM Hartford from 99. *128 Middlewich Road, Sandbach CW11 1FH* Tel (01270) 760191 E-mail geohil.agar@virgin.net

AGASSIZ, David John Lawrence. b 42. St Pet Hall Ox BA64 MA68 Imp Coll Lon PhD94. Oak Hill Th Coll. **d** 66 **p** 67. C Southampton St Mary Extra *Win* 66-71; V Enfield St Jas *Lon* 71-80; P-in-c Grays Thurrock *Chelmsf* 80-83; P-in-c Grays All SS 81-84; P-in-c Lt Thurrock St Mary 81-84; P-in-c W Thurrock 81-83; P-in-c Grays SS Pet and Paul, S Stifford and W Thurrock 83-84; TR Grays Thurrock 84-90; Hon Can Chelmsf Cathl 90-93; Dioc Development Rep 90-93; Perm to Offic 93-94; Kenya 98-00; Perm to Offic *S'wark* from 02. *23 St James's Road, Gravesend DA11 0HF* Tel (01474) 332193 E-mail david@agassiz.worldonline.co.uk

AGBELUSI, Dele Omotayo. b 51. Ahmadu Bello Univ Zaria MSc81. Immanuel Coll Ibadan DipTh85 Oak Hill Th Coll BA99. **d** 86 **p** 87. Nigeria 86-96; C Edmonton All SS w St Mich *Lon* 97-99; V Hornsey Ch Ch from 99. *Christ Church Vicarage, 32 Crescent Road, London N8 8AX* Tel (020) 8340 1656 *or* 8340 1566 E-mail agbelusi@aol.com

AGGETT, Miss Vivienne Cecilia. b 33. Sarum & Wells Th Coll 86. **d** 88 **p** 94. C Binley *Cov* 88-91; C Henleaze *Lich* 91-96; rtd 96; Perm to Offic *Cov* from 98; Asst Chapl Gtr Athens *Eur* from 01. *Balsi, Andros, Greece 84503* Tel (0033) (282) 41102

AGGREY, Solomon Samuel. b 49. BSc76. Immanuel Coll Ibadan MA84. **d** 80 **p** 82. Nigeria 80-88; Miss Partner CMS from 88; C Gorton Em *Man* 93-95; C Gorton St Jas 93-95. *58 Darras Road, Gorton, Manchester M18 7PA* Tel 0161-231 4094

AGNEW, Kenneth David. b 33. Jes Coll Cam BA58 MA62. Clifton Th Coll 58. **d** 60 **p** 61. C Lozells St Silas *Birm* 60-63; C Skellingthorpe *Linc* 63-68; C Birchwood 68-72; R Willand *Ex* 72-00; RD Cullompton 89-95; rtd 00; Perm to Offic *B & W* from 01. *Eastgate, 14 Limington Road, Ilchester, Yeovil BA22 8LX* Tel (01935) 842010

AGNEW, Kevin Raymond Christopher. b 59. Chich Th Coll. **d** 94 **p** 95. C Eastbourne St Mary *Chich* 94-98; V Roughey from 98. *Roffey Vicarage, 52 Shepherds Way, Horsham RH12 4LX* Tel (01403) 265333

AGNEW, Stephen Mark. b 54. Univ of Wales (Ban) BSc76 Southn Univ BTh81. Sarum & Wells Th Coll 76. **d** 79 **p** 80. C Wilmslow *Ches* 79-84; V Crewe St Jo 84-90; Chapl Bromsgrove Sch 90-99; V Claines St Jo *Worc* from 99. *The Vicarage, Claines Lane, Worcester WR3 7RN* Tel (01905) 754772 Mobile 07702-211719 E-mail revsmagnew@yahoo.com

AHRENS, Irene Karla Elisabeth. b 40. Berlin Univ Bonn Univ PhD69 Lon Bible Coll BA92 K Coll Lon MTh93. SEITE 93. **d** 95 **p** 96. NSM Kew St Phil and All SS w St Luke *S'wark* 95-99;

Asst Chapl Berlin *Eur* from 00. *Wildpfad 26, 14193 Berlin, Germany* Tel (0049) (30) 8972 7027 *or* 8256 5300 E-mail iahrens@compuserve.com

AIDLEY, Jessica-Jil Stapleton. b 42. Westf Coll Lon BSc67 UEA PhD73 PGCE84. Dioc OLM tr scheme 97. **d** 99 **p** 00. OLM High Oak, Hingham and Scoulton w Wood Rising *Nor* from 00. *The Old Woolpack, Morley St Botolph, Wymondham NR18 9AA* Tel (01953) 603362 Fax as telephone E-mail j.aidley@ttrs.co.uk

AIKEN, Nicholas John. b 58. Sheff Univ BA. Wycliffe Hall Ox 80. **d** 82 **p** 83. C Ashtead *Guildf* 82-86; Dioc Youth Officer 86-93; R Wisley w Pyrford from 93. *The Rectory, Aviary Road, Woking GU22 8TH* Tel (01932) 352914 E-mail rector@wisleywithpyrford.org

AIKEN, Simon Mark. b 62. St Andr Univ MTh85. Ripon Coll Cuddesdon 86. **d** 88 **p** 89. C Burnley St Matt w H Trin *Blackb* 88-91; C Heyhouses on Sea 91-94; V Musbury 94-99; V Longridge from 99. *The Vicarage, Church Street, Longridge, Preston PR3 3WA* Tel (01772) 783281 *or* 786240 Fax 786240 E-mail sridge@dialstart.net

AINGE, Canon David Stanley. b 47. Brasted Place Coll 68 Lon Univ DipTh74. Oak Hill Th Coll 70. **d** 73 **p** 74. C Bitterne *Win* 73-77; C Castle Church *Lich* 77-79; P-in-c Becontree St Alb *Chelmsf* 79-89; P-in-c Becontree St Jo 85-89; TR Becontree S 89-91; RD Barking and Dagenham 86-91; V Leyton St Mary w St Edw 91-96; P-in-c Leyton St Luke 91-96; V Leyton St Mary w St Edw and St Luke 96-03; RD Waltham Forest 94-00; R Gt Dunmow and Barnston from 03; Hon Can Chelmsf Cathl from 97. *The Vicarage, 3 The Charters, Church End, Dunmow CM6 2SJ* Tel (01371) 872504

AINSCOUGH, Malcolm Ralph. b 52. Liv Univ BEd76 Liv Inst of Educn DASE85. St Mich Coll Llan DipTh87. **d** 87 **p** 88. C Fleur-de-Lis *Mon* 87-90; C Chepstow 90-91; TV Cwmbran 91-95; V Newport St Steph and H Trin 95-03; R Hasland *Derby* from 03; V Temple Normanton from 03. *The Rectory, 49 Churchside, Hasland, Chesterfield S41 0JX* Tel (01246) 232486 E-mail ainscoughm@fsmail.net

AINSLEY, Canon Anthony Dixon. b 29. Oriel Coll Ox BA52 MA57 Univ of S Africa BA74. St Steph Ho Ox 53. **d** 55 **p** 56. C Burnley St Cath *Blackb* 55-60; S Africa 60-80; Adn All SS 73-80; Can St Jo Cathl Umtata 73-80; Hon Can from 81; Chapl Bordeaux w Riberac, Cahors, Duras etc *Eur* 81; V Blackpool St Steph *Blackb* 81-94; rtd 94; Perm to Offic *Bradf* 94-99. *187A Filey Road, Scarborough YO11 3AE*

AINSLEY, Peter Dixon. b 32. OBE87. St Steph Ho Ox 58. **d** 60 **p** 61. C Bury St Thos *Man* 60-62; Chapl RN 62-87; Chapl HM Pris Liv 87-88; Chapl HM Pris Garth 88-95; rtd 95; Perm to Offic *Blackb* and *Liv* from 95. *21 Ridge Close, Southport PR9 8JU*

AINSWORTH, Mark John. b 64. Lon Univ MTh92. Wycliffe Hall Ox 86. **d** 89 **p** 90. C Chipping Barnet w Arkley St Alb 89-93; USA from 93. *270 Bent Road, Wyncote, PA 19095, USA* Tel (001) (215) 517 8568 E-mail mjaec@earthlink.net

AINSWORTH, Michael Ronald. b 50. K Coll Lon LLB71 LLM72 Trin Hall Cam BA74 MA79. Westcott Ho Cam 72. **d** 75 **p** 76. C Scotforth *Blackb* 75-78; Chapl St Martin's Coll of Educn 78-82; Chapl N Ord Course 82-89; R Withington St Chris *Man* 89-94; TR Worsley from 94; AD Eccles from 00. *The Rectory, Walkden Road, Worsley, Manchester M28 2WH* Tel 0161-790 2362 Fax as telephone E-mail michael.ainsworth@i12.com

AINSWORTH, Paul Henry. b 46. JP. Man Poly BA81. N Ord Course 85. **d** 88 **p** 89. NSM Salterhebble All SS *Wakef* 88-92; C Golcar 92-96; TV Moor Allerton *Ripon* from 96. *St Stephen's Vicarage, Tynwald Drive, Leeds LS17 5DR* Tel 0113-268 7338 E-mail p.ainsworth@virgin.net

AINSWORTH, Peter. b 34. Lon Univ BD57. Coll of Resurr Mirfield 69. **d** 70 **p** 71. C Leeds St Wilfrid *Ripon* 70-74; TV Tong *Bradf* 74-77; V Fairweather Green 77-94; rtd 94; Perm to Offic *Wakef* 94-02 and *York* from 03. *34 Dulverton Hall, Esplanade, Scarborough YO11 2AR* Tel (01723) 340134

AINSWORTH-SMITH, Canon Ian Martin. b 41. Selw Coll Cam BA64 MA68. Westcott Ho Cam 64. **d** 66 **p** 67. C Mill Hill Jo Keble Ch *Lon* 66-69; USA 69-71; C Purley St Mark *S'wark* 71-73; Chapl St Geo Hosp Lon 73-94; Chapl St Geo Healthcare NHS Trust Lon from 94; Hon Can S'wark Cathl *S'wark* from 95. *107 West Side, London SW4 9AZ* Tel (020) 7223 5302, 8725 3071 *or* 8672 1255

AIPO RONGO, Bishop of. *See* AYONG, The Most Revd James Simon

AIRD, Donald Allan Ross. b 33. BSc84. AKC55. **d** 56 **p** 57. C N Wembley St Cuth *Lon* 56-59; C Sidmouth, Woolbrook and Salcombe Regis *Ex* 59-62; Youth Chapl *Ely* 62-68; V Swaffham Bulbeck 62-69; V Preston Ascension *Lon* 69-79; V St Marylebone St Mark Hamilton Terrace 79-95; rtd 95; Perm to Offic *Worc* from 95. *1 Mews Cottages, 81 Albert Road South, Malvern WR14 3DX* Tel (01684) 569603

AIRD, Robert Malcolm. b 31. Lon Univ BSc54. Westcott Ho Cam 75. **d** 77 **p** 78. C Burnham *B & W* 77-79; P-in-c Taunton Lyngford 79-84; V 84-87; R Dulverton and Brushford 87-94; rtd 96. *Arran Cottage, East Street, Chulmleigh EX18 7DD* Tel (01769) 581042

AIRD, Wendy Elizabeth. b 41. SEITE. **d** 00 **p** 01. NSM Streatham Immanuel and St Andr *S'wark* from 00. *85A Clarence Avenue, London SW4 8LQ* Tel (020) 8671 2592 Mobile 07711-301813

AIREY, Robert William. b 54. OLM course 96. **d** 99 **p** 00. OLM Holcombe *Man* from 99. *4 Pine Street, Haslingden, Rossendale BB4 5ND* Tel (01706) 224743

AIREY, Simon Christopher. b 60. Trin Coll Bris BA87. **d** 87 **p** 88. C Wilton *B & W* 87-90; Chapl Scargill Ho 90-93; TV Kingswood *Bris* 93-96; Asst P Nether Springs Northumbria Community 96-98 and from 02; C Bath Abbey w St Jas *B & W* 98-02. *The Northumbria Community, Nether Springs, Hetton Hall, Chatton, Alnwick NE66 5SD* Tel (01289) 388242

AISBITT, Joanne. *See* LISTER, Mrs Joanne

AISBITT, Michael. b 60. St Pet Coll Ox BA81 MA84. Westcott Ho Cam 81. **d** 84 **p** 85. C Norton St Mary *Dur* 84-87; C Kirkleatham *York* 87-90; V S Bank 90-96; R Whitby 96-97; TR Whitby w Aislaby and Ruswarp 97-00; R Attleborough w Besthorpe *Nor* from 00. *The Rectory, Surrogate Street, Attleborough NR17 2AW* Tel (01953) 453185

AISBITT, Osmond John. b 35. St Chad's Coll Dur BA57 DipTh61. **d** 61 **p** 62. C Ashington *Newc* 61-64; C Blyth St Mary 64-68; V Cleckheaton St Jo *Wakef* 68-75; V Horbury 75-78; V Horbury w Horbury Bridge 78-97; rtd 97; Perm to Offic *Carl* 97-00; P-in-c Nerja and Almuñécar *Eur* 00-02. *8 Stonecross Gardens, Ulverston LA12 7HA* Tel (01229) 585622

AITCHISON, Charles Baillie. b 45. ACP69 Bede Coll Dur TCert67 Newc Univ DAES74 New Coll Dur BEd85. LNSM course 85. **d** 93 **p** 98. NSM Peebles 93; NSM Innerleithen from 93. *Stepping Stones for Life, 76 High Street, Peebles EH45 8AQ* Tel (01896) 831491

AITKEN, Christopher William Mark. b 53. Dur Univ BA75. Westcott Ho Cam 76. **d** 79 **p** 80. C Finchley St Mary *Lon* 79-82; C Radlett *St Alb* 82-85; V Sprowston *Nor* 85-90; R Beeston St Andr 85-90; R Sprowston w Beeston 90-93; Chapl Sherborne Sch from 93. *Rosslyn House, Acreman Street, Sherborne DT9 3NU* Tel (01935) 813846

AITKEN, Leslie St John Robert. b 41. Open Univ BA75. Cranmer Hall Dur 62. **d** 65 **p** 66. C Worc St Barn w Ch Ch *Worc* 65-69; C Halesowen 69-73; P-in-c Wyche 73-80; R Blackley St Pet *Man* 80-99; Chapl Booth Hall Hosp Man 80-89; R Sutton, Huttoft and Anderby *Linc* from 99. *The Vicarage, Huttoft Road, Sutton-on-Sea, Mablethorpe LN12 2RU* Tel (01507) 441169

AITKEN, William Stuart. b 35. FCFI MSIAD CertEd. Cant Sch of Min 79. **d** 82 **p** 83. NSM Roch 82-86; C Orpington All SS 86-88; R Burham and Wouldham 88-96; Dioc Communications Officer 88-96; rtd 96; Perm to Offic *Roch* from 96. *18 Commissioners Road, Rochester ME2 4EB* Tel (01634) 715892

AITON, Jessica Haran. MA79 Jordanhill Coll Glas PGCE85. TISEC 98. **d** 01 **p** 02. C St Andrews St Andr *St And* from 01. *14 Chamberlain Street, St Andrews KY16 8JF* Tel (01334) 479546

AITON, Canon Robert Neilson. b 36. Univ of Wales BA59 DipEd60. Chich Th Coll 74. **d** 76 **p** 77. C E Grinstead St Swithun *Chich* 76-83; R Lavant 83-90; Chapl St Barn Hospice Worthing 90-95; V Durrington *Chich* 90-01; Can and Preb Chich Cathl from 99; rtd 01; Lic to Offic *Chich* from 01. *Fieldings, Joys Croft, Chichester PO19 4NJ* Tel (01243) 781728 E-mail maiton@talk21.com

AIZLEWOOD, John David. b 44. TCert65. LNSM course 95. **d** 98 **p** 99. OLM Winterton Gp *Linc* from 98. *36 King Street, Winterton, Scunthorpe DN15 9TP* Tel (01724) 732268 E-mail g4wzv@aol.com

✠**AJETUNMOBI, The Rt Revd Jacob Ademola.** b 48. Middx Univ BA93. Igbaja Sem Nigeria BTh73 Lon Bible Coll BA80. **d** 83 **p** 83 **c** 99. Bp's Chapl and V Ilesa St Marg Nigeria 83-88; Chapl to Nigerian Students in UK (CMS) 88-99; Miss Partner CMS 88-99; Bp Ibadan S from 99. *59 Milton Avenue, London NW10 8PL, or c/o Bishopscourt, PO Box 166, Ibadan, Nigeria* Tel and fax 020) 8969 2379 Fax (00234) (22) 810 1413 E-mail jacajet@aol.com

AKEHURST, Peter Russell. b 16. Reading Univ BSc38 Trin Hall Cam. Wycliffe Hall Ox. **d** 48 **p** 49. C Tonbridge SS Pet and Paul *Roch* 48-51; C Kennington St Mark *S'wark* 51; S Africa 51-70; R Didsbury St Jas *Man* 70-74; V Totland Bay *Portsm* 75-81; rtd 81; Perm to Offic *Bris* 86-89; Perm to Offic *Ox* 89-90 and from 99. *20 Emmbrook Court, Woolacombe Drive, Reading RG6 5TZ* Tel 0118-986 2946

✠**AKINOLA, The Most Revd Peter Jasper.** b 44. Virginia Th Sem MTS81 Hon DD93. Nigeria from 78; V Abuja St Jas 78-79; V Suleja St Jas 81-84; Prov Missr 84-89; Bp Abuja from 89; Abp Prov III from 97; Primate All Nigeria from 00. *PO Box 212, ADCP, Abuja, Nigeria* Tel (00234) (9) 523 6928 *or* 523 0989 Mobile 90-805853 Fax (9) 523 0986 E-mail abuja@anglican.skannet.com.ng

AKKER, Derek Alexander. b 46. Bradf Univ MA83. N Ord Course 85. **d** 88 **p** 89. C Mossley *Man* 88-90; C Bury St Pet 90-92; V Lever Bridge 92-97; TV Wolstanton *Lich* 97-99; V Hattersley *Ches* from 99. *St Barnabas' Vicarage, Hattersley Road East, Hyde SK14 3EQ* Tel 0161-368 2795

AKRILL, Dean. b 71. York Univ BA97. Ripon Coll Cuddesdon BTh00. **d** 00. C Swinton *Sheff* 00-01; C Wath-upon-Dearne from 01. *74 Doncaster Road, Wath upon Dearne, Rotherham S63 7AF* Tel (01709) 871107

ALBAN-JONES, Timothy Morris. b 64. MBE03. Warwick Univ BA85. Ripon Coll Cuddesdon 85. **d** 88 **p** 89. C Tupsley *Heref* 88-93; TV Ross 93-00; P-in-c Soham *Ely* 00-01; P-in-c Wicken 00-01; V Soham and Wicken from 02. *The Vicarage, Cross Green, Soham, Ely CB7 5DU* Tel (01353) 720423 E-mail vicar@soham.org.uk

ALBERS, Johannes Reynoud (Joop). b 47. Hogeschool Holland BTh92 Amsterdam Univ MTh. EAMTC 99. **d** 00 **p** 01. C Voorschoten *Eur* 00-02; C Amsterdam w Den Helder and Heiloo from 02. *Dorpsweg 134, 1697 KH Schellinkhout, The Netherlands* Tel (0031) (22) 950 1611 E-mail joopalbers@quicknet.nl

ALBIN, Colin Leslie. b 51. Cov Poly BA75 DCG78 Lanc Univ MA97. Cranmer Hall Dur 89. **d** 91 **p** 92. C Chadderton Ch Ch *Man* 91-94; V Witton *Blackb* 94-98; Bp's Adv on Inter-Faith Relns 94-98. *14 Matlock Close, Sale M33 3FA* Tel 0161-969 8929

ALBON, Lionel Frederick Shapland. b 31. CEng MIMechE60. St Alb Minl Tr Scheme 80. **d** 83 **p** 84. NSM Bromham w Oakley *St Alb* 83-88; NSM Bromham w Oakley and Stagsden 88-89; Ind Chapl 89-96; rtd 96; Lic to Offic *St Alb* from 96. *Greenways, 43 High Street, Stagsden, Bedford MK43 8SG* Tel (01234) 825754

ALBY, Harold Oriel. b 45. Witwatersrand Univ BA68 MA77. Sarum Th Coll 68. **d** 71 **p** 72. S Africa 71-89; C-in-c Forton *Portsm* 89-96; V Milton from 96. *St James's Vicarage, 287 Milton Road, Southsea PO4 8PG* Tel (023) 9273 2786

ALCOCK, Edwin James. b 31. AKC57. **d** 58 **p** 59. C Old St Pancras w Bedford New Town St Matt *Lon* 58-62; C Hillingdon St Andr 62-81; V N Acton St Gabr 81-01; rtd 01. *17 Westfields Road, London W3 0AX* Tel (020) 8896 2748

ALCOCK, Mrs Linda Mary. b 45. St Gabr Coll Lon TCert67. St Alb and Ox Min Course 96. **d** 99 **p** 00. OLM Shires' Edge *Ox* from 99. *Copperfields, Swan Lane, Great Bourton, Banbury OX17 1QR* Tel (01295) 750744

ALDCROFT, Malcolm Charles. b 44. Lon Univ DSocSc68 Liv Univ DASS71 Leeds Univ MA94. N Ord Course 79. **d** 82 **p** 83. NSM Alverthorpe *Wakef* 82-85; NSM Horbury Junction 85-93; Sub Chapl HM Pris and YOI New Hall 94-97; Sub Chapl HM Pris Wakef 96-97; R Cupar *St And* from 97; R Ladybank from 97; Chapl Stratheden Hosp Fife from 97. *St James's Rectory, 33 Millbank, Cupar KY15 5DP* Tel (01334) 653548 E-mail malcolm@aldcroft.freeserve.co.uk

ALDEN, Andrew Michael. b 65. Bris Univ BA88 Ex Univ PGCE89 Lon Univ MA98. Wycliffe Hall Ox 01. **d** 03. C Weston-super-Mare St Paul *B & W* from 03. *Somerset House, 20 Addiscombe Road, Weston-super-Mare BS23 4LT* Tel (01934) 620971 E-mail andrewjmalden@aol.com

ALDEN, Mrs Pamela Ann (Pat). b 42. St Gabr Coll Lon TCert67. Dioc OLM tr scheme 99. **d** 02. OLM Camberwell St Giles w St Matt *S'wark* from 02. *189 Upland Road, London SE22 0DG* Tel (020) 8693 5207 Mobile 07710-283710 Fax (020) 8693 6408 E-mail pat@alphaplus.co.uk

ALDER, Mrs Anne-Louise. b 63. STETS 99. **d** 02 **p** 03. C Cowes H Trin and St Mary *Portsm* from 02. *St Faith's Vicarage, St Faith's Road, Cowes PO31 7HH* Tel (01983) 289533 Fax as telephone E-mail louise.alder@lineone.net

ALDER, Eric Reginald Alfred. b 23. St Luke's Coll Ex 47 Lon Univ BA55 Cam Inst of Educn 64. Chich Th Coll 70. **d** 71 **p** 72. C Deal St Leon w Sholden *Cant* 71-80; P-in-c Woodnesborough 80-83; P-in-c Worth 80-83; P-in-c Staple 80-83; V Woodnesborough w Worth and Staple 83-90; rtd 90; Perm to Offic *Cant* from 90. *3 Hackington Terrace, Canterbury CT2 7HE* Tel (01227) 766783

ALDERMAN, Canon John David. b 49. Man Univ BA71 Selw Coll Cam BA79. Ridley Hall Cam 77. **d** 80 **p** 81. C Hartley Wintney, Elvetham, Winchfield etc *Win* 80-83; V Bursledon 83-92; R Dibden from 92; Hon Can Win Cathl from 01. *The Rectory, Beaulieu Road, Dibden Purlieu, Southampton SO45 4PT* Tel (023) 8084 3204

ALDERSLEY, Ian. b 42. FIBMS68. Wycliffe Hall Ox 89. **d** 91 **p** 92. C Allestree *Derby* 91-94; R Brailsford w Shirley and Osmaston w Edlaston from 94. *The Rectory, Church Lane, Brailsford, Derby DE6 3BX* Tel (01335) 360362 E-mail ian@aldersley.fsbusiness.co.uk

ALDERSON, Albert George. b 22. K Coll Lon 46. **d** 50 **p** 51. C Whitworth w Spennymoor *Dur* 50-54; V S Shields St Fran 54-69; P-in-c 69-72; V S Shields St Jude 69-72; R Penshaw 72-79; P-in-c Bilsdale Midcable *York* 79-80; P-in-c Hawnby w Old Byland 79-80; P-in-c Scawton w Cold Kirby 79-80; R Upper Ryedale 80-91; rtd 91; Perm to Offic *York* from 91. *c/o Mrs M E Potts, Chapel Garth, Old Byland, York YO62 5LG*

ALDERSON, Christopher Derek. b 21. AKC55. **d** 55 **p** 56. C Goring-by-Sea *Chich* 55-59; V Gt Bentley *Chelmsf* 59-67; R Lt Bentley 60-67; V Dunster *B & W* 67-82; P-in-c Brompton Regis w Upton and Skilgate 82-83; R 83-86; rtd 86; Perm to Offic *B & W* 86-90. *2 Milne Way, Newport PO30 1YF* Tel (023) 9282 1032

ALDERSON, Mrs Maureen. b 40. WMMTC 90. **d** 93 **p** 94. NSM Yardley St Cypr Hay Mill *Birm* 93-96; P-in-c 96-00; V 00-02; P-in-c Gainford *Dur* from 02; P-in-c Winston from 02. *The Vicarage, Low Green, Gainford, Darlington DL2 3DS* Tel (01325) 730261

ALDERSON, Roger James Ambrose. b 47. Lon Univ BD70 AKC71 Man Univ 76 Liv Inst of Educn PGCE93. St Aug Coll Cant. **d** 71 **p** 72. C Lawton Moor *Man* 71-75; C Barton w Peel Green 75-76; R Heaton Norris St Thos 76-85; V Bedford Leigh 85-92; V Cleadon Park *Dur* from 99. *St Cuthbert's Vicarage, 218 Sunderland Road, South Shields NE34 6AT* Tel 0191-456 2875 Mobile 07710-722817

ALDERTON-FORD, Jonathan Laurence. b 57. Nottm Univ BTh85. St Jo Coll Nottm 82. **d** 85 **p** 86. C Gaywood, Bawsey and Mintlyn *Nor* 85-87; C Herne Bay Ch Ch *Cant* 87-90; Min Bury St Edmunds St Mary *St E* 90-91; Min Moreton Hall Estate CD 91-94; V Bury St Edmunds Ch Ch from 94. *18 Heldhaw Road, Bury St Edmunds IP32 7ER* Tel (01284) 769956 *or* tel and fax 725391 E-mail ccmh@iname.com *or* revdjonathanford@minister.com

ALDIS, John Arnold. b 43. Univ of Wales (Cardiff) BA65 Lon Univ BD67. Clifton Th Coll 65. **d** 69 **p** 70. C Tonbridge SS Pet and Paul *Roch* 69-72; C St Marylebone All So w SS Pet and Jo *Lon* 72-77; Overseas Service Adv CMS 77-80; C Welling *Roch* 77-80; V Leic H Trin w St Jo *Leic* 80-89; Hon Can Leic Cathl 88-89; V W Kowloon St Andr Hong Kong 89-99; Sen Chapl Protestant Ch Oman 00-01; V Watford *St Alb* from 02. *St Mary's Vicarage, 14 Cassiobury Drive, Watford WD1 3AB* Tel (01923) 254005 Mobile 0772-632991 Fax (01923) 229274 E-mail jcaldis@btopenworld.com

ALDOUS, Alexander Charles Victor. b 56. Southn Univ BA81 K Alfred's Coll Win PGCE83. S Dios Minl Tr Scheme 91. **d** 94 **p** 95. Chapl Oundle Sch 94-97; Chapl Benenden Sch 98-01; Chapl Oakham Sch from 02. *75 Station Road, Oakham LE15 6QT* Tel (01572) 723941 *or* 758591 E-mail aa@oakham.rutland.sch.uk

ALDOUS, John Herbert. b 37. Portsm Poly CQSW83. Bp Otter Coll 94. **d** 96 **p** 00. NSM Gosport Ch Ch *Portsm* 96-00; NSM Rowner 00-02; R Sabie St Pet S Africa from 02. *St Peter's Rectory, PO Box 71, Sabie, 1260 South Africa*

ALDRIDGE, Mrs Anne Louise. b 59. Nottm Univ BEd80. EAMTC 96. **d** 99 **p** 00. NSM Milton *Ely* from 99. *8 Sutton Close, Milton, Cambridge CB4 6DU* Tel (01223) 501201 *or* tel and fax 441007 E-mail r.aldridge@ntlworld.com

ALDRIDGE, Christopher John. b 35. Trin Hall Cam BA57 MA61. Ripon Hall Ox 59. **d** 60 **p** 61. C Coalville *Leic* 60-64; P-in-c Clifton St Fran *S'well* 64-72; V Gospel Lane St Mich *Birm* 72-90; V Selly Oak St Mary 90-00; rtd 00; Perm to Offic *Birm* from 00. *22 Woodlands Road, Sparkhill, Birmingham B11 4HE* Tel 0121-449 6196

ALDRIDGE, Harold. b 35. Keble Coll Ox BA61 MA71. Chich Th Coll 61. **d** 62 **p** 63. C Notting Hill All SS w St Columb *Lon* 62-65; C Kensington St Mary Abbots w St Geo 65-69; Chapl Beech Hill Sch Macclesfield 69-82; TV Staveley and Barrow Hill *Derby* 82-86; P-in-c Longford 86-89; P-in-c Radbourne 86-89; P-in-c Dalbury, Long Lane and Trusley 86-89; V Braddan *S & M* 89-94; rtd 94. *21 Windermere Drive, Onchan, Isle of Man IM3 2DN* Tel (01624) 626201

ALDRIDGE, Canon Harold John. b 42. Lon Univ DipTh67. Oak Hill Th Coll 65. **d** 69 **p** 70. C Rawtenstall St Mary *Man* 69-72; CMJ 72-76; C Woodford Wells *Chelmsf* 76-79; TV Washfield, Stoodleigh, Withleigh etc *Ex* 79-86; V Burton *Ches* 86-90; P-in-c Shotwick 90; V Burton and Shotwick from 91; Dioc Clergy Widows and Retirement Officer from 91; RD Wirral S from 96; Hon Can Ches Cathl from 98; Chapl Clatterbridge Hosp Wirral 86-91; Chapl Wirral Hosp NHS Trust 91-97; Chapl Wirral and W Cheshire Community NHS Trust 97-03; Chapl Cheshire and Wirral Partnership NHS Trust from 03. *The Vicarage, Vicarage Lane, Burton, Neston CH64 5TJ* Tel 0151-336 4070

ALDRIDGE, Mark Richard. b 58. Oak Hill Th Coll BA89. **d** 89 **p** 90. C Combe Down w Monkton Combe and S Stoke *B & W* 89-90; C Woodside Park St Barn *Lon* 90-94; P-in-c Cricklewood St Gabr and St Mich 94-99; V from 99. *St Gabriel's Vicarage, 156 Anson Road, London NW2 6BH* Tel (020) 8452 6305 E-mail markaldridge@lineone.net

ALEXANDER, David Graham. b 61. Ridley Hall Cam 87. **d** 89 **p** 90. C New Barnet St Jas *St Alb* 89-93; C Northwood H Trin *Lon* 93-95; V Stopsley *St Alb* from 95. *The Vicarage, 702 Hitchin Road, Luton LU2 7UJ* Tel (01582) 729194 Fax 450375 E-mail stopsley@aol.com

ALEXANDER, Douglas Keith. b 45. Ripon Coll Cuddesdon 87. **d** 89 **p** 90. C Thorpe St Matt *Nor* 89-92; P-in-c Lakenham St Alb 92-97; Chapl Nor City Coll of F&HE 92-97; TV Barnham Broom 97-00; TV Barnham Broom and Upper Yare from 00. *The Rectory, Town Lane, Garvestone, Norwich NR9 4OR* Tel and fax (01362) 858377 Mobile 07876-572724 E-mail revdougalexander@aol.com

ALEXANDER, James Crichton. b 43. Qu Coll Cam BA65 MA69. Cuddesdon Coll 68. **d** 68 **p** 69. C Much Wenlock w Bourton

Heref 68-72; V Oakington *Ely* from 72; P-in-c Dry Drayton 85-95. *The Vicarage, 99 Water Lane, Oakington, Cambridge CB4 5AL* Tel (01223) 232396 E-mail free2live@free2live.worldonline.co.uk

ALEXANDER, Canon James Douglas. b 27. Linc Th Coll 57. **d** 58 **p** 59. C Frodingham *Linc* 58-61; V Alvingham w N and S Cockerington 61-65; V Keddington 61-65; R Gunhouse w Burringham 65-70; R Peterhead *Ab* 70-76; R Aberdeen St Mary 76-95; Miss to Seafarers from 76; Can St Andr Cathl *Ab* from 72; Chapl HM Pris Aber from 82; P-in-c Cove Bay *Ab* 85-90; rtd 95; Dioc Supernumerary *Ab* from 95. *21 Whitehall Road, Aberdeen AB25 2PP* Tel (01224) 643202

ALEXANDER, Jane Louise. *See* MacLAREN, Mrs Jane Louise

ALEXANDER, Julius Erik Louis. b 66. Guildf Co Coll of Tech BTEC NC84 BTEC HNC86. Wycliffe Hall Ox 89. **d** 92 **p** 93. C Hoole *Ches* 92-94; C Offerton 94-98; TV Upper Holloway *Lon* 98-03; Asst Chapl Southn Univ Hosps NHS Trust from 03. *Trust Management Offices, Southampton General Hospital, Tremona Road, Southampton SO16 6YD* Tel (023) 8077 7222 E-mail juliusalexander@compuserve.com

ALEXANDER, Canon Loveday Constance Anne. b 47. Somerville Coll Ox BA69 MA78 DPhil78 DipTh70. N Ord Course 98. **d** 99 **p** 00. NSM Alderley Edge *Ches* from 99; Can Th Ches Cathl from 03; Perm to Offic *Sheff* from 00. *5 Nevill Road, Bramhall, Stockport SK7 3ET* Tel 0161-439 7946 E-mail l.c.alexander@sheffield.ac.uk

ALEXANDER, Michael George. b 47. Open Univ BA90 DipEd91. Sarum & Wells Th Coll 74. **d** 77 **p** 78. C Wednesfield *Lich* 77-80; C Tettenhall Wood 80-83; Distr Min 83-85; Dioc Adv in Adult and Youth Educn *Derby* 85-89; V Hazlewood 85-89; V Turnditch 85-89; Par Educn Adv (Laity Development) 89-96; Dioc Laity Development Adv 96-00; Dioc Dir Studies Bp's Centres of Learning 96-00; P-in-c Ticknall, Smisby and Stanton-by-Bridge 00-01; P-in-c Barrow-on-Trent w Twyford and Swarkestone 00-01; V Ticknall, Smisby and Stanton by Bridge etc from 01; RD Melbourne from 02. *The Vicarage, 7 Church Lane, Ticknall, Derby DE73 1JU* Tel (01332) 862549 E-mail mike.alexander@ticvic.fsnet.co.uk

ALEXANDER, Norman William. b 27. Chich Th Coll 54. **d** 56 **p** 57. C Hatcham St Cath *S'wark* 56-59; C Horley 59-61; V Markington and S Stainley *Ripon* 61-69; R Mutford w Rushmere w Gisleham w N Cove w Barnby *Nor* 69-74; R W Winch 74-81; V Frensham *Guildf* 81-84; V Hemsby *Nor* 84-89; RD Flegg (Gt Yarmouth) 87-89; rtd 89; Perm to Offic *Nor* from 98. *14 Fitton Road, St Germans, King's Lynn PE34 3AU* Tel (01553) 617513

ALEXANDER, Peter John. b 36. CQSW73 DMA74. Oak Hill Th Coll 92. **d** 95 **p** 96. NSM Aspenden, Buntingford and Westmill *St Alb* 95-02; rtd 02; Perm to Offic *Nor* from 02. *Dellgate, 4 The Dell, Bodham, Holt NR25 6NG* Tel (01263) 588126

ALEXANDER, Mrs Rachel Clare. b 57. EAMTC 96. **d** 99 **p** 00. NSM Mattishall w Mattishall Burgh, Welborne etc *Nor* 99-02; Perm to Offic from 02. *Minstrels, 50 Dereham Road, Mattishall, Dereham NR20 3NS* Tel (01362) 858655 Fax 858822 E-mail rachel@ralexander.fsnet.co.uk

ALEXANDER, Robert. b 37. Lon Univ LLB60 St Cath Coll Ox BA62. St Steph Ho Ox 60. **d** 63 **p** 64. C Kensington St Mary Abbots w St Geo *Lon* 63-68; C Notting Hill 71-74; TV 74-79; Australia from 79; rtd 02. *302/27 Neutral Street, North Sydney, NSW, Australia 2060* Tel (0061) (2) 9954 0543 Fax as telephone E-mail robalexand@bigpond.com

ALEXANDER, Wilfred Robert Donald. b 35. TCD BA58 MA80. **d** 63 **p** 63. C Raheny w Coolock *D & G* 63-67; Min Can St Patr Cathl Dublin 65-67; Hon C Herne Hill St Paul *S'wark* 68-70; Asst Master Gosforth Gr Sch 71-76; Hon C Long Benton St Mary *Newc* 74-76; Chapl St Mary and St Anne's Sch Abbots Bromley 76-80; V Cauldon *Lich* 80-83; V Waterfall 80-83; P-in-c Calton 80-83; P-in-c Grindon 80-83; V Blackb St Luke w St Phil *Blackb* 83-89; V Rainhill *Liv* 89-92; R Croft w Southworth 92-99; C Croft w Southworth and Newchurch 99-01; rtd 01. *16 Hawkshaw Close, Birchwood, Warrington WA3 7NF* Tel (01925) 851472

ALEXANDER-YATES, Tristan Nathaniel. b 66. SEITE 99. **d** 03. NSM Eltham H Trin *S'wark* from 03. *St Kentigern House, 31 Fairfield Grove, London SE7 8UA* Tel (020) 8853 2257 Mobile 07970-016009 E-mail tristalex@aol.com

ALFORD, John. b 35. Nottm Univ BSc58 NDA59 DipEd76. Qu Coll Birm 74. **d** 77 **p** 78. NSM Edgmond *Lich* 77-87; C Cheadle 87-88; C Cheadle w Freehay 88-89; P-in-c Wootton Wawen *Cov* 89-95; P-in-c Grafham *Ely* 95-00; P-in-c Ellington 95-00; P-in-c Easton 95-00; P-in-c Spaldwick w Barham and Woolley 95-00; V 00-01; rtd 01; Perm to Offic *Ely* from 01. *4 Armstrong Close, Perry, Huntingdon PE28 0DF* Tel (01480) 812075 E-mail margaretalford@aol.com

ALFORD, Mrs Rosalie Grace. b 40. Bedf Coll Lon BA61 Lon Univ PGCE62. STETS 95. **d** 98 **p** 99. NSM Wadhurst *Chich* from 98; NSM Stonegate from 98. *Content, 1 Ingoldsby Cottages, Faircrouch Lane, Wadhurst TN5 6PP* Tel (01892) 782974

ALKER, Adrian. b 49. Wadh Coll Ox BA70 Lanc Univ MA71. Ripon Coll Cuddesdon DipTh79. **d** 79 **p** 80. C W Derby St Mary *Liv* 79-83; Dioc Youth Officer *Carl* 83-88; V Sheff St Mark

Broomhill *Sheff* from 88; Dioc Dir of In-Service Tr from 90. *St Mark's Vicarage, 4 St Mark's Crescent, Sheffield S10 2SG* Tel 0114-267 0362 Fax as telephone E-mail alker@stmarkssheffield.co.uk

ALLABY, Miss Mary Dorothea. b 60. Bedf Coll Lon BA82 W Sussex Inst of HE PGCE83. Trin Coll Bris DipHE90 ADPS92. **d** 92 **p** 94. Par Dn Ipsley *Worc* 92-94; C 94-96; TV Bloxwich *Lich* 96-02; V Trent Vale from 02. *Trent Vale Vicarage, Crosby Road, Stoke-on-Trent ST4 6JY* Tel (01782) 747669 E-mail mary@allaby.freeserve.co.uk

ALLABY, Simon Arnold Kenworthy. b 65. St Chad's Coll Dur BA88. Trin Coll Bris 88. **d** 90 **p** 91. C Preston on Tees *Dur* 90-93; C Chester le Street 93-99; R Ardingly *Chich* from 99. *The Rectory, Church Lane, Ardingly, Haywards Heath RH17 6UR* Tel (01444) 892332

ALLAIN CHAPMAN, Ms Justine Penelope Heathcote. b 67. K Coll Lon BA88 PGCE89 Nottm Univ MDiv93. Linc Th Coll 91. **d** 93 **p** 94. Par Dn Forest Hill *S'wark* 93-94; C 94-96; TV Clapham TM 96-01; V Clapham St Paul from 02. *St Paul's Vicarage, Rectory Grove, London SW4 0DX* Tel (020) 7622 2128 E-mail tjac@globalnet.co.uk

ALLAN, Andrew John. b 47. Westcott Ho Cam 76. **d** 79 **p** 80. C Whitstable All SS w St Pet *Cant* 79-84; C Whitstable 84-86; P-in-c Littlebourne 86-87; P-in-c Ickham w Wickhambreaux and Stodmarsh 86-87; R Littlebourne and Ickham w Wickhambreaux etc from 87. *The Vicarage, Church Road, Littlebourne, Canterbury CT3 1UA* Tel (01227) 721233

ALLAN, Canon Archibald Blackie. b 35. Edin Th Coll 57. **d** 60 **p** 61. C Aberdeen St Jo *Ab* 60-63; R 82-00; Chapl St Paul's Cathl Dundee *Bre* 63-68; P-in-c Aberdeen St Clem *Ab* 68-76; Vice-Provost St Andr Cathl 76-82; Can 88-00; Hon Can from 01; rtd 00. *32 Craigiebuckler Terrace, Aberdeen AB15 8SX* Tel (01224) 316636

ALLAN, Donald James. b 35. Sarum & Wells Th Coll 63. **d** 65 **p** 66. C Royton St Paul *Man* 65-71; V Middleton Junction 71-78; P-in-c Finmere w Mixbury *Ox* 78-83; R Finmere w Mixbury, Cottisford, Hardwick etc 83; Chapl Westcliff Hosp 83-87; V Westcliff St Andr *Chelmsf* 83-87; R Goldhanger w Lt Totham 87-01; rtd 01; P-in-c St Goran w Caerhays *Truro* from 01. *The Vicarage, Gorran, St Austell PL26 6HN* Tel (01726) 844457 E-mail donald.allan2@btinternet.com

ALLAN, Jeanette Winifred. b 40. ALA63. St And Dioc Tr Course 79. **dss** 81 **d** 86 **p** 94. NSM Hillfoot's TM 81-86; NSM Bridge of Allan *St And* 86-88; NSM Dunblane 88-98; R Glenrothes from 98. *St Luke's Rectory, 60 Ninian Quadrant, Glenrothes KY7 4HP* Tel (01592) 759764 E-mail revdjallan@aol.com

ALLAN, John William. b 58. St Olaf Coll Minnesota BA80 Birm Univ 86. Trin Lutheran Sem Ohio MDiv84 Qu Coll Birm 90. **d** 91 **p** 92. In Lutheran Ch (USA) 84-86; C Newport w Longford and Chetwynd *Lich* 91-94; P-in-c Longdon 94-01; Local Min Adv (Wolverhampton) 94-01; V Alrewas from 01; V Wychnor from 01. *The Vicarage, Church Road, Alrewas, Burton-on-Trent DE13 7BT* Tel (01283) 790486 E-mail john.allan@lichfield.anglican.org

ALLAN, Peter Burnaby. b 52. Clare Coll Cam BA74 MA78 St Jo Coll Dur BA82. Cranmer Hall Dur 80. **d** 83 **p** 84. C Chaddesden St Mary *Derby* 83-86; C Brampton St Thos 86-89; TV Halesworth w Linstead, Chediston, Holton etc *St E* 89-94; TR Trunch *Nor* from 94; P-in-c Ansley and Arley *Cov* from 03. *The Vicarage, 60 Birmingham Road, Ansley, Nuneaton CV10 9PS* E-mail peter@allan49.fsworld.co.uk

ALLAN, Peter George. b 50. Wadh Coll Ox BA72 MA76 Leeds Univ DipTh74. Coll of Resurr Mirfield 72. **d** 75 **p** 76. C Stevenage St Geo *St Alb* 75-78; Chapl Wadh Coll Ox 78-82; C Ox St Mary V w St Cross and St Pet *Ox* 78-82; CR from 85. *Community of the Resurrection, Stocks Bank Road, Mirfield WF14 0BN* Tel (01924) 494318

ALLANDER, William Edward Morgell Kidd. b 15. TCD BA37 MA40. CITC 37. **d** 38 **p** 39. C Knock *D & D* 38-43; Hd of Trin Coll Miss Belf 43-46; Lic to Offic *Lon* 46-51; C Foleshill St Laur *Cov* 53-55; P-in-c Wood End 55-57; V 57-64; V Atherstone 64-73; I Rathcooney Union C, C & R 73-88; rtd 88. *12 Richmond Estate, Blackrock, Cork, Irish Republic* Tel (00353) (21) 429 3352 Fax 429 3642 E-mail wallander@eircom.net

ALLARD, John Ambrose. b 30. Bps' Coll Cheshunt 63. **d** 65 **p** 66. C Leigh-on-Sea St Marg *Chelmsf* 65-69; P-in-c Rawreth w Rettendon 69-70; R 70-72; V Barkingside St Fran 73-84; V E Ham St Geo 84-86; V St Osyth 86-95; rtd 95; Perm to Offic *Nor* and *St E* 97-02. *18 Greystone Place, Newtonhill, Stonehaven AB39 3UL* Tel (01569) 731767

ALLARD, Roderick George. b 44. Loughb Coll of Educn CertEd96 Lon Univ BA77 Sheff Poly MSc88. Nor Ord Course 97. **d** 99 **p** 00. NSM Charlesworth and Dinting Vale *Derby* from 99. *16 Springmeadow, Charlesworth, Glossop SK13 5HP* Tel (01457) 866278 Mobile 07798-843283

ALLARDICE, Alexander Edwin. b 49. SRN. Chich Th Coll 73. **d** 76 **p** 77. C Rugeley *Lich* 76-79; C Felixstowe St Jo *St E* 79-81; TV Ipswich St Fran 81-87; C Lostwithiel *Truro* 87-90; C Boconnoc w Bradoc 87-90; C St Veep 87-90; C St Winnow 87-90;

R Lostwithiel, St Winnow w St Nectan's Chpl etc 90-97; R Mevagissey and St Ewe 97-99; rtd 99; Perm to Offic *Truro* from 99. *4 Pensylva, St Austell PL25 4RW* Tel (01726) 77695 Fax as telephone E-mail alex.allardice@classicfm.net

ALLBERRY, William Alan John. b 49. Ch Coll Cam BA70 MA71. Ripon Coll Cuddesdon 84. **d** 86 **p** 87. C Brixton St Matt *S'wark* 86-90; V Wandsworth St Paul 90-98; R Esher *Guildf* from 98; RD Emly from 01. *The Rectory, 4 Esher Place Avenue, Esher KT10 8PY* Tel (01372) 462611 Fax as telephone E-mail william.allberry@btopenworld.com

ALLBUTT, Mavis Miriam. b 98. OLM Meir *Lich* from 98. *16 Sorrento Grove, Meir Hay, Stoke-on-Trent ST3 5XZ* Tel (01782) 599653

ALLCHIN, Canon Arthur Macdonald (Donald). b 30. Ch Ch Ox BA51 MA55 BLitt56 Univ of Wales 93. Bucharest Th Inst Hon DD77 Cuddesdon Coll 54. **d** 56 **p** 57. C Kensington St Mary Abbots w St Geo *Lon* 56-60; Lib Pusey Ho 60-69; Warden Community of Sisters of the Love of God Ox 68-73; Can Res and Lib Cant Cathl *Cant* 73-87; Hon Prov Can Cant Cathl from 88; Dir St Theosevia Cen for Chr Spirituality 87-94; Hon Prof Univ of N Wales Ban from 93; rtd 94; Lic to Offic *Cant* 94-97; Perm to Offic *Ban* from 97. *1 Trem yr Wyddfa, Bangor LL57 2ER* Tel (01248) 353744

ALLCHIN, Miss Maureen Ann. b 50. Edge Hill Coll of HE CertEd71 Sussex Univ MA93. S Dios Mini Tr Scheme 88. **d** 91 **p** 94. Hd Past Faculty Steyning Gr Sch 79-92; NSM Southwick St Mich *Chich* 91-92; C Storrington 93-95; TV Bridport *Sarum* from 95. *The Vicarage, King's Head Hill, Bradpole, Bridport DT6 3DZ* Tel (01308) 458788 Fax 421048 E-mail mallchin@fish.co.uk

ALLCOCK, Jeremy Robert. b 63. Trin Coll Bris BA92. **d** 92 **p** 93. C Walthamstow St Luke *Chelmsf* 92-96; V E Ham St Paul from 96. *St Paul's Vicarage, 227 Burges Road, London E6 2EU* Tel (020) 8552 9955 *or* 8959 1856 E-mail jeme6@aol.com

ALLCOCK, Peter Michael. b 37. Oak Hill Th Coll 65. **d** 68 **p** 69. C Upper Tulse Hill St Matthias *S'wark* 68-71; C Dunkeswell and Dunkeswell Abbey *Ex* 71-72; P-in-c Luppitt and Monkton 72-75; V Okehampton w Inwardleigh 75-80; TV Solihull *Birm* 80-85; V Highbury New Park St Aug *Lon* 85-99; V E and W Horndon w Lt Warley and Childerditch *Chelmsf* 99-02; rtd 02. *10 Arden Close, Balsall Common, Coventry CV7 7NY* Tel (01676) 533968 E-mail pma946078@aol.com

ALLDRIT, Nicolas Sebastian Fitz-Ansculf. b 41. St Edm Hall Ox BA63 MA69 DPhil69. Cuddesdon Coll 72. **d** 72 **p** 73. C Limpsfield and Titsey *S'wark* 72-81; Tutor Linc Th Coll 81-96; Sub-Warden 88-96; R Witham Gp *Linc* from 97. *The Rectory, 15 Hillview Road, South Witham, Grantham NG33 5QW* Tel (01572) 767240

ALLEN, Andrew Stephen. b 55. MPS Nottm Univ BPharm77. St Steph Ho Ox 78. **d** 81 **p** 82. C Gt Ilford St Mary *Chelmsf* 81-83; C Luton All SS w St Pet *St Alb* 83-86; TV Chambersbury 86-91; TV Brixham w Churston Ferrers and Kingswear *Ex* 91-01; TR from 01. *The Rectory, 16 Holwell Road, Brixham TQ5 9NE* Tel (01803) 851570 E-mail andallen@hotmail.com

ALLEN, Ms Beverley Carole. b 52. Ch Ch Coll Cant CertEd74 Open Univ BA91. Sarum Th Coll 93. **d** 96 **p** 97. NSM Ruislip Manor St Paul *Lon* from 96. *10 Shipley Mill Close, Stone Cross, Pevensey BN24 5PY* Tel (01323) 740283

ALLEN, Brian. See ALLEN, Frank Brian

ALLEN, Brian. b 58. Oak Hill NSM Course 90. **d** 93 **p** 94. NSM W Norwood St Luke *S'wark* 93-02; NSM Gipsy Hill Ch Ch from 02. *76 Bradley Road, London SE19 3NS* Tel (020) 8771 4282

ALLEN, Brian Stanley. b 24. Roch Th Coll 65. **d** 67 **p** 68. C Roch 67-74; P-in-c Drypool St Jo *York* 74-80; TV Drypool 80; V Marlpool *Derby* 80-87; rtd 87; Perm to Offic *York* from 90. *22 Sycamore Terrace, York YO30 7DN* Tel (01904) 653418

ALLEN, Miss Charlotte. b 79. St Jo Coll Dur BA00. Westcott Ho Cam 00. **d** 03. C Southwick St Mich *Chich* from 03. *1 Church House Close, Southwick, Brighton BN42 4WQ* Tel (01273) 592787 Mobile 07971-423589 E-mail charlie.allen@dunelm.org.uk

ALLEN, Christopher Dennis. b 50. Fitzw Coll Cam BA73 MA77. Cuddesdon Coll 74. **d** 76 **p** 77. C Kettering St Andr *Pet* 76-79; C Pet H Spirit Bretton 79-82; R Bardney *Linc* 82-87; V Knighton St Mary Magd *Leic* from 87. *The Vicarage, Church Lane, Leicester LE2 3WG* Tel 0116-270 5730 E-mail callen@leicester.anglican.org

ALLEN, Christopher Leslie. b 56. Leeds Univ BA78. St Jo Coll Nottm 79. **d** 80 **p** 81. C Birm St Martin *Birm* 80-85; Tr and Ed Pathfinders 85-89; Hd 89-92; Midl Youth Dept Co-ord CPAS 85-89; Hon C Selly Park St Steph and St Wulstan *Birm* 86-92; V Hamstead St Bernard 92-95; NSM Kidderminster St Mary and All SS w Trimpley etc *Worc* from 03. *17 Alder Avenue, Kidderminster DY10 2LD* Tel (01562) 820702

ALLEN, David. b 51. Llan Dioc Tr Scheme. **d** 76 **p** 77. C Fairwater *Llan* 76-84; Chapl Bp of Llan High Sch 84-97; Lic to Offic *Llan* from 84. *1 Kenley Close, Llandaff, Cardiff CF5 2PA* Tel (029) 2056 0252

ALLEN, David Edward. b 70. Van Mildert Coll Dur BSc91. Ripon Coll Cuddesdon BA94. **d** 95 **p** 96. C Grantham *Linc* 95-99; C W Hampstead St Jas *Lon* 99-01; C Kilburn St Mary w All So and W Hampstead St Jas 01-02; V Finsbury St Clem w St Barn and St Matt from 02. *St Clement's Vicarage, King Square, London EC1V 8DA* Tel (020) 7253 9140
E-mail davideallen@tinyworld.co.uk

ALLEN, Derek. b 57. MCIOB89. OLM course 96. **d** 99 **p** 00. OLM Bacup Ch *Man* from 99. *180 New Line, Bacup OL13 9RU* Tel (01706) 875960
E-mail allen.newline@cwcom.net

ALLEN, Canon Francis Arthur Patrick. b 26. Em Coll Saskatoon Div Test52. **d** 51 **p** 52. Canada 51-57; C Bishopwearmouth St Nic *Dur* 57-59; Japan 59-63; Hon Can Kobe from 63; V Kingston upon Hull St Matt *York* 63-67; Australia from 67; rtd 91. *136 High Street, Morpeth, NSW, Australia 2321* Tel (0061) (2) 4934 7049

ALLEN, Frank Brian. b 47. K Coll Lon BD AKC71. **d** 71 **p** 72. C Leam Lane *Dur* 71-74; C Tynemouth Ch Ch *Newc* 74-78; Chapl Preston Hosp N Shields 74-78; Chapl Newc Poly *Newc* 78-84; V Newc St Hilda 84-88; Chapl Nottm Mental Illness and Psychiatric Unit 88-89; Chapl for Mental Health Newc Mental Health Unit 89-94; Chapl Newc City Health NHS Trust 94-96; Chapl Team Leader from 96; Visiting Fell Newc Univ *Newc* from 96. *Trust Chaplaincy Centre, St Nicholas Hospital, Gosforth, Newcastle upon Tyne NE3 3XT* Tel 0191-273 6666 ext 28465 Fax 223 2840 E-mail f.b.allen@ncl.ac.uk

ALLEN, Frank John. b 17. FRIC58 Aston Univ BSc66 Birm Univ DipTh75. Qu Coll Birm 75. **d** 76 **p** 76. NSM Hobs Moat *Birm* 76-79; Perm to Offic *Heref* from 79. *Haresfield, Luston, Leominster HR6 0EB* Tel (01568) 615735

ALLEN, The Ven Geoffrey Gordon. b 39. Sarum Th Coll 64. **d** 66 **p** 67. C Langley Marish *Ox* 66-70; Miss to Seafarers from 70; Chapl Rotterdam w Schiedam *Eur* 78-82; Asst Chapl The Hague 84-93; Chapl Voorschoten 84-93; Can Brussels Cathl from 89; Chapl E Netherlands from 93; Adn NW Eur from 93; P-in-c Haarlem 95-02. *IJsselsingel 86, 6991 ZT Rheden, The Netherlands* Tel (0031) (26) 495 3800 Fax 495 4922
E-mail geoffrey@archdeacon.demon.nl

ALLEN, Giles David. b 70. RCM BMus91. Coll of Resurr Mirfield 92. **d** 95 **p** 96. C Palmers Green St Jo *Lon* 95-99; V Lund *Blackb* from 99. *Lund Vicarage, Church Lane, Clifton, Preston PR4 0ZE* Tel (01772) 683617
E-mail giles@lund18.freeserve.co.uk

ALLEN, Gordon Richard. b 29. St Jo Coll Dur BA54 DipTh55 MA58. **d** 55 **p** 56. C N Meols *Liv* 55-58; Uganda 58-63; V Lathom *Liv* 64-68; USA from 68; rtd 94. *237 Emery's Bridge Road, South Berwick, ME 03908, USA*

ALLEN, Hugh Edward. b 47. Sarum & Wells Th Coll 79. **d** 81 **p** 82. C Frome St Jo *B & W* 81-85; R Old Cleeve, Leighland and Treborough 85-97; RD Exmoor 92-97; P-in-c The Stanleys *Glouc* 97-99. *3 Norden's Meadow, Wiveliscombe, Taunton TA4 2JW* Tel (01984) 623078

ALLEN, Mrs Jacqueline Lesley. b 54. EMMTC 99. **d** 02 **p** 03. NSM Huthwaite *S'well* from 02. *63 Main Street, Huthwaite, Sutton-in-Ashfield NG17 2LQ* Tel (01623) 479680 Mobile 07956-050446 E-mail jackie@serv77.netscapeonline.com

ALLEN, Brother James Edward (Brother James Edward). b 40. Emerson Coll BA66. Berkeley Div Sch MDiv69. **d** 69 **p** 69. USA from 69; C Melbourne (Florida) H Trin 69-72; V Orlando St Chris 72-75; SSJE 75-81; V Philadelphia St Elisabeth 82-86; Min Hatboro Advent 86-87; Min Quakertown Em 87-88; Min Rockledge H Nativity 88-89; Novice SSF 89-92; SSF from 92; Perm to Offic *Sarum* from 01. *PO Box 399, Mount Sinai, NY 11766, USA* E-mail amprovoff@aol.com

ALLEN, Jamie. *See* ALLEN, Timothy James

ALLEN, Mrs Jane Rosemary. b 39. Cartrefle Coll of Educn BA83 PGCE84. St As & Ban Minl Tr Course 99. **d** 00 **p** 01. NSM Llandudno *Ban* 00-02; C from 03. *Treetops, Nant-y-Gamar Road, Llandudno LL30 3BD* Tel (01492) 860531
E-mail revmil@hotmail.com

ALLEN, John Catling. b 25. Leeds Univ BA50. Coll of Resurr Mirfield 50. **d** 52 **p** 53. C Knowle H Nativity *Bris* 52-54; C De Beauvoir Town St Pet *Lon* 54-57; C Beckenham St Barn *Roch* 57-60; V Orpington St Andr 60-66; V Linc St Jo *Linc* 66-84; C Tynemouth Ch Ch w H Trin *Newc* 85-87; C N Shields 87-89; rtd 89; Hon C Gt and Lt Torrington and Frithelstock *Ex* from 89. *7 St Barnabas, The Beauchamp Community, Newland WR13 5AX*

ALLEN, John Clement. b 32. K Coll Lon 54. **d** 58 **p** 59. C Middlesbrough St Martin *York* 58-60; C Northallerton w Kirby Sigston 60-64; V Larkfield *Roch* 64-70; R Ash 70-79; R Ridley 70-79; RD Cobham 76-79; R Chislehurst St Nic 79-97; rtd 97; Perm to Offic *Sarum* from 97. *The Peppergarth, 9 Lane Fox Terrace, Penny Street, Sturminster Newton DT10 1DE* Tel (01258) 473754

ALLEN, The Very Revd John Edward. b 32. Univ Coll Ox BA56 MA63 Fitzw Coll Cam BA68. Westcott Ho Cam 66. **d** 68 **p** 69. C Deal St Leon *Cant* 68-71; P-in-c Clifton St Paul *Bris* 71-78; Chapl Bris Univ 71-78; P-in-c Chippenham St Andr w Tytherton

Lucas 78-82; Provost Wakef 82-97; rtd 97; Perm to Offic *York* from 98. *The Glebe Barn, Main Street, Sawdon, Scarborough YO13 9DY* Tel (01723) 859854

ALLEN, John Michael. b 27. Cuddesdon Coll 71. **d** 72 **p** 73. C Shrewsbury St Giles *Lich* 72-75; V Hengoed w Gobowen 75-82; V Burghill *Heref* 82-85; RD Heref Rural 83-85; TV Bracknell *Ox* 85-92; rtd 92; Perm to Offic *Heref* from 93. *15 Mill Street, Ludlow SY8 1BE* Tel (01584) 877769

ALLEN, Mrs Kathleen. b 46. N Ord Course 88. **d** 91 **p** 94. NSM Colne H Trin *Blackb* 91-94; NSM Colne Ch Ch 94-98; NSM Colne and Villages from 98. *St Mary's Vicarage, Burnley Road, Trawden, Colne BB8 8PN* Tel (01282) 864046 Fax as telephone E-mail kathleen@k-allen.fsnet.co.uk

ALLEN, Malcolm. b 60. Hatfield Poly HND82 Open Th Coll BA00. Trin Coll Bris DipTh96. **d** 96 **p** 97. C Skirbeck H Trin *Linc* 96-00; TV Cheltenham St Mark *Glouc* from 00. *St Barnabas' Vicarage, 152 Alstone Lane, Cheltenham GL51 8HL* Tel (01242) 694203 Fax as telephone
E-mail malcolmallen@tesco.net

ALLEN, Michael Edward Gerald. b 26. Selw Coll Cam BA50 MA53. Chich Th Coll 50. **d** 52 **p** 53. C Farncombe *Guildf* 52-56; R Bentley 56-60; V Baswich *Lich* 60-75; V Highbrook and W Hoathly *Chich* 75-91; RD Cuckfield 77-88; rtd 91; Perm to Offic *Chich* from 91. *Flat 2, 13 St John's Road, Eastbourne BN20 7NQ* Tel (01323) 728240

ALLEN, Michael Stephen. b 37. Nottm Univ BA60. Cranmer Hall Dur 60. **d** 62 **p** 63. C Sandal St Helen *Wakef* 62-66; Hon C Tile Cross *Birm* 66-70; V 72-84; Hon C Bletchley *Ox* 70-72; Vice-Prin Aston Tr Scheme 84-91; Hon C Boldmere *Birm* 85-91; P-in-c Easton w Colton and Marlingford *Nor* 91-93; Local Min Officer 91-93; Dioc Adv in Adult Educn *S'well* 93-02; rtd 02. *8 Grenville Rise, Arnold, Nottingham NG5 8EW* Tel 0115-967 9515

ALLEN, Michael Tarrant. b 30. St Cath Coll Cam BA56 MA61. Ely Th Coll 56. **d** 58 **p** 59. C Portslade St Nic *Chich* 58-64; C Folkestone St Sav *Cant* 64-65; V Harston w Hauxton *Ely* 65-91; rtd 91; Perm to Offic *Ely* 91-98. *13 Church End, Rampton, Cambridge CB4 8QA* Tel (01945) 250434

ALLEN, Noel Stephen (Brother Noel). b 38. Kelham Th Coll 58. **d** 63 **p** 64. C Nuneaton St Mary *Cov* 63-67; Australia from 67; P-in-c Tennant Creek 68-75; C Darwin Cathl 75-81; R Alice Springs 81-85; R Fred's Pass 85-89; Can Darwin 86-89; Chapl Qu Eliz Hosp from 90. *12 Francis Street, Peterhead, S Australia 5016* Tel (0061) (8) 8242 2645 E-mail nsallen@senet.com.au or noel.allen@nwahs.sa.gove.au

ALLEN, Patrick Charles Benedict. b 55. Ex Univ 79. St Steph Ho Ox 83 SSC87. **d** 86 **p** 87. C Bethnal Green St Matt w St Jas the Gt *Lon* 86-90; C Kenton 90-92; V Plumstead St Nic *S'wark* 92-94; In RC Ch 94-97; Asst to RD Battersea 97-98; P-in-c Lavender Hill Ascension 97-00; P-in-c Battersea St Pet and St Paul 97-98; P-in-c Battersea St Phil w St Bart 98-00; V Lavender Hill Ascension etc from 00. *The Clergy House, Pountney Road, London SW11 5TU* Tel and fax (020) 7228 5340 *or* tel 7622 1929 E-mail patrickallen@clergyhouse.fsnet.co.uk

ALLEN, Peter Henry. b 34. Nottm Univ BA66. Kelham Th Coll 58. **d** 66 **p** 67. C Salisbury St Martin *Sarum* 66-70; C Melksham 70-73; C Paignton Ch Ch *Ex* 73-76; P-in-c W Holloway St Dav *Lon* 76-77; V Barnsbury St Dav w St Clem 77-84; P-in-c Brentford St Faith 84-87; TV Brentford 87-91; TV Catford (Southend) and Downham *S'wark* 91-01; rtd 01. *17 Mayfield Road, Belvedere DA17 6DX* Tel 07939-580266 (mobile)

ALLEN, Peter John. b 34. Leic Coll of Educn CertEd74 Leic Univ BEd79 MA79. EAMTC 89. **d** 92 **p** 93. NSM Ketton w Tinwell *Pet* 92-94; NSM Easton on the Hill, Collyweston w Duddington etc 94-96; Chapl St Pet Viña del Mar Chile 96-99; NSM Culworth w Sulgrave and Thorpe Mandeville etc *Pet* from 00; NSM Weedon Lois w Plumpton and Moreton Pinkney etc from 02. *18 Scythe Road, Daventry NN11 5WN* Tel (01327) 300596 E-mail peterjallen@tinyworld.co.uk

ALLEN, Canon Peter John Douglas. b 35. Jes Coll Cam BA61 MA64 PGCE67. Westcott Ho Cam 60. **d** 62 **p** 63. C Wyken *Cov* 62-65; USA 65-66; Chapl Jes Coll Cam 66-72; Chapl K Sch Cant 72-87; Hon Min Can Cant Cathl *Cant* 73-87; Second Master and Sen Chapl Sedbergh Sch Cumbria 87-93; P-in-c Edin St Ninian *Edin* from 93; Prec and Can St Mary's Cathl from 94; Tutor Edin Th Coll 94-01; Chapl Edin Academy from 99; Chapl Fettes Coll Edin from 02. *12A Grosvenor Crescent, Edinburgh EH12 5EL* Tel 0131-337 0027 E-mail pa@cathedral.net

ALLEN, Philip Gerald. b 48. Lon Univ DipTh71. Trin Coll Bris 71. **d** 73 **p** 74. C Portsea St Luke *Portsm* 73-75; C-in-c 75-79; C Southsea St Jude 75-79; P-in-c Gatten St Paul 79-85; V from 85. *St Paul's Vicarage, St Paul's Crescent, Shanklin PO37 7AW* Tel (01983) 862027

ALLEN, Richard James. b 46. Wells Th Coll 69. **d** 71 **p** 72. C Upholland *Liv* 71-75; TV 76-79; TV Padgate 79-85; V Weston-super-Mare St Andr Bournville *B & W* 85-93; V Williton from 93; Chapl Taunton and Somerset NHS Trust from 93. *The Vicarage, 16 Bridge Street, Williton, Taunton TA4 4NR* Tel (01984) 632626 E-mail vicarrichard@aol.com

ALLEN, Richard John Slaney. d 00 **p** 01. NSM Tooting All SS *S'wark* from 00; Asst Chapl SW Lon and St George's Mental Health NHS Trust from 03. *9 Roman Rise, London SE19 1JG*

ALLEN, Richard Lee. b 41. Liv Inst of Educn TCert67. N Ord Course 80. **d** 83 **p** 84. NSM Colne Ch Ch *Blackb* 83-90; P-in-c Trawden 91-98; NSM Colne and Villages from 98; Chapl Burnley Health Care NHS Trust from 99. *St Mary's Vicarage, Burnley Road, Trawden, Colne BB8 8PN* Tel (01282) 864046 Fax as telephone

ALLEN, Roger Charles Brews. b 44. Solicitor 77 Loughb Univ BTech66. LNSM course 89. **d** 92 **p** 93. OLM S Elmham and Ilketshall *St E* 92-95; OLM Bungay H Trin w St Mary from 95. *33A Earlsham Street, Bungay NR35 1AF* Tel (01986) 896927 E-mail rallen@zetnet.co.uk

ALLEN, Roy Vernon. b 43. Open Univ BA81 Birm Univ MA84. Sarum Th Coll 67. **d** 70 **p** 71. C Hall Green Ascension *Birm* 70-74; V Temple Balsall 74-78; P-in-c Smethwick St Steph 78-81; V Smethwick St Mich 78-81; V Smethwick SS Steph and Mich 81-86; V Marston Green from 86. *The Vicarage, Elmdon Road, Birmingham B37 7BT* Tel 0121-779 2492

ALLEN, Samuel Joseph. b 25. CITC. **d** 65 **p** 66. C Bray *D & G* 65-75; P-in-c Carbury *M & K* 75-84; rtd 84. *Dargle Valley Nursing Home, Cookstown, Enniskerry, Co Wicklow, Irish Republic*

ALLEN, Canon Stanley Leonard Sidney. b 26. K Coll Lon BD52 AKC52. **d** 53 **p** 54. C Friern Barnet St Jas *Lon* 53-55; Tutor Qu Coll St Johns Canada 55-57; Vice-Prin 57-58; Chapl K Coll Newcastle-upon-Tyne 58-61; P-in-c Woburn Square w Ch Ch *Lon* 61-66; Chapl Gt Ormond Street Hosp for Sick Children *Lon* 61-66; Warden Roch Th Coll and Can Res Roch Cathl 66-70; Hon Can 70-95; V Sidcup St Jo and Chapl Qu Mary's Hosp Sidcup 70-95; RD Sidcup 75-93; rtd 95; Perm to Offic *Nor* from 96. *55 Manor Road, Dersingham, King's Lynn PE31 6LH* Tel (01485) 543425

ALLEN, Canon Steven. b 49. Nottm Univ BA73. St Jo Coll Nottm 73. **d** 75 **p** 76. C Gt Horton *Bradf* 75-80; V 89-02; V Upper Armley *Ripon* 80-89; RD Bowling and Horton *Bradf* 98-02; Hon Can Bradf Cathl from 00; Dioc Tr Officer from 02. *48 Toller Grove, Bradford BD9 5NP* Tel (01274) 482059

ALLEN, Stuart Philip. b 73. St Cath Coll Ox BA95. Oak Hill Th Coll BA02. **d** 02 **p** 03. C Burford w Fulbrook, Taynton, Asthall etc *Ox* from 02. *6 Orchard Row, Fulbrook, Burford OX18 4BT* Tel (01993) 824255 E-mail stuartpallen@yahoo.co.uk

ALLEN, Mrs Susan Rosemary. b 47. Warwick Univ BSc68 Trevelyan Coll Dur PGCE69. Sarum Th Coll 93. **d** 96 **p** 97. C Goldsworth Park *Guildf* 96-01; TV Hemel Hempstead *St Alb* from 01. *33 Craigavon Road, Hemel Hempstead HP2 6BA* Tel (01442) 270585 E-mail revsue@fish.co.uk

ALLEN, Thomas Davidson. b 49. QUB BA. **d** 84 **p** 85. C Magheralin w Dollingstown *D & D* 84-86; I Kilwarlin Upper w Kilwarlin Lower 86-91; I Maghera w Killelagh *D & R* 91-03; I Donaghcloney w Waringstown *D & D* from 03. *The Rectory, 54 Banbridge Road, Waringstown, Craigavon BT66 7QD* Tel (028) 3888 1218 E-mail tallen@talk21.com

ALLEN, Thomas Henry. b 42. N Ord Course 87. **d** 90 **p** 91. C Upholland *Liv* 90-93; TV Walton-on-the-Hill from 93. *51 Queens Drive, Walton, Liverpool L4 6SF* Tel 0151-521 5276

ALLEN, Timothy James. b 71. Warwick Univ BA93. Ripon Coll Cuddesdon BTh99. **d** 99 **p** 00. C Nuneaton St Mary *Cov* 99-02; V Seend, Bulkington and Poulshot *Sarum* from 02. *The Vicarage, High Street, Seend, Melksham SN12 6NR* Tel (01380) 828615 E-mail jamie@boofuls.co.uk

ALLEN, Tom Giles. b 72. Hull Univ BA78 Westhill Coll Birm 84. Carl and Blackb Dioc Tr Inst. **d** 98 **p** 99. C Mirfield *Wakef* 98-01; V Oakworth *Bradf* from 01. *The Vicarage, 18 Sunhurst Drive, Oakworth, Keighley BD22 7RG* Tel (01535) 648496

ALLEN, Zachary Edward. b 52. Warwick Univ BA74. Ripon Coll Cuddesdon 78. **d** 81 **p** 82. C Bognor *Chich* 81-84; C Rusper and Roughey 84-86; TV Carl H Trin and St Barn *Carl* 86-90; Chapl Strathclyde Ho Hosp Carl 86-90; V Findon w Clapham and Patching *Chich* 90-01; V Rustington from 01. *The Vicarage, Claigmar Road, Rustington, Littlehampton BN16 2NL* Tel (01903) 784749

ALLEYNE, Sir John Olpherts Campbell, Bt. b 28. Jes Coll Cam BA50 MA55. **d** 55 **p** 56. C Southampton St Mary w H Trin *Win* 55-58; Chapl Cov Cathl *Cov* 58-62; Chapl Clare Hall Cam 62-66; Chapl Bris Cathl *Bris* 66-68; Area Sec (SW England) Toc H 68-71; V Speke All SS *Liv* 71-73; TR Speke St Aid 73-76; R Win St Matt *Win* 76-93; rtd 93; Perm to Offic *Guildf* from 93. *2 Ash Grove, Guildford GU2 8UT* Tel (01483) 571854

ALLFORD, Judith Mary. b 55. Sheff Univ BA Lon Univ BD. Trin Coll Bris 77. **dss** 86 **d** 87 **p** 94. Par Dn Deptford St Jo w H Trin *S'wark* 87-91; Asst Chapl Dulwich Hosp 91-93; Asst Chapl K Coll Hosp Lon 91-95; Asst Chapl King's Healthcare NHS Trust 93-95; Chapl St Pet's Hosp NHS Trust Chertsey from 95. *St Peter's Hospital, Guildford Road, Chertsey KT16 0PZ* Tel (01932) 872000 ext 3324

ALLIN, Philip Ronald. b 43. Westmr Coll Ox DipTh92 Reading Univ MA96 Birm Univ CQSW. Lich Th Coll 71. **d** 71 **p** 72. C

Sutton in Ashfield St Mary *S'well* 71-74; Chapl to Sutton Cen 74-76; Lic to Offic 74-76; P-in-c Grove 76-77; R Ordsall 76-80; V Mansfield St Mark 81-83; TR Hermitage and Hampstead Norreys, Cold Ash etc *Ox* 83-96; OCF 83-96; Chapl Nine o'clock Service *Sheff* 96-03; rtd 03; Bp's Adv in Past Care and Counselling *Sheff* from 03. *352 Crookesmoor Road, Sheffield S10 1BH* Tel 0114-266 4463

ALLINGTON, Andrew William. b 57. ACA81 Sheff Univ BA78. Cranmer Hall Dur BA95. **d** 95 **p** 96. C Clifton *York* 95-99; P-in-c Stainforth *Sheff* 99-02; V from 02. *The Vicarage, Field Road, Stainforth, Doncaster DN7 5AQ* Tel (01302) 841295 E-mail allingtonandrew@hotmail.com

ALLINGTON-SMITH, Canon Richard. b 28. Lon Univ BA49 MA52. Wells Th Coll 54. **d** 56 **p** 57. C Milton next Gravesend Ch Ch *Roch* 56-61; R Cuxton 61-67; V Rainham 67-79; V Gt Yarmouth *Nor* 79-89; TR 89-91; Hon Can Nor Cathl 86-98; rtd 91; P-in-c Nor St Andr *Nor* 91-98; Perm to Offic from 98. *14 Yare Court, 22A Yarmouth Road, Norwich NR7 0EF* Tel (01603) 437185

ALLINSON, Capt Paul Timothy. b 63. CA Tr Coll 82 Edin Th Coll 89. **d** 91 **p** 92. C Peterlee *Dur* 91-94; Dio Children's Adv from 94; C Shadforth 94-97; C Sherburn w Pittington 94-97; P-in-c Byers Green from 97. *St Peter's Rectory, Byers Green, Spennymoor DL16 7NW* Tel (01388) 606659 Mobile 07753-453583 E-mail revdpaul@lineone.net

ALLISON, Elliott Desmond. b 36. Univ of S Africa BA64 K Coll Lon MTh74. S Africa Federal Th Coll. **d** 69 **p** 70. *Flat 1, 20 Southview Gardens, Worthing BN11 5JA*

ALLISON, James Timothy. b 61. Man Univ BSc83. Oak Hill Th Coll BA89. **d** 89 **p** 90. C Walkden Moor *Man* 89-93; Chapl Huddersfield Univ *Wakef* 93-98; V Erringden from 98. *The Vicarage, Brier Hey Lane, Mytholmroyd, Hebden Bridge HX7 5PJ* Tel (01422) 883130 E-mail j.t.allison@hud.ac.uk

ALLISON, Keith. b 34. Dur Univ BA59. Ely Th Coll 59. **d** 61 **p** 62. C Sculcoates *York* 61-64; C Stainton-in-Cleveland 64-65; C Leeds St Pet *Ripon* 65-70; V Micklefield *York* 70-74; V Appleton-le-Street w Amotherby 74-78; P-in-c Barton le Street 77-78; P-in-c Salton 77-80; R Amotherby w Appleton and Barton-le-Street 78-82; Chapl Lister Hosp Stevenage 82-90; P-in-c St Ippolyts *St Alb* 82-85; V 85-90; Chapl Hitchin Hosp 86-90; Chapl Shotley Bridge Gen Hosp 90-94; Chapl NW Dur HA 90-94; Sen Chapl N Dur Acute Hosps NHS Trust 94-98; Sen Chapl N Dur Healthcare NHS Trust 98-00; rtd 00. *2 Middlewood Road, Lanchester, Durham DH7 0HL* Tel (01207) 529046

ALLISTER, The Ven Donald Spargo. b 52. Peterho Cam BA74 MA77. Trin Coll Bris 74. **d** 76 **p** 77. C Hyde St Geo *Ches* 76-79; C Sevenoaks St Nic *Roch* 79-83; V Birkenhead Ch Ch *Ches* 83-89; R Cheadle 89-02; RD Cheadle 99-02; Adn Ches from 02. *The Rectory, Chester Road, Delamere, Northwich CW8 2HS* Tel (01606) 882184 Fax 301911 E-mail donald.allister@chester.anglican.org

ALLISTON, Cyril John. b 11. Fitzw Ho Cam BA33 MA37. Cuddesdon Coll 33. **d** 35 **p** 36. C Boyne Hill *Ox* 35-37; C Hessle *York* 37-39; S Africa 40-50 and from 71; Chapl S African Ch Railway Miss 40-50; C-in-c Miri Sarawak 50-52; R Jesselton and Adn N Borneo 52-59; Can Kuching 55-59; R Somersham w Pidley and Colne *Ely* 60-63; V Penponds *Truro* 63-70; R Hermanus St Pet 71-76; rtd 76. *Flat 4, Kogelpark, Kleinmond, 7195 South Africa* Tel (0027) (28) 271 3168

ALLMAN, Mrs Susan. b 56. Bris Univ BA77. WEMTC 93. **d** 96 **p** 97. NSM Henleaze *Bris* 96-99; C Southmead 99-02; V Two Mile Hill St Mich from 02. *St Michael's Vicarage, Two Mile Hill, Bristol BS15 8BF* Tel 0117-967 1371

ALLMARK, Leslie. b 48. Open Univ BA90. Man OLM Scheme 98. **d** 01 **p** 02. OLM Halliwell St Luke *Man* from 01. *75 Crosby Road, Bolton BL1 4EJ* Tel (01204) 845795 E-mail leslie@lallmark.freeserve.co.uk

ALLON-SMITH, Roderick David. b 51. Leic Univ BA PhD Cam Univ MA. Ridley Hall Cam 79. **d** 82 **p** 83. C Kinson *Sarum* 82-86; V Westwood *Cov* 86-96; RD Cov S 92-96; P-in-c Radford Semele from 96; Dioc Dir Par Development and Evang from 01. *The Vicarage, 7 Church End, Radford Semele, Leamington Spa CV31 1TA* Tel (01926) 427374 or 452123 Fax 452123 E-mail allonsmith@bigfoot.com

ALLPORT, David Jack. b 55. Ox Univ BA Birm Univ DPS MEd. Qu Coll Birm 78. **d** 80 **p** 81. C Abingdon w Shippon *Ox* 80-83; C-in-c Woodgate Valley CD *Birm* 83-91; Perm to Offic *Lich* from 91. *122 Cherry Tree Avenue, Walsall WS5 4JL* Tel (01922) 640059

ALLRED, Frank. b 23. Tyndale Hall Bris 62. **d** 64 **p** 65. C Halliwell St Pet *Man* 64-67; V Ravenhead *Liv* 67-75; R Chadwell *Chelmsf* 75-82; TV Heworth H Trin *York* 82-86; rtd 87; Perm to Offic *York* from 87. *12 Viking Road, Bridlington YO16 6TW* Tel (01262) 677321

ALLSO, Michael Neal. b 48. FRICS72 MCIArb73 MAE00. SW Minl Tr Course 95. **d** 98 **p** 99. NSM Ex St Thos and Em *Ex* 98-01; NSM Colyton, Southleigh, Offwell, Widworthy etc 01-03; NSM Colyton, Musbury, Southleigh and Branscombe from 03. *70 Roman Way, Honiton EX14 1PT* Tel (01404) 549951 E-mail frmichaelallso@aol.com

ALLSOP, Anthony James. b 37. AKC62. **d** 63 **p** 64. C Leytonstone St Marg w St Columba *Chelmsf* 63-68; V Gt Ilford St Alb 68-80; V Gainsborough St Jo *Linc* 80-85; V Hockerill *St Alb* 85-02; Chapl Herts and Essex Hosp Bp's Stortford 85-95; Chapl Essex and Herts Community NHS Trust 95-01; Chapl N Essex Mental Health Partnership NHS Trust 01-02; rtd 02. *63 Longdown Road, Congleton CW12 4QH* Tel (01260) 280628

ALLSOP, Mrs Beryl Anne. b 45. EMMTC 94. **d** 97 **p** 98. NSM Clipstone *S'well* 97-00; NSM Blidworth w Rainworth from 00. *The Vicarage, 2 Kirks Croft, Blidworth, Mansfield NG21 0QU* Tel (01623) 792306

ALLSOP, David George. b 48. Wycliffe Hall Ox DipMin99. **d** 99 **p** 00. C Chenies and Lt Chalfont, Latimer and Flaunden *Ox* 99-02; P-in-c from 02. *The Rectory, Chenies, Rickmansworth WD3 6ER* Tel (01923) 284433 Mobile 07818-441431 E-mail dgaera@aol.com

ALLSOP, Patrick Leslie Fewtrell. b 52. Fitzw Coll Cam BA74 MA78. Ripon Coll Cuddesdon BA78 MA83. **d** 79 **p** 80. C Barrow St Matt *Carl* 79-82; Chapl Eton Coll 82-88; Chapl K Sch Roch 89-02; Hon PV Roch Cathl Roch 89-97; Chapl St Paul's Sch Barnes from 02. *St Paul's School, Lonsdale Road, London SW13 9JT* Tel (020) 8748 9162

ALLSOP, Peter William. b 33. Kelham Th Coll 58. **d** 58 **p** 59. C Woodford St Barn *Chelmsf* 58-61; C Urmpland *Liv* 61-65; V Wigan St Geo 65-71; P-in-c Marham *Ely* 71-72; TV Fincham 72-76; V Trawden *Blackb* 76-90; C Marton 90-92; C S Shore H Trin 92-98; rtd 98; Perm to Offic *Blackb* from 98. *31 Lomond Avenue, Blackpool FY3 9QL* Tel (01253) 696624 E-mail peter.w.allsop@amserve.net

ALLSOP, Canon Christine. b 47. Aston Univ BSc68. S Dios Minl Tr Scheme 86. **d** 89 **p** 94. C Caversham St Pet and Mapledurham etc *Ox* 89-94; C Bracknell 94; TV 94-98; P-in-c Bourne Valley *Sarum* 98-00; TR from 00; RD Alderbury from 99; Can and Preb Sarum Cathl from 02. *The Rectory, High Street, Porton, Salisbury SP4 0LH* Tel (01980) 610305 E-mail allsopps@globalnet.co.uk

ALLSOPP, Mark Dennis. b 66. Cuddesdon Coll 93. **d** 96 **p** 97. C Hedworth *Dur* 96-98; C Gt Aycliffe 98-00; TV from 00. *St Francis Vicarage, Burnhope, Newton Aycliffe DL5 7ER* Tel (01325) 321533 E-mail mark@dallsopp.fsworld.co.uk

ALLSOPP, Mrs Patricia Ann. b 48. St Mary's Coll Cheltenham CertEd69. Qu Coll Birm. **d** 00 **p** 01. C Upton-on-Severn, Ripple, Earls Croome etc *Worc* from 00. *8 Hillview Gardens, Upton-upon-Severn, Worcester WR8 0QJ* Tel (01684) 594463 E-mail tricia@easynet.co.uk

ALLSOPP, Stephen Robert. b 50. BSc71 MSc72 PhD75. Mon Dioc Tr Scheme 81. **d** 84 **p** 85. NSM Trevethin *Mon* 84-88; Asst Chapl K Sch Roch from 88; Hon PV Roch Cathl *Roch* from 89; Chapl K Prep Sch Roch from 99. *33 St Margarets Street, Rochester ME1 1UF* Tel (01634) 409878 E-mail stephen@theallsopps.freeserve.co.uk

ALLSWORTH, Peter Thomas. b 44. St Mich Coll Llan 93. **d** 93 **p** 94. C Prestatyn *St As* 93-96; V Esclusham from 96. *The Vicarage, Vicarage Hill, Rhostyllen, Wrexham LL14 4AR* Tel (01978) 354438

ALLTON, Canon Paul Irving. b 38. Man Univ BA60 Dur Univ DipTh62. **d** 63 **p** 64. C Kibworth Beauchamp *Leic* 63-66; C Reading St Mary V *Ox* 66-70; R Caston *Nor* 70-75; R Caston w Griston, Mert and Thompson 70-75; P-in-c Sturston w Thompson and Tottington 70-75; V Holme-next-the-Sea 75-80; V Hunstanton St Mary w Lt Ringstead 75-80; V Hunstanton St Mary w Ringstead Parva, Holme etc 80-85; RD Heacham and Rising 81-85; Hon Can Nor Cathl 85-93; TR Lowestoft and Kirkley 85-93; TR Keynsham *B & W* 93-96; TR Gaywood *Nor* 96-01; rtd 01; Perm to Offic *Nor* from 01. *Chalk Bank, Herrings Lane, Burnham Market, King's Lynn PE31 8DW* Tel (01328) 738341

ALLUM, Jeremy Warner. b 32. Wycliffe Hall Ox 60. **d** 62 **p** 63. C Hornchurch St Andr *Chelmsf* 62-67; P-in-c W Derby St Luke *Liv* 67-69; V 69-75; P-in-c Boulton *Derby* 75-90; RD Melbourne 86-90; V Hathersage 90-98; rtd 98; Perm to Offic *Derby* from 98. *32 Sandown Avenue, Mickleover, Derby DE3 0QQ* Tel (01332) 231253

ALLWOOD, Linda Angela Fredrika. b 76. Newc Univ BA00. Cranmer Hall Dur 01. **d** 03. C Northampton St Giles *Pet* from 03. *18 The Avenue, Cliftonville, Northampton NN1 5BT* Tel (01604) 634060 Mobile 07939-001160 E-mail linda_allwood@hotmail.com

ALLWRIGHT, Mrs Janet Margaret. b 40. Oak Hill Th Coll 87. **d** 90 **p** 94. NSM Galleywood Common *Chelmsf* 90-93; NSM Downham w S Hanningfield 93-99; Chapl HM Pris Bullwood Hall 98-03; TV Canvey Is *Chelmsf* from 03. *St Katherine's House, 17 The Ridings, Canvey Island SS8 9QZ* Tel (01268) 681318

ALMOND, Kenneth Alfred. b 36. EMMTC 76 Linc Th Coll 78. **d** 79 **p** 80. C Boston *Linc* 79-82; V Surfleet 82-87; RD Elloe W 86-96; V Spalding St Jo w Deeping St Nicholas 87-98; rtd 98; Perm to Offic *Linc* from 99. *1 Buckingham Close, Fishtoft, Boston PE21 9QB* Tel (01205) 352805 Fax as telephone E-mail kennethhilary@aol.com

ALP, Mrs Elaine Alison. b 54. Oak Hill Th Coll 87. **d** 00. Dn-in-c Blackb St Mich w St Jo and H Trin *Blackb* 00-02; Par Dn Fleetwood St Nic from 02. *15 Leighton Avenue, Fleetwood FY7 8BP* Tel (01253) 777775

ALPIAR, Ronald. b 29. Pemb Coll Cam BA52. Ely Th Coll 52. **d** 54 **p** 55. C Plaistow St Andr *Chelmsf* 54-56; SSF 54-57; rtd 79. *84 Dudsbury Road, Ferndown BH22 8RG* Tel (01202) 590314

ALSBURY, Colin. b 56. Ch Ch Ox BA77 MA81. Ripon Coll Cuddesdon 77. **d** 80 **p** 81. C Oxton *Ches* 80-84; V Crewe All SS and St Paul 84-92; Ind Chapl 92-95; V Kettering St Andr *Pet* 95-02; V Frome St Jo *B & W* from 02; V Woodlands from 02. *St John's Vicarage, Vicarage Close, Frome BA11 1QL* Tel (01373) 472853 E-mail colin.alsbury@zetnet.co.uk

ALSOP, Eric George. b 12. Liv Univ BA. Dorchester Miss Coll 34. **d** 37 **p** 38. C Grimsby All SS *Linc* 37-39; Chapl RAF 39-58; Asst Chapl-in-Chief RAF 58-67; Hon Chapl to The Queen 65-67; V Over *Ely* 67-69; P-in-c Bodiam *Chich* 69-72; V Burwash Weald 72-77; rtd 77; Perm to Offic *Chich* 77-00; *Cant* from 90; *St Alb* from 00. *4 Windsor Road, Barton-le-Clay, Bedford MK45 4LX* Tel (01582) 881444

ALTHAM, Donald. b 40. Liv Univ BA62. N Ord Course 87. **d** 90 **p** 91. NSM Ramsbottom St Jo and St Paul *Man* 90-96; Chapl Asst Burnley Health Care NHS Trust from 93; Lic Preacher *Man* from 96; NSM Holcombe from 99. *387 Whalley Road, Ramsbottom, Bury BL0 0ER* Tel (01706) 822025

✠**ALVAREZ-VELAZQUEZ, The Rt Revd David Andres.** b 41. Inter American Univ Puerto Rico BA62 Caribbean Cen of Advanced Studies. NY Th Sem MDiv65. **d** 65 **p** 65 **c** 87. Puerto Rico from 65; C St Mich 65; Chapl Episc Cathl Sch 65-67; R St Mark 67-70; R St Jo Cathl 70-79; R St Hilda 79-87; Bp Puerto Rico from 87. *PO Box 902, Saint Just Station, Saint Just, 00978, Puerto Rico* Tel (001) (787) 761 9800 Mobile 376 4125 Fax 761 0320 E-mail iep@spiderlinkpr.net

ALVEY, Martyn Clifford. b 53. FTC74 HNC74. EMMTC DTPS99. **d** 99 **p** 00. NSM Burton Joyce w Bulcote and Stoke Bardolph *S'well* 99-02; C Worksop St Jo from 02. *27 Sunnyside, Worksop S81 7LN* Tel (01909) 473998

AMAT-TORREGROSA, Gabriel José. b 42. R Superior Coll of Music Madrid MA63. Bapt Th Sem Ruschlikon Zürich 64. **d** 71 **p** 72. Spain 71-98; Asst Chapl Zürich *Eur* from 98. *Lettenmattstrasse 33, 8903 Birmendsdorf, Switzerland* Tel (0041) (1) 737 4187 Fax 252 6042

AMBANI, Stephen Frederick. b 45. Univ of Wales (Lamp) BA90. St Jo Coll Nottm 86 CA Tr Coll Nairobi 70. **d** 83 **p** 83. Kenya 83-93; C Glan Ely *Llan* 93-95; C Whitchurch 95-97; V Nantymwel w Wyndham 97-99; V Tonyrefail w Gilfach Goch and Llandyfodwg from 99. *The Vicarage, High Street, Tonyrefail, Porth CF39 8PL* Tel (01443) 670330

AMBROSE, Edgar. b 22. N Ord Course 80. **d** 81 **p** 82. NSM Broughton *Blackb* 81-94; Perm to Offic from 94. *76 Conway Drive, Fulwood, Preston PR2 3EQ* Tel (01772) 464288

AMBROSE, James Field. b 51. Newc Univ BA73. Cranmer Hall Dur DipTh80. **d** 80 **p** 81. C Barrow St Geo w St Luke *Carl* 80-83; C Workington St Jo 83-85; Ch Radio Officer BBC Radio Shropshire 85-88; R Montford w Shrawardine and Fitz *Lich* 85-88; Chapl RAF 88-92; Voc and Min Adv CPAS 92-99; TV Syston *Leic* from 99. *The Vicarage, 25 Ling Dale, East Goscote, Leicester LE7 8XW* Tel 0116-260 5938 E-mail jambrose@leicester.anglican.org

AMBROSE, John George. b 30. Lon Univ BD Ox Univ PGCE. **d** 74 **p** 75. C Rayleigh *Chelmsf* 74-79; V Hadleigh St Barn 79-95; rtd 95; Perm to Offic *Chelmsf* from 95. *9 Fairview Gardens, Leigh-on-Sea SS9 3PD* Tel (01702) 474632

AMBROSE, Thomas. b 47. Sheff Univ BSc69 PhD73 Em Coll Cam BA77 MA84. Westcott Ho Cam 75. **d** 78 **p** 79. C Morpeth *Newc* 78-81; C N Gosforth 81-84; R March St Jo *Ely* 84-93; RD March 89-93; P-in-c Witchford w Wentworth 93-99; Dioc Dir of Communications 93-99; Chapl K Sch Ely 94-96; V Trumpington *Ely* from 99. *The Vicarage, Grantchester Road, Trumpington, Cambridge CB2 2LH* Tel (01223) 841262 Mobile 07711-263083 E-mail tom.ambrose@ely.anglican.org

AMES, Jeremy Peter. b 49. K Coll Lon BD71 AKC71. **d** 72 **p** 73. C Kennington St Jo *S'wark* 72-75; Chapl RN from 75; RN Engineering Coll from 86; RN Dir of Studies RAF Chapl Sch from 89; USA 91-93; Naval Base Chapl Portsmouth 96. *Royal Naval Chaplaincy Service, Room 203, Victory Building, HM Naval Base, Portsmouth PO1 3LS* Tel (023) 9272 7903 Fax 9272 7111 E-mail cyberjpa@aol.com

AMES, Reginald John. b 27. Bps' Coll Cheshunt 51. **d** 54 **p** 55. C Edmonton St Alpheege *Lon* 54-58; C Mill Hill Jo Keble Ch 58-60; P-in-c Northwood Hills St Edm 61-64; V 64-92; rtd 92; Hon C Moffat *Glas* from 92. *Oakbank, Lochwood, Beattock, Moffat DG10 9PS* Tel (01683) 300381

AMES-LEWIS, Richard. b 45. Em Coll Cam BA66 MA70. Westcott Ho Cam 76. **d** 78 **p** 79. C Bromley St Mark *Roch* 78-81; C Edenbridge 81-84; V 84-91; P-in-c Crockham Hill H Trin 84-91; P-in-c Barnes St Mary *S'wark* 91-97; TR Barnes 97-00; RD Richmond and Barnes 94-00; TR E Dereham and Scarning *Nor* from 00; P-in-c Swanton Morley w Beetley w E Bilney and

Hoe from 02; RD Dereham in Mitford from 03. *The Vicarage, 1 Vicarage Meadows, Dereham NR19 1TW* Tel (01362) 693680 *or* 693143 E-mail rameslew@fish.co.uk

AMEY, Graham George. b 44. Lon Univ BD70. Tyndale Hall Bris 67. **d** 71 **p** 72. C Hornsey Rise St Mary *Lon* 71-74; C St Helens St Helen *Liv* 74-79; V Liv All So Springwood 79-91; V Whiston 91-02; V Aigburth from 02. *St Anne's Vicarage, 389 Aigburth Road, Liverpool L17 6BH* Tel 0151-727 1101

AMEY, John Mark. b 59. Ripon Coll Cuddesdon. **d** 00 **p** 01. C Winchmore Hill St Paul *Lon* from 00; Chapl ATC from 03. *St Paul's Lodge, 58 Church Hill, London N21 1JA* Tel (020) 8882 3298 Mobile 07905-122090 E-mail mark.amey@london.anglican.org

AMIS, Ronald. b 37. Linc Th Coll 74. **d** 76 **p** 77. C Grantham w Manthorpe *Linc* 76-78; C Grantham 78-79; P-in-c Holbeach Hurn 79-81; V Long Bennington w Foston 81-91; V Corby Glen 91-93; RD Grantham 90-92; rtd 93; Perm to Offic *Pet* 93-03. *11 Green Street, Great Gonerby, Grantham NG31 8LD*

AMOR, Peter David Card. b 28. AKC53. **d** 54 **p** 55. C St Margaret's-on-Thames *Lon* 54; C Leighton Buzzard *St Alb* 54-58; C Toxteth Park St Agnes *Liv* 58-62; C-in-c Aldershot Ascension CD *Guildf* 62-65; V Bingley H Trin *Bradf* 65-72; V The Collingbournes *Sarum* 72-75; R The Collingbournes and Everleigh 75-77; V Thorpe *Guildf* 77-85; P-in-c Monks Risborough *Ox* 85-89; R *Ox* 89-94; rtd 94; Perm to Offic *Ox* 97-00. *1 Culverton Hill, Princes Risborough HP27 0DZ* Tel (01844) 345236

AMOS, Alan John. b 44. OBE79. K Coll Lon BD66 AKC67 MTh67. St Steph Ho Ox 68. **d** 69 **p** 70. C Hoxton H Trin w St Mary *Lon* 69-72; Lebanon 73-82; Lect Liturg Studies Westcott Ho Cam 82-85; Vice-Prin 85-89; Prin Cant Sch of Min 89-94; Co-Prin SEITE 94-96; Hon PV Roch Cathl *Roch* from 95; Chapl Medway NHS Trust from 96. *Medway Hospital, Windmill Road, Gillingham ME7 5NY* Tel (01634) 830000 ext 3561 Fax 815811

AMOS, Brother. See YONGE, James Mohun

AMOS, Colin James. b 62. Univ of Wales (Lamp) BA83 Univ of Wales (Cardiff) CQSW85. Ridley Hall Cam 93. **d** 93 **p** 94. C Aberdare *Llan* 93-96; V Port Talbot St Theodore from 96. *St Theodore's Vicarage, Talbot Road, Port Talbot SA13 1LB* Tel (01639) 883935 Fax 760104 E-mail colinjamos@compuserve.com

AMOS, Gerald. b 31. St Mich Coll Llan. **d** 58 **p** 62. C Rhosymedre *St As* 58-59; C Peckham St Andr w All SS *S'wark* 62-65; C Walworth 65-72; C S Wimbledon H Trin 72-74; C S Wimbledon H Trin and St Pet 74-75; C Warlingham w Chelsham and Farleigh 75-78; TV Speke St Aid *Liv* 78-88; P-in-c Fazakerley St Nath 88-92; TV Walton-on-the-Hill 92-96; rtd 96. *6 Church Walks, Old Colwyn, Colwyn Bay LL29 9RU* Tel (01492) 512602 E-mail gerald.amos@btinternet.com

AMOS, Patrick Henry. b 31. Roch Th Coll 63. **d** 65 **p** 66. C Strood St Nic *Roch* 65-68; C Polegate *Chich* 68-71; V Horam 71-83; R Chiddingly w E Hoathly 83-93; rtd 93; Perm to Offic *Cant* and *Roch* from 93; Clergy Widows' Officer Maidstone Adnry *Cant* from 95. *20 Fauchons Close, Bearsted, Maidstone ME14 4BB* Tel (01622) 736725

AMYS, Richard James Rutherford. b 58. Trin Coll Bris BA90. **d** 90 **p** 91. C Whitnash *Cov* 90-93; P-in-c Gravesend H Family w Ifield *Roch* 93-95; R 95-99; R Eastington, Frocester, Haresfield etc *Glouc* from 99. *The Rectory, Mill End Lane, Eastington, Stonehouse GL10 3AG* Tel and fax (01453) 822437 Mobile 07796-956050 E-mail richardjramys@aol.com

ANAN, Gabriel. b 48. Univ of E Lon MA96 Middx Univ BA03 MCIT92 ICI Univ Amman BA92. NTMTC 00. **d** 03. NSM Victoria Docks St Luke *Chelmsf* from 03. *41 Camel Road, London E16 2DE* Tel (020) 7473 6003 Mobile 07734-707887 E-mail gabriel58@hotmail.com

ANAND, Jessie Nesam Nallammal. b 54. BSc BEd MA BD MTh. EMMTC. **d** 03. NSM Birstall and Wanlip *Leic* from 03. *St Alban's House, Weymouth Street, Leicester LE4 6FN* Tel 0116-266 1002

ANCRUM, John. b 28. Clifton Th Coll 55. **d** 58 **p** 59. C Branksome St Clem *Sarum* 58-61; C Sparkhill St Jo *Birm* 61-63; V Tibshelf *Derby* 63-70; Canada 70-74; P-in-c Salwarpe *Worc* 74-75; P-in-c Tibberton w Bredicot and Warndon 75-76; P-in-c Hadzor w Oddingley 76-78; Lic to Offic *Chelmsf* 78-81; Chapl HM Pris Stafford 81-82; Chapl HM Pris Dartmoor 82-89; Lic to Offic *Ex* 88-89; Perm to Offic *Ex* from 89. *14 Merrivale View Road, Dousland, Yelverton PL20 6NS* Tel (01822) 853909

ANDAYI, Elphas Ombuna. b 57. St Phil Th Coll Maseno 78. **d** 79 **p** 81. Kenya 79-98 and from 99; Provost Butere 92-99; C Sparkhill w Greet and Sparkbrook *Birm* 98-99. *PO Box 199, Bukura, Kenya* Tel (00254) (333) 20038 Fax 20412

ANDERS, Mrs Erika Gertrud. b 45. ACT 88 St Jo Coll Nottm 99. **d** 92 **p** 02. C Proserpine St Paul Australia 92; NSM Hamburg *Eur* from 99. *Niendorfer Kirchenweg 5C, 22459 Hamburg, Germany* Tel (0049) (40) 582850 Mobile 162-700 0404 Fax (40) 582841

ANDERS, Jonathan Cyril. b 36. Wycliffe Hall Ox 69. **d** 71 **p** 72. C Prescot *Liv* 71-74; C-in-c 74-76; R Wavertree St Mary 76-81; V

Aigburth 81-01; rtd 01. *3 Silverleigh, Liverpool L17 5BL* Tel 0151-728 9997

ANDERS, Roger John. b 38. Man Univ LLB61. N Ord Course 91. **d** 94 **p** 95. NSM New Mills *Derby* 94-97; NSM Buxton w Burbage and King Sterndale 97-98; NSM Adderley, Ash, Calverhall, Ightfield etc *Lich* 98-03; R from 03. *The Rectory, Moreton Say, Market Drayton TF9 3RS* Tel (01630) 638110 E-mail anders@u.genie.co.uk

ANDERSEN, Paul John. b 49. Univ of Alabama BA. Protestant Th Sem Virginia MDiv77. **d** 77 **p** 83. USA 77-82; Belize 82-84; Chapl Zagreb *Eur* 84-85; Chapl Belgrade 85-86; USA 86-89; India 89-91; Sierra Leone 92-93; Chapl Valletta *Eur* 94-96; Chapl Skopje 96-98; NSM Worcester St Luke USA from 98. *109 Richmond Avenue, Worcester, MA 01602-1517, USA* E-mail paulandersen@earthlink.net

ANDERSON, Albert Geoffrey (Geoff). b 42. Ex Univ BA65 MA67. Qu Coll Birm DipTh75. **d** 75 **p** 76. C Helsby and Ince *Ches* 75-77; C Helsby and Dunham-on-the-Hill 77-78; TV Gleadless *Sheff* 78-85; V Thorpe Hesley 85-92; R Ribbesford w Bewdley and Dowles *Worc* 92-03; rtd 03. *57 Park Lane, Bewdley DY12 2HA* Tel (01299) 404773 E-mail geoffanderson@bigfoot.com

ANDERSON, Alice Calder. b 50. Moray Ho Coll of Educn DipEd76 Dip Counselling 99. Local Minl Tr Course 90. **d** 93 **p** 95. NSM Dalkeith *Edin* from 93. *54 Eldindean Terrace, Bonnyrigg EH19 2HQ* Tel 0131-663 3371

ANDERSON, Mrs Ann. b 57. Cranmer Hall Dur 01. **d** 03. C Chester le Street *Dur* from 03. *107 Rydal Road, Chester le Street DH2 3DS* Tel 0191-388 4642

ANDERSON, Preb Brian Arthur. b 42. Sarum Th Coll 75. **d** 78 **p** 79. C Plymouth St Jas Ham *Ex* 78-80; Org Sec CECS *B & W, Ex* and *Truro* 80-89; TV Saltash *Truro* 89-94; RD E Wivelshire 91-94; P-in-c St Breoke and Egloshayle 94-96; R 96-02; RD Trigg Minor and Bodmin 95-02; P-in-c Torpoint from 02; P-in-c Antony w Sheviock from 02; Preb St Endellion from 99. *The Rectory, Sheviock, Torpoint PL11 3EH* Tel (01503) 230622 Mobile 07710-231219

ANDERSON, Brian Glaister. b 35. K Coll Lon 57. **d** 79 **p** 79. Chapl St Fran Sch Hooke 79; C Croydon *Cant* 80-83; Dep Chapl HM Youth Cust Cen Glen Parva 83-84; Chapl HM YOI Hewell Grange 84-89; Chapl HM Rem Cen Brockhill 84-89; Chapl HM Pris Parkhurst 89-96; rtd 96. *The Garden Flat, 126A High Street, Portsmouth PO1 2HW* Tel (023) 9236 9441 Mobile 07967-109117 E-mail brianders@aol.com

ANDERSON, David. b 19. Selw Coll Cam BA41 MA45. Wycliffe Hall Ox 47. **d** 49 **p** 50. C Bishopwearmouth St Gabr *Dur* 49-52; Tutor St Aid Birkenhead 52-56; Chapl Heswall Nautical Sch 52-53; Nigeria 56-62; Prin Wycliffe Hall Ox 62-69; Sen Lect Wall Hall Coll Aldenham 70-74; Prin Lect 74-84; rtd 84; Perm to Offic *Dur* 84-02. *24 Old Hall Avenue, Duffield, Belper DE56 4GN* Tel (01332) 840154

ANDERSON, David Graham. b 33. MICE MIStructE. St Mich Coll Llan 85. **d** 88 **p** 89. C Llanishen and Llanedeyrn *Llan* 88-90; C Fazeley *Lich* 90-94; Perm to Offic *Heref* 96-01; rtd 98; Perm to Offic *Llan* from 01. *c/o J Williams Esq, 78 Lakeside Drive, Cardiff CF23 6DG* Tel (029) 2075 5232

ANDERSON, David Lee. b 75. Westmr Coll Ox BTh96. Ripon Coll Cuddesdon MTh99. **d** 98 **p** 99. C Balderton *S'well* 98-02; V Harworth from 02. *The Vicarage, Tickhill Road, Harworth, Doncaster DN11 8PD* Tel (01302) 744157

ANDERSON, David Richard. b 58. Lanc Univ BEd79. EAMTC DipHE99. **d** 99 **p** 00. C N Walsham w Antingham *Nor* 99-02; R Stalham, E Ruston, Brunstead, Sutton and Ingham from 02. *The Vicarage, Camping Field Lane, Stalham, Norwich NR12 9DT* Tel (01692) 580250 E-mail revdanderson@bigfoot.com

ANDERSON, Digby Carter. b 44. PhD. **d** 85 **p** 86. NSM Luton St Sav *St Alb* from 85. *17 Hardwick Place, Woburn Sands, Milton Keynes MK17 8QQ* Tel (01908) 584526

ANDERSON, Donald Whimbey. b 31. Trin Coll Toronto BA54 MA58 LTh57 STB57 ThD71. **d** 56 **p** 57. Canada 57-59, 75-88 and from 96; Japan 59-74; Philippines 74-75; Dir Ecum Affairs ACC 88-96; rtd 96. *Conference on the Religious Life, 31 Island View Drive, RR1, Little Britain ON, Canada K0M 2C0* Tel (001) (705) 786 3330 Fax as telephone E-mail da@ecunet.org

ANDERSON, Francis Hindley. b 20. Ch Coll Cam BA43 MA47. Wycliffe Hall Ox. **d** 44 **p** 45. C Surbiton St Matt *S'wark* 44-48; C Loughborough All SS *Leic* 48-50; C Pimlico St Pet w Westmr Ch Ch *Lon* 50-59; V Upper Chelsea St Sav 59-91; rtd 92; P-in-c Linchmere *Chich* 93-96; C Lynchmere and Camelsdale 96-97; Perm to Offic *Guildf* 96-97; Perm to Offic *Chich* from 97. *35 Oaklands, Tanners Lane, Haslemere GU27 3RD* Tel (01428) 642133

ANDERSON, Geoff. See ANDERSON, Albert Geoffrey

ANDERSON, Canon Gordon Fleming. b 19. TCD BA41 MA46. **d** 42 **p** 43. C Drumholm *D & R* 42-46; C Clooney 46-47; I Termonamongan 47-57; P-in-c Cumber Lower 57-61; I 61-72; I Cumber Lower w Banagher 72-94; Can Derry Cathl 76-94; Preb Howth St Patr Cathl Dublin 86-94; rtd 94. *Woodlands, 85 Dunboe Road, Ardiclave, Coleraine BT51 4JR*

ANDERSON, Gordon Stuart. b 49. St Jo Coll Nottm. **d** 82 **p** 83. C Hattersley *Ches* 82-86; C Dagenham *Chelmsf* 86-91; TV Mildenhall *St E* 91-01; V Southminster *Chelmsf* from 01. *The Vicarage, Burnham Road, Southminster CM0 7ES* Tel (01621) 772300 Mobile 07759-550990 E-mail gordonand42@aol.com

ANDERSON, Graeme Edgar. b 59. Poly of Wales BSc82. St Jo Coll Nottm MTh02. **d** 02 **p** 03. C Brislington St Luke *Bris* from 02. *119 Birchwood Road, Bristol BS4 4RB* Tel 0117-373 0293 Mobile 07762-258393 E-mail graeme.judy@whsmithnet.co.uk

ANDERSON, Hugh Richard Oswald. b 35. Roch Th Coll 68. **d** 70 **p** 71. C Minehead *B & W* 70-76; C Darley w S Darley *Derby* 76-80; R Hasland 80-94; V Temple Normanton 80-94; rtd 94; Perm to Offic *Derby* from 94. *32 Barry Road, Brimington, Chesterfield S43 1PX* Tel (01246) 551020

ANDERSON, James. b 36. Magd Coll Ox BA59 MA64 Leeds Univ MA00. **d** 02 **p** 03. NSM Holme and Seaton Ross Gp *York* from 02. *Lincoln Flatts House, Foggathorpe, Selby YO8 6PZ* Tel (01430) 860106 Fax as telephone

ANDERSON, James Frederick Wale. b 32. G&C Coll Cam BA58 MA62. Cuddesdon Coll 60. **d** 62 **p** 63. C Leagrave St Alb 62-65; C Eastleigh *Win* 65-70; R Sherfield-on-Loddon 70-86; P-in-c Stratfield Saye w Hartley Wespall 75-86; R Sherfield-on-Loddon and Stratfield Saye etc 86-87; R Newton Valence, Selborne and E Tisted w Colemore 87-99; rtd 99; Chapl Surrey Hants Borders NHS Trust from 01; Hon C Farnham *Guildf* from 01. *1 Potter's Gate, Farnham GU9 7EJ* Tel (01252) 710728

ANDERSON, Canon James Raffan. b 33. FRSA90 Edin Univ MA54. Edin Th Coll 56. **d** 58 **p** 59. Chapl St Andr Cathl *Ab* 58-59; Prec St Andr Cathl 59-62; CF (TA) 59-67; Chapl Aber Univ *Ab* 60-62; Chapl Glas Univ *Glas* 62-69; Chapl Lucton Sch 69-71; Chapl Barnard Castle Sch 71-74; Asst Dir of Educn *Blackb* 74-78; P-in-c Whitechapel 74-78; Bp's Officer for Min *Cov* 78-87; Hon Can Cov Cathl 83-87; Miss Sec Gen Syn Bd for Miss and Unity 87-92; rtd 92; Perm to Offic *Blackb* from 98. *Eccles Moss Farm, Bleasdale Road, Whitechapel, Preston PR3 2ER* Tel (01995) 641280 Fax as telephone E-mail jamesanders@onetel.net.uk

ANDERSON (née FLAHERTY), Mrs Jane Venitia. b 68. Oak Hill Th Coll DipHE91 BA92. **d** 93 **p** 94. C Timperley *Ches* 93-97; C Cheshunt *St Alb* 97-99; P-in-c N Springfield *Chelmsf* from 99. *32 Oak Lodge Tye, Springfield, Chelmsford CM1 6GZ* Tel (01245) 466160

ANDERSON, Jeremy. *See* ANDERSON, Brian Glaister

ANDERSON, Jeremy Dudgeon. b 41. Edin Univ BSc63. Trin Coll Bris 75. **d** 77 **p** 78. C Bitterne *Win* 77-81; TV Wexcombe *Sarum* 81-91; Evang Enabler (Reading Deanery) *Ox* 91-96; V Epsom Common Ch Ch *Guildf* 96-00; C Kinson *Sarum* from 00. *80 Pine Vale Crescent, Bournemouth BH10 6BJ* Tel (01202) 520778

ANDERSON, Mrs Joanna Elisabeth. b 53. St Andr Univ MTh75. EMMTC 85. **d** 88 **p** 95. Par Dn Thurgarton *Linc* 88-92; Warden Iona Community *Arg* 92-95; R S Trin Broads *Nor* 95-02; Dir Body, Mind, Spirit Project from 02; Public Preacher *Nor* from 02. *1 Church Cottages, Ranworth, Norwich NR13 6HS* Tel (01603) 270680

ANDERSON, John Michael. b 17. Madras Univ BA38. St Aug Coll Cant 59. **d** 60 **p** 61. C Smethwick St Alb *Birm* 60-62; C Stockland Green 62-65; C Braunstone *Leic* 65-69; Trinidad and Tobago 69-73; V Leic St Sav *Leic* 74-82; rtd 82; Perm to Offic *Leic* 82-97. *3 St Mary's Avenue, Braunstone, Leicester LE3 3FT* Tel 0116-225 0378

ANDERSON, John Robert. b 75. QUB BD96 TCD MPhil98. CITC 96. **d** 98 **p** 99. C Magherafelt *Arm* 98-02; C Ballymena w Ballyclug *Conn* from 02. *6 Rockgrove Brae, Ballymena BT43 5HY* Tel (028) 2564 2805

ANDERSON, Canon Keith Bernard. b 36. Qu Coll Cam BA60 MA64. Tyndale Hall Bris 60. **d** 62 **p** 63. C Bootle St Leon *Liv* 63-65; Burundi 66-74; Kenya 74-83; Hon Can Mt Kenya E from 77; P-in-c Doddington w Wychling *Cant* 83-88; P-in-c Newnham 88; Chapl Cannes w Grasse *Eur* 88-94; Dir and Chapl Mulberry Ho High Ongar 94-95; TV Horley *S'wark* 96-01; rtd 01; Perm to Offic *S'wark* from 01. *93 Rusper Road, Horsham RH12 4BJ* Tel (01403) 262185 E-mail kb.anderson@virgin.net

ANDERSON, Canon Keith Edward. b 42. Fitzw Coll Cam BA77 MA83 MRCS83. Ridley Hall Cam 74. **d** 77 **p** 78. C Goodmayes All SS *Chelmsf* 77-80; Lic to Offic *Truro* 80-87; Chapl Coll of SS Mark and Jo Plymouth *Ex* 80-87; RD Plymouth Moorside 81-86; V Northampton H Sepulchre w St Andr and St Lawr *Pet* 87-98; RD Northn 92-98; Adv for Min Willesden *Lon* 98-03; Adv for Ord Min Development *Win* from 03; Can Res Win Cathl from 03. *Church House, 9 The Close, Winchester SO23 9LS* Tel (01962) 844644 E-mail keithas@amda.fslife.co.uk

ANDERSON, Kenneth. b 38. G&C Coll Cam BA62 MA66. Westcott Ho Cam 63. **d** 65 **p** 66. C Nor St Steph *Nor* 65-68; Chapl Norfolk and Nor Hosp 65-68; C Wareham w Arne *Sarum* 68-71; Chapl Sherborne Sch 71-83; Zimbabwe 83-94; Chapl Van Mildert Coll *Dur* from 95; Chapl Trevelyan Coll from 95; Dioc Vic Adv from 99. *39 Hallgarth Street, Durham DH1 3AT* Tel 091-383 0628 or 374 3770 E-mail kenneth.anderson@durham.ac.uk

ANDERSON, Martin Edward. b 73. Humberside Univ BA95 St Jo Coll Dur BA02. Cranmer Hall Dur 99. **d** 02 **p** 03. C Gt Aycliffe *Dur* from 02. *35 Beechfield, Newton Aycliffe DL5 7AX* Tel (01325) 313699 E-mail martin.anderson@durham.anglican.org

ANDERSON, Canon Michael Garland. b 42. Clifton Th Coll 62. **d** 66 **p** 67. C Fareham St Jo *Portsm* 66-69; C Worting *Win* 69-74; V Hordle from 74; RD Lyndhurst 82-00; Hon Can Win Cathl from 92. *The Vicarage, Stopples Lane, Hordle, Lymington SO41 0HX* Tel (01425) 614428 E-mail canon.m.g.anderson@ukgateway.net

ANDERSON, Canon Michael John Austen. b 35. AKC60. **d** 66 **p** 67. C Southall Ch Redeemer *Lon* 66-69; C Hampstead Garden Suburb 69-73; V S Mimms St Giles 73-80; V The Brents and Davington w Oare and Luddenham *Cant* 80-86; V Margate All SS 86-00; Hon Can Cant Cathl 97-00; rtd 00; Perm to Offic *Cant* from 01. *Camwa Ash, Bull Lane, Boughton under Blean, Faversham ME13 9AH* Tel (01227) 752352 Mobile 07885-211863

ANDERSON, Nicholas Patrick. b 53. Lanc Univ BA87. Allen Hall 79. **d** 81 **p** 82. In RC Ch 81-89; C Gt Crosby St Faith *Liv* 89-92; C Walton-on-the-Hill 92-95; V Pemberton St Fran Kitt Green from 95. *The Vicarage, 42 Sherborne Road, Kitt Green, Wigan WN5 0JA* Tel (01942) 213227 Fax as telephone

ANDERSON, Olaf Emanuel. b 64. Queensland Univ BA88. St Fran Coll Queensland 84. **d** 87 **p** 88. Australia 87-90 and from 94; Hon C Woolloongabba 87; C Cleveland 88-90; C Petersfield *Portsm* 91-93; P-in-c Goodna 94-00; R New Farm from 00. *655 Brunswick Street, New Farm, Qld, Australia 4005* Tel (0061) (7) 3358 1555 Fax 3254 0387 E-mail olaf.anderson@docnet.org.au

ANDERSON, Mrs Pearl Ann. b 46. St Andr Univ MA68 MCIPD74. Cant Sch of Min 90. **d** 93 **p** 00. Par Dn Epping St Jo *Chelmsf* 93-95; Adv to Coun for Soc Resp *Roch* and *Cant* 95-02; Asst Chief Exec Ch in Soc *Roch* and *Cant* from 02; Hon C Biddenden and Smarden from 00. *1 Gibbs Hill, Headcorn, Ashford TN27 9UD* Tel (01622) 890043 or 755014 Fax 693531 E-mail pearlanderson@btopenworld.com *or* pearl@churchinsociety.org

ANDERSON, Peter John. b 44. Nottm Univ BA65 BA73 Ex Univ CertEd66. St Jo Coll Nottm. **d** 74 **p** 75. C Otley *Bradf* 74-77; TV Marfleet *York* 77-84; V Greasbrough *Sheff* 84-95; I Clonmel Union *C, C & R* 95-02; I Rathcooney Union 95-02; Chapl Cannes *Eur* from 02. *Résidence Kent, 4 avenue Général Ferrié, 06400 Cannes, France* Tel (0033) (4) 93 94 54 61 E-mail hmander@oceanfree.net

ANDERSON, Peter Scott. b 49. Nottm Univ BTh72 CertEd. Kelham Th Coll 68. **d** 74 **p** 75. C Sheff Parson Cross St Cecilia *Sheff* 74-77; C Leytonstone St Marg w St Columba *Chelmsf* 77-81; P-in-c Forest Gate St Edm 81-89; V 89-90; P-in-c Plaistow 90-94; V Willesden Green St Andr and St Fran *Lon* from 94. *The Clergy House, St Andrew's Road, London NW10 2QS* Tel (020) 8459 2670

ANDERSON, Canon Roderick Stephen. b 43. Cant Univ (NZ) BSc63 PhD67 New Coll Ox BA72. Wycliffe Hall Ox 70. **d** 74 **p** 74. C Bradf Cathl *Bradf* 73-75; C Allerton 76-78; V Cottingley 78-94; RD Airedale 88-95; Hon Can Bradf Cathl from 94; V Heaton St Barn from 94. *The Vicarage, Parsons Road, Heaton, Bradford BD9 4AY* Tel (01274) 496712 *or* 499354

ANDERSON, Canon Rosemary Ann. b 36. Ex Univ BA59. N Ord Course 83. **dss** 86 **d** 87 **p** 94. Oldham St Paul *Man* 86-87; Hon Par Dn 87-89; Bp's Adv for Women's Min; Par Dn Roughtown 93-94; P-in-c 94-99; Hon Can Man Cathl 96-99; rtd 99; Perm to Offic *Man* 99-03. *11E Rhodes Hill, Lees, Oldham OL4 5EA* Tel 0161-620 1549

ANDERSON, Stuart. b 31. Dur Univ BA52. Linc Th Coll 52. **d** 54 **p** 55. C Billingham St Cuth *Dur* 54-57; C Fulham St Etheldreda *Lon* 57-61; New Zealand from 61. *3 Arataki Road, Havelock North, Hawkes Bay, New Zealand* Tel (0064) (6) 877 8567

ANDERSON, Timothy George. b 59. Ealing Coll of HE BA82. Wycliffe Hall Ox 83. **d** 86 **p** 87. C Harold Wood *Chelmsf* 86-90; C Whitfield *Derby* 90-95; P-in-c Wolverhampton St Luke *Lich* 95-98; V 98-01; I Dundonald *D & D* from 01. *St Elizabeth's Rectory, 26 Ballyregan Road, Dundonald, Belfast BT16 1HY* Tel (028) 9048 3153 *or* 9048 2644

ANDERSON, Timothy James Lane. b 59. Pemb Coll Ox BA81 MA90. St Jo Coll Nottm Dip Th Studies 92. **d** 93 **p** 94. C Reigate St Mary *S'wark* 93-95; Perm to Offic *S'well* from 95. *3 Dale Lane, Beeston, Nottingham NG9 4EA* Tel 0115-922 4773

ANDERTON, David Ernest. b 36. CEng68 MIMechE68. Dioc OLM tr scheme 97. **d** 00 **p** 01. OLM Eccleston Ch Ch *Liv* from 00. *16 Croxteth Drive, Rainford, St Helens WA11 8JZ* Tel (01744) 637600 Mobile 07751-038014

ANDERTON, Frederic Michael. b 31. Pemb Coll Cam MA57 Jung Inst Zürich Dip Analytical Psychology 86 IAAP. Westcott Ho Cam 64. **d** 66 **p** 67. C St John's Wood *Lon* 66-69; C Al Hallows by the Tower etc 70-77; C St Giles Cripplegate w St Bart Moor Lane etc 77-82; C Zürich *Eur* 82-86; Perm to Offic *Lon* from 94; rtd 96. *61 Brassey Road, Winchester SO22 6SB* Tel (01962) 856326 Fax 852851 E-mail robin.anderton@lineone.net

ANDERTON, Peter. b 45. Sarum & Wells Th Coll 80. d 82 p 83. C Adel *Ripon* 82-86; P-in-c Dacre w Hartwith 86-90; P-in-c Thornthwaite w Thruscross and Darley 88-90; V Dacre w Hartwith and Darley w Thornthwaite 90-91; V Owton Manor *Dur* 91-02; V Torrisholme *Blackb* 02-03; P-in-c Hunslet St Mary *Ripon* from 03. *The Vicarage, Church Street, Hunslet, Leeds LS10 2QY* Tel 0113-271 9661 *or* 270 4659
E-mail fr.peter@ntlworld.com

ANDREW, Brian. b 31. Oak Hill Th Coll 75. d 77 p 78. C Broadwater St Mary *Chich* 77-81; R Nettlebed w Bix and Highmore *Ox* 81-87; V Shenstone *Lich* 87-96; rtd 96; Perm to Offic *Ex* from 97; *Derby* from 01. *18 Shaldon Drive, Littleover, Derby DE23 6HZ* Tel (01332) 768259

ANDREW, Christopher John. b 61. Cen Lancs Univ BA87. St Mich Coll Llan 01. d 03. C Bingley H Trin *Bradf* from 03. *6 Woodvale Crescent, Bingley BD16 4AL* Tel (01274) 565789 Mobile 07932-811444 E-mail candrew@fish.co.uk

ANDREW, David Neil. b 62. Down Coll Cam BA83 MA87 PhD88. Ridley Hall Cam 93. d 93 p 94. C Heatherlands St Jo *Sarum* 93-98; P-in-c White Waltham w Shottesbrooke *Ox* from 98. *The Vicarage, Waltham Road, White Waltham, Maidenhead SL6 3JD* Tel (01628) 822000

ANDREW, David Shore. b 39. Liv Univ BA61 CertEd62. OLM course 97. d 99 p 00. NSM Birkenshaw w Hunsworth *Wakef* from 99. *448 Oxford Road, Gomersal, Cleckheaton BD19 4LD* Tel (01274) 873339

ANDREW, Donald. b 35. Tyndale Hall Bris 63. d 66 p 67. C Croydon Ch Ch Broad Green *Cant* 66-69; C Ravenhead *Liv* 69-72; Scripture Union 72-77; V Rushen *S & M* 77-82; TR Heworth H Trin *York* 82-00; rtd 00. *60 Viking Road, Bridlington YO16 6TW* Tel (01262) 601273

ANDREW, Frank. b 17. St D Coll Lamp BA49 Ely Th Coll 50. d 51 p 52. C Howden *York* 51-55; V Mosbrough *Sheff* 55-59; C-in-c Greenhill CD 59-65; V Greenhill 65-69; R March St Jo *Ely* 69-77; R March St Mary 71-77; RD March 73-77; R Catworth Magna 77-83; R Covington 77-83; R Tilbrook 77-83; rtd 83; Perm to Offic *Chich* from 83. *11 Romney Close, Seaford BN25 3TR* Tel (01323) 897352

ANDREW, Jeremy Charles Edward. b 68. St Jo Coll Dur BA01. Cranmer Hall Dur 98. d 01. C Newquay *Truro* from 01. *127 Penmere Drive, Newquay TR7 1NS* Tel (01637) 873241 E-mail curate@st-michaels-newquay.org.uk

ANDREW, John. b 60. St Mich Coll Llan 98. d 00 p 01. C Oystermouth *S & B* from 00. *83 Castle Acre, Mumbles, Swansea SA3 5TH* Tel (01792) 405310

ANDREW, Canon John Gerald Barton. b 31. OBE. Keble Coll Ox BA55 MA58 Cuttington Univ Coll Liberia Hon DD76 Kentucky Sem Hon DD76 Nashotah Ho Wisconsin Hon DD77 Gen Th Sem NY Hon DD96. Cuddesdon Coll 54. d 56 p 57. C Redcar *York* 56-59; USA 59-60 and 72-96; Abp's Dom Chapl *York* 60-61; Abp's Dom Chapl *Cant* 61-65; Abp's Sen Chapl 65-69; Six Preacher Cant Cathl 67-72; V Preston St Jo *Blackb* 69-72; RD Preston 70-72; R St Thos Fifth Avenue 72-96; rtd 96; Perm to Offic *B & W* 97-99. *414 East 52nd Street, New York, NY 10022, USA* Tel (001) (212) 355 0064

ANDREW, Michael Paul. b 51. SSC Leic Univ CertEd73. Chich Th Coll 80. d 83 p 84. C Par *Truro* 83-86; Hon Chapl Miss to Seamen 86; P-in-c Salford Ordsall St Clem *Man* 86-91; P-in-c Hammersmith St Jo *Lon* from 91. *St John's Vicarage, Iffley Road, London W6 0PA* Tel (020) 8748 0079 Mobile 07712-816680 Fax (020) 8741 8933 E-mail sjh@dlondon.anglican.org *or* father.paul@compuserve.com

ANDREW, Philip John. b 62. Nottm Univ BSc84. St Jo Coll Nottm MTh02. d 02 p 03. C Reading Greyfriars *Ox* from 02. *26 Prospect Street, Reading RG1 7YG* Tel 0118-959 9930 E-mail phil.andrew@greyfriars.org.uk

ANDREW, Ronald Arthur. b 27. Sarum Th Coll 64. d 65 p 66. C Darwen St Cuth *Blackb* 65-69; C Padiham 69-71; V Colne H Trin 71-76; V Adlington 76-85; V Goosnargh w Whittingham 85-92; rtd 92; Perm to Offic *Blackb* from 92. *1 Greystone Drive, Fence, Burnley BB12 9PJ* Tel (01282) 617532

ANDREW, Sydney William. b 55. Cranmer Hall Dur 82. d 85 p 86. C Horncastle w Low Toynton *Linc* 85-88; V Worlaby 88-93; V Bonby 88-93; V Elsham 88-93; rtd 93; Lic to Offic *Linc* 93-95; Hon C Brocklesby Park from 95; Hon C Croxton from 96. *10 Bentley Lane, Grasby, Barnetby DN38 6AW* Tel (01652) 628586 E-mail bridget.revdoc@clara.co.uk

ANDREW, Canon William Hugh. b 32. Selw Coll Cam BA56 MA60. Ridley Hall Cam 56. d 58 p 59. C Woking St Mary *Guildf* 58-61; C Farnborough 61-64; V Gatten St Paul *Portsm* 64-71; R Weymouth St Mary *Sarum* 71-76; V Heatherlands St Jo 76-82; Can and Preb Sarum Cathl 81-86; R Alderbury and W Grimstead 82-86; Perm to Offic *Bris* 86-88; Communications Dir Bible Soc 86-94; Communications Consultant 94-97; Hon C The Lydiards *Bris* 88-94; C W Swindon and the Lydiards 94-96; Hon C 96-98; rtd 96; Perm to Offic *Win* from 98. *31 Charnock Close, Hordle, Lymington SO41 0GU* Tel (01425) 627220

ANDREWES, Nicholas John. b 64. Southn Univ BA87 La Sainte Union Coll PGCE88. Cranmer Hall Dur BTh93 DMS93. d 96 p 97. C Dovecot *Liv* 96-00; TV Pendleton *Man* from 00. *The Vicarage, 25 Brindle Heath Road, Salford M6 6GD* Tel 0161-737 2337 Fax as telephone E-mail nick.andrewes@virgin.net

ANDREWES UTHWATT, Henry. b 25. Jes Coll Cam BA49 MA51. Wells Th Coll 49. d 51 p 52. C Fareham H Trin *Portsm* 51-55; C Haslemere *Guildf* 55-59; C Wimbledon *S'wark* 59-61; V W Wimbledon Ch Ch 61-73; V Yeovil St Jo w Preston Plucknett *B & W* 73-76; TR Yeovil 76-82; V Burrington and Churchill 82-90; RD Locking 87-90; rtd 90; Perm to Offic *B & W* from 90; Chapl Partis Coll Bath from 91; Chapl Bath and West Community NHS Trust from 91. *71 Mount Road, Bath BA2 1LJ* Tel (01225) 482220

ANDREWS, Anthony Brian. b 33. Lon Univ BA54 AKC58. Coll of Resurr Mirfield 56. d 58 p 59. C Haggerston St Columba *Lon* 58-60; C N Hammersmith St Kath 60-63; V Goldthorpe *Sheff* 63-74; V Notting Hill St Mich and Ch Ch *Lon* from 74. *St Michael's Vicarage, 35 St Lawrence Terrace, London W10 5SR* Tel (020) 8969 0776 Fax 8969 0805
E-mail archangel@supanet.com *or* papalist@lineone.net

ANDREWS, Anthony Frederick. b 25. K Coll Lon 54. d 55 p 56. C Kentish Town St Jo *Lon* 55-58; C Belmont 58-60; R Eversholt, Frome St Quinton, Melbury Bubb etc *Sarum* 60-66; CF 66-69; C Bridgwater St Mary w Chilton Trinity *B & W* 69-70; R Cossington 70-73; C Highworth w Sevenhampton and Inglesham etc *Bris* 75-84; P-in-c Bishopstone w Hinton Parva 84-88; rtd 88. *Burford House, Highworth, Swindon SN6 7AD* Tel (01793) 762796

ANDREWS, Anthony John. b 35. S'wark Ord Course 75. d 80 p 81. NSM Cheam *S'wark* 80-83; C Epsom St Martin *Guildf* 83-86; V Barton *Portsm* 86-89; Chapl Northwick Park and St Mark's NHS Trust Harrow 90-98; C Regent's Park St Mark *Lon* 98-00; rtd 00. *112 Albury Drive, Pinner HA5 3RG*

ANDREWS, Benjamin. b 75. St Steph Ho Ox 97. d 00 p 01. C Whitchurch *Llan* 00-03; C Newton Nottage from 03. *Ty Dewi Sant, 5B West End Avenue, Nottage, Porthcawl CF36 3NE* Tel (01656) 783762 E-mail frbenandrews@aol.com

ANDREWS, Canon Brian Keith. b 39. Keble Coll Ox BA62 MA69. Coll of Resurr Mirfield 62. d 64 p 65. C Is of Dogs Ch Ch and St Jo w St Luke *Lon* 64-68; C Hemel Hempstead *St Alb* 68-71; TV 71-79; V Abbots Langley from 79; RD Watford 88-94; Hon Can St Alb from 94. *The Vicarage, High Street, Abbots Langley WD5 0AS* Tel (01923) 263013 *or* tel and fax 261795 E-mail brianandrews@abbotslangley.u-net.com

ANDREWS, Christopher Paul. b 47. Fitzw Coll Cam BA70 MA73. Westcott Ho Cam 69. d 72 p 73. C Croydon *Cant* 72-75; C Gosforth All SS *Newc* 75-79; TV Newc Epiphany 80-87; RD Newc Cen 82-87; V Alnwick 87-96; Chapl Alnwick Infirmary 87-96; Chapl United Lincs Hosps NHS Trust 99-01; R Grantham *Linc* from 96. *The Rectory, 4 Church Street, Grantham NG31 6RR* Tel (01476) 563710 *or* 572932 E-mail chris-p-andrews@hotmail.com

ANDREWS, Clive Frederick. b 43. St Jo Coll Nottm 81. d 83 p 84. C Leic St Jas *Leic* 83-86; Ind Chapl 86-90; Hon TV Melton Gt Framland 89-90; TV Clifton *S'well* 90-92; P-in-c Gamston w Eaton and W Drayton 92-94; R from 94; P-in-c Elkesley w Bothamsall from 92; Chapl Bramcote Sch Notts from 92. *The Vicarage, 3 Maple Drive, Elkesley, Retford DN22 8AX* Tel (01777) 838293

ANDREWS, Edward Robert. b 33. St Mich Coll Llan 62. d 64 p 65. C Kingswinford St Mary *Lich* 64-69; Chapl RAF 69-88; R St Just-in-Roseland w Philleigh *Truro* 88-99; rtd 99. *2 Ingleside, Gunsdown Villas, Station Road, South Molton EX36 3EA* Tel (01769) 572386

ANDREWS, Frances. b 24. EMMTC 73. dss 78 d 87 p 94. Porchester *S'well* 78-86; Asst Chapl Nottm City Hosp 86-88; Hon C Gedling *S'well* 88-92; NSM Epperstone 92-95; NSM Gonalston 92-95; NSM Oxton 92-95; rtd 95; Perm to Offic *S'well* from 95. *1 Cromford Avenue, Nottingham NG4 3RU* Tel 0115-961 3857

ANDREWS, Mrs Jennifer Wendy. b 50. SW Minl Tr Course 97. d 00 p 01. C Southway *Ex* from 00. *53 Dayton Close, Crownhill, Plymouth PL6 5DX* Tel (01752) 704828 Mobile 07411-133876

ANDREWS, John Colin. b 47. Open Univ BA93. Sarum & Wells Th Coll 78. d 80 p 81. C Burnham *B & W* 80-84; V Williton 84-92; P-in-c Ashwick w Oakhill and Binegar 92-02; Dioc Communications Officer from 92; TV Yatton Moor from 02. *Cherry Tree House, Ham Lane, Kingston Seymour, Clevedon BS21 6XE* Tel (01934) 830208
E-mail 106664.1024@compuserve.com

ANDREWS, Preb John Douglas. b 19. Keble Coll Ox BA39 MA44. Chich Th Coll 40. d 42 p 43. C S Bermondsey St Aug *S'wark* 42-44; C Lambeth St Jo w All SS 44-46; C Towcester w Easton Neston *Pet* 46-50; C Shrewsbury H Cross *Lich* 50-52; V Ettingshall 52-59; V Walsall St Andr 59-68; V Penkhull 68-80; P-in-c Ellenhall w Ranton 80-86; P-in-c Chebsey 80-86; Preb Lich Cathl 81-86; rtd 86; Perm to Offic *Heref* and *Lich* 86-01;

York from 01. *28 Dulverton Hall, Esplanade, Scarborough YO11 2AR* Tel (01723) 340128

ANDREWS, John Elfric. b 35. Ex Coll Ox BA59 MA63. Wycliffe Hall Ox 59. **d** 61 **p** 62. C Pittville All SS *Glouc* 61-66; Cand Sec Lon City Miss 66-92; Lic to Offic *S'wark* 66-92; R Kingham w Churchill, Daylesford and Sarsden *Ox* 92-99; rtd 99; Perm to Offic *St E* from 01. *4 St George's Road, Felixstowe IP11 9PL* Tel (01394) 283557

ANDREWS, John Francis. b 34. Jes Coll Cam BA58 MA62. S'wark Ord Course 78. **d** 81 **p** 82. NSM Norwood All SS *Cant* 81-82; NSM Upper Norwood All SS w St Marg 82-85; NSM Upper Norwood All SS *S'wark* 85-87; NSM Dulwich St Barn 89-92; NSM S Dulwich St Steph 92-95; Perm to Offic *S'wark* from 95 and *Sarum* from 01. *6 Kennington Square, Wareham BH20 4JR* Tel (01929) 555311

ANDREWS, John George William. b 42. Qu Coll Birm 65. **d** 68 **p** 69. C Smethwick St Matt w St Chad *Birm* 68-71; CF 71-97; P-in-c Lyme Regis *Sarum* 97-98; TV Golden Cap Team from 98. *The Vicarage, West Hill Road, Lyme Regis DT7 3LW* Tel (01297) 443134

ANDREWS, Mrs Judith Marie. b 47. Avery Hill Coll CertEd68. Dioc OLM tr scheme 97. **d** 00 **p** 01. OLM Wilford Peninsula *St E* from 00. *Hillside, Tower Hill, Hollesley, Woodbridge IP12 3QX* Tel (01394) 411642

ANDREWS, Keith. b 47. St Mich Coll Llan 79. **d** 81 **p** 82. C Penarth w Lavernock *Llan* 81-85; V Nantymoel w Wyndham 85-91; RD Bridgend 89-93; R Coychurch w Llangan and St Mary Hill 91-98; V Caerau St Cynfelin from 98. *The Vicarage, Cymmer Road, Caerau, Maesteg CF34 0YR* Tel (01656) 736500

ANDREWS, Morey Alisdair Christopher. b 66. Leic Poly BSc91 ARICS91 MRICS01. St Jo Coll Nottm MA99. **d** 99 **p** 00. C Yate New Town *Bris* 99-02; C Downend from 02. *15 Glendale Road, Downend, Bristol BS16 6EQ* Tel 0117-956 8859 E-mail morey@blueyonder.co.uk

ANDREWS, Paul Douglas. b 54. Univ of Wales (Abth) BLib76 PhD99. St Alb and Ox Min Course. **d** 00 **p** 01. NSM Kempston and Biddenham *St Alb* 00-03; C Leighton Buzzard w Eggington, Hockliffe etc from 03. *138 Brooklands Drive, Leighton Buzzard LU7 3PG* Tel (01525) 850204 E-mail p.d.andrews@btinternet.com

ANDREWS, Peter Alwyne. b 44. Lon Univ BSc67. Westcott Ho Cam 70. **d** 73 **p** 74. C Barnoldswick w Bracewell *Bradf* 73-76; C Maltby *Sheff* 76-78; V Bradf St Oswald Chapel Green *Bradf* 78-85; V Hanwell St Thos *Lon* from 85. *St Thomas's Vicarage, 182 Boston Road, London W7 2AD* Tel (020) 8567 5280 Fax 8566 0665 E-mail thomashanwell@btinternet.com

ANDREWS, Peter Douglas. b 52. SEN72 SRN78. St Steph Ho Ox 86. **d** 88 **p** 89. C Perry Barr *Birm* 88-92; TV Swindon New Town *Bris* 92-98; V Streatham St Pet *S'wark* from 98. *St Peter's Vicarage, 113 Leigham Court Road, London SW16 2NS* Tel (020) 8769 2922

ANDREWS, Raymond Cyril. b 50. SEITE 00. **d** 03. C E Dulwich St Jo *S'wark* from 03. *11 Hinckley Road, London SE15 4HZ* Tel 07930-694221 (mobile) E-mail andrewsrandrews@aol.com

ANDREWS, Richard John. b 57. Bris Univ BA78 CertEd79. Ripon Coll Cuddesdon 82. **d** 84 **p** 85. C Kidderminster St Mary and All SS, Trimpley etc *Worc* 84-87; Hon C Derby Cathl *Derby* 87-89; Chapl Derbyshire Coll of HE 87-89; V Chellaston *Derby* 89-93; V Spondon from 93. *St Werburgh's Vicarage, Gascoigne Drive, Spondon, Derby DE21 7GL* Tel (01332) 673573 Fax as telephone E-mail rjandrews@ukonline.co.uk

ANDREYEV, Michael. b 62. Hatf Coll Dur BA85. Wycliffe Hall Ox BA91. **d** 96 **p** 97. C Surbiton Hill Ch Ch *S'wark* 96-01; Hon C Stapenhill w Cauldwell *Derby* 02-03; P-in-c from 03. *197 Woods Lane, Burton-on-Trent DE15 9DD* Tel (01283) 530320

ANGEL, Andrew Richard. b 67. St Pet Coll Ox BA89 Lon Inst of Educn PGCE90 Surrey Univ MA94. St Jo Coll Nottm 99. **d** 02 **p** 03. C Dartford Ch Ch *Roch* from 02. *102 Chastilian Road, Dartford DA1 3LG* Tel (01322) 229103 E-mail andrew@angelzam.freeserve.co.uk

ANGEL, Gervais Thomas David. b 36. Ch Ch Ox BA59 MA62 Bris Univ MEd78 Lon Univ PGCE72. Wycliffe Hall Ox 57. **d** 61 **p** 62. C Aberystwyth St Mich *St D* 61-65; Tutor Clifton Th Coll 65-71; Dean of Studies Trin Coll Bris 71-81; Dir of Studies 81-90; Area Sec (W and SW) SAMS 90-02; NSM Stoke Gifford *Bris* 92-02; rtd 02; Perm to Offic *Bris* from 02. *82 Oak Close, Little Stoke, Bristol BS34 6RD* Tel (01454) 618081 Mobile 07967-441426 Fax 0117-904 8588 E-mail gervais.angel@blueyonder.co.uk

ANGEL, Robin Alan. b 41. St Mich Coll Llan. **d** 89 **p** 90. C Whitchurch *Llan* 89-94; V Aberpergwm and Blaengwrach 94-01; V Caerau w Ely 01-03; V Porth w Trealaw from 03. *St Paul's Vicarage, 70 Birchgrove Street, Porth CF39 9UU* Tel (01443) 682401

ANGELL, Geoffrey. b 63. St Jo Coll Nottm. **d** 01 **p** 02. C Daventry, Ashby St Ledgers, Braunston etc *Pet* from 01. *48 Trinity Close, Daventry NN11 4RN* Tel (01327) 301474 E-mail revgeoff@artangells.com

ANGELO, Brother. See DEACON, Donald

ANGIER, Patrick John Mark. b 61. Leic Univ BSc83. Trin Coll Bris. **d** 03. C Stratford-upon-Avon, Luddington etc *Cov* from 03. *14 Keats Road, Stratford-upon-Avon CV37 7JL* Tel 07971-923668 (mobile) E-mail patrick.angier@btinternet.com

ANGLE, John Edwin George. b 42. Lon Bible Coll BD65 Liv Univ AdDipEd73 Univ of Wales MEd75 UWE Dip Educn Mgt 85. WEMTC 92. **d** 94 **p** 95. NSM Clevedon St Andr and Ch Ch *B & W* 94-97; NSM Worle 97-98; P-in-c Camelot Par 98-01; R from 01; Warden of Readers Wells Adnry from 02. *The Rectory, 6 The Close, North Cadbury, Yeovil BA22 7DX* Tel (01963) 440469 E-mail johnangle@onetel.net.uk

ANGOVE, Ms Helen Teresa. b 71. Bath Univ BEng93. Ripon Coll Cuddesdon BTh97. **d** 97 **p** 98. C Bridgwater St Mary, Chilton Trinity and Durleigh *B & W* 97-01; P-in-c Elstree *St Alb* 01-03; USA from 03. *255 S Wilson Avenue, Apartment #8, Pasadena, CA 91125, USA* E-mail hangove@tesco.net

ANGUS, Canon Edward. b 39. Man Univ BA60. Qu Coll Birm DipTh61. **d** 62 **p** 63. C Chorley St Geo *Blackb* 62-65; C S Shore H Trin 65-68; R Bretherton 68-76; V Altham w Clayton le Moors 76-90; V Preesall from 90; RD Garstang 96-01; Hon Can Blackb Cathl from 98. *St Oswald's Vicarage, Lancaster Road, Poulton-le-Fylde FY6 0DU* Tel (01253) 810297

ANGWIN, Richard Paul. b 25. ACA49 FCA60 AKC56. **d** 56 **p** 57. C Clacton St Jas *Chelmsf* 56-59; V Brightlingsea 59-69; V Wanstead H Trin Hermon Hill 69-75; Chapl Wanstead Hosp Lon 69-75; Chapl Halstead Hosp 75-87; V Halstead St Andr *Chelmsf* 75-78; P-in-c Greenstead Green 75-78; V Halstead St Andr w H Trin 78-79; V Halstead St Andr w H Trin and Greenstead Green 79-87; RD Halstead and Coggeshall 84-87; rtd 87; Perm to Offic *Lich* from 88. *2 Seckham Road, Lichfield WS13 7AN* Tel (01543) 250848 E-mail skypilot@sagainternet.co.uk

ANKER, George William. b 10. AKC51. **d** 51 **p** 52. C Richmond H Trin and Ch Ch *S'wark* 51-54; C Battersea St Pet 54-57; C Shere *Guildf* 57-62; C Leatherhead 62-68; V Brockley Hill St Sav *S'wark* 68-72; C Sanderstead All SS 72-76; rtd 76; Perm to Offic *S'wark* from 76. *The College of St Barnabas, Blackberry Lane, Lingfield RH7 6NJ* Tel (01342) 870260

ANKER, Malcolm. b 39. Univ of Wales BA61. Bps' Coll Cheshunt 61. **d** 63 **p** 64. C Marfleet *York* 63-66; C Cottingham 66-69; V Skirlaugh w Long Riston 69-74; V Elloughton and Brough w Brantingham 74-84; V Tadcaster 84-86; V Tadcaster w Newton Kyme 86-91; V Oatlands *Guildf* from 91. *The Vicarage, 5 Beechwood Avenue, Weybridge KT13 9TE* Tel (01932) 847963

ANKER-PETERSEN, Robert Brian. b 52. Aber Univ MTh88. Wycliffe Hall Ox BA79 MA88. **d** 93 **p** 94. C Perth St Ninian *St And* 93-96; Bp's Researcher on Ch's Min of Healing from 93; Dir Bield Retreat and Healing Cen from 93; Dioc Dir of Healing from 97. *Blackruthven House, Tibbermore, Perth PH1 1PY* Tel (01738) 583238 Fax as telephone E-mail robinap@sol.co.uk or bieldatblackruthven@yahoo.com

ANKERS, Charles William (Bill). b 42. FIMI. NEOC 89. **d** 93 **p** 95. NSM York St Luke *York* 93-95; C Kexby w Wilberfoss 95-98; Asst Chapl HM Pris Full Sutton 95-98; V Norton juxta Malton *York* from 98. *The Vicarage, 80 Langton Road, Norton, Malton YO17 9AE* Tel (01653) 692741

ANKETELL, Jeyarajan. b 41. MInstP Lon Univ BSc62 PhD64. Coll of Resurr Mirfield 69. **d** 73 **p** 74. Asst Chapl Newc Univ *Newc* 73-75; Asst Chapl Lon Univ *Lon* 75-77; Teacher from 78; Lic to Offic *S'wark* 81-83; Chasetown High Sch from 85; NSM Lich St Mary w St Mich *Lich* 86-96; NSM Lich St Mich w St Mary and Wall from 96. *7 Wissage Lane, Lichfield WS13 6DQ* Tel (01543) 268897

ANN-MARIA, Sister. See STUART, Sister Ann-Marie Lindsay

ANNANCY, Felix. b 62. Hull Univ DipTh87. **d** 87 **p** 88. C Fenton *Lich* 87-88; Ghana 88-98 and from 00; C Stalybridge St Paul *Ches* 98-00; Perm to Offic *Man* from 00. *c/o St Crispin's Rectory, 2 Hart Road, Manchester M14 7LE*

ANNAS, Geoffrey Peter. b 53. Saram & Wells Th Coll. **d** 83 **p** 84. C S'wark H Trin w St Matt *S'wark* 83-87; TV Walworth 87-94; Warden Pemb Coll Miss Walworth 87-94; V Southampton Thornhill St Chris *Win* from 94. *St Christopher's Vicarage, 402 Hinkler Road, Southampton SO19 6DF* Tel (023) 8044 8537

ANNE, Sister. See PROUDLEY, Sister Anne

ANNIS, Herman North. b 28. Lich Th Coll 62. **d** 64 **p** 65. C Kilburn St Aug *Lon* 64-67; C Toxteth Park St Agnes *Liv* 67-70; V 70-82; V Hempton and Pudding Norton *Nor* 82-84; P-in-c Sculthorpe w Dunton and Doughton 82-84; V Northampton H Trin *Pet* 84-95; rtd 95; Hon C Brighton St Bart *Chich* 95-99. *2 rue de la Liberté, 53500 St Denis-de-Gastines, France* Tel (0033) (2) 43 00 69 66

ANNIS, Jennifer Mary. b 49. Middx Univ BA95. Oak Hill Th Coll 92. **d** 95 **p** 97. NSM Digswell and Panshanger *St Alb* 95-97; NSM Codicote 97-98 and 99-00; Tanzania 98-99; Chapl ATC from 99. *Glanafon, Trecwn, Haverfordwest SA62 5XT* Tel (01348) 840459

ANNIS, Rodney James. b 43. Ex Univ BA75 MA79 PhD86. Ripon Coll Cuddesdon 75. **d** 76 **p** 77. C Brixham *Ex* 76-77; Asst

Chapl Ex Univ 77-80; Chapl Ex Sch 77-80; C Boston *Linc* 80-84; Chapl Trin Hall Cam 84-87; Chapl St Edw K and Martyr Cam *Ely* 84-87; V Bush Hill Park St Steph *Lon* from 87. *St Stephen's Vicarage, 43A Village Road, Enfield EN1 2ET*

ANNON, Jacqueline. d 01 **p** 02. OLM Tooting All SS *S'wark* from 01. *31 Hamilton Road, London SE27 9RZ* Tel (020) 8473 2456

ANNS, Pauline Mary. *See* HIGHAM, Mrs Pauline Mary

ANSAH, Kwesi Gyebi Ababio (George). b 54. DipSM87. Simon of Cyrene Th Inst 90 Oak Hill Th Coll DipHE93 BTh97. **d** 93 **p** 94. C Peckham St Mary Magd *S'wark* 93-96; V W Dulwich Em from 96. *Emmanuel Vicarage, 94 Clive Road, London SE21 8BU* Tel (020) 8670 2793 E-mail kgyebiababio@easicom.com

ANSCOMBE, John Thomas. b 51. Ex Univ BA72. Cranmer Hall Dur DipTh73. **d** 74 **p** 75. C Upper Armley *Ripon* 74-77; C Leeds St Geo 78-81; Exec Producer Scripture Union 81-96; Hon C Beckenham Ch Ch *Roch* from 82. *26 Wimborne Way, Beckenham BR3 4DJ* Tel and fax (020) 8658 4037 Mobile 07720-876487 E-mail john@janscombe.fsbusiness.co.uk

ANSCOMBE, Canon Thomas. b 15. Qu Coll Cam BA37 MA41. Ridley Hall Cam 37. **d** 39 **p** 40. C Lenton *S'well* 39-45; V Becontree St Mary *Chelmsf* 45-52; R Nottingham St Nic *S'well* 52-57; Prin Clifton Th Coll 57-64; R Kirkheaton *Wakef* 64-80; Hon Can Wakef Cathl 77-80; rtd 80; Perm to Offic *Bradf* 80-90; Perm to Offic *Wakef* 80-92. *Milton House Nursing Home, Gargrave, Skipton BD23 3NN* Tel (01756) 749289

ANSELL, Antony Michael. b 40. St Jo Coll Nottm 78. **d** 80 **p** 81. C Harrow Weald St Mich *Lon* 80-84; C Harrow Trin St Mich 84; Hon C Ches Square St Mich w St Phil 86-88; Hon C Mayfair Ch Ch from 88. *4 Vincent Square Mansions, Walcott Street, London SW1P 2NT* Tel (020) 7834 3883 Fax 7834 3884 E-mail antony.ansell@dial.pipex.com

ANSELL, Howard. b 36. St Jo Coll Cam BA59 MA62. NW Ord Course 73. **d** 76 **p** 77. C Chapeltown *Sheff* 76-79; V Worsbrough St Thos and St Jas 79-83; R Lt Waltham *Chelmsf* 83-00; P-in-c Gt Leighs 92-00; P-in-c Lt Leighs 95-00; rtd 00; Perm to Offic *Linc* from 00. *5 Roselea Avenue, Welton, Lincoln LN2 3RT* Tel (01673) 860508

ANSELL, John Christopher. b 49. DipAD. Sarum & Wells Th Coll 79. **d** 81 **p** 82. C Dartford St Alb *Roch* 81-84; C Leybourne 84-88; C Larkfield 84-88; TV Mortlake w E Sheen *S'wark* 88-98; V Mitcham SS Pet and Paul from 98. *The Vicarage, 11 Vicarage Gardens, Mitcham CR4 3BL* Tel (020) 8648 1566 E-mail jsansell@hotmail.com

ANSELL, Philip Harding. b 67. LMH Ox BA89 Rob Coll Cam BA92. Ridley Hall Cam. **d** 93 **p** 94. C Rainham w Wennington *Chelmsf* 93-97; C Rodbourne Cheney *Bris* 97-01; V Moseley St Agnes *Birm* from 01. *St Agnes' Vicarage, 5 Colmore Crescent, Birmingham B13 9SJ* Tel 0121-449 0368

ANSELL, Stuart Adrian. b 59. Ripon Coll Cuddesdon DipMin95 St Alb Minl Tr Scheme 81. **d** 97 **p** 98. C Cheadle w Freehay *Lich* 97-00; P-in-c Silverdale from 00. *21 Pepper Street, Silverdale, Newcastle ST5 6QJ* Tel (01782) 616804

ANSELM, Brother. *See* SMYTH, Robert Andrew Laine

ANSON (née DRAX), Mrs Elizabeth Margaret. b 57. St Jo Coll Nottm DipMin93. **d** 94 **p** 95. C Kimberworth *Sheff* 94-95; C Doncaster St Mary 95-97; rtd 97. *164 Park Avenue, Princes Avenue, Hull HU5 3EY* Tel (01482) 343169

ANSON, Harry. b 35. FInstFF79. St Jo Coll Nottm 83. **d** 88. NSM Ayr *Glas* 88-93; Miss to Seamen 91-93. *Back to Fairview, Doonbank Crescent, Patna, Ayr KA6 7JL* Tel (01292) 531238 Mobile 07867-990345

ANSTEY, Nigel John. b 55. Cranmer Hall Dur 84. **d** 87 **p** 88. C Plumstead St Jo w St Jas and St Paul *S'wark* 87-91; TV Ipswich St Fran *St E* 91-97; TV Walthamstow *Chelmsf* from 97. *St Luke's Vicarage, 17A Greenleaf Road, London E17 6QQ* Tel (020) 8520 2885 E-mail nigel@theansteys.freeserve.co.uk

ANSTICE, John Neville. b 39. Lon Univ BSc63. Cuddesdon Coll 69. **d** 71 **p** 72. C Stonebridge St Mich *Lon* 71-74; Chapl Woodbridge Sch 74-76; TV Droitwich *Worc* 76-80; P-in-c Salwarpe 76-79; Perm to Offic *Chich* from 80; rtd 99. *10 Selham Close, Crawley RH11 0EH* Tel (01293) 535654

ANTANANARIVO, Bishop of. *See* RABENIRINA, The Most Revd Remi Joseph

ANTELL, Roger Howard. b 47. Lon Univ BD71 Warwick Univ MSc79 Ox Univ MTh99. Ripon Coll Cuddesdon 97. **d** 99 **p** 00. C Ashchurch *Glouc* 99-03; R Stoke Prior, Wychbold and Upton Warren *Worc* from 03. *The Rectory, Fish House Lane, Stoke Prior, Bromsgrove B60 4JT* Tel (01527) 832501 E-mail roger.antell@btinternet.com

ANTHAPURUSHA. b 53. Bangalore Univ BA77 Jnana Deepa Vidyapeeth Poona BPh80 Delhi Univ MA83 MPhil84 Serampore Th Coll BD87. Bp's Coll Calcutta 85. **d** 87 **p** 88. India 87-99; Bethany Chr Trust Edin 01-02; C Bistre *St As* from 02. *11 Bron yr Eglwys, Mynydd Isa, Mold CH7 6YQ* Tel (01352) 753465 E-mail apurusha@bronyreglwys.fsnet.co.uk

ANTHONY, Gerald Caldecott. b 18. Down Coll Cam BA41 MA44. Wycliffe Hall Ox 41. **d** 43 **p** 44. C Roxeth Ch Ch *Lon* 43-47; C Harlington 47-49; R Grays Inn Road St Bart 49-51; P-in-c Ernesettle *Ex* 51-55; V S Lambeth All SS and St Barn

S'wark 55-58; Chapl Parkstone Sea Tr Sch Poole 58-64; Chapl HMS Ganges 64-65; P-in-c Bulmer *York* 65-66; R 66-72; V Broughton-in-Furness w Woodland *Carl* 72-75; P-in-c Seathwaite w Ulpha 73-75; V Broughton and Duddon 75-83; rtd 83; Perm to Offic *Worc* from 83. *2 Coppice Close, Malvern WR14 1LE* Tel (01886) 832930 Fax 830930 E-mail gacoppice@talk21.com

ANTHONY, Ian Charles. b 47. NW Ord Course 76. **d** 79 **p** 80. NSM Lt Lever *Man* from 79. *36 Meadow Close, Little Lever, Bolton BL3 1LG* Tel (01204) 791437

ANTONY-ROBERTS, Gelert Roderick. b 43. Southn Univ BEd78 Reading Univ MA84 Cert Counselling 99. Sarum & Wells Th Coll 88. **d** 90 **p** 91. C Alton St Lawr *Win* 90-94. *11 Jubilee Court, North Street, Salisbury SP2 7TA* Tel (01722) 338399

ap GWILYM, Gwynn. b 50. Univ of Wales (Ban) BA71 MA76. Wycliffe Hall Ox BA84 MA89 MPhil00. **d** 84 **p** 85. C Ynyscynhaearn w Penmorfa and Porthmadog *Ban* 84-86; R Penegoes and Darowen w Llanbryn-Mair 86-97; R Mallwyd w Cemais, Llanymawddwy, Darowen etc 97-02; P-in-c Penyfai *Llan* from 02. *The Vicarage, Pen-y-Fai, Bridgend CF31 4LS* Tel (01656) 652849

ap IORWERTH, Geraint. b 50. Univ of Wales (Lamp) DipTh72 Univ of Wales (Cardiff) DPS73 MPhil90 Open Univ BA78. Burgess Hall Lamp 69 Westmr Past Foundn 73 St Mich Coll Llan 73. **d** 74 **p** 75. C Holyhead w Rhoscolyn *Ban* 74-78; R Pennal w Corris and Esgairgeiliog from 78; Co-Founder and Ldr Order of Sancta Sophia from 87. *The Rectory, Pennal, Machynlleth SY20 9JS* Tel (01654) 791216 Fax as telephone E-mail apennal@ouvip.com

APPELBE, Canon Frederick Charles. b 52. TCD DipTh87. CITC 87. **d** 87 **p** 88. C Waterford w Killea, Drumcannon and Dunhill *C & O* 87-90; C Taney *D & G* 90-92; I Rathmichael from 92; Can Ch Ch Cathl Dublin from 02. *Rathmichael Rectory, Shankill, Co Dublin, Irish Republic* Tel (00353) (1) 282 2803 Fax as telephone E-mail rathmichael@dublin.anglican.org

APPLEBY, Anthony Robert Nightingale. b 40. K Coll Lon AKC62. St Boniface Warminster 62. **d** 63 **p** 64. C Cov St Mark *Cov* 63-67; CF 67-95; R Dulverton and Brushford *B & W* 95-02; rtd 02. *9 Ashleigh Park, Bampton, Tiverton EX16 9LF* Tel (01398) 331122

APPLEBY, Janet Elizabeth. b 58. Bris Univ BSc80 MSc81 Newc Poly BA90. Cranmer Hall Dur 01. **d** 03. C Newc H Cross *Newc* from 03. *2A Lanercost Drive, Newcastle upon Tyne NE5 2DE* Tel 0191-274 9574

APPLEBY, Miss Janet Mohr. b 32. Lon Univ TCert53 BA79 Sussex Univ MA(Ed)74. Chich Th Coll 90. **d** 91 **p** 95. NSM Rottingdean *Chich* 91-95; NSM Stantonbury and Willen *Ox* 95-02; Perm to Offic from 02. *38 Darwin Close, Milton Keynes MK5 6FF* Tel (01908) 526737

APPLEBY, Ms antonic. b 58. Southlands Coll Lon CertEd81. Cranmer Hall Dur 01. **d** 03. C Marton-in-Cleveland *York* from 03. *37 Lambourne Drive, Marton-in-Cleveland, Middlesbrough TS7 8QF* Tel (01642) 314504 E-mail jidha@aol.co.uk

APPLEBY, Mrs Melanie Jayne. b 65. RGN86. Ripon Coll Cuddesdon 01. **d** 03. C Reddish *Man* from 03. *49 Ilkley Crescent, Reddish, Stockport SK5 6HG* Tel 0161-442 2094 Mobile 07876-191572 E-mail melanieappleby@hotmail.com

APPLEFORD, Kenneth Henry. b 30. Portsm Dioc Tr Course 91. **d** 92. NSM Portsea St Mary *Portsm* 92-00; rtd 00. *124 Stride Avenue, Portsmouth PO3 6HN* Tel (023) 9281 4685

APPLEFORD, Canon Patrick Robert. b 25. Trin Coll Cam BA49 MA54. Chich Th Coll 50. **d** 52 **p** 53. C Poplar All SS w St Frideswide *Lon* 52-58; Chapl Bps' Coll Cheshunt 58-61; Educn Sec USPG 61-66; Dean Lusaka 66-72; P-in-c Sutton St Nicholas w Sutton St Michael *Heref* 73-75; Dir of Educn *Chelmsf* 75-90; Can Chelmsf Cathl 78-90; rtd 90; Perm to Offic *Chelmsf* from 90. *35 Sowerberry Close, Chelmsford CM1 4YB* Tel (01245) 443508

APPLEGARTH, Anthony Edgar. b 44. Chich Th Coll 82. **d** 84 **p** 85. C Cannington, Otterhampton, Combwich and Stockland *B & W* 84-86; C Bridgwater St Mary, Chilton Trinity and Durleigh 86-89; R Stogursey w Fiddington 89-00; P-in-c Devonport St Mark Ford *Ex* 00-02; V from 02. *St Mark's Vicarage, Cambridge Road, Plymouth PL2 1PU* Tel (01752) 565534

APPLEGATE, The Ven John. b 56. Bris Univ BSc78. Trin Coll Bris DipHE81 PhD85. **d** 84 **p** 85. C Collyhurst *Man* 84-87; Asst Chapl Monsall Hosp 84-87; C Broughton St Jas w St Clem and St Matthias 87-94; R Broughton St Jo 94-96; TR Broughton 96-02; Asst Salford 97-02; Research Fell and Lect Man Univ from 00; Bp's Adv Hosp Chapl from 02; Adn Bolton from 02. *45 Rudgwick Drive, Bury BL8 1YA* Tel 0161-761 6117 Fax 763 7973 E-mail archdeacon@rudgwickdr.fsnet.co.uk

APPLETON, Mrs Bonita. b 55. St Jo Coll Nottm DCM93. **d** 93 **p** 94. C Camberley St Paul *Guildf* 93-96; TV Cove St Jo from 96. *Southwood Vicarage, 15 The Copse, Southwood, Farnborough GU14 0QD* Tel (01252) 513422 E-mail bonnieap@aol.com

APPLETON, John Bearby. b 42. Linc Th Coll 74. **d** 76 **p** 77. C Selby Abbey *York* 76-79; C Epsom St Barn *Guildf* 79-82; V Linc

All SS *Linc* 82-94; rtd 02. *33 South End, Osmotherley, Northallerton DL6 3BN*

APPLETON, Canon Ronald Percival. b 15. St Pet Hall Ox BA36 MA40. Ridley Hall Cam 36. **d** 38 **p** 39. C Hunsingore w Cowthorpe *Ripon* 38-39; C High Harrogate Ch Ch 39-42; C Bromley SS Pet and Paul *Roch* 42-44; R Knockholt 44-53; V Bromley Common St Luke 53-62; V Winchcombe, Gretton, Sudeley Manor etc *Glouc* 62-86; RD Winchcombe 83-86; Hon Can Glouc Cathl 80-86; rtd 86; Perm to Offic *Glouc* 86-97; Perm to Offic *Worc* from 97. *1 Abbey Croft, Pershore WR10 1JQ* Tel (01386) 553023

APPLETON, Timothy Charles. b 36. Selw Coll Cam BA60 MA65 K Coll Lon PhD67 Cam Univ ScD81. S'wark Ord Course 69. **d** 72 **p** 73. NSM Harston w Hauxton *Ely* 72-76; Lect Cam Univ 73-88; Lic to Offic *Ely* 76-79 and from 84; P-in-c Gt w Lt Eversden 79-84; Chapl and Cllr Bourn Hall Clinic from 88. *44 Eversden Road, Harlton, Cambridge CB3 7ET* Tel (01223) 262226 Fax 264332 E-mail tca@ifc.co.uk

APPLIN, David Edward. b 39. Oak Hill Th Coll 63. **d** 65 **p** 66. C Ox St Clem *Ox* 65-69; C Felixstowe SS Pet and Paul *St E* 69-71; Lic to Offic *Win* 71-91; Travelling Sec Rwanda Miss 71-74; Home Sec 74-77; Gen Sec 77-81; Dir Overseas Personnel Dept TEAR Fund 82-87; Overseas Dir 87-92; Hon C Kempshott *Win* 91-92; R Awbridge w Sherfield English 92-97; Exec Dir Samaritan's Purse Internat from 95. *Flat 4, 25 Christchurch Road, St Cross, Winchester SO23 9SU* Tel (01962) 865678

APPS, Anthony Howard. b 22. Ch Coll Cam BA47 MA51. **d** 49 **p** 50. C Poplar All SS w St Frideswide Lon 49-55; V Mile End Old Town H Trin 55-66; V Myddleton Square St Mark 66-82; rtd 82; Perm to Offic *York* from 82. *18 Longworth Way, Guisborough TS14 6DG* Tel (01287) 637939

APPS, Bryan Gerald. b 37. Univ of Wales (Lamp) BA59 St Cath Coll Ox BA61 MA65. Wycliffe Hall Ox 59. **d** 61 **p** 62. C Southampton St Alb *Win* 61-65; C Andover w Foxcott 65-69; P-in-c Freemantle 69-72; R 73-78; V Pokesdown All SS 78-03; rtd 03. *14 Bartlett Drive, Bournemouth BH7 7JT* Tel (01202) 417585 E-mail bryanapps@talk21.com

APPS, David Ronald. b 34. Univ of Wales (Lamp) BA59. Sarum Th Coll 57. **d** 59 **p** 60. C Southbourne St Chris *Win* 59-62; C Weeke 62-67; V Alton All SS 67-80; V Charlestown *Truro* 80-97; Miss to Seamen 80-97; rtd 99. *12 Walnut Close, Exminster, Exeter EX6 8SZ* Tel (01392) 823672

APPS, Canon Michael John (Brother Bernard). b 28. Pemb Coll Cam BA52 MA56. Cuddesdon Coll 53. **d** 55 **p** 56. C Spalding *Linc* 55-58; SSF from 58; Perm to Offic *Chelmsf* 59-63 and 67-69; P-in-c Plaistow 63-67; Australia 69-75; Guardian St Nic Friary Harbledown 77-78; Guardian Hilfield Friary Dorchester 78-89; Can and Preb Sarum Cathl *Sarum* 81-89; Perm to Offic *Lon* 93-96 and from 99; rtd 98; Perm to Offic *Cant* from 03. *6A Stour Street, Canterbury CT1 2NR*

APTED, Peter John. b 43. Middx Univ MA01. NTMTC 95. **d** 98 **p** 99. NSM Feltham *Lon* 98-01; TV Horsham *Chich* from 01. *St Leonard's Vicarage, Cambridge Road, Horsham RH13 5ED* Tel (01403) 266903 E-mail peter@revapted.freeserve.co.uk

APTHORP, The Ven Arthur Norman. b 24. Pemb Coll Cam BA47 MA50. Chich Th Coll 48. **d** 50 **p** 51. C Henfield *Chich* 50-52; C Hove All SS 52-56; Australia from 56; R Narembeen 57-60; R Boulder 60-66; R Northam 66-72; R Kalgoorlie and Boulder 72-78; Hon Can Perth 73-77 and 79-89; R Dianella 78-82; R Merredin 82-89; Adn of the Country (Perth) 82-87; Adn of the Goldfields 87-89; rtd 89. *2 Brookton Highway, Brookton, W Australia 6306* Tel (0061) (8) 9642 1046

AQUILINA, Ivan Dominic. b 66. Univ of Malta BA95 BA97 Educn Diploma Malta PGCE96. Coll of Resurr Mirfield 98. **d** 00 **p** 01. C Leam Lane *Dur* 00-01; C Jarrow from 01. *St John the Baptist House, Iona Road, Jarrow NE32 4HY* Tel 0191-420 8334 Mobile 07947-139263 E-mail ivclau@talk21.com

ARBER, Gerald Kenneth. b 37. Open Univ BA87. Oak Hill NSM Course 81. **d** 84 **p** 85. NSM Romford St Edw *Chelmsf* 84-95; NSM Cranham from 95. *5 Hill Grove, Romford RM1 4JP* Tel (01708) 750070

ARBERY, Canon Richard Neil. b 25. AKC49. **d** 50 **p** 51. C Pemberton St Jo *Liv* 50-55; V Roundthorn *Man* 55-59; V Hindley All SS *Liv* 59-78; Chapl HM Youth Cust Cen Hindley 70-84; Asst Chapl HM YOI Hindley 84-90; RD Wigan *Liv* 75-89; Hon Can Liv Cathl 77-92; V Wigan St Andr 78-92; rtd 92; Perm to Offic *Liv* from 92. *11 Gillan Road, Wigan WN6 7HQ* Tel (01942) 491734

ARBUCKLE, Canon James Hugh. b 19. AKC49. **d** 49 **p** 50. C Seaford w Sutton *Chich* 49-52; C Crosby *Linc* 52-54; V Barnetby le Wold 54-76; P-in-c Bigby 64-76; Can and Preb Linc Cathl 70-00; RD Yarborough 70-76; P-in-c Somerby w Humby 74-76; Sec Linc Dioc Syn and Past Cttee 76-84; rtd 85. *Orchard Court, 7 Wrawby Road, Brigg DN20 8DL*

ARBUTHNOT, Canon James. b 19. QUB BA42. CITC 44. **d** 44 **p** 45. C Belfast St Aid *Conn* 44-47; C Belfast St Simon 47-51; I Ardglass w Dunsford *D & D* 51-60; I Belfast St Phil *Conn* 60-70; I Belfast St Paul 70-87; Can Conn Cathl 83-87; rtd 87. *20 St Colman's Crescent, Carrickfergus BT38 7XN* Tel (028) 9335 9226

ARCH, Ian Michael. b 75. Univ Coll Dur MSc97 Peterho Cam BA02. Westcott Ho Cam 00. **d** 03. C Bromborough *Ches* from 03. *193 Allport Road, Wirral CH62 6BA* Tel 0151-334 4181 E-mail ian.arch@dunelm.org.uk

ARCHER, Alan Robert. b 38. AKC56. Lich Th Coll 65. **d** 68 **p** 69. C Lower Mitton *Worc* 68-71; C Foley Park 71-74; V Warndon 74-79; P-in-c Clifton upon Teme 79-81; P-in-c Lower Sapey 79-81; P-in-c The Shelsleys 79-81; V Malvern Wells and Wyche 81-83; TV Braunstone *Leic* 83-91; P-in-c Bemerton *Sarum* 91-03; Dioc Link Officer for ACUPA 92-94; rtd 03. *15 Summerfield Road, Stourport-on-Severn DY13 9BE*

ARCHER, Graham John. b 58. Lanc Univ BSc79. St Jo Coll Nottm DipTh. **d** 85 **p** 86. C Ipswich St Matt *St E* 85-89; C Walton 89-95; P-in-c 95-99; Chapl Local Health Partnerships NHS Trust 96-99; P-in-c Portswood Ch Ch *Win* from 99; P-in-c Portswood St Denys from 00. *The Vicarage, 36 Brookvale Road, Southampton SO2 1QR* Tel (023) 8055 4277 E-mail vicarbiker@aol.com

ARCHER, John Thomas. b 28. Birm Coll of Commerce GIMechE68 Birm Poly CQSW83. EMMTC 79. **d** 80 **p** 81. NSM Derby St Thos *Derby* 80-86; V Edlington *Sheff* 87-98; rtd 98. *Gwarcwm, Cwmduad, Carmarthen SA33 6AU* Tel (01559) 370139

ARCHER, Keith Malcolm. b 40. Man Univ BA61 MA80 Magd Coll Cam BA67 MA72. Ridley Hall Cam 66. **d** 68 **p** 69. C Newland St Jo *York* 68-72; Hon C Kersal Moor *Man* 72-79; Ind Chapl 72-93; V Weaste from 93. *The Vicarage, 43 Derby Road, Salford M50 2DW* Tel 0161-736 5819 E-mail keitharcher@weaste.in2home.co.uk

ARCHER, Michael James. b 67. St Jo Coll Dur BA90 St Edm Coll Cam PhD95. Ridley Hall Cam CTM92. **d** 94 **p** 95. C Littleover *Derby* 94-97; C Edgware *Lon* 97-98; TV 98-01; P-in-c Bletchley *Ox* from 01. *101 Whalley Drive, Bletchley, Milton Keynes MK3 6HX* Tel (01908) 630305

ARCHER, Michael John. b 37. Trin Coll Bris 76. **d** 78 **p** 79. C Kinson *Sarum* 78-81; C Harpenden St Nic *St Alb* 81-88; P-in-c Rashcliffe and Lockwood *Wakef* 88-00; rtd 00; Perm to Offic *Truro* from 02. *Seaview Cottage, Porthallow, Helston TR12 6PW* Tel (01326) 280502

ARCHER, Neill John. b 61. UEA BA82. NTMTC 96. **d** 99 **p** 00. C Ripley *Derby* 99-02; C Forster Tuncurry Australia from 02. *47 Bent Street, Tuncurry, NSW, Australia 2428* Tel (0061) (2) 6555 5044 E-mail neillarcher@tsn.cc

ARCHER, Ms Sarah Elizabeth. b 66. MB, BS89 MRCGP95. Ripon Coll Cuddesdon BA99. **d** 00 **p** 01. C Dulwich St Barn *S'wark* 00-03; C Shepherd's Bush St Steph w St Thos *Lon* from 03. *The Parsonage, 1 Commonwealth Avenue, London W12 7QR* Tel (020) 8743 7100 Mobile 07901-551854 E-mail searcher@doctors.org.uk

ARCHER, Stanley Edwin. b 21. St Jo Coll Dur 80. **d** 81 **p** 82. C Upper Nidderdale *Ripon* 81-83; P-in-c Wensley 83-89; P-in-c W Witton 83-89; rtd 89; Perm to Offic *Ripon* 89-02; *Ox* from 02. *5 Eaton Close, Faringdon SN7 7FG* Tel (01367) 244423

ARCUS, Jeffrey. b 40. NW Ord Course 72. **d** 75 **p** 76. C Halliwell St Thos *Man* 75-78; C Walmsley 78-81; P-in-c Bury Ch King 81-82; TV Bury Ch King w H Trin 82-93; V Ramsbottom St Jo and St Paul from 93. *St Paul's Vicarage, Maple Grove, Ramsbottom, Bury BL0 0AN* Tel (01706) 821036

ARDAGH-WALTER, Christopher Richard. b 35. Univ of Wales (Lamp) BA58. Chich Th Coll 58. **d** 60 **p** 61. C Heavitree *Ex* 60-64; C Redcar *York* 64-67; C King's Worthy *Win* 67-69; C-in-c Four Marks CD 70-73; V Four Marks 73-76; P-in-c Eling, Testwood and Marchwood 76-78; TR Totton 78-84; R The Sherbornes w Pamber 84-88; V Froyle and Holybourne 88-95; C Verwood *Sarum* 95-97; rtd 97; Perm to Offic *Ex* from 01. *2 Bunkers Hill, Newbury RG14 6TF* Tel (01635) 41128

✠**ARDEN, The Rt Revd Donald Seymour.** b 16. CBE81. Leeds Univ BA37. Coll of Resurr Mirfield 37. **d** 39 **p** 40 **c** 61. C Hatcham St Cath *S'wark* 39-40; C Potten End w Nettleden *St Alb* 41-43; S Africa 44-61; Can Zululand 59-61; Bp Nyasaland 61-64; Bp S Malawi 71-81; Abp Cen Africa 71-80; Asst Bp Willesden *Lon* 81-94; Hon Asst Bp Lon from 94; P-in-c Uxbridge St Marg 81-86; rtd 86; Hon C N Harrow St Alb *Lon* from 86. *6 Frobisher Close, Pinner HA5 1NN* Tel (020) 8866 6009 Fax 8868 8013 E-mail djarden@fish.co.uk

ARDFERT AND AGHADOE, Archdeacon of. See SHANNON, The Ven Malcolm James Douglas

ARDILL, Robert William Brian. b 40. QUB BSc63 PhD67 SOSc. Ox NSM Course 80 St Jo Coll Nottm DipTh85. **d** 83 **p** 85. NSM Sunninghill *Ox* 83-84; Hon Chapl R Holloway Coll Lon 83-84; C Lenton *S'well* 85-87; Perm to Offic *Leic* 92-95; C Harpenden St Nic *St Alb* 95-00; R N Tawton, Bondleigh, Sampford Courtenay etc *Ex* from 00. *The Rectory, Essington, North Tawton EX20 2EX* Tel (01837) 82645 E-mail brian.ardill@ntlworld.com

ARDING, Richard. b 52. ACIB84. Oak Hill Th Coll DipHE92. **d** 92 **p** 93. C Bromley Common St Aug *Roch* 92-96; V Wilmington from 96. *The Vicarage, 1 Curate's Walk, Dartford DA2 7BJ* E-mail richarddarding@btopenworld.com

ARDIS, Edward George. b 54. Dur Univ BA76. CITC 76. **d** 78 **p** 79. C Dublin Drumcondra w N Strand and St Barn *D & G* 78-81; C Dublin St Bart w Leeson Park 81-84; I Ardamine w Kiltennel, Glascarrig etc *C & O* 84-89; Can Tuam Cathl *T, K & A* 89-03; Dean Killala 89-03; I Killala w Dunfeeny, Crossmolina etc 89-94; I Killala w Dunfeeny, Crossmolina, Kilmoremoy etc 94-03; Dir of Ords 95-03; I Dublin Irishtown w Donnybrook *D & G* from 03. *St Mary's Rectory, 4 Ailesbury Grove, Donnybrook, Dublin 4, Irish Republic* Tel (00353) (1) 269 2090 E-mail donnybrook@dublin.anglican.org

ARDLEY, Canon John Owen. b 39. Lon Univ BD70. S'wark Ord Course 70. **d** 72 **p** 73. C Caterham Valley *S'wark* 72-76; V Abbey Wood 76-84; Sub-Dean Woolwich 77-84; P-in-c Lower Sydenham St Mich 84-95; P-in-c Sydenham All SS 84-95; V from 95; RD W Lewisham from 87; Hon Can S'wark Cathl from 95; Borough Dean Lewisham from 00. *All Saints' Vicarage, 41 Trewsbury Road, London SE26 5DP* Tel (020) 8778 3065 E-mail ardley@se26.fsbusiness.co.uk

ARGENTINA, Bishop of. See VENABLES, The Most Revd Gregory James

ARGLES, Mrs Christine. b 57. Bris Univ BA00. Trin Coll Bris 00. **d** 02 **p** 03. C Nailsea Ch Ch w Tickenham *B & W* from 02. *75 The Maples, Nailsea, Bristol BS48 4RY* Tel (01275) 855051 Mobile 07763-476127 E-mail chrisargles@aol.com

ARGUILE, Canon Roger Henry William. b 43. Dur Univ LLB64 Keble Coll Ox BA70 MA75. St Steph Ho Ox 69 Ripon Hall Ox 70. **d** 71 **p** 72. C Walsall *Lich* 71-76; TV Blakenall Heath 76-83; TV Stafford 83-95; P-in-c St Neots *Ely* 95-97; V from 97; Hon Can Ely Cathl from 01; RD St Neots from 02. *The Vicarage, Church Street, St Neots PE19 2BU* Tel (01480) 472297 E-mail roger.arguile@snpc.freeserve.co.uk

ARGYLE, Douglas Causer. b 17. St Jo Coll Cam BA39 MA43. Ridley Hall Cam 39. **d** 41 **p** 42. C Somercotes *Derby* 41-44; CF (EC) 44-47; Chapl Repton Sch Derby 47-59; Chapl Gresham's Sch Holt 59-74; P-in-c Eastleach w Southrop *Glouc* 74-82; rtd 82; Perm to Offic *Glouc* from 82. *East Lynn, London Road, Fairford GL7 4AR* Tel (01285) 713235

ARGYLE, Edward Charles. b 55. Edith Cowan Univ (Aus) BSocSc99. St Barn Coll Adelaide 77 ACT DipTh80. **d** 80 **p** 80. Australia 80-83 and from 94; C Whitford 80-82; C Gt Yarmouth *Nor* 83-85; I Kilcooley w Littleon, Crohane and Fertagh *C & O* 85-94; Can Ossory and Leighlin Cathls 90-94; NY USA 92; Min Cranbrook w Mt Barker from 95; R Albany from 02. *Peel Place, Collie Street, PO Box 5520, Albany, W Australia 6332* Tel (0061) (8) 9842 6215 or 9841 5015 Mobile 428-514119 Fax 9841 3360 E-mail eargyle@telstra.easymail.com.au

ARGYLL AND THE ISLES, Bishop of. See CAMERON, The Rt Revd Douglas MacLean

ARGYLL AND THE ISLES, Dean of. See FLATT, The Very Revd Roy Francis Ferguson

ARKELL, Kevin Paul. b 53. Preston Poly BTh86 Leeds Univ MA95. Sarum & Wells Th Coll 84. **d** 86 **p** 87. C S Petherton w the Seavingtons *B & W* 86-88; P-in-c Gt Harwood St Bart *Blackb* 88-90; V 90-95; TR Darwen St Pet w Hoddlesden from 95; Acting RD Darwen 97-98; AD Blackb and Darwen 98-03. *The Rectory, St Peter's Close, Darwen BB3 2EA* Tel (01254) 702411 Fax as telephone E-mail kevin.arkell@ntlworld.com

ARLOW, Canon William James. b 26. Edin Th Coll 59. **d** 59 **p** 60. C Ballymacarrett St Patr *D & D* 59-61; Cen Adv on Chr Stewardship to Ch of Ireland 61-66; I Newry St Patr 66-70; I Belfast St Donard 70-74; Dep Sec Irish Coun of Chs 74-75; Sec 75-79; Can for Ecum Affairs Belf Cathl from 79; Treas 85-89; P-in-c Ballyphilip w Ardquin 86-89; rtd 89; Lic to Offic *D & D* from 90. *13 Ashford Park, Bangor BT19 6DD* Tel (028) 9146 9758 E-mail william.arlow@talk21.com

ARMAGH, Archbishop of. See EAMES, The Most Revd and Rt Hon Lord

ARMAGH, Archdeacon of. See HOEY, The Ven Raymond George

ARMAGH, Dean of. See CASSIDY, The Very Revd Herbert

ARMAN, Canon Brian Robert. b 54. St Jo Coll Dur BA77 LTh78. Cranmer Hall Dur 74. **d** 78 **p** 79. C Lawrence Weston *Bris* 78-82; C Bishopston 82-88; R Filton from 88; Hon Can Bris Cathl from 01. *The Rectory, Station Road, Bristol BS34 7BX* Tel 0117-979 1128

ARMES, John Andrew. b 55. SS Coll Cam BA77 MA81 Man Univ PhD96. Sarum & Wells Th Coll 77. **d** 79 **p** 80. C Walney Is *Carl* 79-82; Chapl to Agric 82-86; TV Greystoke, Matterdale and Mungrisdale 82-86; TV Watermillock 82-86; TV Man Whitworth *Man* 86-88; TV Man 88-94; Chapl Man Univ 86-94; P-in-c Goodshaw and Crawshawbooth 94-98; AD Rossendale 94-98; R Edin St Jo from 98. *1 Ainslie Place, Edinburgh EH3 6AR* Tel 0131-225 5004

ARMFELT, Julian Roger. b 31. K Coll Cam BA53. Wells Th Coll 54. **d** 56 **p** 58. C Stocksbridge *Sheff* 56-57; C Cantley 57-59; P-in-c Clayton w Frickley 59-61; C Eglingham *Newc* 61-63; V Alkborough w Whitton *Linc* 63-64; C Corringham 69-73; TV Fincham *Ely* 73-75; V Freckleton *Blackb* 75-79; P-in-c Sherburn *York* 79-80; P-in-c W and E Heslerton w Knapton 79-80; P-in-c Yedingham 79-80; R Sherburn and W and E Heslerton w Yedingham 80-83; TV York All SS Pavement w St Crux and St Martin etc 83-84; P-in-c York St Mary Bishophill Junior w All SS 83-84; C Howden 84-86; P-in-c Laughton w Throapham *Sheff* 86-88; rtd 88; Perm to Offic *Newc* 88-02. *29 Dulverton Hall, Esplanade, Scarborough YO11 2AR* Tel (01723) 340129

ARMITAGE, Bryan Ambrose. b 28. K Coll Lon AKC55 BD58. **d** 56 **p** 57. C High Harrogate St Pet *Ripon* 56-59; S Africa 59-61; Uganda 61-73; Chapl Sutton Valence Sch Kent 73-75; Chapl Qu Ethelburga's Sch Harrogate 76-91; V Weaverthorpe w Helperthorpe, Luttons Ambo etc *York* 91-99; Chapl Qu Ethelburga's Coll York from 99. *5 York Road, Harrogate HG1 2QA* Tel (01423) 536547

ARMITAGE, Richard Norris. b 51. AKC. St Aug Coll Cant 73. **d** 74 **p** 75. C Chapelthorpe *Wakef* 74-77; C W Bromwich All SS *Lich* 77-82; P-in-c Ketley 82-83; V Oakengates 82-83; V Ketley and Oakengates 83-89; V Evesham *Worc* 89-96; V Evesham w Norton and Lenchwick from 96; RD Evesham from 00. *The Vicarage, 5 Croft Road, Evesham WR11 4NE* Tel (01386) 446219 or 442213 Fax 761214 E-mail office@allsaintsevesham.swinternet.co.uk

ARMITAGE, Susan. b 46. Th Ext Educn Coll 91. **d** 92 **p** 95. S Africa 92-97; C Fawley *Win* 97-00; C Chandler's Ford from 00. *45 Pantheon Road, Chandlers Ford, Eastleigh SO53 2PD* Tel (023) 8026 8433 E-mail sue.armitage@dial.pipex.com

ARMITSTEAD, Margaretha Catharina Maria. b 65. **d** 03. C Littlemore *Ox* from 03. *20 Vicarage Close, Littlemore, Oxford OX4 4PL* Tel (01865) 779885 Mobile 07761-549548 E-mail mail@armitstead34.free-online.co.uk

ARMITT, Andy John. b 68. Moorlands Bible Coll 88 Trin Coll Bris BA00. **d** 00 **p** 01. C Millhouses H Trin *Sheff* from 00. *59 Endowood Road, Sheffield S7 2LY* Tel 0114-221 9330 Mobile 07811-909782 E-mail andyarmitt@hotmail.com

ARMSON, Canon John Moss. b 39. Selw Coll Cam BA61 MA64 St Andr Univ PhD65. Coll of Resurr Mirfield 64. **d** 66 **p** 67. C Notting Hill St Jo *Lon* 66-69; Chapl and Fell Down Coll Cam 69-73; Chapl Westcott Ho Cam 73-76; Vice-Prin 76-82; Prin Edin Th Coll 82-89; Can St Mary's Cathl *Edin* 82-89; Can Res Roch Cathl *Roch* 89-01; rtd 01; Hengrave Community of Reconciliation from 01. *Mill Bank, Rowlestone, Hereford HR2 0DS* Tel (01981) 241046 E-mail j.armson@virgin.net *or* j.armson@hengravehallcentre.org.uk

ARMSTEAD, Geoffrey Malcolm. b 32. K Coll Lon BD56 AKC56 Nottm Univ AdDipEd73. St Boniface Warminster 56. **d** 57 **p** 57. C Weymouth H Trin *Sarum* 57-60; C Mortlake w E Sheen *S'wark* 60-63; Chapl Em Sch Wandsworth 63-74; Dep Hd Master Harriet Costello Sch 74-91; Acting Hd Master 91-92; Perm to Offic *Win* 74-92; V Win St Bart 92-01; rtd 01. *Polecat Cottage, Polecat Corner, Tunworth, Basingstoke RG25 2LA* Tel (01256) 471650 E-mail geoffrey@armstead.freeserve.co.uk

ARMSTEAD, Gordon. b 33. Oak Hill Th Coll DPS74. **d** 74 **p** 75. C Woodside *Ripon* 74-76; C Heaton Ch Ch *Man* 76-79; Australia 79-81; R Levenshulme St Mark *Man* 81-86; V Borth and Eglwysfach w Llangynfelyn *St D* 86-92; rtd 93; Perm to Offic *Blackb* 93-99; Perm from 99. *4 School Lane, Ripley, Derby DE5 3GT* Tel (01773) 741642

ARMSTRONG, Adrian Christopher. b 48. LSE BSc70 K Coll Lon PhD80. EAMTC 84. **d** 87 **p** 88. NSM Linton *Ely* 87-95; P-in-c N and S Muskham *S'well* 95-00; P-in-c Averham w Kelham 95-00; Perm to Offic *B & W* 01-02; Hon C Wiveliscombe w Chipstable, Huish Champflower etc from 02. *The Rectory, Lydeard St Lawrence, Taunton TA4 3SF* Tel (01984) 667220 E-mail wheelievicar@aol.com

ARMSTRONG, Alexander Milford. b 57. Local Minl Tr Course 87 96. **d** 95 **p** 95. NSM Livingston LEP *Edin* 95-97; C Cleator Moor w Cleator *Carl* 97-98; C Frizington and Arlecdon 97-98; C Crosslacon 98-99; V Westfield St Mary from 99. *St Mary's Vicarage, Salisbury Street, Workington CA14 3TA* Tel (01900) 603227 Fax as telephone E-mail amvarmstrong@hotmail.com

ARMSTRONG, The Very Revd Christopher John. b 47. Nottm Univ BTh75. Kelham Th Coll 72. **d** 75 **p** 76. C Maidstone All SS w St Phil and H Trin *Cant* 76-79; Chapl St Hild and St Bede Coll *Dur* 79-84; Abp's Dom Chapl and Dir of Ords *York* 85-91; V Scarborough St Martin 91-01; Dean Blackb from 01. *The Deanery, Preston New Road, Blackburn BB2 6PS* Tel (01254) 52502 *or* 51491 Fax 689666 E-mail dean@blackburn.anglican.org

ARMSTRONG, Christopher John Richard. b 35. Fribourg Univ LTh60 Ch Coll Cam BA64 MA68 PhD79. Edin Th Coll 74. **d** 59 **p** 59. In RC Ch 59-71; Lect Aber Univ *Ab* 68-74; C Ledbury *Heref* 74-76; P-in-c Bredenbury and Wacton w Grendon Bishop 76-79; P-in-c Edwyn Ralph and Collington w Thornbury 76-79; P-in-c Pencombe w Marston Stannett and Lt Cowarne 76-79; R Cherry Burton *York* 79-80; Tutor Westcott Ho Cam 80-85; V Bottisham *Ely* 85-89; P-in-c Lode and Longmeadow 85-89; P-in-c Cropthorne w Charlton *Worc* 89-93; Dioc Local Min Sec 89-93; R Aberdaron w Rhiw and Llanfaelrhys etc *Ban* 93-99; rtd 99; Perm to Offic *Heref* and *Ban* from 99. *Rowlstone Mill, Pontrilas, Hereford HR2 0DP* Tel (01981) 240346

ARMSTRONG, Colin John. b 32. St Cath Soc Ox BA59 MA65. Wells Th Coll 59. **d** 61 **p** 62. C Acomb St Steph *York* 61-64; C Newland St Jo 64-67; Chapl and Tutor All SS Coll Tottenham 67-78; Chapl and Tutor Middx Poly *Lon* 78-85; rtd 97; Perm to

Offic *St E* from 97. *Mead House, The Street, Preston St Mary, Sudbury CO10 9NQ* Tel (01787) 248218

ARMSTRONG, Eileen. d 95 p 96. NSM *M & K* from 95. *Hennigan, Nobber, Co Meath, Irish Republic* Tel (00353) (46) 905 2314

ARMSTRONG, John Edwin. b 51. Leic Univ CertEd73 BEd74 Homerton Coll Cam AEdRD87. Ridley Hall Cam CTM93. d 93 p 94. C Gt Wilbraham *Ely* 93-96; P-in-c Bassingbourn 96-02; V from 02; P-in-c Whaddon 96-02; V from 02. *The Vicarage, 21 North End, Bassingbourn, Royston SG8 5NZ* Tel (01763) 243119 E-mail revarmstrong@yahoo.com

ARMSTRONG, John Gordon. b 64. Man Poly BSc86 MSc91. Wycliffe Hall Ox 95. d 97 p 98. C Pennington *Man* 97-01; P-in-c Holcombe from 01; P-in-c Hawkshaw Lane from 01. *The Rectory, 12 Carrwood Hey, Ramsbottom, Bury BL0 9QT* Tel (01706) 822312 Fax as telephone E-mail john.armstrong4@tesco.net

ARMSTRONG, Canon John Hammond. b 24. MBE98. Dur Univ BA47 DipTh48. d 49 p 50. C Bishopwearmouth St Gabr *Dur* 49-52; C Cockfield w Staindrop 52-54; V Skipwith *York* 54-59; V Thorganby 54-59; V N Ferriby 59-63; R Sutton upon Derwent 63-71; Dioc Stewardship Adv 63-75; P-in-c York All SS and St Crux w St Sav etc 71-72; R 72-76; P-in-c York St Denys 74-76; TR York All SS Pavement w St Crux and St Denys 76-77; TR York All SS Pavement w St Crux and St Martin etc 77-91; Can and Preb York Minster 72-97; RD City of York 76-86; rtd 91; Perm to Offic *York* from 91; OStJ from 97. *20 Hempland Avenue, Stockton Lane, York YO31 1DE* Tel (01904) 421312

ARMSTRONG, John James. b 15. TCD BA38 MA42. TCD Div Sch Div Test 40. d 40 p 41. C Ballymacarrett St Patr *D & D* 40-46; C Neasden cum Kingsbury St Cath *Lon* 46-49; Ceylon 49-52; C St Marylebone w H Trin *Lon* 52-55; Hd of Trin Coll Miss Belfast 55-58; Miss to Seamen 58-77; Sudan 58-59; Dunkirk 60-62; Belfast 55-77; C Derriaghy *Conn* 62-71; C Seagoe *D & D* 71-73; Hd of S Ch Miss Belfast 73-75; C Belfast St Simon w St Phil *Conn* 77-80; rtd 80. *60 The Green, Dunmurry, Belfast BT17 0QA* Tel (028) 9062 3032

ARMSTRONG, Mrs Margaret Betty. b 48. SRN70 RSCN71. Westcott Ho Cam CTM92. d 92 p 94. NSM Linton *Ely* 92-95; NSM Shudy Camps 92-95; NSM Castle Camps 92-95; NSM Bartlow 92-95; NSM N and S Muskham and Averham w Kelham *S'well* 95-00; P-in-c Lydeard St Lawrence w Brompton Ralph etc *B & W* from 01. *The Rectory, Lydeard St Lawrence, Taunton TA4 3SF* Tel (01984) 667220 E-mail wheelievicar@aol.com

ARMSTRONG, Maurice Alexander. b 62. Ulster Poly BA84 TCD DipTh87. CITC 84. d 87 p 88. C Portadown St Mark *Arm* 87-90; I Sixmilecross w Termonmaguirke 90-95; I Richhill 95-01; I Tempo and Clabby *Clogh* from 01. *The Rectory, Clabby, Fivemiletown BT75 0RD* Tel (028) 8952 1697

ARMSTRONG, Nicholas Paul. b 58. Bris Univ BSc79. Trin Coll Bris DipHE93. d 93 p 94. C Filey *York* 93-97; P-in-c Alveley and Quatt *Heref* R from 98. *The Rectory, Alveley, Bridgnorth WV15 6ND* Tel (01746) 780326 Fax as telephone E-mail nicka@fish.co.uk

ARMSTRONG, Canon Robert Charles (Robin). b 24. TCD BA46 HDipEd52 MA57. CITC 47. d 47 p 48. C Belfast St Luke *Conn* 48-50; Warden Gr Sch Dub 50-59; Succ St Patr Cathl Dublin 50-59; I Dublin Finglas *D & G* 59-67; I Dun Laoghaire 67-94; Dir of Ords (Dub) 74-84; USPG Area Sec 77-94; Can Ch Ch Cathl Dublin 84-88; Treas 88-94; rtd 94. *1 Glenageary Terrace, Dun Laoghaire, Co Dublin, Irish Republic* Tel (00353) (1) 284 6941

ARMSTRONG, Samuel David. b 48. BD MTh. d 86 p 87. C Cambridge H Trin w St Andr Gt *Ely* 86-89; V Cambridge St Martin 89-00; I Carrigaline Union *C, C & R* from 00. *The Rectory, Carrigaline, Co Cork, Irish Republic* Tel (00353) (21) 437 2224

ARMSTRONG, Samuel George. b 39. Ox Univ Inst of Educn TCert65 CYCW65 AdCertEd71 Open Univ BA72 Reading Univ MSc89. S Dios Minl Tr Scheme 90. d 93 p 94. NSM N Tadley St Mary *Win* from 93. *The Cedars, Blakes Lane, Tadley, Basingstoke RG26 3PU* Tel 0118-981 6593 E-mail sammie@armstrongsg.freeserve.co.uk

ARMSTRONG, William. b 29. Sarum Th Coll 52. d 54 p 55. C Hebburn St Cuth *Dur* 54-55; C Ferryhill 55-57; C Gateshead H Trin 57-60; V Cassop cum Quarrington 60-66; Australia 66-81; Asst Dir of Educn *Liv* 81-90; V Aintree St Pet 81-88; TV Speke St Aid 88-90; rtd 90. *10 Blenheim Court, Horn Lane, Woodford Green IG8 9AQ* Tel (020) 8504 1874

ARMSTRONG-MacDONNELL, Mrs Vivienne Christine. b 42. Open Univ BA89 Ex Univ MEd01. Ripon Coll Cuddesdon 88. d 90 p 94. C Crediton and Shobrooke *Ex* 90-93; Dioc Adv in Adult Tr 93-00; rtd 00; Perm to Offic *Ex* from 00. *Strand House, Woodbury, Exeter EX5 1LZ* Tel (01395) 232790 Fax as telephone E-mail viv.a-macdonnell@tiscali.co.uk

ARNDT, Miss Sarah. b 76. Univ of Wales (Abth) BTh98. St Jo Coll Nottm 98. d 00 p 01. C Flint *St As* 00-02. *Address temp unknown*

ARNESEN, Christopher Paul. b 48. Lon Univ BA70. Sarum & Wells Th Coll 78. d 80 p 81. C Dalton-in-Furness *Carl* 80-83; C Ranmoor *Sheff* 83-86; R Distington *Carl* 86-93; TV Sheff Manor *Sheff* 93-97; Mental Health Chapl Community Health Sheff NHS Trust from 98. *21 Horndean Road, Sheffield S5 6UJ* Tel 0114-244 2171 E-mail paul@arnies.org.uk

ARNESEN, Raymond Halfdan (Brother Ælred). b 25. Qu Coll Cam BA49 MA54. Linc Th Coll 50. d 52 p 53. C Newc St Fran *Newc* 52-55; SSF 55-66; Cistercian Monk from 66; Ewell Monastery from 66; rtd 95. *Ewell Monastery, Water Lane, West Malling, Maidstone ME19 6HH* Tel (01732) 843089

ARNOLD, Adrian Paul. b 69. St Steph Ho Ox. d 01 p 02. C Staincliffe and Carlinghow *Wakef* from 01. *St John's House, 8A Amber Street, Batley WF17 8HH* Tel (01924) 472576 Mobile 07951-873597

ARNOLD, Alan Roy. b 33. Lon Univ BD79. S'wark Ord Course 75. d 78 p 79. C Fleet *Guildf* 78-81; V Hinchley Wood 81-84; C Cobham 84-89; C Addlestone 89-92; rtd 93; Perm to Offic *Guildf* 92-94; Perm to Offic *Win* 94-98. *Flat 9, 68 West Cliff Road, Bournemouth BH4 8BE* Tel (01202) 752018

ARNOLD, Brother. See NODDER, Thomas Arthur

ARNOLD, David Alun. b 78. St Andr Univ MTheol00. Coll of Resurr Mirfield 01. d 03. C Ribbleton *Blackb* from 03. *5 Langdale Crescent, Ribbleton, Preston PR2 6AJ* Tel 07786-168261 (mobile)

ARNOLD, Derek John. b 59. Wycliffe Hall Ox. d 03. C St Jo in Bedwardine *Worc* from 03. *4 Ogilvy Square, Worcester WR3 7LU*

ARNOLD, Elisabeth Anne Truyens. b 44. TCert66. LNSM course 88. d 91 p 94. OLM Ipswich St Thos *St E* 91-00; Chapl Dioc Min Course 00-01; OLM Tutor from 01. *66 Bromeswell Road, Ipswich IP4 3AT* Tel (01473) 257406

ARNOLD, Ernest Stephen. b 27. d 64 p 65. C Aberavon *Llan* 64-68; V Ferndale 68-74; Cyprus 81-85; rtd 94; Perm to Offic *Portsm* from 94. *Barn Cottage, Apse Manor Road, Shanklin PO37 7PN* Tel (01983) 866324

ARNOLD, Graham Thomas. b 62. S Kent Coll of Tech OND80. Aston Tr Scheme 87 Ripon Coll Cuddesdon 89. d 92 p 93. C Margate St Jo *Cant* 92-95; TV Whitstable 95-00. *117 Falcon Road, London SW11 2PE* Tel (020) 7738 9099

ARNOLD, Jennifer Anne. b 54. Univ Coll Lon BSc75 MB, BS78 FRCR85. Qu Coll Birm 00. d 02. C Aston SS Pet and Paul *Birm* from 02. *68 Manor Road, Aston, Birmingham B6 6QT* Tel 0121-326 7390 E-mail arnolds68@btopenworld.com

ARNOLD, The Very Revd John Robert. b 33. OBE02. SS Coll Cam BA57 MA61 Lambeth DD99. Westcott Ho Cam 58. d 60 p 61. C Millhouses H Trin *Sheff* 60-63; Chapl and Lect Southn Univ *Win* 63-72; Gen Sec Gen Syn Bd for Miss and Unity 72-78; Hon Can Win Cathl *Win* 74-78; Dean Roch 78-89; Dean Dur 89-02; rtd 03; Perm to Offic *Cant* from 02. *26 Hawks Lane, Canterbury CT1 2NU* Tel (01227) 764703

✠**ARNOLD, The Rt Revd Keith Appleby.** b 26. Trin Coll Cam BA50 MA55. Westcott Ho Cam 50. d 52 p 53 c 80. C Haltwhistle *Newc* 52-55; C Edin St Jo *Edin* 55-61; R 61-69; CF (TA) 58-62; V Kirkby Lonsdale w Mansergh *Carl* 69-73; RD Berkhamsted *St Alb* 73-80; TR Hemel Hempstead 73-80; Suff Bp Warw *Cov* 80-90; Hon Can Cov Cathl 80-90; rtd 90. *9 Dingleberry, Olney MK46 5ES* Tel (01234) 713044

ARNOLD, Michael John. b 44. Rhodes Univ BA68 St Edm Hall Ox BA72 MA77. St Jo Coll Nottm 93. d 98 p 98. Asst Chapl St Jo Coll Johannesburg S Africa 98-99; Chapl from 01; Chapl Claysemore Sch Blandford 98-01. *St John's College, St David's Road, Houghton Estate, Johannesburg, 2198 South Africa* Tel (0027) (11) 648 9932 *or* 648 1350 Mobile (0) 72 3134315 Fax 487 2227 E-mail arnoldmj@hotmail.com

ARNOLD, Richard Nicholas. b 54. AKC76. S'wark Ord Course 76. d 77 p 78. C Nunhead St Antony *S'wark* 77-80; C Walworth 80-82; P-in-c Streatham Hill St Marg 82-84; V 84-89; P-in-c Oseney Crescent St Luke *Lon* 89-93; P-in-c Kentish Town St Jo 89-93; P-in-c Kentish Town St Benet and All SS 89-93; V Kentish Town from 93; AD S Camden from 00. *Kentish Town Vicarage, 43 Lady Margaret Road, London NW5 2NH* Tel (020) 7485 4231 Mobile 07802-730974 Fax 7482 7222 E-mail fr.arnold@lineone.net

ARNOLD, Canon Roy. b 36. St D Coll Lamp BA62 DipTh63. d 63 p 64. C Brislington St Luke *Bris* 63-66; C Ches St Mary *Ches* 67-70; V Brinnington w Portwood 71-75; V Sale St Paul 75-82; R Doddleston 82-84; V Sheff St Oswald *Sheff* 84-90; Dioc Communications Officer 84-97; Chapl w the Deaf 90-97; Hon Can Sheff Cathl 95-97; rtd 97; Perm to Offic *Ches* from 97. *49 Crossfield Road, Bollington, Macclesfield SK10 5EA* Tel (01625) 575472

ARNOLD, Ms Sonja Marie. b 63. Wycliffe Hall Ox BTh98. d 98 p 99. C Hammersmith St Simon *Lon* from 98; Dean of Women's Min Kensington Area from 02. *Flat 2, 176 Holland Road, London W14 8AH* Tel (020) 7603 8475 *or* 7603 1418

ARNOLD, Victor Norman. b 45. Oak Hill Th Coll 91. d 94 p 95. NSM Chigwell and Chigwell Row *Chelmsf* 94-98; C W Ham from 98. *Spring Cottage, 6 Spring Grove, Loughton IG10 4QA* Tel

(020) 8508 6572 Fax as telephone
E-mail norman@ediblehedge.freeserve.co.uk

ARNOTT, Preb David. b 44. Em Coll Cam BA66. Qu Coll Birm 68. **d** 69 **p** 70. C Charlton St Luke w St Paul *S'wark* 69-73; C S Beddington St Mich 73-78; Chapl Liv Poly *Liv* 78-82; V Bridgwater St Fran *B & W* 86-02; Preb Wells Cathl 00-02; V Yealmpton and Brixton *Ex* from 02; RD Ivybridge from 03. *The Vicarage, Bowden Hill, Yealmpton, Plymouth PL8 2JX* Tel (01752) 880979

ARNOTT, Eric William. b 12. Cranmer Hall Dur 67. **d** 68 **p** 69. C Gosforth St Nic *Newc* 68-71; C Wooler 71-74; TV Wooler Gp 74-78; rtd 78. *Forge Cottage, Hoopers Lane, Puncknowle, Dorchester DT2 9BE* Tel (01308) 897768

ARRAND, The Ven Geoffrey William. b 44. K Coll Lon BD66 AKC66. **d** 67 **p** 68. C Washington *Dur* 67-70; C S Ormsby w Ketsby, Calceby and Driby *Linc* 70-73; TV Gt Grimsby St Mary and St Jas 73-79; TR Halesworth w Linstead and Chediston *St E* 79-80; TR Halesworth w Linstead, Chediston, Holton etc 80-85; R Hadleigh w Layham and Shelley 85-94; Dean Bocking 85-94; RD Hadleigh 86-94; Hon Can *St E* Cathl from 91; Adn Suffolk from 94. *Glebe House, The Street, Ashfield, Stowmarket IP14 6LX* Tel (01728) 685497 Fax 685969
E-mail geoffrey@stedmundsbury.anglican.org

ARRANDALE, Richard Paul Matthew. b 63. BA87. Chich Th Coll 87. **d** 90 **p** 91. C E Grinstead St Swithun *Chich* 90-94; C Crawley 94. *6 Main Drive, Bognor Regis PO22 7TN*

ARRANTASH, Canon Reginald Thomas. b 12. Linc Th Coll 33. **d** 36 **p** 37. C Kennington St Jo *S'wark* 36-37; Australia 37-48 and from 52; R Kenchester and Bridge Sollers *Heref* 48-52; R Bishopstone 48-52; rtd 83. *16 Loton Close, Kojonup, W Australia 6395* Tel (0061) (8) 9831 0343

ARRIDGE, Leonard Owen. b 22. Univ of Wales (Ban) BA51. St Deiniol's Hawarden 64. **d** 67 **p** 68. Tutor Ches Coll of HE 67-79; Hon C Hope *St As* 67-69; Hon C Wrexham 69-79; Min Can Ban Cathl *Ban* 79-87; C Ban Cathl *Ban* 79-87; rtd 87; Perm to Offic *Ban* from 87. *8 Ffordd Islwyn, Bangor LL57 1AR* Tel (01248) 362233

ARSCOTT, Barry James. b 36. AKC59. **d** 60 **p** 61. C Walthamstow St Andr *Chelmsf* 60-65; P-in-c Leyton St Luke 65-67; V 67-77; P-in-c Lt Ilford St Barn 77-86; V 86-01; rtd 01. *232 Fencepiece Road, Ilford IG6 2ST* Tel (020) 8502 6853

ARTHINGTON, Sister Muriel. b 23. dss 67 **d** 87. St Etheldreda's Children's Home Bedf 64-84; Hon Par Dn Bedford St Paul *St Alb* 87-94; Perm to Offic from 94; rtd 97. *Paddock House, 6 Linford Lane, Willen, Milton Keynes MK15 9DL*

ARTHUR, Graeme Richard. b 52. Univ of NSW BCom78. Linc Th Coll 93. **d** 93 **p** 94. C Witney *Ox* 93-97; R Westcote Barton w Steeple Barton, Duns Tew etc from 97. *The Rectory, 29 Enstone Road, Westcote Barton, Chipping Norton OX7 7AA* Tel (01869) 340510 E-mail graeme@arfa.clara.net

ARTHUR, Canon Ian Willoughby. b 40. Lon Univ BA63 BA66 PGCE64 Lambeth STh94 Kent Univ MA98. Ripon Coll Cuddesdon 78. **d** 80 **p** 81. C Kempston Transfiguration *St Alb* 80-83; R Potton w Sutton and Cockayne Hatley 83-96; P-in-c Sharnbrook and Knotting w Souldrop from 96; RD Sharnbrook from 97; Hon Can St Alb from 99. *The Rectory, 81 High Street, Sharnbrook, Bedford MK44 1PE* Tel (01234) 781444 Fax 782074 E-mail iwarthur@supanet.com

ARTHUR, Mrs Joan Diane. b 42. St Alb and Ox Min Course. **d** 00 **p** 01. Non-Stip Min High Wycombe *Ox* from 00. *34 Hithercroft Road, High Wycombe HP13 5LS* Tel (01494) 534582 Mobile 07961-840420 Fax (01494) 523311

ARTHUR, Kenneth Paul. b 64. Univ of Wales (Cardiff) BScEcon86 Roehampton Inst PGCE87. St Steph Ho Ox 98. **d** 00 **p** 01. C Bodmin w Lanhydrock and Lanivet *Truro* 00-02; P-in-c Treverbyn from 02; P-in-c Boscoppa from 02. *The Vicarage, Treverbyn Road, Stenalees, St Austell PL26 8TL* Tel (01726) 851923 E-mail father.paul@bigfoot.com

ARTHY, Ms Nicola Mary. b 64. St Jo Coll Ox BA85 MA93. SEITE. **d** 00 **p** 01. C Guildf H Trin w St Mary *Guildf* 00-01; C Farncombe from 01. *71 Fern Road, Godalming GU7 3ER* Tel (01483) 426140 Mobile 07904-721835
E-mail nikkiarthy@tesco.net

ARTISS, Joseph Sturge. b 28. Dur Univ BSc52. Cranmer Hall Dur DipTh67. **d** 67 **p** 68. C Dur St Cuth *Dur* 67-68; C Chester le Street 68-70; V Walsall St Pet *Lich* 71-94; rtd 94. *89 Bloxwich Road, Walsall WS2 8BP* Tel (01922) 23995

ARTLEY, Clive Mansell. b 30. St Jo Coll Dur BA56 Leeds Univ MA(Theol)01. Cranmer Hall Dur DipTh58. **d** 58 **p** 59. C Eston *York* 58-61; R Burythorpe w E Acklam and Leavening 61-64; CF 64-73; Teacher 73-93; Perm to Offic *York* from 73; rtd 93. *56 High Street, Castleton, Whitby YO21 2DA* Tel (01287) 660470

ARTLEY, Miss Pamela Jean. b 47. Worc Coll of Educn CertEd68 Hull Univ MEd91. NEOC 99. **d** 02. NSM Bridlington Priory *York* from 02. *Broxa, 11 Bempton Drive, Bridlington YO16 7HG* Tel (01262) 602044 E-mail pjartley@fish.co.uk

ARTUS, Stephen James. b 60. Man Poly BA82 W Midl Coll of Educn PGCE84. St Jo Coll Nottm MA95. **d** 95 **p** 96. C Altrincham St Geo *Ches* 95-99; P-in-c Norton from 99. *The*

Vicarage, Windmill Hill, Runcorn WA7 6QE Tel (01928) 715225 E-mail stephen@nortonvicarage.fsnet.co.uk

ARUNDEL, Canon Michael. b 36. Qu Coll Ox BA60 MA64. Linc Th Coll 60. **d** 62 **p** 63. C Hollinwood *Man* 62-65; C Leesfield 65-69; R Newton Heath All SS 69-80; RD N Man 75-80; P-in-c Eccles St Mary 80-81; TR Eccles 81-91; R Man St Ann 91-01; Hon Can Man Cathl 82-01; rtd 01. *20 Kiln Brow, Bromley Cross, Bolton BL7 9NR* Tel (01204) 591156

ARVIDSSON, Carl Fredrik. b 66. Regents Th Coll DipTh91. **d** 92 **p** 93. C Southsea H Spirit *Portsm* 92-94; C Botley, Curdridge and Durley 94-96; P-in-c Ringwould w Kingsdown *Cant* 96-97; R 97-01; Hon Min Can Cant Cathl from 01; Sen Chapl K Sch Cant from 01. *The King's School, Canterbury CT1 2ES* Tel (01227) 595613 E-mail chaplainkings@aol.com

ASBRIDGE, Preb John Hawell. b 26. Dur Univ BA47. Bps' Coll Cheshunt 47. **d** 49 **p** 50. C Barrow St Geo *Carl* 49-52; C Fort William *Arg* 52-54; C Lon Docks St Pet w Wapping St Jo *Lon* 54-55; C Kilburn St Aug 55-59; V Northolt Park St Barn 59-66; V Shepherd's Bush St Steph w St Thos 66-96; Preb St Paul's Cathl 89-96; rtd 96. *Crystal Glen, The Old Mineral Line, Roadwater, Watchet TA23 0RL* Tel (01984) 640211

ASBRIDGE, Nigel Henry. b 58. Bris Univ BA80. Chich Th Coll 87. **d** 89 **p** 90. C Tottenham St Paul *Lon* 89; C W Hampstead St Jas 89-94; P-in-c Hornsey H Innocents from 94; P-in-c Stroud Green H Trin from 02. *99 Hillfield Avenue, London N8 7DG* Tel (020) 8340 1300

ASBURY, William. b 35. Sheff Univ CertEd61 Lon Univ DipTh62 Liv Univ MA89. All Nations Chr Coll 57. **d** 97 **p** 98. NSM Southport Ch Ch *Liv* 97-00; Town Cen Chapl 97-00; Perm to Offic from 00. *117 The Causeway, Southport PR9 8JA* Tel (01704) 213383

ASH, Arthur Edwin. b 44. St Jo Coll Nottm 85. **d** 87 **p** 88. C Attleborough *Cov* 87-91; V Garretts Green *Birm* 91-02; rtd 02; Perm to Offic *Birm* from 02. *1 Margetts Close, Kenilworth CV8 1EN* Tel (01926) 853547 E-mail aash@tinyworld.co.uk

ASH, Brian John. b 32. ALCD62. **d** 62 **p** 63. C Plymouth St Andr *Ex* 62-66; Area Sec CMS *Cant* and *Roch* 66-73; V Bromley Common St Aug *Roch* 73-97; rtd 97; Perm to Offic *Chelmsf* 97-00. *The Vines, 95 Green Lane, Leigh-on-Sea SS9 5QU* Tel (01702) 523644

ASH, Christopher Brian Garton. b 53. Trin Hall Cam MA76. Wycliffe Hall Ox BA92. **d** 93 **p** 94. C Cambridge H Sepulchre *Ely* 93-97; P-in-c Lt Shelford 97-02; R from 02. *The Rectory, 2 Manor Road, Little Shelford, Cambridge CB2 5HF* Tel (01223) 843710 Fax as telephone E-mail allsaints.office@talk21.com or ash@home.cam.net.uk

ASH, David Nicholas. b 61. Southlands Coll Lon BA82. Wycliffe Hall Ox BTh03. **d** 03. C Walsall *Lich* from 03. *164 Birmingham Road, Walsall WS1 2NJ* E-mail revdavidash@fish.co.uk

ASH, Nicholas John. b 59. Bath Univ BSc81 Nottm Univ BTh88. Linc Th Coll 85. **d** 88 **p** 89. C Hersham *Guildf* 88-93; P-in-c Flookburgh *Carl* 93-97; Dioc Officer for Stewardship 94-97; TV Cartmel Peninsula 97-98; Dir of Ords from 97; P-in-c Dalston 98-00; P-in-c Wreay 98-00; P-in-c Raughton Head w Gatesgill 98-00; V Dalston w Cumdivock, Raughton Head and Wreay from 01. *The Vicarage, Townhead Road, Dalston, Carlisle CA5 7JF* Tel and fax (01228) 710215 or tel 711993 E-mail nickash405@hotmail.com

ASHBURNER, David Barrington. b 26. Ch Coll Cam BA51 MA55. Wycliffe Hall Ox 51. **d** 53 **p** 54. C Coalville *Leic* 53-56; C Leic H Apostles 56-58; V Bucklebury w Marlston *Ox* 58-70; V Belton *Leic* 70-75; P-in-c Osgathorpe 73-75; R Belton and Osgathorpe 75-79; V Frisby-on-the-Wreake w Kirby Bellars 79-82; V Uffington w Woolstone and Baulking *Ox* 82-91; P-in-c Shellingford 83-91; RD Vale of White Horse 87-91; rtd 91; Perm to Offic *Glouc* from 91; Perm to Offic *Ox* from 91. *Buckleberry, 188 Fosseway Avenue, Moreton-in-Marsh GL56 0EH* Tel (01608) 650347

ASHBY, Eric. b 37. EMMTC 78. **d** 81 **p** 82. C Hucknall Torkard *S'well* 81-85; V Lowdham 85-93; V Lowdham w Caythorpe, and Gunthorpe 93-02; rtd 02. *33 Chartwell Road, Kirkby-in-Ashfield, Nottingham NG17 7HB* Tel (01623) 723830

✠**ASHBY, The Rt Revd Godfrey William Ernest Candler.** b 30. Lon Univ AKC54 BD58 PhD69. **d** 55 **p** 56 **c** 80. C St Helier *S'wark* 55-57; S Africa 57-88 and from 95; Can Grahamstown Cathl 69-75; Dean and Adn Grahamstown 75-80; Bp St John's 80-85; Prof Div Witwatersrand Univ 85-88; Asst Bp Johannesburg 85-88; Asst Bp Leic 88-95; P-in-c Newtown Linford 92-95; Hon Can Leic Cathl 93-95; rtd 95; Asst Bp George from 95. *PO Box 2685, Knysna, 6570 South Africa* Tel (0027) (445) 827059

ASHBY, Mrs Judith Anne Stuart. b 53. Man Univ BSc74 MSc76. STETS 96. **d** 99 **p** 00. Hon C Swindon Ch Ch *Bris* from 99. *97 Bath Road, Swindon SN1 4AX* Tel (01793) 617794

ASHBY, Kevin Patrick. b 53. Jes Coll Ox BA76 MA80. Wycliffe Hall Ox 76. **d** 78 **p** 79. C Market Harborough *Leic* 78-82; C Horwich H Trin *Man* 82-84; C Horwich 84; TV 84-90; R Billing *Pet* 90-01; RD Northn 98-01; R Buckingham *Ox* from 01. *The*

ASHBY

Rectory, 39 Fishers Field, Buckingham MK18 1SF Tel (01280) 813178 Fax 820901 E-mail kevinp.ashby@virgin.net

ASHBY, Peter George. b 49. Univ of Wales (Cardiff) BSc(Econ)70 Nottm Univ DipTh71. Linc Th Coll 70. **d** 73 **p** 74. C Bengeo *St Alb* 73-75; Chapl Hatf Poly 76-79; C Apsley End 80; TV Chambersbury 80-82; Zimbabwe 82-87; Adn N Harare 84-87; V Eskdale, Irton, Muncaster and Waberthwaite *Carl* 87-93; TR Sedgley All SS *Worc* 93-99; TV Tettenhall Regis *Lich* from 99. *76 Tyningham Avenue, Tettenhall, Wolverhampton WV6 9PW* Tel and fax (01902) 753562 *or* tel 751622 E-mail peter@christtheking-aldersley.co.uk

ASHCROFT, Mrs Ann Christine. b 46. Cov Coll of Educn TCert68. N Ord Course 82. **d** 87 **p** 94. Chapl Trin High Sch Man 86-91; Burnage St Nic *Man* 86-95; Hon Par Dn 87-95; Dio Adv Man Coun for Educn 91-95; TV Wareham and Chapl Purbeck Sch *Sarum* 95-02; TR By Brook *Bris* from 02. *The Rectory, The Street, Yatton Keynell, Chippenham SN14 7BA* Tel (01249) 782663

ASHCROFT, Mark David. b 54. Worc Coll Ox BA77 MA82 Fitzw Coll Cam BA81. Ridley Hall Cam 79. **d** 82 **p** 83. C Burnage St Marg *Man* 82-85; CMS 86-96; Kenya 86-96; R Harpurhey Ch Ch *Man* from 96; R Harpurhey St Steph from 96; AD N Man from 00. *95 Church Lane, Manchester M9 5BG* Tel 0161-205 4020

ASHDOWN, Andrew William Harvey. b 64. K Coll Lon BD88 AKC88. Sarum & Wells Th Coll 88. **d** 90 **p** 91. C Cranleigh *Guildf* 90-94; V Ryhill *Wakef* 94-98; P-in-c Denmead *Portsm* 98-99; V from 99. *The Vicarage, Ludcombe, Denmead PO7 6TL* Tel (023) 9225 5490 Fax as telephone E-mail vicar@aashdown.fsnet.co.uk

ASHDOWN, Anthony Hughes. b 37. AKC63. **d** 64 **p** 65. C Tettenhall Regis *Lich* 64-67; P-in-c Bassaleg *Mon* 67-70; Rhodesia 70-77; P-in-c Longton St Jas *Lich* 77-78; P-in-c Longton St Jo 77-78; R Longton 78-80; TR Cove St Jo *Guildf* 80-87; Chapl Lisbon *Eur* 87-90; V Wanstead H Trin Hermon Hill *Chelmsf* 90-00; Perm to Offic *Chich* from 00; rtd 02. *49 Broyle Road, Chichester PO19 4BA* Tel (01243) 532405

ASHDOWN, Barry Frederick. b 42. St Pet Coll Ox BA65 MA69. Ridley Hall Cam 66. **d** 68 **p** 69. C Shipley St Pet *Bradf* 68-71; C Rushden w Newton Bromswold *Pet* 71-74; R Haworth *Bradf* 74-82; V Ore Ch Ch *Chich* 82-87; C Southwick St Mich 91-93. *2 Marlott Road, Shipley BD18 1DJ*

ASHDOWN, Philip David. b 57. Imp Coll Lon BSc79 NW Univ Chicago MS80 Cranfield Inst of Tech PhD85 ARCS79 CMath MIMA87. Ripon Coll Cuddesdon 91. **d** 93 **p** 94. C Houghton le Spring *Dur* 93-96; C Stockton and Chapl Stockton Campus Dur Univ 96-02; V Stockton St Pet *Dur* from 02. *St Peter's Vicarage, 11 Lorne Court, Stockton-on-Tees TS18 3UB* Tel (01642) 670981 E-mail philip.ashdown@durham.anglican.org

ASHE, Francis John. b 53. Sheff Univ BMet74. Ridley Hall Cam 77. **d** 79 **p** 80. C Ashtead *Guildf* 79-82; S Africa 82-87; R Wisley w Pyrford *Guildf* 87-93; V Godalming 93-01; TR from 01; RD Godalming 96-02. *The Rectory, Westbrook Road, Godalming GU7 1ET* Tel (01483) 414135 E-mail john.ashe@talk21.com *or* john.ashe@godalming.org.uk

ASHE, Francis Patrick Bellesme. b 15. St Jo Coll Cam BA37 MA41. Westcott Ho Cam 37. **d** 40 **p** 41. C Woolwich St Mary w H Trin *S'wark* 40-44; Greece 44-46; Youth Chapl *S'wark* 46-50; V Blindley Heath 49-56; V Otley *Bradf* 56-64; V Leamington Priors St Mary *Cov* 64-72; R Church Stretton *Heref* 72-74; Chmn Admin Project Vietnam Orphanage 75-81; rtd 80; Perm to Offic *Guildf* from 81. *62 Busbridge Lane, Godalming GU7 1QQ* Tel (01483) 422435

ASHENDEN, Canon Gavin Roy Pelham. b 54. Bris Univ LLB76 Oak Hill Th Coll BA80 Heythrop Coll Lon MTh89 Sussex Univ DPhil98. **d** 80 **p** 81. C Bermondsey St Jas w Ch Ch *S'wark* 80-83; TV Sanderstead All SS 83-89; Chapl and Lect Sussex Univ *Chich* from 89; Can and Preb Chich Cathl from 03. *The Meeting House, Sussex University, Southern Ring Road, Falmer, Brighton BN1 9RH* Tel (01273) 678217 Fax 678918 E-mail g.ashenden@sussex.ac.uk

ASHFORTH, David Edward. b 37. Lon Univ BSc ARCS59 Birm Univ DipTh61. Qu Coll Birm. **d** 61 **p** 62. C Scarborough St Columba *York* 61-65; C Northallerton w Kirby Sigston 65-67; V Keyingham 67-73; Chapl Imp Coll *Lon* 73-89; V Balderstone *Blackb* 89-01; Dir Post-Ord Tr 89-01; rtd 01. *Sunny Holme Cottage, Preston under Scar, Leyburn DL8 4AH* Tel (01969) 622438 E-mail d.ashforth@btinternet.com

ASHLEY, Brian. b 36. S'wark Ord Course 75. **d** 77 **p** 78. NSM Horsell *Guildf* from 77. Starston, Church Hill, Horsell, Woking GU21 4QE* Tel (01483) 761232

ASHLEY, Brian Christenson. b 33. Roch Th Coll 68. **d** 70 **p** 71. C New Sleaford *Linc* 70-72; Min Basegreen CD 72-74; TV Gleadless *Sheff* 74-77; R Dinnington 77-85; RD Laughton 82-85; V Mosbrough 85-88; P-in-c Curbar and Stoney Middleton *Derby* 88-91; rtd 91; Perm to Offic *Pet* from 95. *15 Eliot Close, Saxon Fields, Kettering NN16 9XR* Tel (01536) 524457

ASHLEY, Clive Ashely. b 54. Croydon Coll of Art and Design LSIAD75 Lon Hosp SRN80 E Ham Coll of Tech FE TCert82

NE Lon Poly NDN83. Aston Tr Scheme 81 Cranmer Hall Dur 84. **d** 86 **p** 87. C Withington St Paul *Man* 86-89; Asst Chapl Freeman Hosp Newc 89-92; Chapl St Rich and Graylingwell Hosps Chich 92-98; Chapl Bognor Regis War Memorial Hosp 95-98; Chapl and Bereavement Cllr R W Sussex Trust 98-01; R New Fishbourne *Chich* from 01; P-in-c Appledram from 01. *The Rectory, 12 Fishbourne Road, Chichester PO19 3HX* Tel (01243) 783364 Mobile 07765-290619 E-mail fishbourne.rectory@virgin.net

ASHLEY, John Michael. b 28. Worc Coll BA51 MA54. Linc Th Coll 52. **d** 54 **p** 55. Australia 54-60; C Anderby w Cumberworth *Linc* 60-66; P-in-c Huttoft 60-61; V 61-66; R Woolsthorpe 66-93; R W w E Allington and Sedgebrook 66-93; CF (TAVR) 79-93; rtd 93; Perm to Offic *Linc* 93-99. *35 Gregory Close, Harlaxton, Grantham NG32 1JG* Tel (01476) 561846

ASHLEY-ROBERTS, James. b 53. Lon Univ BD77. Oak Hill Th Coll 75 Wycliffe Hall Ox 79. **d** 80 **p** 81. C Gt Warley Ch Ch *Chelmsf* 80-83; C E Ham St Paul 83-85; TV Holyhead w Rhoscolyn w Llanfair-yn-Neubwll *Ban* 85-88; R 88-91; V Penrhyndeudraeth w Llanfrothen w Beddgelert 91-97; V Ffestiniog w Blaenau Ffestiniog 97-01. *11 Simon's Close, Crowborough TN6 2XU*

ASHLING, Raymond Charles. b 32. Dur Univ BA58. Linc Th Coll 58. **d** 60 **p** 61. C Halifax St Aug *Wakef* 60-63; C Farlington *Portsm* 63-65; Rhodesia 65-71; Chapl Rishworth Sch Ripponden 71-75; Lesotho 75-85; V Somercotes *Linc* 85-88; Ethiopia 88-89; R Gt w Lt Snoring w Kettlestone and Pensthorpe *Nor* 89-94; rtd 94. *14 Abbey Court, Norwich NR1 2AW*

ASHMAN, Peter Nicholas. b 52. CSS81 SEN73. Sarum & Wells Th Coll 87. **d** 89 **p** 90. C Stafford *Lich* 89-93; R Dymchurch w Burmarsh and Newchurch *Cant* 93-99; R Lyminge w Paddlesworth, Stanford w Postling etc from 99. *The Rectory, Rectory Lane, Lyminge, Folkestone CT18 8EG* Tel (01303) 862432

ASHMAN, Mrs Vanessa. **d** 03. OLM Lyminge w Paddlesworth, Stanford w Postling etc *Cant* from 03. *The Rectory, Rectory Lane, Lyminge, Folkestone CT18 8EG* Tel (01303) 862432

ASHTON, Anthony Joseph. b 37. Oak Hill Th Coll 62. **d** 65 **p** 66. C Crookes St Thos *Sheff* 65-68; C Heeley 68-73; V Bowling St Steph *Bradf* 73-78; R Chesterfield H Trin *Derby* 78-92; rtd 93; Perm to Offic *Derby* 93-00. *19 High Park, Stafford ST16 1BL* Tel (01785) 223943

✠**ASHTON, The Rt Revd Cyril Guy.** b 42. Lanc Univ MA86. Oak Hill Th Coll 64. **d** 67 **p** 68 **c** 00. C Blackpool St Thos *Blackb* 67-70; Voc Sec CPAS 70-74; V Lancaster St Thos *Blackb* 74-91; Lanc Almshouses 76-90; Dioc Dir of Tr *Blackb* 91-00; Hon Can Blackb Cathl 91-00; Suff Bp Doncaster *Sheff* from 00. *Bishop's House, 3 Farrington Court, Wickersley, Rotherham S66 1JQ* Tel (01709) 730130 Fax 730230 E-mail cyril.ashton@virgin.net

ASHTON, David. b 52. Sarum Th Coll 93. **d** 96 **p** 97. NSM St Leonards Ch Ch and St Mary *Chich* 96-98; NSM Upper St Leonards St Jo 98-99; C Uckfield 99-02; V Langney from 02. *St Richard's Rectory, 7 Priory Road, Eastbourne BN23 7AX* Tel (01323) 761158

ASHTON, David William. b 51. Reading Univ BA74 Lanc Univ PGCE75. Wycliffe Hall Ox 79. **d** 82 **p** 83. C Shipley St Pet *Bradf* 82-85; C Tadley St Pet *Win* 85-88; V Sinfin *Derby* 88-91; Chapl Sophia Antipolis *Eur* 91-94; P-in-c Swanwick and Pentrich *Derby* 95-00; V 00-02; RD Alfreton 95-02; Chapl S Derbyshire Acute Hosps NHS Trust from 02. *Chaplaincy Services, Derby City General Hospital, Uttoxeter Road, Derby DE22 3NE* Tel (01332) 340131 E-mail david.ashton@sdah-tr.trent.nhs.uk

ASHTON, Grant. *See* ASHTON, William Grant

✠**ASHTON, The Rt Revd Jeremy Claude.** b 30. Trin Coll Cam BA53 MA57. Westcott Ho Cam 53. **d** 55 **p** 56 **c** 76. C Bury St Mary *Man* 55-60; CF (TA) 57-60; CF (TA - R of O) 60-70; Papua New Guinea 60-86; Asst Bp Papua 76-77; Bp Aipo Rongo 77-86; rtd 86; Australia from 86. *PO Box 113, Maldon, Vic, Australia 3463* Tel (0061) (3) 5475 2696 Fax as telephone

ASHTON, Miss Joan Elizabeth. b 54. Eaton Hall Coll of Educn CertEd76. Cranmer Hall Dur 93. **d** 93 **p** 94. Par Dn Darnall-cum-Attercliffe *Sheff* 93-94; C Hillsborough and Wadsley Bridge 94-96; P-in-c Stainforth 96-98; P-in-c Arksey from 98; Chapl Doncaster R Infirmary and Montagu Hosp NHS Trust 98-01; Chapl Doncaster and Bassetlaw Hosps NHS Trust from 01. *1 Chadwick Gardens, Arksey, Doncaster DN5 0UP*

ASHTON, Joseph Patrick Bankes (Pat). b 27. Jes Coll Cam BA49 MA52. Wells Th Coll 53. **d** 55 **p** 56. C Cheadle *Lich* 55-59; C Caverswall 59-61; C-in-c Werrington CD 61-64; V Werrington 64-66; R Eyke w Bromeswell and Rendlesham *St E* 66-76; R Eyke w Bromeswell, Rendlesham, Tunstall etc 76-86; Chapl Seckford Foundn 86-92; Hon C Woodbridge St Mary 86-92; rtd 92. *45 Crown Place, Woodbridge IP12 1BU* Tel (01394) 384299

ASHTON, Mrs Margaret Lucie. b 40. St Jo Coll Nottm DPS79. **dss** 83 **d** 87 **p** 94. Billericay and Lt Burstead *Chelmsf* 83-99; NSM 87-99; rtd 99; Hon C Fordingbridge and Breamore and Hale etc *Win* from 99. *3 Stephen Martin Gardens, Fordingbridge SP6 1RF* Tel (01425) 656205 E-mail peterashton@email.msn.com

ASHTON, Mark Hewett. b 48. Ch Ch Ox BA70 MA74 Trin Coll Cam BA72. Ridley Hall Cam 71. **d** 73 **p** 74. C Beckenham Ch Ch

22

Roch 73-77; Win Coll 78-81; Lic to Offic *S'wark* 81-87; Hd of CYFA (CPAS) 81-87; V Cambridge H Sepulchre w All SS *Ely* 87-92; V Cambridge H Sepulchre from 92. *The Round Church Vicarage, Manor Street, Cambridge CB1 1LQ* Tel (01223) 518218 Fax 327331 E-mail staff@stag.org

ASHTON, Neville Anthony. b 45. Sarum & Wells Th Coll 78. **d** 80 **p** 81. C Hattersley *Ches* 80-82; C Lancaster Ch Ch w St Jo and St Anne *Blackb* 82-84; R Church Kirk from 84. *Church Kirk Rectory, 434 Blackburn Road, Accrington BB5 0DE* Tel (01254) 236946

ASHTON, Nigel Charles. b 49. SW Minl Tr Course. **d** 78 **p** 79. NSM St Stephen by Saltash *Truro* 78-94; Perm to Offic *Ex* from 95. *9 Bunn Road, Exmouth EX8 5PP* Tel (01395) 224345

ASHTON, Canon Peter Donald. b 34. Lon Univ BD62. ALCD61. **d** 62 **p** 63. C Walthamstow St Mary *Chelmsf* 62-68; V Girlington *Bradf* 68-73; Dir Past Studies St Jo Coll Nottm 73-80; TR Billericay and Lt Burstead *Chelmsf* 80-99; Chapl Mayflower Hosp Billericay 80-99; Chapl St Andr Hosp Billericay 80-93; Chapl Thameside Community Healthcare NHS Trust 93-99; RD Basildon *Chelmsf* 89-99; Hon Can Chelmsf Cathl 92-99; rtd 99; Hon C Fordingbridge and Breamore and Hale etc *Win* from 01. *3 Stephen Martin Gardens, Fordingbridge SP6 1RF* Tel (01425) 656205 E-mail peterashton@email.msn.com

ASHTON, Preb Samuel Rupert. b 42. Sarum & Wells Th Coll. **d** 83 **p** 84. C Ledbury w Eastnor *Heref* 83-86; R St Weonards w Orcop, Garway, Tretire etc 86-98; RD Ross and Archenfield 91-95 and 96-98; Preb Heref Cathl from 97; P-in-c Cradley w Mathon and Storridge 98-99; R from 99. *The Rectory, Cradley, Malvern WR13 5LQ* Tel (01886) 880438

ASHTON, Stephen Robert. b 55. BA BPhil Lon Univ MA99 FRSA03 FGMS03. Sarum & Wells Th Coll. **d** 84 **p** 85. C Penzance St Mary w St Paul *Truro* 84-86; C Tewkesbury w Walton Cardiff *Glouc* 86-89; P-in-c Newton Heath St Wilfrid and St Anne *Man* 89-92; V Breage w Germoe *Truro* 92-94; Perm to Offic *Ox* from 03. *20 Tregarrick Close, Helston TR13 8YA* Tel (01326) 563127 E-mail sashton44@hotmail.com

ASHTON, William Grant. b 57. St Chad's Coll Dur BA79. Oak Hill Th Coll BA85. **d** 85 **p** 86. C Lancaster St Thos *Blackb* 85-89; CF from 89. *clo MOD Chaplains (Army)* Tel (01980) 615804 Fax 615800

ASHWELL, Anthony John. b 42. CChem74 MRSC74 St Andr Univ BSc65. Sarum & Wells Th Coll 86. **d** 88 **p** 89. C Plymstock *Ex* 88-91; C Axminster, Chardstock, Combe Pyne and Rousdon 91-92; TV 92-95; C Crediton and Shobrooke 95-97; TV Bride Valley *Sarum* from 97. *The Vicarage, Litton Cheney, Dorchester DT2 9AG* Tel (01308) 482302

ASHWIN, Canon Vincent George. b 42. Worc Coll Ox BA65. Coll of Resurr Mirfield 65. **d** 67 **p** 68. C Shildon *Dur* 67-70; V 79-85; C Newc St Fran *Newc* 70-72; Swaziland 72-79; V Fenham St Jas and St Basil *Newc* 85-97; RD Newc W 89-97; V Haydon Bridge and Beltingham w Henshaw from 97; RD Hexham 97-02; Hon Can Newc Cathl from 00. *The Vicarage, Station Yard, Haydon Bridge, Hexham NE47 6LL* Tel (01434) 684307 Fax 684152 E-mail vashwin@lineone.net

ASHWORTH, Canon David. b 40. Nottm Univ BPharm62. Linc Th Coll 63. **d** 65 **p** 66. C Halliwell St Thos *Man* 65-69; C Heywood St Jas 69-72; C-in-c Heywood St Marg CD 72-78; V Hale *Ches* 78-87; V Hale and Ashley 87-96; RD Bowdon 87-95; Hon Can Ches Cathl from 94; V Prestbury from 96; RD Macclesfield 98-03. *The Vicarage, Prestbury, Macclesfield SK10 4DG* Tel (01625) 829288 or 827625 E-mail david@ashworth39.freeserve.co.uk

ASHWORTH, Edward James. b 33. Clifton Th Coll 60. **d** 63 **p** 64. C Spitalfields Ch Ch w All SS *Lon* 63-65; C Pennycross *Ex* 65-69; C Blackb St Ch *Blackb* 69-72; V Camerton H Trin W Seaton *Carl* 72-79; V Tunstead *Man* 79-97; rtd 97; Perm to Offic *Man* from 00. *187 Bacup Road, Rawtenstall, Rossendale BB4 7NW*

ASHWORTH, James Nigel. b 55. York Univ BA77. Cranmer Hall Dur 93. **d** 93 **p** 94. C Rothwell *Ripon* 93-96; Chapl Campsfield Ho Oxon 96-99; Hon C Akeman *Ox* 96-99; V Kemsing w Woodlands *Roch* from 99. *The Vicarage, High Street, Kemsing, Sevenoaks TN15 6NA* Tel (01732) 761351 Fax as telephone E-mail nigelashworth@btinternet.com

ASHWORTH, John Russell. b 33. Lich Th Coll 57. **d** 60 **p** 61. C Castleford All SS *Wakef* 60-62; C Luton St Sav *St Alb* 63-67; V Clipstone *S'well* 67-70; V Bolton-upon-Dearne *Sheff* 70-82; V Thornhill Lees *Wakef* 82-98; rtd 98. *Walsingham, 2 Vicarage Road, Savile Town, Dewsbury WF12 9PD* Tel (01924) 461269

ASHWORTH, Keith Benjamin. b 33. NW Ord Course 76. **d** 79 **p** 80. C Pennington *Man* 79-83; P-in-c Bolton St Bede 83-88; V 88-95; V Hillock 95-01; rtd 01; Perm to Offic *Man* from 01. *52 Longsight Lane, Bolton BL2 3JS* Tel (01204) 302833

ASHWORTH, Martin. b 41. AKC63. **d** 64 **p** 65. C-in-c Wythenshawe Wm Temple Ch CD *Man* 64-71; R Haughton St Anne 71-83; V Prestwich St Marg from 83. *St Margaret's Vicarage, St Margaret's Road, Prestwich, Manchester M25 5QB* Tel 0161-773 2698

ASHWORTH, Timothy. b 52. Worc Coll of Educn CertEd74. Trin Coll Bris DipHE79 Oak Hill Th Coll BA81. **d** 82 **p** 83. C

Tonbridge St Steph *Roch* 82-85; C-in-c Whittle-le-Woods *Blackb* 85-90; Chapl Scargill Ho 90-96; V Ingleton w Chapel le Dale *Bradf* 96-03; TV Yate New Town *Bris* from 03. *22 Hampden Close, Yate, Bristol BS37 5UW* Tel (01454) 319416 E-mail timashworth@lineone.net

ASHWORTH, Mrs Vivien. b 52. Worc Coll of Educn CertEd73. Trin Coll Bris DipHE81 Oak Hill Th Coll BA82. **dss** 82 **d** 87 **p** 94. Tonbridge St Steph *Roch* 82-85; Whittle-le-Woods *Blackb* 85-90; Hon Par Dn 87-90; Chapl Scargill Ho 90-96; Hon C Ingleton w Chapel le Dale *Bradf* 96-03; Dioc Youth Adv 96-01; Hon C Yate New Town *Bris* from 03. *22 Hampden Close, Yate, Bristol BS37 5UW* Tel (01454) 319416 E-mail viv.ashworth@lineone.net

ASIR, The Very Revd Anand. b 53. Madurai Univ BSc75 Serampore Univ BD79 New Coll Edin MTh93 Trin & All SS Coll Leeds PGD93 Annamalai Univ MA99. **d** 80 **p** 81. India 80-91 and 95-00; C Nayaith St Jo 80-82; R Tuticorin St Paul 82-84; Sec Tirunelveli Children's Miss 84-91; C Edin St Pet *Edin* 91-92; Hon C Burmantofts St Steph and St Agnes *Ripon* 92-93; C Edin St Mark *Edin* 93-95; Provost Palayamcottai Cathl 95-99; C Leic Resurr *Leic* from 00. *St Alban's Vicarage, Weymouth Street, Leicester LE4 6FN* Tel 0116-266 1002 E-mail anandjessie@hotmail.com

ASKEW, Miss Alison Jane. b 57. Dur Univ BA78 PGCE79. S Dios Minl Tr Scheme DipTh96. **d** 95 **p** 96. NSM Kingsclere *Win* 95-96; Asst Chapl N Hants Hosps NHS Trust 95-99; Chapl from 99. *6 Worcester Block, North Hampshire Hospital, Basingstoke RG24 9NA* Tel (01256) 473202

ASKEW, Canon Dennis. b 30. Open Univ BA76. Kelham Th Coll 45 Lich Th Coll 55. **d** 58 **p** 59. C Garforth *Ripon* 58-61; C Seacroft 61-64; V Holland Fen *Linc* 64-69; R Folkingham w Laughton 69-77; V Aswarby w Swarby 69-77; R Osbournby w Scott Willoughby 69-77; R Pickworth w Walcot 69-77; V Threckingham 69-77; P-in-c Newton w Haceby 72-77; P-in-c Aunsby w Dembleby 72-77; R S Lafford 77-87; Can and Preb Linc Cathl from 86; R Ruskington 87-96; rtd 96; Perm to Offic *Linc* from 96. *Langford House, 4 Hereford Close, Sleaford NG34 8TP* Tel (01529) 305645

ASKEW, Peter Timothy. b 68. Ridley Hall Cam 00. **d** 02 **p** 03. C Bilton *Ripon* from 02. *59 Coppice Way, Harrogate HG1 2DJ* Tel (01423) 560983 Mobile 07754-046029 E-mail peteaskew@hotmail.com

ASKEW, Canon Reginald James Albert. b 28. CCC Cam BA51 MA55. Linc Th Coll 55. **d** 57 **p** 58. C Highgate St Mich *Lon* 57-61; Lect and Vice-Prin Wells Th Coll 61-69; PV Wells Cathl *B & W* 61-69; V Paddington Ch Ch *Lon* 69-73; Member Corrymeela Community from 71; Prin Sarum & Wells Th Coll 73-87; Chmn S Dios Minl Tr Scheme 73-87; Can and Preb Sarum Cathl *Sarum* 75-87; Dean K Coll Lon 88-93; rtd 93; Perm to Offic *B & W* from 93; Perm to Offic *Lon* 93-96. *Carters Cottage, North Wootton, Shepton Mallet BA4 4AF* Tel (01749) 890728

ASKEW, Preb Richard George. b 35. BNC Ox BA59 MA63. Ridley Hall Cam 62. **d** 64 **p** 65. C Chesham St Mary *Ox* 64-66; C Mossley Hill St Matt and St Jas *Liv* 66-67; Chapl Ox Pastorate 67-72; Asst Chapl BNC Ox 67-71; R Ashtead *Guildf* 72-83; RD Leatherhead 80-83; Can Res and Treas Sarum Cathl *Sarum* 83-90; Dioc Adv on Miss and Min *B & W* 83-90; R Bath Abbey w St Jas 90-00; Preb Wells Cathl 92-00; Perm to Offic *Sarum* 00-01; TV Cley Hill Warminster from 01. *Easter Cottage, 133 Foxholes, Crockerton, Warminster BA12 7DB* Tel (01985) 219367

ASKEW, Sydney Derek. b 29. Roch Th Coll 66. **d** 68 **p** 69. C Kirkstall *Ripon* 68-73; V Markington w S Stainley and Bishop Thornton 73-94; rtd 94. *6 Mallorie Close, Ripon HG4 2QE* Tel (01765) 603309

ASKEY, Gary Simon. b 64. K Coll Lon LLB99 Univ Coll Lon LLM00. St Steph Ho Ox 88. **d** 91 **p** 92. SSM 87-99; Prior SSM Priory Kensington 96-98; C Middlesbrough All SS *York* 91-94; Sub-Chapl HM Pris Holme Ho 92-94; C Whitby 94-96; Missr Whitby Miss and Seafarer's Trust 94-96; Lic to Offic *S'wark* from 96; Hon C Angell Town St Jo 98-03. *115 Metro Central Heights, Newington Causeway, London SE1 6BB* Tel (020) 7407 6131 E-mail simon@askey.gs

ASKEY, John Stuart. b 39. Chich Th Coll 63. **d** 66 **p** 67. C Feltham *Lon* 66-69; C Epsom Common Ch Ch *Guildf* 69-72; C Chesterton Gd Shep *Ely* 72-74; R Stretham w Thetford 74-93; Dioc Spirituality Officer 75-98; Dioc Youth Officer 80-99; P-in-c Brinkley, Burrough Green and Carlton 93-97; P-in-c Westley Waterless 93-97; P-in-c Dullingham 93-97; P-in-c Stetchworth 93-97; R Raddesley Gp 97-99; Chapl Gothenburg w Halmstad, Jönköping etc *Eur* from 99. *Norra Liden 15, 411-18 Gothenburg, Sweden* Tel (0046) (31) 711 1915

ASKEY, Mrs Susan Mary. b 44. N Ord Course MA99. **d** 99 **p** 00. C Golcar *Wakef* 99-02; P-in-c Drighlington from 02. *The Vicarage, Back Lane, Drighlington, Bradford BD11 1LS* Tel 0113-285 2402

ASKEY, Thomas Cyril. b 29. Sheff Univ BSc50 Man Univ MA(Theol)81 ACIPA58 MITMA76. NW Ord Course 70. **d** 73

p 74. NSM Gawsworth *Ches* 73-76; Perm to Offic 76-80; rtd 81; Perm to Offic *Derby* from 99. *Park Cottage, Nether End, Baslow, Bakewell DE45 1SR* Tel (01246) 583780

ASPDEN, Peter George. b 28. Univ of Wales (Lamp) BA50. Ely Th Coll 52. **d** 53 **p** 54. C Morecambe St Barn *Blackb* 53-55; C Marton 55-58; V Tockholes 58-63; P-in-c St Annes St Marg 63-66; V 66-75; V Lancaster Ch Ch 75-79; R Eccleston 79-94; rtd 94; Perm to Offic *Liv* from 94. *21 Glencoyne Drive, Southport PR9 9TS* Tel (01704) 214066
E-mail revpgandema@bushinternet.com

ASPINALL, Philip Norman. b 51. Cam Univ MA ATI. WMMTC 86. **d** 89 **p** 90. NSM Cov E *Cov* 89-98. *139 Wiltshire Court, Nod Rise, Mount Nod, Coventry CV5 7JP* Tel (024) 7646 7509

ASQUITH, Barbara Rosemary. b 37. Dioc OLM tr scheme. **d** 03. OLM S Ossett *Wakef* from 03. *115 Teall Street, Ossett WF5 0HS* Tel (01924) 271302

ASQUITH, Eric Lees. b 24. St Aid Birkenhead 55. **d** 56 **p** 57. C Hanging Heaton *Wakef* 56-59; V Netherthong 59-68; rtd 89. *15 Heycroft Way, Nayland, Colchester CO6 4LN* Tel (01206) 262593

ASQUITH, Michael John. b 60. St D Coll Lamp BA82 MPhil91 Ch Ch Coll Cant PGCE83. Cant Sch of Min 91. **d** 94 **p** 95. C S Ashford Ch Ch *Cant* 94-98; P-in-c Weldon w Deene *Pet* 98-00; P-in-c Corby Epiphany w St Jo from 98. *64 South Road, Corby NN17 1XD* Tel (01536) 203671 Fax 262491
E-mail mikeasq@aol.com

ASSON, Geoffrey Ormrod. b 34. Univ of Wales (Ban) BA54 St Cath Coll Ox BA56 MA61. St Steph Ho Ox 54. **d** 57 **p** 58. C Aberdare *Llan* 57-59; C Roath 59-61; R Hagworthingham w Asgarby and Lusby *Linc* 61-65; P-in-c Mavis Enderby w Raithby 62-65; V Friskney 65-69; R S Ormsby w Ketsby, Calceby and Driby 69-74; R Harrington w Brinkhill 69-74; R Oxcombe 69-74; R Ruckland w Farforth and Maidenwell 69-74; R Somersby w Bag Enderby 69-74; R Tetford and Salmonby 69-74; P-in-c Belchford 71-74; P-in-c W Ashby 71-74; V Riverhead w Dunton Green *Roch* 75-80; R Kington w Huntington *Heref* 80-82; RD Kington and Weobley 80-86; P-in-c Almeley 81-82; P-in-c Knill 81-82; P-in-c Old Radnor 81-82; R Kington w Huntington, Old Radnor, Kinnerton etc 82-86; V Mathry w St Edren's and Grandston etc *St D* 86-97; Bp's Rural Adv and Tourist Officer 91-95; rtd 96. *Sincerity, St Dogmaels, Cardigan SA43 3JZ* Tel (01239) 615591

ASTILL, Cyril John. b 33. Lon Univ DipTh64. Oak Hill Th Coll 62. **d** 65 **p** 66. C Carl St Jo *Carl* 65-68; C St Helens St Helen *Liv* 68-71; V Blackb Sav *Blackb* 71-81; P-in-c Blackb Ch Ch w St Matt 81-83; TR N Ferriby *York* 85-97; V 97-99; rtd 99; P-in-c Burton Agnes w Harpham and Lowthorpe etc *York* from 99. *The Rectory, Burton Agnes, Driffield YO25 4NE* Tel (01262) 490217

ASTIN, Alfred Ronald. b 18. St Pet Hall Ox BA43 MA45. Ridley Hall Cam. **d** 47 **p** 48. C Weaste *Man* 47-50; C Harpurhey Ch Ch 50-51; V Leesfield 51-57; V Earlham St Anne *Nor* 57-70; V Sheringham 70-84; rtd 84; Perm to Offic *Nor* 84-99. *c/o The Revd T R Astin, 1 Cowslip Crescent, Thatcham RG18 4DE* Tel (01635) 869940

ASTIN, Howard Keith. b 51. Warwick Univ LLB DipHE. Trin Coll Bris 83. **d** 83 **p** 84. C Kirkheaton *Wakef* 83-88; V Bowling St Jo *Bradf* from 88. *St John's Vicarage, 96 Lister Avenue, Bradford BD4 7QS* Tel (01274) 727355

ASTIN, Mrs Moira Anne Elizabeth. b 65. Clare Coll Cam BA86 MA90. Wycliffe Hall Ox BA94 DipMin95. **d** 95 **p** 96. C Newbury *Ox* 95-99; C Thatcham 99-01; TV from 01. *1 Cowslip Crescent, Thatcham RG18 4DE* Tel (01635) 869940

ASTIN, Timothy Robin. b 58. St Edm Hall Ox BA79 Darw Coll Cam PhD82 FGS. Ox Min Course CBTS93. **d** 93 **p** 94. NSM Reading St Jo *Ox* 93-95; NSM Newbury 95-99; NSM Beedon and Peasemore w W Ilsley and Farnborough from 99. *1 Cowslip Crescent, Thatcham RG18 4DE* Tel (01635) 869940
E-mail t.r.astin@reading.ac.uk

ASTLEY, Prof Jeffrey. b 47. Down Coll Cam BA68 MA72 Birm Univ DipTh69 Dur Univ PhD79. Qu Coll Birm 68. **d** 70 **p** 71. C Cannock *Lich* 70-73; Lect and Chapl St Hild Coll Dur 73-75; Sen Lect and Chapl SS Hild and Bede Coll Dur 75-77; Prin Lect & Hd Relig Studies Bp Grosseteste Coll 77-81; Lic to Offic *Linc* 78-81; Dir N England Inst for Chr Educn from 81. *Carter House, Pelaw Leazes Lane, Durham DH1 1TB* Tel 0191-384 1034 or 374 7807 Fax 384 7529 E-mail jeff.astley@durham.ac.uk

ASTON, Glyn. b 29. Univ of Wales (Abth) BA54 TCert55. Sarum & Wells Th Coll 84. **d** 79 **p** 80. Hon C Maindee *Mon* 79-85; C 85-86; V Llangwm Uchaf and Llangwm Isaf w Gwernesney etc 86-99; rtd 99; Lic to Offic *Mon* from 99. *Flat 4, 47 Caerau Road, Newport NP20 4HH*

ASTON, John Bernard. b 34. Leeds Univ BA55 PGCE56. Qu Coll Birm 72. **d** 75 **p** 76. NSM Shenstone *Lich* from 75; Chapl HM YOI Swinfen Hall 90-99; NSM Stonnall *Lich* from 00. *4 Footherley Road, Shenstone, Lichfield WS14 0NJ* Tel (01543) 480388

ASTON, John Leslie. b 47. Oak Hill Th Coll 77. **d** 80 **p** 81. C Trentham *Lich* 80-83; C Meir Heath 83-85; V Upper Tean 85-91; CF 91-02; C Andover w Foxcott *Win* from 02. *6 Osborne Road, Andover SP10 3EU* Tel (01264) 323968

ASTON, Mrs Kim Elizabeth. b 57. Colchester Inst of Educn BA78 LRAM78. SEITE 00. **d** 03. *61 Boundary Way, Croydon CR0 5AU* Tel (01689) 843669 E-mail astonkim@hotmail.com

ASTON, Michael James. b 48. Loughb Univ BSc70 DIS70 MBCS85. NTMTC 98. **d** 01 **p** 02. NSM Writtle w Highwood *Chelmsf* from 01. *15 Weller Grove, Chelmsford CM1 4YJ* Tel (01245) 442547 Mobile 07940-417418
E-mail mikaston@globalnet.co.uk

ASTON, Roger. b 52. Ox Poly BEd83. St Alb and Ox Min Course 96. **d** 99 **p** 00. OLM Eynsham and Cassington *Ox* from 99. *30 Meadow Way, Yarnton, Kidlington, Oxford OX5 1TA* Tel (01865) 378773

ASTON SMITH, Anthony. b 29. Trin Coll Cam BA52 MA56 PhD56 CEng MIM FIDiagE MICorrST AMIMechE. Ox NSM Course 86. **d** 93 **p** 94. NSM Ox St Giles and SS Phil and Jas w St Marg *Ox* 93-99; rtd 99; Perm to Offic *Ox* from 99. *32 Chalfont Road, Oxford OX2 6TH* Tel (01865) 557090

ASTON, Archdeacon of. *See* BARTON, The Ven Charles John Greenwood

ASTON, Suffragan Bishop of. *See* AUSTIN, The Rt Revd John Michael

ATACK, John Philip. b 49. Lanc Univ MA91. Linc Th Coll 86. **d** 88 **p** 89. C Cleveleys *Blackb* 88-92; V Appley Bridge 92-96; P-in-c Mostyn w Ffynnongroyw *St As* from 99; Hon Chapl Miss to Seafarers from 01. *The Vicarage, Hafod y Ddol Lane, Mostyn, Holywell CH8 9EJ* Tel (01745) 560513
E-mail phil.atack@btopenworld.com

ATFIELD, Gladys. Univ Coll Lon BSc53 DipTh76. Gilmore Course. **dss** 79 **d** 87 **p** 94. Bexley St Mary *Roch* 79-01; Hon C 87-01; rtd 01. *7 Clarendon Mews, High Street, Bexley DA5 1JS* Tel (01322) 551741

ATHERFOLD, Mrs Evelyne Sara. b 43. Leeds Inst of Educn CertEd64. N Ord Course 82. **dss** 85 **d** 92 **p** 94. Kirk Sandall and Edenthorpe *Sheff* 85-87; NSM Fishlake w Sykehouse and Kirk Bramwith etc 87-00; P-in-c from 00; V from 03; Chapl HM YOI Hatfield 96-03. *The Vicarage, Church Street, Fishlake, Doncaster DN7 5JW* Tel (01302) 350224

ATHERLEY, Keith Philip. b 56. St Steph Ho Ox 77. **d** 80 **p** 81. C Armley w New Wortley *Ripon* 80-82; C Harrogate St Wilfrid and St Luke 82-85; V Forcett and Stanwick w Aldbrough 85-89; CF 89-03. *Address temp unknown*

ATHERSTONE, Andrew Castell. b 74. Ch Coll Cam BA95 MA98 Wycliffe Hall Ox MSt99 DPhil01. **d** 01 **p** 02. C Abingdon *Ox* from 01. *33 Mattock Way, Abingdon OX14 2PQ* Tel (01235) 555083 E-mail c&a@atherstone53.freeserve.co.uk

ATHERSTONE, Canon Castell Hugh. b 45. Natal Univ BA67 St Chad's Coll Dur DipTh69 MA79. **d** 70 **p** 70. S Africa 70-83; Dioc Stewardship Adv *Ely* 83-87; P-in-c Doddington w Benwick 83-87; R Frant w Eridge *Chich* 87-95; P-in-c Mark Cross 94-95; RD Rotherfield 90-94; V Seaford w Sutton from 95; RD Lewes and Seaford from 97; Can and Preb Chich Cathl from 02. *The Vicarage, 46 Sutton Road, Seaford BN25 1SH* Tel (01323) 893508 Fax as telephone E-mail hugh@atherstoneweb.org

ATHERTON, Albert. b 26. CQSW71. St Aid Birkenhead 60. **d** 62 **p** 63. C Northenden *Man* 62-64; C Newall Green CD 64-66; V Patricroft 66-70; Lic to Offic 71-72; V Mossley 77-83; V Ockbrook *Derby* 83-86; P-in-c Newall Green St Fran *Man* 86-91; V 91-94; rtd 94; Perm to Offic *Man* from 94. *50 Belmont Drive, Bury BL8 2HU* Tel 0161-764 8397

ATHERTON, Graham Bryson. b 47. GRSM69 FTCL69. Edin Th Coll 77. **d** 79 **p** 80. C Orford St Marg *Liv* 79-82; V Warrington St Barn 82-88; V Leeds Halton St Wilfrid *Ripon* 88-95; RD Whitkirk 92-95; TR Guiseley w Esholt *Bradf* from 95. *The Rectory, The Green, Guiseley, Leeds LS20 9BB* Tel (01943) 874321 E-mail graham.atherton@ntlworld.com

ATHERTON, Henry Anthony. b 44. Univ of Wales BSc67 DipEd68 Fitzw Coll Cam BA72 MA75 Heythrop Coll Lon MTh00 FGS68. Westcott Ho Cam 70. **d** 72 **p** 73. C Leamington Priors All SS *Cov* 72-75; C Orpington All SS *Roch* 75-78; V Gravesend St Mary 78-87; Chapl St Jas Hosp Gravesend 82-87; V Bromley St Andr *Roch* from 87. *The Vicarage, 1 Lake Avenue, Bromley BR1 4EN* Tel (020) 8460 0481 Fax as telephone

ATHERTON, Canon John Robert. b 39. Lon Univ BA60 Man Univ MA74 PhD79. Coll of Resurr Mirfield 60. **d** 62 **p** 63. C Aberdeen St Marg *Ab* 62-64; C Bury St Mark *Man* 64-67; P-in-c Glas St Marg 65-67-68; R Hulme St Geo *Man* 68-74; Ind Chapl 68-74; Asst Dir Wm Temple Foundn 74-79; Dir from 79; Lic to Offic 74-84; Can Res Man Cathl from 84. *3 Booth Clibborn Court, Salford M7 4PJ* Tel 0161-792 0973

ATHERTON, Lionel Thomas. b 45. Univ of Wales (Ban) BA74 St Luke's Coll Ex. St Steph Ho Ox 74. **d** 76 **p** 77. C Chenies and Lt Chalfont *Ox* 76-79; C Fleet *Guildf* 79-84; V S Farnborough 84-89; TR Alston Team *Newc* 89-96; V Chorley St Pet *Blackb* from 96; Bp's Adv on New Relig Movements from 02. *St Peter's*

Vicarage, Harpers Lane, Chorley PR6 0HT Tel (01257) 263423
Fax as telephone E-mail lionelatherton@hotmail.com
ATHERTON, Paul Christopher. b 56. Chich Th Coll. **d** 82 **p** 83. C
Orford St Marg *Liv* 82-86; Chapl Univ of Wales (Cardiff) *Llan*
88-89; TV Walton St Mary *Liv* 89-92; C Westmr St Matt *Lon*
92-96; C Somers Town 96-97; V Bush Hill Park St Mark from 97;
Chapl N Middx Hosp NHS Trust from 97. *The Vicarage,
St Mark's Road, Enfield EN1 1BE* Tel (020) 8363 2780
ATHERTON, Philip Andrew. b 51. Wycliffe Hall Ox. **d** 84 **p** 85. C
Ox St Clem *Ox* 84-87; Lic Preacher *Man* 87-99; Ind Missr 87-99;
Perm to Offic from 00. *Address temp unknown*
ATHERTON, Timothy Edward John. b 60. Middx Poly
DipHE83. Cranmer Hall Dur 83. **d** 86 **p** 87. C S Molton w
Nymet St George, High Bray etc *Ex* 86-89; Canada from 89. *Box
515, Yellowknife NT, Canada, X1A 2N4* Tel (001) (867) 669 9874
ATKIN, Arthur Courtney Qu'apelle. b 19. Dur Univ BA44. Lich
Th Coll 59. **d** 59 **p** 60. Chapl Bromsgrove Jun Sch 59-64; C
Kidderminster St Geo *Worc* 59-60; C Bromsgrove All Sts 62-64;
Chapl RN 64-69; Chapl R Hosp Sch Holbrook 69-72; P-in-c
Brixham *Ex* 72-74; Chapl Colston's Sch Bris 74-79; P-in-c
Pitcombe w Shepton Montague and Bratton St Maur *B & W*
79-85; rtd 86; Perm to Offic *B & W* 86-93; Perm to Offic *Heref*
from 93. *8 St Katherine's, High Street, Ledbury HR8 1DZ*
ATKIN, John Anthony. b 33. Glouc Th Course 70. **d** 72 **p** 73. NSM
Leamington Priors All SS *Cov* 72-77; NSM Barford 77-78; NSM
Barford w Wasperton and Sherbourne 78-80; P-in-c Exford w
Exmoor *B & W* 80-82; P-in-c Hawkridge w Withypool 80-82;
P-in-c Exford, Exmoor, Hawkridge and Withypool 82-83; R
83-92; RD Exmoor 86-92; rtd 93; Perm to Offic *B & W* from 93.
Halsgrove Farm, Withypool, Minehead TA24 7RX Tel (01643)
83388
ATKINS, Anthony John. b 58. Nottm Univ BSc80 SS Paul &
Mary Coll Cheltenham PGCE82. Cranmer Hall Dur 87. **d** 90
p 91. C Shipley St Paul and Frizinghall *Bradf* 90-92; C Baildon
92-93; Chapl Asst Hope Hosp Salford 93-95; Chapl Asst
Ladywell Hosp 93-95; Chapl Rotherham Gen Hosps NHS Trust
from 96; Chapl Rotherham Priority Health Services NHS Trust
from 96. *18 Oakwood Hall Drive, Rotherham S60 3AQ* Tel
(01709) 820000 ext 5732
E-mail anthony.atkins@rgh-tr.trent.nhs.uk
ATKINS, Austen Shaun. b 55. St Pet Coll Ox MA82 Selw Coll
Cam MA85. Ridley Hall Cam 79. **d** 82 **p** 83. C S Mimms Ch Ch
Lon 82-86; C Fulham St Matt 86-91; P-in-c Fulham St Dionis
Parson's Green 91-03; V from 03. *St Dionis' Vicarage, 18 Parson's
Green, London SW6 4UH* Tel (020) 7736 2585 *or* 7384 3459
ATKINS, Canon David John. b 43. Lon Univ DipTh68. Kelham
Th Coll 64. **d** 68 **p** 69. C Lewisham St Mary *S'wark* 68-72; Min
Motspur Park 72-77; P-in-c Mitcham Ascension 77-82; V 82-83;
P-in-c Downham w S Hanningfield *Chelmsf* 83-88; R 88-01; Asst
RD Chelmsf 88-93; RD Chelmsf S 93-01; P-in-c W
Hanningfield 90-93; Hon Can Chelmsf Cathl from 00; V
Maldon All SS w St Pet from 01. *All Saints' Vicarage, Church
Walk, Maldon CM9 4PY* Tel (01621) 854179
ATKINS, Dean John. b 70. Univ of Wales (Cardiff) BD93.
St Steph Ho Ox 93. **d** 95 **p** 96. C Merthyr Dyfan *Llan* 95-99; V
Aberaman and Abercwmboi w Cwmaman 99-01; C Roath
St German from 01; Dioc Youth Officer from 01. *St Agnes, The
Clergy House, Metal Street, Cardiff CF24 1LA* Tel (029) 2049
9867
ATKINS, Mrs Diana. b 31. K Coll Lon BD54 DipEd55. Qu Coll
Birm 81. **dss** 83 **d** 87. De Beauvoir Town St Pet *Lon* 83-85;
Gleadless *Sheff* 85-87; Par Dn 87-93; rtd 93; Perm to Offic *Sheff*
from 93. *27 Stannington Glen, Sheffield S6 6NA* Tel 0114-234
0543
ATKINS, Forrest William (Bill). b 52. Selw Coll Cam MA85 Lon
Univ BD84. Ridley Hall Cam 83. **d** 86 **p** 87. C Normanton
Derby 86-90; C Stratford St Jo and Ch Ch w Forest Gate St Jas
Chelmsf 90-97; Asst Chapl Dubai and Sharjah w N Emirates
97-03; 1 Mohill w Farnaught, Aughavas, Oughteragh etc
K, E & A from 03. *Address temp unknown*
ATKINS, Francis John. b 47. CEng MIStructE. S Dios Minl Tr
Scheme. **d** 89 **p** 90. NSM Studley *Sarum* 89-92; Lic to RD
Bradford from 92. *Church Cottage, 344 Frome Road, Trowbridge
BA14 0EF* Tel (01225) 761757
ATKINS, Graham Anthony Hazlewood. b 28. Selw Coll Cam
BA52 MA57. Coll of Resurr Mirfield 52. **d** 54 **p** 55. C
St Marychurch *Ex* 54-57; Chapl Prestfelde Sch Shrewsbury
58-76; P-in-c Ash *Lich* 76-77; P-in-c Tenbury St Mich *Heref*
77-84; R Hinstock and Sambrook *Lich* 85-94; rtd 94. *9 Weston
Heath, Weston, Shrewsbury SY4 5XE* Tel (01939) 200664
ATKINS, Jane Elizabeth. b 51. EMMTC 98. **d** 01 **p** 02. NSM
Fenn Lanes Gp *Leic* from 01. *84 Leicester Road, Hinckley
LE10 1LT* Tel (01455) 448464
ATKINS, Nicholas Steven. b 60. Oak Hill Th Coll BA88. **d** 88
p 89. C Shepton Mallet w Doulting *B & W* 88-91; C Combe
Down w Monkton Combe and S Stoke 91-93; TV N Wingfield,
Clay Cross and Pilsley *Derby* 93-98; V Essington *Lich* from 98.
*The Vicarage, Wolverhampton Road, Essington, Wolverhampton
WV11 2BX* Tel (01922) 478540

ATKINS, Canon Paul Henry. b 38. Univ of Wales DipTh65.
St Mich Coll Llan 62. **d** 65 **p** 66. C Sheringham *Nor* 65-68; V
Southtown 68-84; RD Flegg (Gt Yarmouth) 78-84; R Aylmerton
w Runton 84-99; P-in-c Beeston Regis 98-99; P-in-c Gresham
98-99; R Aylmerton, Runton, Beeston Regis and Gresham
99-03; RD Repps 86-95; Hon Can Nor Cathl 88-03; rtd 03; Perm
to Offic *Nor* from 03. *34 Regis Avenue, Beeston Regis, Sheringham
NR26 8SW* Tel (01263) 820147
E-mail amdd24@dial.pipex.com
ATKINS, Peter. b 29. Edin Univ MA52. Edin Th Coll 52. **d** 54
p 55. C Edin Old St Paul *Edin* 54-59; P-in-c Edin St Dav 59-64;
Chapl Fulbourn Hosp Cam 64-66; R Galashiels *Edin* 66-69;
Perm to Offic 69-72; Divisional Dir Soc Services Brighton 72-83;
Asst Dir Soc Services E Sussex from 83. *11 South Street, Lewes
BN7 2BT* Tel (01273) 476230
ATKINS, Robert Brian. b 49. CIPFA78 Open Univ BA94. St Alb
and Ox Min Course 94. **d** 97 **p** 98. NSM Bicester w Bucknell,
Caversfield and Launton *Ox* from 97. *8 Tubb Close, Bicester
OX6 8BN* Tel (01869) 253448 Mobile 07973-713149
E-mail frbob@fish.co.uk
ATKINS, Roger Francis. b 30. AKC54. **d** 55 **p** 56. C Bromley All
Hallows *Lon* 55-58; C Eastleigh *Win* 58-62; Australia 62-71;
V Wolverley *Worc* 71-76; V S Hackney St Mich w Haggerston St
Paul *Lon* 76-85; TV Gleadless *Sheff* 85-93; rtd 93; Perm to Offic
Sheff from 93. *27 Stannington Glen, Sheffield S6 6NA* Tel
0114-234 0543
ATKINS, Shaun. *See* ATKINS, Austen Shaun
ATKINS, Timothy David. b 45. Ridley Hall Cam 71. **d** 74 **p** 75. C
Stoughton *Guildf* 74-79; C Chilwell *S'well* 79-84; R Eastwood
84-91; V Finchley Ch Ch *Lon* from 91; Chapl Barnet Healthcare
NHS Trust 92-01; Chapl Enfield Primary Care Trust from 01.
Christ Church Vicarage, 616 High Road, London N12 0AA Tel
(020) 8445 2377 *or* 8445 2532
ATKINS, Timothy James. b 38. Worc Coll Ox BA62. Cuddesdon
Coll 62. **d** 64 **p** 65. C Stafford St Mary *Lich* 64-67; C
Loughborough St Pet *Leic* 67-69; C Usworth *Dur* 69-71; Lic to
Offic *Newc* 71-76; P-in-c Slaley 76-87; P-in-c Shotley from 87.
St John's Vicarage, Snods Edge, Consett DH8 9TL Tel (01207)
255665
ATKINS, Timothy Samuel. b 22. DSC44. Em Coll Cam BA46
MA52. Ridley Hall Cam 47. **d** 49 **p** 50. C Melton Mowbray w
Burton Lazars, Freeby etc *Leic* 49-51; C Preston St Jo *Blackb*
51-54; V Baxenden 54-58; R Mildenhall *St E* 58-63; V Bunbury
Ches 63-87; RD Malpas 85-87; rtd 87; Perm to Offic *Ches* 87-01.
22 Stuart Court, High Street, Kibworth, Leicester LE8 0LR Tel
0116-279 6321
ATKINS, William. *See* ATKINS, Forrest William
ATKINSON, Albert Edward. b 35. St Deiniol's Hawarden 79. **d** 79
p 80. C Ellesmere Port *Ches* 79-81; TV 81-84; P-in-c Kirkby
Malzeard w Grewelthorpe and Mickley etc *Ripon* 84-88; P-in-c
Fountains 88-90; R Fountains Gp 90-92; V Aysgarth and Bolton
cum Redmire 92-96; rtd 96; Perm to Offic *Ripon* from 96; Hon
Min Can Ripon Cathl from 01. *79 Hillshaw Park Way, Ripon
HG4 1JU* Tel (01765) 607964
ATKINSON, Brian Colin. b 49. Sarum & Wells Th Coll 85. **d** 87
p 88. C Up Hatherley *Glouc* 87-90; R Upper Stour *Sarum* 90-95;
TR Trowbridge H Trin from 95. *Holy Trinity Rectory, 2B
Broadmead, Trowbridge BA14 9AA* Tel (01225) 753326
ATKINSON, Christopher John. b 57. Man Univ BA80 DipTh84.
Qu Coll Birm 82. **d** 85 **p** 86. C Stalybridge *Man* 85-88; P-in-c
Westhall w Brampton and Stoven *St E* 88-89; P-in-c Sotterley,
Willingham, Shadingfield, Ellough etc 88-90; P-in-c Hundred
River Gp of Par 90-92; R Fountains Gp 92-97; P-in-c Eye w
Braiseworth and Yaxley 97-00; P-in-c Occold 97-00; P-in-c
Bedingfield 97-00; R Eye 00-03; RD Hartismere 97-03; V Bourne
Linc from 03. *The Vicarage, Church Walk, Bourne PE10 9UQ* Tel
(01778) 422412 E-mail chris_atk@yahoo.com
ATKINSON, Canon Christopher Lionel Varley. b 39. K Coll Lon
63. Chich Th Coll 65. **d** 67 **p** 68. C Sowerby Bridge w Norland
Wakef 67-70; P-in-c Flushing *Truro* 70-73; Dioc Adv in RE
70-73; Perm to Offic *Worc* 74-78; TR Halesowen 78-88; RD
Dudley 79-87; Hon Can Worc Cathl 83-88; V Cartmel *Carl*
88-97; TV Cartmel Peninsula 97-98; RD Windermere 94-98;
Hon Can Carl Cathl 94-98; TR Bensham *Dur* 98-03; AD
Gateshead 99-03; Bp's Adv Spiritual Development from 03; Hon
Can Dur Cathl from 03. *4 Attwood Place, Tow Law, Bishop
Auckland DL13 4ER* Tel (01388) 731749
ATKINSON, Clive James. b 68. QUB BSc90. CITC 90. **d** 93
p 94. C Belfast H Trin and Ardoyne *Conn* 93-97; 1 Belfast
Upper Falls 97-02; Chapl Vevey w Château d'Oex and Villars
Eur from 02. *The Parsonage, Chemin de Champsavaux 1,
1807 Blonay, Vaud, Switzerland* Tel (0041) (21) 943 2334
E-mail info@allsaints.ch
ATKINSON, Canon David James. b 41. Lon Univ BD AKC63
Selw Coll Cam BA65 MA72. Linc Th Coll 65. **d** 66 **p** 67. C Linc
St Giles *Linc* 66-70; Asst Chapl Newc Univ *Newc* 70-73; Adult
Educn Officer *Lich* 73-75; P-in-c Acklam *Bradf* 73-80; Dir of
Educn *Lich* 75-82; Preb Lich Cathl *Lich* 82-87; Chapl Hull Univ *York* 82-87; Dir
of Educn *Linc* 87-94; Can and Preb Linc Cathl from 89; P-in-c

Bishop Norton, Wadingham and Snitterby 94-01; Perm to Offic from 01. *4 The Orchard, Middle Rasen, Market Rasen LN8 3TL* Tel (01673) 849979

✠ATKINSON, The Rt Revd David John. b 43. MSOSc K Coll Lon BSc65 AKC65 PhD69 Bris Univ DipTh70 MLitt73 Ox Univ MA85. Trin Coll Bris and Tyndale Hall Bris 69. **d** 72 **p** 73 **c** 01. C Halliwell St Pet *Man* 72-74; C Harborne Heath *Birm* 74-77; Lib Latimer Ho Ox 77-80; Chapl CCC Ox 80-93; Fell 84-93; Visiting Lect Wycliffe Hall Ox 84-93; Can Res and Chan S'wark Cathl *S'wark* 93-96; Adn Lewisham 96-01; Suff Bp Thetford *Nor* from 01. *Rectory Meadow, Bramerton, Norwich NR14 7DW* Tel (01508) 538251 Fax 538371

ATKINSON, Derek Arthur. b 31. K Coll Lon BD59 AKC59. **d** 60 **p** 61. C Ashford *Cant* 60-64; C Deal St Leon 64-68; R E w W Ogwell *Ex* 68-81; Asst Dir of RE 68-78; Dep Dir and Children's Adv 78-88; R Ogwell and Denbury 81-84; R Kenton w Mamhead and Powderham 84-88; rtd 88; Perm to Offic *Ex* 88-98. *High Trees, Fulford Road, Fulford, Stoke-on-Trent ST11 9QT* Tel (01782) 397156 E-mail derek-atkinson@lineone.net

ATKINSON, Ian. b 33. BNC Ox BA58 MA63. Coll of Resurr Mirfield 56. **d** 58 **p** 59. C Welling *S'wark* 58-62; C Camberwell St Giles 62-63; V Wandsworth Common St Mary 63-67; S Africa 67-68; C Oxted *S'wark* 68-69; Asst Chapl Ch Hosp Horsham 70-85; NSM Dalmahoy *Edin* 85-91; Asst Master Clifton Hall Sch 85-91; NSM Dunkeld *St And* 92-98; rtd 98. *2 Pinel Lodge, Druids Park, Murthly, Perth PH1 4ES* Tel (01738) 710561

ATKINSON, Canon Prof James. b 14. St Jo Coll Dur BA36 MA39 MLitt50 Univ of Munster DTh55 Hull Univ Hon DD97. **d** 37 **p** 38. C Newc H Cross *Newc* 37-41; Succ Sheff Cathl *Sheff* 41-42; Prec 42-44; V Shiregreen St Jas and St Chris 44-51; Fell Sheff Univ from 51; Can Th Leic Cathl *Leic* 54-70; Lect Th Hull Univ 56-64; Reader 64-67; Prof Bibl Studies Sheff Univ 67-79; Lic to Offic *Sheff* from 68; Can Th Sheff Cathl 70-93; rtd 79; Latimer Ho Ox 81-84. *Leach House, Leadmill Bridge, Hathersage, Hope Valley S32 1BA* Tel (01433) 650570

ATKINSON, Canon John Dudley. b 38. ACA60 FCA71. Qu Coll Birm 63. **d** 66 **p** 67. C Bishop's Stortford St Mich *St Alb* 66-70; C Norton 70-73; V Markyate Street 73-80; R Baldock w Bygrave 80-94; RD Stevenage 83-89; TR Bride Valley *Sarum* from 94; RD Lyme Bay from 98; Can and Preb Sarum Cathl from 02. *The Rectory, Church Street, Burton Bradstock, Bridport DT6 4QS* Tel (01308) 897359

ATKINSON, Ms Judith Angela. b 70. Leeds Univ BA92 Fitzw Coll Cam BA95. Ridley Hall Cam CTM93. **d** 96 **p** 97. C Chester le Street *Dur* 96-00; Community Employment Development Worker 00-01; NSM Dunston 01-02; Perm to Offic *Newc* 01-02. *73 Farquhar Road, Edgbaston, Birmingham B15 2QP* Tel 0121-452 2607 E-mail cat-nt@zetnet.co.uk

ATKINSON, Mrs Kate Bigwood. b 56. Cranmer Hall Dur 94. **d** 96 **p** 97. C Woking St Jo *Guildf* 96-00; NSM Haslemere and Grayswood 00-03; Assoc Min Nevada St Patr USA from 03. *818 Barbara Street, Incline Village, NV, USA* E-mail revkotty@aol.com

ATKINSON, Canon Lewis Malcolm. b 34. St Jo Coll Dur. **d** 82 **p** 83. C Chapeltown *Sheff* 82-85; V Sheff St Paul 85-93; Ind Chapl 85-99; RD Ecclesfield 90-93; V Oughtibridge 93-99; RD Tankersley 96-99; Hon Can Sheff Cathl 98-99; rtd 99; Perm to Offic *Sheff* from 99. *14 Rowan Close, Chapeltown, Sheffield S35 1QE*

ATKINSON, Mrs Marianne Rose. b 39. Girton Coll Cam BA61 CertEd62 MA64. Linc Th Coll 86. **d** 88 **p** 94. C S w N Hayling *Portsm* 88-91; C Rainham *Roch* 91-92; Asst Chapl Salford R Hosps NHS Trust 92-97; Hon C Prestwich St Marg *Man* 94-97; Chapl United Hosp Bath NHS Trust 97-00; rtd 00; Perm to Offic *E W* 00-03 and *St E* from 03. *68 Barons Road, Bury St Edmunds IP33 2LW* Tel (01284) 752075

ATKINSON, Megan Annice. b 37. SRN58. STETS DipCTM95. **d** 98 **p** 11. NSM Bridgemary *Portsm* 98-02; NSM Locks Heath from 01. *23 Home Rule Road, Locks Heath, Southampton SO31 6LH* Tel (01489) 575331

ATKINSON, Michael Hubert. b 33. Qu Coll Ox BA57 MA60. Ripon Hall Ox 56. **d** 58 **p** 59. C Attercliffe w Carbrook *Sheff* 58-60; Chapl 60-66; C Sharrow St Andr 60-66; Ind Chapl *Pet* 66-70; Sen Ind Chapl *Cant* 71-79; Research Officer Gen Syn Bd for Resp 79-87; Representation Sec USPG 88-92; TV High Wycombe Ox 92-97; Chapl Bucks Coll of HE 94-97; rtd 97. *7 The Court, Old Bridge Rise, Ilkley LS29 9HH* Tel (01943) 601...

ATKINSON, Nigel Terence. b 60. Sheff Univ BA82 St Jo Coll Dur MA85 Westmr Th Sem (USA) MDiv87 Cranmer Hall Dur 87. **d** 89 **p** 90. C Oakwood St Thos *Lon* 89-92; P-in-c Dolton *Ex* 92; P-in-c Iddesleigh w Dowland 92-95; P-in-c Hatherleigh, Meeth and Okehampton 92-95; Warden Latimer Ho Ox 95-98; V Knutsford *Ches* from 98. *The Vicarage, 11 Gough's ...nutsford WA16 8QL* Tel (01565) 632834 Fax 755160 E-mail nigelatk@btopenworld.com

ATKINSON, Mrs Patricia Anne. b 47. EAMTC 86. **d** 89 **p** 01. ... Nor St Steph *Nor* 89-94; Lic to Offic from 94; Chapl Norwich Primary Care Trust from 00; Chapl Norfolk and Nor Univ Hosp NHS Trust from 01; NSM Brundall w Braydeston and Postwick *Nor* from 01. *32 Berryfields, Brundall, Norwich NR13 5QE* Tel (01603) 714720 E-mail patriciaatkinson46@yahoo.co.uk

ATKINSON, Peter Duncan. b 41. Univ Coll Dur BA62. Linc Th Coll 63. **d** 65 **p** 66. C Beckenham St Geo *Roch* 65-69; C Caversham *Ox* 69-75; P-in-c Millfield St Mark *Dur* 76-86; V Dedworth *Ox* 86-93; TV Aylesbury w Bierton and Hulcott from 93. *St Peter's House, 18 Bronte Close, Aylesbury HP19 8LF* Tel (01296) 432677 Fax as telephone

ATKINSON, Peter Geoffrey. b 50. Sarum & Wells Th Coll 81. **d** 83 **p** 84. C Aylesbury *Ox* 83-86; C Dorchester 86-87; TV 87-91; V Cropredy w Gt Bourton and Wardington 91-96; V Shires' Edge 96-03; R Burstow w Horne *S'wark* from 03. *The Rectory, 5 The Acorns, Smallfield, Horley RH6 9QJ* Tel (01342) 842224 E-mail peter g atkinson@lineone.net

ATKINSON, Canon Peter Gordon. b 52. St Jo Coll Ox BA74 MA78. Westcott Ho Cam 77. **d** 79 **p** 80. C Clapham Old Town *S'wark* 79-83; P-in-c Tatsfield 83-90; R Bath H Trin *B & W* 90-91; Prin Chich Th Coll 91-94; Can and Preb Chich Cathl *Chich* 91-97; R Lavant 94-97; Can Res and Chan Chich Cathl from 97. *The Residentiary, Canon Lane, Chichester PO19 1PX* Tel (01243) 782961 *or* 782595 E-mail peterg@kinson20.freeserve.co.uk

ATKINSON, Philip Charles. b 50. Hull Univ BA71 PhD76 Chorley Coll of Educn CertEd77. N Ord Course 84. **d** 84 **p** 85. NSM Bolton SS Simon and Jude *Man* 84-87; Chapl R Wolv Sch from 87. *Royal Wolverhampton School, 179 Penn Road, Wolverhampton WV3 0EQ* Tel (01902) 341230

ATKINSON, Philip Stephen. b 58. K Coll Lon BD80 AKC80 Dur Univ MA97. Ridley Hall Cam 81. **d** 83 **p** 84. C Barrow St Matt *Carl* 83-86; C Kirkby Lonsdale 86-89; R Redmarshall *Dur* 89-95; V Bishopton w Gt Stainton 89-95; C Kirkby Lonsdale *Carl* 95-97; Chapl Casterton Sch Lancs from 95; NSM Kirkby Lonsdale *Carl* from 97. *Beckside, Casterton, Kirkby Lonsdale, Carnforth LA6 2SB* Tel (01524) 279248

ATKINSON, The Ven Richard William Bryant. b 58. OBE02. Magd Coll Cam MA. Ripon Coll Cuddesdon. **d** 84 **p** 85. C Abingdon w Shippon *Ox* 84-87; TV Sheff Manor *Sheff* 87-91; TR 91-96; Hon Tutor Ripon Coll Cuddesdon 87-92; V Rotherham *Sheff* 96-02; Hon Can Sheff Cathl 98-02; Adn Leic from 02. *46 Southernhay Road, Leicester LE2 3TJ* Tel and fax 0116-270 4441 *or* tel 0116-248 7419 E-mail archdeacon.richard@chouse.leicester.anglican.org

ATKINSON, Canon Samuel Charles Donald. b 30. TCD BA53. **d** 55 **p** 56. C Belfast St Simon *Conn* 55-62; I Ballynaclough *L & K* 62-68; I Cloughjordan w Modreeny 68-87; Dioc Youth Adv (Killaloe) 75-83; Dioc Info Officer 76-88; Can Killaloe Cathl 76-82; Chan 82-96; I Cloughjordan w Borrisokane etc 87-96; rtd 96. *Dromore Lodge, Rockcorry, Co Monaghan, Irish Republic* Tel (00353) (42) 42356

ATKINSON, Simon James. b 71. St Chad's Coll Dur BA93. St Steph Ho Ox 93. **d** 95 **p** 96. C Norton St Mary *Dur* 95-96; C Hartlepool H Trin 96-99; TV Jarrow 99-01; V Chich St Wilfrid *Chich* from 01. *St Wilfrid's House, 7 Durnford Close, Chichester PO19 3AG* Tel (01243) 783853

ATKINSON, Terence Harry. b 52. Coll of Resurr Mirfield 88. **d** 90 **p** 91. C Bottesford w Ashby *Linc* 90-93; TV Cleethorpes 93-98; C-in-c Cleethorpes St Fran CD 98-01; V Chapel St Leonards w Hogsthorpe 01-03; P-in-c Gt Grimsby St Andr w St Luke and All SS from 03. *St Andrew's Vicarage, 2A Albion Street, Grimsby DN32 7DY* Tel (01472) 348200

ATKINSON, Wendy Sybil. b 53. Man Univ BA95. N Ord Course 95. **d** 97 **p** 98. NSM Brinnington w Portwood *Ches* 97-99; C 99-01; NSM Werneth from 01. *8 Freshfield Close, Marple Bridge, Stockport SK6 5ES* Tel 0161-427 5612

ATKINSON-JONES, Mrs Susan Florence. b 64. Univ of Wales (Cardiff) BD93. St Mich Coll Llan 96. **d** 98 **p** 99. C Bargoed and Deri w Brithdir *Llan* from 98. *61 Park Road, Bargoed CF81 8SR* Tel (01443) 829374

ATLING, Edwood Brian. b 46. ACIB FIMgt. Westcott Ho Cam 00. **d** 02 **p** 03. C Godmanchester *Ely* from 02. *Blue Cedars, 70 Common Lane, Hemingford Abbots, Huntingdon PE28 9AW* Tel (01480) 493975 Mobile 07775-544679 Fax (01480) 496240 E-mail brian.atling@talk21.com

ATTA-BAFFOE, Victor Reginald. b 59. Trin Coll Toronto BTh88 Episc Div Sch Cambridge (USA) MA92 Yale Univ STM93. St Nic Th Coll Ghana LTh87. **d** 88 **p** 89. Ghana 88-90 and 93-98; USA 90-93; Lect St Nic Th Coll 88-90 and 93-98; NSM Finsbury Park St Thos *Lon* from 99. *20 Great Peter Street, London SW1P 2BU* Tel (020) 7222 3704 Fax 7233 0255

ATTAWAY, Mrs Elizabeth Ann. b 53. Cant Hill CertEd56. Cant Sch of Min 93 Bp Otter Coll 57. **d** 96 **p** 97. NSM Maidstone St Paul *Cant* 96-02; NSM Boxley w Detling from 02. *1 Staplers Court, Penenden Heath, Maidstone ME14 2XB* Tel (01622) 762656 E-mail glattaway@btinternet.com

ATTFIELD, David George. b 31. Magd Coll Ox BA54 MA58 BD61 K Coll Lon MPhil72 Dur Univ MA81. Westcott Ho Cam

57. **d** 58 **p** 59. C Edgbaston St Aug *Birm* 58-61; C Ward End 61-62; Lect Div St Kath Coll Tottenham 62-64; All SS Coll Tottenham 64-68; Sen Lect St Bede Coll Dur 68-75; St Hild and St Bede Coll 75-80; TV Drypool *York* 80-86; R Newton Heath All SS *Man* 86-96; rtd 97; Perm to Offic *Dur* from 97. *19 Laburnum Avenue, Durham DH1 4HA* Tel 0191-383 0509

ATTLEY, Ronald. b 46. Open Univ BA87 Dur Univ CCSk90. Brasted Th Coll 66 Chich Th Coll 68. **d** 70 **p** 71. C Heworth St Mary *Dur* 70-73; C Hulme Ascension *Man* 73-75; Belize 76-79 and 00; V Leadgate *Dur* 79-84; Chapl HM Rem Cen Ashford 84-87; Chapl HM Pris Ashwell and Stocken 87-89; Chapl HM Pris Frankland 89-92; Chapl HM YOI Deerbolt 92-96; V Bath St Barn w Englishcombe *B & W* 96-00; V Brinnington w Portwood *Ches* from 01. *St Luke's Vicarage, Brinnington Road, Stockport SK5 8BS* Tel 0161-430 4164

ATTRILL, Norman Edmund Charles. b 16. K Coll Lon BA37. Wm Temple Coll Rugby 65 Ripon Hall Ox 67. **d** 68 **p** 69. C Portsea St Mary *Portsm* 68-72; V Sea View 72-83; rtd 81; Perm to Offic *Ox* from 83. *27 Church Street, Henley-on-Thames RG9 1SE* Tel (01491) 574268

ATTWATER, Mrs Sallyanne. b 48. Westmr Coll Ox MTh98. S Dios Minl Tr Scheme 86. **d** 94 **p** 95. Chapl Asst Eastbourne Distr Gen Hosp 94-95; Asst Chapl Princess Alice Hosp and All SS Hosp 94-95; C E Grinstead St Swithun *Chich* 95-98; P-in-c Bishop's Cannings, All Cannings etc *Sarum* from 98. *The Vicarage, The Street, Bishop's Cannings, Devizes SN10 2LD* Tel (01380) 860650 E-mail sally@cannings1.freeserve.co.uk

ATTWATER, Stephen Philip. b 47. ALCM67. Linc Th Coll 85. **d** 87 **p** 88. C Warrington St Elphin *Liv* 87-90; P-in-c Eccleston St Thos 90-94; V 94-99; V Padgate from 99. *The Rectory, Station Road, Padgate, Warrington WA2 0PD* Tel (01925) 821555

ATTWOOD, Andrew Michael. b 66. Derby Coll of Educn BEd91. Trin Coll Bris BA02. **d** 02 **p** 03. C Leamington Priors St Mary *Cov* from 02. *12 Otters Rest, Leamington Spa CV31 1AD* Tel (01926) 315399 Mobile 07884-136816 E-mail a.attwood@talk21.com

ATTWOOD, Anthony Norman. b 47. Univ of Wales (Abth) BSc(Econ)69 Birm Univ DipTh71 Hull Univ MA82. Qu Coll Birm 69. **d** 72 **p** 73. C Greenhill *Sheff* 72-75; V Elsecar 76-81; Ind Missr 81-95; TV Maltby 81-86; Ind Chapl 86-96; RD Adwick 89-95; Teesside Ind Miss *Dur* 95-99; P-in-c Swindon St Aug *Bris* from 99. *St Augustine's Vicarage, Morris Street, Swindon SN2 2HT* Tel (01793) 522741 Mobile 07801-260865

ATTWOOD, Preb Carl Norman Harry. b 53. Bris Univ BA74 Ox Univ BA76 MA80. Cuddesdon Coll 74. **d** 77 **p** 78. C Tupsley *Heref* 77-82; R Colwall w Upper Colwall and Coddington from 82; Perm to Offic *Worc* from 82; Bp's Voc Officer *Heref* 83-89; Chapl St Jas Sch Malvern from 86; RD Ledbury *Heref* 90-96; Preb Heref Cathl from 97. *The Rectory, Walwyn Road, Colwall, Malvern WR13 6EG* Tel (01684) 540330 Fax 540083 E-mail carl@attwoods.demon.co.uk

ATTWOOD, David John Edwin. b 51. Dur Univ BA76 Em Coll Cam BA73 MA77. Cranmer Hall Dur 74. **d** 77 **p** 78. C Rodbourne Cheney *Bris* 77-79; C Lydiard Millicent w Lydiard Tregoz 79-85; Dir and Lect Trin Coll Bris 85-97; V Prenton *Ches* 97-02; R Sundridge w Ide Hill *Roch* from 02. *The Rectory, Chevening Road, Sundridge, Sevenoaks TN14 6AB* Tel (01959) 563749 E-mail david@attwood27.freeserve.co.uk

ATTWOOD, Leslie Thomas. b 42. Univ of W of England MA94 Cranfield Univ MBA MCIPD76. St Steph Ho Ox. **d** 83 **p** 84. C Ascot Heath *Ox* 83-86; Dioc Tr Officer *Truro* 86-88; C Walkasey St Hilary *Ches* 98-00; C Devizes St Pet *Sarum* 00-02; TV Godrevy *Truro* from 02. *The Vicarage, 43 School Lane, St Erth, Hayle TR27 4HN* Tel (01736) 753194 E-mail attwood99@lineone.net

ATTWOOD, Peter John. b 44. ACIB68. SEITE 00. **d** 03. NSM Langton Green *Roch* from 03. *Podlea, Colemans Hatch, Hartfield TN7 4EN* Tel (01342) 822428 Mobile 07714-026402 E-mail rev@podlea.co.uk

ATWELL, The Very Revd James Edgar. b 46. Ex Coll Ox BA68 MA73 BD94 Harvard Univ ThM70. Cuddesdon Coll 68. **d** 70 **p** 71. C E Dulwich St Jo *S'wark* 70-74; C Cambridge Gt St Mary w St Mich *Ely* 74-77; Chapl Jes Coll Cam 77-81; V Towcester w Easton Neston *Pet* 81-95; RD Towcester 83-91; Provost St E 95-00; Dean St E from 00. *The Provost's House, Bury St Edmunds IP33 1RS* Tel (01284) 754852 *or* 754933 Fax 768655 E-mail provost@btconnect.com

ATWELL, Robert Ronald. b 54. St Jo Coll Dur BA75 Dur Univ MLitt79. Westcott Ho Cam 76. **d** 78 **p** 79. C Mill Hill Jo Keble Ch *Lon* 78-81; Chapl Trin Coll Cam 81-87; OSB 87-98; Lic to Offic *Ox* 87-97; Perm to Offic *Ely* 97-98; V Primrose Hill St Mary w Avenue Road St Paul *Lon* from 98. *St Mary's Vicarage, 44 King Henry's Road, London NW3 3RP* Tel (020) 7722 3062 *or* tel and fax 7722 3238 Fax 7722 4833 E-mail robert@44kinghenry.freeserve.co.uk

AUCHMUTY, John Robert. b 67. ACCA Athlone Regional Tech Coll NC(BS)89. CITC 89. **d** 92 **p** 93. C Dundela St Mark *D & D* 92-96; I Eglish w Killylea *Arm* 96-01; I Killaney w Carryduff *D & D* from 01. *The Rectory, 700 Saintfield Road, Carryduff, Belfast BT8 8BU* Tel (028) 9081 2342 *or* 9081 3489 Fax 9081 2830 E-mail cofi@carryduff70.freeserve.co.uk

AUCKLAND, Bishop of. *See* PATERSON, The Rt Revd John Campbell

AUCKLAND, Archdeacon of. *See* JAGGER, The Ven Ian

AUDEN, Lawson Philip. b 45. Qu Coll Birm 73. **d** 78 **p** 81. C Spalding *Linc* 78-81; TV Wordsley *Lich* 81-82; TV Kidderminster St Mary and All SS, Trimpley etc *Worc* 82-87; Ind Chapl 82-87; Perm to Offic *Cov* and *Worc* 87-91; *Birm, Lich* and *Glouc* 94-97; Chapl Worcs Community Healthcare NHS Trust 91-97; P-in-c Pebworth w Dorsington and Honeybourne *Glouc* 97-99; Perm to Offic *Cov* 98-01; *B & W* from 00; Chapl Miss to Seafarers from 99; Millennium Officer *Glouc* 99-01; Perm to Offic *Glouc* from 01. *4 Penlea Court, Shirehampton, Bristol BS11 0BY* Tel 0117-982 7879 *or* (01275) 372926 E-mail philipauden@ukf.net

AUDIBERT, Mrs Janice Elizabeth. b 56. OLM course 98. **d** 99 **p** 00. OLM Oakdale *Sarum* 99-02; C from 02. *24 Blackbird Close, Poole BH17 7YA* Tel (01202) 389751 Fax as telephone E-mail janice.audibert@christ-church-creekmoor.org.uk

AULD, Mrs Sheila Edith. b 38. Newc Poly BA87 Univ of Northumbria at Newc MA99. NEOC 91. **d** 94 **p** 95. Project Worker Cedarwood Trust 88-02; NSM Newc St Gabr *Newc* 94-02; rtd 02. *5 Gibson Fields, Hexham NE46 1AS* Tel (01434) 602297

AUST, Arthur John. b 14. St Aug Coll Cant 62. **d** 63 **p** 64. C Dagenham *Chelmsf* 63-65; Kenya 65-67; P-in-c Skidbrooke *Linc* 67-69; R Theddlethorpe w Mablethorpe 67-71; Nigeria 71-74; S Africa 74-77; TV Clyst St George, Aylesbeare, Clyst Honiton etc *Ex* 79-81; rtd 81; Perm to Offic *Cant* from 81. *20 Campbell Road, Deal CT14 7EQ* Tel (01304) 361583

AUSTEN, Glyn Benedict. b 54. UEA BA77 MPhil80 Ox Univ BA81 MA85. Ripon Coll Cuddesdon 79. **d** 82 **p** 83. C Newport w Longford and Chetwynd *Lich* 82-85; C Hawley H Trin *Guildf* 85-87; R Barnack w Ufford and Bainton *Pet* 87-03. *Address temp unknown* E-mail austen@globalnet.co.uk

AUSTEN, John. b 46. St Cath Coll Cam BA69 MA72. Qu Coll Birm DipTh70. **d** 71 **p** 72. C Thornaby on Tees *York* 71-74; C Aston St Jas *Birm* 74-82; Chapl Aston Univ 82-88; C Handsworth St Andr from 88. *151 Church Lane, Birmingham B20 2RU* Tel 0121-554 8882 E-mail johnausten@iname.com

AUSTEN, Simon Neil. b 67. Warwick Univ BSc88. Wycliffe Hall Ox BA93 MA97 DipMin94. **d** 94 **p** 95. C Gt Chesham *Ox* 94-98; Chapl Stowe Sch 98-02; V Houghton *Carl* from 02. *The Vicarage, Houghton, Carlisle CA6 4HZ* Tel (01228) 810076 *or* 515972 E-mail simon.austen@ukgateway.net

AUSTERBERRY, Preb David Naylor. b 35. Birm Univ BA58. Wells Th Coll 58. **d** 60 **p** 61. C Leek St Edw *Lich* 60-63; Iran 64-70; Chapl CMS Foxbury 70-73; V Walsall Pleck and Bescot *Lich* 73-82; R Brierley Hill 82-88; R Kinnerley w Melverley and Knockin w Maesbrook 88-99; RD Oswestry 92-95; Preb Lich Cathl 96-00; rtd 00; Perm to Offic *Lich* from 00. *Chad Cottage, Dovaston, Kinnerley, Oswestry SY10 8DT* Tel (01691) 682039

AUSTERBERRY, John Maurice. b 62. Birm Univ BA83. Sarum & Wells Th Coll 84. **d** 86 **p** 87. C Clayton *Lich* 86-89; Asst Chapl Withington Hosp Man 89-95; Chapl Tameside and Glossop NHS Trust 95-99; Chapl N Staffs Hosp NHS Trust from 99. *City General Hospital, Newcastle Road, Stoke-on-Trent ST4 6QG* Tel (01782) 715444 *or* 552252

AUSTIN, Canon Alfred George. b 36. Ridley Coll Melbourne ThL61. **d** 61 **p** 62. Australia 61-77; C Dartford St Alb *Roch* 77-79; Australia from 79; R Tatura 79-84; R W Bend 84-90; R Kyneton 90-93; Can 83-97; I Essendon Ch Ch 97-01; rtd 01. *Brooklyn, 3 Alpina Place, Kangaroo Flat, Vic, Australia 3555* Tel (0061) (3) 5447 0174

AUSTIN, Mrs Catherine Brenda. b 57. **d** 00 **p** 01. OLM Henley, Claydon and Barham St E from 00. *Fait Accompli, 7 Freeman Avenue, Henley, Ipswich IP6 0RZ* Tel (01473) 830100

AUSTIN, The Ven George Bernard. b 31. St D Coll Lamp BA53 Chich Th Coll 53. **d** 55 **p** 56. C Chorley St Pet *Blackb* 55-57; C Notting Hill St Clem *Lon* 57-60; Asst Chapl Lon Univ 60-61; C Dunstable *St Alb* 61-64; V Eaton Bray 64-70; V Bushey Heath 70-88; Hon Can St Alb 78-88; Adn York 88-99; Can and Preb York Minster 98-99; rtd 99; Perm to Offic *York* from 99. *North Back House, 3B Main Street, Wheldrake, York YO19 6AG* Tel (01904) 448509 Fax 448002 E-mail george.austin@virgin.net

AUSTIN, Miss Jane. b 43. SRN64 SCM66. Trin Coll Bris DipTh81. **dss** 81 **d** 87 **p** 94. Tonbridge SS Pet and Paul *Roch* 81-98; Par Dn 87-94; C 94-98; Hon Can Roch Cathl 96-98; P-in-c Meltham *Wakef* 98-01; P-in-c Helme 00-01; V Meltham from 01; RD Almondbury from 01. *The Vicarage, 150 Huddersfield Road, Meltham, Huddersfield HD7 3AL* Tel (01484) 850050

✠**AUSTIN, The Rt Revd John Michael.** b 39. St Edm Hall Ox BA63. St Steph Ho Ox 62. **d** 64 **p** 65 **c** 92. C E Dulwich St Jo *S'wark* 64-68; USA 68-69; Warden Pemb Ho and Missr Walworth St Chris CD *S'wark* 69-76; TV Walworth 75-76; Soc Resp Adv *St Alb* 76-84; Dir Dioc Bd for Soc Resp *Lon* 84-92; Preb St Paul's Cathl 89-92; Suff Bp Aston *Birm* from 92; Warden CSMV from 98. *Strensham House, 8 Strensham Hill, Birmingham B13 8AG* Tel 0121-449 0675 *or* 426 0448 Mobile 07973-523702 Fax 449 7310 *or* 428 1114 E-mail bishopofaston@birmingham.anglican.org

AUSTIN, Leslie Ernest. b 46. Trin Coll Bris 72. **d** 74 **p** 75. C Paddock Wood *Roch* 74-79; C Upper Armley *Ripon* 79-81; V Horton *Bradf* 81-85; V Long Preston w Tosside 85-97; TR Shirwell, Loxhore, Kentisbury, Arlington, etc *Ex* from 97. *The Rectory, 2 Barnfield, Bratton Fleming, Barnstaple EX31 4RT* Tel (01598) 710807 E-mail les@austin85.freeserve.co.uk

AUSTIN, Margaret Rose. b 41. Qu Coll Birm 01. **d** 03. NSM Farewell *Lich* 03; NSM Gentleshaw from 03; NSM Hammerwich from 03. *137 Highfields Road, Chasetown, Burntwood WS7 4QT* Tel (01543) 686883
E-mail margaret1693.freeserve.co.uk

AUSTIN, Canon Michael Ridgwell. b 33. FRHistS Lon Univ BD57 PhD69 Birm Univ MA66. Lon Coll of Div ALCD56 LTh. **d** 57 **p** 58. C Ward End *Birm* 57-60; PC Derby St Andr *Derby* 60-66; Lect Th Derbyshire Coll of HE 66-73; Prin Lect 73-85; Chapl Derby Cathl *Derby* 86-88; Can Res Derby Cathl 81-85; Bp's Adv on Tr *S'well* 85-88; Dir Post-Ord Tr 86-94; Can Res S'well Minster 88-94; Dioc Dir of Tr 88-94; Abps' Adv for Bps' Min 94-98; rtd 98. *7 Dudley Doy Road, Southwell NG25 0NJ* Tel (01636) 812604

AUSTIN, Ronald Glyn. b 52. Univ of Wales (Cardiff) BD90 Univ of Wales MPhil98. St Mich Coll Llan 88. **d** 90 **p** 91. C Llangynwyd w Maesteg *Llan* 90-91; C Barry All SS 91-93; V Nantymoel w Wyndham 93-97; V Pontyclun w Talygarn 97-02; St Mich Coll Llan from 02. *3 Heol y Pavin, Llandaff, Cardiff CF5 2EG* Tel (029) 2056 5366

AUSTIN, Mrs Susan Frances. b 47. Open Univ BA81. Cant Sch of Min 87. **d** 92 **p** 94. Chapl Ch Ch High Sch Ashford 90-94; C Gt Chart *Cant* 92-94; C Ashford 92-94; C Estover *Ex* 94-96; V Stevenage All SS Pin Green *St Alb* 96-98; P-in-c Bredgar w Bicknor and Frinsted w Wormshill etc *Cant* from 00. *The Vicarage, Parsonage Lane, Bredgar, Sittingbourne ME9 8HA* Tel (01622) 884387 E-mail susanaustin@talk21.com

AUSTRALIA, Primate of. *See* CARNLEY, The Most Revd Peter Frederick

AVANN, Canon Penelope Joyce. b 46. Trin Coll Bris DipTh71. dss 83 **d** 87 **p** 98. Southborough St Pet w Ch Ch and St Matt *Roch* 83-89; Par Dn 87-89; Warden Past Assts from 89; Par Dn Beckenham St Jo 89-94; C 94-02; Hon Can Roch Cathl from 94; C Green Street Green and Pratts Bottom from 94. *9 Ringwood Avenue, Orpington BR6 7SY* Tel and fax (01689) 861742 Mobile 07710-418839

AVENT, Raymond John. b 28. St D Coll Lamp BA55 Coll of Resurr Mirfield 55. **d** 57 **p** 58. C Bury H Trin *Man* 57-60; C Holborn St Alb w Saffron Hill St Pet *Lon* 60-66; C Munster Square St Mary Magd 66-67; V Tottenham St Paul 67-77; RD E Haringey 73-77; V Kilburn St Aug w St Jo 77-87; AD Westmr Paddington 79-84; R St Vedast w St Mich-le-Querne etc 87-94; rtd 94; Perm to Offic *Lon* 94-00; *Glouc* from 00. *Maryvale House, Catbrook, Chipping Campden GL55 6DE* Tel (01386) 841323 E-mail avent@campadene.fsnet.co.uk

AVERY, Richard Julian. b 52. Keble Coll Ox BA73. St Jo Coll Nottm 74. **d** 77 **p** 78. C Macclesfield St Mich *Ches* 77-80; Canada 82-83 and 87-97; C Becontree St Mary *Chelmsf* 84-87; TV Chelmsford St Mark *Glouc* from 97. *154 Arle Road, Cheltenham GL51 8LH* Tel (01242) 700105

AVERY, Robert Edward. b 69. Magd Coll Cam BA90. Ripon Coll Cuddesdon 90. **d** 93 **p** 94. C Cen Telford *Lich* 93-96; C Cambridge Gt St Mary w St Mich *Ely* 96-99; V Tamerton Foliot *Ex* from 99. *St Mary's Vicarage, Tamerton Foliot, Plymouth PL5 4NT* Tel (01752) 771033
E-mail robert.avery@btinternet.com

AVERY, Russel Harrold. b 46. JP74. ACT ThDip75 Moore Th Coll Sydney 66. **d** 77 **p** 77. Australia 77-78, 88-98 and from 02; C Prenton *Ches* 78-79; Egypt 79-82; Chapl Maisons-Laffitte *Eur* 82-88; Chapl Nord Pas de Calais 98-02; rtd 02. *Address temp unknown*

AVES, Canon John Albert. b 51. K Coll Lon AKC73 BD74 PGCE79 PhD02 Hull Univ MA82. **d** 75 **p** 76. C Plaistow St Andr *Chelmsf* 75-77; Perm to Offic *Lon* 77-79; C Nor St Pet Mancroft *Nor* 79-82; R Attleborough w Besthorpe 82-99; RD Thetford and Rockland 98-99; P-in-c Nor St Giles from 99; Asst Dir CME 99-01; Dioc Dir CME from 01; Hon Can Nor Cathl from 02. *St Giles's Vicarage, 44 Heigham Road, Norwich NR2 3AU* Tel (01603) 623724 Fax as telephone
E-mail johnaves@norwich.anglican.org

AVES, Peter Colin. b 57. Qu Mary Coll Lon BSc79 CertEd80 Lon Univ BD89. Wycliffe Hall Ox 85. **d** 88 **p** 89. C Thames Ditton *Guildf* 88-90; C Chertsey 90-93; R Stockbridge and Longstock and Leckford *Win* 93-00; Chapl to the Deaf *Sarum* from 00. *23 Bridport Road, Verwood BH31 6UP* Tel (01202) 826364

AVESON, Ian Henry. b 55. Jes Coll Ox BA77 MA81 Univ Coll Dur PGCE78 Birkbeck Coll Lon MSc85. St Mich Coll Llan BD97. **d** 97 **p** 98. C Penarth All SS *Llan* 97-99; TV Aberystwyth *St D* from 99. *Holy Trinity Vicarage, Buarth Road, Aberystwyth SY23 1NB* Tel (01970) 617015

AVEYARD, Ian. b 46. Liv Univ BSc68 Sheff Univ MEd00. ALCD72 St Jo Coll Nottm 71. **d** 71 **p** 72. C Bradley *Wakef* 71-74; C Knowle *Birm* 74-79; P-in-c Cofton Hackett 79; P-in-c

Barnt Green 79; V Cofton Hackett w Barnt Green 80-94; Dioc Dir of Reader Tr 85-94; Warden of Readers 91-94; Course Leader St Jo Coll Nottm 96-99; P-in-c Thanington *Cant* from 99; Dioc Dir of Ords from 99. *The Vicarage, 70 Thanington Road, Canterbury CT1 3XE* Tel (01227) 464516 Fax 785894
E-mail ian@iaveyard.freeserve.co.uk

AVIS, Preb Paul David Loup. b 47. Lon Univ BD70 PhD76. Westcott Ho Cam 73. **d** 75 **p** 76. C S Molton, Nymet St George, High Bray etc *Ex* 75-80; V Stoke Canon, Poltimore w Huxham and Rewe etc 80-98; Preb Ex Cathl from 93; Sub Dean Ex Cathl from 97; Gen Sec Coun for Chr Unity from 98. *Church House, Great Smith Street, London SW1P 3NZ, or 48 Trinity Rise, London SW2 2QR* Tel (020) 7898 1470 Fax 7898 1483
E-mail paul.avis@c-of-e.org.uk

AWRE, Richard William Esgar. b 56. Univ of Wales BA78. Wycliffe Hall Ox 78. **d** 81 **p** 82. C Blackpool St Jo *Blackb* 81-84; Asst Dir of Ords and Voc Adv 84-89; C Altham w Clayton le Moors 84-89; V Longridge 89-99; V Kenilworth St Nic *Cov* from 99; RD Kenilworth from 01. *The Vicarage, 7 Elmbank Road, Kenilworth CV8 1AL* Tel (01926) 854367 or 857509
E-mail stnicholasken@aol.com

AXFORD, Mrs Christine Ruth. b 53. Glam Coll of Educn BEd75. STETS BTh00. **d** 00 **p** 02. NSM Yeovil w Kingston Pitney *B & W* 00-01; NSM N Hartismere *St E* from 02. *The Rectory, Oakley, Diss IP21 4BW* Tel (01379) 742708 Fax as telephone
E-mail robaxford@onetel.net.uk

AXFORD, Robert Henry. b 50. CEng85 Univ of Wales BEng72. Sarum & Wells Th Coll 89. **d** 91 **p** 92. C Castle Cary w Ansford *B & W* 91-95; P-in-c Queen Camel w W Camel, Corton Denham etc 95-01; R 01-02; R N Hartismere *St E* from 02. *The Rectory, Oakley, Diss IP21 4BW* Tel (01379) 742708 Fax as telephone
E-mail robaxford@onetel.net.uk

AXON, Andrew John. b 76. Univ of Wales (Lamp) BTh97. Trin Coll Bris 99. **d** 01 **p** 02. C Sevenhampton w Charlton Abbots, Hawling etc *Glouc* from 01. *The Rectory, Withington, Cheltenham GL54 4BG* Tel (01242) 890242
E-mail mail@ajaxon.freeserve.co.uk

AXTELL, Ronald Arthur John. b 33. Lon Univ BSc54 St Cath Soc Ox BA58 MA62. Wycliffe Hall Ox 56. **d** 58 **p** 59. C Walton Breck *Liv* 58-61; Iran 63-78; Chapl Tehran 63-67; Chapl Kerman 67-68; Chapl Shiraz 69-78; Chr Witness to Israel Miss in Man 78-82; Perm to Offic *Man* 79-82; TV Man Resurr 82; TV Man Gd Shep 82-88; R Levenshulme St Pet 88-98; rtd 98; Perm to Offic *Man* from 98. *15 Berwick Avenue, Stockport SK4 3AA* Tel 0161-432 5943 E-mail axtell@ntlworld.com

AXTELL, Stephen Geoffrey. b 57. Open Univ BSc96. St Jo Coll Nottm 00. **d** 02 **p** 03. C Coseley Ch Ch *Worc* from 02. *12 Ribbesford Crescent, Coseley, Bilston WV14 8XU* Tel (01902) 493600 Mobile 07887-544776 E-mail saxtell@globalnet.co.uk

AYAD, Karl. b 25. Cairo Univ BA50 Lon Univ MSc53 PhD55. St Steph Ho Ox 80. **d** 81 **p** 82. C Allerton *Liv* 81-83; V Knowsley 83-90; rtd 90; Perm to Offic *Ches* and *Liv* from 90. *46/2 Stanley Road, Hoylake, Wirral CH47 1HY* Tel 0151-632 5519

AYERS, Canon John. b 40. FCollP Bris Univ BEd75 Newton Park Coll Bath MEd89 FRSA94. **d** 77 **p** 78. NSM Corsham *Bris* 77-79; NSM Gtr Corsham 79-88; NSM Ditteridge 88-92; NSM Box w Hazlebury and Ditteridge from 93; Hon Can Bris Cathl from 94. *Toad Hall, Middlehill, Box, Corsham SN13 8QP* Tel (01225) 742123 E-mail johnayers@middlehill.netlineuk.net

AYERS, Paul Nicholas. b 61. St Pet Coll Ox BA82 MA86. Trin Coll Bris 83. **d** 85 **p** 86. C Clayton *Bradf* 85-88; C Keighley St Andr 88-91; V Wrose 91-97; V Pudsey St Lawr and St Paul from 97. *The Vicarage, Vicarage Drive, Pudsey LS28 7RL* Tel 0113-257 7843 or 256 4197

AYERST, Edward Richard. b 25. Leeds Univ BA51. Coll of Resurr Mirfield 51. **d** 53 **p** 54. C Bethnal Green St Jo w St Simon *Lon* 53-57; C Hayes St Mary 58-60; V Edmonton St Mary w St Jo 60-66; R Whippingham w E Cowes *Portsm* 66-77; V Bridgwater St Mary w Chilton Trinity *B & W* 77-84; V Durleigh 77-84; V Bridgwater St Mary, Chilton Trinity and Durleigh 84-90; Chapl to The Queen 87-95; rtd 90; Perm to Offic *B & W* from 90. *56 Maple Drive, Burham-on-Sea TA8 1DH* Tel (01278) 780701

AYERST, Gabrielle Mary. b 52. St Luke's Coll Ex BEd74. SEITE 97. **d** 00 **p** 01. NSM Surbiton St Andr and St Mark *S'wark* from 00. *Flat 3, 11 Claremont Gardens, Surbiton KT6 4TN* Tel (020) 8390 2166 E-mail gadrillea@paff.nsf.org.uk

AYKROYD, Harold Allan. b 22. DFC. Man Univ BA48. Qu Coll Birm 73. **d** 76 **p** 76. NSM Moseley St Agnes *Birm* 76-82; NSM Bournville 82-96; Perm to Offic from 96. *108 Middleton Hall Road, Birmingham B30 1DG* Tel 0121-451 1365 or 569 4687

AYLEN, George Richard. b 24. Chich Th Coll 48. **d** 52 **p** 53. C Cant St Greg *Cant* 52-55; C Margate All SS 55-58; V Spring Park 58-61; V Newington 61-67; V Whitstable St Pet 67-75; R Petham w Waltham and Lower Hardres w Nackington 75-78; rtd 78; Perm to Offic *Cant* 80-98. *c/o Mark Aylen Esq, Sylvan, Minstead, Lyndhurst SO43 7FY* Tel (01703) 282334

AYLETT, Graham Peter. b 59. Qu Coll Cam BA81 MA84 PhD83 St Jo Coll Dur BA88. Cranmer Hall Dur 86 All Nations Chr

BACKHOUSE

Coll 96. **d** 90 **p** 91. C Wilton *B & W* 90-94; C Runcorn All SS *Ches* 94-96; C Thetford *Nor* 97-98; Mongolia from 98. *clo JCS, PO Box 49/532, Ulaanbaatar 210349, Mongolia*

AYLETT, Mrs Nicola Jane. b 63. St Anne's Coll Ox BA84 St Jo Coll Dur BA89. Cranmer Hall Dur 87 All Nations Chr Coll 96. **d** 90 **p** 94. C Wilton *B & W* 90-94; NSM Runcorn All SS *Ches* 94-96; Perm to Offic *Nor* 97-98; Mongolia from 98. *clo JCS, PO Box 49/532, Ulaanbaatar 210349, Mongolia*

AYLING, Arnold <u>Paul</u>. b 38. Ball Coll Ox BA61. Wells Th Coll 65. **d** 67 **p** 68. C Weymouth H Trin *Sarum* 67-70; Chapl K Alfred Coll *Win* 70-73; Miss to Seamen 73-84; Dunkirk 73; Nigeria 74-82; S Africa 82-84; Perm to Offic *Sarum* 85-86; *Chich* from 85; Chapl Tunbridge Wells HA 86-94; Chapl Kent and Sussex Weald NHS Trust 94-99; rtd 99. *Elmcroft, 36 The Green, Southwick, Brighton BN42 4FR* Tel (01273) 592329 Mobile 07770-967339 E-mail paul.ayling@virgin.net

AYLING, Miss Dallas Jane. b 53. Trin Coll Bris BA94. **d** 98 **p** 99. C Ellesmere Port *Ches* 98-02; TV Birkenhead Priory from 02. *10 Cavendish Road, Birkenhead CH41 8AX* Tel 0151-653 6092

AYLING, Canon John Michael. b 37. St Cath Coll Cam BA60 MA64. Linc Th Coll 60. **d** 62 **p** 63. C Stoke upon Trent *Lich* 62-66; C Codsall 66-67; Australia 67-71; Solomon Is 71-72; Lic to Offic *St Alb* 72-91; TR Boscastle w Davidstow *Truro* 91-98; R 98-02; RD Stratton 98-02; Hon Can Truro Cathl 01-02; rtd 02. *Pencliffe, Old Road, Boscastle PL35 0AQ* Tel (01840) 250608 E-mail john.ayling@virgin.net

AYLING, Mrs Susan Pamela. b 48. OBE03. City of Lon Poly Dip Civil Law 68 Kent Univ DTM98. SEITE 95. **d** 98 **p** 99. NSM Oxshott *Guildf* 98-02; NSM Cuddington from 02. *114 Edenfield Gardens, Worcester Park KT4 7DY* Tel (020) 8337 6347 *or* 7438 6589 E-mail sue.ayling@btinternet.com

AYLWARD, James Gareth. b 45. St Cath Coll Cam BA68 MA72. St As Minl Tr Course 94. **d** 97 **p** 98. NSM Wrexham *St As* 97-00; V Broughton from 00. *The Vicarage, Bryn-y-Gaer Road, Pentre Broughton, Wrexham LL11 6AT* Tel (01978) 756210

AYNSLEY, Ernest Edgar. b 02. FRIC Dur Univ BSc23 MSc24 PhD34 DSc62. Westcott Ho Cam 42. **d** 42 **p** 43. Hon C Long Benton St Mary *Newc* 42-54; Hon C Newc St Barn and St Jude 54-57; Hon C Gosforth St Nic 57-62; Lic to Offic 63-95; Prof Chemistry Newc Univ 63-67; rtd 67. *7 Manor Court, Ulgham, Morpeth NE61 3BG* Tel (01670) 790197

AYOK-LOEWENBERG, Joseph. b 60. DipEd91. Trin Coll Bris 85. **d** 88 **p** 89. C Swanage and Studland *Sarum* 88-90; Cam Univ Miss Bermondsey 90; C Barnes St Mary *S'wark* 91-92; CMS Uganda 92-95; P-in-c Symondsbury and Chideock *Sarum* 96-98; TV Golden Cap Team 98-01; CMS from 01. *CMS, Partnership House, 157 Waterloo Road, London SE1 8UU* Tel (020) 7928 8681

✠**AYONG, The Most Revd James Simon.** b 44. Newton Th Coll DipTh Martin Luther Sem BTh. **d** 82 **p** 84 **c** 96. Papua New Guinea from 82; Asst P Popondetta Resurr 85-86; Lect Newton Th Coll 87-88; Prin 89-93; Par P Gerehu 94-95; Bp Aipo Rongo from 95; Abp Papua New Guinea from 96. *PO Box 893, Mount Hagen, Western Highlands Province, Papua New Guinea* Tel (00675) 542 1131 *or* 542 3727 Fax 542 1181 E-mail acpnghgn@global.net.pg

AYRES, Anthony Lawrence. b 47. Trin Coll Bris 69. **d** 73 **p** 74. C Plumstead All SS *S'wark* 73-77; Hon C 77-00; Member of Counselling Team CA from 83. *37 Donaldson Road, London SE18 4JZ* Tel (020) 8856 1542

AYRES, Dean Matthew. b 68. Bris Univ BSc89 Spurgeon's Coll CertHE96. Ridley Hall Cam 00. **d** 02 **p** 03. C Epsom Common Ch Ch *Guildf* from 02. *278 The Greenway, Epsom KT18 7JF* Tel (01372) 803916 Mobile 07779-584045 E-mail dma@ntlworld.com

✠**AZARIAH, The Rt Revd Samuel.** Bp Raiwind; Moderator Ch of Pakistan. *17 Warris Road, PO Box 2319, Lahore 3, Pakistan* Tel (0092) (42) 758 8950 Fax 757 7255 E-mail bishop@nexlinx.net.pk *or* azariahs@lhr.comsats.net.pk

B

BAAR, Canon William Henry. b 19. Yale Univ BA42 BD45 MA48 PhD53 DD77. Seabury-Western Th Sem STM55. **d** 54 **p** 54. USA 54-60; Chapl Chicago Univ 54-60; R Glencoe St Eliz 60-66; R La Grange Em 66-86; Chapl Venice w Trieste *Eur* 86-93; Can Malta Cathl 89-93; USA from 93; R Chicago St Eliz from 99. *114 Briarwood Lakes, Oak Brook, IL 60523, USA* Tel (001) (603) 654 1893

BABB, Canon Geoffrey. b 42. Man Univ BSc64 MA74 Linacre Coll Ox BA67. Ripon Hall Ox 65. **d** 68 **p** 69. C Heywood St Luke *Man* 68-71; P-in-c Loundsley Green Ascension CD *Derby* 71-76; TV Old Brampton and Loundsley Green 76-77; TV Stafford St Mary and St Chad *Lich* 77-79; TV Stafford 79-88; Soc Resp Officer 77-88; Preb Lich Cathl 87-88; P-in-c Salford Sacred Trin *Man* 88-99; Dir CME 88-99; Hon Can Man Cathl from 89; P-in-c Wythenshawe St Martin 99; P-in-c Newall Green St Fran 99; TR Wythenshawe from 99. *St Martin's Vicarage, 2 Blackcarr Road, Manchester M23 1LX* Tel 0161-998 3408 E-mail geoff@gbabb.fsnet.co.uk

BABBAGE, Canon Stuart Barton. b 16. AM95. St Jo Coll Auckland 35 Univ of NZ BA35 MA36 K Coll Lon PhD42. Tyndale Hall Bris 37 ACT ThD50. **d** 39 **p** 40. C Havering-atte-Bower *Chelmsf* 39-41; Tutor and Lect Oak Hill Th Coll 39-41; Chapl-in-Chief RAF 42-46; Australia 46-63; Dean Sydney 47-53; Dean Melbourne 53-62; Prin Ridley Coll Melbourne 53-63; USA 63-73; V Atlanta and Austell 63-65; Visiting Prof Columbia Th Sem 63-67; Pres Conwell Th Sch Philadelphia 67-69; Vice-Pres and Dean Gordon-Conwell Th Sem 69-73; Australia from 73; Master New Coll Univ of NSW 73-82; Registrar ACT 77-92; rtd 83; Hon Can Sydney from 83. *46 St Thomas Street, Waverley, NSW, Australia 2024* Tel (0061) (2) 9665 1882

BABINGTON, Canon Gervase Hamilton. b 30. Keble Coll Ox BA57 MA57. Wells Th Coll 55. **d** 57 **p** 58. C Sheff St Geo and St Steph *Sheff* 57-60; P-in-c Manor Park CD 60-65; R Waddington *Linc* 65-81; RD Graffoe 74-81; Can and Preb Linc Cathl 77-95; V Gainsborough All SS 81-90; RD Corringham 82-87; R Walesby 90-95; rtd 95; Perm to Offic *Linc* 95-98. *15 Highfields, Nettleham, Lincoln LN2 2ST* Tel (01522) 595702

BABINGTON, Peter Gervase. b 69. Aston Univ BSc91 Birm Univ MPhil03. Cuddesdon Coll BTh98. **d** 98 **p** 99. C Salter Street and Shirley *Birm* 98-02; V Bournville from 02. *The Vicarage, 61 Linden Road, Birmingham B30 1JT* Tel 0121-472 1209 *or* 472 7215 E-mail pb@fish.co.uk

BACH, Mrs Frances Mary. b 48. Open Univ BA AIL. CITC BTh. **d** 94 **p** 95. NSM Ballynure and Ballyeaston *Conn* 94-96; C Larne and Inver 96-99; C Glynn w Raloo 96-99; I Armoy w Loughguile and Drumtullagh from 99. *The Rectory, 181 Glenshesk Road, Armoy, Ballymoney BT53 8RJ* Tel (028) 2075 1226 *or* 2082 3348

BACH, John Edward Goulden. b 40. JP. Dur Univ BA66 DipH69. Cranmer Hall Dur 66. **d** 69 **p** 70. C Bradf Cathl *Bradf* 69-72; Chapl and Lect NUU 73-84; Chapl and Lect Ulster Univ from 84. *The Anglican Chaplaincy, 70 Hopefield Avenue, Portrush BT56 8HE* Tel (028) 2075 1226, 2032 4549 *or* 2082 3348 Fax 2032 4904 E-mail revjegbach@hotmail.com

BACHELL, Kenneth George. b 22. Lon Univ BD49. K Coll Lon 55. **d** 56 **p** 57. C Bitterne Park *Win* 56-60; C-in-c Andover St Mich CD 60-64; V Andover St Mich 64-68; V Southampton St Alb 68-76; Warden Dioc Conf Ho Crawshawbooth *Man* 76-79; P-in-c Crawshawbooth 76-79; Inchinhurst *Win* 79-83; V Froyle and Holybourne 83-87; rtd 87; Perm to Offic *Blackb* 88-98. *18 Cherrylea, Auchterarder PH3 1QG* Tel (01764) 663824

BACHMANN, Douglas Paul. b 49. **d** 75 **p** 76. USA 75-77 and from 79; C Alverstoke *Portsm* 77-79. *1141 Roxie Lane, Walnut Creek, CA 94596-1806, USA*

BACK, Esther Elaine. *See* McCAFFERTY, Mrs Esther Elaine

BÄCKELIN, Miss Maria <u>Katarina</u>. b 63. Lund Univ Sweden MDiv92. Lund Inst Past Th 92. **p** 93. Sweden 93-97; C Åre 93-95; Asst P Barkåkra 95-97; Asst P Swedish Seamen's Ch from 97; NSM Bermondsey Deanery *S'wark* from 02. *Swedish Seamen's Church, 120 Lower Road, London SE16 2UB* Tel (020) 7237 1956 Fax 7231 0235

BACKHOUSE, Alan Eric. b 37. Keble Coll Ox BA61 MA67. Tyndale Hall Bris 61. **d** 64 **p** 65. C Burnage St Marg *Man* 64-67; C Cheadle Hulme St Andr *Ches* 67-70; V Buglawton 70-80; V New Ferry 80-87; V Tarvin 87-93; V Knypersley *Lich* 93-99; Patr Sec Ch Soc Trust 99-00; C Watford *St Alb* 99-02; rtd 02. *Perelandra, Church Pitch, Llandyssil, Montgomery SY16 6LQ* Tel (01686) 669963

BACKHOUSE, Colin. b 41. MCSD82 Birm Poly BA67. Oak Hill Th Coll DipHE87. **d** 87 **p** 88. C Branksome St Clem *Sarum* 87-91; P-in-c Bluntisham cum Earith w Colne and Woodhurst *Ely* 91-92; R from 92. *The Rectory, Rectory Road, Bluntisham, Huntingdon PE28 3LN* Tel (01487) 740456 Fax 842233 E-mail c.backhouse@ntlworld.com

BACKHOUSE, John. b 30. Univ Coll Southn BA50. Wycliffe Hall Ox 51. **d** 53 **p** 54. C Eccleston St Luke *Liv* 53-55; C Maghull 55-58; V Lathom 58-64; Area Sec CMS 64-78; Dios Linc and Ely 64-71; Leic 72-78; Pet 72-75; Cov 75-78; V Thorpe Acre w Dishley *Leic* 78-83; R Ab Kettleby Gp 83-89; P-in-c Bitteswell 89-94; RD Guthlaxton II 90-94; rtd 94; Perm to Offic *Leic* from 94. *29 Peashill Close, Sileby, Loughborough LE12 7PT* Tel (01509) 812016

BACKHOUSE, Jonathan Roland. b 60. Jes Coll Cam BA82 MA85. Trin Coll Bris 01. **d** 03. C Nailsea H Trin *B & W* from 03. *26 St Mary's Grove, Nailsea, Bristol BS48 4NQ* E-mail jcbackhouse@bigfoot.com

BACKHOUSE, Robert. b 35. ALCD70. **d** 70 **p** 71. C Harold Wood *Chelmsf* 70-74; Publicity Sec CPAS 74-78; rtd 00; Perm to Offic *Sarum* from 01. *4 Silver Street, Wilton, Salisbury SP2 0HX* Tel (01722) 741358

BACON, David Gary. b 62. Leic Univ BA83 Southn Univ BTh88. Sarum & Wells Th Coll 85. **d** 88 **p** 89. C Bromley St Mark *Roch* 88-92; C Lynton, Brendon, Countisbury, Lynmouth etc *Ex* 92; TV 92-95; P-in-c Lapford, Nymet Rowland and Coldridge 95-99; P-in-c Dartford St Alb *Roch* from 99. *St Alban's Vicarage, 51 Watling Street, Dartford DA1 1RW* Tel (01322) 224052
E-mail david.bacon@tesco.net

BACON, Derek Robert Alexander. b 44. Birkbeck Coll Lon DAC87 CACP89 BA92 MSc94. TCD Div Sch 69. **d** 71 **p** 72. C Templemore *D & R* 71-73; V Choral Derry Cathl 72-73; C Heeley *Sheff* 74-76; V Sheff Abbeydale St Pet 76-82; Chapl Gt Ormond Street Hosp for Children NHS Trust 82-95; Visiting Fell Ulster Univ 95-97. *14A Heathmount, Portstewart BT55 7AP* Tel (028) 7083 4987 E-mail d.bacon@ulst.ac.uk

BACON, Eric Arthur. b 23. Qu Coll Birm 68. **d** 69 **p** 70. C Linc St Pet-at-Gowts and St Andr *Linc* 69-71; C Asterby Gp 71-74; V Anwick 74-78; V S Kyme 74-78; P-in-c Kirkby Laythorpe w Asgarby 76-78; P-in-c Ewerby w Evedon 76-78; P-in-c Burton Pedwardine 76-78; V Messingham 78-89; rtd 89; Perm to Offic *Linc* 89-01. *2 Curtois Close, Branston, Lincoln LN4 1LJ* Tel (01522) 794265

BACON, Janet Ann. b 57. Man Univ LLB78. NTMTC 95. **d** 98 **p** 99. NSM Stifford *Chelmsf* 98-01; P-in-c Sandbach Heath w Wheelock *Ches* from 01. *Heath Vicarage, School Lane, Sandbach CW11 2LS* Tel (01270) 768826 E-mail j.bacon@virgin.net

BACON, John Martindale. b 22. St Aid Birkenhead 54. **d** 57 **p** 58. C Bury St Paul *Man* 57-59; C-in-c Clifton Green St Thos CD 59-71; V Astley Bridge 71-87; rtd 87; Perm to Offic *Man* from 87-00 and *Blackb* from 87. *21 Lichen Close, Charnock Richard, Chorley PR7 5TT* Tel (01257) 792535
E-mail johnandon.bacon@virgin.net

BACON, Lionel William Rupert. b 06. OBE95. Univ Coll Dur LTh31 BA32 MA40. St Paul's Coll Burgh 27. **d** 33 **p** 34. C Auckland St Pet *Dur* 33-35; Argentina 35-39; Hon C Kentish Town St Martin w St Andr *Lon* 39-40; Hon C Castle Bromwich SS Mary and Marg *Birm* 40-41; Org Sec (SW Area) CCCS 41-47; Kenya 47-52; R Whitfield *Newc* 53-55; V Ninebanks 53-55; PC Carshield 53-55; R Laceby *Linc* 55-59; V Irby on Humber 55-59; V Ancaster 59-73; V Honington 59-73; rtd 73; Perm to Offic *Chich* from 77. *Lomas House, 43 Wordsworth Road, Worthing BN11 3JA* Tel (01903) 213647

BADDELEY, The Ven Martin James. b 36. Keble Coll Ox BA60 MA64. Linc Th Coll 60. **d** 62 **p** 63. C Stretford St Matt *Man* 62-64; Lect Linc Th Coll 65-66; Tutor 66-69; Chapl 68-69; Chapl Fitzw Coll and New Hall Cam 69-74; Can Res Roch Cathl *Roch* 74-80; Hon Can 80-96; Prin S'wark Ord Course 80-94; Co-Prin SEITE 94-96; Adn Reigate *S'wark* 96-00; rtd 00. *2 Glendower, Fossil Bank, Upper Colwall, Malvern WR13 6PJ* Tel (01684) 569761

BADEN, Peter Michael. b 35. CCC Cam BA59 MA62. Cuddesdon Coll 58. **d** 60 **p** 61. C Hunslet St Mary and Stourton *Ripon* 60-63; Lic to Offic *Wakef* 63-64; C E Grinstead St Swithun *Chich* 65-68; V Brighton St Martin 68-74; TR Brighton Resurr 74-76; R Westbourne 76-84; V Stansted 76-84; V Copthorne 84-91; V Clifton *Carl* 91-00; P-in-c Mosser 99-00; rtd 00; Perm to Offic *Pet* from 00; *Carl* from 01. *3 Poppyfield Court, Thrapston, Kettering NN14 4TS* Tel (01832) 734897

BADGER, Canon Edwin. b 09. Bris Univ BA32 MA86 Lon Univ BD57. St Boniface Warminster 28. **d** 34 **p** 35. C Kidderminster St Jo *Worc* 34-36; Japan 36-40; Australia from 40; Hon Can Wangaratta 69-76; rtd 76. *Providence Village, Griffiths Street, Bacchus Marsh, Vic, Australia 3340* Tel (0061) (3) 5367 2316

BADGER, Mark. b 65. Birm Univ BTh96. Qu Coll Birm 93. **d** 96 **p** 97. C Barbourne *Worc* 96-01; P-in-c *Worc* St Geo w St Mary Magd from 01. *St George's Vicarage, St George's Square, Worcester WR1 1HX* Tel (01905) 22698
E-mail revmarkb@ukonline.co.uk

BADHAM, Prof Paul Brian Leslie. b 42. Jes Coll Ox BA65 MA69 Jes Coll Cam BA68 MA72 Birm Univ PhD73. Westcott Ho Cam 66. **d** 68 **p** 69. C Edgbaston St Bart *Birm* 68-69; C Rubery 69-73; Lic to Offic *St D* from 73; Lect Th Univ of Wales (Lamp) 73-83; Sen Lect 83-88; Reader 88-91; Prof Th from 91. *University of Wales, Lampeter SA48 7ED* Tel (01570) 424708

BAGE, Damon John. b 71. Teesside Univ BA95. St Steph Ho Ox 01. **d** 03. C Stockton St Jo *Dur* from 03. *243 Darlington Lane, Stockton-on-Tees TS19 8AA* Tel (01642) 676323
E-mail damon_j_bage@hotmail.com

BAGGALEY, Canon Dennis. b 31. Dur Univ BA53 Liv Univ MA79. St Jo Coll Dur DipTh56. **d** 56 **p** 57. C Pennington *Man* 56-59; C N Meols *Liv* 59-60; V Bacup Ch Ch *Man* 60-65; R Burnage St Nic 65-71; V Onchan *S & M* 71-80; Can St German's Cathl 80-89; RD Douglas 82-86; rtd 96; Perm to Offic *S & M* from 96. *Little Hamlet, The Level, Colby, Isle of Man IM9 4AL* Tel (01624) 836828

BAGLEY, Canon John Marmaduke Erskine. b 08. G&C Coll Cam BA30 MA36. Ely Th Coll 30. **d** 32 **p** 33. C Swindon New Town *Bris* 32-36; C Cambridge St Mary Less *Ely* 36-38; Chapl Jubbulpore Ch 38-44; C Littleham w Exmouth *Ex* 44-46; R Huntingdon All SS w St Jo *Ely* 46-63; Chapl HM Borstal Gaynes Hall 52-55; V Ely 63-74; Chapl Ely Cathl 63-74; RD Ely 66-71; Hon Can Ely Cathl 68-74; P-in-c Chettisham 68-74; rtd 74; Perm to Offic *St E* 74-77; *Ely* from 77; *Nor* from 91. *18 Slade Court, Runton House Close, West Runton, Cromer NR27 9RA* Tel (01263) 837685

BAGLEY, Richard Alexander. b 25. New Coll Ox BA51 MA55 K Coll Cam MA57. Cuddesdon Coll 51. **d** 53 **p** 54. C Cambridge St Mary Less *Ely* 53-58; Hon C Pimlico St Mary Graham-street *Lon* 58-64. *Flat 2, 73 Sinclair Road, London W14 0NR* Tel (020) 7602 1951

BAGLEY, Roy Victor. b 33. **d** 03. OLM Chasetown *Lich* from 03. *65 Oakdene Road, Chasetown, Burntwood WS7 8SA* Tel (01543) 686000 E-mail roy.bagley@lineone.net

BAGOTT, Paul Andrew. b 61. Leeds Univ BA85. Westcott Ho Cam 86. **d** 88 **p** 89. C Chingford SS Pet and Paul *Chelmsf* 88-91; C Pimlico St Sav *Lon* 91-95; P-in-c Clerkenwell H Redeemer and St Mark 95-01; V Clerkenwell H Redeemer from 02; V Clerkenwell St Mark from 02. *Holy Redeemer Clergy House, 24 Exmouth Market, London EC1R 4QE* Tel (020) 7837 1861 Fax 7278 0829 E-mail holyredeemer@freeuk.com

BAGSHAW, Paul Stanley. b 55. Selw Coll Cam BA78 MA81 Man Univ CQSW80. N Ord Course 85. **d** 88 **p** 89. Ind Missr *Sheff* 86-90; C Handsworth Woodhouse 88-90; NSM 91-93; C Newark S'well 93-96; P-in-c Ordsall from 96. *The Rectory, All Hallows Street, Retford DN22 7TP* Tel (01777) 702515

BAGSHAWE, John Allen. b 45. Dur Univ BA70 DipTh71. Cranmer Hall Dur 67. **d** 71 **p** 72. C Bridlington Priory *York* 71-75; C N Ferriby 75-79; V Kingston upon Hull St Matt w St Barn from 79; AD W Hull from 00. *St Matthew's Vicarage, Boulevard, Hull HU3 2TA* Tel (01482) 326573
E-mail allen@stmatthews.karoo.co.uk

BAGULEY, Henry. b 23. Qu Coll Birm 55. **d** 58 **p** 59. C Wilmslow *Ches* 58-61; V Kelsall 61-75; V New Brighton St Jas 75-88; rtd 88; Perm to Offic *Ches* from 88 and *Lich* from 93. *The Meadows, Nantwich Road, Whitchurch SY13 4AA* Tel (01948) 662692

BAGULEY, Paul. b 36. NTMTC 94. **d** 98 **p** 99. NSM N Harrow St Alb *Lon* from 98. *86 Central Avenue, Pinner HA5 5BP* Tel (020) 8866 3454

BAHAMAS AND THE TURKS AND CAICOS ISLANDS, Bishop of the. See GOMEZ, The Most Revd Drexel Wellington

BAILES, Kenneth. b 35. Dur Univ BA69 DipTh71 DPhil. **d** 71 **p** 72. C Redcar *York* 71-73; TV Redcar w Kirkleatham 73-74; P-in-c Appleton Roebuck w Acaster Selby 74-80; P-in-c Sutton on the Forest 80-82; R Stamford Bridge Gp of Par 82-90; V Healaugh w Wighill, Bilbrough and Askham Richard 90-95; rtd 95; Perm to Offic *York* from 98. *The Peace Centre, Inholmes, Leeds Road, Tadcaster LS24 9LP* Tel 07764-614139 (mobile) E-mail kb13@btinternet.com

BAILEY, Adrian Richard. b 57. St Jo Coll Dur 89. **d** 91 **p** 92. C Oswestry St Oswald *Lich* 91-94; C Shobnall 94-99; C Burton 94-99; Town Cen Chapl 94-99; P-in-c Shobnall 99-01; P-in-c Hengoed w Gobowen from 01; Chapl Robert Jones/Agnes Hunt Orthopaedic NHS Trust from 01. *The Vicarage, Old Chirk Road, Gobowen, Oswestry SY11 3LL* Tel (01691) 661226
E-mail arb2@totalise.co.uk

BAILEY, Alan George. b 40. Open Univ BA93. Ripon Hall Ox 62. **d** 64 **p** 65. C Formby H Trin *Liv* 64-67; C Upholland 67-70; P-in-c Edgehill St Dunstan 70-74; V 74-81; RD Toxteth 78-81; Perm to Offic 81-83; Asst Chapl Liv Cathl 83-85; C Liv Our Lady and St Nic w St Anne 85-89; V Waddington *Bradf* from 89. *The Vicarage, Slaidburn Road, Waddington, Clitheroe BB7 3JQ* Tel (01200) 423589

BAILEY, Andrew Henley. b 57. AKC78. Sarum & Wells Th Coll 79. **d** 80 **p** 81. C Romsey *Win* 80-83; V Bournemouth St Alb 83-93; R Milton from 93. *The Rectory, Church Lane, New Milton BH25 6QN* Tel (01425) 615150 Fax as telephone
E-mail andrew@miltonrectory.freeserve.co.uk

BAILEY, Andrew John. b 37. Trin Coll Cam BA61 MA. Ridley Hall Cam 60. **d** 63 **p** 64. C Drypool *York* 63-66; C Melton Mowbray w Thorpe Arnold *Leic* 66-69; C-in-c Skelmersdale Ecum Cen *Liv* 69-79; V Langley Mill *Derby* 79-90; V Gt Faringdon w Lt Coxwell *Ox* 90-02; AD Vale of White Horse 97-01; rtd 02; Perm to Offic *Ches* from 02. *58 Manor Road, Sandbach CW11 2ND* Tel (01270) 764076
E-mail baileyaj@talk21.com

BAILEY, Canon Angela. b 61. Kent Univ BA82. Qu Coll Birm 83. **dss** 85 **d** 87 **p** 94. Reculver and Herne Bay St Bart *Cant* 85-88; Par Dn 87-88; Asst Chapl Hull Univ *York* 88-92; Sen Chapl 94-98; Perm to Offic 92-94; P-in-c Rowley w Skidby from 98; Sen Chapl E Riding Community Health Trust from 98; Can and Preb York Minster *York* from 03. *Rowley Rectory, Old Village Road, Little Weighton, Cottingham HU20 3US* Tel (01482) 843317
E-mail angela@petermichael.karoo.co.uk

BAILEY, Anthony. b 27. Univ of Wales (Lamp) BA51. Ely Th Coll 51. **d** 53 **p** 54. C Barkingside H Trin *Chelmsf* 53-55; Chapl W Buckland Sch Barnstaple 55-59; R Machen *Mon* 59-66; Min Can Bris Cathl *Bris* 66-84; Chapl Bris Cathl Sch 66-84; Succ Bris Cathl *Bris* 66-84; P-in-c Maenclochog w Henry's Moat and Mynachlogddu etc *St D* 83-90; V 90-92; rtd 92; P-in-c Llanglydwen and Llanfyrnach *St D* from 94. *Charing Cross, Llangolman, Clunderwen SA66 7XN* Tel (01437) 532430 Mobile 07974-557912 E-mail anthony_bailey@lineone.net

BAILEY, Bertram Arthur. b 20. Tyndale Hall Bris 65. **d** 67 **p** 68. C Bath St Luke *B & W* 67-72; C Bickenhill w Elmdon *Birm* 72-73; R N Tawton *Ex* 73-79; R N Tawton and Bondleigh 79-87; rtd 87; Perm to Offic *B & W* from 87; Clergy Retirement and Widows' Officer from 89. *4 Uphill Road South, Uphill, Weston-super-Mare BS23 4SD* Tel (01934) 633552

BAILEY, Brendan John. b 61. Strathclyde Univ BSc83 K Coll Lon MA99. Ripon Coll Cuddesdon BTh93. **d** 94 **p** 95. C Purley *Ox* 94-99; R Nettlebed w Bix, Highmoor, Pishill etc from 99. *The Rectory, High Street, Nettlebed, Henley-on-Thames RG9 5DD* Tel (01491) 641575 E-mail baileybj@freeuk.com

BAILEY, Canon Brian Constable. b 36. K Coll Lon AKC62. **d** 63 **p** 64. C Mill Hill Jo Keble Ch *Lon* 63-66; C Gt Stanmore 66-69; C Gt Marlow *Ox* 69-72; R Burghfield 72-81; R Wokingham All SS 81-96; Hon Can Ch Ch 94-96; TV Pinhoe and Broadclyst *Ex* 96-00; rtd 00; V of Close Sarum Cathl *Sarum* 00-01. *2 Rose Cottages, Maudlin Road, Totnes TQ9 5TG* Tel (01803) 865992 E-mail bcbailey@ukonline.co.uk

BAILEY, Darren Stephen. b 65. Poly of Wales BA87 Sheff Poly CertTESOL89 Nottm Univ BTh. Linc Th Coll. **d** 95 **p** 96. C Mexborough *Sheff* 95-98; P-in-c St Weonards w Orcop, Garway, Tretire etc *Heref* 98-03. *Address temp unknown*

BAILEY, Canon David Charles. b 52. Linc Coll Ox BA75 MA78 MSc77. St Jo Coll Nottm BA79. **d** 80 **p** 81. C Worksop St Jo *S'well* 80-83; C Edgware *Lon* 83-87; V S Cave and Ellerker w Broomfleet *York* 87-97; RD Howden 91-97; V Beverley Minster from 97; P-in-c Routh from 97; Can and Preb York Minster from 98. *The Minster Vicarage, Highgate, Beverley HU17 0DN* Tel (01482) 881434 E-mail dbailey_52@hotmail.com

BAILEY, Dennis. b 53. Man Univ BEd74 BMus74. St Jo Coll Nottm BTh79. **d** 79 **p** 80. C Netherley Ch Ch CD *Liv* 79-83; S Africa from 83. *PO Box 635, Hilton, 3245 South Africa* Tel (0027) (331) 431093

BAILEY, Derek Gilbert. b 42. Div Hostel Dub 65. **d** 68 **p** 69. C Cork St Luke w St Ann *C, C & R* 68-72; CF from 72; Perm to Offic *York* from 98. *clo MOD Chaplains (Army)* Tel (01980) 615804 Fax 615800

BAILEY, Derek William. b 39. Lon Univ DipTh64 Man Univ BA96. Cranmer Hall Dur 64. **d** 67 **p** 68. C Sutton *Liv* 67-69; C Chapel-en-le-Frith *Derby* 69-73; V Hadfield 73-90; R Collyhurst *Man* 90-95; V Chaddesden St Mary *Derby* 95-02; rtd 02; Perm to Offic *York* from 03. *187 Bishopthorpe Road, York YO23 1PD* Tel (01904) 628080

BAILEY, Canon Edward Ian. b 35. CCC Cam BA59 MA63 Bris Univ MA69 PhD77. United Th Coll Bangalore 59 Westcott Ho Cam 61. **d** 63 **p** 64. C Newc St Jo *Newc* 63-65; Asst Chapl Marlborough Coll 65-68; Perm to Offic *Bris* 69-70; R Winterbourne from 70; P-in-c Winterbourne Down 75-81; RD Stapleton 77-83; Chapl Frenchay Hosp Bris 79-84; Hon Can Bris Cathl *Bris* from 84; Warden of Readers from 95; Visiting Prof Middx Univ *Lon* from 97. *The Rectory, 58 High Street, Winterbourne, Bristol BS36 1JQ* Tel (01454) 772131 or 776518 E-mail eibailey@csircs.freeserve.co.uk

BAILEY, Edward Peter. b 35. Nottm Univ MA93. Qu Coll Birm. **d** 62 **p** 63. C Ordsall *S'well* 62-66; C Clifton w Glapton 66-71; V Lady Bay 71-83; Relig Affairs Adv to Radio Trent 83-85; C Gedling 86-89; C Bilborough St Jo 89-00; rtd 00; Perm to Offic *York* from 00. *Cragside Cottage, 18 Egton Road, Aislaby, Whitby YO21 1SU*

BAILEY, Mrs Elizabeth Carmen. b 45. EAMTC 89. **d** 93 **p** 94. NSM Roughton and Felbrigg, Metton, Sustead etc *Nor* 93-95 and 99-02; NSM Gresham 95-99; P-in-c Roughton and Felbrigg, Metton, Sustead etc from 02. *5 Warren Road, Southrepps, Norwich NR11 8UN* Tel (01263) 834525

BAILEY, Eric Arthur. b 14. AKC37. **d** 37 **p** 38. C S'wark St Geo *S'wark* 37-39; C Waltham Cross *St Alb* 39-41; C Diss *Nor* 41-42; Chapl CF (EC) 42-43; C Kingsbury *Birm* 44-45; V Dordon 45-52; R Londesborough *York* 52-60; P-in-c Nunburnholme 53-54; R 54-60; P-in-c Burnby 53-54; R 54-60; V Gt w Lt Ouseburn *Ripon* 60-65; V Stonegate *Chich* 65-79; rtd 79; Perm to Offic *St E* 81-88. *Hill End, Sapiston, Bury St Edmunds IP31 1RR* Tel (01359) 269518

BAILEY, Frederick Hugh. b 18. Keble Coll Ox BA40. Linc Th Coll 40. **d** 42 **p** 43. C Boultham *Linc* 42-49; Chapl Rauceby Hosp Lincs from 49; R Quarrington w Old Sleaford *Linc* 49-84; R Silk Willoughby 57-84; rtd 84; Perm to Offic *Linc* 99-02. *1 Willow Close, Scopwick, Lincoln LN4 3PJ* Tel (01522) 321127

BAILEY, Ian Arthur. b 53. **d** 01 **p** 02. NSM Clifton H Trin, St Andr and St Pet *Bris* from 01. *5 Queens Gate, Stoke Bishop, Bristol BS9 1TZ* Tel 0117-968 6251

BAILEY, Canon Ivan John. b 33. Keble Coll Ox BA57 MA65. St Steph Ho Ox DipTh59. **d** 59 **p** 60. C Ipswich All Hallows *St E* 59-62; Clerical Sec CEMS 62-66; V Cringleford *Nor* 66-81; RD Humbleyard 73-81; R Colney 80-81; Relig Adv Anglia TV 81-91; P-in-c Kirby Bedon w Bixley and Whitlingham *Nor* 81-92; Hon Can Nor Cathl 84-98; Chapl St Andr Hosp Norwich 92-94; Chapl Mental Health Unit Nor HA 92-94; Chapl Norfolk Mental Health Care NHS Trust 94-98; rtd 98; Perm to Offic *Nor* from 98. *21 Cranleigh Rise, Norwich NR4 6PQ* Tel (01603) 453565

BAILEY, Ms Jane Rome. b 50. Univ of Wales (Ban) BA99 BTh03. Ban Ord Course 00. **d** 03. C Deanery of Llifon and Talybolion *Ban* from 03. *17 Maes Cynlas, Ty Croes, Rhosneigr LL63 5SN* Tel (01407) 811064 E-mail jane@charity.fslife.com

BAILEY, John Ernest. b 32. Leeds Univ BA57. Coll of Resurr Mirfield 57. **d** 59 **p** 60. C Newbury St Nic *Ox* 59-62; Australia 62-63; V Uffington w Woolstone and Baulking *Ox* 63-70; P-in-c Gt w Lt Oakley *Pet* 70-72; TV Corby SS Pet and Andr w Gt and Lt Oakley 70-72; Chapl Cen Hosp Warw 72-94; Chapl Cen Weston and Abbeyfields 82-90; Chapl Cen Weston 90-94; Chapl S Warks Mental Health Services NHS Trust 94-96; rtd 96; Perm to Offic *Cov* from 96. *22 Hill Wootton Road, Leek Wootton, Warwick CV35 7QL* Tel (01926) 853528

BAILEY, John Robert. b 40. St Jo Coll Cam BA62 MA66 Nottm Univ MEd77. S'wark Ord Course 68. **d** 69 **p** 70. NSM Plumstead Wm Temple Ch Abbey Wood CD *S'wark* 69-70; Lon Sec Chr Educn Movement 69-71; NSM Markyate Street *St Alb* 71-72; RE Adv *Linc* 72-80; Distr Insp Man 80-83; Co Chief Insp Beds Co Coun 83-90; Dioc Schs Officer 91-94; Dioc Dir of Educn from 95; Gen Preacher from 97. *Juniper Cottage, Vicarage Lane, Wellingore, Lincoln LN5 0JF* Tel (01522) 810317 or 569600 E-mail john.bailey@lincoln.anglican.org

✠**BAILEY, The Rt Revd Jonathan Sansbury.** b 40. Trin Coll Cam BA61 MA65. Ridley Hall Cam 62. **d** 65 **p** 66 **c** 92. C Sutton *Liv* 65-68; C Warrington St Paul 68-71; Warden Marrick Priory *Ripon* 71-76; V Wetherby 76-82; Adn Southend *Chelmsf* 82-92; Suff Bp Dunwich *St E* 92-95; Bp Derby from 95; Clerk of the Closet from 96. *The Bishop's House, 6 King Street, Duffield, Belper DE56 4EU* Tel (01332) 840132 or 346744 Fax 842743 or 295810 E-mail bishopderby@clara.net

BAILEY, Joyce Mary Josephine. See OUTEN, Mrs Joyce Mary Josephine

BAILEY, Judith Elizabeth Anne. b 61. RGN RSCN84. Trin Coll Carmarthen DipHE00. **d** 99 **p** 00. OLM Blyth Valley *St E* from 99. *13 Oak Way, Halesworth IP19 8EB* Tel (01986) 872747

BAILEY, Justin Mark. b 55. Birm Univ BA77 Wolv Poly PGCE78 Southn Univ MTh97. Ripon Coll Cuddesdon 90. **d** 92 **p** 93. C Oakdale *Sarum* 92-96; P-in-c Milton Abbas, Hilton w Cheselbourne etc from 96; P-in-c Piddletrenthide w Plush, Alton Pancras etc from 02. *The Rectory, Lower Ansty, Dorchester DT2 7PX* Tel (01258) 880372

BAILEY, Mark David. b 62. Ripon Coll Cuddesdon 87. **d** 90 **p** 91. C Leigh Park *Portsm* 90-93; C Fleet *Guildf* 93-95; TV Basingstoke *Win* 95-00; P-in-c Twyford and Owslebury and Morestead from 00. *The Vicarage, Church Lane, Twyford, Winchester SO21 1NT* Tel (01962) 712208 E-mail the.baileys@ukgateway.net

BAILEY, Mark Robert. b 60. St Paul's Cheltenham BA81. Trin Coll Bris BA89. **d** 89 **p** 90. C Heigham H Trin *Nor* 89-94; Chapl UEA 92-93; TV Cheltenham St Mary, St Matt, St Paul and H Trin *Glouc* from 94. *100 Hewlett Road, Cheltenham GL52 6AR* Tel (01242) 582398 or 262306 Fax 581459 E-mail mark.bailey@trinityuk.org

BAILEY, Martin Tristram. b 57. Oak Hill Th Coll DipHE91. **d** 91 **p** 92. C Brundall w Braydeston and Postwick *Nor* 91-95; TV Plymouth St Andr and St Paul Stonehouse *Ex* from 95; Chapl St Dunstan's Abbey Sch Plymouth from 02. *88 Durnford Street, Plymouth PL1 3QW* Tel (01752) 228114 E-mail martin@standrewschurch.org.uk

BAILEY, Nicholas Andrew. b 55. Nottm Univ CertEd80 Open Univ BA84. Ripon Coll Cuddesdon 88. **d** 90 **p** 91. C Guisborough *York* 90-92; Chapl Foremark Prep Sch Derby from 92. *Sycamore Cottage, Foremark, Milton, Derby DE65 6TB* Tel (01283) 703558

BAILEY, Norman Gerald. b 25. **d** 83 **p** 84. Hon C Kingswood *Bris* 83-90; Hon C E Bris 90-97; Perm to Offic from 97. *71 Lincombe Road, Downend, Bristol BS16 5US* Tel 0117-957 2822

BAILEY, Patricia Laura. b 49. CertEd72. NTMTC 95. **d** 98 **p** 99. NSM Hackney Marsh *Lon* 98-01; NSM S Hackney St Jo w Ch Ch from 01. *20 Bushberry Road, London E9 5SX* Tel (020) 8533 5423

BAILEY, Peter. See BAILEY, Edward Peter

BAILEY, Canon Peter Robin. b 43. St Jo Coll Dur BA64. Trin Coll Bris 72. **d** 74 **p** 75. C Corby St Columba *Pet* 74-77; C Bishopsworth *Bris* 77-82; V Sea Mills 82-97; RD Westbury and Severnside 91-97; P-in-c Bishopston 97-98; P-in-c Bris St Andr w St Bart 97-98; TR Bishopston and St Andrews from 98; Hon Can Bris Cathl from 97. *The Vicarage, Walsingham Road, St Andrews, Bristol BS6 5BT* Tel 0117-924 8683 Fax as telephone E-mail peterandheather@blueyonder.co.uk

BAILEY, Richard William. b 38. Man Univ BSc59. Ripon Hall Ox 63. d 65 p 66. C Tonge *Man* 65-68; C Stretford St Matt 68-71; R Abbey Hey 71-80; V E Crompton 80-86; V Chadderton St Matt 86-98; R Stand from 98. *Stand Rectory, Church Lane, Whitefield, Manchester M45 7NF* Tel 0161-766 2619
E-mail bailey.ditchash@tesco.net

BAILEY, Richard William. b 47. All Nations Chr Coll DBMS75 Oak Hill Th Coll BA84. d 84 p 85. C Huyton St Geo *Liv* 84-87; V Wombridge *Lich* 87-97; P-in-c Shenstone from 97; P-in-c Stonnall from 97. *The Vicarage, St John's Hill, Shenstone, Lichfield WS14 0JB* Tel (01543) 480286 Fax 480864
E-mail ricthevic@madasafish.com

BAILEY, Robert Henry. b 45. FCA69. N Ord Course 99. d 02 p 03. NSM Dewsbury *Wakef* from 02; Sub Chapl HM Pris Leeds from 02. *16 Lumley Road, Dewsbury WF12 7DU* Tel (01924) 460072 Mobile 07973-697954
E-mail robertbailey.minster@btopenworld.co.uk

BAILEY, Robert William. b 49. Open Univ BA91. Bernard Gilpin Soc Dur 68 Lich Th Coll 69. d 72 p 73. C Stoke *Cov* 72-75; Chapl RAF 75-99; RD Calne *Sarum* 97-98; TV Cartmel Peninsula *Carl* from 99. *The Vicarage, Priest Lane, Cartmel, Grange-over-Sands LA11 6PU* Tel (01539) 536261 Fax as telephone
E-mail vicar.cartmel@virgin.net

BAILEY, Ronald William. b 12. Linc Coll Ox BA35 BSc36 MA45. Ripon Hall Ox 57. d 58 p 59. C N Stoneham *Win* 58-61; V Lamberhurst *Roch* 61-77; rtd 77. *c/o Mrs J Vernon, The Vicarage, 12 Harewood Avenue, Pokesdown BH7 6NQ*

BAILEY, Simon. b 56. Man Univ MusB Nottm Univ BCombStuds. Linc Th Coll. d 83 p 84. C Armley w New Wortley *Ripon* 83-86; C Harrogate St Wilfrid and St Luke 86-90; R Harby, Long Clawson and Hose *Leic* 90-94; V Woodhall *Bradf* 94-03; RD Calverley 98-01; R N Adelaide Ch Ch Australia from 03. *Christ Church Rectory, 35 Palmer Place, North Adelaide, S Australia 5006*

BAILEY, Stephen. b 39. Leic Univ BA61. Clifton Th Coll 61. d 62 p 63. C Wellington w Eyton *Lich* 62-66; C Rainham *Chelmsf* 66-69; V Ercall Magna *Lich* 69-75; V Rowton 69-75; RD Wrockwardine 72-75; V W Bromwich Gd Shep w St Jo 75-83; P-in-c W Bromwich St Phil 80-81; V 81-83; R Chadwell *Chelmsf* 83-96; Area Warden Ords Brentwood, Basildon & Thurrock 91-96; RD Thurrock 92-96; V Galleywood Common from 96. *Galleywood Vicarage, 450 Beehive Lane, Chelmsford CM2 8RN* Tel (01245) 353922
E-mail jenniferbailey@thevicarage450.fsnet.co.uk

BAILEY, Stephen John. b 57. NE Surrey Coll of Tech HNC78. Sarum & Wells Th Coll 88. d 90 p 91. C Redhill H Trin *S'wark* 90-95; Chapl E Surrey Coll 91-93; P-in-c Betchworth *S'wark* 95-00; V from 00; P-in-c Buckland 95-00; R from 00. *The Rectory, Old Reigate Road, Betchworth RH3 7DE* Tel (01737) 842102 E-mail stephenbaileyrev@compuserve.com

BAILEY, Mrs Susan Mary. b 40. F L Calder Coll Liv CertEd61. EAMTC 89. d 92 p 94. NSM Chelmsf Cathl *Chelmsf* 92-93; NSM Needham Market w Badley *St E* 93-95; NSM Belper *Derby* 96-00; NSM Allestree St Nic from 00; NSM Quarndon from 00; Morley Retreat and Conf Ho Derby from 00. *6 King Street, Duffield, Belper DE56 4EU* Tel (01332) 840132 Fax 842743

BAILEY, Mrs Yvonne Mary. b 45. Ex Univ BTh03. SW Minl Tr Course 00. d 03. C St Illogan *Truro* from 03. *Church House, 46 Bosmeor Park, Redruth TR15 3JN* Tel (01209) 218753

BAILIE, Alison Margaret. b 62. Leeds Univ LLB83. Trin Coll Bris BA98. d 98 p 99. C Halliwell St Pet *Man* from 98. *70 Orwell Road, Bolton BL1 6ET* Tel (01204) 844160

BAILLIE, Canon Frederick Alexander. b 21. FRGS Open Univ BA75 QUB MA86 PhD87. CITC 53. d 55 p 56. C Belfast St Paul *Conn* 55-59; C Dunmurry 59-61; V RAChD 57-84; I Eglantine *Conn* 61-69; I Belfast Whiterock 69-74; Hd of S Ch Miss Ballymacarrett 74-79; I Magheraculmoney *Clogh* 79-87; Dioc Communications Officer 80-86; Hon CF from 84; Can Clogh Cathl *Clogh* 85-87; rtd 87. *2 Raasay Court, Portree IV51 9TG* Tel (01478) 611376 E-mail f.baillie@amserve.com

BAILLIE, Terence John. b 46. New Coll Ox BA69 MA78 Man Univ MSc72. St Jo Coll Nottm 74. d 77 p 78. C Chadwell *Chelmsf* 77-80; C Bickenhill w Elmdon *Birm* 80-84; V Bedminster St Mich *Bris* 84-96; V Clevedon St Andr and Ch Ch *B & W* from 96. *The Vicarage, 10 Coleridge Road, Clevedon BS21 7TB* Tel (01275) 872982 E-mail terry.baillie@tesco.net

BAILY, Canon Robert Spencer Canning. b 21. G&C Coll Cam BA42 MA46. Westcott Ho Cam 42. d 44 p 45. C Sherborne w Castleton and Lillington *Sarum* 44-46; C Heacham *Nor* 46-47; C Bedford All SS *St Alb* 48-50; C-in-c Hayes St Edm CD *Lon* 50-56; R Blofield w Hemblington *Nor* 56-69; P-in-c Perlethorpe *S'well* 69-87; Dir of Educn 69-87; Hon Can S'well 87-00; rtd 87; Perm to Offic *Linc* 87-02; *S'well* 87-00. *17 Ravendale Close, Grantham NG31 8BS* Tel (01476) 568614

BAIN, Alan. b 48. Thames Poly BSc72. St Jo Coll Nottm DipTh75. d 77 p 78. C Wakef St Andr and St Mary *Wakef* 77-81; V Bath Odd Down *B & W* 81-82; P-in-c Combe Hay 81-82; V Bath Odd Down w Combe Hay from 82. *The Vicarage, 39 Frome Road, Bath BA2 2QF* Tel (01225) 832838 *or* tel and fax 835228
E-mail alanbain@stphilipstjames.org

BAIN, Andrew John. b 55. Newc Poly BA77 Edin Univ MTh89. Edin Th Coll 86. d 88 p 89. Chapl St Mary's Cathl *Edin* 88-91; C Edin St Mary 88-91; R Edin St Jas 91-98; P-in-c Edin St Marg 93-98; Dioc Dir of Ords 95-98; R Haddington from 98. *The Rectory, Church Street, Haddington EH41 3EX* Tel (01620) 822203 Fax as telephone
E-mail trinity@haddington6.freeserve.co.uk

BAIN, David Roualeyn Findlater (Roly). b 54. Bris Univ BA75. Ripon Coll Cuddesdon 76. d 78 p 79. C Perry Hill St Geo *S'wark* 78-81; Chapl Asst Guy's Hosp Lon 81-84; Succ S'wark Cathl *S'wark* 81-84; V Streatham St Paul 84-90; Perm to Offic *Bris* and *Lon* from 90. *The Vicarage, The Street, Olveston, Bristol BS35 4DA* Tel (01454) 616593 Fax as telephone

BAIN, The Ven John Stuart. b 55. Van Mildert Coll Dur BA77. Westcott Ho Cam 78. d 80 p 81. C Washington *Dur* 80-84; C Dunston 84-86; V Shiney Row 86-92; V Herrington 86-92; P-in-c Whitworth w Spennymoor 92-97; P-in-c Merrington 94-97; AD Auckland 96-02; V Spennymoor, Whitworth and Merrington 97-02; Hon Can Dur Cathl 98-02; Adn Sunderland from 02; P-in-c Hedworth 02-03; P-in-c from 03. *St Nicholas' Vicarage, Hedworth Lane, Boldon Colliery NE35 9JA* Tel 0191-536 2300 Fax 519 3369
E-mail archdeacon.of.sunderland@durham.anglican.org

BAINBRIDGE, Ms Christine Susan. b 48. St Aid Coll Dur BA70 K Coll Lon MA99. SEITE 93. d 96 p 97. C S'wark H Trin w St Matt *S'wark* 96-99; Asst to Bp Woolwich (Greenwich Area) 99-03; C Lee Gd Shep w St Pet 99-03; P-in-c Deptford St Jo w H Trin from 03. *St John's Vicarage, St John's Vale, London SE8 4EA* Tel (020) 8692 2857 E-mail christine.bainbridge@dswark.org.uk

BAINBRIDGE, David George. b 42. Wadh Coll Ox BA63 MA67 Lon Univ CertEd67. Ridley Hall Cam 84. d 86 p 87. C Downend *Bris* 86-90; TV Yate New Town 90-01; Lee Abbey Internat Students' Club Kensington from 01; Perm to Offic *Lon* from 01. *Lee Abbey International Students' Club, 57-67 Lexham Gardens, London W8 6JJ* Tel (020) 7373 7242
E-mail dandmbainbridge@tinyworld.co.uk

BAINBRIDGE, John Richard. b 35. Pemb Coll Cam BA59 MA63. Clifton Th Coll 65. d 67 p 68. C Ex St Leon w H Trin *Ex* 67-70; P-in-c Penge St Paul *Roch* 70-73; Chapl Uppingham Sch Leics 73-87; V Stevenage St Nic and Graveley *St Alb* 87-98; rtd 98. *Willowdown Cottage, 8 Laxton, Corby NN17 3AT* Tel (01780) 450308

BAINBRIDGE, Norman Harold. b 15. St Jo Coll Dur LTh38. ALCD38. d 38 p 39. C Morden *S'wark* 38-46; CF (EC) 43-46; V Bayswater *Lon* 46-58; V Muswell Hill St Jas 58-66; V Boscombe St Jo *Win* 66-80; rtd 80; Perm to Offic *Sarum* and *Win* 81-93; *Ex* 95-98. *Manormead, 12 Tilford Road, Hindhead GU26 6RA* Tel (01428) 602500

BAINBRIDGE, Richard Densham. b 49. Ch Coll Cam BA71 MA75 Edge Hill Coll of HE PGCE72 Roehampton Inst DCCD91. S'wark Ord Course 91. d 94 p 95. C Bermondsey St Jas w Ch Ch S'wark 94-99; V Lee Gd Shep w St Pet from 99. *47 Handen Road, London SE12 8NR* Tel (020) 8318 2363 E-mail revrdb@yahoo.com

BAINES, Alan William. b 50. S Bank Poly BSc72. Trin Coll Bris DipHE94. d 94 p 95. C Chenies and Lt Chalfont, Latimer and Flaunden *Ox* 94-98; V Eye *Pet* from 98; Post Ord Tr Co-ord from 00. *The Vicarage, 4 Fountains Place, Eye, Peterborough PE6 7XP* Tel (01733) 222334 E-mail alan.baines@talk21.com

BAINES, Bernard Frederick. b 20. JP. ACP. St Jo Coll Nottm 83. d 84 p 85. NSM Nottingham All SS *S'well* 84-90; rtd 90; Perm to Offic *S'well* from 90. *18 Forest Road East, Nottingham NG1 4HH* Tel 0115-978 4191

BAINES, Derek Alfred. b 53. MCSP75. Carl and Blackb Dioc Tr Inst 99. d 02 p 03. NSM Lostock Hall *Blackb* from 02. *16 Middlefield, Leyland PR26 7AE* Tel and fax (01772) 641521 Mobile 07774-200885 E-mail baines@fish.co.uk

BAINES, John Charles. b 68. Ripon Coll Cuddesdon 00. d 02 p 03. C Morton and Stonebroom w Shirland *Derby* from 02. *Ash Tree House, 18 Wellington Park, Shirland, Alfreton DE55 6EQ* Tel (01773) 830561

BAINES, John Edmund. b 22. Down Coll Cam BA47 MA50 Lon Univ BD51. New Coll Lon. d 58 p 59. C Penistone w Midhope *Wakef* 58-60; V Batley St Thos 60-69; V Cawthorne 69-89; rtd 89; Perm to Offic *Wakef* from 90. *3 Huskar Close, Silkstone, Barnsley S75 4SX* Tel (01226) 791088

BAINES, Keith. b 46. Bolton Inst of Tech HNC69. OLM course 96. d 99 p 00. OLM Atherton and Hindsford *Man* 99-02; OLM Atherton and Hindsford w Howe Bridge from 02. *6 Marton Drive, Atherton, Manchester M46 9WA* Tel (01942) 897668 E-mail kjh@baines1.netlineuk.net

✠**BAINES, The Rt Revd Nicholas.** b 57. Bradf Univ BA80. Trin Coll Bris BA87. d 87 p 88 c 03. C Kendal St Thos *Carl* 87-91; C Leic H Trin w St Jo *Leic* 91-92; V Rothley 92-00; RD Goscote 96-00; Adn Lambeth *S'wark* 00-03; Area Bp Croydon from 03.

53 Stanhope Road, Croydon CR0 5NS Tel (020) 8681 5496 Fax 8686 2074 E-mail nick.baines@dswark.org.uk

BAINES, Noel Edward (Ted). b 29. St Jo Coll Dur BSc52 DipTh54 MA62. **d** 54 **p** 55. C Rainham *Chelmsf* 54-58; C Surbiton Hill Ch Ch *S'wark* 58-61; V Southborough St Matt *Roch* 61-67; V Beckenham St Jo 67-74; Hd RE Taunton Manor High Sch Caterham 74-83; Keston Coll 85-91; Perm to Offic *Roch* 74-91; Hon C Bromley Ch Ch 91-98; Hon C New Beckenham St Paul from 98; rtd 94; Perm to Offic *Roch* from 98. *10 Bromley Avenue, Bromley BR1 4BQ* Tel (020) 8460 8256 Fax as telephone E-mail xfz73@dial.pipex.com

BAIRD, Agnes Murry (Nancy). Man Univ CertEd70. St Jo Coll Nottm Dip Past Counselling 92 EAMTC 93. **d** 96 **p** 97. NSM Bramford *St E* 96-98; NSM Haughley w Wetherden and Stowupland from 98. *32 Maple Road, Stowupland, Stowmarket IP14 4DG* Tel (01449) 674734

BAIRD, Edward Simpson. b 17. Lon Univ BD58 Wisconsin Univ MLitt65 DLitt68. Yorkshire United Th Coll 42 Selly Oak Coll 47 Sarum Th Coll 54. **d** 55 **p** 56. C S Westoe *Dur* 55-58; V Swalwell 58-66; R Harrington *Carl* 66-75; V Barton w Peel Green *Man* 75-80; R Jarrow Grange *Dur* 80-83; rtd 83. *5 Hemsley Road, South Shields N34 6HW* Tel 0191-456 1389

BAIRD, Paul Drummond. b 48. Newc Univ CertEd71 Open Univ BA85. Ripon Coll Cuddesdon 88. **d** 90 **p** 91. C Chandler's Ford *Win* 90-93; V Hythe from 93. *The Vicarage, 14 Atheling Road, Hythe, Southampton SO45 6BR* Tel (023) 8084 2461 Fax as telephone E-mail paulhythe@aol.com

BAIRD, Robert Douglas. b 21. ERD56. Cam Univ MA64. Ripon Coll Cuddesdon. **d** 85 **p** 86. NSM Charlbury w Shorthampton *Ox* 85-87; Asst Chapl HM Pris Grendon and Spring Hill 85; Lic to Offic *Ox* from 87. *Glebe House, Ibstone, High Wycombe HP14 3XZ* Tel (01491) 638642

BAIRD, Canon William Stanley. b 33. TCD BA54 Div Test. **d** 56 **p** 57. C Carlow *C & O* 56-59; I Dunganstown *D & G* 59-64; C Knock *D & D* 64-69; P-in-c Kilwarlin Upper w Kilwarlin Lower 69-71; I 71-72; Warden Ch Min of Healing (Ireland) 72-79; I Dublin Drumcondra w N Strand *D & G* 79-91; Dir of Ords (Dub) 84-99; Can Ch Ch Cathl Dublin 88-99; I Swords w Donabate and Kilsallaghan 91-99; rtd 99. *5 Weavers Way, Wheaton Hall, Dublin Road, Drogheda, Co Louth, Irish Republic* Tel (00353) (41) 984 6445

BAISLEY, George. b 45. Sarum & Wells Th Coll 78. **d** 80 **p** 81. C Glouc St Geo w Whaddon *Glouc* 80-83; R Welford w Weston and Clifford Chambers 83-87; Chapl Myton Hamlet Hospice 87-91; Chapl Warw Univ *Cov* 87-91; R Berkswell 91-03; RD Kenilworth 96-01; Chapl Bromley Coll from 03. *The Chaplain's House, Bromley College, London Road, Bromley BR1 1PE* Tel (020) 8460 4712 *or* tel and fax 8464 3558 E-mail rev@baisley.co.uk *or* bromcoll@aol.com

BAKER, Alan. b 42. Liv Univ BA64. Carl Dioc Tr Inst 93. **d** 96 **p** 97. NSM Cartmel Peninsula *Carl* from 96; Perm to Offic *Blackb* from 98. *1 Church View, Priest Lane, Cartmel, Grange-over-Sands LA11 6PU* Tel (01539) 536551

BAKER, Albert George. b 30. Qu Coll Birm. **d** 61 **p** 62. C Merton St Mary *S'wark* 61-64; C Limpsfield and Titsey 64-65; C Chapel-en-le-Frith *Derby* 65-68; R Odd Rode *Ches* 68-76; V Holme Cultram St Mary *Carl* 76-78; R Blofield w Hemblington *Nor* 78-94; rtd 94. *240 Raedwald Drive, Bury St Edmunds IP32 7DN* Tel (01284) 701802

BAKER, Alicia Mary. b 63. Trin Coll Bris BA03. **d** 03. C E Ham St Paul *Chelmsf* from 03. *St Paul's Church, 227 Burges Road, London E6 2EU* E-mail aliciabakeruk@hotmail.com

BAKER, Angela Mary. b 42. **d** 91. Par Dn Battersea St Sav and St Geo w St Andr *S'wark* 91-94; C 94-96; C Battersea Fields 96-02; rtd 02. *Finches, Ide Hill, Sevenoaks TN14 6JW* Tel (01732) 750470

BAKER, Mrs Ann Christine. b 49. Edin Univ BEd71 Moray Ho Coll of Educn HDipRE71. Carl and Blackb Dioc Tr Inst 98. **d** 01 **p** 02. NSM St Bees *Carl* from 01. *The Vicarage, Oakbank, Whitehaven CA28 6HY* Tel (01946) 692630 Mobile 07752-154083 E-mail j.baker@can-online.org.uk

BAKER, Anne-Marie Clare. See BIRD, Mrs Anne-Marie Clare
BAKER, Anthony Peter. b 38. Hertf Coll Ox BA59 MA63. Clifton Th Coll 60. **d** 63 **p** 64. C Ox St Ebbe w St Pet *Ox* 63-66; C Welling *Roch* 66-70; V Redland *Bris* 70-79; Lect Tyndale Hall Bris 70-71; Lect Trin Coll Bris 71-77; V Beckenham Ch Ch *Roch* 79-94; Chapl Beckenham Hosp 79-94; V Hove Bp Hannington Memorial Ch *Chich* 94-03; rtd 03. *12 Paradise Close, Eastbourne BN20 8BT* Tel (01323) 438783 E-mail tony@apmjbaker.freeserve.co.uk

BAKER, Miss Barbara Ann. b 36. Linc Th Coll 85. **d** 87 **p** 94. Par Dn Hornchurch St Andr *Chelmsf* 87-94; C 94-97; rtd 97; Perm to Offic *Chelmsf* from 97. *120 Devonshire Road, Hornchurch RM12 4LN* Tel (01708) 477759

BAKER, Benedict. See BAKER, Henry Blandford Benedict
BAKER, Canon Bernard George Coleman. b 36. Lon Univ BD61. Oak Hill Th Coll 61. **d** 63 **p** 64. C Broadwater St Mary *Chich* 63-66; Tanzania 66-84 and 96-01; BCMS Miss P and Chapl Morogoro Em Ch 66-79; V Moshi St Marg 79-84; Hon Can

Morogoro from 77; Hon Can Mt Kilimanjaro from 82; C-in-c Ryde St Jas Prop Chpl *Portsm* 84-96; Crosslinks 96-01; Asst P Ruaha Cathl and Teacher Amani Chr Tr Cen 96-01; rtd 01. *104 Merafield Road, Plympton, Plymouth PL7 1SJ* Tel (01752) 339879

BAKER, Brian Ernest Harry. b 38. Sarum & Wells Th Coll 74. **d** 76 **p** 77. C Cannock *Lich* 76-79; C Penkridge w Stretton 79-80; C Dunston w Coppenhall 79-80; P-in-c Earl Stonham w Stonham Parva and Creeting St Pet *St E* 80-89; V Staincliffe *Wakef* 89-93; rtd 00. *Address withheld by request*

BAKER (formerly BARTON), Mrs Caroline Janet. b 61. Ex Univ BA83 Lon Univ 86. Westcott Ho Cam 93. **d** 96 **p** 97. C Ivybridge w Harford *Ex* 96-02; P-in-c Torquay St Luke from 02; Dioc Adv in Adult Tr from 02. *St Luke's Vicarage, 1 Mead Road, Torquay TQ2 6TE* Tel (01803) 690539

BAKER, Charles Edward. b 47. **d** 87 **p** 88. NSM Dublin Clontarf *D & G* 87-90; NSM Delgany 90-94; NSM Dublin Sandford w Milltown 94-97; NSM Dublin St Patr Cathl Gp from 97. *12 Aranleigh Vale, Rathfarnham, Dublin 14, Irish Republic* Tel (00353) (1) 494 6465

BAKER, Prof Christopher James. b 54. St Cath Coll Cam BA75 MA78 PhD78 CEng83 FICE96 FIHT95. EMMTC 85. **d** 88 **p** 89. NSM Matlock Bath *Derby* 88-95; NSM Matlock Bath and Cromford 95; NSM Beeston *S'well* 95-98; Perm to Offic *Lich* 98-00; NSM Lich St Mich w St Mary and Wall from 00. *28 Grosvenor Close, Lichfield WS14 9SR* Tel (01543) 256320 *or* 262211 E-mail cjsmbaker@aol.com

BAKER, Christopher. b 64. St Cuth Soc Dur BA95 Heythrop Coll Lon MA02 Greenwich Univ PGCE96. SEITE 99. **d** 02. C Kennington St Mark *S'wark* from 02. *73 Baytree Road, London SW2 5RR* Tel (020) 7274 6907 Fax as telephone

BAKER, Christopher Richard. b 61. Man Univ BA83 Southn Univ BTh90 Heythrop Coll Lon MTh92. Sarum & Wells Th Coll 86. **d** 89 **p** 93. C Dulwich St Barn *S'wark* 89-92; Tutor Sarum & Wells Th Coll 92-94; Dir Chr Tr Milton Keynes *Ox* 94-98; Stantonbury and Willen 95-98; Dir Tr OLM 98-99; Development Officer Wm Temple Foundn from 01. *Luther King House, Brighton Grove, Rusholme, Manchester M14 5JP* Tel 0161-256 1142 Fax 248 9201 E-mail temple@wtf.org.uk

BAKER, David. b 63. SW Minl Tr Course 99. **d** 02. N Devon Coll Barnstaple from 02. *4 Ashley Terrace, Bideford EX39 3AL* Tel (01237) 473453 E-mail davidbaker5@hotmail.com

BAKER, David Ayshford. b 66. St Aid Coll Dur BA88 Univ of Wales (Cardiff) Dip Journalism 89. Wycliffe Hall Ox BTh97. **d** 98. C Chadwell Heath *Chelmsf* 97-01; C Surbiton Hill Ch Ch *S'wark* from 01. *181 Elgar Avenue, Surbiton KT5 9JX* Tel (020) 8399 1503 E-mail david_dawn.baker@virgin.net

BAKER, David Clive. b 47. Sarum & Wells Th Coll 76. **d** 78 **p** 79. C Shirley *Birm* 78-82; P-in-c Croft *Linc* 82-83; R Wainfleet All SS w St Thos 82-83; P-in-c Wainfleet St Mary 82-83; R The Wainfleets and Croft 83-86; V Stirchley *Birm* 86-96; Perm to Offic 97-98; V Handsworth St Mich 98-02; Chapl Aston Univ 99-02; C Codsall *Lich* from 02. *Church House, 7 Bilbrook Road, Wolverhampton WV8 1EV* Tel (01902) 842912 Mobile 07958-468819

BAKER, David Frederick. b 32. Clifton Th Coll 67. **d** 69 **p** 70. C Bilton *Ripon* 69-71; C Heworth w Peasholme St Cuth *York* 71-75; V Sand Hutton w Gate and Upper Helmsley 75-77; P-in-c Bossall w Buttercrambe 75-77; V Sand Hutton 77-80; R Preston in Holderness 80; C Topcliffe w Dalton and Dishforth 89; V Baldersby w Dalton, Dishforth etc 89-96; rtd 96; Perm to Offic *York* from 96; Perm to Offic *Ripon* from 96. *Chinkoa, 15 Williamson Gardens, Ripon HG4 2QB* Tel (01765) 601822

BAKER, David John. b 27. LRAM50 GRSM51. Ely Th Coll 53. **d** 55 **p** 56. C Swanley St Mary *Roch* 55-58; C Guildf St Nic *Guildf* 58-63; Prec St Alb Abbey *St Alb* 63-67; P-in-c Colney St Pet 67-68; V 68-73; V Tattenham Corner and Burgh Heath *Guildf* 73-84; R Fetcham 84-96; rtd 96; Perm to Offic *Guildf* from 96. *1 Terra Cotta Court, Quennels Hill, Wrecclesham, Farnham GU10 4SL* Tel (01252) 734202

BAKER, David Jordan. b 35. Univ of Wales (Lamp) BA59. Ely Th Coll 59. **d** 61 **p** 62. C Spalding *Linc* 61-66; C Gainsborough All SS 66-69; V Wrawby 69-78; V Melton Ross w New Barnetby 70-78; V Linc St Pet-at-Gowts and St Andr 78-94; rtd 98; Perm to Offic *Linc* from 01. *Fartherwell, The Paddock, Canwick, Lincoln LN4 2RX* Tel (01522) 526903

BAKER, Dilly. See BAKER, Ms Hilary Mary
BAKER, Frank Thomas. b 36. Selw Coll Cam BA61. Coll of Resurr Mirfield. **d** 63 **p** 64. C Mackworth St Fran *Derby* 63-66; C Leeds St Pet *Ripon* 66-73; P-in-c Stanley *Dur* 73-74; R Crook 73-74; Chapl Bucharest *Eur* 74-75; C Tewkesbury w Walton Cardiff *Glouc* 75-81; Min Can Windsor 81-86; rtd 86. *15 Hartford Court, 33 Filey Road, Scarborough YO11 2TP* Tel (01723) 352466

BAKER, Frederick Peter. b 24. Bps' Coll Cheshunt 58. **d** 60 **p** 61. C Peckham St Jude *S'wark* 60-63; C Mitcham St Mark 63-66; C Northampton St Pet w Upton *Pet* 66-69; P-in-c Northampton St Lawr 69-71; V Northampton St Edm 71-78; V Spratton 78-83; R Walgrave w Hannington and Wold 83-89; rtd 89; Perm to Offic

Win 89-98; Perm to Offic *Ely* from 00. *73 Five Arches, Orton Wistow, Peterborough PE2 6FQ* Tel (01733) 371349

BAKER, Canon Gerald Stothert. b 30. Univ of NZ MA54. St Jo Coll Auckland LTh56. **d** 56 **p** 57. New Zealand 56-87 and from 92; Hon Can Wellington 80-87; Adn Wairarapa 95-96; TV Kidderminster St Mary and All SS w Trimpley etc *Worc* 87-92; rtd 95. *83 Kuratawhiti Street, Greytown, New Zealand* Tel (0064) (6) 304 8367

BAKER, Gillian Devonald. b 40. S Dios Minl Tr Scheme 88. **d** 91 **p** 94. NSM Redhorn *Sarum* 91-02; NSM TV from 02; Chapl HM Pris Erlestoke 94-01. *11 The Street, Chirton, Devizes SN10 3QS* Tel (01380) 848170 Fax 840152

BAKER, The Very Revd Graham Brinkworth. b 26. AKC54. **d** 55 **p** 56. C Wandsworth St Anne *S'wark* 55-58; Canada from 58. *1280 Tracksell Avenue, Victoria BC, Canada, V8P 2C9*

BAKER, Harry Hallas. b 16. Bps' Coll Cheshunt 51. **d** 53 **p** 54. C Killingworth *Newc* 53-58; V Mickley 58-63; V Howdon Panns 63-73; C Alnwick St Mich 73-74; C Alnwick 74-84; rtd 84; Perm to Offic *Newc* from 84. *clo J Curtis Esq, 58 Easterly Avenue, Leeds LS8 2TD*

BAKER, Mrs Heather Elizabeth. b 48. WEMTC 94. **d** 97 **p** 98. NSM Ewyas Harold w Dulas, Kenderchurch etc *Heref* 97-98; C 98-00; C Burghill and Stretton Sugwas 00-01; P-in-c Glasbury and Llowes w Clyro and Betws *S & B* from 02. *The Vicarage, 4 The Birches, Glasbury, Hereford HR3 5NW*

BAKER, Henry Blandford Benedict. b 26. Univ of NZ BA49 MA50. Coll of Resurr Mirfield 51. **d** 53 **p** 54. C New Mills *Derby* 53-56; New Zealand 56-57; CSWG 57-66; Father Superior 65-66; Perm to Offic *Chich* 81-86; R Beckington w Standerwick, Berkley, Rodden etc *B & W* 86-92; rtd 92. *Coed Glas, Talgarth Road, Bronllys, Brecon LD3 0HN* Tel (01874) 711964
E-mail benedict.baker@btinternet.co.uk

BAKER, Ms Hilary Mary (Dilly). b 61. Man Univ BA83 Univ of Wales (Cardiff) CQSW86. Sarum & Wells Th Coll 86. **d** 89 **p** 94. Par Dn E Dulwich St Jo *S'wark* 89-92; Tutor Sarum & Wells Th Coll 92-94; TV Stantonbury and Willen *Ox* 94-01; Warden Scargill Ho from 01. *Scargill House, Kettlewell, Skipton BD23 5HU* Tel (01756) 760234
E-mail warden@scargillhouse.co.uk

BAKER, Hugh Crispin. b 58. Open Univ BA92. Linc Th Coll 95. **d** 95 **p** 96. C Birstall and Wanlip *Leic* 95-99; V Middlestown *Wakef* from 99. *The Vicarage, 2 Netherton Hall Gardens, Netherton, Wakefield WF4 4JA* Tel (01924) 278384

BAKER, Hugh John. b 46. Birm Univ BSocSc68 Nottm Univ DipTh69. Cuddesdon Coll 69. **d** 71 **p** 72. C Bilston *Cov* 71-74; C Pemberton St Mark Newtown *Liv* 74-78; TV Sutton 78-90; V Fazeley *Lich* from 90; R Drayton Bassett from 90; V Canwell from 90; P-in-c Hints from 90; Chapl S Staffs Healthcare NHS Trust from 00. *St Paul's Vicarage, 9 West Drive, Bonehill, Tamworth B78 3HR* Tel (01827) 287701 or 289414
E-mail elizabethatthevicarage@supanet.com

BAKER, Iain. b 70. St D Coll Lamp BA91. Oak Hill Th Coll BA99. **d** 99 **p** 00. C Gt Clacton *Chelmsf* from 99. *6 Peter Bruff Avenue, Clacton-on-Sea CO16 8UA* Tel (01255) 432431
E-mail ib.ib@virgin.net

BAKER, Ivon Robert. b 28. St Aug Coll Cant 59. **d** 60 **p** 61. C Sutton in Ashfield St Mary *S'well* 60-62; V Gringley-on-the-Hill 62-94; Chapl HM YOI Gringley 82-91; RD Bawtry *S'well* 85-90; rtd 94; Perm to Offic *York* from 94. *2 Willowgate, Pickering YO18 7BE* Tel (01751) 472281

BAKER, Canon James Henry. b 39. MBE02. Lon Univ DipTh66. Kelham Th Coll 62. **d** 67 **p** 68. C Sheff Arbourthorne *Sheff* 67-70; C Pemberton St Jo *Liv* 70-71; Chapl and Prec St Mary's Cathl *Edin* 71-74; R Lochgelly *St And* 74-84; P-in-c Rosyth 76-84; P-in-c Inverkeithing 76-84; Can St Ninian's Cathl Perth 83-84; TR Whitehaven *Carl* from 84; RD Calder 96-01; Hon Can Carl Cathl from 96. *The Vicarage, Oakbank, Whitehaven CA28 6HY* Tel (01946) 692630 or 62572
E-mail j.baker@can-online.org.uk

BAKER, Jean Margaret. b 47. Sheff Univ BSc69 DipEd70 Lon Univ DipTh75 BD78. All Nations Chr Coll 75 Gilmore Course 81. **dss** 82 **d** 87 **p** 97. Liv Our Lady and St Nic w St Anne *Liv* 82-87; Chapl Huyton Coll 87; Chapl St Mary and St Anne's Sch Abbots Bromley 87-91; Chapl Howell's Sch Denbigh 91-98; C Denbigh *St As* from 97. *34 Trewen, Denbigh LL16 3HF* Tel (01745) 812262 E-mail margaret@smallrev.demon.co.uk

BAKER, John Albert. b 29. St Edm Hall Ox BA52 MA56 Lon Univ BSc68 S Bank Poly MSc76. Cuddesdon Coll 52. **d** 54 **p** 55. C Battersea St Luke *S'wark* 54-58; Hon C from 84; C Richmond St Mary 58-62; V Battersea Park All SS 62-83; Tutor Roehampton Inst 83-91; rtd 94. *44 Wroughton Road, London SW11 6BG* Tel (020) 7585 2492

BAKER, John Alfred. b 41. Dioc OLM tr scheme 99. **d** 02 **p** 03. OLM Herne *Cant* from 02. *Oakfield, 219 Canterbury Road, Herne Bay CT6 7HB* Tel (01227) 362519 Mobile 07960-107169 E-mail john-baker@kent35.fslife.co.uk

✠**BAKER, The Rt Revd John Austin.** b 28. Oriel Coll Ox BA52 MA55 BLitt55 MLitt. Lambeth DD91 Cuddesdon Coll 52. **d** 54 **p** 55 **c** 82. C Cuddesdon *Ox* 54-57; Tutor Cuddesdon Coll 54-57;

C Hatch End St Anselm *Lon* 57-59; Lect K Coll Lon 57-59; Chapl CCC Ox 59-73; Lect Th Ox Univ 59-73; Can Westmr Abbey 73-82; Sub-Dean Westmr 78-82; R Westmr St Marg 78-82; Chapl to Speaker of Ho of Commons 78-82; Bp Sarum 82-93; Can and Preb Sarum Cathl 82-93; rtd 93. *4 Mede Villas, Kingsgate Road, Winchester SO23 9QQ* Tel (01962) 861388 Fax 843089

BAKER, John Carl. b 55. Chich Th Coll 77. **d** 80 **p** 81. C Wigan St Andr *Liv* 80-83; V Hollinfare 83-85; TV Seacroft *Ripon* 85-89; TV Bottesford w Ashby *Linc* 89-94; V Liv St Paul Stoneycroft *Liv* 94-02; V Altcar and Hightown from 02. *St Stephen's Vicarage, St Stephen's Road, Liverpool L38 0BL* Tel 0151-926 2469

BAKER, John Reginald. b 62. Hatf Coll Dur BSc83. Wycliffe Hall Ox 86. **d** 89 **p** 90. C Amersham *Ox* 89-92; C Greenford H Cross *Lon* 92-97. *11A Lakeside Road, London W14 0DX* Tel (020) 8574 3762

BAKER, Jonathan Mark Richard. b 66. St Jo Coll Ox BA88 MPhil90. St Steph Ho Ox BA92. **d** 93 **p** 94. C Ascot Heath *Ox* 93-96; C Reading St Mark 96; P-in-c Reading 96-99; V 99-02; P-in-c Reading H Trin 96-99; V 99-02; Prin Pusey Ho Ox from 03. *Pusey House, Oxford OX1 3LZ* Tel (01865) 278415 Fax 278416

BAKER, Jonathan William. b 61. SS Coll Cam MA85. Wycliffe Hall Ox BA91. **d** 92 **p** 93. C Sanderstead All SS *S'wark* 92-96; P-in-c Scalby w Ravenscar and Staintondale *York* 96-97; P-in-c Hackness w Harwood Dale 96-97; V Scalby from 97; V Hackness w Harwood Dale from 97. *The Vicarage, Scalby, Scarborough YO13 0PS* Tel (01723) 362740

BAKER, Kenneth William. b 38. Nottm Univ DTPS95. EMMTC 92. **d** 96 **p** 97. NSM Welford w Sibbertoft and Marston Trussell *Pet* 96-99; P-in-c 98-01; P-in-c N w S Kilworth and Misterton *Leic* 01-03; P-in-c Swinford w Catthorpe, Shawell and Stanford 01-03; TR Gilmorton, Peatling Parva, Kimcote etc from 03. *The Rectory, Kilworth Road, Swinford, Lutterworth LE17 6BQ* Tel (01788) 860221

BAKER, Marc Crispin. b 75. Westmr Coll Ox BTh96. Oak Hill Th Coll. **d** 02 **p** 03. C Upton (Overchurch) *Ches* from 02. *43 Grafton Drive, Wirral CH49 0TX* Tel 0151-678 1235 or 677 1186 Fax 606 1935 E-mail office@stmupton.freeserve.co.uk

BAKER, Canon Michael Robert Henry. b 39. Keele Univ MA88. Lich Th Coll 63. **d** 66 **p** 67. C Wellingborough All SS *Pet* 66-68; C Pet All SS 68-73; V Earls Barton 73-87; RD Wellingborough 76-87; P-in-c Gt Doddington 77-82; Can Pet Cathl from 85; TR Kingsthorpe w Northampton St Dav 87-95; V Towcester w Easton Neston from 95; RD Towcester from 98. *The Vicarage, Chantry Lane, Towcester NN12 6YY* Tel (01327) 350459 E-mail makemargbaker@aol.com

BAKER, Michael William. b 38. Roch Th Coll 68. **d** 70 **p** 71. C Woodmansterne *S'wark* 70-75; TV Danbury *Chelmsf* 75-78; P-in-c Barrington *Ely* 78-90; V 90-97; P-in-c Shepreth 78-90; V 90-97; rtd 97; Perm to Offic *Nor* from 98. *The White House, Church Street, Elsing, Dereham NR20 3EB* Tel (01362) 637370

BAKER, Miles Anthony. b 71. Brunel Univ BA92. Ridley Hall Cam 99. **d** 02 **p** 03. C Paignton Ch Ch and Preston St Paul *Ex* from 02. *The Vicarage, 133 Torquay Road, Paignton TQ3 2AG* Tel (01803) 664227 E-mail dawnmiles@dbaker16.fsnet.co.uk

BAKER, Canon Neville Duff. b 35. St Aid Birkenhead 60. **d** 63 **p** 64. C Stranton *Dur* 63-66; C Houghton le Spring 66-68; V Tudhoe Grange from 68; RD Auckland 83-94; Hon Can Dur Cathl from 90; P-in-c Merrington 91-94. *St Andrew's Vicarage, Tudhoe Grange, Spennymoor DL16 6NE* Tel (01388) 814817

BAKER, Noel Edward Lloyd. b 37. Sarum & Wells Th Coll 73. **d** 75 **p** 76. C Charlton Kings St Mary *Glouc* 75-79; V Clearwell 79-81; R Eastington and Frocester 81-97; RD Stonehouse 90-94; P-in-c Eastington and Frocester 97-98; P-in-c Standish w Haresfield and Moreton Valence etc 97-98; rtd 98; Perm to Offic *Glouc* from 00. *46 Dozule Close, Leonard Stanley, Stonehouse GL10 3NL* Tel (01453) 823569
E-mail noel_brenda@yahoo.co.uk

BAKER, Paul Anthony. b 64. St Chad's Coll Dur BA85. St Steph Ho Ox BA88 MA98. **d** 89 **p** 90. C Hartlepool St Aid *Dur* 89-93; TV Jarrow 93-98; V Sunderland Pennywell St Thos from 98. *St Thomas's Vicarage, Parkhurst Road, Sunderland SR4 9DB* Tel 0191-534 2100

BAKER, Peter Colin. b 43. Sarum & Wells Th Coll. **d** 82 **p** 83. C Bridgemary *Portsm* 82-86; V Ash Vale *Guildf* 86-99; P-in-c Earlham St Anne *Nor* from 99; P-in-c Earlham St Mary from 99. *The Vicarage, Bluebell Road, Norwich NR4 7LP* Tel (01603) 452922 E-mail peterbaker84@hotmail.com

BAKER, Peter Graham. b 55. MA PhD. St Steph Ho Ox. **d** 82 **p** 83. C Ches H Trin *Ches* 82-86; C Holborn St Alb w Saffron Hill St Pet *Lon* 86-91; V Golders Green 91-01; AD W Barnet 95-00; V Regent's Park St Mark from 01. *St Mark's Vicarage, 4 Regent's Park Road, London NW1 7TX* Tel (020) 7586 1694 or 7485 6340

BAKER, Canon Peter Malcolm. b 21. Lich Th Coll 40. **d** 44 **p** 45. C Bedminster St Aldhelm *Bris* 43-47; C Charlton Kings H Apostles *Glouc* 47-49; C Halesowen *Worc* 49-53; CF (TA) 53-75; V Dudley St Luke *Worc* 53-59; R Hindlip w Martin Hussingtree 59-67; V Inkberrow 67-75; P-in-c Kington w Dormston 74-75; R Inkberrow w Cookhill and Kington w Dormston 75-77; P-in-c

Wilden 77-80; R Mamble w Bayton 80-82; RD Stourport 80-88; R Teme Valley N 82-88; Hon Can Worc Cathl 84-88; rtd 88; Perm to Offic *Heref* from 88; Perm to Offic *Worc* from 88. *The Ryelands, Menith Wood, Worcester WR6 6UG* Tel (01584) 881227

BAKER, Robert John Kenneth. b 50. MICE79 Southn Univ BSc71. Oak Hill Th Coll 88. d 90 p 91. C Cromer *Nor* 90-94; P-in-c Pakefield 94; R from 94. *The Rectory, The Causeway, Pakefield, Lowestoft NR33 0JZ* Tel (01502) 574040

BAKER, Canon Robert Mark. b 50. Bris Univ BA73. St Jo Coll Nottm 74. d 76 p 77. C Portswood Ch Ch *Win* 76-80; R Witton w Brundall and Braydeston *Nor* 80-89; P-in-c Buckenham w Hassingham and Strumpshaw 80-86; R Brundall w Braydeston and Postwick from 89; RD Blofield 89-94; Hon Can Nor Cathl from 93. *The Rectory, 73 The Street, Brundall, Norwich NR13 5LZ* Tel (01603) 715136 E-mail bob-baker@clara.net

BAKER, Canon Robin Henry. b 31. Man Univ BA52 MPhil00. Cuddesdon Coll 54. d 56 p 57. C Swinton St Pet *Man* 56-59; C Birch St Jas 59-61; R Stretford All SS 61-66; Chapl High Royds Hosp Menston 66-72; P-in-c Simpson w Woughton on the Green *Ox* 72-73; P-in-c Woughton 74; TR 74-79; RD Milton Keynes 78-86; C-in-c Milton Keynes City Cen 79-80; V Milton Keynes 80-86; Hon Can Ch Ch 84-91; TR Banbury 86-91; P-in-c Scorton *Blackb* 91-96; Bp's Adv on Healing and Hosp Chapl 91-96; rtd 96; Perm to Offic *Man* from 99. *12 Paxton Crescent, Shenley Lodge, Milton Keynes MK5 7PY* Tel (01908) 236582

BAKER, Ronald Harry. b 21. Ely Th Coll 62. d 64 p 65. C Crediton *Ex* 64-66; R Thornbury 66-73; R Bradford 67-73; R Black Torrington, Bradf and Thornbury 73-77; P-in-c Broadhempston and Woodland 77-78; P-in-c Lt Hempston 77-78; P-in-c Berry Pomeroy 77-78; V Broadhempston, Woodland, Berry Pomeroy etc 78-86; rtd 86; Chapl Marseille w St Raphaël, Aix-en-Provence etc *Eur* 87-88; Perm to Offic *Ex* from 88. *95 Barton Avenue, Paignton TQ3 3HY* Tel (01803) 557462

BAKER, Ronald Kenneth. b 43. Open Univ BA80 LTh. St Jo Coll Nottm 85. d 87 p 88. C Paddock Wood *Roch* 87-90; V Ramsgate St Mark *Cant* 90-95; P-in-c Ewhurst *Chich* 95-98; R from 98; P-in-c Bodiam 95-98; R from 98. *The Rectory, Ewhurst Green, Robertsbridge TN32 5TB* Tel (01580) 830268

BAKER, Roy David. b 36. Lon Univ DipTh61. St Aid Birkenhead 59. d 62 p 63. C Garston *Liv* 62-64; C N Meols 64-68; V Newton-le-Willows 68-73; V Crossens 73-82; V Blundellsands St Nic 82-01; rtd 01. *18 Ennersdale Road, Formby, Liverpool L37 2EA* Tel (01704) 830622

BAKER, Sarah Jane. b 59. Lon Univ MB, BS82 DRCOG87 Sheff Univ MPhil00 Coll of Ripon & York St Jo MA02. N Ord Course 99. d 02 p 03. NSM Kinsley w Wragby *Wakef* from 02. *12 Ingswell Drive, Notton, Wakefield WF4 2NF* Tel (01226) 728336 E-mail sarahrekab@aol.com

BAKER, Simon Nicholas Hartland. b 57. K Coll Lon BD78 Trin Hall Cam DipTh79. Qu Coll Birm 79. d 81 p 82. C Tupsley *Heref* 81-85; V Shinfield *Ox* 85-98; Prin Berks Chr Tr Scheme 93-98; Lay Min Adv and Warden of Readers *Win* 98-02; Dir of Min Development from 02. *The Rectory, Trinity Hill, Medstead, Alton GU34 5LT* Tel (01420) 568191

BAKER, Stephen Anthony. b 55. St Luke's Coll Ex BEd80. Sarum & Wells Th Coll 88. d 91 p 92. C Guildf H Trin w St Mary *Guildf* 91-97; Chapl Guildf Coll of Tech 91-97; Chapl Eliz Coll Guernsey 97-01. *Address temp unknown*

BAKER, Stuart. b 44. MATA63 AIAT65. Spurgeon's Coll DipTh71 Bapt Tr Coll DipMin75 Ripon Coll Cuddesdon 92. d 93 p 94. C Whitchurch *Bris* 93-97; R Brightling, Dallington, Mountfield etc *Chich* from 97. *The Rectory, Brightling, Robertsbridge TN32 5HE* Tel (01424) 838281

BAKER, William Alfred Douglas. b 31. Lon Univ BSc52 MSc56. Qu Coll Birm 72. d 75 p 76. NSM Bridgnorth w Tasley *Heref* 75-78; NSM Bridgnorth, Tasley, Astley Abbotts, etc 78-97; Perm to Offic 97-00. *Oaklea, Astley Abbotts, Bridgnorth WV16 4SW* Tel (01746) 762980

BAKER, William John. b 45. FCII80. Cranmer Hall Dur 87. d 89 p 90. C Sale St Anne *Ches* 89-93; V Crewe St Andr 93-94; P-in-c Crewe St Jo 93-94; V Crewe St Andr w St Jo from 94. *St John's Vicarage, 14 Dane Bank Avenue, Crewe CW2 8AA* Tel (01270) 569000 Fax 650209 E-mail revbake@supanet.com

BAKERE, The Very Revd Ronald Duncan. b 35. TCD BA58 HDipEd60 MA61 BD62 Ch Ch Ox MA66 FRSA68 FBIM79. CITC 59. d 59 p 60. C Knockbreda *D & D* 59-61; C Dublin Zion Ch *D & G* 61-63; Min Can St Patr Cathl Dublin 62-64; CF (TA) 65-67; Lect Th Plymouth Univ 67-72; Nigeria 73-77; Cen Org Ex Red Cross 78-81; Perm to Offic *Ex* 82-85; P-in-c Chew Magna w Dundry *B & W* 86-87; Hd Relig Studies Sir Jo Cass Foundn Lon 88-93; Perm to Offic *Lon* 88-93; Dean Port Moresby 93-96; ChStJ from 95; rtd 96; Perm to Offic *Lon* from 96. *12 Dumbarton Road, London SW2 5LU* Tel (020) 7674 0283 Fax as telephone

BAKKER, Gregory Kendall. b 66. California State Univ BA89. Trin Episc Sch for Min Penn MDiv92 Trin Coll Bris 99. d 92 p 93. C Tariffville USA 92-96; Lect St Phil Coll Kongwa Tanzania 96-99; C Wroughton *Bris* 00-02; TV Stratton

St Margaret w S Marston etc from 02. *The Vicarage, South Marston, Swindon SN3 4SR* Tel (01793) 827021 E-mail gkbakker@hotmail.com

BALCH, John Robin. b 37. Lon Univ BSc61 Bris Univ CertEd62. ALCD68. d 68 p 69. C Bath Walcot *B & W* 68-71; C Fulwood *Sheff* 71-76; V Erith St Paul *Roch* 76-93; RD Erith 90-93; P-in-c Fairlight *Chich* 93-94; R Fairlight, Guestling and Pett 94-01; rtd 01; Perm to Offic *Derby* from 01. *29 Whitecotes Park, Chesterfield S40 3RT* Tel (01246) 297099

BALCHIN, Michael John. b 38. Selw Coll Cam BA60 MA64. Wells Th Coll 60. d 62 p 63. C Bournemouth H Epiphany *Win* 62-65; C Bris St Mary Redcliffe w Temple etc *Bris* 65-69; R Norton sub Hamdon *B & W* 69-70; P-in-c Chiselborough w W Chinnock 69-70; R Norton sub Hamdon w Chiselborough 70-77; P-in-c Chipstable w Huish Champflower and Clatworthy 77-82; R 82-88; Perm to Offic *Ban* from 88; rtd 03. *Gartheiniog, Aberangell, Machynlleth SY20 9QG* Tel (01650) 511659

BALDOCK, Andrew Robert. b 67. St Jo Coll Dur BA00. Cranmer Hall Dur 98. d 00 p 02. C Peterlee *Dur* 00-01; C Felling 01-03; C Dur St Nic from 03. *95 Rochester Road, Durham DH1 5PN* Tel 0191-386 5605 E-mail andrew.baldock@lineone.net

BALDOCK, Charles William Martin. b 52. Nottm Univ BPharm73. St Jo Coll Nottm LTh. d 85 p 86. C Nailsea Ch Ch *B & W* 85-89; V Brampton Bierlow *Sheff* 89-00; RD Wath 95-00; Hon Can Sheff Cathl 98-00; V Dringhouses *York* from 00. *The Vicarage, Tadcaster Road, Dringhouses, York YO24 1QG* Tel (01904) 706120 Fax 709111 E-mail mserz@baldock13.fsnet.co.uk

BALDOCK, Canon Norman. b 29. K Coll Lon BD52 AKC52. d 53 p 54. C Cant St Pet w H Cross *Cant* 53-54; C Thornton Heath St Jude 54-58; V Ash w W Marsh 58-67; V Sheerness H Trin w St Paul 67-75; V Margate St Jo 75-94; RD Thanet 80-86; Hon Can Cant Cathl 82-94; Chapl Margate Gen Hosp 82-94; rtd 94; Perm to Offic *Cant* from 94. *9 Beach Avenue, Birchington CT7 9VS* Tel (01843) 841173

BALDOCK, Reginald David. b 48. Oak Hill Th Coll 72. d 75 p 76. C Plymouth St Jude *Ex* 75-79; C Ardsley *Sheff* 79-85; V Rawthorpe *Wakef* 85-96; C Salterhebble All SS 96-98; P-in-c Bournemouth St Jo w St Mich *Win* from 98. *The Vicarage, 13 Durley Chine Road South, Bournemouth BH2 5JT* Tel (01202) 761962

BALDRY, John Netherway. b 19. Lon Univ BA53. d 79 p 80. Hon C Brighton St Paul *Chich* from 79. *26 Braybon Avenue, Brighton BN1 8HG* Tel (01273) 501268

BALDRY, Ralph Yorke. b 18. St Jo Coll Ox BA40 MA44. Wycliffe Hall Ox 40. d 41 p 42. C Southall H Trin *Lon* 41-45; C Oakwood St Thos 45-47; V Clay Hill St Jo 47-52; V Stonebridge St Mich 52-58; V Finchley St Luke 64-72; V Golders Green St Alb 72-80; P-in-c Golders Green St Mich 77-80; V Golders Green 80-83; rtd 84; Perm to Offic *Lon* from 84. *159 Falloden Way, London NW11 6LG* Tel (020) 8455 6926

BALDWICK, Frank Eric. b 24. Ripon Hall Ox 54. d 55 p 56. C Newark Ch Ch *S'well* 55-58; C Hawton 55-58; C W Bridgford 58-60; V Oldham St Barn *Man* 60-65; R Gt Lever 65-78; V Hindsford 78-81; TV Clifton *S'well* 81-89; rtd 89; Perm to Offic *S'well* from 89. *35 Ladybay Road, Nottingham NG2 5BJ* Tel 0115-982 1273

BALDWIN, Colin Steven. b 61. Brighton Poly BA85 Thames Poly DipArch90 Nottm Univ MTh01. St Jo Coll Nottm 99. d 01 p 02. C Billericay and Lt Burstead *Chelmsf* from 01. *9 Arundel Close, Billericay CM12 0FN* Tel (01277) 632822 Mobile 07714-048450 E-mail colin.baldwin@ntlworld.com

BALDWIN, David Frederick Beresford. b 57. Wolv Univ 91. Ripon Coll Cuddesdon DipMin95. d 95 p 96. C Uttoxeter w Bramshall *Lich* 95-97; C Uttoxeter Area 97-98; V Tilstock, Edstaston and Whixall from 98; Rural Chapl (Salop Adnry) from 00. *The Vicarage, Tilstock, Whitchurch SY13 3JL* Tel (01948) 880552 Fax as telephone E-mail revddavidbaldwin@lichfield.net

BALDWIN, Derek Wilfred Walter. b 23. Lon Univ LTh74. ALCD56. d 52 p 53. C Sharrow St Andr *Sheff* 52-54; C Woodlands 54-56; V Shepley *Wakef* 56-59; V Earl's Heaton 59-66; Org Sec CECS *B & W*, *Ex* and Truro 66-72; R Morchard Bishop *Ex* 72-73; Org Sec CECS *St Alb* and *Ox* 73-77; C Portishead *B & W* 77-79; R Wymondham w Edmondthorpe *Leic* 79-80; P-in-c St Mewan *Truro* 80-81; V Crowan w Godolphin 81-83; C Cockington *Ex* 83-87; rtd 87; Perm to Offic *Ex* from 90. *53 Higher Woolbrook Park, Sidmouth EX10 9ED*

BALDWIN, Mrs Frances Mary. b 49. SRN71. SEITE 99. d 02. NSM Caterham *S'wark* from 02. *3 Hillhurst Gardens, Caterham CR3 5HX* Tel (020) 8660 7534 E-mail francesb3@btinternet.com

BALDWIN, John Charles. b 39. FBCS CEng Bris Univ BSc61 Sussex Univ DPhil65. St Steph Ho Ox 82. d 83 p 84. C Llandaff w Capel Llanilltern *Llan* 83-90; V Ewenny w St Brides Major 90-92; Lic to Offic from 92; Hon Chapl Llan Cathl from 94. *60 Llantrisant Road, Llandaff, Cardiff CF5 2PX* Tel (029) 2055 4457 Fax 2038 7835 E-mail johnbaldwin@rb.churchinwales.org.uk

BALDWIN, Jonathan Michael. b 58. Chich Th Coll 92. **d** 94 **p** 95. C Crawley Chich 94-96; C New Shoreham 96-02; C Old Shoreham 96-02; Chapl Gatwick Airport from 02; C Crawley from 02. *18 Aldingbourne Close, Ifield, Crawley RH11 0QJ* Tel (01293) 447221

BALDWIN, Peter Alan. b 48. Bede Coll Dur BA70 Birm Univ DipTh72. Qu Coll Birm 72. **d** 73 **p** 74. C Hartlepool St Oswald *Dur* 73-75; C Darlington H Trin 75-78; OGS from 77; C-in-c Bishop Auckland Woodhouse Close CD *Dur* 78-82; V Ferryhill 82-88; P-in-c Charlestown *Man* 88-89; V Pendleton St Thos 88-89; TR Pendleton St Thos w Charlestown 89-90; TR Newton Aycliffe *Dur* 90-96; TR Gt Aycliffe 96-97; AD Sedgefield 96-99; V The Trimdons 97-99; P-in-c Bramley *Ripon* 99-00; TR 00-02; rtd 02; Hon C Harrogate St Wilfrid *Ripon* from 02. *St Wilfrid's Cottage, York Road, Harrogate HG1 2QL* Tel (01423) 561415 E-mail peter.baldwin5@virgin.net

BALDWIN, Mrs Vivien Lindsay. b 50. DipHE99. St Alb and Ox Min Course 97. **d** 98 **p** 99. NSM Westbury w Turweston, Shalstone and Biddlesden *Ox* 98-00; C W Buckingham 00-02; P-in-c Stoneleigh w Ashow *Cov* from 02; Rural Life Officer from 02. *The Parsonage, Church Lane, Stoneleigh, Coventry CV8 3DN* Tel (024) 7641 5506 Mobile 07720-811477 E-mail viv@vivbaldwin.worldonline.co.uk

BALDWIN, William. b 48. RMN73 FRSH83. NW Ord Course 75. **d** 78 **p** 79. C Royton St Anne *Man* 78-82; V Halliwell St Thos 82-87; TR Atherton 87-99; TR Atherton and Hindsford 99-02; TV Atherton and Hindsford w Howe Bridge from 02; AD Leigh from 01; OStJ from 88. *Atherton Rectory, Bee Fold Lane, Atherton, Manchester M29 0BL* Tel (01942) 874666

BALE, Edward William Carre. b 22. AKC55 Leic Univ DSRS67. **d** 55 **p** 56. C Mansfield St Pet *S'well* 55-59; C Corby St Jo *Pet* 59-61; R Corby SS Pet and Andr 61-69; V Wollaston and Strixton 69-87; rtd 88; Perm to Offic *Ox* from 88. *27 The Crescent, Haversham, Milton Keynes MK19 7AN* Tel (01234) 391443

BALE, Kenneth John. b 34. Univ of Wales (Lamp) BA58. Qu Coll Birm DipTh60. **d** 60 **p** 61. C Mitcham St Olave *S'wark* 60-63; C Warlingham w Chelsham and Farleigh 63-67; V Battersea Rise St Mark 67-85; Perm to Offic 85-88; Hon C Balham St Mary and St Jo 88-90; V S Wimbledon All SS 90-01; Dioc Adv Min of Healing 91-01; rtd 01; Perm to Offic *Sheff* from 01. *23 Selhurst Crescent, Bessacarr, Doncaster DN4 6EF* Tel (01302) 539100 Fax 371850 E-mail kbale@mistral.co.uk

BALFOUR, Andrew Crispin Roxburgh. b 49. Coll of Resurr Mirfield 93. **d** 95 **p** 96. C S Lafford *Linc* 95-99; P-in-c St Neot and Warleggan *Truro* 99-00; P-in-c Cardynham 99-00; R St Neot and Warleggan w Cardynham from 00. *The Vicarage, St Neot, Liskeard PL14 6NG* Tel (01579) 320472

BALFOUR, Hugh Rowlatt. b 54. SS Coll Cam BA76. Ridley Hall Cam 78. **d** 81 **p** 82. C Bedford Ch Ch *St Alb* 81-86; P-in-c Camberwell Ch Ch *S'wark* 86-92; V from 92. *Christ Church Vicarage, 79 Asylum Road, London SE15 2RJ* Tel (020) 7639 5662

BALFOUR, Mark Andrew. b 66. York Univ BA88 R Holloway Coll Lon PhD98. Trin Coll Bris BA01. **d** 02 **p** 03. C Churchdown *Glouc* from 02. *11 Chapel Hay Lane, Churchdown, Gloucester GL3 2ET* Tel (01452) 713080 E-mail thebalfours@btinternet.com

BALFOUR, Mrs Penelope Mary. b 47. St Andr Univ MA69 St Jo Coll York DipEd72. Coates Hall Edin 89 St Jo Coll Nottm 84. **d** 88 **p** 95. C Dundee St Marg *Bre* 88-94; Dioc AIDS Officer 90-94; NSM Invergowrie 94-96; Chapl Abertay Univ from 94; C Dundee St Marg from 96. *10 Strathaird Place, Dundee DD2 4TN* Tel (01382) 643114 E-mail p.balfour@tay.ac.uk

BALKWILL, Michael Robert. b 69. Univ of Wales (Lamp) BD89 Univ of Wales (Cardiff) DPS90 MTh92. St Mich Coll Llan 89 Bp Tucker Coll Mukono 91. **d** 91 **p** 92. C Llanrhos *St As* 91-97; Dioc RE Adv from 94; R Llanfyllin and Bwlchycibau from 97; Perm to Offic *Ban* from 97; Dioc Co-ord Dept of Development and Tr for Miss *St As* from 99. *The Rectory, Coed Llan Lane, Llanfyllin SY22 5BW* Tel (01691) 648306

BALKWILL, Roger Bruce. b 41. Univ of Wales DipTh64 DPS66. St Mich Coll Llan 61. **d** 64 **p** 65. C Llantrisant *Llan* 64-68; C Caerphilly 68-73; Rhodesia 73-76; P-in-c Idaln w Blore Ray and Okeover *Lich* 76-81; P-in-c Albrighton 81-82; V from 82; P-in-c Beckbury 89-90; P-in-c Badger 89-90; P-in-c Ryton 89-90; P-in-c Kemberton, Sutton Maddock and Stockton 89-90; RD Shifnal 89-98; P-in-c Boningale from 97. *The Vicarage, High Street, Albrighton, Wolverhampton WV7 3EQ* Tel (01902) 372701

BALL, Alan. b 26. Qu Coll Birm 72. **d** 75 **p** 75. NSM Hamstead St Paul *Birm* 75-93; rtd 93; Perm to Offic *Portsm* from 93. *25 Tebourba Drive, Alverstoke, Gosport PO12 2NT* Tel (023) 9260 1694

BALL, Andrew Thomas. b 54. K Coll Lon BD75 AKC75. Sarum & Wells Th Coll 76. **d** 77 **p** 78. C Ribbleton *Blackb* 77-80; C Sedgley All SS *Lich* 80-84; V Pheasey 84-90; Chapl Gd Hope Distr Gen Hosp Sutton Coldfield 90-94; Chapl Gd Hope Hosp NHS Trust Sutton Coldfield from 94. *Chaplain's Office, Good Hope*

Hospital, Rectory Road, Sutton Coldfield B75 7RR Tel 0121-378 2211 ext 2676

BALL, Anthony Charles. b 46. Lon Univ BD71. Chich Th Coll 72. **d** 73 **p** 74. C Heref St Martin *Heref* 73-76; C Ealing St Pet Mt Park *Lon* 76-82; V Ruislip Manor St Paul from 82. *St Paul's Vicarage, Thurlstone Road, Ruislip HA4 0BP* Tel (01895) 633499

BALL, Anthony James. b 68. St Chad's Coll Dur BA89. NTMTC 97. **d** 00 **p** 01. NSM Madrid *Eur* 00-03. *FCO (Madrid), King Charles Street, London SW1A 2AH* Tel (0034) (91) 700 8218 Fax 700 8309 E-mail anthony.ball@fco.gov.uk

BALL, Anthony Michael. b 46. Kelham Th Coll 66. **d** 70 **p** 71. C Kingswinford St Mary *Lich* 70-74; C W Bromwich All SS 74-76; P-in-c Priorslee 76-80; V 80-82; Asst Chapl HM Pris Liv 82-83; Chapl 88-95; Chapl HM Pris Lewes 83-88; Chapl HM Pris Featherstone 95-00; Chapl HM Pris The Verne from 00. *The Chaplain's Office, HM Prison, The Verne, Portland DT5 1EG* Tel (01305) 820124 Fax 823724

BALL, Christopher Rowland. b 40. Wycliffe Hall Ox. **d** 82 **p** 83. C Heysham *Blackb* 82-86; TV Swanborough *Sarum* 86-90; R Llanyblodwel and Trefonen *Lich* 90-99; rtd 99; Perm to Offic *Lich* from 01. *5 Maes y Celyn, Guilsfield, Welshpool SY21 9BL* Tel (01938) 559049

BALL, Canon Frank. b 21. Leeds Univ BA47. Coll of Resurr Mirfield 46. **d** 48 **p** 49. C Shiregreen St Hilda *Sheff* 48-50; C Attercliffe w Carbrook 50-53; V Handsworth Woodhouse 53-61; V Sheff Norwood St Leon 61-87; RD Ecclesfield 80-87; Hon Can Sheff Cathl 85-93; rtd 87; Gov and Chapl Shrewsbury Hosp Sheff 87-93; Perm to Offic *Sheff* from 93. *40 Seagrave Road, Sheffield S12 2JS* Tel 0114-264 4931

BALL, Geoffrey Williams. b 32. FLIA80 FInstSMM81. SW Minl Tr Course 82. **d** 85 **p** 86. NSM Sampford Spiney w Horrabridge *Ex* 85-87; TV Yelverton, Meavy, Sheepstor and Walkhampton 87-91; V Marystowe, Coryton, Stowford, Lewtrenchard etc 91-99; rtd 99; Perm to Offic *Ex* from 00. *22 Chapel Lane, Horrabridge, Yelverton PL20 7SP* Tel (01822) 855731

BALL, George Raymond. b 15. Univ of Wales (Lamp) BA40. St Mich Coll Llan 40. **d** 42 **p** 43. C Llansamlet *S & B* 42-46; C Swansea St Nic 46-50; R Bosherston w St Twynells *St D* 50-85; rtd 85. *1 Meadow Bank, St Twynnells, Pembroke SA71 5HZ* Tel (01646) 661432

BALL, Glynne Howell James. b 47. ACIS DMA. Llan Dioc Tr Scheme. **d** 90 **p** 91. NSM Llangynwyd w Maesteg *Llan* 90-95; NSM Tonyrefail w Gilfach Goch and Llandyfodwg 95; C 96-99; R Maenordeifi and Capel Colman w Llanfihangel etc *St D* from 99. *The Rectory, Llechryd, Cardigan SA43 2PJ* Tel (01239) 682830 E-mail glynne@goch.freeserve.co.uk

BALL, Ian Raymond. b 45. CertEd Univ of Wales MPhil. Glouc Th Course 81. **d** 85 **p** 87. NSM Churchstoke w Hyssington and Sarn *Heref* from 85; Lic to Bp Ludlow from 87; Lic to Offic *St As* from 93. *Bachaethlon Cottage, Sarn, Newtown SY16 4HH* Tel (01686) 670505 Fax as telephone E-mail iball@compuserve.com

BALL, Mrs Jane. b 68. Charlotte Mason Coll of Educn BEd91. St Steph Ho Ox 01. **d** 03. C Bedale and Leeming *Ripon* from 03. *44 Haig Road, Catterick Garrison DL9 3AH* Tel (01748) 830158 Mobile 07764-349957 E-mail jjball@oneltel.net.uk

BALL, John Kenneth. b 42. Lon Univ BSc64 AKC64. Linc Th Coll 69. **d** 71 **p** 72. C Garston *Liv* 71-74; C Eastham *Ches* 74-75; C Barnston 75-77; V Over St Jo 77-82; V Helsby and Dunham-on-the-Hill 82-94; RD Frodsham 88-94; P-in-c Alvanley 92-94; V Hoylake 94-98; rtd 98; P-in-c Downholme and Marske *Ripon* from 00. *5 Belle Vue Terrace, Bellerby, Leyburn DL8 5QL* Tel (01969) 623357

BALL, John Roy. b 47. Fitzw Coll Cam MA71. Wycliffe Hall Ox 83. **d** 85 **p** 86. C Stockport St Mary *Ches* 85-88; C Fazeley *Lich* 88-94; Res Min Drayton Bassett 89-94; Chapl Grenoble *Eur* 94-00; P-in-c Lithuania from 00. *Valstieciu gatve 13-1, 5808 Klaipeda, Lithuania* Tel (00370) (6) 351068 E-mail jroyball@klaipeda.omnitel.net

BALL, Jonathan. b 63. BNC Ox BA85 Leeds Univ BA87. Coll of Resurr Mirfield 85. **d** 88 **p** 89. C Blakenall Heath *Lich* 88-92; TV Rugeley 92-96; CF from 96; Perm to Offic *Cant* 97-99; *Ox* from 01. *c/o MOD Chaplains (Army)* Tel (01980) 615804 Fax 615800

BALL, Mrs Judith Anne. b 48. Nottm Univ BA70 Liv Univ PGCE71. N Ord Course 98. **d** 01 **p** 02. C Upholland *Liv* from 01. *8 Beacon View Drive, Upholland, Skelmersdale WN8 0HL* Tel (01695) 622181

BALL, Kevin Harry. b 55. Linc Th Coll 92. **d** 94 **p** 95. C New Mills *Derby* 94-96; C Walthamstow St Sav *Chelmsf* 96-98; V Stocksbridge *Sheff* 98-00; C Barnsley St Mary *Wakef* 00-01; Chapl Barnsley Coll 00-01; P-in-c Sneinton St Cypr *S'well* from

✠**BALL, The Rt Revd John Martin.** b 34. Univ of Wales BA55. Tyndale Hall Bris. **d** 59 **p** 60 **c** 95. C Blackb St Jude *Blackb* 59-63; Kenya 63-79; Dep Gen Sec BCMS 79-81; Gen Sec 81-93; Gen Sec Crosslinks 93-95; Hon C Sidcup Ch Ch *Roch* 81-95; Hon Can Karamoja from 88; Asst Bp Tanzania 95-00; rtd 00; Hon Asst Bp Chelmsf from 00. *5 Hill View Road, Springfield, Chelmsford CM1 7RS* Tel (01245) 268296 E-mail ball_john@onetel.net.uk

01. *St Cyprian's Vicarage, Marston Road, Nottingham NG3 7AN* Tel 0115-987 3425

BALL, Mrs Marion Elaine. b 68. Hertf Coll Ox BA90 St Jo Coll Dur BA99. Cranmer Hall Dur 97. **d** 02 **p** 03. C Kingston upon Hull H Trin from 02. *67 Adelaide Street, Hull HU3 2EZ* E-mail meandpj@fish.co.uk

BALL, Mark Francis. b 72. St Jo Coll Dur BA94. St Steph Ho Ox BA00. **d** 01 **p** 02. C Poulton-le-Fylde *Blackb* from 01. *24 Roylen Avenue, Poulton-le-Fylde FY6 7PH* Tel (01253) 884535 Mobile 07958-982482 E-mail thereverendmarkball@hotmail.com

✠**BALL, The Rt Revd Michael Thomas.** b 32. Qu Coll Cam BA55 MA59. **d** 71 **p** 71 **c** 80. CGA from 60; Prior Stroud Priory 64-76; C Whiteshill *Glouc* 71-76; Lic to Offic 76; P-in-c Stanmer w Falmer *Chich* 76-80; Chapl Sussex Univ 76-80; Suff Bp Jarrow *Dur* 80-90; Angl Adv Tyne Tees TV 84-90; Bp Truro 90-97; rtd 97; Perm to Offic *B & W* from 01. *Manor Lodge, Aller, Langport TA10 0QN*

BALL, Nicholas Edward. b 54. Man Univ BA75 Ox Univ MA85. Ripon Coll Cuddesdon 79. **d** 80 **p** 81. C Yardley Wood *Birm* 80-83; C Moseley St Mary 83-86; Chapl Cen 13 83-85; V Bartley Green 86-95; P-in-c Hall Green St Pet 95-97. *Address withheld by request*

BALL, Norman. b 41. Liv Univ BA63 Ch Coll Liv CertEd72. Cuddesdon Coll 65. **d** 68 **p** 69. C Broseley w Benthall *Heref* 68-72; Hd RS Christleton High Sch 72-75; V Plemstall w Guilden Sutton *Ches* 75-79; Hd RS Neston Co High Sch 79-94; NSM Dodleston 86-91; NSM Buckley *St As* 91-94; TV Hawarden 94-00; rtd 00; Perm to Offic *St As* from 00. *White Cottage, Lower Mountain Road, Penyffordd, Chester CH4 0EX* Tel (01244) 661132

BALL, Peter Edwin. b 44. Lon Univ BD65 DipEd. Wycliffe Hall Ox 75. **d** 77 **p** 78. C Prescot *Liv* 77-80; R Lawford *Chelmsf* 80-99; RD Harwich 91-96; P-in-c Broomfield from 99. *Broomfield Vicarage, 10 Butlers Close, Chelmsford CM1 7BE* Tel (01245) 440318 E-mail peter.ball@theworboys.freeserve.co.uk

✠**BALL, The Rt Revd Peter John.** b 32. Qu Coll Cam BA54 MA58. Wells Th Coll 54. **d** 56 **p** 57 **c** 77. C Rottingdean *Chich* 56-58; Novice SSM 58-60; CGA from 60; Prior CGA 60-77; Lic to Offic *Birm* 65-66; P-in-c Hoar Cross *Lich* 66-69; Lic to Offic *B & W* 69-77; Suff Bp Lewes *Chich* 77-84; Area Bp Lewes 84-92; Can and Preb Chich Cathl 78-92; Bp Glouc 92-93; rtd 93; Perm to Offic *B & W* from 01. *Manor Lodge, Aller, Langport TA10 0QN*

BALL, Canon Peter Prior. b 25. St Jo Coll Ox BA50 MA55. Ridley Hall Cam 51. **d** 53 **p** 54. C Gt Baddow *Chelmsf* 53-56; C Farnborough *Guildf* 56-60; Chapl Cannes *Eur* 76-80; Visiting Chapl Eur (& N Africa) ICS 80-86; Eur Rep SOMA UK from 86; rtd 90; Hon Can Malta Cathl *Eur* from 91. *Château d'Azur, 44 Boulevard d'Italie, Monte Carlo MC98000, Monaco* Tel (00377) 93 30 40 19 Fax as telephone E-mail pball@monaco.mc

BALL, Canon Peter William. b 30. Worc Coll Ox BA53 MA57. Cuddesdon Coll 53. **d** 55 **p** 56. C Poplar All SS w St Frideswide *Lon* 55-61; V Preston Ascension 61-68; R Shepperton 68-84; RD Staines 72-74; RD Spelthorne 74-83; Preb St Paul's Cathl 76-84; Can Res and Chan *Sarum* 84-95; Perm to Offic *Sarum* from 90; rtd 95. *Whittonedge, Whittonditch Road, Ramsbury, Marlborough SN8 2PX* Tel (01672) 20259

BALL, Philip John. b 52. Bris Univ BEd75 Ox Univ MTh98. Ripon Coll Cuddesdon 79. **d** 82 **p** 83. C Norton St Mich *Dur* 82-84; C Greenford H Cross *Lon* 84-88; V Hayes St Edm 88-97; AD Hillingdon 94-97; TR Bicester w Bucknell, Caversfield and Launton *Ox* from 97; RD Bicester and Islip from 01. *St Edburg's Vicarage, Victoria Road, Bicester OX26 6PQ* Tel (01869) 253222 Fax 246949 E-mail philipball@lineone.net

BALL, Philip John. b 63. Coll of Ripon & York St Jo BA91. Cranmer Hall Dur DTM99. **d** 99 **p** 00. C Linthorpe *York* 99-02; C Kingston upon Hull H Trin from 02. *67 Adelaide Street, Hull HU3 2EZ* Tel and Fax as above E-mail meandpj@fish.co.uk

BALL, Mrs Rita Enid. b 49. Sheff Univ LLB69. St Alb and Ox Min Course 94. **d** 97 **p** 98. NSM Newbury *Ox* from 97. *Monastery Lodge, 240 Andover Road, Newbury RG14 6PT* Tel (01635) 230352 E-mail ball@totalserve.co.uk

BALL, Roy. *See* BALL, John Roy

BALL, Timothy William. b 60. Trin Coll Bris 96. **d** 96 **p** 97. C Harlow St Mary and St Hugh w St Jo the Bapt *Chelmsf* 96-99; V Springfield H Trin from 99; Ind Chapl from 00. *The Vicarage, 61 Hill Road, Chelmsford CM2 6HW* Tel (01245) 353389 E-mail timmyball@tesco.net

BALL, Vernon. b 34. Ox Min Course 87. **d** 90 **p** 91. NSM Banbury *Ox* 90-99. *20 Springfield Avenue, Banbury OX16 9HT* Tel (01295) 265740

BALLAMAN, Ms Pauline Margaret. b 54. Goldsmiths' Coll Lon BA89 Lon Univ MA90. Oak Hill Th Coll 93 Ridley Hall Cam CTM95. **d** 95 **p** 96. C New Addington *S'wark* 95-97; World Ch Links Officer *Bradf* 97-00; C Keighley St Andr 97-00; Tutor United Coll of Ascension Selly Oak from 00. *The United College of the Ascension, Weoley Park Road, Selly Oak, Birmingham B29 6RD*

BALLANTINE, Peter Sinclair. b 46. Nottm Univ MTh85. K Coll Lon BA68 AKC68 St Jo Coll Nottm 70 Lon Coll of Div ALCD71 BD73 LTh74. **d** 73 **p** 74. C Rainham *Chelmsf* 73-77; C Wennington 73-77; TV Barton Mills *St E* 77-80; TV Barton Mills, Beck Row w Kenny Hill etc 80-82; Chapl Liv Poly *Liv* 83-86; Tr Officer Rugby Deanery *Cov* 86-97; P-in-c Churchover w Willey 86-97; P-in-c Clifton upon Dunsmore and Newton 86-97; Dir Buckingham Adnry Chr Tr Sch *Ox* 97-02; TV Stantonbury and Willen from 02. *The Rectory, The Green, Great Linford, Milton Keynes MK14 5BD* Tel (01908) 605892 Mobile 07984-902641

BALLANTINE, Roderic Keith. b 44. Chich Th Coll 66. **d** 69 **p** 70. C Nunhead St Antony *S'wark* 69-72; C S Hackney St Jo w Ch Ch *Lon* 72-75; P-in-c Kensal Town St Thos w St Andr and St Phil 75-79; V Stoke Newington St Andr from 79. *St Andrew's Vicarage, 106 Bethune Road, London N16 5DU* Tel (020) 8800 2900

BALLANTYNE, Jane Elizabeth. *See* KENCHINGTON, Mrs Jane Elizabeth Ballantyne

BALLARD, The Ven Andrew Edgar. b 44. Dur Univ BA66. Westcott Ho Cam 66. **d** 68 **p** 69. C St Marylebone St Mary *Lon* 68-72; C Portsea St Mary *Portsm* 72-76; V Haslingden w Haslingden Grane *Blackb* 76-82; V Walkden Moor *Man* 82-93; TR Walkden Moor w Lt Hulton 93-98; Chapl Salford Coll 82-92; AD Farnworth *Man* 90-98; P-in-c Rochdale 98-99; TR 00; Hon Can Man Cathl from 98; Adn Rochdale from 00. *57 Melling Road, Oldham OL4 1PN* Tel 0161-678 1454 Fax 678 1455 E-mail andrew.ballard@virgin.net

BALLARD, Miss Anne Christina. b 54. LRAM76 HonRCM93 ARAM94. Wycliffe Hall Ox 82. **dss** 85 **d** 87 **p** 94. Hove Bp Hannington Memorial *Chich* 85-87; Chapl St Mich Sch Burton Park 87-89; Chapl RCM *Lon* 89-93; Chapl Imp Coll 89-93; Prec Ch Ch *Ox* 93-98; P-in-c Ivinghoe w Pitstone and Slapton 98-03; P-in-c Llanbadarn Fawr, Llandegley and Llanfihangel etc *S & B* from 03. *The Rectory, Rock Road, Crossgates, Llandrindod Wells LD1 6RU* Tel (01597) 851204 Mobile 07958-571914 E-mail annieballard@supanet.com

BALLARD, Charles Martin. b 29. Jes Coll Cam BA52 MA56. **d** 58 **p** 59. C Doncaster St Geo *Sheff* 58-61; V Balne 61-62; rtd 94; Perm to Offic *Ely* 95-00. *35 Abbey Road, Cambridge CB5 8HH*

BALLARD, Duncan Charles John. b 65. Sheff Univ BSc87. St Mich Coll Llan 00. **d** 02 **p** 03. C Worc St Barn w Ch Ch *Worc* from 02. *96 Hollymount, Worcester WR4 9SF* Tel (01905) 29129 E-mail st.marys@virgin.net

BALLARD, Canon Michael Arthur. b 44. Lon Univ BA66. Westcott Ho Cam 68. **d** 70 **p** 71. C Harrow Weald All SS *Lon* 70-73; C Aylesbury *Ox* 73-78; V Eastwood *Chelmsf* 78-90; RD Hadleigh 83-90; Hon Can Chelmsf Cathl from 89; R Southchurch H Trin from 90; RD Southend-on-Sea 94-00. *The Rectory, 8 Pilgrims Close, Southend-on-Sea SS2 4XF* Tel (01702) 466423

BALLARD, Nigel Humphrey. b 48. Linc Th Coll 92. **d** 94 **p** 95. C Old Brumby *Linc* 94; C Bottesford w Ashby 94-97; P-in-c Helpringham w Hale 97-01; rtd 02. *10 Channings, 215 kingsway, Hove BN3 4FT* Tel (01273) 202584

BALLARD, Canon Peter James. b 55. SS Hild & Bede Coll Dur BEd78 Lon Univ DipTh85. Sarum & Wells Th Coll 85. **d** 87 **p** 88. C Grantham *Linc* 87-90 and 91; Australia 90; V Lancaster Ch Ch *Blackb* 91-98; RD Lancaster 94-98; Can Res Blackb Cathl and Dioc Dir of Educn from 98. *Wheatfield, 7 Dallas Road, Lancaster LA1 1TN* Tel (01524) 32897 *or* (01254) 54421 Mobile 07970-923141 Fax (01524) 66095 *or* (01254) 699963 E-mail peter.ballard@blackburn.anglican.org

BALLARD, Richard Ernest. b 37. Linc Coll Ox BA60 MA66 Lon Univ BD68. Wells Th Coll 62. **d** 62 **p** 63. C Farnham *Guildf* 62-67; Chapl Pierrepont Sch Frensham 67-69; Asst Chapl Eton Coll 69-74; P-in-c Stogursey *B & W* 74-76; P-in-c Fiddington 74-76; R Stogursey w Fiddington 76-78; R Trull w Angersleigh 78-80; Chapl Qu Coll Taunton 78-80; Chapl Wells Cathl Sch 81-86; Chapl Haileybury Coll 86-91; Chapl Westmr Sch and PV Westmr Abbey 91-98; Hon C Westmr St Matt *Lon* 94-98; rtd 98. *17 rue du Port, 17350 Crazannes, France* Tel (0033) (5) 46 91 01 10

BALLARD, Steven Peter. b 52. Man Univ BA73 MA74 Philipps Univ Marburg DrTheol98. St Steph Ho Ox 76. **d** 78 **p** 79. C Lancaster St Mary *Blackb* 78-81; C Blackpool St Mich 81-84; V Brierfield 84-94; Perm to Offic *Carl* from 95. *1 St Catherines Court, Drovers Lane, Penrith CA11 9EJ* Tel (01768) 890976 Fax as telephone

BALLENTINE, Ian Clarke. b 46. Aston Univ BSc71 CEng. BTh. **d** 91 **p** 92. C Lurgan St Jo *D & D* 91-95; I Mallusk *Conn* from 95. *The Rectory, 6 Carwood Drive, Glengormley, Newtownabbey BT36 5LP* Tel (028) 9083 3773 *or* 9087 9029 E-mail ian_ballentine@bigfoot.com

BALLENTYNE, Mrs Fiona Virginia Grace. b 61. ALAM80 R Holloway Coll Lon BA83 Dur Univ PGCE90. EAMTC 95. **d** 97 **p** 98. NSM Halesworth w Linstead, Chediston, Holton etc *St E* 97-98; C Sole Bay 98-00; Chapl St Felix Sch Southwold 99-00; Chapl HM YOI Castington from 00; Chapl Northumbria

Healthcare NHS Trust from 00. *27 Polwarth Drive, Newcastle upon Tyne NE3 5NH* Tel 0191-236 3788

BALLINGER, Francis James. b 43. AKC70. **d** 71 **p** 85. C Weston-super-Mare St Sav *B & W* 71-72; Dir Bd Soc Resp *Leic* 85-88; Hon C Bringhurst w Gt Easton 85-88; TV Melksham *Sarum* 88-93; P-in-c Spernall, Morton Bagot and Oldberrow *Cov* 93-98; P-in-c Coughton 93-98; Dioc Rural Adv 93-98; R Kingstone w Clehonger, Eaton Bishop etc *Heref* from 98. *The Rectory, Kingstone, Hereford HR2 9EY* Tel (01981) 250350 E-mail f.ballinger@midnet.com

BALMER, Walter Owen. b 30. N Ord Course 83. **d** 86 **p** 87. NSM Gateacre *Liv* 86-91; NSM Hale 91-00; Perm to Offic from 00. *38 Grangemeadow Road, Liverpool L25 4SU* Tel 0151-421 1189

BALMFORTH, The Ven Anthony James. b 26. BNC Ox BA50 MA51. Linc Th Coll 50. **d** 52 **p** 53. C Mansfield St Pet *S'well* 52-55; V Skegby 55-61; V Kidderminster St Jo *Worc* 61-65; V Kings Norton *Birm* 65-72; TR 73-79; RD Kings Norton 73-79; Hon Can Birm Cathl 75-79; Hon Can Bris Cathl *Bris* 79-90; Adn Bris 79-90; rtd 90; Perm to Offic *Glouc* from 90. *Slipper Cottage, Stag Hill, Yorkley, Lydney GL15 4TB* Tel (01594) 564016

BAMBER, David Beverley. b 51. Univ of Wales (Lamp) BA75. St Steph Ho Ox 75. **d** 77 **p** 78. C Altrincham St Geo *Ches* 77-80; C Oxton 80-81; Perm to Offic *Derby* 85-87; C Staveley and Barrow Hill 87-88; C W Retford *S'well* 89-90; C E Retford 89-90 and 91-92. *Address temp unknown*

BAMBER, Patrick Herbert. b 71. Dundee Univ MA93. Wycliffe Hall Ox BTh02. **d** 02 **p** 03. C St Austell *Truro* from 02. *St Luke's House, 5 Penhaligon Way, St Austell PL25 3AR* Tel (01726) 69857 E-mail patrick.bamber@virgin.net

BAMBER, Ms Sheila Jane. b 54. Univ of Wales (Lamp) BA75 Sheff Univ MA77 Open Univ MBA94. Ripon Coll Cuddesdon 96. **d** 98 **p** 99. C Dur St Cuth *Dur* 98-01; C Sacriston and Kimblesworth 01-02; TV Dur N from 02. *The Vicarage, 19 Church Parade, Sacriston, Durham DH7 6AD* Tel 0191-371 9024

BAMBERG, Robert William. b 43. Chu Coll Cam BA65 PGCE68. SW Minl Tr Course 98. **d** 01 **p** 02. NSM Kingsteignton *Ex* from 01. *11 Portland Avenue, Teignmouth TQ14 8RR* Tel (01626) 773711 E-mail sllbmbrg@aol.com

BAMFORD, Geoffrey Belk. b 35. Lon Univ BA57 Leic Coll of Educn PGCE58. Dioc OLM tr scheme 97. **d** 99 **p** 00. OLM Upper Holme Valley *Wakef* from 99. *11 Flushouse, Holmbridge, Holmfirth HD9 2QY* Tel (01484) 682532 E-mail judibamford@supanet.com

BAMFORD, Mrs Marion. b 35. K Coll Lon BA56 AKC56. N Ord Course 81. **dss** 84 **d** 90 **p** 94. Baildon *Bradf* 84-85; S Kirkby *Wakef* 85-90; Chapl Pontefract Gen Infirmary Wakef 89-96; Dn-in-c Brotherton *Wakef* 90-94; P-in-c 94-96; rtd 96; Perm to Offic *Wakef* 96-97 and from 96; *Bradf* from 96. *170 Warren Lane, Eldwick, Bingley BD16 3BY* Tel (01274) 564925

BAMFORTH, Marvin John. b 48. N Ord Course 78. **d** 81 **p** 82. C Barnoldswick w Bracewell *Bradf* 81-84; V Cullingworth 84-88; New Zealand 88-89; V Thornton in Lonsdale w Burton in Lonsdale *Bradf* 89-98; Dioc Chapl MU 91-94; P-in-c Bentham St Jo 93-98; Cyprus from 98. *The Anglican Church of Paphos, PO Box 61083, 8130 Paphos, Cyprus* Tel (00357) (26) 952684

BAMFORTH, Stuart Michael. b 35. Hertf Coll Ox BA58 MA61. Sarum Th Coll 60. **d** 62 **p** 63. C Adel *Ripon* 62-67; V Hempton and Pudding Norton *Nor* 67-71; V Toftrees w Shereford 67-71; P-in-c Pensthorpe 67-71; P-in-c Colkirk 69-70; Lic to Offic *Derby* 72-77; Lic to Offic *Ripon* from 77; rtd 95; Perm to Offic *York* from 01. *52 Beverley Road, Market Weighton, York YO43 3JP*

BANBURY, David Paul. b 62. Coll of Ripon & York St Jo BA84. Ridley Hall Cam 85. **d** 88 **p** 89. C Blackb St Jas *Blackb* 88-90; C Preston St Cuth 90-95; P-in-c Bradf St Clem *Bradf* 95-00; V 00; CPAS Evang from 01; Perm to Offic *Cov* from 01. *6 Kingland Drive, Leamington Spa CV32 6BL* Tel (01926) 771097 E-mail david@cpas.org.uk

BANFIELD, Andrew Henry. b 48. AKC71. St Aug Coll Cant 72. **d** 73 **p** 74. C Crayford *Roch* 73-76; Youth Chapl *Glouc* 77-89; Soc Services Development Officer Glos Co Coun from 89; Perm to Offic from 02. *Rosemary Cottage, Oakwood Close, Bream, Lydney GL15 6HU* Tel (01594) 563295

BANFIELD, The Ven David John. b 33. ALCD56. **d** 57 **p** 58. C Middleton *Man* 57-62; Chapl Scargill Ho 62-65; Asst Warden 65-67; V Addiscombe St Mary *Cant* 67-80; V Luton St Mary *St Alb* 80-90; Hon Can St Alb 89-90; RD Luton 89-90; Adn Bris 90-98; Hon Can Bris Cathl 90-98; rtd 98; Perm to Offic *Bris* from 98. *47 Avon Way, Stoke Bishop, Bristol BS9 1SL* Tel 0117-968 4227

BANGAY, Edward Newman. b 37. CQSW75 HNC94 CertRS97. New Coll Lon BD60. **d** 98 **p** 98. NSM Yeovil w Kingston Pitney *B & W* from 98; Chapl E Somerset NHS Trust from 98. *Castle Cottage, Main Street, Mudford, Yeovil BA21 5TE* Tel (01935) 850452

BANGAY (formerly REAST), Mrs Eileen Joan. b 40. Open Univ BA93. EMMTC 81. **dss** 84 **d** 87 **p** 94. Linc St Mary-le-Wigford w St Benedict etc *Linc* 84-87; C Stamford All SS w St Jo 90-93; NSM Walesby 93-95; P-in-c Sutton Bridge 95-00; V 00; RD Elloe E 99-00; rtd 01; Perm to Offic *Linc* from 01. *7 Chesham Drive, Baston, Peterborough PE6 9QW* Tel (01778) 560327

BANGLADESH, Moderator of the Church of. *See* BAROI, The Rt Revd Michael

BANGOR, Archdeacon of. *See* HAWKINS, The Ven Alun John

BANGOR, Bishop of. *See* DAVIES, The Rt Revd Francis James Saunders

BANGOR, Dean of. *See* EVANS, The Very Revd Trevor Owen

BANISTER, Jane Catherine. b 67. Man Univ BA90. Westcott Ho Cam BA96 CTM97. **d** 97 **p** 98. C Addington *S'wark* 97-00; C Wisley w Pyrford *Guildf* 00-02; Lic to Offic *St Alb* from 03. *The Rectory, Station Road, Aldbury, Tring HP23 5RS* Tel (01442) 851200 E-mail jbanister@fish.co.uk

BANISTER, Martin John. b 39. Worc Coll Ox BA62 MA68. Chich Th Coll 62. **d** 64 **p** 65. C Wellingborough All Hallows *Pet* 64-67; C Heene *Chich* 67-70; V Denford w Ringstead *Pet* 70-78; P-in-c Wilshamstead *St Alb* 78-80; P-in-c Houghton Conquest 78-80; V Wilshamstead and Houghton Conquest 80-89; RD Elstow 86-89; V Waltham Cross from 89; RD Cheshunt from 00. *The Vicarage, 5 Longlands Close, Waltham Cross EN8 8LW* Tel (01992) 633243

BANKS, Aleck George. b 18. Lon Univ BD42 AKC42. **d** 42 **p** 43. C Colchester St Jas, All SS, St Nic and St Runwald *Chelmsf* 42-45; C Leigh St Clem 45-51; V Bradfield 51-56; PC Becontree St Geo 56-61; V S Benfleet 61-83; rtd 83; Perm to Offic *Chelmsf* from 83; Perm to Offic *St E* from 85. *5 Gosford Close, Clare, Sudbury CO10 8PT* Tel (01787) 277088

BANKS, Allen James. b 48. Carl and Blackb Dioc Tr Inst 98. **d** 01 **p** 02. OLM Kells *Carl* from 01. *36 Basket Road, Whitehaven CA28 9AH* Tel (01946) 61470

BANKS, Brian William Eric. b 35. Lon Univ BD69 Birm Univ DPS70 Open Univ BA63. Wycliffe Hall Ox 63. **d** 65 **p** 66. C Swindon Ch Ch *Bris* 65-68; C Halesowen *Worc* 68-71; R Wychbold and Upton Warren 71-77; V Bengeworth 77-87; RD Evesham 81-87; R Freshwater *Portsm* 87-90; R Yarmouth 95-00; rtd 00; Perm to Offic *Sarum* from 01. *Candleford, 16 Malthouse Meadow, Portesham, Weymouth DT3 4NS* Tel (01305) 871126

BANKS, Geoffrey Alan. b 43. St Andr Univ MA66. N Ord Course 84. **d** 87 **p** 88. NSM Shelley and Shepley *Wakef* 87-89; C Halifax 89-91; V Holmfield 91-98; TV Upper Holme Valley from 98. *The Vicarage, Ash Grove Road, Holmfirth, Huddersfield HD9 3JR* Tel (01484) 683131

BANKS, John Alan. b 32. Hertf Coll Ox BA54 MA58. Westcott Ho Cam 56. **d** 58 **p** 59. C Warsop *S'well* 58-61; C Ox St Aldate w H Trin *Ox* 61-64; V Ollerton *S'well* 64-75; V Boughton 64-75; R Wollaton 75-83; RD Beeston 77-81; Lic to Offic 83-85; C Bramcote 85-86; C Arnold 86-95; rtd 95; Perm to Offic *S'well* from 95. *247 Oxclose Lane, Nottingham NG5 6FB* Tel 0115-926 6814

BANKS, Michael Lawrence. b 40. Open Univ BA72 Brunel Univ MA82. Westcott Ho Cam 84. **d** 86 **p** 87. C Cheshunt *St Alb* 86-89; Chapl HM Pris Blundeston 89-90; V Leagrave *St Alb* 90-94; V Hatfield Hyde 95-01; rtd 01; Perm to Offic *Nor* 01-03; P-in-c Barningham w Matlaske w Baconsthorpe etc from 03. *The Rectory, The Street, Matlaske, Norwich NR11 7AQ* Tel (01263) 577420 E-mail mbanks@pastoral.demon.co.uk

BANKS, Canon Michael Thomas Harvey. b 35. Ushaw Coll Dur 58 Open Univ BA75. **d** 63 **p** 64. In RC Ch 63-69; C Winlaton *Dur* 69-71; P-in-c Bishopwearmouth Gd Shep 71-75; TV Melton Mowbray w Thorpe Arnold *Leic* 75-80; TR Loughborough Em 80-88; Dir of Ords 83-97; Hon Can Leic Cathl 83-87; Can Res and Chan 87-03; Assoc P Christianity S 93-95; Hon C Leic H Spirit 01-03; rtd 03. *Harvard House, 7 Harvard Close, Moreton-in-Marsh GL56 0JT* Tel (01608) 650706

BANKS, Norman. b 54. Oriel Coll Ox BA76 MA80. St Steph Ho Ox 79. **d** 82 **p** 83. C Newc Ch Ch w St Ann *Newc* 82-87; P-in-c 87-90; V Tynemouth Cullercoats St Paul 90-00; V Walsingham, Houghton and Barsham *Nor* from 00. *The Vicarage, Church Street, Walsingham NR22 6BP* Tel (01328) 821316

BANKS, Philip Charles. b 61. NE Lon Poly BSc85 Nottm Univ BTh93 ARICS87 MRICS01. Linc Th Coll 90. **d** 93 **p** 94. C Chelmsf Ascension *Chelmsf* 93-94; C Brentwood St Thos 94-98; P-in-c Elmstead 98-03; V Coggeshall w Markshall from 03; Bp's Press Officer from 97; Bp's Dom Chapl from 01. *The Vicarage, 4 Church Green, Coggeshall, Colchester CO6 1UD* Tel (01376) 561234 *or* (01277) 352001 Mobile 07798-681886 E-mail pbanks@chelmsford.anglican.org

BANKS, Stephen John. b 65. Newc Univ BSc87. St Jo Coll Nottm MA96 DipMM97. **d** 97 **p** 98. C Sheldon *Birm* 97-00; P-in-c Austrey and Warton from 00; AD Polesworth from 02. *The Vicarage, 132 Main Road, Austrey, Atherstone CV9 3EB* Tel (01827) 839022 E-mail sbanks.home@ukgateway.net

BANKS, Susan Angela. *See* GRIFFITHS, Mrs Susan Angela

BANNARD-SMITH, Dennis Ronald. b 22. Birm Univ BSc42. St Alb Minl Tr Scheme 80. **d** 83 **p** 84. NSM Pavenham *St Alb* 83-88; NSM Odell and Pavenham 88-92; Perm to Offic from 92. *Goodly Heritage, 10 The Bury, Pavenham, Bedford MK43 7PX* Tel (01234) 822992

BANNER, John William. b 36. Open Univ BA78. Tyndale Hall Bris 61. **d** 64 **p** 65. C Bootle St Leon *Liv* 64-66; C Wigan St Jas 66-69; C Stapleton *Bris* 69-70; Australia 70-72; V Liv Ch Ch Norris Green *Liv* 72-82; V Tunbridge Wells H Trin w Ch Ch

Roch from 82. *The Vicarage, 63 Claremont Road, Tunbridge Wells TN1 1TE* Tel (01892) 526644 Fax 529300 E-mail crossandcrown@compuserve.com

BANNER, Prof Michael Charles. b 61. Ball Coll Ox BA83 MA86 DPhil87. **d** 86 **p** 87. Fell St Pet Coll Ox 85-88; Dean Peterho Cam 88-94; Prof Moral and Soc Th K Coll Lon from 94; NSM Balsham, Weston Colville, W Wickham etc *Ely* from 01. *King's College, Strand, London WC2R 2LS* Tel (020) 7848 2073 *or* (01223) 290001 Fax (020) 7848 2255

BANNISTER, Preb Anthony Peter. b 40. Ex Univ BA62. Clifton Th Coll 63. **d** 65 **p** 66. C Uphill *B & W* 65-69; C Hove Bp Hannington Memorial Ch *Chich* 69-74; V Wembdon *B & W* 74-91; Youth Chapl 80-83; RD Bridgwater 80-89; V Taunton St Jas from 91; Preb Wells Cathl from 97. *St James's Vicarage, 3 Richmond Road, Taunton TA1 1EN* Tel (01823) 333194 E-mail prebpeter@bannister1.freeserve.co.uk

BANNISTER, Clifford John. b 53. Hatf Coll Dur BA76. Ripon Coll Cuddesdon 84. **d** 86 **p** 87. C Weymouth H Trin *Sarum* 86-89; TV Basingstoke *Win* 89-94; V Hedge End St Jo from 94. *The Vicarage, Vicarage Drive, Hedge End, Southampton SO30 4DU* Tel (01489) 782288 E-mail cliff.bannister@fish.co.uk

BANNISTER, Grattan Eric McGillycuddy Colm Brendon. TCD BA50 MA53. **d** 52 **p** 57. C Rainbow Hill St Barn *Worc* 57-58; C Cork St Luke *C, C & R* 61-63; P-in-c Schull 63-75; rtd 75. *Ballydehob, Co Cork, Irish Republic*

BANNISTER, John Leslie. b 55. Kent Univ CertMS76 Lanc Univ MA99. Carl and Blackb Dioc Tr Inst 95. **d** 98 **p** 99. C Flimby and Netherton *Carl* 98-00; C Whitehaven 00-02; TV from 02. *The Vicarage, Oakfield Court, Hillcrest, Whitehaven CA28 6TG* Tel (01946) 693474 Mobile 07788-562488 E-mail johnlbannister@onetel.net.uk

BANNISTER, Lesley. b 30. **d** 99 **p** 00. OLM Gt Cornard *St E* from 99. *58 Broom Street, Great Cornard, Sudbury CO10 0JT* Tel (01787) 372889

BANNISTER, Peter Edward. b 38. Leeds Univ BSc60. Linc Th Coll 72. **d** 74 **p** 75. C Norbury St Steph *Cant* 74-77; C Allington and Maidstone St Pet 77-80; R Temple Ewell w Lydden 80-86; TV Bracknell *Ox* 86-93; P-in-c Swallowfield from 93. *The Vicarage, Swallowfield Street, Swallowfield, Reading RG7 1QY* Tel 0118-988 3786 Fax as telephone E-mail peter.bannister@virgin.net

BANNISTER, Simon Monro. b 38. St Jo Coll Ox BA62 MA69. Linc Th Coll 61. **d** 63 **p** 64. C Prestwich St Marg *Man* 63-66; C Farnborough *Roch* 66-70; V Bury St Mark *Man* 70-78; V Oldham St Mary w St Pet 78; TR Oldham 78-87; Hon Can Man Cathl 81-87; V Hatfield Hyde *St Alb* 87-94; P-in-c Brasted *Roch* 94-02; Dioc Adv on CME 94-02; rtd 02. *23 Donnington Road, Dunton Green, Sevenoaks TN13 2TN* Tel and fax (01732) 462764 Mobile 07959-562929 E-mail sbanni@aol.com

BANNON, Canon Richard Babington. b 20. TCD BA42 MA47. CITC 48. **d** 48 **p** 49. C Bangor Abbey *D & D* 48-51; C Belfast St Luke *Conn* 51-55; I Ardclinis w Tickmacrevan 55-86; Can Belf Cathl 85-86; rtd 86. *Dean's Cottage, 7 Whin Road, Ballygally, Larne BT40 2QJ* Tel (028) 2858 3230

BANTING, David Percy. b 51. Magd Coll Cam MA74. Wycliffe Hall Ox MA79. **d** 80 **p** 81. C Ox St Ebbe w H Trin and St Pet *Ox* 80-83; Min St Jos Merry Hill CD *Lich* 83-90; V Chadderton Ch Ch *Man* 90-98; V Harold Wood *Chelmsf* from 98. *The Vicarage, 15 Athelstan Road, Harold Wood, Romford RM3 0QB* Tel (01708) 376400 *or* 342080 E-mail office@stpetersharoldwood.org

BANTING, The Ven Kenneth Mervyn Lancelot Hadfield. b 37. Pemb Coll Cam BA61 MA65. Cuddesdon Coll 64. **d** 65 **p** 66. Asst Chapl Win Coll 65-70; C Leigh Park *Portsm* 70-72; TV Hemel Hempstead *St Alb* 73-79; V Goldington 79-88; P-in-c Renhold 80-82; RD Bedford 84-87; V Portsea St Cuth *Portsm* 88-96; RD Portsm 94-96; Hon Can Portsm Cathl 95-96; Adn Is of Wight from 96; Can Res Portsm Cathl from 02; rtd 03. *Furzend, 38A Bosham Hoe, Bosham PO18 8ET* Tel (01243) 572340 E-mail merlin.banting@fish.co.uk

BANYARD, Douglas Edward. b 21. S'wark Ord Course 69. **d** 71 **p** 72. NSM Selsdon St Jo w St Franc *Cant* 71-77; Perm to Offic *Portsm* from 77; Perm to Offic *Chich* from 77. *22 Lower Wardown, Petersfield GU31 4NY* Tel (01730) 261004

BANYARD, Michael George. b 47. Ch Ch Coll Cant CertEd69 Birm Univ BPhil79 Open Univ MA92. Westcott Ho Cam 01. **d** 01. NSM Chippenham *Ely* from 01. *Chippenham Vicarage, High Street, Chippenham, Ely CB7 5PP* Tel (01353) 659125 E-mail banyardmg1@yahoo.co.uk

BANYARD, Peter Vernon. b 35. Sarum Th Coll 57. **d** 59 **p** 60. C Southampton Maybush St Pet *Win* 59-63; C Tilbury Docks *Chelmsf* 63-65; Miss to Seamen 63-65; Namibia 65-68; V Chesterfield St Aug *Derby* 68-74; TV Grantham w Manthorpe *Linc* 74-78; TV Grantham 78-79; Chapl Warminster Sch 79-85; V Hykeham *Linc* 85-88; rtd 88; Perm to Offic *Linc* from 88. *56 Western Avenue, Lincoln LN6 7SY* Tel (01522) 829026 E-mail ppbanyard@hotmail.com

BANYARD (or BRUNSKILL), Canon Sheila Kathryn. b 53. Univ of Wales (Ban) BA75 K Coll Lon MA83 Ox Univ MTh99.

Cranmer Hall Dur 76. **dss** 82 **d** 92 **p** 94. Sunbury *Lon* 82-85; Asst Chapl Ch Hosp Horsham 85-90; Chapl Malvern Girls' Coll 90-95; TV Droitwich Spa *Worc* 95-00; TR from 00; RD Droitwich 99-02; Hon Can Worc Cathl from 03. *The Rectory, 205 Worcester Road, Droitwich WR9 8AS* Tel (01905) 773134 Fax as telephone E-mail sk.banyard@virgin.net

✠**BARAHONA, The Most Revd Martin de Jesus. c** 92. Bp El Salvador from 92; Primate Cen America from 02. *47 Avenida Sur, 723 Col Flor Blanca, Apt Postal (01), 274 San Salvador, El Salvador* Tel (00503) 223 2252 *or* 224 6136 Fax 223 7952 E-mail anglican@saltel.net

BARBER, Ann. *See* BARBER, Mrs Margaret Ann

BARBER, Charles William Walters. b 60. Pemb Coll Cam BA81 MA85. Wycliffe Hall Ox 83. **d** 86 **p** 87. C Wolverhampton St Matt *Lich* 86-90; C Hornsey Rise Whitehall Park Team *Lon* 90-94; Sub Chapl HM Pris Holloway 95; V Bowling St Steph *Bradf* from 96. *St Stephen's Vicarage, 48 Newton Street, Bradford BD5 7BH* Tel (01274) 720784

BARBER, Canon Christopher Albert. b 33. Ch Coll Cam BA53 MA57. Coll of Resurr Mirfield 56. **d** 58 **p** 59. C Cov St Pet *Cov* 58-61; C Stokenchurch and Cadmore End *Ox* 61-64; V Royston St Paul *Man* 64-70; V Stapleford *Ely* 70-80; RD Shelford 76-80; V Cherry Hinton St Andr 80-88; Hon Can Ely Cathl 88-98; R Cottenham 88-92; RD N Stowe 90-92; V Terrington St John 92-98; V Tilney All Saints 92-98; rtd 98; Perm to Offic *Ely* from 98; Asst Rtd Clergy and Clergy Widow(er)s' Officer from 00. *20 King Edgar Close, Ely CB6 1DP* Tel (01353) 612338

BARBER, Craig John Francis. b 71. STETS 99. **d** 02 **p** 03. NSM Brighton St Bart *Chich* from 02. *20 Sudeley Place, Brighton BN2 1HF* Tel (01273) 687420

BARBER, Garth Antony. b 48. Southn Univ BSc69 Lon Univ MSc79 FRAS MSOSc. St Jo Coll Nottm LTh76. **d** 76 **p** 77. C Hounslow H Trin *Lon* 76-79; Chapl City of Lon Poly 79-86; P-in-c Twickenham All Hallows 86-97; Chapl Richmond Coll 87-97; Chapl UEA *Nor* 97-02; P-in-c Kingswood *S'wark* from 02. *The Vicarage, Woodland Way, Kingswood, Tadworth KT20 6NW* Tel (01737) 832164 E-mail garth.barber@virgin.net

BARBER, Geoffrey Thomas. b 23. Univ of Wales (Lamp) BA51. Ridley Hall Cam 51. **d** 53 **p** 54. C Walthamstow St Mary *Chelmsf* 53-55; C Woking St Pet *Guildf* 56-57; V Chelsea St Jo *Lon* 57-66; V Rushden St Pet 66-75; V Leyton Em *Chelmsf* 75-81; rtd 81; Perm to Offic *Sarum* from 81. *22 Longacre Drive, Ferndown BH22 9EE* Tel (01202) 873626

BARBER, Hilary John. b 65. Aston Tr Scheme 92 Sarum Th Coll 94. **d** 96 **p** 97. C Moston St Jo *Man* 96-00; Adnry Liturg Adv from 98; R Chorlton-cum-Hardy St Clem from 00. *The Rectory, 6 Edge Lane, Manchester M21 9JF* Tel 0161-881 3063 E-mail barberhilary@hotmail.com

BARBER, John Eric Michael. b 30. Wycliffe Hall Ox 63. **d** 65 **p** 66. C Lupset *Wakef* 65-68; C Halifax St Jo Bapt 68-70; V Dewsbury St Matt and St Jo 70-80; V Perry Common *Birm* 80-95; rtd 95; Perm to Offic *Sarum* from 95. *21A Westhill Road, Weymouth DT4 9NB* Tel (01305) 786553

BARBER, Mrs Margaret Ann. b 31. GTCL52. Dalton Ho Bris 55 Sarum & Wells Th Coll 82. **dss** 83 **d** 87 **p** 94. Wimborne Minster and Holt *Sarum* 83-90; Par Dn 87-90; rtd 90; Hon Par Dn Hampreston *Sarum* 90-94; Hon C 94-02. *22 Longacre Drive, Ferndown BH22 9EE* Tel (01202) 873626

BARBER, Martin John. b 35. Univ Coll Lon BA61. Linc Th Coll 61. **d** 63 **p** 64. C Stepney St Dunstan and All SS *Lon* 63-67; Chapl K Sch Bruton 67-93; rtd 93; Perm to Offic *B & W* from 93. *1 Plox Green, Bruton BA10 0EY* Tel (01749) 812290

BARBER, Michael. b 40. Open Univ BA83. Oak Hill Th Coll 69. **d** 71 **p** 72. C Rothley *Leic* 71-74; C Leic Martyrs 74-76; V Queniborough 76-82; V Monkwearmouth All SS *Dur* 82-92; V Mirehouse *Carl* from 92. *The Vicarage, Hollins Close, Mirehouse, Whitehaven CA28 8EX* Tel (01946) 693565

BARBER, Neil Andrew Austin. b 63. Ealing Coll of Educn BA85. NTMTC 94. **d** 98 **p** 98. St Mary's Chr Workers' Trust from 95; NSM Eastrop *Win* 98-01; V Normanton *Derby* from 01. *St Giles's Vicarage, 16 Browning Street, Derby DE23 8DN* Tel (01332) 767483 E-mail neil_barber@bigfoot.com

✠**BARBER, The Rt Revd Paul Everard.** b 35. St Jo Coll Cam BA58 MA66. Wells Th Coll 58. **d** 60 **p** 61 **c** 89. C Westborough *Guildf* 60-63; V York Town St Mich 66-73; V Bourne 73-80; RD Farnham 74-79; Hon Can Guildf Cathl 80-89; Adn Surrey 80-89; Suff Bp Brixworth *Pet* 89-01; Can Pet Cathl 89-01; rtd 01; Hon Asst Bp *B & W* from 01. *Hillside, 41 Somerton Road, Street BA16 0DR* Tel (01458) 442916

BARBER, Philip. d 01. OLM Edensor *Lich* from 01. *125 Cobden Street, Stoke-on-Trent ST3 4EZ* Tel (01782) 769386 *or* 598366

BARBER, Philip Kenneth. b 43. St Jo Coll Dur BA65 Sheff Univ DipEd66. NW Ord Course 74. **d** 76 **p** 77. NSM Burscough Bridge *Liv* 76-84; Asst Master Ormskirk Gr Sch 76-84; P-in-c Brigham *Carl* 84-85; V 85-89; P-in-c Mosser 84-85; V 85-89; P-in-c Borrowdale 89-94; Chapl Keswick Sch 89-94; P-in-c Beetham *Carl* 94-99; Educn Adv 94-99; P-in-c Brampton and Farlam and Castle Carrock w Cumrew 99-02; P-in-c Irthington, Crosby-on-Eden and Scaleby 99-02; P-in-c Hayton w Cumwhitton 99-02; TR Eden, Gelt and Irthing from 02.

St Martin's Vicarage, Main Street, Brampton CA8 1SH Tel (01697) 742182 Fax as telephone
E-mail pbarber@crowdenlea.demon.co.uk

BARBER, Royston Henry. b 38. Univ of Wales (Abth) BD86. United Th Coll Abth 83. **d** 86 **p** 87. NSM Tywyn w Aberdyfi *Ban* 86-92; NSM Cannington, Otterhampton, Combwich and Stockland *B & W* 93-98; Perm to Offic from 98; Perm to Offic *Ex* from 00. *Brambledown, Silver Street, Culmstock, Cullompton EX15 3JE* Tel (01884) 841041

BARBER, Sheila. b 50. N Ord Course 96. **d** 99 **p** 00. C Dinnington *Sheff* 99-02; V Woodhouse St Jas from 02. *St James's Vicarage, 65 Cardwell Avenue, Sheffield S13 7XB* Tel 0114-269 4146

BARBER, William Ewart Worsley. b 15. Leeds Univ BA38. Coll of Resurr Mirfield 38. **d** 40 **p** 41. C Auckland St Helen *Dur* 40-41; C Heworth St Mary 41-44; C Winlaton 44-47; C Cov H Trin *Cov* 47-53; V Dean Forest H Trin *Glouc* 53-59; V Sandhurst 59-64; Asst Youth Chapl 60-64; Min Lower Tuffley St Geo CD 64-67; V Tuffley 67-74; R Huntley 74-79; Hon C Bromsberrow 79-90; rtd 79; Hon C Redmarley D'Abitot, Bromesberrow w Pauntley etc *Glouc* 79-90; Perm to Offic from 90. *37 St Mary's Square, Gloucester GL1 2QT* Tel (01452) 330842

BARBOUR, Mrs Jennifer Louise. b 32. JP67. Barrister-at-Law 55 St Hugh's Coll Ox BA54 MA57. Gilmore Course 80. **dss** 81 **d** 87 **p** 94. Bray and Braywood *Ox* 81-84; Hermitage and Hampstead Norreys, Cold Ash etc 84-87; Chapl Leeds Poly *Ripon* 87-92; Chapl Leeds Metrop Univ 92-95; rtd 95; NSM Shipton Moyne w Westonbirt and Lasborough *Glouc* 95-99; Perm to Offic *Bris* from 95; *Glouc* from 99; *Cov* and *Worc* from 00. *Cheriton, Aston Road, Chipping Campden GL55 6HR* Tel (01386) 840279

BARBOUR, Walter Iain. b 28. FICE65 Pemb Coll Cam BA48 MA53. Ox Min Course 78. **d** 81 **p** 82. NSM Bray and Braywood *Ox* 81-84; NSM Thatcham 84-87; TV Moor Allerton *Ripon* 87-95; rtd 95; NSM Shipton Moyne w Westonbirt and Lasborough *Glouc* 95-98; Perm to Offic *Bris* from 95; *Glouc* 98-01; *Cov* and *Worc* from 00. *Cheriton, Aston Road, Chipping Campden GL55 6HR* Tel (01386) 840279

BARBY, Canon Sheana Braidwood. b 38. Bedf Coll Lon BA59. EMMTC 81. **dss** 84 **d** 87 **p** 94. Derby St Paul *Derby* 84-87; NSM Derby Cathl 87-03; Dioc Dir of Ords 90-97; Par Educn Adv 93-01; rtd 03; Hon Can Derby Cathl *Derby* from 96; RD Derby N from 00. *2 Margaret Street, Derby DE1 3FE* Tel (01332) 383301 E-mail sheana@barbyr.freeserve.co.uk

BARCLAY, Ian Newton. b 33. Clifton Th Coll 58. **d** 61 **p** 62. C Cullompton *Ex* 61-63; C Ashill w Broadway *B & W* 63-66; V Chatham St Phil and St Jas *Roch* 66-69; C St Helen Bishopsgate w St Martin Outwich *Lon* 70-73; V Prestonville St Luke *Chich* 73-81; Lic to Offic 82-93; rtd 93; P-in-c Cannes *Eur* 98-02. *35 Marine Avenue, Hove BN3 4LH*
E-mail barclayican@compuserve.com

BARCLAY, Mrs Susan Molly. Wycliffe Hall Ox. **d** 87 **p** 99. Hon Par Dn March St Wendreda *Ely* 87-96; Tutor Past Studies Ridley Hall Cam from 96. *42 Greystoke Road, Cambridge CB1 8DS* Tel (01223) 246877 or 741058
E-mail sue.barclay@btopenworld.com

BARCROFT, Ambrose William Edgar. b 17. TCD BA40 MA46. TCD Div Sch Div Test41. **d** 41 **p** 42. C Drumachose *D & R* 41-46; Chapl RN 46-70; R Pitlochry *St And* 70-82; rtd 82; Perm to Offic *St And* from 82. *Farragon, The Terrace, Blair Atholl, Pitlochry PH18 5SZ* Tel (01796) 481691

BARCROFT, Ian David. b 60. UMIST BSc83 Edin Univ BD88. Edin Th Coll 85. **d** 88 **p** 89. Prec St Ninian's Cathl Perth *St And* 88-92; Min Perth St Ninian 88-92; P-in-c Aberdeen St Clem *Ab* 92-97; R Hamilton *Glas* from 97. *The Rectory, 4C Auchingramont Road, Hamilton ML3 6JT* Tel (01698) 429895 Fax as telephone E-mail 106107.2014@compuserve.com

BARD, Canon Christopher Frederick James. b 52. AKC75 Open Univ BA88. St Aug Coll Cant 75. **d** 76 **p** 77. C Billingham St Cuth *Dur* 76-79; C Egglescliffe and Chapl to Arts and Recreation *York* and *Dur* 79-81; P-in-c Epping Upland *Chelmsf* 81-95; Dioc Communications Officer 81-91; BBC Essex Relig Progs Producer from 89; TV Epping Distr from 95; Hon Can Chelmsf Cathl from 03. *The Vicarage, Epping Green, Epping CM16 6PN* Tel (01992) 572949 Fax 578892 E-mail chrisbard@hotmail.com *or* chris.bard@bbc.co.uk

BARDELL, Alan George. City Univ BSc. Guildf Dioc Min Course 89. **d** 92 **p** 93. OLM Addlestone *Guildf* from 92. *14 Dickens Drive, Addlestone KT15 1AW* Tel (01932) 847574

BARDELL, Terence Richard. b 51. Dioc OLM tr scheme 98. **d** 01 **p** 02. OLM Coningsby w Tattershall *Linc* from 01. *23 Hoplands Road, Coningsby, Lincoln LN4 4NE* Tel (01526) 342133

BARDSLEY, Warren Nigel Antony. b 52. AKC74. St Aug Coll Cant 74. **d** 75 **p** 76. C Leeds St Aid *Ripon* 75-78; C Cov St Jo *Cov* 78-80; P-in-c Stoke Golding w Dadlington *Leic* 80-89; TV Swinton and Pendlebury *Man* 90-94. *Orchard House, 22 Upper Olland Street, Bungay NR35 1BH* Tel (01986) 895760

BARDWELL, Mrs Elaine Barbara. b 60. K Coll Lon BA81 AKC81. St Steph Ho Ox BA85 MA90. **dss** 86 **d** 87 **p** 95. Heref H Trin *Heref* 86-89; C 87-89; Dir Past Studies St Steph Ho Ox 89-96; V New Marston *Ox* from 96; AD Cowley from 02. *The*

Vicarage, 8 Jack Straws Lane, Headington, Oxford OX3 0DL Tel (01865) 434340 E-mail elaine.bardwell@virgin.net

BARDWELL, John Edward. b 53. Jes Coll Cam BA75 MA79 Ox Univ BA85 MA90. St Steph Ho Ox 83. **d** 86 **p** 87. C Heref H Trin *Heref* 86-89; Perm to Offic *Ox* 90-96. *The Vicarage, 8 Jack Straws Lane, Headington, Oxford OX3 0DL* Tel (01865) 434340

BAREHAM, Miss Sylvia Alice. b 36. Hockerill Coll Cam CertEd59 Open Univ BA83 Ox Univ DipEd84. Ox Min Course 86. **d** 89 **p** 94. NSM N Leigh *Ox* 89-93; NSM Bampton w Clanfield 93-95; NSM Kedington *St E* 95-97; NSM Hundon w Barnardiston 95-97; NSM Haverhill w Withersfield, the Wrattings etc 95-97; NSM Stourhead from 97; NSM Hundon from 97; NSM Haverhill w Withersfield from 97. *St Mary's Cottage, Little Wratting, Haverhill CB9 7UQ* Tel (01440) 762303

BARFF, John Robert. b 43. Ch Coll Cam BA66 MA70 K Coll Lon MTh69. ALCD68. **d** 69 **p** 70. C Fulham St Mary N End *Lon* 69-73; CMS 73-83; Sudan 75-83; P-in-c Compton Greenfield *Bris* 83-85; P-in-c Pilning 83-85; V Pilning w Compton Greenfield 85-92; rtd 92; Perm to Offic *Bris* from 92. *10 Cote Park, Stoke Bishop, Bristol BS9 2AD* Tel 0117-968 5889

BARFORD, Patricia Ann. b 47. Univ of Wales (Cardiff) BSc68 PhD73. WMMTC 95. **d** 98 **p** 99. NSM Stoke Prior, Wychbold and Upton Warren *Worc* from 98. *Greenfields, Church Road, Dodford, Bromsgrove B61 9BY* Tel (01527) 871614

BARGE, Mrs Ann Marina. b 42. S'wark Ord Course 89. **d** 96 **p** 97. C Ludlow, Ludford, Ashford Carbonell etc *Heref* from 96. *8 Old Street, Ludlow SY8 1NP* Tel (01584) 877307

BARGE, David Robert. b 45. S Dios Minl Tr Scheme 92. **d** 95 **p** 96. NSM Westfield *B & W* 95-00; C Frome St Jo and St Mary 00; V Frome St Mary from 01. *St Mary's House, 40 Innox Hill, Frome BA11 2LN* Tel (01373) 455996 E-mail barge@innox.fsnet.co.uk

BARGE, Marian. **d** 00. OLM Mynyddislwyn *Mon* from 00. *8 Pinewood Court, Pontllanfraith, Blackwood NP12 2PA* Tel (01495) 227208

BARGH, George Edward Norman. b 25. St Jo Coll Cam BA48 MA53 Leeds Univ LLB51. Carl Dioc Tr Course 80. **d** 83 **p** 84. NSM Ulverston St Mary w H Trin *Carl* 83-86; P-in-c Egton w Newland 86-87; P-in-c Blawith w Lowick 86-87; P-in-c Egton-cum-Newland and Lowick 87-89; rtd 90; Perm to Offic *Carl* from 90. *1 Willowdene Gardens, Old Hall Road, Ulverston LA12 7WD* Tel (01229) 588051

BARHAM, Ian Harold. b 40. Clifton Th Coll 64. **d** 66 **p** 67. C Broadwater St Mary *Chich* 66-69 and 72-76; Burundi 71-72; R Beyton and Hessett *St E* 76-79; Perm to Offic 79-81; Hon C Bury St Edmunds St Mary 81-84; Chapl St Aubyn's Sch Tiverton 84-96; Chapl Lee Abbey 96-99; rtd 00; Perm to Offic *Ex* from 00. *53 Sylvan Road, Exeter EX4 6EY* Tel (01392) 251643

BARHAM, Mrs Jennifer Mary. b 43. RN65. Oak Hill Th Coll 92. **d** 95 **p** 96. NSM Leigh-on-Sea St Aid *Chelmsf* 95-02; NSM Gt Burstead from 02; Chapl Basildon and Thurrock Gen Hosps NHS Trust from 01. *47 Walker Drive, Leigh-on-Sea SS9 3QT* Tel (01702) 558766 E-mail jen-john@barham47.freeserve.co.uk

✠**BARHAM, The Rt Revd Kenneth Lawrence.** b 36. OBE01. Clifton Th Coll BD63. **d** 63 **p** 64 **c** 93. C Worthing St Geo *Chich* 63-65; C Sevenoaks St Nic *Roch* 65-67; C Cheltenham St Mark *Glouc* 67-70; V Maidstone St Luke *Cant* 70-79; S Area Sec Rwanda Miss 79-84; P-in-c Ashburnham w Penhurst *Chich* 84-01; Asst Bp Cyangugu (Rwanda) 93-96; Bp 96-01; rtd 01. *Rosewood, Canadia Road, Battle TN33 0LR* Tel (01424) 773073 Fax 777409 E-mail bishopken@compuserve.com

BARHAM, Canon Peter. b 62. Selw Coll Cam MA83. Linc Th Coll BTh94. **d** 94 **p** 95. C Fornham All SS and Fornham St Martin w Timworth *St E* 94-97; P-in-c Cockfield w Bradfield St Clare, Felsham etc 97-01; Min Can *St E* Cathl 98-03; Chapl 01-03; Can Res St E Cathl from 03. *2 Abbey Precincts, Bury St Edmunds IP33 1RS* Tel (01284) 701472 Fax as telephone E-mail revpeterbarham@aol.com

BARKER, Arthur John Willoughby. b 10. Lon Coll of Div 46. **d** 48 **p** 49. C Addiscombe St Mary *Cant* 48-53; V Westgate St Jas 53-58; Warden Scargill Ho 58-61; V Dent w Cowgill *Bradf* 61-76; rtd 76; Perm to Offic *Bradf* 76-99. *2-3 Capel Court, The Burgage, Prestbury, Cheltenham GL52 3GL* Tel (01253) 736411

BARKER, Arundel Charles. b 24. Tyndale Hall Bris 54. **d** 56 **p** 57. C Rodbourne Cheney *Bris* 56-58; V Islington St Steph w St Bart and St Matt *Lon* 58-65; R Passenham *Pet* 65-90; P-in-c Cosgrove 65-66; rtd 90; Perm to Offic *Derby* from 90. *7 Bull Farm Mews, Bull Lane, Matlock DE4 5NB* Tel (01629) 580321

BARKER, Brian Wallwork. b 26. G&C Coll Cam BA50 MA55. Wells Th Coll 51. **d** 52 **p** 53. C Bradford cum Beswick *Man* 52-55; Singapore 55-61; Malaya 62-63; Malaysia 63-64; V Ashton St Jas *Man* 65-71; R Burnage St Nic 71-85; R Heaton Reddish 85-91; rtd 91; Perm to Offic *Man* and *Ches* from 91. *105 Crossfield Road, Cheadle Hulme, Cheadle SK8 5PD* Tel 0161-486 0334

BARKER, Cameron Timothy. b 62. Rhodes Univ BA83 Nottm Univ MA(TS)96. St Jo Coll Nottm 94. **d** 96 **p** 97. C W Streatham St Jas *S'wark* 96-00; V Herne Hill from 00. *The Vicarage, 1 Finsen Road, London SE5 9AX* Tel (020) 7771 0381
E-mail cbarker@fish.co.uk

BARKER, Prof Charles Philip Geoffrey. b 50. Lon Univ MB, BS75 FRCS79 Lon Univ MS92. STETS 95. **d** 98 **p** 99. NSM Alverstoke *Portsm* 98-02. *Address temp unknown*
E-mail revdocpb@compuserve.com

✠**BARKER, The Rt Revd Clifford Conder.** b 26. TD71. Oriel Coll Ox BA50 MA55. St Chad's Coll Dur DipTh52. **d** 52 **p** 53 **c** 76. C Falsgrave *York* 52-55; C Redcar 55-57; V Sculcoates 57-63; CF (TA) 58-74; P-in-c Sculcoates St Silas *York* 59-61; V Rudby in Cleveland w Middleton 63-70; RD Stokesley 65-70; V York St Olave w St Giles 70-76; RD City of York 71-75; Can and Preb York Minster 73-76; Suff Bp Whitby 76-83; Suff Bp Selby 83-91; rtd 91; Hon Asst Bp York from 95. *15 Oak Tree Close, Strensall, York YO32 5TE* Tel (01904) 490406

BARKER, David Robert. b 45. Worc Coll Ox BA67 MA70. Virginia Th Sem BD72. **d** 72 **p** 73. C Roehampton H Trin *S'wark* 72-75; Chapl Goldsmiths' Coll Lon 75-79; Min Tr Officer *Cov* 79-85; Selection Sec ACCM 85-90; Sec for Continuing Minl Educn ACCM 85-90; V Sutton Valence w E Sutton and Chart Sutton *Cant* from 90. *The Vicarage, Chart Road, Sutton Valence, Maidstone ME17 3AW* Tel (01622) 843156

BARKER, Edward. *See* BARKER, William Edward

BARKER, Canon Francis Howard. b 41. St Deiniol's Hawarden. **d** 84 **p** 85. NSM Capesthorne w Siddington and Marton *Ches* 84-86; NSM Wilmslow 86-93; C 93-96; P-in-c Woodford from 96; Hon Can Ches Cathl from 02. *The Vicarage, Wilmslow Road, Woodford, Stockport SK7 1RH* Tel 0161-439 2286
E-mail church@christchurchwoodfordsfnet.co.uk

BARKER, Mrs Gillian Ann. b 52. Portsm Dioc Tr Course 91. **d** 92 **p** 98. NSM Alverstoke *Portsm* 92-95; NSM Bridgemary 95-96; Asst Chapl Portsm Hosps NHS Trust 96-98; Chapl 98-01; Chapl Ox Radcliffe Hosps NHS Trust from 01. *The Horton Hospital, Oxford Road, Banbury OX16 9AL* Tel (01295) 229104 *or* 275500

BARKER, Gordon Frank. b 43. Heriot-Watt Univ MSc75 Sheff Univ MA98. S & M Dioc Tr Inst 91. **d** 94 **p** 95. NSM Malew *S & M* 94-00; V Grain w Stoke *Roch* from 00; Through Faith Miss Ev from 00. *The Parsonage, High Street, Isle of Grain, Rochester ME3 0BS* Tel (01634) 270263 Mobile 07867-532658
E-mail revgfbgrainstoke@lineone.net

BARKER, Canon Hugh Remington. b 19. Pemb Coll Cam BA41 MA45. Chich Th Coll 41. **d** 43 **p** 44. C Mill Hill St Mich *Lon* 43-48; C Welling *S'wark* 48-51; V Walworth All SS and St Steph 51-62; V Wisbech St Mary *Ely* 62-75; RD Wisbech 72-75; P-in-c Walpole St Andrew 75-77; V 77-84; P-in-c Walpole St Peter 75-77; R 77-84; RD Lynn Marshland 76-84; Hon Can Ely Cathl 81-84; rtd 84; Perm to Offic Ely from 84. *39 Dowgate Road, Leverington, Wisbech PE13 5DJ* Tel (01945) 585385

BARKER, James Gavin. b 33. Kelham Th Coll 54. **d** 58 **p** 59. C Greenford H Cross *Lon* 58-61; C Bournemouth St Clem w St Mary *Win* 61-66; C Pokesdown St Jas 66-70; V Stanmore 70-77; Chapl Besselsleigh Sch Abingdon 77-86; Hon C S Hinksey Ox 77-79; Hon C Wootton (Boars Hill) 79-86; V Southbourne St Chris *Win* 86-98; rtd 98. *11 Beaconsfield Road, Christchurch BH23 1QT* Tel (01202) 479828

BARKER, Canon John Howard. b 36. Southn Univ BA58. Ripon Coll Cuddesdon 80. **d** 82 **p** 83. C W Leigh *Portsm* 82-84; V Cosham 84-88; Bp's Dom Chapl 88-96; Hon Can Portsm Cathl 93-02; V St Helens and Sea View 96-02; rtd 02; Perm to Offic *Portsm* from 02. *Coniston Lodge, 3 Coniston Drive, Ryde PO33 3AE* Tel (01983) 618674 Mobile 07802-281797
E-mail jhbarker@netcomuk.co.uk

BARKER, John Lawrence. b 26. Middx Poly BA74 NE Lon Poly MSc84. Oak Hill NSM Course 86. **d** 88 **p** 89. NSM Prittlewell *Chelmsf* 88-91; Perm to Offic *Linc* from 91. *Rose Cottage, Back Lane, Bilsby, Alford LN13 9PT* Tel (01507) 462644

BARKER, John Stuart. b 30. Keele Univ BA55. Wells Th Coll 55. **d** 57 **p** 58. C Oswestry St Oswald *Lich* 57-60; C Portishead *B & W* 60-63; V Englishcombe 63-69; R Priston 63-69; V Chew Magna w Dundry 70-85; rtd 94. *9 West Street, Axbridge BS26 2AA* Tel (01934) 732740

BARKER, Jonathan. b 55. Hull Univ BA79. Westcott Ho Cam 79. **d** 83 **p** 84. C Sketty *S & B* 83-86; Chapl Sport and Leisure 83-86; C Swansea St Mary w H Trin 85-86; Bermuda 86-90; TV Liv Our Lady and St Nic w St Anne *Liv* 90-93; P-in-c S Shore St Pet *Blackb* 93-98; Chapl Blackpool Victoria Hosp NHS Trust 93-98; V Cleckheaton St Jo *Wakef* from 98. *St John's Vicarage, 33 Ashbourne Avenue, Cleckheaton BD19 5JH*

BARKER, Julian Roland Palgrave. b 37. Magd Coll Cam BA61 MA65. Westcott Ho Cam 61. **d** 63 **p** 64. C Stafford St Mary *Lich* 63-66; Chapl Clare Hall Cam 66-69; Chapl Clare Coll Cam 66-70; Tutor St Aug Coll Cant 70-71; TV Raveningham *Nor* 71-78; TR 78-82; V Foremark *Derby* 82-02; V Repton 82-02; P-in-c Newton Solney 01-02; V Foremark and Repton w Newton Solney from 02; RD Repton 91-95. *St Wystan's Vicarage, Willington Road, Repton, Derby DE65 6FH* Tel (01283) 703317

BARKER, Canon Leonard Roy. b 24. Selw Coll Cam BA49 MA53. Ridley Hall Cam 49. **d** 51 **p** 52. C Harrogate St Luke *Ripon* 51-53; Prec Bradf Cathl *Bradf* 53-54; V Eccleston St Luke *Liv* 55-62; V Upton (Overchurch) *Ches* 62-80; Hon Can Ches Cathl 78-80; Dir Past Studies Ridley Hall Cam 80-84; Dioc Dir

of Ords *Ches* 84-90; Can Res Ches Cathl 84-89; rtd 90; Perm to Offic *Ches* from 90. *6 Dee Hills Park, Chester CH3 5AR* Tel (01244) 344104

BARKER, Mark. b 62. ACIB90. St Jo Coll Nottm BTh95. **d** 95 **p** 96. C Barking St Marg w St Patr *Chelmsf* 95-98; C Cranham Park from 98. *226 Moor Lane, Upminster RM14 1HN* Tel (01708) 221711 E-mail mark@barkerm.freeserve.co.uk

BARKER, Neil Anthony. b 52. St Andr Univ BSc73. Ridley Hall Cam 74. **d** 77 **p** 78. C Leic H Apostles *Leic* 77-81; C Camberley St Paul *Guildf* 81-86; R Bradfield *Ox* 86-88; P-in-c Stanford Dingley 88; R Bradfield and Stanford Dingley 88-92; R Woodmansterne *S'wark* from 92; Chapl Mother's Union from 96. *The Rectory, Woodmansterne, Banstead SM7 3NL* Tel (01737) 352849 E-mail revneil@i.am

BARKER, Canon Nicholas John Willoughby. b 49. Oriel Coll Ox BA73 BA75 MA77. Trin Coll Bris 75. **d** 77 **p** 78. C Watford *St Alb* 77-80; TV Didsbury St Jas and Em *Man* 80-86; TR Kidderminster St Geo *Worc* from 86; RD Kidderminster from 01; Hon Can Worc Cathl from 03. *The Rectory, 30 Leswell Street, Kidderminster DY10 1RP* Tel (01562) 822131 Fax as telephone E-mail nbarker@wfcsmail.com

BARKER, Canon Roy Thomas. b 33. K Coll Lon BD57 AKC57. **d** 58 **p** 59. C Headingley *Ripon* 58-62; C Hawksworth Wood 62-66; S Africa 66-92; Sub-Dean Cape Town 73-80; Can 74-80; Dean and Adn Grahamstown 80-92; Hon Can from 92; V Southmead *Bris* 92-98; rtd 98; Perm to Offic *Bris* from 98. *7 Cleeve Avenue, Downend, Bristol BS16 6BT* Tel 0117-956 9057 E-mail roy@cleeveave.freeserve.co.uk

BARKER, Stephen Luke Remington. b 20. Cant Sch of Min. **d** 82 **p** 83. NSM Cranbrook *Cant* 82-90; rtd 90; Perm to Offic *Cant* from 91. *St Damian's, High Street, Cranbrook TN17 3LH* Tel (01580) 712048

BARKER, Timothy Reed. b 56. Qu Coll Cam BA79 MA82. Westcott Ho Cam 78. **d** 80 **p** 81. C Nantwich *Ches* 80-83; V Norton 83-88; V Runcorn All SS 88-94; Urban Officer 89-90; Dioc Communications Officer 91-98; Bp's Chapl 94-98; Hon P Asst Ches Cathl 94-98; V Spalding *Linc* from 98; RD Elloe W from 00. *The Parsonage, 8 Church Street, Spalding PE11 2PB* Tel (01775) 722772 *or* 722675 Mobile 07775-833426 Fax (01775) 710273 E-mail tim.barker@spaldingchurches.org

BARKER, Walter Frederick. b 25. Lon Univ BD48 ALCD48. St Jo Coll Lon 44. **d** 51 **p** 52. C Worthing St Geo *Chich* 51-53; C Leeds St Geo *Ripon* 53-56; V Tollington Park St Anne Lon 56-63; V Tollington Park St Mark 56-63; Midl Sec CMJ 63-66; Home Sec CMJ 66-71; Gen Sec CMJ 71-86; Min at Large CMJ 86-89; rtd 89. *72 Lime Grove, Ruislip HA4 8RY* Tel (020) 8866 6941

BARKER, William Edward. b 28. Kelham Th Coll 49. **d** 54 **p** 55. C Warsop *S'well* 54-55; C Bawtry w Austerfield 55-57; V Frizington *Carl* 57-64; V Barrow St Jas 64-70; V Applethwaite 70-93; P-in-c Troutbeck 78-93; rtd 93; Perm to Offic *Carl* from 93. *114 Burneside Road, Kendal LA9 4RZ* Tel (01539) 734787

BARKING, Area Bishop of. *See* HAWKINS, The Rt Revd David John Leader

BARKS, Jeffrey Stephen. b 45. Cranmer Hall Dur 66. **d** 71 **p** 72. C Wootton *St Alb* 71-74; C Boscombe St Jo *Win* 74-76; C Ringwood 76-80; P-in-c Spaxton w Charlynch *B & W* 80; P-in-c Enmore w Goathurst 80; P-in-c Spaxton w Goathurst, Enmore and Charlynch 80-81; R 81-92; RD Bridgwater 89-94; V Wembdon from 92. *The Vicarage, 12 Greenacre, Wembdon, Bridgwater TA6 7RD* Tel (01278) 423468 E-mail stephenbarks@dsl.pipex.com

BARLEY, Ann Christine. b 47. Nottm Univ Dip Past Counselling 98. LNSM course 91. **d** 93 **p** 94. OLM Walton *St E* 93-00; OLM Walton and Trimley from 00. *13 New Road, Trimley St Mary, Felixstowe IP11 0TQ* Tel (01394) 283752 E-mail ann.carmel@lineone.net

BARLEY, Christopher James. b 56. St Steph Ho Ox DipMin93. **d** 93 **p** 94. C Upton cum Chalvey *Ox* 93-96; TV High Wycombe 96-01; V Swinton *Sheff* from 01. *The Vicarage, 50 Golden Smithies Lane, Swinton, Mexborough S64 8DL* Tel (01709) 582259

BARLEY, Gordon Malcolm. b 59. Aston Tr Scheme 94 Oak Hill Th Coll 96. **d** 98 **p** 99. C Walthamstow St Jo *Chelmsf* 98-02; TV Barking St Marg w St Patr from 02. *St Patrick's Vicarage, 79 Sparsholt Road, Barking IG11 7YG* Tel (020) 8594 1960 E-mail revgbarley@eggconnect.net

BARLEY, Ivan William. b 48. Lough Univ MA01 CEng74 MIEE74 Suffolk Poly DMS80. LNSM course 91. **d** 93 **p** 94. OLM Walton *St E* 93-00; OLM Walton and Trimley from 00; Dioc NSM/OLM Officer from 02. *13 New Road, Trimley St Mary, Felixstowe IP11 0TQ* Tel (01394) 283752 E-mail ivanbarley@stmarys.junglelink.co.uk

BARLEY, Lynda Mary. b 53. York Univ BA74 PGCE75 Lon Univ MSc76 FSS77. S'wark Ord Course 93. **d** 96 **p** 97. NSM Lower Nutfield *S'wark* 96-97; NSM Littleham w Exmouth *Ex* 97-98; NSM Tedburn St Mary, Whitestone, Oldridge etc 98-00; Hd Research and Statistics Abps' Coun from 00; NSM Cullompton, Willand, Uffculme, Kentisbeare etc *Ex* from 03.

Church House, Great Smith Street, London SW1P 3NZ Tel (020) 7898 1542 Fax 7898 1532 E-mail lynda.barley@c-of-e.org.uk

BARLEY, Victor Laurence. b 41. St Jo Coll Cam MA66 Ch Ch Ox DPhil72 FRCR76. **d** 02 **p** 03. NSM Flax Bourton *B & W* from 02; NSM Barrow Gurney from 02. *North Archway Cottage, Barrow Court, Barrow Gurney, Bristol BS48 3RW* Tel (01275) 463006 Pager 07654-630255 E-mail victor_barley@talk21.com

BARLING, Michael Keith. b 38. Oak Hill Th Coll 63. **d** 66 **p** 67. C Portman Square St Paul *Lon* 66-70; C Enfield Ch Ch Trent Park 70-74; V Sidcup St Andr *Roch* 74-78; Dir Fountain Trust 78-81; Chapl Bethany Fellowship and Roffey Place 81-88; Hon C Kennington St Mark *S'wark* 88-89; Prin Kingdom Faith Bible Coll 89-99; Pastor from 99. *Roffey Place, Horsham RH12 4RU* Tel (01293) 851543 Mobile 07818-405858 Fax (01293) 854610 E-mail church@kingdomfaith.com

BARLOW, Alan David. b 36. Worc Coll Ox BA59 MA65. Wycliffe Hall Ox 59. **d** 61 **p** 62. C Wealdstone H Trin *Lon* 61-67; V Neasden cum Kingsbury St Cath 67-73; Chapl Cranleigh Sch Surrey 73-81; Chapl Cheltenham Ladies' Coll 82-01; rtd 01; Perm to Offic *Glouc* from 02. *22 Moorend Road, Leckhampton, Cheltenham GL53 0EU* Tel (01242) 584668 Fax as telephone E-mail revdavid@globalnet.co.uk

BARLOW, Canon Charles William Moore. b 32. ALCM50 Man Univ BA57 Hon FGCM94 Hon RSCM98. Cuddesdon Coll 56. **d** 58 **p** 59. C Atherton *Man* 58-61; C Swinton St Pet 61-64; V Dobcross 64-76; V Dobcross w Scouthead 76-98; Hon Can Man Cathl 96-98; AD Saddleworth 97-98; rtd 99; Perm to Offic *Man* 99-03. *18 Mount Road, Marsden, Huddersfield HD7 6HP* Tel (01484) 844494

BARLOW, Clive Christopher. b 42. Linc Th Coll 67. **d** 70 **p** 71. C Surbiton St Mark *S'wark* 70-74; C Spring Park *Cant* 74-77; V Ash w Westmarsh 77-92; RD E Bridge 86-92; R Chartham from 92; RD W Bridge 95-01. *The Rectory, The Green, Chartham, Canterbury CT4 7JW* Tel (01227) 738256 Fax 732282 E-mail cbarlow@btinternet.com

BARLOW, Darren. b 65. Ridley Hall Cam CTM98. **d** 98 **p** 99. C Rayleigh *Chelmsf* 98-01; TV Billericay and Lt Burstead from 01. *The Vicarage, 7A Horace Road, Billericay CM11 1AA* Tel (01277) 656266 E-mail darren@revbarlow.freeserve.co.uk

BARLOW, David. b 50. Leeds Univ BA71 MA. Wycliffe Hall Ox 71. **d** 73 **p** 74. C Horninglow *Lich* 73-75; C Wednesfield St Thos 75-77; C Bloxwich 77-78; Chapl RN from 78. *Royal Naval Chaplaincy Service, Room 203, Victory Building, HM Naval Base, Portsmouth PO1 3LS* Tel (023) 9272 7903 Fax 9272 7111

BARLOW, Canon Edward Burnley. b 29. St Aid Birkenhead 56. **d** 58 **p** 59. C Lenton Abbey *S'well* 58-61; C Ipswich All SS *St E* 61-63; R Fishtoft *Linc* 63-76; V Linc St Giles 76-96; Can and Preb Linc Cathl from 92; rtd 96; Perm to Offic *Linc* 96-99. *8 Pynder Close, Washingborough, Lincoln LN4 1EX* Tel (01522) 793762

BARLOW, Paul Andrew. b 59. Imp Coll Lon BSc80 UMIST PhD84 Bolton Inst of HE PGCE85. Aston Tr Scheme 89 Chich Th Coll 91. **d** 93 **p** 94. C Hale *Guildf* 93-97; C Christchurch Win 97-01; P-in-c Alton All SS from 01. *All Saints' Vicarage, Queen's Road, Alton GU34 1HU* Tel (01420) 83458 E-mail paul@paulbarlow.plus.com

BARLOW, Paul Benson. b 31. Fitzw Coll Cam BA73 MA77 FRSA94. **d** 64 **p** 65. C Bath Abbey w St Jas *B & W* 64-74; Dep Hd Master Leys High Sch Redditch 74-81; Hd Master Jo Kyrle High Sch Ross-on-Wye 82-96; Perm to Offic *Heref* 82-85; Lic to Offic 85-92; NSM Walford and St John w Bishopswood, Goodrich etc 92-97; Perm to Offic from 97. *The Coach House, Hentland, Ross-on-Wye HR9 6LP*

BARLOW, Robert Mark. b 53. Nottm Univ PGDTMM97. St Jo Coll Nottm 84. **d** 86 **p** 87. C Colwich w Gt Haywood *Lich* 86-91; R Crick and Yelvertoft w Clay Coton and Lilbourne *Pet* from 91; Bp's Rural Officer from 98. *The Rectory, Main Road, Crick, Northampton NN6 7TU* Tel (01788) 822147 E-mail robert.barlow@zetnet.co.uk

BARLOW, Thomas Frank. b 24. WMMTC. **d** 84 **p** 85. NSM Dudley St Jas *Worc* 84-88; NSM Belbroughton w Fairfield and Clent 88-93; Perm to Offic from 93. *30 The Glebe, Belbroughton, Stourbridge DY9 9TH* Tel (01562) 730426

BARLOW, Timothy David. b 46. Univ Coll Ox BA67 MA71 Lon Univ BD71. Oak Hill Th Coll 71. **d** 71 **p** 72. C Marple All SS *Ches* 71-74; C Northwood Em *Lon* 74-78; Chapl Vevey w Château d'Oex and Villars *Eur* 78-84; Switzerland 84-89; V Chadkirk *Ches* from 89. *St Chad's Vicarage, Chadkirk Road, Romiley, Stockport SK6 3JY* Tel 0161-430 4652 E-mail tbarlow@tbarlow.freeserve.co.uk

BARLOW, William George. b 40. Liv Univ BSc62 Univ of Wales BD65. St Mich Coll Llan 76. **d** 76 **p** 77. C Roath *Llan* 76-79; TV Cyncoed *Mon* 79-83; R Radyr *Llan* from 83; RD Llan from 95. *The Rectory, 52 Heol Isaf, Radyr, Cardiff CF15 8DY* Tel (029) 2084 2417

BARNACLE, Ronald William. b 20. Wells Th Coll 66. **d** 66 **p** 67. C Emscote *Cov* 66-67; C Nuneaton St Nic 67-69; C Camp Hill w Galley Common 69-70; R Etton w Dalton Holme *York* 70-76; R Hinderwell w Roxby 76-78; P-in-c Buckland Newton *Sarum*

78-80; P-in-c Wootton Glanville and Holnest 78-80; P-in-c Pulham 78-80; R Radwinter w Hempstead *Chelmsf* 80-83; V Blackfordby *Leic* 83-84; Perm to Offic *Worc* 84-92; *Cov* from 87 and *Leic* from 97. *12 Larch Close, Bilton, Rugby CV22 7PJ* Tel (01788) 810390

BARNARD, Canon Anthony Nevin. b 36. St Jo Coll Cam BA60 MA64. Wells Th Coll 61. **d** 63 **p** 64. C Cheshunt *St Alb* 63-65; Tutor Wells Th Coll 65-66; Chapl 66-69; Vice-Prin 69-71; Dep Prin Sarum & Wells Th Coll 71-77; Dir S Dios Minl Tr Scheme 74-77; Can Res and Chan Lich Cathl *Lich* from 77; Warden of Readers 77-91; Dir of Tr 86-91. *13 The Close, Lichfield WS13 7LD* Tel (01543) 306210 or 306240 Fax 306109 E-mail tony.barnard@lichfield-cathedral.org

BARNARD, Catherine Elizabeth. b 54. York Univ BA76 Dur Univ BA79. Cranmer Hall Dur 77. **dss** 80 **d** 87 **p** 94. Mexborough *Sheff* 80-83; Sheff Manor 83-90; Hon Par Dn 87-90; Hon Par Dn Bolsterstone 90-94; C from 94. *The Vicarage, Stone Moor Road, Bolsterstone, Sheffield S36 3ZN* Tel 0114-288 2149 Fax as telephone

BARNARD, Canon John Stuart. b 19. Em Coll Cam BA41 MA45. Ridley Hall Cam 41. **d** 43 **p** 44. C Erith St Jo *Roch* 43-46; C Tonbridge SS Pet and Paul 46-49; C Ox St Aldate *Ox* 49-53; C Bromley Common St Aug *Roch* 53-58; V 58-73; Hon Can Roch Cathl 70-82; V Seal St Pet 73-82; Perm to Offic *Chich* from 82; rtd 84. *31 Haig Court, Cambridge CB4 1TT*

BARNARD, Jonathan Dixon. b 46. St Cath Coll Cam BA68. Cuddesdon Coll 69. **d** 71 **p** 72. C Silksworth *Dur* 71-74; C Hatfield Hyde *St Alb* 74-78; TV Hitchin 78-86; TR Penrith w Newton Reigny and Plumpton Wall *Carl* 86-91; rtd 91. *4 Hallin Croft, Penrith CA11 8AA* Tel (01768) 63000

BARNARD, Kevin James. b 52. Keble Coll Ox BA77 MA79. Cranmer Hall Dur 77. **d** 79 **p** 80. C Swinton *Sheff* 79-83; TV Sheff Manor 83-90; V Bolsterstone from 90; Bp's Adv on Issues Relating to Ageing from 94. *The Vicarage, Stonemoor Road, Bolsterstone, Sheffield S36 3ZN* Tel 0114-288 2149 Fax as telephone

BARNARD, Leslie William. b 24. St Cath Coll Ox BA50 MA55 Southn Univ PhD70. Cuddesdon Coll 51. **d** 51 **p** 52. C Portswood Ch Ch *Win* 51-55; V Shaw and Whitley *Sarum* 55-61; R Chilcomb w Win All SS and Chesil *Win* 61-68; Sen Lect Leeds Univ 69-83; Dioc Dir of Tr *Ripon* 70-76; Chapl Harrogate Gen Hosp 83-89; rtd 89; Perm to Offic *Ripon* from 89. *68 Park Place, Park Parade, Harrogate HG1 4NS* Tel (01423) 560038

BARNARD, Canon William Henry. b 09. Dorchester Miss Coll 37. **d** 39 **p** 40. C Leic St Paul *Leic* 39-43; C Brighton All So *Chich* 43-51; C Barrowhill *Derby* 51-52; C Newbold w Dunston 51-53; R Hinton Martel *Sarum* 53-93; V Wimborne 75-79; Can and Preb Sarum Cathl 79-93; rtd 93; Perm to Offic *B & W* from 94. *Halcyon, 94 Park Road, Congresbury, Bristol BS49 5HH*

BARNDEN, Saskia Gail. b 50. Waterloo Univ (Canada) BA70 Victoria Univ (BC) MA71 Indiana Univ PhD87. St Alb and Ox Min Course 97. **d** 00. Asst Chapl Wycombe Abbey Sch 00-01; Chapl Haberdasher's Monmouth Sch for Girls from 01. *47 Elvetham Road, Birmingham B15 2LY* Tel 0121-440 5677 or (01494) 524582

BARNES, Alan Duff. b 42. St Steph Ho Ox 75. **d** 77 **p** 78. C Wanstead H Trin Hermon Hill *Chelmsf* 77-80; C Clacton St Jas 80-82; R Cranham 82-89; V Calcot *Ox* from 89. *St Birinus' House, Langley Hill, Calcot, Reading RG31 4QX* Tel 0118-942 2828

BARNES, Canon Brian. b 42. Sussex Univ MA82. Cant Sch of Min 79. **d** 82 **p** 83. NSM Maidstone All SS and St Phil w Tovil *Cant* 82-89; C 89-92; FE Adv Gen Syn Bd of Educn 86-92; R Staplehurst *Cant* 92-02; V Hythe from 02; RD W Charing 95-99; AD Cranbrook from 01; Hon Can Cant Cathl from 01. *St Leonard's Vicarage, Oak Walk, Hythe CT21 5DN* Tel (01303) 266217

BARNES, Brian. b 49. St Mich Coll Llan 93. **d** 93 **p** 94. C Betws w Ammanford *St D* 93-96; V Llanwnda, Goodwick w Manorowen and Llanstinan from 96. *The Vicarage, Dyffryn, Goodwick SA64 0AN* Tel (01348) 873758

BARNES, Canon Bryan Peter. b 24. Leeds Univ BA50. Coll of Resurr Mirfield 50. **d** 52 **p** 53. C Swindon New Town *Bris* 52-59; S Rhodesia 59-65; Rhodesia 65-66; V Moorfields *Bris* 66-71; P-in-c Winterbourne Down 71-75; V Fishponds St Mary 75-87; Hon Can Bris Cathl 80-87; rtd 87; NSM Duloe w Herodsfoot *Truro* 91-95; Warden Jes Hosp Cant 95-98. *St Katharine's House, Ormond Road, Wantage OX12 8EA* Tel (01235) 762100

BARNES, Canon Charles Peter Kentish. b 19. Ch Coll Cam BA40 MA44. Ridley Hall Cam 40. **d** 42 **p** 43. C Reading St Jo *Ox* 42-45; C Sutton Coldfield H Trin *Birm* 45-49; Sub-Dean Cairo Cathl Egypt 49-52; R Wavertree St Mary *Liv* 52-56; R Maghull 56-69; R Stratford-on-Avon w Bishopton *Cov* 69-75; TR 75-81; Hon Can Cov Cathl 73-84; V Priors Hardwick, Priors Marston and Wormleighton 81-84; rtd 84; Perm to Offic *Cov* and *Glouc* from 84. *1 Capel Court, The Burgage, Prestbury, Cheltenham GL52 3EL* Tel (01242) 516591

BARNES, Christopher Charles. b 51. Victoria Univ Wellington BA79 TDip79. Trin Coll Bris. **d** 00 **p** 01. C Langport Area Chs

B & W 00-03; P-in-c Burton and Rosemarket *St D* from 03. *The Rectory, Burton, Milford Haven SA73 1NX* Tel (01646) 600877 Mobile 07932-165719 E-mail chris.barnes@ukonline.co.uk

BARNES, Colin. b 33. St Jo Coll York CertEd58. St Aid Birkenhead 61. **d** 64 **p** 65. C Eccles St Mary *Man* 64-66; C Barrow St Geo w St Luke *Carl* 66-68; V Goodshaw *Man* 68-80; P-in-c Wythenshawe St Martin 80-83; New Zealand 83-98; rtd 98; Perm to Offic *Man* from 98. *5 Worston Close, Rawtenstall, Rossendale BB4 8UP* Tel (01706) 215199

BARNES, Cyril Arthur. b 26. Edin Th Coll 47. **d** 50 **p** 51. C Aberdeen St Jo *Ab* 50-53; R Forres *Mor* 53-55; C Darrington *Wakef* 55-58; V Ripponden 58-67; V Thorpe 66-67; R Huntly *Mor* 67-83; R Aberchirder 67-83; Hon Can St Andr Cathl Inverness 71-80; Dioc Sec 71-83; R Keith 74-83; Syn Clerk 77-80; Dean *Mor* 80-83; rtd 83; Perm to Offic *Ab* from 83; Perm to Offic *Mor* from 90. *Tillyramont Cottage, Parish of Isla, Huntly AB54 4SP* Tel (01466) 711370 Fax as telephone

BARNES, David John. b 37. Lon Univ DipRS65 Kent Univ MA96. Chich Th Coll 65. **d** 68 **p** 69. C Crayford *Roch* 68-71; Chapl RAF 71-75; Chapl Sutton Valence Sch Kent 75-87; C Minster-in-Sheppey *Cant* 87-93; V Ash w Westmarsh 93-01; RD E Bridge 98-01; R Aberchirder 67-83; rtd 98. *Home Farm Cottage, School Lane, Higham, Rochester ME3 7JG* Tel (01474) 822589 Fax as telephone E-mail davidbarnes@pgen.net

BARNES, David Keith. b 53. Linc Th Coll. **d** 89 **p** 90. C E Crompton *Man* 89-93; V Belfield 93-99; V Honley *Wakef* from 99. *The Vicarage, St Mary's Road, Honley, Huddersfield HD7 6AZ* Tel (01484) 661178

BARNES, Derek Ian. b 44. Leeds Univ BA66. Westcott Ho Cam 66. **d** 68 **p** 69. C Far Headingley St Chad *Ripon* 68-71; Chapl Qu Eliz Coll *Lon* 72-77; Warden Lee Abbey Internat Students' Club Kensington 77-81; Hon C Willesden Green St Gabr *Lon* 81-83; P-in-c Southall H Trin 84-98; P-in-c Southall St Geo 89-92; Perm to Offic from 99; Chapl W Lon Mental Health NHS Trust from 02. *West London Mental Health NHS Trust, Uxbridge Road, Southall UB1 3EU* Tel (020) 8354 8354 E-mail derekibarnes@yahoo.com

BARNES, Preb Donald Edward. b 26. K Coll Lon BD51 AKC51. **d** 52 **p** 53. C Willesden St Matt *Lon* 52-59; V Cricklewood St Pet 59-79; Lect Bps' Coll Cheshunt 63-68; V Belsize Park *Lon* 79-96; Preb St Paul's Cathl 84-96; AD N Camden 88-93; rtd 96; Perm to Offic *Lon* from 96. *94 Hamilton Road, London NW11 9DY* Tel (020) 8731 9860

BARNES, Duncan Christopher. b 64. Warwick Univ BA90. Trin Coll Bris BA93. **d** 93 **p** 94. C Hornchurch St Andr *Chelmsf* 93-98; V Bicker *Linc* 98-00; V Donington 98-00; TV Woughton *Ox* from 00. *2 Braunston, Woughton Park, Milton Keynes MK6 3AU* Tel (01908) 674742 E-mail dunc@classicfm.net

✠**BARNES, The Rt Revd Edwin Ronald.** b 35. Pemb Coll Ox BA58 MA62. Cuddesdon Coll 58. **d** 60 **p** 61 **c** 95. C Portsea N End St Mark *Portsm* 60-64; C Woodham *Guildf* 64-67; R Farncombe 67-78; V Hessle *York* 78-85; AD W Hull 85-87; Prin St Steph Ho Ox 87-95; Hon Can Ch Ch Ox 94-95; Suff Bp Richborough (PEV) *Cant* 95-01; Hon Asst Bp St Alb 96-01; Hon Asst Bp Chelmsf 99-01; rtd 01; Hon Asst Bp Win from 01. *1 Queen Elizabeth Avenue, Lymington SO41 9HN* Tel (01590) 610133 E-mail bishedwin@aol.com

BARNES, Mrs Enid Mabel. b 38. Homerton Coll Cam Dip Teaching58. WMMTC 87. **d** 90 **p** 94. Par Dn Walsall St Paul *Lich* 90-94; C 94-96; TV Chell 96-02; rtd 02; Perm to Offic *Lich* from 02. *16 Thatcher Grove, Biddulph, Stoke-on-Trent ST8 6SW* Tel (01782) 522591 E-mail enidbarnes@hotmail.com

BARNES, Jennifer. b 45. AdDipCrim Open Univ MA97. N Ord Course 94. **d** 96 **p** 97. C Thorne *Sheff* 96-99; C Clifton St Jas 99-01; Chapl HM Pris Featherstone from 01. *HM Prison, New Road, Featherstone, Wolverhampton WV10 7PU* Tel (01902) 790991 ext 325

BARNES, Jeremy Paul Blissard. b 70. Southn Univ BSc92. Wycliffe Hall Ox BTh99. **d** 99 **p** 00. C Brompton H Trin w Onslow Square St Paul *Lon* from 99. *St Paul's Vicarage Flat, Onslow Square, London SW7 3NX* Tel (020) 7460 5474 E-mail jez.barnes@htb.org.uk

BARNES, Canon John Barwick. b 32. AKC58. **d** 59 **p** 60. C Brentwood St Thos *Chelmsf* 59-65; R Arkesden w Wicken Bonhunt 65-71; V Gt Ilford St Mary 71-99; Hon Can Chelmsf Cathl 91-99; rtd 99; Perm to Offic *Chelmsf* from 99. *352 Henley Road, Ilford IG1 1TJ* Tel (020) 8478 1954

BARNES, John Christopher. b 43. MA ATI DMS. Linc Th Coll 78. **d** 80 **p** 81. C Guiseley *Bradf* 80-83; TV Guiseley w Esholt 83-86; V Rawdon 86-92; R Armthorpe *Sheff* 92-98; TR Maltby 98-01; RD Doncaster 96-98; Hon Can Sheff Cathl 00-01; TR Blakenall Heath *Lich* from 01. *Christ Church Rectory, Blakenall Heath, Walsall WS3 1HT* Tel (01922) 479593

BARNES, John Seymour. b 30. Qu Coll Birm 58. **d** 61 **p** 62. C Bromsgrove St Jo *Worc* 61-64; C Kingsthorpe *Pet* 64-66; C Styvechale *Cov* 66-69; P-in-c Avon Dassett w Farnborough 69-75; P-in-c Cov St Alb 75-84; R Weddington and Caldecote 84-89; P-in-c Wilnecote *Lich* 89-90; V Bentley 90-96; rtd 96;

Perm to Offic *Lich* from 96. *16 Thatcher Grove, Biddulph, Stoke-on-Trent ST8 6SW* Tel (01782) 522591

BARNES, Katrina Crawford. b 52. Oak Hill NSM Course 90 K Coll Lon BA98 AKC98. **d** 93 **p** 94. NSM Bromley H Trin *Roch* 93-98; C Meopham w Nurstead 98-00; Assoc Staff Tutor SEITE from 99; R Longfield *Roch* from 01. *The Rectory, 67 Main Road, Longfield DA3 7PQ* Tel (01474) 702201 E-mail katrina_barnes@talk21.com

BARNES, Mrs Mary Jane. b 48. St Jo Coll Nottm 97. **d** 99 **p** 00. C Harefield *Lon* 99-02; TV New Windsor *Ox* from 02. *The Vicarage, 73 Alma Road, Windsor SL4 3HD* Tel (01753) 861757 Mobile 07930-337407 E-mail mary@harefield9.fsnet.co.uk

BARNES, Matthew John. b 68. Leeds Univ MA99. St Jo Coll Nottm BA93. **d** 96 **p** 97. C Stanley *Wakef* 96-99; TV N Wingfield, Clay Cross and Pilsley *Derby* from 99. *The Vicarage, Stretton Road, Clay Cross, Chesterfield S45 9AQ* Tel (01246) 250110 Mobile 07977-976348 E-mail mjbarnes@talk21.com

BARNES, Neal Duncan. b 63. Leeds Univ BSc84 Cranfield Inst of Tech PhD92. Oak Hill Th Coll DipHE95. **d** 95 **p** 96. C Biggleswade *St Alb* 95-99; V Anlaby St Pet *York* from 99; Hon Chapl Ambulance Service Hull from 99. *The Vicarage, Church Street, Anlaby, Hull HU10 7DG* Tel (01482) 653024 E-mail neal@anvic.karoo.co.uk

BARNES, Canon Neil. b 42. Kelham Th Coll 61 Bps' Coll Cheshunt 65. **d** 68 **p** 69. C Poulton-le-Fylde *Blackb* 68-72; C Ribbleton 72-75; V Knuzden 75-81; Chapl Prestwich Hosp Man 81-88; Chapl Salford Mental Health Services NHS Trust from 88; Manager Chapl Services from 94; Hon Can Man Cathl *Man* from 96. *Mental Health Services of Salford, Bury New Road, Prestwich, Manchester M25 3BL* Tel 0161-772 3675, 773 9121 ext 3675 *or* (01282) 451533

BARNES, Paul. See BYLLAM-BARNES, Preb Paul William Marshall

BARNES, Paul Nicholas. b 58. Qu Coll Birm 89. **d** 91 **p** 92. C Weymouth H Trin *Sarum* 91-95; P-in-c Studley from 95. *The Vicarage, 340 Frome Road, Studley, Trowbridge BA14 0ED* Tel (01225) 753162

BARNES, Peter. See BARNES, Canon Charles Peter Kentish

BARNES, Peter Frank. b 52. St Jo Coll Nottm LTh81. **d** 81 **p** 82. C Colne St Bart *Blackb* 81-83; C Melton Mowbray w Thorpe Arnold *Leic* 83-86; P-in-c Barlestone 86-89; V Broughton and Duddon *Carl* 89-98; V Shrewsbury St Geo w Greenfields *Lich* from 98; P-in-c Bicton, Montford w Shrawardine and Fitz 98-00. *The Vicarage, St George's Street, Shrewsbury SY3 8QA* Tel (01743) 235461 E-mail peter.barnes@lineone.net

BARNES, Philip Richard. b 73. Westmr Coll Ox BTh94 Heythrop Coll Lon MA99. St Steph Ho Ox. **d** 00 **p** 01. C Ruislip St Martin *Lon* 00-03; Shrine P Shrine of Our Lady of Walsingham from 03. *The Shrine of Our Lady of Walsingham, The College, Knight Street, Walsingham NR22 6EF* Tel (01328) 824203 E-mail p.barnes@olw-shrine.org.uk

BARNES, Roland Peter. b 59. Ban Ord Course 01. **d** 03. *Penygeulan, Llanymawddwy, Machynlleth SY20 9AJ* Tel (01650) 531219

BARNES, Stephen. b 46. Hull Univ BA69 Bris Univ DipTh71. Clifton Th Coll 69. **d** 72 **p** 73. C Girlington *Bradf* 72-74; TV Glyncorrwg w Afan Vale and Cymmer Afan *Llan* 74-79; R 79-86; V Aberavon 86-01; V Dulais Valley from 01. *The Vicarage, 86 Church Road, Seven Sisters, Neath SA10 9DT* Tel (01639) 700286 Fax as telephone E-mail sbarnes.cwmdulais@btinternet.com

BARNES, Stephen John. b 59. Univ of Wales (Cardiff) BSc80. Chich Th Coll 83. **d** 86 **p** 87. C Neath w Llantwit *Llan* 86-89; C Coity w Nolton 89-95; V Troedyrhiw w Merthyr Vale from 95. *The Vicarage, Nixonville, Merthyr Vale, Merthyr Tydfil CF48 4RF* Tel (01443) 690249

BARNES, Stephen Martin Leonard. b 60. St Steph Ho Ox. **d** 87. C N Hinksey *Ox* 87-88; In RC Ch 88-98; Perm to Offic *Birm* from 98; NSM Kingstanding St Mark from 98. *All Saints Clergy House, 85 Jenkins Street, Small Heath, Birmingham B10 0PR* Tel 0121-772 0624

BARNES, Stephen William. b 53. Man Univ BSc. St Jo Coll Nottm DipTh82. **d** 83 **p** 84. C Chadwell Heath *Chelmsf* 83-87; C Becontree St Alb 88-89; Deanery Youth Chapl 88-91; C Becontree S 89-91; TV Worth *Chich* 91-98; Chapl Willen Hospice Milton Keynes from 99. *23 White Horse Drive, Milton Keynes MK4 2AZ* Tel (01908) 508896 *or* 663636

BARNES, Mrs Sylvia Frances. b 43. Shoreditch Coll Lon CertEd75. S Tr Scheme 92. **d** 96 **p** 97. Hon C Cusop w Blakemere, Bredwardine w Brobury etc *Heref* from 96. *Pwll Cwm, Arthur's Stone Lane, Dorstone, Hereford HR3 6AY* Tel (01981) 500252

BARNES, Timothy. b 56. Birm Univ BSc78. Westcott Ho Cam 96 Lon Bible Coll 82. **d** 98 **p** 99. C Shrub End *Chelmsf* 98-02; V Leigh-on-Sea St Aid from 02. *St Aidan's Vicarage, 78 Moor Park Gardens, Leigh-on-Sea SS9 4PY* Tel (01702) 512531 E-mail timbarnes@timbo7.fsnet.co.uk

BARNES, William Joseph Athanasius. b 57. St Andr Univ MTh84 Newc Univ MA02 RGN89. Westcott Ho Cam 91. **d** 92 **p** 93. C S Bank *York* 92-95; C Northallerton w Kirby Sigston 95-97; V

Dormanstown 97-01; P-in-c Netherton St Andr *Worc* from 01. *St Andrew's Vicarage, Highbridge Road, Netherton, Dudley DY2 0HT* Tel (01384) 257097
E-mail bja.barnes@btopenworld.com

BARNES, Canon William Thomas. b 39. Dur Univ BA60. Wycliffe Hall Ox 60. **d** 62 **p** 63. C Scotforth *Blackb* 62-66; C Cleveleys 66-67; V Colne Ch Ch 67-74; V Bamber Bridge St Sav from 74; Hon Can Blackb Cathl from 00. *St Saviour's Vicarage, Church Road, Bamber Bridge, Preston PR5 6AJ* Tel (01772) 335374

BARNES-CLAY, Peter John Granger. b 43. MCollP Cam Univ CertEd69. Chich Th Coll 72. **d** 75 **p** 82. C Earlham St Anne *Nor* 75-76; Asst Master Hewett Sch Nor 76-83; Hon C Eaton 81-83; C 83-87; R Winterton w E and W Somerton and Horsey 87-92; R Weybourne Gp 92-03; RD Holt 95-02; rtd 03; Perm to Offic *Nor* from 03. *Reverie Chase, 7 Churchill Crescent, Sheringham NR26 8NQ* Tel (01263) 824775

BARNETT, Alec James Leon. b 44. Em Coll Cam BA66 MA70 PGCE71. Cuddesdon Coll 66. **d** 69 **p** 70. C Preston St Jo *Blackb* 69-72; Asst Master Hutton Grammar Sch 70-72; Asst Chapl Uppingham Sch Leics 72-80; Hd of RE 73-80; Dir of Farmington/Ampleforth Project 79-83; C Witney *Ox* 83-84; P-in-c Lt Compton w Chastleton, Cornwell etc 84-88; Prin Ox Chr Tr Scheme 84-88; P-in-c St Michael Penkevil *Truro* 88-95; P-in-c Lamorran and Merther 88-95; Dioc Tr Officer 88-95; Chapl Strasbourg *Eur* 95-01; Abp Cant's Rep at Eur Inst from 95; Perm to Offic *Truro* from 95; rtd 01. *La Croix, 17800 St Léger, France* Tel (0033) (5) 46 94 99 25 Fax 46 94 95 01
E-mail james.barnett@wanadoo.fr

BARNETT, Ann. *See* BARNETT, Miss Patricia Ann

BARNETT, David John. b 33. Magd Coll Ox BA56 BTh58 MA61. St Steph Ho Ox 56. **d** 59 **p** 60. C Styvechale *Cov* 59-62; S Africa 62-69; Rhodesia 70-76; V Colindale St Matthias *Lon* 77-90; R Finchley St Mary 90-98; rtd 98; Perm to Offic *Ex* from 98. *2 Curlew Way, Exeter EX4 4SW* Tel (01392) 431486

BARNETT, Dudley Graham. b 36. Ch Ch Ox BA62 MA65. St Steph Ho Ox 62. **d** 64 **p** 65. C Abbey Hey *Man* 64-68; V Swinton H Rood 68-90; R Old Trafford St Hilda 90-01; R Firswood and Gorse Hill 01-02; rtd 02; Perm to Offic *Man* from 02. *6A Gilda Crescent Road, Eccles, Manchester M30 9AG* Tel 0161-707 9767

BARNETT, James Andrew McWilliam. b 76. Leeds Univ BA99. Trin Coll Bris BA01. **d** 02 **p** 03. C Bolton St Paul w Em *Man* from 02. *26 Northfield Street, Bolton BL3 5JH* Tel (01204) 439636 Mobile 07780-787694 E-mail barnettsbarnet@yahoo.co.uk

BARNETT, Canon John Raymond. b 51. Lon Univ LLB74 BD86 Birm Univ MA98. Westcott Ho Cam 74. **d** 77 **p** 78. C Northfield *Birm* 77-81; V Hamstead St Bernard 81-91; R The Quinton 91-03; AD Edgbaston 98-03; P-in-c Langley St Jo from 03; P-in-c Langley St Mich from 03; Hon Can Birm Cathl from 01. *The Vicarage, St John's Road, Oldbury, Warley B68 9RP* Tel 0121-552 5005

BARNETT, John Richard. b 28. Open Univ BA99. Portsm Dioc Tr Course 86. **d** 88 **p** 98. NSM Droxford and Meonstoke w Corhampton cum Exton *Portsm* 88-91; NSM W Meon and Warnford 91-01; rtd 01; Perm to Offic *Chich* from 01. *5 The Croft, 10 St Annes Road, Eastbourne BN21 2DL* Tel (01323) 731711

BARNETT, Canon Norman. b 19. Univ of Wales BA41. St Mich Coll Llan 41. **d** 43 **p** 44. C Roath St German *Llan* 43-49; Chapl Llan Cathl 49-53; R Liss *Portsm* 53-85; RD Petersfield 70-75; Hon Can Portsm Cathl 76-85; rtd 85; Perm to Offic *Portsm* from 85. *Banbury House, Burton Street, Marnhull, Sturminster Newton DT10 1PS* Tel (01258) 820260

BARNETT, Miss Patricia Ann. b 38. Whitelands Coll Lon CertEd. St Jo Coll Dur 75. **dss** 78 **d** 87 **p** 94. Gateacre *Liv* 78-82; Litherland St Paul Hatton Hill 82-87; Par Dn 87-88; Par Dn Platt Bridge 88-94; C 94-95; V Skelmersdale Ch at Cen 95-98; rtd 98. *93 Alderhey Road, Eccleston, St Helens WA10 4DW* Tel (01744) 25518

BARNETT, Peter Geoffrey. b 46. AKC71. St Aug Coll Cant 71. **d** 72 **p** 73. C Wolverhampton *Lich* 72-77; P-in-c Caldmore 77-83; TR Bris St Agnes and St Simon w St Werburgh *Bris* 83-87; P-in-c Bris St Paul w St Barn 83-87; TR Bris St Paul's 87-94; Warden Pilsdon Community from 94. *Pilsdon Manor, Pilsdon, Bridport DT6 5NZ* Tel (01308) 868308 Fax 868161

BARNETT, Peter John. b 36. N Ord Course 82. **d** 85 **p** 86. C New Bury *Man* 85-87; TV 87-94; P-in-c Clifton 94-99; P-in-c Clifton Green 99; V Clifton from 99. *St Anne's Vicarage, 237 Manchester Road, Manchester M27 6PP* Tel 0161-794 1939 Fax as telephone E-mail vicarpeter@aol.com

BARNETT, Preb Raymond Michael. b 31. Man Univ BA54. Wells Th Coll 54. **d** 56 **p** 57. C Fallowfield *Man* 56-59; Madagascar 59-60; V Blackrod *Man* 60-67; V Woolavington *B & W* 67-76; RD Bridgwater 72-76; V St Decumans 76-96; RD Quantock 78-86 and 93-95; Preb Wells Cathl 89-96; rtd 96; Perm to Offic *B & W* from 96. *4 Foster Close, Wells BA5 3NB* Tel (01749) 672983

BARNETT, Russell Scott. b 20. Oak Hill Th Coll 56. **d** 58 **p** 59. C Ulverston St Mary *Carl* 58-61; V Kirkdale St Paul N Shore *Liv*

61-67; V Salterhebble All SS *Wakef* 67-77; R Aikton *Carl* 77-85; R Orton St Giles 77-85; rtd 86; Perm to Offic *Carl* from 86. *8 Jackson Road, Houghton, Carlisle CA3 0NW* Tel (01228) 531721

BARNFATHER, Thomas Fenwick. b 52. Linc Th Coll 86. **d** 88 **p** 89. C Sedgefield *Dur* 88-91; TV E Darlington 91-92; CF 92-96; V Heybridge w Langford *Chelmsf* 96-98; Chapl HM YOI Dover 98-00; Chapl HM Pris Swaleside 00-01; P-in-c Aylesham w Adisham *Cant* from 01; Asst Dir of Ords from 02. *The Vicarage, Dorman Avenue North, Aylesham, Canterbury CT3 3JB* Tel and fax (01304) 840266 E-mail tom@barnfather.freeserve.co.uk

BARNSLEY, Mrs Angela Vera. b 47. St Hild Coll Dur BA70. St Alb Minl Tr Scheme 90. **d** 93. NSM Codicote St Alb 93-94. *1 All Saints Road, Weymouth DT4 9EZ* Tel (01305) 770406

BARNSLEY, David Edward. b 75. Ox Brookes Univ BSc97. Oak Hill Th Coll BA03. **d** 03. C Kilnhurst *Sheff* from 03. *30 Buckthorn Close, Swinton, Mexborough S64 8QY* Tel (01709) 577453 E-mail davidb@rnsley.freeserve.co.uk

BARNSLEY, Canon Melvyn. b 46. Dur Univ BA67 DipTh69 CertEd. St Chad's Coll Dur 64. **d** 71 **p** 72. C Cov St Thos *Cov* 71-74; C Cov St Jo 71-75; V New Bilton 75-82; R Stevenage St Andr and St Geo *St Alb* from 82; RD Stevenage 89-99; Hon Can St Alb from 00. *The Rectory, Cuttys Lane, Stevenage SG1 1UP* Tel (01438) 351631

BARNSLEY, Mrs Valerie Anne (Anna). b 48. Sussex Univ BEd71. WMMTC 91. **d** 94 **p** 95. NSM Tettenhall Regis *Lich* 94-99; Perm to Offic from 99. *The Retreat, Clive Road, Pattingham, Wolverhampton WV6 7BU* Tel (01902) 701713

BARNSTAPLE, Archdeacon of. *See* GUNN-JOHNSON, The Ven David Allan

✠**BAROI, The Rt Revd Michael.** Bp Dhaka and Moderator Ch of Bangladesh from 03. *St Thomas's Church, 54 Johnson Road, Dhaka-1, Bangladesh* Tel and fax (00880) (2) 238218 E-mail cob@citechco.net *or* cbdacdio@bangla.net

BARON, Noel Spencer Peter. b 15. K Coll Cam BA39 MA42. Linc Th Coll 40. **d** 41 **p** 42. C Welwyn Garden City *St Alb* 41-43; C Welwyn 43-48; V Holcombe Rogus w Hockworthy *Ex* 48-52; V W Malvern *Worc* 52-83; rtd 83; Perm to Offic *Heref* from 85; *Glouc* from 98. *Brindley, 21 The Crescent, Colwall, Malvern WR13 6QN* Tel (01684) 540477

BARON, Peter Murray. b 56. New Coll Ox MA78. Cranmer Hall Dur 91. **d** 93 **p** 94. C Monkseaton St Pet *Newc* 93-95; C Guildf St Sav *Guildf* 96-98; V Northwood H Trin *Lon* from 98. *Holy Trinity Vicarage, Gateway Close, Northwood HA6 2RP* Tel (01923) 825732 E-mail peter@htrinity.freeserve.co.uk

BARON, Thomas Michael. b 63. St Steph Ho Ox 85. **d** 88 **p** 89. C Hartlepool St Paul *Dur* 88-92; Chapl Asst Hartlepool Gen Hosp 89-92; Asst Chapl Whittington Hosp Lon 92-95; Chapl Enfield Community Care NHS Trust 95-01; Chapl Chase Farm Hosps NHS Trust 95-99; Chapl Barnet and Chase Farm Hosps NHS Trust from 99; Perm to Offic *St Alb* from 99; Chapl Barnet, Enfield and Haringey Mental Health Trust from 01; Chapl Enfield Primary Care Trust from 01. *Chase Farm Hospital, The Ridgeway, Enfield EN2 8JL* Tel (020) 8366 6600 ext 5078 *or* 8882 1195 E-mail frtom.baron@btinternet.com

BARON, Mrs Vanessa Lillian. b 57. SRN79 City Univ BSc79 Fitzw Coll Cam MA85. Ridley Hall Cam 83. **dss** 86 **d** 87 **p** 94. Roxbourne St Andr *Lon* 86-89; Par Dn 87-89; NSM Roxeth 92-95; Lic Preacher from 95; Asst Chapl Harrow Sch from 95. *3 High Street, Harrow HA1 3HT* Tel (020) 8872 8254

BARR, John Gourlay Crichton. b 23. Edin Univ BL46. Edin Dioc NSM Course 81. **d** 84 **p** 85. NSM Edin St Mark *Edin* 84-91; rtd 91; NSM Brechin *Bre* from 92. *Grove House, 22 St Andrew Street, Brechin, Angus DD9 6JJ* Tel (01356) 624412

BARR (née Hayter), Mary Elizabeth. b 58. Jes Coll Ox BA80 CertEd81 MA84 Qu Coll Ox DPhil85. Ridley Hall Cam 84. **dss** 86 **d** 87 **p** 94. Chapl Cam Univ Pastorate 86-91; Cambridge H Trin w St Andr Gt *Ely* 86-87; Par Dn 87-91; Perm to Offic 91-92; Perm to Offic *Ex* 92-94; NSM Torquay St Luke 94-97; NSM Gt Malvern St Mary *Worc* from 97; Chapl Worcs Community Healthcare NHS Trust 99-01; Chapl Worcs Community and Mental Health Trust from 01. *Priory Vicarage, Clarence Road, Malvern WR14 3EN* Tel (01684) 563707 *or* 561020 Fax as telephone E-mail jmbarr@ukonline.co.uk *or* gmpriory@hotmail.com

BARR, Michael John Alexander. b 60. Qu Coll Ox BA82 MA86 Pemb Coll Cam BA86 MA90. Ridley Hall Cam 84. **d** 87 **p** 88. C Earley St Pet *Ox* 87-89; C Cambridge Gt St Mary w St Mich *Ely* 89-92; Chapl Girton Coll Cam 90-92; P-in-c Torquay St Luke *Ex* 92-97; Dioc Communications Officer 92-97; P-in-c Gt Malvern St Mary *Worc* 97-99; V from 99; RD Malvern from 01. *Priory Vicarage, Clarence Road, Malvern WR14 3EN* Tel (01684) 563707 *or* 561020 Fax as telephone E-mail jmbarr@ukonline.co.uk *or* gmpriory@hotmail.com

BARR, Norma. **d** 01. C Aberdour *St And* from 01. *37 Cherry Banks, Dunfermline KY12 7RG*

BARR, The Very Revd William Norman Cochrane. b 20. TCD BA44 MA50 BD50. CITC 45. **d** 46 **p** 46. C Ballymena *Conn* 46-52; C Belf Cathl 52-54; R Duneane w Ballyscullion 54-58; Bp's Dom Chapl 56-71; P-in-c Belfast Whiterock 58-61; I

Derriaghy w Colin 61-90; Can Conn Cathl 80-82; Dean Conn 82-90; rtd 90. *45 Killeaton Crescent, Dunmurry, Belfast BT17 9HB* Tel (028) 9062 1746
E-mail wncbarr@btinternet.com

BARRACLOUGH, Mrs Barbara Amanda Juliet. b 61. Stirling Univ BA83 Chester Coll of HE MA00. N Ord Course 97. **d** 00 **p** 01. C Lupset *Wakef* from 00. *19 Woodland Rise, Wakefield WF2 9DN* Tel (01924) 372352 Mobile 07808-382016
E-mail amanda.barraclough@blueyonder.co.uk

BARRACLOUGH, Dennis. b 35. St Jo Coll York CertEd58 Lambeth STh68 LCP62 FCP74. Ripon Hall Ox 66. **d** 68 **p** 69. C Woodhouse *Wakef* 68-71; V Gildersome 71-83; V Kirkburton 83-00; RD Kirkburton 92-98; rtd 00; Perm to Offic *Wakef* from 00. *8 Clough Park, Fenay Bridge, Huddersfield HD8 0JH* Tel (01484) 325515

BARRACLOUGH, Canon Owen Conrad. b 32. Pemb Coll Cam BA55 MA59. Westcott Ho Cam 56. **d** 57 **p** 58. C Chippenham St Andr w Tytherton Lucas *Bris* 57-62; V Harringay St Paul *Lon* 62-70; Bp's Chapl for Community Relns *Cov* 70-77; P-in-c Baginton 72-77; V Swindon Ch Ch *Bris* 77-97; Chapl Princess Marg Hosp Swindon 77-89; Hon Can Bris Cathl *Bris* 87-97; rtd 98; Perm to Offic *Bris* from 98; *Glouc* 98-01; Joint Perm to Offic *Glouc* from 01. *Robin Hollow, 10A Church Road, Cheltenham GL51 7AN* Tel (01242) 230855

BARRALL, John Henry. b 31. BEd. Bps' Coll Cheshunt. **d** 61 **p** 62. C Digswell *St Alb* 61-65; C Aldershot St Mich *Guildf* 65-70; TV Hemel Hempstead *St Alb* 70-82; Perm to Offic 83-91; R Meppershall w Campton and Stondon 91-98; rtd 98; Perm to Offic *Ely* from 99; *St Alb* from 01; OCF 97-03. *10 Caldecote Road, Ickwell, Biggleswade SG18 9EH* Tel (01767) 627407
E-mail john@barrall.fsnet.co.uk

BARRAND, George William (Bill). b 33. HNC55. Lon Coll of Div 59. **d** 62 **p** 63. C Bucknall and Bagnall *Lich* 62-65; C Parr *Liv* 65-69; Australia from 70; rtd 98. *2/20 Riversdale Road, Yarra Junction, Vic, Australia 3797* Tel (0061) (3) 5967 2592

BARRATT, The Ven Anthony John. b 19. Glas Univ MRCVS. Bible Churchmen's Coll Bris. **d** 49 **p** 50. C Slough *Ox* 49-52; SAMS Miss Cholchol Falkland Is 52-64; Hon Can Port Stanley 57-64; SAMS Miss Asunción Paraguay 64-70; Argentina 70-84; Adn Tucuman 73-84; rtd 84. *Couchill Villa, Couchill Farm Lane, Seaton EX12 3AL* Tel (01297) 21118

BARRATT, Mrs Elizabeth June. b 32. ACP65. Trin Coll Bris 75. **dss** 78 **d** 87 **p** 94. W Kilburn St Luke w St Simon and St Jude *Lon* 78-87; Par Dn 87-94; C 94-98; rtd 98; Hon C Kensal Rise St Mark and St Martin *Lon* from 99. *68A Bathhurst Gardens, London NW10 5HY* Tel (020) 8968 5951

BARRATT, Peter. b 29. Down Coll Cam BA53 MA57. Ridley Hall Cam 53. **d** 55 **p** 56. C Bebington *Ches* 55-58; C-in-c Cam St Martin CD *Ely* 58-61; V Cambridge St Martin 61-68; V Rawtenstall St Mary *Man* 68-83; AD Rossendale 80-83; V Bosley and N Rode w Wincle and Wildboarclough *Ches* 83-94; rtd 94; Perm to Offic *Ches* from 94. *10 Snab Wood Close, Little Neston, Neston CH64 0UP* Tel 0151-336 6641

BARRATT, Philip Norman. b 62. Aston Tr Scheme 87 St Steph Ho Ox 89 Coll of Resurr Mirfield 90. **d** 92 **p** 93. C Heywood St Luke w All So *Man* 92-96; V Thornham St Jas from 96. *St James's Vicarage, 120 Shaw Road, Rochdale OL16 4SQ* Tel (01706) 645256 Mobile 07775-646733 E-mail pn.barratt@zen.co.uk

BARRELL, Adrian Edward. b 36. Keble Coll Ox BA59. Ely Th Coll 59. **d** 62 **p** 63. C Plymouth St Jas Ham *Ex* 62-66; C Bideford 66-70; V Walkhampton 70-80; rtd 01. *Cartref, Dousland, Yelverton PL20 6PA* Tel (01822) 852612

BARRETT, Alan. b 48. Southn Univ BA69. Wycliffe Hall Ox 74. **d** 77 **p** 78. C Conisbrough *Sheff* 77-80; C Lower Homerton St Paul *Lon* 80-81; C-in-c Hounslow Gd Shep Beavers Lane CD 81-87; R Langdon Hills *Chelmsf* 87-97; P-in-c Tamworth *Lich* 97-03; V from 03; RD Tamworth from 99. *The Vicarage, Hospital Street, Tamworth B79 7EE* Tel and fax (01827) 62446 *or* tel 68339 E-mail alan.barrett@breathemail.net

BARRETT, Alastair David. b 75. Fitzw Coll Cam BA97 MA01 Birm Univ BD00. Qu Coll Birm MA01. **d** 01. C Sutton Coldfield St Chad *Birm* from 01. *20 Trenchard Close, Sutton Coldfield, Birmingham B75 7QP* Tel 0121-311 1450
E-mail alastairb@ukonline.co.uk

BARRETT, Mrs Alexandra Mary. b 75. Clare Coll Cam BA96 MA99. Westcott Ho Cam 03. **d** 03. C Godmanchester *Ely* from 03. *59 London Road, Godmanchester, Huntingdon PE29 2HZ* Tel (01480) 450852 Mobile 07769-673546

BARRETT, Arthur. *See* BARRETT, Kenneth Arthur Lambart

BARRETT, Christopher Paul. b 49. AKC71 St Aug Coll Cant 71. **d** 72 **p** 73. C Tupsley *Heref* 72-75; C St Thos *Ex* 75-79; R Atherington and High Bickington 79-83; V Burrington 79-83; Asst Dir of Educn 79-87; P-in-c Sticklepath 83-85; P-in-c Barnstaple 83-85; TV 85-90; V Whipton 90-99; TV Ex St Thos and Em from 99. *St Andrew's Vicarage, 78 Queens Road, Exeter EX2 9EW* Tel (01392) 43901

BARRETT, Clive. b 55. Ox Univ BA76 MA80 CertEd77 Leeds Univ PhD98. St Steph Ho Ox 80. **d** 83 **p** 84. C Wakef Cathl *Wakef* 83-87; Asst Chapl Leeds Univ *Ripon* 87-97; Dioc

Development Rep 89-92; P-in-c Middleton St Cross from 98. *St Cross Vicarage, Middleton Park Avenue, Leeds LS10 4HT* Tel 0113-271 6398 Mobile 07966-540699
E-mail clivebarrett@hotmail.com

BARRETT, David Brian. b 27. Clare Coll Cam BA48 MA50 BD69 Columbia Univ (NY) PhD65. Union Th Sem (NY) STM63 PhD65 Ridley Hall Cam 52. **d** 54 **p** 55. Succ Bradf Cathl *Bradf* 54-56; CMS 57-92; Kenya 57-62 and 65-85; USA 62-63; Guatemala 63-65; Research Sec ACC 70-87; Lic to Offic *Lon* 70-87; USA from 87; rtd 92. *2503 Prestwick Circle, Richmond, VA 23294, USA* Tel (001) (804) 747 7455 Fax 358 0504

BARRETT, Canon Derek Leonard. b 25. St Fran Coll Brisbane ThL57. **d** 57 **p** 58. Australia 57-63; C Ramsgate St Geo *Cant* 64-65; C Putney St Mary *S'wark* 65-67; V Kidderminster St Jo *Worc* 67-77; V Stourbridge St Thos 77-90; RD Stourbridge 83-89; Hon Can Worc Cathl 87-90; rtd 90; Perm to Offic *Glouc*; *Worc* from 90. *Lotty Leven, Crystal Waters, MlS 16, Maleny, Qld, Australia 4552*

BARRETT, Gary John. b 46. Sarum & Wells Th Coll 87. **d** 90 **p** 91. NSM Guernsey St Peter Port *Win* 90-97; Chapl Eliz Coll Guernsey 93-97; P-in-c Westham *Chich* 97-98; V from 98. *The Vicarage, 6 Rattle Road, Westham, Pevensey BN24 5DE* Tel (01323) 762294

BARRETT, Graham Crichton. b 51. IEng76 FIMEMME78. Linc Th Coll 88. **d** 90 **p** 91. C Torpoint *Truro* 90-94; Dio Youth and Voc Officer 94-95; C St Columb Major w St Wenn 94-95; P-in-c St Issey w St Petroc Minor 95-00; Dioc Children's Adv 95-00. *Address unknown*

BARRETT, John Joseph James. b 38. Lon Univ BD65. Sarum & Wells Th Coll. **d** 78 **p** 78. C Danbury *Chelmsf* 78-80; Ind Chapl 80-89; C Dovercourt 80-83; TV Dovercourt and Parkeston 83-89; V Rubery *Birm* from 89. *St Chad's Vicarage, 160A New Road, Rednal, Birmingham B45 9JA* Tel 0121-453 3255

BARRETT, Jonathan Murray. b 68. Oak Hill Th Coll BA98. **d** 98 **p** 99. C Pennycross *Ex* 98-02; TV Plymouth Em, St Paul Efford and St Aug from 02. *28A Sefton Avenue, Plymouth PL4 7HB* Tel (01752) 661797

BARRETT, Canon Kenneth. b 42. Univ of Wales (Lamp) BA64. St Steph Ho Ox 65. **d** 67 **p** 68. C Poulton-le-Fylde *Blackb* 67-69; C S Shore H Trin 69-72; V Brierfield 72-83; V Chorley St Geo from 83; Hon Can Blackb Cathl from 03. *St George's Vicarage, Letchworth Place, Chorley PR7 2HJ* Tel (01257) 263064

BARRETT, Kenneth Arthur Lambart. b 60. CITC BTh94. **d** 97 **p** 98. C Seagoe *D & D* 97-00; I Dublin Booterstown *D & G* from 00; I Dublin Mt Merrion from 00. *The Rectory, Cross Avenue, Blackrock, Co Dublin, Irish Republic* Tel (00353) (1) 288 7118 E-mail booterstown@dublin.anglican.org

BARRETT, Canon Kenneth Sydney. b 26. Roch Th Coll 60. **d** 62 **p** 63. C Wollaton *S'well* 62-65; C Hucknall Torkard 65-67; Australia from 67; Can Bunbury 76-92; rtd 92. *PO Box 818, 2 Loxton Street, Mandurah, W Australia 6210* Tel (0061) (8) 9581 2519 Fax as telephone E-mail joykenb@iinet.net.au

BARRETT, Mrs Marion Lily. b 54. SRN75. SW Minl Tr Course 91. **d** 94 **p** 95. C St Mawgan w St Ervan and St Eval *Truro* 94-97; C St Breoke and Egloshayle 97-98; Asst Chapl R Cornwall Hosps Trust 98-00; Chapl from 00. *Royal Cornwall Hospital, Treliske, Truro TR1 3LJ* Tel (01872) 274242

BARRETT, Paul. *See* BARRETT, Christopher Paul

✠**BARRETT, The Rt Revd Peter Francis.** b 56. TCD BA78 MA81 DipTh81 MPhil84. CITC 78. **d** 81 **p** 82 **c** 03. C Drumachose *D & R* 81-83; C Dublin St Ann *D & G* 83-85; I Conwal Union w Gartan *D & R* 85-90; I Belfast St Geo *Conn* 90-94; Chapl TCD 94-98; Min Can St Patr Cathl Dublin 94-96; Succ 96-98; Dean Waterford *C & O* 98-03; Prec Lismore Cathl 98-03; Prec Cashel Cathl 98-03; I Waterford w Killea, Drumcannon and Dunhill 98-03; Bp C & O from 03. *Wellbrook, Freshford, Co Kilkenny, Irish Republic* Tel (00353) (56) 883 2868 *or* 776 1910 Fax 776 4399 E-mail dean@waterford.anglican.org

BARRETT, Mrs Rachel Jeanne Alexandra. b 56. Ex Univ BA78 PGCE79. SW Minl Tr Course 92. **d** 95 **p** 96. NSM Ex St Mark *Ex* 95-96; NSM Ex St Mark, St Sidwell and St Matt 96-00; Chapl St Margaret's Sch Ex from 00. *St Andrew's Vicarage, 78 Queens Road, Exeter EX2 9EW* Tel (01392) 43901

BARRETT, Ronald Reginald. b 30. Roch Th Coll 61. **d** 64 **p** 65. C Spring Park *Cant* 64-66; C Thornton Heath St Jude 66-68; V Greengates *Bradf* 68-73; V Shelf 73-79; V Embsay w Eastby 79-87; V Farndon and Coddington *Ches* 87-92; rtd 92; Perm to Offic *Bradf* from 92. *12 Craigmore Drive, Ben Rhydding, Ilkley LS29 8PG* Tel (01943) 609713

BARRETT, Stephen David Norman. b 54. Aber Univ BSc75 Edin Univ BD78. Edin Th Coll 75. **d** 78 **p** 79. C Ardrossan *Glas* 78-80; R Peterhead *Ab* 80-81; Chapl HM Pris Peterhead 80-81; R Renfrew *Glas* 81-87; R Bishopbriggs 87-94; Chapl HM Pris Glas (Barlinnie) 87-94; Chapl Stobhill Gen Hosp 87-94; P-in-c Port Glas 94-99; R from 99. *St Mary's Rectory, Bardrainney Avenue, Port Glasgow PA14 6HB* Tel (01475) 707444

BARRIBAL, Richard James Pitt. b 45. Trin Coll Bris DipTh80. **d** 80 **p** 81. C Northampton St Giles *Pet* 80-82; V Long Buckby w Watford 82-86; Perm to Offic from 86; Perm to Offic *Leic* from

00. *45 Knights End Road, Great Bowden, Market Harborough LE16 7EY* Tel (01858) 431495 Fax 468852
E-mail richard.barribal@lineone.net

BARRIE, John Arthur. b 38. K Coll Lon 58 Bps' Coll Cheshunt 59. **d** 63 **p** 64. C Southgate St Mich Lon 63-66; CF 66-88; Sen CF 88-93; QHC 91-93; P-in-c Heref H Trin *Heref* 93-96; P-in-c Breinton 95-96; V St Marylebone St Mark Hamilton Terrace *Lon* from 96. *St Mark's Vicarage, 114 Hamilton Terrace, London NW8 9UT* Tel (020) 7328 4373 *or* 7624 4065
E-mail john.barrie1@btopenworld.com

BARRINGTON, Dominic Matthew Jesse. b 62. Hatf Coll Dur BA84 MSc85 LTCL. Ripon Coll Cuddesdon BA94 MA98 Ch Div Sch of Pacific MTS95. **d** 95 **p** 96. C Mortlake w E Sheen *S'wark* 95-98; Chapl St Chad's Coll Dur 98-03; P-in-c Kettering SS Pet and Paul *Pet* from 03. *The Rectory, Church Walk, Kettering NN16 0DJ* Tel (01536) 513385 Mobile 07720-704953
E-mail dominicb@applicabroadband.net

✠**BARRINGTON-WARD, The Rt Revd Simon.** b 30. KCMG01. Magd Coll Cam BA53 MA57. Wycliffe Coll Toronto Hon DD Westcott Ho Cam 54. **d** 56 **p** 57 **c** 85. Chapl Magd Coll Cam 56-60; Nigeria 60-63; Fell and Dean of Chpl Magd Coll Cam 63-69; Prin Crowther Hall CMS Tr Coll Selly Oak 69-74; Gen Sec CMS 75-85; Hon Can Derby Cathl *Derby* 75-85; Chapl to The Queen 84-85; Bp Cov 85-97; rtd 97; Hon Fell Magd Coll Cam from 87; Hon Can Ely from 98; Hon Asst Bp Ely from 97. *4 Searle Street, Cambridge CB4 3DB* Tel (01223) 740460
E-mail sb292@cam.ac.uk

BARRODALE, Canon George Bryan. b 44. Univ of Wales (Ban) DipTh DipMin88. St Mich Coll Llan 67. **d** 69 **p** 70. C Maindee *Mon* 69-72; TV Merthyr Tydfil and Cyfarthfa *Llan* 72-76; R Cotgrave *S'well* 76-00; P-in-c Owthorpe 76-00; CF (TA) 76-86; RD Bingham *S'well* 94-00; Hon Can S'well Minster from 97; V Beeston from 00. *The Vicarage, Middle Street, Beeston, Nottingham NG9 1GA* Tel 0115-925 4571
E-mail bbarrodale@aol.com

BARRON, Arthur Henry. b 45. Solicitor 72. SEITE 99. **d** 02. NSM Addiscombe St Mary Magd w St Martin *S'wark* from 02. *23 Little Woodcote Lane, Purley CR8 3PZ* Tel (020) 8660 1921
E-mail arthur-barron@vivash-hunt.freeserve.co.uk

BARRON, Kurt Karl. b 60. Chich Th Coll BTh92. **d** 92 **p** 93. C Bulwell St Mary *S'well* 92-97; TV Southwell *Chelmsf* 97-01; P-in-c Mansfield St Lawr *S'well* from 01. *St Lawrence's Vicarage, 3 Shaw Street, Mansfield NG18 2NP* Tel (01623) 623698

BARRON, Leslie Gill. b 44. ACII69. Lich Th Coll 67. **d** 70 **p** 71. C Bishopwearmouth Ch Ch *Dur* 70-72; C Bishopwearmouth St Mary V w St Pet CD 72-75; C Harton 75-77; V Lumley 77-88; P-in-c Hendon and Sunderland 88-90; R Hendon 90-94; V Ushaw Moor 94-95; V Bearpark and Ushaw Moor from 95. *The Vicarage, 8 Woodland Close, Bearpark, Durham DH7 7EB* Tel 0191-373 3886

BARRON, Richard Davidson. b 51. Lon Univ BSc74. Trin Coll Bris 75. **d** 78 **p** 79. C Bradley *Wakef* 78-81; C Heworth H Trin *York* 81-82; TV 82-89; Chapl York Distr Hosp 82-86; R Greenhithe St Mary *Roch* from 89. *The Rectory, Mounts Road, Greenhithe DA9 9ND* Tel (01322) 382031
E-mail rbarron@smgreenhithe.freeserve.co.uk

BARRON, Canon Victor Robert. b 45. Lon Bible Coll DipTh68 St Luke's Coll Ex CertEd70. Trin Coll Bris 76. **d** 78 **p** 79. C Rainham *Chelmsf* 78-81; V Easton H Trin w St Gabr and St Lawr *Bris* 81-82; V Easton H Trin w St Gabr and St Lawr and St Jude 82-89; TR Kinson *Sarum* 89-00; RD Poole 94-00; Can and Preb Sarum Cathl 98-00; rtd 00. *April Cottage, 159 Middlehill Road, Wimborne BH21 2HJ* Tel (01202) 848236 Fax as telephone
E-mail vicandjill@barron19.fsnet.co.uk

BARRY, Colin Lionel. Open Univ BSc94. Bp Attwell Tr Inst 85. **d** 96 **p** 97. NSM Arbory *S & M* from 96. *80 Ballanorris Crescent, Ballabeg, Castletown, Isle of Man IM9 4ER* Tel (01624) 823080

BARRY, Herbert Brian. b 25. QUB 46. Edin Th Coll 46. **d** 48 **p** 49. C Edin Old St Paul *Edin* 48-52; R Burntisland *St And* 52-55; C Hayes St Anselm *Lon* 56-63; C Hayes St Mary 56-63; R Edin St Salvador *Edin* 63-68; C Northolt Park St Barn *Lon* 69-72; P-in-c S Acton All SS 72-82; V Acton Green St Alb 75-82; V Acton St Alb w All SS 82-88; V Acton Green 88-90; Sub-Warden Guild of St Raphael from 85; rtd 90; Perm to Offic *Ex* 90-97 and *Truro* from 97. *4 Hendra Close, Truro TR1 3SL* Tel (01872) 260076

BARRY, Ms Jackie Françoise. Univ de Bordeaux II LSocEth86 MSoc87 York Univ PGCE91. Ridley Hall Cam CTM99. **d** 99 **p** 00. C Sydenham H Trin *S'wark* from 99. *56 Sydenham Park Road, London SE26 4DL* Tel (020) 8699 8776

BARRY, Canon John. b 15. TCD BA38 BA37 TCD MA41. CITC 38. **d** 38 **p** 39. C Belfast St Matt *Conn* 38-41; C Dundela St Mark *D & D* 41-45; I Dunluce *Conn* 45-49; I Hillsborough *D & D* 49-83; Can Belf Cathl 56-64; Chan Down Cathl *D & D* 64-73; Preb St Patr Cathl Dublin 73-83; rtd 83. *16 West Park, Lisburn BT28 2BQ* Tel (028) 9267 0664

BARRY, Canon Jonathan Peter Oulton. b 47. TCD BA70 MA73 Hull Univ BA73 QUB PhD83. Ripon Hall Ox 73. **d** 74 **p** 75. C Dundela St Mark *D & D* 74-79; I Ballyphilip w Ardquin 79-85; Dioc Info Officer 80-90; I Comber from 85; Preb St Audoen

St Patr Cathl Dublin from 01. *The Rectory, 12 Windmill Hill, Comber, Newtownards BT23 5WH* Tel (028) 9187 2283
E-mail comber@down.anglican.org *or* rector@comberparish.fsnet.co.uk

BARRY, Keith Gordon. b 67. TCD BA92. CITC 92. **d** 94 **p** 95. C Templemore *D & R* 94-97; V Choral Derry Cathl 94-97; CF from 97. *c/o MOD Chaplains (Army)* Tel (01980) 615804 Fax 615800

BARRY, Nicholas Brian Paul. b 61. Leic Univ BA83. St Steph Ho Ox 84. **d** 87 **p** 88. C St John's Wood *Lon* 87-90; Chapl RAF from 90. *Chaplaincy Services (RAF), HQ, Personnel and Training Command, RAF Innsworth, Gloucester GL3 1EZ* Tel (01452) 712612 ext 5164 Fax 510828

BARSLEY, Canon Margaret Ann. b 39. Totley Hall Coll CertEd60. EMMTC 79. **dss** 83 **d** 87 **p** 94. Kirton in Holland *Linc* 83-89; NSM 87-89; NSM Skirbeck Quarter 89-96; P-in-c Swineshead 96-99; V from 99; RD Holland W from 97; Can and Preb Linc Cathl from 00. *The Vicarage, Church Lane, Swineshead, Boston PE20 3JA* Tel (01205) 820271
E-mail margaretbarsley@care4free.net

BARTER, Christopher Stuart. b 49. Chich Th Coll. **d** 84 **p** 85. C Margate St Jo Cant 84-88; R Whitwood *Wakef* 88-95; Chapl Castleford, Normanton and Distr Hosp 88-95; P-in-c Ravensthorpe *Wakef* 95-98; AIDS Cllr W Yorks HA 95-98; TV Gt Yarmouth *Nor* 98-02; R Somersham w Pidley and Oldhurst *Ely* from 02. *The Rectory, Rectory Lane, Somersham, Huntingdon PE28 3EL* Tel (01487) 840676 E-mail chrisbarter@talk21.com

BARTER, The Very Revd Donald. b 34. St Fran Coll Brisbane ThL69 ACT ThSchol74. **d** 69 **p** 70. Australia 69-90 and from 93; C Townsville 69-72; R Mareeba 72-76; R Ingham 76-81; Adn of the W and R Mt Isa 81-86; Dean Townsville 86-90; Chapl Miss to Seamen 86-90; Chapl HM Police Service 88-90; Appeals Dir SPCK 90-93; Lic to Offic *Leic* 90-93; Asst to Dean St Jas Cathl 94-00. *6 Sixth Avenue, South Townsville, Qld, Australia 4810* Tel and fax (0061) (7) 4772 7036 Mobile 414-989593
E-mail donbarter@optusnet.com.au

BARTER, Geoffrey Roger. b 41. Bris Univ BSc63. Clifton Th Coll 65. **d** 67 **p** 68. C Normanton *Derby* 67-70; C Rainham *Chelmsf* 70-75; V Plumstead St Jo w St Jas and St Paul *S'wark* 75-82; V Frogmore *St Alb* 82-01; rtd 01; Perm to Offic *Chich* from 02. *45 West Front Road, Pagham, Bognor Regis PO21 4SZ* Tel (01243) 262522

BARTER, Leonard. **d** 95. OLM St Stythians w Perranarworthal and Gwennap *Truro* from 95. *1 Valandrucia, Foundry, Stithians, Truro TR3 7BU* Tel (01209) 860341

BARTER, Susan Kathleen. b 53. Open Univ MBA97. Ridley Hall Cam 01. **d** 03. C Happisburgh, Walcott, Hempstead w Eccles etc *Nor* from 03. *Atherstone House, Lighthouse Lane, Happisburgh, Norwich NR12 0QA* Tel (01692) 652248
E-mail sbarter777@aol.com

BARTHOLOMEW, Craig Gerald. b 61. UNISA DipTh81 BTh82 Wycliffe Hall Ox BA84 MA88 Potchefstroom Univ MA92 Bris Univ PhD97. **d** 86 **p** 87. S Africa 86-92; C Pinetown Ch Ch 87-89; Lect OT Studies Geo Whitefield Coll Cape Town 89-92; Research Fell Glos Univ from 97; Perm to Offic *Glouc* from 98. *School of Theology and Relig Studies, Francis Close Hall, Swindon Road, Cheltenham GL50 4AZ* Tel (01242) 532884 Mobile 07788-413755 Fax (01242) 543314
E-mail cbartholomew@chelt.ac.uk

BARTHOLOMEW, David Grant. b 50. Univ of Wales (Lamp) BA77 Brighton Poly DMS78. Chich Th Coll 91. **d** 93 **p** 94. C Petersfield *Portsm* 93-96; R Etton w Helpston and Maxey *Pet* 96-98; R Burghclere w Newtown and Ecchinswell w Sydmonton *Win* from 98. *The Rectory, Well Street, Burghclere, Newbury RG20 9HS* Tel (01635) 278470

BARTLAM, Alan Thomas. b 51. Bris Univ BEd74. Linc Th Coll 88. **d** 90 **p** 91. C Longdon-upon-Tern, Rodington, Uppington etc *Lich* 90-92; C Tilstock and Whixall 92-95; V Tilstock, Edstaston and Whixall 95-98; R Bewcastle, Stapleton and Kirklinton etc *Carl* from 98. *The Rectory, Stapleton, Carlisle CA6 6LD* Tel (01697) 748660
E-mail alanbartlam@stapletonrectory.freeserve.co.uk

BARTLE, Alan. b 45. Ridley Hall Cam 82. **d** 84 **p** 85. C Ely 84-88; V 87-93; V Chettisham 87-93; V Prickwillow 87-93; P-in-c Thorney Abbey 93-95. *Address temp unknown*

BARTLE, Canon David Colin. b 29. Em Coll Cam BA53 MA57. Ridley Hall Cam 53. **d** 55 **p** 56. C Birm St Martin *Birm* 55-57; C Boscombe St Jo *Win* 57-60; V Lowestoft St Jo *Nor* 60-70; P-in-c Thetford St Cuth w H Trin 70-72; P-in-c Thetford St Mary 70-72; P-in-c Thetford St Pet w St Nic 70-72; TR Thetford 72-75; P-in-c Kilverstone 70-75; P-in-c Croxton 70-75; Teacher Bournemouth Sch 75-83; R Brantham w Stutton *St E* 83-90; RD Samford 86-90; P-in-c Roxwell *Chelmsf* 90-93; Dioc Dir of Ords 90-93; Dioc Lay Min Adv 90-93; Hon Can Chelmsf Cathl 91-93; rtd 93; Perm to Offic *Win* 93-98; Chapl R Bournemouth and Christchurch Hosps NHS Trust 98-00. *40 Blue Waters Drive, Paignton TQ4 6JE* Tel (01803) 843456
E-mail dbartle8@aol.com

BARTLE, Reginald Stephen. b 24. K Coll Lon AKC51 BD52. **d** 52 **p** 53. C Penge Ch Ch w H Trin *Roch* 52-55; SAMS 55-79; Chile 55-70; Adn Chile and Can St Andr Cathl Santiago 64-70; NW Area Sec SAMS 70-73; Home Sec 73-79; C Tunbridge Wells St Jas *Roch* 80-83; rtd 83; Perm to Offic St *D* 84-94; *Chelmsf* 94-00; S'wark 00-01; *Cant* 01-03. *20 Bromley College, London Road, Bromley BR1 1PE* Tel (020) 8460 7128

BARTLE-JENKINS, Canon Leonard Christmas. b 13. Univ of Wales (Lamp) BA35. Lich Th Coll 35. **d** 38 **p** 39. C Fleur-de-Lis *Mon* 38-41; C Trevethin 41-47; V Llangattock-vibon-Avel 47-55; V Bassaleg 55-74; Can St Woolos Cathl 64-82; RD Bassaleg 67-82; R Michaelston-y-Fedw and Rudry 74-82; rtd 82; Lic to Offic *Mon* from 82; Perm to Offic *Llan* from 82. *3 St Teilo's Court, Sturminster Road, Roath, Cardiff CF23 5AX* Tel (029) 2048 9378

BARTLE-JENKINS, Paul. b 43. Bris & Glouc Tr Course. **d** 84 **p** 86. NSM Bris St Agnes and St Simon w St Werburgh *Bris* 84-87; NSM Bris St Paul's from 87. *188A Henleaze Road, Westbury-on-Trym, Bristol BS9 4NE* Tel 0117-975 4147

BARTLES-SMITH, The Ven Douglas Leslie. b 37. St Edm Hall Ox BA61 MA65. Wells Th Coll 61. **d** 63 **p** 64. C Westmr St Steph w St Jo *Lon* 63-68; P-in-c Camberwell St Mich w All So w Em S'wark 68-72; V 72-75; V Battersea St Luke 75-85; RD Battersea 81-85; Adn S'wark from 85; Chapl to The Queen from 96. *1A Dog Kennel Hill, London SE22 8AA* Tel (020) 7274 6767 Fax 7274 0889 E-mail douglas.bartles-smith@dswark.org.uk

BARTLETT, Alan. b 38. Qu Coll Birm 76. **d** 79 **p** 80. Hon C Perry Beeches *Birm* 79-81; Hon C Kingstanding St Mark from 82. *43 Delhurst Road, Birmingham B44 9UT* Tel 0121-360 7878

BARTLETT, Alan Bennett. b 58. G&C Coll Cam BA81 MA85 Birm Univ PhD87 St Jo Coll Dur BA90. Cranmer Hall Dur 88. **d** 91 **p** 92. C Newc H Cross *Newc* 91-94; C Newburn 94-96; Tutor Cranmer Hall Dur from 96. *Cranmer Hall, St John's College, 3 South Bailey, Durham DH1 3RJ* Tel 0191-374 3579 Fax 374 3573 E-mail a.b.bartlett@durham.ac.uk

BARTLETT, Anthony Martin. b 43. Cranmer Hall Dur 74. **d** 77 **p** 78. C Heworth St Mary *Dur* 77-80; V Cleadon 80-84; CF (TA) 81-90; Prec Dur Cathl *Dur* 85-87; V Harton 87-95; P-in-c Hendon 95-96; R 96-97; V Greenlands *Blackb* from 01. *St Anne's House, Salmesbury Avenue, Blackpool FY2 0PR* Tel (01253) 353900 E-mail bcressell@aol.com

BARTLETT, David John. b 36. Pemb Coll Ox BA61. Linc Th Coll 63. **d** 65 **p** 66. C Wollaton *S'well* 65-70; V Woodthorpe 70-83; V Farnsfield 83-01; P-in-c Kirklington w Hockerton 83-01; RD S'well 83-93; Chapl Rodney Sch Kirklington 83-01; rtd 01. *6 De Havilland Way, Farndon Road, Newark NG24 4RF* Tel (01636) 651582

BARTLETT, David William. b 59. Trin Coll Bris 89. **d** 91 **p** 92. C Frinton *Chelmsf* 91-95; TV Easton w Normanby *York* 95-96; Assoc P Worksop St Jo *S'well* 96-01; TV Trunch *Nor* from 01. *The Rectory, Clipped Hedge Lane, Southrepps, Norwich NR11 8NS* Tel (01263) 833404 E-mail ccc@supanet.com

BARTLETT, George Frederick. b 34. Clifton Th Coll 61. **d** 64 **p** 65. C Branksome St Clem *Sarum* 64-71; V Gt Baddow *Chelmsf* 71-72; Perm to Offic *Win* 81-87; rtd 99. *8 Glencarron Way, Southampton SO16 7EF* Tel (023) 8032 5162 E-mail george.bartlett@cwcom.net

BARTLETT, Canon John Raymond. b 37. BNC Ox BA59 MA62 BLitt62 TCD MA70 LittD94. Linc Th Coll 61. **d** 63 **p** 64. C W Bridgford *S'well* 63-66; Lect Div TCD 66-86; Assoc Prof Bibl Studies 86-92; Fell 75-92; Prof Past Th 90-01; Prin CITC 89-01; Treas Ch Ch Cathl Dublin *D & G* 86-88; Prec 88-01; rtd 01. *102 Sorrento Road, Dalkey, Co Dublin, Irish Republic* Tel (00353) (1) 284 7786 E-mail jrbartlett@eircom.net

BARTLETT, Kenneth Vincent John. b 36. OBE93. Oriel Coll Ox BA61 BTh63. Ripon Hall Ox 61. **d** 63 **p** 64. C Paddington St Jas Lon 63-67; Lic to Offic from 67; rtd 01. *13 Shaa Road, London W3 7LN* Tel (020) 8743 3989 E-mail shaa4949@aol.com

BARTLETT, Canon Maurice Edward. b 33. G&C Coll Cam BA59 MA63. Wells Th Coll 59. **d** 60 **p** 61. C Batley All SS *Wakef* 60-64; Bp's Dom Chapl 64-66; Dir of Ords 64-66; Asst Chapl HM Pris Wakef 64-66; V Allerton *Liv* 66-81; V Lancaster St Mary *Blackb* 81-97; Sub-Chapl HM Pris Lanc 81-97; Hon Can Blackb Cathl 87-97; rtd 97. *Waverley House, West Common, Bowness-on-Solway, Carlisle CA7 5AG*

BARTLETT, Michael Fredrick. b 52. Ex Univ BA74 Liv Univ BPhil75 Ox Univ BA79 MA. Ripon Coll Cuddesdon 76 Ven English Coll Rome 78. **d** 79 **p** 80. C Kirkby *Liv* 79-82; C Wordsley *Lich* 82-83; Chapl Wordsley Hosp 82-88; TV Wordsley Lich 83-88; TV Redditch, The Ridge *Worc* from 88. *St Peter's House, Littlewoods, Crabbs Cross, Redditch B97 5LB* Tel (01527) 545709

BARTLETT, Preb Michael George. b 35. S Dios Minl Tr Scheme 84. **d** 87 **p** 88. NSM Wimborne Minster and Holt *Sarum* 87-90; C Charlestown *Truro* 90-91; R St Endellion w Port Isaac and St Kew from 91; Preb St Endellion from 96. *The Rectory, St Endellion, Port Isaac PL29 3TP* Tel (01208) 880442

BARTLETT, Richard Charles. b 68. St Kath Coll Liv BA90 Surrey Univ MA01. Westcott Ho Cam CTM94. **d** 94 **p** 95. C Wareham

Sarum 94-98; Assoc V Ealing All SS *Lon* 98-02; Chapl Twyford C of E High Sch Acton 98-02; USPG from 02; Chapl Brasilia Cathl Brazil from 02. *SQSW 301, Bl E, Ed Porto Rico, Apt 101, Sudoeste, DF, 70673-105, Brazil* Tel (0055) (61) 342 3463 E-mail brasiliaanglicanchaplaincy@yahoo.com.br

BARTON, Andrew Edward. b 53. MRSC St Jo Coll Ox MA77 DPhil80. Ridley Hall Cam 87. **d** 90 **p** 91. C Ringwood *Win* 90-94; R Baughurst, Ramsdell, Wolverton w Ewhurst etc from 95; Lect K Alfred's Coll Win 95-98. *The Rectory, Wolverton, Tadley RG26 5RU* Tel and fax (01635) 298008 Mobile 07778-771651 E-mail andrew.e.barton@ntlworld.com

BARTON, Anne. See BARTON, Margaret Anne

BARTON, Canon Arthur Michael. b 33. CCC Cam BA57 MA61. Wycliffe Hall Ox 57. **d** 59 **p** 60. Min Can Bradf Cathl *Bradf* 59-61; C Maltby *Sheff* 61-63; V Silsden *Bradf* 63-70; V Moor Allerton *Ripon* 70-81; TR 81-82; V Wetherby 82-98; Chapl HM YOI Wetherby 82-89; RD Harrogate *Ripon* 88-95; Hon Can Ripon Cathl 89-98; rtd 98. *22 Ash Road, Harrogate HG2 8EG* Tel (01423) 870799

BARTON, The Ven Charles John Greenwood. b 36. ALCD63. **d** 63 **p** 64. C Cant St Mary Bredin *Cant* 63-66; V Whitfield w W Langdon 66-75; V S Kensington St Luke *Lon* 75-83; AD Chelsea 80-83; Chief Broadcasting Officer for C of E 83-90; Adn Aston *Birm* from 90; Can Res Birm Cathl 90-02; P-in-c Bickenhill St Pet from 02. *26 George Road, Edgbaston, Birmingham B15 1PJ* Tel 0121-454 5525 *or* 426 0436 Mobile 07976-747535 Fax 455 6085 *or* 428 1114 E-mail venjb@globalnet.co.uk

BARTON, Canon Cyril Albert. b 28. St Pet Hall Ox BA50 MA54. Ridley Hall Cam. **d** 52 **p** 53. C Maghull *Liv* 52-55; Min Can Bradf Cathl *Bradf* 55-58; V Oldham St Paul *Man* 58-68; V Norbury *Ches* 68-90; Hon Can Ches Cathl 85-95; R Aldford and Bruera 90-95; rtd 95; Perm to Offic *Ches* from 95. *5 Calder Close, Bollington, Macclesfield SK10 5LJ* Tel (01625) 572601

BARTON, Dale. b 49. Selw Coll Cam BA71 MA76. Linc Th Coll 71. **d** 73 **p** 74. C Gosforth All SS *Newc* 73-77; Lesotho 77-81; Dep Warden CA Hostel Cam 82-83; C Shepton Mallet w Doulting *B & W* 83-88; TV Preston St Steph *Blackb* 88-96; V 96-99; Bp's Adv on Inter-Faith Relns from 99. *5 Vincent Court, Blackburn BB2 4LD* Tel (01254) 672744 E-mail st.barton@ukonline.co.uk

BARTON, David Gerald Story. b 38. Selw Coll Cam BA62 MA66. Cuddesdon Coll 63. **d** 65 **p** 66. C Cowley St Jas *Ox* 65-67; C Hambleden 67-70; Hon C Hammersmith St Jo *Lon* 72-77; Hon C Paddington St Jas 77-81; Hd Master Soho Par Sch 81-88; Hon C Westmr St Jas 81-92; RE Project Officer Lon Dioc Bd for Schs 88-92; Dioc Schs Adv *Ox* 93-99; NSM Iffley from 93; rtd 00. *254 Iffley Road, Oxford OX4 1SE* Tel (01865) 240059 E-mail david.barton@dial.appleinter.net

BARTON, Edward. b 23. **d** 75 **p** 76. C Budock *Truro* 75-79; P-in-c St Stithians w Perranarworthal *Truro* 79-80; V St Stythians w Perranarworthal and Gwennap 80-82; rtd 88; Perm to Offic *Truro* from 98. *Riverside, 5 Riviera Terrace, Malpas, Truro TR1 1SR* Tel (01872) 271686

BARTON, Eric Alfred. b 13. Clifton Th Coll 38. **d** 40 **p** 41. C Stratford New Town St Paul *Chelmsf* 40-42; C S Mimms Ch Ch Lon 42-44; V Holloway St Mary Magd 45-48; V Ripon H Trin Ripon 48-53; V Clifton *York* 53-59; R Haworth *Bradf* 59-61; V Buttershaw St Paul 61-70; V Nailsea Ch Ch *B & W* 70-82; rtd 82; Perm to Offic *Ex* from 82. *22 Woolbrook Rise, Sidmouth EX10 9UD* Tel (01395) 514841

BARTON, Canon Geoffrey. b 27. Oriel Coll Ox BA48 MA52. Chich Th Coll 49. **d** 51 **p** 52. C Arnold *S'well* 51-53; C E Retford 53-54; V Mirfield Eastthorpe St Paul *Wakef* 54-60; V Boroughbridge w Roecliffe *Ripon* 60-73; V Aldborough w Boroughbridge and Roecliffe 73; P-in-c Farnham w Scotton and Staveley and Copgrove 73-74; R 74-77; Chapl Roundway Hosp Devizes 77-92; Can and Preb Sarum Cathl *Sarum* 86-92; rtd 92; Perm to Offic *Sarum* from 01. *4B Willow House, Downlands Road, Devizes SN10 5EA* Tel (01380) 725311

BARTON, Mrs Jean Valerie. b 42. Wycliffe Hall Ox BTh01. **d** 02 **p** 03. NSM Harwell w Chilton *Ox* from 02. *Woodside, Drayton Road, Sutton Courtenay, Abingdon OX14 4HA* Tel (01235) 523702 E-mail pj1barton@ad.com

BARTON, John. See BARTON, The Ven Charles John Greenwood

BARTON, Canon John. b 25. MBE91. Keble Coll Ox BA48 MA50. Ely Th Coll 48. **d** 50 **p** 51. C Worksop St Anne *S'well* 50-53; C Harrogate St Wilfrid *Ripon* 53-56; V Beeston Hill H Spirit 56-60; Chapl Stanley Royd & Pinderfields Hosps Wakef 60-72; RD Wakef 68-72; Chapl Jo Radcliffe Hosp & Radcliffe Infirmary 72-90; Chapl Chu Hosp Ox 72-89; Hon Can Ch Ch Ox 77-94; RD Cowley 89-94; rtd 90; Perm to Offic Ox 94-01; Perm to Offic *Roch* from 01. *150A Longlands Road, Sidcup DA15 7LF* Tel (020) 8300 7073

BARTON, Prof John. b 48. Keble Coll Ox BA69 MA73 Mert Coll Ox DPhil74 St Cross Coll Ox DLitt88. **d** 73 **p** 73. Jun Research Fell Mert Coll Ox 73-74; Lect St Cross Coll Ox 74-89; Fell 74-91; Chapl 79-91; Lect Th Ox Univ 74-89; Reader 89-91; Oriel and Laing Prof of Interpr of H Scrip from 91; Fell Oriel Coll Ox from

91; Can Th Win Cathl *Win* from 91. *11 Withington Court, Abingdon OX14 3QA* Tel (01235) 525925

BARTON, Canon John Christopher Peter. b 28. Trin Hall Cam BA51 MA56. Ridley Hall Cam 51. **d** 53 **p** 54. C Erith St Paul *Roch* 53-56; C Cockfosters Ch Ch CD *Lon* 56-64; V Welling *Roch* 64-75; P-in-c Malmesbury w Westport *Bris* 75-84; P-in-c Charlton w Brokenborough and Hankerton 80-84; V Malmesbury w Westport and Brokenborough 84-94; Hon Can Kigezi from 92; rtd 94; Perm to Offic *B & W* from 94. *Orchard House, Orchard Road, Crewkerne TA18 7AF* Tel (01460) 72536

BARTON, Canon John Michael. b 40. TCD BA62 Div Test. **d** 63 **p** 64. C Coleraine *Conn* 63-68; C Portadown St Mark *Arm* 68-71; I Carnteel and Crilly 71-83; I Derryloran 83-97; Bp's C Acton and Drumbanagher from 97; Can Arm Cathl from 94; Treas 98-01; Chan from 01. *Drumbanagher Vicarage, 128 Tandragee Road, Newry BT35 6LW* Tel (028) 3082 1298

BARTON, Mrs Margaret Ann Edith. b 48. Newc Univ BA71. EMMTC 95. **d** 98 **p** 99. NSM Castle Bytham w Creeton *Linc* from 98. *Blanchland House, Swinstead Road, Corby Glen, Grantham NG33 4NU* Tel (01476) 550763

BARTON, Margaret Anne. b 54. St Anne's Coll Ox BA76 MA80 DPhil81 Selw Coll Cam BA89 MA94. Ridley Hall Cam 87. **d** 90 **p** 94. Par Dn Burley Ville *Win* 90-94; Chapl K Alfred Coll 94-98; Dioc Development and Research Officer for Liturg Matters 99-01; NSM Baughurst, Ramsdell, Wolverton w Ewhurst etc 99-01; Asst Chapl Gen Synod 96-00; rtd 01. *The Rectory, Wolverton, Tadley RG26 5RU* Tel (01635) 298008 Fax as telephone E-mail rev.anne.barton@ntlworld.com

BARTON, Michael. *See* BARTON, Canon Arthur Michael

BARTON, Canon Samuel David. b 45. DipTh. **d** 84 **p** 85. C Ballywillan *Conn* 84-86; I Aghadowey w Kilrea *D & R* 86-92; Bp's C Fahan Lower and Upper from 92; Dioc Educn Co-ord from 94; Dioc Communications Officer from 98; Can Raphoe Cathl from 98. *The Rectory, Cahir O'Doherty Avenue, Buncrana, Co Donegal, Irish Republic* Tel (00353) (74) 936 1154 Fax 936 3726 E-mail dco@derry.anglican.org *or* sbarton@iol.ie

BARTON, Stephen Christian. b 52. Macquarie Univ (NSW) BA75 DipEd75 Lanc Univ MA78 K Coll Lon PhD92. Cranmer Hall Dur 91. **d** 93 **p** 94. NSM Neville's Cross St Jo CD *Dur* 93-00; NSM Dur St Marg and Neville's Cross St Jo from 00. *33 Nevilledale Terrace, Durham DH1 4QG* Tel 0191-386 4983 E-mail s.c.barton@durham.ac.uk

BARTON, Stephen William. b 50. St Jo Coll Cam BA73 MA76 Leeds Univ MPhil81. Coll of Resurr Mirfield 75. **d** 77 **p** 78. C Horton *Bradf* 77-80; USPG 80-92; Bangladesh 81-92; TV Southampton (City Cen) *Win* 92-98; Chapl Manager Birm Women's Healthcare NHS Trust from 99. *The Chaplaincy, Birmingham Women's Hospital, Edgbaston, Birmingham B15 2TG* Tel 0121-472 1377

BARTON, Timothy Charles. b 47. Sarum & Wells Th Coll 73. **d** 76 **p** 77. C Upholland *Liv* 76-80; V Dalton from 80. *88 Lyndhurst Avenue, Skelmersdale WN8 6UH* Tel (01695) 733148

BARTON, Trevor James. b 50. St Alb Minl Tr Scheme 79. **d** 87 **p** 88. NSM Hemel Hempstead *St Alb* from 87. *46 Crossfell Road, Hemel Hempstead HP3 8RQ* Tel (01442) 251537 E-mail trevorbarton@hotmail.com

BARWELL, Brian Bernard Beale. b 30. Preston Poly CertEd79. AKC59 St Boniface Warminster 59. **d** 60 **p** 61. C Heywood St Jas *Man* 60-63; V Smallbridge 63-69; V Farington *Blackb* 69-72; C-in-c Blackb St Luke w St Phil 72-75; C Standish 75-76; Lic to Offic 76-92; rtd 92; Perm to Offic *Blackb* from 92. *70 Claytongate, Coppull, Chorley PR7 4PS* Tel (01257) 794251

BARZEY, Ms Michele Alison Lesley. b 63. Trin Coll Bris BA94. **d** 94. C Gravelly Hill *Birm* 94-96. *40 Holly Park Drive, Birmingham B24 9LQ* Tel 0121-241 2480

BASAVARAJ, Mrs Patricia Margaret. b 37. SRN61 SCM62. **d** 00. OLM Verwood *Sarum* from 00. *Hope Cottage, Church Hill, Verwood BH13 6HT* Tel (01202) 822920

BASFORD HOLBROOK, Colin Eric. b 42. St Steph Ho Ox 73. **d** 75 **p** 76. C Dovecot *Liv* 75-78; V Hollinfare 79-83; CMS 83-88; Cyprus 83-91; Chapl Athens w Kifissia, Patras, Thessaloniki etc *Eur* 91-93; Chapl Athens w Patras, Thessaloniki and Voula 93-94; rtd 02. *PO Box 42786, Larnaca 6503, Cyprus* Tel (00357) (24) 620864

BASH, Anthony. b 52. Bris Univ LLB73 LLM76 Glas Univ BD89 Clare Hall Cam PhD96. Westcott Ho Cam CTM94. **d** 96 **p** 97. C Kingston upon Hull H Trin *York* 96-99; V N Ferriby from 99. *The Vicarage, 20 Aston Hall Drive, North Ferriby HU14 3EB* Tel (01482) 631306 E-mail vicar@northferribychurch.org.uk

BASHFORD, Richard Frederick. b 36. Lon Univ DipTh68. Clifton Th Coll. **d** 68 **p** 69. C Bedworth *Cov* 68-71; C Lower Homerton St Paul *Lon* 71-75; V Bordesley Green *Birm* 75-81; R Birm Bishop Latimer w All SS from 81. *The Vicarage, 28 Handsworth New Road, Birmingham B18 4PT* Tel 0121-554 2221

BASHFORD, Robert Thomas. b 49. Ch Coll Cam BA70 CertEd72 MA74 Lon Univ BD84 MPhil89. Oak Hill Th Coll 86. **d** 88 **p** 89. C Frinton *Chelmsf* 88-91; C Galleywood Common 91-96; V Clapham *St Alb* 96-02; P-in-c Westgate St Jas *Cant* from

02. *St James's Vicarage, Orchard Gardens, Margate CT9 5JT* Tel (01843) 832380

BASHFORTH, Alan George. b 64. Cuddesdon Coll BTh93. **d** 96 **p** 97. C Calstock *Truro* 96-98; C St Ives 98-01; V St Agnes and Mithian w Mount Hawke from 01. *The Vicarage, 6 Penwinnick Parc, St Agnes TR5 0UG* Tel (01872) 553391

BASINGSTOKE, Suffragan Bishop of. *See* WILLMOTT, The Rt Revd Trevor

BASKERVILLE, John. b 45. Open Univ BA78. Sarum & Wells Th Coll 92. **d** 93 **p** 94. C Wanstead St Mary w Ch Ch *Chelmsf* 93-96; C Chingford SS Pet and Paul 96-98; V Felkirk w Brierley *Wakef* from 98. *Felkirk Vicarage, George Street, South Hiendley, Barnsley S72 9BX* Tel (01226) 715315 Mobile 07710-209469

BASKERVILLE, Philip Duncan. b 58. St Chad's Coll Dur BSc79 Oriel Coll Ox PGCE80. Trin Coll Bris BA87. **d** 88 **p** 89. C Roby *Liv* 88-93; Kenya 93-97; C Barnston *Ches* from 98. *8 Antons Road, Pensby, Wirral CH61 9PT* Tel 0151-648 1512 *or* 648 2404 Fax 648 2407 E-mail phil@kabare.freeserve.co.uk

BASON, Brian Vaudrey. b 27. Leeds Univ BA49 Lon Univ BD69 AMusTCL97. Coll of Resurr Mirfield 49. **d** 51 **p** 52. C Haggerston St Aug w St Steph *Lon* 51-55; C Bow w Bromley St Leon 55-56; V Audenshaw St Hilda *Man* 56-89; Perm to Offic *Ches* from 89; Perm to Offic *Man* 89-95; Audenshaw High Sch 89-92; rtd 92; Perm to Offic *Man* from 99. *78 Windsor Road, Denton, Manchester M34 2HE* Tel 0161-320 4408

BASS, Colin Graham. b 41. Liv Univ BSc62 Fitzw Ho Cam BA64 MA68. Ox NSM Course 84. **d** 87 **p** 88. Dir of Studies Leighton Park Sch Reading 87-97; NSM Earley St Pet *Ox* 87-92; NSM Reading Deanery from 92. *9 Bramley Close, Reading RG6 7PL* Tel 0118-966 3732 E-mail colin.bass@lineone.net

BASS, George Michael. b 39. Ely Th Coll 62. **d** 65 **p** 66. C Romaldkirk *Ripon* 65-68; C Kenton Ascension *Newc* 68-71; CF 71-94; Chapl N Tyneside Health Care NHS Trust 94-01; Chapl Northumbria Healthcare NHS Trust 01-02; rtd 02. *North Tyneside General Hospital, Rake Lane, North Shields NE29 8NH* Tel 0191-259 6660 ext 2153 E-mail pupsbass@yahoo.co.uk

BASS, Mrs Rosemary Jane. b 38. Linc Th Coll 76. **dss** 79 **d** 87 **p** 94. Bedford All SS *St Alb* 79-84; Leavesden All SS 84-95; Par Dn 87-94; C W Luton St Andr 95-01; rtd 01; Perm to Offic *St Alb* from 01. *41 Darlow Drive, Biddenham, Bedford MK40 4AY* Tel (01234) 219812 Fax as telephone

BASSETT, John Edmund. b 33. St Aid Birkenhead 63. **d** 66 **p** 67. C Guiseley *Bradf* 66-67; C Stechford *Birm* 67-71; C Ross *Heref* 71-72; P-in-c Brampton Abbotts 73-75; P-in-c Weston under Penyard 73-75; P-in-c Hope Mansell 73-75; TR Halesworth w Linstead and Chediston *St E* 75-78; R Laceby *Linc* 78-83; V Sale St Paul *Ches* 83-88; P-in-c Southport All SS *Liv* 88-94; P-in-c Southport All So 88-94; V Southport All SS and All So 94-98; P-in-c Aspull 98-99; V Aspull and New Springs 99-02; rtd 02; Hon C Pool w Arthington *Ripon* 02-03; Hon C Lower Wharfedale from 03. *The Vicarage, Old Pool Bank, Pool in Wharfedale, Otley LS21 1EJ* Tel 0113-284 3706

BASSETT, Mrs Rosemary Louise. b 42. STETS. **d** 00 **p** 01. NSM The Winterbournes and Compton Valence *Sarum* from 00; P-in-c from 03. *Hengistbury, Winterbourne Steepleton, Dorchester DT2 9LQ* Tel (01305) 889466 E-mail rose_trevor@trbassett.freeserve.co.uk

BASTEN, Richard Henry. b 40. Codrington Coll Barbados 60. **d** 63 **p** 64. C Honduras 63-67; Barbados 68-72; C Hartlepool H Trin *Dur* 72-73; Chapl Bedstone Coll 73-88; C Clun w Chapel Lawn *Heref* 73-77; P-in-c Clungunford 77-78; R Clungunford w Clunbury and Clunton, Bedstone etc 78-88; R Rowde and Poulshot *Sarum* 88-95; rtd 95; Perm to Offic *Glouc* 95-02. *41 Bewley Way, Churchdown, Gloucester GL3 2DU* Tel (01452) 859738

BASTIDE, Derek. b 44. Dur Univ BA65 Reading Univ DipEd66 Sussex Univ MA77. Chich Th Coll 76. **d** 77 **p** 78. Hon C Lewes All SS, St Anne, St Mich and St Thos *Chich* 77-84; Prin Lect Brighton Poly 80-92; Prin Lect Brighton Univ from 92; P-in-c Hamsey *Chich* from 84. *The Rectory, Offham, Lewes BN7 3PX* Tel (01273) 474356

BASTOCK, Kenneth William. b 22. Launde Abbey 75. **d** 76 **p** 77. C Glen Parva and S Wigston *Leic* 76-80; V Orton-on-the-Hill w Twycross etc 80-92; rtd 92; Perm to Offic *Leic* from 92. *18 Beech Road, Oadby, Leicester LE2 5QL* Tel 0116-271 0454

BASTON, Canon Caroline. b 56. Birm Univ BSc78 CertEd79. Ripon Coll Cuddesdon 87. **d** 89 **p** 94. Par Dn Southampton Thornhill St Chris *Win* 89-94; C 94-95; R Win All SS w Chilcomb and Chesil from 95; Dioc Communications Officer 95-98; Dioc Dir of Ords from 99; Hon Can Win Cathl from 00. *All Saints' Rectory, 19 Petersfield Road, Winchester SO23 0JD* Tel (01962) 853777 Fax 841714 E-mail caroline.baston@ukgateway.net

BATCHELOR, Alan Harold. b 30. Bris Univ BA54 Hull Univ MA63 Dip Personnel Mgt 68 LSE. Linc Th Coll 54. **d** 56 **p** 57. C Kingston upon Hull St Alb *York* 56-60; C Attercliffe w Darnall *Sheff* 60-62; India 63-87; Ind Chapl *Ripon* 87-95; C Kirkstall 92-95; rtd 95. *16 Moor Grange Rise, Leeds LS16 5BP* Tel 0113-275 6553

BATCHELOR, John Millar. CITC 76. **d** 78 **p** 79. C Belfast All SS *Conn* 78-80; I Eglish w Killylea *Arm* 80-96; I Ballyhalbert w Ardkeen *D & D* 96-01; rtd 01. *Rhone Brae, 102 Eglish Road, Dungannon BT70 1LB* Tel (028) 8775 0177
E-mail jm_batchelor@lineone.net

BATCHELOR, Martin John. b 67. Plymouth Poly BSc91. St Jo Coll Nottm Dip Th Studies 94 MA95. **d** 95 **p** 96. C Brecon St Mary and Battle w Llanddew *S & B* 95-97; Min Can Brecon Cathl 95-97; C Sketty 97-00; TV Hawarden *St As* from 00. *102A Hawarden Way, Mancot, Deeside CH5 2EW* Tel (01244) 539901
E-mail martin.batchelor@bigfoot.com

BATCHFORD, Philip John. b 71. Sheff Univ BA99. Ridley Hall Cam 00. **d** 02 **p** 03. C Sheff St Mary Bramall Lane *Sheff* from 02. *5 Colver Road, Sheffield S2 4UP* Tel 0114-225 7985

BATCOCK, Neil Gair. b 53. UEA BA74. Westcott Ho Cam CTM96. **d** 96 **p** 97. C Barton upon Humber *Linc* 96-99; TV Totnes w Bridgetown, Berry Pomeroy etc *Ex* from 99. *The Vicarage, Week, Dartington, Totnes TQ9 6JL* Tel (01803) 868304
E-mail nbatcock@compuserve.com

BATE, Dylan Griffin. b 48. Glam Poly HNC71. Mon Dioc Tr Scheme 91. **d** 94 **p** 95. NSM Fleur-de-Lis *Mon* 94-96; NSM Bedwellty 96-97; C Pontypool 97-99; C Tenby *St D* 99-02; R Begelly w Ludchurch and Crunwere from 02. *The Rectory, New Road, Begelly, Kilgetty SA68 0YG* Tel (01834) 812348

BATE, Preb Lawrence Mark. b 40. Univ Coll Ox BA63. Coll of Resurr Mirfield 65. **d** 67 **p** 68. C Benwell St Jas *Newc* 67-69; C Monkseaton St Pet 69-72; TV Withycombe Raleigh *Ex* 72-84; RD Aylesbeare 83-84; R Alphington 84-00; RD Christianity 95-99; TV Heavitree w Ex St Paul 00-02; TV Heavitree and St Mary Steps from 02; Preb Ex Cathl from 02. *Chapple Court, Kenn, Exeter EX6 7UR* Tel (01392) 833485
E-mail morleybate@freeuk.com

BATE, Michael Keith. b 42. Lich Th Coll 67. **d** 69 **p** 70. C W Bromwich St Jas *Lich* 69-73; C Thornhill *Wakef* 73-76; V Wrenthorpe 76-82; V Upper Gornal *Lich* 82-93; V Upper Gornal *Worc* from 93; Chapl Burton Rd Hosp Dudley 82-94; Chapl Dudley Gp of Hosps NHS Trust 94-00. *St Peter's Vicarage, 35 Eve Lane, Upper Gornal, Dudley DY1 3TY* Tel (01902) 883467

BATEMAN, James Edward. b 44. Lon Univ BSc65 Bris Univ DipTh74. Trin Coll Bris 71. **d** 74 **p** 75. C Woodlands *Sheff* 74-77; C Rushden w Newton Bromswold *Pet* 77-84; R Vange *Chelmsf* 84-94; V Southminster 94-01; P-in-c Nazeing and Roydon 01-03; Warden Stacklands Retreat Ho W Kingsdown from 03. *Stacklands Retreat House, West Kingsdown, Sevenoaks TN15 6AN* Tel (01474) 852247
E-mail warden@stacklands.org.uk

BATEMAN, Kenneth William. b 34. ACII58. N Ord Course 85. **d** 88 **p** 89. Hon C Pilling *Blackb* 88-91; Chapl Lanc Moor Hosp 88-92; Chapl Lanc Priority Services NHS Trust 92-95; C Kirkby Lonsdale *Carl* 91-95; NSM 95-98; rtd 95; Perm to Offic *Carl* from 98. *Greenside, Barbon, Carnforth LA6 2LT* Tel (015242) 76318

BATEMAN, Martyn Henry. b 31. Jes Coll Cam BA54 MA58. Clifton Th Coll 54. **d** 56 **p** 57. C Heatherlands St Jo *Sarum* 56-59; C New Malden and Coombe *S'wark* 59-60; Iran 60-62; V Charsfield *St E* 62-69; R Monewden and Hoo 62-69; V Wickham Market 69-82; Hon Can St E Cathl 80-85; V Felixstowe SS Pet and Paul 82-85; TR Lydford, Brent Tor, Bridestowe and Sourton 85-92; RD Tavistock 90-92; rtd 92. *Ardochy, Whitebridge, Inverness IV2 6UR* Tel (01456) 486273

BATEMAN, Patrick John. b 64. St Jo Coll Nottm 99. **d** 01 **p** 02. C Wallington H Trin *S'wark* from 01. *54 Stanley Park Road, Carshalton SM5 3HW* Tel (020) 8404 3918 Mobile 07764-171400 E-mail patrickbateman@blueyonder.co.uk

BATEMAN, Richard George. b 46. St Jo Coll Dur. **d** 82 **p** 83. C Wolviston *Dur* 82-85; C Greenside 85-87; V Newburn *Newc* 87-00; TV Cramlington from 00. *24 Lindsey Close, Cramlington NE23 8EJ* Tel (01670) 738078 E-mail rick@bate146.fsnet.co.uk

BATEMAN, Richard William. b 36. AKC61. **d** 62 **p** 63. C Pennywell St Thos and Grindon St Oswald CD *Dur* 62-66; Trinidad and Tobago 66-70; R Etherley *Dur* 70-77; Ind Chapl *Roch* 77-83; Hon C Chatham St Steph 78-83; Chapl RN 79-83; V Kemsing w Woodlands *Roch* 83-90; P-in-c Petham and Waltham w Lower Hardres etc *Cant* 90-98; P-in-c Elmsted w Hastingleigh 98; rtd 01. *Stoneyridge, Waddem Hall Lane, Petham, Canterbury CT4 5PX* Tel (01227) 709318 *or* 700440

BATEMAN-CHAMPAIN, John Nicholas. b 30. G&C Coll Cam BA53 DipRS85. S'wark Ord Course 83. **d** 85 **p** 86. CStJ from 80; C Harpenden St Jo *St Alb* 85-88; V Northaw 88-97; rtd 97; Perm to Offic *Guildf* from 97. *Littleworth, Surrey Gardens, Effingham, Leatherhead KT24 5HF* Tel (01483) 282461

BATES, Derek Alvin. b 27. St Mich Coll Llan 57. **d** 59 **p** 60. C Bishop's Cleeve *Glouc* 59-63; V Shebbear *Ex* 67-71; R Buckland Filleigh 67-71; R Highampton w Sheepwash 71; R Coates *Ely* 72-80; R Clovelly *Ex* 80-92; V Woolfardisworthy and Buck Mills 80-92; rtd 92; Perm to Offic *Ex* from 92. *Two Old Road, Shepherds Meadow, Abbotsham, Bideford EX39 5BP*

✠**BATES, The Rt Revd Gordon.** b 34. Kelham Th Coll 54. **d** 58 **p** 59 **c** 83. C New Eltham All SS *S'wark* 58-62; Asst Youth Chapl *Glouc* 62-64; Youth Chapl *Liv* 65-69; Chapl Liv Cathl 65-69; V Huyton St Mich 69-73; Can Res and Prec Liv Cathl 73-83; Dir of Ords 73-83; Suff Bp Whitby *York* 83-99; rtd 99; Perm to Offic *Blackb* from 99. *2 Loyne Park, Whittington, Carnforth LA6 2NL* Tel (015242) 72010

BATES, James. b 46. Linc Th Coll 73. **d** 75 **p** 76. C Ewell *Guildf* 75-77; C Farncombe 77-80; V Pet St Mary Boongate *Pet* 80-92; V Kingston All SS w St Jo *S'wark* from 92. *All Saints' Vicarage, 15 Woodbine Avenue, Kingston upon Thames KT1 2AZ* Tel (020) 8546 2644 E-mail j.bates@kingston.ac.uk

BATES, Michael. b 33. Dur Univ BSc57 Hull Univ Ad Dip Maths Educn 84. Clifton Th Coll 57. **d** 59 **p** 60. C Drypool St Columba w St Andr and St Pet *York* 59-62; C Cheadle *Ches* 62-67; V Newbottle *Dur* 67-75; Chapl Nat Coal Bd 68-75; Teacher Bilton Grange High Sch Hull 76-88; Tutor Wilberforce Coll Hull 88-94; Hon C Kingston upon Hull H Trin *York* 81-96; rtd 96; Perm to Offic *York* from 96. *5 Fernland Close, Brough HU15 1DQ* Tel (01482) 669023

BATES, Miss Phyllis Edith. b 29. S'wark Ord Course 80. **dss** 83 **d** 87 **p** 94. Registrar S'wark Ord Course 83-89; Fulham St Dionis Parson's Green 83-87; Hon Par Dn 87-94; rtd 89; NSM Hammersmith St Paul *Lon* from 94; Perm to Offic *S'wark* from 89. *26 St Dionis Road, London SW6 4UF* Tel (020) 7731 6935

BATES, Robert John. b 50. FRICS81. EAMTC 99. **d** 02 **p** 03. NSM Pet St Mary Boongate *Pet* from 02. *1 Park Crescent, Peterborough PE1 4DX* Tel (01733) 560249
E-mail bates.parkcrescent@virgin.net

BATES, Mrs Rosemary Eileen Hamilton. b 45. Ripon Coll Cuddesdon 87. **d** 89 **p** 94. Par Dn Brackley St Pet w St Jas *Pet* 89-94; C 94-95; P-in-c N Hinksey and Wytham *Ox* from 95. *The Vicarage, 81 West Way, Oxford OX2 9JY* Tel (01865) 242345
E-mail revrosie@ehbates.fsnet.co.uk

BATES, Stuart Geoffrey. b 61. Univ of Wales (Lamp) BA82. St Steph Ho Ox 83. **d** 85 **p** 86. C Bromley St Mark *Roch* 85-88; C Westmr St Matt *Lon* 88-89; C Gt Ilford St Mary *Chelmsf* 89-95; C Crofton Park St Hilda w St Cypr *S'wark* from 95. *St Hilda's Vicarage, 35 Buckthorne Road, London SE4 2DG* Tel (020) 8699 1277

BATES, William Frederic. b 49. St Jo Coll Dur BSc72 BA74 MA97. Cranmer Hall Dur DipTh75. **d** 75 **p** 76. C Knutsford St Jo and Toft *Ches* 75-78; C Ripley *Derby* 78-80; R Nether and Over Seale 81-93; V Lullington 81-93; V Allestree St Nic from 93; Bp's Adv on New Relig Movements from 99; P-in-c Quarndon from 00. *The Vicarage, 4 Lawn Avenue, Allestree, Derby DE22 2PE* Tel (01332) 550224
E-mail wjbates@rosemary10.fsnet.co.uk

BATES, William Hugh. b 33. Keble Coll Ox BA56 MA59. Westcott Ho Cam 59. **d** 60 **p** 61. C Horsforth *Ripon* 60-63; Tutor St Chad's Coll Dur 63-70; V Bishop Wilton *York* 70-76; RD Pocklington 74-76; V Pickering 76-82; Prin NEOC 79-94; P-in-c Crayke w Brandsby and Yearsley 82-94; P-in-c Stillington and Marton w Moxby 82-94; rtd 94; Perm to Offic *York* from 94. *Jessibrook, Main Street, Bugthorpe, York YO41 1QG* Tel (01759) 368402

BATESON, Canon Geoffrey Frederick. b 27. K Coll Lon BD51 AKC51. **d** 52 **p** 53. C Tynemouth Cullercoats St Paul *Newc* 52-56; C Gosforth All SS 56-60; V Monkseaton St Pet 60-68; V Newc St Geo 68-77; RD Newc 75-77; Chapl St Geo and Cottage Hosp Morpeth 77-89; R Morpeth *Newc* 77-89; Hon Can Newc Cathl 80-89; rtd 89; Perm to Offic *York* from 91. *1 Netherby Close, Sleights, Whitby YO22 5HD* Tel (01947) 810997

BATESON, Canon James Howard. b 36. MSOSc88 Qu Mary Coll Lon BSc57. EMMTC 85. **d** 87 **p** 88. NSM W Bridgford *S'well* 87-88; NSM Wilford Hill 88-95; Dioc Officer for NSMs from 94; P-in-c Staunton w Flawborough from 96; P-in-c Kilvington from 96; Hon Can S'well Minster from 99. *45 Stamford Road, West Bridgford, Nottingham NG2 6GD* Tel 0115-923 1820 Fax as telephone E-mail h_bateson@primeuk.net

BATESON, Keith Nigel. b 43. **d** 00 **p** 01. OLM Wonersh w Blackheath *Guildf* from 00. *Advent Cottage, Blackheath Lane, Wonersh, Guildford GU5 0PN* Tel (01483) 892753
E-mail k_bateson@engineer.com

BATEY, Canon Herbert Taylor. b 22. Qu Coll Ox BA46 MA48. Linc Th Coll 48. **d** 48 **p** 49. C Dalton-in-Furness *Carl* 48-50; C Egremont 50-52; V Cleator Moor w Cleator 52-59; Chapl St Bees Sch Cumbria 59-64; Chapl Culham Coll Abingdon 64-68; Prin Lect 68-75; P-in-c Culham *Ox* 68-75; Vice-Prin Coll of Ripon and York St Jo from 75; Hon Can Ripon Cathl *Ripon* 85-92; rtd 87; Perm to Offic *Ripon* from 92. *29 College Road, Ripon HG4 2HE* Tel (01765) 607096

BATEY, William Abbott. b 20. Cranmer Hall Dur 62. **d** 63 **p** 64. C Appleby and Murton cum Hilton *Carl* 63-66; R Moresby 66-77; P-in-c Arnside 77-85; V 85-90; rtd 90; Perm to Offic *Carl* from 90. *33 Greengate, Levens, Kendal LA8 8NF* Tel (01539) 566791

BATH, David James William. b 43. Oak Hill NSM Course 87. **d** 89 **p** 90. NSM Henley *Ox* 89-90; Gen Manager Humberside

Gd News Trust 90-96; NSM Anlaby St Pet *York* from 96. *24 Lawnswood, Hessle HU13 0PT* Tel (01482) 644780 E-mail bath@pobox.quza.com

BATH AND WELLS, Bishop of. *See* PRICE, The Rt Revd Peter Bryan

BATH, Archdeacon of. *See* EVENS, The Ven Robert John Scott

BATHURST, Bishop of. *See* HURFORD, The Rt Revd Richard Warwick

BATLEY-GLADDEN, Dane Christopher. b 68. St Steph Ho Ox 96. **d** 99 **p** 00. C Hendon St Alphage *Lon* 99-01; C-in-c Grahame Park St Aug CD from 01. *St Augustine's House, Great Field, London NW9 5SY* Tel (020) 8205 1979 E-mail frdane@dlondon.org.uk

BATSLEER, Canon Albert. b 21. Selw Coll Cam BA46 MA54. Cuddesdon Coll 46. **d** 48 **p** 49. C Leic St Phil *Leic* 48-50; C Hope St Jas *Man* 50-52; V Heap Bridge 52-56; V Glossop *Derby* 56-65; R Staveley 65-72; V Riddings 72-81; RD Alfreton 76-81; V New Mills 81-85; RD Glossop 81-83; Hon Can Derby Cathl 81-85; rtd 85; Perm to Offic *Pet* from 95. *23 The Gables, Kettering NN15 7JW* Tel (01536) 416758

BATSON, David Frederick Edward. b 38. K Coll Lon AKC61 BD69 FSAScot97. St Boniface Warminster. **d** 62 **p** 63. C Southport H Trin *Liv* 62-64; Asst Chapl Hurstpierpoint Coll 64-65; C Cleator Moor w Cleator *Carl* 65-66; Asst Master K Geo V Sch Southport 66-67; NSM Leigh w Bransford *Worc* 68-79; Hon Asst Chapl Convent of H Name Malvern Link 68-72; Prin Soc Work Tr Dept Dumfries and Galloway Coun 84-94; Lect and Tutor Langside Coll Glas 95-97; Lect Soc Studies Dumfries and Galloway Coll from 96; Visiting Lect Paisley Univ from 02; Perm to Offic *Glas* from 03. *Kindar House, New Abbey, Dumfries DG2 8DB* Tel (01387) 850514 Fax 850556

BATSON, John Gordon Kemp. b 38. Kelham Th Coll 60 Bps' Coll Cheshunt 64. **d** 65 **p** 66. C Lamorbey H Redeemer *Roch* 65-69; Trinidad and Tobago 69-74; V Borough Green *Roch* 74-83; V Perry Street 83-92; V Yalding w Collier Street 92-97; V Woodnesborough w Worth and Staple *Cant* 97-03; rtd 03; Perm to Offic *Cant* from 03. *21 Selsey Avenue, Herne Bay CT6 8SB* Tel (01227) 368780

BATSON, Paul Leonard. b 47. Southn Univ BTh79. Sarum & Wells Th Coll 73. **d** 75 **p** 76. C Chesham St Mary *Ox* 75-79; Dioc Youth Adv *Newc* 79-85; V Earley St Pet *Ox* 85-93; Perm to Offic *Sarum* from 01. *Maple Cottage, 78 Murhill, Limpley Stoke, Bath BA2 7FB* Tel (01225) 722721

BATSON, William Francis Robert (Bob). b 43. Nottm Univ Dip Town Planning 69 St Jo Coll Dur BA72. **d** 73 **p** 74. C Eastwood *S'well* 74-77; R Long Marton w Dufton and w Milburn *Carl* 77-79; V Flimby 79-85; TR Raveningham *Nor* 85-91; R Kinver and Enville *Lich* 91-00; V Ledsham w Fairburn *York* from 00. *The Vicarage, 11 Main Street, Ledston, Castleford WF10 2AA* Tel (01977) 556946

BATSTONE, Bruce. b 70. Bris Univ BA92. St Steph Ho Ox 98. **d** 00. C Leigh-on-Sea St Marg *Chelmsf* from 00. *45 Eaton Road, Leigh-on-Sea SS9 3PF* Tel (01702) 477863 E-mail bruce.batstone@ic24.net

BATT, Canon Joseph William. b 39. Keele Univ BA62 DipSS62. Ripon Hall Ox 63. **d** 64 **p** 65. C Bushbury *Lich* 64-68; C Walsall 68-71; Nigeria 71-75; Area Sec CMS *Guildf* and *Chich* 75-84; V Ottershaw *Guildf* from 84; Hon Can Oke-Osun from 94. *Christ Church Vicarage, Cross Lane, Ottershaw, Chertsey KT16 0PA* Tel (01932) 873160

BATT, Kenneth Victor. b 41. Wycliffe Hall Ox 68. **d** 71 **p** 72. C Yateley *Win* 71-76; R The Candover Valley 76-82; R Durrington *Sarum* 82-89; V Kempshott *Win* 89-00; P-in-c Bournemouth H Epiphany from 00. *The Vicarage, 81 Castle Lane West, Bournemouth BH9 3LH* Tel (01202) 512481

BATTE, Mrs Kathleen. b 47. Homerton Coll Cam TCert68. NEOC 91. **d** 94 **p** 95. NSM Newc St Gabr *Newc* 94-96; NSM Wilford Hill *S'well* 96-99; P-in-c Cinderhill from 99. *Christ Church Vicarage, 587 Nuthall Road, Cinderhill, Nottingham NG8 6AD* Tel 0115-970 8151 E-mail kath.batte@talk21.com

BATTEN, Graham John. b 39. Open Univ BA81 Univ of Wales (Cardiff) DipTh65. St D Coll Lamp 65. **d** 66 **p** 67. C Llangynwyd w Maesteg *Llan* 66-70; C St Andrews Major w Michaelston-le-Pit 70-72; Chapl RN 72-91; Asst Chapl of the Fleet 91-94; V Dover St Mary *Cant* 94-00; rtd 00; Perm to Offic *B & W* from 01. *Parsonage House, Tower Hill Road, Crewkerne TA18 8BJ* Tel (01460) 271069

BATTEN, Stuart William. b 73. Univ of Wales (Abth) BD94 MTh96. Trin Coll Bris 96. **d** 98 **p** 99. C Northolt W End St Jos *Lon* 98-01; TV Hucknall Torkard *S'well* from 01. *St Peter and Paul's Vicarage, Ruffs Drive, Hucknall, Nottingham NG15 6JG* Tel 0115-963 3640 E-mail stuart.batten@btinternet.com

BATTERSBY, David George Sellers. b 32. AKC57. St Boniface Warminster 57 Lambeth STh80. **d** 58 **p** 59. C Glas St Marg *Glas* 58-60; C Burnley St Pet *Blackb* 60-62; V Warton St Paul 62-71; Chapl K Wm's Coll Is of Man 71-91; C Ashchurch *Glouc* 91-97; rtd 97; Perm to Offic *Glouc* and *Worc* from 97. *Shill Brook Cottage, Buckland Road, Bampton OX18 2AA*

BATTERSBY, Paul Clifford. b 49. Bede Coll Dur TCert70 St Jo Coll Dur BA74. Cranmer Hall Dur DipTh75. **d** 75 **p** 76. C

Sunderland St Chad *Dur* 75-78; Argentina 78-81; P-in-c Holme and Dioc Youth Officer *Carl* 81-85; Nat Officer for Youth Work Gen Syn Bd of Educn 85-92; TR Darwen St Pet w Hoddlesden *Blackb* 92-94; Soc Resp Officer 95-99; V Witton 99-03; V Leyland St Ambrose from 03. *St Ambrose Vicarage, 85 Moss Lane, Leyland, Preston PR25 4XA* Tel (01772) 462204 E-mail email@reverend.co.uk

BATTERSBY, Simon Charles. b 64. Wycliffe Hall Ox BTh01. **d** 01 **p** 02. C Askern *Sheff* 01-03; Chapl Bethany Sch Goudhurst from 03. *Providence Cottage, Curtisden Green, Goudhurst, Cranbrook TN17 1LD* Tel (01580) 211579 Mobile 07956-576737 E-mail pastasimon@hotmail.com

BATTERSHELL, Mrs Anne Marie. b 33. Ox Poly BEd83. St Alb and Ox Min Course 95. **d** 98 **p** 99. NSM Goring w S Stoke *Ox* 98-01; NSM Brafferton w Pilmoor, Myton on Swale etc *York* 01-03; rtd 03. *1 Hollygarth, Brafferton, York YO61 2NZ* Tel (01423) 360339

BATTIN (née WEBB), Mrs Frances Mary. b 52. WEMTC 92. **d** 95 **p** 96. NSM Inkberrow w Cookhill and Kington w Dormston *Worc* 95-98; Asst Chapl HM Pris Brockhill from 98. *HM Prison and YOI, Brockhill, Redditch B97 6RD* Tel (01527) 552650

BATTLE, Dean of. *See* CUMMINGS, The Very Revd William Alexander Vickery

BATTMAN, John Brian. b 37. ALCD61. **d** 61 **p** 62. C Fulham Ch Ch *Lon* 61-64; Argentina 64-69; Paraguay 69-76; Adn Paraguay 70-76; Ext Sec SAMS 77-80; V Romford Gd Shep Collier Row *Chelmsf* 80-92; V Werrington *Pet* 92-02; rtd 02; Perm to Offic *St E* from 02. *1 Butley Close, Ipswich IP2 9TR* Tel (01473) 680141 E-mail jnbattman@aol.com

BATTY, John Ivan. b 35. Clifton Th Coll 59. **d** 62 **p** 63. C Clayton *Bradf* 62-67; V Toxteth Park St Clem *Liv* 67-73; R Darfield *Sheff* 73-90; Chapl Düsseldorf *Eur* 90-95; V The Marshland *Sheff* 95-00; rtd 00; Perm to Offic *Sheff* from 00; *Linc* from 00. *4 St Lawrence Way, Tallington, Stamford PE9 4RH* Tel (01780) 740151

BATTY, Mark Alan. b 56. BSc. Ripon Coll Cuddesdon. **d** 82 **p** 83. C Bottesford w Ashby *Linc* 82-86; V Scunthorpe All SS 86-95; P-in-c N Wolds Gp 95-97; V from 97. *The Vicarage, St Barnabas Road, Barnetby DN38 6JE* Tel (01652) 688182

BATTY, Stephen Roy. b 58. Chich Th Coll 88. **d** 90 **p** 91. C Wimborne Minster and Holt *Sarum* 90-94; P-in-c Yetminster w Ryme Intrinseca and High Stoy 94-02; V Branksome St Aldhelm from 02. *The Vicarage, St Aldhelm's Road, Poole BH13 6BT* Tel (01202) 764420

BATTYE, Canon John Noel. b 42. TCD BA64 MA73. CITC 66. **d** 66 **p** 67. C Drumglass *Arm* 66-69; C Ballynafeigh St Jude *D & D* 70-73; Chapl Pemb Coll Cam 73-78; Bp's C Knocknagoney *D & D* 78-80; I Cregagh from 80; Preb Castleknock St Patr Cathl Dublin from 94. *St Finnian's Rectory, 3 Upper Knockbreda Road, Belfast BT6 9QH* Tel (028) 9079 3822

BATTYE, Ms Lisa Katherine. b 55. Man Univ BN78 MA(Theol)96 RM79 Man Poly Dip Counselling 84 Liv Univ MTh00. N Ord Course 96. **d** 99 **p** 00. C Clifton *Man* 99-02; R Kersal Moor from 02. *St Paul's Rectory, 1 Moorside Road, Salford M7 3PJ* Tel 0161-792 5362 E-mail lisa@battye.fsbusiness.co.uk

BATY, Edward. b 30. ARICS59 Open Univ BA77 UEA PhD88 MRICS01. St Aid Birkenhead 60. **d** 62 **p** 63. C Acomb St Steph *York* 62-64; Succ Chelmsf Cathl *Chelmsf* 64-67; V Becontree St Cedd 67-71; R Hope Bowdler w Eaton-under-Heywood *Heref* 71-79; R Rushbury 71-79; P-in-c Cardington 71-79; R Fincham *Ely* 79-82; OCF 79-94; R Long Stanton w St Mich *Ely* 82-94; P-in-c Lolworth 85-88; CF(V) 86-95; rtd 95; Perm to Offic *Guildf* from 95. *25 Martindale Avenue, Camberley GU15 1BB* Tel (01276) 20315

BATY, Ernest John. b 20. Univ of Wales BA42. St Mich Coll Llan 42. **d** 44 **p** 45. C Swansea St Thos and Kilvey *S & B* 44-47; C Defynnog w Rhydybriw and Llandeilo'r Fan 47-49; C Caerphilly *Llan* 49-52; V Huyton St Geo *Liv* 53-56; V Wigan St Cath 53; V Pemberton St Mark Newtown 56-62; V Lydiate 62-67; Hon C Sefton 69-85; rtd 85. *7 Delph Park Avenue, Ormskirk L39 5DE* Tel (01695) 423711

BAUERSCHMIDT, John Crawford. b 59. Kenyon Coll Ohio BA81. Gen Th Sem (NY) MDiv84. **d** 84 **p** 85. USA 84-87 and from 92; Lib Pusey Ho 87-91. *120 South New Hampshire, Covington, LA 70433, USA*

BAUGHAN, Mrs Emma Louise Langley. b 70. Bris Univ BA93 MA98. STETS 01. **d** 03. C Horfield H Trin *Bris* from 03. *31 Rosling Road, Bristol BS7 8SX* Tel 0117-951 9771 Mobile 07974-658619 E-mail emmalang@aol.com

BAUGHEN, Andrew Jonathan. b 64. Lon Guildhall Univ BA87. Wycliffe Hall Ox BTh94. **d** 94 **p** 95. C Battersea Rise St Mark *S'wark* 94-97; P-in-c Clerkenwell St Jas and St Jo w St Pet *Lon* 97-00; V from 00. *St James's Church, Clerkenwell Close, London EC1R 0EA* Tel (020) 7251 1190 E-mail vicar@jc-church.org

⊁BAUGHEN, The Rt Revd Michael Alfred. b 30. Lon Univ BD55. Oak Hill Th Coll 51. **d** 56 **p** 57 **c** 82. C Hyson Green *S'well* 56-59; C Reigate St Mary *S'wark* 59-61; Ord Cand Sec CPAS 61-64; R Rusholme H Trin *Man* 64-70; TV

St Marylebone All So w SS Pet and Jo *Lon* 70-75; R 75-82; AD Westmr St Marylebone 78-82; Preb St Paul's Cathl 79-82; Bp Ches 82-96; rtd 96; Hon Asst Bp Lon from 96; Perm to Offic *S'wark* from 97. *99 Brunswick Quay, London SE16 1PX* Tel (020) 7237 0167

BAULCOMB, Canon Geoffrey Gordon. b 46. K Coll Lon BD86 AKC68. **d** 69 **p** 70. C Crofton Park St Hilda w St Cypr *S'wark* 69-74; TV Padgate *Liv* 74-79; R Whitton and Thurleston w Akenham *St E* from 79; Hon Can St E Cathl from 03. *The Rectory, Whitton Church Lane, Ipswich IP1 6LT* Tel (01473) 741389

✠**BAVIN, The Rt Revd Timothy John.** b 35. Worc Coll Ox BA59 MA61. Cuddesdon Coll 59. **d** 61 **p** 62 **c** 74. S Africa 61-69 and 73-85; C Uckfield *Chich* 69-71; V Brighton Gd Shep Preston 71-73; Dean and Adn Johannesburg 73-74; Bp Johannesburg 74-85; Bp Portsm 85-95; OGS from 87; Community of Our Lady and St John from 96; Perm to Offic *Win* from 96; rtd 98. *Alton Abbey, Abbey Road, Beech, Alton GU34 4AP* Tel (01420) 562145 *or* 563575 Fax 561691

BAVINGTON, John Eduard. b 68. Loughb Univ BEng91. Trin Coll Bris BA99. **d** 99 **p** 00. C W Ealing St Jo w St Jas *Lon* 99-02; V Bradf St Clem *Bradf* from 02. *St Clement's Vicarage, 294A Barkerend Road, Bradford BD3 9DF* Tel (01274) 665109

BAWTREE, Andrew James. b 66. Univ of Wales BD91 Nottm Univ MA95 Ch Ch Coll Cant PGCE92. St Jo Coll Nottm 94. **d** 96 **p** 97. C Hoddesdon *St Alb* 96-99; USA from 99. *Trinity Church, 515 Yancey Street, South Boston, VA 24592, USA* Tel (001) (804) 572 4513

BAWTREE, Canon Robert John. b 39. Oak Hill Th Coll 62. **d** 67 **p** 68. C Foord St Jo *Cant* 67-70; C Boscombe St Jo *Win* 70-73; C Kinson *Sarum* 73-75; TV Bramerton w Surlingham *Nor* 76-82; R Arborfield w Barkham *Ox* 82-91; V Hildenborough *Roch* from 91; RD Tonbridge 95-01; Hon Can Roch Cathl from 02. *The Vicarage, 194 Tonbridge Road, Hildenborough, Tonbridge TN11 9HR* Tel (01732) 833596

BAXANDALL, Peter. b 45. Tyndale Hall Bris 67. **d** 70 **p** 72. C Kidsgrove *Lich* 70-71; C St Helens St Mark *Liv* 71-75; C Ardsley *Sheff* 76-77; Rep Leprosy Miss E Anglia 77-86; P-in-c March St Wendreda *Ely* 86-87; R from 87; RD March from 93. *St Wendreda's Rectory, 21 Wimblington Road, March PE15 9QW* Tel (01354) 653377 Fax as telephone
E-mail peter.baxandall@ely.anglican.org

BAXENDALE, John Richard. b 48. Cranmer Hall Dur 89. **d** 91 **p** 92. C Carl St Jo *Carl* 91-94; C Dalston 94-95; P-in-c Monton *Man* 95-96; TV Eccles from 96. *The Vicarage, 3 Egerton Road, Monton, Eccles, Manchester M30 9LR* Tel 0161-789 2420

BAXENDALE, Paul Gordon. b 70. Leeds Univ BA91. Ridley Hall Cam 93. **d** 96 **p** 97. C Kendal St Thos *Carl* 96-01; P-in-c Burton and Holme from 01. *St James's Vicarage, Glebe Close, Burton, Carnforth LA6 1PL* Tel (01524) 781391

BAXENDALE, Rodney Douglas. b 45. Ex Univ BA66 Nottm Univ DipTh79. Linc Th Coll 78. **d** 80 **p** 81. C Maidstone All SS and St Phil w Tovil *Cant* 80-83; Chapl RN 83-03. *Addresss temp unknown*

BAXTER, Anthony. b 54. SEITE 99. **d** 02. NSM Romford Ascension Collier Row *Chelmsf* from 02. *54 South Drive, Brentwood CM14 5DL* Tel (01277) 210937 Mobile 07909-984675 Fax (01277) 211926
E-mail tonybaxter54@aol.com

BAXTER, Brian Raymond. b 31. Tyndale Hall Bris. **d** 58 **p** 59. C Heworth H Trin *York* 58-61; C Belper *Derby* 61-65; R Leverton *Linc* 65-67; C Mile Cross *Nor* 74-76; C Farnborough *Guildf* 76-79; Ldr Southgate Chr Project Bury St Edmunds 79-84; Chapl W Suffolk Hosp 79-81; R Ringsfield w Redisham, Barsham, Shipmeadow etc *St E* 82-88; V Nor Heartsease St Fran *Nor* 88-91; rtd 91; Perm to Offic *Nor* from 91. *1 Clovelly Drive, Norwich NR6 5EY* Tel (01603) 413622

BAXTER, David Norman. b 39. Open Univ BA87. Kelham Th Coll 59. **d** 64 **p** 65. C Tonge Moor *Man* 64-68; Chapl RN 68-84; P-in-c Becontree St Pet *Chelmsf* 84-85; TV Becontree W 85-86; TR 86-94; Spain from 94; rtd 99. *Cl Vidal i Barraquer, 10, Escalera B, 1-2, 08870 Sitges, Barcelona, Spain* Tel (0034) 93 894 6151 Fax 93 894 3800 E-mail dnbaxter@teleline.es

BAXTER (née AVIS), Mrs Elizabeth Mary. b 49. Coll of Ripon & York St Jo Cert Counselling 91 Leeds Poly DipHE91 Leeds Metrop Univ BA93. N Ord Course 81. **d** 84 **d** 87 **p** 94. Leeds St Marg *Ripon* 84-87; Chapl Abbey Grange High Sch 85-93; Leeds All Hallows w Wrangthorn 85-87; Par Dn Leeds St Marg and All Hallows 87-93; Par Dn Topcliffe *York* 93-94; C 94-96; Jt Dir H Rood Ho Cen for Health and Past Care from 93; Perm to Offic *Ripon* from 93; *Dur* and *Newc* from 94; *Bradf* 95-00; *Sheff* from 95; *Wakef* from 97; C Thirsk *York* from 96. *Holy Rood House, 10 Sowerby Road, Sowerby, Thirsk YO7 1HX* Tel (01845) 522580 E-mail holyroodhouse@centrethirsk.fsnet.co.uk

BAXTER, Harold Leslie. b 11. Roch Th Coll 62. **d** 64 **p** 65. C Corsham *Bris* 64-67; C Bath Lyncombe *B & W* 67-70; V Shapwick w Ashcott 70-88; P-in-c Burtle 75-88; V Shapwick w Ashcott and Burtle 88-95; rtd 96; Perm to Offic *Truro* from 97.

Tredole, Prussia Cove Lane, Rosudgeon, Penzance TR20 9AX Tel (01736) 762133

BAXTER, Jane Elizabeth. b 51. Univ of Wales (Ban) DipHE01. EAMTC 98. **d** 01 **p** 02. C Clare w Poslingford, Cavendish etc *St E* from 01. *20 March Place, Clare, Sudbury CO10 8RH* Tel (01787) 277552 E-mail revjanebaxter@btinternet.com

BAXTER, John Richard. b 44. ACII66. STETS DipHE99. **d** 99 **p** 00. NSM Banstead *Guildf* 99-03; TV Surrey Weald from 03. *High Lea, 54 The Street, Capel, Dorking RH5 5LE* Tel 07974-692334 (mobile)
E-mail johnbaxter@eastewell.freeserve.co.uk

BAXTER, Peter James. b 29. St Chad's Coll Dur BA53 DipTh55. **d** 55 **p** 56. C Stanground *Ely* 55-58; C Paddington St Mich w All SS *Lon* 58; C Woodston *Ely* 59-62; R Eynesbury 62-89; rtd 89. *15 Bromley College, London Road, Bromley BR1 1PE*

BAXTER, Canon Richard David. b 33. Kelham Th Coll 53. **d** 57 **p** 58. C Carl St Barn *Carl* 57-59; C Barrow St Matt 59-64; V Drighlington *Wakef* 64-73; V Penistone 73-80; V Carl St Aid and Ch *Carl* 80-86; Can Res Wakef Cathl *Wakef* 86-97; Prec from 86; Vice-Provost 92-97; rtd 97; Perm to Offic *Carl* from 97. *20 Summerfields, Dalston, Carlisle CA5 7NW* Tel (01228) 710496 Fax as telephone
E-mail canondavidbaxter@btinternet.com

BAXTER, Stanley Robert. b 31. Leeds Univ MA90 FRSA96 MInstD97 MCMI98 FRSH99. Chich Th Coll 79. **d** 80 **p** 81. In Lutheran Ch 71-79; C Far Headingley St Chad *Ripon* 80-82; P-in-c Leeds St Marg and All Hallows 82-87; P-in-c Leeds All Hallows w Wrangthorn 85-87; P-in-c Leeds St Marg and All Hallows 87-93; Dir Leeds Cen for Urban Th Studies 88-93; Assoc Chapl Leeds Univ 91-93; P-in-c Topcliffe *York* 93-95; Jt Dir H Rood Ho Cen for Health and Past Care from 93; Perm to Offic *Ripon* from 93; *Dur* and *Newc* from 94; NSM Topcliffe *York* 95-96; NSM Thirsk from 96; Perm to Offic *Bradf* and *Sheff* from 95; *Wakef* from 97. *Holy Rood House, 10 Sowerby Road, Sowerby, Thirsk YO7 1HX* Tel (01845) 522580 *or* 522004 Fax 527300
E-mail holyroodhouse@centrethirsk.fsnet.co.uk

BAXTER, Stuart. b 43. Liv Univ BA65 Nottm Univ PGCE66. Cuddesdon Coll 66. **d** 70 **p** 71. C Kirkby *Liv* 70-73; C Ainsdale 73-76; Sierra Leone 77-83; CMS 83-84; V Nelson in Lt Marsden *Blackb* 84-92; V Lostock Hall 92-99; P-in-c Hatton *Derby* from 99; Asst Chapl HM Pris Sudbury 99-03; Asst Chapl HM Pris Foston Hall from 03. *All Saints' Vicarage, 2A Eaton Close, Hatton, Derby DE65 5ED* Tel (01283) 521053 *or* 584325

BAXTER, Terence Hugh. b 48. Leeds Poly BSc74. N Ord Course 89. **d** 92 **p** 93. NSM Guiseley w Esholt *Bradf* from 92. *2 Flatfield Cottage, Kelcliffe Lane, Guiseley, Leeds LS20 9DD* Tel (01943) 875170 Fax as telephone E-mail terry.baxter@tesco.net

BAYCOCK, Philip Louis. b 33. Wells Th Coll 64. **d** 66 **p** 67. C Kettering SS Pet and Paul *Pet* 66-68; C St Peter-in-Thanet *Cant* 68-72; V Bobbing w Iwade 72-73; Perm to Offic 73-76; V Thanington w Milton 77-84; R Chagford w Gidleigh and Throwleigh *Ex* 84-01; rtd 01. *7 Grove Meadow, Sticklepath, Okehampton EX20 2NE* Tel (01837) 840617
E-mail louisb@care4free.net

BAYES, Frederick Alan. b 60. Imp Coll Lon BSc81. St Jo Coll Dur BA92 Cranmer Hall Dur 93. **d** 93 **p** 94. C Talbot Village *Sarum* 93-97; Chapl St Hild and St Bede Coll *Dur* from 97; Bp's Adv in Interfaith Matters from 02. *3 Ravensworth Terrace, Durham DH1 1QP* Tel 0191-383 9376

BAYES, Paul. b 53. Birm Univ BA75 DipTh78. Qu Coll Birm 76. **d** 79 **p** 80. C Tynemouth Cullercoats St Paul *Newc* 79-82; Chapl Qu Eliz Coll *Lon* 82-87; Chapl Chelsea Coll 85-87; TV High Wycombe *Ox* 87-90; TR 90-94; TR Totton *Win* from 95; AD Lyndhurst from 00. *Testwood Rectory, 92 Salisbury Road, Totton, Southampton SO40 3JA* Tel (023) 8086 5103
E-mail paul.bayes@ukgateway.net

BAYFORD, Mrs Daphne Jean. b 32. Lon Univ TCert53. Qu Coll Birm 84. **d** 87 **p** 94. NSM Brinklow *Cov* 87-95; NSM Harborough Magna 87-95; NSM Monks Kirby w Pailton & Stretton-under-Fosse 87-95; Perm to Offic from 95; *Leic* from 97. *Warwick House, 36 Lutterworth Road, Pailton, Rugby CV23 0QE* Tel (01788) 832797

BAYFORD, Terence Michael. b 48. Westmr Coll Ox MTh96. Wilson Carlile Coll 70 N Ord Course 97. **d** 99 **p** 00. Dep Chapl HM Pris Wakef 99-01; NSM Alverthorpe *Wakef* 99-01; Chapl HM Pris Moorland from 01; Perm to Offic *Wakef* from 01. *HM Prison Moorland, Bawtry Road, Hatfield Woodhouse, Doncaster DN7 6BW* Tel (01302) 351500

BAYLEY, Anne Christine. b 34. OBE86. MB, ChB58 FRCS66 FRCSEd86 Girton Coll Cam BA55. St Steph Ho Ox 90. **d** 91 **p** 94. NSM Wembley Park St Aug *Lon* 91-97; Perm to Offic *York* from 97. *Michaelmas Barn, Farndale, Kirkbymoorside, York YO62 7LA* Tel (01751) 433445 Fax as telephone

BAYLEY, David Francis. b 47. LNSM course 98. **d** 99 **p** 00. OLM Wriggle Valley *Sarum* from 99. *Stoneleigh, High Street, Yetminster, Sherborne DT9 6LF* Tel (01935) 872893 Mobile 0797-0889489

BAYLEY, Canon John Benson. b 39. K Coll Cam BA60 MA64. Qu Coll Birm 61. **d** 63 **p** 64. C Clee *Linc* 63-68; V Gainsborough H Trin 68-73; P-in-c Linc St Mich 73-75; P-in-c Linc St Pet in Eastgate w St Marg 73-75; P-in-c Linc St Mary Magd w St Paul 73-75; R Linc Minster Gp 75-02; Can and Preb Linc Cathl 75-02; Hon PV 77-02; rtd 02. *16 Bexmore Drive, Streethay, Lichfield WS13 8LB*

BAYLEY, Michael John. b 36. CCC Cam BA60 MA64 Sheff Univ DSS67 PhD73. Linc Th Coll 60. **d** 62 **p** 63. C Leeds Gipton Epiphany *Ripon* 62-66; NSM Sheff St Mark Broomhill *Sheff* 67-93; C Sheff St Mary w Highfield Trin 93-95; C Sheff St Mary Bramall Lane 95-00; rtd 00. *27 Meadowbank Avenue, Sheffield S7 1PB* Tel 0114-258 5248

BAYLEY, Oliver James Drummond. b 49. Mansf Coll Ox MA PGCE. St Jo Coll Nottm 81. **d** 83 **p** 84. C Bath Weston St Jo w Kelston *B & W* 83-88; P-in-c Bathampton 88-93; P-in-c Claverton 92-93; R Bathampton w Claverton 93-96; Chapl Dauntsey's Sch Devizes 96-02; rtd 02. *20 High Street, West Lavington SN10 4HQ* Tel (01380) 818973

BAYLEY, Raymond. b 46. Keble Coll Ox BA68 MA72 Dur Univ DipTh69 Ex Univ PhD86. St Chad's Coll Dur 68. **d** 69 **p** 70. C Mold *St As* 69-74; C Llandaff w Capel Llanilltern *Llan* 74; PV Llan Cathl 74-77; C Cwmbach 77-80; Dir Past Studies St Mich Coll Llan 80-84; V Ynysddu *Mon* 84-86; V Griffithstown 86-92; V Rhosymedre *St As* 92-96; Warden and R Ruthin w Llanrhydd from 96; Warden of Readers from 02. *The Cloisters, School Road, Ruthin LL15 1BL* Tel (01824) 702068
E-mail othniel@amserve.net

BAYLIS (née LOFTS), Mrs Sally Anne. b 55. Kent Univ BA78 K Coll Lon MA80 Nottm Univ PGCE93. St Jo Coll Nottm 01. **d** 03. C Gedling *S'well* from 03. *7 Berkeley Avenue, Mapperley, Nottingham NG3 5BU* Tel 0115-962 1077 Fax as telephone
E-mail k.baylis@ntlworld.com

BAYLISS, Geoffrey Brian Tudor. b 60. R Holloway Coll Lon BSc83 Univ of Wales (Swansea) PGCE85. EAMTC DipHE99. **d** 99 **p** 00. NSM Panfield and Rayne *Chelmsf* from 99. *62 Brunwin Road, Rayne, Braintree CM77 6BU* Tel (01376) 325454
E-mail geoff@bayliss41.freeserve.co.uk

BAYLISS, Grant David. b 75. Ex Univ BA96. Ripon Coll Cuddesdon BA99. **d** 03. C Prestbury and All SS *Glouc* from 03. *8 Boulton Road, Cheltenham GL50 4RZ* Tel (01242) 238601
E-mail gdbayliss@ukonline.co.uk

BAYLOR, Nigel Peter. b 58. NUI BA80 TCD DipTh84 MPhil88. **d** 84 **p** 86. C Carrickfergus *Conn* 84-87; C Dundela St Mark *D & D* 87-89; I Galloon w Drummully *Clogh* 89-94; Adult Educn Adv 91-94; I Carnmoney *Conn* 94-03; I Jordanstown from 03. *The Rectory, 120A Circular Road, Jordanstown, Newtownabbey BT37 0RH* Tel (028) 9086 2119
E-mail nigel.baylor@ukgateway.net

BAYLY, Samuel Niall Maurice. b 36. TCD BA64 MA. CITC Div Test65. **d** 65 **p** 66. C Belfast St Matt *Conn* 65-68; Miss to Seamen 68-69; C Belfast St Pet *Conn* 69-74; I Belfast Ch Ch 74-02. *25 Beechlands, Belfast BT9 5HU* Tel (028) 9066 8732

BAYNE, Canon David William. b 52. St Andr Univ MA75. Edin Th Coll 88. **d** 90 **p** 91. C Dumfries *Glas* 90-92; P-in-c 92-93; R 93-99; Chapl Dumfries and Galloway R Infirmary 92-99; Chapl Crichton R Hosp Dumfries 92-99; Chapl HM Pris Dumfries 96-99; P-in-c Castle Douglas *Glas* from 99; Can St Mary's Cathl from 99. *The Rectory, 68 St Andrew Street, Castle Douglas DG7 1EN* Tel (01556) 503818 E-mail dwbayne@aol.com

BAYNE, Mrs Felicity Meriel. b 47. WEMTC 91. **d** 94 **p** 95. NSM Cheltenham Ch Ch *Glouc* 94-98; NSM Leckhampton St Pet from 98. *Hamfield House, Ham Road, Charlton Kings, Cheltenham GL52 6NG* Tel (01242) 237074

BAYNE-JARDINE, Anthea Mary. See GRIGGS, Mrs Anthea Mary

BAYNES, Matthew Thomas Crispin. b 62. UEA BA83 Qu Coll Cam BA86 MA91. Westcott Ho Cam 85. **d** 87 **p** 88. C Southgate Ch Ch *Lon* 87-90; C Gt Berkhamsted *St Alb* 90-95; V Coseley Ch Ch *Worc* 95-99; R Bredon w Bredon's Norton from 99. *The Rectory, Bredon, Tewkesbury GL20 7LT* Tel (01684) 772237

BAYNES, Simon Hamilton. b 33. New Coll Ox BA57 DipTh58 MA62. Wycliffe Hall Ox 57. **d** 59 **p** 60. C Rodbourne Cheney *Bris* 59-62; Japan 63-80; C Keynsham *B & W* 80-84; P-in-c Winkfield *Ox* 84-85; V Winkfield and Cranbourne 85-99; rtd 99; Lic to Offic *Ox* 99-02; Hon C Thame from 02. *23 Moorend Lane, Thame OX9 3BQ* Tel (01844) 213673
E-mail baynes@psa-online.com

BAYNES, Timothy Francis de Brissac. b 29. Ely TColl 59. **d** 61 **p** 62. C Hockerill *St Alb* 61-65; C Mansfield Woodhouse *S'well* 65-67; Ind Chapl *Man* 67-94; P-in-c Miles Platting St Jo 67-72; rtd 94; Perm to Offic *Man* 94-97. *5 Stainbank Green, Brigsteer Road, Kendal LA9 5RP* Tel (01539) 740605

BAYNES, William Hendrie. b 39. Adelaide Univ BA60. S'wark Ord Course 77. **d** 79 **p** 80. C Notting Hill All SS w St Columb *Lon* 79-85; Perm to Offic 86-87 and 99-00; Hon C Paddington St Sav 88-98; Asst Chapl St Mary's NHS Trust Paddington 94-99; Convenor Lon NSMs/MSE *Lon* from 95; Hon C Paddington

St Jas from 00. *39E Westbourne Gardens, London W2 5NR* Tel (020) 7727 9530 Fax as telephone
E-mail will.baynes@london.anglican.org

BAYNHAM, Matthew Fred. b 57. BNC Ox BA78 Birm Univ MPhil00. Wycliffe Hall Ox 80. **d** 83 **p** 84. C Yardley St Edburgha *Birm* 83-87; TV Bath Twerton-on-Avon *B & W* 87-93; V Reddal Hill St Luke *Worc* 93-00; RD Dudley 98-00; Chapl Bp Grosseteste Coll Linc from 00; NSM Linc St Nic w St Jo Newport *Linc* from 00. *Chaplain's House, 7 Riseholme Road, Lincoln LN1 3SN* Tel (01522) 527923

BAYS, Mrs Helen Margaret. b 48. Kent Univ BA69 RGN71 RHV73. STETS 97. **d** 00 **p** 01. NSM Calne and Blackland *Sarum* 00-02; NSM Sampford Peverell, Uplowman, Holcombe Rogus etc *Ex* from 02. *14 Stockton Hill, Dawlish EX7 9LP* Tel (01626) 862860

BAZELY, William Francis. b 53. Sheff Univ BEng75. St Jo Coll Nottm DipTh79 DPS81. **d** 81 **p** 82. C Huyton St Geo *Liv* 81-84; TV Netherthorpe *Sheff* 84-92; Chapl Lambeth Healthcare NHS Trust 92-98; Chapl Guy's and St Thos' Hosps NHS Trust Lon 98-01; C Rotherham *Sheff* 01-03; Chapl Rotherham Gen Hosps NHS Trust 01-03; Chapl Rotherham Priority Health Services NHS Trust 01-03; Sen Chapl Norfolk Mental Health Care NHS Trust from 03. *34 Woodcock Road, Norwich NR3 3TX* Tel (01603) 421345 Mobile 07702-974680
E-mail bill_bazely@hotmail.com

✠**BAZLEY, The Rt Revd Colin Frederick.** b 35. St Pet Coll Ox BA57 MA61. Tyndale Hall Bris 57. **d** 59 **p** 60 **c** 69. C Bootle St Leon *Liv* 59-62; SAMS Miss Chile 62-00; Adn Cautin and Malleco 67-69; Asst Bp Cautin and Malleco 69-75; Asst Bp Santiago 75-77; Bp Chile 77-00; Primate CASA 77-83; Primate Iglesia Anglicana del Cono Sur 89-95; rtd 00; Hon Asst Bp Ches from 00; Warden of Readers from 00. *121 Brackenwood Road, Higher Bebington, Wirral CH63 2LU* Tel 0151-608 1193 Mobile 07866-391333 E-mail colin@colbarb.fsnet.co.uk

BAZLINTON, Stephen Cecil. b 46. Lon Univ BDS RCS LDS. Ridley Hall Cam 78. **d** 85 **p** 86. NSM Stebbing w Lindsell *Chelmsf* from 85. *St Helens, High Street, Stebbing, Dunmow CM6 3SE* Tel (01371) 856495 E-mail revbaz@care4free.co.uk

BEACH, Jonathan Mark. b 67. Essex Univ BSc89. Trin Coll Bris BA94. **d** 94 **p** 95. C Oulton Broad *Nor* 94-97; Chapl RAF from 97; Perm to Offic *Nor* 98-00. *Chaplaincy Services (RAF), HQ, Personnel and Training Command, RAF Ainsworth, Gloucester GL3 1EZ* Tel (01452) 712612 ext 5164 Fax 510828

BEACH, Mark Howard Francis. b 62. Kent Univ BA83 Nottm Univ MA95. St Steph Ho Ox 85. **d** 87 **p** 88. C Beeston *S'well* 87-90; C Hucknall Torkard 90-93; R Gedling 93-01; R Netherfield 96-01; Bp's Chapl *Wakef* from 01. *24 Pledwick Lane, Sandal, Wakefield WF2 6DN* Tel (01924) 240547 Mobile 07930-577248 Fax (01924) 251921
E-mail mark.beach@wakefield.anglican.org

BEACH, Stephen John. b 58. Man Univ BA81 BD88 Didsbury Coll of Educn PGCE82. N Ord Course 92. **d** 93 **p** 94. C Harwood *Man* 93-97; TV Westhoughton and Wingates 97-01; P-in-c Devonport St Budeaux *Ex* 01-02; V from 02. *St Budeaux Vicarage, Agaton Road, Plymouth PL5 2EW* Tel (01752) 361019

BEACHAM, Peter Martyn. b 44. Ex Coll Ox BA65 MA70 Lon Univ MPhil67 FSA92 MRTPI69. Sarum Th Coll 70. **d** 73 **p** 74. NSM Ex St Martin, St Steph, St Laur etc *Ex* 73-74; NSM Cen Ex 74-90; Perm to Offic from 99. *Bellever, Barrack Road, Exeter EX2 6AB* Tel (01392) 35074

BEACOM, Canon Thomas Ernest. b 12. TCD BA33 MA40 BD40. **d** 36 **p** 36. C Limerick St Lawr w H Trin and St Jo *L & K* 36-38; C Seapatrick *D & D* 38-44; P-in-c Belfast St Kath *Conn* 44-58; I 58-82; Dioc Registrar 63-82; Can Belf Cathl 66-82; rtd 82. *4955-41 Avenue, Drayton Valley AB, Canada, T7A 1V4* Tel (001) (780) 542 3488

BEACON, Canon Ralph Anthony. b 44. Univ of Wales (Ban) DipTh70. St Mich Coll Llan 70. **d** 71 **p** 72. C Neath w Llantwit *Llan* 71-74; TV Holyhead w Rhoscolyn *Ban* 74-78; R Llanenddwyn w Llanddwywe, Llanbedr w Llandanwg 78-99; V Harlech and Llanfair-juxta-Harlech etc from 99; RD Ardudwy 89-01; AD from 01; Hon Can Ban Cathl 91-97; Can Cursal from 97. *The Rectory, Môn Dirion, Ffordd Uchaf, Harlech LL46 2SS* Tel (01766) 781336 Mobile 07713-421858

BEACON, Mrs Stephanie Kathleen Nora. b 49. Univ of Wales (Ban) BA70 PGCE71. NW Ord Course 94. **d** 96 **p** 97. NSM Llanenddwyn w Llanddwywe, Llanbedr w Llandanwg *Ban* 96-98; C Ardudwy 98-99; P-in-c Llanenddwyn w Llanddwywe, Llanbedr w Llandanwg 99-01; R from 01. *The Rectory, Môn Dirion, Ffordd Uchaf, Harlech LL46 2SS* Tel (01766) 781336 Mobile 07713-421858

BEADLE, David Alexander. b 37. St And Dioc Tr Course. **d** 88 **p** 89. NSM St Andrews St Andr *St And* from 88. *48 Clayton Caravan Park, St Andrews KY16 9YB* Tel (01334) 870001

BEADLE, Ms Janet Mary. b 52. Philippa Fawcett Coll CertEd74. EAMTC 91. **d** 94 **p** 95. C Kingston upon Hull H Trin *York* 94-98; V Ness Gp *Linc* from 98; Bp's Adv in Women's Min from 01. *The Vicarage, 10 Church Street, Thurlby, Bourne PE10 0EH* Tel (01778) 422475 E-mail janet.beadle@talk21.com

BEADLE, Mrs Lorna. b 40. NEOC DipHE95. **d** 95 **p** 96. NSM Ashington *Newc* from 95. *9 Arundel Square, Ashington NE63 8AW* Tel (01670) 816467

✠**BEAK, The Rt Revd Robert Michael Cawthorn.** b 25. OBE90. Lon Bible Coll DipTh51. **d** 53 **p** 54 **c** 84. C Tunbridge Wells St Jo *Roch* 53-55; BCMS 55-56 and 84-89; Kenya 56-69 and 84-89; R Heanton Punchardon *Ex* 70-84; Offg Chapl RAF 70-80; RD Barnstaple *Ex* 77-81; R Heanton Punchardon w Marwood 79-84; Preb Ex Cathl 82-84; Asst Bp Mt Kenya E 84-89; rtd 90; Hon Asst Bp Derby from 91. *Ashcroft Cottage, Butts Road, Ashover, Chesterfield S45 0AX* Tel (01246) 590048

BEAK, Stephen Robert. b 64. City Univ BSc86 MBCO87. Wycliffe Hall Ox BTh94. **d** 94 **p** 95. C Lache cum Saltney *Ches* 94-97; C Howell Hill *Guildf* 97-01; NSM Woking St Mary from 01. *44 High Street, Old Woking, Woking GU22 9LW* Tel (01483) 830291 Mobile 07715-361841
E-mail stephen.beak@ntlworld.com

BEAKE, Christopher Martyn Grandfield. b 36. K Coll Lon BA60 AKC60. **d** 61 **p** 62. C Berwick H Trin *Newc* 61-66; V Tynemouth H Trin W Town 66-78; V Hanslope w Castlethorpe *Ox* 78-01; rtd 01. *8 Radstone Road, Brackley NN13 5GB* Tel (01280) 706543

BEAKE, Canon Stuart Alexander. b 49. Em Coll Cam BA72 MA76. Cuddesdon Coll 72. **d** 74 **p** 75. C Hitchin St Mary *St Alb* 74-76; C Hitchin 77-79; TV Hemel Hempstead 79-85; Bp's Dom Chapl *S'well* 85-87; V Shottery St Andr *Cov* 87-00; RD Fosse 93-99; Dioc Dir of Ords 96-00; Hon Can Cov Cathl 98-00; Can Res and Sub-Dean Cov Cathl from 00. *109 Beechwood Avenue, Coventry CV5 6FQ* Tel (024) 7667 8752 *or* 7622 7597
E-mail sabeake@msn.com *or*
heather@coventrycathedral.org.uk

BEAKEN, Robert William Frederick. b 62. SS Paul & Mary Coll Cheltenham BA83 Lambeth STh90 MA01 FSAScot01. Ripon Coll Cuddesdon 85 Ven English Coll & Pontifical Gregorian Univ Rome 87. **d** 88 **p** 89. C Forton *Portsm* 88-92; C Shepshed *Leic* 92-94; V Colchester St Barn *Chelmsf* 94-02; P-in-c Gt and Lt Bardfield w Gt and Lt Saling from 02. *The Vicarage, Braintree Road, Great Bardfield, Braintree CM7 4RN* Tel (01371) 810267
E-mail robert@webform.com

BEAL, David Michael. b 61. Nottm Univ BTh89. St Jo Coll Nottm 86. **d** 89 **p** 90. C Marston *Blackb* 89-92; C Darwen St Pet w Hoddlesden 92-93; TV 93-97; R Itchingfield w Slinfold *Chich* from 97. *The Rectory, The Street, Slinfold, Horsham RH13 0RR* Tel (01403) 790197

BEAL, Malcolm. b 31. Bris Univ BA52. Ridley Hall Cam 57. **d** 59 **p** 60. C Keynsham w Queen Charlton *B & W* 59-62; C Speke All SS *Liv* 62-65; Uganda 65-74; V Salford Priors *Cov* 74-83; R Jersey St Clem *Win* 83-97; rtd 97; Perm to Offic *Ex* from 97. *3 Redwoods Close, Hemyock, Cullompton EX15 3QQ* Tel (01823) 680853

BEAL, Royston David. b 35. K Coll Lon BD60 AKC60. **d** 61 **p** 62. C Chesterfield St Mary and All SS *Derby* 61-64; C Chiswick St Nic w St Mary *Lon* 64-70; V Kensal Green St Jo from 70. *St John's Vicarage, Kilburn Lane, London W10 4AA* Tel (020) 8969 2615

BEALES, Christopher Leader Day. b 51. St Jo Coll Dur BA72. Cranmer Hall Dur DipTh75. **d** 76 **p** 77. C Upper Armley *Ripon* 76-79; Ind Chapl 76-79; Ind Chapl *Dur* 79-84; Sen Chapl 82-84; Sec Ind Cttee of Gen Syn Bd for Soc Resp 85-91; Sec Inner Cities Relig Coun (DOE) 92-94; Dir Churches' Regional Commn in the NE *Newc & Dur* 94-97; Consultant Dir 98; C Thamesmead *S'wark* 99-01. *169 Westmount Road, London SE9 1XY* Tel (020) 8859 6733 E-mail chris@c-beales.freeserve.co.uk

BEALES, John David. b 55. SS Hild & Bede Coll Dur BA77 Univ of W Aus DipEd79 Nottm Univ DipTh82. St Jo Coll Nottm DPS83. **d** 83 **p** 84. Australia 83-89 and 90; V Scarborough 83-86; Dioc Youth Chapl Perth 86-89; Dir Educn and Tr Philo Trust 89-90; NSM Nottingham St Nic *S'well* 89-95; Dir Evang Melbourne 95-00; Perm to Offic *Chelmsf* 99-01. *52 Wellesley Road, Colchester CO3 3HF* Tel (01206) 530934
E-mail davidbeales@ntlworld.com

BEALING, Andrew John. b 42. Sarum Th Coll 67. **d** 69 **p** 70. C Auckland St Andr and St Anne *Dur* 69-73; P-in-c Eastgate 73-76; P-in-c Rookhope 73-76; V Frosterley 76-85; V Rekendyke from 85; Chapl S Tyneside Distr Hosp 90-93; Chapl S Tyneside Healthcare Trust from 93; Chapl Miss to Seafarers from 02. *The Vicarage, St Jude's Terrace, South Shields NE33 5PB* Tel 0191-455 2338

BEALING, Mrs Patricia Ramsey. b 39. Lightfoot Ho Dur IDC63. **dss** 63 **d** 87 **p** 94. Rekendyke *Dur* 85-87; Par Dn 87-94; C from 94; Chapl S Tyneside Distr Hosp 88-93; Chapl S Tyneside Healthcare Trust from 93. *The Vicarage, St Jude's Terrace, South Shields NE33 5PB* Tel 0191-455 2338

BEAMENT, Canon Owen John. b 41. MBE01. Bps' Coll Cheshunt 61. **d** 64 **p** 65. C Deptford St Paul *S'wark* 64-68; C Peckham St Jo 69-73; C Vauxhall St Pet 73-74; V Hatcham Park All SS from 74; Hon Can S'wark Cathl from 97. *All Saints Vicarage, 22 Erlanger Road, London SE14 5TG* Tel (020) 7639 3497 E-mail owenbeament@aol.com

BEAMER, Neville David. b 40. Univ of Wales (Lamp) BA62 Jes Coll Ox BA65 MA70. Wycliffe Hall Ox 64. **d** 65 **p** 66. C Hornchurch St Andr *Chelmsf* 65-68; C Warwick St Mary *Cov* 68-72; V Holton-le-Clay *Linc* 72-75; P-in-c Stoneleigh w Ashow *Cov* 75-79; P-in-c Baginton 77-79; V Fletchamstead 79-86; Warden Whatcombe Ho Blandford Forum 86-90; V Jersey Millbrook St Matt *Win* 90-95; R Jersey St Lawr 90-95; V Yateley 95-03; P-in-c Eversley 98-03; R Yateley and Eversley from 03; RD Odiham from 95. *The Vicarage, 99 Reading Road, Yateley GU46 7LR* Tel (01252) 873133 Fax 878809
E-mail ndbeamer@hotmail.com

BEAMISH, Canon Frank Edwin. b 28. TCD BA49 MA. TCD Div Sch. **d** 50 **p** 52. C Templecorran *Conn* 50-53; C Drumglass *Arm* 53-61; C Caledon w Brantry 61-90; Preb Arm Cathl from 88; Treas Arm Cathl from 92; rtd 94. *214 Killylea Road, Caledon BT68 4TN* Tel (028) 3756 8609

BEAN, Alan Evison. b 13. Ch Coll Cam BA35 MA39. Ely Th Coll 35. **d** 36 **p** 37. C Hendon St Ignatius *Dur* 36-40; Perm to Offic *Ox* 41-50; CF 42-45; SSJE from 47; India 50-55 and 57-64; Lic to Offic *Ox* from 65. *SSJE Priory, 228 Iffley Road, Oxford OX4 1SE* Tel (01865) 248116

BEAN, Douglas Jeyes Lendrum. b 25. Worc Coll Ox BA50 MA53. Ely Th Coll 50. **d** 51 **p** 52. C Croydon Woodside *Cant* 51-54; Min Can Windsor 54-59; V Reading St Laur *Ox* 59-68; Chapl HM Borstal Reading 61-68; RD Reading *Ox* 65-68; Min Can St Paul's Cathl *Lon* 68-72; Hon Min Can from 72; V St Pancras w St Jas and Ch Ch 72-93; PV Westmr Abbey 75-80; rtd 93; Perm to Offic *Lon* from 99. *3 Bishop Street, London N1 8PH* Tel (020) 7226 8340

BEAN, James Corey. b 35. Centenary Coll New Jersey BA58 Long Is Univ MS74. Seabury-Western Th Sem LTh61. **d** 61 **p** 62. USA 61-79 and from 90; Chapl Wiesbaden *Eur* 79-90. *968 High Street, Box 490, Pomeroy, WA 99347, USA* Tel (001) (509) 843 1871

BEAN, Canon John Victor. b 25. Down Coll Cam BA47 MA51. Sarum Th Coll 48. **d** 50 **p** 51. C Milton *Portsm* 50-55; C Fareham SS Pet and Paul 55-59; V St Helens 59-66; V Cowes St Mary 66-91; RD W Wight 68-72; Hon Can Portsm Cathl 70-91; P-in-c Cowes St Faith 77-80; C-in-c Gurnard All SS CD 78-91; Chapl to The Queen 80-95; rtd 91; Perm to Offic *Portsm* from 91. *Magnolia, 23 Seldon Avenue, Ryde PO33 1NS* Tel (01983) 812516 Fax as telephone

BEAN, Kevin Douglas. b 54. Edin Univ BD78. Edin Th Coll 75. **d** 81 **p** 82. USA 81-88 and from 89; C Edin St Marg *Edin* 88-89; C Edin Old St Paul 88-89. *54 Robert Road, Marblehead, MA 01945, USA*

BEANE, Andrew Mark. b 72. St Jo Coll Nottm BA02. **d** 02 **p** 03. C Thorpe St Matt *Nor* from 02. *15 Stanley Avenue, Norwich NR7 0BE* Tel (01603) 439113
E-mail andrewbeane@onetel.net.uk

BEANEY, John. b 47. Trin Coll Bris DipHE79. **d** 79 **p** 80. C Bromley Ch *Roch* 79-84; V Broadheath *Ches* from 84; Chapl Altrincham Gen Hosp 91-94; Chapl Trafford Healthcare NHS Trust 94-98. *The Vicarage, Lindsell Road, West Timperley, Altrincham WA14 5NX* Tel 0161-928 4820
E-mail johnbeaney@broadheath99.freeserve.co.uk

BEARCROFT, Bramwell Arthur. b 52. Homerton Coll Cam BEd82. EAMTC 87. **d** 90 **p** 91. Chapl and Hd RS Kimbolton Sch Cambs 88-94; NSM Tilbrook *Ely* 90-94; NSM Covington 90-94; NSM Catworth Magna 90-94; NSM Keyston and Bythorn 90-94; NSM Cary Deanery *B & W* 94-02; Hd Master Hazlegrove Sch 94-02. *Clé de Tève, Devillac, 47210 Lot et Garonne, France* Tel (0033) (5) 53 71 46 24
E-mail jenniferbearcroft@hotmail.com

BEARD, Christopher Robert. b 47. Chich Th Coll 81. **d** 83 **p** 84. C Chich St Paul and St Pet *Chich* 83-86; TV Ifield 86-91; V Haywards Heath St Rich 91-99; P-in-c Donnington from 99; Chapl St Wilfrid's Hospice Eastbourne from 99. *The Vicarage, 34 Graydon Avenue, Donnington, Chichester PO19 8RF* Tel (01243) 776395

BEARD, Laurence Philip. b 45. Lon Univ BA68. Trin Coll Bris 88. **d** 90 **p** 91. C Trentham *Lich* 90-94; V Wolverhampton St Matt 94-01; P-in-c Hartshill *Cov* from 01. *The New Vicarage, Church Road, Hartshill, Nuneaton CV10 0LY* Tel (024) 7639 2266
E-mail lpbeard@talk21.com

BEARD, Robert John Hansley. b 61. St Andr Univ BD85. Ripon Coll Cuddesdon 86 Ch Div Sch of the Pacific (USA) 87. **d** 88 **p** 89. C Sheff Manor *Sheff* 88-91; C Rotherham 91-94; V Sheff Abbeydale St Pet 94-02; Assoc Chapl Sheff Hallam Univ 95-98; Bp's Adv on Interfaith Issues 96-02; Intercultural Regeneration Development Worker *Simunye* from 02. *18 Arnside Road, Sheffield S8 0UX* Tel 0114-255 6335
E-mail arjay61@hotmail.com

BEARDALL, Raymond. b 32. St Jo Coll Nottm 70. **d** 72 **p** 73. C Ilkley All SS *Bradf* 72-74; C Seasalter *Cant* 74-79; V Farndon *S'well* 79-84; R Thorpe 79-84; V Blidworth 84-97; rtd 97. *4 Winster Avenue, Ravenshead, Nottingham NG15 9DD*

BEARDMORE, John Keith. b 42. FCP85 Bris Univ BEd74 K Coll Lon MA90. **d** 77 **p** 78. NSM Maindee *Mon* from 77. *16 Hove Avenue, Newport NP9 7QP* Tel (01633) 263272

BEARDSHAW, David. b 37. JP. DPS. Wells Th Coll 65. **d** 67 **p** 68. C Wood End *Cov* 67-69; C Stoke 70-73; V Whitley 73-77; Dioc Educn Officer 77-87; P-in-c Offchurch 87-93; Warden Offa Retreat Ho 87-93; rtd 93. *188 Ashington Grove, Coventry CV3 4DB*

BEARDSLEY, Christina. b 51. Sussex Univ BA73 St Jo Coll Cam PhD99. Westcott Ho Cam 76. **d** 78 **p** 79. C Portsea N End St Mark *Portsm* 78-85; V Catherington and Clanfield 85-00; Chapl Worthing and Southlands Hosps NHS Trust 00-01; Asst Chapl Chelsea and Westmr Healthcare NHS Trust from 01. *403 Mile Oak Road, Portslade, Brighton BN41 2RD* Tel (01273) 413696 E-mail parsons@portslade.fsnet.co.uk

BEARDSLEY, Daniel Graham Richard. b 55. Liv Univ BA86. St Steph Ho Ox 90. **d** 92 **p** 93. C Stanley *Liv* 92-95; V Dovecot from 95. *Holy Spirit Vicarage, Dovecot Avenue, Liverpool L14 7QJ* Tel 0151-220 6611

BEARDSLEY, Nigel Andrew. b 61. Sheff Hallam Univ BSc88 Nottm Univ MA00. EMMTC 97. **d** 00 **p** 01. C Bath Bathwick *B & W* from 00. *64 St John's Road, Bathwick, Bath BA2 6PT* Tel (01225) 466375 E-mail beardsley@lanj.freeserve.co.uk

BEARDSMORE, Alan. b 45. Wycliffe Hall Ox 67. **d** 70 **p** 71. C Prittlewell St Mary *Chelmsf* 70-72; C Epsom St Martin *Guildf* 72-78; P-in-c Burbage and Savernake Ch *Sarum* 78-79; P-in-c E Grafton, Tidcombe and Fosbury 78-79; TV Wexcombe 79-80; Chapl RN 80-83; TV Haverhill w Withersfield, the Wrattings etc *St E* 83-87; V Gt Barton 87-95; V Eaton *Nor* from 95. *The Vicarage, 210 Newmarket Road, Norwich NR4 7LA* Tel (01603) 250915 E-mail ab@eatonparish.com *or* office@eatonparish.com

BEARDSMORE, John. b 19. Kelham Th Coll 46. **d** 51 **p** 51. C Caldmore *Lich* 51-53; C Otley *Bradf* 53-55; V Burley in Wharfedale 55-69; V Bromley H Trin *Roch* 69-70; V Buttershaw St Paul *Bradf* 70-88; rtd 88; Perm to Offic *Bradf* from 88. *41 Nab Wood Grove, Shipley BD18 4HR* Tel (01274) 596197

BEARE, The Very Revd William. b 33. TCD BA58 DipCSM77. **d** 59 **p** 60. C Waterford St Patr *C & O* 59-62; C Cork H Trin w Shandon St Mary *C, C & R* 62-64; I Rathcormac 64-68; I Marmullane w Monkstown 68-76; Dioc C 76-82; I Stradbally w Ballintubbert, Coraclone etc *C & O* 82-99; Can Ossory and Leighlin Cathls 88-90; Chan 90-92; Prec 92-99; Preb Stagonil St Patr Cathl Dublin from 95; Dean Lismore *C & O* from 99; I Lismore w Cappoquin, Kilwatermoy, Dungarvan etc from 99. *The Deanery, The Mall, Lismore, Co Waterford, Irish Republic* Tel and fax (00353) (58) 54105 Mobile 87-233 1508

BEARN, Hugh William. b 62. Man Univ BA84. Cranmer Hall Dur 86. **d** 89 **p** 90. C Heaton Ch Ch *Man* 89-92; Chapl RAF Coll Cranwell 92-96; V Tottington *Man* from 96. *St Anne's Vicarage, Chapel Street, Tottington, Bury BL8 4AP* Tel (01204) 883713

BEARPARK, Canon John Michael. b 36. Ex Coll Ox BA59 MA63. Linc Th Coll 59. **d** 61 **p** 62. C Bingley H Trin *Bradf* 61-64; C Baildon 64-67; V Fairweather Green 67-77; Chapl Airedale Gen Hosp 77-94; V Steeton 77-94; Hon Can Bradf Cathl 89-01; V Bentham St Marg 94-01; P-in-c Bentham St Jo 99-01; RD Ewecross 94-00; rtd 01; Perm to Offic *Bradf* from 01. *31 Northfields Crescent, Settle BD24 9JP* Tel (01729) 822712

BEASLEY, Canon Arthur James. b 12. Hertf Coll Ox BA33 MA38. Ridley Hall Cam 34. **d** 36 **p** 37. C Harpurhey Ch Ch *Man* 36-39; C Flixton St Mich 39-42; P-in-c Stand 42-43; R Moss Side Ch Ch 43-48; Chapl Man R Infirmary 43-48; V Heaton Ch Ch *Man* 48-81; Hon Can Man Cathl 72-81; rtd 81; Perm to Offic *Man* from 81. *40 Chorley New Road, Lostock, Bolton BL6 4AL* Tel (01204) 494450

BEASLEY, Michael John. b 41. St Jo Coll Dur BA63. Sarum Th Coll 63. **d** 65 **p** 66. C Weston St Jo *B & W* 65-67; C Pinner *Lon* 67-69; C E Grinstead St Swithun *Chich* 69-72; Chapl Mayday, Qu and St Mary's Hosps Croydon 72-77; TV Swanborough *Sarum* 77-82; V Stourbridge St Mich Norton *Worc* 82-98; V Abertillery w Cwmtillery w Six Bells *Mon* from 98; RD Blaenau Gwent from 00. *St Michael's Vicarage, Church Street, Abertillery NP13 1DA* Tel (01495) 212246

BEASLEY, Noel Michael Roy. b 68. Imp Coll Lon BSc91 Oriel Coll Ox DPhil96 St Jo Coll Dur BA98. Cranmer Hall Dur. **d** 99 **p** 00. C Newport w Longford, Chetwynd and Forton *Lich* 99-03; Chapl Westcott Ho Cam from 03. *Westcott House, Jesus Lane, Cambridge CB5 8BP* Tel (01223) 741000

BEASLEY, Canon Walter Sydney. b 33. Nottm Univ BA57. Linc Th Coll 57. **d** 59 **p** 60. C Harworth *S'well* 59-64; V Forest Town 64-70; R Bulwell St Mary 70-97; Hon Can S'well Minster 85-97; rtd 97. *3 Clayton's Drive, Nottingham NG7 2PF* Tel 0115-970 2717 Mobile 07889-350442

BEATER, David MacPherson. b 41. Chich Th Coll 66. **d** 69 **p** 70. C Withington St Crispin *Man* 69-72; C Lightbowne 72-74; V Prestwich St Hilda 74-81; V Northfleet *Roch* 81-85; C Bickley 86-90; TV Stanley *Dur* 90-97; SSF 97-01; C Seaton Hirst *Newc*

from 01. *St Andrew's Vicarage, Hawthorn Road, Ashington NE63 9AU* Tel (01670) 818691

BEATSON, Christine. b 32. Wolv Teacher Tr Coll TCert68. WMMTC 95. **d** 96 **p** 97. OLM Huntley and Longhope *Glouc* 96-99; NSM Rugeley *Lich* from 01. *The Retreat, 11 Green Lane, Rugeley WS15 2AP* Tel (01889) 804773

BEATTIE, Ian David. b 36. Univ of NZ BA58. St Jo Coll Auckland LTh60. **d** 60 **p** 61. New Zealand 60-64 and from 71; C Shirley St Jo *Cant* 64-65; V S Wimbledon St Andr *S'wark* 65-71. *1/148A Tasman Street, Nelson 7001, New Zealand* Tel (0064) (3) 546 7507

BEATTIE, Margaret. *See* BREWSTER, Margaret

BEATTIE, Canon Noel Christopher. b 41. TCD BTh65 Cranfield Inst of Tech MSc86. **d** 68 **p** 69. C Belfast H Trin *Conn* 68-70; C Belfast St Bart 70-73; C Doncaster St Mary *Sheff* 73-77; TV Northampton Em *Pet* 77-88; Ind Chapl 85-88; Ind Chapl *Linc* 88-92; Ind Chapl *Roch* from 92; Hon Can Roch Cathl from 00. *181 Maidstone Road, Chatham ME4 6JG* Tel (01634) 844867 Fax as telephone E-mail noelbt@globalnet.co.uk

BEATTY, Robert Harold. b 27. W Ontario Univ BA48 Keble Coll Ox BA55 MA58 McGill Univ Montreal PhD62. **d** 51 **p** 52. Canada 51, 55-57 and 58-67; Perm to Offic *Ox* 52-55; Tutor Bps' Coll Cheshunt 57-58; C W Byfleet *Guildf* 67-71; C Oseney Crescent St Luke w Camden Square St Paul *Lon* 71-72; R Cosgrove *Pet* 72-83; V Hebburn St Oswald *Dur* 83-93; rtd 93; Perm to Offic *Dur* and *Newc* from 93. *60 Briarwood Avenue, Gosforth, Newcastle upon Tyne NE3 5DB* Tel 0191-285 2429

BEAUCHAMP, Anthony Hazlerigg Proctor. b 40. Trin Coll Cam BA62 MA66 MICE68. St Jo Coll Nottm 73. **d** 75 **p** 76. C New Humberstone *Leic* 75-77; C-in-c Polegate *Chich* 77-80; Chapl Bethany Sch Goudhurst 80-86; Chapl Luckley-Oakfield Sch Wokingham 86-88; Chapl Clayesmore Sch Blandford 89-93; R Kirby-le-Soken w Gt Holland *Chelmsf* 93-00; Asst P Wetheral w Warwick *Carl* 00-01; rtd 01; Perm to Offic *Carl* from 00; *Chich* from 01. *2 Stelvio Cottages, 17 Beachy Head Road, Eastbourne BN20 7QP* Tel (01323) 732743

BEAUCHAMP, Gerald Charles. b 55. Hull Univ BA78 K Coll Lon MA96. Coll of Resurr Mirfield 78. **d** 80 **p** 81. C Hatcham St Cath *S'wark* 80-83; S Africa 83-86; C Ealing St Steph Castle Hill *Lon* 86-88; P-in-c Brondesbury St Anne w Kilburn H Trin 88-89; V 89-93; Chapl Kilburn Coll 88-93; C Chelsea St Luke and Ch Ch *Lon* 93-96; V W Brompton St Mary w St Pet from 96; AD Chelsea from 02. *The Vicarage, 24 Fawcett Street, London SW10 9EZ* Tel (020) 7352 5880 *or* 7835 1440 Fax 7370 6562 E-mail gerald@leviathan2.demon.co.uk

BEAUCHAMP, John Nicholas. b 57. Wycliffe Hall Ox 92. **d** 94 **p** 95. C Ipswich St Jo *St E* 94-97; TV Beccles St Mich from 97. *Hillcrest, 17 Upper Grange Road, Beccles NR34 9NU* Tel (01502) 712317

BEAUMONT, Canon Brian Maxwell. b 34. Nottm Univ BA56. Wells Th Coll 58. **d** 59 **p** 60. C Clifton *S'well* 59-62; C E Stoke w Syerston 62; C Edgbaston St Geo *Birm* 62-65; V Smethwick St Alb 65-70; Asst Dir RE *Blackb* 70-73; V Blackb H Trin 70-77; Hon Can Blackb Cathl 73-77 and 92-99; Can Res 77-92; Dir RE 73-92; V Goosnargh w Whittingham 92-99; Bp's Adv for Rural Areas 92-99; rtd 99; Perm to Offic *Blackb* from 00. *14 Green Drive, Barton, Preston PR3 5AT* Tel (01772) 861131

BEAUMONT, Canon John Philip. b 32. Leeds Univ BA55. Coll of Resurr Mirfield 55. **d** 57 **p** 58. C Leeds St Marg *Ripon* 57-60; C Wellingborough All Hallows *Pet* 60-64; Chapl HM Borstal Wellingborough 64-70; V Wellingborough St Andr *Pet* 64-70; V Finedon 70-96; Can Pet Cathl 80-96; RD Higham 83-87; rtd 96; Perm to Offic *Pet* from 96. *9 Warren Bridge, Oundle, Peterborough PE8 4DQ* Tel (01832) 273863 E-mail john@beaumont.plus.com

BEAUMONT, John William. b 19. MBE48. RMC 38. Qu Coll Birm 48. **d** 51 **p** 52. C Portsea N End St Mark *Portsm* 51-54; C-in-c Leigh Park St Fran CD 54-59; V S w N Hayling 59-74; R Droxford 74-86; R Meonstoke w Corhampton cum Exton 78-86; rtd 86; Perm to Offic *Portsm* from 86. *134 The Dale, Widley, Waterlooville PO7 5DF* Tel (023) 9237 7492

BEAUMONT, Stephen Martin. b 51. K Coll Lon BD73 AKC74. St Aug Coll Cant 73. **d** 74 **p** 75. C Benwell St Jas *Newc* 74-77; Asst Chapl Marlborough Coll 77-81; R Ideford, Luton and Ashcombe *Ex* 81-84; Bp's Dom Chapl 81-84; Chapl Taunton Sch 85-91; Chapl Haileybury Coll 92-00; Second Chapl and Hd Div Tonbridge Sch from 00. *Tonbridge School, High Street, Tonbridge TN9 1JP* Tel (01732) 365555

BEAUMONT, Terence Mayes. b 41. Lon Univ BA63 Nottm Univ DipTh69. Linc Th Coll 68. **d** 71 **p** 72. C Hitchin St Mary *St Alb* 71-74; C Harpenden St Nic 75-79; V Stevenage St Pet Broadwater 79-87; V St Alb St Mich from 87. *St Michael's Vicarage, St Michael's Street, St Albans AL3 4SL* Tel (01727) 835037

BEAUMONT, Mrs Veronica Jean. b 38. Ox Min Course CBTS93. **d** 93 **p** 94. NSM High Wycombe *Ox* from 93; Fundraising Manager (Oxon) Children's Soc from 95. *Edgehill, Upper Stanley Road, High Wycombe HP12 4DB* Tel (01494) 523697 E-mail veronica.beaumont@virgin.net

BEAUMONT OF WHITLEY, The Revd and Rt Hon Lord (Timothy Wentworth). b 28. Ch Ch Ox BA52 MA56. Westcott Ho Cam 54. **d** 55 **p** 56. Asst Chapl Hong Kong Cathl 55-59; Hon C Westmr St Steph w St Jo *Lon* 60-63; Lic to Offic 63-73; Hon C Balham Hill Ascension *S'wark* 85-86; P-in-c Richmond St Luke 86-87; P-in-c N Sheen St Phil and All SS 86-87; V Kew St Phil and All SS w St Luke 87-91; Perm to Offic from 91; rtd 93. *40 Elms Road, London SW4 9EX* Tel (020) 7498 8664 Fax as telephone E-mail beaumontt@parliament.uk

BEAVAN, Charles Kenneth. b 15. JP63. Lon Univ BA49. St Deiniol's Hawarden 66. **d** 67 **p** 68. Hd Master Meole Brace Sch 53-76; Hon C Meole Brace *Lich* 67-71; P-in-c Shrewsbury St Alkmund 71-89; Perm to Offic 89-00. *School House, 5 Vicarage Road, Shrewsbury SY3 9EZ* Tel (01743) 344172

BEAVAN, Canon Edward <u>Hugh</u>. b 43. Ex Coll Ox BA70 MA74 Solicitor 66. Cuddesdon Coll 69. **d** 71 **p** 72. C Ashford St Hilda *Lon* 71-74; C Newington St Mary *S'wark* 74-76; R Sandon *Chelmsf* 76-86; V Thorpe Bay 86-98; P-in-c Bradwell on Sea from 98; P-in-c St Lawrence from 98; Ind Chapl from 98; RD Maldon and Dengie from 00; Hon Can Chelmsf Cathl from 02. *The Rectory, East End Road, Bradwell-on-Sea, Southminster CM0 7PX* Tel (01621) 776203

BEAVER, William Carpenter. b 45. Colorado Coll BA Wolfs Coll Ox DPhil76. Ox NSM Course 79. **d** 82 **p** 83. NSM Kennington St Jo w St Jas *S'wark* 82-95; NSM Avonmouth St Andr *Bris* 96-97; NSM Bris St Mary Redcliffe w Temple etc from 95; NSM St Andr Holborn *Lon* from 01; Dir Communications for C of E 97-02; Dir Communications for Br Red Cross from 02. *British Red Cross, 9 Grosvenor Crescent, London SW1X 7EJ* Tel (020) 7235 5454 E-mail william.beaver@btinternet.com

BEAVIS, Adrian Neill. b 74. Worc Coll Ox BA97. Wycliffe Hall Ox MTh00. **d** 00 **p** 01. C E Twickenham St Steph *Lon* from 00. *308 Richmond Road, Twickenham TW1 2DP* Tel (020) 8892 8869 E-mail adrian@st-stephens.org.uk

BEAVIS, Mrs Sandra. **d** 98. NSM Southbourne w W Thorney *Chich* from 98. *Lavande, Gordon Road, Southbourne, Emsworth PO10 8AZ* Tel (01243) 371853 E-mail s.lavande@tesco.net

BEAZLEY, Prof John Milner. b 32. DRCOG59 MRCOG62 FRCOG73 FACOG89 Man Univ MB, ChB57 MD64. St Deiniol's Hawarden 83. **d** 86 **p** 87. NSM W Kirby St Bridget *Ches* 86-89; NSM Newton 89-92; NSM Hayton w Cumwhitton *Carl* 92-98; rtd 99; Perm to Offic *Carl* from 99. *High Rigg, Faugh, Heads Nook, Carlisle CA8 9EA* Tel (01228) 70353

BEAZLEY, Miss Margaret Sheila Elizabeth Mary. b 32. Nor City Coll CertEd59. St Alb Minl Tr Scheme 86. **d** 89 **p** 94. NSM Ware St Mary *St Alb* from 89. *38 Fanshawe Crescent, Ware SG12 0AS* Tel (01920) 462349

BEBBINGTON, Ms Julia. b 69. Man Univ BA98 St Jo Coll Dur MA00. Cranmer Hall Dur. **d** 00 **p** 01. C Langley and Parkfield *Man* from 00. *The Vicarage, 316 Windermere Road, Middleton, Manchester M24 4LA* Tel 0161-654 8562 E-mail julia@bebbington50.freeserve.co.uk

BEBBINGTON, Myles. b 35. Kelham Th Coll 56. **d** 61 **p** 62. C Horbury *Wakef* 61-64; C Ardwick St Benedict *Man* 64-66; V Cudworth *Wakef* 66-73; P-in-c Kensington St Jo *Lon* 73-78; P-in-c Walthamstow St Mich *Chelmsf* 78-80; V 80-89; V Sunderland Red Ho *Dur* 89-95; P-in-c S Moor 95-00; rtd 00. *78 Marina Avenue, Sunderland SR6 9AH* Tel 0191-549 3503

BECK, Alan. b 28. AKC50. **d** 53 **p** 54. C N Harrow St Alb *Lon* 53-56; C Northolt St Mary 56-59; C Loughborough All SS *Leic* 59-61; V Crookham *Guildf* 61-69; V Puriton *B & W* 69-78; P-in-c Pawlett 74-78; V Puriton and Pawlett 78-79; P-in-c Staplegrove 79-84; R 84-88; rtd 88; Perm to Offic *B & W* 88-97. *Redwing, Creech Heathfield, Taunton TA3 5EG* Tel (01823) 443030

BECK, Amanda Ruth. b 68. Liv Univ BA91 Birm Univ BD93. Qu Coll Birm 91. **d** 94 **p** 95. C W Derby Gd Shep *Liv* 94-99; Asst Chapl Voorschoten *Eur* 99-02; P-in-c Kingston Vale St Jo *S'wark* from 03. *St John's Vicarage, Robin Hood Lane, London SW15 3PY* Tel (020) 8546 4079 E-mail mandy.beck@iname.com

BECK, Mrs Gillian Margaret. b 50. Sheff Univ CertEd71 Nottm Univ BTh78. Linc Th Coll 74. **dss** 78 **d** 87. C Gt Grimsby St Mary and St Jas *Linc* 78-83; St Paul's Cathl *Lon* 84-87; Hon Par Dn St Botolph Aldgate w H Trin Minories 87-88; Par Dn Monkwearmouth St Andr *Dur* 88-94; C 94-97; NSM Eppleton and Hetton le Hole from 97. *The Rectory, Houghton Road, Hetton-le-Hole, Houghton le Spring DH5 9PH* Tel 0191-517 2488 Fax 526 5173 E-mail mgtbex@zoom.co.uk

BECK, John Edward. b 28. ARCM52 FRCO59 St Jo Coll Ox BA56 MA59. Wells Th Coll 56. **d** 58 **p** 59. C Dursley *Glouc* 58-61; C Glouc St Paul 61-63; S Rhodesia 63-65; Rhodesia 65-70; C Cheltenham Ch Ch *Glouc* 70-77; C Cirencester 77-93; rtd 93; Perm to Offic *Glouc* from 93. *25 Bowling Green Road, Cirencester GL7 2HD* Tel (01285) 653778

BECK, Michael Leonard. b 50. K Coll Lon BD77 AKC77. Linc Th Coll 77. **d** 78 **p** 79. C Gt Grimsby St Mary and St Jas *Linc* 78-83; Min Can and Succ St Paul's Cathl *Lon* 83-88; V Monkwearmouth St Andr *Dur* 88-96; TR Monkwearmouth 97; R Eppleton and Hetton le Hole from 97; AD Houghton from 97;

BECK, Peter George Cornford. b 36. Dur Univ BA61. Ridley Hall Cam 61. **d** 63 **p** 64. C Slade Green *Roch* 63-65; C Aylesford 65-68; C-in-c Brampton St Mark CD *Derby* 68-70; V Brampton St Mark 71-75; P-in-c Alvaston 75-89; rtd 00. *Journeys End, 6 Peddars Way North, Ringstead, Hunstanton PE36 5JP* Tel (01485) 525344

BECK, The Very Revd Peter John. b 48. Mert Coll Ox BA69 MA73. Sarum Th Coll 69. **d** 72 **p** 73. C Bangor *Ox* 72-75; TV 75-78; Dioc Youth and Community Officer 75-78; P-in-c Linc St Mary-le-Wigford w St Benedict etc *Linc* 78-81; City Cen Chapl 78-81; New Zealand from 81; TV Glenfield 81-85; V Mt Albert St Luke 86-93; Adn Waitemata 87-93; V Auckland St Matt 93-00; Adn Auckland 98-00; Hon Asst P Wellington Cathl 00-02; Dir Vaughan Park Retreat Cen 02; Dean Christchurch from 02; V Gen from 03. *25 Springfield Road, St Albans, Christchurch, New Zealand* Tel (0064) (3) 377 6095 *or* 366 0046 Mobile 21-654445 E-mail beckwest@paradise.net.nz *or* peterbeck@xtra.co.nz

BECK, Roger William. b 48. Chich Th Coll 79. **d** 81 **p** 82. C St Marychurch *Ex* 81-85; TV Torre 85-88; V Torquay St Jo and Ellacombe 88-94; C Plympton St Mary from 94. *27 Pinewood Close, Plympton, Plymouth PL7 2DW* Tel (01752) 336393

BECK, Mrs Sandra Veronica. b 52. St Jo Coll Nottm 97. **d** 00 **p** 01. NSM Digswell and Panshanger *St Alb* from 00. *48 Grange Rise, Codicote, Hitchin SG4 8YR* Tel (01438) 820191 E-mail beck@colinsandie.freeserve.co.uk

BECK, Canon Stephen. b 16. St Pet Hall Ox BA44 MA45. Westcott Ho Cam 45. **d** 47 **p** 48. C Portsea N End St Mark *Portsm* 45-47; RAChD 56-59; V Moseley St Agnes *Birm* 59-83; RD Moseley 71-81; Hon Can Birm Cathl 76-83; rtd 83; Perm to Offic *Ban* from 83. *Artro View, Moelfre Terrace, Llanbedr LL45 2DQ* Tel (01341) 23545

BECKERLEG, Barzillai. b 20. Selw Coll Cam BA43 MA46. Westcott Ho Cam 42. **d** 44 **p** 45. C Golders Green St Alb *Lon* 44-48; Chapl St Jo Coll Dur 48-52; Lic to Offic *Dur* 49-52; V Battersea St Mary *S'wark* 52-58; V Wentworth *Sheff* 58-59; Hd Master Newc Cathl Choir Sch 59-62; Prec Newc Cathl *Newc* 59-62; R Duncton *Chich* 62-64; R Burton w Coates 62-64; V Kippington *Roch* 64-75; R E Bergholt *St E* 75-79; Chapl St Mary's Sch Wantage 79-85; rtd 85; Perm to Offic *Truro* from 85; *Roch* 86-93; *Chich* from 93; *S'wark* and *Roch* from 00. *15 St Mary's House, Normandy, Horsham RH12 1JL* Tel (01403) 258008

BECKETT, George. b 26. Scawsby Coll of Educn CertEd76 Sheff Univ BEd77 Hull Univ MEd84. **d** 91 **p** 92. NSM Hatfield *Sheff* from 91. *10 Norman Drive, Hatfield, Doncaster DN7 6AQ* Tel (01302) 841091

BECKETT, Graham. b 49. St As Minl Tr Course 95. **d** 99 **p** 00. NSM Hawarden *St As* 99-01; C from 01. *Hillview, Church Lane, Ewloe, Deeside CH5 3BF* Tel (01244) 535269

BECKETT, John Adrian. b 61. Bris Univ BVSc85. Trin Coll Bris. **d** 00 **p** 01. C Harrogate St Mark *Ripon* from 00. *30 Halstead Road, Harrogate HG2 8BP* Tel (01423) 870593

BECKETT, Michael Shaun. b 55. ACA79. Oak Hill Th Coll BA88. **d** 88 **p** 89. C Cambridge St Barn *Ely* 88-93; P-in-c Cambridge St Paul 93-94; V from 94. *St Paul's Vicarage, 15 St Paul's Road, Cambridge CB1 2EZ* Tel (01223) 354186 *or* 315832 Fax 576899

BECKETT, Mrs Patricia Anne. b 44. **d** 00 **p** 01. NSM Cheddleton *Lich* from 00. *5 Deepdale Close, Milton, Stoke-on-Trent ST6 8XF* Tel (01782) 542703

BECKETT, Canon Stanley. b 20. Linc Th Coll. **d** 64 **p** 65. C Barnston *Ches* 64-71; V Daresbury 71-87; Hon Can Ches Cathl 82-87; P-in-c Aston by Sutton 86-87; Hon C 87-90; rtd 87; Hon C Grappenhall *Ches* 90-98; Perm to Offic *Linc* from 98. *82, Fairfields, Holbeach, Spalding PE12 7JE* Tel (01406) 490191

BECKHAM, John Francis. b 25. Bps' Coll Cheshunt 65. **d** 67 **p** 68. C Leytonstone St Jo *Chelmsf* 67-70; C Colchester St Mary V 70-73; R Lawford 73-80; V Gt w Lt Chesterford 80-90; rtd 90; Perm to Offic *St E* from 91. *North Barn, Reckford Road, Westleton, Saxmundham IP17 3BE* Tel (01728) 648969

BECKINSALE, Mrs Pamela Rachel. b 46. Man Univ BSc69. Cant Sch of Min 88. **d** 91 **p** 94. NSM Sittingbourne St Mich *Cant* 91-96; Perm to Offic 96-98; Lic to Offic from 98; Hon Chapl N Kent Health Care NHS Trust 96-98; Chapl Thames Gateway NHS Trust from 98. *8 Glovers Crescent, Bell Road, Sittingbourne ME10 4DU* Tel (01795) 471632

BECKLEY, Peter William (Pedr). b 52. Lon Univ BSc73 CertEd. Trin Coll Bris 76. **d** 79 **p** 80. C Plymouth St Jude *Ex* 79-83; C Ecclesall *Sheff* 83-88; V Greystones from 88. *The Vicarage, 1 Cliffe Farm Drive, Sheffield S11 7JW* Tel 0114-266 7686

BECKLEY, Simon Richard. b 38. Lon Univ BA61. Oak Hill Th Coll 58. **d** 63 **p** 64. C Watford St Luke *St Alb* 63-67; C New Ferry *Ches* 67-70; C Chadderton Ch Ch *Man* 70-73; V Friarmere 73-80; V Tranmere St Cath *Ches* 80-03; Chapl Wirral Community Healthcare NHS Trust 80-97; Chapl Wirral and W

Cheshire Community NHS Trust 97-03; rtd 03. *162 Heathbank Avenue, Wirral CH61 4YG* Tel 0151-648 7767

BECKWITH, Ian Stanley. b 36. Nottm Univ BA58 Selw Coll Cam CertEd59 Westmr Coll Ox MTh96. Linc Th Coll 78. **d** 79 **p** 80. NSM Linc Cathl *Linc* 79-85; Sen Lect Bp Grosseteste Coll Linc 80-86; NSM Wallingford w Crowmarsh Gifford etc *Ox* 91-97; OLM Tr Officer (Berks) 96-02; P-in-c Gt Coxwell w Buscot, Coleshill etc 97-02; rtd 02. *2 Affcot Mill, Affcot, Church Stretton SY6 6RL* Tel (01694) 781667

BECKWITH, Canon John Douglas. b 33. AKC57. **d** 58 **p** 65. C Streatham St Leon *S'wark* 58-59; Lic to Offic *Ripon* 59-60; Nigeria 60-62; C Bedale *Ripon* 62-63; C Mottingham St Andr *S'wark* 64-69; Chapl Gothenburg w Halmstad and Jönköping *Eur* 69-70; Chapl to Suff Bp Edmonton 70-77; Dir of Ords *Lon* 70-77; V Brookfield St Anne, Highgate Rise 77-88; Can Gib Cathl *Eur* 84-88; Hon Can Gib Cathl from 88; P-in-c Bladon w Woodstock *Ox* 88-93; P-in-c Wootton by Woodstock 88; P-in-c Kiddington w Asterleigh 88; C Kidlington w Hampton Poyle 93-94; Perm to Offic *Lon* from 94; rtd 98; Perm to Offic *Eur* from 98. *4 St James Close, Bishop Street, London N1 8PH* Tel and fax (020) 7226 6672 Mobile 07710-277124 E-mail malbis@dircon.co.uk

BECKWITH, John James. b 53. UMIST BSc74 Newc Univ PGCE88. Dioc OLM tr scheme 98. **d** 02 **p** 03. OLM Bothal and Pegswood w Longhirst *Newc* from 02. *5 Coquetdale Close, Pegswood, Morpeth NE61 6YG* Tel (01670) 505076

BECKWITH, Roger Thomas. b 29. St Edm Hall Ox BA52 MA56 BD85 Lambeth DD92. Ripon Hall Ox 51 Tyndale Hall Bris 52 Cuddesdon Coll 54. **d** 54 **p** 55. C Harold Wood *Chelmsf* 54-57; C Bedminster St Luke w St Silas *Bris* 57-59; Tutor Tyndale Hall Bris 59-63; Lib Latimer Ho Ox 63-73 and from 94; Warden 73-94; Lect Wycliffe Hall Ox 71-94; Hon C Wytham *Ox* 88-90; Hon C N Hinksey and Wytham 90-96; rtd 94; Hon C Ox St Mich w St Martin and All SS *Ox* from 97. *310 Woodstock Road, Oxford OX2 7NR* Tel (01865) 557340 Fax as telephone

BEDDINGTON, Peter Jon. b 36. ACP68 DipEd81. NW Ord Course 71. **d** 74 **p** 75. C Bury St Pet *Man* 74-77; Hon C Bury CK King 77-82; Hon C Elton All SS from 82. *18 Throstle Grove, Bury BL8 1EB* Tel 0161-764 3292

BEDDOW, Arthur Josiah Comyns. b 13. Ch Coll Cam BA35 MA41. Linc Th Coll 38. **d** 40 **p** 41. C Sherborne w Castleton and Lillington *Sarum* 40-46; C Bideford *Ex* 46-54; R Nymet Rowland w Coldridge 54-63; Dioc Youth Officer and Asst Dir Relig Educn 56-62; R Bere Ferrers 63-78; rtd 78; Perm to Offic *Sarum* 79; *B & W* 84-94. *4 Gracey Court, Woodland Road, Broadclyst, Exeter EX5 3LP* Tel (01392) 461714

BEDEAU (née MILLS), Mrs Melina. b 40. Local Minl Tr Course. **d** 00. NSM W Bromwich St Phil *Lich* 00-03; NSM W Bromwich Gd Shep w St Jo from 03. *4 Jervoise Street, West Bromwich B70 9LY* Tel 0121-553 6833

BEDELL, Anthony Charles. b 59. Worc Coll Ox BA81 ACA84. Linc Th Coll BTh90. **d** 90 **p** 91. C Newbold w Dunston *Derby* 90-94; C Bedford Leigh *Man* 94-98; V Blackb St Luke w St Phil *Blackb* 98-03; Min Partnership Development Officer *Pet* from 03. *11 Mountbatten Drive, Ringstead, Kettering NN14 4TX* Tel (01933) 626911 E-mail anthonybedell@stlv.freeserve.co.uk

BEDFORD, The Ven Colin Michael. b 35. ALCD60. **d** 61 **p** 62. C Woking St Mary *Guildf* 61-63; C Guildf St Sav 63-65; C Morden *S'wark* 65-69; V Toxteth Park St Philemon *Liv* 69-75; P-in-c Toxteth Park St Gabr 69-75; P-in-c Toxteth Park St Jas and St Matt 69-75; P-in-c Prince's Park St Paul 70-75; P-in-c Toxteth Park St Cleopas 73-78; TR Toxteth St Philemon w St Gabr 75-89; TR Toxteth St Philemon w St Gabr and St Cleopas 89-91; R Edgware *Lon* 91-98; TR 98-00; rtd 00; Can Akoke from 96; Adn Ondo from 99. *44 Arbour Street, Southport PR8 6SQ* Tel (01704) 535811

BEDFORD, Michael Anthony. b 38. Reading Univ BSc59 Heythrop Coll Lon MA00. **d** 01 **p** 02. NSM Ruislip St Martin *Lon* from 01. *7 Chandos Road, Eastcote, Pinner HA5 1PR* Tel (020) 8866 4332 E-mail mabedford@tesco.net

BEDFORD, Richard Derek Warner. b 27. Clare Coll Cam BA52. ALCD54. **d** 54 **p** 55. C Wallington H Trin *S'wark* 54-57; C Sanderstead All SS 57; C Weybridge *Guildf* 57-59; C Addlestone 59-62; C-in-c New Haw CD 62-66; V Epsom Common Ch Ch 66-81; R Walton-on-the-Hill 81-87; Asst Chapl Burrswood Home of Healing 87-92; rtd 92; Perm to Offic *Chich* from 92; Perm to Offic *Roch* from 92. *2 Lealands Close, Groombridge, Tunbridge Wells TN3 9ND* Tel (01892) 864550

BEDFORD, Archdeacon of. See HUGHES, The Ven Paul Vernon

BEDFORD, Suffragan Bishop of. See INWOOD, The Rt Revd Richard Neil

BEDWELL, Stanley Frederick. b 20. MPS42. Ox NSM Course 77. **d** 80 **p** 81. NSM Farnham Royal *Ox* 80-81; NSM Farnham Royal w Hedgerley from 81. *18 Ingleglen, Farnham Common, Slough SL2 3QA* Tel (01753) 644522

BEEBEE, Meyrick Richard Legge. St Alb and Ox Min Course 99. **d** 02. NSM Gerrards Cross and Fulmer *Ox* from 02. *Oak House, 86 Fulmer Road, Gerrards Cross SL9 7EG* Tel (01753) 882524 E-mail mbeebee@aol.com

BEEBY, Lawrence Clifford. b 28. S'wark Ord Course 70. **d** 73 **p** 74. C Notting Hill St Jo *Lon* 73-74; C Sunbury 74-76; C-in-c Hounslow Gd Shep Beavers Lane CD 76-80; Chapl Botleys Park Hosp Chertsey 80-96; rtd 96; Perm to Offic *Guildf* 96-99; Perm to Offic *Lon* from 96. *54 Bingley Road, Sunbury-on-Thames TW16 7RB* Tel (01932) 788922

BEECH, Miss Ailsa. b 44. N Co Coll Newc TDip65. Trin Coll Bris DipHE80. dss 80 **d** 87 **p** 94. Pudsey St Lawr *Bradf* 80-82; Pudsey St Lawr and St Paul 82-87; Par Dn 87-88; C Attleborough *Cov* 88-89; Par Dn Cumnor *Ox* 89-92; Asst Chapl Walsgrave Hosp Cov 92-94; Asst Chapl Walsgrave Hosps NHS Trust Cov 94-96; Chapl from 96. *Walsgrave Hospital, Clifford Bridge Road, Coventry CV2 2DX* Tel (024) 7660 2020 *or* 7653 8950

BEECH, Mrs Charmian Patricia. b 45. RGN66 RHV70 TCert74. St As Minl Tr Course 99. **d** 02 **p** 03. C Connah's Quay *St As* from 02. *Ty'r Llan, 3 Firbrook Avenue, Connah's Quay, Deeside CH5 4PF* Tel (01244) 814537 Mobile 07989-925996

BEECH, Derek Charles. b 49. EMMTC 99. **d** 02 **p** 03. NSM Horsley and Denby *Derby* from 02. *39 Brook Street, Heage, Belper DE56 2AG* Tel (01773) 850168 Mobile 07967-582661

BEECH, Frank Thomas. b 36. Tyndale Hall Bris 64. **d** 66 **p** 67. C Penn Fields *Lich* 66-70; C Attenborough w Chilwell *S'well* 70-74; P-in-c 74-75; P-in-c Attenborough 75-76; V 76-84; V Worksop St Anne from 84; Chapl Welbeck Coll from 84. *The Vicarage, 11 Poplar Close, Worksop S80 3BZ* Tel (01909) 472069 E-mail frank.beech@lineone.net

BEECH, Canon Harold. b 17. Univ of Wales BA39. Chich Th Coll 39. **d** 41 **p** 42. C Abertillery *Mon* 41-51; P-in-c Abercwmboi *Llan* 51-56; V 56-59; Chapl Cell Barnes Hosp and Hill End Hosp St Alb 59-82; Hon Can St Alb 77-83; rtd 82; Perm to Offic *St Alb* 83-86; Perm to Offic from 00. *clo Dr C A Leek, 232 High Street, London Colney, St Albans AL2 1HP*

BEECH, John. b 41. St Jo Coll Nottm. **d** 83 **p** 83. C York St Paul *York* 83-84; P-in-c Bubwith w Ellerton and Aughton 84-85; P-in-c Thorganby w Skipwith and N Duffield 84-85; V Bubwith w Skipwith 85-87; V Acomb H Redeemer 87-00; P-in-c Westleigh St Pet *Man* 00-01; rtd 01. *7 Pear Tree Lane, Dunnington, York YO19 5QG* E-mail jobe@cwcom.net

BEECH, John Thomas. b 38. St Aid Birkenhead 64. **d** 67 **p** 68. C Burton St Paul *Lich* 67-70; Chapl RN 70-83; V Ellingham and Harbridge and Ibsley *Win* 83-94; Chapl Whiteley Village *Guildf* 94-03; rtd 03. *10 Friars Walk, Barton-on-Sea, New Milton BH25 7DA*

BEECH, Peter John. b 34. Bps' Coll Cheshunt 58. **d** 61 **p** 62. C Fulham All SS *Lon* 61-64; S Africa 64-67; V S Hackney St Mich *Lon* 68-71; P-in-c Haggerston St Paul 68-71; V S Hackney St Mich w Haggerston St Paul 71-75; V Wanstead H Trin Hermon Hill *Chelmsf* 75-89; P-in-c St Mary-at-Latton 89-90; V 90-99; rtd 99; Perm to Offic *Ely* from 99. *9 Fitzgerald Close, Ely CB7 4QB* Tel (01353) 666269

BEECHAM, Clarence Ralph. b 35. S'wark Ord Course. **d** 83 **p** 84. NSM Leigh-on-Sea St Jas *Chelmsf* 83-86. *27 Scarborough Drive, Leigh-on-Sea SS9 3ED* Tel (01702) 574923

BEECROFT, Benjamin Harold. b 77. Trin Coll Bris BA98. **d** 00 **p** 01. C Stapleford *S'well* from 00. *3 Ash Grove, Stapleford, Nottingham NG9 7GL* Tel 0115-939 2643

BEECROFT, Mrs Christine Mary. b 62. RGN85. Trin Coll Bris BA97 MA99. **d** 98 **p** 99. C Roxeth *Lon* 98-00; Perm to Offic *S'well* 00-02; C Stapleford from 02. *3 Ash Grove, Stapleford, Nottingham NG9 7GL* Tel 0115-877 6175 E-mail christine.beecroft@ntlworld.com

BEEDELL, Trevor Francis. b 31. ALCD65. **d** 65 **p** 66. C Walton St E 65-68; R Hartshorne *Derby* 68-79; RD Repton 74-79; V Doveridge 79-86; Chapl HM Det Cen Foston Hall 79-80; Dioc Dir of Chr Stewardship *Derby* 79-97; rtd 97; Perm to Offic *Derby* from 97. *185 High Lane West, West Hallam, Ilkeston DE7 6HP* Tel 0115-932 5589

BEEDON, David Kirk. b 59. Birm Univ BA89 MPhil93. Qu Coll Birm 86. **d** 89 **p** 90. C Cannock *Lich* 89-92; V Wednesbury St Bart 92-99; R Lich St Mich w St Mary and Wall from 99. *St Michael's Rectory, St Michael Road, Lichfield WS13 6SN* Tel and fax (01543) 262420 *or* 262211 E-mail dkbeedon@aol.com

BEEK, Canon Michael Peter. b 27. Em Coll Cam BA50 MA55. Linc Th Coll 50. **d** 52 **p** 53. C Mitcham St Barn *S'wark* 52-55; C Talbot Village *Sarum* 55-58; V Higham and Merston *Roch* 58-66; R Gravesend St Geo 66-74; R Gravesend St Jas 66-74; RD Gravesend 70-74; Hon Can Roch Cathl 73-92; RD Tunbridge Wells 74-83; R Speldhurst w Groombridge 74-77; P-in-c Ashurst 77; R Speldhurst w Groombridge and Ashurst 77-83; V Bromley SS Pet and Paul 83-92; rtd 92; Perm to Offic *Nor* from 92; RD Hartismere *St E* 93-97; Perm to Offic from 97. *18 Henry Ward Road, Harleston IP20 9EZ* Tel (01379) 854003

BEER, Mrs Janet Margaret. b 43. Goldsmiths' Coll Lon CertEd64. Oak Hill Th Coll 83. dss 86 **d** 87 **p** 94. Colney St Pet *St Alb* 86-87; Hon C London Colney St Pet 87-97; Chapl St Alb High Sch for Girls 87-89; Chapl Middx Univ *Lon* from 94; NSM Northaw and Cuffley *St Alb* from 99. *Northaw Vicarage, 58 Hill Rise, Cuffley, Potters Bar EN6 4RG* Tel (01707) 874126

BEER, The Ven John Stuart. b 44. Pemb Coll Ox BA65 MA70 Fitzw Coll Cam MA78. Westcott Ho Cam 69. **d** 71 **p** 72. C Knaresborough St Jo *Ripon* 71-74; Chapl Fitzw Coll and New Hall Cam 74-80; Fell Fitzw Coll 77-80; Bye-Fell from 01; P-in-c Toft w Caldecote and Childerley *Ely* 80-83; R 83-87; P-in-c Hardwick 80-83; R 83-87; V Grantchester 87-97; Dir of Ords, Post-Ord Tr and Student Readers from 88; Hon Can Ely Cathl from 89; Adn Huntingdon from 97; Acting Adn Wisbech from 02. *The Rectory, Hemingford Abbots, Huntingdon PE28 9AN* Tel (01480) 469856 *or* fax and tel 496073
E-mail archdeacon.huntingdon@ely.anglican.org

BEER, Michael Trevor. b 44. Chich Th Coll 66. **d** 69 **p** 70. C Leagrave *St Alb* 69-73; St Vincent 73-74; C Thorley w Bishop's Stortford H Trin *St Alb* 74-80; V London Colney St Pet 80-97; V Northaw and Cuffley from 97. *Northaw Vicarage, 58 Hill Rise, Cuffley, Potters Bar EN6 4RG* Tel (01707) 874126

BEER, Nigel David. b 62. Portsm Poly BSc84. St Jo Coll Nottm Dip Th Studies 92 MA93. **d** 93 **p** 94. C Rastrick St Matt *Wakef* 93-96; C Bilton *Ripon* 96-98; TV Moor Allerton from 98. *73 The Avenue, Leeds LS17 7NP* Tel 0113-267 8487
E-mail nbeer@lineone.net

BEER, William Barclay. b 43. ACT ThA68 St Steph Ho Ox. **d** 71 **p** 72. C St Marychurch *Ex* 71-76; V Pattishall w Cold Higham *Pet* 76-82; V Northampton St Benedict 82-85; V Chislehurst Annunciation *Roch* from 85. *The Vicarage, 2 Foxhome Close, Chislehurst BR7 5XT* Tel (020) 8467 3606 Fax as telephone
E-mail wbeer@lineone.net

BEESLEY, Michael Frederick. b 37. K Coll Cam BA59. Westcott Ho Cam 60. **d** 61 **p** 64. C Eastleigh *Win* 61-69; rtd 02. *24 Charmouth Grove, Poole BH14 0LP* Tel (01202) 773471

BEESLEY, Ramon John. b 27. Magd Coll Ox BA51 MA55. Wycliffe Hall Ox 51. **d** 53 **p** 56. C Gerrards Cross *Ox* 53-54; Asst Chapl Embley Park Sch Romsey 54-58; Perm to Offic *Win* 54-58; Asst Master Farnham Sch 58-62; Perm to Offic *Guildf* 58-62; Perm to Offic *Win* from 63; Hd Science Gore Sch New Milton 63-69; Dep Hd Applemore Sch Dibden Purlieu 69-74; Hd Master Bellemoor Sch Southn 74-84; rtd 84. *Wayfarers, Burley, Ringwood BH24 4HW* Tel (01425) 402284

BEESON, Christopher George. b 48. Man Univ BSc70. Qu Coll Birm 72. **d** 75 **p** 76. C Flixton St Mich *Man* 75-78; C Newton Heath All SS 78-80; R Gorton St Jas 80-90; Dioc Communications Officer *Blackb* 91-92; C Ribbleton 92-93; rtd 93; Perm to Offic *Blackb* from 93. *24 Arnold Close, Ribbleton, Preston PR2 6DX* Tel (01772) 702675
E-mail cbeeson@cix.co.uk

BEESON, The Very Revd Trevor Randall. b 26. OBE97. K Coll Lon MA76 FKC87 Southn Univ Hon DLitt99. **d** 51 **p** 52. C Leadgate *Dur* 51-54; C Norton St Mary 54-56; C-in-c Stockton St Chad CD 56-60; V Stockton St Chad 60-65; C St Martin-in-the-Fields *Lon* 65-71; V Ware St Mary *St Alb* 71-76; Can Westmr Abbey 76-87; Treas 78-82; R Westmr St Marg 82-87; Chapl to Speaker of Ho of Commons 82-87; Dean Win 87-96; rtd 96; Perm to Offic *Win* from 96. *69 Greatbridge Road, Romsey SO51 8FE* Tel (01794) 514627

BEESTON, Andrew Bernard. b 41. RMN64 RGN67. NEOC 99. **d** 01 **p** 02. NSM Cullercoats St Geo *Newc* from 01. *21 Deepdale Road, Cullercoats, North Shields NE30 3AN* Tel 0191-259 0431

BEET, Duncan Clive. b 65. Ridley Hall Cam 98. **d** 01 **p** 02. C Northampton Em *Pet* from 01. *12 Jersey Court, Northampton NN3 9TB*

BEETHAM, Anthony. b 32. Lon Univ BSc53. Ox NSM Course. **d** 75 **p** 76. Dir Chr Enquiry Agency 88-97; NSM Ox St Clem *Ox* 75-02. *44 Rose Hill, Oxford OX4 4HS* Tel (01865) 770923

BEETON, David Ambrose Moore. b 39. Chich Th Coll 62. **d** 65 **p** 66. C Forest Gate St Edm *Chelmsf* 65-71; V Rush Green 71-81; V Coggeshall w Markshall 81-02; rtd 02. *Le Strange Cottages, 2 Hunstanton Road, Heacham, King's Lynn PE31 7HH* Tel (01485) 572150

BEETY, Arthur Edward. b 38. Sheff Univ BA60. Cant Sch of Min 92. **d** 95 **p** 96. NSM Cobham w Luddesdowne and Dode *Roch* from 95. *The Old Forge, 4 The Street, Cobham, Gravesend DA12 3BN* Tel (01474) 816684
E-mail arthur.beety@btinternet.com

BEEVER, Miss Alison Rosemary. b 59. Man Univ BA80. Linc Th Coll 88. **d** 90 **p** 94. Par Dn Watford Ch Ch *St Alb* 90-94; C 94-96; V Tilehurst St Cath *Ox* 96-01; P-in-c Cen Ex from 01; Dioc Dir of Ords from 01. *The Rectory, 3 Spicer Road, Exeter EX1 1SX* Tel (01392) 272450

BEEVERS, Preb Colin Lionel. b 40. K Coll Lon BSc62 PhD66 CEng70 MIEE70 MBIM73 DMS72. Sarum & Wells Th Coll 87. **d** 89 **p** 90. C Ledbury w Eastnor *Heref* 89-93; C Lt Marcle 89-93; Asst Dir of Tr 92-96; P-in-c Kimbolton w Hamnish and Middleton-on-the-Hill 93-96; P-in-c Bockleton w Leysters 93-96; P-in-c Ledbury w Eastnor 96-98; P-in-c Much Marcle 96-98; TR Ledbury from 98; RD Ledbury 96-02; Preb Heref Cathl from 02. *The Rectory, Worcester Road, Ledbury HR8 1PL* Tel (01531) 632571 Fax 633792
E-mail ledbury.ministry@virgin.net

BEEVERS, Reginald. b 22. Dur Univ BA48. Qu Coll Birm 48. **d** 50 **p** 51. C Stockton H Trin *Dur* 50-52; C Esh 52-53; C-in-c Peterlee CD 53-57; V Peterlee 57-60; Chapl Worc R Infirmary 60-63; Lic to Offic *Man* 63-65; Chapl Hulme Gr Sch Oldham 63-65; Chapl Guy's Hosp Lon 65-70; Chapl Liv Coll 70-81; R Hatch Beauchamp w Beercrocombe, Curry Mallet etc *B & W* 81-88; rtd 88; P-in-c Oare w Culbone *B & W* 90-93; Perm to Offic 93-99. *18 Abbey Close, Curry Rivel, Langport TA10 0EL* Tel (01458) 253676

BEGBIE, Jeremy Sutherland. b 57. Edin Univ BA77 Aber Univ BD80 PhD87 LRAM80 ARCM77 MSSTh. Ridley Hall Cam 80. **d** 82 **p** 83. C Egham *Guildf* 82-85; Chapl Ridley Hall Cam 85-87; Dir Studies 87-92; Vice-Prin 89-00; Prin from 00; Hon Reader St Andr Univ from 00. *Ridley Hall, Ridley Hall Road, Cambridge CB3 9HG* Tel (01223) 741075 *or* 360995 Fax 741081 E-mail jb215@cam.ac.uk

BEGGS, Norman Lindell. b 32. N Lon Poly CQSW77. S Dios Minl Tr Scheme 86. **d** 89 **p** 90. NSM Milborne St Andrew w Dewlish *Sarum* 89-92; C 92-95; C Piddletrenthide w Plush, Alton Pancras etc 92-95; C Puddletown and Tolpuddle 92-95; rtd 95; Perm to Offic *Sarum* from 95. *Wallingford House, Dewlish, Dorchester DT2 7LX* Tel (01258) 837320

BEGLEY, Frank William. b 18. Univ of Wales (Lamp) BA48. Sarum Th Coll 48. **d** 49 **p** 50. C Ebbw Vale *Mon* 49-55; C Richmond St Jo *S'wark* 55-57; Tanganyika 57-63; C-in-c Boxmoor St Fran Hammerfield CD *St Alb* 64-66; Guyana 66-70; C Roath *Llan* 70-74; V Cardiff St Dyfrig and St Samson 74-83; R Llanwenarth Ultra *Mon* 83-87; rtd 87; Perm to Offic *Llan* from 87. *24 St Teilo's Court, Sturminster Road, Roath, Cardiff CF23 5AX* Tel (029) 2048 9375

BEGLEY, Mrs Helen. b 59. Kingston Poly BA81. N Ord Course 87. **d** 89 **p** 94. Par Dn Leeds H Trin *Ripon* 89-90; Chapl to the Deaf 89-96; Par Dn Leeds City 90-94; C 94-96; Chapl to the Deaf (Wilts) *Sarum* from 96; C Upper Wylye Valley from 03. *The Vicarage, Green Lane, Codford, Warminster BA12 0NY* Tel (01985) 850019

BEHENNA, Preb Gillian Eve. b 57. CertEd78. St Alb Minl Tr Scheme 82. **dss** 85 **d** 87 **p** 94. Chapl to the Deaf *Sarum* 85-90; Chapl with Deaf People *Ex* from 90; Preb Ex Cathl from 02. *1B The Cloisters, Exeter EX1 1JS* Tel (01392) 459376 Mobile 07715-707137 Fax (01392) 459380
E-mail gill@signsofgod.fsnet.co.uk

BEHREND, Michael Christopher. b 60. St Jo Coll Cam BA82 MA86 PGCE83. Oak Hill Th Coll DipHE95. **d** 97 **p** 98. C Hensingham *Carl* 97-02; TV Horwich and Rivington *Man* from 02. *St Catherine's House, Richmond Street, Horwich, Bolton BL6 5QT* Tel (01204) 697162

BELCHER, David John. b 44. Ch Ch Ox BA65 MA69. Cuddesdon Coll 68. **d** 70 **p** 71. C Gateshead St Mary *Dur* 70-73; C Stockton St Pet 73-76; Lic to Offic *Lich* 76-81; P-in-c W Bromwich Ch Ch 81-85; P-in-c W Bromwich Gd Shep w St Jo 85-89; V 89-95; RD W Bromwich 90-94; R Bratton, Edington and Imber, Erlestoke etc *Sarum* 95-03; rtd 03; Hon C Smestow Vale *Lich* from 03. *The Vicarage, 59 Six Ashes Road, Bobbington, Stourbridge DY7 5BZ* Tel (01384) 221580

BELCHER, Canon Derek George. b 50. MRSH73 MBIM82 Univ of Wales Dip Dietetics 73 MEd86 Lon Univ PGCE82. Chich Th Coll 74. **d** 77 **p** 78. C Newton Nottage *Llan* 77-81; PV Llan Cathl 81-87; V Margam 87-01; Hon Can Llan Cathl from 97; RD Margam 90-01; TR Cowbridge from 01. *The Rectory, 85 Broadway, Llanblethian, Cowbridge CF71 7EY* Tel (01446) 775597 Mobile 07768-980471
E-mail derek.belcher@ntlworld.com

BELCHER, Frederick William. b 30. Kelham Th Coll 50 Chich Th Coll 53. **d** 54 **p** 55. C Catford St Laur *S'wark* 54-58; C-in-c Plumstead Wm Temple Ch Abbey Wood CD 58-62; V Eltham Park St Luke 62-64; Lic to Offic 65-81; NSM Charminster and Stinsford *Sarum* 88-94; Perm to Offic from 94; rtd 95. *Little Mead, North Street, Charminster, Dorchester DT2 9QZ* Tel (01305) 260688

BELFAST, Dean of. See McKELVEY, The Very Revd Robert Samuel James Houston

BELHAM, John Edward. b 42. K Coll Lon BSc65 AKC65 PhD70. Oak Hill Th Coll 69. **d** 72 **p** 73. C Cheadle Hulme St Andr *Ches* 72-75; C Cheadle 75-83; R Gressenhall w Longham w Wendling etc *Nor* from 83. *The Rectory, Bittering Street, Gressenhall, Dereham NR20 4EB* Tel (01362) 860211

BELHAM, Michael. b 23. Lon Univ BScEng50. **d** 67 **p** 68. C Northwood Hills St Edm *Lon* 67-69; C Hendon St Mary 69-73; V Tottenham H Trin 73-78; V Hillingdon St Jo 78-85; P-in-c Broughton *Ox* 85; R Broughton w N Newington and Shutford 85-90; Chapl Horton Gen Hosp 85-90; rtd 90; Perm to Offic *Pet* from 90; *Ox* 90-00; Sec DBP *Ox* 95-01; Perm to Offic *B & W* from 01. *14 Holly Court, Frome BA11 2SQ* Tel (01373) 462941
E-mail michael-belham@supanet.com

BELING, David Gibson. b 30. Fitzw Ho Cam BA54 MA58. **d** 56 **p** 57. C Radipole *Sarum* 56-59; C Broadwater St Mary *Chich* 59-61; R W Knighton w Broadmayne *Sarum* 61-73; V Paignton St Paul Preston *Ex* 73-91; rtd 91; Perm to Offic *Ex* from 91. *51 Manor Road, Paignton TQ3 2HZ*

BELITHER, John Roland. b 36. Oak Hill Th Coll 83. **d** 86 **p** 87. NSM Bushey Heath *St Alb* 86-91; V Marsh Farm from 91. *The Vicarage, 40 Purway Close, Marsh Farm, Luton LU3 3RT* Tel (01582) 575757

BELL, Adrian Christopher. b 48. AKC70. St Aug Coll Cant 70. **d** 71 **p** 72. C Sheff St Aid w St Luke *Sheff* 71-74; C Willesborough w Hinxhill *Cant* 74-78; P-in-c Wormshill 78; P-in-c Hollingbourne w Hucking 78-82; P-in-c Leeds w Broomfield 79-82; V Hollingbourne and Hucking w Leeds and Broomfield 82-84; V Herne Bay Ch Ch 84-91; R Washingborough w Heighington and Canwick *Linc* 91-01; R Fakenham w Alethorpe *Nor* from 01. *The Rectory, Gladstone Road, Fakenham NR21 9BZ* Tel (01328) 862268 Fax as telephone

BELL, Alan. b 29. Handsworth Coll Birm 55 Linc Th Coll 64. **d** 65 **p** 65. C Spilsby w Hundleby *Linc* 65-67; R Ludford Magna w Ludford Parva 67-76; V Burgh on Bain 68-76; V Kelstern, Calcethorpe and E Wykeham 68-76; Clerical Org Sec CECS 76-78; rtd 94. *116 The Birches, Crawley RH10 1RZ* Tel (01293) 407195

BELL, Alan John. b 47. Liv Univ BA68. Ridley Hall Cam 69. **d** 72 **p** 73. C Speke St Aid *Liv* 72-77; P-in-c Halewood 77-81; R Wavertree St Mary 81-88; Chapl Mabel Fletcher Tech Coll Liv 81-88; Chapl Olive Mt Hosp 81-88; R Fakenham w Alethorpe *Nor* 88-00; RD Burnham and Walsingham 92-00; TR Stockport SW *Ches* from 00. *St George's Vicarage, 7 Corbar Road, Stockport SK2 6EP*

BELL, Allan McRae. b 49. Moray Ho Teacher Tr Coll Edin CertEd80 E Lon Univ BA90. S'wark Ord Course 86. **d** 92 **p** 95. NSM Bow H Trin and All Hallows *Lon* 91-93; NSM R Foundn of St Kath in Ratcliffe 93-95; USA 95-97; Chapl Univ of California 95-96; P-in-c Bolinas St Aidan 96-97. *177 Well Street, London E9 6QU* Tel (020) 8985 1978

BELL, Andrew Thomas. b 58. Ripon Coll Cuddesdon 93. **d** 95 **p** 96. C Leighton Buzzard w Eggington, Hockliffe etc *St Alb* 95-98; TV Schorne *Ox* from 98. *The Vicarage, Church Street, North Maston, Buckingham MK18 3PH* Tel (01296) 670298

BELL, Anthony Lawson. b 47. AKC72. St Aug Coll Cant 71. **d** 72 **p** 73. C Peterlee *Dur* 72-77; C-in-c Stockton St Jas CD 82-89; P-in-c Byers Green 89-96; Ind Chapl Teesside 89-96; V Ault Hucknall *Derby* 96-99; V Ault Hucknall and Scarcliffe from 99. *The Vicarage, 59 The Hill, Glapwell, Chesterfield S44 5LX* Tel (01246) 850371 Fax 857530 E-mail glapwell@tonybell.co.uk *or* glapwell@btconnect.com

BELL, Antony Fancourt. b 28. Magd Coll Ox BA51 MA58. Wells Th Coll 54. **d** 56 **p** 57. C Clapham H Trin *S'wark* 56-59; C Gillingham *Sarum* 59-61; R Stanway *Chelmsf* 61-94; RD Dedham and Tey 81-91; rtd 94. *Walsingham House, Ilchester Road, Charlton Mackrell, Somerton TA11 6AN* Tel (01458) 223657

BELL, Arthur Francis. b 17. Leeds Univ BA39. Bps' Coll Cheshunt 40. **d** 41 **p** 42. C Bedford H Trin *St Alb* 41-43; C Chesterfield St Mary and All SS *Derby* 43-45; C Barrowhill 45-46; C Westbury-on-Trym H Trin *Bris* 46-48; C Knowle H Nativity 48-50; R Priston *B & W* 50-61; V Englishcombe 55-61; R Charlcombe 61-85; rtd 85; Perm to Offic *B & W* from 86. *Water House, Watehouse Lane, Monkton Combe, Bath BA2 7JB* Tel (01225) 720271

BELL, Arthur James. b 33. Ch Coll Cam BA57 MA60. Coll of Resurr Mirfield 57. **d** 59 **p** 60. C New Cleethorpes *Linc* 59-63; C Upperby St Jo *Carl* 63-66; P-in-c Wabasca Canada 67-72 and 77-83; Perm to Offic *Ely* 73-75; Lic to Offic *Carl* 75-76; Warden Retreat of the Visitation Rhandirmwyn 83-99; Perm to Offic *Dur* from 00. *Burnside, 22 Rose Terrace, Stanhope, Bishop Auckland DL13 2PE* Tel (01388) 526514

BELL, Barnaby. See BELL, Simon Barnaby

BELL, Bede. See BELL, William Wealands

BELL, Brian Thomas Benedict. b 64. Newc Poly BA87 Dip French Studies 91 Newc Univ PGCE88 Univ of Northumbria at Newc MA93. Coll of Resurr Mirfield 88. **d** 97 **p** 98. C Tynemouth Cullercoats St Paul *Newc* 97-01; V Horton from 01. *St Benedict's Vicarage, Brierley Road, Blyth NE24 5AU* Tel (01670) 367035

BELL, Catherine Ann. See MOSS, Mrs Catherine Ann

BELL, Charles William. b 43. TCD Div Test 66 BA66 MA69. CITC 64. **d** 67 **p** 68. C Newtownards *D & D* 67-70; C Larne and Inver *Conn* 70-74; C Ballymena w Ballyclug 74-80; Bp's C Belfast Ardoyne 80-88; Bp's C Belfast Ardoyne w H Redeemer 88-89; I Eglantine from 89; Dioc Info Officer (S Conn) from 89. *All Saints' Rectory, 16 Eglantine Road, Lisburn BT27 5RQ* Tel (028) 9266 2634 Fax 9266 8651 E-mail rev.cwb@bell297.freeserve.co.uk

BELL, Colin Ashworth. b 52. FCCA83. Westcott Ho Cam 89. **d** 91 **p** 92. C Lytham St Cuth *Blackb* 91-93; C Whittle-le-Woods 93-97; V Stalybridge H Trin and Ch Ch *Ches* from 97. *The Vicarage, 277 Mottram Road, Stalybridge SK15 2RT* Tel 0161-303 1984 *or* 304 9308 E-mail pastors@holytrinitystalybridge.co.uk

BELL, Colin Douglas. b 65. QUB DipTh90 BTh94 TCD MPhil96. CITC 94. **d** 96 **p** 97. C Dundonald *D & D* 96-98; C

Knock 98-00; I Lack *Clogh* 00-02; I Rathcoole *Conn* from 02. *7 Oaklands Meadow, Newtownabbey BT37 0XN* Tel (028) 9086 7714

BELL, Cyril John. b 22. Lon Univ BA48. Wycliffe Hall Ox 52. **d** 53 **p** 54. C Monkwearmouth St Pet *Dur* 53-56; Ch of S India 56-60; Hon C Westlands St Andr *Lich* 66-71; Lic to Offic *Ches* 71-82; Perm to Offic 82-90 and from 91; Perm to Offic *Lich* 90-97. *49 Delamere Road, Nantwich CW5 7DF* Tel (01270) 628910

BELL, David James. b 62. QUB BSc84 BTh. **d** 91 **p** 92. C Ballyholme *D & D* 91-94; C Coleraine *Conn* 94-00; I Ardtrea w Desertcreat *Arm* from 00. *Tullyhogue Rectory, 50 Lower Grange Road, Cookstown BT80 8SL* Tel (028) 8676 1163 Fax as telephone E-mail bell.david@talk21.com

BELL, Canon David Owain. b 49. Dur Univ BA69 Nottm Univ DipTh70 Fitzw Coll Cam BA72 MA80. Westcott Ho Cam 70. **d** 72 **p** 73. C Houghton le Spring *Dur* 72-76; C Norton St Mary 76-78; P-in-c Worc St Clem *Worc* 78-84; R 84-85; R Old Swinford Stourbridge 85-97; RD Stourbridge 90-96; Hon Can Worc Cathl from 96; TR Kidderminster St Mary and All SS w Trimpley etc from 97. *The Vicarage, 22 Roden Avenue, Kidderminster DY10 2RF* Tel (01562) 823265

BELL, Canon Donald Jon. b 50. Sarum & Wells Th Coll 73. **d** 76 **p** 77. C Jarrow *Dur* 76-80; C Darlington St Cuth w St Hilda 80-83; V Wingate Grange 83-89; V Sherburn w Pittington 89-95; AD Dur from 93; R Shadforth 94-95; P-in-c Dur St Cuth 95-97; V 97-02; R Witton Gilbert 97-02; TR Dur N from 02; Chapl Dur and Darlington Fire and Rescue Brigade from 95; Hon Can Dur Cathl from 01. *St Cuthbert's Vicarage, 1 Aykley Court, Durham DH1 4NW* Tel and fax 0191-386 4526 Mobile 07973-829491 E-mail aread@djonbell.freeserve.co.uk

BELL, Dorothy Jane. b 53. Teesside Univ BSc93. Cranmer Hall Dur 01. **d** 03. C Washington *Dur* from 03. *38 Brancepeth Road, Washington NE38 0LA* Tel 0191-483 2360

BELL, Edwin Lucius Wyndham. b 19. Worc Coll Ox BA41 MA45. Westcott Ho Cam 41. **d** 43 **p** 44. C Croydon *Cant* 43-50; CF 50-54; V Bapchild w Tonge and Rodmersham *Cant* 54-63; P-in-c Murston 54-56; V Maidstone St Paul 63-78; P-in-c Nonington w Barfreystone 78-85; P-in-c Womenswold 78-85; rtd 85; Perm to Offic *Cant* from 85. *2 Boarley Court, Sandling Lane, Maidstone ME14 2NL* Tel (01622) 756924

BELL, Mrs Evelyn Ruth. b 52. Univ of Wales (Cardiff) BSc(Econ). St Alb and Ox Min Course 97. **d** 00 **p** 01. C Waltham Cross *St Alb* from 00. *18 Shalcross Drive, Cheshunt, Waltham Cross EN8 8UX* Tel (01992) 622924

BELL, Canon Francis William Albert. b 28. TCD BA52 MA57 BD57. **d** 53 **p** 54. C Belfast St Mich *Conn* 53-55; C Belfast All SS 55-61; C Ballynafeigh St Jude *D & D* 61-63; P-in-c Ballyhalbert 63-71; P-in-c Ardkeen 67-71; I Ballyhalbert w Ardkeen 71-95; Miss to Seamen 71-95; Can Belf Cathl 89-95; rtd 95. *Stationbanks, 18 Kilmore Road, Crossgar, Downpatrick BT30 9HJ* Tel (028) 4483 1665

BELL, Mrs Glynis Mary. b 44. Leeds Univ BA66. St Alb and Ox Min Course 99. **d** 02 **p** 03. OLM Newport Pagnell w Lathbury and Moulsoe *Ox* from 02. *6 Kipling Drive, Newport Pagnell MK16 8EB* Tel (01908) 612971

BELL, Godfrey Bryan. b 44. Oak Hill Th Coll 72. **d** 75 **p** 76. C Penn Fields *Lich* 75-79; R Dolton *Ex* 79-89; R Iddesleigh w Dowland 79-89; R Monkokehampton 79-89; R Tollard Royal w Farnham, Gussage St Michael etc *Sarum* 89-96; TV Washfield, Stoodleigh, Withleigh etc *Ex* from 96. *The Vicarage, 3 Court Gardens, Stoodleigh, Tiverton EX16 9PL* Tel (01398) 351373 E-mail gomar@stoodleigh.freeserve.co.uk

BELL, Graham Dennis Robert. b 42. K Coll Lon BSc63 AKC63 Nottm Univ MTh73 ALCM76 Lambeth STh01. Tyndale Hall Bris 63. **d** 68 **p** 69. C Stapleford *S'well* 68-71; C Barton Seagrave *Pet* 71-73; C Barton Seagrave w Warkton 73-76; Perm to Offic *Nor* 76-82; V Wickham Market *St E* 82-86; V Wickham Market w Pettistree and Easton 86-98; R Thrapston *Pet* from 98. *The Rectory, 48 Oundle Road, Thrapston, Kettering NN14 4PD* Tel (01832) 732393 E-mail graham@bellgood.fsnet.co.uk

BELL, Canon Jack Gorman. b 23. Lon Univ BSc48. Oak Hill Th Coll 51. **d** 53 **p** 54. C Blackpool Ch Ch *Blackb* 53-55; C Chadderton Ch Ch *Man* 55-59; R Man St Jerome w Ardwick St Silas 59-69; V Mosley Common 69-89; Hon Can Man Cathl 87-89; rtd 89; Perm to Offic *Carl* from 89. *36 Sandgate, Kendal LA9 6HT* Tel (01539) 725807

BELL, Canon James Harold. b 50. St Jo Coll Dur BA72 St Pet Hall Ox BA74 MA78. Wycliffe Hall Ox 72. **d** 75 **p** 76. Hon C Ox St Mich w St Martin and All SS *Ox* 75-76; Chapl and Lect BNC Ox 76-82; R Northolt St Mary *Lon* 82-93; AD Ealing 91-93; Adv for Min Willesden 93-97; Dioc Dir of Tr *Ripon* 97-99; Dioc Dir of Miss from 99; Can Res Ripon Cathl 99-99; Hon Can Ripon Cathl from 99. *12 Clotherholme Road, Ripon HG4 2DA* Tel (01765) 604835 E-mail j.h.bell@btinternet.com

BELL, James Samuel. b 40. MBE71. RMA 59 St Chad's Coll Dur BA69. Coll of Resurr Mirfield 71. **d** 72 **p** 73. C Lambeth St Phil *S'wark* 72-74; C N Lambeth 74; P-in-c Invergordon St Ninian *Mor* 74-77; P-in-c Dornoch 74-77; P-in-c Brora 74-77; V Pet H

Spirit Bretton *Pet* 77-83; P-in-c Marholm 82-83; Sen Chapl Tonbridge Sch 83-00; rtd 00. *Clocktower House, Edderton, Tain IV19 1LJ* Tel (01862) 821305

BELL, Jane. *See* BELL, Dorothy Jane

BELL, Canon Jeffrey William. b 37. Buckingham Univ MA94. Sarum Th Coll 60. **d** 63 **p** 64. C Northampton St Matt *Pet* 63-66; C Portishead *B & W* 66-68; C Digswell *St Alb* 68-72; V Pet St Jude *Pet* 72-79; V Buckingham *Ox* 79-93; RD Buckingham 84-88 and 89-90; V Portsea N End St Mark *Portsm* 93-03; Hon Can Portsm Cathl 00-03; rtd 03; Hon C The Bourne and Tilford *Guildf* from 03; Perm to Offic *Portsm* from 03. *All Saints' Vicarage, Tilford, Farnham GU10 2DA* Tel (01252) 792333 E-mail thebells2000@hotmail.com

BELL, John. *See* BELL, Canon Donald Jon

BELL, John Christopher. b 33. TCD BA56 MA66. TCD Div Sch Div Test. **d** 56 **p** 57. C Newtownards *D & D* 56-59; C Willowfield 59-62; I Carrowdore 62-70; I Drumbo 70-98; Chapl Young Offender Cen Belf 79-98; Can Down Cathl *D & D* 87-98; Treas 91-98; rtd 98. *Ashwell House, 6 Ballywillin Road, Crossgar, Downpatrick BT30 9LE* Tel (028) 4483 1907

BELL, John Edward. b 34. Cranmer Hall Dur. **d** 67 **p** 68. C Harraby *Carl* 67-70; C Dalton-in-Furness 70-72; V Pennington 72-75; V Carl St Herbert w St Steph 75-84; V Wreay 84-85; rtd 99; Perm to Offic *Carl* from 01. *189 Brampton Road, Carlisle CA3 9AX* Tel (01228) 522746

BELL, John Holmes. b 50. Sheff City Coll of Educn CertEd71. Oak Hill Th Coll DipHE79 BA80. **d** 80 **p** 81. C Leic St Phil *Leic* 80-83; C Portswood Ch Ch *Win* 83-86; TV S Molton w Nymet St George, High Bray etc *Ex* 86-01; V Stoke Fleming, Blackawton and Strete from 01. *Church House, 6 Glebe Park, Stoke Fleming, Dartmouth TQ6 0RD* Tel (01803) 771050 E-mail john@ding-dong.fsnet.co.uk

BELL, Joseph William. b 30. St Cath Coll Ox BA53 Pemb Coll Cam MA57. Wycliffe Hall Ox 53. **d** 55 **p** 56. C Blundellsands St Nic *Liv* 55-58; CF 58-68; V Roby *Liv* 68-70; CF 70-86; P-in-c Fovant, Sutton Mandeville and Teffont Evias etc *Sarum* 86-88; Perm to Offic from 89; rtd 95. *61 St Ann's Place, Salisbury SP1 2SU* Tel (01722) 322576

BELL, Karl Edwin. b 33. Minnesota Univ BA56. Seabury-Western Th Sem MDiv61. **d** 61 **p** 62. USA 61-71 and 76-92; Venezuela 71-76; Chapl Wiesbaden *Eur* from 92. *St Augustine of Canterbury, Frankfurterstrasse 3, 65189 Wiesbaden, Germany* Tel (0049) (611) 306674 Fax 372270 E-mail bell@wiesbaden.netsurf.de

BELL, Kenneth Murray. b 30. Sarum & Wells Th Coll 75. **d** 74 **p** 76. Perm to Offic *Guildf* 74-76; C Hartley Wintney and Elvetham *Win* 76-77; C Hartley Wintney, Elvetham, Winchfield etc 77-80; V Fair Oak 80-95; rtd 96; Perm to Offic *Win* from 96. *12 Hill Meadow, Overton, Basingstoke RG25 3JD* Tel (01256) 770890

BELL, Kevin David. b 58. Newc Univ MA93. Selly Oak Coll CPS82 Aston Tr Scheme 78 Sarum & Wells Th Coll 80. **d** 83 **p** 84. C Weoley Castle *Birm* 83-87; C Acocks Green 87-89; CF from 89; Perm to Offic *Guildf* 97-00. *c/o MOD Chaplains (Army)* Tel (01980) 615804 Fax 615800

BELL, Canon Nicholas Philip Johnson. b 46. St Jo Coll Dur BSc69 Nottm Univ DipTh72. St Jo Coll Nottm 70. **d** 73 **p** 74. C Chadderton Ch Ch *Man* 73-77; C Frogmore *St Alb* 77-81; V Bricket Wood 81-91; RD Aldenham 87-91; V Luton St Mary from 91; Hon Can St Alb from 01. *The Vicarage, 48 Crawley Green Road, Luton LU2 0QX* Tel (01582) 728925 Fax as telephone E-mail nickbell@stmarysluton.org

BELL, Owain. *See* BELL, Canon David Owain

BELL, Paul Joseph. b 35. Dur Univ BA56 DipEd57. Trin Coll Bris 77. **d** 77 **p** 78. Burundi 77-81; C Highbury Ch Ch w St Jo and St Sav Lon 82-85; V Middleton w E Winch *Nor* 85-95; P-in-c Barningham w Matlaske w Baconsthorpe etc 95-99; R 99-02; rtd 02; Perm to Offic *Portsm* from 02. *21 Hurst Point View, Totland Bay PO39 0AQ* Tel (01983) 756180

BELL, Philip Harold. b 19. Leeds Univ BA45 K Alfred's Coll Win PGCE69. Coll of Resurr Mirfield 38. **d** 44 **p** 45. C Barrow St Matt *Carl* 44-49; C Lewisham St Jo Southend *S'wark* 50-56; Tristan da Cunha 56-61; R Crawley w Littleton *Win* 61-72; V Holdenhurst 72-78; P-in-c Hilperton w Whaddon *Sarum* 78-84; P-in-c Staverton 78-84; R Hilperton w Whaddon and Staverton etc 85-86; rtd 86; Perm to Offic *Sarum* from 86; Perm to Offic *Cov* from 92. *31 Duxford Close, Bowerhill, Melksham SN12 6XN* Tel (01225) 709732 E-mail phildil@talk21.com

BELL, Reginald Leslie. b 13. Trin Coll Bris 72. **d** 74 **p** 75. NSM Stoke Bishop Bris 74-75 and 78-94; NSM Horfield H Trin 75-77; Perm to Offic from 94. *September Cottage, 14 Pitch and Pay Lane, Bristol BS9 1NH* Tel 0117-968 1510

BELL, Richard Herbert. b 54. Univ Coll Lon BSc75 PhD79 Tubingen Univ DrTheol91. Wycliffe Hall Ox BA82 MA87. **d** 83 **p** 84. C Edgware *Lon* 83-86; W Germany 86-90; Lect Th Nottm Univ 90-97; Sen Lect from 97; Perm to Offic *S'well* 92-01. *14 Anderson Crescent, Beeston, Nottingham NG9 2PT* Tel 0115-917 4955 *or* 951 5858 E-mail richard.bell@nottingham.ac.uk

BELL, Robert Clarke. b 30. Roch Th Coll 63. **d** 65 **p** 66. C Leeds All SS *Ripon* 65-67; C Claxby w Normanby-le-Wold *Linc* 67-69; R Newark St Leon *S'well* 69-71; V Gosberton Clough *Linc* 71-74; P-in-c Quadring 73-74; Chapl to the Deaf 74-85; V Harmston 85-94; V Coleby 85-94; RD Graffoe 92-94; rtd 94; Perm to Offic *Blackb* from 94 and *Carl* 94-98. *33 Mill Lane, Bolton le Sands, Carnforth LA5 8EZ* Tel (01524) 735619

BELL, Robert Mason. b 35. Lon Coll of Div 66. **d** 68 **p** 69. C Burgess Hill St Andr *Chich* 68-78; R Lewes St Jo sub Castro 78-00; rtd 00. *10 Rufus Close, Lewes BN7 1BG* Tel (01273) 470561

BELL, Ross K. b 64. Bradf and Ilkley Coll BA87. Aston Tr Scheme 89 Westcott Ho Cam 91. **d** 94 **p** 95. C W Bromwich All SS *Lich* 94-98; TV Cen Wolverhampton 98-02. *283 Henwood Road, Tettenhall Wood, Wolverhampton WV6 8PU* Tel (01902) 684927 *or* 684944 Mobile 07976-157022 Fax 684927 E-mail rotinkerbell@aol.com

BELL, Mrs Shena Margaret. b 49. EAMTC. **d** 00 **p** 01. C Earls Barton *Pet* from 00. *16 Riverwell, Northampton NN3 5EG* Tel (01604) 414757 Mobile 07980-584839 E-mail bell@ecton-brook.u-net.com

BELL, Simon Barnaby. b 48. Bris Univ CertEd70. Sarum & Wells Th Coll 87. **d** 89 **p** 90. C Ewyas Harold w Dulas *Heref* 89-90; C Ewyas Harold w Dulas, Kenderchurch etc 90-93; P-in-c Clungunford w Clunbury and Clunton, Bedstone etc 93-01; R from 01. *The Rectory, Clungunford, Craven Arms SY7 0PN* Tel (01588) 660342

BELL, Canon Stuart Rodney. b 46. Ex Univ BA67. Tyndale Hall Bris 69. **d** 71 **p** 72. C Henfynyw w Aberaeron and Llanddewi Aberarth *St D* 71-74; V 81-88; V Llangeler 74-80; R Aberystwyth from 88; Chapl Univ of Wales (Abth) from 94; Ev St Teilo Trust from 95; Can St D Cathl from 01. *The Rectory, Laura Place, Aberystwyth SY23 2AU* Tel and fax (01970) 617184 *or* tel 625080

BELL, Terrance James. b 63. Toronto Univ BA92. Trin Coll Toronto MDiv97. **d** 97 **p** 98. C Wedmore w Theale and Blackford *B & W* 97-01; C Hampstead St Jo *Lon* from 01; Chapl Eden Hall Marie Curie Hospice from 01. *3 Holly Bush Vale, London NW3 6TX* Tel (020) 7433 1115

BELL, Timothy John Keeton. b 59. All Nations Chr Coll. Trin Coll Bris BA02. **d** 02 **p** 03. C Saltford w Corston and Newton St Loe *B & W* from 02. *2 Fenton Close, Saltford, Bristol BS31 3AT* Tel (01225) 873027 E-mail tim@tmpsbell.fsnet.co.uk

BELL, William Weealands (Bede). b 38. York Univ BA86 Dur Univ PGCE87 Leeds Univ BA99. Coll of Resurr Mirfield 97. **d** 99 **p** 00. C Jarrow *Dur* 99-02; Novice CR from 03. *House of the Resurrection, Stocks Bank Road, Mirfield WF14 0BN* Tel (01924) 483316 E-mail bbell@mirfield.org.uk

BELL-RICHARDS, Douglas Maurice. b 23. St Steph Ho Ox 59. **d** 61 **p** 62. C Chipping Campden *Glouc* 61-62; C Thornbury 62-67; V Dymock w Donnington 67-75; V Fairford 75-91; rtd 91. *5 Palace Yard, Hereford HR4 9BJ* Tel (01432) 341070

BELLAMY, Charles Gordon. b 15. St Chad's Coll Dur BA42. St Deiniol's Hawarden 36. **d** 42 **p** 43. C Howdon Panns *Newc* 42-44; C Byker St Ant 44-46; C Horton 46-50; C Sighill 50-56; V Burnley St Matt w H Trin *Blackb* 56-67; V Overton 67-80; rtd 80; Hon C Monkseaton St Mary *Newc* 80-94; Hon C Tynemouth Cullercoats St Paul 94-96; Perm to Offic from 96. *60 Davison Avenue, Whitley Bay NE26 1SH* Tel 0191-251 3355

BELLAMY, David Quentin. b 62. Univ of Wales (Cardiff) BMus84 Univ of Wales (Ban) MA93. Ripon Coll Cuddesdon 87 Ch Div Sch of the Pacific (USA). **d** 90 **p** 91. C Rhyl w St Ann *St As* 90-94; V Llay from 94. *The Vicarage, First Avenue, Llay, Wrexham LL12 0TN* Tel (01978) 852262 E-mail quentinbellamy@cwcom.net

BELLAMY, Mrs Dorothy Kathleen. b 33. Gilmore Course 74. **dss** 82 **d** 87 **p** 94. Feltham *Lon* 82-84; Twickenham St Mary 84; Hampton St Mary 84-85; Hampton Wick 85-87; Par Dn 87-88; Par Dn Teddington St Mark and Hampton Wick St Jo 88-90; Par Dn Westbury *Sarum* 90-94; C 94-96; rtd 97; NSM Freshwater *Portsm* from 97; NSM Yarmouth from 97. *1 Meadows Close, Brighstone, Newport PO30 4BQ* Tel (01983) 740788

BELLAMY, John Stephen. b 55. Jes Coll Ox BA77 MA81 DipTh82 DPS84. St Jo Coll Nottm. **d** 84 **p** 85. C Allerton *Liv* 84-87; C Southport Ch Ch 87-89; Bp's Dom Chapl 89-91; V Birkdale St Jas from 91. *St James's Vicarage, 26 Lulworth Road, Southport PR8 2BQ* Tel (01704) 566255 Fax 564907 E-mail jsbellamy@onetel.net.uk

BELLAMY, Mervyn Roger Hunter. b 47. Sussex Univ CertEd. St Mich Coll Llan DipTh81. **d** 81 **p** 82. C Frecheville and Hackenthorpe *Sheff* 81-85; V Shiregreen St Hilda 85-94; RD Ecclesfield 93-94; R Rawmarsh w Parkgate 94-01; P-in-c King's Sutton and Newbottle and Charlton *Pet* from 01. *The Vicarage, Church Avenue, King's Sutton, Banbury OX17 3RD* Tel (01295) 811364

BELLAMY, Peter Charles William. b 38. Dip Past Counselling 65 Birm Univ MA70 Dip Child Psychology75 PhD79 AKC61. K Coll Lon 58. **d** 62 **p** 63. C Allestree *Derby* 62-65; Chapl All SS Hosp Birm 65-73; Chapl St Pet Coll of Educn Saltley 73-78;

Chapl Qu Eliz Psychiatric Hosp Birm 78-90; Lect Past Studies Birm Univ 79-92; Manager HIV Services Birm Cen HA 90-92; Research Fell Birm Univ *Birm* from 97; Local Min Development Adv *Heref* from 01. *Orchard House, Diddlebury, Craven Arms SY7 9DH* Tel 0121-475 6363 *or* (01584) 841511

BELLAMY, Robert John. b 40. Ripon Hall Ox 64. **d** 66 **p** 67. C Fishponds St Jo *Bris* 66-70; C Oldland 70-74; P-in-c Coalpit Heath 74-76; TV Cannock *Lich* 90-96; Perm to Offic 96-98; NSM Longdon from 98. *10 Meadowlark Close, Hednesford, Cannock WS12 1UE* Tel (01543) 876809

BELLENES, Peter Charles. b 49. Pontifical Univ Salamanca DipPhil68 Thurrock Coll Essex CQSW72. Linc Th Coll 79. **d** 81 **p** 90. C Penistone *Wakef* 81-82; Hon C Liskeard, St Keyne, St Pinnock, Morval etc *Truro* 89-91; Hon C Menheniot 91-99; P-in-c Marldon *Ex* 99-03; TV Totnes w Bridgetown, Berry Pomeroy etc from 03. *The Vicarage, 1 Love Lane Close, Marldon, Paignton TQ3 1TH* Tel (01803) 557294 Fax as telephone E-mail pbellenes@aol.com

BELLINGER, Canon Denys Gordon. b 29. Sheff Univ BA49. Westcott Ho Cam 51. **d** 53 **p** 54. C Ribbleton *Blackb* 53-56; C Lancaster St Mary 56-58; V Colne H Trin 58-68; V Scotforth 68-93; RD Lancaster 82-89; Hon Can Blackb Cathl 86-93; rtd 93; Perm to Offic *Blackb* from 93. *40 Yewlands Drive, Garstang, Preston PR3 1JP* Tel (01995) 601539

BELLINGER, Richard George. b 47. Univ of Wales (Abth) BSc(Econ)69. S Dios Minl Tr Scheme 91. **d** 94 **p** 95. NSM Guernsey St Steph *Win* 94-96; NSM Guernsey St Martin from 96. *La Maison des Vinaires, Rue des Vinaires, St Peter's, Guernsey GY7 9EZ* Tel (01481) 63203 Fax 66989

BELLINGHAM, Charles Eric William. b 06. Sydney Univ BA26 MA28 DipEd41. Ridley Hall Cam 30. **d** 30 **p** 31. C W Ham All SS *Chelmsf* 30-32; Australia 33 and from 61; CMS 33-61; Ch of S India 33-61; Chapl RAF 42-46; rtd 74. *98 Hopetoun Village, Castle Hill, NSW, Australia 2154* Tel (0061) (2) 9889 1548

BELLIS, Huw. b 72. Univ of Wales (Lamp) BA94. Westcott Ho Cam 96. **d** 98 **p** 99. C Merrow *Guildf* 98-02; TV Tring *St Alb* from 02. *The Rectory, Station Road, Aldbury, Tring HP23 5RS* Tel (01442) 851200 E-mail hbellis@fish.co.uk

BELOE, Robert Francis. b 39. Sarum Th Coll. **d** 65 **p** 71. C Nor Heartsease St Fran *Nor* 65-66; C Edmonton St Mary w St Jo *Lon* 68-70; C St Marylebone Ch Ch w St Paul 70-74; P-in-c Wicken *Ely* 74-76; V 76-00; rtd 00; Perm to Offic *Ely* from 00. *29 Juniper Drive, Ely CB7 3TT* Tel (01353) 667704

BEMENT, Peter James. b 43. Univ of Wales (Cardiff) BA64 PhD69. Wycliffe Hall Ox 92. **d** 94 **p** 95. C Hubberston *St D* 94-97; V Llandeilo Fawr and Taliaris from 97. *The Vicarage, 10 Carmarthen Road, Llandeilo SA19 6RS* Tel (01558) 822421

BENBOW, Susan Catherine. See TURNER, Mrs Susan Catherine

BENCE, Canon Graham Edwin. b 16. Lon Univ BA54. Sarum Th Coll 64. **d** 65 **p** 66. C Clacton St Jas *Chelmsf* 65-68; R Barlborough *Derby* 68-86; RD Bolsover 70-73; RD Bolsover and Staveley 73-78; Hon Can Derby Cathl 78-86; rtd 86; Perm to Offic *Lich* from 87. *Flat 3, 4 Quarry Place, Shrewsbury SY1 1JN* Tel (01743) 233533

BENCE, Helen Mary. b 44. Leic Univ BA65 PGCE66. EMMTC 93. **d** 97 **p** 98. NSM Humberstone *Leic* 97-02; NSM Thurnby Lodge 01-02; TV Oadby from 03. *The Grange, 126 Shanklin Drive, Leicester LE2 3QB* Tel 0116-270 7820 E-mail helenbence@leicester.freeserve.co.uk

BENCE, Norman Murray. b 34. Ripon Hall Ox 63. **d** 63 **p** 64. C Eling *Win* 63-66; Australia 66 and 75; NSM Holdenhurst and Iford *Win* from 81. *72 Corhampton Road, Bournemouth BH6 5PB* Tel (01202) 421992 Fax 420154

BENCE, Roy. b 21. Chich Th Coll 55. **d** 57 **p** 58. C Stepney St Dunstan and All SS *Lon* 57-60; V Notting Hill St Mark 61-66; Chapl Zürich w St Gallen and Winterthur *Eur* 66-68; V Bethnal Green St Jas the Gt w St Jude *Lon* 69-72; V Bush Hill Park St Mark 72-79; V Highgate St Aug 79-86; rtd 87; Perm to Offic *Lon* from 87. *5 St James's Close, Bishop Street, London N1 8PH* Tel (020) 7359 0885

BENDELL, David James. b 38. S'wark Ord Course. **d** 87 **p** 88. NSM Surbiton Hill Ch Ch *S'wark* from 87. *3 Pine Walk, Surbiton KT5 8NJ* Tel (020) 8399 7143 E-mail dbendell@aol.com

BENDING, Richard Clement. b 47. Sussex Univ BSc68. Ridley Hall Cam 87. **d** 89 **p** 90. Par Dn St Neots *Ely* 89-92; V Buckden 92-99; P-in-c Hail Weston 97-99; P-in-c Terrington St John 99-02; P-in-c Tilney All Saints 99-02; P-in-c Wiggenhall St Germans and Islington 99-02; P-in-c Wiggenhall St Mary Magd 99-02; V E Marshland from 02. *The Vicarage, Church Road, Terrington St John, Wisbech PE14 7SA* Tel (01945) 880259 E-mail rcbending@hotmail.com

BENEDICT, Brother. See WINSPER, Arthur William

BENFIELD, Gordon. b 29. OBE95. Lon Univ BD60 STh79 Birm Univ MA81 LGSM Leeds Univ DipEd60. **d** 80 **p** 81. NSM Warwick *Cov* 80-85; Prin Westhill Coll of HE Birm 85-90; Perm to Offic *Birm* 85-90; Chmn Ch Educn Movement 86-96; R Barford w Wasperton and Sherbourne *Cov* 90-96; Chapl S Warks Health Care NHS Trust 96-99; RD Shipston *Cov* 97-99; P-in-c

Witchford w Wentworth *Ely* 99-00; Perm to Offic from 01. *Rye House, Holme Lane, Little Downham, Ely CB6 2TR* Tel (01353) 698145 E-mail 106562.2126@compuserve.com

BENFIELD, Paul John. b 56. Newc Univ LLB77 Southn Univ BTh89 Barrister-at-Law (Lincoln's Inn) 78. Chich Th Coll 86. **d** 89 **p** 90. C Shiremoor *Newc* 89-92; C Hexham 92-93; TV Lewes All SS, St Anne, St Mich and St Thos *Chich* 93-97; R Pulborough 97-00; V Fleetwood St Nic *Blackb* from 00. *St Nicholas's Vicarage, Highbury Avenue, Fleetwood FY7 7DJ* Tel (01253) 874402 Fax as telephone E-mail benfield@btinternet.com

BENFORD, Brian. b 47. Sheff Univ BA Hull Univ MEd PhD88. N Ord Course 82. **d** 85 **p** 86. NSM Stocksbridge *Sheff* 85-90; NSM Gawber *Wakef* from 90. *Address temp unknown*

BENFORD, Steven Charles. b 61. Leic Univ MB, ChB86. NEOC 97. **d** 00 **p** 01. NSM Northallerton w Kirby Sigston *York* from 00. *61 Thirsk Road, Northallerton DL6 1PP* Tel (01609) 772400 E-mail steve.benford@lineone.net

BENGE, Charles David. b 40. Cranmer Hall Dur 63. **d** 68 **p** 69. C Millfield St Mark *Dur* 68-72; C Hensingham *Carl* 72-75; TV Maghull *Liv* 75-82; V Bootle St Leon 82-97; NSM Ormskirk 97-01; rtd 01. *26 Drummersdale Lane, Scarisbrick, Ormskirk L40 9RB* Tel (01704) 880956

BENGE, Ian Roger. b 48. STETS 98. **d** 01. NSM Langney *Chich* from 01. *35 Gainsborough Crescent, Eastbourne BN23 7NE* Tel and fax (01323) 763324 *or* tel 731755 Mobile 07713-706069 E-mail revianbenge@btopenworld.com

BENIAMS, Alec Charles. b 28. AKC52. **d** 53 **p** 54. C Gosforth All SS *Newc* 53-56; C Cullercoats St Geo 56-58; C Eltham St Jo *S'wark* 58-59; C-in-c Lynemouth St Aid CD *Newc* 59-61; C (TA) 60-67; V Lynemouth *Newc* 61-63; V Whittingham 63-67; V Willington 67-71; CF (TA - R of O) from 67; V Haydon Bridge *Newc* 71-85; R Yardley Hastings, Denton and Grendon etc *Pet* 85-90; rtd 90; Perm to Offic *Newc* from 90. *12 Dickson Drive, Highford Park, Hexham NE46 2RB* Tel (01434) 600226

BENIANS, Martin Ackland. b 19. St Jo Coll Cam BA41 MA45. Ridley Hall Cam 59. **d** 59 **p** 60. C Headstone St Geo *Lon* 59-62; R Rackheath *Nor* 62-89; V Salhouse 62-89; rtd 89; Perm to Offic *Nor* from 89. *26 Victoria Street, Sheringham NR26 8JZ* Tel (01263) 822563

BENISON, Canon Brian. b 41. K Coll Lon 61. Bps' Coll Cheshunt 63. **d** 66 **p** 67. C Tynemouth Ch Ch *Newc* 66-70; C Gosforth All SS 70-72; TV Cullercoats St Geo 73-81; V Denton 81-93; V Blyth St Mary from 93; RD Bedlington 98-03; Chapl Cheviot and Wansbeck NHS Trust 93-98; Chapl Northumbria Healthcare NHS Trust from 98; Hon Can Newc Cathl *Newc* from 01. *St Mary's Vicarage, 51 Marine Terrace, Blyth NE24 2JP* Tel (01670) 353417 E-mail revbenison@aol.com

BENJAMIN, Adrian Victor. b 42. Wadh Coll Ox BA66 MA68. Cuddesdon Coll 66. **d** 68 **p** 69. C Gosforth All SS *Newc* 68-71; C Stepney St Dunstan and All SS *Lon* 71-75; V Friern Barnet All SS from 75; Relig Ed ITV Oracle from 83. *All Saints' Vicarage, 14 Oakleigh Park South, London N20 9JU* Tel (020) 8445 4654 *or* 8445 8388 Mobile 07889-83298 Fax 8445 6831 E-mail allsaints@mcmail.com

✠**BENN, The Rt Revd Wallace Parke.** b 47. UCD BA69 Lon Univ DipTh71. Trin Coll Bris 69. **d** 72 **p** 73 **c** 97. C New Ferry *Ches* 72-76; C Cheadle 76-82; V Audley (*Lich* 82-87; V Harold Wood *Chelmsf* 87-97; Chapl Harold Wood Hosp Chelmsf 87-96; Area Bp Lewes *Chich* from 97; Can and Preb Chich Cathl from 97. *Bishop's Lodge, 16A Prideaux Road, Eastbourne BN21 2NB* Tel (01323) 648462 Fax 641514 E-mail lewes@clara.net

BENNELL, Canon Richard. b 25. Leeds Univ BA45 DipEd45. Coll of Resurr Mirfield 46. **d** 48 **p** 49. C Bedminster *Bris* 48-51; C Brislington St Anne 51-56; V Fishponds St Jo 56-68; V Knowle St Martin 68-73; TR Knowle 73-80; RD Brislington 73-79; Hon Can Bris Cathl 76-91; Chapl St Monica Home Bris 80-91; rtd 91; Perm to Offic *Bris* from 91. *1B Cooper Road, Bristol BS9 3QZ* Tel 0117-962 2364

BENNET, Gordon Duncan Affleck. b 31. Lon Univ BSc(Econ)55. Clifton Th Coll 55. **d** 57 **p** 58. C Carl St Jo *Carl* 57-60; C Kilburn St Luke w St Simon and St Jude *Lon* 60-63; C-in-c Dallam CD *Liv* 63-69; Lic to Offic *Man* 69-75; NW Area Sec CPAS 69-75; R Edgware *Lon* 75-91; V Walton le Soken *Chelmsf* 91-97; rtd 97; Perm to Offic *Leic* and *Derby* from 99. *140 Woodside, Ashby-de-la-Zouch LE65 2NU* Tel (01530) 417864

BENNET, Mark David. b 62. SS Coll Cam BA84 MA92 ACA89. Westcott Ho Cam 98. **d** 01 **p** 02. C Chapel Allerton *Ripon* from 01. *21 Carr Manor Grove, Leeds LS17 5AH* Tel 0113-266 8806 E-mail mandsbennet@compuserve.com

BENNETT, Alan Robert. b 31. Roch Th Coll 62. **d** 64 **p** 65. C Asterby w Goulceby *Linc* 64-67; C St Alb St Pet *St Alb* 67-70; R Banham *Nor* 70-72; CF 72-77; P-in-c Colchester St Mary Magd *Chelmsf* 77; TV Colchester St Leon, St Mary Magd and St Steph 77-81; R Colne Engaine 81-88; P-in-c Stoke Ferry w Wretton *Ely* 88-89; V Whittington 88-96; rtd 96; Perm to Offic *Nor* from 96; P-in-c Wimbotsham w Stow Bardolph and Stow Bridge etc *Ely* 96-00; Perm to Offic from 00. *34 West Way, Wimbotsham, King's Lynn PE34 3PZ* Tel (01366) 385958

BENNETT, Canon Alan William. b 42. Sarum Th Coll 65. **d** 68 **p** 69. C Fareham H Trin *Portsm* 68-71; C Brighton St Matthias *Chich* 71-73; C Stanmer w Falmer and Moulsecoomb 73-75; C Moulsecoomb 76; V Lower Sandown St Jo *Portsm* 76-80; V Soberton w Newtown 80-87; R Aston Clinton w Buckland and Drayton Beauchamp *Ox* from 87; RD Wendover from 94; Hon Can Ch Ch from 03. *The Rectory, New Road, Aston Clinton, Aylesbury HP22 5JD* Tel (01296) 631626 Fax as telephone E-mail alanbennett@s-michaels.org.uk

BENNETT, Alexander Steven Frederick. b 69. Hull Univ BA91. Westcott Ho Cam CTM95. **d** 95 **p** 96. C Whitton and Thurleston w Akenham *St E* 95-99; OGS from 99; C Oswestry *Lich* 99-01; V Oswestry H Trin from 01. *Holy Trinity Vicarage, 29 Balmoral Crescent, Oswestry SY11 2XQ* Tel (01691) 679306 E-mail asfb@clara.co.uk

BENNETT, Anthony. b 31. Qu Coll Birm 72. **d** 74 **p** 74. C Hobs Moat *Birm* 74-76; C Hill 76-79; R Grendon 79-82; R Upwell St Pet w Welney *Ely* 82-86; R Welney 82-86; P-in-c Coates 86-88; R 88-93; rtd 93; Perm to Offic *Ely* from 93. *77 Snoots Road, Whittlesey, Peterborough PE7 1NN* Tel (01733) 208214

BENNETT, Anton Wayne. b 69. SW Poly Plymouth BSc90. Westcott Ho Cam 00. **d** 02 **p** 03. C Pendleton *Man* from 02. *16 Lower Seedley Road, Salford M6 5WL* Tel 0161-737 6426 Mobile 07715-112147 E-mail antonbennett@archaggeloi.freeserve.co.uk

BENNETT, Arnold Ernest. b 29. K Coll Lon BD59 AKC53. **d** 54 **p** 55. C S w N Hayling *Portsm* 54-59; C Stevenage *St Alb* 59-64; R N w S Wootton *Nor* 64-74; V Hykeham *Linc* 74-85; V Heckfield w Mattingley and Rotherwick *Win* 85-99; rtd 99. *24 Cricket Green, Hartley Wintney, Basingstoke RG27 8PP* Tel (01252) 843147

BENNETT, Arthur Harling. b 22. Ripon Hall Ox 70. **d** 71 **p** 72. C Standish *Blackb* 71-74; TV Darwen St Pet w Hoddlesden 75-79; V Whitechapel 79-89; V Whitechapel w Admarsh-in-Bleasdale 89-90; rtd 90; Perm to Offic *Blackb* from 90. *1 Eden Gardens, Longridge, Preston PR3 3WF* Tel (01772) 784924

BENNETT, Avril Elizabeth Jean. b 63. BEd. **d** 00 **p** 01. C Dublin Crumlin w Chapelizod *D & G* from 00. *17 Ardeevin Court, Lucan, Co Dublin, Irish Republic* Tel (00353) (1) 628 2353

BENNETT, Ben. *See* BENNETT, Stuart

BENNETT, Bernard Michael. b 27. Leeds Univ CertEd52 DipPE54. St Aid Birkenhead 55. **d** 58 **p** 59. C Hemsworth *Wakef* 58-60; C Chapelthorpe 60-62; V Birkenhead St Bede w All SS *Ches* 62-71; V Latchford St Jas 71-75; Chapl HM Pris Appleton Thorn 75-82; V Appleton Thorn and Antrobus *Ches* 75-86; Chapl HM Rem Cen Risley 81-84; rtd 86; Perm to Offic *Ches* from 86-01 and June 91-03. *8 Hanover Close, Prenton CH43 1XR* Tel 0151-652 8968

BENNETT, Charles William. b 38. LTh. St Jo Coll Auckland 60. **d** 63 **p** 64. New Zealand 63-80 and from 81; C Tauranga 63-68; V Clive 68-71; C Cathl 71-74; V Waipaoa 74-79; C N Walsham w Antingham *Nor* 80-81; V Waipaoa 81-82; V Te Puke 82-87; V Dannevirke and P-in-c Woodville 87-91; V Westshore 91-93; Min Enabler from 94. *59 McGrath Street, Napier, New Zealand* Tel (0064) (6) 835 9924 Fax 835 9920 E-mail w.bennett@clear.net.nz

BENNETT, Christopher Ian. b 75. TCD BA98 BTh00. CITC 97. **d** 00 **p** 01. C Larne and Inver *Conn* 00-03; C Holywood *D & D* from 03. *30 Abbots Wood, Holywood BT18 9PL* Tel (028) 9042 4319 Mobile 07980-885991 E-mail cands@care4free.net

BENNETT, Clifford Orford. b 32. St Mich Coll Llan 73. **d** 75 **p** 76. C Holywell *St As* 73-79; V Pontbidyddyn 79-99; rtd 99. *4 Bryn Teg, Brynford, Holywell CH8 8AP* Tel (01352) 719028

BENNETT, David Edward. b 35. Fitzw Ho Cam BA56 MA60 Lon Univ PGCE. Wells Th Coll 58. **d** 60 **p** 61. C Lightcliffe *Wakef* 60-62; NE Area Sec Chr Educn Movement 62-68; Gen Insp RE Nottm Co Coun 68-00; Hon C Holme Pierrepont w Adbolton *S'well* 71-85; NSM Radcliffe-on-Trent and Shelford etc 85-00; rtd 00. *The Old Farmhouse, 65 Main Street, Gunthorpe, Nottingham NG14 7EY* Tel 0115-966 3451

BENNETT, Donovan Harry. b 27. Qu Mary Coll Lon BScEng52 FGS61 AMICE61 CEng61 FICE72. Moray Ord Course 88. **d** 92 **p** 93. Hon C Dingwall *Mor* 92-93; Hon C Strathpeffer 92-93; Hon C Inverness St Mich 93-95; P-in-c Grantown-on-Spey from 96. *St Columba's Rectory, Grant Road, Grantown-on-Spey PH26 3LD* Tel (01479) 872866

BENNETT, Edwin James. b 23. St Barn Coll Adelaide ThL47 STh52. **d** 47 **p** 48. Australia 47-74; V Oldham St Barn *Man* 74-78; V Alderney *Win* 78-84; V Heatherlie w Tangley, Weyhill and Penton Mewsey 84-89; rtd 89; Perm to Offic *Win* from 89. *Kalgoorlie, 35 Hatherden Road, Charlton, Andover SP10 4AP* Tel (01264) 356358

BENNETT, Garry Raymond. b 46. K Coll Lon 66 St Aug Coll Cant 69. **d** 70 **p** 71. C Mitcham St Mark *S'wark* 70-73; C Mortlake w E Sheen 73-75; TV 76-78; V Herne Hill St Paul 78-88; P-in-c Ruskin Park St Sav and St Matt 82-88; V Herne Hill 89; Sen Dioc Stewardship Adv *Chelmsf* 89-94; TR Southend 94-98. *177 South Croxted, London SE21 8AY* Tel (020) 8670 5434

BENNETT, Geoffrey Kenneth. b 56. Ex Univ MA01. Oak Hill Th Coll. **d** 89 **p** 90. C Ipswich St Matt *St E* 89-92; R St Ruan w St Grade and Landewednack *Truro* 92-98; V Budock from 98; P-in-c Mawnan from 02. *The Vicarage, School Lane, Budock Water, Falmouth TR11 5DJ* Tel (01326) 372227 E-mail g.k.bennett@amserve.net

BENNETT, George Darley. b 21. ACIS47. **d** 66 **p** 67. Zambia 66-76; R Hulland, Atlow and Bradley *Derby* 76-78; P-in-c Hulland, Atlow, Bradley and Hognaston 76-78; R 78-86; RD Ashbourne 81-86; rtd 87; Perm to Offic *Derby* from 87. *11 Freemantle Road, Mickleover, Derby DE3 9HW* Tel (01332) 510212

BENNETT, Canon George Edward. b 51. Univ of Wales (Abth) BA72. St Steph Ho Ox 73. **d** 76 **p** 77. C Clifton All SS w Tyndalls Park *Bris* 76-78; C Clifton All SS w St Jo 78-82; Chapl Newbury and Sandleford Hosps 82-93; TV Newbury *Ox* 82-93; V Llwynderw *S & B* from 93; RD Clyne from 98; Hon Can Brecon Cathl 00-02; Can Res Brecon Cathl from 02. *Llwynderw Vicarage, Fairwood Road, West Cross, Swansea SA3 5JP* Tel (01792) 401903

BENNETT, Graham Eric Thomas. b 53. Sarum & Wells Th Coll 88. **d** 90 **p** 91. C Baswich *Lich* 90-94; C Codsall 94-00; P-in-c Willenhall St Steph from 00. *St Stephen's Vicarage, 27 Wolverhampton Street, Willenhall WV13 2PS* Tel (01902) 605239 Fax as telephone E-mail grahambennett@tinyworld.co.uk

BENNETT, Handel Henry Cecil. b 33. MCIM. Cant Sch of Min 79. **d** 82 **p** 83. NSM St Margarets-at-Cliffe w Westcliffe etc *Cant* 82-85; Dir Holy Land Chr Tours 85-94; Holy Land Consultant F T Tours 95-96; Sen Travel Consultant Raymond Cook Chr Tours from 96; Perm to Offic *St Alb* 85-99; Perm to Offic *Ex* from 99. *Camps Bay, 2 Victoria Road, Sidmouth EX10 8TZ* Tel and fax (01395) 514211 Mobile 07774-981569

BENNETT, Miss Helen Anne. b 69. Coll of Ripon & York St Jo BEd91 Bris Univ BA01. Trin Coll Bris 99. **d** 01 **p** 02. C Beverley Minster *York* from 01. *23 Outer Trinities, Beverley HU17 0HN* Tel (01482) 888249 Mobile 07887-681771 E-mail habennett@bigfoot.com

BENNETT, Canon Ian Frederick. b 30. Ch Coll Cam BA54 MA62. Westcott Ho Cam 61. **d** 63 **p** 64. C Hemel Hempstead *St Alb* 63-68; Asst Chapl Man Univ *Man* 69-73; Sen Chapl 73-79; C Chorlton upon Medlock 69-73; P-in-c 73-79; TR Man Whitworth 79; Dioc Tr Officer *Birm* 79-88; Hon Can Birm Cathl 86-88; Can Res Newc Cathl *Newc* 88-98; Dioc Dir of Min and Tr 90-98; Dir Post-Ord Tr 97-98; rtd 98; Perm to Offic *Newc* from 98. *21 Otterburn Avenue, Gosforth, Newcastle upon Tyne NE3 4RR* Tel 0191-285 1967

BENNETT, James Kenneth Bretherton. b 11. St Jo Coll Ox BA33 DipTh34 MA37. Wycliffe Hall Ox 33. **d** 35 **p** 36. C Leic H Apostles *Leic* 35-38; C-in-c Westwood and Wingfield *Sarum* 38-40; RAChD 40-46; V Lythe *York* 46-49; V Bainton 49-57; V N Dalton 49-57; Chapl Glebe Ho Sch Hunstanton 57-59; Hd Master 59-67; Lic to Offic *Nor* 57-67; Asst Master Loretto Sch Musselburgh 67-73; Chapl Caldicott Sch Farnham Royal 73-76; rtd 76. *c/o Mrs E Harling, The Acorns, Church Lane, Oakley, Bedford MK43 7RJ*

BENNETT, John David. b 58. Ox Univ BA79 MA83. Westcott Ho Cam 81. **d** 83 **p** 84. C Taunton St Andr *B & W* 83-86; Chapl Trowbridge Coll *Sarum* 86-90; Asst P Studley 86-90; V Yeovil H Trin *B & W* 90-95; R Yeovil H Trin w Barwick 95-02; R Sprowston w Beeston *Nor* from 02. *The Vicarage, 2 Wroxham Road, Norwich NR7 8TZ* Tel (01603) 426492

BENNETT, John Seccombe. b 59. Wye Coll Lon BSc81 Leic Poly CertEd84. Th Coll Bris. **d** 00 **p** 01. C Llanrhian w Llanhywel and Carnhedryn etc *St D* 00-01; C Dewisland 01-02; TV from 02; Chapl St D Cathl from 00. *The Vicarage, Llanrhian, Haverfordwest SA62 5BG* Tel (01348) 831354

BENNETT, Joyce Mary. b 23. OBE79. Westf Coll Lon BA44 DipEd45 K Coll Lon DipTh61 Hong Kong Univ Hon DSocSc84. **d** 62 **p** 71. Hong Kong 62-83; NSM St Martin-in-the-Fields *Lon* 84-87; Perm to Offic *Ox* from 87; Perm to Offic *Lon* 87-88 and from 99. *The Cornerstone, 72 The Crescent, High Wycombe HP13 6JP* Tel (01494) 539016

BENNETT, Lee. b 70. RGN93 Leeds Univ BA00. Coll of Resurr Mirfield 97. **d** 00 **p** 01. C Hemsworth *Wakef* from 00. *St Michael's House, 13 Little Hemsworth, Hemsworth, Pontefract WF9 4BH* Tel (01977) 625596 E-mail frlee.bennett@btopenworld.com

BENNETT, Mark Ian. b 61. K Coll Cam BA83 MA86. Trin Coll Bris BA94 PGDTheol00. **d** 94 **p** 95. C Selly Park St Steph and St Wulstan *Birm* 94-97; C Harrow Trin St Mich *Lon* 97-99; Hon C Redland *Bris* 99-00; Chapl United Bris Healthcare NHS Trust 00; TV Kingswood *York* from 00. *Victoria Dock Vicarage, 22 Corinthian Way, Hull HU9 1UF* Tel (01482) 610584 Mobile 07866-680535 E-mail mark@thebennetts.karoo.co.uk

BENNETT, Canon Michael Edgar. b 32. Keble Coll Ox BA53 MA58 DipEd. Wells Th Coll 59. **d** 61 **p** 62. C Calne and Blackland *Sarum* 61-64; C Tewkesbury w Walton Cardiff *Glouc* 64-69; R Swindon w Uckington and Elmstone Hardwicke 69-92;

Ed *Glouc Dioc Gazette* 73-98; Chapl Sue Ryder Home Cheltenham 80-92; R Toddington, Stanton, Didbrook w Hailes etc 92-98; Hon Can Glouc Cathl 96-98; rtd 98; Perm to Offic *Glouc* from 98. *36 Althorp Close, Tuffley, Gloucester GL3 0XP* Tel (01452) 304640

BENNETT, Michael John. b 43. K Coll Lon AKC66. St Boniface Warminster 66. **d** 67 **p** 68. C Chester le Street *Dur* 67-71; C Portland All SS w St Pet *Sarum* 71-74; Chapl Portland Hosp Weymouth 74-85; V Portland St Jo *Sarum* 74-85; R Alveley and Quatt *Heref* 85-92; Dep Chapl HM YOI Glen Parva 93-95; TV Wrexham *St As* 95-99; V Llansantffraid-ym-Mechain and Llanfechain from 99. *The Vicarage, Bronhyddon, Llansantffraid SY22 6TZ* Tel (01691) 828244

BENNETT, Nigel John. b 47. Lon Univ DipTh69. Oak Hill Th Coll 66. **d** 71 **p** 72. C Tonbridge St Steph *Roch* 71-75; C Heatherlands St Jo *Sarum* 75-79; P-in-c Kingham w Churchill, Daylesford and Sarsden *Ox* 79; R 80-85; Chapl Blue Coat Sch Reading from 85. *13 Wilmington Close, Woodley, Reading RG5 4LR* Tel 0118-969 9223

BENNETT, Osmond Shirley. b 36. Oriel Coll Ox BA67. Ripon Hall Ox 64. **d** 68 **p** 69. C Stocking Farm *Leic* 68-71; C Thurcaston 71-72; V Leic St Marg 72-82; V Leic St Marg and All SS 83-89; R Houghton-on-the-Hill, Keyham and Hungarton 89-00; rtd 00. *48 Wide Lane, Hathern, Loughborough LE12 5LN* Tel (01509) 569240

BENNETT, Paul. b 55. Southn Univ BTh94. St Steph Ho Ox 95. **d** 97 **p** 98. C Willingdon *Chich* 97-00; C Hangleton from 00. *St Richard's House, 139 Godwin Road, Hove BN3 7FS* Tel (01273) 422810 E-mail fr.paul@cwcom.net

BENNETT, Paul John. b 47. Univ of Wales (Cardiff) DPS89. St Mich Coll Llan 88 Llan Dioc Tr Scheme 79. **d** 85 **p** 86. NSM Ystrad Rhondda w Ynyscynon *Llan* 85-89; C Tylorstown w Ynyshir 89-93; V Llanwynno 93-02; V Aberdare St Fagan from 02. *St Fagan's Vicarage, Windsor Street, Trecynon, Aberdare CF44 8LL* Tel (01656) 881435

BENNETT, Paul Jonathan. b 61. Ex Univ BA85. Cuddesdon Coll 85. **d** 87 **p** 88. C Henleaze *Bris* 87-91; P-in-c Swindon All SS 91-94; V Swindon All SS w St Barn 94-96; V Patrick, Foxdale and German St Jo *S & M* 96-00. *60 Teign View Road, Bishopsteignton, Teignmouth TQ14 9SZ* Tel (01626) 774474 E-mail pbennett1961@yahoo.co.uk

BENNETT, Paul William. b 61. DCR92. Linc Th Coll 95. **d** 95 **p** 96. C Thornton-le-Fylde *Blackb* 95-00; V Wesham 00-03; P-in-c Treales 00-03; V Wesham and Treales from 03. *The Vicarage, Mowbreck Lane, Wesham, Preston PR4 3HA* Tel (01772) 682206

BENNETT, Peter Hugh. b 22. K Coll Lon 46. **d** 50 **p** 51. C Newington Transfiguration *York* 50-53; C Bottesford *Linc* 53-57; V Tile Hill *Cov* 58-64; V Hillmorton 64-76; R Beaudesert w Henley-in-Arden 76-81; P-in-c Ullenhall cum Aspley 76-81; R Beaudesert and Henley-in-Arden w Ullenhall 81-87; rtd 87; Perm to Offic *Cov* from 87. *20 Avon Crescent, Stratford-upon-Avon CV37 7EY* Tel (01789) 296278

BENNETT, Richard Edward Stuart. b 24. St Jo Coll Ox BA49 MA55. Wells Th Coll 50. **d** 51 **p** 52. C Twerton *B & W* 51-56; V Gt Staughton *Ely* 56-63; Chapl HM Youth Cust Cen Gaynes Hall 56-63; R Camerton *B & W* 63-80; R Dunkerton 63-80; R Camerton w Dunkerton, Foxcote and Shoscombe 80-88; RD Midsomer Norton 86-88; rtd 88; Perm to Offic *B & W* 88-94. *Xlendi, 21 King's Oak Meadow, Clutton, Bristol BS39 5SU*

BENNETT, Roger Sherwood. b 35. Nottm Univ BA56. Wells Th Coll 58. **d** 59 **p** 60. C Mansfield Woodhouse *S'well* 59-60; C Spalding *Linc* 60-63; V Gedney 63-69; Chapl RNR 65-68; Chapl RN 69-90; V Amport, Grateley, Monxton and Quarley *Win* 90-95; rtd 96; Perm to Offic *Win* 96-00. *Le Reduit, School Lane, Nether Wallop, Stockbridge SO20 8EH* Tel (01264) 782336

BENNETT, Roy Donald. b 40. Nottm Univ MA97. St Jo Coll Nottm 78. **d** 80 **p** 81. C Fletchamstead *Cov* 80-83; C Bedworth 83-87; P-in-c Studley 87-93; Chapl Univ Hosp Nottm 93-96; Chapl Qu Medical Cen Nottm 94-96; Chapl Bassetlaw Hosp and Community Services NHS Trust 96-01; Chapl Doncaster and Bassetlaw Hosps NHS Trust from 01. *Bassetlaw Hospital, Kilton Road, Worksop S81 0BD, or 51 Blyth Road, Worksop S81 0JJ* Tel (01909) 500990 ext 2846 *or* 472925 Fax 502685 E-mail roydbennett@cwcom.net

BENNETT, Shirley. *See* BENNETT, Osmond Shirley

BENNETT (née FORD), Ms Simone Louise. b 70. Warwick Univ BA92. Westcott Ho Cam 00. **d** 02 **p** 03. C Stockingford *Cov* from 02. *47 Beverley Avenue, Stockingford, Nuneaton CV10 9JP*

BENNETT, Stuart (Ben). b 61. St Jo Coll Nottm BA02. **d** 02 **p** 03. C Consett *Dur* from 02. *Church House, 1C Aynsley Terrace, Consett DH8 5LX* Tel (01207) 590731 E-mail stubennett@bigfoot.com

BENNETT, Ms Toni Elizabeth. b 56. Worc Coll of Educn BA81 Sheff Poly 87. St Jo Coll Nottm MA94. **d** 96 **p** 97. C Heanor *Derby* 96-00; TV Bedworth *Cov* from 00. *2 Bryony Close, Bedworth CV12 0GG* Tel (024) 7664 4693 E-mail bnntoni1@aol.com

BENNETT, William Leslie. b 52. TCD Div Sch DipTh90. **d** 90 **p** 91. C Carrickfergus *Conn* 90-93; I Lisnaskea *Clogh* 93-00; I Newcastle w Newtownmountkennedy and Calary *D & G* from 00. *The Rectory, Church Lane, Newcastle, Greystones, Co Wicklow, Irish Republic* Tel (00353) (1) 281 9300 E-mail revwilliambennett@eircom.net

✠**BENNETTS, The Rt Revd Colin James.** b 40. Jes Coll Cam BA63 MA67. Ridley Hall Cam 63. **d** 65 **p** 66 **c** 94. C Tonbridge St Steph *Roch* 65-69; Chapl Ox Pastorate 69-79; C Ox St Aldate w H Trin *Ox* 69-73; Lic to Offic 73-78; Asst Chapl Jes Coll Ox 73-75; Chapl 75-78; P-in-c Ox St Andr *Ox* 79; V 80-90; RD Ox 84-89; Can Res Ches Cathl and Dioc Dir of Ords *Ches* 90-94; Area Bp Buckm *Ox* 94-98; Bp Cov from 98. *The Bishop's House, 23 Davenport Road, Coventry CV5 6PW* Tel (024) 7667 2244 Fax 7671 3271 E-mail bishcov@clara.net

BENNETTS, Gordon Vivian. b 15. TD62. Open Univ BA78. **d** 77 **p** 78. NSM Phillack w Gwithian and Gwinear *Truro* 77-79; NSM Redruth 79-80; NSM Redruth w Lanner 80-82; Chapl Tehidy Hosp Camborne 82-87; Lic to Offic *Truro* from 82; Chapl Duchy Hosp Truro 87-02. *66 Tregolls Road, Truro TR1 1LD* Tel (01872) 241857

BENNETTS, John Barrington. b 32. LNSM course 85. **d** 92 **p** 93. NSM Falmouth K Chas *Truro* from 92. *39 Budock Terrace, Falmouth TR11 3NE* Tel (01326) 314961 *or* 312111 E-mail kcmvestry@onetel.net.uk

BENNETTS, Ms Rachel Mary. b 69. Homerton Coll Cam BEd91. Trin Coll Bris BA01. **d** 02 **p** 03. C Wroughton *Bris* from 02. *21 Anthony Road, Wroughton, Swindon SN4 9HN* Tel (01793) 813929 Mobile 07881-563215 E-mail racheagle@yahoo.co.uk

BENNETTS, William Rawling. b 28. Univ of W Aus BSc48 BA54 Adelaide Univ DipEd56. Cuddesdon Coll 56. **d** 58 **p** 59. C Portsea St Mary *Portsm* 58-60; Australia from 60; rtd 93. *8 Kapok Court, Parkwood, W Australia 6147* Tel (0061) (8) 9354 3536

BENNIE, Stanley James Gordon. b 43. Edin Univ MA65. Coll of Resurr Mirfield 66. **d** 68 **p** 69. C Ashington *Newc* 68-70; Prec St Andr Cathl Inverness *Mor* 70-74; Itinerant Priest 74-81; R Portsoy *Ab* 81-84; R Buckie 81-84; R Stornoway *Arg* from 84; R Eorropaidh 84-95; Miss to Seafarers from 84. *St Peter's House, 10 Springfield Road, Stornoway HS1 2PT* Tel (01851) 703609 E-mail gm4ptq@zetnet.co.uk

BENNISON, Philip Owen. b 42. Dur Univ BA64. Coll of Resurr Mirfield 64. **d** 66 **p** 67. C Guisborough *York* 66-67; C S Bank 67-71; C Thornaby on Tees St Paul 71-72; TV Thornaby on Tees 72-74; R Skelton in Cleveland 74-78; R Upleatham 75-78; Chapl Freeman Hosp Newc 78-84; V Ashington *Newc* 84-93; Chapl N Tees Health NHS Trust Stockton-on-Tees 93-02; P-in-c Newton Flowery Field *Ches* from 02; P-in-c Hyde St Thos from 02. *St Stephen's Vicarage, 154 Bennett Street, Hyde SK14 4SS* Tel 0161-368 3333 Fax as telephone E-mail philip_bennison@hotmail.com

BENNISON, Timothy Paul. b 63. Aber Univ BD94. Edin Th Coll 95. **d** 97 **p** 98. C St Andr Cathl *Ab* 97-00; Asst Chapl Aberdeen Univ 97-00; P-in-c Aberdeen St Jas *Ab* from 00; Dioc Miss 21 Co-ord from 00. *31 Gladstone Place, Aberdeen AB10 6UX* Tel (01224) 322631 *or* tel and fax 322708 Mobile 07050-395100 E-mail tim@bennison.ws

BENOY, Stephen Michael. b 66. Clare Coll Cam BA87 MA90. Trin Coll Bris BA93. **d** 96 **p** 97. C New Malden and Coombe *S'wark* 96-02; Kingston Borough Youth Project 00-02; V Kettering Ch the King *Pet* from 02. *The Vicarage, Deeble Road, Kettering NN15 7AA* Tel (01536) 512828 E-mail steve.benoy@virgin.net

BENSON, Christopher Hugh. b 53. Bath Academy of Art BA75 Keble Coll Ox BA78 MA87. Chich Th Coll 78. **d** 80 **p** 81. C Heavitree w Ex St Paul *Ex* 80-83; P-in-c Broadclyst 83-85; TV Pinhoe and Broadclyst 85-90; V Kingsteignton from 90; Chapl Plymouth Univ 92-95; RD Newton Abbot and Ipplepen from 01. *The Vicarage, Daws Meadow, Kingsteignton, Newton Abbot TQ12 3UA* Tel (01626) 354915 E-mail ccsjbbenson2@netscapeonline.co.uk

BENSON, David. *See* BENSON, John David

BENSON, Gareth Neil. b 47. HNC71 Jordan Hill Coll Glas FE TCert80. St And NSM Tr Scheme 77. **d** 81 **p** 82. NSM Glenrothes *St And* 81-88; NSM Kinghorn from 88; NSM Kirkcaldy from 88. *129 Waverley Drive, Glenrothes KY6 2LZ* Tel (01592) 759278

BENSON, George Patrick (Paddy). b 49. Ch Ch Ox BA70 Lon Univ BD77 Open Univ MPhil94. All Nations Chr Coll 78 St Jo Coll Nottm 89. **d** 91 **p** 92. C Upton (Overchurch) *Ches* 91-95; V Barnston from 95; RD Wirral N from 98. *The Vicarage, 87 Barnston Road, Heswall, Wirral CH61 1BW* Tel 0151-648 1776 *or* 648 2404 Fax 648 2407 E-mail muhunjia@aol.com

BENSON, Mrs Hilary Christine. b 51. Man Univ BA72 Hughes Hall Cam PGCE73. Trin Coll Bris DipHE83. **dss** 84 **d** 87 **p** 94. Starbeck *Ripon* 84-86; Birm St Martin w Bordesley St Andr *Birm* 86-91; NSM 87-91; NSM Brandwood 91-97; Chapl Birm Univ 92-97; Chapl St Edw Sch Ox 97-00; Chapl Qu Anne's Sch Caversham from 00. *Queen Anne's School, Henley Road, Caversham, Reading RG4 6DX* Tel 0118-947 1582 *or* 954 5026 E-mail saintbede@ntlworld.com

ENSON, John David. b 36. Lon Univ DipTh61 Hull Univ DipTh82. St Aid Birkenhead 58. **d** 61 **p** 62. C Kingston upon Hull St Martin *York* 61-65; C Marfleet 65-68; V Ingleby Greenhow 68-72; P-in-c Kildale 68-72; Asst Youth Chapl 68-72; Dioc Youth Chapl *Sheff* 72-78; V Thorne 78-91; V Totley 91-98; rtd 98; Perm to Offic *Sheff* from 98. *14 Ash Hill Crescent, Hatfield, Doncaster DN7 6HY* Tel (01302) 846359

ENSON, John Patrick. b 51. Univ of Wales (Ban) BSc72. Trin Coll Bris 83. **d** 85 **p** 86. C Stoke Damerel *Ex* 85-88; P-in-c Petrockstowe, Petersmarland, Merton and Huish 88; TV Shebbear, Buckland Filleigh, Sheepwash etc 89-94; RD Torrington 93-94; P-in-c Newport, Bishops Tawton and Tawstock 94-97; TV Barnstaple from 97. *The Vicarage, 40 Chichester Road, Newport, Barnstaple EX32 9EH* Tel (01271) 72733

ENSON, The Very Revd John Patrick. b 52. Ch Coll Cam BA73 MA76 PhD76. Trin Coll Bris 78. **d** 81 **p** 82. C Walmley *Birm* 81-84; C Chadkirk *Ches* 84-86; Singapore from 87; V St Geo Singapore 87-95; Dir of Tr from 95; Dean Cambodia from 95. *Anglican Retreat Centre, 41 Ceylon Road, Singapore 429630* Tel (0065) 447 4416 Fax 447 0842

ENSON, Nicholas Henry. b 53. Man Univ BSc75 Leeds Univ MSc77. Trin Coll Bris 81. **d** 84 **p** 85. C Starbeck *Ripon* 84-86; C Birm St Martin w Bordesley St Andr *Birm* 86-91; Chapl to the Markets 86-91; V Brandwood 91-97; Perm to Offic *Ox* 99-01; NSM Reading St Jo from 01. *Hillside, 2 Henley Road, Caversham, Reading RG4 6DS* Tel 0118-954 5026 E-mail saintbede@ntlworld.com

ENSON, Paddy. *See* BENSON, George Patrick

ENSON, Peter Leslie. b 60. Leeds Univ BA81. Westcott Ho Cam 81. **d** 85 **p** 86. C Kippax w Allerton Bywater *Ripon* 85-88; C Potternewton 88-91; Asst Chapl St Jas Univ Hosp Leeds 91-94; Chapl Dewsbury Health Care NHS Trust 94-98; P-in-c Batley St Thos *Wakef* 98-99; V from 99. *The Vicarage, 16 Stockwell Drive, Batley WF17 5PA* Tel (01924) 473901 Mobile 07712-554218 E-mail peter_benson@ntlworld.com

ENSON, Philip Steven. b 59. ACertCM79 LLCM80 Ulster Univ BSc81. S Dios Minl Tr Scheme 88. **d** 92 **p** 93. Producer Relig Broadcasting Dept BBC 91-94; NSM W Ealing St Jo w St Jas *Lon* 92-94; Lic to Offic *Ches* from 94; Relig Progr Producer BBC Man from 94. *4 Cranford Avenue, Knutsford WA16 0EB* Tel (01565) 652513 Fax 641695 E-mail ps@fish.co.uk

ENSON, Mrs Rachel Candia. b 43. JP76. TCD MA66 Lon Univ PGCE67 DipRS87. S'wark Ord Course 84. **d** 87 **p** 94. NSM Putney St Marg *S'wark* 87-97; NSM Sand Hutton *York* from 97; NSM Whitwell w Crambe, Flaxton and Foston from 97. *Grange Farm, Westow, York YO60 7NJ* Tel (01653) 658296 Fax 658456

BENSON, Richard John. b 55. Birm Coll of Educn CertEd78. Ripon Coll Cuddesdon DipMin94. **d** 94 **p** 95. C Alford w Rigsby *Linc* 94-97; R Partney Gp from 97. *The Rectory, Partney, Spilsby PE23 4PG* Tel (01790) 753570

BENT, David Michael. b 55. Leeds Univ BA83. Trin Coll Bris BA94. **d** 96 **p** 97. C Gorleston St Andr *Nor* 96-00; TR Brinsworth w Catcliffe and Treeton *Sheff* from 00. *The Vicarage, 61 Whitehill Lane, Brinsworth, Rotherham S60 5JR* Tel (01709) 363850

BENT, Mrs Helen Margaret. b 56. Sheff Univ BMus77 Trent Poly PGCE78. Trin Coll Bris DipHE94 EAMTC 97. **d** 98 **p** 99. C Gorleston St Mary *Nor* 98-00; C Brightside w Wincobank *Sheff* from 00. *The Vicarage, 61 Whitehill Lane, Brinsworth, Rotherham S60 5JR* Tel (01709) 363850

BENT, James. b 31. St Deiniol's Hawarden 79. **d** 81 **p** 82. C Prenton *Ches* 81-84; V W Derby St Jas *Liv* 84-88; NSM Newchurch and Glazebury 93-94; NSM Glazebury w Hollinfare 94-96; rtd 96. *13 Blair Avenue, Hindley, Wigan WN2 4HQ* Tel (01942) 514394

BENT, Michael Charles. b 31. Kelham Th Coll 51. **d** 55 **p** 56. C Wellingborough St Mary *Pet* 55-60; New Zealand 60-85, 89-94 and from 96; Papua New Guinea 94-96; Adn Taranaki 76-85; Dean H Trin Cathl Suva Fiji 85-89; Can St Pet Cathl Hamilton 90-94. *34 Brooklands Road, New Plymouth, New Zealand* Tel (0064) (6) 753 5507 E-mail miro@clear.net.nz

BENTALL, Mrs Jill Margaret. b 44. MCSP66. S Dios Minl Tr Scheme 91. **d** 94 **p** 95. NSM Knights Enham *Win* 94-02; C Andover w Foxcott from 02. *Old Farm Cottage, 102 Charlton, Andover SP10 4AN* Tel (01264) 365143

BENTHAM, John William. b 58. Loughb Univ BSc80 Nottm Univ LTh85. St Jo Coll Nottm DipPS85. **d** 85 **p** 86. C Burmantofts St Steph and St Agnes *Ripon* 85-88; C Horsforth 88-90; P-in-c Nottingham St Sav *S'well* 90-92; V 92-98; Chapl Nottm Univ from 98. *51 Chaworth Road, West Bridgford, Nottingham NG2 7AE* Tel 0115-846 1054 or 846 6037 E-mail john.bentham@nottingham.ac.uk

BENTHAM, Philip John (Ben). b 55. Hull Univ BA83 PGCE85. Trin Coll Bris MA96. **d** 96 **p** 97. C Wrockwardine Deanery *Lich* 96-00; Zimbabwe from 00. *4 Woodrough Drive, Birmingham B13 9EP* Tel 0121-449 1336

✠**BENTLEY, The Rt Revd David Edward.** b 35. Leeds Univ BA56. Westcott Ho Cam 58. **d** 60 **p** 61 **c** 86. C Bris St Ambrose Whitehall *Bris* 60-62; C Guildf H Trin w St Mary *Guildf* 62-66; R Headley All SS 66-73; R Esher 73-86; RD Emly 77-82; Hon Can Guildf Cathl 80-86; Chmn Dioc Coun Soc Resp 80-86; Suff Bp Lynn *Nor* 86-93; Chmn Cand Cttee ACCM 87-91; ABM 91-93; Bp Glouc from 93. *Bishopscourt, Pitt Street, Gloucester GL1 2BQ* Tel (01452) 524598 Fax 310025 E-mail bshpglos@star.co.uk

BENTLEY, Edward John. b 35. Bris Univ BA61. Tyndale Hall Bris 58. **d** 63 **p** 64. C Wolverhampton St Luke *Lich* 63-66; BCMS 66-72; C Cheltenham St Mark *Glouc* 72-78; V Wallasey St Nic *Ches* 78-02; rtd 02. *8 Caithness Drive, Wallasey CH45 7PW* Tel 0151-637 1923

BENTLEY, Frank Richard. b 41. K Coll Lon BD67 AKC67. **d** 68 **p** 69. C Feltham *Lon* 68-72; P-in-c Bethnal Green St Bart 72-77; R Bow w Bromley St Leon 77-88; P-in-c Mile End Old Town H Trin 77-88; P-in-c Bromley All Hallows 77-88; AD Tower Hamlets 83-88; TR E Ham w Upton Park St Alb *Chelmsf* 88-97; P-in-c Petersham *S'wark* from 97; Chapl HM Pris Latchmere Ho from 97. *The Vicarage, Bute Avenue, Richmond TW10 7AX* Tel (020) 8940 8435

BENTLEY, The Ven Frank William Henry. b 34. AKC57. **d** 58 **p** 59. C Shepton Mallet *B & W* 58-62; R Kingston w Podymore-Milton 62-66; P-in-c Yeovilton 62-66; P-in-c Babcary 64-66; V Wiveliscombe 66-76; RD Tone 73-76; V St Jo in Bedwardine *Worc* 76-84; RD Martley and Worc W 80-84; Hon Can Worc Cathl 81-84; P-in-c Worc St Mich 82-84; Adn Worc and Can Res Worc Cathl 84-99; Chapl to The Queen from 94; rtd 99. *The Chaplain's House, St Oswald's Close, The Tything, Worcester WR1 1HR* Tel (01905) 616619

BENTLEY, Graham James. b 29. S'wark Ord Course 77. **d** 80 **p** 81. NSM Merton St Mary *S'wark* 80-83; C Balham St Mary 83-84; C Wimbledon 85-86; V Raynes Park St Sav 86-95; rtd 95; Perm to Offic *Guildf* from 95. *61 Clarence Road, Fleet, Aldershot GU51 3RY* Tel (01252) 682464

BENTLEY, Ian Robert. b 55. Sheff Univ BA76 Sheff City Poly PGCE78. St Jo Coll Dur 95. **d** 95 **p** 96. C Mattishall w Mattishall Burgh, Welborne etc *Nor* 95-98; R Ditchingham, Hedenham and Broome from 98; R Earsham w Alburgh and Denton from 98. *The Rectory, School Road, Earsham, Bungay NR35 2TF* Tel (01986) 892147 E-mail ian@revbentley.freeserve.co.uk

BENTLEY, Ian Ronald. b 51. BA79. Oak Hill Th Coll 76. **d** 79 **p** 80. C Northwood Em *Lon* 79-85; C St Marylebone All So w SS Pet and Jo 85-88; C Langham Place All So 88-91; V Eynsham and Cassington *Ox* from 91. *The Vicarage, 45 Acre End Street, Eynsham, Witney OX29 4PF* Tel (01865) 881323 E-mail st_leonards_eynsham@compuserve.com

BENTLEY, Lesley. b 55. RMN80 Univ of Wales (Lamp) BA76 Nottm Univ MTh82. St Jo Coll Nottm DPS83. **dss** 82 **d** 87 **p** 94. Mickleover St Jo *Derby* 82-84; Thornton *Liv* 84-89; Par Dn 87-89; Dir Diaconal Mins 89-92; Par Dn Farnworth 92-94; C 94-95; V Westbrook St Phil 95-01; Hon Can Liv Cathl 99-01; V Bilton *Ripon* 01-03; TR from 03. *Bilton Vicarage, Bilton Lane, Harrogate HG1 3DT* Tel (01423) 527811

BENTLEY, Paul. b 48. Sarum & Wells Th Coll DipTh93. **d** 93 **p** 94. C Ex St Dav *Ex* 93-96; P-in-c Marlpool *Derby* 96-01; V 01-02; Chapl Derbyshire Community Health Services 96-00; Chapl Amber Valley Primary Care Trust 00-02; Chapl Mansfield Distr Primary Care Trust from 02. *The Pilgrim Centre, Mansfield Community Hospital, Stockwell Gate, Mansfield NG18 5QJ* Tel (01623) 785011 E-mail paul.bentley@mansfield-pct.nhs.uk *or* revpaulb@aol.com

BENTLEY, Richard. *See* BENTLEY, Frank Richard

BENTLEY, William. Univ Coll Dur BA39 DipTh40 MA42. St Andr Whittlesford 40. **d** 41 **p** 42. C Chesterle Street *Dur* 41-46; C Bishopwearmouth St Mich 46-49; V Auckland St Pet 49-59; R Hartlepool St Hilda 59-82; Chapl St Hilda's Hosp Hartlepool 59-82; rtd 82. *4 Lindisfarne, High Shincliffe, Durham DH1 2PH* Tel 0191-384 9876

BENTON, John Anthony. b 27. Ex Coll Ox BA48 MA52. Sarum Th Coll 49. **d** 50 **p** 51. C N Keyham *Ex* 50-52; C Tavistock and Gulworthy 52-55; C Heavitree 55-56; R Lower Gravenhurst *St Alb* 56-61; V Silsoe 56-61; V Upper Gravenhurst 56-61; S Africa 61-68; R Moretonhampstead *Ex* 68-74; RD Moreton 73-74; R Holsworthy w Cookbury and Hollacombe 74-80; TR Withycombe Raleigh 80-92; RD Aylesbeare 84-89; rtd 92; Perm to Offic *Ex* from 92. *38 Wreford's Close, Exeter EX4 5AY* Tel (01392) 211428

BENTON, Canon Michael John. b 38. Lon Univ BSc60 FRSA93 MSOSc. Sarum & Wells Th Coll 72. **d** 74 **p** 74. Sen Lect K Alfred Coll *Win* 74-76; NSM Weeke 74-76; C Burslendon 76-78; R Over Wallop w Nether Wallop 78-83; Dir of Educn 79-96; R Win St Lawr and St Maurice w St Swithun 83-90; Hon Can Win Cathl 89-03; P-in-c Kingsclere 96-03; Chapl to The Queen from 98; rtd 03. *South Lodge, Auchterarder House, Auchterarder PH3 1ER* Tel (01764) 662991

BENTON-EVANS, Martin James William. b 69. K Coll Lon BA90 Anglia Poly Univ PGCE97. Ripon Coll Cuddesdon BTh03. **d** 03. C Ivybridge w Harford *Ex* from 03. *12 Buddle Close, Ivybridge PL21 0JU* Tel (01752) 691742 Mobile 07984-122774 E-mail jim@benton-evans.demon.co.uk

BENWELL, John Desmond. Jes Coll Cam BA54 MA58 Sheff Univ DSS58 Lon Univ CASS59. St Jo Coll Nottm CertCS89. **d** 89 **p** 89. Somalia 89-90; Chapl Fontainebleau *Eur* 91-93; Hon C Portswood Ch Ch *Win* 93-99; rtd 99. *14 Furzedown Road, Southampton SO17 1PN* Tel (023) 8055 7622

BENWELL, Michael Patrick. b 55. Jes Coll Cam BA77 Glas Univ PhD80. Sarum & Wells Th Coll BTh92. **d** 92 **p** 93. C Eastleigh *Win* 92-95; Chapl Leeds Metrop Univ *Ripon* 95-99; TV Seacroft from 99. *St Luke's Vicarage, Stanks Lane North, Leeds LS14 5AS* Tel 0113-273 1302 E-mail benwell@ndirect.co.uk

BENZIES, Neil Graham. Bede Coll Dur. Cranmer Hall Dur 93. **d** 95 **p** 96. NSM Stockton St Pet *Dur* from 95. *62 Fairwell Road, Stockton-on-Tees TS19 7HX* Tel (01642) 582322

BERDINNER, Clifford. b 24. SS Mark & Jo Coll Plymouth BA88 Ex Univ MPhil95. **d** 64 **p** 65. C Leic St Pet *Leic* 64-67; R Heather 67-72; NSM Totnes and Berry Pomeroy *Ex* 86-91; NSM Totnes, Bridgetown and Berry Pomeroy etc 91-94; rtd 89; Perm to Offic *Ex* from 89. *Little Croft, 30 Droridge, Dartington, Totnes TQ9 6JG* Tel (01803) 732518

BERESFORD, Charles Edward. b 45. St Jo Coll Nottm. **d** 86 **p** 87. C Bushbury *Lich* 86-90; TV Glascote and Stonydelph 90-98; TR N Wingfield, Clay Cross and Pilsley *Derby* from 98. *The Rectory, St Lawrence Road, North Wingfield, Chesterfield S42 5HX* Tel (01246) 851181 E-mail rev-ceb@north-wingfield.freeserve.co.uk

BERESFORD, Canon Eric Brian. b 57. Liv Univ BSc78. Wycliffe Hall *Ox* BA82 MA86. **d** 82 **p** 83. C Upton (Overchurch) *Ches* 82-85; Canada from 85; Asst Prof Ethics McGill Univ Montreal 88-96; Consultant Ethics and Interfaith Relns Gen Syn from 96; Hon Can Montreal from 99; Consultant Ethics ACC from 99. *600 Jarvis Street, Toronto ON, Canada, M4Y 2J6* Tel (001) (416) 924 9199 ext 209 Fax 924 0211 E-mail eberesford@national.anglican.ca

BERESFORD, Mrs Florence. b 33. Cranmer Hall Dur 75. **dss** 78 **d** 87 **p** 94. Eighton Banks *Dur* 78-86; Lobley Hill 86-87; Par Dn 87-90; Par Dn Chester le Street 90-91; rtd 91. *Gilead, 39 Picktree Lodge, Chester-le-Street DH3 4SJ* Tel 0191-388 7425

BERESFORD, Peter Marcus de la Poer. b 49. Cranmer Hall Dur 74. **d** 77 **p** 78. C Walney Is *Carl* 77-80; C Netherton 80-83; TV Wednesfield *Lich* 83-88; TV Rugby St Andr *Cov* 88-97; Chapl Rugby Hosps 88-97; R Barby w Kilsby *Pet* from 97. *The Rectory, Barby, Rugby CV23 8TZ* Tel (01788) 890252

BERESFORD-DAVIES, Thomas. b 14. Univ of Wales (Lamp) BD67. **d** 42 **p** 43. C Glouc St Mary de Lode and St Nic *Glouc* 42-46; C Langley Marish *Ox* 46; C Glouc St Jas *Glouc* 46-48; V Church Honeybourne w Cow Honeybourne 48-51; P-in-c Pauntley w Upleadon 51-62; V Twigworth w Down Hatherley 63-85; rtd 85; P-in-c Glouc St Mark *Glouc* 86-87; Perm to Offic from 87. *Islwyn, Tewkesbury Road, Twigworth, Gloucester GL2 9PQ* Tel (01452) 730362

BERESFORD JONES, Gareth Martin. b 70. Ex Univ BA93 Fitzw Coll Cam BTh01. Westcott Ho Cam 98. **d** 01 **p** 02. C Sidcup St Jo *Roch* from 01. *5 Orchard Cottages, Old Perry Street, Chislehurst BR7 6PZ* Tel (01689) 827465 0455

BERESFORD-PEIRSE, Mark de la Poer. b 45. Qu Coll Birm 73. **d** 76 **p** 77. C Garforth *Ripon* 76-79; C Beeston 79-83; V Barton and Manfield w Cleasby 83-90; V Pannal w Beckwithshaw 90-91; Dioc Chapl MU from 91; R W Tanfield and Well w Snape and N Stainley from 01. *The Rectory, Main Street, West Tanfield, Ripon HG4 5JJ* Tel (01677) 470321

BERG, John Russell. b 36. MBE78. Sarum Th Coll 57. **d** 60 **p** 61. C Ipswich St Aug *St E* 60-64; C Whitton and Thurleston w Akenham 64-65; Miss to Seafarers from 65; Hong Kong 65-68; Japan from 68; rtd 01. *Yokohama Newport Building 10Fl, 191 Yamashita-cho, Naka-ku, Yokohama 231-0023, Japan* Tel and fax (081) (45) 641 6684 E-mail johnberg@gol.com

BERG, Canon Paul Michael. b 31. Lon Univ BA53. Oak Hill Th Coll 54. **d** 56 **p** 57. C Woodford Wells *Chelmsf* 56-60; V Tittensor *Lich* 60-65; V Rainham *Chelmsf* 65-74; R Wennington 65-74; V Chn Ch w Em *Bris* 74-97; Hon Can Bris Cathl 82-97; RD Chn 87-93; rtd 97; Perm to Offic *B & W* from 97. *32 Old Farm, Nether Stowey, Bridgwater TA5 1PE* Tel (01278) 733032 E-mail langham@ision.co.uk

BERER, Otto. b 19. CEng FIMechE. Oak Hill Th Coll. **d** 83 **p** NSM Dovercourt and Parkeston *Chelmsf* 83-93; Perm to Offic from 93. *35 Gordon Road, Dovercourt, Harwich CO12 3TL* Tel (01255) 502806

BERGQUIST, Anders Karim. b 58. Peterho Cam BA79 MA83 PhD90. St Steph Ho Ox BA85 MA90. **d** 86 **p** 87. C Abbots Langley *St Alb* 86-89; Hon C Cambridge St Mary Less *Ely* 89-97; Tutor Westcott Ho Cam 89-95; Vice-Prin 95-97; Can Res St Alb 97-02; Minl Development Officer 97-02; V St John's Wood *Lon* from 02. *St John's House, St John's Wood High Street, London NW8 7NE* Tel (020) 7722 4378 *or* 7586 3864 E-mail andersb@waitrose.com

BERGSHIRE, Archdeacon of. *See* RUSSELL, The Ven Norman Atkinson

BERMUDA, Archdeacon of. *See* HOLLIS, The Ven Arnold Baldeus

BERMUDA, Bishop of. *See* RATTERAY, The Rt Revd Alexander Ewen

BERNARD, Brother. *See* APPS, Canon Michael John

BERNARDI, Frederick John. b 33. JP75. Chich Th Coll 55. **d** 58 **p** 59. C Blackb St Luke *Blackb* 58-60; C Ribbleton 60-63; V Brinsley w Underwood *S'well* 63-66; Barbados 67-71; V Sparkbrook St Agatha *Birm* 71-77; P-in-c Sparkbrook Ch Ch 73-75; V Haywards Heath St Wilfrid *Chich* 77-80; TR 80-87; Chapl Madrid *Eur* 87-90; NSM Tooting All SS *S'wark* 90-91; V Hanger Hill Ascension and W Twyford St Mary *Lon* 91-95; rtd 95; Perm to Offic *Chich* from 95. *13 Kingmere, South Terrace, Littlehampton BN17 5LD* Tel (01903) 713543 E-mail stella@knights-templar.org.uk *or* john@bernardi.co.uk

BERNERS-WILSON, Mrs Angela Veronica Isabel. b 54. St Andr Univ MTh76 St Jo Coll Dur DipTh78. **dss** 79 **d** 87 **p** 94. Southgate Ch Ch *Lon* 79-82; St Marylebone Ch 82-84; Ind Chapl 82-84; Chapl Thames Poly *S'wark* 84-91; Chapl Bris Univ *Bris* 91-95; C Bris St Mich and St Paul 94-95; P-in-c Colerne w N Wraxall 95-01; R from 01. *The Rectory, Colerne, Chippenham SN14 8DF* Tel (01225) 742742

BERRETT, Paul Graham. b 49. St Chad's Coll Dur BA70 St Steph Ho Ox 71. **d** 74 **p** 75. C Hockerill *St Alb* 74-77; C Leighton Buzzard 77-81; C Leighton Buzzard w Eggington, Hockliffe etc 81-83; V Bournemouth St Fran *Win* from 83. *St Francis's Clergy House, Charminster Road, Bournemouth BH8 9SH* Tel (01202) 529336

BERRIDGE, Grahame Richard. b 38. S'wark Ord Course 71. **d** 72 **p** 73. NSM S Beddington St Mich *S'wark* 72-75; NSM Merton St Jas 75-81; Perm to Offic from 81. *11 Cedar Walk, Kingswood, Tadworth KT20 6HW* Tel (01737) 358882

BERRIMAN, Brinley John. b 50. Univ Coll Lon BSc71. SW Minl Tr Course 95. **d** 98 **p** 99. NSM St Ives and Halsetown *Truro* 98-00; P-in-c Lanteglos by Camelford w Advent from 00. *The Rectory, Trefrew, Camelford PL32 9TP* Tel (01840) 211040 E-mail bberriman@bigfoot.com

BERRIMAN, Gavin Anthony. b 60. S'wark Ord Course 87. **d** 90 **p** 91. C Greenwich St Alfege w St Pet and St Paul *S'wark* 90-94; V Lee St Aug from 94. *St Augustine's Vicarage, 336 Baring Road, London SE12 0DU* Tel (020) 8857 4941

BERROW, Philip Rees. b 36. St Coll Lamp 58. **d** 62 **p** 63. C Neath w Llantwit *Llan* 62-66; CF 67-87; R Welford w Weston and Clifford Chambers *Glouc* 87-94; P-in-c Badminton w Lt Badminton, Acton Turville etc from 94. *The Vicarage, Badminton GL9 1ET* Tel (01454) 218427 E-mail prberrow@hotmail.com

BERRY, Canon Adrian Charles. b 50. Mert Coll Ox BA71 MA78. Cuddesdon Coll 72. **d** 75 **p** 76. C Prestbury *Glouc* 75-79; C Cirencester 79-83; V Cam w Stinchcombe 83-88; Dioc Ecum Officer 83-95; P-in-c Twyning 88-95; R Leckhampton St Pet 95-02; Dioc Min Development Officer *Llan* from 02; P-in-c Wenvoe and St Lythans from 02; Can Llan Cathl from 02. *The Rectory, 2 Port Road, Wenvoe, Cardiff CF5 6DF* Tel (029) 2059 3392

BERRY, Alan Peter. b 36. NW Ord Course 74. **d** 77 **p** 78. NSM Headingley *Ripon* 77-78; NSM Chapel Allerton 78-91; Perm to Offic from 91. *17 High Street, Spofforth, Harrogate HG3 1BQ* Tel (01937) 590503

BERRY, Anthony Nigel. b 53. Lon Bible Coll BA80 Sarum & Wells Th Coll 84. **d** 87 **p** 88. NSM Howell Hill *Guildf* 87-90; C 90; C Farnham 90-93; R Abinger cum Coldharbour from 93; Dioc Tr Officer for Past Assts from 94. *The Rectory, Abinger Common, Dorking RH5 6HZ* Tel (01306) 730746 E-mail revanberry@aol.com

BERRY, David Llewellyn Edward. b 39. St Jo Coll Cam BA61 MA65. Wells Th Coll 64. **d** 66 **p** 67. C Poplar All SS w St Frideswide *Lon* 66-69; C Ellesmere Port *Ches* 69-73; V Brafferton w Pilmoor and Myton on Swale *York* 73-79; P-in-c Thormanby 78-79; R Skelton w Upleatham 79-87; V Barrow St Aid *Carl* 87-97; Chapl Rotterdam *Eur* 97-99; rtd 99. *2 The Croft, Warcop, Appleby-in-Westmorland CA16 6PH* Tel (01768) 342175

BERRY, Frank John. b 47. Lon Univ BSc72 PhD75 DSc88 FRSC84. Qu Coll Birm 96. **d** 99 **p** 00. Prof Inorganic Chemistry Open Univ from 91; NSM Rednal *Birm* from 99. *44 Middle Park Road, Selly Oak, Birmingham B29 4BJ* Tel 0121-475 2718

BERRY, Geoffrey Wilbur Ronald. b 22. Ridley Hall Cam 54. **d** 56 **p** 57. C Northwood Em *Lon* 56-59; V Poplar St Matthias 59-70; V Westacre *Nor* 70-79; R Gayton Thorpe w E Walton 71-79; P-in-c Maresfield *Chich* 79; R 79-87; V Nutley 79-87; rtd 87; Perm to Offic *Bris* from 87. *13 Manor Park, Great Somerford, Chippenham SN15 5EQ* Tel (01249) 720530

BERRY, Miss Heather Evelyn. b 45. Lon Univ BA67 Ex Univ PGCE68. Dioc OLM tr scheme 98. **d** 00 **p** 01. OLM Gaywood *Nor* from 00. *29 Suffolk Road, King's Lynn PE30 4AH* Tel (01553) 764098

BERRY, Ian Thomas Henry. b 73. QUB BSc94. CITC BTh98. **d** 98 **p** 99. C Bangor Abbey *D & D* 98-02; I Monaghan w

Tydavnet and Kilmore *Clogh* from 02. *The Rectory, Clones Road, Monaghan, Irish Republic* Tel (00353) (47) 81136
E-mail monaghan@clogher.anglican.org

BERRY, John. b 41. Dur Univ BA62. Oak Hill Th Coll 63. **d** 65 **p** 66. C Burnage St Marg *Man* 65-68; C Middleton 68-70; Travelling Sec IVF 70-73; V Derby St Pet *Derby* 73-76; P-in-c Derby Ch Ch and H Trin 73-76; V Derby St Pet and Ch Ch w H Trin 76-81; Bp's Officer for Evang *Carl* 81-86; P-in-c Bampton and Mardale 81-86; TR N Wingfield, Pilsley and Tupton *Derby* 86-89; Evang Sec Evang Alliance 89-92; V Guernsey H Trin *Win* 92-98; TR Broadwater St Mary *Chich* from 98. *The Rectory, 8 Sompting Avenue, Worthing BN14 8HN* Tel (01903) 823996

BERRY, Paul Edward. b 56. N Ord Course 91. **d** 94 **p** 95. C Halliwell St Luke *Man* 94-98; TV Horwich and Rivington from 98. *St Elizabeth's Vicarage, Cedar Avenue, Horwich, Bolton BL6 6HT* Tel (01204) 669120 E-mail st.liz@xalt.co.uk

~~BERRY, The Very Revd Peter Austin.~~ b 35. Keble Coll Ox BA59 BTh61 MA63 Birm Univ Hon DD97. St Steph Ho Ox 59. **d** 62 **p** 63. C Cov St Mark *Cov* 62-66; Dioc Community Relns Officer 64-70; C Cov Cathl 66-73; Can Res Cov Cathl 73-86; Vice-Provost Cov Cathl 77-86; Bp's Adv for Community Relns 77-86; Provost Birm 86-99; rtd 99; Perm to Offic *Cov* from 99. *Reed Lodge, D5 Kenilworth Court, Hagley Road, Birmingham B16 9NU* Tel 0121-454 0021

BERRY, Philipa Raines. b 51. Man Univ BA72 Univ of Wales (Cardiff) CertEd73. St Jo Coll Nottm 82. **d** 95 **p** 96. NSM Leic H Apostles *Leic* from 95. *273 Fosse Road South, Leicester LE3 1AE* Tel 0116-291 8272

BERRY, Sister Susan Patricia (Sister Sue). b 49. Bris Univ BA70 Hughes Hall Cam PGCE72. Qu Coll Birm 77. **dss** 86 **d** 87 **p** 94. Chapl Barn Fellowship Whatcombe Ho 86-89; Chapl Lee Abbey 89-91; NSM Thatcham *Ox* 93-95; CSF from 95; Perm to Offic *B & W* 96-97 and from 98; Chapl Guy's and St Thos' Hosps NHS Trust Lon 97-98; Perm to Offic *S'wark* 97-98. *Community of St Francis, Compton Durville, South Petherton TA13 5ES* Tel (01460) 240153 Fax 242360

BERRY, Timothy Hugh. b 50. Reading Univ BA72. Oak Hill NSM Course 81. **d** 84 **p** 85. NSM Swanley St Paul *Roch* 84-88; C Gorleston St Andr *Nor* 88-93; V Grain w Stoke *Roch* 93-95; rtd 95. *26 Cyclamen Road, Swanley BR8 8HJ* Tel (01322) 613385

BERRY-DAVIES, Charles William Keith. b 48. MIOT71. Linc Th Coll. **d** 83 **p** 84. C Hythe *Cant* 83-86; Chapl RAF from 86; Perm to Offic *Linc* 93-96. *Chaplaincy Services (RAF), HQ, Personnel and Training Command, RAF Innsworth, Gloucester GL3 1EZ* Tel (01452) 712612 ext 5164 Fax 510828

BERRYMAN, William Arthur David. b 47. Lon Univ BD69 St Pet Coll Ox CertEd71. Sarum & Wells Th Coll 72. **d** 76 **p** 77. Asst Master Preston Sch Yeovil 76-80; Hon C Yeovil St Mich *B & W* 76-80; C Ex St Dav *Ex* 80-83; Chapl Ex Coll 80-83; Chapl RN 83-89; V Highertown and Baldhu *Truro* 89-95; TR Cov E *Cov* 95-97; TR The Abbey Leic 97-01; P-in-c Leic St Paul 97-01; R Banchory *Ab* from 01; P-in-c Kincardine O'Neil from 01. *The Rectory, High Street, Banchory AB31 5TB*

BERSON, Alan Charles. b 31. Univ of Michigan BA52 MA53 Lon Univ PhD62. St Steph Ho Ox 63. **d** 65 **p** 66. C Leeds St Pet *Ripon* 65-68; C St Giles-in-the-Fields *Lon* 68; Lic to Offic 69-80; Perm to Offic 80-88; rtd 96. *74 Ridgmount Gardens, London WC1E 7AX* Tel (020) 7636 1990

BERSWEDEN, Judith Anne. b 63. St Jo Coll Dur BA84. Ripon Coll Cuddesdon BA91. **d** 92 **p** 94. Par Dn Mirfield *Wakef* 92-94; NSM Robert Town 94-97; NSM Roberttown w Hartshead 97-00; NSM Alderbury Deanery from 00; Chapl Bp Wordsworth Sch Salisbury from 01. *The Rectory, Winterslow, Salisbury SP5 1RE* Tel (01980) 862231
E-mail judith.bersweden@breathemail.net

BERSWEDEN, Nils Herry Stephen. b 57. Newc Univ BSc78. Ripon Coll Cuddesdon 88. **d** 90 **p** 91. C Mirfield *Wakef* 90-93; P-in-c Purlwell 93-94; P-in-c Robert Town 94-97; V Roberttown w Hartshead 97-00; P-in-c Winterslow *Sarum* 00-01; TV Clarendon from 01. *The Rectory, Winterslow, Salisbury SP5 1RE* Tel (01980) 862231 E-mail nils.bersweden@breathemail.net

BERTRAM, Canon Richard Henry. b 27. TCD BA50 MA64. CITC 50. **d** 53 **p** 54. C Sligo Cathl *K, E & A* 53-56; C Dublin Booterstown *D & G* 56-58; I Stranorlar w Meenglas and Kilteevogue *D & R* 58-65; I Dublin St Cath w St Jas *D & G* 65-73; I Dublin Irishtown 73-74; I Dublin Irishtown w Donnybrook 74-02; Can Ch Ch Cathl Dublin 86-02; Treas Ch Ch Cathl 02; rtd 02. *Glencoe, The Harbour, North Beach, Greystones, Co Wicklow, Irish Republic* Tel (00353) (1) 287 5320

BESSANT, Brian Keith. b 32. Roch Th Coll 65. **d** 67 **p** 68. C Chatham St Wm *Roch* 67-70; C Cove St Jo *Guildf* 71-74; V Frimley Green 74-97; rtd 97; Perm to Offic *Guildf* from 97. *14 Tray Close, Farnborough GU14 9NB* Tel (01252) 376530

BESSANT, Canon Idwal Brian. b 39. Cardiff Coll of Art NDD61 ATD62 Univ of Wales DipTh68. St Mich Coll Llan 68. **d** 68 **p** 69. C Llantwit Major and St Donat's *Llan* 68-73; R Llangammarch w Garth, Llanlleonfel etc *S & B* 73-77; V Crickhowell 77-78; CMS Miss 78-83; Cyprus 80-83; V Crickhowell w Cwmdu and Tretower *S & B* 83-91; RD Crickhowell 86-91; V Llanwrtyd w Llanddulas in Tir Abad etc from 91; Can Res Brecon Cathl from

98; RD Builth from 02. *The Vicarage, Llanwrtyd Wells LD5 4SA* Tel (01591) 610231

BESSANT, Simon David. b 56. Sheff Univ BMus77 MA00. St Jo Coll Nottm DipTh79. **d** 81 **p** 82. C Litherland St Jo and St Jas *Liv* 81-84; C Holloway Em w Hornsey Road St Barn *Lon* 84-86; C Holloway St Mark w Em 86-91; V Blackb Redeemer *Blackb* 91-98; Acting RD Blackb 97-98; Dir Miss and Evang from 98; Dir CME from 02. *1 Swallowfields, Blackburn BB1 8NR* Tel (01254) 580176 Fax 279883 E-mail s.d.bessant@dial.pipex.com

BESSENT, Stephen Lyn. b 53. Bris Univ BA75. Wycliffe Hall Ox 75. **d** 77 **p** 78. C Patchway *Bris* 77-80; TV Swindon St Jo and St Andr 80-83; TV Eston w Normanby *York* 83-90; V Cogges *Ox* 90-94; P-in-c S Leigh 90-94; V Cogges and S Leigh 94-01; P-in-c Alphington *Ex* from 01. *The Rectory, Rectory Drive, Alphington, Exeter EX2 8XJ* Tel (01392) 437662

BEST, Miss Karen Belinda. b 62. Qu Coll Birm 92. **d** 94 **p** 95. C Southall Green St Jo *Lon* 94-97; C Northolt Park St Barn 97-00; V Gillingham St Barn *Roch* from 00. *The Vicarage, 1 St Barnabas Close, Gillingham ME7 4BU* Tel (01634) 851010
E-mail kbest36310@aol.com

BEST, Canon Raymond. b 42. Sarum & Wells Th Coll 71. **d** 74 **p** 75. C Whorlton *Newc* 74-78; C Seaton Hirst 78-83; C Benwell St Jas 83-85; TV Benwell Team 85-89; V Walker 89-00; P-in-c Byker St Martin 96-99; Hon Can Newc Cathl from 97; V Haltwhistle and Greenhead from 00; AD Hexham from 02. *The Vicarage, Edens Lawn, Haltwhistle NE49 0AB* Tel (01434) 320215 E-mail canonbest@aol.com

BESTELINK, Canon William Meindert Croft. b 48. Hull Univ BA70 FRSA78. Cuddesdon Coll 71. **d** 73 **p** 74. C Holt *Nor* 73-74; C E Dereham w Hoe 74-76; C Thorpe 76-80; R Colby w Banningham and Tuttington 80-90; R Felmingham 80-90; R Suffield 80-90; P-in-c Roydon St Remigius from 90; Dioc Rural Officer from 99; RD Redenhall 00-03; Hon Can Nor Cathl from 02; P-in-c Scole, Brockdish, Billingford, Thorpe Abbots etc from 02. *The Rectory, High Road, Roydon, Diss IP22 5RD* Tel (01379) 642180 Mobile 07966-549638
E-mail wmcbestelink@hotmail.com

BESTLEY, Peter Mark. b 60. Qu Coll Cam MA Univ of Wales (Cardiff) MPhil92. St Mich Coll Llan 89. **d** 92 **p** 93. C Hampton All SS *Lon* 92-95; Chapl W Middx Univ Hosp NHS Trust 95-99. *Address temp unknown*

BESWETHERICK, Andrew Michael. b 55. Ex Univ BEd80. S'wark Ord Course 87. **d** 90 **p** 91. Dep Hd Maze Hill Sch Greenwich 88-98; NSM Blackheath St Jo *S'wark* from 90; Hd Sixth Form Rosemary Sch Islington from 98. *112 Charlton Road, London SE7 7EY* Tel (020) 8853 0853

BESWICK, Canon Gary Lancelot. b 38. ALCD63. **d** 63 **p** 64. C Walthamstow St Mary *Chelmsf* 63-67; C Laisterdyke *Bradf* 67-70; V Idle H Trin 70-78; Area Sec (NW England) SAMS 78-92; Area Sec (N Thames) 92-97; Hon Can N Argentina from 87; R Gt Smeaton w Appleton Wiske and Birkby etc *Ripon* from 97. *The Rectory, Great Smeaton, Northallerton DL6 2EP* Tel (01609) 881205

BESWICK, Jonathan Warwick. b 67. Westcott Ho Cam. **d** 95 **p** 96. C Dudley St Fran *Worc* 95-96; C Brookfield St Anne, Highgate Rise *Lon* 96-99; C Brookfield St Mary 96-99; C St John's Wood 99-02; R Catsfield and Crowhurst *Chich* from 02. *The Rectory, Church Lane, Catsfield, Battle TN33 9DR* Tel (01424) 892319

BESWICK, Joseph Hubert. b 25. Birm Univ MB, ChB48 Lon Univ DipTh58. **d** 59 **p** 60. Lic to Offic *S'well* from 59. *38 Hallams Lane, Beeston, Nottingham NG9 5FH* Tel 0115-925 6719

BETSON, Stephen. b 53. Sarum & Wells Th Coll 89. **d** 91 **p** 92. C Sittingbourne St Mich *Cant* 91-95; V Fairweather Green *Bradf* 95-01; R Hockwold w Wilton *Ely* from 01; R Weeting from 01. *The Rectory, 25 South Street, Hockwold, Thetford IP26 4JG* Tel (01842) 828469 E-mail betson1@tesco.net

BETTELEY, Canon John Richard. b 46. Sarum & Wells Th Coll 81. **d** 83 **p** 84. C Auchterarder *St And* 83-85; C Dunblane 83-85; Chapl RAF 85-89; R Callander *St And* 89-94; P-in-c Aberfoyle 89-94; P-in-c Doune 89-94; R Ballachulish *Arg* from 94; R Glencoe from 94; R Onich from 94; Dioc Youth Officer 94-01; Syn Clerk from 99; Can St Jo Cathl Oban from 99; Can Cumbrae from 99. *The Rectory, Glencoe, Argyll PH49 2HP* Tel (01855) 811335 Fax 811976 E-mail glencoe@argyll.anglican.org

BETTERIDGE, Simon Frank. b 66. St Jo Coll Nottm. **d** 00 **p** 01. C Studley *Cov* 00-02; C Leamington Priors St Paul from 02. *49 Wathen Road, Leamington Spa CV32 5UY* Tel (01926) 451439 Mobile 07867-527291 E-mail porters88@yahoo.co.uk

BETTIS, Canon Margaret Jean. b 42. Gilmore Ho 72. **dss** 77 **d** 87 **p** 94. Kenya 74-79; Tutor Crowther Hall CMS Tr Coll Selly Oak 79-82; Hodge Hill *Birm* 82-87; Par Dn 87; Par Dn Flitwick *St Alb* 87-93; P-in-c Westoning w Tingrith 93-94; V from 94; Hon Can St Alb from 99. *The Vicarage, Church Road, Westoning, Bedford MK45 5JW* Tel (01525) 713703

BETTRIDGE, Canon Winston Graham. b 39. Kelham Th Coll 60. **d** 65 **p** 66. C Burley in Wharfedale *Bradf* 65-67; C Baildon 67-70; V Harden and Wilsden 70-81; TR Kirkby Lonsdale *Carl* from 81; Hon Can Carl Cathl from 89; Chapl Cumbria

Constabulary from 96. *The Rectory, Vicarage Lane, Kirkby Lonsdale, Carnforth LA6 2BA* Tel (01524) 271320 *or* 72044

BETTS, Alan John. b 55. Portsm Poly BSc77 St Martin's Coll Lanc PGCE81. St Jo Coll Nottm 93. **d** 93 **p** 94. C Cannock *Lich* 93-01; P-in-c Endon w Stanley from 01. *St Luke's Vicarage, Leek Road, Endon, Stoke-on-Trent ST9 9BH* Tel (01782) 502166

BETTS, Anthony Clive. b 40. Wells Th Coll 63. **d** 65 **p** 66. C Leeds All Hallows w St Simon *Ripon* 65-67; C Wetherby 67-70; C Adel 70-73; V Leeds All SS 73-79; V Leeds Richmond Hill 79-84; R Knaresborough 84-03; TR from 03; RD Harrogate 95-98. *The Rectory, High Bond End, Knaresborough HG5 9BT* Tel (01423) 865273 E-mail tonybetts@bettst.freeserve.co.uk

BETTS, Canon Anthony Percy. b 26. Lon Univ BD52. ALCD52. **d** 52 **p** 53. C Guildf St Sav *Guildf* 52-56; C Hanworth St Geo *Lon* 56-59; V Derby St Aug *Derby* 59-74; RD Derby 71-74; V Bracebridge *Linc* 74-83; R Fenny Bentley, Kniveton, Thorpe and Tissington *Derby* 83-91; RD Ashbourne 86-91; Hon Can Derby Cathl 87-91; rtd 91; Perm to Offic *Derby* from 91. *Otterbourne House, Windley, Belper DE56 2LP* Tel (01773) 550677

BETTS, David John. b 38. Lon Univ BSc61. Oak Hill Th Coll 63. **d** 65 **p** 66. C Slough *Ox* 65-70; C Welling *Roch* 70-75; V Swanley St Paul 75-93; R Nottingham St Nic *S'well* 93-98; TV Canford Magna *Sarum* ibetts from 98. *The Rectory, Canford Magna, Wimborne BH21 3AF* Tel (01202) 886230

BETTS, Canon Edmund John. b 51. St Chad's Coll Dur BA72 Lanc Univ MA81. Qu Coll Birm DipTh75 DPS76. **d** 76 **p** 77. C Leagrave *St Alb* 76-79; Asst Chapl R Albert Hosp Lanc 79-81; Chapl Lea Castle Hosp and Kidderminster Gen Hosp 81-86; Prov Officer Educn for Min Ch in Wales 86-88; Exec Sec for Min 88-90; TR Haverhill w Withersfield, the Wrattings etc *St E* 90-97; V Haverhill w Withersfield from 97; RD Clare from 91; Hon Can St E Cathl from 02; CUF Link Officer from 02. *The Rectory, 10 Hopton Rise, Haverhill CB9 7FS* Tel (01440) 708768 Fax as telephone E-mail edmund.betts@talk21.com

BETTS, George William John. b 23. Ex Univ BA51. Westcott Ho Cam 51. **d** 53 **p** 54. C Wallsend St Luke *Newc* 53-54; C Benwell St Jas 54-56; C Plumstead St Jas w St Jo *S'wark* 56; C Peckham St Andr w All SS 56; C Eltham St Jo 57-60; C Findon *Chich* 60-67; Rhodesia 67-68; C Sherborne w Castleton and Lillington *Sarum* 68-69; C Brookfield St Anne, Highgate Rise *Lon* 69; rtd 88. *72 Westmount Road, London SE9 1JE* Tel (020) 8850 2116

BETTS, Ivan Ringland. b 38. TCD BA61 MA67. **d** 62 **p** 63. C Ballyholme *D & D* 62-65; C Dundela St Mark 65-69; Miss to Seamen 69-73; Sudan 69-71; Trinidad and Tobago 71-73; C Drumglass *Arm* 73-81; I Augher w Newtownsaville and Eskrahoole *Clogh* 81-86; Bp's C Ballymacarrett St Martin *D & D* 86-02; rtd 02. *56 Norwood Drive, Belfast BT4 2EB* Tel (028) 9065 0723 E-mail ibetts@compuserve.com

BETTS, Mrs Patricia Joyce. b 43. St Kath Coll Lon CertEd64 DipTLSA85 FRSA96. S Dios Minl Tr Scheme 90. **d** 96 **p** 97. NSM Bath Widcombe *B & W* 96-00; P-in-c from 00. *Hunters Lodge, North Road, Bath BA2 6HP* Tel (01225) 464918 Mobile 07974-799809 Fax (01225) 445732 E-mail candpbetts@aol.com

BETTS, Paul Robert. b 31. Lon Univ BSc51. Oak Hill Th Coll 53. **d** 56 **p** 57. C Plymouth St Jude *Ex* 56-59; C Cheltenham St Mark *Glouc* 59-63; V Finchley St Paul Long Lane *Lon* 63-76; Warden St Columba Cen Cam 76-79; R Datchworth w Tewin *St Alb* 79-96; rtd 96; Perm to Offic *Ex* from 96. *2 Penny Close, Exminster, Exeter EX6 8SU* Tel (01392) 824403

BETTS, Richard Alan. b 56. ACA83 UEA BA77. Sarum & Wells Th Coll 93. **d** 93 **p** 94. C Mile Cross *Nor* 93-97; TV Dorchester *Sarum* from 97. *St George's Vicarage, 59 Fordington High Street, Dorchester DT1 1LB* Tel (01305) 262394

BETTS, Steven James. b 64. York Univ BSc86. Ripon Coll Cuddesdon 89. **d** 90 **p** 91. C Bearsted w Thurnham *Cant* 90-94; Bp's Chapl *Nor* 94-97; V Old Catton from 97; RD Nor N from 01. *St Margaret's Vicarage, 1 Parkside Drive, Norwich NR6 7DP* Tel (01603) 425615 E-mail s-s.betts@ukgateway.net

BEUKES, Douglas. b 22. Oak Hill Th Coll 45. **d** 51 **p** 52. C Walthamstow St Andr *Chelmsf* 51-53; C E Barnet *St Alb* 53-55; Chapl RAF 55-58; Chapl Utrecht w Arnhem, Zwolle, Amersfoort etc *Eur* 59-90; rtd 90. *De Wartburg, Kennedylaan 16, 3533 KJ Utrecht, The Netherlands* Tel (0031) (30) 271 1997

BEVAN, Alan John. b 29. Bris Univ BA54. Oak Hill Th Coll 54. **d** 56 **p** 59. C Penn Fields *Lich* 56-57; C Corsham *Bris* 58-61; C Wath-upon-Dearne w Adwick-upon-Dearne *Sheff* 61-68; C Darfield 68-71; C Drypool St Columba w St Andr and St Pet *York* 71-79; Chapl HM Pris Wandsworth 79-83; Chapl HM Pris Kirkham 83-86; rtd 86; Perm to Offic *Ex* from 86. *c/o Mrs D G Ancrum, 14 Merrivale Road, Dousland, Yelverton PL20 6NS* Tel (01822) 853909

BEVAN, Bryan David. Lon Univ BD60 MA70 CertEd65 DipEd66 MPhil84. Lambeth STh62 St Aug Coll Cant 62. **d** 64 **p** 66. C E Dereham w Hoe *Nor* 64-65; C Hove All SS *Chich* 65-67; Lect St Mich Coll Salisbury 67-70; The Coll Bedf from 70. *4A De Parys Lodge, De Parys Avenue, Bedford MK40 2TZ* Tel (01234) 343622

BEVAN, Canon Charles Joseph Godfrey. b 22. TCD BA44 MA52. **d** 45 **p** 46. C Dublin St Geo *D & G* 45-49; I Rathvilly *C & O*

49-59; I Carbury *M & K* 59-64; I Drogheda St Pet w Ballymakenny, Beaulieu etc *Arm* 64-90; I Drogheda w Ardee, Collon and Termonfeckin 90-95; Miss to Seamen 64-95; Can Arm Cathl *Arm* 83-95; Chan 88-92; Prec 92-95; rtd 95. *13 St Peter's Place, Drogheda, Co Louth, Irish Republic* Tel (00353) (98) 414 4622

BEVAN, David Graham. b 34. Univ of Wales (Lamp) BA54 LTh56. Gen Th Sem (NY) MDiv57. **d** 57 **p** 58. C Llanelli *St D* 57-60; CF 60-76; rtd 99. *148 Bromley Heath Road, Downend, Bristol BS16 6JJ* Tel 0117-956 0946

BEVAN, Gordon Richard. b 26. NW Ord Course. **d** 75 **p** 76. C Spondon *Derby* 75-80; R Upper Langwith w Langwith Bassett etc 80-94; TV E Scarsdale 94-96; rtd 96; Perm to Offic *Derby* from 96. *8 Whaley Common, Langwith, Mansfield NG20 9HY* Tel (01623) 742413

BEVAN, Herbert Richard. b 28. Birm Univ DipTh56 MA67. **d** 57 **p** 58. C Sutton Coldfield H Trin *Birm* 57-60; C Chelsea All SS *Lon* 60-62; R Abberley w Pensax 62-92; RD Mitton 72-74; P-in-c Pensax 80-84; rtd 92. *Redlake Reach, Bucknell SY7 0AL* Tel (01547) 4427

BEVAN, Hubert Basil Henry. b 24. Univ of Wales (Lamp) BA52 LTh54 MTh75 PhD78. **d** 54 **p** 55. C Knighton and Heyope *S & B* 54-60; C Toxteth Park St Marg *Liv* 60-61; V Walsall St Mary and All SS Palfrey *Lich* 61-64; R Sunderland *Dur* 64-66; V Hendon St Paul 64-66; V Gilfach Goch w Llandyfodwg *Llan* 66-73; R Cregina *S & B* 73-78; V Bettws Disserth w Llansantffraed in Elwell 73-78; V Glascwm and Rhulen 76-78; R Llanferres, Nercwys and Eryrys *St As* 78-80; Tutor St Deiniol's Lib Hawarden 79-89; V Treuddyn and Nercwys and Eryrys *St As* 80-85; R Llanfynydd 85-89; rtd 89. *Bryn Heulog, Bryniau Duon, Old Llandegfan, Menai Bridge LL59 5PP*

BEVAN (née BYWATERS), Ms Janet Mary. b 46. Bris Poly CertEd86. WMMTC DipApTh98. **d** 98 **p** 99. C Bishop's Cleeve *Glouc* 98-02; V Overbury w Teddington, Alstone etc *Worc* from 02. *The Vicarage, Station Road, Beckford, Tewkesbury GL20 7AD* Tel (01386) 881349

BEVAN, Noel Haden. b 34. St Aid Birkenhead 61. **d** 63 **p** 64. C Girlington *Bradf* 63-66; C Worksop St Jo *S'well* 66-68; V Everton w Mattersey 68-70; R Everton and Mattersey w Clayworth 70-77; TV Barton Mills *St E* 77-80; TV Barton Mills, Beck Row w Kenny Hill etc 80-85; TV Mildenhall 85-86; P-in-c Sternfield w Benhall and Snape 86-89; R 89-98; rtd 98. *6 Benhall Green, Saxmundham IP17 1HU* Tel (01728) 604169

BEVAN, Paul John. b 49. Bris Sch of Min 84. **d** 87. NSM Bishopsworth *Bris* 87-96. *10 Brookdale Road, Headley Park, Bristol BS13 7PZ* Tel 0117-964 6330

BEVAN, Peter John. b 54. K Coll Lon BA76 AKC76 MA86. St Steph Ho Ox BA79. **d** 80 **p** 81. C Brighouse *Wakef* 80-83; C Chapelthorpe 83-86; V Scholes 86-95; V Potters Bar *St Alb* from 95. *The Vicarage, 15 The Walk, Potters Bar EN6 1QN* Tel (01707) 644539 *or* 645080

BEVAN, Philip Frank. b 41. Brasted Th Coll 63 Chich Th Coll 65. **d** 67 **p** 68. C Walton St Mary *Liv* 67-71; Bahamas 71-78; P-in-c Long Is SS Pet and Paul 71-73; R Nassau St Matt 73-78; Perm to Offic *Lon* and *S'wark* from 00. *5 Dunstable Road, Richmond TW9 1UH* Tel (020) 8940 3622 Mobile 07970-961539 E-mail fr.philip@btinternet.com

BEVAN, Richard. *See* BEVAN, Herbert Richard

BEVAN, Canon Richard Justin William. b 22. LTh42 St Chad's Coll Dur BA45 DTh72 PhD80. St Aug Coll Cant 39. **d** 45 **p** 46. C Stoke upon Trent *Lich* 45-49; Chapl Aberlour Orphanage 49-51; Lic to Offic *Mor* 49-51; Lic to Offic *Blackb* 51-52; C Church Kirk 52-56; C Whalley 56-61; R Dur St Mary le Bow w St Mary the Less *Dur* 61-64; Chapl Dur Univ 61-74; V Dur St Oswald 64-74; P-in-c Dur St Mary le Bow w St Mary the Less 64-67; R 67-74; R Grasmere *Carl* 74-82; Can Res, Lib and Treas Carl Cathl 82-89; Vice-Dean Carl 86-89; Chapl to The Queen 86-93; rtd 89; Perm to Offic *Carl* from 89. *Beck Cottage, West End, Burgh-by-Sands, Carlisle CA7 6BT* Tel (01228) 576781

BEVAN, Rodney. b 57. Leeds Univ BA80 Keele Univ PGCE81 Open Univ MA99. St Jo Coll Dur 97. **d** 99 **p** 00. C Ogley Hay *Lich* from 99. *50 Lichfield Road, Brownhills, Walsall WS8 6HT* Tel (01543) 371170 E-mail rjdr@uk.packardbell.org

BEVER, Canon Michael Charles Stephen. b 44. Selw Coll Cam BA66 MA70. Cuddesdon Coll. **d** 69 **p** 70. C Steeton *Bradf* 69-72; C Northampton St Mary *Pet* 72-74; Niger 75-79; P-in-c Elmstead *Chelmsf* 80-83; V 83-85; V Bocking St Pet 85-96; P-in-c Odiham *Win* from 96; Hon Can Awka from 93. *The Vicarage, The Bury, Odiham, Hook RG29 1ND* Tel (01256) 703896 Fax as telephone E-mail mcsb@ozala.fsnet.co.uk

BEVERIDGE, Mrs Freda Joy. b 38. Qu Mary Coll Lon BA59 Lon Inst of Educn PGCE60. Ripon Coll Cuddesdon 83. **dss** 85 **d** 87 **p** 94. Ox St Giles and SS Phil and Jas w St Marg *Ox* 85-88; Par Dn 87-88; Par Dn Woughton 88-94; C 94-95; TR 95-97; C Woodham *Guildf* 97-00; rtd 00; Perm to Offic *Sarum* from 01. *Moonraker Cottage, 27 New Road, Chiseldon, Swindon SN4 0LY* Tel (01793) 741064

BEVERIDGE, Simon Alexander Ronald. b 61. Nottm Univ BA84. Chich Th Coll 84. **d** 87 **p** 88. C Braunton *Ex* 87-90; TV N

Creedy 90-93; Chapl RN from 93. *Royal Naval Chaplaincy Service, Room 203, Victory Building, HM Naval Base, Portsmouth PO1 3LS* Tel (023) 9272 7903 Fax 9272 7111

BEVERLEY, David John. b 46. Univ of Wales (Lamp) BA68. Linc Th Coll 71. **d** 73 **p** 74. C Cov E *Cov* 73-76; C Immingham *Linc* 76-84; V Bracebridge Heath 84-86; Ind Chapl 86-97; P-in-c Scunthorpe Resurr 97-01; V 01-02; R Trentside E from 02. *The Vicarage, Mirfield Road, Scunthorpe DN15 8AN* Tel (01724) 842196

BEVERLEY, Suffragan Bishop of (Provincial Episcopal Visitor). *See* JARRETT, The Rt Revd Martyn William

BEVINGTON, Canon Colin Reginald. b 36. ALCD63. **d** 63 **p** 64. C Devonport St Budeaux *Ex* 63-65; C Attenborough w Chilwell *S'well* 65-68; R Benhall w Sternfield *St E* 68-74; P-in-c Snape w Friston 73-74; V Selly Hill St Steph *Birm* 74-81; P-in-c Selly Oak St Wulstan 80-81; V Selly Park St Steph and St Wulstan 81-88; Dioc Adv on Miss *St E* 88-95; Dioc and Co Ecum Officer 88-99; Hon Can St E Cathl 93-00; Bp's Dom Chapl and Personal Asst 95-99; R Holbrook, Freston, Woolverstone and Wherstead 99-00; RD Samford 99-00; rtd 01; Perm to Offic *St E* from 01. *44 Thorney Road, Capel, Ipswich IP9 2LH* Tel (01473) 310069 E-mail bevington@capel19.freeserve.co.uk

BEVINGTON, David John. b 51. Ch Coll Cam BA72 MA76. Trin Coll Bris 73. **d** 76 **p** 77. C Tulse Hill H Trin *S'wark* 76-79; C Galleywood Common *Chelmsf* 79-82; TV Hanley H Ev *Lich* 82-90; TV Hemel Hempstead *St Alb* 90-99; V Calbourne w Newtown *Portsm* from 99; V Shalfleet from 99. *The Vicarage, 4 Manor Green, Shalfleet, Newport PO30 4QT* Tel (01983) 531238 E-mail dbevington@lineone.net

BEVIS, Anthony Richard. b 34. Chich Th Coll 87. **d** 87 **p** 89. NSM Hamble le Rice *Win* 87-94; NSM Woolston from 94; Chapl Southampton Community Services NHS Trust from 90. *Lynwood, High Street, Hamble, Southampton SO31 4HA* Tel (023) 8045 3102 *or* 8047 2258

BEVIS, Derek Harold. b 23. FCIS. **d** 90 **p** 91. OLM Guildf Ch Ch *Guildf* 90-97; rtd 98; Perm to Offic *Guildf* from 99. *94 Wodeland Avenue, Guildford GU2 4LD* Tel (01483) 561968

BEWES, Anthony Charles Neill. b 71. Birm Univ BA93. Wycliffe Hall Ox 96. **d** 99 **p** 00. C Sevenoaks St Nic *Roch* from 99. *40 South Park, Sevenoaks TN13 1EJ* Tel (01732) 454221 E-mail anthonybewes@hotmail.com

BEWES, Helen Catherine. *See* SCAMMAN, Mrs Helen Catherine

BEWES, Preb Richard Thomas. b 34. Em Coll Cam BA58 MA61. Ridley Hall Cam 57. **d** 59 **p** 60. C Beckenham Ch Ch *Roch* 59-65; V Harold Wood *Chelmsf* 65-74; V Northwood Em *Lon* 74-83; R St Marylebone All So w SS Pet and Jo 83-88; P-in-c Portman Square St Paul 87-88; R Langham Place All So from 88; Preb St Paul's Cathl from 88. *12 Weymouth Street, London W1W 5BY* Tel (020) 7580 6029 *or* 7580 3522 E-mail richard.bewes@allsouls.org

BEWLEY, Albert Latham. b 38. Leeds Univ BA61. Ely Th Coll 61. **d** 63 **p** 64. C Wigan St Mich *Liv* 63-65; C Caister *Nor* 65-69; R W Lynn 69-76; V Lakenham St Jo 76-97; rtd 97; Perm to Offic *Nor* from 97. *37 St Mary's Road, Poringland, Norwich NR14 7SR* Tel (01508) 492685

BEWLEY, Robin John. b 63. St Jo Coll Ox BA86 MA95 Fitzw Coll Cam BA99. Ridley Hall Cam. **d** 00 **p** 01. NSM Impington *Ely* from 00; NSM Histon from 00. *31 Lone Tree Avenue, Impington, Cambridge CB4 9PG* Tel (01223) 232469 E-mail r.bewley@btinternet.com

BEYNON, Malcolm. b 36. Univ of Wales (Lamp) BA56 Univ of Wales (Swansea) DipSocSc59 Univ of Wales (Cardiff) PGCE71. St Mich Coll Llan 56. **d** 59 **p** 60. C Aberavon *Llan* 59-62; C Whitchurch 63-68; V Llanwynno 68-73; Chapl Old Hall Sch Wellington Shropshire 74-75; Chapl Nevill Holt Sch Market Harborough 75-82; Chapl Denstone Coll Prep Sch Uttoxeter 82-93; V Dale and St Brides w Marloes *St D* 93-01; rtd 01. *22 Ostrey Bank, St Clears, Carmarthen SA33 4AH*

BEYNON, Nigel David. b 68. Collingwood Coll Dur BSc90. Ridley Hall Cam BA94. **d** 95 **p** 96. C Fulham St Matt *Lon* 95-98; C St Helen Bishopsgate w St Andr Undershaft etc from 98; Student Team Ldr from 01. *12 Merrick Square, London SE1 4JB* Tel (020) 7378 0229

BEYNON, Vincent Wyn. b 54. CertEd76 Univ of Wales DipTh81 Lambeth STh97. St Mich Coll Llan 78. **d** 81 **p** 82. C Llantrisant *Llan* 81-83; C Caerphilly 84-85; R Gelligaer 85-88; TV Gtr Corsham *Bris* 88-97; R Potton w Sutton and Cockayne Hatley *St Alb* from 97; RD Biggleswade from 01. *The Rectory, Hatley Road, Potton, Sandy SG19 2RP* Tel (01767) 260782 E-mail wynbeynon@benefice.swinternet.co.uk

BIANCHI, Mrs Margaret Ruth. b 56. St Mary's Coll Dur BA77. Cranmer Hall Dur 78. **dss** 80 **d** 91 **p** 94. Chester le Street *Dur* 80-83; W Pelton 83-91; NSM 91-95; Perm to Offic from 95. *8 Lindisfarne, Washington NE38 7JR* Tel 0191-417 0852

BIANCHI, Robert Frederick. b 56. St Jo Coll Dur BA77. Cranmer Hall Dur 78. **d** 80 **p** 81. C Chester le Street *Dur* 80-83; C W Pelton 83-86; P-in-c 86-95; Perm to Offic from 95. *8 Lindisfarne, Washington NE38 7JR* Tel 0191-417 0852

BIBBY, Canon Frank. b 37. ACP60 K Coll Lon BD64 AKC64. **d** 65 **p** 66. C Upholland *Liv* 65-67; Lect Birm Coll of Educn 67-72; V Prestwich St Gabr *Man* 72-76; Dir of Ords 72-76; V Hope St Jas 76-86; AD Salford 82-86; R Prestwich St Mary 86-02; Hon Can Man Cathl 96-02; AD Radcliffe and Prestwich 99-02; rtd 02; Perm to Offic *Man* from 02. *65 Leyton Drive, Bury BL9 9TS* Tel 0161-766 3123

BIBBY, Paul Benington. b 27. Magd Coll Cam BA51 MA56. Westcott Ho Cam 55. **d** 57 **p** 58. C Flixton St Mich *Man* 57-60; C Woolwich St Mary w H Trin *S'wark* 60-62; V Hurst *Man* 62-69; Hd of Cam Ho Camberwell 69-76; R Shepton Mallet *B & W* 76-81; P-in-c Doulting w E and W Cranmore and Downhead 78-81; R Shepton Mallet w Doulting 81-82; Sen Chapl Eton Coll 82-87; R Hambleden Valley *Ox* 87-93; rtd 93; Perm to Offic *Nor* from 94. *Vine Cottage, Cross Lane, Stanhoe, King's Lynn PE31 8PS* Tel (01485) 518291

BICK, David Jim. b 33. ALCD59 LTh74. **d** 59 **p** 60. C Glouc St Cath *Glouc* 59-61; C Coleford w Staunton 61-63; R Blaisdon w Flaxley 63-72; V Coaley 72-83; P-in-c Arlingham 80-83; P-in-c Frampton on Severn 80-83; Hon C Saul w Fretherne and Framilode 83-84; Perm to Offic from 84; rtd 98. *St Joseph's, Prinknash Park, Cranham, Gloucester GL4 8EU* Tel (01452) 812973

BICKERDYKE, James Clifford. b 17. St Jo Coll Dur BA42 MA45. Oak Hill Th Coll LTh41. **d** 42 **p** 43. C Stockport St Geo *Ches* 42-43; C Cannock *Lich* 43-45; Normanton Sch Buxton 45-48; Chadderton Gr Sch 48-51; CF 51-67; Launceston Coll 67-75; Grove Sch Hindhead 75-81. *Manesty, Springs Garth, Keswick CA12 4BG* Tel (01768) 773537

BICKERSTETH, Anthony Cyril. b 33. K Coll Lon 54. Bps' Coll Cheshunt 55. **d** 58 **p** 59. C Middlesbrough St Oswald *York* 58-61; S Africa 61-64; V Stillington w Marton and Farlington *York* 64-68; V Stoke Newington Common St Mich *Lon* 68-74; V Nayland w Wiston *St E* 74-82; R Tolleshunt Knights w Tiptree *Chelmsf* 82-87; rtd 87; Perm to Offic *Chelmsf* 87-90. *42 Roman Road, Colchester CO1 1UP* Tel (01206) 544517

BICKERSTETH, David Craufurd. b 50. Wycliffe Hall Ox 71. **d** 75 **p** 76. C Beverley Minster *York* 75-79; C Farnborough *Guildf* 79-81; P-in-c Dearham *Carl* 81-85; R Gosforth w Nether Wasdale and Wasdale Head 86-93; P-in-c Harraby 93-97; V Maryport from 98; Dioc Chapl Mother's Union 94-97. *The Vicarage, Church Street, Maryport CA15 6HE* Tel (01900) 813077 Mobile 07790-088421 E-mail david.bickersteth@whsmithnet.co.uk

BICKERSTETH, Edward Piers. b 56. R Agric Coll Cirencester DipREM78 ARICS80 MRICS01. Wycliffe Hall Ox 89. **d** 91 **p** 92. NSM Bebington *Ches* 91-92; C 92-94; Proclamation Trust 94-98; P-in-c Arborfield w Barkham *Ox* 98-02; R from 02. *The Rectory, Church Lane, Arborfield, Reading RG2 9HZ* Tel 0118-976 0285

✠**BICKERSTETH, The Rt Revd John Monier.** b 21. KCVO89. Ch Ch Ox BA49 MA53. Wells Th Coll 48. **d** 50 **p** 51 **c** 70. C Moorfields *Bris* 50-54; C-in-c Hurst Green CD *S'wark* 54-62; V Chatham St Steph *Roch* 62-70; Hon Can Roch Cathl 68-70; Suff Bp Warrington *Liv* 70-75; Bp B & W 75-87; ChStJ and Sub-Prelate from 77; Clerk of the Closet 79-89; rtd 87. *Beckfords, Newtown, Tisbury, Salisbury SP3 6NY* Tel (01747) 870479

BICKERSTETH, Simon Craufurd. b 77. St Jo Coll Dur BA98. Wycliffe Hall Ox 99. **d** 01 **p** 02. C Windermere *Carl* from 01. *Burnthwaite, 24 Kendal Road, Bowness-on-Windermere, Windermere LA23 3EW* Tel (01539) 444301 Mobile 07752-853148 E-mail simon.bickersteth@btinternet.com

BICKNELL, Jonathan Richard. b 62. Wycliffe Hall Ox. **d** 00 **p** 01. C Chesham Bois *Ox* 00-02. *210 High Street, Berkhamsted HP4 1AG* Tel (01442) 872447

BICKNELL (née RIDING), Mrs Pauline Alison. b 61. SEN82. Oak Hill Th Coll BA90. **d** 90 **p** 96. Par Dn Moor Allerton *Ripon* 90-93; Par Dn Leeds St Aid 93-94; C 94-96; C Rothwell 96-99; TV Drypool *York* from 99. *383 Southcoates Lane, Hull HU9 3UN* Tel (01482) 781090 E-mail pauline@bicknells.freeserve.co.uk

BIDDELL, Canon Christopher David. b 27. Ch Coll Cam BA48 MA52. Ridley Hall Cam 51. **d** 51 **p** 52. C Hornchurch St Andr *Chelmsf* 51-54; Succ S'wark Cathl *S'wark* 54-56; P-in-c Wroxall *Portsm* 56-61; R Bishop's Waltham 62-75; RD Bishop's Waltham 69-74; V Stockport St Geo *Ches* 75-86; Hon Can Ches Cathl 81-86; Can Res 86-93; RD Stockport 85-86; Vice-Dean Ches 91-93; rtd 93; P-in-c Duncton *Chich* 95-98; P-in-c Tillington 95-98; P-in-c Up Waltham 95-98; Perm to Offic from 98. *3 Park Terrace, Tillington, Petworth GU28 9AE* Tel (01798) 342008

BIDDELL, John Herman. b 15. Worc Coll Ox BA38 MA45. Wells Th Coll 38. **d** 47 **p** 48. C Basingstoke *Win* 47-51; V Pennington 51-58; R Merstham and Gatton *S'wark* 58-65; V Milverton *B & W* 65-80; R Fitzhead 77-80; rtd 80; Perm to Offic *B & W* 81-02. *c/o P R Baker Esq, Springfold, 22 Gatton Road, Reigate RH2 0EX* Tel (01737) 245262

BIDDER, John. b 19. Cuddesdon Coll. **d** 62 **p** 63. C Birstall *Leic* 62-65; R Croft 65-71; R Witcham w Mepal *Ely* 71-80; R Coates

80-85; rtd 85; Perm to Offic *Blackb* from 86. *Carinya, 83 Main Street, Nether Kellett, Carnforth LA6 1EF* Tel (01524) 734993

BIDDINGTON, Terence Eric. b 56. MCollP83 Hull Univ BA77 Trin & All SS Coll Leeds PGCE78 Leeds Univ PhD86 Nottm Univ BTh88 Man Univ MA(Theol)96. Linc Th Coll 85. **d** 88 **p** 89. C Harpenden St Jo *St Alb* 88-90; Chapl Keele Univ *Lich* 90-93; Freelance Th Educator and Asst Lect Keele Univ 94-99; Assoc Min Betley and Keele 90-93; Asst Dir Cornerstone St Aug *Man* 95-96; Mental Health Advocate Stockport 96-98; Dir and Sen Advocate Stockport MIND from 98; Perm to Offic *Man* 99-01; P-in-c Heaton Norris Ch w All SS 01-02; C Heatons from 02; Asst Chapl Man Mental Health Partnership 01-03; Chapl Man Univ *Man* from 03; Chapl Man Metrop Univ from 03. *St Agnes's Rectory, 551 Gorton Road, Stockport SK5 6NX* Tel 0161-233 0692 *or* 0161-275 2894 E-mail tbjp2000@fish.co.uk

BIDDLE, Nicholas Lawrence. b 71. K Coll Lon BA94 Leeds Univ MA98. Coll of Resurr Mirfield 96. **d** 98 **p** 99. C Bedford St Andr *St Alb* 98-01; Bp's Dom Chapl and Research Asst *Chich* from 01. *Monk's Cottage, Canon Lane, Chichester PO19 1PX* Tel (01243) 839379 Mobile 07790-287280 E-mail n.biddle@ntlworld.com *or* chaplain@diochi.freeserve.co.uk

BIDDLE, Rodney William Dennis. b 44. St Jo Coll Nottm. **d** 85 **p** 86. C Penn *Lich* 85-89; P-in-c Shrewsbury St Geo 89-90; V 90-98; P-in-c Montford w Shrawardine and Fitz 89; Chapl HM Pris Shrewsbury 90-96; RD Shrewsbury *Lich* 91-97; P-in-c Bicton, Montford w Shrawardine and Fitz 97-98; R Newport w Longford, Chetwynd and Forton from 98. *The Rectory, 10 Forton Glade, Newport TF10 8BU* Tel (01952) 810089

BIDDLE, Miss Rosemary. b 44. CertEd67. St Jo Coll Dur 76. **dss** 79 **d** 87 **p** 94. Sheldon *Birm* 79-83; Burntwood *Lich* 83-87; Par Dn 87-89; Par Dn Gt Wyrley 89-94; C 94-99; rtd 99; Perm to Offic *Lich* from 00. *8 Brook Lane, Great Wyrley, Walsall WS6 6BQ* Tel (01922) 419032

BIDDLECOMBE, Francis William. b 30. St Mich Coll Llan 57. **d** 59 **p** 60. C Llangynwyd w Maesteg *Llan* 59-62; C Roath 62-65; V Llanddewi Rhondda w Bryn Eirw 65-71; V Berse and Southsea *St As* 71-79; P-in-c Teme Valley S *Worc* 79-85; rtd 92; Perm to Offic *Heref* from 92; Perm to Offic *Worc* from 92. *Four Winds, New Road, Highley, Bridgnorth WV16 6NN* Tel (01746) 861746

BIDDLESTONE, Joseph. b 15. Wycliffe Hall Ox 67. **d** 68 **p** 68. C Woodley St Jo the Ev *Ox* 68-71; P-in-c Dunsden 71-77; P-in-c Kiddington w Asterleigh 77-85; P-in-c Wootton by Woodstock 77-85; rtd 85; Perm to Offic *Ox* from 85. *6 Dashwood Rise, Duns Tew, Oxford OX25 6JQ* Tel (01869) 340350

BIDE, Mrs Mary Elizabeth. b 53. St Anne's Coll Ox BA74 MA78. S Dios Minl Tr Scheme 91. **d** 94 **p** 95. NSM Bookham *Guildf* 94-95; C 95-98; Past Tutor Dioc Min Course 97-03; P-in-c Frimley Green 98-01; V Frimley Green and Mytchett 02-03; Prec Ch Ch *Ox* from 03. *Christ Church, Oxford OX1 1DP* Tel (01865) 276214 E-mail mary.bide@christ-church.oxford.ac.uk

BIDE, Peter William. b 12. St Cath Soc Ox BA39 MA45. Wells Th Coll 38. **d** 49 **p** 50. C Portslade St Nic *Chich* 49-55; PC Hangleton 55-57; V Goring-by-Sea 57-59; Asst Gen Sec BCC 59-61; R Lt Hadham *St Alb* 61-64; V Battersea St Luke *S'wark* 64-68; Chapl LMH Ox 68-80; Fell 78-80; rtd 80; Prec Ch Ch *Ox* 80-82; Perm to Offic *Chich* from 80; *Portsm* 84-88. *Meadow Corner, The Street, Boxgrove, Chichester PO18 0DY* Tel (01243) 774134

BIDEN, Neville Douglas. b 31. Lon Univ DipRS80. S'wark Ord Course 76. **d** 79 **p** 80. C Ash *Guildf* 79-82; NSM Surbiton St Andr and St Mark *S'wark* 87-91; Chapl Asst Long Grove Hosp Epsom 90-91; Perm to Offic *Guildf* 90-91 and from 97; C Coulsdon St Jo *S'wark* 91-96; rtd 96; Perm to Offic *Heref* 95-97. *5 Taylor Drive, Bramley, Tadley RG26 5XB* Tel (01256) 880459

BIDGOOD, Julian Paul. b 71. Oak Hill Th Coll. **d** 03. C Ox St Ebbe w H Trin and St Pet *Ox* from 03. *48 Town Furze, Headington, Oxford OX3 7EW* Tel (01865) 765755 *or* 240438 E-mail julianbidgood@hotmail.com

BIELBY, Elaine Elizabeth. b 57. Surrey Univ MSc83. Ripon Coll Cuddesdon DipMin98. **d** 98 **p** 99. C Marton-in-Cleveland *York* 98-01; P-in-c Welton w Melton from 01; Tr Officer E Riding from 01. *The Vicarage, Cowgate, Welton, Brough HU15 1ND* Tel (01482) 666677 E-mail ebielby@fish.co.uk

BIENFAIT, Alexander. b 61. Hatf Poly BSc86. Sarum & Wells Th Coll BTh94. **d** 94 **p** 95. C Battersea St Luke *S'wark* 94-96; C Clapham TM 96-99; TV Whitstable *Cant* from 99. *The Vicarage, Saddleton Road, Whitstable CT5 4JH* Tel (01227) 263152 E-mail alex.bienfait@virgin.net

BIERBAUM, Ms Ruth Anne. b 67. RN89. Trin Coll Bris BA98. **d** 99 **p** 00. C Filey *York* 99-02; C Coxheath, E Farleigh, Hunton, Linton etc *Roch* from 02. *19 Westerhill Road, Coxheath, Maidstone ME17 4DQ* Tel (01622) 743866 Mobile 017984-803728 E-mail ruth@bierbaum.freeserve.co.uk

BIGG, Howard Clive. b 40. Jes Coll Cam BA68 MA72. Ridley Hall Cam 73. **d** 74 **p** 75. C Worksop St Jo *S'well* 74-76; Min Can St Alb 76-77; Perm to Offic *Ches* 78-82; *Ely* 82-99; Vice-Prin Romsey Ho Cam 86-89; NSM Cambridge St Benedict *Ely* 99-01; Perm to Offic from 01. *55 Hemingford Road, Cambridge CB1 3BY* Tel (01223) 514155

BIGGAR, Prof Nigel John. b 55. Worc Coll Ox BA76 MA88 Chicago Univ PhD86 AM80 Regent Coll Vancouver MCS81. **d** 90 **p** 91. Lib Latimer Ho Ox 85-91; Asst Lect Chr Ethics Wycliffe Hall Ox 87-94; Chapl Oriel Coll Ox 90-99; Prof Th Leeds Univ *Ripon* from 99. *Dept of Theology & Religious Studies, University of Leeds, Woodhouse Lane, Leeds LS2 9JT* Tel 0113-233 3652 Fax 233 3654 E-mail n.j.biggar@leeds.ac.uk

BIGGIN, Ronald. b 20. NW Ord Course 70. **d** 73 **p** 74. C Thelwall *Ches* 73-79; V 79-87; rtd 87; NSM Lt Leigh and Lower Whitley *Ches* 90-93; Perm to Offic from 93. *12 Wilmslow Crescent, Thelwall, Warrington WA4 2JE* Tel (01925) 261531

BIGGS, David James. b 55. St Jo Coll Auckland LTh82. **d** 81 **p** 82. New Zealand 81-86; C Stevenage St Andr and St Geo *St Alb* 86-89; TV Moulsecoomb *Chich* 89-99; C Brighton St Pet w Chpl Royal 99-02; P-in-c from 02. *4 Parochial Mews, Princes Street, Brighton BN2 1WF* Tel (01273) 774492

BIGGS, George Ramsay. b 45. Liv Univ BA67 Qu Coll Cam BA73. Westcott Ho Cam 72. **d** 74 **p** 75. C Lee St Aug *S'wark* 74-78; TV Eling, Testwood and Marchwood *Win* 78; TV Totton 78-93; V E and W Wellow 93-98; V E w Wellow and Sherfield English from 98; Hosp Chapl Adv (Bournemouth Adnry) from 02. *Wellow Vicarage, 1 The Beeches, West Wellow, Romsey SO51 6RN* Tel (01794) 323562

BIGGS, Laurence John. b 60. Leeds Univ BSc81. Trin Coll Bris DipHE94. **d** 94 **p** 95. C St Alb St Paul *St Alb* 94-99; V Codicote from 99. *The Vicarage, 4 Bury Lane, Codicote, Hitchin SG4 8XT* Tel (01438) 820266 Fax 822007 E-mail lbiggs@enterprise.net

BIGGS, Laurence Walter. b 23. ACT DipTh73 Roch Th Coll 64. **d** 66 **p** 67. C Cleethorpes *Linc* 66-69; C St Germans *Truro* 69-70; Australia from 70; rtd 88. *Lamport Lane, Old Sale Road, Brandy Creek, via Warragul, Vic, Australia 3820* Tel (0061) (3) 5626 8454

BIGGS, Philip John. b 51. Ripon Hall Ox 74 Ripon Coll Cuddesdon 75. **d** 77 **p** 78. C Maidstone All SS w St Phil and H Trin *Cant* 77-80; Dioc Youth Officer *Truro* 80-84; Australia from 84; Hon Chapl Miss to Seafarers from 84; Chapl St Hilda's Angl Sch Perth 84-87; R Bicton 87-91; R Mosman Park from 92; AD Claremont 98-01. *8 Vlamingh Place, Mosman Park, W Australia 6012* Tel (0061) (8) 9384 4279 *or* 9384 0108 Fax 9384 0108 E-mail bigger@opera.iinet.net.au

BIGGS, Stewart Richard. b 58. SEITE. **d** 01 **p** 02. C Tunbridge Wells St Jas w St Phil *Roch* from 01. *3 Andrews Close, Tunbridge Wells TN2 3PA* Tel (01892) 531297 Mobile 07967-979559 E-mail biggsstewart@hotmail.com

BIGMORE, Graeme Paul. b 57. Univ of Wales (Cardiff) BTh95. St Mich Coll Llan DipTh92. **d** 92 **p** 93. C Cardiff St Jo *Llan* 92-96; Cardiff City Cen Chapl 94-96; C Rhondda 96-98; V Tylorstown w Ynyshir from 98. *The Vicarage, Graig Road, Ynyshir, Porth CF39 0NS* Tel (01443) 684148

BIGNELL, Alan Guy. b 39. Lon Univ BA64. Ox NSM Course 78. **d** 81 **p** 82. NSM Upton cum Chalvey *Ox* 81-90; NSM Burnham and Slough Deanery from 90. *Little Gidding, 2 Wheatlands Road, Slough SL3 7PB* Tel (01753) 523005 E-mail abignell@waitrose.com

BIGNELL, David Charles. b 41. EMMTC 76. **d** 79 **p** 80. C Porchester *S'well* 79-82; V Awsworth w Cossall 82-86; Bp's Ecum Officer from 84; V Edwalton from 86. *The Vicarage, Village Street, Edwalton, Nottingham NG12 4AB* Tel 0115-923 2034

BIGWOOD, Kate Elizabeth. See ATKINSON, Mrs Kate Bigwood

BILES, David George. b 35. AKC58 Open Univ BA75 Lambeth STh91 Leeds Univ MA96. **d** 59 **p** 60. C Cockerton *Dur* 59-62; C Winlaton 62-67; P-in-c Dipton 67-74; R Wolviston 74-89; P-in-c Thirkleby w Kilburn and Bagby *York* 89-90; V 90-00; RD Thirsk 90-91; RD Mowbray 91-00; rtd 00; Perm to Offic *York* from 00. *10 King Rudding Close, Riccall, York YO19 6RY* Tel (01757) 248829 Fax as telephone

BILES, Canon Timothy Mark Frowde. b 35. Univ of Wales DipTh64. St Mich Coll Llan 60. **d** 64 **p** 66. C Middleton St Cross *Ripon* 64-66; Chapl St Fran Sch Hooke 66-72; P-in-c Toller Porcorum w Hooke *Sarum* 72-79; P-in-c Melplash w Mapperton 74-79; P-in-c Beaminster 77-79; TR Beaminster Area 79-00; Can and Preb Sarum Cathl 83-00; RD Beaminster 84-89; rtd 00; Perm to Offic *Sarum* from 01. *36 Hound Street, Sherborne DT9 3AA* Tel (01935) 816247

BILL, Alan. b 29. K Coll Lon BD66 AKC66. **d** 67 **p** 68. C Gt Burstead *Chelmsf* 67-70; TV Thornaby on Tees *York* 71-76; R E Gilling 76-81; V Ormesby 81-91; rtd 91; Perm to Offic *Newc* from 91. *13 Wilmington Close, Tudor Grange, Newcastle upon Tyne NE3 2SF* Tel 0191-242 4467

BILL, Denis Aubrey. b 20. Coll of Resurr Mirfield 48. **d** 50 **p** 51. C Shieldfield Ch Ch *Newc* 50-59; V Cambois 59-64; V Holy Is 64-89; rtd 89; Perm to Offic *Newc* from 89. *The Annex, Etal Manor, Berwick-upon-Tweed TD15 2PU* Tel (01890) 820378

BILL, Thomas Andrew Graham. b 47. Dur Univ BA76 DipTh78. Cranmer Hall Dur 78. **d** 77 **p** 78. C Penwortham St Mary *Blackb* 77-80; C Torrisholme 80-82; P-in-c Accrington St Pet 82-89; P-in-c Haslingden St Jo Stonefold 82-89; V Skerton St Chad from

89. *St Chad's Vicarage, 1 St Chad's Drive, Lancaster LA1 2SE* Tel (01524) 63816 Fax as telephone E-mail tom.bill@lineone.net

BILLETT, Anthony Charles. b 56. Bris Univ BEd. Wycliffe Hall Ox 82. **d** 85 **p** 86. C Waltham Abbey *Chelmsf* 85-88; C Nor St Pet Mancroft w St Jo Maddermarket *Nor* 88-91; V Stalham and E Ruston w Brunstead 91-00; R Stalham, E Ruston, Brunstead, Sutton and Ingham 00-01; R Diss from 01. *The Rectory, 26 Mount Street, Diss IP22 3QG* Tel (01379) 642072 E-mail billett@btinternet.com

BILLETT (née RANDALL), Mrs Elizabeth. b 55. RGN75 SCM81. EAMTC 94. **d** 97 **p** 98. C Loddon, Sisland w Hales and Heckingham *Nor* 97-98; C Loddon, Sisland, Chedgrave, Hardley and Langley 98-01; TV Hempnall from 02. *The Flat, George's House, The Street, Woodton, Bungay NR35 1LZ* Tel (01508) 482366

BILLINGHAM, Canon Peter Charles Geoffrey. b 34. Leeds Univ BA56. Westcott Ho Cam 61. **d** 62 **p** 63. C Halesowen *Worc* 62-66; R Addingham *Bradf* 66-70; R Droitwich St Nic w St Pet *Worc* 70-72; TR Droitwich 72-83; P-in-c Salwarpe 76-80; RD Droitwich 78-83; P-in-c Gt Malvern H Trin 83; P-in-c W Malvern 83; V Malvern H Trin and St Jas 84-99; RD Malvern 92-98; Hon Can Worc Cathl 93-99; rtd 99; Perm to Offic *Sarum* from 00. *57 Foxcroft Drive, Wimborne BH21 2JY* Tel (01202) 840094

BILLINGHURST, Richard George. b 48. St Jo Coll Cam BA70 MA74 FIA76. Ridley Hall Cam 76. **d** 79 **p** 80. C Caverswall *Lich* 79-81; C Cullompton *Ex* 81-84; R Redgrave cum Botesdale w Rickinghall *St E* 84-92; R Skellingthorpe w Doddington *Linc* from 92; RD Graffoe 94-02. *The Rectory, 50 Lincoln Road, Skellingthorpe, Lincoln LN6 5UY* Tel (01522) 682520 Mobile 07971-590378 Fax (01522) 693330 E-mail acorns@clara.co.uk

BILLINGS, Alan Roy. b 42. Em Coll Cam BA65 MA69 Bris Univ PGCE66 Leic Univ MEd75. NY Th Sem DMin87 Linc Th Coll 66. **d** 68 **p** 69. C Knighton St Mary Magd *Leic* 68-72; P-in-c Sheff Gillcar St Silas *Sheff* 72-76; V Beighton 76-77; Hd RE Broadway Sch Barnsley 77-81; Perm to Offic 77-81; V Walkley 81-86; Dir Ox Inst for Ch and Soc 86-92; Perm to Offic *Ox* 86-92; Vice-Prin Ripon Coll Cuddesdon 88-92; Prin WMMTC 92-94; V Kendal St Geo *Carl* from 94; Dir Centre for Ethics and Relig Lanc Univ from 00. *St George's Vicarage, 3 Firbank, Sedbergh Road, Kendal LA9 6BE* Tel (01539) 723039 *or* 720018 Fax 737180 E-mail alan.billings@yahoo.co.uk

BILLINGS, Derek Donald. b 30. Fitzw Ho Cam BA54 MA59. Tyndale Hall Bris 55. **d** 56 **p** 57. C Attenborough w Bramcote and Chilwell *S'well* 56-58; R Ashley w Silverley *Ely* 59-66; V Bottisham 66-80; R Houghton w Wyton 80-97; rtd 97; Perm to Offic *Ely* from 97. *The Limes, 59 Cambridge Street, Godmanchester, Huntingdon PE29 2AY* Tel (01480) 414244

BILLINGS, Roger Key. b 41. AIB. Oak Hill Th Coll BA80. **d** 80 **p** 81. C Tunbridge Wells St Jas *Roch* 80-84; V Chatham St Paul w All SS 84-95; V Carterton *Ox* 95-03; TR Carterton and Brize Norton from 03. *St John's Vicarage, 6 Burford Road, Carterton OX18 3AA* Tel (01993) 846996 *or* 842429 E-mail rkbcar@tinyonline.co.uk

BILLINGSLEY, Raymond Philip. b 48. FCMA80 Open Univ BA98 DASS98. Qu Coll Birm 87. **d** 89 **p** 90. C Yardley St Edburgha *Birm* 89-92; V Ward End 92-96; V Brymbo *St As* from 96. *The Vicarage, Vicarage Road, Brymbo, Wrexham LL11 5LF* Tel (01978) 758107 Mobile 08315-39896

BILLINGTON, Charles Alfred. b 30. Leeds Univ BA55. Coll of Resurr Mirfield 53. **d** 55 **p** 56. C Carl H Trin *Carl* 55-59; CR 59-64; Lic to Offic *Wakef* 60-64; R Man St Aid *Man* 64-66; V Gt Crosby St Faith *Liv* 66-72; R Harrold and Carlton w Chellington *St Alb* 72-80; R Tintinhull w Chilthorne Domer, Yeovil Marsh etc *B & W* 80-81; Chapl Leybourne Grange Hosp W Malling 81-85; Lic to Offic *Roch* 81-85; V Walsden *Wakef* 85-88; R Llanfair Talhaearn and Llansannan etc *St As* 88-97; rtd 97. *27 Lon-y-Mes, Abergele LL22 7JG* Tel (01745) 824563

BILLINGTON, George. b 45. St Jo Coll Nottm Dip Th & Min 94. **d** 94 **p** 95. C Accrington St Jo w Huncoat *Blackb* 94-98; C Whittle-le-Woods 98-00; V Stalmine w Pilling from 00. *St John's Vicarage, Lancaster Road, Pilling, Preston PR3 6AE* Tel (01253) 799170 E-mail george.billington@ukonline.co.uk

BILLOWES, David. b 20. Chich Th Coll. **d** 76 **p** 77. NSM Cowes St Mary *Portsm* 76-91; Chapl St Mary's Hosp Newport 82-91; rtd 91; Perm to Offic *Portsm* from 91. *45 Solent View Road, Gurnard, Cowes PO31 8JZ* Tel (01983) 297366

BILLS, Reginald. b 18. TCert47. Lich Th Coll 68 Wm Temple Coll Rugby DipTh68. **d** 70 **p** 71. C Wednesfield St Thos *Lich* 70-73; C Wolverhampton St Pet 73-79; Chapl St Pet Colleg Sch 73-79; C Wolverhampton St Andr 79-81; P-in-c Brockmoor 81-87; rtd 87. *43 Kewstoke Road, Willenhall WV12 5DY* Tel (01922) 405049

BILNEY, Kenneth Henry. b 25. FBCS. St Deiniol's Hawarden 75. **d** 75 **p** 76. Hon C Knighton St Mary Magd *Leic* 75-78; C St Jas 78-80; R Leire w Ashby Parva and Dunton Bassett 80-90; rtd 90; Perm to Offic *Leic* from 90. *20 Ferndale Road, Leicester LE2 6GN* Tel 0116-257 0436

BILSTON, Barbara Bradley. b 35. Man Univ BA58 Essex Univ MA75. EAMTC 96. **d** 97 **p** 98. NSM Bacton w Wyverstone and Cotton *St E* 97-00; NSM Bacton w Wyverstone, Cotton and Old Newton etc from 00. *Boy's Hall, Ward Green, Old Newton, Stowmarket IP14 4EY* Tel and fax (01449) 781253 Mobile 07889-516674 E-mail b.b.bilston@open.ac.uk

BILTON, Paul Michael. b 52. AKC74. St Aug Coll Cant 74. **d** 75 **p** 76. C Skipton Ch Ch *Bradf* 75-79; Ind Chapl Worc 79-81; V Greetland and W Vale *Wakef* 81-88; R Mablethorpe w Trusthorpe *Linc* 88-91; V Bradf St Wilfrid Lidget Green *Bradf* from 91; P-in-c Bradf St Columba w St Andr from 01; RD Bowling and Horton from 02. *St Wilfrid's Vicarage, Lidget Green, Bradford BD7 2LU* Tel (01274) 572504

BIMSON, Sarah Margaret. b 56. St Jo Coll Nottm BA. **d** 03. C Maidstone St Martin *Cant* from 03. *85 Loose Road, Maidstone ME15 7DA* Tel (01622) 679432 E-mail sara.bimson@btopenworld.com

BINDING, Ms Frances Mary. b 59. York Univ BA81 Newc Poly PGCE82. WEMTC 98. **d** 02. C Bromyard *Heref* from 02. *12 Lower Thorn, Bromyard HR7 4AZ* Tel (01885) 482620 E-mail franbinding@lineone.net

BINDOFF, Ms Anna. b 70. Leeds Univ BA94. Ripon Coll Cuddesdon BA97. **d** 98 **p** 99. Asst Chapl New Coll Ox 98-01; Hon C Blackbird Leys *Ox* 98-01; C from 01. *23 Brook Street, Watlington OX49 5JH* Tel (01491) 613327

BINDOFF, Stanley. b 54. Sarum & Wells Th Coll 79. **d** 82 **p** 83. C Thirsk 82-86; Chapl HM YOI Northallerton 85-89; P-in-c Rounton w Welbury *York* 86-89; Chapl HM Pris Gartree 89-92; Chapl HM Pris Frankland 92-96; Chapl HM YOI Deerbolt 96-03; TR Castleford *Wakef* from 03. *The Rectory, 15 Barnes Road, Castleford WF10 5AA* Tel (01977) 733796 Pager 07693-277628 E-mail fr_stan@blueyonder.co.uk

BINDON, Joan Vereker. b 19. K Coll Lon DipTh47. St Chris Coll Blackheath 47. **d** 67. New Zealand from 67; rtd 79. *3/149 Church Street, Onehunga, Auckland 1006, New Zealand* Tel (0064) (9) 634 3920

BING, Alan Charles. b 56. St Edm Hall Ox BA78 MA91 DipInstM83 Ex Univ MA96. Oak Hill Th Coll DipHE91. **d** 91 **p** 92. C Fremington *Ex* 91-94; C-in-c Roundswell CD 94-97; TV Barnstaple 97-99; Chapl N Devon Coll Barnstaple 96-99; P-in-c Ulverston St Mary w H Trin *Carl* from 99. *The Rectory, 15 Ford Park Crescent, Ulverston LA12 7JR* Tel (01229) 584331 Fax as telephone E-mail alanbing@fish.co.uk

BINGHAM, Mrs Marie Joyce Phyllis. b 27. Glouc Sch of Min 80. **dss** 84 **d** 87 **p** 94. Glouc St Mary de Crypt w St Jo and Ch Ch *Glouc* 84-85; Glouc St Mary de Lode and St Nic 85-87; Hon C 87-95; Hon C Glouc St Mary de Crypt w St Jo and Ch Ch 94-95; Hon C Glouc St Mary de Crypt w St Jo, Ch Ch etc 95-98; Perm to Offic from 98. *Hazel Cottage, Sandhurst, Gloucester GL2 9NP* Tel (01452) 730285

BINGHAM, Norman James Frederick. b 26. Lon Univ BSc51. Tyndale Hall Bris 61. **d** 63 **p** 64. C Chell *Lich* 63-67; C Macclesfield St Mich *Ches* 67-71; P-in-c Macclesfield St Pet 71-73; V Leyton St Mary w St Edw *Chelmsf* 73-91; RD Waltham Forest 81-86; P-in-c Leyton St Luke 82-91; rtd 91; Perm to Offic *St Alb* from 91. *97 Monks Walk, Buntingford SG9 9DP* Tel (01763) 272275

BINKS, Canon Edmund Vardy. b 36. K Coll Lon BD61 AKC61 Liv Univ Hon LLD98 FRSA89. **d** 62 **p** 63. C Selby Abbey *York* 62-65; Asst Chapl Univ Coll of Ripon and York St Jo 65-83; Hd St Kath Coll 83-87; Prin Ches Coll *Ches* from 87; Hon Can Ches Cathl 95-98; Perm to Offic *Chich* from 98; rtd 01. *2 Lodge Close, Lewes BN7 1AR* Tel (01273) 487136

BINLEY, Miss Teresa Mary. b 37. Dalton Ho Bris 61. **d** 87 **p** 94. Par Dn Ashton-upon-Mersey St Mary *Ches* 87-92; Bp's Officer for Women in Min 87-92; C Chaddesden St Mary *Derby* 92-98; rtd 98; Perm to Offic *Derby* from 98. *27 Hindscarth Crescent, Mickleover, Derby DE3 9NN* Tel (01332) 511146

BINNEY, Mark James Gurney. b 58. K Coll Lon BD80. Qu Coll Birm 84. **d** 86 **p** 87. C Hornchurch St Andr *Chelmsf* 86-89; C Hutton 89-91; V Pheasey *Lich* 91-96; TV Wombourne w Trysull and Bobbington 96-99; V Wilnecote from 99. *The Vicarage, Glascote Lane, Wilnecote, Tamworth B77 2PH* Tel (01827) 280806 Mobile 07703-359204

BINNIAN, Mrs Jennifer Ann. b 34. Qu Coll Birm 81. **dss** 84 **d** 87 **p** 94. Chaddesley Corbett and Stone *Worc* 84-85; Bewdley Far Forest 85-87; Chapl Kemp Hospice 87-96; Chapl Asst Kidderminster Gen Hosp 87-94; rtd 96; Perm to Offic *Worc* from 96. *Bodenham Farm, Wolverley, Kidderminster DY11 5SY* Tel (01562) 850382

BINNS, David John. b 39. Moore Th Coll Sydney ThL64. **d** 64 **p** 65. Australia 64-67 and from 70; C Norbiton *S'wark* 67-69; R Adelaide St Luke 80-98; Assoc Min 98-00; rtd 00. *Unit 4/2 Spence Avenue, Myrtle Bank, S Australia 5064* Tel (0061) (8) 8338 5779 Mobile 0417-860560 E-mail djb29@ozemail.com.au

BINNS, John Richard. b 51. Cam Univ MA70 Lon Univ PhD89. Coll of Resurr Mirfield 74. **d** 76 **p** 77. C Clapham H Trin *S'wark* 76-78; C Clapham Old Town 78-80; TV Mortlake w E Sheen 80-87; V Upper Tooting H Trin 87-94; V Cambridge Gt St Mary w St Mich *Ely* from 94. *Great St Mary's Vicarage, 39 Madingley Road, Cambridge CB3 0EL* Tel (01223) 355285 *or* 741716 Fax 462914 E-mail bep21@cam.ac.uk

BINNS, Peter Rodney. b 44. St Andr Univ MA66. Ox NSM Course 72. d 75 p 76. NSM Amersham on the Hill *Ox* 75-90; NSM Wingrave w Rowsham, Aston Abbotts and Cublington 90-97; NSM Hawridge w Cholesbury and St Leonard 90-97; NSM Amersham on the Hill from 97. *16 Turnfurlong Row, Turnfurlong Lane, Aylesbury HP21 7FF* Tel (01296) 330836 Fax 337965

BINNY, John Wallace. b 46. Univ of Wales (Lamp) BA70. St Mich Coll Llan 69. d 71 p 72. C Llantrisant *Llan* 71-77; V Troedyrhiw w Merthyr Vale 77-82; R Eglwysbrewis w St Athan, Flemingston, Gileston 82-95; R Eglwysbrewis w St Athan w Gileston 95-03; V Pentyrch w Capel Llanilltterne from 03. *The Vicarage, Church Road, Pentyrch, Cardiff CF15 9QF* Tel (029) 2089 0318

BIRBECK, Anthony Leng. b 33. MBE90. Linc Coll Ox BA59 MA61. Linc Th Coll 58. d 60 p 61. C Redcar *York* 60-62; C Teesside Ind Miss 62-74; Can Res and Treas Wells Cathl *B & W* 74-78; NSM Wells St Thos w Horrington 89-98; rtd 98; Perm to Offic *B & W* from 98. *Beeches, Cannard's Grave Road, Shepton Mallet BA4 4LX* Tel (01749) 330382 Mobile 07802-725024 E-mail tony-birbeck@msn.com

BIRBECK, John Trevor. b 49. AIB77. St Jo Coll Nottm 86. d 88 p 89. C Eccleshill *Bradf* 88-92; V Hurst Green and Mitton 92-03; R Rawmarsh w Parkgate *Sheff* from 03. *The Rectory, 2 High Street, Rawmarsh, Rotherham S62 6NE* Tel (01709) 527160 E-mail john.birbeck@ntlworld.com

BIRCH, Arthur James Fleet. b 14. Univ Coll Dur BA36 MA39. d 37 p 38. C W Bromwich Ch Ch *Lich* 37-41; C Wroxeter 41-43; C Crewe St Jo *Ches* 43-46; V Lostock Gralam 46-55; V Plemstall w Guilden Sutton 55-59; V Hooton 59-70; R Lymm 70-79; rtd 79; Perm to Offic *Ches* from 79. *21 Arran Drive, Frodsham WA6 6AL* Tel (01928) 733709

BIRCH, Arthur Kenneth. b 15. Qu Coll Birm 46. d 48 p 49. C St Alb St Paul *St Alb* 48-50; Area Sec (Dios Ely, Nor and St E & I) CMS 50-55; V New Catton Ch Ch *Nor* 55-60; V Buxton w Oxnead 60-71; R Lammas w Lt Hautbois 60-71; Uganda 71-75; V Fence in Pendle *Blackb* 75-76; C Bollington St Jo *Ches* 77-79; R Church Lawton 79-81; rtd 81; Perm to Offic *Sarum* 81-95; Perm to Offic *Nor* from 95. *26 Smugglers Lane, Reepham, Norwich NR10 4QT* Tel (01603) 871405

BIRCH, Derek. b 31. Univ of Wales (Lamp) BA58. Coll of Resurr Mirfield 58. d 60 p 61. C S Elmsall *Wakef* 60-62; C Penistone w Midhope 62-66; V Silkstone 66-89; Chapl Stainborough 76-89; P-in-c Hoyland Swaine 85-89; V Hoylandswaine and Silkstone w Stainborough 89-97; rtd 98; Perm to Offic *Wakef* from 98. *46 Pengeston Road, Penistone, Sheffield S36 6GW* Tel (01226) 761523

BIRCH, Graham James. b 62. N Ord Course BTh94. d 97 p 98. C Southport St Phil and St Paul *Liv* 97-01; P-in-c Wigan St Cath from 01. *St Catharine's Vicarage, St Catharine Terrace, Wigan WN1 3JW* Tel (01942) 820668

BIRCH, Henry Arthur. b 24. St Jo Coll Dur BA48. Tyndale Hall Bris 48. d 49 p 50. C Edin St Thos *Edin* 49-51; C Surbiton Hill Ch Ch *S'wark* 51-54; R Uphill *B & W* 54-69; Australia 69-81 and from 84; S Africa 81-84; rtd 91. *9/87 Yathong Road, Carringbah, NSW, Australia 2229* Tel (0061) (2) 9525 1763

BIRCH, Janet Ann. St Alb Minl Tr Scheme 77. dss 80 d 87 p 94. Luton St Mary *St Alb* 80-87; Par Dn Streatley 87-91; rtd 91; NSM Aldeburgh w Hazlewood *St E* 91-01; Perm to Offic from 01. *Market Cross House, Wentworth Road, Aldeburgh IP15 5BJ* Tel (01728) 453371

BIRCH, Mark Russell. b 70. Bris Univ BVSc93 Em Coll Cam 99. Westcott Ho Cam 97. d 00 p 01. C Cirencester *Glouc* from 00. Chapl and Fell Ex Coll Ox from 03. *Exeter College, Oxford OX1 3DP* Tel (01865) 279600 E-mail markrbirch@netscapeonline.co.uk

BIRCH, Richard Arthur. b 51. d 01 p 02. NSM Foord St Jo *Cant* from 01. *38 Martello Drive, Hythe CT21 6PJ* Tel (01303) 267155 E-mail richarda.birch@virgin.net

BIRCH, Shirley Anne. b 34. EMMTC 88. d 91 p 94. Hon Par Dn Bottesford w Muston *Leic* 91-93; NSM Melton Mowbray 93-01; NSM Minster-in-Sheppey *Cant* from 02. *St Peter's House, 2 St Clare's Close, Minster on Sea, Sheerness ME12 3DD* Tel (01795) 872199

BIRCHALL, John Dearman. b 70. St Andr Univ MA93. Wycliffe Hall Ox BTh99. d 99 p 00. C Purley Ch Ch *S'wark* 99-02; C Merton Anger *Sarum* from 02. *14 Wyndham Park, Salisbury SP1 3BA* Tel (01722) 416577 E-mail john@jssbirchall.freeserve.co.uk

BIRCHALL, Robert Gary. b 59. Sheff Univ BA81. St Jo Coll Nottm 85. d 88 p 89. C Manston *Ripon* 88-91; C Leic Martyrs 91-94; C New Humberstone 94-95; V Burnopfield *Dur* from 95. *The Vicarage, Front Street, Burnopfield, Newcastle upon Tyne NE16 6HQ* Tel (01207) 270261 E-mail gmsr@globalnet.co.uk

BIRCHARD, Canon Thaddeus Jude. b 45. Louisiana State Univ 66 Nottm Univ DipTh68. Kelham Th Coll 66. d 70 p 71. C

Devonport St Mark Ford *Ex* 70-73; C Southend St Jo w St Mark, All SS w St Fran etc *Chelmsf* 73-76; TV Poplar *Lon* 76-80; V Paddington St Jo w St Mich 80-01; Hon Can Louisiana from 90; rtd 01. *142 Dibdin House, Maida Vale, London W9 1QG* Tel (020) 7328 2380

BIRCHMORE, Brian Leonard. b 35. ALCD59. d 59 p 60. C Rusthall *Roch* 59-62; C Rainham 62-64; C Belvedere All SS 64-66; V Meopham 66-74; R Chatham St Mary w St Jo 74-75; Perm to Offic *Chelmsf* 81-83; Ind Chapl Harlow 83-89; P-in-c Bush End and Hatfield Broad Oak 83-89; P-in-c Greenstead 89-97; C All Hallows by the Tower etc *Lon* 97-01; rtd 01. *39 Elmbrook Drive, Bishop's Stortford CM23 4JB* Tel (01279) 507612

BIRD, Mrs Ann Maud. b 39. d 00 p 01. OLM W Bromwich All SS *Lich* from 00. *16 Caldwell Street, West Bromwich B71 2DN* Tel 0121-588 4335

BIRD (née BAKER), Mrs Anne-Marie Clare. b 56. Wye Coll Lon BSc78 Glas Univ MSc80. St Jo Coll Nottm 88. d 90 p 94. Par Dn Levenshulme St Pet *Man* 90-94; C 94-95; P-in-c Crumpsall 95-03; TV Keynsham *B & W* from 03. *9 Chelmer Grove, Keynsham, Bristol BS31 1QA* Tel 0117-986 1837

BIRD, Anthony Peter. b 31. St Jo Coll Ox BA54 BTh55 MA57 Birm Univ MB, ChB70. Cuddesdon Coll 55. d 57 p 58. C Stafford St Mary *Lich* 57-60; Chapl Cuddesdon Coll 60-61; Vice-Prin 61-64; C Selly Oak St Wulstan *Birm* 64-68; Lic to Offic 68-79; Prin Qu Coll Birm 74-79; Perm to Offic *Birm* from 85; rtd 96. *93 Bournbrook Road, Birmingham B29 7BX*

BIRD, Brian Edward. b 37. Rhodes Univ BA. d 75. S Africa 75-99; Bp's C Mt Merrion *D & D* from 99. *122 Mount Merrion Avenue, Belfast BT6 0FS* Tel (028) 9029 4471 Fax as telephone

BIRD, The Ven Colin Richard Bateman. b 33. Selw Coll Cam BA56 MA61. Cuddesdon Coll 56. d 58 p 59. S Africa 58-70; C Limpsfield and Titsey *S'wark* 70-75; V Hatcham St Cath 75-88; RD Deptford 80-85; Hon Can S'wark Cathl 82-88; Adn Lambeth 88-99; P-in-c Brixton Hill St Sav 91-94; rtd 00; Perm to Offic *St E* from 00; *Chelmsf* and *Nor* from 01. *32 Bristol Road, Bury St Edmunds IP33 2DL* Tel (01284) 723810 E-mail dick_val@hotmail.com

BIRD, David John. b 46. Univ of Wales (Lamp) BA70 Duquesne Univ PhD87. Gen Th Sem (NY) STM74. d 70 p 71. C Kidderminster St Geo *Worc* 70-72; USA from 72. *3933 Idaho Avenue North West, Washington, DC 20008-3107, USA* Tel (001) (202) 537 6072 *or* 333 7100 E-mail david3933@aol.com

BIRD, Canon David Ronald. b 55. York Univ BA76. St Jo Coll Nottm 83. d 86 p 87. C Kinson *Sarum* 86-90; R Thrapston *Pet* 90-97; P-in-c Islip 94-95; RD Higham 94-97; V Northampton St Giles from 97; Can Pet Cathl from 01. *St Giles's Vicarage, 2 Spring Gardens, Northampton NN1 1LX* Tel (01604) 634060 Fax 628623 E-mail david@dbird.freeserve.co.uk

BIRD, Donald Wilfred Ray. b 27. Dur Univ BA52. Linc Th Coll 61. d 63 p 64. C E w W Barkwith *Linc* 63-65; Rhodesia 66-80; R Scotter w E Ferry *Linc* 80-92; rtd 92; Zimbabwe 94; Perm to Offic *Ban* from 97 and *Bradf* from 00. *18 Park Place, Hellifield, Skipton BD23 4HB* Tel (01729) 850310

BIRD, Douglas Norman. b 38. LNSM course 89. d 92 p 93. OLM New Bury *Man* from 92. *10 Hawthorne Avenue, Horwich, Bolton BL6 6JD* Tel (01204) 480000

BIRD, Canon Frederick Hinton. b 38. St Edm Hall Ox BA62 MA66 Univ of Wales MEd81 PhD86. St D Coll Lamp BD65. d 65 p 66. C Mynyddislwyn *Mon* 65-67; Min Can St Woolos Cathl 67-70; Chapl Anglo-American Coll Farringdon 70-71; Perm to Offic *Ox* 70-78; Perm to Offic *Cant* 72-78; Perm to Offic *Mon* 76-82; V Rushen *S & M* from 82; Can St German's Cathl from 93. *Kirk Rushen Vicarage, Barracks Road, Port St Mary, Isle of Man IM9 5LP* Tel (01624) 832275

BIRD, Geoffrey. b 44. Dioc OLM tr scheme 97. d 99 p 00. Asst Chapl HM YOI and Remand Cen Brinsford 99; Sen Chapl from 99. *HM YOI Brinsford, New Road, Featherstone, Wolverhampton WV10 7PY* Tel (01902) 791118

BIRD, Canon Geoffrey Neville. b 22. AKC48. St Boniface Warminster 48. d 49 p 50. C Berkeley *Glouc* 49-53; C Malder St Jo *S'wark* 53-54; C Glouc St Aldate *Glouc* 54-56; R Edge w Pitchcombe 56-82; P-in-c Brookthorpe w Whaddon and Harescombe 76-82; V The Edge, Pitchcombe, Harescombe and Brookthorpe 82-90; Hon Can Glouc Cathl 83-90; RD Bisley 84-90; rtd 90; Perm to Offic *Glouc* from 90. *Ivycroft, Winstone, Cirencester GL7 7JZ* Tel (01285) 821664

BIRD, Henry John Joseph. b 37. ARCO58 Qu Coll Cam BA59 MA63. Linc Th Coll 62. d 64 p 65. C Harbledown *Cant* 64-68; C Skipton H Trin *Bradf* 68-70; V Oakworth 70-81; Chapl Abingdon Sch 81-82; P-in-c Doncaster St Geo *Sheff* 82-85; V 85-02; rtd 02. *278 Thorne Road, Doncaster DN2 5AJ* Tel (01302) 326041

BIRD, Hugh Claud Handley. b 24. FRCGP SS Coll Cam MA MB BCh. Ridley Hall Cam. d 86 p 86. NSM Coxheath w E Farleigh Hunton and Linton *Roch* 86-95; Perm to Offic *Cant* from 95. *The Slate Barn, Seamark Road, Brooksend, Birchington CT7 0JL* Tel (01843) 846619

BIRD, Jeffrey David. b 54. Nottm Univ BCombStuds85. Linc Th Coll 82. **d** 85 **p** 86. C Frome St Jo *B & W* 85-88; Asst Chapl HM Pris Pentonville 88-89; Chapl HM Pris Dartmoor 89-95; Chapl HM Pris Albany 95-03; Chapl HM Pris Linc from 03. *The Chaplain's Office, HM Prison, Greetwell Road, Lincoln LN2 4BD* Tel (01522) 663090 Fax 663001

BIRD, Jeremy Paul. b 56. Ex Univ BSc77 DipTh78 Hull Univ MA88. Sarum Th Coll 78. **d** 80 **p** 81. C Tavistock and Gulworthy *Ex* 80-83; Chapl Teesside Poly *York* 83-88; R Chipstable w Huish Champflower and Clatworthy *B & W* 88-93; Rural Affairs Officer 88-93; V Uffculme *Ex* 93-01; P-in-c Dawlish from 01. *The Vicarage, 13 West Cliff Road, Dawlish EX7 9EB* Tel (01626) 862021

BIRD, John Anthony. b 45. EMMTC. **d** 03. NSM Thringstone St Andr *Leic* from 03. *8 Buckingham Road, Thorpe Acre, Loughborough LE11 4TE* Tel (01509) 234962

BIRD, Maurice Pidding. b 19. Linc Coll Ox BA40 MA44. Cuddesdon Coll 40. **d** 42 **p** 43. C Malden St Jo *S'wark* 42-43; C Headington *Ox* 43-46; C Eastney *Portsm* 47-55; Chapl Hostel of God Clapham 55-59; R Winterton w E Somerton *Nor* 59-71; V Heigham St Barn 71-75; V Heigham St Barn w St Bart 75-82; P-in-c Edington and Imber *Sarum* 82-83; P-in-c Erlestoke and Gt Cheverell 82-83; P-in-c Edington and Imber, Erlestoke and E Coulston 83-88; rtd 88; Perm to Offic *Ripon* from 88; Perm to Offic *Wakef* 88-97 and from 98. *61 Beechwood, Woodlesford, Leeds LS26 8PQ* Tel 0113-282 0865

BIRD, Norman David. b 32. CQSW73. Coll of Resurr Mirfield 87. **d** 89 **p** 90. NSM Willesden Green St Andr and St Fran *Lon* 89-92; NSM Preston Ascension 93-98; rtd 98. *5 Oldfield Road, London NW10 9UD* Tel (020) 8451 4160

BIRD, Peter Andrew. b 40. Wadh Coll Ox BA62 MA68. Ridley Hall Cam 63. **d** 65 **p** 66. C Keynsham w Queen Charlton *B & W* 65-68; C Strood St Nic *Roch* 68-72; TV Strood 72-79; V S Gillingham 79-89; V Westerham 89-02; Hon Can Roch Cathl 01-02. *Iona Prospect View, Stanedge Road, Bakewell DE45 1DG* Tel (01629) 813087

BIRD, Rex Alan. b 30. Trin Coll Bris 54. **d** 57 **p** 58. C Wellington Ch Ch *Lich* 57-59; C St Alb St Paul *St Alb* 59-61; V Rainham *Chelmsf* 61-65; R Wennington 61-65; R Lavenham *St E* 65-75; CF (TA) from 65; RD Lavenham *St E* 72-75; Dean and V Battle *Chich* 75-84; V Castle Hedingham *Chelmsf* 84-91; R Monks Eleigh w Chelsworth and Brent Eleigh etc *St E* 91-99; rtd 99; Perm to Offic *St E* from 00. *6 Deacons Close, Lavenham, Sudbury CO10 9SZ* Tel (01787) 247657

BIRD, Richard. *See* BIRD, The Ven Colin Richard Bateman

BIRD, Canon Roger Alfred. b 49. AKC72. St Aug Coll Cant 72. **d** 73 **p** 74. C Prestatyn *St As* 73-78; R Llandysilio and Penrhos and Llandrinio etc 78-92; Dioc RE Adv from 84; Dioc Dir of Educn from 89; R Guilsfield 92-97; R Guilsfield w Pool Quay 97-02; V Guilsfield w Buttington from 02; Hon Can St As Cathl from 93; RD Pool 96-01. *The Vicarage, Guilsfield, Welshpool SY21 9NF* Tel (01938) 554245 Fax as telephone
E-mail rogerb@infinnet.co.uk

BIRDSEYE, Miss Jacqueline Ann. b 55. Sussex Univ BEd78 Southn Univ BTh88 K Coll Lon MTh93. Sarum & Wells Th Coll 85. **d** 88 **p** 94. C Egham Hythe *Guildf* 88-91; C Fleet 91-92; C Shottermill 92-95; C Leavesden All SS *St Alb* 95-98; R Ashwell w Hinxworth and Newnham from 98. *The Rectory, Hodwell, Ashwell, Baldock SG7 5QQ* Tel (01462) 742277

BIRDWOOD, William Halhed. b 51. St Jo Coll Dur BA73. Sarum & Wells Th Coll 76. **d** 78 **p** 79. C Royston *St Alb* 78-82; C Thorley w Bishop's Stortford H Trin 82-89; Chapl HM Pris Ex 89-96; Chapl HM Pris Dartmoor from 96; Lic to Offic Ex from 89. *HM Prison Dartmoor, Princetown, Yelverton PL20 6RR* Tel (01822) 890261 Fax 890679

BIRKENHEAD, Suffragan Bishop of. *See* URQUHART, The Rt Revd David Andrew

BIRKET, Cyril. b 28. ACIS70. NW Ord Course 71. **d** 74 **p** 75. C Broughton *Blackb* 74-79; V Wesham 79-86; V Overton 86-96; rtd 96; Perm to Offic *Blackb* from 96 and *Bradf* 96-01. *61 Twemlow Parade, Heysham, Morecambe LA3 2AL* Tel (01524) 852870
E-mail cyril@clerical.freeserve.co.uk

BIRKETT, Mrs Joyce. b 38. WMMTC 84. **d** 87 **p** 94. Par Dn Hill *Birm* 87-91; Asst Chapl Highcroft Hosp Birm 87-91; Par Dn Rowley Regis *Birm* 91-94; C 94-96; V Londonderry 96-01; rtd 01. *83 Callowbrook Lane, Rubery, Rednal, Birmingham B45 9HP* Tel 0121-457 9759

BIRKETT, Neil Warren. b 45. Lanc Univ BEd74 Southn Univ MA84. Kelham Th Coll 65. **d** 77 **p** 77. NSM Win St Matt *Win* from 77. *Corrymeela, 132 Teg Down Meads, Winchester SO22 5NS* Tel (01962) 864910

BIRKETT, Peter. b 13. Univ Coll Dur BA35 MA39. **d** 36 **p** 37. C Boxley *Cant* 36-38; C Birchington w Acol 38-40; Chapl RAFVR 40-46; V Charing *Cant* 46-51; R Crowcombe *B & W* 51-64; P-in-c Bicknoller 60-62; V Castle Cary w Ansford 64-69; R Holford w Dodington 69-77; rtd 78; Perm to Offic *B & W* 82-87. *14 Long Street, Williton, Taunton TA4 4NQ*

BIRKIN, Mrs Elspeth Joyce (Joy). b 36. CertEd58. WMMTC 95. **d** 96 **p** 97. NSM Hanley Castle, Hanley Swan and Welland *Worc*

96-01; NSM Berrow w Pendock, Eldersfield, Hollybush etc from 01. *9 Hastings Road, Malvern WR14 2SS* Tel (01684) 569493

BIRKINSHAW, Ian George. b 58. Pemb Coll Ox BA81 Leeds Univ MA97 Sheff Univ PGCE82. N Ord Course 93. **d** 96 **p** 97. NSM Chapeltown *Sheff* 96-97; C Normanton *Wakef* 98-01; C York St Mich-le-Belfrey *York* from 01. *13 Hempland Drive, York YO31 1AY* Tel (01924) 422418

BIRLEY, John Lindsay. b 19. Kelham Th Coll 37. **d** 43 **p** 44. C Coulsdon St Andr *S'wark* 43-46; Asst Chapl Wellingborough Sch 46-48; Asst Master Choristers' Sch Ex 48-50; Chapl Reed's Sch Cobham 50-54; Asst Chapl St Jo Sch Leatherhead 54-64; Asst Master Wellington Coll Berks 64-76; rtd 76. *Abtei Himmerod, D 54534 Grosslittgen, Germany* Tel (0049) (6575) 96075

BIRMINGHAM, Archdeacon of. *See* OSBORNE, The Ven Hayward John

BIRMINGHAM, Bishop of. *See* SENTAMU, The Rt Revd John Mugabi

BIRMINGHAM, Dean of. *See* MURSELL, The Very Revd Alfred Gordon

BIRT, David Edward. b 26. St Steph Ho Ox 86. **d** 86 **p** 87. NSM Ealing Ch the Sav *Lon* 86-99; Perm to Offic from 99. *10 Manor Court Road, London W7 3EL* Tel (020) 8579 4871

BIRT, Patrick. b 34. Glouc Th Course 71. **d** 75 **p** 75. NSM Bisley *Glouc* 75-76; NSM Whiteshill 76-81; C Stroud H Trin 81; R Ruardean 81-86; V Newbridge-on-Wye and Llanfihangel Brynpabuan *S & B* 86-88; TV Gillingham *Sarum* 88-99; rtd 99; Perm to Offic *Sarum* from 01. *Hornbeam Cottage, Green Lane, Stour Row, Shaftesbury SP7 0QD* Tel (01747) 839716

BIRT, Richard Arthur. b 43. Ch Ch Ox BA66 MA69. Cuddesdon Coll 67. **d** 69 **p** 70. C Sutton St Mich *York* 69-71; C Wollaton *S'well* 71-75; R Kirkby in Ashfield 75-80; P-in-c Duxford *Ely* 80-87; R 87-88; P-in-c Hinxton 80-87; V 87-88; P-in-c Ickleton 80-87; V 87-88; V Weobley w Sarnesfield and Norton Canon *Heref* 88-00; P-in-c Letton w Staunton, Byford, Mansel Gamage etc 88-00; rtd 00. *18 Ingestre Street, Hereford HR4 0DU*

BIRTWISTLE, Canon James. b 53. FCA66. Ely Th Coll 57. **d** 59 **p** 60. C Southport St Luke *Liv* 59-63; V Cleator Moor w Cleator *Carl* 63-70; R Letchworth *St Alb* 70-73; P-in-c Wareside 73-80; Dep Dir of Educn 77-80; Dioc Dir of Educn 80-98; Hon Can St Alb 85-98; P-in-c Hertingfordbury 89-98; rtd 98; Perm to Offic *Ex* from 99. *9 Stoneborough Lane, Budleigh Salterton EX9 6HL* Tel (01395) 442517

BIRTWISTLE, Lesley Sutherland. b 44. LLB. EMMTC 00. **d** 00 **p** 01. NSM Appleby Gp *Leic* from 00. *14 Nethercroft Drive, Packington, Ashby-de-la-Zouch LE65 1WT* Tel (01530) 833333 or 413309

BISASO-SEKITOLEKO, Capt Samuel. b 66. St Paul's Coll Limuru DipTh93 Cheltenham & Glouc Coll of HE BA99. **d** 99 **p** 02. NSM Matson *Glouc* 99; NSM Ponders End St Matt *Lon* 01-02; NSM Brownswood Park from 02. *St John's Vicarage, 2A Gloucester Drive, London N4 2LW* Tel 07944-800605 (mobile) E-mail sambisaso@aol.com

BISCOE, Clive. b 45. St Deiniol's Hawarden 85. **d** 87 **p** 87. C Llansamlet *S & B* 86-90; V Landore 90-91. *6 Hazelwood Row, Cwmavon, Port Talbot SA12 9DP*

BISH, Donald. b 26. Ripon Hall Ox. **d** 75 **p** 75. C S Gillingham *Roch* 75-79; R Wateringbury w Teston and W Farleigh 79-92; rtd 92; Perm to Offic *Cant* from 92; Perm to Offic *Roch* 92-98 and from 00. *5 Eynesford Road, Allington, Maidstone ME16 0TD* Tel (01622) 661847

BISHOP, Mrs Alice Margaret Marion. b 67. Newnham Coll Cam BA89 MA93 Lon Univ MTh92. St Steph Ho Ox 92. **d** 94. C Stepney St Dunstan and All SS *Lon* 94-99. *The Vicarage, Church Lane, Old Basing, Basingstoke RG24 7DJ* Tel (01256) 473762

BISHOP, Andrew Scott. b 70. Leeds Univ BA93 Heythrop Coll Lon MTh02. St Steph Ho Ox BTh93. **d** 96 **p** 97. C Westmr St Steph w St Jo *Lon* 96-99; C Kensington St Mary Abbots w St Geo 99-03; V Basing *Win* from 03. *The Vicarage, Church Lane, Old Basing, Basingstoke RG24 7DJ* Tel (01256) 473762
E-mail andrew_bishop@talk21.com

BISHOP, Canon Anthony John. b 43. G&C Coll Cam BA66 MA69 Lon Univ MTh69. ALCD67. **d** 69 **p** 70. C Eccleston St Luke *Liv* 69-73; C Gt Baddow *Chelmsf* 73-77; Nigeria 77-84; Lect Lon Bible Coll 84-85; TV Chigwell *Chelmsf* 85-93; P-in-c Walthamstow St Jo 93-98; V from 98; Hon Can Kano from 00. *St John's Vicarage, Brookscroft Road, London E17 4LH* Tel (020) 8531 6249 E-mail bishop@fish.co.uk

BISHOP, The Ven Anthony Peter. b 46. CB01. Nottm Univ LTh74 MPhil84 ALCD71 FRSA87. St Jo Coll Nottm 71. **d** 71 **p** 72. C Beckenham St Geo *Roch* 71-75; Chapl RAF 75-91; Command Chapl RAF 91-98; Chapl-in-Chief RAF 98-01; Can and Preb Linc Cathl *Linc* 98-01; Hon C Tewkesbury w Walton Cardiff and Twyning *Glouc* from 01. *The Vicarage, Churchend, Twyning GL20 6DA* Tel (01684) 290765

BISHOP, Miss Cecil Marie. b 18. Lon Univ LLB40 DipTh48. St Chris Coll Blackheath 46 Gilmore Ho 56. **dss** 57 **d** 87. Jamaica 57-74; The Gambia 74-76; Lic to Offic *Ex* 76-87; rtd 78; Hon Par Dn Paignton St Jo *Ex* 87-94; Perm to Offic from 94. *Flat 5,*

Lancaster House, Belle Vue Road, Paignton TQ4 6HD Tel (01803) 523522

BISHOP, Canon Christopher. b 48. K Coll Lon. St Aug Coll Cant 71. **d** 72 **p** 73. C Gt Ilford St Mary *Chelmsf* 72-75; C Upminster 75-78; Adn's Youth Chapl 77-80; Dioc Youth Officer 80-86; Chapl Stansted Airport from 86; P-in-c Manuden w Berden from 86; RD Newport and Stansted from 89; Hon Can Chelmsf Cathl from 99. *24 Mallows Green Road, Manuden, Bishop's Stortford CM23 1DG* Tel (01279) 812228
E-mail chrismitre@hotmail.com

BISHOP, David. b 65. St Jo Coll Nottm 01. **d** 03. C Boulton *Derby* from 03. *2 Rosemary Drive, Alvaston, Derby DE24 0TA* Tel (01332) 576042

BISHOP, Canon David Harold. b 28. ARIBA53 FRSA75 DipArch. Westcott Ho Cam 55. **d** 57 **p** 58. C Cannock *Lich* 57-61; C Gt Barr 61-67; V All Hallows Lon Wall *Lon* 67-80; Architectural Adv CCC 67-80; Can Res Nor Cathl *Nor* 80-92; Vice-Dean 84-92; rtd 92; Perm to Offic *Sarum* from 92. *Coneycote, 6 Coneygar Park, Bridport DT6 3BA* Tel (01308) 424673

BISHOP, David Henry Ryder. b 27. R Agric Coll Cirencester MRAC50. Tyndale Hall Bris DipTh57. **d** 57 **p** 58. C Sevenoaks St Nic *Roch* 57-59; C Branksome St Clem *Sarum* 59-63; Uganda 64-67; Dep Sec CCCS 68; R Ox St Clem *Ox* 69-73; Zimbabwe 91-93; rtd 93; Perm to Offic *Ox* from 93. *38 Sandfield Road, Headington, Oxford OX3 7RJ* Tel (01865) 760099

BISHOP, Donald. b 22. Lon Univ BSc48. Qu Coll Birm 56. **d** 57 **p** 58. C Trowbridge H Trin *Sarum* 57-60; CF (TA) 58-68; V Bodicote *Ox* 60-87; P-in-c Broughton 71-85; rtd 87; Perm to Offic *Cov* 87-01 and *Wakef* from 01. *17 Westminster Road, Halifax HX3 8DH* Tel (01422) 200844

BISHOP, Huw Daniel. b 49. Univ of Wales (Lamp) BA71 DipTh73. Bp Burgess Hall Lamp CPS73. **d** 73 **p** 74. C Carmarthen St Pet *St D* 73-77; Prov Youth Chapl Wales 77-79; V Llanybydder and Llanwenog w Llanwnnen 79-80; Youth and Community Officer 80-81; Hd RS Carre's Gr Sch Sleaford 81-85; Hd RS K Sch Pet 85-92; Lic to Offic *Linc* 83-95; CF (TA) from 85; Perm to Offic *Pet* 86-92; *Lich* 92-00. *Address temp unknown*

BISHOP, Ian Gregory. b 62. ARICS87 Portsm Poly BSc84 MRICS01. Oak Hill Th Coll BA91. **d** 91 **p** 92. C Purley Ch Ch *S'wark* 91-95; P-in-c Saxlingham Nethergate and Shotesham *Nor* 95-97; TR Newton Flotman, Swainsthorpe, Shotesham, etc 98-01; V Middlewich w Byley *Ches* from 01. *St Michael's Vicarage, 37 Queen's Street, Middlewich CW10 9AR* Tel (01606) 833124 E-mail ian@bishopfamily.fsnet.co.uk

BISHOP, Jeremy Simon. b 54. Nottm Univ BSc75 Yonsei Univ S Korea 84. All Nations Chr Coll 82 Wycliffe Hall Ox 89. **d** 91 **p** 92. C Macclesfield Team Par *Ches* 91-98; R Carlton Colville w Mutford and Rushmere *Nor* 98-99; V Carlton Colville and Mutford from 99. *The Rectory, Rectory Road, Carlton Colville, Lowestoft NR33 8BB* Tel (01502) 565217

BISHOP, John Baylis. b 32. Selw Coll Cam BA54 MA58. Cuddesdon Coll 54. **d** 56 **p** 57. C Middlesbrough St Oswald *York* 56-59; C Romsey *Win* 59-62; Chapl RN 62-66; P-in-c Linc St Mary-le-Wigford w St Martin *Linc* 66-67; V Linc St Faith 66-68; V Linc St Faith and St Martin w St Pet 69-71; Lic to Offic *Bris* 72-84; C Henbury 84-87; TV Bris St Agnes and St Simon w St Werburgh 87; TV Bris St Paul's 87-92; P-in-c Barrow Gurney *B & W* 92-94; P-in-c Flax Bourton 92-98; Asst Resources Adv 92-94; rtd 98. *56 Darren View, Crickhowell NP8 1DS* Tel (01873) 812167

BISHOP, John Charles Simeon. b 46. Chich Th Coll 77. **d** 79 **p** 79. SSF 66-86; P-in-c Edin St Dav *Edin* 82-86; Chapl to the Deaf *Birm* 86-99; C Portsea N End St Mark *Portsm* 99-01; Chapl to the Deaf *Linc* from 01. *220 Boultham Park Road, Lincoln LN6 7SU* Tel (01522) 787136 Fax as telephone E-mail jcsb@aol.com

BISHOP, John David. b 36. Liv Univ BEng MIMechE. EMMTC. **d** 85 **p** 86. NSM Ockbrook *Derby* from 85. *143 Victoria Avenue, Borrowash, Derby DE7 3HF* Tel (01332) 663828

BISHOP, Joy. **d** 01. NSM Penkridge Team *Lich* from 01. *21 Farmdown Road, Stafford ST17 0AP* Tel (01785) 603074

BISHOP, Keith William. b 45. SEITE 00. **d** 03. NSM Balham St Mary and St Jo *S'wark* from 03. *43 Magdalen Road, London SW18 3ND* Tel (020) 8870 7267
E-mail keithwilliambishop@hotmail.com

BISHOP, Mark Andrew. b 58. Down Coll Cam BA80 MA83 Barrister 81. EAMTC 99. **d** 02 **p** 03. Dep Chan *Roch* from 01; NSM Cambridge St Mary Less *Ely* from 02. *10 Wordsworth Grove, Cambridge CB3 9HH* Tel (01223) 362281 Fax 323247 E-mail markbishop@ukonline.co.uk

BISHOP, Michael George. b 27. Wycliffe Hall Ox 63. **d** 65 **p** 66. C Cheltenham St Mary *Glouc* 65-68; P-in-c Edale *Derby* 68-71; V Doveridge 71-79; Chapl HM Det Cen Foston Hall 73-79; V Cotmanhay *Derby* 79-81; Chapl Ilkeston Gen Hosp 79-81; USA 81-89; Perm to Offic *Chich* 89-02; rtd 92; Perm to Offic *Nor* from 03. *Cherry Tree Cottage, Gormans Lane, Colkirk, Fakenham NR21 7NP* Tel (01328) 853461

BISHOP, Philip Michael. b 47. Lon Univ BD69 AKC69. St Aug Coll Cant 70. **d** 71 **p** 72. C Mansfield Woodhouse *S'well* 71-76; C

Liscard St Mary w St Columba *Ches* 76-78; V Thornton-le-Moors w Ince and Elton 78-90; V Sutton w Carlton and Normanton upon Trent etc *S'well* 90-96; P-in-c Ch Broughton w Barton Blount, Boylestone etc *Derby* 96-98; P-in-c Longford, Long Lane, Dalbury and Radbourne 96-98; R Boylestone, Church Broughton, Dalbury, etc from 98. *The Vicarage, Chapel Lane, Church Broughton, Derby DE65 5BB* Tel (01283) 585296 E-mail p.michael.bishop@ntlworld.com

BISHOP, Phillip Leslie. b 44. K Coll Lon BD66 AKC66. **d** 67 **p** 68. C Albrighton *Lich* 67-70; C St Geo-in-the-East St Mary *Lon* 70-71; C Middlesbrough Ascension *York* 71-73; P-in-c Withernwick 73-77; Ind Chapl 73-82; V Gt Ayton w Easby and Newton in Cleveland 82-89; RD Stokesley 85-89; R Guisborough from 89; Chapl S Tees Community and Mental NHS Trust 90-99; Chapl Tees and NE Yorks NHS Trust from 99; Chapl Langbaurgh Primary Care Trust from 02. *The Rectory, Church Street, Guisborough TS14 6BS* Tel (01287) 632588 Fax as telephone E-mail phillip@guisrec.fsnet.co.uk

BISHOP, Stephen John. b 62. Hull Univ BA84 PGCE86. Ripon Coll Cuddesdon 90 Ch Div Sch of the Pacific (USA) 90. **d** 92 **p** 93. C Syston *Leic* 92-95; C Market Harborough 95-97; TV Market Harborough and The Transfiguration etc 97-00; R Six Saints circa Holt from 00; Rural Officer (Leic Adnry) from 01. *The Rectory, Rectory Lane, Medbourne, Market Harborough LE16 8DZ* Tel (01858) 565419

BISHOP, Stephen Patrick. b 60. Dioc OLM tr scheme 99. **d** 02. OLM Purley Ch Ch *S'wark* from 02. *Elmwood, 117 Mitchley Avenue, South Croydon CR2 9HP* Tel (020) 8651 2840 E-mail elmwood@tinyonline.co.uk

BISHOP, Miss Waveney Joyce. b 38. Westf Coll Lon BSc60. Cranmer Hall Dur DipTh72. **dss** 82 **d** 87 **p** 94. Leyton St Mary w St Edw *Chelmsf* 82-84; Bishopsworth *Bris* 84-96; Hon Par Dn 87-94; Hon C 94-96; rtd 96; Perm to Offic *Bris* 96-99; and *B &W* from 98. *14 Saxby Close, Clevedon BS21 7YF* Tel (01275) 343533

BISHTON, Gerald Arthur. b 32. MRSH76 Ruskin Coll Ox Dip Economics 56 St Pet Hall Ox BA59 MA63. Qu Coll Birm 60. **d** 61 **p** 62. C Forest Gate St Edm *Chelmsf* 61-64; Asst Chapl Lon Univ *Lon* 64-67; Chapl NE Lon Poly 68-73; Sen Lect 73-80; Chapl St Mary's Hosp Gt Ilford 68-80; Ind Chapl *Chelmsf* 80-97; P-in-c Shopland 80-89; P-in-c Sutton 80-89; P-in-c Sutton w Shopland 89-97; rtd 97; Perm to Offic *Leic* and *Pet* from 97. *32 Horsefair Close, Market Harborough LE16 9QP* Tel (01858) 466141

BISIG (née BOULNOIS), Linda Dianne. b 59. Trin Coll Bris 92. **d** 96 **p** 97. C Brampton Bierlow *Sheff* 96-99; Asst Chapl Berne w Neuchâtel *Eur* from 00. *Bernstrasse, 95B Stetten CH-3066, Switzerland*

BISSET, Michael Davidson. b 55. NTMTC DipTS99. **d** 99 **p** 00. C Ickenham *Lon* 99-03; P-in-c Penn *Ox* from 03; P-in-c Tylers Green from 03. *Twichels, Church Road, Penn HP10 8NU* Tel (01895) 676092 E-mail mike.bisset@talk21.com

BISSET, Canon Robert McBain. b 05. Glas Univ MA30. Edin Th Coll 30. **d** 32 **p** 33. C Glas Ch Ch *Glas* 32-37; I Glas St Luke 37-41; R Lanark 41-47; R Bearsden 47-73; R Milngavie 56-73; Can St Mary's Cathl 62-73; rtd 73; Hon Can St Mary's Cathl *Glas* from 77. *Rannoch Lodge, Rannoch Drive, Cumbernauld, Glasgow G67 4EP* Tel (01236) 729273

BISSEX, Mrs Janet Christine Margaret. b 50. Westhill Coll Birm CertEd72. Trin Coll Bris 76. **dss** 86 **d** 87 **p** 94. Toxteth Park St Bede *Liv* 86-93; Par Dn 87-93; Dn-in-c Kirkdale St Mary and St Athanasius 93-94; P-in-c 94-03; C Litherland St Andr from 03. *The Vicarage, 4 St Andrews Road, Bootle L20 5EX* Tel 0151-944 1121

BISWAS, Aloke. b 44. **d** 01. NSM W Drayton *Lon* from 01. *12 Cherry Orchard, West Drayton UB7 7JR* Tel (01895) 447904

BLACK, Canon Alexander Stevenson. b 28. Glas Univ MA53. Edin Th Coll 53. **d** 55 **p** 56. C Dumfries *Glas* 55-58; Chapl Glas Univ 58-61; C Glas St Mary 58-61; P-in-c E Kilbride 61-69; R Edin St Columba *Edin* 69-79; TV Edin St Jo 79-83; R Haddington 83-93; R Dunbar 83-93; Can St Mary's Cathl from 88; rtd 93. *3 Bass Rock View, Canty Bay, North Berwick EH39 5PJ* Tel (01620) 894771

BLACK, Dominic Paul. b 70. Teesside Poly HND90 S Bank Univ BSc95. Cranmer Hall Dur BA98. **d** 98 **p** 99. C N Hull St Mich *York* from 98. *2 St Michael's Church, Orchard Park Road, Hull HU6 9BX* Tel (01482) 802079 E-mail stmaapc@aol.com

BLACK, Douglas John. b 58. Middx Poly BA80 CertMS84 Ridley Hall Cam 89. **d** 91 **p** 92. C Wrexham *St As* 91-01; Chapl NE Wales Inst HE 93-01; V Thelwall *Ches* from 02. *All Saints Vicarage, Bell Lane, Thelwall, Warrington WA4 2SX* Tel (01925) 261166 E-mail revdouglasblack@aol.com

BLACK, Mrs Elizabeth Anne. b 47. Qu Coll Birm 80 Cranmer Hall Dur 81. **dss** 82 **d** 87 **p** 03. Cleadon *Dur* 82-85; S Westoe 85-88; Par Dn 87-88; Par Dn Chester le Street 88-92; Emmaus Chr Healing Trust 93-02; Perm to Offic *Dur* from 95; NE Regional Co-ord Acorn Chr Foundn from 00; Lic to Offic *Car* from 02; NSM Barony of Burgh from 02. *The Gables, Monkhill Road, Moorhouse, Carlisle CA5 6ER* Tel (01228) 575064 E-mail eabgables@aol.com

BLACK, Ian Christopher. b 62. Kent Univ BA85 Nottm Univ MDiv93. Linc Th Coll 91. **d** 93 **p** 94. C Maidstone All SS and

St Phil w Tovil *Cant* 93-96; P-in-c The Brents and Davington w Oare and Luddenham 96-02; Hon Min Can Cant Cathl 97-02; Asst Dir Post-Ord Tr 98-02; V Whitkirk *Ripon* from 02. *Whitkirk Vicarage, 386 Selby Road, Leeds LS15 0AA* Tel 0113-264 5790 E-mail icblack@btinternet.com

BLACK, Ian Forbes. b 29. St Aid Birkenhead 55. **d** 58 **p** 59. C Bramhall *Ches* 58-61; C Witton 61-63; P-in-c Prestonpans *Edin* 63-68; R Edin Ch Ch-St Jas 68-71; Asst Chapl HM Pris Liv 71-72; Chapl HM Pris Haverigg 72-73; R Bootle w Corney *Carl* 73-75; P-in-c Whicham w Whitbeck 73-75; R Bootle, Corney, Whicham and Whitbeck 75-86; P-in-c Orton St Giles 86-89; R 89-94; P-in-c Aikton 86-89; R 89-94; rtd 94; Perm to Offic *Carl* from 98. *Solwayside, Port Carlisle, Wigton CA7 5BU* Tel (01697) 351964

BLACK (formerly NAPIER), Lady Jennifer Beryl. b 39. S Dios Minl Tr Scheme 89. **d** 93 **p** 96. NSM Itchen Valley *Win* 93-01. *Woodlands, Martyr Worthy, Winchester SO21 1AJ* Tel (01962) 779307 Fax as telephone

BLACK, Canon Leonard Albert. b 49. Edin Th Coll 69. **d** 72 **p** 73. C Aberdeen St Marg *Ab* 72-75; Chapl St Paul's Cathl Dundee *Bre* 75-77; P-in-c Aberdeen St Ninian *Ab* 77-80; N Area Chapl Miss to Seafarers from 80; R Inverness St Mich *Mor* from 80; P-in-c Balloch New Town Distr 80-87; R Inverness St Jo 80-87; Relig Progr Producer Moray Firth Radio from 87; Syn Clerk *Mor* from 92; Can St Andr Cathl Inverness from 92. *St Michael's Rectory, 28 Abban Street, Inverness IV3 8HH* Tel and fax (01463) 233797 Mobile 07836-365719 E-mail st.michael@angelforce.co.uk

BLACK, Canon Neville. b 36. MBE97. DMS86 DASHE97. Oak Hill Th Coll 61. **d** 64 **p** 65. C Everton St Ambrose w St Tim *Liv* 64-69; P-in-c Everton St Geo 69-71; V 71-81; P-in-c Everton St Benedict 70-72; P-in-c Everton St Chad w Ch Ch 70-72; Nat Project Officer Evang Urban Tr Project 74-81; TR St Luke in the City from 81; Chapl Liv Women's Hosp 82-92; Chapl Liv Women's Hosp NHS Trust from 92; Tutor N Ord Course 82-89; Dir Gp for Urban Min and Leadership *Liv* 84-95; Hon Can Liv Cathl from 87; P-in-c Edgehill St Dunstan 98-02. *445 Aigburth Road, Liverpool L19 3PA* Tel 0151-427 9803 Pager 07699-727640 Fax 494 0736

BLACK, Canon Robert John Edward Francis Butler. b 41. TCD BA65 HDipEd70 DipG&C80 MA85. CITC 66. **d** 66 **p** 67. C Jordanstown *Conn* 66-68; C Dublin St Steph and St Ann *D & G* 68-73; C Stillorgan w Blackrock 73-85; Hd Master Dundalk Gr Sch *Arm* 85-96; Lic to Offic from 85; Hd Master Kilkenny Coll *C & O* from 96; Can Ossory Cathl from 96. *Kilkenny College, Kilkenny, Co Kilkenny, Irish Republic* Tel (00353) (56) 772 2213 *or* 776 1544 Fax 777 0918

BLACK, Samuel James. b 38. CITC. **d** 68 **p** 69. C Cloughfern *Conn* 68-72; C Lisburn St Paul 72-78; I Rasharkin w Finvoy 78-82; I Belfast Upper Malone (Epiphany) 82-95; I Ballymore *Arm* from 95. *The Rectory, Glebe Hill Road, Tandragee, Craigavon BT62 2EP* Tel (028) 3884 0234

BLACK, William Henry. St Deiniol's Hawarden. **d** 88 **p** 89. NSM Malahide w Balgriffin *D & G* 88-89; NSM Dublin St Ann and St Steph 89-94; C 94-00; Hon Asst Chapl Miss to Seamen 89-00; I Dublin Drumcondra w N Strand *D & G* from 00. *The Rectory, 74 Grace Park Road, Drumcondra, Dublin 9, Irish Republic* Tel (00353) (1) 837 2505 Fax as telephone

BLACKALL, Mrs Margaret Ivy. b 38. St Kath Coll Lon CertEd58. EAMTC 82. **dss** 86 **d** 87 **p** 94. NSM Wickham Market w Pettistree and Easton *St E* 86-88; Par Dn Leiston 88-92; Par Dn Gt and Lt Glemham, Blaxhall etc 92-94; P-in-c 94-96; R 96-02; P-in-c Sternfield w Benhall and Snape 98-02; rtd 03; Perm to Offic *St E* from 03. *6 Orchard Place, Wickham Market, Woodbridge IP13 0RU* Tel (01728) 747326 Mobile 07850-632900 E-mail mgtblack@globalnet.co.uk

BLACKALL, Robin Jeremy McRae. b 35. Ridley Hall Cam 67. **d** 69 **p** 70. C Stowmarket *St E* 69-72; R Stanstead w Shimplingthorne and Alpheton 72-77; R Bradwell on Sea *Chelmsf* 77-79; R St Lawrence 77-79; Warden Bede Ho Staplehurst 79-81; Chapl HM Det Cen Blantyre Ho 81-82; R Edith Weston w N Luffenham and Lyndon w Manton *Pet* 86-95; P-in-c Upwell St Pet *Ely* 95-99; P-in-c Outwell 95-99; Dioc Rural Miss Officer 95-01; P-in-c Barton Bendish w Beachamwell and Shingham 99-01; P-in-c Boughton 99-01; P-in-c Wereham 99-01; rtd 01; Perm to Offic *Ely* from 01 and *Nor* from 02. *The Pightle House, Eastmoor Road, Eastmoor, Oxborough, King's Lynn PE33 9PZ* Tel (01366) 328663 Fax 328163 E-mail rjmb@globalnet.co.uk

BLACKALL, Susan Elizabeth. b 52. Qu Univ Kingston Ontario BA74 MA75 CCC Ox DPhil82. SEITE 00. **d** 03. NSM Eltham St Barn *S'wark* from 03. *8 Park Place House, Park Vista, London SE10 9ND* Tel (020) 8853 3302 E-mail s.blackall@research-int.com

BLACKBURN, David James. b 45. Hull Univ BA67. Trin Coll Bris DipHE87. **d** 87 **p** 88. C Bromsgrove St Jo *Worc* 87-90; V Cradley 90-01; R Kinver and Enville *Lich* from 01. *The Vicarage, Vicarage Drive, Kinver, Stourbridge DY7 6HJ* Tel (01384) 872556

BLACKBURN, Frederick John Barrie. b 28. TD73. Lich Th Coll 52. **d** 55 **p** 56. C Hebburn St Cuth *Dur* 55-58; C Bishopwear-

mouth St Mary V w St Pet CD 58-61; V Hunwick 61-64; CF (TA) 61-87; V Eighton Banks *Dur* 64-75; R Stella 75-87; TV Bellingham/Otterburn Gp *Newc* 87-89; rtd 89. *26 Kepier Close, Ryton NE40 4UW* Tel and fax 0191-413 7365 Mobile 07808-795817

BLACKBURN, Helen Claire. b 55. Leeds Univ BA76 MA00 PGCE78 ARCM75. Nor Ord Course 96. **d** 99 **p** 00. C Sheff Cathl *Sheff* 99-01; CA from 00; Asst Chapl Cen Sheff Univ Hosps NHS Trust from 01. *Royal Hallamshire Hospital, Glossop Road, Sheffield S10 2JF* Tel 0114-271 1900 E-mail helen.blackburn@sth.nhs.uk

BLACKBURN, The Ven John. b 47. Univ of Wales (Cardiff) DipTh69 DPS71 Open Univ BA88. St Mich Coll Llan 66. **d** 71 **p** 72. C Risca *Mon* 71-76; CF (TA) 73-76; CF 76-99; Dep Chapl Gen 99-00; Chapl Gen from 00; Adn for the Army from 99; QHC from 96; Hon Can Ripon Cathl *Ripon* from 01. *MOD Chaplains (Army), Trenchard Lines, Upavon, Pewsey SN9 6BE* Tel (01980) 615804 Fax 615800

BLACKBURN, Sister Judith Elizabeth. b 58. SEITE 99. **d** 02. NSM Old Ford St Paul and St Mark *Lon* from 02. *St Saviour's Priory, 18 Queensbridge Road, London E2 8NX* Tel (020) 7739 9976 Mobile 07855-510393

BLACKBURN, Keith Christopher. b 39. K Coll Lon BD63 AKC63. St Boniface Warminster 63. **d** 64 **p** 65. C Surbiton St Andr *S'wark* 64-66; C Battersea St Mary 67-70; Teacher Sir Walter St Jo Sch Battersea 67-70; Hon C Eltham H Trin 70-76; Hd of Ho Crown Woods Sch Eltham 70-76; Dep Hd Master Altwood C of E Sch 76-82; Lic to Offic *Ox* 76-82; Chapl and Hd Master St Geo Sch Gravesend 83-93; Hon C Fawkham and Hartley *Roch* 83-93; V Seal St Pet from 93. *The Vicarage, Church Street, Seal, Sevenoaks TN15 0AR* Tel (01732) 762955 E-mail revkcb@aol.com

BLACKBURN, Peter James Whittaker. b 47. Sydney Univ BA69. Coll of Resurr Mirfield DipTh71. **d** 72 **p** 73. C Felixstowe St Jo *St E* 72-76; C Bournemouth St Pet w St Swithun, H Trin etc *Win* 76-79; R Burythorpe, Acklam and Leavening w Westow *York* 79-85; Chapl Naples Ch Ch *Eur* 85-91; Chapl Algarve 91-97. *12 rue de la Cave Forte, 49730 Parnay, France*

BLACKBURN, The Ven Richard Finn. b 52. St Jo Coll Dur BA74 Hull Univ MA97. Westcott Ho Cam 81. **d** 83 **p** 84. C Stepney St Dunstan and All SS *Lon* 83-87; P-in-c Isleworth St Jo 87-92; V Mosbrough *Sheff* 92-99; RD Attercliffe 96-99; Hon Can Sheff Cathl 98-99; Adn Sheff from 99; Can Res Sheff Cathl from 99. *34 Wilson Road, Sheffield S11 8RN* Tel 0114-266 6009 *or* (01709) 309110 Fax (01709) 309107 E-mail archdeacon.of.sheffield@sheffield-diocese.org.uk

BLACKBURN, William Ross. b 67. NW Univ Illinois BA90. Trin Episc Sch for Min Penn MDiv95. **d** 95. USA 95-01; NSM St Andrews St Andr from 01. *South Bowhill Farmhouse, Peat Inn, Cupar KY15 5LL* Tel (01334) 840567 E-mail wrossblackburn@yahoo.com

BLACKBURN, Archdeacon of. See HAWLEY, The Ven John Andrew

BLACKBURN, Bishop of. See CHESTERS, The Rt Revd Alan David

BLACKBURN, Dean of. See ARMSTRONG, The Very Revd Christopher John

BLACKER, Herbert John. b 36. Bris Univ BSc59. Cranmer Hall Dur DipTh61. **d** 61 **p** 62. C Wednesbury St Bart *Lich* 61-63; C Chasetown 63-65; C Chigwell *Chelmsf* 65-69; TV Barnham Broom w Kimberley, Bixton etc *Nor* 69-76; R Burgh Parva w Briston 76-92; P-in-c Melton Constable w Swanton Novers 86-92; R Briston w Burgh Parva and Melton Constable 92-01; rtd 01; Perm to Offic *Nor* from 01. *227 Church Road, Kessingland, Lowestoft NR33 7SF* Tel (01502) 740554

BLACKETT, James Gilbert. b 27. Tyndale Hall Bris 52. **d** 55 **p** 56. C Heworth H Trin *York* 55-57; C Newburn *Newc* 57-58; C Newc St Barn and St Jude 58-61; V Broomfleet *York* 61-67; V Ledsham 67-74; V Burton All SS *Lich* 74-82; V Burton All SS w Ch Ch 82-92; rtd 92; Perm to Offic *Pet* from 92. *103 Milford Avenue, Stony Stratford, Milton Keynes MK11 1EZ* Tel (01908) 265149

BLACKETT, Robert Peter. b 63. Dur Univ BSc85. Ripon Coll Cuddesdon BTh95. **d** 95 **p** 96. C Wigton *Carl* 95-00; R Bowness-on-Solway, Kirkbride and Newton Arlosh from 00. *The Rectory, Church Road, Kirkbride, Carlisle CA7 5HY* Tel (01697) 351256

BLACKFORD, David Walker. b 25. Univ of Wales DipTh69. **d** 70 **p** 71. C Holyhead w Rhoscolyn w Llanfair-yn-Neubwll *Ban* 70-72; Lic to Offic *Blackb* 72-80; Hon C Bassaleg *Mon* 80-85; V Treuddyn and Nercwys and Eryrys *St As* 85-90; Lic to Offic *Mon* from 99. *11 Whitechapel Walk, Undy, Magor, Newport NP26 3NS* Tel (01633) 880507

BLACKHAM, Paul. b 70. BD PhD. AKC. **d** 97 **p** 98. C Langham Place All So *Lon* from 97. *20 Holcroft Court, Clipstone Street, London W1P 7DL* Tel (020) 7580 1033 *or* 7580 3522 E-mail paul.blackham@allsouls.org

BLACKIE, Richard Footner (Brother Edmund). b 37. St Cath Coll Cam BA59 MA63 Worc Coll Ox BA59 BSc61. Ely Th Coll 60. **d** 62 **p** 63. C Saffron Walden *Chelmsf* 62-65; SSF from 66. *138A Station Road, New Milton BH25 6LW, or The Friary, Hilfield, Dorchester DT2 7BE* Tel (01425) 615014

BLACKLEDGE, David John. b 51. Oak Hill Th Coll 89. d 92 p 93. NSM Woodford Wells *Chelmsf* from 92. *Hornbeam, 143 Monkhams Lane, Woodford Green IG8 0NW* Tel (020) 8262 7690 E-mail djblackled@aol.com

BLACKLEDGE, Philip Vincent Patrick. b 74. Edin Univ BMus92 BD02. TISEC 99. d 02. C Edin St Mary *Edin* from 02. *8 Grosvenor Street, Edinburgh EH12 5EG* Tel 0131-346 7653

BLACKMAN, Brian David Eric. b 38. Ox NSM Course 82. d 85 p 86. NSM Reading St Luke *Ox* 85-86; NSM Reading St Luke w St Bart from 86. *13 Avebury Square, Reading RG1 5JH* Tel 0118-926 0345

BLACKMAN (née PRATT), Christine Fiona. b 60. Reading Univ BSc81. Ox Min Course 88. d 91 p 94. NSM Reading St Luke w St Bart *Ox* 91-94; NSM Earley St Pet 94-95; NSM Reading St Luke w St Bart from 95. *13 Avebury Square, Reading RG1 5JH* Tel 0118-926 0345

BLACKMAN, Clive John. b 51. Hull Univ BSc73 MSc74 Birm Univ DipTh77. Qu Coll Birm 75. d 78 p 79. C Folkestone St Sav *Cant* 78-81; Chapl Birm Univ *Birm* 81-86; V Thorpe St Matt *Nor* 86-94; R Cringleford w Colney and Bawburgh 94-98; Asst Dir Lay and Reader Tr from 98; Chapl Nor City Coll of F&HE from 03. *13 Norvic Drive, Eaton, Norwich NR4 7NN* Tel (01603) 505776

BLACKMAN, James Bentley. b 57. SS Hild & Bede Coll Dur BEd80 Nottm Univ BTh88. Linc Th Coll 85. d 88 p 89. C Nether Hoyland St Pet *Sheff* 88-91; C Harrogate St Wilfrid and St Luke *Ripon* 91-94; V Leyburn w Bellerby 94-01; Asst Chapl S Derbyshire Community and Mental Health Trust from 01. *42 Robincroft Road, Allestree, Derby DE22 2FR* Tel (01332) 554769 E-mail cyra@blackmanj57.fsnet.co.uk

BLACKMAN, John Franklyn. b 34. LRAM70 DipRS75. S'wark Ord Course 72. d 75 p 76. NSM Cov H Trin *Cov* 75-81; Succ Cov Cathl 81-95; TV Cov E 88-95; Perm to Offic *Newc* 98-01. *1 Old Deanery Close, Minster Road, Ripon HG4 1LZ*

BLACKMAN, Michael Orville. b 46. Univ of W Ontario BMin80 Univ of W Indies LTh70. Codrington Coll Barbados 67. d 71 p 71. C St Jo Cathl Antigua 71-73; R H Innocents w St Sav Barbados 73-78; Hon C Westminster St Jas Canada 78-80; P-in-c St Patr Barbados 80-86; TV E Ham w Upton Park St Alb *Chelmsf* 86-91; R St Pet Barbados 91-97; V Dalton *Sheff* 97-03; P-in-c S Wimbledon All SS *S'wark* from 03; P-in-c Raynes Park St Sav from 03. *St Saviour's Vicarage, Church Walk, London SW20 9DW* Tel (020) 8542 2787

BLACKMAN, Peter Richard. b 28. Sarum Th Coll 52. d 55 p 56. C Aylestone *Leic* 55-60; V Ratby cum Groby 60-84; TR 84-93; rtd 93; Perm to Offic *Chich* from 93. *25 Turnbull Road, Chichester PO19 7LY* Tel (01243) 787299

BLACKMORE, Cuthbert. b 17. Qu Coll Birm 57. d 59 p 60. C Acomb St Steph *York* 59-62; V Hackness w Harwood Dale 62-66; V Seamer w E Ayton 66-83; rtd 84; Perm to Offic *York* from 99. *85 West Garth, Cayton, Scarborough YO11 3SD* Tel (01723) 585156

BLACKMORE, Frank Ellis. b 43. Univ of Wales (Lamp) BA66. Wells Th Coll 65. d 67 p 68. C S'wark St Geo *S'wark* 67-70; Hon C Camberwell St Giles 70-79; NSM Paddington St Sav *Lon* from 79. *65 Sutherland Avenue, London W9 2HF* Tel (020) 7289 3020

BLACKMORE, Robert Ivor. b 37. Univ of Wales (Lamp) 59 Open Univ BA74 Univ of Wales MTh94. d 62 p 63. C Llangynwyd w Maesteg *Llan* 62-65; C Dowlais 65-67; C Neath w Llantwit 67-71; V Fochriw w Deri 71-73; V Troedrhiwgarth 73-80; V Seven Sisters 80-00; rtd 02. *Cefnforest, Bethlehem, Llandeilo SA19 6YL* Tel (01550) 777543

BLACKMORE, Vernon John. b 50. Southn Univ BSc Man Univ MSc Lon Univ DipTh K Coll Lon MTh. Oak Hill Th Coll DipHE. d 82 p 83. C Ecclesall *Sheff* 82-87; Bp's Adv on Youth 85-87; Ed Lion Publishing 87-90; Dir Publications, Tr and Sales CPAS from 90; Perm to Offic *Cov* 90-98. *Write Connection, 53 Coten End, Warwick CV34 4NU* Tel (01926) 775024 Fax 410571

BLACKSHAW, Alfred. b 14. St Jo Coll Dur BA39 DipTh40 MA42. d 40 p 41. C Darwen St Barn *Blackb* 40-43; C Crookes St Thos *Sheff* 43-44; R Collyhurst *Man* 44-48; V Haydock St Mark *Liv* 48-55; V Blackpool Ch Ch *Blackb* 55-66; V Chesham Ch Ch *Ox* 66-72; V Copp *Blackb* 72-79; rtd 79; Perm to Offic *Blackb* 79-02. *5 Capel Court, The Burgage, Prestbury, Cheltenham GL52 3EL* Tel (01242) 571812

BLACKSHAW, Brian Martin. b 43. Lanc Univ MA74 Ch Ch Ox BA95 MA96. Ox NSM Course 87. d 90 p 91. NSM Amersham *Ox* 90-93; C Hatch End St Anselm *Lon* 93-95; V Cheshunt *St Alb* from 96. *The Vicarage, Churchgate, Cheshunt EN8 9DY* Tel (01992) 623121 E-mail brianandpatsy@cheshunt99.freeserve.co.uk

BLACKSHAW, Trevor Roland. b 36. GIMechE59. Lon Coll of Div 67. d 69 p 70. C New Catton St Luke *Nor* 69-73; C Luton Lewsey St Hugh *St Alb* 73-78; V Llandinam w Trefeglwys w Penstrowed *Ban* 78-85; Dioc Dir of Adult Educn 83-85; Consultant Dir Wholeness Through Ch Min 86-92; Midl Regional Co-ord Crosslinks 92-97; Dir and Warden Divine

Healing Miss Crowhurst 97-02; rtd 02. *Mayland, 2 Balmoral Crescent, Oswestry SY11 2XG* Tel (01691) 659645 E-mail trevor@blackshawt.freeserve.co.uk

BLACKTOP, Graham Leonard. b 33. St Alb Minl Tr Scheme 82. d 85 p 86. NSM Rickmansworth *St Alb* 85-92; Perm to Offic *Sarum* from 92. *Dairy House, Wolfeton, Dorchester DT2 9QN* Tel (01305) 262184 Fax as telephone

BLACKWALL, David D'Arcy Russell. b 35. Southn Univ BSc60 Imp Coll Lon DIC62. Wycliffe Hall Ox 63. d 65 p 66. C Southampton Thornhill St Chris *Win* 65-68; V Long Sutton 69-72; Chapl Ld Wandsworth Coll Hants 69-74; Hon C Odiham w S Warnborough *Win* 72-75; Chapl St Lawr Coll Ramsgate 75-95; Hd Jun Sch 95-97; Lic to Offic *Cant* 75-98; Perm to Offic *Sarum* from 98; rtd 00. *Cookwell, Back Lane, Okeford Fitzpaine, Blandford Forum DT11 0RD* Tel (01258) 860157

BLACKWELL, Geoffrey Albert. b 27. Lon Coll of Div 62. d 65 p 66. C Clifton *York* 65-69; Chapl R N 69-73; Warden St Mich Home of Healing Cleadon 73-75; V S Hetton *Dur* 75-82; CSWG 83-94; P-in-c Burpham *Chich* 95-96; rtd 96; Perm to Offic *Chich* from 96. *1 Highfield Gardens, Rustington, Littlehampton BN16 2PZ* Tel (01903) 782219

BLACKWELL, Geoffrey David. b 34. Jes Coll Ox BA57 MA61. Chich Th Coll 57. d 59 p 60. C Romford St Edw *Chelmsf* 59-62; C Africa 62-68; Chapl Westcott Ho Cam 68-73; V Forest Gate St Edm *Chelmsf* 73-81; Pilsdon Community 83-95; rtd 94; Perm to Offic *Pet* from 94. *15 Chatsfield, Werrington, Peterborough PE4 5DJ* Tel (01733) 324278

BLACKWELL, Nicholas Alfred John. b 54. Warwick Univ MA97. St Jo Coll Nottm BTh85. d 85 p 86. C Birkenhead Priory *Ches* 85-88; C Stratford-on-Avon w Bishopton *Cov* 88-91; TV Cov E 91-98; Perm to Offic from 98. *74 Brays Lane, Coventry CV2 4DW* Tel (024) 7645 6175

BLACKWELL-SMYTH, Charles Peter Bernard. b 42. TCD BA64 MA71 MB73. Gen Th Sem (NY) MDiv65. d 65 p 66. C Bangor Abbey *D & D* 65-67; C Dublin Ch Ch Leeson Park *D & G* 67-69; P-in-c Carbury *M & K* 73-75; Hon C St Stephen in Brannel Truro 87-94; Perm to Offic from 94. *Parcgwyn, Rectory Road, St Stephen, St Austell PL26 7RL* Tel (01726) 822465

BLACOE, Canon Brian Thomas. b 36. Open Univ DipEH BA. Oak Hill Th Coll 63. d 66 p 67. C Dundonald *D & D* 66-69; C Drumcree *Arm* 69-74; I Ardtrea w Desertcreat 74-78; I Annalong *D & D* 78-95; I Knocknamuckley from 95; Can Dromore Cathl from 93; Prec from 02. *30 Mossbank Road, Ballynagarrick, Portadown BT63 5SL* Tel (028) 3883 1227 Fax 3883 2934 E-mail elizabethanne@knockrectory.fs.co.uk

BLADE, Brian Alan. b 24. ACCS55 ASCA66. Roch Th Coll 67. d 69 p 70. C Barnehurst *Roch* 69-71; C Crayford 71-76; V Buttershaw St Aid *Bradf* 76-80; R Etton w Helpston *Pet* 80-86; V Hardingstone and Horton and Piddington 86-90; rtd 90; Perm to Offic *Cant* from 90; Perm to Offic *Roch* from 90. *25 Dan Drive, Faversham ME13 7SW* Tel (01795) 531842

BLADE, Mrs Susan Joan. b 58. SEITE. d 00 p 01. NSM Wateringbury and Teston *Roch* 00-02; Asst Chapl Maidstone and Tunbridge Wells NHS Trust 00-02; Chapl from 02. *Eagle Lodge, Mill Lane, Wateringbury, Maidstone ME18 5PE* Tel (01622) 812581

BLAGDEN, Ms Susan. b 64. Ox Min Course 89 Ripon Coll Cuddesdon DipMin99. d 99 p 00. C Grantham *Linc* 99-03; Asst Chapl Stoke Mandeville Hosp NHS Trust from 03. *Stoke Mandeville Hospital, Mandeville Road, Aylesbury HP21 8AL* Tel (01296) 315000 E-mail sbwulfram@aol.com

BLAGDON-GAMLEN, Peter Eugene. b 20. KLJ. SSC. AKC48. St Boniface Warminster 48. d 49 p 50. C Wellington w W Buckland *B & W* 49-51; C Torquay St Martin Barton *Ex* 51-52; C Evesham *Worc* 52-53; V Swinefleet *Sheff* 53-56; PC Derby St Bart *Derby* 56-64; CF (R of O) 59-75; R Harrold and Carlton w Chellington *St Alb* 64-68; R Eastchurch *Cant* 68-71; R Eastchurch w Leysdown and Harty 71-87; CF (TA) 78-85; rtd 87; Perm to Offic *Ex* 87-93; *Pet* from 93; *Leic* from 96. *Blagdon House, 110 Neale Avenue, Kettering NN16 9HD* Tel (01536) 484885

BLAGG, Colin. b 31. Leeds Univ BA57. Coll of Resurr Mirfield 57. d 59 p 60. C Edin Old St Paul *Edin* 59-63; R Gourock *Glas* 63-68; Chapl to the Deaf RADD Lon 68-74; Hon C Stoke Newington St Olave Lon 73-74; Chapl to the Deaf *Chich* 74-80; V Shoreham Beach 80-96; rtd 97; Perm to Offic *Chich* from 97. *55 Roedean Road, Worthing BN13 2BT* Tel (01903) 695321

BLAIN, Anne Sharon. b 46. RGN89. Dioc OLM tr scheme 98. d 01 p 02. OLM Tadworth *S'wark* from 01. *Watts Cottage, Watts Lane, Tadworth KT20 5RW* Tel (01737) 355347 Mobile 07811-267238 Fax (01737) 351546 E-mail breusis@aol.com

BLAIN, Michael Winston. b 44. Cant Univ (NZ) BA65 MA66. Coll of Resurr Mirfield 66. d 67 p 68. C Goldthorpe *Sheff* 67-70; New Zealand 70-87, 90-95 and from 97; Zimbabwe 87-90; Chapl New Guinea 95-97; V Kelburn from 97. *PO Box 28087, Kelburn, Wellington, New Zealand* Tel (0064) (4) 934 9338 E-mail mwblain@paradise.net.nz

BLAIR, Mrs Catherine Jill. b 62. Nottm Univ BA84 BArch87 RIBA88. St Jo Coll Nottm MA02. d 02 p 03. C Goldsworth Park

Guildf from 02. *52 Eastmead, Woking GU21 3BP* Tel (01483) 755351

BLAIR, John Wallace. b 48. Lon Univ BSc70 Birm Univ DipTh82. Qu Coll Birm 79. **d** 81 **p** 82. C Chorlton-cum-Hardy St Werburgh *Man* 81-83; CF 83-97; I Faughanvale *D & R* from 97. *21 Main Street, Eglinton, Londonderry BT47 3AB* Tel (028) 7181 0217

BLAIR, Jonathan Lewis. b 62. Nottm Univ BA84 ACA88. St Jo Coll Nottm. **d** 02 **p** 03. C Goldsworth Park *Guildf* from 02. *52 Eastmead, Woking GU21 3BP* Tel (01483) 755026
E-mail jonnyblair@jonnyblair.fsnet.co.uk

BLAIR, The Very Revd Patrick Allen. b 31. Trin Coll Cam BA54 MA58. Ridley Hall Cam 54. **d** 56 **p** 57. C Harwell *Ox* 56-59; Chapl Oundle Sch 59-64; Jerusalem 64-66; Sudan 67-71; Provost Khartoum 67-71; R Chester le Street *Dur* 71-77; TR Barking St Marg w St Patr *Chelmsf* 77-87; Chapl Barking Hosp 77-87; Tunisia 87-91; Cyprus 91-96; Provost Nicosia 91-96; rtd 96. *Grace Cottage, Pilley Green, Boldre, Lymington SO41 5QG* Tel (01596) 677015

BLAIR, Philip Hugh. b 39. St Edm Hall Ox BA62 MA67. Ridley Hall Cam 62. **d** 64 **p** 65. C Camborne *Truro* 64-68; C Kenwyn 68-70; Sudan 70-73 and from 78; P-in-c St Enoder *Truro* 73-76; Tutor Ex Univ *Ex* 76-77. *PO Box 322, Khartoum, Sudan*

BLAIR-BROWN, Dennis. b 17. Em Coll Saskatoon LTh52. **d** 56 **p** 56. Canada 56-63; C Lymington *Win* 63-70; V E and W Wellow 70-93; rtd 93; Perm to Offic *Sarum* from 98. *135 The Close, Salisbury SP1 2EY* Tel (01722) 334008

BLAIR-CHAPPELL, Mrs Elcineide Menezes. b 47. Sao Paulo Univ Brazil 74 Birm Poly PGCE88. WMMTC 00. **d** 03. NSM Erdington *Birm* from 03. *18 Kempson Avenue, Sutton Coldfield B72 1HJ* Tel 0121-682 5340

BLAIR-FISH, Canon John Christopher. b 20. Linc Coll Ox BA46 MA47. Cuddesdon Coll 48. **d** 49 **p** 50. C Mottingham St Andr *S'wark* 49-51; C Warlingham w Chelsham 51-55; V Surbiton St Mark 55-72; R Chipstead 73-89; Hon Can S'wark Cathl 79-88; rtd 89; Perm to Offic *Chich* from 93. *39 Beehive Lane, Ferring, Worthing BN12 5NR* Tel (01903) 241480
E-mail cblair@fish.co.uk

BLAKE, Colin David. b 52. Rolle Coll CertEd Ex Univ BEd Lon Univ BD. Trin Coll Bris 81. **d** 84 **p** 85. C Hucclecote *Glouc* 84-88; C Patchway and Min Bradley Stoke N CD *Bris* 88-00; TV Worle *B & W* from 00. *6 Gannet Road, Worle, Weston-super-Mare BS22 8UR* Tel (01934) 521765 E-mail colinblake1@aol.com

BLAKE, Derek Gordon. b 10. St Jo Coll Dur 32. **d** 36 **p** 37. C Bermondsey St Crispin *S'wark* 36-39; C Plumstead St Marg 39-42; V Maryport *Carl* 42-57; V Carl St Aid and Ch Ch 57-69; V Holme Cultram St Cuth 69-88; P-in-c Allonby 77-81; rtd 89; Perm to Offic *Carl* 89-95. *Holmewood Residential Home, Lamplugh Road, Cockermouth CA13 0DP* Tel (01900) 827483

BLAKE, Ian Martyn. b 57. BA79. Oak Hill Th Coll 76. **d** 80 **p** 81. C Widford *Chelmsf* 80-84; C Barton Seagrave w Warkton *Pet* 84-90; V Sneinton St Chris w St Phil *S'well* 90-01; V Howell Hill *Guildf* from 01. *18 Nonsuch Walk, Cheam SM2 7NG* Tel (020) 8873 1961 Fax 8224 9961 E-mail ian-anne@msk.net

BLAKE, Mrs Margaret. b 48. Open Univ BA87. S'wark Ord Course 92. **d** 95 **p** 96. NSM Farnham *Guildf* 95-96; C 96-01; P-in-c Farncombe from 01. *The Rectory, 38 Farncombe Hill, Godalming GU7 2AU* Tel (01483) 416091

BLAKE, Preb Patrick John. b 30. Univ of Wales BA51 DipEd52 St Edm Hall Ox BA54 MA58. St Mich Coll Llan 54. **d** 55 **p** 56. C Buckley *St As* 55-59; C Oystermouth *S & B* 59-63; V Cleeve *B & W* 63-71; R Bruton w Lamyatt, Wyke and Redlynch 71-83; Dioc Ecum Officer 79-84; Preb Wells Cathl 79-03; TR Yeovil 83-88; R Yeovil w Kingston Pitney 88; P-in-c Backwell 88-89; R 89-92; R Backwell w Chelvey and Brockley 92-95; RD Portishead 92-95; rtd 95; Perm to Offic *B & W* from 95; Clergy Retirement and Widows' Officer from 96. *The Firs, 47 Lower Street, Merriott TA16 5NN* Tel (01460) 78932

BLAKE, Peta Ruth. b 44. Lambeth STh89 Episc Div Sch Cam Mass MA89 DMin90 Trin Coll Bris 82. **dss** 83 **d** 87. New Swindon St Barn Gorse Hill *Bris* 83-87; Par Dn 87-88; Perm to Offic from 88. *10 Elmer Close, Malmesbury SN16 9UE* Tel (01666) 823722

BLAKE, Canon Peter Douglas Stuart. b 27. BNC Ox BA52 MA57. Westcott Ho Cam 52. **d** 54 **p** 55. C Armley St Bart *Ripon* 54-58; N Rhodesia 58-64; Zambia 64-65; V Cropthorne w Charlton *Worc* 65-69; V Leek St Edw *Lich* 70-76; P-in-c Hartfield *Chich* 76-78; R Hartfield w Coleman's Hatch 78-87; rtd 87; P-in-c Breamore *Win* 89-90; Perm to Offic *Glas* from 91. *Holmhouse Cottage, Tynron, Thornhill DG3 4LE* Tel (01848) 200417

BLAKE, Philip Charles. b 29. FAIWCM88 MACC88 Lon Univ DipTh57 Mitchell Coll of Adv Educn (NSW) BA80 Macquarie Univ (NSW) MA86 PhD91. Melbourne Coll of Div DipRE76 DipPS80 Oak Hill Th Coll 56. **d** 58 Southl *Ox* 57-60; C Uphill *B & W* 60-62; V Branston *Lich* 62-69; Australia from 69; rtd 94. *412 Gravelly Beach Road, Gravelly Beach, Tas, Australia 7276* Tel (0061) (03) 6394 3582 Fax 6394 3112
E-mail philipblake@bigpond.com

BLAKE, Canon Roy Harold David. b 25. Chich Th Coll 54. **d** 57 **p** 58. C Westbury-on-Trym H Trin *Bris* 57-61; C Bishopston

61-65; V Bris St Agnes w St Simon 65-72; TR Bris St Agnes and St Simon w St Werburgh 72-74; RD Bris City 73-74; V Purton 74-93; RD Cricklade 76-82; Hon Can Bris Cathl 77-93; rtd 93. *10 Elmer Close, Malmesbury SN16 9UE* Tel (01666) 823722

BLAKE, Steven Robert (Max). b 53. Furzedown Coll of Educn CertEd74 Brentwood Coll of Educn BEd91. NTMTC 98. **d** 01 **p** 02. NSM Orsett and Bulphan and Horndon on the Hill *Chelmsf* from 01. *Oakfield, Victoria Road, Horndon-on-the-Hill, Stanford-le-Hope SS17 8ND* Tel (01375) 360522
E-mail maxbla@lineone.net

BLAKELEY, Julian Graham. b 60. Oak Hill Th Coll BA88. **d** 88 **p** 89. C Bedworth *Cov* 88-91; C Harlow St Mary and St Hugh w St Jo the Bapt *Chelmsf* 91-95; R Darfield *Sheff* from 95. *The Rectory, Church Street, Darfield, Barnsley S73 9JX* Tel (01226) 752236

BLAKELEY, Robert Daniel. b 29. Saskatchewan Univ BA63 St Pet Coll Ox BA66 MA70. Em Coll Saskatchewan LTh56. **d** 56 **p** 57. Canada 56-59; USA 59-68; C High Wycombe *Ox* 68-71; USA 71-75; C St Marylebone St Mary *Lon* 75-82; Chapl Hill Ho Sch Knightsbridge 75-82; P-in-c Tasburgh *Nor* 82-85; P-in-c Tharston 82-85; P-in-c Forncett St Mary w St Pet 82-85; P-in-c Flordon 82-85; Hd Master and Chapl Corona Ravenscourt Sch *Lon* 85-92; rtd 92. *37 Nunnery Road, Canterbury CT1 3LS* Tel (01227) 453872

BLAKELY, Miss Denise Irene. b 69. QUB BD91 PGCE92. CITC DPS95. **d** 95 **p** 96. C Holywood *D & D* 95-99; C Portadown St Columba *Arm* 99-00; I Carrowdore w Millisle *D & D* from 00. *Carrowdore Rectory, 40 Woburn Road, Millisle, Newtownards BT22 2HY* Tel (028) 9186 2219

BLAKEMAN, Mrs Janet Mary. b 36. Man Univ BA57 CertEd58. Carl Dioc Tr Course 87. **d** 90 **p** 97. NSM Wetheral w Warwick *Carl* 90-97; NSM Thornthwaite cum Braithwaite, Newlands etc 97-01; Perm to Offic from 01. *Langstrath, Greenfield Lane, Brampton CA8 1AU* Tel (01697) 72008

BLAKEMAN, Walter John. b 37. Qu Coll Birm 74. **d** 76 **p** 77. C Gnosall *Lich* 76-83; C Cheadle 83-86; Res Min Hednesford 86-90; Min Roundshaw LEP *S'wark* 90-94; TV E Scarsdale *Derby* 94-98; rtd 98. *Llandyn House, High Street, Glyn Ceiriog, Llangollen LL20 7EH* Tel (01691) 718173

BLAKESLEY, Ms Christine Marilyn. b 50. St Hugh's Coll Ox BA73 MA75 PGCE74. NEOC 93. **d** 95 **p** 96. C Darlington H Trin *Dur* 95-98; TV E Darlington from 98. *343 Yarm Road, Darlington DL1 1BD* Tel (01325) 382860
E-mail christine.blakesley@durham.anglican.org

BLAKESLEY, John. b 50. Keble Coll Ox BA72 MA76. St Steph Ho Ox 72. **d** 74 **p** 75. C Egremont *Carl* 74-77; C Doncaster Ch Ch *Sheff* 77-79; V Auckland St Helen *Dur* 79-94; Chapl Tindale Crescent Hosp Dur 90-94; Lect Th Dur Univ from 91; Tutor St Chad's Coll Dur 95-00; C Ch the King *Newc* 00-03; V Cambois and Sleekburn from 03. *St John's Vicarage, North View, Bedlington NE22 7ED* Tel (01670) 822309

BLAKEWAY-PHILLIPS, Richard John. b 19. St Chad's Coll Dur BA43. **d** 43 **p** 44. C Ledbury *Heref* 43-45; C Cirencester *Glouc* 45-50; C Lydney w Aylburton 50-52; R Dumbleton w Wormington 52-58; V Crawley Down All SS *Chich* 58-69; V Arrington *Ely* 69-77; R Orwell 69-77; R Wimpole 69-77; P-in-c Gt w Lt Abington 77-86; P-in-c Hildersham 77-86; rtd 86; Perm to Offic *Heref* from 86. *Church Cottage, Clun, Craven Arms SY7 8JW* Tel (01588) 640494

BLAKEY, Canon Cedric Lambert. b 54. Fitzw Coll Cam BA76 MA80. St Jo Coll Nottm 77. **d** 79 **p** 80. C Cotmanhay *Derby* 79-83; C-in-c Blagreaves St Andr CD 83-89; P-in-c Sinfin Moor 84-89; V Heanor 89-97; RD Heanor 94-97; Bp's Dom Chapl from 97; Hon Can Derby Cathl from 02. *50 Park Road, Duffield, Belper DE56 4GR* Tel (01332) 841047 Fax 843147
E-mail c.blakey@btinternet.com

BLAKEY, William George. b 51. Southn Univ BSc72 PGCE73. Oak Hill Th Coll BA82. **d** 82 **p** 83. C Cheltenham St Mark *Glouc* 82-85; P-in-c Parkham, Alwington, Buckland Brewer etc *Ex* 85-86; R 86-94; TR 94-01; P-in-c Lundy Is 92-01; RD Hartland 89-96; TR Wareham *Sarum* from 01. *The Rectory, 19 Pound Lane, Wareham BH20 4LQ* Tel (01929) 552684 or 550905
E-mail billblakey@fish.co.uk

BLAMEY, Mark Kendall. b 62. Bris Poly BSc84 ARICS86 MRICS01. Ripon Coll Cuddesdon. **d** 01 **p** 02. C Cowley St Jo *Ox* from 01. *58 Magdalen Road, Oxford OX4 1RB* Tel (01865) 793919 E-mail mark@blamey.fslife.co.uk

BLAMIRE, Jean. See PROSSER, Jean

BLAMIRE, Philip Gray. b 50. St Pet Coll Birm CertEd71 Wall Hall Coll Aldenham BEd76 UEA MA91. EAMTC 00. **d** 03. NSM Swaffham *Nor* from 03. *50 Rosewood Cottage, The Street, Sporle, King's Lynn PE32 2DR* Tel (01760) 721785
E-mail philgb@lineone.net

BLAMIRE-BROWN, Charles Richard. b 21. St Cath Soc Ox BA49 MA53. Cuddesdon Coll 49. **d** 51 **p** 52. C Bedale *Ripon* 51-53; C Welwyn *St Alb* 53-58; P-in-c Tewin 58-67; R 67-75; RD Hatfield 71-75; V Chipperfield St Paul 75-86; rtd 86; Perm to Offic *Cov* 87-01. *7 Willoughby Avenue, Kenilworth CV8 1DG* Tel (01926) 850808

BLANCH, Paul Frederick. b 56. St Cuth Soc Dur BA97. Chich Th Coll 83. **d** 86 **p** 87. C Chaddesden St Phil *Derby* 86-88; C Auckland St Andr and St Anne *Dur* 88-91; P-in-c Hunwick 91-94; Chapl HM Pris Edin 98-02; P-in-c Edin St Salvador *Edin* 98-00; R 00-02; P-in-c Wester Hailes St Luke 00-02; P-in-c Melton and Ufford w Bredfield and Hasketon *St E* 02-03; R Melton and Ufford from 03. *The Rectory, Station Road, Melton, Woodbridge IP12 1PX* Tel (01394) 380279 E-mail frpaul@meltuff.freeserve.co.uk

BLANCHARD, Christopher John. b 46. Univ of Wales (Lamp) BA70. St Mich Coll Llan 86. **d** 79 **p** 80. NSM Chepstow *Mon* 79-81; NSM Itton and St Arvans w Penterry and Kilgwrrwg etc 81-86; TV Ebbw Vale 87-89; R Llangenni and Llanbedr Ystrad Yw w Patricio *S & B* 89-98; V Chepstow *Mon* from 98. *The Vicarage, 25 Mount Way, Chepstow NP16 5NF* Tel (01291) 620980

BLANCHARD, Frank Hugh. b 30. St Jo Coll Dur BA54 DipTh55 MA62. **d** 55 **p** 56. C Bottesford *Linc* 55-58; CMS 58-65; C Kirby Grindalythe *York* 65-67; V 67-71; C N Grimston w Wharram Percy and Wharram-le-Street 65-67; V 67-71; P-in-c Thorpe Bassett 67-71; P-in-c Settrington 67-68; V Scarborough St Jas 71-79; P-in-c Scarborough H Trin 78-79; V Scarborough St Jas and H Trin 79-86; R Stockton-on-the-Forest w Holtby and Warthill 87-94; rtd 94; P-in-c Rothesay *Arg* 94-96; Perm to Offic *York* from 00. *23 Front Street, Sowerby, Thirsk YO7 1JG* Tel (01845) 574446

BLANCHARD, Mrs Jean Ann. b 43. St Alb Minl Tr Scheme 79. **dss** 85 **d** 87 **p** 94. Mill End and Heronsgate w W Hyde *St Alb* 85-92; Hon Par Dn 87-92; Par Dn Luton All SS w St Pet 92-94; C 94-95; P-in-c Skirbeck Quarter *Linc* 96-97; V 97-01; P-in-c Digby Gp from 01. *The Rectory, 1 Thomas à Becket Close, Digby, Lincoln LN4 3GA* Tel (01526) 321099

BLANCHARD, Canon Lawrence Gordon. b 36. Edin Univ MA60. Linc Th Coll 63. **d** 65 **p** 66. C Woodhouse *Wakef* 65-67; C Cannock *Lich* 67-70; Swaziland 70-76; TV Raveningham *Nor* 76-80; V Ancaster *Linc* 80-87; Dir LNSM 80-87; Can and Preb Linc Cathl 85-88; Dir of Tr CA 88-93; V Roxton w Gt Barford *St Alb* 93-98; rtd 98. *The Old Post Office, Post Office Road, Knodishall, Saxmundham IP17 1UG* Tel (01728) 830580

BLAND, Albert Edward. b 14. St Mich Coll Llan. **d** 62 **p** 63. C Darwen St Cuth *Blackb* 62-65; P-in-c Over Darwen St Jo 65-66; V 66-67; V Feniscowles 67-84; rtd 85; Perm to Offic *Blackb* from 85; *Derby* from 96. *18 Royal Oak Place, Matlock Street, Bakewell DE45 1HD* Tel (01629) 813370

BLAND, Jean Elspeth. b 42. K Coll Lon BA63. Glouc Sch of Min 87. **d** 90 **p** 94. Par Dn Cen Telford *Lich* 90-94; Asst Chapl HM Pris Shrewsbury 92-94; Chapl HM Pris Doncaster 94-98; C Goole *Sheff* 99; P-in-c Purleigh, Cold Norton and Stow Maries *Chelmsf* from 99. *All Saints' Rectory, The Street, Purleigh, Chelmsford CM3 6QH* Tel (01621) 826905

BLAND, Thomas. b 12. Clifton Th Coll 39. **d** 42 **p** 43. C Bishopston *Bris* 42-44; C Styvechale *Cov* 44-45; V 45-61; V Stratford-on-Avon 61-63; R Stratford-on-Avon w Bishopton 63-69; Hon Can Cov Cathl 67-69; rtd 77. *1 Costard Avenue, Shipston-on-Stour CV36 4HW* Tel (01608) 663284

BLANDFORD-BAKER, Neil James. b 64. Dundee Univ BSc86 Nottm Univ BTh92. St Jo Coll Nottm DipMM93. **d** 93 **p** 94. C The Quinton *Birm* 93-96; V E Acton St Dunstan w St Thos *Lon* from 96; Dir of Ords Willesden Area from 02. *The Vicarage, 54 Perryn Road, London W3 7NA* Tel (020) 8743 4117 E-mail jamesbb@btinternet.com

BLANEY, Laurence. b 41. Lon Univ DipTh69 Open Univ BA85 Essex Univ MA88 PhD95. Oak Hill Th Coll 66. **d** 69 **p** 70. C Leyton St Mary w St Edw *Chelmsf* 69-73; P-in-c Wimbish w Thunderley 73-77; P-in-c Steeple 77-82; P-in-c Mayland 77-82; R Pitsea 82-95; R Pitsea w Nevendon 95-96; P-in-c Mayland from 96; P-in-c Steeple from 96. *The Vicarage, 31 Imperial Avenue, Mayland, Chelmsford CM3 6AH* Tel (01621) 740943 E-mail vicar.mayland@onnet.co.uk

BLANKENSHIP, Charles Everett. b 42. Santa Clara Univ BA64. Cuddesdon Coll 71. **d** 74 **p** 75. C Catford (Southend) and Downham *S'wark* 74-78; P-in-c Battersea St Phil w St Bart 78-83; V 83-85; TV Wimbledon 85-91; P-in-c Welling 91-92; V 92-99; P-in-c S Norwood St Alb from 99; RD Croydon N from 02. *The Vicarage, 6 Dagmar Road, London SE25 6HZ* Tel (020) 8653 6092 E-mail chuck@blankenship.demon.co.uk

BLANKLEY, Roger Henry. b 32. ARICS60 MRICS01. Clifton Th Coll 62. **d** 66 **p** 67. C Peckham St Mary Magd *S'wark* 66-69; SAMS 70-74; Brazil 74-80; R Gillingham w Geldeston, Stockton, Ellingham etc *Nor* 80-91; P-in-c Charmouth and Catherston Leweston *Sarum* 91-97; rtd 97; Perm to Offic *Glouc* from 97; *Cov* 98-00; and from 02; *Ox* from 00; Area Sec SAMS 98-00. *12 Hubbard Close, Buckingham MK18 1YS* Tel (01280) 814710 E-mail mblankley@rblankley.freeserve.co.uk

BLANT, Edgar. b 18. St Chad's Coll Dur BA47 DipTh48. **d** 48 **p** 49. C Meir *Lich* 48-54; Antigua 55-60; St Kitts-Nevis 60-85; Adn St Kitts 78-85; rtd 86; Perm to Offic *Lich* 86-98. *326 Sandon Road, Stoke-on-Trent ST3 7EB* Tel (01782) 398300

BLATCHLEY, Ms Elizabeth Palmer. b 62. Wycliffe Hall Ox 01. **d** 03. C Northolt W End St Jos *Lon* from 03. *341 Balmoral Drive, Hayes UB4 8DL* Tel (020) 8561 1434 E-mail betsyblatchley@hotmail.com

BLATCHLY, Owen Ronald Maxwell. b 30. Bps' Coll Cheshunt 62. **d** 64 **p** 65. C Boxmoor St Jo *St Alb* 64-67; C Boreham Wood All SS 67-69; C Frimley *Guildf* 69-77; V Manaccan w St Anthony-in-Meneage *Truro* 77-82; R Binfield *Ox* 82-97; rtd 97; Perm to Offic *Truro* from 97. *1 Rose Cottages, East Road, Stithians, Truro TR3 7BD* Tel (01209) 860845

BLAY, Ian. b 65. Man Univ BA88. Westcott Ho Cam 89. **d** 88 **p** 92. C Withington St Paul *Man* 91-94; C Elton All SS 94-96; R Droylsden St Andr from 96; Dioc Ecum Officer from 98. *St Andrew's Rectory, Merton Drive, Droylsden, Manchester M43 6BH* Tel 0161-370 3242 Mobile 07879-004033 E-mail ian@blay.freeserve.co.uk

BLAY, Ms Linda Jean. Warwick Univ DipEd89 Essex Coll of Educn CertEd. Trin Coll Bris. **d** 00 **p** 01. C Foleshill St Paul *Cov* from 00. *11 Pennington Way, Coventry CV6 5TE* Tel (024) 7658 1203 Mobile 07710-160144 E-mail lindablay@hotmail.com

BLEAKLEY, Melvyn Thomas. b 43. K Coll Lon BD66 AKC66. **d** 67 **p** 68. C Cross Heath *Lich* 67-70; TV High Wycombe *Ox* 70-77; Perm to Offic from 77. *294 Hughenden Road, High Wycombe HP13 5PE* Tel (01494) 529315

BLEE, Peter Michael. b 64. St Jo Coll Cam BA86. St Steph Ho Ox BTh94. **d** 94 **p** 95. C Guildf St Nic *Guildf* 94-97; C Whipton *Ex* 97-03; P-in-c Berwick w Selmeston and Alciston *Chich* from 03. *The Parsonage, Berwick, Polegate BN26 6SR* Tel (01323) 870512 E-mail pn.blee@virgin.net

BLENCOE, Charles Dennis. b 17. Lon Univ BA38. Bps' Coll Cheshunt 38. **d** 41 **p** 42. C Sutton in Ashfield St Mary *S'well* 41-43; Chapl RAF 43-61; Canada from 61. *Address temp unknown*

BLENKIN, Hugh Linton. b 16. Trin Coll Cam BA39 MA43. Lambeth STh56 Westcott Ho Cam 39. **d** 40 **p** 41. C Hitchin St Mary *St Alb* 40-43; Prec St Alb Abbey 43-48; Chapl and Lect Hockerill Coll Bishop's Stortford 48-66; Lect St Mich Coll Salisbury 66-78; Lect Sarum Th Coll 78-83; rtd 81. *Amesbury Abbey, Amesbury, Salisbury SP4 7EX* Tel (01980) 624813

BLENNERHASSETT, Canon Richard Noel Rowland. b 09. TCD BA33 MA52. **d** 33 **p** 34. C Clonmel *C & O* 33-37; I Kilrossanty 37-39; I Kilrossanty w Stradbally and Monksland 39-45; I Knappagh *T, K & A* 45-47; I Aughaval w Burrishoole 47-68; I Aughaval w Burrishoole w Achill w Dugort 68-69; Dom Chapl to Bp Tuam 51-57; Can Tuam Cathl 52-69; Adn Tuam 56-69; Preb Kilmactalway St Patr Cathl Dublin 60-67; I Timoleague *C, C & R* 69-73; rtd 73. *The Moorings, Fenit, Tralee, Co Kerry, Irish Republic* Tel (00353) (66) 36198

BLEWETT, Roy. b 32. K Coll Lon BSc54 MPhil74 Leeds Inst of Educn 66 Newc Univ DipRS81. Edin Th Coll 81. **d** 82 **p** 83. C Newc St Fran *Newc* 82-85; P-in-c Cornhill w Carham 85-91; P-in-c Branxton 85-91; rtd 92; Perm to Offic *Truro* from 92. *Bryn Mawr, Lower Broad Lane, Redruth TR15 3HT* Tel (01209) 313152

BLEWETT, Canon Timothy John. b 67. Surrey Univ BA88 Cam Univ BA92 MA92 Coll of Ripon & York St Jo MA96. Westcott Ho Cam 89. **d** 92 **p** 93. C Knaresborough *Ripon* 92-95; V Hanmer, Bronington, Bettisfield, Tallarn Green *St As* 95-98; Can Res and Can Cursal St As Cathl from 98; Asst Dioc Dir of Ords 98-00; Dioc Dir of Ords from 00; Dioc Officer for Min and Adv for CME from 00. *13 Llys Chwyd, Elwy Park, St Asaph LL17 0UA* Tel (01745) 582560 *or* (01978) 314134 Fax (01978) 290454 E-mail tim.blewett@virgin.net

BLICK, John Harold Leslie. b 36. Univ of Wales (Lamp) BA61. Bps' Coll Cheshunt 61. **d** 63 **p** 64. C Radlett *St Alb* 63-66; Min St Cem Miss Labrador Canada 66-71; Min Marsh Farm CD *St Alb* 71-76; R Shaw cum Donnington *Ox* 76-89; rtd 96; Perm to Offic *Mon* from 99. *Springwood, Cleddon, Trelleck NP25 4PN* Tel (01600) 860094 Fax 869045 E-mail revdjblick@aol.com

BLIGH, Philip Hamilton. b 36. Lon Univ BSc57 PhD61 MEd79 St Cath Coll Ox BA63 MInstP75. S'wark Ord Course 86. **d** 88 **p** 89. C Abingdon *Pet* 88-90; V Bozeat w Easton Maudit 90-99; R Hackett Australia 99-01; rtd 01; Perm to Offic *Nor* from 02. *35 Norwich Road, Cromer NR27 0EX* Tel (01263) 511385 E-mail philaud@bligh.freeserve.co.uk

BLISS, Alan Ernest Newport. b 29. K Coll Lon AKC50. St Boniface Warminster 54. **d** 54 **p** 57. C Wooburn *Ox* 54-56; C Whitley Ch 56-58; C Hatcham Park All SS *S'wark* 63-68; C Sundon w Streatley *St Alb* 68-73; P-in-c Caldecote All SS 74-78; V 78-91; V Old Warden 81-91; Perm to Offic from 91. *6 Jubilee Gardens, Biggleswade SG18 0JW* Tel (01767) 313797

BLISS, David Charles. b 52. Aston Univ BSc75 Cranfield Inst of Tech MSc82. St Jo Coll Nottm 87. **d** 89 **p** 90. C Burntwood *Lich* 89-93; TV Aston cum Aughton w Swallownest, Todwick etc *Sheff* 93-02; V Todwick from 02; Chapl among Deaf People from 97. *The Rectory, 15 Rectory Gardens, Todwick, Sheffield S26 1JU* Tel (01909) 770283 Fax 774873

BLISS, John Derek Clegg. b 40. Sarum Th Coll. **d** 68 **p** 69. C Wymondham *Nor* 68-73; V Easton 73-80; R Colton 73-80; USA from 80; rtd 01. *4 Edgewater Hillside, Westport, CT 06880, USA* Tel (001) (203) 222 1879 E-mail jb106600@aol.com

BLISS, Neil Humberstone. b 29. TCD BA54 MA59. Coll of Resurr Mirfield 55. **d** 57 **p** 58. C N Keyham *Ex* 57-60; Swaziland 61-65 and 68-80; S Africa 65-67; P-in-c Osmington w Poxwell *Sarum* 80-81; TV Preston w Sutton Poyntz and Osmington w Poxwell 81-84; V Ernesettle *Ex* 84-88; R S Tawton and Belstone 88-93; rtd 94. *Jordan House, Jordan, Lyme Regis DT7 3AQ* Tel (01297) 445189

BLISSARD-BARNES, Christopher John. b 36. ARCO55 Linc Coll Ox BA61 MA64. Ridley Hall Cam 61. **d** 63 **p** 64. C Woking St Paul *Guildf* 63-67; C Orpington Ch Ch *Roch* 67-71; P-in-c Heref St Jas *Heref* 71-78; Chapl Heref Gen Hosp 71-78; R Hampreston *Sarum* 78-88; TR 88-89; RD Wimborne 80-85; P-in-c Hambledon *Guildf* 89-94; R Newdigate 94-01; Warden of Readers 93-99; rtd 01; Perm to Offic *Win* from 02. *148 Olivers Battery Road South, Winchester SO22 4LF* Tel (01962) 862082 Fax as telephone E-mail cf@blissard-barnes.freeserve.co.uk

BLOCK, Robert Allen. b 62. Univ of Wales (Lamp) BA84. Coll of Resurr Mirfield 86. **d** 88 **p** 89. C Hampton *Worc* 88-91; C Notting Hill St Mich and Ch Ch *Lon* 91-96; P-in-c Hammersmith St Luke 96-02; C-in-c Hammersmith SS Mich and Geo White City Estate CD 96-02. *Bentwitchen House, South Molton EX36 3HA* Tel (01598) 740258 E-mail robertblock@zoom.co.uk

BLOFELD, Thomas Guest. *See* GUEST-BLOFELD, Thomas

BLOGG, Kevin Derek. b 55. Ch Ch Coll Cant BSc82 PGCE87. Franciscan Ho of Studies. **d** 84 **p** 85. NSM Eythorne and Elvington w Waldershare etc *Cant* 89-92; Orchard Sch Cant 89-90; Harbour Sch Dover 92-93; NSM Colkirk w Oxwick w Pattesley, Whissonsett etc *Nor* 95-02; NSM Gressenhall w Longham w Wendling etc from 02; Sidestrand Hall Sch Nor from 94. *The Rectory Barn, Rectory Road, Gressenhall, Dereham NR19 2QG* Tel (01362) 861084

BLOOD, David John. b 36. G&C Coll Cam BA60 MA64. Westcott Ho Cam 60. **d** 62 **p** 63. C Rushmere *St E* 62-66; C Harringay St Paul *Lon* 66-70; Lic to Offic 71-81; rtd 01. *42 Churston Gardens, London N11 2NL*

BLOOD, Canon Michael William. b 44. AKC67. **d** 69 **p** 70. C Moseley St Agnes *Birm* 69-75; V Cotteridge from 75; Relig Progr Producer BBC Radio W Midl from 76; Hon Can Birm Cathl from 97. *118 Northfield Road, Birmingham B30 1DX* Tel 0121-458 2815 Fax 459 6909

BLOOD, Stephen John. b 28. Keble Coll Cam BA53 MA58. Coll of Resurr Mirfield 53. **d** 55 **p** 56. C Greenford H Cross *Lon* 55-58; C Forest Gate St Edm *Chelmsf* 58-61; C-in-c Ashford St Hilda CD *Lon* 61-73; V Ashford St Hilda 73-00; rtd 00; Perm to Offic *St Alb* from 00. *69 Hampstead Road, Kings Langley WD4 8BS* Tel (01923) 268453

BLOOMER, Ms Sherry Lesley. b 50. TD. Liv Jo Moores Univ BA91 Lon Univ Dip Nursing82 Wolv Poly CertEd83 RN73 RM74 RHV78 DipHV78. Westcott Ho Cam CTM97. **d** 97 **p** 98. C Llangollen w Trevor and Llantysilio *St As* 97-00; R Cilcain and Nannerch and Rhyd-y-mwyn from 00. *The Rectory, 9 Pen y Coed, Nannerch, Mold CH7 5RS* Tel (01352) 741376

BLOOMFIELD, Mrs Gillian. b 38. Leeds Univ BA59. WMMTC 84. **d** 87 **p** 94. Par Dn Highters Heath *Birm* 87-89; TD Chelmsley Wood 89-94; TV 94-95; Chapl Chelmsley Hosp Birm 89-95; Chapl Marston Green Hosp Birm 89-95; P-in-c Pattingham w Patshull *Lich* 95-01; rtd 01; Perm to Offic *Lich* from 01. *14 Garridge Close, Albrighton, Wolverhampton WV7 3PZ* Tel (01902) 372153

BLOOMFIELD, John Michael. b 35. Univ of Wales (Lamp) BA57. Sarum Th Coll 59. **d** 61 **p** 62. C Fordington *Sarum* 61-64; C Branksome St Aldhelm 64-66; Youth Chapl *Win* 66-69; R Win All SS w Chilcomb and Chesil 71-79; P-in-c Corsley *Sarum* 79-81; P-in-c Studland 83-86; Chapl HM Pris Dorchester 87-89; C Dorchester *Sarum* 87-89; Chapl HM Pris The Verne 89-00; rtd 00. *Green Acres, Valley Road, Corfe Castle, Wareham BH20 5HU* Tel (01929) 480924 Fax 481699 E-mail swanbeck@aol.com

BLOOMFIELD, John Stephen. b 56. Southn Univ. Chich Th Coll 83. **d** 86 **p** 87. C Chich St Paul and St Pet *Chich* 86-89; TV Littlehampton and Wick 89-98; V Hunstanton St Edm w Ringstead *Nor* from 98. *St Edmund's Vicarage, 53 Northgate, Hunstanton PE36 6DS* Tel (01485) 532157

BLOOR, Terence Bernard. b 62. Liv Univ BTh02. N Ord Course 99. **d** 02. C Hadley *Lich* from 02. *10 Partridge Close, Leegomery, Telford TF1 4WF* Tel (01952) 240146 Mobile 07890-980749 E-mail terry.bloor@supanet.com

BLORE, John Francis. b 49. Jes Coll Ox BA72 MA76. Wycliffe Hall Ox 73. **d** 75 **p** 76. C Waltham Abbey *Chelmsf* 75-78; C E Ham St Geo 78-81; R Colchester St Mich Myland 81-00; Chapl Oxley Parker Sch Colchester 81-00; P-in-c Halstead St Andr w H Trin and Greenstead Green *Chelmsf* from 00; RD Hinckford from 03. *The Vicarage, Parsonage Street, Halstead CO9 2LD* Tel (01787) 472171 E-mail john@johnfblore.freeserve.co.uk

BLOUNT, Robin George. b 38. Lon Univ DipTh68. Lon Coll of Div 61 Wycliffe Hall Ox 67. **d** 68 **p** 69. C Bletchley *Ox* 68-71; C Washington *Dur* 71-74; TV Chelmsley Wood *Birm* 74-76; Ind

Chapl *Worc* 76-89; Asst P Dudley St Jo 76-89; Asst P Dudley St Thos and St Luke 88-89; Ind Chapl (Eurotunnel Development) *Cant* 89-03; rtd 03; Perm to Offic *Cant* from 03. *6 Lyn Court, Shorncliffe Road, Folkestone CT20 2PE* Tel (01303) 250028 E-mail robin.blount@freeuk.com

BLOWERS, Canon Ralph Barrie. b 28. Fitzw Ho Cam BA50 MA61. Ridley Hall Cam 51. **d** 53 **p** 54. C Higher Openshaw *Man* 53-56; R Man Albert Memorial Ch 56-68; RD Cheetham 63-69; R Man Albert Memorial Ch w Newton Heath 68-69; V Normanton *Derby* 69-93; RD Derby 74-79; RD Derby S 79-89; Hon Can Derby Cathl 85-93; rtd 93; Perm to Offic *Derby* from 93. *8 Portland Close, Mickleover, Derby DE3 9BQ* Tel (01332) 517114

BLOWS, Canon Derek Reeve. b 26. SAP75 Linc Coll Ox BA50 MA52. Cuddesdon Coll 50. **d** 52 **p** 53. C Cov St Mark *Cov* 52-56; Lic to Offic *Sarum* 56-58; Chapl Warlingham Park Hosp Croydon 58-65; V Purley St Mark *S'wark* 65-70; Dir Past Care and Counselling 70-80; Lic to Offic from 70; Hon Can S'wark Cathl 72-80; Dir Westmr Past Foundn 80-91; rtd 91; Perm to Offic *Roch* from 91. *2 Blackmoor House, Four Elms, Edenbridge TN8 6PG* Tel (01732) 700770

BLOXAM-ROSE, Canon Simon Franklyn. b 61. HonFLCM88 Southn Univ BTh MA PhD99. Chich Th Coll 85. **d** 88 **p** 89. C Bassaleg *Mon* 88-89; Chapl Aldenham Sch Herts 89-94; Perm to Offic *Ex* from 94; Chapl (Sen) Millfield Sch Somerset from 94; Can St Jo Pro-Cathl Katakwa from 95. *The Chaplaincy, Butleigh Road, Street BA16 0DA* Tel (01458) 447276 E-mail sbr@millfield.somerset.sch.uk

BLOXHAM, Oliver. b 27. Ely Th Coll 60. **d** 62 **p** 63. C Newc H Cross *Newc* 62-65; C Ponteland 65-69; V Dudley 69-79; P-in-c Balkwell 79-81; V 81-92; rtd 92; Perm to Offic *Newc* from 92. *23 Lambley Avenue, North Shields NE30 3SL* Tel 0191-296 1785

BLUNDELL, Catherine. b 62. St Alb and Ox Min Course 96. **d** 99 **p** 00. C Furze Platt *Ox* 99-03; TV Bracknell from 03. *St Paul's Vicarage, 58 Harmans Water Road, Bracknell RG12 9PT* Tel (01344) 422819 E-mail catherine.blundell@btinternet.com

BLUNDELL, Canon Derek George. b 32. Tyndale Hall Bris 58. **d** 61 **p** 62. C Fazakerley Em *Liv* 61-64; C-in-c Bath Odd Down *B & W* 64-69; V 69-74; V Tulse Hill H Trin *S'wark* 74-81; Org and Admin African Pastor Fund 81-98; Perm to Offic *Cov* 81-98; and from 01; Hon Can Mityana from 90; rtd 98. *12 Ibex Close, Binley, Coventry CV3 2FB* Tel (024) 7645 2536 Fax as telephone

BLUNDELL, Peter Grahame. b 61. Ealing Coll of Educn BA83. Oak Hill NSM Course 91. **d** 94 **p** 95. NSM Kensington St Barn *Lon* 94-97; Zimbabwe 97-99; Assoc Min Romford Gd Shep Collier Row *Chelmsf* from 99. *470 Mawney Road, Collier Row, Romford RM7 8QB* Tel (01708) 728720 E-mail megandpeter@clara.co.uk

BLUNDEN, Jacqueline Ann. *See* MILLER, Mrs Jacqueline Ann

BLUNDEN, Jeremy Augustine. b 61. BSc CEng88. SEITE DipTM99. **d** 99 **p** 00. NSM Sydenham St Bart *S'wark* 99-01; C 01-03; V Clapham H Spirit from 03. *15 Elms Road, London SW4 9ER* Tel (020) 7622 8703 E-mail jeremy.blunden@virgin.net

BLUNSUM, Charles Michael. b 28. ACIB51 MBIM86. **d** 74 **p** 75. C Stoke Bishop *Bris* 74-79; Chapl Brunel Manor Chr Cen Torquay 79-94; rtd 94; Perm to Offic *Ex* from 94. *16A Hollywater Close, Torquay TQ1 3TN* Tel (01803) 214371

BLUNT, The Ven Paul David. b 44. Lon Univ BSc65 Leeds Univ DipTh70. Coll of Resurr Mirfield 67. **d** 70 **p** 71. C Norbury St Steph *Lon* 70-73; Canada from 73. *1234 Prescone Drive, Orleans ON, Canada, K1E 3X6* E-mail st.helen@on.aibn.com

BLYDE, Ian Hay. b 52. Liv Univ BSc74 Edin Univ BD80. Edin Th Coll 77. **d** 80 **p** 81. C Ainsdale *Liv* 80-83; Chapl Birkenhead Sch Merseyside 83-90; V Over St Chad *Ches* 90-93; Chapl Ex Sch 93-98; Chapl St Marg Sch Ex 93-98. *2 Hulham Road, Exmouth EX8 3HR* Tel (01395) 264339

BLYTH, Andrew Kenneth Eric. b 63. Surrey Univ BA86 Middx Univ PGCE87. Ridley Hall Cam 98. **d** 00 **p** 01. C Luton St Mary *St Alb* from 00. *34 Wychwood Avenue, Luton LU2 7HU* Tel (01582) 729902 E-mail theblyths@yahoo.com

BLYTH, Bryan Edward Perceval. b 22. Linc Coll Ox BA49 MA52. Wells Th Coll 48. **d** 50 **p** 51. C Timperley *Ches* 50-52; C Talbot Village *Sarum* 52-55; C-in-c Weymouth St Edm 55; P-in-c 56-63; Asst Dir of Educn *Chelmsf* 64-67; Hon C Mountnessing 67-68; Hon C Ingatestone w Buttsbury 67-68; Teacher Ingatestone Sec Modern Sch 67-68; Teacher Westwood Co Jun Sch 68-72; Dep Hd 72-87; Hon C Thundersley 80-84; rtd 87; Perm to Offic *Sarum* and *Win* from 98. *Greenways, 19 Chiltern Drive, New Milton BH25 7JY* Tel (01425) 611140

BLYTH, Canon Drummond Gwyn. b 26. K Coll Lon 53. **d** 54 **p** 55. C N Lynn w St Marg and St Nic *Nor* 54-59; C Sheff Parson Cross St Cecilia *Sheff* 59-62; R Carlton Colville *Nor* 62-70; V Stalham w Brunstead 70-77; P-in-c E Ruston 76-77; RD Waxham 77-89; V Stalham and E Ruston w Brunstead 77-91; Hon Can Nor Cathl 87-91; rtd 91; Perm to Offic *Nor* from 91. *Pegg's Close, 6 St Nicholas Close, Sheringham NR26 8LE* Tel (01263) 822611

BLYTH, Mrs Geraldine Anne. b 50. Llan Dioc Tr Scheme 90. **d** 94 **p** 97. C Llantrisant *Llan* 94-01; P-in-c Llanharry from 01; Chapl

Pontypridd and Rhondda NHS Trust from 01. *The Rectory, Llanharry, Pontyclun CF72 9LH* Tel (01443) 223140

BLYTH, Ian John. b 40. Rhodes Univ BA66 Natal Univ BEd81 MEd96. **d** 82 **p** 83. S Africa 82-01; Dioc Educn Officer Natal 83-85; R Pietermaritzburg St Luke 85-87; Lic to Offic 88-01; NSM W Woodhay w Enborne, Hampstead Marshall etc *Ox* from 02. *St Laurence's Rectory, West Woodhay, Newbury RG20 0BL* Tel and fax (01488) 669233 Mobile 07900-857096 E-mail ian@blythkin.fsnet.co.uk

BLYTH, John Reddie. b 25. Wadh Coll Ox BA48 MA50. Ridley Hall Cam 48. **d** 50 **p** 51. C Southport Ch Ch *Liv* 50-52; C Enfield Ch Ch Trent Park *Lon* 52-55; V Plymouth St Jude *Ex* 55-63; E Midl Area Sec CPAS 63-70; V Parkstone St Luke *Sarum* 70-90; Chapl Uplands Sch Parkstone 70-73; rtd 90; Perm to Offic *Chich* from 90. *5 Powell Road, Newick, Lewes BN8 4LS* Tel (01825) 722011

BLYTH, Kenneth Henry. b 35. Lon Univ DipTh60. Oak Hill Th Coll 58. **d** 61 **p** 62. C St Alb St Paul *St Alb* 61-65; P-in-c Aspenden and Layston w Buntingford 65-66; R 66-72; R Washfield, Stoodleigh, Withleigh etc *Ex* 72-82; P-in-c Cruwys Morchard 72-74; RD Tiverton 76-82; V Eastbourne H Trin *Chich* 82-00; rtd 00; Perm to Offic *Ex* from 00. *Hamslade House, Bampton, Tiverton EX16 9JA*

BLYTH, Michael Graham. b 53. Jes Coll Ox BA75 MA78 Dur Univ PhD79. Qu Coll Birm 82. **d** 84 **p** 85. C Nantwich *Ches* 84-86; C Coppenhall 86-88; TV Southend *Chelmsf* 88-95; P-in-c Danbury from 95; RD Chelmsf S from 01. *St John's Rectory, 55 Main Road, Danbury, Chelmsford CM3 4NG* Tel (01245) 223140 E-mail graham@revdoc.fsnet.co.uk

BOAG, David. b 46. Edin Th Coll 69. **d** 72 **p** 73. C Edin Old St Paul *Edin* 72-76; P-in-c Edin St Andr and St Aid 75-88; Lic to Offic from 88. *7 Starch Mill, Ford Road, Haddington EH41 4AR* Tel (01620) 826839

BOAG, Michael John. b 61. Leeds Univ BA00. Coll of Resurr Mirfield 98. **d** 00 **p** 01. C Howden *York* from 00. *6 Sandholme Way, Howden, Goole DN14 7LN* Tel (01430) 432276 E-mail michael.boag@macunlimited.net

BOAK, Canon Donald Kenneth. b 30. MBAOT53. S'wark Ord Course DipRS85. **d** 85 **p** 86. C Tulse Hill H Trin and St Matthias *S'wark* 85-88; C Surbiton St Matt 88-91; Intercon Ch Soc, SAMS and Miss to Seamen 91-95; Peru 91-95; Dean Lima 93-95; rtd 95; Hon Can Peru from 95; Hon C Bournemouth St Andr *Win* 96-99; Perm to Offic *Sarum* 98-01; *Win* from 99. *96 Shelley Road East, Boscombe, Bournemouth BH7 6HB* Tel (01202) 303706

BOAKES, Norman. b 50. Univ of Wales (Swansea) BA71 Univ of Wales (Lamp) LTh73 Ox Univ MTh96. Bp Burgess Hall Lamp 71. **d** 73 **p** 74. C Swansea St Mary w H Trin *S & B* 73-78; Chapl Univ of Wales (Swansea) 76-78; Chapl K Alfred Coll *Win* 78-82; V Colbury 82-91; Chapl Ashurst Hosp 82-91; Chapl Mental Handicap Services Unit 82-91; V Southampton Maybush St Pet *Win* from 91; Bp's Adv for Hosp Chapl 87-00; AD Southn from 02. *Maybush Vicarage, Sedgerup Road, Southampton SO16 9HJ* Tel (023) 8070 3443 E-mail nboakes@fish.co.uk

BOAR, Alan Bennett. b 23. Sarum Th Coll 56. **d** 58 **p** 59. C E Dereham w Hoe *Nor* 58-60; C Gorleston St Andr 60-63; V Tibenham 63-67; P-in-c Tivetshall 64-67; R Beeston St Laurence w Ashmanhaugh and Hoveton 67-78; P-in-c Tunstead w Sco' Ruston 67-78; P-in-c Marsham 78-89; P-in-c Burgh 78-89; rtd 89; Perm to Offic *Nor* from 89. *20 Emelson Close, Dereham NR19 2ES* Tel (01362) 698944

BOARDMAN, Frederick Henry. b 25. Liv Univ BSc46 St Cath Soc Ox BA49 MA54 Birm Univ MEd71 PhD77. Wycliffe Hall Ox 47. **d** 50 **p** 51. C Bootle Ch Ch *Liv* 50-52; C-in-c Netherton CD 52-57; V Stechford *Birm* 57-63; Lic to Offic 63-69; Lic to Offic *Liv* from 71; Hon C Sutton 76-89; Hon C Burtonwood from 89; rtd 90. *Woodside, Burtonwood Road, Great Sankey, Warrington WA5 3AN* Tel (01925) 635079

BOARDMAN, Jonathan. b 63. Magd Coll Cam BA89 Magd Coll Ox MA90. Westcott Ho Cam 87. **d** 90 **p** 91. C W Derby St Mary *Liv* 90-93; Prec St Alb Abbey *St Alb* 93-96; TR Catford (Southend) and Downham *S'wark* 96-99; RD E Lewisham 99; Chapl Rome *Eur* from 99. *All Saints, via del Babuino 153, 00187 Rome, Italy* Tel (0039) (06) 3600 2171 *or* 3600 1881 E-mail j.boardman@agora.stm.it

BOARDMAN, Preb Philippa Jane. b 63. Jes Coll Cam BA85 MA89. Ridley Hall Cam 87. **d** 90 **p** 94. Par Dn Walthamstow St Mary w St Steph *Chelmsf* 90-93; C Hackney Wick St Mary of Eton w St Aug *Lon* 93-96; P-in-c Old Ford St Paul and St Mark 96-03; V from 03; Dean of Women's Min Stepney Area 94-02; Preb St Paul's Cathl from 02. *The Vicarage, St Stephen's Road, London E3 5JL* Tel (020) 8980 9020

BOASE, David John. b 49. St Jo Coll Dur BA71 Trin Coll Ox PGCE73. Cuddesdon Coll 71. **d** 73 **p** 74. C Penrith *Carl* 73-76; Tutor Greystoke Coll Carl 76-78; Chapl Miss to Seamen and Prec Gib Cathl *Eur* 78-80; Chapl Gothenburg w Halmstad and Jönköping 80-82; TV Thornaby on Tees *York* 82-88; V Kirkby-in-Cleveland from 88; P-in-c Whorlton w Carlton and Faceby from 03; Min Development Officer (Cleveland Adnry) from 88.

18 Church Lane, Swainby, Northallerton DL6 3EA Tel (01642) 700887 Fax 700595 E-mail david.boase@dunelm.org.uk

BOCKING (Essex), Dean of. See NEED, The Very Revd Philip Alan

BOCKING (Suffolk), Dean of. See STRANACK, The Very Revd David Arthur Claude

BODDINGTON, Canon Alan Charles Peter. b 37. Lon Univ DipTh65. Oak Hill Th Coll 63. **d** 66 **p** 67. C Bedworth *Cov* 66-69; Bp's Officer for Min 69-75; Bp's Chapl for Miss 69-73; P-in-c Wroxall and Honiley 72-75; V Westwood 75-85; Asst Chapl Warw Univ 78-85; TR N Farnborough *Guildf* 85-02; RD Aldershot 88-93; Hon Can Guildf Cathl 92-02; rtd 02; Perm to Offic *Cov* from 02. *Tremar, Hathaway Lane, Stratford-upon-Avon CV37 9BJ* Tel (01789) 263643 Mobile 07866-909092

BODDY, Alan Richard. b 47. Ripon Coll Cuddesdon. **d** 84 **p** 85. C Eastcote St Lawr *Lon* 84-87; C Kensington St Mary Abbots w St Geo 87-90; Chapl HM Pris Brixton 90-91; Chapl HM Pris Send and Downview 91-92; Chapl HM Pris High Down 92-98; Chapl HM Pris Wormwood Scrubs 98-02; rtd 02; PV Westmr Abbey from 02; Perm to Offic *Lon* and *Ox* from 02. *105 Valiant House, Vicarage Crescent, London SW11 3LX*

BODDY, David. b 57. SSF. Linc Th Coll 92. **d** 92 **p** 93. C Peterlee *Dur* 92-95; C Penshaw 95-97; P-in-c Shiney Row 95-98; P-in-c Herrington 95-98; TV S Shields All SS from 98. *The Vicarage, St Oswin's Street, South Shields NE33 4SE* Tel 0191-455 3072 Mobile 07971-304622 E-mail davidboddy@lineone.net

BODKIN, Thomas Patrick Joseph. b 45. Richmond Fellowship Coll Dip Human Relns 78 Open Univ BA77 BA90. St Hyacinth's Coll & RC Sem Mass 64 Franciscan Ho of Studies DipPhil67 DipTh70. **d** 80 **p** 80. In RC Ch 80-86; NSM Littlehampton and Wick *Chich* 91-93; Visiting Tutor Moral Th Chich Th Coll 92-99; P-in-c Bishopstone 97-99. *6 Pinehurst Park, Bognor Regis PO21 3DL*

BODLE, Richard Talbot. b 70. Southn Univ LLB91. Wycliffe Hall Ox BTh98. **d** 98 **p** 99. C S Mimms Ch Ch *Lon* 98-02; TV Edgware from 02. *1 Beulah Close, Edgware HA8 8SP* Tel (020) 8958 9730

BODMIN, Archdeacon of. See COHEN, The Ven Clive Ronald Franklin

BODY, Andrew. b 46. Pemb Coll Cam BA68 MA71. Ridley Hall Cam 68. **d** 70 **p** 71. C New Bury *Man* 70-73; TV Droylsden St Mary 73-78; V Low Harrogate St Mary *Ripon* 78-92; Trustee FLAME from 90; TR Redhorn *Sarum* 92-97; V Chobham w Valley End *Guildf* from 97. *Chobham Vicarage, Bagshot Road, Chobham, Woking GU24 8BY* Tel (01276) 858197 E-mail andrew@abody.freeserve.co.uk

BODY, Mrs Shuna Jane. b 67. SEITE 98. **d** 01 **p** 02. NSM Appledore w Brookland, Fairfield, Brenzett etc *Cant* from 01. *Hope Farm, Snargate, Romney Marsh TN29 9UQ* Tel (01797) 343977 Mobile 07786-543711 E-mail shunabody@hotmail.com

BODYCOMBE, Stephen John. b 58. Lanchester Poly BA. St Mich Coll Llan DipTh83. **d** 83 **p** 84. C Cardiff St Jo Llan 83-86; V Dinas and Penygraig w Williamstown 86-00; V Dyffryn from 00. *The Vicarage, Dyffryn, Neath SA10 7AZ* Tel (01792) 814237

BOFF, Charles Roy. b 31. Pemb Coll Ox BA57 MA60. Clifton Th Coll 55. **d** 57 **p** 58. C Plumstead All SS *S'wark* 57-61; V Gipsy Hill Ch Ch 61-68; V Felbridge 68-79; V Steyning *Chich* 79-84; R Ashurst 79-84; RD Storrington 81-84; R Romaldkirk w Laithkirk *Ripon* 84-94; RD Richmond 90-93; rtd 94; Perm to Offic *Carl* from 94. *9 Edenfold, Bolton, Appleby-in-Westmorland CA16 6BQ* Tel (01768) 362328

BOFFEY, Ian. b 40. Glas Univ MA63. Glas NSM Course 75. **d** 78 **p** 78. Hon C Dalry *Glas* 75-78; P-in-c from 78. *2 Kinloch Avenue, Stewarton, Kilmarnock KA3 3HF* Tel (01560) 482586

BOGA, Bishop of. See NJOJO, The Rt Revd Patrice Byankya

BOGGIS, Miss Christine Louise. b 38. R Holloway Coll Lon BA60 Cam Univ CertEd61 Hull Univ BTh94. EMMTC DTPS94. **d** 94 **p** 95. NSM Scartho *Linc* 94-98; NSM Gt and Lt Coates w Bradley from 98. *90 Waltham Road, Grimsby DN33 2NA* Tel (01472) 822108

BOGGUST, Mrs Patricia Anne. b 42. Portsm Dioc Tr Course. **d** 90 **p** 98. NSM Hook w Warsash *Portsm* 90-94; NSM Locks Heath from 94. *21 Beverley Close, Park Gate, Southampton SO31 6QU* Tel (01489) 573586

BOGLE, Ms Elizabeth. b 47. York Univ BA68 Leeds Univ PGCE69. S'wark Ord Course 93. **d** 96 **p** 97. NSM E Greenwich *S'wark* 96-00; NSM Hatcham St Jas from 00. *8 Waller Road, London SE14 5LA* Tel (020) 7732 9420 *or* 8305 2339 E-mail elizabethbogle@hotmail.com

BOGLE, James Main Lindam Linton. b 33. Peterho Cam BA56 MA60. Wells Th Coll 59. **d** 61 **p** 62. C Bermondsey St Anne *S'wark* 61-65; Chapl York Univ *York* 65-72; V Brayton 72-76; V Forest Hill St Aug *S'wark* 76-83; C Hatcham St Cath 83-85; NSM from 91; C Herne Hill St Paul 86-87; rtd 87. *8 Waller Road, London SE14 5LA* Tel (020) 7732 9420 E-mail james.bogle@btinternet.com

BOHUN, Brother Roger Alexander. b 32. Lon Univ BSc58. Cuddesdon Coll 65. **d** 68 **p** 69. C Rugby St Andr *Cov* 68-74; SSF from 74; Perm to Offic *Sarum* 74-76, 88-93 and from 00; *Newc*

76-78; Tanzania 78-86; Zimbabwe 86-88 and 93-00; P-in-c Waruka Ch Distr 86-88; R Bonda Miss 93-95; P-in-c Chimanimani and Chipinge Miss Distr 96-00; rtd 00. *The Friary, Hilfield, Dorchester DT2 7BE* Tel (01300) 341345 Fax 341293

BOIT, Mervyn Hays. b 38. Univ of Wales (Lamp) BA59. St Mich Coll Llan 59. **d** 61 **p** 62. C Roath St German *Llan* 61-63; C Skewen 63-69; V Pontycymer and Blaengarw from 69. *The Vicarage, St David Street, Pontycymer, Bridgend CF32 8LT* Tel (01656) 870280

BOLAND, Christopher Paul. b 75. Hertf Coll Ox MPhys97. Ridley Hall Cam BTh01. **d** 01 **p** 02. C Skirbeck H Trin *Linc* from 01. *11 Hope Gardens, Boston PE21 9HJ* Tel (01205) 351727 Mobile 07791-702537 E-mail chrisboland@fish.co.uk

BOLAND, Geoffrey. b 56. DipHE89. Oak Hill Th Coll 87. **d** 89 **p** 90. C Ormskirk *Liv* 89-94; C Woodside Park St Barn *Lon* 94-99; TV Canford Magna *Sarum* from 99. *11 Plantagenet Crescent, Bournemouth BH11 9PL* Tel (01220) 573872

BOLD, Peter Edward. b 64. Sheff Univ BEng86 PhD90. Cranmer Hall Dur BA94 DMS95. **d** 95 **p** 96. C Grenoside *Sheff* 95-97; Dioc Communications Officer 97-01; C Rotherham 97-01; P-in-c Brampton Bierlow from 01. *Brampton Vicarage, Christchurch Road, Wath-upon-Dearne, Rotherham S63 6NW* Tel (01709) 873210 E-mail pebold@talk21.com

BOLE, Malcolm Dennis. b 30. Oak Hill Th Coll 65. **d** 67 **p** 68. C Bridlington Priory *York* 67-70; Rwanda 71-73; P-in-c Combe Hay *B & W* 74-81; V Bath Odd Down 74-81; P-in-c Taunton St Jas 81-84; V 84-90; R Bicknoller w Crowcombe and Sampford Brett 90-98; rtd 98; Perm to Offic *B & W* from 01. *7 Putsham Mead, Kilve, Bridgwater TA5 1DZ* Tel (01278) 741297

BOLLARD, Canon Richard George. b 39. Fitzw Ho Cam BA61 MA65 K Coll Lon BD63 AKC63. **d** 64 **p** 65. C Southampton Maybush St Pet *Win* 64-68; Chapl Aston Univ *Birm* 68-74; TR Chelmsley Wood 74-82; V Coleshill from 82; V Maxstoke from 82; RD Coleshill 82-92; Hon Can Birm Cathl from 85; Dioc Ecum Officer 97-02. *The Vicarage, High Street, Coleshill, Birmingham B46 3BP* Tel (01675) 462188

BOLLEN, Bryan Hayward. b 26. **d** 77 **p** 78. NSM Chippenham St Pet *Bris* 77-94; Perm to Offic from 94. *27 The Tinings, Chippenham SN15 3LY* Tel (01249) 652515

BOLLEY, Michael Francis. b 55. St Cath Coll Ox BA76 MSc77 MA92. Ripon Coll Cuddesdon 90. **d** 92 **p** 93. C Pinner *Lon* 92-95; C Eastcote St Lawr 95-99; P-in-c Southall H Trin from 99. *Holy Trinity Vicarage, Park View Road, Southall UB1 3HJ* Tel (020) 8574 3839 E-mail michael@bolley.freeserve.co.uk

BOLSTER, David Richard. b 50. BA. St Jo Coll Nottm. **d** 84 **p** 85. C Luton Lewsey St Hugh *St Alb* 84-87; V Woodside w E Hyde 87-01; V Edmonton St Aldhelm *Lon* from 01. *St Aldhelm's Vicarage, Windmill Road, London N18 1PA* Tel (020) 8807 5336 E-mail bolster@milestonenet.co.uk

BOLT, David Dingley. b 53. Jo Coll Cam LLB58 LLM85. Westcott Ho Cam 66. **d** 68 **p** 69. Malawi 68-70; C Chesterton Gd Shep *Ely* 70-71; P-in-c Gt Wilbraham 71-74; V 74-86; P-in-c Lt Wilbraham 71-74; R 74-86; RD Quy 75-81; rtd 86; Perm to Offic *Ely* from 86. *24 Warwick Road, Cambridge CB4 3HN* Tel (01223) 366361

BOLT, George Henry. b 34. MInstP75 CPhys75 Lon Univ BSc60 Bath Univ MSc75. S Dios Minl Tr Scheme 85. **d** 88 **p** 89. NSM Oldbury *Sarum* 88-89; Chapl Chippenham Tech Coll 89-90; C Kington St Michael *Bris* 90-92; P-in-c Aldenham *St Alb* 90-97; rtd 98; Perm to Offic *Ban* from 98. *Ty Capel Ffrwd, Llanfachreth, Dolgellau LL40 2NR* Tel (01341) 422006

BOLT, Mrs Mary Veronica. b 36. S Dios Minl Tr Scheme 90. **d** 93 **p** 94. NSM Aldenham *St Alb* 93-98; Sub-Chapl HM Pris The Mount 93-98; rtd 98; Perm to Offic *Ban* 98-99; P-in-c Maentwrog w Trawsfynydd 99-03. *Ty Capel Ffrwd, Llanfachreth, Dolgellau LL40 2NR* Tel (01341) 422006 E-mail mary.bolt@care4free.net

BOLTON, Christopher Leonard. b 60. St Mich Coll Llan DipTh83. **d** 83 **p** 84. C Lampeter *St D* 83-86; P-in-c Llanarth and Capel Cynon w Talgarreg etc 86-87; V from 87; RD Glyn Aeron from 02. *The Vicarage, Llanarth SA47 0NJ* Tel (01545) 580745

BOLTON, Mrs Jane Elizabeth. b 53. Leic Univ BA75. Ripon Coll Cuddesdon DipMin95. **d** 97 **p** 98. C Sheff St Mark Broomhill *Sheff* 97-02; P-in-c Dinnington from 02; P-in-c Laughton w Throapham from 03. *The Rectory, 217 Nursery Road, Dinnington, Sheffield S25 2QU* Tel (01909) 562335

BOLTON, John. b 43. SS Paul & Mary Coll Cheltenham DipEd64. Trin Coll Bris 83. **d** 85 **p** 86. C Minehead *B & W* 85-89; R Winford w Felton Common Hill 89-98; C-in-c Locking Castle CD from 98. *The Vicarage, 78 Bransby Way, Weston-super-Mare BS24 7BW* Tel (01934) 516565 Fax 513218 E-mail john20011ccp@aol.com

BOLTON, Kelvin. b 53. Wilson Carlile Coll 88 Trin Coll Bris BA98. **d** 98 **p** 99. C Walton Breck Ch Ch *Liv* 98-01; V Goose Green from 01. *St Paul's Vicarage, Warrington Road, Wigan WN3 6QB* Tel (01942) 242984

BOLTON, Paul Edward. b 71. St Jo Coll Ox BA94 MA98 Peterho Cam BA97. Ridley Hall Cam 95. **d** 98 **p** 99. C Lowestoft Ch Ch

Nor 98-01; Titus Trust from 01. *93 Morrell Avenue, Oxford OX4 1NQ* Tel (01865) 248955 E-mail paul_bolton@lineone.net

BOLTON, Peter Richard Shawcross. b 58. Warwick Univ BA79. Sarum & Wells Th Coll 80. **d** 83 **p** 84. C Beckenham St Jas *Roch* 83-86; C Bedford Leigh *Man* 86-88; V Royton St Paul 88-94; AD Tandle 93-94; P-in-c Lower Broughton Ascension 95-01; P-in-c Salford Ordsall St Clem 98-01; P-in-c Ardwick St Benedict 99-01; V Leavesden All SS *St Alb* from 01. *All Saints' Vicarage, Horseshoe Lane, Watford WD25 7HJ* Tel (01923) 672375 E-mail peterbolton@btconnect.com

BOLTON, Richard David Edward. b 52. MA. St Steph Ho Ox 79. **d** 81 **p** 82. C Rawmarsh w Parkgate *Sheff* 81-84; Chapl Wellingborough Sch 85-92; Chapl Merchant Taylors' Sch Northwood from 91; Lic to Offic *St Alb* from 91; Perm to Offic *Lon* from 91; P in O from 96. *1 Askew Road, Sandy Lodge, Northwood HA6 2JE* Tel (01923) 821136 or 820644

BOLTON, Archdeacon of. *See* APPLEGATE, The Ven John

BOLTON, Suffragan Bishop of. *See* GILLETT, The Rt Revd David Keith

BOMFORD, Canon Rodney William George. b 43. BNC Ox BA64 DipTh66 MA68. Coll of Resurr Mirfield 67 Union Th Sem (NY) STM69. **d** 69 **p** 70. C Deptford St Paul *S'wark* 69-77; V Camberwell St Giles w St Matt 77-01; RD Camberwell 87-97; Hon Can S'wark Cathl 93-01; rtd 01. *The Manor House, Modbury, Ivybridge PL21 0RA* Tel (01548) 831277

BOMYER, Julian Richard Nicholas Jeffrey. b 55. AKC78 Sarum & Wells Th Coll 78. **d** 79 **p** 80. C Rugby St Andr *Cov* 79-84; TV 85-88; P-in-c Clifton upon Dunsmore w Brownsover 84-85; Prec Ch Ch *Ox* 88-93; V Hampton *Worc* 93-01; P-in-c Sedgeberrow w Hinton-on-the-Green 00-01; R Hampton w Sedgeberrow and Hinton-on-the-Green from 01; Chapl Evesham Coll from 93. *St Andrew's Vicarage, Pershore Road, Evesham WR11 2PQ* Tel (01386) 446381 Fax 49224 E-mail vicar@hamptonchurch.org.uk

BOND, Alan Richard. b 49. Lon Univ BSc71 Imp Coll Lon ARCS71 Portsm Poly DMS74 MCMI75 MIMA75 CMath98. S Dios Minl Tr Scheme 80. **d** 83 **p** 84. NSM Westbourne *Chich* 83-86. *26 Victoria Court, Castle Cary BA7 7NL*

✠**BOND, The Rt Revd Charles Derek.** b 27. AKC51. **d** 52 **p** 53 **c** 76. C Friern Barnet St Jas *Lon* 52-56; Lic to Offic *Birm* 56-58; Midl Sch Sec SCM 56-58; V Harringay St Paul *Lon* 58-62; V Harrow Weald All SS 62-72; P-in-c Pebmarsh *Chelmsf* 72-73; Adn Colchester 72-76; Suff Bp Bradwell 76-84; Area Bp Bradwell 84-92; rtd 92; Hon Asst Bp *Glouc* and *Worc* from 92. *Ambleside, 14 Worcester Road, Evesham WR11 4JU* Tel (01386) 446156

BOND, Charles Robert. b 25. Trin Coll Bris DipHE80. **d** 80 **p** 81. C Wythenshawe Wm Temple Ch *Man* 80-82; TV Cwmbran *Mon* 82-88; Chapl Corfu *Eur* 88-91; Chapl Playa de Las Americas Tenerife 91-93; rtd 93. *Urbanizacion Club Miraverde, Apartment 1, Edificio Iris, 38660 Playa de Las Americas, Tenerife, Canary Islands* Tel (0034) (22) 791082

BOND, Clifford Frank. b 24. St Aid Birkenhead 60. **d** 62 **p** 63. C Kirkham *Blackb* 62-64; C Wallingford St Mary w All Hallows and St Leon *Ox* 64-69; P Missr Reading St Barn CD 69-73; R Reading St Barn 73-95; rtd 95; Perm to Offic *Ox* from 01. *Devonia, St James's Close, Pangbourne, Reading RG8 7AP* Tel 0118-984 3793

BOND, Daniel Michael. b 75. Bp Grosseteste Coll BA(QTS)97 Cam Univ BTh02. Ridley Hall Cam 99. **d** 02 **p** 03. C Ranworth w Panxworth, Woodbastwick etc *Nor* from 02. *The Rectory, 23 The Street, South Walsham NR13 6DQ* E-mail dmb40@cam.ac.uk

BOND, David. b 36. Oak Hill Th Coll 72. **d** 74 **p** 75. C Leyton St Mary w St Edw *Chelmsf* 74-78; C Slough *Ox* 78-80; V Selby St Jas *York* 80-93; P-in-c Wistow 80-82; V 82-93; RD Selby 89-93; P-in-c Northiam *Chich* 93-94; R 94-99; rtd 99; Perm to Offic *Chich* from 00. *109 Pebsham Lane, Bexhill-on-Sea TN40 2RP* Tel (01424) 731845

BOND, David Matthew. b 38. Leic Univ BA59 Leeds Univ PGCE67 Nottm Univ MA85. Sarum Th Coll 59. **d** 61 **p** 62. C Leic St Anne *Leic* 61-64; E England Sec SCM 64-66; Hon C Nor St Pet Mancroft *Nor* 64-67; Lect and Hd of Section Pet Regional Coll 67-96; Lect Pet Coll of Adult Educn from 96; Hon C Stamford All SS w St Pet *Linc* 74-81; Hon C Stamford All SS w St Jo from 81; Perm to Offic *Pet* from 85. *2 The Courtyard, Cotterstock, Peterborough PE8 5HD* Tel (01832) 226255

BOND, David Warner. b 32. MA BSc(Econ). Cant Sch of Min 79. **d** 82 **p** 83. NSM Otham w Langley *Cant* from 82. *6 Denton Close, Willington Street, Maidstone ME15 8ER* Tel (01622) 202239 Fax 205149 E-mail dwbond@denton44.freeserve.co.uk

BOND, Douglas Gregory. b 39. FVCM. Edin Th Coll 74. **d** 76 **p** 77. NSM Edin St Paul and St Geo *Edin* 76-83; P-in-c Abthorpe w Slapton *Pet* 83-84; P-in-c Silverstone and Abthorpe w Slapton 84; R 84-89; V Pet St Jude 89-95; R Kislingbury and Harpole from 95. *The Rectory, School Lane, Harpole, Northampton NN7 4DR* Tel and fax (01604) 830322 Mobile 07802-736409 E-mail father.d@highrev.fsnet.co.uk

BOND, Gordon. b 44. Chich Th Coll 68. **d** 71 **p** 72. C Wisbech St Aug *Ely* 71-74; C Wembley Park St Aug *Lon* 74-77; C York Town St Mich *Guildf* 77-80; C Haywards Heath St Wilfrid *Chich* 80; TV 80-82; V Lower Beeding 82-86; V E Grinstead St Mary from 86; RD E Grinstead from 98. *The Vicarage, Windmill Lane, East Grinstead RH19 2DS* Tel (01342) 323439 E-mail bond_st_mary_eg@yahoo.co.uk

BOND, Canon John Albert. b 35. LRAM55 GGSM56 St Cath Soc Ox BA61 MA65 MPhil77 Seabury-Western Th Sem BD62. Wycliffe Hall Ox 58. **d** 62 **p** 63. C Chelmsf Cathl *Chelmsf* 62-63; Succ 63-64; Prec 64-66; Lect St Osyth Coll Clacton-on-Sea 66-69; Lect Ch Ch Coll Cant 69-73; Sen Lect 73-85; Prin Lect and Hd RS Cant Ch Ch Univ Coll 85-00; Hon Min Can Cant Cathl *Cant* 70-85; Hon Can 85-00; rtd 00. *St Lawrence Priory, 136 Old Dover Road, Canterbury CT1 3NX* Tel (01227) 765575

BOND, The Very Revd John Frederick Augustus. b 45. Open Univ BA75. CITC 64. **d** 67 **p** 69. C Lisburn St Paul *Conn* 67-70; C Finaghy 70-77; I Ballynure and Ballyeaston 77-99; I Skerry w Rathcavan and Newtowncrommelin from 99; Can Conn Cathl 96-98; Prec 98-01; Dean Conn from 01. *The Rectory, 49 Rectory Gardens, Broughshane, Ballymena BT42 4LF* Tel and fax (028) 2586 1215 Mobile 07711-285728 E-mail skerry@connor.anglican.org *or* dean@connor.anglican.org

BOND, Kim Mary. *See* BURGESS, Mrs Kim Mary

BOND, Lawrence. b 53. ACIB77. Sarum & Wells Th Coll 92. **d** 92 **p** 93. C Saffron Walden w Wendens Ambo and Littlebury *Chelmsf* 92-95; TV 96-00; P-in-c Takeley w Lt Canfield from 00; RD Dunmow from 02. *The Rectory, Parsonage Road, Takeley, Bishop's Stortford CM22 6QX* Tel (01279) 870837 Fax as telephone E-mail lbd.littlebury@virgin.net

BOND, Linda. b 52. Nottm Univ BEd80 Lon Inst of Educn MA89 ACertCM87 Univ of Wales (Ban) DipHE99. EAMTC 96. **d** 99 **p** 00. C Brackley St Pet w St Jas *Pet* from 99. *12 Bannerman Drive, Brackley NN13 6HS* Tel (01280) 704263 E-mail linda@revdbond.fsnet.co.uk

BOND, Mark Francis Wilson. b 53. Sarum & Wells Th Coll 89. **d** 91 **p** 92. C Taunton Lyngford *B & W* 91-95; V Highbridge 95-02; R Jersey St Brelade *Win* from 02. *The Rectory, La Marquanderie Hill, St Brelade, Jersey JE3 8EP* Tel (01534) 742302

BOND, Norman. b 23. Wycliffe Hall Ox. **d** 70 **p** 71. C Warrington St Ann *Liv* 70-73; P-in-c 73-77; P-in-c Warrington St Pet 73-77; V Wigan St Cath 77-88; rtd 88; Perm to Offic *Carl* 88-01; *Liv* 88-98; *S & M* from 00. *5 Bradda Glen Close, Port Erin, Isle of Man IM9 6PG* Tel (01624) 832817

BOND, Paul Maxwell. b 36. TD73. Open Th Coll BA00 ACIB56. Oak Hill Th Coll 76. **d** 79 **p** 80. NSM Wisley w Pyrford *Guildf* 79-91; Org Children's Soc SW Lon 88-91; C Egham *Guildf* 91-93; C Horsell 93-94; V Rockfield and St Maughen's w Llangattock etc *Mon* 94-99; rtd 99; Hon C Islip w Charlton on Otmoor, Oddington, Noke etc *Ox* 99-01; Hon C Ray Valley from 01. *St Mary's House, High Street, Charlton on Otmoor, Kidlington OX5 2UQ* Tel (01865) 331124 Fax as telephone E-mail paul.bond@bigfoot.com

BOND, Robert. *See* BOND, Charles Robert

BOND, Mrs Susan Fraser. b 55. SS Hild & Bede Coll Dur BEd78. N Ord Course 96. **d** 99 **p** 00. C Tickhill w Stainton *Sheff* 99-02; R Warmsworth from 02. *Warmsworth Rectory, 187 Warmsworth Road, Doncaster DN4 0TW* Tel (01302) 853324

BOND, The Ven Thomas James. b 18. TCD BA41 MA68. CITC 41. **d** 42 **p** 43. C Annagh w Drumaloor and Cloverhill *K, E & A* 42-44; C Sligo Cathl 44-47; I Kilgobbin *L & K* 47-49; I Bourney w Dunkerrin 49-52; I Kilkeevin w Kiltullagh *K, E & A* 52-55; I Bailieborough 55-60; I Templemichael w Clongish, Clooncumber etc 60-91; Preb Elphin Cathl 67-91; Adn Elphin and Ardagh 78-91; rtd 91. *Halstow, Drumelis, Cavan, Co Cavan, Irish Republic* Tel (00353) (49) 61812

BOND-THOMAS, David Harradence. b 23. Ch Coll Cam BA44 MA51. **d** 59 **p** 60. C Langley Marish *Ox* 59-62; C Earley St Pet 62-71; P-in-c Middleton Stoney 71-77; C Bucknell 71-76; P-in-c Weston on the Green 72-76; P-in-c Chesterton w Wendlebury 76-77; V Chesterton w Middleton Stoney and Wendlebury 77-89; rtd 89; Perm to Offic *Glouc* from 89. *35 Greet Road, Winchcombe, Cheltenham GL54 5JT* Tel (01242) 603150

✠**BONE, The Rt Revd John Frank Ewan.** b 30. St Pet Coll Ox BA54 MA59 Whitelands Coll Lon PGCE71. Ely Th Coll 54. **d** 56 **p** 57 **c** 89. C Pimlico St Gabr *Lon* 56-60; C Henley *Ox* 60-63; V Datchet 63-76; RD Burnham 74-77; R Upton cum Chalvey 76-78; Adn Buckingham 77-89; Area Bp Reading 89-96; rtd 97; Hon Asst Bp Ox from 97. *4 Grove Road, Henley-on-Thames RG9 1DH* Tel (01491) 413482 E-mail jfebone@breathemail.net

BONHAM, Mrs Valerie. b 47. ALA94. St Alb and Ox Min Course 94. **d** 97 **p** 98. NSM Newbury *Ox* 97-98; C Cookham 98-02; P-in-c Coleford w Holcombe *B & W* from 02. *The Vicarage, Church Street, Coleford, Radstock BA3 5NG* Tel (01373) 813382

BONHAM-CARTER, Gerard Edmund David. b 31. Lon Univ BSc53 DCAe55. S'wark Ord Course 84. **d** 87 **p** 88. NSM Wandsworth St Paul *S'wark* from 87; Perm to Offic *St E* from 87;

Chapl R Hosp for Neuro-Disability from 92. *7 Fleur Gates, Princes Way, London SW19 6QQ* Tel (020) 8788 1230 *or* 8780 4500 ext 5075 Fax as telephone E-mail gerard.bonham-carter@ukgateway.net

BONIFACE, Lionel Ernest George. b 36. Lon Coll of Div ALCD63 BD64. **d** 64 **p** 65. C Attenborough w Chilwell *S'well* 64-69; C Farndon 69-71; C Thorpe 69-71; P-in-c Mansfield St Aug 71-77; V Oughtibridge *Sheff* 77-92; Ind Chapl 79-81; P-in-c Treeton 92-93; TV Brinsworth w Catcliffe and Treeton 93-98; rtd 98; Perm to Offic *Sheff* from 99. *30 Everard Avenue, Bradway, Sheffield S17 4LZ* Tel 0114-235 0415

BONIWELL, Timothy Richard. b 51. AKC73. St Aug Coll Cant 74. **d** 75 **p** 76. C Walthamstow St Mich *Chelmsf* 75-78; C Wigmore Abbey *Heref* 78-83; C Studley and Chapl Trowbridge Coll *Sarum* 83-86; V Bath St Barn w Englishcombe *B & W* 86-95; R Tintinhull w Chilthorne Domer, Yeovil Marsh etc 95-02; V Enfield St Geo *Lon* from 02. *St George's Vicarage, 706 Hertford Road, Enfield EN3 6NR* Tel (01992) 762581 Fax as telephone E-mail boniwell@netcomuk.co.uk

BONNER, David Robert. b 28. ASCA66 FCIS72 FCIB74 Lon Univ DipRS78. S'wark Ord Course 74. **d** 77 **p** 78. NSM Hampton All SS *Lon* 77-84; P-in-c Twickenham All SS 84-91; rtd 91; Perm to Offic *Lon* from 91. *17 St James's Road, Hampton Hill, Hampton TW12 1DH* Tel (020) 8979 1565

BONNER, James Maxwell Campbell. Sydney Univ BSc49 DipEd49. Oak Hill Th Coll BD59. **d** 60 **p** 61. C Walthamstow St Mary *Chelmsf* 60-63; C Morden *S'wark* 63-65; Australia from 65; rtd 98. *1206/5 Albert Road, Strathfield, NSW, Australia 2135* Tel (0061) (2) 9763 7535

BONNET, Tom. b 51. Univ of Wales (Ban) DipTh89 Univ of Wales (Cardiff) BTh90. St Mich Coll Llan 90. **d** 90 **p** 91. C Criccieth w Treflys *Ban* 90-91; C Denio w Abererch 91-93; R Llanfachraeth 93-94; P-in-c Valley w Llanfachraeth 94; R 94-98; R Valley w Llechylched and Caergeiliog from 98. *The Rectory, London Road, Valley, Holyhead LL65 3DP* Tel and fax (01407) 741242 Mobile 07713-548941 E-mail rev@tbonnet.freeserve.co.uk

BONNEY, Mark Philip John. b 57. St Cath Coll Cam BA78 MA82. St Steph Ho Ox BA84 MA89. **d** 85 **p** 86. C Stockton St Pet *Dur* 85-88; Chapl St Alb Abbey *St Alb* 88-90; Prec 90-92; V Eaton Bray w Edlesborough 92-96; R Gt Berkhamsted from 96. *The Rectory, Rectory Lane, Berkhamsted HP4 2DH* Tel (01442) 864194 Fax as telephone E-mail m.bonney@c-of-e.freeserve.co.uk

BONNEY, Prof Richard John. b 47. Ox Univ DPhil73. **d** 96 **p** 97. NSM Knighton St Mary Magd *Leic* from 96. *7 Carisbrooke Park, Leicester LE2 3PQ* Tel 0116-212 5677 E-mail bon@leicester.anglican.org

BONNEY, Stuart Campbell. b 51. Edin Univ BD83. Edin Th Coll 81. **d** 83 **p** 84. C Edin St Luke *Edin* 83-86; C Edin St Martin 83-86; P-in-c Auchterarder *St And* 86-90; P-in-c Muthill 86-90; Dep Chapl HM Pris Leeds 90-91; Chapl HM Pris Moorland 91-96; P-in-c Bathgate *Edin* 96-01; P-in-c Linlithgow 96-01. *Circleway Cottage, 259 Main Street, Pathhead EH37 5SQ* E-mail scbonney@aol.com

BONNEYWELL, Miss Christine Mary. b 57. Univ of Wales (Lamp) BA78 LTh80. Sarum & Wells Th Coll 80. **d** 81 **p** 94. C Swansea St Pet *S & B* 81-84; C Llangyfelach 84-86; Chapl Univ of Wales (Lamp) *St D* 86-90; Educn Officer Wells Cathl *B & W* 90-95; V Yeovil H Trin w Barwick 95-97; Chapl Yeovil Distr Hosp 95-97; Chapl Pilgrim Health NHS Trust Boston 97-01; Chapl United Lincs Hosps NHS Trust from 01. *The Chaplaincy, Pilgrim Hospital, Sibsey Road, Boston PE21 9QT, or 4 Hospital Lane, Boston PE21 9BY* Tel (01205) 364801 ext 2243 *or* 355151 Fax 354395

BONSALL, Charles Henry Brash. b 42. Ex Univ BA66. Ridley Hall Cam 66. **d** 68 **p** 69. C Cheltenham St Mary *Glouc* 68-72; Sudan 72-77 and 79-83; Perm to Offic *Nor* 78; Development and Miss Sec Intercon Ch Soc 83-93; Perm to Offic *Birm* from 91; rtd 93. *3 Pakenham Road, Birmingham B15 2NE* Tel 0121-440 6143

✠**BONSER, The Rt Revd David.** b 34. Man Univ MA75 AKC61. **d** 62 **p** 63 **c** 91. C Heckmondwike *Wakef* 62-65; C Sheff St Geo *Sheff* 65-68; R Chorlton-cum-Hardy St Clem *Man* 68-82; Bp's Ecum Adv 73-81; Hon Can Man Cathl 81-82; AD Hulme 81-82; Adn Rochdale 82-91; TR Rochdale 82-91; Suff Bp Bolton 91-99; rtd 99. *82 Birchfield Drive, Rochdale OL11 4NY* Tel (01706) 352522

BONSEY, Hugh Richmond Lowry. b 49. Sarum & Wells Th Coll 74. **d** 76 **p** 77. C Bris St Mary Redcliffe w Temple etc *Bris* 76-80; TV Sutton *Liv* 80-88; P-in-c Yatton Keynell *Bris* 88-89; P-in-c Biddestone w Slaughterford 88-89; P-in-c Castle Combe 88-89; P-in-c W Kington 88-89; P-in-c Nettleton w Littleton Drew 88-89; C Westbury-on-Trym H Trin 89-90; V Peasedown St John w Wellow *B & W* from 90. *The Vicarage, Church Road, Peasedown St John, Bath BA2 8AA* Tel (01761) 432293 E-mail hbonsey@blueyonder.co.uk

BONSEY, Thory Richmond. b 18. St Chad's Coll Dur 37. Cuddesdon Coll 46. **d** 47 **p** 48. C Salisbury St Martin *Sarum* 47-50; C Kingsthorpe *Pet* 50-53; PC Ashwick w Oakhill *B & W*

53-57; V Desborough *Pet* 57-61; R Teigh w Whissendine 61-67; R Ecton 67-73; V Ketton 73-77; Australia from 77; rtd 83. *PO Box 548, Heathcote, Vic, Australia 3523* E-mail tfbonsey@austarmetro.com.au

BONTING, Prof Sjoerd Lieuwe. b 24. Amsterdam Univ BSc44 MSc50 PhD52 Lon Univ BD58 SOSc. Washington Dioc Course 63. **d** 63 **p** 64. C Bethesda St Luke USA 63-65; Prof Biochemistry Nijmegen Univ 65-85; Chapl Nijmegen, Eindhoven, Arnhem, and Twenthe *Eur* 80-85; Consultant NASA USA 85-98; Asst Sunnyvale St Thos 85-90; Asst Palo Alto St Mark 90-93; Perm to Offic *Eur* from 93. *Specreyse 12, 7471 TH Goor, The Netherlands* Tel (0031) (547) 260947 E-mail s.l.bonting@wxs.nl

BOOCOCK, John Walter. b 31. Wells Th Coll 63. **d** 65 **p** 66. C Guisborough *York* 65-67; C Bottesford *Linc* 67-73; TV Bottesford w Ashby 73-74; V Riddlesden *Bradf* 74-83; V Darlington H Trin *Dur* 83-91; P-in-c Ingleton w Denton 91-96; Dioc Par Development Officer 91-95; rtd 96; Perm to Offic *Wakef* 96-01; *B & W* from 02. *46 Southfield Road, Shepton Mallet BA4 5XG* Tel (01749) 343732 E-mail jbmir31@yahoo.co.uk

BOOKER, Gerald Dennis. b 30. St Pet Coll Ox BA52 MA56. Ridley Hall Cam 53 Oak Hill Th Coll 80. **d** 81 **p** 82. Hon C Hertford All SS *St Alb* 81-83; R Bramfield w Stapleford and Waterford 83-96; Chapl Herts Univ 90-96; rtd 96; Perm to Offic *St Alb* from 96. *The Garden House, Churchfields, Hertford SG13 8AE*

BOOKER, James Howard. b 57. Edin Th Coll 88. **d** 90 **p** 91. C Peterhead *Ab* 90-92; C Old Deer 90-92; C Longside 90-92; C Strichen 90-92; Bp's Chapl Peterhead 92-93; Miss to Seamen 92-00; R Peterhead *Ab* 93-00; Chapl HM Pris Peterhead 93-00. *Address temp unknown*

BOOKER, Mrs Margaret Katharine. b 20. MCSP42. Westcott Ho Cam 82. **dss** 83 **d** 87 **p** 94. Stansted Mountfitchet *Chelmsf* 83-95; Par Dn 87-90; NSM 90-95; rtd 90; Perm to Offic *Ely* from 95. *49 Home Farm Road, Houghton, Huntingdon PE17 2BN* Tel (01480) 469167

BOOKER, Michael Charles. b 36. LLCM57 ARCO58. Lon Coll of Div LTh63. **d** 63 **p** 64. C Royston *St Alb* 63-66; C Mildenhall *St E* 66-68; Min Can St E Cathl 68-83; Prec 70-83; Chapl Framlingham Coll 84-99; rtd 99; Perm to Offic *St E* from 99. *29 The Mowbrays, Framlingham, Woodbridge IP13 9DL* Tel (01728) 723122

BOOKER, Michael Paul Montague. b 57. Jes Coll Ox BA79 Bris Univ CertEd80. Trin Coll Bris 84. **d** 87 **p** 88. C Cant St Mary Bredin *Cant* 87-91; V Leamington Priors St Mary *Cov* 91-96; Dir Miss and Past Studies Ridley Hall Cam from 96. *Ridley Hall, Sidgwick Avenue, Cambridge CB3 9HG* Tel (01223) 741059 Fax 741081 E-mail mpmb2@cam.ac.uk

BOOKLESS, Andrew Pitcairn. b 63. Sheff Univ BA85. St Jo Coll Nottm DipMM92. **d** 92 **p** 93. C Llantrisant *Llan* 92-95; C Llangynwyd w Maesteg 95-97; V Bargoed and Deri w Brithdir from 97. *The Vicarage, Vicarage Lane, Bargoed CF81 8TR* Tel (01443) 831069

BOOKLESS, David John Charles. b 62. Jes Coll Cam MA83 PGCE. Trin Coll Bris DipHE90 MA91. **d** 91 **p** 92. C Southall Green St Jo *Lon* 91-99; P-in-c Southall St Geo 99-01; Nat Dir A Rocha UK (Christians in Conservation) from 01; Hon C Southall Green St Jo from 03. *13 Avenue Road, Southall UB1 3BL* Tel (020) 8571 0981 E-mail arochauk@arocha.org

BOOKLESS, John Guy. b 19. Clare Coll Cam BA40 MA46 Serampore Univ MTh72. Ridley Hall Cam 47. **d** 49 **p** 50. C Toxteth Park Ch Ch *Liv* 49-50; C Fazakerley Em 50-51; Tutor Ridley Hall Cam 51-52; India 53-72; Miss Bhagalpur 53-60; Tutor Bp's Coll Calcutta 61-65; Lect United Th Coll Bangalore 66-72; C St Alb St Mich *St Alb* 73-76; C Harlow New Town w Lt Parndon *Chelmsf* 76-78; TV 78-79; V Willoughby-on-the-Wolds w Wysall *S'well* 79-85; P-in-c Widmerpool 79-85; rtd 85; Perm to Offic *S'well* 85-88; *Leic* 85-93. *7 Oakland Gardens, Bargoed CF81 8QF* Tel (01443) 832166

BOOKLESS, Mrs Rosemary. b 26. Westf Coll Lon BA47 DipEd49 Serampore Univ BD72. St Mich Ho Ox 56. **dss** 80 **d** 91 **p** 94. Willoughby-on-the-Wolds w Wysall and Widmerpool *S'well* 80-85; rtd 85; Perm to Offic *Leic* 85-89; Loughborough Em 89-91; NSM 91-95; NSM Loughborough Em and St Mary in Charnwood 95-97; Perm to Offic 97-03. *7 Oakland Gardens, Bargoed CF81 8QF* Tel (01443) 832166 E-mail rosemary@rbookless.freeserve.co.uk

BOON, Marion. *See* SIMMONS, Ms Marion

BOON, Nigel Francis. b 39. St Jo Coll Nottm. **d** 83 **p** 84. C St Helens St Helen *Liv* 83-86; V Kirkdale St Lawr 86-92; V Huyton Quarry 92-99; rtd 01. *20 Reynards Close, Tadley, Basingstoke RG26 4LR* Tel 0118-981 9102 Mobile 07989-011938 Fax 0118-981 4441 E-mail nigelboon@aol.com

BOON, William John. b 54. Glouc Sch of Min 84. **d** 88 **p** 89. Hon C Matson *Glouc* 88-91; NSM Gt Witcombe 91; C 91-95; C Brockworth 91-96; P-in-c Slimbridge 97-99; R Sharpness, Purton, Brookend and Slimbridge from 00; RD Dursley from 02. *The Vicarage, Sanigar Lane, Newtown, Berkeley GL13 9NF* Tel (01453) 811360 E-mail bill_boon@lineone.net

BOOT, Felicity Olivia. b 43. TCert64. S Tr Scheme 94. **d** 97 **p** 98. NSM Lyndhurst and Emery Down and Minstead *Win* from 97. *Pikes Hill Cottage, Pikes Hill Avenue, Lyndhurst SO43 7AX* Tel (023) 8028 2616 E-mail redfoxyachts@btinternet.com

BOOTES, Michael Charles Edward. b 35. ACP70. Sarum Th Coll 58. **d** 61 **p** 62. C Winchmore Hill St Paul *Lon* 61-64; Switzerland 64-67; C St Marylebone All SS *Lon* 67-68; OGS from 68; Chapl Kingsley St Mich Sch W Sussex 69-75; V Brandon *Dur* 75-78; Chapl Shoreham Gr Sch 78-79; C Clayton w Keymer *Chich* 80-84; TV Ovingdean w Rottingdean and Woodingdean 84-85; TR Ovingdean 85-88; V Lundwood *Wakef* 88-92; C Pontefract St Giles 92-95; P-in-c Kellington w Whitley 95-00; rtd 00; Hon C Castleford *Wakef* from 00. *10A Lumley Street, Castleford WF10 5LB* Tel (01977) 557080 Mobile 07720-296297 E-mail mb@ogs.net

BOOTH, Charles Robert. b 48. Leeds Univ CertEd75. N Ord Course 79. **d** 82 **p** 83. C Eccleshill *Bradf* 82-84; C Jersey St Brelade *Win* 84-88; Australia 88-90 and from 93; C Newman 88-90; V Blurton *Lich* 90-93; Chapl Frederick Irwin Angl Communion Sch Mandurah 94-98; R Spearwood from 99. *10 Fallow Crescent, Spearwood, W Australia 6163* Tel (0061) (8) 9418 1005

BOOTH, David. b 44. Coll of Resurr Mirfield 72. **d** 74 **p** 75. C Osmondthorpe St Phil *Ripon* 74-77; C Armley w New Wortley 77-79; V Leeds St Wilfrid 79-95; V Royton St Paul *Man* from 95. *St Paul's Vicarage, 2 Low Meadows, Royton, Oldham OL2 6YB* Tel 0161-624 2388

BOOTH, Derek. b 36. LTCL ALCM AKC61. **d** 62 **p** 63. C Woodchurch *Ches* 62-65; C Penrith St Andr *Carl* 65-67; C Tranmere St Paul *Ches* 67-70; C Wilmslow 70-72; V Micklehurst 73-97; C Staveley and Barrow Hill *Derby* 97-01; rtd 01; Perm to Offic *Derby* from 01. *9 Ilam Close, Inkersall, Chesterfield S43 3EW* Tel (01246) 475421

BOOTH, Eric James. b 43. Open Univ BA84. N Ord Course 86. **d** 89 **p** 90. NSM Nelson St Phil *Blackb* 89-93; NSM Fence and Newchurch-in-Pendle 93-97; NSM Padiham w Hapton and Padiham Green 97-03; rtd 03. *5 Round Hill Place, Park Road, Cliviger, Burnley BB10 4UA* Tel (01282) 450708

BOOTH, Ewart Charles. b 67. LTCL85 K Coll Lon LLB88. Sarum & Wells Th Coll BTh93. **d** 93 **p** 95. NSM Tadley St Pet *Win* 93-95; C Highcliffe w Hinton Admiral 95-00; R W Parley Sarum from 00. *The Rectory, 250 New Road, West Parley, Ferndown BH22 8EW* Tel (01202) 873561

BOOTH, Graham Richard. b 55. Birm Univ BSocSc75. St Jo Coll Nottm 89. **d** 91 **p** 92. C Woodthorpe *S'well* 91-96; P-in-c Trowell 96-02; P-in-c Awsworth w Cossall 00-02; R Trowell, Awsworth and Cossall from 02. *The Rectory, Nottingham Road, Trowell, Nottingham NG9 3PF* Tel 0115-849 5195 Fax 849 5196 E-mail g.booth@ntlworld.com

BOOTH, Ian George. b 64. Chich Th Coll 85 Linc Th Coll 87. **d** 88 **p** 89. C Pet St Mary Boongate *Pet* 88-90; C Hawley H Trin *Guildf* 90-94; V Willesden St Mary *Lon* 94-03; P-in-c Gosport H Trin *Portsm* from 03; RD Gosport from 03. *9 Britannia Way, Gosport PO12 4FZ* Tel (01329) 239722

BOOTH, James Roger. b 46. Keble Coll Ox BA71 MA74 BTh77. Wycliffe Hall Ox 75. **d** 78 **p** 79. C Bridlington Priory *York* 78-83; V Nafferton w Wansford from 83. *The Vicarage, 3 Middle Street, Nafferton, Driffield YO25 4JS* Tel (01377) 254372 Mobile 07703-968047

BOOTH, Jon Alfred. b 42. Nottm Univ BA64 Lon Univ MPhil72. Coll of Resurr Mirfield 78. **d** 80 **p** 81. C Elland *Wakef* 80-84; C Royston from 84. *The Vicarage, Church Street, Royston, Barnsley S71 4QZ* Tel (01226) 722410

BOOTH, Kenneth Neville. b 41. Otago Univ BA62 MA63 BD66 MTh69 St Andr Univ PhD74. St Jo Coll Auckland 63. **d** 65 **p** 66. New Zealand 65-71; C St Paul's Cathl Dunedin 65-69; Perm to Offic *St And* 70-71; Lect St Andr Univ 70-71; New Zealand 72-80; Lect St Jo Coll Auckland 72-80; Asst P Tamaki St Thos 73-80; Perm to Offic *Ox* 80-81; New Zealand from 81; Warden Selwyn Coll Dunedin 81-85; Lect 81-97; V Roslyn 85-97; Adn Dunedin 86-95; V Gen 92-97; Dir Coll Ho Inst of Th from 97. *30 Church Lane, Merivale, Christchurch 8001, New Zealand* Tel (0064) (3) 355 9145 Fax 355 6140 E-mail chit@cyberxpress.co.nz

BOOTH, Leonard William. b 46. K Coll Lon BD70 AKC70. **d** 71 **p** 72. C Cockerton *Dur* 72-75; C Hove St Barn *Chich* 75-77; TV Brighton Resurr 77-78; C E Grinstead St Mary 78-81; USA from 81. *254 St Joseph Avenue, Long Beach, CA 90803, USA* Tel (001) (562) 433 6531 E-mail fatherleo@fatherleo.com

BOOTH, Michael Kevin. b 47. Louvain Univ Belgium BA. St Jo Coll Nottm 88 Oscott Coll (RC) 65. **d** 71 **p** 72. In RC Ch 71-87; C N Reddish *Man* 88-89; R Heaton Norris Ch w All SS 89-99; rtd 99; Perm to Offic *Man* from 00. *3 Potter Road, Hadfield, Hyde SK13 2RA* Tel (01457) 853963

BOOTH, Paul Harris. b 49. St Jo Coll Nottm LTh79. **d** 79 **p** 80. C Thorpe Edge *Bradf* 79-82; P-in-c Frizinghall 82-83; TV Shipley St Paul and Frizinghall 83-97; rtd 97; Perm to Offic *Bradf* from 97. *3 Gilstead Court, Gilstead, Bingley BD16 3LA* Tel (01274) 551071 E-mail paul@gilcourt.freeserve.co.uk

BOOTH, Terrence Richard. b 44. Edith Cowan Univ (Aus) BA98. St Jo Coll Morpeth ThDip70. **d** 69 **p** 70. Australia 69-79 and from 81; C Corowa 69-71; Asst Broken Hill 72-74; P-in-c Urana/Jerilderie 74-79; C Chesterfield St Mary and All SS *Derby* 79-81; Chapl Chesterfield R Hosp 79-81; R Coolamon/Ganmain 82; RD Murrumbidgee 83-84; Chapl Bunbury Cathl Gr Sch 85-93; Chapl Edith Cowan Univ 86-92; R Casino 94-98; R Ithaca-Ashgrove 98-01; AD from 01. *286 Waterworks Road, PO Box 31, Ashgrove, Qld, Australia 4060* Tel (0061) (7) 3366 2320 Fax 3366 9793 E-mail stpaulsash@iprimus.com.au

BOOTH, Wallace. b 14. **d** 62 **p** 63. C Croydon Woodside *Cant* 62-66; V Woodnesborough 66-79; P-in-c Staple 77-79; rtd 79; Perm to Offic *Chich* from 87. *3 St Augustine's Close, Bexhill-on-Sea TN39 3AZ* Tel (01424) 214524

BOOTH, Preb William James. b 39. LVO99. TCD BA60 MA75. **d** 62 **p** 63. C Belfast St Luke *Conn* 62-64; Chapl Cranleigh Sch Surrey 65-74; Chapl Westmr Sch 74-91; Lic to Offic *Lon* 74-93; P in O 76-93; PV Westmr Abbey 87-93; Sub-Dean HM Chpls R and Dep Clerk of the Closet from 91; Sub-Almoner and Dom Chapl to The Queen from 91; Preb St Paul's Cathl *Lon* from 00. *Marlborough Gate, St James's Palace, London SW1A 1BG* Tel (020) 7930 6609

BOOTHBY, Frank. b 29. St D Coll Lamp 56. **d** 58 **p** 59. C Maghull *Liv* 58-61; C N Meols 61-64; Miss to Seamen 64; rtd 94. *7 Belsfield Drive, Hesketh Bank, Preston PR4 6YB*

BOOTHMAN, Ms Olive. b 31. TCD BA. **d** 94 **p** 95. NSM Clondalkin w Rathcoole *D & G* from 94. *Miley Hall, Blessington, Co Wicklow, Irish Republic* Tel (00353) (45) 865119

BOOTHMAN, Canon Samuel. b 09. TCD BA34 Div Test35 MA37. **d** 35 **p** 35. C Enniskillen and Trory *Clogh* 35-37; C Win St Thos and St Clem w St Mich etc *Win* 37-40; CF (EC) 40-46; Hon CF 46; R Farley Chamberlayne w Braishfield *Win* 46-81; RD Romsey 71-79; Hon Can Win Cathl 73-81; R Michelmersh, Timsbury, Farley Chamberlayne etc 81; rtd 81; Perm to Offic *Win* 81-99. *Boldbrook Lodge, Pound Lane, Ampfield, Romsey SO51 9BP* Tel (01794) 368143

BOOTS, Claude Donald Roy. b 26. Roch Th Coll 67. **d** 69 **p** 70. C Midsomer Norton *B & W* 69-73; V Westfield 73-80; P-in-c Hambridge w Earnshill and Isle Brewers 80; R Ilton w Hambridge, Earnshill, Isle Brewers etc 80-91; rtd 91; Perm to Offic *B & W* from 91. *41 Furlong Close, Midsomer Norton, Bath BA3 2PR* Tel (01761) 419263

BOOYS, Mrs Susan Elizabeth. b 56. Bris Univ BA78 LMH Ox PGCE79. St Alb and Ox Min Course 92. **d** 95 **p** 96. C Kidlington w Hampton Poyle *Ox* 95-99; TV Dorchester from 99. *The Vicarage, The Green North, Warborough, Wallingford OX10 7DW* Tel (01865) 858381 E-mail sue@booys.fsnet.co.uk

BOREHAM, Harold Leslie. b 37. S'wark Ord Course. **d** 72 **p** 73. C Whitton and Thurleston w Akenham *St E* 72-77; R Saxmundham 77-85; V Felixstowe SS Pet and Paul 85-96; Chapl Felixstowe Hosp 85-96; Chapl Bartlet Hosp Felixstowe 95-96; P-in-c Ramsgate St Mark *Cant* 96-01; V 01-03; Chapl E Kent Community NHS Trust 98-03; rtd 03; Perm to Offic *St E* from 03. *313 St John's Road, Colchester CO4 0JR* Tel (01206) 853769

BORRILL, John. b 19. Lon Univ BD41 AKC41. Westcott Ho Cam 41. **d** 42 **p** 43. C Hanwell St Thos *Lon* 42-45; C Ealing St Pet Mt Park 45-48; New Zealand 48-51; Lon Dioc Home Missr Whitton St Aug *Lon* 49-51; P-in-c 51-58; V 58-59; V St Pancras w St Jas and Ch Ch 59-71; Chapl Elizabeth Garrett Anderson Hosp 62-71; Nat Temperance Hosp 62-71; Lon Ho Mecklenburgh 62-63; V Hendon St Mary 71-82; Chapl Puerto de la Cruz Tenerife *Eur* 82-84; rtd 84; Hon C Tenerife *Eur* 84-87; Perm to Offic *Chich* 87-02. *25 Dulverton Hall, The Esplanade, Scarborough YO11 2AR* Tel (01723) 340125

BORROWDALE, Geoffrey Nigel. b 61. Southn Univ BSc83 W Sussex Inst of HE PGCE94. Chich Th Coll 87. **d** 90 **p** 99. C Tilehurst St Mich *Ox* 90-91; Perm to Offic *Chich* 93-97; NSM Sunninghill *Ox* 98-99; C Bracknell 99-01; P-in-c Theale and Englefield from 01. *The Rectory, Englefield Road, Theale, Reading RG7 5AS* Tel 0118-930 2759
E-mail geoffrey.borrowdale@tesco.net

BORSBEY, Alan. b 38. Linc Th Coll 71. **d** 73 **p** 73. C Bardsley *Man* 73-75; C Elton All SS 75-78; V Bury St Paul 78-96; P-in-c Bolton St Bede from 96. *St Bede's Vicarage, 92 Normanby Street, Bolton BL3 3QR* Tel (01204) 61496

BORTHWICK, Alexander Heywood. b 36. Open Univ BA80 Surrey Univ MSc89 MBPsS90. Lich Th Coll 57. **d** 60 **p** 61. C Glas Ch Ch *Glas* 60-62; C Landore *S & B* 62-64; C Swansea St Thos and Kilvey 64-65; Br Guiana 65-66; Guyana 66-70; C Oystermouth *S & B* 70-71; USPG 71-83; Area Sec *Man* and *Liv* 71-76; Area Sec *Blackb* and *S & M* 73-76; Sch and Children's Work Sec 76-83; Chapl Tooting Bec Hosp Lon 83-91; Chapl Charing Cross Hosp Lon 92-94; Chapl Hammersmith Hosps NHS Trust 94-00; TR Catford (Southend) and Downham *S'wark* from 00. *St John's Rectory, 353 Bromley Road, London SE6 2RP* Tel (020) 8698 3600

BOS, Ronald Diederik. b 45. Cranmer Hall Dur 99. **d** 00 **p** 01. NSM Haltwhistle and Greenhead *Newc* from 00. *Stonecrop,*

Eals, Slaggyford CA8 7PG Tel (01434) 322532
E-mail stonecrop@aol.com

BOSHER, Philip Ross. b 61. Sarum & Wells Th Coll 84. **d** 87 **p** 88. C Warminster St Denys *Sarum* 87-90; P-in-c Farley w Pitton and W Dean w E Grimstead 90-91; TV Alderbury Team 91-96; CF from 96. *c/o MOD Chaplains (Army)* Tel (01980) 615804 Fax 615800

BOSS, Ann. b 42. **d** 02 **p** 03. NSM Scorton and Barnacre and Calder Vale *Blackb* from 02. *School House Barn, Inglewhite Road, Inglewhite, Preston PR3 2LD* Tel (01995) 640026 Fax as telephone

BOSSOM, Peter Emery. b 28. St D Dioc Tr Course. **d** 82 **p** 83. NSM Llandysilio w Egremont and Llanglydwen etc *St D* 82-86; rtd 86; Lic to Offic *St D* 86-90. *Address temp unknown*

BOSSWARD, Eric Paul. b 63. Nottm Poly CQSW90. Trin Coll Bris BA99. **d** 99 **p** 00. C Ecclesall *Sheff* 99-01; C Netherthorpe St Steph from 01. *77 Glebe Road, Crookes, Sheffield S10 1FB* Tel 0114-268 0315 E-mail eric@bossward.freeserve.co.uk

BOSTOCK, Peter Anthony. b 64. Nottm Univ BA85 Fitzw Coll Cam BA89. Westcott Ho Cam 87. **d** 90 **p** 91. C Brighton St Matthias *Chich* 90-94; C Leytonstone St Marg w St Columba *Chelmsf* 94-98; P-in-c Bishopwearmouth Gd Shep *Dur* 98-02; V Monk Bretton *Wakef* from 02. *The Vicarage, Burton Road, Barnsley S71 2HQ* Tel (01226) 203159 Mobile 07752-886039

BOSTON, Jonathan Bertram. b 40. Ely Th Coll 61. **d** 64 **p** 65. C Eaton *Nor* 64-70; Sen Chapl ACF Norfolk from 70; V Horsham St Faith w Newton St Faith 70-90; V Horsford 71-90; V Horsford and Horsham w Newton St Faith 90-97; P-in-c Litcham w Kempston, E and W Lexham, Mileham etc from 97. *Bevan House, Front Street, Litcham, King's Lynn PE32 2QG* Tel (01328) 700760

BOSWELL, Canon Colin John Luke. b 47. Sarum & Wells Th Coll 72. **d** 74 **p** 75. C Upper Tooting H Trin *S'wark* 74-78; C Sydenham St Phil 78-79; C St Helier 80-83; P-in-c Caterham 83-95; P-in-c Chaldon 85-95; RD Caterham 85-95; V Croydon St Jo from 95; Hon Can S'wark Cathl from 99; RD Croydon Cen from 00. *Croydon Vicarage, 22 Bramley Hill, Croydon CR2 6LT* Tel (020) 8688 1387 *or* 8688 8104 Mobile 07931-850905 E-mail croydon.parishchurch@lineone.net

BOTHAM, Arthur. b 53. St Jo Coll Nottm. **d** 00 **p** 01. C Hartley Wintney, Elvetham, Winchfield etc *Win* from 00. *40 Pool Road, Hartley Wintney, Basingstoke RG27 8RD* Tel (01252) 843389 E-mail arthur.botham@talk21.com

BOTHAM, Norman. Nottm Univ MPhil80 Lon Univ CertEd55 DBRS66 MRTvS84. S'wark Ord Course 63. **d** 66 **p** 67. Lect Coll SS Mark & Jo Chelsea 66-69; C Englefield Green *Guildf* 66-69; Sen Lect Shoreditch Coll Egham 69-74; C Bagshot 69-73; C-in-c Bath H Trin *B & W* 74; Asst Dir RE 74; Sen Lect Doncaster Inst of HE 74-82; Public Preacher *S'well* from 75; Perm to Offic *Sheff* 75; Hon AP Bawtry w Austerfield and Misson 75-85; Offg Chapl RAF from 85; rtd 94; Perm to Offic *Sheff* from 98. *Rufford, Mattersey Road, Ranskill, Retford DN22 8NF* Tel (01777) 818234

BOTSWANA, Bishop of. See NALEDI, The Rt Revd Theophilus Tswere

BOTT, Graham Paul. b 49. Staffs Univ MBA95. N Ord Course 00. **d** 03. NSM Rickerscote *Lich* from 03. *24 Wayfield Drive, Stafford ST16 1TR* Tel (01785) 255658

BOTT, Theodore Reginald. b 27. MBE03. Birm Univ BSc52 PhD68 DSc84 CEng58 FIChemE68. WMMTC 85. **d** 86 **p** 87. NSM Harborne St Faith and St Laur *Birm* 86-97; Perm to Offic from 97. *17 Springavon Croft, Harborne, Birmingham B17 9BJ* Tel 0121-427 4209

BOTTERILL, David Darrell. b 45. Open Univ BA. Sarum & Wells Th Coll. **d** 83 **p** 84. C Blandford Forum and Langton Long etc *Sarum* 83-86; TV Shaston 86-00; Chapl HM YOI Guys Marsh 89-91; P-in-c Portland St Jo *Sarum* from 00. *St John's Vicarage, Ventnor Road, Portland DT5 1JE* Tel (01305) 820103

BOTTING, Canon Michael Hugh. b 25. K Coll Lon BSc51 AKC K Coll Lon PGCE52. Ridley Hall Cam 54. **d** 56 **p** 57. C Onslow Square St Paul *Lon* 56-61; V Fulham St Matt 61-72; RD Hammersmith 67; V Leeds St Geo *Ripon* 72-84; RD Headingley 81-84; Hon Can Ripon Cathl 82-84; R Aldford and Bruera *Ches* 84-90; rtd 90; Jt Dir Lay Tr *Ches* 90-95; Perm to Offic from 95. *25 Woodfield Grove, Hoole, Chester CH2 3NY* Tel (01244) 321133

BOTTING, Paul Lloyd. b 43. Brasted Th Coll 67 St Mich Coll Llan 69. **d** 71 **p** 72. C Hucknall Torkard *S'well* 71-74; C Cen Torquay *Ex* 74-76; P-in-c Sutton in Ashfield St Mich *S'well* 76; V 77-88; Chapl King's Mill Hosp Sutton-in-Ashfield 85-88; Perm to Offic *Leic* 95-97; NSM Vale of Belvoir Gp 95-97; C High Framland Par 97-01; C Waltham on the Wolds, Stonesby, Saxby etc 97-01; C Wymondham w Edmondthorpe, Buckminster etc 97-01; P-in-c High Framland Par from 01. *High Framland Rectory, 5 Croxton Lane, Harston, Grantham NG32 1PP* Tel (01476) 870188 E-mail plb@pixie-cat.fslife.co.uk

BOTTOMLEY, Gordon. b 31. Oak Hill Th Coll 51. **d** 55 **p** 56. C Kinson *Sarum* 55-58; Lic to Offic *Man* 58-63; N Area Sec BCMS 58-63; V Hemswell w Harpswell *Linc* 63-72; V Glentworth 63-72; Chapl RAF 63-71; R Bucknall and Bagnall *Lich* 72-80; TR

80-82; P-in-c Worthing H Trin *Chich* 82-88; V Camelsdale 88-96; rtd 96; Perm to Offic *Portsm* from 98. *6 Jay Close, Fareham PO14 3TA*

BOTTOMLEY, Philip. b 45. Cranmer Hall Dur BA67 DipTh69. **d** 70 **p** 71. C Harlow New Town w Lt Parndon *Chelmsf* 70-74; C W Kilburn St Luke w St Simon and St Jude *Lon* 74-78; Midl Sec CMJ 78-84; Hon C Selly Park St Steph and St Wulstan *Birm* 81-84; USA from 84. *211 Elizabeth, Avalon, PA 15202-2977, USA*

BOTWRIGHT, Canon Adrian Paul. b 55. St Jo Coll Ox MA PGCE. Westcott Ho Cam 80. **d** 82 **p** 83. C Chapel Allerton *Ripon* 82-85; Chapl Chapel Allerton Hosp 82-85; C Bourne *Guildf* 85-88; V Weston 88-94; R Skipton H Trin *Bradf* from 94; Hon Can Bradf Cathl from 02. *The Rectory, Rectory Lane, Skipton BD23 1ER* Tel (01756) 793622 *or* 700773
E-mail rector@holytrinityskipton.org.uk

BOUCHER, Brian Albert. b 39. Univ of Wales (Lamp) BA61. Chich Th Coll 61. **d** 63 **p** 64. C Hoxton H Trin w St Mary *Lon* 63-67; Chapl RN 67-68; Asst Chapl Harrow Sch 68-73; Chapl 73-86; P-in-c Clerkenwell H Redeemer w St Phil *Lon* 86-91; P-in-c Myddleton Square St Mark 86-91; Chapl Hurstpierpoint Coll 92-96; rtd 96; Perm to Offic *Chich* from 01. *20 Summervale Road, Tunbridge Wells TN4 8JB* Tel (01892) 530342

BOUCHER, Geoffrey John. b 61. Warwick Univ BA82 K Coll Lon 94. Ridley Hall Cam 94. **d** 96 **p** 97. C Tavistock and Gulworthy *Ex* 96-01; P-in-c W Monkton *B & W* from 01. *The Rectory, West Monkton, Taunton TA2 8QT* Tel (01823) 412226

BOUGHEY, Richard Keith. b 26. Man Univ. Qu Coll Birm 77. **d** 80 **p** 82. NSM Upper Tean *Lich* 80-81; NSM Stoke-upon-Trent 80-81; NSM Uttoxeter w Bramshall 82-88; rtd 88; Perm to Offic *Lich* from 88. *Kontokali, The Old Lane, Deadman's Green, Checkley, Stoke-on-Trent ST10 4NQ* Tel (01538) 722013

BOUGHTON, Mrs Elisabeth Mary Victoria. b 66. St Anne's Coll Ox BA87 MA93. Ridley Hall Cam 89. **d** 91 **p** 94. C Guildf Ch Ch *Guildf* 91-95; Chapl St Cath Sch Bramley 92-97; NSM Fetcham *Guildf* from 97. *The Rectory, 10A The Ridgeway, Fetcham, Leatherhead KT22 9AZ* Tel (01372) 372598

BOUGHTON, Canon Michael John. b 37. Kelham Th Coll 57. **d** 62 **p** 63. C Grantham St Wulfram *Linc* 62-66; C Kingsthorpe *Pet* 66-68; C Linc St Nic w St Jo Newport *Linc* 68-72; V Scunthorpe All SS 72-79; V Crowle 79-89; R Epworth 80-89; TR Bottesford w Ashby 89-02; Can and Preb Linc Cathl from 00; rtd 02. *45 Albion Crescent, Lincoln LN1 1EB* Tel (01552) 569653

BOUGHTON, Paul Henry. b 55. ACA80 Imp Coll Lon BScEng77 ARSM77. Ridley Hall Cam 89. **d** 91 **p** 92. C Guildf Ch Ch *Guildf* 91-96; R Fetcham from 96. *The Rectory, 10A The Ridgeway, Fetcham, Leatherhead KT22 9AZ* Tel (01372) 372598

BOULCOTT, Thomas William. b 16. Bps' Coll Cheshunt 47. **d** 49 **p** 50. C Hitchin St Mary *St Alb* 49-51; C Kempston 51-54; Chapl Bedf Gen Hosp 52-54; V Newfoundpool *Leic* 54-61; V N Evington 61-73; Chapl Leic Gen Hosp 62-73; V Loppington w Newtown *Lich* 73-85; RD Wem and Whitchurch 78; rtd 85; Perm to Offic *Lich* 85-94. *Silver Birch, Tilley Road, Wem, Shrewsbury SY4 5HA* Tel (01939) 233602

BOULD, Preb Arthur Roger. b 32. Selw Coll Cam BA54 MA58 Wadh Coll Ox BA55 DipTh56 DipEd57 MA58. St Steph Ho Ox 54. **d** 57 **p** 58. C Wednesfield St Thos *Lich* 57-64; V Wellington Ch Ch 64-71; R Cheadle 71-88; P-in-c Freehay 84-88; R Cheadle w Freehay 88-91; Chapl Cheadle Hosp 71-91; Chapl HM Pris Moorcourt 72-82; RD Cheadle 72-91; Preb Lich Cathl 83-99; Asst to Bp Wolv 91-97; Bp Lich's Past Aux 97-99; C Stafford 97-99; rtd 99; Perm to Offic *Lich* from 00. *4 Mansell Close, Castlefields, Stafford ST16 1AG* Tel (01785) 220860 Fax as telephone

BOULD, Stephen Frederick. b 49. Dartmouth Coll (USA) 77 K Coll Lon BD78 AKC78. Sarum & Wells Th Coll 78. **d** 79 **p** 80. C Cantril Farm *Liv* 79-82; AV Hindley St Pet 82-85; C Wigan All SS 85; Hon C Leic H Spirit *Leic* 85-88; Chapl Leic Univ 85-88; V Leic St Pet 88; P-in-c Leic St Sav 88; V Leic Ch Sav 88-96; P-in-c New Humberstone 94-96; TR Leic Resurrection 96-98; TR Bruton and Distr *B & W* from 98. *The Rectory, Plox, Bruton BA10 0EF* Tel (01749) 812372 Fax 812863
E-mail stephen.bould@which.net

BOULLIER, Kenneth John. b 51. Lon Bible Coll 79 Trin Coll Bris DipHE84. **d** 84 **p** 85. C Heref St Pet w St Owen and St Jas *Heref* 84-87; V Nutley *Chich* 89-93; R Maresfield 89-93; New Zealand 93-97; R Nailsea H Trin *B & W* from 97. *The Rectory, 2 Church Lane, Nailsea, Bristol BS48 4NG* Tel (01275) 853227 Fax 852291
E-mail kenboullier@htnailsea.swinternet.co.uk

BOULNOIS, Linda Dianne. *See* BISIG, Linda Dianne

BOULSOVER, Philip John. b 16. ACT ThL55 Kelham Th Coll 34. **d** 40 **p** 41. C Middlesbrough St Cuth *York* 40-41; C Northallerton 41-43; C Bexhill St Pet *Chich* 43-51; Australia from 51; R Atherton 51-56; R Rockhampton 56-67; R Canberra St Luke 67-81; rtd 81. *21 Chillagoe Street, Fisher, Canberra, ACT, Australia 2611* Tel (0061) (2) 6288 7589

BOULT, Geoffrey Michael. b 56. Southn Univ BTh88 Bris Univ MA90 Birm Univ MSc97. Sarum & Wells Th Coll 77. **d** 80 **p** 81. C Newark w Hawton, Cotham and Shelton *S'well* 80-83; TV Melksham *Sarum* 83-90; P-in-c Charminster and Stinsford

90-95; Perm to Offic *Birm* 95-96; Perm to Offic *Sarum* 95-98. *Address temp unknown*

BOULTBEE, John Michael Godolphin. b 22. Oak Hill Th Coll 66. **d** 68 **p** 69. C Hawkwell *Chelmsf* 68-71; C St Keverne *Truro* 71-73; V Constantine 74-79; P-in-c St Merryn 79-81; V 81-87; rtd 87; Perm to Offic *Ex* from 87. *July Cottage, 8 Williams Close, Dawlish EX7 9SP* Tel (01626) 865761

BOULTER, Michael Geoffrey. b 32. Lon Univ BD56. Tyndale Hall Bris 53. **d** 57 **p** 58. C Tranmere St Cath *Ches* 57-60; R Cheetham Hill *Man* 60-65; R Tollard Royal w Farnham *Sarum* 65-66; Chapl Alderney Hosp Poole 66-96; V Branksome St Clem *Sarum* 66-96; rtd 96. *7 Temple Trees, 13 Portarlington Road, Bournemouth BH4 8BU* Tel (01202) 768718

BOULTER, Robert George. b 49. Man Univ BA90. St Aug Coll Cant 72. **d** 75 **p** 76. C Langley All SS and Martyrs *Man* 75-80; V Lower Kersal 80-84; Oman 84-86; Slough Community Chapl *Ox* 86-87; R Whalley Range St Marg *Man* 87-99; P-in-c from 99. *St Margaret's Rectory, Rufford Road, Manchester M16 8AE* Tel 0161-226 1289

BOULTON, Christopher David. b 50. Keble Coll Ox BA71 MA80. Cuddesdon Coll 71. **d** 74 **p** 75. C Harlow St Mary and St Hugh w St Jo the Bapt *Chelmsf* 74-77; C Shrub End 77-80; P-in-c Gt Bentley 80-83; V 83-89; C Cherry Hinton St Andr *Ely* from 89; P-in-c Teversham from 90. *Cherry Hinton Vicarage, Fulbourn Old Drift, Cambridge CB1 9LR* Tel (01223) 247740
E-mail chris@boultonc.fsnet.co.uk

BOULTON, Wallace Dawson. b 31. MCIJ86. Lon Coll of Div 65. **d** 67 **p** 68. C Bramcote *S'well* 67-71; Dioc Public Relns Officer 69-71; Hon C St Bride Fleet Street w Bridewell etc *Lon* 71-86; Guild Chapl from 86; Publicity Sec CMS 71-79; Media Sec 79-86; Ed *C of E Newspaper* 86-88; Lic to Offic *Chich* 84-94; Perm to Offic 94-96; rtd 96; NSM St Leonards St Leon *Chich* 96-01; P-in-c from 01. *44 Winterbourne Close, Hastings TN34 1XQ* Tel (01424) 713743 E-mail revw.boulton@virgin.net

BOULTON-LEA, Peter John. b 46. St Jo Coll Dur BA68. Westcott Ho Cam 69. **d** 71 **p** 72. C Farlington *Portsm* 72-75; C Darlington St Jo *Dur* 75-77; R E and W Horndon w Lt Warley *Chelmsf* 77-82; V Hersham *Guildf* 82-91; R Kirk Sandall and Edenthorpe *Sheff* 91-96; RD Doncaster 95-96; V Campsall 96-97; R Burghwallis and Campsall 97-98; V Tattenham Corner and Burgh Heath *Guildf* from 98. *St Mark's Vicarage, St Mark's Road, Epsom KT18 5RD* Tel (01737) 353011

BOULTON-REYNOLDS, Mrs Jean. b 49. Sarum Th Coll 93. **d** 96 **p** 97. C Harnham *Sarum* 96-99; C Salisbury St Mark 99-01; TV Westborough *Guildf* from 01. *St Clare's Vicarage, 242 Cabell Road, Guildford GU2 6JW* Tel (01483) 301349
E-mail revjbr@sarum26.freeserve.co.uk

BOUNDY, David. b 34. Kelham Th Coll 55. **d** 59 **p** 60. C Stirchley *Birm* 59-64; Chapl E Birm Hosp 64-74; V Bordesley St Oswald 64-70; V S Yardley St Mich 70-74; R Bideford *Ex* 74-82; RD Hartland 80-82; R Northfield *Birm* 82-88; P-in-c Penzance St Mary w St Paul *Truro* 88-90; V 90-94; rtd 94; Chapl Convent of St Mary at the Cross Edgware 94-99; Perm to Offic *Ex* from 00. *5 Retreat Road, Topsham EX3 0LF* Tel (01392) 874349

BOUNDY, Canon Gerald Neville. b 36. BA. Linc Th Coll. **d** 65 **p** 66. C Bris St Mary Redcliffe w Temple etc *Bris* 65-70; P-in-c Southmead 70-72; V 72-81; V Cotham St Sav w St Mary 81-99; Hon Can Bris Cathl 96-99; rtd 99; Perm to Offic *Bris* from 99. *10 Morley Road, Southville, Bristol BS3 1DT* Tel 0117-966 3337

BOURDEAUX, Canon Michael Alan. b 34. St Edm Hall Ox BA57 MA61 Lambeth DD96. Wycliffe Hall Ox BA59. **d** 60 **p** 61. C Enfield St John *Lon* 60-64; P-in-c Charlton St Luke w St Paul *S'wark* 64-65; Lic to Offic *Roch* 65-91; Lic to Offic *Ox* from 91; Visiting Prof St Bernard's Sem Rochester NY 69; Gen Dir Keston Inst 69-99; Hon Can Roch Cathl *Roch* 90-99; rtd 99. *101 Church Way, Iffley, Oxford OX4 4EG* Tel (01865) 777276
E-mail michael.bourdeaux@keston.org

✠**BOURKE, The Rt Revd Michael Gay.** b 41. CCC Cam BA63 MA67. Cuddesdon Coll 65. **d** 67 **p** 68 **c** 93. C Gt Grimsby St Jas *Linc* 67-71; C Digswell *St Alb* 71-73; C-in-c Panshanger CD 73-78; Course Dir St Alb Minl Tr Scheme 75-87; V Southill 78-86; Adn Bedford 86-93; Area Bp Wolverhampton *Lich* from 93. *61 Richmond Road, Wolverhampton WV3 9JH* Tel (01902) 824503 Fax 824504
E-mail bishop.wolverhampton@lichfield.anglican.org

BOURKE, Canon Ronald Samuel James. b 50. MA HDipEd. **d** 79 **p** 80. C Portadown St Mark *Arm* 79-83; I Carnteel and Crilly 83-90; I Mountmellick w Coolbanagher, Rosenallis etc *M & K* 90-97; I Kingscourt w Drumconrath, Syddan and Moybologue from 97; Chan Kildare Cathl from 00; Can Meath from 00; Preb Tipper St Patr Cathl Dublin from 00. *St Ernan's Rectory, Kingscourt, Co Cavan, Irish Republic* Tel (00353) (42) 966 7255 Fax 966 7947

BOURKE, Stanley Gordon. b 48. CITC 78. **d** 78 **p** 79. C Dundonald *D & D* 78-80; C Lurgan Ch the Redeemer 81-82; I Dungiven w Bovevagh *D & R* 82-89; I Lurgan St Jo *D & D* 89-03; I Inishmacsaint *Clogh* from 03. *The Rectory, Derrygonnelly, Enniskillen, Co Fermanagh BT93 6HW* Tel (028) 6864 1638

BOURNE, Mrs Carole Sylvia. b 47. York Univ BA68 LSE MSc79 PhD85. SEITE 99. **d** 02 **p** 03. C Epsom St Martin *Guild* from 02. *12 Worple Road, Epsom KT18 5EE* Tel (01372) 727380 Mobile 07957-295842 E-mail carolebourne@kt70rt.freeserve.co.uk

BOURNE, David James. b 54. Reading Univ BA76. Trin Coll Bris 77. **d** 79 **p** 80. C W Bromwich Gd Shep w St Jo *Lich* 79-84; V Riseley w Bletsoe *St Alb* from 84; Perm to Offic *Nor* from 01. *The Vicarage, Church Lane, Riseley, Bedford MK44 1ER* Tel (01234) 708234

BOURNE, Canon Dennis John. b 32. Loughb Coll of Educn DLC55. Ridley Hall Cam 58. **d** 60 **p** 61. C Gorleston St Andr *Nor* 60-64; Min Gorleston St Mary CD 64-79; V Costessey 79-86; R Hingham w Wood Rising w Scoulton 86-97; RD Hingham and Mitford 90-95; Hon Can Nor Cathl 93-97; rtd 97; Perm to Offic *Nor* from 97. *Amron, Star Lane, Long Stratton, Norwich NR15 2XH* Tel (01508) 530863 E-mail johnbourne@onetel.net.uk

BOURNE, Mrs Diana Mary. b 46. St Jo Coll York BEd68. S Dios Minl Tr Scheme 92. **d** 95 **p** 96. C Pinner *Lon* 95-00; V Lamberhurst and Matfield *Roch* from 00. *The Vicarage, Old Town Hill, Lamberhurst, Tunbridge Wells TN3 8EL* Tel (01892) 890324

BOURNE, Henry. b 34. Spurgeon's Coll 55. **d** 64 **p** 65. C Handsworth St Mary *Birm* 64-67; Chapl RAF 67-85; Asst Chapl-in-Chief RAF 85-87; P-in-c Bourn *Ely* 87-88; V 88-89; P-in-c Kingston 87-88; R 88-89; V Caxton 88-89; R Bourn and Kingston w Caxton and Longstowe 89-91; rtd 91; Perm to Offic *Truro* 95-00 and from 01; Hon C Sampford Peverell, Uplowman, Holcombe Rogus etc *Ex* 00-01. *13 The Bowjey Hill, Newlyn, Penzance TR18 5LW* Tel (01736) 330742

BOURNE, The Ven Ian Grant. b 32. Univ of NZ BA55 Otago Univ BD75 Univ of NZ LTh61. **d** 56 **p** 57. New Zealand 56-65 and from 67; Adn Wellington 78-86 and 90-95; C Epsom St Martin *Guild* 65-67. *26 Annan Grove, Papakowhai, Porirua, New Zealand* Tel (0064) (4) 233 0466

BOURNE, John Mark. b 49. Cant Sch of Min 88. **d** 91 **p** 92. C Allington and Maidstone St Pet *Cant* 91-94; V Marden from 94; Chapl HM Pris Blantyre Ho 94-02. *The Vicarage, Haffenden Close, Marden, Tonbridge TN12 9DR* Tel (01622) 831379 E-mail revjohnbourne@classicfm.net

BOURNE, Nigel Irvine. b 60. St Jo Coll Ox BA82 MA86. Trin Coll Bris BA92. **d** 92 **p** 93. C Bedhampton *Portsm* 92-94; C Newport St Jo 94-98; V Chalk *Roch* from 98. *The Vicarage, 2A Vicarage Lane, Gravesend DA12 4TF* Tel (01474) 567906 Fax 745147 E-mail vicarofchalk@hotmail.com

BOURNE, Philip John. b 61. Sussex Univ BEd83 Aber Univ MLitt86 Ex Univ MEd96 FRSA97. Cranmer Hall Dur 85. **d** 87 **p** 88. C Gildersome *Wakef* 87-89; Chapl Ex Univ *Ex* 89-93; Assoc Chapl The Hague and Voorschoten *Eur* 94 and 95; Chapl Voorschoten from 96. *Zwaluwweg 83, 2251 NC Voorschoten, The Netherlands* Tel (0031) (71) 561 2762 or 561 1528 Fax 561 1645 E-mail pjbourne@wanadoo.nl

BOURNEMOUTH, Archdeacon of. *See* HARBIDGE, The Ven Adrian Guy

BOURNER, Paul. b 48. CA Tr Coll. **d** 90 **p** 91. CA from 79; C Ipswich St Mary at Stoke w St Pet *St E* 90-93; R Ufford w Bredfield and Hasketon 93-01; V Ipswich St Thos from 01. *St Thomas's Vicarage, 102 Cromer Road, Ipswich IP1 5EP* Tel (01473) 741215 E-mail paul.bourner@ntlworld.com

BOURNON, Dennis Harry. b 20. St Cuth Soc Dur LTh48 BA49. Oak Hill Th Coll 46. **d** 49 **p** 50. C Heworth H Trin *York* 49-51; C Bebington *Ches* 51-54; V Everton St Jo *Liv* 54-58; R Gunton St Pet *Nor* 58-65; R Eastrop *Win* 65-80; R Nursling and Rownhams 80-85; rtd 85. *17 Wessex Avenue, New Milton BH25 6NG* Tel (01425) 614016

BOUSFIELD, Andrew Michael. b 70. Middx Univ BA92. Oak Hill Th Coll BA00. **d** 00 **p** 01. C Beckenham Ch Ch *Roch* from 00. *78 The Drive, Beckenham BR3 1EG* Tel (020) 8650 7669 E-mail andybou@yahoo.com

BOUSKILL, David Walter. b 72. Ox Brookes Univ HND95. Westcott Ho Cam 95. **d** 98 **p** 99. C Henley w Remenham *Ox* 98-02; TV Bicester w Bucknell, Caversfield and Launton from 02. *75 Ravencroft, Bicester OX26 6YE* Tel (01869) 321048 E-mail rev.bouskill@virgin.net

BOUTAN, Marc Robert. b 53. Univ of Iowa BA74. Fuller Th Sem California MD87 Virginia Th Sem 90. **d** 91 **p** 92. USA 91-96 and from 99; Asst Chapl Brussels *Eur* 96-99. *St James Episcopal Church, 1872 Camp Road, Charleston, SC 29412, USA*

BOUTFLOWER, David Curtis. b 45. Man Univ BSc67 Linacre Coll Ox BA69. Ripon Hall Ox 67. **d** 70 **p** 71. C Shard End *Birm* 70-73; C Mortlake w E Sheen *S'wark* 73-74; C Caldecot *Mon* from 98. *29 Wentwood View, Caldicot NP26 4QG* Tel (01291) 423229

BOUTLE, David Francis. b 44. Leeds Univ BSc67 Lon Univ DipTh72. Cuddesdon Coll 69. **d** 72 **p** 73. C Boston *Linc* 72-77; C Waltham 77-80; P-in-c Morton 80-81; V 81-94; Chapl W Lindsey NHS Trust 80-94; Local Mental Health Chapl 88-94; P-in-c Heckington *Linc* from 94. *The Vicarage, 10 Cameron Street, Heckington, Sleaford NG34 9RW* Tel (01529) 460302

BOVEY, Denis Philip. b 29. Ely Th Coll 50. **d** 53 **p** 54. C Southwick St Columba *Dur* 53-57; Perm to Offic *Ox* 57-59; Lic to Offic *Chich* 62-64; C W Hartlepool St Aid *Dur* 64-66; R Aberdeen St Jas *Ab* 66-74; R Old Deer 74-89; R Longside 74-89; R Strichen 74-89; Can St Andr Cathl 75-88; Syn Clerk 78-83; Dean Ab 83-88; I Alford 89-94; R Auchindoir 89-94; R Inverurie 89-94; P-in-c Dufftown 89-94; P-in-c Kemnay 89-94; rtd 94. *15 Loskin Drive, Glasgow G22 7QW* Tel 0141-574 3603

BOVILL, Francis William. b 34. Lon Univ DipTh58. St Aid Birkenhead 55. **d** 58 **p** 59. C Bispham *Blackb* 58-61; C Crosthwaite Keswick *Carl* 61-66; V Radcliffe St Andr *Man* 66-68; P-in-c Woodside St Steph *Glouc* 68; V 69-73; V Scotby *Carl* 73-96; P-in-c Cotehill and Cumwhinton 94-96; rtd 96; Perm to Offic *Carl* from 96. *16 Summerfields, Dalston, Carlisle CA5 7NW* Tel (01228) 710682

BOWCOTT, Jonathan Michael William. b 67. Trin Coll Bris. **d** 01 **p** 02. C Cricklewood St Gabr and St Mich *Lon* from 01. *31 Olive Road, London NW2 6TY* Tel (020) 8450 8707

BOWDEN, Andrew David. b 59. Newc Univ BA80 BArch83. Cranmer Hall Dur 95. **d** 97 **p** 98. C Monkseaton St Pet *Newc* 97-01; V Whorlton from 01. *St John's Vicarage, Whorlton, Westerhope, Newcastle upon Tyne NE5 1NN* Tel 0191-286 9648

BOWDEN, John Stephen. b 35. CCC Ox BA59 MA62 Edin Univ Hon DD81 Lambeth DD96. Linc Th Coll 59. **d** 61 **p** 62. C Nottingham St Mary *S'well* 61-64; Hon C 64-66; Lect Nottm Univ 64-66; Ed and Managing Dir SCM Press from 66; Hon C Highgate All SS *Lon* 66-00; Hon C Brentford St Faith 80-87; Perm to Offic from 87; rtd 00. *20 Southwood Avenue, London N6 5RZ* Tel (020) 8340 7548 Fax as telephone

BOWDEN, John-Henry David. b 47. MIL78 Magd Coll Cam BA69 MA73 Man Poly DMS77. S Dios Minl Tr Scheme 81. **d** 84 **p** 85. NSM Redlynch and Morgan's Vale *Sarum* 84-88; NSM Cuckfield *Chich* 88-92; Perm to Offic 92-98; NSM St Mary le Bow w St Pancras Soper Lane etc *Lon* 92-98; NSM Chailey *Chich* from 98. *Dene House, South Chailey, Lewes BN8 4AB* Tel (01273) 401076

BOWDEN, Canon Robert Andrew. b 38. Worc Coll Ox BA62 DipTh63 MA67 BDQ68. Cuddesdon Coll 63. **d** 65 **p** 66. C Wolverhampton St Geo *Lich* 65-69; C Duston *Pet* 69-72; R Byfield 72-79; Chapl R Agric Coll Cirencester 79-93; R Coates, Rodmarton and Sapperton etc *Glouc* from 79; Bp's Adv on Rural Soc 81-93; Hon Can Glouc Cathl from 90; Chapl to The Queen from 92; Local Min Officer *Glouc* from 93. *The Rectory, Coates, Cirencester GL7 6NR* Tel (01285) 770235 E-mail bowdencoates@care4free.net

BOWDER, Reginald William Maxwell (Bill). b 46. TCD BA68 MA81 Lon Univ DipRS80 Irish Sch of Ecum MPhil99. S'wark Ord Course 78. **d** 81 **p** 82. C Bush Hill Park St Steph *Lon* 81-84; I Fiddown w Clonegam, Guilcagh and Kilmeaden *C & O* 84-87; I Lismore w Cappoquin, Kilwatermoy, Dungarvan etc 87-89; Dean Lismore 87-89; Chapl Kent Univ and Kent Inst of Art and Design *Cant* 90-97; I Donoughmore and Donard w Dunlavin *D & G* 97-01; Reporter *Church Times* from 01; Perm to Offic *Ox* from 02. *122 Greys Hill, Henley-on-Thames RG9 1SL* Tel (01491) 576725 E-mail bill.bowder@talk21.com *or* bill@churchtimes.com

BOWEN, Canon Colin Wynford. b 48. St D Coll Lamp DipTh71. **d** 71 **p** 72. C Hubberston *St D* 71-75; R Cosheston w Nash and Upton 75-77; V Carew w Cosheston w Nash and Upton 77-85; V Pembroke St Mary w St Mich 85-01; V Haverfordwest St Martin w Lambston from 01; Can St D Cathl from 01. *St Martin's Vicarage, Barn Street, Haverfordwest SA61 1TD* Tel (01437) 762509 Mobile 07770-572464

BOWEN, Daniel Joseph George. b 51. Univ of Wales (Cardiff) Dip Past Th 98. St Mich Coll Llan CertMS98. **d** 98 **p** 99. C Gorseinon *S & B* 98-00; C Cen Swansea 00-01; TV 01-02; V Birchfield *Birm* from 02. *Holy Trinity Vicarage, 213 Birchfield Road, Birmingham B20 3DG* Tel 0121-356 4241 Mobile 07890-265429

BOWEN, David Gregory. b 47. Lanchester Poly BSc69. Cuddesdon Coll 70. **d** 74 **p** 75. C Rugby St Andr *Cov* 74-77; C Charlton St Luke w H Trin *S'wark* 78-80; V Stantonbury *Ox* 80-82; Perm to Offic from 89. *17 Chapel Hill, Clevedon BS21 7NL* Tel (01275) 878962

BOWEN, David John. b 46. Glouc Th Course 83. **d** 86 **p** 88. NSM Ross w Brampton Abbotts, Bridstow and Peterstow *Heref* 86-88; C Kingstone w Clehonger, Eaton Bishop etc 88-93; P-in-c Lugwardine w Bartestree and Weston Beggard 93-94; V Lugwardine w Bartestree, Weston Beggard etc from 94; RD Heref Rural from 99. *The Vicarage, Lugwardine, Hereford HR1 4AE* Tel (01432) 850244 Fax as telephone E-mail david@djbowen.demon.co.uk

BOWEN, Ms Delyth. b 54. St D Coll Lamp BA90. St Mich Coll Llan DPS91. **d** 91 **p** 97. C Llandybie *St D* 91-95; Dn-in-c Llanllwni 95-97; V Llanybydder and Llanwenog w Llanllwni 97-02; V Betws w Ammanford from 02. *The Rectory, 78 High Street, Ammanford SA18 2NB* Tel (01269) 592084

BOWEN, Gareth James. b 60. Lon Guildhall Univ BA99 ARPS00. NTMTC 99. **d** 02. C Leyton St Cath and St Paul

Chelmsf from 02. *114 Hainault Road, London E11 1EL* Tel and fax (020) 8558 7294 Mobile 07775-674504 E-mail gareth@bowen.to

BOWEN, Canon Jennifer Ethel. b 46. Liv Univ BSc68 CertEd69. N Ord Course 80. **dss** 83 **d** 87 **p** 94. Blundellsands St Nic *Liv* 83-86; W Derby St Mary 86-87; Par Dn 87-94; C from 94; AD W Derby from 01; Hon Can Liv Cathl from 03. *4 The Armoury, West Derby, Liverpool L12 5EL* Tel 0151-256 6600

BOWEN, John. b 39. **d** 68 **p** 69. C Aberavon *Llan* 68-73; Australia from 73. *3 Sculptor Street, Giralang, ACT, Australia 2617* Tel (0061) (2) 6241 5317 *or* 6234 2252 Fax 6234 2263 E-mail john.bowen@radford.com.au

BOWEN, John Roger. b 34. St Jo Coll Ox BA59 MA62. Tyndale Hall Bris 59. **d** 61 **p** 62. C Cambridge St Paul *Ely* 61-65; Tanzania 65-76; Kenya 76-80; Dir Past Studies St Jo Coll Nottm 80-85; Tutor 85-95; Gen Sec Crosslinks 96-00; rtd 99; Perm to Offic *Ely* from 01. *26 Lingholme Close, Cambridge CB4 3HW* Tel (01223) 352592 E-mail bowenrw@onetel.net.uk

BOWEN, Lionel James. b 16. S'wark Ord Course 63. **d** 64 **p** 65. C Vauxhall St Pet *S'wark* 64-67; C Sanderstead All SS 67-74; V Pill *B & W* 74-79; Perm to Offic *Chich* from 79; rtd 81. *43 Sussex Court, Eaton Road, Hove BN3 3AS* Tel (01273) 775945

BOWEN, Roger William. b 47. Magd Coll Cam BA69 MA73 Hatf Poly Cert Counselling 91. St Jo Coll Nottm 69 Selly Oak Coll 76. **d** 72 **p** 73. C Rusholme H Trin *Man* 72-75; Rwanda Miss 75-84; Burundi 77-84; Tutor and Lect All Nations Chr Coll Ware 85-91; Hon C Ware Ch Ch *St Alb* 86-91; Gen Sec Mid-Africa Min (CMS) 91-97; V Lt Amwell *St Alb* from 97; RD Hertford and Ware from 99. *The Vicarage, 17 Barclay Close, Hertford Heath, Hertford SG13 7RW* Tel (01992) 589140

BOWEN, Stephen Allan. b 51. Leic Univ BA72. Glouc Sch of Min 88. **d** 91 **p** 92. NSM Bream *Glouc* 91-92; NSM Tidenham w Beachley and Lancaut 91-94; C Glouc St Jas and All SS 94-97; P-in-c Woodchester and Brimscombe 97-00; R from 00. *The Vicarage, Walls Quarry, Brimscombe, Stroud GL5 2PA* Tel (01453) 882204 E-mail bowen stephen@hotmail.com

BOWEN, Stephen Guy. b 47. Qu Coll Cam BA68 MA72 Bris Univ MA72. Clifton Th Coll 69. **d** 71 **p** 72. C Chelsea St Jo *Lon* 71-73; C Chelsea St Jo w St Andr 73; C Guildf St Sav *Guildf* 73-76; C Guildf St Sav w Stoke-next-Guildford 76-77; C Wallington H Trin *S'wark* 77-79; V Felbridge from 79. *The Vicarage, The Glebe, Felbridge, East Grinstead RH19 2QT* Tel (01342) 321524 Fax (0870) 162 9334 E-mail sg@bowenfelbridge.idps.co.uk

BOWEN, Thomas Raymond. b 20. Univ of Wales (Lamp) BA42. **d** 48 **p** 49. C Monkton St D 48-52; C Haverfordwest St Mary w St Thos 52; Chapl RAF 53-75; Chapl Gresham's Sch Holt 75-83; rtd 83; Perm to Offic *St D* from 83. *35 Gail Rise, Llangwm, Haverfordwest SA62 4HW* Tel (01437) 891179

BOWEN, Vincent Paul. b 26. Qu Coll Cam BA50 MA55. Ely Th Coll 51. **d** 53 **p** 54. C Cowley St Jo *Ox* 53-56; C Brentwood St Thos *Chelmsf* 56-61; R Cranham 61-71; R Wanstead St Mary 71-91; rtd 91; Perm to Offic *Cant* from 92. *44 Nunnery Fields, Canterbury CT1 3JT* Tel (01227) 472036

BOWEN, Brian Mark. b 60. QUB BA. DipTh. **d** 85 **p** 86. C Orangefield w Moneyreagh *D & D* 85-87; I Inver w Mountcharles, Killaghtee and Killybegs *D & R* 87-93; Miss to Seafarers from 87; I Augher w Newtownsaville and Eskrahoole *Clogh* from 93. *16 Knockmay Road, Augher BT77 0DF* Tel (028) 8254 8008 Fax as telephone

BOWER, James Hugh Marsh. b 17. St Chad's Coll Dur BA39 DipTh40 MA43. **d** 40 **p** 41. C Shrewsbury St Mary *Lich* 40-41; C Rugeley 41-42; C Wolverhampton St Pet 42-48; V Northwood 48-54; V Caldmore 54-58; V Wolverhampton St Andr 58-74; R Cavendish *St E* 74-83; P-in-c Stansfield 78-83; RD Clare 82-83; rtd 83; Perm to Offic *St E* from 83; Perm to Offic *Chelmsf* 83-99. *142 Melford Road, Sudbury CO10 1JZ* Tel (01787) 372683

BOWER, Jonathan James. b 72. Bp Grosseteste Coll BA96. Ripon Coll Cuddesdon. **d** 00 **p** 01. C Spalding *Linc* 00-02; C Sanderstead St Mary *S'wark* 02-03; P-in-c from 03. *St Mary's Vicarage, 85 Purley Oaks Road, South Croydon CR2 0NY* Tel (020) 8657 1725 E-mail jontybower@ntlworld.com

BOWERING, John Anthony (Tony). b 34. SS Coll Cam BA57 MA. Wycliffe Hall Ox 57. **d** 59 **p** 60. C Hornchurch St Andr *Chelmsf* 59-62; Succ Chelmsf Cathl 62; Prec 63; V Brampton Bierlow *Sheff* 64-70; V Norton Woodseats St Paul 70-80; V Tickhill w Stainton 80-97; RD W Doncaster 87-92; rtd 97; Perm to Offic *S'well* from 97; Perm to Offic *Sheff* from 97. *Linthwaite Cottage, Main Street, Kirklington, Newark NG22 8ND* Tel (01636) 816995 E-mail john.bowering@which.net

BOWERING, The Ven Michael Ernest. b 35. Kelham Th Coll 55. **d** 59 **p** 60. C Middlesbrough St Oswald *York* 59-62; C Huntington 62-64; V Brayton 64-72; RD Selby 71-72; V Saltburn-by-the-Sea 72-81; Can Res York Minster 81-87; Sec for Miss and Evang 81-87; Adn Lindisfarne *Newc* 87-00; rtd 00; Perm to Offic from 00. *Old Timbers, Westway, Crayke, York YO61 4TE* Tel (01347) 823682

BOWERMAN, Andrew. b 67. Southn Univ BSc88 Brunel Univ MSW91. Wycliffe Hall Ox 00. **d** 02 **p** 03. C Bradf St Aug

Undercliffe Bradf from 02. *37 Pollard Lane, Bradford BD2 4RN* Tel (01274) 638377 Mobile 07720-398659 E-mail andy.bowerman@virgin.net

BOWERS, David. b 55. Man Univ BA79. Wycliffe Hall Ox 82. **d** 84 **p** 85. C Lawton Moor *Man* 84-87; C Walmsley 87-93; V Milnrow 93-98; P-in-c Deerhurst, Apperley w Forthampton and Chaceley *Glouc* from 98; Dir of Ords from 98. *The Vicarage, 1 The Green, Apperley, Gloucester GL19 4DQ* Tel (01452) 780880 E-mail dbowers@tinyworld.co.uk

BOWERS, Canon Francis Malcolm. b 44. Chan Sch Truro 79. **d** 82 **p** 83. NSM Penzance St Mary w St Paul *Truro* 82-83; C 86-88; NSM Madron 83-86; TV Redruth w Lanner and Treleigh 88-91; V St Blazey from 91; P-in-c Lanlivery w Luxulyan from 01; P-in-c Tywardreath w Tregaminion from 02; RD St Austell from 96; Hon Can Truro Cathl from 01. *Church House, 2 Nursery Close, Tywardreath, Par PL24 2QW* Tel and fax (01726) 817665 Mobile 07974-818631 E-mail fathermalcolm@arktume.freeserve.co.uk

BOWERS, Canon John Edward. b 23. TD68. AKC50. **d** 51 **p** 52. C Leic St Pet *Leic* 51-55; Sacr S'wark Cathl *S'wark* 55-57; CF (TA) 56-67; V Loughborough St Pet *Leic* 57-63; V Ashby-de-la-Zouch St Helen w Coleorton 63-88; CF (R of O) 67-78; RD Akeley W *Leic* 76-88; Hon Can Leic Cathl 78-88; rtd 88; Perm to Offic *Derby* and *Leic* 88-94; *Ely* 94-00. *19 Curtis Drive, Heighington, Lincoln LN4 1GF* Tel (01522) 791330

BOWERS, Canon John Edward William. b 32. St Aid Birkenhead 60. **d** 63 **p** 64. C Bromborough *Ches* 63-68; Ind Chapl 68-74; P-in-c Crewe St Pet 69-71; V Crewe St Mich 71-74; TR Ellesmere Port 74-79; V Hattersley 79-91; Hon Can Ches Cathl 80-02; RD Mottram 88-91; V Bunbury and Tilstone Fearnall 91-98; P-in-c Leasowe 98-02; rtd 02; Perm to Offic *Ches* from 02. *2 Shalford Grove, Wirral CH48 9XY* Tel 0151-625 4831

BOWERS, Julian Michael. b 48. Middx Univ BA97 Goldsmiths' Coll Lon MA00. Edin Th Coll 69. **d** 72 **p** 73. C Chippenham St Andr w Tytherton Lucas *Bris* 72-74; C Henbury 74-77; Sri Lanka 77-82; P-in-c Evercreech w Chesterblade and Milton Clevedon *B & W* 82-83; V 83-89; V Enfield St Jas *Lon* from 89. *St James's Vicarage, 144 Hertford Road, Enfield EN3 5AY* Tel (020) 8804 1966

BOWERS, Michael Charles. b 52. Sarum & Wells Th Coll 89. **d** 91 **p** 92. C St Peter-in-Thanet *Cant* 91-95; V Reculver and Herne Bay St Bart 95-02; P-in-c Fen Ditton *Ely* from 02; P-in-c Horningsea from 02. *The Rectory, 29 High Street, Fen Ditton, Cambridge CB5 8ST* Tel (01223) 295927

BOWERS, Peter. b 47. Linc Th Coll 72. **d** 76 **p** 77. C Mackworth St Fran *Derby* 76-78; C Maidstone St Martin *Cant* 78-83; V Elmton *Derby* 83-89; R Swimbridge w W Buckland and Landkey *Ex* from 89; RD Shirwell from 01. *The Rectory, Barnstaple Hill, Swimbridge, Barnstaple EX32 0PH* Tel (01271) 830068 E-mail revpebo@hotmail.com

BOWERS, Peter William Albert. b 36. K Coll Lon BD61 AKC61. **d** 62 **p** 63. C Chorley St Pet *Blackb* 62-64; C New Sleaford *Linc* 64-67; C Folkestone H Trin w Ch Ch *Cant* 67-72; V Deal St Geo 72-80; Dir Galilee Community 80-85; R River 86-02; RD Dover 93-00; rtd 02; Perm to Offic *Cant* from 02. *7 River Street, River, Dover CT16 0RB* Tel (01304) 822808 E-mail pbowers4@aol.com

BOWERS, Mrs Rosemary Christine. b 49. Ripon Coll Cuddesdon. **d** 01 **p** 02. C Rossendale Middle Valley *Man* from 01. *Tunstead Vicarage, 33 Booth Road, Bacup OL13 0QP*

BOWERS, Stanley Percival. b 20. Lon Univ BD45 AKC45. Hartley Victoria Coll 40 Wells Th Coll 66. **d** 66 **p** 66. In Methodist Ch 45-66; C Lawrence Weston *Bris* 66-69; V Two Mile Hill St Mich 69-91; rtd 91; Perm to Offic *Bris* from 91; Perm to Offic *B & W* 91-95. *1 Windsor Road, Longwell Green, Bristol BS30 9AF* Tel 0117-932 4051

BOWES, Mrs Beryl Sylvia. b 48. SRN70 RSCN71 Hull Univ BTh89. NEOC 89. **d** 91 **p** 94. NSM Kirk Ella *York* 91-99; Chapl R Hull Hosps NHS Trust 93-99; P-in-c Kexby w Wilberfoss *York* from 99. *The Vicarage, 19 Ings Road, Wilberfoss, York YO41 5NG* Tel (01759) 388288 Fax 388857 E-mail bsbowes@bigfoot.com

BOWES, Canon John Anthony Hugh. b 39. Ch Ch Ox BA62 DipTh63 MA65. Westcott Ho Cam 63. **d** 65 **p** 66. C Langley All SS and Martyrs *Man* 65-68; Asst Chapl Bris Univ *Bris* 68-73; TV Cramlington *Newc* 73-76; P-in-c Oldland *Bris* 76-80; TR 80-84; V Westbury-on-Trym St Alb from 84; Hon Can Bris Cathl from 02. *St Alban's Vicarage, 21 Canowie Road, Bristol BS6 7HR* Tel and fax 0117-973 5844 *or* 973 1562

BOWES, Peter Hugh. b 48. Hull Univ LLB69. Cranmer Hall Dur 02. **d** 03. Warden of Readers *York* from 95; NSM Pocklington and Owsthorpe and Kilnwick Percy etc from 03. *The Vicarage, 19 Ings Road, Wilberfoss, York YO41 5NG* Tel (01759) 388288 Mobile 07775-757723 E-mail phbowes@zetnet.co.uk

BOWES-SMITH, Edward Michael Crispin. b 67. K Coll Lon LLB89 AKC89 Solicitor 90 Selw Coll Cam BA96. Ridley Hall Cam 94. **d** 97 **p** 98. C Combe Down w Monkton Combe and S Stoke *B & W* 97-00; C Enfield Ch Ch Trent Park *Lon* from 00. *2 Chalk Lane, Cockfosters, Barnet EN4 9JQ* Tel (020) 8449 4042

BOWETT, Richard Julnes. b 45. EAMTC 86. **d** 89 **p** 90. C Hunstanton St Mary w Ringstead Parva, Holme etc *Nor* 89-93;

C King's Lynn St Marg w St Nic 93-95; V Watton w Carbrooke and Ovington 95-02; RD Breckland 99-02; P-in-c Ashill w Saham Toney 00-01; Dioc Sec from 02. *Swiss Cottage, High Street, Thornham, Hunstanton PE36 6LY* Tel (01485) 512220 E-mail richardbowett@norwich.anglican.org

BOWIE, Michael Nicholas Roderick. b 59. Sydney Univ BA78 CCC Ox DPhil90. St Steph Ho Ox MA90. **d** 91 **p** 92. C Swanley St Mary *Roch* 91-93; C Penarth w Lavernock *Llan* 93-96; Australia 96-00; R Norton *Sheff* from 00. *The Rectory, Norton Church Road, Norton, Sheffield S8 8JQ* Tel 0114-274 5066 Fax as telephone E-mail mnrbowie@hotmail.com

BOWIE, Sara. b 53. Open Univ BA83 Surrey Univ BA02 MSSCh MBChA. STETS 99. **d** 02 **p** 03. NSM Camberley St Mich Yorktown *Guildf* from 02. *23 Green Farm Road, Bagshot GU19 5LB* Tel (01276) 475677
E-mail sara@bowie-bagshot.fsnet.co.uk

BOWKER, Prof John Westerdale. b 35. Worc Coll Ox BA58. Ripon Hall Ox. **d** 61 **p** 62. C Endcliffe *Sheff* 61-62; Fell Lect and Dir of Studies CCC Cam 62-74; Lect Div Cam Univ 70-74; Prof RS Lanc Univ 74-86; Hon Prov Can Cant Cathl *Cant* from 85; Dean of Chpl Trin Coll Cam 86-91; rtd 91; Lic to Offic *Cant* 91-94; Perm to Offic *Ely* 94-00. *14 Bowers Croft, Cambridge CB1 8RP*

✠**BOWLBY, The Rt Revd Ronald Oliver.** b 26. Trin Coll Ox BA50 MA54. Westcott Ho Cam 50. **d** 52 **p** 53 **c** 73. C Pallion *Dur* 52-56; C Billingham St Cuth 56-57; C-in-c Billingham St Aid CD 57-60; V Billingham St Aid 60-66; V Croydon *Cant* 66-73; Hon Can Cant Cathl 70-73; Bp Newc 73-80; Bp S'wark 80-91; rtd 91; Asst Bp Lich from 91. *4 Uppington Avenue, Shrewsbury SY3 7JL* Tel (01743) 244192 E-mail rebowl@tinyworld.co.uk

BOWLER, Christopher William. See JAGE-BOWLER, Christopher William

BOWLER, David Henderson. b 54. Kent Univ BA75. St Jo Coll Nottm 75. **d** 78 **p** 79. C Bramcote *S'well* 78-82; TV Kirby Muxloe *Leic* 82-88; V Quorndon from 88. *Quorn Vicarage, 6 Loughborough Road, Quorn, Loughborough LE12 8DX* Tel (01509) 412593

BOWLER, Denis Charles Stanley. b 16. **d** 66 **p** 67. C Bishop's Cleeve *Glouc* 66-69; C Coleford w Staunton 69-72; V Coney Hill 72-77; V Lydbrook 77-82; rtd 82; Perm to Offic *Glouc* 82-96. *c/o Mrs P M Hatfield, 47 Welland Lodge Road, Cheltenham GL52 3HB*

BOWLER, Preb Kenneth Neville. b 37. K Coll Lon 57. **d** 61 **p** 62. C Buxton *Derby* 61-67; R Sandiacre 67-75; V E Bedfont *Lon* 75-87; AD Hounslow 82-87; V Fulham All SS 87-02; Preb St Paul's Cathl 85-02; rtd 02. *62 Ickleford Road, Hitchin SG5 1TZ* Tel (01462) 454794

BOWLER, Roy Harold. b 27. Wadh Coll Ox BA48 MA57. Wells Th Coll 52. **d** 53 **p** 54. C Clerkenwell H Redeemer w St Phil *Lon* 53-55; C Tottenham All Hallows 55-57; Lic to Offic *Cant* 57-61; S Rhodesia 61-65; Rhodesia 65-80; Zimbabwe from 80. *Box 537, Mutare, Zimbabwe*

BOWLES, Arthur William. b 36. Loughb Coll of Educn DLC59. LNSM course 94. **d** 96 **p** 97. OLM Gt Yarmouth *Nor* from 96. *4 Onslow Avenue, Great Yarmouth NR30 4DT* Tel (01493) 842360

BOWLES, David Anthony. b 44. Kelham Th Coll 63. **d** 68 **p** 69. C Bilborough w Strelley *S'well* 68-72; C Beeston 72-75; Ascension Is 75-77; V Wellingborough St Mark *Pet* 77-83; P-in-c Wilby 78-83; R Burton Latimer 83-90; V Sheff St Oswald *Sheff* 90-91; Perm to Offic *Derby* 93-95 and *Roch* 95-98. *Address temp unknown*

BOWLES, Preb Michael Hubert Venn. b 36. Selw Coll Cam BA59 MA63. Ridley Hall Cam 59. **d** 61 **p** 62. C Woodside Park St Barn *Lon* 61-64; C Swanage *Sarum* 64-67; Lect St Mich Coll Llan 67-72; Chapl 67-70; Lib 70-72; Lect Th Univ of Wales (Cardiff) 67-72; R Gt Stanmore *Lon* 72-01; Preb St Paul's Cathl 85-01; rtd 01. *15 The Limes, St Albans AL1 4AT* Tel (01727) 832555

BOWLES, Peter John. b 39. Lon Univ BA60. Linc Th Coll 71. **d** 73 **p** 74. C Clay Cross *Derby* 73-76; C Boulton 76-79; R Brailsford w Shirley 79-85; P-in-c Osmaston w Edlaston 81-85; R Brailsford w Shirley and Osmaston w Edlaston 85-89; TR Old Brampton and Loundsley Green 89-98; V Hope, Castleton and Bradwell from 98. *The Vicarage, Church Street, Bradwell, Hope Valley S33 9HJ* Tel (01433) 620485

BOWLES, Ronald Leonard. b 24. K Coll Lon BD52 AKC52. **d** 53 **p** 54. C Berwick H Trin *Newc* 53-56; C Christchurch *Win* 56-60; R Nursling and Rownhams 60-66; V Woolston 66-75; V Moordown 75-89; rtd 89; Perm to Offic *Win* 89-99; *Portsm* from 89. *25 Cherry Tree Avenue, Cowplain, Waterlooville PO8 8BA* Tel (023) 9226 7376

BOWLEY, Canon John Richard Lyon. b 46. MRTPI76 Dur Univ BA68 QUB MSc72. CITC. **d** 79 **p** 80. C Knock *D & D* 79-81; Bp's C Knocknagoney 81-90; I Ballywalter w Inishargie from 90; Can Down Cathl from 03. *The Vicarage, 2 Whitechurch Road, Ballywalter, Newtownards BT22 2JY* Tel (028) 9175 8416

BOWMAN, Miss Alison Valentine. b 57. St Andr Univ MA79. St Steph Ho Ox 86. **d** 89 **p** 94. Par Dn Peacehaven *Chich* 89-94; C 94-95; Chapl to Bp Lewes 93-95; TV Rye from 95. *St Michael's House, 21 Fair Meadow, Rye TN31 7NL* Tel (01797) 225769

BOWMAN, Clifford William. b 57. St Jo Coll Dur BA78 Nottm Univ MA96. Ridley Hall Cam 80. **d** 82 **p** 83. C Sawley *Derby* 82-85; C Hucknall Torkard *S'well* 85-89; R Warsop 89-00; Dioc Chapl amongst Deaf People from 00. *45 Clumber Avenue, Edwinstowe, Mansfield NG21 9PE* Tel, minicom and fax (01623) 825700 E-mail c.bowman@dunelm.org.uk

BOWMAN, Ivelaw Alexander. b 46. LNSM course 94. **d** 97 **p** 98. OLM Stockwell Green St Andr *S'wark* from 97. *16 Horsford Road, London SW2 5BN* Tel (020) 7733 2309 *or* 7276 5746

BOWMAN, Prof John. b 16. Glas Univ MA38 BD41 Ch Ch Ox DPhil45. **d** 50 **p** 54. Hon C Leeds St Geo *Ripon* 51-53; Hon C Kirkstall 53-54; Perm to Offic *York* 54-59; Australia from 59; rtd 73. *15 Haines Street, North Melbourne, Vic, Australia 3051* Tel (0061) (3) 9329 0794 Fax as telephone
E-mail mbowman@vicnet.net.au

BOWMAN-EADIE, Preb Russell Ian. b 45. ACP68 K Coll Lon BD71 AKC71. St Aug Coll Cant 71. **d** 72 **p** 73. C Hammersmith St Pet *Lon* 72-74; V Leic St Nic *Leic* 74-81; Chapl Leic Univ 74-81; Adult Educn Adv *Dur* 81-84; Dir of Tr *B & W* from 84; Preb Wells Cathl from 90. *2 The Liberty, Wells BA5 2SU* Tel (01749) 674702 *or* 670777 Fax 674240
E-mail russell.bowman-eadie@bathwells.anglican.org

BOWN, Canon John Frederick Olney. b 13. TD50. BA36 MA70. Cuddesdon Coll 36. **d** 37 **p** 38. C Prittlewell St Mary *Chelmsf* 37-39; CF (TA) 39-44; CF 44-70; V Dover St Mary *Cant* 44-45; Hon Chapl Edin St Mary *Edin* 55-57; Can Mombasa 56-58; QHC 67-70; R Fordingbridge w Ibsley *Win* 70-79; RD Christchurch 74-78; rtd 79; Hon P-in-c Longstock w Leckford *Win* 79-87. *Dawlish House, 7 Trafalgar Way, Stockbridge SO20 6ET* Tel (01264) 810672

BOWNESS, William Gary. b 48. Warwick Univ BSc69 Chicago State Univ DMin98. Ripon Coll Cuddesdon 80. **d** 82 **p** 83. C Lancaster St Mary *Blackb* 82-86; V Lostock Hall 86-91; V Whittington w Arkholme and Gressingham 91-02; RD Tunstall 93-99; Dir Post-Ord Tr 00-02; R Alderley w Birtles *Ches* from 02. *St Mary's Rectory, Congleton Road, Nether Alderley, Macclesfield SK10 4TW* Tel (01625) 583134

BOWRING, Stephen John. b 55. R Holloway Coll Lon BMus77 St Mary's Coll Twickenham PGCE78. EMMTC 89. **d** 92 **p** 93. C Thurmaston *Leic* 92-95; V Shepshed 95-02; R River *Cant* from 02; AD Dover from 03. *The Vicarage, 23 Lewisham Road, Dover CT17 0QG* Tel (01304) 822287 E-mail bowring@fish.co.uk

BOWRON, Hugh Mark. b 52. Cant Univ (NZ) BA74 MA76 Leeds Univ DipTh78. Coll of Resurr Mirfield 76. **d** 79 **p** 80. C Northampton St Mary *Pet* 79-82; New Zealand from 82; V Ellesmere 82-86; V Addington St Mary 86-95; V Wellington St Pet from 95. *PO Box 27 110, Wellington, New Zealand* Tel (0064) (4) 972 3250 *or* 382 8486
E-mail hugh.bowron@clear.net.nz

BOWSER, Alan. b 35. Univ of Wales (Lamp) BA60 DipTh62. **d** 63 **p** 64. C Gateshead St Chad Bensham *Dur* 63-67; C Owton Manor CD 67-72; V Horden 72-02; rtd 02. *Kengarth House, Coast Road, Blackhall Colliery, Hartlepool TS27 4HF*

BOWSHER, Andrew Peter. b 59. Reading Univ BA81 Nottm Univ DipTh84. St Jo Coll Nottm DPS86. **d** 86 **p** 87. C Grenoside *Sheff* 86-89; C Darfield 89-91; P-in-c Haley Hill *Wakef* 91-96; V Bradf St Aug Undercliffe *Bradf* 96-99; Chapl Bradf Coll from 99; Chapl Bradf Univ *Bradf* from 99. *Faith Sawrey's House, 41 Little Horton Green, Bradford BD5 0NG* Tel 01274 727034 *or* 415910 Mobile 07876-401339
E-mail anglican-chaplain@bradford.ac.uk

BOWSKILL, Mrs Amanda. b 49. Dip Counselling 93. STETS DipTh99. **d** 99 **p** 00. NSM Winklebury *Win* 99-03; NSM Tadley S and Silchester from 03. *St Mary's House, 10 Roman's Field, Silchester, Reading RG7 2QH* Tel 0118-970 2353

BOWSKILL, Robert Preston. b 48. S Dios Minl Tr Scheme 88. **d** 91 **p** 92. NSM Eastrop *Win* 91-94; NSM Winklebury from 94. *St Mary's House, 10 Roman's Field, Silchester, Reading RG7 2QH* Tel 0118-970 2353 E-mail bob.bowskill@boltblue.com

BOWTELL, Paul William. b 47. Lon Univ BSc68. St Jo Coll Nottm 80. **d** 82 **p** 83. C Gorleston St Andr *Nor* 82-85; TV Forest Gate St Sav w W Ham St Matt *Chelmsf* 85-91; R Spitalfields Ch Ch w All SS *Lon* 91-02; Newham Employment Project from 02; Perm to Offic *Chelmsf* from 02. *23 Gardner Road, London E13 8LN* Tel (020) 7476 2564 *or* 8548 4676 Fax 8548 4110
E-mail paul@bowtellp.freeserve.co.uk

BOWYER, Arthur Gustavus Frederick. b 36. Dioc OLM tr scheme 97. **d** 00 **p** 01. NSM Kingswood *S'wark* from 00. *41 Tattenham Grove, Epsom KT18 5QT* Tel (01737) 357913 Mobile 07939-533506 E-mail abowyer@onetel.net.uk

BOWYER, Frank. b 28. Man Univ BA49 BD56. Oak Hill Th Coll 53. **d** 55 **p** 56. C Halliwell St Paul *Man* 55-57; C Crosthwaite Keswick *Carl* 57-59; V Thornham w Gravel Hole *Man* 59-63; R Burnage St Marg 63-81; R Egworth w Nether Wasdale and Wasdale Head *Carl* 81-85; R Holcombe *Man* 85-93; rtd 93; Perm to Offic *Man* from 93. *43 New Church Road, Bolton BL1 5QQ* Tel (01204) 844547

BOWYER, Geoffrey Charles. b 54. ACA79 ATII82 Lanc Univ BA76. St Jo Coll Nottm 85. **d** 87 **p** 88. C Walton *St E* 87-89; C

Macclesfield Team Par *Ches* 89-91; V Cinderford St Steph w Littledean *Glouc* 91-95; V Brockenhurst *Win* 95-98; Hon C Trull w Angersleigh *B & W* from 00. *36 Bakers Close, Bishops Hull, Taunton TA1 5HD* Tel (01823) 335289
E-mail us4bowyers@aol.com

BOX, David Norman. b 28. K Coll Lon BD48 AKC48. **d** 51 **p** 52. C Grays Thurrock *Chelmsf* 51-53; Hon C Aldershot St Mich *Guildf* 53-55; Asst Master St Benedict's Sch Aldershot 53-55; C Weston 55-58; C Camberley St Paul 58-61; V Blackheath and Chilworth 61-69; V Allerton *Bradf* 69-75; R Exford w Exmoor *B & W* 75-80; V Castle Cary w Ansford 80-90; P-in-c Childe Okeford, Manston, Hammoon and Hanford *Sarum* 90-91; R Childe Okeford, Okeford Fitzpaine, Manston etc 91-94; rtd 94; Perm to Offic *Carl* from 94. *Granary House, 1 Castle Street, Hilton, Appleby-in-Westmorland CA16 6LX* Tel (01768) 352689

BOX, Reginald Gilbert (Brother Reginald). b 20. Lon Univ BD41 AKC41 Em Coll Cam BA52 MA57 Lambeth STh91. Westcott Ho Cam 41. **d** 43 **p** 44. C Chingford SS Pet and Paul *Chelmsf* 43-47; Chapl Bps' Coll Cheshunt 47-50; SSF from 51; Lic to Offic *Ely* 51-55; Lic to Offic *Sarum* 55-61; C Cambridge St Benedict *Ely* 61-67; Chapl Coll of SS Mark and Jo Chelsea 67-69; New Zealand, Australia and Melanesia 69-84; Perm to Offic *Sarum* from 84; Perm to Offic *Ely* 85-97; rtd 90; Chapl Chich Th Coll 90-93. *The Friary, Hilfield, Dorchester DT2 7BE* Tel (01300) 341345 Fax 341293

BOXALL, David John. b 41. Dur Univ BA63 DipTh65. Sarum Th Coll 65. **d** 66 **p** 67. C Ipswich St Aug *St E* 66-69; C Bourne *Linc* 69-71; C Woodside Park St Barn *Lon* 71-72; C Thundersley *Chelmsf* 72-76; P-in-c Farcet *Ely* 76-77; TV Stanground and Farcet 77-85; V Guyhirn w Ring's End 85-90; V Southea w Murrow and Parson Drove 85-90; P-in-c Fletton 90-94; Perm to Offic 94-00; rtd 99. *11 Plover Drive, March PE15 9HY* Tel (01354) 659905

BOXALL, Keith Michael. b 37. Trin Coll Bris. **d** 82 **p** 83. C Staines St Pet *Lon* 82-83; C Staines St Mary and St Pet 83-85; C Lydiard Millicent w Lydiard Tregoz *Bris* 85-86; TV The Lydiards 86-93; V Mangotsfield 93-03; rtd 03. *25 Parc Plas, Blackwood NP12 1SJ* Tel (01495) 222572 Mobile 07745-016038
E-mail keith.boxall1@btinternet.com

BOXALL, Canon Martin Alleyne. b 37. Wells Th Coll 65. **d** 67 **p** 68. C Crowthorne *Ox* 67-70; C Tilehurst St Mich 70-76; V Tilehurst St Cath 76-78; V Padstow *Truro* 78-00; Miss to Seafarers from 78; rtd 01; Dioc Officer for Unity *Truro* from 01. *Goonhilland Farmhouse, Burnthouse, St Gluvias, Penryn TR10 9AS* Tel (01872) 863241

BOXALL, Simon Roger. b 55. St Jo Coll Cam BA76. Ridley Hall Cam 77. **d** 79 **p** 80. C Eaton *Nor* 79-82; SAMS Brazil from 82. *rua Real Grandeza 99, Botafogo, Rio de Janeiro, RJ 22281-030, Brazil* Tel (0055) (21) 226 9488 or 226 2978 Fax 538 2978
E-mail christchurch@openlink.com.br

BOXLEY, Christopher. b 45. K Coll Lon BD68 AKC68 Southn Univ CertEd73 Reading Univ MA84. **d** 69 **p** 70. C Bitterne Park *Win* 69-73; Perm to Offic *Chich* 73-78; Hd of Relig Studies Midhurst Gr Sch from 73; Dir Midhurst and Petworth Relig Studies Cen from 78; P-in-c Heyshott from 78. *The Rectory, Heyshott, Midhurst GU29 0DH* Tel (01730) 814405

BOYCE, Canon Brian David Michael. b 32. Fitzw Ho Cam BA55 MA62. Wells Th Coll 55. **d** 57 **p** 58. C Tavistock and Gulworthy *Ex* 57-60; C Paignton St Jo 60-62; C Germiston S Africa 62-64; R Ermelo 64-67; R Primrose 67-75; R Springs and Adn SE Transvaal 75-86; rtd 97; Perm to Offic *B & W* 98-03. *PO Box 44108, Linden, Johannesburg, 2104 South Africa*

BOYCE, Christopher Allan. b 44. Brighton Coll of Art DipArch66 ARIBA69. S Dios Minl Tr Scheme 84. **d** 87 **p** 88. NSM Eastbourne All SS *Chich* 87-93; C Upton (Overchurch) *Ches* 93-96; V New Brighton St Jas w Em 96-02; P-in-c New Brighton All SS 98-02; C Bicester w Bucknell, Caversfield and Launton *Ox* from 02. *4 Orpine Close, Bicester OX26 3ZJ* Tel (01869) 244918 Mobile 07989-269175
E-mail revcab@lineone.net

BOYCE, John Frederick. b 33. ALCD57. **d** 57 **p** 58. C Earlsfield St Andr *S'wark* 57-60; C Westerham *Roch* 60-63; C Farnborough 63-66; V Sutton at Hone 66-73; P-in-c Chiddingstone 73-74; R Chiddingstone w Chiddingstone Causeway 74-84; V Brenchley 84-98; rtd 98; Perm to Offic *Chich* from 99. *3 Orchard Rise, Groombridge, Tunbridge Wells TN3 9RU*

BOYCE, Kenneth Albert. b 51. St Edm Hall Ox BA72 MA76 Selw Coll Cam BA75 MA79. Westcott Ho Cam 73. **d** 75 **p** 76. C Evington *Leic* 75-78; P-in-c Gt Bowden w Welham 78-81; Dioc Stewardship Adv 78-81; Chapl Leic Poly 81-86; TV Leic H Spirit 82-86; Chapl to the Deaf *Worc* 86-93; P-in-c Astwood Bank 86-93; R Fladbury, Wyre Piddle and Moor 93-98; P-in-c Cropthorne w Charlton 94-98; R Fladbury w Wyre Piddle and Moor etc 98-00; RD Pershore 97-00; TR Worc SE from 00. *The Rectory, St Catherine's Hill, Worcester WR5 2EA* Tel (01905) 355119 or 358083

BOYCE, Robert Albert Wright. b 19. BA. St Alb Minl Tr Scheme. **d** 82 **p** 83. NSM Bp's Hatfield *St Alb* 82-89; Perm to Offic from

89; rtd 90. *92 Park Meadow, Hatfield AL9 5HE* Tel (01707) 267531

BOYCE, William. d 03. C Willowfield *D & D* from 03. *21 Loopland Crescent, Belfast BT6 9EE* Tel (028) 9045 2165

BOYD, Alan McLean. b 50. St Jo Coll Nottm BTh79. **d** 79 **p** 80. C Bishop's Waltham *Portsm* 79-83; Chapl Reading Univ *Ox* 83-88; Chapl E Birm Hosp 88-94; Chapl Birm Heartlands and Solihull NHS Trust from 94. *Solihull Hospital, Lode Lane, Solihull B91 2JL* Tel 0121-766 6611 ext 4700

BOYD, Alexander Jamieson. b 46. MIBiol FSAScot St Chad's Coll Dur BSc68 Nottm Univ PGCE69. Coll of Resurr Mirfield 69. **d** 79 **p** 80. NSM Musselburgh *Edin* 79-83; CF 83-00; P-in-c Loddington *Leic* from 00; Warden Launde Abbey from 00. *Launde Abbey, Launde, Leicester LE7 9XB* Tel (01572) 717254
E-mail laundeabbey@leicester.anglican.org

BOYD, Allan Gray. b 41. St Jo Coll Nottm 84. **d** 87 **p** 88. Hon Chapl Miss to Seafarers from 87; NSM Glas St Gabr *Glas* 87-93; NSM Greenock 93-96; NSM Paisley St Barn from 96; NSM Paisley H Trin from 96. *47 Holms Crescent, Erskine PA8 6DJ* Tel 0141-812 2754

BOYD, Allan Newby. b 31. Ball Coll Ox BA53 MA59 MInstM73. St Alb Minl Tr Scheme 81. **d** 84 **p** 85. NSM Watford St Luke *St Alb* 84-88; C Ardsley *Sheff* 88-91; V Barrow St Jo *Carl* 91-94; rtd 94; Perm to Offic *Ripon* from 96. *Bishop Fold, Thoralby, Leyburn DL8 3SU* Tel (01969) 663474

BOYD, Canon David Anthony. b 42. Sarum & Wells Th Coll 72. **d** 75 **p** 76. C Ches H Trin *Ches* 75-79; R 85-93; V Congleton St Jas 79-85; V Farndon and Coddington from 93; RD Malpas from 97; Hon Can Ches Cathl from 02. *The Vicarage, Church Lane, Farndon, Chester CH3 6QD* Tel (01829) 270270 Fax as telephone

BOYD, David George. b 37. Cant Univ (NZ) BSc62 LTh64. St Aug Coll Cant. **d** 63 **p** 64. New Zealand 63-66; St Aug Coll Cant 66-67; Chapl RAF 67-71; New Zealand from 71; Adn Mid-Canterbury 92-96. *PO Box 178, Eltham, New Zealand* Tel (0064) (6) 764 8119 E-mail daboyd@xtra.co.nz

BOYD, Michael Victor. b 33. St Chad's Coll Dur BA57 DipAdEd69 MEd77 PhD81. Coll of Resurr Mirfield 57. **d** 59 **p** 60. C Warsop *S'well* 59-61; Chapl St Geo Coll Quilmes Argent 62-63; Chapl Wolsingham Sch 63-67; Lect St Hild Coll Dur 67-75; Lect SS Hild and Bede Dur 75-79; Lect Dur Univ 79-84; rtd 98. *4 Aykley Green, Durham DH1 4LN* Tel 0191-384 9473

BOYD, Robert Henry. b 36. **d** 66 **p** 67. C Drumcree *Arm* 66-69; I Annaghmore 69-83; Bp's C Lissan 83-90; I from 90. *The Rectory, 150 Moneymore Road, Cookstown BT80 8PY* Tel (028) 7976 6112

BOYD, Samuel Robert Thomas. b 62. **d** 90 **p** 91. NSM Derryloran *Arm* 90-95; C 95-97; I Woodschapel w Gracefield from 97. *140 Ballyronan Road, Magherafelt BT45 6HT* Tel (028) 7941 8230

BOYD, Stephen William. b 71. Aston Tr Scheme DipHE97 Ripon Coll Cuddesdon BTh00. **d** 00 **p** 01. C Walton-on-the-Hill *Liv* from 00. *The Curate's House, Walton Village, Liverpool L4 6TJ* Tel 0151-523 0683

BOYD, Canon William John Peter. b 28. Lon Univ BA48 BD53 PhD77 Birm Univ MA60. **d** 57 **p** 58. C Aston SS Pet and Paul *Birm* 57-60; V Smethwick 60-63; V St Breward *Truro* 63-68; Adult Educn Chapl 64-85; Dioc Ecum Officer 65-83; R St Ewe 68-73; Preb St Endellion 73-85; V St Kew 73-77; R Falmouth K Chas 77-85; RD Carnmarth S 84-85; Dir of Tr 85-93; Prin SW Minl Tr Course 85-93; Can Res and Chan Truro Cathl *Truro* 85-93; rtd 93; Perm to Offic *Truro* from 93. *7 Chapel Crescent, Zelah, Truro TR4 9HN*

BOYD-WILLIAMS, Anthony Robert. b 46. Univ of Wales (Cardiff) DPS88. St Mich Coll Llan 86. **d** 88 **p** 89. C Tonyrefail w Gilfach Goch *Llan* 88-91; V Treharris w Bedlinog 91-96; V Ocker Hill *Lich* from 96; RD Wednesbury from 03. *St Mark's Vicarage, Ocker Hill Road, Tipton DY4 0UT* Tel 0121-556 0678
E-mail tonybw@stmarksvicarage.fsnet.co.uk

BOYDEN, Peter Frederick. b 41. Lon Univ BSc62 AKC62 Em Coll Cam BA64 MA68 MLitt69. Ridley Hall Cam 63. **d** 66 **p** 67. C Chesterton St Andr *Ely* 66-68; C Wimbledon *S'wark* 68-72; Chapl K Sch Cant 72-89; Asst Chapl Radley Coll 89-02; rtd 02. *30 Chesterfield Road, Shirland, Alfreton DE55 6BN* Tel (01773) 830552

BOYES, Canon David Arthur Stiles. b 30. Lon Coll of Div 62. **d** 63 **p** 64. C Islington St Mary *Lon* 63-71; V Canonbury St Steph 71-75; V St Paul's Cray St Barn *Roch* 75-85; P-in-c Earl Soham w Cretingham and Ashfield *St E* 85-96; Dioc Development Officer 86-92; RD Loes 91-95; Hon Can St E Cathl 95-96; rtd 96; Perm to Offic *St E* from 96. *13 Magdalen Drive, Woodbridge IP12 4EF* Tel (01394) 383389

BOYES, Matthew John. b 70. Roehampton Inst BA91. Wycliffe Hall Ox BTh99. **d** 99 **p** 00. C Bury St Edmunds Ch Ch *St E* 99-02; P-in-c Penn Street *Ox* from 02. *The Vicarage, Penn Street, Amersham HP7 0PX* Tel (01494) 712194
E-mail mattboyz@dial.pipex.com

BOYES, Michael Charles. b 27. Lon Univ BA53 BD58. Wells Th Coll 53. **d** 55 **p** 56. C Heavitree *Ex* 55-61; C Exwick 61-68; V Broadclyst 68-83; RD Aylesbeare 77-81; TV Sampford Peverell,

Uplowman, Holcombe Rogus etc 83-85; TR 85-92; rtd 92; Perm to Offic *Ex* from 92. *Southdown, Burlescombe, Tiverton EX16 7LB* Tel (01884) 840492

BOYLAND, Alice Teresa. b 41. **d** 99. NSM Llangybi and Coedypaen w Llanbadoc *Mon* from 99. *2 Catherine Cottages, Ton Road, Llangybi, Usk NP15 1NU* Tel (01633) 450647

BOYLAND, David Henry. b 58. TCD BA79 BAI79. TCD Div Sch BTh91. **d** 91 **p** 92. C Seapatrick *D & D* 91-94; I Celbridge w Straffan and Newcastle-Lyons *D & G* 94-98; I Kilmakee *Conn* from 98. *Kilmakee Rectory, 60 Killeaton Park, Dunmurry, Belfast BT17 9HE* Tel (028) 9061 0505

BOYLAND, Henry Hubert. b 23. Dip Mgt. CITC. **d** 84 **p** 85. NSM Dunboyne Union *M & K* 84-87; Bp's C Carrickmacross w Magheracloone *Clogh* 87-90; I 90-93; rtd 93. *2 Spring View, Wheaton Hall, Dublin Road, Drogheda, Co Louth, Irish Republic* Tel (00353) (41) 44724

BOYLE, Andrew McKenzie. b 45. Down Coll Cam BA67 MA71 CEng72 MICE72. WMMTC 82. **d** 85 **p** 86. NSM Woodthorpe *S'well* 85-87; Perm to Offic *Roch* 88-90; 91-96; Hon C Sevenoaks St Luke CD 90-91; NSM Sundridge w Ide Hill from 96. *Greenridge, 35 Garth Road, Sevenoaks TN13 1RU* Tel (01732) 456546 Fax 450060 E-mail andrewboyle1@compuserve.com

✠**BOYLE, The Rt Revd Christopher John.** b 51. AKC75. St Aug Coll Cant 75. **d** 76 **p** 77 **c** 01. C Wylde Green *Birm* 76-80; Bp's Dom Chapl 80-83; R Castle Bromwich SS Mary and Marg 83-01; AD Coleshill 92-99; P-in-c Shard End 96-97; Hon Can Birm Cathl 96-01; Bp N Malawi from 01. *PO Box 120, Mzuzu, Malawi* Tel (00265) 34930 Mobile 825097 Fax 333805 E-mail biggers@malawi.net

BOYLE, Paul. b 01 **p** 02. C Cen Cardiff *Llan* from 01. *41 Colum Road, Cardiff CF10 3EE* Tel (029) 2022 4036

BOYLE, Robert Leslie. b 52. EMMTC. **d** 00 **p** 01. NSM Derby St Anne and St Jo *Derby* from 00. *61 Rowditch Avenue, Derby DE22 3LE* Tel (01332) 349044

BOYLES, Peter John. b 59. Univ of Wales (Lamp) BA84. Sarum & Wells Th Coll 86. **d** 88 **p** 89. C Ches St Mary *Ches* 88-91; C Neston 91-95; R Lavendon w Cold Brayfield, Clifton Reynes etc *Ox* 95-99; V Dent w Cowgill *Bradf* from 99. *The Vicarage, Dent, Sedbergh LA10 5QR* Tel (01539) 625226 E-mail peter.boyles@btinternet.com

BOYLING, Canon Denis Hudson. b 16. Keble Coll Ox BA38 DipTh39 MA42. Cuddesdon Coll 39. **d** 40 **p** 41. C Sheff St Cuth *Sheff* 40-46; Chapl K Coll Hosp Lon 46-49; Chapl United Sheff Hosps 49-57; V Endcliffe *Sheff* 57-68; Hon Can Sheff Cathl 58-68; V Almondbury *Wakef* 68-75; RD Almondbury 68-75; Hon Can Wakef Cathl 72-75; Can Res Wakef Cathl 75-82; rtd 82; Perm to Offic *Heref* from 82. *7 St Mary's Close, Tenbury Wells WR15 8ES* Tel (01584) 811633

BOYLING, Canon Mark Christopher. b 52. Keble Coll Ox BA74 BA76 MA78. Cuddesdon Coll 74. **d** 77 **p** 78. C Kirkby *Liv* 77-79; P-in-c 79-80; TV 80-83; Bp's Dom Chapl 85-89; V Formby St Pet 89-94; Can Res and Prec Liv Cathl from 94. *3 Cathedral Close, Liverpool L1 7BR* Tel 0151-708 0934

BOYNS, Martin Laurence Harley. b 26. St Jo Coll Cam BA49 MA51. Ridley Hall Cam 50. **d** 52 **p** 53. C Woodmansterne *S'wark* 52-55; C Folkestone H Trin w Ch Ch *Cant* 55-58; V Duffield *Derby* 58-71; V Rawdon *Bradf* 71-76; Chapl Woodlands Hosp Rawdon 71-76; R Melton *St E* 76-85; R Gerrans w St Anthony in Roseland *Truro* 85-92; Miss to Seamen 85-92; rtd 92; Perm to Offic *Truro* from 92. *Bojunda, Boscaswell Village, Pendeen, Penzance TR19 7EP* Tel (01736) 788390

BOYNS, Timothy Martin Harley. b 58. Warwick Univ BA80 Nottm Univ BCombStuds84. Linc Th Coll 81. **d** 84 **p** 85. C Oxhey St Matt *St Alb* 84-87; TV Solihull *Birm* 87-94; V Lillington *Cov* from 94; RD Warwick and Leamington from 99. *The Vicarage, Lillington, Leamington Spa CV32 7RH* Tel (01926) 424214 or 470449 E-mail tim.boyns@talk21.com

BOYS, Mrs Margaret Ann. b 34. Lon Univ TCert56 Liv Univ DipPE59. Oak Hill Th Coll 91. **d** 94 **p** 95. NSM Hadleigh St Barn *Chelmsf* 94-98; NSM Thundersley from 98. *10 Seymour Road, Westcliff-on-Sea SS0 8NJ* Tel (01702) 475997

BOYSE, Felix Vivian Allan. b 17. LVO78. CCC Cam BA39 MA42. Cuddesdon Coll 39. **d** 40 **p** 41. C New Mills *Derby* 40-43; P-in-c 43-45; Vice-Prin Cuddesdon Coll 46-51; V Kingswood *S'wark* 51-58; V St Mary Abchurch *Lon* 58-61; Prin St Geo Coll Jerusalem 61-64; Chapl Chpl Royal Hampton Court Palace 65-82; Preacher Lincoln's Inn 82-93; rtd 93; Perm to Offic *Chich* from 83. *Rose Cottage, Rookwood Road, West Wittering, Chichester PO20 8LT* Tel (01243) 514320

BRACE, Alistair Andrew. b 53. Newc Univ MB, BS76 DRCOG77. WMMTC 90. **d** 94. NSM Broseley w Benthall, Jackfield, Linley etc *Heref* 94-98. *58 Spout Lane, Benthall, Broseley TF12 1QY* Tel (01952) 884031

BRACE, Stuart. b 49. Open Univ DipMgt00 BSc01. Bp Burgess Hall Lamp DipTh74. **d** 74 **p** 75. C Llanelli Ch Ch *St D* 74-76; C Tenby w Gumfreston *St D* 76-77; V Ystradmeurig and Strata Florida 77-79; CF 79-86; CF(V) 86-93; Chapl HM Youth Cust Cen Everthorpe 86-88; Chapl HM Pris Stafford 88-93; Chapl HM Pris Long Lartin 93-95; Ecum Tr Officer HM Pris Service Chapl 95-99; Chapl HM Pris Glouc from 99; Perm to Offic *Worc* from 99. *The Chaplaincy, HM Prison Gloucester, Barrack Square, Gloucester GL1 2JN* Tel (01452) 529551 E-mail brace3@chap0.freeserve.co.uk

BRACEGIRDLE, Christopher Andrew. b 56. Dur Univ BEd79 St Edm Ho Cam BA84 MA89. Ridley Hall Cam 82. **d** 85 **p** 86. C Livesey *Blackb* 85-88; TV E Farnworth and Kearsley *Man* 88-92; V Astley 92-98; Chapl Wigan and Leigh Health Services NHS Trust 92-98; Tutor Dioc OLM Scheme *Man* from 97; P-in-c Walkden Moor w Lt Hulton 98-99; TR Walkden and Lt Hulton from 99. *St Paul's Vicarage, 10 Old Vicarage Gardens, Walkden, Manchester M28 3JR* Tel 0161-790 2483 Fax as telephone E-mail chris@bracegirdles.fsworld.co.uk

BRACEGIRDLE, Canon Cynthia Wendy Mary. b 52. LMH Ox BA73 MA77 Liv Univ DipAE82. N Ord Course. **d** 87 **p** 94. Chapl Asst Man R Infirmary 85-88; Dir Dioc OLM Scheme *Man* 89-02; Hon Can Man Cathl 98-02; rtd 03. *The Vicarage, St George's Road, Millom LA18 4JA* Tel (01229) 772889 E-mail ignatius@globalnet.co.uk

BRACEGIRDLE, Robert Kevin Stewart. b 47. Univ Coll Ox BA69 MA73. Cuddesdon Coll 69. **d** 73 **p** 74. C Dorchester *Sarum* 73-75; C Woodchurch *Ches* 75-78; V Bidston 78-82; P-in-c Salford St Ignatius *Man* 82-86; R Salford St Ignatius and Stowell Memorial 86-02; P-in-c Salford Ordsall St Clem 99-02; P-in-c Millom *Carl* from 02. *The Vicarage, St George's Road, Millom LA18 4JA* Tel (01229) 772889 E-mail ignatius@globalnet.co.uk

BRACEWELL, David John. b 44. Leeds Univ BA66 Man Univ MA82. Tyndale Hall Bris 67. **d** 69 **p** 70. C Tonbridge St Steph *Roch* 69-72; C Shipley St Pet *Bradf* 72-75; V Halliwell St Paul *Man* 75-84; R Guildf St Sav *Guildf* from 84. *St Saviour's Rectory, Wharf Road, Guildford GU1 4RP* Tel (01483) 577811 *or* 455333 E-mail st.saviours@dial.pipex.com

BRACEWELL, Howard Waring. b 35. FRGS73. Tyndale Hall Bris. **d** 63 **p** 63. Canada 63-72; Travel Missr World Radio Miss Fellowship 72-77; P-in-c Ashill *Nor* 72-74; Hon C Bris St Phil and St Jacob w Em *Bris* 77-84; Perm to Offic *St Alb* 84-86; R Odell 86-88; V Pavenham *St Alb* 88-93; Assoc Min St Andrew's Street Bapt Ch Cambridge 94-99; Assoc Min Halliwell St Luke *Man* 99-01; rtd 01; Perm to Offic *Man* from 01. *10 Fairfields, Egerton, Bolton BL7 9EE* Tel (01204) 304028 E-mail howard@igloovut.fsnet.co.uk

BRACEY, David Harold. b 36. AKC63 Man Univ DPST83. **d** 64 **p** 65. C Westleigh St Pet *Man* 64-67; C Dunstable *St Alb* 67-70; V Benchill *Man* 70-76; V Elton St Steph 76-87; V Howe Bridge 87-00; rtd 00. *Rhiw Awel, Sarn, Pwllheli LL53 8EY* Tel (01758) 730381

BRACHER, Paul Martin. b 59. Solicitor 84 Ex Univ LLB80. Trin Coll Bris BA90. **d** 90 **p** 91. C Sparkhill St Jo *Birm* 90; C Sparkhill w Greet and Sparkbrook 90-93; Chapl Birm Women's Hosp 92-93; P-in-c Lea Hall *Birm* 93-98; V from 98. *St Richard's Vicarage, Hallmoor Road, Birmingham B33 9QY* Tel 0121-783 2319

BRACK, Edward James. b 37. Sarum Th Coll 67. **d** 69 **p** 70. C Gravesend St Aid *Roch* 69-73; C Woodside Park St Barn *Lon* 73-77; C Wood Green St Mich 77-80; V Whitton SS Phil and Jas 80-83; TV Bethnal Green St Jo w St Bart 83-86; TV St Jo on Bethnal Green 87-94; C W Hackney St Barn 94-96; rtd 96. *8 Surrey Gardens, Hermitage Road, London N4 1UD*

BRACKENBURY, The Ven Michael Palmer. b 30. Linc Th Coll 64. **d** 66 **p** 67. C S Ormsby w Ketsby, Calceby and Driby *Linc* 66-69; V Scothern w Sudbrooke 69-77; RD Lawres 73-78; Bp's Personal Asst 77-88; Dioc Dir of Ords 77-87; Can and Preb Linc Cathl 79-95; Dioc Lay Min Adv 88-95; Adn Linc 88-95; rtd 95. *18 Lea View, Ryhall, Stamford PE9 4HZ* Tel (01780) 752415

✠**BRACKLEY, The Rt Revd Ian James.** b 47. Keble Coll Ox BA69 MA73. Cuddesdon Coll 69. **d** 71 **p** 72 **c** 96. C Bris Lockleaze St Mary Magd w St Fran *Bris* 71-74; Asst Chapl Bryanston Sch 74-77; Chapl 77-80; V E Preston w Kingston Chich 80-88; RD Arundel and Bognor 82-86; TR Haywards Heath St Wilfrid 88-96; RD Cuckfield 89-95; Suff Bp Dorking *Guildf* from 96; Hon Can Guildf Cathl from 96. *13 Pilgrim's Way, Guildford GU4 8AD* Tel (01483) 570829 Fax 567268 E-mail bishop.ian@cofeguildford.org.uk

BRACKLEY, Mark Ozanne. b 53. Boro Road Teacher Tr Coll CertEd75. S'wark Ord Course 90. **d** 93 **p** 94. C Hampstead St Steph w All Hallows *Lon* 93-97; V W Green Ch Ch w St Pet from 97. *Christ Church Vicarage, Waldeck Road, London N15 3EP* Tel (020) 8889 9677

BRADBERRY, John. b 20. Clifton Th Coll 46. **d** 47 **p** 48. C Hinckley H Trin *Leic* 47-50; C Earlham St Anne *Nor* 50-51; V Leyton Ch Ch *Chelmsf* 51-55; Argentina 55-61; V Siddal *Wakef* 61-72; R Bentham St Jo *Bradf* 72-85; rtd 85; Perm to Offic *Bradf* 86-92. *18 Moor Bottom Road, Halifax HX2 9SR* Tel (01422) 244944

BRADBERRY, John Stephen. b 47. Hull Univ BSc70 Leeds Univ CertEd71 MEd86 Bradf Univ PhD91. NW Ord Course 76. **d** 79 **p** 80. NSM Warley *Wakef* from 79. *129 Paddock Lane, Halifax HX2 0NT* Tel (01422) 358282

BRADBROOK, Mrs Averyl. b 46. Girton Coll Cam BA67 MA88 Man Univ PGCE69 MA(Theol)96. N Ord Course 90. **d** 93 **p** 94. C Heaton Ch Ch *Man* 93-96; P-in-c Elton St Steph 96-02; Bp's Adv for Women's Min 01-02; V Moseley St Mary *Birm* from 02. *St Mary's Vicarage, 18 Oxford Road, Moseley, Birmingham B13 9EH* Tel 0121-449 1459 *or* 449 2243 Mobile 07808-290817 E-mail bradbrook@onetel.net.uk

BRADBROOK, Peter David. b 33. Kelham Th Coll 54. **d** 60 **p** 61. C Ches St Oswald St Thos *Ches* 60-63; C Fulham St Etheldreda *Lon* 64-65; V Congleton St Jas *Ches* 65-79; V Wheelock 79-92; V Crewe All SS and St Paul 92-98; rtd 98; Perm to Offic *Ches* from 00. *20 Magdelen Court, College Fields, Dane Bank Avenue, Crewe CW2 8FF* Tel (01270) 669420

BRADBURY, George Graham. b 35. AKC58. **d** 59 **p** 60. C Portsea St Mary *Portsm* 59-62; C Melksham *Sarum* 62-64; R Winfrith Newburgh w Chaldon Herring 64-68; CF 68-71; rtd 99. *Wayside, Brook Street, Shipton Gorge, Bridport DT6 4NA* Tel (01308) 897714

BRADBURY, Canon Herbert Cedric. b 30. FPS Man Univ PhC53. Linc Th Coll 64. **d** 66 **p** 67. C Blackpool St Steph *Blackb* 66-71; TV Hempnall *Nor* 71-75; TR 75-81; R Fritton w Morningthorpe w Shelton and Hardwick 74-77; RD Depwade 77-81; V Wroxham w Hoveton 81; P-in-c Belaugh 81; R Wroxham w Hoveton and Belaugh 81-92; RD Tunstead 83-91; Hon Can Nor Cathl 90-97; R Gt and Lt Massingham and Harpley 92-97; P-in-c South Raynham, E w W Raynham, Helhoughton, etc 94-97; rtd 97; Perm to Offic *Nor* from 97; Bp's Officer for Rtd Clergy and Widows from 99. *Morningthorpe, 66 Grove Lane, Holt NR25 6ED*

BRADBURY, Julian Nicholas Anstey. b 49. BNC Ox BA71 MA75 Birm Univ MA84. Cuddesdon Coll 71. **d** 73 **p** 74. C S'wark H Trin *S'wark* 73-76; In RC Ch in USA 76-79; V Tottenham H Trin *Lon* 79-85; Dir Past Th Sarum & Wells Th Coll 85-90; P-in-c Yatton Keynell *Bris* 90-97; P-in-c Biddestone w Slaughterford 90-97; P-in-c Castle Combe 90-97; P-in-c W Kington 90-97; P-in-c Nettleton 90-97; R Horfield H Trin 97-02; Fell K Fund from 02; Perm to Offic *Ox* from 02. *12 St Bernards Road, Oxford OX2 6EH* Tel (020) 7307 2610 E-mail n.bradbury@kingsfund.org.uk

BRADBURY, Kenneth James Frank. b 23. Qu Coll Birm 72. **d** 75 **p** 76. NSM Cen Telford 75-77; C 77-80; V Chirbury *Heref* 80-88; V Marton 80-88; V Trelystan 80-88; rtd 88; Perm to Offic *Heref* 90-99. *Elm Tree Cottage, Treflach, Oswestry SY10 9HG* Tel (01691) 637407

BRADBURY, Matthew Laurence. b 58. Kent Univ BA79 Solicitor 83. EAMTC 00. **d** 03. NSM Sutton *Ely* from 03; NSM Witcham w Mepal from 03. *70 The Brook, Sutton, Ely CB6 2QQ* Tel 07775-937951 (mobile) E-mail m-brad@supanet.com

BRADBURY, Norman Lunn. b 15. K Coll Lon BA36 AKC36. N Ord Course 76. **d** 77 **p** 78. NSM Paddock *Wakef* 77-81; NSM Rashcliffe and Lockwood 81-84; Perm to Offic from 84. *23 Springwood Hall Gardens, Huddersfield HD1 4HA* Tel (01484) 427548

BRADBURY, Robert Douglas. b 50. Ripon Coll Cuddesdon 75. **d** 76 **p** 77. C Harlescott *Lich* 76-81; V Ruyton 81-88; P-in-c Gt w Lt Ness 84-88; V Ruyton XI Towns w Gt and Lt Ness 88-99. *Cysegr, Holyhead Road, Froncysyllte, Llangollen LL20 7PU*

BRADBURY, Roy Albert. b 30. Chich Th Coll 72. **d** 74 **p** 75. C Earlsdon *Cov* 74-76; C Coventry Caludon 76-78; P-in-c Calow *Derby* 78-82; V Pensnett *Lich* 82-90; V Pattingham w Patshull 90-94; V Ocker Hill 94-95; rtd 95; Perm to Offic *Derby* from 95. *2 Stretton Close, Mickleover, Derby DE3 9NW* Tel (01332) 513380

BRADDICK-SOUTHGATE, Charles Anthony Michael. b 70. K Coll Lon BD92. Chich Th Coll 92. **d** 94 **p** 95. C Catford St Laur *S'wark* 94-97; V Nunhead St Antony w St Silas from 97. *St Antony with St Silas Vicarage, Athenlay Road, London SE15 3EP* Tel (020) 7639 4261 Fax 7252 8152 E-mail cambs@aol.com

BRADDOCK, Andrew Jonathan. b 71. SS Coll Cam BA92 Cam Univ MA96. Ridley Hall Cam 95. **d** 98 **p** 99. C Ranworth w Panxworth, Woodbastwick etc *Nor* 98-01; R Cringleford and Colney from 01. *The Vicarage, Newmarket Road, Cringleford, Norwich NR4 6UE* Tel (01603) 458467

BRADDOCK, Arthur Derek. b 25. Bolton Inst of Educn BA90. Lich Th Coll 56. **d** 59 **p** 60. C Droylsden St Mary *Man* 59-61; C New Bury 61-65; V Kearsley Moor 65-79; C Ellesmere Port *Ches* 79-85; rtd 85; Perm to Offic *Man* from 85. *1 Corrie Drive, Kearsley, Bolton BL4 8RG* Tel 0161-794 8953

BRADFORD, Daphne Marcelle. b 28. LNSM course 95. **d** 97 **p** 98. OLM Martham and Repps with Bastwick, Thurne etc *Nor* 97-01; rtd 01; Perm to Offic *Nor* from 01. *13 Pine Close, Martham, Norwich NR29 4SG* Tel (01493) 740579

BRADFORD, John. b 34. FRSA FRGS Lon Univ BA60 Birm Univ MEd81 Ox Univ AdCertEd70. Oak Hill Th Coll 55. **d** 60 **p** 61. C Walcot *B & W* 60-64; Ass Master Wendover C of E Primary Sch 64-65; Hd RE Dr Challoner's High Sch Lt Chalfont 65-69; Perm to Offic *Ox* 66-70; Lect St Pet Coll of Educn Saltley 70-77; Perm to Offic *Birm* 70-71; Lic to Offic from 71; Perm to Offic *Cov* from 77; Nat Chapl-Missr CECS 77-99; Gen Perm to

Offic Ch in Wales from 89; rtd 99. *27 Marsh Lane, Solihull B91 2PG* Tel 0121-704 9895 E-mail revjohnbradford@aol.com

BRADFORD, Peter. b 38. Sarum Th Coll 69. **d** 70 **p** 71. C Holdenhurst *Win* 70-73; C Stanmore 73-77; P-in-c Eling, Testwood and Marchwood 77-78; R Marchwood 78-86; C Christchurch 86-90; C Andover w Foxcott 90-92; V E and W Worldham, Hartley Mauditt w Kingsley etc from 92. *The Vicarage, East Worldham, Alton GU34 3AS* Tel (01420) 82392

BRADFORD, Archdeacon of. See WILKINSON, The Ven Guy Alexander

BRADFORD, Bishop of. See JAMES, The Rt Revd David Charles

BRADFORD, Dean of. See HANCOCK, The Very Revd Christopher David

BRADING, Jeremy Clive. b 74. Birm Univ BA95 MPhil98. Westcott Ho Cam 00. **d** 02 **p** 03. C Man Clayton St Cross w St Paul *Man* from 02. *14 Heather Street, Manchester M11 4FW* Tel and fax 0161-230 6848 Mobile 07786-567140 E-mail jeremycbrading@yahoo.co.uk

BRADLEY, Andrew Robert. b 65. Clare Coll Cam BA88. St Jo Coll Nottm Dip Th Studies 93 MA94. **d** 94 **p** 95. C Burnage St Marg *Man* 94-98; TV Didsbury St Jas and Em from 98. *The Vicarage, 453 Parrs Wood Road, Didsbury, Manchester M20 5NE* Tel 0161-445 1310

BRADLEY, Anthony David. b 56. Wye Coll Lon BSc76. St Jo Coll Nottm DPS88. **d** 88 **p** 89. C Southchurch Ch Ch *Chelmsf* 88-91; C Cov H Trin *Cov* 91-97; Dioc Lay Tr Adv from 93; P-in-c Budbrooke from 97. *The Vicarage, Budbrooke, Warwick CV35 8QL* Tel (01926) 494002 E-mail tony.bradley@dial.pipex.com

BRADLEY, Anthony Edward. b 39. Perth Bible Coll 93. **d** 89 **p** 96. Australia 89-99; Dn-in-c Ravensthorpe 95-96; P-in-c 96-99; C Wotton St Mary *Glouc* from 00. *30 Simon Road, Longlevens, Gloucester GL2 0TP* Tel (01452) 523803 Fax as telephone E-mail anthonybradley@onetel.net.uk

BRADLEY, Brian Hugh Granville. b 32. Univ Coll Ox 51. Lon Coll of Div 59. **d** 62 **p** 63. C E Twickenham St Steph *Lon* 62-65; C Herne Bay Ch Ch *Cant* 65-69; Miss to Seamen Teesside 69-71; Ceylon 71-72; Sri Lanka 72-74; Chapl Amsterdam w Haarlem and Den Helder *Eur* 75-79; chapl Lyon w Grenoble and Aix-les-Bains 79-85; TV Bucknall and Bagnall *Lich* 87-93; Assoc Chapl Dubai and Sharjah w N Emirates 93-97; rtd 97; Perm to Offic *Win* from 97. *7 Clos d'Elise, Rue de la Cache, St Andrew, Guernsey GY6 8TQ* Tel (01481) 256348

BRADLEY, Cecil Robert Jones. b 23. TCD BA47 MA50. CITC 48. **d** 48 **p** 49. C Clooney *D & R* 48-50; C Derry Cathl 50-67; Dean's V St Patr Cathl Dublin 67-96; Preb Maynooth St Patr Cathl Dublin 81-96; rtd 96. *Gascoigne House, Cowper Road, Rathmines, Dublin 6, Irish Republic*

BRADLEY, Clifford David. b 36. Lon Univ BA60. St Aid Birkenhead 60. **d** 62 **p** 63. C Stoneycroft All SS *Liv* 62-65; C Chipping Sodbury and Old Sodbury *Glouc* 65-68; Br Honduras 68-70; C Leckhampton SS Phil and Jas *Glouc* 70-71; V Badgeworth w Shurdington 71-79; Dioc Missr *S & M* 79-84; V Santan 79-84; V Braddan 79-84; Bp's Dom Chapl 81-84; V Stroud and Uplands w Slad *Glouc* 84-89; C Shepshed *Leic* 90-92; R Leire w Ashby Parva and Dunton Bassett 92-99; rtd 99; P-in-c Renhold *St Alb* from 99. *The Vicarage, 46 Church End, Renhold, Bedford MK41 0LU* Tel (01234) 771317

BRADLEY, Colin John. b 46. Edin Univ MA69 Hertf Coll Ox 71. Sarum & Wells Th Coll 72. **d** 75 **p** 76. C Easthampstead *Ox* 75-79; V Shawbury *Lich* 79-90; R Moreton Corbet 80-90; P-in-c Stanton on Hine Heath 81-90; Can Res Portsm Cathl *Portsm* 90-98; Dir of Ords 90-98; C Chich 98-00; C Chich St Paul and Westhampnett 00-01; P-in-c Cocking, Bepton and W Lavington from 01. *The Rectory, Mill Lane, Cocking, Midhurst GU29 0HJ* Tel (01730) 817340

BRADLEY, Connla John Osman. b 08. Bible Churchmen's Coll Bris. **d** 47 **p** 47. C Tunbridge Wells H Trin *Roch* 47-49; V Camberwell Ch Ch *S'wark* 49-55; V Frogmore *St Alb* 55-68; V Havering-atte-Bower *Chelmsf* 68-76; rtd 76; Perm to Offic *Chich* 76-88. *Lyndon Eventide Home, 2 High Street, Sandridge, St Albans AL4 9DH* Tel (01727) 851050

BRADLEY, Canon Donald John Walter. b 19. Em Coll Cam BA40 MA44. Westcott Ho Cam 40. **d** 42 **p** 43. C Purley St Mark *S'wark* 42-44; Succ S'wark Cathl 44-48; Chapl and Tutor Saltley Tr Coll Birm 48-49; Public Preacher *Birm* 48-49; Chapl Cuddesdon Coll 49-53; Vice Prin 51-53; Chapl Ch Ch Ox 51-53; V Battersea St Luke *S'wark* 53-63; Hon Bp's Chapl 59-63; Dir of Educn *Birm* 63-71; Lic to Offic 63-70; Hon Can Birm Cathl 70-84; V Edgbaston St Geo 71-84; RD Edgbaston 77-84; Hon Bp's Chapl 78-84; Warden of Readers 78-84; Hon Can Offic *Sarum* from 84. *32 St Mark's Road, Salisbury SP1 3AZ* Tel (01722) 334653

BRADLEY (née DRAPER), Mrs Elizabeth Ann. b 38. Nottm Univ BTh75 Birm Univ DipTh77. Linc Th Coll 71. **dss** 84 **d** 87 **p** 94. Ind Chapl *Linc* 84-91; Bracebridge 84-91; Hon C 87-91; GFS Ind Chapl *Lon* 91-96; Hon Chapl GFS 96-98; Riverside Chapl *S'wark* 96; Perm to Offic *St Alb* 97-98 and 01-02; C Leighton Buzzard w Eggington, Hockliffe etc 98-01; Chapl

Luton and Dunstable Hosp NHS Trust from 02. *The Chaplain's Office, Luton and Dunstable Hospital, Lewsey Road, Luton LU4 0DZ* Tel (01582) 497370 Fax as telephone
E-mail elizabeth.bradley@ldh-tr.anglox.nhs.uk

BRADLEY, Gary Scott. b 53. Lon Univ LLB75. Ripon Coll Cuddesdon 75. **d** 78 **p** 79. C St John's Wood *Lon* 78-83; V Paddington St Sav from 83; P-in-c Paddington St Mary from 95; P-in-c Paddington St Mary Magd from 98. *6 Park Place Villas, London W2 1SP* Tel (020) 7723 1968 Mobile 07957-140371 Fax (020) 7724 5332 E-mail bottlerot@aol.com

BRADLEY, John Owen. b 30. Jes Coll Ox BA55 MA56. St Mich Coll Llan 52. **d** 56 **p** 57. C Cardiff St Mary *Llan* 56-59; Lect St Mich Coll Llan 59-61; C Caerau w Ely *Llan* 60; C Newton Nottage 61-64; V Aberavon H Trin 65-69; Lic to Offic *Cov* 70-76; C W Kirby St Bridget *Ches* 76-79; TV Knowle *Bris* 79-80; TR 80-91; RD Brislington 83-89; Chapl St Monica Home Westbury-on-Trym 91-00; Perm to Offic *Bris* from 00. *20 Home Ground, Bristol BS9 4UB* Tel and fax 0117-907 1503
E-mail johnbra@aol.com

BRADLEY, Joy Elizabeth. *See* COUSANS, Mrs Joy Elizabeth

BRADLEY, Mrs Julie Caroline. b 59. Ex Univ BSc80. WEMTC 00. **d** 03. NSM Stoke Gifford *Bris* from 03. *113 North Road, Stoke Gifford, Bristol BS34 8PF* Tel 0117-979 3418
E-mail cjcbradley@deltats.co.uk

BRADLEY, Michael Frederick John. b 44. Qu Coll Birm 76. **d** 77 **p** 78. C Sheff St Cuth *Sheff* 77-78; C Alford w Rigsby *Linc* 78-83; V Bracebridge 83-90; V Flitwick *St Alb* from 90. *The Vicarage, 26 Dew Pond Road, Flitwick, Bedford MK45 1RT* Tel (01525) 712369 Fax (0870) 125 9827
E-mail michael.bradley@lineone.net

BRADLEY, The Ven Peter David Douglas. b 49. Nottm Univ BTh79. Ian Ramsey Coll 74 Linc Th Coll 75. **d** 79 **p** 80. C Upholland *Liv* 79-83; TR 94-01; V Dovecot 83-94; Dir CME 89-02; Hon Can Liv Cathl from 00; Adn Warrington from 01; TR Upholland from 01. *The Rectory, 1A College Road, Upholland, Skelmersdale WN8 0PY* Tel (01695) 622936 Fax 625865 E-mail archdeacon@peterbradley.fsnet.co.uk

BRADLEY, Peter Edward. b 64. Trin Hall Cam BA86 MA90. Ripon Coll Cuddesdon 86. **d** 88 **p** 89. C Northampton St Mich w St Edm *Pet* 88-91; Chapl G&C Coll Cam 91-95; TV Abingdon *Ox* 95-98; TV High Wycombe from 98. *All Saints' Vicarage, 6 Priory Avenue, High Wycombe HP13 6SH* Tel (01494) 525602 Fax (0870) 705 9930 E-mail peter@bradley.plus.com

BRADLEY, Ronald Percival. b 25. ACP51 FRSA52 TCert49. Ex & Truro NSM Scheme 80. **d** 83 **p** 84. C Honiton, Gittisham, Combe Raleigh, Monkton etc *Ex* 83-86; P-in-c Halberton 86-87; rtd 90. *Haddon House, 20 Moorland Road, Plympton, Plymouth PL7 2BH* Tel (01752) 337667

BRADNUM, Canon Ella Margaret. b 41. CertEd64 St Hugh's Coll Ox MA65. **dss** 69 **d** 87 **p** 94. Illingworth *Wakef* 69-72; Batley All SS 72-73; Lay TV Officer 77-82; Min Tr Officer 82-88; Sec Dioc Bd of Min from 88; Warden of Readers 88-02; Co-ord Lay Tr 88-02; Hon Can Wakef Cathl from 94; Prin Wakef Min Scheme from 97. *13 Boothtown Road, Halifax HX3 6EU* Tel (01422) 321740

BRADNUM, Richard James. b 39. Pemb Coll Ox BA62 MA67. Ridley Hall Cam 62. **d** 64 **p** 65. C Birm St Martin *Birm* 64-68; C Sutton St Jas *York* 68-69; Perm to Offic *Wakef* 71-72; C Batley All SS 72-74; V Gawthorpe and Chickenley Heath 74-86; V Mixenden 86-97; rtd 97; Perm to Offic *Wakef* 97-99; Hon Retirement Officer from 99. *13 Boothtown Road, Halifax HX3 6EU* Tel (01422) 321740

BRADSHAW, Charles Anthony. b 44. Birm Univ MA76. Qu Coll Birm DipTh74. **d** 75 **p** 76. C Whickham *Dur* 75-78; C Bilton *Cov* 78-81; TV Coventry Caludon 81-89; V Birstall and Wanlip *Leic* 89-99; TR Vale of Belvoir Par from 00. *The Rectory, 4 Rutland Lane, Bottesford, Nottingham NG13 0DG* Tel (01949) 842335 Fax 842533 E-mail cbradshaw@leicester.anglican.org

BRADSHAW, Denis Matthew. b 52. Chich Th Coll 77. **d** 80 **p** 81. C Ruislip St Martin *Lon* 80-84; C Northolt Park St Barn 84-86; V Northolt W End St Jos 86-01; P-in-c Hayes St Nic CD 94-00; V Kennington St Jo w St Jas *S'wark* from 01. *The Vicarage, 92 Vassall Road, London SW9 6JA* Tel (020) 7735 9340 Fax 7735 4548 E-mail dmb6161@compuserve.com

BRADSHAW, Graham. b 58. Edin Univ BD86. Edin Th Coll 83. **d** 86 **p** 87. C Thornton-le-Fylde *Blackb* 86-89; C Kirkby Lonsdale *Carl* 89-91; V Langford *St Alb* 91-97; Papua New Guinea 97-99; R Aspley Guise w Husborne Crawley and Ridgmont *St Alb* from 00. *The Rectory, Church Street, Aspley Guise, Milton Keynes MK17 8HN* Tel (01908) 583169

BRADSHAW, Miss Jennie McNeille. b 47. UEA BA69. Cranmer Hall Dur 85. **d** 90 **p** 94. Par Dn Herne *Cant* 90-94; C 94-95; P-in-c Claybrooke cum Wibtoft and Frolesworth *Leic* 95-96; R from 96. *The Vicarage, Main Road, Claybrook Parva, Lutterworth LE17 5AE* Tel (01455) 202262

BRADSHAW, (née DAY), Mrs Jennifer Ann. b 67. Aber Univ BSc89. Wycliffe Hall Ox BTh95. **d** 95 **p** 96. C Whitburn *Dur* 95-98; C Monkwearmouth 98-99; TV 99-01. *St Matthew's*

Vicarage, Silksworth Road, Sunderland SR3 2AA Tel 0191-521 1167

BRADSHAW, Jolyon Anthony. b 51. St Jo Coll Dur BA73. Trin Coll Bris 73. **d** 76 **p** 77. C Normanton *Wakef* 76-82; TV Wreningham *Nor* 82-89; P-in-c Bermondsey St Mary w St Olave, St Jo etc *S'wark* 89-96; R 96-01; V Tyseley *Birm* from 01. *St Edmund's Vicarage, 277 Reddings Lane, Tyseley, Birmingham B11 3DD* Tel 0121-777 2433 Mobile 07966-276841
E-mail jolyonbradshaw@hotmail.com

BRADSHAW, Kenneth Allan. b 23. Roch Th Coll 60. **d** 62 **p** 63. C Cheam Common St Phil *S'wark* 62-65; C Portslade St Nic *Chich* 65-67; C Preston 67-71; C Haywards Heath St Wilfrid 71-82; C Sidley 82-88; rtd 88; Perm to Offic *Llan* from 88. *The Cottage, 115A Splott Road, Cardiff CF24 2BY* Tel (029) 2046 5998

BRADSHAW, Canon Malcolm McNeille. b 45. Lon Univ DipTh69. Kelham Th Coll 65. **d** 70 **p** 71. C New Addington *Cant* 70-76; Chapl Milan w Cadenabbia, Varese and Lugano *Eur* 77-82; V Boxley w Detling *Cant* 82-99; Sen Chapl Gtr Athens *Eur* from 99; Hon Can Malta Cathl from 01. *c/o The British Embassy, Plutarchou 1, 106-75 Athens, Greece* Tel (0030) (10) 721 4906 Fax as telephone

BRADSHAW, Canon Prof Paul Frederick. b 45. Clare Coll Cam BA66 MA70 K Coll Lon PhD71 FRHistS91 Ox Univ DD94. Westcott Ho Cam 67. **d** 69 **p** 70. C W Wickham St Jo *Cant* 69-71; C Cant St Martin and St Paul 71-73; Tutor Chich Th Coll 73-78; V Flamstead *St Alb* 78-82; Dir of Minl Tr Scheme 78-82; Vice-Prin Ripon Coll Cuddesdon 83-85; USA 85-95; Prof Th Notre Dame Univ from 85; Hon Can N Indiana from 90; PV Westmr Abbey from 95; Perm to Offic *Guildf* from 95. *Notre Dame London Centre, 1 Suffolk Street, London SW1Y 4HG* Tel (020) 7484 7811 Fax 7484 7853 E-mail bradshaw.1@nd.edu

BRADSHAW, Philip Hugh. b 39. Qu Coll Ox BA64 MA67 Lon Univ DipRS91. S'wark Ord Course 88. **d** 91 **p** 92. NSM Bletchingley *S'wark* 91-98; Ldr Community of Celebration 91-98; NSM Redhill St Jo from 98. *35 Cavendish Road, Redhill RH1 4AL* Tel (01737) 778760

BRADSHAW, Richard Gordon Edward. b 66. Southn Univ LLB90. Wycliffe Hall Ox BTh94. **d** 97 **p** 98. C Bishopwearmouth St Gabr *Dur* 97-00; C Silksworth 00-01; P-in-c from 01. *St Matthew's Vicarage, Silksworth Road, Sunderland SR3 2AA* Tel 0191-521 1167

BRADSHAW, Roy John. b 49. Sarum & Wells Th Coll 85. **d** 87 **p** 88. FSJ from 84; C Gainsborough All SS *Linc* 87-90; V New Waltham 90-94; R Killamarsh *Derby* from 94. *The Rectory, Sheepcote Road, Killamarsh, Sheffield S21 1DU* Tel 0114-248 2769

BRADSHAW, Timothy. b 50. Keble Coll Ox BA72 MA78 PhD. St Jo Coll Nottm BA75. **d** 76 **p** 77. C Clapton Park All So *Lon* 76-79; Lect Trin Coll Bris 80-91; Hon C Sea Mills *Bris* 83-91; Tutor Regent's Park Coll Ox from 91; NSM Ox St Aldate w St Matt *Ox* 91-94; NSM Ox St Matt from 95. *54 St Giles, Oxford OX1 3LU* Tel (01865) 288147
E-mail timothy.bradshaw@regents.ox.ac.uk

BRADSHAW, Veronica. *See* CAROLAN, Mrs Veronica

BRADWELL, Area Bishop of. *See* GREEN, The Rt Revd Laurence Alexander

BRADY, Frederick Herbert James. b 33. Sydney Univ BSc55 DipEd56 Lon Univ BD65. Moore Th Coll Sydney ThL59. **d** 60 **p** 60. Australia 60-63 and from 69; Lic to Offic *Lon* 63-69; rtd 00. *18 Capel Street, West Melbourne, Vic, Australia 3003* Tel (0061) (3) 9328 8487 *or* (3) 9650 3791 Fax (3) 9650 4718
E-mail brady@ioville.net.au

BRADY, Ian. b 59. Ridley Hall Cam. **d** 01 **p** 02. C Cromer *Nor* from 01. *18 Vicarage Road, Cromer NR27 9DQ* Tel (01263) 514352 Mobile 07801-173480

BRADY, Mrs Madalaine Margaret. b 45. Univ of Wales (Ban) BD88 CertEd91 MA92. **d** 89 **p** 97. Asst Chapl Univ of Wales (Ban) Bangor 89-96; Dioc Communications Officer from 94; Dioc Lay Min Officer from 95; C Arllechwedd 96-97; P-in-c Llanfaelog 97-02; R Llanfaelog and Llangwyfan from 02. *The Rectory, Station Road, Rhosneigr LL64 5JX* Tel and fax (01407) 810412 *or* tel (01248) 354999 Fax (01248) 353882
E-mail dmbrady@lineone.net

BRAGG, Mrs Rosemary Eileen. b 41. Plymouth Coll of Tech MRPharmS64. St Steph Ho Ox 99. **d** 00 **p** 01. NSM Maidenhead St Andr and St Mary *Ox* from 00. *2 Aldwick Drive, Maidenhead SL6 4JQ* Tel (01628) 629577

BRAILSFORD, Matthew Charles. b 64. Newc Univ BSc86. Cranmer Hall Dur BA95. **d** 95 **p** 96. C Hull Newland St Jo *York* from 95. *892 Beverley High Road, Hull HU6 7DG* Tel (01482) 854526 E-mail matthew.brailsford@ukgateway.net

BRAIN, Mrs Marina. **d** 01 **p** 02. OLM Wokingham St Sebastian *Ox* from 01. *71 Kiln Ride, Wokingham RG40 3PJ* Tel 0118-973 3246

BRAIN, Michael Charles. b 39. ACP65 Culham Coll Ox 59 Ox Univ Inst of Educn TCert61. Lich Th Coll 68. **d** 70 **p** 71. C Stone St Mich *Lich* 70-73; C Harlescott 73-76; C Longton St Jas 76-77; P-in-c Dudley St Edm *Worc* 77-79; V from 79; Chapl Dudley Coll of Tech from 77. *St Edmund's Vicarage, 9 Ednam Road, Dudley DY1 1JX* Tel (01384) 252532

BRAITHWAITE, Albert Alfred. b 24. Clifton Th Coll. **d** 59 **p** 60. C Bestwood St Matt *S'well* 59-62; Chapl RN 62-81; QHC from 77; C Southsea St Jude *Portsm* 82-90; Perm to Offic from 90; rtd 90. *3 Lorne Road, Southsea PO5 1RR* Tel (023) 9273 8753

BRAITHWAITE, Canon Michael Royce. b 34. Linc Th Coll 71. **d** 73 **p** 74. C Barrow St Geo w St Luke *Carl* 73-77; V Kells 77-88; RD Calder 84-88; V Lorton and Loweswater w Buttermere 88-99; Ldr Rural Life and Agric Team 93-96; Member Rural Life and Agric Team 96-99; RD Derwent 94-98; Hon Can Carl Cathl 94-99; rtd 99; Perm to Offic *Carl* from 00. *High Green Farm, Bothel, Carlisle CA7 2JA* Tel (01697) 32349

BRAITHWAITE, Canon Roy. b 34. Dur Univ BA56. Ridley Hall Cam 58. **d** 60 **p** 61. C Blackb St Gabr *Blackb* 60-63; C Burnley St Pet 63-66; V Accrington St Andr 66-74; V Blackb St Jas 74-95; RD Blackb 86-91; Hon Can Blackb Cathl 93-98; V Garstang St Helen Churchtown 95-98; Dioc Ecum Officer 95-98; rtd 98; Perm to Offic *Blackb* from 98. *9 Barker Lane, Mellor, Blackburn BB2 7ED* Tel (01254) 240724

BRAITHWAITE, Wilfrid. b 14. St Chad's Coll Dur BA41 MA44. **d** 42 **p** 43. C Harrington *Carl* 42-45; C Kendal H Trin 45-46; R Soulby w Crosby Garrett 46-51; V Ireleth w Askam 51-62; V Lanercost w Kirkcambeck 62-79; P-in-c Walton 78-79; rtd 79; Perm to Offic *Carl* 82-99. *Brougham Lodge, Eamont Bridge, Penrith CA10 2BZ* Tel (01768) 862939

BRALESFORD, Nicholas Robert. b 53. St Jo Coll Nottm LTh79 BTh79. **d** 79 **p** 80. C Leic St Chris *Leic* 79-82; C Heeley *Sheff* 82-85; TV Kings Norton *Birm* 85-90; V Chapel-en-le-Frith *Derby* from 90. *The Vicarage, 71 Manchester Road, Chapel-en-le-Frith, High Peak SK23 9TH* Tel (01298) 812134

BRALEY, Robert James. See RILEY-BRALEY, Robert James

BRAMELD, Peter John. b 40. AKC62. **d** 63 **p** 64. C Hucknall Torkard *S'well* 63-66; C Ordsall 66-70; C Carlton 70-74; C Colwick 70-74; P-in-c Overton w Fyfield and E Kennett *Sarum* 74-75; TV Upper Kennet 75-80; R Hickling w Kinoulton and Broughton Sulney *S'well* 80-94; RD S Bingham 86-91; rtd 00. *St Mary's House, 108 Westgate, Southwell NG25 0LT* Tel (01636) 816226

BRAMHALL, Eric. b 39. St Cath Coll Cam BA61 MA65. Tyndale Hall Bris 61. **d** 63 **p** 64. C Eccleston St Luke *Liv* 63-66; C Bolton Em *Man* 66-69; Perm to Offic *Ches* 70-74; Chapl Ormskirk Children's Hosp 75-92; V Aughton Ch Ch *Liv* 75-92; V Childwall All SS from 92. *All Saints' Vicarage, Childwall Abbey Road, Liverpool L16 0JW* Tel 0151-737 2169

BRAMLEY, Thomas Anthony. b 44. BSc PhD. TISEC. **d** 96 **p** 97. NSM Penicuik *Edin* from 96; NSM W Linton from 96. *44 Bavelaw Crescent, Penicuik EH26 9AT*

BRAMMER, David John. b 62. **d** 99 **p** 00. C Acton St Mary *Lon* 99-02; C Ealing All SS from 02; Chapl Twyford C of E High Sch Acton from 02. *All Saints' Vicarage, Elm Grove Road, London W5 3JH* Tel (020) 8567 8166
E-mail david.brammer@london.anglican.org

BRAMPTON, Ms Fiona Elizabeth Gordon. b 56. St Jo Coll Dur BA78. Cranmer Hall Dur BA83. **dss** 84 **d** 87 **p** 94. Bris St Andr Hartcliffe *Bris* 84-87; Par Dn 87-90; C Orton Waterville *Ely* 90-96; C-in-c Orton Goldhay CD 90-96; TV The Ortons, Alwalton and Chesterton 96-00; V Haddenham from 00; V Wilburton from 00. *The Vicarage, Church Lane, Haddenham, Ely CB6 3TB* Tel (01353) 740309
E-mail fiona.brampton@ely.anglican.org

BRANCHE, Brian Maurice. b 37. Chich Th Coll 73. **d** 75 **p** 76. C Brighton Resurr *Chich* 75-78; C Upper Norwood St Jo *Cant* 78-81; P-in-c Croydon St Martin 81-84; V Croydon St Martin *S'wark* 85-88; V St Helier 88-93; V New Eltham All SS 93-97; V Barkingside H Trin *Chelmsf* 97-02; rtd 02. *113 Tong Road, Little Lever, Bolton BL3 1PU* Tel (01204) 410227
E-mail bbranche@aol.com

BRAND, Frank Ronald Walter. b 25. Lon Coll of Div ALCD56 LTh74. **d** 56 **p** 57. C Brondesbury St Anne w Kilburn H Trin *Lon* 56-58; Br Guiana 58-66; Guyana 66-67; V N Greenford All Hallows *Lon* 67-91; rtd 91; Perm to Offic *B & W* from 91. *23 Hawthorn Grove, Combe Down, Bath BA2 5QA* Tel (01225) 834572

BRAND, Peter John. b 32. Lon Univ BSc54. Edin Dioc NSM Course 75. **d** 83 **p** 84. NSM Edin St Jo *Edin* from 83. *24 Drum Brae Park, Edinburgh EH12 8TF* Tel 0131-339 4406

BRAND, Richard Harold Guthrie. b 65. Dur Univ BA87. Ripon Coll Cuddesdon 87. **d** 89 **p** 90. C N Lynn w St Marg and St Nic *Nor* 89-92; C King's Lynn St Marg w St Nic 92-93; C Croydon St Jo *S'wark* 93-96; New Zealand 96-98; P-in-c Hambledon *Portsm* from 98; Dir of Ords from 98. *The Vicarage, Church Lane, Hambledon, Waterlooville PO7 4RT* Tel (023) 9263 2717
Fax as telephone E-mail richard.brand@virgin.net

BRAND, Stuart William. b 30. Leeds Univ BSc53. Coll of Resurr Mirfield 53. **d** 55 **p** 56. C Stepney St Dunstan and All SS *Lon* 55-59; C Acton Green St Pet 59-60; C-in-c Godshill CD *Portsm* 60-63; Malawi 63-67; V Widley w Wymering *Portsm* 67-72; Chapl Fieldhead Hosp Wakef 72-80; Chapl Pinderfields &

Stanley Royd Hosps Wakef 72-80; Chapl Brook Gen Hosp Lon 80-95; Chapl Greenwich Distr Hosp Lon 80-95; rtd 95; Perm to Offic *Ox* from 96. *17 Hayfield Road, Oxford OX2 6TX* Tel (01865) 316456

BRANDES, Simon Frank. b 62. Univ of Wales (Ban) BA83. Edin Th Coll 83. **d** 85 **p** 86. C Barton w Peel Green *Man* 85-88; C Longsight St Jo w St Cypr 88-90; R 90-94; Asst Dioc Youth Officer 88-94; V Lt Lever 94-02; P-in-c Lydgate w Friezland 02-03; TR Saddleworth from 03. *The Vicarage, Stockport Road, Lydgate, Oldham OL4 4JJ* Tel (01457) 872117 Mobile 07775-526285

BRANDIE, Canon Beaumont Lauder. b 40. K Coll Lon AKC64 BD66 SSC. **d** 65 **p** 66. C Whitton St Aug *Lon* 65-71; C Portsea St Mary *Portsm* 71-77; TR Brighton Resurr *Chich* from 77; Can and Preb Chich Cathl from 87; RD Brighton 97. *St Martin's Rectory, Upper Wellington Road, Brighton BN2 3AN* Tel (01273) 604687 Fax 621090
E-mail team.rector@resurrection-brighton.org.uk

BRANDON, Miss Vera Eileen. b 12. Univ of Wales (Abth) CertEd35 BSc40 Lon Univ DipEd42 BD53. St Mich Ho Ox 51. **dss** 60 **d** 87 **p** 98. Lect and Tutor St Mich Ho Ox 51-61; Rushden St Pet 61-63; Tutor Wilson Carlile Coll of Evang 64-74; Community of the Word of God from 75; Lower Homerton St Paul *Lon* 75-80; Clapton Park All So 75-80; Hanger Lane St Ann 80-83; rtd 83; Tunbridge Wells St Pet *Roch* 83-87; Hon Par Dn 87-89; Perm to Offic 89-98; Chapl Florence Balls Ho & Halliwell Nursing Home 98-00. *Mount Ephraim House, Mount Ephraim Road, Tunbridge Wells TN1 1ET*

BRANNAGAN, Alan McKenzie. b 34. Chich Th Coll 66. **d** 68 **p** 69. C N Hull St Mich *York* 68-70; C Dunstable *St Alb* 70-75; R E w W Rudham *Nor* 75-81; V Houghton 75-81; TV Wolverhampton *Lich* 81-87; R W Felton 87-96; Chapl Ypres *Eur* 96-97; Perm to Offic *St Alb* from 97; rtd 99. *8 Park Lane, Blunham, Bedford MK44 3NH* Tel (01767) 640868

BRANSCOMBE, Michael Peter. b 65. Cranmer Hall Dur BA95. **d** 95 **p** 96. C Ogley Hay *Lich* 95-01; Dioc Voc Officer 99-01; Asst R Palm Harbor USA from 01. *2807 Paddock Drive, Palm Harbor, FL 34684-3242, USA* Tel (001) (727) 771 1844 *or* 785 1601
E-mail frmike@stalfred.org

BRANSON, Robert David. b 46. Linc Th Coll 74. **d** 77 **p** 78. C Kempston Transfiguration *St Alb* 77-80; C Goldington 80-82; V Marsh Farm 82-91; V Aylsham *Nor* from 91; RD Ingworth from 00; Chapl Norwich Primary Care Trust from 99. *The Vicarage, 64 Holman Road, Aylsham, Norwich NR11 6BZ* Tel (01263) 733871

BRANT, Anthony Richard. b 44. S Dios Minl Tr Scheme. **d** 82 **p** 83. NSM Felpham w Middleton *Chich* 82-84; C Clymping 84-85; NSM 85-87; Perm to Offic from 88. *Fairholme, Barnham Road, Eastergate, Chichester PO20 3RS* Tel (01243) 544735

BRANT, Anthony William. b 31. Linc Th Coll 73. **d** 75 **p** 76. C Cove St Jo *Guildf* 75-79; P-in-c Puttenham and Wanborough 79-83; V Lightwater 83-93; rtd 93; Perm to Offic *Chich* from 93. *2 Southcourt Avenue, Bexhill-on-Sea TN39 3AR* Tel (01424) 217526

BRANT, Ms Karlyn Lee. b 72. Birm Univ BA99 MA01. Ripon Coll Cuddesdon 01. **d** 03. C Gaywood *Nor* from 03. *The Church Bungalow, Gayton Road, Kings Lynn PE30 4DZ* Tel (01553) 765167 E-mail lee@ciborium.fsnet.co.uk

BRANT, Leslie Harold. b 11. **d** 71 **p** 72. C Lower Sandown St Jo *Portsm* 71-74; P-in-c Newchurch 75-80; rtd 80; Perm to Offic *Portsm* from 82. *1 Dean's Court, Solent View, Ryde PO33 2AQ*

BRANWELL, Edward Bruce. b 20. St Cath Coll Cam BA42 MA46. Linc Th Coll 42. **d** 44 **p** 45. C S Hampstead St Sav *Lon* 44-46; Trinidad and Tobago 46-49; C Rugby St Andr *Cov* 49-51; V Glossop *Derby* 51-56; Area Sec (SE England) UMCA 56-57; V Lavender Hill Ascension *S'wark* 58-64; Chapl Aldenham Sch Herts 64-70; Asst Master Burlington Sch *Lon* 70-77; Perm to Offic *St Alb* 81-84 and *Ches* from 84; rtd 85. *16 King's Crescent West, Chester CH3 5TQ* Tel (01244) 313641

BRASIER, Ralph Henry (Jim). b 30. Cant Sch of Min 82. **d** 85 **p** 86. C S Ashford Ch Ch *Cant* 85-89; V Pembury *Roch* 89-95; rtd 95; Perm to Offic *Portsm* and *Win* from 95. *72 Jenkyns Close, Botley, Southampton SO30 2UU* Tel (01489) 788332

BRASSELL, Canon Kenneth William. b 23. Kelham Th Coll 46. **d** 50 **p** 51. C Woodbridge St Mary *St E* 50-53; C-in-c Bury St Edmunds All SS CD 53-57; V Ipswich St Thos 57-63; V Beckenham St Jas *Roch* 63-88; P-in-c Beckenham St Aug 66-77; P-in-c Beckenham St Mich 77-78; P-in-c Beckenham St Mich w St Aug 77-78; Hon Can Roch Cathl 82-88; rtd 88; Perm to Offic *Glouc* from 88. *20 College Green, Gloucester GL1 2LR* Tel (01452) 309080

BRASSIL, Seán Adrian. b 56. Westf Coll Lon BSc79. STETS 97. **d** 00 **p** 01. NSM Westborough *Guildf* from 00. *15 Clinton Close, Knaphill, Woking GU21 2AL* Tel (01483) 838526 Mobile 07932-068249 E-mail sean.brassil@ntlworld.com

BRATLEY, David Frederick. b 42. Linc Th Coll 80. **d** 82 **p** 83. C Holbeach *Linc* 82-85; R Fleet w Gedney from 85; RD Elloe E from 01. *The Rectory, Church End, Fleet, Spalding PE12 8NQ* Tel (01406) 423795

BRATTON, Mark Quinn. b 62. Lon Univ BA84 City Univ DipLaw85 Barrister-at-Law (Middle Temple) 87 K Coll Lon MA98. Wycliffe Hall Ox BA94 DipMin94. **d** 94 **p** 95. C W Ealing St Jo w St Jas *Lon* 94-98; Chapl Warw Univ *Cov* from 98; AD Cov S from 02. *92 De Montfort Way, Coventry CV4 7DT* Tel (024) 7669 0216 *or* 7652 3519 E-mail cpsad@csv.warwick.ac.uk *or* mark.bratton@talk21.com

BRAUN, Thom. b 53. St Jo Coll Ox BA76 MA76 Univ Coll Lon PhD80. S'wark Ord Course 89. **d** 92 **p** 93. Hon C Surbiton St Andr and St Mark *S'wark* from 92. *8 Kings Drive, Surbiton KT5 8NG* Tel (020) 8399 6898

BRAVINER, William Edward. b 66. Leic Poly BSc88 St Jo Coll Dur BA94 Dip Minl Studies 95 ACA91. Cranmer Hall Dur 92. **d** 95 **p** 96. C Royton St Anne *Man* 95-99; R Lansallos and V Talland *Truro* 99-03; P-in-c Duloe, Herodsfoot, Morval and St Pinnock 01-03; TR Jarrow *Dur* from 03. *St Andrew's House, Borough Road, Jarrow NE32 5BL* Tel 0191-489 3279

BRAY, Christopher Laurence. b 53. Leeds Univ BSc74 Qu Univ Kingston Ontario MSc76. St Jo Coll Nottm DipTh79 DPS81. **d** 81 **p** 82. C Aughton Ch Ch *Liv* 81-84; Hon C Scarborough St Mary w Ch Ch and H Apostles *York* 84-88; Chapl Scarborough Coll 84-88; V St Helens St Matt Thatto Heath *Liv* 88-98; V Southport All SS and All So 98-02; rtd 02. *4 The Mallards, Southport PR9 8RJ* Tel (01704) 224648 E-mail chrislbray@aol.com

BRAY, Gerald Lewis. b 48. McGill Univ Montreal BA69 Sorbonne Univ Paris LittD73. Ridley Hall Cam 76. **d** 78 **p** 79. C Canning Town St Cedd *Chelmsf* 78-80; Tutor Oak Hill Th Coll 80-92; Ed *Churchman* from 83; Perm to Offic *Ely* from 92; Angl Prof Div Beeson Div Sch Samford Univ Alabama from 93. *16 Manor Court, Cambridge CB3 9BE* Tel (01223) 311804 *or* (001) (205) 726 2585 Fax (01223) 566608/(001) (205) 726 2234 E-mail glbray@samford.edu

BRAY, Jason Stephen. b 69. SS Hild & Bede Coll Dur BA90 MA91 Fitzw Coll Cam PhD96 DipTh96 MSOTS97. Westcott Ho Cam 95. **d** 97 **p** 98. C Abergavenny St Mary w Llanwenarth Citra *Mon* 97-99; Min Can St Woolos Cathl 99-02; V Blaenavon w Capel Newydd from 02. *The Vicarage, Llanover Road, Blaenavon, Pontypool NP4 9HR* Tel (01495) 790292

BRAY, Jeremy Grainger. b 40. Man Univ BA62. Wells Th Coll 62. **d** 64 **p** 65. C Bris St Andr w St Bart *Bris* 64-67; C Bris H Cross Inns Court 67-71; C-in-c Stockwood CD 71-73; V Bris Ch the Servant Stockwood 73-83; RD Brislington 79-83; P-in-c Chippenham St Pet 83-88; V 88-93; V Fishponds St Jo from 93. *St John's Vicarage, Mayfield Park, Bristol BS16 3NW* Tel 0117-965 4130 E-mail jg bray@blueyonder.co.uk

BRAY, Joyce. b 32. CA Tr Coll. **dss** 80 **d** 87 **p** 94. Bloxwich *Lich* 80-84; Derringham Bank *York* 84-03; Par Dn 87-94; Hon C 94-03; rtd 94; Perm to Offic *York* from 03. *413 Willerby Road, Hull HU5 5JD* Tel (01482) 502193

BRAY, Kenneth John. b 31. St Mich Coll Llan 65. **d** 67 **p** 72. C Killay *S & B* 67-68; C S Harrow St Paul *Lon* 71-73; C Hillingdon St Jo 73-76; C Chipping Sodbury and Old Sodbury *Glouc* 76-79; C Worle *B & W* 79-80; Lic to Offic *Ches* 80-83; TV Wrexham *St As* 83-85; V Llay 85-94; rtd 94. *21 Glenthorn Road, Bexhill-on-Sea TN39 3QH* Tel (01424) 213965

BRAY, Richard. b 29. Linc Th Coll 55. **d** 57 **p** 58. C Lt Ilford St Barn *Chelmsf* 57-62; R Tye Green w Netteswell 62-93; rtd 93; Perm to Offic *Chelmsf* from 93. *14 The Wayback, Saffron Walden CB10 2AX* Tel (01799) 526901

BRAY, Thomas Chadwick. b 08. Qu Coll Birm 46. **d** 48 **p** 49. C Gnosall w Knightley *Lich* 48-51; C Shifnal 51-55; R Ryton 55-69; P-in-c Badger 55-56; R 56-69; P-in-c Beckbury 55-56; R 56-69; RD Shifnal 65-69; V Bolam *Newc* 69-74; rtd 74. *33 Heron Way, Newport TF10 8QF* Tel (01952) 825872

BRAYBROOKE, Marcus Christopher Rossi. b 38. Magd Coll Cam BA62 MA65 Lon Univ MPhil68. Wells Th Coll 63. **d** 64 **p** 65. C Highgate St Mich *Lon* 64-67; C Frindsbury w Upnor *Roch* 67-72; TV Frindsbury w Upnor 72-73; P-in-c Swainswick w Langridge and Woolley *B & W* 73-76; R 76-79; Dir of Tr 79-84; Hon C Bath Ch Ch Prop Chpl 84-91; Exec Dir Coun of Chrs and Jews 84-87; rtd 88; Perm to Offic *Bris* 88-93; Preb Wells Cathl *B & W* 90-93; Chapl Bath St Mary Magd Holloway 92-93; Perm to Offic 93; Hon C Dorchester *Ox* from 93. *The Rectory, Marsh Baldon, Oxford OX44 9LS* Tel (01865) 343215 Fax 343575 E-mail marcusbray@aol.com

BRAZELL, Denis Illtyd Anthony. b 42. Trin Coll Cam BA64 MA68. Wycliffe Hall Ox 78. **d** 80 **p** 81. C Cheltenham Ch Ch *Glouc* 80-84; V Reading St Agnes w St Paul *Ox* 84-96; Perm to Offic *Guildf* 96-97; Warden and Chapl Acorn Chr Healing Trust 97-99; rtd 99; Ldr and Miss Movt for Life Trust from 99. *Word for Life Trust, The House of Bread, Ross Road, Christchurch, Coleford GL16 7NS* Tel (01594) 837744 E-mail wflt@wflt.org

BRAZELL, Mrs Elizabeth Jane. b 44. LRAM64 ARCM65 GGSM65 AGSM65. Wycliffe Hall Ox 85. **dss** 86 **d** 87 **p** 94. Reading St Agnes w St Paul *Ox* 86-96; Par Dn 87-94; C 94-96; Dir Word for Life Trust from 96. *Word for Life Trust, The House of Bread, Ross Road, Christchurch, Coleford GL16 7NS* Tel (01594) 837744 Fax 837742 E-mail elizabeth@wflt.org

BRAZIER, Eric James Arthur. b 37. Qu Coll Birm 84. **d** 86 **p** 87. C Lighthorne *Cov* 86-89; P-in-c 89-92; P-in-c Chesterton 89-92; P-in-c Newbold Pacey w Moreton Morrell 89-92; R Astbury and Smallwood *Ches* 92-99; rtd 99; Perm to Offic *Ches* from 99; *Lich* and *Heref* from 00. *Wolf's Head Cottage, Chirbury, Montgomery SY15 6BP* Tel (01938) 561450

BRAZIER, Canon Raymond Venner. b 40. Wells Th Coll 68. **d** 71 **p** 72. C Horfield St Greg *Bris* 71-75; P-in-c Bris St Nath w St Kath 75-79; V 79-84; P-in-c Kingsdown 80-84; V Bris St Matt and St Nath from 84; RD Horfield 85-91; P-in-c Bishopston 93-97; Hon Can Bris Cathl from 94; Chapl to The Queen from 98. *The Vicarage, 11 Glentworth Road, Bristol BS6 7EG* Tel 0117-942 4186 *or* 944 1598

BREADEN, The Very Revd Robert William. b 37. Edin Th Coll 58. **d** 61 **p** 62. C Broughty Ferry *Bre* 61-65; R from 72; R Carnoustie 65-72; Can St Paul's Cathl Dundee from 77; Dean Bre from 84. *46 Seafield Road, Broughty Ferry, Dundee DD5 3AN* Tel (01382) 477477 Fax 477434 E-mail ateallach@aol.com

BREADMORE, Martin Christopher. b 67. Lon Univ LLB89. Wycliffe Hall Ox BTh93. **d** 93 **p** 94. C Herne Bay Ch Ch *Cant* 93-97; C Camberley St Paul *Guildf* 97-01; Chapl Elmhurst Ballet Sch 97-98; C Wallington H Trin *S'wark* from 01. *47 Park Hill Road, Wallington SM6 0RU*

BREADON, John Desmond. b 73. St Andr Univ BD96. Westcott Ho Cam 99. **d** 01. C W Bromwich All SS *Lich* from 01. *50 Wilford Road, West Bromwich B71 1QN* Tel 0121-588 3440 E-mail brazil@waitrose.com

BREAR, Alvin Douglas. b 33. **d** 87 **p** 96. NSM Leic H Spirit *Leic* 87-88; NSM Leic Ch Sav 88-96; NSM Leic Presentation 96-98; Finland from 98. *Sahurintie 44, 28800 Pori, Finland* Tel (00358) (2) 648 2060 E-mail douglas.brear@tukkk.fi

BREARLEY, Mrs Janet Mary. b 48. Cranmer Hall Dur 88. **d** 90 **p** 94. C Prudhoe *Newc* 90-91; C Fenham St Jas and St Basil 91-95; V Warkworth and Acklington from 95. *The Vicarage, 11 Dial Place, Warkworth, Morpeth NE65 0UR* Tel (01665) 711217 Fax as telephone E-mail jmbrearley@stlawrence-church.org.uk

BREBNER, Martin James. b 47. ARCS68 Imp Coll Lon BSc68. St Alb Minl Tr Scheme 87. **d** 90 **p** 91. Hon C Letchworth St Paul w Willian *St Alb* 90-94; Hon C St Ippolyts 95-01; Perm to Offic from 01. *Willowcroft, Greatford, Stamford PE9 4QA* Tel (01778) 561145 Fax 561157 E-mail martin.brebner@net.ntl.com

BRECHIN, Bishop of. *See* CHAMBERLAIN, The Rt Revd Neville

BRECHIN, Dean of. *See* BREADEN, The Very Revd Robert William

BRECKLES, Robert Wynford. b 48. St Edm Hall Ox BA72 MA74 CertEd. St Jo Coll Dur DipTh79. **d** 79 **p** 80. C Bulwell St Mary *S'well* 79-84; P-in-c Lady Bay 84; V from 84. *The Vicarage, 121 Holme Road, Nottingham NG2 5AG* Tel 0115-981 3565

BRECKNELL, David Jackson. b 32. Keble Coll Ox BA57. St Steph Ho Ox 56. **d** 58 **p** 59. C Streatham St Pet *S'wark* 58-62; C Sneinton St Steph w St Alb *S'well* 62-64; C Solihull *Birm* 64-68; V Streatham St Paul *S'wark* 68-75; R Rumboldswhyke *Chich* 75-81; P-in-c Portfield 79-81; R Whyke w Rumboldswhyke and Portfield 81-95; rtd 95; Perm to Offic *Chich* from 95; P-in-c Boxgrove 98-99. *8 Priory Close, Boxgrove, Chichester PO18 0EA* Tel (01243) 784841 E-mail david.brecknell@talk21.com

BRECKWOLDT, Peter Hans. b 57. Man Poly BA79. Oak Hill Th Coll BA88. **d** 88 **p** 89. C Knutsford St Jo and Toft *Ches* 88-92; V Moulton *Pet* from 92. *The Vicarage, 30 Cross Street, Moulton, Northampton NN3 1RZ* Tel (01604) 491060 E-mail peterbreckwoldt@cs.com

BRECON, Archdeacon of. *See* THOMAS, The Ven Alfred James Randolph

BRECON, Dean of. *See* DAVIES, The Very Revd John David Edward

BREED, Kenneth Wilfred. b 11. Leeds Univ BA33. Coll of Resurr Mirfield 33. **d** 35 **p** 36. C Cov H Trin *Cov* 35-37; C Parkstone St Pet w Branksea *Sarum* 37-43; Chapl RNVR 43-46; C Eastleigh *Win* 46-49; C Cheam *S'wark* 49-51; V Shirley *Birm* 51-77; rtd 77; Hon C St Andr Holborn *Lon* 77-79; Perm to Offic *Sarum* from 80 and *B & W* 86-94. *4 Yard Court, East Street, Warminster BA12 9NY* Tel (01985) 213230

BREEDS, Christopher Roger. b 51. LGSM83 ACertCM87 Lon Univ CertEd73. Chich Th Coll 84. **d** 87 **p** 88. C E Grinstead St Swithun *Chich* 87-90; TV Aldrington 90-92; P-in-c Hove St Andr Old Ch 92-93; TV Hove 93-99; V Wivelsfield from 99. *New Vicarage, Church Lane, Wivelsfield, Haywards Heath RH17 7RD* Tel (01444) 471783 E-mail christopher.breeds@virgin.net

BREEN, Michael James. b 58. Oak Hill Th Coll BA79 MA85 LTh Cranmer Hall Dur 81. **d** 83 **p** 84. C Cambridge St Martin *Ely* 83-87; V Clapham Park All SS *S'wark* 87-92; USA 92-94; TR Crookes St Thos *Sheff* from 94. *The Rectory, 18A Hallam Gate Road, Sheffield S10 5BT* Tel 0114-268 6362 E-mail mike@stthomascrookes.org.uk

BREENE, Timothy Patrick Brownell. b 59. Kent Univ BA81 CCC Cam BA89. Ridley Hall Cam 87. **d** 90 **p** 93. C Hadleigh w Layham and Shelley *St E* 90-95; C Martlesham w Brightwell from 95. *4 Sadlers Place, Martlesham Heath, Ipswich IP5 3SS* Tel (01473) 625433

BREFFITT, Geoffrey Michael. b 46. CChem MRIC72 Trent Poly CertEd77 DipPSE82. Qu Coll Birm 87. **d** 89 **p** 90. C Prenton *Ches* 89-92; V Frankby w Greasby 92-01; Dioc Ecum Officer 00-01; V German St Jo *S & M* from 01; V Foxdale from 01; V Patrick from 01. *The Vicarage, Patrick, Peel, Isle of Man IM5 1AW* Tel (01624) 842637 Fax 843374

BRENCHLEY, Royston Harry Peter. b 32. Lon Inst CertEd73 Lon Inst of Educn BEd77. Dioc OLM tr scheme 99. **d** 02. OLM Mitcham St Olave *S'wark* from 02. *74 Manor Way, Mitcham CR4 1EE* Tel (020) 8764 3797 E-mail roy.brenchley@ukgateway.net

BRENDON-COOK, John Lyndon. b 37. FRICS. SW Minl Tr Course. **d** 81 **p** 82. NSM Bodmin *Truro* 81-82; NSM St Breoke and Egloshayle 82-90; NSM Helland 90-94; P-in-c 94-98; NSM Cardynham 90-94; rtd 98; Perm to Offic *Truro* from 98. *Treworder Byre, 119 Egloshayle Road, Wadebridge PL27 6AG* Tel (01208) 812488

BRENNAN, John Lester. b 20. MRCP51 FRCPath77 Barrister-at-Law (Middle Temple) 71 Lon Univ MB, BS44 DipTh47 MD52 LLM86. St Aug Coll Cant 54. **d** 55 **p** 56. India 55-65; Hon C Woodside Park St Barn *Lon* 65-69; Lic to Offic *Lich* 69-88; P-in-c Chrishall *Chelmsf* 88-89; Hon C 89-91; Hon C Heydon, Gt and Lt Chishill, Chrishall etc 91-93; Perm to Offic *St Alb* from 93. *16 Butterfield Road, Wheathampstead AL4 8PU* Tel (01582) 832230

BRENNAN, Samuel James. b 16. St Aid Birkenhead. **d** 57 **p** 58. C Magheralin *D & D* 57-60; C Down H Trin 60-63; Min Can Down Cathl 60-63; I Scarva 63-69; I Aghalee 69-84; rtd 84. *71 Bangor Road, Newtownards BT23 7BZ* Tel (028) 9181 9139

BRENNAND (née PUNSHON), Ms Carol Mary. b 59. Liv Inst of Educn BEd83. Ridley Hall Cam CTM94. **d** 94 **p** 95. C Bushey *St Alb* 94-97; C Watford Ch Ch 97-00; P-in-c Ash Vale *Guildf* from 00. *The Vicarage, 203 Vale Road, Ash Vale, Aldershot GU12 5JE* Tel (01252) 325295

BRENNEN, Canon Colin. b 15. Lon Univ BA47 BD56 Dur Univ PhD88. Linc Th Coll 46. **d** 48 **p** 49. C Seaton Hirst *Newc* 48-50; C Bishopwearmouth Ch Ch *Dur* 50-52; V Grangetown 52-58; V Whitworth w Spennymoor 58-78; RD Auckland 74-82; Hon Can Dur Cathl 78-93; V Hamsterley 78-82; rtd 82. *1 Royton Close, Wrexham LL13 7EP* Tel (01978) 357747

BRENT, Prof Allen Leonard. b 40. Em Coll Cam BA66 Lon Univ MA72 Leeds Univ PhD78. N Queensland Coll of Min 82. **d** 84 **p** 85. Australia 84-95; Hon Can N Queensland 91-95; Sen Lect Coll of SS Mark and Jo Plymouth 95-01; Perm to Offic *Ex* 95-98; Lic to Offic 98-01; Perm to Offic *Ely* from 01. *18 St Albans Road, Cambridge CB4 2HG* Tel (01223) 362671

BRENT, Philip. b 68. K Coll Lon BD89. Cuddesdon Coll 94. **d** 96 **p** 97. C Sawbridgeworth *St Alb* 96-99; C Skegness and Winthorpe *Linc* 99-03; Chapl United Lincs Hosps NHS Trust 00-03; R Market Deeping *Linc* from 03. *The Rectory, 13 Church Street, Market Deeping, Peterborough PE6 8DA* Tel (01778) 342237

BRENTNALL, David John. b 53. UEA BA75 MPhil82. Ridley Hall Cam 84. **d** 86 **p** 87. C Eaton *Nor* 86-90; V Stevenage St Pet Broadwater *St Alb* 90-96; V St Alb St Pet from 96. *The Vicarage, 23 Hall Place Gardens, St Albans AL1 3SB* Tel (01727) 851464 E-mail david.brentnall@btinternet.com

BRERETON, Ms Catherine Louise. b 69. St Aid Coll Dur BSc90 Cranfield Univ MSc92. Ridley Hall Cam BTh00. **d** 00 **p** 01. C S Bank *York* 00-03; V Middlesbrough St Chad from 03. *St Chad's Vicarage, 9 Emerson Avenue, Middlesbrough TS5 7QW* Tel (01642) 819854 E-mail cathi.brereton@talk21.com

BRETEL, Keith Michael. b 51. St Mich Coll Llan 79. **d** 81 **p** 82. C Thundersley *Chelmsf* 81-84; CF from 84. *c/o MOD Chaplains (Army)* Tel (01980) 615804 Fax 615800

BRETHERTON, Donald John. b 18. Lon Univ BD57. Handsworth Coll Birm 38 Headingley Coll Leeds 38 St Aug Coll Cant 59. **d** 60 **p** 61. In Methodist Ch 42-59; C Cant St Martin w St Paul *Cant* 60-62; V Thornton Heath St Jude 62-70; V Herne 70-82; RD Reculver 74-80; rtd 82; Perm to Offic *Cant* from 84. *Martin's, The Green, Chartham, Canterbury CT4 7JW* Tel (01227) 730255

BRETHERTON, Canon William Alan. b 22. St Cath Coll Cam BA43 MA47. Lon Coll of Div BD49 ALCD49. **d** 49 **p** 50. C Fazakerley Em *Liv* 49-52; V Everton St Chrys 52-65; V Ince Ch Ch 65-72; V Kirkdale St Mary 72-73; V Kirkdale St Mary and St Athanasius 73-87; RD Liv 81-87; Hon Can Liv Cathl 81-87; rtd 87; Perm to Offic *Liv* from 87. *3 Bradville Road, Liverpool L9 9BH* Tel 0151-525 0866

BRETT, Dennis Roy Anthony. b 46. Sarum & Wells Th Coll 86. **d** 88 **p** 89. C Bradford-on-Avon *Sarum* 88-92; P-in-c Bishopstrow and Boreham 92-01; R from 01; Chapl Warminster Hosp from 92. *The Rectory, 8 Rock Lane, Warminster BA12 9JZ* Tel (01985) 213000

BRETT, Canon Paul Gadsby. b 41. St Edm Hall Ox BA62 MA66. Wycliffe Hall Ox 64. **d** 65 **p** 66. C Bury St Pet *Man* 65-68; Asst Ind Chapl 68-72; Ind Chapl *Worc* 72-76; Sec Ind Cttee of Gen

Syn Bd for Soc Resp 76-84; Dir Soc Resp *Chelmsf* 85-94; Can Res Chelmsf Cathl 85-94; R Shenfield from 94. *The Rectory, 41 Worrin Road, Shenfield, Brentwood CM15 8DH* Tel (01277) 220360 E-mail paul.brett@btinternet.com

BRETT, Canon Peter Graham Cecil. b 35. Em Coll Cam BA59 MA63. Cuddesdon Coll 59. **d** 61 **p** 62. C Tewkesbury w Walton Cardiff *Glouc* 61-64; C Bournemouth St Pet *Win* 64-66; Chapl Dur Univ *Dur* 66-72; R Houghton le Spring 72-83; RD Houghton 80-83; Can Res Cant Cathl *Cant* 83-01; rtd 01; Perm to Offic *Cant* from 01. *3 Appledore Road, Tenterden TN30 7AY* Tel (01580) 761794 E-mail pandgbrett@btinternet.com

BRETT YOUNG (née ROBIN), Ms Helen Mary Kathleen. b 67. St Martin's Coll Lanc BEd90. Cranmer Hall Dur BA98. **d** 98 **p** 99. C Gd Shep TM *Carl* 98-02; TV from 02. *The Rectory, Patterdale, Penrith CA11 0NL* Tel (01768) 482209 E-mail hmbrettyoung@hotmail.com

BRETTELL, Robert Michael. b 20. St Cath Soc Ox BA49 MA54. Lon Coll of Div 46 Wycliffe Hall Ox 47. **d** 49 **p** 50. C Blackheath St Jo *S'wark* 49-51; C Norbiton 51-53; V Woking St Mary *Guildf* 53-62; V Clifton Ch Ch w Em *Bris* 62-73; V Eastbourne H Trin *Chich* 73-82; V Bexhill St Steph 82-86; rtd 86; Perm to Offic *Chich* 86-00; *Glouc* from 01. *16 Capel Court, The Burgage, Prestbury, Cheltenham GL52 3EL* Tel (01242) 510972

BREW, William Kevin Maddock. b 49. BA MSc. **d** 78 **p** 79. C Raheny w Coolock *D & G* 78-80; Bp's C Dublin Finglas 80-83; I Mountmellick w Coolbanagher, Rosenallis etc *M & K* 83-89; I Ahoghill w Portglenone *Conn* from 89. *42 Church Street, Ahoghill, Ballymena BT42 2PA* Tel (028) 2587 1240 E-mail brewk@lineone.net

BREW, William Philip. b 43. Derby Coll of Educn CertEd64 Liv Univ Dip Special Educn 72 FCollP84. N Ord Course 84. **d** 87 **p** 88. In Independent Methodist Ch 70-83; Hd Master Birtenshaw Sch 78-90; NSM Holcombe *Man* 87-90; TV Horwich 91-93; TV Horwich and Rivington 93-97; V Lostock St Thos and St Jo from 97; AD Deane from 98. *Lostock Vicarage, 9 Lowside Avenue, Lostock, Bolton BL1 5XQ* Tel (01204) 848631 E-mail lostockvicar@aol.com

BREWER, Barry James. b 44. Oak Hill Th Coll 72. **d** 75 **p** 76. C Hove Bp Hannington Memorial Ch *Chich* 75-78; C Church Stretton *Heref* 78-81; TV Bishopsnympton, Rose Ash, Mariansleigh etc *Ex* 81-87; R Swynnerton and Tittensor *Lich* from 87; RD Trentham from 01. *3 Rectory Gardens, Swynnerton, Stone ST15 0RT* Tel (01782) 796564 E-mail barry.brewer@talk21.com

BREWER, Mrs Susan Comport. b 55. LMH Ox MA76. SEITE 99. **d** 02 **p** 03. C Dartford St Edm *Roch* from 02. *Burr Lea, Church Hill, Wilmington, Dartford DA2 7EH* Tel (01322) 281838 Mobile 07930-492323 E-mail suec@brewer86.freeserve.co.uk

BREWIN, David Frederick. b 39. Leic Poly BSc PhD. Lich Th Coll 63. **d** 66 **p** 67. C Shrewsbury H Cross *Lich* 66-69; C Birstall *Leic* 69-73; V Eyres Monsell 73-79; V E Goscote 79-82; V E Goscote w Ratcliffe and Rearsby 82-90; R Thurcaston 90-91; R Thurcaston w Cropston from 92. *6 Vinehouse Close, Thurcaston, Leicester LE7 7JU* Tel 0116-230 1700

BREWIN, Donald Stewart. b 41. Ch Coll Cam BA62 MA66. Ridley Hall Cam 68. **d** 71 **p** 72. C Ecclesall *Sheff* 71-75; V Anston 75-81; V Walton H Trin *Ox* 81-89; TR 89-94; RD Aylesbury 90-94; Nat Dir SOMA UK from 94; Perm to Offic *St Alb* from 94. *Wickham Cottage, Gaddesden Turn, Billington, Leighton Buzzard LU7 9BW* Tel (01525) 373644 *or* 237953 Fax 237954 E-mail donbrewin@compuserve.com *or* don.brewin@somauk.org

BREWIN, Canon Eric Walter. b 16. Hertf Coll Ox BA38 MA42. Ripon Hall Ox 38. **d** 40 **p** 41. C Leic St Marg *Leic* 40-42; Ind Sec SCM 42-46; C Ox St Mary V *Ox* 46-48; Sub-Chapl Nuff Coll Ox 46-48; V Coleford w Staunton *Glouc* 48-70; RD Forest S 57-70; Hon Can Glouc Cathl 65-81; R Leckhampton St Pet 70-81; rtd 81; Perm to Offic *Glouc* 82-00. *The Pleck, Llangrove, Ross-on-Wye HR9 6EU* Tel (01989) 770487

BREWIN, Karan Rosemary. b 42. Jordan Hill Coll Glas DCE68. CA Tr Coll 77 Glas NSM Course 80. **dss** 84 **d** 85. Clarkston *Glas* 84-89; Hon C 86-89 and 91-97; OHP 89 and from 98; Perm to Offic *York* from 01. *St Hilda's Priory, Sneaton Castle, Whitby YO21 3QN* Tel (01947) 602079

BREWIN, Wilfred Michael. b 45. Nottm Univ BA69. Cuddesdon Coll 69. **d** 70 **p** 71. C Walker *Newc* 70-73; C Alnwick St Paul 73-74; C Alnwick w Edlingham and Bolton Chpl 74-77; Fell Sheff Univ 77-79; C Greenhill *Sheff* 79; P-in-c Eggleston *Dur* 79-81; V Norton St Mich 81-87; V Headington *Ox* from 87. *The Vicarage, 33 St Andrew's Road, Oxford OX3 9DL* Tel (01865) 761094 E-mail michaelbrewin@btinternet.com

BREWSTER, Miss Christine Elaine. b 45. Newc Univ BA67 CertEd68 ALCM76 LTCL78 Lon Univ DipEd82 MA84. St Alb and Ox Min Course DipMin95. **d** 98 **p** 99. NSM Aylesbury w Bierton and Hulcott *Ox* 98-00; NSM Dacre w Hartwith and Darley w Thornthwaite *Ripon* 00-01; C Wetherby from 01. *3 Holly Villas, Dacre Banks, Harrogate HG3 4EG* Tel (01423) 780125

BREWSTER, David Pearson. b 30. Clare Coll Cam BA54 MA58 Lon Univ BA65 Oriel Coll Ox MA66 DPhil76. Ridley Hall Cam. **d** 58 **p** 59. C Southampton St Mary w H Trin *Win* 58-61; C N Audley Street St Mark *Lon* 61-62 and 63-65; Tunisia 62-63; Home Sec JEM 65-66; C Ox St Mary V w St Cross and St Pet *Ox* 66-68; Lect Lady Spencer-Churchill Coll Ox 68-71; New Zealand 71-78; V Brockenhurst *Win* 78-95; rtd 95; Perm to Offic *Win* from 95. *4 Saxonford Road, Christchurch BH23 4ES* Tel (01425) 277860

BREWSTER, David Thomas. b 68. GLCM90 ALCM89. Cranmer Hall Dur BA99. **d** 99 **p** 00. C Bidston *Ches* 99-03; TV Stockport SW from 03. *St Mark's Vicarage, 66 Berlin Road, Stockport SK3 9QF* Tel 0161-480 5896

BREWSTER, Jonathan David. b 67. Bucks Coll of Educn BA89 Bris Univ BA94 K Coll Lon MA01. Trin Coll Bris 91. **d** 94 **p** 95. C Gt Horton *Bradf* 94-98; Chapl Univ Westmr *Lon* 98-03; V Highbury Ch Ch w St Jo and St Sav Lon from 03. *Christ Church Vicarage, 155 Highbury Grove, London N5 1SA* Tel (020) 7226 4544 Mobile 07977-127244

BREWSTER (née BEATTIE), Margaret. b 43. S'wark Ord Course 90. **d** 93 **p** 94. NSM S'wark H Trin w St Matt *S'wark* 93-97; NSM Newington St Paul from 97. *1 Charleston Street, London SE17 1NG* Tel (020) 7701 4010 E-mail brew95906@aol.com

BREWSTER, Mrs Susan Jacqueline. b 48. SEITE 94. **d** 97 **p** 98. NSM Goodmayes St Paul *Chelmsf* 97-01; TV Loughton St Jo from 01. *20 Wellfields, Loughton IG10 1NX* Tel (020) 8508 6441

BRIAN, Brother. See HARLEY, Brother Brian Mortimer

BRIAN, Stephen Frederick. b 54. Brighton Coll of Educn CertEd76 Sussex Univ BEd77 Birm Univ DipTh84 Open Univ MA90 Lanc Univ MPhil97. Qu Coll Birm 82. **d** 85 **p** 86. C Scotforth *Blackb* 85-88; V Freckleton 88-97; V Bagshot *Guildf* from 97. *The Vicarage, 43 Church Road, Bagshot GU19 5EQ* Tel (01276) 473348 E-mail sfb4510@aol.com

BRICE, Christopher John. b 48. St Edm Ho Cam MA80. Wycliffe Hall Ox 82. **d** 82 **p** 83. C N Hinksey *Ox* 82-86; Chapl Nuff Coll Ox 84-86; V S Hackney St Mich w Haggerston St Paul *Lon* 86-93; Dir Dioc Bd for Soc Resp 93-01; Adv for Soc Justice from 01; Hon C De Beauvoir Town St Pet from 93. *9 Beresford Road, London N5 2HS* Tel (020) 7226 3834 E-mail chris.brice@london.anglican.org

BRICE, Derek William Fred. b 39. Poly Cen Lon MA87 Kingston Poly DMS84 MCIM89 FCMI82. Dioc OLM tr scheme 99. **d** 02. OLM Cheam *S'wark* from 02. *Mallow, Parkside, Cheam, Sutton SM3 8BS* Tel (020) 8642 0241

BRICE, Jonathan Andrew William. b 61. **d** 92 **p** 93. C Buckhurst Hill *Chelmsf* 92-96; V Victoria Docks Ascension 96; P-in-c 96-98; V from 98. *5 Broadgate Road, London E16 3TL* Tel (020) 7476 6887

BRICE, Neil Alan. b 59. Man Univ BA81 Hughes Hall Cam CertEd87. Westcott Ho Cam 82. **d** 84 **p** 85. C Longton *Lich* 84-86; Hd of Relig Studies Coleridge Community Coll Cam 87-89; NSM Cherry Hinton St Andr *Ely* 88-89; C Fulbourn 89-92; C Gt Wilbraham 89-92; C Lt Wilbraham 89-92; V Arrington 92-00; R Orwell 92-00; R Wimpole 92-00; R Croydon w Clopton 92-00; P-in-c Barrington 98-00; R Orwell Gp from 00. *The Rectory, Fishers Lane, Orwell, Royston SG8 5QX* Tel (01223) 208653 Fax as telephone E-mail revnab@aol.com

BRICE, Paul Earl Philip. b 54. Bath Univ BSc77. Wycliffe Hall Ox 83. **d** 86 **p** 87. C Gt Baddow *Chelmsf* 86-89; Chapl Imp Coll Lon 89-95; St Mary's Hosp Med Sch 89-95; Chapl RCA 90-95; Sec HE/Chapl C of E Bd of Educn 95-02; Hon C S Kensington St Jude *Lon* 95-02; R Hartfield w Coleman's Hatch *Chich* from 02. *The Rectory, Church Street, Hartfield TN7 4AG* Tel (01892) 770850 E-mail anglican@pb.cix.co.uk

BRIDGE, The Very Revd Antony Cyprian. b 14. FSA. Linc Th Coll 53. **d** 55 **p** 56. C Hythe *Cant* 55-58; V Paddington Ch Ch *Lon* 58-68; Dean Guildf 68-86; rtd 86; Perm to Offic *Cant* 86-02. *34 London Road, Deal CT14 9TE* Tel (01304) 366792

BRIDGE, Miss Helen Cecily. b 25. SRN47 SCM49 Open Univ BA80 Ox Univ BTh98. Lambeth STh78 Dalton Ho Bris 70 Trin Coll Bris 70. **dss** 74 **d** 87 **p** 94. Tonbridge St Steph *Roch* 74-75; Countess of Ches Hosp 75-84; Plemstall w Guilden Sutton *Ches* 85-87; Hon Par Dn 87-98; NSM Stockport St Mary 88-98; Perm to Offic *Ches* and *Man* from 00. *25 Rectory Fields, Stockport SK1 4BX* Tel 0161-477 2154

BRIDGE, Martin. b 45. Lon Univ BA66 Linacre Coll Ox BA71 MA73. St Steph Ho Ox 69. **d** 72 **p** 73. C St Peter-in-Thanet *Cant* 72-77; New Zealand from 77. *PO Box 87-145, Meadowbank, Auckland, New Zealand* Tel (0064) (9) 521 5013 *or* 521 0636 Fax as telephone E-mail martin.bridge@xtra.co.nz

BRIDGEN, Andrew Grahame. b 57. Aston Univ BSc81 Surrey Univ BA03 FCCA95. STETS 00. **d** 03. NSM Portchester *Portsm* from 03. *18 Froxfield Gardens, Fareham PO16 8DN* Tel (023) 9234 8617

BRIDGEN, John William. b 40. K Coll Cam BA62 MA66. Ripon Hall Ox 66. **d** 70 **p** 72. C Headstone St Geo *Lon* 70-71; C Hanwell St Mary 71-75; C Tolladine *Worc* 75; TV Worc St Barn w Ch Ch 76; R Barrow *St E* 76-83; V Denham St Mary 76-83; Perm to

Offic *Ely* 84-88 and from 91; rtd 88; Perm to Offic *Glas* 89-91. *57 St Philip's Road, Cambridge CB1 3DA* Tel (01223) 571748

BRIDGEN, Mark Stephen. b 63. K Coll Lon BD85. Cranmer Hall Dur 86. **d** 88 **p** 89. C Kidderminster St Jo *Worc* 88-90; C Kidderminster St Jo and H Innocents 90-92; C Nor St Pet Mancroft w St Jo Maddermarket *Nor* 92-94; V Longbridge *Birm* 94-00; V Wednesbury St Bart *Lich* from 00. *The Vicarage, Little Hill, Wednesbury WS10 9DE* Tel 0121-556 9378

BRIDGER, Francis William. b 51. Pemb Coll Ox BA73 MA78 Bris Univ DipTh75 PhD80. Trin Coll Bris 74. **d** 78 **p** 79. C Islington St Jude Mildmay Park *Lon* 78-82; C Mildmay Grove St Jude and St Paul 82; Lect St Jo Coll Nottm 82-90; Dir of Courses 88-89; Dir of Studies 89-90; V Woodthorpe *S'well* 90-99; Prin Trin Coll Bris from 99. *Trinity College, Stoke Hill, Bristol BS9 1JP* Tel 0117-968 2803 *or* 968 2646

BRIDGER, Canon Gordon Frederick. b 32. Selw Coll Cam BA53 MA58. Ridley Hall Cam 54. **d** 56 **p** 57. C Islington St Mary *Lon* 56-60; C Cambridge St Sepulchre *Ely* 60-62; V Fulham St Mary N End *Lon* 62-69; C Edin St Thos *Edin* 69-76; R Heigham H Trin *Nor* 76-87; RD Nor S 79-86; Hon Can Nor Cathl 84-87; Prin Oak Hill Th Coll 87-96; rtd 96; Perm to Offic *Nor* from 96. *The Elms, 4 Common Lane, Sheringham NR26 8PL* Tel (01263) 823522

✠**BRIDGES, The Rt Revd Dewi Morris.** b 33. Univ of Wales (Lamp) BA54 CCC Cam BA56 MA60. Westcott Ho Cam 57. **d** 57 **p** 58 **c** 88. C Rhymney *Mon* 57-60; C Chepstow 60-63; V Tredegar St Jas 63-65; Lect Kidderminster Coll 65-69; Lic to Offic *Worc* 65-69; V Kempsey 69-79; RD Upton 74-79; RD Narberth *St D* 80-82; R Tenby 79-88; Adn St D 82-88; Bp S & B 88-98; rtd 98. *Hafan Dawel, 2 Cooksyeat View, Kilgetty SA68 0UA* Tel (01834) 811630

BRIDGES, Mrs Gillian Mary. b 43. EAMTC 85. **d** 88 **p** 94. Hon C Hellesdon *Nor* 88-96; Hon C Lakenham St Jo *Nor* 96-97; Assoc V Lakenham St Alb 97-99; Assoc V Sprowston w Beeston from 99. *2 Vera Road, Norwich NR6 5HU* Tel (01603) 789634

BRIDGES, The Ven Peter Sydney Godfrey. b 25. ARIBA51 Birm Univ DLA67. Linc Th Coll 56. **d** 58 **p** 59. C Hemel Hempstead *St Alb* 58-64; Warden Angl Chapl Birm Univ 64-68; Perm to Offic *Birm* 65-72; Lect Aston Univ 68-72; Adn Southend *Chelmsf* 72-77; P-in-c Southend St Jo w St Mark, All SS w St Fran etc 72-73; Dir Dioc Research and Development Unit 73-77; Adn Cov 77-83; Can Th Cov Cathl 77-90; Adn Warwick 83-90; rtd 90; Dioc Adv for Chr Spirituality 90-93; Perm to Offic *Win* from 01. *St Clare, 25 Rivermead Close, Romsey SO51 8HQ* Tel (01794) 512889

BRIDGEWATER, Canon Guy Stevenson. b 60. Ch Ch Ox BA83. Trin Coll Bris BA87. **d** 87 **p** 88. C Radipole and Melcombe Regis *Sarum* 87-90; Chapl Lee Abbey 90-93; V Cranbrook *Cant* 93-98; Dioc Officer for Par Resources (Miss and Lay Tr) *Glouc* from 98; Dioc Can Res Glouc Cathl from 02. *10 College Green, Gloucester GL1 2LX* Tel (01452) 410022 ext 248 Fax 308324 E-mail gbridgewater@glosdioc.org.uk

BRIDGEWOOD, Bruce William. b 41. St Paul's Coll Grahamstown LTh67. **d** 67 **p** 68. S Africa 67-81; Hon C Stanmer w Falmer *Chich* 81-86; Perm to Offic *Lon* from 90; Assoc P Westmr St Matt 90-94; Assoc P Alexandra Park from 94. *81 Warwick Road, London N11 2SP* Tel (020) 8368 6770 E-mail bridgewood@tesco.net

BRIDGLAND, Cyril John Edwin. b 21. Trin Coll Bris 42. **d** 45 **p** 46. C Illogan *Truro* 45-47; C Northwood Em *Lon* 47-50; V Islington H Trin Cloudesley Square 50-58; V Redhill H Trin *S'wark* 58-87; rtd 87; Perm to Offic *Cant* 89-99; Perm to Offic *Roch* 89-98. *3 Barned Court, Barming, Maidstone ME16 9EL* Tel (01622) 728451

BRIDGMAN, Canon Gerald Bernard. b 22. St Cath Coll Cam BA50 MA55. Bible Churchmen's Coll Bris 46 Wycliffe Hall Ox 50. **d** 51 **p** 52. C Broadwater St Mary *Chich* 51-54; C Ox St Aldate *Ox* 54-56; C-in-c Southgate CD *Chich* 56-59; V Southgate 59-67; V Kingston upon Hull H Trin *York* 67-87; Chapl Hull R Infirmary 67-87; Area Dean Cen and N Hull 81-86; Can and Preb York Minster 83-87; OStJ from 76; rtd 87; Perm to Offic *Chich* from 87. *129 The Welkin, Lindfield, Haywards Heath RH16 2PL* Tel (01444) 484563

BRIDGWATER, Philip Dudley. b 31. St Alb Minl Tr Scheme 88. **d** 91 **p** 92. NSM Buxton w Burbage and King Sterndale *Derby* 91-94 and 98-01; NSM Fairfield 94-98; Perm to Offic from 01. *Millstone, 9 College Road, Buxton SK17 9DZ* Tel (01298) 72876

BRIDLE, Geoffrey Peter. b 52. CITC 87. **d** 87 **p** 88. C Lurgan Ch the Redeemer *D & D* 87-91; I Carnteel and Crilly *Arm* 91-99; I Cleenish w Mullaghdun *Clogh* from 99. *Cleenish Rectory, Bellanaleck, Enniskillen BT92 2BA* Tel (028) 6634 8259 Fax 6634 8620 E-mail geoffreypbridle@email.com

BRIDSON, Canon Raymond Stephen. b 58. Southn Univ BTh82. Chich Th Coll. **d** 82 **p** 83. C St Luke in the City *Liv* 82-86; TV Ditton St Mich 86-98; V Anfield St Columba from 98; AD Walton from 02; Hon Can Liv Cathl from 03. *St Columba's Vicarage, Pinehurst Avenue, Liverpool L4 2TZ* Tel 0151-474 7231

BRIDSTRUP, Juergen Walter. b 44. St Alb Minl Tr Scheme 84. **d** 87 **p** 88. C Leagrave *St Alb* 87-90; V Goff's Oak St Jas from 90.

St James's Vicarage, St James's Road, Goffs Oak, Waltham Cross EN7 6TP Tel (01707) 872328 Fax as telephone
E-mail juergen.bridstrup@ukgateway.net

BRIEN, John Richard. b 57. Kingston Poly BSc80. EAMTC 98. **d** 01 **p** 02. NSM Mistley w Manningtree and Bradfield *Chelmsf* from 01. *1 East View, Crown Street, Dedham, Colchester CO7 6AN* Tel (01206) 322706
E-mail briens@dedham.fsworld.co.uk

BRIERLEY, Charles Ian. b 46. MIMI69. S Dios Minl Tr Scheme 90. **d** 93 **p** 94. NSM Wellington and Distr *B & W* from 93. *46 Oakfield Park, Wellington TA21 8EY* Tel (01823) 666101
E-mail brierley@aol.com

BRIERLEY, Canon David James. b 53. Bris Univ BA75. Oak Hill Th Coll 75. **d** 77 **p** 78. C Balderstone *Man* 77-80; P-in-c Eccles St Andr 80-81; TV Eccles 81-85; Bp's Ecum Adv 81-88; V Harwood 85-95; AD Walmsley 95-02; V Walmsley 95-01; P-in-c Belmont 97-01; TV Turton Moorland Min 01-02; Can Res Bradf Cathl *Bradf* from 02; Dioc Adv in Evang from 02. *2 Cathedral Close, Bradford BD1 4EG* Tel (01274) 727806 *or* 777218 Mobile 07748-942183 E-mail david.brierley@bradford.anglican.ord

BRIERLEY, John Michael. b 32. Lon Univ BD71. Lich Th Coll 57. **d** 60 **p** 61. C Lower Mitton *Worc* 60-62; C-in-c Dines Green St Mich CD 62-68; V Worc St Mich 69-71; R Eastham w Rochford 71-79; P-in-c Knighton-on-Teme 76-79; P-in-c Reddal Hill St Luke 79-81; V 81-92; rtd 92; Perm to Offic *Worc* from 92. *10 Woodhouse Way, Cradley Heath, Warley B64 5EL* Tel (01384) 633527

BRIERLEY, Michael William. b 73. CCC Cam BA94 MA98. Ripon Coll Cuddesdon BA98 DipMin98. **d** 98 **p** 99. C Marnhull *Sarum* 98-01; C Okeford 98-01; Bp's Dom Chapl *Ox* from 01. *55 Marsh Lane, Marston, Oxford OX3 0NQ* Tel (01865) 767946 *or* 208221 E-mail michael.brierley@oxford.anglican.org

BRIERLEY, Philip. b 49. CChem80 MRSC80 Salford Univ BSc74. LNSM course 89. **d** 92 **p** 93. OLM Stalybridge *Man* from 92. *Burnside, 30 Cranworth Street, Stalybridge SK15 2NW* Tel 0161-303 0809

BRIERLEY, William David. b 64. Kent Univ BA87 New Coll Ox DPhil93. Ripon Coll Cuddesdon DipMin93. **d** 93 **p** 94. C Amersham *Ox* 93-97; TV Wheatley from 97. *The New Vicarage, Cox Lane, Stanton St John, Oxford OX33 1HW* Tel (01865) 351142 E-mail william.brierley@tesco.net

BRIGGS, Christopher Ronald. b 58. K Coll Lon BD79 AKC79 PGCE80. Sarum & Wells Th Coll 87. **d** 89 **p** 90. C Horsell *Guildf* 89-93; Hong Kong 93-97; V Norton *St Alb* 97-00; Sen Chapl Haileybury Coll from 00. *Lawrence Cottage, 2 Hailey Lane, Hertford Heath, Hertford SG13 7NX* Tel and fax (01992) 462922 *or* tel 706314 E-mail chrisbriggs@freenet.co.uk

BRIGGS, Derek. b 26. Lon Univ DipTh55. St Aid Birkenhead 52. **d** 55 **p** 56. C Brownhill *Wakef* 55-57; C Trowbridge St Jas *Sarum* 57-60; R Levenshulme St Pet *Man* 60-67; V Farsley *Bradf* 67-90; rtd 90; Perm to Offic *Bradf* 90-99. *6 College Court, Bradley, Keighley BD20 9EA* Tel (01535) 630085

✠**BRIGGS, The Rt Revd George Cardell.** b 10. CMG80. SS Coll Cam BA33 MA37. Cuddesdon Coll 33. **d** 34 **p** 35 **c** 73. C Stockport St Alb Hall Street *Ches* 34-37; Tanzania 37-73; OGS from 39; Adn Newala 55-64; Can Zanzibar 64-65; Can Dar-es-Salaam 65-69; Can Masasi 69-73; Bp Seychelles 73-79; Asst Bp Derby 79-80; C Matlock and Tansley 79-80; rtd 80; Asst Bp Worc 91-00. *c/o P J Anderson Esq, Exchange House, White Friars, Chester CH1 1NZ*

BRIGGS, George William. b 76. Wadh Coll Ox BA98 Fitzw Coll Cam BA02. Ridley Hall Cam 00. **d** 03. C Stretford St Bride *Man* from 03. *38 Prestage Street, Old Trafford, Manchester M16 9JU* Tel 0161-226 4513

BRIGGS, Gordon John. b 39. CIPFA. St Alb and Ox Min Course 95. **d** 98 **p** 99. OLM Farnham Royal w Hedgerley *Ox* from 98. *52 Freemans Close, Stoke Poges, Slough SL2 4ER* Tel (01753) 662536

BRIGGS, Canon John. b 39. Edin Univ MA61. Ridley Hall Cam 61. **d** 63 **p** 64. C Jesmond Clayton Memorial *Newc* 63-66; Schs Sec Scripture Union 66-79; Tutor St Jo Coll Dur 67-74; Lic to Offic *Dur* 67-74; Lic to Offic *Edin* 74-79; V Chadkirk *Ches* 79-88; RD Chadkirk 85-88; TR Macclesfield Team Par from 88; Hon Can Ches Cathl from 96; Chapl W Park Hosp Macclesfield 90-99. *The Rectory, 85 Beech Lane, Macclesfield SK10 2DY* Tel (01625) 426110 *or* 421984 E-mail jbriggs@fish.co.uk

BRIGGS, Michael Weston. b 40. Edin Th Coll 61. **d** 64 **p** 65. C Sneinton St Steph w St Alb *S'well* 64-67; C Beeston 67-70; P-in-c Kirkby Woodhouse 70-74; V Harworth 74-81; R Harby w Thorney and N and S Clifton 81-94; R N Wheatley, W Burton, Bole, Saundby, Sturton etc from 94; P-in-c Clarborough w Hayton from 03; CF (ACF) from 73. *The Rectory, Middlefield Road, North Wheatley, Retford DN22 9DA* Tel (01427) 880293 Fax as telephone E-mail m_w_briggs@lineone.net

BRIGGS, The Very Revd Roger Edward. b 36. ALCD61. **d** 61 **p** 61. Canada 61-71; C Upper Armley *Ripon* 71-72; Canada 72-99; Dean Arctic 96-99; rtd 99. *Apartment 1207, 415 Greenview Avenue, Ottawa ON, Canada, K2B 8G5*

BRIGHAM, John Keith. b 48. FSAScot Man Univ CertEd70. St Steph Ho Ox 71. **d** 74 **p** 75. C Ches H Trin *Ches* 74-77; C Ealing Ch the Sav *Lon* 77-85; P-in-c Fulwell St Mich and St Geo 85-88; P-in-c Upper Teddington SS Pet and Paul 85-88; V Southport St Luke *Liv* 88-94; Dioc Chapl to the Deaf 88-94; V Lund *Blackb* 94-98. *17 South Meade, Timperley, Altrincham WA15 6QC* Tel 0161-976 2644

BRIGHOUSE, George Alexander (Alex). b 46. N Ord Course 87. **d** 90 **p** 91. NSM Ingrow cum Hainworth *Bradf* 90-91; NSM Keighley All SS 92; NSM Bradf St Wilfrid Lidget Green from 92. *38 Thirsk Grange, Clayton, Bradford BD14 6HS* Tel 07768-618562 (mobile)

BRIGHT, George Frank. b 50. Peterho Cam BA71 MA75 Leeds Univ DipTh73 LSE MSc83 SAP99. Coll of Resurr Mirfield 71. **d** 74 **p** 75. C Notting Hill *Lon* 74-77; Perm to Offic 77-84; P-in-c Kentish Town St Benet and All SS 84-89; P-in-c Kensington St Jo 89-93; V from 93. *The Vicarage, 176 Holland Road, London W14 8AH* Tel (020) 7602 4655 E-mail gfb@dircon.co.uk

BRIGHT, Reginald. b 26. Tyndale Hall Bris 57. **d** 60 **p** 61. C Toxteth Park St Philemon w St Silas *Liv* 60-63; P-in-c Everton St Polycarp 63-65; R Orton St Giles *Carl* 65-72; V Holme 72-79; P-in-c W Newton 79-81; V Bromfield w Waverton 79-81; R Bowness 81-93; rtd 93; Perm to Offic *Carl* from 93. *Spinney House, Cannonfield, Roadhead, Carlisle CA6 6NB* Tel (01697) 748645

BRIGHTMAN, Peter Arthur. b 30. Lon Coll of Div ALCD61 LTh74. **d** 64 **p** 65. C Westgate St Jas *Cant* 64-67; C Lydd 67-70; C Lt Coates *Linc* 70; C Heaton Ch Ch *Man* 71-72; V Bolton SS Simon and Jude 72-77; R Bath St Sav *B & W* 77-85; R Farnborough, Marksbury and Stanton Prior 85-90; C Coney Hill *Glouc* 90-93; C Hardwicke, Quedgeley and Elmore w Longney 93-95; rtd 95; Perm to Offic *B & W* from 95. *2 Westmead Cottages, Dean Hill Lane, Weston, Bath BA1 4DT* Tel (01225) 315076

BRIGHTON, Terrence William. b 43. SW Minl Tr Course 85. **d** 88 **p** 89. C Dawlish *Ex* 88-92; P-in-c Newton Poppleford w Harpford 92-94; V Newton Poppleford, Harpford and Colaton Raleigh 94-98; RD Ottery 96-98; P-in-c W Lavington and the Cheverells *Sarum* 98-02; Rural Officer (Ramsbury Area) 98-02; P-in-c Charleton w Buckland Tout Saints etc *Ex* from 02; RD Woodleigh from 03. *The Rectory, West Charleton, Kingsbridge TQ7 2AJ* Tel (01548) 531211 E-mail twb@surfaid.org

BRIGHTWELL, Ms Johanna Clare. b 64. Bris Univ BSc66 Heythrop Coll Lon MA98. Ridley Hall Cam CTM99. **d** 99 **p** 00. C Coulsdon St Jo *S'wark* 99-02; TV Morden from 02. *5 Willows Avenue, Morden SM4 5SG* Tel (020) 8646 2002
E-mail jcbrightwell@yahoo.com

BRIGNALL, Simon Francis Lyon. b 54. St Jo Coll Dur BA78. Wycliffe Hall Ox 80. **d** 83 **p** 84. C Colne St Bart *Blackb* 83-86; SAMS 86-96; Peru 86-96; P-in-c Tetsworth, Adwell w S Weston, Lewknor etc *Ox* 96-98; TV Thame from 98. *The Rectory, 46 High Street, Tetsworth, Thame OX9 7AS* Tel (01844) 281267 Mobile 07718-627674 E-mail brignall@fish.co.uk

BRIGNELL, Roger. b 39. CertEd65 ACP88 MCollP89. St Aid Birkenhead 60 St As Minl Tr Course 95. **d** 98 **p** 99. NSM Montgomery and Forden and Llandyssil *St As* from 98. *Minevia, Kerry Road, Montgomery SY15 6PD* Tel (01686) 668539 Fax as telephone

BRIMACOMBE, Keith John. b 59. Open Univ BA92 Westmr Coll Ox MTh00. SW Minl Tr Course 99. **d** 01 **p** 03. NSM Ottery St Mary, Alfington, W Hill, Tipton etc *Ex* from 00. *Banklea, Exeter Road, Newton Poppleford, Sidmouth EX10 0BJ* Tel (01395) 568404 E-mail brims@kjbrims.fsnet.co.uk

BRIMICOMBE, Mark. b 44. Nottm Univ BA66 CertEd. SW Minl Tr Course 83. **d** 85 **p** 86. NSM Plympton St Mary *Ex* from 85. *4 Dad Close, Stoggy Lane, Plympton, Plymouth PL7 3BQ* Tel (01752) 338454

BRINDLE, John Harold. b 21. St Jo Coll Dur LTh42 BA43 MA46. St Aid Birkenhead 39. **d** 42 **p** 43. C Ashton-on-Ribble St Mich *Blackb* 44-47; C Sandylands 47-51; V Grimsargh 51-88; rtd 88; Perm to Offic *Blackb* from 88. *8 Sussex Drive, Garstang, Preston PR3 1ET* Tel (01995) 606588

BRINDLE, Peter John. b 47. MIStructE72. N Ord Course 78. **d** 81 **p** 82. NSM Bingley All SS *Bradf* 81-84; NSM Bingley H Trin 84-86; V Keighley All SS 86-91; V Kirkstall *Ripon* 91-96; V Beeston 96-02; TR from 02. *Beeston Vicarage, 16 Town Street, Leeds LS11 8PN* Tel and fax 0113-270 5529 *or* 277 1494 Mobile 07860-157363

BRINDLEY, Miss Angela Mary. b 44. Oak Hill Th Coll 93 N Ord Course 99. **d** 00 **p** 01. C Handforth *Ches* 00-03; R Whaley Bridge from 03. *St James's Rectory, Taxal Road, Whaley Bridge, High Peak SK23 7DY*

BRINDLEY, The Very Revd David Charles. b 53. K Coll Lon BD75 AKC75 MTh76 MPhil81. St Aug Coll Cant 75. **d** 76 **p** 77. C Epping St Jo *Chelmsf* 76-79; Lect Coll of SS Paul and Mary Cheltenham 79-82; Dioc Dir of Tr *Leic* 82-86; V Quorndon 82-86; Prin Glouc Sch for Min *Glouc* 87-92; Prin WEMTC 92-94; Dir of Minl Tr 87-94; Dioc Officer for NSM 88-94; Hon Can Glouc Cathl 92-94; TR Warwick *Cov* 94-02; Dean Portsm from 02. *The Deanery, 13 Pembroke Road, Portsmouth PO1 2NS* Tel (023) 9282 4400 *or* 9234 7605 Fax 9229 5480 E-mail dean@portsmouthcathedral.org.uk

BRINDLEY, Canon Stuart Geoffrey Noel. b 30. St Jo Coll Dur BA53 DipTh55. **d** 55 **p** 56. C Newc St Anne *Newc* 55-58; C Tynemouth Cullercoats St Paul 58-60; C Killingworth 60-63; V Newsham 63-69; W Germany 69-76; Asst Master Wyvern Sch Weston-super-Mare 76-80; V Stocksbridge *Sheff* 80-88; RD Tankersley 85-88; V Rotherham 88-96; Hon Can Sheff Cathl 95-96; rtd 96; Perm to Offic *Newc* from 96. *Hanbury, Backcrofts, Rothbury, Morpeth NE65 7XY* Tel (01669) 621472

BRINKWORTH, Canon Christopher Michael Gibbs. b 41. Lanc Univ BA70. Kelham Th Coll 62 SSC. **d** 67 **p** 68. C Lancaster St Mary *Blackb* 67-70; C Milton *Portsm* 70-74; V Ault Hucknall *Derby* 74-84; V Derby St Anne and St Jo from 84; Hon Can Derby Cathl from 00. *The Vicarage, 25 Highfield Road, Derby DE22 1GX* Tel (01332) 332681 E-mail cbrink5565@aol.com

BRION, Martin Philip. b 33. Ex Univ BA55. Ridley Hall Cam 57. **d** 59 **p** 60. C Balderstone *Man* 59-62; C Morden *S'wark* 62-66; V Low Elswick *Newc* 66-73; P-in-c Giggleswick *Bradf* 73-77; V 77-80; V Camerton H Trin W Seaton *Carl* 80-86; V Dearham 86-95; rtd 95; Perm to Offic *Carl* from 95. *7 Falcon Place, Moresby Parks, Whitehaven CA28 8YF* Tel (01946) 691912

BRISCOE, Allen. b 42. Liv Univ BSc64 CertEd65. Coll of Resurr Mirfield 90. **d** 92 **p** 93. C Shiremoor *Newc* 92-95; V Barnsley St Pet and St Jo *Wakef* from 95. *The Vicarage, 1 Osborne Mews, Barnsley S70 1UU* Tel (01226) 282220

BRISCOE, Canon Frances Amelia. b 35. Univ of Wales CertEd55 Leeds Univ DipRE62 Man Univ BA71 MA74. Gilmore Course 74. **dss** 77 **d** 87 **p** 94. Gt Crosby St Luke *Liv* 77-81; Dioc Lay Min Adv 81-87; Chapl Liv Cathl 81-89; Dir Diaconal Mins 87-89; Lect St Deiniol's Minl Tr Scheme 88-00; Hon Can Liv Cathl *Liv* 88-00; AD Sefton 89-00; Dir of Reader Studies 89-00; Dn-in-c Hightown 92-94; P-in-c 94-00. *5 Derwent Avenue, Formby, Liverpool L37 2JT* Tel (01925) 221049

BRISCOE, Gordon Michael. b 24. Leeds Univ CertEd50. Ely Th Coll 51. **d** 53 **p** 54. C Isleworth St Fran *Lon* 53-54; Hon C 66-67; C Ealing Ch the Sav 54-57; W Germany 57-62; C Twickenham St Mary *Lon* 62-65; Chapl Fortescue Ho Sch Twickenham 62-65; Hon C Brookfield St Anne, Highgate Rise *Lon* 67-77; Hon C Paddington St Steph w St Luke 77-80; Hon C St Marylebone Annunciation Bryanston Street 80-83; Chapl Bedford Modern Sch 83-84; Hon Chapl 84-94; R Dunton w Wrestlingworth and Eyeworth *St Alb* 84-94; rtd 94. *59 Furland Road, Crewkerne TA18 8DD* Tel (01460) 78812 E-mail briskel@btinternet.com

BRISON, The Ven William Stanly. b 29. Alfred Univ NY BSc51 Connecticut Univ MDiv57 STM71. Berkeley Div Sch. **d** 57 **p** 57. USA 57-72; V Davyhulme Ch Ch *Man* 72-81; R Newton Heath All SS 81-85; AD N Man 81-85; Hon Can Man Cathl 82-85; Adn Bolton 85-92; TV E Farnworth and Kearsley 85-89; C Bolton St Thos 89-92; CMS 92-94; Nigeria 92-94; P-in-c Pendleton St Thos w Charlestown *Man* 94-95; TR Pendleton 95-98; rtd 98; Perm to Offic *Man* from 99. *2 Scott Avenue, Bury BL9 9RS* Tel 0161-764 3998

BRISTOL, Archdeacon of. *See* McCLURE, The Ven Timothy Elston

BRISTOL, Bishop of. *See* HILL, The Rt Revd Michael Arthur

BRISTOL, Dean of. *See* GRIMLEY, The Very Revd Robert William

BRISTOW, Arthur George Raymond. b 09. Lich Th Coll 32. **d** 35 **p** 36. C Longton St Mary and St Chad *Lich* 35-38; Perm to Offic *Roch* 38; Perm to Offic *Ox* 38-39 and 41; Perm to Offic *Lich* 39-40; C Sheff St Matt *Sheff* 41-43; V Saltley *Birm* 43-52; R Wednesbury St Jo *Lich* 52-57; V Willenhall St Steph 57-75; rtd 75; Perm to Offic *Lich* from 85; Hon C Emscote *Cov* 75-03. *41 Badgers Way, Heath Hayes, Cannock WS12 3XQ* Tel (01543) 275530

BRISTOW, Keith Raymond Martin. b 56. Ex Univ BA78. Chich Th Coll 87. **d** 89 **p** 90. C Kirkby *Liv* 89-93; C Portsea St Mary *Portsm* 93-03; R Ash *Guildf* from 03. *The Rectory, Ash Church Road, Ash, Aldershot GU12 6LU* Tel (01252) 321517 E-mail frkeithbristow@aol.com

BRISTOW, Peter Edmund. b 49. Pontificium Institutum Internationale Angelicum Rome JCL77 St Jos Coll Upholland 67. **d** 72 **p** 73. In RC Ch 72-87; C Poplar *Lon* 89-92; Lay Tr Officer 89-90; TV Droitwich Spa *Worc* 92-94; TR 94-00; V Boston Spa *York* from 00; P-in-c Thorp Arch w Walton from 00. *The Vicarage, High Street, Boston Spa, Wetherby LS23 6EA* Tel (01937) 842454

BRISTOW, Roger. b 60. Aston Tr Scheme 81 Ridley Hall Cam 83. **d** 86 **p** 87. C Leyton St Mary w St Edw *Chelmsf* 86-90; TV Kings Norton *Birm* 90-98; V Bromley H Trin *Roch* from 98. *Holy Trinity Vicarage, Church Lane, Bromley BR2 8LB* Tel (020) 8462 1280 Mobile 07778-397224 E-mail rb3in1@lineone.co.uk *or* htc-bc@tiscali.co.uk

BRITT, Eric Stanley. b 47. St Jo Coll Nottm LTh74 BTh75. **d** 74 **p** 75. C Chorleywood Ch Ch *St Alb* 74-78; C Frimley *Guildf* 78-80; P-in-c Alresford *Chelmsf* 80-88; R Takeley w Lt Canfield

88-93; Asst Chapl R Free Hosp Lon 93-96; Chapl Mid-Essex Hosp Services NHS Trust 96-00; Chapl Algarve *Eur* from 01. *Apartado 135, Casa Sao Vicente, Boliqueime, 8100 Loule, Portugal* Tel (00351) (289) 366720 Fax 362231 E-mail britt.st.vincents@ip.pt

BRITTAIN, John. b 23. St Aug Coll Cant 59. **d** 60 **p** 61. C Heref St Martin *Heref* 60-62; V Highley 62-88; rtd 88. *26 Stuart Court, High Street, Kibworth, Leicester LE8 0LR*

BRITTON, Christine Mary. *See* BEECROFT, Mrs Christine Mary

BRITTON, John Anthony. b 39. Dur Univ BA60. Wycliffe Hall Ox 61. **d** 63 **p** 64. C Sheff St Swithun *Sheff* 63-64; C Sheff St Aid w St Luke 64-66; C Doncaster St Geo 66-68; C Grantham St Wulfram *Linc* 68-72; V Surfleet 72-76; V Bolsover *Derby* 76-86; V Harworth *S'well* 86-01; RD Bawtry 96-01; rtd 01. *Beaver Lodge, 10 Weirside, Oldcotes, Worksop S81 8HW* Tel (01909) 540735 E-mail jabritton@btinternet.com

BRITTON, John Timothy Hugh. b 50. Dundee Univ BSc73. Trin Coll Bris 73. **d** 76 **p** 77. C Cromer *Nor* 76-79; P-in-c Freethorpe w Wickhampton 79-82; P-in-c Beighton and Moulton 79-82; P-in-c Halvergate w Tunstall 79-82; CMS 82-89; Uganda 83-89; R Allesley *Cov* 89-02; P-in-c Long Itchington and Marton from 02; P-in-c Wappenbury w Weston under Wetherley from 02; P-in-c Hunningham from 02; P-in-c Offchurch from 02. *The Vicarage, Leamington Road, Long Itchington, Southam CV47 9PL* Tel (01926) 812518 E-mail timbritton@myrealbox.com

BRITTON, Neil Bryan. b 35. Em Coll Cam BA59 MA63. Clifton Th Coll 61. **d** 63 **p** 64. C Eastbourne All SS *Chich* 63-67; C Ashtead *Guildf* 67-70; Chapl Scargill Ho 70-74; Asst Chapl Villars *Eur* 74-81; rtd 00. *Mercy Ships CDTS, PO Box 2020, Lindale, TX 75771, USA* Tel (001) (903) 882 0887

BRITTON, Canon Paul Anthony. b 29. SS Coll Cam BA52 MA57. Linc Th Coll 52. **d** 54 **p** 55. C Upper Norwood St Jo *Cant* 54-57; C Wantage *Ox* 57-61; V Stanmore *Win* 61-70; V Bitterne Park 70-80; Can Res Win Cathl 80-94; Lib 81-85; Treas 85-94; rtd 94; Perm to Offic *Sarum* from 94. *Pemberton, High Street, Hindon, Salisbury SP3 6DR* Tel (01747) 820406

BRITTON, Robert. b 37. Oak Hill Th Coll 78. **d** 79 **p** 80. C St Helens St Helen *Liv* 79-83; V Lowton St Mary 83-02; AD Winwick 89-01; rtd 02; Perm to Offic *Man* from 03. *15 Balmoral Avenue, Lowton, Warrington WA3 2ER* Tel (01942) 711135

BRITTON, Ronald George Adrian Michael (Robert). b 24. Univ of State of NY BSc78 Lambeth STh82. St D Coll Lamp 63. **d** 82 **p** 82. Arabia 82-85; Chapl Alassio *Eur* 85-90 and 92-93; Chapl San Remo 86; Hon C Southbourne St Kath *Win* 90-92; rtd 96; Perm to Offic *Bris* from 97. *2 Cherry Tree Road, Bristol BS16 4EY* Tel 0117-965 5734 E-mail robert@britton320.fsnet.co.uk

BRIXTON, Miss Corinne Jane. b 63. Ex Univ BSc84. Wycliffe Hall Ox BTh95. **d** 95. C Leytonstone St Jo *Chelmsf* 95-00; C Buckhurst Hill from 00. *63 High Road, Buckhurst Hill IG9 5SR* Tel (020) 8504 6652 E-mail cbrixton@aol.com

BRIXWORTH, Suffragan Bishop of. *See* WHITE, The Rt Revd Francis

BROAD, David Nicholas Andrew. b 59. Man Univ BA. Edin Th Coll. **d** 87 **p** 88. C Fulham All SS *Lon* 87-90; TV Clare w Poslingford, Cavendish etc *St E* 90-93; TV Totton *Win* 93-99; R Abbotts Ann and Upper and Goodworth Clatford from 99. *The Rectory, Upper Clatford, Andover SP11 7QP* Tel (01264) 352906 Fax as telephone E-mail dna.broad@virgin.net

BROAD, Canon Hugh Duncan. b 37. Lich Th Coll 64. **d** 67 **p** 68. C Heref H Trin *Heref* 67-72; Asst Master Bp's Sch Heref 72-73; C Fareham SS Pet and Paul *Portsm* 74-76; V Heref All SS *Heref* 76-90; R Matson *Glouc* 90-97; V Glouc St Geo w Whaddon 97-03; Hon Can Glouc Cathl 02-03; rtd 03; P-in-c Mojacar *Eur* from 03. *Apartado 617, Mojacar Playa, 04638 Almeria, Spain* Tel (0034) 950 478432 Mobile 617 779327 E-mail hughbroad996@hotmail.com

BROAD, Hugh Robert. b 49. St Mich Coll Llan 67. **d** 72 **p** 73. C Tenby w Gumfreston *St D* 72-75; C Caerau w Ely *Llan* 75-79; V Llanharan w Peterston-super-Montem 79-89; RD Bridgend 88-89; Ex-Paroch Officer 90; V Whatborough Gp of Par *Leic* from 90. *The Vicarage, Oakham Road, Tilton on the Hill, Leicester LE7 9LB* Tel 0116-259 7244 E-mail hbroad@hbro.freeserve.co.uk

BROAD, Canon William Ernest Lionel. b 40. Ridley Hall Cam 64. **d** 66 **p** 67. C Ecclesfield *Sheff* 66-69; Chapl HM Pris Wormwood Scrubs 69; Chapl HM Pris Albany 70-74; Chapl HM Rem Cen Risley 74-76; V Ditton St Mich *Liv* 76-83; P-in-c Mayland *Chelmsf* 83-91; P-in-c Steeple 83-91; V Blackhall *Dur* 91-97; TR Gt Aycliffe from 97; P-in-c Chilton from 03; Hon Can Dur Cathl from 02. *St Clare's Vicarage, St Cuthbert's Way, Newton Aycliffe DL5 5NT* Tel (01325) 313613 Fax 308824 E-mail bill@deagol.fsnet.co.uk

BROADBENT, Mrs Doreen. b 36. Local Minl Tr Course 91. **d** 94 **p** 95. OLM Stalybridge *Man* 94-02; Perm to Offic from 02. *37 Ladysmith Road, Ashton-under-Lyne OL6 9DJ* Tel 0161-330 9085

BROADBENT, Edward Ronald. b 23. Man Univ BSc44. Westcott Ho Cam 53. **d** 55 **p** 56. C Runcorn St Mich *Ches* 55-59; C Ches

St Pet 59-62; Youth Chapl 59-62; V Bredbury St Mark 62; SPCK Staff 63-87; Hon C Wilton w Netherhampton and Fugglestone *Sarum* 78-80; P-in-c S Newton 80-83; Hon C Chalke Valley W 84-91; rtd 88; Perm to Offic *Sarum* from 92. *3 Archers Court, Castle Street, Salisbury SP1 3WE* Tel (01722) 326809

BROADBENT, Hugh Patrick Colin. b 53. Selw Coll Cam BA75 MA. Wycliffe Hall Ox DipTh78. **d** 78 **p** 79. C Chatham St Steph *Roch* 78-82; C Shortlands 82-84; C Edenbridge 84-87; C Crockham Hill H Trin 84-87; V Bromley H Trin 87-97; Chapl St Olave's Gr Sch Orpington from 95; V Bromley St Jo *Roch* from 97. *St John's Vicarage, 9 Orchard Road, Bromley BR1 2PR* Tel (020) 8460 1844 E-mail hughbroadbent@hotmail.com

BROADBENT, Neil Seton. b 53. Qu Coll Birm DipTh80. **d** 81 **p** 82. C Knaresborough *Ripon* 81-84; C Leeds Gipton Epiphany 84-87; Lic to Offic 87-89; Chapl Minstead Community *Derby* 89; Perm to Offic from 89; Dir Sozein from 93. *The Old Vicarage, Church Lane, Horsley Woodhouse, Ilkeston DE7 6BB* Tel (01332) 780598

BROADBENT, Paul John. b 41. Oak Hill Th Coll DipTh83. **d** 85 **p** 86. C Duston *Pet* 85-88; TV Ross w Brampton Abbotts, Bridstow and Peterstow *Heref* 88-91; R Pattishall w Cold Higham and Gayton w Tiffield *Pet* from 91. *The Rectory, Pattishall, Towcester NN12 8NB* Tel and fax (01327) 830043 Mobile 07786-865015 E-mail pjbroadbent@aol.com

✠**BROADBENT, The Rt Revd Peter Alan.** b 52. Jes Coll Cam BA74 MA78. St Jo Coll Nottm DipTh75. **d** 77 **p** 78 **c** 01. C Dur St Nic *Dur* 77-80; C Holloway Em w Hornsey Road St Barn *Lon* 80-83; Chapl N Lon Poly 83-89; Hon C Islington St Mary 83-89; V Harrow Trin St Mich 89-94; AD Harrow 94; Adn Northolt 95-01; P-in-c Southall H Trin 98-99; Area Bp Willesden from 01. *173 Willesden Lane, London NW6 7YN* Tel (020) 8451 0189 Mobile 07957-144674 Fax (020) 8451 4606 E-mail bishop.willesden@btinternet.com

BROADBENT, Ralph Andrew. b 55. K Coll Lon BD76 AKC76. Chich Th Coll 77. **d** 78 **p** 79. C Prestwich St Mary *Man* 78-82; R Man Miles Platting 82-84; CF 84-87; TV Wordsley *Lich* 88-93; Chapl Wordsley and Ridge Hill Hosps 88-93; V Wollescote *Worc* from 93. *St Andrew's Vicarage, Oakfield Road, Wollescote, Stourbridge DY9 9DG* Tel (01384) 422695

BROADBENT, Thomas William. b 45. Chu Coll Cam BA66 MA70 PhD70. Ridley Hall Cam 75. **d** 78 **p** 79. C Allington and Maidstone St Pet *Cant* 78-82; Chapl Mid Kent Coll of H&FE 80-82; C Kings Heath *Birm* 82-84; Hon C Pendleton St Thos *Man* 84-89; TV Pendleton St Thos w Charlestown 89-92; Chapl Salford Univ 84-92; Chmn Man Coun of Chr and Jews 89-92; P-in-c Claydon and Barham *St E* from 92; P-in-c Henley from 99; Chapl Suffolk Coll of HE 92-00; P-in-c Gt Blakenham from 02. *The Rectory, 7 Back Lane, Claydon, Ipswich IP6 0EB* Tel (01473) 830362

BROADBERRY, Canon Richard St Lawrence. b 31. TCD BA53 BD59 MLitt66. **d** 54 **p** 55. C Dublin St Thos *D & G* 54-56; C Dublin Grangegorman 56-62; Min Can St Patr Cathl Dublin 58-62; Hon Clerical V Ch Ch Cathl Dublin *D & G* 62-64; C Dublin Clontarf 62-64; C Thornton Heath St Jude *Cant* 64-66; V Norwood All SS 66-82; V Upper Norwood All SS w St Marg 82-84; RD Croydon N 81-84; Hon Can Can Cathl 82-84; V Merton St Mary *S'wark* 85-92; RD Croydon N 85; Hon Can S'wark Cathl 85-01; V Riddlesdown 92-01; rtd 01; Perm to Offic *S'wark* from 01. *73 Court Avenue, Coulsden CR5 1HG* Tel (01737) 551109

BROADHEAD, Alan John. b 38. Lon Univ MD62. Cuddesdon Coll 65. **d** 66 **p** 67. C Willenhall H Trin *Lich* 66-68; USA from 71. *517 3rd Avenue Southeast, Jamestown, ND 58402, USA*

✠**BROADHURST, The Rt Revd John Charles.** b 42. AKC65. Lambeth STh82. **d** 66 **p** 67 **c** 96. C Southgate St Mich *Lon* 66-70; C Wembley Park St Aug 70-73; P-in-c 73-75; V 75-85; AD Brent 82-85; TR Wood Green St Mich w Bounds Green St Gabr etc 85-96; AD E Haringey 85-91; Suff Bp Fulham from 96. *26 Canonbury Park South, London N1 2FN* Tel (020) 7354 2334 Fax 7354 2335 E-mail bpfulham@aol.com

BROADHURST, John James. b 08. Birm Univ BA31. **d** 32 **p** 33. C Heckmondwike *Wakef* 32-37; V Shelley 37-42; V Newton in Makerfield St Pet *Liv* 42-59; Chapl Red Bank Schs 43-59; R S Hill w Callington *Truro* 59-73; rtd 73; Perm to Offic *Sarum* from 01. *18 Monmouth Gardens, Beaminster DT8 3BT* Tel (01308) 862509

BROADHURST, Jonathan Robin. b 58. Univ Coll Ox BA81 MA86. Wycliffe Hall Ox 85. **d** 88 **p** 89. C Hull Newland St Jo *York* 88-91; P-in-c Burton Fleming w Fordon, Grindale etc 91-92; V 92-98; C Kingston upon Hull H Trin 98-01; P-in-c Rastrick St Jo *Wakef* from 01. *St John's Vicarage, 2 St John Street, Brighouse HD6 1HN* Tel (01484) 715889 Mobile 07790-899195 E-mail jonathan@broadhurst-jr.freeserve.co.uk

BROADHURST, Kenneth. b 33. Lon Coll of Div 56. **d** 59 **p** 60. C Bucknall and Bagnall *Lich* 59-63; R Rodington 63-67; C Longdon-upon-Tern 63-67; R Clitheroe St Jas *Blackb* 67-82; V Leyland St Andr 82-88; rtd 89; Perm to Offic *Blackb* from 89. *Paris House, 12 Ramsgreave Road, Ramsgreave, Blackburn*

BB1 9BH Tel (01254) 240924 E-mail kbroadhurst@btinternet.com

BROADLEY, Michael John. b 66. Roehampton Inst BA87. Trin Coll Bris 93. **d** 96 **p** 97. C Egham *Guildf* 96-01; TV Horsham *Chich* from 01. *St Mark's House, North Heath Lane, Horsham RH12 5PJ* Tel (01403) 254964 E-mail broadley@bigfoot.com

BROCK, Michael John. b 52. Birm Univ BSc74 Nottm Univ BA77. St Jo Coll Nottm 75. **d** 78 **p** 79. C Stapleford *S'well* 78-82; C Bestwood St Matt 82-86; TV Bestwood 86-90; R Epperstone from 90; R Gonalston from 90; V Oxton from 90; RD S'well 93-96; Dioc Adv in Rural Affairs 97-02; P-in-c Woodborough from 02. *The Rectory, Main Street, Epperstone, Nottingham NG14 6AG* Tel 0115-966 4220

BROCK, Preb Patrick Laurence. b 18. MBE45. Trin Coll Ox BA46 MA48. Ripon Hall Ox 55. **d** 57 **p** 58. C Gt Malvern St Mary *Worc* 57-59; C St Martin-in-the-Fields *Lon* 59-62; V Belsize Park 62-72; R Finchley St Mary 72-89; Preb St Paul's Cathl 80-89; AD Cen Barnet 80-85; rtd 89; Perm to Offic *Lon* from 89. *10 Albert Street, London NW1 7NZ* Tel (020) 7383 0198

BROCKBANK, Arthur Ross. b 51. Wigan Coll of Tech BTEC ND85. N Ord Course 87. **d** 90 **p** 91. C Haughton St Mary *Man* 90-93; V Bircle from 93; Chapl Bury Healthcare NHS Trust 93-03. *The Vicarage, 33 Castle Hill Road, Bury BL9 7RW* Tel 0161-764 3853

BROCKBANK, Donald Philip. b 56. Univ of Wales (Ban) BD78. Sarum & Wells Th Coll 79. **d** 81 **p** 82. C Prenton *Ches* 81-85; TV Birkenhead Priory 85-91; V Altrincham St Jo 91-96; Urban Officer 91-96; Dioc Ecum Officer *Lich* 96-98; C Lich St Mich w St Mary and Wall 96-98; V Acton and Worleston, Church Minshull etc *Ches* from 98. *St Mary's Vicarage, Chester Road, Acton, Nantwich CW5 8LG* Tel (01270) 628864 E-mail donald@brockbankrev.freeserve.co.uk

BROCKBANK, John Keith. b 44. Dur Univ BA65. Wells Th Coll 66. **d** 68 **p** 69. C Preston St Matt *Blackb* 68-71; C Lancaster St Mary 71-73; V Habergham All SS 73-83; P-in-c Gannow 81-83; V W Burnley 83-86; Dioc Stewardship Adv 86-92; P-in-c Shireshead 86-92; V Kirkham from 92. *The Vicarage, Kirkham, Preston PR4 2SE* Tel (01772) 683644 Fax as telephone E-mail revjkb@kirkvicarage.freeserve.co.uk

BROCKBANK, John Stanley. b 41. Carl and Blackb Dioc Tr Inst 97. **d** 00 **p** 01. OLM Arnside *Carl* from 00. *Hough Close, 5 Ash Meadow Road, Arnside, Carnforth LA5 0AE* Tel (01524) 761634

BROCKBANK, Leslie David. b 35. Auckland Univ CertSS77 MRIN53. St Aid Birkenhead 60. **d** 63 **p** 64. C Corby SS Pet and Andr *Pet* 63-66; C Darley w S Darley *Derby* 66-72; New Zealand from 72; Chapl Flying Angel Miss to Seamen 72-81; V Paparoa 81-91; V Bryant Park Hamilton 91-95; rtd 95; Titoki Healing Cen 95-96. *14 View Road, Te Kuiti, New Zealand* Tel (0064) (7) 8785904

BROCKHOUSE, Grant Lindley. b 47. Adelaide Univ BA71 Ex Univ MA81. St Barn Coll Adelaide 70 ACT ThL72. **d** 73 **p** 74. Australia 73-78; C Ex St Jas *Ex* 78-80; Asst Chapl Ex Univ 80-83; Dep PV Ex Cathl 81-98; V Marldon 83-98; RD Torbay 95-98; V Higham Ferrers w Chelveston *Pet* from 98; RD Higham from 03. *The Vicarage, Wood Street, Higham Ferrers, Rushden NN10 8DL* Tel (01933) 312433 E-mail grantbrockhouse@care4free.net

BROCKIE, Canon William James Thomson. b 36. Pemb Coll Ox BA58 MA62. Linc Th Coll 58. **d** 60 **p** 61. C Lin St Jo Bapt CD *Linc* 60-63; V Gt Staughton *Ely* 63-68; Chapl HM Borstal Gaynes Hall 63-68; TV Edin St Jo *Edin* 68-76; Chapl Edin Univ 71-76; USA 76; R Edin St Martin *Edin* 76-01; P-in-c Edin St Luke 79-90; Hon Can St Mary's Cathl from 98; rtd 00. *St Hilda's House, 1B Oxgangs Avenue, Edinburgh EH13 9HZ* Tel 0131-441 1235 E-mail billjennybrockie@hotmail.com

BROCKLEBANK, John. b 32. N Ord Course 83. **d** 86 **p** 87. NSM Warrington St Barn *Liv* 86-93; NSM Orford St Marg 93-97; rtd 97; Perm to Offic *Ches* and *Liv* from 99. *53 St Mary's Road, Penketh, Warrington WA5 2DT* Tel (01925) 722063

BROCKLEHURST, John Richard. b 51. Univ Coll Ox BA72 Lon Univ CertEd74. Oak Hill Th Coll BA81. **d** 81 **p** 82. C Harwood *Man* 81-85; V Hopwood 85-97; P-in-c Friarmere 97-03; TV Saddleworth from 03. *The Vicarage, 1 Cobblers Hill, Delph, Oldham OL3 5HT* Tel (01457) 874209

BROCKLEHURST, Simon. b 63. Cranmer Hall Dur 86. **d** 89 **p** 90. C Clifton *S'well* 89-93; TV 93-96; P-in-c Mabe *Truro* 96-99; Miss to Seamen 96-99; V Ham St Andr *S'wark* from 99; Inland Hon Chapl Miss to Seafarers from 00. *St Andrew's Vicarage, Church Road, Ham, Richmond TW10 5HG* Tel (020) 8940 9017 Fax as telephone

BRODDLE, Christopher Stephen Thomas. b 57. **d** 87 **p** 88. C Lisburn St Paul *Conn* 87-90; CF from 90. *c/o MOD Chaplains (Army)* Tel (01980) 615804 Fax 615800

BRODIE, Frederick. b 40. Leic Teacher Tr Coll TCert61. St Jo Coll Nottm DCM92. **d** 92 **p** 93. C Lutterworth w Cotesbach *Leic* 92-95; P-in-c Mountsorrel Ch Ch and St Pet 95-97; V 97-03; rtd 03. *11 Cooper Lane, Ratby, Leicester LE6 0QG* Tel 0116-238 7959 E-mail fbrodie@leicester.anglican.org

BRODY, Paul. b 40. N Ord Course 85. **d** 88 **p** 89. C Leigh St Mary *Man* 88-90; C Peel 90-91; TR 91-97; TV Worsley from 97. *8 Landrace Drive, Worsley, Manchester M28 1UY* Tel 0161-799 1208 E-mail paul.brody@amserve.net

BROGGIO, Bernice Muriel Croager. b 35. Bedf Coll Lon BA57 K Coll Lon BD66 IDC66 Glas Univ DSS71 DASS72. **dss** 84 **d** 87 **p** 94. Bris St Paul w St Barn *Bris* 84-87; Hon Par Dn Bris St Paul's 87-88; C Charlton St Luke w H Trin *S'wark* 88-95; V Upper Tooting H Trin 95-03; Hon Can S'wark Cathl 95-03; RD Tooting 96-02; TV Bensham *Dur* from 03. *St Chad's Vicarage, Dunsmuir Grove, Gateshead NE8 4QL* Tel 0191-478 6338 Fax as telephone E-mail bernicebroggio@hotmail.com

BROMAGE, Kenneth Charles. b 51. EAMTC. **d** 90 **p** 91. NSM Woolpit w Drinkstone *St E* 90-92; Chapl RN from 92. *Royal Naval Chaplaincy Service, Room 203, Victory Building, HM Naval Base, Portsmouth PO1 3LS* Tel (023) 9272 7903 Fax 9272 7111

BROMFIELD, Michael. b 32. Kelham Th Coll 54 Lich Th Coll 59. **d** 62 **p** 63. C Sedgley All SS *Lich* 62-64; C Tunstall Ch Ch 64-67; P-in-c Grindon 67-70; R 70-80; P-in-c Butterton 67-70; V 70-80; R Hope Bowdler w Eaton-under-Heywood *Heref* 80-97; R Rushbury 80-97; V Cardington 80-97; rtd 98; Perm to Offic *Lich* from 98. *11 Walklate Avenue, Newcastle ST5 0PR* Tel (01782) 630716 E-mail bromfield@stoke54.freeserve.co.uk

BROMFIELD, Nicholas Robert. b 60. St Jo Coll Cam MA82. WEMTC 98. **d** 02 **p** 03. NSM Tidenham w Beachley and Lancaut *Glouc* from 02. *Forest Edge House, The Purples, Coalway, Coleford GL16 7JL* Tel (01594) 835092 Fax 835533 E-mail bromfields@email.msn.com

BROMFIELD, Richard Allan. b 47. LVCM85 Sussex Univ MA96. Chich Th Coll 86. **d** 88 **p** 89. C Durrington *Chich* 88-95; V Woodingdean from 95. *The Vicarage, 2 Downsway, Brighton BN2 6BD* Tel (01273) 681582

BROMILEY, Paul Nigel. b 49. Univ of Wales (Cardiff) BSc71. Oak Hill Th Coll 88. **d** 90 **p** 91. C Gee Cross *Ches* 90-94; P-in-c Millbrook from 94. *St James's Vicarage, 28 Buckton Vale Road, Stalybridge SK15 3LW* Tel (01457) 833295

BROMILEY, Philip Arthur. b 73. Westmr Coll Ox BTh94 St Jo Coll Dur MA98. Cranmer Hall Dur 95. **d** 98 **p** 99. C Marton *Blackb* 98-01; Assoc P Calne and Blackland *Sarum* from 01. *7 Richmond Road, Calne SN11 9UW* Tel (01249) 818677 E-mail philbromiley@cybernail.uk.com

BROMLEY, Mrs Janet Catherine Gay. b 45. Surrey Univ BSc68 Bradf Univ MSc72 Brunel Tech Coll Bris FE TCert86. S Dios Minl Tr Scheme 91. **d** 94 **p** 96. C Westbury-on-Trym H Trin *Bris* 94-96; C Wroughton 96-00; Dean of Women's Min 98-00; R Dursley *Glouc* from 00. *The Rectory, Broadwell, Dursley GL11 4JE* Tel (01453) 542053 E-mail revjanet@dursleyparishchurch.freeserve.co.uk

BROMLEY, William James. b 44. Edin Univ BD74. Edin Th Coll 70. **d** 74 **p** 75. C Glas St Mary *Glas* 74-77; Bangladesh 77-80; R Glas H Cross *Glas* 80-89; R Stottesdon w Farlow, Cleeton St Mary, etc *Heref* from 89. *The Rectory, Stottesdon, Kidderminster DY14 8UE* Tel (01746) 718297 E-mail billbromley@talk21.com

BROMLEY AND BEXLEY, Archdeacon of. *See* NORMAN, The Ven Garth

BRONNERT, Preb David Llewellyn Edward. b 36. Ch Coll Cam BA57 MA61 PhD61 Lon Univ BD62. Tyndale Hall Bris 60. **d** 63 **p** 64. C Cheadle Hulme St Andr *Ches* 63-67; C Islington St Mary *Lon* 67-69; Chapl N Lon Poly 69-75; V Southall Green St Jo 75-01; Preb St Paul's Cathl 89-01; P-in-c Southall St Geo 92-99; AD Ealing W 84-90; rtd 01. *101 Walton Way, Aylesbury HP21 7JP* Tel (01296) 484048 E-mail david.bronnert@talk21.com

BRONNERT, John. b 33. Man Univ MA(Theol)84 Univ of Wales (Lamp) PhD98 Lon Univ DipTh68 ACA57 FCA68. Tyndale Hall Bris 65. **d** 68 **p** 69. C Hoole *Ches* 68-71; P-in-c Parr *Liv* 71-73; TV 73-85; V Runcorn St Jo Weston *Ches* 85-98; rtd 98; Perm to Offic *Liv* from 85; *Man* from 98. *Tyndale, 15 Craig Avenue, Flixton, Urmston, Manchester M41 5JS* Tel 0161-748 7061 E-mail bronnert-revddrjohn@tyndale.freeserve.co.uk

BROOK, Kathleen Marjorie. b 23. IDC. Lightfoot Ho Dur 57. **dss** 84 **d** 87 **p** 94. Linthorpe *York* 64-75; Ormesby 75-83; rtd 83; Perm to Offic *York* from 83. *6 Station Square, Saltburn-by-the-Sea TS12 1AG* Tel (01287) 624006

BROOK, Peter Geoffrey (Brother Simon). b 47. N Ord Course 91. **d** 94 **p** 95. CGA from 71; NSM Heywood and Middleton Deanery 94-96; Perm to Offic *Ex* from 96. *The Priory, Lamacraft Farm, Start Point, Chivelstone, Kingsbridge TQ7 2NG* Tel (01548) 511474

BROOK, Stephen Edward. b 44. Univ of Wales (Abth) BSc65 DipEd66 Lisbon Univ 89. Wycliffe Hall Ox 71 All Nations Chr Coll 85. **d** 74 **p** 75. C Heworth H Trin *York* 74-77; C Linthorpe 77-80; TV Deane *Man* 80-85; BCMS 86-93; Crosslinks 93-96; Portugal 88-96; P-in-c Bacup St Sav *Man* from 96; P-in-c Tunstead from 99. *St Saviour's Vicarage, 10 Park Crescent, Bacup OL13 9RL* Tel (01706) 873362

BROOK, William Neville. b 31. S'wark Ord Course 66. **d** 69 **p** 70. C Maidstone St Martin *Cant* 69-75; V Hartlip w Stockbury 75-80; R Willesborough w Hinxhill 80-86; R Willesborough 87-89; V Gt Staughton *Ely* 89-96; V Hail Weston 89-96; rtd 96; Perm to Offic *Chich* from 96. *27 Middleton Drive, Eastbourne BN23 6HD* Tel (01323) 731243

BROOKE, Miss Bridget Cecilia. b 31. DBO51. Coll of Resurr Mirfield 88. **d** 89 **p** 94. Hon Par Dn Ranmoor *Sheff* 89-94; Hon C from 94; Bp's Adv for NSMs 94-01. *166 Tom Lane, Sheffield S10 3PG* Tel 0114-230 2147

BROOKE, David Fewsdale. b 43. St Paul's Coll Grahamstown 80. **d** 90 **p** 90. S Africa 90-99; Asst Chapl Dioc Coll Cape Town 90-92; NSM Crawford St Jo 93-97; NSM Sea Point St Jas 98-99; Perm to Offic *Newc* 00; C Norham and Duddo from 01; C Cornhill w Carham from 01; C Branxton from 01. *The Vicarage, The Old School House, Branxton, Cornhill-on-Tweed TD12 4SW* Tel and fax (01890) 820308 Mobile 07801-751136 E-mail david@fruitspree.freeserve.co.uk

BROOKE, David Martin. b 58. Selw Coll Cam BA80 MA83 Lon Inst of Educn PGCE81. St Alb and Ox Min Course 96. **d** 99 **p** 00. C Luton Lewsey St Hugh *St Alb* 99-00; NSM Sunnyside w Bourne End 00-02; C from 02. *1 Westview Rise, Hemel Hempstead HP2 5DQ* Tel (01442) 389297 Mobile 07967-326085 E-mail rev.david.brooke@ntlworld.com

BROOKE, Canon Robert. b 44. Birm Univ DPS77. Qu Coll Birm 70. **d** 73 **p** 74. C Man Resurr *Man* 73-76; C Bournville *Birm* 76-77; Chapl Qu Eliz Coll *Lon* 77-82; C Bramley *Ripon* 82-85; TV 85-86; V Hunslet Moor St Pet and St Cuth 86-93; Chapl People w Learning Disabilities from 86; TV Seacroft 93-03; TV Beeston from 03; Chapl Leeds Mental Health Teaching NHS Trust 94-03; Hon Can Ripon Cathl *Ripon* from 01. *St David's House, Waincliffe Drive, Leeds LS11 8ET* Tel 0113-2829 E-mail bob.brooke@another.com

BROOKE, Rosemary Jane. b 53. Cam Univ BEd75 Open Univ BA83. N Ord Course 86. **d** 89 **p** 94. NSM Poynton *Ches* from 89; Bp's Adv for Women in Min from 96. *45 Brookfield Avenue, Poynton, Stockport SK12 1JE* Tel (01625) 872822

BROOKE, Timothy Cyril. b 38. Jes Coll Cam BA60 MA70 Middx Poly CQSW76. Ripon Coll Cuddesdon 84. **d** 86 **p** 87. C Hillmorton *Cov* 86-90; V Earlsdon 90-98; V Cov St Fran N Radford from 98. *St Francis's Vicarage, 110 Treherne Road, Coventry CV6 3DY* Tel (024) 7659 5178 E-mail brookenet@zetnet.co.uk

BROOKE, Vernon. b 41. St Aid Birkenhead 62. **d** 65 **p** 66. C Crofton Park St Hilda w St Cypr *S'wark* 65-68; C Eccleshill *Bradf* 68-70; Ind Chapl *Linc* 70-84; Ind Chapl *Derby* 84-97; Ind Chapl *Chich* from 97. *6 Patcham Grange, Brighton BN1 8UR* Tel (01273) 564057 Fax as telephone E-mail vernonbrooke@yahoo.co.uk

BROOKE, Canon William Edward. b 13. Birm Univ BA34 MA35. Westcott Ho Cam 35. **d** 37 **p** 38. C Wylde Green *Birm* 37-40; C Sparkbrook St Agatha 40-44; P-in-c Birm St Jude 44-50; V 50-60; R Castle Bromwich SS Mary and Marg 60-78; Hon Can Birm Cathl 61-78; rtd 78; Perm to Offic *Heref* from 78. *Ivy Cottage, Tarrington, Hereford HR1 4HZ*

BROOKER, Mrs Anna Lesley. b 56. York Univ BA78 MA79 Homerton Coll Cam PGCE80. Ridley Hall Cam 01. **d** 03. C Brentford *Lon* from 03. *14 Heatham Park, Twickenham TW2 7SF* Tel (020) 8892 2580 Mobile 07960-120753 E-mail albrooker@email.com

BROOKER, Miss Ruth Muriel. b 53. Wycliffe Hall Ox 96. **d** 98 **p** 99. C Beverley Minster *York* 98-02; R Haddlesey w Hambleton and Birkin 02-03. *Bawtry Hall, South Parade, Bawtry, Doncaster DN10 6JH* Tel (01302) 710020 Fax 710027

BROOKER, Mrs Wendy Ann. b 41. St Alb Minl Tr Scheme 82. **dss** 85 **d** 87 **p** 94. Pinner *Lon* 85-87; Greenhill St Jo 87; Par Dn 87-88; Ind Chapl 89-94; NSM Hayes St Edm 94; C 95-99; Chapl R Nat Orthopaedic Hosp NHS Trust from 99. *Royal National Orthopaedic Hospital, Brockley Hill, Stanmore HA7 4LP* Tel (020) 8954 2300

BROOKES, Arthur George. b 21. ACIB52. Worc Ord Coll 64. **d** 66 **p** 67. C Lower Mitton *Worc* 66-67; C Fladbury w Throckmorton, Wyre Piddle and Moor 67-70; C Abberton w Bishampton 67-70; R 70-73; V Cradley 73-78; P-in-c Castle Morton 78-79; P-in-c Holly Bush w Birtsmorton 78-79; P-in-c Castlemorton, Hollybush and Birtsmorton 79-80; P-in-c Norton w Whittington 80-81; TV Worc St Martin w St Pet, St Mark etc 81-86; rtd 86; Perm to Offic *Worc* from 86; *Glouc* from 96. *13 Capel Court, The Burgage, Prestbury, Cheltenham GL52 3EL* Tel (01242) 580523

BROOKES, Colin Stuart. b 70. Lon Bible Coll BA93. Ridley Hall Cam 00. **d** 02 **p** 03. C Cambridge St Barn *Ely* from 02. *80 St Barnabas Road, Cambridge CB1 2DE* Tel (01223) 367578 Mobile 07973-840340 E-mail curate@stbs.org.uk

BROOKES, David Charles. b 45. St Mich Coll Llan 84. **d** 86 **p** 87. C Llanishen and Lisvane *Llan* 86-88; TV Brighouse St Martin *Wakef* 89-92; TV Brighouse and Clifton 92-94; V Hollingbourne and Hucking w Leeds and Broomfield *Cant* from 94. *The Vicarage, Hollingbourne, Maidstone ME17 1UJ* Tel (01622) 880243 E-mail david@dcbrookes.freeserve.co.uk

BROOKES, Derrick Meridyth. b 17. Trin Hall Cam BA38 MA42. Westcott Ho Cam 39. **d** 40 **p** 41. C Macclesfield St Mich *Ches* 40-44; Chapl RAFVR 44-47; C Wilmslow *Ches* 47-49; V Chipping Sodbury and Old Sodbury *Glouc* 49-53; Youth Chapl 51-53; Chapl RAF 53-72; Master Bris Cathl Sch 72-73; Master XIV Prep Sch Bris 73-78. *Woodpeckers, Pilcorn Street, Wedmore BS28 4AW* Tel (01934) 712988

BROOKES, Edwin William. b 39. St Mark & St Jo Coll Lon TCert63 Birm Univ BPhil(Ed)85 Open Univ BA73 BA93. OLM course 95. **d** 98 **p** 99. OLM Cen Wolverhampton *Lich* from 98. *23 Chetwynd Road, Blakenhall, Wolverhampton WV2 4NZ* Tel (01902) 654979 *or* 428491 Fax 562616
E-mail edbrookes@bleak23.freeserve.co.uk

BROOKES, Geoffrey John Denis. b 24. CMS Tr Coll Crowther Hall 78 Ridley Hall Cam 84. **d** 85 **p** 86. Bahrain 85-88; Project Officer Ch Action w the Unemployed 88-91; Hon C Hastings All So *Chich* 88-91; Asst Chapl Milan w Genoa and Varese *Eur* 91-94; Canada 94-97; Perm to Offic *Chich* 97-99; and from 01. *Flat 3, 11 Warrior Square Terrace, St Leonards-on-Sea TN37 6BN* Tel (01424) 430943

BROOKES, Jean. b 37. St Jo Coll Auckland LTh69 Selly Oak Coll 74. **d** 69 **p** 77. New Zealand 69-74 and from 76; C E Coast Bays 69-71; C Glenfield 72-74; C Shenley Green *Birm* 74-76; C Howick 76-77; Asst P 77-81; V Mangere E 81-89; Prov Bicultural Unit 89-92; Field Worker Chr World Service 92-95; Co-ord Warren's Cen Auckland 95-97; Lic to Offic from 97. *3/130B Balmoral Road, Mount Eden, Auckland 1003, New Zealand* Tel (0064) (9) 630 0455

BROOKES, Keith Roy. b 37. JP74. MHCIMA MRSH Leeds Univ DipEd72. St Aid Birkenhead 64. **d** 80 **p** 81. Hon C Stockport St Thos *Ches* 80-86; Hon C Stockport St Thos w St Pet 86-91; C 91-98; Hon C from 99. *42 Derby Road, Stockport SK4 4NE* Tel 0161-442 0301

BROOKES, Laurence. b 33. Dioc OLM tr scheme 01. **d** 02 **p** 03. OLM Flockton cum Denby Grange *Wakef* from 02; OLM Emley from 02. *Treetops, 6 Chessington Drive, Flockton, Wakefield WF4 4TJ* Tel (01924) 848238

BROOKES, Robin Keenan. b 47. Trin Coll Bris 72. **d** 75 **p** 76. C Livesey *Blackb* 75-78; C Burnley St Pet 78-80; P-in-c Bawdeswell w Foxley *Nor* 80-83; I Donagh w Tyholland and Errigal Truagh *Clogh* 83-91; Dioc Communications Officer 90-91; I Dublin Drumcondra w N Strand *D & G* 91-99; Chapl Ayia Napa Cyprus from 99. *PO Box 33873, 5318 Paralimni, Cyprus* Tel (00357) (23) 742955 *or* 742956 Mobile 99-698049 Fax (23) 742957
E-mail angfam@spidernet.com.cy

BROOKES, Steven David. b 60. Lanc Univ BA81. Ripon Coll Cuddesdon 82. **d** 85 **p** 86. C Stanley *Liv* 85-88; C W Derby St Mary 88-90; Chapl RN 90-94; R Weybridge *Guildf* 94-03; P-in-c Liv Our Lady and St Nic w St Anne *Liv* from 03. *Apartment 19, 15 Hatton Garden, Liverpool L3 2HA* Tel 0151-236 5287 *or* 724 1284 E-mail weystjam@surfaid.org

BROOKFIELD, Alun John. b 50. Lon Univ BMus72 Spurgeon's Coll Lon BA82. **d** 00 **p** 01. NSM Stratton St Margaret w S Marston etc *Bris* 00-02; P-in-c Cwmtawe Uchaf *S & B* from 03. *The Vicarage, Heol Tawe, Abercrave, Swansea SA9 1TJ* Tel (01639) 730640 E-mail a.brookfield@ntlworld.com

BROOKFIELD, Patricia Anne. See HARDACRE, Patricia Anne

BROOKHOUSE, Leslie. b 28. Ridley Hall Cam 69 St Aid Birkenhead 68. **d** 70 **p** 71. C Tonge *Man* 70-72; C Didsbury Ch Ch 72-74; V Newall Green St Fran 74-80; V High Crompton 80-86; R Ashwater, Halwill, Beaworthy, Clawton etc *Ex* 86-98; RD Holsworthy 94-99; rtd 98; P-in-c Pyworthy, Pancrasweek and Bridgerule *Ex* 98-03. *9 St Andrew's Close, Sutcombe, Holsworthy EX22 7PL* Tel (01409) 240021
E-mail lbrookhouse@talk21.com

BROOKS, Alan Leslie. b 43. Nor City Coll TCert65. Dioc OLM tr scheme 98. **d** 01 **p** 02. OLM Waterloo Ch Ch and St Jo *Liv* from 01. *6 Kingsway, Waterloo, Liverpool L22 4RQ* Tel 0151-920 8770

BROOKS, Mrs Alison Margaret. b 46. EMMTC. **d** 03. Asst Chapl Qu Medical Cen Nottm Univ Hosp NHS Trust from 03. *12 Russell Avenue, Wollaton, Nottingham NG8 2BL*

BROOKS, Mrs Christine Ellen. b 43. Sheff Univ BA65 Lon Univ BD81. Lambeth STh81 EAMTC 86. **d** 88 **p** 94. NSM Palgrave w Wortham and Burgate *St E* 88-89; Par Dn Thorndon w Rishangles, Stoke Ash, Thwaite etc 89-94; P-in-c Aldringham w Thorpe, Knodishall w Buxlow etc from 94; Asst P Sternfield w Benhall and Snape 98-03; P-in-c from 03; P-in-c Gt and Lt Glemham, Blaxhall etc from 03. *The Rectory, Aldeburgh Road, Friston, Saxmundham IP17 1NP* Tel (01728) 688972 Mobile 07752-652833

BROOKS, Dorothy Anne. See MOORE BROOKS, Dorothy Anne

BROOKS, Canon Francis Leslie. b 35. Kelham Th Coll 55. **d** 59 **p** 60. C Woodlands *Sheff* 59-61; Ind Missr S Yorkshire Coalfields 61-66; V Moorends 66-72; Chapl HM Borstal Hatf 67-72; Chapl HM Pris Acklington 72-75; Chapl HM Borstal Wellingborough 75-79; Chapl HM Pris Wakef 79-83; Area Sec USPG *Wakef* and *Bradf* 83-88; V Carleton *Wakef* 88-96; V E Hardwick 88-96; Can

Mara (Tanzania) from 88; rtd 96. *4 Ennerdale Drive, Elland HX5 9QJ* Tel (01422) 375571

BROOKS, Ian George. b 47. Selw Coll Cam BA68 MA72. Chich Th Coll 68. **d** 70 **p** 71. C Stoke Newington St Mary *Lon* 70-74; C Hoxton St Anne w St Sav and St Andr 74-75; C Hoxton St Anne w St Columba 75-80; P-in-c Croxteth St Paul CD *Liv* 80-81; V Croxteth from 81. *St Paul's Vicarage, Delabole Road, Liverpool L11 6LG* Tel 0151-548 9009 Fax as telephone

BROOKS, Jeremy Paul. b 67. Leic Univ LLB88 Clare Coll Cam BA96 MA01 K Coll Lon MA00. Ridley Hall Cam 94. **d** 97 **p** 98. C Highgate St Mich *Lon* 97-01; P-in-c Hoddesdon *St Alb* from 01. *11 Oxenden Drive, Hoddesdon EN11 8QF* Tel (01992) 464335
E-mail jeremy.brooks@btinternet.com

BROOKS, Jonathan Thorburn. b 53. Solicitor 76 G&C Coll Cam BA75 DipHE. Trin Coll Bris 84. **d** 86 **p** 87. C Dagenham *Chelmsf* 86-88; Perm to Offic *Glouc* from 03. *12 Hyde Avenue, Thornbury, Bristol BS35 1JA* Tel (01454) 411853

BROOKS, Malcolm David. b 45. Univ of Wales (Lamp) DipTh71. **d** 71 **p** 72. C Pontllottyn w Fochriw *Llan* 71-72; C Caerphilly 72-78; V Ferndale w Maerdy 78-81; C Port Talbot St Theodore 82-84; V Ystrad Mynach 84-85; V Ystrad Mynach w Llanbradach from 85. *The Vicarage, Nelson Road, Ystrad Mynach, Hengoed CF82 7EG* Tel (01443) 813246

BROOKS, Patrick John. b 27. Man Univ BA49 DipEd. Oak Hill Th Coll 78. **d** 77 **p** 79. Burundi 77-80; Perm to Offic *Ex* 80-83; P-in-c Phillack w Gwithian and Gwinear *Truro* 83-88; R 88-93; rtd 93; Perm to Offic *Chich* from 93. *Abbots, Claigmar Road, Rustington, Littlehampton BN16 2NL*

BROOKS, Paul John. b 59. Loughb Univ BSc81 Dip Th Studies 89 DPS90. St Jo Coll Nottm 87. **d** 90 **p** 91. C Long Eaton St Jo *Derby* 90-94; Min Jersey St Paul Prop Chpl *Win* from 94. *5 Claremont Avenue, St Saviour, Jersey JE2 7SF* Tel (01534) 880393 E-mail pjbvic@aol.com

BROOKS, Peter. b 55. St Mich Coll Llan DMS99. **d** 99 **p** 00. C Morriston *S & B* 99-01; P-in-c Rhayader and Nantmel 01-02; P-in-c Cwmddauddwr w St Harmon's and Llanwrthwl from 02. *The Vicarage, Dark Lane, Rhayader LD6 5DA* Tel (01597) 810223

BROOKS, Peter Joseph. b 54. **d** 83 **p** 84. C Portslade St Nic and St Andr *Chich* 83-86; C Kingstanding St Luke *Birm* 86-91; V Nork *Guildf* from 91. *The Vicarage, Warren Road, Banstead SM7 1LG* Tel (01737) 353849
E-mail fatherpeter@craggyisland.co.uk

BROOKS, Philip David. b 52. MA Cam Univ MTh. St Jo Coll Nottm 80. **d** 83 **p** 84. C Ipsley *Worc* 83-87; V Fulford w Hilderstone *Lich* 87-95; Chapl Stallington Hosp 87-95; P-in-c Crich *Derby* 95-01; V Crich and S Wingfield from 01. *The Vicarage, 19 Coasthill, Crich, Matlock DE4 5DS* Tel (01773) 852449 E-mail philipdbro@aol.com

BROOKS, Roger John. b 46. Nottm Univ PhD71 MRPharmS70 FFARCS81. N Ord Course 98. **d** 01 **p** 02. C Burley in Wharfedale *Bradf* from 01. *7 Rose Bank, Burley in Wharfedale, Ilkley LS29 7PQ* Tel (01943) 864890
E-mail rjb@fonticulus.org.uk

BROOKS, Mrs Susan Margaret. b 50. Philippa Fawcett Coll CertEd71 Open Univ BA95. SEITE 00. **d** 03. *189 Malling Road, Snodland ME6 5EE* Tel (01634) 241350
E-mail suebrooks@talk21.com

BROOKS, Mrs Susan Vera. b 51. N Ord Course 87. **d** 90 **p** 94. Par Dn Carleton and E Hardwick *Wakef* 90-93; TV Almondbury w Farnley Tyas 93-98; Chapl Huddersfield NHS Trust 98-01; Chapl Calderdale and Huddersfield NHS Trust from 01. *Huddersfield Royal Infirmary, Acre Street, Lindley, Huddersfield HD3 3EA* Tel (01484) 422191 *or* 323839

BROOKS, Mrs Vivien June. b 47. Univ of Wales (Ban) BA68 Southn Univ MA70. Ridley Hall Cam 87. **d** 89 **p** 95. C Exning St Martin w Landwade *St E* 89-92; Par Dn Hermitage and Hampstead Norreys, Cold Ash etc *Ox* 92-94; C 94-95; P-in-c Cox Green 95-03; Co Ecum Officer (Berks) 00-03; P-in-c Earls Colne w White Colne and Colne Engaine *Chelmsf* from 03. *The Rectory, 5 Shut Lane, Earls Colne, Colchester CO6 2RE* E-mail vbrooks@minnieb.com

BROOKS, Vivienne Christine. See ARMSTRONG-MacDONNELL, Mrs Vivienne Christine

BROOKSBANK, Alan Watson. b 43. Univ of Wales (Lamp) BA64 Edin Univ MEd76. Edin Th Coll 64. **d** 66 **p** 67. C Cleator Moor w Cleator *Carl* 66-70; V Dalston 70-80; P-in-c Greystoke, Matterdale and Mungrisdale 80-81; R 81-83; R Watermillock 81-83; R Hagley *Worc* 83-95; Bp's Officer for NSM 88-95; V Claines St Jo 95-98; rtd 98. *169 Northfields Lane, Brixham TQ5 8RD*

BROOKSHAW, Miss Janice Chitty. b 48. MIPD90. Ripon Coll Cuddesdon 96. **d** 98 **p** 99. C Beaconsfield *Ox* 98-02; P-in-c The Stodden Churches *St Alb* from 02. *The Stodden Rectory, High Street, Upper Dean, Huntingdon PE28 0ND* Tel (01234) 708531 Fax as telephone E-mail jan@revbrookshaw.freeserve.co.uk

BROOKSTEIN, Canon Royston. b 29. Qu Coll Birm 60. **d** 62 **p** 63. C Rubery *Birm* 62-66; V Cotteridge 66-75; V Hall Green St Pet 75-94; Hon Can Birm Cathl 84-94; rtd 94; Perm to Offic

Birm from 94. *257 Wake Green Road, Birmingham B13 9XH* Tel 0121-777 7989

BROOM, Andrew Clifford. b 65. Keele Univ BSocSc86. Trin Coll Bris BA92. **d** 92 **p** 93. C Wellington, All SS w Eyton *Lich* 92-96; C Brampton St Thos *Derby* 96-00; V Walton St Jo from 00. *6 Medlock Road, Walton, Chesterfield S40 3NH* Tel (01246) 205993 E-mail a.broom@ukonline.co.uk

BROOM, Jacqueline Anne. b 52. R Holloway Coll Lon BSc73. Trin Coll Bris DipHE81. **dss** 82 **d** 95 **p** 95. Easton H Trin w St Gabr and St Lawr and St Jude *Bris* 82-86; OMF Internat 87-01; Hong Kong 87-95; Macao China 96-01; rtd 01. *25 Coralberry Drive, Weston-super-Mare BS22 6SQ* Tel (01934) 520439

BROOME, David Curtis. b 36. Leeds Univ BA63. Coll of Resurr Mirfield. **d** 65 **p** 66. C Winshill *Derby* 65-69; C Leigh-on-Sea St Marg *Chelmsf* 69-74; V Leeds St Marg *Ripon* 74-81; V Stoke H Cross w Dunston *Nor* 81-93; P-in-c Arminghall 92-93; P-in-c Caistor w Markshall 92-93; R Stoke H Cross w Dunston, Arminghall etc 93-00; rtd 00; Perm to Offic *Nor* from 00. *13 Greenacres Drive, Poringland, Norwich NR14 7JG* Tel (01508) 493201

BROOME, Mildred Dorothy. **d** 00 **p** 01. NSM Malden St Jo *S'wark* from 00. *124 The Manor Drive, Worcester Park KT4 7LW* Tel (020) 8337 1572

BROOMFIELD, David John. b 37. Reading Univ BA59. Oak Hill Th Coll 64. **d** 66 **p** 67. C Gresley *Derby* 66-71; C Rainham *Chelmsf* 71-77; R High Ongar w Norton Mandeville 77-88; RD Ongar 83-88; P-in-c Stanford Rivers 84-86; P-in-c Loughton St Mary and St Mich 88-95; P-in-c Loughton St Mary 95-97; R 97-03; rtd 03. *15 Oriel Grove, Moreton-in-Marsh GL56 0ED* Tel (01608) 651023 E-mail david@dabroomfield.freeserve.co.uk

BROOMFIELD, Iain Jonathan. b 57. Univ Coll Ox MA87. Wycliffe Hall Ox 80. **d** 83 **p** 84. C Beckenham Ch Ch *Roch* 83-87; Sen Schs Worker Titus Trust 87-00; V Bromley Ch Ch *Roch* from 00. *Christ Church Vicarage, 18 Highland Road, Bromley BR1 4AD* Tel (020) 8313 9882

BROSNAN, Mark. b 61. St Martin's Coll Lanc BA83 RMN88 Otley Agric Coll. EAMTC 92. **d** 95 **p** 96. C Rushmere *St E* 95-98; NSM Shrub End *Chelmsf* from 01. *100 Old Heath Road, Colchester CO1 2HB* Tel (01206) 797478

BROSTER, Godfrey David. b 52. Ealing Tech Coll BA75. Ripon Coll Cuddesdon 78. **d** 81 **p** 82. C Crayford *Roch* 81-82; C Brighton Resurr *Chich* 82-86; C-in-c The Hydneye CD 86-91; R Plumpton w E Chiltington 91-93; R Plumpton w E Chiltington cum Novington from 93. *The Rectory, Station Road, Plumpton Green, Lewes BN7 3BU* Tel (01273) 890570

BROTHERSTON, Miss Isabel Mary. b 42. Cranmer Hall Dur 81. **dss** 83 **d** 87 **p** 94. Coleshill *Birm* 83-87; Par Dn Duddeston w Nechells 87-92; Par Dn Harlescott *Lich* 92-94; C from 94. *Emmanuel Vicarage, Mount Pleasant Road, Shrewsbury SY1 3HY* Tel (01743) 350907 Fax as telephone

BROTHERTON, The Ven John Michael. b 35. St Jo Coll Cam BA59 MA63. Cuddesdon Coll 59. **d** 61 **p** 62. C Chiswick St Nic w St Mary *Lon* 61-65; Trinidad and Tobago 65-75; V Cowley St Jo *Ox* 76-81; Chapl St Hilda's Coll Ox 76-81; RD Cowley *Ox* 78-81; V Portsea St Mary *Portsm* 81-91; Hon Can Kobe Japan from 86; Adn Chich 91-02; rtd 02. *Flat 2, 23 Gledhow Gardens, London SW5 0AZ* Tel (020) 7373 5147 E-mail jmbrotherton@hotmail.com

BROTHERTON, Michael. b 56. MBE93. Univ of Wales (Abth) BD80. Wycliffe Hall Ox 80. **d** 81 **p** 82. Hon Chapl Miss to Seamen 81-84; C Pembroke Dock *St D* 81-84; Chapl RN from 84. *Royal Naval Chaplaincy Service, Room 203, Victory Building, HM Naval Base, Portsmouth PO1 3LS* Tel (023) 9272 7903 Fax 9272 7111

BROTHERWOOD, Nicholas Peter. b 50. Oak Hill Th Coll BA83. **d** 83 **p** 84. C Nottingham St Nic *S'well* 83-86; Canada from 86; Dir Quebec Lodge 86-89; Angl Chapl McGill Univ 89-91; Assoc R Westmount St Steph from 91. *3498 Harvard Avenue, Montreal PQ, Canada, H4A 2W3* Tel (001) (514) 489 4158 Fax 932 0550 E-mail st.stephens@qc.aira.com

BROTHWELL, Paul David. b 37. Lich Th Coll 62. **d** 65 **p** 66. C Honley *Wakef* 65-68; Min Can Wakef Cathl 68-71; V Whittington St Giles *Lich* 71-83; P-in-c Weeford 78-83; V Whittington w Weeford 83-92; Chapl Kidderminster Gen Hosp 92-94; Chapl Kidderminster Health Care NHS Trust 94-01; Chapl Worcs Community and Mental Health Trust 01-02; Hon Can Antananarivo 02; rtd 02. *8 Hillside Close, Stourport-on-Severn DY13 0JW* Tel (01299) 823495 or (01562) 823424 ext 3306

BROTHWOOD, Ian Sidney. b 56. K Coll Lon BD84. Linc Th Coll 87. **d** 89 **p** 90. C Selsdon St Jo w St Fran *S'wark* 89-93; P-in-c S Norwood St Alb 93-97; V 97-99; V Reigate St Mark from 99. *St Mark's Vicarage, 8 Alma Road, Reigate RH2 0DA* Tel (01737) 241161 E-mail iansb@aol.com

BROTHWOOD, John. b 31. Peterho Cam MA55 MB, BChir55. S'wark Ord Course 89. **d** 91 **p** 92. NSM Dulwich St Barn *S'wark* from 91. *98 Woodwarde Road, London SE22 8UT* Tel (020) 8693 8273

BROUGH, Gerald William. b 32. Trin Coll Cam BA55 MA59. Ridley Hall Cam 55. **d** 57 **p** 58. C Westgate St Jas *Cant* 57-60; C

New Addington 60-62; V Mancetter *Cov* 62-73; P-in-c Bourton w Frankton and Stretton on Dunsmore etc 73-74; R 74-93; rtd 93; Perm to Offic *Cov* from 93. *17 Brookhurst Court, Beverley Road, Leamington Spa CV32 6PB* Tel (01926) 430759 E-mail gwbrls@aol.com

BROUGHALL, Rodney John. b 32. LNSM course 95. **d** 96 **p** 97. OLM Watton w Carbrooke and Ovington *Nor* 96-02; rtd 02; Perm to Offic *Nor* from 02. *15 Garden Close, Watton, Thetford IP25 6DP* Tel (01953) 881989

BROUGHTON, James Roger. b 48. Leeds Univ BA71 Nottm Univ CertEd72. Wycliffe Hall Ox 87. **d** 89 **p** 90. C Stoneycroft All SS *Liv* 89-92; P-in-c Carr Mill 92-94; V 94-96; Chapl Duke of York's R Mil Sch Dover from 96. *Kent House, Duke of York's Royal Military School, Guston, Dover CT15 5DR* Tel (01304) 202437 or 245059 E-mail duke@easynet.co.uk

BROUGHTON, Lynne Mary. b 46. Melbourne Univ BA67 PhD79. EAMTC 99. **d** 00 **p** 01. Hon C Wood Ditton w Saxon Street *Ely* from 00; Hon C Kirtling from 00; Hon C Cheveley from 00; Hon C Ashley w Silverley from 00. *85 Richmond Road, Cambridge CB4 3PS* Tel (01223) 322014 E-mail lmb2@hermes.cam.ac.uk

BROUGHTON, Stuart Roger. b 36. Univ of Wales DipTh65. St Mich Coll Llan 61 Wilson Carlile Coll 59. **d** 64 **p** 65. C Bromley Ch Ch *Roch* 64-67; SAMS 67-79 and 86-95; Miss Paraguayan Chaco Paraguay 67-70; R Salvador Gd Shep Brazil 70-79; V Stoke sub Hamdon *B & W* 79-83; Hon CF 82-86; V Blackb Ch Ch w St Matt *Blackb* 83-86; R Alcacer do Sal Portugal 86-91; Chapl Rio de Janeiro Brazil 91-95; rtd 96; Chapl Agia Napa Cyprus 96; Chapl Ch Ch Cathl Falkland Is 97-98; P-in-c Corfu *Eur* 98-01; Hon C Jersey St Paul Prop Chpl *Win* from 01. *1 Highgrove Mews, La rue du Boulivot, Grouville, Jersey JE3 9DP* Tel (01534) 851466 E-mail kathrynbroughton@tinyworld.co.uk

BROUN, Canon Claud Michael. b 30. BNC Ox BA55. Edin Th Coll 56. **d** 58 **p** 59. Chapl St Mary's Cathl *Edin* 58-62; Can St Mary's Cathl *Glas* 84-95; Hon Can from 95; P-in-c Cambuslang 62-70; R 70-75; R Hamilton 75-88; R Gatehouse of Fleet 88-95; R Kirkcudbright 88-95; rtd 95. *Martin Lodge, Ardross Place, Alness IV17 0PX* Tel (01349) 882442

BROWN, Canon Alan. b 37. Tyndale Hall Bris 59. **d** 63 **p** 64. C Braintree *Chelmsf* 63-66; C Tooting Graveney St Nic *S'wark* 66-68; C Chesham St Mary *Ox* 68-70; V Hornsey Rise St Mary *Lon* 70-75; V Sidcup Ch Ch *Roch* 75-88; V Newport St Jo *Portsm* 88-01; RD W Wight 91-96; Hon Can Portsm Cathl 95-01; P-in-c Newport St Thos 96-99; V 99-01; rtd 01. *Beatrice Cottage, 4 Victoria Mews, Cowes PO31 7PH* Tel (01983) 281133

BROWN, Alan George. b 51. Bradf Univ BSc84 Leeds Univ CertEd81 MBA92 SRN72 RMN75 RNT81. N Ord Course 92. **d** 95 **p** 96. NSM Ilkley St Marg *Bradf* from 95; Hd of Division Applied Health Studies Leeds Univ from 98. *Waverley, Wheatley Road, Ilkley LS29 8TS* Tel (01943) 601115 Fax as telephone E-mail a.g.brown@leeds.ac.uk

BROWN, Alan Michael Ernest. b 52. St Chad's Coll Dur BA74. St Jo Coll Nottm 81. **d** 83 **p** 84. C Bridlington Priory *York* 83-86; V Morton St Luke *Bradf* 86-02; Mental Health Worker Bradf City Primary Care Trust from 02. *Bradford City Primary Care Trust, 1st Floor, Joseph Brennan House, Sunbridge Road, Bradford BD1 2SY* Tel (01274) 424780

BROWN, Albert Harry Alfred Victor. b 12. **d** 81 **p** 83. OLM Kennington Park St Agnes *S'wark* 81-92; Perm to Offic from 92. *378 IIP Ward 23, Berth 20 Royal Hospital, London SW3 4SI* Tel (020) 7274 5982

BROWN, Alec Charles. b 33. AKC58. **d** 59 **p** 60. C S Mimms St Mary and Potters Bar *Lon* 59-63; C S Ashford Ch Ch *Cant* 63-66; Bahamas 66-71; New Zealand from 71. *151 Tasman Street, Nelson, New Zealand* Tel (0064) (3) 548 3644

BROWN, Alec George. b 53. Univ of Zimbabwe DipSW80 Univ of Wales (Cardiff) MSc(Econ)87. St Deiniol's Hawarden 88 N Ord Course 90. **d** 93 **p** 94. C Stockton Heath *Ches* 93-96; C Thelwall 96-97; V 97-01; V Gt Budworth from 01. *The Vicarage, High Street, Great Budworth, Northwich CW9 6HF* Tel (01606) 891324

BROWN, Alexander Peter-Aidan. b 48. Sarum & Wells Th Coll. **d** 82 **p** 83. C Ifield *Chich* 82-86; TV 86-91; V St Leonards SS Pet and Paul from 91. *The Vicarage, 10 Bloomfield Road, St Leonards-on-Sea TN37 6HH* Tel (01424) 445606

BROWN, Allan James. b 47. K Coll Lon BD69 AKC69 MTh70. St Aug Coll Cant 69. **d** 73 **p** 74. Jerusalem 73-75; Chapl St Geo Sch 73-74; Chapl St Marg Sch Nazareth 74-75; C Clifton *S'well* 75-77; CF 77-00; Asst Chapl Gen 99-00; V Ilkeston St Mary *Derby* from 00. *The Vicarage, 63B Manners Road, Ilkeston DE7 5HB* Tel 0115-932 4725

BROWN, Canon Andrew. b 55. St Pet Hall Ox BA80 MA82. Ridley Hall Cam 79. **d** 80 **p** 81. C Burnley St Pet *Blackb* 80-82; C Elton All SS *Man* 82-86; P-in-c Ashton St Pet 86-93; V 94-96; V Halliwell St Luke 96-03; Dioc CME Adv *Derby* from 03; Can Th Derby Cathl from 03. *149 Church Road, Quarndon, Derby DE22 5JA* Tel (01332) 553424 E-mail andie.brown@virgin.net

BROWN, Andrew. b 65. LNSM course 94. **d** 95 **p** 96. OLM Heywood *Man* from 95. *24 Honiton Close, Heywood OL20 3PF* Tel (01706) 623091

BROWN, Andrew (Bod). b 66. Man Univ BSc87. Oak Hill Th Coll BA02. **d** 03. C Hyde St Geo *Ches* from 03. *121 Dowson Road, Hyde SK14 5HJ* Tel 0161-367 9353
E-mail bod77@hotmail.com

BROWN, Anthony Frank Palmer. b 31. Fitzw Ho Cam BA56 Fitzw Coll Cam MA84. Cuddesdon Coll 56. **d** 58 **p** 59. C Aldershot St Mich *Guildf* 58-61; C Chiswick St Nic w St Mary *Lon* 61-66; Asst Chapl Lon Univ 65-70; Lic to Offic 70-72; C-in-c Hammersmith SS Mich and Geo White City Estate CD 72-74; P-in-c Upper Sunbury St Sav 74-80; V 80-01; rtd 01; Perm to Offic *Chich* from 02. *6 Church Lane, Ditchling, Hassocks BN6 8TB* Tel (01273) 843847

BROWN, Anthony Paul. b 55. Reading Univ BSc75 MRICS87. Qu Coll Birm 77. **d** 80 **p** 81. C Pelsall *Lich* 80-83; C Leighton Buzzard w Eggington, Hockliffe etc *St Alb* 83-87; TV Langley Marish *Ox* 87-93; V Pet St Mary Boongate *Pet* 93-98; TR Wombourne w Trysull and Bobbington *Lich* 98-02; TR Smestow Vale from 02. *The Vicarage, School Road, Wombourne, Wolverhampton WV5 9ED* Tel (01902) 892234 *or* 897700
E-mail revpbrown@aol.com

BROWN, Antony William Keith. b 26. RN Coll Dartmouth 43. Trin Coll Bris 86. **d** 87 **p** 88. NSM Lawrence Weston *Bris* 87-89; Chapl Casablanca *Eur* 89-93; Asst Chapl Paris St Mich 94-00; rtd 00; Perm to Offic *Bris* from 01. *13 Marklands, 37 Julian Road, Bristol BS9 1NP* Tel 0117-377 6543 Fax as telephone
E-mail brownantony@talk21.com

BROWN, Arthur Basil Etheredge. b 17. Reading Univ BA39. Wycliffe Hall Ox 46. **d** 47 **p** 48. C Camborne *Truro* 47-50; Org Sec (Midl) CPAS 50-53; PC Scarborough H Trin *York* 53-58; V Heworth H Trin 58-66; R Camborne *Truro* 66-82; rtd 82; Perm to Offic *Truro* from 82. *14 Tregenna Fields, Camborne TR14 7QS* Tel (01209) 716196

BROWN, Arthur William Stawell. b 26. St Jo Coll Ox BA50 MA51. Cuddesdon Coll 63. **d** 65 **p** 66. C Edin St Jo *Edin* 65-66; C Petersfield w Sheet *Portsm* 67-75; V Portsea St Alb 75-79; R Smithfield St Bart Gt *Lon* 79-91; R St Sepulchre w Ch Ch Greyfriars etc 81-91; Chapl Madeira *Eur* 90-91; rtd 91; Perm to Offic *Ex* from 93. *9 Little Silver, Exeter EX4 4HU* Tel (01392) 217630

BROWN, Barry Ronald. b 48. Ridley Coll Melbourne ThL72. **d** 73 **p** 74. Australia 73-77 and 82-95; C Richmond St Mary *S'wark* 78-79; C Richmond St Mary w St Matthias and St Jo 79; C Edin Old St Paul *Edin* 79-80; Chapl Belgrade w Zagreb *Eur* 81-82; Canada from 95. *46 Granby Street, Toronto ON, Canada, M5B 2J5* Tel (001) (416) 979 6766

BROWN, Canon Bernard Herbert Vincent. b 26. Mert Coll Ox BA50 MA52. Westcott Ho Cam 50. **d** 52 **p** 53. C Rugby St Andr *Cov* 52-56; C Stoke Bishop *Bris* 56-59; Youth Chapl 56-62; Ind Chapl *Roch* 62-73; Bp's Dom Chapl 66-73; R Crawley *Chich* 73-79; TR 79-83; Ind Chapl *Bris* 83-92; Bp's Soc and Ind Adv 84-92; Hon Can Bris Cathl 85-92; RD Bris City 85-91; rtd 92; Perm to Offic *Sarum* from 92. *33B London Road, Dorchester DT1 1NF* Tel (01305) 260806

BROWN, Bernard Maurice Newall. b 26. Oak Hill Th Coll Coll 47. **d** 51 **p** 52. C Penn Fields *Lich* 51-53; S Area Sec BCMS 53-55; Kenya 55-62; R Hartshorne *Derby* 62-68; V Stapenhill w Cauldwell 68-72; C Weston-super-Mare Ch Ch *B & W* 72-74; R Spaxton w Charlynch 74-80; rtd 80. *12 Ewart Road, Weston-super-Mare BS22 8NU* Tel (01934) 412170

BROWN, Bill Charles Balfour. b 44. Linc Th Coll 87. **d** 89 **p** 90. C Moulsham St Luke *Chelmsf* 89-91; C Prittlewell 91-94; V Worksop St Paul *S'well* from 95. *St Paul's Vicarage, Cavendish Road, Worksop S80 2ST* Tel (01909) 473289

BROWN, Brian Ernest. b 36. ALA64. Oak Hill NSM Course 82. **d** 85 **p** 86. NSM Wallington H Trin *S'wark* 85-91; C 91-00; rtd 00; Perm to Offic *Nor* from 00. *6 Burnside, Necton, Swaffham PE37 8ER* Tel (01760) 721292

BROWN, Charles Henry. b 48. Tulane Univ (USA) BA70 Ch Coll Cam BA75 MA81. Westcott Ho Cam. **d** 00 **p** 01. C Boston *Linc* 00-03; Lect from 03. *5 Irby Street, Boston PE21 8SA* Tel (01205) 369266

BROWN, Charles Hubert. b 21. S'wark Ord Course 82. **d** 84 **p** 85. NSM Shortlands *Roch* 84-86; P-in-c Seal St Lawr 86-90; P-in-c Underriver 86-90; rtd 90; Perm to Offic *Roch* from 90. *Barton Croft, 11 St Mary's Close, Sevenoaks TN15 8NH* Tel (01732) 882893

BROWN, Christopher. b 38. AKC62 CQSW68. St Boniface Warminster 62. **d** 63 **p** 64. C Crofton Park St Hilda w St Cypr *S'wark* 63-64; C S Beddington St Mich 64-67; C Herne Hill St Paul 67-68; Lic to Offic *S'wark* 68-72; *Lich* 72-74; *Birm* 74-76; *Worc* 76-79; *Ox* 79-86; Perm to Offic *Chelmsf* from 86; Dir and Chief Exec NSPCC 89-95. *7 Baronia Croft, Colchester CO4 9EE* Tel (01206) 852904 E-mail chribrow@yahoo.co.uk

BROWN, Christopher. b 43. Linc Th Coll 79. **d** 81 **p** 82. C Stafford St Jo *Lich* 81-85; C Stafford St Jo and Tixall w Ingestre 85; V Alton w Bradley-le-Moors and Oakamoor w Cotton 85-94; Chapl Asst Nottm City Hosp NHS Trust from 94. *The Chaplain's Office, Nottingham City Hospital, Hucknall Road, Nottingham NG5 1PB* Tel 0115-969 1169 *or* 962 7616

BROWN, Christopher Charles. b 58. Solicitor 82 Univ of Wales (Cardiff) LLB79. Westcott Ho Cam 87. **d** 90 **p** 91. C Taunton St Mary *B & W* 90-94; R Timsbury and Priston 94-00; P-in-c Urmston *Man* from 00. *St Clement's Vicarage, 24 Stretford Road, Urmston, Manchester M41 9JZ* Tel (0161-748 3972

BROWN, Christopher David. b 49. Birm Univ CertEd71 BEd72 Univ of Wales (Cardiff) Dip Practical Th 94. St Mich Coll Llan 93. **d** 94 **p** 95. C Swansea St Thos and Kilvey *S & B* 94-96; C Swansea St Jas 96-98; St Helena 98-01; Asst Chapl and Hd of RS Epsom Coll from 01. *Epsom College, Epsom KT17 4JQ* Tel (01372) 820104 E-mail kristophdavid@hotmail.com

BROWN, Christopher Edgar Newall. b 31. Oak Hill Th Coll 51. **d** 55 **p** 56. C Surbiton Hill Ch Ch *S'wark* 55-57; C Gipsy Hill Ch Ch 57-61; V Plumstead All SS 61-70; V Sissinghurst *Cant* 70-73; P-in-c Frittenden 72-73; V Sissinghurst w Frittenden 73-76; Perm to Offic *S & M* 84-91 and from 96; Bp's Dom Chapl 91-95; rtd 96. *21 College Green, Castletown, Isle of Man IM9 1BE* Tel (01624) 822364

BROWN, Canon Christopher Francis. b 44. Sarum Th Coll 68. **d** 71 **p** 72. C High Wycombe *Ox* 71-74; C Sherborne w Castleton and Lillington *Sarum* 74-77; P-in-c Wylye, Fisherton Delamere and the Langfords 77-79; R Yarnbury 79-82; R Portland All SS w St Pet 82-88; RD Weymouth 85-88; R Trowbridge St Jas from 88; Chapl Trowbridge and Distr Hosp 88-95; RD Bradford 94-02; Can and Preb Sarum Cathl from 98. *The Rectory, Union Street, Trowbridge BA14 8RU* Tel (01225) 755121
E-mail stjames@trowbridge1.fsnet.co.uk

BROWN, Christopher Howard. b 49. **d** 03. OLM Uttoxeter Area *Lich* from 03. *21 Carter Street, Uttoxeter ST14 8EY* Tel (01889) 567492

BROWN, Christopher James. b 50. Open Univ BA92. Trin Coll Bris DipHE93. **d** 93 **p** 94. C Skelmersdale St Paul *Liv* 93-97; Chapl Asst Salford R Hosps NHS Trust from 97. *Chaplaincy Department, Stott Lane, Salford, Manchester M6 8HD* 0161-787 5167 *or* 789 7373

BROWN, Clive Lindsey. b 33. Southn Univ BA55. Oak Hill Th Coll 57. **d** 59 **p** 60. C Becontree St Mary *Chelmsf* 59-62; Australia from 62; rtd 98. *80 Bower Street, Manly, NSW, Australia 2095* Tel (0061) (2) 9977 2546

BROWN, Prof Colin. b 32. Liv Univ BA53 Lon Univ BD58 Nottm Univ MA61 DD94 Bris Univ PhD70. Tyndale Hall Bris 55. **d** 58 **p** 59. C Chilwell *S'well* 58-61; Lect Tyndale Hall Bris 61-78; Vice Prin 67-70; Dean Studies 70-71; USA from 78; Prof Systematic Th Fuller Th Sem California from 78; Assoc R Altadena St Mark from 80; Assoc Dean Adv Th Studies 88-97; rtd 00. *1024 Beverly Way, Altadena, CA 91001-2516, USA* Tel (001) (626) 798 7180 E-mail colbrn@fuller.edu

BROWN, David Charles Girdlestone. b 42. Solicitor 67. S'wark Ord Course 87. **d** 90 **p** 91. NSM Milford *Guildf* 90-92; NSM Haslemere 92-00; NSM Haslemere and Grayswood 00-01; Perm to Offic *Chich* from 02. *Southdowns, Red House Court, Rogate, Petersfield GU31 5HE* Tel (01730) 821192 Fax 821937
E-mail dcgbrown@dircon.co.uk

BROWN, David Frederick. b 38. Illinois Univ BA60. Seabury-Western Th Sem MDiv67. **d** 67 **p** 67. USA 67-78; Hon C Battersea Ch Ch and St Steph *S'wark* 78-83; Sen Chapl R Marsden NHS Trust Lon and Surrey from 83; Perm to Offic *S'wark* 83-00. *The Royal Marsden NHS Trust, Fulham Road, London SW3 6JJ* Tel (020) 7352 8171 ext 2818 *or* 7351 6082 Fax 7351 2191

BROWN, David Lloyd. b 44. TCD DipTh86 BTh90. **d** 86 **p** 87. C Cregagh *D & D* 86-91; Bp's C Knocknagoney from 91. *19 Old Holywood Road, Belfast BT4 2HJ* Tel (028) 9076 3343

BROWN, David Victor Arthur. b 44. Em Coll Cam BA66 MA70 DCG69 Em Coll Cam CertEd Bp Grosseteste Coll 74 Dip Counselling 98. Linc Th Coll 72. **d** 74 **p** 75. C Bourne *Linc* 74-77; Chapl St Steph Coll Broadstairs 77-79; Chapl Asst N Gen Hosp Sheff 81-84; C Sheff St Cuth *Sheff* 81-84; Chapl Ridge Lea Hosp Lanc 84-92; Chapl Lanc Moor Hosp 84-92; Chapl Lanc Priority Services NHS Trust 92-98; Chapl Lanc R Infirmary 87-92; Chapl Lanc Acute Hosps NHS Trust 92-98; Chapl Morecambe Bay Hosps NHS Trust from 98; Chapl Bay Community Trust from 98. *Chaplain's Office, Royal Lancaster Infirmary, Ashton Road, Lancaster LA1 4RP* Tel (01524) 583955, 762800 *or* 400308 E-mail dbrown1586@aol.com

BROWN, Canon David William. b 48. Edin Univ MA70 Oriel Coll Ox BA72 Clare Coll Cam PhD76. Westcott Ho Cam 75. **d** 76 **p** 77. Chapl, Fell and Tutor Oriel Coll Ox 76-90; Van Mildert Prof Div Dur Univ from 90; Can Res Dur Cathl *Dur* from 90. *14 The College, Durham DH1 3EQ* Tel 0191-386 4657

BROWN, Dennis Cockburn. b 27. Hatf Coll Dur BSc48 K Coll Dur PhD54. WMMTC 79. **d** 82 **p** 83. C Bilton *Cov* 82-84; V Wolford w Burmington 84-96; R Cherington w Stourton 84-96; R Barchestton 84-96; rtd 96; Perm to Offic *Cov* from 96; Dioc Rtd Clergy and Widows Officer from 98. *13 Cleveland Court, 41 Kenilworth Road, Leamington Spa CV32 6JA* Tel (01926) 423771

BROWN, Canon Derek Frederick. b 27. St Fran Coll Brisbane ThL52. **d** 52 **p** 54. Australia 52-58; C Merstham and Gatton

S'wark 59-61; R Deptford St Paul 61-69; Chapl RNR from 62; R Havant *Portsm* 69-00; rtd 00; Perm to Offic *Portsm* from 00. *Christ Church Bungalow, Rowan Road, Havant PO9 2XA* Tel (023) 9248 1730

BROWN, Derek Henry Pridgeon. b 46. Cam Coll of Art and Tech BA67 Leeds Univ PGCE71. St Steph Ho Ox 90. **d** 92 **p** 93. C Finchley St Mary *Lon* 92-95; C W Hampstead St Jas 95-99; V Eyres Monsell *Leic* from 99. *St Hugh's Vicarage, 51 Pasley Road, Leicester LE2 9BU* Tel 0116-278 6288

BROWN, Canon Donald Fryer. b 31. St Jo Coll Dur BA56 DipTh61. Cranmer Hall Dur 60. **d** 61 **p** 62. Min Can Bradf Cathl *Bradf* 61-64; C Bingley All SS 64-66; V Low Moor H Trin 66-97; Hon Can Bradf Cathl 85-97; RD Bowling and Horton 87-95; rtd 97; Perm to Offic *Bradf* from 98. *3 Northfield Gardens, Wibsey, Bradford BD6 1LQ* Tel (01274) 671869

BROWN, Mrs Doreen Marion. b 39. Cam Univ CertEd67 Dip Counselling 85. N Ord Course 85. **d** 88 **p** 94. Par Dn Axminster, Chardstock, Combe Pyne and Rousdon *Ex* 88-92; Ind Chapl *Linc* 92-98; TV Brumby from 98. *The Vicarage, 36 Dorchester Road, Scunthorpe DN17 1YG* Tel (01724) 847671 E-mail doreen.bn@lineone.net

BROWN, Douglas Adrian Spencer. b 29. Univ of W Aus BA50 MA71 K Coll Lon MTh90. St Mich Th Coll Crafers 50. **d** 53 **p** 54. Australia 53-60, 66-88 and from 02; SSM 54-00; Chapl and Tutor St Mich Th Coll Crafers 54-60; Tutor and Chapl Kelham Th Coll 60-66; Chapl Univ of W Aus 66-71; P-in-c Canberra St Alb 71-75; Warden St Mich Th Coll Crafers 75-82; P-in-c Adelaide St Jo 78-82; Academic Dean Adelaide Coll of Div 79-81; President 88; Visiting Scholar Union Th Sem NY 82; Perm to Offic *Lon* 88-90; Chapl Bucharest w Sofia *Eur* 90-91; Dir Angl Cen Rome 91-95; Chapl Palermo w Taormina *Eur* 95-96; Lect Newton Th Coll Papua New Guinea 97; Perm to Offic *Dur* 97-00; *S'wark* 99-00; Dir Nor Cathl Inst and Hon PV Nor Cathl *Nor* 00-02. *75/6 Manning Terrace, South Perth, W Australia 6151*

BROWN, Ms Elizabeth Ann. b 43. **d** 00 **p** 01. OLM W Bromwich All SS *Lich* from 01. *307 Beaconview Road, West Bromwich B71 3PS* Tel 0121-588 7530

BROWN, Miss Elizabeth Charlotte (Beth). b 54. Bris Univ BSc76 PGCE77. Trin Coll Bris DipHE95. **d** 95 **p** 96. C Taunton Lyngford *B & W* 95-99; TV Bath Twerton-on-Avon from 99. *20A Bellotts Road, Bath BA2 3RT* Tel (01225) 443940

BROWN, Eric. b 28. Leeds Univ BA98. NW Ord Course 73. **d** 76 **p** 77. NSM S Kirkby *Wakef* 76-83; NSM Knottingley 83-94; NSM Kellington w Whitley 89-94; Sub Chapl HM Pris Lindholme 90-94; Perm to Offic from 94. *Wynberg, Barnsley Road, South Kirby, Pontefract WF9 3BG* Tel (01977) 643683

BROWN, Canon Ernest George. b 23. Em Coll Cam BA51 MA56. Oak Hill Th Coll 52. **d** 53 **p** 54. C Darfield *Sheff* 53-56; V Ardsley 56-66; V Thurnby w Stoughton *Leic* 67-90; RD Gartree II 78-90; Hon Can Leic Cathl 82-90; rtd 90; Perm to Offic *Leic* from 90. *16 Holbeck Drive, Broughton Astley, Leicester LE9 6UR* Tel (01455) 285458

BROWN, Ernest Harry. b 32. St Mich Coll Llan. **d** 59 **p** 60. C Swansea St Pet *S & B* 59-62; CF (TA) 62-68; C Gowerton w Waunarlwydd *S & B* 62-68; Chapl to the Deaf 68-98; rtd 98. *Montreaux, 30 Lon Cedwyn, Sketty, Swansea SA2 0TH* Tel (01792) 207628

BROWN, Frank Seymour. b 10. S'wark Ord Course 62 St Aug Coll Cant 65. **d** 65 **p** 66. C Bexleyheath Ch Ch *Roch* 65-70; R Cratfield w Heveningham and Ubbeston *St E* 70-76; rtd 76; Perm to Offic *St E* 76-86; P-in-c Ixworth and Ixworth Thorpe 78; P-in-c Euston w Barnham and Fakenham 80; Perm to Offic *St Alb* from 86. *3 Windsor Gardens, Kimbolton Road, Bedford MK40 3BU* Tel (01234) 210999

BROWN, Geoffrey Alan. b 34. Dioc OLM tr scheme DipHE00. **d** 99 **p** 00. OLM Bury St Edmunds St Mary *St E* from 99. *Rodenkirchen, 12 Sharp Road, Bury St Edmunds IP33 2NB* Tel (01284) 769725

BROWN, Geoffrey Gilbert. b 38. FBIS Dur Univ BA62 DipEd63 Fitzw Coll Cam BA69 MA73. Westcott Ho Cam 67. **d** 70 **p** 71. C Gosforth All SS *Newc* 70-73; Chapl Dauntsey's Sch Devizes 73-76; New Zealand 76-78 and 86-90; V Barrow St Aid *Carl* 79-86; C Digswell and Panshanger *St Alb* 91-93; Chapl E Herts Hospice Care from 94; Lic to Offic *St Alb* from 94. *Isabel Wing, Douglas Tilbe House, Hall Grove, Welwyn Garden City AL7 4PH* Tel (01707) 330686 *or* 327565 Fax 393132

BROWN, Canon Geoffrey Harold. b 30. Trin Hall Cam BA54 MA58. Cuddesdon Coll 54. **d** 56 **p** 57. C Plaistow St Andr *Chelmsf* 56-60; C Birm St Pet *Birm* 60-63; R Birm St Geo 63-73; TR Gt Grimsby St Mary and St Jas *Linc* 73-85; Can and Preb Linc Cathl 79-85; V St Martin-in-the-Fields *Lon* 85-95; rtd 95; Perm to Offic *Worc* from 95. *8 Worcester Close, Hagley, Stourbridge DY9 0NP* Tel (01562) 886921

BROWN, Mrs Glenys. b 57. St D Coll Lamp BA78 Coll of Ripon & York St Jo PGCE79. N Ord Course 96. **d** 99 **p** 00. C Wythenshawe *Man* 99-02; V Over St Chad *Ches* from 02. *The Vicarage, 1 Over Hall Drive, Winsford CW7 1EY* Tel (01606) 593222

BROWN, Graeme Eric. b 37. St Jo Coll Auckland LTh61. **d** 62 **p** 63. New Zealand 62-74 and from 75; C Nor Heartsease St Fran *Nor* 74-75. *104 Masters Avenue, Hamilton 2001, New Zealand* Tel (0064) (7) 856 0074 E-mail gebrown@wave.co.nz

BROWN, Graham Stanley. b 51. Sarum & Wells Th Coll 82. **d** 84 **p** 85. C Crediton and Shobrooke *Ex* 84-87; Chapl RAF 87-93 and from 99; R Elgin w Lossiemouth *Mor* 93-98; R Castle Douglas *Glas* 98-99. *Chaplaincy Services (RAF), HQ, Personnel and Training Command, RAF Innsworth, Gloucester GL3 1EZ* Tel (01452) 712612 ext 5164 Fax 510828

BROWN, Harold. b 53. SEN74 SRN77 RMN82 RCN CCT84. Edin Th Coll 86. **d** 88 **p** 89. C Upperby St Jo *Carl* 88-90; C Carl H Trin and St Barn 90-91; C Workington St Mich 91-93; TV 93-95; P-in-c Crosscrake and Preston Patrick 95-03. *Address temp unknown* E-mail harry@hbrown77.freeserve.co.uk

BROWN, Mrs Harriet Nina. b 37. Open Univ BA77 Lon Univ CertEd57. Gilmore Course 80 Oak Hill Th Coll 83. **dss** 83 **d** 87 **p** 94. Greenstead *Chelmsf* 83-90; Par Dn 87-90; Asst Chapl R Hosp Sch Holbrook 90-93; Perm to Offic *Chelmsf* from 93; Perm to Offic *St E* 93-96; P-in-c Gt and Lt Blakenham w Baylham and Nettlestead 96-01; rtd 01. *22 Gainsborough Road, Colchester CO3 4QN* Tel (01206) 523072

BROWN, Henry. b 27. Lon Univ BSc51 BSc52. NW Ord Course 72. **d** 75 **p** 76. NSM Padiham *Blackb* 75-80; V Warton St Paul 80-90; rtd 90; Perm to Offic *Blackb* from 90. *18 Windsor Gardens, Garstang, Preston PR3 1EG* Tel (01995) 606592

BROWN, Ian. b 48. N Ord Course 89. **d** 91 **p** 92. C Burnage St Marg *Man* 91-94; P-in-c Halliwell St Paul 94-98; TV Halliwell 98-01; Chapl Bolton Hosps NHS Trust 94-01; TV Melbury *Sarum* from 01. *The Vicarage, Corscombe, Dorchester DT2 0NU* Tel (01935) 891247

BROWN, Ian Barry. b 53. Ruskin Coll Ox 75 St Cuth Soc Dur BA80 PGCE81. Westmr Past Foundn Cert Counselling 90 Sarum & Wells Th Coll 84. **d** 86 **p** 87. C Winchmore Hill St Paul *Lon* 86-89; Hon Chapl Chase Farm Hosp Enfield 86-88; Hon Chapl Harley Street Area Hosps 88-90; Hon Chapl RAM 89; C St Marylebone w H Trin 89-94; rtd 94; Perm to Offic *Lon* from 96; Hon Chapl Regent's Coll from 96; Gov 97-99. *Flat 4, 9 Welbeck Street, London W1G 9YB* Tel (020) 7935 6687

BROWN, Ian David. b 53. UEA BA76. Wycliffe Hall Ox BA80. **d** 81 **p** 82. C Southsea St Jude *Portsm* 81-84; Chapl Coll of SS Paul and Mary Cheltenham 84-89; V Lt Heath *St Alb* from 89. *The Vicarage, Thornton Road, Potters Bar EN6 1JJ* Tel (01707) 654414 E-mail cclh@cclh.freeserve.co.uk

BROWN, Ivan James. b 24. Cant Sch of Min 84. **d** 86 **p** 87. NSM St Nicholas at Wade w Sarre and Chislet w Hoath *Cant* 86-94; rtd 94; Perm to Offic *Cant* 94-02. *Horseshoe Cottage, Elms Ride, West Wittering, Chichester PO20 8LP* Tel (01243) 514896

BROWN, Canon Jack Robin. b 44. Linc Th Coll 67. **d** 69 **p** 70. C Canning Town St Cedd *Chelmsf* 69-72; C Dunstable *St Alb* 72-78; V Luton St Andr 78-85; V Kempston Transfiguration 85-00; RD Bedford 92-98; Hon Can St Alb from 97; Dioc Officer for Local Min from 00; Lic to Offic *Chelmsf* from 00. *St John's House, High Street, Markyate, St Albans AL3 8PD* Tel (01582) 842150 Fax as telephone E-mail imo@stalbans.anglican.org.

BROWN, James Douglas. b 52. S'wark Ord Course 93. **d** 96 **p** 97. NSM Shooters Hill Ch Ch *S'wark* 96-01; P-in-c E Malling *Roch* from 02; P-in-c Wateringbury and Teston from 02. *The Vicarage, 2 The Grange, East Malling, West Malling ME19 6AH* Tel (01732) 843282 Fax as telephone E-mail jamesbrown2@tinyworld.co.uk

BROWN, Canon James Michael. b 49. Newc Univ Aus BA90. St Jo Coll Morpeth ThL78. **d** 77 **p** 78. Australia 77-81 and 83-02; C Gosford 77-79; C Cessnock 79-81; C Eyres Monsell *Leic* 81-83; C Entrance 83; P-in-c Windale 83-88; R Morpeth 88-97; Acting Registrar Wangaratta 98-00; Dom Chapl to Bp Wangaratta and Dir Min Tr 98-02; Adn The Hume 99-02; V Knowle H Nativity *Bris* from 02; P-in-c Easton All Hallows from 02; Hon Can Wangaratta from 02. *Holy Nativity Vicarage, 41 Lilymead Avenue, Bristol BS4 2BY* Tel 0117-977 4260 Fax as telephone E-mail frjames@holynativity.org.uk

BROWN, Canon James Philip. b 30. St Cath Coll Ox BA54 MA55. Westcott Ho Cam 54. **d** 56 **p** 57. C Hemel Hempstead *St Alb* 56-63; V Hellesdon *Nor* 63-71; P-in-c Kirkley w Lowestoft St Jo 71-79; TV Lowestoft St Marg 76-79; TV Lowestoft and Kirkley 79-81; P-in-c Northleach w Hampnett and Farmington *Glouc* 81-95; RD Northleach 83-92; P-in-c Cold Aston w Notgrove and Turkdean 86-95; Hon Can Glouc Cathl 91-95; rtd 95; Perm to Offic *Ex* from 95. *The Priest's House, 1 St Scholactica's Abbey, Teignmouth TQ14 8FF* Tel (01626) 773623

BROWN, Jane Madeline. *See* **SHARP, Mrs Jane Madeline**

BROWN, Jenny. b 78. St Martin's Coll Lanc BA99. Oak Hill Th Coll BA03. **d** 03. C Hyde St Geo *Ches* from 03. *121 Dowson Road, Hyde SK14 5HJ* Tel 0161-367 9353

BROWN, Mrs Joan Leslie. b 31. SS Hild & Bede Coll Dur CertEd55. Oak Hill Th Coll BA85. **dss** 85 **d** 87 **p** 94. Fulwood *Sheff* 85-87; Par Dn 87-88; TD Netherthorpe 88-93; rtd 93; NSM Ellesmere St Pet *Sheff* 93-99; Perm to Offic from 00. *2 Kingston Street, Sheffield S4 7SU* Tel 0114-243 3534

BROWN, John. b 21. **d** 50 **p** 51. C Tydavnet *Clogh* 50-51; P-in-c Drum 51-58; I Clontibret w Tullycorbet 58-62; I Clabby 62-75; V Dunham w Darlton and Ragnall *S'well* 75-87; R Fledborough 76-87; rtd 87; Perm to Offic *Heref* from 87. *Swallows Croft, 12 The Ridge, Bishops Castle SY9 5AB* Tel (01588) 638898

BROWN, John. b 64. Kent Univ BA86. Westcott Ho Cam 87. **d** 90 **p** 91. C Lt Ilford St Mich *Chelmsf* 90-94; C E Ham w Upton Park St Alb 94; TV 94-01; P-in-c St Ilford St Luke from 01. *St Luke's Vicarage, Baxter Road, Ilford IG1 2HN* Tel (020) 8478 1104

BROWN, Canon John Bruce. b 32. Nottm Univ BA64 MA68. Cuddesdon Coll 64. **d** 66 **p** 67. C Warwick St Nic *Cov* 66-71; C Bp's Hatfield *St Alb* 71-78; V Watford St Mich from 78; RD Watford 94-99; Hon Can St Alb from 02. *St Michael's Vicarage, 5 Mildred Avenue, Watford WD18 7DY* Tel (01923) 232460 E-mail john.brown420@ntlworld.com

BROWN, Canon John Derek. b 41. Linc Th Coll 71. **d** 73 **p** 74. C Rotherham *Sheff* 73-76; P-in-c W Pinchbeck *Linc* 76-78; V Surfleet 76-82; R Boultham 83-94; RD Christianity 85-92; Can and Preb Linc Cathl from 88; P-in-c Epworth and Wroot 94-97; RD Is of Axholme from 96; R Epworth Gp from 97. *St Andrew's Rectory, Belton Road, Epworth, Doncaster DN9 1JL* Tel (01427) 872471 E-mail derek@cbepworth.freeserve.co.uk

BROWN, John Dixon. b 28. Pemb Coll Cam BA52. Oak Hill Th Coll 52. **d** 54 **p** 55. C Worthing St Geo *Chich* 54-57; C S w N Bersted 57-63; V W Hampnett 63-91; rtd 91; Perm to Offic *Chich* from 91. *3 Manor Way, Elmer, Bognor Regis PO22 6LA* Tel (01243) 583449

BROWN, Canon John Duncan. b 43. St Pet Coll Ox BA64 BA66 MA68 Lon Univ BSc. Wycliffe Hall Ox 65. **d** 67 **p** 68. C Kingston upon Hull H Trin *York* 67-69; C St Leonards St Leon *Chich* 69-72; Hon C Norbiton *S'wark* 72-75; C Kirkcaldy *St And* 75-78; Prec and Chapl Chelmsf Cathl *Chelmsf* 78-86; P-in-c Kelvedon Hatch 86-92; P-in-c Navestock 86-92; P-in-c Fryerning w Margaretting 92-99; Bp's ACORA Officer 92-99; Hon Can Chelmsf Cathl from 93; rtd 99. *556 Galleywood Road, Chelmsford CM2 8BX* Tel (01245) 358185

⚓**BROWN, The Rt Revd John Edward.** b 30. Lon Univ BD68. Kelham Th Coll 50. **d** 55 **p** 56 **c** 87. Jerusalem 55-57; C Reading St Mary V *Ox* 57-60; Sudan 60-64; V Stewkley *Ox* 64-69; V Maidenhead St Luke 69-73; V Bracknell 73-77; RD Sonning 73-77; Adn Berks 78-87; Warden Ascot Priory 80-87; Bp Cyprus and the Gulf 87-95; rtd 95; Asst Bp Linc from 95; RD Grimsby and Cleethorpes from 03. *130 Oxford Street, Cleethorpes DN35 0BP* Tel (01472) 698840

BROWN, Canon John Roger. b 37. AKC60. **d** 61 **p** 62. C New Eltham All SS *S'wark* 61-64; C Bexhill St Pet *Chich* 64-68; V Eastbourne St Eliz 68-75; V E Grinstead St Swithun 75-97; Chapl Qu Victoria Hosp NHS Trust East Grinstead 75-97; RD E Grinstead *Chich* 82-93; Can and Preb Chich Cathl 89-98; Perm to Offic 97-99; TV Worth from 00. *11 Gregory Close, Maidenbower, Crawley RH10 7LB* Tel (01293) 881638

BROWN, John William Etheridge. b 13. St Pet Hall Ox BA35 MA39. Wycliffe Hall Ox 35. **d** 37 **p** 38. C Stratford New Town St Paul *Chelmsf* 37-40; C Rawtenstall St Mary *Man* 40-42; C Thame *Ox* 42-45; OCF 43-45; V St Keverne *Truro* 45-51; V Hoo All Hallows w Stoke *Roch* 51-55; V Crich *Derby* 55-61; V Leusden *Ex* 61-79; V Widecombe in the Moor 61-79; P-in-c Holne 70-74; P-in-c Princetown 74-79; RD Moreton 74-80; Asst Chapl HM Pris Dartmoor 75-82; V Widecombe, Leusden and Princetown etc *Ex* 79-82; rtd 82; Lic to Offic *Ex* from 82. *8 Emmetts Park, Ashburton, Newton Abbot TQ13 7DB* Tel (01364) 653072

BROWN, Jonathan. b 60. Univ Coll Dur BA83 MA85 Ex Univ CertEd86. Ripon Coll Cuddesdon 86 Ch Div Sch of the Pacific (USA) 88. **d** 89 **p** 90. C Esher *Guildf* 89-97; TV Crawley *Chich* from 97; Chapl St Cath Hospice from 97. *St Richard's Vicarage, 1 Crossways, Crawley RH10 1QF* Tel (01293) 533727

BROWN, Jonathan Alexander Iain. b 75. SS Hild & Bede Coll Dur BSc96 Leeds Univ BA99. Coll of Resurr Mirfield 97. **d** 00 **p** 01. C Accrington Ch the King *Blackb* 00-03; P-in-c Merthyr Cynog and Dyffryn Honddu etc *S & B* from 03; Min Can Brecon Cathl from 03. *The Vicarage, Lower Chapel, Brecon LD3 9RE* Tel (01874) 690238

BROWN, Julian Keith. b 57. Magd Coll Ox BA79. St Jo Coll Nottm 82. **d** 85 **p** 86. C Eydon w Hampton Poyle *Ox* 85-88; C Luton All SS w St Pet *St Alb* 88-91; Hon Asst Chapl Versailles *Eur* from 94. *5 rue Pierre Curie, 94170 Le Perreux, France*

BROWN, Canon Kathleen Margaret. b 40. QUB BD BTh. **d** 88 **p** 90. C Carrickfergus *Conn* 88-92; I Belfast St Paul w St Barn from 92; Can Belf Cathl from 01. *The Rectory, 50 Sunningdale Park, Belfast BT14 6RW* Tel (028) 9071 5413

BROWN, Kenneth Arthur Charles. b 27. ACP65. LNSM course 85. **d** 84 **p** 85. OLM Ingoldsby *Linc* 84-97. *11 Ingoldsby Road, Lenton, Grantham NG33 4HB* Tel (01476) 85763

BROWN, Kenneth Roger. b 48. St Chad's Coll Dur BA69 DipTh72. Liturg Inst Trier Dip Liturg Studies 73. **d** 73 **p** 74. C Patchway *Bris* 73-77; C Fishponds St Jo 77-79; Chapl RAF 79-95; Chapl HM Pris Pentonville 95-96; Chapl HM Pris Wellingborough 96-98; Perm to Offic *B & W* 99-00; P-in-c Crook

Peak from 00. *The Rectory, Sparrow Hill Way, Weare, Axbridge BS26 2LE* Tel (01934) 733140 E-mail rev ken brown@hotmail.com

BROWN (née BOWERS), Lady (Denise Frances). b 50. City Univ BSc72. St Alb and Ox Min Course 99. **d** 02. NSM Beedon and Peasemore w W Ilsley and Farnborough *Ox* from 02. *Bridleway Cottage, Stanmore, Beedon, Newbury RG20 8SR* Tel and fax (01635) 281825 Mobile 07901-914975

BROWN, Miss Louise Margaret. b 53. Trin Coll Bris DipHE82. **dss** 83 **d** 87 **p** 94. Woodley St Jo the Ev *Ox* 84-87; Par Dn Woodley 87-92; Asst Chapl Reading Hosps 92-94; C Shinfield 93-94; P-in-c Dedworth from 94. *The Vicarage, 3 Pierson Road, Windsor SL4 5RJ* Tel (01753) 864591

BROWN, Malcolm Arthur. b 54. Oriel Coll Ox BA76 MA82 Man Univ PhD00. Westcott Ho Cam 77. **d** 79 **p** 80. C Riverhead w Dunton Green *Roch* 79-83; TV Southampton (City Cen) *Win* 83-91; Assoc Dir Wm Temple Foundn 91-93; Exec Sec 93-00; Hon C Heaton Moor *Man* 95-00; Prin EAMTC *Ely* from 00. *Chadkirk, School Lane, Impington, Cambridge CB4 9NS* Tel (01223) 741030 *or* 741026 E-mail mbrown@eamtc.cam.ac.uk

BROWN (née PATTERSON), Mrs Marjorie Jean. b 54. Wooster Coll USA BA76 St Andr Univ 77. S Dios Minl Tr Scheme 92. **d** 95 **p** 96. C Poplar *Lon* 95-99; P-in-c Stamford Hill St Thos 99-02; V from 02; Dean of Women's Min Stepney Area from 02. *The Vicarage, 37 Clapton Common, London E5 9AA* Tel (020) 8806 1463 Fax 07092-189271 E-mail mjb@nworb.com

BROWN, Canon Mark Edward. b 61. Southn Univ BSc83 Cam Univ PGCE84 Brunel Univ MTh98. Trin Coll Bris DipHE87 BA88. **d** 88 **p** 89. C Egham *Guildf* 88-92; Assoc V Northwood Em *Lon* 92-02; Bp's Officer for Evang 96-02; Can Missr *S'well* from 02; Hon Can S'well Minster from 02. *5 Vicar's Court, Southwell NG25 0HP* Tel (01636) 815056 E-mail revmbrown@aol.com

BROWN, Michael Brian. b 56. Trin Coll Bris BA97 Coll of Resurr Mirfield 98. **d** 99 **p** 00. C Trowbridge St Jas *Sarum* 99-02; C Bruton and Distr *B & W* from 02. *The Parsonage, Gold Hill, Batcombe, Shepton Mallet BA4 6HF* Tel (01749) 850671 E-mail fr.michaelbrown@btopenworld.com

BROWN, The Ven Michael Rene Warneford. b 15. St Pet Coll Ox BA37 MA41. St Steph Ho Ox 38. **d** 41 **p** 42. C W Grinstead *Chich* 41-43; Chapl RNVR 43-46; Chapl St Pet Hall Ox 46; C Ox St Mary V *Ox* 46; RN Coll Greenwich 46-47; Fell St Aug Coll Cant 48-52; Lib 48-50; P-in-c Bekesbourne *Cant* 49-50; Asst Sec CACTM 50-60; Chapl Ch Ho Westmr 55-60; Adn Nottingham *S'well* 60-77; Perm to Offic *Cant* 77-02; rtd 80; Hon OCF R Marines Sch of Music Deal from 85. *Faygate, 72 Liverpool Road, Walmer, Deal CT14 7LR* Tel (01304) 361326

BROWN, Murray. See BROWN, Phillip Murray

BROWN, Nicholas Francis Palgrave. b 23. Fitzw Ho Cam BA51 MA54. **d** 53 **p** 54. C Warwick St Nic *Cov* 53-55; C Birm St Paul *Birm* 55-60; V Temple Balsall 60-66; Gen Sec Ind Chr Fellowship 66-76; V St Kath Cree *Lon* 66-71; Chapl and Dir of Studies Holland Ho Cropthorne 76-80; P-in-c Cropthorne w Charlton *Worc* 76-88; Adult Educn Officer 80-85; rtd 88; Perm to Offic *Worc* from 88. *Bredon Vine, Rear of 40 Bridge Street, Pershore WR10 1AT* Tel (01386) 556816

BROWN, Nina. See BROWN, Mrs Harriet Nina

BROWN, Canon Norman Charles Harry. b 27. Univ of Wales BSc46. St Mich Coll Llan 48. **d** 50 **p** 51. C Canton St Jo *Llan* 50-57; C Llanishen and Lisvane 58-63; V Miskin 63-97; RD Aberdare 82-97; Can Llan Cathl 86-97; rtd 97. *33 Bron y Deri, Mountain Ash CF45 4LL* Tel (01443) 476631

BROWN, Canon Norman John. b 34. Thames Poly MA90. Ripon Hall Ox 74. **d** 74 **p** 75. C High Wycombe *Ox* 74-78; V Tilehurst St Cath 78-82; V Boyne Hill from 82; Chapl Windsor and Maidenhead Coll 87-89; Hon Can Ch Ch *Ox* from 03. *All Saints' Vicarage, Westmorland Road, Maidenhead SL6 4HB* Tel (01628) 626921 Fax 623193 E-mail revbrown@waitrose.com

BROWN, Patricia Valerie. b 37. CertEd58. STETS BTh95. **d** 98 **p** 99. NSM Tadley St Pet *Win* 98-02; NSM Tadley S and Silchester from 02. *58 Bowmonts Road, Tadley, Basingstoke RG26 3SB* Tel 0118-981 6109

BROWN, Paul. See BROWN, Anthony Paul

BROWN, Paul David Christopher. b 50. Lon Univ LLB71. EMMTC 81. **d** 84 **p** 85. NSM Wollaton *S'well* from 84. *32 Benington Drive, Wollaton, Nottingham NG8 2TF* Tel 0115-928 4493

BROWN, Penelope Jane. b 57. St Steph Ho Ox DipMin94. **d** 96 **p** 97. C Croydon St Jo *S'wark* 96-99; V Croydon St Matt from 99. *The Vicarage, 7 Brownlow Road, Croydon CR0 5JT* Tel (020) 8688 5055 E-mail revpennyb@st-matthews.fsnet.co.uk

BROWN, Peter. b 38. Leeds Univ BSc62 PhD65. Nashotah Ho 85. **d** 87 **p** 88. USA 87-89; C Sprowston *Nor* 89-90; C Sprowston w Beeston 90-92; P-in-c W Winch w Setchey and N Runcton 92-98; P-in-c Middleton w E Winch 96-98; P-in-c Nor St Andr 98-99; P-in-c Norwich St Geo Colegate 98-99; Chapl Norfolk and Nor Health Care NHS Trust 98-99; rtd 00; Perm to Offic *Leic* from 00. *41 Main Street, Cosby, Leicester LE9 1UW* Tel 0116-286 6184 E-mail peterbrown@tesco.net

BROWN, Canon Peter. b 47. RMN69. Kelham Th Coll 69. **d** 74 **p** 75. C Hendon *Dur* 74-80; C Byker St Ant *Newc* 80-90; C Brandon *Dur* from 90; Hon Can Dur Cathl from 01. *The Clergy House, Sawmill Lane, Brandon, Durham DH7 8NS* Tel 0191-378 0845

BROWN, Peter. b 53. St Chad's Coll Dur BA75. Sarum & Wells Th Coll 75. **d** 77 **p** 78. C Tunstall Ch Ch *Lich* 77-79; C Tunstall 79-80; C Willenhall H Trin 80-83; V Weston Rhyn 83-88; Australia 88-90; R Hubberston *St D* 90-01; V Chilvers Coton w Astley *Cov* from 01. *Chilvers Coton Vicarage, Coventry Road, Nuneaton CV11 4NJ* Tel (024) 7638 3010

BROWN, Peter Russell. b 43. Oak Hill Th Coll. **d** 71 **p** 72. C Gt Faringdon w Lt Coxwell *Ox* 71-73; C Reading Greyfriars 73-74; V Forty Hill Jes Ch *Lon* 74-81; V Laleham from 81. *The Vicarage, The Broadway, Laleham, Staines TW18 1SB* Tel (01784) 457330

BROWN, Peter Thomas. b 43. Leic Univ BSc64. WEMTC 00. **d** 03. OLM Prestbury and All SS *Glouc* from 03. *32 Gallops Lane, Prestbury, Cheltenham GL52 5SD* Tel (01242) 529774 E-mail pete.brown@tinyworld.co.uk

BROWN, Philip. *See* BROWN, Canon James Philip

BROWN, Philip Anthony. b 54. Oak Hill Th Coll BA91. **d** 91 **p** 92. C Rock Ferry *Ches* 91-95; V Hattersley 95-98; V Harold Hill St Geo *Chelmsf* from 98. *St George's Vicarage, Chippenham Road, Romford RM3 8HX* Tel (01708) 343415 E-mail browns@globalnet.co.uk

BROWN, Canon Philip Roy. b 41. St Steph Ho Ox 78. **d** 80 **p** 81. C Highters Heath *Birm* 80-83; P-in-c Washwood Heath 83-87; V Tysoe w Oxhill and Whatcote *Cov* 87-93; R Harbury and Ladbroke from 93; RD Southam 95-97 and 99-02; Hon Can Cov Cathl from 00. *The Rectory, 2 Vicarage Lane, Harbury, Leamington Spa CV33 9HA* Tel (01926) 612377 Fax 614668 E-mail canon.roybrown@lineone.net

BROWN, Phillip Murray. b 59. Keele Univ BSc80. Trin Coll Bris DipTh86 ADPS87. **d** 87 **p** 88. C Greasbrough *Sheff* 87-91; Ind Chapl 87-93; V Thorne 91-99; V Norton Lees St Paul from 99. *St Paul's Vicarage, 6 Angerford Avenue, Sheffield S8 9BG* Tel 0114-255 1945 E-mail murray-b@fish.co.uk

BROWN, Raymond Isaac Harry. b 14. Kelham Th Coll 36. **d** 42 **p** 43. C Romford St Andr *Chelmsf* 42-48; Metrop Area Sec UMCA 48-52; V Wellingborough St Mary *Pet* 52-66; V Tintinhull *B & W* 66-74; RD Martock 70-75; Lesotho from 76; rtd 79. *Convent of the Holy Name, PO Box 43, Leribe 300, Lesotho* Tel (00266) 2240 0249

BROWN, Raymond John. b 49. Ox Univ BEd71. Wycliffe Hall Ox 72. **d** 75 **p** 76. C Barking St Marg w St Patr *Chelmsf* 75-78; C Walton H Trin *Ox* 78-82; V Enfield St Mich *Lon* 82-91; Chapl St Mich Hosp Enfield 82-91; R Springfield All SS *Chelmsf* from 91. *The Rectory, 4 Old School Field, Chelmsford CM1 7HU* Tel (01245) 356720

BROWN, Richard George. b 38. Dur Univ BSc63. Wells Th Coll 63. **d** 65 **p** 66. C Norton St Mary *Dur* 65-69; C N Gosforth *Newc* 69-71; Chapl Wells Cathl Sch 71-81; P-in-c Dulverton and Brushford *B & W* 81-83; R 83-86; Chapl Millfield Jun Sch Somerset 86-89; Chapl Brighton Coll 89-92; Chapl Benenden Sch 92-94; Perm to Offic *Chich* 94-97; P-in-c Poynings w Edburton, Newtimber and Pyecombe from 97. *The Rectory, Poynings, Brighton BN45 7AQ* Tel (01273) 857494 E-mail richardgb@ukgateway.net

BROWN, Richard Lessey. b 27. Keble Coll Ox BA51 MA55. Qu Coll Birm 51. **d** 53 **p** 54. C York St Lawr w St Nic *York* 53-55; C Fulford 55-57; V Fridaythorpe w Fimber and Thixendale 57-61; V York St Luke 61-75; V Barlby 75-92; rtd 92; Perm to Offic *York* from 92. *1 Kings Court, King Street, Cottingham HU16 5RW* Tel (01482) 845299

BROWN, Robert. b 47. Man Univ BSc72 Open Univ BA86 Dur Univ MA87 Sunderland Univ DipHE98. NEOC 95. **d** 98 **p** 99. C Yarm *York* 98-01; V Ormesby from 01. *The Vicarage, 54 Church Lane, Ormesby, Middlesbrough TS7 9AU* Tel (01642) 314443

BROWN, Robert Peter Cameron. b 63. K Coll Lon BSc84 Imp Coll Lon MSc87. Lon Bible Coll BA97 Cranmer Hall Dur 01. **d** 03. C Stanhope w Frosterley *Dur* from 03. *14 Burnfoot, St John's Chapel, Bishop Auckland DL13 1QH* Tel (01388) 537996

BROWN, Robin. *See* BROWN, Canon Jack Robin

BROWN, Robin. b 38. Leeds Univ BA60 MPhil69. Qu Coll Birm 89. **d** 91 **p** 92. C Far Headingley St Chad *Ripon* 91-94; V Hawksworth Wood 94-00; rtd 00. *Dale Edge, 2A Harbour View, Bedale DL8 2DQ* Tel and fax (01677) 425483 E-mail rob.stel@virgin.net

BROWN, Roger. *See* BROWN, Canon John Roger

BROWN, Capt Roger George. b 37. CA Tr Coll SEITE 92. **d** 95 **p** 96. C Maidstone St Martin *Cant* 95-97; C Oakham, Hambleton, Egleton, Braunston and Brooke *Pet* from 97; Chapl Leics and Rutland Healthcare NHS Trust from 97. *The Vicarage, 67 Church Street, Langham, Oakham LE15 7JE* Tel (01572) 722969

BROWN, Roger Lee. b 42. Univ of Wales (Lamp) BA63 Univ Coll Lon MA73. Wycliffe Hall Ox 66. **d** 68 **p** 69. C Dinas w

Penygraig *Llan* 68-70; C Bargoed and Deri w Brithdir 70-72; TV Glyncorrwg w Afan Vale and Cymmer Afan 72-74; R 74-79; V Tongwynlais 79-93; R Welshpool w Castle Caereinion *St As* from 93; RD Pool from 01. *The Vicarage, Church Street, Welshpool SY21 7DP* Tel (01938) 553164

✠**BROWN, The Rt Revd Ronald.** b 26. St Jo Coll Dur BA50 DipTh52. **d** 52 **p** 53 **c** 74. C Chorley St Laur *Blackb* 52-56; V Whittle-le-Woods 56-61; V Halliwell St Thos *Man* 61-69; R Ashton St Mich 69-74; RD Ashton-under-Lyne 69-74; Suff Bp Birkenhead *Ches* 74-92; rtd 92; Perm to Offic *Ches* 92-00. *Hurst Cottage, Moss Lane, Burscough, Ormskirk L40 4BA* Tel (01704) 897314

BROWN, Rosalind. b 53. Lon Univ BA74 Univ of Cen England in Birm Dip Town Planning 82. Yale Div Sch MDiv97. **d** 97 **p** 97. V Canonsburg St Thos USA 97-99; Vice-Prin OLM Scheme *Sarum* from 99; Tutor STETS from 99. *6 Lime Kiln Way, Salisbury SP2 8RN* Tel (01722) 341103 E-mail rosalind.brown@salisbury.anglican.org

BROWN, Mrs Rosémia. b 53. Ripon Coll Cuddesdon 97. **d** 99 **p** 00. C Shoreditch St Leon and Hoxton St Jo *Lon* 99-00; C Shoreditch St Leon w St Mich 00-02; TV Hackney 02-03; V Clapton St Jas from 03. *134 Rushmore Road, London E5 0EY* Tel (020) 8985 1750

BROWN, Roy. *See* BROWN, Canon Philip Roy

BROWN, Simon John. b 66. Birm Univ BSc87 PGCE88 Nottm Univ MA93. St Jo Coll Nottm Dip Th Studies 92. **d** 93 **p** 94. C Holbrooks *Cov* 93-97; C Leamington Priors All SS 97-00; C Leamington Spa H Trin and Old Milverton 97-00; P-in-c Woolavington w Cossington and Bawdrip *B & W* 00-01; V from 01. *The Rectory, Woolavington, Bridgwater TA7 8DX* Tel (01278) 683408 E-mail simon@vicar.plus.com

BROWN, Canon Simon Nicolas Danton. b 37. Clare Coll Cam BA61 MA65. S'wark Ord Course 61 Linc Th Coll 63. **d** 64 **p** 65. C Lambeth St Mary the Less *S'wark* 64-66; Chapl and Warden LMH Settlement 66-72; P-in-c Southampton St Mary w H Trin *Win* 72-73; TV Southampton (City Cen) 73-79; R Gt Brickhill w Bow Brickhill and Lt Brickhill *Ox* 79-84; TR Burnham w Dropmore, Hitcham and Taplow from 84; RD Burnham and Slough 87-02; Hon Can Ch Ch from 94; Dioc Consultant for Deanery Development from 97; Sen Exec Asst to Bp Buckingham from 02. *The Rectory, The Precincts, Burnham, Slough SL1 7HU* Tel (01628) 604173 E-mail sndbrown@csi.com

BROWN, Stanley George. b 19. Bps' Coll Cheshunt 66. **d** 67 **p** 68. C Shrub End *Chelmsf* 67-71; R Dengie w Asheldham 71-89; V Tillingham 71-89; RD Maldon and Dengie 82-89; rtd 89; Perm to Offic *Ely* from 90. *134 Lynn Road, Ely CB6 1DE* Tel (01353) 662888

BROWN, Stephen Charles. b 60. Leeds Univ BA83 BA89 Reading Univ PGCE89. Coll of Resurr Mirfield 87. **d** 90 **p** 91. C Whitkirk *Ripon* 90-93; Asst Youth Chapl 92-95; C Chapel Allerton 93-95; R Stanningley St Thos 95-01; V Laneside *Blackb* from 01; Hon Chapl ATC from 03. *St Peter's Vicarage, Laneside, Haslingden, Rossendale BB4 4BG* Tel (01706) 213838 E-mail stephenbrown@supanet.com

BROWN, Stephen James. b 44. Bradf Univ BSc69. Westcott Ho Cam 71. **d** 72 **p** 73. C Seaton Hirst *Newc* 72-75; C Marton-in-Cleveland *York* 75-77; Dioc Youth Adv *Dur* 77-82; V Thorner *Ripon* 82-92; Chapl Yorkshire TV from 89; Dioc Officer for Local Min 90-01; P-in-c Ripley from 92. *The Rectory, Ripley, Harrogate HG3 3AY* Tel (01423) 770147 Fax 772217 E-mail stephenjamesbrown@compuserve.com

BROWN, Susan Gertrude. b 48. Univ of Wales (Swansea) BA71 Roehampton Inst PGCE72. St Mich Coll Llan 98. **d** 02 **p** 03. NSM Gelligaer *Llan* from 02. *27 Tenby Court, Hendredenny, Caerphilly CF83 2UE* Tel (029) 2086 2736 E-mail suebrown27 uk@yahoo.com

✠**BROWN, The Rt Revd Thomas John.** b 43. St Jo Coll Auckland LTh72 STh76 San Francisco Th Sem DMin84. **d** 72 **p** 73 **c** 91. New Zealand 72-74 and from 76; C Christchurch St Alban 72-74; C Leic St Jas *Leic* 74-76; V Upper Clutha 76-79; V Roslyn 79-85; V Lower Hutt St Jas 85-91; Adn Belmont 87-91; Asst Bp Wellington 91-97; Bp Wellington from 98. *20 Eccleston Hill, Wellington 6001, New Zealand* Tel (0064) (4) 473 2183 *or* 472 1057 Fax 499 1360

BROWN, Mrs Verity Joy. b 68. Qu Mary Coll Lon BA89. Ripon Coll Cuddesdon BTh93. **d** 93 **p** 94. C Barnard Castle w Whorlton *Dur* 93-95; C Bensham 95-97; Perm to Offic from 97. *75 Eamont Gardens, Hartlepool TS26 9JE* Tel (01429) 423186

BROWN, Victor Charles. b 31. S'wark Ord Course 67. **d** 71 **p** 72. C Pinhoe *Ex* 71-73; C Egg Buckland 73-74; C Oakdale St Geo *Sarum* 74-77; R Old Trafford St Hilda *Man* 77-83; R Chigwell Row *Chelmsf* 83-92; R Fenny Bentley, Kniveton, Thorpe and Tissington *Derby* 92-96; rtd 96; Perm to Offic *Sarum* from 96. *377 Sopwith Crescent, Wimborne BH21 1XJ* Tel (01202) 841274

BROWN, Canon Wallace. b 44. Oak Hill Th Coll 77. **d** 79 **p** 80. C Oadby *Leic* 79-85; V Quinton Road W St Boniface *Birm* from 85; Hon Can Birm Cathl from 01. *St Boniface Vicarage, Quinton Road West, Birmingham B32 2QD* Tel 0121-427 1939

BROWN, William Martyn. b 14. Pemb Coll Cam BA36 MA47. Nor Ord Course 76. d 76 p 77. NSM Thornage w Brinton w Hunworth and Stody *Nor* 76-77; NSM Field Dalling w Saxlingham 77-84; RD Holt 84-88; NSM Gunthorpe w Bale w Field Dalling, Saxlingham etc 84-88; Perm to Offic from 88. *Lodge Cottage, Field Dalling, Holt NR25 7AS* Tel (01328) 830403

BROWNBRIDGE, Bernard Alan. b 19. NW Ord Course 74. d 77 p 78. NSM Huntington *York* 77-80; V Sand Hutton 80-86; rtd 87; Hon C Birdsall w Langton *York* 87-92; Perm to Offic from 92. *2 Duncombe Close, Malton YO17 7YY* Tel (01653) 697626

BROWNBRIDGE, Peter John. b 31. BD. d 81 p 82. NSM Wingham w Elmstone and Preston w Stourmouth *Cant* 81-87; V 87-99; rtd 99; Perm to Offic *Cant* from 01. *Woodland St Mary, The Street, Ickham, Canterbury CT3 1QN* Tel (01227) 722958

BROWNE, Arnold Samuel. b 52. St Jo Coll Ox BA73 MA77 SS Coll Cam PhD87 Surrey Univ MSc89 MBPsS92. Westcott Ho Cam 76. d 78 p 79. C Esher *Guildf* 78-81; C Worplesdon 81-86; Chapl R Holloway and Bedf New Coll 86-92; Fell and Dean of Chpl Trin Coll Cam from 92. *Trinity College, Cambridge CB2 1TQ* Tel (01223) 338563 Fax 338564 E-mail asb32@cam.ac.uk

BROWNE, Aubrey Robert Caulfeild. b 31. Moore Th Coll Sydney 54. d 55 p 56. Australia 55-71; Producer of Relig Radio Progr USPG 72-84; Hon C S Kensington St Steph *Lon* 78-88; Hd of Area Sec Dept USPG 84-87; P-in-c Nunhead St Antony *S'wark* 88-90; V Nunhead St Antony w St Silas 90-96; rtd 97; Australia from 97. *15 Caroma Avenue, Kyeemagh, NSW, Australia 2216*

BROWNE, Miss Christine Mary. b 53. Nottm Univ BEd75. EMMTC 87. d 90 p 94. Par Dn Bulwell St Mary *S'well* 90-94; C 94-95; TV Hucknall Torkard 95-00; Dep Chapl HM Pris Nor 00-01; Chapl HM YOI Swinfen Hall 01-03; Perm to Offic *Derby* from 03. *42 Thoresby Crescent, Draycott, Derby DE72 3PH* Tel (01332) 872802

BROWNE, George William. b 42. CITC 99. d 02. NSM Kilmore w Ballintemple, Kildallon etc *K, E & A* from 02. *Rose Villa, Corgar, Ballinamore, Co Leitrim, Irish Republic* Tel (00353) (71) 964 4415 Mobile 86-351 7700 E-mail gwbrowne@oceanfree.net

BROWNE, Canon Herman Beseah. b 65. Cuttington Univ Coll BTh86 K Coll Lon BD90 AKC90 Heythrop Coll Lon DPhil94. d 87 p 91. C N Lambeth *S'wark* 90-91; Tutor Simon of Cyrene Th Inst 90-96; Abp's Asst Sec for Ecum and Angl Affairs *Cant* 96-01; Abp's Officer for Angl Communion from 01; Perm to Offic *S'wark* from 96; Hon Prov Can Cant Cathl *Cant* from 01. *Cottage 3, Lambeth Palace, London SE1 7JU* Tel (020) 7898 1219 E-mail herman.browne@c-of-e.org.uk

BROWNE, Ian Cameron. b 51. St Cath Coll Ox BA74 MA78 Fitzw Coll Cam BA76 MA80. Ridley Hall Cam 74. d 77 p 78. C Cheltenham Ch Ch *Glouc* 77-80; Hon C Shrewsbury St Chad *Lich* 80-83; Asst Chapl Shrewsbury Sch 80-83; Chapl Bedford Sch 83-96; Sen Chapl Oundle Sch from 97. *The School, Oundle, Peterborough PE8 4EN* Tel (01832) 273372 *or* 273541

BROWNE, Leonard Joseph. b 58. St Cath Coll Cam BA81 MA84. Trin Coll Bris 87. d 89 p 90. C Reading Greyfriars *Ox* 89-92; V Cambridge St Barn *Ely* 92-00; Sen Chapl and Hd Div Dean Close Sch Cheltenham from 00. *25 Hatherley Road, Cheltenham GL51 6EB* Tel (01242) 513088 *or* 258062 Fax 258003 E-mail leonard@brownes.f9.co.uk *or* lj-browne@supanet.com

BROWNE, Peter Clifford. b 59. Bris Univ BA80 SRN82. Ripon Coll Cuddesdon 88. d 90 p 91. C Southgate Ch Ch *Lon* 90-92; NSM Kemp Town St Mary *Chich* 93-95; Chapl United Bris Healthcare NHS Trust 96-98; NSM Southmead *Bris* 98-02; Chapl HM Pris Preston from 02. *HM Prison, 2 Ribbleton Lane, Preston PR1 5AB* Tel (01772) 257734

BROWNE, Robert. *See* BROWNE, Aubrey Robert Caulfeild

BROWNING, Edward Barrington Lee (Barry). b 42. St Pet Coll Saltley TCert65. Ripon Coll Cuddesdon 90. d 92 p 93. C Falmouth K Chas *Truro* 92-96; R Roche and Withiel 96-01; P-in-c Manaccan w St Anthony-in-Meneage and St Martin from 01; P-in-c Cury and Gunwalloe w Mawgan from 01. *The Rectory, Mawgan, Helston TR12 6AD* Tel (01326) 221696

BROWNING, Mrs Jacqueline Ann. b 44. Sarum Th Coll 93. d 96 p 97. NSM New Alresford w Ovington and Itchen Stoke *Win* from 96; Past Asst Win Cathl from 02. *1 Paddock Way, Alresford SO24 9PN* Tel (01962) 734372

BROWNING, Canon John William. b 36. Keele Univ BA61. Ripon Hall Ox 61. d 63 p 64. C Baswich *Lich* 63-66; Chapl Monyhull Hosp Birm 67-72; Chapl Wharncliffe Hosp Sheff 72-78; Chapl Middlewood Hosp Sheff 72-94; Hon Can Sheff Cathl *Sheff* 84-97; Chapl Sheff Mental Health Unit 85-94; Chapl Community Health Sheff NHS Trust from 94; Chapl Sheff (South) Mental Health Centres 94-97; rtd 97; Perm to Offic *Sheff* from 97. *131 Low Road, Stannington, Sheffield S6 5FZ* Tel 0114-234 3740 E-mail johnpatbrowning@hotmail.com

BROWNING, Julian. b 51. St Jo Coll Cam BA72 MA76. Ripon Coll Cuddesdon 77. d 80 p 81. C Notting Hill *Lon* 80-81; C W Brompton St Mary w St Pet 81-84; Perm to Offic 84-91; NSM Paddington St Sav from 99. *82 Ashworth Mansions, Grantully Road, London W9 1LN* Tel (020) 7286 6034

BROWNING, Kevin John. b 56. Ridley Hall Cam CTM96. d 98 p 99. C Northampton Em *Pet* 98-01; P-in-c Hardwick *Ely* from 01. *The Rectory, Main Street, Hardwick, Cambridge CB3 7QS* Tel (01954) 210695

BROWNING, Canon Richard Geoffrey Claude. b 25. Selw Coll Cam BA50 MA55. Lon Coll of Div BD53 ALCD53. d 53 p 54. C Walthamstow St Mary *Chelmsf* 53-56; V E Ham St Paul 56-65; V Old Hill H Trin *Worc* 65-91; Hon Can Worc Cathl 77-91; rtd 91; Perm to Offic *Ban* from 91. *Llwyn Rhug, Ffordd Dewi Sant, Nefyn, Pwllheli LL53 6EG* Tel (01758) 720834

BROWNING, Robert Derek. b 42. Guildf Dioc Min Course 98. d 01 p 02. OLM Lightwater *Guildf* from 01. *16 Guildford Road, Lightwater GU18 5SN* Tel (01276) 474345 E-mail derekandcarol@btinternet.com

BROWNING, Thomas Clive. b 35. Lon Univ DipTh65 BD67. Wycliffe Hall Ox 63. d 67 p 68. C Ipswich St Jo *St E* 67-69; Chapl Scargill Ho 69-70; C Downend *Bris* 70-73; C Hagley *Worc* 73-76; Asst Master Bay Ho Sch Gosport 77-00; rtd 00. *30 Norfolk Road, Shirley, Southampton SO15 5AS* Tel (023) 8036 6891

BROWNING, Canon Wilfrid Robert Francis. b 18. Ch Ch Ox BA40 MA44 BD49. Cuddesdon Coll 40. d 41 p 42. C Towcester w Easton Neston *Pet* 41-44; C Woburn Square Ch Ch *Lon* 44-46; Chapl St Deiniol's Lib Hawarden 46-48; Chapl Heswall Nautical Sch 46-48; C-in-c Hove St Rich CD *Chich* 48-51; Lect Cuddesdon Coll 51-59; R Gt Haseley *Ox* 51-59; Ed *Bulletin Anglican* 55-60; Warden Whalley Abbey 59-63; Can Res Blackb Cathl *Blackb* 59-65; Dir Post-Ord Tr 62-65; Lect Cuddesdon Coll 65-70; Can Res Ch Ch *Ox* 65-87; Hon Can 87-89; Dir Post-Ord Tr 65-85; Dir of Ords 65-85; Dir Ox NSM Course 72-89; rtd 87; Tutor Westmr Coll Ox 93-99. *42 Alexandra Road, Oxford OX2 0DB* Tel (01865) 723464

BROWNLESS, Brian Paish. b 25. TD72. Keble Coll Ox BA50 MA50. Wells Th Coll 50. d 52 p 53. C Man St Aid *Man* 52-54; C Chorlton-cum-Hardy St Clem 54-56; C Swinton St Pet 56-58; V Elton St Steph 58-66; CF (TA) 60-66; Area Sec USPG *Lich* 66-77; Lic to Offic *Lich* 66-77; CF (TA - R of O) 66-72; R Yoxall *Lich* 77-82; V S Ramsey St Paul *S & M* 82-87; rtd 87; Perm to Offic *Heref* from 87. *10 Caple Avenue, Kings Caple, Hereford HR1 4UL* Tel (01432) 840246

BROWNLESS, Philip Paul Stanley. b 19. Selw Coll Cam BA41 MA45. Ridley Hall Cam 46. d 47 p 48. C Prittlewell St Mary *Chelmsf* 47-50; Min Prittlewell St Mary CD 50-54; Chapl & Hd Master Lambrook Sch Bracknell 54-71; V Heckfield cum Mattingley *Win* 71-74; V Heckfield w Mattingley and Rotherwick 74-84; RD Odiham 83-84; rtd 85; Perm to Offic *Chich* from 85. *The Hornpipe, Oak Meadow, Birdham, Chichester PO20 7BH* Tel (01243) 512177

BROWNLIE, Miss Caroline Heddon. b 47. Suffolk Poly CQSW75. St Jo Coll Nottm DPS80 Qu Coll Birm IDC81. d 87 p 94. Asst Chapl Fairfield Hosp Hitchin 87-91; NSM Ashwell w Hinxworth and Newnham *St Alb* 92-98; Chapl HM Rem Cen Low Newton 99-01. *Priory of Our Lady, Priory Lane, Burford OX18 4SQ* Tel (01993) 823605

BROWNRIDGE, Canon Allan John Michael. b 32. Chan Sch Truro 80. d 82 p 83. C St Keverne *Truro* 82-86; P-in-c Werrington, St Giles in the Heath and Virginstow 86-92; R Boyton, N Tamerton, Werrington etc 92-02; RD Trigg Major from 94; Hon Can Truro Cathl from 98; rtd 02. *6 Cotehele View, Calstock PL18 9RJ* Tel (01822) 832006

BROWNRIDGE, David Leonard Robert. b 76. Univ of Wales (Lamp) BA97. Trin Coll Bris 98. d 00 p 01. C Henfynyw w Aberaeron and Llanddewi Aberarth *St D* from 00. *Dyffryn, Lampeter Road, Aberaeron SA46 0ED* Tel (01545) 571579 E-mail davidbecky@brownridge97.freeserve.co.uk

BROWNRIGG, Canon Ronald Allen. b 19. Em Coll Cam BA47 MA50 FRSA91. Westcott Ho Cam 47. d 49 p 50. C Beverley Minster *York* 49-51; Dean Jerusalem 51-54; C Stanmore *Win* 54-60; R Bletchingley *S'wark* 60-74; V Petersham 74-85; Hon Can S'wark Cathl 78-85; Consultant Inter-Ch Travel from 83; rtd 85. *Marlborough Lodge, 13 Marlborough Lane, Bath BA1 2NQ* Tel (01225) 334831

BROWNSELL, Preb John Kenneth. b 48. Hertf Coll Ox BA69 BA72 MA89. Cuddesdon Coll 70. d 73 p 74. C Notting Hill All SS w St Columb *Lon* 73-74; C Notting Hill 74-76; TV 76-82; V Notting Hill All SS w St Columb from 82; AD Kensington 84-92; Preb St Paul's Cathl from 92; Dir of Ords from 95. *The Vicarage, Powis Gardens, London W11 1JG* Tel (020) 7727 5919

BROXTON, Alan. b 40. UMIST BSc72 CEng MICE79 MIStructE77. LNSM course 93. d 96 p 97. OLM Rhodes *Man* from 96. *241 Heywood Old Road, Middleton, Manchester M24 4QR* Tel 0161-643 6319 Fax as telephone

BRUCE, David Ian. b 47. Univ of Wales (Cardiff) DipTh73. St Mich Coll Llan 70. d 73 p 74. C Bordesley St Benedict *Birm* 73-74; C Llanishen and Lisvane *Llan* 74-81; V Canley *Cov* 81-90;

V Longford 90-97; rtd 97; Perm to Offic *Cov* from 97. *122 Hugh Road, Coventry CV3 1AF* Tel (024) 7644 5789

BRUCE, Francis Bernard. b 30. Trin Coll Ox BA52 MA56. Westcott Ho Cam 52. **d** 54 **p** 55. C Bury St Mary *Man* 54-59; C Sherborne w Castleton and Lillington *Sarum* 59-61; R Croston *Blackb* 61-86; V Bibury w Winson and Barnsley *Glouc* 86-95; rtd 95; Perm to Offic *Glouc* from 95. *6 Gloucester Street, Cirencester GL7 2DG* Tel (01285) 641954

BRUCE, James Hamilton. b 57. Dur Univ BSc78 Newc Univ MSc79 St Andr Univ PhD99. Trin Coll Bris DipTh84. **d** 84 **p** 85. C Walmley *Birm* 84-86; Perm to Offic *Carl* 87-95; W Cumbria Sch Worker N Schs Chr Union 87-93; Nat Development Officer Wales Scripture Union 93-94; Chapl Turi St Andr Kenya 95-96; NSM St Andrews St Andr *St And* 96-99; R Penicuik *Edin* from 99; R W Linton from 99. *23 Broomhill Road, Penicuik EH26 9EE* E-mail rector@stjamespenicuik.freeserve.co.uk

BRUCE, John. b 26. **d** 50 **p** 51. Canada 50-62; V Broughton Moor *Carl* 63-66; V Carl St Herbert w St Steph 66-74; P-in-c Kendal St Geo 74-76; V 76-83; V Coundon *Dur* 83-86; rtd 86; Perm to Offic *Carl* 86-93. *9 Penton Close, Carlisle CA3 0PX*

BRUCE, John Cyril. b 41. EMMTC 95. **d** 98 **p** 99. NSM Spalding *Linc* from 98. *Cae Canol, 15 Holland Road, Spalding PE11 1UL* Tel (01775) 725648 E-mail john.bruce@spaldingchurches.org

BRUCE, Ms Katherine Sarah. b 68. Leeds Univ BA89 St Jo Coll Dur BA01 Trin & All SS Coll Leeds PGCE91. Cranmer Hall Dur 98. **d** 01 **p** 02. C Ripon H Trin *Ripon* from 01. *8 Kirkby Road, Ripon HG4 2ET* Tel (01765) 698758

BRUCE, Leslie Barton. b 23. Liv Univ MB, ChB48. **d** 71 **p** 72. Hon C Wavertree H Trin *Liv* from 71. *3 Childwall Park Avenue, Liverpool L16 0JE* Tel 0151-722 7664

BRUECK, Ms Jutta. b 61. LSE MSc89 Heythrop Coll Lon MA92 Fitzw Coll Cam BA96. Westcott Ho Cam 94. **d** 97 **p** 98. C Is of Dogs Ch Ch and St Jo w St Luke *Lon* 97-01; Chapl Guildhall Sch of Music and Drama from 01. *The Vicarage, Manchester Road, London E14 3BN* Tel (020) 7538 1766

BRUMWELL, Francis John Thomas. b 33. Lich Th Coll 57. **d** 61 **p** 62. C Birm St Geo *Birm* 61-63; C Gorton St Mark *Man* 63-64; V Calderbrook 65-73; V Bradley St Martin *Lich* 73-89; P-in-c Bilston St Mary 75-78; R Gorton St Phil *Man* 89-95; rtd 95. *53 Audmore Road, Gnosall, Stafford ST20 0HE* Tel (01785) 822808

BRUNDLE, Michael Roy. b 52. Qu Coll Birm. **d** 84 **p** 85. C Swindon New Town *Bris* 84-88; TV Halifax *Wakef* 88-92; Chapl HM YOI Feltham 92-94; C Notting Dale St Clem w St Mark and St Jas *Lon* 94-95; V Swanley St Mary *Roch* from 95. *St Mary's Vicarage, London Road, Swanley BR8 7AQ* Tel (01322) 662201 Fax as telephone E-mail frbrundle@ntlworld.com

BRUNNING, Canon David George. b 32. St D Coll Lamp BA53. St Mich Coll Llan 53. **d** 55 **p** 56. C Llantwit Major and St Donat's *Llan* 55-59; C Usk and Monkswood w Glascoed Chpl and Gwehelog *Mon* 59-62; V Abercarn 62-71; V Pontnewydd 71-89; RD Pontypool 89-97; R Panteg 90-98; Can St Woolos Cathl from 94; rtd 98; Lic to Offic *Mon* from 98. *6 Spitzkop, Llantwit Major CF61 1RD* Tel (01446) 792124

BRUNNING, Neil. b 29. NW Ord Course 73. **d** 76 **p** 77. C Cheadle Hulme All SS *Ches* 76-79; V 79-88; V Glentworth *Linc* 88-93; P-in-c Hemswell w Harpswell 88-93; V Glentworth Gp 93-94; rtd 94; Perm to Offic *Linc* from 94. *11 Drovers Court, Lea Road, Gainsborough DN21 1AN* Tel (01427) 617938 Fax as telephone E-mail neilbrun@aol.com

BRUNO, Canon Allan Allan David. b 34. AKC59. St Boniface Warminster 59. **d** 60 **p** 61. C Darlington H Trin *Dur* 60-64; S Africa 64-65 and 76-80; Rhodesia 65-70; Overseas Chapl Scottish Episc Ch 70-75; C Edin Old St Paul *Edin* 75-76; Namibia 80-86; Dean Windhoek 81-86; R Falkirk *Edin* 86-95; Hon Can Kinkizi from 95; Bp's Dom Chapl *Bradf* 96-99; Bp's Past Asst 99-01; rtd 01; Lic to Offic *Bradf* from 01. *Pump Cottage, 2 Waterside Potteries, Burton in Lonsdale, Carnforth LA6 3LL* Tel (01524) 261616 E-mail david@bruno81.freeserve.co.uk

BRUNSDON, Canon Thomas Kenneth. b 08. Univ of Wales BA33. St Mich Coll Llan 33. **d** 34 **p** 35. C Knighton *S & B* 34-40; V Llandegley 40-47; V Builth w Alltmawr and Llanynys 47-61; RD Builth 55-61; V Newton St Pet 61-76; Can Brecon Cathl 58-72; Treas 72-76; rtd 76. *Albert Edward Prince of Wales Court, Penylan Avenue, Porthcawl CF36 3LY* Tel (01656) 772105

BRUNSKILL, Mrs Sheila Kathryn. *See* BANYARD, Canon Sheila Kathryn

BRUNSWICK, Canon Robert John. b 38. TD86. St Aid Birkenhead 60. **d** 63 **p** 64. C Neston *Ches* 63-66; CF (TA - R of O) from 65; C Warrington St Paul *Liv* 66-68; V Liv St Paul Stoneycroft 68-78; V Southport St Luke 78-87; R Croston *Blackb* 87-01; R Croston and Bretherton from 01; Chapl Bp Rawstorne Sch Preston from 88; Hon Can Koforidua from 94. *St Michael's Rectory, 19 Westhead Road, Croston, Leyland PR26 9JQ* Tel (01772) 600877

BRUNT, Prof Peter William. OBE. Liv Univ MB59 MD67 Lon Univ FRCP74. Ab Dioc Tr Course. **d** 96 **p** 97. NSM Bieldside *Ab* from 96. *17 Kingshill Road, Aberdeen AB15 5JY* Tel (01224) 314204 *or* 681818 ext 52287 Fax 840711

BRUNT, Mrs Philippa Ann. b 53. Leeds Univ BA74 Leeds and Carnegie Coll PGCE75. WEMTC 95. **d** 98 **p** 99. C Cinderford St Steph w Littledean *Glouc* 98-01; V Parkend and Viney Hill from 01. *The Vicarage, Lower Road, Yorkley, Lydney GL15 4TN* Tel (01594) 562828 E-mail pabrunt@ukonline.co.uk

BRUNYEE, Miss Hilary. b 46. Linc Th Coll 76. **dss** 81 **d** 87 **p** 94. Longsight St Jo w St Cypr *Man* 81-87; Par Dn Peel 87-94; TV 94-99; TV Walkden and Lt Hulton 99-00; rtd 00. *38 Holly Avenue, Worsley, Manchester M28 3DW* Tel 0161-790 7761

BRUSH, Canon Sally. b 47. Lon Univ BD75 Univ of Wales MPhil96. Trin Coll Bris 73. **dss** 76 **d** 80 **p** 97. Flint *St As* 76-83; C 80-83; C Cefn 83-87; C St As and Tremeirchion 83-87; Chapl St As Cathl 83-87; Dn-in-c Cerrigydrudion w Llanfihangel Glyn Myfyr etc 87-97; V from 97; RD Edeirnion from 98; Hon Can St As Cathl from 01. *The Rectory, 1 Tyddyn Terrace, Cerrigydrudion, Corwen LL21 9NT* Tel (01490) 420313

BRUTON, Keith Leslie. b 39. S Dios Minl Tr Scheme 91. **d** 94 **p** 96. NSM Camelot Par *B & W* 94-98; Vlissingen (Flushing) Miss to Seamen *Eur* 98-99; P-in-c Toddington, Stanton, Didbrook w Hailes etc *Glouc* 99-02. *15 Fairway, Northway, Tewkesbury GL20 8QD* Tel (01684) 291359 E-mail kbruton@fish.co.uk

BRUTTON, Robert Springett. b 14. Trin Coll Cam BA34 MA55. Cuddesdon Coll 54. **d** 55 **p** 56. C Wendover *Ox* 55-57; V Radley 57-65; V Sonning 65-74; rtd 74; Perm to Offic *Sarum* from 75. *7 North Street, Langton Matravers, Swanage BH19 3HL* Tel (01929) 425681

BRYAN, Canon Cecil William. b 43. TCD BA66 MA73. CITC 66. **d** 68 **p** 69. C Dublin Zion Ch *D & G* 68-72; Chapl RAF 72-75; Dioc Info Officer *D & G* 75-90; I Castleknock w Mulhuddart, Clonsilla etc 75-89; Chapl K Hosp Sch Dub 89-99; I Tullow *D & G* from 99; Can Ch Ch Cathl Dublin from 03. *Tullow Rectory, Brighton Road, Carrickmines, Dublin 18, Irish Republic* Tel (00353) (1) 289 3154

BRYAN, Christopher Paul. b 75. Univ Coll Ox BA96 St Jo Coll Dur BA99. Cranmer Hall Dur 97. **d** 00 **p** 01. C Old Swinford Stourbridge *Worc* from 00. *58 Arlington Court, Stourbridge DY8 1NN* Tel (01384) 373286 E-mail cpbryan@hotmail.com

BRYAN, David John. b 56. Liv Univ BSc77 Hull Univ BTh85 Qu Coll Ox DPhil89. Ox Min Course 89. **d** 90 **p** 91. C Abingdon *Ox* 90-93; Tutor Qu Coll Birm 93-01; Dean of Studies 95-01; R Haughton le Skerne *Dur* from 01. *The Rectory, Haughton Green, Darlington DL1 2DD* Tel (01325) 468142 E-mail david@portessbryan.freeserve.co.uk

BRYAN, Judith Claire. b 57. Aston Univ BSc79 PhD82 Trent Poly PGCE83. St Jo Coll Nottm BTh94 LTh95. **d** 95 **p** 96. C Wolverhampton St Matt *Lich* 95-99; Chapl Hull Univ *York* from 99. *21 Southwood Road, Cottingham HU16 5AE* Tel (01482) 847151

BRYAN, Leslie Harold. b 48. Div Hostel Dub 70. **d** 73 **p** 74. C Cork St Fin Barre's Cathl *C, C & R* 73-75; I Templebreedy w Tracton and Nohoval 75-79; CF 79-03. *Address temp unknown*

BRYAN, Michael John Christopher. b 35. Wadh Coll Ox BA58 BTh59 MA63 Ex Univ PhD83. Ripon Hall Ox 59. **d** 60 **p** 61. C Reigate St Mark *S'wark* 60-64; Tutor Sarum & Wells Th Coll 64-69; Vice-Prin 69-71; USA 71-74 and from 83; Sen Officer Educn and Community Dept *Lon* 74-79; Chapl Ex Univ *Ex* 79-83; rtd 95; Perm to Offic *Ex* from 95. *148 Proctors Hall Road, Sewanee, TN 37383-1000, USA*

BRYAN, Nigel Arthur. b 39. Univ of Wales (Lamp) BA61. Burgess Hall Lamp 61. **d** 63 **p** 64. C Llanstadwel *St D* 63-69; Chapl RAF 69-94; R Gt w Lt Milton and Gt Haseley *Ox* 94-98; R Newport w Cilgwyn and Dinas w Llanllawer *St D* from 98. *The Rectory, Long Street, Newport SA42 0TJ* Tel (01239) 820380

BRYAN, Patrick Joseph. b 41. St Jo Coll Cam BA63 MA67. St Steph Ho Ox 73. **d** 75 **p** 76. C Rushall *Lich* 75-78; C Brierley Hill 78-80; P-in-c Walsall St Mary and All SS Palfrey 80-87. *49 Hawthorn Road, Shelfield, Walsall WS5 4NB* Tel (01922) 963234

BRYAN, Canon Percival John Milward. b 19. St Pet Coll Ox BA40 MA46 BTh47. Wycliffe Hall Ox 46. **d** 48 **p** 49. C Belvedere All SS *Roch* 48-51; Australia 51-52; C Blindley Heath *S'wark* 53-54; R Warkton and Weekley *Pet* 54-56; R King's Cliffe 56-85; Can Pet Cathl 73-86; rtd 86; Perm to Offic *Pet* from 86; *Linc* 91-00. *3 Saxon Road, Barnack, Stamford PE9 3EQ*

BRYAN, Canon Philip Richard. b 40. Dur Univ BA61. Wycliffe Hall Ox 72. **d** 74 **p** 75. C Macclesfield St Mich *Ches* 74-77; V St Bees *Carl* from 77; Chapl St Bees Sch Cumbria from 77; RD Calder *Carl* 88-96; Hon Can Carl Cathl 91-00. *The Priory, St Bees CA27 0DR* Tel (01946) 822279

BRYAN, Canon Sherry Lee. b 49. WMMTC 88. **d** 91 **p** 94. Par Dn St Columb Minor and St Colan *Truro* 91-94; C 94-96; P-in-c St Teath from 96; RD Trigg Minor and Bodmin from 02; Hon Can Truro Cathl from 03; Chapl Cornwall Healthcare Trust 99-02. *The Vicarage, Whitewell Lane, St Teath, Bodmin PL30 3LH* Tel (01208) 850292 Fax as telephone E-mail sherry@whitewelllane.fsnet.co.uk

BRYAN, Timothy Andrew. b 56. St Edm Hall Ox MA80. S'wark Ord Course 93. **d** 96 **p** 97. NSM Morden *S'wark* 96-99; NSM Carshalton Beeches from 99; Perm to Offic *Guildf* from 99.

39 Highfield Road, Sutton SM1 4JY Tel (020) 8642 0576 *or* 7230 1212 E-mail timbryan@tinyworld.co.uk

BRYAN, William Terence. b 38. Birm Univ CertEd68. Chich Th Coll 73. **d** 75 **p** 76. C Shrewsbury St Giles *Lich* 75-79; V Churchstoke w Hyssington and Sarn *Heref* from 79. *The Vicarage, Church Stoke, Montgomery SY15 6AF* Tel (01588) 620228

BRYANS, Joseph. b 15. TCD BA39 MA43. CITC 40. **d** 42 **p** 43. C Kirby Moorside w Gillamoor *York* 42-45; C Thornaby on Tees St Luke 45-47; C Seapatrick *D & D* 47-54; I Gleneely w Culdaff *D & R* 54-60; I Tamlaghtard w Aghanloo 60-90; rtd 90. *1 Eventide Gardens, Limavady BT49 0AX* Tel (028) 7176 2768

BRYANT, Andrew Watts. b 57. St Jo Coll Dur BA78 Birm Univ MA81 DipTh82. Qu Coll Birm 80. **d** 83 **p** 84. C Pelsall *Lich* 83-87; NSM 91-94; Perm to Offic 87-92; NSM Streetly 94-96; NSM Beckbury, Badger, Kemberton, Ryton, Stockton etc 96-99; R Worplesdon *Guildf* from 99; Chapl Merrist Wood Coll of Agric and Horticulture from 01. *The Rectory, Perry Hill, Worplesdon, Guildford GU3 3RE* Tel (01483) 234616 Fax as telephone E-mail worplesdon.rectory@virgin.net

BRYANT, Canon Christopher. b 32. K Coll Lon AKC60. **d** 61 **p** 62. C Fareham H Trin *Portsm* 61-65; C Yatton Keynell *Bris* 65-71; C Biddestone w Slaughterford 65-71; C Castle Combe 65-71; V Chirton, Marden and Patney *Sarum* 71-76; V Chirton, Marden, Patney, Charlton and Wilsford 76-78; P-in-c Devizes St Jo w St Mary 78-79; R 79-97; RD Devizes 83-93; Can and Preb Sarum Cathl from 87; rtd 97; Master St Nic Hosp Salisbury from 97. *The Master's House, St Nicholas Hospital, St Nicholas Road, Salisbury SP1 2SW* Tel (01722) 336874

BRYANT, David Charles. b 48. St Andr Univ BSc71. St Mich Coll Llan 71. **d** 74 **p** 75. C Llanilid w Pencoed *Llan* 74-78; C Caerphilly 78-79; V Crynant 79-84; V Llanegryn and Llanfihangel-y-Pennant etc *Ban* 84-93; V Llandwrog and Llanwnda from 93. *The Vicarage, Groeslon, Caernarfon LL54 7DL* Tel (01286) 830584 Fax 830614 E-mail davidbryant@netmatters.co.uk

BRYANT, David Henderson. b 37. K Coll Lon BD60 AKC60. **d** 61 **p** 62. C Trowbridge H Trin *Sarum* 61-63; C Ewell *Guildf* 63-67; V Leiston *St E* 67-73; Chapl RN 73; C Northam *Ex* 74-75; P-in-c Clavering w Langley *Chelmsf* 76-77; Teacher Mountview High Sch Harrow 77-85; P-in-c Boosbeck w Moorsholm *York* 85-89; V 89-90; V Sowerby 90-95; P-in-c Sessay 90-95; V Lastingham w Appleton-le-Moors, Rosedale etc 95-99; rtd 99. *35 West End, Kirkbymoorside, York YO62 6AD* Tel (01751) 430269

✠**BRYANT, The Rt Revd Denis William.** b 18. DFC42. Qu Coll Birm 56. **d** 58 **p** 59 **c** 67. C Bourne *Guildf* 58-60; C Cuddington 60-61; Australia from 61; Adn Goldfields 67-72; Bp Kalgoorlie 67-72; Adn Northam 72-75; Asst Bp Perth 74-75; rtd 94. *Unit 3, Dorothy Genders Village, 99 McCabe Street, Mosman Park, W Australia 6012* Tel (0061) (8) 9385 4515

BRYANT, Donald Thomas. b 29. FSS59 SE Essex Coll BSc64 Birkbeck Coll Lon BSc58 Dip Counselling 99. S'wark Ord Course 85. **d** 88 **p** 89. NSM Redhill St Matt *S'wark* 88-99; Perm to Offic from 99. *21 Windermere Way, Reigate RH2 0LW* Tel (01737) 762382

BRYANT, Canon Edward Francis Paterson. b 43. S'wark Ord Course 75. **d** 78 **p** 79. NSM Hadlow *Roch* 78-84; C Dartford St Alb 84-87; R Hollington St Leon *Chich* 87-93; V Bexhill St Aug 93-99; TR Bexhill St Pet from 99; P-in-c Sedlescombe w Whatlington from 02; RD Battle and Bexhill from 98; Can and Preb Chich Cathl from 00. *The Rectory, Old Town, Bexhill-on-Sea TN40 2HE* Tel (01424) 211115 Mobile 07710-295453 Fax 07970-991268 E-mail ebryant@hotpop.com

BRYANT, Graham Trevor. b 41. Keble Coll Ox BA63 DipTh64 MA67. Chich Th Coll 64. **d** 66 **p** 67. C Leeds St Wilfrid *Ripon* 66-69; C Haywards Heath St Wilfrid *Chich* 69-74; V Crawley Down All SS 74-79; V Bexhill St Aug 79-85; V Charlton Kings St Mary *Glouc* 85-02; rtd 02. *6 The Close, Cheltenham GL53 0PQ* Tel (01242) 520313

BRYANT, John. *See* BRYANT, Sidney John

BRYANT, The Ven Mark Watts. b 49. St Jo Coll Dur BA72. Cuddesdon Coll 72. **d** 75 **p** 76. C Addlestone *Guildf* 75-79; C Studley *Sarum* 79-83; V 83-88; Chapl Trowbridge Coll 79-83; Voc Development Adv *Cov* 88-96; Dioc Dir of Ords 88-96; Hon Can Cov Cathl 93-01; TR Coventry Caludon 96-01; AD Cov E 99-01; Adn Cov from 01. *9 Armorial Road, Coventry CV3 6GH* Tel (024) 7641 7750 *or* 7667 4328 Fax 7641 4640 E-mail archdeacon.mark@covdioc.org

BRYANT, Patricia Ann. b 36. Qu Mary Coll Lon BA58. St Mich Coll Llan 94. **d** 91 **p** 97. NSM Llanbadoc *Mon* 91-93; NSM Llangybi and Coedypaen w Llanbadoc 93-94; C 94-98; Asst Chapl Gwent Tertiary Coll 94-98; V Merthyr Cynog and Dyffryn Honddu etc *S & B* from 98. *5 Trebarried Court, Llandefalle, Brecon LD3 0NB* Tel (01874) 754087 E-mail bryants@surfaid.org

BRYANT, Peter James. b 35. Jes Coll Cam BA58 MA64 UWIST 59 FInstM. St Deiniol's Hawarden 86 St Mich Coll Llan 96. **d** 97 **p** 98. NSM Raglan-Usk *Mon* 97-98; NSM Merthyr Cynog and Dyffryn Honddu etc *S & B* 98-02. *5 Trebarried Court,*

Llandefalle, Brecon LD3 0NB Tel (01874) 754087 E-mail bryants@surfaid.org

BRYANT, Canon Richard Kirk. b 47. Ch Coll Cam BA68 MA72 Nottm Univ DipTh70. Cuddesdon Coll 70. **d** 72 **p** 73. C Newc St Gabr *Newc* 72-75; C Morpeth 75-78; C Benwell St Jas 78-82; V Earsdon and Backworth 82-93; V Wylam 93-97; Hon Can Newc Cathl from 97; Prin Local Min Scheme from 97; Prin Reader Tr from 97. *2 Burlington Court, Hadrian Park, Wallsend NE28 9YH* Tel 0191-263 7922 *or* 281 9930 Fax 212 1184 E-mail r.bryant@newcastle.anglican.org *or* r.bryant@lineone.net

BRYANT, Richard Maurice. b 46. MAAIS80. WMMTC 90. **d** 93 **p** 94. NSM The Stanleys *Glouc* 93-98; NSM Glouc St Geo w Whaddon from 98. *6 Church Street, Kings Stanley, Stonehouse GL10 3HW* Tel (01453) 823172

BRYANT, Sidney John. b 29. Linc Coll Ox BA52 MA56. St Steph Ho Ox 52. **d** 54 **p** 55. C Southgate St Andr *Lon* 54-58; C Tottenham Ch Ch W Green 58-60; V New Southgate St Paul 60-71; R Gt Leighs *Chelmsf* 71-92; P-in-c Lt Leighs 71-92; rtd 92; Perm to Offic *St E* from 92. *16 Rydal Avenue, Felixstowe IP11 9SE* Tel (01394) 275822

BRYARS, Peter John. b 54. BA MEd PhD. St Jo Coll Nottm. **d** 84 **p** 85. C Kingston upon Hull St Martin *York* 84; C Hull St Martin w Transfiguration 84-87; TV Drypool 87-90; TV Glendale Gp *Newc* 90-94; P-in-c Heddon-on-the-Wall 94-01; Adult Educn Adv 94-01; V Delaval from 01; AD Bedlington from 03. *The Vicarage, The Avenue, Seaton Sluice, Whitley Bay NE26 4QW* Tel 0191-237 1982 E-mail pjbryars@aol.com

BRYCE, Michael Adrian Gilpin. b 47. TCD BA. CITC 74. **d** 77 **p** 78. C Dublin Ch Ch Cathl Gp *D & G* 77-79; Chapl Univ Coll Dub 79-82; I Ardamine w Kiltennel, Glascarrig etc *C & O* 82-84; CF 84-00; I Lisbellaw *Clogh* from 00. *The Rectory, Faughard, Lisbellaw, Enniskillen BT94 5ES* Tel (028) 6638 7219

BRYDON, Michael Andrew. b 73. St Chad's Coll Dur BA95 MA96 PhD00. St Steph Ho Ox BA01. **d** 02 **p** 03. C Bexhill St Pet *Chich* from 02. *14 Barrack Road, Bexhill-on-Sea TN40 2AT* Tel (01424) 212453

BRYER, Anthony Colin. b 51. Lon Univ BSc72 Bris Univ DipTh75. Trin Coll Bris 72. **d** 75 **p** 76. C Preston St Cuth *Blackb* 75-78; C Becontree St Mary *Chelmsf* 78-81; TV Loughton St Mary and St Mich 81-88; C Clifton St Paul *Bris* 88-91; P-in-c 91-94; R Bris St Mich and St Paul 94-96; Dir of Outreach Edin SS Andr and Geo (C of S) from 96; Lic to Offic *Edin* from 96. *St Andrew's and St George's Church, 13 George Street, Edinburgh EH2 2PA* Tel 0131-225 3847 Mobile 07814-832004 Fax 0131-225 5921 E-mail tsbryer@waitrose.com

BRYER, Paul Donald. b 58. Sussex Univ BEd80 Nottm Univ MA96. St Jo Coll Nottm DipTh90. **d** 90 **p** 91. C Tonbridge St Steph *Roch* 90-94; TV Camberley St Paul *Guildf* 94-99; V Camberley St Mary 99-01; V Dorking St Paul from 01. *St Paul's Vicarage, South Terrace, Dorking RH4 2AB* Tel (01306) 881988 E-mail paulandfiona.bryer@virgin.net

BRYN-THOMAS, John. b 37. Lich Th Coll 63. **d** 66 **p** 67. C Stoke upon Trent *Lich* 66-71; R Wotton *Guildf* 71-79; P-in-c Holmbury St Mary 78-79; R Wotton and Holmbury St Mary 79-86; C Easthampstead *Ox* 86-88; TV Chambersbury *St Alb* 88-01; rtd 01. *5 Richmond Road, Godalming GU7 2ET* Tel (01483) 429782 E-mail brynjthom.@aol.com

BUBBERS, David Bramwell. b 23. Lambeth MA84 Oak Hill Th Coll 51. **d** 54 **p** 55. C Beckenham St Jo *Roch* 54-58; V Wandsworth St Mich *S'wark* 58-65; V Northwood Em *Lon* 65-74; Perm to Offic *St Alb* 74-93; Lic to Offic *Lon* 74-88; Gen Sec CPAS 74-88; rtd 88; Perm to Offic *Chich* from 88. *2 Earlsmead Court, 15 Granville Road, Eastbourne BN20 7HE* Tel (01323) 737077

BUCHAN, Geoffrey Herbert. b 38. CEng MIMechE. Nor Ord Course 91. **d** 94 **p** 95. NSM Barnton *Ches* 94-96; NSM Goostrey 96-99; C Stretton and Appleton Thorn from 99. *12 Hough Lane, Anderton, Northwich CW9 6AB* Tel (01606) 74512 E-mail ghbuchan@tiscali.co.uk

BUCHAN, Matthew Alexander John. b 69. St Andr Univ MA92. Wycliffe Hall Ox BTh95. **d** 98 **p** 99. C Horninglow *Lich* 98-01; TV Moulsecoomb *Chich* from 01. *Holy Nativity Vicarage, Norwich Drive, Brighton BN2 4LA* Tel (01273) 602325

BUCHANAN, Andrew Derek. b 64. Stirling Univ BA90. Wycliffe Hall 98. **d** 01 **p** 02. C Plas Newton *Ches* 01-03; C Ches Ch Ch from 03. *The Vicarage, Gloucester Street, Chester CH1 3HR* E-mail rev_buchanan@hotmail.com

✠**BUCHANAN, The Rt Revd Colin Ogilvie.** b 34. Linc Coll Ox BA MA Lambeth DD93. Tyndale Hall Bris 59. **d** 61 **p** 62 **c** 85. C Cheadle *Ches* 61-64; Tutor St Jo Coll Nottm 64-85; Lib 64-69; Registrar 69-74; Dir of Studies 74-75; Vice-Prin 75-78; Prin 79-85; Hon Can St well Minster *S'well* 84-85; Suff Bp Aston *Birm* 85-89; Asst Bp Roch 89-96; Asst Bp S'wark 90-91; V Gillingham St Mark *Roch* 91-96; Area Bp Woolwich *S'wark* from 96. *37 South Road, London SE23 2UJ* Tel (020) 8699 7771 Fax 8699 7949 E-mail bishop.colin@dswark.org.uk

BUCHANAN, Eoin George. b 59. Qu Coll Birm 98. **d** 00 **p** 01. C Dovercourt and Parkeston w Harwich *Chelmsf* from 00; C

Ramsey w Lt Oakley and Wrabness from 02. *The Vicarage, Church Hill, Ramsey, Harwich CO12 5EU* Tel (01255) 880291 Mobile 07947-793558 E-mail eion@eion.fsworld.co.uk

BUCHANAN, Canon Eric. b 32. Leeds Univ BA54. Coll of Resurr Mirfield 54. **d** 56 **p** 57. C Cov St Mark *Cov* 56-59; Asst Chapl Lon Univ *Lon* 59-64; C Bloomsbury St Geo w St Jo 59-64; V Duston *Pet* 64-79; RD Wootton 75-79; Can Pet Cathl 77-97; V Wellingborough All Hallows 79-90; V Higham Ferrers w Chelveston 90-97; Chapl to The Queen from 92; rtd 97; Perm to Offic *Pet* from 97. *8 College Street, Higham Ferrers, Wellingborough NN10 8DZ* Tel (01933) 411232

BUCHANAN, George Rowland. b 15. St Aug Coll Cant. **d** 59 **p** 60. C Sherborne w Castleton and Lillington *Sarum* 59-63; V Bradford Abbas w Clifton Maybank 63-67; R Gt Wishford 67-73; R Lt Langford 67-73; RD Wylye and Wilton 69-73; Org Sec CECS *Ex* and *B & W* 73-77; rtd 77; Perm to Offic *Sarum* from 77. *6 Pageant Drive, Sherborne DT9 3LP* Tel (01935) 812263

BUCHANAN, John Fraser Walter. b 32. Em Coll Cam BA55. LNSM course 91. **d** 93 **p** 94. OLM Wainford *St E* from 93. *The Hermitage, Bridge Street, Beccles NR34 9BA* Tel (01502) 712154

BUCHANAN, Stephanie Joan. b 65. Linc Coll Ox BA88 MA02 Goldsmiths' Coll Lon PGCE93 Selw Coll Cam BA01. Ridley Hall Cam 99. **d** 02 **p** 03. C Mirfield *Wakef* from 02. *10 Greenside Road, Mirfield WF14 0AU* Tel (01924) 492684

BUCK, David Andrew. b 64. GRNCM88 Birm Univ DipHE97. Ripon Coll Cuddesdon DipMin99. **d** 99 **p** 00. C Poulton-le-Sands w Morecambe St Laur *Blackb* from 99. *31 Dallam Avenue, Morecambe LA4 5BB* Tel (01524) 426704 E-mail davidbuck@care4free.net

BUCK (née JONES), Mrs Kathryn Mary. b 59. Birm Univ BA81 MEd91 Sheff Univ PGCE82. Ripon Coll Cuddesdon DipMin99. **d** 99 **p** 00. C Uttoxeter Area *Lich* 99-00; C Scotforth *Blackb* from 00. *31 Dallam Avenue, Morecambe LA4 5BB* Tel (01524) 426704

BUCK, Nicholas John. b 57. Leic Univ BScEng79. Ridley Hall Cam 81. **d** 84 **p** 85. C Oakwood St Thos *Lon* 84-87; C Darnall and Attercliffe *Sheff* 87-90; V Kimberworth 90-96; Chapl Scargill Ho 96-01; P-in-c Bassingham Gp *Linc* from 01. *The Rectory, 11 Torgate Lane, Bassingham, Lincoln LN5 9HF* Tel (01522) 788383 E-mail the-bucks@supanet.com

BUCK, Canon Richard Peter Holdron. b 37. AKC64. Lambeth Hon MA93. **d** 65 **p** 66. C Mill Hill Jo Keble Ch *Lon* 65-68; C St Marylebone All SS 68-74; Can Res and Treas Truro Cathl *Truro* 74-76; V Primrose Hill St Mary w Avenue Road St Paul *Lon* 76-84; Bp's Ecum Adv *S'wark* 84-91; P-in-c Dulwich Common St Pet 84-86; Hon Can S'wark Cathl from 90; C Rotherhithe St Kath w St Barn 91-92; C Bermondsey St Kath w St Barn 92-94; C Greenwich St Alfege w St Pet and St Paul 94-98; rtd 98. *64 Britannia Court, The Strand, Brighton Marina Village, Brighton BN2 5SF* Tel (01273) 671580

BUCK, William Ashley. b 61. Man Univ BA82 Ox Univ BA86 MA91. Ripon Coll Cuddesdon 84. **d** 87 **p** 88. C Addington *S'wark* 87-91; C Pimlico St Pet w Westmr Ch Ch *Lon* 91-94; TV Wenlock *Heref* 94-03; RD Condover 00-03; R Cleobury Mortimer w Hopton Wafers etc from 03. *The Rectory, The Hurst, Cleobury Mortimer, Kidderminster DY14 8EG* Tel (01299) 270264

BUCKBY, Gary. b 69. Leeds Univ BA90. Coll of Resurr Mirfield 93. **d** 95 **p** 96. C Wolverhampton St Steph *Lich* 95-98; V Longford *Cov* from 98. *St Thomas's Vicarage, Hurst Road, Coventry CV6 6EL* Tel (024) 7636 4078 E-mail frgary@tesco.net

BUCKETT, Canon James Frederick. b 27. MBE97. ACP. Roch Th Coll 60. **d** 62 **p** 63. C Rowner *Portsm* 62-64; Lic to Offic 64-66; Chapl Highbury Tech Coll Portsm 64-66; V St Helens *Portsm* 66-72; CF (TA) 72-95; V Newport St Thos *Portsm* 72-95; Hon Can Portsm Cathl 81-95; rtd 95; Perm to Offic *Portsm* from 95. *The Coach House, 140A Staplers Road, Newport PO30 2DP* Tel (01983) 521847 or 527298 Mobile 07889-784376 E-mail jamesbuckett@cs.com

BUCKINGHAM, The Ven Hugh Fletcher. b 32. Hertf Coll Ox BA57 MA60. Westcott Ho Cam 55. **d** 57 **p** 58. C Halliwell St Thos *Man* 57-60; C Sheff Gillcar St Silas *Sheff* 60-65; V Hindolveston *Nor* 65-70; V Guestwick 65-70; R Fakenham w Alethorpe 70-88; Chmn Dioc Bd Soc Resp 81-88; RD Burnham and Walsingham 81-87; Hon Can Nor Cathl 85-88; Adn E Riding *York* 88-98; Can and Preb York Minster 88-01; rtd 98; Perm to Offic *York* from 01. *2 Rectory Corner, Brandsby, York YO61 4RJ* Tel (01347) 888202

BUCKINGHAM, Paul John. b 63. Bris Univ BVSc87. WMMTC 94. **d** 98. NSM Kington w Huntington, Old Radnor, Kinnerton etc *Heref* from 98. *The Cottage, Prospect Lane, Kington HR5 3BE* Tel (01544) 231357

BUCKINGHAM, Richard Arthur John. b 49. Univ of Wales (Cardiff) BA71 PGCE72. Chich Th Coll 73. **d** 76 **p** 77. C Llantwit Major *Llan* 76-80; C Leigh-on-Sea St Marg *Chelmsf* 80-84; C Westmr St Matt *Lon* 84-87; R Stock Harvard *Chelmsf* 87-02. *3 Priory Close, London N3 1BB* Tel (020) 8371 0178

BUCKINGHAM, Terence John. b 52. Aston Univ BSc73 MSc75 PhD78 FCOptom74. Coll of Resurr Mirfield 01. **d** 03. NSM Harrogate St Wilfrid *Ripon* from 03. *29 Dalesway, Guiseley, Leeds LS20 8JN* Tel (01943) 876066 E-mail terry.j.buckingham@btopenworld.com

BUCKINGHAM, Archdeacon of. *See* WATSON, The Ven Sheila Anne

BUCKINGHAM, Area Bishop of. *See* WILSON, The Rt Revd Alan Thomas Lawrence

BUCKLE, Graham Martin. b 62. Southn Univ BTh89. Sarum & Wells Th Coll 85. **d** 89 **p** 90. C Paddington St Jas *Lon* 89-94; P-in-c Paddington St Pet 94-00; Assoc Dir of Ords Two Cities Area from 99; R St Marylebone St Paul from 00. *St Paul's House, 9 Rossmore Road, London NW1 6NJ* Tel and fax (020) 7262 9443 Pager 07654-327687 E-mail buckle@freeuk.com

BUCKLER, Andrew Jonathan Heslington. b 68. Trin Coll Ox BA89 MA96. Wycliffe Hall Ox BTh93. **d** 96 **p** 97. C Ox St Aldate *Ox* 96-00; Crosslinks France from 00. *64 rue Compans, 75019 Paris, France* Tel (0033) (1) 42 06 28 97 E-mail bucklers@clara.net

BUCKLER, George Anthony (Tony). b 35. Open Univ BA74. Lich Th Coll 58. **d** 61 **p** 62. C Old Swinford *Worc* 61-65; C Droitwich St Nic w St Pet 65-67; C Droitwich St Andr w St Mary 65-67; Chapl Claybury Hosp Woodford Bridge 67-78; Chapl St Geo and Co Hosps Linc 78-87; Chapl Lawn Hosp Linc 78-81; Chapl Wexham Park Hosp Slough 87-90; Chapl Mapperley Hosp Nottm 90-94; Chapl Nottm Mental Illness and Psychiatric Unit 90-96; Chapl Wells Rd Cen Nottm 94-96; Chapl Qu Medical Cen Nottm 94-96; Chapl Highbury Hosp Nottm 94-96; rtd 96. *73 Westfield Drive, Nottingham NG3 4RE*

BUCKLER, Guy Ernest Warr. b 46. ACA69 FCA79. Linc Th Coll 71. **d** 74 **p** 75. C Dunstable *St Alb* 74-77; C Houghton Regis 77-86; TV Willington Team *Newc* 86-88; TR 88-95; Chapl N Tyneside Coll of FE 88-95; R Bedford St Pet w St Cuth *St Alb* from 95. *St Peter's Rectory, 36 De Parys Avenue, Bedford MK40 2TP* Tel (01234) 354543 E-mail guybuckl@hotmail.com

BUCKLER, Kenneth Arthur. b 50. Bucks Coll of Educn DPSN91 S Bank Univ MSc94. NTMTC 95. **d** 98 **p** 99. C Welwyn w Ayot St Peter *St Alb* 98-01; P-in-c Kimpton w Ayot St Lawrence from 01; Asst Chapl E Herts NHS Trust 99-00; Asst Chapl E and N Herts NHS Trust from 00. *The Vicarage, 11 High Street, Kimpton, Hitchin SG4 8RA* Tel and fax (01438) 833419 Mobile 07909-970545 E-mail kenabuckler@yahoo.co.uk

BUCKLER, Canon Philip John Warr. b 49. St Pet Coll Ox BA70 MA74. Cuddesdon Coll 70. **d** 72 **p** 73. C Bushey Heath *St Alb* 72-75; Chapl Trin Coll Cam 75-81; Min Can and Sacr St Paul's Cathl *Lon* 81-87; V Hampstead St Jo 87-99; AD N Camden 93-98; Can Res St Paul's Cathl from 99; Treas from 00. *2 Amen Court, London EC4M 7BU* Tel (020) 7248 3312 Fax 7489 8579 E-mail buckler@stpaulcath.fsnet.co.uk

BUCKLEY, Alan. b 40. Tyndale Hall Bris. **d** 67 **p** 68. C Owlerton *Sheff* 67-70; C Mansfield St Pet *S'well* 70-73; P-in-c Whitfield *Derby* 73-75; P-in-c Whitfield 76-84; V Moldgreen *Wakef* 84-90; V Hadfield *Derby* 90-03; rtd 03. *St Andrew's Vicarage, 122 Hadfield Road, Hadfield, Glossop SK13 2DR* Tel (01457) 852431

BUCKLEY, Alexander Christopher Nolan. b 67. Univ of Wales (Abth) BD89. St Mich Coll Llan DPS91. **d** 91 **p** 94. C Llandudno *Ban* 91-92; C Ynyscynhaearn w Penmorfa and Porthmadog 92-93 and 94-96; Jesuit Volunteer Community Manchester 93-94; C Caerau w Ely *Llan* 96-01; V Trowbridge Mawr *Mon* from 01; Chapl ATC from 96. *St Hilary's Vicarage, 38 Rhyl Road, Rumney, Cardiff CF3 3NZ* Tel (029) 2079 2352

BUCKLEY, Anthony Graham. b 63. Keble Coll Ox BA84 MA90 PGCE85 DipMin98. Wycliffe Hall Ox 96. **d** 98 **p** 99. C Foord St Jo *Cant* 98-00; V from 00. *St John's Vicarage, 4 Cornwallis Avenue, Folkestone CT19 5JA* Tel (01303) 250280 E-mail antmon64@hotmail.com

BUCKLEY, Christopher Ivor. b 48. Chich Th Coll. **d** 86 **p** 87. C Felpham w Middleton *Chich* 86-89; C Jersey St Brelade *Win* 89-93; V Jersey St Mark from 93; Chapl Jersey Airport from 00. *54 Millennium Court, La Greve d'Azette, St Clement, Jersey JE2 6GT* Tel and fax (01534) 720595 Mobile 07797-714595 E-mail christopher.buckley@jerseymail.co.uk

BUCKLEY, David Rex. b 47. Ripon Coll Cuddesdon 75. **d** 77 **p** 78. C Witton *Ches* 77-81; V Backford 81-85; Youth Chapl from 81; V Barnton 85-93; P-in-c Bickerton w Bickley 93-97; P-in-c Harthill and Burwardsley 93-97; V Bickerton, Bickley, Harthill and Burwardsley 97-01; P-in-c Sandbach from 01. *The Vicarage, 15 Offley Road, Sandbach CW11 1GY* Tel (01270) 762379 E-mail rex@chazandrex.freeserve.co.uk

BUCKLEY, Ernest Fairbank. b 25. Jes Coll Cam BA49 MA50 Jes Coll Ox BLitt53. Westcott Ho Cam 55. **d** 55 **p** 56. C Rochdale *Man* 55-58; V Hey 58-64; V Baguley 64-79; V Clun w Chapel Lawn, Bettws-y-Crwyn and Newcastle *Heref* 79-87; RD Clun Forest 82-87; rtd 88. *Hawthorn Bank, Clunton, Craven Arms SY7 0HP* Tel (01588) 660281

BUCKLEY, John. b 42. **d** 95 **p** 96. C Macclesfield Team Par *Ches* 95-01; P-in-c Pott Shrigley from 01. *The Vicarage, Spuley Lane, Pott Shrigley, Macclesfield SK10 5RS* Tel (01625) 573316

BUCKLEY, Michael. b 49. St Jo Coll Dur Cranmer Hall Dur 77. **d** 79 **p** 80. C Birkdale St Jo *Liv* 79-82; TV Maghull 82-88; V Earlestown 88-98; V Gt Sankey from 98. *The Parsonage, Parsonage Way, Great Sankey, Warrington WA5 1RP* Tel (01925) 723235

BUCKLEY, Canon Michael Richard. b 20. Lon Univ BD42 AKC42. Cuddesdon Coll 42. **d** 43 **p** 44. C Whitton St Aug *Lon* 43-45; C Bp's Hatfield *St Alb* 45-48; C Leatherhead *Guildf* 48-52; V Stoneleigh 52-67; R Weybridge 67-85; Hon Can Guildf Cathl 76-85; rtd 85; Perm to Offic *Chelmsf* from 85; Perm to Offic *Ely* from 86. *Bourn Cottage, High Street, Great Chesterford, Saffron Walden CB10 1PL* Tel (01799) 530398

BUCKLEY, Richard Francis. b 44. Ripon Hall Ox 69. **d** 72 **p** 73. C Portsea St John *Portsm* 72-75; C Portsea All SS w St Jo Rudmore 75-79; Chapl RN 79-00; Perm to Offic *B & W* from 00. *Ste Croix, Coryate Close, Higher Odcombe, Yeovil BA22 8UJ* Tel and fax (01935) 864039 Mobile 07810-123065 E-mail rfbuckley@onetel.net.uk

BUCKLEY, Richard John. b 43. Hull Univ BSc(Econ)64 PhD87 Strathclyde Univ MSc69. Sarum Th Coll 64. **d** 66 **p** 67. C Huddersfield St Jo *Wakef* 66-68; C Sutton St Jas *York* 69-71; TV Sutton St Jas and Wawne 71-75; V Handsworth Woodhouse *Sheff* 75-85; R Adwick-le-Street 85-91; V Wentworth 91-97; Perm to Offic *York* from 88; *Sheff* from 97; Area Co-ord (S and E Yorkshire) Chr Aid from 97. *2 Kirkstead Abbey Mews, Thorpe Hesley, Rotherham S61 2UZ* Tel 0114-246 5064

BUCKLEY, Richard Simon Fildes. b 63. WMMTC 97. **d** 00 **p** 01. NSM Moseley St Mary *Birm* from 00. *285 Moor Green Lane, Birmingham B13 8QR* Tel 0121-471 2229 Fax as telephone E-mail puppet.buckley@virgin.net

BUCKLEY, Robert William. b 50. Grey Coll Dur BSc70 PhD73 DipEd73 CPhys75 MInstE91 FCollP92 FInstP97. N Ord Course 85. **d** 87 **p** 88. NSM N Greenford All Hallows *Lon* 87-91; P-in-c 91-94; NSM W Acton St Martin 94-95; NSM Ealing All SS 94-95; C 95-97; P-in-c Preston Ascension 97-99; TR Wembley Park from 99. *The Vicarage, 319 Preston Road, Harrow HA3 0QQ* Tel (020) 8904 4062 Fax 8908 2207 E-mail brobert@fish.co.uk

BUCKLEY, Stephen Richard. b 45. Cranmer Hall Dur 82. **d** 84 **p** 85. C Iffley *Ox* 84-88; TV Halesowen *Worc* 88-00; TR Sedgley All SS from 00. *All Saints' Vicarage, Vicar Street, Sedgley, Dudley DY3 3SD* Tel (01902) 883255 E-mail stephen@presbyter.freeserve.co.uk

BUCKLEY, Timothy Denys. b 57. BA. St Jo Coll Nottm DipTh. **d** 83 **p** 84. C S Westoe *Dur* 83-85; C Paddington Em Harrow Road *Lon* 85-88; C Binley *Cov* 88-98; Min Binley Woods LEP 88-98; V Belton Gp *Linc* from 98. *The Vicarage, 118 High Street, Belton, Doncaster DN9 1NS* Tel (01427) 872207 E-mail timothybuckley@tinyworld.co.uk

BUCKLEY, Timothy John. b 67. Jes Coll Cam BA90 MA94 ACA94. Wycliffe Hall Ox BTh99. **d** 99 **p** 00. C Langdon Hills *Chelmsf* 99-02; P-in-c Devonport St Mich and St Barn *Ex* from 02. *St Barnabas' Vicarage, 10 De la Hay Avenue, Plymouth PL3 4HU* Tel (01752) 666544 E-mail revtim@fish.co.uk

BUCKMAN, Rossly David. b 36. TCD BA64 MA67 St Pet Coll Ox BA65. Moore Th Coll Sydney ACT ThL59. **d** 59 **p** 60. Australia 59-61, 76-80 and 89-00; C Dublin Harold's Cross *D & G* 61-64; C Ox St Mich *Ox* 64-65; Lect Th Bris Univ 65-69; CF 69-76; P-in-c Mid Marsh Gp *Linc* 81-82; R 82-89; Chapl Düsseldorf *Eur* from 00. *Mulvany House, Rotterdamer Strasse 135, 40475 Dusseldorf, Germany* Tel (0049) (211) 452759 Fax 454 2216

BUCKNALL, Ms Alison Mary. b 55. Leeds Univ BA76 Trin Coll Bris MA94. Qu Coll Birm 94. **d** 96 **p** 97. C The Quinton *Birm* 96-00; C Sutton Coldfield H Trin 00-01; Asst Chapl N Bris NHS Trust from 01. *North Bristol NHS Trust, Beckspool Road, Frenchay, Bristol BS16 1LE* Tel 0117-970 1070

BUCKNALL, Allan. b 35. ALCD62. Lon Coll of Div 62. **d** 62 **p** 63. C Harlow New Town w Lt Parndon *Chelmsf* 62-69; Chapl W Somerset Miss to Deaf 69-71; Perm to Offic *Bris* 71-77; P-in-c Wisborough Green *Chich* 77-79; R Tillington 78-86; R Duncton 82-86; R Up Waltham 82-86; C Henfield w Shermanbury and Woodmancote 86-89; Asst Chapl Princess Marg Hosp Swindon 89-96; Angl Chapl Swindon and Marlborough NHS Trust 96-00; rtd 00; Perm to Offic *Bris* from 00. *5 The Willows, Highworth, Swindon SN6 7PG* Tel (01793) 762721

BUCKNALL, Miss Ann Gordon. b 32. K Coll Lon BSc53 Hughes Hall Cam DipEd54. Qu Coll Birm 94. **dss** 81 **d** 87 **p** 94. Birm St Aid Small Heath *Birm* 81-85; Balsall Heath St Paul 85-92; Par Dn 87-92; C Handsworth St Jas 92-95; rtd 95; Perm to Offic *Lich* from 95. *20 St Margaret's Road, Lichfield WS13 7RA* Tel (01543) 257382

BUCKNALL, William John. b 44. Lon Univ DipTh67. Kelham Th Coll 63. **d** 68 **p** 69. C Carl H Trin *Carl* 68-71; C Baswich *Lich* 71-73; P-in-c Ilam w Blore Ray and Okeover 73-76; V Wednesbury St Paul Wood Green 76-84; RD Wednesbury 78-84; TR Wordsley 84-90. *3 Woodville Gardens, Sedgley, Dudley DY3 1LB* Tel (01902) 882436

BUDD, John Christopher. b 51. QUB BA73 DLIS77 TCD DipTh82. CITC. **d** 82 **p** 83. C Ballymena *Conn* 82-85; C Jordanstown w Monkstown 85-88; I Craigs w Dunaghy and Killagan 88-97; Dioc Info Officer 89-97; Bp's Dom Chapl from 94; I Derriaghy w Colin from 97. *Derriaghy Rectory, 20 Derriaghy Road, Magheralave, Lisburn BT28 3SH* Tel (028) 9061 0859

BUDD, John Victor. b 31. CCC Ox BA55 MA58 Open Univ BSc98. Bps' Coll Cheshunt 57. **d** 59 **p** 60. C Friern Barnet St Jas *Lon* 59-64; C Harrow Weald All SS 64-70; Lic to Offic *St Alb* 70-73; V Lt Amwell 73-96; RD Hertford 83-88; rtd 96; Perm to Offic *Worc* from 96. *37 Wykewane, Malvern WR14 2XD* Tel (01684) 566174

BUDD, Philip John. b 40. St Jo Coll Dur BA63 DipTh65 MLitt71 Bris Univ PhD78. Cranmer Hall Dur. **d** 66 **p** 67. C Attenborough w Chilwell *S'well* 66-69; Lect Clifton Th Coll 69-71; Lect Trin Coll Bris 72-80; Tutor Ripon Coll Cuddesdon 80-88; Asst Chapl and Tutor Westmr Coll Ox from 80; Lect from 88. *4 Clover Close, Oxford OX2 9JH* Tel (01865) 863682

BUDDEN, Clive John. b 39. Liv Univ BA. Chich Th Coll. **d** 84 **p** 86. C Gaywood, Bawsey and Mintlyn *Nor* 84-87; TV Brixham w Churston Ferrers and Kingswear *Ex* 87-90; R Exton and Winsford and Cutcombe w Luxborough *B & W* 90-99; Perm to Offic *Truro* 00-02; P-in-c Veryan w Ruan Lanihorne from 02. *The Vicarage, Veryan, Truro TR2 5QA* Tel (01872) 501618

BUDGE, Leonard Percival. b 11. Dur Univ LTh40. St Aug Coll Cant 37. **d** 40 **p** 41. C Easington w Skeffling and Kilnsea *York* 40-43; C Hertford St Andr *St Alb* 43-45; Tanganyika 45-48; C Stourbridge St Thos *Worc* 48-51; V Castle Morton 51-58; V Amblecote 58-64; V Frithelstock *Ex* 64-76; V Monkleigh 64-76; P-in-c Littleham 64-70; R 70-76; rtd 76; Perm to Offic *Ex* from 76. *2 Chestnut Close, Braunton EX33 2EH* Tel (01271) 814313

BUDGELL, Peter Charles. b 50. Lon Univ BD. **d** 83 **p** 84. C Goodmayes All SS *Chelmsf* 83-86; C Chipping Barnet w Arkley *St Alb* 86-88; V Luton St Anne from 88. *St Anne's Vicarage, 7 Blaydon Road, Luton LU2 0RP* Tel (01582) 720052 Fax as telephone

BUDGELL, Rosemary Anne. b 51. Lon Bible Coll BD73 CertEd76. **dss** 83 **d** 87 **p** 94. Goodmayes All SS *Chelmsf* 83-86; Chipping Barnet w Arkley *St Alb* 86-88; Hon Par Dn 87-88; Hon Par Dn Luton St Anne 88-95; Perm to Offic 95-98. *32 Hobbs Hill Road, Hemel Hempstead HP3 9QA* Tel (01442) 390556

BUDGETT, Preb Anthony Thomas. b 26. TD60. Oriel Coll Ox BA50 MA57. Wells Th Coll 57. **d** 59 **p** 60. C Hendford *B & W* 59-63; PC Lopen 63-68; R Seavington St Mich w St Mary 63-68; V Somerton 68-80; RD Ilchester 72-81; P-in-c Compton Dundon 76-80; R Somerton w Compton Dundon 80-81; R Somerton w Compton Dundon, the Charltons etc 81-84; Preb Wells Cathl 83-90; P-in-c Bruton w Lamyatt, Wyke and Redlynch 84-85; P-in-c Batcombe w Upton Noble 84-85; P-in-c S w N Brewham 84-85; TR Bruton and Distr 85-90; rtd 90; Perm to Offic *Ex* from 90; Perm to Offic *B & W* from 90. *Cornerways, White Ball, Wellington TA21 0LS* Tel (01823) 672321

BUFFEE, Canon Leslie John. b 30. AKC53 Open Univ BA88. **d** 54 **p** 55. C Lewisham St Swithun *S'wark* 54-57; Australia 57-62; C Cheam *S'wark* 63-65; P-in-c Becontree St Pet *Chelmsf* 65-67; V 67-72; Min Parkeston CD 72-83; TV Dovercourt and Parkeston 83-89; Miss to Seamen 83-89; C Southend St Sav Westcliff *Chelmsf* 89-95; rtd 95; Perm to Office *Cant* and *Chelmsf* from 95. *46 Stonebridge Way, Faversham ME13 7SB* Tel (01795) 535970

BUFFREY, Canon Samuel John Thomas. b 28. Keble Coll Ox BA52 MA57. Cuddesdon Coll 52. **d** 54 **p** 55. C Lower Tuffley St Geo CD *Glouc* 54-56; C Branksome St Aldhelm *Sarum* 56-61; R Gussage St Michael and Gussage All Saints 61-69; V Amesbury 69-80; RD Avon 77-80; P-in-c Broadstone 80-82; V 82-93; Can and Preb Sarum Cathl 87-93; rtd 93; Perm to Offic *Sarum* from 93. *34 Woolslope Road, West Moors, Ferndown BH22 0PD* Tel (01202) 875522

BUFTON (née FORSHAW), Mrs Janet Elisabeth. b 41. Redland Coll of Educn CertEd61. Dioc OLM tr scheme 96. **d** 99 **p** 00. OLM Debenham w Aspall and Kenton *St E* from 99; OLM Helmingham w Framsden and Pettaugh w Winston from 99. *Harkaway Cottage, 9 Fenn Street, Winston, Stowmarket IP14 6LD* Tel (01728) 860535

BUGBY, Timothy. b 53. AKC75. Chich Th Coll 76. **d** 77 **p** 78. C Hockerill *St Alb* 77-81; C Pimlico St Mary Graham-street *Lon* 81-87; V Highgate St Aug from 87; Dir Educn, Min and Voc Confraternity of the Blessed Sacrament from 00. *St Augustine's Vicarage, Langdon Park Road, London N6 5BH* Tel (020) 8340 3567 Fax as telephone E-mail timbugby@aol.com

BUGDEN, Ernest William. b 16. Lich Th Coll 56. **d** 58 **p** 59. C Esher *Guildf* 58-68; Hon C 68-81; rtd 81; Perm to Offic *Ely* from 91. *32 French's Road, Cambridge CB4 3LA* Tel (01223) 311306

BUGG, Canon Peter Richard. b 33. Univ of BC BA62. Wells Th Coll 63. **d** 64 **p** 64. C Whitley Ch Ch *Ox* 64-67; C Ludlow *Heref* 67-69; Zambia 69-72; P-in-c Brill w Boarstall *Ox* 72-78; P-in-c Chilton w Dorton 77-78; V Brill, Boarstall, Chilton and Dorton 78-97; Hon Can Ch Ch 92-97; rtd 97. *66 Windmill Street, Brill, Aylesbury HP18 9TG* Tel (01844) 238204 Fax as telephone

BUGLER, Canon Derek Leslie. b 25. Gen Th Sem NY LTh64. **d** 64 **p** 64. USA 64-90; rtd 90; Lic to Offic *Win* from 90. *Wintney House, London Road, Hartley Wintney, Basingstoke RG27 8RN* Tel (01252) 844239 E-mail dbugler@gwi.net

BUIK, Allan David. b 39. St Andr Univ BSc61 SSC. Coll of Resurr Mirfield 66. **d** 68 **p** 69. Perm to Offic *Win* 68-69; C Eastleigh 69-72; C Brighton St Bart *Chich* 72-74; C Lavender Hill Ascension *S'wark* 74-78; V Kingstanding St Mark *Birm* 78-86; Guyana 86-91; V Tunstall *Lich* from 91. *Christchurch Vicarage, 26 Stanley Street, Tunstall, Stoke-on-Trent ST6 6BW* Tel (01782) 838288 Mobile 07703-479715 E-mail abuik@bigfoot.com

BUIKE, Desmond Mainwaring. b 32. Ex Coll Ox BA55 MA69 Leeds Univ CertEd72. Qu Coll Birm DipTh57. **d** 57 **p** 58. C Man St Aid *Man* 57-60; C Ox SS Phil and Jas *Ox* 60-63; V Queensbury *Bradf* 63-71; Perm to Offic 71-85; V Glaisdale *York* 85-93; rtd 93; Perm to Offic *York* from 93. *Wayside, 3 White Bridge Road, Whitby YO21 3JQ* Tel (01947) 821440

BULCOCK, Andrew Marcus. b 62. Man OLM Scheme. **d** 03. OLM Elton St Steph *Man* from 03. *5 Fieldhead Avenue, Bury BL8 2LX* Tel 0161-761 6347 E-mail kemamb@beeb.net

BULL, Christine. b 45. Bedf Coll Lon BA67. N Ord Course 91. **d** 94 **p** 95. NSM High Lane *Ches* 94-98; NSM Stockport SW 98-99; Perm to Offic from 99; *Derby* from 98; *Man* from 00. *67 Buxton Road, Whaley Bridge, High Peak SK23 7HX* Tel (01663) 734851 E-mail christine@c-k-l.freeserve.co.uk

BULL (née ADAMS), Mrs Christine Frances. b 53. Cam Inst of Educn CertEd74. NEOC. **d** 00 **p** 01. NSM St Oswald in Lee w Bingfield *Newc* from 00. *East Side Lodge, Bingfield, Newcastle upon Tyne NE19 2LE* Tel (01434) 672303

BULL, Christopher Bertram. b 45. Lon Bible Coll BA87. Wycliffe Hall Ox 88. **d** 90 **p** 91. C Leominster *Heref* 90-95; P-in-c Westbury 95-02; R from 02; P-in-c Yockleton 95-02; R from 02; P-in-c Gt Wollaston 95-02; V from 02. *The Rectory, Westbury, Shrewsbury SY5 9QX* Tel (01743) 884216 E-mail cbbull@anglican.fslife.co.uk

BULL, Christopher David. b 59. St Jo Coll Nottm 89. **d** 91 **p** 92. C Bowbrook S *Worc* 91-95; P-in-c Flackwell Heath *Ox* 95-00; V from 00; RD Wycombe from 97. *The Vicarage, 9 Chapel Road, Flackwell Heath, High Wycombe HP10 9AA* Tel (01628) 522795 E-mail christopher.bull@virgin.net

BULL, George. *See* BULL, William George

BULL, Malcolm George. b 35. Portsm Dioc Tr Course 87. **d** 87 **p** 98. NSM Farlington *Portsm* 87-90; NSM Widley w Wymering 92-93; NSM S Hayling 93-97; NSM Hayling Is St Andr 97-00; Bp's Adv for Cults and New Relig Movements 99-00; rtd 00; Perm to Offic *Portsm* 00-01; P-in-c Greatworth and Marston St Lawrence etc *Pet* from 01. *The Rectory, Marston St Lawrence, Banbury OX17 2DA* Tel (01295) 712279 E-mail bullmg@bushinternet.com

BULL, Malcolm Harold. b 44. BDS. St Alb Minl Tr Scheme. **d** 83 **p** 84. NSM Bedford St Paul *St Alb* 83-93. *27 Cardington Road, Bedford MK42 0BN* Tel (01234) 368163

BULL, Martin Wells. b 37. Worc Coll Ox BA61 MA68. Ripon Hall Ox 61. **d** 63 **p** 64. C Blackley St Andr *Man* 63-67; C Horton *Bradf* 67-68; V Ingrow cum Hainworth 68-78; RD S Craven 74-77; V Bingley All SS 78-80; TR 80-92; P-in-c Gargrave 92-02; rtd 02. *Mallard Cottage, Grewelthorpe HG4 3BT* Tel (01765) 650473

BULL, Michael John. b 35. Roch Th Coll 65. **d** 67 **p** 68. C N Wingfield *Derby* 67-69; C Skegness *Linc* 69-72; R Ingoldmells w Addlethorpe 72-79; Area Sec USPG *S'wark* 79-85; Area Org RNLI (Lon) 86-88; C Croydon St Jo *S'wark* 89-93; P-in-c Mitcham Ch Ch 93-97; V Colliers Wood Ch Ch 97-00; rtd 00; Perm to Offic *Nor* from 00. *Broadview, West Carr Road, Attleborough NR17 1AA* Tel (01953) 451475

BULL, Norman John. b 16. Trin Coll Ox BTh38 BA39 MA48 Reading Univ PhD67. Linc Th Coll 38. **d** 39 **p** 40. C Colchester St Botolph w H Trin and St Giles *Chelmsf* 39-41; C Loughton St Mary 41-43; P-in-c Petersfield w Sheet *Portsm* 44-45; C Croydon *Cant* 45-46; Dioc Youth Chapl 46-48; Chapl St Luke's Coll Ex 49-60; Lect 49-75. *21 Wonford Road, Exeter EX4 2LH* Tel (01392) 55806

BULL, Robert David. b 51. Man Univ DSPT86. Ripon Coll Cuddesdon 74. **d** 77 **p** 78. C Worsley *Man* 77-80; C Peel 80-81; TV 81-86; P-in-c Wisbech St Aug *Ely* 86-88; V 88-02; RD Wisbech 92-02; RD Wisbech Lynn Marshland 02; R Lich St Chad *Lich* from 02. *St Chad's Rectory, The Windings, Lichfield WS13 7EX* Tel (01543) 262254 E-mail robert@augustine99.freeserve.co.uk

BULL, Stephen Andrew. b 58. St Jo Coll Nottm DCM93. **d** 93 **p** 94. C Wroughton *Bris* 93-96; P-in-c Eyemouth *Edin* 96-98; NSM 98; Lic to Offic from 98. *12 Craigs Court, Torphichen, Bathgate EH48 4NU* Tel (01506) 650070 E-mail steve@scotiabahn.com

BULL, Miss Susan Helen. b 58. Qu Mary Coll Lon BSc79 ACIS84. STETS BTh98. **d** 98 **p** 99. NSM Epsom St Barn *Guildf* from 98. *41 Stamford Green Road, Epsom KT18 7SR* Tel (01372) 742703 E-mail rev@suebull.freeserve.co.uk

BULL, Timothy Martin. b 65. Worc Coll Ox BA87 MA93 Dur Univ PhD94 Fitzw Coll Cam BA98 FRSA96. Ridley Hall Cam 96. **d** 99 **p** 00. C Bath Walcott *B & W* 99-03; P-in-c Langham w Boxted *Chelmsf* from 03; Colchester Area CME Adv from 03. *The Rectory, Wick Road, Langham, Colchester CO4 5PG* Tel (01206) 230666 E-mail tim@revbull.freeserve.co.uk

BULL, William George. b 28. Sarum Th Coll 65. **d** 66 **p** 67. C Salisbury St Mich *Sarum* 66-69; V Swallowcliffe w Ansty 69-75; Dioc Youth Officer 69-71; P-in-c Laverstock 75-81; V 81-93; rtd 94; Perm to Offic *Sarum* from 94. *Bungalow 1, Boreham Field, Warminster BA12 9EB* Tel (01985) 847830

BULLAMORE, John Richard. b 41. Linc Coll Ox BA69 MA69. Wycliffe Hall Ox 74. **d** 95 **p** 95. NSM Eorropaidh *Arg* 95-98; NSM Bath St Sav w Swainswick and Woolley *B & W* from 98. *St Mary's House, Upper Swainswick, Bath BA1 8BX* Tel (01225) 851159 E-mail johnbullamore@btinternet.com

BULLIMORE, Christine Elizabeth. b 46. Nottm Univ BA67 Dip Counselling 92. St Jo Coll Nottm 96. **d** 96 **p** 97. Bp's Adv Past Care and Counselling *Wakef* 92-99 and from 01; NSM S Ossett 96-99; P-in-c Emley from 99; P-in-c Flockton cum Denby Grange from 99. *The Rectory, 14 Grange Drive, Emley, Huddersfield HD8 9SF* Tel (01924) 849161 Mobile 07778-022163 Fax 849219 E-mail jcbullimor@aol.com

BULLIVANT, Ronald. b 32. CertEd Dip Counselling. St Mich Coll Llan. **d** 59 **p** 60. C Roath St German *Llan* 59-61; P-in-c Bradf H Trin *Bradf* 61-66; V Horbury *Wakef* 66-69; Lic to Offic *Ripon* 70-78; Perm to Offic *Nor* 78-81; Lic to Offic 81-98; Perm to Offic *Man* from 99. *107 Waterloo Road, Manchester M8 8BY* Tel 0161-832 2428 *or* 832 2423

BULLOCH, William Gillespie. b 68. St Steph Ho Ox. **d** 01. C Bognor *Chich* from 01. *2 Shelley Road, Bognor Regis PO21 2SL*

BULLOCK, Andrew Belfrage. b 50. Univ of Wales (Ban) BSc73 MEd81 Westmr Coll Ox PGCE79. Wycliffe Hall Ox DipMin94. **d** 97 **p** 98. C Sandhurst *Ox* 97-02; P-in-c Alfrick, Lulsley, Suckley, Leigh and Bransford *Worc* from 02. *The Rectory, Leigh, Worcester WR6 5LE* Tel (01886) 832355

BULLOCK, Andrew Timothy. b 56. Southn Univ BTh91. Sarum & Wells Th Coll 89. **d** 91 **p** 92. C Erdington St Barn *Birm* 91-94; TV Solihull 94-03; P-in-c Acocks Green from 03. *The Vicarage, 34 Dudley Park Road, Acocks Green, Birmingham B27 6QR* Tel 0121-706 9764 E-mail andrewbullock@tinyonline.co.uk

BULLOCK, Jude Ross. b 58. Heythrop Coll Lon BD89. Allen Hall 84. **d** 89 **p** 90. In RC Ch 89-97; C Lt Ilford St Mich *Chelmsf* from 01. *The Curate's Flat, 3 Toronto Avenue, London E12 5JF* Tel (020) 8553 4627 Mobile 07976-395732 E-mail judebullock@hotmail.com

BULLOCK, Kenneth Poyser. b 27. Down Coll Cam BA50 MA55. Ridley Hall Cam 50. **d** 52 **p** 53. C Aston SS Pet and Paul *Birm* 52-56; R Openshaw *Man* 56-63; V Ainsworth 63-91; rtd 91. *26 Plas Penrhyn, Penrhyn Bay, Llandudno LL30 3EU* Tel (01492) 543343

BULLOCK, Canon Michael. b 49. Hatf Coll Dur BA71. Coll of Resurr Mirfield 72. **d** 75 **p** 76. C Bart St Jo *Pet* 75-79; Zambia 79-86; V Longthorpe *Pet* 86-91; Chapl Naples *Eur* 91-99; OGS from 93; P-in-c Liguria *Eur* 99-00; Chapl Gtr Lisbon from 00; Can Malta Cathl from 98. *rua Joao de Deus 5, Alcoitão, 2645-128 Alcabideche, Portugal* Tel (00351) (21) 469 2303 Fax as telephone E-mail gl-chaplaincy@clix.pt

BULLOCK, Miss Rosemary Joy. b 59. Portsm Poly BA81 Southn Univ BTh94. Sarum & Wells Th Coll 89. **d** 91 **p** 94. Par Dn Warblington w Emsworth *Portsm* 91-94; C 94-95; C Gt Parndon *Chelmsf* 95-98; TV Beaminster Area *Sarum* 98-03; P-in-c Ridgeway from 03. *The Rectory, 3 Butts Road, Chiseldon, Swindon SN4 0NN* Tel (01793) 740369

BULLOCK (née WHEALE), Mrs Sarah Ruth. b 64. Surrey Univ BA86 St Jo Coll Dur BA93. Cranmer Hall Dur 90. **d** 93 **p** 94. C Kersal Moor *Man* 93-98; P-in-c Whalley Range St Edm from 98; P-in-c Moss Side St Jas w St Clem from 99. *St Edmund's Rectory, 1 Range Road, Whalley Range, Manchester M16 8FS* Tel 0161-226 1291

BULLOCK, Stephanie Clair. b 46. St Mary's Hosp Medical Sch Lon MB, BS70. Ripon Coll Cuddesdon 90. **d** 92 **p** 94. Par Dn Cuddesdon *Ox* 92-94; Tutor Ripon Coll Cuddesdon 92-94; Asst Chapl Ox Radcliffe Hosp NHS Trust 94-97; Chapl Ox Radcliffe Hosps NHS Trust 97-03; Hon C Headington St Mary *Ox* from 03. *Church Farm, Church Lane, Old Marston, Oxford OX3 0PT* Tel (01865) 722926

BULLOCK, Victor James Allen. b 67. Southn Univ BTh90 St Mary's Coll Twickenham PGCE91. St Steph Ho Ox DipMin94. **d** 94 **p** 95. C Cowley St Jas *Ox* 94-95; C Reading St Giles 95-99; V Fenny Stratford from 99. *The Vicarage, Manor Road, Milton Keynes MK2 2HW* Tel (01908) 372825

BULLOCK-FLINT, Peter. b 22. Kelham Th Coll 39. **d** 45 **p** 46. C Deptford St Paul *S'wark* 45-48; C Streatham Ch Ch 48-50; C Boyne Hill *Ox* 50-56; C-in-c Tilehurst St Mary CD 56-72; V Hughenden 72-83; V Ivinghoe w Pitstone and Slapton 83-91; RD Mursley 86-91; rtd 91; Perm to Offic *Sarum* from 91. *1 Wellow Cottage, Salisbury Road, Pimperne, Blandford Forum DT11 8UW* Tel (01258) 450142

BULMAN, Mrs Madeline Judith. b 61. K Coll Lon BD AKC. **dss** 86 **d** 87 **p** 94. Shepperton *Lon* 86-87; Par Dn 87-88; Par Dn Brentford 88-94; C 94-96; V Cobbold Road St Sav w St Mary from 96; Dean of Women's Min from 99. *St Saviour's Vicarage, Cobbold Road, London W12 9LN* Tel (020) 8743 4769 Mobile 07973-954802 Fax 8740 1501
E-mail madeline.bulman@london.anglican.org

BULMAN, Michael Thomas Andrew. b 34. Jes Coll Cam BA59 MA61. Ridley Hall Cam 58. **d** 60 **p** 61. C Blackpool St Mark *Blackb* 60-63; C Branksome St Clem *Sarum* 63-67; V York St Barn *York* 67-84; CMJ Israel 84-93; R Jerusalem Ch Ch 85-87; Can Jerusalem 87-93; R Maresfield and V Nutley *Chich* 94-00; rtd 00. *15 Beechcroft Road, Alverstoke, Gosport PO12 2EP* Tel (023) 9252 7353 E-mail michael.bulman@btopenworld.com

BUNCE, Michael John. b 49. St Andr Univ MTh79 PhD91 FRSA FSA. Westcott Ho Cam DipTh80. **d** 80 **p** 81. C Grantham *Linc* 80-83; TV 83-85; R Tarfside *Bre* 85-92; R Brechin 85-92; R Auchmithie 91-92; Provost St Paul's Cathl Dundee 92-97; Chapl Menorca *Eur* from 00. *Apartado de Correos 102, 07720 Es Castell, Menorca, Spain* Tel (0034) (971) 352378

BUNCE, Raymond Frederick. b 28. Lon Univ DipSocSc53. Ely Th Coll 54. **d** 57 **p** 58. C Hillingdon St Andr *Lon* 57-62; C Greenford H Cross 62-67; V Ealing All SS 67-89; rtd 89; Chapl Ascot Priory 89-90; Perm to Offic *Portsm* from 91; Perm to Offic *Chich* from 99. *45 Guillards Oak, Midhurst GU29 9JZ* Tel (01730) 816282

BUNCH, Andrew William Havard. b 53. Selw Coll Cam BA74 MA78 PhD79. Ox NSM Course 84. **d** 87 **p** 88. NSM Wantage *Ox* 87-91; C New Windsor 91-93; TV 93-97; V Ox St Giles and SS Phil and Jas w St Marg from 97. *The Vicarage, Church Walk, Oxford OX2 6LY* Tel (01865) 510460
E-mail awh@awhbunch.freeserve.co.uk

BUNDAY, Canon Paul. b 30. Wadh Coll Ox BA54 MA58. ALCD56. **d** 56 **p** 57. C Woking St Jo *Guildf* 56-60; Chapl Reed's Sch Cobham 60-66; R Landford w Plaitford *Sarum* 66-77; RD Alderbury 73-77; TR Radipole and Melcombe Regis 77-86; RD Weymouth 82-85; Can and Preb Sarum Cathl 83-95; TV Whitton 86-91; TR 91-95; Chapl Duchess of Somerset Hosp Froxfield 86-94; rtd 95; Perm to Offic *Sarum* from 95. *16 St John's Close, Tisbury, Salisbury SP3 6PN* Tel (01747) 871530

BUNDAY, Richard William. b 76. Lanc Univ BA98. Cranmer Hall Dur 98. **d** 00 **p** 01. C Redcar *York* 00-01; C Marton *Blackb* from 01. *74 Worcester Road, Marton, Blackpool FY3 9SZ* Tel (01253) 792118 E-mail bunday@btopenworld.com *or* bunday@blueyonder.co.uk

BUNDOCK, Anthony Francis. b 49. Qu Coll Birm 81. **d** 83 **p** 84. C Stansted Mountfitchet *Chelmsf* 83-86; TV Borehamwood *St Alb* 86-94; TR Seacroft *Ripon* from 94; AD Whitkirk from 00. *The Rectory, 47 St James Approach, Leeds LS14 6JJ* Tel 0113-294 0414 E-mail tony.pat.bundock@virgin.net

BUNDOCK, Edward Leigh. b 52. Keble Coll Ox BA73 Open Univ PhD94 MAAT. St Steph Ho Ox 74. **d** 76 **p** 77. C Malvern Link w Cowleigh *Worc* 76-80; C-in-c Portslade Gd Shep CD *Chich* 80-88; V Wisborough Green 88-94; Perm to Offic *Guildf* 96-97; P-in-c E and W Rudham, Houghton-next-Harpley etc *Nor* 97-99; R E w W Rudham, Helhoughton etc from 99. *The Rectory, South Raynham Road, West Raynham, Fakenham NR21 7HH* Tel (01328) 838385

BUNDOCK, John Nicholas Edward. b 45. Wells Th Coll 66. **d** 70 **p** 71. C Chingford SS Pet and Paul *Chelmsf* 70-74; P-in-c Gt Grimsby St Matt Fairfield CD *Linc* 74-81; V Hindhead *Guildf* 81-99; RD Farnham 91-96; V Bramley and Grafham from 99; Chapl Gosden Ho Sch from 99. *The Vicarage, Birtley Rise, Bramley, Guildford GU5 0HZ* Tel (01483) 892109
E-mail johnbundock@lineone.net

BUNDOCK, Nicholas John. b 73. Sheff Univ BSc94 PhD98 Fitzw Coll Cam BA01. Ridley Hall Cam 99. **d** 02 **p** 03. C Mortomley St Sav High Green *Sheff* from 02. *23 Eyre Gardens, High Green, Sheffield S35 4NU* Tel 0114-286 9781
E-mail nick_bundock@hotmail.com

BUNDOCK, Ronald Michael. b 44. Leeds Univ BSc65. Ox NSM Course 87. **d** 90 **p** 91. NSM Buckingham *Ox* 90-98; NSM Stowe 98-03; P-in-c from 03. *1 Holton Road, Buckingham MK18 1PQ* Tel (01280) 813887 E-mail ron@bundock.com

BUNKER, Harry. b 28. Oak Hill Th Coll. **d** 59 **p** 60. C Longfleet *Sarum* 59-63; R Blisworth *Pet* 63-97; rtd 97; Perm to Offic *Pet* from 97. *14 Wardlow Close, West Hunsbury, Northampton NN4 9YQ* Tel (01604) 450230

BUNKER, John Herbert George. b 31. AKC56. **d** 57 **p** 58. C Newc St Jo *Newc* 57-60; C Cullercoats St Geo 61-65; V Byker St Mich 65-74; V Ashington 74-84; V Halifax St Aug *Wakef* 84-93; rtd 93; Perm to Offic *Wakef* from 93. *1 Hebble Dean, Hebble Lane, Halifax HX3 5JL*

BUNKER, The Very Revd Michael. b 37. Oak Hill Th Coll 59. **d** 63 **p** 64. C Alperton *Lon* 63-66; C St Helens St Helen *Liv* 66-70; V Muswell Hill St Matt *Lon* 70-79; V Muswell Hill St Jas 78-79; V Muswell Hill St Jas w St Matt 79-92; AD W Haringey 85-90; Preb St Paul's Cathl 90-92; Dean Pet from 92. *The Deanery, Minster*

Precincts, Peterborough PE1 1XS Tel (01733) 562780 Fax 897874 E-mail deanbunker@aol.com

BUNKER, Neil John. b 59. K Coll Lon BD80 AKC80. Ripon Coll Cuddesdon 82. **d** 83 **p** 84. C Bromley St Andr *Roch* 83-87; Chapl Farnborough Psychiatric Unit 85-87; Chapl Farnborough and Orpington Hosps 87-95; Distr Chapl Bromley HA 89-95; Perm to Offic *S'wark* from 89; Chapl Thameslink NHS Trust 91-98; Chapl Dartford and Gravesham NHS Trust 91-99; Chapl Ravensbourne NHS Trust 91-99; Dioc Adv for Hosp Chapl *Roch* 92; Chapl Oxleas NHS Trust from 93; Relig, Spiritual and Cultural Care Co-ord Chapl from 02; Chapl Cane Hill Secure Unit 89-97; Chapl Lewisham and Guy's Mental Health NHS Trust 98-99; P-in-c Clopton w Otley, Swilland and Ashbocking *St E* 01. *15 Charles Court, 20 Avenue Road, Erith DA8 3BY*

BUNN, Mrs Rosemary Joan. b 60. EAMTC 94. **d** 97 **p** 98. NSM Sprowston w Beeston *Nor* 97-01; R Stoke H Cross w Dunston, Arminghall etc from 01. *Holy Cross Vicarage, Mill Road, Stoke Holy Cross, Norwich NR14 8PA* Tel (01508) 492305
E-mail rev.rosie@venta-group.org.uk

BUNNELL, Adrian. b 49. Univ of Wales (Abth) BSc72. St Mich Coll Llan 74. **d** 75 **p** 76. C Wrexham *St As* 75-78; C Rhyl w St Ann 78-79; CF 79-95; R Aberfoyle *St And* from 95; R Callander from 95. *St Mary's Rectory, Main Street, Aberfoyle, Stirling FK8 3UJ* Tel (01877) 382887 Fax as telephone
E-mail st.mary@lineone.net

BUNT, Brian William. b 34. Bris Univ BA63 Lon Univ BD67. Tyndale Hall Bris. **d** 68 **p** 69. C Chich St Pancras and St Jo *Chich* 68-72; C Camborne *Truro* 72-75; P-in-c Kenwyn St Jo 75-93; P-in-c Penzance St Jo 93-94; rtd 94; Perm to Offic *Truro* from 01. *44 Daniell Road, Truro TR1 2DA* Tel (01872) 270063

BUNTING, Edward Garth. b 70. TCD BTh99. CITC 96. **d** 99 **p** 00. C Clooney w Strathfoyle *D & R* 99-02; I Leckpatrick w Dunnalong from 02. *The Rectory, 1 Lowertown Road, Ballymagorry, Strabane BT82 0LE* Tel (028) 7188 3545 Fax as telephone E-mail egbunting@aol.com

BUNTING, Canon Ian David. b 33. Ex Coll Ox BA58 MA61. Tyndale Hall Bris 57 Princeton Th Sem ThM60. **d** 60 **p** 61. C Bootle St Leon *Liv* 60-63; V Waterloo St Jo 64-71; Dir Past Studies St Jo Coll Dur 71-78; R Chester le Street *Dur* 78-87; RD Chester-le-Street 79-84; Kingham Hill Fellow 87-89; Dioc Dir of Ords *S'well* 90-00; C Lenton 90-97; Hon Can S'well Minster 93-99; Bp's Research Officer 97-00; rtd 00; Perm to Offic *S'well* from 00. *8 Crafts Way, Southwell NG25 0BL* Tel (01636) 813868 E-mail ibunting@waitrose.com

BUNTING, Jeremy John. b 34. St Cath Coll Cam BA56 MA60. Worc Coll Ox BA58 MA60. St Steph Ho Ox 57. **d** 59 **p** 60. C Bickley *Roch* 59-62; C Cambridge St Mary Less *Ely* 62-66; Fell and Tutor Gen Th Sem New York USA 66-68; R Stock Harvard *Chelmsf* 68-87; RD Wickford 73-79; V Hampstead Garden Suburb *Lon* 87-94; rtd 99. *Fairview, 82 New Road, Haslingfield, Cambridge CB3 7LP* Tel (01223) 871602

BUNYAN, David Richard. b 48. Edin Th Coll 93. **d** 96 **p** 97. NSM Musselburgh *Edin* 96-98; NSM Prestonpans 96-98; C Edin St Dav 98-00; R Grangemouth from 00; P-in-c Bo'ness from 00. *The Rectory, 33 Carronflats Road, Grangemouth FK3 9DG* Tel (01324) 482438 Fax as telephone
E-mail david.bunyan@btinternet.com

BUNYAN, Richard Charles. b 43. Oak Hill Th Coll 63 Ridley Hall Cam 69. **d** 71 **p** 72. C Luton Ch Ch *Roch* 71-74; C Bexleyheath Ch Ch 74-76; C Bexley St Jo 76-79; TV Northampton Em *Pet* 79-81; V Erith St Jo *Roch* 81-86; V S Woodham Ferrers *Chelmsf* 86-89; Chapl Scargill Ho 89-91; Sub-Chapl HM Pris Swaleside 91-94; Perm to Offic *Cant* from 91; Dep Chapl HM Pris Belmarsh 94-96; Chapl HM Pris Littlehey from 96. *HM Prison Littlehey, Perry, Huntingdon PE28 0SR* Tel (01480) 812202 ext 252 Fax 812151 E-mail rcbunyan@waitrose.com

BUR, Patricia Margaret. b 59. SEITE. **d** 99 **p** 01. C Clapham TM *S'wark* 99-01; C Nunhead St Antony w St Silas 01-03. *72 Harlescott Road, London SE15 3BZ* Tel (020) 7635 8626

BURBERY, Ian Edward. b 37. Univ of Wales (Lamp) BA59. Coll of Resurr Mirfield 59. **d** 61 **p** 62. C Penarth w Lavernock *Llan* 61-68; V Porth 68-77; V Cainscross w Selsley *Glouc* 77-89; P-in-c Cheltenham Em 89-95; V Cheltenham Em w St Steph 95-98; rtd 98. *21 Fairy Grove, Killay, Swansea SA2 7BY* Tel (01792) 204460

BURBIDGE, Barry Desmond. b 52. S Tr Scheme DipTh97. **d** 97 **p** 98. NSM Fleet *Guildf* 97-03; NSM Crondall and Ewshot from 03. *34 Ashbury Drive, Hawley, Camberley GU17 9HH* Tel (01276) 32776 E-mail barry.burbidge@ntlworld.com

BURBRIDGE, The Very Revd John Paul. b 32. FSA89 K Coll Cam BA54 MA58 New Coll Ox BA54 MA58. Wells Th Coll 58. **d** 59 **p** 60. C Eastbourne St Mary *Chich* 59-62; V Choral York Minster *York* 62-66; Can Res and Prec 66-76; Adn Richmond *Ripon* 76-83; Can Res Ripon Cathl 76-83; Dean Nor 83-95; rtd 95; Perm to Offic *Ripon* from 95. *The School House, High Fremington, Richmond DL11 6AS*

BURBRIDGE, Richard James. b 47. Univ of Wales (Ban) BSc68. Oak Hill Th Coll 68. **d** 72 **p** 73. C Rodbourne Cheney *Bris* 72-75; C Downend 75-78; P-in-c Bris H Cross Inns Court 78-83; P-in-c Fishponds All SS 83-86; V 86-97; RD Stapleton 89-95; C

111

Bishopston 97-98; C Bris St Andr w St Bart 97-98; TV Bishopston and St Andrews from 98. *25 Morley Square, Bristol BS7 9DW* Tel 0117-942 4359

BURCH, Cyril John. b 18. AKC49. **d** 49 **p** 50. C Milton next Sittingbourne *Cant* 49-51; C Croydon St Mich 51-52; PV Wells Cathl *B & W* 52-57; Chapl Prestfelde Sch Shrewsbury 57-58; Chapl Llan Cathl Sch 58-63; V Stoke Mandeville *Ox* 63-86; rtd 86. *c/o K E Burch, 31 Forbes Road, Faversham ME13 8QG* Tel (01795) 535715

BURCH, John Anthony. b 37. Open Univ BA75. Wycliffe Hall Ox 67. **d** 69 **p** 70. C Guild Ch Ch *Guildf* 69-72; C Cove St Jo 72-75; TV Fincham *Ely* 75-79; V Huntingdon St Barn 79-81; Perm to Offic 82-90; rtd 99. *13 Hawthorn Road, Kearsley, Bolton BL4 8SD*

BURCH, Canon John Christopher (Chris). b 50. Trin Coll Cam BA71 MA76 Leeds Univ MPhil95. St Jo Coll Nottm 73. **d** 76 **p** 77. C Sheff St Jo *Sheff* 76-79; C Holbeck *Ripon* 79-82; V Burmantofts St Steph and St Agnes 82-95; Can Res and Prec Cov Cathl *Cov* 95-02; Chapl to Clergy of UPA 99-02; C-in-c Braunstone Park CD *Leic* from 02. *The Vicarage, Main Street, Leicester LE3 3AL* Tel 0116-289 3377

BURCH, Canon Peter John. b 36. ACA60 FCA71. Ripon Hall Ox 62. **d** 64 **p** 65. C Brixton St Matt *S'wark* 64-67; Sierra Leone 68-72; P-in-c Chich St Pet *Chich* 72-76; V Broadwater Down 76-85; V Steyning 85-94; R Ashurst 85-94; Hon Can Bauchi from 93; V Broadway *Worc* 94-96; V Broadway w Wickhamford 96-02; rtd 02; Perm to Offic *Glouc* from 03. *6 Jordan's Close, Willersey, Broadway WR12 7QD* Tel (01386) 853837
E-mail canonburch@stmichaels95.freeserve.co.uk

BURCH, Stephen Roy. b 59. St Jo Coll Nottm LTh82. **d** 85 **p** 86. C Ipswich St Aug *St E* 85-89; P-in-c Kinwarton w Gt Alne and Haselor *Cov* 89-99; R from 99; Youth Chapl 89-94; RD Alcester from 99; P-in-c Coughton from 02. *The Rectory, Sternall Lane, Great Alne, Alcester B49 6HY* Tel (01789) 488344
E-mail stephen.burch@btinternet.com

BURCHILL, Jane. b 31. Dalhousie Univ Canada BSc54 Aber Univ PhD81. Moray Ho Edin CertEd56 St Jo Coll Nottm 85. **d** 88 **p** 94. NSM Inverurie *Ab* from 88; NSM Auchindoir from 88; NSM Alford from 88; NSM Kemnay from 88. *5 Hopetoun Avenue, Bucksburn, Aberdeen AB2 9QU* Tel (01224) 712931

BURDEN, Miss Anne Margaret. b 47. Ex Univ BSc69 CQSW72. Linc Th Coll 89. **d** 91 **p** 94. Par Dn Mill Hill Jo Keble Ch *Lon* 91-94; C 94; TV Basingstoke *Win* 94-02; Dioc Adv for Women's Min 00-02; TV Brixham w Churston Ferrers and Kingswear *Ex* from 02. *6 Durleigh Road, Brixham TQ5 9JJ* Tel (01803) 954924

BURDEN, Derek. b 29. St Edm Hall Ox BA52 MA56. Wells Th Coll 56. **d** 58 **p** 59. C Mitcham St Mark *S'wark* 58-61; V Coombe Bissett w Homington *Sarum* 61-69; V N Bradley 69-79; V Steeple Ashton w Semington 79-84; V Keevil 79-84; V Steeple Ashton w Semington and Keevil 84-89; rtd 89; Perm to Offic *Sarum* from 89. *9 Farleigh Avenue, Trowbridge BA14 9DS* Tel (01225) 754759

BURDEN, Derek Ronald. b 37. Sarum Th Coll 59. **d** 62 **p** 63. C Cuddington *Guildf* 62-64; C Leamington Priors All SS *Cov* 64-66; C Stamford All SS w St Pet *Linc* 66-74; C-in-c Stamford Ch Ch CD 71-74; P-in-c Ashbury w Compton Beauchamp *Ox* 74-77; V 77-81; V Ashbury, Compton Beauchamp and Longcot w Fernham 81-84; V Wokingham St Sebastian 84-97; P-in-c Wooburn 97-02; rtd 02. *42 North Street, Wareham BH20 4AQ* Tel (01929) 550260

BURDEN, Michael Henry. b 38. Selw Coll Cam BA59 MA62 Hull Univ MEd79. Ridley Hall Cam 59. **d** 61 **p** 62. C Ashton-upon-Mersey St Mary *Ches* 62-65; Chapl St Pet Sch York 65-70; Asst Master Beverley Gr Sch 70-74; R Walkington *York* 74-77; Chapl Asst Berwick R Infirmary 82-94; P-in-c Berwick H Trin *Newc* 82-87; V 87-89; P-in-c Berwick St Mary 82-87; V Berwick H Trin and St Mary 89-94; P-in-c Skirwith, Ousby and Melmerby w Kirkland *Carl* 94-98; Sec Guild of St Raphael 94-98; rtd 99; Perm to Offic *Newc* from 99. *The White House, Fenkle Street, Holy Island, Berwick-upon-Tweed TD15 2SR* Tel (01289) 389302 Fax as telephone

BURDEN, Paul. b 62. AMIMechE87 Rob Coll Cam BA84 MA88. Wycliffe Hall Ox BA91. **d** 92 **p** 93. C Clevedon St Andr and Ch Ch *B & W* 92-96; R Bathampton w Claverton from 96. *The Vicarage, Bathampton Lane, Bath BA2 6SW* Tel (01225) 463570 E-mail p.burden@talk21.com

BURDETT, John Fergusson. b 25. Pemb Coll Cam BA47 MA79. **d** 79 **p** 80. C Edin St Jo *Edin* 79-87 and 90-95; Cyprus 87-90; rtd 95. *80/1 Barnton Park View, Edinburgh EH4 6HJ* Tel 0131-339 7226 Fax 317 1179 E-mail rev@johnburdett.demon.co.uk

BURDETT, Stephen Martin. b 49. AKC72. St Aug Coll Cant 73. **d** 74 **p** 75. C Walworth St Pet *S'wark* 74-75; C Walworth 75-77; C Benhilton 77-80; P-in-c Earlsfield St Jo 80-83; V 83-89; V N Dulwich St Faith 89-99; Ldr Post Ord Tr Woolwich Episc Area 96-99; TR Southend *Chelmsf* from 99. *144 Alexandra Road, Southend-on-Sea SS1 1HB* Tel (01702) 342687
E-mail stephenburdett@waitrose.com

BURDON, Anthony James. b 46. Ex Univ LLB67 Lon Univ BD73. Oak Hill Th Coll 71. **d** 73 **p** 74. C Ox St Ebbe w St Pet *Ox* 73-76; C Church Stretton *Heref* 76-78; Cand Sec CPAS 78-81; Hon C Bromley Ch Ch *Roch* 78-81; V Filkins w Broadwell,

Broughton, Kelmscot etc *Ox* 81-84; R Broughton Poggs w Filkins, Broadwell etc 84-85; V Reading St Jo 85-96; C California 96-98; Warden and P-in-c Cumbrae (or Millport) *Arg* from 98. *The College, College Street, Millport, Isle of Cumbrae KA28 0HE* Tel (01475) 530353 Mobile 07957-336432 Fax 530204
E-mail tccumbrae@argyll.anglican.org

BURDON, Christopher John. b 48. Jes Coll Cam BA70 MA74 Leeds Univ DipTh73 Glas Univ PhD95. Coll of Resurr Mirfield 71. **d** 74 **p** 75. C Chelmsf All SS *Chelmsf* 74-78; TV High Wycombe *Ox* 78-84; P-in-c Olney w Emberton 84-90; R 90-92; Lic to Offic *Glas* 92-94; Lay Tr Officer *Chelmsf* 94-99; Prin N Ord Course from 00; Lic Preacher *Man* from 00. *75 Framingham Road, Sale M33 3RH* Tel 0161-962 8900 *or* 249 2511
E-mail chris@thenoc.org.uk

BURDON, Edward Arthur. b 11. Linc Th Coll 44. **d** 46 **p** 47. C Taunton H Trin *B & W* 46-48; C Mayfield *Chich* 48-54; V Gosfield *Chelmsf* 54-72; V Coggeshall w Markshall 72-80; rtd 80; Perm to Offic *St E* from 81. *c/o Dr C J Burdon, 75 Framingham Road, Sale M33 3RH*

BURDON, Mrs Pamela Muriel. b 46. Ex Univ BA68 Reading Univ DipEd69. Wycliffe Hall Ox 88. **d** 90 **p** 94. Par Dn Reading St Jo 90-94; C 94-96; P-in-c California 96-98; NSM Cumbrae (or Millport) *Arg* from 98. *The College, College Street, Millport, Isle of Cumbrae KA28 0HE* Tel (01475) 530353 Fax 530204
E-mail tccumbrae@aol.com *or* tccumbrae@argyll.anglican.org

BURDON, William. b 23. Leeds Univ BA51. Coll of Resurr Mirfield 51. **d** 53 **p** 54. C Derby St Anne *Derby* 53-57; C Weston-super-Mare All SS *B & W* 57-62; C Clifton All SS *Bris* 63-64; V Skirwith *Carl* 64-73; V Skirwith w Ousby and Melmerby 73-84; R Maidwell w Draughton, Scaldwell, Lamport etc *Pet* 84-88; rtd 88; Perm to Offic *Leic* 97-98. *25 Stuart Court, High Street, Kibworth, Leicester LE8 0LR* Tel 0116-279 6326

BURFITT, Edward Ronald. b 42. MIMA64 Liv Univ CSocSc67 Newc Univ DASS68. Cranmer Hall Dur 91. **d** 93 **p** 94. C Monkseaton St Mary *Newc* 93-97; rtd 97. *Eden House, 11 St Nicholas Road, Hexham NE46 2EZ* Tel (01434) 603073 Mobile 07870-762522 E-mail revburf@aol.com

BURFORD, Anthony Francis. b 55. Oak Hill Th Coll BA98. **d** 98 **p** 99. C Cov H Trin *Cov* 98-02; P-in-c Rye Park St Cuth *St Alb* from 02. *The Vicarage, 8 Ogard Road, Hoddesdon EN11 0NU* Tel (01992) 302222 E-mail abur118268@aol.com

BURGE, Edward Charles Richard. b 70. Liv Univ BA92. Ridley Hall Cam CTM93. **d** 96 **p** 97. C Cayton w Eastfield *York* 96-99; P-in-c Lythe w Ugthorpe from 99; Children's Officer from 99; Hon Chapl Miss to Seafarers from 02. *The Vicarage, Lythe, Whitby YO21 3RL* Tel (01947) 893479
E-mail richardburge@ecrb.fsnet.co.uk

BURGER, David Joseph Cave. b 31. Selw Coll Cam BA58 MA62 Leic Univ 68. Coll of Resurr Mirfield 58. **d** 60 **p** 61. C Chiswick St Paul Grove Park *Lon* 60-63; C Charlton St Luke w H Trin *S'wark* 63-65; Warden St Luke Tr Ho Charlton 63-65; Chapl Moor Park Coll Farnham 66; Teacher Ysgol y Gader Dolgellau 68-85; Resettlement Officer Ches Aid to the Homeless 88-92; rtd 92; Perm to Offic *Ban* from 96. *Pwllygele Mawr, Llanfachreth, Dolgellau LL40 2DP* Tel (01341) 450350

BURGESS, Alan James. b 51. Ridley Hall Cam 87. **d** 89 **p** 90. C Glenfield *Leic* 89-92; V Donisthorpe and Moira w Stretton-en-le-Field from 92; RD Akeley W from 00. *St John's Vicarage, Donisthorpe, Swadlincote DE12 7PX* Tel (01530) 271456
E-mail admos@supanet.com

BURGESS, Alfred George. b 18. Univ of Wales BA39. St Mich Coll Llan 39. **d** 41 **p** 42. C Swansea Ch Ch *S & B* 41-44; C Llandrindod w Cefnllys 44-47; C Stratford-on-Avon *Cov* 47-49; V Longford 49-58; V Alveston 58-81; RD Stratford-on-Avon 69-73; R Ilmington w Stretton on Fosse and Ditchford 81-84; rtd 84; Perm to Offic *Cov* from 84; *Glouc* 84-97. *139 Evesham Road, Stratford-upon-Avon CV37 9BP* Tel (01789) 293321

BURGESS, Clive Brian. b 63. Trin Coll Bris BA00. **d** 00 **p** 01. C Oxton *Ches* from 00. *St Saviour's House, 36 Noctorum Dell, Prenton CH43 9UL* Tel 0151-652 8050
E-mail revdcliveburgess@btinternet.com

BURGESS, David James. b 58. Southn Univ BSc80. St Jo Coll Nottm LTh89 DPS89. **d** 89 **p** 90. C S Mimms Ch Ch *Lon* 89-93; C Hanwell St Mary w St Chris 93-97; P-in-c The Lee *Ox* from 97; P-in-c Hawridge w Cholesbury and St Leonard from 97. *The Vicarage, The Lee, Great Missenden HP16 9LZ* Tel (01494) 837315 E-mail d.burgess@clara.net

BURGESS, David John. b 39. Trin Hall Cam BA62 MA66 Univ Coll Ox MA66 FRSA91. Cuddesdon Coll 62. **d** 65 **p** 66. C Maidstone All SS w St Phil *Cant* 65; Asst Chapl Univ Coll Ox 66-70; Chapl 70-78; Can and Treas Windsor 78-87; Chapl to The Queen from 87; V St Lawr Jewry *Lon* from 87. *St Lawrence Jewry Vicarage, Next Guildhall, London EC2V 5AA* Tel (020) 7600 9478

BURGESS, Mrs Denise. b 49. **d** 00 **p** 01. OLM Glascote and Stonydelph *Lich* from 00. *22 Melmerby, Wilncote, Tamworth B77 4LP* Tel (01827) 897098

BURGESS, Derek Mark. b 31. Brasted Place Coll 61 St Mich Coll Llan 61. **d** 89 **p** 90. Australia 89-92; P-in-c Knowbury *Heref*

93-98; P-in-c Coreley and Doddington 93-98; rtd 98; Perm to Offic *Win* from 99. *1 Leighwood, 275 Leigh Road, Chandler's Ford, Eastleigh SO53 3LA* Tel (023) 8025 4677
E-mail revmburgess@onetel.net.uk

BURGESS, Edwin Michael. b 47. Ch Coll Cam BA69 MA73. Coll of Resurr Mirfield 70. **d** 72 **p** 73. C Beamish *Dur* 72-77; C Par *Truro* 77-80; P-in-c Duloe w Herodsfoot 80-83; R 83-86; Jt Dir SW Minl Tr Course 80-86; Subwarden St Deiniol's Lib Hawarden 86-91; R Oughtrington *Ches* from 91; P-in-c Warburton from 93; CME Officer from 99; Dioc Chapl Mother's Union from 02. *The Rectory, Oughtrington, Lymm WA13 9JB* Tel (01925) 752388 E-mail m.e.burgess@tesco.net

BURGESS, Canon Henry James. b 08. Lon Univ BA31 MA49 PhD54. Wycliffe Hall Ox 35. **d** 36 **p** 37. C Bath St Paul *B & W* 36-38; C Tunbridge Wells St Jo *Roch* 38-39; Chapl Weymouth Coll 39-40; V Poughill *Truro* 40-44; V Sidcup Ch Ch *Roch* 44-50; V Cudham 50-61; Dioc Schs Adv 55-61; V Lucton w Eyton *Heref* 61-66; R Hooton Roberts *Sheff* 66-70; Hon Can Sheff Cathl 66-70; Can Res 70-75; Dioc Dir of Educn 70-75; rtd 75; Perm to Offic *Truro* 75-85; Perm to Offic *Roch* 85-95. *Flat 17, Bromley College, London Road, Bromley BR1 1PE* Tel (020) 8290 1362

BURGESS, Canon Henry Percival. b 21. Leeds Univ BA48. Coll of Resurr Mirfield 48. **d** 50 **p** 51. C Northfield *Birm* 50-54; V Shaw Hill 54-62; V Wylde Green 62-89; Hon Can Birm Cathl 75-90; RD Sutton Coldfield 76-88; rtd 90; Perm to Offic *Birm* from 90. *39 Chestnut Drive, Birmingham B36 9BH* Tel 0121-747 9926

BURGESS, Mrs Jean Ann. b 62. EMMTC. **d** 03. C Gresley *Derby* from 03. *Chapel End, Chapel Street, Church Gresley, Swadlincote DE11 9LX* Tel (01283) 551015

BURGESS, The Ven John Edward. b 30. Lon Univ BD57. ALCD56. **d** 57 **p** 58. C Bermondsey St Mary w St Olave and St Jo *S'wark* 57-60; C Southampton St Mary w H Trin *Win* 60-62; V Dunston w Coppenhall *Lich* 62-67; Chapl Stafford Coll of Tech 63-67; V Keynsham w Queen Charlton *B & W* 67-75; R Burnett 67-75; RD Keynsham 72-75; Adn Bath and Preb Wells Cathl 75-95; rtd 96; Perm to Offic *B & W* and *Sarum* from 96. *12 Berryfield Road, Bradford-on-Avon BA15 1SX* Tel (01225) 868905

BURGESS, John Henry William. b 35. Westhill Coll Birm CYCW72. Wells Th Coll 65. **d** 67 **p** 68. C Teddington St Alb *Lon* 67-72; C Northolt W End St Jos 72-74; Perm to Offic *B & W* 93-99 and from 00; rtd 95; C Bruton and Distr *B & W* 99-00. *10 Pendragon Park, Glastonbury BA6 9PQ* Tel (01458) 833287

BURGESS, John Michael. b 36. ALCD61. **d** 61 **p** 62. C Eccleston St Luke *Liv* 61-64; S Rhodesia 64-65; Rhodesia 65-74; V Nottingham St Andr *S'well* 74-79; Bp's Adv on Community Relns 77-79; V Earlestown *Liv* 79-87; RD Warrington 82-87; TR Halewood 87-94; V Southport St Phil and St Paul 94-01; AD N Meols 95-00; rtd 01. *3 Glencoyne Drive, Southport PR9 9TS* Tel (01704) 506843

BURGESS, John Mulholland. b 32. Cranmer Hall Dur 58. **d** 61 **p** 62. C Frimley *Guildf* 61-67; C Cheltenham St Luke and St Jo *Glouc* 67-69; P-in-c Withington w Compton Abdale 69-74; R Woolstone w Gotherington and Oxenton 74-75; Chapl Rotterdam w Schiedam etc *Eur* 75-78; Chapl Sliema 78-80; C Nottingham All SS *S'well* 80; C Rolleston w Morton 80-83; C Rolleston w Fiskerton, Morton and Upton 83-84; V Mansfield St Aug 84-99; Asst RD Mansfield 88-92; RD 92-98; rtd 99. *278 Westfield Lane, Mansfield NG19 6NQ* Tel (01623) 421163

BURGESS, Sister Kate Lamorna. b 64. Man Poly BA86 Leeds Univ MA97. NEOC 99. **d** 02 **p** 03. OHP from 92; C Hessle *York* from 02. *167 First Lane, Hessle, Hull HU13 9EY* Tel (01482) 645745 E-mail klb6@klb6.karoo.co.uk

BURGESS (née BOND), Mrs Kim Mary. b 58. SRN79. Trin Coll Bris BA87. **d** 87 **p** 94. Par Dn Cullompton *Ex* 87-91; Asst Chapl N Staffs R Infirmary Stoke-on-Trent 91-95; NSM Audley *Lich* from 95. *6 Quarry Cottages, Nantwich Road, Audley, Stoke-on-Trent ST7 8DW* Tel (01782) 722961

BURGESS, Miss Laura Jane. b 74. Imp Coll Lon BSc95 ARSM95. Ripon Coll Cuddesdon BTh00. **d** 00 **p** 01. C St Alb Abbey *St Alb* 00-01; C Boxmoor St Jo from 01. *23 Beechfield Road, Hemel Hempstead HP1 1PP* Tel (01442) 253102
E-mail laura.burgess@telinco.co.uk

BURGESS, Mark. *See* BURGESS, Derek Mark

BURGESS, Michael. *See* BURGESS, John Michael

BURGESS, Michael Anglin. b 34. St Deiniol's Hawarden 81. **d** 83 **p** 84. C Habergham Eaves St Matt *Blackb* 83-85; C Burnley St Matt w H Trin 85-86; V Preston St Matt 86-93; V Nelson St Bede 93-99; rtd 99; Perm to Offic *Blackb* from 99. *39 Reedley Road, Reedley, Burnley BB10 2LU* Tel (01282) 449727
E-mail revmab@globalnet.co.uk

BURGESS, Michael James. b 42. Coll of Resurr Mirfield 74. **d** 76 **p** 77. C Leigh-on-Sea St Marg *Chelmsf* 76-79; C St Peter-in-Thanet *Cant* 79-82; Canada from 82. *66 Spencer Avenue, Toronto ON, Canada, M6K 2J6* Tel (001) (416) 531 4037

BURGESS, Michael Walter. Bps' Coll Cheshunt 66. **d** 68 **p** 70. C Hammersmith St Matt *Lon* 68-70; C Boreham Wood All SS

St Alb 70-73; V Flamstead 74-77; V St Marylebone Annunciation Bryanston Street *Lon* from 77. *4 Wyndham Place, London W1H 1AP* Tel (020) 7262 4329

BURGESS, Neil. b 53. Univ of Wales (Lamp) BA75 Nottm Univ MTh87 PhD93. St Mich Coll Llan 75. **d** 77 **p** 78. C Cheadle *Lich* 77-79; C Longton 79-82; TV Hanley H Ev 82-86; C Uttoxeter w Bramshall 86-87; Lect Linc Th Coll 87-95; Hon C Linc Minster Gp *Linc* 88-95; Dioc Dir of Clergy Tr *S'well* 95-00; C Newark 97-00; Perm to Offic *Linc* from 00. *23 Drury Lane, Lincoln LN1 3BN* Tel (01522) 539408
E-mail ann.burgess@btinternet.com

BURGESS, Sister Patricia Jean. b 16. Edin Univ BSc38. New Coll Edin 65. **dss** 69 **d** 86. NSM Roslin (Rosslyn Chpl) *Edin* 69-73; Community of the Transfiguration Midlothian from 73. *Hermitage of the Transfiguration, 70E Clerk Street, Loanhead EH20 9RG*

BURGESS, Paul Christopher James. b 41. Qu Coll Cam BA63 MA67. Lon Coll of Div 66. **d** 68 **p** 69. C Islington St Mary *Lon* 68-72; C Church Stretton *Heref* 73-74; Pakistan 74-83; Warden Carberry Tower (Ch of Scotland) 84-86; Progr Co-ord 86-88; TV Livingston LEP *Edin* 88-92. *Address temp unknown*

BURGESS, Peter Alan. b 40. St Edm Ho Cam BA86 MA89 MPhil86 St Jo Coll York MA99. Cranmer Hall Dur 02. **d** 03. NSM Wheldrake w Thorganby *York* from 03. *2 Derwent Drive, Wheldrake, York YO19 6AL* Tel (01904) 448309
E-mail burgesspr@btinternet.com

BURGESS, Roy. b 32. S Dios Minl Tr Scheme 80. **d** 83 **p** 84. NSM Bentworth and Shalden and Lasham *Win* 83-89; R Ingoldsby *Linc* 89-97; RD Beltisloe 93-97; rtd 97; Perm to Offic *Nor* from 98. *4 Melton Gate, Wymondham NR18 0PQ* Tel (01953) 606449

BURGESS, Roy Graham. b 47. Birm Univ CertCYW72 Bulmershe Coll of HE DMS81. Ox Min Course CBTS94. **d** 94 **p** 95. C Easthampstead *Ox* 94-99; C Wokingham St Paul from 99. *St Nicholas House, Brook Close, Wokingham RG41 1ND* Tel 0118-978 0034 E-mail revroy@compriest.freeserve.co.uk

BURGHALL, Kenneth Miles. b 34. Selw Coll Cam BA57 MA61. Qu Coll Birm 57. **d** 59 **p** 60. C Macclesfield St Mich *Ches* 59-63; CF 63-66; P-in-c Birkenhead Priory *Ches* 67-71; V Macclesfield St Paul 71-87; V Nether Peover from 87; P-in-c Over Peover from 92. *The Vicarage, Lower Peover, Knutsford WA16 9PY* Tel (01565) 722304

BURGIN, Henry Kenneth. b 36. FRSA95. S'wark Ord Course 70. **d** 71 **p** 72. C Caterham Valley *S'wark* 71-73; C Benhilton 73-77; V Cheam Common St Phil 77-82; P-in-c Blackheath All SS 82-89; V 89-99; Tutor and Chapl Whittington Coll Felbridge from 99. *32 Whittington College, London Road, Felbridge, East Grinstead RH19 2QU* Tel (01342) 322790 Fax 302431
E-mail henryb@mercers.co.uk

BURGON, Canon George Irvine. b 41. Edin Th Coll. **d** 65 **p** 66. C Dundee St Mary Magd *Bre* 65-68; C Wellingborough All Hallows *Pet* 68-71; P-in-c Norton 71-73; TV Daventry w Norton 73-75; V Northampton St Mary 75-98; Can Pet Cathl from 95; R Rothwell w Orton, Rushton w Glendon and Pipewell from 98; Hon Chapl ATC from 02. *The Vicarage, High Street, Rothwell, Kettering NN14 6BQ* Tel (01536) 710268
E-mail george@squireshill1.freeserve.co.uk

BURKE, Charles Michael. b 28. Keble Coll Ox BA51 MA54 Ox Univ DipEd52. Glouc Th Course. **d** 84 **p** 85. C Colwall w Upper Colwall and Coddington *Heref* 84-88; V Canon Pyon w Kings Pyon and Birley 88-98; P-in-c Wellington 98; rtd 98; Perm to Offic *Heref* from 98. *Pyons, 7 Stretton Close, Fayre Oakes, Hereford HR4 0QN* Tel (01432) 270068

BURKE, Christopher Mark. b 65. Cov Poly LLB87. Ripon Coll Cuddesdon 89. **d** 92 **p** 93. C Nunthorpe *York* 92-96; V S Bank 96-02; R Stepney St Dunstan and All SS *Lon* from 02. *St Dunstan and All Saints Rectory, Rectory Square, London E1 3NQ* Tel (020) 7791 3545 Fax as telephone
E-mail christopher.burke@btinternet.com

BURKE, Colin Douglas. b 41. Bp Otter Coll CertEd64 LNSM course. **d** 92 **p** 93. OLM Fressingfield, Mendham etc *St E* 92-99; NSM Oare w Culbone *B & W* from 99. *The Rectory, Oare, Lynton EX35 6NX* Tel (01598) 741270

BURKE, Eric John. b 44. Llan Dioc Tr Scheme 81. **d** 85 **p** 86. NSM Cardiff St Jo *Llan* 85-95; Chapl Asst Univ Hosp of Wales and Llandough NHS Trust from 95. *The University Hospital of Wales, Heath Park, Cardiff CF4 4XW* Tel (029) 2074 7747 ext 3230 *or* 2079 8147

BURKE, Kelvin Stephen. b 56. Man Univ BA77 FCA81. Cranmer Hall Dur DTM99. **d** 99 **p** 00. C Stanley *Wakef* 99-02; P-in-c Wakef St Andr and St Mary from 02. *25 Barratts Road, Wakefield WF1 3RT* Tel (01924) 375229 Mobile 07802-677785
E-mail kelvinburke@hotmail.com

BURKE, Michael Robert. b 61. Leeds Univ BA83. Trin Coll Bris BA89. **d** 89 **p** 90. C Anston *Sheff* 89-92; V Crosspool 92-00; V Hucclecote *Glouc* from 00. *128 Hucclecote Road, Gloucester GL3 3SB* Tel (01452) 610568 E-mail mikburke@aol.com

BURKE, Wayne Jackson. b 51. San Francisco State Univ BA76 MA78 Univ of Wales (Cardiff) PhD91. St Steph Ho Ox 01. **d** 02

p 03. NSM Gtr Athens *Eur* from 02. *Stratigou Eindou 14, 185 36 Piraeus, Greece* Tel (0030) (10) 418 2251 E-mail burke@hol.gr

BURKE, William Spencer Dwerryhouse. b 46. Ripon Coll Cuddesdon 90. **d** 92 **p** 93. C Watford St Mich *St Alb* 92-95; R Castor w Sutton and Upton w Marholm *Pet* from 95. *The Rectory, 5 Church Hill, Castor, Peterborough PE5 7AU* Tel (01733) 380244

BURKETT, Canon Christopher Paul. b 52. Warwick Univ BA75 Birm Univ DipTh77 Westmr Coll Ox DipApTh92 MTh93. Qu Coll Birm 75. **d** 78 **p** 79. C Streetly *Lich* 78-81; C Harlescott 81-83; TV Leek and Meerbrook 83-89; Chapl Leek Moorlands Hosp 83-89; Area Sec USPG *Ches* 89-92; V Whitegate w Lt Budworth *Ches* 92-00; Asst CME Officer 93-00; Can Res Ches Cathl from 00; Bp's Chapl from 00. *5 Abbey Green, Chester CH1 2JH* Tel (01244) 347500 E-mail burkett@chestercathedral.org.uk

BURKILL, Mark Edward. b 56. MA PhD. Trin Coll Bris. **d** 84 **p** 85. C Cheadle *Ches* 84-88; C Harold Wood *Chelmsf* 88-91; V Leyton Ch Ch from 91. *The Vicarage, 52 Elm Road, London E11 4DW* Tel (020) 8539 4980 E-mail mark.burkill@talk21.com

BURKITT, Paul Adrian. b 49. RMN75 SRN77 Coll of Ripon & York St Jo Cert Counselling 89. St Steph Ho Ox 84. **d** 86 **p** 87. C Whitby *York* 86-90; V Egton w Grosmont 90-93; V Newington w Dairycoates 93-96; P-in-c Kingston upon Hull St Mary from 96. *223 Cottingham Road, Hull HU5 4AU* Tel (01482) 343182

BURKITT, Richard Francis. b 49. Leeds Univ BA71 CertEd72. Sarum & Wells Th Coll 82. **d** 90 **p** 90. R Fraserburgh w New Pitsligo *Ab* 90-95; R Fortrose *Mor* from 95; R Cromarty from 95; R Arpafeelie from 95. *St Andrew's Rectory, 1 Deans Road, Fortrose IV10 8TJ* Tel (01381) 620255

BURLAND, Clive Beresford. b 37. Sarum & Wells Th Coll 81. **d** 85 **p** 86. C Warblington w Emsworth *Portsm* 85-87; C Cowes St Mary 87-92; V Gurnard 92-98; R Northwood 93-98; rtd 98; Perm to Offic *Portsm* from 98. *5A Orchard Close, Freshwater PO40 9BQ* Tel (01983) 753949

BURLEIGH, David John. b 42. FCII69. St Deiniol's Hawarden 84. **d** 87 **p** 88. NSM Lache cum Saltney *Ches* 87-88; NSM Eastham 89-92; C Birkenhead Priory 92-95; P-in-c Duloe w Herodsfoot *Truro* 95-99; TV Liskeard, St Keyne, St Pinnock, Morval etc 95-99; R Duloe, Herodsfoot, Morval and St Pinnock 99-01; V Bath St Barn w Englishcombe *B & W* from 01. *The Vicarage, Mount View, Southdown, Bath BA2 1JX* Tel (01225) 478952

BURLEIGH, Walter Coleridge. b 41. WMMTC 89. **d** 89 **p** 90. NSM N Evington *Leic* 90-96; Perm to Offic from 96. *20 Border Drive, Leicester LE4 2JH* Tel 0116-235 9320

BURLES, Robert John. b 54. Bris Univ BSc75. St Jo Coll Nottm LTh86. **d** 88 **p** 89. C Mansfield St Pet *S'well* 88-91; C The Lydiards *Bris* 91-92; TV W Swindon and the Lydiards 92-97; TR Swindon St Jo and St Andr from 97. *The Vicarage, Verwood Close, Swindon SN3 2LE* Tel (01793) 611473

BURLEY, John Roland James. b 46. St Jo Coll Cam BA67 MA70 Ball Coll Ox Dip Geochemistry 68. Trin Episc Sch for Min Ambridge Penn MDiv88. **d** 81 **p** 82. SAMS Chile 81-90; TV Southgate *Chich* 93-99; R Alfold and Loxwood *Guildf* from 99. *The Rectory, Vicarage Hill, Loxwood, Billingshurst RH14 0RG* Tel (01403) 752320 Fax as telephone E-mail john@burleys.co.uk

BURLEY, Michael. b 58. Ridley Hall Cam 86. **d** 89 **p** 90. C Scarborough St Mary w Ch Ch and H Apostles *York* 89-92; C Drypool 93; TV 93-97; V Sutton St Mich from 97. *St Michael's Vicarage, 751 Marfleet Lane, Hull HU9 4TJ* Tel (01482) 374509 E-mail burley@standrews.karoo.co.uk

BURLTON, Aelred Harry. b 49. Sarum & Wells Th Coll 75. **d** 78 **p** 79. C Feltham *Lon* 78-82; Chapl Heathrow Airport 83-94; P-in-c Harmondsworth 92-94; R St Buryan, St Levan and Sennen *Truro* from 94. *The Rectory, St Buryan, Penzance TR19 6BB* Tel (01736) 810216

BURLTON, William Frank. b 12. K Coll Lon. **d** 43 **p** 44. C Glouc St Mark *Glouc* 43-46; C Northleach and Hampnett w Stowell and Yanworth 46-48; C St Briavels 48-51; R Cromhall 51-78; Chapl HM Pris Leyhill 54-89; R Cromhall w Tortworth *Glouc* 78-82; rtd 82; Perm to Offic *Glouc* 82-89 and *Truro* from 89. *24 Godolphin Terrace, Marazion, Penzance TR17 0EX* Tel (01736) 710699

BURMAN, Philip Harvey. b 47. Kelham Th Coll 66. **d** 70 **p** 71. C Huyton St Mich *Liv* 70-75; C Farnworth 75-77; TV Kirkby 77-83; V Hindley All SS 83-93; V Middlesbrough St Martin *York* 93-97; V Middlesbrough St Martin w St Cuth 97-99; P-in-c Eccleston St Thos *Liv* from 99. *St Thomas's Vicarage, 21 St George's Road, St Helens WA10 4LH* Tel (01744) 22295

BURMAN, Thomas George. b 41. S'wark Ord Course 86. **d** 89 **p** 90. NSM Forest Hill *S'wark* from 90. *131 Como Road, London SE23 2JN* Tel (020) 8699 8929

BURMAN, William Guest. b 26. St Cath Coll Cam MA55 Worc Coll Ox MA63. St Steph Ho Ox 81. **d** 83 **p** 84. C Weymouth H Trin *Sarum* 83-86; R Exton and Winsford and Cutcombe w Luxborough *B & W* 86-89; TV Langport Area Chs 89-91; rtd 91;

Perm to Offic *B & W* 91-98; Master Bath St Mary Magd Holloway from 94. *8 Stoneleigh Court, Lansdown Road, Bath BA1 5TL* Tel (01225) 312140

BURMESTER, Stephen John. b 66. Leeds Univ BSc87. Wycliffe Hall Ox 96. **d** 98 **p** 99. C Lenton *S'well* 98-02; C Bebington *Ches* from 02. *2 Wellington Road, Bebbington, Wirral CH63 7NF* Tel 0151-645 9584 E-mail burmester@hotmail.com

BURN, Geoffrey Livingston. b 60. Sydney Univ BSc83 Imp Coll Lon PhD87 St Jo Coll Dur BA95. Cranmer Hall Dur DipMin96. **d** 96 **p** 97. C St Austell *Truro* 96-03; Perm to Offic *Cant* from 03. *Barramundi, Bewsbury Cross Lane, Whitfield, Dover CT16 3EZ* Tel (01304) 820314

BURN, Mrs Helen Mary. b 64. Down Coll Cam BA86 Ox Univ PGCE88 Ex Univ MA02. SW Minl Tr Course 00. **d** 03. C Eythorne and Elvington w Waldershare etc *Cant* from 03. *Barramundi, Bewsbury Cross Lane, Whitfield, Dover CT16 3EZ* Tel (01304) 820314

BURN, Ms Kathleen Doreen. b 48. Bp Grosseteste Coll CertEd69. NY Th Sem MDiv82. **d** 82 **p** 83. USA 82-93 and from 95; TV Dunstable *St Alb* 94-95. *Address temp unknown*

BURN, Leonard Louis. b 44. K Coll Lon BD67 AKC67. **d** 68 **p** 69. C Kingswinford St Mary *Lich* 68-70; C S Ascot *Ox* 70-72; C Caversham 72-76; Chapl Selly Oak Hosp Birm 76-81; Bris City Hosp 81-82; P-in-c Bris St Mich *Bris* 81-83; R Peopleton and White Ladies Aston w Churchill etc *Worc* 83-88; V Bengeworth 88-97; Chapl St Richard's Hospice Worc 88-97; Chapl Evesham Coll 90-97; rtd 97; Perm to Offic *Glouc* from 97; *Worc* 97-98; Chapl Worcs Community and Mental Health Trust from 98. *Beckford Rise, Beckford, Tewkesbury GL20 7AN* Tel (01386) 881160

BURN, Richard James Southerden. b 34. Pemb Coll Cam BA56. Wells Th Coll 56. **d** 58 **p** 59. C Cheshunt *St Alb* 58-62; C Leighton Buzzard 65-66; C Glastonbury St Jo *B & W* 66-68; P-in-c Prestonpans *Edin* 68-71; P-in-c Stokesay *Heref* 71-75; P-in-c Dorrington 75-81; P-in-c Stapleton 75-81; P-in-c Leebotwood w Longnor 75-81; P-in-c Smethcott w Woolstaston 81; TR Melbury *Sarum* 81-87; P-in-c Quendon w Rickling and Wicken Bonhunt *Chelmsf* 87-92; R Quendon w Rickling and Wicken Bonhunt etc 92-95; rtd 95; NSM Isleworth St Fran *Lon* 95-00. *Les Grandes Vignes, Litout, 24610 Minzac, France* Tel (0033) (5) 53 80 05 81

BURN, Robert Pemberton. b 34. Peterho Cam BA56 MA60 Lon Univ PhD68. CMS Tr Coll Chislehurst 60. **d** 63 **p** 81. India 63-71; Perm to Offic *Ely* 71-81; P-in-c Foxton 81-88; Perm to Offic *Ex* from 89. *Sunnyside, Barrack Road, Exeter EX2 6AB* Tel (01392) 430028

BURN-MURDOCH, Aidan Michael. b 35. Trin Coll Cam BA60 MA63. Ridley Hall Cam 59. **d** 61 **p** 62. C Bishopwearmouth St Gabr *Dur* 61-63; Tutor Ridley Hall Cam 63-67; CMS Miss 67-70; India 68-70; R Hawick *Edin* 70-77; Bp's Co-ord of Evang *S & B* 77-81; R Reynoldston w Penrice and Llangennith 77-83; R Port Eynon w Rhosili and Llanddewi and Knelston 83-89; R Uddingston *Glas* 89-97; R Cambuslang 89-97; rtd 97; Missr Eyemouth *Edin* 98-00. *1 Hundalee Farm Cottages, Jedburgh TD8 6PA* Tel (01835) 864167

BURNET, Norman Andrew Gray. b 32. Aber Univ BEd77 Cam Univ MLitt92. Edin Th Coll 53. **d** 55 **p** 56. C Ayr *Glas* 55-58; S Africa 58-69; C St Jo Cathl Umtata 58-63; R Mt Frere 63-69; R Leven *St And* 69-72; Perm to Offic *Ab, Bre* and *Ely* 73-81; P-in-c Brinkley, Burrough Green and Carlton *Ely* 82-83; P-in-c Westley Waterless 82-83; Australia 83-84; R Fraserburgh w New Pitsligo *Ab* 85-89; P-in-c Bicker *Linc* 89; V Bicker and Wigtoft 89-97; rtd 97; Perm to Offic *Nor* 97-99; *Linc* 97-00. *61 Westlode Street, Spalding PE11 2AE* Tel (01775) 767429 Fax as telephone

BURNETT, Canon John Capenhurst. b 19. AKC49. **d** 49 **p** 50. C Shirehampton *Bris* 49-53; C Stoke Bishop 53-56; V Wroughton 56-76; RD Cricklade 70-76; Hon Can Bris Cathl 74-85; V Bris St Andr w St Bart 76-85; rtd 85; Perm to Offic *Bris* from 85. *57 Upper Cranbrook Road, Bristol BS6 7UR* Tel 0117-924 5284

BURNETT, Mrs Patricia Kay. b 38. Newnham Coll Cam MA60. Sarum Th Coll 94. **d** 97 **p** 98. NSM Jarvis Brook *Chich* from 97. *20 St Richards Road, Crowborough TN6 3AT* Tel (01892) 655668

BURNETT, Susan Mary. b 50. Lon Univ BEd73 St Jo Coll Dur DipTh76. **dss** 78 **d** 87 **p** 94. Welling *S'wark* 78-83; E Greenwich Ch Ch w St Andr and St Mich 83-91; Par Dn 87-91; Par Dn Sydenham All SS 91-94; C 94-95; C Lower Sydenham St Mich 91-95; V from 95. *St Michael's Vicarage, Champion Crescent, London SE26 4HH* Tel (020) 8778 7196

BURNETT-HALL, Mrs Karen. b 46. Bp Grosseteste Coll CertEd68 Lon Univ BD82. Oak Hill Th Coll 86. **d** 89 **p** 94. Par Dn Norbury *Ches* 89-92; NSM York St Paul *York* 93-95; NSM York St Barn 95-99; P-in-c from 00. *5 Grosvenor Terrace, York YO30 7AG* Tel (01904) 638935 E-mail karen.bh@btinternet.com

✠**BURNHAM, The Rt Revd Andrew.** b 48. New Coll Ox BA69 BA71 MA73 Westmr Coll Ox CertEd72 ARCO(CHM). St Steph Ho Ox 81. **d** 83 **p** 84 **c** 00. Hon C Clifton *S'well* 83-85; C Beeston 85-87; V Carrington 87-94; Vice-Prin St Steph Ho Ox 95-00; Suff Bp Ebbsfleet (PEV) *Cant* from 00; Hon Asst Bp *B & W, Ex, Lich* and Ox from 01. *Bishop's House, Church Lane, Dry Sandford, Abingdon OX13 6JP* Tel (01865) 390746 Fax 390611 E-mail bishop.andrew@ebbsfleet.org.uk

BURNHAM, Frank Leslie. b 23. Edin Th Coll 52. **d** 55 **p** 56. C York St Mary Bishophill Senior *York* 55-58; C Marfleet 58-62; V 62-72; TR 72-74; V Acomb St Steph 74-85; C Fulford 85-88; rtd 88; Perm to Offic *York* from 88. *Dulverton Hall, Esplanade, Scarborough YO11 2AR* Tel (01723) 340101

BURNHAM, Stephen Patrick James. b 75. Ch Ch Ox BA97. Westcott Ho Cam 00. **d** 02 **p** 03. C Vale of Belvoir Par *Leic* from 02. *The Rectory, 2 Church Lane, Redmile, Nottingham NG13 0GE* Tel (01949) 844137 Mobile 07905-882805

BURNINGHAM, Frederick George. b 34. ALCD60. **d** 60 **p** 61. C New Beckenham St Paul *Roch* 60-63; Canada 63-68 and 89-95; C Wisley w Pyrford *Guildf* 68-69; P-in-c Sydenham H Trin *S'wark* 69-71; C Broadwater St Mary *Chich* 72-77; R Sotterley, Willingham, Shadingfield, Ellough etc *St E* 77-82; R Ipswich St Clem w H Trin 82-89; P-in-c Thorndon w Rishangles, Stoke Ash, Thwaite etc 95-99; rtd 99; Perm to Offic *Bradf* from 99. *8 Meadow Rise, Skipton BD23 1BT* Tel (01756) 794440

BURNINGHAM, Richard Anthony. b 47. Keele Univ BA70 Aber Univ CQSW77 Roehampton Inst PGCE85. All Nations Chr Coll 82 Oak Hill Th Coll 94. **d** 96 **p** 97. C Reigate St Mary *S'wark* 96-00; V Weston *Win* from 00. *The Vicarage, Weston Lane, Southampton SO19 9HG* Tel (023) 8044 8421

BURNISTON, Aubrey John. b 53. St Jo Coll Dur BA. Cranmer Hall Dur. **d** 83 **p** 84. C Owton Manor *Dur* 83-86; TV Rugby St Andr *Cov* 86-93; V Heaton St Martin *Bradf* from 93; Bp's Adv in Liturgy from 00. *St Martin's Vicarage, 130 Haworth Road, Bradford BD9 6LL* Tel (01274) 543004 Fax 0870-161 7424 E-mail john@saintmartin.demon.co.uk

BURNLEY, Suffragan Bishop of. *See* GODDARD, The Rt Revd John William

BURNS, Dane. b 51. DipTh. **d** 85 **p** 86. C Enniskillen *Clogh* 85-87; I Augher w Newtownsaville and Eskrahoole 87-92; Dioc Communications Officer 91-92; I Camus-juxta-Bann *D & R* 92-96. *86 Donneybrewer Road, Eglinton, Londonderry BT47 3PD*

BURNS, Canon Edward Joseph. b 38. Liv Univ BSc58 St Cath Soc Ox BA61 MA64. Wycliffe Hall Ox 58. **d** 61 **p** 62. C Leyland St Andr *Blackb* 61-64; C Burnley St Pet 64-67; V Chorley St Jas 67-75; V Fulwood Ch Ch from 75; RD Preston 79-86; Chapl Sharoe Green Hosp Preston 81-94; Hon Can Blackb Cathl *Blackb* from 86; Bp's Adv on Hosp Chapls 89-94. *Christ Church Vicarage, 19 Vicarage Close, Fulwood, Preston PR2 8EG* Tel (01772) 719210 E-mail eddieandsheila@ejburns.freeserve.co.uk

BURNS, Canon James Denis. b 43. Lich Th Coll 69. **d** 72 **p** 73. C Gt Wyrley *Lich* 72-75; C Aldermoor *Man* 75-76; Asst Chapl Sheff Ind Miss *Sheff* 76-79; C-in-c Masborough St Paul w St Jo 76-78; C-in-c Northfield St Mich 76-78; V Rotherham St Paul, St Mich and St Jo Ferham Park 78-79; V Lancaster Ch Ch *Blackb* 79-81; V Lancaster Ch Ch w St Jo and St Anne 81-86; V Chorley St Pet 86-96; R Rufford from 96; Warden Past Assts from 96; Hon Can Blackb Cathl from 99. *St Mary's Rectory, 17 Church Road, Rufford, Ormskirk L40 1TA* Tel (01704) 821261

BURNS, John Macdonald. *See* ODA-BURNS, John Macdonald

BURNS, Michael John. b 53. AKC76. Chich Th Coll 76. **d** 77 **p** 78. C Broseley w Benthall *Heref* 77-81; C Stevenage All SS Pin Green *St Alb* 81-84; V Tattenham Corner and Burgh Heath *Guildf* 84-92; C and Chapl Younger People Milton Keynes *Ox* 92-00; P-in-c Potters Bar K Chas *St Alb* from 00. *The Vicarage, 42 Pinewood Drive, Potters Bar EN6 2BD* Tel (01707) 661266

BURNS, Robert Joseph. b 34. Wycliffe Hall Ox 67. **d** 71 **p** 72. C Portswood Ch Ch *Win* 71-73; C Woking St Jo *Guildf* 73-77; C Glas St Mary *Glas* 77; Bp's Dom Chapl 77-78; R Glas Gd Shep and Ascension 78-92; rtd 92. *clo Seaman, 25 Westfield Drive, Glasgow G52 2SG* Tel 0141-882 3363

BURNS, Stephen. b 70. Grey Coll Dur BA92 MA94 Clare Coll Cam MLitt96 Dur Univ PhD03. Ridley Hall Cam 93. **d** 96 **p** 97. C Houghton le Spring *Dur* 96-99; TV Gateshead 99-02; Dir Urban Miss Cen Cranmer Hall 99-02; Tutor Qu Coll Birm from 03. *73 Farquhar Road, Edgbaston, Birmingham B15 2QP* Tel 0121-452 2607 or 454 1527 E-mail sburns@queens.ac.uk

BURNS, Stuart Keith. b 66. Bp Grosseteste Coll BEd88 Lon Univ BD94 Leeds Univ MA95 PhD99. St Jo Coll Nottm. **d** 03. C Gt Bowden w Welham, Glooston and Cranoe etc *Leic* from 03. *The Rectory, 3 Stonton Road, Church Langton, Market Harborough LE16 7SZ* Tel (01858) 545740 E-mail s.k.burns@zetnet.co.uk

BURNS, The Rt Revd Stuart Maitland. b 46. Leeds Univ BA67. Coll of Resurr Mirfield 67. **d** 69 **p** 70. C Wyther Ven Bede *Ripon* 69-73; Asst Chapl Leeds Univ 73-77; Asst Chapl Leeds Poly 73-77; P-in-c Thornthwaite w Thruscross and Darley 77-84; V Leeds Gipton Epiphany 84-89; OSB from 89; Burford Priory from 89; Prior 96-01; Abbot from 01; Lic to Offic *Ox* from 89. *Burford Priory, Priory Lane, Burford, Oxford OX18 4SQ* Tel (01993) 823605 E-mail abbot@burfordosb.org.uk

BURNS, Stuart Sandeman. b 62. Natal Univ BA85 Ball Coll Ox BA89 MA94. St Paul's Coll Grahamstown. **d** 89 **p** 90. S Africa 89-99; C Stanger 90-91; Dir Scripture Union Ind Schs 92-94; R Drakensberg 95-97; Chapl W Prov Prep Sch 98-99; I Kinneigh

Union *C, C & R* 99-02; TV Bourne Valley *Sarum* from 02. *The Vicarage, Winterbourne Earls, Salisbury SP4 6HA* Tel (01980) 611350

BURNS, Susan Janice Cronbach. b 55. Sheff Univ BA75 CertEd76. **dss** 80 **d** 83 **p** 88. Maidenhead St Andr and St Mary *Ox* 80-82; New Zealand from 82. *Reynolds Road, RD 3, Roto-o-Rangi, Cambridge, New Zealand* Tel (0064) (7) 827 8352

BURR, Mrs Ann Pamela. b 39. S Dios Minl Tr Scheme 83. **dss** 86 **d** 87 **p** 94. Fareham H Trin *Portsm* 86-87; Hon C from 87; Hon Asst Chapl Knowle Hosp Fareham 86-90; Asst Chapl Qu Alexandra Hosp Portsm 90-92; Chapl Portsm Hosps NHS Trust from 92. *3 Bruce Close, Fareham PO16 7QJ* Tel (01329) 281375

BURR, Brian Gilbert. b 23. AKC49. St Boniface Warminster 50. **d** 50 **p** 51. C Babbacombe *Ex* 50-52; C Brixham 52-55; Lic to Offic 55; V Tideford *Truro* 56-58; V Kingswear *Ex* 58-63; V Churston Ferrers w Goodrington 63-76; RD Ipplepen 69-77; V Brixham 76-77; V Brixham w Churston Ferrers 77; R Cen Torquay 77-81; TR Torre 81-87; rtd 87; Perm to Offic *Ex* 89-91; Chapl Beauchamp Community 91-96; Perm to Offic *Worc* 97-98. *5 St Barnabas, Beauchamp Community, The Quadrangle, Newland, Malvern WR13 5AX* Tel (01684) 561044

BURR, Christopher Edward. b 68. Univ of Wales (Cardiff) BTh01. St Mich Coll Llan 98. **d** 01 **p** 02. C Llantrisant *Llan* from 01. *The Rise, Talbot Road, Talbot Green, Pontyclun CF72 8AD* Tel (01443) 239092 Fax as telephone E-mail chris.burr1@ntlworld.com

BURR, Paul David. b 62. Birm Univ LLB83. St Jo Coll Nottm MA99. **d** 99 **p** 00. C Newark *S'well* 99-02; C Eaton *Nor* from 02. *24 Carnoustie, Norwich NR4 6AY* Tel (01603) 458912

BURR, Raymond Leslie. b 43. NEOC 82 Edin Th Coll 84. **d** 85 **p** 86. C Hartlepool St Paul *Dur* 85-87; C Sherburn w Pittington 87-89; R Lyons 89-95; RD Houghton 94-96; V S Shields St Hilda w St Thos from 95. *St Hilda's Vicarage, 40 Lawe Road, South Shields NE33 2EU* Tel 0191-454 1414 E-mail ray.burr@talk21.com

BURRELL, David Philip. b 56. Southn Univ BTh90. Sarum & Wells Th Coll 85. **d** 88 **p** 89. C Ixworth and Bardwell *St E* 88-91; P-in-c Haughley w Wetherden 91-96; P-in-c Culford, W Stow and Wordwell w Flempton etc 96-98; R Lark Valley from 98. *The Rectory, West Stow, Bury St Edmunds IP28 6ET* Tel (01284) 728556

BURRELL, Godfrey John. b 49. Reading Univ BSc70 Qu Coll Ox CertEd71. Wycliffe Hall Ox 84 Th Educn Coll Johannesburg DipTh00. **d** 86 **p** 87. C Didcot All SS *Ox* 86-89; S Africa 90-01; Chapl St Alb Coll Pretoria 90-95; Chapl Pretoria Cen Prison 94-97; R Lynnwood Trin 96-01; Adn Pretoria E 00-01; R Lighthorne *Cov* from 01; V Chesterton from 01; V Newbold Pacey w Moreton Morrell from 01. *The Rectory, Church Lane, Lighthorne, Warwick CV35 0AR* Tel (01926) 651279 E-mail burrell@lighthorne.fsnet.co.uk

BURRELL, Martin John. b 61. ARCM71. Trin Coll Bris BA95. **d** 95 **p** 96. C Cant St Mary Bredin *Cant* 95-99; V Cranbrook from 99. *The Vicarage, Waterloo Road, Cranbrook TN17 3JQ* Tel (01580) 712150 E-mail mburrell@classicfm.net

BURRELL, Canon Maurice Claude. b 30. Bris Univ BA54 MA63 Lanc Univ PhD78. Tyndale Hall Bris. **d** 55 **p** 56. C Wandsworth St Steph *S'wark* 55-57; C Whitehall Park St Andr Hornsey Lane *Lon* 57-59; R Kirby Cane *Nor* 59-63; R Ellingham 61-63; Chapl K Sch Gutersloh, W Germany 63-67; R Widford *Chelmsf* 67-71; Chapl and Lect St Mary's Coll Cheltenham 71-75; Dir of Educn *Nor* 75-86; Hon Can Nor Cathl 77-95; Dioc Dir of Tr 87-95; rtd 95; Perm to Offic *Nor* from 95. *37 Ireton Close, Thorpe St Andrew, Norwich NR7 0TW* Tel (01603) 702510 E-mail maurice@37iretoncl.freeserve.co.uk

BURRIDGE, Stephen John. b 55. Univ Coll Ox BA77 MA81 Nottm Univ CertEd78 DipTh83 PhD89 SNTS95. St Jo Coll Nottm 82. **d** 85 **p** 86. C Bromley SS Pet and Paul *Roch* 85-87; Chapl Ex Univ *Ex* 87-94; Dean K Coll Lon from 94; Lic Preacher *Lon* from 94; Perm to Offic *S'wark* from 98. *King's College, Strand, London WC2R 2LS* Tel (020) 7848 2333 Fax 7848 2344 E-mail richard.burridge@kcl.ac.uk

BURRIDGE-BUTLER, Paul David. *See* BUTLER, Paul David

BURROUGHS, Edward Graham. b 35. K Coll Lon BD AKC. **d** 60 **p** 61. C Walton St Mary *Liv* 60-63; S Rhodesia 63-65; Rhodesia 65-80; Zimbabwe from 80. *Box 8045, Belmont, Bulawayo, Zimbabwe* Tel (00263) (9) 78711

BURROW, Miss Alison Sarah. b 59. Homerton Coll Cam BEd82. Westcott Ho Cam 84. **d** 87 **p** 03. Par Dn Hebden Bridge *Wakef* 87-88; Par Dn Prestwood and Gt Hampden *Ox* 88-90; Par Dn Olney w Emberton 90-92; rtd 92; Hon C Bedford St Pet w St Cuth *St Alb* from 02. *2A Waterloo Road, Bedford MK40 3PQ* Tel (01234) 315579

BURROW, Ronald. b 31. Univ Coll Dur BA55. St Steph Ho Ox 83. **d** 85 **p** 86. C Dawlish *Ex* 85-87; TV Ottery St Mary, Alfington, W Hill, Tipton etc 87-91; P-in-c Pyworthy, Pancrasweek and Bridgerule 91-95; rtd 95; Perm to Offic *Ex* from 95. *3 Riverside, Dolphin Street, Colyton EX24 6LU* Tel (01297) 553883 Fax as telephone

BURROWS, Canon Brian Albert. b 34. Lon Univ DipTh59 Atlantic Sch of Th BTh83. St Aid Birkenhead 56. **d** 59 **p** 60. C Sutton St Geo *Ches* 59-62; Canada 62-69 and from 74; V Stratton St Margaret *Bris* 70-74; Hon Can Frobisher Bay 78-80; rtd 99. *334 Mary Street, Niagara on the Lake ON, Canada, L0S 1J0*

BURROWS, Prof Clifford Robert. b 37. Univ of Wales BSc62 Lon Univ PhD69 DSc(Eng)89 MIMechE68 FIMechE82 FIEE98. Chich Th Coll 75. **d** 76 **p** 77. NSM Brighton St Pet *Chich* 76-78; NSM Brighton St Pet w Chpl Royal 78-80; NSM Brighton St Pet w Chpl Royal and St Jo 80-82; Perm to Offic *Glas* 82-85 and 86-89; NSM Clarkston 85-86; NSM Bath Ch Ch Prop Chpl *B & W* from 90. *Stonecroft, Entry Hill Drive, Bath BA2 5NL* Tel (01225) 334743 Fax 429990

BURROWS, David. b 62. Leeds Univ BA85 MA03. Linc Th Coll 86. **d** 88 **p** 89. C Kippax w Allerton Bywater *Ripon* 88-91; C Manston 91-95; Chapl Killingbeck Hosp 94; V Halifax St Anne Southowram *Wakef* 95-00; P-in-c Charlestown 95-00; V Southowram and Claremount 00-02; TV Elland from 02. *All Saints' Vicarage, Charles Street, Elland HX5 0JF* Tel (01422) 373184 E-mail fatherdavid@micromundi.net

BURROWS, David MacPherson. b 43. N Ord Course. **d** 82 **p** 83. NSM Newburgh *Liv* 82-93; NSM Newburgh w Westhead from 93. *34 Woodrow Drive, Newburgh, Wigan WN8 7LB* Tel (01257) 462948

BURROWS, Canon George Henry Jerram. b 10. TCD BA31 MA37. TCD Div Sch 31. **d** 33 **p** 38. Dioc C (Leigh) and Hd Master D'Israeli Sch 33-34; Hd Master Villiers Endowed Sch Limerick 34-47; Dioc C 41-47; Hd Master Gr High Sch Cork 47-71; Min Can Cork Cathl C, C & R 67-69; Can Cork and Ross Cathls 69-71; P-in-c Dublin St Luke *D & G* 71-78; Succ St Patr Cathl Dublin 71-77; Chan V 77-81; rtd 78; Clerical V Ch Ch Cathl Dublin *D & G* 81-90. *Gascoigne House, 33-39 Cowper Road, Rathmines, Dublin 6, Irish Republic* Tel (00353) (1) 496 9399

BURROWS, Graham Charles. b 47. Leeds Univ CertEd69 Open Univ BA81. N Ord Course 87. **d** 90 **p** 91. C Chorlton-cum-Hardy St Clem *Man* 90-93; TV Horwich 93; TV Horwich and Rivington 93-94. *29 Heaton Road, Lostock, Bolton BL6 4EE* Tel (01204) 494826

BURROWS, Jean. b 54. CertEd75. Trin Coll Bris 89. **d** 91 **p** 94. C Allesley *Cov* 91-95; C Thorley St Alb 95-99; P-in-c Harrold and Carlton w Chellington from 99. *The Rectory, 3 The Moor, Carlton, Bedford MK43 7JR* Tel (01234) 720262 E-mail jeanburrows@jeanius.me.uk

BURROWS, Canon John Edward. b 36. Leeds Univ BA60 PGCE63. Coll of Resurr Mirfield. **d** 63 **p** 65. C Much Hadham *St Alb* 63-65; Hon C Haggerston St Mary w St Chad *Lon* 65-73; P-in-c Finsbury St Clem w St Barn and St Matt 73-76; Chapl Woodbridge Sch 76-83; V Ipswich St Bart *St E* 83-03; Hon Can St E Cathl 01-03; rtd 03; Perm to Offic *St E* from 03. *55 Berners Street, Ipswich IP1 3LN* Tel (01473) 216629 E-mail burrows@freenetname.co.uk

BURROWS, Joseph Atkinson. b 32. St Aid Birkenhead 58. **d** 61 **p** 62. C Hoole *Ches* 61-67; Jamaica 67-68; C Ayr *Glas* 68-74; R Prestwick 74-78; Hon Chapl RAF 74-78; Hon Chapl RN 74-78; Australia from 78; rtd 97. *3B Cowan Road, St Ives, NSW, Australia 2075* Tel (0061) (2) 9488 9393 *or* 9488 9855 Fax 9983 9352

BURROWS, The Very Revd Michael Andrew James. b 61. TCD BA82 MA85 MLitt86 DipTh87. **d** 87 **p** 88. C Douglas Union w Frankfield C, C & R 87-91; Dean of Res TCD 91-94; Min Can St Patr Cathl Dublin 91-94; I Bandon Union C, C & R 94-02; Can Cork and Cloyne Cathls 96-02; Dean Cork from 02; I Cork St Fin Barre's Union from 02. *The Deanery, 9 Dean Street, Cork, Irish Republic* Tel and fax (00353) (21) 496 4742 *or* tel 496 3387 E-mail dean@cork.anglican.org

BURROWS, Canon Paul Anthony. b 55. Nottm Univ BA77. Gen Th Sem (NY) STM88 St Steph Ho Ox 77. **d** 79 **p** 80. C Camberwell St Giles *S'wark* 79-81; C St Helier 81-83; C Fareham SS Pet and Paul *Portsm* 83-85; USA from 85; V Union St Luke and All SS New Jersey 85-90; R Des Moines St Mark Iowa 95-01; Can Des Moines Cathl 98-01; R San Francisco Advent of Ch the K California from 01. *162 Hickory Street, San Francisco, CA 94102, USA* E-mail canonpab@earthlink.net

BURROWS, Canon Peter. b 55. BTh. Sarum & Wells Th Coll 80. **d** 83 **p** 84. C Baildon *Bradf* 83-87; R Broughton Astley *Leic* 87-95; TR Broughton Astley and Croft w Stoney Stanton 95-00; RD Guthlaxton I 94-00; Dir of Ords from 97; Hon Can Leic Cathl from 98; Par Development Officer from 00. *1 Finch Way, Narborough, Leicester LE19 2TP* Tel 0116-275 0082 E-mail pbddo@leicester.anglican.org

BURROWS, Philip Geoffrey. b 59. Birm Univ BSc80. Oak Hill Th Coll DipHE92. **d** 92 **p** 93. C Poynton *Ches* 92-96; Min Cheadle Hulme Em CD 96-03; V Mottram in Longdendale from 03. *30A Broadbottom Road, Mottram, Hyde SK14 6JB* E-mail emmanuel@domini.com

BURROWS, Samuel Reginald. b 30. AKC57. **d** 58 **p** 59. C Shildon *Dur* 58-62; C Heworth St Mary 62-67; C-in-c Leam Lane CD

67-72; C-in-c Bishopwearmouth St Mary V w St Pet CD 72-77; R Bewcastle and Stapleton *Carl* 77-82; R Harrington 82-90; P-in-c Millom 90; V 90-95; rtd 95. *40 Lindisfarne Road, Durham DH1 5YQ*

✠**BURROWS, The Rt Revd Simon Hedley.** b 28. K Coll Cam BA52 MA56. Westcott Ho Cam 52. **d** 54 **p** 55 **c** 74. C St John's Wood *Lon* 54-57; Chapl Jes Coll Cam 57-60; V Wyken *Cov* 60-67; V Fareham H Trin *Portsm* 67-71; TR 71-74; Suff Bp Buckingham *Ox* 74-87; Area Bp Buckm 87-94; rtd 94. *8 Quarry Road, Winchester SO23 0JF* Tel (01962) 853332

BURSELL, His Honour Judge Rupert David Hingston. b 42. QC86. Ex Univ LLB63 St Edm Hall Ox BA67 MA72 DPhil72. St Steph Ho Ox 67. **d** 68 **p** 69. NSM St Marylebone w H Trin *Lon* 68-69; NSM Almondsbury *Bris* 69-71; NSM Bedminster St Fran 71-75; NSM Bedminster 75-82; NSM Bris Ch Ch w St Ewen and All SS 83-88; NSM City of Bris 83-88; Lic to Offic 88-95; Lic to Offic *B & W* 72-92; Chan *Our* from 89; Chan *B & W* 92; Chan *St Alb* from 92; NSM Cheddar *B & W* from 93; Hon Can St Alb 96-02; Hon Cf from 97; Chan *Ox* from 02. *Brookside, 74 Church Road, Winscombe BS25 1BP*

BURSLEM, Christopher David Jeremy Grant. b 35. AKC85. **d** 59 **p** 60. C Bocking St Mary *Chelmsf* 59-63; C Glouc All SS *Glouc* 64-67; R Amberley 67-87; P-in-c Withington and Compton Abdale w Haselton 87-98; rtd 98; Perm to Offic *Derby* from 98. *44 Vestry Road, Oakwood, Derby DE21 2BL* Tel (01332) 830154

BURSON-THOMAS, Michael Edwin. b 52. Sarum & Wells Th Coll 84. **d** 86 **p** 87. C Bitterne Park *Win* 86-89; V Lockerley and E Dean w E and W Tytherley 89-95; P-in-c Fotherby *Linc* 95-99; Asst Local Min Officer 95-99; V Horncastle w Low Toynton from 99; R Greetham w Ashby Puerorum from 99; V High Toynton from 99; RD Horncastle from 01. *The Vicarage, 9 Langton Drive, Horncastle LN9 5AJ* Tel and fax (01507) 525564 *or* 525600 E-mail m.bursonthomas@btinternet.com

BURSTON, Richard John. b 46. ARICS70 MRTPI73 MRICS01. S Dios Minl Tr Scheme 89. **d** 93 **p** 94. Hon C Stratton St Margaret w S Marston etc *Bris* from 93. *17 Crawley Avenue, Swindon SN3 4LB* Tel (01793) 822403

BURSTON, Canon Robert Benjamin Stuart. b 45. St Chad's Coll Dur BA68 DipTh70. **d** 70 **p** 71. C Whorlton *Newc* 70-77; V Alwinton w Holystone and Alnham 77-83; TR Glendale Gp from 83; Hon Can Newc Cathl from 95. *The Rectory, 5 Fenton Drive, Wooler NE71 6DT* Tel (01668) 281551 Fax as telephone

BURT, David Alan. b 44. K Alfred's Coll Win BTh98. STETS 95. **d** 98 **p** 99. NSM Goring-by-Sea *Chich* 98-03; C from 03. *15 Fernhurst Drive, Goring-by-Sea, Worthing BN12 5AU* Tel (01903) 248671 Fax as telephone

BURT, Leslie Reginald. b 22. ACIS49. St Aug Coll Cant 65. **d** 66 **p** 67. C Petersfield w Sheet *Portsm* 66-70; Perm to Offic from 82. *44B Victoria Road South, Southsea PO5 2BT* Tel (023) 9273 0989

BURT, Noel Bryce. b 21. Clare Coll Cam BA49 MA53. Cuddesdon Coll 49. **d** 51 **p** 52. C York St Olave w St Giles *York* 51-54; C Scarborough St Martin 54-56; V Scarborough St Sav 56-61; V Sledmere 61-67; R Cowlam 61-67; R Invergowrie *Bre* 67-76; R Glencarse 71-76; V Denton and Ingleton *Dur* 76-88; rtd 88. *49 Balmer Hill, Gainford, Darlington DL2 3EL* Tel (01325) 730075

BURT, Paul Andrew. b 52. Leeds Univ BA74 K Coll Lon MA02. Ridley Hall Cam 82. **d** 84 **p** 85. C Edin St Thos *Edin* 84-88; CMS Bahrain 88-90; R Melrose *Edin* 91-00; Chapl Borders Gen Hosp NHS Trust 93-98; Ho Master Win Coll from 00; Hd RS Pilgrims' Sch from 00. *53-64 Kingsgate Street, Winchester SO23 9PE* Tel (01962) 853435 E-mail pburt@pilgrims-winchester.hants.sch.uk

BURT, Roger Malcolm. b 45. MBE91. St Jo Coll Auckland LTh74 SSC. **d** 73 **p** 74. V Tinui New Zealand 73-80; P-in-c Colton *Nor* 80; P-in-c Easton 80; V Easton w Colton and Marlingford 80-88; CF 88-01; P-in-c E Coker w Sutton Bingham and Closworth *B & W* from 01. *The Vicarage, East Coker, Yeovil BA22 9JG* Tel (01935) 862125

BURTON, Andrew John. b 63. St Kath Coll Liv BA84 Cert Div84. Cranmer Hall Dur 86. **d** 88 **p** 89. C Harlescott *Lich* 88-91; C Ches H Trin *Ches* 91-94; P-in-c Congleton St Jas 94-01; R Calton, Cauldon, Grindon, Waterfall etc *Lich* from 01; RD Alstonfield from 03; SBStJ from 01. *The Vicarage, Waterfall Lane, Waterhouses, Stoke-on-Trent ST10 3HT* Tel (01538) 308506 E-mail ajburton@fish.co.uk

BURTON, Antony William James. b 29. Ch Coll Cam BA52 MA56. Cuddesdon Coll 52. **d** 54 **p** 55. C Linc St Nic w St Jo Newport *Linc* 54-57; C Croydon *Cant* 57-62; V Winterton *Linc* 62-82; V Roxby w Risby 70-82; RD Manlake 76-82; V Nettleham 82-94; rtd 94; Perm to Offic *Linc* from 94-02. *28 Eastfield Road, Messingham, Scunthorpe DN17 3PG* Tel (01724) 763916

BURTON, Christopher Paul. b 38. FCA75 Bris Univ PhD00. Clifton Th Coll 64. **d** 69 **p** 70. C Wandsworth All SS *S'wark* 69-72; C York St Paul *York* 72-75; V Castle Vale *Birm* 75-83; R Gt Parndon *Chelmsf* 82-99; TR 99-03; rtd 03. *The Hermitage, Constitution Hill, Sudbury CO10 2PT*

BURTON, Daniel John Ashworth. b 63. Regent's Park Coll Ox BA88 MA93 Heythrop Coll Lon MTh93. St Mich Coll Llan 93. **d** 94 **p** 95. C Mountain Ash *Llan* 94-97; R St Brides Minor w Bettws 97-02; R St Brides Minor w Bettws w Aberkenfig 02-03; P-in-c Cheetham *Man* from 03. *The Vicarage, 105 Brideoak Street, Manchester M8 0AY* E-mail daniel.burton2@virgin.net

BURTON, David Alan. b 53. St Jo Coll Dur BA. Westcott Ho Cam 81. **d** 84 **p** 85. C Bedford St Andr *St Alb* 84-87; C Leighton Buzzard w Eggington, Hockliffe etc 87-91; V Kingsbury Episcopi w E Lambrook *B & W* 91-94; V Kingsbury Episcopi w E Lambrook, Hambridge etc 94-95; R Bishops Lydeard w Bagborough and Cothelstone 95-03. *1 Summer Close, Hemyock, Cullompton EX15 3PA* E-mail david.burton@dial.pipex.com

BURTON, Desmond Jack. b 49. Sarum & Wells Th Coll 70. **d** 73 **p** 74. C Lakenham St Jo *Nor* 73-77; C Gt Yarmouth 77-80; R Tidworth *Sarum* 80-83; Chapl HM Pris Pentonville 83-84; Chapl HM Pris Standford Hill 84-88; Chapl HM Pris Swaleside 88-93; Chapl HM Pris Roch 93-99; Chapl HM Pris Whitemoor from 99. *HM Prison Whitemoor, Longhill Road, March PE15 0PR* Tel (01354) 650783 Fax 660653

BURTON, Edward Arthur. b 15. Tyndale Hall Bris 39. **d** 42 **p** 43. C Tipton St Martin *Lich* 42-45; P-in-c W Derby St Nath Windsor *Liv* 45-46; C Morden *S'wark* 46-49; V Birm Bp Ryder *Birm* 49-51; V Tipton St Paul *Lich* 51-55; V Tibshelf *Derby* 55-63; V Beckford w Ashton under Hill *Glouc* 63-78; rtd 78; Perm to Offic *Chich* from 83. *B5 Hatfield Court, Salisbury Road, Hove BN3 3AA* Tel (01273) 727560

BURTON, Graham John. b 45. Bris Univ BA69. Tyndale Hall Bris 69. **d** 71 **p** 72. C Leic St Chris *Leic* 71-75; C Southall Green St Jo *Lon* 75-79; CMS Pakistan 80-92; P-in-c Basford w Hyson Green *S'well* 92-99; P-in-c Hyson Green and Forest Fields 99-01; Assoc P from 01; Dir Rainbow Project from 01. *All Saints' Vicarage, 16 All Saints Street, Radford NG7 4DP* Tel 0115-978 2760

BURTON, Hugh Anthony. b 56. Edin Univ BD79. Cranmer Hall Dur 81. **d** 83 **p** 84. C Coalville and Bardon Hill *Leic* 83-87; P-in-c Packington w Normanton-le-Heath 87-92; V 92-96; TV Kidderminster St Geo *Worc* from 96. *38 Comberton Avenue, Kidderminster DY10 3EG* Tel (01562) 824490 E-mail hburton@wfcsmail.com

BURTON, Leslie Samuel Bertram. b 23. **d** 91 **p** 92. NSM St Cleer *Truro* 91-93; Perm to Offic 93-00. *29 Vivian Court, Truro TR1 2TR*

BURTON, Michael John. b 55. Leeds Univ BSc76 Leeds Poly BSc80. St Jo Coll Nottm LTh88. **d** 88 **p** 89. C Charles w Plymouth St Matthias *Ex* 88-92; V Paignton St Paul Preston 92-99; TV Almondbury w Farnley Tyas *Wakef* 99-02; V Roade and Ashton w Hartwell *Pet* from 02. *The Vicarage, 18 Hartwell Road, Roade, Northampton NN7 2NT* Tel (01604) 862284

BURTON, Nicholas John. b 52. St Steph Ho Ox 77. **d** 80 **p** 81. C Leic St Matt and St Geo *Leic* 80-82; C Leic Resurr 82-83; TV 83-88; C Narborough and Huncote 88-90; R from 90. *All Saints' Rectory, 15 Church View, Narborough, Leicester LE19 2GY* Tel 0116-275 0388

BURTON, Norman George. b 30. N Ord Course. **d** 83 **p** 84. C Rothwell w Lofthouse *Ripon* 83-86; C Rothwell 86-87; V Lofthouse 87-96; rtd 96; Perm to Offic *Ripon* from 96. *28 Temple Row Close, Colton, Leeds LS15 9HR* Tel 0113-260 1129

BURTON, Richard Peter. b 56. Nottm Univ BA80. Cranmer Hall Dur 80. **d** 82 **p** 83. C Linthorpe *York* 82-85; R Bishop Burton w Walkington 85-91; V Tadcaster w Newton Kyme from 91; RD New Ainsty from 01. *The Vicarage, 78 Station Road, Tadcaster LS24 9JR* Tel (01937) 833394 E-mail richard@burtclan.freeserve.co.uk

BURTON, Mrs Virginia Ann. b 55. St As Minl Tr Course 00. **d** 03. C Llanrhos *St As* from 03. *Siabod, Tyddyn Mali, Llanddoged, Llanrwst LL26 0DZ* Tel (01492) 640636 E-mail ginny_burton@hotmail.com

BURTON EVANS, David. See EVANS, David Burton

BURTON-JONES, Simon David. b 62. Em Coll Cam BA84 MA88 Nottm Univ BTh92 MA93. St Jo Coll Nottm 90. **d** 93 **p** 94. C Darwen St Pet w Hoddlesden *Blackb* 93-96; C Biggin Hill *Roch* 96-98; P-in-c Plaistow St Mary 98-00; V from 00; RD Bromley from 01. *St Mary's Vicarage, 74 London Lane, Bromley BR1 4HE* Tel (020) 8460 1827 Fax as telephone E-mail sburtonjo@aol.com

BURTT, Andrew Keith. b 50. Massey Univ (NZ) BA72 MA74 DipEd76. St Jo Coll (NZ) LTh82. **d** 81 **p** 82. New Zealand 81-83; CF 84-92; Sen Chapl Brighton Coll 93-03; Chapl Portsm Gr Sch from 03. *8 Penny Street, Portsmouth PO1 2NH*

BURTWELL, Stanley Peter. b 32. Leeds Univ BA55. Coll of Resurr Mirfield 55. **d** 57 **p** 58. C Leeds St Hilda *Ripon* 57-61; S Africa 61-72; P-in-c Gt Hanwood *Heref* 72-78; R 78-83; RD Pontesbury 80-83; V Upper Norwood St Jo *Cant* 83-84; V Upper Norwood St Jo *S'wark* 85-90; RD Croydon N 85-90; TR Bourne Valley *Sarum* 90-97; rtd 97; Perm to Offic *Sarum* from 97. *Splinters, 116 High Street, Swanage BN19 2NY* Tel (01929) 421785

BURUNDI, Archbishop of. *See* NDAYISENGA, The Most Revd Samuel

BURY, Miss Dorothy Jane. b 53. St Hild Coll Dur CertEd75 Lanc Univ BA96 MA98. Ripon Coll Cuddesdon 00. **d** 02 **p** 03. C Thornton-le-Fylde *Blackb* from 02. *2 Blackthorn Close, Thornton-Cleveleys FY5 2ZA* Tel (01253) 862451 Mobile 07715-560031 E-mail tillybury@tiscali.co.uk

BURY, Herbert John Malcolm. b 28. Linc Coll Ox BA52 MA56. Roch Th Coll 68. **d** 69 **p** 70. C Bexleyheath Ch Ch *Roch* 69-72; V Ryarsh w Birling 72-83; P-in-c Addington w Trottiscliffe 76-83; R Knockholt w Halstead 83-93; rtd 93; Perm to Offic *Chich* from 93. *Star Cottage, High Street, Burwash, Etchingham TN19 7HA* Tel (01435) 882326

BURY, The Very Revd Nicholas Ayles Stillingfleet. b 43. Qu Coll Cam BA65 MA69 Ch Ch Ox MA71. Cuddesdon Coll. **d** 68 **p** 69. C Liv Our Lady and St Nic *Liv* 68-71; Chapl Ch Ch Ox 71-75; V Stevenage St Mary Shephall *St Alb* 75-84; V St Peter-in-Thanet *Cant* 84-97; RD Thanet 93-97; Hon Can Cant Cathl 94-97; Dean Glouc from 97. *The Deanery, 1 Miller's Green, Gloucester GL1 2BP* Tel (01452) 524167 E-mail deanglos@uk.gateway.net

BUSBY, Ian Frederick Newman. b 32. Roch Th Coll 61. **d** 64 **p** 65. C Bedale *Ripon* 64-67; C Stevenage St Geo *St Alb* 67-71; V Stevenage St Mary Shephall 71-75; V Kildwick *Bradf* 75-92; rtd 93; Perm to Offic *Bradf* from 93. *65 Main Street, Farnhill, Keighley BD20 9BJ* Tel (01535) 633001

BUSBY, Jack Wright. b 12. Leeds Univ BA35. Coll of Resurr Mirfield 35. **d** 37 **p** 38. C Sneinton St Steph *S'well* 37-41; C Hucknall Torkard 41-47; Chapl Newstead Abbey and Colliery 47-56; V Blidworth 56-66; V Goxhill *Linc* 66-70; R Barkestone cum Plungar and Redmile *Leic* 70-77; rtd 77; Perm to Offic *Linc* from 77. *c/o Mrs V Hargrave, 110 Woodhall Drive, Waltham, Grimsby DN37 0DF*

BUSBY, John. b 38. St Cath Coll Cam MA60 CEng. Local Minl Tr Course. **d** 93 **p** 94. OLM Worplesdon *Guildf* 93-02; NSM Pirbright from 02. *Iona, Fox Corner, Worplesdon, Guildford GU3 3PP* Tel (01483) 234562

BUSFIELD, Miss Lynn Maria. b 60. Trin Coll Bris ADPS97 BA99. **d** 99 **p** 00. C Scartho *Linc* from 99. *25 Waltham Road, Grimsby DN33 2LY* Tel (01472) 870373 E-mail lynn.busfield@virgin.net

BUSH, Mrs Ann Kathleen. b 47. MATCA65. Marlow Past Foundn Dip Counselling 90 Ox Min Course 90. **d** 93 **p** 94. NSM Warfield *Ox* 93-96; Dep Chapl HM Pris Wormwood Scrubs 96-97; Chapl HM Pris Reading 97-99; Sen Chapl HM Pris Feltham 99-01; Canada from 01. *PO Box 24, Fort Smith NT, Canada, X0E 0P0* Tel (001) (867) 872 3438 E-mail abush@auroranet.nt.ca

BUSH, David. b 25. FRIBA47 Liv Univ BArch47. S'wark Ord Course 73. **d** 77 **p** 77. C Douglas St Geo and St Barn *S & M* 77-80; Chapl Ballamona Hosp and Cronk Grianagh 80-86; V Marown 80-87; R The Rissingtons *Glouc* 87-92; rtd 92; Perm to Offic *Glouc* 92-98; Perm to Offic *Ely* from 99. *12 Kentwell Place, Burwell, Cambridge CB5 0RT* Tel (01638) 741839

BUSH, George Raymond. b 57. St Jo Coll Cam BA81 MA84 Univ of Wales LLM95. Ripon Coll Cuddesdon BA84 MA88. **d** 85 **p** 86. C Leeds St Aid *Ripon* 85-89; Chapl St Jo Coll Cam 89-94; V Hoxton St Anne w St Columba *Lon* 94-02; R St Mary le Bow w St Pancras Soper Lane etc from 02. *The Rector's Lodgings, Cheapside, London EC2V 6AU* Tel (020) 7248 5139 E-mail grbush@london.anglican.org

BUSH, Mrs Glenda. b 41. N Ord Course 92. **d** 95 **p** 96. NSM Bolton St Phil *Man* 95-99; C 99-02; C Bolton SS Simon and Jude 99-02; P-in-c from 02. *46 Mary Street West, Horwich, Bolton BL6 7JU* Tel (01204) 691539

BUSH, Mrs Kathryn Ann. b 60. OLM course 95. **d** 99 **p** 00. OLM Mareham-le-Fen and Revesby *Linc* from 99; OLM Mareham on the Hill from 99; OLM Hameringham w Scrafield and Winceby from 99. *Wheatsheaf Farm, Chapel Lane, New Bolingbroke, Boston PE22 7LF* Tel (01205) 480631 Mobile 07775-736344

BUSH, Canon Roger Charles. b 56. K Coll Lon BA78 Leeds Univ BA85. Coll of Resurr Mirfield 83. **d** 86 **p** 87. C Newbold w Dunston *Derby* 86-90; TV Leic Resurr *Leic* 90-94; TR Redruth w Lanner and Treleigh *Truro* from 94; RD Carnmarth N from 96; Hon Can Truro Cathl from 03. *The Rectory, 53 Clinton Road, Redruth TR15 2LP* Tel (01209) 215258 E-mail roger.bush@btinternet.com

BUSHAU, Reginald Francis. b 49. Shimer Coll Illinois AB71. St Steph Ho Ox BA73 MA98. **d** 74 **p** 75. C Deptford St Paul *S'wark* 74-77; C Willesden St Andr *Lon* 77; C Gladstone Park St Fran 77-82; P-in-c Brondesbury St Anne w Kilburn H Trin 83-88; V Paddington St Mary Magd 88-97; AD Westmr Paddington 92-97; P-in-c S Kensington St Steph 96-98; V from 98. *9 Eldon Road, London W8 5PU* Tel (020) 7937 5083 E-mail rfbushau@compuserve.com

BUSHBY, Michael Reginald. b 42. LSE BSc70 Leeds Univ MA97. **d** 02 **p** 03. NSM S Cave and Ellerker w Broomfleet *York* from 02. *The Vicarage, Mill Hill, Ellerker, Brough HU15 2DG* Tel (01430) 422757

BUSHELL, Anthony Colin. b 59. Pemb Coll Ox MA82 Barrister 83. S'wark Ord Course 93. **d** 96 **p** 97. NSM Felsted and Lt Dunmow *Chelmsf* 96-98; NSM Stanway from 98. *Pump Hall,*

Middle Green, Wakes Colne, Colchester CO6 2BJ Tel (01787) 222487 Fax 222361

BUSHELL, Roy. b 32. NW Ord Course 75. **d** 79 **p** 80. NSM Croft w Southworth *Liv* 79-87; C Netherton 87-89; R Newton in Makerfield Em 89-97; rtd 97; Perm to Offic *Bradf* from 98. *34 Maple Avenue, Whitley Bay NE25 8JS* Tel 0191-251 9816

BUSHELL, Stephen Lionel. b 60. K Coll Lon BA84. Ripon Coll Cuddesdon 92. **d** 94 **p** 95. C Exhall *Cov* 94-97; Asst Chapl Aylesbury Vale Community Healthcare NHS Trust from 97; Asst P Shelswell *Ox* from 97. *St Fergus Cottage, Cottisford, Brackley NN13 5SW* Tel (01280) 847979
E-mail tostephenbushell@hotmail.com

BUSK, David Westly. b 60. Magd Coll Cam BA. Cranmer Hall Dur. **d** 89 **p** 90. C Old Swinford Stourbridge *Worc* 89-93; USPG Japan from 94; V Nagasaki H Trin from 95. *Holy Trinity Church, Oura-Machi 1-6, Nagasaki 850-90-21, Japan* Tel (0081) (958) 230455

BUSK, Horace. b 34. Clifton Th Coll 56. **d** 60 **p** 61. C Burton All SS *Lich* 60-63; Paraguay 63-66; C Silverhill St Matt *Chich* 66-67; Lic to Offic *Sarum* 67-69; C W Kilburn St Luke w St Simon and St Jude *Lon* 69-74; TV Ashwellthorpe w Wreningham *Nor* 74-81; TV Wreningham 81; P-in-c Meysey Hampton w Marston Meysey and Castle Eaton *Glouc* 81-82; R from 82. *The Rectory, Church Street, Meysey Hampton, Cirencester GL7 5JX* Tel (01285) 851249

BUSS, Gerald Vere Austen. b 36. CCC Cam PhD87. St Steph Ho Ox 59. **d** 63 **p** 64. C Petersham *S'wark* 63-66; C Brompton H Trin *Lon* 66-69; Asst Chapl Hurstpierpoint Coll 70-73; Chapl 74-90; Ho Master 90-94; History teacher 94-96; rtd 96. *Souches, The Street, Albourne, Hassocks BN6 9DJ* Tel (01273) 832465 Fax as telephone

BUSS, Philip Hodnett. b 37. Ch Coll Cam BA59 MA63. Tyndale Hall Bris 61. **d** 63 **p** 64. Tutor Lon Coll of Div 62-66; Chapl 66-69; Hon C Northwood Em *Lon* 63-70; V Fulham Ch Ch 74-82; V Handsworth Woodhouse *Sheff* 70-74; V Woking St Pet *Guildf* 82-88; Hon C Ham St Rich *S'wark* 94-98; rtd 02. *5 Kings Square, Bridport DT6 3QE* Tel 07748-912380 (mobile)

BUSSELL, Ian Paul. b 62. Reading Univ BA84 Kingston Poly PGCE85. Qu Coll Birm MA98. **d** 98 **p** 99. C Twickenham St Mary *Lon* 98-01; TV Godalming *Guildf* from 01. *St Mark's Vicarage, 29 Franklyn Road, Godalming GU7 2LD* Tel (01483) 424710 E-mail st-marks@supanet.com

BUSSELL, Ronald William. b 34. CA Tr Coll 57 St Deiniol's Hawarden 81. **d** 83 **p** 84. C Claughton cum Grange *Ches* 83-85; P-in-c Preston St Oswald *Blackb* 85-87; V Fleetwood St Nic 87-93; Dioc Chapl MU 91-95; R Tarleton 93-95; rtd 95; Perm to Offic *Blackb* from 95. *4 Willoughby Avenue, Thornton-Cleveleys FY5 2BW* Tel (01253) 820067 E-mail ron.bussell@talk21.com

BUSSEY, Norman. b 22. Clifton Th Coll 63. **d** 65 **p** 66. C Upton (Overchurch) *Ches* 65-69; V Bradley *Wakef* 69-88; rtd 88; Perm to Offic *Glouc* from 88. *43 Crispin Road, Winchcombe, Cheltenham GL54 5JX* Tel (01242) 602754

BUSSEY, Rachel Anne. STETS. **d** 03. NSM Durrington *Sarum* from 03. *3 Birchwood Drive, Durrington, Salisbury SP4 8ER* Tel 07899-926034 (mobile) E-mail rachel.bussey@ntlworld.com

BUSTARD, Guy Nicholas. b 51. K Coll Lon BD77 AKC77. St Steph Ho Ox 77. **d** 78 **p** 79. C Hythe *Cant* 78-81; Chapl RN 81-85; V Haddenham and Wilburton *Ely* 85-89; Chapl Qu Eliz Hosp Welwyn Garden City 89-92; Chapl E Herts NHS Trust 92-00; Chapl E and N Herts NHS Trust from 00. *The Chaplain's Office, Queen Elizabeth II Hospital, Welwyn Garden City AL7 4HQ* Tel (01707) 328111

BUSTIN, Canon Peter Ernest. b 32. Qu Coll Cam BA56 MA60. Tyndale Hall Bris 56. **d** 57 **p** 58. C Welling *Roch* 57-60; C Farnborough *Guildf* 60-62; V Hornsey Rise St Mary *Lon* 62-70; R Barnwell *Pet* 70-88; RD Oundle 76-84; P-in-c Luddington w Hemington and Thurning 77-78; R Barnwell w Thurning and Luddington 78-84; V Southwold *St E* 84-97; RD Halesworth 90-95; Hon Can St E Cathl 91-97; rtd 97; Perm to Offic *St E* from 97. *55 College Street, Bury St Edmunds IP33 1NH* Tel (01284) 767708 E-mail bustin@saintedmunds.vispa.com

BUSTIN, Peter Laurence. b 54. St Steph Ho Ox. **d** 83 **p** 84. C Northolt St Mary *Lon* 83-86; C Pimlico St Pet w Westmr Ch Ch 86-88; C Heston 88-91; P-in-c Twickenham All SS 91-98; V from 98. *All Saints' Vicarage, 18 Belmont Road, Twickenham TW2 2DA* Tel (020) 8894 3580 Fax as telephone
E-mail 040471@email.msn.com

BUTCHER, Andrew John. b 43. Trin Coll Cam BA66 MA69. Cuddesdon Coll 66. **d** 68 **p** 69. C Sheff St Mark Broomhall *Sheff* 68-70; P-in-c Louth H Trin *Linc* 70-72; Chapl RAF 72-87; Lic to Offic *Ox* 85-87; TR Cove St Jo *Guildf* 87-91; V Egham Hythe 91-98; V Docking, the Birchams, Stanhoe and Sedgeford *Nor* from 98. *The Vicarage, Sedgeford Road, Docking, King's Lynn PE31 8PN* Tel and fax (01485) 518247 Mobile 07887-506876
E-mail andrewj.butcher@virgin.net

BUTCHER, David John. b 46. STETS 00. **d** 03. NSM Fareham SS Pet and Paul *Portsm* from 03. *44 Old Turnpike, Fareham PO16 7HA* Tel (01329) 235186 E-mail d.j.butcher@tesco.net

BUTCHER, Edwin William. b 39. Portsm Dioc Tr Course 91. **d** 92. NSM Ryde All SS *Portsm* from 92. *23 Quarry Road, Ryde PO33 2TX* Tel (01983) 616889

BUTCHER, Hubert Maxwell. b 24. Ch Coll Cam BA48 MA53. Trin Coll Toronto BD68 San Francisco Th Sem DMin78 Wycliffe Hall Ox 49. **d** 51 **p** 52. C Tunbridge Wells St Jo *Roch* 51-53; India 54-58; P-in-c Bradf St Jo *Bradf* 58-62; Canada from 63; rtd 88. *Box 129, Sorrento BC, Canada, V0E 2W0* Tel (001) (250) 675 2783

BUTCHER, Philip Warren. b 46. Trin Coll Cam BA68 MA70. Cuddesdon Coll 68. **d** 70 **p** 71. C Bris St Mary Redcliffe w Temple etc *Bris* 70-73; Hon C W Wickham St Fran *Cant* 73-78; Chapl Abingdon Sch 78-85; Chapl Nor Sch 85-98; V Horsford and Horsham w Newton St Faith *Nor* from 98. *The Vicarage, 35 Corner Lane, Horsford, Norwich NR10 3DG* Tel (01603) 893537

BUTCHER, Richard Peter. b 50. St Chad's Coll Dur BA71. Chich Th Coll 73. **d** 74 **p** 75. C Yeovil St Mich *B & W* 74-77; Chapl Wellingborough Sch 77-83; R Gt w Lt Billing *Pet* 83-88; Chapl Bp Stopford Sch Kettering 88-90; Perm to Offic *Pet* 90-01. *55 Field Street, Kettering NN16 8EN*

BUTCHERS, Mark Andrew. b 59. Trin Coll Cam BA81 Southn Univ BTh87 K Coll Lon MTh90. Chich Th Coll 84. **d** 87 **p** 88. C Chelsea St Luke *Lon* 87; C Chelsea St Luke and Ch Ch 87-90; C Mitcham SS Pet and Paul *S'wark* 90-93; R N Tawton, Bondleigh, Sampford Courtenay etc *Ex* 93-99; Chapl and Fell Keble Coll Ox from 99. *Keble College, Oxford OX1 3PG, or 7 Osberton Road, Oxford OX2 7NU* Tel (01865) 272725 *or* 428738
E-mail mark.butchers@keble.ox.ac.uk

BUTLAND, Cameron James. b 58. BA. Ripon Coll Cuddesdon 81. **d** 84 **p** 85. C Tettenhall Regis *Lich* 84-88; V Bodicote *Ox* 88-95; TR Witney from 95; RD Witney 97-02; AD from 03. *The Rectory, 13 Station Lane, Witney OX8 6BH* Tel (01993) 200323
E-mail cbutland@ukgateway.net

BUTLAND, Canon Godfrey John. b 51. Grey Coll Dur BA72. Wycliffe Hall Ox 73. **d** 75 **p** 76. C Much Woolton *Liv* 75-78; Bp's Dom Chapl 78-81; V Everton St Geo 81-94; AD Liv N 89-94; V Allerton from 94; AD Liv S from 00; Hon Can Liv Cathl from 03. *Allerton Vicarage, Harthill Road, Liverpool L18 3HU* Tel 0151-724 1561

BUTLAND, William Edwin (Joe). b 09. St Andr Coll Pampisford 48 Lon Coll of Div 49. **d** 51 **p** 52. C Kentish Town *Lon* 51-54; C Chorleywood Ch Ch *St Alb* 54-58; P-in-c Colney Heath St Mark 58-59; V 59-80; rtd 80; Perm to Offic *St Alb* 80-01. *4 The Spinney, Long Lawford, Rugby CV23 9SH* Tel (01788) 578245

BUTLER, Alan. b 53. Carl Dioc Tr Inst 89. **d** 89 **p** 90. NSM Flookburgh *Carl* 89-93; C Maryport 93-96; C Flimby 93-96; P-in-c 96-98; TV Saltash *Truro* from 98. *The Vicarage, St Stephen by Saltash, Saltash PL12 4AB* Tel (01752) 842323

BUTLER, Alan. b 57. Leic Univ BA78. Coll of Resurr Mirfield 80. **d** 83 **p** 84. C Skerton St Luke *Blackb* 83-87; C Birch w Fallowfield *Man* 87-90; V Claremont H Angels 90-95; Chapl Pendleton Coll 95-99; TV Pendleton *Man* 95-99; P-in-c High Crompton from 99. *St Mary's Vicarage, 18 Rushcroft Road, Shaw, Oldham OL2 7PR* Tel and fax (01706) 847455
E-mail alanbutler@freenetname.co.uk

BUTLER, Canon Alan John. b 30. Kelham Th Coll 51. **d** 56 **p** 57. S Africa 56-65 and 79-95; Bechuanaland 65-66; Botswana 66-70; V Fletchamstead *Cov* 71-79; Adn Griqualand W 79-85; Adn Kuruman 79-85; Dir Moffat Miss, Kuruman 81-95; TV Hanley H Ev *Lich* 95; rtd 95; Perm to Offic *Sarum* from 95; Perm to Offic *Win* from 95. *4 Osborne Road, Wimborne BH21 1BL* Tel (01202) 848859

BUTLER, Ms Angela Elizabeth. b 31. Studley Coll Dip Horticulture 53. Gilmore Ho 60 DipTh64 Lambeth STh64. **dss** 81 **d** 87 **p** 94. Cookham *Ox* 81-86; Wheatley w Forest Hill and Stanton St John 86-97; Hon Par Dn 87-89; NSM 89-97; NSM Wheatley 97-01; Perm to Offic from 02. *10 River Gardens, Purley-on-Thames, Reading RG8 8BX* Tel 0118-942 2055

BUTLER, Angela Madeline. b 47. Oak Hill NSM Course 87. **d** 90 **p** 94. Hon Par Dn Chipperfield St Paul *St Alb* 90-93; Dn-in-c 93-94; P-in-c 94-01; Staff Oak Hill Th Coll 93-97; Springboard Missr 97-01; Dioc Springboard Missr *Glouc* from 01; P-in-c Hempsted from 01. *The Rectory, Rectory Lane, Hempsted, Gloucester GL2 5LW* Tel (01452) 523025 Fax 524592
E-mail angela.butler@talk21.com

BUTLER, Betty. b 47. **d** 96. NSM Sully *Llan* 96-97; NSM Merthyr Dyfan from 98. *10 Nurston Close, Rhoose, Barry CF62 3EF* Tel (01446) 710822

BUTLER, Christopher. b 67. St Jo Coll Nottm. **d** 01 **p** 02. C Retford *S'well* from 01. *1 Chapel Gate, Retford DN22 6PL* Tel (01777) 719908 E-mail crbutler@bigfoot.com

BUTLER, Christopher John. b 25. Leeds Univ BA50. Chich Th Coll 50. **d** 52 **p** 53. C Kensington St Mary Abbots w St Geo *Lon* 52-57; Australia 57-59; V Blackmoor *Portsm* 60-70; V Wellingborough St Andr *Pet* 70-79; P-in-c Garsington *Ox* 79-83; R Garsington and Horspath 83-95; rtd 95; Perm to Offic *Portsm, Chich, Guildf* and *Win* from 95. *33 Oak Tree Road, Whitehill, Bordon GU35 9DF* Tel (01420) 475311

BUTLER, Colin Sydney. b 59. Bradf Univ BSc81. Wycliffe Hall Ox 81. **d** 84 **p** 85. C Farsley *Bradf* 84-87; C Bradf St Aug Undercliffe 87-89; P-in-c Darlaston All SS *Lich* 89-95; Ind Missr 89-95; TR Chell 95-99; CF from 99. *c/o MOD Chaplains (Army)* Tel (01980) 615804 Fax 615800

BUTLER, The Ven Cuthbert Hilary. b 13. St Jo Coll Cam BA35 MA39. Westcott Ho Cam 37. **d** 40 **p** 41. C Preston *Chich* 40-42; Chapl RNVR 42-46; P-in-c Brighton St Matthias *Chich* 46-47; V 47-51; R Crawley 51-58; Canada 58-84; Adn Colombia 77-78; rtd 78; Perm to Offic *Ex* 85-98. *Running Waters, Winsford, Minehead TA24 7JF* Tel (01643) 851250

BUTLER, David Edwin. b 56. ACA83 Jes Coll Ox BA79 BA86. St Steph Ho Ox MA87. **d** 87 **p** 88. C Hulme Ascension *Man* 87-90; V Patricroft 90-94; Perm to Offic *Liv* from 97; Hon C Prestwich St Hilda *Man* from 00. *30 Windsor Road, Prestwich, Manchester M25 0FF*

BUTLER, Derek John. b 53. Aston Univ BSc74 St Jo Coll York PGCE75. St Jo Coll Dur 79. **d** 82 **p** 83. C Bramcote *S'well* 82-86; Perm to Offic *Roch* 86-88; Perm to Offic *Portsm* 86-92; Lon and SE Co-ord CPAS 86-88; NSM Bromley Ch Ch *Roch* 88-91; NSM Chesham Bois *Ox* from 92. *121 Woodside Road, Amersham HP6 6AL* Tel (01494) 724577

BUTLER, Donald Arthur. b 31. **d** 79 **p** 80. Hon C Apsley End *St Alb* 79-80; Hon C Chambersbury from 80. *143 Belswains Lane, Hemel Hempstead HP3 9UZ*

BUTLER, George James. b 53. AKC74 Kent Univ MA95. St Aug Coll Cant 75. **d** 76 **p** 77. C Ellesmere Port *Ches* 76-79; C Eastham 79-81; Chapl RAF 81-83; C W Kirby St Bridget *Ches* 83-84; V Newton 84-86; CF 86-91; V Folkestone St Sav *Cant* 91-99; P-in-c Wool and E Stoke *Sarum* from 99. *The Vicarage, Wool, Wareham BH20 6EB* Tel (01929) 462215

BUTLER, George William. b 52. CITC DipTh. **d** 90 **p** 91. C Drung w Castleterra, Larah and Lavey etc *K, E & A* 90-93; I 93-95; I Castlemacadam w Ballinaclash, Aughrim etc *D & G* from 95. *The Rectory, Castlemacadam, Avoca, Co Wicklow, Irish Republic* Tel and fax (00353) (402) 35127 Mobile 087-679 5625

BUTLER, Henry. b 25. Ridley Hall Cam 73. **d** 75 **p** 76. C Cambridge St Paul *Ely* 75-77; P-in-c Stilton w Denton and Caldecote 77-83; P-in-c Folksworth w Morborne 77-83; V Histon 83-90; P-in-c Impington 84-90; rtd 90; Perm to Offic *Ely* from 90. *48 Church Road, Hauxton, Cambridge CB2 5HS* Tel (01223) 874183

BUTLER, Huw. b 63. Univ of Wales (Ban) BSc84. St Mich Coll Llan DipTh94 BTh95. **d** 95 **p** 96. C Llantwit Fardre *Llan* 95-00; R Llangynhafal w Llanbedr DC and Llanychan *St As* 00-02; R Llanbedr DC w Llangynhafal, Llanychan etc from 02. *The Rectory, Llanbedr Dyffryn Clwyd, Ruthin LL15 1UP* Tel (01824) 704160 E-mail huw.butler@tesco.net

BUTLER, Ian Malcolm. b 39. Bris Univ BA67 BA69. Clifton Th Coll 67. **d** 69 **p** 70. C Clapham Common St Barn *S'wark* 69-73; C Reigate St Mary 73-78; V Sissinghurst w Frittenden *Cant* 78-91; rtd 92; Chapl Dulwich Prep Sch Cranbrook from 90; Perm to Offic *Cant* from 91. *High Cedars, Theobalds, Hawkhurst, Cranbrook TN18 4AJ* Tel (01580) 752366 Fax 754904 E-mail mail@ianbutler.net

BUTLER, John. b 38. Univ of Wales DipTh67 DPS68 Gwent Coll Newport CertEd77. St Mich Coll Llan. **d** 68 **p** 69. C Ebbw Vale *Mon* 68-70; TV 70-75; Perm to Offic 76-77 and 79-88; P-in-c Crumlin 77-78; R Gt and Lt Casterton w Pickworth and Tickencote *Pet* 88-91; R Woolstone w Gotherington and Oxenton etc *Glouc* 91-97; Hon C Dawlish *Ex* 98-01; P-in-c Chevington w Hargrave, Chedburgh w Depden etc *St E* 01-02; R 02-03; rtd 03; C Shaldon, Stokeinteignhead, Combeinteignhead etc *Ex* from 03. *The Rectory, Stoke in Teignhead, Newton Abbot TQ12 4QB* Tel (01626) 871013

BUTLER, John Philip. b 47. Leeds Univ BA70. Coll of Resurr Mirfield 70. **d** 72 **p** 73. C Elton All SS *Man* 72-75; C Bolton St Pet 75-78; Chapl Bolton Colls of H&FE 75-78; Hon C Clifton St Paul *Bris* 78-81; Asst Chapl Bris Univ 78-81; V Llansawel w Briton Ferry *Llan* 81-84; Warden Bp Mascall Cen *Heref* 84-88; Vice-Prin Glanc Sch for Min 85-88; Chapl Univ of Wales (Ban) from 88. *Anglican Chaplaincy Centre, Prince's Road, Bangor LL57 2BD* Tel (01248) 370566 Fax 354472 E-mail angchap@lineone.net

BUTLER, Mrs Linda. b 51. Liv Univ CertEd72. Cranmer Hall Dur 01. **d** 03. C Middlewich w Byley *Ches* from 03. *27 St Ann's Road, Middlewich CW10 9BN* Tel (01606) 835132 E-mail butlers@fish.co.uk

BUTLER, Linda Jane. b 56. SRN77. St Jo Coll Nottm 85. **d** 88 **p** 94. C Burbage w Aston Flamville *Leic* 88-91; Asst Chapl Leic R Infirmary 91-93; Asst Chapl Towers Hosp Humberstone 93-95; Chapl 95-97; Chapl Leics and Rutland Healthcare NHS Trust 97-03; Chapl to the Deaf *Pet* from 03. *5 Gray Lane, Sileby, Loughborough LE12 7GS* Tel (01509) 812705

BUTLER, Malcolm. b 40. Linc Th Coll 76. **d** 78 **p** 79. C Whickham *Dur* 78-82; V Leam Lane 82-87; R Penshaw 87-90; rtd 90. *2 Lapwing Court, Barcus Close Lane, Burnopfield, Newcastle upon Tyne NE16 4DZ* Tel (01207) 271559

BUTLER, Canon Michael. b 41. Univ of Wales (Ban) DipTh62. St Mich Coll Llan 62 St Deiniol's Hawarden 63. **d** 64 **p** 65. C Welshpool *St As* 64; C Welshpool w Castle Caereinion 65-73; TV Aberystwyth *St D* 73-80; Chapl Univ of Wales (Abth) 73-80; V St Issell's and Amroth from 80; RD Narberth from 94; Can St D Cathl from 01. *St Issell's Vicarage, Saundersfoot SA69 9BD* Tel (01834) 812375

BUTLER, Canon Michael John. b 32. Keble Coll Ox BA58 MSW. Coll of Resurr Mirfield. **d** 59 **p** 60. C Poplar All SS w St Frideswide *Lon* 59-68; Hon C St Steph Walbrook and St Swithun etc 68-73; C Godalming *Guildf* 73-76; P-in-c Brighton St Anne *Chich* 77-79; Dioc Communications Officer and Dir Soc Resp 77-83; Dir Dioc Bd of Soc Resp 83-94; Soc Resp Adv 94-00; Hon C Brighton St Pet w Chpl Royal 94-00; Can and Preb Chich Cathl 85-00; rtd 00; Perm to Offic *Nor* from 00. *Railway Cottages, 2 Buxton Road, Aylsham, Norwich NR11 6JD* Tel (01263) 734820

BUTLER, Canon Michael Weeden. b 38. Clare Coll Cam BA60 MA65. Westcott Ho Cam 63. **d** 65 **p** 66. C Bermondsey St Mary w St Olave, St Jo etc *S'wark* 65-68; Ind Chapl 68-72; Sierra Leone 73-77; Ind Chapl *Cant* 77-86; R Gt Chart 77-86; RD E Charing 81-86; V Glouc St Jas and All SS *Glouc* from 86; RD Glouc City 94-99; Hon Can Glouc Cathl from 96. *The Vicarage, 1 The Conifers, Gloucester GL1 4LP* Tel (01452) 422349 E-mail michaelbutler@michaelbutler.freeserve.co.uk

BUTLER, Ms Pamela. b 53. Nottm Univ BTh86 CertEd74. Linc Th Coll 83. **dss** 86 **d** 87 **p** 94. Rotherhithe H Trin *S'wark* 86-87; Par Dn 87-88; Par Dn Old Trafford St Jo *Man* 88-89; Par Dn Claremont H Angels 90-94; C 94-95; C Pendleton 95-97; Chapl Asst S Man Univ Hosps NHS Trust from 96. *St Mary's Vicarage, 18 Rushcroft Road, Shaw, Oldham OL2 7PR* Tel (01706) 847455, 0161-291 2298 *or* 998 7070

BUTLER, Paul David. b 67. Sheff Univ BA88. Linc Th Coll 92. **d** 92 **p** 93. C Handsworth Woodhouse *Sheff* 92-96; V Bellingham St Dunstan *S'wark* from 96; RD E Lewisham from 99. *St Dunstan's Vicarage, 32 Bellingham Green, London SE6 3JB* Tel (020) 8698 3291 E-mail paulredbutler@compuserve.com

BUTLER, Canon Paul Roger. b 55. Nottm Univ BA77. Wycliffe Hall Ox BA82. **d** 83 **p** 84. C Wandsworth All SS *S'wark* 83-87; Inner Lon Ev Scripture Union 87-92; Dep Hd of Miss 92-94; NSM E Ham St Paul *Chelmsf* 87-94; P-in-c Walthamstow St Mary w St Steph 94-97; P-in-c Walthamstow St Luke 94-97; P-in-c Walthamstow St Gabr 97; TR Walthamstow from 97; AD Waltham Forest from 00; Hon Can Byumba from 01. *St Mary's Rectory, 117 Church Hill, London E17 3BD* Tel (020) 8520 4281 Fax as telephone E-mail butler@fish.co.uk

BUTLER, Perry Andrew. b 49. FRHistS York Univ BA70 Lon Univ PGCE75 Jes Coll Ox DPhil78 Nottm Univ DipTh79. Linc Th Coll 78. **d** 80 **p** 81. C Chiswick St Nic w St Mary *Lon* 80-83; C S Kensington St Steph 83-87; V Bedford Park 87-95; Angl Adv Lon Weekend TV 91-99; P-in-c Bloomsbury St Geo w Woburn Square Ch Ch *Lon* 95-02; R from 02; Dioc Dir of Ords from 96. *The Rectory, 6 Gower Street, London WC1E 6DP* Tel (020) 7580 4010 E-mail stgeorgebloomsbury@hotmail.com *or* holmado@aol.com

BUTLER, Richard Charles Burr. b 34. St Pet Hall Ox BA59 MA62. Linc Th Coll 58. **d** 60 **p** 61. C St John's Wood *Lon* 60-63; V Kingstanding St Luke *Birm* 63-75; R Lee St Marg *S'wark* 75-00; rtd 00. *21 Defoe House, Barbican, London EC2Y 8DN* Tel (020) 7628 0527 E-mail eleanorandrichardbutler@btinternet.com

BUTLER, Robert Clifford. b 25. AKC54. **d** 55 **p** 56. C Gt Berkhamsted *St Alb* 55-59; C Dunstable 59-63; V Stanbridge w Tilsworth 63-73; R Maulden 73-80; R Oldbury *Sarum* 80-93; rtd 93; Perm to Offic *Sarum* from 93. *3 Mithras Close, Dorchester DT1 2RF* Tel (01305) 264817

BUTLER, Canon Robert Edwin. b 37. Ely Th Coll 60. **d** 62 **p** 63. C Lewisham St Jo Southend *S'wark* 62-65; C Eastbourne St Eliz *Chich* 65-69; V Langney 69-86; TR 86-96; Can and Preb Chich Cathl 94-97; rtd 96; Perm to Offic *Chich* from 97. *10 Langdale Close, Langney, Eastbourne BN23 8HS* Tel (01323) 461135

BUTLER, (née McVEIGH), Mrs Sandra. b 58. Reading Univ BA80. Cranmer Hall Dur 95. **d** 95 **p** 96. C Stranton *Dur* 95-98; P-in-c Blackhall, Castle Eden and Monkhesleden 98-99; R 99-02. *Tansy Cottage, 15 Lidgett, Colne BB8 7AF* Tel (01282) 865858 E-mail revsandie@aol.com

BUTLER, Simon. b 64. UEA BSc86 RN Coll Dartmouth 86. St Jo Coll Nottm Dip Th Studies 91 MA92. **d** 92 **p** 93. C Chandler's Ford *Win* 92-94; C Northolt W End St Jos *Lon* 94-97; V Streatham Immanuel and St Andr *S'wark* from 97; Lambeth Adnry Ecum Officer from 99; RD Streatham from 02. *Immanuel Vicarage, 51A Guildersfield Road, London SW16 5LS* Tel (020) 8764 5103 E-mail immanvic@aol.com

BUTLER, Stephen Ian. b 59. Edin Univ BA BSc80. Trin Coll Bris BA84. **d** 97 **p** 98. C Edin St Pet *Edin* 97-99; R Edin St Jas from 99. *71 Restalrig Road, Edinburgh EH6 8BG* Tel 0131-554 3520 E-mail sibutler01@yahoo.com

✠**BUTLER, The Rt Revd Thomas Frederick.** b 40. Leeds Univ BSc61 MSc62 PhD72. Coll of Resurr Mirfield 62. **d** 64 **p** 65 **c** 85.

C Wisbech St Aug *Ely* 64-66; C Folkestone St Sav *Cant* 66-67; Zambia 68-73; Chapl Kent Univ *Cant* 73-80; Six Preacher Cant Cathl 79-84; Adn Northolt *Lon* 80-85; Area Bp Willesden 85-91; Bp Leic 91-98; Bp S'wark from 98. *Bishop's House, 38 Tooting Bec Gardens, London SW16 1QZ* Tel (020) 8769 3256 Fax 8769 4126 E-mail bishop.tom@dswark.org.uk

BUTLER, Valerie Joyce. b 58. EAMTC 99. **d** 02 **p** 03. NSM Southminster *Chelmsf* from 02. *6 Coastguard Cottages, Mill End, Bradwell-on-Sea, Southminster CM0 7HN* Tel (01621) 776513 E-mail val_butler@lineone.net

BUTLER-SMITH, Basil George (Bob). b 30. Bps' Coll Cheshunt 66. **d** 67 **p** 68. C Bray and Braywood *Ox* 67-71; R Norton *St E* 71-74; P-in-c Tostock 71-74; R Rotherfield Peppard *Ox* 76-02; P-in-c Rotherfield Greys 79-80; R 80-02; rtd 02. *40 Westleigh Drive, Sonning Common, Reading RG4 9LB* Tel 0118-972 1871

BUTLIN, David Francis Grenville. b 55. Bris Univ BA77 Ox Univ CertEd78. Sarum & Wells Th Coll 85. **d** 87 **p** 88. C Bedford St Andr *St Alb* 87-90; C Milton *Portsm* 90-92; V Hurst Green *S'wark* from 92. *The Vicarage, 14 Oast Road, Oxted RH8 9DU* Tel (01883) 712674 E-mail dfgbutlin@14oastroad.freeserve.co.uk

BUTLIN, Timothy Greer. b 53. St Jo Coll Dur BA75 Ox Univ CertEd76. Wycliffe Hall Ox 85. **d** 87 **p** 88. C Eynsham and Cassington *Ox* 87-91; V Loudwater from 91. *The Vicarage, Loudwater, High Wycombe HP10 9QL* Tel (01628) 526087 Fax 529354 E-mail vicar@loudwater.org

BUTT, Adrian. b 37. **d** 71 **p** 72. S Africa 71-76; C Ilkeston St Mary *Derby* 76-79; P-in-c Sturton w Littleborough *S'well* 79-84; P-in-c Bole w Saundby 79-84; R N and S Wheatley w W Burton 79-84; R N Wheatley, W Burton, Bole, Saundby, Sturton etc 84-85; R Kirkby in Ashfield from 85. *The Rectory, 12 Church Street, Kirkby-in-Ashfield, Nottingham NG17 8LE* Tel (01623) 753790

BUTT, Mrs Catherine. b 76. St Hilda's Coll Ox BA99 MA02 St Jo Coll Dur BA02. Cranmer Hall Dur 00. **d** 03. C Bletchley *Ox* from 03. *1 Ashburnham Close, Bletchley, Milton Keynes MK3 7TR* Tel (01908) 631050 Mobile 07971-714223 E-mail butties01@yahoo.co.uk

BUTT, Christopher Martin. b 52. St Pet Coll Ox BA74 Fitzw Coll Cam BA77. Ridley Hall Cam 75. **d** 79 **p** 80. C Cambridge St Barn *Ely* 79-82; Hong Kong 82-89; P-in-c Windermere *Carl* 89-98; TR S Gillingham *Roch* from 98. *The Rectory, 4 Drewery Drive, Wigmore, Gillingham ME8 0NX* Tel (01634) 231071 E-mail office@parishofsgill.freeserve.co.uk

BUTT, Edward. b 46. Huddersfield Poly CQSW80. Trin Coll Bris DipHE88. **d** 88 **p** 89. C Erith St Paul *Roch* 88-92; C Shirley *Win* 92-99; V Stourbridge St Mich Norton *Worc* from 99. *St Michael's House, Westwood Avenue, Stourbridge DY8 3EN* Tel (01384) 393647

BUTT, Martin James. b 52. Sheff Univ LLB75. Trin Coll Bris 75. **d** 78 **p** 79. C Aldridge *Lich* 78-81; C Walsall 84-87; TV 87-94; P-in-c Farewell from 94; P-in-c Gentleshaw from 94; C Hammerwich 96-03; P-in-c from 03. *The Vicarage, Budds Road, Rugeley WS15 4NB* Tel (01543) 684329

BUTT, William Arthur. b 44. Kelham Th Coll 70 Linc Th Coll 71. **d** 71 **p** 72. C Mackworth St Fran *Derby* 71-75; C Aston cum Aughton *Sheff* 76-79; V Dalton 79-88; TR Staveley and Barrow Hill *Derby* from 88. *The Rectory, Staveley, Chesterfield S43 3XZ* Tel (01246) 472270

BUTTANSHAW, Graham Charles. b 59. TCD BA(Econ)80 BA85. St Jo Coll Nottm 88. **d** 91 **p** 92. C Toxteth St Cypr w Ch Ch *Liv* 91-94; CMS Mar 95-99; V Otley *Bradf* from 99. *The Vicarage, Burras Lane, Otley LS21 3HR* Tel (01943) 462240 E-mail buttansh@fish.co.uk

BUTTERFIELD, David John. b 52. Lon Univ BMus73. St Jo Coll Nottm DipTh75. **d** 77 **p** 78. C Southport Ch Ch *Liv* 77-81; Min Aldridge St Thos CD *Lich* 81-91; V Lilleshall, Muxton and Sheriffhales from 91; RD Edgmond 97-01; RD Shifnal 99-01; RD Edgmond and Shifnal from 01. *The Vicarage, 25 Church Road, Lilleshall, Newport TF10 9HE* Tel (01952) 604281 Fax as telephone E-mail davidb@fish.co.uk

BUTTERFIELD, John Kenneth. b 52. Nottm Univ BCombStuds. Linc Th Coll 79. **d** 82 **p** 83. C Cantley *Sheff* 82-84; C Doncaster St Leon and St Jude 84-86; TV Ilfracombe, Lee, Woolacombe, Bittadon etc *Ex* 86-88; V Thurcroft *Sheff* 88-96; Perm to Offic from 96; Chapl Chesterfield and N Derbyshire NHS Trust from 96. *Chesterfield and North Derbyshire Royal Hospital, Calow, Chesterfield S44 5BL* Tel (01246) 277271 ext 3398

BUTTERWORTH, Antony James. b 51. Hull Univ BSc73 Bris Univ DipTh76. Trin Coll Bris 73. **d** 76 **p** 77. C Halliwell St Pet *Man* 76-81; V Werneth 81-90; V Tonge Fold from 90. *St Chad's Vicarage, 9 Tonge Fold Road, Bolton BL2 6AW* Tel (01204) 525809 E-mail stchads@clara.net

BUTTERWORTH, David Frederick. b 48. Oak Hill Th Coll DipHE87 BA88. **d** 88 **p** 89. Canada 88-98; C Hanmer, Bronington, Bettisfield, Tallarn Green *St As* from 98. *The Vicarage, Hanmer, Whitchurch SY13 3DE* Tel (01948) 830468 Fax 830010

BUTTERWORTH, Derek. b 27. Wells Th Coll 63. **d** 65 **p** 65. C Bottesford *Linc* 65-73; TV Bottesford w Ashby 73-83; Chapl

St Hilda's Sch Whitby 83-85; V Derringham Bank *York* 85-90; rtd 90; Perm to Offic *York* from 90; Perm to Offic *Ripon* from 90. *26 St Mary's Gate, Ripon HG4 1LX*

BUTTERWORTH, Elsie. b 27. Linc Th Coll 81. **dss** 83 **d** 87 **p** 94. OHP 83-85; Derringham Bank *York* 85-87; Par Dn 87-88; Par Dn Filey 88-94; C 94-97; rtd 93; Perm to Offic *York* from 97. *3 Brooklands Close, Filey YO14 9BJ* Tel (01723) 515781

BUTTERWORTH, George John. b 58. Liv Univ BA85. Chich Th Coll 92. **d** 92 **p** 93. C Mayfield *Chich* 92-93; C Hastings St Clem and All SS 93-96; TV Brighton Resurr 96-02; P-in-c Saltdean from 02. *St Nicholas' Vicarage, Saltdean Vale, Saltdean, Brighton BN2 8HE* Tel (01273) 302345

BUTTERWORTH, Canon George Michael. b 41. Man Univ BSc63 Lon Univ BD67 PhD89 Nottm Univ MPhil71. Tyndale Hall Bris. **d** 67 **p** 68. C S Normanton *Derby* 67-71; India 72-79; Lect Oak Hill Th Coll 80-96; Prin St Alb and Ox Min Course *Ox* from 97; Perm to Offic *St Alb* from 80; Hon Can St Alb from 02. *9 Fulmar Court, Bicester OX26 4FG* Tel (01869) 240932 or (01865) 790084 E-mail mikebutterworth@waitrose.com

BUTTERWORTH, Mrs Gillian. b 49. Man Univ BA71 Dur Univ PGCE72. N Ord Course 96. **d** 99. C Barnsley St Mary *Wakef* 99-03; Min Development Officer from 03. *Outwood Vicarage, 424 Leeds Road, Wakefield WF1 2JB* Tel (01924) 823150

BUTTERWORTH, Ian Eric. b 44. Aber Univ MA67 MTh79. Edin Th Coll 67. **d** 69 **p** 70. C Langley All SS and Martyrs *Man* 69-71; Prec St Andr Cathl *Ab* 71-75; V Bolton St Matt w St Barn *Man* 75-85; C-in-c Lostock CD 85-92; Laity Development Officer (Bolton Adnry) 85-92; Teacher Fairfield High Sch Droylsden 92-99; Perm to Offic *Man* 96-99; P-in-c Castleton Moor from 00; Hon C Sudden St Aidan from 00. *St Martin's Vicarage, Vicarage Road North, Rochdale OL11 2TE* Tel (01706) 632353 E-mail i.butterworth@tesco.net

BUTTERWORTH, Preb James Frederick. b 49. St Chad's Coll Dur BA70 Birm Univ MA99. Cuddesdon Coll 70. **d** 72 **p** 73. C Kidderminster St Mary *Worc* 72-76; P-in-c Dudley St Barn 76-79; V 79-82; Prec and Min Can Worc Cathl 82-88; TR Bridgnorth, Tasley, Astley Abbotts, etc *Heref* 88-94; Can Res and Treas Heref Cathl 94-99; Preb Heref Cathl from 94; P-in-c Ewyas Harold w Dulas, Kenderchurch etc from 99; RD Abbeydore from 02. *The Rectory, Ewyas Harold, Hereford HR2 0EY* Tel (01981) 240079

BUTTERWORTH, James Kent. b 49. Southn Univ BTh79. Chich Th Coll 75. **d** 79 **p** 80. C Heckmondwike *Wakef* 79-83; V Wrenthorpe 83-95; V Staincross from 95. *St John's Vicarage, 48 Greenside, Staincross, Barnsley S75 6GU* Tel (01226) 382261 E-mail jim@butterworth.uk.net

BUTTERWORTH, John Walton. b 49. St Jo Coll Dur BSc70 DipTh73. **d** 74 **p** 75. C Todmorden *Wakef* 74-77; Chapl Wakef Cathl 77-78; C Wakef Cathl 77-78; V Outwood from 78. *Outwood Vicarage, 424 Leeds Road, Wakefield WF1 2JB* Tel (01924) 823150

BUTTERWORTH, Canon Julia Kay. b 42. Edin Univ MA64 Bris Univ CertEd66 Nottm Univ DipTh75. Linc Th Coll 73. **dss** 77 **d** 87 **p** 94. Cov E *Cov* 77-79; Cant Cathl *Cant* 79-84; Dioc Adv in Women's Min 82-92; Faversham 84-87; Par Dn 87-92; TD Whitstable 92-94; TV 94-97; Hon Can Cant Cathl from 96; P-in-c Tenterden St Mich from 97; Dioc Adv in Spirituality from 97. *The Vicarage, Ashford Road, St Michaels, Tenterden TN30 6PY* Tel (01580) 764670 Fax as telephone E-mail jbutterworth@clara.co.uk

BUTTERWORTH, Mildred Jean. b 42. Leeds Univ MB, ChB65 FRCOG84. St Jo Coll Nottm. **d** 00 **p** 01. NSM Moldgreen and Rawthorpe *Wakef* from 00. *1 Furnbrook Gardens, Kirkheaton, Huddersfield HD5 0DY* Tel (01484) 421375 E-mail mildred@fish.co.uk

BUTTERWORTH, Roy. b 31. Selw Coll Cam BA55 MA59. Wells Th Coll 55. **d** 57 **p** 58. C Bathwick w Woolley *B & W* 57-61; Prec St Paul's Cathl Dundee *Bre* 61-63; V Dearnley *Man* 63-81; V Tyldesley w Shakerley 81-83; V Healey 83-94; rtd 94. *102 Greenbank Road, Rochdale OL12 0EN* Tel (01706) 350808

BUTTERY, Bernard. b 36. Culham Coll Ox CertEd58 LCP75. OLM course 96. **d** 99 **p** 00. OLM Stafford *Lich* from 99. *7 Dearnsdale Close, Tillington, Stafford ST16 1SD* Tel (01785) 244771

BUTTERY, Graeme. b 62. York Univ BA84. St Steph Ho Ox 85. **d** 88 **p** 89. C Peterlee *Dur* 88-91; C Sunderland 91-92; TV 92-94; V Horsley Hill St Lawr from 94; AD Jarrow from 01. *St Lawrence House, 84 Centenary Avenue, South Shields NE34 6SF* Tel 0191-456 1747 E-mail buttery.stl@virgin.net

BUTTERY, Nathan James. b 72. Em Coll Cam BA94 MA97. Wycliffe Hall Ox BA98. **d** 00 **p** 01. C Hull Newland St Jo *York* from 00. *75 Desmond Avenue, Hull HU6 7JX* Tel (01482) 343789 E-mail nathan.debbie@ukgateway.net

BUTTIMORE, Canon John Charles. b 27. St Mich Coll Llan 55. **d** 57 **p** 58. C Treherbert *Llan* 57-60; C Aberdare St Fagan *Llan* 60-64; V Llanwonno 64-71; Chapl Ely Hosp Cardiff 71-98; V Caerau w Ely *Llan* 71-97; RD Cardiff 83-89; Can Llan Cathl 87-97; rtd 97; Perm to Offic *Llan* from 97. *3 Nant y Pepra, Cardiff CF5 4UB* Tel (029) 2065 9333

BUTTLE, Leslie Albert. b 32. Open Univ BA89. Edin Th Coll 61. **d** 64 **p** 65. C Sowerby Bridge w Norland *Wakef* 64-66; C Plymstock *Ex* 66-69; C Ilfracombe H Trin 69-71; V Woolfardisworthy and Buck Mills 71-76; C Sticklepath 76-77; Asst Chapl HM Pris Leeds 77-80; Lic to Offic *Ripon* 77-80; Chapl HM Youth Cust Cen Hindley 80-84; Perm to Offic *Ex* 86-93; Hon C Braunton from 93; rtd 97. *Church House, Saunton, Braunton EX33 1LG* Tel (01271) 817022

BUTTLE, Leslie Ronald Frank. b 07. Lon Univ BA28. **d** 34 **p** 35. C Wanstead St Mary *Chelmsf* 34-36; Asst Master R Wanstead Sch 31-36; Asst Chapl 34-36; Chapl K Coll Otahuhu New Zealand 36-38; R Water Stratford *Ox* 38-39; Asst Chapl Felsted Sch 40; Chapl RNVR 41-47; R Goldhanger w Lt Totham *Chelmsf* 47-50; R Purleigh 50-55; V Gt w Lt Packington *Cov* 55-58; V Maxstoke *Birm* 55-58; R Fordham *Chelmsf* 58-63; V Hatfield Broad Oak 63-66; V Bush End 63-66; R Lowick w Sudborough and Slipton *Pet* 67-73; rtd 73; Perm to Offic *Truro* from 73. *5 Castle Street, Launceston PL15 8BA* Tel (01566) 772052

BUTTON, David Frederick. b 27. St Chad's Coll Dur BA53 DipTh54. **d** 54 **p** 55. C S Shields St Mary *Dur* 54-58; C Seacroft *Ripon* 58-60; V Holland Fen *Linc* 60-64; V Surfleet 64-71; R Belton SS Pet and Paul 71-78; V Barkston w Syston 72-78; V Honington 73-78; R Gunhouse w Burringham 78-82; P-in-c Gt w Lt Hockham w Wretham w Illington *Nor* 82-84; P-in-c Shropham w Larling and Snetterton 82-84; V Hockham w Shropham Gp of Par 84-91; rtd 91; Perm to Offic *Nor* 91-96. *6 Vallibus Close, Oulton, Lowestoft NR32 3DS*

BUTTREY, Anne Stella Ivy. b 40. Dioc OLM tr scheme 99. **d** 02. OLM Brandon and Santon Downham w Elveden *St E* from 02; OLM Lakenheath from 02. *8 Mount Road, Brandon IP27 0DT* Tel (01842) 810172 E-mail annebuttrey@mailacc.fsnet.co.uk

BUXTON, Alyson Christina. b 65. Chelt & Glouc Coll of HE BA00 RGN86. St Jo Coll Nottm MTh01. **d** 02 **p** 03. C New Sleaford *Linc* from 02. *West Hall, Grantham Road, Coleby, Lincoln LN5 0AP* Tel (01522) 810973 Mobile 077132-490240 E-mail alybux@aol.com

BUXTON, Canon Derek Major. b 31. Lon Univ BD63. Ripon Hall Ox 58. **d** 60 **p** 61. C Leic St Nic *Leic* 60-64; Chapl Leic Univ 60-64; Chapl Leic Coll of Art and Tech 64-65; Min Can Leic Cathl 64-69; Prec 67; R Ibstock 69-76; R Ibstock w Heather 76-87; Chapl ATC from 78; OCF and Cen and E Regional Chapl from 87; RD Akeley S *Leic* 84-87; P-in-c Woodhouse Eaves 87-91; V Woodhouse and Woodhouse Eaves 91-98; Chapl Roecliffe Manor Cheshire Home from 87; Chapl Coun OStJ from 87; Hon Can Leic Cathl *Leic* from 88; rtd 98; Perm to Offic *Leic* from 99. *Shepherd's Hill, 74 Pitsford Drive, Loughborough LE11 4NY* Tel (01509) 216663

BUXTON, Edmund Francis. b 42. Trin Coll Cam BA65 MA68 DPS74 Sheff Univ MMinTheol93. Linc Th Coll 65. **d** 67 **p** 68. C Wanstead St Mary *Chelmsf* 67-70; C Cambridge Gt St Mary w St Mich *Ely* 70-73; C Barking St Marg w St Patr *Chelmsf* 74-75; India 75-79; Chapl Bath Univ *B & W* 79-89; TR Willenhall H Trin *Lich* 89-96; Chapl Team Leader Univ Hosp Birm NHS Trust from 96. *The Chaplaincy Office, Queen Elizabeth Hospital, Edgbaston, Birmingham B15 2TH* Tel 0121-472 1311 ext 3104/3437 Fax 627 2211

BUXTON, Graham. b 45. York Univ BA66 Bradf Univ MSc71. St Jo Coll Nottm 83 Melbourne Coll of Div MMin97. **d** 83 **p** 84. C Ealing Dean St Jo *Lon* 83-84; C W Ealing St Jo w St Jas 84-86; C S Harrow St Paul 86-89; P-in-c 89-91; Sen Lect Tabor Coll Australia from 91. *5 Heron Place, Flagstaff Hill, S Australia 5159* Tel (0061) (8) 8370 6038 or 8373 8777 Fax 8373 1766 E-mail gbuxton@adelaide.tabor.edu.au

BUXTON, James Andrew Denis. b 64. Newc Univ BA86. Westcott Ho Cam 95. **d** 97 **p** 98. C Portsea St Mary *Portsm* 97-01; Succ S'wark Cathl *S'wark* from 01; Chapl Medical and Dental Students K Coll Lon from 01. *St Paul's Vicarage, 54 Kipling Street, London SE1 3RU* Tel (020) 7367 6705 E-mail james@buxton9.fsnet.co.uk

BUXTON, Richard Fowler. b 40. Lon Univ BSc62 Linacre Coll Ox BA67 MA71 Ex Univ PhD73. St Steph Ho Ox 65. **d** 68 **p** 69. C Whitley Ch Ch *Ox* 68-70; C Pinhoe *Ex* 70-71; Asst Chapl Ex Univ 71-73; Tutor Sarum & Wells Th Coll 73-77; Vice-Prin 77; Perm to Offic *Ches* 77-97; Lect Liturgy Man Univ 80-94; Subwarden St Deiniol's Lib Hawarden 94-97; Perm to Offic *Ban* from 96; *St As* from 97; rtd 00. *Golygfa'r Orsaf, 6 Rhesdai Garth, Porthmadog LL49 9BE* Tel (01766) 514782

BUXTON, Canon Trevor George. b 57. Ex Univ BEd78. Chich Th Coll 81. **d** 83 **p** 84. C Hove All SS *Chich* 83-87; C Burgess Hill St Jo 87-91; V Brighton St Aug and St Sav 91-03; P-in-c Sidley from 02; Can and Preb Chich Cathl from 01. *All Saints' Vicarage, All Saints Lane, Sidley, Bexhill-on-Sea TN39 5HA* Tel (01424) 221071 Mobile 07885-942901 E-mail hojoe@waitrose.com

BUXTON, William Arnold Greaves (Paddy). b 33. FBIM78 FInstD78 FInstM79. Sarum & Wells Th Coll 80. **d** 82 **p** 83. C Durrington *Chich* 82-85; R Kingston Buci 85-89; TR Rye 89-94; rtd 94; Perm to Offic *Cant* and Chich from 95. *The Old House, 45 The Mint, Rye TN31 7EN* Tel (01797) 223191

BUYE, Bishop of. *See* NDAYISENGA, The Most Revd Samuel

BUYERS, Stanley. b 39. Leeds Univ CertEd71 Sunderland Poly BEd78 Newc Univ MEd90. NEOC 97. **d** 00 **p** 01. NSM E Boldon *Dur* from 00. *37 Tarragon Way, South Shields NE34 8TB* Tel 0191-519 0370 Mobile 07979-693153 E-mail stanbuyers@eggconnect.net

BYATT, John William. b 55. St Jo Coll Nottm. **d** 01 **p** 02. C Heanor *Derby* from 01. *46 Johnson Drive, Heanor DE75 7SU* Tel (01773) 716865 Mobile 07773-906919

BYE, Canon Peter John. b 39. Lon Univ BD65. Clifton Th Coll 62. **d** 67 **p** 68. C Hyson Green *S'well* 67-70; C Dur St Nic *Dur* 70-73; V Lowestoft Ch Ch *Nor* 73-80; V Carl St Jo *Carl* from 80; Chapl Carl Gen Hosp 80-94; Chapl Carl Hosps NHS Trust 94-98; Hon Can Carl Cathl *Carl* from 98; RD Carl from 00. *St John's Vicarage, London Road, Carlisle CA1 2QQ* Tel (01228) 521601 or 595792 E-mail peterbye@st-johns-carlisle.co.uk

BYERS, Canon Christopher Martin. b 33. Jes Coll Ox BA59 MA62. Wycliffe Hall Ox 59. **d** 60 **p** 61. C Bermondsey St Mary w St Olave, St Jo etc *S'wark* 60-66; R Mottingham St Andr 66-86; TR Thamesmead 86-99; C 99-00; Hon Can S'wark Cathl 96-00; rtd 01; Perm to Offic *Cant* from 01. *36 Faversham Road, Whitstable CT5 4AR* Tel (01227) 272786

BYFORD, Canon David Charles. b 30. Bps' Coll Cheshunt 58. **d** 61 **p** 62. C Short Heath *Birm* 61-63; C Londonderry 63-65; Chapl Selly Oak Hosp Birm 65-70; V Rowley Regis *Birm* 70-78; V Polesworth 78-95; RD Polesworth 84-91; Hon Can Birm Cathl 87-95; rtd 95; Perm to Offic *Sarum* from 95. *Rose Cottage, Stratford sub Castle, Salisbury SP1 3LB* Tel (01722) 322569

BYFORD, The Ven Edwin Charles. b 47. Aus Nat Univ BSc70 Melbourne Coll of Div BD73 Univ of Chicago MA76 Man Univ PhD85. Trin Coll Melbourne 70. **d** 73 **p** 73. C Qeanbeyan Ch Ch Australia 73-75; Chapl Univ of Chicago USA 75-76; Hon C Chorlton-cum-Hardy St Werburgh *Man* 76-79; Australia from 79; Chapl Woden Valley Hosp 80-83; Asst P Wagga Wagga 83-84; Asst P Ainslie All SS 84-87; Chapl Aus Nat Univ 87-91; R Binda 91-95; R Broken Hill St Pet and Adn The Darling from 95. *PO Box 185, Broken Hill, NSW, Australia 2880* Tel and fax (0061) (8) 8087 3221 Mobile 409-467981 E-mail e-byford-4@alumni.uchicago.edu

BYLES, Canon Raymond Vincent. b 30. Univ of Wales (Lamp) BA52. St Mich Coll Llan 52. **d** 54 **p** 55. C Llanfairisgaer *Ban* 54-57; C Llandudno 57-59; V Carno 59-64; V Trefeglwys 63; V Newmarket and Gwaenysgor *St As* 64-72; V Llysfaen 72-80; V Bodelwyddan and St George 80-85; V Bodelwyddan 85-95; Hon Can St As Cathl from 89; rtd 95. *20 Lon Dderwen, Tan-y-Goppa Parc, Abergele LL22 7DW* Tel (01745) 833604

BYLLAM-BARNES, Preb Paul William Marshall. b 38. Birm Univ BCom Lon Univ MSc. Sarum & Wells Th Coll. **d** 84 **p** 85. C Gt Bookham *Guildf* 84-87; R Cusop w Blakemere, Bredwardine w Brobury etc *Heref* 87-03; RD Abbeydore 96-00; Preb Heref Cathl 99-03; rtd 03. *Myrtle Cottage, 1 Wantz Chase, Maldon CM9 5DN* Tel (01621) 858978

BYNON, William. b 43. St Aid Birkenhead 63. **d** 66 **p** 67. C Huyton St Mich *Liv* 66-69; C Maghull 69-72; TV 72-75; V Highfield 75-82; V Southport All SS 82-88; P-in-c Southport All So 86-88; V Newton in Makerfield St Pet 88-94; V Caerhun w Llangelynin w Llanbedr-y-Cennin *Ban* from 94. *Caerhun Vicarage, Tyn-y-Groes, Conwy LL32 8UG* Tel (01492) 650250

BYRNE, Bryn. *See* BYRNE, Ronald Brendan Anthony

BYRNE, David Patrick. b 48. PGCE96. St Jo Coll Nottm 74. **d** 77 **p** 78. C Bordesley Green *Birm* 77-79; C Weoley Castle 79-82; TV Kings Norton 82-92; TV Hodge Hill 92-94; Perm to Offic 94-97; Chapl Asst Birm Heartlands and Solihull NHS Trust 96-98; Chapl NW Lon Hosp NHS Trust from 98; Chapl Harrow and Hillingdon Healthcare NHS Trust from 98. *Staff Residence, Northwick Park Hospital, Watford Road, Harrow HA1 3UJ* Tel (020) 8864 2113

BYRNE, David Rodney. b 47. St Jo Coll Cam BA70 MA73. Cranmer Hall Dur 71. **d** 73 **p** 74. C Maidstone St Luke *Cant* 73-77; C Patcham *Chich* 77-83; TV Stantonbury *Ox* 83-87; TV Stantonbury and Willen 87-92; TV Woodley 92-02; V Patchway *Bris* from 02. *St Chad's Vicarage, 1B Southsea Road, Patchway, Bristol BS34 5DP* Tel 0117-969 2935 or 979 3978 E-mail dbyrne@fish.co.uk

BYRNE, Miss Georgina Ann. b 72. Trin Coll Ox BA92 MA96 CCC Cam MPhil98. Westcott Ho Cam. **d** 97 **p** 98. NSM W Bromwich All SS *Lich* 97-98; C 98-01; Hon Asst Chapl CCC Cam 97-98; Chapl to Bp Kensington *Lon* from 01; Hon C Twickenham St Mary from 01. *St Mary's Lodge, Church Street, Hampton TW12 2EB*

BYRNE, Ian Barclay. b 53. Ripon Coll Cuddesdon 01. **d** 03. C Blyth Valley St E from 03. *St Ursula's House, 64 Old Station Road, Halesworth IP19 8JQ* Tel (01986) 874128

BYRNE, Canon John Victor. b 47. FCA. St Jo Coll Nottm LTh73. **d** 73 **p** 74. C Gillingham St Mark *Roch* 73-76; C Cranham Park *Chelmsf* 76-80; V Balderstone *Man* 80-87; V Southsea St Jude *Portsm* from 87; P-in-c Southsea St Pet 95-03; Hon Can Portsm Cathl from 97; RD Portsm from 01; Chapl to The Queen from

03. *St Jude's Vicarage, 7 Hereford Road, Southsea PO5 2DH* Tel and fax (023) 9282 1071 *or* tel 9275 0442
E-mail john@byrne07.freeserve.co.uk

BYRNE, The Very Revd Matthew. b 27. Man Univ MA69 TCD HDipEd81. Tyndale Hall Bris 47. **d** 51 **p** 52. C Rawtenstall St Mary *Man* 51-54; OCF 54-57; R Moss Side St Jas *Man* 57-62; R Whalley Range St Marg 62-80; P-in-c Chapelizod *D & G* 80-83; Chapl K Hosp Sch Dub 83-89; Dean Kildare *M & K* 89-93; I Kildare w Kilmeague and Curragh 89-93; Producer Relig Dept RTE 83-92; Chapl Defence Forces 89-92; rtd 92. *5 Fairfield Park, Greystones, Co Wicklow, Irish Republic* Tel (00353) (1) 287 3622 Fax as telephone

BYRNE, The Very Revd Miriam Alexandra Frances. b 46. Westcott Ho Cam. **d** 87 **p** 94. Par Dn Beoley *Worc* 87-90; C Ayr *Glas* 90-92; Dn-in-c Dumbarton 92-94; P-in-c 94-98; Provost St Paul's Cathl Dundee *Bre* from 98; R Dundee St Paul from 98. *The Cathedral Rectory, 4 Richmond Terrace, Dundee DD2 1BQ* Tel (01382) 646296 Fax as telephone

BYRNE, Robert James Matthew. b 64. Oak Hill Th Coll BA95. **d** 95 **p** 96. C Tonbridge St Steph *Roch* 95-99; C Coxheath w E Farleigh, Hunton and Linton 99-01; rtd 01. *5A John Street, Tunbridge Wells TN4 9RR* Tel (01892) 540565 Mobile 07973-523966 E-mail revbobbyrne@hotmail.com

BYRNE, Rodney Edmund. b 18. **d** 84 **p** 84. Hon C Leckhampton SS Phil and Jas w Cheltenham St Jas *Glouc* 84-88; rtd 88; Perm to Offic *Glouc* from 88. *39 Collum End Rise, Cheltenham GL53 0PA* Tel (01242) 526428

BYRNE, Ronald Brendan Anthony (Bryn). b 31. Reading Univ BA72. Westcott Ho Cam 86. **d** 64 **p** 65. Chapl Cov Cathl *Cov* 87-91; Chapl Lanchester Poly 87-91; Lic to Offic 91-94; Chapl Limerick Univ *L & K* 94-98; Chapl Villier's Sch Limerick 95-98; rtd 96; Chapl Lanzarote *Eur* 98-00. *28 Hendon Lane, London N3 1TR* Tel and fax (020) 8343 2526 Mobile 07960-319294

BYRNE, Roy Harold. b 71. Westmr Coll Ox BTh97 Irish Sch of Ecum MPhil00. CITC 97. **d** 99 **p** 00. C Dublin Ch Ch Cathl Gp *D & G* 99-03; I Killeshin w Cloydagh and Killabban *C & O* from 03. *The Rectory, Ballickmoyler, Carlow, Irish Republic* Tel (00353) (059) 862 5321 E-mail roybyrne@eircom.net

BYROM, Alan. b 51. Magd Coll Ox BA72 Leeds Univ PGCE73 Bris Univ MA85 Man Univ MPhil99. Trin Coll Bris DipHE84 N Ord Course 97. **d** 99 **p** 00. C Leyland St Andr *Blackb* 99-03; TV Solway Plain *Carl* from 03. *The Vicarage, Wigton Road, Silloth, Wigton CA7 4NR* Tel (016973) 31413
E-mail arm@abyrom.freeserve.co.uk

BYROM, Canon John Kenneth. b 20. Selw Coll Cam BA41 MA45. Westcott Ho Cam 41. **d** 43 **p** 44. C Neston *Ches* 43-48; C Stockport St Matt 48-50; V Cheadle Hulme All SS 50-63; Warden Brasted Place Coll Westerham 64-74; V Swaffham Prior *Ely* 74-88; Dir of Ords 75-87; Dir Post-Ord Tr 75-87; Hon Can Ely Cathl 78-88; RD Fordham 78-83; rtd 88; Perm to Offic *Ely* from 88. *62 Cambridge Road, Great Shelford, Cambridge CB2 5JS* Tel (01223) 844015

BYROM, Canon Malcolm Senior. b 37. Edin Th Coll 65. **d** 67 **p** 68. C Allerton *Bradf* 67-69; C Padstow *Truro* 69-72; V Hessenford 72-77; P-in-c St Martin by Looe 72-77; V Kenwyn 77-91; R Kenwyn w St Allen 91-99; Hon Can Truro Cathl 92-00; RD Powder 88-90; Sub-Warden Community of the Epiphany Truro 85-00; Warden from 00; rtd 99; Perm to Offic *Truro* from 00. *West Haven, Dobbin Road, Trevone, Padstow PL28 8QP* Tel (01841) 520242

BYRON, Frederick. b 14. Dur Univ BA38. St Jo Coll Dur 38. **d** 39 **p** 40. C Openshaw *Man* 39-43; C Oldham St Paul 43-46; C Moston St Mary 46-50; R Old Trafford St Cuth 50-56; V Bolton St Barn 56-68; V Out Rawcliffe *Blackb* 68-78; C Standish 78-79; rtd 79. *18 Scott Avenue, Hindley, Wigan WN2 4DG* Tel (01942) 53807

BYRON, Terence Sherwood. b 26. Keble Coll Ox BA50 MA54. Linc Th Coll 50. **d** 52 **p** 53. C Melton Mowbray w Burton Lazars, Freeby etc *Leic* 52-55; C Whitwick St Jo the Bapt 55-60; India 60-76; C-in-c Beaumont Leys (Extra-paroch Distr) *Leic* 76-85; V Beaumont Leys 85-86; RD Christianity N 86-92; P-in-c Leic St Phil 86-88; V 88-92; rtd 93; Perm to Offic *Leic* from 93. *84 Flax Road, Leicester LE4 6QD* Tel 0116-266 1922

BYRON-DAVIES, Peter. b 49. K Coll Lon BD75 AKC75 Nottm Univ MTh85. St Aug Coll Cant 75. **d** 76 **p** 77. C Wootton Bassett *Sarum* 76-79; Chapl Charterhouse Sch Godalming 79-80; R Bassingham *Linc* 80-85; V Aubourn w Haddington 80-85; V Carlton-le-Moorland w Stapleford 80-85; R Thurlby w Norton Disney 80-85; Canada 85-88; R Chalke Valley E *Sarum* 88-96; Perm to Offic 96; Perm to Offic *B & W* from 96. *PO Box 2400, Bradford-on-Avon BA15 2YN*

BYSOUTH, Paul Graham. b 55. Oak Hill Th Coll. **d** 84 **p** 85. C Gorleston St Andr *Nor* 84-87; C Ripley *Derby* 87-91; TV N Wingfield, Clay Cross and Pilsley 91-00; V Blagreaves from 00. *St Andrew's Vicarage, 5 Greenburn Close, Littleover, Derby DE23 1FF* Tel (01332) 773877

BYTHEWAY, Phillip James. b 35. MIIExE89 BA93. **d** 97. OLM Church Stretton *Heref* 97-00; rtd 00; Perm to Offic *Heref* from 00. *Ivy Glen, 55 Watling Street South, Church Stretton SY6 7BQ* Tel (01694) 723901 Mobile 07778-391088 Fax 724440

BYWORTH, Canon Christopher Henry Briault. b 39. Oriel Coll Ox BA61 MA65 Bris Univ BA63. Lon Coll of Div 64. **d** 65 **p** 66. C Low Leyton *Chelmsf* 65-68; C Rusholme H Trin *Man* 68-70; Lic to Offic *Lon* 71-75; TR Thetford *Nor* 75-79; Warden Cranmer Hall Dur 79-83; TR Fazakerley Em *Liv* 83-90; P-in-c St Helens St Helen 90-94; TR from 94; AD St Helens 90-00; Hon Can Liv Cathl from 99. *The Vicarage, 51A Rainford Road, St Helens WA10 6BZ* Tel (01744) 22067

BYWORTH, Mrs Ruth Angela. b 49. Cranmer Hall Dur BA82. dss 83 **d** 92 **p** 94. Kirkby *Liv* 83-89; Aintree St Pet 89-97; Dn-in-c 92-94; P-in-c 94-97; P-in-c St Helens St Mark 97-98; C Sutton 98-03; TV from 03. *The Vicarage, 51A Rainford Road, St Helens WA10 6BZ* Tel (01744) 23806

C

CABLE, Patrick John. b 50. AKC72. **d** 74 **p** 75. C Herne *Cant* 74-78; CF from 78; Lic to Offic *Cant* from 78. *c/o MOD Chaplains (Army)* Tel (01980) 615804 Fax 615800

CACKETT, Janice Susan. b 39. Goldsmiths' Coll Lon BA76 Surrey Univ MSc83. SW Minl Tr Course 99. **d** 99 **p** 00. NSM Clyst St Mary, Clyst St George etc *Ex* 99-03; P-in-c E Budleigh w Bicton and Otterton from 03. *Manor House, Clyst St George, Exeter EX3 0NS* Tel (01392) 877468
E-mail jcackett@ukgateway.net

CADDELL, Richard Allen. b 54. Auburn Univ Alabama BIE77. Trin Coll Bris BA88. **d** 88 **p** 89. C Uphill *B & W* 88-94; Perm to Offic 94-96; TV Beaconsfield *Ox* from 96. *St Thomas's House, Mayflower Way, Beaconsfield HP9 1UF* Tel (01494) 672750

CADDEN, Brian Stuart. b 58. BSc BTh TCD. **d** 89 **p** 90. C Lecale Gp *D & D* 89-92; C Killowen *D & R* 92-95; I Muckamore *Conn* from 95. *The Rectory, 5 Ballycraigy Road, Muckamore, Antrim BT41 1QP* Tel (028) 9446 2073
E-mail muckamore@conner.anglican.org

CADDEN, Terence John. b 60. TCD BTh89. CITC 86. **d** 89 **p** 90. C Coleraine *Conn* 89-92; C Lurgan Ch the Redeemer *D & D* 92-93; Past Dir 93-01; I Gilford from 01. *The Vicarage, 18 Scarva Road, Gilford, Craigavon BT63 6BG* Tel (028) 3832 6040
E-mail gilford@dromore.anglican.org

CADDICK, Jeremy Lloyd. b 60. St Jo Coll Cam BA82 MA86 K Coll Lon MA93. Ripon Coll Cuddesdon BA86 MA91. **d** 87 **p** 88. C Kennington St Jo w St Jas *S'wark* 87-90; Chapl Lon Univ *Lon* 90-94; Chapl R Free Medical Sch 90-94; Chapl R Veterinary Coll Lon 90-94; PV Westmr Abbey 92-94; Dean Em Coll Cam from 94. *Emmanuel College, Cambridge CB2 3AP* Tel (01223) 334264 *or* 330195 Fax 334426 E-mail jlc24@cam.ac.uk

CADDICK, Canon Lloyd Reginald. b 31. Bris Univ BA56 St Cath Coll Ox BA58 MA62 Nottm Univ MPhil73 K Coll Lon PhD78 Open Univ Hon MA79. St Steph Ho Ox 56. **d** 59 **p** 59. C N Lynn w St Marg and St Nic *Nor* 59-62; Chapl Oakham Sch 62-66; P-in-c Bulwick, Harringworth w Blatherwycke and Laxton *Pet* 66-67; R Bulwick, Blatherwycke w Harringworth and Laxton 67-77; V Oundle 77-96; Can Pet Cathl 94-96; rtd 96; Perm to Offic *Pet* from 96. *18A Glapthorn Road, Oundle, Peterborough PE8 4JQ* Tel (01832) 273616

CADDY, Canon Michael George Bruce Courtenay. b 45. K Coll Lon. **d** 71 **p** 72. C Walton St Mary *Liv* 71-76; C Solihull *Birm* 76-79; TV 79-81; V Shard End 81-87; TR Shirley 87-00; P-in-c Tanworth St Patr Salter Street 97-00; TR Salter Street and Shirley from 00; AD Shirley 97-02; Hon Can Birm Cathl from 99. *The Vicarage, 2 Bishopton Close, Shirley, Solihull B90 4AH* Tel 0121-744 3123 *or* 745 8896

CADDY, Ms Susan. b 50. Westcott Ho Cam 99. **d** 01 **p** 02. C Sutton in Ashfield St Mary *S'well* from 01. *Grosvenor House, Grosvenor Avenue, Sutton-in-Ashfield NG17 1FG* Tel (01623) 552572 E-mail suecee@fish.co.uk

CADE, Mrs Margaret Elizabeth. b 34. Dioc OLM tr scheme 99. **d** 00. OLM Portland All SS w St Pet *Sarum* from 00. *27 Avalanche Road, Portland DT5 2DJ* Tel (01305) 821317 Mobile 07974-696892 Fax 826453

CADE, Simon Peter Vincent. b 69. Univ of Wales BA90. Westcott Ho Cam CTM94. **d** 94 **p** 95. C Calne and Blackland *Sarum* 94-98; Chapl St Mary's Sch Calne 94-97; TV Basingstoke *Win* from 98. *45 Beaconsfield Road, Basingstoke RG21 3DG* Tel (01256) 464616 E-mail simon@cade.u-net.com

CADMAN, Kenneth Claude. b 14. St Jo Coll Dur BA40. **d** 40 **p** 41. C Harpurhey Ch Ch *Man* 40-44; C Rochdale 44-45; C Worsley 45-47; R Heaton Norris All SS 47-52; CF (TA) 49-52; CF (TA - R of O) 52-69; V Rainow w Saltersford and Forest *Ches* 52-54; R

Higher Broughton *Man* 54-59; R Guernsey St Michel du Valle *Win* 59-65; V Alderney 65-69; R Guernsey St Pierre du Bois 69-81; R Guernsey St Philippe de Torteval 80-81; Vice Dean Guernsey 70-81; rtd 81; Perm to Offic *Win* 82-98. *Summerland House Nursing Home, St Peter Port, Guernsey GY1 1DX* Tel (01481) 724196

CADMAN, Robert Hugh. b 49. Nottm Univ DipTh76. St Jo Coll Nottm 77. **d** 78 **p** 79. C Ecclesall *Sheff* 78-82; C Worting *Win* 82-84; C-in-c Winklebury CD 84-87; R Widford *Chelmsf* 87-94; Chapl Anglia Poly Univ 94-95; NSM Brentwood St Thos 01-03; TV Southend from 03. *All Saints' Vicarage, 1 Sutton Road, Southend-on-Sea SS2 5PA*
E-mail robcadman@blueyonder.co.uk

CADMORE, Albert Thomas. b 47. Open Univ BA81 NE Lon Poly Nor City Coll DMS84 SS Mark & Jo Coll Plymouth Lon Inst of Educn CertEd68 UEA MA94. EAMTC 85. **d** 88 **p** 89. NSM Gorleston St Andr *Nor* 88-96; NSM Winterton w E and W Somerton and Horsey 94-96; NSM Flegg Coastal Benefice from 96. *10 Upper Cliff Road, Gorleston, Great Yarmouth NR31 6AL* Tel (01493) 668762

CADOGAN, Paul Anthony Cleveland. b 47. AKC74. **d** 75 **p** 76. C Fishponds St Jo *Bris* 75-79; C Swindon New Town 79-81; P-in-c Swindon All SS 81-82; V 82-90; R Lower Windrush *Ox* 90-94. *2 Malthouse Close, Ashbury SN6 8PB* Tel (01793) 710488

CADOGAN, Percil Lavine. WMMTC. **d** 01 **p** 02. NSM Bournville *Birm* from 01. *76 Highbury Road, Birmingham B14 7QW* Tel 0121-680 9595

CAESAR, Canon Anthony Douglass. b 24. LVO87 CVO91. Magd Coll Cam BA47 MA49 MusB47 FRCO47. St Steph Ho Ox 59. **d** 61 **p** 62. C Kensington St Mary Abbots w St Geo *Lon* 61-65; Chapl RSCM Addington 65-70; Asst Sec CACTM 65-66; ACCM 65-70; Dep P in O 67-68; P-in-O 68-70; C Bournemouth St Pet *Win* 70-73; Prec and Sacr Win Cathl 74-79; Hon Can 75-76 and 79-91; Can Res 76-79; Dom Chapl to The Queen 79-91; Extra Chapl to The Queen from 91; Sub Almoner and Dep Clerk of the Closet 79-91; Sub Dean of HM Chpls Royal 79-91; rtd 91; Chapl St Cross Hosp Win 91-93; Perm to Offic *Portsm* from 93. *Flat 2, Old Kiln, Brading, Sandown PO36 0BP* Tel (01983) 406435

CAFFYN, Douglas John Morris. b 36. ACIS77 Peterho Cam MA60 Nairobi Univ MSc69 Westmr Coll Ox DipEd61. S Dios Minl Tr Scheme 87. **d** 90 **p** 91. NSM Hampden Park *Chich* 90-94; Chapl among Deaf People 94-97; Jt Sec Cttee for Min among Deaf People 95-97; Perm to Offic from 97; rtd 01. *255 King's Drive, Eastbourne BN21 2UR* Tel (01323) 500977

CAHILL, Nigel. b 59. St Mich Coll Llan DipTh80 DPS82. **d** 82 **p** 83. C Whitchurch *Llan* 82-86; V Tonypandy w Clydach Vale 86-96; RD Rhondda 93-96; V Fairwater 96-03; V Caerau w Ely from 03. *The Vicarage, Cowbridge Road West, Ely, Cardiff CF5 5BQ* Tel (029) 2056 3254

CAIN, Andrew David. b 63. Aber Univ BSc86. Ripon Coll Cuddesdon BA89. **d** 90 **p** 91. C Walworth St Jo *S'wark* 90-94; Bp's Dom Chapl *Ox* 94-98; P-in-c Kilburn St Mary w All So *Lon* 98-01; P-in-c W Hampstead St Jas 98-01; V Kilburn St Mary w All So and W Hampstead St Jas from 01. *St Mary's Vicarage, 134A Abbey Road, London NW6 4SN* Tel (020) 7624 5434 Fax as telephone E-mail acain@acain.screaming.net

CAIN, Canon Frank Robert. b 56. Oak Hill Th Coll BA88. **d** 88 **p** 89. C Aughton Ch Ch *Liv* 88-91; P-in-c Toxteth Park St Clem 91-99; V Toxteth St Bede w St Clem from 99; AD Toxteth and Wavertree from 01; Hon Can Liv Cathl from 03; Chapl N Mersey Community NHS Trust from 96. *The Vicarage, 76 Beaumont Street, Liverpool L8 0XA* Tel 0151-709 9880 Fax as telephone E-mail frankandsuecain@ukgateway.net

CAIN, Michael Christopher. b 68. St Jo Coll Dur BA90 K Coll Lon MA92 Selw Coll Cam BA94. Ridley Hall Cam 93. **d** 95 **p** 96. C Wimbledon Em Ridgway Prop Chpl *S'wark* 95-99; Asst Chapl Leipzig *Eur* 99-02; C Clifton Ch Ch w Em *Bris* from 02. *60 Clifton Park Road, Bristol BS8 3HN* Tel 0117-973 3729

CAIN, Michael John Patrick. b 62. Chich Th Coll 88. **d** 91 **p** 92. C Cainscross w Selsley *Glouc* 91-94; C Mackworth St Fran *Derby* 94-97; V Derby St Luke 97-02; C Paignton St Jo *Ex* from 02. *St Boniface House, Belfield Road, Paignton TQ3 3UZ* Tel (01803) 556612

CAINK, Richard David Somerville. b 37. Lich Th Coll 68. **d** 71 **p** 72. C Prittlewell St Mary *Chelmsf* 71-74; C Gt Yarmouth *Nor* 74-76; P-in-c Blickling w Ingworth 76-80; P-in-c Saxthorpe and Corpusty 76-80; P-in-c Oulton SS Pet and Paul 76-80; R Cheddington w Mentmore and Marsworth *Ox* 80-87; P-in-c Wooburn 87-90; V 90-96; P-in-c Lacey Green 96-98; TV Risborough 98-02; rtd 02. *1 Whitlock Drive, Great Yeldham, Halstead CO9 4EE* Tel (01787) 236091

✠**CAIRD, The Rt Revd Prof Donald Arthur Richard.** b 25. TCD BA49 MA55 BD55 HDipEd59 Hon DD88 Hon LLD93. TCD Div Sch 49. **d** 50 **p** 51 **c** 70. C Dundela St Mark *D & D* 50-53; Chapl and Asst Master Portora R Sch Enniskillen 53-57; Lect St D Coll Lamp 57-59; I Rathmichael *D & G* 60-69; Asst Master St Columba's Coll Dub 60-62; Lect TCD 62-64; Lect in Philosophy of Relig Div Hostel Dub 64-69; Dean Ossory *C & O* 69-70; Can Leighlin Cathl 69-70; I Kilkenny 69-70; Bp Limerick,

Ardfert and Aghadoe *L & K* 70-76; Bp M & K 76-85; Abp Dublin *D & G* 85-96; Preb Cualaun St Patr Cathl Dublin 85-96; rtd 96; Visiting Prof Gen Th Sem New York from 97. *3 Crofton Avenue, Dun Laoghaire, Co Dublin, Irish Republic* Tel (00353) (1) 280 7869 Fax 230 1053

CAIRNS, Henry Alfred (Jim). Melbourne Univ BA49 Ridley Coll Melbourne. ACT ThL43. **d** 42 **p** 43. Australia 42-81; Can Gippsland 59-60; Perm to Offic *Cant* 81-83; Perm to Offic *St Alb* 81-83 and from 85; Hon C Radlett 83-85. *47 Westminster Court, St Stephen's Hill, St Albans AL1 2DX* Tel (01727) 850949

CALAMINUS, Peter Andrew Franz. b 14. Lon Univ BA44. Cuddesdon Coll 69. **d** 71 **p** 71. C Westbury *Sarum* 71-73; P-in-c Pitcombe w Shepton Montague and Bratton St Maur *B & W* 73-76; V 76-78; rtd 79. *Hibiscus Gardens, 2 Sissy Street, South Gladstone, Qld, Australia 4680* Tel (0061) (7) 4979 0156

CALCOTT-JAMES, Colin Wilfrid. b 25. Bris Univ BSc48. S'wark Ord Course 77. **d** 80 **p** 81. NSM Barnes H Trin *S'wark* 80-85; C Hykeham *Linc* 85-88; R Barrowby 88-92; rtd 92; Perm to Offic *Lon* 93-94; Perm to Offic *S'wark* from 93. *23 Gwendolen Avenue, London SW15 6ET* Tel (020) 8788 6591

CALDER, David Ainsley. b 60. NE Lon Poly BSc86 Dur Univ BA93. St Jo Coll Dur DMS95. **d** 96 **p** 97. C Ireland Wood *Ripon* 96-00; V Woodhouse and Wrangthorn from 00; Chapl Leeds Metrop Univ from 02. *2 Halcyon Hill, Leeds LS7 3PU* Tel 0113-269 0448 Mobile 07947-535044
E-mail david.calder1@virgin.net

CALDER, Canon Ian Fraser. b 47. York Univ BA68 CertEd69. Glouc Sch of Min 84. **d** 87 **p** 88. NSM Lydney w Aylburton *Glouc* 87-91; C Cirencester 91-95; V Coney Hill 95-01; RD Glouc City 99-01; R Bishop's Cleeve from 01; RD Tewkesbury and Winchcombe from 02; Hon Can Glouc Cathl from 03. *The Rectory, 4 Church Approach, Bishops Cleeve, Cheltenham GL52 8NG* Tel (01242) 675103
E-mail ian.calder@cableinet.co.uk

CALDER, Roger Paul. b 53. Hatf Coll Dur BA75 SSC. Chich Th Coll 76. **d** 79 **p** 80. C Addlestone *Guildf* 79-82; C Grangetown *Dur* 82-84; TV Brighton Resurr *Chich* 84-87; CF 87-92; P-in-c Cocking, Bepton and W Lavington *Chich* 92-95; P-in-c Bognor 95-98; V from 98. *The Vicarage, 17 Victoria Drive, Bognor Regis PO21 2RH* Tel (01243) 821965 E-mail fr.roger@wilfrid.com *or* roger.p.calder@btinternet.com

CALDERHEAD, Christopher Conrad. b 62. Princeton Univ AB84. Seabury-Western Th Sem MDiv98. **d** 98 **p** 99. C Chesterton Gd Shep *Ely* 98-02; USA from 02. *Address temp unknown*
E-mail calderhead@windmillweb.net

CALDICOTT, Anthony. b 31. ARCO52 FRCO62 ADCM66 St Jo Coll Dur BA53. Ripon Hall Ox 55. **d** 57 **p** 58. C Finham *Cov* 57-61; C Bedford St Andr *St Alb* 61-64; Chapl Lindisfarne Coll 64-67; C W Bromwich All SS *Lich* 67-69; Lic to Offic *Cov* 69-75; Hon C Twickenham St Mary *Lon* 75-89; Perm to Offic from 91; rtd 96. *38 Lyndhurst Avenue, Twickenham TW2 6BX* Tel (020) 8894 6859

CALDWELL, Alan. b 29. Oak Hill Th Coll 65. **d** 67 **p** 68. C Aldershot H Trin *Guildf* 67-69; C New Malden and Coombe *S'wark* 69-73; C Edgware St Andr CD *Lon* 73-78; P-in-c Pettaugh and Winston St E 78; R Helmingham w Framsden and Pettaugh w Winston 78-87; R Cowden w Hammerwood *Chich* 87-94; rtd 94; Perm to Offic *Ban* from 94. *Ael-y-Bryn, Druid Road, Menai Bridge LL59 5BY* Tel (01248) 713550
E-mail alancldwll@aol.com

CALDWELL, David Denzil. b 24. TD70. Bps' Coll Cheshunt 53. **d** 55 **p** 56. C Carnmoney *Conn* 55-59; CF (TA) 57-67; C Antrim All SS w Muckamore *Conn* 59-61; I Kilwaughter w Cairncastle 61-90; CF (TAVR) 67-70; CF (R of O) 70-80; SB OStJ from 80; Sub-Chapl from 90; rtd 90. *30 Shandon Park, Ballymena BT42 2ED* Tel (028) 2564 2650

CALDWELL, Ian Charles Reynolds. b 43. St Mich Coll Llan 68. **d** 70 **p** 71. C Oakham w Hambleton and Egleton *Pet* 70-74; C Swindon New Town *Bris* 74-78; P-in-c Honicknowle *Ex* 78-80; V 80-88; V Norton St Mich *Dur* 88-94; rtd 03. *Address withheld by request*

CALDWELL, Mrs Jill. b 47. Lon Univ BPharm69 MRPharmS70. S Dios Minl Tr Scheme 89. **d** 92 **p** 94. NSM Yiewsley *Lon* 92-97; NSM St Marylebone w H Trin 97-02; Chapl St Marylebone Girls' Sch Lon 97-98; Chapl R Academy of Music 97-98; Chapl Lon Sch of Pharmacy 97-98; Chapl Liv Cathl *Liv* from 03. *Liverpool Cathedral, St James's Mount, Liverpool L1 7AZ* Tel 0151-709 6271

CALDWELL, Canon John Donaldson. b 19. TCD BA41. **d** 42 **p** 43. C Belfast St Aid *Conn* 42-47; C Magheralin *D & D* 47-50; I Drumgath 50-55; I Kilmegan w Maghera 55-89; Can Dromore Cathl 85-89; rtd 89; Lic to Offic *D & D* from 90. *66 Castlewellan Road, Newcastle BT33 0JP* Tel (028) 4472 4874

CALDWELL, Roger Fripp. b 31. Cranmer Hall Dur. **d** 64 **p** 65. C Gosforth St Nic *Newc* 64-67; C Sugley 67-74; R Helmdon w Stuchbury and Radstone *Pet* 74-91; R Greatworth 74-91; rtd 91. *Quiet Waters, Station Road, Heyford, Oxford OX5 3PD*

CALE, Canon Clifford Roy Fenton. b 38. St Mich Coll Llan 65. **d** 67 **p** 68. C Griffithstown *Mon* 67-72; V Cwm 72-73; V

Abersychan 73-79; V Abersychan and Garndiffaith 79-82; R Goetre w Llanover and Llanfair Kilgeddin 82-85; R Goetre w Llanover 85-01; RD Raglan-Usk 90-01; Can St Woolos Cathl 98-01; rtd 01. *Long Mynd, 3 Fayre Oak, Raglan, Usk NP15 2HA* Tel (01291) 690544

CALE, Nicholas. b 66. St Mich Coll Llan DipTh92. **d** 92 **p** 93. C Tenby *St D* 92-95; R Begelly w Ludchurch and Crunwere 95-01; V Wiston w Walton E and Clarbeston from 01. *The Vicarage, Wiston, Haverfordwest SA62 4PL* Tel (01437) 731266 E-mail cale@tinyonline.co.uk

CALITIS, Juris. Maryland Univ BA Latvia Univ DD. Harvard Div Sch STB. **d** 98 **p** 98. Chapl Riga, Latvia *Eur* from 98; Dean Faculty of Th Univ of Latvia from 99; Assoc Prof Bibl Studies from 99; Co-ord Bible Translation (Latvian Bible Soc) from 99. *Anglikanu iela 2A, Riga, LV1050, Latvia* Tel (00371) 721 1390 Fax as telephone E-mail calitis@latnet.lv

CALLADINE, Joanne Elizabeth. b 71. Liv Inst of Educn BA93. Cranmer Hall Dur 95. **d** 97 **p** 98. NSM Blurton *Lich* 97-98; C Stoke-upon-Trent 98-01; NSM Moston St Mary *Man* from 01. *St Mary's Rectory, 47 Nuthurst Road, Moston, Manchester M10 0EW* Tel 0161-681 1201 E-mail jo.calladine@lineone.net

CALLADINE, Matthew Robert Michael. b 65. St Jo Coll Dur BSc87 Reading Univ MSc89. Cranmer Hall Dur BA93 DMS93. **d** 96 **p** 97. C Blurton *Lich* 96-01; P-in-c Moston St Mary *Man* from 01. *St Mary's Rectory, 47 Nuthurst Road, Moston, Manchester M10 0EW* Tel 0161-681 1201 E-mail matthew.calladine@lineone.net

CALLAGHAN, Canon Harry. b 34. AKC59 Open Univ BA83. **d** 60 **p** 61. C Sheff Parson Cross St Cecilia *Sheff* 60-63; Br Guiana 63-66; Guyana 66-70; Barbados 70-74; Lic to Offic *Man* 74-84; Miss to Seamen 74-76; Area Sec USPG *Blackb, Man* and *S & M* 76-84; P-in-c Wythenshawe St Martin *Man* 84-85; V 85-91; V Bolton St Jo 91-98; Hon Can Massachusetts from 92; rtd 98; Perm to Offic *Man* from 98 and *Derby* from 99. *5 Manor Park View, Glossop SK13 7TL* Tel (01457) 868886 Mobile 07778-988523 E-mail hcallaghan@compuserve.com

CALLAGHAN, Martin Peter. b 57. Edin Th Coll 91. **d** 93 **p** 94. C Ayr *Glas* 93-96; C Girvan 93-96; C Maybole 93-96; P-in-c Gretna from 96; P-in-c Eastriggs from 96; P-in-c Annan from 97; P-in-c Lockerbie from 97; P-in-c Moffat from 97. *The Vicarage, 4 Kingfisher Lane, Gretna DG16 5JS* Tel (01461) 338176 or 338773

CALLAGHAN, Michael James. b 63. Clare Coll Cam BA85. SEITE 94. **d** 97 **p** 98. NSM Blackheath Park St Mich *S'wark* from 97. *81 St Joseph's Vale, London SE3 0XG* Tel (020) 8318 7561 or 7919 0928 E-mail mikecall@netcomuk.co.uk

CALLAGHAN, Robert Paul. b 59. K Coll Lon BD81. Linc Th Coll 81. **d** 83 **p** 85. C Winchmore Hill St Paul *Lon* 83-85; C Paddington St Jo w St Mich 85-91; V Dartford St Edm *Roch* from 91. *The Vicarage, St Edmund's Road, Temple Hill, Dartford DA1 5ND* Tel (01322) 225335 E-mail st.edmunds@mcmail.com

CALLAN, Canon Terence Frederick. b 26. CITC 55. **d** 57 **p** 58. C Monaghan Clogh 57-58; I Clogh 58-64; C Derriaghy *Conn* 64-66; P-in-c Ballymacash 67-70; I Belfast St Aid 70-79; I Agherton 79-94; Can Conn Cathl from 86; Treas from 90; rtd 94. *18 Central Avenue, Portstewart BT93 0DN* Tel (028) 7083 2704

CALLAN, Ms Wendy Mary. b 52. Ox Brookes Univ BA93. St Alb and Ox Min Course 96. **d** 99 **p** 00. C Bicester w Bucknell, Caversfield and Launton *Ox* 99-03; V Shipton-under-Wychwood w Milton, Fifield etc from 03. *The Vicarage, Church Street, Shipton-under-Wychwood, Chipping Norton OX7 6BP* Tel and fax (01993) 830257 Mobile 07788-442946

CALLAN-TRAVIS, Anthony. b 46. N Ord Course 90. **d** 93 **p** 94. C Tong *Bradf* 93-97; C Harrogate St Wilfrid *Ripon* 97-03; TV Knaresborough from 03. *9 Castle Yard, Knaresborough HG5 8AS* Tel (01423) 869845

CALLARD, Canon David Kingsley. b 37. St Pet Coll Ox BA61 MA65. Westcott Ho Cam 61. **d** 63 **p** 64. C Leamington Priors H Trin *Cov* 63-66; U Wyken 66-68; C Bp's Hatfield *St Alb* 68-73; R Bilton *Cov* 73-83; TR Swanage and Studland *Sarum* 83-93; TR Oakdale 93-02; Can and Preb Sarum Cathl 95-02; rtd 02. *Woodlands, 29 Folkestone Road, Salisbury SP2 8JP* Tel (01722) 501200

CALLENDER, Francis Charles. b 48. TCD BA70 DipEd71 MA73. TCD Div Sch 76. **d** 79 **p** 80. C Bandon *C, C & R* 79-82; New Zealand 82-88 and from 90; USA 88-90. *41 Bellvue Avenue, Christchurch 8005, New Zealand* Tel (0064) (3) 352 9335 Fax as telephone

CALLER, Laurence Edward Harrison. b 19. Lon Univ BMus77 MA82. Lich Th Coll 39. **d** 42 **p** 43. C Ipswich St Matt *St E* 42-45; C Walsall St Pet *Lich* 45-46; C Hednesford 46-48; R Stafford St Mary 48-55; Subchanter Lich Cathl 55-57; V Shrewsbury St Alkmund 57-63; V Harlescott 63-67; rtd 84. *103 Fronks Road, Dovercourt, Harwich CO12 4EG* Tel (01255) 504501

CALLON, Andrew McMillan. b 56. Chich Th Coll 77. **d** 80 **p** 81. C Wigan All SS *Liv* 80-85; V Abram 85-90; V Bickershaw 89-90; Chapl RN from 90. *Royal Naval Chaplaincy Service, Room 203, Victory Building, HM Naval Base, Portsmouth PO1 3LS* Tel (023) 9272 7903 Fax 9272 7111

CALVELEY, Mrs Susan. b 47. Dioc OLM tr scheme. **d** 02. OLM Birkdale St Pet *Liv* from 02. *19 Nolan Street, Southport PR8 6QQ* Tel (01704) 546746 Fax 540969 E-mail calveley@btclick.com

CALVER, Mrs Gillian Margaret. b 47. Qu Eliz Coll Lon BSc68. Cant Sch of Min 89. **d** 92 **p** 94. NSM Folkestone H Trin w Ch Ch *Cant* 92-95; P-in-c Alkham w Capel le Ferne and Hougham 95-01; V 01-02; Chapl Dover Coll 95-99; R Staplehurst *Cant* from 02. *The New Rectory, High Street, Staplehurst, Tonbridge TN12 0BJ* Tel (01580) 891258

CALVER, Nicholas James. b 58. Nottm Univ BTh83 Dur Univ MA90. Cranmer Hall Dur 86. **d** 88 **p** 89. C Forest Hill Ch Ch *S'wark* 88-91; C Forest Hill 91-92; P-in-c Mottingham St Edw 92-95; V 95-97; Voc Adv Lewisham Adnry 94-97; V Redhill St Jo from 97. *St John's Vicarage, Church Road, Redhill RH1 6QA* Tel (01737) 766562

CALVERT, Geoffrey Richard. b 58. Edin Univ BSc79 PhD84 Leeds Univ BA86. Coll of Resurr Mirfield 84. **d** 87 **p** 88. C Curdworth w Castle Vale *Birm* 87-90; C Barnsley St Mary *Wakef* 90-92; TV Halifax 92-94; V Halifax H Trin 95-99; V Luton St Aug Limbury *St Alb* from 99. *The Vicarage, 215 Icknield Way, Luton LU3 2JR* Tel (01582) 572415 Fax as telephone E-mail geoff.calvert@dial.pipex.com

CALVERT, Canon Jean. b 34. Lightfoot Ho Dur IDC63. **dss** 78 **d** 87 **p** 94. S Bank *York* 78-84; Chapl Asst Rampton Hosp Retford 84-88; Dn-in-c Dunham w Darlton and Ragnall *S'well* 88-89; Dn-in-c E Drayton w Stokeham 88-89; Dn-in-c Fledborough 88-89; Dn-in-c Dunham-on-Trent w Darlton, Ragnall etc 89-94; P-in-c from 94; Hon Can S'well Minster from 93. *The Vicarage, Dunham-on-Trent, Newark NG22 0UL* Tel (01777) 228707

CALVERT, John Raymond. b 42. Lon Coll of Div 64. **d** 67 **p** 68. C Kennington St Mark *S'wark* 67-70; C Southborough St Pet *Roch* 70-72; C Barton Seagrave *Pet* 72-75; Asst Master Shaftesbury High Sch 78-79; Dioc Children's Officer *Glouc* 79-87; P-in-c S Cerney w Cerney Wick and Down Ampney 87-89; V from 89; P-in-c Siddington w Preston from 02. *The Vicarage, Silver Street, South Cerney, Cirencester GL7 5TP* Tel (01285) 860221

CALVERT, John Stephen. b 27. Lon Univ BSc53. Wycliffe Coll Toronto BTh61. **d** 61 **p** 62. Canada 61-63; C Preston St Jo *Blackb* 63-70; rtd 92; Perm to Offic *Blackb* from 92. *17 Leyster Street, Morecambe LA4 5NF* Tel (01524) 424491

CALVERT, Canon Peter Noel. b 41. Ch Coll Cam BA63 MA67. Cuddesdon Coll 64. **d** 66 **p** 67. C Brighouse *Wakef* 66-71; V Heptonstall 71-82; V Todmorden from 82; P-in-c Cross Stone 83-93; RD Calder Valley from 84; Hon Can Wakef Cathl from 92; Chapl to The Queen from 98. *Christ Church Vicarage, Burnley Road, Todmorden OL14 7BS* Tel (01706) 813180

CALVERT, Philip. b 62. St Steph Ho Ox 00. **d** 02 **p** 03. C Holbrooks *Cov* from 02. *The Rosary, 4 Cloverdale Close, Coventry CV6 4PZ* Tel (024) 7636 0397 Mobile 07866-878278 E-mail frphilipcarlvert@aol.com

CALVIN-THOMAS, David Nigel. b 43. Univ of Wales (Cardiff) BSc64 Lon Univ BD77 Leeds Univ DipC&G88. St Mich Coll Llan 77. **d** 78 **p** 79. C Pontypridd St Cath *Llan* 78-80; Malawi 81-84; V Rastrick St Matt *Wakef* 84-88; V Birchencliffe 88-93; Chapl Huddersfield R Infirmary 88-93; R Aberdeen St Pet *Ab* 93-01; P-in-c Cove Bay 93-01; TV Glenrothes *St And* from 01. *141 Napier Road, Glenrothes KY6 1AU* Tel (01592) 754141 E-mail david.calvin-thomas4@which.net

CALWAY, Geoffrey. b 45. Bris Sch of Min. **d** 87 **p** 88. NSM Cotham St Sav w St Mary *Bris* 87-94; NSM Horfield H Trin 94-97; P-in-c Publow w Pensford, Compton Dando and Chelwood *B & W* from 97. *The Rectory, Old Road, Pensford, Bristol BS39 4BB* Tel (01761) 490221

CAM, Julian Howard. b 48. York Univ BA69 Birm Univ DipTh74 Man Univ MA99. Qu Coll Birm 73. **d** 75 **p** 76. C St Ives *Truro* 75-80; C Lelant 78-80; V Flookburgh *Carl* 80-82; V St Stephen by Saltash *Truro* 82-83; V Low Marple *Ches* from 83. *St Martin's Vicarage, 15 Brabyns Brow, Marple Bridge, Stockport SK6 5DT* Tel 0161-427 2736 E-mail julian.cam@talk21.com

CAMBRIDGE, Benedict Howard. b 73. Westmr Coll Ox BTh95. Cranmer Hall Dur 99. **d** 01 **p** 02. C Chilwell *S'well* from 01. *29 Farm Road, Chilwell, Nottingham NG9 5BZ* Tel 0115-875 2875

✠**CAMERON, The Most Revd Andrew Bruce.** b 41. New Coll Edin CPS72. Sheff Urban Th Unit 82 Edin Th Coll 61. **d** 64 **p** 65 **c** 92. C Helensburgh *Glas* 64-67; C Edin H Cross *Edin* 67-71; Prov and Dioc Youth Chapl 69-75; Chapl St Mary's Cathl 71-75; R Dalmahoy 75-82; Chapl Heriot-Watt Univ 75-82; TV Livingston LEP 82-88; R Perth St Jo *St And* 88-92; Convener Prov Miss Bd 88-92; Bp Ab from 92; Primus from 00. *Diocesan Office, 39 King's Crescent, Aberdeen AB24 3HP* Tel (01224) 636653 or 208142 Fax 636186 or 312141 E-mail bishop@aberdeen.anglican.org

CAMERON, David Alan. b 59. Glas Univ MA81 DipEd82 PGCE82. Ripon Coll Cuddesdon 88. **d** 91 **p** 92. C Farncombe *Guildf* 91-93; C Guildf H Trin w St Mary 93-96; V Fenton *Lich* from 96. *The Vicarage, 65 Glebedale Road, Stoke-on-Trent ST4 3AQ* Tel (01782) 412417 Fax as telephone

CAMERON, David Alexander. b 42. MRTPI Reading Univ BA63 Leeds Art Coll Dip Town Planning 69. St And Dioc Tr Course 80. **d** 90 **p** 93. NSM Blairgowrie *St And* from 90; NSM Coupar Angus from 90; NSM Alyth from 90. *Firgrove, Golf Course Road, Blairgowrie PH10 6LF* Tel (01250) 873272 *or* 874583 E-mail dacameron@talk21.com

CAMERON, Donald Eric Nelson. b 29. St Jo Coll Dur 68. **d** 70 **p** 71. C Kingston upon Hull H Trin *York* 70-73; V Eston 73-82; R Balerno *Edin* 82-87; rtd 94. *The Granary, Crauchie, East Linton EH40 3EB* Tel (01620) 860067

✠**CAMERON, The Rt Revd Douglas MacLean.** b 35. Univ of S Tennessee 61. Edin Th Coll 59. **d** 62 **p** 63 **c** 93. C Falkirk *Edin* 62-65; Papua New Guinea 66-74; Adn New Guinea Mainland 72-74; P-in-c Edin St Fillan *Edin* 74-78; R 78-88; R Edin St Hilda 77-88; R Dalkeith 88-92; R Lasswade 88-92; Can St Mary's Cathl 90-91; Syn Clerk 90-91; Dean Edin 91-92; Bp Arg from 93. *Bishop's Office, The Pines, Ardconnel Road, Oban PA34 5DR* Tel (01631) 566912 Fax as telephone E-mail bishop@argyll.anglican.org

CAMERON, Canon Gregory Kenneth. b 59. Linc Coll Ox BA80 MA84 Down Coll Cam BA82 MA85 Univ of Wales (Cardiff) DPS83 MPhil92 LLM95. St Mich Coll Llan 82. **d** 83 **p** 84. C Newport St Paul *Mon* 83-86; Tutor St Mich Coll Llan 86-89; C Llanmartin *Mon* 86-87; TV 87-88; Chapl Wycliffe Coll Glos 88-94; Dir Bloxham Project 94-00; Research Fell Cardiff Univ Cen for Law and Relig 98-00; Chapl to Abp Wales 00-03; Dir Ecum Relns ACC from 03; Hon Can St Woolos Cathl *Mon* from 03. *Anglican Communion Office, Partnership House, 157 Waterloo Road, London SE1 8UT* Tel (020) 7620 1110 E-mail gregory@cofia.fsnet.co.uk

CAMERON, Mrs Janice Irene. b 43. Reading Univ BA. TISEC 93. **d** 96 **p** 96. C Blairgowrie *St And* 96-98; C Coupar Angus 96-98; C Alyth 96-98; R Dunblane from 99. *The Rectory, Smithy Loan, Dunblane FK15 0HQ* Tel (01786) 824225

CAMERON, Mrs Margaret Mary. b 48. Qu Mary Coll Lon BA69 Liv Univ DAA70 Ex Univ MA95. SW Minl Tr Course 87. **d** 90 **p** 94. NSM Budleigh Salterton *Ex* 90-95; C Whipton 95-97; R Hemyock w Culm Davy, Clayhidon and Culmstock 97-03; RD Cullompton 99-03; V Plympton St Mary from 03. *St Mary's Vicarage, 58 Plymbridge Road, Plympton, Plymouth PL7 4QG* Tel (01752) 336157 *or* 348525 E-mail revd.cameron@tesco.net

CAMERON, Michael John. b 41. Sheff Tech Coll HNC63 DipM66 Nottm Univ Cert Th & Past Studies 90. Linc Th Coll 91. **d** 92 **p** 93. C Dinnington *Sheff* 92-96; V Beighton from 96; AD Attercliffe from 99. *The Vicarage, 27 Tynker Avenue, Beighton, Sheffield S20 1DX* Tel 0114-248 7635 E-mail beighton2000@netscapeonline.co.uk

CAMERON, Peter Scott. b 45. Edin Univ LLB67 BD76 Cam Univ PhD79 LRAM64. **d** 97 **p** 97. C Perth St Jo *St And* 97-98; R Dunkeld from 98; R Strathtay from 98. *Hope Cottage, Strathtay, Pithlochry PH9 0PG* Tel (01887) 840212 Fax as telephone

CAMERON, Ms Sheila. b 34. TCert54. Gilmore Ho 65. **d** 98 **p** 99. NSM Catford St Laur *S'wark* 98-02; Perm to Offic from 02. *52 Engleheart Road, London SE6 2HW* Tel (020) 8698 9282

CAMERON, William Hugh Macpherson. b 59. Edin Univ LLB82 BD86. Edin Th Coll 83. **d** 86 **p** 87. C Cheadle Hulme All SS *Ches* 86-89; Asst Chapl and Hd RS Wellington Coll Berks 89-93; Chapl K Sch Bruton 93-00; Perm to Offic *Chich* from 01. *Cranesden, West Street, Mayfield TN20 6DS* Tel (01435) 872991

CAMERON, William James. b 35. Brasted Th Coll 60 St Aid Birkenhead 62. **d** 64 **p** 65. C Halewood *Liv* 64-66; C-in-c Halewood St Mary CD 66-68; Asst Chapl Leeds Univ *Ripon* 68-71; Ind Chapl *Liv* 71-77; Tr Officer Gen Syn Bd of Educn 77-84; V Hickling and Waxham w Sea Palling *Nor* 84-95; P-in-c Ludham w Potter Heigham 94-95; V Ludham, Potter Heigham and Hickling 95-00; RD Waxham 93-96; rtd 00; Perm to Offic *Nor* from 00. *Forge Bungalow, The Street, Lessingham, Norwich NR12 0DG* Tel (01692) 582790

CAMIER, Canon James. b 12. TCD BA33 MA67 Div Test. **d** 35 **p** 36. I Borrisokane w Ardcroney, Aglishclohane etc *L & K* 61-86; Can Killaloe Cathl from 65; Prec 72-86; rtd 86. *Ferndale, Shillelagh, Co Wicklow, Irish Republic* Tel (00353) (55) 29227

CAMMELL, William John. b 36. Glouc Sch of Min 89. **d** 92 **p** 93. OLM Ruardean *Glouc* from 92. *The Beeches, High Beech, The Pludds, Ruardean GL17 9UD* Tel (01594) 860603

CAMP, Brian Arthur Leslie. b 50. St Jo Coll Nottm. **d** 83 **p** 84. C Blackheath *Birm* 83-86; TV Halesowen *Worc* 86-96; P-in-c Sheldon *Birm* 96-97; R from 97. *The Rectory, 165 Church Road, Sheldon, Birmingham B26 3TT* Tel 0121-743 2033

CAMP, Frederick Walter. b 19. Sarum Th Coll 47. **d** 49 **p** 50. C Brookfield St Mary *Lon* 49-54; CF 54-58; V Brigham *Carl* 58-80; V Whittingham *Newc* 80-84; V Whittingham and Edlingham w Bolton Chapel 84-85; rtd 85; Perm to Offic *Carl* from 85. *2 Ellen Court, Church Terrace, Ellenborough, Maryport CA15 7PR* Tel (01900) 817936

CAMP, John Edward. b 44. Barrister 69 Jes Coll Ox MA68 Brunel Univ MTech91 Univ Coll Lon Dip Forensic Psychotherapy 98. Ripon Coll Cuddesdon DipTh88. **d** 88 **p** 89. NSM High Wycombe *Ox* 88-89; Chapl Three Shires Hosp Northn 89-98;

Chapl St Andr Hosp Northn 89-98; Visiting Chapl 98-01; P-in-c Turvey *St Alb* 00-01. *4 Elwes Way, Great Billing, Northampton NN3 9EA* Tel (01604) 788831 Fax 413670 E-mail camp@bigfoot.com

CAMP, Michael Maurice. b 52. Southn Univ BTh83 Brentwood Coll of Educn CertEd70 K Coll Lon MA99. Sarum & Wells Th Coll 78. **d** 81 **p** 82. C Loughton St Jo *Chelmsf* 81-84; C Chingford SS Pet and Paul 84-87; V Northfleet *Roch* 87-94; V Hadlow 94-01; RD Paddock Wood 99-01; V Bromley SS Pet and Paul from 01. *The Vicarage, 9 St Paul's Square, Bromley BR2 0XH* Tel (020) 8460 6275 Fax as telephone E-mail mmcamp@zetnet.co.uk

CAMPBELL, Allan. b 14. Selw Coll Cam BA36 MA40. Westcott Ho Cam 36. **d** 38 **p** 39. C Crosthwaite Keswick *Carl* 38-39; Chapl RNVR 39-46; R Bletchley *Ox* 46-63; RD Bletchley 56-63; R Amersham 63-86; Chapl Amersham Gen Hosp 63-86; rtd 86; Perm to Offic *Carl* 86-99. *Bridge House, Cockermouth CA13 0HW* Tel (01900) 826748

CAMPBELL, Mrs Brenda. b 47. St Jo Coll Nottm DipTh94. **d** 94 **p** 95. C Rothley *Leic* 94-97; C Market Bosworth, Cadeby w Sutton Cheney etc 97-00; TV Bosworth and Sheepy Gp from 00. *4 Springfield Avenue, Market Bosworth, Nuneaton CV13 0NS* Tel (01455) 292157 E-mail campbell@leicester.anglican.org

CAMPBELL, David. b 70. St Andr Univ MTheol92 New Coll Edin MTh94. Edin Th Coll CECM94. **d** 94 **p** 95. C Perth St Jo *St And* 94-96; P-in-c Newport-on-Tay from 96; P-in-c Tayport 96-99; Dioc Youth Officer from 96; R Dunfermline from 99. *St Mary's Rectory, High Street, Newport-on-Tay DD6 8DA* Tel and fax (01382) 543311 Mobile 07976-151538 E-mail frcampbell@hotmail.com

CAMPBELL, Frederick David Gordon. b 15. Ex Coll Ox BA39. Wells Th Coll 39. **d** 40 **p** 41. C Portsea St Mary *Portsm* 40-45; Chapl RNVR 45-48; C Fareham SS Pet and Paul *Portsm* 48-49; Bp's Press Sec *Lon* 49-51; V Isleworth St Mary 51-54; SSJE from 57; Superior Gen SSJE 76-91; Lic to Offic *Lon* 69-97; Perm to Offic from 99. *St Edward's House, 22 Great College Street, London SW1P 3QA* Tel (020) 7222 9234

CAMPBELL, George St Clair. b 32. Lon Univ BSc53. Clifton Th Coll 58. **d** 60 **p** 61. C Tunbridge Wells St Pet *Roch* 60-64; C Clitheroe St Jas *Blackb* 64-70; V Tibshelf *Derby* 70-86; V W Bromwich H Trin *Lich* 86-97; Chapl Heath Lane Hosp 87-97; rtd 97; Perm to Offic *Guildf* from 98. *2 Doreen Close, Farnborough GU14 9HB* Tel (01276) 31639

CAMPBELL, Mrs Hilary Anne. b 58. UMIST BSc80. St Alb and Ox Min Course. **d** 01 **p** 02. C Goring w S Stoke *Ox* from 01. *11 Westway, Goring, Reading RG8 0BX* Tel (01491) 873890 E-mail hilary@thecampbells.demon.co.uk

CAMPBELL, Ian George. b 47. FRICS74 FBEng93. SEITE 96. **d** 99 **p** 00. NSM Chilham w Challock and Molash *Cant* 99-01; P-in-c Crundale w Godmersham from 01. *The Forge, Godmersham Park, Godmersham, Canterbury CT4 7DT* Tel (01227) 730925 E-mail campbellkent@another.com

CAMPBELL, James Duncan. b 55. Qu Eliz Coll Lon BSc77. St Jo Coll Dur 85 Oak Hill Th Coll MA00. **d** 87 **p** 88. C Hendon St Paul Mill Hill *Lon* 87-92; V Stevenage St Hugh and St Jo *St Alb* from 92. *St Hugh's House, 4 Mobbsbury Way, Chells, Stevenage SG2 0HL* Tel (01438) 354307 E-mail shsj@nildram.co.uk

CAMPBELL, James Larry. b 46. Indiana Univ BSc69 E Kentucky Univ MA73 Hull Univ MA91. Linc Th Coll 86. **d** 88 **p** 89. C N Hull St Mich *York* 88-92; C Hessle 92-95; V Burton Pidsea and Humbleton w Elsternwick from 95. *The New Vicarage, Back Lane, Burton Pidsea, Hull HU12 9AN* Tel (01964) 671074 E-mail campbell822@aol.com

CAMPBELL, James Malcolm. b 55. ARICS81 R Agric Coll Cirencester DipREM77 MRICS01. Wycliffe Hall Ox 89. **d** 91 **p** 92. C Scole, Brockdish, Billingford, Thorpe Abbots etc *Nor* 91-95; R Bentley and Binstead w Binsted *Nor* from 95; RD Alton from 02. *Holy Cross Vicarage, Church Street, Binsted, Alton GU34 4NX* Tel (01420) 22174 E-mail jmcampbell@binsted6.freeserve.co.uk

CAMPBELL, James Norman Thompson. b 49. BTh MA. **d** 86 **p** 87. C Arm St Mark w Aghavilly *Arm* 86-89; I Belfast H Trin and Ardoyne *Conn* 89-95; I Dundela St Mark *D & D* 95-01; I Portadown St Mark *Arm* from 01. *The Rectory, Brownstown Road, Portadown, Craigavon BT62 3QA* Tel (028) 3833 2368 E-mail jim.campbell1@btinternet.com

CAMPBELL, Ms Jane Judith. b 68. Trin Coll Bris BA01. **d** 01 **p** 02. NSM Lyddington and Wanborough and Bishopstone etc *Bris* from 01. *The Vicarage, South Marston, Swindon SN3 4SR* Tel (01793) 827021 E-mail jcampbell@fish.co.uk

CAMPBELL, Kenneth Scott. b 47. BA82. Oak Hill Th Coll. **d** 82 **p** 83. C Aughton St Mich *Liv* 82-85; V Brough w Stainmore *Carl* 85-90; R Brough w Stainmore, Musgrave and Warcop 90-92; rtd 92. *4 Quarry Close, Kirkby Stephen CA17 4SS* Tel (01768) 372390

CAMPBELL, Lawrence Henry. b 41. TCD BA63 MA66. **d** 63 **p** 65. C Larne and Inver *Conn* 63-66; C Finaghy 66-67; Chapl RN 67-83; R Brancaster w Burnham Deepdale and Titchwell *Nor* 83-95; P-in-c Hunstanton St Mary w Ringstead Parva, Holme etc 94-95; R Hunstanton St Mary w Ringstead Parva etc from 95; RD Heacham and Rising from 01. *St Mary's Rectory,*

Church Road, Hunstanton PE36 6JS Tel (01485) 532169 Fax 534719

CAMPBELL, Mrs Margaret Ruth. b 62. Trin Coll Bris BA02. **d** 02 **p** 03. C Yeovil w Kingston Pitney *B & W* from 02. *67 Preston Grove, Yeovil BA20 2BJ* Tel (01935) 425452

CAMPBELL, Patrick Alistair. b 36. Qu Coll Birm 64. **d** 67 **p** 68. C Paston *Pet* 67-71; C Stockton Heath *Ches* 71-73; V Egremont St Jo 73-78; V Bredbury St Mark 78-85; R Astbury and Smallwood 85-91; V Wybunbury w Doddington 91-97; rtd 97; Perm to Offic *Ches* from 97; Warden Coll of St Barn Lingfield from 01. *The Lodge, College of St Barnabas, Blackberry Lane, Lingfield RH7 6NJ* Tel (01342) 870260 Fax 870193

CAMPBELL, Robin William. b 41. TCD BA63 MA67. Ridley Hall Cam 63. **d** 65 **p** 66. C Netherton *Liv* 65-68; C Liv Our Lady and St Nic w St Anne 68-70; V Hooton *Ches* 70-99; rtd 99. *77 Seaview Parade, Lakes Entrance, Vic, Australia 3909* Tel (0061) (3) 5155 2157

CAMPBELL, Roger Stewart. b 40. Birm Univ BSc61 PhD65 St Jo Coll Dur BA71. Cranmer Hall Dur 68. **d** 71 **p** 72. C Jesmond Clayton Memorial *Newc* 71-77; Singapore 78-85; C Nottingham St Nic *S'well* 86-90; V Holloway St Mark w Em *Lon* 90-92; TR Tollington 92-97; Asst Chapl Leeds Teaching Hosps NHS Trust from 97. *St James's University Hospital, Beckett Street, Leeds LS9 7TF* Tel 0113-206 4365 E-mail sjuh.chap@dial.pipex.com

CAMPBELL, Stephen James. b 60. **d** 91 **p** 92. C Lisburn Ch Ch *Conn* 91-95; I Kilcronaghan w Draperstown and Sixtowns *D & R* 95-00; I Dunluce *Conn* 00-03. *Address temp unknown*

CAMPBELL, Stephen Lloyd. b 46. St Andr Univ LLB67 Solicitor 72. SEITE 95. **d** 98 **p** 99. NSM Quantoxhead *B & W* from 98. *Hodderscombe Lodge, Holford, Bridgwater TA5 1SA* Tel and fax (01278) 741329 Mobile 07808-967046 E-mail stephencampbell0@tinyonline.co.uk

CAMPBELL, William George. Toronto Univ BA54 MA57. Wycliffe Coll Toronto LTh57 BTh57 BD73. **d** 57 **p** 58. Canada 57-96; Bp's C Sallaghy *Clogh* 97-01. *c/o Martha McLary, 8452 64th Avenue NW, Calgary AB, Canada 73B 4H3*

CAMPBELL-SMITH, Robert Campbell. b 38. CCC Cam BA61 MA66 Ibadan Univ Nigeria 62. Linc Th Coll 61. **d** 63 **p** 64. C Norbury St Steph *Cant* 63-66; C W Wickham St Mary 66-71; Ind Chapl 65-76; V Croydon St Aug 71-81; Acting RD Croydon Cen 77-81; Spiritual Development Adv Nat Assn of Boys' Clubs 77-89; V Goudhurst *Cant* 81-87; Chapl Kent Assn of Boys' Clubs 81-97; RD W Charing *Cant* 82-89; P-in-c Kilndown 83-87; V Goudhurst w Kilndown 87-99; Hon Can Cant Cathl 94-99; Chapl Kent Youth Trust 97-99; TR Modbury, Bigbury, Ringmore w Kingston etc *Ex* from 99. *The Vicarage, Church Lane, Modbury, Ivybridge PL21 0QN* Tel (01548) 830260

CAMPBELL-TAYLOR, William Goodacre. b 65. Ox Univ BA87 Cam Univ BA93. Westcott Ho Cam 90. **d** 94 **p** 95. C Chingford SS Pet and Paul *Chelmsf* 94-97; Chapl Lon Guildhall Univ *Lon* 97-02; Chapl Lon Metrop Univ from 02. *London Guildhall University, Calcutta House, Old Castle Street, London E1 7NT* Tel (020) 7320 2379 E-mail awtaylor@igu.ac.uk

CAMPBELL-WILSON, Allan. b 43. Dur Univ BEd74. NEOC 79. **d** 82 **p** 83. NSM Boosbeck w Moorsholm *York* 82-85; R Easington w Skeffling, Kilnsea and Holmpton 85-87; P-in-c Middlesbrough St Jo the Ev 89-95; V 95-99; V Cayton w Eastfield from 99. *90 Main Street, Cayton, Scarborough YO11 3RP* Tel (01723) 586569 E-mail frallancayton@aol.com

CAMPEN, William Geoffrey. b 50. Liv Univ CertEd71 Southn Univ BTh81. Sarum & Wells Th Coll 76. **d** 79 **p** 80. C Peckham St Jo w St Andr *S'wark* 79-83; P-in-c Mottingham St Edw 83-92; R Charlwood from 92; R Sidlow Bridge from 92. *The Rectory, The Street, Charlwood, Horley RH6 0EE* Tel (01293) 862343

CAMPION, Keith Donald. b 52. S Dios Minl Tr Scheme. **d** 84 **p** 87. NSM Is of Scilly *Truro* 84-96. *20 Launceston Close, St Mary's TR21 0LN* Tel (01720) 422606

CAMPION (formerly HOUSEMAN), Mrs Patricia Adele. b 39. St D Coll Lamp DipTh90 St Mich Coll Llan Dip Practical Th 93. **d** 93 **p** 97. C St Issell's and Amroth *St D* 93-95; C Llanegryn w Aberdyfi w Tywyn *Ban* 95-97; rtd 97. *3 Mariners Reach, The Strand, Saundersfoot SA69 9EX* Tel (01834) 811047

CAMPION, Peter Robert. b 64. Bp's Univ Canada BA87 TCD BTh90 MA93 MPhil97 Homerton Coll Cam PGCE94. **d** 90 **p** 91. C Belfast H Trin and Ardoyne *Conn* 90-93; C Taney *D & G* 94-00; Dean's V St Patr Cathl Dublin 96-00; Canada from 00; Chapl Netherwood Sch Rothesday from 00. *RCS Netherwood School, 40 College Hill Road, Rothesday NB, Canada, E2E 5H1* Tel (001) (506) 847 8224 Fax 848 0851 E-mail campionp@rcsn.nb.ca

CAMPLING, The Very Revd Christopher Russell. b 25. St Edm Hall Ox BA50 MA54. Cuddesdon Coll 50. **d** 51 **p** 52. C Basingstoke *Win* 51-55; Min Can Ely Cathl *Ely* 55-60; Chapl K Sch Ely 55-60; Chapl Lancing Coll 60-68; P-in-c Birlingham w Nafford *Worc* 68-75; V Pershore w Wick 68-75; RD Pershore 70-76; Hon Can Worc Cathl 74-84; V Pershore w Pinvin, Wick and Birlingham 75-76; Dioc Dir of Educn 76-84; Adn Dudley 76-84; P-in-c Dodderhill 76-84; Dean Ripon 84-95; Chmn CCC

88-94; rtd 95; Perm to Offic *Chich* from 95. *Pebble Ridge, Aglaia Road, Worthing BN11 5SW* Tel (01903) 246598

CAMPLING, Doreen Elizabeth. b 31. K Coll Lon BSc55. Dioc OLM tr scheme. **d** 01 **p** 02. OLM Bridport *Sarum* from 01. *Harbour Lights, Coneygar Park, Bridport DT6 3BA* Tel (01308) 425670

CAMPLING, Michael. b 27. Trin Coll Cam BA50 MA61. Wells Th Coll 51. **d** 53 **p** 54. C Calne *Sarum* 53-57; C Roehampton H Trin *S'wark* 57-61; V Crowthorne *Ox* 61-75; P-in-c Foleshill St Laur *Cov* 75-81; V 81-83; R Old Alresford and Bighton *Win* 83-92; rtd 92; Chapl St Marg Convent E Grinstead 92-99; Hon C Bexhill St Pet *Chich* from 99. *4 Calverley Court, 10 Collington Avenue, Bexhill-on-Sea TN39 3QA* Tel (01424) 215483

CANADA, Primate of All. *See* PEERS, The Most Revd Michael Geoffrey

CANDELAND, Thomas Blyde. b 37. **d** 99 **p** 00. OLM Lyng, Sparham, Elsing, Bylaugh, Bawdeswell etc *Nor* from 99. *2 Hammond Place, Lyng, Norwich NR9 5RQ* Tel (01603) 871674

CANDLER, David Cecil. b 24. Cape Town Univ BSc47 Keble Coll Ox BA50 MA55. St Paul's Coll Grahamstown 56. **d** 56 **p** 57. S Rhodesia 57-65; Rhodesia 65-80; Zimbabwe 80-85; R Barningham w Matlaske w Baconsthorpe etc *Nor* 85-94; rtd 94; Perm to Offic *Nor* from 94. *Millstone, Mill Lane, Aldborough, Norwich NR11 7NS* Tel (01263) 577420

CANE, Anthony William Nicholas Strephon. b 61. Cape Town Univ BA81 Birm Univ MPhil93 PhD03. Westcott Ho Cam 87. **d** 90 **p** 91. C Kings Heath *Birm* 90-93; Chapl Brighton Univ *Chich* 93-99; P-in-c Torquay St Luke *Ex* 99-01; Dioc Adv in Adult Tr 99-01; Dioc Adv for Educn and Tr of Adults *Chich* from 01; C Ringmer from 01. *Cley House, Lewes Road, Ringmer, Lewes BN8 5QF* Tel (01273) 812967 *or* 421021 E-mail anthony cane@lineone.net *or* anthony.cane@diochi.org.uk

CANEY, Canon Robert Swinbank. b 37. St Jo Coll Cam 57. Lich Th Coll 58. **d** 61 **p** 62. C Kingswinford H Trin *Lich* 61-64; C Castle Church 64-67; V Bradwell *Derby* 67-73; V Fairfield 73-84; RD Buxton 78-84; P-in-c Peak Forest and Wormhill 79-83; R Wirksworth w Alderwasley, Carsington etc 84-92; TR Wirksworth 92-02; Hon Can Derby Cathl 93-02; rtd 02. *2 Erica Drive, South Normanton, Alfreton DE55 2ET* Tel (01773) 581106

CANHAM, John Graham. b 33. Univ of Wales (Lamp) BA55. Chich Th Coll 55. **d** 57 **p** 58. C Hawarden *St As* 57-64; Asst Chapl Ellesmere Coll Shropshire 64-66; Chapl Ches Cathl Choir Sch 66-73; Chapl Choral Ches Cathl 66-73; Asst Chapl Rossall Sch Fleetwood 73-76 and 83-93; Chapl 76-83; V Minera *St As* from 93; RD Minera from 01. *The Vicarage, Church Road, Minera, Wrexham LL11 3DA* Tel (01978) 753133

CANHAM, Philip Edward. b 15. St Aid Birkenhead 46. **d** 46 **p** 47. C Bury St Paul *Man* 46-49; India 49-52; P-in-c Carl St Herbert w St Steph *Carl* 52-56; R Clayhidon *Ex* 56-58; P-in-c Inverkeithing *St And* 58-60; P-in-c Rosyth 58-60; R Aikton *Carl* 60-65; V Dalston 65-70; V Irthington 70-76; P-in-c Addingham 76-79; P-in-c Edenhall w Langwathby and Culgaith 76-79; P-in-c Greenhead *Newc* 79-80; P-in-c Lambley w Knaresdale 79-80; rtd 80. *6 Eden Park Crescent, Carlisle CA1 2UF* Tel (01228) 547236

CANHAM, Robert Edwin Francis. b 24. FRCO59 ARCM. **d** 74 **p** 75. NSM Newlyn St Pet *Truro* 74-75; C Phillack w Gwithian 75-79; P-in-c Phillack w Gwithian and Gwinear 79-83; V Greenham *Ox* 83-93; rtd 93; Perm to Offic *Chich* from 93. *Cross Way, 1A Torton Hill Road, Arundel BN18 9HF* Tel (01903) 883614

CANHAM, William Alexander. b 26. Clare Coll Cam BA47 MA56. Roch Th Coll 65. **d** 67 **p** 68. C Orpington St Andr *Roch* 67-70; C Guernsey St Steph *Win* 70-75; Chapl Eliz Coll Guernsey 72-75; R Tadley St Pet *Win* 75-83; V Bournemouth St Luke 83-91; R Guernsey St Marguerite de la Foret 91-96; rtd 96; Perm to Offic *Win* from 96; Perm to Offic *Portsm* from 96. *56 The Causeway, Petersfield GU31 4JS* Tel (01730) 269413

CANN, Christopher James. b 64. St Andr Univ BA MA. St Steph Ho Ox. **d** 91 **p** 92. C Newport St Julian *Mon* 91-93; Chapl Smallwood Manor Sch Uttoxeter 93-99; Hd Master from 97. *Smallwood Manor Preparatory School, Uttoxeter ST3 3BS* Tel (01889) 563666

CANNAM, Martin Stafford John. b 68. Jes Coll Ox BA90 MA95. Wycliffe Hall Ox 93. **d** 96 **p** 97. C Childwall All SS *Liv* 96-00; V Biddulph *Lich* from 00. *The Vicarage, 7 Wrexham Close, Biddulph, Stoke-on-Trent ST8 6RJ* Tel (01782) 513247 *or* 513891 E-mail martin@cannam.fsnet.co.uk

CANNELL, Anthea Marjorie. b 45. UEA MA85. EAMTC 01. **d** 02. NSM Theydon Bois *Chelmsf* from 02. *118 High Street, Roydon, Harlow CM19 5EF* Tel (01279) 792543 E-mail acannell@fish.co.uk

CANNER, Canon Peter George. b 24. St Chad's Coll Dur BA49 DipTh51 MA55. **d** 51 **p** 52. C Stoke *Cov* 51-54; S Africa 53-63; V Tynemouth Ch Ch *Newc* 63-77; V Ponteland 77-89; Hon Can Newc Cathl 80-89; rtd 89; Perm to Offic *Newc* from 89. *The Rigg, 4 Back Croft, Rothbury, Morpeth NE65 7YB* Tel (01669) 21319

CANNING, Arthur Brian. b 12. St Jo Coll Dur BA37 MA40. **d** 37 **p** 38. C Darlington St Cuth *Dur* 37-42; V Sellack and King's Caple *Heref* 42-50; V Lugwardine w Bartestree 50-66; Bp's Dom Chapl 54-65; V New Romney w Hope and St Mary's Bay etc *Cant* 66-71; V Boughton Monchelsea 71-79; rtd 79; Perm to Offic *Heref* 81-96. *Harp Cottage, Old Radnor, Presteigne LD8 2RH* Tel (01544) 350312

CANNING, Canon Arthur James. b 45. St Jo Coll Dur BA66 Linacre Coll Ox BA70 MA74 Lambeth STh90. Ripon Hall Ox 67. **d** 71 **p** 72. C Coleshill *Birm* 71-74; C Frome St Jo *B & W* 75-76; V Frizington and Arlecdon *Carl* 76-80; P-in-c Foleshill St Paul *Cov* 80-81; V from 81; Hon Can Cov Cathl from 00. *St Paul's Vicarage, 13 St Paul's Road, Coventry CV6 5DE* Tel (024) 7668 8283

CANNING, Graham Gordon Blakeman. b 33. S'wark Ord Course 73. **d** 76 **p** 77. NSM Mill Hill Jo Keble Ch *Lon* 76-78; TV Dorchester *Ox* 78-85; V Shipton-under-Wychwood w Milton, Fifield etc 85-98; RD Chipping Norton 95-00; rtd 98; Perm to Offic *Ox* from 00. *Moredays, 36 The Slade, Oxford OX7 3SJ* Tel (01608) 810421 Fax as telephone
E-mail gcanning@gcanning.u-net.com

CANNING, John Graham. b 21. Edin Th Coll 47. **d** 49 **p** 50. C Penton Street St Silas w All SS *Lon* 49-54; C Poplar 54-55; N Rhodesia 55-62; V Hammersmith St Jo *Lon* 62-90; rtd 90; Perm to Offic *B & W* from 90. *11 Circus Field, Glastonbury BA6 9PE* Tel (01458) 833708

CANNING, Peter Christopher. b 52. Birm Poly CQSW. St Jo Coll Nottm 87. **d** 89 **p** 90. C Cov St Mary *Cov* 89-93; V Hartshill 93-96; rtd 96. *11 Thackeray Close, Galley Common, Nuneaton CV10 9RT* Tel (024) 7639 8828

CANNON, Elizabeth Mary. b 50. EAMTC 94. **d** 97 **p** 98. NSM New Catton Ch Ch *Nor* 97-00; P-in-c Cross Roads cum Lees *Bradf* from 00. *St James's Vicarage, Haworth Road, Cross Roads, Keighley BD22 9DL* Tel (01535) 642210
E-mail rev-liz@fish.co.uk

CANNON, Mark Harrison. b 60. Keble Coll Ox BA82. Cranmer Hall Dur 83. **d** 85 **p** 86. C Skipton Ch Ch *Bradf* 85-88; Dioc Youth Officer 88-92; C Baildon 88-92; P-in-c Church Coniston *Carl* 92-00; P-in-c Torver 92-00; P-in-c Brindle *Blackb* from 00; Dioc Voc Adv from 00. *The Rectory, Sandy Lane, Brindle, Chorley PR6 8NJ* Tel (01254) 854130
E-mail mhcannon@fsmail.net

CANNON, Tony Arthur. b 57. Oak Hill Th Coll 94. **d** 96 **p** 97. C Church Stretton *Heref* 96-00; P-in-c Kingham w Churchill, Daylesford and Sarsden *Ox* 00-01; TV Chipping Norton from 01. *6 The Grange, Kingham, Chipping Norton OX7 6XY* Tel (01608) 658164 Fax 08700-940150
E-mail tonycannon@tiscali.co.uk

CANSDALE, George Graham. b 38. Mert Coll Ox BA60 MA64 DipEd61. Clifton Th Coll 62. **d** 64 **p** 65. C Heatherlands St Jo *Sarum* 64-67; Kenya 68-76; P-in-c Clapham *St Alb* 76-80; V 80-89; Bedford Sch 89-97; Lic to Offic *St Alb* 93-01; Perm to Offic *Wakef* from 01; rtd 01. *7 Stubbins Close, Mytholmroyd, Hebden Bridge HX7 5HP* Tel (01422) 881693

CANSDALE, Philip John. b 73. Keble Coll Ox BA95 MA99. Trin Coll Bris BA98 MA99. **d** 99 **p** 00. C Cant St Mary Bredin *Cant* 99-03; C Penn Fields *Lich* from 03. *100 Bellencroft Gardens, Merry Hill, Wolverhampton WV3 8DU* Tel (01902) 763603
E-mail curate@smb.org.uk

CANSDALE, Simon James Lee. b 68. Keble Coll Ox BA90. Wycliffe Hall Ox 93. **d** 95 **p** 96. C Bletchley *Ox* 95-98; C Cambridge H Trin *Ely* 98-01; R W Bridgford *S'well* from 01. *The Rectory, 86 Bridgford Road, West Bridgford, Nottingham NG2 6AX* Tel 0115-981 1112 E-mail rector@stgiles.org.uk

CANT, Christopher Somerset Travers. b 51. Keble Coll Ox BA72 MA76 Ex Univ PGCE77. All Nations Chr Coll 80 Wycliffe Hall Ox 93. **d** 87 **p** 90. Pakistan 87-92; Lic to Offic *Cov* 92-93; Warden St Clem Family Cen Ox 93-95; C Gt Ilford St Andr *Chelmsf* 95-98; V Hainault from 98. *St Paul's Vicarage, 143 Arrowsmith Road, Chigwell IG7 4NZ* Tel (020) 8500 3366
E-mail chriscant@tiscali.co.uk

CANT, David Edward. b 49. Sheff Univ LLB70. Oak Hill Th Coll DipTh89. **d** 89 **p** 90. C Newburn *Newc* 89-92; C N Shields 92-93; TV 93-98; Chapl Tynemouth Coll 94-98; P-in-c Wylam *Newc* from 98. *The Vicarage, Church Road, Wylam NE41 8AT* Tel (01661) 853254 E-mail david@stoswin.totalserve.co.uk

CANTERBURY, Archbishop of. *See* WILLIAMS, The Most Revd and Rt Hon Rowan Douglas

CANTERBURY, Archdeacon of. *See* EVANS, The Ven Patrick Alexander Sidney

CANTERBURY, Dean of. *See* WILLIS, The Very Revd Robert Andrew

CANTI, Mrs Christine. b 24. St Alb Minl Tr Scheme 82. **dss** 85 **d** 87 **p** 94. Radlett *St Alb* 85-86; Hon C Pitminster w Corfe *B & W* 87-90; Perm to Offic from 90. *Brook Farm House, Corfe, Taunton TA3 7BU* Tel (01823) 421623

CANTRELL, David Grindon. b 59. Bris Univ BSc80 Nottm Univ PhD83 Pemb Coll Cam BA88. Ridley Hall Cam 86. **d** 89 **p** 90. C Low Harrogate St Mary *Ripon* 89-90; C Horsforth 90-94; Chapl

Nottm Trent Univ *S'well* 94-97; V Porchester 97-00; Chapl York Univ *York* from 00. *Bede House, Heslington, York YO1 5ED* Tel (01904) 413925 E-mail david.cantrell@ukgateway.net

CANTRILL, Mark James. b 67. Lanc Univ BEd89. St Jo Coll Nottm 00. **d** 02 **p** 03. C Warsop *S'well* from 02. *Heather Villas, 23 Main Street, Blidworth, Mansfield NG21 0PX* Tel (01623) 460978 Mobile 07759-305766 E-mail markojay@ntlworld.com

CAPE TOWN, Dean of. *See* SMITH, The Very Revd Rowan Quentin

CAPE TOWN (Saldanah Bay), Suffragan Bishop of. *See* MARCUS, The Rt Revd Justus Mauritius

CAPE TOWN, Archbishop of. *See* NDUNGANE, The Most Revd Winston Hugh Njongonkulu

CAPEL, Luke Thomas. *See* IRVINE-CAPEL, Luke Thomas

CAPEL-EDWARDS, Maureen. b 36. Southn Univ BSc60 Reading Univ PhD69. St Alb Minl Tr Scheme 84. **d** 87 **p** 94. NSM Ware St Mary *St Alb* 87-90; Chapl Hertf Regional Coll of FE 87-00; NSM Hertford All SS *St Alb* 90-94; NSM Aspenden and Layston w Buntingford 94-95; NSM Aspenden, Buntingford and Westmill 95-00; P-in-c Ardeley from 00; P-in-c Cottered w Broadfield and Throcking from 00. *The Rectory, Warren Lane, Cottered, Buntingford SG9 9QA* Tel (01763) 281218 E-mail capeland@waitrose.com

CAPELIN-JONES, Kevin Stuart. b 73. Huddersfield Univ BMus96. Ox Minl Tr Coll BA02. **d** 02 **p** 03. C Croglin *Carl* from 02; C Holme Eden from 02; C Wetheral w Warwick from 02. *The Rectory, Plains Road, Wetheral, Carlisle CA4 8LA* Tel (01228) 560216 E-mail wetheral.rectory@virgin.net

CAPERON, John Philip. b 44. Bris Univ BA66 Open Univ MPhil80 Ox Univ MSc83 Kent Univ MA99. Ox NSM Course 80. **d** 83 **p** 84. NSM Hook Norton w Gt Rollright, Swerford etc *Ox* 83-86; NSM Knaresborough *Ripon* 86-92; Dep Hd St Aid Sch Harrogate 86-92; Hd and Chapl Bennett Memorial Dioc Sch Tunbridge Wells from 92; Perm to Offic *Chich* 98-03; Hon C Mayfield from 03. *Bennett Memorial Diocesan School, Culverden Down, Tunbridge Wells TN4 9SH* Tel (01892) 521595 Fax 514424 E-mail head@bennett.kent.sch.uk *or* jcaperon@fish.co.uk

CAPES, Arthur Geoffrey. b 33. Bps' Coll Cheshunt 58. **d** 61 **p** 62. C Seacroft *Ripon* 61-66; Guyana 66-80; V Claremont H Angels *Man* 80-85; V Blyton w Pilham *Linc* 85-90; V E Stockwith 86-90; V Laughton w Wildsworth 86-90; R Broad Town, Clyffe Pypard and Tockenham *Sarum* 90-94; rtd 99. *45 Leigh Road, Westbury BA13 3QW* Tel (01373) 859163

CAPES, Dennis Robert. b 34. Linc Th Coll 65 Handsworth Coll Birm DipTh58. **d** 64 **p** 65. In Methodist Ch (Sarawak) 59-63; C Lt Coates *Linc* 64-66; Malaysia 66-69; V Gosberton Clough *Linc* 69-71; V Kirton in Holland 71-80; Area Sec USPG *Cov, Heref* and *Worc* 80-87; Chapl Copenhagen w Aarhus *Eur* 87-93; TV Liv Our Lady and St Nic w St Anne *Liv* 93-99; rtd 99. *35 Hardwick Avenue, Newark NG24 4AW* Tel (01636) 672874

CAPIE, Fergus Bernard. b 47. Auckland Univ BA68 MA71. Wycliffe Hall Ox BA77. **d** 77 **p** 78. C Ox St Mich w St Martin and All SS *Ox* 77-80; Chapl Summer Fields Sch Ox 80-91; Hon C Wolvercote w Summertown *Ox* 87-91; Perm to Offic *St E* 91; TV E Ham w Upton Park St Alb *Chelmsf* 91-95; P-in-c Brondesbury St Anne w Kilburn H Trin *Lon* 95-01; V from 01; Chapl NW Lon Coll from 95. *125 Salusbury Road, London NW6 6RG* Tel (020) 7625 7470, 7372 6864 *or* 7604 3053 Fax 7604 3052
E-mail fergus.capie@dlondon.org.uk

CAPITANCHIK, Sophie Rebecca. *See* JELLEY, Mrs Sophie Rebecca

CAPLE, Stephen Malcolm. b 55. Chich Th Coll 86. **d** 88 **p** 89. C Newington St Mary *S'wark* 88-92; V Eltham St Sav 92-97; V Salfords from 97. *The Vicarage, Honeycrock Lane, Redhill RH1 5DF* Tel (01737) 762232
E-mail stephen@caple.fsnet.co.uk

CAPON, Canon Anthony Charles. b 26. Trin Coll Cam BA51 MA55. Wycliffe Coll Toronto BD65 DD82 Oak Hill Th Coll 51. **d** 53 **p** 54. C Portman Square St Paul *Lon* 53-56; Canada from 56; Hon Can Montreal from 78; Prin Montreal Dioc Th Coll 78-91; rtd 91. *5 Loradean Crescent, Kingston ON, Canada, K7K 6X9* Tel (001) (613) 545 9781 E-mail acapon@cgocable.net

CAPON, Gerwyn Huw. b 65. Liv Jo Moores Univ BSc92. St Steph Ho Ox 01. **d** 03. C W Derby St Mary *Liv* from 03. *St Paul's Vicarage, Carlton Lane, Stoneycroft, Liverpool L13 6QS* Tel 0151-228 0307 E-mail gerwyn@hermes7.fsnet.co.uk

CAPPER, Mrs Elizabeth Margaret. b 31. St Chris Coll Blackheath 52. **dss** 79 **d** 87 **p** 94. The Dorothy Kerin Trust Burrswood 79; Whitstable *Cant* 80-96; Hon Par Dn 87-94; Perm to Offic 94-96; rtd 91. *11 North Road, Loughor, Swansea SA4 6QE* Tel (01792) 892834

CAPPER, Canon Richard. b 49. Leeds Univ BSc70 Fitzw Coll Cam BA72 MA79. Westcott Ho Cam 70. **d** 73 **p** 74. C Wavertree H Trin *Liv* 73-76; P-in-c Ince St Mary 76-79; V 79-83; V Gt Crosby St Faith 83-97; AD Bootle 89-97; Can Res Wakef Cathl *Wakef* from 97. *3 Cathedral Close, Wakefield WF1 2DP* Tel (01924) 210007 E-mail capper@3cathedralclose.freeserve.co.uk

CAPPER, Robert Melville. b 52. Chu Coll Cam BA74 MA80. Wycliffe Hall Ox 74. **d** 77 **p** 78. C Maindee *Mon* 77-81; TV Aberystwyth *St D* 81-87; Chapl Univ of Wales (Abth) 81-87; V Malpas *Mon* 87-00; V Gabalfa *Llan* from 00. *St Mark's Vicarage, 208 North Road, Gabalfa, Cardiff CF14 3BL* Tel (029) 2061 3286

CAPPER, William Alan. QUB BTh. **d** 88 **p** 89. C Dundonald *D & D* 88-91; C Lisburn Ch Ch *Conn* 91-94; I Tamlaght O'Crilly Upper w Lower *D & R* 94-96; I Lack *Clogh* from 03. *The Rectory, Lack, Enniskillen BT93 0DN* Tel (028) 6863 1360

CAPPLEMAN, Graham Robert (Sam). b 56. Chelsea Coll Lon BSc79 Sheff Univ PhD83. ADipR92 St Alb and Ox Min Course 94. **d** 97 **p** 98. NSM Bedf St Mark *St Alb* from 97. *107 Dover Crescent, Bedford MK41 8QR* Tel (01234) 266952 Mobile 07836-784051 Fax 402624 E-mail samc@tesco.net

CAPPLEMAN, Mrs Jennifer Margaret. b 53. Liv Univ CertEd74. St Alb and Ox Min Course 97. **d** 00 **p** 01. NSM Bedford St Pet w St Cuth *St Alb* 00-03; C Goldington from 03. *107 Dover Crescent, Bedford MK41 8QR* Tel (01234) 405253 Mobile 07714-701008 Fax (01234) 402624 E-mail jennie.cappleman@ntlworld.com

CAPRON, David Cooper. b 45. Open Univ BA80. Sarum & Wells Th Coll 71. **d** 75 **p** 76. C Cov St Mary *Cov* 75-79; V Shottery St Andr 79-86; TV Stratford-on-Avon w Bishopton 79-86; V Shottery St Andr 86; V Newton Aycliffe *Dur* 86-89; TR 89-90; P-in-c Alcester and Arrow w Oversley and Weethley *Cov* 90-95; R from 95; Chapl Warks Fire and Rescue Service from 93. *St Nicholas' Rectory, Old Rectory Garden, Alcester B49 5DB* Tel and fax (01789) 764261 Mobile 07780-707521 E-mail caprons@ntlworld.com

CAPRON, Ronald Beresford. b 35. Clifton Th Coll. **d** 62 **p** 63. Canada 62-65; C Evington *Leic* 65-67; R Gaddesby w S Croxton 67-71; R Beeby 67-71; Chapl RAF 71-83; rtd 95. *107 Coverside Road, Great Glen, Leicester LE8 9EB* Tel 0116-259 2809

CAPSTICK, John Nowell. b 30. AKC54. **d** 55 **p** 56. C Skipton Ch Ch *Bradf* 55-57; C Buxton *Derby* 57-61; V Codnor and Loscoe 61-63; C-in-c Rawthorpe CD *Wakef* 63-64; V Rawthorpe 64-70; V Netherthong 70-89; TV Upper Holme Valley 89-95; rtd 96; Perm to Offic *Wakef* from 96. *8 Town End Avenue, Holmfirth, Huddersfield HD7 1YW* Tel (01484) 688708

CAPSTICK, William Richard Dacre. b 32. Pemb Coll Ox. Chich Th Coll 61. **d** 64 **p** 65. C Hunslet St Mary and Stourton St Andr *Ripon* 64-67; C Knaresborough H Trin 67-71; V Stratfield Mortimer *Ox* 71-76; P-in-c St Marylebone Ch Ch w St Paul *Lon* 76-78; TV St Marylebone Ch Ch 78-79; TR Newbury *Ox* 79-89; TV Brighton St Pet and St Nic w Chpl Royal *Chich* 89-97; rtd 97. *28 Bloomsbury Street, Brighton BN2 1HQ* Tel (01273) 681171

CARBERRY, Derek William. b 65. SEN88 Leeds Univ BA03. Coll of Resurr Mirfield 01. **d** 03. C Tynemouth Cullercoats St Paul *Newc* from 03. *14 Naters Street, Whitley Bay NE26 2PG* Tel 0191-253 2781 Mobile 07814-049605 E-mail d_carberry@hotmail.com

CARBERRY, Leon Carter. b 54. Penn State Univ BSc76. St Steph Ho Ox 81. **d** 84 **p** 85. C Peterlee *Dur* 84-87; C Newton Aycliffe 87-89; V Choral York Minster *York* 89-94; Chapl St Pet Sch York 94-95; V Fylingdales and Hawsker cum Stainsacre *York* 95-01; Chapl Burrswood Chr Cen *Roch* 01-03; V Beckenham St Jas from 03. *The Vicarage, 15 St James Avenue, Beckenham BR3 4HF* Tel (020) 8650 0420 Fax as telephone E-mail leoncarberry@tinyworld.co.uk *or* leoncarberry@hotmail.co

CARBY, Stuart Graeme. b 51. CBiol77 MIBiol77 LRSC78 Man Univ BSc73 Leeds Univ PGCE74 Open Univ MA96. St Jo Coll Nottm 92. **d** 92 **p** 93. C Magor w Redwick and Undy *Mon* 92-96; TV Cyncoed from 96. *100 Hillrise, Llanedeyrn, Cardiff CF23 6UL* Tel (029) 2073 3915

CARD, Terence Leslie. b 37. K Coll Lon BD68 AKC68 Heythrop Coll Lon MTh84. **d** 69 **p** 70. C Thundersley *Chelmsf* 69-72; Lic to Offic *Bradf* 72-75; V Chingford St Anne *Chelmsf* 75-81; RD Waltham Forest 78-81; R Springfield All SS 81-83; C Becontree St Jo 85-87; rtd 87; Perm to Offic *Ely* 96-00. *11 Harvey Goodwin Gardens, Cambridge CB4 3EZ* Tel (01223) 367715

CARD, Thomas Ian. b 36. RD76. Master Mariner 66. Portsm Dioc Tr Course 88. **d** 89. NSM Binstead *Portsm* 89-95; Miss to Seafarers from 89; NSM Swanmore St Mich w Havenstreet *Portsm* 89-92; NSM Havenstreet St Pet 92-95; NSM Ryde All SS from 95. *Dolphins, 49 Mayfield Road, Ryde PO33 3PR* Tel (01983) 564749

CARD-REYNOLDS, Charles Leonard. b 67. Lon Univ BD92 Hughes Hall Cam BA94 MA98. St Steph Ho Ox 96. **d** 98 **p** 99. C Reading H Trin *Ox* from 98; C Reading St Mark from 98; FSJ from 01. *St Mark's Vicarage, 88 Connaught Road, Reading RG30 2UF* Tel 0118-958 7400 Fax as telephone E-mail clcardreynolds@btinternet.com

CARDALE, Charles Anthony. b 21. St D Coll Lamp BA47 Lich Th Coll 55. **d** 56 **p** 57. C Honicknowle CD *Ex* 56-58; C Bideford 58-60; R Wembworthy w Eggesford 60-69; V Brushford 63-69; V Staverton w Landscove 69-87; R Broadhempston, Woodland, Staverton etc 88-89; Perm to Offic from 89; rtd 90. *Keyberry,*

13 Woodland Close, Staverton, Totnes TQ9 6PQ Tel (01803) 762277

CARDALE, Edward Charles. b 50. CCC Ox BA72 MA73. Cuddesdon Coll 72 Union Th Sem (NY) STM74. **d** 74 **p** 75. C E Dulwich St Jo *S'wark* 74-77; Asst P Bainbridge Is USA 77-80; V Ponders End St Matt *Lon* 80-84; V Lytchett Minster *Sarum* 84-98; Dir Past Studies Coll of the Resurr Mirfield 98-02; P-in-c Lemsford *St Alb* from 02; Tutor St Alb and Ox Min Course from 02. *7 High Oaks Road, Welwyn Garden City AL8 7BJ* Tel (01707) 327621 E-mail edward.cardale@btopenworld.com

CARDELL-OLIVER, John Anthony. b 43. Em Coll Cam BA67 MA72 Univ of W Aus BEd75 MEd85. Westcott Ho Cam 86. **d** 86 **p** 88. Australia 86-88; Perm to Offic *Ely* 88-89; C Stansted Mountfitchet *Chelmsf* 89-92; R Langham w Boxted 92-02; rtd 02. *1 Burt Street, Albany, W Australia 6330* Tel (0061) (8) 9383 7381 Fax as telephone E-mail jco@graduate.uwa.edu.au

CARDEN, Edwin William. b 54. Cranmer Hall Dur 85. **d** 87 **p** 88. C Thundersley *Chelmsf* 87-91; CUF 91-93; NSM Poplar *Lon* 91-93; Chapl Pathfinder Mental Health Services NHS Trust 93-99; Chapl SW Lon and St George's Mental Health NHS Trust 99-00; Selection Sec Min Division from 00; NSM Maldon St Mary w Mundon *Chelmsf* from 00. *21 Plume Avenue, Maldon CM9 6LB* Tel (01621) 854908 *or* (020) 7898 1402 E-mail eddie.carden@mindiv.c-of-e.org.uk

CARDEN, John Brumfitt. b 24. Lon Coll of Div 48. **d** 52 **p** 53. Pakistan 52-55, 57-60 and 65-69; C Leeds Halton St Wilfrid *Ripon* 56-57; Lit Sec CMS 60-65; Asia Sec CMS 70-76; Hon C Croydon St Sav *Cant* 75-76; C-in-c Bath St Steph *B & W* 76-82; V 82-84; CMS 84-89; Jerusalem 84-87; Exec Asst WCC Geneva 87-89; rtd 89; Miss Partner CMS from 89; Perm to Offic *York* from 89. *81 The Village, Haxby, York YO32 2JE* Tel (01904) 750035

CARDIGAN, Archdeacon of. *See* JONES, The Ven Benjamin Jenkin Hywel

CARDINAL, Ian Ralph. b 57. Qu Coll Birm 81. **d** 84 **p** 85. C Whitkirk *Ripon* 84-87; C Knaresborough 87-89; P-in-c Wilsford *Linc* 89; P-in-c Ancaster 89; R Ancaster Wilsford Gp 89-94; P-in-c Wigginton *Lich* from 94; Warden of Readers from 96. *The Vicarage, Main Road, Wigginton, Tamworth B79 9DN* Tel (01827) 64537 Mobile 07778-055993 E-mail ian.cardinal@lichfield.anglican.org

CARDWELL, Edward Anthony Colin. b 42. Trin Coll Cam BA63 MA68. St Jo Coll Nottm 73. **d** 75 **p** 76. C Stapenhill w Cauldwell *Derby* 75-78; C Bramcote *S'well* 78-82; V S'well H Trin 81-92; R Eastwood from 92. *The Rectory, 5A Woodland Way, Eastwood, Nottingham NG16 3BU* Tel (01773) 712395 E-mail cardwell@eastwood88.freeserve.co.uk

CARDWELL, Joseph Robin. b 47. Qu Coll Cam BA68 MA77. Trin Coll Bris 73. **d** 76 **p** 77. C Bromley Ch Ch *Roch* 76-79; C Shirley *Win* 79-82; V Somborne w Ashley 82-90; V Derry Hill *Sarum* 90-94; V Derry Hill w Bremhill and Foxham 94-00; Community Affairs Chapl 90-94; V Lyddington and Wanborough and Bishopstone etc *Bris* from 00. *The Vicarage, 19 Church Road, Wanborough, Swindon SN4 0BZ* Tel (01793) 790242 E-mail robin@cardwell99.fsnet.co.uk

CARE, Canon Charles Richard. b 21. Univ of Wales (Lamp) BA42. St Mich Coll Llan 42. **d** 44 **p** 45. C Grangetown *Llan* 44-57; R St Brides Minor 57-88; RD Bridgend 75-88; Can Llan Cathl 83-88; Prec 87-88; rtd 88; Perm to Offic *Llan* from 88. *31 Laburnum Drive, Porthcawl CF36 5UA* Tel (01656) 785446

CAREW, Bryan Andrew. b 38. AIB63 ACIB87. St D Coll Lamp DipTh69. **d** 67 **p** 68. C Pembroke Dock St D 67-70; CF 70-74; P-in-c Gt and Lt Henny w Middleton *Chelmsf* 74-76; P-in-c Wickham St Paul w Twinstead 75-76; R Gt and Lt Henny w Middleton, Wickham St Paul etc 76-99; P-in-c Alphamstone w Lamarsh 99; V Alphamstone w Gt and Lt Henny, Lamarsh etc 99-03; rtd 03. *Branfields, The Street, Belchamp Otten, Sudbury CO10 7BG* Tel (01787) 278730

CAREY, Alan Lawrence. b 29. K Coll Lon AKC53. **d** 54 **p** 55. C Radford *Cov* 54-57; C Burnham *Ox* 57-65; C-in-c Cippenham CD 65-77; rtd 94. *12 Ormsby Street, Reading RG1 7YR* Tel 0118-961 2309

CAREY, Charles John. b 29. K Coll Lon BD53 AKC53. St Aug Coll Cant 71. **d** 72 **p** 73. C Spring Park *Cant* 72-74; C Ifield *Chich* 74-78; C Burgess Hill St Jo 78-80; Chapl Rush Green Hosp Romford 80-94; Chapl Oldchurch Hosp Romford 80-94; rtd 94. *Address withheld by request*

CAREY, Christopher Lawrence John. b 38. St Andr Univ BSc61 Lon Univ BD64. Clifton Th Coll 61. **d** 64 **p** 65. C Battersea Park St Sav *S'wark* 64-67; CMS Kenya 68-79; Overseas Regional Sec for E Africa CMS 79-98; NSM Chislehurst Ch Ch *Roch* 79-98; R Stickney Gp *Linc* from 99; RD Bolingbroke 02-03. *The Rectory, Horbling Lane, Stickney, Boston PE22 8DQ* Tel (01205) 480049 Fax 480044 E-mail chris@horblinglane.freeserve.co.uk

CAREY, Mark Jonathan. b 65. St Jo Coll Nottm BTh94. **d** 94 **p** 95. C Ossett *Wakef* 94-97; C Chapeltown *Sheff* 97-99; V Grenoside from 99. *St Mark's Vicarage, 19 Graven Close, Grenoside, Sheffield S35 8QT* Tel 0114-246 7513 E-mail mpjcarey@aol.com

CAREY, Canon Ronald Clive <u>Adrian</u>. b 21. K Coll Cam BA46 MA48. Chich Th Coll 47. **d** 48 **p** 49. C Harborne St Pet *Birm* 48-50; Bp's Dom Chapl *Chelmsf* 50-52; C Keighley *Bradf* 52-55; V Illingworth *Wakef* 55-59; Perm to Offic *S'wark* 59-68; Asst in Relig Broadcasting *S'wark* 59-68; V Claygate *Guildf* 68-78; RD Emly 72-77; Hon Can Guildf Cathl 78-86; R Guildf H Trin w St Mary 78-86; RD Guildf 84-86; rtd 86; Perm to Offic *Roch* from 86. *4 Chart View, Kemsing, Sevenoaks TN15 6PP* Tel (01732) 762629

CAREY, Mrs Wendy Marion. b 45. Bris Univ BA66 Lon Inst of Educn CertEd67. WMMTC 90. **d** 93 **p** 94. NSM Milton Keynes *Ox* 93-96; Sub Chapl HM Pris Woodhill 93-96; Chapl HM Pris Bullingdon 96-00; Ecum Tr Officer HM Pris Service Chapl from 00; Lic to Offic *Cov* from 00; Perm to Offic *Ox* from 00. *Prison Service College, Newbold Revel, Rugby CV23 0TH* Tel (01788) 834162

✠**CAREY OF CLIFTON, The Rt Revd and Rt Hon Lord (George Leonard).** b 35. PC91. Lon Univ BD62 MTh65 PhD71 Dur Univ Hon DD93 Open Univ Hon DD95 FRSA91 FKC93. ALCD61. **d** 62 **p** 63 **c** 87. C Islington St Mary *Lon* 62-66; Lect Oak Hill Th Coll 66-70; Lect St Jo Coll Nottm 70-75; V Dur St Nic *Dur* 75-82; Chapl HM Rem Cen Low Newton 77-81; Prin Trin Coll Bris 82-87; Hon Can Bris Cathl *Bris* 84-87; Bp B & W 87-91; Abp Cant 91-02; rtd 02. *4 Royal Park Mews, Vyvyan Road, Bristol BS8 3AD*

CARGILL THOMPSON, Edmund Alwyn James. b 72. St Jo Coll Ox BA94. Cranmer Hall Dur 98. **d** 00 **p** 01. C St Jo on Bethnal Green *Lon* 00-03; V Barkingside H Trin *Chelmsf* from 03. *Barkingside Vicarage, 36 Mossford Green, Ilford IG6 2BJ* Tel (020) 8550 2669 E-mail father.edmund@virgin.net

CARHART, John Richards. b 29. Bris Univ BA50 Salford Univ MSc77 Liv Univ MTh99 FRSA. St Deiniol's Hawarden 63. **d** 65 **p** 66. C Ches St Oswald w Lt St Jo *Ches* 65-72; Lect Ches Coll of HE 65-72; Prin Lect from 72; Dean Academic Studies 88-94; C Ches 72; Lic to Offic 73-85; Hon C Ches St Mary 85-00; rtd 00; Perm to Offic *Ches* from 00. *29 Abbot's Grange, Chester CH2 1AJ* Tel (01244) 380923

CARLESS, Canon Frank. b 22. Lon Univ BD56. St Aid Birkenhead 53. **d** 56 **p** 57. C Normanton *Wakef* 56-59; V Rashcliffe 59-64; V Warley 64-87; RD Halifax 82-86; Hon Can Wakef Cathl 86-87; rtd 87; Perm to Offic *Wakef* from 87. *130 Savile Park Road, Halifax HX1 2EX* Tel (01422) 348379

CARLILL, Adam Jonathan. b 66. Keble Coll Ox BA88. Linc Th Coll 88. **d** 90 **p** 91. C Romford St Edw *Chelmsf* 90-94; C Uckfield *Chich* 94-98; V Tilehurst St Geo *Ox* from 98; P-in-c Tilehurst St Mary from 02. *St George's Vicarage, 98 Grovelands Road, Reading RG3 2PD* Tel 0118-958 8354

CARLILL, Richard Edward. b 38. Westcott Ho Cam 77. **d** 79 **p** 80. C Prittlewell *Chelmsf* 79-83; TV Saffron Walden w Wendens Ambo and Littlebury 83-89; V Austwick w Foxholes, Butterwick, Cottam etc *York* 89-94; V Gt and Lt Driffield 94-03; RD Harthill 99-02; rtd 03. *31 Riverdene, Tweedmouth, Berwick-upon-Tweed TD15 2JD* Tel (01289) 303701

CARLIN, William Patrick <u>Bruce</u>. b 53. St Steph Ho Ox 75. **d** 78 **p** 79. C Penistone *Wakef* 78-81; C Barnsley St Mary 81-83; V Stockton St Chad *Dur* 83-93; V Hedworth 93-01; TR Kippax w Allerton Bywater *Ripon* from 01. *The Rectory, Church Lane, Kippax, Leeds LS25 7HF* Tel 0113-286 2710 Fax 286 7339 E-mail brucecarlin@freeuk.com *or* rector@stmarykippax.org.uk

CARLING, Mrs Bronwen Noel. b 43. SRN65 SCM73. Linc Th Coll 89. **d** 91 **p** 94. C Blakeney w Cley, Wiveton, Glandford etc *Nor* 91-94; C Trunch 94-96; TV 96-01; rtd 01; Perm to Offic *Nor* from 01. *3 Stranger's Court, Pottergate, Norwich NR2 1EX* Tel (01603) 763578 E-mail bncarling@sagainternet.co.uk

CARLISLE, Christopher John. b 39. Sheff Univ BEng62. NW Ord Course 72. **d** 75 **p** 76. C Bury St Paul *Man* 75-80; C Walkden Moor 80-82; V Lytham St Jo *Blackb* 82-02; rtd 02. *2 Reedy Acre Place, Lytham, Lytham St Annes FY8 4PR* Tel (01253) 739562

CARLISLE, John Patrick. b 66. St Andr Univ MTh89 Hughes Hall Cam PGCE90. St Steph Ho Ox 93. **d** 95 **p** 96. C Hendon St Alphage *Lon* 95-99; TV Ribbleton *Blackb* 99-03; V New Rossington *Sheff* from 03. *St Luke's Vicarage, The Circle, New Rossington, Doncaster DN11 0QP* Tel (01302) 868288 E-mail jpcarlisle@aol.com

CARLISLE, Matthew David. b 74. Man Univ BA96. Westcott Ho Cam 99. **d** 02 **p** 03. C Crompton *Man* from 02. *9 Scarr Lane, Shaw, Oldham OL2 8HQ* Tel (01706) 291366 Mobile 07870-760746 E-mail matthew.carlisle@ntlworld.com

CARLISLE, Archdeacon of. *See* THOMSON, The Ven David

CARLISLE, Bishop of. *See* DOW, The Rt Revd Geoffrey Graham

CARLISLE, Dean of. *See* KNOWLES, The Very Revd Graeme Paul

CARLOS, Francis John. b 29. Jes Coll Cam BA54 MA57. Wells Th Coll 52. **d** 55 **p** 56. C Canning Town St Matthias *Chelmsf* 55-57; C-in-c Thundersley CD *St E* 57-64; V New Thundersley *Chelmsf* 64-65; R Wentnor and Ratlinghope w Myndtown and Norbury *Heref* 65-89; P-in-c More w Lydham 82-89; P-in-c

Snead 85-89; R Wentnor w Ratlinghope, Myndtown, Norbury etc 89-94; rtd 94; Perm to Offic *Heref* from 94. *16 Springfield Park, Clee Hill, Ludlow SY8 3QY* Tel (01584) 891253

CARLSON, Blair Truett. b 52. Wheaton Coll Illinois BA74. Cranmer Hall Dur 00. **d** 02 **p** 03. C Hailsham *Chich* from 02. *19 St Wilfrid's Green, Hailsham BN27 1DR* Tel (01323) 442132 Fax as telephone E-mail bcarlson@onetel.net.uk

CARLSSON, Miss Siw. b 43. **d** 92 **p** 94. Par Dn Barnes St Mary *S'wark* 92-93; C Mitcham SS Pet and Paul 93-98; Asst Chapl SW Lon and St George's Mental Health NHS Trust 99-00; Chapl Ipswich Hosp NHS Trust from 00. *Ipswich Hospital, Heath Road, Ipswich IP4 5PD* Tel (01473) 712223 *or* 704100 Fax 703400

CARLTON, Roger John. b 51. **d** 80 **p** 81. NSM Downend *Bris* 80-83; NSM Heavitree w Ex St Paul *Ex* 83-87; Chapl St Marg Sch Ex 83-87; Chapl Ex Sch 83-87; TV Bickleigh (Plymouth) *Ex* 87-91; TR 91-93; TR Bickleigh and Shaugh Prior from 94; RD Ivybridge 93-98. *The Vicarage, 2 Blackeven Close, Roborough, Plymouth PL6 7AX* Tel (01752) 702119 Fax 768882 E-mail roger.carlton@btinternet.com

CARLYON, Miss Catherine Rachel. b 67. RN89 Plymouth Univ DipN97. Ripon Coll Cuddesdon 00. **d** 02 **p** 03. C Launceston *Truro* from 02. *11 Summerhill Road, Launceston PL15 7DU* Tel (01566) 779846 E-mail crcarlyon@hotmail.com

CARLYON (née ENGLAND), Mrs Jessie Marguerite <u>Tarie</u>. b 44. Westf Coll Lon BA66 K Coll Lon PGCE67. WMMTC 92. **d** 95 **p** 97. C Pontypool *Mon* 95-97; TV 97-00; V Bedwellty from 00. *The Rectory, Church Street, Aberbargoed, Bargoed CF81 9FF* Tel (01443) 829555

CARMAN, Jill Youde. b 37. Cartrefle Coll of Educn CertEd69 Liv Univ DipEd86. St Alb and Ox Min Course 97. **d** 99 **p** 00. NSM Markyate Street *St Alb* 99-02; NSM Quinton *Glouc* from 02. *The Vicarage, Lower Quinton, Stratford-upon-Avon CV37 8SG* Tel (01789) 720756

CARMAN, Roger Eric. b 40. Univ of Wales BSc62 MIEE. TISEC 92. **d** 97 **p** 98. C Dollar *St And* from 97. *7 Park Place, Dollar FK14 7AA* Tel (01259) 742485 *or* 0131-333 2000 Fax 0131-333 3607 E-mail roger_carman@classic.msn.com

CARMARTHEN, Archdeacon of. *See* CROCKETT, The Ven Phillip Anthony

CARMICHAEL, Elizabeth Dorothea Harriet. b 46. MBE95. LMH Ox MA73 BM73 BCh73 Worc Coll Ox BA83 Ox Univ DPhil91. **d** 91 **p** 92. S Africa 91-96; Chapl and Tutor St Jo Coll Ox from 96. *St John's College, Oxford OX1 3JP* Tel (01865) 277300 Fax 277435 E-mail liz.carmichael@sjc.ox.ac.uk

CARMICHAEL, Peter Iain. b 28. Chich Th Coll 75. **d** 75 **p** 76. C Rye w Rye Harbour and Playden *Chich* 75-79; C Rye, Rye Harbour and Playden and Iden 79-80; R Earnley and E Wittering 80-94; rtd 94; Perm to Offic *Chich* from 94. *20 East Street, Selsey, Chichester PO20 0BJ* Tel (01243) 606194

CARMODY, Canon Dermot <u>Patrick</u> Roy. b 41. CITC 77. **d** 77 **p** 78. C Dublin Zion Ch *D & G* 77-79; I Dunganstown w Redcross 79-84; TV Dublin Ch Ch Cathl Gp 84-93; Can Ch Ch Cathl Dublin 84-92; Preb Ch Ch Cathl Dublin 92-93; I Mullingar, Portnashangan, Moyliscar, Kilbixy etc *M & K* from 93; Dir of Ords (Meath) from 97; Can Meath from 98; Can Kildare Cathl from 98; Treas from 00; P-in-c Rathmolyon w Castlerickard, Rathcore and Agher from 00. *All Saints' Rectory, Mullingar, Co Westmeath, Irish Republic* Tel (00353) (44) 48376 Fax as telephone E-mail pcarmody@dmcwebs.com

CARMYLLIE, Robert Jonathan. b 63. Cov Poly BSc85. St Jo Coll Dur 85. **d** 88 **p** 89. C Horwich *Man* 88-92; P-in-c Edgeside 92-99; P-in-c Astley from 99. *St Stephen's Vicarage, 7 Holbeck, Astley, Tyldesley, Manchester M29 7DU* Tel (01942) 883313

CARNALL, Mrs Nicola Jane. b 66. St Jo Coll Nottm 99. **d** 01 **p** 02. C Edwinstowe *S'well* from 01. *46 Occupation Lane, Edwinstowe, Mansfield NG21 9HU* Tel (01623) 824278 E-mail njcarnall@aol.com

CARNE, Canon Brian George. b 29. FSA Liv Univ BCom50. Qu Coll Birm 53. **d** 55 **p** 56. C Swindon St Aug *Bris* 55-58; C Bris St Andr w St Bart 58-60; R Lydiard Millicent w Lydiard Tregoz 60-68; V Bris St Andr Hartcliffe 68-74; V Almondsbury 74-91; RD Westbury and Severnside 80-86; Hon Can Bris Cathl 82-91; P-in-c Littleton on Severn w Elberton 83-91; P-in-c Olveston 83-91; rtd 91; Perm to Offic *Bris* from 92; *Glouc* 92-98 and from 01. *Whitehouse Farm, English Bicknor, Coleford GL16 7PA* Tel (01594) 860200

CARNE, Norman David <u>John</u>. b 27. Roch Th Coll 59. **d** 62 **p** 63. C Roch St Justus *Roch* 62-66; C Strood St Mary 66-68; R Westcote Barton and Steeple Barton *Ox* 68-74; P-in-c Enstone and Heythrop 74-81; V 82-92; rtd 92; Perm to Offic *Leic* 93-98. *45 Beckingthorpe Drive, Bottesford, Nottingham NG13 0DN* Tel (01949) 843890

CARNE-ROSS, Stewart Pattison. b 24. Wycliffe Hall Ox 58. **d** 59 **p** 60. C Brockley Hill St Sav *S'wark* 59-62; C Dulwich St Barn 62-64; V Champion Hill St Sav 64-70; P-in-c Stanton Lacy *Heref* 70-72; V 72-77; V Bromfield 70-77; R Culmington w Onibury 70-77; V Hambledon *Portsm* 77-79; Chapl HM Pris Kingston (Portsm) 79-90; C Portsea St Mary *Portsm* 86-90; rtd 90; Perm to

Offic *Portsm* from 90. *7 Hanover Court, Highbury Street, Portsmouth PO1 2BN* Tel (023) 9275 2698

CARNELL, Canon Geoffrey Gordon. b 18. St Jo Coll Cam BA40 MA44. Cuddesdon Coll 40. **d** 42 **p** 43. C Abington *Pet* 42-49; Chapl and Lect St Gabr Coll Camberwell 49-53; R Isham *Pet* 53-71; V Gt w Lt Harrowden 53-71; Dir of Post-Ord Tr and Dir of Ords 62-85; Can Pet Cathl 65-85; R Boughton 71-85; Dioc Lib Ecton Ho 67-93; Chapl to The Queen 81-88; rtd 85; Perm to Offic *Pet* from 86. *52 Walsingham Avenue, Kettering NN15 5ER* Tel (01536) 511415

CARNELLEY, The Ven Desmond. b 29. Open Univ BA77 Leeds Univ CertEd Ex Univ CertRE. Ripon Hall Ox 59. **d** 60 **p** 61. C Aston cum Aughton *Sheff* 60-63; C-in-c Ecclesfield St Paul CD 63-67; V Balby w Hexthorpe 67-73; P-in-c Mosbrough 73-74; V 74-85; RD Attercliffe 79-84; Adn Doncaster 85-94; Dioc Dir of Educn 91-94; rtd 94; Perm to Offic *Sheff* and *Derby* from 94. *7 Errwood Avenue, Buxton SK17 9BD* Tel (01298) 71460

CARNELLEY, Ms Elizabeth Amy. b 64. St Aid Coll Dur BA85 Selw Coll Cam MPhil87. Ripon Coll Cuddesdon 88. **d** 90 **p** 94. Par Dn Sharrow St Andr *Sheff* 90-93; Par Dn Is of Dogs Ch Ch and St Jo w St Luke *Lon* 93-94; C 94-95; P-in-c Woolfold *Man* 95-99; TV Man Whitworth 99-02; Chapl Man Univ and Man Metrop Univ 99-02; Policy Officer Chs' Regional Commn for Yorks and the Humber from 02. *30 New Hey Road, Huddersfield HD3 4AJ* Tel (01484) 303374
E-mail liz.carnelley@yorkshirechurches.org.uk

CARNEY, David Anthony. b 42. Salford Univ BSc77. Linc Th Coll 77. **d** 79 **p** 80. C Wythenshawe St Martin *Man* 79-81; CF 81-84; Canada 84-91; P-in-c Whaplode *Linc* 91-97; V 97-02; P-in-c Holbeach Fen 91-97; V 97-02; R Colsterworth Gp from 02. *The Rectory, Church Street, Skillington, Grantham NG33 5HQ* Tel (01476) 861443

CARNEY, Mrs Mary Patricia. b 42. Univ of Wales (Ban) BSc62 DipEd63. Wycliffe Hall Ox. **d** 90 **p** 94. Par Dn Carterton *Ox* 90-93; Par Dn Harwell w Chilton 93-94; C 94-01; P-in-c Ray Valley from 01. *The Vicarage, Church Walk, Ambrosden, Bicester OX26 2UJ* Tel (01869) 247813 E-mail mary_carney@lineone.net

CARNEY, The Ven Richard Wayne. b 52. Lon Teachers Coll Ontario TCert73 Toronto Univ BA79. Trin Coll Toronto MDiv84. **d** 84 **p** 85. Canada 84-95; I Clonfert Gp of Par *L & K* from 95; Adn Killaloe, Kilfenora, Clonfert etc from 02. *The Rectory, Banagher, Birr, Co Offaly, Irish Republic* Tel (00353) (90) 51269 Mobile 087-677 3196 E-mail rwcarney@iol.ie *or* clonfert@clonfert.anglican.org

✠**CARNLEY, The Most Revd Peter Frederick.** b 37. AO98. Melbourne Univ BA66 Cam Univ PhD69 Gen Th Sem NY Hon DD84 Newc Univ Aus Hon DLitt00 Univ of W Aus Hon DLitt00. St Jo Coll Morpeth ThL62 ACT 62. **d** 62 **p** 64 **c** 81. Australia 63-66, 69-71 and from 72; C Parkes 66; Lic to Offic *Ely* 66-69; Chapl Mitchell Coll Bathurst 70-71; Research Fell St Jo Coll Cam 71-72; Warden St Jo Coll Brisbane 72-81; Can Res Brisbane 75-81; Abp Perth from 81; Primate of Australia from 00; ChStJ from 82; Sub Prelate from 91. *GPO Box W2067, Perth, W Australia 6846* Tel (0061) (08) 9322 1253 *or* 9325 7455 Fax 9325 6741 E-mail abcsuite@perth.anglican.org

CAROLAN (née STUART-BLACK), Mrs Veronica. b 52. St Jo Coll Dur BA75. Cranmer Hall Dur. **dss** 82 **d** 87. Borehamwood *St Alb* 82-84; Watford Ch Ch 84-85; Stevenage St Mary Shephall 85-87; Par Dn Stevenage St Mary Sheppall w Aston 87-88; Perm to Offic from 98. *18 Randalls Hill, Shephall, Stevenage SG2 9YN* Tel (01438) 235597

CARPANI, Karl Augustus. b 65. St Jo Coll Nottm 96. **d** 98 **p** 99. C Biggin Hill *Roch* 98-01; V Green Street Green and Pratts Bottom from 01. *The Vicarage, 46 World's End Lane, Orpington BR6 6AG* Tel (01689) 852905 E-mail karl@carpani.org

CARPENTER, Bruce Leonard Henry. b 32. Lon Univ BA54 St Chad's Coll Dur DipTh59. **d** 59 **p** 60. C Portsea N End St Mark *Portsm* 59-63; C Fareham SS Pet and Paul 63-67; V Locks Heath 67-74; TR Fareham H Trin 74-84; RD Alverstoke 71-76; Hon Can Portsm Cathl 79-84; V Richmond St Mary w St Matthias and St Jo *S'wark* 84-91; Chapl Ch Ch High Sch Ashford 91-93; P-in-c S Ashford Ch Ch *Cant* 94-97; rtd 97; Chapl Huggens Coll Northfleet 97-02; Perm to Offic *Portsm* from 02. *Pistachio, 96 Festing Grove, Southsea PO4 9QF* Tel (023) 9229 4128

CARPENTER, David James. b 52. Trin Coll Carmarthen CertEd74. St Steph Ho Ox 74. **d** 76 **p** 77. C Newport St Julian *Mon* 76-77; C Pontypool 77-79; C Ebbw Vale 79-81; TV 81-85; V Pontnewynydd 85-88; V Bedwellty 88-00; Chapl Aberbargoed Hosp 88-99; V Staincliffe and Carlinghow *Wakef* from 00. *The Vicarage, Staincliffe Hall Road, Batley WF17 7QX* Tel and fax (01924) 473143 Mobile 07702-400766
E-mail carpenterdj@aol.com

CARPENTER, Canon Derek George Edwin. b 40. K Coll Lon BD62 AKC62. **d** 63 **p** 64. C Friern Barnet All SS *Lon* 63-66; C Chingford SS Pet and Paul *Chelmsf* 66-70; V Dartford St Alb *Roch* 70-79; R Crayford 79-90; RD Erith 82-90; R Beckenham St Geo 90-02; Hon Can Roch Cathl 97-02; rtd 02. *39 Chatfield Way, East Malling, West Malling ME19 6QD* Tel (01732) 874420

CARPENTER, Donald Arthur. b 35. Roch Th Coll 65. **d** 67 **p** 68. C Thornton Heath St Jude *Cant* 67-73; V Earby *Bradf* 73-78; V Skipton Ch Ch 78-88; V Baildon 88-91; P-in-c Perivale *Lon* 91-96; rtd 96; Perm to Offic *Lon* from 96. *9 Drew Gardens, Greenford UB6 7QF* Tel (020) 8903 9697

CARPENTER, Mrs Judith Margaret. b 47. Bris Univ BA68 CertEd69. Trin Coll Bris BA95. **d** 95 **p** 96. C Warmley, Syston and Bitton *Bris* 95-99; V Withywood from 99. *Withywood Church House, 63 Turtlegate Avenue, Bristol BS13 8NN* Tel 0117-964 7763

CARPENTER, Leonard Richard. b 32. EMMTC 82. **d** 85 **p** 86. NSM Leic H Apostles *Leic* 85-90; P-in-c Barlestone 90-98; rtd 98; Perm to Offic *Leic* and *Derby* from 98. *10 Main Street, Albert Village, Swadlincote DE11 8EW* Tel (01283) 229335

CARPENTER, Michael John Anselm. b 77. Leeds Univ BA02. Coll of Resurr Mirfield 99. **d** 02. C Cudworth and Lundwood *Wakef* 02-03; C Castleford from 03. *The Vicarage, Churchfield Lane, Glasshoughton, Castleford WF10 4BP* Tel (01977) 734075

CARPENTER, William Brodie. b 35. St Alb Minl Tr Scheme 76. **d** 79 **p** 80. NSM Hemel Hempstead *St Alb* 79-85; C Bp's Hatfield 85-88; C Caversham St Pet and Mapledurham etc *Ox* 88-89; V Caversham St Andr 89-99; rtd 99; Perm to Offic *St Alb* 00-02; P-in-c Wigginton from 02. *33 Elm Tree Walk, Tring HP23 5EB* Tel (01442) 824585 E-mail billcarp@supanet.com

CARR, Alan Cobban. b 49. Nottm Univ BTh88. Linc Th Coll 85. **d** 88 **p** 89. C Rustington *Chich* 88-92; V Highbrook and W Hoathly from 92. *The Vicarage, North Lane, West Hoathly, East Grinstead RH19 4QF* Tel (01342) 810494

CARR, Anthony Howard. b 62. Ex Univ BA. **d** 92 **p** 93. C Taverham w Ringland *Nor* 92-97; P-in-c S Darley, Elton and Winster *Derby* 97-03; R E Peckham and Nettlestead *Roch* from 03. *The Rectory, Bush Road, East Peckham, Tonbridge TN12 5LL* Tel (01622) 871278

CARR, The Very Revd Arthur Wesley. b 41. Jes Coll Ox BA64 MA67 Jes Coll Cam BA66 MA70 Sheff Univ PhD75. Ridley Hall Cam 65. **d** 67 **p** 68. C Luton w E Hyde *St Alb* 67-71; Tutor Ridley Hall Cam 70-71; Chapl 71-72; Hon C Ranmoor *Sheff* 72-74; Chapl Chelmsf Cathl *Chelmsf* 74-78; Can Res Chelmsf Cathl 78-87; Dep Dir Cathl Cen for Research and Tr 74-82; Dioc Dir of Tr 76-84; Dean Bris 87-97; Dean Westmr from 97. *The Deanery, Dean's Yard, London SW1P 3PA* Tel (020) 7654 4801 Fax 7654 4883 E-mail wesley.carr@westminster-abbey.org

CARR, Derrick Charles. b 43. MCIPD. St Alb and Ox Min Course 99. **d** 02. NSM Amersham *Ox* from 02. *52 Warren Wood Drive, High Wycombe HP11 1EA* Tel and fax (01494) 452389 Mobile 07768-507391 E-mail dcarr@globalnet.co.uk

CARR, Douglas Nicholson. b 20. Jes Coll Cam BA47 MA50. Cranmer Hall Dur. **d** 65 **p** 66. C Reigate St Mary *S'wark* 65-69; Home Dir OMF 69-85; Lic to Offic *S'wark* 77-85; rtd 85; Perm to Offic *Glouc* from 85. *Willow Cottage, 435 Paiswick Road, Gloucester GL4 9BY* Tel (01452) 507455

CARR, Mrs Elaine Susan. b 46. LTCL82. St Alb and Ox Min Course 99. **d** 02. NSM High Wycombe *Ox* from 02. *52 Warren Wood Drive, High Wycombe HP11 1EA* Tel (01494) 452389 Fax as telephone E-mail e.carr@fish.co.uk

CARR, Miss Eveline. b 45. St Jo Coll Dur 91. **d** 93 **p** 95. NSM Eighton Banks *Dur* 93-98; NSM Gateshead from 98. *10 Lanchester Avenue, Gateshead NE9 7AJ* Tel 0191-482 1157 E-mail e-carr@supnet.com

CARR, John Henry Percy. b 52. NTMTC AdDipTh98 ADPS98. **d** 98 **p** 99. C Hackney Wick St Mary of Eton w St Aug *Lon* 98-01; R Walesby *Linc* from 01. *The Rectory, Otby Lane, Walesby, Market Rasen LN8 3UT* Tel (01673) 838513 E-mail carr.ide@boltblue.com

CARR, John Robert. b 40. ACII62. Oak Hill Th Coll 63. **d** 66 **p** 67. C Tonbridge St Steph *Roch* 66-70; C Cheadle Hulme St Andr *Ches* 70-79; R Widford *Chelmsf* 79-87; TV Becontree W 87-93; V Basildon St Andr w H Cross from 93. *St Andrew's Vicarage, 3 The Fremnells, Basildon SS14 2QX* Tel (01268) 520516

CARR, Miss Joy Vera. b 32. DipEd52. Dalton Ho Bris 56. **dss** 80 **d** 87 **p** 94. Scarborough St Jas and H Trin *York* 80-82; Kingston upon Hull St Matt w St Barn 82-87; Par Dn 87-89; Par Dn Elloughton and Brough w Brantingham 89-92; rtd 92; Perm to Offic *York* from 92. *15 Sea View Gardens, Scarborough YO11 3JD* Tel (01723) 376986

CARR, Paul Anthony. b 62. Oak Hill Th Coll DipHE95 Aston Tr Scheme 93. **d** 97 **p** 98. C Handforth *Ches* 97-01; V Chadwell Heath *Chelmsf* from 01. *The Vicarage, 10 St Chad's Road, Romford RM6 6JB* Tel (020) 8590 2054 E-mail revpaulcarr@onetel.net.uk

CARR, Wesley. *See* CARR, The Very Revd Arthur Wesley

CARRE, Canon John Trenchard. b 23. Lich Th Coll 42 Linc Th Coll 45. **d** 46 **p** 47. C Gt Bookham *Guildf* 46-48; C Hodnet w Weston under Redcastle *Lich* 48-50; C Cannock 50-53; V Bodicote *Ox* 53-60; V Steeple Morden *Ely* 60-74; V Guilden Morden 60-74; RD Shingay 67-74; V Wendy w Shingay 69-74; R Croydon w Clopton 69-74; R Hatley 69-74; V Litlington w Abington Pigotts 69-74; V Tadlow w E Hatley 69-74; V Chesterton St Andr 74-88; Hon Can Ely Cathl 79-88; rtd 88;

Perm to Offic *Ely* from 88. *North Barn, 17 Cromwell Road, Ely CB6 1AS* Tel (01353) 662471

CARRICK, Canon Ian Ross. b 13. Clare Coll Cam BA35 MA39. Chich Th Coll 35. **d** 37 **p** 38. C Sculcoates St Paul *York* 37-39; C Staveley *Derby* 39-43; Min St Barn CD Northolt 43-54; V Northolt Park St Barn *Lon* 54-58; S Africa from 59; R Irene 59-62; P-in-c Sekhukhuniland and Prin St Fran Coll 62-66; Adn Barberton 64-66; Adn Pretoria 67-76; R Pretoria St Wilfred 68-75; R Pretoria Trin 76-80; Dir Min Tr Dioc of Pretoria 80-84; rtd 84. *65 First Crescent, Fish Hoek, 7975 South Africa* Tel (0027) (21) 782 5586 E-mail mary@carrick.dynagen.co.za

CARRINGTON, Mrs Elizabeth Ashby. b 46. EMMTC 86. **d** 90 **p** 94. NSM Nottingham St Ann w Em *S'well* 90-91; C Basford w Hyson Green 92-97; Lect Nottingham St Mary and St Cath 97-00; Assoc P W Bingham Deanery 00; Perm to Offic 00-01; Chapl Woodford Ho Sch New Zealand from 01. *Woodford House, Iona Road, Havelock North, New Zealand* Tel (0064) (6) 873 0722 E-mail elizabethcarrington@hotmail.com

CARRINGTON, Philip John. b 48. MBE03. Leeds Univ MA96 MCMI Leeds Poly CEng SBStJ02. Chich Th Coll 83. **d** 85 **p** 86. C W Acklam *York* 85-88; V Middlesbrough St Agnes 88-92; Chapl S Cleveland Hosp 88-92; Trust Chapl S Tees Hosps NHS Trust from 92. *The James Cook University Hospital, Marton Road, Middlesbrough TS4 3BW* Tel (01642) 850850 *or* 854802 Fax 854802 E-mail rev.carrington@stees.nhs.uk

CARRIVICK, Derek Roy. b 45. Birm Univ BSc66. Ripon Hall Ox 71. **d** 74 **p** 75. C Enfield St Jas *Lon* 74-78; C-in-c Woodgate Valley CD *Birm* 78-83; TR Chelmsley Wood 83-92; Dioc Ecum Officer 86-96; R Baxterley w Hurley and Wood End and Merevale etc 92-99; AD Polesworth 96-99; P-in-c Blisland w St Breward *Truro* from 99; P-in-c Helland from 99. *The Rectory, Limehead, St Breward, Bodmin PL30 4LU* Tel (01208) 850869 E-mail pjc7@truro.open.ac.uk

CARROLL, The Ven Charles William Desmond. b 19. TCD BA43 MA46. St Chad's Coll Dur. **d** 48 **p** 49. C Stanwix *Carl* 48-50; V 50-59; Hon Can Blackb Cathl *Blackb* 59-64; Dir RE 59-73; Can Res Blackb Cathl 64-75; Adn Blackb 73-86; V Balderstone 73-86; rtd 86; Perm to Offic *Blackb* 86-00. *11 Assheton Road, Blackburn BB2 6SF* Tel (01254) 51915

CARROLL, Frederick Albert. b 16. Worc Coll Ox BA51 MA55. Ripon Hall Ox 46. **d** 51 **p** 52. C Oldbury *Birm* 51-56; V Cotteridge 56-65; C-in-c Castle Vale CD 65-68; V Castle Vale 68-74; V Coughton *Cov* 74-87; R Spernall, Morton Bagot and Oldberrow 74-87; RD Alcester 84-87; rtd 87. *8 Gracey Court, Woodland Road, Broadclyst, Exeter EX5 3GA* Tel (01392) 460788

CARROLL, James Thomas. b 41. Pittsburgh Univ MA85. St Deiniol's Hawarden 89 Oblate Fathers Sem Dub 59. **d** 63 **p** 64. C Dublin St Patr Cathl Gp *D & G* 89-92; Min Can St Patr Cathl Dublin 90-96; I Raheny w Coolock *D & G* from 92; Chan V St Patr Cathl Dublin from 96. *403 Howth Road, Raheny, Dublin 5, Irish Republic* Tel (00353) (1) 831 3929 E-mail midnight@indigo.ie

CARROLL, John Hugh. b 31. Bris Univ BA57. Tyndale Hall Bris 54. **d** 58 **p** 59. C Slough *Ox* 54-61; V S Lambeth St Steph *S'wark* 61-72; V Norwood St Luke 72-81; P-in-c Purley Ch Ch 81-85; V 85-93; rtd 93; Perm to Offic *S'wark* from 93. *75 Court Avenue, Coulsdon CR5 1HJ* Tel (01737) 553471

CARROLL, Laurence William. b 44. Birm Univ CertEd66 Open Univ BA73 Leic Univ BEd74 FRHS66 ACP67 LCP68. LNSM course 92. **d** 95 **p** 96. OLM Mark Gp *Linc* from 95. *Hall Farm Barn, Church Lane, Manby, Louth LN11 8HL* Tel (01507) 327630

CARROLL WALLIS, Ms Joy Ann. b 59. SS Mark & Jo Coll Plymouth BEd82. Cranmer Hall Dur 85. **d** 88 **p** 94. Par Dn Hatcham St Jas *S'wark* 88-93; Par Dn Streatham Immanuel and St Andr 93-94; C 94-97; USA from 97. *2629 13th Street NW, Washington, DC 20009, USA* Tel (001) (202) 483 0119 E-mail joycwallis@aol.com

CARRUTHERS, Arthur Christopher (Kester). b 35. Lon Coll of Div ALCD60 LTh73. **d** 60 **p** 61. C Addiscombe St Mary *Cant* 60-62; Prec Bradf Cathl *Bradf* 62-64; CF 64-92; R W Tanfield and Well w Snape and N Stainley *Ripon* 92-00; rtd 00; Perm to Offic *Guildf* from 00. *3 Park View Court, Woking GU22 7SE* Tel (01483) 721995

CARRY, Canon Edward Austin. b 18. TCD BA41 MA47. **d** 42 **p** 43. I Killiney H Trin *D & G* 56-86; Preb St Patr Cathl Dublin 83-86; rtd 86. *2 Roxboro Close, Ballinclea Road, Killiney, Co Dublin, Irish Republic* Tel (00353) (1) 285 8847

CARSON, Christopher John. b 69. QUB BA91 TCD BTh94. **d** 94 **p** 95. C Bangor St Comgall *D & D* 94-97; Bp's C Kilmegan w Maghera 97-98; I from 98. *50 Main Street, Dundrum, Newcastle BT33 0LY* Tel (028) 4375 1225

CARSON, Ms Claire. b 76. St Martin's Coll Lanc BA98 Birm Univ MA99. Qu Coll Birm 00. **d** 03. C Streetly *Lich* from 03. *20 Trenchard Close, Sutton Coldfield, Birmingham B75 7QP* Tel 0121-311 2745 E-mail claire.c@fish.co.uk

CARSON, Ernest. b 17. S'wark Ord Course 68. **d** 71 **p** 72. C Baldock w Bygrave and Clothall *St Alb* 71-75; R

Hertingfordbury 75-86; rtd 86; Perm to Offic *Worc* from 86. *16 Woodward Close, Pershore WR10 1LP* Tel (01386) 553511

CARSON, Gerald James Alexander. b 24. TCD BA49 MA52. **d** 49 **p** 50. C Belfast St Phil *Conn* 49-51; C Derry Cathl *D & R* 51-54; I Kilteevogue 54-57; I Dunfanaghy 57-68; Can Raphoe Cathl 67-81; I Urney w Sion Mills 68-85; Can Derry Cathl 81-85; I Clonallon w Warrenpoint *D & D* 85-90; rtd 90. *84 Avonbrook Gardens, Mountsandel, Coleraine BT52 1SS* Tel (028) 7035 6047

CARSON, Herbert Moore. b 22. TCD BA43 BD45. **d** 45 **p** 46. C Belfast St Phil *Conn* 45-48; CSSM N Ireland 48-53; V Blackheath Park St Mich *S'wark* 53-58; V Cambridge St Paul *Ely* 58-65; rtd 87. *c/o D Boyd-Carson Esq, 28 Parkmount Road, Belfast BT15 4EQ*

CARSON, James Irvine. b 59. TCD BA DipTh84 MTh. **d** 84 **p** 85. C Willowfield *D & D* 84-87; C Lecale Gp 87-89; I Devenish w Boho *Clogh* 89-95; Dioc Youth Adv 91-95; Dioc Communications Officer 93-95; I Belfast Upper Malone (Epiphany) *Conn* 95-99; I Lisburn St Paul from 99. *St Paul's Rectory, 3 Ballinderry Road, Lisburn BT28 1UD* Tel (028) 9266 3520 E-mail ji.carson@breathemail.net

CARSON-FEATHAM, Lawrence William. b 53. AKC DipTh74. **d** 78 **p** 79. SSM w St Mary *Liv* 78-82; Chapl Bolton Colls of H&FE 82-87; C Bolton St Pet *Man* 82-87; TV Oldham 87-92; V Ashton St Jas 92-95; Perm to Offic *Liv* 95-97; C Leeds Belle Is St Jo and St Barn *Ripon* 97-01; TV Accrington Ch the King *Blackb* from 01. *St Mary Magdalen's Vicarage, 5 Queen's Road, Accrington BB5 6AR* Tel (01254) 233763

CARTER, Arthur. b 32. CITC. **d** 97 **p** 98. C Clonmel w Innislounagh, Tullaghmelan etc *C & O* from 97. *Suir Villa, Barnora, Cahir, Co Tipperary, Irish Republic* Tel (00353) (52) 41524

CARTER, Barry Graham. b 54. K Coll Lon BD76 AKC76. St Steph Ho Ox 76. **d** 77 **p** 78. C Evesham *Worc* 77-81; C Amblecote 81-84; TV Ovingdean w Rottingdean and Woodingdean *Chich* 84-85; V Woodingdean 85-95; V Lancing St Mich from 95. *The Vicarage, 117 Penhill Road, Lancing BN15 8HD* Tel (01903) 753653

CARTER, Celia. b 38. JP74. Glouc Sch of Min 86. **d** 89 **p** 94. NSM Avening w Cherington *Glouc* from 89; Asst Chapl Stroud Gen Hosp 89-93; Asst Chapl Severn NHS Trust from 93. *Avening Park, West End, Avening, Tetbury GL8 8NE* Tel (01453) 836390

CARTER, Canon Charles Trevelyan Aubrey. b 14. TCD BA36 MA46. TCD Div Sch Div Test37. **d** 37 **p** 38. C Dublin Sandford *D & G* 37-43; Chapl Female Orphanage Ho Dublin 43-55; I Dublin St Steph 52-59; I Dublin Crumlin 59-67; I Dublin Sandford 67-82; I Dublin Sandford w Milltown 82-85; Can Ch Ch Cathl Dublin 71-85; rtd 85. *7 South Hill, Dartry, Dublin 6, Irish Republic* Tel (00353) (1) 497 1171

CARTER (née SMITH), Mrs Christine Lydia. b 43. Lon Hosp SRN64 Bristol Hosp SCM67 Bris Poly Dip Nursing76 Wolv Poly CertFE84. Trin Coll Bris DipHE91. **d** 91 **p** 94. Par Dn Penkridge Team *Lich* 91-94; C 94-96; Perm to Offic *Blackb* 96-97; NSM Blackb Sav 97-01; Chapl Asst St Helen's and Knowsley Hosps Trust 97-01; NSM Elmdon St Nic *Birm* from 01. *Elmdon Rectory, Tanhouse Farm Road, Solihull B92 9EY* Tel 0121-743 6336 E-mail paulandchris@tworevs.freeserve.co.uk

CARTER, Christopher Franklin (Kit). b 37. Wadh Coll Ox BA59 MA63. Wycliffe Hall Ox 60. **d** 64 **p** 65. C Clifton St Jas *Sheff* 64-67; C Handsworth 67-70; C Clun w Chapel Lawn *Heref* 70-74; Lic to Offic 74-76; P-in-c Ironbridge 76-78; C Coalbrookdale, Iron-Bridge and Lt Wenlock 78-80; V Llansilin w Llangadwaladr and Llangedwyn *St As* from 88; RD Llanfyllin from 88. *The Vicarage, Llansilin, Oswestry SY10 7PX* Tel (01691) 791209

CARTER, Colin John. b 56. Fitzw Coll Cam BA77 MB, BChir80 MA81 FRCS86 FRCOphth89. Trin Coll Bris BA93. **d** 93 **p** 94. C Ripley *Derby* 93-97; TV Horsham *Chich* 97-00; St Geo Healthcare NHS Trust Lon from 00. *St George's Hospital, Blackshaw Road, London SW17 0QT* Tel (020) 8672 1255 Fax 8672 5304

CARTER, David John. b 37. Chich Th Coll 64. **d** 67 **p** 68. C Plaistow St Andr *Chelmsf* 67-70; C Wickford 70-73; Chapl Asst Runwell Hosp Wickford 71-73; Chapl Basingstoke Distr Hosp 73-80; R E Woodhay and Woolton Hill *Win* 80-02; rtd 02. *24 Sandford Close, Kingsclare RG20 5QZ* Tel (01635) 299455

CARTER, Dudley Herbert. b 25. Peterho Cam BA49 MA51. Ridley Hall Cam 49. **d** 51 **p** 52. C Longfleet *Sarum* 51-53; C Rainham *Chelmsf* 54-56; R Tollard Royal w Farnham *Sarum* 60-64; Chapl Colston's Sch Bris 65-67; Lic to Offic *B & W* 67-85; Perm to Offic from 85; rtd 90. *24 Caernarvon Way, Burnham-on-Sea TA8 2DQ* Tel (01278) 789572

CARTER, Duncan Robert Bruton. b 58. Univ of Wales (Cardiff) BA79 Cam Univ BA83 MA89. Ridley Hall Cam 81. **d** 84 **p** 85. C Harold Wood *Chelmsf* 84-88; C S Kensington St Luke *Lon* 88-90; V Henley H Trin *Ox* from 90; AD Henley from 02. *Holy Trinity Vicarage, Church Street, Henley-on-Thames RG9 1SE* Tel (01491) 574822 E-mail drbcarter@hotmail.com

CARTER, Edward John. b 67. Ex Univ BA88. Ripon Coll Cuddesdon BA96. **d** 97 **p** 98. C Thorpe St Matt *Nor* 97-00; Min Can and Dean's V Windsor from 00. *5 The Cloisters, Windsor Castle, Windsor SL4 1NJ* Tel (01753) 848757 Fax 848798 E-mail revdedward.carter@ukgateway.net

CARTER, Eric. b 17. **d** 58 **p** 59. C S Shore H Trin *Blackb* 58-62; V Preesall 62-69; RD Garstang 68-69; V Adlington 69-75; V Garstang St Thos 75-84; rtd 84; Perm to Offic *Ripon* from 84. *1 Arncliffe Road, Harrogate HG2 8NQ* Tel (01423) 884867

CARTER, Frank Howard James. b 23. Chich Th Coll 58. **d** 59 **p** 60. C Bethnal Green St Matt *Lon* 59-64; V Ipstones *Lich* 64-65; V Haggerston All SS *Lon* 65-75; V Alexandra Park St Andr 75-88; rtd 88; Perm to Offic *Lon* 91-98. *53 Naylor Road, London N20 0HE* Tel (020) 8445 0982

CARTER, Grayson Leigh. b 53. Univ of S California BSc76 Ch Ch Ox DPhil90. Fuller Th Sem California MA84 Wycliffe Hall Ox 89. **d** 90 **p** 91. C Bungay H Trin w St Mary *St E* 90-92; Chapl BNC Ox 92-96; Hon C Ox St Mary V w St Cross and St Pet *Ox* 93-96; USA from 96; Assoc Prof Methodist Coll Fayetteville 96-03; Asst R Fayetteville H Trin 96-03; Assoc Prof Fuller Th Sem from 03. *1602 Palmcroft Drive SW, Phoenix, AZ 75996, USA* Tel (001) (602) 252 5582 *or* (408) 517 1414 Fax (408) 517 1492 E-mail gcarter10@yahoo.com *or* gcarter@fuller.edu

CARTER, Hazel June. b 48. Doncaster Coll of Educn CertEd72. Carl Dioc Tr Inst 89. **d** 92 **p** 94. C Wreay *Carl* 92-98; C Dalston and Raughton Head w Gatesgill 92-98; TV Carl H Trin and St Barn 98-02; TR from 02. *Holy Trinity Rectory, 25 Wigton Road, Carlisle CA2 7BB* Tel (01228) 526284

CARTER, Ian Sutherland. b 51. Trin Coll Ox BA73 MA77 DPhil77 Leeds Univ BA80. Coll of Resurr Mirfield 78. **d** 81 **p** 82. C Shildon *Dur* 81-84; C Darlington H Trin 84-87; Chapl Liv Univ 87-93; V Hindley St Pet 93-98; Chapl Oldham NHS Trust from 98. *Royal Oldham Hospital, Rochdale Road, Oldham OL1 2JH* Tel 0161-624 0420 *or* 627 8796 E-mail chaplaincy@oldham-tr.nwest.nhs.uk

CARTER (née O'NEILL), Mrs Irene. b 44. Worc Coll of Educn CertEd65. EMMTC 92. **d** 93. NSM N and S Leverton *S'well* from 93. *25 Mill Close, North Leverton, Retford DN22 0AT* Tel (01427) 880451

CARTER, Mrs Jacqueline Ann. b 50. St Mich Coll Llan 01. **d** 03. C Ebbw Vale *Mon* from 03. *The Vicarage, 177 Badminton Grove, Beaufort, Ebbw Vale NP23 5UN* Tel (01495) 304516 E-mail jackiecarter16@hotmail.com

CARTER, John Howard Gregory. b 55. York Univ BA76 Leeds Univ CertEd77 Nottm Univ MA96. St Jo Coll Nottm LTh87. **d** 87 **p** 88. C Nailsea H Trin *B & W* 87-91; TV Camberley St Paul *Guildf* 91-97; Chapl Elmhurst Ballet Sch 91-97; Dioc Communications Officer *Ripon* from 97; Bp's Dom Chapl from 00. *7 Blenheim Court, Harrogate HG2 9DT* Tel (01423) 530369 Mobile 07798-652707 Fax (01423) 538557 E-mail jhgcarter@aol.com

✠**CARTER, The Rt Revd John Stanley.** b 21. Lon Univ BA47. Oak Hill Th Coll 46 Wycliffe Hall Ox 48. **d** 49 **p** 50 **c** 68. C Walthamstow St Mary *Chelmsf* 49-52; C Streatham Immanuel w St Anselm *S'wark* 52-53; S Africa from 53; Suff Bp Johannesburg 68-77. *80 The Ridge, Clifton, Cape Town, 8005 South Africa* Tel (0027) (21) 438 5606 Fax 438 0793

CARTER, Leslie Alfred Arthur. b 27. K Coll Lon 50 St Boniface Warminster 53. **d** 54 **p** 55. C Northolt Park St Barn *Lon* 54-56; S Africa 57-62; C Wimbledon *S'wark* 63-68; Chapl Quainton Hall Sch Harrow 68-77; TV Brighton Resurr *Chich* 77-81; TV Southend *Chelmsf* 81-88; V Gt Waltham w Ford End 88-93; rtd 94; Perm to Offic *Sarum* from 94; and *B & W* from 00. *The Garden Flat, 11 Bathwick Street, Bath BA2 6NX*

CARTER, Ms Marian. b 40. Whitelands Coll Lon TCert61 Lon Univ DipTh62 BD67 Reading Univ DASE73 Nottm Univ MPhil79 Man Univ MA84. Nor Bapt Coll 81. **d** 92 **p** 94. Par Dn Kempshott *Win* 92-93; Tutor SW Minl Tr Course 92-96; Tutor Coll of SS Mark and Jo Plymouth 93-00; NSM Plymstock and Hooe *Ex* 94-98; NSM Widecombe-in-the-Moor, Leusdon, Princetown etc 98-00; Chapl St Eliz Hospice Ipswich from 00. *Shalom, 80 Woodlands, Chelmondiston, Ipswich IP9 1DU* Tel (01473) 780259

CARTER, Canon Michael John. b 32. St Alb Minl Tr Scheme 81. **d** 84 **p** 85. NSM Radlett *St Alb* 84-88; Chapl SW Herts HA 88-94; Chapl Watford Gen Hosp 88-94; Lic to Offic *St Alb* 88-99; Chapl Mt Vernon and Watford Hosps NHS Trust 94-99; Bp's Adv for Hosp Chapl *St Alb* 95-99; Hon Can St Alb 96-99; rtd 99; Perm to Offic *St Alb* from 99; Hon Chapl Peace Hospice Watford from 99. *Greenford, 42 Oakridge Avenue, Radlett WD7 8ER* Tel (01923) 856009 E-mail michael_carter_2@compuserve.com

CARTER, Michael William. b 33. Newland Park Teacher Tr Coll TCert56. Dioc OLM tr scheme 98. **d** 01 **p** 02. OLM Lingfield and Crowhurst *S'wark* from 01. *Redwood House, 76 Godstone Road, Lingfield RH7 6BT* Tel (01342) 833843

CARTER, Nicholas Adrian. b 48. Ripon Hall Ox 71. **d** 74 **p** 75. C Sowerby *Wakef* 74-79; V Hanging Heaton 79-83; CF 83-86; V Elton All SS *Man* 86-90; C Milton *Win* 90-94; P-in-c Boscombe

St Andr 94-00; V from 00. *St Andrew's Vicarage, 3 Wilfred Road, Bournemouth BH5 1NB* Tel (01202) 394575

CARTER, Nigel John. b 53. N Staffs Poly C&G80 Bolton Inst of Educn CertEd89. Sarum & Wells Th Coll DCM93. **d** 93 **p** 94. C Burntwood *Lich* 93-96; V Bentley from 96; RD Wolverhampton 00-02. *The Vicarage, Cairn Drive, Bentley, Walsall WS2 0HP* Tel (01922) 624200 Fax as telephone E-mail nigel.carter@genie.co.uk

CARTER, Noel William. b 53. Birm Univ BSc75 Bris Univ CertEd76 Nottm Univ BSc83. Linc Th Coll. **d** 83 **p** 84. C Penrith w Newton Reigny and Plumpton Wall *Carl* 83-86; C Barrow St Matt 86-87; V Netherton 87-91; TR Penrith w Newton Reigny and Plumpton Wall 91-97; P-in-c Jersey St Brelade *Win* 97-98; R 98-01; Vice-Dean Jersey 00-01. *Address temp unknown*

CARTER, Canon Norman. b 23. Leeds Univ BSc48. Coll of Resurr Mirfield 48. **d** 50 **p** 51. C Liv Our Lady and St Nic w St Anne *Liv* 50-54; C Orford St Marg 54-56; V 56-71; PC Knotty Ash H Spirit 71-74; V Dovecot 74-83; RD W Derby 78-83; Hon Can Liv Cathl 82-88; V Formby St Pet 83-88; rtd 88; Perm to Offic *Liv* from 88. *34 Granby Close, Southport PR9 9QG* Tel (01704) 232821

CARTER, Canon Paul Brian. b 22. AKC49. **d** 50 **p** 51. C Scarborough St Columba *York* 50-53; C Pocklington w Yapham-cum-Meltonby, Owsthorpe etc 53-55; V Kingston upon Hull St Jo Newington 55-60; R Ainderby Steeple and Scruton *Ripon* 60-79; P-in-c Yafforth 76-79; R Ainderby Steeple w Yafforth and Scruton 79-87; Hon Can Ripon Cathl 86-87; rtd 87; Perm to Offic *Ripon* from 87. *Cliffe Cottage, West Tanfield, Ripon HG4 5JR* Tel (01677) 470203

CARTER, Paul Joseph. b 67. St Chad's Coll Dur BA88. St Steph Ho Ox 89. **d** 91 **p** 92. C Ipswich All Hallows *St E* 91; C Newmarket St Mary w Exning St Agnes 91-94; V Thorpe-le-Soken *Chelmsf* from 94. *The Vicarage, Mill Lane, Thorpe-le-Soken, Clacton-on-Sea CO16 0ED* Tel (01255) 861234 E-mail frpaul@saintmikes.freeserve.co.uk

CARTER, Paul Mark. b 56. BA78 MA90. Ridley Hall Cam 79. **d** 81 **p** 82. C Kidsgrove *Lich* 81-84; CF 84-00; Asst P Vancouver St Phil Canada 00-03. *1655 West 41st Avenue, Vancouver, BC, Canada V6M 1X9* Tel (001) (604) 222 4497 E-mail paulcarter@acinw.org

CARTER, Paul Rowley. b 45. Lon Univ BD69 Lon Bible Coll ALBC69 Southn Univ PGCE70. Trin Coll Bris. **d** 91 **p** 92. C Penkridge Team *Lich* 91-96; V Blackb Sav *Blackb* 96-01; R Elmdon St Nic *Birm* from 01. *Elmdon Rectory, Tanhouse Farm Road, Solihull B92 9EY* Tel 0121-743 6336 E-mail vicar@tworevs.co.uk

CARTER, Robert Desmond. b 35. Cranmer Hall Dur 62. **d** 65 **p** 66. C Otley *Bradf* 65-69; C Keighley 69-73; V Cowling 73-00; rtd 00; Perm to Offic *Bradf* from 00. *1 Quincy Close, Eccleshill, Bradford BD2 2EP* Tel (01274) 638385

CARTER, Robert Edward. b 44. Univ of Wales (Ban) BSc66. St Jo Coll Nottm 79. **d** 81 **p** 82. C Caverswall *Lich* 81-86; V Biddulph 86-94; V Wolverhampton St Jude from 94. *St Jude's Vicarage, St Jude's Road, Wolverhampton WV6 0EB* Tel (01902) 753360 E-mail stjudes@zoom.co.uk

CARTER, Robert Thomas. b 49. Moore Th Coll Sydney 72 Ridley Coll Melbourne ThL75. **d** 75 **p** 76. Australia 75-00 and from 02; C Traralgon St Jas 75-76; P-in-c Endeavour Hills St Matt 77-79; V 80-84; Assoc Min Kew St Hilary 85-91; V Blackburn N St Alfred 92-00; C Fisherton Anger *Sarum* 00-02. *224 Maroondah Highway, Croydon, Melbourne, Vic, Australia 3136*

CARTER, Robin. b 46. Chich Th Coll 71. **d** 74 **p** 75. C Wortley de Leeds *Ripon* 74-76; C Hutton *Chelmsf* 76-78; C Wickford 78-81; TV Wickford and Runwell 81-83; Chapl HM Pris Leeds 83-85; Chapl HM Pris Reading 85-89; Chapl HM YOI Huntercombe and Finnamore Wood 85-89; Chapl HM YOI Finnamore Wood Camp 86-89; Gov 5, Hd of Operations, HM Pris Channings Wood 89-94; Gov 4, Régime and Throughcare, HM Pris Woodhill 94-99; Gov HM Pris E Sutton Park from 99. *Prison Service Headquarters, Cleland House, Page Street, London SW1P 4LN* Tel (020) 7217 3000

CARTER, Ronald George. b 31. Leeds Univ BA58. Coll of Resurr Mirfield 58. **d** 60 **p** 61. C Wigan St Anne *Liv* 60-63; Prec Wakef Cathl *Wakef* 63-66; V Woodhall *Bradf* 66-77; Chapl Qu Marg Sch Escrick Park 77-83; Min Can, Prec and Sacr Pet Cathl *Pet* 83-88; R Upper St Leonards St Jo *Chich* 88-94; rtd 94; Perm to Offic *York* from 95. *5 Greenwich Close, York YO30 5WN* Tel (01904) 610237

CARTER, Russell James Wigney. b 29. Chich Th Coll 80. **d** 82 **p** 83. C Aldwick *Chich* 82-86; R Buxted and Hadlow Down 86-90; rtd 90; Perm to Offic *Chich* from 90. *6 Lucerne Court, Aldwick, Bognor Regis PO21 4XL* Tel (01243) 862858

CARTER, Samuel. b 49. St Jo Coll Dur BA71 DipTh72. Cranmer Hall Dur 73. **d** 74 **p** 75. C Kingswinford St Mary *Lich* 74-77; C Shrewsbury H Cross 77-84; V Normacot 84-94. *Address excluded by request*

CARTER, Sarah Helen Buchanan. See GORTON, Sarah Helen Buchanan

CARTER, Stanley Reginald. b 24. St Jo Coll Dur BA49 DipTh50. **d** 50 **p** 51. C Stoughton *Guildf* 50-53; C Bucknall and Bagnall

Lich 53-56; R Salford St Matthias w St Simon *Man* 56-62; V Highbury New Park St Aug *Lon* 62-69; V Sneinton St Chris w St Phil *S'well* 69-89; rtd 89; Perm to Offic *S'well* from 89. *31 Pateley Road, Nottingham NG5 5QF* Tel 0115-953 2122
E-mail stan.carter@dunelm.org.uk

CARTER, Stephen. b 56. Univ of Wales (Lamp) BA77 Southn Univ BTh81. Sarum & Wells Th Coll 78. **d** 81 **p** 82. C Halstead St Andr w H Trin and Greenstead Green *Chelmsf* 81-84; C Loughton St Jo 84-89; V N Shoebury 89-95; R Lexden from 95; RD Colchester from 01. *The Rectory, 2 Wroxham Close, Colchester CO3 3RQ* Tel (01206) 575966

CARTER, Stephen Howard. b 47. City Univ BSc72. St Jo Coll Nottm LTh85. **d** 85 **p** 86. C Hellesdon *Nor* 85-88; Chapl Asst Birm Children's Hosp 88-91; Chapl Asst Birm Maternity Hosp 88-91; Lic to Offic *Birm* 88-91; TV Tettenhall Wood *Lich* 91-98; Chapl Compton Hall Hospice Wolv 91-98; P-in-c Coalbrookdale, Iron-Bridge and Lt Wenlock *Heref* 98-00; R from 00; Asst Dioc Co-ord for Evang from 00. *The Rector's House, Paradise, Coalbrookdale, Telford TF8 7NR* Tel (01952) 433309 Fax 432137 E-mail stevecarter@bigfoot.com

CARTER, Stuart Conway. b 58. Lon Bible Coll DipRS83 St Jo Coll Nottm DipMM92. **d** 92 **p** 93. C Birm St Luke *Birm* 92-96; C The Quinton from 96. *95 Oak Road, Quinton, Birmingham B68 0BH* Tel 0121-422 3621

CARTER, Terence John. b 31. K Coll Lon BD57 AKC57 Lon Univ BA68 PGCE69. **d** 58 **p** 59. C Winchmore Hill H Trin *Lon* 58-60; PV S'wark Cathl *S'wark* 60-63; Sacr S'wark Cathl 60-63; Succ S'wark Cathl 61-63; R Ockham w Hatchford *Guildf* 63-69; Lic to Offic *S'wark* 69-78; Lic to Offic *Portsm* 78-82; Perm to Offic from 82; rtd 91. *15 Balliol Road, Portsmouth PO2 7PP* Tel (023) 9269 9167 Mobile 07811-474020
E-mail terence.carter@euphony.net

CARTLEDGE, Margery. *See* TOLLER, Elizabeth Margery

CARTLEDGE, Mark John. b 62. Lon Bible Coll BA85 Univ of Wales PhD00. Oak Hill Th Coll MPhil89. **d** 88 **p** 89. C Formby H Trin *Liv* 88-91; Miss Partner CMS 91-93; Nigeria 91-93; Chapl Liv Univ *Liv* 93-98; Chapl and Tutor St Jo Coll Dur 98-03; Lect Univ of Wales (Lamp) from 03. *Department of Theology, University of Wales, Lampeter SA48 7ED*

CARTMELL, Canon Richard Peter Watkinson. b 43. Cranmer Hall Dur 77. **d** 79 **p** 80. C Whittle-le-Woods *Blackb* 79-85; V Lower Darwen St Jas 85-03; RD Darwen 91-96; P-in-c S Shore H Trin from 03; Hon Can Blackb Cathl from 98. *92 Watson Road, Blackpool FY4 2DE* Tel (01253) 347140

CARTMILL, Canon Ralph Arthur. b 40. St Jo Coll Dur BA62 Em Coll Cam MA64. Ridley Hall Cam 63. **d** 65 **p** 66. C Dukinfield St Jo *Ches* 65-68; C Wilmslow 68-69; Warden Walton Youth Cen Liv 69-70; Asst Master Aylesbury Gr Sch 70-74; Perm to Offic *Ox* 72-74; V Terriers 74-85; P-in-c Chinnor w Emmington and Sydenham 85-86; R Chinnor w Emmington and Sydenham etc 86-98; Hon Can Ch 97-98; rtd 98; Perm to Offic *Nor* from 00. *6 Longview Close, Snettisham, King's Lynn PE31 7RD* Tel (01485) 543357

CARTWRIGHT, Mrs Amanda Jane. b 58. St Jo Coll Nottm 00. **d** 02 **p** 03. C Beeston *S'well* from 02. *46 Bramcote Road, Beeston, Nottingham NG9 1DW* Tel 0115-854 3628
E-mail p.a.cartwright@tinyworld.co.uk

CARTWRIGHT, John Walter Deryk. b 25. Lon Univ BSc. Ox NSM Course. **d** 82 **p** 83. NSM Welford w Wickham and Gt Shefford *Ox* 82-85; TV Newbury 85-93; rtd 93; Perm to Offic *Ox* from 99. *70 Walton Way, Newbury RG14 2LJ* Tel (01635) 49339

CARTWRIGHT, Julia Ann. b 58. Nottm Univ BA80. Linc Th Coll 84. **dss** 86 **d** 87 **p** 94. Asst Chapl HM Pris Morton Hall 85-90; Linc St Jo *Linc* 86-88; Hon C 87-88; Hon C Bardney 88-97; Chapl Linc Co Hosp 90-93; Chapl St Geo Hosp Linc 90-93; Chapl Linc Distr Health Services and Hosps NHS Trust 93-97; Chapl S Bucks NHS Trust from 97; Lic to Offic *Ox* from 97. *Wycombe General Hospital, Queen Alexandra Road, High Wycombe HP11 2TT* Tel (01494) 526161 *or* 425072

CARTWRIGHT, Michael John. b 42. Birm Univ DLA70. Qu Coll Birm 67. **d** 70 **p** 71. C Astwood Bank w Crabbs Cross *Worc* 70-75; P-in-c Worc St Mich 75-77; V Stockton St Paul *Dur* 77-87; V Market Rasen *Linc* from 87; R Linwood from 87; V Legsby from 87; RD W Wold 90-01; R Wickenby *Gp* 95-00; V Lissington from 00. *The Vicarage, 13 Lady Frances Drive, Market Rasen LN8 3JJ* Tel (01673) 843424

✠**CARTWRIGHT, The Rt Revd Richard Fox.** b 13. Pemb Coll Cam BA35 MA39 Univ of the South (USA) Hon DD69. Cuddesdon Coll 35. **d** 36 **p** 37. C Kennington Cross St Anselm *S'wark* 36-40; C Kingswood 40-45; V Surbiton St Andr 45-52; V Bris St Mary Redcliffe w Temple etc *Bris* 52-72; Hon Can Bris Cathl 67-72; rtd 72. C Kennington Cross St Anselm *S'wark* 36-40; C Kingswood 40-45; V Surbiton St Andr 45-52; V Bris St Mary Redcliffe w Temple etc *Bris* 52-72; Hon Can Bris Cathl 67-72; Suff Bp Plymouth *Ex* 72-81; rtd 82; Asst Bp Truro 82-91; Asst Bp Ex from 88. *5 Old Vicarage Close, Ide, Exeter EX2 9RE* Tel (01392) 211270

CARTWRIGHT, Roy Arthur. b 29. CCC Cam BA52 MA56. Wycliffe Hall Ox. **d** 54 **p** 55. C Hornchurch St Andr *Chelmsf* 54-56; C Gt Clacton 56-60; C-in-c Prittlewell St Steph CD 60-69; V Prittlewell St Steph 69-72; rtd 72; Hon C S Shoebury *Chelmsf* 77-94; Perm to Offic *Glouc* from 94. *21 Winfield, Newent GL18 1QB* Tel (01531) 821335

CARTWRIGHT, Samuel. b 27. Cuddesdon Coll 71. **d** 72 **p** 72. C Rochdale *Man* 72-76; V Roundthorn 76-83; V Ashton Ch Ch 83-93; rtd 93; Perm to Offic *Derby* from 93. *8 Wentworth Avenue, Walton, Chesterfield S40 3JB* Tel (01246) 232252

CARTWRIGHT, Sidney Victor. b 22. Launde Abbey 73. **d** 74 **p** 75. C Braunstone *Leic* 74-78; P-in-c Arnesby w Shearsby 78-86; R Arnesby w Shearsby and Bruntingthorpe 86-87; rtd 87; Perm to Offic *Leic* from 87; Perm to Offic *Pet* from 87. *32 Northleigh Grove, Market Harborough LE16 9QX* Tel (01858) 463915

CARTWRIGHT, William Michael. b 44. Birm Univ CertEd67. Coll of Resurr Mirfield 83. **d** 83 **p** 84. Hd Master Chacombe Sch 83-95; Hon C Middleton Cheney w Chacombe *Pet* 83-85; Hd Master Chacombe Sch Banbury 83-85; C Kettering SS Pet and Paul *Pet* 85-86; Perm to Offic 86-87; Chapl Northaw Prep Sch Win 89-92; P-in-c Altarnon w Bolventor, Laneast and St Clether *Truro* 92-97; V Treverbyn 97-01; V Bempton w Flamborough, Reighton w Speeton *York* 01-03; V Ampleforth w Oswaldkirk, Gilling E etc from 03. *The Rectory, West End, Ampleforth, York YO62 4DU* Tel (01439) 788264

CARUANA, Mrs Rosemary Anne. b 38. St Alb Minl Tr Scheme 81. **dss** 84 **d** 87 **p** 94. Hertford St Andr *St Alb* 84-87; Par Dn Hertingfordbury 87-94; C 94-98; P-in-c from 98. *36 Holly Croft, Sele Farm Estate, Hertford SG14 2DR* Tel (01992) 306427 Mobile 07769-658756 E-mail r.caruana@ntlworld.com

CARVER, Arthur Tregarthen. r 15. Lon Univ 37. Tyndale Hall Bris 37. **d** 41 **p** 42. C Southport Ch Ch *Liv* 41-43; P-in-c 43-44; P-in-c St Helens St Matt Thatto Heath 44-48; V St Helens St Mark 48-53; V Marple All SS *Ches* 53-69; R Uphill *B & W* 69-80; rtd 80; Perm to Offic *Ches* from 80. *Copinsay, 20 Hayton Street, Knutsford WA16 0DR* Tel (01565) 651622

CARVER, Miss Elizabeth Ann. b 36. ACIB73. Bp Otter Coll BA00. **d** 99. NSM Littlehampton and Wick *Chich* from 99. *13 Hearnfield Road, Littlehampton BN17 7PR* Tel (01903) 713169

CARVOSSO, John Charles. b 45. ACA71 FCA79. Oak Hill Th Coll 75. **d** 78 **p** 79. C Chelsea St Jo w St Andr *Lon* 78-81; Chapl RAF 81-84; P-in-c Tawstock *Ex* 84-85; TV Newport, Bishops Tawton and Tawstock 85-96; TV Newton Tracey, Horwood, Alverdiscott etc from 96; RD Torrington 97-02. *The Rectory, Tawstock, Barnstaple EX31 3HZ* Tel (01271) 374963
E-mail devoncarvossos@classicfm.net

CASE, Preb Catherine Margaret. b 44. Ripon Coll Cuddesdon 86. **d** 88 **p** 94. C Blurton *Lich* 88-92; Min to Hanley Care Agencies 92-94; TD Hanley H Ev 92-94; P-in-c Wrockwardine Wood 95-98; R 98-00; V Gnosall from 00; Preb Lich Cathl from 02. *The Vicarage, Gnosall, Stafford ST20 0ER* Tel (01785) 822213

CASE, Philip Thomas Charles. b 17. Lon Univ BSc(Econ)51. Sarum Th Coll 51. **d** 53 **p** 54. C Westmr St Steph w St Jo *Lon* 53-56; C Ashford St Matt 56-58; C-in-c Ashford St Hilda CD 58-61; V St Helier *S'wark* 61-66; V Witley *Guildf* 66-84; RD Godalming 79-84; rtd 84; Perm to Offic *Ex* 85-98. *15 Lawpool Court, Wells BA5 2AN* Tel (01749) 670859

CASEBOW, Ronald Philip. b 31. Roch Th Coll 59. **d** 61 **p** 62. C Southgate Ch Ch *Lon* 61-64; C Oseney Crescent St Luke w Camden Square St Paul 64-70; Warden St Paul's Ho Student Hostel 64-70; V Colchester St Steph *Chelmsf* 70-74; V Burnham 74-89; rtd 89; Perm to Offic *Nor* from 95. *The Priory, Priory Road, Palgrave, Diss IP22 1AJ* Tel (01379) 651804

CASEY, Christopher Noel. b 61. Open Univ BA95 Nottm Univ BA01. St Jo Coll Nottm 98. **d** 01 **p** 02. C Penrith w Newton Reigny and Plumpton Wall *Carl* from 01. *18 Skirsgill Close, Penrith CA11 8QF* Tel (01768) 899540
E-mail kc.family@btopenworld.com

CASEY, Ernest George. b 14. St Chad's Coll Dur BA36 DipTh. **d** 37 **p** 38. C Benfieldside *Dur* 37-40; C Winlaton 40-44; P-in-c Cassop cum Quarrington 44-45; V Chilton Moor 45-59; V Dur St Giles 59-79; rtd 79. *8 Hampshire Road, Belmont, Durham DH1 2DJ* Tel 0191-384 9228

CASH, Simon Andrew. b 62. St Jo Coll Nottm 99. **d** 01 **p** 02. C Aston cum Aughton w Swallownest and Ulley *Sheff* from 01. *The Rectory, 36 Union Street, Harthill, Sheffield S26 7YH* Tel (01909) 771412 E-mail s.cash@messages.co.uk

CASHEL, Dean of. *See* KNOWLES, The Very Revd Philip John

CASHEL, WATERFORD AND LISMORE, Archdeacon of. *See* MURRAY, The Ven John Grainger

CASHEL, WATERFORD, LISMORE, OSSORY, FERNS AND LEIGHLIN, Bishop of. *See* BARRETT, The Rt Revd Peter Francis

CASIOT, David John. b 39. St Pet Coll Ox BA63 MA67. Clifton Th Coll 63. **d** 65 **p** 66. C Drypool St Columba w St Andr and St Pet *York* 65-67; C Barking St Marg *Chelmsf* 67-71; R Whalley Range St Edm *Man* 71-84; V Wandsworth St Mich *S'wark* 84-00; Perm to Offic *Roch* from 00. *57 Knighton Road, Otford, Sevenoaks TN14 5LE* Tel (01959) 522588
E-mail david@oakside.idps.co.uk

CASON, Preb Ronald Arthur. b 28. Kelham Th Coll 48. **d** 53 **p** 54. C Fenton *Lich* 53-56; V Brereton 56-63; V Wednesbury w Donington *Leic* 63-67; R Blakenall Heath *Lich* 67-74; R Stoke upon Trent 74-80; Preb Lich Cathl 75-93; RD Stoke 78-88; TR

Stoke-upon-Trent 80-91; Lect Tettenhall Par 91-93; rtd 93; Perm to Offic *Lich* 93-00. *130 Main Road, Brereton, Rugeley WS15 1EB* Tel (01889) 582267

CASSAM, Victor Reginald. b 33. Chich Th Coll 59. **d** 62 **p** 63. C Portsea St Jo Rudmore *Portsm* 62-64; C W Leigh CD 64-66; C Torquay St Martin Barton *Ex* 66-69; C Stanmer w Falmer and Moulsecoomb *Chich* 69-73; P-in-c Catsfield 73-76; R Catsfield and Crowhurst 76-81; R Selsey 81-01; RD Chich 96-01; rtd 01; Perm to Offic *Chich* from 01; *Portsm* from 02. *195 Oving Road, Chichester PO19 7ER* Tel and fax (01243) 783998 Mobile 07976-757451 Fax (08701) 209548 E-mail vrc@vicas.demon.co.uk

CASSELTON, John Charles. b 43. Univ of Wales (Swansea) MA95 E Lon Univ Dip Counselling 98. Oak Hill Th Coll DipTh67. **d** 68 **p** 69. C Upton *Ex* 68-73; C Braintree *Chelmsf* 73-80; V Ipswich St Jo *St E* 80-92; RD Ipswich 86-92; Chapl St Clem Hosp Ipswich 92-98; Chapl St Eliz Hospice Ipswich 92-00; Dir Inspire Chr Counselling from 00; Perm to Offic *St E* from 00. *Rose Cottage, 41 North Hill Road, Ipswich IP4 2PN* Tel (01473) 401638

CASSIDY, Brian Ross. b 31. Cape Town Univ. St Bede's Coll Umtata 88. **d** 89 **p** 91. S Africa 89-92; C Lymington *Win* 92-93; P-in-c Hyde Common 93-96; P-in-c Ellingham and Harbridge and Ibsley 95-96; V Ellingham and Harbridge and Hyde w Ibsley 96-03; rtd 03. *The Vicarage, Hyde, Fordingbridge SP6 2QJ* Tel (01425) 653216 E-mail cassidy@btinternet.com

✠**CASSIDY, The Rt Revd George Henry.** b 42. QUB BSc65 Lon Univ MPhil67. Oak Hill Th Coll 70. **d** 72 **p** 73 **c** 99. C Clifton Ch Ch w Em *Bris* 72-75; V Sea Mills 75-82; V Portman Square St Paul *Lon* 82-87; Adn Lon and Can Res St Paul's Cathl 87-99; P-in-c St Ethelburga Bishopgate 89-91; Bp S'well from 99. *Bishop's Manor, Bishop's Drive, Southwell NG25 0JP* Tel (01636) 812112 Fax 815401 E-mail bishop@southwell.anglican.org

CASSIDY, The Very Revd Herbert. b 35. TCD BA57 MA65. CITC 58. **d** 58 **p** 59. C Belfast H Trin *Conn* 58-60; C Londonderry Ch Ch *D & R* 60-62; I Aghavilly w Derrynoose *Arm* 62-65; Hon V Choral Arm Cathl 63-85; C Portadown St Columba 65-67; I 67-85; Dean Kilmore *K, E & A* 85-89; I Kilmore w Ballintemple 85-86; I Kilmore w Ballintemple, Kildallon etc 86-89; Dir of Ords 89; Dean Arm and Keeper of Public Lib *Arm* from 89; I Arm St Patr from 89; Hon Sec Gen Syn from 90. *The Library, 43 Abbey Street, Armagh BT61 7DY* Tel (028) 3752 3142 Fax 3752 4177 E-mail armroblib@aol.com *or* dean@armagh.anglican.org

CASSIDY, Ian David. b 59. N Ord Course 94. **d** 97 **p** 98. NSM Everton St Geo *Liv* from 97. *79 Gilroy Road, Liverpool L6 6BG* Tel 0151-263 9751 Mobile 0780-1933654

CASSIDY, Canon Joseph Patrick. b 54. Concordia Univ Montreal BA76 Detroit Univ MA80 Toronto Univ STB86 MDiv86 St Paul Univ Ottawa LTh89 DTh95 Ottawa Univ PhD95 FRSA. Toronto Bible Coll 82. **d** 85 **p** 86. Canada 85-96; NSM Laverstock *Sarum* 96-97; NSM Salisbury St Martin 96-97; Prin St Chad's Coll Dur from 97; Hon Can Dur Cathl *Dur* from 01. *St Chad's College, University of Durham, 18 North Bailey, Durham DH1 3RH* Tel 0191-374 3364 *or* 374 3367 Fax 374 3309 E-mail j.p.cassidy@durham.ac.uk

CASSIDY, Patrick Nigel. b 40. TCD BA63 MA66. Sarum Th Coll 64. **d** 66 **p** 67. C Heaton St Barn *Bradf* 66-68; Asst Chapl Brussels *Eur* 68-70; Chapl SW France 70-72; V Oseney Crescent St Luke w Camden Square St Paul *Lon* 72-83; Chapl Strasbourg w Stuttgart and Heidelberg *Eur* 83-84; Perm to Offic *Chich* 86-90; Chapl Marseille w Aix-en-Provence *Eur* from 90; Hon Chapl Miss to Seafarers from 90. *18 rue du Jeune Anacharsis, 13001 Marseille, France* Tel (0033) (4) 91 55 57 38

CASSIDY, Canon Ronald. b 43. Lon Univ BD66 Man Univ MPhil85. Tyndale Hall Bris 63. **d** 68 **p** 69. C Kirkdale St Lawr *Liv* 68-70; C Bolton Em Man 70-74; V Roughtown 74-89; R Denton St Lawr from 89; AD Ashton-under-Lyne 97-03; Hon Can Man Cathl from 02. *St Lawrence's Rectory, 131 Town Lane, Denton, Manchester M34 2DJ* Tel 0161-320 4895 E-mail roncass-99@yahoo.com

CASSON, David Christopher. b 41. Qu Coll Cam BA64 MA68. Ridley Hall Cam 65. **d** 67 **p** 68. C Birm St Martin *Birm* 67-72; C Luton St Mary *St Alb* 72-77; P-in-c 77; V Luton St Fran 77-84; V Richmond H Trin and Ch Ch *S'wark* 84-97; R Acle w Fishley, N Burlingham, Beighton w Moulton *Nor* from 97. *The Rectory, Acle, Norwich NR13 3BU* Tel (01493) 750393

CASSON, Canon James Stuart. b 32. Liv Univ BA54 Nottm Univ MPhil70. Ridley Hall Cam. **d** 61 **p** 62. C Eccleston Ch Ch *Liv* 61-64; C Littleover *Derby* 64-67; V Dearham *Carl* 67-76; V Holme Eden 76-98; RD Brampton 91-96; Hon Can Carl Cathl 93-98; P-in-c Croglin 93-98; rtd 98; Perm to Offic *Carl* from 01. *5 High Woodbank, Brisco, Carlisle CA4 0QR* Tel (01228) 525692

CASSWELL, David Oriel. b 52. Loughb Coll of Educn DipEd74 Leeds Univ CQSW79. Oak Hill Th Coll DipHE87. **d** 87 **p** 88. C Acomb St Steph *York* 87-91; Dep Chapl HM Pris Leeds 91-92; Chapl HM Pris Everthorpe 92; Chapl HM Pris Wolds 92-95; V Clifton *York* from 98. *Clifton Vicarage, Clifton, York YO30 6BH* Tel (01904) 655071 Fax 654796 E-mail davcass@fish.co.uk

CASSWELL, Canon Peter Joyce. b 22. Trin Coll Cam BA48 MA50. Ridley Hall Cam 48. **d** 50 **p** 51. C Addiscombe St Mildred *Cant* 50-53; C-in-c New Addington CD 53-55; V New Addington 55-64; Chapl Forest Gate Hosp Lon 64-78; R Buckhurst Hill *Chelmsf* 64-78; Hon Can Chelmsf Cathl 75-78; R Lutterworth w Cotesbach *Leic* 78-90; RD Guthlaxton II 89-90; rtd 90; Perm to Offic *Leic* from 90. *1 Spring Close, Lutterworth LE17 4DD* Tel (01455) 554197

✠**CASTLE, The Rt Revd Brian Colin.** b 49. Lon Univ BA72 Ox Univ BA77 MA80 Birm Univ PhD89. Cuddesdon Coll 74. **d** 77 **p** 78 **c** 02. C Sutton St Nic *S'wark* 77; C Limpsfield and Titsey 77-81; USPG Zambia 81-84; Lect Ecum Inst WCC Geneva 84-85; V N Petherton w Northmoor Green *B & W* 85-92; Dir Past Studies and Vice-Prin Cuddesdon Coll 92-01; Suff Bp Tonbridge *Roch* from 02; Hon Can Roch Cathl from 02. *Bishop's Lodge, 48 St Botolph's Road, Sevenoaks TN13 3AG* Tel (01732) 456070 Fax 741449 E-mail bishop.tonbridge@rochester.anglican.org

CASTLE, Brian Stanley. b 47. Oak Hill Th Coll 70. **d** 73 **p** 74. C Barnsbury St Andr w St Thos and St Matthias *Lon* 73-76; C Lower Homerton St Paul 76-79; P-in-c Bethnal Green St Jas Less 79-98; V Tile Cross *Birm* from 98. *The Vicarage, Haywood Road, Birmingham B33 0LH* Tel and fax 0121-779 2739 Mobile 07710-251790 E-mail revbcastle@adl.com

CASTLE, Daphne Susan (Dee). b 39. Lon Inst of Educn TCert60 Open Univ BA88. Ox Min Course CBTS93. **d** 93 **p** 94. NSM Newbury *Ox* 93-00; Perm to Offic from 00. *20 Falkland Garth, Newbury RG14 6PB*

CASTLE, John Arthur. b 61. G&C Coll Cam BA83 S Bank Univ DMS88. Aston Tr Scheme 90 Cranmer Hall Dur BA95. **d** 95 **p** 96. C Southborough St Pet w Ch Ch and St Matt *Roch* 95-99; Miss Partner CMS from 99. *CMS, Partnership House, 157 Waterloo Road, London SE1 8UU* Tel (020) 7928 8681

CASTLE, Michael David. b 38. Wells Th Coll 69. **d** 71 **p** 72. C Acocks Green *Birm* 71-75; C Weoley Castle 76-78; V from 78. *St Gabriel's Vicarage, 83 Marston Road, Birmingham B29 5LS* Tel 0121-475 1194

CASTLE, Phillip Stanley. b 43. LNSM course 94. **d** 97 **p** 98. OLM E Farnworth and Kearsley *Man* from 97. *73 Bradford Street, Farnworth, Bolton BL4 9JY* Tel (01204) 571439

CASTLE, Roger James. b 39. St Jo Coll Cam BA62 MA66. Clifton Th Coll 63. **d** 65 **p** 66. C Rushden w Newton Bromswold *Pet* 65-68; C Stapenhill w Cauldwell *Derby* 68-72; V Hayfield 72-89; R Coxheath, E Farleigh, Hunton, Linton etc *Roch* from 89; Chapl Invicta Community Care NHS Trust from 91. *The Rectory, 144 Heath Road, Coxheath, Maidstone ME17 4PL* Tel (01622) 747570 E-mail rjcastle@fish.co.uk

CASTLE, Vincent Clifton. b 15. ALCD37 St Jo Coll Dur LTh38 BA39. **d** 39 **p** 40. C Moulsham St Jo *Chelmsf* 39-42; CF (EC) 42-47 and 54-58; C-in-c Oakdale St Geo CD *Sarum* 47-50; P-in-c Coalpit Heath *Bris* 50-54; V Avonmouth St Andr 58-63; Miss to Seamen 63-71; V Creeksea w Althorne *Chelmsf* 71-79; RD Dengie 74-82; V Creeksea w Althorne, Latchingdon and N Fambridge 80-82; rtd 82; Perm to Offic *Chelmsf* from 82. *49 Winstree Road, Burnham-on-Crouch CM0 8ET* Tel (01621) 782807

CASTLETON, David Miles. b 39. Oak Hill Th Coll 69. **d** 72 **p** 73. C Canonbury St Steph *Lon* 72-76; C Guildf St Sav w Stoke-next-Guildford *Guildf* 76-89. *2 Lyne Cottages, Lyne Close, Virginia Water GU25 4EA*

CASWELL, Roger John. b 47. St Chad's Coll Dur BA70. St Steph Ho Ox 75. **d** 77 **p** 78. C Brighton Resurr *Chich* 77-83; TV Crawley 83-90; TR Littlehampton and Wick from 90; Chapl Littlehampton Hosp 90-93; Chapl Worthing Priority Care NHS Trust from 93. *St Mary's Vicarage, 34 Fitzalan Road, Littlehampton BN17 5ET* Tel (01903) 724410 *or* 726875

CASWELL, Thomas Hubert. b 55. Aston Tr Scheme 90 Coll of Resurr Mirfield 92. **d** 94 **p** 95. C Sheff Norwood St Leon *Sheff* 94-97; P-in-c Sheff Parson Cross St Cecilia from 97. *St Cecilia's Priory, 98 Chaucer Close, Sheffield S5 9QE* Tel 0114-232 1084 Fax as telephone

CATCHPOLE, Geoffrey Alan. b 53. AKC. Westcott Ho Cam 76. **d** 77 **p** 78. C Camberwell St Luke *S'wark* 77-80; C Dulwich St Barn 80-82; TV Canvey Is *Chelmsf* 82-87; Ind Chapl 83-87; P-in-c Bradwell on Sea 87-92; P-in-c St Lawrence 87-92; V Holland-on-Sea 92-00; P-in-c Witchford w Wentworth *Ely* 00-02; Adult Educn and Tr Officer 00-02; R Colchester St Mich Myland *Chelmsf* from 02. *Myland Rectory, Rectory Close, Colchester CO4 5DN* Tel (01206) 853076 E-mail mail@pole97.fsnet.co.uk

CATCHPOLE, Guy St George. b 30. **d** 82 **p** 83. Kenya 82-89; C Woodford Wells *Chelmsf* 89-95; rtd 95; Perm to Offic *Cant* from 95. *67 Trevor Drive, Allington, Maidstone ME16 0QW* Tel (01622) 761378

CATCHPOLE, Canon Keith William. b 30. MBE98. AKC56. St Boniface Warminster 54. **d** 57 **p** 58. C Woodchurch *Ches* 57-61; C W Kirby St Bridget 61-64; C-in-c Upton Priory CD 64-72; R Lavant *Chich* 72-82; RD Chich 80-96; Can and Preb Chich Cathl 82-99; V Chich St Paul and St Pet 82-95; P-in-c W

Hampnett 91-95; TR Chich 95-99; rtd 99; Perm to Offic *Chich* from 01. *23 Ninevah Shipyard, Arundel BN18 9SU* Tel (01903) 885340

CATCHPOLE, Richard James Swinburne. b 65. St Steph Ho Ox 92. **d** 95 **p** 96. C Eastbourne St Andr *Chich* 95-98; C Eastbourne St Mary 98-00; C E Grinstead St Swithun from 00. *St Luke's House, Holtye Avenue, East Grinstead RH19 3EG* Tel (01342) 323800

CATCHPOLE, Roy. b 46. Sheff Univ MMinTheol95. St Jo Coll Nottm LTh74 ALCD74. **d** 74 **p** 75. C Rainham *Chelmsf* 74-76; C Hyson Green *S'well* 76-79; V Broxtowe 79-86; V Calverton 86-94; Hilfield Friary Dorchester 95-01; rtd 01. *60 Gainsborough, Milborne Port, Sherborne DT9 5BB* Tel (01963) 250040
E-mail rev.catch@virgin.net

CATER, Lois May. b 37. S Dios Minl Tr Scheme 81. **dss** 84 **d** 87 **p** 94. Calne and Blackland *Sarum* 84-89; Hon Par Dn 87-89; Hon Par Dn Devizes St Jo w St Mary 89-94; Hon C 94-96; Hon TV Alderbury Team 96-01; Hon TV Clarendon from 01. *18 St Margaret's Close, Calne SN11 0UQ* Tel (01249) 819432
E-mail 106257.17@compuserve.com

CATERER, James Albert Leslie Blower. b 44. New Coll Ox BA67 MA81. Sarum & Wells Th Coll 79. **d** 81 **p** 82. C Cheltenham St Luke and St Jo *Glouc* 81-85; V Standish w Haresfield and Moreton Valence etc 85-96; P-in-c Glouc St Steph from 96. *St Stephen's Vicarage, 84 Frampton Road, Gloucester GL1 5QB* Tel (01452) 524694 Fax as telephone
E-mail jcaterer@atlas.co.uk

CATHCART, Adrian James. *See* MATTHEWS, Adrian James

CATHERALL, Mark Leslie. b 64. Chich Th Coll BTh93. **d** 93 **p** 94. C Lancing w Coombes *Chich* 93-95; C Selsey 95-98; Chapl RN from 98. *Royal Navy Chaplaincy Service, Room 203, Victory Building, HM Naval Base, Portsmouth PO1 3LS* Tel (023) 9272 7903 Fax 9272 7111

CATHIE, Sean Bewley. b 43. Dur Univ BA67. Cuddesdon Coll 67. **d** 69 **p** 70. C Kensal Rise St Martin *Lon* 69-73; C Paddington H Trin w St Paul 73-75; P-in-c Bridstow w Peterstow *Heref* 76-79; Hon C Westmr St Jas *Lon* 85-97; Hon C St Marylebone w H Trin from 99; Hon C St Marylebone St Cypr from 99. *23 Brookfield Mansions, Highgate West Hill, London N6 6AS* Tel (020) 8340 6603

CATLEY, John Howard. b 37. AKC60. K Coll Lon 57 St Boniface Warminster 60. **d** 61 **p** 62. C Sowerby Bridge w Norland *Wakef* 61-64; C Almondbury 64-67; V Earl's Heaton 67-75; V Brownhill 75-86; V Morley St Pet w Churwell 86-92; V St Annes St Marg *Blackb* 92-98; RD Kirkham 94-98; rtd 98; Perm to Offic *Blackb* from 98. *Flat 6, Herne Hill Lodge, 598 Lytham Road, Blackpool FY4 1RB* Tel (01253) 408129

CATLING, Michael David. b 56. Goldsmiths' Coll Lon CertEd77 DipEd84 Whitelands Coll Lon DipC&S88. Cranmer Hall Dur 88. **d** 90 **p** 91. C Cullercoats St Geo *Newc* 90-94; TV Glendale Gp 94-01; V Whittingham and Edlingham w Bolton Chapel from 01. *The Vicarage, Whittingham, Alnwick NE66 4UP* Tel (01665) 574704 E-mail mike@catlingfamily.fsnet.co.uk

CATLING, Canon Robert Mason. b 19. St Jo Coll Ox BA41 MA44. St Steph Ho Ox 41. **d** 43 **p** 44. C Falmouth All SS *Truro* 43-57; Lib Pusey Ho 57-61; Asst Chapl Univ Coll Ox 57-61; C Falmouth All SS *Truro* 61-64; V Beckenham St Barn *Roch* 64-72; V Devoran *Truro* 72-87; Hon Can Truro Cathl 77-87; rtd 87; Perm to Offic *Ex* and *Truro* from 87. *Ground Floor Flat, 31 Cranford Avenue, Exmouth EX8 2QA* Tel (01395) 267896

CATO (formerly LEGGETT), Ms Vanessa Gisela. b 51. St Osyth Coll of Educn TCert75. Westcott Ho Cam 93. **d** 93 **p** 94. C Southchurch H Trin *Chelmsf* 93-97; R Orsett and Bulphan and Horndon on the Hill from 97; Chapl Basildon and Thurrock Gen Hosps NHS Trust from 99. *The Rectory, Orsett, Grays RM16 3JT* Tel (01375) 891254 E-mail vgcato@lineone.net

CATON, David Arthur. b 25. Trin Coll Ox BA50 MA50. St Steph Ho Ox 49. **d** 51 **p** 52. C Seaton Hirst *Newc* 51-55; S Africa 55-61; V Stapleford *Ely* 61-69; V Hurst *Man* 69-75; V Hanwell St Thos *Lon* 75-84; AD Ealing W 82-84; V Staincross *Wakef* 84-95; rtd 95; Perm to Offic *Lon* from 95. *39 Beardsley Way, London W3 7YQ* Tel (020) 8743 2126

CATON, Philip Cooper. b 47. Oak Hill Th Coll 79. **d** 81 **p** 82. C Much Woolton *Liv* 81-85; V Birkdale St Jo from 98. *St John's Vicarage, 17 Kirkstall Road, Southport PR8 4RA* Tel (01704) 568318 E-mail caton@dircon.co.uk

CATT, Albert Henry. b 08. St Steph Ho Ox 34. **d** 37 **p** 38. C Somers Town *Lon* 37-40; CF (EC) 40-46; Hon CF from 46; C Harrow St Pet *Lon* 46-48; V Hornsey St Geo 49-74; rtd 74; Perm to Offic *Ely* 75-88. *c/o A Catt Esq, 3 The Conifers, Oundle Road, Peterborough PE2 5WL* Tel (01733) 234329 *or* 372148 Fax 372402

CATT, Douglas Gordon. b 23. MCSP49 SRP67. Roch Th Coll 61. **d** 63 **p** 64. C Cant St Martin w St Paul *Cant* 63-66; R Croughton *Pet* 66-75; R Hinton in the Hedges w Steane 66-75; V Evenley 72-75; Chapl St Andr Hosp Northn 75-89; Lic to Offic *Pet* 75-88; rtd 88; Perm to Offic *Pet* from 88. *195 Billing Road, Northampton NN1 5RS* Tel (01604) 27710

CATTELL, The Ven Jack. b 15. Univ Coll Dur BA37 DipTh38 MA40 Lon Univ BD53. Sarum & Wells Th Coll 38. **d** 39 **p** 40. C Royston *Wakef* 39-41; Perm to Offic *Sarum* 41-42; CF (EC) 42-46; Lic to Offic *Ripon* 46-49; Chapl R Wanstead Sch 49-53; Bermuda 53-82; Adn Bermuda 61-82; Perm to Offic *Mon* 82-89. *39A Risca Road, Newport NP9 4HX* Tel (01633) 54529

CATTERALL, David Arnold. b 53. Lon Univ BSc74 ARCS74. Cranmer Hall Dur DipTh78. **d** 78 **p** 79. C Swinton St Pet *Man* 78-81; C Wythenshawe St Martin 81-83; R Heaton Norris Ch w All SS 83-88; I Fanlobbus Union *C, C & R* 88-95; Can Cork and Ross Cathls 93-95; Warden Ch's Min of Healing in Ireland 95-02; I Templemichael w Clongish, Clooncumber etc *K, E & A* from 02. *St John's Rectory, Battery Road, Longford, Irish Republic* Tel (00353) (43) 46442 E-mail djcatt@eircom.net

CATTERALL, Mrs Janet Margaret. b 53. Univ of Wales (Ban) BA74. Cranmer Hall Dur DipTh77. **dss** 81 **d** 87 **p** 90. Wythenshawe St Martin *Man* 81-83; Heaton Norris Ch w All SS 83-87; Par Dn 87-88; C Bandon Union *C, C & R* 88-89; Dioc Youth Adv (Cork) 89-94; Dioc Youth Chapl 94-95; I Drung w Castleterra, Larah and Lavey etc *K, E & A* 95-02; P-in-c Mostrim w Granard, Clonbroney, Killoe etc from 02. *St John's Rectory, Battery Road, Longford, Irish Republic* Tel (00353) (43) 46442 E-mail djcatt@eircom.net

CATTERICK, Matthew John. b 68. W Sussex Inst of HE BA92. St Steph Ho Ox BTh95. **d** 95 **p** 96. C Colchester St Jas, All SS, St Nic and St Runwald *Chelmsf* 95-98; C Leic Resurr *Leic* 98-99; TV from 99. *St Gabriel's House, Kerrysdale Avenue, Leicester LE4 7GH* Tel 0116-266 1452
E-mail matthew.catterick@ntlworld.com

CATTLE, Canon Richard John. b 40. WMMTC 88. **d** 90 **p** 91. NSM Brixworth Deanery *Pet* 90-91; NSM Welford w Sibbertoft and Marston Trussell 91-92; V 92-97; Bp's Dioc Chapl 97-00; Dioc Sec 98-00; Can Pet Cathl 98-02; rtd 01; Perm to Offic *Pet* from 02. *PO Box 1617, Newport Pagnell MK16 0ZU* Tel (01908) 830250

CATTLEY, Richard Melville. b 49. Trin Coll Bris DipTh73. **d** 73 **p** 74. C Kendal St Thos *Carl* 73-77; Nat Sec Pathfinders CPAS 77-82; Exec Sec 82-85; V Dalton-in-Furness *Carl* 85-90; V Dulwich St Barn *S'wark* 90-99; Chapl Alleyn's Foundn Dulwich 90-99; V Milton Keynes *Ox* from 99; AD Milton Keynes from 01. *1 Cottage Common, Loughton, Milton Keynes MK5 8AE* Tel (01908) 692575 Fax 200216

CATTON, Canon Cedric Trevor. b 36. JP. Lambeth STh94 Wells Th Coll 70. **d** 72 **p** 73. C Solihull *Birm* 72-74; R Whepstead w Brockley *St E* 74-75; R Hawstead and Nowton w Stanningfield etc 74-79; Dioc Stewardship Adv 77-83; R Cockfield 79-83; V Exning St Martin w Landwade 83-99; Chapl Newmarket Gen Hosp 85-93; Chapl Mid Anglia Community Health NHS Trust 93-99; Hon Can St E Cathl *St E* 90-02; Chapl Dioc MU from 94; Dioc Par Resources and Stewardship Officer 99-02; Asst Can Past St E Cathl 02; rtd 02. *60 Sextons Meadows, Bury St Edmunds IP33 2SB* Tel (01284) 749429 Fax as telephone

CATTON, Stanley Charles. b 44. OLM course 96. **d** 99 **p** 00. OLM Bermondsey St Jas w Ch Ch and St Crispin *S'wark* from 99. *4 Reverdy Road, London SE1 5QE* Tel (020) 7237 7703

CAUDWELL, Juliet Lesley. *See* STRAW, Mrs Juliet Lesley

CAUNT, Mrs Margaret. b 55. N Ord Course DipTh97. **d** 97 **p** 98. NSM Brightside w Wincobank *Sheff* 97-00; C Ecclesfield 00-02; TV Gleadless from 02. *St Peter's Vicarage, 51 White Lane, Sheffield S12 3ED* Tel 0114-239 6132

CAVAGAN, Raymond. b 35. Hull Univ MA86 PhD87. Oak Hill Th Coll DipTh62. **d** 63 **p** 64. C Upper Holloway St Pet *Lon* 63-66; C Hurworth *Dur* 66-68; V New Shildon 68-76; P-in-c Toxteth Park St Andr Aigburth Road *Liv* 76-77; V Toxteth Park St Mich 76-77; V Toxteth Park St Mich w St Andr 78-88; V Stamfordham w Matfen *Newc* from 88; Hon CF from 90. *The Vicarage, Stamfordham, Newcastle upon Tyne NE18 0QQ* Tel (0661) 886456 Fax as telephone E-mail min.stam@virgin.net

CAVAGHAN, Dennis Edgar. b 45. Ex Univ MA99. St Jo Coll Nottm BTh74. **d** 74 **p** 75. C Hartford *Ches* 74-77; C Plymouth St Andr w St Paul and St Geo *Ex* 77-80; V Cofton w Starcross 80-88; P-in-c Exe 88-93; Perm to Offic *B & W* 93-02; Hon C Taunton St Mary from 02. *7 Elm Grove, Taunton TA1 1EG* Tel (01823) 282634

CAVALCANTI, Joabe Gomes. b 69. Federal Univ of Pernambuco BA97 Trin Coll Bris MA00. Nordeste Th Sem BA91. **d** 98 **p** 98. Perm to Offic *Bris* 99-00; *S'wark* from 00. *24 Pilgrims Cloisters, 116 Sedgmoor Place, London SE1 7RQ* Tel 07740-931387 (mobile) E-mail joabecavalcanti@hotmail.com

CAVALIER, Mrs Sandra Jane. b 48. Guildf Dioc Min Course 98. **d** 00 **p** 01. OLM Guildf Ch Ch w St Martha-on-the-Hill *Guildf* from 00. *10 The Greenwood, Guildford GU1 2ND* Tel (01483) 822496 Mobile 07990-658445
E-mail sandycavalier@ntlworld.com

CAVAN, Lawrence Noel. b 38. Trin Coll Bris 72. **d** 75 **p** 76. C Lurgan Ch the Redeemer *D & D* 75-78; C Chorleywood Ch Ch *St Alb* 78-82; I Durrus *C, C & R* 82-85; I Portarlington w Cloneyhurke and Lea *M & K* 85-90; TV Eston w Normanby

York from 90. *The Vicarage, 73A High Street, Eston, Middlesbrough TS6 9EH* Tel (01642) 456755

CAVANAGH, Anthony James. b 49. Ushaw Coll Dur 72. **d** 79 **p** 80. In RC Ch 79-95; C Goole *Sheff* 99-01; TV Cullercoats St Geo *Newc* from 01. *St Hilda's Vicarage, Preston Gate, North Shields NE29 9QB* Tel 0191-257 6595

CAVANAGH, Capt Kenneth Joseph. b 41. CA Tr Coll 60. **d** 77 **p** 77. CA from 64; Paraguay 70-83; P-in-c Gt w Lt Snoring *Nor* 83-85; R Gt w Lt Snoring w Kettlestone and Pensthorpe 85-88; R Glencarse *Bre* 88-94; CA Co-ord (Scotland/Ireland) & Regional Voc Adv from 90; R Dundee St Luke from 95. *The Rectory, 4 St Luke's Road, Downfield, Dundee DD3 0LD* Tel (01382) 825165 Fax as telephone
E-mail cavanagh@tinyworld.co.uk

CAVANAGH, Mrs Lorraine Marie. b 46. Lucy Cavendish Coll Cam BA97 MA01. Ridley Hall Cam 00. **d** 01 **p** 02. Perm to Offic *Ely* 01-03; Chapl Fitzw Coll Cam from 03. *Cae Hedd, Llantilio Crossney, Abergavenny NP7 8TL*, or *112 Coton Road, Grantchester, Cambridge CB3 9NX* Tel (01600) 780244, (01223) 847115 *or* (01223) 332013 E-mail lmc1005@cam.ac.uk

CAVANAGH, Michael Richard. b 49. MIDPM78. N Ord Course 89. **d** 92 **p** 93. NSM Stalybridge H Trin and Ch Ch *Ches* 92-98; P-in-c Over Tabley and High Legh from 98. *The Vicarage, The Avenue, High Legh, Knutsford WA16 6ND* Tel (01925) 759132 *or* 759037 E-mail michael@balmoralconsulting.co.uk

CAVANAGH, Canon Peter Bernard. b 49. Sarum & Wells Th Coll 71. **d** 73 **p** 74. C Gt Crosby St Faith *Liv* 73-76; C Stanley 76-79; V Anfield St Columba 79-97; V Lancaster St Mary w St John and St Anne *Blackb* from 97; Hon Can Blackb Cathl from 00. *The Vicarage, Priory Close, Lancaster LA1 1YZ* Tel (01524) 63200 Fax as telephone E-mail lancasterpriory@yahoo.co.uk

CAVE, Anthony Sidney. b 32. EMMTC. **d** 84 **p** 85. C Immingham *Linc* 84-88; V Keelby 88-89; V Riby 88-89; V Keelby w Riby and Aylesby 89-98; rtd 99; Perm to Offic *Linc* from 00. *Polruan, The Bungalow, Cherry Lane, Barrow-upon-Humber DN19 7AX* Tel (01469) 532350

CAVE, Bill. *See* CAVE-BROWNE-CAVE, Bernard James William

CAVE, Brian Malcolm. b 37. St Cath Soc Ox BA60 MA64. Oak Hill Th Coll. **d** 63 **p** 64. C Streatham Park St Alb *S'wark* 63-66; C Ruskin Park St Sav and St Matt 66-68; C Tunbridge Wells St Jas *Roch* 68-71; V Bootle St Leon *Liv* 71-75; Min St Mary w St John Bootle 73-75; Area Sec Leprosy Miss 75-81; V Hurst Green *Bradf* 81-82; P-in-c Mitton 81-82; V Hurst Green and Mitton 82-91; rtd 91; Perm to Offic *B & W* from 91. *63 Westway, Nailsea, Bristol BS48 2NB* Tel (01275) 654892

CAVE, Cyril Hayward. b 20. Nottm Univ MA60 BD63. AKC49. **d** 50 **p** 51. C Upholland *Liv* 50-53; P-in-c Darley w S Darley *Derby* 53-56; V Ticknall 56-65; Lic to Offic *Ex* 65-95; Lect Th Ex Univ 65-80; Sen Lect 80-85; rtd 85; Perm to Offic *Ex* from 95. *Berry House, Cheriton Fitzpaine, Crediton EX17 4HZ* Tel (01363) 866548

CAVE, Douglas Lionel. b 26. Lon Bible Coll 50 Lon Coll of Div 64. **d** 66 **p** 67. C Upper Holloway St Jo *Lon* 66-69; C Barking St Marg *Chelmsf* 69-73; V Blackb St Barn *Blackb* 73-81; Ind Chapl *Lon* 81-91; rtd 91; Perm to Offic *Lon* from 93. *8 Wood Rise, Pinner HA5 2JD* Tel (01895) 677426

CAVE, The Ven Guy Newell. b 19. TCD BA41 MA58. CITC 41. **d** 42 **p** 43. C Knockbreda *D & D* 42-45; P-in-c Kildrumferton w Ballymachugh *K, E & A* 45-73; Preb St Patr Cathl Dublin 65-72; Adn Kilmore *K, E & A* 72-87; P-in-c Ballymachugh w Kildrumferton and Ballyjamesduff 73-87; rtd 87. *5 Yew Point, Hodson's Bay, Athlone, Co Westmeath, Irish Republic* Tel (00353) (90) 649 2718

CAVE, John Edwin Dawson. b 43. Cranmer Hall Dur 71. **d** 74 **p** 75. C Gt Ayton w Easby and Newton in Cleveland *York* 74-77; C Redcar w Kirkleatham 77-78; C Redcar 78-80; P-in-c Aislaby and Ruswarp 80-81; V 81-87; V Dormanstown 87-97; V Marton-in-Cleveland 97-00; P-in-c Bilborough St Jo *S'well* from 01; P-in-c Bilborough w Strelley from 01. *St John's Vicarage, Graylands Road, Nottingham NG8 4FD* Tel 0115-929 3320

CAVE, Mrs Rachel Mary. b 53. Warwick Univ BA75. N Ord Course 98. **d** 01 **p** 02. NSM Gomersal *Wakef* from 01. *Yew Tree Hall, 13 Leeds Road, Mirfield WF14 0BY* Tel (01924) 480666 E-mail robertcave@msn.com

CAVE, Robert Philip. b 23. Roch Th Coll 64. **d** 67 **p** 68. C York Town St Mich *Guildf* 67-71; C Yaxley *Ely* 71-75; R Cottenham 75-88; rtd 88; Perm to Offic *Pet* from 89. *14 St Mary's Way, Roade, Northampton NN7 2PQ* Tel (01604) 864420

CAVE BERGQUIST, Julie Anastasia. b 59. St Jo Coll Dur BA80 Franciscan Univ Rome STL87. St Steph Ho Ox 85. **d** 87 **p** 98. Par Dn Kennington *Cant* 87-89; Chapl Trin Coll Cam 89-94; Chapl Westcott Ho Cam 94-97; C St Alb St Steph *St Alb* 98-02; P-in-c S Kensington H Trin w All SS *Lon* from 02; Dir of Ords Two Cities Area from 02. *St John's House, St John's Wood High Street, London NW8 7NE* Tel (020) 7722 4378 E-mail julescb@london.anglican.org

CAVE-BROWNE-CAVE, Bernard James William (Bill). b 54. Trin Hall Cam BA76 MA80 Bradf Univ MA90. Westcott Ho

Cam 77. **d** 79 **p** 80. C Chesterton Gd Shep *Ely* 79-83; Chapl Lanc Univ *Blackb* 83-95; Chapl HM Pris Service from 95. *HM Prison Service Chaplaincy, Abell House, John Islip Street, London SW1P 4LH* Tel (020) 7217 5685 Fax 7217 5090

CAVEEN, David Francis. b 44. Univ of Wales (Cardiff) BSc66 DipEd67. STETS DipTh95. **d** 98 **p** 99. C Swaythling *Win* 98-02; V Lord's Hill from 02. *1 Tangmere Drive, Southampton SO16 8GY* Tel (023) 8073 1182 E-mail davidcaveen@tinyonline.co.uk

✠**CAVELL, The Rt Revd John Kingsmill.** b 16. Qu Coll Cam BA39 MA44. Wycliffe Hall Ox 39. **d** 40 **p** 41 **c** 72. C Folkestone H Trin *Cant* 40; C Addington 40-44; Lic to Offic *Ox* 45-52; Area Sec (Dio Ox) CMS 44-52; Dio Post 44-49; Tr Officer 49-52; V Cheltenham Ch Ch *Glouc* 52-62; V Plymouth St Andr *Ex* 62-72; RD Plymouth 67-72; Preb Ex Cathl 67-72; V E Stonehouse 68-72; Suff Bp Southampton *Win* 72-84; Hon Can Win Cathl 72-84; rtd 84; Perm to Offic *Win* from 84; Asst Bp Sarum from 88; Can and Preb Sarum Cathl from 88. *5 Constable Way, West Harnham, Salisbury SP2 8LN* Tel (01722) 334782 Fax 413112

CAVELL-NORTHAM, Canon Cavell Herbert James. b 32. St Steph Ho Ox 53. **d** 56 **p** 57. C W Wycombe *Ox* 56-61; CF (TA) 60-63; V Lane End *Ox* 61-68; V Stony Stratford 68-97; P-in-c Calverton 69-72; R 72-97; Hon Can Ch Ch 91-97; rtd 97. *The Glebe House, Finnings Road, Lane End, High Wycombe HP14 3EU* Tel (01494) 881552

CAW (née FINLAY), Alison Mary. b 40. Natal Univ BA62 Ox Univ PGCE64. Ox Min Course CBTS93. **d** 93 **p** 94. NSM Beaconsfield *Ox* from 93. *1 Westway, Beaconsfield HP9 1DQ* Tel (01494) 674524

CAW, Hannah Mary. *See* JEFFERY, Mrs Hannah Mary

CAWDELL, Mrs Sarah Helen Louise. b 65. St Hugh's Coll Ox BA88 St Hugh's Coll Ox MA91 Trin Coll Cam BA94 MA99 K Coll Lon MA99. Ridley Hall Cam CTM95. **d** 95 **p** 96. C Belmont *S'wark* 95-98; Perm to Offic *Heref* 98-00; NSM Claverley w Tuckhill from 00. *The Vicarage, Lodge Park, Claverley, Wolverhampton WV5 7DP* Tel (01746) 710268 E-mail s.h.cawdell@btinternet.com

CAWDELL, Simon Howard. b 65. Univ Coll Dur BA86 K Coll Lon MA99. Ridley Hall Cam CTM94. **d** 94 **p** 95. C Cheam Common St Phil *S'wark* 94-98; V Claverley w Tuckhill *Heref* from 98. *The Vicarage, Lodge Park, Claverley, Wolverhampton WV5 7DP* Tel (01746) 710268 E-mail s.h.cawdell@btinternet.com

CAWLEY, David Lewis. b 44. FSA81. AKC71 St Aug Coll Cant 71. **d** 72 **p** 73. C Sprowston *Nor* 72-75; Chapl HM Pris Nor 74-75; C Wymondham *Nor* 75-77; C Buckland in Dover w Buckland Valley *Cant* 77-83; V Eastville St Anne w St Mark and St Thos *Bris* 83-95; V Leic St Mary *Leic* from 95; TV Leic H Spirit from 97; Chapl Trin Hosp Leic from 96. *The Vicarage, 15 Castle Street, Leicester LE1 5WN* Tel 0116-262 8727

CAWLEY, Stephen. b 42. GRSM63 ARMCM63. St Deiniol's Hawarden 81. **d** 84 **p** 85. C Tranmere St Paul w St Luke *Ches* 84-88; TV Hawarden *St As* 88-93; V Gwernaffield and Llanferres 93-02; V Gorsedd w Brynford, Ysgeifiog and Whitford from 02. *The Vicarage, Babell Road, Gorsedd, Holywell CH8 8RB* Tel (01352) 711675

CAWRSE, Christopher William. b 60. Univ of Wales (Cardiff) DipTh82 Birkbeck Coll Lon BA97 Qu Mary and Westf Coll Lon MA00. Westcott Ho Cam 82. **d** 84 **p** 85. C Stoke Newington St Mary *Lon* 84-86; Chapl St Mark's Hosp Lon 86-90; C Islington St Jas w St Pet *Lon* 86-90; Chapl Asst Charing Cross Hosp Lon 90-93; rtd 93; Perm to Offic *Lon* 93-97. *8 Hayhurst Court, Dibden Street, London N1 8RQ*

CAWTE, Canon David John. b 30. St Mich Coll Llan. **d** 65 **p** 66. C Chorley St Laur *Blackb* 65-67; C Boyne Hill *Ox* 67-74; C-in-c Cox Green CD 75-78; V Cox Green 78-94; Hon Can Ch Ch 88-94; rtd 94; Perm to Offic *Win* from 94. *6 Broadfields Close, Milford on Sea, Lymington SO41 0SE* Tel (01590) 642793

CAWTE, Martin Charles. b 51. Jes Coll Ox BA73 MA77 Lanchester Poly IPFA77. SEITE 97. **d** 00 **p** 01. NSM Sanderstead All SS *S'wark* from 00. *47 Farm Fields, Sanderstead CR2 0HQ* Tel and fax (020) 8657 8753 Mobile 07808-143809 E-mail martin cawte@hotmail.com

CAWTHORNE, Jack. b 22. ATD50 Lon Univ DipTh58. Cuddesdon Coll 69. **d** 71 **p** 72. NSM Newchurch *Man* 71-86; NSM Garforth *Ripon* 87-88; Perm to Offic from 88. *15 Arran Drive, Garforth, Leeds LS25 2BU* Tel 0113-286 9527

CAWTHORNE, Paul Howarth. b 66. St Hild Coll Dur BA88. Cuddesdon Coll 98. **d** 98 **p** 99. C Cen Telford *Lich* 98-01; TV Wrockwardine Deanery from 01. *The Vicarage, Eaton Constantine, Shrewsbury SY5 6RF* Tel (01952) 510333 E-mail paul@cawthorne52.fsnet.co.uk

CAYTON, John. b 32. Bps' Coll Cheshunt 54. **d** 57 **p** 58. C Hindley All SS *Liv* 57-59; C Littleham w Exmouth *Ex* 59-63; V Burnley St Cath *Blackb* 63-72; V Marton 72-87; V Fleetwood 87-97; Miss to Seamen 87-97; rtd 97; Perm to Offic *Blackb* from 97. *19 Parkstone Avenue, Thornton-Cleveleys FY5 5AE* Tel (01253) 854088

CECIL, Kevin Vincent. b 54. BA PGCE. St Mich Coll Llan DipTh82. **d** 82 **p** 83. C Llanilid w Pencoed *Llan* 82-85; C Coity w Nolton 85-88; Area Co-ord CMS *St D, Llan, Mon* and *S & B* from 88. *Gronow House, Llanharry, Pontyclun CF72 9LH* Tel (01443) 225035 Fax 223147

CECILE, Sister. *See* HARRISON, Sister Cécile

CEELY, Ms Sandra Elizabeth. b 44. N Ord Course 94. **d** 97 **p** 98. C Gt and Lt Driffield *York* 97-98; C S Cave and Ellerker w Broomfleet 98-01; Chapl Hull and E Yorks Hosps NHS Trust from 02. *The Chaplaincy, Castle Hill Hospital, Castle Road, Cottingham HU16 5JQ* Tel (01482) 875875

CENTRAL AFRICA, Archbishop of. *See* MALANGO, The Most Revd Bernard Amos

CENTRAL MELANESIA, Bishop of. *See* POGO, The Most Revd Sir Ellison Leslie

CERMAKOVA, Helena Maria Alija. b 43. **d** 88 **p** 95. NSM Roath *Llan* 88-91; Westcott Ho Cam 91-92; Asst Chapl Univ Hosp of Wales Cardiff 92-95; Chapl United Bris Healthcare NHS Trust 95-99; Chapl Jersey Gp of Hosps from 99. *Chaplain's Office, General Hospital, Gloucester Street, St Helier, Jersey JE1 3QS* E-mail hss34@psilink.co.uk

CERRATTI, Christa Elisabeth. b 54. Ox Coll FE NNEB93. Wycliffe Hall Ox DipMin94. **d** 97 **p** 98. C Chipping Norton *Ox* 97-00; P-in-c Lavendon w Cold Brayfield, Clifton Reynes etc from 00; Deanery Youth Co-ord from 00. *The New Rectory, 7A Northampton Road, Lavendon, Olney MK46 4EY* Tel (01234) 240013

CHADD, Jeremy Denis. b 55. Jes Coll Cam BA77 MA81. Coll of Resurr Mirfield 78. **d** 81 **p** 82. C Seaton Hirst *Newc* 81-84; C N Gosforth 84-88; V Sunderland St Chad *Dur* from 88. *St Chad's Vicarage, Charter Drive, Sunderland SR3 3PG* Tel 0191-528 2397

CHADD, Canon Leslie Frank. b 19. Leeds Univ BSc41. Coll of Resurr Mirfield 41. **d** 43 **p** 44. C Portsea All SS w St Jo Rudmore *Portsm* 43-46; Chapl RNVR 46-48; C Greenford H Cross *Lon* 48-54; C Littlehampton St Mary *Chich* 54-58; V Hanworth All SS *Lon* 58-65; V Fareham SS Pet and Paul *Portsm* 65-92; Relig Adv STV 72-81; Hon Can Portsm Cathl 81-92; rtd 92; Perm to Offic *Portsm* from 92. *Tree Tops, Hoads Hill, Wickham, Fareham PO17 5BX* Tel (01329) 834397

CHADDER, Philip Thomas James. b 66. Ex Univ BA88. Oak Hill Th Coll 01. **d** 03. C Gt Chesham *Ox* from 03. *31 Chapmans Crescent, Chesham, Buckingham HP5 2QT* Tel (01494) 786686 Mobile 07796-815285 E-mail philchadder@yahoo.co.uk

CHADWICK, Alan Michael. b 61. St Cath Coll Cam BA83 MA87. Wycliffe Hall Ox DipMin98. **d** 98 **p** 99. C Hubberston *St D* 98-01; R from 01. *Hubberston Rectory, 35 Westaway Drive, Hubberston, Milford Haven SA73 3EQ* Tel (01646) 692251

CHADWICK, Charles John Peter. b 59. Birm Univ BA81 Slough Coll DMS84 Southn Univ BTh90. Sarum & Wells Th Coll 85. **d** 88 **p** 89. C Chalfont St Peter *Ox* 88-91; C Gt Marlow 91-93; TV Gt Marlow w Marlow Bottom, Lt Marlow and Bisham 93-95; P-in-c Stokenchurch and Ibstone 95-01; Asst Dir Children Ch Tr Course 95-01; V Bridgwater St Mary, Chilton Trinity and Durleigh *B & W* from 01. *The Vicarage, 7 Durleigh Road, Bridgwater TA6 7HU* Tel (01278) 422443 *or* 424972 E-mail charles@chad0205.fsnet.co.uk

CHADWICK, David Emmerson. b 73. Lincs & Humberside Univ BA96. Ridley Hall Cam BTh00. **d** 00 **p** 01. C Whickham *Dur* from 00. *7A Coalway Drive, Whickham, Newcastle upon Tyne NE16 4BT* Tel 0191-488 3015

CHADWICK, David Guy Evelyn St Just. b 36. Bps' Coll Cheshunt 61. **d** 68 **p** 69. C Edmonton All SS *Lon* 68-71; C Edmonton St Mary w St Jo 71-72; C Greenhill St Jo 72-74; Bp's Dom Chapl *Truro* 74-79; Chapl Community of the Epiphany Truro 77-78; P-in-c Crantock *Truro* 79-83; R Clydebank *Glas* 83-87; R Renfrew 87-94; rtd 94. *Alverna, 1 Nithsdale Crescent, Bearsden, Glasgow G61 4DF*

CHADWICK, Francis Arnold Edwin. b 30. AKC54. **d** 55 **p** 56. C Chapel Allerton *Ripon* 55-58; C Hayes *Roch* 58-61; V Arreton *Portsm* 61-67; V Newchurch 61-67; V Kingshurst *Birm* 67-73; V York Town St Mich *Guildf* 73-83; P-in-c Long Sutton w Long Load *B & W* 83-87; R Stockbridge and Longstock and Leckford *Win* 87-93; rtd 93; Chapl Helsinki w Tallinn *Eur* 95-98; Perm to Offic *B & W* from 98. *Hillway, Wickfield, Devizes SN10 5DU* Tel (01380) 721489

✠**CHADWICK, The Rt Revd Graham Charles.** b 23. Keble Coll Ox BA49 MA53. St Mich Coll Llan 49. **d** 50 **p** 51 **c** 76. C Oystermouth *S & B* 50-53; Basutoland 53-63; C Masite St Barn 53-54; R Qacha's Nek 54-59; R Mohales Hoek 59-63; Chapl Univ of Wales (Swansea) *S & B* 63-68; Sen Bursar Qu Coll Birm 68-69; Lic to Offic *S'wark* 69-70; Warden Dioc Tr Cen Lesotho 70-76; Bp Kimberley and Kuruman 76-82; Dioc Adv on Spirituality *St As* 83-90; Chapl St As Cathl 83-90; rtd 90; Asst Bp Liv 90-95; Dir Inst for Chr Spirituality Sarum Coll 95-98. *66 Hulse Road, Salisbury SP1 3LY* Tel (01722) 505801 Fax 505802 E-mail gchadwick@aol.com

CHADWICK, Helen Jane. *See* MARSHALL, Mrs Helen Jane

CHADWICK, Canon Henry. b 20. KBE89 OM(Ger)93. Magd Coll Cam BA41 MA45 MusBac41 DD57 Glas Univ Hon DD57

Uppsala Univ Hon DD67 Yale Univ Hon DD70 Man Univ Hon DD75 Leeds Univ Hon DD80 Surrey Univ Hon DD96 Harvard Univ Hon DD97 Nashotah Ho Wisconsin Hon DD98 MRIA FBA60. Ridley Hall Cam 42. **d** 43 **p** 44. C S Croydon Em *Cant* 43-45; Asst Chapl Wellington Coll Berks 45-46; Chapl Qu Coll Cam 46-50; Dean 50-55; Regius Prof Div Ox Univ 59-69; Can Ch Ch *Ox* 59-69; Dean Ch Ch 69-79; Vice-Pres Br Academy 68-69; Regius Prof Div Cam Univ 79-82; Hon Can Ely Cathl *Ely* 79-83; Lic to Offic 83-93; Master Peterho Cam 87-93. *46 St John Street, Oxford OX1 2LH* Tel (01865) 512814

CHADWICK, Peter MacKenzie. b 21. Lich Th Coll 63. **d** 65 **p** 66. C Buckhurst Hill *Chelmsf* 65-66; Jt Hd Master Forres Sch Swanage 56-81; Chapl 66-85; NSM Kingston, Langton Matravers and Worth Matravers *Sarum* 85-92; rtd 89; Perm to Offic *Sarum* from 92. *Cull's, Langton Matravers, Swanage BH19 3HJ* Tel (01929) 422258

CHADWICK, Prof William Owen. b 16. OM83 KBE82. St Jo Coll Cam BA39 MA42 BD51 DD55 St Andr Univ Hon DD60 Ox Univ Hon DD73 Univ of Wales Hon DD93 FBA62. Cuddesdon Coll 39. **d** 40 **p** 41. C Huddersfield St Jo *Wakef* 40-42; Chapl Wellington Coll Berks 42-46; Fell Trin Hall Cam 47-56; Dean 49-56; Master Selw Coll Cam 56-83; Fell from 83; Dixie Prof Ecclesiastical Hist Cam 58-68; Regius Prof Modern Hist Cam 68-83; Pres Br Academy 81-85; Chan UEA 85-94; Perm to Offic *Ely* from 94. *67 Grantchester Street, Cambridge CB7 9HZ* Tel (01223) 314000

CHAFFEY, Jane Frances. b 59. Somerville Coll Ox BA80 MA84 St Jo Coll Dur BA86. Cranmer Hall Dur 84. **d** 88 **p** 94. Par Dn Roby *Liv* 88-90; NSM Finningley w Auckley *S'well* 95-96; Perm to Offic *Pet* 96-99; *Linc* 98-01; Perm to Offic RAF from 98. *Address temp unknown*

CHAFFEY, Jonathan Paul Michael. b 62. St Chad's Coll Dur BA83. Cranmer Hall Dur 84. **d** 87 **p** 88. C Gateacre *Liv* 87-90; Chapl RAF from 90. *Chaplaincy Services (RAF), HQ, Personnel and Training Command, RAF Innsworth, Gloucester GL3 1EZ* Tel (01452) 712612 Ext 5164 Fax 510684

CHAFFEY, Michael Prosser. b 30. Lon Univ BA51. St Steph Ho Ox 53. **d** 55 **p** 56. C Victoria Docks Ascension *Chelmsf* 55-59; C Leytonstone H Trin Harrow Green 59-62; V Walthamstow St Mich 62-69; R Cov St Jo *Cov* 69-85; P-in-c Cov St Thos 69-75; Hon C Bideford *Ex* 85; P-in-c Charlestown *Man* 85-88; V Sutton St Mich *York* 88-96; rtd 96; Perm to Offic *York* from 96. *1 School Lane, Burton Fleming, Driffield YO25 3PX* Tel (01262) 470439

CHALCRAFT, Christopher Warine Terrell (Kit). b 37. Oak Hill Th Coll. **d** 67 **p** 68. C Egham *Guildf* 67-70; P-in-c Slough *Ox* 70-73; TV Bramerton w Surlingham *Nor* 73-87; P-in-c Cockley Cley w Gooderstone 87-95; P-in-c Gt and Lt Cressingham w Threxton 87-95; P-in-c Didlington 87-95; P-in-c Hilborough w Bodney 87-95; P-in-c Oxborough w Foulden and Caldecote 87-95; Perm to Offic from 02. *The Malthouse, London Street, Swaffham PE37 7DD* Tel (01760) 724805 E-mail k.chalcraft@btinternet.com

CHALK, Francis Harold. b 25. Lich Th Coll 61. **d** 62 **p** 63. C Linc St Nic w St Jo Newport *Linc* 62-64; R Kirkby Laythorpe w Asgarby 64-69; V Ewerby w Evedon 65-69; R Gt Gonerby 69-89; rtd 89; Perm to Offic *Truro* from 90. *Chalkleigh, 3 Church Street, St Just, Penzance TR19 7HA* Tel (01736) 787925

CHALK, John Edward. b 33. St D Coll Lamp BA51. **d** 58 **p** 59. C Connah's Quay St As 58-61; C Abergele 61-65; V Cyfarthfa *Llan* 65-72; V Pyle w Kenfig 72-77; Lect in FE 84-92; NSM Mansfield Woodhouse *S'well* 92; Perm to Offic *Lich* 92-94; NSM Salt and Sandon w Burston 94-96; rtd 96. *Hendre Penprys, Pentre Uchaf, Pwllheli LL53 8EZ* Tel (01758) 750306

CHALK, Norman Albert. b 25. S'wark Ord Course 69. **d** 71 **p** 72. C Northwood Hills St Edm *Lon* 71-76; R Cowley 76-90; rtd 91; Perm to Offic *Ox* 94-01. *23 Rushmoor Avenue, Hazelmere, High Wycombe HP15 7NT* Tel (01494) 813438

CHALK, Miss Susan Christine. b 50. Warwick Univ BSc71 Man Univ CETD72. S Dios Minl Tr Scheme 90. **d** 93 **p** 94. NSM Bradford Peverell, Stratton, Frampton etc *Sarum* 93-03. *2 Dorchester Road, Stratton, Dorchester DT2 9RT* Tel (01305) 268464

CHALKLEY, Andrew William Guy. b 64. Aston Tr Scheme 90 St Jo Coll Nottm BTh92. **d** 95 **p** 96. C Liskeard, St Keyne, St Pinnock, Morval etc *Truro* 95-99; C Liskeard and St Keyne 99; TV Uphill *B & W* from 99. *St Barnabas' Vicarage, 2 Westbury Crescent, Weston-super-Mare BS23 4RB* Tel (01934) 623195

CHALKLEY, Henry Roy. b 23. St Aid Birkenhead 58. **d** 59 **p** 60. C Bromborough *Ches* 59-63; Miss to Seamen 63-88; rtd 88; Perm to Offic *St E* from 93. *32 Spriteshall Lane, Felixstowe IP11 9QY* Tel (01394) 277600

CHALLEN, Canon Peter Bernard. b 31. Clare Coll Cam BA56 MA60 FRSA94. Westcott Ho Cam 56. **d** 58 **p** 59. C Goole *Sheff* 58-61; V Dalton 61-67; Sen Ind Chapl *S'wark* 67-96; R S'wark Ch Ch 67-96; Hon Can S'wark Cathl 74-96; rtd 96; Perm to Offic *S'wark* from 96. *21 Bousfield Road, London SE14 5TP* Tel and fax (020) 7207 0509 E-mail peter@southwark.org.uk

CHALLENDER, John Clifford. b 32. CITC 67. **d** 67 **p** 68. C Belfast St Luke *Conn* 67-70; C Kilkenny w Aghour and Odagh

C & O 70-71; Bp's V and Lib Kilkenny Cathl 70-71; Dioc Registrar (Ossory, Ferns and Leighlin) 70-71; I Fenagh w Myshall and Kiltennel 71-76; I Fenagh w Myshall, Aghade and Ardoyne 76-79; I Crosspatrick Gp 79-95; Preb Ferns Cathl 85-88; Dioc Glebes Sec (Ferns) 86-91; Treas Ferns Cathl 88-91; Chan 91-95; I Killeshin w Cloydagh and Killabban 95-02; Can Ossory and Leighlin Cathls 00-02; rtd 02. *3 Adare Close, Killincarrig, Greystones, Co Wicklow, Irish Republic* Tel (00353) (1) 201 7268 *or* 287 6359 Mobile 86-243 3678
E-mail challen1@gofree.indigo.ie

CHALLENGER, Peter Nelson. b 33. St Jo Coll Cam BA57 MA61. Ripon Hall Ox 57. **d** 59 **p** 60. C Bushbury *Lich* 59-62; V Horsley Woodhouse *Derby* 62-67; V Derby St Barn 67-75; Brazil 75-80; TV New Windsor *Ox* 80-89; V Wootton (Oxon Hill) 89-98; rtd 99. *39 Moorland Road, Witney OX8 5LS* Tel (01993) 774630

CHALLICE, John Richard. b 34. ACP65. Sarum & Wells Th Coll 73. **d** 75 **p** 76. C Warminster St Denys *Sarum* 75-78; R Longfield *Roch* 78-00; rtd 00; Perm to Offic *Roch* from 00. *Magnolia, Allhallows Road, Lower Stoke, Rochester ME3 9SL* Tel (01634) 272468

CHALLIS, Douglas James. b 21. Selw Coll Cam BA48 MA55. Cuddesdon Coll 49. **d** 51 **p** 58. Kimbolton Sch Cambs 53-58; Chapl Summer Fields Sch Ox 58-60; Asst Chapl Stowe Sch 60-64; Chapl St Bees Sch Cumbria 64-67; Chapl Ryde's Sch Cobham 67-80; rtd 80; Perm to Offic *Cant* from 89. *20 Ryders Avenue, Westgate-on-Sea CT8 8LW* Tel (01843) 831052

CHALLIS, Ian. b 46. St Jo Coll Nottm 82. **d** 84 **p** 85. C Heatherlands St Jo *Sarum* 84-86; C Lytchett Minster 86-88; Perm to Offic from 88; NSM Canford Magna 95-00. *50 Constitution Hill Road, Poole BH14 0QD* Tel (01202) 691300

CHALLIS, John William Anthony. b 68. St Steph Ho Ox 98. **d** 00 **p** 01. C Ifield *Chich* from 00. *2 Lychgate Cottage, Ifield Street, Ifield, Crawley RH11 0NN* Tel (01293) 515373

CHALLIS, Terence Peter. b 40. St Aid Birkenhead 65. **d** 68 **p** 69. C Billericay St Mary *Chelmsf* 68-71; Admin Sec Dio Maseno S Kenya 72-75; Bp's Chapl 72-74; P-in-c Sparkbrook Ch Ch *Birm* 76-80; V Enfield St Jas *Lon* 80-89; V Astley Bridge *Man* 89-98; P-in-c Leigh St Mary and Leigh St Jo 99-02; rtd 02; Perm to Offic *Blackb* from 03. *48 Wilson Square, Thornton-Cleveleys FY5 1RF* Tel (01253) 864534

CHALLIS, William George. b 52. Keble Coll Ox BA73 K Coll Lon MTh75. Oak Hill Th Coll 73. **d** 75 **p** 76. C Islington St Mary *Lon* 75-79; Lect Trin Coll Bris 79-81; C Stoke Bishop *Bris* 79-81; Lect Oak Hill Th Coll 82; Burundi 82-85; P-in-c Bishopston *Bris* 86-89; TR 89-92; Vice-Prin Wycliffe Hall Ox 93-98; V Bitterne *Win* from 98. *The Vicarage, 2 Bursledon Road, Southampton SO19 7LW* Tel (023) 8044 6488
E-mail william.challis@bitterneparish.free-online.co.uk

CHALMERS, Canon Brian. b 42. Oriel Coll Ox BA64 MA68 DPhil70 BA71. Wycliffe Hall Ox 71. **d** 72 **p** 73. C Luton St Mary *St Alb* 72-76; Chapl Cranfield Inst of Tech 76-81; Chapl Kent Univ *Cant* 81-89; Six Preacher Cant Cathl 85-96; V Charing w Charing Heath and Lt Chart from 89; AD Ashford from 98; Hon Can Cant Cathl from 97. *The Vicarage, Pett Lane, Charing, Ashford TN27 0DL* Tel (01233) 712598
E-mail brian.chalmers@tesco.net

CHALONER, Stephen Mason. b 34. Dur Univ BA57. Ridley Hall Cam 57. **d** 59 **p** 60. C Aspley *S'well* 59-62; Chapl RNR from 61; P-in-c Eakring *S'well* 62-65; R 65-69; R Bilsthorpe 62-69; Chapl Saxondale Hosp Radcliffe-on-Trent 69-73; P-in-c Holme Pierrepont w Adbolton *S'well* 69-73; V Shelford 69-73; V Radcliffe-on-Trent 69-73; C Rowner *Portsm* 73-74; Hon C 74-81; Miss to Seamen 81-86; P-in-c Binstead *Portsm* 86-92; R 92-99; P-in-c Swanmore St Mich w Havenstreet 86-92; V Havenstreet St Pet 92-99; RD E Wight 88-94; rtd 99. *11 Bay Court, Wheelers Bay Road, Ventnor PO38 1HU* Tel (01983) 854659

CHAMBERLAIN, Allen Charles William. b 29. Lon Univ CertEd52 Birkbeck Coll Lon BSc56. LNSM course 95. **d** 96 **p** 97. OLM Gunton St Pet *Nor* 96-99; rtd 99; Perm to Offic *Nor* from 99. *28 Yarmouth Road, Lowestoft NR32 4AG* Tel (01502) 573637

CHAMBERLAIN, David (Bernard). b 28. Fitzw Ho Cam BA51. Linc Th Coll 52. **d** 54 **p** 55. C Brighouse *Wakef* 54-57; C Sheff Parson Cross St Cecilia *Sheff* 57-61; CR 63-85; S Africa 68-70; Bp's Adv on Community Relns *Wakef* 71-85; Bp's Adv Community Relns & Inter-Faith Dialogue *Bris* 86-93; V Easton All Hallows 86-93; rtd 93; Perm to Offic *B & W* from 94. *43 Bath Road, Wells BA5 3HR* Tel (01749) 679369

CHAMBERLAIN, David Murray. b 22. Cuddesdon Coll 55. **d** 57 **p** 58. C Barkingside H Trin *Chelmsf* 57-60; Japan 60-71 and 76-81; V Edgbaston St Germain *Birm* 71-76; Miss to Seamen N Australia 81-88; rtd 88; Perm to Offic *Truro* from 88. *42 Tresawls Road, Truro TR1 3LE* Tel (01872) 272270

CHAMBERLAIN, Eric Edward. b 34. Lon Univ DipTh64. Tyndale Hall Bris 64. **d** 65 **p** 66. C Chell *Lich* 65-73; P-in-c Preston St Mary *Blackb* 73-76; V 76-89; P-in-c Preston St Luke 81-83; R S Normanton *Derby* 89-99; rtd 99; Perm to Offic *Ox*

from 00. *1 The Closes, Haddenham, Aylesbury HP17 8JN* Tel (01844) 299303

CHAMBERLAIN, Frederick George. b 19. Univ of Wales (Lamp) BA50. Chich Th Coll 50. **d** 52 **p** 53. C Weybridge *Guildf* 52-54; C Bourne 54-57; V Blindley Heath *S'wark* 57-63; V Tilshead *Sarum* 63-71; R The Orchestons 66-71; V Chitterne 69-71; R Tilshead, Orcheston and Chitterne 71-80; P-in-c Handley w Pentridge 80-82; R 82-84; rtd 84; Perm to Offic *Sarum* from 84. *Mill Cottage, High Street, Codford, Warminster BA12 0ND* Tel (01985) 850519

CHAMBERLAIN, Malcolm Leslie. b 69. York Univ BA92. Wycliffe Hall Ox 93. **d** 96 **p** 97. C Walsall Pleck and Bescot *Lich* 96-99; C Mossley Hill St Matt and St Jas *Liv* 99-02; Asst Chapl Liv Univ 99-02; Chapl from 02; Dioc 18-30s Officer from 02. *71 Woodlands Road, Aigburth, Liverpool L17 0AL*

✠**CHAMBERLAIN, The Rt Revd Neville.** b 39. Nottm Univ BA61 Ox Univ DPSA62 Nottm Univ MA73 CQSW73. Ripon Hall Ox 61. **d** 63 **p** 64 **c** 97. C Balsall Heath St Paul *Birm* 63-64; C Hall Green Ascension 64-66; C-in-c Gospel Lane CD 66-69; V Gospel Lane St Mich 69-72; Lic to Offic *Linc* 73-74; Soc Resp Sec 74-82; Can and Preb Linc Cathl 79-98; R Edin St Jo *Edin* 82-97; Bp Bre from 97. *The Diocesan Centre, Pine Grove, 334 Perth Road, Dundee DD2 1EQ* Tel (01382) 640007 Fax 630083
E-mail office@brechin.anglican.org

CHAMBERLAIN, Nicholas Alan. b 63. St Chad's Coll Dur BA85 PhD91 New Coll Edin BD91. **d** 91 **p** 92. C Cockerton *Dur* 91-94; C Newton Aycliffe 94-95; TV 95-96; TV Gt Aycliffe 96-98; P-in-c Burnmoor from 98; Bp's Adv for CME from 98. *The Rectory, Burnmoor, Houghton le Spring DH4 6EX* Tel 0191-385 2695 *or* 374 6016 Fax 384 7529
E-mail nick.chamberlain@durham.anglican.org

CHAMBERLAIN, Roger Edward. b 53. BEd76 BA87. Trin Coll Bris 84. **d** 87 **p** 88. C Plymouth Em w Efford *Ex* 87-90; C Selly Park St Steph and St Wulstan *Birm* 90-94; V Yardley St Cypr Hay Mill 94-96; Perm to Offic from 96. *22 Hanbury Croft, Acocks Green, Birmingham B27 6RX* Tel 0121-708 0998

CHAMBERLAIN, Roy Herbert. b 44. Oak Hill Th Coll 91 N Ord Course 95. **d** 96 **p** 97. C Gee Cross *Ches* 96-98; Perm to Offic *Blackb* from 01. *125 Lancaster Road, Morecambe LA4 5QJ* Tel (01524) 409070

CHAMBERLAIN, Russell Charles. b 51. Univ of Wales (Cardiff) LLM00. Oak Hill Th Coll DipHE78. **d** 78 **p** 79. C Harold Hill St Geo *Chelmsf* 78-80; C Uckfield *Chich* 80-83; R Balcombe 83-90; V Okehampton w Inwardleigh *Ex* 90-94; TR Okehampton w Inwardleigh, Bratton Clovelly etc 94-01; RD Okehampton 93-98; R Wolborough and Ogwell from 01. *The Rectory, 5 Coach Place, Newton Abbot TQ12 1ES* Tel (01626) 368889 E-mail russell@chamberlain70.fsnet.co.uk

CHAMBERLIN, David John. b 56. St Jo Coll Nottm Dip Th & Min 94. **d** 94 **p** 95. C Chatham St Phil and St Jas *Roch* 94-97; R Swardeston w E Carleton, Intwood, Keswick etc *Nor* from 97; RD Humbleyard from 03. *The Vicarage, The Common, Swardeston, Norwich NR14 8EB* Tel (01508) 570550
E-mail david@chamberlin.org.uk

CHAMBERLIN, John Malcolm. b 38. Carl Dioc Tr Course 84. **d** 87 **p** 88. NSM Cockermouth w Embleton and Wythop *Carl* 87-97; Master St Mary Magd and H Jes Trust Newc from 97; Hon C Newc St Jo *Newc* from 98. *56 St Mary Magdalene Hospital, Claremont Road, Newcastle upon Tyne NE2 4NN* Tel 0191-261 2648 Fax 0870-133 1974
E-mail jmandmic@surfaid.org

CHAMBERS, Anthony Frederick John. b 40. Sarum Th Coll 69. **d** 71 **p** 72. C Hall Green St Pet *Birm* 71-74; C Holdenhurst *Win* 74-77; P-in-c Ropley w W Tisted 77-79; R Bishop's Sutton and Ropley and W Tisted 79-83; V Pokesdown St Jas 83-99; RD Bournemouth 95-99; P-in-c Heckfield w Mattingley and Rotherwick 99-02; V from 02; Chapl N Foreland Lodge Sch Basingstoke from 99. *The Rectory, Vicarage Lane, Hound Green, Hook RG27 8LF* Tel 0118-932 6385 Fax as telephone
E-mail anthony.chambers1@virgin.net

CHAMBERS, Miss Barbara Ada. b 51. LNSM course 95. **d** 99 **p** 99. OLM Gt Crosby St Luke *Liv* from 98. *12 Vale Road, Crosby, Liverpool LS23 5RZ* Tel 0151-924 5851

CHAMBERS, Mrs Barbara Mary Sinnott. b 43. SRN65 RM67 Birm Poly HVCert55 TCert77. WMMTC 87. **d** 93 **p** 94. Par Dn Blurton *Lich* 93-94; C Hove 94-96; Chapl Asst Qu Medical Cen Nottm Univ Hosp NHS Trust from 96. *Queen's Medical Centre University Hospital, Derby Road, Nottingham NG7 2UH* Tel 0115-942 9924 ext 43799

CHAMBERS, Carl Michael. b 68. Pemb Coll Cam BA90 Oak Hill Th Coll BA00. **d** 01. C Hove Bp Hannington Memorial Ch *Chich* from 01. *47 Nevill Avenue, Hove BN3 7NB* Tel (01273) 739144

CHAMBERS, George William. b 24. TCD BA46 MA57. CITC 47. **d** 47 **p** 48. C Conwall *D & R* 47-50; Chapl Portora R Sch Enniskillen 50-51; I Tullyaughnish w Milford *D & R* 51-61; I Adare *L & K* 61-81; Dioc Registrar (Limerick etc) 62-81; Adn Limerick 69-81; Dean Limerick 81-86; I Limerick City 81-86; I Killeshin w Cloydagh and Killabban *C & O* 86-95; Can Ossory and Leighlin Cathls 90-92; Treas Ossory and Leighlin Cathls 92-95; rtd 95. *12 Rathdown Court, Greystones, Co Wicklow, Irish Republic* Tel (00353) (1) 287 1140

CHAMBERS, Canon Peter Lewis. b 43. Imp Coll Lon BScEng64. St Steph Ho Ox 64. **d** 66 **p** 67. C Llandaff w Capel Llanilltern *Llan* 66-70; Chapl Ch in Wales Youth Coun 70-73; Youth Chapl *Bris* 73-78; V Bedminster St Mich 78-84; RD Bedminster 81-84; Adv Ho of Bps Marriage Educn Panel Gen Syn 84-88; Dir Dioc Coun for Soc Resp *Guildf* 88-94; Hon Can Guildf Cathl 89-94; Dir Tr *Sheff* 95-00; Hon Can Sheff Cathl from 96; P-in-c Harthill and Thorpe Salvin from 00; Dioc Min Teams Officer from 00. *27 Common Road, Thorpe Salvin, Worksop S80 3JJ* Tel (01909) 770279

CHAMBERS, Simon Paul. b 65. Liv Univ BEng87 PhD91. Ripon Coll Cuddesdon 00. **d** 02 **p** 03. C Parkstone St Pet and St Osmund w Branksea *Sarum* from 02. *79 Church Road, Parkstone, Poole BH14 0NS* Tel (01202) 743016 Fax 710591
E-mail simon@simonchambers.com

CHAMP, Darren David. b 60. Kent Univ BA93. Linc Th Coll MA95. **d** 95 **p** 96. C Ashford *Cant* 95-97; Perm to Offic 02-03. *154 Beaver Road, Ashford TN23 7SS* Tel (01233) 663090
E-mail dazchamp@hotmail.com

CHAMPION, Canon John Oswald Cecil. b 27. St Chad's Coll Dur BA49 DipTh51. **d** 51 **p** 52. C Worc St Martin *Worc* 51-53; Chapl RN 53-57; C Cant St Martin w St Paul *Cant* 57-60; C-in-c Stourbridge St Mich Norton CD *Worc* 60-64; V Astwood Bank w Crabbs Cross 64-68; V Redditch St Steph 68-75; R Fladbury, Wyre Piddle and Moor 75-93; RD Pershore 79-85; Hon Can Worc Cathl 81-93; rtd 93; Perm to Offic *Worc* from 93. *Black Horse Cottage, 3 Church Row, Pershore WR10 1BL* Tel (01386) 552403

CHAMPNEYS, Michael Harold. b 46. LRAM66 GRSM67 ARCO67. Linc Th Coll 69. **d** 72 **p** 73. C Poplar *Lon* 72-73; C Bow w Bromley St Leon 73-75; P-in-c Bethnal Green St Barn 75-76; C Tewkesbury w Walton Cardiff *Glouc* 76-78; V Bedford Park *Lon* 78-83; V Shepshed *Leic* 84-87; Community Educn Tutor Bolsover 88-93; Perm to Offic *Derby* 90-92; NSM Bolsover 92-93; V Potterspury, Furtho, Yardley Gobion and Cosgrove *Pet* 93-98; RD Towcester 94-98; V Shap w Swindale and Bampton w Mardale *Carl* 98-01; R Calow and Sutton cum Duckmanton *Derby* from 01. *The Rectory, Top Road, Calow, Chesterfield S44 5AF* Tel (01246) 273486
E-mail michaelchampneys@yahoo.co.uk

CHANCE, David Newton. b 44. Univ of Wales (Lamp) BA68. St Steph Ho Ox 68. **d** 70 **p** 71. C Selsdon St Jo w St Fran *Cant* 70-73; C Plymstock *Ex* 73-77; P-in-c Northam 77-79; TR Northam w Westward Ho! and Appledore 79-93; V Banstead *Guildf* from 93. *The Vicarage, Court Road, Banstead SM7 2NQ* Tel (01737) 351134

CHAND, Wazir. b 29. Punjab Univ BA56 BT59. Ox NSM Course. **d** 90 **p** 91. NSM Cowley St Jas *Ox* from 90. *38 Garsington Road, Oxford OX4 2LG* Tel (01865) 714160 *or* 433015

CHANDA, Daniel Khazan. b 28. Punjab Univ BA57 MA62 Saharanputh Coll. **d** 70 **p** 70. Hon C Handsworth St Jas *Birm* 70-83; Hon C Perry Barr 83-89; C Small Heath 89-98; rtd 98; Perm to Offic *Birm* 98-99 and from 00. *173 Wood Lane, Handsworth, Birmingham B20 2AG* Tel 0121-554 1093

CHANDLER, Anthony. b 43. Lon Inst of Educn CertEd65. EAMTC 94. **d** 97 **p** 98. Dioc Youth Officer *Ely* 96-00; NSM March St Mary 97-00; R from 00; NSM March St Pet 97-00; R from 00. *17 St Peter's Road, March PE15 9NA* Tel (01354) 652894 E-mail anthony.chandler@ely.anglican.org

CHANDLER, Derek Edward. b 67. Southn Univ BTh91 Nottm Univ MDiv93. Linc Th Coll 91. **d** 93 **p** 94. C Bitterne Park *Win* 93-97; C Sholing 97-00; R Emmer Green w Caversham Park *Ox* from 00. *20 St Barnabas Road, Emmer Green, Reading RG4 8RA* Tel 0118-947 8239 E-mail rev.derek.chandler@virgin.net

CHANDLER, Ian Nigel. b 65. K Coll Lon BD89 AKC89. Chich Th Coll 92. **d** 92 **p** 93. C Hove *Chich* 92-96; Bp's Dom Chapl 96-00; V Haywards Heath St Rich from 00. *St Richard's Vicarage, Queen's Road, Haywards Heath RH16 1EB* Tel (01444) 413621 E-mail ianchandler@hotmail.com

CHANDLER, John Charles. b 46. Solicitor. Oak Hill Th Coll 91. **d** 94 **p** 95. C Tonbridge St Steph *Roch* 94-98; V Felsted and Lt Dunmow *Chelmsf* from 98. *The Vicarage, Bury Chase, Felsted, Dunmow CM6 3DQ* Tel (01371) 820242

CHANDLER, John Edmond Owen. b 18. St Cath Soc Ox BA48 MA48. Cuddesdon Coll 68. **d** 68 **p** 69. Hon C Quarndon *Derby* 68-72; Lic to Offic *S'well* 73-78; P-in-c Oxton 79-85; R Epperstone 79-85; R Gonalston 79-85; rtd 85; Perm to Offic *S'well* from 85. *18 Thoresby Dale, Hucknall, Nottingham NG15 7UG* Tel 0115-963 5945

CHANDLER, Canon Michael John. b 45. Lon Univ DipTh75 K Coll Lon PhD87. Lambeth STh80 Linc Th Coll 70. **d** 72 **p** 73. C Cant St Dunstan w H Cross *Cant* 72-75; C Margate St Jo 75-78; V Newington w Bobbing and Iwade 78-83; P-in-c Hartlip w Stockbury 80-83; V Newington w Hartlip and Stockbury 83-88; RD Sittingbourne 84-88; R Hackington 88-95; RD Cant 94-95;

Can Res Cant Cathl from 95. *15 The Precincts, Canterbury CT1 2EL* Tel (01227) 463056

CHANDLER, Quentin David. b 62. Aston Tr Scheme 87 Trin Coll Bris DipHE91 BA92. **d** 92 **p** 93. C Goldington *St Alb* 92-96; TV Rushden w Newton Bromswold *Pet* 96-00; V Rushden St Pet from 00; Dir Tr for Past Assts from 03. *St Peter's Vicarage, 12 Kensington Close, Rushden NN10 6RR* Tel (01933) 356398 E-mail quentin.chandler@talk21.com

CHANDRA, Kevin Douglas Naresh. b 65. Qu Coll Birm 94 Lon Bible Coll BA88. **d** 96 **p** 97. C Walmley *Birm* 96-00; P-in-c Erdington St Chad 00-02; TV Erdington from 02. *1 Abbott's Road, Erdington, Birmingham B24 9HE* Tel 0121-350 3967

CHANDRAN, Nirmalan (Alain). b 68. Trin Coll Bris. **d** 03. C Southborough St Pet w Ch Ch and St Matt etc *Roch* from 03. *54 Holden Park Road, Southborough, Tunbridge Wells TN4 0EP* Tel (01892) 529153 E-mail alainchandran@yahoo.com

CHANDY, Sugu John Mathai. b 40. Kerala Univ BSc61 Serampore Univ BD66. Wycliffe Coll Toronto 67. **d** 66 **p** 68. India 66-74 and from 80; C Ormesby *York* 74-77; C Sutton St Jas and Wawne 78-80; rtd 99. *Matteethra, Muttambalam, Kottayam, Kerala, 686004, India* Tel (0091) (481) 572438 *or* 572590

✠**CHANG-HIM, The Rt Revd French Kitchener.** b 38. Lich Th Coll. **d** 62 **p** 63 **c** 79. C Goole *Sheff* 62-63; R Praslin Seychelles 63-67; C Sheff Norwood St Leon *Sheff* 67-68; C Mahé Cathl Mauritius 68-70; Missr Praslin 70-73; R Anse Royale St Sav and Adn Seychelles 73-79; Bp Seychelles from 79; rtd 03. *PO Box 44, Victoria, Seychelles* Tel (00248) 224242 Fax 224296 E-mail angdio@seychelles.net

CHANNER, Christopher Kendall. b 42. K Coll Lon BD64 AKC64. St Boniface Warminster 64. **d** 65 **p** 66. C Norbury St Steph *Cant* 65-68; C S Elmsall *Wakef* 68-70; V Dartford St Edm *Roch* 70-75; Chapl Joyce Green Hosp Dartford 73-75; V Bromley St Andr *Roch* 75-81; V Langton Green 81-94; Chapl Holmewood Ho Sch Tunbridge Wells 94-98; P-in-c Lewes All SS, St Anne, St Mich and St Thos *Chich* 98-00; R Lewes St Mich and St Thos at Cliffe w All SS from 00. *St Michael's Rectory, St Andrew's Lane, Lewes BN7 1UW* Tel (01273) 474723

CHANT, Edwin John. b 14. Lon Univ BA62. K Coll Lon 39 Clifton Th Coll 46. **d** 47 **p** 48. C Erith St Paul *Roch* 47-49; C Darfield *Sheff* 49-51; C Conisbrough 51-53; C Cliftonville *Cant* 53-56; V Gentleshaw *Lich* 56-80; V Farewell 56-80; rtd 80; Perm to Offic *Lich* from 80. *c/o Mrs D J McLuskey, 17 Diamedes Avenue, Stanwell, Staines TW19 7JE* Tel (01784) 248294

CHANT, Harry. b 40. Oak Hill Th Coll DipHE78. **d** 78 **p** 79. C Heatherlands St Jo *Sarum* 78-81; P-in-c Bramshaw 81-83; P-in-c Landford w Plaitford 81-83; R Bramshaw and Landford w Plaitford 83-87; V Fareham St Jo *Portsm* 87-00; rtd 00; Perm to Offic *Truro* from 00. *Paradise Cottage, 34 Nanscober Place, Helston TR13 0SP* Tel (01326) 561916 Fax as telephone E-mail harrychant@aol.com

CHANT, Kenneth William. b 37. St Deiniol's Hawarden 67. **d** 70 **p** 71. C Ynyshir *Llan* 70-74; C Bargoed and Deri w Brithdir 74; P-in-c Aberpergwm and Blaengwrach 74-77; V 77-81; V Cwmavon 81-02; rtd 02. *22 Chalice Court, Port Talbot SA12 7DA* Tel (01639) 813456

CHANT, Maurice Ronald. b 26. Chich Th Coll 51. **d** 54 **p** 55. C Mitcham St Mark *S'wark* 54-57; C Surbiton St Matt 57-60; P-in-c Cookridge CD Ripon 60-64; V Cookridge H Trin 64-67; Chapl Miss to Seamen Tilbury 67-71; Gt Yarmouth 71-77; Australia 77-84 and from 85; Singapore 84-85; rtd 91. *Unit 2, 99 Charlotte Street, Wynnum, Qld, Australia 4178* Tel (0061) (7) 3893 1251

CHANTER, Canon Anthony Roy. b 37. ACP60 Open Univ BA72 Lon Univ MA75. Sarum Th Coll 64. **d** 66 **p** 67. C W Tarring *Chich* 66-69; Chapl St Andr Sch Worthing 69-70; Hd Master Bp King Sch Linc 70-73; Hon PV Linc Cathl *Linc* 70-73; Hd Master Grey Court Comp Sch Richmond 73-76; Hon C Kingston All SS *S'wark* 73-76; Hd Master Bp Reindorp Sch Guildf 77-84; Dir of Educn *Guildf* 84-01; Hon Can Guildf Cathl 84-01; rtd 02; Perm to Offic *Chich* from 02. *Thalassa, 62 Sea Avenue, Rustington, Littlehampton BN16 2DJ* Tel (01903) 774288 E-mail tonychanter@hotmail.com

CHANTREY, Preb David Frank. b 48. K Coll Cam BA70 PhD73 MA74. Westcott Ho Cam 83. **d** 86 **p** 87. C Wordsley *Lich* 86-89; C Beckbury 89-90; P-in-c 90-93; C Badger 89-90; P-in-c 90-93; C Kemberton, Sutton Maddock and Stockton 89-90; P-in-c 90-93; C Ryton 89-90; P-in-c 90-93; R Beckbury, Badger, Kemberton, Ryton, Stockton etc from 93; Preb Lich Cathl from 99. *The Rectory, Beckbury, Shifnal TF11 9DG* Tel and fax (01952) 750474 Mobile 07785-524495 E-mail chantrey@fish.co.uk

CHANTRY, Ms Helen Fiona. b 59. Bradf Univ BSc82 Leeds Univ CertEd83. Trin Coll Bris BA89. **d** 89 **p** 94. NSM Hyde St Geo *Ches* 89-92; Dioc Youth Officer 92-00; NSM Barrow 94-99; C Acton and Worleston, Church Minshull etc from 00. *The Rectory, Church Lane, Nantwich CW5 5RQ* Tel (01270) 626737 E-mail helenchantry@btopenworld.com

CHANTRY, Peter Thomas. b 62. Bradf Univ BSc83. Trin Coll Bris BA89. **d** 89 **p** 90. C Hyde St Geo *Ches* 89-92; Dioc Youth Officer 91-99; P-in-c Barrow 94-99; R Nantwich from 99. *The*

CHANTRY, Richard Michael. b 31. Hertf Coll Ox BA55 MA57. Ridley Hall Cam 55. **d** 57 **p** 57. C Boulton *Derby* 57-59; C Ox St Aldate w H Trin *Ox* 59-68; P-in-c 74-75; Chapl Hertf Coll Ox from 61; Chapl Ox United Football Club from 65; Chapl Somerville Coll Ox from 95; rtd 96. *11 Talbot Road, Oxford OX2 8LL* Tel (01865) 58286 *or* 279400

CHANTRY, Mrs Sandra Mary. b 41. Cam Inst of Educn CertEd63. EMMTC 83. **dss** 86 **d** 87 **p** 94. Loughb Gd Shep *Leic* 86-87; Par Dn 87-89; Par Dn Belton and Osgathorpe 89-90; Par Dn Hathern, Long Whatton and Diseworth w Belton etc 90-94; C 94-97; P-in-c 97-01; rtd 01. *4 The Toft, Mill Lane, Belton, Loughborough LE12 9UL* Tel (01530) 222578
E-mail sandrachantry@aol.com

CHAPLIN, Ann. b 39. LRAM59 FE TCert75 Em Coll Boston (US) MA93 Cheltenham & Glouc Coll of HE DipHE98. WEMTC 95. **d** 98 **p** 99. NSM Heref S Wye *Heref* 98-03; NSM St Weonards w Orcop, Garway etc from 03. *45 Fonteine Court, Grey Tree Road, Ross-on-Wye HR9 7JU* Tel (01989) 576119

CHAPLIN, Colin. b 33. Edin Dioc NSM Course 74. **d** 76 **p** 77. NSM Penicuik *Edin* 76-91; P-in-c Peebles 89-90; NSM Bathgate 91-95; rtd 95. *26 Broomhill Road, Penicuik, Edinburgh EH26 9EE* Tel (01968) 672050

CHAPLIN, Douglas Archibald. b 59. Em Coll Cam BA81. St Jo Coll Nottm DipTh84. **d** 86 **p** 87. C Glouc St Geo w Whaddon *Glouc* 86-89; C Lydney w Aylburton 89-93; R Worc St Clem *Worc* 93-01; TV Droitwich Spa from 01. *The Vicarage, 29 Old Coach Road, Droitwich WR9 8BB* Tel (01905) 798929
E-mail fatherdoug@faithtofaith.net

CHAPLIN, Paul. b 57. Hull Univ BA80 CertEd81 K Coll Lon MA89. St Steph Ho Ox 85. **d** 87 **p** 88. C Ex St Jas *Ex* 87-90; C Wokingham St Paul *Ox* 90-98; V Stratfield Mortimer 98-99; V Stratfield Mortimer and Mortimer W End etc from 99. *The Vicarage, 10 The Avenue, Mortimer, Reading RG7 3QY* Tel 0118-933 2404 *or* 933 3704

CHAPMAN, Canon Albert Aidan. b 09. TD. Em Coll Cam BA35 MA39. Lon Coll of Div. **d** 37 **p** 38. C Beckenham St Jo *Roch* 37-39; CF (TA) 39-55; V Erith St Paul *Roch* 46-50; R Farnborough 50-64; Chapl Orpington Hosp 52-59; Chapl Farnborough Hosp 59-64; RD Orpington *Roch* 55-64; V Westerham 64-76; RD Sevenoaks 64-74; Hon Can Roch Cathl 64-76; rtd 76; Perm to Offic *Cant* from 96; Perm to Offic *Roch* 98-00. *4 Lorenden Park, Hawkhurst, Cranbrook TN18 4LF* Tel (01580) 754434

CHAPMAN, Ms Ann Beatrice. b 53. Hull Coll of Educn BEd77 Leeds Univ BA87. St Jo Coll Nottm MA95. **d** 95 **p** 96. C Burley *Ripon* 95-98; TV Sheff Manor *Sheff* 98-01; P-in-c Askrigg w Stallingbusk *Ripon* from 01. *The Vicarage, Askrigg, Leyburn DL8 3HZ* Tel (01969) 650301

CHAPMAN, Barry Frank. b 48. Trin Coll Bris 83. **d** 82 **p** 83. NSM Bradford-on-Avon Ch Ch *Sarum* from 82; Assoc Chapl Bath Univ *B & W* from 83. *16 Church Acre, Bradford-on-Avon BA15 1RL* Tel (01225) 866861 *or* 461244
E-mail b.f.chapman@bath.ac.uk

CHAPMAN, Mrs Celia. b 32. Whitelands Coll Lon TCert53 Open Univ BA82. WMMTC 84. **d** 87 **p** 94. NSM Bilston *Lich* 87-93; Ind Chapl Black Country Urban Ind Miss 93-98; Chapl St Pet Colleg Sch Wolv 93-98; rtd 99; Perm to Offic *Glouc* from 00. *5 Tyne Drive, Evesham WR11 7FG* Tel (01386) 765878

CHAPMAN, Canon Christopher Robin. b 37. Nottm Univ DipAddEd71 Cam Univ DipRK74. Ripon Hall Ox 72. **d** 73 **p** 74. C Kidbrooke St Jas *S'wark* 73-77; V Corton *Nor* 77-80; V Hopton 77-80; RD Lothingland 80-86; V Hopton w Corton 80-92; P-in-c Loddon w Sisland 92-93; P-in-c Loddon, Sisland w Hales and Heckingham 93-98; V Loddon, Sisland, Chedgrave, Hardley and Langley 97-98; V Loddon, Sisland, Chedgrave, Hardley and Langley from 98; RD Loddon 95-98; Hon Can Nor Cathl from 96. *The Vicarage, 4 Market Place, Loddon, Norwich NR14 6EY* Tel (01508) 520251

CHAPMAN, Colin Gilbert. b 38. St Andr Univ MA60 Lon Univ BD62 Birm Univ MPhil94. Ridley Hall Cam 62. **d** 64 **p** 65. C Edin St Jas *Edin* 64-67; Egypt 68-73; Tutor Crowther Hall CMS Tr Coll Selly Oak 73-75; Prin 90-97; Lebanon 75-82; Chapl Limassol St Barn 82-83; Lect Trin Coll Bris 83-90; Dir Faith to Faith Consultancy 97-99; Lect Near E Sch of Th Lebanon from 99. *Near East School of Theology, PO Box 13-5780, Chouran, Beirut, Lebanon* Tel (00961) (1) 346708 Fax 347129
E-mail chapman@inco.com.lb

CHAPMAN, David John. b 28. Jes Coll Ox BA52 MA56. Wells Th Coll 52. **d** 54 **p** 55. C Sedgley All SS *Lich* 54-57; C Cannock 57-60; V Tipton St Matt 60-69; R Sawley *Derby* 69-79; P-in-c Holkham w Egmere and Waterden *Nor* 79-83; P-in-c Warham w Wighton 79-83; R Wells next the Sea 79-83; R Holkham w Egmere w Warham, Wells and Wighton 83; V Feltham *Lon* 83-93; rtd 93; Perm to Offic *Worc* from 93. *12 Little Penny Rope, Pershore WR10 1QN* Tel (01386) 561558

CHAPMAN, Canon Derek. b 22. Westcott Ho Cam 52. **d** 53 **p** 54. C Earlsdon *Cov* 53-56; C Rugby St Andr 56-58; V E Malling

Roch 58-79; CF (TA) 60-67; R Hever w Mark Beech *Roch* 79-89; P-in-c Four Elms 80-89; Hon Can Roch Cathl 84-89; rtd 89; Perm to Offic *Roch* 89-98; Perm to Offic *Chich* from 89. *1 Moat Lane, Sedlescombe, Battle TN33 0RZ* Tel (01424) 754455

CHAPMAN, Mrs Dorothy. b 38. Nottm Univ Cert Th & Past Studies. EMMTC. **d** 89 **p** 94. Par Dn Bingham *S'well* 89-92; Sub-Chapl HM Pris Whatton 89-92; C Lenton 92-98; rtd 98. *86 Kenrick Road, Nottingham NG3 6FB* Tel 0115-950 3088

CHAPMAN, Drummond John. b 36. NDD. Cant Sch of Min 80. **d** 83 **p** 86. C Kington w Huntington, Old Radnor, Kinnerton etc *Heref* 83-84; C Llanidloes w Llangurig *Ban* 86-90; V Llanwnnog and Caersws w Carno from 90. *The Vicarage, Llanwnnog, Caersws SY17 5JG* Tel (01686) 688318

CHAPMAN, Edward Thomas. b 32. Man Univ BA60. St Mich Coll Llan 62. **d** 63 **p** 64. C Cleveleys *Blackb* 63-65; C Ox St Mary V w St Cross and St Pet *Ox* 65-67; Chapl LMH Ox 67-68; Asst Dir of Educn *York* 68-75; R E Gilling 68-76; P-in-c Hockley *Chelmsf* 76-77; V 77-82; P-in-c Gosberton Clough and Quadring *Linc* 82-83; Chapl St Cath Sch Bramley 83-86; R Bulmer w Dalby, Terrington and Welburn *York* 86-97; RD Bulmer and Malton 91-97; rtd 97; Perm to Offic *York* from 97. *6 Undercroft, Dunnington, York YO19 5RP* Tel (01904) 488637

CHAPMAN, Canon Eric Ronald. b 19. Man Univ BA41 BD59. Bps' Coll Cheshunt 41. **d** 43 **p** 44. C Chorley St Pet *Blackb* 43-46; C Skerton St Luke 46-51; V Bolton St Mark *Man* 51-58; V Kells *Carl* 58-66; RD Whitehaven 66-70; R Egremont 66-81; Hon Can Carl Cathl 79-85; TR Egremont and Haile 81-85; rtd 85; Perm to Offic *Carl* from 86. *Bernaville, Highfield Road, Grange-over-Sands LA11 7JA* Tel (01539) 534351

CHAPMAN, Gorran. b 55. Dur Univ BA. Westcott Ho Cam 78. **d** 80 **p** 81. C Par *Truro* 80-82; C Kenwyn 82-84; P-in-c Penwerris 84-89; V 89-92; V Torquay St Martin Barton *Ex* from 92; Perm to Offic *Truro* from 92. *St Martin's Vicarage, Beechfield Avenue, Barton, Torquay TQ2 8HU* Tel (01803) 327223

CHAPMAN, Guy Godfrey. b 33. Southn Univ BSc57. Clifton Th Coll 60. **d** 62 **p** 63. C Chadderton Ch Ch *Man* 62-67; V Edgeside 67-70; P-in-c Shipton Bellinger *Win* 70-72; V 72-83; RD Andover 75-85; Hon Can Win Cathl 79-91; R Over Wallop w Nether Wallop 83-91; V Ambrosden w Merton and Piddington *Ox* 91-00; RD Bicester and Islip 95-00; rtd 00. *65 St Ann Place, Salisbury SP1 2SU* Tel (01722) 335339
E-mail gandachapman@fish.co.uk

CHAPMAN, Henry Davison. b 31. Bris Univ BA55. Tyndale Hall Bris 52. **d** 56 **p** 57. C St Helens St Mark *Liv* 56-60; R Clitheroe St Jas *Blackb* 60-67; V Tipton St Martin *Lich* 67-68; SW Area Sec CPAS 68-72; V Eccleston St Luke *Liv* 72-78; P-in-c Ringshall w Battisford, Barking w Darmsden etc *St E* 78-80; R 80-93; RD Bosmere 87-91; rtd 93; Perm to Offic *Sarum* from 93. *Daracombe, 4 The Clays, Market Lavington, Devizes SN10 4AY* Tel (01380) 813774

CHAPMAN, Ian Martin. b 47. Oak Hill Th Coll BA94. **d** 94 **p** 95. C S Mimms Ch Ch *Lon* 94-99. *24 Vicars Close, Enfield EN1 3DN*

CHAPMAN (née CRAVEN), Mrs Janet Elizabeth. b 58. St Jo Coll Dur BSc80 MA92. Cranmer Hall Dur 84. **d** 87 **p** 95. Par Dn Darlington St Cuth *Dur* 87-92; NSM Edin Gd Shep *Edin* 93-95; NSM Long Marston and Rufforth w Moor Monkton and Hessay *York* 95-98; Chapl Qu Ethelburga's Coll York 97-99; Chapl Harrogate Ladies' Coll 00; P-in-c Banbury *Ox* from 01. *The Vicarage, 39 Oxford Road, Banbury OX16 9AJ* Tel (01295) 262370 E-mail janet.chapman@care4free.net

CHAPMAN, John. b 24. St Cuth Soc Dur BA51 St Chad's Coll Dur DipTh53. **d** 53 **p** 54. C Billingham St Cuth *Dur* 53-55; C Harton 55-57; PC Hedgefield 57-63; PC Annfield Plain 63-78; V Bolton All So w St Jas *Man* 78-85; V Baddesley Ensor w Grendon *Birm* 85-91; rtd 91; Perm to Offic *Birm* 91-97; Cov from 91; *Man* from 01. *The Angelus, 49 Alfriston Road, Coventry CV3 6FG* Tel (024) 7641 3758

CHAPMAN, John Brown. b 54. Strathclyde Univ BSc76 Lon Bible Coll BA80. NTMTC 00. **d** 02 **p** 03. C W Ealing St Jo w St Jas *Lon* from 02. *41 Leighton Road, London W13 9EL* Tel (020) 8567 0241 E-mail john.chapman@stjohnsealing.org.uk

CHAPMAN (née WHITFIELD), Mrs Joy Verity. b 46. SRN50 SCM71 Midwife Teacher's Dip 80. Trin Coll Bris BA88. **d** 88 **p** 94. C Littleover *Derby* 88-92; Par Dn Bucknall and Bagnall *Lich* 92-94; C 94; TV 94-97; Chapl LOROS Hospice 97-03; rtd 03; Perm to Offic *Leic* from 03. *The Firs, Main Street, Botcheston, Leicester LE9 9FF* Tel (01455) 828100
E-mail chapman@leicester.anglican.org

CHAPMAN, Mrs Linda. b 46. Lon Univ BSc67 Lon Inst of Educn PGCE68. Guildf Dioc Min Course 98. **d** 00 **p** 01. NSM Ewell St Fran *Guildf* from 00. *21 Overdale, Ashtead KT21 1PW* Tel (01372) 272614 E-mail linda.chapman@tesco.net

CHAPMAN, Mrs Margaret. b 34. Univ Coll Lon BA72 Qu Mary Coll Lon MA74. EAMTC 94. **d** 95 **p** 96. NSM Theydon Bois *Chelmsf* 95-01; P-in-c Gt Hallingbury and Lt Hallingbury from 01. *The Rectory, Wright's Green Lane, Little Hallingbury, Bishop's Stortford CM22 7RE* Tel (01279) 723341
E-mail revdmchapman@xalt.co.uk

CHAPMAN, Mark David. b 60. Trin Coll Ox MA83 DipTh84 DPhil89. Ox Min Course 93. **d** 94 **p** 95. Lect Ripon Coll Cuddesdon from 92; NSM Dorchester *Ox* 94-99; NSM Wheatley from 99. *Ripon College, Cuddesdon, Oxford OX44 9EX* Tel (01865) 874310
E-mail markchapman@ripon-cuddesdon.ac.uk

CHAPMAN, The Ven Michael Robin. b 39. Leeds Univ BA61. Coll of Resurr Mirfield 61. **d** 63 **p** 64. C Southwick St Columba *Dur* 63-68; Chapl RN 68-84; V Hale *Guildf* 84-91; RD Farnham 88-91; Adn Northn *Pet* from 91; Can Pet Cathl from 91. *Westbrook, 11 The Drive, Northampton NN1 4RZ* Tel (01604) 714015 Fax 792016
E-mail michaelrchapman@compuserve.com

CHAPMAN, Miss Patricia Ann. b 42. dss 84 **d** 87 **p** 94. Rainworth *S'well* 84-96; Par Dn 87-94; C 94-96; P-in-c Mansfield Oak Tree Lane from 96. *8 Hartington Court, Mansfield NG18 3QJ* Tel (01623) 645030

CHAPMAN, Peter Harold White. b 40. AKC64. **d** 65 **p** 66. C Havant *Portsm* 65-69; C Stanmer w Falmer and Moulsecoomb *Chich* 69-73; Chapl RN 73-86; Chapl Chigwell Sch Essex 86-90; P-in-c Stapleford Tawney w Theydon Mt *Chelmsf* 87-01; rtd 02. *The Old Rectory, Theydon Mount, Epping CM16 7PW* Tel (01992) 578723 E-mail phwchapman@aol.com

CHAPMAN, Peter John. b 33. Dur Univ BA56. Cranmer Hall Dur DipTh59. **d** 59 **p** 60. C Boulton *Derby* 59-62; Uganda 63-70; P-in-c Southampton St Matt *Win* 71-73; TV Southampton (City Cen) 73-78; V Bilston St Leon *Lich* 78-79; P-in-c Bilston St Mary 78-79; TR Bilston 80-98; RD Wolverhampton 89-98; rtd 99; Perm to Offic *Glouc* from 00. *5 Tyne Drive, Evesham WR11 6FG* Tel (01386) 765878

CHAPMAN, Prof Raymond. b 24. Jes Coll Ox BA45 MA59 Lon Univ MA47 BD75 PhD78. S'wark Ord Course 72. **d** 74 **p** 75. NSM St Mary le Strand w St Clem Danes *Lon* 74-82; NSM Barnes St Mary S'wark 82-94; Perm to Offic from 94; Perm to Offic *Lon* 82-91. *6 Kitson Road, London SW13 9HJ* Tel (020) 8748 9901

CHAPMAN, Raymond. b 41. Linc Th Coll 68. **d** 71 **p** 72. C Dronfield *Derby* 71-74; C Delaval *Newc* 75-76; TV Whorlton 76-79; V Newc St Hilda 79-83; V Blyth St Cuth 83-89; Hon C Fareham SS Pet and Paul *Portsm* 95-98; Perm to Offic 98-00; C Purbrook from 00. *170 White Hart Lane, Fareham PO16 9AX* Tel (023) 9232 4537 Mobile 07944-1245467 Fax 9264 4237

CHAPMAN, Canon Rex Anthony. b 38. Univ Coll Lon BA62 St Edm Hall Ox BA64 MA68 Birm Univ DPS67. Wells Th Coll 64. **d** 65 **p** 66. C Stourbridge St Thos *Worc* 65-68; Chapl Aber Univ *Ab* 68-78; Cantl Adr Cathl 76-78; Bp's Adv for Educn *Carl* 78-85; Dir of Educn from 85; Can Res Carl Cathl from 78; Chapl to The Queen from 97. *1 The Abbey, Carlisle CA3 8TZ* Tel (01228) 597614 *or* 538086 Fax 815409
E-mail rex.chapman@ukgateway.net *or* dir-educ@carlisle-c-of-e.org

CHAPMAN, Robert Bertram. b 68. St Jo Coll Nottm BA00. **d** 00 **p** 01. C Daybrook *S'well* from 00. *5 Blake Close, Arnold, Nottingham NG5 6NB* Tel 0115-926 8517
E-mail robertsarah@chapm64.freeserve.co.uk

CHAPMAN, Rodney Andrew. b 53. AKC75. St Aug Coll Cant 75. **d** 76 **p** 77. C Hartlepool St Aid *Dur* 76-81; Lic to Offic 81-83; C Owton Manor 83-87; P-in-c Kelloe 87-92; V Sharlston *Wakef* 92-01; V Stainland from 01. *The Vicarage, 345 Stainland Road, Stainland, Halifax HX4 9HF* Tel (01422) 311848

CHAPMAN, Roger John. b 34. AKC58. **d** 59 **p** 60. C Guildf Ch Ch *Guildf* 59-61; Kenya 61-67; R S Milford *York* 68-77; RD Selby 72-77; V Beverley St Mary 77-88; RD Beverley 85-88; V Desborough *Pet* 88-95; R Brampton Ash w Dingley and Braybrooke 88-95; rtd 95; Perm to Offic *York* from 95. *14 Scrubwood Lane, Beverley HU17 7BE* Tel (01482) 881267

CHAPMAN, Mrs Sally Anne. b 55. Lancheter Poly BSc76 Univ of Wales (Swansea) PGCE77. WMMTC 87. **d** 90 **p** 94. Par Dn Stoneydelph St Martin CD *Lich* 90; Par Dn Glascote and Stonydelph 90-93; Par Dn Willenhall H Trin 93-94; C 94-96; TV 96-99; V Streetly from 99; Dioc Adv for Women in Min from 99. *All Saints' Vicarage, 2 Foley Church Close, Sutton Coldfield B74 3JX* Tel 0121-353 2292 *or* 353 3582
E-mail robert@furzebank.freeserve.co.uk

CHAPMAN, Mrs Sarah Jean. b 55. Lon Univ DipCOT77. Sarum & Wells Th Coll 86. **d** 89 **p** 94. NSM Rogate w Terwick and Trotton w Chithurst *Chich* 89-94; NSM Easebourne 94-96; Perm to Offic *Portsm* 96-97; V Sheet 97-02; V Bitterne Park *Win* from 02. *Bitterne Park Vicarage, 7 Thorold Road, Southampton SO18 1HZ* Tel (023) 8055 1560 E-mail revsarah@sargil.co.uk

CHAPMAN (formerly WOOD), Canon Sylvia Marian. b 40. Gilmore Ho 77. dss 80 **d** 87 **p** 94. Tolleshunt Knights w Tiptree *Chelmsf* 80-83; Leigh-on-Sea St Jas 83-86; Canvey Is 86-87; Par Dn 87-92; Miss to Seamen 87-92; Warden of Ords *Chelmsf* 89-92; Par Dn Hutton 92-94; CME Officer 92-94; C Hutton 94-97; Ind Chapl 97-99; V Moulsham St Luke from 99; Hon Can Chelmsf Cathl from 01; Perm to Offic *Nor* from 00. *St Luke's House, 26 Lewis Drive, Chelmsford CM2 9EF* Tel (01245) 354479 Fax as telephone E-mail chapman@fish.co.uk

CHAPMAN, Thomas Graham. b 33. Trin Coll Bris 73. **d** 75 **p** 76. C Branksome St Clem *Sarum* 75-81; V Quarry Bank *Lich* 81-93; V Quarry Bank *Worc* 93-99; rtd 99. *8 Somerset Drive, Wollaston, Stourbridge DY8 4RH* Tel (01384) 373921

CHAPMAN, Timothy Mark. b 69. Clare Coll Cam BA91. Oak Hill Th Coll BA02. **d** 02 **p** 03. C Lt Shelford *Ely* from 02. *5 Garden Fields, Little Shelford, Cambridge CB2 5HH* Tel (01223) 844963 *or* 843710 Mobile 07815-686072
E-mail timandlucy@lineone.net

CHAPMAN, William Howard Dale. b 11. Edin Th Coll 33. **d** 38 **p** 39. C Ayr *Glas* 38-41; R Brechin *Bre* 41-47; P-in-c Girvan *Glas* 47; P-in-c Stranraer 47; P-in-c Portpatrick 47; C Ayr 47-49; V Coverham w Horsehouse *Ripon* 49-53; V Askrigg w Stallingbusk 53-60; V Kemble w Poole Keynes *Glouc* 60-71; R Brookthorpe w Whaddon and Harescombe 71-76; rtd 76; Perm to Offic *Glouc* 85-91. *c/o R Anderton Esq, 4 Alderwood Avenue, Chandler's Ford, Eastleigh SO53 4TH* Tel (023) 8025 1367

CHAPMAN, Miss Yvonne Hazel. b 35. Serampore Th Coll BRE63 Brighton Coll of Educn CertEd55. Coll of Ascension 60 EAMTC 95. **d** 96 **p** 97. NSM Duston Team *Pet* 96-02; NSM Officer 99-02; rtd 02. *18 Sundew Court, Northampton NN4 9XH* Tel (01604) 762091 E-mail rev.ychapman@virgin.net

CHAPPELL, Allan. b 27. Selw Coll Cam BA51 MA56. Coll of Resurr Mirfield 51. **d** 53 **p** 54. C Knowle *Bris* 53-57; Zanzibar 57-63; C Long Eaton St Laur *Derby* 64-67; C-in-c Broxtowe CD *S'well* 67-73; P-in-c Flintham 73-82; R Car Colston w Screveton 73-82; V Mansfield St Lawr 82-92; rtd 93; Perm to Offic *S'well* from 93; *Derby* from 00. *43 Hillsway Crescent, Mansfield NG18 5DR* Tel (01623) 654155

CHAPPELL, Edward Michael. b 32. Glouc Sch of Min 84. **d** 87 **p** 88. NSM Wotton-under-Edge w Ozleworth and N Nibley *Glouc* 87-01; Perm to Offic from 01. *5 Parklands, Wotton-under-Edge GL12 7LT* Tel (01453) 844250

CHAPPELL, Eric Richardson. b 08. Keble Coll Ox BA30 MA34. Cuddesdon Coll 30. **d** 31 **p** 32. C Teddington St Mark *Lon* 31-35; C Hillingdon St Andr 35-43; Chapl RAFVR 43-47; Chapl RAF 47-63; V Goodnestone H Cross w Chillenden and Knowlton *Cant* 64-78; P-in-c Adisham 75-78; rtd 78; Perm to Offic *Cant* from 78. *Littlebourne House Nursing Home, 2 High Street, Littlebourne, Canterbury CT3 1UN* Tel (01227) 721527

CHAPPELL, Frank Arnold. b 37. Dur Univ BA58. Bps' Coll Cheshunt. **d** 60 **p** 61. C Headingley *Ripon* 60-65; V Beeston Hill St Luke 65-73; R Garforth 73-91; V Dacre w Hartwith and Darley w Thornthwaite 91-02; rtd 02; Perm to Offic *York* from 02. *14 Nelsons Lane, York YO24 1HD* Tel (01904) 709566

CHAPPELL, Preb George Thomas. b 04. St Jo Coll Dur LTh28 BA29 MA32. Lon Coll of Div 24. **d** 28 **p** 29. C Birkenhead St Mary w St Paul *Ches* 28-31; C Cliftonville *Cant* 31-34; Org Sec (Dios Ox and Cov) CMS 34-41; (Dio Pet) 35-41; P-in-c Paddington St Jas *Lon* 41-43; V 43-71; Chapl St Mary's Hosp Paddington 44-54; RD Paddington 56-67; RD Westmr Paddington 67-69; Preb St Paul's Cathl 63-71; rtd 71; C S Kensington H Trin w All SS *Lon* 71-74; P-in-c Poole 74-75; Perm to Offic 75-85. *Flat 3, 19 Burton Road, Poole BH13 6DT* Tel (01202) 764665

CHAPPELL, Michael Paul. b 35. Selw Coll Cam BA57 MA61 ACertCM65. Cuddesdon Coll 60. **d** 62 **p** 63. C Pershore w Pinvin, Wick and Birlingham *Worc* 62-65; Malaysia 65-67; V Choral and Chapl Heref Cathl *Heref* 67-71; Min Can Dur Cathl *Dur* 71-76; Prec 72-76; Chapl H Trin Sch Stockton 76-87; C-in-c Stockton Green Vale H Trin CD *Dur* 82-87; V Scarborough St Luke *York* 87-01; Chapl Scarborough Gen Hosp 87-97; rtd 01; Perm to Offic *York* from 01. *26 Dulverton Hall, Esplanade, Scarborough YO11 2AR* Tel (01723) 340126

CHARD, Canon Francis Eric. b 24. Dur Univ BA53 MLitt81. St Jo Coll Dur DipTh55. **d** 55 **p** 56. C Cleveleys *Blackb* 55-57; C Preston St Jo 57-60; V Ewood 60-72; V Downham 72-88; RD Whalley 83-89; Hon Can Blackb Cathl 86-93; Co Ecum Officer 88-93; rtd 93; Perm to Offic *Blackb* from 93. *21 Moorland Crescent, Clitheroe BB7 4PY* Tel (01200) 427480

CHARD, Reginald Jeffrey. b 40. Univ of Wales (Lamp) BA62 Birm Poly CQSW75. Coll of Resurr Mirfield 62. **d** 64 **p** 65. C Ystrad Mynach *Llan* 64-67; C Aberdare St Fagan 67-71; V Hirwaun 71-74; Hon C Stechford *Birm* 74-78; TV Banbury *Ox* 78-86; Ind Chapl from 86; P-in-c Claydon w Mollington 86-96; R Ironstone from 96. *The Rectory, Church Street, Wroxton, Banbury OX15 6QE* Tel (01295) 730344 Fax as telephone
E-mail rector.ironstone@cdsinternet.com

CHARE, Frederic Keith. b 16. Hatf Coll Dur LTh38 BA39. Edin Th Coll 35. **d** 39 **p** 40. C Greenock *Glas* 39-43; C Dumfries 43-46; C Forton *Portsm* 46-52; V Camberwell St Phil *S'wark* 52-57; Min Barming Heath CD *Cant* 57-69; V Barming Heath 69-73; V Upchurch 74-75; V Upchurch w Lower Halstow 75-82; rtd 82; Perm to Offic *Cant* 82-00. *c/o Mrs F Scourfield, 19 Queen's Terrace, Otley LS21 3JE*

CHARING CROSS, Archdeacon of. *See* JACOB, The Ven William Mungo

CHARKHAM, Rupert Anthony. b 59. Ex Univ BA81. Wycliffe Hall Ox 83. **d** 89 **p** 89. C Ox St Aldate w St Matt *Ox* 89-92; P-in-c

Fisherton Anger *Sarum* 92-99; R from 99; V Cambridge H Trin *Ely* from 03. *Holy Trinity Vicarage, 1 Selwyn Gardens, Cambridge CB3 9AX* Tel (01223) 354774
E-mail rupert.charkham@htcambridge.org.uk

CHARLES, George Edward. b 41. St Jo Coll Morpeth ThL63. **d** 66 **p** 67. Australia 66-01; C Bentleigh St Jo 66-67; C Broadmeadows 67-70; I Montmorency 70-74; I Mooroolbark 74-81; I Bacchus Marsh 81-86; I Sorrento 86-93; I Altona 93-98; I Inverleigh, Bannockburn and Meredith 98-01; TV Hanley H Ev *Lich* from 02. *19 Widecombe Road, Stoke-on-Trent ST1 6SL* Tel (01782) 267243 E-mail gpsecharles@aol.com

CHARLES, James Richard. b 67. St Edm Hall Ox BA90 CertEd91. Oak Hill Th Coll BA03. **d** 03. C Throop *Win* from 03. *51 Landford Way, Bournemouth BH8 0NY* Tel (01202) 526731 E-mail jimrcharles@yahoo.co.uk

CHARLES, Jonathan. b 42. St Luke's Coll Ex CertEd64. Ripon Hall Ox 72 Ripon Coll Cuddesdon 78. **d** 79 **p** 80. C Leagrave *St Alb* 79-82; Chapl Denstone Coll Uttoxeter 82-86; Chapl Malvern Girls' Coll 86-89; Chapl K Sch Worc 89-95; Min Can Worc Cathl *Worc* 89-95; R Burnham Gp of Par *Nor* from 95; RD Burnham and Walsingham from 00. *The Rectory, The Pound, Burnham Market, King's Lynn PE31 8UL* Tel (01328) 738317 E-mail revj.charles@virgin.net

CHARLES, Mary Cecilia. b 49. Univ of Wales BEd. Trin Coll Carmarthen. **d** 96 **p** 97. NSM Letterston w Llanfair Nant-y-Gof etc *St D* from 96. *Heneglwys Farm, St David's Road, Letterston, Haverfordwest SA62 5SR* Tel (01348) 840452

CHARLES, Meedperdas Edward. b 28. Fitzw Ho Cam BA60 MA64. Bangalore Th Coll BD54. **d** 54 **p** 55. Malaya 54-55; Singapore 55-58 and 64-66; Perm to Offic *Ely* 58-60; V Sheff St Bart Langsett Road *Sheff* 60-64; V Gravelly Hill *Birm* 66-78; V Endcliffe *Sheff* 79-90; rtd 91; Perm to Offic *Sheff* from 91. *60 Ringinglow Road, Sheffield S11 7PQ* Tel 0114-266 4980

CHARLES, Robert Sidney James. b 40. Lon Univ CertEd77 Open Univ BA79 Univ of Wales LLM97. St Mich Coll Llan DipTh65. **d** 65 **p** 66. C Merthyr Tydfil *Llan* 65-68; C Shotton *St As* 68-70; R Stock and Lydlinch *Sarum* 70-74; R Hubberston *St D* 74-76; Perm to Offic *Chelmsf* 81-83; V Crossens *Liv* 83-97; V Budleigh Salterton *Ex* from 97. *St Peter's Vicarage, 4A West Hill Lane, Budleigh Salterton EX9 6AA* Tel (01395) 443195

CHARLES, Robin. b 50. N Staffs Poly HND72. Sarum & Wells Th Coll. **d** 86 **p** 87. C Chesterton *Lich* 86-89; C Rugeley 89-90; TV 90-97; TV E Scarsdale *Derby* 97-01; C Chesterfield St Mary and All SS from 01. *5 Queen Street, Chesterfield S40 4SF* Tel (01246) 229871 Fax as telephone E-mail robin-a@fish.co.uk

CHARLES, William Martin Darrell. b 40. **d** 90 **p** 91. C Market Harborough *Leic* 90-91; P-in-c Higham-on-the-Hill w Fenny Drayton and Witherley 91-99; P-in-c Breedon cum Isley Walton and Worthington 99-02; rtd 02. *37 Whatton Road, Kegworth, Derby DE74 2EZ* Tel (01509) 672040

CHARLES-EDWARDS, David Mervyn. b 38. Trin Coll Cam BA61. Linc Th Coll 62. **d** 64 **p** 89. C Putney St Mary *S'wark* 64-65; Chief Exec Officer Br Assn for Counselling 82-87; Gen Manager Lon Lighthouse AIDS Project 87-88; Consultant in leadership and team building from 88; NSM Rugby St Andr *Cov* 89-99; P-in-c Clifton upon Dunsmore and Newton from 99. *236 Hillmorton Road, Rugby CV22 5BG* Tel (01788) 569212 E-mail cwa.david@btinternet.com

CHARLESWORTH, Eric Charlesworth. b 29. Kelham Th Coll 49. **d** 54 **p** 56. C Woodbridge St Mary *St E* 54-57; Asst Chapl Oslo St John *Eur* 57-59; Canada 60-66; R Huntingfield w Cookley *St E* 66-70; R Slimbridge *Glouc* 70-96; rtd 96; Perm to Offic *Glouc* from 96. *Gardener's Cottage, Fairford Park, Fairford GL7 4JQ* Tel (01285) 712411

CHARLESWORTH, Ian Peter. b 65. Lanc Univ BA87. St Mich Coll Llan DipTh93. **d** 93 **p** 94. C Caereithin *S & B* 93-95; C Oystermouth 95-97; R Llandefalle and Llyswen w Boughrood etc from 97. *The Rectory, Church Lane, Llyswen, Brecon LD3 0UU* Tel (01874) 754255 E-mail ianpcharl@aol.com

CHARLEY, Canon Julian Whittard. b 30. New Coll Ox BA55 MA58. Ridley Hall Cam 55. **d** 57 **p** 58. C St Marylebone All So w SS Pet and Jo *Lon* 57-64; Lect Lon Coll of Div 64-70; Vice-Prin St Jo Coll Nottm 70-74; TR Everton St Pet *Liv* 74-87; Warden Shrewsbury Ho 74-87; P-in-c Gt Malvern St Mary *Worc* 87-97; Hon Can Worc Cathl 91-97; rtd 97; Perm to Offic *Heref* and *Worc* from 97. *155A Old Hollow, Malvern WR14 4NN* Tel (01684) 569801

CHARLTON, Canon Arthur David. b 23. Open Univ BA73 BPhil83. Chich Th Coll. **d** 66 **p** 67. C Rotherfield *Chich* 66-70; C Uckfield 70-72; C Isfield 70-72; C Lt Horsted 70-72; R Cocking w Bepton 72-79; P-in-c W Lavington 78-79; R Cocking, Bepton and W Lavington 79-90; Can and Preb Chich Cathl 88-90; rtd 90; Perm to Offic *Chich* from 91; Perm to Offic *Roch* 91-98. *33 High Cross Field, Crowborough TN6 2SN* Tel (01892) 661351

CHARMAN, Ms Jane Ellen Elizabeth. b 60. St Jo Coll Dur BA81 Selw Coll Cam BA84 MA88. Westcott Ho Cam 82. **d** 87 **p** 94. C Glouc St Geo w Whaddon *Glouc* 87-90; Chapl and Fell Clare Coll Cam 90-95; R Duxford *Ely* from 95; V Hinxton from 95; V Ickleton from 95. *The Rectory, 13 St John's Street, Duxford,*

Cambridge CB2 4RA Tel (01223) 832137 *or* 511944 Fax 07005-963374 E-mail gentianblue@ntlworld.com

CHARMLEY, Mark Richard. b 71. Ex Univ BA93. Qu Coll Birm MA01. **d** 01. C Blurton *Lich* from 01. *St Alban's House, 51 Ripon Road, Stoke-on-Trent ST3 3BS* Tel (01782) 315029 E-mail charmley@totalise.co.uk

CHARNOCK, Deryck Ian. b 47. Oak Hill Th Coll 78. **d** 80 **p** 81. C Rowner *Portsm* 80-84; TV Southgate *Chich* 84-90; V Penge St Paul *Roch* 90-98; V Whitwick St Jo the Bapt *Leic* from 98. *The Vicarage, 37 North Street, Whitwick, Coalville LE67 5HB* Tel (01530) 836904 E-mail dc.whit1@ntlworld.com

CHARRETT, Geoffrey Barton. b 36. ALCM Nottm Univ BSc57. Ridley Hall Cam 65. **d** 67 **p** 68. C Clifton *York* 67-68; Lic to Offic *Blackb* 69-80; C Walthamstow St Mary w St Steph *Chelmsf* 81-82; TV 82-87; Chapl Gordon's Sch Woking 87-94; P-in-c Hambledon *Guildf* 94-97; rtd 97; Perm to Offic *Linc* from 00. *2 Station Road, Sutton-on-Sea, Mablethorpe LN12 2HN* Tel (01507) 443525

CHARRINGTON, Nicholas John. b 36. MA. Cuddesdon Coll 60. **d** 62 **p** 63. C Shrewsbury St Chad *Lich* 62-65; C Gt Grimsby St Mary and St Jas *Linc* 65-72; P-in-c Wellington Ch Ch *Lich* 72-78; R Edgmond 78-89; R Edgmond w Kynnersley and Preston Wealdmoors 89-91; C Plymstock *Ex* 91-94; Chapl St Luke's Hospice Plymouth 91-94; P-in-c Longden and Annscroft w Pulverbatch *Heref* 94-00; rtd 00. *Domas Cottage, Harley, Shrewsbury SY5 6LX* Tel (01952) 510721 E-mail nick@charrington.enta.net

CHARTERIS, Hugo Arundale. b 64. Witwatersrand Univ BA88. Cranmer Hall Dur 90. **d** 93 **p** 94. C Byker St Mark and Walkergate St Oswald *Newc* 93-97; P-in-c New Ferry *Ches* 97-02; V from 02. *St Mark's Vicarage, New Chester Road, Wirral CH62 1DG* Tel 0151-645 2638

CHARTERS, Alan Charles. b 35. Trin Hall Cam BA60 MA63 FCollP88. Linc Th Coll 60. **d** 62 **p** 63. C Gt Grimsby St Mary and St Jas *Linc* 62-65; Chapl and Hd RE Eliz Coll Guernsey 65-70; P-in-c Guernsey St Jas the Less 65-70; Dep Hd Master Park Sen High Sch Swindon 70-73; Chapl St Jo Sch Leatherhead 73-83; Dep Hd Master 76; Visiting Lect and Tutor Lon Univ Inst of Ed 76-80; Headmaster The K Sch Glouc 83-92; V Aberedw w Llandeilo Graban and Llanbadarn etc *S & B* 92-00; Bp's Visitor to Schs 92-00; rtd 00; Perm to Offic *Eur* 00-03; P-in-c Dinard from 03. *Crescent House, Church Street, Talgarth, Brecon LD3 0BL* Tel (01874) 711135

✠**CHARTRES, The Rt Revd and Rt Hon Richard John Carew.** b 47. PC96. Trin Coll Cam BA68 MA73 BD83 Hon DLitt98 Hon DD99 FSA99 Hon FGMS97. Cuddesdon Coll 69 Linc Th Coll 72. **d** 73 **p** 74 **c** 92. C Bedford St Andr *St Alb* 73-75; Bp's Dom Chapl 75-80; Abp's Chapl *Cant* 80-84; P-in-c Westmr St Steph w St Jo *Lon* 84-85; V 86-92; Dir of Ords 85-92; Prof Div Gresham Coll 86-92; Six Preacher Cant Cathl *Cant* 91-97; Area Bp Stepney *Lon* 92-95; Bp Lon from 95; Dean of HM Chpls Royal and Prelate of OBE from 95. *The Old Deanery, Dean's Court, London EC4V 5AA* Tel (020) 7248 6233 Fax 7248 9721 E-mail bishop@londin.clara.co.uk

CHATER, John Leathley. b 29. Qu Coll Cam BA54 MA58. Ridley Hall Cam 54. **d** 56 **p** 57. C Bath Abbey w St Jas *B & W* 56-60; V Bermondsey St Anne *S'wark* 60-64; Ind Chapl 60-64; V Heslington *York* 64-69; Chapl York Univ 64-69; V Lawrence Weston *Bris* 69-73; Perm to Offic 74-80; P-in-c Wraxall *B & W* 80-82; R 82-84; V Battle *Chich* 84-90; Dean Battle 84-90; RD Battle and Bexhill 86-90; R St Marylebone w H Trin *Lon* 90-96; rtd 96; Perm to Offic *Chich* from 96. *75 Braemore Road, Hove BN3 4HA* Tel (01273) 748402

CHATFIELD, Adrian Francis. b 49. Leeds Univ BA71 MA72 MPhil89 PhD97. Coll of Resurr Mirfield 71. **d** 72 **p** 73. Trinidad and Tobago 72-83; TV Barnstaple, Goodleigh and Landkey *Ex* 83-85; TR Barnstaple 85-88; Lect St Jo Coll Nottm 88-98; S Africa from 99. *Tee College, PO Box 74257, Turffontein, 2140 South Africa* Tel (0027) (11) 683 3284 E-mail admin@tee.co.za

CHATFIELD, Mrs Gillian. b 50. Leeds Univ BA71 PGCE72. St Jo Coll Nottm MA94. **d** 94 **p** 95. C Greasley *S'well* 94-98; S Africa from 99. *Tee College, PO Box 74257, Turffontein, 2140 South Africa* Tel (0027) (11) 683 3284

CHATFIELD, Michael Francis. b 75. York Univ BSc96. Ridley Hall Cam BA99. **d** 00 **p** 01. C Attenborough *S'well* from 00. *9 Welbeck Gardens, Toton, Nottingham NG9 6JD* Tel 0115-946 8567 E-mail michael@chatalot.freeserve.co.uk

CHATFIELD, Neil Patrick. b 66. Nottm Univ BTh95. Linc Th Coll 93 Westcott Ho Cam 95. **d** 96 **p** 97. C Bexhill St Pet *Chich* 96-00; V Eastbourne Ch Ch from 00; Chapl Eastbourne Hosps NHS Trust from 01. *Christ Church Vicarage, 18 Addingham Road, Eastbourne BN22 7DY* Tel (01323) 721952

CHATFIELD, Canon Norman. b 37. Fitzw Ho Cam BA59 MA68. Ripon Hall Ox 60. **d** 62 **p** 63. C Burgess Hill St Jo *Chich* 62-65; C Uckfield 65-69; V Lower Sandown St Jo *Portsm* 69-76; V Locks Heath 76-83; Bp's Chapl for Post-Ord Tr 78-85; R Alverstoke 83-91; Chapl HM Pris Haslar 83-90; Chapl Gosport War Memorial Hosp 83-91; Hon Can Portsm Cathl *Portsm*

85-91; Can Res Glouc Cathl *Glouc* 91-02; rtd 02; Perm to Offic *Portsm* from 03. *16 Meadow Gardens, Waltham Chase, Southampton SO32 2NJ* Tel (01489) 891995
E-mail nandjchatfield@ukgateway.net

CHATFIELD, Thomas William. b 19. Lon Univ. Chich Th Coll 44. **d** 46 **p** 47. C Hanworth All SS *Lon* 46-49; C Woolwich St Mich *S'wark* 49-51; C Eastbourne St Andr *Chich* 51-55; V Hastings St Clem 55-68; P-in-c Hastings St Mary Magd 68-71; R 71-78; P-in-c Bishopstone 78-84; rtd 84; Perm to Offic *Chich* from 84. *5 Leeds Close, Victoria Avenue, Ore Village, Hastings TN35 5BX* Tel (01424) 437413

CHATHAM, Richard Henry. b 28. Launde Abbey 71. **d** 71 **p** 72. C Aylestone *Leic* 71-76; R Hoby cum Rotherby 76-77; P-in-c Brooksby 76-77; R Hoby cum Rotherby w Brooksby, Ragdale & Thru'ton 77-85; R Overstrand *Nor* 85-93; rtd 93; Perm to Offic *Nor* from 93. *Sandyside, Sandy Lane, Cromer NR27 9JT* Tel (01263) 513456

CHATTERJI DE MASSEY, Robert Arthur Sovan Lal. b 15. Chich Th Coll 54. **d** 56 **p** 57. C Romford St Edw *Chelmsf* 56-60; R Abberton w Langenhoe 60-90; rtd 90; Perm to Offic *Ely* 96-98. *Clare House, 82 Main Street, Witchford, Ely CB6 2HQ*

CHATTERLEY, Mrs Marion Frances. b 55. Open Univ DipHSW95. Edin Th Coll 95. **d** 98 **p** 99. C Edin Gd Shep *Edin* 98-00; Chapl Napier Coll from 00; C Edin Ch Ch from 00. *102 Relugas Road, Edinburgh EH9 2LZ* Tel 0131-667 6847 Mobile 07771-982163 E-mail marion@chatterleys.demon.co.uk

CHATTERTON, Thomas William. b 50. SEITE. **d** 99 **p** 00. OLM Blackheath All SS *S'wark* from 99. *44 Harland Road, London SE12 0JA* Tel (020) 8851 6813 *or* 7525 7912 ext 4482

CHATWIN, Ronald Ernest. b 34. St Aid Birkenhead 58. **d** 60 **p** 61. C Selsdon *Cant* 60-64; C Crawley *Chich* 64-68; V Coldwaltham 68-74; TV Ovingdean w Rottingdean and Woodingdean 74-83; V Saltdean 83-91; V Hellingly and Upper Dicker 91-02; rtd 02. *Cold Waltham, 29A New Road, Hellingly, Hailsham BN27 4EW* Tel (01323) 843346

CHAVE, Preb Brian Philip. b 51. Open Univ BA. Trin Coll Bris. **d** 84 **p** 85. C Cullompton *Ex* 84-87; TV Bishopsnympton, Rose Ash, Mariansleigh etc 87-93; Chapl for Agric *Heref* 93-96; Communications Adv and Bp's Staff Officer 97-01; Bp's Dom Chapl 97-01; TV W Heref from 01; Preb Heref Cathl from 97; Can 97-01. *The Vicarage, Vowles Close, Hereford HR4 0DF* Tel (01432) 273086 E-mail chave@hfddiocesan.church-of-england.org

CHAVE-COX, Guy. b 56. St Andr Univ BSc79. Wycliffe Hall Ox 83. **d** 86 **p** 87. C Wigmore Abbey *Heref* 86-88; C Bideford *Ex* 88-91; TV Barnstaple from 91. *St Paul's Vicarage, Old Sticklepath Hill, Barnstaple EX31 2BG* Tel (01271) 344400
E-mail vicar@barnstaple-st-paul.org.uk

CHAVNER, Robert. b 59. ALCM82 AGSM85 Guildhall Sch of Music & Drama Cert Ad Study Early Music 86 FGMS00. Linc Th Coll 90. **d** 92 **p** 93. C Beckenham St Geo *Roch* 92-96; Min Sevenoaks St Luke CD 96; V Sevenoaks St Luke from 96. *St Luke's House, 30 Eardley Road, Sevenoaks TN13 1XT* Tel (01732) 452462 Fax as telephone

CHEADLE, Preb Robert. b 24. MBE71 TD66. Leeds Univ BA49. Coll of Resurr Mirfield 49. **d** 51 **p** 52. C Newbury St Jo *Ox* 51-55; C Tunstall Ch Ch *Lich* 55-57; TR Hanley H Ev 57-60; V Bloxwich 60-72; V Penkridge w Stretton 72-89; Preb Lich Cathl 79-89; P-in-c Dunston w Coppenhall 79-82; V 82-89; P-in-c Acton Trussell w Bednall 80-82; V 82-89; rtd 89; Perm to Offic *Lich* from 89. *26 Audley Place, Newcastle ST5 3RS* Tel (01782) 618685

CHEALL, Henry Frederick Knowles. b 34. Ex Coll Ox BA56 MA60. Ripon Hall Ox 58. **d** 60 **p** 61. C Sutton *Liv* 60-63; C Blundellsands St Mich 63-66; Nigeria 66-68; R Crumpsall St Matt *Man* 68-76; R Crumpsall 76-84; V Chipping and Whitewell *Blackb* 84-96; R Wensley *Ripon* 96-00; V W Witton 96-00; rtd 00. *6 Tryfan, Glan Conwy, Colwyn Bay LL28 5NL* Tel (01492) 580250

CHEATLE, Adele Patricia. b 46. York Univ BA73. Trin Coll Bris 76. **d** 87 **p** 98. Par Dn Harborne Heath *Birm* 87; NSM 92-93; Perm to Offic *Heref* 96-97; NSM Burghill 97-99; NSM Stretton Sugwas 97-99; NSM Heref St Pet w St Owen and St Jas from 99. *The Mews House, Mordiford, Hereford HR1 4LN* Tel (01432) 870440

CHEATLE, Christopher Robert David. b 41. Leeds Univ BA63 Birm Univ MSc. Coll of Resurr Mirfield 63. **d** 65 **p** 66. C Hangleton *Chich* 65-66; C Corringham *Chelmsf* 66-70; Bp's Adv on Child Protection from 95; NSM Southend from 96. *28 Park Road, Leigh-on-Sea SS9 2QH* Tel (01702) 479043

CHEDZEY, Derek Christopher. b 67. Trin Coll Bris BA93. **d** 93 **p** 94. C Bedgrove *Ox* 93-95; C Haddenham w Cuddington, Kingsey etc 95-98; TV High Wycombe 98-01; C Washfield, Stoodleigh, Withleigh etc *Ex* from 01; Deanery Tr Officer from 01. *The Rectory, Withleigh, Tiverton EX16 8JQ* Tel (01884) 232033 Fax 251441 E-mail chedzey1@aol.com

CHEEK, Richard Alexander. b 35. Lon Univ LDS60 RCS 60. Ox NSM Course 72. **d** 75 **p** 76. NSM Maidenhead St Luke *Ox* 75-94; Asst Chapl Heatherwood and Wexham Park Hosp NHS Trust

from 94. *Windrush, 26 Sheephouse Road, Maidenhead SL6 8EX* Tel (01628) 628484

CHEESEMAN, Colin Henry. b 47. Reading Univ BA69 Kent Univ PhD00. Sarum & Wells Th Coll 82. **d** 84 **p** 85. C Cranleigh *Guildf* 84-87; C Godalming 87-89; V Cuddington 89-96; Chapl HM Pris Wealstun 96-97; P-in-c Tockwith and Bilton w Bickerton *York* 97-01; RD New Ainsty 99-01; P-in-c Roundhay St Jo *Ripon* from 01. *The Vicarage, 2A Ryder Gardens, Leeds LS8 1JS* Tel 0113-266 9747

CHEESEMAN (née GOODAIR), Ms Janet. b 59. K Coll Lon BA81 Roehampton Inst PGCE82. NEOC 97. **d** 00 **p** 01. NSM Tockwith and Bilton w Bickerton *York* 00-01; NSM York St Olave w St Giles 00-01; Chapl Harrogate Ladies' Coll from 01. *Harrogate Ladies' College, Clarence Drive, Harrogate HG1 2QG* Tel (01423) 504543 Fax 568893 E-mail enquire@hlc.org.uk

CHEESEMAN, John Anthony. b 50. Oriel Coll Ox BA73 MA75. Trin Coll Bris DipTh76. **d** 76 **p** 77. C Sevenoaks St Nic *Roch* 76-79; C Egham *Guildf* 79-82; V Leyton Ch Ch *Chelmsf* 82-90; V Westgate St Jas *Cant* 90-01; V Eastbourne H Trin *Chich* from 01. *Holy Trinity Vicarage, Trinity Trees, Eastbourne BN21 3BE* Tel (01323) 729046

CHEESEMAN, Kenneth Raymond. b 29. Roch Th Coll 63. **d** 66 **p** 67. C Crayford *Roch* 66-69; C Beckenham St Jas 69-75; V Belvedere St Aug 75-83; V Thorley *Portsm* 83-94; R Yarmouth 83-94; rtd 94; Perm to Offic *Portsm* from 94. *10 St Catherine's View, Godshill, Ventnor PO38 3JJ* Tel (01983) 840700

CHEESEMAN, Nicholas James. b 72. Qu Mary and Westf Coll Lon BA94 Leeds Univ BA02. Coll of Resurr Mirfield 00. **d** 03. C Wantage *Ox* from 03. *5 Barnard's Way, Wantage OX12 7EA* E-mail nicholascheeseman3@fish.co.uk

CHEESEMAN, Trevor Percival. b 38. Auckland Univ PhD64 Lon Univ BD67. K Coll Lon and St Boniface Warminster AKC67. **d** 68 **p** 69. C Warmsworth *Sheff* 68-71; New Zealand from 71. *49 Birdwood Avenue, Papatoetoe, New Zealand* Tel (0064) (9) 277 6145 E-mail tpandhmc@internet.co.nz

CHEESMAN, Canon Andrew Walford. b 36. St Mark's Coll Adelaide BA58. Cuddesdon Coll 59. **d** 61 **p** 62. C Man St Aid *Man* 61-63; Australia from 63; P-in-c Keith 64-68; Prec St Pet Cathl Adelaide 68-70; Chapl Flinders Univ 68-70; Asst Chapl St Pet Coll Adelaide 70-73; P-in-c Tea Tree Gully 73-76; R Mitcham Adelaide 76-01; Adn Torrens 85-93; Can Adelaide from 85. *1/4 Torrens Street, Mitcham, S Australia 5062* Tel (0061) (8) 8272 1864 Fax as telephone

CHEESMAN, Ashley Frederick Bruce. b 53. Oak Hill Th Coll. **d** 83 **p** 84. C Tranmere St Cath *Ches* 83-88; R Gaulby *Leic* 88-99; V from 99. *The Rectory, Gaulby Road, Gaulby, Leicester LE7 9BB* Tel 0116-259 6228

CHEESMAN, Peter. b 43. ACA65 FCA76 MCMI. Ridley Hall Cam 66. **d** 69 **p** 70. C Herne Bay Ch Ch *Cant* 69-74; TV Lowestoft St Marg *Nor* 75-78; TV Lowestoft and Kirkley 79-81; Ind Chapl *Glouc* 81-84; P-in-c Saul w Fretherne and Framilode 84-85; V Frampton on Severn, Arlingham, Saul etc from 85. *The Vicarage, The Street, Frampton on Severn, Gloucester GL2 7ED* Tel (01452) 740966 Fax as telephone
E-mail peter@the-cheesman.net

✠**CHEETHAM, The Rt Revd Richard Ian.** b 55. CCC Ox BA77 CertEd78 MA82 Lon Univ PhD99. Ripon Coll Cuddesdon 85. **d** 87 **p** 88 **c** 02. C Newc H Cross *Newc* 87-90; V Luton St Aug Limbury *St Alb* 90-99; RD Luton 95-98; Adn St Alb 99-02; Area Bp Kingston *S'wark* from 02. *24 Albert Drive, London SW19 6LS* Tel (020) 8789 3218 *or* 8392 3741 Fax 8392 3743
E-mail bishop.richard@dswark.org.uk

CHEEVERS, Canon George Alexander. b 42. CITC 70. **d** 73 **p** 74. C Carrickfergus *Conn* 73-81; C Kilroot 78-81; I Kilmakee 82-91; I Magheragall from 91; Can Belf Cathl from 01. *Magheragall Rectory, 70 Ballinderry Road, Lisburn BT28 2QS* Tel (028) 9262 1273

CHELMSFORD, Bishop of. See GLADWIN, The Rt Revd John Warren

CHELMSFORD, Dean of. See JUDD, The Very Revd Peter Somerset Margesson

CHELTENHAM, Archdeacon of. See RINGROSE, The Ven Hedley Sidney

CHENNELL, Capt Arthur John. b 28. St Deiniol's Hawarden 77. **d** 77 **p** 78. CA from 58; C Prenton *Ches* 77-79; V Liscard St Thos 79-82; V Lt Thornton *Blackb* 82-94; rtd 94; Perm to Offic *Ches* from 94. *79 Cobham Road, Moreton, Wirral CH46 0RA* Tel 0151-678 5708

CHERRILL, John Oliver. b 33. Bath Univ MArch75 DipArch61. Sarum & Wells Th Coll 76. **d** 79 **p** 80. NSM Blackmoor *Portsm* 79-83; NSM Headley All SS *Guildf* 83-85; C 86-90; Perm to Offic *Portsm* from 95; rtd 98. *8 Londlandes, Church Crookham, Fleet GU52 6ZS* Tel (01252) 624508

CHERRIMAN, Colin Wilfred (Brother Colin Wilfred). b 37. Leeds Univ BA63. Coll of Resurr Mirfield 63. **d** 65 **p** 66. C Bournemouth St Fran *Win* 65-69; SSF from 69; Prov Min from 97; Lic to Offic *Chelmsf* 73-75; *Cant* 75-77; *Edin* 77-79; *Sarum* 79-82; *Newc* 82-88; Perm to Offic *Lon* 88-91; Adv HIV/AIDS Unit 91-92; HIV Support Worker St Botolph Aldgate *Lon* 92-96;

New Zealand 96-02; rtd 02. *Hermitage of St Bernardine, PO Box 46, Stroud, NSW, Australia 2425*

CHERRY, David. b 30. Roch Th Coll 59. **d** 61 **p** 62. C Seacroft *Ripon* 61-67; R Bamford *Derby* 67-75; Chapl Malaga w Almunecar and Nerja *Eur* 83-91; rtd 91; NSM Waltham St Lawrence *Ox* 97-01. *Knell Cottage, 26 Upper Church Street, Syston, Leicester LE7 1HR*

CHERRY, David Warwick. b 61. Cape Town Univ BMus86 Leeds Univ BA91. Coll of Resurr Mirfield 92. **d** 92 **p** 93. C Hammersmith SS Mich and Geo White City Estate CD *Lon* 92-01; C Hammersmith St Luke 94-01; Chapl Univ of Greenwich *S'wark* 01-03; Chapl Univ of Westmr from 03. *4A Luxborough Street, London W1U 5BF* Tel (020) 7911 5822

CHERRY, Malcolm Stephen. b 28. Open Univ BA81. Sarum Th Coll 51. **d** 54 **p** 55. C Mill Hill Jo Keble CD *Lon* 54-57; C Hendon All SS Childs Hill 57-59; Min Colchester St Anne CD *Chelmsf* 59-68; V Horndon on the Hill 68-79; Ind Chapl 69-79; Voc Officer Southend Adnry 74-79; R Lochgilphead *Arg* 79-82; V Mill End and Heronsgate w W Hyde *St Alb* 82-90; V Chipping Barnet w Arkley 90-94; rtd 94; Perm to Offic *St E* from 94. *Nether Hankleys, Barrow Road, Higham, Bury St Edmunds IP28 6NN* Tel (01284) 810269

CHERRY, Stephen Arthur. b 58. St Chad's Coll Dur BSc79 Fitzw Coll Cam BA85. Westcott Ho Cam 83. **d** 86 **p** 87. C Baguley *Man* 86-89; Chapl K Coll Cam 89-94; R Loughborough All SS w H Trin *Leic* from 94; RD Akeley E 96-99. *The Rectory, 60 Westfield Drive, Loughborough LE11 3QL* Tel (01509) 212780 *or* 217029 E-mail aswht@leicester.anglican.org

CHESHAM, William Gerald. b 23. MIMechE55 Birm Univ DPS66. Wells Th Coll 61. **d** 63 **p** 64. C Ashford *Cant* 63-66; C Edgbaston St Bart *Birm* 66-68; V Smethwick 68-72; Lic to Offic *Heref* 72-78; TV Glendale Gp *Newc* 78-84; rtd 84; Hon Asst Chapl Algarve *Eur* 84-97; Perm to Offic *Sarum* from 97. *1 St Georges Close, Lower Street, West Harnham, Salisbury SP2 8HA* Tel (01722) 323484

CHESHER, Michael. b 52. Open Univ BA84. EAMTC. **d** 00 **p** 01. C Littleport *Ely* 00-03; V Chelmsf All SS *Chelmsf* from 03. *All Saints' Vicarage, 76A Kings Road, Chelmsford CM1 4HP* Tel (01245) 352005 E-mail mchesher@fsmail.net

CHESSUN, The Ven Christopher Thomas James. b 56. Univ Coll Ox BA78 MA82 Trin Hall Cam BA82. Westcott Ho Cam. **d** 83 **p** 84. C Sandhurst *Ox* 83-87; C Portsea St Mary *Portsm* 87-89; Min Can and Chapl St Paul's Cathl *Lon* 89-93; Voc Adv from 90; R Stepney St Dunstan and All SS 93-01; AD Tower Hamlets 97-01; Adn Northolt from 01. *247 Kenton Road, Harrow HA3 0HQ* Tel (020) 8907 5941 Fax 8909 2368 E-mail archdeacon.northolt@london.anglican.org

CHESTER, David Kenneth. b 50. Dur Univ BA73 Aber Univ PhD78 Liv Univ DipTh96 CGeol92 FGS88. Nor Ord Course 93. **d** 96 **p** 97. Hon C Hoylake *Ches* from 96. *Yenda, Grange Old Road, West Kirby, Wirral CH48 4ET* Tel 0151-625 8004 E-mail jg543@liverpool.ac.uk

CHESTER, Mark. b 55. Lanc Univ BA79. Wycliffe Hall Ox 86. **d** 88 **p** 89. C Plymouth St Andr w St Paul and St Geo *Ex* 88-94; V Burney Lane *Birm* 94-99; V Camberley St Paul *Guildf* from 99. *The Vicarage, Sandy Lane, Camberley GU15 2AG* Tel (01276) 21100 *or* 700211 E-mail mzbg@mzchester.freeserve.co.uk

CHESTER, Maureen Olga. b 47. Univ of Wales (Swansea) BA70. NEOC DipHE94. **d** 97 **p** 98. NSM Morpeth *Newc* from 97. *10 Leland Place, Morpeth NE61 2AN* Tel (01670) 514569 E-mail mochester@classicfm.net

CHESTER, Philip Anthony Edwin. b 55. Birm Univ LLB76. St Jo Coll Dur DipTh80. **d** 80 **p** 81. C Shrewsbury St Chad *Lich* 80-85; C St Martin-in-the-Fields *Lon* 85-88; Chapl K Coll Lon 88-95; PV Westmr Abbey from 90; P-in-c Westmr St Matt *Lon* 95-03; V from 03. *St Matthew's Clergy House, 20 Great Peter Street, London SW1P 2BU* Tel (020) 7222 3704

CHESTER, Mrs Violet Grace. b 50. WEMTC 97. **d** 00 **p** 01. OLM Dymock w Donnington and Kempley *Glouc* 00; OLM Redmarley D'Abitot, Bromesberrow, Pauntley etc from 00. *1 Longbridge, Dymock GL18 2JA* Tel (01531) 890633 Fax 635919 E-mail vialanrev@netscapeonline.co.uk

CHESTER, Archdeacon of. See ALLISTER, The Ven Donald Spargo

CHESTER, Bishop of. See FORSTER, The Rt Revd Peter Robert

CHESTER, Dean of. See McPHATE, The Very Revd Gordon Ferguson

CHESTERFIELD, Archdeacon of. See GARNETT, The Ven David Christopher

CHESTERMAN, Canon George Anthony (Tony). b 38. Man Univ BSc62 DipAdEd Nottm Univ PhD89. Coll of Resurr Mirfield 62. **d** 64 **p** 65. C Newbold w Dunston *Derby* 64-68; C Derby St Thos 68-70; Adult Educn Officer 70-79; R Mugginton and Kedleston 70-89; Vice-Prin EMMTC 79-86; Can Res Derby Cathl *Derby* from 89; Dioc Clergy In-Service Tr Adv from 89; Chapl to The Queen from 98. *13 Newbridge Road, Ambergate, Belper DE56 2GR* Tel (01773) 852236 E-mail cmederby@talk21.com

✠**CHESTERS, The Rt Revd Alan David.** b 37. St Chad's Coll Dur BA59 St Cath Soc Ox BA61 MA65. St Steph Ho Ox 59. **d** 62 **p** 63 **c** 89. C Wandsworth St Anne *S'wark* 62-66; Hon C 66-68; Chapl Tiffin Sch Kingston 66-72; Hon C Ham St Rich *S'wark* 68-72; Dioc Dir of Educn *Dur* 72-85; R Brancepeth 72-85; Hon Can Dur Cathl 75-85; Adn Halifax *Wakef* 85-89; Bp Blackb 89-03; rtd 03. *64 Hallfields Road, Tarvin, Chester CH3 8ET*

CHESTERS, Simon. b 66. Rob Coll Cam BA87 MA91. Wycliffe Hall Ox BA94 DipMin95. **d** 95 **p** 96. C Bidston *Ches* 95-99; P-in-c Runcorn St Jo Weston 99-03; Dir Reader Tr from 99; Min Development Officer from 03. *7 Earlsway, Chester CH4 8AX, or Church House, Lower Lane, Aldford, Chester CH4 8AX* Tel (01244) 679311 *or* 620444 E-mail simon@schesters.freeserve.co.uk

CHESTERTON, Robert Eric. b 31. St Aid Birkenhead 63. **d** 65 **p** 66. C Kirby Muxloe *Leic* 65-67; Canada 67-68 and 75-78; C St Annes *Blackb* 68-69; V Southminster *Chelmsf* 69-75; V Wythenshawe Wm Temple Ch *Man* 78-82; TV Marfleet *York* 82-85; V Marshchapel *Linc* 85-88; R N Coates 85-88; V Grainthorpe w Conisholme 85-88; V Langtoft 88-91; V Kingsbury *Birm* 91-94; rtd 94; Perm to Offic *Pet* from 95; *Leic* 96-99. *46 Tyne Road, Oakham LE15 6SJ* Tel (01572) 757222

CHESWORTH, John Martin. b 44. Leeds Univ BSc67 PhD71 FRSC80. S Dios Minl Tr Scheme 90. **d** 92 **p** 93. Oman 92-95; Perm to Offic *Ab* 96-98; Perm to Offic *Ches* from 98. *36 Elgin Drive, Wallasey CH45 7PR* Tel 0151-639 4067 Fax as telephone E-mail johnchesworth@compuserve.com

CHETWYND, Edward Ivor. b 42. Leeds Univ DipTh68. Coll of Resurr Mirfield 68. **d** 70 **p** 71. C Westgate Common *Wakef* 70-74; C Penistone w Midhope 74-75; V Smawthorpe St Mich from 75. *St Michael's Vicarage, St Michael's Close, Castleford WF10 4ER* Tel (01977) 557079

CHEUNG, Anita Yen. b 40. LNSM course 95. **d** 98 **p** 99. OLM St Luke in the City *Liv* from 98. *10 Pine Walks, Prenton, Birkenhead CH42 8LQ* Tel 0151-609 1459 Fax as telephone

CHEVERTON, Miss Jill. b 48. RGN71 RHV77 Leeds Poly DSS73. Cranmer Hall Dur 93. **d** 93 **p** 94. Par Dn Bilton *Ripon* 93-94; C 94-96; V Burmantofts St Steph and St Agnes 96-03; Min Binley Woods LEP *Cov* from 03. *20 Daneswood Road, Binley Woods, Coventry CV3 2BJ* Tel (02476) 543003 E-mail revchev@email.com

CHEW, Philip Vivian Frederick. b 62. St Martin's Coll Lanc BA96. Qu Coll Birm 96. **d** 98 **p** 99. C Chorley St Laur *Blackb* 98-02; V Burnley St Steph from 02. *St Stephen's Vicarage, 154 Todmorden Road, Burnley BB11 3ER* Tel (01282) 424733 E-mail revchew@fsmail.net

CHICHESTER, Archdeacon of. See McKITTRICK, The Ven Douglas Henry

CHICHESTER, Bishop of. See HIND, The Rt Revd John William

CHICHESTER, Dean of. See FRAYLING, The Very Revd Nicholas Arthur

CHICKEN, Canon Peter Lindsay. b 46. St Andr Univ BSc71. Chich Th Coll 77. **d** 79 **p** 80. C High Wycombe *Ox* 79-83; V The Stanleys *Glouc* 83-96; V Leckhampton SS Phil and Jas w Cheltenham St Jas from 96; Bp's Adv for CME from 92; Hon Can Glouc Cathl from 03. *St Philip and St James Vicarage, 80 Painswick Road, Cheltenham GL50 2EU* Tel (01242) 525460 E-mail rev.peterchicken@btopenworld.com

CHIDLAW, Richard Paul. b 49. St Cath Coll Cam BA71 MA. Ripon Hall Ox 72. **d** 74 **p** 81. C Ribbesford w Bewdley and Dowles *Worc* 74-76; NSM Coaley *Glouc* 81-83; NSM Frampton on Severn 81-83; NSM Arlingham 81-83; NSM Saul w Fretherne and Framilode 83-84; NSM Cam w Stinchcombe 85-90; Perm to Offic 90-91; NSM Berkeley w Wick, Breadstone and Newport 91-02; NSM Berkeley w Wick, Breadstone, Newport, Stone etc from 02. *38 May Lane, Dursley GL11 4HU* Tel (01453) 547838

CHIDWICK, Alan Robert. b 49. MIL MA. Oak Hill NSM Course. **d** 84 **p** 85. NSM Pimlico St Pet w Westmr Ch Ch *Lon* from 84. *119 Eaton Square, London SW1W 9AL* Tel (020) 7235 4242 E-mail monsieur@btinternet.com

CHILCOTT, Mark David. b 62. Ch Coll Cam BA83 MA87 PhD88. Ripon Coll Cuddesdon BA92. **d** 93 **p** 94. C Warrington St Elphin *Liv* 93-99; P-in-c Westbrook St Jas 99-01; V 01-02. *Estates Branch, Sedgley Park Centre, Sedgley Park Road, Prestwich, Manchester M25 0JT* Tel 0161-856 0505 Fax 856 0506

CHILD, Corin James. b 73. Man Univ BA95. Trin Coll Bris BA02 MA03. **d** 03. C Sanderstead All SS *S'wark* from 03. *285 Limpsfield Road, Sanderstead CR2 9DG* Tel (020) 8657 0613 E-mail corin.child@ntlworld.com

CHILD, Margaret Mary. See MASLEN, Mrs Margaret Mary

CHILD, Canon Rupert Henry. b 29. St Jo Coll Dur 50 K Coll Lon DipTh56 St Boniface Warminster 57. **d** 58 **p** 59. C Tavistock and Gulworthy *Ex* 58-61; C Dunstable *St Alb* 61-65; V Luton St Chris Round Green 65-74; V Sawbridgeworth 74-95; Hon Can St Alb 86-95; rtd 95; Perm to Offic *St Alb* from 00. *6 Lakes Close, Langford, Biggleswade SG18 9SJ* Tel (01462) 700303

CHILDS, David Robert. b 64. Univ Coll Lon BSc86 Regent's Park Coll Ox MA95. Ripon Coll Cuddesdon 99. **d** 99 **p** 00. C Bloxham w Milcombe and S Newington *Ox* 99-02; TV Witney from 02. *The Vicarage, 292 Thorney Leys, Witney OX28 5PB* Tel (01993) 703507

CHILDS, Emma Jane. *See* WESTERMANN-CHILDS, Miss Emma Jane

CHILDS, Ernest Edmund. b 23. Lich Th Coll 63. **d** 65 **p** 66. C Billesley Common *Birm* 65-68; C Elland *Wakef* 68-69; Clerical Org Sec CECS *Pet, Leic* and *Ely* 69-72; V Staverton w Helidon and Catesby *Pet* 72-76; rtd 77; Perm to Offic *Nor* 77-91; Hon C W Lynn *Ely* 92-94; P-in-c 94-95; Perm to Offic *Ely* from 95; *Nor* from 96. *4 Fieldview Court, Fakenham NR21 8PB* Tel (01328) 856595

CHILDS, Canon Leonard Neil. b 43. Leeds Univ BA65. Wells Th Coll 66. **d** 68 **p** 69. C Matlock and Tansley *Derby* 68-72; C Chesterfield St Mary and All SS 72-74; P-in-c Stonebroom 74-81; P-in-c Morton 78-81; R Morton and Stonebroom 81-84; TV Buxton w Burbage and King Sterndale 84-92; V Derby St Mark from 92; Hon Can Derby Cathl from 02. *St Mark's Vicarage, 119 Francis Street, Derby DE21 6DE* Tel (01332) 340183

CHILDS, Martin James. **d** 99 **p** 00. C Mountain Ash and Miskin *Llan* from 99. *Miskin Vicarage, Llanwonno Road, Mountain Ash CF45 3NE* Tel (01443) 473247

CHILLINGTON, Barbara Anne. b 42. Staffs Poly RGN84. WEMTC. **d** 00 **p** 01. NSM Madley w Tyberton, Peterchurch, Vowchurch etc *Heref* from 00. *Cephas House, 2 Princes Orchard, Peterchurch, Hereford HR2 0RW* Tel and fax (01981) 550979 Mobile 07748-384104

CHILLINGWORTH, The Ven David Robert. b 51. TCD BA73 Oriel Coll Ox BA75 MA81. Ripon Coll Cuddesdon 75. **d** 76 **p** 77. C Belfast St Finn *Conn* 76-79; Ch of Ireland Youth Officer 79-83; C Bangor Abbey *D & D* 83-86; I Seagoe from 86; Dean Dromore 95-02; Adn Dromore from 02. *8 Upper Church Lane, Portadown, Craigavon BT63 5JE* Tel (028) 3833 2538 *or* 3835 0583 Mobile 07802-274187 Fax (028) 3833 0773 E-mail archdeacon@dromore.anglican.org

CHILLMAN, David James. b 59. Southn Univ BA82. Trin Coll Bris ADMT95. **d** 95 **p** 96. C Yateley *Win* 95-99; V Halifax All So and St Aug *Wakef* from 99. *St Augustine's Vicarage, Hanson Lane, Halifax HX1 5PG* Tel (01422) 365552 E-mail david.chillman@tesco.net

CHILONGANI, Dickson David. b 66. Bris Univ BA96 Dur Univ MA99 St Phil Coll (Tanzania) DipTh93. **d** 93 **p** 94. Tanzania 93-94 and 96-98; V Cathl of the H Spirit 93-94; Prin Msalato Bible Coll 96-98. *24 Druid Hill, Stoke Bishop, Bristol BS9 1EN* Tel 0117-968 2902 E-mail dickson@chilongani.freeserve.co.uk

CHIN, Michael Shoon Chion. b 41. Lon Univ BD71 Melbourne Univ BA76 DipEd79. Moore Th Coll Sydney 60 Trin Th Coll Singapore BTh64 Ridley Coll Melbourne 68 Melbourne Coll of Div DipRE74. **d** 64 **p** 65. Malaysia 64-68; Australia 69-80 and 87-91; Miss to Seafarers from 72; USA 81-82; Perm to Offic *Win* 93-98; Gen Sec Internat Chr Maritime Assn from 93. *International Christian Maritime Association, 2-3 Orchard Place, Southampton SO14 3BR* Tel (023) 8033 6111 Fax 8033 3567

CHING, Derek. b 37. St Cath Coll Cam BA58 MA Cam Inst of Educn CertEd59. Qu Coll Birm 81. **d** 83 **p** 84. C Finham *Cov* 83-87; V Butlers Marston and the Pillertons w Ettington 87-96; rtd 96; Perm to Offic *Ripon* from 96. *25 Kirkby Road, Ripon HG4 2EY* Tel (01765) 609419

CHIPLIN, Christopher Gerald. b 53. Lon Univ BSc75. St Steph Ho Ox BA77 MA81. **d** 78 **p** 79. C Chesterfield St Mary and All SS *Derby* 78-80; C Thorpe *Nor* 80-84; V Highbridge *B & W* 84-94; V Midsomer Norton w Clandown from 94. *The Vicarage, 42 Priory Close, Midsomer Norton, Radstock BA3 2HZ* Tel (01761) 412118

CHIPLIN, Gareth Huw. b 50. Worc Coll Ox BA71 MA. Edin Th Coll 71. **d** 73 **p** 74. C Friern Barnet St Jas *Lon* 73-75; C Eastcote St Lawr 76-79; C Notting Hill St Mich and Ch Ch 79-84; V Hammersmith St Matt from 84. *St Matthew's Vicarage, 1 Fielding Road, London W14 0LL* Tel (020) 7603 9769

CHIPLIN, Howard Alan. b 43. Sarum & Wells Th Coll 84. **d** 86 **p** 87. C Caerleon *Mon* 86-89; V Ferndale w Maerdy *Llan* 89-91; V Ysbyty Cynfyn w Llantrisant and Eglwys Newydd *St D* 91-95; R Narberth w Mounton w Robeston Wathen and Crinow 95-02; V Llanfihangel w Llanafan and Llanwnnws etc from 02. *The Vicarage, Llanafon, Aberystwyth SY23 4AZ* Tel (01974) 261101

CHIPLIN, Malcolm Leonard. b 42. Univ of Wales (Cardiff) DPS88. St Mich Coll Llan 86. **d** 88 **p** 89. C Newton Nottage *Llan* 88-91; V Pwllgwaun w Llanddewi Rhondda from 91. *The Vicarage, Lanelay Crescent, Maesycoed, Pontypridd CF37 1JB* Tel (01443) 402417

CHIPPENDALE, Peter David. b 34. Dur Univ BA55. Linc Th Coll 57. **d** 59 **p** 60. C Claines St Jo *Worc* 59-63; V Defford w Besford 63-73; P-in-c Eckington 66-69; V 69-73; V Kidderminster St Geo 73-76; V The Lickey *Birm* 76-96; rtd 96. *1 Fairways, Pershore WR10 1HA* Tel (01386) 553478

CHIPPENDALE, Robert William. b 42. DipTh68 Ox Univ BA79 Dip Teaching84. **d** 67 **p** 68. Australia 67-72 and from 79; V Shaw

Man 72-78. *4 Violet Way, Gaven, Qld, Australia 4211* Tel (0061) (7) 5596 2247 *or* 5532 4922

CHISHOLM, David Whitridge. b 23. Keble Coll Ox BA48 MA48. Linc Th Coll 48. **d** 50 **p** 51. C Sudbury St Andr *Lon* 50-53; C Enfield Jes Chpl 53-57; V Edmonton St Aldhelm 57-66; V N Harrow St Alb 66-72; V Paddington St Jas 72-78; RD Westmr Paddington 74-79; C Paddington St Jas 78-79; V Hurley *Ox* 79-90; rtd 90; Perm to Offic *Ox* 92-01. *32 Herons Place, Marlow SL7 3HP* Tel (01628) 483243

CHISHOLM, Canon Ian Keith. b 36. AKC62. **d** 63 **p** 64. C Lich St Chad *Lich* 63-66; C Sedgley All SS 66-69; V Rough Hills 69-77; V Harrow Weald All SS *Lon* 77-88; V W Moors *Sarum* 88-01; Can and Preb Sarum Cathl 00-01; rtd 01. *33 Meadoway, Shrewton, Salisbury SP3 4HE* Tel (01980) 620579

CHISHOLM, Ian Stuart. b 37. ALCD63. **d** 63 **p** 64. C Worksop St Jo *S'well* 63-66; Succ Sheff Cathl *Sheff* 66-68; Bp's Chapl for Soc Resp 68-72; C Ox St Andr *Ox* 72-76; Tutor Wycliffe Hall Ox 72-76; V Conisbrough *Sheff* 76-94; Chapl Conisbrough Hosp 76-94; RD W Doncaster 82-87 and 93-94; V Chilwell *S'well* 94-99; rtd 99; Perm to Offic *Sheff* from 94 and *Linc* from 00. *72 Broadbank, Louth LN11 0EW* Tel (01605) 605970 E-mail ichisholm@waitrose.com

CHISHOLM, Canon Reginald Joseph. b 13. TCD BA40 MA51. TCD Div Sch 42. **d** 42 **p** 43. C Belfast St Donard *D & D* 42-45; C Bangor St Comgall 45-48; I Ardglass w Dunsford 48-51; I Newtownards 51-82; Min Can Belf Cathl 52-62; Treas Down Cathl *D & D* 80-82; rtd 82. *20 Glendun Park, Bangor BT20 4UX* Tel (028) 9145 0100

CHISHOLM, Samuel James. b 20. Edin Th Coll 74 St Jo Coll Nottm 86. **d** 86 **p** 87. NSM Eastriggs *Glas* 87-92; NSM Gretna 90-91; rtd 92; Perm to Offic *Chich* from 95. *1 Elm Tree House, 5 Hastings Road, Bexhill-on-Sea TN40 2HJ* Tel (01424) 219294

CHISLETT, David Norman Hilton. b 61. Kingston Poly BSc83 UEA PGCE84. Ridley Hall Cam 00. **d** 02. C Highley w Billingsley, Glazeley etc *Heref* from 02. *43 Yew Tree Grove, Highley, Bridgnorth WV16 6DG* Tel (01746) 862588 E-mail davenhchislett@aol.com

CHITHAM, Ernest John. b 57. LSE BSc79 Leeds Univ PGCE80 Dur Univ MA84. NEOC 88. **d** 91 **p** 92. C Swanborough *Sarum* 91-94; CMS Lebanon 95-98; TV Worthing Ch the King *Chich* from 99. *85 Heene Road, Worthing BN11 4PP* Tel (01903) 218026 E-mail chitham@iname.com

CHITTENDEN, John Bertram d'Encer. b 24. ASCA. Lon Coll of Div 56. **d** 58 **p** 59. C St Mary-at-Lambeth *S'wark* 58-64; R Acrise *Cant* 64-82; R Hawkinge 64-82; R Hawkinge w Acrise and Swingfield 82-90; rtd 91; Perm to Offic *Cant* from 91. *19 Hasborough Road, Folkestone CT19 6BQ* Tel (01303) 241773

CHITTENDEN, Nils Philip d'Encer. b 69. St Chad's Coll Dur BA91 Univ of Northumbria at Newc MA99. Westcott Ho Cam 93. **d** 95. C Benfieldside *Dur* 95-97; Chapl Community Health Care N Dur NHS Trust 96-97; Urban Regeneration Chapl Gateshead *Dur* 97-01; Perm to Offic from 01; UK Co-ord Chs Community Work Alliance from 01; Dir Transferable Skills Progr St Chad's Coll Dur from 01. *St Chad's College, North Bailey, Durham DH1 3RH* Tel 0191-334 3346 Mobile 07866-804460 Fax 334-3371 E-mail nilsc@ccwa.org.uk *or* n.p.d.chittenden@durham.ac.uk

CHITTY, Philip Crofts. b 27. Roch Th Coll 61. **d** 63 **p** 64. C Holbrooks *Cov* 63-68; V Long Itchington 68-77; R Ufton 69-77; P-in-c Cov St Marg 77-84; rtd 84. *17 Rotherham Road, Coventry CV6 4FF* Tel (024) 7668 5398

✠**CHIU, The Rt Revd Joshua Ban It.** b 18. K Coll Lon LLB41 AKC41 Barrister-at-Law (Inner Temple) 41. Westcott Ho Cam 43. **d** 45 **p** 46 **c** 66. C Bournville *Birm* 45-47; Malaya 47-50; Singapore 50-59 and 66-82; Hon Can St Andr Cathl Singapore 56-59; Australia 59-62; Service Laymen Abroad WCC Geneva 62-65; Fell St Aug Coll Cant 65-66; Bp Singapore and Malaya 66-70; Bp Singapore 70-82; Member Cen Cttee WCC 68-75; Member ACC 75-79; rtd 82; Perm to Offic *Sarum* 82-00; *Chelmsf* from 02. *40 Beverley Crescent, Woodford Green IG8 9DD* Tel (020) 8924 6490

CHIVERS, Christopher Mark. b 67. Magd Coll Ox BA88 MA92 Selw Coll Cam BTh96. Westcott Ho Cam 94. **d** 97 **p** 98. C Friern Barnet St Jas *Lon* 97-99; Can Prec St Geo Cathl Cape Town 99-01; Min Can and Prec Westmr Abbey from 01. *4B Little Cloister, London SW1P 3PL* Tel (020) 7654 4855 E-mail chris.chivers@westminster-abbey.org

CHIVERS, Ernest Alfred John. b 34. Bris & Glouc Tr Course. **d** 83 **p** 84. NSM Bedminster *Bris* 83-87; NSM Whitchurch 87-98; NSM Knowle St Martin 98-00; Sen Asst P Chard and Distr *B & W* from 00. *The Vicarage, 4 Chard Street, Thorncombe, Chard TA20 4NE* Tel (01460) 30479

CHIVERS, Royston George. b 34. Glouc Th Course. **d** 83 **p** 84. NSM Gorsley w Cliffords Mesne *Glouc* 83-85; NSM Newent and Gorsley w Cliffords Mesne from 85. *Mayfield, Gorsley, Ross-on-Wye HR9 7SJ* Tel (01989) 720492

CHIVERS, Canon William Herbert. b 20. Univ of Wales (Cardiff) BA42. Coll of Resurr Mirfield 42. **d** 44 **p** 45. C Roath St Sav *Llan* 44-48; C Pontlottyn 50-51; C Peterston-super-Ely

51-53; C Bushey *St Alb* 53-58; V Bollington St Jo *Ches* 58-60; R Bushey *St Alb* 60-81; R Carnarvon Australia 81-83; R Llandogo and Tintern *Mon* 83-86; rtd 86; Asst Chapl Athens w Kifissia, Patras, Thessaloniki etc *Eur* 86-91; Perm to Offic *Lon* from 92. *3 Downing Court, Grenville Street, London WC1N 1LX* Tel (020) 7713 7847

CHIVERTON, Dennis Lionel Dunbar. b 26. St D Coll Lamp BA51. **d** 53 **p** 54. C Cardiff St Mary *Llan* 53-54; C Dowlais 54-57; C Bargoed w Brithdir 57-61; P-in-c Cymmer and Abercregan 61-67; R Llanfabon 67-91; rtd 91; Perm to Offic *Llan* from 91. *3 Park Terrace, Trelewis, Treharris CF46 6BT* Tel (01443) 411237

CHO, Paul Hang-Sik. b 61. Kent Univ MA96. Chr Th Sem & Div Sch of Korea BTh93. **d** 00 **p** 01. C Munster Square Ch Ch and St Mary Magd *Lon* from 00; Chapl Angl Korean Community from 00. *4 Silsoe House, 50 Park Village East, London NW1 7QH* Tel (020) 7388 2166 Mobile 07780-682585 Fax 0870-131 7923 E-mail frpaulcho@hotmail.com

CHORLTON, John Samuel Woodard. b 45. Newc Univ BSc67. Wycliffe Hall Ox 89. **d** 89 **p** 91. Jerusalem 82-92; C Ox St Aldate w St Matt *Ox* 92-94; C Ox St Aldate from 95; Voc Adv from 98; AD Ox from 99. *2 Shirelake Close, Oxford OX1 1SN* Tel (01865) 721150 *or* 244713 Fax 201543 E-mail john.chorlton@staldates.org.uk

CHOTANAGPUR, Bishop of. *See* TEROM, The Rt Revd Zechariah James

CHOUFAR, Joseph Oriho Abulemoi. b 63. Nile Th Coll Khartoum BA95 ICI Univ Amman BA98. **d** 87 **p** 88. Sudan 87-96; All SS Cathl Khartoum 87-88 and 91-96; Torit Congregation Lologo Displaced Camp 88-90; NSM Ealing St Pet Mt Park *Lon* from 00. *Moulin House, 24-26 Mount Park Road, London W5 2RT* Tel (020) 8991 6998 E-mail abulemoi@hotmail.com

CHOW, Ting Suie Roy. b 46. Brasted Th Coll 68 Sarum & Wells Th Coll 70. **d** 72 **p** 73. C Weaste *Man* 72-74; C Swinton St Pet 74-78; R Blackley St Paul 78-85; Sec SPCK (Dio Man) from 80; R Burnage St Nic *Man* 85-95; P-in-c Man Gd Shep 95-97; P-in-c Openshaw 95-97; R Manchester Gd Shep and St Barn from 97. *All Soul's Rectory, Every Street, Ancoats, Manchester M4 7DQ* Tel 0161-273 6582

CHOW, Wai Meng. b 65. Bris Univ BSc89 ACA93. Trin Coll Bris BA97 MA02. **d** 02 **p** 03. NSM Westminster St Jas the Less *Lon* from 02. *29 Carillon Court, Oxford Road, London W5 3SX* Tel (020) 8810 1651 Mobile 07968-776557

CHOWN, William Richard Bartlett. b 27. AKC54. **d** 55 **p** 56. C Egremont *Carl* 55-58; C Upminster *Chelmsf* 58-61; R Romford St Andr 61-78; R Newton Longville w Stoke Hammond, Whaddon etc *Ox* 78-83; P-in-c Kidmore End 83-85; V 85-90; rtd 90; NSM Harpsden *Ox* 93-94; Perm to Offic from 94. *26 Lovell Close, Henley-on-Thames RG9 1PX* Tel (01491) 575735

CHRICH, Andrew James. b 70. Girton Coll Cam BA92 MA96. Cranmer Hall Dur BA93. **d** 96 **p** 97. C Gerrards Cross and Fulmer *Ox* 96-99; Chapl Trin Coll Cam from 99. *Trinity College, Cambridge CB2 1TQ* Tel (01223) 338435 E-mail ajc27@cam.ac.uk

CHRICH-SMITH, Joanne Elizabeth. b 71. Qu Coll Cam BA93 MA96. Cranmer Hall Dur BA95 Ripon Coll Cuddesdon 96. **d** 97 **p** 98. C Amersham on the Hill *Ox* 97-99; Perm to Offic *Ely* 99-00; Chapl Girton Coll Cam 00-02. *Address temp unknown* E-mail jec57@cam.ac.uk

CHRISMAN, John Aubrey. b 33. US Naval Academy BS58. Westcott Ho Cam 86. **d** 88 **p** 89. NSM Orwell *Ely* 88-89; NSM Wimpole 88-89; NSM Arrington 88-89; NSM Croydon w Clopton 88-89; Asst Chapl Oslo St Edm *Eur* 89-91; USA from 91. *St George's Episcopal Church, 14 Rhode Island Avenue, Newport, RI 02840, USA* E-mail fatherjack@worldnet.att.net

CHRIST THE KING, Bishop of. *See* LEE, The Rt Revd Peter John

CHRISTCHURCH, Bishop of. *See* COLES, The Rt Revd David John

CHRISTENSEN, Canon Norman Peter. b 37. St D Coll Lamp BA63. Ridley Hall Cam 63. **d** 65 **p** 66. C Barnston *Ches* 65-70; V Over St Jo 70-77; R Bromborough 77-92; RD Wirral S 86-92; Hon Can Ches Cathl 90-02; Chapl Arrowe Park Hosp Wirral 92-96; V Higher Bebington *Ches* 96-02; rtd 02; Perm to Offic *Ches* from 02. *13 Howbeck Close, Prenton CH43 6TH* Tel 0151-652 9869 E-mail canonpc@aol.com

CHRISTIAN, Mrs Alison Jean. b 51. Cen Sch Speech & Drama Dip Acting72. S Dios Minl Tr Scheme 88. **d** 91 **p** 94. Par Dn Uxbridge *Lon* 91-94; C 94-95; Chapl Uxbridge Coll 91-95; V Sudbury St Andr *Lon* 95-02; R Gt Stanmore from 02. *St John's Rectory, Rectory Lane, Stanmore HA7 4AQ* Tel (020) 8954 0276 E-mail alison.christian1@btopenworld.com

CHRISTIAN, Anthony Clive Hammond. b 46. Kent Univ BA74 Sussex Univ MA95 DPhil99 FRSA01. K Coll Lon 74 St Aug Coll Cant 74. **d** 76 **p** 77. C Faversham *Cant* 76-79; C St Laur in Thanet 79-81; P-in-c 81-84; R Gt Mongeham w Ripple and Sutton by Dover 84-88; V Pevensey *Chich* 88-94; P-in-c 94-01; V from 01. *Marsh Hall, Church Lane, Pevensey BN24 5LD* Tel and fax (01323) 762247 Mobile 07711-170350

CHRISTIAN, Brother. *See* PEARSON, Christian David John

CHRISTIAN, Mark Robert. b 58. Linc Th Coll 95. **d** 95 **p** 96. C Stockport SW *Ches* 95-98; CF from 98. *c/o MOD Chaplains (Army)* Tel (01980) 615802 Fax 615800 E-mail mark@padrechristian.demon.co.uk

CHRISTIAN, Paul. b 49. Cant Sch of Min 84. **d** 87 **p** 88. C Folkestone St Sav *Cant* 87-91; R Temple Ewell w Lydden from 91. *The Rectory, Green Lane, Temple Ewell, Dover CT16 3AS* Tel (01304) 822865

CHRISTIAN, Richard. b 37. Nottm Univ DipEd74 Ox Univ MA81. AKC62. **d** 63 **p** 65. C Camberwell St Mich w All So w Em *S'wark* 63-66; C Woolwich St Mary w H Trin 66-70; Chapl and Lect Bp Lonsdale Coll Derby 70-74; P-in-c Hurley *Ox* 76-79; Chapl Lancing Coll 79-81; Chapl Harrow Sch 82-89; Chapl R W Sussex Hosp Chich 89-91; P-in-c Cowley *Lon* 91-95; Chapl Hillingdon Hosp NHS Trust 91-02; rtd 02. *St John's Rectory, Rectory Lane, Stanmore HA7 4AQ* Tel (020) 8954 0276

CHRISTIAN, Canon George. b 20. AKC48. **d** 49 **p** 50. C Mansfield Woodhouse *S'well* 49-52; C Margate St Jo *Cant* 52-56; V Bramford w Burstall *St E* 56-62; V Bramford 62-91; Dioc Ecum Officer 66-88; Hon Can St E Cathl 75-91; Bruges Link Dioc Co-ord from 88; rtd 91; Perm to Offic *St E* from 91. *54 Pine View Road, Ipswich IP1 4HR* Tel (01473) 463031

CHRISTIAN-EDWARDS, Canon Michael Thomas. b 36. Down Coll Cam BA60 MA64. Clifton Th Coll 60. **d** 62 **p** 63. C Ex St Leon w H Trin *Ex* 62-67; V Trowbridge St Thos *Sarum* 67-75; R Wingfield w Rowley 67-75; P-in-c Fisherton Anger 75-81; R 81-92; Ind Chapl 85-92; RD Salisbury 85-90; Can and Preb Sarum Cathl 87-92; V Crofton *Portsm* 92-00; rtd 00. *Rivendell, Westbeams Road, Sway, Lymington SO41 6AE* Tel (01590) 682353

CHRISTIANSON, Canon Rodney John (Bill). b 47. St Paul's Coll Grahamstown DipTh72. **d** 72 **p** 73. S Africa 72-76 and 82-91; C St Sav Cathl Pietermaritzburg 72-76; Miss to Seafarers from 76; Min Sec 93-00; Sec Gen from 00; Hon C Milton next Gravesend Ch Ch *Roch* 78-82; Chapl Miss to Seamen and R St Andr Richard's Bay 82-91; Chapl Hull Miss to Seamen 91-93; Hon Can Bloemfontein Cathl from 93; Lic to Offic *Lon* 94-97; V St Mich Paternoster Royal from 00. *The Mission to Seafarers, St Michael Paternoster Royal, College Hill, London EC4R 2RL* Tel (020) 7248 5202 Fax 7248 4761 E-mail general@missiontoseafarers.org

CHRISTIE, Alexander Robert. b 58. Qu Coll Cam BA79 LLM80. Oak Hill Th Coll DipHE94. **d** 94 **p** 95. C W Norwood St Luke *S'wark* 94-98; C Wandsworth All SS 98-03; V Blackheath Park St Mich from 03. *St Michael's Vicarage, 2 Pond Road, London SE3 9JL* Tel (020) 8852 5287 E-mail ar.christie@virgin.net

CHRISTIE, David James. b 58. York Univ BA80 MA83 PGCE81 Leeds Univ MPhil88. Cranmer Hall Dur 89. **d** 91 **p** 92. C Drypool *York* 91-95; V Patrick Brompton and Hunton *Ripon* from 95; V Hornby from 95; V Crakehall from 95. *The Vicarage, Patrick Brompton, Bedale DL8 1JN* Tel (01677) 450439 E-mail dc@christiepb.fsnet.co.uk

CHRISTIE, Canon Thomas Richard. b 31. CCC Cam BA53 MA57. Linc Th Coll 55. **d** 57 **p** 58. C Portsea N End St Mark *Portsm* 57-60; C Cherry Hinton St Andr *Ely* 60-62; C-in-c Cherry Hinton St Jas CD 62-66; V Wisbech St Aug 66-73; V Whitstable All SS *Cant* 73-75; V Whitstable All SS w St Pet 75-80; Can Res and Treas Pet Cathl *Pet* 80-01; Perm to Offic *Ely* from 00; RD Pet 87-96; Chapl to Rtd Clergy from 00; rtd 01; P-in-c Wittering w Thornhaugh and Wansford *Pet* 01-02; P-in-c Thornhaugh and Wansford from 03. *16 College Park, Peterborough PE1 4AW* Tel (01733) 344228

CHRISTOPHER, Richard. b 53. NTMTC 94 Birm Bible Inst 80. **d** 97 **p** 98. C Southall Green St Jo *Lon* from 97. *22 Witley Gardens, Southall UB2 4ES* Tel (020) 8574 0253

CHRISTOU, Sotirios. b 51. Avery Hill Coll DipHE80. St Jo Coll Nottm 84. **d** 88 **p** 92. C Berechurch St Marg w St Mich *Chelmsf* 88-89; C Goodmayes All SS 89-90; NSM Harston w Hauxton *Ely* 92-94; Lic to Offic 94-95; C Burgess Hill St Andr *Chich* 95-98; Perm to Offic *Ely* from 98. *18 Bullen Close, Cambridge CB1 8YU* Tel (01223) 514593

CHUBB, John Nicholas. b 33. St Cath Soc Ox BA55 MA58. Qu Coll Birm 57. **d** 59 **p** 60. C Kirby Moorside w Gillamoor *York* 59-62; C Scarborough St Mary 62-64; V Potterspury w Furtho and Yardley Gobion *Pet* 64-69; V Brixworth 69-74; P-in-c Holcot 73-74; V Brixworth w Holcot 74-81; V Hampton Hill *Lon* 81-88; Chapl Pet Distr Hosp 88-97; Chapl Edith Cavell Hosp 88-97; rtd 97. *12 Alness Drive, York YO24 2XZ*

CHUBB, Richard Henry. b 45. Univ of Wales (Cardiff) BMus67 Bris Univ PGCE76. Linc Th Coll 67. **d** 70 **p** 71. C Chippenham St Andr w Tytherton Lucas *Bris* 71-72; C-in-c Stockwood CD 72-73; C Bris Ch the Servant Stockwood 73-76; Perm to Offic 76-79; Min Can and Succ Bris Cathl 79-88; Chapl St David People 83-02; Chapl Qu Eliz Hosp Sch Bris 87-92; rtd 02. *17 Southmead Road, Westbury-on-Trym, Bristol BS10 5DL* Tel 0117-962 9508 Fax as telephone E-mail richard.chubb@lineonet.net

CHUDLEY, Cyril Raymond. b 29. Lon Univ BA53 DipEd. Wells Th Coll 70. **d** 72 **p** 73. C Newark St Mary *S'well* 72-75; C Egg Buckland *Ex* 75-77; P-in-c Plymouth St Aug 77-80; V 80-83; V

Milton Abbot, Dunterton, Lamerton etc 83-91; TV Wickford and Runwell *Chelmsf* 91-95; rtd 95; Perm to Offic *Truro* from 95. *Ten Acres, Coxpark, Gunnislake PL18 9BB* Tel (01822) 832345

✢CHUNG, The Most Revd Matthew Chul Bum. c 95. Bp Seoul from 95; Presiding Bp Korea from 02. *3 Chong Dong, Chung Ku, Seoul 100-120, Republic of Korea* Tel (0082) (2) 735 6157 *or* 738 6597 Fax 723 2640 E-mail mcbchung@hotmail.com *or* mcbchung@chollian.net

CHURCH, Mrs Linda Ann. b 51. MCSP73 Open Univ 93. EMMTC 88. **d** 91 **p** 94. NSM Kirkby in Ashfield St Thos *S'well* 91-95; NSM Skegby and Teversal 95-98; P-in-c Annesley w Newstead 98-03; TR Hucknall Torkard from 03. *The Rectory, Annesley Road, Hucknall, Nottingham NG15 7DE* Tel 0115-963 2033 E-mail lawrence@annesleycutting.freeserve.co.uk

CHURCH, William John. b 41. Qu Coll Cam MA62 Solicitor. St Alb and St Mich Ann Course 96. **d** 99 **p** 00. NSM Bengeo St Alb 99-01; NSM Gt Amwell w St Margaret's and Stanstead Abbots from 01. *115 Queen's Road, Hertford SG13 8BJ* Tel (01992) 410469 Fax 583079 E-mail bill.church@hertscc.gov.uk

CHURCHER, Ms Mandy. b 54. RN75 RM77 Surrey Univ PGCE87 Brunel Univ MEd92. NTMTC 96. **d** 99 **p** 00. C Wolverhampton St Matt *Lich* 99-02; Assoc Chapl Plymouth Hosps NHS Trust from 02. *The Chaplaincy, Derriford Hospital, Derriford Road, Plymouth PL6 8DH* Tel (01752) 792022 E-mail mandy.churcher@phntswest.nhs.uk

CHURCHMAN, David Ernest Donald (Don). b 21. Clifton Th Coll 45. **d** 48 **p** 49. C Preston All SS *Blackb* 48-49; C Braintree *Chelmsf* 50-52; V Harold Wood 52-59; V Southsea St Jude *Portsm* 59-74; V Enfield Ch Ch Trent Park *Lon* 74-86; RD Enfield 75-82; rtd 86; Perm to Offic *Portsm* from 87. *Heronsbrook, 158 Havant Road, Hayling Island PO11 0LJ* Tel (023) 9246 3216

CHURCHUS, Eric Richard Ivor. b 28. Lon Univ BSc MSc56. **d** 78 **p** 79. Hon C Withington w Westhide *Heref* 78-82; C Heref St Martin 82-85; P-in-c Woolhope 85-93; rtd 93; Perm to Offic *Heref* from 93. *27 Aconbury Avenue, Hereford HR2 6HR* Tel (01432) 267022

CHYNCHEN, John Howard. b 38. FRICS72. Sarum & Wells Th Coll 88. **d** 89 **p** 90. Bp's Dom Chapl *Sarum* from 89; Hon Chapl Hong Kong Cathl from 90. *64 Courtenay Street, London SE11 5PQ,* or *2044 Fairmont House, 8 Cotton Tree Drive, Hong Kong* Tel (020) 7582 3541 *or* (00852) 2541 4155 Fax (00852) 2544 2638 E-mail chynchen@btinternet.com

CIANCHI, Dalbert Peter. b 28. Lon Univ BSc57. Westcott Ho Cam 69. **d** 70 **p** 71. C Harpenden St Nic *St Alb* 70-74; TV Woughton *Ox* 74-80; P-in-c Wavendon w Walton 74-80; P-in-c Lavendon w Cold Brayfield 80-84; R Lavendon w Cold Brayfield, Clifton Reynes etc 84-94; rtd 94. *20 Fisken Crescent, Kambah, ACT, Australia 2902* Tel (0061) (2) 6231 8556 E-mail pcianchi@cyberone.com.au

CIECHANOWICZ, Edward Leigh Bundock. *See* BUNDOCK, Edward Leigh

CINNAMOND, Andrew Victor. b 71. St Andr Univ MA94. Wycliffe Hall Ox BA00. **d** 01 **p** 02. C Clapham TM *S'wark* 01; C Clapham H Trin and St Pet from 02. *Glebe House, 6 Rectory Grove, London SW4 0DZ* Tel (020) 7498 9957 E-mail andrew_cinnamond@hotmail.com

CIRCUS, Robert William. b 19. Lon Univ BSc(Econ)90. Wycliffe Hall Ox 52. **d** 54 **p** 55. C Rayleigh *Chelmsf* 54-56; V Northampton St Andr *Pet* 56-60; V Werrington 60-70; R The Quinton *Birm* 70-76; P-in-c Wolverley *Worc* 76-82; V Wolverley and Cookley 82-84; rtd 84; Perm to Offic *Worc* from 84. *90 Audley Drive, Kidderminster DY11 5NF* Tel (01562) 750286

CLABON, Ronald Oliver Edwin. b 30. **d** 97. NSM Pontnewydd *Mon* 97-03. *72 Anthony Drive, Caerleon, Newport NP18 3DX* Tel (01633) 420790

CLACEY, Derek Phillip. b 48. LTh. St Jo Coll Nottm 76. **d** 79 **p** 80. C Gt Parndon *Chelmsf* 79-82; C Walton H Trin *Ox* 82-88; R Bramshaw and Landford w Plaitford *Sarum* from 88. *The Rectory, Wych Green, Bramshaw, Lyndhurst SO4 7JF* Tel (01794) 390256

CLACK, Robert John Edmund. b 63. Lanc Univ BA85. Coll of Resurr Mirfield 89. **d** 92 **p** 93. C Bury St Pet *Man* 92-95; Chapl Bury Colls of FE 93-95; TV New Bury 95-97; R Ashton-upon-Mersey St Martin *Ches* from 97. *St Martin's Rectory, 367 Glebelands Road, Sale M33 5GG* Tel 0161-973 4204 E-mail robert@rclack.fsbusiness.co.uk

CLACKER, Martin Alexander. b 56. Trin Coll Bris DipHE95. **d** 95 **p** 96. C Yate New Town *Bris* 95-98; V Southmead 98-00; C Portishead *B & W* 00-02; TV 02-03; rtd 03. *110 Brampton Way, Portishead, Bristol BS20 6 YT* Tel (01275) 847197

CLANCEY, Ms Blanche Elizabeth Fisher. b 28. SRN50 Lon Univ CertEd71. Gilmore Ho 64. **dss** 78 **d** 87 **p** 94. Bromley Common St Aug *Roch* 78-83; Hanley H Ev *Lich* 83-86; Dn-in-c 87-89; rtd 89; NSM Wilford Hill *S'well* 89-91; NSM Gamston and Bridgford 91-97; NSM Cropwell Bishop w Colston Bassett, Granby etc 97-99; Perm to Offic *S'well* from 00. *83 Church Way, South Croydon CR2 0JU* Tel (020) 8657 6376

CLANCY, Michael. b 24. Kensington Univ (USA) BA82. Glas NSM Course 76. **d** 79 **p** 80. Hon C Glas St Silas *Glas* 79-96; Perm

to Offic from 96. *33 Highfield Drive, Clarkston, Glasgow G76 7SW* Tel 0141-638 4469

CLAPHAM, Christopher Charles. b 69. Man Univ BA91 St Jo Coll Dur BA96. Cranmer Hall Dur 94 Union Th Sem (NY) STM98. **d** 99 **p** 00. NSM Withington St Chris *Man* 99-01; C Didsbury Ch Ch 01-03; P-in-c Swinton H Rood from 03. *Holy Rood Vicarage, 33 Moorside Road, Swinton, Manchester M27 3EL* Tel 0161-794 2464 E-mail charlesclapham@lineone.net

CLAPHAM, John. b 47. Open Univ BA76. Sarum & Wells Th Coll 77. **d** 80 **p** 81. Dep PV Ex Cathl *Ex* from 80; C Lympstone 85-87; P-in-c 87-99; P-in-c Woodbury 97-99; RD Aylesbeare 96-01; R Lympstone and Woodbury w Exton from 99. *The Rectory, Lympstone, Exmouth EX8 5HP* Tel (01395) 273343

CLAPHAM, Kenneth. b 47. Trin Coll Bris 76. **d** 78 **p** 79. C Pemberton St Mark Newtown *Liv* 78-81; C Darfield *Sheff* 81-83; P-in-c Over Kellet *Blackb* 83-88; V from 88. *The Vicarage, 3 Kirklands Road, Over Kellet, Carnforth LA6 1DJ* Tel (01524) 734189 Fax as telephone E-mail ukvicar@aol.com

CLAPP, Nicholas Michel Edward. b 48. Univ of Wales (Cardiff) DipTh74. St Mich Coll Llan 71. **d** 74 **p** 75. C Walsall St Gabr Fulbrook *Lich* 74-77; C Burnley St Cath *Blackb* 77-80; R Blackley H Trin *Man* 80-87; V Carl St Aid and Ch Ch *Carl* 87-98; Perm to Offic *Blackb* from 00. *3 Arnold Close, Ribbleton, Preston PR2 6DX* Tel (01772) 798613

CLAPSON, Canon Clive Henry. b 55. Leeds Univ BA76. Trin Coll Toronto MDiv79. **d** 79 **p** 80. Canada 79-83; USA 83-88; C Hawley H Trin *Guildf* 88-90; Miss to Seafarers from 90; R Invergordon St Ninian *Mor* 90-00; Prin Ord and Lay Tr Course 90-94; Can St Andr Cathl Inverness 97-00; Co-ord Dioc Lay Tr Course from 98; R Aberdeen St Mary *Ab* from 00. *St Mary's Rectory, 28 Stanley Street, Aberdeen AB10 6UR* Tel (01224) 584123 E-mail father.clive@virgin.net

CLAPTON, Timothy. b 59. Westmr Coll Ox MTh92. CA Tr Coll 82 Westcott Ho Cam 96. **d** 98 **p** 99. C Wimborne Minster *Sarum* 98-02; Ecum Chapl Milton Keynes Gen NHS Trust from 02. *Milton Keynes General Hospital, Standing Way, Milton Keynes MK6 5LD* Tel (01908) 660033

CLARE, Christopher. b 52. Sheff Univ BSc73 Nottm Univ PGCE74. Ox Min Course 89. **d** 92 **p** 93. NSM Chesham Bois *Ox* from 92. *5 Lime Tree Walk, Amersham HP7 9HY* Tel (01494) 766513

CLARE, Lionel Philip. b 19. St Aid Birkenhead 46. **d** 49 **p** 50. C Far Headingley St Chad *Ripon* 49-52; C Low Harrogate St Mary 52-54; R Addingham *Bradf* 54-66; V Sunnyside w Bourne End *St Alb* 66-74; V Kirkbymoorside w Gillamoor, Farndale etc *York* 74-84; rtd 84; Perm to Offic *Bradf* from 84. *Flat 1, Regent Court, 20 Regent Road, Ilkley LS29 9EA* Tel (01943) 609330

CLARE, Sister. *See* LOCKHART, Clare Patricia Anne

CLARIDGE, Antony Arthur John. b 37. LRAM Hull Univ MA. Bris & Glouc Tr Course. **d** 84 **p** 85. NSM Keynsham *B & W* 84-97; Bp's Officer for NSMs from 90; Min Bath Ch Ch Prop Chpl from 97. *62 Cranwells Park, Bath BA1 2YE* Tel (01225) 427462 E-mail chantrybath@breathemail.net

CLARIDGE, Michael John. b 61. MIEH Matt Bourton Tech Coll Birm DipEH82. Qu Coll Birm 89 Bossey Ecum Inst Geneva Cert Ecum Studies 92. **d** 92 **p** 93. C Harlescott *Lich* 92-95; P-in-c Wellington Ch Ch 95-97; V 97-03; V W Bromwich St Andr w Ch Ch from 03. *St Andrew's Vicarage, Oakwood Street, West Bromwich B70 9SN* Tel 0121-553 1871 E-mail mjc@fish.co.uk

CLARINGBULL, Canon Denis Leslie. b 30. K Coll Lon BD57 AKC57 Univ of Cen England in Birm DUniv98 MCIPD85 FCIPD01. **d** 58 **p** 59. C Croydon St Aug *Cant* 58-62; Ind Chapl to Bp Croydon 62-71; Ind Chapl *Cov* 71-75; Chapl Cov Cathl 71-75; Succ 72-75; V Norbury St Phil *Cant* 75-80; Sen Ind Chapl *Birm* 80-98; P-in-c Birm St Paul 85-98; V 88-98; Hon Can Birm Cathl 87-98; rtd 98; Perm to Office *Birm* and *Heref* from 98. *17 Merrivale Crescent, Ross-on-Wye HR9 5JU* Tel (01989) 567771 E-mail gms58@dial.pipex.com

CLARINGBULL (née DAVID), Mrs Faith Caroline. b 55. St Aid Ripon Coll Cuddesdon 87. **d** 89 **p** 94. Par Dn Is of Dogs Ch Ch and St Jo w St Luke *Lon* 89-93; Asst Chapl R Lon Hosps NHS Trust 93-98; NSM Wheatley *Ox* 98-00; Asst Dioc Dir of Ords *Worc* from 00; Dioc CME Officer from 02. *6 Riverside Way, Droitwich WR9 8UP* Tel (01905) 796740 E-mail claring.bull@virgin.net

CLARINGBULL, Keith. b 49. Ripon Coll Cuddesdon 98. **d** 00 **p** 01. C Droitwich Spa *Worc* from 00. *6 Riverside Way, Droitwich WR9 8UP* Tel (01905) 796740 E-mail claring.bull@virgin.net

CLARK, Albert Percival (Peter). b 17. Hatf Coll Dur LTh39 BA39. St Boniface Warminster 36. **d** 40 **p** 41. C Wildmore *Linc* 40-42; C New Cleethorpes 42-44; C Linc St Botolph 44-46; R Strubby w Woodthorpe and Maltby-le-Marsh 46-50; S Africa 50-61 and 77-80; R The Quinton *Birm* 61-70; V Werrington *Pet* 70-77; R Chipping Warden w Edgcote and Aston le Walls 80-83; rtd 83; Perm to Offic *S'wark* from 83; Perm to Offic *Guildf* from 86. *3 Falconhurst, The Crescent, Surbiton KT6 4BP* Tel (020) 8399 2032

CLARK, Andrew James. b 50. ACIB72 ACIS76. EMMTC 91. d 94 p 95. NSM Allestree *Derby* 94-97; NSM Allenton and Shelton Lock 97-03; NSM Walbrook Epiphany from 03. *44 Crabtree Close, Allestree, Derby DE22 2SW* Tel (01332) 552492

CLARK, Antony. b 61. York Univ BA83. Wycliffe Hall Ox 84. d 88 p 89. C Ashton-upon-Mersey St Mary *Ches* 88-92; Chapl Lee Abbey 92-95; Lic to Offic *Ex* 92-95; Chapl Univ Westmr *Lon* 95-98; C Bletchley *Ox* 98-00. *Divinity School, St Mary's College, St Andrews KY16 9JU or Westerlea, Pittenweem Road, Anstruther KY10 3DT* Tel (01333) 313124

CLARK, Arthur. b 30. MIBiol FRSC Sheff Univ BSc MCB. St D Dioc Tr Course. d 88 p 89. NSM Haverfordwest St Mary and St Thos w Haroldston *St D* 88-91; C 91-92; V Llawhaden w Bletherston and Llanycefn 92-96; rtd 96. *84 Portfield, Haverfordwest SA61 1BT* Tel (01437) 762694

CLARK, Bernard Charles. b 34. Open Univ BA81. S'wark Ord Course 65. d 68 p 69. C Pemberton St Jo *Liv* 68-71; C Winwick 71-73; P-in-c Warrington St Barn 74-76; V 76-78; V Hindley All SS 78-83; Perm to Offic 86-94; R Glazebury w Hollinfare 94-99; rtd 99; Perm to Offic *Man* from 00. *31 Linkfield Drive, Worsley, Manchester M28 1JU* Tel 0161-799 7998 E-mail bckathcain31@aol.com

CLARK, Brian John. b 48. Portsm Poly CQSW89 Portsm Univ MA94. STETS 97. d 00 p 01. NSM Titchfield *Portsm* 00-01; NSM Helston and Wendron *Truro* 01-02; Perm to Offic *Portsm* from 02. *30 Selhurst Way, Fair Oak, Eastleigh SO50 7JX* Tel (023) 8060 0484

CLARK, Cecil. b 44. Sarum Th Coll. d 98 p 99. OLM Canford Magna *Sarum* from 98. *Fermain Cottage, 133 Magna Road, Bearwood, Bournemouth BH11 9NE* Tel (01202) 577898 or 663275

CLARK, Mrs Christine Margaret. b 44. St Alb and Ox Min Course 01. d 01 p 02. NSM Croxley Green St Oswald *St Alb* from 01. *2 Clutterbucks, Church Lane, Sarratt, Rickmansworth WD3 6HL* Tel (01923) 261861 E-mail cmclark@fish.co.uk

CLARK, Daniel Alastair. b 74. St Jo Coll Dur BA96. Wycliffe Hall Ox BA99. d 00 p 01. C Rusholme H Trin *Man* from 00. *2 The Grange, Manchester M14 5NY* Tel 0161-256 3718 or 224 1123 Fax 224 1144 E-mail daniel@plattchurch.org

CLARK, David. b 30. Nottm Univ BSc51 Lon Univ DipTh57. St Aid Birkenhead 55. d 57 p 58. C Tyldesley w Shakerley *Man* 57-60; V Ashton St Jas 60-64; rtd 93. *Roz an Avalou, 22340 Mael-Carhaix, France* Tel (0033) 96 24 65 04

CLARK, Canon David George Neville. b 25. Linc Coll Ox BA49 MA59. Wells Th Coll 49. d 51 p 52. C Sanderstead All SS S'wark 51-54; C Lewisham St Jo Southend 54-59; V Sutton New Town St Barn 59-72; R Charlwood 72-90; P-in-c Sidlow Bridge 76-77; R 77-90; P-in-c Buckland 85-87; P-in-c Leigh 87-90; Hon Can S'wark Cathl 88-90; rtd 90; Perm to Offic *Cov* from 90. *12 Marlborough Road, Coventry CV2 4EP* Tel (024) 7644 2400

CLARK, David Gordon. b 29. Clare Coll Cam BA52 MA57. Ridley Hall Cam 52. d 54 p 55. C Walthamstow St Jo *Chelmsf* 54-57; V 60-69; C Gt Ilford St Andr 57-60; R Stansted *Roch* 69-82; R Stansted w Fairseat and Vigo 82-94; rtd 94; Perm to Offic *Sarum* from 94. *1 Coastguard Cottages, Wareham BH20 5PF* Tel (01929) 480753

CLARK, David Humphrey. b 39. G&C Coll Cam BA60. Wells Th Coll 62. d 64 p 65. C Leigh St Mary *Man* 64-68; Min Can and Prec Man Cathl 68-70; Ind Chapl *Nor* 70-85; P-in-c Nor St Clem and St Geo 70-76; P-in-c Nor St Sav w St Paul 76-85; V Norwich-over-the-Water Colegate St Geo 76-79; Hon Asst P Nor St Pet Mancroft 79-85; TR Oadby *Leic* 85-98; C Leic St Jas from 98. *1 Dixon Drive, Leicester LE2 1RA* Tel 0116-270 0340 E-mail dhclark@leicester.anglican.org

CLARK, David John. b 40. CEng MIStructE Surrey Univ MPhil75. Ridley Hall Cam 81. d 83 p 84. C Combe Down w Monkton Combe and S Stoke *B & W* 83-89; Voc Adv Bath Adnry from 89; R Freshford, Limpley Stoke and Hinton Charterhouse from 89. *The Rectory, Crowe Lane, Freshford, Bath BA3 6EB* Tel (01225) 723135 E-mail david@freshford313.freeserve.co.uk

CLARK, Dennis Henry Graham. b 26. St Steph Ho Ox 52. d 55 p 56. C Southall St Geo *Lon* 55-58; C Barbourne *Worc* 58-61; Chapl RAF 61-78; Asst Chapl-in-Chief RAF 78-82; Chapl St Clem Danes (RAF Ch) 79-82; V Godmanchester *Ely* 82-91; rtd 91; Perm to Offic *Ely* from 91. *8 Arran Way, St Ives PE27 3DT* Tel (01480) 301951

CLARK, Diane Catherine. See FITZGERALD CLARK, Mrs Diane Catherine

CLARK, Edward Robert. b 39. Ex Coll Ox BA61 MA65 Bris Univ CASS69. St Steph Ho Ox 61. d 63 p 64. C Solihull *Birm* 63-67; Perm to Offic *Bris* 67-69; *Leic* 69-71; *Ox* 71-80; *St Alb* 80-84; *Cant* from 84. *2 Hunters Bank, Old Road, Elham, Canterbury CT4 6SS* Tel (01303) 840134 E-mail edward.clark@lineone.net

CLARK, Ellen Jane. See CLARK-KING, Ellen Jane

CLARK, Frederick Albert George. b 15. MBE68. ACP66. d 67 p 68. Hon C Stroud *Glouc* 67-84; Hon C Stroud and Uplands w Slad 84-85; Perm to Offic 85-97. *2 Terrace Cottages, Thrupp, Stroud GL5 2BN* Tel (01453) 882060

CLARK, Harold Clive. b 28. Witwatersrand Univ LTh53. St Paul's Coll Grahamstown. d 54 p 55. S Africa 54-60 and 62-77; C Orange Grove 54-56; R Mayfair 56-60; P-in-c Morden *S'wark* 60-62; R Verulam 62-68; Chapl Michaelhouse 68-77; New Zealand from 77; V Green Island 77-85; V Kaitaia 85-92; Chapl Kristin Sch Albany from 92. *351 East Coast Road, Mairangi Bay 1310, New Zealand* Tel (0064) (9) 479 3434

CLARK, Ian Duncan Lindsay. b 35. K Coll Cam BA59 MA63 PhD64 Linacre Ho Ox DipTh63. Ripon Hall Ox 62. d 64 p 65. C Willington *Newc* 64-66; India 66-76; Lect Bp's Coll Calcutta 66; Vice-Prin 69-74; Chapl St Cath Coll Cam 76; Fell 77-85; Tutor 78-85; Dean of Chpl and Lect 80-85; Select Preacher Cam Univ 82; Hon Asst P Kelso *Edin* from 85. *4 Yewtree Lane, Town Yetholm, Kelso TD5 8RZ* Tel (01573) 420323

CLARK, Miss Janet Elizabeth. b 44. Derby Coll of Educn CertEd65 Open Univ BA75. All Nations Chr Coll CertRS84 Oak Hill Th Coll DipHE91 BA92. d 92 p 94. Par Dn Edmonton All SS w St Mich *Lon* 92-94; C 94-96; V Ealing St Steph Castle Hill from 96. *St Stephen's Vicarage, Sherbourne Gardens, London W13 8AQ* Tel (020) 8810 4929 or 8991 0164 E-mail jan@fortaguada.freeserve.co.uk

CLARK, Mrs Jean Robinson. b 32. K Coll Lon AKC BD79. St Chris Coll Blackheath CertRK53. dss 85 d 87 p 94. Cov E *Cov* 85-87; C 87-88; NSM Upper Mole Valley Gp *S'wark* 89-90; Hon Par Dn Charlwood 89-90; Lic to Offic *Cov* 90-92; rtd 92; Perm to Offic *Cov* from 92. *12 Marlborough Road, Coventry CV2 4EP* Tel (024) 7644 2400

CLARK, Jeremy James. b 66. Cant Univ (NZ) BA88. St Jo Coll Auckland BTh97. d 94 p 95. C Shirley St Steph New Zealand 94-97; C Upton (Overchurch) *Ches* 97-01; P-in-c Ilfracombe SS Phil and Jas w W Down *Ex* from 01. *St James's Vicarage, Kingsley Avenue, Ilfracombe EX34 8ET* Tel (01271) 863519 E-mail pipjimcalix@aol.com

CLARK, John David Stanley. b 36. Dur Univ BA64. Ridley Hall Cam 64. d 66 p 67. C Benchill *Man* 66-69; C Beverley Minster *York* 69-74; Perm to Offic *S'well* 74-76; Lic to Offic 76-77; Miss to Seamen 77-80; Perm to Offic *York* 80-83; V Egton w Grosmont 83-89; R Thornton Dale w Ellerburne and Wilton 89-01; R Thornton Dale w Allerston, Ebberston etc from 01. *The Rectory, Church Hill, Thornton Dale, Pickering YO18 7QH* Tel (01751) 474244

CLARK, John Edward Goodband. b 49. Leeds Univ MA01. Chich Th Coll 70. d 73 p 74. C Thorpe *Nor* 73-76; C Earlham St Anne 76-78; Chapl RN 78-82; P-in-c Tittleshall w Godwick, Wellingham and Weasenham *Nor* 82-85; P-in-c Helhoughton w Raynham 82-85; R South Raynham, E w W Raynham, Helhoughton, etc 85-90; R Taverham w Ringland 90-96; R Middleton-in-Teesdale w Forest and Frith *Dur* from 96; V Eggleston from 96; AD Barnard Castle from 00. *The Rectory, 1 Hude, Middleton-in-Teesdale, Barnard Castle DL12 0QW* Tel (01833) 640267 E-mail hudeshope@rapidial.co.uk

CLARK, John Michael. b 35. Dip Sales Mgt Studies 63 Dip Youth Work 65 Leic Poly Dip Community Educn 80. EMMTC 87. d 90 p 91. Chapl to the Deaf *Linc* 86-00; NSM Bracebridge Heath 90-00; rtd 00; Perm to Offic *Linc* from 00. *3 Hawthorn Road, Cherry Willingham, Lincoln LN3 4JU* Tel (01522) 751759

CLARK, John Patrick Hedley. b 37. St Cath Coll Cam BA61 MA65 Worc Coll Ox BA63 MA72 BD74 Lambeth Hon DD89. St Steph Ho Ox 61. d 64 p 65. C Highters Heath *Birm* 64-67; C Eglingham *Newc* 67-72; P-in-c Newc St Anne 72-77; V Longframlington w Brinkburn 77-95; V Chevington 95-02; rtd 02; Perm to Offic *Dur* from 02. *6 The Cottage, West Row, Greatham, Hartlepool TS25 2HW* Tel (01429) 870203

CLARK, John Ronald Lyons. b 47. TCD BA69 MA72. Div Hostel Dub 67. d 70 p 71. C Dundela St Mark *D & D* 70-72; CF 72-75; C Belfast St Aid *Conn* 75-76; I Stranorlar w Meenglas and Kilteevogue *D & R* 76-81; Chapl Wythenshawe Hosp Man 81-95; I Kilgariffe Union *C, C & R* 95-96; Chapl Blackb, Hyndburn and Ribble Valley NHS Trust from 96; Chapl E Lancs Hospice, Park Hospital, Haslingden Road, Blackburn BB2 3HH Tel (01254) 263555, 294807 or (01706) 830715 Mobile 07774-274410

CLARK, Jonathan Dunnett. b 61. Ex Univ BA83 Bris Univ MLitt90 Southn Univ MA96. Trin Coll Bris 84. d 88 p 89. C Stanwix *Carl* 88-92; Chapl Bris Univ *Bris* 92-93; Dir of Studies S Dios Minl Tr Scheme 94-97; Chapl Univ of N Lon 97-02; Chapl Lon Metrop Univ 02-03; AD Islington 99-03; R Stoke Newington St Mary from 03. *The Rectory, Stoke Newington Church Street, London N16 9ES* Tel (020) 7254 6072 Mobile 07968-845698 E-mail rector@stmaryn16.org.uk

CLARK, Jonathan Jackson. b 57. Linc Coll Ox 79 Down Coll Cam 83. Ridley Hall Cam 81. d 84 p 85. C W Derby St Luke *Liv* 84-87; C Gt Clacton *Chelmsf* 87-93; V Hammersmith St Simon *Lon* from 93; AD Hammersmith and Fulham 96-01. *153 Blyth*

Road, London W14 0HL Tel (020) 7602 1043 *or* 7602 7767 Fax 7602 7227 E-mail jjclark@btinternet.com
CLARK, Kathleen Christine. *See* LEFROY, Mrs Kathleen Christine
CLARK, The Ven Kenneth James. b 22. DSC44. St Cath Soc Ox BA48 MA52. Cuddesdon Coll 52. **d** 52 **p** 53. C Brinkworth *Bris* 52-53; C Cricklade w Latton 53-56; C-in-c Filwood Park CD 56-59; V Bris H Cross Inns Court 59-61; V Westbury-on-Trym H Trin 61-72; V Bris St Mary Redcliffe w Temple etc 72-82; P-in-c Bedminster St Mich 73-78; RD Bedminster 73-79; Hon Can Bris Cathl 74-92; Adn Swindon 82-92; rtd 92; Perm to Offic *Sarum* from 92. *6 Saxon Road, Harnham, Salisbury SP2 8JZ* Tel (01722) 421410
CLARK, Kenneth William. b 69. R Holloway Coll Lon BA92 Trin Coll Cam BA99. Westcott Ho Cam 97. **d** 00 **p** 01. C Bromley St Mark *Roch* from 00. *25 Matfield Close, Bromley BR2 9DY* Tel (020) 8466 5827 E-mail kenofkent@amserve.net
CLARK, Lance Edgar Dennis. b 52. MBE93. Linc Th Coll 74. **d** 77 **p** 78. C Arnold *S'well* 77-82; V Brinsley w Underwood 82-87; Chapl RAF 87-02. *Address temp unknown*
CLARK, Lynn. *See* PURVIS, Lynn
CLARK, Martin Hudson. b 46. K Coll Lon BD68 AKC68 MTh91 Birm Univ PGCE89. **d** 71 **p** 72. C S'wark H Trin *S'wark* 71-74; C Parkstone St Pet w Branksea and St Osmund *Sarum* 74-77; V E Wickham *S'wark* 77-86; V Wandsworth St Anne 86-98; RD Wandsworth 90-95; V Angell Town St Jo from 98; RD Brixton from 01. *St John's Vicarage, 49 Wiltshire Road, London SW9 7NE* Tel (020) 7733 0585 Fax as telephone E-mail martin@jemima.globalnet.co.uk
CLARK, Michael Arthur. b 46. S Dios Minl Tr Scheme. **d** 83 **p** 84. NSM Monkton Farleigh, S Wraxall and Winsley *Sarum* from 83. *62 Tyning Road, Winsley, Bradford-on-Avon BA15 2JW* Tel (01225) 866652
CLARK, Michael David. b 45. Ox Univ MA68. Trin Coll Bris DipTh72. **d** 72 **p** 73. C Cheadle *Ches* 72-76; Brazil 77-86; Bolivia 86-88; C Wilton *B & W* 89-90; TV 90-99; C Tollington *Lon* 99-01; TR Edgware from 01. *The Rectory, Rectory Lane, Edgware HA8 7LG* Tel (020) 8952 1081
CLARK, Michael James. b 71. Univ of Wales (Cardiff) BSc92. Trin Coll Bris BA02. **d** 02 **p** 03. C Tiverton St Geo and St Paul *Ex* from 02. *St George's Vicarage, St Andrew Street, Tiverton EX16 6PH* Tel (01884) 252184 E-mail mjclark@lycos.co.uk
CLARK, Miss Patricia Mary. b 36. Liv Univ BSc. **d** 88 **p** 94. Par Dn Leasowe *Ches* 88-92; Bp's Officer for Women in Min 89-97; Par Dn Davenham 92-94; C 94-97; rtd 97; Perm to Offic *Ches* from 97. *18 Farmstead Way, Great Sutton, Ellesmere Port CH66 2RU* Tel 0151-339 1450
CLARK, Peter. *See* CLARK, Albert Percival
CLARK, Canon Peter. b 38. Ch Coll Cam BA61 MA65. Chich Th Coll 61. **d** 63 **p** 64. C Huddersfield St Pet and St Paul *Wakef* 63-67; C Notting Hill St Jo *Lon* 67-74; Grenada 75-79; C Hove All SS *Chich* 79; P-in-c Hove St Patr 79-82; V Hove St Patr w Ch Ch and St Andr 82-83; V Battersea Ch Ch and St Steph *S'wark* from 83; RD Battersea 90-01; Hon Can S'wark Cathl from 96. *Christ Church Vicarage, Candahar Road, London SW11 2PU* Tel (020) 7228 1225
CLARK, Peter. b 45. Sarum & Wells Th Coll 87. **d** 89 **p** 90. C Portsea St Cuth *Portsm* 89-92; TV Rye *Chich* 92-96; P-in-c Chiddingly w E Hoathly 96-98; R from 98. *The Rectory, Rectory Close, East Hoathly, Lewes BN8 6EG* Tel (01825) 840270 E-mail clucksville@onetel.net.uk
CLARK, Peter Norman. b 53. Qu Coll Cam BA79. Westcott Ho Cam 78. **d** 80 **p** 81. C Bris St Mary Redcliffe w Temple etc *Bris* 80-83; C Potternewton *Ripon* 83-86; R Longsight St Luke *Man* from 86; AD Ardwick from 00. *St Luke's Rectory, Stockport Road, Longsight, Manchester M13 9AB* Tel 0161-273 6662
CLARK, Peter Rodney. b 58. Oriel Coll Ox BA81 MCIH93. N Ord Course 97. **d** 00 **p** 01. C Stone St Mich and St Wulfad w Aston St Sav *Lich* 00-03; TV Hanley H Ev from 03. *Christ Church Vicarage, 10 Emery Street, Stoke-on-Trent ST6 2JJ* Tel (01782) 212639 E-mail rod@prclark.freeserve.co.uk
CLARK, Mrs Prudence Anne. b 44. Man Coll of Educn CertEd78. N Ord Course 89. **d** 92 **p** 94. NSM Royton St Anne *Man* 92-94; Hon C 94-95; NSM Haughton St Anne from 95. *1 Hereford Way, Stalybridge SK15 2TD* Tel 0161-338 5275
CLARK, Reginald Isaac. b 16. AKC47. **d** 47 **p** 48. C Somersham w Pidley and Oldhurst *Ely* 47-49; C Luton St Mary *St Alb* 49-53; C-in-c Luton St Chris Round Green CD 53-59; V Luton St Chris Round Green 59-65; Chapl Shenley Hosp Radlett Herts 65-84; rtd 84; Perm to Offic *Linc* from 84. *1 Monks Walk, Spalding PE11 3LG* Tel (01775) 768304
CLARK, Richard Martin. b 60. Ch Coll Cam MA81 Nottm Univ MA99. Trin Coll Bris BA86. **d** 86 **p** 87. C Orpington Ch Ch *Roch* 86-89; C Marple All SS *Ches* 89-92; V Nottingham St Andr *S'well* from 92. *St Andrew's Vicarage, Chestnut Grove, Nottingham NG3 5AD* Tel 0115-912 0098 Mobile 07970-823462 E-mail richardnottm@onet.co.uk
CLARK, Robert Henry. b 32. Oak Hill Th Coll 61. **d** 64 **p** 65. C Haydock St Mark *Liv* 64-67; C Tranmere St Cath *Ches* 67-75; V

Platt Bridge *Liv* 75-84; V Litherland St Paul Hatton Hill 84-94; rtd 94; Perm to Offic *Liv* from 94. *9 Lime Vale, Ince, Wigan WN3 4PE* Tel (01942) 861751
CLARK, Canon Robin. b 27. Lon Univ BA49 BD69 MPhil77 St Jo Coll Dur DipTh54 Sheff Univ MA00. **d** 54 **p** 55. C Newton Heath All SS *Man* 54-58; Asst Master Woodhouse Gr Sch Sheff 58-61; R Brant Broughton w Stragglethorpe *Linc* 61-90; P-in-c Welbourn 65-66; RD Loveden 72-93; Can and Preb Linc Cathl from 84; R Brant Broughton and Beckingham 90-93; rtd 93; Perm to Offic *Linc* 93-01. *Ravenshurst Cottage, 23 The Green, Ingham, Lincoln LN1 2XT*
CLARK, Preb Roland Mark Allison. b 21. St Cath Coll Cam BA48 MA53. Wells Th Coll 48. **d** 50 **p** 51. C Battersea St Paul *S'wark* 50-52; C Greenwich St Alfege w St Pet 52-56; Chapl RNVR 53-56; V Wilton *B & W* 56-79; RD Taunton S 60-65; Preb Wells Cathl from 63; R Backwell 79-88; RD Portishead 82-86; rtd 88; Perm to Offic *B & W* and *Chich from 88; Bris* from 95. *21 The Chimes, Nailsea, Bristol BS48 4NH* Tel (01275) 852670
CLARK, Ronald. *See* CLARK, John Ronald Lyons
CLARK, Russell John. b 15. LSE BSc(Econ)38. LNSM course. **d** 93 **p** 93. NSM Hoxne w Denham, Syleham and Wingfield *St E* from 93. *Old School, Wingfield, Diss IP21 5RG* Tel (01379) 384537
CLARK, Sarah Elizabeth. b 65. Loughb Univ BA86 Keele Univ MBA94. St Jo Coll Nottm MA97 DipMM98. **d** 98 **p** 99. C Porchester *S'well* 98-02; R Carlton-in-Lindrick and Langold w Oldcotes from 02. *Langold Vicarage, Church Street, Langold, Worksop S81 9NW* Tel (01909) 730398 E-mail sec1@tinyworld.co.uk
CLARK, Simon Peter John. b 68. Westcott Ho Cam 95. **d** 98 **p** 99. C Bocking St Mary *Chelmsf* 98-02; C Edmonton St Alphege *Lon* from 02; C Ponders End St Matt from 02. *St Matthew's Vicarage, Church Road, Enfield EN3 4NT* Tel (020) 8443 2255 E-mail fr.simon@btinternet.com
CLARK, Stephen Kenneth. b 52. Bris Univ BEd74. Wycliffe Hall Ox 80. **d** 83 **p** 84. C Pitsea *Chelmsf* 83-86; Chapl Scargill Ho 86-89; R Elmley Castle w Bricklehampton and Combertons *Worc* 89-96; Chapl Burrswood Chr Cen *Roch* 96-01; Chapl Team Ldr from 01. *Swedish Log House, Burrswood, Groombridge, Tunbridge Wells TN3 9PU* Tel (01892) 863637 Fax 863623 E-mail admin@burrswood.org.uk
CLARK, Terence Paul. b 62. Leeds Univ BSc85 PGCE94 St Jo Coll Ox DPhil91. Wycliffe Hall Ox 98. **d** 00 **p** 01. C Whitfield *Derby* from 00. *1 Cedar Close, Glossop SK13 7BP* Tel (01457) 860412 Fax as telephone E-mail revterry@btinternet.com
CLARK, Trevor Bartholomew. b 44. Qu Coll Birm 68. **d** 71 **p** 72. C Maltby *Sheff* 71-75; V New Rossington 75-80; V Campsall 80-95; rtd 96; Perm to Offic *Sheff* from 96. *44 Elmdale Drive, Edenthorpe, Doncaster DN3 2LE*
CLARK-KING (née CLARK), Ellen Jane. b 62. Newnham Coll Cam BA85 MA89 Reading Univ PCVG86 Lon Univ MA99 Lanc Univ PhD03. Ripon Coll Cuddesdon 89. **d** 92 **p** 94. C Colwall w Upper Colwall and Coddington *Heref* 92-95; Chapl SS Coll Cam 95-00; NSM N Shields *Newc* from 00; Asst Dioc Dir of Ords from 01. *St Anthony's Vicarage, Enslin Gardens, Newcastle upon Tyne NE6 3ST* Tel 0191-265 1605 E-mail ejck@lineone.net
CLARK-KING (formerly KING), Jeremy Norman. b 66. K Coll Lon BD88 AKC88 Lon Univ MA99. Ripon Coll Cuddesdon 88. **d** 90 **p** 91. C Ashby-de-la-Zouch St Helen w Coleorton *Leic* 90-93; C Ledbury w Eastnor *Heref* 93-96; C Cambridge Gt St Mary w St Mich *Ely* 96-00; Chapl Girton Coll Cam 96-99; Chapl Cam Univ 96-99; V Byker St Ant *Newc* from 00. *St Anthony's Vicarage, Enslin Gardens, Newcastle upon Tyne NE6 3ST* Tel 0191-265 1605 E-mail jnck@lineone.net
CLARKE, Alan John. b 55. St Jo Coll Dur BA77 MA85 PGCE. Westcott Ho Cam 78. **d** 80 **p** 81. C Heworth St Mary *Dur* 80-83; C Darlington St Jo 83-87; Asst Chapl Bryanston Sch 87-91; Chapl St Pet High Sch Ex 93-99; Lic to Offic *Ex* 93-99; Chapl and Hd RS Reed's Sch Cobham from 99. *Clover, Reed's School, Sandy Lane, Cobham KT11 2BL* Tel (01932) 869006
CLARKE, Alan Keith. b 38. Leic Coll of Educn DipYL64 Newc Univ DAES73 MA89. SW Minl Tr Course. **d** 87 **p** 88. NSM Wolborough w Newton Abbot *Ex* 87-00; NSM Wolborough and Ogwell from 01. *School House, 20 Coach Place, Newton Abbot TQ12 1ES* Tel (01626) 363515
CLARKE, Miss Alison Clare. b 33. MCST54 Open Univ BA85. EAMTC 90. **d** 93 **p** 94. NSM Lt Ilford St Mich *Chelmsf* 93-98; Asst Chapl Newham Healthcare NHS Trust Lon 93-98; Perm to Offic *Lon* 94-98; NSM Woodford St Mary w St Phil and St Jas *Chelmsf* 98-03; rtd 03. *29 Glengall Road, Woodford Green IG8 0DN* Tel (020) 8504 5106
CLARKE, Andrew John. b 58. New Coll Edin BD82 Graduate Soc Dur PGCE89. Linc Th Coll 84. **d** 86 **p** 87. C High Harrogate Ch Ch *Ripon* 86-88; RE Teacher Royds Hall High Sch Huddersfield 89-91; C Thornbury *Bradf* 91-93; P-in-c Bingley H Trin 93-99; V from 99; RD Airedale from 01. *Holy Trinity Vicarage, Oak Avenue, Bingley BD16 1ES* Tel (01274) 563909 E-mail andrewclarkebd@aol.com

CLARKE, Ann. *See* CLARKE, Geraldine Ann

CLARKE, Arthur. b 34. Lon Univ BD66 Nottm Univ MPhil75 DipEd. Sarum & Wells Th Coll 75. **d** 76 **p** 77. C Wollaton *S'well* 76-79; R Sutton Bonington 79-91; P-in-c Normanton on Soar 79-91; R Sutton Bonington w Normanton-on-Soar 91-93; P-in-c Arnold 93-94; V 94-02; rtd 02. *16 Kegworth Road, Kingston-on-Soar, Nottingham NG11 0DB* Tel (01509) 674545

CLARKE, Miss Audrey May. b 35. Gilmore Ho 65. **dss** 75 **d** 87 **p** 94. Crofton Park St Hilda w St Cypr *S'wark* 75-79; Chapl Asst Middx Hosp Lon 80-84; Mottingham St Andr *S'wark* 84-87; Par Dn 87-89; C Westborough *Guildf* 89-95; rtd 95; Hon C St Mary's Bay w St Mary-in-the-Marsh etc *Cant* 95-98; Hon C New Romney w Old Romney and Midley 95-98; Perm to Offic *Pet* from 98. *47 Lindsay Street, Kettering NN16 8RG* Tel (01536) 410586

CLARKE, Bernard Ronald. b 53. FRGS. Ridley Hall Cam 74. **d** 77 **p** 78. C Leigh Park *Portsm* 77-78; C Petersfield w Sheet 78-81; Chapl RN from 81; Dir of Ords RN 93-03. *Royal Naval Chaplaincy Service, Room 205, Victory Building, HM Naval Base, Portsmouth PO1 3LS* Tel (023) 9272 7900 Fax 9272 7111

CLARKE, Mrs Caroline Anne. b 44. Girton Coll Cam BA75 MA79 K Coll Lon PGCE76. SEITE 97. **d** 00 **p** 01. NSM Clapham H Trin and St Pet *S'wark* from 00. *42 The Chase, London SW4 0NH* Tel (020) 7622 0765 Mobile 07808-858674 Fax (020) 7652 4555 E-mail carolineclarke@lineone.net

CLARKE, Charles David. b 37. Univ of Wales BA76 MA93 PhD98 Cam Univ DipEd77 MEd Lambeth MA95 LCP77. St Mich Coll Llan 88. **d** 90 **p** 91. C Whitchurch *Llan* 90-93; V Graig 93-96; P-in-c Cilfynydd 93-96; TV Cyncoed *Mon* 96-98; R Neath w Llantwit *Llan* 98-01; TR Neath 01-02; rtd 02. *Lough Cutra, 11 Davies Andrews Road, Tonna, Neath SA11 1EU* Tel (01639) 638049

CLARKE, Miss Christine Vera. b 45. Lon Univ CertEd66 Bris Univ MSc00. Qu Coll Birm 79. **dss** 81 **d** 87 **p** 94. Bris St Mary Redcliffe w Temple etc *Bris* 81-86; Ind Chapl 86-95; NSM Westbury-on-Trym St Alb 94-95; P-in-c Wraxall *B & W* 95-97; R 97-03; rtd 03; Perm to Offic *B & W* from 03. *32 St Andrew's Mews, Wells BA5 2LB* Tel (01749) 673675

CLARKE, Canon Christopher George. b 43. Sarum Th Coll 67. **d** 68 **p** 69. C Sprowston *Nor* 68-72; V Hemsby 72-77; V Sutton Courtenay w Appleford *Ox* 77-84; TR Bracknell 84-97; RD Bracknell 90-96; Hon Can Ch Ch from 95; P-in-c Sonning 97-98; V from 98. *The Vicarage, Thames Street, Sonning, Reading RG4 6UR* Tel 0118-969 3298 E-mail chris@cgc.fsnet.co.uk

CLARKE, Daniel. b 17. TCD BA39 MA44 BD66. TCD Div Sch 39. **d** 41 **p** 42. C Dublin St Bart *D & G* 41-44; Dioc C Killaloe *L & K* 44-46; Chapl Roscrea Hosp Inst 46-48; C-in-c Corbally 46-48; I Borrisokane 48-59; Asst Master Robert Bloomfield Sch Shefford 59-62; Hd Relig Studies Reigate Gr Sch 62-82; Chapl 75-84; Chapl Reigate St Mary's Sch 85-92; Hon Chapl 92-97; rtd 97; Perm to Offic *S'wark* 66-80 and from 85. *4 Orchard Way, Reigate RH2 8DY* Tel (01737) 246169

CLARKE, Canon David George Alexander. b 23. TCD BA47 MA51 BD55 PhD57. **d** 48 **p** 49. C Dromore *Clogh* 48-49; P-in-c Drum 49-50; I Cleenish w Killoe *K, E & A* 50-51; I Clogh 52-54; C Abbeystrewry *C, C & R* 55-57; TR Usworth *Dur* 57-61; I Kilrossanty *C & O* 61-73; Preb Newcastle St Patr Cathl Dublin 65-89; Prec Waterford and Lismore *C & O* 67-73; Dean Cashel 73-83; I Cashel St Jo 73-83; I Ballymascanlan w Creggan, Forkhill etc *Arm* 83-89; rtd 89; Lic to Offic *Arm* from 90; Lic to Offic *D & G* from 90. *2 Ashley Court, Warrenpoint, Newry BT34 3RN* Tel (028) 3077 2416

CLARKE, David James. b 55. Univ of Wales (Abth) BSc(Econ)77 Keele Univ MA78 PhD83. Trin Coll Bris DipTh84 **d** 84 **p** 85. C Cardigan w Mwnt and Y Ferwig *St D* 84-87; P-in-c Llansantffraed and Llanbadarn Trefeglwys etc 87-88; V 88-91; Chapl Coll of SS Mark and Jo Plymouth *Ex* 91-96; V Lindfield *Chich* from 96. *The Vicarage, High Street, Lindfield, Haywards Heath RH16 2HR* Tel (01444) 482286

CLARKE, Denis John. b 23. LNSM course. **d** 87 **p** 88. OLM Brothertoft Gp *Linc* 87-98; rtd 98; Perm to Offic *Linc* 98-01. *49 Punchbowl Lane, Boston PE21 8HU* Tel (01205) 363512

CLARKE, Douglas Charles. b 33. Bps' Coll Cheshunt 65. **d** 66 **p** 67. C Chingford SS Pet and Paul *Chelmsf* 66-72; V Romford Ascension Collier Row 72-79; V Bembridge *Portsm* 79-83; V Bournemouth St Mary *Win* 83-87; R High Wych and Gilston w Eastwick *St Alb* 87-00; rtd 00; Perm to Offic *Linc* and *St Alb* from 00. *36 Tennyson Drive, Bourne PE10 9WD* Tel (01778) 394840

CLARKE, Dudley Barrington. b 22. OBE. Em Coll Cam BA46 MA48 PhD. Ridley Hall Cam 46. **d** 48 **p** 49. C Aldershot H Trin *Guildf* 48-50; Chapl Monkton Combe Sch Bath 50-58; Australia from 59; rtd 87. *60 Duke Street, Sandy Bay, Tas, Australia 7005* Tel (0061) (02) 6224 0784 or 6220 2385

CLARKE, Duncan James Edward. b 54. Wycliffe Hall Ox 75. **d** 78 **p** 79. C Newport St Andr *Mon* 78-80; C Griffithstown 80-82; Trinidad and Tobago 82-84 and 95-99; NSM Fleckney and Kilby *Leic* 92-95; USPG 95-99; C Wednesfield *Lich* 99; TV 99-01; Asst Chapl HM Pris Wormwood Scrubs 01-03; Chapl HM Pris

---

Haverigg from 03. *HM Prison, North Lane, Haverigg, Millom LA18 4NA* Tel (01229) 713000 Mobile 07931-111276

CLARKE, Eric Samuel. b 26. Nottm Univ BSc51 St Cath Coll Ox BA69 MA69. Wycliffe Hall Ox 51. **d** 54 **p** 55. C Gedling *S'well* 54-57; C Nottingham St Pet and St Jas 57-69; Perm to Offic *Derby* 63-02; rtd 02. *Hillcrest, Cottington Mead, Sidmouth EX10 8HB*

CLARKE, Frank. b 21. St Jo Coll Nottm. **d** 85 **p** 87. NSM Farnsfield *S'well* 85-97; rtd 98. *Belvedere, Tippings Lane, Farnsfield, Newark NG22 8EP* Tel (01623) 882528

CLARKE, Capt Geoffrey. b 53. CA Tr Coll Dip Evang84 Trin Coll Bris DipHE94. **d** 97 **p** 98. C Belmont *Lon* 97-00; C Tonbridge SS Pet and Paul *Roch* from 00. *14 Salisbury Road, Tonbridge TN10 4PB* Tel (01732) 355200 Fax as telephone E-mail geoff.clarke@diocese-rochester.org

CLARKE, Geraldine Ann. b 46. Hockerill Coll of Educn CertEd68 ACP81. NTMTC 93. **d** 96 **p** 97. NSM Aldersbrook *Chelmsf* 96-01; TR Becontree S from 01. *St Martin's Vicarage, Goresbrook Road, Dagenham RM9 6UX* Tel (020) 8592 0967 Fax as telephone E-mail ann.clarke@virgin.net

CLARKE, Harold George. b 29. St D Coll Lamp 58. **d** 61 **p** 62. C Ebbw Vale Ch Ch *Mon* 61-64; C Roath St German *Llan* 64-73; Chapl Wales Poly 73-74; V Glyntaff 73-84; V Roath St Martin 84-00; RD Cardiff 89-99; Can Llan Cathl 91-99; rtd 00. *12 St Margaret's Crescent, Cardiff CF23 5AU* Tel (029) 2046 2280

CLARKE, Harold Godfrey Codrington. *See* CODRINGTON CLARKE, Harold Godfrey

CLARKE, Hilary James. b 41. JP. Univ of Wales (Lamp) BA64 Ox Univ DipEd65. St Steph Ho Ox 64. **d** 66 **p** 67. C Kibworth Beauchamp *Leic* 66-68; Chapl to the Deaf 68-71; Prin Officer Ch Miss for Deaf Walsall 71-73; Prin Officer & Sec Leic and Co Miss for the Deaf 73-89; Hon C Leic St Anne *Leic* 73-98; TV Leic H Spirit 82-99; Hon Can Leic Cathl 88-96; Bp's Press Relns and Dio Communications Officer 95-96; Sec Gen Syn Coun for the Deaf 88-02; rtd 02. *Visible Communications, 5 Castle Street, Kendal LA9 7AB* Tel 07730-02570 (mobile)

CLARKE, Jason Philip. b 66. Lon Hosp BDS. Oak Hill Th Coll. **d** 01 **p** 02. C Fulwood *Sheff* from 01. *50 Brooklands Crescent, Sheffield S10 4GG* Tel 0114-230 1588 E-mail jason@fulwoodchurch.co.uk

CLARKE, Jason Scott. b 65. Leeds Univ BA87. Coll of Resurr Mirfield 89. **d** 91 **p** 92. C Hendon St Mary *Lon* 91-95; V Enfield St Geo 95-01; V Ditchling *Chich* from 01. *The Vicarage, West Street, Ditchling, Hassocks BN6 8TS* Tel (01273) 843165

CLARKE, John Charles. b 31. St Jo Coll Nottm 91. **d** 92 **p** 93. NSM Winshill *Derby* 92-95; P-in-c Stanley 95-98; rtd 98; Perm to Offic *Win* from 98. *5 The Tyleshades, Tadburn, Romsey SO51 5RJ* Tel (01794) 523945

CLARKE, Canon John David Maurice. b 60. **d** 89 **p** 90. C Dublin Whitechurch *D & G* 89-92; Asst Chapl St Vin Hosp Donnybrook 89-92; I Navan w Kentstown, Tara, Slane, Painestown etc *M & K* from 92; Can Meath from 00; Can Kildare Cathl from 00. *The Rectory, Boyne Road, Navan, Co Meath, Irish Republic* Tel (00353) (46) 902 1172 E-mail johndmclark@eircom.net

CLARKE, Canon John Martin. b 52. Edin Univ BD76 Hertf Coll Ox BA89 MA89. Edin Th Coll 73. **d** 76 **p** 77. C Kenton Ascension *Newc* 76-79; Prec St Ninian's Cathl Perth *St And* 79-82; Info Officer to Scottish Episc Gen Syn 82-87; Greece 87-88; V Battersea St Mary *S'wark* 89-96; Prin Ripon Coll Cuddesdon from 97; Can and Preb Linc Cathl *Linc* from 00. *Ripon College, Cuddesdon, Oxford OX44 9HP* Tel (01865) 874404

CLARKE, John Patrick Hatherley. b 46. Pemb Coll Ox BA68 Man Univ MBA73. St Jo Coll Nottm DipTh83. **d** 83 **p** 84. C Leic H Trin w St Jo *Leic* 83-87; C Selly Park St Steph and St Wulstan *Birm* 87-92; Hon C Woking St Mary *Guildf* 92-94; V Greenham *Ox* from 94. *Greenham Vicarage, New Road, Greenham, Newbury RG19 8RZ* Tel (01635) 41075

CLARKE, Canon John Percival. b 44. TCD BA67 MA98. **d** 69 **p** 70. C Belfast St Simon *Conn* 69-72; C Monkstown *D & G* 72-76; Asst Chapl TCD 76-78; I Durrus *C, C & R* 79-82; I Carrigrohane Union 82-89; Tanzania 89-92; I Wicklow w Killiskey *D & G* from 92; Abp's Dom Chapl 95-97; Can Ch Ch Cathl Dublin from 97. *The Rectory, Wicklow, Irish Republic* Tel (00353) (404) 67132

CLARKE, John Philip. b 31. Trin Hall Cam BA54 MA62. Linc Th Coll. **d** 57 **p** 58. C Walworth Lady Marg w St Mary *S'wark* 57-59; C Warlingham w Chelsham and Farleigh 59-62; C Mottingham St Andr 62-67; C Eltham Park St Luke 67-72; Chapl Leeds Gen Infirmary 72-91; C Far Headingley St Chad *Ripon* 91-96; Bp's Adv on Chr Healing 91-96; rtd 96; Perm to Offic *Ripon* from 96. *2 Raikes View, Wilsill, Harrogate HG3 5EG* Tel (01423) 711646

CLARKE, Mrs Joy Irene. b 44. LNSM course 96. **d** 98 **p** 02. OLM Ditton St Mich w St Thos *Liv* from 98. *55 Spinney Avenue, Widnes WA8 8LB* Tel 0151-424 8747

CLARKE, Judith Irene. b 46. SRN67 SCM69. EAMTC 97. **d** 00 **p** 01. NSM Shingay Gp of Par *Ely* 00-02; P-in-c Gt Staughton from 02. *St Andrew's Vicarage, Causeway, Great Staughton, St Neots PE19 5BF* Tel (01480) 861112

✠**CLARKE, The Rt Revd Kenneth Herbert.** b 49. TCD BA71. **d** 72 **p** 73 **c** 01. C Magheralin *D & D* 72-75; C Dundonald 75-78; Chile 78-81; I Crinken *D & G* 82-86; I Coleraine *Conn* 86-01; Chmn SAMS (Ireland) from 94; Can Conn Cathl 96-98; Adn Dalriada 98-01; Bp K, E & A from 01. *48 Carrickfern, Co Cavan, Irish Republic* Tel (00353) (49) 437 2759 Fax 436 2829 E-mail ken@atnaf.freeserve.co.uk *or* bishop@kilmore.anglican.org

CLARKE, Canon Margaret Geraldine. b 33. Dalton Ho Bris 62. **dss** 68 **d** 87 **p** 94. Wells St Thos w Horrington *B & W* 68-74; Easthampstead *Ox* 74-94; Par Dn 87-94; C 94; Hon Can Ch Ch 90-94; rtd 94; Hon C Bracknell *Ox* from 97. *Hermon, London Road, Bracknell RG12 2XH* Tel (01344) 427451

CLARKE, Martin Geoffrey. b 45. Dur Univ BA66. Wells Th Coll 67. **d** 69 **p** 70. C Atherstone *Cov* 69-72; C Keresley and Coundon 72-75; R Scorborough w Leconfield *York* 75-79; P-in-c Lockington w Lund 78-79; R Lockington and Lund and Scorborough w Leconfield 79-81; R Romsley *Worc* 81-96; Chapl Halesowen Coll 81-96; P-in-c Walsham le Willows and Finningham w Westhorpe *St E* 96-99; P-in-c Badwell Ash w Gt Ashfield, Stowlangtoft etc 96-99; R Badwell and Walsham from 00. *The Rectory, The Causeway, Walsham-le-Willows, Bury St Edmunds IP31 3AB* Tel (01359) 259310

CLARKE, Martin Howard. b 47. AKC70. St Aug Coll Cant 70. **d** 71 **p** 72. C Saffron Walden w Wendens Ambo *Chelmsf* 71-74; C Ely 74-78; V Messing w Inworth *Chelmsf* 78-90; V Layer de la Haye 90-02; R Layer de la Haye and Layer Breton w Birch etc from 03. *The Vicarage, 45 Malting Green Road, Layer-de-la-Haye, Colchester CO2 0JJ* Tel (01206) 734243

CLARKE, Ms Mary Margaret. b 65. K Coll Lon BD86 AKC86. Linc Th Coll 89. **d** 89 **p** 94. Par Dn Northampton St Jas *Pet* 89-93; Chapl Nene Coll of HE Northn 92-93; TD Coventry Caludon *Cov* 93-94; TV 94-01; Perm to Offic *Lon* from 01. *1 Porchester Gardens, London W2 3LA* Tel (020) 7229 6359 E-mail mary-andrew@clarkewillson.fsnet.co.uk

CLARKE, Maurice Fulford Lovell. b 12. Clare Coll Cam BA34 MA38. Wells Th Coll 35. **d** 36 **p** 37. C Benwell St Jas *Newc* 36-46; CF (EC) 40-46; CF (TA) 48-54; Vice-Prin Sarum Th Coll 46-53; V Lewisham St Swithun *S'wark* 54-65; Chapl Hither Green Hosp 54-65; R Ashley *Lich* 65-77; P-in-c Hales 65-73; rtd 77; Perm to Offic *Heref* 77-99. *25 Ramsay Hall, 11-13 Byron Road, Worthing BN11 3HN* Tel (01903) 201830

CLARKE, Maurice Harold. b 30. K Alfred's Coll Win CertEd56 Sussex Univ MA79 LCP69. Cuddesdon Coll 65. **d** 67 **p** 68. Hd Master Co Sec Sch Cowplain (Lower Sch) 67-72; Hon C Waterlooville *Portsm* 67-70; Hon C Fareham SS Pet and Paul 70-72; Hon C Higham and Merston *Roch* 72-83; Dep Hd Master Thamesview High Sch 72-80; Hd Master Eltham Green Comp Sch 80-83; V Hamble le Rice *Win* 83-90; rtd 91; Perm to Offic *Win* from 91; *Chich* from 92. *10 Worcester Road, Chichester PO19 8DJ* Tel (01243) 775646

CLARKE, Michael. b 39. Ely Th Coll 60. **d** 62 **p** 63. C Stoneham *Win* 62-64; C N Greenford All Hallows *Lon* 64-69; Hon C Milton *Portsm* 69-74; Chapl St Jas Hosp Portsm 69-91; Chapl Hurstpierpoint Coll 91-92; R Highnam, Lassington, Rudford, Tibberton etc *Glouc* 92-98; rtd 99; Perm to Offic *Glouc* 99-01; *Portsm* from 02. *Little Barns, 77 Fishbourne Lane, Ryde PO33 4EX* Tel (01983) 883858

CLARKE, Neil Malcolm. b 53. Solicitor 79. WMMTC 89. **d** 92 **p** 93. NSM Desborough, Brampton Ash, Dingley and Braybrooke *Pet* from 92. *53 Breakleys Road, Desborough, Kettering NN14 2PT* Tel (01536) 760667

CLARKE, Nicholas John. b 57. Lon Univ BA78 Lon Inst of Educn PGCE80. Ridley Hall Cam 95. **d** 97 **p** 98. C Attleborough *Cov* 97-00; V Fillongley and Corley from 00. *The Vicarage, Holbeche Crescent, Fillongley, Coventry CV7 8ES* Tel (01676) 540320 E-mail cool.clarkes@virgin.net

CLARKE, Norman. b 28. Keble Coll Ox BA52 MA58. St Steph Ho Ox 52. **d** 54 **p** 55. C Ellesmere Port *Ches* 54-57; C Kettering St Mary *Pet* 57-60; Ghana 60-62; C Friern Barnet All SS *Lon* 62-63; Lic to Offic *Leic* 63-74; C Knighton St Mary Magd 74-81; Dioc Communications Officer 81-88; P-in-c Sproughton w Burstall *St E* 81-88; P-in-c Dunsford and Doddiscombsleigh *Ex* 88-95; P-in-c Cheriton Bishop 88-95; rtd 95; Perm to Offic *Ex* from 95; RD Ottery from 02. *78 Malden Road, Sidmouth EX10 9NA* Tel (01395) 515849

CLARKE, Oswald Reeman. b 12. Liv Univ BA35 St Cath Soc Ox BA37 MA40. Ripon Hall Ox 34. **d** 36 **p** 37. C Whitehaven Ch Ch w H Trin *Carl* 36-37; C Addingham 37-38; Hon C Carl H Trin 38-39; C Wavertree St Mary *Liv* 39-43; P-in-c Widnes St Mary 43-44; V Liv St Sav 44-53; V Tulse Hill H Trin *S'wark* 53-58; V Upper Chelsea St Simon *Lon* 58-85; rtd 85; Perm to Offic *Lon* 85-90; P-in-c St Mary Abchurch from 90. *14 Down, Morden College, 19 St Germans Place, London SE3 0PW* Tel (020) 8293 1181

CLARKE, Canon Peter. b 25. Lon Univ BSc49 St Chad's Coll Dur DipTh51. **d** 51 **p** 52. C Linc St Giles *Linc* 51-53; C Gt Grimsby St Mary and St Jas 53-60; V Linc All SS 60-68; V Bardney 68-75; V Apley w Stainfield 68-75; V Linc St Nic w St Jo Newport 75-88;

RD Christianity 78-85; Can and Preb Linc Cathl 79-99; rtd 88; Perm to Offic *Linc* 88-00. *1 North Croft, Saxilby, Lincoln LN1 2PU* Tel (01522) 702795

CLARKE, Preb Peter Gerald. b 38. Cuddesdon Coll 74. **d** 76 **p** 77. Hon C Marston Magna w Rimpton *B & W* 76-79; Hon C Queen Camel, Marston Magna, W Camel, Rimpton etc 79-87; Hon C Chilton Cantelo, Ashington, Mudford, Rimpton etc 87-88; R Tintinhull w Chilthorne Domer, Yeovil Marsh etc 88-94; TV Weston-super-Mare Cen Par 94-95; V Weston super Mare All SS and St Sav from 96; Preb Wells Cathl from 02. *All Saints' Vicarage, 46 Manor Road, Weston-super-Mare BS23 2SU* Tel (01934) 623230 E-mail peter g clarke@ntlworld.com

CLARKE, Peter John. b 36. Qu Coll Ox BA60 MA64 Lon Univ BD79. Clifton Th Coll 62. **d** 62 **p** 63. C Upper Tulse Hill St Matthias *S'wark* 62-64; CMJ 64-96; Dir for S America 88-96; rtd 97. *Pedro Moran 4414, C 1419 HLH Buenos Aires, Argentina* Tel (0054) (11) 4501 4629 Fax as telephone

CLARKE, Philip John. b 44. Bris Univ BA65 Univ of Wales (Abth) DipEd66. N Ord Course 84. **d** 87 **p** 88. NSM Crewe Ch Ch and St Pet *Ches* 87-88; NSM Coppenhall 88-90; Lic to Offic 90-91; C Altrincham St Geo 91-95; C Odd Rode 95-97; P-in-c Peterchurch w Vowchurch, Turnastone and Dorstone *Heref* 97-98; V Llansantffraid Glyn Ceirog and Llanarmon etc *St As* from 98. *The Vicarage, High Street, Glyn Ceiriog, Llangollen LL20 7EH* Tel (01691) 718245 E-mail pjclarke@barclays.net

CLARKE, Richard Leon. b 37. Sarum Th Coll 62. **d** 65 **p** 66. C Fordington *Sarum* 65-68; C Haywards Heath St Rich *Chich* 68-72; C Goring-by-Sea 72-76; P-in-c Portslade St Andr 76-77; P-in-c Southwick St Pet 76-77; V Portslade St Pet and St Andr 77-79; R Clayton w Keymer 79-02; RD Hurst 90-98; rtd 03. *107 Freshfield Road, Brighton BN2 0BL* Tel (01273) 628006

✠**CLARKE, The Most Revd Richard Lionel.** b 49. TCD BA71 MA79 PhD90 K Coll Lon BD75 AKC75. **d** 75 **p** 76 **c** 96. C Holywood *D & D* 75-77; C Dublin St Bart w Leeson Park *D & G* 77-79; Dean of Residence TCD 79-84; I Bandon Union *C, C & R* 84-93; Dir of Ords 85-93; Cen Dir of Ords 82-97; Can Cork and Ross Cathls 91-93; Dean Cork 93-96; I Cork St Fin Barre's Union 93-96; Chapl Univ Coll Cork 93-96; Bp M & K from 96. *Bishop's House, Moyglare, Maynooth, Co Kildare, Irish Republic* Tel (00353) (1) 628 9354 Fax 628 9696 E-mail bishop@meath.anglican.org

CLARKE, Robert George. b 36. Natal Univ PhD83. Cranmer Hall Dur BA65 DipTh67. **d** 67 **p** 68. C Basingstoke *Win* 67-70; S Africa from 71. *26 Somerset Street, Grahamstown, 6139 South Africa* Tel (0027) (046) 622 7803 E-mail bob@ecumedia.ru.ac.za

CLARKE, Robert Graham. b 28. S Dios Minl Tr Scheme 78. **d** 81 **p** 82. NSM Woolston *Win* 81-89; NSM Portswood St Denys 89-93; Chapl Torrevieja *Eur* 93-95; Perm to Offic *Win* and *Eur* from 95. *10 River Green, Hamble, Southampton SO31 4JA* Tel (023) 8045 4230

CLARKE, Robert Michael. b 45. Oak Hill Th Coll BD71 Sarum & Wells Th Coll 78. **d** 78 **p** 79. Hon C Glastonbury St Jo w Godney *B & W* 78-81; Asst Hd Master Edington Sch 78-81; Chapl Felsted Sch 81-84; Asst Chapl and Hd Master 85-92; Hd Master Brocksford Hall 92-94; Chapl Seaford Coll Petworth 94-99; Hd Master Bredon School 99-00; Perm to Offic *Lich* from 01. *17 Top Street, Whittington, Oswestry SY11 4DR* Tel (01691) 662548

CLARKE, Robert Sydney. b 35. OBE00. AKC64 K Coll Lon MA65. **d** 65 **p** 66. C Hendon St Mary *Lon* 65-69; C Langley Marish *Ox* 69-70; Chapl New Cross Hosp Wolv 70-74; Chapl Dorchester Hosps 74-79; Sen Chapl Westmr Hosp Lon 80-85; Sen Chapl Westm Hosp 88-94; Sen Chapl Win and Eastleigh Healthcare NHS Trust 94-00; Chapl to The Queen from 87; Sec and Dir Tr Gen Syn Hosp Chapl Coun 94-00; rtd 00; Perm to Offic *Lon* and *S'wark* from 95. *3 Brook Court, Middlebridge Street, Romsey SO51 8HR* Tel (01794) 524215

CLARKE, Robert William. b 56. TCD DipTh83. **d** 83 **p** 84. C Cloughfern *Conn* 83-85; C Drumragh w Mountfield *D & R* 85-87; I Edenderry w Clanabogan from 87. *Edenderry Rectory, 91 Crevenagh Road, Omagh BT79 0EZ* Tel (028) 8224 5525

CLARKE, Roger David. b 58. Man Univ BA Ox Univ MA. Ripon Coll Cuddesdon 80. **d** 83 **p** 84. C Frodsham *Ches* 83-86; C Wilmslow 86-88; V High Lane 88-93; V Heald Green St Cath 93-99; R W Kirby St Bridget from 99. *St Bridget's Rectory, Rectory Road, Wirral CH48 7HL* Tel 0151-625 5229

CLARKE, Ronald George. b 31. Oak Hill Th Coll. **d** 64 **p** 65. C Carlton-in-the-Willows *S'well* 64-68; V Bestwood St Matt 68-76; V Barnsbury St Andr w St Thos and St Matthias *Lon* 76-77; V Barnsbury St Andr 77-78; V Barnsbury St Andr w H Trin 79-80; P-in-c Battle Bridge All SS w Pentonville St Jas 79-80; V Barnsbury St Andr and All SS 81-86; TR Bath Twerton-on-Avon *B & W* 86-94; rtd 94; P-in-c Churchstanton, Buckland St Mary and Otterford *B & W* 94-97; Perm to Offic from 97. *Myrtle Cottage, 35 High Street, Chard TA20 1QL* Tel (01460) 65495

CLARKE, Steven Peter. b 61. Oak Hill Th Coll DipHE95. **d** 97 **p** 98. C Frinton *Chelmsf* 97-01; C Woodford Wells from 01.

80 Montalt Road, Woodford Green IG8 9SS Tel (020) 8505 1431
E-mail revsclarke@aol.com

CLARKE, Thomas Percival. b 15. Univ of Wales BA39. Lich Th Coll 39. **d** 41 **p** 42. C Cardiff St Mary *Llan* 41-45; C Walcot *B & W* 45-48; C Bathwick w Woolley 48-49; V Hendford 49-52; Area Sec (E Counties) UMCA 52-56; Metrop Area Sec UMCA 56-59; C S Kensington St Steph *Lon* 56-59; V Blackheath All SS *S'wark* 59-72; Chapl Leighton Hosp Crewe 72-73; Chapl Charing Cross Hosp Lon 73-82; rtd 82. *Flat 1, 29 Westbourne Road, Penarth, Cardiff CF64 3HA* Tel (029) 2030 8864

CLARKE, Timothy John. b 69. Jes Coll Cam BA91 MA95 Barrister 92. WMMTC 00. **d** 03. NSM Birm Cathl *Birm* from 03. *72 Victoria Road, Harborne, Birmingham B17 0AE* Tel 0121-427 7193 E-mail timclarke@waitrose.com

CLARKE, Ms Valerie Diane. b 45. Open Univ BA00. N Ord Course 91. **d** 95 **p** 96. C Sherburn in Elmet w Saxton *York* 95-97; C Brayton 97-99; Chapl Scargill Ho from 00. *Scargill House, Kettlewell, Skipton BD23 5HU* Tel (01756) 760234, 760341, or 796114 Mobile 07974-698468

CLARKE, Vernon Douglas. b 18. Jes Coll Cam BA48 MA50. Bps' Coll Cheshunt 47. **d** 49 **p** 50. C Bulwell St Mary *S'well* 49-51; C Ambleside w Rydal *Carl* 51-54; V Aspatria 54-63; V Millom H Trin 63-71; V Cockermouth All SS w Ch 71-74; P-in-c Kirkland 75-83; P-in-c Gt Salkeld 79-80; C Gt Salkeld w Lazonby 80-83; rtd 83; Perm to Offic *Carl* 84-93. *Birchfield, Great Salkeld, Penrith CA11 9LW* Tel (01768) 898380

CLARKE, Mrs Yvonne Veronica. b 58. CA Tr Coll. **dss** 86 **d** 87 **p** 94. Nunhead St Silas *S'wark* 86-90; Par Dn 87-90; Par Dn Nunhead St Antony w St Silas 90-91; Par Dn Mottingham St Andr 91-94; C 94-98; V Spring Park All SS from 98. *All Saints' Vicarage, 1 Farm Drive, Croydon CR0 8HU* Tel (020) 8777 2775

CLARKSON, The Ven Alan Geoffrey. b 34. Ch Coll Cam BA57 MA61. Wycliffe Hall Ox 57. **d** 59 **p** 60. C Penn *Lich* 59-60; C Oswestry St Oswald 60-63; C Wrington *B & W* 63-65; V Chewton Mendip w Emborough 65-74; Dioc Ecum Officer 65-75; V Glastonbury St Jo w Godney 74-84; P-in-c W Pennard 80-84; P-in-c Meare 81-84; P-in-c Glastonbury St Benedict 82-84; V Glastonbury w Meare, W Pennard and Godney 84; Hon Can Win Cathl *Win* 84-99; Adn Win 84-99; V Burley Ville 84-99; rtd 99; Perm to Offic *Chelmsf* and *Ely* from 99. *Cantilena, 4 Harefield Rise, Linton, Cambridge CB1 6LS* Tel (01223) 892988 E-mail aclarkso@fish.co.uk

CLARKSON, David James. b 42. St Andr Univ BSc66. N Ord Course 85. **d** 88 **p** 89. NSM Slaithwaite w E Scammonden *Wakef* 88-89; C Morley St Pet w Churwell 89-91; R Cumberworth w Denby Dale 91-93; P-in-c Denby 91-93; R Cumberworth, Denby and Denby Dale 93-02; rtd 03. *Waulkmill Cottage, Westerkirk, Langholm DG13 0NJ* Tel (01387) 370279

CLARKSON, Eric George. b 22. St Jo Coll Dur BA48 DipTh50. **d** 50 **p** 51. C Birkdale St Jo *Liv* 50-52; C Grassendale 52-54; PC W Derby St Luke 54-66; V Blackb St Mich *Blackb* 66-75; V Blackb St Mich w St Jo 75; V Chapeltown *Sheff* 75-86; C Ranmoor 86-87; V Crosspool 87-92; rtd 92; Perm to Offic *York* from 92. *2 Harewood Drive, Filey YO14 0DE* Tel (01723) 513957 Fax as telephone

CLARKSON, Geoffrey. b 35. AKC61. **d** 62 **p** 63. C Shildon *Dur* 62-65; Asst Chapl HM Pris Liv 65-66; Chapl HM Pris Borstal Feltham 66-71; Hon C Hampton St Mary *Lon* from 71; Development Officer Br Assn of Settlements 71-74; Chapl HM Rem Cen Ashford 88-90; Chapl HM Pris Coldingley 90-99; Chapl HM Pris Send 92-94; rtd 00. *109 Cambridge Road, Teddington TW11 8DF* Tel (020) 8977 1434 E-mail gfclarkson@aol.com

CLARKSON, Canon John Thomas. b 30. AKC53. St Boniface Warminster 54. **d** 54 **p** 55. C Luton St Sav *St Alb* 54-59; Australia 59-73 and from 77; Brotherhood of St Barn 59-64; R Mundingburra 64-72; V Dallington *Pet* 73-77; R W Wyalong St Barn 77-82; R Blayney Ch Ch 82-95; Hon Can Bathurst 95-96; rtd 96. *134 Mitre Street, Bathurst, NSW, Australia 2795* Tel (0061) (2) 6332 6032 E-mail clarkson@netwit.net.au

CLARKSON, Michael Livingston. b 48. California Univ BA70 Loyola Univ JD73. Wycliffe Hall Ox 87. **d** 89 **p** 90. C Kensington St Barn *Lon* 89-93; Min Oak Tree Angl Fellowship from 93. *41 South Parade, London W4 1JS* Tel (020) 8995 1562 Fax 8742 7801 E-mail mikec@oaktree.org.uk

CLARKSON, Canon Richard. b 33. Man Univ BSc54 Ball Coll Ox DPhil57. Oak Hill Th Coll 89. **d** 91 **p** 92. NSM Sunnyside w Bourne End *St Alb* from 91; RD Berkhamsted from 97; Hon Can St Alb from 02. *Kingsmead, Gravel Path, Berkhamsted HP4 2PH* Tel (01442) 873014 E-mail clarkson@rclarkson.u-net.com

CLARKSON, Richard Michael. b 38. St Jo Coll Dur BA60 DipTh62 Lanc Univ PGCE68. Cranmer Hall Dur 60. **d** 62 **p** 63. C St Annes *Blackb* 62-66; C Lancaster St Mary 66-68; Asst Master Kirkham Gr Sch 68-90; Asst Master Hurstpierpoint Coll 90-91; Asst Master St Mary's Hall Brighton 92-98; Chapl 96-98; rtd 93; Perm to Offic *Chich* 93-00. *121 College Lane, Hurstpierpoint, Hassocks BN6 9AF* Tel (01273) 834117

CLARKSON, Robert Christopher. b 32. Dur Univ BA53 DipEd54. S Dios Minl Tr Scheme 85. **d** 87 **p** 88. NSM Lower Dever Valley *Win* from 87. *27 Wrights Way, South Wonston, Winchester SO21 3HE* Tel (01962) 881692

CLARRIDGE, Donald Michael. b 41. DipOT86. Oak Hill Th Coll 63. **d** 66 **p** 67. C Newc St Barn and St Jude *Newc* 66-70; C Pennycross *Ex* 70-76; R Clayhanger 76-83; R Petton 76-83; R Huntsham 76-83; V Bampton 76-83. *5 Surrey Close, Tunbridge Wells TN2 5RF* Tel (01892) 533796

CLASBY, Michael Francis Theodore. b 37. Univ Coll Lon BA59. Chich Th Coll 59. **d** 61 **p** 62. C Leigh-on-Sea St Marg *Chelmsf* 61-64; C Forest Gate St Edm 64-69; V Walthamstow St Mich 69-70; Chapl Community of Sisters of the Love of God 87-89; Perm to Offic *St Alb* 87-89; NSM Hemel Hempstead 90-93; Perm to Offic 93-98; rtd 02. *14 Richmond Walk, St Albans AL4 9BA* Tel (01727) 853913

CLASPER, John. b 42. AKC67. **d** 68 **p** 69. C Leeds All Hallows w St Simon *Ripon* 68-71; C Hawksworth Wood 72-74; Ind Chapl *Dur* 74-97; TV Jarrow St Paul 75-77; TV Jarrow 77-91; Dioc Urban Development Officer 90-91; TR E Darlington 91-97; V Fenham St Jas and St Basil *Newc* 97-02; RD Newc W 98-02; rtd 03. *103 Warkworth Woods, Newcastle upon Tyne NE3 5RB* Tel 07710-078945 (mobile) E-mail john.clasper@virgin.net

CLASSON, Michael Campbell. b 32. TCD BA52 HDipEd54 MA55. CITC 87. **d** 89 **p** 91. NSM Conwal Union w Gartan *D & R* 89-90; NSM Ardara w Glencolumbkille, Inniskeel etc from 90. *Summy, Portnoo, Co Donegal, Irish Republic* Tel (00353) (74) 954 5242

CLATWORTHY, Jonathan Richard. b 48. Univ of Wales BA70. Sarum & Wells Th Coll 71. **d** 76 **p** 77. C Man Resurr *Man* 76-78; C Bolton St Pet 78-81; V Ashton St Pet 81-85; Chapl Sheff Univ *Sheff* 85-91; V Denstone w Ellastone and Stanton *Lich* 91-98; Chapl Liv Univ *Liv* 98-02; rtd 02. *9 Westward View, Aigburth, Liverpool L17 7EE* Tel 0151-727 6291 E-mail jonathan@clatworthy.org

CLAUSEN, John Frederick. b 37. Sarum Th Coll 65. **d** 68 **p** 69. C Kentish Town St Jo *Lon* 68-71; C Rainham *Roch* 71-77; R Stone 77-89; Lic to Dartford RD 89-02; rtd 02. *24 Spring Vale North, Dartford DA1 2LL*

CLAWSON, Derek George. b 35. AMCST62. Qu Coll Birm 63. **d** 66 **p** 67. C Ditton St Mich *Liv* 66-70; C Speke All SS 70-72; V Hindley Green 72-85; V Wigan St Mich 85-00; rtd 00. *20 Parklands Drive, Aspull, Wigan WN2 1ZA* Tel (01942) 830769

CLAY, Canon Colin Peter. b 32. Ch Coll Cam BA55 MA59. Em Coll Saskatoon Hon DD91 Wells Th Coll 55. **d** 57 **p** 58. C Malden St Jas *S'wark* 57-59; Canada from 59; C Sudbury Epiphany 59-60; R Sudbury St Jas 60-69; R Sudbury St Geo 60-64; R French River St Thos 64-69; Asst Prof RS Laurentian Univ 69-72; R Capreol St Alb 70-77; Chapl Saskatchewan Univ 77-00; Hon Can Saskatoon from 97; Interim St Jo Cathl 00-01; Hon Asst from 01. *812 Colony Street, Saskatoon SK, Canada, S7N 0S1* Tel (001) (306) 664 4628 E-mail clay@sask.usask.ca

CLAY, Canon Elizabeth Jane. b 50. Ridley Hall Cam. **dss** 86 **d** 87 **p** 94. Birstall *Wakef* 86-87; Hon Par Dn Lupset 87-90; Par Dn 90-94; C 94-96; Chapl HM Pris and YOI New Hall from 96; Hon Can Wakef Cathl *Wakef* from 00. *The Vicarage, Broadway, Lupset, Wakefield WF2 8AA* Tel (01924) 373088 Fax 840692

CLAY, Geoffrey. b 51. CertEd. Ridley Hall Cam. **d** 86 **p** 87. C Birstall *Wakef* 86-90; V Lupset from 90. *The Vicarage, Broadway, Lupset, Wakefield WF2 8AA* Tel (01924) 373088 Fax as telephone E-mail gjrstg@aol.com

CLAY, Peter Herbert. b 31. Lich Th Coll 62. **d** 64 **p** 65. C Ross *Heref* 64-67; C Leamington Priors All SS *Cov* 67-70; P-in-c Temple Grafton w Binton 70-73; V 73-75; P-in-c Exhall w Wixford 70-73; R 73-75; TV Cen Telford *Lich* 75-86; USPG 86-90; V Loughb Gd Shep *Leic* 90-96; rtd 96; Perm to Offic *Leic* from 96; Perm to Offic *Cov* from 96. *78 Eastlands Road, Rugby CV21 3RR* Tel (01788) 569138

CLAY, Timothy Francis. b 51. St Mark & St Jo Coll Lon BA85 Ealing Coll of Educn 89. Linc Th Coll 95. **d** 95 **p** 96. C Wickford and Runwell *Chelmsf* 95-98; C S Ockendon 98-01; C S Ockendon and Belhus Park 01-02; P-in-c Ashingdon w S Fambridge from 02. *The Rectory, Church Road, Rochford SS4 3HY* Tel (01702) 549318 E-mail tim@tclay.fslife.co.uk

CLAYDEN, David Edward. b 42. Oak Hill Th Coll 74. **d** 76 **p** 77. C Worksop St Jo *S'well* 76-79; V Clarborough w Hayton 79-84; C Bloxwich *Lich* 87-90; TV 90-93; TV Tollington *Lon* 93-99; P-in-c Thorndon w Rishangles, Stoke Ash, Thwaite etc *St E* 99-00; P-in-c Thornhams Magna and Parva, Gislingham and Mellis 99-00; R Gislingham and Thorndon from 00. *The Rectory, Standwell Green, Thorndon, Eye IP23 7JL* Tel (01379) 678603 E-mail davidclayden@cwcom.net

CLAYDON, Preb Graham Leonard. b 43. K Coll Lon BA65. Clifton Th Coll 66. **d** 68 **p** 69. C Walthamstow St Mary w St Steph *Chelmsf* 68-73; Hon C St Marylebone All So w SS Pet and Jo *Lon* 73-81; V Islington St Mary 81-99; C Highbury Ch Ch w St Jo and St Sav Lon 99-03; TV Hackney Marsh from 03; Preb St Paul's

Cathl from 92. *All Souls' Vicarage, Overbury Street, London E5 0AJ* Tel (020) 8986 5076
E-mail graham@lclaydon.fsnet.co.uk

CLAYDON, John Richard. b 38. St Jo Coll Cam BA61 MA65 Bris Univ DipTh72. Trin Coll Bris 71. **d** 73 **p** 74. C Finchley Ch Ch *Lon* 73-76; Asst Chapl K Edw Sch Witley 76-77; C Macclesfield St Mich *Ches* 77-81; V Marple All SS 81-91; CMJ Israel 91-99; V Blackb Redeemer *Blackb* 99-02; rtd 02. *54 Old Forge Road, Layer-de-la-Haye, Colchester CO2 0LH* Tel (01206) 734056
E-mail vicar@jrclaydon.dabsol.co.uk

CLAYTON, Adam. b 78. Keble Coll Ox BA99. Westcott Ho Cam 00. **d** 02 **p** 03. C Far Headingley St Chad *Ripon* from 02. *64 Becketts Park Crescent, Leeds LS6 3PF* Tel 0113-274 0946
E-mail revdaclayton@aol.com

CLAYTON, Canon Anthony Edwin Hay. b 36. Sarum Th Coll 61. **d** 63 **p** 64. C Tooting All SS *S'wark* 63-68; Perm to Offic *Leic* 69-74; Perm to Offic *S'well* 73-80; Hon C Lockington w Hemington *Leic* 74-80; P-in-c Eastwell 80-83; P-in-c Eaton 80-83; P-in-c Croxton Kerrial, Knipton, Harston, Branston etc 83-84; R 84-93; R High Framland Par 93-96; RD Framland 90-94; Hon Can *Leic* 95-00; rtd 97; Perm to Offic *Leic* 97-00. *18 Commerce Square, Nottingham NG1 1HS* Tel 0115-988 1920 Fax as telephone

CLAYTON, Geoffrey Buckroyd. b 26. Newc Univ BA67. Roch Th Coll 62. **d** 64 **p** 65. C Newc St Geo *Newc* 64-67; C Byker St Ant 67-68; Chapl Salonika *Eur* 68-69; C Cheddleton *Lich* 69-72; V Arbory *S & M* 72-97; RD Castletown 82-97; V Santan 88-97; rtd 97; Perm to Offic *St D* from 97. *Y Rheithordy, Llangeitho, Tregaron SY25 6TR* Tel (01974) 821388

CLAYTON, George Hamilton. b 52. Strathclyde Univ BSc65. S'wark Ord Course 90. **d** 93 **p** 94. NSM Send *Guildf* from 93. *137 Knightswood, Woking GU21 3PX* Tel (01483) 720698

CLAYTON, Canon John. b 11. Leeds Univ BA33 MA43. Wells Th Coll 34. **d** 35 **p** 36. C Dewsbury Moor *Wakef* 35-38; C Halifax St Jo Bapt 38-41; Lect 40-41; V Lupset 41-51; Chapl Snapethorpe Hosp 49-51; V Bolton St Jas *Bradf* 51-65; RD Calverley 56-65; V Otley 65-76; RD Otley 68-73; Hon Can Bradf Cathl 63-76; rtd 76; Perm to Offic *Bradf* and *Ripon* from 76. *10 Sandy Walk, Bramhope, Leeds LS16 9DW* Tel 0113-261 1388

CLAYTON, Melanie Yvonne. b 62. St Aid Coll Dur BA84 Victoria Univ (BC) MA85 Hertf Coll Ox DPhil89. WMMTC 91. **d** 94 **p** 95. C Penn *Lich* 94-97; TV Wolverhampton 97-98; TV Cen Wolverhampton from 98. *St Chad's Vicarage, Manlove Street, Wolverhampton WV3 0HG* Tel (01902) 426580
E-mail snap1@tinyworld.co.uk

CLAYTON, Norman James. b 24. AKC52. **d** 53 **p** 54. C Long Benton St Mary *Newc* 53-55; R Lomagundi S Rhodesia 55-60; Chapl St Geo Home Johannesburg 60-78; Dioc Communications Officer *Derby* 78-88; P-in-c Risley 78-87; R 87-89; rtd 89; Perm to Offic *Derby* and *S'well* from 89. *6 Allendale Avenue, Beeston, Nottingham NG9 6AN* Tel 0115-925 0060

CLAYTON, Sydney Cecil Leigh. b 38. Pemb Coll Ox BA62 MA65 Lon Univ BD65. Linc Th Coll. **d** 65 **p** 66. C Birch St Jas *Man* 65-68; Lect Bolton Par Ch 68-77; V Denshaw from 77. *The Vicarage, Huddersfield Road, Denshaw, Oldham OL3 5SB* Tel (01457) 874575

CLAYTON, William Alan. b 32. Liv Univ BSc54 Lon Univ BD60. **d** 63 **p** 64. C Wallasey St Hilary *Ches* 63-67; R Burton Agnes w Harpham *York* 67-69; V Batley St Thos *Wakef* 69-72; Lic to Offic *Ripon* 73-85; Hon C Grinton 75-85; R Barningham w Hutton Magna and Wycliffe 85-97; rtd 97; Perm to Offic *Newc* from 00. *Halidon View, 1 The Pastures, Tweedmouth, Berwick-upon-Tweed TD15 2NT*

CLAYTON-JONES, Roger Francis. b 39. AKC64. **d** 66 **p** 67. C Oxton *Ches* 66-69; Asst Chapl R Hosp Sch Holbrook 69-71; Jamaica 71-73; CF 73-93; Chapl St Mary's Sch Wantage from 93. *Alma House, 35 Newbury Street, Wantage OX12 8DJ* Tel (01235) 763617

CLEALL-HILL, Malcolm John. b 51. Salford Univ Man Metrop Univ. Dioc OLM tr scheme. **d** 01 **p** 02. OLM Chorlton-cum-Hardy St Werburgh *Man* from 01. *62 Buckingham Road, Chorlton cum Hardy, Manchester M21 0RP* Tel 0161-881 7024 *or* 247 2288
E-mail m.cleall-hill@mmu.ac.uk

CLEASBY, The Very Revd Thomas Wood Ingram. b 20. Magd Coll Ox BA47 MA47. Cuddesdon Coll. **d** 49 **p** 50. C Huddersfield St Pet *Wakef* 49-52; Abp's Dom Chapl *York* 52-56; C Nottingham St Mary *S'well* 56-63; Chapl Nottm Univ 56-63; V Chesterfield St Mary and All SS *Derby* 63-70; Hon Can Derby Cathl 63-78; Adn Chesterfield 63-78; R Morton 70-78; Dean Ches 78-86; rtd 86; Perm to Offic *Carl* from 86; *Bradf* from 87. *Low Barth, Dent, Sedbergh LA10 5SZ* Tel (01539) 625476

CLEATON, John. b 39. Open Univ BA86. S Dios Minl Tr Scheme 89. **d** 92 **p** 93. NSM Wareham *Sarum* from 92. *1 Avon Drive, Wareham BH20 4EL* Tel (01929) 553149

CLEAVER, Gerald. b 20. Lon Univ BSc52. St Jo Coll Nottm 85. **d** 86 **p** 87. NSM W Bridgford *S'well* 86-96; NSM Clifton from 96. *62 South Road, Nottingham NG2 7AH* Tel 0115-981 0196

CLEAVER, Gordon Philip. b 29. SW Minl Tr Course. **d** 78 **p** 79. NSM St Ruan w St Grade *Truro* 78-86; Perm to Offic from 86.

Bryn-Mor, Cadgwith, Ruan Minor, Helston TR12 7JZ Tel (01326) 290328

CLEAVER, John Martin. b 42. K Coll Lon BD64 AKC64. St Boniface Warminster 61. **d** 65 **p** 66. C Bexley St Mary *Roch* 65-69; C Ealing St Steph Castle Hill *Lon* 69-71; P-in-c Bostall Heath *Roch* 71-76; V Green Street Green 76-85; Primary Adv Lon Dioc Bd for Schs *Lon* 85-92; V Teddington St Mary w St Alb from 92. *The Vicarage, 11 Twickenham Road, Teddington TW11 8AQ* Tel (020) 8977 2767

CLEAVER, Stuart Douglas. b 46. ACIS. Oak Hill Th Coll. **d** 83 **p** 84. C Portsdown *Portsm* 83-86; C Blendworth w Chalton w Idsworth etc 86-88; P-in-c Whippingham w E Cowes 88-98; R 98-01; rtd 01. *The Crest, Soake Road, Waterlooville PO7 6HY* Tel (023) 9226 2277

CLEEVE, Admire William. b 43. ACIS78 MBIM81 CPPS83 Ox Univ MTh96. Sierra Leone Th Hall 78. **d** 82 **p** 83. Sierra Leone 82-86; NSM Douglas St Geo and St Barn *S & M* 87-91; TV Langley Marish *Ox* 91-97; P-in-c Tilehurst St Mary 97-02; rtd 02. *St Paul's Episcopal Church, 61 Wood Street, PO Box 165, Hopkinton, MA 01748, USA* Tel (001) (508) 497 6388
E-mail admirecleeve@pastors.com

CLEEVE, Martin. b 43. ACP67 Open Univ BA80. Bp Otter Coll TCert65 Oak Hill Th Coll 69. **d** 72 **p** 73. C Margate H Trin *Cant* 72-76; V Southminster *Chelmsf* 76-86; Teacher Castle View Sch Canvey Is 86-91; Perm to Offic 91-99; Hd RE Bromfords Sch Wickford 91-94; Hd RE Deanes Sch Thundersley 94-98; P-in-c Gt Mongeham w Ripple and Sutton by Dover *Cant* from 99. *The Rectory, Northbourne Road, Great Mongeham, Deal CT14 0HB* Tel (01304) 360170
E-mail martincleeve@mcleeve.freereserve.co.uk

CLEEVES, David John. b 56. Univ of Wales (Lamp) BA Fitzw Coll Cam MA85. Westcott Ho Cam. **d** 82 **p** 83. C Cuddington *Guildf* 82-85; C Dorking w Ranmore 85-87; V Ewell St Fran 87-94; P-in-c Rotherfield w Mark Cross *Chich* 94-01; V Masham and Healey *Ripon* from 01. *The Vicarage, Rodney Terrace, Masham, Ripon HG4 4JA* Tel (01765) 689255

CLEGG, David Kneeshaw. b 46. N Ord Course 77. **d** 80 **p** 81. C Briercliffe *Blackb* 80-83; Chapl Lancs (Preston) Poly 83-89; rtd 89; Perm to Offic *Dur* from 89. *126 York Crescent, Newton Hall, Durham DH1 5QS*

CLEGG, Herbert. b 24. Fitzw Ho Cam BA59 MA63 Bris Univ MA65. Sarum Th Coll 52. **d** 54 **p** 55. C Street *B & W* 54-56; Perm to Offic *Ely* 56-59; Tutor St Pet Th Coll Jamaica 59-61; R Newington Bagpath w Kingscote and Ozleworth *Glouc* 61-65; Prin Bp Willis Coll Uganda 65-69; P-in-c Aldsworth *Glouc* 70-75; P-in-c Sherborne w Windrush 70-75; V Marcham w Garford *Ox* 75-83; R Chipping Warden w Edgcote and Aston le Walls *Pet* 83-89; rtd 89; C Ox St Giles and SS Phil and Jas w St Marg *Ox* 90-94. *3 Case Gardens, Seaton EX12 2AP* Tel (01297) 23103

CLEGG, Jeffrey Thomas. *See* MIDDLEMISS, Jeffrey Thomas

CLEGG, Canon John Anthony Holroyd. b 44. Kelham Th Coll 65. **d** 70 **p** 71. C St Annes *Blackb* 70-74; C Lancaster St Mary 74-76; V Lower Darwen St Jas 76-80; TV Shaston *Sarum* 80-86; Chapl HM Youth Cust Cen Guys Marsh 80-86; R Poulton-le-Sands w Morecambe St Laur *Blackb* 86-97; RD Lancaster 89-94; TR Cartmel Peninsula *Carl* from 97; RD Windermere from 01; Hon Can Carl Cathl from 01. *The Rectory, Hampsfell Road, Grange-over-Sands LA11 6BE* Tel (01539) 532757 Fax as telephone
E-mail anthonyclegg@care4free.net

CLEGG, John Lovell. b 48. Qu Coll Ox BA70 MA74. Trin Coll Bris DipTh75. **d** 75 **p** 76. C Barrow St Mark *Carl* 75-79; R S Levenshulme *Man* 79-98; P-in-c Blackley St Paul from 98. *St Paul's Rectory, Erskine Road, Manchester M9 6RB* Tel 0161-740 1518

CLEGG, Patricia Ann. b 45. STETS 96. **d** 99 **p** 00. NSM Harnham *Sarum* from 99. *28 Bishop's Drive, Salisbury SP2 8NZ* Tel (01722) 333573 Fax as telephone
E-mail pat@newsarum.fsnet.co.uk

CLEGG, Peter Douglas. b 49. Sarum & Wells Th Coll 83. **d** 85 **p** 86. C Hangleton *Chich* 85-88; C-in-c Portslade Gd Shep CD 88-94; V Portslade Gd Shep from 94. *The Vicarage, 35 Stanley Avenue, Portslade, Brighton BN41 2WH* Tel (01273) 419518

CLEGG, Roger Alan. b 46. St Jo Coll Dur BA68 Nottm Univ CertEd69 DipTh76. St Jo Coll Nottm 75. **d** 78 **p** 79. C Harwood *Man* 78-81; TV Sutton St Jas and Wawne *York* 81-87; V Kirk Fenton w Kirkby Wharfe and Ulleskelfe from 87; OCF from 87; Chapl HM Pris Askham Grange from 95. *The Vicarage, Church Street, Church Fenton, Tadcaster LS24 9RD* Tel (01937) 557387
E-mail rogclegg@ntlworld.com

CLELAND, Richard. b 26. Belf Coll of Tech MPS47. St Aid Birkenhead 58. **d** 60 **p** 61. C Lisburn Ch Ch *Conn* 60-63; C Ballynafeigh St Jude *D & D* 63-66; C Portman Square St Paul *Lon* 66-67; V Ilkley All SS *Bradf* 67-83; Master Wyggeston's Hosp Leic 83-97; rtd 97; Perm to Offic *S'well* 97-02. *23 Stuart Court, High Street, Kibworth, Leicester LE8 0LR* Tel 0116-279 6245

CLELAND, Trevor. b 66. QUB BTh94 TCD MPhil97. CITC 94. **d** 96 **p** 97. C Lisburn Ch Ch *Conn* 96-99; C Carrickfergus 99-03; I

Belfast Upper Falls from 03. *31 Dunmurry Lane, Belfast BT17 9RP* Tel (028) 9062 2400

CLEMAS, Nigel Antony. b 53. Wycliffe Hall Ox. **d** 83 **p** 84. C Bootle St Mary w St Paul *Liv* 83-87; V Kirkdale St Mary and St Athanasius 87-91; TV Netherthorpe *Sheff* 91-93; V Netherthorpe St Steph 93-98; R Chapel Chorlton, Maer and Whitmore *Lich* from 98; RD Eccleshall from 00. *The Rectory, Snape Hall Road, Whitmore, Newcastle ST5 5HS* Tel (01782) 680258

CLEMENCE, Paul Robert Fraser. b 50. MRTPI82 Man Univ Dip Town Planning 74 St Edm Hall Ox MA90. Wycliffe Hall Ox 88. **d** 90 **p** 91. C Lancaster St Mary *Blackb* 90-94; Chapl HM Pris Lanc Castle 90-94; V Lt Thornton *Blackb* from 94; AD Poulton from 00. *St John's Vicarage, 35 Station Road, Thornton-Cleveleys FY5 5HY* Tel (01253) 825107 Fax as telephone E-mail p.clemence@ukonline.co.uk

CLEMENT, Miss Barbara Winifred. b 20. Gilmore Ho 49. **dss** 56 **d** 87. Frimley Green *Guildf* 53-66; Hd Dss 66-74; Dioc Adv Lay Min 74-82; Frimley 74-82; Frimley Hosp 74-87; rtd 82; Perm to Offic *Guildf* 82-99 and from 01. *9 Merlin Court, The Cloisters, Frimley, Camberley GU16 5JN* Tel (01276) 22527

CLEMENT, Geoffrey Paul. b 69. Angl Th Inst of Montevideo DipTh99. **d** 94 **p** 96. Uruguay 94-01; Hipodrome Gardens St Aug 94-95; Miss of St Jas the Apostle Colón 95-97; Barruo Fatima Salto St Luke w the H Spirit 97-01; TV Wilford Peninsula *St E* from 01. *The Rectory, Church Lane, Shottisham, Woodbridge IP12 3HG* Tel (01394) 411748 Mobile 07766-601011 E-mail clement@onetel.net.uk

CLEMENT, Peter James. b 64. UMIST BSc88 Man Univ MA98. Qu Coll Birm 89. **d** 92 **p** 93. C Grange St Andr *Ches* 92-95; C Man Apostles w Miles Platting *Man* 95-97; TV Uggeshall w Sotherton, Wangford and Henham *St E* 97-99; TV Sole Bay 99-00; Dioc Youth Officer 01-02; V Fairweather Green *Bradf* from 02. *St Saviour's Vicarage, 25 Ings Way, Bradford BD8 0LU* Tel (01274) 544807 E-mail peter.clement@bradford.anglican.org

CLEMENT, Thomas Gwyn. b 51. Lon Univ BMus73 Goldsmiths' Coll Lon PGCE74. St Steph Ho Ox. **d** 93 **p** 94. C Friern Barnet St Jas *Lon* 93-96; V Edmonton St Alphege from 96; AD Enfield from 01; P-in-c Ponders End St Matt from 02. *St Alphege's Vicarage, Rossdale Drive, London N9 7LG* Tel (020) 8245 3588

CLEMENT, Timothy Gordon. b 54. Usk Coll of Agric NCA75 OND76. Trin Coll Bris DipTh92. **d** 94 **p** 95. C Chepstow *Mon* 94-97; R Bettws Newydd w Trostrey etc from 97; Rural Min Adv from 02. *The Rectory, Bettws Newydd, Usk NP15 1JN* Tel (01873) 880258

CLEMENTS, Alan Austin. b 39. Newc Univ MA93 ACIB66. Linc Th Coll 74. **d** 76 **p** 77. C Woodley St Jo the Ev *Ox* 76-79; C Wokingham All SS 79-83; V Felton *Newc* 83-95; P-in-c Wallsend St Pet 95-01; rtd 01; Perm to Offic *Newc* from 01. *3 Woodkirk Close, Seghill, Cramlington NE23 7TZ* Tel 0191-237 7366 Fax as telephone E-mail alanaclements@aol.com

CLEMENTS, Andrew. b 48. K Coll Lon BD72 AKC72. St Aug Coll Cant 72. **d** 73 **p** 74. C Langley All SS and Martyrs *Man* 73-76; C Westhoughton 76-81; R Thornton Dale w Ellerburne and Wilton *York* 81-89; Prec Leic Cathl *Leic* 89-91; V Market Weighton *York* 91-97; R Goodmanham 91-97; V Osbaldwick w Murton from 97. *The Vicarage, 80 Osbaldwick Lane, York YO10 3AX* Tel (01904) 416763 E-mail andrew@ozmurt.freeserve.co.uk

CLEMENTS, Miss Christine Hilda. b 49. SW Minl Tr Course 99. **d** 02 **p** 03. C Halsetown *Truro* from 02. *St John's-in-the-Fields Vicarage, Hellesvean, St Ives TR26 2HG* Tel (01736) 796035 Mobile 07890-708773 E-mail lamorna21@eurobell.co.uk

CLEMENTS, Doris Thomasina Sara. b 46. TCD BA68 MA90. CITC 92. **d** 95 **p** 96. NSM Killala w Dunfeeny, Crossmolina, Kilmoreney etc *T, K & A* from 95. *Doobeg House, Bunninadden, Ballymote, Co Sligo, Irish Republic* Tel (00353) (71) 918 5425 Fax 918 5255 E-mail dorisc.ias@eircom.net

CLEMENTS, Edwin George. b 41. Chich Th Coll 77. **d** 79 **p** 80. C Didcot St Pet *Ox* 79-83; C Brixham w Churston Ferrers *Ex* 83; TV 84-86; TV Brixham w Churston Ferrers and Kingswear 86-88; P-in-c Hagbourne *Ox* 88; V 88-90; P-in-c Blewbury 89-90; P-in-c Upton 89-90; R Blewbury, Hagbourne and Upton from 90; AD Wallingford from 99. *The Rectory, Blewbury, Didcot OX11 9QH* Tel (01235) 850267 Mobile 07703-342950 Fax 851736 E-mail revedwin@aol.com

CLEMENTS, Miss Mary Holmes. b 43. Bedf Coll Lon BA64 Lon Bible Coll DipTh66 Lon Inst of Educn PGCE69. Ox Min Course 92. **d** 94 **p** 95. NSM High Wycombe *Ox* 94-01; C N Petherton w Northmoor Green *B & W* from 01; C N Newton w St Michaelchurch, Thurloxton etc from 01. *8 Alder Close, North Petherton, Bridgwater TA6 6TT* Tel (01278) 662905 E-mail mary@holmesclements.freeserve.co.uk

CLEMENTS, Philip Christian. b 38. K Coll Lon BD64 AKC64. **d** 65 **p** 66. C S Norwood St Mark *Cant* 65-68; Chapl R Russell Sch Croydon 65-68; Asst Chapl Denstone Coll Uttoxeter 75-76; Chapl 76-81; Chapl Lancing Coll 82-90; R Ninfield *Chich* 90-99; V Hooe 90-99; rtd 99; Perm to Offic *Cant* from 95. *21 Swaynes*

Way, Eastry, Sandwich CT13 0JP Tel (01304) 617413 or 613982 E-mail philip@clements3739.freeserve.co.uk

CLEMENTS, Philip John Charles. b 42. Nottm Univ CertEd64 Loughb Univ DLC64. Ridley Hall Cam. **d** 85 **p** 86. C Aylestone St Andr w St Jas *Leic* 85-87; P-in-c Swinford w Catthorpe, Shawell and Stanford 87-91; V 91-99; Rural Officer (Leic Adnry) 91-96; RD Guthlaxton II 94-99; P-in-c N w S Kilworth and Misterton 96-99; P-in-c Barrowden and Wakerley w S Luffenham *Pet* 99-02; R Barrowden and Wakerley w S Luffenham etc from 03; RD Barnack from 00. *The Rectory, 11 Church Lane, Barrowden, Oakham LE15 8ED* Tel (01572) 747192 Fax as telephone E-mail pipclements@lineone.net

CLEMENTS, Canon Roy Adrian. b 44. Dur Univ BA68 DipTh69 MA. St Chad's Coll Dur 65. **d** 69 **p** 70. C Royston *Wakef* 69-73; V Clifton 73-77; V Rastrick St Matt 77-84; V Horbury Junction 84-92; Dioc Communications Officer 84-98; Bp's Chapl 92-00; Hon Can Wakef Cathl from 94; V Battyeford from 00. *Battyeford Vicarage, 107A Stocksbank Road, Mirfield WF14 9QT* Tel (01924) 493277 E-mail roy@christ-the-king.co.uk

CLEMETT, Peter Thomas. b 33. Univ of Wales (Lamp) BA60. Sarum Th Coll 59. **d** 61 **p** 62. C Tredegar St Geo *Mon* 61-63; Chapl St Woolos Cathl 63-66; CF 66-99; Chapl R Memorial Chpl Sandhurst 84-88; rtd 88; OCF from 99; Perm to Offic *Win* from 01. *Silver Birches, Gardeners Lane, East Wellow, Romsey SO51 6AD* Tel (023) 8081 4261

CLENCH, Brian Henry Ross. b 31. Ripon Coll Cuddesdon. **d** 82 **p** 83. C Fulham All SS *Lon* 82-85; Ind Chapl *Truro* 85-92; P-in-c St Mewan 85-92; rtd 92; Perm to Offic *Sarum* from 96. *Tamworth Barn, Hampton Lane, Whitford, Axminster EX13 7NJ*

CLENDON, David Arthur. b 33. Em Coll Cam BA56 MA61. Wells Th Coll 56. **d** 58 **p** 59. C Hockerill *St Alb* 58-62; C Digswell 62-63; C Luton Ch Ch 63-65; P-in-c 71-76; V Caddington 65-71; P-in-c Pirton 75-85; V 85-91; P-in-c Offley w Lilley 85-88; rtd 91; Perm to Offic *St Alb* from 91. *1 Docklands, Pirton, Hitchin SG5 3QF* Tel (01462) 712741

CLEPHANE, Alexander Honeyman. b 48. LNSM course 94. **d** 97 **p** 98. OLM Flixton St Mich *Man* from 97. *306 Church Road, Urmston, Manchester M41 6JJ* Tel 0161-747 8816 Mobile 07798-613291

CLEVELAND, Mrs Lorna Christina (Dickie). b 39. State Univ NY BSc60. SEITE 99. **d** 02. NSM Wye w Brook *Cant* from 02. *2 Church Street, Wye, Ashford TN25 5BJ* Tel (01233) 813051 E-mail dickie@clevelp.freeserve.co.uk

CLEVELAND, Michael Robin. b 52. Warwick Univ BA73. St Jo Coll Nottm 86 Serampore Th Coll BD88. **d** 88 **p** 89. C Bushbury *Lich* 88-92; V Foleshill St Laur *Cov* from 92. *St Laurence's Vicarage, 142 Old Church Road, Coventry CV6 7ED* Tel (024) 7668 8271

CLEVELAND, Archdeacon of. See FERGUSON, The Ven Paul John

CLEVERLEY, Michael Frank. b 36. Man Univ BScTech57. Wells Th Coll 61. **d** 63 **p** 64. C Halifax St Aug *Wakef* 63; C Huddersfield St Jo 63-66; C Brighouse 66-69; V Gomersal 69-83; P-in-c Clayton W w High Hoyland 83-89; P-in-c Scissett St Aug 83-89; R High Hoyland, Scissett and Clayton W 89-96; rtd 96; NSM Leathley w Farnley, Fewston and Blubberhouses *Bradf* from 96. *The Rectory, Stainburn Lane, Leathley, Otley LS21 2LF* Tel 0113-284 3744 E-mail mclef@argonet.co.uk

CLEVERLY, Charles St George. b 51. Ox Univ MA. Trin Coll Bris. **d** 82 **p** 83. C Cranham Park *Chelmsf* 82-89; V 89-92; Crosslinks from 92; Perm to Offic *Chelmsf* 92-00; R Ox St Aldate *Ox* from 02. *Holy Trinity House, 19 Turn Again Lane, Oxford OX1 1QL* Tel (01865) 250894 Fax 201543 E-mail charlie.cleverly@staldates.org.uk

CLEWS, Nicholas. b 57. CIPFA85 SS Coll Cam BA80 MA84 Leeds Univ BA87. Coll of Resurr Mirfield 85. **d** 88 **p** 89. C S Elmsall *Wakef* 88-91; V Featherstone from 91. *All Saints' Vicarage, Ackton Lane, Featherstone, Pontefract WF7 6AP* Tel (01977) 792280 E-mail clewsclan@btopenworld.com

CLIFF, Frank Graham. b 38. St Paul's Cheltenham TCert60 Lon Univ DipTh66. Clifton Th Coll 63. **d** 66 **p** 67. C Leic St Chris *Leic* 66-69; C Whitton and Thurleston w Akenham *St E* 69-71; USA from 71; Asst R Houston St Thos 71-72; Asst R Waco St Alb 72-74; Asst R Potomac St Jas 74-78; R Denton Ch Ch 78-85; V Pittsburgh St Phil 86-87; R Pittsburgh Advent Ch 87-94; R Honesdale Grace Ch from 94. *210 Spring Hill Road, Honesdale, PA 18431, USA* Tel (001) (570) 253 4535 E-mail cliffam@ptd.net

CLIFF, Julian Arnold. b 41. Cranmer Hall Dur 63. **d** 66 **p** 67. C Bowdon *Ches* 66-69; C Poynton 69-73; P-in-c Crewe St Barn 73-75; V 75-79. *24 Exmoor Close, Wirral L61 9QN* Tel 0151-648 1408

CLIFF, Philip Basil. b 15. Lon Univ BSc61 Birm Univ PhD. Independent Coll Bradf 36. **d** 77 **p** 77. Hon C Northfield *Birm* 77-91; Perm to Offic from 91. *4 Fox Hill Close, Birmingham B29 4AH* Tel 0121-472 1556

CLIFFE, Christopher George. b 47. CITC 94. **d** 97 **p** 98. Bp's Dom Chapl *C & O* from 97; C Fiddown w Clonegam, Guilcagh, and Kilmeaden 97-00; I from 00. *The Rectory, Piltown, Co Kilkenny, Irish Republic* Tel (00353) (51) 643275 Mobile 087-236 8682

CLIFFORD, Raymond Augustine. b 45. Birkbeck Coll Lon CertRS91. Coll of Resurr Mirfield 91. **d** 93 **p** 94. C Saltdean *Chich* 93-96. *124 Arnold Estate, Druid Street, London SE1 2DT* Tel (020) 7232 2439

CLIFTON, Canon Robert Walter. b 39. Solicitor. Westcott Ho Cam 82. **d** 84 **p** 85. C Bury St Edmunds St Geo *St E* 84-87; P-in-c Culford, W Stow and Wordwell 87-88; R Culford, W Stow and Wordwell w Flempton etc 88-95; P-in-c Fornham All SS and Fornham St Martin w Timworth 93-95; RD Thingoe 93-95; P-in-c Orford w Sudbourne, Chillesford, Butley and Iken 95-00; P-in-c Eyke w Bromeswell, Rendlesham, Tunstall etc 98-99; TR Wilford Peninsula from 00; RD Woodbridge from 96; Hon Can St E Cathl from 00. *The Rectory, Rectory Lane, Orford, Woodbridge IP12 2NN* Tel and fax (01394) 450336 Mobile 07713-237754
E-mail robert.clifton@stedmundsbury.anglican.org

CLIFTON, Canon Roger Gerald. b 45. ACA70 FCA. Sarum & Wells Th Coll 70. **d** 73 **p** 74. C Winterbourne *Bris* 73-76; P-in-c Brislington St Cuth 76-83; P-in-c Colerne w N Wraxall 83-95; RD Chippenham 88-94; Hon Can Bris Cathl from 94; TR Gtr Corsham 95-01; TR Gtr Corsham and Lacock from 01. *The Rectory, Newlands Road, Corsham SN13 0BS* Tel (01249) 713232 Fax as telephone

CLIFTON-SMITH, Gregory James. b 52. GGSM73 Lon Univ TCert74 Goldsmiths' Coll Lon BMus82. Sarum & Wells Th Coll 87. **d** 89 **p** 90. C Welling *S'wark* 89-93; V Tattenham Corner and Burgh Heath *Guildf* 93-97; Asst Chapl R Berks and Battle Hosps NHS Trust 97-99; Chapl Isle of Wight Healthcare NHS Trust from 99. *The Chaplaincy, St Mary's Hospital, Parkhurst Road, Newport PO30 5TG* Tel (01983) 534639 *or* 856781 Mobile 07790-089981
E-mail gregory.clifton-smith@lowht.swest.nhs.uk

CLINCH, Christopher James. b 60. Nottm Univ BEd82 BTh89. Linc Th Coll 86. **d** 89 **p** 90. C Newc St Geo *Newc* 89-92; C Seaton Hirst 92-94; TV Ch the King 94-00; V Newc St Fran from 00. *St Francis's Vicarage, 66 Cleveland Gardens, Newcastle upon Tyne NE7 7QH* Tel 0191-266 1071

CLINCH, Kenneth Wilfred. b 22. Bps' Coll Cheshunt 62. **d** 64 **p** 65. C Old Shoreham *Chich* 64-67; C Lancing St Mich 67-73; R Upper St Leonards St Jo 73-88; rtd 88; Perm to Offic *Chich* from 88. *7 The Leas, Essenden Road, St Leonards-on-Sea TN38 0PU* Tel (01424) 438286 Fax as telephone
E-mail ken22@globalnet.co.uk

CLINES, Emma Christine. *See* LOUIS, Ms Emma Christine

CLINES, Jeremy Mark Sebastian. b 55. Cranmer Hall Dur. **d** 97 **p** 98. C Birm St Martin w Bordesley St Andr *Birm* 97-99; Asst Chapl Univ Coll of Ripon and York St Jo from 99; Perm to Offic *Birm* from 99. *University College of Ripon and York, Lord Mayor's Walk, York YO3 7EX* Tel (01904) 716607
E-mail j.clines@ucrysj.ac.uk *or* jmc844@bham.ac.uk

CLITHEROW, Canon Andrew. b 50. St Chad's Coll Dur BA72 Ex Univ MPhil87. Sarum & Wells Th Coll 78. **d** 79 **p** 80. Hon C Bedford Ch Ch *St Alb* 79-84; Asst Chapl Bedford Sch 79-84; Chapl Caldicott Sch Farnham Royal 84-85; C Penkridge w Stretton *Lich* 85-88; Min Acton Trussell w Bednall 85-88; Chapl Rossall Sch Fleetwood 89-94; V Scotforth *Blackb* 94-00; Can Res Blackb Cathl from 00; Dioc Dir of Tr from 00. *St Leonard's House, Potters Lane, Samlesbury, Preston PR5 0UE* Tel (01772) 877229 Fax as telephone
E-mail andrew@clithcan.freeserve.co.uk

CLOCKSIN (née HOYLE), Mrs Pamela Margaret. b 61. Nottm Univ BA82. St Jo Coll Nottm 84. **d** 87 **p** 94. Par Dn Bulwell St Jo *S'well* 87-91; Cam Pastorate Chapl 91-95; Par Dn Cambridge H Trin w St Andr Gt *Ely* 91-92; C Cambridge H Trin 92-95; Perm to Offic from 95. *The Beeches, Manor Farm Court, Lower End, Swaffham Prior, Cambridge CB5 0LJ* Tel (01638) 743698

CLOCKSIN, William Frederick. b 55. BA76 St Cross Coll Ox MA81 Trin Hall Cam MA87 PhD93. EAMTC 91. **d** 94 **p** 95. Asst Chapl Trin Hall Cam from 94. *Trinity Hall, Cambridge CB2 1TJ* Tel (01223) 334628 *or* (01638) 743698 Fax 334678
E-mail wfc@cl.cam.ac.uk

CLODE, Arthur Raymond Thomas. b 35. Roch Th Coll 67. **d** 69 **p** 70. C Blackheath *Birm* 69-72; V Londonderry 73-75; R Kirkbride *S & M* 75-79; UAE 80-83; Min Stewartly LEP 86-90; C Wootton *St Alb* 86-90; C St Alb St Paul 90-94; rtd 94; Perm to Offic *Glouc* from 01. *60 Albemarle Gate, Cheltenham GL50 4PJ* Tel (01242) 577521

CLOETE, Richard James. b 47. AKC71. St Aug Coll Cant 72. **d** 72 **p** 73. C Redhill St Matt *S'wark* 72-76; V Streatham St Paul 76-84; P-in-c W Coker *B & W* 84-88; P-in-c Hardington Mandeville w E Chinnock and Pendomer 84-88; R W Coker w Hardington Mandeville, E Chinnock etc 88; R Wincanton 88-97; R Pen Selwood 88-97; Sec and Treas Dioc Hosp Chapl Fellowship 91-97; Perm to Offic *Lon* 97-98; Perm to Offic *Ex* 99-02; C Sampford Peverell, Uplowman, Holcombe Rogus etc

from 02. *The Retreat, Gravel Walk, Cullompton EX15 1DA* Tel (01884) 38788 Mobile 07855-493868

CLOGHER, Archdeacon of. *See* PRINGLE, The Ven Cecil Thomas

CLOGHER, Bishop of. *See* JACKSON, The Rt Revd Michael Geoffrey St Aubyn

CLOGHER, Dean of. *See* MOORE, The Very Revd Thomas Robert

CLONMACNOISE, Dean of. *See* JONES, The Very Revd Robert William

CLOSE, Brian Eric. b 49. St Chad's Coll Dur BA74 MA76. Ridley Hall Cam 74. **d** 76 **p** 77. C Far Headingley St Chad *Ripon* 76-79; C Harrogate St Wilfrid 79-80; C Harrogate St Wilfrid and St Luke 80-82; P-in-c Alconbury w Alconbury Weston *Ely* 82-83; V 83-86; P-in-c Buckworth 82-83; R 83-86; P-in-c Upton and Copmanford 82-83; Chapl Reed's Sch Cobham 86-96; Chapl Malvern Coll 96-01; Chapl Uppingham Sch Leics from 01. *Uppingham School, Uppingham, Oakham LE15 9QD* Tel (01572) 822216 Fax 821872

CLOSE (née HITCHEN), Mrs Carol Ann. b 47. St Mary's Coll Ban CertEd69 St Martin's Coll Lanc DipEd91 Chester Coll of HE BTh02. N Ord Course 99. **d** 02. NSM Hindley St Pet *Liv* from 02. *271 Warrington Road, Abram, Wigan WN2 5RQ* Tel (01942) 861670

CLOSE, Mrs Jane. b 48. Warwick Univ Dip Counselling 00. WMMTC 00. **d** 03. NSM Fillongley and Corley *Cov* from 03. *316 Allesley Old Road, Coventry CV5 8SH* Tel and fax (024) 7672 2160 Mobile 07957-233502 E-mail j-b.close@ntlworld.com

CLOSE, Timothy John. b 68. QUB BA91 Leic Univ MSc95 TCD BTh00. CITC 97. **d** 00 **p** 01. C Glenageary *D & G* 00-03; Dean's V Belf Cathl from 03. *The Vicarage, 11 Woodfield, Newtownabbey BT37 0ZH* Tel (028) 9086 0023

CLOSS-PARRY, The Ven Selwyn. b 25. Univ of Wales (Lamp) BA50. St Mich Coll Llan 50. **d** 52 **p** 53. C Dwygyfylchi *Ban* 52-58; V Treuddyn *St As* 58-66; R Llangystennin 66-71; V Holywell 71-77; Can St As Cathl 76-82; Prec 82-84; Preb 82-90; V Colwyn 77-84; Adn St As 84-90; R Trefnant 84-90; rtd 91. *3 Llys Brompton, Brompton Avenue, Rhos-on-Sea LL28 4TB* Tel (01492) 545801

CLOTHIER, Gerald Harry. b 34. Oak Hill Th Coll 75. **d** 78 **p** 79. Hon C Highwood *Chelmsf* 78-79; Hon C Writtle w Highwood 79-83; P-in-c Westhall w Brampton and Stoven *St E* 83-86; TV Beccles St Mich 86-93; R Rougham, Beyton w Hessett and Rushbrooke 93-97; rtd 97; Perm to Offic *Nor* from 97; P-in-c Tenerife Sur *Eur* 01-02. *4 Wiggs Way, Corton, Lowestoft NR32 5JJ* Tel (01502) 733231

CLOVER, Canon Brendan David. b 58. LTCL74 G&C Coll Cam BA79 MA83. Ripon Coll Cuddesdon 79. **d** 82 **p** 83. C Friern Barnet St Jas *Lon* 82-85; C W Hampstead St Jas 85-87; Chapl Em Coll Cam 87-92; Dean Em Coll Cam 92-94; P-in-c St Pancras w St Jas and Ch Ch *Lon* 94-99; P-in-c St Pancras H Cross w St Jude and St Pet 96-99; Can Res Bris Cathl *Bris* from 99. *55 Salisbury Road, Redland, Bristol BS5 7AS* Tel 0117-942 1452 Fax 925 3678

CLOW, Laurie Stephen. b 65. Man Univ BA86 MA88. Wycliffe Hall Ox DipMin98. **d** 98 **p** 99. C Trentham *Lich* 98-01; TV Hampreston *Sarum* from 01. *19 Canford Bottom, Wimborne Minster BH21 2HA* Tel (01202) 884796
E-mail w.m.clow@uclan.ac.uk

CLOWES, John. b 45. AKC67. **d** 68 **p** 69. C Corby St Columba *Pet* 68-71; R Itchenstoke w Ovington and Abbotstone *Win* 71-74; V Acton w Gt and Lt Waldingfield *St E* 74-80; Asst Dioc Chr Stewardship Adv 75-80; TV Southend St Jo w St Mark, All SS w St Fran etc *Chelmsf* 80-82; TV Southend 82-85; Ind Chapl 80-85; R Ashwick w Oakhill and Binegar *B & W* 85-91; P-in-c Brompton Regis w Upton and Skilgate 91-97; rtd 98. *The Tythings, Tythings Court, Minehead TA24 5NT* Tel 07808-200619 (mobile)

CLOYNE, Dean of. *See* MARLEY, The Very Revd Alan Gordon

CLUCAS, Anthony John. b 56. WMMTC 96. **d** 99 **p** 00. NSM Erdington *Birm* from 99. *7 Arden Drive, Henley Close, Sutton Coldfield B73 5ND* Tel 0121-382 4461
E-mail clucas@btinternet.com

CLUCAS, Robert David. b 55. Cranmer Hall Dur. **d** 82 **p** 83. C Gateacre *Liv* 82-86; P-in-c Bishop's Itchington *Cov* 86-93; CPAS Staff from 93; Perm to Offic *Cov* from 93. *CPAS, Athena Drive, Tachbrook Park, Warwick CV34 6NG* Tel (01926) 458456 Fax 458459

CLUER, Donald Gordon. b 21. S'wark Ord Course 61. **d** 64 **p** 65. C Malden St Jas *S'wark* 64-68; C Bexhill St Pet *Chich* 68-73; V Shoreham Beach 73-77; V Heathfield St Rich 77-86; C Eastbourne St Mary 86-90; rtd 90; Perm to Offic *Ox* from 90. *10 Windsor Street, Oxford OX3 7AP* Tel (01865) 767270

CLUES, David Charles. b 66. K Coll Lon BD87 Lon Univ PGCE95. St Steph Ho Ox 88. **d** 90 **p** 91. C Notting Hill All SS w St Columb *Lon* 90-94; NSM 94-96; NSM Notting Hill St Mich and Ch Ch 96-98; Asst Chapl HM Pris Wormwood Scrubs 97-98; C Paddington St Mary Magd *Lon* from 98; C Paddington St Mary from 98; C Paddington St Sav from 98; V Willesden

St Mary from 03. *St Mary's Vicarage, 18 Neasden Lane, London NW10 2TT* Tel (020) 8459 2167 E-mail transpontem@aol.com

CLUETT, Michael Charles. b 53. Kingston Poly BSc78. St Steph Ho Ox 84. **d** 86 **p** 87. C Pontesbury I and II *Heref* 86-90; TV Wenlock 90-99; P-in-c Canon Pyon w Kings Pyon and Birley from 99. *The Vicarage, Brookside, Canon Pyon, Hereford HR4 8NY* Tel (01432) 830802 E-mail mccluett@aol.com

CLUNIE, Grace. b 60. Ulster Univ BA82 MA91 QUB Dip Librarianship 85. CITC BTh95. **d** 95 **p** 96. C Newtownards *D & D* 95-99; C Seagoe 99-01; I Belfast St Nic *Conn* from 01. *St Nicholas' Rectory, 15 Harberton Park, Belfast BT9 6TW* Tel (028) 9066 7753 Fax 9068 2924
E-mail belfast.stnicholas@connor.anglican.org

CLUTTERBUCK, Herbert Ivan. b 16. Ch Coll Cam BA38 MA42. Chich Th Coll 38. **d** 39 **p** 40. C Lamorbey H Trin *Roch* 39-41; Hon CF 41-44; Chapl and Sen Classics Master Wellingborough Sch 44-47; Chapl RN 47-62; V Lanteglos by Fowey *Truro* 62-66; Org Sec Ch Union 66-74; Chapl Qu Marg Sch Escrick Park 74-76; Chapl and Dir Relig Studies Roedean Sch Brighton 76-81; rtd 82; Master St Jo Hosp Lich 82-91; Perm to Offic *Truro* from 99 and *Roch* from 00. *7 Springfield Road, St Martin Field, East Looe PL13 1HB* Tel (01503) 263509

CLUTTERBUCK, Miss Marion Isobel. b 56. All Nations Chr Coll DipRS87 Oak Hill Th Coll BA91. **d** 92 **p** 94. C Lindfield *Chich* 92-96; TV Alderbury Team *Sarum* 96-01; TV Clarendon from 01. *The Vicarage, Common Road, Whiteparish, Salisbury SP5 2SU* Tel (01794) 884315

CLYDE, John. b 39. Univ of Wales (Lamp) MA99. CITC. **d** 71 **p** 72. C Belfast St Aid *Conn* 71-74; I Belfast St Barn 74-80; I Belfast H Trin 80-89; Bp's C Acton and Drumbanagher *Arm* 89-94; I Desertlyn w Ballyeglish 94-02; rtd 02. *25 Castleoak, Castledawson, Magherafelt BT45 8RX* Tel (028) 7946 9153
E-mail jc@rclyde.freeserve.co.uk

CLYNES, William. b 33. Sarum & Wells Th Coll 78. **d** 79 **p** 80. C Winterbourne *Bris* 79-83; TV Swindon St Jo and St Andr 83-91; rtd 91. *185A Claverham Road, Claverham, Bristol BS49 4LE*

COAKLEY (née FURBER), Prof Sarah Anne. b 51. New Hall Cam BA73 PhD82. Harvard Div Sch ThM75. **d** 00. Edw Mallinckrotd Jun Prof of Div Harvard Div Sch from 95; Hon C Waban The Gd Shep from 00; Hon C Littlemore *Ox* from 00. *Harvard Divinity School, 45 Francis Avenue, Cambridge, MA 02138, USA* Tel (001) (617) 495 4518

COATES, Alan Thomas. b 55. St Jo Coll Nottm 87. **d** 89 **p** 90. C Heeley *Sheff* 89-90; C Bramley and Ravenfield 90-92; V Askern 92-96; Chapl RAF from 96; Perm to Offic *Ripon* from 96. *Chaplaincy Services (RAF), HQ, Personnel and Training Command, RAF Innsworth, Gloucester GL3 1EZ* Tel (01452) 712612 ext 5164 Fax 510828

COATES, Archie. *See* COATES, Richard Michael

COATES, Christopher Ian. b 59. Qu Coll Birm 81. **d** 84 **p** 85. C Cottingham *York* 84-87; TV Howden 87-91; V Sherburn in Elmet 91-94; V Sherburn in Elmet w Saxton 94-02; V Bishopthorpe 02; V Acaster Malbis from 02. *The Vicarage, 48 Church Lane, Bishopthorpe, York YO23 2QG* Tel (01904) 706476

COATES, Canon Francis Gustav. b 10. OBE63. G&C Coll Cam BA32 MA36. Ridley Hall Cam 32. **d** 52 **p** 54. Uganda 52-65; C Worthing St Paul *Chich* 65-68; P-in-c Wickmere w Wolterton and Lt Barningham *Nor* 68-71; R Heydon w Irmingland 68-82; P-in-c Booton w Brandiston 71-82; Hon Can Busoga from 81; rtd 82; Perm to Offic *Nor* 82-96. *c/o Mrs F M Sullivan, 19 Ashleigh Gardens, Wymondham NR18 0EX* Tel (01953) 602616

COATES, Jean Margaret. b 47. Sussex Univ BSc68 Reading Univ PhD77 MIBiol CBiol. St Alb and Ox Min Course 93. **d** 96 **p** 97. C Wallingford w Crowmarsh Gifford etc *Ox* 96-98; C Wallingford 98-99; P-in-c Watercombe *Sarum* 99-02; R from 02; Rural Officer (Dorset) from 99. *The Rectory, Main Street, Broadmayne, Dorchester DT2 8EB* Tel (01305) 852435
E-mail jeancoates@macunlimited.net

COATES, John David Spencer. b 41. Dur Univ BA64 DipTh66. Cranmer Hall Dur 64. **d** 66 **p** 67. C Chipping Campden w Ebrington *Glouc* 66-69; CF 69-96; rtd 96; Perm to Offic *B & W* from 96; CF(V) from 97. *c/o Lloyds TSB PLC, 19 The Parade, Minehead TA24 5LU* Tel (01643) 862772

COATES, Canon Kenneth Will. b 17. St Jo Coll Dur LTh45 BA46. Bible Churchmen's Coll Bris 39. **d** 42 **p** 43. C Daubhill *Man* 42-44; Perm to Offic *Bris* 44-47; C Cheadle *Ches* 47-49; V Preston All SS *Blackb* 49-60; V St Helens St Helen *Liv* 60-88; Hon Can Liv Cathl 71-88; rtd 88; Perm to Offic *Liv* from 88. *122 Broadway, Eccleston, St Helens WA10 5DH* Tel (01744) 29629

COATES, Maxwell Gordon. b 49. Lon Univ CertEd70 Open Univ BA83 AdDipEd87 UEA MA86. Trin Coll Bris DipTh77. **d** 77 **p** 78. C Blackheath Park St Mich *S'wark* 77-79; Chapl Greenwich Distr Hosp Lon 77-79; Asst Teacher Saintbridge Sch *Glouc* 79-81; Teacher Gaywood Park High Sch King's Lynn 81-85; NSM Lynn St Jo *Nor* 81-85; Dep Hd Teacher Winton Comp Sch Bournemouth 85-90; Hd Teacher St Mark's Comp Sch Bath 90-97; NSM Canford Magna *Sarum* 85-90 and from 99; NSM

Stoke Gifford *Bris* 93-96; rtd 97; Perm to Offic *B & W* 91-96. *3 Oakley Road, Wimborne BH21 1QJ* Tel (01202) 883162

COATES, Michael David. b 60. Chester Coll of HE BTh01. N Ord Course 98. **d** 01 **p** 02. C Orrell Hey St Jo and St Jas *Liv* from 01. *20 Mount Avenue, Bootle L20 6DT* Tel (0151) 570307

COATES, Nigel John. b 51. Reading Univ BSc MA. Trin Coll Bris. **d** 83 **p** 84. C Epsom St Martin *Guildf* 83-86; C Portswood Ch Ch *Win* 86-88; Chapl Southn Univ 89-97; Chapl Southn Inst of HE 89-95; P-in-c Freemantle 97-00; R from 00. *The Rectory, 129 Paynes Road, Southampton SO15 3BW* Tel (023) 8022 1804
E-mail coates@btinternet.com

COATES, Canon Peter Frederick. b 50. K Coll Lon BD79 AKC79. St Steph Ho Ox 79. **d** 80 **p** 81. C Woodford St Barn *Chelmsf* 80-83; C E and W Keal *Linc* 83-86; R The Wainfleets and Croft 86-94; R The Wainfleet Gp 94-03; RD Calcewaithe and Candleshoe 92-03; P-in-c Spilsby Gp from 03; RD Bolingbroke from 03; Can and Preb Linc Cathl from 02. *The Vicarage, 1 Church Street, Spilsby PE23 5DU* Tel (01790) 754560
E-mail peter@candleshoe.freeserve.co.uk

COATES, Richard Michael (Archie). b 70. Birm Univ BA92. Wycliffe Hall Ox BA99. **d** 00 **p** 01. C Ashtead *Guildf* from 00. *17 Loraine Gardens, Ashtead KT21 1PD* Tel (01372) 813366

COATES, Robert. b 63. Aston Tr Scheme 87 St Steph Ho Ox 89. **d** 92 **p** 93. C Heavitree w Ex St Paul *Ex* 92-95; Chapl RN 95-00; V Bexhill St Aug *Chich* from 00. *St Augustine's Vicarage, St Augustine's Close, Bexhill-on-Sea TN39 3AZ* Tel (01424) 210785 Fax as telephone E-mail ert@rcoates42.freeserve.co.uk

COATES, Robert Charles. b 44. Open Univ BA76. Cant Sch of Min 83. **d** 86 **p** 87. C Deal St Leon and St Rich and Sholden *Cant* 86-89; V Loose 89-00; V Barnwood *Glouc* from 00. *The Vicarage, 27A Barnwood Avenue, Gloucester GL4 3AB* Tel (01452) 613760
E-mail robert.coates1@virgin.net

COATES, Stuart Murray. b 49. Lon Univ BA70 Edin Univ MTh91. Wycliffe Hall Ox 72. **d** 75 **p** 76. C Rainford *Liv* 75-78; C Orrell 78-79; V 79-86; Chapl Strathcarron Hospice Denny from 86; Hon C Stirling *Edin* 86-90; NSM Doune *St And* from 89; NSM Aberfoyle 89-94. *Westwood Smithy, Chalmerston Road, Stirling FK9 4AG* Tel (01786) 860531

COATSWORTH, Nigel George. b 39. Trin Hall Cam BA61 MA. Cuddesdon Coll 61. **d** 63 **p** 64. C Hellesdon *Nor* 63-66; Ewell Monastery 66-80; TV Folkestone H Trin and St Geo w Ch Ch *Cant* 83-85; C Milton next Sittingbourne 85-86; P-in-c Selattyn *Lich* 86-91; P-in-c Weston Rhyn 89-91; R Weston Rhyn and Selattyn from 91. *St John's Vicarage, Vicarage Lane, Weston Rhyn, Oswestry SY10 7RE* Tel (01691) 774693
E-mail rev.coatsworth@micro-plus-web.net

COBB, Douglas Arthur. b 25. Kelham Th Coll 49. **d** 54 **p** 55. C Notting Hill St Mich and Ch Ch *Lon* 54-57; C Ruislip St Mary 57-63; V Kentish Town St Silas 63-87; P-in-c Kentish Town St Martin w St Andr 81-85; Chapl Convent of St Mary at the Cross Edgware 87-92; rtd 92; Perm to Offic *Lon* from 97. *Padre Pio House, 10 Buckingham Gardens, Edgware HA8 6NB* Tel (020) 8933 1789 E-mail ddacobb@aol.com

COBB, George Reginald. b 50. Oak Hill Th Coll BA81. **d** 81 **p** 82. C Ware Ch Ch *St Alb* 81-84; C Uphill *B & W* 84-89; R Alresford *Chelmsf* 89-99; Chapl Mt Vernon and Watford Hosps NHS Trust 99-00; Chapl W Herts Hosps NHS Trust from 00. *Mount Vernon Hospital, Rickmansworth Road, Northwood HA6 2RN* Tel (01923) 826111 *or* (020) 8861 2720
E-mail gcobb83618@aol.com

COBB, John Philip Andrew. b 43. Man Univ BSc65 New Coll Ox BA67 MA71. Wycliffe Hall Ox 66. **d** 68 **p** 69. Par Dn Reading St Jo *Ox* 68-71; Par Dn Romford Gd Shep Collier Row *Chelmsf* 71-73; SAMS from 74; Chile from 74. *Iglesia Anglicana del Chile, Casilla 50675, Correo Central, Santiago, Chile* Tel (0056) (2) 696 7107 Fax 639 4581 E-mail jcobb@evangel.cl

COBB, Miss Marjorie Alice. b 24. St Chris Coll Blackheath IDC52. **dss** 61 **d** 87. CSA 56-85; rtd 85; Perm to Offic *Cant* from 87; Chapl Jes Hosp Cant from 90. *2 John Boys Wing, Jesus Hospital, Sturry Road, Canterbury CT1 1BS* Tel (01227) 472615

COBB, Mark Robert. b 64. Lanc Univ BSc86 Derby Univ 96 Keele Univ CertMan99. Ripon Coll Cuddesdon 88. **d** 91 **p** 92. C Hampstead St Jo *Lon* 91-94; Asst Chapl Derbyshire R Infirmary NHS Trust 94-96; Palliative & Health Care Chapl Derbyshire R Infirmary NHS Trust 96-98; Chapl Manager Cen Sheff Univ Hosps NHS Trust from 98; Sen Chapl from 98. *Chaplaincy Services, Royal Hallamshire Hospital, Glossop Road, Sheffield S10 2JF* Tel 0114-271 2718 *or* 271 1900
E-mail mark.cobb@csuh.trent.nhs.uk

COBB, Canon Peter George. b 37. Ch Ch Ox BA59 MA63. St Steph Ho Ox 64. **d** 65 **p** 66. C Solihull *Birm* 65-69; Lib Pusey Ho 69-71; Sen Tutor St Steph Ho Ox 71-76; Cust Lib Pusey Ho 76-78; V Midsomer Norton *B & W* 78-83; V Clandown 78-83; V Midsomer Norton w Clandown 83-84; RD Midsomer Norton 83-84; V Clifton All SS w St Jo *Bris* 84-02; Hon Can Bris Cathl 92-02; rtd 02. *13 Knoll Court, Knoll Hill, Bristol BS9 1QX* Tel 0117-968 7460

COBB, Peter Graham. b 27. St Jo Coll Cam BA48 MA52. Ridley Hall Cam 66. **d** 68 **p** 69. C Porthkerry *Llan* 68-71; P-in-c

Penmark 71-72; V Penmark w Porthkerry 72-81; V Magor w Redwick and Undy *Mon* 82-95; rtd 95. *2 Talycoed Court, Talycoed, Monmouth NP25 5HR* Tel (01600) 780309

COCHLIN, Maurice Reginald. b 19. TCert57 FVCM57 ACP60 FFChM Sussex Univ CertEd70 Lambeth STh74. Chich Th Coll 70. **d** 70 **p** 71. C Rowlands Castle *Portsm* 70-72; Chapl Paulsgrove Sch Cosham 71; C Warblington w Emsworth *Portsm* 72-75; C S w N Bersted *Chich* 76-78; Hd Littlemead Upper Sch Chich 78-79; C Saltdean *Chich* 79-83; V Kirdford 83-88; rtd 88; Perm to Offic *Chich* from 88. *56 Farnhurst Road, Barnham, Bognor Regis PO22 0JW* Tel (01243) 553584

COCHRANE, Alan George. b 28. S'wark Ord Course. **d** 82 **p** 83. NSM Clapham Old Town *S'wark* 82-85; C Spalding St Jo w Deeping St Nicholas *Linc* 85-87; R Southery *Ely* 87-98; V Fordham St Mary 87-91; R Hilgay 87-98; rtd 98; Perm to Offic *Nor* from 99. *38 Broadgate, Taverham, Norwich NR8 6GH* Tel (01603) 869449

COCHRANE, Canon Kenneth Wilbur. b 27. TCD BA58 MA61 Trin Coll Newburgh PhD88. **d** 58 **p** 59. C Belfast St Aid *Conn* 58-61; C Belfast St Nic 61-62; C Lisburn Ch Ch 62-63; P-in-c Lisburn St Paul 63-65; I 65-98; Can Belf Cathl 86-90; Preb Clonmethan St Patr Cathl Dublin 90-98; rtd 98. *3 Knockmore Park, Ballinderry Road, Lisburn BT28 2SJ* Tel (028) 9262 7934

COCHRANE, Canon Roy Alan. b 25. AKC53. **d** 54 **p** 55. C Linc St Faith *Linc* 54-56; C Skegness 56-59; R Thurlby w Norton Disney 59-65; V Swinderby 59-65; Chapl HM Borstal Morton Hall 59-65; R N Coates *Linc* 65-69; Chapl RAF 65-69; V Marshchapel *Linc* 65-69; V Grainthorpe w Conisholme 65-69; V Glanford Bridge 69-89; Chapl Glanford Hosp 69-89; RD Yarborough 76-81; Can and Preb Linc Cathl 77-97; Chapl and Warden St Anne's Bedehouses 89-93; rtd 90. *5 Chippendale Close, Doddington Park, Lincoln LN6 3PR* Tel (01522) 689221

COCKAYNE, Gordon. b 34. RMN73. **d** 92 **p** 93. NSM Owlerton *Sheff* 92-94; Ind Chapl 92-94; NSM Brightside w Wincobank 94-99; Perm to Offic from 99. *6 Austin Close, Loxley, Sheffield S6 6QD* Tel 0114-220 6626

COCKAYNE, Mark Gary. b 61. UEA LLB82. St Jo Coll Nottm BTh92 MA93. **d** 93 **p** 94. C Armthorpe *Sheff* 93-96; V Malin Bridge from 96. *St Polycarp's Vicarage, 33 Wisewood Lane, Sheffield S6 4WA* Tel 0114-234 3450

COCKBILL, Douglas John. b 53. Chicago Univ BA75. Gen Th Sem (NY) MDiv78. **d** 78 **p** 79. Virgin Is 79-80; Bahamas 80-83; USA 84-90; P-in-c Roxbourne St Andr *Lon* 90-92; V from 92. *St Andrew's Vicarage, Malvern Avenue, Harrow HA2 9ER* Tel (020) 8422 3633 Fax 8422 2009
E-mail funkymonkey22@hotmail.com

COCKBURN, Sidney. b 14. Leeds Univ BA36. Coll of Resurr Mirfield 36. **d** 38 **p** 40. C Hartlepool St Jas *Dur* 38-39; Hon C Roath St German *Llan* 39-40; C Gateshead St Cuth w St Paul *Dur* 40-42; C Newc St Mary *Newc* 42-43; RAFVR 43-47; C Heanor *Derby* 47-51; C-in-c Marlpool 47-51; V Long Eaton St Jo 51-85; rtd 85; Perm to Offic *Derby* from 85. *10 Poplar Road, Breaston, Derby DE72 3BH* Tel (01332) 872363

COCKCROFT, Basil Stanley. b 26. CEng MICE Leeds Univ BSc49. Wells Th Coll 64. **d** 66 **p** 67. C Featherstone *Wakef* 66-69; C Norton St Mary *Dur* 69-71; P-in-c Eldon 71-75; NSM Elland *Wakef* 75-92; rtd 91; Perm to Offic *Wakef* from 92. *9 Dene Close, South Parade, Elland HX5 0NS* Tel (01422) 374465

COCKE, James Edmund. b 26. Wadh Coll Ox BA50 MA55. Wells Th Coll 50. **d** 52 **p** 53. C Christchurch *Win* 52-57; V Highfield *Ox* from 57; Chapl Wingfield-Morris Hosp Ox 57-90; Chapl Nuffield Orthopaedic Centre NHS Trust from 90. *All Saints' Vicarage, 85 Old Road, Oxford OX3 7LB* Tel (01865) 62536

COCKELL, Ms Helen Frances. b 69. Trin Hall Cam BA90 MA94. Qu Coll Birm BD94. **d** 95. C Bracknell *Ox* 95-98; NSM Rugby St Andr *Cov* from 00. *St George's House, St John's Avenue, Rugby CV22 5HR* Tel (01788) 577331

COCKELL, Timothy David. b 66. Qu Coll Birm BTheol95. **d** 95 **p** 96. C Bracknell *Ox* 95-98; C Rugby St Andr *Cov* 98-99; TV from 99. *St George's House, St John's Avenue, Rugby CV22 5HR* Tel (01788) 577331 E-mail tim.cockell@btopenworld.com

COCKER (née BENTLEY), Mrs Frances Rymer (Mother Frances Anne). b 22. Man Univ BSc48 TDip49 PGCE49. **d** 95 **p** 95. Mother Superior CSD 87-00; Perm to Offic *Sarum* from 95. *Sarum College, 19 The Close, Salisbury SP1 2EE* Tel (01722) 339761 Mobile 07702-659609

COCKERELL, David John. b 47. Univ of Wales (Cardiff) BA71 Univ of Wales (Swansea) MA74 Qu Coll Cam BA75. Westcott Ho Cam 73. **d** 76 **p** 77. C Chapel Allerton *Ripon* 76-79; C Farnley 79-81; TV Hitchin *St Alb* 81-89; TV Dorchester *Ox* 89-92; Adult Educn and Tr Officer *Ely* 92-00; R Raddesley Gp from 00. *The Rectory, Stetchworth Road, Dullingham, Newmarket CB8 9UJ* Tel (01638) 507263
E-mail david@cockerell.co.uk

COCKERTON, Canon John Clifford Penn. b 27. Liv Univ BA48 St Cath Soc Ox BA54 MA58. Wycliffe Hall Ox 51. **d** 54 **p** 55. C St Helens St Helen *Liv* 54-58; Tutor Cranmer Hall Dur 58-60; Chapl 60-63; Warden 68-70; Vice-Prin St Jo Coll Dur 63-70; Prin 70-78; R Wheldrake *York* 78-84; R Wheldrake w Thorganby

84-92; Can and Preb York Minster 87-92; rtd 92; Perm to Offic *York* from 98. *42 Lucombe Way, New Earswick, York YO32 4DS* Tel (01904) 765505

COCKERTON, Thomas Charles. b 24. **d** 88 **p** 90. NSM Bermondsey St Mary w St Olave, St Jo etc *S'wark* 88-94; Perm to Offic from 94. *30 Carrick Court, Kennington Park Road, London SE11 4EE* Tel (020) 7735 6966

COCKETT, Elwin Wesley. b 59. Aston Tr Scheme 86 Oak Hill Th Coll DipHE90 BA91. **d** 91 **p** 92. C Chadwell Heath *Chelmsf* 91-94; Chapl W Ham United Football Club from 92; C Harold Hill St Paul 94-95; P-in-c 95-97; V 97-00; TR Billericay and Lt Burstead from 00. *The Rectory, 40 Laindon Road, Billericay CM12 9LD* Tel (01277) 658055 Fax 658056
E-mail elwin@billericaychurches.org

COCKING, Martyn Royston. b 53. Trin Coll Bris 83. **d** 85 **p** 86. C Weston-super-Mare Cen Par *B & W* 85-88; C Kingswood *Bris* 88-89; TV 89-93; V Pill w Easton in Gordano and Portbury *B & W* 93-96. *68 Friary Grange Park, Winterbourne, Bristol BS36 1NB* Tel (01454) 886771

COCKMAN, David Willie. b 32. Ex & Truro NSM Scheme 89. **d** 82 **p** 83. C Christow, Ashton, Trusham and Bridford *Ex* 82; NSM Exwick 83-84; Warden Mercer Ho 83-97; Lic to Offic from 83; rtd 97. *4 The Fairway, Pennsylvania, Exeter EX4 5DW* Tel (01392) 278590

COCKRAM, Anthony John. b 44. Leeds Univ BSc65 Birm Univ MEd83. SW Minl Tr Course 98. **d** 01 **p** 02. NSM Seaton *Ex* 01-03; NSM Seaton and Beer from 03. *1 Hillymead, Seaton EX12 2LF* Tel (01297) 20426 Mobile 07989-566641
E-mail suton@ic24.net

COCKS, Howard Alan Stewart. b 46. St Barn Coll Adelaide 78 ACT Th. **d** 80 **p** 81. Australia 80-82; C Prestbury *Glouc* 82-87; P-in-c Stratton w Baunton 87-94; P-in-c N Cerney w Bagendon 91-94; R Stratton, N Cerney, Baunton and Bagendon 95-98; V Leic St Aid *Leic* from 98; rtd 98. *23 Fairfield Avenue, Addington, Christchurch, New Zealand 8020* Tel (0064) (3) 377 7053 Fax as telephone E-mail cocks@ihug.co.nz

COCKS, Michael Dearden Somers. b 28. Univ of NZ MA50 St Cath Coll Ox BA53 MA57. Ripon Hall Ox. **d** 53 **p** 54. New Zealand 53-93 and from 98; Chapl Gothenburg w Halmstad, Jönköping etc *Eur* 93-98; rtd 98. *St Aidan's Vicarage, St Oswald's Road, Leicester LE3 6RJ* Tel 0116-287 2342 Fax 232 2056

COCKSEDGE, Hugh Francis. b 26. Magd Coll Cam BA50 MA52. **d** 88 **p** 89. NSM Alton All SS *Win* 88-89; Lic to Offic 89-91; Chapl Ankara *Eur* 91-96; rtd 96; Perm to Offic *Win* from 96; *Eur* from 97; *Portsm* from 01. *Stancomb, Stancomb Lane, Medstead, Alton GU34 5QB* Tel (01420) 563624
E-mail hfcocksedge@netscapeonline.co.uk

COCKSHAW, Evan David. b 74. Sussex Univ BSc95 Nottm Univ MA99. St Jo Coll Nottm 97. **d** 00 **p** 01. C Horncastle w Low Toynton *Linc* 00-02; C Pennington *Man* from 02. *11 Ruby Grove, Leigh WN7 4JW* Tel (01942) 675832 Mobile 07958-050009
E-mail evan@penningtonchurch.com

COCKSWORTH, Canon Christopher John. b 59. Man Univ BA80 PhD89 PGCE81. St Jo Coll Nottm 84. **d** 88 **p** 89. C Epsom Common Ch Ch *Guildf* 88-92; Chapl R Holloway and Bedf New Coll 92-97; Dir STETS 97-01; Hon Can Guildf Cathl *Guildf* 99-01; Prin Ridley Hall Cam from 01. *The Principal's Lodge, Ridley Hall, Cambridge CB3 9HG* Tel (01223) 353040 or 741060 Fax 301287 E-mail cjcfo@cam.ac.uk

CODLING, Timothy Michael. b 62. Trin Coll Ox BA84 MA91. St Steph Ho Ox 89. **d** 91 **p** 92. C N Shoebury *Chelmsf* 91-97; V Tilbury Docks from 97; Hon Chapl Miss to Seafarers from 97. *St John's Vicarage, Dock Road, Tilbury RM18 7PP* Tel (01375) 842417

CODRINGTON CLARKE, Harold Godfrey. b 26. S'wark Ord Course 71. **d** 74 **p** 75. C Redhill St Jo *S'wark* 74-79; P-in-c Blindley Heath 79-96; rtd 96. *77 Oaklands, South Godstone, Godstone RH9 8HX* Tel (01342) 892905

COE, Andrew Derek John. b 58. Nottm Univ BTh86. St Jo Coll Nottm 83. **d** 86 **p** 87. C Pype Hayes *Birm* 86-88; C Erdington St Barn 88-91; C Birm St Martin w Bordesley St Andr 91-96; P-in-c Hamstead St Bernard 96; V 96-02; P-in-c Newdigate *Guildf* 02-03; TR Surrey Weald from 03. *The Rectory, Church Road, Newdigate, Dorking RH5 5DL* Tel (01306) 631469
E-mail revdandrewdj.coe@btinternet.com

COE, David. b 45. **d** 69 **p** 70. C Belfast St Matt *Conn* 69-72; C Belfast St Donard *D & D* 72-75; I Tullylish 75-81; I Lurgan St Jo 81-89; I Ballymacarrett St Patr 89-02; I Richhill *Arm* from 02. *The Rectory, 15 Annareagh Road, Richhill BT61 9JT* Tel (028) 3887 1322

COE, John Norris. b 31. Oak Hill Th Coll 57. **d** 59 **p** 60. C Stoughton *Guildf* 59-61; C Guernsey St Michel du Valle *Win* 61-63; C Norbiton *S'wark* 63-67; V Bath Widcombe *B & W* 67-84; R Publow w Pensford, Compton Dando and Chelwood 84-96; rtd 96; Perm to Offic *B & W* from 96. *12 Stirtingdale Road, Bath BA2 2NF* Tel (01225) 789752

COE, Michael Stephen. b 63. Bath Univ BSc85. Wycliffe Hall Ox DipMin00. **d** 00 **p** 01. C Moulton *Pet* from 00. *8 Cubleigh Close, Moulton, Northampton NN3 7BG* Tel (01604) 494169
E-mail mikelisac@aol.com

COE, Stephen David. b 49. Ch Coll Cam MA72. Ox Min Course CBTS93. **d** 93 **p** 94. NSM Abingdon *Ox* 93-97; Assoc Min Ox St Andr from 97. *29 Mill Lane, Old Marston, Oxford OX3 0QB* Tel (01865) 241337
E-mail stephen.coe@standrewsoxford.org.uk

COEKIN, Philip James. b 64. Wye Coll Lon BScAgr87. Oak Hill Th Coll BA93. **d** 96 **p** 97. C Eastbourne All SS *Chich* 96-00; V Hastings Em and St Mary in the Castle from 00. *The Vicarage, Vicarage Road, Hastings TN34 3NA* Tel (01424) 421543
E-mail phil@p.coekin.freeserve.co.uk

COEKIN, Richard John. b 61. Solicitor 86 Jes Coll Cam BA83 MA87. Wycliffe Hall Ox 89. **d** 91 **p** 92. C Cheadle *Ches* 91-95; NSM Wimbledon Em Ridgway Prop Chpl *S'wark* from 95. *107 Merton Hall Road, London SW19 3PY* Tel (020) 8542 8739

COFFEY, Hubert William (Bill). b 15. MBE46. TCD BA37 MA40. TCD Div Sch Div Test38. **d** 38 **p** 39. C Errigle Keerogue w Ballygawley and Killeshil *Arm* 38-41; Chapl RN 41-47; I Milltown *Arm* 47-52; Chapl Miss to Seamen 52-64; Australia from 53; V Melbourne S 64-80; rtd 80; Perm to Offic *Melbourne* from 80. *23 Hawthorn Avenue, Caulfield North, Vic, Australia 3161* Tel (0061) (3) 9527 7875

COFFIN, Pamela. See PENNELL, Ms Pamela

COFFIN, Stephen. b 52. Pemb Coll Ox BA74 MA79. Trin Coll Bris 74. **d** 77 **p** 78. C Illogan *Truro* 77-80; C Liskeard w St Keyne and St Pinnock 80-82; CMS Burundi 82-86; V St Germans *Truro* 86-00; Chapl Grenoble *Eur* from 00. *14 rue Gérard Philippe, 38100 Grenoble, France* Tel (0033) (4) 76 25 33 79
E-mail chaplain@grenoble-church.org *or* coffin@onetelnet.fr

COGGINS, Glenn. b 60. Warwick Univ BA81. St Jo Coll Dur CTM95. **d** 95 **p** 96. C Cley Hill Warminster *Sarum* 95-99; R Doddington w Benwick and Wimblington *Ely* from 99. *The Rectory, Ingle's Lane, Doddington, March PE15 0TE* Tel (01354) 740692 E-mail glenn.coggins@ely.anglican.org

COGGINS, Richard James. b 29. Ex Coll Ox BA50 MA54 DipTh53 BD75. St Steph Ho Ox 52. **d** 54 **p** 55. C Withycombe Raleigh *Ex* 54-57; Tutor St Steph Ho Ox 57-60; Chapl 60-62; Asst Chapl Ex Coll Ox 57-62; Chapl Magd Coll Ox 60-62; Lic to Offic *Lon* 64-94; Sub-Warden K Coll Lon 62-67; Lect 62-81; Sen Lect 81-94; rtd 94; Perm to Offic *Win* from 94. *3 de Mowbray Way, Lymington SO41 3PD* Tel (01590) 673626

COGHLAN, Patrick John. b 47. Down Coll Cam BA(Econ)69 Nottm Univ MA73. St Jo Coll Nottm LTh72. **d** 73 **p** 74. C Crookes St Thos *Sheff* 73-78; Brazil 78-92; V Anston *Sheff* from 92. *The Vicarage, 17 Rackford Road, Anston, Sheffield S25 4DE* Tel (01909) 563447

COGMAN, Canon Frederick Walter. b 13. Lon Univ BD38 AKC38. **d** 38 **p** 39. C Upton cum Chalvey *Ox* 38-42; Chapl St Geo Sch Harpenden 42-48; R Guernsey St Martin *Win* 48-76; Dean Guernsey 67-78; Hon Can Win Cathl 67-79; R Guernsey St Peter Port 76-78; rtd 78; Perm to Offic *Win* 78-97. *Duchess of Kent House, Le Vauquiedor, St Andrews, Guernsey GY6 8TW* Tel (01481) 232881

COHEN, The Ven Clive Ronald Franklin. b 46. ACIB71. Sarum & Wells Th Coll 79. **d** 81 **p** 82. C Esher *Guildf* 81-85; R Winterslow *Sarum* 85-00; RD Alderbury 89-93; Can and Preb Sarum Cathl 92-00; Adn Bodmin *Truro* from 00. *Archdeacon's House, Cardinham, Bodmin PL30 4BL* Tel (01208) 821614 Fax 821602
E-mail clive@truro.anglican.org

COHEN, David Mervyn Stuart. b 42. Sydney Univ BA63 MA78. **d** 67 **p** 68. Mauritius 67-69; New Zealand 70-72; Regional Sec (Africa) Bible Soc 73-75; Australia 75-85 and from 94; Gen Dir Scripture Union (England and Wales) 86-93; Perm to Offic *Lon* 92-94; Tear Fund UK 93-96. *PO Box 67, Croydon Park, NSW, Australia 2133* Tel (0061) (2) 9745 2840 Fax 9744 3496
E-mail dcohen1@compuserve.com

COHEN, Ian Geoffrey Holland. b 51. Nottm Univ BA74. Ripon Coll Cuddesdon 77. **d** 79 **p** 80. C Sprowston *Nor* 79-83; TV Wallingford w Crowmarsh Gifford etc *Ox* 83-88; V Chalgrove w Berrick Salome from 88. *The Vicarage, 58 Brinkinfield Road, Chalgrove, Oxford OX44 7QX* Tel (01865) 890392
E-mail ianghcohen@hotmail.com

COHEN, Malcolm Arthur. b 38. Canberra Coll of Min DipTh79. **d** 78 **p** 79. Australia 79-84; C Moruya, Bega and Cootamundra 79-80; R Braidwood 82-83; R Stifford *Chelmsf* 84-92; Chapl Asst Thurrock Community Hosp Grays 84-86; Hon Chapl ATC from 86; P-in-c Mayland and Steeple *Chelmsf* 92-95; C Prittlewell 95-99; C Greenstead from 00; TV Greenstead w Colchester St Anne from 00. *1 Blackwater Avenue, Colchester CO4 3UY* Tel (01206) 861525

COHEN, Michael Neil. b 45. Ripon Coll Cuddesdon 79. **d** 81 **p** 82. C Gt Bookham *Guildf* 81-84; C York Town St Mich 84-93; V Camberley St Martin Old Dean 93-95; Regional Adv (SE) CMJ 96-99; R Jerusalem Ch Ch from 99. *PO Box 14037, Jaffa Gate, Old City, Jerusalem 91140, Israel* Tel (00972) (2) 627 7727

COKE, William Robert Francis. b 46. St Edm Hall Ox BA68 MA79 Lon Univ BD78. Trin Coll Bris 75. **d** 79 **p** 80. C Blackb

Sav *Blackb* 79-83; V Fence in Pendle 83-84; P-in-c Newchurch-in-Pendle 83-84; V Fence and Newchurch-in-Pendle 84-89; Switzerland 89-95; Chapl Ardingly Coll 95-96; V Ambleside w Brathay *Carl* from 96; P-in-c Langdale from 97. *The Vicarage, Millans Park, Ambleside LA22 9AD* Tel (01539) 433205
E-mail randpcoke@cwcom.net

COKE-WOODS, Sylvia Jessie. b 47. Sheff Univ BA79. Qu Coll Birm 81 N Ord Course 98. **d** 99 **p** 00. C Widnes St Mary *Liv* from 99. *19 Hall Avenue, Hough Green, Widnes WA8 8XS* Tel 0151-424 2811

COKER, Alexander Bryan. b 48. Fourah Bay Coll (Sierra Leone) LDiv73 K Coll Lon BD75 MTh76 Brunel Univ MA84 MEd89 AKC76 MCollP84. St Aug Coll Cant 75. **d** 86 **p** 87. NSM Belsize Park *Lon* 86-90; C Croydon Woodside *S'wark* 90-93; C Cheam Common St Phil 93-94. *19 Rosehill Park West, Sutton SM1 3LA* Tel (020) 8641 8690

COKER, Canon Barry Charles Ellis. b 46. K Coll Lon BD69 AKC69. **d** 70 **p** 71. C Newton Aycliffe *Dur* 70-74; Trinidad and Tobago 74-78; R Matson *Glouc* 78-90; V Stroud and Uplands w Slad from 90; RD Bisley from 94; Hon Can Glouc Cathl from 98; P-in-c The Edge, Pitchcombe, Harescombe and Brookthorpe 00-01. *The Vicarage, Church Street, Stroud GL5 1JL* Tel (01453) 764555 Fax 751494 E-mail barrycoker@thevicarage.fsnet.co.uk

COLBOURN, John Martin Claris. b 30. Selw Coll Cam BA52 MA56. Ridley Hall Cam 52. **d** 54 **p** 55. C Cheadle *Ches* 54-58; V Trowbridge St Thos *Sarum* 59-65; V Fareham St Jo *Portsm* 65-87; V Creech *Derby* 87-95; RD Alfreton 88-95; rtd 95; Perm to Offic *Derby* from 95. *Stanton View Cottage, Dale Road North, Darley Dale, Matlock DE4 2HX* Tel (01629) 733284

COLBY, David Allan. b 33. Ox NSM Course 78. **d** 81 **p** 82. NSM Gt Faringdon w Lt Coxwell *Ox* 81-83; TV Ewyas Harold w Dulas, Kenderchurch etc *Heref* 83-91; V Westbury-on-Severn w Flaxley and Blaisdon *Glouc* 91-99; rtd 99; Perm to Offic *Ox* from 01. *Solway House, Faringdon Road, Kingston Bagpuize, Abingdon OX13 5AQ* Tel (01865) 820360

COLBY, Preb Robert James. b 31. Roch Th Coll 62. **d** 64 **p** 65. C Luton Ch Ch *St Alb* 64-68; C Chirbury *Heref* 68-70; P-in-c 70-78; V 78-79; P-in-c Trelystan 70-78; V 78-79; P-in-c Marton 70-78; V 78-79; P-in-c Whitbourne 79-82; P-in-c Tedstone Delamere and Edvin Loach etc 80-82; P-in-c Upper Sapey w Wolferlow 80-82; R Edvin Loach w Tedstone Delamere etc 82-96; Preb Heref Cathl 94-96; rtd 96; Perm to Offic *St Alb* from 96 and *Ox* from 99. *20 Colsons Way, Olney MK46 5EQ* Tel (01234) 713593

COLCHESTER, Archdeacon of. See WALLACE, The Ven Martin William

COLCHESTER, Area Bishop of. See MORGAN, The Rt Revd Christopher Heudebourck

✠**COLCLOUGH, The Rt Revd Michael John.** b 44. Leeds Univ BA69. Cuddesdon Coll 69. **d** 71 **p** 72. C Burslem St Werburgh *Lich* 71-75; C Ruislip St Mary *Lon* 75-79; P-in-c Hayes St Anselm 79-85; V 85-86; AD Hillingdon 85-92; P-in-c Uxbridge St Marg 86-88; P-in-c Uxbridge St Andr w St Jo 86-88; TR Uxbridge 88-92; Adn Northolt 92-94; P-in-c St Vedast w St Mich-le-Querne etc 94-96; Bp Sen Chapl 94-96; Dean of Univ Chapls from 94; Dep P in O 95-96; Area Bp Kensington *Lon* from 96. *Dial House, Riverside, Twickenham TW1 3DT* Tel (020) 8892 7781 Fax 8891 3969 E-mail bishop.kensington@london.anglican.org

COLDERWOOD, Alfred Victor. b 26. Bps' Coll Cheshunt 58. **d** 60 **p** 61. C Oakwood St Thos *Lon* 60-63; C Enfield St Jas 63-66; V Edmonton St Aldhelm 66-91; rtd 91; Perm to Offic *Cant* from 91. *11 Mill Row, Birchington CT7 9TT* Tel (01843) 841544

COLDHAM, Miss Geraldine Elizabeth. b 35. FLA66 Trevelyan Coll Dur BA80. Cranmer Hall Dur 82. dss 83 **d** 87 **p** 94. S Normanton *Derby* 83-87; Par Dn 87; Par Dn Barking St Marg w St Patr *Chelmsf* 87-90; Par Dn Stifford 90-94; C 94-95; rtd 95; Perm to Offic *Glouc* from 01. *27 Capel Court, The Burgage, Prestbury, Cheltenham GL52 3EL* Tel (01242) 576425

COLE, Adrian Peter. See ROBBINS-COLE, Adrian Peter

COLE, Canon Alan John. b 35. Cam Univ Cert Counselling 90. Bps' Coll Cheshunt 63. **d** 66 **p** 67. C Boreham Wood All SS *St Alb* 66-69; C St Alb St Mich 69-72; V Redbourn 72-80; R Thorley w Bishop's Stortford H Trin 80-87; Chapl St Edw K and Martyr Cam *Ely* 87-94; Chapl Arthur Rank Hospice Cam 87-94; SSF from 98; P-in-c Gamlingay w Hatley St Geo and E Hatley *Ely* 94-99; Hon Can Ely Cathl 96-00; P-in-c Everton w Tetworth 98-99; R Gamlingay and Everton 99-00; rtd 01; Perm to Office *St E* and *Ely* from 01. *73 Finchams Close, Linton, Cambridge CB1 6ND* Tel (01223) 892286
E-mail cancole@btopenworld.com

COLE, Alan Michael. b 40. Melbourne Univ DipEd74 BA74 SSC. ACT DipTh67. **d** 66 **p** 67. Australia 66-75 and 90-97; Chapl Bp Otter Coll Chich 76-77; Chapl Ardingly Coll 77-82; Chapl Bonn w Cologne *Eur* 82-86; Chapl Helsinki w Moscow 86-90; P-in-c Ilkeston H Trin *Derby* 97-01; V from 02. *Holy Trinity Vicarage, 1 Cotmanhay Road, Ilkeston DE7 8HR* Tel 0115-932 0833

COLE, Canon Brian Robert Arthur. b 35. Nottm Univ BA57. Ridley Hall Cam 59. **d** 61 **p** 62. C Tye Green w Netteswell

Chelmsf 61-64; C Keighley *Bradf* 64-67; Chapl Halifax Gen Hosp 67-73; V Copley *Wakef* 67-73; R Gt w Lt Dunham *Nor* 73-82; R Gt w Lt Fransham 74-82; P-in-c Sporle w Gt and Lt Palgrave 81-82; R Gt and Lt Dunham w Gt and Lt Fransham and Sporle 83-03; P-in-c from 03; RD Brisley and Elmham from 93; Hon Can Nor Cathl from 98. *The Rectory, Pound Lane, Litcham, King's Lynn PE32 2QR* Tel (01328) 701466 Fax 701338

COLE, Charles Vincent. b 26. Kelham Th Coll 47. **d** 51 **p** 52. C Harton *Dur* 51-54; C Gateshead St Jas 54-56; V Blackhall 56-91; rtd 91; Perm to Offic *Wakef* from 91. *66 Scott Green Crescent, Gildersome, Morley, Leeds LS27 7DF* Tel 0113-253 0021

COLE, David. b 40. Qu Coll Birm 66. **d** 66 **p** 67. C Kensington St Helen w H Trin *Lon* 66-69; C Altham w Clayton le Moors *Blackb* 69-72; P-in-c Preston St Luke 72-75; V Inskip 75-80; C-in-c Chelmsley Wood St Aug CD *Birm* 80-87; C Cannock *Lich* 87-93; I Kinneigh Union *C, C & R* 93-98; Can Cork Cathl 96-98; Can Ross Cathl 96-98; Bp's C Gweedore, Carrickfin and Templecrone *D & R* 98-01; I Carrickmacross w Magheracloone *Clogh* from 01. *The Rectory, Drumconrath Road, Carrickmacross, Co Monaghan, Irish Republic* Tel (00353) (42) 966 1931

COLE, David Henry. *See* GIFFORD-COLE, David Henry

COLE, Denise Helen. b 42. WEMTC 98. **d** 00 **p** 01. OLM Whiteshill and Randwick *Glouc* from 00. *Bethany, The Plain, Whiteshill, Stroud GL6 6AB* Tel (01453) 764504

COLE, Canon Donald Robertson. b 24. Edin Th Coll 57. **d** 59 **p** 60. C Edin Ch Ch *Edin* 59-62; R Lasswade 62-69; R Edin St Cuth 69-94; Hon Can St Mary's Cathl from 91; rtd 94. *92 Spottiswoode Street, Edinburgh EH9 1DJ* Tel 0131-447 9230

COLE, Guy Spenser. b 63. Univ of Wales (Ban) BA84 Jes Coll Cam BA88 MA91. Westcott Ho Cam 85. **d** 88 **p** 89. C Eastville St Anne w St Mark and St Thos *Bris* 88-92; P-in-c Penhill 92-95; V 95-01; R Easthampstead *Ox* from 01. *The Rectory, Crowthorne Road, Easthampstead, Bracknell RG12 7ER* Tel (01344) 423253 *or* 425205 E-mail guycole@guycole.freeserve.co.uk

COLE, Henry Frederick Charles. b 23. ALCD52. **d** 52 **p** 53. C Bexleyheath Ch Ch *Roch* 52-55; C-in-c Wigmore w Hempstead CD 55-59; V Lawkholme *Bradf* 59-67; Ind Chapl *Sheff* 67-72; V Wadsley 72-88; RD Hallam 83-87; rtd 88; Perm to Offic *Sheff* from 88. *Julians, 217 Tullibardine Road, Sheffield S11 7GQ* Tel 0114-268 4719

COLE, John Gordon. b 43. Magd Coll Cam BA65 MA69. Cuddesdon Coll 66. **d** 68 **p** 69. C Leeds St Pet *Ripon* 68-71; C Moor Allerton 71-75; P-in-c Pendleton *Blackb* 75-86; Dioc Communications Officer 75-86; Dioc Missr *Linc* 86-98; Ecum Development Officer 98-02; Nat Adv for Unity in Miss from 03. *Pelham House, Little Lane, Wrawby, Brigg DN20 8RW* Tel (01652) 657484 Fax as telephone E-mail johngcole@lineone.net

COLE, John Spensley. b 39. FCA65 Clare Coll Cam BA62 MA66 Nottm Univ DipTh79. Linc Th Coll 78. **d** 80 **p** 81. C Cowes St Mary *Portsm* 80-83; C Portchester 83-87; V Modbury *Ex* 87-95; R Aveton Gifford 87-95; TR Modbury, Bigbury, Ringmore w Kingston etc 95-98; P-in-c Alne from 98; P-in-c Brafferton w Pilmoor, Myton on Swale etc from 98. *Monk Green House, Main Street, Alne, York YO61 1TB* Tel (01347) 838021 E-mail john@colealne.freeserve.co.uk

COLE, Michael Berkeley. b 44. Cuddesdon Coll. **d** 72 **p** 73. C Shepshed *Leic* 72-76; V Leic St Chad 76-79; Hon C Painswick w Sheepscombe *Glouc* 94-97; Hon C Painswick w Sheepscombe and Cranham 97-98; Hon C Fairford and Kempsford w Whelford from 98. *The Parsonage, Kempsford, Fairford GL7 4ET* Tel (01285) 810130 E-mail mbcole@btinternet.com

COLE, Michael George. b 35. CD75. Wycliffe Th Sem Washington DMin88 Kelham Th Coll 56 Lich Th Coll 57. **d** 60 **p** 61. C Doncaster Ch Ch *Sheff* 60-63; Chapl RAF 63-68; Canada 68-82; USA from 82; rtd 98. *48 Pierpont Court, Pawleys Island, SC 29585, USA* Tel (001) (843) 237 9962 E-mail mcole@sc.rr.com

COLE, Canon Michael John. b 34. St Pet Hall Ox BA56 MA60. Ridley Hall Cam 56. **d** 58 **p** 59. C Finchley Ch Ch *Lon* 58; C Leeds St Geo *Ripon* 58-61; Travelling Sec IVF 61-64; V Crookes St Thos *Sheff* 64-71; R Rusholme H Trin *Man* 71-75; V Woodford Wells *Chelmsf* 75-00; Chapl Leytonstone Ho Hosp 85-00; Hon Can Chelmsf Cathl *Chelmsf* 89-00; RD Redbridge 95-00; rtd 00; Perm to Offic *Chelmsf* from 00. *67 Princes Road, Buckhurst Hill IG9 5DZ* Tel (020) 8506 0702

COLE, Mrs Norma Joan. b 46. EAMTC 93. **d** 96 **p** 97. C Ipswich St Mary at Stoke w St Pet *St E* 96-97; C Ipswich St Mary at Stoke w St Pet and St Fran 97-99; V Gt Cornard from 99. *The Vicarage, 59 Bures Road, Great Cornard, Sudbury CO10 0JE* Tel (01787) 373579 Fax as telephone E-mail thevicarage@lineone.co.uk

COLE, Canon Peter George Lamont. b 27. Pemb Coll Cam BA49 MA52. Cuddesdon Coll 50. **d** 52 **p** 53. C Aldershot St Mich *Guildf* 52-55; S Rhodesia 55-65; V Bromley St Andr *Roch* 65-72; V Folkestone St Mary and St Eanswythe *Cant* 72-87;

Hon Can Cant Cathl 80-87; V E and W Worldham, Hartley Mauditt w Kingsley etc *Win* 87-92; RD Alton 89-92; rtd 92; RD Petworth *Chich* 94-95; Perm to Offic from 95. *Marula Cottage, Lower Street, Fittleworth, Pulborough RH20 1JE* Tel (01798) 865540

COLE, Stanley Westley Tom. b 28. **d** 97 **p** 98. NSM Chalke Valley *Sarum* from 97. *Cranborne Farm, Old Blandford Road, Coombe Bissett, Salisbury SP5 4LF* Tel (01722) 718240

COLE, Timothy Alexander Robertson. b 60. Aber Univ MA83 Edin Univ BD86. Edin Th Coll 83. **d** 86 **p** 87. C Dunfermline *St And* 86-89; Vice-Provost St Andr Cathl Inverness *Mor* 89-90; R Inverness St Andr 89-90; R Edin St Mich and All SS *Edin* 90-95; CF from 95. *c/o MOD Chaplains (Army)* Tel (01980) 615804 Fax 615800

COLE, William. b 45. Oak Hill Th Coll BA96. **d** 96 **p** 97. NSM St Keverne *Truro* 96-99; P-in-c St Ruan w St Grade and Landewednack from 99. *The Rectory, Church Cove, The Lizard, Helston TR12 7PQ* Tel (01326) 291011

COLE-BAKER, Peter Massey. b 58. New Univ of Ulster BSc80 TCD BTh98. CITC 95. **d** 98 **p** 99. C Ballywillan *Conn* 98-01; I Templemore w Thurles and Kilfithmone *C & O* from 01. *The Rectory, Roscrea Road, Templemore, Co Tipperary, Irish Republic* Tel (00353) (504) 31175 Fax as telephone E-mail peter.cole-baker@telinco.co.uk

COLEBROOK, Canon Christopher John. b 36. Qu Mary Coll Lon BA60 BD69. St D Coll Lamp DipTh62. **d** 62 **p** 63. C Llandeilo Tal-y-bont *S & B* 62-66; C Llansamlet 66-71; V Nantmel w St Harmon's and Llanwrthwl 71-76; V Glantawe 76-85; V Gowerton 85-01; RD Llwchwr 93-00; Hon Can Brecon Cathl 97-01; Prec 00-01; rtd 01. *65 Pentregethin Road, Cwmbwrla, Swansea SA5 8BA*

COLEBROOK, Peter Acland. b 29. Coates Hall Edin 52. **d** 55 **p** 56. C Northfield *Birm* 58-62; C Bideford *Ex* 62-66; rtd 89; Perm to Offic *Sarum* from 01. *Vale Cottage, Ham Lane, Marnhull, Sturminster Newton DT10 1JN* Tel (01258) 820246

COLEBROOKE, Andrew. b 50. Imp Coll Lon BSc71 MSc72 PhD75. Ridley Hall Cam 92. **d** 94 **p** 95. C Shrub End *Chelmsf* 94-98; R Mistley w Manningtree and Bradfield from 98. *The Rectory, 21 Malthouse Road, Mistley, Manningtree CO11 1BY* Tel (01206) 392200 E-mail a.colebrooke@btinternet.com

COLEBY, Andrew Mark. b 59. Linc Coll Ox MA85 DPhil85 Dur Univ BA90 FRHistS88. Cranmer Hall Dur 88. **d** 91 **p** 92. C Heeley *Sheff* 91-93; TV Gleadless 94-97; Chapl Ox Brookes Univ *Ox* 97-01; P-in-c Didcot All SS from 01. *The Rectory, 140 Lydalls Road, Didcot OX11 7EA* Tel and fax (01235) 813244 E-mail am.coleby@btopenworld.com

COLEMAN, Aidan William. b 56. St Jo Coll Nottm 97. **d** 99 **p** 00. C Llandudno *Ban* 99-02; TV Bangor from 02; P-in-c Llandegai and Maes y Groes from 02. *The Vicarage, 18 Coed y Castell, Bangor LL57 1PH* Tel (01248) 372417

COLEMAN, Mrs Ann Valerie. b 55. K Coll Lon BD72. St Aug Coll Cant. **dss** 80 **d** 87 **p** 94. Hampstead Garden Suburb *Lon* 80-84; Golders Green 85-87; Selection Sec and Voc Adv ACCM 87-91; Teacher Bp Ramsey Sch 92-93; Chapl from 93; Hon C Eastcote St Lawr *Lon* from 93; Course Leader NTMTC from 99. *St Lawrence's Vicarage, 2 Bridle Road, Pinner HA5 2SJ* Tel (020) 8866 1263 E-mail ann.coleman@london.anglican.org

COLEMAN, Beverley Warren. b 20. Leeds Univ BA41. Coll of Resurr Mirfield 41. **d** 43 **p** 44. C Greenford H Cross *Lon* 43-46; C Stepney St Dunstan and All SS 46-47; CF 47-52; CF (TA) 52-87; PC Barrow Gurney *B & W* 52-54; Malaya 54-56; Indonesia 56-63; P-in-c Albrighton *Lich* 63-64; V 64-71; R Jersey St Sav *Win* 71-84; rtd 87; Perm to Offic *Worc* from 87. *44 Walnut Crescent, Malvern WR14 4AX* Tel (01684) 563535

COLEMAN, Brian James. b 36. K Coll Cam BA58 MA61. Ripon Hall Ox 58. **d** 60 **p** 61. C Allestree *Derby* 60-65; V Allestree St Nic 65-69; Chapl and Lect St Mich Coll Salisbury 69-77; P-in-c Matlock Bank *Derby* 77-86; R Frimley *Guildf* 86-92; V Guildf All SS 92-02; rtd 02. *6 Kingfisher Close, Salisbury SP2 8JE* Tel (01722) 410034

COLEMAN, Brian Ray. b 71. California State Univ Fullerton BPhil94. Seabury-Western Th Sem MDiv98. **d** 98 **p** 99. Assoc R Los Angeles St Jas USA 98-01; C Sheff Norwood St Leon *Sheff* 01-03; Chapl N Gen Hosp NHS Trust Sheff 01-03; P-in-c Sheff Abbeydale St Pet *Sheff* from 03; P-in-c Sheff St Oswald from 03. *St Peter's Vicarage, 21 Ashland Road, Sheffield S7 1RH* Tel 0114-250 9716 E-mail rbrian@dircon.co.uk

COLEMAN, Charles Romaine Boldero. b 10. Clifton Th Coll 46. **d** 39 **p** 40. C Downend *Bris* 39-41; C Keynsham *B & W* 41-43; R Felthorpe w Haveringland *Nor* 43-49; V Waxham w Sea Palling 49-55; R Horsey 52-55; R Buckenham w Hassingham and Strumpshaw 55-61; R Sampford Brett *B & W* 61-77; rtd 78; Perm to Offic *Nor* from 81. *1 The Firs, Redgate Hill, Hunstanton TE36 6LQ* Tel (01485) 532946

COLEMAN, David. b 49. K Coll Lon BD72 AKC72. St Aug Coll Cant 72. **d** 73 **p** 74. C Is of Dogs Ch Ch and St Jo w St Luke *Lon* 73-77; C Greenford H Cross 77-80; V Cricklewood St Pet 80-85; V Golders Green 85-90; V Eastcote St Lawr from 90.

St Lawrence's Vicarage, 2 Bridle Road, Pinner HA5 2SJ Tel (020) 8866 1263 E-mail david.coleman@london.anglican.org

COLEMAN, Frank. b 58. Hull Univ BA79. St Steph Ho Ox BA83 MA87. **d** 83 **p** 84. C Brandon *Dur* 83-85; C Newton Aycliffe 85-88; V Denford w Ringstead *Pet* 88-00; P-in-c Islip 95-00; V Caldecote, Northill and Old Warden *St Alb* from 00. *The Vicarage, 2A Biggleswade Road, Upper Caldecote, Biggleswade SG18 9BL* Tel (01767) 315578 Fax 317988 *or* 08701-612233 E-mail frankcoleman@btinternet.com

COLEMAN, John Edward Noel. b 15. St Chad's Coll Dur BA37 DipTh39 MA49. **d** 39 **p** 40. C Latchford *St Jas Ches* 39-48; V Allithwaite *Carl* 48-55; V Silverdale *Blackb* 55-82; rtd 82; Perm to Offic *Blackb* from 82; *Carl* 83-92. *25 Coach Road, Warton, Carnforth LA5 9PR* Tel (01524) 732368

COLEMAN, John Harold. b 38. Cant Sch of Min 83. **d** 86 **p** 87. NSM Dover St Martin *Cant* 86-92; V St Mary's Bay w St Mary-in-the-Marsh etc 92-95; P-in-c New Romney w Old Romney and Midley 95-03; rtd 03; Perm to Offic *Cant* from 03. *17 Nightingale Avenue, Hythe CT21 6QX* Tel (01303) 268823

COLEMAN, Jonathan Mark. b 59. Kent Univ BA81 Man Poly DMS91. Qu Coll Birm MA99. **d** 99 **p** 00. C Warrington St Elphin *Liv* 99-02; P-in-c Liv St Chris Norris Green from 02. *St Christopher's Vicarage, Lorenzo Drive, Norris Green, Liverpool L11 1BQ* Tel 0151-226 1637 Fax 07092-176537 E-mail markcoleman@bigfoot.com

COLEMAN, Michael. b 28. Glas Bible Coll DipTh85 Nat Coll Div LTh90. **d** 95. NSM E Kilbride *Glas* 95-99; NSM Motherwell from 99; NSM Wishaw from 99. *51 Lammermoor, Calderwood, East Kilbride, Glasgow G74 3SE* Tel (01355) 902523

COLEMAN, Ms Nicola Jane. b 63. Goldsmiths' Coll Lon BA86. Ripon Coll Cuddesdon 99. **d** 01 **p** 02. C Croydon St Jo *S'wark* from 01. *8 The Ridgeway, Croydon CR0 4AB* Tel (020) 8688 5877

COLEMAN, Patrick Francis. b 58. Reading Univ Pontifical Univ Rome STL STB PhB. Ven English Coll Rome 77. **d** 82 **p** 83. In RC Ch 82-91; NSM Abergavenny St Mary w Llanwenarth Citra *Mon* 96-99; Asst Chapl Milan w Genoa and Varese *Eur* 99-01; R Goetre w Llanover *Mon* from 01; Dir CME from 02. *The Rectory, Nantyderry, Abergavenny NP7 9DW* Tel (01873) 880378

COLEMAN, Peter Nicholas. b 42. St Mich Coll Llan 83. **d** 85 **p** 86. C Skewen *Llan* 85-88; R Ystradyfodwg from 88; RD Rhondda from 96. *The Vicarage, St David's Close, Pentre CF41 7AX* Tel (01443) 434201

COLEMAN, Robert William Alfred. b 16. Ch Coll Cam BA39 MA42. Bible Churchmen's Coll Bris 39. **d** 40 **p** 41. C Broadwater St Mary *Chich* 40-42; CF 42-46; V Tiverton St Geo *Ex* 46-50; V Ealing Dean St Jo *Lon* 50-60; Chapl Seaford Coll Petworth 60-81; rtd 81; Perm to Offic *Chich* from 83. *Villa Florence, 24 West Drive, Bognor Regis PO22 7TS* Tel (01243) 583410

COLEMAN, Canon Sybil Jean. b 30. St Deiniol's Hawarden 83. **d** 85 **p** 97. NSM Manselton *S & B* 85-90; C Swansea St Mark and St Jo 90-94; P-in-c 94-98; V 98-00; Hon Can Brecon Cathl 98-00; rtd 00. *Beckley, 25 Beverley Gardens, Fforestfach, Swansea SA5 5DR* Tel (01792) 584280

COLEMAN, Terence Norman. b 37. St Mich Coll Llan 83. **d** 85 **p** 86. C Machen *Mon* 85-87; C Penmaen and Crumlin 87-89; V 89-93; V Newbridge 93-02; rtd 02. *2 Fox Avenue, Newbridge, Newport NP11 4HP*

COLEMAN, Timothy. b 57. Southn Univ BSc79 CEng86 MIChemE86. Ridley Hall Cam 87. **d** 89 **p** 90. C Bisley and W End *Guildf* 89-93; C Hollington St Jo *Chich* 93-97; V Aldborough Hatch *Chelmsf* 97-02; Chapl Princess Alexandra Hosp NHS Trust from 02. *Princess Alexandra Hospital, Hamstel House, Hamstel Road, Harlow CM20 1QX* Tel (01279) 444455 *or* (01708) 730126 E-mail tim.coleman@tesco.net

COLES, Alasdair Charles. b 67. St Andr Univ BSc90 Homerton Coll Cam PGCE91 Ox Univ BTh96 Heythrop Coll Lon PhD03. Ripon Coll Cuddesdon 93. **d** 96 **p** 97. C Wymondham *Nor* 96-99; Min Can and Sacr St Paul's Cathl *Lon* from 99. *7A Amen Court, London EC4M 7BU* Tel and fax (020) 7248 6151 E-mail lilac@paston.co.uk *or* ac@stpaulscathedral.org.uk

COLES, Miss Alison Elizabeth. b 60. St Mary's Coll Dur BA81. Ripon Coll Cuddesdon 95. **d** 97 **p** 98. C Leckhampton SS Phil and Jas w Cheltenham St Jas *Glouc* 97-00; Asst Chapl Dudley Gp of Hosps NHS Trust from 00. *The Russells Hall Hospital, Dudley DY1 2HQ* Tel (01384) 456111

COLES, Christopher Wayne. b 58. St Mich Coll Llan 97. **d** 99 **p** 00. C Coity w Nolton *Llan* 99-02; C Canton Cardiff from 02. *8 Berthwin Street, Pontcanna, Cardiff CF11 9JH*

✠**COLES, The Rt Revd David John.** b 43. Auckland Univ MA67 Otago Univ BD69 MTh71 Man Univ PhD74. St Jo Coll Auckland 66 Melbourne Coll of Div DipRE71. **d** 68 **p** 69 **c** 90. New Zealand 68-71 and from 74; C Remuera 68-71; Chapl Selwyn Coll Dunedin 70-71; Hon C Fallowfield *Man* 72-74; Chapl Hulme Hall 73-74; V Glenfield 74-76; V Takapuna 76-80; Dean Napier 80-84; Dean Christchurch 84-90; Bp Christchurch

from 90. *Bishop's Lodge, 12 Idris Road, Christchurch 8005, New Zealand* Tel (0064) (3) 351 7711 *or* 363 0913 Fax 372 3357 E-mail bishop@chch.ang.org.nz

COLES, Preb Francis Herbert. b 35. Selw Coll Cam BA59 MA63. Coll of Resurr Mirfield 59. **d** 61 **p** 62. C Wolvercote *Ox* 61-65; C Farnham Royal 65-69; V Lynton and Brendon *Ex* 69-73; V Countisbury 70-73; TR Lynton, Brendon, Countisbury, Lynmouth etc 73-76; P-in-c Iffley *Ox* 76-88; V Ivybridge w Harford *Ex* 88-00; Preb Ex Cathl from 98; rtd 00; Perm to Offic *Ex* from 00. *8 Glenthorne Road, Exeter EX4 4QU* Tel (01392) 420238

COLES, Geoffrey Herbert. b 38. Nottm Univ CertEd59 TCert60 Loughb Coll of Educn DLC60. N Ord Course 77. **d** 80 **p** 81. NSM Shelf *Bradf* 80-85; C Manningham 85-86; TV 86-92; P-in-c Wyke 92-97; P-in-c Riddlesden from 97. *The Vicarage, Riddlesden, Keighley BD20 5PA* Tel (01535) 603419

COLES, John Spencer Halstaff. b 50. Hertf Coll Ox BA72 MA76. Wycliffe Hall Ox 72. **d** 75 **p** 76. C Reading Greyfriars *Ox* 75-79; C Clifton Ch Ch w Em *Bris* 79-82; V Woodside Park St Barn *Lon* from 82. *St Barnabas' Vicarage, 68 Westbury Road, London N12 7PD* Tel (020) 8445 3598 *or* 8446 7506 Fax 8343 9406 E-mail johncoles@stbarnabas.co.uk

COLES, Robert Reginald. b 47. Surrey Univ BSc69. Cant Sch of Min 82. **d** 85 **p** 86. NSM Sittingbourne St Mich *Cant* 85-87; C St Laur in Thanet 87-93; P-in-c St Nicholas at Wade w Sarre and Chislet w Hoath from 93; P-in-c Minster w Monkton from 96. *The Vicarage, St Mildred's Road, Minster, Ramsgate CT12 4DE* Tel (01843) 821250

COLES, Stephen Richard. b 49. Univ Coll Ox BA70 MA74 Leeds Univ BA80. Coll of Resurr Mirfield 78. **d** 81 **p** 82. C Stoke Newington St Mary *Lon* 81-84; Chapl K Coll Lon 84-89; V Finsbury Park St Thos *Lon* from 89. *25 Romilly Road, London N4 2QY* Tel (020) 7359 5741 E-mail jeoffry.cardinal@dial.pipex.com

COLEY, Peter Leonard. b 45. CEng MIMechE Bath Univ BSc67 City Univ MSc84. Oak Hill Th Coll 85. **d** 87 **p** 88. C Mile Cross *Nor* 87-91; R Stratton St Mary w Stratton St Michael etc 92-01; R Kirby-le-Soken w Gt Holland *Chelmsf* from 01. *The Rectory, 18 Thorpe Road, Kirby Cross, Frinton-on-Sea CO13 0LT* Tel (01255) 675997 Fax as telephone E-mail rev.petercoley@lineone.net

COLIN WILFRED, Brother. See CHERRIMAN, Colin Wilfred

COLLARD, Canon Harold. b 27. Wycliffe Hall Ox 51. **d** 53 **p** 54. C Rainham *Chelmsf* 53-56; C Kingston upon Hull H Trin *York* 56-59; V Upper Armley *Ripon* 59-68; R Chesterfield H Trin *Derby* 68-77; P-in-c Matlock Bath 77-83; V 83-92; Hon Can Derby Cathl 87-92; RD Wirksworth 88-92; rtd 92; Perm to Offic *Ripon* from 92. *10 Kirkby Avenue, Ripon HG4 2DR* Tel (01765) 606306

COLLARD, John Cedric. b 30. Pemb Coll Cam BA53 MA76. St Alb Minl Tr Scheme 77. **d** 80 **p** 81. NSM Roxton w Gt Barford *St Alb* 80-84; C Liskeard w St Keyne, St Pinnock and Morval *Truro* 84-87; TV Liskeard, St Keyne, St Pinnock, Morval etc 87-93; rtd 93; Perm to Offic *Truro* from 93. *Curlew Cottage, Bohetherick, Saltash PL12 6SZ* Tel (01579) 350560

COLLARD, Norton Harvey. b 22. Open Univ BA80. Roch Th Coll 63. **d** 65 **p** 66. C Swanley St Mary *Roch* 65-67; C Dartford H Trin 67-70; V Grantham St Anne *Linc* 70-87; rtd 87; Perm to Offic *Linc* 87-02. *1 Kenwick Drive, Grantham NG31 9DP* Tel (01476) 577345

COLLAS, Canon Victor John. b 23. Pemb Coll Ox BA44 MA48. Wycliffe Hall Ox 49. **d** 51 **p** 52. C Milton *Win* 51-58; R Guernsey St Andr 58-81; Hon Can Win Cathl 78-81; Perm to Offic from 81; rtd 81. *Paradis, La Rue du Paradis, Vale, Guernsey GY3 5BL* Tel (01481) 244450

COLLEDGE, Christopher Richard. b 58. Chich Th Coll. **d** 82 **p** 83. C Deal St Leon *Cant* 82-83; C Deal St Leon and St Rich and Sholden 83-85; Bermuda 85-88; TV Wickford and Runwell *Chelmsf* 88-90; Chapl Runwell Hosp Wickford 88-90; Chapl RAD from 90; Perm to Offic *Chelmsf* from 90. *243 Brunswick Road, London W5 1AJ* Tel (020) 8810 8471 Mobile 07721-864517 Fax 8810 8879

COLLESS, Mrs Salma. b 55. SRN77 RM80. EAMTC 89. **d** 92 **p** 94. NSM Chesterton St Andr *Ely* 92-93; Australia from 93; Hon Dn Chapman 93; C Curtin 94-96; Chapl Brindabella Gardens 96; P Worker Bernie Court 97; Asst P Woden 97-98. *12 Sollya Place, Rivett, ACT, Australia 2611* Tel (0061) (2) 6288 7835 Mobile 414-755756

COLLETT-WHITE, Thomas Charles. b 36. Trin Coll Cam BA61 MA86. Ridley Hall Cam 60. **d** 62 **p** 63. C Gillingham St Mark *Roch* 62-66; V 79-90; C Normanton *Wakef* 66-69; V Highbury New Park St Aug *Lon* 69-76; Canada 76-79; Chapl Medway Hosp Gillingham 79-85; P-in-c Clerkenwell St Jas and St Jo w St Pet *Lon* 90-96; rtd 01. *77 The Street, Boughton under Blean, Faversham ME13 9BE* Tel (01227) 750770

COLLIE, Canon Bertie Harold Guy. b 28. Glas Univ MB, ChB56. Glas NSM Course 75. **d** 76 **p** 77. NSM Ayr *Glas* 76-84; NSM

Maybole from 76; NSM Girvan from 76; NSM Pinmore from 76; Dioc Supernumerary from 91; Can St Mary's Cathl 96-99; Hon Can from 99. *52 Bellevue Crescent, Ayr KA7 2DR* Tel (01292) 285889 Pager 07625-138817

COLLIE, Canon John Norman. b 25. Em Coll Cam BA51 MA56. Ridley Hall Cam 52. **d** 54 **p** 55. C Leic H Apostles *Leic* 54-57; C Melton Mowbray w Thorpe Arnold 57-59; Chapl Lee Abbey 59-62; V Streatham Immanuel w St Anselm *S'wark* 62-68; V Ecclesall *Sheff* 68-90; Hon Can Sheff Cathl 83-90; RD Ecclesall 85-89; rtd 90; Perm to Offic *Sheff* from 90. *46 Sunnyvale Road, Totley, Sheffield S17 4FB* Tel 0114-235 2249

COLLIER, Anthony Charles. b 45. Peterho Cam BA68 MA72 Oriel Coll Ox DipTh70 Whitelands Coll Lon PGCE76. Cuddesdon Coll 68. **d** 71 **p** 72. C N Holmwood *Guildf* 71-75; Perm to Offic *S'wark* 75-79; Chapl Colfe's Sch Lon from 80; Hon C Shirley St Jo *Cant* 80-84; Perm C Shirley St Jo *S'wark* from 85. *56 Bennetts Way, Croydon CR0 8AB* Tel (020) 8777 6456 E-mail anthony.collier@lineone.net

COLLIER, Mrs Janice Margaret. b 57. Liv Univ GradDipPhys79 MCSP79. Cam Th Federation. **d** 01 **p** 02. C Formby H Trin *Liv* from 01. *19 Hampton Road, Formby, Liverpool L37 6EJ*

COLLIER, Michael Francis. b 29. Wycliffe Hall Ox 71. **d** 73 **p** 74. C Hampstead St Paul *Birm* 73-75; P-in-c Castleton *Derby* 75-80; P-in-c Hope 78-80; V Hope and Castleton 80-97; RD Bakewell and Eyam 90-95; rtd 97; Perm to Offic *Derby* from 90. *Buffers Cottage, Station Road, Hope, Hope Valley S33 6RR* Tel (01433) 620915

COLLIER, Paul Clive. b 53. Trin Coll Bris 80. **d** 82 **p** 83. C Hazlemere *Ox* 82-90; V from 90. *The New Vicarage, 260 Amersham Road, High Wycombe HP15 7PZ* Tel (01494) 439404

COLLIER, Paul Edward (Edge). b 63. Solicitor 93 Mert Coll Ox BA85 Lon Univ PGCE87. S'wark Ord Course 91. **d** 94 **p** 95. C E Dulwich St Jo *S'wark* 94-97; C-in-c Bermondsey St Hugh CD 97-02; Chapl Goldsmiths' Coll Lon from 03. *7 Morval Road, London SW2 1DG* Tel (020) 7733 0278

COLLIER, Richard John Millard. b 45. FRSA92. EAMTC 78. **d** 81 **p** 82. NSM Nor St Pet Mancroft w St Jo Maddermarket *Nor* 81-99; NSM Thurton from 99. *Old Manor Farm, Fox Road, Framingham Pigot, Norwich NR14 7PZ* Tel (01508) 492916

COLLIER, Stephen John. b 46. St Pet Coll Ox MA68 Univ of Wales (Cardiff) DipSW74. Qu Coll Birm DipTh94. **d** 94 **p** 95. C Thorpe *Nor* 94-98; C Nor St Pet Mancroft w St Jo Maddermarket 98-01; R Kessingland, Gisleham and Rushmere from 01. *The Rectory, 1 Wash Lane, Kessingland, Lowestoft NR33 7QZ* Tel (01502) 740256

COLLIER, Susan Margaret. b 47. Cam Univ MB, BChir73. Nor Ord Course 95. **d** 98 **p** 99. NSM Dringhouses *York* from 98. *12 St Helen's Road, York YO24 1HP* Tel (01904) 706064 Fax 708052

COLLIN, Terry. b 39. St Aid Birkenhead 65. **d** 67 **p** 68. C Bolton St Jas w St Chrys *Bradf* 67-71; C Keighley 71-74; V Greengates from 74. *The Vicarage, 138 New Line, Greengates, Bradford BD10 0BX* Tel (01274) 613111

COLLING, Canon James Oliver (Joc). b 30. MBE95. Man Univ BA50. Cuddesdon Coll 52. **d** 54 **p** 55. C Wigan All SS *Liv* 54-59; V Padgate Ch 59-71; R Padgate 71-73; RD Warrington 70-82 and 87-89; AD 89-95; R Warrington St Elphin 73-97; Hon Can Liv Cathl 76-97; Chapl to The Queen 90-00; rtd 97; Perm to Offic *Ches* from 99. *19 King Street, Chester CH1 2AH* Tel (01244) 317557

COLLING, Terence John. b 47. Linc Th Coll 84. **d** 86 **p** 87. C Wood End *Cov* 86-90; V Willenhall 90-02; V Wolvey w Burton Hastings, Copston Magna etc from 02. *St John's Vicarage, School Lane, Wolvey, Hinckley LE10 3LH* Tel (01455) 220385 Fax 221590 E-mail tc@vicwolvey.fsnet.co.uk

COLLINGBOURNE, David Edward. b 42. St D Coll Lamp. **d** 01. Treas Dioc Coun of Educn *Mon* from 94; NSM Bishton from 01. *The Gables, Llanwern, Newport NP18 2DS* Tel (01633) 412742 Fax as telephone E-mail susan.collingbourne@tinyworld.co.uk

COLLINGE, Mrs Christine Elizabeth. b 47. Doncaster Coll of Educn CertEd68. St Alb and Ox Min Course 95. **d** 98 **p** 99. NSM W Slough *Ox* from 98. *26 Bell Close, Wexham, Slough SL2 5UQ* Tel (01753) 575332

COLLINGS, Canon Neil. b 46. K Coll Lon BD69 AKC69. **d** 70 **p** 71. C Littleham w Exmouth *Ex* 70-72; TV 72-74; Chapl Westmr Abbey 74-79; Preb Heref Cathl *Heref* 79-86; Dir of Ords and Post-Ord Tr 79-86; R Heref St Nic 79-86; Bp's Dom Chapl 82-86; R Harpenden St Nic *St Alb* 86-99; Hon Can St Alb 96-99; Can Res and Treas Ex Cathl *Ex* from 99; Chapl Devon and Cornwall Constabulary from 99; Chapl OStJ from 01. *9 Cathedral Close, Exeter EX1 1EZ* Tel (01392) 279367 Fax 498769 E-mail collings@exeter-cathedral.org.uk

COLLINGS, Robert Frank. b 26. Lon Univ BD53. ALCD52. **d** 52 **p** 53. C Bayswater *Lon* 52-55; Australia from 55; rtd 87. *Unit*

5, 2 Wattle Street, Bunbury, W Australia 6230 Tel (0061) (8) 9721 4520

COLLINGTON, Cameron James. b 68. Wycliffe Hall Ox BTh01. **d** 01 **p** 02. C Ealing St Paul *Lon* from 01. *15A Erlesmere Gardens, London W13 9TZ* Tel (020) 8567 3374 Fax as telephone E-mail bagpipes.collington@xalt.co.uk

COLLINGWOOD, Christopher Paul. b 54. Birm Univ BMus76 Ox Univ BA82 MA87 K Coll Lon MA01. Ripon Coll Cuddesdon 80. **d** 83 **p** 84. C Tupsley *Heref* 83-86; Prec St Alb Abbey *St Alb* 86-90; V Bedford St Paul 90-97; Can Res and Prec Guildf Cathl *Guildf* 97-99; Chapl Chigwell Sch Essex from 99; Sen Tutor from 01; Hon C Loughton St Jo *Chelmsf* from 99. *84 Russell Road, Buckhurst Hill IG9 5QB* Tel (020) 8504 4476 *or* 8501 5746 Fax 8500 6232 E-mail ccollingwood@chigwell-school.org

COLLINGWOOD, Deryck Laurence. b 50. St Jo Coll Cam BA72. Edin Th Coll BD85. **d** 85 **p** 85. Chapl Napier Poly *Edin* 85-88; C Edin Ch Ch 85-88; TV from 88; Tutor Edin Th Coll from 89; Asst P Edin St Hilda *Edin* from 94; Asst P Edin St Fillan from 94; Chapl Napier Univ from 95. *St Hilda's House, 1A Oxgangs Avenue, Edinburgh EH13 9JA* Tel 0131-441 1235 *or* 455 4694 Fax 455 4695 E-mail d.collingwood@napier.ac.uk

COLLINGWOOD, Graham Lewis. b 63. Open Univ BA92 Ex Univ MA98. St Steph Ho Ox DipMin95. **d** 95 **p** 96. C Heavitree w Ex St Paul *Ex* 95-97; CF 97-99; C St Marychurch *Ex* 99-00; C Cottingham *York* 00-02; Chapl RAF from 02. *Chaplaincy Services (RAF), HQ, Personnel and Training Command, RAF Innsworth, Gloucester GL3 1EZ* Tel (01452) 712612 ext 5164 Fax 510828

COLLINGWOOD, John Jeremy Raynham. b 37. Barrister 64 CCC Cam BA60 MA68 Lon Univ BD78. Trin Coll Bris 75. **d** 78 **p** 79. C Henleaze *Bris* 78-80; P-in-c Clifton H Trin, St Andr and St Pet 80-81; V 81-91; RD Clifton 84-87; Bp's Officer for Miss and Evang 87-91; V Guildf Ch Ch *Guildf* 91-98; V Guildf Ch Ch w St Martha-on-the-Hill 98-02; RD Guildf 95-00; rtd 02. *The Old Manse, 55 Audley Road, Saffron Walden CB11 3HD* Tel (01799) 529055 E-mail mporokoso@aol.com

COLLINS, Adelbert Andrew. b 15. Lich Th Coll. **d** 61 **p** 62. C Sedgley All SS *Lich* 61-77; P-in-c Enville 77-81 and 86-88; R 81-86; C Kinver and Enville 88-90; rtd 90; Perm to Offic *Lich* and *Worc* from 90. *West Cottage, Bridgnorth Road, Enville, Stourbridge DY7 5JA* Tel (01384) 873733

COLLINS, Barry Douglas. b 47. Kelham Th Coll 66. **d** 70 **p** 71. C Peel Green *Man* 70-73; C Salford St Phil w St Steph 73-75; R Blackley H Trin 75-79; Perm to Offic *Ripon* 80-82; *Pet* 83-93; *Cov* 85-93; *Ox* 93-97; P-in-c Bengeworth *Worc* 98-99; V from 99. *The Vicarage, 1 Broadway Road, Evesham WR11 3NB* Tel (01386) 446164 Fax 421664

COLLINS, Bruce Churton. b 47. BSc. Oak Hill Th Coll. **d** 83 **p** 84. C Notting Hill St Jo *Lon* 83-87; C Notting Hill St Jo and St Pet 87-90; V Roxeth Ch Ch and Harrow St Pet 90-93; P-in-c S Harrow St Paul 91-93; TR Roxeth 93-03; NSM from 03; Overseer New Wine Internat Min from 03. *48 Whitmore Road, Harrow HA1 4AD* Tel (020) 8423 6261 E-mail brucertm@aol.com

COLLINS, Ms Cheryl Anne. b 62. MCA90 Rob Coll Cam BA85 MA89. Ripon Coll Cuddesdon 91. **d** 93 **p** 94. C Sharrow St Andr *Sheff* 93-95; Chapl Sheff Univ 95-01; Hon C Endcliffe 96-01; P-in-c Barton *Ely* from 01; P-in-c Coton from 01; P-in-c Dry Drayton from 01. *70 High Street, Coton, Cambridge CB3 7PL* Tel (01954) 210287 E-mail c.a.collins@shef.ac.uk

COLLINS, Christopher. b 46. K Coll Lon BSc67 AKC67 Pemb Coll Ox BA70. St Steph Ho Ox 68. **d** 71 **p** 72. C Pennywell St Thos and Grindon St Oswald CD *Dur* 71-74; C Pallion 74-76; C Millfield St Mary 74-76; C Bishopwearmouth Gd Shep 74-76; C Harton Colliery 76-78; TV Winlaton 78-85; V Grangetown from 85. *St Aidan's Vicarage, Ryhope Road, Sunderland SR2 9RS* Tel 0191-514 3485

COLLINS, Canon Christopher David. b 43. Sheff Univ BA(Econ)64. Tyndale Hall Bris 65. **d** 68 **p** 69. C Rusholme H Trin *Man* 68-71; C Bushbury *Lich* 71-74; V Fairfield *Liv* 74-81; V Tunbridge Wells St Jo *Roch* 81-92; R Luton Ch Ch from 92; Chapl Thames Gateway NHS Trust from 92; Chapl Medway NHS Trust 92-99; RD Roch 94-00; Hon Can Roch Cathl from 98. *Luton Rectory, Capstone Road, Chatham ME5 7PN* Tel (01634) 843780 E-mail c.d.col@breathe.com

COLLINS, Donard Michael. b 55. TCD. Oak Hill Th Coll BA83. **d** 83 **p** 84. C Lurgan Ch the Redeemer *D & D* 83-87; I Ardmore w Craigavon 87-98; I Killowen *D & R* from 98. *St John's Rectory, 4 Laurel Hill, Coleraine BT51 3AT* Tel (028) 7034 2629

COLLINS, Canon Frederick Spencer. b 36. FACCA Birm Univ DipTh67. Ripon Hall Ox. **d** 67 **p** 68. C Evington *Leic* 67-71; C Hall Green Ascension *Birm* 71-73; V Burney Lane 73-79; Dioc Stewardship Adv 79-84; V Yardley St Edburgha 84-96; RD Yardley 86-92; Hon Can Birm Cathl 89-97; rtd 96; Perm to Offic *Birm* from 96. *237 Old Birmingham Road, Marlbrook, Bromsgrove B60 1HQ* Tel 0121-447 7687

COLLINS, Gavin Andrew. b 66. Trin Hall Cam BA89 MA93. Trin Coll Bris BA96 MA97. **d** 97 **p** 98. C Cambridge St

Barn *Ely* 97-02; V Chorleywood Ch Ch *St Alb* from 02. *Christ Church Vicarage, Chorleywood Common, Rickmansworth WD3 5SG* Tel (01923) 284224 *or* 282149
E-mail gavin-collins@supanet.com

COLLINS, George Martyn. b 36. Bris Univ BA58. Coll of Resurr Mirfield. **d** 62 **p** 63. C Widley w Wymering *Portsm* 62-64; C Kingstanding St Mark CD *Birm* 64-69; V Weoley Castle 69-78; R Curdworth 78-83; TR Curdworth w Castle Vale 83-88; V Westbury-on-Trym H Trin *Bris* 88-01; rtd 01; Perm to Offic *Bris* from 02. *7 Northwick Road, Bristol BS7 0UG* Tel 0117-931 5761

COLLINS, Guy James Douglas. b 74. St Andr Univ MTheol96 Peterho Cam PhD00. Westcott Ho Cam 96. **d** 00 **p** 01. C Barnes *S'wark* 00-03; R Huntington Valley USA from 03. *The Rectory, 2122 Washington Lane, Huntington Valley, Philly, PA 19006, USA*

COLLINS, Canon Ian Geoffrey. b 37. Hull Univ BA60 CertEd. Sarum Th Coll 60. **d** 62 **p** 63. C Gainsborough All SS *Linc* 62-65; Min Can Windsor 65-81; Succ Windsor 67-81; R Kirkby in Ashfield *S'well* 81-85; Can Res S'well Minster 85-02; P-in-c Edingley w Halam 91-00; rtd 02. *2 Marston Moor Road, Newark NG24 2GN* Tel (01636) 702866

COLLINS, James Frederick. b 10. St Jo Coll Cam BA34 MA38. Westcott Ho Cam 34. **d** 35 **p** 36. C Benwell St Jas *Newc* 35-38; Chapl Miss to Seamen Port Sudan 38-41; Chapl RNVR 36-46; C Milford *Win* 46-47; V Rothwell w Orton *Pet* 47-51; R Bromham *Sarum* 51-62; V Chisledon and Draycot Foliatt 62-68; Dir of Ords 68-73; Hon C Devizes St Jo w St Mary 68-75; rtd 75; Perm to Offic *St Alb* 81-99. *3 Parkinson Close, Marford Road, Wheathampstead, St Albans AL4 8DP* Tel (01582) 833944

COLLINS, Miss Janet May. b 55. Qu Mary Coll Lon BA78 St Jo Coll Dur BA84. Cranmer Hall Dur 82. **dss** 85 **d** 87 **p** 94. Willington Team *Newc* 85-88; C 87-88; Par Dn Stevenage St Hugh Chells *St Alb* 88-90; Par Dn Goldington 90-93; TD Witney *Ox* 93-94; TV 94-96; Tutor St Alb and Ox Min Course 96-01; TV Langtree 99-01; P-in-c Weldon w Deene *Pet* from 01; RD Corby from 02. *24 Garston Road, Corby NN18 8NH* Tel (01536) 746560 E-mail revd.jan@btopenworld.com

COLLINS, John. See COLLINS, Peter John.

COLLINS, John Gilbert. b 32. S'wark Ord Course 67. **d** 71 **p** 72. C Coulsdon St Jo *S'wark* 71-75; Chapl St Fran Hosp Haywards Heath 75-84; Chapl Hurstwood Park Hosp Haywards Heath 75-84; R Stedham w Iping, Elsted and Treyford-cum-Didling *Chich* 84-92; rtd 92; Perm to Offic *Chich* 94-00. *12 Exeter Road, Broyle, Chichester PO19 5EF* Tel (01243) 536861

COLLINS, Preb John Theodore Cameron Bucke. b 25. Clare Coll Cam BA49 MA52. Ridley Hall Cam 49. **d** 51 **p** 52. C St Marylebone All So w SS Pet and Jo *Lon* 51-57; V Gillingham St Mark *Roch* 57-71; Chapl Medway Hosp Gillingham 70-71; V Canford Magna *Sarum* 71-80; RD Wimborne 79-80; V Brompton H Trin w Onslow Square St Paul *Lon* 80-85; C 85-89; AD Chelsea 84-88; Preb St Paul's Cathl 85-89; rtd 89; Perm to Offic *Lon* 89-90; Perm to Offic *Win* 89-97. *27 Woodstock Close, Oxford OX2 8DB* Tel (01865) 556228

COLLINS, John William Michael. b 54. Univ Coll Chich Dip Th & Min 99. Bp Otter Coll 95. **d** 98. NSM S Patcham *Chich* from 98. *2 Buxted Rise, Brighton BN1 8FG* Tel (01273) 509388

COLLINS, Ms Kathryne Broncy. b 51. Portland State Univ BSc75 Lon Univ MSc76. Linc Th Coll 92. **d** 94 **p** 95. C Bishop's Castle w Mainstone *Heref* 94-98; P-in-c 98-01; V Bishop's Castle w Mainstone, Lydbury N etc 01-03; TV Wrexham *St As* from 03; Chapl NE Wales NHS Trust from 03. *All Saints' Vicarage, 55 Princess Street, Wrexham LL13 7US* Tel (01978) 266145
E-mail kathy.collins@virgin.net

COLLINS, Ms Linda Kathleen. b 56. Girton Coll Cam BA77 MA80 Bris Univ PGCE78. WMMTC 99. **d** 02. C Harborne St Pet *Birm* from 02. *19 Vicarage Road, Harborne, Birmingham B17 0SN* Tel 0121-426 5431 Mobile 07985-033476
E-mail tobycol@aol.com

COLLINS, Mrs Lindsay Rosemary Faith. b 70. K Coll Lon BD91 AKC91 PGCE92. Ripon Coll Cuddesdon MTh95. **d** 97 **p** 98. C Witney *Ox* 97-99; NSM 00-01; Chapl Cokethorpe Sch Witney 00-01; Chapl and Hd RE St Paul's Girls' Sch Hammersmith from 01. *25 Glebe Road, Barnes SW13 0DZ* Tel (020) 8878 6982

COLLINS, Martyn. See COLLINS, George Martyn

COLLINS, Canon Norman Hilary. b 33. Wert Coll Ox BA55 MA58. Wells Th Coll 58. **d** 60 **p** 61. C Ystrad Mynach *Llan* 60-62; C Gelligaer 62-67; V Maerdy 67-77; R Penarth w Lavernock 77-98; RD Penarth and Barry 87-98; Can Llan Cathl 92-98; rtd 98. *4 Llys Steffan, Llantwit Major CF61 2UF* Tel (01446) 794976

COLLINS, Paul David Arthur. b 50. Lanc Univ MSc91. K Coll Lon BD72 AKC72 St Aug Coll Cant 73. **d** 73 **p** 74. C Rotherhithe St Mary w All SS *S'wark* 73-76; C Stocking Farm *Leic* 76-78; V 78-83; R Husbands Bosworth w Mowsley and Knaptoft etc 83-87; Soc Resp Officer *Blackb* 87-94; R Worc City St Paul and Old St Martin etc *Worc* 94-03; Min Can Worc Cathl 95-03; P-in-c Bishop's Castle w Mainstone, Lydbury N etc *Heref* from 03. *The Vicarage, Church Lane, Bishops Castle SY9 5AF* Tel (01588) 638445

COLLINS, Paul Myring. b 53. St Jo Coll Dur BA75 Ox Univ BA78 MA83 K Coll Lon PhD95. St Steph Ho Ox 76. **d** 79 **p** 80. C Meir *Lich* 79-82; C Fenton 82-83; TV Leek and Meerbrook 83-87; Tutor in Th and Liturgy Chich Th Coll 87-94; Dir of Studies 90-94; V Brighton Gd Shep Preston *Chich* 94-96; Tutor Qu Coll Birm 96-01; V Bournville *Birm* 01-02; Reader Chr Th Univ Coll Chich from 02. *University College, College Lane, Chichester PO19 6PE* Tel (01243) 816000
E-mail p.collins@ucc.ac.uk

COLLINS, Peter John. b 33. Open Univ BA. Oak Hill Th Coll 64. **d** 66 **p** 67. C Low Leyton *Chelmsf* 66-69; C Portsdown *Portsm* 69-72; V Gatten St Paul 72-79; C-in-c Ingrave St Steph CD *Chelmsf* 79-85; V Roydon 85-98; rtd 98; Perm to Offic *S'wark* from 00. *14 Glyndale Grange, Mulgrave Road, Sutton SM2 6LP* Tel (020) 8770 7683

COLLINS, Philip Howard Norton. b 50. AKC73. St Aug Coll Cant 73. **d** 74 **p** 75. C Stamford Hill St Thos *Lon* 74-78; C Upwood w Gt and Lt Raveley *Ely* 78-81; C Ramsey 78-81; R Leverington 81-92; P-in-c Wisbech St Mary 89-92; RD Wisbech 90-92; TR Whittlesey and Pondersbridge 92-95; TR Whittlesey, Pondersbridge and Coates 95-02; R New Alresford w Ovington and Itchen Stoke *Win* from 02. *The Rectory, 37 Jacklyns Lane, Alresford SO24 9LF* Tel (01962) 732105
E-mail philip_nortoncollins@hotmail.com

COLLINS (née SHIRRAS), Rachel Joan. b 66. Univ of Wales (Abth) BSc88. St Jo Coll Nottm 88. **d** 91 **p** 94. Par Dn Ockbrook *Derby* 91-94; C Bris St Matt and St Nath *Bris* 94-97; V Beckton St Mark *Chelmsf* 97-02; NSM Wandsworth St Steph *S'wark* from 02; NSM Wandsworth St Mich from 02. *87 Lambton Road, London SW20 0LW* Tel (020) 8947 7440
E-mail rshirras@aol.com

COLLINS, Richard Andrew. b 65. K Coll Lon BD92 AKC92 Dur Univ MA00. St Steph Ho Ox 92. **d** 94 **p** 95. C Whickham *Dur* 94-97; C Bensham 97-98; TV 98-03; P-in-c Greatham from 03; Local Min Officer from 03; Chapl Greatham Hosp from 03. *Greatham House, 6 Front Street, Greatham, Hartlepool TS25 2HS* Tel (01429) 872626
E-mail richard.collins@durham.anglican.org

COLLINS, Roger Richardson. b 48. Birm Univ BPhil88. WMMTC 78. **d** 81 **p** 82. NSM Cotteridge *Birm* from 81. *6 Chesterfield Court, Middleton Hall Road, Birmingham B30 1AF* Tel 0121-459 4009 E-mail roger@rrcollins.freeserve.co.uk

COLLINS, Ross Nicoll Ferguson. b 64. Edin Univ MA87 Ven English Coll Rome 91 Pontifical Univ Rome 91. Ripon Coll Cuddesdon BA91. **d** 92 **p** 93. C Goring w S Stoke *Ox* 92-96; P-in-c N Leigh 96-01; TR Barnes *S'wark* from 01. *The Rectory, 25 Glebe Road, London SW13 0DZ* Tel (020) 8404 3177 *or* 8741 5422 Fax as telephone E-mail ross@stmarybarnes.org

COLLINS, Canon Stella Vivian. b 32. S Dios Minl Tr Scheme 74. **dss** 77 **d** 87 **p** 94. Harnham *Sarum* 77-88; Hon Par Dn 87-88; Dioc Lay Min Adv 82-97; Adv for Women's Min 82-97; Hon Par Dn Wilton w Netherhampton and Fugglestone 88-94; Hon C 94-97; RD Wylye and Wilton 89-94; Can and Preb Sarum Cathl 93-97; rtd 97; Perm to Offic *Sarum* from 97. *1 Meadowside, Hanging Langford, Salisbury SP3 4NW* Tel (01722) 790743

COLLINS, William Arthur Donovan. b 21. AKC49. **d** 50 **p** 51. C Huddersfield St Jo *Wakef* 50-52; S Africa 52-61; C Friern Barnet All SS *Lon* 61-62; V Kellington w Whitley *Wakef* 62-66; S Africa 66-80; Adn Cape Town 75-80; V Birchington w Acol and Minnis Bay *Cant* 80-85; Warden Coll of St Barn Lingfield 85-88; rtd 88; Perm to Offic *St E* from 88. *The College of St Barnabas, Blackberry Lane, Lingfield RH7 6NJ* Tel (01342) 870350

COLLINS, William Carpenter. b 35. BA55 MA57 MDiv65. Ch Div Sch of the Pacific (USA) 63. **d** 66 **p** 67. USA 66-71; Hon C Newlyn St Pet *Truro* 82-93; Perm to Offic 93-96. *Cape House, Cape Cornwall, St Just, Penzance TR19 7NN* Tel (01736) 787112

COLLINS, William Francis Martin. b 43. St Cath Coll Cam BA66 MA70. Cuddesdon Coll 68. **d** 70 **p** 71. C Man Victoria Park *Man* 70-73; P-in-c Ancoats 73-78; Chapl Abraham Moss Cen 78-91; Hon C Cheetham Hill 81-84; Chs' FE Officer for Gtr Man 84-91; V Norbury *Ches* from 91. *Norbury Vicarage, 75 Chester Road, Hazel Grove, Stockport SK7 5PE* Tel 0161-483 8640
E-mail martin@norbury75.freeserve.co.uk

COLLINS, Winfield St Clair. b 41. Univ of W Indies BA83 Man Univ BA88 MEd91. Codrington Coll Barbados LTh77. **d** 76 **p** 76. Asst Chapl HM Pris Wakef 76; Barbados 76-84; C St Jo 76; P-in-c St Mark and St Cath 77-84; Asst Chapl HM Pris Wandsworth 85; Chapl HM YOI Thorn Cross 85-91; Chapl HM Pris Pentonville 91-01; Can Res Barbados 01-02; rtd 02. *92 Barclay Road, London N18 1EQ* Tel (020) 8245 4145

COLLINSON, Ernest John. b 12. ALCD36. **d** 36 **p** 37. C Southall Green St Jo *Lon* 36-38; Sudan 38-46; R Graveley w Chivesfield *St Alb* 46-48; V Laleham *Lon* 48-52; Africa Inland Miss 52-54; V Penge St Jo *Roch* 54-63; Rwanda Miss 63-66; V Tiverton St Geo *Ex* 66-73; Perm to Offic from 74; rtd 77. *2 St Helens Court, Cotmaton Road, Sidmouth EX10 8SS*

COLLINSON, Leslie Roland. b 47. St Jo Coll Nottm DCM92. **d** 92 **p** 93. C Gorleston St Andr *Nor* 92-96; TV Banbury *Ox* 96-98; V Banbury St Fran 98-00; V Darwen St Barn *Blackb* from

00. *St Barnabas' Vicarage, 68 Park Road, Darwen BB3 2LD* Tel (01254) 702732 E-mail revles@ntlworld.com

COLLINSON, Mark Peter Charles. b 68. City Univ BSc90 Fitzw Coll Cam BA97 MA01. Ridley Hall Cam 95. **d** 98 **p** 99. C Ashton-upon-Mersey St Mary *Ches* 98-01; Chapl Amsterdam w Den Helder and Heiloo *Eur* from 01. *Bouwmeester 2, 1188 DT Amstelveen, The Netherlands* Tel (0031) (20) 441 0355 E-mail mark@christchurch.nl

COLLINSON, Roger Alfred. b 36. St Jo Coll Dur BA58 Cranmer Hall Dur 60. **d** 63 **p** 97. C Liv St Mich *Liv* 63-64; NSM Ormside *Carl* from 97; NSM Appleby from 97. *1 Caesar's View, Appleby-in-Westmorland CA16 6SH* Tel (01768) 352886

COLLIS, Jonathan. b 69. Selw Coll Cam BA91 MA94. Aston Tr Scheme 96 Westcott Ho Cam 97. **d** 99 **p** 00. C St Neots *Ely* 99-02; Chapl Jes Coll Cam from 02. *Jesus College, Cambridge CB5 8BL* Tel (01223) 339339 *or* 359196 E-mail jonathan@collis60.freeserve.co.uk

COLLIS, Michael Alan. b 35. K Coll Lon BD60 AKC60. **d** 61 **p** 62. C Worc St Martin *Worc* 61-63; C Dudley St Thos 63-66; C St Peter-in-Thanet *Cant* 66-70; V Croydon H Trin 70-77; P-in-c Norbury St Steph 77-81; V 81-82; V Sutton Valence w E Sutton and Chart Sutton 82-89; R New Fishbourne *Chich* 89-00; P-in-c Appledram 89-00; rtd 00; Perm to Offic *Chich* from 00. *66 Orchard Way, Barnham, Bognor Regis PO22 0HY* Tel (01243) 552429

COLLIS, Stephen Thomas. b 47. MHCIMA74. Cranmer Hall Dur 80. **d** 82 **p** 83. C Crewe All SS and St Paul *Ches* 82-84; C Wilmslow 84-86 and 95-98; Chapl RAF 86-95; P-in-c Barthomley *Ches* 98-00; S Cheshire Ind Chapl 98-00; Chapl Abu Dhabi UAE from 00. *St Andrew's Church, PO Box 262, Abu Dhabi, United Arab Emirates* Tel (00971) (2) 446 1631 E-mail standrew@emirates.net.ae

COLLIS SMITH, Charles Philip. b 39. St Cath Coll Cam BA61. Lich Th Coll 61. **d** 63 **p** 64. C Wednesfield St Thos *Lich* 63-66; C Hednesford 66-71; V High Offley 71-80; R Myddle 80-92; V Broughton 80-92; rtd 92; Perm to Offic *Lich* from 92. *Trenance, 19 Wellgate, Wem, Shrewsbury SY4 5ES* Tel (01939) 235013

COLLISON, Christopher John. b 48. Oak Hill Th Coll 68. **d** 72 **p** 73. C Cromer *Nor* 72-75; C Costessey 76-78; V 87-95; C Heckmondwike *Wakef* 78-79; P-in-c Shepley 79-83; Dioc Communications Officer 79-83; Chapl Flushing Miss to Seamen *Eur* 83-85; Asst Min Sec Miss to Seamen 85-87; C St Mich Paternoster Royal *Lon* 85-87; P-in-c Swainsthorpe w Newton Flotman *Nor* 95-97; TV Newton Flotman, Swainsthorpe, Tasburgh, etc 98-02; Dioc Evang Officer 95-01; V Henfield w Shermanbury and Woodmancote *Chich* from 02. *The Vicarage, Church Lane, Henfield BN5 9NY* Tel (01273) 492017 Fax as telephone E-mail stpeters.henfield@virgin.net

COLLISON, Ms Elizabeth. b 38. Man Univ CertEd58. N Ord Course 85. **d** 88 **p** 94. C Huyton St Mich *Liv* 88-94; C Rainhill from 94. *25 Lowther Drive, Rainhill, Prescot L35 0NG* Tel 0151-426 3853

COLLYER, Canon David John. b 38. JP. Keble Coll Ox BA61 Ox Univ MA86. Westcott Ho Cam 61. **d** 63 **p** 64. C Perry Beeches *Birm* 63-65; Bp's Chapl for Special Youth Work 65-70; P-in-c Deritend 66-70; Bp's Youth Chapl and Dioc Youth Officer 70-73; R Northfield 73-78; Hon Chapl Birm Cathl 78-81; Hon C Birm St Geo 81-86; V Handsworth St Andr 86-97; Hon Can Birm Cathl from 95; Dioc Development Officer 97-01; Perm to Offic from 01. *24 Sundbury Rise, Northfield, Birmingham B31 2EZ* Tel 0121-477 0429 *or* 426 0400 Fax 428 1114 E-mail d.collyer@birmingham.anglican.org

COLLYER, Leon John. b 72. SS Hild & Bede Coll Dur BSc95 Leeds Univ BA00. Coll of Resurr Mirfield 98. **d** 01 **p** 02. C Airedale w Fryston *Wakef* from 01. *3 Kendal Gardens, Castleford WF10 3NY* Tel (01977) 510551 E-mail lcollyer@genie.co.uk

COLMAN, Geoffrey Hugh. b 29. Univ Coll Ox BA53 MA68. Wells Th Coll 67. **d** 68 **p** 69. C Wanstead St Mary *Chelmsf* 68-72; V Barking St Erkenwald 72-77; Youth Chapl 78-81; C Maidstone All SS and St Phil w Tovil *Cant* 85-88; P-in-c Norton 88-93; R 93-96; P-in-c Teynham 88-93; P-in-c Lynsted w Kingsdown 88-93; V Teynham w Lynsted and Kingsdown 93-96; rtd 96; Perm to Offic *Cant* 98-99. *c/o Georgina Fulcher, Bramble Barn, Binsted Lane, Binsted, Arundel BN18 0LQ*

COLMER, Andrew John. b 68. De Montfort Univ Leic BSc90. St Jo Coll Nottm MA96 LTh97. **d** 97 **p** 98. C Roby *Liv* 97-01; C Litherland St Andr 01-02; P-in-c Liv All So Springwood from 02. *Springwood Vicarage, Mather Avenue, Liverpool L19 4TF* Tel 0151-427 5699

COLMER, The Ven Malcolm John. b 45. Sussex Univ MSc67 Nottm Univ BA73. St Jo Coll Nottm 71. **d** 73 **p** 74. C Egham *Guildf* 73-76; C Chadwell *Chelmsf* 76-79; V S Malling *Chich* 79-85; V Hornsey Rise w St Mary w St Steph *Lon* 85-87; TR Hornsey Rise Whitehall Park Team 87-96; AD Islington 90-94; Adn Middx from 96. *61 Cole Park Road, Twickenham TW1 1HT* Tel (020) 8744 2447 E-mail archdeacon.middlesex@london.anglican.org

COLSON, Major Alexander Francis Lionel. b 21. MBE45. St Jo Coll Cam BA43 MA61. Tyndale Hall Bris 60. **d** 62 **p** 63. C

Slough *Ox* 62-65; R Elmswell *St E* 65-73; V W Kilburn St Luke w St Simon and St Jude *Lon* 73-82; R Thrandeston, Stuston and Brome w Oakley *St E* 82-86; rtd 86; Perm to Offic *Nor* from 86. *10 Soanes Court, Lyng, Norwich NR9 5RE* Tel (01603) 872812

COLSON, Ian Richard. b 65. Wolv Poly BSc86 Nottm Univ BTh89 Westmr Coll Ox DipRE98. Linc Th Coll 86. **d** 89 **p** 90. C Nunthorpe *York* 89-92; C Thornaby on Tees 92-93; Chapl RAF 93-00; V Sunbury *Lon* 00-02; Chapl Ardingly Coll from 02. *Ardingly College, College Road, Haywards Heath RH17 6SQ* Tel (01444) 892577 E-mail ianrcolson@aol.com

COLSTON, John Edward. b 43. Open Univ BA91 Leeds Univ MA94. Lich Th Coll 65. **d** 68 **p** 69. C Bromsgrove All SS *Worc* 68-71; C Tettenhall Wood *Lich* 71-74; V Alrewas 74-88; V Wychnor 74-88; R Ainderby Steeple w Yafforth and Kirby Wiske etc *Ripon* 88-95; Warden of Readers 90-96; V High Harrogate St Cuth from 95; AD Harrogate from 01. *Christ Church Vicarage, 11 St Hilda's Road, Harrogate HG2 8JX* Tel (01423) 883390 *or* 530750 E-mail jecolston@yahoo.com

COLTHURST, The Ven Reginald William Richard. b 22. TCD BA44. CITC 45. **d** 45 **p** 46. C Portadown St Mark *Arm* 45-48; C Belfast All SS *Conn* 48-55; I Ardtrea w Desertcreat *Arm* 55-66; I Richhill 66-94; Adn Arm 85-92; rtd 94. *14 Cabin Hill Gardens, Belfast BT75 7AP* Tel (028) 9047 2288

COLTON, Martin Philip. b 67. Sheff Univ BMus89 MMus92 FRCO92 Open Univ PGCE97. St Mich Coll Llan BA03. **d** 03. C Whitchurch *Llan* from 03. *16 St John's Crescent, Whitchurch, Cardiff CF14 7AF* Tel (029) 2062 5947 E-mail martin.colton@which.net

✠**COLTON, The Rt Revd William Paul.** b 60. NUI BCL81 TCD DipTh84 MPhil87. **d** 84 **p** 85 **c** 99. C Lisburn St Paul *Conn* 84-87; Bp's Dom Chapl 85-90; V Choral Belf Cathl 87-90; Min Can Belf Cathl 89-90; PV, Registrar and Chapter Clerk Ch Ch Cathl Dub *D & G* 90-95; I Castleknock and Mulhuddart, w Clonsilla 90-99; Co-ord Protestant Relig Progr RTE 93-99; Hon Chapl Actors' Ch Union 94-96; Area Chapl (Ireland) Actors' Ch Union 96-97; Can Ch Ch Cathl Dublin 97-99; Bp C, C & R from 99. *The Palace, Bishop Street, Cork, Irish Republic* Tel (00353) (21) 431 6114 Fax 427 3437 E-mail bishop@cork.anglican.org *or* pcolton@iol.ie

COLVILLE, Gary Stanley. b 59. Sarum & Wells Th Coll 90. **d** 92 **p** 93. C Plaistow St Mary *Roch* 92-94; P-in-c Foots Cray 94-96; R 96-00; P-in-c N Cray 97-00; R Footscray w N Cray 00; R Pembroke Bermuda from 00. *PO Box HM 544, Hamilton HM CX, Bermuda* Tel (001441) 292 5308 Fax 292 9173 E-mail stjohnsangch@161.bm

COLWILL, James Patrick (Jay). b 68. Man Poly BA91. St Jo Coll Nottm BTh93 MA94. **d** 94 **p** 95. C Reading St Agnes w St Paul *Ox* 94-97; C Easthampstead 97-03; V Orpington Ch Ch *Roch* from 03. *The Vicarage, 165 Charterhouse Road, Orpington BR6 9EP* Tel (01689) 870923 E-mail j.colwill@ntlworld.com

COMBE, Edward Charles. b 40. Man Univ MSc PhD QUB DSc. N Ord Course. **d** 89 **p** 90. NSM Broadheath *Ches* 89-94; USA from 94. *1760 Southwind Lane, Maplewood, MN 55109, USA* Tel (001) (651) 773 3066 E-mail combe001@gold.tc.umn.edu

COMBE, The Very Revd John Charles. b 33. TCD BA53 MA56 BD57 MLitt65 PhD70. **d** 56 **p** 57. C Cork St Luke w St Ann *C, C & R* 56-58; C Ballynafeigh St Jude *D & D* 58-61; I Crinken *D & G* 61-66; Hon Clerical V Ch Ch Cathl Dublin 63-66; C Belfast St Bart *Conn* 66-70; I Belfast St Barn 70-74; I Portadown St Mark *Arm* 74-84; I Arm St Mark w Aghavilly 84-90; Can Arm Cathl 85-90; Dean Kilmore *K, E & A* 90-96; I Kilmore w Ballintemple, Kildallon etc 90-96; rtd 96. *24 Kensington Park, Maxwell Road, Bangor BT20 3RF* Tel (028) 9146 6123

COMBER, Mrs Alison. LNSM course. **d** 94 **p** 95. OLM New Bury *Man* from 94. *12 Seymour Grove, Farnworth, Bolton BL4 0HF* Tel (01204) 397745

COMBER, The Ven Anthony James. b 27. Leeds Univ BSc49 MSc52. St Chad's Coll Dur 53. **d** 56 **p** 57. C Manston *Ripon* 56-60; V Oulton 60-69; V Hunslet St Mary 69-77; RD Armley 72-75 and 79-81; R Farnley 77-82; Hon Can Ripon Cathl 80-92; Adn Leeds 82-92; rtd 92; Perm to Offic *Ripon* from 92; Perm to Offic *Bradf* 93-99. *10 Tavistock Park, Leeds LS12 4DD* Tel 0113-263 0311

COMBER, Keith Charles. b 15. Wycliffe Hall Ox 71. **d** 73 **p** 74. C Walmley *Birm* 73-76; V Barston 76-79; rtd 80; Perm to Offic *Ely* and *Nor* 80-86; Lic to Offic *Chich* 86-88; Perm to Offic *Chich* from 88. *The Derwent Hotel, 38 Sedlescombe Road South, St Leonards-on-Sea TN38 0TB* Tel (01424) 720334

COMBER, Michael. b 35. Carl Dioc Tr Inst. **d** 72 **p** 72. C Carl H Trin and St Barn *Carl* 72-73; C Upperby St Jo 73-76; V Dearham 76-81; V Harraby 81-84; R Orton and Tebay w Ravenstonedale etc 84-90; I Clonfert Gp of Par *L & K* 90-94; I Convoy w Monellan and Donaghmore *D & R* 94-97; I Tamlaght O'Crilly Upper w Lower 97-02; rtd 02. *87 Pinecroft, Kingstown, Carlisle CA3 0DB* Tel (01228) 401428 Mobile 07703-349923 E-mail m.comber@talk21.com

COMBES, The Ven Roger Matthew. b 47. K Coll Lon LLB69. Ridley Hall Cam 72. **d** 74 **p** 75. C Onslow Square St Paul *Lon* 74-77; C Brompton H Trin 76-77; C Cambridge H Sepulchre w

All SS *Ely* 77-86; R Silverhill St Matt *Chich* 86-03; RD Hastings 98-02; Adn Horsham from 03. *3 Danehurst Crescent, Horsham RH13 5HS* Tel (01403) 262710 Fax 210778
E-mail archhorsham@diochi.org.uk *or* combes@fish.co.uk
COMER, Michael John. b 30. St Mich Coll Llan 79. **d** 81 **p** 82. C Bistre *St As* 81-84; R Llanfyllin and Bwlchycibau 84-91; C Hattersley *Ches* 91; V 91-94; rtd 94. *134 Sycamore Drive, Newtown SY16 2QE* Tel (01686) 624557
COMERFORD, Patrick. b 52. Pontifical Univ Maynooth BD87 FRSAI87. CITC 99. **d** 00 **p** 01. NSM Dublin Whitechurch *D & G* from 00. *75 Glenvara Park, Knocklyon, Dublin 16, Irish Republic* Tel (00353) (1) 495 0934 Mobile 087-663 5116
E-mail theology@ireland.com
COMERFORD, Mrs Suzanne Lyn. b 46. St Alb and Ox Min Course 97. **d** 00 **p** 01. OLM Woodley *Ox* from 00. *35 Southlake Crescent, Woodley, Reading RG5 3QJ* Tel 0118-376 9646
E-mail minister@emmanuel-woodley.org
COMFORT, Alan. b 64. Ridley Hall Cam CTM94. **d** 94 **p** 95. C Chadwell Heath *Chelmsf* 94-97; C Buckhurst Hill 97-98; TV 98-03; R Loughton St Mary from 03. *The Rectory, 203 High Road, Loughton IG10 1BB* Tel (020) 8508 7892
E-mail alan@comfort11.freeserve.co.uk
COMLEY, Thomas Hedges. b 36. Leeds Univ BA62. Coll of Resurr Mirfield 62. **d** 64 **p** 65. C Leadgate *Dur* 64-67; C Shirley *Birm* 67-71; V Smethwick St Alb 71-76; Perm to Offic 76-82; V N Wembley St Cuth *Lon* 82-92; V Taddington, Chelmorton and Flagg, and Monyash *Derby* 92-01; rtd 01. *19 Wentworth Avenue, Walton, Chesterfield S40 3JB* Tel (01246) 270911
E-mail tom_comley@lineone.net
COMMANDER, Reginald Arthur. b 20. RGN Aston Univ DHSA BA. Qu Coll Birm 75. **d** 78 **p** 79. NSM Wolverhampton *Lich* 78-92; Perm to Offic from 92; Perm to Offic *Heref* from 95. *15 Coulter Grove, Perton, Wolverhampton WV6 7UA* Tel (01902) 744276
COMMIN, Robert William. b 47. Cape Town Univ BA79. St Paul's Coll Grahamstown DipTh71. **d** 70 **p** 71. S Africa 70-80 and from 89; Chapl Loretto Sch Musselburgh 80-84; TV Thetford *Nor* 84-89. *The Rectory, 5 Roslyn Road, Rondebosch, Cape Town, 7700 South Africa* Tel (0027) (21) 686 3512 *or* 689 4720
COMPTON, Barry Charles Chittenden. b 33. Linc Th Coll 60. **d** 62 **p** 63. C Beddington *S'wark* 62-65; C Limpsfield and Titsey 66-68; Hon C 71-94; R Ridley *Roch* 69-70; R Ash 69-70; Perm to Offic *S'wark* from 70; rtd 94. *14 Hallsland Way, Oxted RH8 9AL* Tel (01883) 714896 Fax 722842
COMPTON, Penelope. b 55. Bulmershe Coll of HE BEd87. NTMTC 98. **d** 01 **p** 02. C Northolt Park St Barn *Lon* from 01. *3 Vernon Rise, Greenford UB6 0EQ* Tel (020) 8723 8140
E-mail pgcompton@aol.com
COMYNS, Clifford John. b 28. TCD BA50 HDipEd53 MA53 BD67. **d** 51 **p** 52. C Chapelizod *D & G* 51-55; CF 55-75; Asst Master Eastbourne Coll from 75; Asst Chapl from 85; Perm to Offic *Chich* from 75. *Eastbourne College, Old Wish Road, Eastbourne BN21 4JY* Tel (01323) 737411
CONALTY, Julie Anne. b 63. SEITE. **d** 99 **p** 00. NSM E Wickham *S'wark* from 99. *12 Littleheath, London SE7 8HU* Tel (020) 8855 6203 *or* 7740 8500
CONANT, Fane Charles. b 44. Oak Hill Th Coll 83. **d** 85 **p** 86. C Hoole *Ches* 85-89; V Kelsall 89-01; P-in-c Seer Green and Jordans *Ox* from 01. *The Vicarage, 43 Long Grove, Seer Green, Beaconsfield HP9 2YN* Tel (01494) 675013
E-mail fanesue@aol.com
CONAWAY, Barry Raymond. b 41. CertEd69 Nottm Univ BEd70. Sarum & Wells Th Coll 86. **d** 88 **p** 89. C Ross w Brampton Abbotts, Bridstow and Peterstow *Heref* 88-91; R Bishop's Frome w Castle Frome and Fromes Hill 91-96; P-in-c Acton Beauchamp and Evesbatch 91-96; P-in-c Charminster and Stinsford *Sarum* 96-01; rtd 01; Perm to Offic *Glouc* 01-02. *9 Constable Way, West Harnham, Salisbury SP2 8LN* Tel (01722) 334870
CONDELL, Canon Joseph Alfred Ambrose. b 48. CITC 70. **d** 73 **p** 74. C Donaghcloney *D & D* 73-76; I Achonry w Tubbercurry and Killoran *T, K & A* 76-79; I Roscrea w Kyle, Bourney and Corbally *L & K* from 79; Can Killaloe Cathl 83-89; Prec Limerick and Killaloe Cathls from 89; Dioc Sec from 91. *St Conan's Rectory, Roscrea, Co Tipperary, Irish Republic* Tel (00353) (505) 21725 Mobile 087-2435737 Fax 21993
E-mail secretary@limerick.anglican.org *or* condell@iol.ie
CONDER, Paul Collingwood Nelson. b 33. St Jo Coll Cam BA56 MA60. Ridley Hall Cam 56. **d** 58 **p** 59. C Grassendale *Liv* 58-61; Tutor St Jo Coll Dur 61-67; R Sutton *Liv* 67-74; RD 74-75; V Thames Ditton *Guildf* 75-86; RD Emly 82-86; V Blundellsands St Mich *Liv* 86-99; rtd 99. *112 Strensall Road, Earswick, York YO32 9SJ* Tel (01904) 763071
CONDRY, Canon Edward Francis. b 53. UEA BA74 Ex Coll Ox Dip Soc Anthropology 75 BLitt77 DPhil80 Nottm Univ DipTh81 Open Univ MBA02. Linc Th Coll 80. **d** 82 **p** 83. C Weston Favell *Pet* 82-85; V Bloxham w Milcombe and S Newington *Ox* 85-93; TR Rugby St Andr *Cov* 93-02; Dir Post-

Ord Tr *Cant* from 02; Can Res Cant Cathl from 02. *19 The Precincts, Canterbury CT1 2EP* Tel (01227) 865228
E-mail edwardc@canterbury-cathedral.org
CONEY, Christopher Thomas. b 32. Magd Coll Cam BA56 MA60. Cuddesdon Coll 68. **d** 69 **p** 70. C Farnham *Guildf* 69-72; Chapl Pangbourne Coll 72-86; R W Woodhay w Enborne, Hampstead Marshall etc *Ox* 86-90; rtd 97; Lic to Offic *St D* from 97. *Jubilee House, Pen-y-Bryn, Begelly, Kilgetty SA68 0XE* Tel (01834) 814652
CONEY, Joanna Margery. b 39. Culham Coll of Educn CertEd75 Open Univ BA83. Ox Min Course CBTS93. **d** 93 **p** 94. Par Dn Wolvercote w Summertown *Ox* 93-94; C 94-97; OLM Tr Officer (Ox Adnry) 97-00; Dioc Portfolio Officer from 00; Dioc Adv to Lic Lay Min from 02. *4 Rowland Close, Wolvercote, Oxford OX2 8PW* Tel (01865) 556456 Fax as telephone
E-mail portox@oxford.anglican.org
CONEY, Preb Peter Norman Harvey. b 28. Keble Coll Ox BA51 MA55. Cuddesdon Coll 51. **d** 53 **p** 54. C Northallerton w Deighton and Romanby *York* 53-56; C Wakef Cathl *Wakef* 56-59; V Milverton *B & W* 59-65; Chapl K Coll Taunton 65-70; V Martock *B & W* 70-72; V Martock w Ash 72-92; RD Martock 80-90; Dioc Press Officer 83-88; Preb Wells Cathl 85-92; rtd 93; Perm to Offic *Eur* from 92. *Les Aubépines, Le Causse, 46500 Mayrinhac-Lentour, France* Tel (0033) (5) 65 38 22 19
CONEYS, Stephen John. b 61. Sheff Univ LLB82. St Jo Coll Nottm 87. **d** 90 **p** 91. C Plymouth Em w Efford *Ex* 90-92; C Plymouth Em, Efford and Laira 93-94; TV Whitstable *Cant* 94-02; TR from 02. *The Vicarage, 11 Kimberley Grove, Seasalter, Whitstable CT5 4AY* Tel (01227) 276795
E-mail steve@sconeys.freeserve.co.uk
CONGDON, John Jameson. b 30. St Edm Hall Ox BA53 MA57. Wycliffe Hall Ox 53. **d** 55 **p** 56. C Aspley *S'well* 55-58; C-in-c Woodthorpe CD 58-63; V Woodthorpe 63-69; V Spring Grove St Mary *Lon* 70-84; V Woodley St Jo the Ev *Ox* 84-89; Chapl W Middx Univ Hosp Isleworth 89-95; rtd 95; Perm to Offic *Lon* from 95. *23 Pates Manor Drive, Feltham TW14 8JJ* Tel (020) 8893 1823
CONLEY, James Alan. b 29. Dur Univ BSc51. St Jo Coll Nottm. **d** 87 **p** 88. NSM Cropwell Bishop w Colston Bassett, Granby etc *S'well* 87-97; Perm to Offic *Sarum* from 97. *30 The Waldrons, Thornford, Sherborne DT9 6PX* Tel (01935) 872672
CONLON, Shaun. b 69. Birm Univ BA90. Ripon Coll Cuddesdon DipMin93. **d** 93 **p** 94. C Castle Bromwich SS Mary and Marg *Birm* 93-97; C Hockerill *St Alb* 97-00; V St Mary-at-Latton *Chelmsf* from 00. *St Mary-at-Latton Vicarage, The Gowers, Harlow CM20 2JP* Tel (01279) 424005
CONN, Alistair Aberdein. b 37. Down Coll Cam BA60 MA64. Linc Th Coll 60. **d** 62 **p** 63. C W Hartlepool St Paul *Dur* 62-65; Uganda 65-66; Chapl Shrewsbury Sch 66-73; R Coupar Angus *St And* 73-78; V Ravenshead *S'well* 78-93; RD Newstead 90-93; R Collingham w S Scarle and Besthorpe and Girton 93-02; RD Newark 95-02; rtd 02. *17 Beacon Heights, Newark NG24 2JS* Tel (01636) 706291
CONNELL, Frederick Philip Richard John. b 45. **d** 01. NSM Nottingham St Pet and All SS *S'well* from 01. *Colston Basset House, Colston Basset, Nottingham NG12 3FE* Tel (01949) 81424 Fax 81116
CONNELL, Miss Heather Josephine. b 38. SRN60 SCM61 HVCert69 Open Univ BA93. S'wark Ord Course DipRS79. **dss** 79 **d** 87 **p** 94. Heston *Lon* 79-84; Gillingham St Barn *Roch* 84-90; Par Dn 87-90; Distr Chapl Medway NHS Trust 91-96; NSM Gillingham H Trin *Roch* from 94; rtd 98. *31 Brenchley Road, Gillingham ME8 6HD* Tel (01634) 230289
CONNELL, John Richard. b 63. K Coll Lon BD84. St Mich Coll Llan. **d** 94 **p** 96. C Caldicot *Mon* 94-97; C Risca 97-00; V Llantilio Pertholey w Bettws Chpl etc from 00. *St Teilo's Vicarage, Llantilio Pertholey, Abergavenny NP7 6NY* Tel (01873) 854323
CONNELL, Mrs Penelope Clare. b 44. EMMTC. **d** 03. NSM Whatton w Aslockton, Hawksworth, Scarrington etc *S'well* from 03. *Colston Basset House, Church Gate, Colston Basset, Nottingham NG12 3FE*
CONNELL, Ms Sharon Margaret. b 65. St Jo Coll Nottm BA03. **d** 03. C S Hackney St Jo w Ch Ch *Lon* from 03. *19 Valentine Road, London E9 7AD* Tel (020) 8986 6273 Mobile 07710-761385
E-mail sharon.connell@virgin.net
CONNER, Mrs Cathryn. b 42. Birm Univ BSc64. NEOC 91. **d** 94 **p** 95. NSM Bainton w N Dalton, Middleton-on-the-Wolds etc *York* 94-98; NSM Woldsburn from 98. *Centre House, North Dalton, Driffield YO25 9XA* Tel (01377) 217265
CONNER, Charles Borthwick. b 20. Keble Coll Ox BA43 MA49. St Steph Ho Ox 48. **d** 50 **p** 51. C Saltburn-by-the-Sea *York* 50-52; Chapl Ely Th Coll 52-53; CF 53-70; Perm to Offic *Sarum* from 80. *Angel Cottage, West Knighton, Dorchester DT2 8PE* Tel (01305) 852465
✠**CONNER, The Rt Revd David John.** b 47. Ex Coll Ox BA69 MA77. St Steph Ho Ox 69. **d** 71 **p** 72 **c** 94. Asst Chapl St Edw Sch Ox 71-73; Chapl 73-80; Hon C Summertown *Ox* 71-76; TV Wolvercote w Summertown 76-80; Chapl Win Coll 80-87; V

Cambridge Gt St Mary w St Mich *Ely* 87-94; RD Cambridge 89-94; Suff Bp Lynn *Nor* 94-98; Dean Windsor and Dom Chapl to The Queen from 98; Bp HM Forces from 01. *The Deanery, Windsor Castle, Windsor SL4 1NJ* Tel (01753) 865561 Fax 819002 E-mail david.conner@stgeorges-windsor.org

CONNING, Dowell Paul. b 64. Ripon Coll Cuddesdon BTh00. **d** 00 **p** 01. C Leckhampton St Pet *Glouc* 00-03; Chapl RN from 03. *Royal Naval Chaplaincy Service, Room 203, Victory Building, HM Naval Base, Portsmouth PO1 3LS* Tel (01705) 727903 Fax 727112 E-mail dowell@freenet.co.uk

CONNOLL, Miss Helen Dorothy. b 45. Oak Hill Th Coll BA86. **dss** 86 **d** 87 **p** 94. Leytonstone St Jo *Chelmsf* 86-87; Par Dn 87-90; Asst Chapl Grimsby Distr Gen Hosp 90-93; Chapl Kent and Cant Hosp 93-94; Chapl Kent and Cant Hosps NHS Trust 94-99; Chapl E Kent Hosps NHS Trust 99-01; Hon C Aylesham w Adisham *Cant* from 01; Hon C Nonington w Wymynswold and Goodnestone etc from 01. *The Vicarage, Vicarage Lane, Nonington, Dover CT15 4JT* Tel (01304) 840271 E-mail helen.therev@virgin.net

CONNOLLY, Daniel. b 51. BEng. St Jo Coll Nottm DPS84. **d** 84 **p** 85. C Bedgrove *Ox* 84-87; C-in-c Crookhorn Ch Cen CD *Portsm* 87-88; V Crookhorn 88-97; R Sutton Coldfield H Trin *Birm* 97-98; V Reigate St Mary *S'wark* from 98; RD Reigate from 03. *St Mary's Vicarage, 76 Church Street, Reigate RH2 0SP* Tel (01737) 242973 E-mail dancon@ukonline.co.uk

CONNOLLY, Miss Lynne. b 53. Aston Tr Scheme 88 Linc Th Coll 92. **d** 92 **p** 94. Par Dn Hurst *Man* 92-94; C 94-96; R Burnage St Nic 96-02; V Spotland from 02. *10 Little Flatt, Rochdale OL12 7AU* Tel (01706) 648972

CONNOLLY, Sydney Herbert. b 40. Leeds Univ BA66. Coll of Resurr Mirfield 66. **d** 68 **p** 69. C W Derby St Mary *Liv* 68-71; C Prescot 71-74; V Burtonwood 74-80; V Walker *Newc* 80-89; TR Whorlton 89-96; V Chapel House 96-99; TR N Shields from 99. *Christ Church Vicarage, 26 Cleveland Street, North Shields NE29 0NG* Tel 0191-257 1721 E-mail sydandpat@blueyonder.co.uk

CONNOR, Ellis Jones. b 16. Univ of Wales BA38. St Mich Coll Llan 38. **d** 39 **p** 41. C Broughton *St As* 39-43; C Llandegfan and Beaumaris *Ban* 43-48; V Llst Chris Norris Green *Liv* 48-55; R Desford *Leic* 55-73; R N Hill *Truro* 73-75; V Lewannick 73-75; R Llanddewi Skirrid w Llanvetherine etc *Mon* 75-78; C Spalding St Jo *Linc* 79-82; rtd 82; Perm to Offic *Leic* from 82. *35 Sycamore Street, Blaby, Leicester LE8 4FL* Tel 0116-277 7725

CONNOR, Geoffrey. b 46. K Coll Lon BD73 AKC73. St Aug Coll Cant. **d** 74 **p** 75. C Cockerton *Dur* 74-79; Dioc Recruitment Officer 79-87; Chapl St Chad's Coll 84-87; Vice-Provost St Mary's Cathl *Edin* 87-90; R Edin St Mary 87-90; Dioc Dir of Ords *Edin* and *Arg* 87-90; V Whitechapel w Admarsh-in-Bleasdale *Blackb* 90-00; Dir of Ords 90-00; TR Epping Distr *Chelmsf* from 00. *The Rectory, Hartland Road, Epping CM16 4PD* Tel (01992) 572906 Fax as telephone E-mail geoffrey_connor@priest.com

CONNOR, Patrick Francis Latham. b 25. Ex Coll Ox BA47 MA52. Gen Th Sem (NY) STB53. **d** 53 **p** 53. USA 53-55 and 59-62; R N Tamerton *Truro* 55-59; R St Ive 62-64; R Sparkford w Weston Bampfylde *B & W* 64-85; P-in-c Sutton Montis 70-85; R Mawnan *Truro* 85-89; rtd 89; Perm to Offic *Truro* from 89. *Trelatham, Boyton, Launceston PL15 9RJ* Tel (01566) 776078

CONNOR, Archdeacon of. *See* McBRIDE, The Ven Stephen Richard

CONNOR, Bishop of. *See* HARPER, The Rt Revd Alan Edwin Thomas

CONNOR, Dean of. *See* BOND, The Very Revd John Frederick Augustus

CONRAD, Paul Derick. b 54. Worc Coll Ox BA76 MA82. St Steph Ho Ox 78. **d** 80 **p** 81. C Wanstead St Mary *Chelmsf* 80-83; C Somers Town *Lon* 83-85; P-in-c Kentish Town St Martin w St Andr 85-91; V 91-95; P-in-c Hampstead Ch Ch 95-97; V from 97; Chapl R Free Hampstead NHS Trust from 95. *Christ Church Vicarage, 10 Cannon Place, London NW3 1EJ* Tel (020) 7435 6784 Fax as telephone

CONSTABLE, Douglas Brian. b 40. Lon Univ BA62. Linc Th Coll 63. **d** 65 **p** 66. C Stockwood CD *Bris* 65-70; Hon C Clifton St Paul 70-72; Asst Chapl Bris Univ 70-72; Chapl Lee Abbey 72-77; V Derby St Thos *Derby* 77-85; TV Southampton (City Cen) *Win* 85-92; rtd 92; Perm to Offic *Win* from 92. *9 Ordnance Road, Southampton SO15 2AZ* Tel (023) 8022 8953

CONSTABLE, Mrs Sharon Joanne. b 57. STETS 95. **d** 98 **p** 99. NSM Hutton *B & W* 98-01; Bp's Officer for NSMs from 00. 6 Severn Clevedon w Clapton in Gordano etc from 01. *5 Chestnut Grove, Clevedon BS21 7LA* Tel (01275) 795080 E-mail sharon.constable@ntlworld.com

CONSTABLE, Mrs Sybil Margaret. b 43. **d** 00 **p** 01. C Montgomery and Forden and Llandyssil *St As* from 00. *6 Severn Close, Caerhowel, Montgomery SY15 6JE* Tel (01686) 668741

CONSTANTINE, Miss Elaine Muriel. b 50. Univ of Wales (Swansea) BSc72 CertEd73 DipEd75 Lon Univ MEd78. St Alb Minl Tr Scheme. **dss** 86 **d** 87 **p** 94. Bedford St Martin *St Alb* 86-87; Par Dn 87-88; Par Dn Leighton Buzzard w Eggington, Hockliffe etc 88-94; C 94-98; TV Dunstable from 98.

St Fremund's Vicarage, 22 Princes Street, Dunstable LU6 3AX Tel (01582) 668996 E-mail revd.elaine@virgin.net

CONSTANTINE, Leonard. b 30. AKC57. **d** 58 **p** 59. C W Hartlepool St Aid *Dur* 58-61; C Sheff St Geo and St Steph *Sheff* 61-62; Nyasaland 62-64; Malawi 64-69; V W Pelton *Dur* 69-73; V Shotton 73-78; V Stillington 78-80; V Grindon and Stillington 80-82; V Corbridge w Halton and Newton Hall *Newc* 82-95; Chapl Charlotte Straker Hosp 82-95; rtd 95; Perm to Offic *Wakef* from 95. *28 Tenterfield Road, Ossett WF5 0RU* Tel (01924) 276180

CONVERY, Canon Arthur Malcolm. b 42. Sheff Univ BSc63 DipEd64. N Ord Course 79. **d** 82 **p** 83. NSM Parr *Liv* 82-87; V Marown *S & M* from 87; Can St German's Cathl from 99. *The Vicarage, Marown, Crosby, Isle of Man IM4 4BH* Tel (01624) 851378

CONWAY, Alfred Sydney. b 22. Kelham Th Coll 40. **d** 45 **p** 46. C Fulham St Oswald w St Aug *Lon* 45-49; V Allenton and Shelton Lock *Derby* 49-55; P-in-c Chaddesden St Phil 55-63; V Croxley Green All SS *St Alb* 63-81; V Walton St Jo *Liv* 81-89; rtd 89; Perm to Offic *Ex* from 89. *14 Mount Close, Honiton EX14 8QZ* Tel (01404) 46052

CONWAY, Canon Glyn Haydn. b 38. St Mich Coll Llan DipTh65. **d** 65 **p** 66. C Wrexham *St As* 65-71; TV 71-77; V Holywell 77-83; V Upton Ascension *Ches* from 83; Hon Can Accra from 03. *The Vicarage, Demage Lane, Chester CH2 1EL* Tel (01244) 383518

CONWAY, John Arthur. b 67. Leeds Univ BEng90 DipTh93 Edin Univ BD97. Linc Th Coll 94 TISEC 97. **d** 97 **p** 98. C Edin St Mary *Edin* 97-01; R Edin St Martin from 01; Chapl Edin Sick Children's NHS Trust 98-01. *15 Ardmillan Terrace, Edinburgh EH11 2JW* Tel 0131-337 5471 E-mail jconway@fish.co.uk

CONWAY, Canon Owen Arnott. b 35. Dur Univ BA58. St Steph Ho Ox 58. **d** 60 **p** 61. C Manston *Ripon* 60-64; V Osmondthorpe St Phil 64-70; Warden Dioc Ho Barrowby 70-73; V Armley w New Wortley 73-81; V Headingley 81-91; RD Headingley 87-91; Hon Can Ripon Cathl 87-91; Can Res Ches Cathl *Ches* 91-00; rtd 00; Perm to Offic *York* and *Truro* from 00. *20 High Market Place, Kirkbymoorside, York YO62 6BQ* Tel (01751) 432467

CONWAY, Philip James. b 66. Liv Inst of Educn BA91. St Steph Ho Ox DipMin95. **d** 95 **p** 96. C High Harrogate Ch Ch *Ripon* 95-99; P-in-c Menheniot *Truro* from 99. *The Vicarage, Menheniot, Liskeard PL14 3SU* Tel (01579) 342195 E-mail fatherphilip@menheniotvicarage.fsnet.co.uk

CONWAY, Mrs Sandra Coralie. b 45. Bris Univ BA66. S'wark Ord Course DipRS92. **d** 92 **p** 00. NSM Kenley *S'wark* from 92. *28 Russell Hill, Purley CR8 2JA* Tel (020) 8668 2890

CONWAY, The Ven Stephen David. b 57. Keble Coll Ox BA80 MA84 CertEd81 Selw Coll Cam BA85. Westcott Ho Cam 83. **d** 86 **p** 87. C Heworth St Mary *Dur* 86-89; C Bishopwearmouth St Mich w St Hilda 89-90; Hon C Dur St Marg 90-94; Dir of Ords 90-94; P-in-c Cockerton 94-96; V Meadowfield 96-98; Bp's Sen Chapl 98-02; Communications Officer 98-02; Adn Dur and Can Res Dur Cathl from 02. *15 The College, Durham DH1 3EQ* Tel 0191-384 7534 E-mail archdeacon.of.durham@durham.anglican.org

CONWAY, Thomas Robertson. b 36. DipTh. **d** 86 **p** 87. C Bangor Abbey *D & D* 86-95; I Dungiven w Bovevagh *D & R* 89-95; I Carrowdore w Millisle *D & D* 95-00; rtd 00. *17 Neill's Hill Park, Belfast BT5 6FL* Tel (028) 9086 0523

CONWAY-LEE, Stanley. b 17. Linc Th Coll 68. **d** 70 **p** 71. C Dedham *Chelmsf* 70-72; C Lt Ilford St Mich 72-74; V Tollesbury 74-75; V Tollesbury w Salcot Virley 75-79; V Bocking St Pet 79-85; rtd 85; Perm to Offic *Chelmsf* from 85. *10 Northumberland Close, Braintree CM7 9NL* Tel (01376) 550117 Fax as telephone

COOGAN, The Ven Robert Arthur William. b 29. Univ of Tasmania BA51 St Jo Coll Dur DipTh53. **d** 53 **p** 54. C Plaistow St Andr *Chelmsf* 53-56; Australia 56-62; V N Woolwich *Chelmsf* 62-73; P-in-c W Silvertown St Barn 62-73; V Hampstead St Steph *Lon* 73-77; P-in-c N St Pancras All Hallows 74-77; RD S Camden 75-81; P-in-c Old St Pancras w Bedford New Town St Matt 76-80; V Hampstead St Steph w All Hallows 77-85; P-in-c Kentish Town St Martin w St Andr 78-81; AD N Camden 78-83; Preb St Paul's Cathl 82-85; Adn Hampstead 85-94; rtd 94; Perm to Offic *Chich* 94-00; St E from 03. *Salters Hall West, Stour Street, Sudbury CO10 2AX* Tel (01787) 370026

COOK, Alan. b 27. St Deiniol's Hawarden 79. **d** 80 **p** 81. Hon C Gatley *Ches* 80-83; Chapl Man R Eye Hosp 83-86; Chapl Asst Man R Infirmary 80-83 and 86-88; V Congleton St Jas *Ches* 89-93; rtd 93; Perm to Offic *Ches* from 93. *15 Buttermere Road, Gatley, Cheadle SK8 4RQ* Tel 0161-428 4534

COOK, Canon Brian Edwin. b 36. Sarum & Wells Th Coll 78. **d** 80 **p** 81. C E Wickham *S'wark* 80-83; C Petersfield w Sheet *Portsm* 83-86; R Liss 86-01; RD Petersfield 91-96 and 99; Hon Can Portsm Cathl 96-01; rtd 01; Perm to Offic *Chich* from 01. *Daubeney Cottage, Bersted Street, South Bersted, Bognor Regis PO22 9QE* Tel (01243) 828379 E-mail daubeney@tesco.net

COOK, Brian Robert. b 43. Chich Th Coll 83. **d** 85 **p** 86. C Whyke w Rumboldswhyke and Portfield *Chich* 85-87; C Worth 87-90; TV 90-94; P-in-c Chidham 94-99; V from 99; RD Westbourne from 99. *The Vicarage, Cot Lane, Chidham, Chichester PO18 8TA* Tel (01243) 573147

COOK, Canon Charles Peter. b 32. St Jo Coll Dur BA54 DipTh58. **d** 58 **p** 59. C Kingston upon Hull H Trin *York* 58-64; V High Elswick St Paul *Newc* 64-74; V Cheadle Hulme St Andr *Ches* 74-98; Hon Can Ches Cathl 91-98; rtd 98; Perm to Offic *Newc* from 00; *Carl* from 01. *Bel Abri, Leadgate, Alston CA9 3EL* Tel (01434) 381873

COOK, Christopher. b 44. Qu Coll Birm 68. **d** 69 **p** 70. C Gt Ilford St Mary *Chelmsf* 69-72; C Corringham 72-77; R E Donyland 77-84; R Pentlow, Foxearth, Liston and Borley 84-88; Chapl RAD Essex Area 88-89; rtd 89; Perm to Offic *Chelmsf* from 89. *Oak Mill, Field View Drive, Little Totham, Maldon CM9 8ND* Tel (01621) 893280

COOK, Canon Christopher Arthur. Edin Th Coll 53. **d** 56 **p** 58. C Motherwell *Glas* 56-59; S Africa 59-64 and from 70; Clydesdale Miss 59-60; Matatiele St Steph 60-61; Idutywa St Barn 61-64; Area Sec USPG *Wakef* and *Sheff* 65-70; R Grahamstown St Matt Miss 70-95; Adn Grahamstown 80-95; Hon Can Grahamstown from 96; rtd 96. *PO Box 7641, East London, 5200 South Africa* Tel (0027) (431) 385357

COOK, Prof Christopher Charles Holland. b 56. K Coll Lon BSc77 MB, BS81 MD95 MRCPsych87. SEITE 97. **d** 00 **p** 01. Prof Psychiatry Alcohol Misuse Kent Inst of Medicine and Health Science from 97; NSM Otham w Langley *Cant* from 00. *8 Waters Edge, Maidstone ME15 6SG* Tel (01622) 670651 Fax as telephone E-mail cchcook@aol.com

COOK, David. b 46. Hertf Coll Ox BA MA72. Wycliffe Hall Ox 69. **d** 73 **p** 74. C Kingston upon Hull H Trin *York* 74-75; Lect Qu Coll Birm 75-81; Chapl Cranbrook Sch Kent from 81. *33 Oatfield Drive, Cranbrook TN17 3LA* Tel (01580) 713310

COOK David Arthur. b 50. St Jo Coll Dur BA74. St Steph Ho Ox 86. **d** 88 **p** 89. C S Bank *York* 88-91; C Up Hatherley *Glouc* 91-93; P-in-c Cumbernauld *Glas* from 93. *1R Blake Road, Cumbernauld, Glasgow G67 1AG* Tel (01236) 722544

COOK, Canon David Charles Murray. b 41. MA. Wycliffe Hall Ox 65. **d** 67 **p** 68. C Chatham St Phil and St Jas *Roch* 67-71; S Africa 71-89; TR Newbury *Ox* 89-02; RD Newbury 98-02; Hon Can Ch Ch 02; P-in-c Chipping Campden w Ebrington *Glouc* from 02. *The Vicarage, Church Street, Chipping Campden GL55 6JG* Tel (01386) 840671

COOK, David Smith. b 47. Hull Univ BTh88 MA93. Lich Th Coll 68. **d** 71 **p** 72. C Tudhoe Grange *Dur* 71-75; C Bishopwearmouth St Mary V w St Pet CD 75-77; V Copley *Wakef* 77-80; V Birstall 80-83; V Holme upon Spalding Moor *York* 83-98; RD S Wold 96-01; R Holme and Seaton Ross Gp 98-01; V Copmanthorpe from 01; P-in-c Askham Bryan from 01; Chapl Askham Bryan Coll from 01. *The Vicarage, 17 Sutor Close, Copmanthorpe, York YO23 3TX* Tel (01904) 778701 E-mail revcook@btinternet.com

COOK, Canon Derek Edward. b 23. AKC51. **d** 52 **p** 53. C Radlett *St Alb* 52-56; C Hatfield Hyde 56-64; V Luton St Paul 64-78; P-in-c Stanbridge w Tilsworth 78-80; V Totternhoe, Stanbridge and Tilsworth 80-88; Hon Can St Alb 85-88; rtd 88; Perm to Offic *Ely* from 93 and *St Alb* from 00. *8 Ridgeway, Eynesbury, St Neots PE19 2QY* Tel (01480) 475141

COOK, Canon Edward Rouse. b 28. Linc Coll Ox BA51 MA55. Linc Th Coll 51. **d** 53 **p** 54. C Louth w Welton-le-Wold *Linc* 53-56; C Crosby 56-57; Lect Boston 58-60; R Lt Coates 60-67; V Saxilby 67-90; R Broxholme 69-90; P-in-c Burton by Linc 78-94; Can and Preb Linc Cathl 79-03; Chmn Dioc Readers 86-94; RD Corringham 87-93; R Saxilby w Ingleby and Broxholme 90-94; rtd 94; Perm to Offic *Linc* 94-97. *80 Lincoln Road, Dunholme, Lincoln LN2 3QY* Tel (01673) 861534

COOK, Elspeth Jean. b 34. Edin Univ BSc56 PhD66. S Dios Minl Tr Scheme 85. **d** 88 **p** 94. C Yateley *Win* 88-91; Assoc Chapl Ld Mayor Treloar Hosp Alton 91-93; NSM Dunfermline *St And* 93-99; P-in-c Aberdour 96-01. *12 River View, Dalgety Bay, Dunfermline KY11 9YE* Tel (01383) 825222 E-mail tacook@surfaid.org

COOK, Geoffrey John Anderson. b 64. DipBS84. St Steph Ho Ox DipMin97. **d** 97 **p** 98. C St Leonards Ch Ch and St Mary *Chich* 97-99; Hon Asst P Brighton St Mich 00-02; Hon C Southwick St Mich 02-03; Chapl Asst Univ Coll Lon Hosps NHS Trust from 03. *Middlesex Hospital, Mortimer Street, London W1T 3AA* Tel (020) 7387 9300

COOK, Helen. b 50. New Coll Edin BD74 Glas Univ MA92. **d** 96. C Rothiemurchus *Mor* from 96. *Dukeville, Duke Street, Kingussie PH21 1JG* Tel (01540) 661724 E-mail helen.cook@highland.gov.uk

COOK, Ian Bell. b 38. NW Ord Course 70. **d** 73 **p** 74. C Oldham St Paul *Man* 73-75; Ind Chapl 76-79; P-in-c Newton Heath St Wilfrid and St Anne 76-79; V Middleton Junction from 79. *The Vicarage, Greenhill Road, Middleton Junction, Manchester M24 2BD* Tel 0161-643 5064

COOK, Preb Ian Brian. b 38. MBIM73 Aston Univ MSc72 Birm Univ MA76. Kelham Th Coll 58. **d** 63 **p** 64. C Langley Marish *Ox* 63-66; C Stokenchurch and Cadmore End 66-68; V Lane End 68-72; P-in-c Ibstone w Fingest 68-72; Tutor W Bromwich Coll of Comm and Tech 72-74; Sen Tutor 74-80; NSM W Bromwich St Pet *Lich* 77-80; R Wednesbury St Jas and St Jo from 80; Dir St Jas Tr Inst from 81; RD Wednesbury 88-03; Preb Lich

Cathl from 94. *The Rectory, 1 Hollies Drive, Wednesbury WS10 9EQ* Tel 0121-505 1188 *or* 505 1568 Fax 556 0785

COOK, James Christopher Donald. b 49. Ch Ch Ox BA70 MA74. St Steph Ho Ox 79. **d** 80 **p** 81. C Witney *Ox* 80-83; CF from 83. *clo MOD Chaplains (Army)* Tel (01980) 615804 Fax 615800

COOK, Jean. *See* COOK, Elspeth Jean

COOK, Mrs Joan Lindsay. b 46. SRN70. St Jo Coll Dur 86. **d** 88 **p** 94. Par Dn Hartlepool St Hilda *Dur* 88-93; Dn-in-c 93-94; P-in-c 94-96; rtd 96. *10 Peakston Close, Hartlepool TS26 0PN* Tel (01429) 231778

COOK, John. b 32. Linc Th Coll 87. **d** 89 **p** 90. C Bourne *Linc* 89-92; R Colsterworth Gp 92-02; rtd 02. *24 Portrush Drive, Grantham NG31 9GD* Tel (01476) 569063

COOK, John Edward. b 35. AKC61. **d** 62 **p** 63. C York Town St Mich *Guildf* 62-67; Singapore 67-77; P-in-c Beoley *Worc* 78-83; V 83-89; V Bromsgrove All SS 89-01; rtd 01; Perm to Offic *Cov* from 02. *61 Newport Drive, Alcester B49 5BJ* Tel (01789) 762553 Fax 400040 E-mail johnedwardcook@aol.com

COOK, John Henry. b 11. Mert Coll Ox BA34 BSc35 MA39 MSc41. Clifton Th Coll 36. **d** 38 **p** 39. C Gt Faringdon w Lt Coxwell *Ox* 38-42; C Newbury St Nic 42-45; V Winkfield 45-52; V Furze Platt 52-68; R Witney 68-78; rtd 79; Perm to Offic *Ox* from 79. *9 Church View Road, Witney OX8 7HT* Tel (01993) 704609

COOK, John Michael. b 48. Coll of Resurr Mirfield 72. **d** 74 **p** 75. C Weymouth H Trin *Sarum* 74-76; C Felixstowe St Jo *St E* 76-79; P-in-c Gt and Lt Whelnetham 79-84; P-in-c Cockfield 84-85; P-in-c Bradfield St George w Bradfield St Clare etc 84-85; R Cockfield w Bradfield St Clare, Felsham etc 85-87; V Workington St Jo *Carl* from 87. *St John's Vicarage, 59 Thorncroft Gardens, Workington CA14 4DP* Tel (01900) 602383

COOK, John Richard Millward. b 61. St Jo Coll Dur BA. Wycliffe Hall Ox 83. **d** 85 **p** 86. C Brampton St Thos *Derby* 85-89; C Farnborough *Guildf* 89-92; C Langham Place All So *Lon* 92-98; V Chelsea St Jo w St Andr from 98. *The Vicarage, 43 Park Walk, London SW10 0AU* Tel (020) 7352 1675 Fax as telephone E-mail johnrmcook@ukgateway.net

COOK, Kenneth George Thomas. b 36. ACA59 AHA69 FCA70. Coll of Resurr Mirfield 86. **d** 88 **p** 89. C Stocking Farm *Leic* 88-91; Chapl Leics Hospice 91-96; Chapl Hinchingbrooke Health Care NHS Trust 96-01; rtd 01; Perm to Offic *Ely* from 01. *1 Peregrine Close, Hartford, Huntingdon PE29 1UZ* Tel (01480) 451790

COOK, Kenneth Hugh. b 30. ALAM. AKC55. **d** 56 **p** 57. C Netherfield *S'well* 56-59; C Newark w Coddington 59-61; V Basford St Aid 61-67; V Gargrave *Bradf* 67-77; Dir of Ords 77-89; Can Res Bradf Cathl 77-95; rtd 95; Perm to Offic *Ripon* from 95. *25 Hollins Close, Hampsthwaite, Harrogate HG3 2EH* Tel (01423) 772521

COOK, Kenneth Robert. b 42. Huddersfield Poly BA86. Chich Th Coll 66. **d** 68 **p** 69. C Upton *Ox* 68-72; C Duston *Pet* 72-76; V Halifax St Hilda *Wakef* 76-79; Chapl Huddersfield Poly 79-90; V Linc St Mary-le-Wigford w St Benedict etc *Linc* 90-02; P-in-c Skirbeck Quarter 02-03; rtd 03. *25 Western Crescent, Lincoln LN6 7TD*

COOK (née McCLEAN), Mrs Lydia Margaret Sheelagh. b 72. Ball Coll Ox BA94 MA98. Cuddesdon Coll 94. **d** 96 **p** 97. C Brackley St Pet w St Jas *Pet* 96-99; NSM Wallingford *Ox* 99-01; NSM Wallingford Deanery from 01; Chapl and Teacher Cranford Ho Sch Ox from 99. *Chestnut Cottage, The Street, Brightwell-cum-Sotwell, Wallingford OX10 0RR* Tel (01491) 833242 E-mail revrock@brightwell99.freeserve.co.uk

COOK, Marcus John Wyeth. b 41. Chich Th Coll 67. **d** 70 **p** 71. C Friern Barnet St Jas *Lon* 70-73; Hon C St Geo-in-the-East w St Paul 73-00; Perm to Offic 73-00. *St George-in-the-East Church, Cannon Street Road, London E1 0BH* Tel (020) 7481 1345

COOK, Nicholas Leonard. b 59. Nottm Univ BCombStuds84. Linc Th Coll 81. **d** 84 **p** 85. C Leic St Pet *Leic* 84-85; C Knighton St Mich 85-86; Chapl Asst Towers Hosp Humberstone 86-89; Chapl Leics Mental Health Service Unit 89-91; Chapl Quainton Hall Sch Harrow 91-94; CF(V) 88-94; CF from 94. *clo MOD Chaplains (Army)* Tel (01980) 615804 Fax 615800

COOK, Paul Raymond. *See* McLAREN-COOK, Paul Raymond

COOK, Peter John. b 50. Ridley Hall Cam CTM95. **d** 95 **p** 96. C Romford Gd Shep Collier Row *Chelmsf* 95-98; C Colchester St Jo from 98. *3 Northfield Gardens, Highwoods, Colchester CO4 4TL* Tel (01206) 532550 E-mail peter_cook@ntlworld.com

COOK, Peter John Arthur. b 42. Reading Univ BA64 Brandeis Univ (USA) MA65 QUB PhD81. Tyndale Hall Bris 68. **d** 71 **p** 72. C Everton St Chrys *Liv* 71-74; Chapl Stranmillis Coll of Educn Belf 74-87; Hon C Belfast All SS *Conn* 81-87; USA from 87. *123 West Sale Road, Lake Charles, LA 70605, USA*

COOK, Richard John Noel. b 49. Univ Coll Ox BA70 MA74 PGCE72. Wycliffe Hall Ox MA77. **d** 78 **p** 79. C Fulwood *Sheff* 78-80; C Bolton St Paul w Em *Man* 81-86; TV 86-93; V Goldsworth Park *Guildf* from 93; RD Woking from 99. *St Andrew's Vicarage, 8 Cardingham, Woking GU21 3LN* Tel (01483) 764523 E-mail cookingwok@lineone.net

COOK, Canon Robert Bond. b 28. Dur Univ BSc54. Ripon Hall Ox 54. **d** 56 **p** 57. C Benwell St Jas *Newc* 56-60; C Sugley 60-64; V Denton 64-75; V Haltwhistle 75-88; P-in-c Greenhead 84-88; V Haltwhistle and Greenhead 88-93; RD Hexham 88-93; Hon Can Newc Cathl 92-93; rtd 93; Perm to Offic *St E* from 94; RD Lavenham from 03. *Ashcroft, Heath Road, Woolpit, Bury St Edmunds IP30 9RN* Tel (01359) 240670

COOK, Ronald Thomas. b 50. St Steph Ho Ox BA79 MA83. **d** 80 **p** 81. C Willesden St Andr *Lon* 80-83; USA 83-87; C Northolt Park St Barn *Lon* 87-96; Chapl HM Pris Blundeston 90-96; V Kettering All SS *Pet* from 96; RD Kettering from 02. *All Saints' Vicarage, 80 Pollard Street, Kettering NN16 9RP* Tel (01536) 513376 E-mail ronaldcook@supanet.com

COOK, Stephen. b 62. Brunel Univ BSc(Econ)84 Birkbeck Coll Lon DipRS92. S'wark Ord Course 89. **d** 92 **p** 93. Hon C Forest Hill St Aug *S'wark* 92-98; P-in-c Eltham St Barn from 98; CF (TA) from 00. *St Barnabas' Vicarage, 449 Rochester Way, London SE9 6PH* Tel (020) 8856 8294 E-mail cooksca@aol.com

COOK, Stephen William. b 57. BA DipHE Lambeth STh87. Trin Coll Bris. **d** 85 **p** 86. C Heref St Pet w St Owen and St Jas *Heref* 85-89; TV Keynsham *B & W* 89-95; V Hanham *Bris* 95-02; RD Bitton 98-99; AD Kingswood and S Glos 99-02; TR Okehampton w Inwardleigh, Bratton Clovelly etc *Ex* from 02. *The Vicarage, 1 Church Path, Okehampton EX20 1LW* Tel (01837) 659297

COOK, Timothy John. b 62. Cranmer Hall Dur 95. **d** 95 **p** 96. C Dorchester *Sarum* 95-99; TV Ilminster and Distr *B & W* 99-03; R Yeovil H Trin w Barwick from 03. *Holy Trinity Vicarage, 24 Turners Barn Lane, Yeovil BA20 2LM* Tel (01935) 423774 E-mail timcook@tesco.net

COOK, Trevor Vivian. b 43. Sarum Th Coll 67. **d** 69 **p** 70. C Lambeth St Phil *S'wark* 69-73; C St Buryan, St Levan and Sennen *Truro* 73-75; V The Ilketshalls *St E* 75-79; P-in-c Rumburgh w S Elmham 75-79; R Rumburgh w S Elmham w the Ilketshalls 79-84; TR Langport Area Chs *B & W* 84-96; P-in-c Rode Major 96-02; C Hardington Vale from 02. *The Rectory, 38 Church Lane, Rode, Frome BA11 6PN* Tel (01373) 831234

COOKE, Alan. b 50. Nottm Univ BTh74 Lanc Univ PGCE75. Kelham Th Coll 69. **d** 75 **p** 76. C Tyldesley w Shakerley *Man* 75-78; C Salford Ordsall St Clem 78; C Langley All SS and Martyrs 80-82; TV Langley and Parkfield 82-83; P-in-c Chadderton St Mark 83-85; V from 85. *St Mark's Vicarage, Milne Street, Chadderton, Oldham OL9 0HR* Tel 0161-624 2005

COOKE, Angela Elizabeth. b 42. SRN65 SCM67 Midwife Teacher's Dip 72. St Jo Coll Nottm 85. **d** 87 **p** 94. Par Dn Walton H Trin *Ox* 87-92; Par Dn Bexleyheath Ch Ch *Roch* 92-94; C 94-97; V St Mary Cray and St Paul's Cray from 97. *The Vicarage, Main Road, Orpington BR5 3EN* Tel (01689) 827697 E-mail angelacooke@hotmail.com

COOKE (née LEA), Mrs Carolyn Jane. b 65. Nottm Univ BA88 PGCE90. St Jo Coll Nottm MTh02. **d** 02 **p** 03. C Hyson Green and Forest Fields *S'well* from 02. *8 Austen Avenue, Nottingham NG7 6PE* Tel 0115-961 7555 E-mail cookes@northnotts-gofree.co.uk

COOKE, Christopher Stephen. b 54. Lon Univ BA76 MA77 Ox Univ BA81 MA88. Ripon Coll Cuddesdon 79. **d** 82 **p** 83. C Cen Telford *Lich* 82-86; R Uffington, Upton Magna and Withington 86-95; RD Wrockwardine 92-01; TR Wrockwardine Deanery 95-01; P-in-c Wem from 01; P-in-c Lee Brockhurst from 01; P-in-c Loppington w Newtown from 01. *The Rectory, Ellesmere Road, Wem, Shrewsbury SY4 5TU* Tel (01939) 232550 E-mail christopher@csc2000.f9.co.uk

COOKE, David John. b 31. Linc Th Coll 60. **d** 62 **p** 63. C Brighton Gd Shep Shep Preston *Chich* 62-65; C Clayton w Keymer 65-70; R Stone w Hartwell w Bishopstone *Ox* 70-77; R Stone w Dinton and Hartwell from 77. *The Rectory, Stone, Aylesbury HP17 8RZ* Tel (01296) 748215

COOKE, Francis Theodore. b 34. Tyndale Hall Bris 53 Clifton Th Coll 58. **d** 02 **p** 03. Ind Missr Bentley Motors *Ches* from 02; NSM Poynton from 02. *13 Maple Avenue, Poynton, Stockport SK12 1PR* Tel (01625) 859246

COOKE, Frederic Keable. b 35. Selw Coll Cam BA58 MA61. Ridley Hall Cam 59. **d** 61 **p** 62. C Flixton St Mich *Man* 61-64; C-in-c Flixton St Jo CD 64-67; V Flixton St Jo 68-74; R Ashton St Mich 74-77; Jerusalem 77-80; V Walmsley *Man* 80-85; AD Walmsley 81-85; Malaysia 85-90; Prin Ho of Epiphany Th Coll Borneo 85-90; P-in-c Accrington *Blackb* 90-91; TR 91-96; P-in-c Ringley w Prestolee *Man* 96-01; rtd 01. *41 Knights Court, Canterbury Gardens, Salford M5 5AB* Tel 0161-788 7713

COOKE, Geoffrey. b 38. Sarum Th Coll 61. **d** 64 **p** 65. C Eastover *B & W* 64-67; Chapl RAF 67-71; C Bridgwater St Jo *B & W* 71-76; R N Newton w St Michaelchurch and Thurloxton 76-78; R N Newton w St Michaelchurch, Thurloxton etc 78-83; TV Yeovil 83-88; V Yeovil H Trin 88-89; R Staple Fitzpaine, Orchard Portman, Thurlbear etc 89-96; rtd 96. *34 Bluebell Close, Taunton TA1 3XQ* Tel (01823) 324235

COOKE (married name SHEARD), Ms Gillian Freda. b 39. Lon Univ DipTh70 BD73 Leeds Univ MA87. Linc Th Coll IDC75. **dss** 78 **d** 87 **p** 94. Cricklewood St Pet CD *Lon* 78-80; Chapl

Middx Poly 78-80; Chapl Leeds Poly *Ripon* 80-87; N Humberside Ind Chapl *York* 87-90; Asst Chapl HM Pris Hull 90-94; Chapl Keele Univ *Lich* 94-97; Assoc Min Betley and Keele 94-97; Chapl Rampton Hosp Retford 97-99; rtd 99; Perm to Offic *York* from 00. *7 Northfield, Swanland, North Ferriby HU14 3RG* Tel (01482) 633971 Fax as telephone E-mail gilalsrd@surfaid.org

COOKE (née MORRALL), Mrs Heather Lynne. b 55. LMH Ox BA76 MA80 MIPR88. Dioc OLM tr scheme DipHE00. **d** 99 **p** 00. OLM Martlesham w Brightwell *St E* from 99. *9 Swan Close, Martlesham Heath, Ipswich IP5 3SD* Tel (01473) 623770 Mobile 07703-568051 E-mail hcookema@aol.com

COOKE, Canon Hereward Roger Gresham. b 39. ACA64 K Coll Lon BD69 AKC70. **d** 70 **p** 71. C Rugby St Andr *Cov* 70-76; P-in-c St Kath Cree *Lon* 76-82; P-in-c St Botolph without Aldersgate 82-89; AD The City 82-85; P-in-c St Edm the King and St Mary Woolnoth etc 82-89; TV Nor St Pet Parmentergate w St Jo *Nor* 89-93; Ind Miss 89-93; Sen Ind Chapl from 93; Hon C Nor St Pet Mancroft w St Jo Maddermarket from 93; P-in-c Nor St Steph from 03; RD Nor E 93-02; Hon Can Nor Cathl from 97. *St John's Vicarage, 31 Bracondale, Norwich NR1 2AT* Tel (01603) 624827 Fax 477323 E-mail cookehd@paston.co.uk

COOKE, James Percy. b 13. St D Coll Lamp BA51. **d** 52 **p** 54. C Prestatyn *St As* 52-57; R Derwen and Llanelidan 57-83; rtd 83. *28 Maes Cantaba, Ruthin LL15 1YP* Tel (01824) 704905

COOKE, John Stephen. b 35. K Coll Lon BD58 AKC58. **d** 59 **p** 60. C W Bromwich St Fran *Lich* 59-62; C Chalfont St Peter *Ox* 62-66; V Cross Heath *Lich* 66-72; R Haughton 72-86; P-in-c Ellenhall w Ranton 72-80; V Eccleshall 86-00; Sub Chapl HM Pris Drake Hall 89-95; rtd 00. *50 High Street, Eccleshall, Stafford ST21 6BZ* Tel (01785) 850570

COOKE, Canon Kenneth John. b 29. Linc Coll Ox BA53 MA57. Ely Th Coll 53. **d** 55 **p** 56. C Nuneaton St Mary *Cov* 55-58; C Cov St Thos 58-61; V Willenhall 61-66; V Meriden 66-76; V Cov St Geo 76-84; V Leamington Spa H Trin and Old Milverton 84-94; Hon Can Cov Cathl 92-94; rtd 94; Perm to Offic *Cov* from 94. *2 Chantry Crescent, Alcester B49 5BT* Tel (01789) 763460

COOKE, Michael David. b 46. New Coll Ox BA68 MA71 DPhil71. Ox NSM Course 75. **d** 78 **p** 79. NSM Newport Pagnell *Ox* 78-85; NSM Newport Pagnell w Lathbury and Moulsoe 85-88; NSM Beckenham Ch Ch *Roch* 90-96; P-in-c Seal St Lawr from 96; P-in-c Underriver from 96; Perm to Offic *Cant* from 98. *St Lawrence Vicarage, Stone Street, Sevenoaks TN15 0LQ* Tel (01732) 761766 Fax as telephone E-mail mcooke7oaks@btopenworld.com

COOKE, Michael John. b 39. Ab Dioc Tr Course 78. **d** 80 **p** 81. NSM St Andr Cathl *Ab* 80-81; Chapl Miss to Seamen 81-88; Hon C Immingham *Linc* 81-88; Miss to Seamen Tilbury 88-91; Ind Chapl Teesside *Dur* 91-97; V Kelloe and Coxhoe from 97. *8 Mulbery, Coxhoe, Durham DH6 4SN* Tel 0191-377 3722

COOKE, Miss Priscilla Garland Hamel. b 24. Gilmore Ho 69. **dss** 80 **d** 87 **p** 94. Bromsgrove St Jo *Worc* 80-82; Lee Abbey 82-85; Torquay St Matthias, St Mark and H Trin *Ex* 86-87; NSM 87-92 and 94-98; Perm to Offic 92-94 and from 98. *St Nicolas, Woodend Road, Torquay TQ1 2PZ* Tel (01803) 297366

COOKE, Raymond. b 34. Liv Univ BSc56. Wells Th Coll 58. **d** 60 **p** 61. C Newton Heath All SS *Man* 60-64; C-in-c Failsworth H Family CD 64-75; R Failsworth H Family 75-83; P-in-c Man Gd Shep 83-88; V Westleigh St Pet 88-99; rtd 99. *136 Victoria Avenue East, Manchester M9 6HF* Tel 0161-740 0664

COOKE, Richard James. b 60. Pemb Coll Ox BA82 MA88 Bris Univ PhD96. Trin Coll Bris 85. **d** 88 **p** 89. C Rugby St Matt *Cov* 88-92; V Fletchamstead from 92; Dir Initial Tr for Readers from 97; CME Adv from 03. *St James's Vicarage, 395 Tile Hill Lane, Coventry CV4 9DP* Tel (024) 7646 6262 E-mail fletch@surfaid.org

COOKE, Roger. b 39. **d** 99 **p** 00. C Prestonpans *Edin* from 99; C Musselburgh from 99. *2 Cochran Terrace, Edinburgh EH7 4DJ* Tel 0131-558 1110

COOKE, Stephen. See COOKE, John Stephen

COOKSON, Miss Diane Veronica. b 51. N Ord Course 81. **dss** 84 **d** 87 **p** 94. Gt Sutton *Ches* 84-86; Neston 86-87; Par Dn 87-94; C 94-96; V Stockport St Sav from 96; Ecum Adv (Gtr Man) 00-02. *St Saviour's Vicarage, 22 St Saviour's Road, Great Moor, Stockport SK2 7QE* Tel 0161-483 2633 E-mail st.saviours@virgin.net

COOKSON, Graham Leslie. b 37. Sarum Th Coll 64. **d** 67 **p** 68. C Upton Ascension *Ches* 67-69; C Timperley 69-75; V Godley cum Newton Green 75-83; R Tarporley from 83. *The Rectory, High Street, Tarporley CW6 0AG* Tel (01829) 732491

COOKSON, William. b 61. **d** 98 **p** 99. C Haydock St Mark *Liv* 98-02; Min Wallington Springfield Ch *S'wark* from 02. *49 Stanley Park Road, Carshalton SM5 3HT* Tel (020) 8404 6064 E-mail willcookson@blueyonder.co.uk

COOLING, Derrick William. b 35. AKC58 Heref Coll of Educn TCert68 Lon Univ BD69 DipEd71 Univ of Wales (Cardiff) MEd81. St Boniface Warminster 58. **d** 59 **p** 60. C Haydock St Jas *Liv* 59-61; C Hove St Barn *Chich* 61-63; V Llangattock w St Maughan's etc *Mon* 63-68; R Blaina 68-70; Perm to Offic

Sarum 70-74; Chapl Windsor Girls' Sch Hamm 74-75; Asst Master Croesyceiliog Sch Cwmbran 75-81; Perm to Offic *Mon* 79-81; Chapl Epsom Coll 81-84; V Bettws *Mon* 84-95; P-in-c Purleigh, Cold Norton and Stow Maries *Chelmsf* 95-98; rtd 98; Perm to Offic *Mon* from 98. *St Thomas Cottage, The Fence, St Brievels, Lydney GL15 6QG* Tel (01594) 530926 Fax as telephone E-mail clericderrick@aol.com

COOLING (née YOUNG), Mrs Margaret Dorothy. b 37. K Coll Lon BA59 AKC Lon Univ BD69 DipEd71 Univ of Wales (Cardiff) MEd81. Mon Dioc Tr Scheme 89. **d** 90 **p** 95. NSM Bettws *Mon* 90-95; NSM Purleigh, Cold Norton and Stow Maries *Chelmsf* 95-98; rtd 98; Perm to Offic *Mon* from 98; *Glouc* from 01. *St Thomas Cottage, The Fence, St Brievels, Lydney GL15 6QG* Tel (01594) 530926 Fax as telephone E-mail clericderrick@aol.com

COOMBE, James Anthony. b 31. Em Coll Cam BA53 MA57 Lon Univ BD60. Tyndale Hall Bris 57. **d** 60 **p** 61. C Chadderton Ch Ch *Man* 60-63; C Worthing St Geo *Chich* 63-65; V Wandsworth St Mich *S'wark* 65-74; P-in-c Warboys *Ely* 74-76; R 76-87; RD St Ives 83-87; P-in-c Broughton 84-87; P-in-c Wistow 84-87; V Alconbury w Alconbury Weston 87-96; R Buckworth 87-96; rtd 96. *12 Nursery Fields, Hythe CT21 4DL* Tel (01303) 262151

COOMBE, John Morrell (Brother Martin). b 25. Chich Th Coll 56. **d** 57 **p** 58. SSF from 49; Lic to Offic *Sarum* 57-59; C-in-c Hillfield and Hermitage 59-66; Asst Chapl Ellesmere Coll Shropshire 66-69; Chapl Ranby Ho Sch Retford 69-71; V Cambridge St Benedict *Ely* 71-85; Perm to Offic *Jerusalem* 85-86; Prov Sec SSF 86-94; Lic to Offic *Linc* 86-95; Perm to Offic *Ely* from 97; Sec for Miss SSF from 99. *St Francis's House, 14/15 Botolph Lane, Cambridge CB2 3RD* Tel (01223) 321576 E-mail martinssf@franciscans.org.uk

COOMBE, Kenneth Harry Southcott. b 24. Clifton Th Coll 61. **d** 63 **p** 64. C Cullompton *Ex* 63-66; C-in-c Elburton CD 66-73; V Elburton 73-97; rtd 97; Perm to Offic *Ex* from 97. *80 Mewstone Avenue, Wembury, Plymouth PL9 0HT* Tel (01752) 863297 E-mail mewstone@aol.com

COOMBE, Canon Michael Thomas. b 31. Lon Univ BA64. Ox NSM Course 73. **d** 75 **p** 76. Chapl St Piran's Sch Maidenhead 75-81; NSM Furze Platt *Ox* 75-81; C 86-88; Asst Chapl Oslo St Edm *Eur* 81-84; Chapl Belgrade w Zagreb 84-86; Chapl Marseille w St Raphaël, Aix-en-Provence etc 88-89; Chapl Reading Gp of Hosps 89-91; P-in-c Clewer St Andr *Ox* 91-92; C New Windsor 92-93; C Reading St Mark 93-95; C Reading H Trin 93-95; Prec Gib Cathl and Port Chapl *Eur* 95-03; Can Gib Cathl 00-03; rtd 03. *28 Gipsy Lane, Exmouth EX8 3HN* Tel (01395) 272923

COOMBER, Ian Gladstone. b 47. Ch Ch Coll Cant CertEd68 Southn Univ BTh79. Sarum & Wells Th Coll 73. **d** 76 **p** 77. C Weeke *Win* 76-79; TV Saffron Walden w Wendens Ambo and Littlebury *Chelmsf* 79-82; V Weston *Win* 82-90; R Bedhampton *Portsm* 90-96; R Botley from 96; V Curdridge from 96; R Durley from 96; RD Bishop's Waltham 98-03. *The Rectory, 46 High Street, Botley, Southampton SO30 2EA* Tel (01489) 781534 or 782445

COOMBES, Derek Fennessey. b 42. Nottm Univ Cert Counselling 95 Dip Counselling & Psychotherapy 00. Edin Th Coll LTh61. **d** 65 **p** 66. Prec St Andr Cathl Inverness *Mor* 65-68; Bp's Chapl 65-68; Perm to Offic *Nor* 76-79; V Happisburgh w Walcot 79-83; C Tewkesbury Abbey 84-85; Ind Chapl *S'wark* 85-89; R Asterby Gp *Linc* 89-95; Mental Health Chapl Louth 91-95; Perm to Offic *Lich* 95-97; TV Haywards Heath St Wilfrid *Chich* from 97. *The Vicarage, 1 Marylands, New England Road, Haywards Heath RH16 3JZ* Tel (01444) 443450 Fax as telephone

COOMBES, Edward David. b 39. Dur Univ BA61. Qu Coll Birm DipTh63. **d** 63 **p** 64. C Claines St Jo *Worc* 63-65; C Halesowen 65-69; V Beoley 69-77; V Edgbaston St Bart *Birm* from 77; Chapl Birm Univ from 77. *Edgbaston Vicarage, 1B Arthur Road, Birmingham B15 2UW* Tel 0121-454 0070 Fax as telephone

COOMBES, Frederick Brian John. b 34. Nottm Univ BA56 Plymouth Poly MPhil73 Univ Coll Lon Dip Town Planning 63 FRGS. Sw Minl Tr Course 85. **d** 88 **p** 89. NSM Bodmin w Lanhydrock and Lanivet *Truro* from 88. *5 Valley View, Bodmin PL31 1BE* Tel (01208) 73036

COOMBES, Edward Neve. b 66. Bris Univ BSc88. Cranmer Hall Dur BA93. **d** 94 **p** 95. C Edin St Thos *Edin* 94-96; C Dagenham *Chelmsf* 97-01; P-in-c Banbury St Paul *Ox* from 01. *St Paul's House, Bretch Hill, Banbury OX16 0LR* Tel (01295) 264003 E-mail encoombs@tesco.net

COOMBES, John Allen. b 46. Portsm Poly BSc70. Oak Hill Th Coll DipHE88 Sarum & Wells Th Coll 89. **d** 89 **p** 90. C Leverington *Ely* 89-93; C Wisbech St Mary 89-93; P-in-c Emneth 93-96; V Emneth and Marshland St James 96-99; P-in-c Papworth Everard 99-00; TV Papworth 00-02; Chapl Papworth Hosp NHS Trust from 99. *Papworth Hospital, Papworth Everard, Cambridge CB3 8RE* Tel (01480) 830541 Fax 831315 E-mail john.coombs@ely.anglican.org

COOMBS, John Kendall. b 47. Culham Coll Ox BEd73. Sarum & Wells Th Coll 75. **d** 77 **p** 78. C Fareham H Trin *Portsm* 77-80; C

Petersfield w Sheet 80-83; TV Beaminster Area *Sarum* 83-87; TR Preston w Sutton Poyntz and Osmington w Poxwell 87-97; TR Hermitage *Ox* from 97. *The Rectory, High Street, Hermitage, Thatcham RG18 9ST* Tel (01635) 202967

COOMBS, The Ven Peter Bertram. b 28. Bris Univ BA58 MA61. Clifton Th Coll 55. **d** 60 **p** 61. C Beckenham Ch Ch *Roch* 60-63; R Nottingham St Nic *S'well* 63-68; V New Malden and Coombe *S'wark* 68-75; RD Kingston 71-75; Adn Wandsworth 75-88; Adn Reigate 88-95; rtd 95; Perm to Offic *Portsm* from 97. *92 Locks Heath Park Road, Locks Heath, Southampton SO31 6LZ* Tel (01489) 577288

COOMBS, Richard Murray. b 63. St Chad's Coll Dur BSc85 Rob Coll Cam BA89 MA90. Ridley Hall Cam 87. **d** 90 **p** 91. C Enfield Ch Ch Trent Park *Lon* 90-94; C St Helen Bishopsgate w St Andr Undershaft etc 94-98; P-in-c St Pet Cornhill 95-98; V Burford w Fulbrook, Taynton, Asthall etc *Ox* from 98. *The Vicarage, Church Lane, Burford OX18 4SD* Tel (01993) 822275 Fax 824699 E-mail rmcoombs@lineone.net

COOMBS, Stephen John. b 54. Open Univ BA86. Trin Coll Bris 85. **d** 87 **p** 88. C Norton Canes *Lich* 87-90; Chapl Trowbridge Coll *Sarum* 90-94; C Studley 90-94. *48 Whitstone Rise, Shepton Mallet BA4 5QB* Tel (01749) 343750

COOMBS, Canon Walter James Martin. b 33. Keble Coll Ox BA57 MA61. Cuddesdon Coll 59. **d** 61 **p** 62. C Kennington St Jo *S'wark* 61-64; Chapl Em Coll Cam 64-68; Bp's Dom Chapl *S'wark* 68-70; V E Dulwich St Jo 70-77; V Pershore w Pinvin, Wick and Birlingham *Worc* 77-92; Hon Can Worc Cathl 84-92; RD Pershore 85-91; TV Dorchester *Ox* 92-98; rtd 98; Perm to Offic *Ox* from 01. *54 Divinity Road, Oxford OX4 1LJ* Tel (01865) 243865

COONEY, Michael Patrick. b 55. City of Lon Poly BA77. Ripon Coll Cuddesdon 77. **d** 80 **p** 81. C Cov E *Cov* 80-83; C Old Brumby *Linc* 83-85; V Linc St Jo 85-90; V Frodingham from 90; RD Manlake from 99. *The Vicarage, Vicarage Gardens, Scunthorpe DN15 7AZ* Tel (01724) 842726

COONEY, William Barry. b 47. K Coll Lon 69. **d** 70 **p** 71. C W Bromwich All SS *Lich* 70-73; C Wolverhampton St Pet 73-75; C Rugeley 75-78; V Sneyd Green 78-87; R Sandiacre *Derby* from 87. *St Giles's Rectory, Church Drive, Sandiacre, Nottingham NG10 5EE* Tel 0115-939 7163

COOPER, Alfred Philip. b 50. Bris Univ BA71. All Nations Chr Coll 72. **d** 77 **p** 78. Chile from 75; SAMS from 77. *Inglesia Anglicana del Chile, Casilla 50675, Correo Central, Santiago, Chile* Tel (0056) (2) 226 8794

COOPER, Andrew John. b 62. W Sussex Inst of HE BA87. St Steph Ho Ox 88. **d** 91 **p** 92. C Rawmarsh w Parkgate *Sheff* 91-93; C Mosbrough 93-95; P-in-c Donnington Wood *Lich* 95-96; CF from 96. *c/o MOD Chaplains (Army)* Tel (01980) 615804 Fax 615800

COOPER, Andrew John Gearing. b 48. Sir John Cass Coll Lon BSc70. Ripon Coll Cuddesdon 73. **d** 76 **p** 77. C Potternewton *Ripon* 76-79; Antigua 79-81; Anguilla 81-87; V W Bromwich St Andr w Ch Ch *Lich* 88-92. *50 Hunter Avenue, Burntwood WS7 9AQ* Tel (01543) 677817 E-mail andrew.cooper@lichfield.anglican.org

COOPER, Mrs Annette Joy. b 53. Open Univ BA80 Lon Univ DipSW84 CQSW84. S'wark Ord Course DipRS88. **d** 88 **p** 94. NSM Pembury *Roch* 88; Chapl Asst Tunbridge Wells Hosps 88-91; Chapl Asst Kent and Sussex Hosp Tunbridge Wells 88-91; Chapl Asst Leybourne Grange Hosp W Malling 88-91; Chapl Bassetlaw Hosp and Community Services NHS Trust 91-96; P-in-c Edwinstowe *S'well* from 96; Chapl Center Parcs Holiday Village 96-01; AD Worksop from 99. *The Vicarage, 5 West Lane, Edwinstowe, Mansfield NG21 9QT* Tel (01623) 822430 Fax as telephone E-mail vicar@edwinstowestmary.freeserve.co.uk

COOPER, Barrie Keith. b 56. Oak Hill Th Coll. **d** 85 **p** 86. C Partington and Carrington *Ches* 85-89; V Stockport St Mark 89-93; Chapl HM YOI Stoke Heath 93-02; Chapl HM Pris Acklington from 02. *HM Prison Acklington, Morpeth NE65 9XF* Tel (01670) 762300

COOPER, Barry Jack. Sarum Th Coll 59. **d** 61 **p** 62. C Norbury St Oswald *Cant* 61-64; C Crook *Dur* 64-68; R Cheriton *Cant* 68-84; V Cant All SS 84-00; rtd 00; Perm to Offic *Cant* from 01. *11 Windhill Lane, Charing Heath, Ashford TN27 0BG* Tel (01233) 714787

COOPER, Canon Bede Robert. b 42. Ex Univ BA69. Coll of Resurr Mirfield 69. **d** 71 **p** 72. C Weymouth H Trin *Sarum* 71-74; P-in-c Broad Town 74-79; V Wootton Bassett 74-86; R Wilton w Netherhampton and Fugglestone from 86; Can and Preb Sarum Cathl from 88. *The Rectory, 27A West Street, Wilton, Salisbury SP2 0DL* Tel (01722) 743159

COOPER, Benedict Christopher. b 68. K Coll Cam BA90 Wolfs Coll Ox MPhil94 DPhil97. Oak Hill Th Coll BA03. **d** 03. C St Helen Bishopsgate w St Andr Undershaft etc *Lon* from 03. *5 Louisa Gardens, London E1 4NG* Tel (020) 7790 6045 E-mail bc_cooper@hotmail.com

COOPER, Bert. *See* COOPER, Herbert William

COOPER, Brian Hamilton. b 35. Keble Coll Ox BA58 MA67. Ripon Hall Ox 58. **d** 60 **p** 61. C Woolwich St Mary w H Trin

S'wark 60-64; Canada 64-66; Vice-Prin Westcott Ho Cam 66-71; R Downham Market w Bexwell *Ely* 71-82; RD Fincham 80-82; V Chesterfield St Mary and All SS *Derby* 82-91; V Herringthorpe *Sheff* 91-00; RD Rotherham 93-98; rtd 00; Perm to Offic *Sheff* from 00. *51 Ariston Avenue, Worksop S81 7HU* Tel (01909) 479306

✠**COOPER, The Rt Revd Carl Norman.** b 60. Univ of Wales (Lamp) BTh82. d 85 p 86 c 02. C Llanelli *St D* 85-87; P-in-c Llanerch Aeron w Ciliau Aeron and Dihewyd etc 87-88; R 88-93; R Dolgellau w Llanfachreth and Brithdir etc *Ban* 93-02; Warden of Readers 88-02; Adn Meirionnydd 00-02; Bp St D from 02. *Llys Esgob, Abergwili, Carmarthen SA31 2JG* Tel (01267) 236597
E-mail bishop.stdavids@churchinwales.org.uk

COOPER, Cecil Clive. b 26. TD75. AKC52. d 53 p 54. C Chipping Campden *Glouc* 53-55; C Cheltenham St Mary 55-60; V Stroud 60-65; CF (TA) 63-75; R Woodmansterne *S'wark* 65-91; RD Sutton 80-90; rtd 91; Perm to Offic *Cov* and *Pet* from 91. *10 Mill Close, Braunston, Daventry NN11 7HY* Tel (01788) 890596

COOPER, Canon Cecil William Marcus. b 32. TCD BA58 MA66. CITC 57. d 59 p 60. C Cork St Fin Barre and St Nic *C, C & R* 59-62; Bp's V, Lib and Registrar Kilkenny Cathl *C & O* 62-64; C Knockbreda *D & D* 65-67; Asst Ed *Church of Ireland Gazette* 66-82; Ed 82-00; I Magheradroll 67-82; Dioc Registrar 81-90; I Drumbeg 82-00; Can Down Cathl 86-00; Prec 90-91; Chan 91-00; rtd 00. *35 Manor Drive, Lisburn BT28 1JH* Tel (028) 9263 4425

COOPER, Clive Anthony Charles. b 38. Lon Univ BEd74. ALCD62. d 62 p 63. C Morden *S'wark* 62-65; SAMS Argentina 65-71; Asst Master St Nic Sch Cranleigh 74-82; Hon C Cranleigh *Guildf* 78-79; Hon C Ewhurst 80-82; Hon Chapl Duke of Kent Sch 83-92; Chapl Felixstowe Coll 92-93; Perm to Offic *Ex* 94-95; Chapl Puerto Pollensa *Eur* 95-02; P-in-c Instow *Ex* from 03; P-in-c Westleigh from 03. *1 Stanbridge Park, Bideford EX39 3RS* Tel (01237) 473839 E-mail pinc.instow@btopenworld.com

COOPER, Colin. b 55. Open Univ BA. St Jo Coll Nottm 83. d 86 p 87. C Cheadle Hulme St Andr *Ches* 86-89; C Tunbridge Wells St Jo *Roch* 89-93; V Whitfield *Derby* from 93. *The Vicarage, 116 Charlestown Road, Glossop SK13 8LB* Tel (01457) 864938
E-mail colin@glossop.org

COOPER, Colin Charles. b 40. Middx Univ BA94. Oak Hill Th Coll 92. d 66 p 67. C Islington St Andr w St Thos and St Matthias *Lon* 66-69; Bermuda 69-76; V Gorleston St Andr *Nor* 77-94; USA from 94; R Emporia Ch Ch w Purdy Grace Virginia from 94. *111 Battery Avenue, Emporia, VA 23847, USA*
E-mail cooperc@3rddoor.com

COOPER, Mrs Corynne Elizabeth. b 54. Kent Univ BA76 PGCE77 Nottm Univ MA98. EMMTC 95. d 98 p 99. NSM Kneesall w Laxton and Wellow *S'well* 98-01; C Widecombe-in-the-Moor, Leusdon, Princetown etc *Ex* from 01. *The Vicarage, Holne, Newton Abbot TQ13 7RT* Tel (01364) 631522
E-mail corynne.cooper@virgin.net

COOPER, David. b 44. AKC69. d 69 p 70. C Wortley de Leeds *Ripon* 69-73; CF 73-83; Lic to Offic *Ox* from 84; Chapl Eton Coll from 85. *Eton College, Windsor SL4 6DW* Tel (01753) 864587

COOPER, David Jonathan. b 44. Sarum & Wells Th Coll 70. d 74 p 75. C Chard-in-Dover *Cant* 74-79; TV Wednesfield *Lich* 79-83; SSF 83-85; V Grimsby St Aug *Linc* 85-89; TV Trowbridge H Trin *Sarum* 89-98; TV Manningham *Bradf* from 98. *The Vicarage, 16 Wood Street, Bradford BD8 8HY* Tel (01274) 730726

COOPER, David Philip. b 65. York Univ BA86. Qu Coll Birm BTheol94. d 94 p 95. C Burslem *Lich* 94-98; Dioc Inter-Faith Officer 98; TV Cen Wolverhampton from 98. *20 Tettenhall Road, Wolverhampton WV1 4SL* Tel (01902) 771375
E-mail ifofficer@aol.com

COOPER, Derek Edward. b 30. Bps' Coll Cheshunt 61. d 62 p 63. C Bishop's Stortford St Mich *St Alb* 62-66; V Westcliff St Cedd *Chelmsf* 66-89; R Camerton w Dunkerton, Foxcote and Shoscombe *B & W* 89-95; rtd 95; Perm to Offic *Win* from 95. *6 Caerleon Drive, Andover SP10 4DE* Tel (01264) 362807

COOPER, Eric John. b 22. Cam Univ MA47. Chich Th Coll 52. d 53 p 54. V Bedminster Down *Bris* 66-72; rtd 87. *6 Deveron Grove, Keynsham, Bristol BS31 1UJ* Tel 0117-986 7339

COOPER, Frederick. b 30. Cranmer Hall Dur 68. d 70 p 71. C Preston All SS *Blackb* 70-72; C Preston St Jo 72-76; TV 76-78; V Higher Walton 78-91; P-in-c Preston All SS 91-95; rtd 95; Perm to Offic *Blackb* from 95. *31 Churchfields, Fulwood, Preston PR2 8GT* Tel (01772) 713808

COOPER, Ms Gillian Anne. b 55. LMH Ox BA76 CertEd77 MA80 Nottm Univ MEd94. St Jo Coll Nottm 84. dss 86 d 87 p 94. Tutor EMMTC 86-01; Beeston *S'well* 86-91; Hon C 87-91; Hon C Bilborough w Strelley 91-01; Lect St Jo Coll Nottm 87-01; New Zealand from 01. *Address temp unknown*

COOPER, Gordon William. b 54. Aston Tr Scheme 93 Ripon Coll Cuddesdon DipMin95. d 97 p 98. C Kippax w Allerton Bywater *Ripon* 97-01; V Wyther Ven Bede from 01. *Wyther Vicarage, Houghley Lane, Leeds LS13 4AU* Tel 0113-279 8014
E-mail gordon@williamcooper.freeserve.co.uk

COOPER, Graham Denbigh. b 48. Nottm Univ BTh75. St Jo Coll Nottm LTh75. d 75 p 76. C Collyhurst *Man* 75-78; C Stambermill *Worc* 78-80; V The Lye and Stambermill 80-90; P-in-c Frome H Trin *B & W* 90; V 91-95; Appeals Organiser Children's Soc 95-97; Area Manager Save the Children Fund from 97. *2 Coombe View, Shepton Mallet BA4 5YF* Tel (01749) 343157

COOPER, Herbert William. b 29. Chich Th Coll 77. d 79 p 80. C Leigh Park *Portsm* 79-82; C-in-c Hayling St Pet CD 82-85; V Whitwell 85-94; R St Lawrence 85-94; P-in-c Niton 89-94; rtd 94. *10 Henley Orchards, Ludlow SY8 1TN* Tel (01584) 874985

COOPER, Ian. b 57. St Jo Coll Nottm 00. d 02 p 03. C Mildenhall *St E* from 02. *103 Melbourne Drive, Mildenhall, Bury St Edmunds IP28 7BP* Tel (01638) 715112
E-mail icoop@icooper.freeserve.co.uk

COOPER, Ian Clive. b 48. FCA Ex Univ BA76 K Coll Lon MTh94. Linc Th Coll 76. d 78 p 79. C Sunbury *Lon* 78-81; P-in-c Astwood Bank *Worc* 81-85; P-in-c Feckenham w Bradley 82-85; TV Hemel Hempstead *St Alb* 85-95; R Bushey from 95. *The Rectory, High Street, Bushey WD23 1BD* Tel (020) 8950 1546
E-mail iancooperbushey@aol.com

COOPER, Jack. b 44. St Jo Coll Nottm 76. d 78 p 79. C Roundhay St Edm *Ripon* 78-80; C Ripley *Derby* 81-82; V Willington 82-88; V Findern 82-88; P-in-c Marley w Alsop-en-le-Dale 88-94; Perm to Offic *York* from 95. *Park View, 14 Chubb Hill Road, Whitby YO21 1JU* Tel (01947) 604213
E-mail jackanann@btopenworld.com

COOPER, James Peter. b 61. Westf Coll Lon BSc82. Sarum & Wells Th Coll 82. d 85 p 86. C Durrington *Chich* 85-88; C Clayton w Keymer 88-95; TV Chich 95-00; Chapl Chich Coll of Tech from 95; C Chich St Paul and Westhampnett *Chich* 00-01; Chapl R W Sussex Trust from 01. *St Richard's Hospital, Spitalfield Lane, Chichester PO19 6SE* Tel (01243) 788122 Mobile 07989-741004 Fax 531269

COOPER, Jeremy John. b 45. Kelham Th Coll 65 Linc Th Coll 71. d 71 p 72. C Derby St Luke *Derby* 71-76; TV Malvern Link w Cowleigh *Worc* 76-79; P-in-c Claypole *Linc* 79-80; P-in-c Westborough w Dry Doddington and Stubton 79-80; C Eye w Braiseworth and Yaxley *St E* 80-82; R Hundon w Barnardiston 82-97; V Hundon 97-99; Chapl St Marg Convent E Grinstead from 99. *The Chaplain's Cottage, St Margaret's Convent, East Grinstead RH19 3LD* Tel (01342) 322406

COOPER, John. b 34. BEd. N Ord Course. d 83 p 84. C Tong *Bradf* 83-87; V Bingley H Trin 87-92; V Silsden 92-99; rtd 99; Perm to Offic *Bradf* from 01. *58 Cambridge Drive, Otley LS21 1DD* Tel (01943) 463915

COOPER, John. b 47. Sarum & Wells Th Coll 71. d 74 p 75. C Spring Grove St Mary *Lon* 74-77; C Shepherd's Bush St Steph w St Thos 77-82; V Paddington St Pet 82-89; V Darwen St Cuth w Tockholes St Steph *Blackb* 89-96; V Northampton St Mich w St Edm *Pet* 96-99. *29 Turner Way, Bedford MK41 7ND* Tel (01234) 315194 E-mail jco4328743@aol.com

COOPER, John Edward. b 40. K Coll Lon BD63 AKC63. d 64 p 65. C Prittlewell St Mary *Chelmsf* 64-67; C Up Hatherley *Glouc* 67-69; C-in-c Dorridge CD *Birm* 69-71; P-in-c Alkmonton w Yeaveley *Derby* 71-76; V Longford 71-76; TV Canvey Is *Chelmsf* 76-82; R Spixworth w Crostwick *Nor* 82-91; R Frettenham w Stanninghall 82-91; V Gt w Lt Harrowden and Orlingbury *Pet* 91-01; rtd 01. *Staveley House, 30 Brooke Road, Braunston, Oakham LE15 8QR* Tel (01572) 770984

COOPER, Canon John Leslie. b 33. Lon Univ BD65 MPhil78. Chich Th Coll 59. d 62 p 63. C Kings Heath *Birm* 62-65; Asst Chapl HM Pris Wandsworth 65-66; Chapl HM Borstal Portland 66-68; Chapl HM Pris Bris 68-72; P-in-c Balsall Heath St Paul *Birm* 73-81; V 81-82; Adn Aston and Can Res Birm Cathl 82-90; Adn Coleshill 90-93; C Sutton Coldfield H Trin 93-97; Hon Can Birm Cathl 93-97; rtd 97; Perm to Offic *Derby* from 98. *4 Ireton Court, Kirk Ireton, Ashbourne, Derby DE6 3JP* Tel (01335) 370459

COOPER, John Northcott. b 44. Ox Min Course 89. d 92 p 93. NSM Burghfield *Ox* 92-99; P-in-c Wootton (Boars Hill) 99-00; V Wootton and Dry Sandford from 00; AD Abingdon from 02. *The Vicarage, Wootton Village, Boars Hill, Oxford OX1 5JL* Tel (01865) 735661 E-mail cooper@woottonvic.freeserve.co.uk

COOPER, Jonathan. See COOPER, David Jonathan

COOPER, Jonathan Mark Eric. b 62. Man Univ BSc83 Edin Univ BD88. Edin Th Coll 85. d 88 p 89. C Stainton-in-Cleveland *York* 88-91; C W Bromwich All SS *Lich* 91-93; C-in-c Ingleby Barwick CD *York* 93-98; P-in-c Hinderwell w Roxby from 98. *The Rectory, Hinderwell, Saltburn-by-the-Sea TS13 5JH* Tel (01947) 840249 E-mail jonathan@jmec.freeserve.co.uk

COOPER, Joseph Trevor. b 32. Linc Th Coll 65. d 67 p 68. C Fletchamstead *Cov* 67-69; Ind Chapl 69-90; rtd 92; Perm to Offic *Cov* 92-00. *16 Trevor Close, Tile Hill, Coventry CV4 9HP* Tel (024) 7646 2341

COOPER, Kenneth Cantlay. b 17. Qu Coll Cam BA39 MA43. Ridley Hall Cam 39. d 41 p 42. C Radipole and Melcombe Regis *Sarum* 41-46; C Broadwater St Mary *Chich* 46-50; V Cumnor *Ox* 50-65; R Fisherton Anger *Sarum* 65-74; P-in-c Fovant w

Compton Chamberlayne etc 74-79; R Fovant, Sutton Mandeville and Teffont Evias etc 79-82; rtd 82; Perm to Offic *B & W* from 83. *8 Helena Road, East Coker, Yeovil BA20 2HQ* Tel (01935) 862291

COOPER, Ms Louise Helena. b 68. Leeds Univ BA90. Qu Coll Birm. **d** 93 **p** 94. Par Dn Dovecot *Liv* 93-94; C 94-96; Dep Chapl HM YOI Glen Parva 96-01; Chapl HM Pris Styal 01-03; Chapl HM Pris Man from 03. *The Chaplain's Office, HM Prison, Southall Street, Manchester M60 9AH* Tel 0161-834 8626 ext 326 Fax 832 0074

COOPER, Malcolm Tydeman. b 37. Pemb Coll Ox BA61 MA64. Linc Th Coll 63. **d** 63 **p** 64. C Spennithorne *Ripon* 63-66; C Caversham *Ox* 66-71; Hon C Blackbird Leys CD 71-75; Lic to Offic *Sarum* 75-78; Lic to Offic *B & W* 78-82; NSM Sutton *Ely* 82-97; NSM Witcham w Mepal 82-97; rtd 97; P-in-c Coveney *Ely* from 97. *91 The Row, Sutton, Ely CB6 2PB* Tel (01353) 777310 Fax 777422 E-mail mtcm4@waitrose.com

COOPER, Marc Ashley Rex. b 62. Leeds Univ BA85 MA95. Linc Th Coll 92. **d** 92 **p** 93. C Bolton St Jas w St Chrys *Bradf* 92-96; P-in-c Fishtoft *Linc* 96-97; R from 97; RD Holland E from 03. *The Rectory, Rectory Close, Fishtoft, Boston PE21 0RZ* Tel (01205) 363216 Fax as telephone E-mail revmarccooper@lineone.net

COOPER, Sister Margery. b 26. Cam Inst of Educn CertRK52 CA52. CA Tr Coll 49. **dss** 79 **d** 87 **p** 94. Evang Family Miss *Dur, Newc* and *York* 79-86; Perm to Offic *York* 86-91 and from 00; NSM Fulford 91-00; rtd 00. *7 Grange Street, Fulford Road, York YO10 4BH* Tel (01904) 633990

COOPER, Mark Richard. b 69. Kent Univ BA98. St Jo Coll Morpeth DipTh95. **d** 95 **p** 95. Australia 95-96 and from 98; C Hamilton 95-96; C Rainham *Roch* 96-98; Assoc P Kincumber from 98. *167 Avoca Drive, PO Box 1065, Kincumber, NSW, Australia 2251* Tel (0061) (2) 4369 2018 Fax 4369 1204 E-mail markcooper1969@hotmail.com

COOPER, Canon Michael Leonard. b 30. St Jo Coll Cam BA53 MA58. Cuddesdon Coll 53. **d** 55 **p** 56. C Croydon *Cant* 55-61; V Spring Park 61-71; V Boxley 71-82; RD Sutton 74-80; Hon Can Cant Cathl 76-97; V Cranbrook 82-92; Hon Chapl to Bp Dover 93-97; Asst Chapl Kent and Cant Hosps NHS Trust 94-97; Perm to Offic *Roch* from 97; rtd 00. *The Rectory, The Street, Plaxtol, Sevenoaks TN15 0QG* Tel (01732) 810319

COOPER, Canon Michael Sydney. b 41. Univ of Wales (Lamp) BA63. Westcott Ho Cam 63. **d** 65 **p** 66. C Farlington *Portsm* 65-69; Pakistan 70-71; Mauritius 71-73; C-in-c Hayling St Pet CD *Portsm* 74-81; V Carisbrooke St Mary 81-92; V Carisbrooke St Nic 81-92; V Hartplain 92-98; V Portchester from 98; RD Fareham from 99; Hon Can Portsm Cathl from 02. *The Vicarage, 164 Castle Street, Portchester, Fareham PO16 9QH* Tel and fax (023) 9237 6289 *or* tel 9232 1380 E-mail stmary@lineone.net

COOPER, Nigel Scott. b 53. Ox Univ MA Cam Univ MA PGCE MIEEM CBiol FIBiol FLS. Ripon Coll Cuddesdon. **d** 83 **p** 84. C Moulsham St Jo *Chelmsf* 83-88; R Rivenhall from 88. *The Rectory, 40 Church Road, Rivenhall, Witham CM8 3PQ* Tel (01376) 511161 E-mail nscooper@essex.ac.uk

COOPER, Noel. b 49. Oak Hill Th Coll. **d** 88 **p** 89. C Plymouth St Jude *Ex* 88-92; V Clapham Park All SS *S'wark* 92-99; R Bedford St Jo and St Leon *St Alb* from 99. *St John's Rectory, 36 St John's Street, Bedford MK42 0DH* Tel (01234) 354818 E-mail stjohns@nascr.com

COOPER, Peter. *See* COOPER, Wallace Peter

COOPER, Canon Peter David. b 48. Sarum & Wells Th Coll 70. **d** 73 **p** 74. C Yateley *Win* 73-78; C Christchurch 78-81; P-in-c Southampton St Mark 81-83; V Eldene 83-92; R Tadley S and Silchester *Win* from 02. *The Rectory, The Green, Tadley RG26 6PB* Tel 0118-981 4860 E-mail peter.cooper@xaltmail.com

COOPER, Peter Timothy. b 65. Brunel Univ BSc95. Ridley Hall Cam 01. **d** 03. C Edgware *Lon* from 03. *St Peter's Parsonage, Stonegrove, Edgware HA8 8AB* Tel 07900-462505 (mobile) E-mail cooperpeter@btopenworld.com

COOPER, Canon Richard Thomas. b 46. Leeds Univ BA69. Coll of Resurr Mirfield 69. **d** 71 **p** 72. C Rothwell *Ripon* 71-75; C Adel 75-78; C Knaresborough 78-81; P-in-c Croft 81-90; P-in-c Eryholme 81-90; P-in-c Middleton Tyas and Melsonby 81-90; RD Richmond 86-90; V Aldborough w Boroughbridge and Roecliffe 90-98; RD Ripon 93-96; R Richmond w Hudswell from 98; Hon Can Ripon Cathl from 97; Chapl to The Queen from 03. *The Rectory, Church Wynd, Richmond DL10 7AQ* Tel (01748) 823398

COOPER, Robert Gerard. b 68. Univ of Wales (Abth) BD91. Linc Th Coll 93. **d** 93 **p** 94. C Whitkirk *Ripon* 93-96; C Leeds Richmond Hill 96-97; Chapl Agnes Stewart C of E High Sch Leeds 96-97; C Chigwell Sch Essex 97-98; V Lightcliffe *Wakef* from 98. *The Vicarage, Wakefield Road, Lightcliffe, Halifax HX3 8TH* Tel and fax (01422) 202424 Mobile 07931-565516 E-mail robert_cooper@msn.com

COOPER, Robert James. b 52. Bris Univ BA75. Ridley Hall Cam 76. **d** 78 **p** 79. C Street w Walton *B & W* 78-82; C Batheaston w St Cath 82-86; Asst Chapl to Arts and Recreation *York* and *Dur* 86-03; P-in-c Sadberge 86-03; Chapl Arts and Recreation from

03. *24 North Close, Thorpe Thewles, Stockton-on-Tees TS21 3JY* Tel (01740) 630549 E-mail robertj.cooper@ntlworld.com

COOPER, Roger Charles. b 48. GRSM ARMCM69 PGCE70. Coll of Resurr Mirfield 79. **d** 81 **p** 82. C Monkseaton St Mary *Newc* 81-83; C Morpeth 83-87; Min Can and Prec Man Cathl *Man* 87-90; V Blackrod from 90. *St Katharine's Vicarage, Blackhorse Street, Blackrod, Bolton BL6 5EN* Tel (01204) 68150

COOPER, Seth William. b 62. Westcott Ho Cam 94. **d** 96 **p** 97. C Golders Green *Lon* 96-00; TV Uxbridge from 00. *The Rectory, Nursery Waye, Uxbridge UB8 2BJ* Tel (01895) 239055

COOPER, Mrs Shirley Ann. b 58. St Steph Ho Ox 96. **d** 98 **p** 99. C Gt Bookham *Guildf* 98-03; R Long Ditton from 03. *5 Church Meadow, Surbiton KT6 5EP* Tel (020) 8398 1583 Mobile 07736-680737 E-mail mailforshirley@aol.com

COOPER, Stephen. b 54. Bernard Gilpin Soc Dur 73 Chich Th Coll 74. **d** 77 **p** 78. C Horbury *Wakef* 77-78; C Horbury w Horbury Bridge 78-81; C Barnsley St Mary 81-84; TV Elland 84-91; Hon C Huddersfield St Thos 93-94; P-in-c Middlesbrough St Columba w St Paul *York* from 94; Chapl S Tees Hosps NHS Trust from 94. *St Columba's Vicarage, 115 Cambridge Road, Middlesbrough TS5 5HF* Tel (01642) 824779 E-mail fr_s_cooper@hotmail.com

COOPER, Stephen Paul Crossley. b 58. Aston Tr Scheme 89 Trin Coll Bris DipTh93. **d** 93 **p** 94. C Blackb Redeemer *Blackb* 93-95; C Altham w Clayton le Moors 95-98; V Langho Billington 98-03; Chapl Rossall Sch Fleetwood from 03. *2 Sandy Lane Cottages, Broadway, Fleetwood FY7 8SW* Tel (01253) 777440 *or* 774201 E-mail chaplain@rossall-school.lancs.sch.uk

COOPER, Mrs Susan Mary. b 45. Westcott Ho Cam 01. **d** 03. C Syston *Leic* from 03. *1121 Melton Road, Syston, Leicester LE7 2JS* Tel 0116-260 1670 E-mail scoople@yahoo.com

COOPER, Susan Mira. *See* RAMSARAN, Susan Mira

COOPER, Sydney Bernard Nikon. b 27. K Coll Lon BD49 AKC49. **d** 51 **p** 52. C St Marylebone Ch Ch w St Barn *Lon* 51-54; C Palmers Green St Jo 54-58; P-in-c Staines Ch Ch 58-66; V Stoke Newington St Olave 66-76; R Chigwell Row *Chelmsf* 76-83; P-in-c Easton on the Hill, Collyweston w Duddington etc *Pet* 83; R 84-88; rtd 88; Perm to Offic *Ely* from 88. *Chase View, Church Road, Walpole St Peter, Wisbech PE14 7NU* Tel (01945) 780473

COOPER, Thomas Joseph Gerard Strickland. b 46. Lanc Univ PhD85. Ven English Coll & Pontifical Gregorian Univ Rome PhB66 PhL67 STB69 STL71. **d** 70 **p** 70. In RC Ch 70-92; Chapl St Woolos Cathl *Mon* 93-95; V Llandaff N *Llan* from 95. *All Saints' Vicarage, 59 Station Road, Llandaff, Cardiff CF14 2FB* Tel (029) 2056 4096 E-mail teilo@woolos.supanet.com

COOPER, Trevor. *See* COOPER, Joseph Trevor

COOPER, Trevor John. b 51. Ex Univ MA95. Wycliffe Hall Ox 75. **d** 79 **p** 95. C Southsea St Pet *Portsm* 79-80; NSM Heavitree w Ex St Paul *Ex* 93-96; C Standish *Blackb* 96-99; V Burnley St Cuth from 99. *The Vicarage, Barbon Street, Burnley BB10 1TS* Tel (01282) 424978

COOPER, Wallace Peter. b 24. Kelham Th Coll 47. **d** 51 **p** 52. C Watford St Mich *St Alb* 51-52; C Ealing St Barn *Lon* 52-54; C New Brompton St Luke *Roch* 54-56; Perm to Offic *Ox* 62-81; Hon C Earley St Pet 81-83; Hon C Earley St Nic 83-92; rtd 92; Hon C Reading St Mark *Ox* 92-99; Perm to Offic *Ex* from 99. *7 Gracey Court, Woodland Road, Broadclyst, Exeter EX5 3LP* Tel (01392) 460612

COOPER, William Douglas. b 42. ARCST65 Dur Univ CertEd69 Open Univ BA83 Nottm Univ DipMM94. St Jo Coll Nottm 88 Qu Coll Birm 93. **d** 94 **p** 95. NSM Melbourne *Derby* 94-97; C Penwortham St Mary *Blackb* 97-00; P-in-c Smeeth w Monks Horton and Stowting and Brabourne *Cant* from 00. *The Rectory, Church Road, Smeeth, Ashford TN25 6SA* Tel (01303) 812697

COOTE, Anthony John. b 54. Qu Coll Birm 95. **d** 97 **p** 98. C Malvern H Trin and St Jas *Worc* 97-01; TV Heref S Wye *Heref* 01-02; P-in-c Cradley *Worc* from 02. *43 The Poplars, Stourbridge DY8 5SN* Tel (01384) 75665

COOTE, Bernard Albert Ernest. b 28. Lon Univ BD53. Chich Th Coll 54. **d** 55 **p** 56. C Addiscombe St Mary *Cant* 55-57; C Hawkhurst 57-59; C Sanderstead All SS *S'wark* 59-63; Chapl HM Borstal E Sutton Park 63-74; V Sutton Valence w E Sutton *Cant* 63-76; P-in-c Chart next Sutton Valence 71-76; Chapl and Dir R Sch for the Blind Leatherhead 76-91; rtd 91; Perm to Offic *Chich* and *Guildf* from 91. *6 Coxham Lane, Steyning BN44 3JG* Tel (01903) 813762

COPE, James Brian Andrew. b 58. SSC. Chich Th Coll 80. **d** 83 **p** 84. C Poulton-le-Fylde *Blackb* 83-86; C Fleetwood 86-87; V Fleetwood St Dav 87-94; P-in-c Somercotes *Derby* 94-99; V Watford St Jo *St Alb* from 99. *St John's Vicarage, 9 Monmouth Road, Watford WD17 1QW* Tel (01923) 236174 E-mail frjames-copessc@lineone.net

COPE, Judith. b 50. **d** 03. NSM Lt Berkhamsted and Bayford, Essendon etc *St Alb* from 03. *18 Hatherleigh Gardens, Potters Bar EN6 5HZ* Tel (01707) 644391

COPE, Mrs Melia Lambrianos. b 53. Cape Town Univ BSocSc73 Worc Coll of Tech CertMS84. St Jo Coll Nottm 80 WMMTC 83. **dss** 86 **d** 93 **p** 94. W Bromwich All SS *Lich* 86-93; NSM 93-94; NSM W Bromwich St Mary Magd CD 93-94; TV Cen Telford

94-02; Chapl HM Pris Shrewsbury 95-98; P-in-c Stokesay *Heref* from 02; P-in-c Sibdon Carwood w Halford from 02; P-in-c Acton Scott from 02. *Stokesay Vicarage, Clun Road, Craven Arms SY7 9QW* Tel (01588) 673463
E-mail meliacope@fish.co.uk

COPE, Miss Olive Rosemary. b 29. Birm Univ DPS73. Gilmore Ho 63. dss 69 d 87 p 94. Kentish Town St Martin w St Andr *Lon* 69-72; Enfield St Andr 73-87; Par Dn 87-89; Hon Par Dn 89-94; Hon C from 94; rtd 89. *7 Calder Close, Enfield EN1 3TS* Tel (020) 8363 8221 E-mail olivecheshunt@waitrose.com

COPE, Peter John. b 42. Mert Coll Ox BA64 MA68 Lon Univ MSc74 Man Univ PhD91. Cuddesdon Coll 64. d 66 p 67. C Chapel Allerton *Ripon* 66-69; Ind Chapl *Lon* 69-76; Ind Chapl *Worc* 76-85; Min Can Worc Cathl 76-85; P-in-c Worc St Mark 76-81; Min W Bromwich St Mary Magd CD *Lich* 85-94; Ind Chapl 85-94; Telford Town Cen Chapl from 94; W Midl FE Field Officer from 94; Churches Ind Officer from 97; Perm to Offic *Heref* from 96. *Stokesay Vicarage, Clun Road, Craven Arms SY7 9QW* Tel (01588) 673463
E-mail petercope@telfordchristiancouncil.co.uk

COPE, Ralph Bruce. Sir Geo Williams Univ Montreal BA60 McGill Univ Montreal BD62. d 60 p 61. Canada 60-99 and from 00; P-in-c Sophia Antipolis *Eur* 99-00. *Unit 407, 4701 Uplands Drive, Nanaimo BC, Canada, V9T 5Y2* Tel (001) (250) 758 3296
E-mail ralglo@compuserve.com

COPE, Stephen Victor. b 60. St Jo Coll Ox BA81 DipTh84 MA87. Chich Th Coll 86. d 89 p 90. C Newmarket St Mary w Exning St Agnes *St E* 89-92; C Northampton St Matt *Pet* 92-94; V Rudston w Boynton and Kilham *York* 94-98; V Rudston w Boynton, Carnaby and Kilham from 98; P-in-c Burton Fleming w Fordon, Grindale etc from 00; RD Bridlington 98-03. *The Vicarage, Rudston, Driffield YO25 4XA* Tel (01262) 420313
E-mail stephen.cope@dial.pipex.com

COPELAND, Christopher Paul. b 38. AKC64. d 65 p 66. C Luton St Andr *St Alb* 65-67; C Droitwich St Nic w St Pet *Worc* 67-71; C Kings Norton *Birm* 71-72; TV 73-78; V Tyseley 78-88; P-in-c Grimley w Holt *Worc* 88-96; Dioc Stewardship Missr 88-96; P-in-c Forest of Dean Ch Ch w English Bicknor *Glouc* 96-03; rtd 03. *24 Players Avenue, Malvern WR14 1DU* Tel (01684) 563323

COPELAND, Derek Norman. b 38. Worc Coll Ox BA62 MA68. Westcott Ho Cam 63. d 64 p 65. C Portsea St Mary *Portsm* 64-71; P-in-c Avonmouth St Andr *Bris* 71-77; P-in-c Chippenham St Paul w Langley Burrell 78-79; Ind Chapl from 78; TR Chippenham St Paul w Hardenhuish etc 79-89; V Kington St Michael 79-89; Perm to Offic *Bris*; *B & W* and *Sarum* from 89. *51B Lowden, Chippenham SN15 2BG* Tel (01249) 443879

COPELAND, Ian Trevor. b 51. FCA83. OLM course 98. d 99 p 00. NSM Werrington *Lich* from 99. *4 Heather Close, Werrington, Stoke-on-Trent ST9 0LB* Tel (01782) 303525

COPLAND, Miss Carole Jean. b 37. Man Univ BA60. Wm Temple Coll Rugby DipRK67. d 87 p 94. NSM Northallerton w Kirby Sigston *York* 87-90; Dioc Adv in Children's Work 81-90; Par Dn Dunnington 90-94; Faith in the City Link Officer 90-96; C Dunnington 94-96; V Ledsham w Fairburn 96-99; rtd 99; Perm to Offic *York* from 99. *4 Jedwell Close, New Earswick, York YO32 4DQ* Tel (01904) 767110
E-mail carolecopland@hotmail.com

COPLAND, Canon Charles McAlester. b 10. CCC Cam BA33 MA36. Cuddesdon Coll 33. d 34 p 35. C Pet St Jo *Pet* 34-38; India 38-52; Can All SS Cathl Nagpur from 52; R Arbroath *Bre* 53-59; Can St Paul's Cathl Dundee 53-59; R Oban St Jo *Arg* 59-79; Provost St Jo Cathl Oban 59-79; Dean *Arg* 77-79; rtd 79; Hon Can St Jo Cathl Oban *Arg* from 79. *3 West Hill Road, Kirriemuir DD8 4PR* Tel (01575) 575415

COPLETON, Roger Boyd. b 62. Edin Univ BD87. TISEC 97. d 97 p 98. NSM Haddington *Edin* from 97; NSM Dunbar from 97. *6 Traprain Terrace, Haddington EH41 3QD* Tel (01620) 822994 or 895456 E-mail roger@copleton.freeserve.co.uk

COPLEY, Colin. b 30. FRSA85 Nor City Coll HNC49. Kelham Th Coll 51. d 55 p 56. C Linc St Swithin *Linc* 55-58; C Bottesford 58-60; Chapl HM Borstal Hollesley 60-66; Chapl HM Pris Liv 66-70; Chapl HM Pris Styal 70-73; N Regional Chapl HM Pris and Borstals 70-73; Midl Region 73-75; Chapl HM Pris Drake Hall 73-75; Asst Chapl Gen of Pris (Midl) 75-90; Chapl HM Pris Sudbury 90-95; Chapl HM Pris Foston Hall 90-95; Perm to Offic *Lich* from 90; rtd 95. *67 Porlock Avenue, Stafford ST17 0HT* Tel (01785) 663162

COPLEY, David Judd. b 15. Linc Coll Ox BA48 MA53. Wycliffe Hall Ox 48. d 50 p 51. C Old Swinford *Worc* 50-53; Chapl to Bp Worc 52-55; Min Stourbridge St Mich Norton CD 53-56; R Romsley 56-67; Chapl Romsley Hosp 56-67; V Tardebigge 67-81; rtd 81; Perm to Offic *Worc* from 81. *220 Bromsgrove Road, Hunnington, Halesowen B62 0JS* Tel (01562) 710247

COPLEY, Paul. b 58. NEOC DipHE94. d 99 p 00. C Hessle *York* 99-02; TV Sutton St Jas and Wawne from 02. *The Vicarage, 11 Sovereign Way, Kingswood, Hull HU7 3JG*

COPPEN, Colin William. b 53. BCombStuds85. Linc Th Coll. d 85 p 86. C Tokyngton St Mich *Lon* 85-88; C Somers Town 88-90; P-in-c Edmonton St Alphege 90-92; V 92-95; P-in-c W Hampstead St Jas 95-97; P-in-c Kilburn St Mary w All So 95-97;

TR Wood Green St Mich w Bounds Green St Gabr etc from 97. *St Michael's Rectory, 39 Bounds Green Road, London N22 8HE* Tel (020) 8888 1968 E-mail rector@woodgreenparish.com

COPPEN, Martin Alan. b 48. Ex Univ BA69 Nottm Univ DipTh84. St Jo Coll Nottm 83. d 85 p 86. C Bitterne *Win* 85-88; V St Mary Bourne and Woodcott 88-99; V Hurstbourne Priors, Longparish etc from 00; RD Whitchurch 98-03. *The Vicarage, St Mary Bourne, Andover SP11 6AY* Tel (01264) 738308
E-mail martin.coppen@ukgateway.net

COPPEN, Peter Euan. b 39. Ripon Coll Cuddesdon 79. d 81 p 82. C New Sleaford *Linc* 81-86; V Scawby and Redbourne 86-89; V Scawby, Redbourne and Hibaldstow 89-95; rtd 95. *Flete House, Church Street, Greatworth, Banbury OX17 2DU* Tel (01295) 711537

COPPEN, Robert George. b 39. Cape Town Univ BA66. St Jo Coll Dur 79. d 81 p 82. C Douglas St Geo and St Barn *S & M* 81-84; TV Kidlington w Hampton Poyle *Ox* from 84; Chapl HM YOI Campsfield Ho 84-91. *St John's Vicarage, 16 The Broadway, Kidlington OX5 1EF* Tel (01865) 375611
E-mail alacrity@btinternet.com *or* coppen@dunelm.org.uk

COPPIN, Canon Ronald Leonard. b 30. Birm Univ BA52. Ridley Hall Cam 54. d 56 p 57. C Harrow Weald All SS *Lon* 56-59; Bp's Dom Chapl *Man* 59-63; Chapl St Aid Birkenhead 63-65; Vice-Prin 65-68; Selection Sec ACCM 68-74; Sec Cttee for Th Educn 71-74; Can Res and Lib Dur Cathl *Dur* 74-97; Dir of Clergy Tr 74-96; Warden NEOC 76-84; Dir Post-Ord Tr 86-97; rtd 97. *157 Defoe House, London EC2Y 8ND* Tel (020) 7588 9228
E-mail ronald.coppin@virgin.net

COPPING, Adrian Walter Alexander. b 52. Ridley Hall Cam. d 00 p 01. C Royston *St Alb* from 00. *12 Prince Andrew's Close, Royston SG8 9DZ* Tel (01763) 243265
E-mail copping@ukgateway.net

COPPING, John Frank Walter Victor. b 34. K Coll Lon BD58 AKC58. d 59 p 60. C Hampstead St Jo *Lon* 59-62; C Bray and Braywood *Ox* 62-65; V Langley Mill *Derby* 65-71; V Cookham Dean *Ox* 71-03; RD Maidenhead 87-94; rtd 03. *41 Golden Ball Lane, Pinkneys Green, Maidenhead SL6 6NW* Tel (01628) 674433 E-mail john.copping@zoom.co.uk

COPPING, Raymond. b 35. St Mark & St Jo Coll Lon TCert59 St Paul's Cheltenham DivCert60. Wycliffe Hall Ox 72. d 74 p 75. C High Wycombe *Ox* 74-77; TV 77-87; TV Digswell and Panshanger *St Alb* 87-95; P-in-c Charlton Kings H Apostles *Glouc* 95-00; rtd 00. *20 Friars Furlong, Long Crendon, Aylesbury HP18 9DQ* Tel (01844) 208509

COPSEY, Nigel John. b 52. K Coll Lon BD75 AKC75 Surrey Univ MSc88 Middx Univ DProf01. St Aug Coll Cant 72. d 76 p 77. C Barkingside St Fran *Chelmsf* 76-78; C Canning Town St Cedd 78-80; P-in-c Victoria Docks Ascension 80-87; Chapl E Surrey Mental Health Unit 87-90; Hd Past & Spiritual Care E Surrey Priority Care NHS Trust from 90; Co-ord Past Care Surrey Oaklands NHS Trust from 99; Co-ord Relig Care Newham Community Health Services NHS Trust 99-01; Co-ord Relig Care Newham Primary Care Trust from 01. *39 London Road South, Merstham, Redhill RH1 3AX* Tel (01737) 642522 Pager 07625-156656 E-mail n.copsey@btopenworld.com

COPUS, Brian George. b 36. AKC59. d 60 p 61. C Croydon St Mich *Cant* 60-63; C Swindon New Town *Bris* 63-69; V Colebrooke *Ex* 69-73; P-in-c Hittisleigh 69-73; R Perivale *Lon* 73-82; V Ruislip St Mary 82-01; rtd 01. *2 Casterbridge Court, 1 Grosvenor Road, Bournemouth BH4 8BQ* Tel (01202) 752840

COPUS, John Cecil. b 38. TCert64 Maria Grey Coll Lon DipEd71 Open Univ BA78. Cant Sch of Min. d 82 p 84. Hon C Folkestone H Trin and St Geo w Ch Ch *Cant* 83-85; Hon C Midsomer Norton w Clandown *B & W* 85-91; Dioc Adv for Children's Work *Ex* 91-98; Hon C Aylesbeare, Rockbeare, Farringdon etc 95-98; P-in-c 98-01; rtd 01; Perm to Offic *Ex* from 01. *The Sidings, Park Road, Lapford, Crediton EX17 6QJ* Tel (01363) 83408

COPUS, Jonathan Hugh Lambert. b 44. LGSM66 BNC Ox BA66 MA71 MInstPI94. S'wark Ord Course 68. d 71 p 72. C Horsell *Guildf* 71-73; Producer Relig Progr BBC Radio Solent 73-87; Lic to Offic *Win* from 73. *Llys Myrddin, Efailwen, Clynderwen SA66 7XG* Tel (01994) 419792 Mobile 07971-545910 Fax 419796

CORBAN-BANKS, Edrick Hale. b 53. Victoria Univ Wellington BMus74 LTCL79 FTCL81. St Jo Coll Auckland BTh91. d 91 p 92. New Zealand 91-99; P Asst Johnsonville St Jo 92-94; Ct Planter Churton Park 93-94; V Katikati 94-99; P Missr Alicante Spain 99; R Alicante St Paul 99-00; Chapl Ibiza *Eur* 00-03. *Smcd Magon, Port des Torrent 07820, San Antonio, Ibiza, Spain* Tel and fax (0034) (971) 343383 Mobile 646-458205
E-mail corbanks@teleline.es

CORBETT, George. b 18. Bible Churchmen's Coll Bris 47. d 50 p 51. C Wednesfield Heath *Lich* 50-52; R Salford St Matthias w St Simon *Man* 52-55; V S Area Sec BCMS 55-58; V S Lambeth St Steph *S'wark* 58-61; Assoc Home Sec BCMS 61-63; V Hatherleigh *Ex* 63-78; P-in-c Ringmore and Kingston 78-84; R Bigbury, Ringmore and Kingston 84-86; rtd 86; Perm to Offic

Heref from 87. *2 Quantock Close, Hereford HR4 0TD* Tel (01432) 269211

CORBETT, Canon Henry. b 53. CCC Cam BA75. Wycliffe Hall Ox DipTh78. **d** 78 **p** 79. C Everton St Pet *Liv* 78-84; TV 84-87; TR 87-02; R Everton St Pet w St Chrys from 02; AD Liv N from 03; Hon Can Liv Cathl from 03. *Shrewsbury House, Langrove Street, Liverpool L5 3LT* Tel 0151-207 1948

CORBETT, Ian Deighton. b 42. St Cath Coll Cam BA64 MA68 Salford Univ MSc83. Westcott Ho Cam 67. **d** 69 **p** 70. C New Bury *Man* 69-72; C Bolton St Pet 72-75; Chapl Bolton Colls of H&FE 72-75; Dioc FE Officer 74-83; R Man Victoria Park *Man* 75-80; Chapl Salford Univ 80-83; Hon Can Man Cathl 83-87; P-in-c Salford Sacred Trin 83-87; Dir of In-Service Tr 83-87; Lesotho 87-91; Zimbabwe 91-92; Botswana 92-94; S Africa 94-95; Dean Tuam *T, K & A* 97-99; I Tuam w Cong and Aasleagh 97-99; R Whitesands Canada from 02. *Box 1686, Kamsack SK, Canada, S0A 1S0* Tel (001) (306) 542 3868

CORBETT, John David. b 32. Oriel Coll Ox BA55 MA59. St Steph Ho Ox 55. **d** 57 **p** 58. C Plymouth St Pet *Ex* 57-64; V Marldon 64-74; TV Bournemouth St Pet w St Swithun, H Trin etc *Win* 74-83; V Beckenham St Barn *Roch* 83-88; V King's Sutton and Newbottle and Charlton *Pet* 88-97; rtd 97; Perm to Offic *Portsm* and *Win* from 98. *119 St Augustine Road, Southsea PO4 9AA* Tel (023) 9275 3212 E-mail jdc.augustine@virgin.net

CORBETT, Miss Phyllis. b 34. Cranmer Hall Dur 76. **dss** 80 **d** 87 **p** 94. Walsall Wood *Lich* 80-87; Par Dn Baswich 87-94; C 94-95; rtd 95; Perm to Offic *Lich* from 95. *9 Redhill Gorse, Crab Lane, Trinity Fields, Stafford ST16 1SW*

CORBETT, Stephen Paul. b 57. BA80. St Jo Coll Nottm 83. **d** 85 **p** 86. C Tollington Park St Mark w St Anne *Lon* 85-86; C Holloway St Mark w Em 86-91; V Chitts Hill St Cuth 91-93; V Springfield *Birm* from 93; AD Moseley from 02. *The Vicarage, 172 Woodlands Road, Birmingham B11 4ET* Tel and fax 0121-777 4908 *or* tel 702 2934
E-mail stephencorbett@stchrist.freeserve.co.uk

CORBIN, Frederick Athelston. b 42. S Dios Minl Tr Scheme 80. **d** 83 **p** 85. NSM Basingstoke *Win* 83-84; C Hulme Ascension *Man* 84-86; Lic to Hulme Deanery 86-87; C E Crompton 87-89; V Oldham St Barn 89-00; rtd 00; Grenada 00-01; Perm to Offic *Man* from 01. *11 Westminster Close, Shaw, Oldham OL2 7XZ* Tel (01706) 847405

CORBYN, John. b 58. Man Univ BA79 Ven English Coll & Pontifical Gregorian Univ Rome 83. Wycliffe Hall Ox BA83 MA87. **d** 84 **p** 85. C Deane *Man* 84-87; C Lancaster St Mary *Blackb* 87-90; Chapl HM Pris Lanc 89-90; V Blackb St Gabr *Blackb* 90-01; V Bearsted w Thurnham *Cant* from 01. *The Vicarage, Church Lane, Bearsted, Maidstone ME14 4EF* Tel (01622) 737135 E-mail johncorbyn@garlick.net

CORBYN, John Robert. b 54. Qu Coll Birm. **d** 82 **p** 83. C Northolt W End St Jos *Lon* 82-86; Urban Miss P *York* 86-88; C Sutton St Mich 86-88; V Dalton *Sheff* 88-96; R Cressing *Chelmsf* 96-99; R Cressing w Stisted and Bradwell etc from 99. *The House, The Street, Bradwell, Braintree CM77 8EL* Tel (01376) 562398 E-mail frjohn@crestibrad.freeserve.co.uk

CORCORAN, Mrs Valerie A'Court. b 46. UEA BA68 Lon Inst of Educn PGCE69. STETS 99. **d** 02 **p** 03. NSM Boyatt Wood *Win* from 02. *Ashley, Finches Lane, Twyford, Winchester SO21 1QB* Tel (01962) 712951 Mobile 07736-459500 Fax (01962) 715770 E-mail v.corcoran@btinternet.com

CORDELL, Derek Harold. b 34. Chich Th Coll 57. **d** 60 **p** 61. C Whitstable All SS *Cant* 60-63; C Moulsecoomb *Chich* 63-69; Chapl Bucharest *Eur* 69-71; V Brighton St Wilfrid *Chich* 71-74; Chapl HM Borstal Roch 74-80; Asst Chapl HM Pris Man 80-81; Chapl HM Pris The Verne 81-89; Chapl HM Pris Channings Wood 89-90; Chapl Milan w Genoa and Varese *Eur* 90-91; Chapl Mojacar 91-94; Perm to Offic from 95; rtd 97. *49 Tower Way, Dunkeswell, Honiton EX14 4XH* Tel (01404) 891859

CORDINER, Alan Dobson. b 61. HTC83 Westmr Coll Ox BA87. **d** 92 **p** 93. C Upperby St Jo *Carl* 92-98; P-in-c Bootle, Corney, Whicham and Whitbeck from 98; Asst Chapl HM Pris Haverigg 98-03. *The Rectory, Bootle, Millom LA19 5TH* Tel (01229) 718223

CORDINGLEY, Canon Brian Lambert. b 30. St Aid Birkenhead 55. **d** 57 **p** 58. Ind Chapl *Sheff* 57-63; C Clifton St Jas 57-61; C Rotherham 61-63; Ind Chapl *Man* 63-92; R Old Trafford St Cuth 63-81; V Hamer 81-92; Hon Can Man Cathl 87-92; rtd 92; Perm to Offic *Man* from 99. *Wellsprings, 27 Fernthorpe Avenue, Uppermill, Oldham OL3 6EA* Tel (01457) 820130

CORE, Edward. b 54. BTh. Sarum & Wells Th Coll. **d** 82 **p** 83. C Newbold w Dunston *Derby* 82-86; Chapl RAF 86-01; Command Chapl RAF from 01. *Chaplaincy Services (RAF), HQ, Personnel and Training Command, RAF Innsworth, Gloucester GL3 1EZ* Tel (01452) 712612 ext 5164 Fax 510828

CORFE, David Robert. b 35. Pemb Coll Cam BA58 MA60 Lambeth STh70. Cuddesdon Coll 58. **d** 60 **p** 61. C Wigan All SS *Liv* 60-63; SPG Miss India 63-68; V Lucknow Ch Ch w All SS and St Pet 70-75; C Northwood Em *Lon* 75; V Westwell and Eastwell w Boughton Aluph *Cant* 75-80; V Hildenborough *Roch* 80-91; Lic Preacher Stretford St Bride *Man* 91-98; Team Ldr

Interserve 98-00; rtd 00. *1 Hartley Court, 12 Winn Road, Southampton SO17 1EN* Tel (023) 8058 5557

CORK, Ronald Edward. b 43. Plymouth Poly CQSW72. N Ord Course 89. **d** 92 **p** 93. Hon C Altrincham St Geo *Ches* 92-96; P-in-c Altrincham St Jo 96-01; rtd 01. *9 Dodgson Close, Llandudno LL30 1AJ* Tel (01492) 873889
E-mail roncork@aol.com

CORK, CLOYNE AND ROSS, Archdeacon of. *See* WHITE, The Ven Robin Edward Bantry

CORK, CLOYNE AND ROSS, Bishop of. *See* COLTON, The Rt Revd William Paul

CORK, Dean of. *See* BURROWS, The Very Revd Michael Andrew James

CORKE, Andrew John. b 55. Bris Univ LLB77. **d** 98 **p** 00. OLM Canford Magna *Sarum* from 98. *2 Silverwood Close, Wimborne Minster BH21 1QZ* Tel (01202) 882449 Mobile 07711-898723 Fax 786140 E-mail a.corke@talk21.com

CORKE, Bryan Raymond. b 49. Westmr Coll Lon 81. LNSM course 92. **d** 95 **p** 96. OLM Flixton St Jo *Man* from 95. *40 Daresbury Avenue, Manchester M41 8GL* Tel 0161-748 1827

CORKE, Colin John. b 59. St Pet Coll Ox BA81. Cranmer Hall Dur 83. **d** 85 **p** 86. C Chapel Allerton *Ripon* 85-88; C Burmantofts St Steph and St Agnes 88-91; P-in-c Tatsfield *S'wark* 91-01; Reigate Adnry Ecum Officer 92-01; V Longbridge *Birm* from 01; Dioc Ecum Officer from 02. *St John's Vicarage, 220 Longbridge Lane, Birmingham B31 4JT* Tel 0121-475 3484

CORKE, Francis Bonny. *See* RODRIGUEZ-VEGLIO, Francis Bonny

CORKE, John Harry. b 29. AKC55. **d** 56 **p** 57. C Stockingford *Cov* 56-58; C Nuneaton St Nic 58-60; V Hartshill 60-80; R Hampton Lucy w Charlecote and Loxley 80-94; rtd 94; Perm to Offic *Linc* from 95. *18 Haven Close, Fleet, Spalding PE12 8NS* Tel (01406) 426038

CORKE, Louise Dorothy. b 59. Southn Univ BSc80 PGCE81. Trin Coll Bris BA94. **d** 97 **p** 98. C Ipsley *Worc* 97-01; TV Bradgate Team *Leic* from 01. *The Rectory, 58 Pymm Ley Lane, Groby, Leicester LE6 0GZ* Tel 0116-231 3090
E-mail louisecorke@smallvoice.screaming.net

CORKE, Roderick Geoffrey. b 58. UEA BEd79 Open Univ MA96. St Jo Coll Nottm Dip Th Studies 92. **d** 92 **p** 93. C Trimley *St E* 92-95; C Walton 95-00; TR Walton and Trimley from 00. *1 Parsonage Close, Felixstowe IP11 2QR* Tel (01394) 284803 E-mail r.corke@ntlworld.com

CORKER, Mrs Elizabeth Jane. b 42. Dioc OLM tr scheme 96. **d** 99 **p** 00. OLM Martlesham w Brightwell *St E* from 99. *12 Fairfield Avenue, Felixstowe IP11 9JN* Tel (01394) 210793

CORKER, John Anthony. b 37. TD93. ACIB75 AKC63. **d** 64 **p** 65. C Lindley *Wakef* 64-68; V Brotherton 68-72; Perm to Offic 72-82; CF (TA) 80-93; Hon C Askham Bryan *York* 82-91; TV York All SS Pavement w St Crux and St Martin etc 91-96; Asst P Amblecote *Worc* 96-01; C Dudley St Barn 01-02; rtd 02. *69 Lakeside Court, Brierley Hill DY5 3RQ* Tel (01384) 897378

CORKER, Canon Ronald. b 30. Ely Th Coll 51. **d** 54 **p** 55. C Whitworth w Spennymoor *Dur* 54-58; Min Dunstan St Nic ED 58-65; Chapl Dunston Hill Hosp Gateshead 58-68; V Dunston St Nic *Dur* 65-68; R Willington 68-75; P-in-c Sunnybrow 73-75; R Willington and Sunnybrow 75-80; V Billingham St Cuth 80-85; RD Stockton 83-85; TR Jarrow 85-95; Hon Can Dur Cathl 90-00; rtd 95. *195 Beaconsides, Cleadon Manor, South Shields NE34 7PT* Tel 0191-454 2987

CORLESS, Canon Keith Ronald. b 37. Edin Th Coll 58. **d** 61 **p** 62. C Pittville All SS *Glouc* 61-64; C Leckhampton SS Phil and Jas 66-69; R Ashchurch 69-96; Hon Can Glouc Cathl 95-00; V Staverton w Boddington and Tredington etc 96-00; rtd 00; Perm to Offic *Glouc* from 00. *1 Tanners Close, Brockworth, Gloucester GL3 4QN* Tel (01452) 863766

CORLETT, Ewan Christian Brew. b 23. OBE85. FEng74 FIMarE FRINA FRIN FNI Qu Coll Ox MA47 K Coll Dur PhD50. Is of Man Tr Inst 88. **d** 91 **p** 92. NSM Maughold *S & M* from 91. *Cottimans, Port-e-Vullen, Ramsey, Isle of Man IM7 1AP* Tel (01624) 814009 Fax 817248

CORNE, Ronald Andrew. b 51. Sarum & Wells Th Coll 87. **d** 89 **p** 90. C Bitterne Park *Win* 89-93; R Headbourne Worthy and King's Worthy 93-01; P-in-c Broughton, Bossington, Houghton and Mottisfont from 01. *The Rectory, Rectory Lane, Broughton, Stockbridge SO20 8AB* Tel (01794) 301287
E-mail ronandrew@corne10.freeserve.co.uk

CORNECK, Canon Warrington Graham. b 35. FCA62 ACA60. Clifton Th Coll. **d** 65 **p** 66. C Islington St Jude Mildmay Park *Lon* 65-67; C Southgate *Chich* 67-73; P-in-c Deptford St Nic w Ch Ch *S'wark* 73-76; P-in-c Deptford St Luke 73-76; V Deptford St Nic and St Luke from 76; RD Deptford from 85; Hon Can S'wark Cathl from 91. *St Nicholas' Vicarage, 41 Creek Road, London SE8 3BU* Tel (020) 8692 2749 Fax as telephone
E-mail wgcorneck@tesco.net

CORNELIUS, Donald Eric. b 31. K Coll Lon BD52 AKC. Linc Th Coll 84. **d** 84 **p** 85. NSM Crowle *Linc* 84-97; NSM Crowle Gp 97-02; NSM Flixborough w Burton upon Stather 91-02; P-in-c Gunhouse w Burringham 91-02; Perm to Offic from 02.

4 Mulberry Drive, Crowle, Scunthorpe DN17 4JF Tel (01724) 710279

CORNELL, Miss Jean Cranston. b 36. Man Univ CertEd59 BA64 York Univ BPhil71. Ripon Coll Cuddesdon 87 MTh00. **d** 89 **p** 94. C Matson *Glouc* 89-92; C Bishop's Cleeve 92-96; rtd 96; NSM Winchcombe, Gretton, Sudeley Manor etc *Glouc* 96-01; Perm to Offic 01-02. *20 Darent Close, Stone Cross, Pevensey BN24 5PW* Tel (01323) 763171
E-mail naej@chris47.freeserve.co.uk

CORNELL, John Lister. b 12. St Pet Hall Ox BA34 MA39. Wycliffe Hall Ox 35. **d** 35 **p** 36. C Bermondsey St Anne *S'wark* 35-40; C Putney St Mary 40-44; R Spexhall w Wissett *St E* 44-53; R Mickleham *Guildf* 53-78; rtd 78. *Staddles, Windmill Hill, Ashill, Ilminster TA19 9NT* Tel (01823) 480012

CORNELL, Michael Neil. *See* COHEN, Michael Neil

CORNES, Alan Stuart. b 70. Open Univ BA98 Nottm Univ MA00 Chester Coll of HE DipN94. St Jo Coll Nottm 98. **d** 01. C Meole Brace *Lich* from 01. *6 Burnside Gardens, Meole Brace, Shrewsbury SY3 9HH* Tel (01743) 248297

CORNES, Andrew Charles Julian. b 49. CCC Ox BA70 MA73 St Jo Coll Dur DipTh73. Wycliffe Hall Ox 70 Cranmer Hall Dur 72. **d** 73 **p** 74. C York St Mich-le-Belfrey *York* 73-76; C St Marylebone All So w SS Pet and Jo *Lon* 76-85; USA 85-88; V Crowborough *Chich* from 89; RD Rotherfield 97-03; Chapl Eastbourne and Co Healthcare NHS Trust from 89. *All Saints' Vicarage, Chapel Green, Crowborough TN6 1ED* Tel (01892) 667384 *or* 652081

CORNESS, Andrew Stuart. b 69. Bp Otter Coll Chich BA91 Westmr Coll Ox PGCE93. Wycliffe Hall Ox BA00. **d** 01 **p** 02. C Ewood *Blackb* from 01. *17 Douglas Close, Blackburn BB2 4FF* Tel (01254) 696622 Fax as telephone
E-mail andrewcorness@hotmail.com

CORNFIELD, Richard James. b 67. St Jo Coll Nottm BA96. **d** 96 **p** 97. C Cheltenham Ch Ch *Glouc* 96-00; C Aldridge *Lich* from 00. *227 Walsall Road, Aldridge, Walsall WS9 0QA* Tel (01902) 457732 E-mail richard.cornfield@virgin.net

CORNISH, Anthony. b 30. Roch Th Coll 64. **d** 67 **p** 68. C Goodmayes All SS *Chelmsf* 67-71; C Buckhurst Hill 71-73; V Westcliff St Andr 73-83; R Rawreth w Rettendon 83-96; rtd 96. *12 Fleetwood Avenue, Clacton-on-Sea CO15 5SE*

CORNISH, Dennis Henry Ronald. b 31. FCIB72 FCIS81. S'wark Ord Course 83. **d** 86 **p** 87. NSM Uxbridge *Lon* 86-89; R Lurgashall, Lodsworth and Selham *Chich* 89-96; rtd 96; Perm to Offic *Chich* from 96. *Peerley Lodge, 1 Peerley Road, East Wittering, Chichester PO20 8DW* Tel (01243) 672481

CORNISH, Gillian Lesley. b 45. ACIB77. St Jo Coll Nottm 90 LNSM course 93. **d** 96 **p** 97. OLM Moston St Mary *Man* from 96. *11 Rishworth Drive, New Moston, Manchester M40 3PS* Tel 0161-681 2839

CORNISH, Graham Peter. b 42. Dur Univ BA67 FLA. NEOC 82. **d** 84 **p** 85. NSM Harrogate St Wilfrid and St Luke *Ripon* 84-96; Perm to Offic *York* from 84; NSM Bilton *Ripon* from 96. *33 Mayfield Grove, Harrogate HG1 5HD* Tel (01423) 562747 E-mail graham.cornish@bl.uk

CORNISH, Ivor. b 60. Reading Univ BSc61 DipEd62 ADipR79. Ox Min Course 86. **d** 89 **p** 90. NSM Aston Clinton w Buckland and Drayton Beauchamp *Ox* 89-97; NSM The Lee from 97; NSM Hawridge w Cholesbury and St Leonard from 97. *79 Weston Road, Aston Clinton, Aylesbury HP22 5EP* Tel (01296) 630345

CORNISH, John Douglas. b 42. Lich Th Coll 67. **d** 70 **p** 71. C Lt Stanmore St Lawr *Lon* 70-73; C Harefield 73-96; Perm to Offic 96-02; rtd 02. *46 Arnos Grove, London N14 7AR*

CORNISH, Peter Andrew. b 55. Ch Ch Ox BA77 MA80 Ex Univ CertEd78. St Jo Coll Nottm 84. **d** 87 **p** 88. C Sanderstead All SS *S'wark* 87-92; TV Cen Telford *Lich* 92-98; R Sturry w Fordwich and Westbere w Hersden *Cant* from 98. *The Rectory, 2 The Hamels, Sturry, Canterbury CT2 0BL* Tel (01227) 710320
E-mail peter.cornish@amserve.net

CORNISH, Philip Gordon Pym. b 01. K Coll Lon AKC25 BD28. **d** 26 **p** 27. C Roehampton H Trin *S'wark* 26-29; Canada 29-33; C Upper St Leonards St Jo *Chich* 33-37; V Hastings St Clem 37-44; V Danehill 44-59; RD Uckfield 56-59; R Lt Waltham *Chelmsf* 59-67; rtd 67. *c/o Mrs M Courage, Bridge Cottage, Melbury Osmond, Dorchester DT2 0NA* Tel (01935) 83364

CORNWALL, Archdeacon of. *See* WHITEMAN, The Ven Rodney David Carter

CORNWALL, Christopher Richard. b 43. Dur Univ BA67. Cuddesdon Coll 67. **d** 69 **p** 70. C Cannock *Lich* 69-75; P-in-c Hadley 75-80; V 80-81; Bp's Dom Chapl 81-86; Subchanter Lich Cathl 81-86; V Ellesmere 86-89; V Welsh Frankton 86-89; V Ellesmere and Welsh Frankton 89-92; TV Leeds City *Ripon* 92-00; AD Allerton 94-97; V Ireland Wood from 00. *St Paul's Vicarage, Raynel Drive, Leeds LS16 6BS* Tel 0113-267 2907

CORNWALL, Gertrude Florence. b 21. CertEd48 Nottm Univ DipEd72. Gilmore Ho 56 Lambeth STh60. **dss** 62 **d** 87. See Asst Bp Grosseteste Coll Linc 64-81; rtd 81; Perm to Offic *Linc* from 91. *Flat 2A, 14 Minster Yard, Lincoln LN2 1PW* Tel (01522) 527249

CORNWELL, Lisa Michele. b 70. Lon Bible Coll BA94 Westmr Coll Ox PGCE95 K Coll Lon MA99. Ridley Hall Cam 00. **d** 02 **p** 03. C Newport Pagnell w Lathbury and Moulsoe *Ox* from 02. *3 Castle Meadow Close, Newport Pagnell MK16 9EJ* Tel (01908) 613161 Mobile 07789-778885

CORP, Ronald Geoffrey. b 51. Ch Ch Ox MA77. STETS DipTh98. **d** 98 **p** 99. NSM Kilburn St Mary w All So and W Hampstead St Jas *Lon* 98-02; NSM Hendon St Mary and Ch Ch from 02. *76 Brent Street, London NW4 2ES*
E-mail reynaldo@angkor.demon.co.uk

CORRADINE, John. b 29. St Aid Birkenhead. **d** 58 **p** 59. C Tarporley *Ches* 58-61; C Wilmslow 61-64; V Moulton 64-95; rtd 95; Perm to Offic *Ches* from 95. *6 Beach Road, Hoylake, Wirral CH47 1HT* Tel 0151-632 3042

CORRAN, Henry Stanley. b 15. Trin Coll Cam BA36 PhD41. CITC 76. **d** 77 **p** 78. NSM Bray Ch Ch *D & G* 77-85; rtd 85. *71 Alderley Road, Hoylake, Wirral CH47 2AU* Tel 0151-632 2750

CORRIE, Jennifer Sylvia. b 46. RMN68 SRN76 DN77. OLM course 96. **d** 99 **p** 00. OLM Broughton *Man* from 99. *6 Briardene, Back Hilton Street, Salford M7 2GQ*

CORRIE, John. b 48. Imp Coll Lon BScEng69 MSc70 DIC70 PhD73 Lon Univ DipTh77 Nottm Univ MTh86. Trin Coll Bris 74. **d** 77 **p** 78. C Kendal St Thos *Carl* 77-80; C Attenborough *S'well* 80-86; ICS Peru 86-91; Tutor and Lect All Nations Chr Coll Ware 91-02; Lect/Development Officer Cen for Angl Communion Studies Selly Oak from 02. *United College of the Ascension, Weoley Park Road, Birmingham B29 6RD* Tel 0121-415 6810

CORRIE, Paul Allen. b 43. St Jo Coll Nottm 77. **d** 79 **p** 80. C Beverley Minster *York* 79-82; V Derby St Werburgh *Derby* 82-84; V Derby St Alkmund and St Werburgh 84-95; Singapore 95-99; R Hawkwell *Chelmsf* from 00. *The Rectory, Ironwell Lane, Hawkwell, Hockley SS5 4JY* Tel (01702) 200620

CORRIGAN, The Ven Thomas George. b 28. TCD Dip Bibl Studies 56 BTh91. CITC 56. **d** 58 **p** 59. C Cavan and Drung *K, E & A* 58-60; I Drung 60-67; I Belfast St Mich *Conn* 67-70; I Kingscourt w Drumconrath, Syddan and Moybologue *M & K* 70-96; Adn Meath 81-96; Dioc Registrar (Meath) 87-90; rtd 96. *The Beeches, Turner's Hill, Kingscourt, Co Cavan, Irish Republic* Tel (00353) (42) 966 8348 Fax 966 8388
E-mail adncorgn@esatclear.ie

CORRY, Caroline Anne. b 58. St Hilda's Coll Ox BA79 Ox Univ MA97. S Tr Scheme 94. **d** 97 **p** 98. C Weston *Guildf* 97-01; P-in-c N Holmwood from 01. *The Vicarage, Willow Green, North Holmwood, Dorking RH5 4JB* Tel (01306) 882135

CORSIE, Andrew Russell. b 57. Trin Coll Bris DipHE93. **d** 93 **p** 94. C Northolt Park St Barn *Lon* 93-97; C Perivale 97-01; P-in-c from 01; AD Ealing from 03. *Perivale Rectory, Federal Road, Greenford UB6 7AP* Tel (020) 8997 1948
E-mail acorsie@aol.com

CORSTORPHINE, Miss Margaret. b 34. SRN57 SCM59. Cranmer Hall Dur 70. **dss** 84 **d** 87 **p** 94. Colchester St Jo *Chelmsf* 84-87; Par Dn 87-94; C 94; rtd 94; Perm to Offic *Portsm* from 94. *12 Oakmeadow Close, Emsworth PO10 7RL*

CORWIN, Nigel Trevor. b 47. EAMTC 95. **d** 97 **p** 98. NSM Bury St Edmunds St Jo *St E* from 97. *121 Raedwald Drive, Bury St Edmunds IP32 7DG* Tel (01284) 725284 Mobile 07713-769816 Fax (01284) 725391 E-mail ccmh@iname.com
or nigel@corwin.fsnet.co.uk

CORY, Ms Valerie Ann. b 44. CertEd65 Nottm Univ BEd85. EMMTC 85. **d** 88 **p** 94. Area Sec CMS *Linc* and *Pet* 87-91; NSM Grantham *Linc* 88-91; Par Dn Ealing St Mary *Lon* 91-94; Chapl NW Lon Poly 91-92; Chapl Thames Valley Univ 92-96; C Ealing St Mary 94-96; Chapl Birm Cathl *Birm* 96-99; C Surbiton St Andr and St Mark *S'wark* from 99. *The Vicarage, 1 The Mall, Surbiton KT6 4EH* Tel (020) 8399 6806
E-mail valcory@ukgateway.net

COSBY, Ingrid St Clair. b 34. ALCM LLCM DipEd Lon Univ DipTh. **dss** 71 **d** 86 **p** 96. Cumbernauld *Glas* 71-73; Asst CF 73-78; Stromness *Ab* 83-86; NSM from 86. *Quarrybrae, Hillside Road, Stromness KW16 3HR* Tel (01856) 850832 Fax as telephone

COSENS, William Edward Hyde (Ted). b 38. Lich Th Coll 61. **d** 64 **p** 65. C W Drayton *Lon* 64-68; C Roehampton H Trin *S'wark* 68-70; ILEA Youth Ldr 69-70; Miss to Seamen 70-94; Rotterdam 70-72; Tilbury 72-76; Australia 76-81 and 99-03; Dampier 76-81; Auckland New Zealand 81-89; Chapl Immingham Seafarers' Cen 89-94; Hon C Immingham *Linc* 89-94; Chapl Felixstowe Seafarers' Cen 94-97; Chapl Avonmouth Miss to Seamen 97-99; Sen Chapl Melbourne Miss to Seafarers 99-03; Chapl State of Vic 99-03; rtd 03. *6 Sandell Court, The Parkway, Southampton SO16 3PH* Tel (023) 8076 9235 Mobile 07905-782776
E-mail ted.caroline.cosens@virgin.net

COSH, Roderick John. b 56. Lon Univ BSc78. St Steph Ho Ox 78. **d** 81 **p** 82. C Swindon New Town *Bris* 81-86; Chapl Asst R Marsden Hosp Lon and Surrey 86-91; V Whitton St Aug *Lon* 91-00; P-in-c Staines St Mary and St Pet from 00. *St Peter's*

Vicarage, 14 Thames Side, Staines TW18 2HA Tel (01784) 453039 *or* 469155 E-mail rod@stainesparish.fsnet.co.uk

COSLETT, Anthony Allan. b 49. Cuddesdon Coll. **d** 84 **p** 85. C Notting Hill St Clem and St Mark *Lon* 84-85; C Brentford 85-87; C-in-c Hounslow Gd Shep Beavers Lane CD 87-90; V Hounslow W Gd Shep 90-92; CF 92-02. *Address temp unknown*

COSLETT (née SLATER), Mrs Carol Ann. b 63. Univ of Wales (Ban) BD85 Jes Coll Cam PGCE86 Lon Inst of Educn MA92. Ripon Coll Cuddesdon 01. **d** 03. C Horsell *Guildf* from 03. *6A Waldons Park Road, Horsell, Woking GU21 4RN* Tel 07803-671256 (mobile) E-mail carolcoslett@tiscali.co.uk

COSSAR, David Vyvyan. b 34. Lon Univ BA63. Chich Th Coll 63. **d** 65 **p** 66. C Upper Clapton St Matt *Lon* 65-68; C Withycombe Raleigh *Ex* 68-72; V Honicknowle 72-78; V Brixham w Churston Ferrers 78-86; P-in-c Kingswear 85-86; TR Brixham w Churston Ferrers and Kingswear 86-90; V Lamorbey H Trin *Roch* 90-03; rtd 03. *31 Bromley College, London Road, Bromley BR1 1PE* Tel (020) 8464 6911
E-mail diane.cossar@tinyonline.uk

COSSAR, Miss Heather Jillian Mackenzie. b 27. dss 83 **d** 81 **p** 94. Miss Partner CMS 83-90; Kenya 83-90; Slindon, Eartham and Madehurst *Chich* 90-99; NSM 91-99; Perm to Offic from 99. *Gwitu, 38 Spinney Walk, Barnham, Bognor Regis PO22 0HT* Tel (01243) 552718

COSSINS, John Charles. b 43. Hull Univ BSc65. Oak Hill Th Coll 65. **d** 67 **p** 68. C Kenilworth St Jo *Cov* 67-70; C Huyton St Geo *Liv* 70-73; TV Maghull 73-79; Chapl Oakwood Hosp Maidstone 79-85; Maidstone Hosp 85-88; Chapl Park Lane Hosp Liv 88-03; Chapl Moss Side Hosp Liv 88-03; Chapl Ashworth Hosp Magull 88-03; rtd 03. *9 Longton Drive, Liverpool L37 7ET* Tel (01704) 833136 Fax 08700-553669
E-mail jcossins@jcossins.demon.co.uk

COSSINS, Roger Stanton. b 40. K Coll Lon BD67 AKC67. **d** 68 **p** 69. C Bramley *Ripon* 68-71; C W End *Win* 71-76; V Bramley 76-91; P-in-c Bournemouth H Epiphany 91-94; V 94-00; rtd 00. *5 Allen Court, Trumpington, Cambridge CB2 2LU* Tel (01223) 841726

COSSLETT, Dominic Simon. b 72. Univ of Wales (Lamp) BA94 Leeds Univ MA96. Coll of Resurr Mirfield 94. **d** 96 **p** 97. C Newton St Pet *S & B* 96-99; C Abergavenny St Mary w Llanwenarth Citra *Mon* 99-02; V Kingstanding St Mark *Birm* from 02. *St Mark's Clergy House, Bandywood Crescent, Birmingham B44 9JX* Tel 0121-360 7288

COSSLETT, Ronald James. b 38. St D Coll Lamp DipTh70. **d** 70 **p** 71. C Newport St Teilo *Mon* 70-74; C Epsom St Barn *Guildf* 74-78; C Shrewsbury St Mary w All SS and St Mich *Lich* 78-80; V Smallthorne 80-91; V Landore *S & B* 91-02; rtd 03. *24 Bridle Lane, Sutton Coldfield B74 3HB* Tel 0121-580 7546

COSTER, Mrs Catherine Anne. b 47. Bris Poly BEd85. WEMTC 97. **d** 00 **p** 01. NSM Yate New Town *Bris* from 00. *31 Vayre Close, Chipping Sodbury, Bristol BS37 6NT* Tel (01454) 314858 Fax 0117-927 7454 E-mail catherine@ccoster.freeserve.co.uk

COSTERTON, Alan Stewart. b 40. Bris Univ BA67. Clifton Th Coll 67. **d** 69 **p** 70. C Peckham St Mary Magd *S'wark* 69-73; C Forest Gate St Saw w W Ham St Matt *Chelmsf* 73-76; TV 76-79; V Thornton cum Bagworth *Leic* 79-85; V Thornton, Bagworth and Stanton 85-95; TR Sileby, Cossington and Seagrave from 95. *The Rectory, 11 Mountsorrel Lane, Sileby, Loughborough LE12 7NF* Tel (01509) 812493
E-mail alan@costerton.freeserve.co.uk

COTGROVE, Canon Edwin John. b 23. Kelham Th Coll 42. **d** 47 **p** 48. C Bris St Jude w St Matthias *Bris* 47-50; C Southall St Geo *Lon* 50-52; S Africa 52-56; Swaziland 56-57; V Bromley St Mich *Lon* 57-64; V Hampton All SS 64-82; RD Hampton 72-82; R Bartlow *Ely* 82-91; V Linton 82-91; P-in-c Shudy Camps 85-91; P-in-c Castle Camps 85-91; RD Linton 88-93; Hon Can Ely Cathl 89-91; rtd 91; Perm to Offic *Ely* from 91. *96 The High Street, Great Abington, Cambridge CB1 6AE* Tel (01223) 893735

COTMAN, John Sell Granville (Jan). b 44. St Jo Coll Dur BA69. Wells Th Coll 70. **d** 73 **p** 74. C Leigh St Mary *Man* 73-76; P-in-c Coldhurst 76-78; TV Oldham 78-82; TV E Ham w Upton Park St Alb *Chelmsf* 82-85; C Hove All SS *Chich* 88-93; TV Hove 93-00; TV W Slough *Ox* from 01. *298 Stoke Poges Lane, Slough SL1 3LL* Tel (01753) 578503

COTSON, Tony Arthur. b 53. NEOC 00. **d** 03. NSM Kingston upon Hull St Nic *York* from 03. *11 Kipling Walk, Summergroves Way, Hull HU4 6SX* Tel (01482) 504189
E-mail tony@cotson.karoo.co.uk

COTTAM, Kenneth Michael David. b 46. FTC70 Leic Univ NDA70 Brooksby Agric Coll NDFOM70. St Mich Coll Llan 93. **d** 93 **p** 94. Lic to Offic Llangadog and Llandeilo Deanery *St D* 93-96; V Llangadog and Gwynfe w Llanddeusant from 96. *The Vicarage, Walters Road, Llangadog SA19 9AE* Tel (01550) 777604

COTTEE, Christopher Paul. b 54. Newc Univ BSc75. Wycliffe Hall Ox 77. **d** 80 **p** 81. C Much Woolton *Liv* 80-84; C Prescot 84-88; NSM Parr 89-91; V Watford St Pet *St Alb* from 91. *St Peter's Vicarage, 61 Westfield Avenue, Watford WD24 7HF* Tel (01923) 226717 E-mail c.p.cottee@cwcom.net

COTTEE, Mary Jane. b 43. CertEd64 Open Univ BA81. Oak Hill Th Coll 87. **d** 90 **p** 94. NSM Gt Baddow *Chelmsf* 90-95; P-in-c Woodham Ferrers and Bicknacre from 95. *Church House, Main Road, Bicknacre, Chelmsford CM3 4HA* Tel (01245) 224895

COTTELL, Avril Jane. *See* GAUNT, Mrs Avril Jane

COTTER, Graham Michael. b 50. Univ of Wales (Ban) BA72. Ridley Hall Cam 75. **d** 78 **p** 79. C Headley All SS *Guildf* 78-81; C Plymouth St Andr w St Paul and St Geo *Ex* 81-84; V Buckland Monachorum from 84; RD Tavistock 93-98. *The Vicarage, Buckland Monachorum, Yelverton PL20 7LQ* Tel (01822) 852227

COTTER, James England. b 42. G&C Coll Cam BA64 MA67. Linc Th Coll 68. **d** 67 **p** 68. C Stretford St Matt *Man* 67-70; Lect Linc Th Coll 70-73; Lic to Offic *Lon* 73-74; Chapl G&C Coll Cam 74-77; C Leavesden All SS *St Alb* 77-83; Asst Prin St Alb Minl Tr Scheme 77-83; Course Dir 83-86; Perm to Offic *Ex* 86-88 and *Sheff* 88-89; Lic to Offic *Sheff* 89-01; Perm to Offic *Ban* from 99. *Dwylan, Stryd Fawr, Harlech LL46 2YA* Tel (01766) 781368
E-mail jim@cottercairns.co.uk

COTTER, Canon John Beresford Dolmage. b 20. TCD BA47 BD55. **d** 47 **p** 48. C Glencraig *D & D* 47-49; Chile and Bolivia 49-53; Peru 53; I Tempo *Clogh* 54-55; I Garrison 55-60; I Donagh 60-67; Dir of Ords 62-69; Can Clogh Cathl 62-69; I Dromore 67-69; Preb Donaghmore St Patr Cathl Dublin 69; Bahrain 69-75; V Towednack *Truro* 76-89; V Zennor 76-89; Past Tr Chapl 82-89; rtd 89; Perm to Offic *B & W* from 89. *Thimble Cottage, 64 Mount Road, Bath BA2 1LH* Tel (01225) 337414

COTTERELL, Michael Clifford. b 54. Oak Hill Th Coll 81. **d** 84 **p** 85. C Lutterworth w Cotesbach *Leic* 84-87; C Belper *Derby* 87-91; V Locking *B & W* 91-98; V Slough *Ox* from 98. *St Paul's Vicarage, 196 Stoke Road, Slough SL2 5AY* Tel (01753) 521497
E-mail mikecottterell@aol.com

COTTERILL, Joseph Charles. b 17. AMCT38 Lon Univ DipTh BD California Coll Peking MA46. Ox Min Course 92. **d** 93 **p** 94. NSM Marcham w Garford *Ox* 93-98; Perm to Offic from 98. *8 Draycott Road, Southmoor, Abingdon OX13 5BY* Tel (01865) 820436

COTTINGHAM, Peter John Garnet. b 24. Wadh Coll Ox BA48 MA50. Ridley Hall Cam 48. **d** 50 **p** 51. C Cheadle *Ches* 50-55; R Ox St Clem *Ox* 55-68; V S Mimms Ch Ch *Lon* 68-81; V Derby St Pet and Ch Ch w H Trin *Derby* 81-89; rtd 89; Perm to Offic *Ban* from 89. *5 Broadway, Rhos-on-Sea, Colwyn Bay LL28 4AR* Tel (01492) 548840

COTTON, Charles Anthony. b 50. Linc Coll Ox BA72 MA77 PGCE73. Ridley Hall Cam 89. **d** 91 **p** 92. C Hendon St Paul Mill Hill *Lon* 91-96; C Wandsworth All SS *S'wark* 96-97; V Clapham St Jas from 97. *St James's Vicarage, 1 Rodenhurst Road, London SW4 8AE* Tel (020) 8674 3973

COTTON, John. b 44. Newc Univ BSc66. SW Minl Tr Course 99. **d** 02 **p** 03. NSM St Gennys, Jacobstow w Warbstow and Treneglos *Truro* from 02. *24 Bede Haven Close, Bude EX23 8QF* Tel (01288) 352896 Fax as telephone
E-mail thecottons@btinternet.com

COTTON, Canon John Alan. b 24. Qu Coll Ox BA48 MA52. Chich Th Coll 50. **d** 51 **p** 52. C Doncaster St Geo *Sheff* 51-54; C Ifield *Chich* 54-56; P-in-c Jevington 56-57; R 57-60; Chief Org Sec SPCK 60-63; Chapl Sussex Univ 63-69; V Fairwarp 69-82; Dir of Educn 72-78; Can and Preb Chich Cathl 72-89; Bp's Adv on Min 79-89; Dir of Ords 79-89; rtd 89; Perm to Offic *Carl* 91-99. *1 Westhaven, Thursby, Carlisle CA7 6PH* Tel (01228) 711506

COTTON, John Horace Brazel. b 28. MIMechE St Jo Coll Cam BA50 MA76. St Alb Minl Tr Scheme 78. **d** 81 **p** 82. NSM Lt Berkhamsted and Bayford, Essendon etc *St Alb* 81-87; P-in-c 87-96; rtd 96; Perm to Offic *St Alb* from 96. *49 Sherrardspark Road, Welwyn Garden City AL8 7LD* Tel (01707) 321815

COTTON, John Kenneth. b 25. Westcott Ho Cam 57. **d** 58 **p** 59. C S Ormsby w Ketsby, Calceby and Driby *Linc* 58-61; R Wrentham w Benacre, Covehithe and Henstead *St E* 61-68; R Sotterley w Willingham 63-68; R Shadingfield 63-68; Canada 68-71; TV Sandringham w W Newton *Nor* 71-76; P-in-c Assington *St E* 80-86; P-in-c Lt Cornard 80-86; P-in-c Newton 80-86; P-in-c Eyke w Bromeswell, Rendlesham, Tunstall etc 87-92; P-in-c Alderton w Ramsholt and Bawdsey 89-92; rtd 92; Perm to Offic *St E* from 92. *8 Chillesford Lodge Bungalows, Sudbourne, Woodbridge IP12 2AN* Tel (01394) 450740
E-mail john.cotton@btinternet.com

COTTON, Canon John Wallis. b 31. Wells Th Coll 57. **d** 59 **p** 60. C Stepney St Dunstan and All SS *Lon* 59-64; C Hanworth All SS 64-67; V Hammersmith St Sav 67-74; R Lancing w Coombes *Chich* 75-86; RD Worthing 83-85; R Bexhill St Pet 86-90; TR 90-99; RD Battle and Bexhill 92-98; Can and Preb Chich Cathl 96-02; P-in-c Arlington, Folkington and Wilmington 97; rtd 02. *7 Jevington Close, Bexhill-on-Sea TN39 3BB* Tel (01424) 845273

COTTON, John William. b 53. Basford Coll Nottm DipInstBM74. Oak Hill Th Coll DipHE86. **d** 86 **p** 87. C New Clee *Linc* 86-89; Chapl St Andr Hospice Grimsby 88-89; R Middle Rasen Gp 89-95; P-in-c Broughton 95-97; R from 97;

Chapl Humberside Airport 99-00. *The Rectory, 22 Scawby Road, Broughton, Brigg DN20 0AF* Tel (01652) 652506

COTTON, Mrs Margaret Elizabeth. b 30. JP79. Newnham Coll Cam BA53 MA66. St Alb Minl Tr Scheme 78. **dss** 82 **d** 87 **p** 94. Lt Berkhamsted and Bayford, Essendon etc *St Alb* 82-87; Hon Par Dn 87-94; Hon C 94-96; rtd 96; Perm to Offic *St Alb* from 96. *49 Sherrardspark Road, Welwyn Garden City AL8 7LD* Tel (01707) 321815

COTTON, Norman Joseph. b 39. Kelham Th Coll 59. **d** 64 **p** 65. C Auckland St Helen *Dur* 64-67; C Withington St Chris *Man* 67-68; C Hucknall Torkard *S'well* 69-71; TV 71-73; TV Fenny Stratford *Ox* 73-75; TV Fenny Stratford and Water Eaton 75-82; P-in-c Broughton and Milton Keynes 82; P-in-c Wavendon w Walton 82; R Walton 82-90; TR Walton Milton Keynes 90-92; V Stewkley w Soulbury and Drayton Parslow from 92; RD Mursley 94-01. *The Vicarage, High Street North, Stewkley, Leighton Buzzard LU7 0HH* Tel (01525) 240287 Fax as telephone

COTTON, Miss Patricia Constance. b 32. Gilmore Ho 54. **dss** 60 **d** 87 **p** 94. Forest Gate St Edm *Chelmsf* 60-64; Reading St Giles *Ox* 64-65; Basildon St Martin w H Cross and Laindon *Chelmsf* 65-79; Gt Burstead 79-87; Par Dn Maldon All SS w St Pet 87-91; rtd 92; NSM Holland-on-Sea *Chelmsf* 94-96; Perm to Offic from 96. *21 Stallards Crescent, Kirby Cross, Frinton-on-Sea CO13 0TN* Tel (01255) 672711

COTTON, Patrick Arthur William. b 46. Essex Univ BA67 Cam Univ MA73. Linc Th Coll 68. **d** 71 **p** 72. C Earlham St Anne *Nor* 71-73; Chapl Down Coll Cam 73-78; V Eaton Socon *St Alb* 78-84; TR Newc Epiphany *Newc* 84-90; V Tunstall w Melling and Leck *Blackb* 90-95; Chapl Pet High Sch from 01. *Peterborough High School, Westwood House, Thorpe Road, Peterborough PE3 6JF* Tel (01733) 343357

COTTON, Peter John. b 45. BNC Ox BA66 Bris Univ CQSW76. Cuddesdon Coll 67. **d** 69 **p** 70. C Salford St Phil w St Steph *Man* 69-73; Asst Educn Officer *St Alb* 73-75; C Bris St Geo *Bris* 75-76; C-in-c Portsea St Geo CD *Portsm* 76-80; Soc Resp Adv 78-88; Can Res Portsm Cathl 84-88; V St Laur in Thanet *Cant* 88-93; TR 93-97; Hon Min Can Cant Cathl 93-97; TR Hemel Hempstead *St Alb* from 97; RD Hemel Hempstead from 03. *The Rectory, 40 High Street, Hemel Hempstead HP1 3AE* Tel and fax (01442) 213838 *or* 253977 E-mail petercotton2@compuserve

COTTON, Canon Richard William. b 35. Hertf Coll Ox BA58 MA62. Clifton Th Coll 58. **d** 60 **p** 61. C Harold Wood *Chelmsf* 60-64; C Higher Openshaw *Man* 64-67; Lic to Offic 67-71; Ch Youth Fellowships Assn and Pathfinders 67-71; Nat Sec Pathfinders CPAS 71-76; Lic to Offic *St Alb* 73-76; V Chislehurst Ch Ch *Roch* 76-92; V Herne Bay Ch Ch *Cant* 92-01; RD Reculver 93-01; Hon Can Cant Cathl 99-01; rtd 01; Perm to Offic *Cant* from 01. *16 Crundale Way, Cliftonville, Margate CT9 3YH* Tel (01843) 221970 E-mail rwcotton67@hotmail.com

COTTON, Robert Lloyd. b 58. Mert Coll Ox MA79 Louvain Univ Belgium DipTh81. Westcott Ho Cam 81. **d** 83 **p** 84. C Plaistow St Mary *Roch* 83-86; C Bisley and W End *Guildf* 87-89; P-in-c E Molesey St Paul 89-96; Dir of Reader Tr from 90; R Guildf H Trin w St Mary from 96. *Holy Trinity Rectory, 9 Eastgate Gardens, Guildford GU1 4AZ* Tel (01483) 575489 E-mail rector@htsm.demon.co.uk

COTTON, Roy William. b 29. Jes Coll Ox BA53 MA61. Chich Th Coll 66. **d** 66 **p** 67. C Eastney *Portsm* 66-71; R Harting *Chich* 71-74; P-in-c Eastbourne St Andr 74-76; V 76-84; R Brede w Udimore 84-99; rtd 99; Perm to Offic *Chich* from 99. *11 Gregory Walk, Battle TN33 0QZ* Tel (01424) 870783

COTTON, Timothy. b 61. Ripon Coll Cuddesdon 97. **d** 99 **p** 00. C Godrevy *Truro* 99-02; P-in-c St Breoke and Egloshayle from 02. *The Rectory, 31 Trevanion Road, Wadebridge PL27 7NZ* Tel (01208) 812460 E-mail tim@cottonh.fsnet.co.uk

COTTRELL, Canon Stephen Geoffrey. b 58. Poly Cen Lon BA79. St Steph Ho Ox 81. **d** 84 **p** 85. C Forest Hill Ch Ch *S'wark* 84-88; C-in-c Parklands St Wilfrid CD *Chich* 88-93; Asst Dir Past Studies Chich Th Coll 88-93; Dioc Missr *Wakef* 93-98; Bp's Chapl for Evang 93-98; Springboard Missr and Consultant in Evang 98-01; Can Res Pet Cathl *Pet* from 01. *Prebendal House, Minster Precincts, Peterborough PE1 1XX* Tel (01733) 897335 Fax 555342 E-mail stephencottrell@fish.co.uk

COTTRILL, Derek John. b 43. MA. Qu Coll Birm. **d** 82 **p** 83. C Southampton Maybush St Pet *Win* 82-85; V Barton Stacey and Bullington etc 85-92; R Bishopstoke from 92; Asst Chapl Win and Eastleigh Healthcare NHS Trust from 92. *The Rectory, 10 Stoke Park Road, Eastleigh SO50 6DA* Tel (023) 8061 2192

COUCH, Andrew Nigel. b 48. K Coll Lon BD70 AKC70 Ex Coll Ox PGCE72. St Aug Coll Cant 70. **d** 71 **p** 72. C St Ives *Truro* 71-74; C St Martin-in-the-Fields *Lon* 74-78; USPG 78-91; Uruguay 79-84; Argentina 85-91; Chapl Qu Mary Coll *Lon* 91-94; V St Ives *Truro* from 94; P-in-c Halsetown from 98; RD Penwith 98-03. *The Vicarage, St Andrew's Street, St Ives TR26 1AH* Tel (01736) 796404 E-mail andycouch@bigfoot.com

COUCH, Ms Felicity Anne. b 59. CQSW85. SEITE 00. **d** 03. *20 Camsey House, St Matthew's Road, London SW2 1SX* Tel

(020) 7501 9449 Mobile 07745-905417 E-mail fcouch@supanet.com

COUCHMAN, Anthony Denis. b 37. Sarum Th Coll 66. **d** 69 **p** 70. C Barkingside St Fran *Chelmsf* 69-71; C Chingford SS Pet and Paul 71-76; P-in-c Walthamstow St Barn and St Jas Gt 76-80; V from 80. *St Barnabas' Vicarage, St Barnabas Road, London E17 8JZ* Tel (020) 8520 5323

COUGHLIN, Wayne Michael Timothy Vianney. b 77. Writtle Agric Coll BSc99 Leeds Univ BA03. Coll of Resurr Mirfield 00. **d** 03. C Neath *Llan* from 03. *The Presbytery, 18 Woodland Road, Neath SA11 3AL* Tel (01639) 635738

COUGHTREY, Miss Sheila Frances. b 48. RSCN73 SRN73 S Bank Poly BSc79. Qu Coll Birm 79. **dss** 84 **d** 87 **p** 94. Sydenham St Bart *S'wark* 81-85; Roehampton H Trin 85-91; Par Dn 87-91; Par Dn Brixton Hill St Sav 91-94; P-in-c 94-01; Min King's Acre LEP 91-01; RD Brixton 99-01; P-in-c Pleshey *Chelmsf* from 01; Warden Dioc Retreat Ho from 01. *The Vicarage, The Street, Pleshey, Chelmsford CM3 1HA* Tel (01245) 237576 E-mail sheila@scoughtrey.fsnet.co.uk

COULDRIDGE, Janice Evelyn. See FOX, Mrs Janice Evelyn

COULING, Canon David Charles. b 36. Open Univ BA89. Qu Coll Birm 61. **d** 63 **p** 64. C Harborne St Faith and St Laur *Birm* 63-66; C E Grinstead St Mary *Chich* 66-70; V Copthorne 70-75; V Eastbourne St Mich 75-82; V Brighton St Matthias 82-83; C-in-c Harton St Lawr CD *Dur* 84-90; V Horsley Hill St Lawr 91-94; P-in-c Greatham 94-97; V 97-01; AD Hartlepool 95-01; Master Greatham Hosp 94-00; Hon Can Dur Cathl *Dur* 99-01; rtd 01; Perm to Offic *Dur* from 01. *11 Shropshire Drive, Belmont, Durham DH1 2LT* Tel 0191-375 7367

COULSON, Canon Stephen Hugh. b 60. St Edm Hall Ox BA82 MA88 Lon Univ CertEd83. Wycliffe Hall Ox 85. **d** 88 **p** 89. C Summerfield *Birm* 88-91; Perm to Offic 91-92; CMS Uganda 92-01; Asst V Namirembe 92-96; Can from 99; Prin Uganda Martyrs Sem Namugongo 96-01; V Mitcham St Mark *S'wark* from 01. *St Mark's Vicarage, Locks Lane, Mitcham CR4 2JX* Tel (020) 8648 2397 E-mail steve@scoulson.freeserve.co.uk

COULSON, Thomas Stanley. b 32. TCD BA54 MA68. TCD Div Sch 55. **d** 55 **p** 56. C Maghera *D & R* 55-62; I Aghalurcher and Tattykeeran *Clogh* 62-63; I Woodschapel w Gracefield *Arm* 63-97; Preb Arm Cathl 88-97; Treas Arm Cathl 94-96; Chan Arm Cathl 96-97; rtd 97. *Lisadian, 84 Coleraine Road, Portrush BT56 8HN* Tel (028) 7082 4202

COULSON, Tony Erik Frank. b 32. St Edm Hall Ox BA55 DipTh56 MA59. Wycliffe Hall Ox 55. **d** 57 **p** 58. C Walthamstow St Mary *Chelmsf* 57-60; C Reading St Jo *Ox* 60-63; V Iver 63-86; R White Waltham w Shottesbrooke 86-97; rtd 97; Perm to Offic *Ox* from 98. *30 Ravensbourne Drive, Reading RG5 4LH* Tel 0118-969 3556

COULTER, Edmond James. b 60. QUB BSc82 BD96 TCD DipTh87. **d** 87 **p** 88. C Ballymena w Ballyclug *Conn* 87-90; C Knockbreda *D & D* 90-92; I Belfast Upper Falls *Conn* 92-97; I Milltown *Arm* 97-03; Superintendent Dublin Irish Ch Miss *D & G* from 03. *38 Woodpark, Castleknock, Dublin 15, Irish Republic* E-mail ecoulter@lineone.net

COULTER, Ian Herbert Young. b 54. BA HDipEd. **d** 99 **p** 00. Lic to Offic (Cashel, Waterford and Lismore) *C & O* from 99. *22 Rose Hill Court, Kilkenny, Co Kilkenny, Irish Republic* Tel (00353) (56) 776 2675 E-mail coulters@gofree.indigo.ie *or* coulter@ireland.com

COULTER, Mrs Kirsten Ruth. b 43. Univ of Wales (Abth) BSc64 Homerton Coll Cam CertEd65 Lon Univ BD89 Newc Univ MA93. Dioc OLM tr scheme 98. **d** 01 **p** 02. OLM Tweedmouth *Newc* from 01. *90 Shielfield Terrace, Tweedmouth, Berwick-upon-Tweed TD15 2EE* Tel (01289) 308485 E-mail timothy.coulter@btinternet.com

COULTER (née REEVES), Mrs Maria Elizabeth Ann. b 72. Leeds Univ BA95. St Steph Ho Ox DipMin98. **d** 98 **p** 99. C Newington St Mary *S'wark* 98-02; V Dulwich St Clem w St Pet from 02. *St Clement's Vicarage, 140 Friern Road, London SE22 0AY* Tel (020) 8693 1890

COULTER, Richard Samuel Scott. b 09. Dur Univ LTh39. Clifton Th Coll 35. **d** 38 **p** 39. C Parr Mt *Liv* 38-40; CF 40-46; Hon CF from 46; C Huyton St Mich *Liv* 46-50; Chapl Whiston Hosp 47-50; V Wavertree St Bridget *Liv* 50-61; V Upton Snodsbury w Broughton Hackett etc *Worc* 61-77; rtd 77. *29 Greenheart Way, Southmoor, Abingdon OX13 5DF* Tel (01865) 820912

COULTHARD, Miss Nina Marion. b 50. CertEd71 Bp Lonsdale Coll BEd72. Trin Coll Bris DipHE91. **d** 91 **p** 94. Par Dn Cant St Mary Bredin *Cant* 91-94; C 94-95; C Bath Abbey w St Jas *B & W* 95-99; Chapl R Nat Hosp for Rheumatic Diseases NHS Trust 95-99; C Northwood Em *Lon* from 99. *64 Chester Road, Northwood HA6 1AG* Tel (01923) 825019

COULTHURST, Jeffrey Evans. b 38. Man Univ BA61 Leeds Univ PGCE62. LNSM course 85. **d** 84 **p** 85. OLM Ancaster *Linc* 84-89; OLM Ancaster Wilsford Gp from 89. *5 North Drive, Ancaster, Grantham NG32 3RB* Tel (01400) 230280 E-mail jeff@jcoulthurst.fsnet.co.uk

COULTON, David Stephen. b 41. Sarum Th Coll 64. **d** 67 **p** 68. C Guildf H Trin w St Mary *Guildf* 67-70; Asst Chapl Radley Coll 70-83; Sen Chapl 83-01; Chapl Eton Coll from 01. *Eton College, Windsor SL4 6DW* Tel (01753) 671436

COULTON, The Very Revd Nicholas Guy. b 40. Lon Univ BD72. Cuddesdon Coll 65. **d** 67 **p** 68. C Pershore w Wick *Worc* 67-70; Bp's Dom Chapl *St Alb* 71-75; P-in-c Bedford St Paul 75-79; V 79-90; Hon Can St Alb 89-90; Provost Newc 90-01; Dean Newc 01-03; Can Res and Sub-Dean Ch Ch *Ox* from 03. *Christ Church, Oxford OX1 1DP* Tel (01865) 276278 *or* 276155 E-mail nicholas.coulton@chch.ox.ac.uk

COULTON, Philip Ernest. b 31. St Cath Coll Cam BA54 MA58 TCD BD68 Open Univ BA84. Ely Th Coll 55. **d** 57 **p** 58. Asst Master Perse Sch Cam 54-55; Asst Master Bradf Gr Sch 57; C Newark w Coddington *S'well* 57-61; Min Can and Sacr Cant Cathl *Cant* 61-63; Min Can Ripon Cathl *Ripon* 63-68; Hd of RE Ashton-under-Lyne Gr Sch 69-84; Perm to Offic *Ches* 70-71; Lic to Offic 71-84; V Ulceby Gp *Linc* 85-89; P-in-c Ingatestone w Buttsbury *Chelmsf* 89-99; P-in-c Fryerning w Margaretting 89-92; rtd 99; Perm to Offic *Sarum* from 01. *90 Boreham Road, Warminster BA12 9JW* Tel (01985) 219353 Fax 847719 E-mail pecoulton@onetel.net.uk

COUNSELL, Edwin Charles Robert. b 63. Univ of Wales (Cardiff) BA84 MTh97. St Steph Ho Ox 85. **d** 88 **p** 89. C Cardiff St Mary and St Steph w St Dyfrig etc *Llan* 88-94; Sub-Chapl HM Pris Cardiff from 90; V Pendoylan w Welsh St Donats from 94; Dioc Dir Statutory Educn from 00. *The Vicarage, 9 Heol St Cattwg, Pendeulwyn, Bont-Faen CF71 7UG* Tel (01446) 760195 *or* tel and fax 760210 E-mail post@llandaffschools.fs.net.co.uk

COUNSELL, Michael John Radford. b 35. Pemb Coll Cam BA59 MA63. Ripon Hall Ox 59. **d** 61 **p** 62. C Handsworth St Mary *Birm* 61-63; Singapore 64-68; Vietnam and Cambodia 68-71; Seychelles 72-76; Dean Mahe 73-76; V Harborne St Pet *Birm* 76-89; Relig Consultant to Inter-Ch Travel Ltd 89-90; V Forest Hill St Aug *S'wark* 90-00; Perm to Offic *Cant* from 91; rtd 00. *12 Shelley Road, Hove BN3 5FQ*

COUPAR, Thomas. b 50. BA71 ACE80. Edin Dioc NSM Course 77. **d** 80 **p** 81. NSM Dunbar *Edin* 80-86; NSM Haddington 80-86; Hd Master Pencaitland Primary Sch E Lothian 80-81; Hd Master K Meadow Sch E Lothian 81-87; Asst Dioc Supernumerary *Edin* 87-89; Primary Educn Adv Fife from 88; Dioc Supernumerary 90-96. *10 Greenfield Park, Monktonhall, Musselburgh EH21 6SX* Tel 0131-665 1780 Fax as telephone E-mail tcoupar@hotmail.com

COUPER, Jeanette Emily (Jean). b 40. S'wark Ord Course 85. **d** 88. Par Dn Mitcham SS Pet and Paul *S'wark* 88-93; Perm to Offic from 93; Chapl Asst Guy's Hosp Lon 93-94; rtd 00. *56 Grove Road, Mitcham CR4 1SA* Tel (020) 8640 8157

COUPER, Jonathan George. b 51. St Jo Coll Dur BA73. Wycliffe Hall Ox 73. **d** 75 **p** 76. C Clifton *York* 75-78; C Darfield *Sheff* 78-81; V Bridlington Quay Ch Ch *York* from 81. *21 Kingston Road, Bridlington YO15 3NF* Tel (01262) 673538

COUPLAND, Simon Charles. b 59. St Jo Coll Cam BA82 PGCE83 MA85 PhD87. Ridley Hall Cam 88. **d** 91 **p** 92. C Bath St Luke *B & W* 91-95; TV Broadwater St Mary *Chich* from 95. *67 Normandy Road, Broadwater, Worthing BN14 7EA* Tel (01903) 213359

COURT, David Eric. b 58. Southn Univ BSc80 PhD83 PGCE84. Oak Hill Th Coll BA91. **d** 91 **p** 92. C Barton Seagrave w Warkton *Pet* 91-94; C Kinson *Sarum* 94-97; P-in-c Mile Cross *Nor* 97-99; V 99-03; V Cromer from 03. *The Vicarage, 30 Cromwell Road, Cromer NR27 0BE* Tel (01263) 512000

COURT, Canon Kenneth Reginald. b 36. AKC60. **d** 61 **p** 62. C Garforth *Ripon* 61-63; C Harrogate St Wilfrid 63-65; V Thornbury *Bradf* 65-73; Prec Leic Cathl *Leic* 73-76; V Douglas St Matt *S & M* 76-84; V Syston *Leic* 84-93; TR Syston 93-98; RD Goscote 90-95; Hon Can Leic Cathl 92-98; rtd 98; Perm to Offic *Leic* from 99; *Linc* from 01. *12 Lord Burghley's Hospital, Station Road, Stamford PE9 2LD* E-mail kcourt@webbleicester.co.uk

COURT, Martin Jeremy. b 61. GRNCM84 Nottm Univ BTh89. Linc Th Coll 86. **d** 89 **p** 90. C Thurmaston *Leic* 89-92; C Leic St Jas 92-93; TV Leic Resurr 93-98; V Scraptoft from 98; Dioc Info Tech Co-ord from 96. *331 Scraptoft Lane, Scraptoft, Leicester LE5 2HU* Tel 0116-241 3205 Mobile 07798-876837 E-mail mcourt@leicester.anglican.org

COURT, Nicholas James Keble. b 56. SSC. Chich Th Coll 86. **d** 88 **p** 89. C Golders Green *Lon* 88-91; C Westbury-on-Trym H Trin *Bris* 91-94; PV Llan Cathl *Llan* 94-96; V Graig 96-02; P-in-c Cilfynydd 96-01. *Cair Paravel, Ardmuir, Ullapool IV26 2TN*

COURT, Richard Leonard. b 54. UEA 96. EAMTC 94. **d** 97 **p** 98. NSM Framlingham w Saxtead *St E* from 97. *9 Howard Close, Framlingham, Woodbridge IP13 9SH* Tel (01728) 724230 Mobile 07802-797436 E-mail richard.court@btinternet.com

COURTAULD, Augustine Christopher Caradoc. b 34. Trin Coll Cam BA58 MA61. Westcott Ho Cam 58. **d** 60 **p** 61. C Oldham St Mary *Man* 60-63; Chapl Trin Coll Cam 63-68; Chapl The Lon Hosp (Whitechapel) 68-78; V Wilton Place St Paul *Lon* 78-99;

AD Westmr St Marg 92-97; rtd 99. *Broke House, The Drift, Levington, Ipswich IP10 0LF* Tel (01473) 659773

COURTIE, John Malcolm. b 42. BNC Ox BA65 DPhil72 St Jo Coll Dur BA76 DipTh77. Cranmer Hall Dur 74. **d** 77 **p** 78. C Mossley Hill St Matt and St Jas *Liv* 77-80; V Litherland St Paul Hatton Hill 80-84; Wellingborough Sch 84-89; Hon C Wollaston and Strixton *Pet* 84-89; V Woodford Halse w Eydon 89-99; R Blisworth and Stoke Bruerne w Grafton Regis etc 99-02; rtd 02. *The Baptist Manse, Stoke St Gregory, Taunton TA3 6JG* Tel (01823) 490388 E-mail john@courtie.fsnet.co.uk

COURTNEY (née JORDAN), Mrs Avril Marilyn. b 35. Lon Univ DipEd56. SW Minl Tr Course 79. **dss** 82 **d** 87 **p** 94. Highweek and Teingrace *Ex* 82-88; Par Dn 87-88; Par Dn Ottery St Mary, Alfington, W Hill, Tipton etc 88-94; C 94-99; rtd 99; Perm to Offic *Ex* from 00. *Fairholme, Exeter Road, Newton Poppleford, Sidmouth EX10 0JB* Tel (01395)

COURTNEY, Canon Brian Joseph. b 44. BD92 MA97. CITC 70. **d** 73 **p** 74. C Willowfield *D & D* 73-75; P-in-c Knocknagoney 75-78; I Aghavea *Clogh* 78-83; I Carrickfergus *Conn* 83-95; I Enniskillen *Clogh* from 95; Prec Clogh Cathl from 95. *St Macartin's Rectory, 13 Church Street, Enniskillen BT74 7DW* Tel (028) 6632 2465 *or* 6632 2917 E-mail briancourtney@nireland.com

COURTNEY, Miss Louise Anita Hodd. b 48. SW Minl Tr Course 99. **d** 02 **p** 03. C St Keverne *Truro* from 02. *Church House, Chymbloth Way, Coverack, Helston TR12 6TA* Tel (01326) 280816 E-mail louiseah@eurobell.co.uk

COURTNEY, Martin Horace. b 34. St Alb and Ox Min Course 95. **d** 98 **p** 99. OLM Flackwell Heath *Ox* from 98. *1 Green Crescent, Flackwell Heath, High Wycombe HP10 9JQ* Tel (01628) 526354

COURTNEY, Michael Monlas. b 19. Coll of Resurr Mirfield 58. **d** 60 **p** 61. C Shrewsbury St Chad *Lich* 60-63; P-in-c N Keyham *Ex* 63-68; V 68-73; TV Sidmouth, Woolbrook, Salcombe Regis etc 73-84; rtd 84; Perm to Offic *Ex* from 86. *Fairholme, Exeter Road, Newton Poppleford, Sidmouth EX10 0BJ* Tel (01395) 568691

COUSANS (née BRADLEY), Mrs Joy Elizabeth. b 63. Sheff Univ BA85 Fitzw Coll Cam BA91 MA95. Ridley Hall Cam CTM92. **d** 92 **p** 94. Par Dn Wadsley *Sheff* 92-94; C 94-96; C Mosbrough 96-97; V Hillsborough and Wadsley Bridge from 97. *Christ Church Vicarage, 218 Fox Hill Road, Sheffield S6 1HJ* Tel 0114-231 1576

COUSINS, Christopher William. b 44. Oak Hill Th Coll DipHE87. **d** 87 **p** 88. C Wallasey St Hilary *Ches* 87-90; R Rollesby w Burgh w Billockby w Ashby w Oby etc *Nor* 90-94; P-in-c Ormesby w Scratby *Nor* 94; V Ormesby St Marg w Scratby, Ormesby St Mich etc 94-98; RD Gt Yarmouth 94-98; V Altham w Clayton le Moors *Blackb* 98-03; P-in-c Rochford *Chelmsf* from 03; P-in-c Stambridge from 03; P-in-c Sutton w Shopland from 03. *The Rectory, 36 Millview Meadows, Rochford SS4 1EF* Tel (01702) 530621 E-mail c4cousins@yahoo.co.uk

COUSINS, Graham John. b 55. Oak Hill Th Coll BA91. **d** 91 **p** 92. C Birkenhead St Jas w St Bede *Ches* 91-95; C Bebington 95-01; R Moreton from 01. *The Rectory, Dawpool Drive, Moreton, Wirral CH46 0PH* Tel 0151-641 0303

COUSINS, Peter Gareth. b 37. **d** 95 **p** 96. NSM Cwmparc *Llan* 95-02. *15 Conway Road, Cwmparc, Treorchy CF42 6UW* Tel (01443) 773669

COUSINS, Canon Philip John. b 35. K Coll Cam BA58 MA62. Cuddesdon Coll 59. **d** 61 **p** 62. C Marston *Blackb* 61-63; PV Truro Cathl *Truro* 63-67; USPG Ethiopia 67-75; V Henleaze *Bris* 75-84; RD Clifton 79-84; Provost All SS Cathl Cairo 84-89; Chan Malta Cathl *Eur* 89-95; Chapl Valletta w Gozo 89-95; R Llandudno *Ban* from 95. *The Rectory, 27 Church Walks, Llandudno LL30 2HL* Tel (01492) 876624

COUSINS, Stephen Michael. b 53. St Alb and Ox Min Course 98. **d** 01 **p** 02. OLM Caversham St Jo *Ox* from 01. *15 Champion Road, Caversham, Reading RG4 8EL* Tel 0118-948 1679 Mobile 07808-663530 E-mail smcousins@talk21.com

COUSLAND, Andrew Oliver. b 41. Goldsmiths' Coll Lon MA92. Edin Th Coll 62. **d** 65 **p** 66. C Broughty Ferry *Bre* 65-68; C Ayr *Glas* 68-70; R Renfrew 70-75; Perm to Offic *St E* 75-79; CF (TAVR) 76-82; Perm to Offic *Bre* 79-84; Perm to Offic *S'wark* 89-94; R Fraserburgh w New Pitsligo *Ab* 94-99; R Clogherny w Seskinore and Drumnakilly *Arm* 99-03; rtd 03. *Address temp unknown* E-mail ao@land24.freeserve.co.uk

COUSSENS, Mervyn Haigh Wingfield. b 47. St Jo Coll Nottm BTh74. **d** 74 **p** 75. C Clifton Ch Ch w Em *Bris* 74-77; C Morden *S'wark* 77-83; V Patchway *Bris* 83-91; R Lutterworth w Cotesbach *Leic* 91-98; P-in-c Bitteswell 95-98; R Lutterworth w Cotesbach and Bitteswell from 99; RD Guthlaxton II from 01. *The Rectory, Coventry Road, Lutterworth LE17 4SH* Tel (01455) 552669 E-mail rector.stmary.lutterworth@care4free.net

COUSSMAKER, Canon Colin Richard Chad. b 34. OBE. Worc Coll Ox BA57 BSc58 MA63 MSc85. Chich Th Coll 59. **d** 60 **p** 61. C Newtown St Luke *Win* 60-64; C Whitley Ch Ch *Ox* 64-67; Chapl Istanbul *Eur* 67-72; Chapl Sliema 72-77; Chapl Antwerp St Boniface 77-93; Can Brussels Cathl 81-00; Chapl Moscow

93-99; rtd 99; Hon Asst Chapl Nice w Vence *Eur* 99-00; Perm to Offic from 00. *533 Route des Vallettes Sud, 06140 Tourrettes-sur-Loup, France* Tel (0033) (4) 93 59 28 74

COUTTS, Ian Alexander. b 56. Warwick Univ BA77 Jes Coll Ox MSc80 CQSW80. St Jo Coll Nottm DipTh89. **d** 89 **p** 90. C Hamstead St Bernard *Birm* 89-92; C Warlingham w Chelsham and Farleigh *S'wark* 92-97; TV 97-00; Perm to Offic from 02. *116 Farley Road, South Croydon CR2 7NE* Tel (020) 8405 9389

COUTTS, James Allan. b 58. Fitzw Coll Cam MA. St Jo Coll Nottm MTh84. **d** 84 **p** 85. C Thorpe Acre w Dishley *Leic* 84-88; TV Kirby Muxloe 88-99; P-in-c Trowbridge St Thos and W Ashton *Sarum* from 99; Chapl Wilts and Swindon Healthcare NHS Trust from 99. *St Thomas's Vicarage, York Buildings, Trowbridge BA14 8PT* Tel (01225) 754826

COUTTS, Canon James Walter Cargill. b 35. Univ of Wales (Lamp) BA57 CCC Cam BA59. St Mich Coll Llan 59. **d** 60 **p** 61. C Cardiff St Mary *Llan* 60-63; C Greenford H Cross *Lon* 63-67; C Swansea St Gabr *S & B* 67-71; V Llanwrtyd w Llanddulas in Tir Abad etc 71-78; V Brecon St Dav 78-80; V Brecon St David w Llanspyddid and Llanilltyd 80-84; V Monmouth *Mon* 84-02; Can St Woolos Cathl 94-02; RD Monmouth 99-01; rtd 02. *The Reynolds, Penallt, Monmouth NP25 4RX*

COUTTS, Robin Iain Philip. b 52. Portsm Univ MA00. Sarum & Wells Th Coll 80. **d** 83 **p** 84. C Alverstoke *Portsm* 83-86; Min Leigh Park St Clare CD 86-89; V Warren Park 89-91; V Purbrook from 91; RD Havant from 00. *The Vicarage, 9 Marrels Wood Gardens, Purbrook, Waterlooville PO7 5RS* Tel (023) 9226 2307 E-mail robin.rocket@virgin.net

COUVELA, Ms Stephanie Joy. b 68. Sheff City Poly BA89. Ridley Hall Cam 95. **d** 98 **p** 99. C Upper Holloway *Lon* 98-01; TV from 01. *2 Anatola Road, London N19 5HN* Tel (020) 7263 6915 E-mail stephanie.couvela@london.anglican.org

COVE, Kenneth John. b 34. Lich Th Coll 58. **d** 60 **p** 61. C Crosland Moor *Wakef* 60-63; C Halifax St Jo Bapt 63-65; V Wakef St Jo 65-73; V Appleby *Carl* 73-78; RD Appleby 74-78; V Ambleside w Brathay 78-87; V Thames Ditton *Guildf* 87-94; P-in-c Morland, Thrimby and Gt Strickland *Carl* 94-96; V Morland, Thrimby, Gt Strickland and Cliburn 96-99; rtd 99; Perm to Offic *Carl* from 01. *The Barn, Maulds Meaburn, Penrith CA10 3HN* Tel (01931) 715067 E-mail kencove@care4free.net

COVENTRY, Archdeacon of. See BRYANT, The Ven Mark Watts

COVENTRY, Bishop of. See BENNETTS, The Rt Revd Colin James

COVENTRY, Dean of. See IRVINE, The Very Revd John Dudley

COVINGTON, Canon Michael William Rock. b 38. Open Univ BA78. Sarum Th Coll 60. **d** 63 **p** 64. C Daventry *Pet* 63-66; C Woolwich St Mary w H Trin *S'wark* 66-68; C Northampton All SS w St Kath *Pet* 68-71; V Longthorpe 71-86; Hon Min Can Pet Cathl 75-86; Can Pet Cathl from 86; V Warmington, Tansor, Cotterstock and Fotheringhay 86-95; Warden Dioc Assn of Readers from 87; RD Oundle 89-95; V Oakham, Hambleton, Egleton, Braunston and Brooke from 95; P-in-c Langham from 97; RD Rutland from 02. *All Saints' Vicarage, Vicarage Road, Oakham LE15 6EG* Tel (01572) 722108 Fax as telephone E-mail allsaints@oakham-rutland.fsnet.co.uk

COWAN, Helen Jane. b 42. Dioc OLM tr scheme 97. **d** 00 **p** 01. NSM Redhill H Trin *S'wark* from 00. *15 Westway Gardens, Redhill RH1 2JA* Tel (01737) 762543

COWAN, John. b 71. Trin Coll Bris. **d** 03. C Redcar *York* from 03. *34 Ings Road, Redcar TS10 2DL* Tel (01642) 498241

COWAN, Malcolm. b 45. **d** 00 **p** 01. NSM Keswick St Jo *Carl* from 00. *The Spinney, Bridekirk, Cockermouth CA13 0PF* Tel (01900) 823780

COWAN, Paul Hudson. b 69. Ripon Coll Cuddesdon 00. **d** 02 **p** 03. C Wokingham All SS *Ox* from 02. *7 Tamarisk Drive, Wokingham RG40 1WG* Tel 0118-989 2772 E-mail cowans@ukonline.co.uk

COWARD, Colin Charles Malcolm. b 45. Kingston Poly DArch72. Westcott Ho Cam 75. **d** 78 **p** 79. C Camberwell St Geo *S'wark* 78-82; P-in-c Wandsworth St Faith 82-90; V 90-96; Chapl Richmond, Twickenham and Roehampton NHS Trust 96-97; Co-ord Changing Attitude from 97; Perm to Offic *S'wark* from 99. *11 Murfett Close, London SW19 6QB* Tel (020) 8788 1384 Fax 8780 1733

COWARD, Raymond. b 41. NW Ord Course 79. **d** 82 **p** 83. C Turton *Man* 82-84; C Heaton Ch Ch 84-86; V Rochdale St Geo w St Alb 86-92; V Daisy Hill from 92. *46 Parkway, Westhoughton, Bolton BL5 2RY* Tel (01942) 813155

COWBURN, John Charles. b 48. Sarum & Wells Th Coll 88. **d** 90 **p** 91. C Andover w Foxcott *Win* 90-94; C Christchurch 94-96; Chapl to the Deaf *Lich* from 96; P-in-c Church Aston from 01. *St Andrew's Rectory, 7 Wallshead Way, Church Aston, Newport TF10 9JG* Tel (01952) 810942 or 493281 E-mail john.cowburn@lichfield.anglican.org

COWDREY, Herbert Edward John. b 26. Trin Coll Ox BA49 MA51. St Steph Ho Ox 50. **d** 52 **p** 53. Tutor St Steph Ho Ox 52-56; Chapl 54-56; Asst Chapl Ex Coll Ox 52-56; Lic to Offic Ox from 52; Fell St Edm Hall Ox from 56; Chapl 56-78; rtd 91.

30 Oxford Road, Old Marston, Oxford OX3 0PQ Tel (01865) 279015

COWELL, Anthony. See COWELL, Neil Anthony

COWELL, Irene Christine. b 58. RGN80. Ridley Hall Cam CTM94. **d** 94 **p** 95. C Litherland St Phil *Liv* 94-98; R Sefton and Thornton from 98; Dioc Adv on HIV/AIDS and Sexual Health from 97; Dioc Dir CME from 02. *The Vicarage, Water Street, Liverpool L23 1TB* Tel 0151-931 4676 E-mail 101456.77@compuserve.com

COWELL, Neil Anthony. b 61. LNSM course 95. **d** 98 **p** 99. OLM New Bury *Man* from 98. *166 Harrowby Street, Farnworth, Bolton BL4 7DE* Tel (01204) 706957

COWELL, Peter James. b 58. Peterho Cam BA80 MA84. Coll of Resurr Mirfield 80. **d** 82 **p** 83. C Folkestone St Sav *Cant* 82-86; Chapl Asst St Thos Hosp Lon 86-90; Co-ord Chapl R Lon Hosp 90-94; Co-ord Chapl Bart's and The Lon NHS Trust from 94; PV Westmr Abbey from 94. *The Chaplain's Office, The Royal London Hospital, London E1 1BB* Tel (020) 7377 7000 or 7377 7385 E-mail peter.cowell@yahoo.com

COWEN, Canon Brian. b 45. Nottm Univ BTh77. Linc Th Coll 73. **d** 77 **p** 78. C Hexham *Newc* 77-80; C Eastnor *Heref* 80-81; C Ledbury 80-81; TV Glendale Gp *Newc* 81-90; V Lesbury w Alnmouth from 90; V Longhoughton w Howick from 98; AD Alnwick from 93; Hon Can Newc Cathl from 01. *The Vicarage, Lesbury, Alnwick NE66 3AU* Tel (01665) 830281 E-mail brian.cowen@cwcom.net

COWGILL, Michael. b 48. Linc Th Coll 84. **d** 86 **p** 87. C Bolton St Jas w St Chrys *Bradf* 86-89; V Buttershaw St Paul 89-93; P-in-c Cullingworth 93-97; Dir Dioc Foundn Course 93-97; V Sutton from 97. *The Vicarage, Main Street, Sutton-in-Craven, Keighley BD20 7JS* Tel (01535) 633372

COWHAM, Hugh Nicholas Gerard. b 26. MACE81 Selw Coll Cam BA51 MA78 Aber Univ CertEd73. LNSM course 75. **d** 78 **p** 79. Hon C Elgin w Lossiemouth *Mor* 78-81; Asst Chapl Gordonstoun Sch 78-81; Australia from 81; rtd 93. *25 Equinox Court, Mudgeeraba, Qld, Australia 4213* Tel (0061) (7) 5530 2378 Fax 5530 7017 E-mail he@cowham.org

COWIE, Derek Edward. b 33. S'wark Ord Course 70. **d** 73 **p** 74. C Maldon All SS w St Pet *Chelmsf* 73-76; R Bowers Gifford w N Benfleet 76-79; V Chelmsf Ascension 79-84; V Shrub End 84-95; P-in-c Gosfield 95-03; RD Hinckford 01-03; rtd 03. *68 Wash Lane, Kessingland, Lowestoft NR33 7QY* Tel (01502) 740989 Mobile 07788-662011 E-mail decow@lineone.net or derekecowie@tiscali.co.uk

COWIE, John William Stephen. b 64. Wycliffe Hall Ox BTh97. **d** 97 **p** 98. C Shoreditch St Leon and Hoxton St Jo *Lon* 97-00. *Address temp unknown* E-mail williamcowie@onetel.net.uk

COWIE, Leonard Wallace. b 19. Pemb Coll Ox BA41 DipTh43 MA46 Lon Univ PhD54. Ripon Hall Ox 42. **d** 43 **p** 44. C High Wycombe All SS *Ox* 43-45; Tutor Coll SS Mark and Jo Chelsea 45-68; Chapl 45-47; Tutor Whitelands Coll Putney 68-82; Lic to Offic *S'wark* from 68. *38 Stratton Road, London SW19 3JG* Tel (020) 8542 5036

COWLES, Richard Martin. b 53. Birm Univ BSc74 DipT76. Ripon Coll Cuddesdon DipMin93. **d** 93 **p** 94. C Iffley *Ox* 93-96; TV Wheatley w Forest Hill and Stanton St John 96-97; TV Wheatley from 97. *The Rectory, 17 South End, Garsington, Oxford OX44 9DH* Tel (01865) 361381 E-mail vicar@cowles.globalnet.co.uk

COWLEY, Charles Frederick. See HOWARD-COWLEY, Joseph Charles

COWLEY, Mrs Elizabeth Mary. b 47. Bris Univ PQCSW84. WMMTC 89. **d** 92 **p** 94. NSM Wolston and Church Lawford *Cov* 92-97; Soc Resp Officer 97-02; P-in-c Churchover w Willey 97-02; TV Daventry, Ashby St Ledgers, Braunston etc *Pet* from 02. *The Vicarage, 19 Church Street, Staverton, Daventry NN11 6JJ* Tel (01327) 702466 E-mail liz.cowley@btinternet.com

COWLEY, Herbert Kenneth. b 20. Glouc Sch of Min 75. **d** 79 **p** 80. Hon C Lydney w Aylburton *Glouc* 79-89; rtd 89; Perm to Offic *B & W* 89-98. *19 Beechwood Road, Nailsea, Bristol BS48 2AF* Tel (01275) 856198

COWLEY, Ian Michael. b 51. Natal Univ BCom72 BA75 Sheff Univ MA83. Wycliffe Hall Ox 75. **d** 78 **p** 79. S Africa 78-81 and 83-94; C Norton Woodseats St Chad *Sheff* 81-83; R Milton *Ely* from 94; RD Quy 00-02. *The Rectory, Church Lane, Milton, Cambridge CB4 6AB* Tel (01223) 861511 or tel and fax 441007 E-mail iancowley@ukonline.co.uk

COWLEY, Mrs Jean Louie Cameron. See HERRICK, Mrs Jean Louie Cameron

COWLEY, Paul William. b 55. Middx Univ BA02. NTMTC 99. **d** 02 **p** 03. C Brompton H Trin w Onslow Square St Paul *Lon* from 02. *72 Archel Road, London W14 9QP* Tel (020) 7386 5140 Mobile 07860-146552 E-mail paul.cowley@htb.org.uk

COWLEY, Samuel Henry. b 44. St Jo Coll Nottm 85. **d** 87 **p** 88. C Hadleigh w Layham and Shelley *St E* 87-91; P-in-c Ipswich St Mich 91-99; P-in-c Westerfield and Tuddenham w Witnesham

from 99. *The Rectory, Westerfield Road, Westerfield, Ipswich IP6 9AG* Tel (01473) 254483 Fax 236407
E-mail sam.cowley@stedmundsbury.anglican.org

COWLING, Canon Douglas Anderson. b 19. Leeds Univ BA40. Coll of Resurr Mirfield 40. **d** 42 **p** 43. C Linc St Andr *Linc* 42-45; R Candlesby w Scremby 47-53; R Carlton Scroop w Normanton 53-61; V Spalding St Paul 61-84; Can and Preb Linc Cathl 77-93; rtd 84; Perm to Offic *Linc* from 84. *24 Campbell's Close, Spalding PE11 2UH* Tel (01775) 767044

COWLING, John Francis. b 32. K Coll Cam BA56. Linc Th Coll 56. **d** 58 **p** 59. C Leigh St Mary *Man* 58-61; Sec SCM in Schs Liv and Ches 61-65; V Bolton St Matt 65-71; V Bolton St Matt w St Barn 71-75; V Southport St Nath *Liv* 75-91; R St Olave Hart Street w All Hallows Staining etc *Lon* from 91; Dir of Ords 92-02; P-in-c St Kath Cree from 02. *St Olave's Rectory, 8 Hart Street, London EC3R 7NB* Tel (020) 7488 4318 Fax 7702 0811

COWLING, Simon Charles. b 59. G&C Coll Cam BA80 MA88 K Coll Lon PGCE82. Linc Th Coll BTh91. **d** 91 **p** 92. C Potternewton *Ripon* 91-94; C Far Headingley St Chad 94-96; V Roundhay St Edm from 96. *St Edmund's Vicarage, 5A North Park Avenue, Leeds LS8 1DN* Tel 0113-266 2550
E-mail simoncowling@ntlworld.com

COWLING, Wilfred Edmund. b 14. Dur Univ BA38 MA42. St Aid Birkenhead 38. **d** 40 **p** 41. C Benwell St Aid *Newc* 40-43; Chapl Miss to Seamen 43-45; C Leeds St Geo *Ripon* 45-47; P-in-c Scarborough St Thos *York* 47-57; V Kirkburn 57-83; V Garton on the Wolds 57-83; R Harthill 63-73 and 78-80; rtd 83; Perm to Offic *York* from 83. *14 Ashleigh Drive, Beeford, Driffield YO25 8AU* Tel (01262) 488277

COWMEADOW, Derek Lowe. b 28. Wells Th Coll 68. **d** 70 **p** 71. C Ledbury *Heref* 70-72; C Llanrhos *St As* 72-74; V Bringhurst w Gt Easton *Leic* 74-77; P-in-c Coln St Aldwyn w Hatherop and Quenington *Glouc* 77-82; V Coln St Aldwyns, Hatherop, Quenington etc 82-93; rtd 93; Perm to Offic *Glouc* from 93. *2 Hampton Grove, Meysey Hampton, Cirencester GL7 5JN* Tel (01285) 851645

COWPER, Christopher Herbert. b 44. AKC67 Open Univ BA76. **d** 68 **p** 69. C Alnwick *Newc* 68-71; C Ulverston St Mary w H Trin *Carl* 71-74; R Kirklinton w Hethersgill and Scaleby 74-83; V Bridekirk 83-94; Chapl Dovenby Hall Hosp Cockermouth 83-94; P-in-c Wetheral w Warwick *Carl* 94-98; R Barningham w Hutton Magna and Wycliffe *Ripon* from 98. *The Rectory, Barningham, Richmond DL11 7DW* Tel (01833) 621217

COWPER, Peter James. b 67. Wadh Coll Ox BA89. Edin Th Coll BD94. **d** 94 **p** 95. C Kippax w Allerton Bywater *Ripon* 94-97; C Stanningley St Thos 97-02; C W Bromwich All SS *Lich* from 02; Ind Chapl Black Country Urban Ind Miss from 02. *7 Hopkins Drive, West Bromwich B71 3RR* Tel 0121-588 3744

COX, Alan. b 44. St Chad's Coll Dur BSc65 DipTh68 Man Poly PGCE83. St Chad's Coll Dur 66. **d** 68 **p** 69. C N Reddish *Man* 68; C Birch St Agnes 69-71; C Withington St Crispin 71-74; R Ardwick St Thos 74-78; Lic Preacher from 89. *31 St John's Road, Longsight, Manchester M13 0NE* Tel 0161-225 4062
E-mail alancox@dunelm.org.uk

COX, Alan John. b 34. Lon Coll of Div ALCD65 LTh. **d** 65 **p** 66. C Kirkheaton *Wakef* 65-67; C Keynsham w Queen Charlton *B&W* 67-71; R Chipstable w Huish Champflower and Clatworthy 71-76; TV Strood *Roch* 76-80; V Strood St Fran 80-83; R Keston 83-95; rtd 95; Perm to Offic *Roch* from 00. *12 Beech Court, 46 Copers Cope Road, Beckenham BR3 1LD* Tel (020) 8639 0082

COX, Ms Alison Clare. b 63. MHort(RHS)89. Ripon Coll Cuddesdon 01. **d** 03. C Spalding *Linc* from 03. *18 Maple Grove, Spalding PE11 2LE* Tel (01775) 725637

COX, Mrs Alison Hilda. b 57. Coll of Ripon & York St Jo BEd79 Nottm Univ MA02. EMMTC 99. **d** 02 **p** 03. NSM Bakewell *Derby* from 02. *Lynton, The Avenue, Bakewell DE45 1EQ* Tel (01629) 814034 Fax as telephone
E-mail alison.cox@totalise.co.uk

COX, Canon Anthony James Stuart. b 46. BNC Ox BA68 MA74. Qu Coll Birm DipTh70 DPS71. **d** 71 **p** 72. C Smethwick St Matt w St Chad *Birm* 71-74; Chapl Liv Univ *Liv* 74; Malawi 75-87; Chapl Malosa Secondary Sch 75-79; Hd Master 80-87; Hon Can S Malawi from 80; Chapl Loughborough Gr Sch from 87. *Orchard House, 169 Main Street, Willoughby on the Wolds, Loughborough LE12 6SY* Tel (01509) 880861

COX, Brian Leslie. b 49. S Dios Minl Tr Scheme 91. **d** 94 **p** 95. C Southampton Maybush St Pet *Win* 94-98; P-in-c Knights Enham from 98. *The Rectory, 1 Ryon Close, Knights Enham, Andover SP10 4DG* Tel (01264) 357032

COX, David John. b 51. S Bank Poly HNC76 Lon Univ BD97. Qu Coll Birm 76. **d** 79 **p** 80. C Brampton Bierlow *Sheff* 79-82; Miss Partner CMS 82-88; V N Perak W Malaysia 83-88; V Friarmere *Man* 88-96; P-in-c Denton Ch Ch from 96. *Christ Church Rectory, 1 Windmill Lane, Denton, Manchester M34 3RN* Tel 0161-336 2126 Fax as telephone E-mail djcox1779@aol.com

COX, Canon Eric William. b 30. Dur Univ BA54. Wells Th Coll 54. **d** 56 **p** 57. C Sutton in Ashfield St Mary *S'well* 56-59; Asst Chapl Brussels *Eur* 59-62; V Winnington *Ches* 62-71; V Middlewich 71-76; Chapl Mid Cheshire Hosps Trust 73-95;

P-in-c Biley *Ches* 73-76; V Middlewich w Byley 76-95; RD Middlewich 80-94; Hon Can Ches Cathl 84-95; rtd 95; Perm to Offic *Ches* from 95 and *Lich* from 96. *Lovel Hollow, Church Road, Baschurch, Shrewsbury SY4 2EE* Tel (01939) 261258
E-mail canoneric@lovelhollow.fsnet.co.uk

COX, Geoffrey Sidney Randel. b 33. Mert Coll Ox BA56 MA60. Tyndale Hall Bris. **d** 58 **p** 59. C St Paul's Cray St Barn CD *Roch* 58-61; C Bromley Ch Ch 61-64; V Gorsley w Cliffords Mesne *Glouc* 64-79; V Hucclecote 79-89; V Wollaston and Strixton *Pet* 89-96; rtd 96; Perm to Offic *Glouc* from 96; Clergy Widows Officer (Cheltenham Adnry) from 99. *32 Murvagh Close, Cheltenham GL53 7QY* Tel (01242) 251604
E-mail geoffandjunecox@amserve.net

COX, George William. b 25. St Steph Ho Ox 83. **d** 86 **p** 87. NSM Abingdon *Ox* 86-95; rtd 92. *103 Bath Street, Abingdon OX14 1EG* Tel (01235) 521375

COX, Hugh Teversham. b 42. Moore Th Coll Sydney ThL68 ThSchol71 Keble Coll Ox BA76 MA82 Trin Evang Div Sch IL DMin99 Chas Sturt Univ NSW DipAgr63 Melbourne Coll of Div DipRE72. **d** 69 **p** 70. Australia 69-74 and 76-01; C Manuka St Paul 70-71; P-in-c Kameruka 71-74; Perm to Offic *Ox* 75-76; Chapl Commonwealth and Continental Ch Soc 76; P-in-c Canberra Ch Ch 76-82; Tutor and Lect St Mark's Nat Th Cen 77-82; R Lane Cove 82-87; R Castle Hill St Paul 87-01; Chapl Tervuren *Eur* from 01. *St Paul's Church Centre, Dorpsstraat 707A, 3061 Leefdaal, Belgium* Tel (0032) (2) 767 3435 Fax as telephone E-mail chaplain@stpaulstervuren.com *or* info@stpaulstervuren.com

COX, James David Robert. b 65. Lanc Univ BA88. Qu Coll Birm BD92. **d** 93 **p** 94. C Harborne St Pet *Birm* 93-96; C Chelmsley Wood 96-97; TV 97-00; V Smethwick Resurr from 00. *The Vicarage, 69 South Road, Smethwick, Warley B67 7BP* Tel 0121-558 0373

COX, James Edward Thomas. b 20. Sheff Univ BA47. Cuddesdon Coll 47. **d** 49 **p** 50. C Boxley *Cant* 49-52; C-in-c Buckland Valley CD 52-59; R Hawkinge 59-64; R Acrise 59-64; Chapl RAF 59-62; Chapl Abbey Sch Malvern 64-79; V Lt Malvern *Worc* 65-85; P-in-c 85-90; rtd 85; Perm to Offic *Heref* and *Worc* from 93. *4 Lucerne Avenue, Malvern WR14 3QA* Tel (01684) 564392

COX, John Anthony. b 45. Hull Univ BA67 Birm Univ DipTh72. Qu Coll Birm 71. **d** 73 **p** 74. C Buckingham *Ox* 73-76; C Whitley Ch Ch 76-81; V Reading St Agnes w St Paul 81-83; V Chaddesley Corbett and Stone *Worc* from 83. *The Vicarage, Butts Lane, Stone, Kidderminster DY10 4BH* Tel (01562) 69438

COX, John Edgar. b 26. CEng MIEE56 Lon Univ BSc50 MSc69. Bps' Coll Cheshunt 67. **d** 68 **p** 69. NSM Harlow St Mary Magd *Chelmsf* 68-76; C S Petherwin w Trewen *Truro* 77-79; P-in-c 79-82; P-in-c Lawhitton 81-82; P-in-c Lezant 81-82; R Lezant w Lawhitton and S Petherwin w Trewen 82-83; V Breage w Germoe 83-91; rtd 91; Perm to Offic *Truro* from 91. *Manderley, 8 Trewartha Road, Praa Sands, Penzance TR20 9ST* Tel (01736) 762582

COX, The Ven John Stuart. b 40. Fitzw Ho Cam BA62 MA66 Linacre Coll Ox BA67 Birm Univ DPS68. Wycliffe Hall Ox 64. **d** 68 **p** 69. C Prescot *Liv* 68-71; C Birm St Geo *Birm* 71-73; R 73-78; Selection Sec ACCM 78-83; Hon C Orpington All SS *Roch* 78-83; Dioc Dir of Ords *S'wark* 83-91; Can Res and Treas S'wark Cathl 83-91; V Roehampton H Trin 91-95; Adn Sudbury *St E* from 95. *42 Corsbie Close, Bury St Edmunds IP33 3SU* Tel (01284) 766796 Fax as telephone
E-mail archdeacon.john@stedmundsbury.anglican.org

COX, Jonathan James. b 63. Wollongong Univ BA85 Univ of NSW DipEd86. Ridley Hall Cam. **d** 00 **p** 01. C Tonbridge SS Pet and Paul *Roch* 00-03; R Oxley Vale Australia from 03. *95 Glengarvin Drive, Tamworth, NSW, Australia 2340* Tel (0061) (2) 6761 7271 E-mail sean@fish.co.uk

COX, Julie Margaret. b 55. St Alb and Ox Min Course. **d** 00 **p** 01. NSM Luton St Chris Round Green *St Alb* from 00. *29 Maple Close, Pulloxhill, Bedford MK45 5EF* Tel (01525) 717002

COX, Leonard James William. b 27. Sarum & Wells Th Coll 79. **d** 81 **p** 82. C Hythe *Cant* 81-84; V Thanington 84-92; rtd 92; Perm to Offic *Cant* 92-01. *31 Wheatfield Crescent, Mansfield Woodhouse, Mansfield NG19 9HH*

COX, Martin Brian. b 64. Keele Univ BA91 CQSW91. St Jo Coll Nottm 01. **d** 03. C Sale St Anne *Ches* from 03. *3 Windermere Avenue, Sale M33 3FP* Tel 0161-962 0951
E-mail martin_b_cox@btopenworld.com

COX, Martin Lloyd. b 57. Wilson Carlile Coll and Sarum & Wells Th Coll. **d** 88 **p** 89. C Risca *Mon* 88-91; TV Pontypool 91-96; V Monkton *St D* from 96. *Priory Vicarage, Church Terrace, Monkton, Pembroke SA71 4LW* Tel (01646) 682723

COX, Ms Patricia Jean. b 44. WEMTC. **d** 00 **p** 01. Hon C Coleford w Staunton *Glouc* from 00. *67 Primrose Hill, Lydney GL15 5SW* Tel (01594) 843852
E-mail revpat_cox@tinyworld.co.uk

COX, Canon Paul Graham. b 40. Keele Univ BA62 DipEd62 Ibadan Univ Nigeria 63. Westcott Ho Cam 77. **d** 78 **p** 79. NSM Kemsing w Woodlands *Roch* 78-80; Hd Master and Chapl St Mich Sch Otford 81-90; C Petham and Waltham w Lower

Hardres etc *Cant* 90-95; P-in-c 95-97; C Elmsted w Hastingleigh 90-95; P-in-c 95-97; Bp's Officer for NSM 91-98; R Biddenden and Smarden from 97; Dioc Dir of Reader Selection and Tr 98-00; Bp's Officer for OLM from 00; Hon Can Cant Cathl from 01. *The Rectory, High Street, Biddenden, Ashford TN27 8AH* Tel and fax (01580) 291454 Mobile 07799-300589 E-mail pcox@fish.co.uk

COX, Peter Allard. b 55. Univ of Wales (Lamp) BA76. Wycliffe Hall Ox 77. **d** 79 **p** 80. C Penarth All SS *Llan* 79-82; V Aberpergwm and Blaengwrach 82-86; V Bargoed and Deri w Brithdir 86-97; V Penarth All SS from 97. *All Saints' Vicarage, 2 Lower Cwrt-y-Vil Road, Penarth CF64 3HQ* Tel (029) 2070 8952 E-mail petercox6@virgin.net

COX, Philip Gordon. b 36. St Jo Coll Cam MA62 Lon Univ PGCE71. Dioc OLM tr scheme 99. **d** 02 **p** 03. OLM Charing w Charing Heath and Lt Chart *Cant* from 02. *Home Meadow, Little Chart Forstal, Little Chart, Ashford TN27 0PU* Tel (01233) 840274 E-mail philip@homemeadow.plus.com

COX, Miss Rosemary Jennifer. b 54. St Aid Coll Dur BA75 Lon Bible Coll BTh97 Trin Coll Bris MA99. Cranmer Hall Dur 01. **d** 03. C Osmondthorpe St Phil *Ripon* from 03. *31 Richardson Road, Leeds L59 9BQ* Tel 0113-235 9516 E-mail rosemaryjcox@aol.com

COX, Mrs Sheila Margaret. b 54. Nottm Univ BA76 Reading Univ PGCE77. SEITE 00. **d** 03. NSM Cranbrook *Cant* from 03. *12 Westwell Court, Tenterden TN30 6TS* Tel (01580) 764556 Mobile 07985-003095 Fax (01580) 765981 E-mail sheila@medix-uk.com

COX, Mrs Sheila Stuart. b 41. Aber Coll of Educn CertEd63. Edin Univ NSM Course 85. **d** 88 **p** 94. NSM Livingston LEP *Edin* 88-93; Asst Chapl St Jo and Bangour Hosps W Lothian 89-93; Chapl 96-98; Hon C Edin St Mark 93-96; Missr Edin St Andr and St Aid 95-96; NSM Eyemouth from 98. *5 Northfield Farm Cottages, St Abbs, Eyemouth TD14 5QF* Tel (01890) 771764

COX, Simon John. b 53. MIBiol79 CBiol79 Qu Mary Coll Lon BSc74 Liv Univ PhD81 Selw Coll Cam BA81 MA85 Lanc Univ MA87. Ridley Hall Cam 79. **d** 82 **p** 83. C Livesey *Blackb* 82-85; C Cheadle Hulme St Andr *Ches* 85-89; V Disley 89-94; R Bispham *Blackb* from 94. *The Rectory, All Hallows Road, Blackpool FY2 0AY* Tel (01253) 351886 E-mail drscox@aol.com

COX, Stephen. b 38. Open Univ BA80. Bps' Coll Cheshunt 65. **d** 68 **p** 69. C Gaywood, Bawsey and Mintlyn *Nor* 68-72; Youth Chapl 72-82; C N Lynn w St Marg and St Nic 73-82; Chapl Guildf Coll of Tech 82-87; Chapl Surrey Univ *Guildf* 82-91; Tr and Devlpt Manager Jas Paget Hosp Gorleston 91-93; Manager Medical Records 93-96; Consumer Relns and Litigation Manager 96-99; rtd 99. *56 Bately Avenue, Gorleston, Great Yarmouth NR31 6HN* Tel (01493) 662061

COX, Stephen John Wormleighton. b 54. New Coll Ox MA79 Fitzw Coll Cam BA79. Ridley Coll Cam 77. **d** 80 **p** 81. C Clapton Park All So *Lon* 80-85; TV Hackney Marsh 85-87; V Holloway St Mary w St Jas 87-88; P-in-c Barnsbury St Dav w St Clem 87-88; V Holloway St Mary Magd 88-97; AD Islington 95-99; TR Upper Holloway from 97. *St Mary's Vicarage, 3 Highcroft Road, London N19 3AQ* Tel (020) 7272 9084 *or* 7272 1783 Fax 7272 9934 E-mail stephenj.cox@virgin.net

COX, William John Francis. b 24. SW Minl Tr Course. **d** 77 **p** 78. NSM Liskeard w St Keyne and St Pinnock *Truro* 77-82; NSM Liskeard w St Keyne, St Pinnock and Morval 82-86; NSM N Hill w Altarnon, Bolventor and Lewannick 86-87; TV Bolventor 87-92; P-in-c North Hill and Lewannick 92-94; rtd 94; Perm to Offic *Truro* from 94. *9 Trelawney Rise, Callington PL17 7PT* Tel (01579) 384347

COXHEAD, Mrs Margaret. b 40. S Dios Minl Tr Scheme 91. **d** 94 **p** 95. NSM High Hurstwood *Chich* 94-00; P-in-c from 00; P-in-c Fairwarp from 00. *Rock Hall, Chillies Lane, High Hurstwood, Uckfield TN22 4AD* Tel (01825) 733833

COYNE, John Edward. b 55. Sheff Univ MA98. Oak Hill Th Coll BA79. **d** 79 **p** 80. C Cheadle Hulme St Andr *Ches* 79-81; C Macclesfield St Mich 81-83; V Stalybridge H Trin and Ch Ch 83-88; Chapl RAF 88-02; Command Chapl RAF from 02; RAF Adv in Evangelism 93-98; Hon C Hemingford Grey *Ely* 96-98. *Chaplaincy Services (RAF), HQ, Personnel and Training Command, RAF Innsworth, Gloucester GL3 1EZ* Tel (01452) 712612 ext 5164 Fax 510828

COYNE, Terence Roland Harry. b 37. Chich Th Coll 64. **d** 66 **p** 67. C Meir *Lich* 66-69; C Horninglow 69-72; V Walsall St Gabr Fulbrook from 72; C Walsall St Mary and All SS Palfrey 97-02; C Caldmore w Palfrey from 02. *St Gabriel's Vicarage, Walstead Road, Walsall WS5 4LZ* Tel (01922) 622051

COZENS, Mrs Audrey Lilian. b 35. St Hugh's Coll Ox BA56 MA84. Gilmore Course 79. dss 82 **d** 87 **p** 94. Shenfield *Chelmsf* 82-87; Par Dn 87-89; Par Dn Westcliff St Andr 89-94; C 94-95; P-in-c Chelmsf St Andr 95-02; P-in-c The Chignals w Mashbury 95-02; rtd 02. *56 Victoria Road, Writtle, Chelmsford CM1 3PA* Tel (01245) 420165 E-mail revacozens@supanet.com

COZENS, Daniel Harry. b 44. Oak Hill Th Coll DipTh70. **d** 71 **p** 72. C St Paul's Cray St Barn *Roch* 71-74; C Deptford St Nic w Ch Ch *S'wark* 74-76; C Deptford St Nic and St Luke 76-78; Rees Missr *Ely* from 78; Six Preacher Cant Cathl *Cant* from 94. *The Rectory, 73 High Street, Coton, Cambridge CB3 7PL* Tel (01954) 210239 Fax 211983 E-mail walk1000@btinternet.com

COZENS, Michael Graeme. b 59. Chich Th Coll 91. **d** 93 **p** 94. C Emscote *Cov* 93-96; C Prestbury *Glouc* 96-03; TV Prestbury and All SS from 03. *The Vicarage, 66 All Saints Road, Cheltenham GL52 2HA* Tel (01242) 523177

✠**CRABB, The Most Revd Frederick Hugh Wright.** b 15. Lon Univ BD39. Wycliffe Coll Toronto Hon DD60 St Andr Coll Saskatoon Hon DD67 Coll of Em and St Chad Hon DD77 ALCD39. **d** 39 **p** 40 **c** 75. C W Teignmouth *Ex* 39-41; C Plymouth St Andr 41-42; CMS 42-51; Sudan 42-51; Prin Bp Gwynne Coll 42-51; Vice-Prin Lon Coll of Div 51-57; Canada from 57; Prin Em Coll Saskatoon 57-67; Bp Athabasca 75-83; Abp Rupertsland 77-83. *3483 Chippendale Drive, Calgary AB, Canada, T2L 0W7* Tel (001) (403) 284 2333

CRABB, Paul Anthony. b 58. St Chad's Coll Dur BSc79 Leeds Univ PGCE80. Qu Coll Birm 90. **d** 91 **p** 92. C Gomersal *Wakef* 91-95; V Drighlington 95-01; TV Dewsbury from 01. *96 Old Bank Road, Dewsbury WF12 7AJ* Tel (01924) 438577

CRABTREE, Derek. b 32. Leic Univ BSc(Econ)53. Cant Sch of Min 91. **d** 94 **p** 95. NSM Hackington *Cant* 94-02; Asst Chapl Kent Univ 94-02; rtd 02; Perm to Offic *Cant* from 02. *19 Monastery Street, Canterbury CT1 1NJ* Tel (01227) 471503

CRABTREE, Eric. b 30. Chelt & Glouc Coll of HE BA99 ACA55 FCA68. Premontre Community (RC) 58. **d** 64 **p** 64. In RC Ch 64-90; Reader 97-00; Perm to Offic *Glouc* from 00. *3 Hazlitt Croft, Cheltenham GL51 0PN* Tel (01242) 580851

CRABTREE, Martine Charmaine. b 74. Glas Bible Coll BA96 St Jo Coll Nottm MTh02. **d** 02 **p** 03. C Kippax w Allerton Bywater *Ripon* from 02. *55 Goodwood Avenue, Kippax, Leeds LS25 7HS* Tel 0113-286 1442 E-mail martinecrabtree@aol.com

CRABTREE, Stephen. *See* JONES-CRABTREE, Stephen

CRABTREE, Stephen John. b 62. Roehampton Inst BEd85 Surrey Univ MA93. SEITE 93. **d** 96 **p** 97. NSM N Farnborough *Guildf* from 96. *42 Avenue Road, Farnborough GU14 7BL* Tel (01252) 541873

CRADDOCK, Brian Arthur. b 40. Chich Th Coll 67. **d** 70 **p** 71. C Stoke-upon-Trent *Lich* 70-74; Bermuda 75-89; P-in-c Bury and Houghton *Chich* 89-95; Chapl St Mich Sch Burton Park 89-94; Chapl Mojacar *Eur* 95-99; rtd 99. *72 Pacific Road, Trentham, Stoke-on-Trent ST4 8UD*

CRADDOCK, Jeremy Graham. b 37. Lon Univ BSc64 Nottm Univ MPhil72. EAMTC 93. **d** 94 **p** 95. NSM Godmanchester *Ely* 94-99; Perm to Offic from 99. *8 Hall Close, Hartford, Huntingdon PE29 1XJ* Tel (01480) 458011

CRADDUCK, Martin Charles. b 50. Hull Univ BSc71. St Jo Coll Nottm DipTh77. **d** 79 **p** 80. C W Kilburn St Luke w St Simon and St Jude *Lon* 79-83; C Oxhey All SS *St Alb* 83-86; Asst Chapl HM Pris Man 86-87; Dep Chapl HM Young Offender Inst Glen Parva 87-89; Chapl HM Pris Stocken 89-95. *35 Worcester Road, Grantham NG31 8SF* Tel (01476) 571351

CRADDUCK, Stuart William. b 74. Bp Otter Coll Chich BA97. Ripon Coll Cuddesdon BTh00. **d** 00 **p** 01. C W Leigh *Portsm* from 00. *St Alban's House, 4 White Oak Walk, Havant PO9 5PL* Tel (023) 9248 4711 E-mail stuart@cradduckmail.freeserve.co.uk

CRAFER, Mrs Jeanette Angela. b 48. Keswick Hall Coll CertEd78. EAMTC 99. **d** 01 **p** 02. C Ashmanhaugh, Barton Turf etc *Nor* from 01. *The Rectory, School Road, Neatishead, Norwich NR12 8XH* Tel (01692) 630645

CRAFT, William Newham. b 46. MCIPD70 Lon Univ BSc68. Oak Hill Th Coll 87. **d** 89 **p** 90. C Werrington *Pet* 90-93; C-in-c Norfolk Park St Leonard CD *Sheff* 93-02; P-in-c Sheff St Jo 99-02; V 02-03; V Stapleford *S'well* from 03. *The Vicarage, 61 Church Street, Stapleford, Nottingham NG9 8GA* Tel 0115-875 3462 *or* 917 6202 E-mail wncraft@hotmail.com

CRAGG, Adrian. *See* CRAGG, Edward William Adrian

✠**CRAGG, The Rt Revd Albert Kenneth.** b 13. Jes Coll Ox BA34 MA38 DPhil50 Huron Coll Hon DD63 Virginia Th Sem Hon DD85 Leeds Univ Hon DD93 Lambeth DD02. Tyndale Hall Bris 34. **d** 36 **p** 37 **c** 70. C Tranmere St Cath *Ches* 36-39; Lebanon 39-47; R Longworth *Ox* 47-51; USA 51-56; Can Res Jerusalem 56-59; St Aug Coll Cant 59-60; Sub-Warden 60-61; Warden 61-67; Hon Can Cant Cathl *Cant* 61-80; Hon Can Jerusalem 65-73; Asst Bp Jerusalem 70-73; Bye-Fellow G&C Coll Cam 69-70; Asst Bp Chich 73-78; Asst Bp Wakef 78-81; V Helme 78-81; rtd 81; Asst Bp Ox from 82. *3 Goring Lodge, White House Road, Oxford OX1 4QE* Tel (01865) 249895

CRAGG, Edward William Adrian. b 55. St Cath Coll Cam BA77 MA81. Cranmer Hall Dur 97. **d** 99 **p** 00. C Clifton *York* 99-02; R Skelton w Shipton and Newton on Ouse from 02; Chapl York Health Services NHS Trust from 02. *The Rectory, Church Lane, Skelton, York YO30 1XT* Tel (01904) 470045 E-mail acragg@fish.co.uk

CRAGG, Mrs Sandra Anne. b 45. St Hugh's Coll Ox BA67. SEITE 94. **d** 97 **p** 98. NSM Kingston All SS w St Jo *S'wark* from 97. *10 Lingfield Avenue, Kingston upon Thames KT1 2TN* Tel (020) 8546 1997 Fax 8541 5281
E-mail sandy.cragg@cableinet.co.uk

CRAGGS, Colin Frederick. b 41. Open Univ BA80. Sarum & Wells Th Coll 85. **d** 88 **p** 89. NSM Wilton *B & W* 88-90; NSM Taunton St Andr 90-93; Chapl Taunton and Somerset NHS Trust from 90; NSM Wilton *B & W* from 93. *89 Galmington Road, Taunton TA1 5NW* Tel (01823) 271989 Fax as telephone

CRAGGS, Michael Alfred. b 43. Open Univ BA79. St Mich Coll Llan 66. **d** 69 **p** 70. C Clee *Linc* 69-72; C Old Brumby 72-76; TV Kingsthorpe w Northampton St Dav *Pet* 76-83; P-in-c Gt w Lt Addington 83-89; RD Higham 88-89; TR Corby SS Pet and Andr w Gt and Lt Oakley 89-02; V Corby SS Pet and Andr from 02; RD Corby 90-95. *The Rectory, 40 Beanfield Avenue, Corby NN18 0EH* Tel (01536) 267620 *or* 402442
E-mail mikeccorb@aol.com

CRAGO, Geoffrey Norman. b 44. Linc Th Coll. **d** 70 **p** 71. C Matson *Glouc* 70-75; V Drean Forest H Trin 75-80; Relig Progr Producer Radio Severn Sound 80-85; P-in-c Huntley 80-82; Perm to Offic 82-90; Dioc Communications Officer 84; Gen Syn Broadcasting Dept 85-88; Hon C Highnam, Lassington, Rudford, Tibberton etc from 90; Relig Progr Producer BBC Radio Gloucestershire from 94; Bp's Press Officer and Dioc Communications Officer from 97. *Milestones, 2 Two Mile Lane, Highnam, Gloucester GL2 8DW* Tel (01452) 750575 Fax 750105
E-mail glosdco@star.co.uk

CRAIG, Canon Alan Stuart. b 38. Leeds Univ BA59. Cranmer Hall Dur DipTh61. **d** 61 **p** 62. C Newcastle w Butterton *Lich* 61-65; C Scarborough St Mary w Ch Ch, St Paul and St Thos *York* 65-67; V Werrington *Lich* 67-72; Asst Chapl HM Pris Man 72-73; Chapl HM Borstal Hindley 73-78; Chapl HM Pris Acklington 78-84; V Longhirst *Newc* 84-90; R Morpeth 90-99; RD Morpeth 84-95; Hon Can Newc Cathl 90-02; Chapl St Geo and Cottage Hosp Morpeth 90-93; Chapl Northd Mental Health NHS Trust 93-99; Chapl to The Queen from 95; Dir of Ords and Bp's Chapl *Newc* 99-02; rtd 02. *5 Springfield Meadows, Alnwick NE66 2NY* Tel (01665) 602806 Mobile 07779-519040

CRAIG, Andrew John. b 54. Selw Coll Cam BA76 MA80 PhD80 Dur Univ MBA92. NEOC 00. **d** 03. NSM Stranton *Dur* from 03. *25 Egerton Road, Hartlepool TS26 0BW* Tel (01429) 422461
E-mail andrewj.craig@ntlworld.com

CRAIG, David Paul. b 46. Univ of K Coll Halifax NS Hon DD94. ACT ThDip. **d** 84 **p** 85. Australia 84-89; Canada 89-94; Miss to Seamen 89-94; Chapl Immingham Seafarers' Cen from 94; Gen Preacher *Linc* from 97. *The Seafarers' Centre, Lockside Road, Immingham DN40 2NN* Tel (01469) 574195 Fax 574740

CRAIG, Eric. b 39. Birm Univ BA62 DipTh63. Qu Coll Birm 62. **d** 64 **p** 65. C Todmorden *Wakef* 64-68; C Hurstpierpoint *Chich* 68-70; C Cobham *Guildf* 70-73; V Dawley St Jerome *Lon* 73-76; V Stainland *Wakef* 76-87; R Yarnton w Begbroke and Shipton on Cherwell *Ox* from 87. *The Rectory, 26 Church Lane, Yarnton, Kidlington OX5 1PY* Tel (01865) 375749

CRAIG, Gillean Weston. b 49. York Univ BA72 Qu Coll Cam BA76 MA80. Westcott Ho Cam 76. **d** 77 **p** 78. C St Marylebone Ch Ch *Lon* 77-82; C Ealing St Barn 82-88; P-in-c St Geo-in-the-East w St Paul 88-89; R 89-02; V Kensington St Mary Abbots w St Geo from 02. *St Mary Abbots Vicarage, Vicarage Gate, London W8 4HN* Tel (020) 7937 6032

CRAIG, James Owen Maxwell. b 72. Open Univ BA98. Cranmer Hall Dur 99. **d** 02 **p** 03. C Ch the K *Dur* from 02. *St Stephen's House, Hollyhill Gardens East, Stanley DH9 6PG* Tel (01207) 299201 E-mail james.craig@durham.ac.uk

CRAIG, Canon John Newcome. b 39. Selw Coll Cam BA63 MA67. Linc Th Coll 63. **d** 65 **p** 66. C Cannock *Lich* 65-71; V Gt Wyrley 71-79; TR Wednesfield 79-91; Prec Leic Cathl *Leic* 91-03; Hon Can 93-03; Can Res Leic Cathl from 03. *154 Barclay Street, Leicester LE3 0JB* Tel 0116-255 7327
E-mail john.olivia.craig@lineone.net

CRAIG, Judy Howard. b 57. Lon Univ MB, BS81 DRCOG83 MRCGP86. WMMTC 97. **d** 00 **p** 01. NSM Billing *Pet* from 00. *Howard's End, 16A Doddington Road, Earls Barton, Northampton NN6 0NF* Tel (01604) 811045
E-mail judy.craig@virgin.net

CRAIG, Julie Elizabeth. *See* LEAVES, Julie Elizabeth

CRAIG, Julie Elizabeth. *See* EATON, Mrs Julie Elizabeth

CRAIG, Patrick Thomas. b 36. BA. St D Coll Lamp 59 Bps' Coll Cheshunt 59. **d** 61 **p** 62. C Belfast St Mary *Conn* 61-65; C Belfast St Pet 65-69; CF 69-88; R Hartfield w Coleman's Hatch *Chich* 88-01; rtd 01; P-in-c Six Pilgrims *B & W* from 03. *Briars, Broadclose Way, Barton St David, Somerton TA11 6BS* Tel (01458) 850825

CRAIG, Richard Harvey. b 31. Em Coll Cam BA58. Linc Th Coll. **d** 60 **p** 61. C Bottesford *Linc* 60-65; Bp's Ind Chapl 65-69; Dioc Adv on Laity Tr *Bris* 69-74; V Whitchurch 74-86; TV N Lambeth *S'wark* 86-96; Bp's Ecum Adv 88-96; Ecum Officer 90-96; rtd 96; Perm to Offic *St Alb* 96-99; Perm to *S'wark*

from 01. *18 Holst Court, Westminster Bridge Road, London SE1 7JQ* Tel (020) 7928 0495

CRAIG, Robin Joseph. b 43. TCD BA65 Div Test66 Birm Univ CertEd70. **d** 66 **p** 67. C Carrickfergus *Conn* 66-69; Chapl Ld Wandsworth Coll Hants 75-85; Chapl K Sch Macclesfield 85-01; Lic to Offic *Ches* 85-01; rtd 01. *5 Winston Court, Lavant Road, Chichester PO19 5RG*

CRAIG-WILD, Ms Dorothy Elsie (Dhoe). b 54. Birm Univ BA77. Qu Coll Birm 79. dss 81 **d** 87 **p** 94. Middleton St Mary *Ripon* 81-87; Par Dn Chapeltown *Sheff* 88-94; C 94-96; P-in-c Bruntcliffe *Wakef* 96-02; Jt P-in-c Morley St Paul 00-02; P-in-c Roberttown w Hartshead from 02; RD Birstall from 98. *The Vicarage, 3 Vicarage Meadow, Mirfield WF14 9JL* Tel (01924) 505791 Fax as telephone E-mail dhoecraigwild@hotmail.com

CRAIG-WILD, Peter John. b 55. Leeds Univ BA77. Qu Coll Birm 77. **d** 80 **p** 81. C Rothwell w Lofthouse *Ripon* 80-83; C Beeston 83-87; V Chapeltown *Sheff* 87-96; RD Tankersley 93-96; V Mirfield *Wakef* from 96; P-in-c Eastthorpe and Upper Hopton from 03. *The Vicarage, 3 Vicarage Meadow, Mirfield WF14 9JL* Tel (01924) 505790 Fax 505791
E-mail peter.craig-wild@ntlworld.com

CRAM, Mrs Ruth Frances Isobel. b 52. Kingston Poly BA87 Poly Cen Lon MA92. N Ord Course 94. **d** 97 **p** 98. C E Crompton *Man* 97-99; C Cirencester *Glouc* 99-02; C Broad Blunsdon *Bris* 02; V N Swindon St Andr from 02. *8 Figsbury Close, Swindon SN25 1UA* Tel (01793) 701353 E-mail rc.cram@btinternet.com

CRAMERI, Mrs Mary Barbara. b 44. K Coll Lon BD65 AKC91 Lon Inst of Educn PGCE66. S Dios Minl Tr Scheme 86. **d** 88 **p** 94. C Whitton SS Phil and Jas *Lon* 88-91; Staff Member S Dios Minl Tr Scheme 91-97; Minl Development Officer STETS 97-98; Vice-Prin Sarum & Wells Th Coll 93-98; Par Dn Bemerton *Sarum* 91-92; TV Pewsey and Swanborough 98-00; TR Whitton 00-01; rtd 01. *2 Richards Way, Salisbury SP2 8NT* Tel (01722) 415342

CRAMPTON, John Leslie. b 41. CITC 64. **d** 67 **p** 68. C Lurgan Ch the Redeemer *D & D* 67-71; C Dundela St Mark 71-73; C Rhodesia 73-80; Zimbabwe 80-82; I Killanne w Killegney, Rossdroit and Templeshanbo *C & O* 82-88; Preb Ferns Cathl 85-88; Chapl Wilson's Hosp Sch Multyfarnham *M & K* 88-91; C Mullingar, Portnashangan, Moyliscar, Kilbixy etc 89-91; I Athy w Kilberry, Fontstown and Kilkea *D & G* 91-01; Can Ch Ch Cathl Dublin 95-01; I Geashill w Killeigh and Ballycommon *M & K* from 01. *The Rectory, Geashill, Tullamore, Co Offaly, Irish Republic* Tel (00353) (506) 43242 Mobile 87-907 7981 E-mail geashill@kildare.anglican.org

CRANE, John Walter. b 32. Chich Th Coll. **d** 58 **p** 59. C Forest Town *S'well* 58-60; C Primrose Hill St Mary w Avenue Road St Paul *Lon* 60-64; R Greenford H Cross 64-67; Min Can and Chapl Windsor 67-79; Chapl St Geo Sch Ascot 67-79; Warden Dioc Retreat Ho (Holland Ho) Cropthorne *Worc* 79-83; P-in-c Harvington and Norton and Lenchwick 84-87; rtd 87. *16 Allesborough Drive, Pershore WR10 1JH* Tel (01386) 556444

CRANE, Mrs Judith. b 53. Matlock Coll of Educn BCombStuds81. Cranmer Hall Dur 94. **d** 96 **p** 97. C Tadcaster w Newton Kyme *York* 96-99; TV Brayton 99-02; V Blackwell w Tibshelf *Derby* from 02. *The Vicarage, 67 High Street, Tibshelf, Alfreton DE55 5NU* Tel (01773) 872243

CRANE, Ronald Edward. b 48. SSC. Wilson Carlile Coll 73 St Steph Ho Ox 83. **d** 85 **p** 86. C Bicester w Bucknell, Caversfield and Launton *Ox* 85-88; P-in-c Washwood Heath *Birm* 88-92; V 92-01; V Wylde Green from 01. *Emmanuel Vicarage, 17 Greenhill Road, Sutton Coldfield B72 1DS* Tel 0121-373 8348 Fax as telephone E-mail whr@rcrane9.fsnet.co.uk

CRANE, Vincent James. b 10. St Aid Birkenhead 62. **d** 64 **p** 65. C Penn *Lich* 64-70; R Himley 70-78; V Swindon 70-78; rtd 78; Perm to Offic *Worc* from 78; *Lich* from 01. *14 Holcroft Road, Wall Heath, Kingswinford DY6 0HP* Tel (01384) 292208

CRANFIELD, Nicholas William Stewart. b 56. Mert Coll Ox BA77 MA81 DPhil88 Leeds Univ BA81 Selw Coll Cam PhD95. Coll of Resurr Mirfield 79 Union Th Sem (NY) STM84. **d** 86 **p** 87. C Ascot Heath *Ox* 86-89; Prin Berks Chr Tr Scheme 89-92; Hon C Reading St Mary w St Laur 89-92; Chapl and Fell Selw Coll Cam 92-99; Dean of Chpl 94-99; Chapl Newnham Coll Cam 92-99; V Blackheath All SS *S'wark* from 99. *All Saints' Vicarage, 10 Duke Humphrey Road, London SE3 0TY* Tel (020) 8852 4280 E-mail vicar blackheath@hotmail.com

CRANIDGE, Mrs Wendy Ann. b 31. Sheff Univ CertEd52. Community Sch of Min 81. dss 84 **d** 87 **p** 94. Roch 84-88; Hon Par Dn 87-88; Soc Resp Adv *Cant* and *Roch* 86-88; Hon C Washingborough w Heighington and Canwick *Linc* 88-92; Perm to Offic 92-93; Roch 93-94; C Farnborough *Roch* 94-96; rtd 96; Perm to Offic *Roch* 96-02. *Ashburton House, 948 Rochdale Road, Walsden, Todmorden OL14 6TY* Tel (01706) 815062

CRANKSHAW, Ronald. b 41. Coll of Resurr Mirfield 74. **d** 76 **p** 77. C Orford St Andr *Liv* 76; C N Meols 76-79; V Abram 79-85; V Wigan St Anne 85-99; AD Wigan W 94-99; V Heston *Lon* from 99. *The Vicarage, 147 Heston Road, Hounslow TW5 0RD* Tel (020) 8570 2288

CRANMER, Ms Elaine. b 56. Hockerill Coll Cam CertEd77. SEITE 97. **d** 00 **p** 01. C Charlton *S'wark* from 00. *73 Elliscombe Road, London SE7 7PF* Tel (020) 8858 4336
E-mail cranmer@ic24.net

CRANMER, John Abery. b 33. K Alfred's Coll Win CertEd56 Southn Univ MPhil69. **d** 94 **p** 00. NSM Crawley and Littleton and Sparsholt w Lainston *Win* 94-02; rtd 02; Perm to Offic *Win* from 02. *The Coach House, Crawley, Winchester SO21 2PU* Tel (01962) 776214

CRANSHAW, Trevor Raymond. b 58. Trin Coll Bris 00. **d** 03. C Westbury-on-Trym H Trin *Bris* from 03. *16 Southfield Road, Westbury-on-Trym, Bristol BS9 3BH* Tel 0117-962 5693 Mobile 07734-304116

CRANSWICK, James Harvard. b 22. Melbourne Univ BA47 St Cath Coll Ox BA50 MA54 Birm Univ MA76. Wycliffe Hall Ox 49. **d** 50 **p** 51. C Werneth *Man* 50-51; C St Pancras H Cross w St Jude and St Pet *Lon* 52-54; P-in-c Dartford St Alb *Roch* 54-56; Australia 56-66 and from 70; C Raynes Park St Sav *S'wark* 68-70; rtd 88. *8 Locarno Avenue, Kallista, Vic, Australia 3791* Tel (0061) (3) 9752 1136 Fax 9754 3518
E-mail jimcranswick@hotmail.com

CRANWELL, Brian Robert. b 32. Sheff Poly MSc. Cranmer Hall Dur. **d** 84 **p** 85. C Ecclesfield *Sheff* 84-86; V Handsworth Woodhouse 86-99; rtd 99; Perm to Offic *Sheff* from 99; *Derby* from 00. *9 Westview Close, Totley, Sheffield S17 3LT* Tel 0114-262 1499 E-mail brian_cranwell@lineone.net

CRASKE, Leslie Gordon Hamilton. b 29. AKC54 Lambeth STh80. **d** 55 **p** 56. C Malden St Jo *S'wark* 55-58; C Streatham St Leon 58-60; S Rhodesia 60-65; Rhodesia 65-66; V Upper Norwood St Jo *Cant* 67-83; R Guernsey St Sav *Win* 83-97; rtd 97; Perm to Offic *Win* from 97. *La Gruterie, 3 Mount Row, St Peter Port, Guernsey GY1 1NS* Tel (01481) 716027

CRASTON (née FULLALOVE), Mrs Brenda Hurst. b 33. Open Univ BA75 Man Univ MPhil86. St Mich Ho Ox 58. **dss** 80 **d** 87 **p** 94. Bolton St Paul w Em *Man* 80-87; Par Dn 87-93; rtd 93; Perm to Offic *Man* from 94. *12 Lever Park Avenue, Horwich, Bolton BL6 7LE* Tel (01204) 699972

CRASTON, Canon Richard Colin. b 22. Bris Univ BA49 Lon Univ BD51 Lambeth DD92. Tyndale Hall Bris 46. **d** 51 **p** 52. C Dur St Nic *Dur* 51-54; V Bolton St Paul *Man* 54-76; P-in-c Bolton Em 64-66; V 66-76; Hon Can Man Cathl 68-95; RD Bolton 72-92; V Bolton St Paul w Em 77-86; TR 86-93; Chapl to The Queen 85-92; rtd 93; Perm to Offic *Man* from 93. *12 Lever Park Avenue, Horwich, Bolton BL6 7LE* Tel (01204) 699972

CRATE, Canon George Frederick Jackson. b 28. Lon Univ BD56. ALCD55. **d** 56 **p** 57. C Penge St Jo *Roch* 56-58; C Tonbridge St Steph 58-60; R Knossington and Cold Overton *Leic* 60-64; V Owston and Withcote 60-64; V Mountsorrel Ch Ch 64-83; RD Akeley E 75-92; Hon Can Leic Cathl 80-94; V Mountsorrel Ch Ch and St Pet 83-94; rtd 94; Perm to Offic *Leic* from 94. *115 Nanpantan Road, Loughborough LE11 3YB* Tel (01509) 269505

CRAVEN, Canon Allan. b 35. LTCL77 Univ of Wales (Lamp) BA57 Lon Univ BD72. Chich Th Coll 57. **d** 59 **p** 60. C Blaenau Ffestiniog *Ban* 59-61; C Milford Haven *St D* 61-65; V Llwynhendy 65-68; R Nolton w Roch 68-00; RD Roose 85-99; Can St D Cathl from 91; rtd 00. *25 West Lane Close, Keeston, Haverfordwest SA62 6EW* Tel (01437) 710709

CRAVEN, Colin Peter. b 48. Dartmouth RN Coll. St Steph Ho Ox 83. **d** 85 **p** 86. C Holbeach *Linc* 85-88; Chapl Fleet Hosp 86-97; TV Grantham *Linc* 88-97; P-in-c Fairfield *Derby* 97-03; OCF 88-03; CF from 03. *c/o MOD Chaplains (Army)* Tel (01980) 615804 Fax 615800

CRAVEN, Gordon Forster. b 26. Qu Coll Cam BA50 MA55. Wells Th Coll 51. **d** 53 **p** 54. C Castleford All SS *Wakef* 53-57; V King Sterndale *Derby* 57-72; V Fairfield 57-72; Perm to Offic *B & W* from 81; rtd 91. *Kingfisher Cottage, 41 Southover, Wells BA5 1UH* Tel (01749) 672282

CRAVEN, Janet Elizabeth. See CHAPMAN, Mrs Janet Elizabeth

CRAVEN, Rebecca Clare. b 58. Bris Univ BDS80 Glas Univ MPH90 Man Univ PhD97 RCS DDPH90 RCPS FDS97. Dioc OLM tr scheme 98. **d** 01 **p** 02. OLM Reddish *Man* from 01. *35 Middleton Road, Reddish, Stockport SK5 6SH* Tel 0161-443 2701

CRAVEN, Archdeacon of. See GRUNDY, The Ven Malcolm Leslie

CRAWFORD, Duncan Alexander. b 59. Newc Univ BA81 MA83 K Coll Lon CertEd83. St Jo Coll Nottm 86. **d** 89 **p** 90. C Hatcham St Jas *S'wark* 89-92; Perm to Offic from 93. *42 Furzefield Road, London SE3 8TX*

CRAWFORD, Canon Ivy Elizabeth. b 50. Trin Coll Bris DipTh85. **d** 88 **p** 94. C Collier Row St Jas *Chelmsf* 88; Collier Row St Jas and Havering-atte-Bower 86-87; Par Dn 87-89; Par Dn Harlow New Town w Lt Parndon 89-94; C Harlow Town Cen w Lt Parndon 94-95; V Blackmore and Stondon Massey from 95; Hon Can Chelmsf Cathl from 98. *The Vicarage, Church Street, Blackmore, Ingatestone CM4 0RN* Tel (01277) 821464
E-mail ivy@vicarage50.fsnet.co.uk

CRAWFORD, James Robert Harry. b 55. Carl and Blackb Dioc Tr Inst 00. **d** 03. OLM Lower Darwen St Jas *Blackb* from 03. *31 Tynwald Road, Blackburn BB2 3NS* Tel (01254) 693822

CRAWFORD, John. b 22. TCD BA50. **d** 51 **p** 53. C Dunmurry *Conn* 51-58; C Monaghan *Clogh* 58-60; C S Kensington St Luke *Lon* 60-63; C Stoke Newington St Mary 63-65; C Wickford *Chelmsf* 65-67; C Lt Marlow *Ox* 67-83; rtd 83. *33 Wenlock Edge, Charvil, Reading RG10 9QG* Tel 0118-934 1848

CRAWFORD, Canon John William Rowland. b 53. AKC75 Open Univ BA81 NUI MA95. CITC 75. **d** 76 **p** 77. C Dundela St Mark *D & D* 76-79; C Taney Ch Ch *D & G* 79-84; V Dublin St Patr Cathl Gp from 84; Preb Tipperkevin St Patr Cathl Dublin from 84. *248 South Circular Road, Dolphin's Barn, Dublin 8, Irish Republic* Tel (00353) (1) 454 2274
E-mail jwrcrawf@iol.ie

CRAWFORD, Kenneth Ian. b 48. Melbourne Univ BMus77 Columbia Univ MA79 MEd80 MACE84. Trin Coll Melbourne BD86. **d** 87 **p** 87. Australia 87-97; C Ringwood St Paul 87-89; C Cheltenham St Matt 89-90; P-in-c Vermont S H Name 90-93; Can Prec Melbourne Cathl 93-97; P-in-c Warndon St Nic *Worc* from 97. *The Vicarage, 4 Daty Croft, Home Meadow, Worcester WR4 0JB* Tel (01905) 616109 Fax 22413
E-mail kennethandkim@tiscali.co.uk

CRAWFORD, Louise Dorothy Anita. b 60. Oak Hill Th Coll BA91 Princeton Th Sem MDiv00. Irish Sch of Ecum MPhil02. **d** 02. C Drumragh w Mountfield *D & R* from 02. *38 Orangefield Park, Omagh BT79 0DE* Tel (028) 8224 7862
E-mail anamchara00@yahoo.com

CRAWFORD, Michael Davis. b 45. Oak Hill Th Coll BA97 K Coll Lon PGCE98. **d** 00 **p** 01. NSM New Barnet St Jas *St Alb* from 00. *159 Victoria Road, New Barnet, Barnet EN4 7PB* Tel (020) 8449 2306 Mobile 07890-487569
E-mail michaecrawford@barnet58.freeserve.co.uk

CRAWFORD, Peter. b 22. Trin Coll Cam BA49 MA54. Wycliffe Hall Ox 49. **d** 51 **p** 52. C Ashton St Mich *Man* 51-54; V Pendlebury St Jo 54-60; Chapl R Man Children's Hosp 54-60; V Masham *Ripon* 60-75; RD Ripon 70-75; V Masham and Healey 75-79; R E Bergholt *St E* 79-87; RD Samford 82-86; rtd 87; Perm to Offic *St E* from 87. *3 Burl's Yard, Crown Street, Needham Market, Ipswich IP6 8AJ* Tel (01449) 722343

CRAWFORD, Canon Robin. b 33. Pemb Coll Cam BA57 MA61. Roch Th Coll. **d** 67 **p** 80. Ghana 67-69; Dep Sec Chrs Abroad 69-73; Dep Hd Priory Sch Lewes 74-76; Nigeria 77-79; Dep Sec Buttle Trust 79-86; Sec 86-90; Dir 90-92; Hon C Win H Trin *Win* 80-82; Hon C Notting Hill All SS w St Columb *Lon* 82-87; Hon C Westmr St Matt from 87; Hon Can Tamale from 01. *52 Dean Abbott House, 70 Vincent Street, London SW1P 4BS* Tel (020) 7931 8013 Fax as telephone

CRAWLEY, David. b 47. TD. St Steph Ho Ox 75. **d** 78 **p** 79. C Solihull *Birm* 78-81; TV Newbury *Ox* 81-84; Lic to Offic 84-95; Chapl Stoke Mandeville Hosp Aylesbury 84-95; Distr Chapl 88-95; Hd Chapl Services W Suffolk Hosps NHS Trust from 95; Bp's Adv on Hosp Chapl *St E* from 00. *22 Westbury Avenue, Bury St Edmunds IP33 3QE, or West Suffolk Hospital, Hardwick Lane, Bury St Edmunds IP33 2QZ* Tel (01284) 750526 *or* 713486 Fax 701993

CRAWLEY, John Lloyd Rochfort. b 22. Selw Coll Cam BA47 MA52. Cuddesdon Coll 47. **d** 49 **p** 50. C Newc H Cross *Newc* 49-52; V Byker St Ant 52-59; V Longhoughton w Howick 59-69; Chapl Newc Univ 69-74; Master Newc St Thos Prop Chpl 69-74; P-in-c Cockermouth All SS w Ch Ch *Carl* 74-77; TR Cockermouth w Embleton and Wythop 77-86; Perm to Offic *Arg* from 86; rtd 87. *Croft House, Cove Road, Tarbert, Argyll PA29 6TX* Tel (01880) 820842

CRAWLEY, Nicholas Simon. b 58. ACIB82 AIIM85 Southn Univ BSc79. Wycliffe Hall Ox 85. **d** 88 **p** 89. C E Twickenham St Steph *Lon* 88-93; R Avondale Zimbabwe 93-99; P-in-c Netherthorpe St Steph *Sheff* from 99. *The Rectory, 115 Upperthorpe Road, Sheffield S6 3EA* Tel 0114-276 7130
E-mail lpep@dialstart.net

CRAWLEY, Simon Ewen. b 31. Em Coll Cam BA57 MA60. Ridley Hall Cam 56. **d** 58 **p** 59. C Denton Holme *Carl* 58-61; P-in-c Cinderford St Steph w Littledean *Glouc* 61-67; V Margate H Trin *Cant* 67-74; V Folkestone H Trin w St Geo 74-81; R Patterdale *Carl* 81-87; RD Penrith 83-86; R Culworth w Sulgrave and Thorpe Mandeville etc *Pet* 87-95; RD Brackley 89-95; rtd 95; Perm to Offic *York* from 03. *The Old Vicarage, Main Street, Healaugh, Tadcaster LS24 8DB* Tel (01937) 830160
E-mail secraddock@aol.com

CRAWLEY-BOEVEY, Robert Arthur. b 12. Hertf Coll Ox BA34 MA38. Cuddesdon Coll 35. **d** 37 **p** 38. C Farnham Royal *Ox* 37-43; Chapl RNVR 43-46; R Waltham on the Wolds and Stonesby *Leic* 47-51; V Cuddington w Dinton *Ox* 51-59; V Seer Green 59-78; rtd 78; Perm to Offic *Sarum* from 78. *3 St Michael's Close, Urchfont, Devizes SN10 4QJ* Tel (01380) 840635

CRAWSHAW, Clinton. b 70. St Steph Ho Ox. **d** 02 **p** 03. C Hendon St Alphage *Lon* from 02. *18 Montrose Avenue, Edgware HA8 0DW* Tel (020) 8952 1635
E-mail fathercrawshaw@email.com

CRAWTE, William Richard. b 30. TCD BA54. **d** 55 **p** 56. C Belfast St Aid *Conn* 55-57; C Newcastle *D & D* 57-59; CF 59-79. *23 Gotsfield Close, Acton, Sudbury CO10 0AS* Tel (01787) 377356

✠**CRAY, The Rt Revd Graham Alan.** b 47. Leeds Univ BA68. St Jo Coll Nottm 69. **d** 71 **p** 72 **c** 01. C Gillingham St Mark *Roch* 71-75; N Area Co-ord CPAS Youth Dept 75-78; C York St Mich-le-Belfrey *York* 78-82; V 82-92; Prin Ridley Hall Cam 92-01; Six Preacher Cant Cathl *Cant* 97-01; Suff Bp Maidstone from 01. *Bishop's House, Pett Lane, Charing, Ashford TN27 0DL* Tel (01233) 712950 Fax 713543
E-mail bishmaid@diocant.clara.net

CREAN, Patrick John Eugene. b 38. TCD BA81 MA84. Edin Th Coll 82. **d** 84 **p** 85. C Perth St Jo *St And* 84-86; P-in-c Liv St Phil w St Dav *Liv* 86-87; V 87-90; R Cupar *St And* 90-92; R Ladybank 90-92; P-in-c Sefton *Liv* 92-97; Dioc Children's Officer 92-03; V Aintree St Giles 97-98; V Aintree St Giles w St Pet 98-03; rtd 03. *Lingfield, 36 Park Lane, Netherton, Bootle L30 1BB*

CREASER, Canon David Edward. b 35. St Cath Coll Cam BA58 MA62. Clifton Th Coll 59. **d** 61 **p** 62. C Cheadle *Ches* 61-67; V Weston *Bradf* 67-69; P-in-c Denton 67-69; V Weston w Denton 69-74 and 82-02; Dir Educn 73-96; V Frizinghall 74-82; V Weston w Denton 82-02; Hon Can Bradf Cathl 80-02; P-in-c Leathley w Farnley, Fewston and Blubberhouses 96-02; rtd 02. *Rose Cottage, Pant Lane, Austwick, Lancaster LA2 8BH* Tel (01542) 51536

CREASEY, Graham. *See* GOLDSTONE-CREASEY, Graham

CREBER, Arthur Frederick. b 45. Lon Univ DipTh67. N Ord Course 84. **d** 87 **p** 88. C Rickerscote *Lich* 87-91; V Gt Wyrley 91-99; RD Rugeley 94-98; P-in-c Newcastle w Butterton from 99. *The Rectory, Seabridge Road, Newcastle ST5 2HS* Tel (01782) 616397 E-mail afcreber1@hotmail.com

CREDITON, Suffragan Bishop of. *See* HAWKINS, The Rt Revd Richard Stephen

CREE, John Richard. b 44. Open Univ BA74 Lanc Univ MA92. Coll of Resurr Mirfield. **d** 83 **p** 84. C Blackb St Jas *Blackb* 83-86; V Feniscowles 86-01; Chapl Blackb Coll 86-01; R Chorley St Laur *Blackb* from 01. *The Rectory, Rectory Close, Chorley PR7 1QW* Tel (01257) 263114 E-mail johnrcree@hotmail.com

CREER, Irene. *See* SHAW, Mrs Irene

CREERY-HILL, Anthony Thomas. b 23. BNC Ox BA49 MA54. Ridley Hall Cam 49. **d** 51 **p** 52. C Highbury Ch Ch *Lon* 51-53; Travelling Sec CSSM 53-58; Chapl Dean Close Sch Cheltenham 59-74; Dep Hd Master Larchfield Sch Helensburgh 75-77; Kenya 77-83; Chapl Chantilly *Eur* 83-86; rtd 87; Perm to Offic *Heref* from 87. *Under Down, Gloucester Road, Ledbury HR8 2JE* Tel (01531) 635608

CREES, David Paul. b 68. Southn Univ BSc89. Trin Coll Bris BA99 MA00. **d** 00 **p** 01. C Patcham *Chich* from 00. *70 Overhill Drive, Patcham, Brighton BN1 8WJ* Tel (01273) 554791

CREES, Geoffrey William. b 35. ONC Open Univ BA85. Cranmer Hall Dur 65. **d** 67 **p** 68. C Hoddesdon *St Alb* 67-70; C Harwell *Ox* 70-73; C Chilton All SS 70-73; V Greenham 73-82; TR Marfleet *York* 82-88; AD E Hull 82-88; TR Rodbourne Cheney *Bris* 88-99; rtd 99; Perm to Offic *Glouc* from 99. *The Thatch, New Road, Popes Hill, Newnham GL14 1JT* Tel (01452) 760843

CREGAN, Mark. b 59. Lon Bible Coll BA91. Wycliffe Hall Ox 95. **d** 97 **p** 98. C Chippenham St Pet *Bris* 97-01; P-in-c Stapleton from 01; Asst Chapl Colston's Sch Bris from 01. *Stapleton Rectory, 21 Park Road, Bristol BS16 1AZ* Tel 0117-958 3858

CREGEEN, Gary Marshall. b 62. Oak Hill Th Coll BA00. **d** 00 **p** 01. C Carl St Jo *Carl* 00-03; P-in-c Scotby and Cotehill w Cumwhinton from 03. *The Vicarage, Lambley Bank, Scotby, Carlisle CA4 8BX* Tel (01228) 513205
E-mail gary@gandjcregeen.co.uk

CREIGHTON, Frederick David. b 50. TCD BTh88 ACII74. **d** 88 **p** 89. C Lisburn Ch Ch *Conn* 88-91; I Drumclamph w Lower and Upper Langfield *D & R* 91-00; I Glendermott from 00. *Glendermott Rectory, Church Brae, Altnagelvin BT47 2LS* Tel (028) 7134 3001

CREIGHTON, Mrs Judith. b 36. Reading Univ BSc57. Trin Coll Bris 80 Edin Th Coll 81. **dss** 83 **d** 87 **p** 94. Greenock *Glas* 83-85; Lawrence Weston *Bris* 85-87; Par Dn Kingswood 87-90; Chapl Stoke Park and Purdown Hosps Stapleton 90-93; Hon C Marshfield w Cold Ashton and Tormarton etc *Bris* 93-97; rtd 96; Perm to Offic *Bris* from 97. *Rose Cottage, West Littleton, Marshfield, Chippenham SN14 8JE* Tel (01225) 891021

CREIGHTON, Ms Rachel Margaret Maxwell. b 64. Br Is Nazarene Coll BTh86 BD87. Cranmer Hall Dur 94 Lon Bible Coll MA89. **d** 94 **p** 95. C Basford w Hyson Green *S'well* 94-96; C Nottingham All SS 96-98; P-in-c Broxtowe 98-02; Chapl HM Pris Bedf from 02. *HM Prison, St Loyes Street, Bedford MK40 1HG* Tel (01234) 358671 *or* 373000 ext 3053 Fax 273568

CRELLIN, Howard Joseph. b 30. Magd Coll Cam BA52 MA56 Magd Coll Ox BA54 DipTh55 MA56. Wycliffe Hall Ox 53. **d** 55 **p** 56. C Dovercourt *Chelmsf* 55-58; R Theydon Garnon 58-70; Select Preacher Ox Univ 68; Perm to Offic *Ox* 70-82; Hon C High Wycombe 72-77; Asst Master K Chas I Sch Kidderminster 74-80; Caldicott Sch Farnham 80-82; Perm to Offic *Chelmsf* 82-91; Asst Master Fryerns Sch Basildon 82-88; St Anselm's Sch Basildon 88-91; P-in-c Whatfield w Semer, Nedging and Naughton *St E* 91-98; rtd 98; Perm to Offic *St E* from 98 and *Eur* from 02. *10 Green Willows, Lavenham, Sudbury CO10 9SP* Tel (01787) 247588

CREMIN (née LAKE), Mrs Eileen Veronica. b 58. Lon Univ Cert Counselling 93. Aston Tr Scheme 83 Sarum & Wells Th Coll 85. **d** 88 **p** 94. Par Dn Islington St Mary *Lon* 88-92; Asst Chapl Homerton Hosp Lon 92-94; Asst Chapl Hackney Hosp Gp 92-94; P-in-c Brondesbury Ch Ch and St Laur *Lon* 94-01; C Douglas Union w Frankfield *C, C & R* from 01. *64 Willowbank, Church Road, Blackrock, Co Cork, Irish Republic* Tel (00353) (21) 435 8226 E-mail evcremin@eircom.net *or* ecremin@hotmail.com

CRESSALL, Paul Richard. b 51. UEA BA74. Ripon Coll Cuddesdon 86. **d** 88 **p** 89. C Stevenage H Trin *St Alb* 88-91; V Caldecote All SS 91-95; V Old Warden 91-95; V Rothwell *Ripon* from 95. *The Vicarage, Beech Grove, Rothwell, Leeds LS26 0EF* Tel 0113-282 2369 Mobile 07801-582503
E-mail cressall1@netscapeonline.co.uk

CRESSEY, Canon Roger Wilson. b 35. Chich Th Coll 72. **d** 74 **p** 75. C Pontefract St Giles *Wakef* 74-77; Hon C Dewsbury All SS 77-80; Chapl Pinderfields Gen Hosp Wakef 80-94; Chapl Carr Gate Hosp Wakef 80-94; Chapl Fieldhead Hosp Wakef 80-94; Chapl Pinderfields and Pontefract Hosps NHS Trust 94-00; Hon Can Wakef Cathl *Wakef* 98-00; rtd 00. *1 Wellhead Mews, Chapelthorpe, Wakefield WF4 3JG* Tel (01924) 258972
E-mail roger-cressey@supanet.com

CRESSWELL, Howard Rex. b 31. Ely Th Coll 56. **d** 59 **p** 60. C Dovercourt *Chelmsf* 59-61; C Victoria Docks Ascension 61-64; V 64-71; R E w W Harling *Nor* 71-72; TV Quidenham w Eccles and Snetterton 72-75; V Arminghall 75-82; R Caistor w Markshall 75-82; V Trowse 75-82; V Heigham St Barn w St Bart 82-91; rtd 91; Perm to Offic *Nor* from 91. *28 Penryn Close, Norwich NR4 7LY* Tel (01603) 455591

CRESSWELL, Canon Jeremy Peter. b 49. St Jo Coll Ox BA72 MA78 Lon Univ MA93. Ridley Hall Cam 73. **d** 75 **p** 76. C Wisley w Pyrford *Guildf* 75-78; C Weybridge 78-82; P-in-c E Clandon 82-83; P-in-c W Clandon 82-83; R E and W Clandon 83-90; V Oxshott from 90; Hon Can Owerri from 01. *The Vicarage, Steel's Lane, Oxshott, Leatherhead KT22 0QH* Tel (01372) 842071 E-mail vicar@oxshott.co.uk

CRESSWELL, Preb Kenneth Benjamin. b 17. St D Coll Lamp BA50. **d** 51 **p** 52. C Porthill *Lich* 51-55; R Longton St Jo 55-67; V Horninglow 67-81; Preb Lich Cathl 80-83; TV Stoke-upon-Trent 81-83; rtd 83; Perm to Offic *Lich* 83-95; Perm to Offic *Worc* from 95. *1 Chartwell Close, Woodsetton, Dudley DY1 4LY* Tel (01902) 663354

CRETNEY, Mrs Antonia Lois. b 48. York Univ BA69 Bris Univ BA87 PGCE89. S Dios Minl Tr Scheme 92. **d** 94 **p** 95. NSM Bedminster *Bris* 94-96; C 96-97; P-in-c Beedon and Peasemore w W Ilsley and Farnborough *Ox* 97-99; R from 99. *The Rectory, 3 Drakes Farm, Peasemore, Newbury RG20 7DF* Tel (01635) 248925 E-mail peasemorecretney@aol.com

CRIBB, Robert John. b 22. Spurgeon's Coll 45. **d** 85 **p** 86. NSM Curry Rivel w Fivehead and Swell *B & W* 85-89; rtd 89; Perm to Offic *B & W* 89-94. *4 Heale Lane, Curry Rivel, Langport TA10 0PG* Tel (01458) 252333

CRICHTON, James Kenneth. b 35. Glouc Sch of Min 78. **d** 80 **p** 80. NSM Minchinhampton *Glouc* 80-83; NSM Nailsworth 83-86; Dep Chapl HM Pris Pentonville 86-87; Chapl HM Pris The Mount 87-97; rtd 97. *Pennant, Horeb, Llandysul SA44 4JG* Tel (01559) 362448

CRICK, Peter. b 39. Lon Univ BD68 NY Univ DMin84. Wells Th Coll 66. **d** 67 **p** 68. C Horsham *Chich* 67-71; Asst Dioc Youth Officer *Ox* 71-75; R Denham 75-88; Bp's Adv for CME *Dur* 88-97; P-in-c Coniscliffe 88-97; Hon Can Dur Cathl 93-97; R City of Bris from 97. *City Rectory, 2 Fremantle Square, Bristol BS6 5TL* Tel 0117-942 7546 E-mail crick@cix.co.uk

CRICK, Philip Benjamin Denton (Ben). b 33. Bris Univ BA63. Clifton Th Coll 60. **d** 64 **p** 65. C Clerkenwell St Jas and St Jo w St Pet *Lon* 64-67; CF 67-72; C Southall Green St Jo *Lon* 72-75; P-in-c Southall H Trin 75-83; P-in-c Kidbrooke St Jas *S'wark* 83-85; TV 85-92; C E Acton St Dunstan w St Thos *Lon* 92-95; Sub-Chapl HM Pris Wormwood Scrubs 92-95; rtd 95; Perm to Offic *Cant* from 95; Sub-Chapl HM Pris Cant from 97. *232 Canterbury Road, Birchington CT7 9TD* Tel (01843) 864049 E-mail ben.crick@argonet.co.uk

CRINKS, Kevin David. b 63. Aston Tr Scheme 86 Sarum & Wells Th Coll BTh91. **d** 93 **p** 94. C Aylesford *Roch* 93-96; C Hessle *York* 96-97; TV Upholland *Liv* 97-00; V Platt Bridge from 00. *Abram Vicarage, 9 Lee Lane, Abram, Wigan WN2 5QU* Tel (01942) 866269 Fax 866396 E-mail kevin.crinks@talk21.com

CRIPPS, Harold Ernest. b 04. AKC47. **d** 47 **p** 48. C Warrington St Elphin *Liv* 47-52; P-in-c New Springs 52-53; V 53-59; V Burtonwood 59-74; rtd 74; Perm to Offic *Chich* 77-92; Perm to Offic *Sarum* from 93. *144 Wessex Oval, Wareham BH20 4BT* Tel (01929) 550926

CRIPPS, Keith Richard John. b 21. Trin Coll Cam BA43 MA47 Newc Univ PhD80. Ridley Hall Cam 43. **d** 45 **p** 47. Inter-Colleg Sec SCM (Man) 45-47; C Man Victoria Park *Man* 45-47; C Aston SS Pet and Paul *Birm* 47-50; R Chorlton upon Medlock *Man* 50-60; Chapl Man Univ 51-60; Lect 52-60; Chapl and Lect Ripon Coll of Educn 60-65; Sen Lect Kenton Lodge Coll of Educn 65-71; Sen Lect City of Newc Coll of Educn 71-84; Lect Newc Poly 74-79; Chapl Jes Coll Cam 84-88; rtd 88; Perm to Offic *Ely* 92-95. *24 Mowbray Court, Butts Road, Exeter EX2 5TQ*

CRIPPS, Martyn Cyril Rowland. b 46. Birm Univ LLB68 Solicitor 71. Wycliffe Hall Ox 80. **d** 82 **p** 83. C Canford Magna *Sarum* 82-86; V Preston St Cuth *Blackb* 87-94; Warden Les Cotils *Win* 94-96; V Gipsy Hill Ch Ch *S'wark* 96-00; R Horning w Beeston St Laurence and Ashmanhaugh *Nor* 00-01; R Neatishead, Barton Turf and Instead 00-01; R Ashmanhaugh, Barton Turf etc from 01. *St Benedict's Vicarage, Church Road, Horning, Norwich NR12 8PZ* Tel (01692) 630216
E-mail mandmc.gh@talk21.com

CRIPPS, Michael Frank Douglas. b 28. Ch Ch Ox BA50 MA53. Ridley Hall Cam 58. **d** 59 **p** 60. C Cambridge Gt St Mary w St Mich *Ely* 59-62; Ceylon 62-66; C-in-c Swindon Covingham CD *Bris* 66-72; V Swindon St Paul 72-73; P-in-c Aldbourne and Baydon *Sarum* 73; TV Whitton 73-81; C Marlborough 81-94; rtd 94; Chapl Pau *Eur* 94-96; Perm to Offic *Sarum* from 96. *9 Silverless Street, Marlborough SN8 1JQ* Tel (01672) 512748

CRITCHELL, Denise Eileen. b 49. St Alb and Ox Min Course 96. **d** 99 **p** 00. C Flackwell Heath *Ox* 99-03; TV Risborough from 03. *The Vicarage, Church Lane, Lacey Green, Princes Risborough HP27 0QX* Tel (01844) 347741
E-mail denise@dncritchell.fsnet.co.uk

CRITCHLEY, Colin. b 41. Dur Univ BA63 Liv Univ MA69 AFBPsS94. NW Ord Course 75. **d** 78 **p** 79. NSM Halewood *Liv* from 78; Dioc Child Protection Adv from 96. *53 Elwyn Drive, Halewood, Liverpool L26 0UX* Tel 0151-487 5710

CRITCHLOW, Trevor Francis. b 61. Lanc Univ BA83 K Coll Lon MA96. Westcott Ho Cam 88. **d** 90 **p** 91. C Croydon St Jo *S'wark* 90-92; C Lewisham St Mary 92-94; Development Dir Westmr St Matt 95-99. *73 Newmarket Road, Cambridge CB5 8EG* Tel (01223) 351919 Fax 07092-205002
E-mail trevor@bird-in-hand.fsnet.co.uk

CRITTALL, Richard Simon. b 47. Sussex Univ BA69 Linacre Coll Ox BA71. St Steph Ho Ox 69. **d** 72 **p** 73. C Oswestry H Trin *Lich* 72-75; C E Grinstead St Mary *Chich* 75-78; TV Brighton Resurr 78-83; R E Blatchington 83-95; V Heathfield St Rich from 95. *St Richard's Vicarage, Hailsham Road, Heathfield TN21 8AF* Tel (01435) 862744 E-mail simon.crittall@breathemail.net

CROAD, Arthur Robert. b 35. Down Coll Cam BA58 MA61. Clifton Th Coll 58. **d** 61 **p** 62. C Sneinton St Chris w St Phil *S'well* 61-64; C Kinson *Sarum* 64-72; R Sherfield English *Win* 72-74; R Awbridge w Sherfield English 74-92; P-in-c Hinton Ampner w Bramdean and Kilmeston 92-01; rtd 01. *48 Woodfield Drive, Winchester SO22 5PU* Tel (01962) 851978

CROAD, David Richard. b 31. Reading Univ BSc55. Clifton Th Coll. **d** 57 **p** 58. C Iver *Ox* 57-60; C Rushden *Pet* 60-63; V Loudwater *Ox* 63-72; SW Area Sec CPAS 72-78; V Bovingdon *St Alb* 78-91; Min Hampstead St Jo Downshire Hill Prop Chpl *Lon* 91-94; rtd 94; Perm to Offic *Guildf* and *Win* from 00. *5 Berryfield Road, Hordle, Lymington SO41 0HQ* Tel (01425) 614613

CROCKER, Jeremy Robert. b 67. MCIM92 S Bank Univ MA94 Heythrop Coll Lon MA98. Westcott Ho Cam 94 CITC 96. **d** 97 **p** 98. C Stevenage H Trin *St Alb* 97-00; TV Bp's Hatfield from 00. *St John's Vicarage, Bishop's Rise, Hatfield AL10 9BZ* Tel (01707) 262689 E-mail jeremy.crocker@tesco.net

CROCKER, Keith Gwillam. b 49. Lanchester Poly BSc70 DipTh78. Oak Hill Th Coll 74. **d** 77 **p** 78. C Whitnash *Cov* 77-80; C Gt Horton *Bradf* 80-83; C Grays SS Pet and Paul, S Stifford and W Thurrock *Chelmsf* 83-84; TV Grays Thurrock 84-88; TR Wreningham *Nor* 88-95; P-in-c New Catton Ch Ch 95-99; V from 99. *Christ Church Vicarage, 65 Elm Grove Lane, Norwich NR3 3LF* Tel (01603) 408332 E-mail keith.crocker@which.net

CROCKER, Peter David. b 56. Lon Univ MB, BS80 MRCGP. Mon Dioc Tr Scheme 93. **d** 96 **p** 97. NSM Bassaleg *Mon* 96-02; TV from 02. *St John's Vicarage, Wern Terrace, Rogerstone, Newport NP10 9FG* Tel (01633) 893357

CROCKER, Richard Campbell. b 54. BSc Nottm Univ MA. Wycliffe Hall Ox. **d** 82 **p** 83. C Summerfield *Birm* 82-84; Chapl K Edw Sch Birm 84-91; USA from 91. *821 Ironwood Court, Council Bluffs, IA 51503, USA* E-mail rccrocker@juno.com

CROCKETT, Peter James Sinclair. b 44. Sarum & Wells Th Coll 74. **d** 77 **p** 78. C Heavitree *Ex* 77; C Heavitree w Ex St Paul 78-80; TV Ex St Thos and Em 80-87; V Countess Wear from 87; Chapl St Loyes Tr Coll for the Disabled from 87; Chapl W of England Sch for those w little or no sight from 87; CF (TA) from 88. *The Vicarage, 375 Topsham Road, Exeter EX2 6HB* Tel (01392) 873263

CROCKETT, The Ven Phillip Anthony. b 45. K Coll Lon BA67 BD70 AKC70 Univ of Wales MA91. St Mich Coll Llan DPS71. **d** 71 **p** 72. C Aberdare *Llan* 71-74; C Whitchurch 74-78; V Llanfihangel-y-Creuddyn, Llanafan w Llanwnnws *St D* 78-86; Sec Prov Selection Panel 83-87; V Ysbyty Ystwyth 84-86; R Dowlais *Llan* 86-91; Sec for Bd of Min 91-99; V Cynwil Elfed and Newchurch *St D* from 99; Adn Carmarthen from 99; Warden of Readers from 00. *The Vicarage, Cynwyl Elfed, Carmarthen SA33 6LU* Tel (01267) 281605
E-mail ministry@rb.churchinwales.org.uk

CROFT, James Stuart. b 57. K Coll Lon BD80 Leeds Univ MA95. Ripon Coll Cuddesdon 83. **d** 85 **p** 86. C Friern Barnet St Jas *Lon* 85-88; R Lea *Linc* 88-93; V Knaith 88-93; V Upton 88-93; R Gate Burton 88-93; R Lea Gp 93-97; Chapl N Lincs Coll 90-93; V Froyle and Holybourne *Win* from 97. *The Vicarage, Church Lane, Holybourne, Alton GU34 4HD* Tel (01420) 83240

CROFT, John Armentieres. b 15. MC44. Sarum Th Coll 56. **d** 57 **p** 58. C Madron w Morvah *Truro* 57-60; V Gwinear 60-70; rtd 70; Perm to Offic *Truro* and *Sarum* from 70; *B & W* 70-98. *Vine House, Common Road, Wincanton BA9 9RB* Tel (01963) 32253

CROFT, Michael Peter. b 60. GradIPM. Trin Coll Bris BA88. **d** 88 **p** 89. C Drypool *York* 88-91; P-in-c Sandal St Cath *Wakef* 91-95; V from 95; Chapl Manygates Maternity Hosp Wakef from 91. *9 Sandal Cliff, Wakefield WF2 6AU* Tel and fax (01924) 256108 Mobile 07866-367182 E-mail mike@croftie.fsnet.co.uk

CROFT, Ronald. b 30. St Aid Birkenhead 61. **d** 63 **p** 64. C Lawton Moor *Man* 63-65; C Withington St Crispin 65-66; R 74-86; C Prestwich St Marg 66-67; V Oldham St Ambrose 67-71; P-in-c Oldham St Jas 67-68; V 68-71; V Prestwich St Hilda 71-74; P-in-c 96-00; R Heaton Norris St Thos 86-96; rtd 00. *St Hilda's Vicarage, 55 Whittaker Lane, Prestwich, Manchester M25 5ET* Tel 0161-773 1642

CROFT, Simon Edward Owen. b 51. Ch Ch Coll Cant CertEd73. St Steph Ho Ox 75. **d** 78 **p** 79. C Heavitree w Ex St Paul *Ex* 78-83; V Seaton 83-93; P-in-c Ex St Mark 93-96; P-in-c Ex St Sidwell and St Matt 96; R Ex St Mark, St Sidwell and St Matt from 96. *St Mark's Rectory, 8 Lamacraft Drive, Exeter EX4 8QS* Tel (01392) 421050

CROFT, Steven John Lindsey. b 57. MA PhD. Cranmer Hall Dur 80. **d** 83 **p** 84. C Enfield St Andr *Lon* 83-87; V Ovenden *Wakef* 87-96; Dioc Miss Consultant 91-96; Warden Cranmer Hall Dur from 96. *16 Briardene, Durham DH1 4QU,* or *St John's College, 3 South Bailey, Durham DH1 3RJ* Tel 0191-334 3866 Fax 334 3501

CROFT, Canon Warren David. b 36. ACT ThL62. **d** 61 **p** 62. Australia 61-69 and from 79; Papua New Guinea 69-77; C Mottingham St Andr *S'wark* 77-78; Hon Can Dogura 86; C Hunters Hill 87; R Kogarah 87-01; rtd 01. *43 Sierra Avenue, PO Box 3078, Bateau Bay, NSW, Australia 2261* Tel (0061) (2) 4333 3967 Mobile 425-206621 Fax 9553 8594
E-mail isandwas@bigpond.com

CROFT, Canon William Stuart. b 53. Trin Hall Cam BA76 MA79 K Coll Lon MTh88. Ripon Coll Cuddesdon BA80. **d** 80 **p** 81. C Friern Barnet St Jas *Lon* 80-83; Tutor Chich Th Coll 83-92; Vice-Prin 88-92; V Fernhurst *Chich* 92-98; Dir of Ords *Pet* 98-03; Prec and Min Can Pet Cathl 98-01; Can Res and Prec from 01; Liturg Officer from 03. *18 Minster Precincts, Peterborough PE1 1XX* Tel (01733) 343389 E-mail williamsbill croft@hotmail.com

CROFTON, Canon Edwin Alan. b 46. Univ Coll Ox BA68 MA72. Cranmer Hall Dur DipTh72. **d** 73 **p** 74. C Hull Newland St Jo *York* 73-77; C Worksop St Jo *S'well* 77-81; Chapl Kilton Hosp Worksop 80-81; V Scarborough St Mary w Ch Ch and H Apostles *York* 81-91; Miss to Seamen 81-91; Chapl St Mary's Hosp Scarborough 82-91; V Cheltenham Ch Ch *Glouc* 91-02; RD Cheltenham 95-00; Hon Can Glouc Cathl from 01; TR Eccles *Man* from 02. *The Rectory, 12B Westminster Road, Eccles, Manchester M30 9EB* Tel 0161-281 5739
E-mail ea_crofton@msn.com

CROFTS, Charles Arthur. b 14. Ball Coll Ox BA38 MA48. Lich Th Coll 38. **d** 39 **p** 40. C Shrewsbury St Chad *Lich* 39-41; C Tettenhall Regis 42-48; Min Can Worc Cathl *Worc* 48-50; Asst Master K Sch Worc 48-50; V Ox St Cross *Ox* 51-62; CF (TA) 54-64; V Crowhurst *S'wark* 62-68; Sen Insp of Schools 62-68; V Hexton *St Alb* 69-77; Hon Can St Alb 69-76; Dir RE 69-71; Teacher Herts and Beds Secondary Schools 71-76; N Herts FE Coll 76; Chapl St Bede's Ecum Sch Reigate 77-80; C Merstham and Gatton *S'wark* 77-80; rtd 80; Perm to Offic *Chich* from 80. *5 Manaton Close, Haywards Heath RH16 3HS* Tel (01444) 457190

CROFTS, David Thomas. b 47. Cheshire Coll of Educn CertEd68 Open Univ BA76. Dioc OLM tr scheme. **d** 99 **p** 00. OLM Bury St Edmunds St Mary *St E* from 99. *8 Linton Gardens, Bury St Edmunds IP33 2DZ* Tel (01284) 761801 Mobile 0780-8020316 Fax 765501 E-mail david@croftsdt.demon.co.uk

CROFTS, Ian Hamilton. b 55. BSc. St Jo Coll Nottm 79. **d** 82 **p** 83. C Leamington Priors St Paul *Cov* 82-86; C Oadby *Leic* 86; TV 86-91; V Maidstone St Faith *Cant* from 91. *St Faith's Vicarage, Moncktons Lane, Maidstone ME14 2PY* Tel (01622) 201164 E-mail ian_crofts@msn.com

CROMPTON, Holly Jo. b 74. Bath Coll of HE BA95. Wycliffe Hall Ox BTh01. **d** 01 **p** 02. C Luton Lewsey St Hugh *St Alb* from 01. *247 Leagrave High Street, Luton LU4 0NA* Tel (01582) 593402 Mobile 07761-628335 E-mail hollycrompton@hotmail.com

CROMPTON, Roger Martyn Francis. b 47. Sheff Univ BA69 PGCE73. St Jo Coll Dur Cranmer Hall Dur BA84. **d** 85 **p** 86. C Woodford Wells *Chelmsf* 85-89; V Golcar *Wakef* from 89; RD Huddersfield from 99. *The Vicarage, Church Street, Golcar, Huddersfield HD7 4PX* Tel (01484) 654647

CRONK, Simon Nicholas. b 59. CQSW85 Poly of Wales BA82. Wycliffe Hall Ox 89. **d** 92 **p** 93. C Cheltenham Ch Ch *Glouc* 92-96; V Cinderford St Steph w Littledean 96-02; V Hughenden *Ox* from 02. *The Vicarage, Valley Road, Hughenden Valley, High Wycombe HP14 4PF* Tel (01494) 563439

CROOK, Colin. b 44. JP78. Brighton Poly ALA67 FLA93 Lon Univ BSc(Econ)74 DMS81. S'wark Ord Course 87. **d** 90 **p** 91. NSM Dartford Ch Ch *Roch* 90-97; Dioc Ecum Officer from 96; P-in-c Crockenhill All So from 97. *The Vicarage, Eynsford Road, Crockenhill, Swanley BR8 8JS* Tel (01322) 662157 Fax as telephone

CROOK, David Creighton. b 37. Trin Coll Cam BA61 MA68. Cuddesdon Coll 61. **d** 63 **p** 64. C Workington St Mich *Carl* 63-66; C Penrith St Andr 66-70; V Barrow St Jas 70-78; V Maryport 78-81; TV Greystoke, Matterdale and Mungrisdale 81-87; TV Watermillock 84-87; V Hesket-in-the-Forest and Armathwaite 87-98; rtd 98; Perm to Offic *Carl* from 01. *11 Lowther Street, Penrith C11 7UW* Tel (01768) 866773

CROOK, Mrs Diana Elizabeth. b 47. Hull Univ BA73 Open Univ BSc93 City Univ MSc97 Middx Univ BA03 RGN70 MBPsS. NTMTC 00. **d** 03. NSM Waltham H Cross *Chelmsf* from 03. *Great Chalks, High Street, Hatfield Broad Oak, Bishop's Stortford CM22 7HQ* Tel (01279) 718201 Fax 718109 E-mail diana@famille.demon.co.uk

CROOK, Graham Leslie. b 49. Chich Th Coll 74. **d** 76 **p** 77. C Withington St Crispin *Man* 76-79; C Prestwich St Marg 79-82; V Nelson St Bede *Blackb* 82-92; Chapl Southend Health Care NHS Trust from 92; Bp's Adv for Hosp Chapl *Chelmsf* from 98. *Southend Hospital, Prittlewell Chase, Westcliff-on-Sea SS0 0RY* Tel (01702) 435555

✠**CROOK, The Rt Revd John Michael.** b 40. Univ of Wales (Lamp) BA62. Coll of Resurr Mirfield 62. **d** 64 **p** 65 **c** 99. C Horninglow *Lich* 64-66; C Bloxwich 66-70; R Inverness St Mich *Mor* 70-78; R Inverness St Jo 74-78; Dioc Youth Chapl *St And* 78-86; R Aberfoyle 78-87; R Doune 78-87; R Callander 78-87; Can St Ninian's Cathl Perth 85-99; R Bridge of Allan 87-99; Syn Clerk 97-99; Bp Mor from 99. *Diocesan Office, 11 Kenneth Street, Inverness IV3 5NR* Tel (01463) 231059 *or* tel and fax 226255 E-mail office@moray.anglican.org

CROOK, Malcolm Geoffrey. b 53. St Steph Ho Ox 88. **d** 90 **p** 91. C Pet St Jude *Pet* 90-93; C Barrow St Matt *Carl* 93-96; TV Langley and Parkfield *Man* 96-97; R Man Apostles w Miles Platting from 97. *77 Ridgeway Street, Manchester M40 7DT* Tel 0161-205 4371

CROOK, Rowland William. b 39. Lon Univ DipTh63. Tyndale Hall Bris 61. **d** 64 **p** 65. C Penn Fields *Lich* 64-68; C Lower Broughton St Clem w St Matthias *Man* 68-70; C Bucknall and Bagnall *Lich* 70-76; V New Shildon *Dur* 76-86; V Northwich St Luke and H Trin *Ches* 86-99; P-in-c Helsby and Dunham-on-the-Hill from 99. *St Paul's Vicarage, Vicarage Lane, Helsby, Warrington WA6 9AB* Tel (01928) 722151 Fax as telephone E-mail rowland@rpwland.co.uk

CROOK, Timothy Mark. b 68. Oak Hill Th Coll BA00. **d** 00 **p** 01. C Charles w Plymouth St Matthias *Ex* from 00. *18 Dale Gardens, Mutley, Plymouth PL4 6PX* Tel (01752) 669087 E-mail timothycrook@hotmail.com

CROOKS, Christopher John (Kip). b 53. St Bede's Coll Dur CertEd75. Trin Coll Bris BA90. **d** 90 **p** 91. C The Quinton *Birm* 90-93; V Ince Ch Ch *Liv* 93-03; R Much Woolton from 03. *The Rectory, 67 Church Road, Woolton, Liverpool L25 6DA* Tel 0151-428 1853

CROOKS, Canon David William Talbot. b 52. TCD BA75 MA78 BD83. **d** 77 **p** 78. C Glendermott *D & R* 77-81; C Edin Old St Paul *Edin* 81-84; I Taughboyne, Craigadooish, Newtowncunningham etc *D & R* from 84; Bp's Dom Chapl from 88; Can Raphoe Cathl from 91. *Taughboyne Rectory, Churchtown, Carrigans, Lifford, Co Donegal, Irish Republic* Tel (00353) (74) 914 0135 E-mail dcrooks@eircom.net

CROOKS, Eric. b 34. Oak Hill Th Coll 68. **d** 70 **p** 71. C Chadderton Ch Ch *Man* 70-73; C Bolton St Paul 73-75; C Lurgan Ch the Redeemer *D & D* 75-77; I Aghaderg w Donaghmore 77-80; I Donnaald 80-01; rtd 01. *15 Cairnshill Court, Saintfield Road, Belfast BT8 4TX* Tel (028) 9070 1449

CROOKS, Frederick Walter (Mike). b 18. TCD BA41 MA45. TCD Div Sch Div Test41. **d** 41 **p** 42. C Kilkenny *C & O* 41-43;

Dean's V St Canice's Cathl 41-43; Chapl RNVR 43-46; C High Wycombe All SS *Ox* 46-48; V Whitechapel St Paul w St Mark *Lon* 48-52; V Cobham *Guildf* 52-62; R Haslemere 62-69; RD Godalming 67-69; V Epsom St Martin 69-74; Hon Can Guildf Cathl 69-74; V Shalfleet *Portsm* 74-80; V Thorley 75-80; Perm to Offic from 80; rtd 83; Perm to Offic *Chich* from 83. *68 Homeheights House, Clarence Parade, Southsea PO5 3NW* Tel (023) 9287 0470

CROOKS, Henry Cecil. b 15. Edin Th Coll 71. **d** 72 **p** 72. P-in-c Kinross *St And* 72-75; R 75-81; P-in-c Dollar 76-81; rtd 81; Perm to Offic *Bris* 81-86 and *Chich* from 87. *Terry's Cross, Bungalow 8, Brighton Road, Woodmancote, Henfield BN5 9SX* Tel (01273) 493802

CROOKS, Kenneth Robert. b 36. CEng FIEE FCMI. S'wark Ord Course 80. **d** 83 **p** 84. NSM Wisley w Pyrford *Guildf* from 83; Perm to Offic *Ex* from 98. *Foxes Corner, Peak Hill Road, Sidmouth EX10 0NW* Tel (01395) 577558

CROOKS, Peter James. b 50. St Jo Coll Cam BA72. Cranmer Hall Dur DipTh76. **d** 76 **p** 77. C Onslow Square St Paul *Lon* 76-77; C Brompton H Trin w Onslow Square St Paul 77-79; C Wembley St Jo 79-82; CMS 82-92; Lebanon 83-89; Syria 85-89; Dean Jerusalem 89-92; P-in-c Hunningham *Cov* 92-01; P-in-c Wappenbury w Weston under Wetherley 92-01; P-in-c Offchurch 96-01; V Long Itchington and Marton 96-01; CMS 01-02; TV Dolgellau w Llanfachreth and Brithdir etc *Ban* from 02. *Tangnefedd, Friog Terrace, Fairbourne LL38 2SQ* Tel (01341) 251031 E-mail pncrooks@ukonline.com.uk

CROSBIE, Andrew Moncrieff. b 62. St Steph Ho Ox DipTh98. **d** 98 **p** 99. C St Paul's Cathl St Helena 98-00; CF from 00. *c/o MOD Chaplains (Army)* Tel (01980) 615804 Mobile 07769-973129 Fax (01980) 615800 E-mail fathercrosbie@hotmail.com

CROSBIE, Timothy John. b 44. ACMA72. **d** 00 **p** 01. OLM Shotley *St E* from 00. *27 Kitchener Way, Shotley Gate, Ipswich IP9 1RN* Tel (01473) 787316 E-mail tim@tcrosbie.freeserve.co.uk

CROSBY, Bernard Edward. b 47. Oak Hill Th Coll 86. **d** 88 **p** 89. C Springfield H Trin *Chelmsf* 88-91; C Penn Fields *Lich* 91-94; V St Leonards St Ethelburga *Chich* 94-02; R Fairlight, Guestling and Pett from 02. *The Rectory, Battery Hill, Fairlight, Hastings TN35 4AP* Tel (01424) 812799 E-mail bernardcrosby@supanet.com

CROSBY, David Edward. b 48. St Alb and Ox Min Course 96. **d** 99 **p** 00. NSM Newbury *Ox* 99-01; C The Bourne and Tilford *Guildf* from 01. *Heavitree, 5 Dene Lane, Lower Bourne, Farnham GU10 3PN* Tel (01252) 733563 Mobile 07966-367707 E-mail davidc@fish.co.uk

CROSFIELD, Canon George Philip Chorley. b 24. OBE90. Selw Coll Cam BA50 MA55. Edin Th Coll 46. **d** 51 **p** 52. C Edin St Dav *Edin* 51-53; C St Andrews St Andr *St And* 53-55; R Hawick *Edin* 55-60; Chapl Gordonstoun Sch 60-67; Can St Mary's Cathl 68-91; Vice-Provost 68-70; Provost 70-90; R Edin St Mary 70-90; rtd 90; Hon Can St Mary's Cathl *Edin* from 91. *21 Biggar Road, Silverburn, Penicuik EH26 9LQ* Tel (01968) 676607

CROSS, Canon Alan. b 43. Chich Th Coll 68. **d** 70 **p** 71. C Bordesley St Oswald *Birm* 70; C S Yardley St Mich 70-73; C Colchester St Jas, All SS, St Nic and St Runwald *Chelmsf* 73-77; V Leigh-on-Sea St Jas 77-89; V Woodford St Barn from 89; Hon Can Chelmsf Cathl from 97. *127 Snakes Lane East, Woodford Green IG8 7HX* Tel (020) 8504 4687

CROSS, Preb Elizabeth Mary. b 46. Leeds Univ BA69 CertEd70. Sarum Th Coll 80. **dss** 83 **d** 87 **p** 94. Wootton Bassett *Sarum* 83-86; Westbury 86-87; Par Dn 87-89; C Glastonbury w Meare, W Pennard and Godney *B & W* 89-95; Asst Dir of Ords 89-95; Preb Wells Cathl from 93; V Wedmore w Theale and Blackford from 95. *The Vicarage, Manor Lane, Wedmore BS28 4EL* Tel (01934) 713566 Fax 713437

CROSS, Greville Shelly. b 49. Birm Univ DPS80. Sarum & Wells Th Coll 73. **d** 76 **p** 77. C Kidderminster St Mary *Worc* 76-80; P-in-c Worc St Mark 80-81; TV Worc St Martin w St Pet, St Mark etc 81-85; R Inkberrow w Cookhill and Kington w Dormston 85-98; RD Evesham 93-97; R Old Swinford Stourbridge from 98; RD Stourbridge from 01. *The Rectory, Rectory Road, Stourbridge DY8 2HA* Tel (01384) 395410 E-mail stmaryos@fish.co.uk

CROSS, James Stuart. b 36. Magd Coll Ox BA65 MA71. Ripon Hall Ox 62. **d** 65 **p** 66. C Leckhampton SS Phil and Jas *Glouc* 65-66; CF 66-92; QHC 89-92; R Stretford St Pet *Man* 92-00; rtd 00. *St Davids, Redbrook Road, Monmouth NP25 3LY* Tel (01600) 715977 Fax as telephone E-mail jimcross1@aol.com

CROSS, Jeremy Burkitt. b 45. St Pet Coll Ox BA68 MA71. Wycliffe Hall Ox 67. **d** 69 **p** 70. C Mildenhall *St E* 69-72; C Lindfield *Chich* 72-77; V Framfield 77-89; R St Leonards St Leon 89-01; R Birling, Addington, Ryarsh and Trottiscliffe *Roch* from 01. *The Vicarage, Birling Road, Ryarsh, West Malling ME19 5AW* Tel (01732) 842249 E-mail j-scross@81afilsham.freeserve.co.uk

CROSS, John Henry Laidlaw. b 30. Peterho Cam BA53 MA57. Ridley Hall Cam 53. **d** 55 **p** 56. C Ealing Dean St Jo *Lon* 55-58; C Gt Baddow *Chelmsf* 58-60; V Maidenhead St Andr and St Mary *Ox* 60-68; News Ed *C of E Newspaper* 68-71; Assoc Ed 71-72; Ed 72-75; Hon C St Pet Cornhill *Lon* 68-87; P-in-c 87-95; Hon C Chelsea All SS 76-93; rtd 95. *8 Pinetum Close, Devizes SN10 5EW* Tel (01380) 722997 E-mail revjhlcross@aol.com

CROSS, Michael Anthony. b 45. Leeds Univ BA67 BA69. Coll of Resurr Mirfield 68. **d** 70 **p** 71. S Africa 70-73; C Adel *Ripon* 74-76; Chapl Birm Univ *Birm* 76-81; V Chapel Allerton *Ripon* 81-92; V Headingley from 92; AD Headingley from 96. *Headingley Vicarage, 16 Shire Oak Road, Leeds LS6 2DE* Tel 0113-275 1526 E-mail michael@anncross.freeserve.co.uk

CROSS, Canon Michael Harry. b 28. Liv Univ BVSc50. Cuddesdon Coll 74. **d** 76 **p** 77. C Ledbury *Heref* 76-79; P-in-c Bosbury 79-82; P-in-c Coddington 79-82; P-in-c Wellington Heath 79-82; V Bosbury w Wellington Heath etc 82-83; V Bishop's Castle w Mainstone 83-84; P-in-c Snead 83-84; V Morland, Thrimby and St Strickland *Carl* 84-93; RD Appleby 91-93; Hon Can Carl Cathl 92-93; rtd 93; Perm to Offic *Carl* from 93. *Hollin Knowle, Kilmidyke Road, Grange-over-Sands LA11 7AQ* Tel (01539) 535908

CROSS, Stephanie. b 53. Essex Univ BSc74 Loughb Univ MSc76 Bris Univ BA01 Reading Univ PGCE93. Trin Coll Bris 99. **d** 01 **p** 02. C Lytchett Minster *Sarum* from 01. *15 Guest Road, Upton, Poole BH16 5LQ* Tel (01202) 623637 E-mail crossstevie@hotmail.com

CROSSE, Anne-Marie. b 49. NSM W Worthing St Jo *Chich* 99-02; NSM Arundel w Tortington and S Stoke from 02. *25 Strathmore CLose, Worthing BN13 1PQ* Tel (01903) 247706 E-mail topaz@across.freeserve.co.uk

CROSSEY, Nigel Nicholas. b 59. Cam Univ BA TCD DipTh84. **d** 84 **p** 85. C Drumglass w Moygashel *Arm* 84-87; I Magheraculmoney *Clogh* 87-93; CF from 93. *c/o MOD Chaplains (Army)* Tel (01980) 615804 Fax 615800

CROSSLAND, Felix Parnell. b 20. CEng MIMechE57 Univ of Wales (Swansea) BSc49. St Deiniol's Hawarden 73. **d** 75 **p** 76. Hon C Skewen *Llan* 75-78; Hon C Neath w Llantwit 78-85; rtd 85; Perm to Offic *Llan* from 85. *21 Cimla Road, Neath SA11 3PR* Tel (01639) 643560

CROSSLAND, Sister Joyce. b 19. Gilmore Ho IDC48. **dss** 54 **d** 87. CSA 49-78; St Etheldreda's Children's Home Bedf 62-90; Hon Par Dn Bedford St Paul *St Alb* 87-91; rtd 91; Perm to Offic *St Alb* from 91 and *Ox* from 94. *6 Linford Lane, Willen, Milton Keynes MK15 9DL* Tel (01908) 661554

CROSSLAND, June. **d** 01. OLM Monk Bretton *Wakef* from 01. *St Paul's Vicarage, Monk Bretton, Barnsley S71 2HQ*

CROSSLAND, Richard Henry. b 49. Ex Univ BA72. S'wark Ord Course 91. **d** 94 **p** 96. NSM Surbiton St Andr and St Mark *S'wark* 94-95; NSM Linc Cathl Linc 95-98. *3 Vicars' Court, Minster Yard, Lincoln LN2 1PT* Tel (01522) 535225

CROSSLEY, Dennis Thomas. b 23. AKC52 St Boniface Warminster. **d** 53 **p** 54. C Crofton Park St Hilda *S'wark* 53-56; C Beddington 56-59; C Talbot Village *Sarum* 59-62; R Finchampstead *Ox* 62-97; rtd 97. *1 Larkswood Close, Sandhurst, Camberley GU47 8QJ*

CROSSLEY, George Alan. b 34. St Jo Coll Dur BA56. Cranmer Hall Dur DipTh60. **d** 60 **p** 61. C Blackb St Steph *Blackb* 60-63; C Ashton-on-Ribble St Andr 63-65; V Oswaldtwistle St Paul 65-72; R Dufton *Carl* 72-73; P-in-c Milburn w Newbiggin 72-73; R Long Marton w Dufton and w Milburn 73-76; P-in-c Beckermet St Jo 76-78; V Beckermet St Jo and Ponsonby 78-84; Chapl Furness Gen Hosp 84-89; TV Newbarns w Hawcoat *Carl* 84-89; Chapl Princess R Hosp Telford 89-97; rtd 95; P-in-c Bilsborrow *Blackb* 97-99; Perm to Offic from 00. *6 Eden Mount Way, Carnforth LA5 9XN* Tel (01524) 734568

CROSSLEY, George John. b 57. Bradf Univ BA81 PhD84. N Ord Course 91. **d** 94 **p** 95. C Balderstone *Man* 94-98; V Branston w Tatenhill *Lich* 98-02; RD Tutbury 00-02. *81 Ash Street, Burton-on-Trent DE14 3PX* Tel (01283) 516804 E-mail georgecrossley@fish.co.uk

CROSSLEY, Hugh Vaughan. b 20. AKC42. Bps' Coll Cheshunt. **d** 47 **p** 48. C Loughton St Jo *Chelmsf* 47-49; S Africa 49-52; Portuguese E Africa 52-57; Org Sec Miss to Seamen E Distr 57-58; V Shalford *Chelmsf* 58-60; S Africa 60-73; Adn Mafeking 66-70; R Crosett *Chelmsf* 73-85; P-in-c Bulphan 77-85; rtd 85; Perm to Offic *Nor* 86-96; *Chich* from 99. *Flat 4, 7 Chatsworth Gardens, Eastbourne BN20 7JP* Tel (01323) 412966

CROSSLEY, James Salter Baron. b 47. Linc Th Coll 70. **d** 72 **p** 74. C Chesterfield St Mary and All SS *Derby* 72-75; Chapl Doncaster R Infirmary 75-92; Chapl Doncaster R Infirmary and Montagu Hosp NHS Trust 92-95; Chapl Asst Tickhill Road and St Cath Hosps 75-92; Hon C Doncaster Intake *Sheff* 78-95; rtd 95; Perm to Offic *Sheff* 95-99. *The Gables, Low Row, Richmond DL11 6NH* Tel (01748) 886429

CROSSLEY, Joan Winifred. b 57. Sussex Univ BA78 Leic Univ MA80 Univ Coll Lon PhD85. St Alb and Ox Min Course 97. **d** 00 **p** 01. C Goldington *St Alb* 00-02; C Bedf St Mark from 02;

Asst Chapl Gt Ormond Street Hosp for Children NHS Trust from 03. *30 Cutcliffe Grove, Bedford MK40 4DD* Tel (01234) 346820 *or* 344536 E-mail jwcrossley@aol.com

CROSSLEY, John Eric. b 51. St Martin's Coll Lanc BA92. Carl Dioc Tr Inst 92. **d** 94 **p** 95. C Westfield St Mary *Carl* 94-97; P-in-c Penrith w Newton Reigny and Plumpton Wall 97-02; Chapl Newton Rigg Coll of H&FE 97-02; TV Cartmel Peninsula *Carl* from 02. *The Vicarage, Station Road, Flookburgh, Grange-over-Sands LA11 7JY* Tel (01539) 558245

CROSSLEY, Kenneth Ernest. b 38. NEOC 01. **d** 03. NSM Ripon Cathl *Ripon* from 03. *11 Station Drive, Ripon HG4 1JA* Tel (01765) 692499

CROSSLEY, Canon Robert Scott. b 36. Lon Univ BSc61 BD68 PhD75. ALCD64. **d** 64 **p** 65. C Beckenham St Jo *Roch* 64-68; C Morden *S'wark* 68-72; Chapl Ridley Hall Cam 72-75; V Camberley St Paul *Guildf* 75-83; TR 83-98; RD Surrey Heath 81-84; Hon Can Guildf Cathl 89-98; rtd 98; Perm to Offic *Guildf* 98-01; NSM Camberley St Mich Yorktown from 01. *20 Highbury Crescent, Camberley GU15 1JZ* Tel (01276) 500036

CROSSLEY, Mrs Ruth Joy. b 54. Cranmer Hall Dur 00. **d** 02 **p** 03. C Cartmel Peninsula *Carl* from 02. *The Vicarage, Station Road, Flookburgh, Grange-over-Sands LA11 7JY* Tel (01539) 558245

CROSSLEY, William Jeremy Hugh. b 55. St Jo Coll Dur BA76. Cranmer Hall Dur 81. **d** 84 **p** 85. C Gillingham St Mark *Roch* 84-87; C Ches Square St Mich w St Phil *Lon* 87-94; V Westminster St Jas the Less from 94-00; R St Marg Lothbury and St Steph Coleman Street etc from 00. *The Rectory, 1 St Olave's Court, London EC2V 8EX* Tel (020) 7600 2379 Fax 7606 1204 E-mail the.rector@stml.org.uk

CROSSMAN, Mrs Charmian Jeanette. b 27. Lon Univ BA48 Lanc Univ MA81 Edin Univ DipMin84. **d** 91 **p** 94. NSM Carl St Jo *Carl* 91-94; P-in-c Thursby 95-97; Perm to Offic *Sheff* from 97. *12 Ashfurlong Road, Sheffield S17 3NL* Tel 0114-236 0731

CROSSMAN, Miss Sharon Margaret Joan. b 65. St Loyes Sch of Occupational Therapy DipCOT87. Linc Th Coll BTh93. **d** 93 **p** 94. Par Dn Chippenham St Andr w Tytherton Lucas *Bris* 93-94; C 94-96; Chapl UWE 96-02; Hon C Almondsbury 97-98; Hon C Almondsbury and Olveston 98-02; Chapl Würzburg Univ Germany 02-03; Lic to Offic *Sarum* from 03. *25 Lambourne Way, Portishead, Bristol BS20 7LQ* Tel (01275) 840526 E-mail sharon.crossman@fsmail.net

CROSTHWAITE, George Roger. b 38. Dur Univ BSc62. Ridley Hall Cam 62 Fuller Th Sem California DMin83. **d** 65 **p** 66. C Bradf Cathl Par *Bradf* 65-67; C Ox St Aldate w H Trin *Ox* 67-70; Youth Adv CMS 70-73; P-in-c Derby St Werburgh *Derby* 73-78; V 78-82; C La Crescenta St Luke USA 77-78; V Anston *Sheff* 82-83; Registrar St Giles-in-the-Fields *Lon* 83-86; V Barnes St Mich *S'wark* 86-88; Perm to Offic *Guildf* 88-93; Dir Cen Essential Psychology from 92. *31 Upper High Street, Worthing BN11 1DR* Tel (01903) 529478

CROSTHWAITE, Howard Wellesley. b 37. St Cuth Soc Dur BA59. St Steph Ho Ox 59. **d** 61 **p** 62. C Workington St Mich *Carl* 61-63; Grenada 63-64; C Barnsley St Mary *Wakef* 64-68; V Milnsbridge 68-70; V Thurgoland 70-79; rtd 99. *50 Low Road West, Warmsworth, Doncaster DN4 9LE* Tel (01302) 859213 Mobile 07370-966629

CROUCH, Prof David Bruce. b 53. Univ of Wales (Cardiff) BA75 PhD84 FRHistS86. NEOC DipTh98. **d** 98 **p** 99. NSM Scarborough St Martin *York* 98-01; NSM Scarborough St Columba from 01. *29 Royal Avenue, Scarborough YO11 2LS* Tel (01723) 374867 Fax 378015 E-mail david@ucscarb.ac.uk

CROUCH, Keith Matheson. b 45. Whitelands Coll Lon CertEd71 Westhill Coll Birm BPhil00. K Coll Lon AKC70. **d** 72 **p** 73. C Hill *Birm* 72-75; C-in-c Woodgate Valley CD 75-77; V Bishop's Castle w Mainstone *Heref* 91-98; Vice-Prin WEMTC from 98; TV Tenbury 98-02; Public Preacher from 02. *The Vicarage, Orleton, Ludlow SY8 4HN* Tel (01568) 780881

CROUCHMAN, Eric Richard. b 30. Bps' Coll Cheshunt 64. **d** 66 **p** 67. C Ipswich H Trin *St E* 66-69; C Ipswich All Hallows 69-72; R Crowfield w Stonham Aspal and Mickfield 72-81; R Combs 81-90; RD Stowmarket 84-90; P-in-c Lydgate w Ousden and Cowlinge 90-95; R Wickhambrook w Lydgate, Ousden and Cowlinge 95-96; rtd 96; Perm to Offic *St E* from 97. *6 Mitre Close, Woolpit, Bury St Edmunds IP30 9SJ* Tel (01359) 240070 Fax as telephone

CROW, Arthur. b 26. St Chad's Coll Dur BA51 DipTh52. **d** 52 **p** 53. C Thornhill *Wakef* 52-54; C Holmfirth 54-57; V Shelley 57-63; V Flockton cum Denby Grange 63-91; rtd 91; Perm to Offic *York* from 91. *2 Thatchers Croft, Copmanthorpe, York YO23 3YD* Tel (01904) 709861

CROW, Michael John. b 35. AKC63. **d** 64 **p** 65. C Welwyn Garden City *St Alb* 64-67; C Sawbridgeworth 67-69; C Biscot 69-71; V Luton St Aug Limbury 71-79; TR Borehamwood 79-87; V Markyate Street 87-00; P-in-c Flamstead 98-00; rtd 00; Perm to Offic *Ex* from 00. *216 Pinhoe Road, Exeter EX4 7HH* Tel (01392) 424804

CROWDER, The Ven Norman Harry. b 26. St Jo Coll Cam BA48 MA52. Westcott Ho Cam 50. **d** 52 **p** 53. C Radcliffe-on-Trent

S'well 52-55; Bp's Res Chapl Portsm 55-59; Asst Chapl Canford Sch Wimborne 59-64; Chapl 64-72; V Oakfield St Jo Portsm 72-75; Can Res Portsm Cathl 75-85; Dir RE 75-85; Adn Portsm 85-93; rtd 93; Perm to Offic Portsm and Sarum from 94. 37 Rectory Road, Salisbury SP2 7SD Tel (01722) 320052
E-mail pauleen@pcrowder.freeserve.co.uk

CROWE, Anthony Murray. b 34. St Edm Hall Ox BA58 MA61. Westcott Ho Cam 57. d 59 p 60. C Stockingford Cov 59-62; C New Eltham All SS S'wark 62-66; V Clapham St Jo 66-73; R Charlton St Luke w H Trin 73-94; rtd 94; Sub-Chapl HM Pris Elmley 94-97; Sub-Chapl HM Pris Swaleside 94-99; Perm to Offic Cant from 94. 9 Park Avenue, Whitstable CT5 2DD Tel (01227) 273046

CROWE, Brian David. QUB BA92 PhD95 TCD BA98. d 98 p 99. C Ballynure and Ballyeaston Conn 98-01; I Galloon w Drummully Clogh 01-02. Address temp unknown

CROWE, Eric Anthony. b 29. St Jo Coll Dur BA53 MA98. Cuddesdon Coll 53. d 55 p 56. C Huddersfield St Jo Wakef 55-58; C Barnsley St Pet 58-60; R High Hoyland w Clayton W 60-68; V Battyeford 68-74; P-in-c Pitminster w Corfe B & W 75-76; V 76-90; rtd 90; Perm to Offic Ex 95-01. 5 Minster Close, Galmington, Taunton TA1 4LB Tel (01823) 257197

CROWE, Grant Norman. b 74. Keele Univ LLB96. Cranmer Hall Dur 00. d 03. C Burton All SS w Ch Ch Lich from 03. 1A Moor Street, Burton-on-Trent DE14 3AU Tel (01283) 538149

CROWE, Canon John Yeomans. b 39. Keble Coll Ox BA62 MA66. Linc Th Coll 62. d 64 p 65. C Tettenhall Regis Lich 64-67; C Caversham Ox 67-71; V Hampton Worc 72-76; P-in-c Leek St Edw Lich 76-79; TR Leek 79-83; TR Leek and Meerbrook 83-87; RD Leek 82-87; TR Dorchester Ox from 87; RD Aston and Cuddesdon 93-02; Hon Can Ch Ch from 94. The Rectory, Manor Farm Road, Dorchester-on-Thames, Wallingford OX10 7HZ Tel (01865) 340007 Fax as telephone
E-mail dorchesterabbey@enterprise.net

CROWE, Leonard Charles. b 25. S Dios Minl Tr Scheme 80. d 82 p 83. NSM Buxted and Hadlow Down Chich 82-84; NSM Fairlight 84-86; P-in-c 86-89; V 89-92; RD Rye 93-95; Perm to Offic 95-98; P-in-c Ashburnham w Penhurst 98-99; rtd 99; Perm to Offic Chich from 99. 3 St Kitts, West Parade, Bexhill-on-Sea TN39 3DR Tel (01424) 218676

CROWE, Canon Norman Charles. b 23. ADipR62. Launde Abbey. d 63 p 64. C Leic Martyrs Leic 63-66; C-in-c Leic St Chad CD 66-68; V Leic St Chad 68-73; V Market Harborough 73-88; RD Gartree I 76-81; Hon Can Leic Cathl 80-88; rtd 88; Perm to Offic Leic and Pet from 88. 8 Wilton Close, Desborough, Kettering NN14 2QJ Tel (01536) 760820

CROWE, Canon Philip Anthony. b 36. Selw Coll Cam BA60 MA64. Ridley Hall Cam 60. d 62 p 63. Tutor Oak Hill Th Coll 62-67; C Enfield Ch Ch Trent Park Lon 62-65; Ed C of E Newspaper 67-71; Lect Birm St Martin 71-76; R Breadsall Derby 77-88; Prin and Tutor Sarum & Wells Th Coll 88-95; Can and Preb Sarum Cathl Sarum 91-95; R Overton and Erbistock and Penley St As 95-97; Dir St As and Ban Minl Tr from 96; rtd 97; Perm to Offic Lich from 01. Alder Lea, Babbinswood, Whittington, Oswestry SY11 4PQ Tel (01691) 671698

CROWE, Canon Sydney Ralph. b 32. Edin Th Coll 61. d 63 p 64. C Bingley H Trin Bradf 63-66; C Bierley 66-69; V Toller Lane St Chad from 69; Hon Can Bradf Cathl from 85; RD Airedale 95-99. The Vicarage, St Chad's Road, Toller Lane, Bradford BD8 9DE Tel (01274) 543957

CROWHURST, Preb David Brian. b 40. Qu Coll Birm 77. d 80 p 81. NSM Ribbesford w Bewdley and Dowles Worc 80-82; Hon Chapl Birm Cathl Birm 81-82; C Kidderminster St Jo Worc 82-83; C-in-c Wribbenhall 83-84; P-in-c 84-87; V Oswestry St Oswald Lich 87-94; P-in-c Oswestry H Trin 93-94; V Oswestry from 94; P-in-c Rhydycroesau 90-91; R from 91; RD Oswestry 95-01; Preb Lich Cathl from 00. The Vicarage, Penylan Lane, Oswestry SY11 2AJ Tel (01691) 653467 or 652861 Fax 655235
E-mail d.crowhurst@btinternet.com

CROWIE, Hermon John. b 41. Kelham Th Coll 61. d 69 p 73. C Sneinton St Cypr S'well 69; C Balderton 72-75; V Basford St Aid 75-78; R Everton and Mattersey w Clayworth 78-84; St Helena 84-89; Chapl HM Pris Nor 89-91; Chapl HM Pris Cant 91-02; Bulgaria from 02. Zora 23, Nickolaevo, Stara Zagora, Bulgaria

CROWLE, Miss Sarah Ann. b 65. Ripon Coll Cuddesdon BTh99. d 99 p 00. C Godalming Guildf 99-03; Chapl Godalming Coll 01-03; R Chiddingfold Guildf from 03. The Rectory, Coxcombe Lane, Chiddingfold, Godalming GU8 4QA Tel (01428) 682008 Mobile 07747-031534 E-mail sarahcrowle@zoom.co.uk

CROWLEY, Jennifer. d 03. C Waterford w Killea, Drumcannon and Dunhill C & O from 03. Glen, Stradbally, Kilmacthomas, Co Waterford, Irish Republic Tel (00353) (51) 293143

CROWSON, Richard Charles Marriott. b 39. Down Coll Cam BA62 MA66. Lich Th Coll 62. d 64 p 65. C Smethwick Birm 64-67; V Nottingham St Andr S'well 67-74; Chapl Community Relns Pet 74-80; Perm to Offic Lon 80-92; Asst Sec for Race and Community Relns Gen Syn 92-97; Public Preacher Lon from 93; rtd 97. 11 Ellington Street, London N7 8PP Tel (020) 7609 1984

✠CROWTHER, The Rt Revd Clarence Edward. b 29. Leeds Univ BA50 LLB52 LLM53 California Univ PhD75. Cuddesdon Coll 55. d 56 p 57 c 65. C Ox SS Phil and Jas Ox 56-59; USA 59-64 and from 67; Episc Chapl California Univ 59-64; Dean Kimberley S Africa 64-65; Bp Kimberley and Kuruman 65-70; Asst Bp California 70-84; Asst Bp Los Angeles from 84. PO Box 1559, Summerland, CA 93067, USA E-mail cctravel@west.net

CROWTHER, Donald James. b 23. Oak Hill NSM Course 80. d 82 p 83. NSM Seal St Lawr Roch 82-85; NSM Sevenoaks St Nic 85-87; P-in-c Sevenoaks Weald 87-90; Perm to Offic from 90. Midhope, Pilgrims Way, Kemsing, Sevenoaks TN15 6LS Tel (01732) 761035

CROWTHER, Frank. b 28. Qu Coll Birm 68. d 69 p 70. C Bulwell St Mary S'well 69-72; TV Clifton 72-77; V Kirkby in Ashfield St Thos 77-85; rtd 86; Perm to Offic S'well from 86; Perm to Offic Derby 86-00. 30 Bramley Court, Sutton-in-Ashfield NG17 4AT Tel (01623) 443251

CROWTHER, Gordon Allan. b 63. Rhodes Univ BA85 LLB87. Spurgeon's Coll BD94 St Jo Coll Dur MA98. d 00 p 01. C Lancaster St Thos Blackb from 00. 6 Jackson Close, Lancaster LA1 5EY Tel (01524) 33741 E-mail gordon@st.tees.org.uk

CROWTHER, Stephen Alfred. b 59. TCD DipTh87. d 87 p 88. C Willowfield D & D 87-89; I Belfast St Chris 89-92; I Kiltegan w Hacketstown, Clonmore and Moyne C & O 93-99; Philippines 99-00; C Kill D & G 00-01; I Lisnaskea Clogh from 01. The Rectory, Castlebalfour, Lisnaskea BT92 0LT Tel (028) 6772 1237 E-mail crowther@oceanfree.net

CROWTHER-ALWYN, Benedict Mark. b 53. Kent Univ BA74. Qu Coll Birm 74. d 77 p 78. C Fenny Stratford and Water Eaton Ox 77-80; C Moulsecoomb Chich 80-81; TV 81-83; R Glas St Serf and Baillieston Glas 83-87; R Bassingham Linc 87-90; V Aubourn w Haddington 87-90; R Thurlby w Norton Disney 87-90; V Elmton Derby 90-03; P-in-c Matlock from 03. The Rectory, Church Street, Matlock DE4 3BZ Tel (01629) 582199

CROWTHER-GREEN, Canon John Patrick Victor. b 18. Hatf Coll Dur LTh41 BA42. St Boniface Warminster 39. d 42 p 44. C Croydon H Trin Cant 42-44; C New Windsor H Trin Ox 44-49; V Shackerstone and Congerstone Leic 49-53; R Willoughby Waterleys, Peatling Magna etc 53-58; V Leic St Sav 58-73; V Blaby 73-87; RD Guthlaxton I 81-87; Hon Can Leic Cathl 82-87; rtd 87; Perm to Offic Leic from 87. 40 Craighill Road, Knighton, Leicester LE2 3FB Tel 0116-270 7615

CROWTHER-GREEN, Michael Leonard. b 36. K Coll Lon 56. d 60 p 61. C Caterham S'wark 60-64; C Lewisham St Jo Southend 64-69; Chr Aid Area Sec (Berks, Oxon and Bucks) 69-78; Lic to Offic Ox 78-83; Dioc Stewardship Adv 83-92; rtd 92; Perm to Offic Ox from 92. 8 Egerton Road, Reading RG2 8HQ Tel 0118-987 2502

CROYDON, Archdeacon of. See DAVIES, The Ven Vincent Anthony

CROYDON, Area Bishop of. See BAINES, The Rt Revd Nicholas

CRUICKSHANK, Jonathan Graham. b 52. K Coll Lon BD74 AKC74 Keble Coll Ox PGCE75. St Aug Coll Cant 75. d 76 p 77. C Stantonbury Ox 76-79; C Burnham 79-82; Chapl RNR 80-83; C Burnham w Dropmore, Hitcham and Taplow Ox 82-83; Chapl RN 83-89; TV New Windsor Ox 89-01; R Itchen Valley Win from 01; RD Alresford from 01; Corps Chapl Sea Cadet Corps from 95. Itchen Valley Rectory, Chillandham Lane, Itchen Abbas, Winchester SO21 1AS Tel (01962) 779832 Fax as telephone E-mail jcruickshank@btclick.com

CRUISE, Brian John Alexander. Bris Univ BA TCD BTh. d 88 p 89. C Lurgan Ch the Redeemer D & D 88-92; I Kildress w Altedesert Arm from 92. Kildress Rectory, 6 Rectory Road, Cookstown BT80 9RX Tel (028) 7965 1215
E-mail brian@aonet.org.uk

CRUMPTON, Colin. b 38. AKC61 Sheff Univ Dip Leadership, Renewal & Miss Studies 97. d 64 p 65. C Billingham St Cuth Dur 64-66; C Shirley Birm 66-69; V Mossley Ches 69-75; Miss to Seamen 75-77; V Burslem St Paul Lich 77-82; V Edensor 82-97; V Llanrhaeadr-ym-Mochnant etc St As 97-00; Dir Accra Retreat Cen Ghana 00-01; rtd 02; Hon C Redmarley D'Abitot, Bromesberrow, Pauntley etc Glouc 02-03; Perm to Offic Lich from 03. 60 Craig Walk, Alsager ST7 2RJ Tel (01270) 882666 Mobile 07799-183971

CRUSE, Jack. b 35. ARIBA67. Sarum & Wells Th Coll 76. d 79 p 80. NSM W Teignmouth Ex 79-85; C Ideford, Luton and Ashcombe 85-89; C Bishopsteignton 85-89; R Broadhempston, Woodland, Staverton etc 90-98; RD Totnes 94-98; rtd 98; Perm to Offic Ex from 98. 41 Butts Close, Honiton EX14 2FS Tel (01404) 46567 E-mail jack@jcruse.freeserve.co.uk

CRUSE, John Jeremy. b 58. Univ of Wales (Lamp) BA79 Hughes Hall Cam CertEd87. Sarum & Wells Th Coll 81. d 82 p 83. C Newton St Pet K & B 82-84; P-in-c Newbridge-on-Wye and Llanfihangel Brynpabuan 84-86; Perm to Offic Heref 88-89; C Waltham H Cross Chelmsf 89-91; TV Yatton Moor B & W 91-00; V Shalford Guildf from 00. The Vicarage, East Shalford

Lane, Shalford, Guildford GU4 8AE Tel and fax (01483) 562396 Mobile 07889-919928 E-mail john@cruse60.freeserve.co.uk

CRUTCHLEY, John Hamilton. b 62. Kingston Poly LLB85. Trin Coll Bris 99. **d** 01 **p** 02. C Barnstaple *Ex* from 01. *28 Old School Road, Barnstaple EX32 9DP* Tel (01271) 325553
E-mail crutchleyfam@tesco.net

CRUTTENDEN, Leslie Roy. b 39. Cant Sch of Min. **d** 84 **p** 85. NSM Maidstone St Luke *Cant* 84-86; NSM Charlton-in-Dover 86-90; NSM River 90-01. *Address temp unknown*

CRYER, Gordon David. b 34. St D Coll Lamp BA63 DipTh64. **d** 64 **p** 65. C Mortlake w E Sheen *S'wark* 64-67; C Godstone 67-70; Chapl St Dunstan's Abbey Sch Plymouth 71-02; R Stoke Damerel *Ex* 71-02; P-in-c Devonport St Aubyn 88-02; rtd 02; Perm to Offic *Truro* from 02. *9 St Stephens Road, Saltash PL12 4BG* Tel (01752) 510436

CRYER, Neville Barker. b 24. Hertf Coll Ox BA48 MA52. Ridley Hall Cam. **d** 50 **p** 51. C Derby St Werburgh *Derby* 50-53; C Ilkeston St Mary 53-54; R Blackley St Pet *Man* 55-59; V Addiscombe St Mary *Cant* 59-67; Sec Conf Br Miss Socs 67-70; Gen Sec BFBS 70-86; rtd 86; Perm to Offic *York* from 90. *14 Carmires Road, Haxby, York YO32 3NN* Tel (01904) 763371

CUBA, Bishop of. *See* HURTADO, The Rt Revd Jorge A Perera

CUBITT, Paul. b 64. Sheff Univ BA86. Cranmer Hall Dur 95. **d** 97 **p** 98. C Bromyard *Heref* 97-01; V Elloughton and Brough w Brantingham *York* from 01. *The Vicarage, Church Street, Elloughton, Brough HU15 1HN* Tel (01482) 667431

CUDBY, Paul Edward Frank. b 66. Hatf Poly BSc88. Ridley Hall Cam 99. **d** 02 **p** 03. C Bedford St Andr *St Alb* from 02. *5 St Minver Road, Bedford MK40 3DQ* Tel (01234) 217330

CUERNAVACA, Bishop of. *See* GARCIA-MONTIEL, The Rt Revd Martiniano

CUFF, Gregor John. b 61. Keele Univ BSc82. Ridley Hall Cam Cert Th & Min 95. **d** 95 **p** 96. C Stanley *Liv* 95-99; V Waterloo Ch Ch and St Jo from 99. *The Vicarage, 22 Crosby Road South, Liverpool L22 1RQ* Tel 0151-920 7791 Fax as telephone

CUFF, Mrs Pamela. b 47. MCSP68. S Dios Minl Tr Scheme 89. **d** 92 **p** 94. NSM Nether Stowey w Over Stowey *B & W* 92-93; NSM Quantoxhead from 93; Asst Chapl Taunton Hosps 93-94; Asst Chapl Taunton and Somerset NHS Trust from 94. *Millands, Kilve, Bridgwater TA5 1EA* Tel (01278) 741229

CULBERTSON, Eric Malcolm. b 54. Ch Ch Ox BA76 MA80 K Coll Lon PhD91. Edin Th Coll 78. **d** 80 **p** 81. C Edin St Thos *Edin* 80-83; C Ealing St Mary *Lon* 83-87; R Clarkston *Glas* 87-89; Area Sec Crosslinks 89-94; I Tullaniskin w Clonoe *Arm* from 94. *215 Brackaville Road, Newmills, Dungannon BT71 4EJ* Tel (028) 8774 7154 E-mail ericculbertson@compuserve.com

CULL, Ernest Geoffrey. b 20. Coll of Resurr Mirfield 57. **d** 57 **p** 58. C Heref H Trin *Heref* 57-61; PC Barrowhill *Derby* 61-70; V Derby St Paul 71-80; V Mackworth St Fran 80-90; rtd 90; Perm to Offic *Derby* from 90. *15 Lodge Lane, Spondon, Derby DE21 7GD* Tel (01332) 674562

CULL, John. b 31. Oak Hill Th Coll 56. **d** 59 **p** 60. C Radipole *Sarum* 59-66; Chapl Mariners' Ch Glouc 66-70; R Woodchester *Glouc* 70-90; RD Stonehouse 85-89; V Walton *St E* 90-94; rtd 94; Perm to Offic *Glouc* from 94. *Hillgrove Stables, Bear Hill, Woodchester, Stroud GL5 5DH* Tel (01453) 872145

CULLEN, Canon John Austin. b 43. Auckland Univ BA67 Otago Univ BD76 Keble Coll Ox DPhil86 FRSA89. St Jo Coll Auckland 66. **d** 69 **p** 70. New Zealand 69-78; Asst Chapl Keble Coll Ox 79-82; Perm to Offic *Lon* 82-84; Chapl and Lect Worc Coll Ox 84-86; C St Botolph Aldgate w H Trin Minories *Lon* 86-87; Hon C St Marylebone All SS 87-91; Dir Inst of Chr Studies 87-91; Dir of Min Development *Win* 91-97; Dir of Min Development 97-01; Hon Can Win Cathl 96-02; Sen Asst to Bp Lon from 02; P-in-c St Geo-in-the-East w St Paul from 03. *60 Cephas Avenue, London E1 4AR* Tel (020) 7265 9028
E-mail john.cullen@ukgateway.net

CULLIFORD, Michael. b 26. Qu Coll Birm 56. **d** 58 **p** 59. C Birkenhead St Jas *Ches* 58-60; C Bollington St Jo 60-62; V Heald Green St Cath 62-80; Perm to Offic *Man* from 89; rtd 91. *23 Field Vale Drive, Stockport SK5 6XZ* Tel 0161-432 1706

CULLING, Elizabeth Ann. *See* HOARE, Elizabeth Ann

CULLINGWORTH, Anthony Robert. b 42. BSc. Ox NSM Course. **d** 83 **p** 84. NSM Slough *Ox* 83-99; NSM Denham 99-02; NSM Morton St Luke *Bradf* from 02. *2 Thurleston Court, East Morton, Keighley BD20 5RG* Tel (01535) 601187
E-mail theculllies@aol.com

CULLIS, Andrew Stanley Weldon. b 48. Hertf Coll Ox BA69 LTh. St Jo Coll Nottm 70. **d** 73 **p** 74. C Reigate St Mary *S'wark* 73-78; C Yateley *Win* 78-82; V Dorking St Paul *Guildf* 82-00; RD Dorking 94-00; P-in-c Chilwell *S'well* from 00. *Christ Church Vicarage, 8 College Road, Beeston, Nottingham NG9 4AS* Tel 0115-925 2585

CULLWICK, Christopher John. b 53. Hull Univ BA75 Reading Univ Ox Univ BA80 MA85. Wycliffe Hall Ox 78. **d** 81 **p** 82. C Nottingham St Jude *S'well* 81-84; C York St Mich-le-Belfrey *York* 84-87; TV Huntington 87-03; Ind Chapl from 02. *The Vicarage, 64 Strensall Road, Huntington, York YO32 9SH* Tel (01904) 764608

CULLY, Miss Elizabeth Faith. b 46. SRN67 SCM69 RGN72. Trin Coll Bris BA88. **d** 88 **p** 94. Par Dn Filton *Bris* 88-92; Par Dn Fishponds St Jo 92-94; C 94-95; P-in-c Brinsley w Underwood *S'well* 95-98; V 98-02; P-in-c Farnsfield from 02; P-in-c Kirklington w Hockerton from 02; P-in-c Bilsthorpe from 02; P-in-c Eakring from 02; P-in-c Maplebeck from 02; P-in-c Winkburn from 02. *The Vicarage, Beck Lane, Farnsfield, Newark NG22 8ER* Tel (01623) 882247
E-mail faith.cully@btopenworld.com

CULROSS, James Fred. b 17. Lon Univ BD51. Bps' Coll Cheshunt 47. **d** 50 **p** 51. C Pateley Bridge *Ripon* 50-54; C Romaldkirk 54-55; V Middleton St Cross 55-62; R Glas St Jas *Glas* 62-65; C Bramley and Grafham *Guildf* 65-67; Chapl R Wanstead Sch 67-71; Chapl Sir Roger Manwood's Sch Sandwich 71-79; R Barrowden and Wakerley w S Luffenham *Pet* 79-82; rtd 82; Perm to Offic *B & W* 82-97; Perm to Offic *Pet* from 77. *1 St Christopher's Walk, Abington Park Crescent, Northampton NN3 3AD* Tel (01604) 234388

CULVERWELL, Martin Phillip. b 48. Sarum & Wells Th Coll 72. **d** 75 **p** 76. C Ashford St Hilda *Lon* 75-78; C Chelsea St Luke 78-80; Chapl RN 80-83; TV Yeovil *B & W* 83-87; P-in-c Sarratt *St Alb* 87-90; NSM Bradford w Oake, Hillfarrance and Heathfield *B & W* 90-92; R Rode Major 92-96. *The Old Ebenezer, High Street, Rode, Frome BA11 6NZ* Tel (01373) 830476 E-mail mpcul@aol.com

CUMBERLAND, The Very Revd Barry John. b 44. Birm Univ BA67 Worc Coll Ox DipEd68 Trin Coll Singapore MDiv88. **d** 88 **p** 89. NSM Westmr St Matt *Lon* 88-90; Perm to Offic 90-96; Philippines 90-96 and 98-01; Dean Manila 92-96; Chapl Stockholm w Gävle and Västerås *Eur* 96-98; P-in-c Las Palmas 01-03. *Address temp unknown*

CUMBERLAND, Leslie Hodgson. b 15. Leeds Univ BA37. Coll of Resurr Mirfield 37. **d** 39 **p** 40. C Birtley *Dur* 39-44; C Medomsley 44-49; Min Kimblesworth 49-55; V Bradf St Columba *Bradf* 55-64; Lic to Offic 64-85; rtd 80; Perm to Offic *Bradf* 85-90. *Amerdale, 2 Cam Lodge Lane, Kettlewell, Skipton BD23 5RW* Tel (01756) 761141

CUMBERLEGE, Francis Richard. b 41. AKC65. **d** 66 **p** 67. C Leigh Park St Fran CD *Portsm* 66-71; Papua New Guinea 71-81; Adn N Papua 74-81; C Portsea St Mary *Portsm* 81; R Hastings St Clem and All SS *Chich* 81-86; V Broadwater Down 86-91; V Tunbridge Wells St Mark *Roch* 91-99; RD Tunbridge Wells 96-99; P-in-c Brockenhurst *Win* from 99. *The Vicarage, Meerut Road, Brockenhurst SO42 7TD* Tel (01590) 623309

CUMBERLIDGE, Anthony Wynne. b 49. ACIB75. Sarum & Wells Th Coll 79. **d** 82 **p** 83. C Llanrhos *St As* 82-85; R Llanfair Talhaearn and Llansannan etc 85-87; CF from 87. *c/o MOD Chaplains (Army)* Tel (01980) 615804 Fax 615800

CUMBRAE, Provost of. *Vacant*

CUMING, Mark Alexander. b 53. AKC75. Westcott Ho Cam 76. **d** 77 **p** 78. C Newc H Cross *Newc* 77-80; Perm to Offic *Birm* 87-93; Perm to Offic *Newc* 93-95; R Blanchland w Hunstanworth and Edmundbyers etc 95-98; V Eastbourne St Phil *Chich* from 98. *The Vicarage, 1 St Philip's Avenue, Eastbourne BN22 8LU* Tel (01323) 732381
E-mail mark.c@clara.co.uk

CUMINGS, Llewellyn Frank Beadnell. b 29. Natal Univ BA50 St Cath Coll Cam CertEd53. Ridley Hall Cam 65. **d** 67 **p** 68. C Leamington Priors St Mary *Cov* 67-70; V Lobley Hill *Dur* 70-74; R Denver *Ely* 74-82; V Ryston w Roxham 74-82; R St Leonards St Leon *Chich* 82-88; V Billinghay *Linc* 88-93; rtd 93. *Y Bwthyn, Coedllan, Llanfyllin SY22 5BP* Tel (01691) 648013

CUMMING, Canon Nigel Patrick. b 42. St Jo Coll Nottm 73. **d** 75 **p** 76. C Castle Hall *Ches* 75-77; C Stalybridge H Trin and Ch Ch 77-78; C Tadley St Pet *Win* 78-82; R Overton w Laverstoke and Freefolk from 82; RD Whitchurch 89-98; Hon Can Win Cathl from 99. *The Rectory, 54 Lordsfield Gardens, Overton, Basingstoke RG25 3EW* Tel (01256) 770207 Fax as telephone
E-mail nigel.cumming@ukgateway.net

CUMMING, Ms Susan Margaret. b 47. Man Univ BSc68 Makerere Univ Kampala DipEd69. EMMTC 82. **dss** 82 **d** 87 **p** 95. Cinderhill *S'well* 82-85; Dioc Adv in Adult Educn 85-92; Par Dn Nottingham St Mary and St Cath 93-95; Lect 95-97; Asst Chapl Qu Medical Cen Nottm Univ Hosp NHS Trust 97-03; Sen Chapl from 03. *569 Farnborough Road, Clifton, Nottingham NG11 9DG* Tel 0115-974 9389

CUMMING-LATTEY, Mrs Susan Mary Ruth. b 47. Open Univ BA77 SRN69. STETS 00. **d** 03. NSM Ash Vale *Guildf* from 03. *38A Elms Road, Fleet GU51 3EQ* Tel (01252) 621295 Mobile 07761-126354 Fax (01252) 815882
E-mail reinboy@totalise.co.uk

CUMMINGS, Mrs Elizabeth. b 45. St Jo Coll Dur BA84. NEOC 85. **d** 94 NSM Dur St Giles *Dur* 87-89; Chapl HM Pris Dur 89-90; Chapl HM Rem Cen Low Newton 90-95; Chapl HM Pris Stocken 95-96; Chapl HM Pris Frankland from 96. *HM Prison Frankland, Finchale Avenue, Durham DH1 5YD* Tel 0191-384 5544 Fax 384 9203

CUMMINGS, Richard Vivian Payn. b 21. Lon Univ BSc41. Chich Th Coll 51. **d** 53 **p** 54. C Pet All SS *Pet* 53-55; C

Wellingborough All SS 55-60; V Wollaston and Strixton 60-69; V Wellingborough St Barn 69-73; RD Wellingborough 70-73; R Collingtree w Courteenhall 73-80; P-in-c Milton Malsor 73-80; R Collingtree w Courteenhall and Milton Malsor 80-90; rtd 90; Perm to Offic *Pet* from 90. *55 Watersmeet, Northampton NN1 5SQ* Tel (01604) 37027

CUMMINGS, The Very Revd William Alexander Vickery. b 38. Ch Ch Ox BA62 MA64. Wycliffe Hall Ox 61. **d** 64 **p** 65. C Leytonstone St Jo *Chelmsf* 64-67; C Writtle 67-71; R Stratton St Mary w Stratton St Michael *Nor* 71-73; R Wacton Magna w Parva 71-73; R Stratton St Mary w Stratton St Michael etc 73-91; RD Depwade 81-91; Hon Can Nor Cathl 90-91; V Battle *Chich* from 91; Dean Battle from 91. *The Deanery, Mount Street, Battle TN33 0JY* Tel (01424) 772693

CUMMINS, Ashley Wighton. b 56. St Andr Univ BD83. Coates Hall Edin DipMin84. **d** 84 **p** 85. C Broughty Ferry *Bre* 84-87; P-in-c Dundee St Ninian 87-92; P-in-c Invergowrie from 92; Chapl Angl Students Dundee Univ from 92. *27 Errol Road, Invergowrie, Dundee DD2 5AG* Tel (01382) 562525

CUMMINS, Daphne Mary. *See* GREEN, Daphne Mary

CUMMINS, James Ernest. b 32. Brasted Th Coll 56 Westcott Ho Cam 57. **d** 60 **p** 61. C Baswich *Lich* 60-64; V Hales w Heckingham *Nor* 64-70; V Raveningham 70-76; Perm to Offic *Heref* and *S & B* from 76; rtd 97. *Skyborry, Knighton LD7 1TW* Tel (01547) 528369 Fax 640677

CUMMINS, Julian Peter Francis. b 55. TD91. K Coll Cam BA77 MA80 Bradf Univ MBA91 Leeds Univ PhD99 MCIM84 FCIM99. N Ord Course 94. **d** 97 **p** 98. NSM Lower Wharfedale *Ripon* 97-01; C Bramley 01-02; Perm to Offic from 03. *50 Lane End, Pudsey LS28 9AD* Tel 0113-255 0909 Mobile 07957-357634 Fax 0113-255 0910 E-mail julian@avista.co.uk

CUMMINS, The Very Revd Nicholas Marshall. b 36. CITC 65. **d** 67 **p** 68. C Ballymena *Conn* 67-70; C Belfast St Nic 70-73; I Buttevant Union *C, C & R* 73-78; I Mallow Union 78-83; I Kilmoe Union 83-96; Can Cork Cathl 90-96; Treas Cork Cathl 95-96; Preb Tymothan St Patr Cathl Dublin 95-01; Dean Killaloe and Clonfert *L & K* 96-01; Dean Kilfenora and Provost Kilmacduagh 96-01; I Killaloe w Stradbally 96-01; rtd 01. *Ard Mhuire, Annabella, Mallow, Co Cork, Irish Republic* Tel (00353) (22) 20329

CUMPSTY, Prof John Sutherland. b 31. K Coll Dur BSc54 PhD56 Barrister-at-Law (Middle Temple) 56 Carnegie-Mellon Univ MS58 St Jo Coll Dur DipTh60. Cranmer Hall Dur 58. **d** 60 **p** 61. C Normanton *Wakef* 60-62; Tutor St Jo Coll Dur 62-66; Lect Glas Univ 66-69; S Africa from 70; Prof RS Cape Town Univ from 70; rtd 96. *University of Cape Town, Dept of Religious Studies, Rondebosch, 7700 South Africa* Tel (0027) (21) 650 3454 Fax 650 3761

CUNDIFF, Mrs Margaret Joan. b 32. Man Univ DMS60. St Mich Ho Ox 51. **dss** 77 **d** 87 **p** 94. Broadcasting Officer *York* 75-99; Angl Adv Yorkshire TV 79-90; Selby St Jas *York* 77-01; Par On 87-94; Assoc Min 94-01; rtd 01; Perm to Offic *York* from 01. *37 Oaklands, Camblesforth, Selby YO8 8HH* Tel (01757) 618148

✠**CUNDY, The Rt Revd Ian Patrick Martyn.** b 45. Trin Coll Cam BA67 MA71. Tyndale Hall Bris 67. **d** 69 **p** 70 **c** 92. C New Malden and Coombe *S'wark* 69-73; Lect Oak Hill Th Coll 73-77; TR Mortlake w E Sheen *S'wark* 78-83; Warden Cranmer Hall Dur 83-92; Area Bp Lewes *Chich* 92-96; Bp Pet from 96. *The Palace, Peterborough PE1 1YA* Tel (01733) 562492 Fax 890077 E-mail bishop@peterborough-diocese.org.uk

CUNLIFFE, Christopher John. b 55. Ch Ch Ox BA77 MA81 DPhil81 Trin Coll Cam BA86 MA86 ARHistS94. Westcott Ho Cam 80. **d** 83 **p** 84. C Chesterfield St Mary and All SS *Derby* 83-85; Chapl Linc Coll Ox 85-89; Chapl City Univ *Lon* 89-91; Chapl Guildhall Sch of Music and Drama 89-91; Voc Officer and Selection Sec ABM 91-97; Dir Professional Min *Lon* from 97. *London Diocesan House, 36 Causton Street, London SW1P 4AU* Tel (020) 7932 1100

CUNLIFFE, Harold. b 28. St Aid Birkenhead 57. **d** 60 **p** 61. C Hindley All SS *Liv* 60-64; V Everton St Chad w Ch Ch 64-69; R Golborne 70-93; rtd 93; Perm to Offic *Liv* from 93. *51 Greenfields Crescent, Ashton-in-Makerfield, Wigan WN4 8QY* Tel (01942) 202956 E-mail cunliffe@cableinet.co.uk

CUNLIFFE, The Ven Helen Margaret. b 54. St Hilda's Coll Ox BA77 MA78. Westcott Ho Cam 81. **dss** 83 **d** 87 **p** 94. Chesterfield St Mary and All SS *Derby* 83-85; Ox St Mary V w St Cross and St Pet *Ox* 86-89; Par On 87-89; Chapl Nuff Coll Ox 86-89; TD Clapham TM *S'wark* 89-94; TV 94-96; Can Res S'wark Cathl 96-03; Chapl Welcare 96-03; Adn St Alb from 03. *6 Sopwell Lane, St Albans AL1 1RR* Tel (01727) 847212 Fax 848311 E-mail archdstalbans@stalbans.anglican.org

CUNLIFFE, Peter Henry. b 54. SRN77 RSCN79 RCNT83 Univ of Wales MA93 Lon Univ DN84. Trin Coll Bris DipHE94. **d** 94 **p** 95. C Carshalton Beeches *S'wark* 94-95; C Reigate St Mary 95-99; Sen C 99-02; P-in-c Hemingford Grey *Ely* from 02. *The Vicarage, 6 Braggs Lane, Hemingford Grey, Huntingdon PE28 9BW* Tel (01480) 394378 E-mail peter.cunliffe@ukonline.co.uk

CUNNINGHAM, Arthur. b 48. Man Univ PhD95. Inst of Chr Tr Dallas DipMin79 Oak Hill Th Coll DipHE87 BA88 Lon Bible

Coll MA89 N Ord Course 92. **d** 93 **p** 94. C Walkden Moor *Man* 93; C Walkden Moor w Lt Hulton 93-96; Chapl Salford Coll 93-96; C Camelot Par *B & W* 96-98; Chapl Yeovil Coll 96-97; R Berrow w Pendock, Eldersfield, Hollybush etc *Worc* from 98; Dioc Warden of Readers and Moderator of Reader Tr from 98. *The Vicarage, Berrow, Malvern WR13 6JN* Tel (01684) 833237 E-mail artcunningham@compuserve.com

CUNNINGHAM, Brian James. b 65. York Univ BA88. Ripon Coll Cuddesdon BA91. **d** 92 **p** 93. C Merrow *Guildf* 92-96; C Kennington St Jo w St Jas *S'wark* 96-99; Chapl Pangbourne Coll from 99. *Sunbeam, Pangbourne College, Pangbourne, Reading RG8 8LA* Tel 0118-984 2101

CUNNINGHAM, John James. b 50. Belf Coll of Tech ONC70. TCD Div Sch BTh98. **d** 98 **p** 99. C Drumachose *D & R* 98-01; I Camus-juxta-Bann from 01. *19 Dunderg Road, Macosquin, Coleraine BT51 4PN* Tel (028) 7034 3918 E-mail revon50@aol.com

CUNNINGHAM, Philip John. b 52. St Jo Coll Dur BA74 PGCE75 MA85. N Ord Course 93. **d** 95 **p** 96. NSM York St Luke *York* 95-97; NSM York St Olave w St Giles 97-99; TV Haxby w Wigginton 99-02; V Gosforth St Nic *Newc* from 02. *The Vicarage, 17 Rectory Road, Gosforth, Newcastle upon Tyne NE3 1XR* Tel 0191-285 1326

CUNNINGHAM, Richard Martin. b 61. Goldsmiths' Coll Lon BEd84. St Alb and Ox Min Course 95. **d** 98 **p** 99. NSM Kingham w Churchill, Daylesford and Sarsden *Ox* 98-01; NSM Chipping Norton 01-02; NSM Ox St Andr from 01. *Churchill Mill, Sarsden Halt, Churchill, Chipping Norton OX7 6NT* Tel (01608) 659426 Fax 659134 E-mail richard.cunningham@standrewsoxford.org.uk

CUNNINGHAM, Robert Stewart. b 16. **d** 59 **p** 60. C Belfast St Mary *Conn* 59-62; C Belfast All SS 62-63; I Portglenone 63-74; I Belfast Whiterock 74-83; I Sallaghy *Clogh* 83-86; I Monaghan w Tydavnet and Kilmore 86-91; Can Clogh Cathl 88-89; Preb Clogh Cathl 89-91; rtd 91. *19 Edenaveys Crescent, Newry Road, Armagh BT60 1NT* Tel (028) 3752 7868

CUNNINGTON, Andrew Thomas. b 56. Southn Univ BA79. Sarum & Wells Th Coll 82. **d** 85 **p** 86. C Ifield *Chich* 85-89; TV Haywards Heath St Wilfrid 89-94; V Midhurst from 94; R Woolbeding from 94; RD Midhurst from 03. *The Vicarage, June Lane, Midhurst GU29 9EW* Tel (01730) 813339

CUNNINGTON, Miss Averil. b 41. St Mary's Coll Cheltenham CertEd61 Man Univ BA68 MEd73. N Ord Course 93. **d** 95 **p** 96. Hd Mistress Counthill Sch Oldham 84-96; NSM Milnrow *Man* 95-98; NSM Hey 98-02; Lic Preacher from 02. *Alston Londes, 629 Huddersfield Road, Lees, Oldham OL4 3PY* Tel 0161-624 9614

CUNNINGTON, Edgar Alan. b 37. Oak Hill Th Coll 68. **d** 70 **p** 71. C Highbury Ch Ch *Lon* 70-73; P-in-c W Holloway St Dav 73-76; V Martham *Nor* 76-83; V W Somerton 76-83; V Martham w Repps w Bastwick 83-89; RD Flegg (Gt Yarmouth) 84-87; TV Trunch 89-96; P-in-c Lyng, Sparham, Elsing and Bylaugh 96-97; P-in-c Bawdeswell w Foxley 96-97; R Lyng, Sparham, Elsing, Bylaugh, Bawdeswell etc 97-02; rtd 02; Perm to Offic *Nor* from 03. *35 Station Road, Reedham, Norwich NR13 3TB* Tel (01493) 701141

CUNNINGTON, Howard James. b 56. Southn Univ BA77 St Jo Coll Dur PGCE78. Trin Coll Bris ADMT92. **d** 92 **p** 93. C Ex St Leon w H Trin *Ex* 92-96; V Sandown Ch Ch *Portsm* from 96; V Lower Sandown St Jo from 96. *The Vicarage, 26 Nunwell Street, Sandown PO36 9DE* Tel (01983) 402548 E-mail howard@jcunnington2.freeserve.co.uk

CUPITT, Don. b 34. Trin Hall Cam BA55 MA58 Bris Univ Hon DLitt84. Westcott Ho Cam 57. **d** 59 **p** 60. C Salford St Phil w St Steph *Man* 59-62; Vice-Prin Westcott Ho Cam 62-66; Dean Em Coll Cam 66-91; Asst Lect Div Cam Univ 68-73; Lect 73-96; Lic to Offic *Ely* 63-94; rtd 96; Life Fell Em Coll Cam from 96. *Emmanuel College, Cambridge CB2 3AP* Tel (01223) 334200

CURD, Ms Christine Veronica. b 51. Bris Univ BA. Oak Hill Th Coll 84 WMMTC 88. **d** 89 **p** 94. NSM Widecombe-in-the-Moor, Leusdon, Princetown etc *Ex* 89-93; Asst Chapl HM Pris Channings Wood 92-02; NSM Bovey Tracey SS Pet, Paul and Thos w Hennock *Ex* 94-97; Lic to Offic from 98; Chapl HM Pris Ex from 02. *HM Prison Exeter, New North Road, Exeter EX4 4EX* Tel (01392) 278321 ext 325 Fax 422647

CURD, Clifford John Letsom. b 45. RNT Qu Eliz Coll Lon SRN. Oak Hill Th Coll 84. **d** 86 **p** 87. C Stone Ch Ch *Lich* 86-89; C Stone Ch Ch and Oulton 89; TV Widecombe-in-the-Moor, Leusdon, Princetown etc *Ex* 89-93; P-in-c Ilsington from 93. *The Vicarage, Ilsington, Newton Abbot TQ13 9RW* Tel (01364) 661245 E-mail cliff-chris@ccurd.freeserve.co.uk

CURL, Roger William. b 50. BA BD DPhil. Oak Hill Th Coll. **d** 82 **p** 83. C Cromer *Nor* 82-86; C Sevenoaks St Nic *Roch* 86-88; V Fulham St Mary N Kend *Lon* from 88. *St Mary's Vicarage, 2 Edith Road, London W14 9BA* Tel (020) 7602 1996 E-mail stmarys.westken@london.anglican.org

CURNEW, Preb Brian Leslie. b 48. Qu Coll Ox BA69 DPhil77 MA77 DipTh78. Ripon Coll Cuddesdon 77. **d** 79 **p** 80. C Sandhurst *Ox* 79-82; Tutor St Steph Ho Ox 82-87; V Fishponds St Mary *Bris* 87-94; TR Ludlow, Ludford, Ashford Carbonell etc

Heref from 94; Preb Heref Cathl from 02. *The Rectory, 4 College Street, Ludlow SY8 1AN* Tel (01584) 874988 *or* 872073 Fax 875138

CURNOCK, Canon Karen Susan. b 50. Linc Th Coll BTh74. **d** 95 **p** 97. NSM Graffoe Gp *Linc* 95-96; Dioc Sec *Sarum* 96-03; NSM Chalke Valley 96-03; V Buckland Newton, Cerne Abbas, Godmanstone etc from 03; Can and Preb Sarum Cathl from 02. *The Vicarage, 4 Back Lane, Cerne Abbas, Dorchester DT2 7LW* Tel (01300) 341251 E-mail karen@curnock.screaming.net

CURNOW, Terence Peter. b 37. Univ of Wales (Lamp) BA62 DipTh63. **d** 63 **p** 64. C Llanishen and Lisvane *Llan* 63-71; Youth Chapl 67-71; Asst Chapl K Coll Taunton 71-74; Chapl Taunton Sch 74-84; Ho Master 84-98; Perm to Offic *B & W* from 84; rtd 02. *19 Stonegallows, Taunton TA1 5JW* Tel (01823) 330003

CURRAH, Michael Ewart. b 31. Down Coll Cam BA54 MA58. Sarum Th Coll 54. **d** 56 **p** 57. C Saltash Sarum 56-60; V Southbroom 60-69; Perm to Offic 70-88; Asst Master Woodroffe Sch Lyme Regis 71-85; Hon C Taunton H Trin *B & W* 88-96; rtd 96; Perm to Offic *B & W* from 96. *123 South Road, Taunton TA1 3ED* Tel (01823) 284057

CURRAN, John Henry. b 77. Nottm Univ BA00. Wycliffe Hall Ox 00. **d** 02 **p** 03. C W Bridgford *S'well* from 02. *9 Church Drive, West Bridgford, Nottingham NG2 6AY* Tel 0115-878 0434 E-mail curate@stgiles.org.uk

CURRAN, The Ven Patrick Martin Stanley. b 56. K Coll (NS) BA80 Southn Univ BTh84. Chich Th Coll 80. **d** 84 **p** 85. C Heavitree w Ex St Paul *Ex* 84-87; Bp's Chapl to Students *Bradf* 87-93; Chapl Bonn w Cologne *Eur* 93-00; Chapl Vienna from 00; Can Malta Cathl from 00; Adn E Adnry from 02. *The British Embassy, Jauresgasse 12, A-1010 Vienna, Austria* Tel and fax (0043) (1) 714 8900 *or* 718 5902

CURRAN, Thomas Heinrich. b 49. Toronto Univ BA72 Dalhousie Univ Canada MA75 Hatf Coll Dur PhD91. Atlantic Sch of Th MTS80. **d** 78 **p** 79. Canada 77-81 and from 92; Chapl Hatf Coll Dur 88-92. *Tacoma RPO, Box 28010, Dartmouth NS, Canada, B2W 6E2*

CURRELL, Linda Anne. *See* SCOTT, Mrs Linda Anne

CURRIE, Alan Richard. b 58. St Andr Univ MA82 Aber Univ DipEd83. NEOC 97. **d** 00 **p** 01. NSM Haydon Bridge and Beltingham w Henshaw *Newc* from 00. *35 Dotland Close, Eastwood Grange, Hexham NE46 1UF* Tel (01434) 607614

CURRIE, John Stuart. b 47. SEITE 94. **d** 97 **p** 98. C S Chatham H Trin *Roch* 97-01; TV from 01. *The Team Vicarage, 18 Marion Close, Walderslade, Chatham ME5 9QA* Tel and fax (01634) 684888 Mobile 07803-283917 E-mail john.currie@blueyonder.co.uk

CURRIE, Stuart William. b 53. Hertf Coll Ox MA79 Fitzw Coll Cam BA85 CertEd. Westcott Ho Cam 82. **d** 85 **p** 86. C Whitley Ch Ch *Ox* 85-89; TV Banbury 89-94; V Barbourne *Worc* from 94. *St Stephen's Vicarage, 1 Beech Avenue, Worcester WR3 8PZ* Tel (01905) 452169

CURRIE, Walter. b 39. Lon Univ DipTh66. Tyndale Hall Bris 64. **d** 67 **p** 68. C Cromer *Nor* 67-70; C Macclesfield St Mich *Ches* 70-74; R Postwick *Nor* 74-87; Chapl Jas Paget Hosp Gorleston 87-94; Chapl Jas Paget Hosp NHS Trust Gorleston 94-01; rtd 01; Perm to Offic *Nor* from 01. *11 Langham Green, Blofield, Norwich NR13 4LD* Tel (01603) 713484 E-mail w.and.m.currie@barclays.net

CURRIN, John. b 56. Keele Univ CertEd78 Birm Poly Dip Maths Educn 87. St Jo Coll Nottm Dip Th Studies 92 MA93. **d** 93 **p** 94. C Eastwood *S'well* 93-97; P-in-c Matlock Bath and Cromford *Derby* 97-02; V from 02. *Holy Trinity Vicarage, 8 Derby Road, Matlock DE4 3PU* Tel (01629) 582947

CURRY, Anthony Bruce. b 31. ARCO49 St Edm Hall Ox BA53 MA56. Wells Th Coll 53. **d** 55 **p** 56. C Northfleet *Roch* 55-56; Chapl K Sch Cant 56-61; R Penshurst *Roch* 61-75; Dir Music Kelly Coll Tavistock 75-85; Hon C Calstock *Truro* 75-85; R Brasted *Roch* 85-93; rtd 93. *Monta Rosa, King Street, Gunnislake PL18 9JU* Tel (01822) 834133 Fax as telephone

CURRY, Canon Bruce. b 39. Dur Univ BA61. Wells Th Coll 61. **d** 63 **p** 64. C Shepton Mallet *B & W* 63-67; C Cheam *S'wark* 67-71; R W Walton *Ely* 71-78; V St Neots 78-94; RD St Neots 90-02; P-in-c Everton w Tetworth 94-98; P-in-c Abbotsley 94-99; P-in-c Waresley 94-99; P-in-c Gt w Lt Gransden 98-99; R Gt Gransden and Abbotsley and Lt Gransden etc from 99; Hon Can Ely Cathl from 98. *The Vicarage, 4 Webb's Meadow, Great Gransden, Sandy SG19 3BL* Tel (01767) 677227 E-mail bruce@jcurry.fsnet.co.uk

CURRY, Canon George Christopher. b 14. TCD BA42 MA55 Div Test. **d** 44 **p** 45. I Edenderry *D & R* 57-64; I Edenderry w Clanabogan 64-86; Can Derry Cathl 79-86; rtd 86. *8 Rutherglen Park, Bangor BT19 1DX* Tel (028) 9145 5970

CURRY, George Robert. b 51. JP90. Bede Coll Dur BA72 Newc Univ MA97. Cranmer Hall Dur DipTh74 Oak Hill Th Coll DPS76. **d** 76 **p** 77. C Denton Holme *Carl* 76-81; V Low Elswick *Newc* from 81; P-in-c High Elswick St Paul from 97. *St Stephen's Vicarage, Clumber Street, Newcastle upon Tyne NE4 7ST* Tel 0191-273 4680 E-mail g.r.curry@btinternet.com

CURRY, James Sebastian. b 63. Hatf Coll Dur BA84. Ripon Coll Cuddesdon BTh93. **d** 93 **p** 94. C Four Oaks *Birm* 93-96; C Erdington St Barn 96-99; TV Jarrow *Dur* from 99. *St Peter's House, York Avenue, Jarrow NE32 5LP* Tel 0191-489 0946

CURRY, Thomas Christopher. b 47. Sarum & Wells Th Coll 71. **d** 74 **p** 75. C Bradford-on-Avon *Sarum* 74-78; Asst Chapl Hurstpierpoint Coll 78-82; P-in-c The Donheads *Sarum* from 82; RD Chalke 87-92. *The Rectory, Donhead St Andrew, Shaftesbury SP7 9DZ* Tel (01747) 828370

CURSON, James Desmond. b 30. Keble Coll Ox BA54 MA60. St Steph Ho Ox 54. **d** 56 **p** 57. C Teddington St Alb *Lon* 56-58; C Ruislip St Martin 58-62; V Tottenham St Paul 62-67; V Hockley *Chelmsf* 67-75; Chapl HM Borstal Bullwood Hall 68-75; V Treverbyn *Truro* 75-79; P-in-c Marazion 79-85; P-in-c St Hilary w Perranuthnoe 81-83; R 83-93; rtd 93; Perm to Offic *Nor* 93-01; *Chich* from 00. *Marriott House, Tollhouse Close, Chichester PO19 1FG* Tel (01243) 536652

CURTIS, Bert. b 20. Lon Univ BCom42 BA46. Ripon Hall Ox. **d** 46 **p** 47. Perm to Offic *Carl* from 74. *Greystones, Embleton, Cockermouth CA13 9YP* Tel (01768) 776503

CURTIS, Colin. b 47. ALA69 Open Univ BA80. LNSM course 80 St Jo Coll Nottm CertCS91. **d** 93 **p** 94. Hon C Clarkston *Glas* from 93. *78 Auldhouse Road, Glasgow G43 1UR* Tel 0141-569 4206

CURTIS, Frederick John. b 36. SS Coll Cam MA64. Ridley Hall Cam 77. **d** 79 **p** 80. C Chilvers Coton w Astley *Cov* 79-82; V Claverdon w Preston Bagot 82-87; V Allesley Park and Whoberley 87-98; rtd 98; Perm to Offic *York* from 98. *29A Undercliffe, Pickering YO18 7BB*

CURTIS, Canon Geoffrey John. b 35. Dur Univ BA57. Ripon Hall Ox 59. **d** 61 **p** 62. C Gosport Ch Ch *Portsm* 61-65; C Bedhampton 65-68; Producer Schs Broadcasting Dept BBC Lon 68-75; Dioc Communications Adv *Guildf* 75-00; P-in-c Grayswood 75-91; Dir Grayswood Studio 84-00; Hon Can Guildf Cathl 87-00; rtd 00; Perm to Offic *Guildf* from 00. *1 Clairville, Woodside Road, Chiddingfold, Godalming GU8 4QY* Tel (01428) 685943

CURTIS, Gerald Arthur. b 46. Lon Univ BA69. Sarum & Wells Th Coll 85. **d** 87 **p** 88. C Allington and Maidstone St Pet *Cant* 87-90; TV Gt Grimsby St Mary and St Jas *Linc* 90-95; P-in-c Morton w Hacconby 95-96; R Ringstone in Aveland Gp 96-02; rtd 03. *Le Val, 61560 St Germain de Martigny, France* E-mail gacurt@btinternet.com

CURTIS, Mrs Jacqueline Elaine. b 60. Sarum & Wells Th Coll 87. **d** 90 **p** 94. Par Dn Bridport *Sarum* 90-94; C 94-95; TV Melbury 95-00; TV Maltby *Sheff* 00-02; TR from 02. *The Rectory, 69 Blyth Road, Maltby, Rotherham S66 7LF* Tel (01709) 812684 E-mail j.curtis@dogcollar.org.uk

CURTIS, Mrs Jane Darwent. b 64. Leic Univ BA86. Linc Th Coll BTh93. **d** 93 **p** 94. Par Dn Oadby *Leic* 93-94; C 94-96; Chapl De Montfort Univ from 96; C Leic H Spirit 96-97; TV from 97. *4 Purbeck Close, Wigston LE18 2JY* Tel 0116-220 7068 E-mail jcurtis@leicester.anglican.org

CURTIS, John Durston. b 43. Lich Th Coll 65. **d** 68 **p** 69. C Coseley Ch Ch *Lich* 68-71; C Sedgley All SS 71-74; CF 74-79; P-in-c Newton Valence *Win* 79-82; P-in-c Selborne 79-82; R Newton Valence, Selborne and E Tisted w Colemore 82-87; R Marchwood from 87. *St John's Vicarage, Vicarage Road, Marchwood, Southampton SO40 4SX* Tel (023) 8086 1496 Fax as telephone E-mail john.curtis@care4free.net

CURTIS, Layton Richard. b 61. Leic Univ BSc84 PGCE85. Linc Th Coll BTh93. **d** 93 **p** 94. C Knighton St Mary Magd *Leic* 93-96; C Leic St Phil 96-01; P-in-c Wigston Magna from 01. *4 Purbeck Close, Wigston LE18 2JY* Tel 0116-220 7068 E-mail rcurtis@leicester.anglican.org

CURTIS, Peter Bernard. b 35. St Pet Hall Ox BA60 MA64. Westcott Ho Cam 60. **d** 62 **p** 63. C Warsop *S'well* 62-65; Chapl Dur Univ *Dur* 65-69; V Worle *B & W* 69-78; R Crewkerne w Wayford 78-00; rtd 00; Perm to Offic *B & W* from 01. *The Old Farmhouse, 28 Millstream Gardens, Wellington TA21 0AA* Tel (01823) 662638

CURTIS, Ronald Victor. b 47. St Alb and Ox Min Course 98. **d** 01 **p** 02. NSM Shipton-under-Wychwood w Milton, Fifield etc *Ox* from 01. *14 Chestnut Close, Witney OX28 1PD* Tel (01993) 209249

CURTIS, Thomas John. b 32. Pemb Coll Ox BA55 MA59 Lon Univ BD58. Clifton Th Coll 55. **d** 58 **p** 59. C Wandsworth All SS *S'wark* 58-61; Chile 61-71; R Saxmundham *St E* 71-77; V Cheltenham St Mark *Glouc* 77-84; TR 84-86; V Chipping Norton *Ox* 86-95; rtd 95; Hon Dioc Rep SAMS *St E* 95-01; Perm to Offic *Glouc* and *Worc* from 01. *60 Courtney Close, Tewkesbury GL20 5FB* Tel (01684) 295298 E-mail curtistomjon@aol.com

CURTIS, The Very Revd Wilfred Frank. b 23. AKC51. d 52 p 53. C High Wycombe All SS *Ox* 52-55; Area Sec CMS *Ex* and *Truro* 55-65; Lic to Offic *Ex* 55-74; SW Sec CMS 62-65; Home Sec CMS 65-74; Provost Sheff 74-88; Hon Can N Maseno from 82; rtd 88; Perm to Offic *Ex* from 88; RD Okehampton 89-92. *17 Norwood Avenue, Exeter EX2 4RT* Tel (01392) 427740

CURWEN, Canon David. b 38. St Cath Coll Cam BA62. Cuddesdon Coll 62. d 64 p 65. C Orford St Andr *Liv* 64-67; Ind Chapl *Cant* 67-77 and 83-84; C S'wark Ch Ch *S'wark* 78-83; Ind Chapl *S'wark* 78-83 and 85-88; Dioc Soc Resp Adv St E 88-93; Dioc Adv for CME 93-97; R Capel St Mary w Lt and Gt Wenham 97-03; Hon Can St E Cathl 97-03; rtd 03. *41 Cuckfield Avenue, Ipswich IP3 8SA* Tel (01473) 272706

CURZEN, Prof Peter. b 31. MRCOG62 FRCOG70 Lon Univ BSc52 MB, BS55 MD66. Sarum & Wells Th Coll 93. d 94 p 95. NSM Bemerton *Sarum* 94-98; NSM Wylye and Till Valley 98-00; rtd 01. *2 Bishop's Drive, Harnham Wood, Salisbury SP2 8NZ* Tel (01722) 412713

CUTCLIFFE, Neil Robert. b 50. NUU BA72 TCD BA72. d 75 p 76. C Belfast St Mary *Conn* 75-78; C Lurgan Ch the Redeemer *D & D* 78-80; I Garrison w Slavin and Belleek *Clogh* 80-86; I Mossley *Conn* from 86. *558 Doagh Road, Mossley, Newtownabbey BT36 6TA* Tel (028) 9083 2726

CUTHBERT, John. b 52. Edin Univ BSc76 PhD80. Coates Hall Edin BD92. d 92 p 93. Chapl St Mary's Cathl *Edin* 92-98; C Edin St Mary 92-98; R Forres *Mor* from 98. *St John's Rectory, Victoria Road, Forres IV36 3BN* Tel (01309) 672856
E-mail john@cuth100.freeserve.co.uk

CUTHBERT, John Hamilton. b 34. Univ of Wales (Lamp) BA59. Coll of Resurr Mirfield 59. d 61 p 62. C Cov St Pet *Cov* 61-64; Australia 64-69; C Willesden St Andr *Lon* 69-72; C Sheff Parson Cross St Cecilia *Sheff* 72-74; V Lavender Hill Ascension *S'wark* 74-97; rtd 97; Perm to Offic *St Alb* from 97. *29 The Cloisters, Welwyn Garden City AL8 6DU* Tel (01707) 376748

CUTHBERT, Victor. b 46. Dioc OLM tr scheme 98. d 01 p 02. OLM Surbiton St Matt *S'wark* from 01. *4 St Thomas Close, Surbiton KT6 7TU* Tel (020) 8399 8722

CUTHBERTSON, Mrs Amanda. b 54. ALCM85 LLCM87 K Coll Lon BD92 AKC92 Open Univ PGCE98 Loughb Univ MA00. EAMTC 98. d 00 p 01. C Northampton St Benedict *Pet* from 00. *75 High Street, Potterspury, Towcester NN12 7PG* Tel (01908) 542684 E-mail revacuthbertson@talk21.com

CUTHBERTSON, Christopher Martin. b 48. K Coll Lon BD74 AKC74 CertEd75 MTh80. St Aug Coll Cant 75. d 76 p 77. C Whitstable All SS w St Pet *Cant* 76-79; Chapl Princess Marg R Free Sch Windsor 79-84; Perm to Offic *Win* from 84; Chapl Bp Wordsworth Sch Salisbury 84-01. *14 Stephen Martin Gardens, Parsonage Park, Fordingbridge SP6 1RF* Tel (01425) 655865

CUTHBERTSON, John Dickon. b 19. Lon Univ BSc49. Oak Hill Th Coll 51. d 53 p 54. C Penn Fields *Lich* 53-56; R High Halstow w All Hallows and Hoo St Mary *Roch* 56-62; V W Hampstead St Cuth *Lon* 62-69; V Upper Holloway St Jo 69-77; R Stanstead w Shimplingthorne and Alpheton *St E* 77-84; P-in-c Lawshall 80-84; rtd 84; Perm to Offic *Ox* from 84. *86 Evans Road, Eynsham, Witney OX29 4QS* Tel (01865) 880904

CUTHBERTSON, Raymond. b 52. AKC75. Coll of Resurr Mirfield 74. d 77 p 78. C Darlington St Mark w St Paul *Dur* 77-81; C Usworth 81-83; C Darlington St Cuth 83-86; V Shildon w Eldon 86-00; V Shildon from 00; RD Auckland 94-96. *St John's Vicarage, Central Parade, Shildon DL4 1DW* Tel (01388) 772122

CUTLER, Robert Francis. b 37. Lon Univ BSc57. Clifton Th Coll 62. d 64 p 65. C Peckham St Mary Magd *S'wark* 64-68; C Redhill H Trin 68-70; Travel Sec Inter-Coll Chr Fellowship of IVF 70-74; Hon C Selly Hill St Steph *Birm* 70-74; Interserve Internat Bangladesh 74-93; Internat Fellowship Evang Students 74-85; Bible Students Fellowship of Bangladesh 85-93; V Rochdale Deeplish St Luke *Man* 94-99; TV S Rochdale 00-02; rtd 02. *17 Woodlands, Park Street, St Albans AL2 2AD* Tel (01727) 872248 E-mail rfcutler@zetnet.co.uk

CUTLER, Roger Charles. b 49. Sussex Univ MInstPkg76. Coll of Resurr Mirfield 86. d 88 p 89. C Walney Is *Carl* 88-91; Chapl RN 91-98; Perm to Offic *Glas* 91-98; Hon C Challoch w Newton Stewart 95-98; V Gosforth St Nic *Newc* 98-01; P-in-c Wanlen w Newbrough from 01; P-in-c St John Lee from 01. *St John Lee Rectory, Acomb, Hexham NE46 4PE* Tel (01434) 601024
E-mail cogito@ergo-sum.greeserve.co.uk

CUTMORE, Simon Giles. b 72. Trin Coll Bris BA95 Dur Univ MA00. Cranmer Hall Dur DMS99. d 99 p 00. C Biggleswade *St Alb* from 99. *St Andrew's House, 46 Wilsheres Road, Biggleswade SG18 0DN* Tel (01767) 314240
E-mail simonandalexc@aol.com

CUTT, Canon Samuel Robert. b 25. Selw Coll Cam BA50 MA54. Cuddesdon Coll 51. d 53 p 54. C W Hartlepool St Aid *Dur* 53-56; Tutor St Boniface Coll Warminster 56-59; Sub Warden 59-65; Tutor Chich Th Coll 65-71; PV Chich Cathl *Chich* 66-71; Min Can St Paul's Cathl *Lon* 71-79; Lect K Coll Lon 73-79; P in O 75-79; Can Res Wells Cathl *B & W* 79-93; Chan 79-85; Treas 85-93; Dir of Ords 79-86; Warden CSD 87-93; rtd 93; Perm to

Offic *Pet* from 94. *clo J C Cutt Esq, 37 Sallows Road, Peterborough PE1 4EX* Tel (01733) 562796

CUTTELL, Jeffrey Charles. b 59. Birm Univ BSc80 PhD83 Sheff Univ MA91. Trin Coll Bris DipHE86. d 87 p 88. C Normanton *Wakef* 87-91; V 91-95; Producer Relig Progr BBC Radio Stoke 95-97; Presenter Relig Progr BBC 97-99; CF (TA) from 97; R Astbury and Smallwood *Ches* from 99; Assoc Lect Th Univ of Wales (Cardiff) from 01; Tutor St Mich Coll Llan from 01. *The Rectory, Astbury, Congleton CW12 4RQ* Tel (01260) 272625 Mobile 07941-373578 E-mail rector@astburychurch.org.uk

CUTTER, John Douglas. b 31. Lon Univ BD61. Chich Th Coll 56. d 59 p 60. C Blyth St Mary *Newc* 59-62; C Rugeley *Lich* 62-65; V Rocester 65-73; V Shrewsbury St Giles 73-83; R Yoxall 83-91; Dean's V Lich Cathl 83-91; rtd 91; Perm to Offic *Win* from 91; Hon Chapl Win Cathl from 98. *Little Wykeham, 111 Teg Down Meads, Winchester SO22 5NN* Tel (01962) 852203

CUTTING, Alastair Murray. b 60. Westhill Coll Birm BEd83. St Jo Coll Nottm LTh86 DPS87. d 87 p 88. C Woodlands *Sheff* 87-88; C Wadsley 89-91; C Uxbridge *Lon* 91-96; Chapl to the Nave and Uxbridge Town Cen 91-96; V Copthorne *Chich* from 96. *St John's Vicarage, Copthorne, Crawley RH10 3RD* Tel (01342) 712063 E-mail acutting@mac.com

CUTTS, Canon David. b 52. Van Mildert Coll Dur BSc73 Nottm Univ BA79. St Jo Coll Nottm BA77. d 80 p 81. C Ipswich St Matt *St E* 80-82; Bp's Dom Chapl 82-85; R Coddenham w Gosbeck and Hemingstone w Henley 85-94; RD Bosmere 92-94; V Ipswich St Marg from 94; RD Ipswich 96-01; Hon Can St E Cathl from 00. *St Margaret's Vicarage, 32 Constable Road, Ipswich IP4 2UW* Tel (01473) 253906 Mobile 07711-370702 Fax 413348 E-mail cutts.family@tesco.net

CUTTS, Elizabeth Joan Gabrielle. See STRICKLAND, Mrs Elizabeth Joan Gabrielle

CUTTS, Nigel Leonard. b 57. Sheff Univ BA86 BTh. Linc Th Coll 83. d 87 p 88. C Old Brampton and Loundsley Green *Derby* 87-89; C Chesterfield St Mary and All SS 89-91; V Morecambe St Barn *Blackb* 91-99; V Colwyn *St As* 99-03; rtd 03. *2 Cwm Road, Dyserth, Rhyl LL18 6BB* Tel (01745) 571496

CYPRUS AND THE GULF, Bishop of. See HANDFORD, The Most Revd George Clive

CYSTER, Canon Raymond Frederick. b 13. CCC Ox BA35 MA40. Wycliffe Hall Ox 40. d 42 p 43. C Ipswich St Jo *St E* 42-45; Chapl Norwich Tr Coll 45-64; R Fenny Compton and Wormleighton *Cov* 64-76; Hon Can Cov Cathl 74-80; P-in-c Hampton Lucy w Charlecote 76-79; R Hampton Lucy w Charlecote and Loxley 79-80; rtd 80; Perm to Offic *Cov* from 80. *47 Cherry Orchard, Stratford-upon-Avon CV37 9AP* Tel (01789) 295012

CZERNIAWSKA EDGCUMBE, Mrs Irena Christine. b 59. Trin Coll Ox BA82. Oak Hill Th Coll 93. d 95 p 96. NSM De Beauvoir Town St Pet *Lon* 95-99; Chapl Raines Foundn Sch Tower Hamlets from 99; C Bow Common from 00. *24 Calabria Road, London N5 1JA* Tel (020) 7359 7526

D

DABBS, Norman. d 03. OLM Hollingbourne and Hucking w Leeds and Broomfield *Cant* from 03. *Address unknown*

DABBS, Roger Stevens. b 09. Bp Wilson Coll 29. d 32 p 33. C Birm St Thos *Birm* 32-35; Toc H Padre (E Midl) 35-38; V Cosby *Leic* 38-47; V Ashby-de-la-Zouch H Trin 47-53; RD Akeley W 48-53; R Jersey Grouville *Win* 53-74; rtd 74; Perm to Offic *Ex* from 74. *Flat 21, Bedford Park, Pearn Road, Plymouth PL3 5JF* Tel (01752) 774677

DABORN, Robert Francis. b 53. Keble Coll Ox BA74 MA78 Fitzw Coll Cam BA77. Ridley Hall Cam 75. d 78 p 79. C Mortlake w E Sheen *S'wark* 78-81; Chapl Collingwood and Grey Coll *Dur* 82-86; V Lapley w Wheaton Aston *Lich* 86-91; P-in-c Blymhill w Weston-under-Lizard 89-91; P-in-c Tibberton w Bolas Magna and Waters Upton 91-99; Shropshire Local Min Adv 91-99; P-in-c Childs Ercall 92-95; P-in-c Stoke upon Tern 92-95; Dir Local Min Development from 99. *3 Dungarven Drive, Newport TF10 7UR* Tel (01952) 810673 *or* (01543) 306225 Fax (01543) 306229 E-mail harbinger@cix.co.uk *or* deb.daborn@lichfield.anglican.org

DACK, Miss Margaret Patricia. b 39. Offley Teacher Tr Coll TCert61 DipRS82. Oak Hill NSM Course 91. d 93 p 94. NSM Letchworth St Paul w Willian *St Alb* from 93. *91 Penn Way, Letchworth Garden City SG6 2SH* Tel (01462) 634956

DACK, Paul Marven. K Coll Lon AKC51 BD51. St Boniface Warminster. d 52 p 53. C Leckhampton St Pet *Glouc* 52-55; R

DADD, Alan Edward. b 50. St Jo Coll Nottm 77. **d** 78 **p** 79. C Bishopsworth *Bris* 78-81; V Springfield *Birm* 81-85; Chapl Poly Cen *Lon* 85-86; V Hanger Lane St Ann 86-93; rtd 93. *124 Chelsfield Lane, Orpington BR5 4PZ* Tel (01689) 570558

DADD, Canon Peter Wallace. b 38. Sheff Univ BA59. Qu Coll Birm 59. **d** 61 **p** 62. C Grays Thurrock *Chelmsf* 61-65; C Grantham St Wulfram *Linc* 65-70; C Grantham w Manthorpe 70-72; TV 72-73; V Haxey 73-90; RD Is of Axholme 82-90; V Gainsborough All SS 90-98; Can and Preb Linc Cathl from 91; P-in-c Flixborough w Burton upon Stather 98-00; V from 00. *The Vicarage, 12 Darby Road, Burton-upon-Stather, Scunthorpe DN15 9DZ* Tel (01724) 720276

DADSON, Lawrence Michael (Mike). b 29. G&C Coll Cam MA56 Lon Univ BSc(Econ)64. St Deiniol's Hawarden 80. **d** 92 **p** 92. NSM Bramhall *Ches* from 92; Perm to Offic from 97. *14 Yew Tree Park Road, Cheadle Hulme, Cheadle SK8 7EP* Tel 0161-485 2482

DADSWELL, David Ian. b 58. New Coll Ox BA80 MA83 Brunel Univ MPhil97. Westcott Ho Cam 80. **d** 83 **p** 84. C W Derby St Mary *Liv* 83-87; Chapl Brunel Univ *Lon* 87-96; Perm to Offic from 96; Perm to Offic St Alb *Ox* from 98. *243 St Leonards Road, Windsor SL4 3DR* Tel (01753) 864827 Fax (01895) 2707701 E-mail david.dadswell@dial.pipex.com

DADSWELL, Richard Edward. b 46. CITC BTh98. **d** 98 **p** 99. C Cork St Fin Barre's Union *C, C & R* 98-01; Min Can Cork Cathl 00-01; I Ballisodare w Collooney and Emlaghfad *T, K & A* from 01. *The Rectory, Ballisodare, Co Sligo, Irish Republic* Tel (00353) (71) 67260

DAFFERN, Canon Adrian Mark. b 68. St Jo Coll Dur BA89 FRCO98 FRSA99. St Steph Ho Ox 90. **d** 92 **p** 93. C Lich St Chad *Lich* 92-95; TV Stafford 95-00; V Walsall Wood 00-03; Treas V Lich Cathl 97-03; Can Res and Prec Cov Cathl *Cov* from 03. *22 Radcliffe Road, Coventry CV5 6AA* Tel (024) 7622 7597 E-mail precentor@coventrycathedral.org.uk

DAFFURN, Lionel William. b 19. DFC43. AKC49. **d** 50 **p** 51. C Rugby St Andr *Cov* 50-53; V Cov St Thos 53-57; R Brampton St Thos *Derby* 57-74; P-in-c Hindon w Chicklade w Pertwood *Sarum* 74-76; R E Knoyle, Hindon w Chicklade and Pertwood 76-84; rtd 84; Perm to Offic *Cov* from 84. *Bankside, 9 Quineys Road, Stratford-upon-Avon CV37 9BW* Tel (01789) 292703

DAGGER, John Henry Kynaston. b 07. Selw Coll Cam BA31 MA35. Cuddesdon Coll. **d** 32 **p** 34. C Wolverhampton St Pet *Lich* 32-37; C W Bromwich All SS 37-40; Chapl RAFVR 40-46; Chapl RAF 46-61; R Sutton w Bignor *Chich* 61-77; R Barlavington 62-77; rtd 77; Perm to Offic *Win* from 78. *Greenways, Copthorne Lane, Fawley, Southampton SO45 1DP* Tel (023) 8089 1582

DAGGER, Kenneth. b 46. Bernard Gilpin Soc Dur 72 Cranmer Hall Dur 73. **d** 76 **p** 77. C Blackb St Jas *Blackb* 76-79; C Colne St Bart 79-81; R Hesketh w Becconsall 81-85; Deputation Appeals Org Children's Soc 85-89; C Lowton St Mary *Liv* 89-91; C Rainhill 91-94; TV Maghull 94-00; TV Kirkby 00-02; C W Derby Gd Shep from 02. *345 Utting Avenue East, Liverpool L11 1DF* Tel 0151-256 0510 E-mail rev.ken@btopenworld.com

DAGGETT, Michael Wayne. b 47. Portland State Univ BSc72. Ridley Hall Cam 84. **d** 86 **p** 87. C Tyldesley w Shakerley *Man* 86-90; V Swinton H Rood 90-02; Chapl Eccles Sixth Form Coll 90-02; rtd 02. *138 Elliott Street, Tyldesley, Manchester M29 8FJ* Tel (01942) 883437

DAGLEISH, John. b 38. Goldsmiths' Coll Lon MA01 ACIB74 BAC Acc85 Lon Univ DipRS78 UKRC Reg Ind Cllr 96. S'wark Ord Course 75. **d** 78 **p** 79. NSM Riddlesdown *S'wark* 78-99; NSM All Hallows by the Tower etc *Lon* 79-89; Chapl Asst Guy's Hosp Lon 87-89. *42 Brancaster Lane, Purley CR8 1HF* Tel (020) 8660 6060 Fax as telephone

DAGLISH, John Davis. b 44. RMCS BSc70. Cranmer Hall Dur 74. **d** 77 **p** 78. C Ormesby *York* 77-79; C Kirk Ella 79-82; V Hull St Cuth 82-97; NSM Beverley St Mary 00-01; P-in-c Thorpe Edge *Bradf* from 01. *The Vicarage, Northwood Crescent, Bradford BD10 9HX* Tel (01274) 613246 E-mail john@jdaglish.fsnet.co.uk

DAGNALL, Bernard. b 44. K Coll Lon BSc65 AKC65 Ox Univ BA75 MA78 CChem MRSC MSOSc88. St Steph Ho Ox 72. **d** 75 **p** 76. C Stanningley St Thos *Ripon* 75-76; C Lightbowne *Man* 76-78; C-in-c Grahame Park St Aug CD *Lon* 78-84; V Earley St Nic *Ox* 84-91; Ind Chapl 85-91; TR N Huddersfield *Wakef* 91-93; TV Newbury *Ox* from 93; Chapl W Berks Priority Care Services NHS Trust 93-01; Chapl Newbury and Community Primary Care Trust from 01. *The Vicarage, 1 Chesterfield Road, Newbury RG14 7QB* Tel (01635) 230216 Fax 230215 E-mail dagnall@boltblue.com

DAILEY, Arthur John Hugh. b 25. Lon Univ BScEng45. Clifton Th Coll 63. **d** 65 **p** 66. C Wandsworth All SS *S'wark* 65-70; V Frogmore St Alb 70-81; RD Aldenham 75-79; St Alb St Paul 82-90; rtd 90; Perm to Offic *St Alb* 90-00. *24 Clifton Street, St Albans AL1 3RY* Tel (01727) 850639

DAILEY, Douglas Grant. b 56. Nottm Univ BTh88. Linc Th Coll 85. **d** 88 **p** 89. C Leominster *Heref* 88-91; USA from 91. *PO Box 1103, Statesville, NC 28677, USA* E-mail trinity@vnet.net

DAIMOND, John Ellerbeck. b 39. St Cuth Soc Dur BA61. Ripon Hall Ox 61. **d** 63 **p** 64. C Caverswall *Lich* 63-66; Chapl RAF 66-85; Asst Chapl-in-Chief RAF 85-91; QHC 89-91; V Shawbury *Lich* 91-95; R Moreton Corbet 91-95; V Stanton on Hine Heath 91-95; rtd 99; P-in-c Pattingham w Patshull *Lich* from 02. *The Vicarage, 20 Dartmouth Avenue, Pattingham, Wolverhampton WV6 7DP* Tel (01902) 700257 Fax as telephone

DAINTREE, Canon Geoffrey Thomas. b 54. Bris Univ BSc77. Trin Coll Bris 78. **d** 81 **p** 82. C Old Hill H Trin *Worc* 81-85; C Tunbridge Wells St Jo *Roch* 85-89; V Framfield *Chich* 89-00; RD Uckfield 96-00; Hon Can Cyanguqu (Rwanda) from 97; V Eastbourne St Jo *Chich* from 00. *St John's Vicarage, 9 Buxton Road, Eastbourne BN20 7LL* Tel (01323) 721105 Fax as telephone E-mail gdaintree@aol.com

DAINTY, James Ernest. b 46. Open Univ BA86 Liv Univ MA01 Lon Univ DipTh68 Lon Bible Coll ALBC68. Cranmer Hall Dur 71. **d** 73 **p** 74. C Normanton *Wakef* 73-76; C Gillingham St Mark *Roch* 76-78; V Barnsley St Geo *Wakef* 78-88; Chapl Barnsley Distr Gen Hosp 78-88; Chapl Seacroft Hosp Leeds 88-94; Chapl Killingbeck and Meanwood Park Hosps Leeds 88-94; P-in-c Turnham Green Ch Ch *Lon* 94-97; V from 97. *The Vicarage, 2 Wellesley Road, London W4 4BL* Tel (020) 8994 1617 Fax 0870-168 0680 E-mail jimdainty@dunelm.org.uk

DAKIN (née HOLLETT), Mrs Catherine Elaine. b 53. Qu Eliz Coll Lon BSc74. St Jo Coll Nottm DipTh90. **d** 90. Par Dn Horley *S'wark* 90-93; NSM Heydon, Gt and Lt Chishill, Chrishall etc *Chelmsf* 93-97; NSM Gt and Lt Maplestead w Gestingthorpe 97-99; NSM Knights and Hospitallers Par 99-01; NSM Fulford w Hilderstone *Lich* from 01. *20 Tudor Hollow, Fulford, Stoke-on-Trent ST11 9NP* Tel (01782) 397073

DAKIN, Peter David. b 57. Wye Coll Lon BSc79. St Jo Coll Nottm 91. **d** 91 **p** 92. NSM Southgate *Chich* 91-93; C Heydon, Gt and Lt Chishill, Chrishall etc *Chelmsf* 93-97; P-in-c Gt and Lt Maplestead w Gestingthorpe 97-99; P-in-c Pebmarsh 99; V Knights and Hospitallers Par 99-01; P-in-c Fulford w Hilderstone *Lich* from 01; Rural Officer for Staffs from 01. *20 Tudor Hollow, Fulford, Stoke-on-Trent ST11 9NP* Tel (01782) 397073 Fax (01780) 761764 E-mail pdakin@waitrose.com

DAKIN, Reginald James Blanchard. b 25. S'wark Ord Course 66. **d** 70 **p** 71. C Preston Ascension *Lon* 70-74; C Greenhill St Jo 74-76; P-in-c Littleton 76-80; R 80-95; CF (ACF) 78-95; Warden for Readers (Kensington Episc Area) 88-95; rtd 95; Perm to Offic *Nor* 95-00; Chapl Malta 97-99. *22 Heywood Avenue, Diss IP22 3DN* Tel (01379) 641167

DAKIN, Canon Stanley Frederick. b 30. CA52. Roch Th Coll 63. **d** 65 **p** 66. C Meole Brace *Lich* 65-68; V 68-72; R Sutton 68-72; Hosp Chapl Nairobi Kenya 72-75; P-in-c Nettlebed *Ox* 75-81; P-in-c Bix w Pishill 77-81; P-in-c Highmore 78-81; R Nettlebed w Bix and Highmore 81; V Ealing Dean St Jo *Lon* 81-84; V W Ealing St Jo w St Jas 84-92; Hon Can Mombasa from 89; Gen Sec CA Africa from 92; rtd 99; Perm to Offic *Lich* 99-02; *Ox* from 02. *71 Rectory Crescent, Middle Barton, Chipping Norton OX7 7BP* Tel (01869) 349983

DAKIN, Canon Timothy John. b 58. SS Mark & Jo Coll Plymouth BA86 K Coll Lon MTh87. **d** 93 **p** 94. Kenya 93-00; Prin Carlile Coll 93-00; C Nairobi Cathl 94-00; Gen Sec CMS from 00; Hon C Ruscombe and Twyford *Ox* from 00; Can Th Cov Cathl *Cov* from 01. *3 Highgrove Place, Ruscombe, Reading RG10 9LF* Tel 0118-934 3909 Fax as telephone E-mail timsal@tinyworld.co.uk

DALAIS, Duncan John. b 56. St Paul's Coll Grahamstown. **d** 83 **p** 84. C Pinetown St Jo B S Africa 83-87; C Chingford SS Pet and Paul *Chelmsf* 87-92; V Aldersbrook 92-02; P-in-c Leytonstone St Andr from 02; Asst Chapl Forest Healthcare NHS Trust Lon from 02. *St Andrew's Vicarage, 7 Forest Glade, London E11 1LU* Tel (020) 8989 0942 or 8520 6328 Mobile 07714-760068 E-mail duncan.dalais@virgin.net

DALBY, The Ven John Mark Meredith. b 38. Ex Coll Ox BA61 MA65 Nottm Univ PhD77. Ripon Hall Ox 61. **d** 63 **p** 64. C Hambleden *Ox* 63-68; C Medmenham 66-68; V Birm St Pet *Birm* 68-75; RD Birm City 73-75; Hon C Tottenham All Hallows *Lon* 75-80; Selection Sec and Sec Ctee for Th Educn ACCM 75-80; V Worsley *Man* 80-84; TR 84-91; AD Eccles 87-91; Adn Rochdale 91-00; rtd 00; Chapl Beauchamp Community from 00. *The Chaplain's House, The Beauchamp Community, Newland, Malvern WR13 5AX* Tel (01684) 899198 Fax as telephone E-mail markdalby@dalbyj.fsnet.co.uk

DALE, Miss Barbara. b 48. Cranmer Hall Dur 78. **dss** 81 **d** 87 **p** 94. N Wingfield, Pilsley and Tupton *Derby* 81-87; Par Dn 87-90; Par Dn N Wingfield, Clay Cross and Pilsley 90-94; TV 94-00; C Eckington and Ridgeway from 00. *17 Penny Engine Lane, Eckington, Sheffield S21 4BF* Tel (01246) 431643

DALE, Ms Christine. b 62. Ox Poly DipCart82. Trin Coll Bris BA94. **d** 94 **p** 95. C Thatcham *Ox* 94-98; TV Bracknell 98-02; R E Woodhay and Woolton Hill *Win* from 02. *The Rectory, The*

Mount, Highclere, Newbury RG20 9QZ Tel (01635) 253323 E-mail cdale5@compuserve.com
DALE, Eric Stephen. b 24. Roch Th Coll 63. **d** 65 **p** 66. C Kippax *Ripon* 65-67; C Fulford *York* 67-69; V Askham Bryan 69-70; V Askham Richard 69-70; V Askham Bryan w Askham Richard 70-78; Chapl HM Pris Askham Grange 69-78; Chapl HM Pris Wakef 78-79; Chapl HM Pris Gartree 79-82; Chapl HM Pris Leeds 82-89; rtd 89. *31 Kirkwood Lane, Leeds LS16 7EN* Tel 0113-230 0766
DALE, John Anthony. b 42. Qu Coll Birm 72. **d** 75 **p** 76. C Elmley Castle w Bricklehampton and Combertons *Worc* 75-81; P-in-c 81-83; R 83-88; Hon Can Worc Cathl 87-92; V Hallow 88-92; Dioc Registrar 92; P-in-c Michaelston-y-Fedw *Mon* from 03. *The Rectory, Michaelston-y-Fedw, Cardiff CF3 9XS* Tel (01633) 680414
DALE, Martin Nicholas. b 55. Chelsea Coll Lon BSc76 CPA83. Wycliffe Hall Ox. **d** 01 **p** 02. C Stiffkey and Cockthorpe w Morston, Langham etc *Nor* from 01. *The Rectory, Slade Road, Bale, Fakenham NR21 0QJ* Tel (01328) 878292 E-mail mndale@aol.com
DALE, Miss Olive Sylvia. b 44. Stockwell Coll of Educn TCert66. Faculté de Théologie Évangélique Vaux-sur-Seine France MScRel76 WMMTC 91. **d** 94 **p** 97. C Highley *Heref* 94-96; C Leominster 96-98; Chapl Asst Linc and Louth NHS Trust 98-00; rtd 00; Perm to Offic *Heref* from 00. *7A Pilley Road, Hereford HR1 1NA* Tel (01432) 352406
DALES, Douglas John. b 52. FRHistS90 Ch Ch Ox BA74 MA78 BD89. Cuddesdon Coll 74. **d** 77 **p** 78. C Shepperton *Lon* 77-81; C Ely 81-83; Chapl Marlborough Coll from 84; Hd of RE from 84. *Hillside, Bath Road, Marlborough SN8 1NN* Tel (01672) 514557
DALEY, David Michael. b 50. Oak Hill Th Coll BA90. **d** 92 **p** 92. C Enfield Ch Ch Trent Park *Lon* 92-94; V Chitts Hill St Cuth from 94. *St Cuthbert's Vicarage, 85 Wolves Lane, London N22 5JD* Tel (020) 8888 6178
DALEY, Preb Victor Leonard. b 38. Chich Th Coll 76. **d** 78 **p** 79. C Durrington *Chich* 78-81; C Somerton w Compton Dundon, the Charltons etc *B & W* 81-87; V Cheddar 87-88; V from 88; P-in-c Rodney Stoke w Draycott 02-03; RD Axbridge 91-03; Preb Wells Cathl from 97. *The Vicarage, Church Street, Cheddar BS27 3RF* Tel (01934) 742535 Fax as telephone E-mail victor@daley4395.freeserve.co.uk
DALLAWAY, Philip Alan. b 48. Chich Th Coll 80. **d** 81 **p** 82. C Newbury *Ox* 81-83; C Newport Pagnell w Lathbury 83-85; V Stewkley w Soulbury and Drayton Parslow 85-92; P-in-c Didcot All SS 92-97; R 97-00; V Caversham St Jo from 00. *The Vicarage, St John's Road, Caversham, Reading RG4 5AN* Tel 0118-947 1814
DALLING, Roger Charles. b 26. Lon Univ BSc53 DChemEng55. S Dios Minl Tr Scheme 79. **d** 83 **p** 84. NSM Lewes St Jo sub Castro *Chich* 83-84; NSM Uckfield 84-98; NSM Isfield 84-98; NSM Lt Horsted 84-98; rtd 98; Perm to Offic *Chich* from 98. *1 Avis Close, Denton, Newhaven BN9 0DN* Tel (01273) 515970
DALLOW, Gillian Margaret. b 45. Univ of Wales (Ban) BA66 DipEd67 Bris Univ MEd87 Univ Coll of SW CertMS88. Oak Hill Th Coll 93. **d** 96 **p** 97. NSM W Ealing St Jo w St Jas *Lon* 96-99; P-in-c Barlestone *Leic* from 99; Dioc Children's Min Adv from 99. *The New Vicarage, 22 Bosworth Road, Barlestone, Nuneaton CV13 0EL* Tel (01455) 290249 Mobile 07801-650187 Fax 242450 E-mail gdallow@leicester.anglican.org
DALLY, Keith Richard. b 47. FCCA77. St Jo Coll Nottm 80. **d** 82 **p** 83. C Southend St Sav Westcliff *Chelmsf* 82-85; Ind Chapl 85-93; C Southend 85-86; TV 86-92; C Harold Hill St Geo 92-93; Cen Co-ord Langham Place All So Clubhouse *Lon* 97-02; Perm to Offic *Ox* from 02. *172 Grasmere Way, Leighton Buzzard LU7 2QJ* Tel (01525) 378668
DALRIADA, Archdeacon of. *See* PATTERSON, The Ven John Norton
DALTON, Anthony Isaac. b 57. Em Coll Cam BA78 MA82 Leeds Univ BA82. Coll of Resurr Mirfield. **d** 82 **p** 83. C Carl St Aid and Ch Ch *Carl* 82-86; C Caversham St Pet and Mapledurham etc *Ox* 86-88; P-in-c Accrington St Mary *Blackb* 88-91; V 91-92; Chapl Victoria Hosp Accrington 88-92; V Sheff Parson Cross St Cecilia *Sheff* 92-96; P-in-c Burnley St Cath w St Alb and St Paul *Blackb* 96-98; V 98-01; R Orton and Tebay w Ravenstonedale etc *Carl* from 01. *The Vicarage, Orton, Penrith CA10 3RQ* Tel (01539) 624532 E-mail tony@dalton101.globalnet.co.uk
DALTON, Bertram Jeremy (Tod). b 32. AIB64. Sarum & Wells Th Coll 81. **d** 83 **p** 84. C Ringwood *Win* 83-86; R Norton sub Hamdon, W Chinnock, Chiselborough etc *B & W* 86-97; rtd 97;

Perm to Offic *B & W* from 97. *Meadow Cottage, 8 Woodbarton, Milverton, Taunton TA4 1LU* Tel (01823) 400302
DALTON, Derek. b 40. N Ord Course. **d** 84 **p** 85. NSM Pool w Arthington *Ripon* 84-87; P-in-c Thornton Watlass w Thornton Steward 87-90; C Bedale 87-90; R Wensley 90-95; V Watton 90-95; R Romaldkirk w Laithkirk 95-97; rtd 97. *North Wing, Thornton Watlass Hall, Ripon HG4 4AS* Tel (01677) 425302
DALTON, Kevin. b 32. TCD BA65. Ch Div Sch of the Pacific (USA) BD67 CITC 66. **d** 66 **p** 67. C Stillorgan *D & G* 66-72; I Dublin Drumcondra w N Strand 72-79; I Monkstown from 79. *62 Monkstown Road, Monkstown, Blackrock, Co Dublin, Irish Republic* Tel (00353) (1) 280 6596 Mobile (00353) 87-6633232 Fax as telephone E-mail monkstown@dublin.anglican.org
DALTRY, Paul Richard. b 56. Tottenham Coll of Tech DipEH79. St Jo Coll Nottm DCM92. **d** 92 **p** 93. C Ipswich St Matt *St E* 92-96; P-in-c Needham Market w Badley from 96; RD Bosmere from 01. *The Vicarage, 3 Stowmarket Road, Needham Market, Ipswich IP6 8DR* Tel (01449) 720316 Fax as telephone E-mail paul@daltrys.freeserve.co.uk
DALY, Ms Bernadette Theresa. b 45. TCD BTh94. **d** 97 **p** 98. C Taney *D & G* 97-00; Chan's V St Patr Cathl Dublin from 00; Dir Past St CITC from 00. *CITC, Braemor Park, Dublin 14, Irish Republic* Tel (00353) (1) 492 3506
DALY, Jeffrey. b 50. Bris Univ BA73 Jes Coll Cam PGCE74 Fitzw Coll Cam BA82 MA86. Ridley Hall Cam 80. **d** 83 **p** 84. C Tilehurst St Mich *Ox* 83-89; P-in-c Steventon w Milton 89-92; Asst Chapl Sherborne Sch 92-96; Chapl St Pet Sch York from 96. *St Peter's School, York YO30 6AB* Tel (01904) 623213 ext 412
DAMIAN, Brother. *See* KIRKPATRICK, Roger James
DAMMERS, The Very Revd Alfred Hounsell. b 21. Pemb Coll Cam BA45 MA47. Westcott Ho Cam 46. **d** 48 **p** 49. C Adlington *Blackb* 48-50; Lect Qu Coll Birm 50-53; C Edgbaston St Bart *Birm* 50-53; India 53-57; V Millhouses H Trin *Sheff* 57-65; Can Res Cov Cathl *Cov* 65-73; Dean Bris 73-87; rtd 87; Perm to Offic *Bris* from 87. *4 Bradley Avenue, Bristol BS11 9SL* Tel 0117-982 9121
DANCE, Peter Patrick. b 31. Em Coll Saskatoon 66. **d** 69 **p** 69. Canada 69-71; C Hednesford *Lich* 71-75; P-in-c Westcote Barton and Steeple Barton *Ox* 76-77; P-in-c Sandford St Martin 76-77; R Westcote Barton w Steeple Barton, Duns Tew etc 77-89; R Castle Douglas 89-97; rtd 97. *Mannville, High Street, Adderbury, Banbury OX17 3NA* Tel (01295) 811989
DAND, Mrs Angela Jane. b 49. St Andr Univ BSc70 Newc Univ PGCE71. LNSM course 95. **d** 98 **p** 99. OLM Astley Man from 98. *20 Acresfield, Astley, Tyldesley, Manchester M29 7NL* Tel (01942) 879608
DAND, Robert William Scrymgour. b 17. Pemb Coll Ox BA MA45. Cuddesdon Coll. **d** 47 **p** 48. C Portsea St Mary *Portsm* 47-50; V Finchingfield *Chelmsf* 50-59; R Woodbridge St Mary *St E* 59-60; Portugal 60-67; V Bracknell *Ox* 68-72; C Upton cum Chalvey 73-82; rtd 82; Perm to Offic *Cov* 82-00. *1 Stuart Court, High Street, Kibworth, Leicester LE8 0LR* Tel 0116-279 6347
DANDO, Ms Elaine Vera. b 53. Coll of Resurr Mirfield 94 N Ord Course 98. **d** 00 **p** 01. C Luddenden w Luddenden Foot *Wakef* 00-03; C Halifax from 03. *St Mary's Vicarage, 157 Keighley Road, Halifax HX2 9LL* Tel (01422) 244322
DANDO, Stephen. b 49. Goldsmiths' Coll Lon TCert70. Coll of Resurr Mirfield 81. **d** 83 **p** 84. C Wandsworth St Anne *S'wark* 83-87; V Stainland *Wakef* 87-99; V Illingworth from 99. *St Mary's Vicarage, 157 Keighley Road, Halifax HX2 9LL* Tel (01422) 244322
DANES, Charles William. b 28. Chich Th Coll 54. **d** 56 **p** 57. C N Greenford All Hallows *Lon* 56-59; C Caversham *Ox* 59-63; V Walsgrave on Sowe *Cov* 63-65; P-in-c Hanworth All SS *Lon* 65-67; V 68-76; P-in-c Wick *Chich* 76-78; V Littlehampton St Jas 76-78; P-in-c Littlehampton St Mary 76-78; V Worthing St Jo 78-87; Chapl Monte Carlo *Eur* 87-93; rtd 93; Perm to Offic *Chelmsf* from 93; Perm to Offic *Eur* from 93. *31 Oakley Road, Braintree CM7 5QS* Tel (01376) 324586
DANGERFIELD, Andrew Keith. b 63. Univ of Wales (Ban) BD87. St Steph Ho Ox 87. **d** 89 **p** 90. C St Marychurch *Ex* 89-93; C-in-c Grahame Park St Aug CD *Lon* 93-96; V Tottenham St Paul from 96; P-in-c Edmonton St Mary w St Jo from 98; AD E Haringey from 00. *St Paul's Vicarage, 60 Park Lane, London N17 0JR* Tel (020) 8808 7297 Mobile 07767-687954 Fax (020) 8376 0446 E-mail danger@stpaulstottenham.org.uk
DANIEL, Arthur Guy St John. b 12. K Coll Cam BA33 MA37. Cuddesdon Coll 34. **d** 35 **p** 36. C Blandford Forum *Sarum* 35-38; C Reading St Giles *Ox* 38-40; C Gt Marlow 40-46; V Colnbrook 46-78; TV Riverside 78-80; rtd 80; Perm to Offic *Ox* 80-87. *2 Gervis Court, Penwerris Avenue, Osterley TW7 4QU* Tel (020) 8572 1848
DANIEL, Mrs Gaynor Elizabeth. b 46. NNEB65. Llan Ord Course 94. **d** 98 **p** 99. NSM St Brides Minor w Bettws *Llan* 98-01; C 01-02; C St Brides Minor w Bettws w Aberkenfig from 02. *5 Coronation Street, Bryn, Port Talbot SA13 2SE* Tel (01639) 891871
DANIEL, Canon Herrick Haynes. b 38. Open Univ BA81. Trin Coll Bris 73. **d** 75 **p** 76. C Harlesden St Mark *Lon* 75-78; C

Livesey *Blackb* 78-81; V Blackb St Barn from 81; Hon Can Blackb Cathl from 98. *St Barnabas' Vicarage, 20 Buncer Lane, Blackburn BB2 6SE* Tel (01254) 56587

DANIEL, Mrs Joy. b 44. Gilmore Course 81 Oak Hill Th Coll 82. **dss** 84 **d** 87 **p** 94. Luton St Fran *St Alb* 84-02; Par Dn 87-94; C 94-02; P-in-c Woodside w E Hyde from 02. *St Andrew's Vicarage, Church Road, Slip End, Luton LU1 4BJ* Tel (01582) 424363 E-mail joy@daniel67.freeserve.co.uk

DANIEL, Philip Sharman. b 62. Man Univ BA83 Rob Coll Cam CertEd84. Wycliffe Hall Ox 84. **d** 86 **p** 87. C Macclesfield Team Par *Ches* 86-89; C Cheadle 89-94; V Disley from 94. *Disley Vicarage, Red Lane, Disley, Stockport SK12 2NP* Tel (01663) 762068 E-mail revpsdan@daniel192.freeserve.co.uk

DANIEL, Rajinder Kumar. b 34. St Steph Coll Delhi 55 Westcott Ho Cam 61. **d** 63 **p** 64. C Purley St Barn *S'wark* 63-66; C Battersea St Pet 66-67; C N Harrow St Alb *Lon* 67-72; TV Beaconsfield *Ox* 72-75; V Smethwick St Matt w St Chad *Birm* 75-87; Dioc Adv on Black Min 87-92; Chapl Birm Gen Hosp 91-92; TR Braunstone *Leic* 92-01; rtd 01; USPG and R Arima St Jude Trinidad and Tobago from 03. *16 Highgate Drive, Leicester LE2 6HH* Tel 0116-288 2644

DANIEL, Robert. b 37. **d** 87 **p** 88. C Camberwell St Giles w St Matt *S'wark* 90-92; V Lewisham St Swithun from 92. *St Swithun's Vicarage, 191 Hither Green Lane, London SE13 6QE* Tel (020) 8852 5088

DANIELS, Geoffrey Gregory. b 23. St Pet Coll Ox BA48 MA53. Lambeth STh60 Linc Th Coll 73. **d** 73 **p** 75. NSM Diss *Nor* 73-74; NSM Bexhill St Pet *Chich* 74-83; C Eastbourne St Andr 83-84; V Horam 84-88; rtd 88; Chapl Convent of Dudwell St Mary from 88; NSM Bexhill St Andr CD *Chich* 90-95; Perm to Offic from 95. *20 Richmond Grove, Bexhill-on-Sea TN39 3EQ* Tel (01424) 211719

DANIELS, Canon John Wyn. b 60. Southn Univ BSc82 PhD87 Bris Univ MA92. Trin Coll Bris DipHE91 United Th Coll Bangalore 96. **d** 92 **p** 93. C Roundhay St Edm *Ripon* 92-95; India 96; C Ambleside w Brathay *Carl* 97-01; Chapl St Martin's Coll Lanc 97-01; Res Can Ban Cathl *Ban* from 01. *Y Canondy, Cathedral Close, Bangor LL57 1LH* Tel (01248) 362840 E-mail jd001@supanet.com

DANIELS, Lee Martin. b 61. Coll of Resurr Mirfield 99. **d** 01 **p** 02. C Toxteth Park St Agnes and St Pancras *Liv* from 01. *St Agnes Flat, 51 Heysmoor Heights, Liverpool L8 3SW* Tel 0151-727 2458 E-mail lmartindaniels@aol.com

DANIELS, Norman. b 38. Leeds Univ BA60. St Mich Coll Llan 71. **d** 73 **p** 74. C Pontnewynydd *Mon* 73-76; W Germany 76-82; Chapl Giggleswick Sch 82-93; P-in-c Keighley All SS *Bradf* 93-03; V from 03. *All Saints' Vicarage, 21 View Road, Keighley BD20 6JN* Tel (01535) 607002 E-mail norman.daniels@btopenworld.com

DANKS, Alan Adam. b 41. Edin Th Coll 61. **d** 64 **p** 65. C Dumfries *Glas* 64-67; C Earl's Court St Cuth w St Matthias *Lon* 68-71; C St Steph Walbrook and St Swithun etc 71-74; C Brookfield St Mary 75-76; C Hendon St Mary 76-85. *33 Park Road, London W4 3EY* Tel (020) 8994 3131

DANSIE, Bruce John. b 40. Woolwich Poly BSc67 Univ Coll Lon MSc71 CEng72. Linc Th Coll 92. **d** 92 **p** 93. C Ivybridge w Harford *Ex* 92-96; P-in-c Charleton w Buckland Tout Saints etc 96-01; rtd 01. *c/o Andy and Sue Dansie, RR#1, Site #8, Box #3, Head Jeddore NS, Canada B0J 1P0*

DANSON, Mrs Mary Agatha. MPS48 Strathclyde Univ PhC48. St Jo Coll Nottm 82. **d** 88 **p** 94. NSM Uddingston *Glas* from 88; NSM Cambuslang from 88. *3 Golf Road, Rutherglen, Glasgow G73 4JW* Tel 0141-634 4330

DAPLYN, Timothy James. b 52. Ripon Coll Cuddesdon DipMin94. **d** 94 **p** 95. C Southmead *Bris* 94-97; P-in-c Abbots Leigh w Leigh Woods 97-99; Dioc Communications Officer 97-99; R Clutton w Cameley *B & W* from 99; RD Chew Magna from 03. *The Rectory, Main Road, Temple Cloud, Bristol BS39 5DA* Tel (01761) 451315 E-mail tim@tdaplyn.freeserve.co.uk

DARBY, Canon Anthony Ernest. b 26. Linc Th Coll 74. **d** 76 **p** 77. C Chilvers Coton w Astley *Cov* 76-79; P-in-c Longford 79-81; V 81-84; V Cov St Mary 84-91; RD Cov S 88-91; rtd 91; Chapl Cov Cathl from 91; Hon Can Th 00. *53 Ivybridge Road, Styvechale, Coventry CV3 5PF* Tel (024) 7641 4174 E-mail darby@bushinternet.com

DARBY, Michael Barwick. b 34. St D Coll Lamp BA61 Tyndale Hall Bris 61. **d** 63 **p** 64. C Islington St Andr w St Thos and St Matthias *Lon* 63-66; C Ealing Dean St Jo 66-68; V Broomfleet *York* 68-73; Area Sec CCCS *York* and *Sheff* 68-73; V Paddington Em Harrow Road *Lon* 73-78; Iran 78-79; Brazil 80-83; Perm to Offic *Carl* 80-84; from 01; V Maidstone St Faith 84-90; UAE 90-92; V Platt Bridge *Liv* 93-99; rtd 99. *Paqueta, 79 Sandwich Road, Cliffsend, Ramsgate CT12 5JA* Tel (01843) 597228 Mobile 07947-582469

DARBY, Nicholas Peter. b 50. Kent Univ BA82 Surrey Univ MSc02. Sarum & Wells Th Coll 71. **d** 74 **p** 75. C Walton-on-Thames *Guildf* 74-78; C Horsell 78-80; USA 82-84; Chapl Lon Univ *Lon* 84-89; Chapl R Lon Hosp (Whitechapel) 90-91; Perm

to Offic *S'wark* 90-91; Perm to Offic *Lon* 90-91; V Kew St Phil and All SS w St Luke *S'wark* from 91. *St Philip's Vicarage, 70 Marksbury Avenue, Richmond TW9 4JF* Tel (020) 8392 1425 *or* 8332 1324 Fax 8948 1015 E-mail npdarby@btopenworld.com

DARBY, Preb Philip William. b 44. Bede Coll Dur TCert66. Qu Coll Birm DipTh70. **d** 70 **p** 71. C Kidderminster St Geo *Worc* 70-74; P-in-c Dudley St Jo 74-79; V 79-80; P-in-c Catshill 80-82; V Catshill and Dodford 82-88; V Ipplepen w Torbryan *Ex* 88-00; V Ipplepen, Torbryan and Denbury 01-02; RD Newton Abbot and Ipplepen 93-01; V Ashburton w Buckland in the Moor and Bickington from 02; Preb Ex Cathl from 02. *The Vicarage, Copperwood Close, Ashburton, Newton Abbot TQ13 7JQ* Tel (01364) 652506 E-mail pwdarby@supanet.com

DARBYSHIRE, Brian. b 48. Kent Univ DipTh81 BA83. Oak Hill Th Coll. **d** 83 **p** 84. C Enfield St Jas *Lon* 83-86; R Slaidburn *Bradf* 86-92; V Gt Harwood St Jo *Blackb* 92-02; V Douglas St Ninian *S & M* from 02. *58 Ballanard Road, Douglas, Isle of Man IM2 5HE* Tel (01624) 621694

DARCH, John Henry. b 52. Univ of Wales (Lamp) BA73 PhD97 Lon Univ PGCE74 MA77 DipHE82. Trin Coll Bris 80. **d** 82 **p** 83. C Meole Brace *Lich* 82-85; C Hoole *Ches* 85-88; V Hyde St Geo 88-99; P-in-c Godley cum Newton Green 89-93; RD Mottram 91-99; Lect St Jo Coll Nottm from 99; Chapl from 03; Public Preacher *S'well* from 99; Perm to Offic *Derby* from 03. *St John's College, Chilwell Lane, Bramcote, Nottingham NG9 3DS* Tel 0115-925 1114 Fax 943 6438 E-mail j.darch@stjohns-nottm.ac.uk

DARK, Nicholas John. b 62. Leic Univ BA83 ACIB92. CITC BTh98. **d** 98 **p** 99. C Ballyholme *D & D* from 98. *34 Beverley Gardens, Bangor BT20 4NQ* Tel (028) 9127 1922 *or* 9127 4912 Fax 9146 6357

DARK, Ronald Henry Richard. b 31. Oak Hill Th Coll. **d** 85 **p** 86. NSM Fyfield *Chelmsf* 85-89; NSM Fyfield and Moreton w Bobbingworth 90-93; NSM Fyfield, Moreton w Bobbingworth etc 93-94; Perm to Offic from 94. *74 Warescot Road, Brentwood CM15 9HE* Tel (01277) 214797

DARLEY, Canon Shaun Arthur Neilson. b 36. Dur Univ BA61 DipTh63 Reading Univ MSc75. Cranmer Hall Dur 61. **d** 63 **p** 64. C Luton w E Hyde *St Alb* 63-67; Chapl Bris Tech Coll 67-69; Chapl Bris Poly *Bris* 69-92; Sen Chapl UWE 92-01; Lect 69-75; Sen Lect 75-01; Dir Cen for Performing Arts 82-02; Bp's Cathl Chapl 69-76; Hon Can Bris Cathl 89-01; rtd 01; Perm to Offic *B & W* from 98 and *Bris* from 02. *Church Paddock, Winscombe Hill, Bristol BS25 1DE* Tel (01934) 843633

DARLING, David Francis (Brother David Francis). b 55. TISEC 93. **d** 96 **p** 97. SSF from 88; Novice Guardian from 99; NSM Edin St Ninian *Edin* 96-98; Chapl W Gen Hosps NHS 96-98; Chapl Edin Sick Children's NHS Trust 96-98; Lic Preacher *Lon* from 03. *Glasshampton Monastery, Shrawley, Worcester WR6 6TQ* Tel (01299) 896345

✠**DARLING, The Rt Revd Edward Flewett.** b 33. TCD BA55 MA58. CITC. **d** 56 **p** 57 **c** 85. C Belfast St Luke *Conn* 56-59; C Orangefield *D & D* 59-62; C-in-c Carnalea 62-72; Chapl Ban Hosp 63-72; I Belfast Malone St Jo *Conn* 72-85; Min Can Belf Cathl 78-85; Chapl Ulster Independent Clinic 81-85; Bp L & K 85-00. *15 Beechwood Park, Moira, Craigavon BT67 0LL* Tel (028) 9261 2982 E-mail darling.moira@churchofireland.net

DARLINGTON, Paul Trevor. b 71. Imp Coll Lon BSc92 K Coll Lon PGCE93. Oak Hill Th Coll BA99 MPhil00. **d** 00 **p** 01. C Bispham *Blackb* from 00. *Church Villa, All Hallows Road, Blackpool FY2 0AY* Tel (01253) 353648 E-mail paul.t.darlington@ntlworld.com

DARLISON, Geoffrey Stuart. b 49. Liv Poly DipTP74 MRTPI80. St Jo Coll Nottm DCM91. **d** 91 **p** 92. C Horncastle w Low Toynton *Linc* 91-95; P-in-c Welton and Dunholme w Scothern 95-97; V from 97. *The New Vicarage, Holmes Lane, Dunholme, Lincoln LN2 3QT* Tel (01673) 862820 E-mail stuart@darlisons.freeserve.co.uk

DARMODY, Richard Arthur. b 52. Lon Univ DipTh77 BD90. Linc Th Coll MDiv94. **d** 94 **p** 95. C Cherry Hinton St Jo *Ely* 94-97; I Belfast St Aid *Conn* 97-99; TR The Ramseys and Upwood *Ely* from 99; RD St Ives from 02. *The Rectory, Hollow Lane, Ramsey, Huntingdon PE26 1DE* Tel (01487) 813271 E-mail darmodyrichard@hotmail.com

DARRALL, Charles Geoffrey. b 32. Nottm Univ BA55 MA57. Qu Coll Birm 56. **d** 57 **p** 58. C Cockermouth All SS w Ch Ch *Carl* 57-63; Chapl Dioc Youth Cen 63-95; V St John's in the Vale w Wythburn 63-95; P-in-c Threlkeld 85-95; rtd 96; Perm to Offic *Carl* from 98. *Piper House, Naddle, Keswick CA12 4TF* Tel (01768) 774500

DARRALL, John Norman. b 34. Nottm Univ BA57. Ripon Hall Ox 57. **d** 60 **p** 61. C Nottingham St Mary *S'well* 60-65; Chapl Nottm Children's Hosp 64-65; V Bole w Saundby *S'well* 65-66; V Sturton w Littleborough 65-66; Chapl Oakham Sch 84-99; rtd 99. *Grange Cottage, 69 Main Street, Cottesmore, Oakham LE15 7DH* Tel (01572) 812443

DARRANT, Louis Peter. b 77. Aber Univ BD00 Leeds Univ MA03. Coll of Resurr Mirfield 01. **d** 03. C Kennington St Jo w

St Jas *S'wark* from 03. *96 Vassall Road, London SW9 6JA* Tel (020) 7582 2162 Mobile 07949-765523

DARROCH, Ronald Humphrey. b 45. Trin Coll Cam BA67 MA71 Ch Ch Ox BA67 MA71. Ripon Hall Ox 67. **d** 70 **p** 71. C Kingston upon Hull St Nic *York* 70-73; Hon C 73-74; Hon C Perth St Jo *St And* from 74; Chapl Stancliffe Hall Derby 84-87; Perm to Offic *Worc* 87-98; Chapl Old Swinford Hosp Sch Worc 89-98. *17 Viewlands Terrace, Perth PH1 1BN* Tel (01738) 628880

DART, John Peter. b 40. St Jo Coll Ox BA63. Cuddesdon Coll 62. **d** 64 **p** 65. C W Hartlepool St Aid *Dur* 64-67; C Alverthorpe *Wakef* 67-70; Lic to Offic 70-84. *3 Springhill Avenue, Crofton, Wakefield WF4 1HA* Tel (01924) 863782

DARVILL, Christopher Mark. b 61. Ox Univ BA83. St Steph Ho Ox 84. **d** 86 **p** 87. C Tottenham St Paul *Lon* 86-88; C Oystermouth *S & B* 88-90; Chapl Univ of Wales (Swansea) 90-94; Asst Dioc Warden of Ords from 92; V Llansamlet from 94. *The Vicarage, 61 Church Road, Llansamlet, Swansea SA7 9RL* Tel (01792) 771420

DARVILL, Geoffrey. b 43. Aston Univ DipHE81. Oak Hill Th Coll 79. **d** 81 **p** 82. C Barking St Marg w St Patr *Chelmsf* 81-84; C Widford 84-86; P-in-c Ramsden Crays w Ramsden Bellhouse 86-90; Dep Chapl HM Pris Pentonville 90-91; Chapl HM YOI Onley 91-97; Chapl HM Pris Nor 97-01; Chapl HM Pris Man 01-02; P-in-c Chadderton Em *Man* 02-03; V from 03. *Emmanuel Vicarage, 15 Chestnut Street, Chadderton, Oldham OL9 8HB* Tel 0161-681 1310

DARVILL, Canon George Collins. b 36. Kelham Th Coll 56. **d** 61 **p** 62. C Middlesbrough St Chad *York* 61-64; C Manston *Ripon* 64-66; V Kippax 66-79; V Catterick 79-88; RD Richmond 80-86; P-in-c Adel 88-89; R 89-01; RD Headingley 91-96; Hon Can Ripon Cathl 91-01; rtd 01. *39 Woodlea Lane, Meanwood, Leeds LS6 4SX* Tel 0113-275 7973

✠**DARWENT, The Rt Revd Frederick Charles.** b 27. JP87. ACIB. Wells Th Coll 61. **d** 63 **p** 64 **c** 78. C Pemberton St Jo *Liv* 63-65; R Strichen *Ab* 65-71; R New Pitsligo 65-71; R Fraserburgh w New Pitsligo 71-78; Can St Andr Cathl 71-78; Dean Ab 73-78; Bp Ab 78-92; rtd 92; Lic to Offic *Ab* from 92. *107 Osborne Place, Aberdeen AB25 2DD* Tel (01224) 646497

DASH, Mrs Janet Eleanor Gillian. b 47. SRN69. Cant Sch of Min 89. **d** 93 **p** 94. C Morden *S'wark* 93-96; C S Croydon Em 96-98; Chapl HM Pris Cookham Wood from 98; P-in-c Borstal *Roch* from 98. *The Vicarage, 76 Borstal Street, Rochester ME1 3HL* Tel and fax (01634) 845948 Mobile 07770-741291 E-mail jan@jdash.fsnet.co.uk

DASHFIELD, Edward Maurice. b 26. LTh65. **d** 51 **p** 52. New Zealand 51-55 and from 57; C Masterton 51-55; C Cannock *Lich* 55-57; V Tinui 57-64; P-in-c 83-88; V Carterton 64-69; Hd Master St Matt Sch Masterton 69-80; rtd 88. *53 Miro Street, Masterton, New Zealand* Tel (0064) (6) 377 0418

DATE, Stephen James. b 69. LSE BA90 Dur Univ MA92. SEITE 99. **d** 02 **p** 03. NSM Brighton Gd Shep Preston *Chich* from 02. *67 Stanford Road, Brighton BN1 5PR* Tel (01273) 565927 Mobile 07747-895213 E-mail stephend@yahoo.co.uk

DATSON, Mrs Sheila Mary. b 24. CertEd67. S'wark Ord Course 76. **dss** 78 **d** 87 **p** 94. Bexleyheath Ch Ch *Roch* 78-91; Hon Par Dn 87-91; rtd 91; Perm to Offic *Worc* 91-94 and from 95; NSM Stourport and Wilden 94-95. *17 Moorhall Lane, Stourport-on-Severn DY13 8RB* Tel (01299) 823044

DAUBNEY, Howard. b 49. Woolwich Poly BA70. S'wark Ord Course 86. **d** 89 **p** 90. NSM Roch 89-02; C from 02. *Trehaun, 20 City Way, Rochester ME1 2AB* Tel (01634) 401691 Mobile 0790-952 6415 E-mail h daubney@hotmail.com

DAUBUZ, Michael Claude. b 19. Trin Coll Cam BA40 MA53. Wells Th Coll 40. **d** 42 **p** 43. C Fareham SS Pet and Paul *Portsm* 42-47; Hon C Blandford Forum *Sarum* 47-50; C Gillingham 50-53; R Brading w Yaverland *Portsm* 53-59; Perm to Offic *Win* 62-64; C Twyford 64-70; V Colden 70-84; rtd 84. *31 St Osmund Close, Yetminster, Sherborne DT9 6LU* Tel (01935) 872584

DAUGHTERY, Stephen John. b 61. Kent Univ BSc82. Trin Coll Bris BA94. **d** 96 **p** 97. C Guildf Ch Ch *Guildf* 96-98; C Guildf Ch Ch w St Martha-on-the-Hill 98-03; R Southover *Chich* from 03. *The Rectory, Southover High Street, Lewes BN7 1HT* Tel (01273) 472018 E-mail steve@daughtery.freeserve.co.uk

DAULMAN, John Henry. b 33. Lich Th Coll 60. **d** 62 **p** 63. C Monkseaton St Mary *Newc* 62-65; Min Can Newc Cathl 65-67; Chapl Crumpsall and Springfield Hosp 67-73; V Tyldesley w Shakerley *Man* 73-81; V Turton 81-00; rtd 00; Perm to Offic *Blackb* from 01. *17 Higher Bank Street, Withnell, Chorley PR6 8SF* Tel (01254) 832597

DAUNTON-FEAR, Andrew. b 45. Univ of Tasmania BSc64 Qu Coll Cam BA67 MA72 ACT ThL68 St Andr Univ BPhil76 K Coll Lon PhD00 Dip Librarianship 74. Ridley Hall Cam 67. **d** 68 **p** 70. C Thomastown Australia 68-71; P-in-c Islington H Trin Cloudesley Square *Lon* 71-75; Hon C Islington St Mary 71-75; C Stoke Bishop *Bris* 76-79; R Rampton *Pet* 79-89; R Barming *Roch* 89-03; Lect St Andr Th Sem Philippines from 03. *PO Box 3167, 1099 Manila, Philippines* Tel (0063) (2) 722 2571 E-mail nothingdaunted@hotmail.com

DAVAGE, William Ernest Peter. b 50. MA94. St Steph Ho Ox 89. **d** 91 **p** 92. C Eyres Monsell *Leic* 91-94; P Lib Pusey Ho Ox from 94. *Pusey House, St Giles, Oxford OX1 3LZ* Tel (01865) 278415 Fax 278416

DAVENPORT (née HILL), Ms Elizabeth Jayne Louise. b 55. St Hugh's Coll Ox BA77 MA81. Fuller Th Sem California ThM89 N Ord Course 79. **dss** 82 **d** 87 **p** 91. Halliwell St Pet *Man* 82-83; Paris St Mich *Eur* 83-85; Lic to Offic *St Alb* 85-87; Hon Par Dn Chorleywood St Andr 87-89; USA from 89. *University of Southern California, Student Union 202, Los Angeles, CA 90089-0890, USA* E-mail ejld@usc.edu

DAVENPORT, Ian Arthan. b 54. Linc Th Coll 85. **d** 87 **p** 88. C Ches H Trin *Ches* 87-91; V Newton 91-97; V Oxton from 97. *Oxton Vicarage, 8 Wexford Road, Prenton CH43 9TB* Tel 0151-652 1194 Fax 653 9211

DAVENPORT, Michael Arthur. b 38. Kelham Th Coll 58 Lich Th Coll 60. **d** 62 **p** 63. C Bilborough w Strelley *S'well* 62-66; C Kettering St Mary *Pet* 66-69; V Tottenham St Benet Fink *Lon* from 69; Chapl ATC from 79; Wing Chapl Middx 83-96; Regional Chapl Lon and SE 86-96. *St Benet's Vicarage, Walpole Road, London N17 6BH* Tel (020) 8888 4541 Fax 8829 9593

DAVENPORT, Ms Sally Elizabeth. b 59. Lon Bible Coll BA99. Ripon Coll Cuddesdon 99. **d** 01 **p** 02. C Bishop's Stortford St Mich *St Alb* from 01. *Cowell House, 24 Apton Road, Bishop's Stortford CM23 3SN* Tel (01279) 654414 Mobile 07956-911356 E-mail sdavenport@sur.co.uk

DAVENPORT, Miss Sybil Ann. b 36. Nottm Univ CertEd54 DipTh88. EMMTC 85. **d** 89 **p** 94. NSM Thurgarton w Hoveringham and Bleasby etc *S'well* 89-94; NSM Collingham w S Scarle and Besthorpe and Girton 94-02; rtd 02. *Holmedale, North Muskham, Newark NG23 6HQ* Tel (01636) 701552

DAVEY, Andrew John. b 53. Univ of Wales (Cardiff) DPS77. St Mich Coll Llan DipTh76. **d** 77 **p** 78. C Gt Stanmore *Lon* 77-79; NSM Watford St Jo *St Alb* 87-92; C Potters Bar 92-95; P-in-c Clenchwarton *Ely* 95-96; P-in-c W Lynn 95-96; R Clenchwarton and W Lynn from 96; ChLJ from 97. *The Rectory, Clenchwarton, King's Lynn PE34 4DT* Tel (01553) 772089 Fax as telephone E-mail andrewdavey@route56.co.uk

DAVEY, Andrew John. b 57. Magd Coll Ox BA78 MA83. Wycliffe Hall Ox 80. **d** 83 **p** 84. C Bermondsey St Jas w Ch Ch *S'wark* 83-87; Chapl Trin Coll Cam 87-92; Pilsdon Community from 94. *Pilsdon Manor, Pilsdon, Bridport DT6 5NZ* Tel (01308) 868308 Fax 868161

DAVEY, Andrew Paul. b 61. Southn Univ BA82 Sheff Univ DMinTh99. Westcott Ho Cam 85. **d** 87 **p** 88. C S'wark H Trin w St Matt *S'wark* 87-91; V Camberwell St Luke 91-96; Min Development Officer Woolwich Area Miss Team 96-98; Ho of Bps' Officer for UPAs from 98; Asst Sec Abps' Coun Bd for Soc Resp from 98; Lic to Offic *S'wark* from 98. *7 Bousfield Road, London SE14 5TP* Tel (020) 7277 9688 *or* 7898 1446 E-mail andrew.davey@c-of-e.org.uk

DAVEY, Christopher Mark. b 64. EN(G)84 RGN89. St Steph Ho Ox DipMin95. **d** 95 **p** 96. C Leeds Belle Is St Jo and St Barn *Ripon* 95-97; C-in-c Grahame Park St Aug CD *Lon* 97-01; V St Alb St Mary Marshalswick *St Alb* from 01. *The Vicarage, 1 Sherwood Avenue, St Albans AL4 9QA* Tel (01727) 851544 E-mail cdavey2776@aol.com

DAVEY, Colin Hugh Lancaster. b 34. Em Coll Cam BA56 MA60 PhD89. Cuddesdon Coll 59. **d** 61 **p** 62. C Moseley St Agnes *Birm* 61-64; Lic to Offic *Eur* 64-65; Sub Warden St Boniface Coll Warminster 66-69; C Bath Weston St Jo *B & W* 69-70; Asst Chapl Abp Cant's Cllrs on Foreign Relns 70-74; Angl Sec ARCIC 70-74; Hon C St Dunstan in the West *Lon* 71-73; Hon C Kennington St Jo *S'wark* 73-74; V S Harrow St Paul *Lon* 74-80; V Paddington St Jas 80-83; Sec Ecum Affairs BCC 83-90; Ch Life Sec CCBI 90-99; rtd 00; Perm to Offic *St Alb* from 97. *20 Honeysuckle Way, Bedford MK41 0TF* Tel (01234) 360851 E-mail colinandjan-davey8.freeserve.co.uk

DAVEY, Eric Victor. b 28. Wycliffe Hall Ox 53 Ridley Hall Cam. **d** 56 **p** 57. C Stockton St Thos *Dur* 56-59; C Stretford St Matt *Man* 59-61; V Slaithwaite w E Scammonden *Wakef* 61-68; V Pontefract St Giles 68-83; V Wakef St Jo 83-93; rtd 93; Perm to Offic *Wakef* from 93. *Croft House, 15B St John's Croft, Wakefield WF1 2RQ*

DAVEY, Canon Frederick Hutley David. b 14. Cranmer Hall Dur 58. **d** 60 **p** 62. C Bishopwearmouth St Nic *Dur* 60-62; C Dur St Giles 62-64; India 64-69; E Pakistan 69-71; Bangladesh 71-76; Chapl De Beer Miss to Seamen *Eur* 77-82; rtd 82; Perm to Offic *B & W* 82-95. *126 Ashtree Road, Frome BA11 2SF* Tel (01373) 467545

DAVEY, Mrs Hilary Margaret. b 49. Bris Univ BSc70. EAMTC 98. **d** 01 **p** 02. NSM Saffron Walden w Wendens Ambo, Littlebury etc *Chelmsf* from 01. *3 Springhill Road, Saffron Walden CB11 4AH* Tel (01799) 522616 E-mail st.mary's@virgin.net

DAVEY, James Garland. b 21. **d** 75 **p** 76. C Liskeard w St Keyne and St Pinnock *Truro* 75-77; Perm to Offic *B & W* 77-80; TV S Molton w Nymet St George, High Bray etc *Ex* 80-86; rtd 86;

Perm to Offic *B & W* from 86. *43 Tree Field Road, Clevedon BS21 6JD* Tel (01275) 540648

DAVEY, John. b 35. FRSH89 CPsychol92 AFBPsS92 Birkbeck Coll Lon BSc84 MPhil87 PhD91. Chich Th Coll 67. **d** 69 **p** 70. C Eastbourne St Eliz *Chich* 69-72; C Eastbourne St Mary 72-74; V W Wittering 74-77; Min Can and Chapl Windsor 77-81; R The Rissingtons *Glouc* 81-85; R Alfriston w Lullington, Litlington and W Dean *Chich* 85-92; Chapl Bramshill Police Coll *Win* 92-96; rtd 97; P-in-c Amberley w N Stoke and Parham, Wiggonholt etc *Chich* 97-98; Perm to Offic from 98. *Bewick, 13 Fairfield Close, Bosham, Chichester PO18 8JQ*

DAVEY, John Michael. b 31. St Chad's Coll Dur BA54 Sunderland Poly DMS76. St Chad's Coll Dur DipTh56. **d** 56 **p** 61. C Southwick H Trin *Dur* 56-57; C Harton 60-64; C Bawtry w Austerfield *S'well* 64-67; V Stillington *Dur* 67-70; Lic to Offic 70-78; Perm to Offic *Sheff* 78-93; rtd 96. *11 Darfield Close, Owlthorpe, Sheffield S20 6SW* Tel 0114-248 0917

DAVEY, Julian Metherall. b 38. Jes Coll Ox BA62 MA65. Wells Th Coll 62. **d** 64 **p** 65. C Weston-super-Mare St Jo *B & W* 64-66; Perm to Offic *St Alb* 66-68; Chapl St Alb Sch 68-73; Chapl Merchant Taylors' Sch Crosby 73-82; Perm to Offic *Truro* 82-83; P-in-c Meavy w Sheepstor *Ex* 83-85; P-in-c Walkhampton 83-85; R Meavy, Sheepstor and Walkhampton 85; Chapl Warw Sch 86-89; P-in-c The Winterbournes and Compton Valence *Sarum* 89-94; TV Marshwood Vale 96-98; P-in-c St Gennys, Jacobstow w Warbstow and Treneglos *Truro* 98-02; rtd 02; Perm to Offic *Truro* from 02. *18 Pondfield Road, Latchbrook, Saltash PL12 4UA* Tel (01752) 840086

DAVEY, Julian Warwick. b 45. LRCPI DCH DRCOG. Qu Coll Birm 78. **d** 81 **p** 82. NSM Ipsley *Worc* from 81. *The Field House, Allimore Lane, Alcester B49 5PR* Tel (01789) 764640

DAVEY, Kenneth William. b 41. Lanc Coll HNC. Qu Coll Birm 84. **d** 86 **p** 87. C Baswich *Lich* 86-90; V Lostock Gralam *Ches* 90-96; P-in-c Thornton-le-Moors w Ince and Elton from 96. *The Vicarage, Ince Lane, Elton, Chester CH2 4QB* Tel (01928) 724028 E-mail kenzor@daveyk1.fsnet.co.uk

DAVEY, Nathan Paul. *See* PAINE DAVEY, Nathan Paul

DAVEY, Peter Francis. b 40. Trin Coll Cam BA63 MA68. Cuddesdon Coll 63. **d** 65 **p** 66. C Atherton *Man* 65-69; C Leesfield 69-72; V High Crompton 72-79; V Blackrod 79-89; P-in-c Ringley 89-91; V Ringley w Prestolee 91-95; P-in-c Dearnley from 95. *The Vicarage, Arm Road, Littleborough OL15 8NJ* Tel (01706) 378466

DAVEY, Peter James. b 59. Bris Univ BSc81 Loughb Univ MBA91. Trin Coll Bris BA00. **d** 00 **p** 01. C Long Eaton St Jo *Derby* from 00. *10 Brecon Close, Long Eaton, Nottingham NG10 4JW* Tel 0115-972 0459 Mobile 07720-756955 E-mail petedavey@aol.com

DAVEY, Peter William. b 44. Culham Coll of Educn TCert65. Linc Th Coll 93. **d** 93 **p** 94. C Cheadle w Freehay *Lich* 93-96; P-in-c Calton, Cauldon, Grindon and Waterfall 96-99; R Calton, Cauldon, Grindon, Waterfall etc 99-00. *St John's Vicarage, High Street, Alsagers Bank, Stoke-on-Trent ST7 8BQ* Tel (01782) 720808

DAVEY, Piers Damer. b 57. Dur Univ BSc. Coll of Resurr Mirfield 80. **d** 83 **p** 84. C Heworth St Mary *Dur* 83-86; C Barnard Castle w Whorlton 86-89; V Aycliffe 89-95; V Chilton Moor from 95. *St Andrew's Vicarage, Chilton Moor, Houghton le Spring DH4 6LU* Tel 0191-385 8747

DAVEY, Canon Richard Henry. b 66. Man Univ BA88. Linc Th Coll BTh93. **d** 93 **p** 94. C Parkstone St Pet w Branksea and St Osmund *Sarum* 93-96; Chapl and Min Can St E Cathl *St E* 96-99; Can Res S'well Minster *S'well* from 99. *3 Vicar's Court, Southwell NG25 0HP* Tel (01636) 813767 E-mail rdavey1175@aol.com

DAVID, Brother. *See* JARDINE, David John

DAVID, Faith Caroline. *See* CLARINGBULL, Mrs Faith Caroline

DAVID, Canon Kenith Andrew. b 39. Natal Univ BA(Theol)64. Coll of Resurr Mirfield 64. **d** 66 **p** 67. C Harpenden St Nic *St Alb* 66-69; S Africa 69-71; P-in-c Southwick St Mich *Chich* 71-72; Th Educn Sec Chr Aid 72-75; Project Officer India and Bangladesh 76-81; Hon C Kingston All SS *S'wark* 72-76; Hon C Kingston All SS w St Jo 76-81; Botswana 81-83; Hon C Geneva *Eur* 83-95; Co-ord Urban Rural Miss WCC 83-94; Can Dio Lundi Zimbabwe from 93; V Hessle *York* from 95. *The Vicarage, 4 Chestnut Avenue, Hessle HU13 0RH* Tel (01482) 648555 Fax as telephone

DAVID, Michael Anthony Louis. b 29. AKC58. **d** 59 **p** 60. C Greenhill St Jo *Lon* 59-63; V Gravesend St Mary *Roch* 63-78; V Foremark w Repton *Derby* 78-81; V Repton w Burbage and King Sterndale 81-85; R Warlingham w Chelsham and Farleigh *S'wark* 85-90; rtd 91; Perm to Offic *Sarum* from 91. *95 Lulworth Avenue, Hamworthy, Poole BH15 4DH* Tel (01202) 684475

DAVID, Philip Evan Nicholl. b 31. Jes Coll Ox BA53 MA57 Univ of Wales BA61 Nottm Univ MPhil86 Leic Univ MEd88. St Mich Coll Llan 56. **d** 57 **p** 58. C Llanblethian w Cowbridge *Llan* 57-60; C Cardiff St Jo 60-64; Chapl Ch Coll Brecon 64-75; P-in-c

Aberyscir and Llanfihangel Nantbran *S & B* 70-75; Chapl Loretto Sch Musselburgh 75-82; Lic to Offic *Derby* 80-91; Chapl Trent Coll Nottm 83-91; R Llanfyllin and Bwlchycibau *St As* 91-96; P-in-c Llangynog 95-96; rtd 96; P-in-c Newbridge-on-Wye and Llanfihangel Brynpabuan etc *S & B* 98-00. *Woodside Cottage, The Bron, Cross Gates, Llandrindod Wells LD1 6RS* Tel (01597) 851401

DAVID COLUMBA, Brother. *See* HARE, David

DAVID FRANCIS, Brother. *See* DARLING, David Francis

DAVID STEPHEN, Brother. *See* STEVENS, Canon David Johnson

DAVIDGE-SMITH, Mrs Margaret Kathleen. b 53. Trent Poly CQSW77. STETS 99. **d** 02 **p** 03. NSM E Acton St Dunstan w St Thos *Lon* from 02. *36 Newburgh Road, London W3 6DQ* Tel (020) 8993 0868 Fax as telephone E-mail mdavidge_s@hotmail.com

DAVIDSON, Canon Charles Hilary. b 29. St Edm Hall Ox BA52 MA56 Leic Univ MPhil89. Lich Th Coll 52. **d** 54 **p** 55. C Abington *Pet* 54-59; C Pet St Jo 59-60; R Sywell w Overstone 60-66; P-in-c Lamport w Faxton 66-76; R Maidwell w Draughton and Scaldwell 67-76; R Maidwell w Draughton, Scaldwell, Lamport etc 77-80; RD Brixworth 77-79; Can Pet Cathl 79-94; V Roade 80-87; V Roade and Ashton w Hartwell 87-94; RD Towcester 91-94; rtd 94; Perm to Offic *Pet* from 94. *Croftside, Butlins Lane, Roade, Northampton NN7 2PU* Tel (01604) 863016

DAVIDSON, Christopher John. b 45. St Luke's Coll Ex CertEd67 CertRE67 St Martin's Coll Lanc BEd74. EAMTC. **d** 91 **p** 92. NSM Taverham w Ringland *Nor* 91-93; Dir of Educn 87-93; P-in-c Whixley w Green Hammerton *Ripon* 93-96; RE Adv 93-96; Dioc Dir of Educn *Ex* 97-01; Assoc P Exminster and Kenn 97-01; R Quidenham Gp *Nor* from 01. *The Rectory, Church Street, Banham, Norwich NR16 2HN* Tel (01953) 887562

DAVIDSON, Graeme John. b 42. Victoria Univ Wellington BA64 BA66 Ox Univ MA70. St Steph Ho Ox 67. **d** 70 **p** 71. C Maidenhead St Luke *Ox* 70-73; New Zealand 73-77 and from 93; USA 77-88. *103 Upland Road, Kelburn, Wellington, New Zealand* Tel (0064) (4) 475 8228 Fax 475 8219 E-mail davidson@betterlearn.co.nz

DAVIDSON, Ian George. b 32. LSE BSc(Econ)54. Linc Th Coll 55. **d** 58 **p** 59. C Waltham Cross *St Alb* 58-60; C St Alb Abbey 61-63; Hon PV S'wark Cathl *S'wark* 63-67; V Gt Cornard *St E* 67-72; R Lt Cornard 67-70; Lic to Offic 72-79; Student Counsellor Suffolk Coll 72-79; P-in-c Witnesham w Swilland and Ashbocking 79-83; Warden Scargill Ho 83-88; Chapl Chr Fellowship of Healing *Edin* 88-97; rtd 97. *28 Fox Spring Crescent, Edinburgh EH10 6NQ* Tel 0131-445 3381 E-mail iangill@foxspring.freeserve.co.uk

DAVIDSON, John Lindsay. b 27. LRCP51 St Cath Soc Ox DipTh57. St Steph Ho Ox. **d** 58 **p** 59. C Croydon St Mich *Cant* 58-61; P-in-c H Cross Miss 62-66; V Lewisham St Steph *S'wark* 67-70; V Croydon St Mich *Cant* 70-80; V Croydon St Mich w St Jas 80-81; TR N Creedy *Ex* 81-92; RD Cadbury 86-90; rtd 92; Perm to Offic *Ex* from 92. *12 Highfield, Lapford, Crediton EX17 6PY* Tel (01363) 83764

DAVIDSON, Ralph. b 38. Dioc OLM tr scheme 98. **d** 01 **p** 02. OLM Birkenshaw w Hunsworth *Wakef* from 01. *Bedale, Moorhouse Lane, Birkenshaw, Bradford BD11 2BA* Tel (01274) 681955

DAVIDSON, Trevor John. b 49. CertEd DipHE. Oak Hill Th Coll 80. **d** 85 **p** 86. C Drypool *York* 85-88; V Bessingby 88-97; V Carnaby 88-97; Chapl Bridlington and Distr Gen Hosp 88-94; Chapl E Yorks Community Healthcare NHS Trust 94-97; V Felling *Dur* from 97; CUF Projects Officer from 97. *The Vicarage, Carlisle Street, Felling, Gateshead NE10 0HQ* Tel 0191-420 3434 E-mail trevor@christchurch5.freeserve.co.uk

DAVIDSON, William Watkins. b 20. Wadh Coll Ox BA48 MA53. Westcott Ho Cam 49. **d** 50 **p** 51. C Radcliffe-on-Trent *S'well* 50-53; Chapl RN 53-57; R Esher *Guildf* 57-65; V Westmr St Steph w St Jo *Lon* 65-83; rtd 85. *32 Hamilton Avenue, Woking GU22 8RS* Tel (01932) 342711

DAVIE (née JONES), Mrs Alyson Elizabeth. b 58. Ex Univ BA86. Wycliffe Hall Ox 86. **d** 88 **p** 94. Par Dn Ipswich St Fran *St E* 88-92; Perm to Offic *Ox* 92-93; Perm to Offic *St Alb* 93-94; NSM E Barnet 94-97; Asst Chapl Oak Hill Th Coll 94-96; P-in-c The Mundens w Sacombe *St Alb* from 97. *2 Forge Cottages, Munden Road, Dane End, Ware SG12 0LP* Tel (01920) 438736 E-mail alyson.davie@btopenworld.com

DAVIE, Peter Edward Sidney. b 36. Lon Univ BSc57 MPhil78 Birm Univ MA73 Kent Univ PhD91. Coll of Resurr Mirfield 57. **d** 60 **p** 61. C De Beauvoir Town St Pet *Lon* 60-63; C-in-c Godshill CD *Portsm* 63-67; R Upton St Leonards *Glouc* 67-73; Sen Lect Ch Ch Coll of HE Cant 73-98; Hon C Cant St Pet w St Alphege and St Marg etc *Cant* from 73; Prin Lect Cant Ch Ch Univ Coll 98-01; rtd 01. *8 Brockenhurst Close, Canterbury CT2 7RX* Tel (01227) 451572

DAVIE, Stephen Peter. b 52. S Bank Poly BA75 MRTPI77 Cam Univ DipRS90. Oak Hill Th Coll BA93. **d** 93 **p** 94. C Luton Ch Ch *Roch* 93-97; R Cobham w Luddesdowne and Dode from 97.

The Vicarage, Battle Street, Cobham, Gravesend DA12 3DB Tel (01474) 814332 Fax as telephone
E-mail steve.davie@btinternet.com

DAVIES, Adrian Paul. b 43. K Coll Lon. **d** 69 **p** 70. C Nottingham St Mary *S'well* 69-74; C Gt w Lt Billing *Pet* 74-75; P-in-c Marholm 75-82; R Castor 75; R Castor w Sutton and Upton 76-82; V Byker St Mich w St Lawr *Newc* 82-94; rtd 95. *9 Arrow Lane, Halton, Lancaster LA2 6QW* Tel (01524) 811141

DAVIES, Alan. *See* DAVIES, James Alan

DAVIES, Alan Arthur. b 35. Sarum & Wells Th Coll 83. **d** 85 **p** 86. C Eastleigh *Win* 85-88; C Portsea N End St Mark *Portsm* 88-90; V Lydiate *Liv* 90-00; rtd 00; Perm to Offic *Sarum* from 01. *25 St Catherine's, Wimborne BH21 1BE* Tel (01202) 848233

DAVIES, Alastair John. b 56. Nottm Univ BA MTh. Westcott Ho Cam. **d** 84 **p** 85. C Eltham St Jo *S'wark* 84-87; C Dulwich St Barn 87-89; Chapl RAF from 89; P-in-c Lyneham w Bradenstoke *Sarum* 01-03. *Chaplaincy Services (RAF), HQ, Personnel and Training Command, RAF Innsworth, Gloucester GL3 1EZ* Tel (01452) 712612 ext 5032 Fax 510828

DAVIES, Canon Alfred Joseph. b 23. St D Coll Lamp BA49. **d** 50 **p** 51. C Llanegwad *St D* 50-53; C Llanelli Ch Ch 53-54; V Llangeler 54-74; RD Emlyn 70-73; Chapl Cardigan Hosp 74-88; V Cardigan w Mwnt and Y Ferwig *St D* 74-88; Can St D Cathl 79-88; rtd 88; Hon Can St D Cathl *St D* from 88. *Isfoel, Heol Llynyfran, Llandysul SA44 4JW* Tel (01559) 362040

DAVIES, Mrs Alison Margaret. b 57. Nottm Univ BA78. STETS Dip Th & Min 99. **d** 99 **p** 00. NSM Win St Barn *Win* from 99. *13 Silwood Close, Winchester SO22 6EN* Tel (01962) 856432 Fax 862642

DAVIES, Alun Edwards. b 13. Univ of Wales BA40. St D Coll Lamp 45. **d** 46 **p** 47. C Treharris *Llan* 46-48; C Cardigan *St D* 48-50; CF 50-56; Hon CF 56; R Byford w Mansel Gamage *Heref* 56-58; P-in-c Preston-on-Wye w Blakemere 56-58; V Birch St Mary *Man* 58-62; R Lower Crumpsall 62-84; rtd 84; Perm to Offic *Man* from 84. *48 Ashtree Road, Crumpsall, Manchester M8 5AT* Tel 0161-720 8345

DAVIES, Andrew James. b 53. Univ of Wales (Cardiff) BD00. St Mich Coll Llan 01. **d** 03. C Caerphilly *Llan* from 03. *St Andrew's House, 26 Troed y Bryn, Penyrheol, Caerphilly CF83 2PX* Tel (029) 2088 4103 Mobile 07931-370054
E-mail daviesaj8@hotmail.com

DAVIES, Andrew John. b 54. Univ of Wales (Abth) BMus76 St Martin's Coll Lanc PGCE78. Sarum & Wells Th Coll 79. **d** 81 **p** 82. C Tenby w Gumfreston *St D* 81-84; C Llanelli 84-86; V Monkton 86-91; V Fairfield *Derby* 91-96; P-in-c Barlborough 96-01; R Barlborough and Renishaw from 01; V Pembroke Dock *St D* from 03. *The Vicarage, Church Street, Pembroke Dock SA72 6AR* Tel (01646) 682943
E-mail andrewdavies19@aol.com

DAVIES, Anthony. *See* DAVIES, The Ven Vincent Anthony

DAVIES, Anthony. *See* DAVIES, David Anthony

DAVIES, Canon Arthur Cadwaladr. b 19. Univ of Wales BA41. Wells Th Coll 41. **d** 43 **p** 44. C Broughton *St As* 43-48; C Llanrhos 48-52; V Spalding St Paul *Linc* 52-57; V Ches Ch Ch *Ches* 57-64; V Stockton Heath 64-85; RD Gt Budworth 81-85; rtd 85; Perm to Offic *Ban* from 85. *1 The Paddock, Treforris Road, Penmaenmawr LL34 6RH* Tel (01492) 623739

DAVIES, Arthur Gerald Miles. b 29. Univ of Wales (Ban) BA51. St Mich Coll Llan 51. **d** 53 **p** 54. C Shotton *St As* 53-60; R Nannerch 60-63; V Llansilin and Llangadwaladr 63-68; V Llansilin w Llangadwaladr and Llangedwyn 68-71; V Llanfair Caereinion w Llanllugan 71-75; TV Wrexham 75-83; V Hanmer, Bronington, Bettisfield, Tallarn Green 83-94; rtd 94. *Elland, School Lane, Bronington, Whitchurch SY13 3HN* Tel (01948) 780296

DAVIES, Arthur Lloyd. *See* LLOYD-DAVIES, Arthur

DAVIES, Benjamin John. b 27. Glouc Sch of Min 80 Trin Coll Bris 87. **d** 88 **p** 89. NSM Cinderford St Steph w Littledean *Glouc* 88-98; Perm to Offic 98-00. *Address temp unknown*

DAVIES, Bernard. b 24. St D Coll Lamp BA49. **d** 51 **p** 52. C New Tredegar *Mon* 51-53; C Gelligaer *Llan* 53-54; V Deeping Fen *Linc* 56-58; R Beswick *Man* 58-63; V Stand Lane St Jo 63-66; rtd 84. *7 Manitoba Close, Cardiff CF23 6HD*

DAVIES, Canon Bernard. b 34. Lon Univ BD63. Oak Hill Th Coll 59. **d** 63 **p** 64. C Rawtenstall St Mary *Man* 63-69; Sec Rwanda Miss 69-71; R Widford *Chelmsf* 71-78; V Braintree 78-00; RD Braintree 87-95; Hon Can Chelmsf Cathl 92-00; rtd 00; Perm to Offic *Nor* from 00 and *St E* from 01. *3 Brookwood Close, Worlingham, Beccles NR34 7RJ* Tel (01502) 719739

DAVIES, Carol Ann. b 52. Bp Otter Coll 94. **d** 96 **p** 98. NSM Oakfield St Jo *Portsm* 96-00; NSM Bonchurch from 00; NSM Ventnor St Cath from 00; NSM Ventnor H Trin from 00. *Little Dean Lodge, 49A Madeira Road, Ventnor PO38 1QY* Tel (01983) 854249 E-mail revcarol@stablehouse31a.freeserve.co.uk

DAVIES, Catharine Mary. *See* FURLONG, Mrs Catharine Mary

DAVIES, Ceri John. b 61. Univ of Wales (Lamp) BA91 Univ of Wales (Abth) PGCE92 Univ of Wales (Cardiff) BTh00. St Mich Coll Llan 97. **d** 00 **p** 01. C Carmarthen St Dav *St D* 00-03; TV

Llanelli from 03. *St Peter's Vicarage, St Peter's Terrace, Llanelli SA15 2RT* Tel (01554) 752378
E-mail ruth_ceri2000@coleg88.freeserve.co.uk

DAVIES, Chris. *See* DAVIES, Canon David Christopher

DAVIES, Christopher. b 51. NE Lon Poly BA72. SEITE 99. **d** 02. NSM Peckham St Sav *S'wark* from 02. *5 Wyleu Street, London SE23 1DU* Tel and fax (020) 8291 3831 Mobile 07941-392682
E-mail christopherscott@tinyworld.co.uk

DAVIES, Christopher Edward. b 72. **d** 03. OLM Bilston *Lich* from 03. *10 Wroxham Glen, Willenhall WV13 3HU* Tel (01902) 655305 Mobile 07952-196204 E-mail cedavies424@hotmail.com

DAVIES, Christopher John. b 55. St Alb Minl Tr Scheme 83. **d** 86 **p** 87. C Tooting All SS *S'wark* 86-90; V Malden St Jas 90-96; RD Kingston 92-96; TR Wimbledon from 96. *St Mary's Rectory, 14 Arthur Road, London SW19 7DZ* Tel (020) 8946 2830 or 8946 2605 Fax 8946 6293
E-mail church@stmaryswimbledon.fsnet.co.uk

DAVIES, Clifford Morgan. b 19. Univ of Wales BA41. St Mich Coll Llan 41. **d** 43 **p** 44. C Gabalfa *Llan* 43-46; C Pontypridd St Cath 46-51; C Pokesdown All SS *Win* 51-56; V Shipton Bellinger w S Tidworth 56-61; Chapl Duke of York's R Mil Sch Dover 61-77; rtd 84. *37 Applegarth Avenue, Guildford GU2 8LX* Tel (01483) 579415

DAVIES, Canon Clifford Thomas. b 41. Glouc Th Course. **d** 84 **p** 84. NSM Dean Forest H Trin *Glouc* 83-87; C Huntley and Longhope 87; R Ruardean from 87; Hon Can Glouc Cathl from 02. *The Rectory, High Street, Ruardean GL17 9US* Tel (01594) 542214

DAVIES, David Anthony (Tony). b 57. ARICS84 Thames Poly BSc81 MRICS01. Coll of Resurr Mirfield 85. **d** 88 **p** 89. C Stalybridge *Man* 88-91; C Swinton and Pendlebury 91-92 and 01-02; TV 92-01; V Tonge Moor from 02. *St Augustine's Vicarage, Ainsworth Lane, Tonge Moore, Bolton BL2 2QW* Tel and fax (01204) 523899 Mobile 07866-359864
E-mail tony@davieses.co.uk

DAVIES, David Arthur Guy Hampton. b 27. St Jo Coll Ox BA50 DipTh51 MA55. Ely Th Coll 51. **d** 53 **p** 54. C Somers Town *Lon* 53-55; C Cranford 55-60; C Shrewsbury H Cross *Lich* 60-62; R Stamford St Mary and St Mich *Linc* 62-90; rtd 90; Perm to Offic *Lich* 97-01. *8 Holywell Terrace, Shrewsbury SY2 5DF* Tel (01743) 245086

DAVIES, David Barry Grenville. b 38. St Jo Coll Dur BA60 MA77. Sarum Th Coll 61. **d** 63 **p** 64. C Aberystwyth St Mich *St D* 63-66; Min Can St D Cathl 66-72; R Stackpole Elidor w St Petrox 72-83; V Laugharne w Llansadwrnen and Llandawke 83-03; rtd 03. *Ty Seisyll, Penrhiwnewydd, Penrhyncock, Aberystwyth SY23 3EY* Tel (01970) 828370

DAVIES, David Berwyn. b 42. SSC Univ of Wales Dip Past Th 66. St Mich Coll Llan 95. **d** 96 **p** 97. C Llanelli *St D* 96-98; R Llanerch Aeron w Ciliau Aeron and Dihewyd etc from 98. *The Rectory, Ciliau Aeron, Lampeter SA48 7SG* Tel (01570) 471283
E-mail taddavid@aol.com

DAVIES, Canon David Christopher (Chris). b 52. Lon Univ BSc73 Leeds Univ DipTh75. Coll of Resurr Mirfield 73. **d** 76 **p** 77. C Bethnal Green St Jo w St Simon *Lon* 76-78; C Bethnal Green St Jo w St Bart 78-80; C-in-c Portsea St Geo CD *Portsm* 80-81; Relig Affairs Producer Radio Victory 81-86; V Portsea St Geo 81-87; Chapl Ham Green Hosp Bris 87-94; Chapl Southmead Hosp Bris 87-94; Chapl Southmead Health Services NHS Trust 94-99; Chapl N Bris NHS Trust from 99; Perm to Offic *B & W* from 94; Hon Can Bris Cathl *Bris* from 99. *Southmead Hospital, Westbury-on-Trym, Bristol BS10 5NB, or 28 Hortham Lane, Almondsbury, Bristol BS32 4JL* Tel 0117-950 5050 or 959 5447

DAVIES, David Geoffrey George. b 24. Univ of Wales (Ban) BA49 Lon Univ BD55 Chorley Coll of Educn PGCE75. St Mich Coll Llan 49. **d** 51 **p** 52. C Brecon St Mary w Battle and Llanhamlach *S & B* 51-55; Min Can Brecon Cathl 53-55; C Oystermouth 55-59; V Cwm *St As* 59-63; Warden of Ords 62-70; V Ruabon 63-70; Hon Can St As Cathl 66-69; Cursal Can 69-70; NSM W Derby St Jo *Liv* 70-81; Chapl to Welsh Speaking Angl in Liv 74-81; TV Bourne Valley *Sarum* 81-87; TR 87-89; Bp's Chapl to Schs 83-89; RD Alderbury 86-89; rtd 89; Hon Chapl Liv Cathl *Liv* from 89; Sub-Chapl HM Pris Risley 90-96. *55 Hattons Lane, Liverpool L16 7QR* Tel 0151-722 1415

DAVIES, David Islwyn. b 42. St Deiniol's Hawarden 83. **d** 85 **p** 86. C Llangiwg *S & B* 85-87; C Swansea St Pet 87-89; Miss to Seamen 89-94; The Netherlands *Eur* 89-92; Chapl Schiedam Miss to Seamen 89-92; Chapl Milford Haven Miss to Seamen 92-94; V Pontyates and Llangyndeyrn *St D* 94-99; R Ystradgynlais *S & B* from 99. *The Rectory, 2 Heol Eglwys, Ystradgynlais, Swansea SA9 1EY* Tel (01639) 843200

DAVIES, Canon David Jeremy Christopher. b 46. CCC Cam BA68 MA72. Westcott Ho Cam 68. **d** 71 **p** 72. C Stepney St Dunstan and All SS *Lon* 71-74; Chapl Qu Mary Coll 74-78; Chapl Univ of Wales (Cardiff) *Llan* 78-85; Can Res Sarum Cathl *Sarum* from 85. *Hungerford Chantry, 54 The Close, Salisbury SP1 2EL* Tel (01722) 330914 E-mail djcdavies@aol.com

DAVIES, David Leslie Augustus. b 25. St D Coll Lamp BA50. **d** 51 **p** 52. C Aberystwyth *St D* 51-55; C Llanelli St Paul 55-56; V Castlemartin and Warren 56-61; R Eglwysilan *Llan* 61-65; Chapl Mayday, Qu and St Mary's Hosps Croydon 65-71; V Penrhyncoch and Elerch *St D* 71-74; Chapl R Berks and Reading Distr Hosps 74-89; rtd 90; Perm to Offic *Win* from 90. *Basset Down, 31 Three Acre Drive, New Milton BH25 7LG* Tel (01425) 610376

DAVIES, Canon David Michael Cole. b 44. St D Coll Lamp DipTh69. **d** 68 **p** 69. C Carmarthen St Pet *St D* 68-72; R Dinas 72-77; V Ty-Croes w Saron 77-80; V Llanedi w Tycroes and Saron 80-90; RD Dyffryn Aman 85-90; V Dafen and Llwynhendy 90-94; V Dafen from 94; Hon Can St D Cathl from 00. *The Vicarage, Bryngwyn Road, Dafen, Llanelli SA14 8LW* Tel (01554) 774730 E-mail dcmcd@aol.com

DAVIES, Prof David Protheroe. b 39. CCC Cam BA62 MA66 CCC Ox MA69 BD69. Ripon Hall Ox 62. **d** 64 **p** 65. C Swansea St Mary w H Trin *S & B* 64-67; Lect Th Univ of Wales (Lamp) 67-75; Sen Lect 75-86; Dean Faculty of Th 75-77 and from 81; Hd Th and Relig Studies from 84; Prof Th Univ of Wales (Lamp) from 86; Pro Vice-Chan from 88; Bp's Chapl for Th Educn *S & B* from 79. *University of Wales, Lampeter SA48 7ED* Tel (01570) 422351

DAVIES, David Vernon. b 14. AFBPsS68 Univ of Wales (Swansea) BA35 BD38 St Cath Coll Ox MA40 K Coll Lon PhD56. St D Coll Lamp 41. **d** 41 **p** 42. C Llanelli Ch Ch *St D* 41-46; Chapl St John's Coll Nassau Bahamas 46-50; Chapl Cane Hill Hosp Coulsdon 50-61; Lect St Luke's Coll Ex 61-65; Lic to Offic *Ex* 61-68; Sen Lect St Luke's Coll Ex 65-68; Lic to Offic *Llan* from 68; Prin Lect Llan Coll of Educn 68-77; Sen Lect Univ of Wales (Cardiff) 77-79; rtd 79. *41 Cefn Coed Avenue, Cyncoed, Cardiff CF23 6HF* Tel (029) 2075 7635

DAVIES, David William. b 64. **d** 90 **p** 91. C Newton St Pet *S & B* 90-93; V Llywel and Traean-glas w Llanulid 93-97; CF from 97. *c/o MOD Chaplains (Army)* Tel (01980) 615804 Fax 615800

DAVIES, Dennis William. b 24. Leeds Univ BA46 K Coll Lon AKC54 BD65 Open Univ BA92. **d** 54 **p** 55. C Aylesbury *Ox* 54-58; Lic to Offic from 60; rtd 90. *45 Green End Street, Aston Clinton, Aylesbury HP22 5JE* Tel (01296) 630989

DAVIES, Derwent. *See* DAVIES, Preb Derwent

DAVIES, Dewi Caradog. b 14. St D Coll Lamp BA35. **d** 38 **p** 39. C Abercynon *Llan* 38-44; C Cilybebyll 44-49; C-in-c Crynant 49-54; V Tonypandy w Clydach Vale 54-66; R Canton St Jo 66-79; rtd 79. *10 Insole Gardens, Llandaff, Cardiff CF5 2HW* Tel (029) 2056 3743

DAVIES, Dewi Gwynfor. b 56. Thames Poly DipArch80 RIBA82 Univ of Wales (Abth) BD92 MTh98. **d** 98 **p** 99. C Llangunnor w Cwmffrwd *St D* 98-99; P-in-c Elerch w Penrhyncoch w Capel Bangor and Goginan 99-00; P-in-c Cil-y-Cwm and Ystrad-ffin w Rhandir-mwyn etc 00-01; V 01-03; V Llanedi w Tycroes and Saron from 03. *The Vicarage, 37 Hendre Road, Tycroes SA18 3LA* Tel (01269) 592384

DAVIES, Dillwyn. b 30. St Mich Coll Llan 52. **d** 54 **p** 55. C Laugharne w Llansadwrnen and Llandawke *St D* 54-57; Lic to Offic *Dur* 57-58; Miss to Seamen 57-58; Ceylon 58-62; R Winthorpe *S'well* 62-71; V Langford w Holme 62-71; V Mansfield Woodhouse 71-85; R Gedling 85-92; RD Gedling 85-90; Hon Can S'well Minster 90-92; rtd 92. *7 Norbury Drive, Mansfield NG18 4HT* Tel (01623) 458594

DAVIES, Dorrien Paul. b 64. Univ of Wales (Ban) DipTh86 Univ of Wales (Lamp) BA95. Llan Dioc Tr Scheme 86 St Mich Coll Llan DPS88. **d** 88 **p** 89. C Llanelli *St D* 88-91; V Llanfihangel Ystrad and Cilcennin w Trefilan etc 91-99; V St Dogmael's w Moylgrove and Monington from 99. *The Vicarage, St Dogmael's, Cardigan SA43 3DX* Tel (01239) 612030

DAVIES, Prof Douglas James. b 47. St Jo Coll Dur BA69 St Pet Coll Ox MLitt72 Nottm Univ PhD80 Uppsala Univ DTh98. Cranmer Hall Dur 71. **d** 75 **p** 76. Lect Nottm Univ 75-97; Sen Lect 90-97; Hon C Wollaton *S'well* 75-83; Hon C Attenborough 83-85; Hon C E Leake 85-91; Hon C Daybrook 91-97; Prof RS Nottm Univ 95-97; Prin SS Hild and Bede Coll Dur 97-00; Prof Th Dur Univ from 97; Prof Study of Relig Dur Univ from 00; Perm to Offic *Dur* from 97. *Department of Theology, Abbey House, Palace Green, Durham DH1 3RS* Tel 0191-375 7697 E-mail douglas.davies@durham.ac.uk

DAVIES, Canon Douglas Tudor. b 20. Univ of Wales (Ban) BA44. Coll of Resurr Mirfield 44. **d** 46 **p** 47. C Swansea Ch Ch *S & B* 46-52; C Oystermouth 52-57; R Llangynllo and Bleddfa 57-63; C-in-c Treboeth CD 63-65; V Treboeth 65-90; RD Penderi 78-90; Hon Can Brecon Cathl 82-83; Can from 83; rtd 90. *245A Swansea Road, Waunarlwydd, Swansea SA5 4SN* Tel (01792) 879587

DAVIES, Edward Earl. b 40. Llan Dioc Tr Scheme 88. **d** 90 **p** 91. C Pontypridd St Cath w St Matt *Llan* 90-93; V Ferndale w Maerdy 93-00; V Cardiff Ch Ch Roath Park from 00. *154 Lake Road East, Cardiff CF23 5NQ* Tel (029) 2075 7190

DAVIES, Edward Trevor. b 37. MRSC62 MInstE74 CEng78. N Ord Course 92. **d** 95 **p** 96. NSM Waverton *Ches* 95-99; NSM Hargrave 99-00; C Bunbury and Tilstone Fearnall 00-02; NSM from 02; Hon Asst Chapl Countess of Chester Hosp NHS Trust 95-02; Chapl from 02. *Athergreen, 5 Allansford Avenue, Waverton, Chester CH3 7QH* Tel (01244) 332106 Fax as telephone E-mail e.trevordavies@virgin.net

DAVIES, Edward William Llewellyn. b 51. Nottm Univ BTh77. St Jo Coll Nottm 74. **d** 78 **p** 79. C Southsea St Jude *Portsm* 78-81; C Alverstoke 81-84; R Abbas and Templecombe w Horsington *B & W* 84-89; Perm to Offic *Ches* 89-99; V Sutton St Jas from 99; Asst Warden of Readers from 02. *St James's Vicarage, Church Lane, Macclesfield SK11 0DS* Tel (01260) 252228 E-mail taffy@parishpump.co.uk

DAVIES, Ms Elizabeth Jane. b 58. Man Univ BA97 RGN82 RSCN88. Qu Coll Birm 99. **d** 01 **p** 02. C Spotland *Man* from 01. *16 Ashbourne Avenue, Middleton, Manchester M24 2NZ* Tel 0161-643 2781

DAVIES, Mrs Elizabeth Jean. b 39. MRCS63 LRCP63 Lon Univ MB, BS63. S Dios Minl Tr Scheme 86 Chich Th Coll 86. **d** 89 **p** 95. Par Dn Southwick St Mich *Chich* 89-91; Par Dn Littlehampton and Wick 91-95; C Seaford w Sutton 95-97; NSM E Preston w Kingston from 97. *1 The Roystons, East Preston, Littlehampton BN16 2TR* Tel (01903) 784581

DAVIES, Eric Brian. b 36. St Jo Coll Nottm. **d** 87 **p** 89. NSM Castle Donington and Lockington cum Hemington *Leic* 87-88; Hon C Hathern, Long Whatton and Diseworth 89-90; Hon C Hathern, Long Whatton and Diseworth w Belton etc 90-93; C Minster-in-Sheppey *Cant* 93-00; rtd 00; NSM Walsall St Gabr Fulbrook *Lich* 00-03; NSM Caldmore 00-02; NSM Caldmore w Palfrey 02-03; NSM Kinver and Enville from 03. *The Vicarage, The Close, Enville, Stourbridge DY7 5HX* Tel (01384) 878228

DAVIES, Evelyn Dorothy. MBE99. BEd72 Lin Univ CertEd56 Dip Psychology 58. **d** 96 **p** 97. NSM Llangynog *St As* 96-00; P-in-c Aberdaron w Rhiw and Llanfaelrhys etc *Ban* from 00. *Dyffryn, Aberdaron, Pwllheli LL53 8BG* Tel (01758) 760229 Fax as telephone E-mail melangell@pennant1.demon.co.uk

DAVIES, Frances Elizabeth. b 38. BA CertEd Napier Poly Edin DipC&G. Moray Ord Course. **d** 95. Hon C Thurso *Mor* from 95; Hon C Wick from 95. *22 Granville Crescent, Thurso, Caithness KW14 7NP* Tel (01847) 892386

✠**DAVIES, The Rt Revd Francis James Saunders.** b 37. Univ of Wales (Ban) BA60 Selw Coll Cam BA62 MA66 Bonn Univ 63. St Mich Coll Llan 62. **d** 63 **p** 64 **c** 00. C Holyhead w Rhoscolyn *Ban* 63-67; Chapl Ban Cathl 67-69; R Llanllyfni 69-75; Can Missr Ban Cathl 75-78; V Gorseinon *S & B* 78-86; RD Llwchwr 83-86; V Cardiff Dewi Sant *Llan* 86-93; R Criccieth w Treflys *Ban* 93-99; Adn Meirionnydd 93-99; Bp Ban from 99. *Ty'r Esgob, Upper Garth Road, Bangor LL57 2SS* Tel (01248) 362895 Fax 354866 E-mail bishop.bangor@churchinwales.org.uk

DAVIES, Gareth Rhys. b 51. DipHE. Oak Hill Th Coll. **d** 83 **p** 84. C Gt Warley Ch Ch *Chelmsf* 83-86; C Oxhey All SS *St Alb* 86-90; C Aldridge *Lich* 90-99; V Colney Heath St Mark *St Alb* 99-00; V Sneyd Green *Lich* from 00. *St Andrew's Vicarage, 42 Granville Avenue, Sneyd Green, Stoke-on-Trent ST1 6BH* Tel (01782) 215139

DAVIES, Geoffrey. *See* DAVIES, David Geoffrey George

✠**DAVIES, The Rt Revd Geoffrey Francis.** b 41. Cape Town Univ BA62 Em Coll Cam BA67 MA71. Cuddesdon Coll 67. **d** 69 **p** 70 **c** 87. C W Brompton St Mary *Lon* 69-72; Serowe St Aug Botswana 72-76; S Africa from 77; R Kalk Bay H Trin Cape Town 77-80; Dir Dept of Miss 81-87; Suff Bp St John 88-91; Bp Umzimvubu from 91. *PO Box 644, Kokstad, 4700 South Africa* Tel (0027) (39) 727 3351 Fax 727 4117 E-mail umzimvubu@cosa.org.za

DAVIES, Canon Geoffrey Lovat. b 30. St Aid Birkenhead. **d** 62 **p** 63. C Davenham *Ches* 62-65; C Higher Bebington 65-67; V Witton 67-80; R Lymm 80-96; Dioc Clergy Widows and Retirement Officer 87-91; Hon Can Ches Cathl 88-96; RD Gt Budworth 91-96; P-in-c Weaverham 96; rtd 96; Perm to Offic *Liv* from 96; Perm to Offic *Ches* from 96. *21 Howbeck Close, Prenton CH43 6TH* Tel 0151-653 2441

DAVIES, Geoffrey Michael. b 43. St D Coll Lamp DipTh70. **d** 70 **p** 71. C Brynmawr *S & B* 70-73; Coll of Ascension Selly Oak 73-74; S Africa 74-91; C Roath *Llan* 91-95; V Llanishen w Trellech Grange and Llanfihangel etc *Mon* 95-99; S Africa from 99. *12 Bluegum Avenue, Bordeaux, Randburg, Gauteng, 2194 South Africa*

DAVIES, George Vivian. b 21. CCC Cam BA47 MA49. Ely Th Coll. **d** 49 **p** 50. C Maidstone St Martin *Cant* 49-51; C Folkestone St Mary and St Eanswythe 51-56; V Leysdown w Harty 56-59; R Warehorne w Kenardington 59-74; R Rounton w Welbury *York* 74-86; rtd 86; Perm to Offic *Derby* 86-99. *12 Rectory Drive, Wingerworth, Chesterfield S42 6RT* Tel (01246) 279222

DAVIES, George William. b 51. Open Univ BA74 MPhil89 Liv Univ DMS76 MIPD. Sarum & Wells Th Coll 83. **d** 85 **p** 86. C Mansfield St Pet *S'well* 85-89; Chapl Cen Notts HA 86-89; P-in-c Fobbing *Chelmsf* 89-96; Ind Chapl 89-96; Chapl Thurrock Lakeside Shopping Cen 93-96; R Mottingham St Andr *S'wark* from 96. *The Rectory, 233 Court Road, London SE9 4TQ* Tel (020) 8851 1909 E-mail office@standrewschurch.freeserve.co.uk

DAVIES, Glanmor Adrian. b 51. St D Coll Lamp DipTh73. **d** 73 **p** 75. C Llanstadwel *St D* 73-78; R Dinas w Llanllawer and Pontfaen w Morfil etc 78-84; V Lamphey w Hodgeston 84-85; V Lamphey w Hodgeston and Carew 85-03; V Borth and Eglwysfach w Llangynfelyn from 03. *The Vicarage, Swn y Mor, The Cliff, Borth SY24 5NG* Tel (01970) 871594

✠**DAVIES, The Rt Revd Glenn Naunton.** b 50. Sydney Univ BSc72 Sheff Univ PhD88. Westmr Th Sem (USA) BD78 ThM79. **d** 81 **p** 81 **c** 01. Australia 81-85; C Fulwood *Sheff* 85-87; Hon C Lodge Moor St Luke 86-87; Australia from 87; Lect Moore Th Coll 83-95; R Miranda 95-01; Bp N Sydney from 01. *PO Box Q190, Queen Victoria Buildings, Sydney, NSW, Australia 1230* Tel (0061) (2) 9265 1527 *or* 9419 6761 Fax 9265 1543

DAVIES, Glyn Richards. b 28. Solicitor 52. Mon Dioc Tr Scheme 76. **d** 79 **p** 80. NSM Michaelston-y-Fedw and Rudry *Mon* 79-88; NSM St Mellons and Michaelston-y-Fedw 88-96; NSM St Mellons from 96. *Ty Golau, 8 Tyr Winch Road, St Mellons, Cardiff CF3 5UX* Tel (029) 2041 3426

DAVIES, Glyndwr George. b 36. Glouc Sch of Min 88. **d** 91 **p** 92. NSM Clodock and Longtown w Craswall, Llanveynoe etc *Heref* 91-02; rtd 02; Perm to Offic *Heref* from 02. *White House Farm, Llanfihangel Crucorney, Abergavenny NP7 8HW* Tel (01873) 890251

DAVIES, The Ven Graham James. b 35. Univ of Wales BD72 St D Coll Lamp BA56. St Mich Coll Llan 56 Episc Th Sch Cam Mass 58. **d** 59 **p** 60. C Johnston w Steynton *St D* 59-62; C Llangathen w Llanfihangel Cilfargen 62-64; Min Can St D Cathl 64-66; R Burton 66-71; R Hubberston 71-74; Hon C Lenham w Boughton Malherbe *Cant* 74-80; V Cwmddauddwr w St Harmon's and Llanwrthwl *S & B* 80-86; V Cydweli and Llandyfaelog *St D* 86-97; Can St D Cathl 92-02; Adn St D 96-02; V Steynton 97-02; rtd 02. *Mistral, 4 Lloyd George Lane, Pembroke SA71 4EZ*

DAVIES, Canon Henry Joseph. b 38. Univ of Wales (Cardiff) BSc61. St Mich Coll Llan 75. **d** 76 **p** 77. C Griffithstown *Mon* 76-79; TV Cwmbran 79-85; V Newport St Andr 85-03; Can St Woolos Cathl 98-03; rtd 03. *14 Morden Road, Newport NP19 7EU*

DAVIES, Canon Henry Lewis. b 20. St Jo Coll Dur BA42 DipTh43 MA45. **d** 43 **p** 44. C Upton on Severn *Worc* 43-47; C Dudley St Jo 47-49; C Halesowen 49-52; V Cradley 52-65; R Old Swinford 65-78; R Old Swinford Stourbridge 78-85; rtd 85; Perm to Offic *Worc* from 87. *15 Bramley Way, Bewdley DY12 2PU* Tel (01299) 402713

DAVIES, Herbert John. b 30. Cheltenham & Glouc Coll of HE BA97. Glouc Sch of Min 84. **d** 87 **p** 88. NSM Cheltenham St Mark *Glouc* 87-01; Perm to Offic from 01. *45 Farmington Road, Benhall, Cheltenham GL51 6AG* Tel (01242) 515996

✠**DAVIES, The Rt Revd Howell Haydn.** b 27. ARIBA55 DipArch54. Tyndale Hall Bris 56. **d** 59 **p** 60 **c** 81. C Heref St Pet w St Owen *Heref* 59-61; Kenya 61-79; Adn N Maseno 71-74; Provost Nairobi 74-79; V Woking St Pet *Guildf* 79-81; Bp Karamoja Uganda 81-87; V Wolverhampton St Jude *Lich* 87-93; rtd 93; Perm to Offic *Heref* 93-99. *3 Gilberts Wood, Ewyas Harold, Hereford HR2 0JL* Tel (01981) 240984

DAVIES, Huw. *See* DAVIES, Philip Huw

DAVIES, Huw. *See* DAVIES, Philip Huw

DAVIES, Hywel John. b 45. Univ of Wales (Abth) BA67 Univ of Wales (Ban) DipEd68 Univ of Wales (Cardiff) MA90 Univ of Wales (Ban) BTh99. St Mich Coll Llan Qu Coll Birm. **d** 97 **p** 98. Min Can Ban Cathl *Ban* 97-98; C Llandudno 98-99; Hd RS Ysgol Gyfun Llanhari from 99; NSM Canton Cardiff *Llan* from 03. *24 Fairfield Avenue, Cardiff CF5 1BS* Tel (029) 2056 1741

DAVIES, Ian. b 45. Man Coll of Educn TCert74 Open Univ BA79. Carl Dioc Tr Inst 88. **d** 91 **p** 92. NSM Harraby *Carl* 91-95; C Barrow St Jo 95-96; P-in-c 96-00; P-in-c Beetham from 00; Youth and Sch Support Officer from 00. *The Parsonage, Stanley Street, Beetham, Milnthorpe LA7 7AL* Tel (01539) 562216 Fax 562450 E-mail reviand@aol.com

DAVIES, Ian Charles. b 51. Sarum & Wells Th Coll 78. **d** 81 **p** 82. C E Bedfont *Lon* 81-84; C Cheam *S'wark* 84-87; V Merton St Jas 87-96; RD Merton 91-96; Chapl Tiffin Sch Kingston 96-97; P-in-c Kingston St Luke *S'wark* 96-98; V S Beddington St Mich 98-99. *111 Milton Road, London W7 1LG* Tel (020) 8621 4450

DAVIES, Ian Elliott. b 64. Univ of Wales (Ban) BD85. Ridley Hall Cam 86. **d** 88 **p** 89. C Baglan *Llan* 88-90; C Skewen 90-96; C St Marylebone All SS *Lon* 96-01. *Address temp unknown* E-mail frianed@aol.com

DAVIES, Ion. *See* DAVIES, Johnston ap Llynfi

DAVIES, Islwyn. *See* DAVIES, David Islwyn

DAVIES, Canon Ivor Llewellyn. b 35. Univ of Wales BA56 St Cath Soc Ox BA58 MA63. Wycliffe Hall Ox 56. **d** 62 **p** 63. C Wrexham *St As* 62-64; India 65-71; V Connah's Quay *St As* 71-79; P-in-c Gorsley w Cliffords Mesne *Glouc* 79-84; P-in-c Hempsted 84-90; Dir of Ords 84-90; Hon Can Glouc Cathl 89-01; V Parkend 90-01; P-in-c Viney Hill 97-01; rtd 01; Perm to Offic *Glouc* from 01. *Rose Cottage, Church Walk, Parkend, Lydney GL15 4HQ* Tel (01594) 564512

DAVIES, Canon Ivor Llewelyn. b 23. Univ of Wales (Swansea) BA49 St Cath Soc Ox DipTh52 Fitzw Coll Cam BA56 MA60. Wycliffe Hall Ox 49. **d** 51 **p** 52. C Knighton and Heyope *S & B* 51-54; Hon C Cambridge St Andr Gt *Ely* 54-56; C-in-c Llanwrthwl *S & B* 56-59; R Llanfeugan w Llanddetty and Glyncollwg 59-70; P-in-c Llansantffraed-juxta-Usk 67-70; V Hay 70-72; V Hay w Llanigon and Capel-y-Ffin 72-87; V Knighton and Norton 87-89; RD Hay 73-82 and 85-87; Hon Can Brecon Cathl 76-79; Can 79-89; Treas 88-89; rtd 89; Perm to Offic *Heref* from 95. *Bracken Lea, Hazler Road, Church Stretton SY6 7AQ* Tel (01694) 724459

DAVIES, James Alan. b 38. St D Coll Lamp BA39 AKC41. **d** 41 **p** 42. C Fletchamstead *Cov* 83-87; P-in-c Hartshill 87-89; V 89-93; Asst RD Nuneaton 90-93; V E Green from 93. *St Andrew's Vicarage, Church Lane, Eastern Green, Coventry CV5 7BX* Tel (024) 7642 2856 Fax as telephone E-mail alan.davies@ukonline.co.uk

DAVIES, James Owen. b 26. St Aid Birkenhead 60. **d** 61 **p** 62. C Drayton in Hales *Lich* 61-65; V Tipton St Jo 65-69; P-in-c Lt Drayton 70-73; V 73-97; rtd 97; Perm to Offic *Lich* from 99. *64 Grove Gardens, Market Drayton TF9 1HQ*

DAVIES, Canon James Trevor Eiddig. b 17. St D Coll Lamp BA39 AKC41. **d** 41 **p** 42. C Rhymney *Mon* 41-44; C Newport St Andr 44-47; P-in-c 47-51; P-in-c Nash 50-51; R Llanfeugan w Trostrey and Kemeys Commander 51-58; V Blaenavon w Capel Newydd 58-68; V Llantarnam 68-71; TR Cwmbran 71-86; Hon Can St Woolos Cathl 83-86; rtd 86; Lic to Offic *Mon* from 86. *34 Rockfield Road, Monmouth NP25 5BA* Tel (01600) 716649

DAVIES, James William. b 51. Trin Hall Cam BA72 MA76 St Jo Coll Dur BA79. **d** 80 **p** 81. C Croydon Ch Ch Broad Green *Cant* 80-83; CMS 83-86; Chapl Bethany Sch Goudhurst 86-90; P-in-c Parkstone St Luke *Sarum* 90-00. *1 Alexandra Terrace, Cowlease, Swanage BH19 2QQ*

DAVIES, Mrs Jane Ann. b 58. Heref Coll of FE ONC77 Coll of Ripon & York St Jo MA97. N Ord Course 94 Aston Tr Scheme 91 WMMTC 93. **d** 96 **p** 97. NSM Heref S Wye *Heref* 96-97; C 97-00; P-in-c Bishop's Frome w Castle Frome and Fromes Hill from 00; P-in-c Acton Beauchamp and Evesbatch w Stanford Bishop from 00; P-in-c Stoke Lacy, Moreton Jeffries w Much Cowarne etc from 00. *The Vicarage, Bishop's Frome, Worcester WR6 5AP* Tel (01885) 490204

DAVIES, Mrs Jaqueline Ann. b 42. Bris Univ BA64 CertEd65 Univ of Wales (Lamp) MA99. EMMTC 84 St As Minl Tr Course 97. **d** 98 **p** 99. NSM Llanfair DC, Derwen, Llanelidan and Efenechtyd *St As* 98-00; Perm to Offic from 00. *The Vicarage, Llanrhaeadr-ym-Mochnant, Oswestry SY10 0JZ* Tel (01691) 780247

DAVIES, Jeremy. *See* DAVIES, Canon David Jeremy Christopher

DAVIES, Sister Joan Margaret. b 06. Bedf Coll Lon BA28 Maria Grey Coll Lon DipEd29. St Andr Ho Ox 31. **dss** 37 **d** 87. CSA from 34; Notting Hill St Clem *Lon* 37-43; Paddington St Steph w St Luke 48-69; Shadwell St Paul w Ratcliffe St Jas 69-73; R Foundn of St Kath in Ratcliffe 69-73; Abbey Ho Malmesbury 76-79; Lic to Offic *Bris* 76-79. *St Andrew's House, 2 Tavistock Road, London W11 1BA* Tel (020) 7229 2662

DAVIES, John. *See* DAVIES, Herbert John

DAVIES, John. *See* DAVIES, Benjamin John

DAVIES, John. *See* PAGE DAVIES, David John

DAVIES, John. b 62. Univ of Wales (Cardiff) BA88. Ridley Hall Cam 98. **d** 00 **p** 01. C Wavertree H Trin *Liv* from 00. *66 Grant Avenue, Liverpool L15 5AY* Tel 0151-733 6733 Fax as telephone E-mail johndavies.liverpool@blueyonder.co.uk

DAVIES, John Atcherley. b 27. St Jo Coll Dur BA55. Wycliffe Hall Ox 55. **d** 57 **p** 58. C Eastbourne St Jo *Chich* 57-61; Chapl RN 61-82; V Hyde Common *Win* 82-92; rtd 92; Perm to Offic *Win* from 96. *6 Durlston Crescent, St Catherine's Hill, Christchurch BH23 2ST* Tel (01202) 484398

DAVIES, John Barden. b 47. Univ of Wales (Ban) DipTh70. St D Coll Lamp 70. **d** 71 **p** 72. C Rhosllannerchrugog *St As* 71-75; R Llanbedr-y-Cennin *Ban* 75-86; Adult Educn Officer 86-93; V Betws-y-Coed and Capel Curig w Penmachno etc 86-93; R Llanfrwog and Clocaenog and Gyffylliog *St As* from 93; RD Dyffryn Clwyd from 95. *The Rectory, Mwrog Street, Ruthin LL15 1LE* Tel (01824) 704866 Mobile 07050-152824 Fax 702724 E-mail jbarden@btinternet.com

DAVIES, John Daniel Lee. b 55. Trin Coll Carmarthen BEd79 CertRE91. **d** 00 **p** 00. C Leverburgh *Arg* 00-01; P-in-c Lochgilphead from 01. *3A Cluer, Isle of Harris HS3 3EP* Tel (01859) 530344

DAVIES, The Very Revd John David Edward. b 53. Southn Univ LLB74 Univ of Wales (Cardiff) DipTh84 LLM95. St Mich Coll Llan 82. **d** 84 **p** 85. C Chepstow *Mon* 84-86; C-in-c Michaelston-y-Fedw and Rudry 86-89; R Bedwas and Rudry 89-95; V Maindee 95-00; Dean Brecon *S & B* from 00; V Brecon St Mary w Llanddew from 00. *The Deanery, Cathedral Close, Brecon LD3 9DP* Tel (01874) 623344

✠**DAVIES, The Rt Revd John Dudley.** b 27. Trin Coll Cam BA51 MA63. Linc Th Coll 52. **d** 53 **p** 54 **c** 87. C Leeds Halton St Wilfrid *Ripon* 53-56; S Africa 57-71; Sec Chapls in HE Gen

Syn Bd of Educn 71-74; P-in-c Keele *Lich* 74-76; Chapl Keele Univ 74-76; Prin USPG Coll of the Ascension Selly Oak 76-81; Preb Lich Cathl *Lich* 76-87; Can Res, Preb and Sacr St As Cathl *St As* 82-85; Dioc Missr 82-87; V Llanrhaeadr-ym-Mochnant, Llanarmon, Pennant etc 85-87; Suff Bp Shrewsbury *Lich* 87-92; Area Bp 92-94; rtd 94. *Nyddfa, By-Pass Road, Gobowen, Oswestry SY11 3NG* Tel (01691) 653434 Fax as telephone E-mail sddjdd@sddjdd.free-online.co.uk

DAVIES, John Edwards Gurnos. b 18. Ch Coll Cam BA41 MA45. Westcott Ho Cam 40. d 42 p 43. C Portwood St Paul *Ches* 42-44; CF (EC) 44-46; CF 46-73; Asst Chapl Gen 70; Hon Chapl to The Queen 72; R Monk Sherborne and Pamber *Win* 73-76; P-in-c Sherborne 76; R The Sherbornes w Pamber 76-83; rtd 83. *3 Parsonage Lane, Edington, Westbury BA13 4QS* Tel (01380) 830479

DAVIES, John Gwylim. b 27. Ripon Hall Ox 67. d 70 p 71. C Ox St Mich *Ox* 70-71; C Ox St Mich w St Martin and All SS 71-72; TV New Windsor 73-77; R Hagley *Worc* 77-83; TV Littleham w Exmouth *Ex* 83-92; Asst Dioc Stewardship Adv 83-92; rtd 92; Perm to Offic *Ex* from 92. *5 The Retreat, The Retreat Drive, Topsham, Exeter EX3 0LS* Tel (01392) 876995

DAVIES, John Gwyn. b 12. St Cath Coll Cam BA36 MA40. Ely Th Coll 36. d 37 p 38. C Fleetwood *Blackb* 37-39; C Wyken *Cov* 39-44; P-in-c 44-45; V 45-54; V Rowington 54-77; rtd 78; Perm to Offic *Cov* from 78. *Lapwater, Pinley, Claverdon, Warwick CV35 8NA* Tel (01926) 842597

DAVIES, John Harverd. b 57. Keble Coll Ox BA80 MA84 CCC Cam MPhil82 Lanc Univ PhD. Westcott Ho Cam 82. d 84 p 85. C Liv Our Lady and St Nic w St Anne *Liv* 84-87; C Pet St Jo *Pet* 87-90; Min Can Pet Cathl 88-90; V Anfield St Marg *Liv* 90-94; Chapl, Fell and Lect Keble Coll Ox 94-99; V Melbourne *Derby* from 99; Dioc Dir of Ords from 00. *The Vicarage, Church Square, Melbourne, Derby DE73 1EN* Tel (01332) 862347 E-mail jhd@rdplus.net

DAVIES, Canon John Howard. b 29. St Jo Coll Cam BA50 MA54 Nottm Univ BD62. Westcott Ho Cam 54. d 55 p 56. Succ Derby Cathl *Derby* 55-58; Chapl Westcott Ho Cam 58-63; Lect Th Southn Univ 63-81; Lic to Offic *Win* 63-81; Sen Lect 74-81; Dir Th and RS Southn Univ 81-94; Can Th Win Cathl *Win* 81-91; Hon C Southampton St Alb 88-91; Hon C Swaythling 91-94; rtd 94. *13 Glen Eyre Road, Southampton SO16 3GA* Tel (023) 8067 9359

DAVIES, Canon John Howard. b 35. Brasted Th Coll 60 Ely Th Coll 62. d 64 p 65. C Bromsgrove All SS *Worc* 64-67; C Astwood Bank w Crabbs Cross 67-70; R Worc St Martin 70-74; P-in-c Worc St Pet 72-74; R Worc St Martin w St Pet 74-79; RD Worc E 77-79; TR Malvern Link w Cowleigh 79-93; Hon Can Worc Cathl 81-00; RD Malvern 83-92; V Bromsgrove St Jo 93-00; rtd 00. *10 Baveney Road, Worcester WR2 6DS* Tel (01905) 428086

DAVIES, John Howard. b 51. EAMTC. d 01 p 02. NSM Walsingham, Houghton and Barsham *Nor* from 01. *The Anchorage, Whissonsett Road, Colkirk, Fakenham NR21 7NL* Tel (01328) 863385 Mobile 07870-509439 E-mail john_davies@hotmail.com

DAVIES, John Hugh Conwy. b 42. Bris Univ BSc64 PhD67 CEng72 MICE72. Linc Th Coll 84. d 86 p 87. C Limber Magna w Brocklesby *Linc* 86-89; R Wickenby Gp 89-94; R Denbigh and Nantglyn *St As* 94-99; R Denbigh 99-00; V Llanrhaeadr-ym-Mochnant etc from 01. *The Vicarage, Llanrhaeadr ym Mochnant, Oswestry SY10 0JZ* Tel (01691) 780247

DAVIES, John Hywel Morgan. b 45. St D Coll Lamp BA71 LTh73. d 73 p 74. C Milford Haven *St D* 73-77; V from 89; R Castlemartin w Warren and Angle etc 77-82; R Walton W w Talbenny and Haroldston W 82-89. *St Katharine's Vicarage, 1 Sandhurst Road, Milford Haven SA73 3JU* Tel (01646) 693314 E-mail johnmorgandavies@talk21.com

DAVIES, John Ifor. b 20. ACP DipEd. d 80 p 81. Hon C Allerton *Liv* 80-84; Hon C Ffynnongroyw *St As* 84-87; Hon C Whitford 87-88. *Hafan Deg, Ffordd-y-Graig, Lixwm, Holywell CH8 8LY* Tel (01352) 781151

DAVIES, John Keith. b 33. St Mich Coll Llan 80. d 82 p 83. C Llanbadarn Fawr w Capel Bangor and Goginan *St D* 82-84; V Llandygwydd and Cenarth w Cilrhedyn etc 84-89; V Abergwili w Llanfihangel-uwch-Gwili etc 89-98; RD Carmarthen 93-98; rtd 98. *Tanyfron, 81 Hafod Cwnin, Carmarthen SA31 2AS* Tel (01267) 242551

DAVIES, John Melvyn George. b 37. Wycliffe Hall Ox 68. d 71 p 72. C Norbury *Ches* 71-75; C Heswall 76-78; V Claughton cum Grange 78-83; R Waverton 83-02; RD Malpas 90-97; rtd 02. *15 Tattenhall Road, Tattenhall, Chester CH3 9QQ* Tel (01829) 770184

DAVIES, Canon John Oswell. b 27. St D Coll Lamp 74. d 75 p 76. C Henfynyw w Aberaeron and Llanddewi Aberarth *St D* 75-76; P-in-c Eglwyswenydd w Ysbyty Ystwyth 76-77; V 77-83; R Maenordeifi and Capel Colman w Llanfihangel etc 83-93; RD Cemais and Sub-Aeron 84-93; Hon Can St D Cathl 92-93; rtd 93. *Hafod, Carregwen, Llechryd, Cardigan SA43 2PJ* Tel (01239) 682568

✠**DAVIES, The Rt Revd John Stewart.** b 43. Univ of Wales BA72 Qu Coll Cam MLitt74. Westcott Ho Cam 72. d 74 p 75 c 99. C Hawarden *St As* 74-78; Tutor St Deiniol's Lib Hawarden 76-83; V Rhosymedre *St As* 78-87; Dir Dioc Minl Tr Course 83-93; Warden of Ords 83-91; Hon Can St As Cathl 86-91; V Mold 87-92; Adn St As 91-99; R Llandyrnog and Llangwyfan 92-99; Bp St As from 99. *Esgobty, St Asaph LL17 0TW* Tel (01745) 583503 Fax 584301 E-mail bishop.stasaph@churchinwales.org.uk

DAVIES, Johnston ap Llynfi (Ion). b 28. St D Coll Lamp BA51 St Mich Coll Llan 51. d 53 p 54. C Swansea Ch Ch *S & B* 53-55; C Sketty 55-57; Nigeria 57-61; R Whittington *Derby* 61-64; Chapl Broadmoor Hosp Crowthorne 64-66; Perm to Offic *Ox* 67-72; Perm to Offic *York* 72-86; V Creeksea w Althorne, Latchingdon and N Fambridge *Chelmsf* 86-88; rtd 88; Asst Chapl Costa Blanca *Eur* 89-92; Chapl 92-93; Lic to Offic 93-95. *Apartmentos Esmeralda 41A, Playa de Levante, 03710 Calpe, Alicante, Spain* Tel (0034) (96) 583 8063

DAVIES, Jonathan Byron. b 69. Univ of Wales DipTh94 BTh95. St Mich Coll Llan Dip Past Th 96. d 96 p 97. C Betws w Ammanford *St D* 96-00. *Address temp unknown*

DAVIES, Judith. b 54. Man Univ BA75. WEMTC 97. d 00 p 01. C Harlescott *Lich* from 00. *19 Heron Drive, Shrewsbury SY1 4UG* Tel (01743) 465431 E-mail judyd@fish.co.uk

DAVIES, Julian Edward. b 60. Jes Coll Ox BA82 MA86 DPhil87 Selw Coll Cam BA92 MA96. Ridley Hall Cam 90. d 94 p 95. C Hucknall Torkard *S'well* 94-96; C Eglwysilan *Llan* 96-99; Assoc R St Marylebone w H Trin *Lon* from 99. *16 Clarence Gate Gardens, Glentworth Street, London NW1 6AY* Tel (020) 7724 7883 or 7563 1684 E-mail jdavies@stmarylebone.org

DAVIES, Keith. *See* DAVIES, John Keith

DAVIES, Keith. *See* BERRY-DAVIES, Charles William Keith

DAVIES, Kenneth John. b 42. Ripon Coll Cuddesdon 79. d 80 p 81. C Buckingham *Ox* 80-83; V Birstall *Wakef* 83-91; TV Crookes St Thos *Sheff* 91-94; TR Huntington *York* from 94. *The Rectory, New Lane, Huntington, York YO32 9NU* Tel (01904) 768160 E-mail johnsuedavies@aol.com

DAVIES, Kevin Godfrey. b 62. Univ Coll Ox BA84 MA87. Trin Coll Bris BA93. d 93 p 94. C Otley *Bradf* 93-97; P-in-c Scotby *Carl* 97-00; P-in-c Scotby and Cotehill w Cumwhinton 00-02; TR Langtree *Ox* from 02; P-in-c Whitchurch St Mary from 02. *The Rectory, Checkendon, Reading RG8 0SR* Tel (01491) 680252 E-mail langtreerector@hotmail.com

DAVIES, Laurence Gordon. b 28. Down Coll Cam BA52 MA56. Linc Th Coll 52. d 54 p 55. C E Dulwich St Jo *S'wark* 54-57; C Boyne Hill *Ox* 57-61; V Brigstock w Stanion *Pet* 61-69; R Gt w Lt Billing 69-83; V Welton w Ashby St Ledgers 83-88; rtd 88; Perm to Offic *Ox* from 89. *Cherry Pie, 56 Couching Street, Watlington OX9 5PU* Tel (01491) 612446

DAVIES, The Ven Lorys Martin. b 36. JP78. ALCM52 Univ of Wales (Lamp) BA57. Wells Th Coll 57. d 59 p 60. C Tenby w Gumfreston *St D* 59-62; Asst Chapl Brentwood Sch Essex 62-66; Chapl Solihull Sch 66-68; V Moseley St Mary *Birm* 68-81; Can Res Birm Cathl 81-92; Dioc Dir of Ords 82-90; Adn Bolton *Man* 92-01; Bp's Adv Hosp Chapl 92-01; Warden of Readers 94-01; rtd 02. *Heol Cerrig, 28 Penshurst Road, Bromsgrove B60 2SN* Tel (01527) 577337

DAVIES (née ROACH), Mrs Lynne Elisabeth. b 44. WMMTC 95. d 98 p 99. NSM Snitterfield w Bearley *Cov* 98-01; NSM Salford Priors from 01; NSM Exhall w Wixford from 01; NSM Temple Grafton w Binton from 01. *19 Garrard Close, Salford Priors, Evesham WR11 8XG* Tel (01789) 773711 Fax 490231

DAVIES, Malcolm. b 35. St Mich Coll Llan 82. d 84 p 85. C Roath *Llan* 84-88; C Pentre 88-94; V Llancarfan w Llantrithyd 94-02; rtd 02. *141 Fontygary Road, Rhoose, Barry CF62 3DU* Tel (01446) 710509

DAVIES, Malcolm Thomas. b 36. Open Univ BA81. St Mich Coll Llan 71. d 73 p 74. C Betws w Ammanford *St D* 73-76; V Cil-y-Cwm and Ystrad-ffin w Rhandir-mwyn etc 76-80; V Llangyfelach *S & B* 80-85; V Loughor 85-94; V Llanelli St Paul *St D* 94-95; V Llanelli St Pet 95-01; rtd 01. *25 Walters Road, Llanelli SA15 1LR* Tel (01554) 770295

DAVIES, Mrs Margaret Adelaide. b 45. Weymouth Coll of Educn CertEd67 DipTh96. S Dios Minl Tr Scheme 92. d 95 p 96. NSM Westbury *Sarum* 95-02; NSM White Horse from 02. *60 Newtown, Westbury BA13 3EF* Tel (01373) 823735

DAVIES, Canon Mark. b 62. BA85. Coll of Resurr Mirfield 86. d 89 p 90. C Barnsley St Mary *Wakef* 89-95; R Hemsworth from 95; Dioc Vocations Adv and Asst Dir of Ords from 98; RD Pontefract from 00; Hon Can Wakef Cathl from 02. *The Rectory, 3 Church Close, Hemsworth, Pontefract WF9 4SJ* Tel (01977) 610507 E-mail sthelen@dialstart.net

DAVIES, Martin. *See* DAVIES, William Martin

DAVIES, Martyn John. b 60. Chich Th Coll 82. d 85 p 86. C Llantrisant *Llan* 85-87; C Whitchurch 87-90; P-in-c Trealaw 90-01; R Merthyr Tydfil St Dav from 01. *The Rectory, Bryntirion Road, Merthyr Tydfil CF47 0ER* Tel (01685) 722992 E-mail msd@learnfree.co.uk

DAVIES, Melvyn. *See* DAVIES, John Melvyn George
DAVIES, Canon Mervyn Morgan. b 25. Univ of Wales BA49. Coll of Resurr Mirfield 49. **d** 51 **p** 52. C Penarth w Lavernock *Llan* 51-58; Lic to Offic *Wakef* 58-60; C Port Talbot St Theodore *Llan* 60-63; V Pontycymer and Blaengarw 63-69; V Fairwater 69-95; RD Llan 81-95; Jt Ed *Welsh Churchman* 82-95; Can Llan Cathl 84-89; Prec 89-95; rtd 95; Perm to Offic *Llan* from 95. *20 Palace Avenue, Llandaff, Cardiff CF5 2DW* Tel (029) 2057 5327
DAVIES, Miss Moira Kathleen. b 41. Cant Sch of Min. **d** 88 **p** 94. Par Dn Walmer *Cant* 88-94; C 94-96; P-in-c Somercotes and Grainthorpe w Conisholme *Linc* 96-99; R from 99. *The Rectory, Keeling Street, North Somercotes, Louth LN11 7QU* Tel (01507) 358829
DAVIES, Canon Mostyn David. b 37. AKC64. **d** 65 **p** 66. C Corby St Columba *Pet* 65-69; Ind Chapl 69-03; P-in-c Pet St Barn 80-03; Can Pet Cathl from 95; rtd 03; Perm to Offic *Pet* from 03. *16 Swanspool, Peterborough PE3 7LS* Tel (01733) 262034
E-mail mostyn@zetnet.co.uk
DAVIES, Canon Myles Cooper. b 50. Sarum & Wells Th Coll 71. **d** 74 **p** 75. C W Derby St Mary *Liv* 74-77; C Seaforth 77-80; V 80-84; V Stanley from 84; Chapl Rathbone Hosp *Liv* 84-92; Chapl N Mersey Community NHS Trust from 92; Dir of Ords *Liv* from 94; Hon Can Liv Cathl from 01. *St Anne's Vicarage, 8 Derwent Square, Liverpool L13 6QT* Tel 0151-228 5252 Fax as telephone E-mail frmyles@saint-anne.freeserve.co.uk
DAVIES, Neil Anthony Bowen. b 52. Ex Univ BSc74. Westcott Ho Cam 75. **d** 78 **p** 79. C Llanblethian w Cowbridge and Llandough etc *Llan* 78-80; C Aberdare 80-82; V Troedyrhiw w Merthyr Vale 82-88; Min Lower Earley LEP *Ox* 88-92; V Earley Trinity 92-95; P-in-c Reading St Luke w St Bart 95-99; Perm to Offic from 99. *14 Measham Way, Lower Earley, Reading RG6 4ES* Tel 0118-931 4847 E-mail neil@daviesuk30.freeserve.co.uk
DAVIES, Nigel Lawrence. b 55. Lanc Univ BEd77. Sarum & Wells Th Coll 84. **d** 87 **p** 88. C Heywood St Luke w All So *Man* 87-91; V Burnside *Carl* from 91. *St Oswald's Vicarage, Burneside, Kendal LA9 6QX* Tel (01539) 722015 Fax (07974) 010223 E-mail vicar_stoswald@hotmail.com
DAVIES, Noel Paul. b 47. Chich Th Coll 83. **d** 85 **p** 86. C Milford Haven *St D* 85-89; R Jeffreyston w Reynoldston and E Williamston etc from 89. *The Rectory, Jeffreyston, Kilgetty SA68 0SG* Tel (01646) 651269
DAVIES, Canon Patricia Elizabeth. b 36. Westf Coll Lon BA58 Hughes Hall Cam CertEd59 Leeds Univ MA74. NEOC 83. **dss** 86 **d** 87 **p** 94. Killingworth *Newc* 86-90; Hon C 87-90; Hon C Newc H Cross 91-96; NSM Newc Epiphany 96-99; NSM Gosforth St Hugh 99-00; P-in-c 00-01; Hon Can Newc Cathl 00-01; rtd 01; Perm to Offic *York* from 01. *Applegarth, Middlewood Lane, Fylingthorp, Whitby YO22 4TT* Tel (01947) 881175
DAVIES, Patrick Charles Steven. b 59. RGN86 RMN92 RHV94 Man Poly DN92 Man Metrop Univ DipHE94 Man Univ DipTh97 Leeds Univ BA99. Coll of Resurr Mirfield 97. **d** 99 **p** 00. C Reddish *Man* from 99. *2 Rowsley Grove, Stockport SK5 7AH* Tel 0161-443 1949 E-mail fatherpat@btinternet.com
DAVIES, Paul. *See* DAVIES, Richard Paul
DAVIES, Paul Lloyd. b 46. Solicitor 71 Bris Univ LLB68 Trin Coll Carmarthen 84. **d** 87 **p** 88. NSM Newport w Cilgwyn and Dinas w Llanllawer *St D* 87-97; P-in-c Mathry w St Edren's and Grandston etc 97-01; V from 01. *The Rectory, St Nicholas, Goodwick SA64 0LG* Tel (01348) 891230
DAVIES, Paul Martin. b 35. Lon Univ BD75. Sarum & Wells Th Coll 75. **d** 75 **p** 76. C Walthamstow St Mary w St Steph *Chelmsf* 75-79; Kenya 79-86; R Leven w Catwick *York* 86-95; RD N Holderness 90-95; rtd 95; Perm to Offic *York* from 95. *54 The Meadows, Cherry Burton, Beverley HU17 7SD* Tel (01964) 551739
DAVIES, Paul Scott. b 59. Cranmer Hall Dur 85. **d** 88 **p** 89. C New Addington *S'wark* 88-91; C Croydon H Sav 91-94; P-in-c Norton in the Moors *Lich* 94-99; R from 99. *The New Rectory, Norton Lane, Stoke-on-Trent ST6 8BY* Tel (01782) 534622 E-mail paul@zippor.com
DAVIES, Peter Huw. b 57. Crewe & Alsager Coll BEd79. Wycliffe Hall Ox 87. **d** 89 **p** 90. C Moreton *Ches* 89-93; V Weston-super-Mare St Paul *B & W* from 93. *St Paul's Vicarage, 33 Clarence Road North, Weston-super-Mare BS23 4AW* Tel (01934) 412687 E-mail huwdavies@wsm500.freeserve.co.uk
DAVIES, Peter Richard. b 32. St Jo Coll Ox BA55 MA58. Westcott Ho Cam 56. **d** 58 **p** 59. C Cannock *Lich* 58-62; Kenya 63-76; Chapl Bedford Sch 76-85; V Dale and St Brides w Marloes *St D* 85-92; rtd 92. *Canthill Cottage, Dale, Haverfordwest SA62 3QZ* Tel (01646) 636535
DAVIES, Peter Timothy William. b 50. Leeds Univ BSc74. Oak Hill Th Coll 75. **d** 78 **p** 79. C Kingston Hill St Paul *S'wark* 78-81; C Hove Bp Hannington Memorial Ch *Chich* 81-88; V Audley *Lich* from 88. *The Vicarage, Wilbraham Walk, Audley, Stoke-on-Trent ST7 8HL* Tel (01782) 720392
DAVIES, The Ven Philip Bertram. b 33. Cuddesdon Coll 61. **d** 63 **p** 64. C Atherton *Man* 63-66; V Winton 66-71; R Salford St Phil

w St Steph 71-76; V Radlett *St Alb* 76-87; RD Aldenham 79-87; Adn St Alb 87-98; rtd 98. *Stone Cottage, 34 School Road, Finstock, Chipping Norton OX7 3DJ* Tel (01993) 868207
DAVIES, Philip Huw. b 64. Aston Univ BSc86 MRPharmS87. St Mich Coll Llan 00. **d** 02 **p** 03. C Llangynwyd w Maesteg *Llan* 02-03; C Betws w Ammanford *St D* from 03. *19 Llwyn-y-Bryn, Bonllwyn, Ammanford SA18 2ES* Tel (01269) 595753
DAVIES, Philip James. b 58. UEA BA79 Keswick Hall Coll PGCE80 K Coll Lon MA92. Ridley Hall Cam 86. **d** 89 **p** 90. C Rainham *Roch* 89-90; C Gravesend St Geo and Rosherville 90-95; V Rosherville 95-98; P-in-c King's Cliffe *Pet* from 98; Dioc Schs Development Officer from 98. *The Rectory, 3 Hall Yard, King's Cliffe, Peterborough PE8 6XQ* Tel (01780) 470314 E-mail p.j.davies@tesco.net
DAVIES, Philip Simon. b 65. Trin Coll Ox BA87 MA91. Aston Tr Scheme 93 Ridley Hall Cam 95. **d** 97 **p** 98. C Burntwood *Lich* 97-00; TV Cheswardine, Childs Ercall, Hales, Hinstock etc 00-03; TR from 03. *The Vicarage, Childs Ercall, Market Drayton TF9 2DA* Tel (01952) 840229 E-mail davies1@ukonline.co.uk
DAVIES, Philip Wyn. b 50. Univ of Wales BA72 MA82 DAA82. St D Dioc Tr Course 93 St Mich Coll Llan BD96. **d** 96 **p** 97. C Llandysul *St D* 96-98; V Tregaron w Ystrad Meurig and Strata Florida from 98. *The Vicarage, Tregaron SY25 6HL* Tel (01974) 299010
DAVIES, Raymond Emlyn Peter. b 25. St Mich Coll Llan 51. **d** 53 **p** 54. C Llangeinor *Llan* 53-58; C Llanishen and Lisvane 58-62 and 65-68; R Glyncorrwg w Afan Vale and Cymmer Afan 62-65; V Penrhiwceiber w Matthewstown and Ynysboeth 68-72; C Whitchurch 72-73; V Childs Ercall *Lich* 73-81; R Stoke upon Tern 73-81; P-in-c Hamstall Ridware w Pipe Ridware 81-82; P-in-c Kings Bromley 81-82; P-in-c Mavesyn Ridware 81-82; R The Ridwares and Kings Bromley 83-90; rtd 90; Perm to Offic *B & W* from 95. *51 Vereland Road, Hutton, Weston-super-Mare BS24 9TH* Tel (01934) 814680
DAVIES, Rebecca Jane. b 75. Clare Coll Cam MA96. St Mich Coll Llan 01. **d** 03. C Llandeilo Fawr and Taliaris *St D* from 03. *19 Llwyn-y-Bryn, Ammanford SA18 2ES* Tel (01269) 595753
DAVIES, Reginald Charles. b 33. Tyndale Hall Bris 58. **d** 64 **p** 65. C Heywood St Jas *Man* 64-66; C Drypool St Columba w St Andr and St Pet *York* 66-69; V Denaby Main *Sheff* from 69. *The Vicarage, Church Road, Denaby Main, Doncaster DN12 4AD* Tel (01709) 862297
DAVIES, Rendle Leslie. b 29. St Chad's Coll Dur BA52 DipTh54 CertFE DipSS. **d** 54 **p** 55. C Monmouth *Mon* 54-58; V Llangwm Uchaf w Llangwm Isaf w Gwernesney etc 58-63; V Usk and Monkswood w Glascoed Chpl and Gwehelog 63-99; Chapl HM YOI Usk and Prescoed 63-94; rtd 99. *12 Ridgeway, Wyesham, Monmouth NP25 3JX*
DAVIES, Rhiannon Mary Morgan. *See* JOHNSON, Rhiannon Mary Morgan
DAVIES, Richard James. b 42. Peterho Cam BA64 MA68. St Steph Ho Ox 67. **d** 69 **p** 70. Rhodesia 69-72 and 75-80; Zimbabwe from 80; C Southwick St Mich *Chich* 72-74; P-in-c Malmesbury w Westport *Bris* 75. *Address temp unknown*
DAVIES, Richard Paul. b 48. Wycliffe Hall Ox 72. **d** 75 **p** 76. C Everton St Sav w St Cuth *Liv* 75-78; Chapl Asst Basingstoke Distr Hosp 78-80; TV Basingstoke *Win* 80-85; V Southampton Thornhill St Chris 85-94; V Eastleigh from 94. *The Vicarage, 1 Cedar Road, Eastleigh SO50 9DB* Tel (023) 8061 2073
DAVIES, Richard Paul. b 73. Univ of Wales (Lamp) BA94 Ox Univ MTh98. Ripon Coll Cuddesdon 94. **d** 97 **p** 98. Min Can St D Cathl *St D* from 97; TV Dewisland from 01. *The Vicarage, Whitchurch, Solva, Haverfordwest SA62 6UD* Tel (01437) 721281 E-mail rpledavies@aol.com
DAVIES, Robert Emlyn. b 56. N Staffs Poly BA79. Coll of Resurr Mirfield 83. **d** 86 **p** 87. C Cardiff St Jo *Llan* 86-90; V Cwmparc 90-97; V Aberdare from 97; AD Cynon Valley from 02. *The Vicarage, 26 Abernant Road, Aberdare CF44 0PY* Tel (01685) 884769
DAVIES, Roger Charles. b 46. Univ of Wales BD73. St Mich Coll Llan 69. **d** 73 **p** 74. C Llanfabon *Llan* 73-76; CF (TAVR) 75-94; C Llanblethian w Cowbridge and Llandough etc *Llan* 76-78; TV Halesworth w Linstead, Chediston, Holton etc *St E* 84-87; R Claydon and Barham 87-91; R Lavant *Chich* 91-94; Chapl Lavant Ho Sch W Sussex 91-94. *Address temp unknown*
✠**DAVIES, The Rt Revd Ross Owen.** b 55. Melbourne Univ BA71 LLB79. ACT ThL81. **d** 81 **p** 82 **c** 02. Australia 81-91 and from 97; P-in-c Mundford w Lynford *Nor* 91-94; P-in-c Ickburgh w Langford 91-94; P-in-c Cranwich 91-94; C Somerton w Compton Dundon, the Charltons etc *B & W* 94-97; R Hindmarsh 97-00; Vic Gen and Adn The Murray 00-02; Bp from 02. *23 Ellendale Avenue, PO Box 269, Murray Bridge, S Australia 5253* Tel (0061) (8) 8532 2270 Mobile 428-891850 Fax (8) 8532 5760 E-mail r.davies@murray.anglican.org
DAVIES, Miss Rowan. b 55. Univ of Wales (Swansea) BA78 PGCE79. WMMTC 00. **d** 03. NSM Wigginton *Lich* from 03. *16 Queen's Way, Tamworth B79 8QD* Tel (01827) 69651 E-mail hedgerow@tinyworld.co.uk

DAVIES, Preb Roy Basil. b 34. Bris Univ BA55. Westcott Ho Cam 57. **d** 59 **p** 60. C Ipswich St Mary le Tower *St E* 59-63; C Clun w Chapel Lawn *Heref* 63-70; V Bishop's Castle w Mainstone 70-83; RD Clun Forest 72-83; Preb Heref Cathl 82-99; P-in-c Billingsley w Sidbury 83-86; P-in-c Chelmarsh 83-86; P-in-c Chetton w Deuxhill and Glazeley 83-86; P-in-c Middleton Scriven 83-86; R Billingsley w Sidbury, Middleton Scriven etc 86-89; RD Bridgnorth 87-89; TR Wenlock 89-99; rtd 99; Perm to Offic *Heref* from 00. *13 Courtnay Rise, Hereford HR1 1BP* Tel (01432) 341154

✠**DAVIES, The Rt Revd Roy Thomas.** b 34. St D Coll Lamp BA55 Jes Coll Ox DipTh58 BLitt59. St Steph Ho Ox 57. **d** 59 **p** 60 **c** 85. C Llanelli St Paul *St D* 59-64; V Llanafan y Trawscoed and Llanwnnws 64-67; Chapl Univ of Wales (Abth) 67-73; C Aberystwyth 67-69; TV 70-73; Sec Ch in Wales Prov Coun for Miss and Unity 73-79; V Carmarthen St Dav *St D* 79-83; Adn Carmarthen 82-85; V Llanegwad w Llanfynydd 83-85; Bp Llan 85-99; rtd 99. *25 Awel Tywi, Llangunnor, Carmarthen SA31 2NL*

DAVIES, Miss Sally Jane. b 63. Linc Coll Ox BA86. Trin Coll Bris BA92. **d** 92 **p** 94. C E Molesey St Paul *Guildf* 92-96; C Chalfont St Peter *Ox* 96-99; Chapl RN Coll Greenwich from 99; Hon C Greenwich St Alfege *S'wark* from 99. *The Chaplain's Lodging, The Old Royal Naval College, London SE10 9LW* Tel (020) 8858 2154 *or* 8269 4766

DAVIES, Sarah Isabella. b 39. Llan Dioc Tr Scheme 87. **d** 91 **p** 97. NSM Pontypridd St Cath w St Matt *Llan* 91-93; NSM Ferndale w Maerdy 93-97; C 97-00; Chapl Univ Hosp of Wales and Llandough NHS Trust 98-00; Chapl Pontypridd and Rhondda NHS Trust 98-00; C Cardiff Ch Ch Roath Park *Llan* 00-02; Dioc Child Protection Officer from 02. *154 Lake Road East, Cardiff CF23 5NQ* Tel (029) 2075 7190

DAVIES, Saunders. See DAVIES, The Rt Revd Francis James Saunders

DAVIES, Sidney. b 16. St D Coll Lamp BA40. **d** 41 **p** 42. C Llandysul *St D* 41-44; C Llanfihangel-ar-arth 44-53; V Llanerch Aeron w Ciliau Aeron 53-69; R Llanerch Aeron w Ciliau Aeron and Dihewyd 69-82; rtd 82. *12 Pontfaen, Porthyrhyd, Carmarthen SA32 8PE* Tel (01267) 275525

DAVIES, Simon Stanley Miles. b 65. Cranfield Univ BEng88 MSc95. Seabury-Western Th Sem 97 Westcott Ho Cam 98. **d** 00 **p** 01. C Llanrhos *St As* from 00. *Birkrigg, 66 Rhuddlan Avenue, Llandudno LL30 1LN* Tel (01492) 871502

DAVIES, Stanley James. b 18. MBE54. St Chad's Coll Dur BA40 DipThA1 MA44. **d** 41 **p** 42. C Walton St Marg Belmont Road *Liv* 41-42; C Wigan All SS 42-45; CF 45-68; Asst Chapl Gen Lon 68-70; BAOR 70-73; Hon Chapl to The Queen from 72; R Uley w Owlpen and Nympsfield *Glouc* 73-84; rtd 84; Perm to Offic from 86. *Peverell Cottage, Doddiscombsleigh, Exeter EX6 7PR* Tel (01647) 252616

DAVIES, Stephen. b 56. Nottm Univ BSc77. Wycliffe Hall Ox 01. **d** 03. C Crawley and Littleton and Sparsholt w Lainston *Win* from 03. *13 Silwood Close, Winchester SO22 6EN* Tel (01962) 856432 E-mail sd@fish.co.uk

DAVIES, Stephen John. b 55. Bp Otter Coll Chich BA01 IEng77. St Steph Ho Ox DipMin98. **d** 98 **p** 99. C Leigh Park and Warren Park *Portsm* 98-02; C Durrington *Chich* from 02; Chapl Chich Cathl from 02. *26 Vancouver Close, Durrington, Worthing BN13 2SH* Tel (01903) 693075 E-mail frsteve@stsymphorians.freeserve.co.uk

DAVIES, Stephen John. b 65. Nottm Univ BA86 Reading Univ MPhil88 Wycliffe Hall Ox BTh94 ARICS90 MRICS01. **d** 97 **p** 98. C Barton Seagrave w Warkton *Pet* 97-01; P-in-c Enderby w Lubbesthorpe and Thurlaston *Leic* from 01. *The Rectory, 16A Desford Road, Leicester LE9 7TE* Tel (0116) 2386 545 (sic) 888488

DAVIES, Stephen Walter. b 26. AKC54. **d** 55 **p** 56. C Plympton St Mary *Ex* 55-58; C Ex St Mark 58-61; Chapl RAF 61-77; R Feltwell *Ely* 78-84; R N Newton w St Michaelchurch, Thurloxton etc *B & W* 84-91; rtd 91. *5 Manchester Road, Exmouth EX8 1DE*

DAVIES, Mrs Susan Anne. b 48. N Co Coll Newc CertEd69. St Mich Coll Llan 98. **d** 01 **p** 02. NSM Overmonnow w Wonastow and Michel Troy *Mon* 01-03; NSM Monmouth w Overmonnow etc from 03. *8 Toynbee Close, Osbaston, Monmouth NP25 3NU* Tel (01600) 713708 E-mail susanannedavies@aol.com

DAVIES, Taffy. See DAVIES, Edward William Llewellyn

DAVIES, Mrs Teresa Ann. b 71. St Steph Ho Ox BTh02. **d** 02 **p** 03. C Barbourne *Worc* from 02. *5 Keats Avenue, Worcester WR3 8DU* Tel (01905) 455486 Mobile 07887-550770

DAVIES, Preb Thomas Derwent. b 16. St D Coll Lamp BA38. St Mich Coll Llan 39. **d** 39 **p** 41. C Pontypridd St Cath *Llan* 39-45; C Bideford *Ex* 45-48; Lic to Offic 48-51; Asst Sec DBF 48-51; V Devonport St Mark Ford 51-58; R Bideford 58-74; Preb Ex Cathl 69-97; V Cadbury 74-81; V Thorverton 74-81; rtd 82; Perm to Offic *Ex* from 82. *17 Lennard Road, Crediton EX17 2AP* Tel (01363) 773765

DAVIES, Canon Thomas Philip. b 27. Univ of Wales (Ban) BEd73. St Mich Coll Llan 55. **d** 56 **p** 57. C Ruabon *St As* 56-59; C Prestatyn 59-62; V Penley 62-69; V Bettisfield 66-69; V Holt

and Isycoed 69-77; Dioc Dir of Educn 76-92; Dioc RE Adv 76-92; RD Wrexham 76-77; TR Hawarden 77-92; Can St As Cathl 79-92; rtd 93. *53 Muirfield Road, Buckley CH7 2NN* Tel (01244) 547099

DAVIES, Timothy Robert. b 64. Bradf Univ BSc87. Wycliffe Hall Ox BTh93. **d** 93 **p** 94. C Eynsham and Cassington *Ox* 93-97; C Fulwood *Sheff* from 97. *1 Silver Birch Avenue, Sheffield S10 3TA* Tel 0114-263 0926

DAVIES, Trevor. See DAVIES, Edward Trevor

DAVIES, Canon Trevor Gwesyn. b 28. Univ of Wales (Ban) BEd73. St Mich Coll Llan 55. **d** 56 **p** 57. C Holywell *St As* 56-63; V Cwm 63-74; V Colwyn Bay 74-95; Can St As Cathl from 79; rtd 95. *Dalkeith, 37 Brompton Avenue, Rhos on Sea, Colwyn Bay LL28 4TF* Tel (01492) 548044

DAVIES, The Ven Vincent Anthony (Tony). b 46. Brasted Th Coll 69 St Mich Coll Llan 71. **d** 73 **p** 74. C Owton Manor CD *Dur* 73-76; C Wandsworth St Faith *S'wark* 76-78; P-in-c 78-81; V Walworth St Jo 81-94; RD S'wark and Newington 88-93; Adn Croydon from 94; Bp's Adv for Hosp Chapl from 00. *246 Pampisford Road, South Croydon CR2 6DD* Tel (020) 8688 2943 *or* 8681 5496 Fax 8686 2074 E-mail tony.davies@dswark.org.uk

DAVIES, Walter Hugh. b 28. St Deiniol's Hawarden 64. **d** 66 **p** 67. C Ban St Mary *Ban* 66-69; P-in-c Rhosybol and Llandyfrydog 70; TV Amlwch, Rhosybol and Llandyfrydog 71-74; R Llanfaethlu w Llanfwrog and Llanrhuddlad etc 74-93; RD Llifon and Talybolion 85-93; rtd 93; Perm to Offic *Ban* from 93. *14 Y Fron, Cemaes Bay LL67 0HU* Tel (01407) 710333

DAVIES, Canon William David. b 19. Bris Univ BA41. St Mich Coll Llan 48. **d** 43 **p** 44. C Ebbw Vale Ch Ch *Mon* 43-46; C Buckley *St As* 46-48; Chapl Llan Cathl *Llan* 48-50; C-in-c Fairwater CD 50-67; V Fairwater 67-68; R Porthkerry 68-72; R Barry All SS 72-85; RD Penarth and Barry 75-85; Can Llan Cathl 82-85; rtd 85; Perm to Offic *Llan* from 85. *3 Brookfield Park Road, Cowbridge CF71 7HJ* Tel (01446) 775259

DAVIES, William Martin. b 56. Univ of Wales (Cardiff) BSc78. Wycliffe Hall Ox 78. **d** 81 **p** 82. C Gabalfa *Llan* 81-84; P-in-c Beguildy and Heyope *S & B* 84-85; V 85-87; V Swansea St Thos and Kilvey 87-93; Asst Chapl Miss to Seafarers from 89; V Belmont *Lon* from 93. *St Anselm's Vicarage, Ventnor Avenue, Stanmore HA7 2HU* Tel and fax (020) 8907 3186 or tel 8907 5899 Mobile 07050-042586 E-mail martin.davies@london.anglican.org

DAVIES, William Morris. b 19. LCP56 Univ of Wales (Lamp) BA41 Jes Coll Ox BA43 MA47 Man Univ DipEd61 Liv Univ MEd68. St Mich Coll Llan 43. **d** 44 **p** 45. C Ysbyty Ystwyth w Ystradmeurig *St D* 44-49; V 49-57; Chapl Sandbach Sch 57-65; Lect Div Crewe Coll Educn 65-68; Sen Lect 68-71; Hd Div Dept 71-75; Tutor Th and Educn Crewe and Alsager Coll of HE 75-79; Tutor Open Univ 78-81; V Norley *Ches* 79-85; Tutor St Deiniol's Lib Hawarden 83-85; rtd 85; Sub-Chapl HM Young Offender Inst Thorn Cross 85-89; Lic to Offic *Ches* 85-89; Perm to Offic from 90. *Eastwood, Willington, Tarporley CW6 0NE* Tel (01829) 752181

DAVIES-COLE, Charles Sylester. b 38. New Coll Dur BA BD. Edin Th Coll 66. **d** 66. Hon C Edin Old St Paul *Edin* from 66; Prin Teacher Jas Gillespie's High Sch from 82. *121 Mayburn Avenue, Loanhead EH20 9ER* Tel 0131-440 4190

DAVIES-HANNEN, Robert John. b 65. W Glam Inst of HE DipHE87 BEd89. St Mich Coll Llan DipTh91 BTh92. **d** 92 **p** 93. C Gorseinon *S & B* 92-95; P-in-c Swansea St Jude 95-02; V Llangyfelach from 02. *The Vicarage, 64 Heol Pentrefelin, Morriston, Swansea SA6 6BY* Tel (01792) 774120

DAVILL, Robin William. b 51. SS Paul & Mary Coll Cheltenham CertEd73 BEd74 Leic Univ MA79. Westcott Ho Cam 86. **d** 88 **p** 89. C Broughton *Blackb* 88-91; C Howden *York* 91-93; NSM Crayke w Brandsby and Yearsley 93-97; P-in-c 97-03; P-in-c Thirkleby w Kilburn and Bagby from 03. *Leyland House, 44 Uppleby, Easingwold, York YO61 3BB* Tel (01347) 823472

DAVINA, Sister. See WILBY, Mrs Jean

DAVIS, Alan. b 34. Birm Univ BSc56. Ox NSM Course. **d** 75 **p** 76. NSM Chesham St Mary *Ox* 75-80; NSM St Chesham from 80. *18 Cheyne Walk, Chesham HP5 1AY* Tel (01494) 782124

DAVIS, Alan John. b 33. St Alb Minl Tr Scheme 77. **d** 80 **p** 81. NSM Goldington *St Alb* 80-84; C Benchill *Man* 84-86; R Gt Chart *Cant* 86-02; rtd 02; Perm to Offic *Cant* from 02. *8 Roberts Road, Greatstone, New Romney TN28 8RL* Tel (01797) 361917

DAVIS, The Ven Alan Norman. b 38. Open Univ BA75. Lich Th Coll 63. **d** 65 **p** 66. C Kingstanding St Luke *Birm* 65-68; C-in-c Ecclesfield St Paul CD *Sheff* 68-73; V Sheff St Paul 73-75; V Shiregreen St Jas and St Chris 75-80; R Maltby 80-81; TR 81-89; Abp's Officer for UPA 90-92; Lic to Offic *St Alb* 90-92; P-in-c Carl St Cuth w St Mary *Carl* 92-96; Dioc Communications Officer 92-96; Adn W Cumberland from 96; Hon Can Carl Cathl from 96; RD Solway 98-99. *50 Stainburn Road, Workington CA14 1SN* Tel (01900) 66190 Fax 603534 E-mail archdeacon.west@carlislediocese.org.uk

DAVIS, Andrew Fisher. b 46. St Chad's Coll Dur BA67. St Steph Ho Ox 68. **d** 70 **p** 71. C Beckenham St Jas *Roch* 70-74; C

Kensington St Mary Abbots w St Geo *Lon* 74-80; V Sudbury St Andr 80-90; AD Brent 85-90; V Ealing Ch the Sav from 90. *The Clergy House, The Grove, London W5 5DX* Tel (020) 8567 1288 Fax as telephone E-mail christ.the.saviour@mcmail.com

DAVIS, Andrew George. b 63. Bath Univ BSc Edin Univ BD. Edin Th Coll. **d** 89 **p** 90. C Alverstoke *Portsm* 89-92; C Portsea N End St Mark 92-96; Bp's Dom Chapl 96-98; R Bishop's Waltham from 98; R Upham from 98. *The Rectory, Free Street, Bishops Waltham, Southampton SO32 1EE* Tel (01489) 892618

DAVIS, Anne. *See* DAVIS, Mrs Maureen Anne

DAVIS, Arthur Vivian. b 24. Clifton Th Coll 60. **d** 62 **p** 63. C Derby St Chad *Derby* 62-65; C Cambridge St Andr Less *Ely* 65-68; V 68-75; V Kirtling 75-86; V Wood Ditton w Saxon Street 75-86; P-in-c Cheveley 83-86; P-in-c Ashley w Silverley 83-86; rtd 86; Perm to Offic *St E* from 93. *408 Studland Park, Newmarket CB8 7BB* Tel (01638) 661709

DAVIS, Canon Bernard Rex. b 33. Sydney Univ BA55 Gen Th Sem (NY) MDiv60 Newc Univ MA67 FRSA87. Coll of Resurr Mirfield 55. **d** 57 **p** 58. R Guildf St Nic *Guildf* 57-59; USA 59-61; Australia 62-68; Exec Sec Unit 3 WCC Geneva 68-77; Warden Edw K Ho from 77; Can Res and Subdean Linc Cathl *Linc* from 77; Perm to Offic *S'well* from 01; rtd 03. *51 Parma Crescent, London SW11 1LT* Tel (020) 7223 4342

DAVIS, Canon Brian. b 40. AKC69 BD69. St Aug Coll Cant 69. **d** 70 **p** 71. C Humberstone *Leic* 70-73; C Kirby Muxloe 73-74; V Countesthorpe w Foston 74-91; RD Guthlaxton I 90-91; V Hinckley St Mary from 91; RD Sparkenhoe W 92-02; Hon Can Leic Cathl from 94. *St Mary's Vicarage, St Mary's Road, Hinckley LE10 1EQ* Tel (01455) 234241 E-mail bdavis@leicester.anglican.org

DAVIS, Mrs Bryony Elizabeth. b 64. DipCOT86. EAMTC 99. **d** 02 **p** 03. C Beccles St Mich *St E* from 02. *The New House, Queen's Road, Beccles NR34 9DU* Tel (01502) 715258

DAVIS, Christopher Eliot. b 28. Pemb Coll Cam BA50 MA55. Wells Th Coll 52. **d** 54 **p** 55. C Dudley St Aug Holly Hall *Worc* 54-56; C Bromyard *Heref* 57; Min Can Carl Cathl *Carl* 57-59; Prec Worc Cathl *Worc* 60-62; Perm to Offic *Lich* 62-95; P-in-c Lich St Mary 65-66; PV Lich Cathl 65-67; Chapl Magd Coll Ox 71-74; rtd 93. *28 Newbridge Crescent, Wolverhampton WV6 0LH* Tel (01902) 759220

DAVIS, Christopher James. b 63. Worc Coll Ox BA85. Cranmer Hall Dur 88. **d** 91 **p** 92. C Margate H Trin *Cant* 91-94; C Cambridge H Sepulchre *Ely* 94-00; C Wimbledon Em Ridgway Prop Chpl *S'wark* from 00. *207 Cottenham Park Road, London SW20 0SY* Tel (020) 8946 1006 E-mail cjdavis@ukonline.co.uk

DAVIS, Clinton Ernest Newman. b 46. Solicitor 71. Wycliffe Hall Ox 78. **d** 80 **p** 81. C Margate H Trin *Cant* 80-84; C St Laur in Thanet 84-87; V Sandgate St Paul 87-92; P-in-c Folkestone St Geo 92; V Sandgate St Paul w Folkestone St Geo 92-97; Chapl HM Pris Standford Hill from 97. *HM Prison Standford Hill, Church Road, Eastchurch, Sheerness ME12 4AA* Tel (01795) 880441 Fax 880267

E-mail ernir@ernestnewman.freeserve.co.uk

DAVIS, Colin Anthony John. b 65. St Jo Coll Nottm DTM99. **d** 99 **p** 00. C Bletchley *Ox* 99-02; C S Molton w Nymet St George, High Bray etc *Ex* from 02. *The Vicarage, Chittlehampton, Umberleigh EX37 9QL* Tel (01769) 540654 Mobile 07768-781357 E-mail revcol@btinternet.com

DAVIS, David John. b 35. St Steph Ho Ox 79. **d** 81 **p** 82. C Reading St Mark *Ox* 81-84; C Gt Grimsby St Mary and St Jas *Linc* 84-85; TV 85-89; V Caistor w Clixby 89-94; TV Louth 98-01; rtd 01. *19 Cow Lane, Tealby, Market Rasen LN8 3YB* Tel (01673) 838869

DAVIS, Donald Cyril. b 26. Open Univ BA79. NTMTC 94. **d** 96 **p** 97. NSM N Greenford All Hallows *Lon* from 96. *33 Sherwood Avenue, Greenford UB6 0PG* Tel (020) 8864 1060

E-mail dondavis@dondavis.force9.co.uk

DAVIS, Donald Richard. b 59. Oak Hill Th Coll DipHE94. **d** 94 **p** 95. C Plymouth St Jude *Ex* 94-99; C Devonport St Boniface and St Phil from 99. *St Philip's Vicarage, Bridewell Lane North, Plymouth PL5 1AN* Tel (01752) 212091

DAVIS, Edward Gabriel Anastasius. b 75. R Holloway Coll Lon BA97. Trin Coll Bris BA02 MA03. **d** 03. C Boldmere *Birm* from 03. *19 Southam Drive, Sutton Coldfield B73 5PD* Tel 0121-354 8432

DAVIS, Edwin John Charles. b 36. Dur Univ BA60 St Cath Soc Ox BA62 MA66. Ripon Hall Ox 60. **d** 62 **p** 63. C Kington w Huntington *Heref* 62-65; Lect Lich Th Coll 65-66; Chapl Edin Th Coll 66-70; Hon Chapl St Mary's Cathl *Edin* 66-70; P-in-c Hope w Shelve *Heref* 70-78; R 78-81; P-in-c Middleton 70-78; V 78-81; P-in-c Worthen 75-78; R 78-81; V S Hinksey *Ox* 81-01; Dep Dir Tr Scheme for NSM 84-01; rtd 01. *13 Kennett Road, Headington, Oxford OX3 7BH* Tel (01865) 763383

E-mail ejcdavis@uk.packardbell.com

DAVIS, Mrs Elizabeth Jane. b 42. S'wark Ord Course 91. **d** 94 **p** 95. NSM Plaistow St Mary *Roch* 94-99; NSM Bromley St Andr from 99. *3 Kinnaird Avenue, Bromley BR1 4HG* Tel (020) 8460 4672

DAVIS, Felicity Ann. *See* SMITH, Felicity Ann

DAVIS, Geoffrey. *See* DAVIS, Ronald Geoffrey

DAVIS, Canon Herbert Roger. b 36. Kelham Th Coll 60. **d** 65 **p** 66. C Barkingside St Fran *Chelmsf* 65-69; C Harpenden St Nic *St Alb* 69-73; P-in-c Eaton Bray 73-75; V Eaton Bray w Edlesborough 75-81; RD Dunstable 77-81; R Gt Berkhamsted 81-95; Hon Can St Alb 93-95; rtd 99. *6 St Thomas Terrace, St Thomas Street, Wells BA5 2XG* Tel (01749) 677195

DAVIS, Ian Andrew. b 58. MIBiol85 CBiol85 Sheff Univ BSc79 PGCE80. St Jo Coll Nottm LTh89 DPS90. **d** 90 **p** 91. C Hatfield *Sheff* 90-92; C Beighton 92-95; R Thurnscoe St Helen 95-99; P-in-c Chesterfield St Aug *Derby* 99-01; V from 01. *St Augustine's Vicarage, 1 Whitecotes Lane, Chesterfield S40 3HJ* Tel (01246) 273942 E-mail reviandavis@compuserve.com

DAVIS, Jack. b 35. LRSC63 CChem80 MRSC80 Sheff City Poly HNC59 Sheff Univ MSc88. Oak Hill Th Coll DipHE88. **d** 88 **p** 89. C Owlerton *Sheff* 88-91; V Manea *Ely* 91-93; R Wimblington 91-93; P-in-c Walsoken 93-94; R 94-00; rtd 00. Perm to Offic *Sheff* from 00. *5 Pinfold Court, Barnby Dun, Doncaster DN3 1RQ* Tel (01302) 888065 Fax as telephone E-mail revjackdavis@aol.com

DAVIS, John Basil. b 20. Lon Univ BA69. Bps' Coll Cheshunt 46. **d** 49 **p** 50. V Bacton w Edingthorpe *Nor* 61-66; Perm to Offic *S'well* 71-86; rtd 85; Hon C Bingham *S'well* 86-90. *1 Banks Crescent, Bingham, Nottingham NG13 8BP* Tel (01949) 837721

DAVIS, John Brian. b 33. Linc Th Coll 72. **d** 75 **p** 76. Hon C Bungay H Trin w St Mary *St E* 75-84; P-in-c Barrow 84-85; P-in-c Denham St Mary 84-85; R Barrow w Denham St Mary and Higham Green 85-98; rtd 98; Perm to Offic *Nor* from 98. *Cherry Tree House, Outney Road, Bungay NR35 1DY* Tel (01986) 895574

DAVIS, John George. b 65. Roehampton Inst BSc87 S Glam Inst HE PGCE88. St Steph Ho Ox BTh96. **d** 96 **p** 97. C Newton Nottage *Llan* 96-00; V Tredegar St Geo *Mon* from 00. *St George's Vicarage, Church Street, Tredegar NP22 3DU* Tel (01495) 722672

DAVIS, John Harold. b 54. St Jo Coll Dur BSc76 DipTh78 MA86. Cranmer Hall Dur 76. **d** 79 **p** 80. C Marske in Cleveland *York* 79-82; P Pocklington w Yapham-cum-Meltonby, Owsthorpe etc 82-83; TV Pocklington Team 84-86; V Carlton and Drax 86-95; Ind Chapl from 88; V Sowerby from 95; P-in-c Sessay 95-98; R from 98. *The Vicarage, 5 The Close, Sowerby, Thirsk YO7 1JA* Tel (01845) 523546 E-mail jdavis@fish.co.uk

DAVIS, John Stephen. b 51. N Staffs Poly BSc75. Wycliffe Hall Ox 75. **d** 78 **p** 79. C Meole Brace *Lich* 78-81; C Bloxwich 81-85; V Walsall St Paul 85-96; Development Officer Prince's Trust from 96. *15 Heygate Way, Aldridge, Walsall WS9 8SD* Tel (01922) 58510

DAVIS, Preb Kenneth William. b 25. Ripon Hall Ox 60. **d** 62 **p** 63. C Lyngford *B & W* 62-65; R Axbridge 65-72; V Wells St Cuth 72-73; V Wells St Cuth w Wookey Hole 73-92; RD Shepton Mallet 79-86; Preb Wells Cathl from 83; rtd 92; Perm to Offic *B & W* from 92. *Beach Lawns, 67 Beach Road, Weston-super-Mare BS23 4BG* Tel (01934) 629130

DAVIS, Mrs Maureen Anne. b 59. St Hilda's Coll Ox BA80 MA84. N Ord Course 96. **d** 99 **p** 00. NSM Plemstall w Guilden Sutton *Ches* 99-01; C Ches St Mary 01-03; R Woodchurch from 03. *The Rectory, Church Lane, Upton, Wirral CH49 7LS*

E-mail annedavis@tinyworld.co.uk

DAVIS, Michael James Burrows. b 36. ED JP87. St Deiniol's Hawarden Ridley Hall Cam. **d** 72 **p** 72. Bermuda from 72. *PO Box SN 74, Southampton SN BX, Bermuda* Tel (001441) 238 0236 Fax 238 3767

DAVIS, Nicholas Anthony Wylie. b 56. BA. Chich Th Coll. **d** 84 **p** 85. C N Lambeth *S'wark* 84-88; TV Catford (Southend) and Downham 88-94; V Camberwell St Phil and St Mark from 94. *St Philip's Vicarage, Avondale Square, London SE1 5PD* Tel (020) 7237 3239 E-mail nicholas_a.davis@virgin.net

DAVIS, Nicholas Edward. b 75. Univ of Wales (Ban) BD96. Coll of Resurr Mirfield 98. **d** 00 **p** 01. C Darwen St Cuth w Tockholes St Steph *Blackb* from 00. *14 The Meadows, Darwen BB3 0PF* Tel (01254) 701180 E-mail clergy@st-cuthberts.co.uk

DAVIS, Canon Norman. b 38. FCII66. Oak Hill Th Coll 77. **d** 79 **p** 80. C Walton *St E* 79-82; P-in-c Bredfield w Boulge 86-91; P-in-c Grundisburgh w Burgh 82-91; RD Woodbridge 90-96; R Boulge w Burgh and Grundisburgh 91-03; P-in-c Hasketon 01-03; R Boulge w Burgh, Grundisburgh and Hasketon from 03; Hon Can St E Cathl from 01. *The Rectory, Woodbridge Road, Grundisburgh, Woodbridge IP13 6UF* Tel (01473) 735749

DAVIS, Norman John. b 41. Oak Hill Th Coll 63. **d** 66 **p** 67. C Wellington w Eyton *Lich* 66-70; C Higher Openshaw *Man* 70-72; R S Levenshulme 72-79; P-in-c Berrow w Pendock and Eldersfield *Worc* 79-81; R 81-87; R Churchill-in-Halfshire w Blakedown and Broome from 87. *The Rectory, 5 Mill Lane, Blakedown, Kidderminster DY10 3ND* Tel (01562) 700293

E-mail norsuedavis@ic24.net

DAVIS, Peter Thomas. b 61. Flinders Univ Aus BTh87. Adelaide Coll of Div DPS88 St Barn Coll Adelaide 83. **d** 87 **p** 87. Adelaide 87-91 and 92-01; TV Gt and Lt Coates w Bradley *Linc* 91-92; Dioc Youth Officer Adelaide 92-94; P-in-c Parafield Gardens St Barbara 94-98; R Elizabeth H Cross 98-01; Chapl Anglicare S

Australia 98-01; V Satley, Stanley and Tow Law *Dur* from 01. *The Vicarage, 3 Church Lane, Tow Law, Bishop Auckland DL13 4HE* Tel (01388) 730335 E-mail peter.davis@flinders.edu.au

DAVIS, Roger. *See* DAVIS, Canon Herbert Roger

DAVIS, Ronald Frank. b 26. Oak Hill Th Coll 62. **d** 64 **p** 65. C Bilton *Ripon* 64-67; V N and S Otterington *York* 67-77; C Rainham *Chelmsf* 77-82; V Hainault 82-88; rtd 88; Perm to Offic *Bradf* from 90. *Home View, Westview Grove, Keighley BD20 6JJ* Tel (01535) 681294

DAVIS, Ronald Geoffrey (Geoff). b 47. St Jo Coll Nottm 79. **d** 81 **p** 81. C Maidstone St Luke *Cant* 81-84; P-in-c Lostwithiel *Truro* 84-86; P-in-c Lanhydrock 84-86; Asst Dioc Youth Officer 84-86; P-in-c Boughton Monchelsea *Cant* 86-88; V from 88; Six Preacher Cant Cathl 94-99; C-in-c Parkwood CD 95-98; AD N Downs 99-02. *The Vicarage, Church Hill, Boughton Monchelsea, Maidstone ME17 4BU* Tel (01622) 743321 Fax as telephone E-mail stpeters.church@btinternet.com

DAVIS, Russell Earls. b 14. Sydney Univ LLB50. Moore Th Coll Sydney ThL52. **d** 52 **p** 53. Australia 52-88; C Launceston Holy Trin 54-60; Prec St Geo Cathl 60-66; Chapl Hale Sch 66-88; P-in-c Brislington St Luke *Bris* 76-77; rtd 88. *66B Dover Road, Scarborough, W Australia 6019* Tel (0061) (8) 9205 1684

DAVIS, Ruth Elizabeth. *See* TAIT, Ruth Elizabeth

DAVIS, Simon Charles. b 63. Plymouth Poly BSc86. Trin Coll Bris BA92. **d** 92 **p** 93. C Bollington St Jo *Ches* 92-96; P-in-c Abbots Bromley w Blithfield *Lich* from 96. *The Vicarage, Market Place, Abbots Bromley, Rugeley WS15 3BP* Tel (01283) 840242 E-mail simon.davis@freeuk.com

DAVIS, Stephen Charles. b 19. AKC48 St Cath Soc Ox BA50 MA54. Wycliffe Hall Ox 48. **d** 50 **p** 51. C Slough *Ox* 50-52; S Africa 52-57; V Leic H Trin *Leic* 58-64; Chapl HM Pris Leic 58-64; R Dur St Marg *Dur* 64-87; rtd 87. *6 Juniper Way, Malvern WR14 4XG* Tel (01684) 561039

DAVIS, Thomas Edward. b 20. **d** 83 **p** 84. NSM Cen Telford *Lich* 83-91; Perm to Offic 91-00. *14 Bembridge, Telford TF3 1NA* Tel (01952) 592352

DAVIS, Thomas Henry. b 60. SSC01. Dioc OLM tr scheme DipHE00. **d** 99 **p** 00. OLM Stadhampton and Chilton *St E* 99-03; NSM Preston St Jo and St Geo *Blackb* from 03. *Glebe House, 33 Bairstow Street, Preston PR1 3TN* Tel and fax (01772) 884921 Mobile 07929-654764 E-mail father-davis@tinyworld.co.uk

DAVIS, Timothy Alwyn. b 74. Trin Coll Bris BTh. **d** 01 **p** 02. C Crich and S Wingfield *Derby* from 01. *6 Dowie Way, Crich, Matlock DE4 5NJ* Tel (01773) 853923

DAVIS, Timothy Charles. b 59. Reading Univ BA81 Homerton Coll Cam PGCE82. Trin Coll Bris DipHE91. **d** 91 **p** 92. C Normanton *Wakef* 91-95; C Fisherton Anger *Sarum* 95-99; TV Abingdon *Ox* from 99. *69 Northcourt Road, Abingdon OX14 1NH* Tel (01235) 520115 or 539172 Fax 522549 E-mail chch@clara.net

DAVIS, Trevor Lorenzo. b 45. Simon of Cyrene Th Inst 92. **d** 94 **p** 95. NSM Upper Norwood St Jo *S'wark* 94-00. *31B Thornlaw Road, London SE27 0SH* Tel (020) 8766 6238

DAVIS, William Henry. b 17. Open Univ BA84. Bps' Coll Cheshunt. **d** 67 **p** 68. C Sudbury St Andr *Lon* 67-70; V Wickhambrook *St E* 70-72; V Wickhambrook w Stradishall and Denston 72-91; V Wickhambrook 91-95; P-in-c Stansfield 76-78; rtd 95. *Folly Barn, 10 Bellevue Road, Weymouth DT4 8RX* Tel (01305) 784853

DAVIS, Mrs Yvonne Annie. b 30. CQSW75. LNSM course 93. **d** 96 **p** 97. OLM Purley St Barn *S'wark* 96-00; Perm to Offic from 00. *1 Hurnford Close, Sanderstead CR2 0AN* Tel (020) 8657 2097

DAVISON, Andrew Paul. b 74. Mert Coll Ox BA96 MA99 DPhil00 CCC Cam BA02. Westcott Ho Cam 00. **d** 03. C Bellingham St Dunstan *S'wark* from 03. *38 Playgreen Way, London SE6 3HU* Tel (020) 8697 3878 E-mail email@apdavison.co.uk

DAVISON, Miss Beryl. b 37. Lightfoot Ho Dur 62. **d** 87 **p** 94. Par Dn Consett *Dur* 87-92; Dn-in-c Holmside 92-94; P-in-c 94-97; rtd 97. *48 Deanery View, Lanchester, Durham DH7 0NJ* Tel (01207) 520137

DAVISON, Canon George Thomas William. b 65. St Andr Univ BD88. Oak Hill Th Coll 88 CITC BTh92. **d** 92 **p** 93. C Portadown St Mark *Arm* 92-95; I Kinawley w H Trin *K, E & A* from 95; Dir of Ords from 97; Preb Kilmore Cathl from 02. *The Rectory, Cloghan, Derrylin, Enniskillen BT92 9LD* Tel (028) 6674 8994 Fax as telephone E-mail kinawley@kilmore.anglican.org

DAVISON, Philip Anthony. b 66. Magd Coll Cam BA88 MA93. Cuddesdon Coll BA98 DipMin98. **d** 98 **p** 99. C Lancaster St Mary w St John and St Anne *Blackb* 98-02; P-in-c Feniscowles from 02. *The Vicarage, 732 Preston Old Road, Feniscowles, Blackburn BB2 5EN* Tel (01254) 201236

DAVISON, Canon Richard Ireland. b 42. St Chad's Coll Dur BSc63. Linc Th Coll 64. **d** 66 **p** 67. C Cockerton Dur 66-70; C Houghton le Spring 70-73; V Heworth St Alb 73-80; Ascension Is 80-82; V Dunston *Dur* 82-85; V Bishopwearmouth Ch Ch 85-98; AD Wearmouth 94-99; Hon Can Dur Cathl from 97; P-in-c Dur

St Giles 99-00; V from 00. *St Giles's Vicarage, Gilesgate, Durham DH1 1QH* Tel 0191-384 2452 E-mail atthevicarage@hotmail.com

DAVISON, Richard John. b 32. St Andr Univ MA56. Linc Th Coll 56. **d** 58 **p** 59. C S Shields St Hilda *Dur* 58-61; C Dur St Cuth 61-63; R Wyberton *Linc* 63-86; RD Holland W 84-86; TR Swan *Ox* 86-91; V Streatley w Moulsford 91-96; rtd 97; Perm to Offic *Linc* from 00. *37 Stirling Road, Stamford PE9 2XF* Tel (01780) 766794

DAVISON, Canon Roger William. b 20. Kelham Th Coll 46. **d** 51 **p** 52. C Tonge Moor *Man* 51-55; V 55-65; Hon Can Man Cathl 63-65; V Higham Ferrers w Chelveston *Pet* 65-88; rtd 88; Perm to Offic *Roch* from 88. *17 Hermitage Road, Higham, Rochester ME3 7DB* Tel (01474) 823824

DAVISON, Thomas Alfred. b 28. St Aug Coll Cant 48 St Chad's Coll Dur 52. **d** 60 **p** 61. C Tetbury w Beverston *Glouc* 60-62; C Malvern Link St Matthias *Worc* 62-65; R Coates *Glouc* 65-76; R Coates, Rodmarton and Sapperton etc 76-78; Chapl R Agric Coll Cirencester 67-78; P-in-c Bleadon *B & W* 78-81; Chapl HM Pris Leeds 81-84; Chapl HM Pris Channings Wood 84-89; P-in-c Pyworthy, Pancrasweek and Bridgerule *Ex* 89-91; P-in-c Otterton and Colaton Raleigh 91-94; rtd 94; Perm to Offic *Ex* from 94. *6 Grosvenor Terrace, Ferndale Road, Teignmouth TQ14 8NE* Tel (01626) 779202

DAVISON, William. b 18. St D Coll Lamp 58. **d** 60 **p** 61. C Horsington w Stixwould *Linc* 60-62; R Welby 62-65; V Heydour and Culverthorpe 62-65; R Offord D'Arcy w Offord Cluny *Ely* 65-66; R Mareham le Fen *Linc* 66-76; Lic to Offic 77-78; R Barkestone cum Plungar and Redmile *Leic* 78-81; rtd 82; Perm to Offic *Linc* 82-02. *28 Stoney Way, Tetney, Grimsby DN36 5PG* Tel (01472) 814252

DAVOLL, Ivan John (Snowy). b 33. Dip Youth Work 67. LNSM course 87. **d** 88 **p** 90. NSM Bermondsey St Jas w Ch Ch *S'wark* 88-93; C 93-98; rtd 98; Perm to Offic *S'wark* 98-03. *42 Ecroyd Park, Credenhill, Hereford HR4 7EL*

DAVY, Peter Geoffrey. b 31. St Pet Coll Saltley TCert54 DipPE56. SW Minl Tr Course 93. **d** 94 **p** 94. NSM St Columb Minor and St Colan *Truro* 94-99; rtd 99; Perm to Offic *Truro* from 00. *9 Tredour Road, Newquay TR7 2EY* Tel (01637) 872241

DAW, Geoffrey Martin. b 57. Oak Hill Th Coll 81. **d** 84 **p** 85. C Hollington St Leon *Chich* 84-87; C Seaford w Sutton 87-90; V Iford w Kingston and Rodmell from 90. *The Rectory, 14 Lockitt Way, Kingston, Lewes BN7 3LG* Tel (01273) 473665

DAWE, David Fife Purchas. b 20. Keble Coll Ox BA41 MA45. Wells Th Coll 41. **d** 43 **p** 44. C Wolstanton *Lich* 43-46; C Meole Brace 46-47; C Leek All SS 47-50; C Tardebigge *Worc* 50-52; R Stoke Bliss w Kyre Wyard 52-54; R Jackfield *Heref* 54-61; V Criftins *Lich* 61-77; V Dudleston 63-77; P-in-c Alkmonton w Yeaveley *Derby* 77-81; P-in-c Cubley w Marston Montgomery 77-81; V Alkmonton, Cubley, Marston, Montgomery etc 81-85; rtd 85; Perm to Offic *Derby* 85-94; Perm to Offic *Lich* 85-94; Perm to Offic *Pet* from 94. *11 Coaching Walk, Northampton NN3 3EU* Tel (01604) 414083

DAWES, Dori Katherine. b 37. ARCM. Oak Hill Th Coll 85. **d** 88 **p** 94. Par Dn Watford St Luke *St Alb* 88-90; Par Dn Watford 90-94; C 94-96; P-in-c Dunton w Wrestlingworth and Eyeworth 96-01; rtd 01. *Orchard House, Upway, Porlock, Minehead TA24 8QE* Tel (01643) 862474

DAWES, Mrs Helen Elizabeth. b 74. Trin Coll Cam BA96 MA00. Westcott Ho Cam 99. **d** 02 **p** 03. C Chesterton St Andr *Ely* from 02. *258 Milton Road, Cambridge CB4 1LQ* Tel (01223) 740110 E-mail helen.dawes@ely.anglican.org

DAWES, Hugh William. b 48. Univ Coll Ox BA71 MA76. Cuddesdon Coll 71. **d** 74 **p** 75. C Purley St Mark *S'wark* 74-77; Chapl G&C Coll Cam 77-82; Chapl Em Coll Cam 82-87; V Cambridge St Jas *Ely* 87-00; V N Dulwich St Faith *S'wark* from 00. *St Faith's Vicarage, 62 Red Post Hill, London SE24 9JQ* Tel (020) 7274 1338 E-mail hugh@tcpost.fsnet.co.uk

DAWES, Julian Edward. b 27. RAF Coll Cranwell 49. Bps' Coll Cheshunt 58. **d** 59 **p** 60. C Whitton St Aug *Lon* 59-62; Chapl RAF 62-65; V Overbury w Alstone, Teddington and Lt Washbourne *Worc* 65-70; V Cropthorne w Charlton 70-76; Chapl Dioc Conf Cen 70-76; Chapl Exe Vale Hosp Gp 76-84; Chapl Bromsgrove and Redditch Distr Gen Hosp 84-86; rtd 91; Perm to Offic *Ex* from 91. *Maranatha, Exeter Road, Rewe, Exeter EX5 4AE* Tel (01392) 841877 Fax 841577

DAWES, Peter Martin. b 24. Westmr Coll Cam 52. **d** 81 **p** 81. C Dunscroft Ch Ch *Sheff* 81-83; V 83-89; rtd 89; Perm to Offic *Bris* from 89. *2 Holway Cottages, 71B The Mall, Swindon SN1 4JB* Tel (01793) 615878

✠**DAWES, The Rt Revd Peter Spencer.** b 28. Hatf Coll Dur BA52. Tyndale Hall Bris 53. **d** 54 **p** 55 **c** 88. C Whitehall Park St Andr Hornsey Lane *Lon* 54-57; C Ox St Ebbe *Ox* 57-60; Tutor Clifton Th Coll 60-65; V Romford Gd Shep Collier Row *Chelmsf* 65-80; Hon Can Chelmsf Cathl 78-80; Adn W Ham 80-88; Dioc Dir of Ords 80-86; Bp Derby 88-95; rtd 95; Hon Asst Bp Ely from 95. *45 Arundell, Ely CB6 1BQ* Tel (01353) 661241

DAWES, Peter. b 31. Roch Th Coll 64. **d** 66 **p** 67. C Newbold w Dunston *Derby* 66-69; C Buxton 69-72; V Somercotes 72-93; rtd 93; Hon C Kenton, Mamhead, Powderham, Cofton and

Starcross *Ex* from 93. *115 Exeter Road, Dawlish EX7 0AN* Tel (01626) 862593

DAWKIN, Peter William. b 60. Nottm Univ BTh88 Open Univ BA91. St Jo Coll Nottm 85. **d** 88 **p** 89. C Birkdale St Jo *Liv* 88-91; C Netherton 91-93; V Liv Ch Ch Norris Green from 93. *62 Longview Drive, Liverpool L36 6EF* Tel 07947-164207

DAWKINS, Canon Alan Arthur Windsor. b 26. Lon Univ DipTh54. St Aid Birkenhead 53. **d** 55 **p** 56. C Preston Em *Blackb* 55-57; C S Shore H Trin 57-59; V Slade Green *Roch* 59-61; V St Mary Cray and St Paul's Cray 61-63; V White Colne *Chelmsf* 63-66; R Pebmarsh 63-66; P-in-c Mt Bures 65-66; V Westgate St Jas *Cant* 66-74; V Herne Bay Ch Ch 74-83; Hon Can Cant Cathl 79-91; P-in-c Chilham 85-91; Adv for Miss and Unity 85-91; rtd 91; Perm to Offic *Cant* from 96; Chapl St Jo Hosp Cant from 96. *St John's House, 40 Northgate, Canterbury CT1 1BE* Tel (01227) 764935

DAWKINS, John Haswell. b 47. Lon Univ DipTh70. NEOC 98. **d** 01 **p** 02. NSM Barmby Moor Gp *York* from 01. *9 Fossbeck Close, Wilberfoss, York YO41 5PR* Tel (01759) 388144

DAWKINS, Michael Howard. b 44. Bris Univ BTh68 Man Univ MA96. Tyndale Hall Bris 67. **d** 69 **p** 69. C Drypool St Columba w St Andr and St Pet *York* 69-73; CF 74-80; P-in-c Bulford *Sarum* 80-81; P-in-c Figheldean w Milston 80-81; R Meriden *Cov* from 85. *The Rectory, The Green, Meriden, Coventry CV7 7LN* Tel (01676) 522719 E-mail mhdawkins@aol.com

DAWN, Maggi Eleanor. b 59. Fitzw Coll Cam MA96 Selw Coll Cam PhD02. Ridley Hall Cam CTM96. **d** 99 **p** 00. C Ely 99-01; Chapl K Coll Cam 01-03; Chapl Rob Coll Cam from 03. *Robinson College, Cambridge CB3 9AN* Tel (01223) 339140 Mobile 07743-351467 E-mail med1000@cam.ac.uk

DAWSON, Alan. b 28. St Jo Coll Dur BA54 Liv Univ MA67. Clifton Th Coll 54. **d** 56 **p** 57. C Bowling St Steph *Bradf* 56-59; C Attenborough w Bramcote *S'well* 59-62; V Everton St Jo *Liv* 62-69; V Birkdale St Pet 69-91; rtd 91. *8 Dunbar Avenue, Kirkcudbright DG6 4HD* Tel (01557) 330017

DAWSON, Andrew. See DAWSON, Canon William James Andrew

DAWSON, Andrew. See DAWSON, Francis Andrew Oliver Duff

DAWSON, The Very Revd Arthur Roger. b 38. Sarum Th Coll 64. **d** 66 **p** 66. C Addiscombe St Mildred *Cant* 66-67; C Cove St Jo *Guildf* 67-69; C-in-c Newton-in-Makerfield Em CD *Liv* 75-77; R Newton in Makerfield Em 77-83; BCC 83-87; Hon C Dulwich St Barn *S'wark* 84-92; R Hockering, Honingham, E and N Tuddenham *Nor* 92-97; Dean Caracas, Venezuela from 97. *Iglesia Anglicana de Caracas, Aptdo 61.116 (Chacao), Caracas 1060, Venezuela* Tel (0058) (2) 991 4727 Fax 993 8170 E-mail dawson@cantv.net

DAWSON, Barry. b 38. Lon Univ DipTh65. Oak Hill Th Coll 63. **d** 66 **p** 67. C Fulham St Mary N End *Lon* 66-69; C St Marylebone All So w SS Pet and Jo 69-73; Bp's Chapl *Nor* 73-76; Gen Sec CEMS 76-81; V Rye Park St Cuth *St Alb* 81-89; V Attenborough *S'well* 89-98; rtd 98; Perm to Offic *S'well* from 98. *88 Conway Crescent, Carlton, Nottingham NG4 2PZ*

DAWSON, Brian. b 33. Leeds Univ BA54 Lon Univ DipTh57 Man Univ MA84 Newc Univ MPhil01. Coll of Resurr Mirfield 56. **d** 58 **p** 59. C Hollinwood *Man* 58-62; C Rawmarsh w Parkgate *Sheff* 62-63; V Royton St Anne *Man* 63-75; V Urswick *Carl* 75-86; V Bardsea 75-86; R Skelton and Hutton-in-the-Forest w Ivegill 86-98; RD Penrith 91-96; Hon Can Carl Cathl 94-98; rtd 98; Perm to Offic *Carl* from 98. *Apple Croft, High Hesket, Carlisle CA4 0HS* Tel (01697) 473069

DAWSON, Christopher John Rowland. b 26. OBE QPM. Lon Univ DipTh86. S'wark Ord Course 82. **d** 86 **p** 87. NSM Sevenoaks St Jo *Roch* 86-98; Perm to Offic 98-99. *Craggan House, 58 Oak Hill Road, Sevenoaks TN13 1NT* Tel (01732) 458037

DAWSON, Canon Cyril. b 34. St Chad's Coll Dur BA58 DipTh59. **d** 59 **p** 60. C Honicknowle *Ex* 59-63; C Paignton St Jo 63-66; V Heptonstall *Wakef* 66-71; V Todmorden 71-82; RD Calder Valley 75-82; Can Res Wakef Cathl 82-92; Vice-Provost 86-92; Hon Can 92-99; V Bridlington 92-99; rtd 99; Perm to Offic *York* and *Linc* from 00. *24 Beacon Road, Bridlington YO16 6UX* Tel (01262) 672911

DAWSON, David. b 57. TISEC 99. **d** 99 **p** 00. NSM Kirkwall *Ab* from 99. *Cottage of Ronaldsvoe, St Margaret's Hope, Orkney KW17 2TN* Tel (01856) 831596 Mobile 07881-932657 Fax 831451

DAWSON, Edward. b 81 **p** 83. NSM Newington St Paul *S'wark* 81-85; NSM Walworth St Jo 85-00; Chapl Asst Maudsley Hosp Lon from 87. *3 Ethel Street, London SE17 1NH* Tel (020) 7701 8923

DAWSON, Francis Andrew Oliver Duff. b 48. Keble Coll Ox BA70 MA74. St Jo Coll Nottm 74. **d** 76 **p** 77. C Billericay St Mary *Chelmsf* 76-77; C Billericay and Lt Burstead 77-80; C Childwall All SS *Liv* 80-84; Chapl St Kath Coll 80-84; V Shevington *Blackb* 84-97; Internat Officer & Team Ldr for Evang Affairs *Man* from 97; Lic to Offic from 99. *14 Longbrook, Shevington, Wigan WN6 8DB* Tel (01257) 404373 *or* 0161-832 5253 Fax 832 2869 E-mail adawson@manchester.anglican.org

DAWSON, Frederick William. b 44. St Chad's Coll Dur BA66 Nottm Univ MTh74. Linc Th Coll 67. **d** 69 **p** 70. C Caversham *Ox* 69-72; C Ranmoor *Sheff* 72-79; R Kibworth Beauchamp *Leic* 79-82; R Kibworth and Smeeton Westerby and Saddington 82-94; R Tilehurst St Mich *Ox* from 94. *Tilehurst Rectory, Routh Lane, Reading RG30 4JY* Tel 0118-941 1127 Fax as telephone E-mail freddawson@ukonline.co.uk

DAWSON, Ian Douglas. b 52. Liv Univ BSc73. N Ord Course 83. **d** 86 **p** 87. NSM Southport SS Simon and Jude *Liv* 86-93; NSM Birkdale St Jas 93-95; NSM Southport St Phil and St Paul 96-01; Perm to Offic *Linc* from 01. *18 Park View, Barton-upon-Humber DN18 6AX* Tel (01652) 637554

DAWSON, John William Arthur. b 43. EMMTC DipTh95. **d** 95 **p** 96. NSM Breedon cum Isley Walton and Worthington *Leic* from 95. *Orchard House, 2 Manor Drive, Worthington, Ashby-de-la-Zouch LE65 1RN* Tel (01530) 222673

DAWSON, Miss Mary. b 51. Loughb Coll ALA73. EMMTC 85. **d** 90 **p** 94. Par Dn Braunstone *Leic* 90-92; Par Dn Shrewsbury H Cross *Lich* 92-94; C 94-95; P-in-c Glentworth Gp *Linc* 95-97; V from 97. *The Vicarage, 1 Stoney Lane, Glentworth, Gainsborough DN21 5DF* Tel (01427) 668203 Fax as telephone

DAWSON, Neil. b 49. Ripon Hall Ox 71. **d** 74 **p** 75. C Putney St Mary *S'wark* 74-78; C Camberwell St Giles 78-80; TV N Lambeth 84-86; V E Dulwich St Clem 86; V Dulwich St Clem w St Pet 86-89; NSM Wilton Place St Paul *Lon* from 92. *5 Clitheroe Road, London SW9 9DY* Tel (020) 7326 4682 *or* 7235 3460

DAWSON, Nicholas Anthony. b 52. St Jo Coll Nottm 88. **d** 90 **p** 91. C Mortomley St Sav High Green *Sheff* 90-95; V Owlerton from 95. *Owlerton Vicarage, Forbes Road, Sheffield S6 2NW* Tel 0114-234 3560

DAWSON, Canon Norman William. b 41. MBE99. K Coll Lon BD63 AKC63. **d** 65 **p** 66. C Salford St Phil w St Steph *Man* 65-68; C Heaton Ch Ch 68-70; R Longsight St Jo 70-75; R Longsight St Jo w St Cypr 75-82; R Withington St Paul 82-99; AD Withington 91-99; Hon Can Man Cathl from 98; P-in-c Davyhulme St Mary from 99. *St Mary's Vicarage, Vicarage Road, Manchester M41 5TP* Tel 0161-748 2210

DAWSON, Paul Christopher Owen. b 61. Leeds Univ BA82. Ripon Coll Cuddesdon 83. **d** 85 **p** 86. C Dovecot *Liv* 85-89; V Westbrook St Phil 89-94; Bp's Dom Chapl 94-98; V Witton *Ches* from 98. *The Vicarage, 61 Church Road, Northwich CW9 5PB* Tel (01606) 42943 E-mail pauldawson@pcod.fsnet.co.uk

DAWSON, Paul Richard. b 67. Bris Univ BSc89. Oak Hill Th Coll 99. **d** 01 **p** 02. C Wimbledon Em Ridgway Prop Chpl *S'wark* from 01. *41 Circle Gardens, London SW19 3JX* Tel (020) 8404 3894 E-mail paul.dawson@dundonald.org

DAWSON, The Ven Peter. b 29. Keble Coll Ox BA52 MA56. Ridley Hall Cam 52. **d** 54 **p** 55. C Morden *S'wark* 54-59; R 68-77; V Barston *Birm* 59-63; R Higher Openshaw *Man* 63-68; RD Merton *S'wark* 75-77; Adn Norfolk *Nor* 77-93; rtd 93; Perm to Offic *Nor* from 93; *Carl* from 98. *The Coach House, Harmony Hill, Milnthorpe LA7 7QA* Tel (01539) 562020

DAWSON, Peter Rodney. b 44. MIMI. Guildf Dioc Min Course 96. **d** 98 **p** 99. OLM Ashtead *Guildf* from 98. *28 Sunny Bank, Epsom KT18 7DX* Tel (01372) 727761

DAWSON, Ronald Eric John. b 27. St Mark & St Jo Coll Lon TCert54 Lon Univ BD64. Bps' Coll Cheshunt 62. **d** 62 **p** 63. C Dartford H Trin *Roch* 62-66; C Fulham St Etheldreda 66-74; V Brentford St Faith 74-80; rtd 92. *13 Birkbeck Road, London W5 4ES* Tel (020) 8560 3564

DAWSON, Thomas Douglas. b 52. Newc Univ BA. St Steph Ho Ox. **d** 80 **p** 82. C N Gosforth *Newc* 80-81; C Leic St Chad *Leic* 82-85; TV Catford (Southend) and Downham *S'wark* 85-88; V Chevington *Newc* 88-94; V Cowgate 94-96; P-in-c Cresswell and Lynemouth 96-98; C Blyth St Mary 98-01; rtd 01; Perm to Offic *Newc* from 02. *Iona, 2 Hillside, Lesbury, Alnwick NE66 3NR* Tel (01665) 830412 Mobile 07763-122259 E-mail fr_tom_dawson@hotmail.com

DAWSON, Canon William James Andrew. b 48. TCD MA72. CITC 88. **d** 88 **p** 89. NSM Killyman *Arm* 88-91; NSM Pomeroy from 91; Can Arm Cathl from 98; Preb 00. *Tamlaght, Coagh, Cookstown BT80 0AB* Tel (028) 8676 2227 Fax as telephone

DAWSON, William John. b 26. TEng74 ACP74 MTh96. CITC 77. **d** 80 **p** 81. NSM Lisburn St Paul *Conn* 80-85; Dioc C 85-99; Aux Min Glenavy w Tunny and Crumlin 99-01; rtd 01. *55 Thornleigh Drive, Lisburn BT28 2DA* Tel (028) 9267 0252

DAWSON-CAMPBELL, Olive Sheila. b 57. ACIB70. WEMTC 99. **d** 00 **p** 01. OLM Longden and Annscroft w Pulverbatch *Heref* from 00. *Sheaves, Lyth Bank, Lyth Hill, Shrewsbury SY3 0BE* Tel (01743) 872071

DAWSWELL, Jonathan Andrew. b 65. Jes Coll Cam BA86. Wycliffe Hall Ox BA91. **d** 92 **p** 93. C Childwall All SS *Liv* 92-96; C Leyland St Andr *Blackb* 96-99; V Knypersley *Lich* from 99. *St John's Vicarage, 62 Park Lane, Knypersley, Stoke-on-Trent ST8 7AU* Tel (01782) 512240 E-mail andrew@dawswell.freeserve.co.uk

DAWTRY, Anne Frances. b 57. Westf Coll Lon BA79 PhD85. Ripon Coll Cuddesdon DipMin93. **d** 93 **p** 94. C Corfe Mullen *Sarum* 93-96; C Parkstone St Pet w Branksea and St Osmund

96-97; Chapl Bournemouth Univ *Win* 97-99; Prin OLM and Integrated Tr *Sarum* 99-03; Prin Dioc OLM Scheme *Man* from 03. *173 Rochdale Road East, Heywood OL10 1QU* Tel (01706) 620642

DAXTER, Preb Gregory. b 42. Chelmer Inst of HE PGCE76. Oak Hill Th Coll 64. **d** 68 **p** 69. C Paignton St Paul Preston *Ex* 68-72; C Woodford Wells *Chelmsf* 72-75; Hon C Harold Hill St Paul 75-77; Hon C Wilmington *Roch* 77-87; PV Ex Cathl and Chapl Ex Cathl Sch 87-03; Preb Ex Cathl *Ex* from 02; rtd 03. *36 Lyncombe Crescent, Higher Lincombe Road, Torquay TQ1 2HP*

DAY, Audrey. b 30. CA Tr Coll IDC57. **d** 88 **p** 94. Par Dn Mildenhall *St E* 88-91; Dioc Officer for the Care of the Elderly 91-95; NSM Blackbourne 94-95; rtd 95; Perm to Offic *St E* from 95. *Peace Haven, Duke Street, Stanton, Bury St Edmunds IP33 2AB* Tel (01359) 250742

DAY, Charles George. b 28. Keble Coll Ox BA51 MA63. Cuddesdon Coll 51. **d** 53 **p** 54. C Hythe *Cant* 53-56; C S Norwood St Alb 56-59; R Stisted *Chelmsf* 59-65; V Brenchley *Roch* 65-75; rtd 93. *Sparks Hall, Forsham Lane, Sutton Valence, Maidstone ME17 3EW* Tel (01622) 843248 Fax 844298

DAY, Charles Ian. b 48. Univ of Wales (Ban) BA72. St Mich Coll Llan 73. **d** 75 **p** 76. C Llanrhos *St As* 75-79; V Mochdre 79-83; CF 80-91; V Minera *St As* 83-92; Dioc Soc Resp Officer 89-94; V Mold from 92. *The Vicarage, Church Lane, Mold CH7 1BW* Tel and fax (01352) 752960 Mobile 07977-001692
E-mail friday@cwcom.net

DAY, Canon Colin Michael. b 40. Lon Univ BSc62 AKC62 Em Coll Cam BA66 MA71. Ridley Hall Cam 65. **d** 67 **p** 68. C Heworth w Peasholme St Cuth *York* 65-70; C Ox St Clem *Ox* 70-76; V Kidsgrove *Lich* 76-86; Exec Officer Angl Evang Assembly and C of E Coun 86-90; Adv on Miss and Evang *Sarum* 90-95; Can and Preb Sarum Cathl from 94; P-in-c Branksome Park All SS 95-01; V from 01; Dioc Tr in Evang from 95. *The Vicarage, 28 Western Road, Poole BH13 7BP* Tel (01202) 708202 E-mail colin.m.day@tesco.net

DAY, David John. b 44. CEng72 MICE72. Trin Coll Bris DipHE. **d** 90 **p** 91. C Stratton St Margaret w S Marston etc *Bris* 90-94; Perm to Offic from 94; Manager SA Alcohol Rehabilitation Cen Highworth from 98. *56 Beechcroft Road, Swindon SN2 7PX* Tel (01793) 725721

DAY, David Vivian. b 36. Lon Univ BA57 Nottm Univ MEd73 MTh77. **d** 99 **p** 00. NSM Dur St Nic *Dur* from 99. *35 Orchard Drive, Durham DH1 1LA* Tel 0191-386 6909
E-mail dv.day@virgin.net

DAY, Canon David William. b 37. St Andr Univ MA58 BD61 CertEd73. St And Dioc Tr Course 74. **d** 76 **p** 77. St Andrews All SS *St And* 76-77; P-in-c Dundee St Ninian *Bre* 77-84; Itinerant Priest *Arg* from 84; R Duror from 84; P-in-c Gruline from 84; P-in-c Kentallen from 84; P-in-c Kinlochleven from 84; P-in-c Kinlochmoidart 84-96; P-in-c Lochbuie 84-96; P-in-c Portnacrois from 84; P-in-c Strontian 84-96; Can St Jo Cathl Oban from 99. *St Adamnan's Rectory, Duror of Appin, Argyll PA38 4BS* Tel (01631) 740218 Fax as telephone
E-mail duror@argyll.anglican.org

DAY, George Chester. b 45. Ex Univ BA66 Lon Univ BD70. Clifton Th Coll 67. **d** 71 **p** 72. C Reading St Jo *Ox* 71-75; C Morden *S'wark* 75-81; Sec for Voc and Min CPAS 81-86; Hon C Bromley Ch Ch *Roch* 83-86; V St Paul's Cray St Barn from 86; RD Orpington from 01. *The Vicarage, Rushet Road, Orpington BR5 2PU* Tel (01689) 821353
E-mail vicar@st-barnabas-cray.org.uk

DAY, Canon James Alfred. b 23. DFC44. AKC49. **d** 50 **p** 51. C Wembley Park St Aug *Lon* 50-52; Mauritius 52-57; V E and W Ravendale w Hatcliffe *Linc* 57-60; R Beelsby 57-60; PC Gt Grimsby St Paul 60-66; V Tattershall 66-80; R Coningsby 66-80; RD Horncastle 73-80; Can and Preb Linc Cathl from 77; V Heckington 80-89; rtd 89. *22 Ancaster Drive, Sleaford NG34 7LY* Tel (01529) 305318

DAY, Prof James Meredith. b 55. Oberlin Coll (USA) AB77 Harvard Univ EdM81 Univ of Penn PhD87. Westcott Ho Cam 01. **d** 03. C Antwerp St Boniface *Eur* from 03; C Ostend from 03. *Address temp unknown* Tel (0032) 486-141323 (mobile)
E-mail james.day@psp.ucl.ac.be

DAY, Jennifer Ann. See BRADSHAW, Mrs Jennifer Ann

DAY, John. b 44. Oak Hill NSM Course 87. **d** 90 **p** 91. NSM Bexleyheath St Pet *Roch* 90-93; C Erith Ch Ch and Erith St Jo 93-95; P-in-c Erith St Jo 95-97; V 97-03; rtd 03. *56 Barrington Road, Bexleyheath DA7 4UW* Tel (020) 8331 5177

DAY, Canon John Alfred. b 25. TCD BA51. **d** 51 **p** 52. C Enniskillen and Trory *Clogh* 51-54; I Clontibret w Tullycorbet 54-58; I Drumkeeran 58-67; I Maguiresbridge w Derrybrusk 67-91; Can Clogh Cathl from 78; rtd 91. *Killeenifinane Cottage, 40 Ballylucas Road, Tamlaght, Enniskillen BT74 4HD* Tel (028) 6638 7835

DAY, John Cuthbert. b 36. Sarum Th Coll 66. **d** 68 **p** 69. C Bedhampton *Portsm* 68-72; V Froxfield 72-73; V Froxfield w Privett 73-77; V Warminster Ch Ch *Sarum* 77-81; R Pewsey 81-90; Chapl Pewsey Hosp 81-90; P-in-c Sturminster Newton

and Hinton St Mary *Sarum* 90-01; P-in-c Stock and Lydlinch 90-01; rtd 01; Perm to Offic *B & W* from 01. *Kingfisher Cottage, Clements Lane, Mere, Warminster BA12 6DF* Tel (01347) 860984

DAY, John Kenneth. b 58. Hull Univ BA85. Cranmer Hall Dur 85. **d** 87 **p** 88. C Thornbury *Bradf* 87-90; V 90-96; V Whitkirk *Ripon* 96-01; New Zealand from 01. *7 Makora Street, Fendalton, Christchurch 8004, New Zealand* Tel (0064) (3) 351 7392
E-mail johnkday@btinternet.com

DAY, John Nathaniel. b 36. Kelham Th Coll 59. **d** 64 **p** 65. C Mansfield St Mark *S'well* 64-69; C W Wycombe *Ox* 69-75; TV High Wycombe 75-77; C-in-c Britwell St Geo CD 77-78; TV W Slough 78-87; TV Langley Marish 87-96; Warden St Columba's Retreat and Conf Cen 96-97; Chapl Community of St Pet Woking 96-97; rtd 97; TV Chipping Barnet w Arkley *St Alb* 97-01. *12 Racecourse Road, Mansfield NG18 4EZ* Tel (01623) 429672

DAY, Miss Mary Elizabeth. b 57. Leic Poly BEd79. St Jo Coll Nottm 93. **d** 93 **p** 94. C Newbarns w Hawcoat *Carl* 93-98; P-in-c Allonby 98-03; P-in-c Cross Canonby 98-03; P-in-c Dearham 02-03; V Allonby, Cross Canonby and Dearham from 03. *The Vicarage, Crosscanonby, Maryport CA15 6SJ* Tel (01900) 812146
E-mail mary.day1@tesco.net

DAY, Michael. b 37. AKC61 RCA(Lon) MA75. **d** 62 **p** 63. C Hulme St Phil *Man* 62-65; Asst Chapl Newc Univ *Newc* 65-70; Chapl Chelsea Coll and Chapl R Coll of Art 70-90; Chapl Cen, Chelsea and St Martin's Schs of Art *Lon* 85-90; P-in-c Bloomsbury St Geo w Woburn Square Ch Ch 91-95; C St Pancras w St Jas and Ch Ch 95-02; Chapl Lon Art Colls 95-02; rtd 02. *40 Thistlewaite Road, London E5 0QQ* Tel (020) 8985 8568

DAY, Paul Geoffrey. b 51. Dur Univ BEd75. Trin Coll Bris 76. **d** 78 **p** 79. C Roxeth Ch *Lon* 78-82; TV Barking St Marg w St Patr *Chelmsf* 82-87; V Barrow St Mark *Carl* 87-00; V Eccleston St Luke *Liv* from 00. *St Luke's Vicarage, Mulberry Avenue, St Helens WA10 4DE* Tel (01744) 21173
E-mail paulgday@btinternet.com

DAY, Paul Geoffrey. b 56. St Pet Coll Ox BA77. St Jo Coll Nottm 87. **d** 89 **p** 90. C Mildmay Grove St Jude and St Paul *Lon* 89-92; C Loughborough Em *Leic* 92-95; TV Loughborough Em and St Mary in Charnwood 95-98; Lic to Adn Loughb 98. *Address temp unknown*

DAY, Peter. b 50. BPharm71. Coll of Resurr Mirfield 85. **d** 87 **p** 88. C Eastcote St Lawr *Lon* 87-91; C Wembley Park St Aug 91-94; V Glen Parva and S Wigston *Leic* from 94. *The Vicarage, 1 St Thomas's Road, Wigston LE18 4TA* Tel 0116-278 2830
E-mail peterday@leicester.anglican.org

DAY, Robert Murray. b 63. St Jo Coll Dur BA87. Trin Coll Bris BA95. **d** 97 **p** 98. C Beckenham St Geo *Roch* 97-01; TV Gillingham *Sarum* 01-02; Chapl Sexey's Sch Bruton 02-03. *Address temp unknown*

DAY, Roy Frederick. b 24. S'wark Ord Course 63. **d** 67 **p** 68. C Newington St Paul *S'wark* 67-70; C Radlett *St Alb* 70-72; P-in-c Ponsbourne 72-76; R Campton 76-82; V Shefford 76-82; R Shenley 82-89; rtd 89; Perm to Offic *St Alb* from 89. *11 Hill End Lane, St Albans AL4 0TX* Tel (01727) 845782

DAY, Canon Samuel Richard. b 14. Reading Univ BSc36 Ch Ch Ox BA48 MA52 DPhil56. St D Coll Lamp 37. **d** 38 **p** 39. C Birkdale St Jo *Liv* 38-40; CF (EC) 40-46; C Ox St Mich *Ox* 46-49; R Chinnor 49-66; R Emmington 50-66; P-in-c Sydenham 51-66; Lect Ripon Hall Ox 57-62; V Gt Marlow 66-89; RD Wycombe 68-74; Hon Can Ch Ch 70-89; rtd 89. *3 Leighton House, Glade Road, Marlow SL7 1EA* Tel (01628) 484922

DAY, Terence Patrick. b 30. Lon Univ BD60 K Coll Lon MTh63 PhD66. Lon Coll of Div ALCD59. **d** 60 **p** 61. C Polegate *Chich* 60-63; India 63-71; CMS 66-71; Kenya 71-73; Canada from 73; Prof Religions Univ of Manitoba 74-95; rtd 95. *7 Hazel Park Drive, Winnipeg MB, Canada, R3T 5H5* E-mail tmday@shaw.ca

DAY, William Charles. b 47. Portsm Poly BEd86. Ripon Coll Cuddesdon 88. **d** 90 **p** 91. C Bishop's Waltham *Portsm* 90-93; P-in-c Greatham w Empshott and Hawkley w Prior's Dean 93-95; R 95-98; V Titchfield from 98. *The Vicarage, 24 Frog Lane, Titchfield, Fareham PO14 4DU* Tel (01329) 842324 *or* tel and fax 847003 E-mail bill@stpittchfield.freeserve.co.uk

DAYKIN, Timothy Elwin. b 54. R Holloway Coll Lon BSc75 St Jo Coll Dur DipTh77 MA81 K Coll Lon MPhil93 MEHS89. Cranmer Hall Dur 75. **d** 78 **p** 79. C Bourne *Guildf* 78-81; Chapl K Alfred Coll *Win* 82-87; C-in-c Valley Park CD 87-91; V Valley Park 91-92; P-in-c Fordingbridge 92-98; V 98-01; P-in-c Hale w S Charford 94-01; P-in-c Breamore 99-01; TR Fordingbridge and Breamore and Hale etc from 01. *71 Church Street, Fordingbridge SP6 1BB* Tel (01425) 653163 Fax 656709
E-mail rector@fordingbridge.com

DAYNES, Andrew John. b 47. Jes Coll Cam BA69 MA73. Westcott Ho Cam 69. **d** 72 **p** 73. C Radlett *St Alb* 72-76; Chapl St Alb Abbey 76-80; Chapl Bryanston Sch from 80. *Bryanston School, Blandford Forum DT11 0PX* Tel (01258) 484655 *or* 452411

DAZELEY, Mrs Lorna. b 31. CertEd53 New Hall Cam BA82 MA86. EAMTC 82. **dss** 84 **d** 87 **p** 94. Chesterton St Andr *Ely* 84-87; C 87-97; rtd 97; Perm to Offic *Ely* from 01. *Chesterton*

House, Church Street, Chesterton, Cambridge CB4 1DT Tel (01223) 356243

DE ALWIS, Anthony Clarence. b 39. Nottm Univ MA99. EAMTC 96. **d** 99 **p** 00. NSM Carrington *S'well* from 99. *85 Marlborough Road, Beeston, Nottingham NG9 2HL* Tel 0115-922 0443 Mobile 07974-084514 E-mail t.dealwis@clarendon.ac.uk

de BERRY, Andrew Piers. b 44. St Jo Coll Dur BA66. Ripon Hall Ox 70. **d** 74 **p** 75. C Aylesbury *Ox* 74-77; USA 78; TV Clyst St George, Aylesbeare, Clyst Honiton etc *Ex* 78-80; Asst Chapl HM Pris Wormwood Scrubs 80-82; Chapl HM Pris Sudbury 82-84; V Blackwell *Derby* 84-91; V Thurgarton w Hoveringham and Bleasby etc *S'well* from 91. *The Vicarage, Southwell Road, Thurgarton, Nottingham NG14 7QP* Tel (01636) 830234 E-mail de_berry@totalise.co.uk

de BERRY, Barnabas John de la Tour. b 75. Heythrop Coll Lon BA99. Wycliffe Hall Ox 99. **d** 01 **p** 02. C Derby St Alkmund and St Werburgh *Derby* from 01. *58 Cedar Street, Derby DE22 1GE* Tel 07968-728840 (mobile) E-mail barneydeb@hotmail.com

DE BERRY, Robert Delatour. b 42. Qu Coll Cam BA64 MA68. Ridley Hall Cam 65. **d** 67 **p** 68. C Bradf Cathl *Bradf* 67-70; Uganda 71-75; V Attercliffe *Sheff* 75-83; V W Kilburn St Luke w St Simon and St Jude *Lon* 83-97; Gen Sec Mid-Africa Min (CMS) 97-99; P-in-c Kennington St Mark *S'wark* 99-01; V from 01. *St Mark's Vicarage, 56 Kennington Oval, London SE11 5SW* Tel (020) 7735 1801 Fax as telephone E-mail 100646@compuserve.com

de BOWEN, Alfred William. b 24. KStJ KLJ. Leeds Univ Dip Horticulture. St Paul's Coll Grahamstown 76. **d** 78 **p** 86. S Africa 78-86; NSM Cil-y-Cwm and Ystrad-ffin w Rhandir-mwyn etc *St D* 86-88; Lic to Offic *Linc* 88-92; rtd 90. *Elmham House, Bay Hill, Ilminster TA19 0AT* Tel (01460) 52694

de BURGH-THOMAS, George Albert. b 30. Univ of Wales (Ban) BA50. St Mich Coll Llan 51. **d** 53 **p** 54. C Hawarden *St As* 53-56 and 60-63; C Roath St Martin *Llan* 56-58; C Llangeinor 58-60; V Bampton and Mardale *Carl* 63-70; V Fritwell *Ox* 70-83; R Souldern 70-83; R Fritwell w Souldern and Ardley w Fewcott 83-87; R Hawridge w Cholesbury and St Leonard 87-96; V The Lee 87-96; rtd 96; Perm to Offic *Ox* from 01. *6 Priory Orchard, Wantage OX12 9EL* Tel (01235) 767780

de CHAZAL, John Robert. b 16. Bris Univ. Wycliffe Hall Ox 53. **d** 55 **p** 56. C Redland *Bris* 55-57; C Brislington St Anne 57; C Boxwell w Leighterton *Glouc* 58-60; C Newington Bagpath w Kingscote and Ozleworth 58-60; P-in-c 60; Iraq 61-64; R Caldecote *Cov* 64-71; R Bradford Peverell w Stratton *Sarum* 72-77; P-in-c Sydling St Nic 77; P-in-c Frampton 77; R Bradford Peverell, Stratton, Frampton etc 77-80; rtd 81; Perm to Offic *Sarum* from 81. *Lavender Cottage, East Street, Sydling, Dorchester DT2 9NX* Tel (01300) 341693

de CHAZAL, Mrs Nancy Elizabeth. b 28. Bedf Coll Lon BA52 Lambeth STh90. Sarum & Wells Th Coll 81. **dss** 84 **d** 87 **p** 94. NSM Melbury *Sarum* 84-98; Perm to Offic from 98. *Lavender Cottage, East Street, Sydling St Nicholas, Dorchester DT2 9NX* Tel (01300) 341693

de COSTOBADIE, James Palliser. b 72. G&C Coll Cam BA94 MA98. Oak Hill Th Coll BA01. **d** 02. C St Helen Bishopsgate w St Andr Undershaft etc *Lon* from 02; C Mayfair Ch Ch from 02. *21B Down Street, London W1J 7AW* Tel (020) 7629 5993 E-mail jdecostobadie@hotmail.com

de GARIS, Jean Helier Thomson. b 60. K Alfred's Coll Win BA82 PGCE83. Sarum & Wells Th Coll BTh93. **d** 93 **p** 94. C Chandler's Ford *Win* 93-98; P-in-c Lytchett Minster *Sarum* from 98. *The Vicarage, New Road, Lytchett Minster, Poole BH16 6JQ* Tel (01202) 622253 E-mail jdg@fish.co.uk

de GREY-WARTER, Philip. b 67. Leeds Univ BEng89. Ridley Hall Cam BA94 CTM94. **d** 94 **p** 95. C Bromley Ch Ch *Roch* 94-97; C Sevenoaks St Nic 97-02; P-in-c Fowey *Truro* 02; P-in-c St Sampson from 02. *The Vicarage, Church Avenue, Fowey PL23 1BU* Tel (01726) 833535 E-mail pdgw@btinternet.com

DE HOOP, Brother Thomas Anthony. b 38. Bp's Univ Lennox BA63 LTh63. **d** 68 **p** 69. Canada 68-79; C Fort George w Painthills 68-70; I Mistassini 70-72; R La Tuque 72-75; Assoc P Pierrefonds 75-79; SSF from 79; Perm to Offic *Sarum* 79-80; Hon C Toxteth St Marg *Liv* 80-85; Chapl Newsham Gen Hosp Liv 82-85; P-in-c Cambridge St Benedict *Ely* 85-88; V 88-92; Perm to Offic *Liv* 92-94 and *Eur* from 94. *Glasshampton Monastery, Shrawley, Worcester WR6 6TQ* Tel (01299) 896345 E-mail glasshamptonssf@franciscans.org.uk

DE KEYSER, Nicholas David Llewellyn. b 49. Nottm Univ BTh75 MTh86. St Jo Coll Nottm 71. **d** 75 **p** 76. C Portswood Ch Ch *Win* 75-77; C Yateley *Win* 77-81; TV Grantham *Linc* 81-86; V Heyside *Man* 86-91; R Charlton-in-Dover *Cant* 91-03; R Stock Harvard *Chelmsf* from 03. *The Rectory, 61 High Street, Stock, Ingatestone CM4 9BN* Tel (01277) 840453 Mobile 07050-155481 Fax 08701-249842 E-mail nickdekeyser@btopenworld.com

de la BAT SMIT, Reynaud. b 50. St Edm Hall Ox BA80 MA86 Dur Univ PhD94 FRSA94. Ripon Coll Cuddesdon. **d** 82 **p** 83. C Headington *Ox* 82-85; Chapl St Hild and St Bede Coll *Dur* 85-96; Chapl Cheltenham Coll from 96; Sec Chs' Peace Forum CTBI

from 97. *Cheltenham College, Bath Road, Cheltenham GL53 7LD* Tel (01242) 513540 *or* 230800 E-mail reynaud@ukonline.co.uk

de la HOYDE, Canon Denys Ralph Hart. b 33. G&C Coll Cam BA57 MA61. Westcott Ho Cam 57. **d** 59 **p** 60. C Moss Side Ch Ch *Man* 59-60; Chapl G&C Coll Cam 60-64; India 64-68; C Eltham H Trin *S'wark* 68-69; Chapl Bromsgrove Sch 69-71; Lic to Offic *Ripon* 71-78; V Pool w Arthington 86-98; Dioc Dir of Ords 86-98; Hon Can Ripon Cathl 92-98; rtd 98; Assoc Dir of Ords *Ripon* from 98. *36 Hookstone Chase, Harrogate HG2 7HS* Tel (01423) 548146

de la MARE, Benedick James Hobart. b 38. Trin Coll Ox BA63 MA67. Cuddesdon Coll 63. **d** 65 **p** 66. C Gosforth All SS *Newc* 65-68; Chapl Trin Coll Cam 68-73; V Newc St Gabr *Newc* 73-81; V Dur St Oswald *Dur* 81-02; rtd 02; Chapl Collingwood Coll from 95. *216 Gilesgate, Durham DH1 1QN* Tel 0191-383 2634

de la MOUETTE, Norman Harry. b 39. Southn Univ BEd73 MA98. Sarum & Wells Th Coll 76. **d** 79 **p** 80. NSM Win St Lawr and St Maurice w St Swithun *Win* 79-99; Deputation Appeals Org CECS *Win* and *Portsm* 83-96; Chapl St Jo Win Charity 96-99; NSM Win St Lawr and St Maurice w St Swithun *Win* from 99. *146 Greenhill Road, Winchester SO22 5DR* Tel (01962) 853191

DE LACEY, Thomas. b 46. HNC68. Carl Dioc Tr Inst 88. **d** 91 **p** 92. NSM Ingol *Blackb* 91-93; NSM Ribbleton 93-94. *5 Fulwood Hall Lane, Fulwood, Preston PR2 8DA* Tel (01772) 700923

de MELLO, Gualter Rose. b 34. MBE96. Ridley Hall Cam 63. **d** 64 **p** 65. C S Hackney St Jo w Ch Ch *Lon* 64-66; Toc H Chapl (Hackney) 66-72; Hon C All Hallows by the Tower etc *Lon* from 73; Dir Friends Anonymous Service from 73; Dir Community of Reconciliation and Fellowship from 88; rtd 99. *Prideaux House, 10 Church Crescent, London E9 7DL*

DE MURALT, Robert Willem Gaston. b 25. Utrecht Univ LLM48 DLSc54. Chich Th Coll 90. **d** 90 **p** 91. Hon Asst Chapl The Hague *Eur* 90-02; rtd 02. *Burgemeester de Monchyplein 73, 2585 DH The Hague, The Netherlands* Tel (0031) (70) 383 8520

✠**de PINA CABRAL, The Rt Revd Daniel Pereira dos Santos.** b 24. Lisbon Univ LLB47. Lon Coll of Div. **d** 47 **p** 49 **c** 67. Portugal 47-67; Portuguese E Africa 67-75; Mozambique 75-76; Asst Bp Lebombo 67-68; Bp Lebombo 68-76; Asst Bp Eur from 76; Hon Can Gib Cathl 79-87; Adn Gib 87-93; rtd 89. *Rua Henrique Lopes de Mendonça, 253-42 Dto hab 42, 4150-396 Porto, Portugal* Tel (00351) (22) 617 7772

DE POE SILK, Ronald Charles. b 32. Lich Th Coll 65. **d** 67 **p** 68. C Tottenham St Phil *Lon* 67-68; C Edmonton St Mary w St Jo 68-70; V Stamford Hill St Bart 70-74; rtd 97. *122 Kings Hedges Road, Cambridge CB4 2PB* Tel (01223) 424190

de POMERAI, David Ian Morcamp. b 50. Edin Univ BSc72 Univ Coll Lon PhD75. EMMTC 90. **d** 93 **p** 94. NSM Sutton in Ashfield St Mary *S'well* 93-96; NSM Clifton 96-02; NSM Walton-on-Trent w Croxall, Rosliston etc *Derby* from 02. *The Rectory, 2 Station Lane, Walton-on-Trent, Swadlincote DE12 8NA* Tel (01283) 711350 E-mail david.depomerai@nottingham.ac.uk

de POMERAI, Mrs Lesley Anne. b 60. ACIPD82. St Jo Coll Nottm BTh90. **d** 92 **p** 94. Par Dn Sutton in Ashfield St Mary *S'well* 92-94; C 94-96; TV Clifton 96-02; R Walton-on-Trent w Croxall, Rosliston etc *Derby* from 02. *The Rectory, 2 Station Lane, Walton-on-Trent, Swadlincote DE12 8NA* Tel (01283) 712442 E-mail ddepomerai@aol.com

DE PURY, Andrew Robert. b 28. K Coll Lon BD57 AKC57. **d** 58 **p** 59. C Epping St Jo *Chelmsf* 58-60; C Loughton St Jo 60-65; V Harold Hill St Geo 65-72; Missr Swan Par Gp *Ox* 72-76; TR Swan 76-85; R Worminghall w Ickford, Oakley and Shabbington 85-95; rtd 95; Perm to Offic *B & W* from 95. *8 Russell Pope Avenue, Chard TA20 2JN* Tel (01460) 66714

de QUIDT, Mrs Fiona Margaret Munro. b 53. St Andr Univ MTheol76. NTMTC 97. **d** 00 **p** 01. NSM Kingston Hill St Paul *S'wark* from 00. *10 Norbiton Avenue, Kingston-upon-Thames KT1 3QS* Tel (020) 8549 4175

DE ROBECK, Miss Fiona Caroline. b 74. St Martin's Coll Lanc BA96. St Jo Coll Nottm MA(TS)99. **d** 00 **p** 01. C Bitterne *Win* from 00. *4 Aberdour Close, Bitterne, Southampton SO18 5PF* Tel (023) 8047 3436 E-mail fiona@derobeck.freeserve.co.uk

DE SAUSMAREZ, Canon John Havilland Russell. b 26. Lambeth MA81 Wells Th Coll 54. **d** 56 **p** 57. C N Lynn w St Marg and St Nic *Nor* 56-58; C Flitwick *Cant* 58-61; V Maidstone St Martin 61-68; V St Peter-in-Thanet 68-81; RD Thanet 74-81; Hon Can Cant Cathl 78-81; Can Res Cant Cathl 81-94; rtd 94; Perm to Offic *Cant* from 94. *9 St Peter's Court, Broadstairs CT10 2UU* Tel (01843) 867050

DE SILVA, David Ebenezer Sunil. b 48. DipTh. **d** 72 **p** 73. Sri Lanka 72-84; C Elm Park St Nic Hornchurch *Chelmsf* 84-87; R Mistley w Manningtree and Bradfield 87-90; TR Stanground and Farcet *Ely* 90-01; V Stanground from 01. *The Rectory, 9 Mace Road, Stanground, Peterborough PE2 8RQ* Tel (01733) 890552 E-mail rector@amserve.com

DE SMET, Andrew Charles. b 58. Ex Univ BSc79 Southn Univ BTh88. Sarum & Wells Th Coll 85. **d** 88 **p** 89. C Portsea St Mary

Portsm 88-93; R Shipston-on-Stour w Honington and Idlicote *Cov* 93-00; Warden Offa Retreat Ho and Dioc Spirituality Adv from 00. *The Vicarage, School Hill, Offchurch, Leamington Spa CV33 9AL* Tel (01926) 424401 *or* 423309
E-mail offahouse@btconnect.com

DE VERNY, David Dietrich. b 55. Trier Univ MTh81 DTh89. **d** 83 **p** 83. Asst Chapl Bonn *Eur* 83; C Henfield w Shermanbury and Woodmancote *Chich* 84-86; C Westmr St Sav and St Jas Less *Lon* 86-88; P-in-c Cheddington w Mentmore and Marsworth *Ox* 88-90; Gen Sec Fellowship of St Alb and St Sergius 90-92. *Address temp unknown*

de VIAL, Raymond Michael. b 39. Oak Hill Th Coll 77. **d** 80 **p** 81. NSM Beckenham St Jo *Roch* 80-84; C Morden *S'wark* 84-88; TV 88-94; V Kingston Hill St Paul from 94. *The Vicarage, 33 Queen's Road, Kingston upon Thames KT2 7SF* Tel (020) 8549 8597 *or* 8549 5444 Fax 8974 9158 E-mail raydevial@msn.com *or* ray.devial@stpauls-kingstonhill.co.uk

de VOIL, Paul Walter. b 29. FTII64 Solicitor 67 Hertf Coll Ox BA50 MA87. LNSM course. **d** 92 **p** 93. NSM Denston w Stradishall and Stansfield *St E* 92-02. *Water Lane Barn, Denston, Newmarket CB8 8PP* Tel (01440) 820181 Fax as telephone

✠**de WAAL, The Rt Revd Hugo Ferdinand.** b 35. Pemb Coll Cam BA58 MA63. Ridley Hall Cam 59. **d** 60 **p** 61 **c** 92. C Birm St Martin *Birm* 60-64; Chapl Pemb Coll Cam 64-68; P-in-c Dry Drayton *Ely* 64-68; R 68-74; Min Bar Hill LEP 68-74; V Blackpool St Jo *Blackb* 74-78; Prin Ridley Hall Cam 78-92; Hon Can Ely Cathl *Ely* 86-92; Suff Bp Thetford *Nor* 92-00; rtd 01; Perm to Offic *St E* from 01; Hon Asst Bp Eur from 02. *Folly House, The Folly, Haughley, Stowmarket IP14 3NS* Tel (01449) 774915

de WAAL, Victor Alexander. b 29. Pemb Coll Cam BA49 MA53 Nottm Univ Hon DD83. Ely Th Coll 50. **d** 52 **p** 53. C Isleworth St Mary *Lon* 52-56; Lic to Offic *Ely* 56-59; Chapl Ely Th Coll 56-59; Chapl K Coll Cam 59-63; Hon C Nottingham St Mary *S'well* 63-69; Chapl Nottm Univ 63-69; Can Res and Chan Linc Cathl *Linc* 69-76; Dean Cant 76-86; Perm to Offic *Heref* 88-99; rtd 90; Chapl Soc of Sacred Cross Tymawr 90-00; Lic to Offic *Mon* 90-02. *6 St James Close, Bishop Street, London N1 8PH* Tel (020) 7354 2741 E-mail victor.dewaal@care4free.net

DE WIT, John. b 47. Oriel Coll Ox BA69 MA73 Clare Coll Cam BA78 MA84. Westcott Ho Cam 75. **d** 78 **p** 79. C The Quinton *Birm* 78-81; TV Solihull 81-85; V Kings Heath 85-94; RD Moseley 91-94; P-in-c Hampton in Arden from 94. *The Vicarage, Hampton-in-Arden, Solihull B92 0AE* Tel (01675) 442604

DE WOLF, Mark Anthony. b 32. BA55. Ely Th Coll 56. **d** 59 **p** 60. C Hackney Wick St Mary of Eton w St Aug *Lon* 59-64; USA from 64; rtd 97. *9 Weetamoe Farm Drive, Bristol, RI 02809, USA*

DEACON, Charles Edward. b 57. Westf Coll Lon BSc78. Ridley Hall Cam CTM94. **d** 94 **p** 95. C Ex St Jas *Ex* 94-98; V Shiphay Collaton from 98. *St John's Vicarage, 83 Cadewell Lane, Torquay TQ2 7HP* Tel (01803) 613361

DEACON, Donald (Brother Angelo). Chich Th Coll 66. **d** 68 **p** 69. SSF from 63; Lic to Offic *Man* 69-70; USA 70-72; C Kennington St Jo *S'wark* 72-74; V Wilton Place St Paul *Lon* 74-75; Angl-Franciscan Rep Ecum Cen Assisi *Eur* 75; Franciscanum Sem 76-78; Perm to Offic *Sarum* 78-82; Lic to Offic *Chelmsf* 82-90; *Birm* 90-93; *Linc* 94-97; rtd 98; Lic to Offic *Lon* from 98. *Society of St Francis, Alverna, 110 Ellesmere Road, London NW10 1JS* Tel (020) 8452 7285 Fax as telephone

DEACON, Frederick George Raymond. b 15. Tyndale Hall Bris 63. **d** 65 **p** 66. C Kingswood *Bris* 65-69; C Leckhampton SS Phil and Jas *Glouc* 69-71; V Longcot *Ox* 71-72; V Longcot w Fernham and Bourton 72-77; Zambia 77-80; P-in-c Cressage w Sheinton *Heref* 80-81; P-in-c Harley w Kenley 80-81; TV Wenlock 81-85; rtd 85; Perm to Offic *Heref* 85-90; *Glouc* from 1986 and *Worc* from 90. *29 Robinson Meadow, Ledbury HR8 1SU* Tel (01531) 634500

DEACON, John. b 37. Arm Aux Min Course 87. **d** 90 **p** 91. NSM Enniscorthy w Clone, Clonmore, Monart etc *C & O* from 90. *The Rectory, Creagh, Gorey, Co Wexford, Irish Republic* Tel (00353) (55) 20354

DEACON, Mrs Selina Frances. b 52. SRN74. Ripon Coll Cuddesdon 01. **d** 03. C White Horse *Sarum* from 03. *37 Timor Road, Westbury BA13 2GA* Tel (01373) 826509 Mobile 07867-521909 E-mail selinadeacon@hotmail.com

DEACON, Timothy Randall. b 55. Ex Univ BA78. Chich Th Coll 79. **d** 80 **p** 81. C Whitleigh *Ex* 80-83; P-in-c Devonport St Aubyn 83-88; P-in-c Newton Ferrers w Revelstoke 88-94; R from 94; P-in-c Holberton from 93; RD Ivybridge 98-03. *The Rectory, Court Road, Newton Ferrers, Plymouth PL8 1DL* Tel (01752) 872530 Fax as telephone E-mail timdeacon@bigfoot.com

DEADMAN, Richard George Spencer. b 63. Ex Univ BA85. Coll of Resurr Mirfield 86. **d** 88 **p** 89. C Grangetown *York* 88-91; P-in-c 91-93; V 93-96; V Wallsend St Luke *Newc* 96-01; V Newc St Phil and St Aug and St Matt w St Mary from 01. *St Matthew's Vicarage, 10 Winchester Terrace, Newcastle upon Tyne NE4 6EY* Tel 0191-232 9039

DEAKIN, John David. b 58. Qu Coll Birm BA03. **d** 03. C Blakenall Heath *Lich* from 03. *St Aidan's Vicarage, 78A Chestnut Road, Walsall WS3 1AP* Tel (01922) 494655

DEAKIN, Preb John Hartley. b 27. K Coll Cam BA50 MA63. Cranmer Hall Dur DipTh65. **d** 65 **p** 66. C Newcastle St Geo *Lich* 65-70; V Cotes Heath 70-84; RD Eccleshall 82-92; R Standon and Cotes Heath 84-95; Preb Lich Cathl 88-02; Sub-Chapl HM Pris Drake Hall *Birm* 89-95; rtd 95; Hon C Kinver and Enville *Lich* 95-02. *8C Cliff Road, Bridgnorth WV16 4EY* Tel (01746) 762574

DEAMER, Mrs Carylle. b 40. St Alb and Ox Min Course 96. **d** 99 **p** 00. OLM Riverside *Ox* from 99. *6 Parkland Avenue, Slough SL3 7LQ* Tel (01753) 543818 Mobile 07711-611318

DEAN, The Ven Alan. b 38. Hull Univ BA61. Qu Coll Birm DipTh63. **d** 63 **p** 64. C Clitheroe St Mary *Blackb* 63-67; C Burnley St Pet 67-68; CF 68-93; Dep Chapl Gen and Adn for the Army 93-95; rtd 96; QHC from 93; Perm to Offic *York* from 95. *1 Midway Avenue, Nether Poppleton, York YO26 6NT* Tel (01904) 785305

DEAN, Andrew James. b 40. FCII ACIArb. WEMTC 92. **d** 95 **p** 96. NSM Rodbourne Cheney *Bris* from 95. *Koinonia, 2 Wicks Close, Haydon Wick, Swindon SN25 1QH* Tel (01793) 725526

DEAN, Archibald Charles. b 13. Wycliffe Hall Ox 52. **d** 54 **p** 55. C Yeovil St Jo w Preston Plucknett *B & W* 54-61; R Odcombe 61-91; R Brympton 61-91; R Lufton 61-91; P-in-c Montacute 78-86; rtd 91; Perm to Offic *B & W* from 91. *3 Chur Lane, West Coker, Yeovil BA22 9BH* Tel (01935) 862224

DEAN, Canon Arthur. b 32. Southn Univ CQSW80. Wesley Coll Leeds 55 S Dios Minl Tr Scheme 89. **d** 90 **p** 90. NSM Eastney *Portsm* 90-96; P-in-c Portsea St Alb 96-02; Hon Can Portsm Cathl from 02; rtd 02; Perm to Offic *Portsm* from 02. *9 Kingsley Road, Southsea PO4 8HJ* Tel (023) 9273 5773 Mobile 07855-146929 Fax (023) 9222 1910
E-mail annenarthur.dean@btopenworld.com

DEAN, Francis John Michael. b 15. Univ Coll Ox BA38 MA42. Cuddesdon Coll 38. **d** 39 **p** 40. C Clifton All SS *Bris* 39-46; Hd Master All SS Sch Clifton 43-46; Chapl Ch Ch *Ox* 46-52; P Lib Pusey Ho Ox 46-52; V Bournemouth St Steph *Win* 52-57; R Cranford *Lon* 57-64; V Regent's Park St Mark 61; rtd 81. *35 Spencer Hill Road, London SW19 4EL* Tel (020) 8947 6187

DEAN, John Milner. b 27. S'wark Ord Course 69. **d** 72 **p** 73. C Lewisham St Mary *S'wark* 72-75; C Merton St Mary 75-77; V S Beddington St Mich 77-97; rtd 97. *69 Groveside Close, Carshalton SM5 2ER* Tel (020) 8669 9369

DEAN, Malcolm. b 34. Tyndale Hall Bris 67. **d** 69 **p** 70. C Daubhill *Man* 69-73; P-in-c Constable Lee 73-74; V 74-79; P-in-c Everton St Sav w St Cuth *Liv* 79-86; P-in-c Anfield SS Simon and Jude 81-86; V Walton Breck Ch Ch 86-89; rtd 89; Perm to Offic *Man* from 89. *40 Grasmere Road, Haslingden, Rossendale BB4 4EB* Tel (01706) 215953

DEAN, Preb Raymond Charles. b 27. Bris Univ BA51. Wycliffe Hall Ox 51. **d** 53 **p** 54. C Weston-super-Mare St Jo *B & W* 53-59; V Lyngford 59-70; V Burnham 70-93; Preb Wells Cathl from 73; RD Burnham 82-91; RD Axbridge 87-91; rtd 93; Perm to Offic *B & W* from 93. *258 Berrow Road, Berrow, Burnham-on-Sea TA8 2JH* Tel (01278) 780979

DEAN, Simon Timothy Michael Rex. b 62. Liv Univ BEng83. Ridley Hall Cam 86. **d** 89 **p** 90. C St German's Cathl *S & M* 89-92; V Castletown from 92. *The Vicarage, Arbory Road, Castletown, Isle of Man IM9 1ND* Tel (01624) 823509

DEANE, John. **d** 02. Lic to Offic *D & R* from 02. *Copany, Donegal PO, Donegal, Irish Republic* Tel (00353) (74) 972 2101

DEANE, Nicholas Talbot Bryan. b 46. Bris Univ BA69. Clifton Th Coll 70. **d** 72 **p** 73. C Accrington Ch Ch *Blackb* 72-75; OMF 75-89; Korea 75-89; P-in-c Newburgh *Liv* 90-93; P-in-c Westhead 90-93; V Newburgh w Westhead 93-97; R Chadwell *Chelmsf* from 97. *The Rectory, 10 Rigby Gardens, Grays RM16 4JJ* Tel (01375) 842176 E-mail nic.deane@virgin.net

DEANE, Robert William. b 52. DipTh85. CITC 85. **d** 85 **p** 86. C Raheny w Coolock *D & G* 85-88; I Clonsast w Rathangan, Thomastown etc *M & K* 88-00; Can Kildare Cathl 97-00; Can Meath Cathl 98-00; I Swords w Donabate and Kilsallaghan *D & G* from 00. *The Rectory, Church Road, Swords, Co Dublin, Irish Republic* Tel (00353) (1) 840 2308

DEANE, Stuart William. b 45. Sarum & Wells Th Coll 86. **d** 88 **p** 89. C Bromyard *Heref* 88-92; V Astley, Clive, Grinshill and Hadnall *Lich* 92-98; TV Cen Telford 98-00; TR from 00. *Holy Trinity Vicarage, 20 Burlington Close, Telford TF4 3TD* Tel (01952) 595915

DEANE-HALL, Henry Michael. b 21. Leeds Univ BA46. Coll of Resurr Mirfield 47. **d** 49 **p** 50. C Poplar St Sav w St Gabr and St Steph *Lon* 49-51; C Kirkley *Nor* 51-53; C Reading St Mary V *Ox* 53-56; Chapl St Gabr Convent Sch Newbury 56-62; V Hermitage *Ox* 58-65; V Patrick *S & M* 65-67; R Bughton *Pet* 67-71; R Duloe w Herodsfoot *Truro* 71-79; V Morval 71-79; P-in-c Donhead St Mary *Sarum* 79-80; R The Donheads 80-82; rtd 82; Perm to Offic *B & W* 82-95; Warden CJGS 82-95. *The College of St Barnabas, Blackberry Lane, Lingfield RH7 6NJ* Tel (01342) 870260

DEAR, Graham Frederick. b 44. St Luke's Coll Ex CertEd66. Wycliffe Hall Ox 67. **d** 70 **p** 71. C Chigwell *Chelmsf* 70-73; C Chingford SS Pet and Paul 73-75; V Southchurch Ch Ch 75-82; CF 82-89; P-in-c The Cowtons *Ripon* 89-94; RE Adv 89-94; V

Startforth and Bowes and Rokeby w Brignall 94-97; Chapl HM Pris Garth 97-01; Perm to Offic *Ripon* from 01. *1 The Old Wynd, Bellerby, Leyburn DL8 5QJ* Tel (01969) 623960

DEAR, Neil Douglas Gauntlett. b 35. Linc Th Coll 87. **d** 89 **p** 90. C Framlingham w Saxtead *St E* 89-92; P-in-c Eyke w Bromeswell, Rendlesham, Tunstall etc 92-98; Chapl Local Health Partnerships NHS Trust 98-02; Chapl Cen Suffolk Primary Care Trust from 02; P-in-c Worlingworth, Southolt, Tannington, Bedfield etc *St E* from 02. *The Rectory, Church Street, Worlingworth, Woodbridge IP13 7NT* Tel (01728) 628032

DEARDEN, James Varley. b 22. Wycliffe Hall Ox 61. **d** 62 **p** 63. C Drypool St Columba w St Andr and St Pet *York* 62-66; V Newington Transfiguration 66-75; V Huddersfield H Trin *Wakef* 75-87; rtd 87; Perm to Offic *Wakef* from 87. *26 Sycamore Avenue, Meltham, Huddersfield HD7 3EE* Tel (01484) 852519

DEARDEN, Canon Philip Harold. b 43. AKC65. **d** 66 **p** 67. C Haslingden w Haslingden Grane *Blackb* 66-69; C Burnley St Pet 69-71; V Langho Billington 71-78; TR Darwen St Pet w Hoddlesden 78-91; RD Darwen 86-91; V Altham w Clayton le Moors 91-97; RD Accrington 95-97; Hon Can Blackb Cathl from 96; V Clitheroe St Mary from 97. *St Mary's Vicarage, Church Street, Clitheroe BB7 2DD* Tel (01200) 423317 *or* 22828 Fax as telephone E-mail philipdearden@aol.com

DEARING, Henry Ernest. b 26. Lon Univ BD53. St Deiniol's Hawarden 55. **d** 55 **p** 56. C Skerton St Chad *Blackb* 55-57; V Huncoat 57-60; rtd 95. *7 Troon Way, Abergele LL22 7TT* Tel (01745) 826714

DEARING, Trevor. b 33. Lon Univ BD58. Qu Coll Birm MA63. **d** 61 **p** 62. C Todmorden *Wakef* 61-63; V Silkstone 63-66; V Northowram 66-68; C Harlow New Town w Lt Parndon *Chelmsf* 68-70; V Hainault 70-75; Dir Healing Miss 75-79; Hon C Gt Ilford St Andr 75-79; Perm to Offic *Linc* 80-81; 99-02; USA 81-83; rtd 83. *4 Rock House Gardens, Radcliffe Road, Stamford PE9 1AS* Tel (01780) 751680

DEARNLEY, Miss Helen Elizabeth. b 77. De Montfort Univ LLB98 Cam Univ BTh02. Westcott Ho Cam 99. **d** 02 **p** 03. C Knighton St Mary Magd *Leic* from 02. *39 Woodcroft Avenue, Leicester LE2 6HU* Tel 0116-288 6443 E-mail helen.dearnley@ukgateway.net

DEARNLEY, John Wright. b 37. Open Univ BA81 Bris Univ CASS65 Univ of Wales (Lamp) DipTh91. **d** 99. NSM Llandogo w Whitebrook Chpl and Tintern Parva *Mon* from 99. *2 Greenbanks, Llandogo, Monmouth NP25 4TG* Tel (01594) 530080

DEARNLEY, Mark Christopher. b 59. Cranmer Hall Dur 84. **d** 87 **p** 88. C Purley Ch Ch *S'wark* 87-91; C Addiscombe St Mary 91-93; C Addiscombe St Mary Magd w St Martin 93-94; V Hook 94-02; R Wendover and Halton *Ox* from 02. *The Vicarage, 34 Dobbins Lane, Wendover, Aylesbury HP22 6DH* Tel (01296) 622230 E-mail dearnley@ukgateway.net

DEARNLEY, Preb Patrick Walter. b 34. Nottm Univ BA55 LTh75. ALCD64. **d** 64 **p** 65. C New Malden and Coombe *S'wark* 64-68; C Portswood Ch Ch *Win* 68-71; C Leeds St Geo *Ripon* 71-74; Hon C Nottingham St Nic *S'well* 74-77; P-in-c Holloway Em w Hornsey Road St Barn *Lon* 77-85; AD Islington 80-85; Abp's Officer for UPA 85-90; Preb St Paul's Cathl *Lon* 86-91; P-in-c Waterloo St Jo *Liv* 91-99; rtd 99; Perm to Offic *Bradf* from 00. *14 Beanlands Parade, Ilkley LS29 8EW* Tel (01943) 603927

DEAS, Leonard Stephen. b 52. New Coll Ox BA75 CertEd76 MA78. St Mich Coll Llan 81. **d** 82 **p** 83. C Dowlais *Llan* 82-84; Chapl St Mich Coll Llan 84-85; Chapl Univ of Wales (Cardiff) *Llan* 85-86; V Newbridge *Mon* 86-93; Can Res St Woolos Cathl 92-96; Master of the Charterhouse Kingston upon Hull from 96. *The Charterhouse, Charterhouse Lane, Hull HU2 8AF* Tel (01482) 329307

DEAVE, Mrs Gillian Mary. b 31. EMMTC 79. **dss** 82 **d** 87 **p** 94. Nottingham St Pet and St Jas *S'well* 82-87; Par Dn 87-91; rtd 91; Perm to Offic *S'well* from 91; Perm to Offic *Leic* from 91. *Greensmith Cottage, 8 City Road, Stathern, Melton Mowbray LE14 4HE* Tel (01949) 860340 E-mail g.deave@leicester.anglican.org

DEBENHAM, Peter Mark. Nottm Univ BSc PhD. EAMTC. **d** 01. NSM Burwell *Ely* from 01; NSM Swaffham Bulbeck and Swaffham Prior w Reach from 01. *23 Burleigh Rise, Burwell, Cambridge CB5 0RS* Tel (01638) 603142

DEBNEY, Canon Wilfred Murray. b 26. ACA48 FCA60. Wycliffe Hall Ox 58. **d** 60 **p** 61. C Leic H Apostles *Leic* 60-65; V Thorpe Edge *Bradf* 65-69; TV Wendy w Shingay *Ely* 69-75; R Brampton 75-94; Offg Chapl RAF 75-94; RD Huntingdon *Ely* 81-94; Hon Can Ely Cathl 85-94; rtd 94; Lic to Offic *Eur* 94-01; Chapl Lugano 98-02; Perm to Offic *Ely* from 02. *3 Hoo Close, Buckden, St Neots PE19 5TX*

DEBOO, Alan John. b 45. Qu Coll Cam BA73 MA77. Westcott Ho Cam 72. **d** 74 **p** 75. C Brackley St Pet w St Jas *Pet* 74-77; Perm to Offic *Sarum* 85-94; NSM Wexcombe 94-02; NSM Savernake from 02. *Mayzells Cottage, Collingbourne Kingston, Marlborough SN8 3SD* Tel (01264) 850683 Fax 850151 E-mail alandeboo@aol.com

DEBOYS, David Gordon. b 54. QUB BD76 Wolfs Coll Ox MLitt. Ridley Hall Cam 90. **d** 92 **p** 93. C Ipswich St Aug *St E* 92-93; C Whitton and Thurleston w Akenham 93-95; R Hardwick *Ely* 95-00; R Toft w Caldecote and Childerley 95-00; V Cambridge St Jas from 00; Dir Focus Chr Inst Cambridge from 00. *St James's Vicarage, 110 Wulfstan Way, Cambridge CB1 8QJ* Tel (01223) 246419 E-mail daviddeboys@btinternet.com

DEDMAN, Canon Roger James. b 45. Oak Hill Th Coll 68. **d** 71 **p** 72. C Gresley *Derby* 71-74; C Ipswich St Fran *St E* 74-79; P-in-c Bildeston w Wattisham 79-92; P-in-c Bramford from 92; P-in-c Somersham w Flowton 94-02; RD Bosmere 96-01; Hon Can St E Cathl from 01; P-in-c Lt Blakenham, Baylham and Nettlestead from 02. *The Vicarage, Vicarage Lane, Bramford, Ipswich IP8 4AE* Tel (01473) 741105 E-mail roger.dedman@virgin.net

DEE, Clive Hayden. b 61. Ripon Coll Cuddesdon 86. **d** 89 **p** 90. C Bridgnorth, Tasley, Astley Abbotts, etc *Heref* 89-93; P-in-c Wellington w Pipe-cum-Lyde and Moreton-on-Lugg 93-96. *Ross Cottage, Crumpton Hill Road, Storridge, Malvern WR13 5HE* Tel (01886) 832639

DEEDES, Canon Arthur Colin Bouverie. b 27. Bede Coll Dur BA51. Wells Th Coll 51. **d** 53 **p** 54. C Milton *Portsm* 53-58; C Worplesdon *Guildf* 58-60; V Weston 60-66; V Fleet 66-73; RD Aldershot 69-73; TR Bournemouth St Pet w St Swithun, H Trin etc *Win* 73-80; RD Bournemouth 74-80; Hon Can Win Cathl 78-92; Master Win St Cross w St Faith 80-92; rtd 92; Perm to Offic *Win* from 92; Hon Chapl Win Cathl from 97. *Dolphins, 17 Chesil Street, Winchester SO23 0HU* Tel (01962) 861617

DEEDES, Ms Rosie Anne. b 66. Birm Univ BA87 City Univ 90. Westcott Ho Cam 94. **d** 96 **p** 97. C St Botolph Aldgate w H Trin Minories *Lon* 96-99; Asst Chapl HM Pris Holloway 99-02; Chapl HM Pris Downview from 02. *HM Prison Downview, Sutton Lane, Sutton SM2 5PD* Tel (020) 8929 3300

DEEGAN, Arthur Charles. b 49. CertEd71 Birm Univ BEd86. Qu Coll Birm 86. **d** 88 **p** 89. C Leic St Jas *Leic* 88-91; C Melton Gt Framland 91-92; TV 92-93; TV Melton Mowbray 93-96; CF (TA) from 95; Chapl ACF Leics, Northants, and Rutland from 95; R Barwell w Potters Marston and Stapleton *Leic* from 96. *The Rectory, 14 Church Lane, Barwell, Leicester LE9 8DG* Tel (01455) 444927 Fax 444928 E-mail ac.deegan@barwell-parish.org.uk

DEELEY, Mrs Elke Christiane. b 58. Birm Univ BA81. SW Minl Tr Course 99. **d** 02 **p** 03. NSM Roche and Withiel *Truro* from 02. *44 Duporth Bay, St Austell PL26 6AQ* Tel (01726) 63083 E-mail elke1@tinyonline.co.uk

DEEMING, Paul Leyland. b 44. CA Tr Coll 65 CMS Tr Coll Selly Oak 70. **d** 80 **p** 80. CMS 71-82; Pakistan 71-82; R E and W Horndon w Lt Warley *Chelmsf* 83-89; V Gt Ilford St Andr 89-01; Co-ord Chapl Heatherwood and Wexham Park Hosp NHS Trust from 01. *Wexham Park Hospital, Wexham, Slough SL2 4HL* Tel (01753) 633000

DEER, Diane Antonia. b 45. SEITE. **d** 00 **p** 01. C Hackington *Cant* from 00. *6 Monks Close, Canterbury CT2 7EH* Tel (01227) 379362 Mobile 07957-758721

DEERING, Alan George. b 36. **d** 99 **p** 00. OLM Blyth Valley *St E* from 99. *11 Walpole Road, Halesworth IP19 8DL* Tel (01986) 873388

DEES, Miss Marilyn Monica (Mandy). b 34. Nottm Univ BSc55 PGCE56. WEMTC 94. **d** 96 **p** 97. NSM Fownhope w Mordiford, Brockhampton etc *Heref* from 96. *Hazelbank, 24 Nover Wood Drive, Fownhope, Hereford HR1 4PN* Tel (01432) 860369

DEETH, William Stanley. b 38. St Pet Coll Ox BA59 MA67. St Steph Ho Ox 66. **d** 68 **p** 69. C Eastbourne St Mary *Chich* 68-71; C Benwell St Jas *Newc* 71-75; C-in-c Byker St Martin CD 75-76; P-in-c Byker St Martin 76; V 76-89; P-in-c Bothal 89-91; R Bothal and Pegswood w Longhirst 91-94; rtd 94; Perm to Offic *Newc* from 94. *17 Osborne Gardens, North Sunderland, Seahouses NE68 7UF* Tel (01665) 720067

DeGROOSE, Leslie John. b 28. Oak Hill Th Coll 62. **d** 64 **p** 65. C Gunton St Pet *Nor* 64-67; Chapl RN 67-83; P-in-c Gt Oakley *Chelmsf* 83-85; R Gt Oakley w Wix 85-92; rtd 92. *1 Queensberry Mews, Newmarket CB8 9AE* Tel (01638) 660599

✠**DEHQANI-TAFTI, The Rt Revd Hassan Barnaba.** b 20. Tehran Univ BA43. Virginia Th Sem DD81 Ridley Hall Cam 47. **d** 49 **p** 50 **c** 61. Iran 49-61; Bp Iran 61-90; Pres Bp Episc Ch Jerusalem and Middle E 76-86; Asst Bp Win from 82; rtd 90. *Sohrab House, 1 Camberry Close, Basingstoke RG21 3AG* Tel (01256) 327457

DEIGHTON, Ian Armstrong. b 19. Glas Univ MA40. Edin Th Coll 40. **d** 43 **p** 44. C Paisley H Trin *Glas* 43-45; Bp's Dom Chapl *Arg* 45-47; P-in-c Nether Lochaber 45-47; P-in-c Kinlochleven 45-47; P-in-c Glas St Mark 47-52; R Clydebank *Glas* 52-57; R Musselburgh *Edin* 57-84; P-in-c Prestonpans 76-84; rtd 84. *6 Duddingston Park South, Edinburgh EH15 3PA* Tel 0131-669 5108

DEIGHTON, William John. b 44. K Coll Lon AKC68 Plymouth Poly CQSW74. St Boniface Warminster 68. **d** 69 **p** 70. C Kenwyn

Truro 69-72; Hon C Winterbourne *Bris* from 90. *22 Salem Road, Winterbourne, Bristol BS36 1QF* Tel (01454) 778847

DEIMEL, Margaret Mary. b 49. CertEd71. WMMTC 91. **d** 94 **p** 95. NSM Bidford-on-Avon *Cov* 94-97; NSM Studley from 97. *The Vicarage, 3 Manor Mews, Manor Road, Studley B80 7PR* Tel (01527) 852830 E-mail studley.vic@virgin.net

DEIMEL, Richard Witold. b 49. Lon Univ BA84. Cranmer Hall Dur 86. **d** 88 **p** 89. C Bilton *Cov* 88-93; P-in-c Studley 93-97; V from 97. *The Vicarage, Manor Mews, Manor Road, Studley B80 7PR* Tel (01527) 852830 E-mail studley.vic@virgin.net

DELAMERE, Allen Stephen. BTh. **d** 90 **p** 91. C Bangor Abbey *D & D* 90-93; I Saintfield 93-03. *Address temp unknown* E-mail allen@sonow.com

DELAMERE, Isaac George. b 71. CITC BTh02. **d** 02. C Newtownards *D & D* from 02. *10 Londonderry Road, Newtownards BT23 3AY* Tel (028) 9181 4750

DELANEY, Anthony. b 65. St Jo Coll Nottm BTh95. **d** 95 **p** 96. C Cullompton *Ex* 95-98; C Maidstone St Luke *Cant* 98-01; P-in-c W Horsley *Guildf* 01-03; R from 03. *The Rectory, 80 East Lane, West Horsley, Leatherhead KT24 6LQ* Tel (01483) 283783 E-mail antdelaney@tesco.net

DELANEY, The Ven Peter Anthony. b 39. MBE01. AKC65. **d** 66 **p** 67. C St Marylebone w H Trin *Lon* 66-70; Chapl Nat Heart Hosp Lon 66-70; Res Chapl Univ Ch Ch the K 70-73; Can Res and Prec S'wark Cathl *S'wark* 73-77; V All Hallows by the Tower etc *Lon* from 77; P-in-c St Kath Cree 98-02; Can Cyprus and the Gulf from 88; Preb St Paul's Cathl *Lon* 95-99; Adn Lon from 99. *43 Trinity Square, London EC3N 4DJ* Tel (020) 7488 2335 Fax 7488 2648 E-mail archdeacon.london@london.anglican.org

DELANY, Michael Edward. b 34. Lon Univ BSc55 PhD58. S'wark Ord Course 80. **d** 83 **p** 84. NSM Hampton St Mary *Lon* 83-87; R Copythorne and Minstead *Win* 87-94; rtd 94; Perm to Offic *Win* 94-00. *Littlecott, Tytherley Road, Winterslow, Salisbury SP5 1PZ* Tel (01980) 862183

DELFGOU, John. b 35. Oak Hill Th Coll 81. **d** 84 **p** 85. NSM Loughton St Mary and St Mich *Chelmsf* 84-90; NSM Loughton St Jo 90-93; C 93-94; TV 94-00; rtd 01; Perm to Offic *Chelmsf* from 01. *20 Carroll Hill, Loughton IG10 1NN* Tel (020) 8508 6333 E-mail john@delfgou.freeserve.co.uk

DELFGOU, Jonathan Hawke. b 63. Aston Tr Scheme 89 Linc Th Coll BTh94. **d** 94 **p** 95. C Greenstead *Chelmsf* 94-98; TV Wickford and Runwell from 98; Chapl Southend Community Care Services NHS Trust 98-99; Chapl S Essex Mental Health & Community Care NHS Trust from 00. *St Mary's Vicarage, Church End Lane, Runwell, Wickford SS11 7JQ* Tel (01268) 732068 E-mail delfgou@fish.co.uk

DELIGHT, The Ven John David. b 25. Liv Univ CSocSc48 Open Univ BA75. Oak Hill Th Coll 49. **d** 52 **p** 53. C Tooting Graveney St Nic *S'wark* 52-55; C Wallington H Trin 55-58; Lic to Offic *Man* 58-61; Travelling Sec IVF 58-61; C-in-c Leic St Chris CD *Leic* 61-68; Chapl HM Pris Leic 64-67; V Leic St Chris *Leic* 68-69; R Aldridge *Lich* 69-82; Preb Lich Cathl 80-90; RD Walsall 81-82; Adn Stoke 82-90; Dir Th Educn Machakos Kenya 90-94; Hon Can Machakos 90-94; Perm to Offic *Ches* and *Lich* from 99. *Karibuni, 17 Hillside Drive, Macclesfield SK10 2PL* Tel (01625) 428117 E-mail delight@fish.co.uk

DELL, Murray John. b 31. Cape Town Univ BA51 BSc54 Edin Univ MB, ChB59. Westcott Ho Cam 63. **d** 65 **p** 65. S Africa 65-70; Dean Windhoek 71-80; V Lyme Regis *Sarum* 80-96; Chapl Lyme Regis Hosp 96; rtd 96. *3 Empsons Close, Dawlish EX7 9BG* Tel (01626) 866193

DELL, The Ven Robert Sydney. b 22. Em Coll Cam BA46 MA50. Ridley Hall Cam 46. **d** 48 **p** 49. C Islington St Mary *Lon* 48-50; C Cambridge H Trin *Ely* 50-53; Lic to Offic *Lich* 53-55; Asst Chapl Wrekin Coll Telford 53-55; R Mildenhall *St E* 55-57; Vice-Prin Ridley Hall Cam 57-65; V Chesterton St Andr *Ely* 66-73; Adn Derby 73-92; Hon Can Derby Cathl 73-81; Can Res 81-92; rtd 92; Perm to Offic *Ely* 92-00; *Derby* from 92. *Pinehurst Lodge, 35 Grange Road, Cambridge CB3 9AU* Tel (01223) 365466

DELMEGE, Andrew Mark. b 68. Essex Univ BA91 Southn Univ MTh98. SW Minl Tr Course 94. **d** 97 **p** 98. C Kings Heath *Birm* 97-01; V Brandwood from 01; Chapl to Deaf People from 01. *The Vicarage, 77 Doversley Road, Birmingham B14 6NN* Tel 0121-693 0217 E-mail adelmege@compuserve.com

DELVE, Eric David. b 42. Trin Coll Bris. **d** 89 **p** 90. NSM Bris St Matt and St Nath *Bris* 89-92; P-in-c Kirkdale St Lawr *Liv* 93-96; V Maidstone St Luke *Cant* from 96; AD Maidstone 99-03; Six Preacher Cant Cathl from 99. *The Vicarage, 24 Park Avenue, Maidstone ME14 5HN* Tel (01622) 754856 E-mail ericdelve@stlukes.org.uk

DELVES, Canon Anthony James. b 47. Birm Univ BSocSc70 Hull Univ PhD94. St Steph Ho Ox 83. **d** 85 **p** 86. C Cantley *Sheff* 85-90; V Goldthorpe w Hickleton from 90; Hon Can Sheff Cathl from 98; AD Wath from 00. *Goldthorpe Presbytery, Lockwood Road, Goldthorpe, Rotherham S63 9JY* Tel (01709) 898426

DELVES BROUGHTON, Simon Brian Hugo. b 33. Ex Coll Ox BA56 MA64. Kelham Th Coll 56. **d** 59 **p** 60. Ox Miss to Calcutta 60-64; C Skirbeck St Nic *Linc* 64-67; E Pakistan/Bangladesh 67-74; Chapl Chittagong 67-69; V St Thos Cathl Dhaka 69-74; V

Northampton Ch Ch *Pet* 74-95; Chapl Northn Gen Hosp 77-87; rtd 95; Perm to Offic *Ox* 95-00. *71A Observatory Street, Oxford OX2 6EP* Tel (01865) 515463

DEMERY, Rupert Edward Rodier. b 72. Trin Hall Cam BA94 MA01 BTh01. Ridley Hall Cam 98. **d** 01 **p** 02. C New Borough and Leigh *Sarum* from 01. *7 Ethelbert Road, Wimborne BH21 1BH* Tel (01202) 889405 Mobile 07801-825671 E-mail rdemery@clara.net

DENBY, Canon Paul. b 47. NW Ord Course 73. **d** 76 **p** 77. C Stretford All SS *Man* 76-80; V Stalybridge 80-87; Chapl Tameside Distr Gen Hosp Ashton-under-Lyne 82-87; Dir of Ords *Man* 87-95; LNSM Officer 91-95; Hon Can Man Cathl 92-95; Bp's Dom Chapl 94-95; Can Admin and Prec Man Cathl from 95. *2 Booth Clibborn Court, Salford M7 4PJ* Tel 0161-792 0979 *or* 833 2220 Fax 839 6226 E-mail paul.denby@manchestercathedral.com

DENCH, Christopher David. b 62. RGN83. Aston Tr Scheme 86 Sarum & Wells Th Coll 88. **d** 91 **p** 92. C Crayford *Roch* 91-94; P-in-c Leybourne 94-98; R from 98; Dioc Lay Tr Adv from 01. *The Rectory, 73 Rectory Lane, Leybourne, Maidstone ME19 5HD* Tel (01732) 842187 Fax as telephone E-mail chris@cdench.freeserve.co.uk

DENERLEY, John Keith Christopher. b 34. Qu Coll Ox BA58 MA61. St Steph Ho Ox 58. **d** 61 **p** 62. C Airedale w Fryston *Wakef* 61-64; Chapl Sarum Th Coll 64-68; Min Can Cov Cathl *Cov* 68-76; Chapl Lanchester Poly 70-76; Chapl The Dorothy Kerin Trust Burrswood 76-85; V Trellech and Cwmcarvan *Mon* 85-87; V Penallt 85-87; V Penallt and Trellech 87-99; Chapl Ty Mawr Convent (Wales) 85-90; R Monmouth *Mon* 93-99; rtd 99; Perm to Offic *Glouc* from 00. *1 The Pales, English Bicknor, Coleford GL16 7PQ* Tel (01594) 860028

DENFORD, Keith Wilkie. b 35. AKC62. **d** 63 **p** 64. C Gunnersbury St Jas *Lon* 63-66; C Brighton St Pet *Chich* 66-71; Min Can Cant Cathl *Cant* 71-75; R W Tarring *Chich* 75-85; V Burgess Hill St Jo 85-90; R Pulborough 90-96; rtd 96; Perm to Offic *Chich* from 96. *31 John Street, Shoreham-by-Sea BN43 5DL* Tel (01273) 464251

DENGATE, Richard Henry. b 39. Cant Sch of Min 82. **d** 85 **p** 86. NSM Wittersham w Stone-in-Oxney and Ebony *Cant* 85; R Sandhurst w Newenden 90-01; rtd 01; Perm to Offic *Cant* from 01. *Apuldrum, Main Street, Peasemarsh, Rye TN31 6UL* Tel (01797) 230980

DENHAM, Anthony Christopher (Chris). b 43. Keble Coll Ox BA65 MA70. Oak Hill Th Coll DipHE93. **d** 93 **p** 94. C Hythe *Cant* 93-97; V Haddenham w Cuddington, Kingsey etc *Ox* from 97. *The Vicarage, 27A The Gables, Haddenham, Aylesbury HP17 8AD* Tel (01844) 291244 E-mail chris@revdenham.freeserve.co.uk

DENHAM, Nicholas Philip. b 50. Salford Univ BSc72 Birm Univ CertEd74. Wycliffe Hall Ox 87. **d** 89 **p** 90. C Bishopwearmouth St Gabr *Dur* 89-90; C Chester le Street 90-92; TV Rushden w Newton Bromswold *Pet* 92-95; R Teigh w Whissendine and Market Overton 95-02; P-in-c Thistleton 01-02; RD Rutland 01-02; TR Bedworth *Cov* from 02. *The Rectory, 1 Linden Lea, Bedworth, Nuneaton CV12 8UD* Tel (024) 7631 0219 E-mail revnpdenham@whissendine333.freeserve.co.uk

DENHAM, Thomas William. b 17. Wycliffe Hall Ox 58. **d** 59 **p** 60. C Bexley St Jo *Roch* 59-62; Area Sec CMS 62-73; Perm to Offic *Liv* 62-73; P-in-c Bishopwearmouth St Gabr *Dur* 73-82; rtd 82. *Forresters Cottage, Nether Ervie, Parton, Castle Douglas DG7 3NG* Tel (01644) 470314

DENHOLM, Canon Robert Jack. b 31. Edin Th Coll 53. **d** 56 **p** 57. C Dundee St Mary Magd *Bre* 56-59; C Edin St Pet *Edin* 59-61; R Bridge of Allan *St And* 61-69; Chapl Stirling Univ 67-69; R N Berwick *Edin* 69-80; R Gullane 76-80; R Edin St Mark 80-90; Can St Mary's Cathl from 88; rtd 90. *15 Silverknowes, Midway, Edinburgh EH4 5PP* Tel 0131-312 6462

DENING, John Cranmer. b 21. Clare Coll Cam BA48 MA52. Qu Coll Birm 50. **d** 52 **p** 53. C Allerton *Liv* 52-55; C Bournemouth St Andr *Win* 55-58; C Lillington *Cov* 59-60; C Yeovil St Jo w Preston Plucknett *B & W* 61-67; C Moulsham St Jo *Chelmsf* 69-70; C W Teignmouth *Ex* 70-73; C N Stoneham *Win* 73-80; C Sholing 80-85; rtd 86. *27 The Paddocks, Brandon IP27 0DX*

DENISON, Canon Keith Malcolm. b 45. Down Coll Cam BA67 MA71 PhD70. Westcott Ho Cam 70. **d** 71 **p** 72. C Chepstow *Mon* 71-72; C Bassaleg 72-75; Post-Ord Tr Officer 75-85; V Mathern and Mounton 75-80; V Mathern and Mounton w St Pierre 80-85; RD Chepstow 82-85; V Risca 85-91; V Goldcliffe and Whitson and Nash 91-96; Dioc Dir of Educn from 91; Hon Can St Woolos Cathl 91-94; Can from 94; Can Res from 96. *Canon's House, Stow Hill, Newport NP20 4EA* Tel (01633) 264919

DENISON, Philip. b 55. York Univ BA77 CertEd. St Jo Coll Nottm 83. **d** 86 **p** 87. C Barnoldswick w Bracewell *Bradf* 86-88; P-in-c Basford St Leodegarius *S'well* 88-91; C Basford w Hyson Green 91-94; V Nether Stowey w Over Stowey *B & W* from 94; RD Quantock from 01. *St Mary's Vicarage, 25 St Mary Street, Nether Stowey, Bridgwater TA5 1LJ* Tel (01278) 732247 E-mail denisonphil@hotmail.com

DENMAN, Frederick George. b 46. Chich Th Coll 67. **d** 70 **p** 71. C Stafford St Mary *Lich* 70-72; C Ascot Heath *Ox* 72-75; P-in-c Culham 75-77; P-in-c Sutton Courtenay w Appleford 75-77; P-in-c Clifton Hampden 77; TV Dorchester 78-81; C Ox St Mich w St Martin and All SS 80; Chapl Henley Memorial Hosp 81-82; P-in-c W Hill *Ex* 82; TV Ottery St Mary, Alfington and W Hill 82-87; V Sparkwell from 87; V Shaugh Prior 87-93; P-in-c Cornwood from 98. *The Vicarage, Sparkwell, Plymouth PL7 5DB* Tel (01752) 837218
E-mail freddie@sparkwell.fsnet.com

DENNEN, The Ven Lyle. b 42. Harvard Univ LLB67 Trin Coll Cam BA70 MA75. Cuddesdon Coll 70. **d** 72 **p** 73. C S Lambeth St Ann *S'wark* 72-75; C Richmond St Mary 75-78; P-in-c Kennington St Jo 78-79; V Kennington St Jo w St Jas 79-99; P-in-c Brixton Road Ch Ch 81-89; RD Brixton 90-99; Hon Can S'wark Cathl 99; Adn Hackney *Lon* from 99; V St Andr Holborn from 99. *St Andrew's Vicarage, 5 St Andrew's Street, London EC4A 3AB* Tel (020) 7353 3544 Fax 7538 2750
E-mail archdeacon.hackney@london.anglican.org

DENNESS, Mrs Linda Christine. b 51. Portsm Dioc Tr Course. **d** 89 **p** 01. NSM Milton *Portsm* 89-93; NSM Portsea St Mary 93-96; Lic to Offic 96-98; NSM Widley w Wymering from 98. *19 Fourth Avenue, Cosham, Portsmouth PO6 3HX* Tel (023) 9278 1381

DENNETT, John Edward. b 36. Tyndale Hall Bris 66. **d** 68 **p** 69. C Chell *Lich* 68-71; C Bispham *Blackb* 71-73; C Cheltenham Ch Ch *Glouc* 73-75; V Coppull *Blackb* 75-79; P-in-c Parkham, Alwington and Buckland Brewer *Ex* 79-80; R 80-84; V Blackpool St Thos *Blackb* 84-92; rtd 92; Chapl Trin Hospice in the Fylde from 88; Perm to Offic *Blackb* from 92. *37 Village Way, Bispham, Blackpool FY2 0AH* Tel (01253) 358039
E-mail johnann.dennett@virgin.net

DENNIS, Mrs Barbara Christine. b 56. NTMTC 94. **d** 97 **p** 98. NSM Romford St Edw *Chelmsf* 97-01; C from 01. *4 Oaklands Avenue, Romford RM1 4DB* Tel (01708) 739676

DENNIS, Miss Drucilla Lyn. b 49. Culham Coll of Educn BEd71 Southn Univ MA82. S Dios Minl Tr Scheme 92. **d** 95 **p** 96. NSM Cowes H Trin and St Mary *Portsm* 95-01; TV Dorchester *Sarum* from 01. *2 Longmoor Street, Poundbury, Dorchester DT1 3GN* Tel (01305) 259355

✠**DENNIS, The Rt Revd John.** b 31. St Cath Coll Cam BA54 MA59. Cuddesdon Coll 54. **d** 56 **p** 57 **c** 79. C Armley St Bart *Ripon* 56-60; C Kettering SS Pet and Paul *Pet* 60-62; V Is of Dogs Ch Ch and St Jo w St Luke *Lon* 62-71; V Mill Hill Jo Keble Ch 71-79; RD W Barnet 73-79; Preb St Paul's Cathl 77-79; Suff Bp Knaresborough *Ripon* 79-86; Dioc Dir of Ords 80-86; Bp St E 86-96; rtd 96; Perm to Offic *St E* from 96. *7 Conifer Close, Winchester SO22 6SH* Tel (01962) 868881
E-mail dennis@johndor.fslife.co.uk

DENNIS, Canon John Daniel. b 20. LLCM. St D Coll Lamp BA41 LTh43. **d** 43 **p** 44. C Haverfordwest St Mary w St Thos *St D* 43-48; C Newport St Mark *Mon* 48-54; V New Tredegar 54-62; R Worthenbury w Tallarn Green *St As* 62-71; V Chirk 71-86; RD Llangollen 74-86; Hon Can St As Cathl 83-86; rtd 86; Perm to Offic *St As* from 86. *Mount Cottage, Chirk, Wrexham LL14 5HD* Tel (01691) 773382

DENNIS, Keith Aubrey Lawrence. b 55. City of Lon Poly BA79. Cranmer Hall Dur 88. **d** 90 **p** 91. C Bushbury *Lich* 90-94; P-in-c Newcastle St Geo 94-99; TV Kirby Muxloe *Leic* 99-03; C Ashby-de-la-Zouch St Helen w Coleorton from 03; C Breedon cum Isley Walton and Worthington from 03. *The Rectory, Rectory Close, Breedon on the Hill, Derby DE73 1AP* Tel (01332) 864845

DENNIS, Patrick John. b 44. Linc Th Coll 67. **d** 70 **p** 71. C Eccleshill *Bradf* 70-72; C Ponteland *Newc* 73-75; Chr Aid Org Leic and Linc 75-78; TV Cullercoats St Geo *Newc* 78-82; Dioc Ecum Officer 79-82; R Bradfield *Sheff* 82-91; Dioc Ecum Adv 82-93; Sec & Ecum Officer S Yorkshire Ecum Coun 91-93; R Braithwell w Bramley 91-93. *Address excluded by request*

DENNIS, Canon Trevor John. b 45. St Jo Coll Cam BA68 MA71 PhD74. Westcott Ho Cam 71. **d** 72 **p** 73. C Newport Pagnell *Ox* 72-74; Chapl Eton Coll 75-82; Tutor Sarum & Wells Th Coll 82-94; Vice-Prin 89-94; Can Res Ches Cathl *Ches* from 94. *13 Abbey Street, Chester CH1 2JF* Tel (01244) 314408
E-mail dennis@chestercathedral.org.uk

DENNISON, Philip Ian. b 52. Nottm Univ BTh81. St Jo Coll Nottm 77. **d** 81 **p** 82. C Stalybridge H Trin and Ch Ch *Ches* 81-84; C Heswall 84-91; TV Bushbury *Lich* from 91. *131 Taunton Avenue, Wolverhampton WV10 6PN* Tel (01902) 781944
E-mail revd.pidennison@tinyworld.co.uk

DENNISS, Mrs Amanda Jane. b 57. Univ Coll Lon LLB78. Oak Hill Th Coll 98 NTMTC 00. **d** 03. C Turnham Green Ch Ch *Lon* from 03. *27 Stratford Road, London W8 6RA* Tel (020) 7937 6761
E-mail amandadenniss@aol.com

DENNISTON, James Keith Stuart. b 49. Barrister-at-Law 70 Down Coll Cam MA70. Oak Hill Th Coll DipEd92. **d** 93 **p** 94. C Harborne Heath *Birm* 93-97; Chapl Lee Abbey 97-02. *Cutland House, Chulmleigh EX18 7AJ*
E-mail james@thedennistons.freeserve.co.uk

DENNISTON, Robin Alastair. b 26. Ch Ch Ox MA48 Edin Univ MSc92 Univ Coll Lon PhD96. **d** 78 **p** 79. NSM Clifton upon Teme *Worc* 78-81; NSM Clifton-on-Teme, Lower Sapey and the Shelsleys 81-85; NSM S Hinksey *Ox* 85-87; NSM Gt w Lt Tew 87-90; NSM Aberdour *St And* 90-94; NSM W Fife Team Min 90-94; NSM St Marylebone St Mark Hamilton Terrace *Lon* 94-95; P-in-c Gt w Lt Tew and Over w Nether Worton *Ox* 95-02; rtd 02. *112 Randolph Avenue, London W9 1PQ* Tel (020) 7286 0880

DENNO, Basil. b 52. Dundee Univ BSc74. Oak Hill Th Coll BA81. **d** 81 **p** 83. C Chaddesden St Mary *Derby* 81-83; Hon C 83-84. *21 Parkside Road, Chaddesden, Derby DE21 6QR* Tel (01332) 672687

DENNY, John Peter Sekeford. b 43. RIBA69 Portsm Sch of Architecture DipArch67. Chich Th Coll 90. **d** 91 **p** 92. C Aylmerton w Runton *Nor* 91-95; P-in-c Barney, Fulmodeston w Croxton, Hindringham etc 95-96; R 96-98; rtd 98; Perm to Offic *Truro* from 98. *Little Penkelly, Pelynt, Looe PL13 2QH* Tel (01503) 220335

DENNY, Lorne Robert. b 58. Pemb Coll Ox MA84. St Alb and Ox Min Course 98. **d** 01 **p** 02. NSM Ox St Barn and St Paul *Ox* from 01. *35 Stapleton Road, Oxford OX3 7LX* Tel (01865) 768009

DENNY, Michael Thomas. b 47. Kelham Th Coll 68 St Jo Coll Nottm 71. **d** 73 **p** 74. C Gospel Lane St Mich *Birm* 73-77; P-in-c Frankley 77-82; R from 82. *The Rectory, Frankley Green, Birmingham B32 4AS* Tel 0121-475 3724

DENNY, Peter Bond. b 17. Lon Univ BA41. Bps' Coll Cheshunt 41. **d** 43 **p** 44. C Bushey Heath *St Alb* 43-45; C Calstock *Truro* 52-56; V Newlyn St Newlyn 56-83; RD Pydar 61-64 and 74-81; rtd 83; Perm to Offic *Truro* from 83. *Tralee, The Crescent, Truro TR1 3ES* Tel (01872) 274492

DENT, Canon Christopher Mattinson. b 46. K Coll Lon BA68 AKC68 MTh69 Jes Coll Cam BA72 MA76 New Coll Ox MA76 DPhil80. Westcott Ho Cam 70. **d** 72 **p** 73. C Chelsea St Luke *Lon* 72-76; Asst Chapl New Coll Ox 76-79; Fell Chapl and Dean Div 79-84; V Hollingbourne and Hucking w Leeds and Broomfield *Cant* 84-93; V Bedford St Andr *St Alb* from 93; Hon Can St Alb from 01. *St Andrew's Vicarage, 1 St Edmond Road, Bedford MK40 2NQ* Tel (01234) 354234 *or* 216881
E-mail dent@tinyworld.co.uk

DENT, Joseph Michael. b 73. Jes Coll Cam BA94. Wycliffe Hall Ox 96. **d** 99 **p** 00. C Plymouth St Andr and St Paul Stonehouse *Ex* 99-03; C Sevenoaks St Nic *Roch* from 03. *6 Sackville Close, Sevenoaks TN13 3QD* Tel (01732) 779140

DENT, Michael Leslie. b 54. Leeds Univ BEd76. St Steph Ho Ox DipMin95. **d** 95 **p** 96. C Cockerton *Dur* 95-98; V Escomb from 98; R Etherley from 98; V Witton Park from 98; Chapl Dur Constabulary from 02. *The Vicarage, Escomb, Bishop Auckland DL14 7ST* Tel (01388) 602861

DENT, Raymond William. b 47. Birm Coll of Educn CertEd68 Open Univ BA84. Ridley Hall Cam 70. **d** 73 **p** 74. C Hyde St Geo *Ches* 73-76; C Eastham 76-79; TV E Runcorn w Halton 79-80; V Hallwood 80-83; V New Brighton Em 83-94; V Willaston from 94. *The Vicarage, 13 Hooton Road, Willaston, Neston CH64 1SE* Tel 0151-327 4737 E-mail raymond@raydent.freeserve.co.uk

DENT, Richard William. b 32. Down Coll Cam BA56 MA LLB59. Bris Sch of Min 73. **d** 77 **p** 78. NSM Southmead *Bris* 77-81; NSM Henleaze 81-85; V Highworth w Sevenhampton and Inglesham etc 85-88; TV Oldland 88-91; V Longwell Green 91-93; C Bedminster St Mich 93-94; C 94-97; Chapl Asst Frenchay Healthcare NHS Trust Bris 94-97; rtd 97; Perm to Offic *Bris* from 99. *1 Bakers Buildings, Station Road, Wrington, Bristol BS40 5LQ* Tel (01934) 861070

DENTON, Kenneth Percival. b 14. Clifton Th Coll 54. **d** 55 **p** 56. C Buttershaw St Paul *Bradf* 55-57; C Otley 57-59; C Morpeth *Newc* 59-62; R Winteringham *Linc* 62-69; V Middlesbrough St Thos *York* 69-73; C Rufforth w Moor Monkton and Hessay 73-76; P-in-c Escrick 76-80; rtd 80; Perm to Offic *B & W* from 81. *46 Pedlars Grove, Frome BA11 2SX* Tel (01373) 463875

DENTON, Peter Brian. b 37. Kelham Th Coll 57. **d** 62 **p** 63. C Ellesmere Port *Ches* 62-66; Chapl HM Borstal Hollesley 66-69; CF 69-90; Warden Bridge Gen from 90; C Hounslow H Trin w St Paul *Lon* 90-92; V Northolt Park St Barn from 92; P-in-c Southall Green St Jo 97-03; P-in-c N Greenford All Hallows from 00. *The Vicarage, Raglan Way, Northolt UB5 4SX* Tel (020) 8422 3775 Fax as telephone E-mail revdenton@aol.com

DENTON, Peter Charles. b 52. St Jo Coll Dur BA52. Oak Hill Th Coll 49. **d** 52 **p** 53. C Ushaw Moor *Dur* 52-54; C-in-c Throckley St Mary CD *Newc* 54-58; V Long Horsley 58-67; Lect City of Néwc Coll of Educn 67-75; Sen Lect Newc Poly 75-90; rtd 90. *11 Cornwall Walk, Belmont, Durham DH1 2DD* Tel 0191-384 3247

DENYER, Alan Frederick. b 31. Wycliffe Hall Ox 80. **d** 82 **p** 83. C Rodbourne Cheney *Bris* 82-84; P-in-c Garsdon w Lea and Cleverton 84-87; R Garsdon, Lea and Cleverton and Charlton 87-91; R Lydbury N w Hopesay and Edgton *Heref* 91-97; Asst Dioc Soc Resp Officer 91-97; rtd 97; Hon C Long Preston w Tosside *Bradf* 97-02. *25 Lupton Close, Glasshouses, Harrogate HG3 5QX* Tel (01423) 711667

DENYER, Canon Paul Hugh. b 46. Lon Univ BA68. Ripon Coll Cuddesdon 74. **d** 77 **p** 78. C Horfield H Trin *Bris* 77-82; TV Yate New Town 82-88; V Bris Lockleaze St Mary Magd w St Fran 88-95; Dioc Dir of Ords 95-02; Hon Can Bris Cathl 99-02; R Warmley, Syston and Bitton from 02. *The Rectory, Church Avenue, Warmley, Bristol BS30 5JJ* Tel 0117-967 3965

DENZIL, Sister. *See* ONSLOW, Sister Denzil Octavia

DEO, Paul. b 60. Coll of Ripon & York St Jo CertEd81. St Jo Coll Nottm 95. **d** 97 **p** 98. C Tong *Bradf* 97-00; P-in-c Laisterdyke 00-02; V from 02. *The Vicarage, Parsonage Road, Laisterdyke, Bradford BD4 8PY* Tel (01274) 661449
E-mail pauldeo@blueyonder.co.uk

DERBRIDGE, Roger. b 39. Clifton Th Coll 63. **d** 66 **p** 69. C Surbiton Hill Ch Ch *S'wark* 66-67; C Richmond Ch Ch 67-70; C Toxteth Park St Philemon *Liv* 70-75; TV Toxteth St Philemon w St Gabr 75-84; V Woking St Mary *Guildf* from 84. *St Mary of Bethany Vicarage, West Hill Road, Woking GU22 7UJ* Tel (01483) 761269

DERBY, Archdeacon of. *See* GATFORD, The Ven Ian

DERBY, Bishop of. *See* BAILEY, The Rt Revd Jonathan Sansbury

DERBY, Dean of. *See* PERHAM, The Very Revd Michael Francis

DERBYSHIRE, Alan George. b 16. Lon Univ BA41. Linc Th Coll 41. **d** 43 **p** 44. C Swinton *St Alb* 43-47; CF 47-67; R Merrow *Guildf* 67-81; rtd 81; Perm to Offic *Heref* 81-94. *7 Lansdowne Road, Navenby, Lincoln LN5 0EY* Tel (01522) 811091

DERBYSHIRE, Mrs Anne Margaret. b 31. Lon Univ CertEd75 Open Univ BA87. SW Minl Tr Course. **dss** 84 **d** 87 **p** 01. NSM Tiverton St Pet *Ex* 87-90; Perm to Offic 90-01 and from 02; NSM Washfield, Stoodleigh, Withleigh etc 01-02. *38 Greenway Gardens, Tiverton EX16 5JL* Tel (01884) 255966

DERBYSHIRE, Douglas James. b 26. **d** 81 **p** 82. Hon C Heald Green St Cath *Ches* 81-86; Hon C Stockport St Geo 86-89; C 89-91; rtd 91; Perm to Offic *Man* 92-95; *Ches* from 92; *Man* from 00. *91 East Avenue, Heald Green, Cheadle SK8 3BR* Tel 0161-437 3748

DERBYSHIRE, Philip Damien. b 50. Sarum & Wells Th Coll 80. **d** 82 **p** 83. C Chatham St Wm *Roch* 82-86; Zimbabwe 86-88; TV Burnham w Dropmore, Hitcham and Taplow *Ox* 88-92; Chapl HM Pris Reading 92-97; Chapl HM Pris Holloway 97-00; Chapl HM Pris Bullingdon from 00. *HM Prison Bullingdon, PO Box 50, Bicester OX6 0PR* Tel (01869) 322111

DERHAM, Miss Hilary Kathlyn. b 50. Nottm Univ BPharm71 MRPharmS71. Chich Th Coll 89. **d** 91 **p** 95. Par Dn Stevenage H Trin *St Alb* 91-94; C 94-98; P-in-c London Colney St Pet 98-03; rtd 03; Perm to Offic *St Alb* from 03. *39 Brecken Close, St Albans AL4 9LF* Tel (01727) 842089
E-mail h.derham@btopenworld.com

DERISLEY, Canon Albert Donald. b 20. Ely Th Coll 60. **d** 62 **p** 63. C Gt Yarmouth *Nor* 62-66; V Gt w Lt Plumstead 66-72; V N Elmham w Billingford 72-85; RD Brisley and Elmham 77-85; Hon Can Nor Cathl 78-85; rtd 85; Perm to Offic *Nor* from 85. *22 Stuart Road, Aylsham, Norwich NR11 6HN* Tel (01263) 734579

DEROY-JONES, Philip Antony (Tony). b 49. St Mich Coll Llan 92. **d** 92 **p** 93. C Neath w Llantwit *Llan* 92-95; V Caerau St Cynfelin 95-98; V Pontlottyn w Fochriw from 98. *The Vicarage, Picton Street, Pontlottyn, Bargoed CF81 9PS* Tel (01685) 841322 Fax as telephone
E-mail tony@deroy-jones.freeserve.co.uk

DERRICK, David John. b 46. S'wark Ord Course. **d** 84 **p** 85. NSM Angell Town St Jo *S'wark* 84-98; NSM St Mary le Strand w St Clem Danes *Lon* 86-93. *Weavers Cottage, 8 Bellvue Place, London E1 4UG* Tel (020) 7791 2943

DERRICK, Mrs Dorothy Margaret. b 41. St Mary's Coll Cheltenham CertEd63 RTC63. Ox Min Course CBTS92. **d** 92 **p** 94. NSM Gt Missenden w Ballinger and Lt Hampden *Ox* 92-98; NSM Drayton St Pet (Berks) from 98. *The Vicarage, 8 Gravel Lane, Drayton, Abingdon OX14 4HY* Tel (01235) 531374
E-mail jdderrick@compuserve.com

DERRIMAN, Canon Graham Scott. b 39. Bps' Coll Cheshunt 63. **d** 66 **p** 67. C Wandsworth St Mich *S'wark* 66-70; C Merton St Mary 70-74; P-in-c Earlsfield St Andr 75-81; V Camberwell St Luke 81-90; V Croydon St Aug from 90; Voc Adv Croydon Adnry from 93; RD Croydon Cen from 95; Hon Can S'wark Cathl from 01. *The Vicarage, 23A St Augustine's Avenue, Croydon CR2 6JN* Tel (020) 8688 2663
E-mail gderriman@staug.fsnet.co.uk

DERRY AND RAPHOE, Bishop of. *See* GOOD, The Rt Revd Kenneth Raymond

DERRY, Archdeacon of. *See* McLEAN, The Ven Donald Stewart

DERRY, Dean of. *See* MORTON, The Very Revd William Wright

DESBRULAIS, Mrs Patricia Mary. b 27. Qu Coll Birm 77. **dss** 79 **d** 87. Gt Bowden w Welham *Leic* 79-83; Market Harborough 83-87; Hon Par Dn 87-89; rtd 89; Perm to Offic *Leic* 89-00. *78 Rainsborough Gardens, Market Harborough LE16 9LW* Tel (01858) 466766

DESERT, Thomas Denis. b 31. Bps' Coll Cheshunt 54. **d** 56 **p** 57. C Goldington *St Alb* 56-60; C-in-c Luton St Hugh Lewsey CD 60-63; C St Alb St Sav 63-65; C Cheshunt 65-68; V Bedford All SS 68-89; R Northill w Moggerhanger 89-96; rtd 96; Perm to Offic *St Alb* from 96. *2 Phillpotts Avenue, Bedford MK40 3UJ* Tel (01234) 211413

DESHPANDE, Lakshmi Anant. *See* JEFFREYS, Mrs Lakshmi Anant

DESICS, Robert Anthony. b 77. Bp Grosseteste Coll BA99 Open Univ MA00. St Jo Coll Nottm 99. **d** 01 **p** 02. C Potters Bar *St Alb* from 01. *11 Otways Close, Potters Bar EN6 1TE* Tel (01707) 646505

DESMOND, Mrs Elspeth Margaret. b 49. Trin Coll Bris CPS90 S Dios Minl Tr Scheme 90. **d** 93 **p** 95. NSM Filton *Bris* from 93; Asst Chapl HM Pris Bris from 98. *The Chaplain's Office, HM Prison, Cambridge Road, Bristol BS7 8PS* Tel 0117-980 8246 Fax 980 8153

DESON, Rolston Claudius. b 39. Qu Coll Birm 85. **d** 84 **p** 85. NSM Saltley *Birm* 84-86; C Edgbaston SS Mary and Ambrose 86-90; V W Bromwich St Phil *Lich* from 90. *The Vicarage, 33 Reform Street, West Bromwich B70 7PF* Tel 0121-525 1985

DESPARD, Canon Eric Herbert. b 17. TCD BA40 BD48. CITC 41. **d** 41 **p** 42. C Roscommon *K, E & A* 41-43; C Dublin St Pet *D & G* 43-51; I Blessington w Kilbride 51-65; I Lucan w Leixlip 65-92; Can Ch Ch Cathl Dublin 73-92; rtd 92. *59 Sweetmount Park, Dundrum, Dublin 14, Irish Republic* Tel (00353) (1) 298 2489

DESROSIERS, Jacques Thomas Maurice. b 55. Qu Univ Kingston Ontario BCom77. S'wark Ord Course 91. **d** 94 **p** 95. NSM Benenden *Cant* 94-97; C Maidstone All SS and St Phil w Tovil 97-01; TV Pewsey and Swanborough *Sarum* from 01. *The Vicarage, Wilcot, Pewsey SN9 5NS* Tel (01672) 562282 Fax 569215 E-mail stodesro@surfaid.org

DETTMER, Douglas James. b 64. Univ of Kansas BA86 Yale Univ MDiv90. Berkeley Div Sch 90. **d** 90 **p** 91. C Ilfracombe, Lee, Woolacombe, Bittadon etc *Ex* 90-94; Bp's Dom Chapl 94-98; P-in-c Thorverton, Cadbury, Upton Pyne etc from 98. *The Rectory, School Lane, Thorverton, Exeter EX5 5NR* Tel (01392) 860332

DEUCHAR, Andrew Gilchrist. b 55. Southn Univ BTh86. Sarum & Wells Th Coll 81. **d** 84 **p** 85. C Alnwick *Newc* 84-88; TV Heref St Martin w St Fran *Heref* 88-90; Adv to Coun for Soc Resp *Roch* and *Cant* 90-94; Sec for Angl Communion Affairs 94-00; Hon Prov Can Cant Cathl 95-00; R Nottingham St Pet and St Jas *S'well* 00-02; R Nottingham St Pet and All SS from 02. *St Peter's Rectory, 3 King Charles Street, Nottingham NG1 6GB* Tel 0115-947 4891

DEVAL, Mrs Joan Margaret. b 38. Southlands Coll Lon TDip58 Lon Univ CertRK59 Lon Bible Coll DipTh71. St Alb and Ox Min Course 95. **d** 98 **p** 99. OLM Chinnor w Emmington and Sydenham etc *Ox* from 98. *3 Orchard Way, Chinnor OX9 4UD* Tel (01844) 353404

DEVAMANIKKAM, Trevor. b 47. Ripon Hall Ox 74. **d** 76 **p** 77. C Manston *Ripon* 76-79; P-in-c Moor Allerton 79-81; P-in-c Harrogate St Wilfrid and St Luke 81-84; V Buttershaw St Aid *Bradf* 84-85; Succ St D Cathl *St D* 85-87; V Llanwnda, Goodwick w Manorowen and Llanstinan 87-90; Chapl RN 90-94; Chapl Fuengirola St Andr *Eur* 94-96; rtd 96. *6 Centurion Close, Sleaford NG34 7PH*

DEVENNEY, Raymond Robert Wilmont. b 47. TCD BA69 MA73. CITC 70. **d** 70 **p** 71. C Ballymena *Conn* 70-75; C Ballyholme *D & D* 75-81; I Killinchy w Kilmood and Tullynakill 81-00; I Drumbeg from 00. *The Rectory, 64 Drumbeg Road, Dunmurry, Belfast BT17 9LE* Tel (028) 9061 0255
E-mail raydev@hotmail.com

✠**DEVENPORT, The Rt Revd Eric Nash.** b 26. Open Univ BA74. Kelham Th Coll 46. **d** 51 **p** 52 **c** 80. C Leic St Mark *Leic* 51-54; C Barrow St Matt *Carl* 54-56; Succ Leic Cathl *Leic* 56-59; V Shepshed 59-64; R Oadby 64-73; Hon Can Leic Cathl 73-80; Dioc Missr 73-80; Suff Bp Dunwich *St E* 80-92; rtd 92; Chapl Adn Italy and Malta *Eur* 92-97; Florence w Siena 92-97; Asst Bp *Eur* 93-97; Perm to Offic *Nor* from 97; Hon PV Nor Cathl from 98; Hon Asst Bp Nor from 00. *32 Bishopgate, Norwich NR1 4AA* Tel (01603) 664121

DEVERELL, William Robert Henry. b 61. CITC 88 St Jo Coll Nottm CertCS92. **d** 92 **p** 93. C Agherton *Conn* 92-95; I Sixmilecross w Termonmaguirke *Arm* 95-99; I Tallaght *D & G* from 99. *St Maelruain's Rectory, 6 Sally Park, Firhouse Road, Tallaght, Dublin 24, Irish Republic* Tel (00353) (1) 462 1044 *or* 462 6006 Mobile 086-803 0239 Fax as telephone
E-mail tallaght@dublin.anglican.org

DEVEREUX, Canon John Swinnerton. b 32. Lon Univ BSc53. Wells Th Coll. **d** 58 **p** 59. C Wigan St Mich *Liv* 58-60; C Goring-by-Sea *Chich* 60-69; Ind Chapl 69-97; Can and Preb Chich Cathl 90-97; rtd 97; Perm to Offic *Chich* from 97. *40 Hillside Avenue, Worthing BN14 9QT* Tel (01903) 234044

DEVERILL, Jennifer. b 40. Auckland Medical Sch MSR62. LNSM course 93. **d** 96 **p** 97. OLM Battersea St Luke *S'wark* from 96; Chapl St Geo Healthcare NHS Trust Lon from 96.

60 Badminton Road, London SW12 8BL Tel (020) 8675 0503 *or* 8725 3285 E-mail jenny@deverill.fsnet.co.uk

DEVINE, Margaret Rose. b 50. Sunderland Poly BEd76. NEOC 00. **d** 03. NSM E Boldon *Dur* from 03. *22 Dunelm Street, South Shields NE33 3JT* Tel 0191-455 6125

DEVINE, Maureen Mary. b 37. Cheltenham & Glouc Coll of HE TCert74. St Alb and Ox Min Course 95. **d** 98 **p** 99. NSM Reading St Jo *Ox* 98-01; NSM Beech Hill, Grazeley and Spencers Wood from 01. *33 Radstock Lane, Earley, Reading RG6 5RX* Tel 0118-921 2767 E-mail julmar99@aol.com

DEVONISH, Clive Wayne. b 51. Ridley Hall Cam. **d** 96 **p** 97. C Meole Brace *Lich* from 96. *2 Perivale Close, Radbrook, Shrewsbury SY3 6DH* Tel (01743) 367707 *or* 362399 E-mail rev.cw.devo@cwcom.net

DEVONSHIRE, Roger George. b 40. AKC62. **d** 63 **p** 64. C Rotherhithe St Mary w All SS *S'wark* 63-67; C Kingston Hill St Paul 67-71; Chapl RN 71-95; Hon Chapl to The Queen 92-95; R Pitlochry *St And* from 95; R Kilmaveonaig from 95. *The Rectory, 16A Lettoch Terrace, Pitlochry PH16 5BA* Tel (01796) 472539 Fax as telephone E-mail devonshire@supanet.com

DEVONSHIRE JONES, Thomas Percy Norman. *See* JONES, Thomas Percy Norman Devonshire

DEW, Glyn. b 55. Worc Coll of Educn BEd90. St Jo Coll Nottm MA97. **d** 97 **p** 98. C Beoley *Worc* 97-01; TV Redditch, The Ridge from 01. *The Vicarage, Church Road, Webheath, Redditch B97 5PD* Tel (01527) 403939

DEW, Lindsay Charles. b 52. Cranmer Hall Dur 85. **d** 86 **p** 86. C Knottingley *Wakef* 86-89; V Batley St Thos 89-97; RD Dewsbury from 96; R Thornhill and Whitley Lower from 97. *The Rectory, 51 Frank Lane, Dewsbury WF12 0JW* Tel (01924) 465064 Mobile 07767-367483 E-mail allangels@lineone.net

DEW, Maureen. b 51. Univ of Wales MA98. Qu Coll Birm BA99. **d** 99 **p** 00. C Inkberrow w Cookhill and Kington w Dormston *Worc* 99-02; C Redditch, The Ridge from 02. *The Vicarage, Church Road, Webheath, Redditch B97 5PD* Tel (01527) 402404

DEW, Robert David John. b 42. St Pet Coll Ox BA63. St Steph Ho Ox 63. **d** 65 **p** 66. C Abington *Pet* 65-69; Chapl Tiffield Sch Northants 69-71; Ind Chapl *Pet* 71-79; Ind Chapl *Liv* 79-87; Sen Ind Missr 88-91; V Skelsmergh w Selside and Longsleddale *Carl* from 91; Bp's Research Officer 91-95; CME Adv from 95. *The Vicarage, Skelsmergh, Kendal LA9 6NU* Tel (01539) 724498 Fax 734655 E-mail bob.dew@virgin.net

DEWAR, Francis John Lindsay. b 33. Keble Coll Ox BA56 MA59. Cuddesdon Coll 58. **d** 60 **p** 61. C Hessle *York* 60-63; C Stockton St Chad *Dur* 63-66; V Sunderland St Chad 66-81; Org Journey Inward, Journey Outward Project from 82; Perm to Offic *B & W* from 01. *Wellspring, Church Road, Wookey, Wells BA5 1JX* Tel (01749) 675365 E-mail francisdewar@yahoo.com

DEWAR, Ian John James. b 61. Kingston Poly BA83. Cranmer Hall Dur 89. **d** 92 **p** 93. C Blackb St Gabr *Blackb* 92-95; C Darwen St Cuth w Tockholes St Steph 95-97; V Appley Bridge from 97. *The Vicarage, Finch Lane, Appley Bridge, Wigan WN6 9DT* Tel (01257) 252875 E-mail ijjdewar@hotmail.com

DEWAR, John. b 32. Chich Th Coll 58. **d** 61 **p** 62. C Leeds St Hilda *Ripon* 61-65; C Cullercoats St Geo *Newc* 65-69; V Newsham 69-76; V Kenton Ascension 76-86; R Wallsend St Pet 86-92; V Longhorsley and Hebron 92-96; rtd 96. *51 Bonner Lane, Calverton, Nottingham NG14 6FU* Tel 0115-965 2599

DEWES, Ms Deborah Mary. b 59. Homerton Coll Cam BEd81 St Jo Coll Dur BA90 MA93. Cranmer Hall Dur 88. **d** 92 **p** 94. C Stockton St Pet *Dur* 92-96; C Knowle *Birm* 96-03; C Bath Abbey w St Jas *B & W* from 03. *7 Holloway, Bath BA2 4PS* Tel (01225) 484469

DEWEY, David Malcolm. b 43. Lon Univ BA72 LSE MSc(Econ)87 Fitzw Coll Cam MPhil94. Westcott Ho Cam 76. **d** 78 **p** 79. Sen Lect Middx Poly 72-92; Sen Lect Middx Univ from 92; Hon C Enfield St Mich *Lon* 78-79; Hon C Bush Hill Park St Steph 79-84; Hon C Palmers Green St Jo 84-90; Perm to Offic 90-95; Perm to Offic *St Alb* 95-98; Hon C Hertford All SS 98-01; P-in-c St Paul's Walden from 01. *The Vicarage, Bendish Lane, Whitwell, Hitchin SG4 8HX* Tel (01438) 871658 Mobile 07713-328780 E-mail david47@nw.mdx.ac.uk

DEWEY, Peter Lewis. b 38. Wycliffe Hall Ox 69. **d** 71 **p** 72. C Hammersmith St Sav *Lon* 71-73; Chapl to Bp Kensington 73-75; C Isleworth All SS 75-81; TV Hounslow *Lon* 81-91; CF (TA) 86-91; Chapl Gordonstoun Sch 92-97; TR St Laur in Thanet *Cant* 97-03; rtd 03; P-in-c Sulhamstead Abbots and Bannister w Ufton Nervet *Ox* from 03. *The Rectory, Sulhamstead Road, Ufton Nervet, Reading RG7 4DH* Tel 0118-983 2328

DEWEY, Sanford Dayton. b 44. Syracuse Univ AB67 MA72. Gen Th Sem (NY) MDiv79. **d** 79 **p** 80. Hon C St Mary le Bow w St Pancras Soper Lane etc *Lon* 87-92; C Hampstead St Steph w All Hallows 92-94; Co-Dir Hampstead Counselling Service 94-00; Dir from 00; NSM Hampstead Ch Ch 94-96; Hon C Grosvenor Chpl from 96; Prov Past Consultant URC from 96; Perm to Offic from 97. *43 Shirlock Road, London NW3 2HR* Tel (020) 7482 1527

DEWHIRST, Janice. b 50. EMMTC 99. **d** 02 **p** 03. NSM Forest Town *S'well* from 02. *26 King Street, Mansfield Woodhouse, Mansfield NG19 9AU* Tel (01623) 454471

DEWHURST, Gabriel George. b 30. **d** 59 **p** 60. In RC Ch 60-69; C Darlington St Jo *Dur* 70; C Bishopwearmouth St Nic 71-73; C-in-c Stockton St Mark CD 73-81; V Harton 81-86; R Castle Eden w Monkhesleden 86-97; rtd 97; Perm to Offic *Dur* from 98. *9 Knott Lane, Easingwold, York YO61 3LX* Tel (01347) 823526

DEWHURST, George. b 34. TD76. AKC58. **d** 59 **p** 60. C Chorley St Pet *Blackb* 59-61; C-in-c Oswaldtwistle All SS CD 61-65; CF (TA) 63-67; V Shevington *Blackb* 65-83; CF (TAVR) 67-83; CF (TA - R of O) 83-88; V Horsley and Newington Bagpath w Kingscote *Glouc* 83-96; rtd 96; Perm to Offic *Glouc* from 96. *St Nicholas House, Cherington, Tetbury GL8 8SN* Tel (01285) 841367 E-mail gdewhurst@hotmail.com

DEWHURST, Russell James Edward. b 77. Magd Coll Ox MPhys99 Selw Coll Cam BTh03. Westcott Ho Cam 00. **d** 03. C Blewbury, Hagbourne and Upton *Ox* from 03. *St Andrew's House, 1 Saxon's Way, Didcot OX11 9RA* Tel (01235) 814792 E-mail russell dewhurst@yahoo.co.uk

DEWICK, David Richard. b 36. St Alb and Ox Min Course CBTS99. **d** 99 **p** 00. NSM Risborough *Ox* from 99. *The Rectory, Church End, Bledlow, Princes Risborough HP27 9PD* Tel (01844) 344162

DEWING, Robert Mark Eastwood. b 68. Bris Univ BA90 PGCE91. Ridley Hall Cam BA98. **d** 99 **p** 00. C Alverstoke *Portsm* 99-03; V Sheet from 03. *Sheet Vicarage, 2 Pulens Lane, Petersfield GU31 4DB* Tel (01730) 263673 E-mail robdewing@hotmail.com

DEWING, William Arthur. b 52. NEOC 99. **d** 02. NSM Middlesbrough St Oswald *York* from 02. *19 Monarch Grove, Marton, Middlesbrough TS7 8QQ* Tel (01642) 321074 Mobile 07966-191640 Fax (01642) 500661 E-mail w.dewing@ntlworld.com

DEWIS, Harry Kenneth. b 19. NW Ord Course 75. **d** 78 **p** 79. NSM Bedale *Ripon* 78-89; Perm to Offic from 89. *11 Masham Road, Bedale DL8 2AF* Tel (01677) 423588

DEWSBURY, Michael Owen. b 31. St Aid Birkenhead 54 St Jo Coll Dur 53. **d** 57 **p** 58. C Hellesdon *Nor* 57-60; C Speke All SS *Liv* 60-62; R Gt and Lt Glemham *St E* 62-67; R W Lynn *Nor* 67-68; Australia from 68; rtd 99. *6B Livingstone Street, Beaconsfield, W Australia 6162* Tel (0061) (8) 9335 6852 *or* (8) 9386 3675 E-mail dewsbury@iinet.net.au

DEXTER, Canon Frank Robert. b 40. Cuddesdon Coll 66. **d** 68 **p** 69. C Newc H Cross *Newc* 68-71; C Whorlton 71-73; V Pet Ch Carpenter *Pet* 73-80; V High Elswick St Phil *Newc* 80-85; RD Newc W 81-85; V Newc St Geo from 85; Hon Can Newc Cathl from 94; P-in-c Newc St Hilda 95-98. *St George's Vicarage, St George's Close, Jesmond, Newcastle upon Tyne NE2 2TF* Tel 0191-281 1628 Fax as telephone E-mail frank.dexter@talk21.com

DEY, Canon Charles Gordon Norman. b 46. Lon Coll of Div DipTh70. **d** 71 **p** 72. C Almondbury *Wakef* 71-76; V Mixenden 76-85; TR Tong *Bradf* from 85; Hon Can Bradf Cathl from 00. *The Rectory, Holmewood Road, Tong, Bradford BD4 9EJ* Tel (01274) 682100 E-mail gordon@thedeyteam.freeserve.co.uk

DEY, John Alfred. b 33. ALCD57 ALCM57. **d** 57 **p** 58. C Man Albert Memorial Ch *Man* 57-60; C Pennington 60-62; V Mosley Common 62-69; V Chadderton Em 69-79; V Flixton St Jo 79-96; rtd 96; Perm to Offic *Man* from 96. *8 Woodlands Avenue, Urmston, Manchester M41 6NE*

DHAKA Bishop of. *See* BAROI, The Rt Revd Michael

DI CASTIGLIONE, Nigel Austin. b 57. St Jo Coll Dur BA78. St Jo Coll Nottm MA94. **d** 94 **p** 95. C Tamworth *Lich* 94-97; P-in-c Trentham 97-01; V from 02. *The Vicarage, Trentham Park, Stoke-on-Trent ST4 8AE* Tel (01782) 658194 E-mail nigel@dicastiglione.fsnet.co.uk

DI CHIARA, Miss Alessandra Maddalena. b 59. Univ of Wales (Swansea) BA80. Wycliffe Hall Ox 00. **d** 02 **p** 03. C Hooton *Ches* from 02. *419 Chester Road, Little Sutton, Ellesmere Port CH66 3RH* Tel 0151-339 0839 E-mail alessandra_di chiara@hotmail.com

DIALI, The Ven Daniel Chukwuma. b 47. Portsm Univ BA80. Immanuel Coll Ibadan 88. **d** 84 **p** 86. Nigeria 84-01; V Lagos St Bart 86-92; V Bp Tugwell Ch 92-96; Can Lagos W 96-99; Adn St Paul's 00-01; Perm to Offic *S'wark* from 02. *9 Springall Street, London SE15 2TY* Tel (020) 7732 6639 E-mail dcdvnd@yahoo.com

DIAMOND, Canon Michael Lawrence. b 37. St Jo Coll Dur BA60 MA74 Sussex Univ DPhil84. Lon Coll of Div ALCD62 LTh74. **d** 62 **p** 63. C Wandsworth St Mich *S'wark* 62-64; C Patcham Chich 64-69; R Hamsey 70-75; P-in-c Cambridge St Andr Less *Ely* 75-86; V from 86; Hon Can Ely Cathl from 94; RD Cambridge from 96. *The Vicarage, Parsonage Street, Cambridge CB5 8DN* Tel (01223) 353794 Fax 412202

DIAMOND, Capt Richard Geoffrey Colin. b 49. MBE00. CA Tr Coll Dip Evang89. **d** 93 **p** 93. Miss to Seafarers Kenya 90-01; rtd 01. *209A Priory Road, Southampton SO17 2LR* Tel (02380) 678558 E-mail rgcdiamond@ic24.net

DIAPER, James Robert (Bob). b 30. Portsm Dioc Tr Course 84. **d** 85. NSM Portsea St Sav *Portsm* 85-89 and 91-95; NSM Milton

89-91; rtd 95; Perm to Offic *Portsm* from 95. *48 Wallington Road, Portsmouth PO2 0HB* Tel (023) 9269 1372

DIAPER, Trevor Charles. b 51. ALA79. Coll of Resurr Mirfield 88. **d** 90 **p** 91. C N Walsham w Antingham *Nor* 90-94; P-in-c Ardleigh *Chelmsf* 94-95; P-in-c The Bromleys 94-95; R Ardleigh and The Bromleys 95-97; V Bocking St Pet from 97. *The Vicarage, 6 St Peter's in the Fields, Bocking, Braintree CM7 9AR* Tel (01376) 322698 E-mail father.trevor@btinternet.com

DIBB SMITH, John. b 29. Ex & Truro NSM Scheme 78. **d** 81 **p** 82. NSM Carbis Bay *Truro* 81-82; NSM Carbis Bay w Lelant 82-84; Warden Trelowarren Fellowship Helston 84-89; Chapl 89-91; NSM Halsetown *Truro* 91-97; rtd 98; Perm to Offic *Truro* from 00. *Cargease Cottage, Cockwells, Penzance TR20 8DG* Tel (01736) 740707

DIBBENS, Canon Hugh Richard. b 39. Lon Univ BA63 MTh67 St Pet Coll Ox BA65 MA74. Oak Hill Th Coll 60. **d** 67 **p** 68. C Holborn St Geo w H Trin and St Bart *Lon* 67-72; CMS 73-74; Japan 74-77; TR Chigwell *Chelmsf* 78-92; V Hornchurch St Andr from 92; RD Havering from 98; Hon Can Chelmsf Cathl from 01. *222 High Street, Hornchurch RM12 6QP* Tel (01708) 454594 *or* 441571 E-mail hughandruth@dibbens10.freeserve.co.uk

DIBBS, Canon Geoffrey. b 24. Man Univ BA51 ThD69. Wycliffe Hall Ox 51. **d** 53 **p** 54. C Droylsden St Mary *Man* 53-56; V Chadderton St Luke 56-59; R Burton Agnes w Harpham *York* 59-66; Canada 66-88; rtd 88. *13414 Desert Glen Drive, Sun City West, AZ 85375, USA* Tel (001) (623) 546 1920

DIBDEN, Alan Cyril. b 49. Hull Univ LLB70 Fitzw Coll Cam BA72 MA76. Westcott Ho Cam 70. **d** 73 **p** 74. C Camberwell St Luke *S'wark* 73-77; TV Walworth 77-79; TV Langley Marsh *Ox* 79-84; C Chalfont St Peter 84-90; TV Burnham w Dropmore, Hitcham and Taplow from 90. *The Rectory, Rectory Road, Taplow, Maidenhead SL6 0ET* Tel (01628) 661182

DICK, Alexander Walter Henry. b 20. Lon Univ BSc49 BSc(Econ)56. Sarum & Wells Th Coll 73. **d** 74 **p** 75. C Totnes *Ex* 74-77; Min Estover LEP 77-80; V Estover 80-81; P-in-c Broadwoodwidger 81-83; V 83-86; P-in-c Kelly w Bradstone 81-83; R 83-86; P-in-c Lifton 81-83; R 83-86; rtd 86; Perm to Offic *Ex* from 86; Perm to Offic *Lon* 86-94. *Flat 1, Fairfield, Huxtable Hill, Torquay TQ2 6RN* Tel (01803) 605126

DICK, Miss Angela. b 62. Sheff Univ BA92. St Jo Coll Nottm MA94. **d** 96 **p** 97. C Mixenden *Wakef* 96-97; C Mount Pellon 97-99; P-in-c Bradshaw 99-00; P-in-c Holmfield 99-00; V Bradshaw and Holmfield from 00. *The Vicarage, Pavement Lane, Bradshaw, Halifax HX2 9JJ* Tel (01422) 244330 E-mail ange@dix110.freeserve.co.uk

DICK, Canon Caroline Ann. b 61. Nottm Univ BTh88. Linc Th Coll 85. **d** 88 **p** 94. Par Dn Houghton le Spring *Dur* 88-93; Par Dn Hetton le Hole 93-94; C 94-96; Asst Chapl Sunderland Univ 94-98; C Harton from 96; Development Officer Dioc Bd of Soc Resp from 98; Adv for Women's Min from 02; Hon Can Dur Cathl from 03. *Harton Vicarage, 182 Sunderland Road, South Shields NE34 6AH* Tel 0191-427 5538 Fax as telephone E-mail bsr.development.officer@durham.anglican.org

DICK, Cecil Bates. b 42. TD97. Selw Coll Cam BA68 MA72. EMMTC 73. **d** 76 **p** 78. NSM Cinderhill *S'well* 76-79; Chapl Dame Allan's Schs Newc 79-85; CF (TA) 84-99; C Gosforth All SS *Newc* 85-87; Chapl HM Pris Dur 88-89; Chapl HM Pris Hull 89-03; rtd 03. *26 New Walk, Beverley HU17 7DJ* Tel (01482) 862985

DICK, Norman MacDonald. b 32. ACIB. Ox NSM Course 87. **d** 90 **p** 91. NSM Bedgrove *Ox* 90-95; NSM Ellesborough, The Kimbles and Stoke Mandeville 95-01; Perm to Offic from 01. *21 Camborne Avenue, Aylesbury HP21 7UH* Tel (01296) 85530

DICK, Raymond Owen. b 53. Edin Univ BD77. Edin Th Coll 73. **d** 77 **p** 78. C Glas St Mary *Glas* 77-84; Perm to Offic *St Alb* 84-85; P-in-c Edin St Paul and St Geo *Edin* 85; P-in-c Edin St Marg 85-87; TV Edin Old St Paul 87-88; R Hetton le Hole *Dur* 88-96; V Harton from 96. *Harton Vicarage, 182 Sunderland Road, South Shields NE34 6AH* Tel 0191-427 5538 Fax as telephone E-mail rodick182@aol.com *or* raymond.dick@durham.anglican.org

DICKENS, Adam Paul. b 65. Man Univ BA89 Nottm Univ MDiv93. Linc Th Coll 91. **d** 93 **p** 94. C Pershore w Pinvin, Wick and Birlingham *Worc* 93-98; C Portsea St Mary *Portsm* from 98. *2 Glebe Flats, Nutfield Place, Portsmouth PO1 4JF* Tel (023) 9282 6892

DICKENS, Timothy Richard John. b 45. Leeds Univ BSc68. Westcott Ho Cam 68. **d** 71 **p** 72. C Meole Brace *Lich* 71-74; C-in-c Stamford Ch Ch CD *Linc* 74-80; V Anlaby St Pet *York* 80-91; V Egg Buckland w Eggbuckland w from 91; RD Plymouth Moorside from 03. *The Vicarage, 100 Church Hill, Plymouth PL6 5RD* Tel (01752) 701399 E-mail tim.dickens@lineone.net

DICKENSON, Charles Gordon. b 29. Bps' Coll Cheshunt 53. **d** 56 **p** 57. C Ellesmere Port *Ches* 56-61; R Egremont St Columba 61-68; V Latchford *Ch* 68-74; P-in-c Hargrave 74-79; V Birkenhead St Jas w St Bede 79-83; R Tilston and Shocklach 83-94; rtd 94; Perm to Offic *Ches* from 94. *58 Kingsway, Crewe CW2 7ND* Tel (01270) 560722 E-mail cgordon.dickenson@care4free.net

DICKENSON, Geoffrey. b 20. Kelham Th Coll 38. **d** 44 **p** 45. C Averham w Kelham *S'well* 44-47; C Sedgley All SS *Lich* 47-49; C Fenton 49-53; S Africa 53-57; C Greenford H Cross *Lon* 57-59; R Sandiacre *Derby* 59-67; PC Frecheville 67-70; RD Staveley 68-70; V Scarcliffe 70-75; R Walton on Trent w Croxall 75-83; Perm to Offic *Heref* 83-98; rtd 85. *c/o C E Dickenson Esq, Home-Lea, Hyde Lea, Stafford ST18 9BG* Tel (01785) 251455

DICKENSON, Robin Christopher Wildish. b 44. Lon Univ CertEd67 Ex Univ BPhil81 MA98. SW Minl Tr Course 94. **d** 97 **p** 98. NSM Week St Mary w Poundstock and Whitstone *Truro* 97-98; P-in-c week from 98; P-in-c St Gennys, Jacobstow w Warbstow and Treneglos from 02. *The Rectory, The Glebe, Week St Mary, Holsworthy EX22 6UY* Tel (01288) 341134 Fax as telephone E-mail parsonrob@aol.com

DICKER, Canon David. b 31. St Pet Hall Ox BA57 MA58. Linc Th Coll 55. **d** 57 **p** 58. C Wootton Bassett *Sarum* 57-60; C Broad Town 57-60; C Weymouth H Trin 60-63; Antigua 63-64; R Tisbury *Sarum* 64-71; Argentina 71-77; Miss to Seamen 77-81; Chapl Dunkerque w Lille Arras etc Miss to Seamen *Eur* 81-86; TR Shaston *Sarum* 86-96; RD Blackmore Vale 90-95; Can and Preb Sarum Cathl 95-96; rtd 96; Perm to Offic *Linc* from 00. *25 Dunholme Road, Welton, Lincoln LN2 3RS* Tel (01673) 863233

DICKER, Ms Jane Elizabeth. b 64. Whitelands Coll Lon BA87. Linc Th Coll 87. **d** 89 **p** 94. Par Dn Merton St Jas *S'wark* 89-93; C Littleham w Exmouth *Ex* 93-97; Chapl Plymouth Univ 93-97; Ecum Chapl for F&HE Grimsby *Linc* 97-02; Chapl Univ of Greenwich *Roch* from 02; Chapl Kent Inst of Art and Design from 02. *15 Oaks Dene, Chatham ME5 9HN* Tel (01634) 684155 Mobile 07932-166426

DICKER, Miss Mary Elizabeth. b 45. Girton Coll Cam BA66 MA70 Sheff Univ MSc78. Cranmer Hall Dur 83. **dss** 85 **d** 87 **p** 94. Mortlake w E Sheen *S'wark* 85-87; Par Dn 87-88; Par Dn Irlam *Man* 88-92; Par Dn Ashton Ch 92-94; C 94-97; P-in-c Hopwood 97-98; TV Heywood from 98. *St John's Vicarage, Manchester Road, Heywood OL10 2EQ* Tel (01706) 369324

DICKERSON, Richard Keith. b 31. Sir Geo Williams Univ Montreal BA60 McGill Univ Montreal BD60. Montreal Dioc Th Coll. **d** 60 **p** 60. Canada 60-69 and from 78; C Hampstead St Matt 60-63; R Waterloo St Luke 63-69; Perm to Offic *Cant* 72; C Canvey Is *Chelmsf* 73-75; Perm to Offic Montreal 75-78; C Georgeville St Geo 78-82; P-in-c 82-91; R Lennoxville St Geo 91-01; rtd 96. *84 Queen Street, Lennoxville PQ, Canada, J1M 1J4* Tel (001) (819) 346 5564 Fax 346 0219 E-mail stgeorgeslennox@qc.aibn.com

DICKIE, James Graham Wallace. b 50. Worc Coll Ox BA72 MA BLitt77. Westcott Ho Cam 78. **d** 81 **p** 82. C Bracknell *Ox* 81-84; Lic to Offic *Ely* 84-89; Chapl Trin Coll Cam 84-89; Chapl Clifton Coll Bris 89-96; Sen Chapl Marlborough Coll from 96. *The Old Rectory, High Street, Marlborough SN8 1HQ* Tel (01672) 892204 E-mail chaplain@marlboroughcollege.wilts.sch.uk

DICKINSON, Anthony William. b 48. New Coll Ox BA71 MA74 Nottm Univ DipHE82. Linc Th Coll 80. **d** 82 **p** 83. C Sanderstead All SS *St Alb* 82-86; TV Upton cum Chalvey *Ox* 86-94; P-in-c Terriers 94-99; V from 99. *St Francis's Vicarage, Amersham Road, High Wycombe HP13 5AB* Tel (01494) 520676 E-mail tony.dickinson@ukonline.co.uk

DICKINSON, David Charles. b 58. BA79 Lanc Univ MA97. Carl and Blackb Dioc Tr Inst. **d** 99 **p** 00. NSM Ewood *Blackb* from 99. *12 Kirkdale Road, Langho, Blackburn BB6 8EW* Tel (01254) 245289

DICKINSON, Dyllis Annie. b 52. **d** 01 **p** 02. OLM Stalmine w Pilling *Blackb* from 01. *Springfield, Moss Side Lane, Stalmine, Poulton-le-Fylde FY6 0JP* Tel (01253) 700011 E-mail dyljohn@lineone.net

DICKINSON, Henry. b 29. St Deiniol's Hawarden 84. **d** 86 **p** 87. NSM Blackb St Mich w St Jo and H Trin *Blackb* 86-89; NSM Burnley St Cath w St Alb and St Paul 89-95; Perm to Offic from 98. *22 Notre Dame Gardens, Blackburn BB1 5EF* Tel (01254) 693414

DICKINSON, Hugh. b 34. **d** 58 **p** 59. USA 58-97 and from 99; C Portarlington w Cloneyhurke and Lea *M & K* 97-99. *19 West Baltimore Avenue, Lansdowne, PA 19050, USA*

DICKINSON, The Very Revd the Hon Hugh Geoffrey. b 29. Trin Coll Ox BA53 DipTh54 MA56. Cuddesdon Coll 54. **d** 56 **p** 57. C Melksham *Sarum* 56-58; Chapl Trin Coll Cam 58-63; Chapl Win Coll 63-69; P-in-c Milverton *Cov* 69-77; V St Alb St Mich *St Alb* 77-86; Dean Sarum 86-96; rtd 96; Perm to Offic *Glouc* from 96. *22 St Peter's Road, Cirencester GL7 1RG* Tel (01285) 657710

DICKINSON, Canon Robert Edward. b 47. Nottm Univ BTh74. St Jo Coll Nottm 70. **d** 74 **p** 75. C Birm St Martin *Birm* 74-78; P-in-c Liv St Bride w St Sav *Liv* 78-81; TV St Luke in the City 81-86; Chapl Liv Poly 86-92; Chapl Liv Jo Moores Univ from 92; Hon Can Liv Cathl from 03. *45 Queen's Drive, Liverpool L18 2DT* Tel 0151-722 1625 *or* 231 2121

DICKINSON, Simon Braithwaite Vincent. b 34. St Alb and Ox Min Course. **d** 97 **p** 98. OLM Waddesdon w Over Winchendon and Fleet Marston *Ox* 97-02; OLM Schorne from

02. *The White House, Waddesdon, Aylesbury HP18 0JA* Tel (01296) 651693 *or* 658038

DICKINSON, Stephen Paul. b 54. SRN75. N Ord Course 85. **d** 88 **p** 89. Hon C Purston cum S Featherstone *Wakef* 88-91; C Goldthorpe w Hickleton *Sheff* 91-94; V New Bentley from 94. *The Vicarage, Victoria Road, Bentley, Doncaster DN5 0EZ* Tel (01302) 875266

DICKINSON, Victor Tester. b 48. Univ of Wales (Cardiff) BSc70. St Steph Ho Ox 70. **d** 73 **p** 74. C Neath w Llantwit *Llan* 73-76; Asst Chapl Univ of Wales (Cardiff) 76-79; TV Willington Team *Newc* 79-86; V Kenton Ascension 86-97; V Lowick and Kyloe w Ancroft from 97; R Ford and Etal from 97. *The Vicarage, 1 Main Street, Lowick, Berwick-upon-Tweed TD15 2UD* Tel (01289) 388229

DICKSON, Anthony Edward. b 59. Nottm Univ BTh88. Linc Th Coll 85. **d** 88 **p** 89. C Portsea St Alb *Portsm* 88-91; C Cleobury Mortimer w Hopton Wafers *Heref* 91-94; R Fownhope w Mordiford, Brockhampton etc 94-99. *27 Grosvenor Place, Bath BA1 1BA* Tel (01225) 428514
E-mail anthony@fownhope.kc3ltd.co.uk

DICKSON, Brian John. b 19. Reading Univ BSc41 Birm Univ DipTh51. Qu Coll Birm 49. **d** 51 **p** 52. C S Wimbledon H Trin *S'wark* 51-53; C Golders Green St Alb *Lon* 53-55; Sec SCM Th Colls Dept 53-55; Chapl Hulme Gr Sch Oldham 55-59; Min Can Worc Cathl *Worc* 60-67; Chapl K Sch Worc 60-67; Lic to Offic *Bris* 67-74; Chapl Colston's Sch Bris 67-74; V Bishopston *Bris* 74-85; RD Horfield 80-85; rtd 85; Perm to Offic *Worc* from 85. *One Acre Cottage, Abberley, Worcester WR6 6BS* Tel (01299) 896442

DICKSON, Colin James. b 74. St Andr Univ MA96 MPhil00 Leeds Univ BA01. Coll of Resurr Mirfield 99. **d** 02 **p** 03. C Tottenham St Paul *Lon* from 02. *The Curate's Flat, St Paul's Vicarage, 60 Park Lane, London N17 0JR* Tel (020) 8885 1395
E-mail frcolin@stpaulstottenham.org.uk

DICKSON, Colin Patrick Gavin. b 56. **d** 96 **p** 97. C Grays Thurrock *Chelmsf* 96-00; V Glantawe *S & B* from 00. *The Vicarage, 122 Mansel Road, Bonymaen, Swansea SA1 7JR* Tel (01792) 652839

DICKSON, Richard Arthur. b 67. LSE BSc(Econ)88. Ripon Coll Cuddesdon BA92. **d** 93 **p** 94. C Sale St Anne *Ches* 93-96; Sweden from 96. *Snapphanev 92, 177 54 Jarfalla, Sweden* Tel (0046) (8) 580 386 92 E-mail dickson@swipnet.se

DICKSON, Canon Samuel Mervyn James. b 41. CITC. **d** 66 **p** 67. C Ballyholme *D & D* 66-70; C Knockbreda 70-75; I Clonallon w Warrenpoint 75-84; I Down H Trin w Hollymount from 84; Bp's C Rathmullan w Tyrella from 00; Bp's C Lecale Gp from 01; Bp's C Loughinisland from 01; Can Down Cathl from 91; Treas 98-00; Prec 00-01; Chan from 01. *12 The Meadows, Strangford Road, Downpatrick BT30 6LN* Tel (028) 4461 2286

DIGGLE, Richard James. b 47. Lon Inst BA69 Man Poly CertEd74. Dioc OLM tr scheme 98. **d** 01 **p** 02. OLM Chorlton-cum-Hardy St Werburgh *Man* from 01. *6 Ellesmere Road, Manchester M21 0SR* Tel 0161-860 4814
E-mail diggles@ntlworld.com

DIL, The Very Revd Pierre Joseph. b 37. Bp Gray Coll Cape Town LTh63. **d** 63 **p** 64. S Africa 64-66; USPG 66-98; V Weybridge *Guildf* 67; Zambia from 67; Dean Lusaka 89-98; rtd 98. *Post Box RW51313, Ridgeway, Lusaka, Zambia* Tel (260) (1) 274991 Fax 272437 E-mail mecdil@zamnet.zm

DILL, Nicholas Bayard Botolf. b 63. Toronto Univ BA86 Lon Univ LLB89 Barrister 91. Wycliffe Hall Ox 96. **d** 98 **p** 99. C Lindfield *Chich* from 98. *2 Church Close, Frances Road, Lindfield RH16 2JP* Tel (01444) 483945 Fax as telephone
E-mail nifidill@surfaid.org

DILL, Peter Winston. b 41. ACP66 K Coll Lon BD72 AKC72. St Aug Coll Cant 72. **d** 73 **p** 74. C Warsop *S'well* 73-75; C Rhyl w St Ann *St As* 75-77; C Oxton *Ches* 77-78; V Newton in Mottram 78-82; P-in-c Shelton and Oxon *Lich* 82-84; V 84-87; Chapl Clifton Coll Bris 87-00; C Thorverton, Cadbury, Upton Pyne etc *Ex* 00-01; Perm to Offic *Bris* from 02. *85B Pembroke Road, Clifton, Bristol BS8 3EB* Tel 0117-973 9769

DILNOT, Canon John William. b 36. Selw Coll Cam BA60 MA64. Cuddesdon Coll 60. **d** 62 **p** 63. C Stafford St Mary *Lich* 62-66; C Stoke upon Trent 66-67; V Leek All SS 67-74; V Leeds w Broomfield *Cant* 74-79; P-in-c Aldington 79-81; P-in-c Bonnington w Bilsington 79-81; P-in-c Fawkenhurst 79-81; R Aldington w Bonnington and Bilsington 81-87; RD N Lympne 82-87; Hon Can Cant Cathl 85-99; V Folkestone St Mary and St Eanswythe 87-99; rtd 99; Perm to Offic *Cant* from 99. *Underhill Cottage, The Undercliff, Sandgate, Folkestone CT20 3AT* Tel (01303) 248000

DILWORTH, Anthony. b 41. St Deiniol's Hawarden 87. **d** 90 **p** 91. NSM Gt Saughall *Ches* 90-93; P-in-c Cwmcarn *Mon* 93-95; V 95-99; V Abercarn and Cwmcarn 99-01; TV Upholland *Liv* from 01. *158 Back Lane, Skelmersdale WN8 9BX* Tel (01695) 728091 Mobile 07773-389179

DIMES, Stuart Christopher Laurence. b 60. Warwick Univ BSc81. St Jo Coll Nottm. **d** 01 **p** 02. C Branksome St Clem *Sarum* from 01. *29 Croft Road, Parkstone, Poole BH12 3LB* Tel (01202) 721056

DIMMICK, Mrs Margaret Louisa. b 44. Keswick Hall Coll TCert66 Open Univ BA75. St Alb and Ox Min Course 97. **d** 00 **p** 02. Oxfam from 95; OLM Caversham St Pet and Mapledurham etc *Ox* 00-03; OLM Emmer Green w Caversham Park from 03. *12 Lowfield Road, Caversham, Reading RG4 6PA* Tel 0118-947 0258 E-mail margaret@dimmick33.freeserve.co.uk

DIMOLINE, Keith Frederick. b 22. Clifton Th Coll 48. **d** 51 **p** 52. C Watford Ch Ch *St Alb* 51-54; C Corsham *Bris* 54-59; C-in-c Swindon St Jo Park CD 59-62; V Swindon St Jo 62-65; V Coalpit Heath 65-74; V Hanham 74-83; C Cudworth w Chillington *B & W* 83-84; P-in-c Dowlishwake w Chaffcombe, Knowle St Giles etc 83-84; R Dowlishwake w Chaffcombe, Knowle St Giles etc 84-88; rtd 88; Perm to Offic *B & W* from 88. *16 Exeter Road, Weston-super-Mare BS23 4DB* Tel (01934) 635006

DINES, Anthony Bernard. b 25. Clifton Th Coll 57. **d** 60 **p** 61. C Highbury Ch Ch *Lon* 60-63; C Weymouth St Jo *Sarum* 63-67; R Glas St Silas *Glas* 67-78; R Gunton St Pet *Nor* 78-90; rtd 90; NSM Flixton w Homersfield and S Elmham *St E* 90-92; NSM S Elmham and Ilketshall 92-93; Perm to Offic *Glouc* 93-97; and from 01. *215 Prestbury Road, Cheltenham GL52 3ES* Tel (01242) 525840

DINES, The Very Revd Philip Joseph (Griff). b 59. Univ Coll Lon BScEng80 Clare Coll Cam PhD84 Man Univ MA(Theol)93. Westcott Ho Cam 83. **d** 86 **p** 87. C Northolt St Mary *Lon* 86-89; C Withington St Paul *Man* 89-91; V Wythenshawe St Martin 91-98; P-in-c Newall Green St Fran 95-98; Provost St Mary's Cathl *Glas* from 98; R Glas St Mary from 98. *45 Rowallan Gardens, Glasgow G11 7LH* Tel 0141-339 4956 *or* 339 6691 Fax 357 0929 *or* 334 5669 E-mail griff@dines.org *or* provost@glasgow.anglican.org

DINNEN, The Very Revd John Frederick. b 42. TCD BA65 BD72 QUB MTh91. CITC. **d** 66 **p** 67. C Belfast All SS *Conn* 66-68; ICM Dub 69-71; C Carnmoney 71-73; Asst Dean of Residences QUB 73-74; Dean 74-84; I Hillsborough *D & D* from 84; Preb Down Cathl 93-96; Dir of Ords 96-98; Dean Down from 96. *17 Dromore Road, Hillsborough BT26 6HS* Tel (028) 9268 2366 Fax as telephone

DINSMORE, Ivan. b 71. TCD BTh01. CITC 98. **d** 01 **p** 02. C Glendermott *D & R* from 01. *2 Duncastle Park, Newbuildings, Londonderry BT47 2QL* Tel (028) 7131 8426
E-mail ivandinsmore@hotmail.com

DINSMORE, Stephen Ralph. b 56. Wye Coll Lon BSc78. Cranmer Hall Dur 82. **d** 85 **p** 86. C Haughton le Skerne *Dur* 85-88; C Edgware *Lon* 88-93; V Plymouth St Jude *Ex* from 93; RD Plymouth Sutton 96-01. *St Jude's Vicarage, Knighton Road, Plymouth PL4 9BU* Tel (01752) 661232
E-mail judeplym@aol.com

DISLEY, Mrs Edith Jennifer. b 51. Sheff Univ BSc72 Man Univ BD79. N Ord Course 99. **d** 01 **p** 02. NSM Man Victoria Park *Man* from 01. *49 Broadstone Hall Road North, Heaton Chapel, Stockport SK4 5LA* Tel 0161-432 5114
E-mail sisteredith@priest.com

DISNEY, Peter James. b 13. Univ of BC BA36. Angl Th Coll (BC) LTh37. **d** 37 **p** 38. Canada 37-46; C Wandsworth Common St Mary *S'wark* 46-47; C Dufton *Carl* 47-48; V Godmanchester *Ely* 48-57; V Ipswich All SS *St E* 57-63; Distr Sec (Essex and Herts) BFBS 63-69; (Surrey) 65-69; V Halstead H Trin *Chelmsf* 69-78; rtd 78; Perm to Offic *St E* from 78. *c/o Mr R Disney, Beggars Cottage, Westridge Edge, Aldworth RG8 9RG* Tel (01491) 873158

DISS, Canon Ronald George. b 31. Sarum Th Coll 58. **d** 61 **p** 62. C Greenwich St Alfege w St Pet *S'wark* 61-65; Lic to Offic 65-80; Lic to Offic *Lon* 68-77; Chapl Lon Univ 68-71; Bp's Dom Chapl *Win* 78-80; V Southampton Maybush St Pet 80-91; Hon Can Win Cathl 85-96; R Freemantle 91-96; rtd 96; Hon Chapl to Bp Dover *Cant* from 97. *35 Castle Row, Canterbury CT1 2QY* Tel (01227) 462410

DITCH, David John. b 45. St Cath Coll Cam BA67 MA70 Leeds Univ PGCE68. WMMTC 88. **d** 91 **p** 92. C Biddulph *Lich* 91-94; V Hednesford 94-02; V Chasetown from 02. *The Vicarage, 158A High Street, Chasetown, Burntwood WS7 3XG* Tel (01543) 686276 *or* 686111

DITCHBURN, Canon Hazel. b 44. NEOC 82. **dss** 84 **d** 87 **p** 94. Scotswood *Newc* 84-86; Ind Chapl *Dur* 86-95; AD Gateshead 92-98; TV Gateshead 95-98; Hon Can Dur Cathl from 94; P-in-c Stella from 98; AD Gateshead W 98-00; P-in-c Swalwell from 01. *St Cuthbert's Rectory, Shibdon Road, Blaydon-on-Tyne NE21 5AE* Tel 0191-414 2720 Fax as telephone
E-mail hazel.ditchburn@durham.anglican.org

DITCHFIELD, Timothy Frederick. b 61. CCC Cam BA83. Cranmer Hall Dur 85. **d** 88 **p** 89. C Accrington St Jo *Blackb* 88-89; C Accrington St Jo w Huncoat 89-91; C Whittle-le-Woods 91-95; Chapl K Coll Lon from 95; Perm to Offic *S'wark* from 98. *19 Maunsel Street, London SW1P 2QN*, or *King's College, Strand, London WC2R 2LS* Tel (020) 7828 1772 *or* 7848 2373 Fax 7848 2344 E-mail tim.ditchfield@kcl.ac.uk

DITTMER, Canon Michael William. b 17. St Edm Hall Ox BA39 MA43. Sarum Th Coll 40. **d** 41 **p** 42. C Bromley St Andr *Roch*

41-43; C Horfield H Trin *Bris* 43-49; C-in-c Lockleaze St Fran CD 49-52; V Yatton Keynell 52-88; R Biddestone w Slaughterford 53-88; R Castle Combe 53-88; RD Chippenham 66-76; R W Kington 75-88; Hon Can Bris Cathl 84-88; P-in-c Nettleton w Littleton Drew 85-88; rtd 88; Perm to Offic *B & W* from 88. *Greenacres, Summerhedge Lane, Othery, Bridgwater TA7 0JD* Tel (01823) 698288

DIVALL, David Robert. b 40. New Coll Ox BA64 Sussex Univ DPhil74. Sarum & Wells Th Coll 75. **d** 77 **p** 78. Hon C Catherington and Clanfield *Portsm* 77-92; Hon C Rowlands Castle 92-93; Perm to Offic from 01. *17 Pipers Mead, Clanfield, Waterlooville PO8 0ST* Tel (023) 9259 4845

DIVALL, Stephen Robert. b 70. Pemb Coll Ox MA92. Ridley Hall Cam BA97. **d** 98 **p** 99. C Cheadle *Ches* 98-01; UCCF from 01. *UCCF, 38 De Montfort Street, Leicester LE1 7GP* Tel 0116-255 1700 Fax 255 5672 E-mail stmary@cheadle.org

DIXON, Ms Anne Elizabeth. b 56. Leeds Univ LLB77 Solicitor 80. Westcott Ho Cam. **d** 01 **p** 02. C Guildf H Trin w St Mary *Guildf* from 01. *27 Pewley Way, Guildford GU1 3PX* Tel (01483) 568477

DIXON, Bruce Richard. b 42. Lon Univ BScEng63. Sarum Th Coll 66. **d** 68 **p** 69. C Walton St Mary *Liv* 68-70; C Harnham *Sarum* 70-73; C Streatham St Leon *S'wark* 73-77; R Thurcaston *Leic* 77-83; R Cranborne w Boveridge, Edmondsham etc *Sarum* 83-02. *East Heddon, Filleigh, Barnstaple EX32 0RY* Tel (01598) 760513

DIXON, Bryan Stanley. b 61. St Jo Coll Nottm BTh93. **d** 93 **p** 94. C Beverley Minster *York* 93-96; C Kingston upon Hull St Aid Southcoates 96-97; Asst Chapl HM Pris Dur 97-98; R Mid Marsh Gp *Linc* from 98. *Mid Marsh Rectory, 37 Tinkle Street, Grimoldby, Louth LN11 8SW* Tel (01507) 327429

DIXON, Charles William. b 41. NW Ord Course 78. **d** 81 **p** 82. C Almondbury *Wakef* 81-82; C Almondbury w Farnley Tyas 82-84; P-in-c Shepley 84-88; P-in-c Shelley 84-88; V Shelley and Shepley 88-89; V Ripponden 89-94; V Barkisland w W Scammonden 89-94; P-in-c Thornes St Jas w Ch Ch 94-98; Chapl among Deaf People *Chelmsf* from 98. *156C Rayleigh Road, Hutton, Brentwood CM13 1PH* Tel (01277) 216544 E-mail dchas58@aol.com

DIXON, Canon David. b 19. Lich Th Coll 57. **d** 58 **p** 59. C Barrow St Luke *Carl* 58-61; V Westfield St Mary 61-68; Warden Rydal Hall 68-84; P-in-c Rydal 78-84; rtd 84; Perm to Offic *Carl* from 84; Hon Can Carl Cathl 84-85. *Rheda, The Green, Millom LA18 5JA* Tel (01229) 774300

DIXON, David Hugh. b 40. Chich Th Coll 90. **d** 92 **p** 93. C Launceston *Truro* 90-95; TV Probus, Ladock and Grampound w Creed and St Erme from 95. *The Rectory, Ladock, Truro TR2 4PL* Tel (01726) 882554 E-mail ddixon@fish.co.uk

DIXON, David Michael. b 58. Preston Poly BA82 Barrister 83. Coll of Resurr Mirfield BA98. **d** 98 **p** 99. C Goldthorpe w Hickleton *Sheff* 98-01; P-in-c W Kirby St Andr *Ches* from 01. *St Andrew's Vicarage, 2 Lingdale Road, West Kirby, Wirral CH48 5DQ* Tel 0151-632 4728

DIXON, Edward Michael (Mike). b 42. St Chad's Coll Dur BA64 DipTh66 Newc Univ MA93. **d** 66 **p** 67. C Hartlepool H Trin *Dur* 66-70; C Howden *York* 70-73; Chapl HM Pris Liv 73; Chapl HM Pris Onley 74-82; Chapl HM Pris Frankland 82-87; Chapl HM Pris Dur 87-97; Chapl HM Pris Acklington 97-98; Asst Chapl 98-02; P-in-c Shilbottle *Newc* from 98; P-in-c Chevington from 03. *The Vicarage, Shilbottle, Alnwick NE66 2XR* Tel and fax (01665) 575800 E-mail mdixon@fish.co.uk

DIXON, Eric. b 31. MPS. EMMTC 78. **d** 81 **p** 82. NSM Kirk Langley *Derby* 81-96; NSM Mackworth All SS 81-96; Perm to Offic from 96. *Silverdale, 105 Lower Road, Mackworth, Derby DE22 4NG* Tel (01332) 824543

DIXON, Mrs Francesca Dorothy. b 52. Cam Univ MA73 Birm Univ DipTh83. Qu Coll Birm 81. **dss** 84 **d** 87 **p** 94. W Bromwich All SS *Lich* 84-94; Par Dn 87-94; C 94; Chapl Burrswood Chr Cen *Roch* 95; Perm to Offic *Chich* from 97. *46 Arun Vale, Coldwaltham, Pulborough RH20 1LP* Tel (01798) 872177

DIXON, John Kenneth (Ken). b 40. Linc Th Coll 79. **d** 81 **p** 82. C Goldington *St Alb* 81-85; V Cardington 85-94; RD Elstow 89-94; R Clifton 94-95; P-in-c Southill 94-95; R Clifton and Southill from 95; RD Shefford 95-01. *The Rectory, 8 Rectory Close, Clifton, Shefford SG17 5EL* Tel (01462) 850150 Fax 815740 E-mail eidyn@cainnech.fsworld.co.uk

DIXON, John Martin. b 42. SSC75 York Univ DMS96 ACMI96. Kelham Th Coll Lich Th Coll. **d** 72 **p** 73. C Ellesmere Port *Ches* 72-74; C Bredbury St Barn 74-75; P-in-c Greenlands *Blackb* 75-78; Chapl Victoria Hosp Blackpool 75-78; Chapl RAF 78-81; Asst Chapl HM Pris Featherstone 81-85; Dep Chapl HM Pris Wormwood Scrubs 85-87; Chapl HM Pris Rudgate and Thorp Arch 87-89; Chapl HM Pris Leeds 89-93; Chapl HM Pris Stafford from 93. *HM Prison, 54 Gaol Road, Stafford ST16 3AW* Tel (01782) 254421 ext 327 Fax 227734

DIXON, John Scarth. b 69. Aber Univ MA92. Westcott Ho Cam CTM98. **d** 98 **p** 99. C Walney Is *Carl* 98-01; R Harrington from 01. *The Rectory, Rectory Close, Harrington, Workington CA14 5PN* Tel (01946) 830215 E-mail jjcdixon@btinternet.com

DIXON, Lorraine. b 65. Leeds Univ BA96. CA Tr Coll Dip Evang 89 Qu Coll Birm BD98. **d** 98 **p** 99. C Potternewton *Ripon* 98-01; Chapl Ches Coll *Ches* from 01. *85 Parkgate Road, Chester CH1 4AJ* Tel (01244) 372002 or 375444 Fax 392820

DIXON, Nicholas Scarth. b 30. G&C Coll Cam BA54 MA63. Westcott Ho Cam 54. **d** 56 **p** 57. C Walney Is *Carl* 56-59; CF 59-62; V Whitehaven Ch Ch w H Trin *Carl* 62-70; R Blofield w Hemblington *Nor* 70-77; P-in-c Bowness *Carl* 77-79; R 79-81; V Frizington and Arlecdon 81-87; V Barton, Pooley Bridge and Martindale 87-95; rtd 95; Perm to Offic *Carl* from 95. *7 Mayburgh Avenue, Penrith CA11 8PA* Tel (01768) 892864

DIXON, Canon Peter. b 36. Qu Coll Ox BA58 MA62 Birm Univ BD65 PhD75. Qu Coll Birm DipTh60. **d** 60 **p** 61. C Mountain Ash *Llan* 60-63; C Penrhiwceiber w Matthewstown and Ynysboeth 63-68; P-in-c 68-70; V Bronllys w Llanfilo *S & B* 70-02; Bp's Chapl for Readers 80-02; Bp's Chapl for Th Educn 83-02; Warden of Readers 92-02; RD Hay 90-02; Can Res Brecon Cathl 98-02; rtd 02. *22 Caerpound, Hay-on-Wye, Hereford HR3 5DU*

DIXON, Peter David. b 48. Edin Univ BSc71 MIMechE. Edin Dioc NSM Course 75. **d** 79 **p** 80. NSM Prestonpans *Edin* 79-89; NSM Musselburgh 79-89; NSM Edin St Luke 90; P-in-c Edin St Barn from 91. *8 Oswald Terrace, Prestonpans EH32 9EG* Tel (01875) 812985

DIXON, Philip. b 48. Leeds Univ BSc69 Open Univ BA91. St Jo Coll Nottm 77. **d** 80 **p** 81. C Soundwell *Bris* 80-82; C Stoke Bishop 82-84; TV Hemel Hempstead *St Alb* 84-85; Chapl Westonbirt Sch from 85; Perm to Offic *Bris* from 86. *East Lodge, Westonbirt School, Tetbury GL8 8QG* Tel (01666) 880333

DIXON, Philip Roger. b 54. CCC Ox BA77 MA80. Oak Hill Th Coll BA80. **d** 80 **p** 81. C Droylsden St Mary *Man* 80-84; TV Rochdale 84-91; V Audenshaw St Steph from 91; AD Ashton-under-Lyne from 03. *St Stephen's Vicarage, 176 Stamford Road, Audenshaw, Manchester M34 5WW* Tel 0161-370 1863 E-mail ssaudenshaw@aol.com

DIXON, Robert. b 50. Univ of Wales (Lamp) BA80. Chich Th Coll 80. **d** 81 **p** 82. C Maidstone St Martin *Cant* 81-84; Chapl HM Youth Cust Cen Dover 84-88; C All Hallows by the Tower etc *Lon* 88-90; P-in-c Southwick H Trin *Dur* 90-97; R 97; R Etchingham *Chich* from 97; V Hurst Green from 97. *9 McMichaels Way, Hurst Green, Etchingham TN19 7HJ* Tel (01580) 860105 Mobile 07779-121169 E-mail sussexrob@aol.com

DIXON, Roger John. b 33. Magd Coll Cam BA58 MA61. EAMTC 78. **d** 79 **p** 80. NSM Fakenham w Alethorpe *Nor* 79-82; C Brandeston w Kettleburgh *St E* 82-84; P-in-c 84-99; Asst Chapl Framlingham Coll 82-99; RD Loes *St E* 97-98; rtd 99; Perm to Offic *Nor* from 99. *Hunters Light, Hall Lane, Knapton, North Walsham NR28 0SG* Tel (01263) 721050

DIXON, Ms Sheila. b 46. Open Univ BA78 Trent Poly CertEd79. St Jo Coll Nottm 93. **d** 93 **p** 94. Par Dn Ordsall *S'well* 93-94; C 94-97; P-in-c Sutton w Carlton and Normanton upon Trent etc from 97. *The Vicarage, Old North Road, Sutton-on-Trent, Newark NG23 6PL* Tel (01636) 821797

DIXON, Stephen William. b 53. Nottm Univ BA75 Man Metrop Univ PGCE88 Liv Univ MTh00. Nor Ord Course 96. **d** 99 **p** 00. NSM Meltham *Wakef* from 99; Lic Preacher *Man* from 01. *83 Totties, Holmfirth, Huddersfield HD7 1UJ* Tel (01484) 687376

DIXON, Mrs Teresa Mary. b 61. Southn Univ BSc82 Ball Coll Ox PGCE83. EAMTC 99. **d** 02 **p** 03. NSM Sutton *Ely* from 02; NSM Witcham w Mepal from 02. *Ash Tree Farm, Furlong Drove, Little Downham, Ely CB6 2EW* Tel (01353) 699552 E-mail teresa@ashtreefarm.freeserve.co.uk

DIXON-SWINNEY, Fergus William Henry. b 37. Edin Th Coll 67. **d** 69 **p** 70. C Benwell St Jas *Newc* 69-72; C Willington 72-75; V Longhirst 75-80; rtd 97. *23A West Street, Berwick-upon-Tweed TD15 1AS* Tel (01289) 302863

DIZERENS, Charles Robert (Frère François). b 18. Lausanne Univ. **d** 97. Asst Chapl Montreux w Gstaad *Eur* from 97. *Avenue de Valmont 16, Lausanne 1010, Switzerland* Tel (0041) (21) 653 1090 or 963 43654 Fax 963 4391

DNISTRIANSKYJ, Stefan Mykola. b 61. Leic Univ BSc82 Chester Coll of HE BTh02. N Ord Course 99. **d** 02. C Halliwell St Luke *Man* from 02. *Karis, Stowell Street, Bolton BL1 3RQ* Tel (01204) 522810 Mobile 07931-785598 E-mail dnist@hotmail.com

DOBB, Canon Arthur Joseph. b 31. ARIBA54 Man Coll of Art DA52 ACertCM80 Hon FGMS93. Oak Hill Th Coll 56. **d** 58 **p** 59. C Bolton St Paul *Man* 58-60; C Rawtenstall St Mary 60-62; V Bircle 62-72; V Harwood 72-84; Hon Can Man Cathl 81-96; V Wingates 84-96; rtd 96; Perm to Offic *Man* from 96. *97 Turton Heights, Bromley Cross, Bolton BL2 3DU* Tel (01204) 308419

DOBB, Christopher. b 46. Dur Univ BA68. Cuddesdon Coll 68. **d** 70 **p** 71. C Portsea St Mary *Portsm* 70-73; Lic to Offic *S'wark* 73-77; Perm to Offic *Bris* 77-79; Lic to Offic 79-81; V Swindon St Aug 81-98; rtd 98. *Kingsbury Hall, The Green, Calne SN11 8DG* Tel (01249) 821521 Fax 817246 E-mail kingsburyhallcd@aol.com

DOBBIE, Charles William Granville. b 49. OBE92. Wycliffe Hall Ox 94. **d** 96 **p** 97. C Morriston *S & B* 96-00; Asst Chapl Morriston Hosp/Ysbyty Treforys NHS Trust 97-00; V Lyonsdown H Trin *St Alb* from 00. *Holy Trinity Vicarage, 18 Lyonsdown Road, Barnet EN5 1JE* Tel (020) 8216 3786
E-mail charles@holytrinitylyonsdown.org.uk
DOBBIE, Gary William. b 51. St Andr Univ MA75 BD77 Magd Coll Cam CertEd80 FRSA98 FSAScot. Coll of Resurr Mirfield 83. **d** 83 **p** 83. Kimbolton Sch Cambs 83-84; Hon C Kimbolton *Ely* 83-84; Sen Chapl Ch Hosp Horsham 86-96; Asst Chapl 96-03; Housemaster 93-03; Chapl Shrewsbury Sch from 03. *Shrewsbury School, Kingsland, Shrewsbury SY3 7BA* Tel (01743) 280550 Mobile 07879-426056
E-mail chaplain@shrewsbury.org.uk
DOBBIN, Canon Charles Philip. b 51. Jes Coll Cam BA73 MA77 Oriel Coll Ox BA75 MA83. St Steph Ho Ox 74. **d** 76 **p** 77. C New Addington *Cant* 76-79; C Melton Mowbray w Thorpe Arnold *Leic* 79-83; V Loughb Gd Shep 83-89; V Ashby-de-la-Zouch St Helen w Coleorton 89-00; RD Akeley W 93-00; Hon Can Leic Cathl 94-00; TR Moor Allerton *Ripon* from 00. *St John's Rectory, 1 Fir Tree Lane, Leeds LS17 7BZ* Tel 0113-268 4598
E-mail cdobbin@aol.com
DOBBIN, Harold John. b 47. Liv Univ BSc69. St Steph Ho Ox 70. **d** 73 **p** 74. C Newbold w Dunston *Derby* 73-77; C Leckhampton SS Phil and Jas w Cheltenham St Jas *Glouc* 77-80; V Hebburn St Cuth *Dur* 80-86; R Barlborough *Derby* 86-95; P-in-c Alfreton 95-00; V from 00; RD Alfreton from 02. *The Vicarage, 13 Church Street, Alfreton DE55 7AH* Tel (01773) 833280
DOBBIN, Miss Penelope Jane. b 59. Slough Coll GRSC88. St Alb and Ox Min Course CBTS99. **d** 99 **p** 00. C Bideford, Northam, Westward Ho, Appledore etc *Ex* from 99. *61 Hanson Park, Bideford EX39 3SB* Tel (01237) 429468
E-mail penny@entropytoo.freeserve.co.uk
DOBBINS, Lorraine Sharon. b 72. Ripon Coll Cuddesdon BTh01. **d** 01 **p** 02. C Talbot Village *Sarum* from 01. *St Saviour's House, 18 Hillside Road, Poole BH12 5DY* Tel (01202) 513646
E-mail lorrainedobbins@hotmail.com
DOBBS, George Christopher. b 43. Linc Th Coll 66. **d** 68 **p** 69. C Hykeham *Linc* 68-71; Asst Master Heneage Sch Grimsby 71-78; Perm to Offic S'well 78-80; TV Chelmsley Wood *Birm* 80-84; TV Rochdale *Man* 84-99; V Sudden St Aidan from 00; C Castleton Moor from 00. *St Aidan's Vicarage, 498 Manchester Road, Rochdale OL11 3HE* Tel (01706) 631812
E-mail g3rjv@gqpr.demon.co.uk
DOBBS, Michael John. b 48. Linc Th Coll 74. **d** 77 **p** 78. C Warsop S'well 77-82; V Worksop St Paul 82-89; P-in-c Mansfield St Mark from 89. *St Mark's Vicarage, Nottingham Road, Mansfield NG18 1BP* Tel (01623) 655548
DOBELL, Richard Frank. b 53. Ex Univ BA83 PGCE84 ARCO83. WMMTC 96. **d** 99 **p** 00. Asst Master Alcester Gr Sch 85-02; Bursar from 02; NSM Alveston *Cov* 99-03; NSM Alcester and Arrow w Oversley and Weethley from 03. *40 Fairwater Crescent, Alcester B49 6RB* Tel (01789) 762584 *or* 762494
DOBLE, Mrs Maureen Mary Thompson. b 44. RGN65. S Dios Minl Tr Scheme CECM93. **d** 93 **p** 94. NSM Kingston St Mary w Broomfield etc *B & W* from 93. *Rosebank, Lyngford Lane, Taunton TA2 7LL* Tel (01823) 286772
DOBLE, Peter. b 29. Univ of Wales (Cardiff) BA51 Fitzw Coll Cam BA54 MA58 St Edm Hall Ox MA68 Leeds Univ PhD92. Wesley Ho Cam 52. **d** 55 **p** 58. In Ch of S India 55-60; In Meth Ch 60-64; Hd of RE Qu Mary Sch Lytham St Annes *Blackb* 64-67; Lect RS Culham Coll Abingdon *Ox* 67-69; Sen Lect 69-74; Prin Lect and Hd Relig Studies 74-80; Perm to Offic *York* from 80; Dir York RE Cen 80-94; Sen Fell Th and RS Leeds Univ *Ripon* 95-98; Hon Lect from 98. *3 Sandholme, Usher Park, Haxby, York YO3 8LW* Tel (01904) 761288
E-mail peter.doble@btinternet.com
DOBSON, Christopher John. b 62. Univ of Wales (Abth) BA83. Wycliffe Hall Ox BA88. **d** 89 **p** 90. C Biggin Hill *Roch* 89-92; C Tunbridge Wells St Jas w St Phil 92-95; USPG Zimbabwe 95-99; V Paddock Wood *Roch* from 00. *The Vicarage, 169 Maidstone Road, Paddock Wood, Tonbridge TN12 6DZ* Tel and fax (01892) 833917 *or* tel 837617
E-mail cdobson@supanet.com
DOBSON, Geoffrey Norman. b 46. ACP70. Leeds Univ CertEd68 BA77 Open Univ BA73. Wells Th Coll 71. **d** 74 **p** 75. C S Woodford H Trin CD *Chelmsf* 74-76; Colchester Adnry Youth Chapl 76-78; C Halstead St Andr w H Trin and Greenstead Green 76-78; Asst Dir Educn (Youth) *Carl* 78-82; P-in-c Kirkandrews-on-Eden w Beaumont and Grinsdale 78-82; V Illingworth *Wakef* 82-86; V Roxton w Gt Barford *St Alb* 86-93; Chapl N Man Health Care NHS Trust 93-98; P-in-c Newton Heath St Wilfrid and St Anne *Man* 93-97; C Newton Heath 97-98; P-in-c Alconbury w Alconbury Weston *Ely* 98-00; P-in-c Buckworth 98-00; P-in-c Gt w Lt Stukeley 98-00; Perm to Offic from 02. *30 Lees Lane, Southoe, Huntingdon PE19 5YG* Tel (01480) 890284
DOBSON, Canon John Francis Alban. b 12. **d** 38 **p** 45. Australia 47-57; S Africa 57; V New Groombridge *Chich* 57-58; Bahamas

58-60; Canada from 60. *10 Kensington Road, Bramalea ON, Canada, L6T 3V4* Tel (001) (905) 792 8601
DOBSON, John Haselden. b 29. Mert Coll Ox BA52 MA55 Lon Univ BD58. Oak Hill Th Coll 54. **d** 56 **p** 57. C Rugby St Matt *Cov* 56-59; C W Hampstead St Luke Lon 59-60; Uganda 60-72; C Gorleston St Andr *Nor* 73-77; R Saxlingham Nethergate w Saxlingham Thorpe 77-90; V Shotesham 77-90; R Saxlingham Nethergate and Shotesham 90-93; rtd 94; Perm to Offic *Nor* from 94. *Karanga, The Street, Hardwick, Norwich NR15 2AB* Tel (01508) 530611
DOBSON, John Richard. b 64. Van Mildert Coll Dur BA87. Ripon Coll Cuddesdon 87. **d** 89 **p** 90. C Benfieldside *Dur* 89-92; C Darlington St Cuth 92-96; C-in-c Blackwell All SS and Salutation CD 96-98; V Blackwell All SS and Salutation from 98; AD Darlington from 01. *104 Blackwell Lane, Darlington DL3 8QQ* Tel (01325) 354503
E-mail john.dobson@durham.anglican.org
DOBSON, Kenneth Shuard. b 26. Oak Hill Th Coll 53. **d** 56 **p** 57. C Hatcham St Jas *S'wark* 56-59; C Wimbledon 59-62; R W Lynn *Nor* 62-66; Lic to Offic 66-68; P-in-c Deopham w Hackford 68-74; Chapl Eccles Hall Sch Quidenham 74-78; R Elvedon *St E* 78-84; R Eriswell 78-84; R Icklingham 78-84; RD Mildenhall 80-81; RD Newmarket 80-81; rtd 84; Chapl Wayland Hosp Norfolk 84-87; Lic to Offic *Nor* 84-97. *St Joseph's, 14 Salthouse Close, Crofty, Swansea SA4 3SN* Tel (01792) 851652
DOBSON, Philip Albert. b 52. Lanc Univ BA73 CertEd74. Trin Coll Bris DipHE89. **d** 89 **p** 90. C Grenoside *Sheff* 89-92; C Cove St Jo *Guildf* 92-93; TV 93-96; V Camberley St Martin Old Dean from 96. *St Martin's Vicarage, 2A Hampshire Road, Camberley GU15 4DW* Tel (01276) 23958
E-mail philip.dobson@ntlworld.com
DOBSON, Stuart Joseph. b 51. Westmr Coll Ox BA85. Chich Th Coll 86. **d** 88 **p** 89. C Costessey *Nor* 88-90; C Chaddesden St Phil *Derby* 90-92; C Friern Barnet St Jas *Lon* 92-93; TV Plymouth Em, Efford and Laira *Ex* 93-96; P-in-c Laira 96; R Withington St Crispin *Man* 96-98; P-in-c Beguildy and Heyope *S & B* 98-00; P-in-c Llangynllo and Bleddfa 99-00; TV Bruton and Distr *B & W* 00-01. *Whitecroft, Ulsta, Yell, Shetland ZE2 9BG* E-mail stuart.dobson@btinternet.com
✠**DOCKER, The Rt Revd Ivor Colin.** b 25. Birm Univ BA46 St Cath Soc Ox BA49 MA52. Wycliffe Hall Ox 46. **d** 49 **p** 50 c 75. C Normanton *Wakef* 49-52; C Halifax St Jo Bapt 52-54; Area Sec (Dios Derby Linc and S'well) CMS 54-58; Metrop Sec (S) 58-59; V Midhurst *Chich* 59-64; RD Midhurst 61-64; R Woolbeding 61-64; V Seaford w Sutton 64-71; RD Seaford 64-71; Can and Preb Chich Cathl 66-91; V Eastbourne St Mary 71-75; RD Eastbourne 71-75; Suff Bp Horsham 75-84; Area Bp Horsham 84-91; rtd 91; Asst Bp Ex from 91. *Braemar, Bradley Road, Bovey Tracey, Newton Abbot TQ13 9EU* Tel (01626) 832468
DODD, Alan Henry. b 42. Man Univ BA70 MA79. Chich Th Coll 82. **d** 82 **p** 83. C Fareham H Trin *Portsm* 82-84; TV 84-89; V Osmotherley w Harlsey and Ingleby Arncliffe *York* from 89; Chapl Northallerton Health Services NHS Trust from 92. *Orchard House, Ingleby Arncliffe, Northallerton DL6 3LN* Tel (01609) 882189
DODD, Andrew Patrick. b 68. Hatf Poly BEng91. Westcott Ho Cam 97. **d** 00 **p** 01. C New Addington S'wark from 00. *27 Burford Way, New Addington, Croydon CR0 0RR*
DODD, Charles Nathanael. b 30. Westcott Ho Cam. **d** 57 **p** 58. C Milton *Portsm* 57-62; Australia 62-91; P-in-c Bretby w Newton Solney *Derby* 91-96; Bp's Ind Adv 91-00; rtd 00. *6 Sylvia Avenue, Hatch End, Pinner HA5 4QE* Tel (020) 8428 3275
DODD, Graham Michael. b 38. St Jo Coll York CertEd61 Hull Coll of Educn DipEd67 Leeds Univ DipTh97. Nor Ord Course 93. **d** 96 **p** 97. NSM Golcar *Wakef* 96-99; NSM N Huddersfield from 99. *9 Broombank, Huddersfield HD2 2DJ* Tel (01484) 539832 E-mail mikedodd@compuserve.com
DODD, James Henry Birchenough. b 25. CPsychol AFBPsS Ox Univ MA. Westcott Ho Cam 85. **d** 85 **p** 86. NSM Epping Upland *Chelmsf* 85-95; NSM Epping Distr 95-96; Perm to Offic from 96. *The Chequers, Epping Upland, Epping CM16 6PH* Tel (01992) 572561
DODD, Jane. b 33. Loughb Univ ALA51 FLA51. LNSM course 97. **d** 98 **p** 99. OLM Wroxham w Hoveton and Belaugh *Nor* from 98. *Locheil, Tunstead Road, Hoveton St John, Norwich NR12 8QN* Tel (01603) 782509
DODD, Mrs Jean. b 47. LNSM course 95. **d** 98 **p** 99. OLM Irlam *Man* from 98. *75 Harewood Road, Manchester M44 6DL* Tel 0161-775 9125
DODD, John Dudley. b 15. Liv Univ BA36 Lon Univ BD51 DipEd54. Westcott Ho Cam 54. **d** 54 **p** 55. C Jersey St Helier *Win* 54-78; rtd 78; P-in-c Jersey Gouray St Martin *Win* 78-93; NSM Jersey St Luke 94-96; Perm to Offic from 96. *10 Clos de Gouray, Gorey Village, Jersey JE3 9EN* Tel (01534) 854713
DODD, John Stanley. b 24. Huron Coll Ontario 46. **d** 50 **p** 51. Canada 50-52; Leeds St Jo Ev *Ripon* 52-54; C High Harrogate Ch Ch 54-58; V Stainburn 58-65; V Weeton 58-64; V Meanwood 65-89; rtd 89; Perm to Offic *Ripon* from 89. *3 Shawdene, Burton Crescent, Leeds LS6 4DN* Tel 0113-278 9069

DODD, Malcolm Ogilvie. b 46. Dur Univ BSc67 Loughb Univ MSc90. Edin Th Coll 67. **d** 70 **p** 71. C Hove All SS *Chich* 70-73; C Crawley 73-78; P-in-c Rusper 79-83; Chapl Brighton Coll Jun Sch 83; Chapl Stancliffe Hall Sch 84-97; rtd 01. *Résidence Dodd, 210 Chemin des Villecrozes, Buis les Baronnies, 26170 Drome, France* Tel (0033) (4) 7528 0599
E-mail m.et.j.dodd@wanadoo.fr

DODD, Michael Christopher. b 33. Ch Coll Cam BA55 MA59. Ridley Hall Cam 57. **d** 59 **p** 60. C Stechford *Birm* 59-62; V Quinton Road W St Boniface 62-72; TV Paston *Pet* 72-77; TR Hodge Hill *Birm* 77-89; rtd 90; Perm to Offic *Birm* from 90. *39 Regency Gardens, Birmingham B14 4JS* Tel 0121-474 6945

DODD, Canon Peter Curwen. b 33. St Jo Coll Cam BA57 FRSA93. Linc Th Coll 58 Wm Temple Coll Rugby 59. **d** 60 **p** 61. C Eastwood *Sheff* 60-63; Ind Chapl 63-67; Ind Chapl *Newc* 67-98; RD Newc E 78-83 and 92-95; Hon Can Newc Cathl 82-98; rtd 98; Perm to Offic *Newc* from 98. *Glenesk, 26 The Oval, Benton, Newcastle upon Tyne NE12 9PP* Tel 0191-266 1293

DODDS, Alan Richard. b 46. Greenwich Univ K Coll Lon MA94. **d** 95 **p** 96. C Deal St Geo *Cant* 95-99; C-in-c Deal, The Carpenter's Arms 98-99; Prin OLM Course 99-01; TV Cullompton, Willand, Uffculme, Kentisbeare etc *Ex* from 02. *The Vicarage, Bridge Street, Uffculme, Cullompton EX15 3AX* Tel (01884) 841001 E-mail alandoddss@eegconnect.net

DODDS, Canon Arthur Whitfield. b 20. FRMetS Qu Coll Ox BA48 MA53. Wells Th Coll 49. **d** 50 **p** 51. C Horley *S'wark* 50-53; R Honiley *Cov* 53-58; V Atherstone 58-64; V Chedworth w Yanworth and Stowell *Glouc* 64-75; R Northleach 73-83; V Chedworth, Yanworth and Stowell, Coln Rogers etc 75-85; Hon Can Glouc Cathl 78-90; rtd 86; Perm to Offic *Glouc* 90-97. *Watermoor House, Watermoor Road, Cirencester GL7 1TR* Tel (01285) 659385

DODDS, Brian Martin. b 37. AKC62. **d** 63 **p** 64. C Morpeth *Newc* 63-67; Guyana 67-71; V Willington *Newc* 71-74; TV Brayton *York* 75-79; V Gravelly Hill *Birm* 79-83; V Winterton *Linc* 83-85; V Winterton Gp 85-90; V Gainsborough St Jo 90-96; V Morton 95-96; R Walesby 96-00; rtd 00; Perm to Offic *Linc* from 01. *69 Pennell Street, Lincoln LN5 7TD* Tel (01522) 512593
E-mail bmdodds@talk21.com

DODDS, Preb Graham Michael. b 58. GTCL80. Trin Coll Bris. **d** 84 **p** 85. C Reigate St Mary *S'wark* 84-91; P-in-c Bath Walcot *B & W* 91-93; R 93-96; Lay Tr Adv from 96; Dir Reader Studies from 96; Preb Wells Cathl from 03. *25 Wood Close, Wells BA5 2GA* Tel (01749) 677531 or 670777 Fax 674240
E-mail general@bathwells.anglican.org

DODDS, Canon Neil Sutherland. b 35. ARCO59 Keble Coll Ox BA59 DipTh61 MA63. Linc Th Coll 60. **d** 62 **p** 63. C Handsworth St Jas *Birm* 62-65; V Highters Heath 65-75; V Olton 75-00; RD Solihull 79-89; Hon Can Birm Cathl 82-00; rtd 00; Perm to Offic *Birm* and *Cov* from 00. *29 Stuart Close, Warwick CV34 6AQ* Tel (01926) 402909
E-mail neil.jean.dodds@talk21.com

DODDS, Canon Norman Barry. b 43. Open Univ BA. CITC 73. **d** 76 **p** 77. C Ballynafeigh St Jude *D & D* 76-80; I Belfast St Mich *Conn* from 80; Chapl HM Pris Belf from 84; Can Belf Cathl from 98. *5 Sunningdale Park, Belfast BT14 6RU* Tel (028) 9071 5463 Fax as telephone E-mail doddscavehill@yahoo.com

DODDS, Peter. b 35. WMMTC 88 Qu Coll Birm 88. **d** 91 **p** 92. NSM Hartshill *Cov* 91-93; NSM Nuneaton St Mary 94-95; Hon Chapl Geo Eliot Hosp NHS Trust Nuneaton from 95; Hon Chapl Mary Ann Evans Hospice from 95; NSM Camp Hill w Galley Common *Cov* 99-01; Perm to Offic from 02. *Wem House, 51 Magyar Crescent, Nuneaton CV11 4SQ* Tel (024) 7638 4061

DODGE, Robin Dennis. b 58. Cornell Univ NY BA80 Boston Univ JD83. Virginia Th Sem MDiv99. **d** 98 **p** 99. C Arlington St Mary USA 98-02; C Bris St Mary Redcliffe w Temple etc *Bris* from 02. *2 Colston Parade, Bristol BS1 6RA* Tel 0117-929 8458 Fax 929 1487 E-mail rdodge@stmaryredcliffe.co.uk

DODGSON, Ronald. b 27. Sarum & Wells Th Coll 72. **d** 74 **p** 75. Sub Warden Barn Fellowship Blandford Forum 74-85; Hon C Canford Magna *Sarum* 78-85; C Hartley Wintney, Elvetham, Winchfield etc *Win* 85-92; rtd 92. *84 Tavistock Road, Fleet, Aldershot GU13 8EZ* Tel (01252) 624991

DODHIA, Hitesh Kishorilal. b 57. Cranmer Hall Dur 85. **d** 88 **p** 89. C Leamington Priors All SS *Cov* 88-91; Chapl HM YOI Glen Parva 91-92; Asst Chapl 94-98; Chapl HM Pris Roch 92-94; Chapl HM Pris The Mount from 98; Lic to Offic *St Alb* from 98. *HM Custody Centre, The Mount, Molyneux Avenue, Bovingdon, Hemel Hempstead HP3 0NZ* Tel (01442) 834363

DODSON, Canon Gordon. b 31. Barrister 56 Em Coll Cam BA54 LLB55 MA58. Ridley Hall Cam 57. **d** 59 **p** 60. C Belhus Park *Chelmsf* 59-60; C Barking St Marg 60-63; CMS 63-67; C New Malden and Coombe *S'wark* 67-69; V Snettisham *Nor* 69-81; RD Heacham and Rising 76-81; P-in-c Reepham and Hackford w Whitwell and Kerdiston 81-83; P-in-c Salle 81-83; P-in-c Thurning w Wood Dalling 81-83; R Reepham, Hackford w Whitwell, Kerdiston etc 83-94; Hon Can Nor Cathl 85-94; rtd 94; Perm to Offic *Nor* from 94. *Poppygate, 2 The Loke, Cromer NR27 9DH* Tel (01263) 511811

DODSON, James Peter. b 32. DipMin88. Lich Th Coll 58. **d** 61 **p** 62. C Chasetown *Lich* 61-63; C Hednesford 63-68; V Halifax

St Hilda *Wakef* 68-76; V Upperthong 76-85; TV York All SS Pavement w St Crux and St Martin etc *York* 85-90; rtd 92; Perm to Offic *Ripon* from 92. *Roseville, Studley Road, Ripon HG4 2QH* Tel (01756) 602053

DODSWORTH, George Brian Knowles. b 34. Univ of Wales DipTh62 Birm Univ DPS66 Open Univ AdDipCrim92 BSc94. St Mich Coll Llan 59. **d** 62 **p** 63. C Kidderminster St Mary *Worc* 62-67; Asst Chapl HM Pris Man 67-68; Chapl HM Pris Eastchurch 68-70; Chapl HM Pris Wakef 70-74; Chapl HM Pris Wormwood Scrubs 74-83; Asst Chapl Gen of Pris (SE) 83-90; Asst Chapl Gen of Pris (HQ) 90-94; Chapl HM Pris Brixton 94-95; Lic to Offic *Lon* 83-94; Lic to Offic *S'wark* from 94; rtd 99. *1C Underhill Road, London SE22 0BT* Tel (020) 8693 9976 Fax as telephone E-mail brian.gbkd@lineone.net

DOE, Martin Charles. b 54. Lon Univ BSc(Econ)75 PGCE87 MA95. St Steph Ho Ox 89. **d** 91 **p** 92. C Portsea St Mary *Portsm* 91-94; Chapl Abbey Grange High Sch Leeds 94-00; Sen Angl Chapl Scarborough and NE Yorks Healthcare NHS Trust from 00. *Scarborough Hospital, Woodlands Drive, Scarborough YO12 6QL* Tel (01723) 368111

✠**DOE, The Rt Revd Michael David.** b 47. St Jo Coll Dur BA69 Bath Univ Hon LLD02. Ripon Hall Ox 69. **d** 72 **p** 73 **c** 94. C St Helier *S'wark* 72-76; Youth Sec BCC 76-81; C-in-c Blackbird Leys CD *Ox* 81-88; V Blackbird Leys 88-89; RD Cowley 86-89; Soc Resp Adv *Portsm* 89-94; Can Res Portsm Cathl 89-94; Suff Bp Swindon *Bris* from 94. *Mark House, Field Rise, Old Town, Swindon SN1 4HP* Tel (01793) 538654 Fax as telephone E-mail bishop.michael@bristol.anglican.org

DOE, Mrs Priscilla Sophia. b 41. LRAM61. SEITE 97. **d** 00 **p** 01. NSM Maidstone All SS and St Phil w Tovil *Cant* from 00. *Mount St Laurence, High Street, Cranbrook TN17 3EW* Tel (01580) 712330

DOEL, Patrick Stephen. b 71. Wycliffe Hall Ox BA03. **d** 03. C Blackheath St Jo *S'wark* from 03. *Flat A, 15 St John's Park, London SE3 7TD* Tel (020) 8305 0520
E-mail steve.doel@ntlworld.com

DOGGETT, Margaret Ann. b 36. Open Univ BA78 Homerton Coll Cam PGCE79. LNSM course 94. **d** 96 **p** 97. OLM Pulham Market, Pulham St Mary and Starston *Nor* 96-99; OLM Dickleburgh and The Pulhams 99-01; rtd 02; Perm to Offic *Nor* from 02. *Antares, Station Road, Pulham St Mary, Diss IP21 4QT* Tel and fax (01379) 676662 Mobile 07710-621547
E-mail john.doggett@btinternet.com

DOHERTY, Mrs Christine. b 46. SEN72. STETS 97. **d** 00 **p** 01. NSM Framfield *Chich* 00-03; C Seaford w Sutton from 03. *St Luke's House, 16 Saltwood Road, Seaford BN25 3SP* Tel (01323) 892969 E-mail christinedoherty@chyngton.fsnet.co.uk

DOHERTY, Deana Rosina Mercy. b 21. St Aid Coll Dur BA55. dss 82 **d** 87 **p** 94. Sutton St Jas and Wawne *York* 82-95; Par Dn 87-94; C 94-95; Perm to Offic 95-99; rtd 98. *18 Cecil Road, Weston-super-Mare BS23 2HT* Tel (01934) 626299

DOHERTY, Terence William. b 30. Shoreditch Coll Lon TCert St Jo Coll Dur BA56. Ripon Hall Ox 56. **d** 58 **p** 59. C Church Stretton *Heref* 58-60; C Halesowen *Worc* 60-62; Lic to Offic 62-64 and 69-78; R Hagley 64-69; Warden Dioc Conf Cen *Ches* 69-78; Lic to Offic *B & W* 70-78; TR Sutton St Jas and Wawne *York* 78-99; rtd 99. *18 Cecil Road, Weston-super-Mare BS23 2HT* Tel (01934) 626299

DOHERTY, Thomas Alexander. b 48. Chich Th Coll 73. **d** 76 **p** 77. V Choral Derry Cathl *D & R* 76-79; C Llandaff w Capel Llanilltern *Llan* 79-80; PV Llan Cathl 80-84; V Penmark w Porthkerry 84-90; R Merthyr Dyfan 90-02; V Margam from 02. *Margam Vicarage, 59A Bertha Road, Margam, Port Talbot SA13 2AP* Tel (01639) 891067

DOIDGE, Charles William. b 44. Univ Coll Lon BSc65 MSc67 PhD72. EMMTC 93. **d** 93 **p** 94. NSM Blaby *Leic* 93-96; P-in-c Willoughby Waterleys, Peatling Magna etc from 96. *32 Peveril Road, Ashby Magna, Lutterworth LE17 5NG* Tel (01455) 209800
E-mail doidge@dmu.ac.uk

DOIDGE, Valerie Gladys. b 49. STETS 98. **d** 01. NSM St Leonards St Ethelburga *Chich* from 01. *6 Collinswood Drive, St Leonards-on-Sea TN38 0NU* Tel (01424) 425651

DOIG, Allan George. b 51. Univ of BC BA69 K Coll Cam BA73 MA80 PhD82 FSA98. Ripon Coll Cuddesdon 86. **d** 88 **p** 89. C Abingdon *Ox* 88-91; Chapl LMH Ox from 91; Fell from 96; Select Preacher *Ox* 95-96. *Lady Margaret Hall, Oxford OX2 6QA* Tel (01865) 274300 Fax 511069
E-mail allan.doig@lmh.ox.ac.uk

DOLAN, Miss Louise. b 68. St Paul's Cheltenham BA89 Reading Univ PGCE90. Aston Tr Scheme 92 Linc Th Coll 94 Westcott Ho Cam MA95. **d** 96 **p** 97. C N Stoneham *Win* 96-99. *Address temp unknown*

DOLBY, Mrs Christine Teresa. b 54. SRN80 Nottm Univ MA01. EMMTC 98. **d** 01 **p** 02. NSM Cropwell Bishop w Colston Bassett, Granby etc *S'well* from 01. *1 Granby Hill, Granby, Nottingham NG13 9PN* Tel (01949) 850127
E-mail chri270@aol.com

DOLL, Peter Michael. b 62. Yale Univ BA84 Ch Ch Ox DPhil89. Cuddesdon Coll BA94 DipMin95. **d** 95 **p** 96. C Cowley St Jo *Ox* 95-99; Chapl Worc Coll Ox 98-02; TV Abingdon *Ox* from 02. *39 The Motte, Abingdon OX14 3NZ* Tel (01235) 520297

DOLMAN, Derek Alfred George Gerrit. b 40. ALCD64. d 64
p 65. C St Alb St Paul *St Alb* 65-68; C Bishopwearmouth St Gabr
Dur 68-72; R Jarrow Grange 72-80; V New Catton St Luke *Nor*
80-98; V New Catton St Luke w St Aug 98-00; R S Croxton Gp
Leic from 00. *The Rectory, 19 Main Street, South Croxton,
Leicester LE7 3RJ* Tel (01664) 840245
DOMINIC MARK, Brother. *See* IND, Dominic Mark
DOMINY, Canon Peter John. b 36. Qu Coll Ox BA60 MA64 Aber
Univ MLitt83. Oak Hill Th Coll 60. d 62 p 63. C Bedworth *Cov*
62-66; Nigeria 67-84; Sudan United Miss 67-72; V Jos St Piran
72-84; R Broadwater St Mary *Chich* 84-92; TR 92-98; P-in-c
Danehill 98-99; V 99-03; Can and Preb Chich Cathl 93-03; RD
Uckfield 00-03; rtd 03. *5 St Nicholas Gardens, Durweston,
Blandford Forum DT11 0QH* Tel (01258) 450975
DOMMETT, Canon Richard Radmore. b 19. St Jo Coll Ox BA41
MA45. Wells Th Coll 41. d 43 p 44. C E Dulwich St Jo *S'wark*
43-48; C Peckham St Jo 48-52; V Clapham St Pet 52-60; R Caister
Nor 60-81; P-in-c Saxthorpe and Corpusty 81-85; P-in-c Oulton
SS Pet and Paul 81-85; P-in-c Blickling w Ingworth 81-85; P-in-c
Heydon w Irmingland 82-85; Hon Can Nor Cathl 77-85; rtd 85;
Perm to Offic *Nor* and *St E* from 85. *14 Norwich Road,
Halesworth IP19 8HN* Tel (01986) 873778
DOMMETT, Simon Paul. b 58. Warwick Univ BSc79. St Jo Coll
Nottm MA99. d 99 p 00. C Weston Favell *Pet* 99-02; P-in-c Gt w
Lt Harrowden and Orlingbury from 02. *The Vicarage, 18 Kings
Lane, Little Harrowden, Wellingborough NN9 5BL* Tel (01933)
678225 E-mail thedommetts@fish.co.uk
DONAGHY, Paul Robert Blount. b 56. Guildf Dioc Min Course
97. d 00 p 01. OLM Goldsworth Park *Guildf* from 00.
5 Knightswood, Woking GU21 3PU Tel (01483) 835503
DONALD, Andrew William. b 19. St Jo Coll Morpeth 47 ACT
ThL50. d 49 p 50. Australia 49-57; C St Pet Park Road Lon
57-58; Gothenburg *Eur* 58-65; Chapl Lausanne 65-68; Australia
from 68; rtd 84. *Eriswell, 18A Cobham Way, Westfield Park,
W Australia 6111* Tel (0061) (8) 9390 8425
DONALD, Brother. *See* GREEN, Donald Pentney
DONALD, Dennis Curzon. b 38. Oak Hill Th Coll 68. d 70 p 71. C
Carl St Jo *Carl* 70-73; Lic to Offic 73-77; Warden Blaithwaite Ho
Chr Conf Cen Wigton 73-98; Perm to Offic *Carl* from 77; Chapl
Eden Valley Hospice Carl 92-98; rtd 98. *Windyfell, Raughton
Head, Carlisle CA5 7DG* Tel (01697) 476246
DONALD, Robert Francis. b 49. St Jo Coll Nottm BTh75 LTh.
d 75 p 76. C New Barnet St Jas *St Alb* 75-79; C St Alb St Paul
79-86; C St Alb St Mary Marshalswick 86-87; Lic to Offic from
87; Dir Chr Alliance Housing Assn Ltd 87-98. *24 Meadowcroft,
St Albans AL1 1UD* Tel (01727) 841647
DONALD, Rosemary Anne. b 52. STETS 99. d 02 p 03. NSM
Blendworth w Chalton w Idsworth *Portsm* from 02. *3 Havant
Road, Horndean, Waterlooville PO8 0DB* Tel (023) 9259 1719
E-mail rdonald@fish.co.uk
DONALD, Steven. b 55. CertEd76. Oak Hill Th Coll BA88. d 88
p 89. C Cheadle All Hallows *Ches* 88-91; C Ardsley *Sheff* 91; V
Kendray 92-99; P-in-c Chadderton Ch Ch *Man* 99-03; V from
03. *Christ Church Vicarage, Block Lane, Chadderton, Oldham
OL9 7QB* Tel 0161-624 2326 E-mail stevedon1@aol.com
DONALD, William. b 30. Lon Univ DipTh61. Tyndale Hall Bris
58. d 61 p 62. C Stapenhill w Cauldwell *Derby* 61-63; Perm to
Offic *Ox* 63-66; Lic to Offic *Bris* 66-70; C Cheltenham St Mark
Glouc 70-77; C Glouc St Jas 77-82; Lic to Offic 82-95; rtd 95;
Perm to Offic *Glouc* from 95. *82 Forest View Road, Gloucester
GL4 0BY* Tel (01452) 506993
DONALDSON, Miss Elizabeth Anne. b 55. Univ of Wales (Ban)
BSc76 Surrey Univ MSc80 Nottm Univ BA82. St Jo Coll Nottm
DPS83. dss 83 d 87 p 94. Guildf Clch *Guildf* 83-86;
Cuddington 86-90; C 87-90; C Keresley and Coundon *Cov*
90-99; V Gt Amwell w St Margaret's and Stanstead Abbots
St Alb from 00; Perm to Offic *S'wark* from 00. *The Vicarage,
25 Hoddesdon Road, Stanstead Abbotts, Ware SG12 8EG* Tel
(01920) 870115 Pager 07666-545248
E-mail anne.donaldson@ntlworld.com
DONALDSON, Mrs Janet Elizabeth. b 53. GTCL74 Whitelands
Coll Lon CertEd75. EAMTC 95. d 98 p 99. NSM Tolleshunt
Knights w Tiptree and Gt Braxted *Chelmsf* 98-02; V Knights
and Hospitallers Par from 02. *The Rectory, Church Street, Great
Maplestead, Halstead CO9 2RG* Tel (01787) 463106
E-mail janet@amdonaldson.freeserve.co.uk
DONALDSON, Malcolm Alexander. b 48. Cranmer Hall Dur 84.
d 86 p 87. C Heworth H Trin *York* 86-89; Chapl York Distr Hosp
86-89; C Marfleet *York* 89-90; TV 90-96; R Collyhurst *Man* from
96. *The Rectory, Eggington Street, Collyhurst, Manchester
M40 7RN* Tel 0161-205 2808
DONALDSON, Maurice Coburne. b 19. Univ of Wales BA40
Lon Univ BD47. St Mich Coll Llan 41. d 42 p 43. C Blaenau
Ffestiniog *Ban* 42-44; C Conwy w Gyffin 44-47; C Llandysilio
47-49; P-in-c Llanfachraeth 49-53; V Ynyscynhaearn w
Penmorfa 53-57; V Ysbyty Ystwyth w Ystradmeurig *St D* 57-70;
V Ruabon *St As* 70-77; V Abergele 77-84; rtd 84; Perm to Offic
St As from 84; Perm to Offic *Ban* from 84. *7 Llys Mair, Bryn
Eithinog, Bangor LL57 2LA* Tel (01248) 354589

DONALDSON, Roger Francis. b 50. Jes Coll Ox BA71 MA75.
Westcott Ho Cam 72. d 74 p 75. C Mold *St As* 74-78; V Denio w
Abererch *Ban* 78-95; R Llanbeblig w Caernarfon and Betws
Garmon etc from 95. *The Rectory, 4 Ffordd Menai, Caernarfon
LL55 1LF* Tel (01286) 673750
DONALDSON, William Richard. b 56. St Cath Coll Cam BA78
MA81. Ridley Hall Cam 79. d 82 p 83. C Everton St Sav w
St Cuth *Liv* 82-85; C Reigate St Mary *S'wark* 85-89; V Easton H
Trin w St Gabr and St Lawr and St Jude *Bris* 89-99; V W Ealing
St Jo w St Jas *Lon* from 99. *23 Culmington Road, London
W13 9NJ* Tel (020) 8566 3507
DONCASTER, Archdeacon of. *See* FITZHARRIS, The Ven
Robert Aidan
DONCASTER, Suffragan Bishop of. *See* ASHTON, The Rt Revd
Cyril Guy
DONE, Mrs Margaret. b 43. LNSM course 84 Linc Th Coll 91.
d 92 p 94. OLM Coningsby w Tattershall *Linc* from 92. *43 Park
Lane, Coningsby, Lincoln LN4 4SW* Tel (01526) 343013
DONE, Nigel Anthony. b 68. Wye Coll Lon BSc89. St Jo Coll Dur
BA98. d 98 p 99. C Pilton w Croscombe, N Wootton and Dinder
B & W 98-02; R Hardington Vale from 02. *The Rectory, Vicarage
Lane, Norton St Philip, Bath BA3 6LY* Tel (01373) 834447
E-mail nigel.done@btinternet.com
DONEGAN-CROSS, Guy William. b 68. St Aid Coll Dur BA90.
Trin Coll Bris BA98. d 99 p 00. C Swindon Ch Ch *Bris* 99-03; V
Saltburn-by-the-Sea *York* from 03. *The Vicarage, Greta Street,
Saltburn-by-the-Sea TS12 1LS* Tel (01287) 622007
E-mail guy@donegan-cross.freeserve.co.uk
DONELLA, Mother. *See* MATHIE, Patricia Jean
DONKERSLEY, Mrs Christine Mary. b 44. STETS 98. d 01.
NSM Baltonsborough w Butleigh, W Bradley etc *B & W* from
01. *Pinewood, Church Street, Barton St David, Somerton
TA11 6BX* Tel (01458) 850695 Fax as telephone
E-mail cm.donkersley@route56.co.uk
DONKIN, Robert. b 50. Univ of Wales (Cardiff) DipTh74.
St Mich Coll Llan 71. d 74 p 75. C Mountain Ash *Llan* 74-77; C
Coity w Nolton 77-79; V Oakwood 79-84; V Aberaman and
Abercwmboi 84-91; V Aberaman and Abercwmboi w
Cwmaman 91-99; R Penarth w Lavernock from 99. *The Rectory,
13 Hickman Road, Penarth CF64 2AJ* Tel (029) 2070 9463
E-mail robert.donkin@ntlworld.com
DONNELLY, Trevor Alfred. b 71. K Coll Lon BA93 AKC93.
Cuddesdon Coll 94. d 97 p 98. C Southgate Ch Ch *Lon* 97-01; V
Hinchley Wood *Guildf* from 01. *The Vicarage, 98 Manor Road
North, Esher KT10 0AE* Tel (020) 8786 6391
E-mail fr.trev.blessed@virgin.net
DONOHOE, Olive Mary Rose. b 58. TCD BA79 BTh94 MA95
CPA83. CITC 91. d 95 p 96. C Bandon Union *C, C & R* 95-98; I
Mountmellick w Coolbanagher, Rosenallis etc *M & K* from 98.
The Rectory, Mountmellick, Portlaoise, Co Laois, Irish Republic
Tel (00353) (502) 24143 Fax as telephone E-mail revol@elive.ie
DONOVAN, Mrs Rosalind Margaret. b 48. Birm Univ LLB69
Bedf Coll Lon DASS73. St Alb and Ox Min Course 95. d 98
p 99. NSM Seer Green and Jordans *Ox* 98-03; P-in-c Wexham
from 03. *2 The Dell, Chalfont St Peter, Gerrards Cross SL9 0JA*
Tel (01494) 870039 E-mail rosdonovan@ntlworld.com
DONOVAN, Mrs Rosemary Ann. b 71. La Sainte Union Coll
BTh92 Birm Univ PGCE93. Qu Coll Birm MA01. d 01. C Kings
Heath *Birm* from 01. *14 All Saints Road, Kings Heath,
Birmingham B14 7LL* Tel 0121-444 2491
E-mail rosemary@donovan123.freeserve.co.uk
DONSON, Miss Helen Cripps. b 32. Somerville Coll Ox DipEd55
MA58. Dalton Ho Bris 58 Gilmore Ho 69. dss 79 d 87. Staines
St Pet *Lon* 80-83; Staines St Mary and St Pet 83-90; Par Dn 87-90;
Par Dn Herne Bay Ch Ch *Cant* 90-92; rtd 93; Hon Par Dn Bexhill
St Aug *Chich* 93-97; Perm to Offic from 97. *St Augustine's Close,
Cooden Drive, Bexhill-on-Sea TN39 3AZ* Tel (01424) 734640
DOODES, Peter John. b 45. STETS 98. d 01. NSM Ninfield
Chich from 01; NSM Hooe from 01. *Catslide, The Common,
Hooe, Battle TN33 9ET* Tel (01424) 892329 Mobile 07718-
302115 E-mail pjdoodes@hotmail.com
DOOGAN, Simon Edward. b 70. Univ of Wales (Abth) LLB92
Univ of Wales (Cardiff) LLM01 TCD BTh97. CITC 94. d 97
p 98. C Cregagh *D & D* 97-01; Dom Chapl to Bp Horsham
Chich from 01. *108 Clarence Road, Horsham RH13 5SG* Tel
(01403) 240129 *or* 242759 Mobile 07810-638748
DOOLAN, Leonard Wallace. b 57. St Andr Univ MA79 Ox Univ
BA82 MA88. Ripon Coll Cuddesdon 80. d 83 p 84. C High
Wycombe *Ox* 83-85; C Bladon w Woodstock 85-88; C Wootton
by Woodstock 85-88; P-in-c 88-90; C Kiddington w Asterleigh
85-88; P-in-c 88-90; P-in-c Glympton 88-90; R Wootton w
Glympton and Kiddington 90-91; TR Halesworth w Linstead,
Chediston, Holton etc *St E* 91-98; RD Halesworth 95-98; V
Ifield *Chich* from 98. *The Vicarage, Ifield, Crawley RH11 0NN*
Tel (01293) 520187 *or* 520843 Fax 537578
E-mail ifield_parish@lineone.net
DOORES, Peter George Herbert. b 46. DipYESTB71 Hull Univ
BSc67 Birm Univ PGCE68. Linc Th Coll 92. d 92 p 93. C N
Stoneham *Win* 92-96; V St Leonards and St Ives 96-03; P-in-c

Alton St Lawr from 03. *St Lawrence's Vicarage, Church Street, Alton GU34 2BW* Tel (01420) 83234

DORAN, Clive. b 58. St Jo Coll Nottm 99. **d** 01 **p** 02. C Maghull *Liv* from 01. *6 Deyes End, Maghull, Liverpool L31 6DP* Tel 0151-286 3063 E-mail revclive@yahoo.com

DORAN, Edward Roy. b 47. St Jo Coll Nottm. **d** 85 **p** 86. C Roby *Liv* 85-88; V Ravenhead from 88. *St John's Vicarage, Crossley Road, Ravenhead, St Helens WA10 3ND* Tel (01744) 23601

DORANS, Robert Marshall. b 47. Open Univ BA82 Ex Univ MEd85 Dur Univ MA96. **d** 01 **p** 02. OLM Longhorsley and Hebron *Newc* from 01. *14 The Grange, Nedderton Village, Bedlington NE22 6BQ* Tel (01670) 832022 *or* 534300 E-mail bdurans@tiscali.co.uk

DORBER, Canon Adrian John. b 52. St Jo Coll Dur BA74 K Coll Lon MTh91. Westcott Ho Cam 76. **d** 79 **p** 80. C Easthampstead *Ox* 79-85; P-in-c Emmer Green 85-88; Chapl Portsm Poly *Portsm* 88-92; Chapl Portsm Univ 92-97; Lect 91-97; Public Orator 92-97; Hon Chapl Portsm Cathl 92-97; P-in-c Brancepeth *Dur* 97-01; Dir Min and Tr 97-01; Hon Can Dur Cathl from 97; Dir Min and Tr from 01. *The Rectory, Brancepeth, Durham DH7 8EL,* or *Carter House, Pelaw Leazes Lane, Durham DH1 1TB* Tel 0191-378 0503 *or* 374 6012 Fax 384 7529 E-mail adrian.dorber@durham.anglican.org

DORCHESTER, Area Bishop of. *See* FLETCHER, The Rt Revd Colin William

DORÉ, Eric George. b 47. S Dios Minl Tr Scheme 87. **d** 90 **p** 91. NSM Hove Bp Hannington Memorial Ch *Chich* 90-92; C Burgess Hill St Andr 92-95; R Frant w Eridge 95-00; V Framfield from 00. *The Vicarage, Framfield, Uckfield TN22 5NH* Tel (01825) 890365 Fax 891064 E-mail ericdore@onetel.net.uk

DOREY, Trevor Eric. b 30. ACIS53. S Dios Minl Tr Scheme 87. **d** 90 **p** 91. NSM E Woodhay and Woolton Hill *Win* 90-96; P-in-c Manaccan w St Anthony-in-Meneage and St Martin *Truro* 96-99; rtd 99; Perm to Offic *Sarum* from 01. *Pear Tree House, 40 Saint Martin's, Marlborough SN8 1AS* Tel (01672) 511958

DORGU, Woyin Karowei. b 58. MB, BS85. Lon Bible Coll BA93 Oak Hill Th Coll DipHE95. **d** 95 **p** 96. C Tollington *Lon* 95-98; C Upper Holloway 98-00; TV from 00. *51 Tytherton Road, London N19 4PZ* Tel (020) 7272 5309 Fax as telephone E-mail karmos.timsim@virgin.net

DORKING, Archdeacon of. *See* WILSON, The Ven Mark John Crichton

DORKING, Suffragan Bishop of. *See* BRACKLEY, The Rt Revd Ian James

DORMANDY, Richard Paul. b 59. Univ Coll Lon BA81 St Edm Ho Cam BA88. Ridley Hall Cam 86. **d** 89 **p** 90. C Sydenham H Trin *S'wark* 89-93; V 93-01; V Westminster St Jas the Less *Lon* from 01. *56 Tachbrook Street, London SW1V 2NA* Tel (020) 7630 6282 E-mail richdorm@connectfree.co.uk

DORMER, Christopher Robert. b 39. Bris Univ BA61. Lich Th Coll 61. **d** 63 **p** 64. C Sheff Parson Cross St Cecilia *Sheff* 63-67; C Greenford H Cross *Lon* 67-69; Australia 69-74; Sec (Ireland) USPG 74-75; R Catton *York* 75-78; R Stamford Bridge Gp of Par 78-81; RD Pocklington 80-81; Itinerant Priest *Mor* 81-98; P-in-c Lochalsh 81-98; P-in-c Poolewe 81-98; P-in-c Ullapool 81-98; P-in-c Kishorn 81-98; Miss to Seamen 81-98; Can St Andr Cathl Inverness *Mor* 94-98; R Kelso *Edin* from 98. *The Rectory, Forestfield, Kelso TD5 7BX* Tel (01573) 224163 Fax 228924

DORMOR, Duncan James. b 67. Magd Coll Ox BA88 Lon Univ MSc89. Ripon Coll Cuddesdon BA94 DipMin95. **d** 95 **p** 96. C Wolverhampton *Lich* 95-98; Chapl St Jo Coll Cam 98-02; Fell and Dean from 02. *St John's College, Cambridge CB2 1TP* Tel (01223) 338633 E-mail djd28@cam.ac.uk

DORMOR, Preb Duncan Stephen. b 34. St Edm Hall Ox BA60. Cuddesdon Coll 60. **d** 62 **p** 63. C Headington *Ox* 62-66; USA 66-72; R Hertford St Andr *St Alb* 72-88; RD Hertford 77-83; TR Tenbury *Heref* 88-01; R Burford I 88-01; R Burford II w Greete and Hope Bagot 88-01; R Burford III w Lt Heref 88-01; V Tenbury St Mich 94-01; RD Ludlow 96-01; Preb Heref Cathl 99-02; C Tenbury 01-02; C Burford I 01-02; C Burford II w Greete and Hope Bagot 01-02; C Burford III w Lt Heref 01-02; C Tenbury St Mich 01-02; rtd 02; Perm to Offic *Heref* from 02. *Brantwood, Hereford Road, Leominster HR6 8JU* Tel (01568) 610897

DORRINGTON, Brian Goodwin. b 32. Leeds Univ CertEd55. St Deiniol's Hawarden 65. **d** 66 **p** 67. C Poynton *Ches* 66-71; Perm to Offic *Truro* 71-78; Hd Master Veryan Sch Truro 71-84; Hon C Veryan *Truro* 78-84; C N Petherwin 84-87; C Boyton w N Tamerton 84-87; TV Bolventor 87-90; R Kilkhampton w Morwenstow 90-97; RD Stratton 92-97; rtd 97; Perm to Offic *Truro* from 00. *Southcroft, 18 Elm Drive, Bude EX23 8EZ* Tel (01288) 352467

DORRINGTON, Richard Bryan. b 48. Linc Th Coll 79. **d** 81 **p** 82. C Stretely *Lich* 81-84; C Badger 84-85; R Ryton 84-85; R 85-88; C Beckbury 84-85; R 85-88; V Geddington w Weekley *Pet* 88-98; P-in-c Bradworthy *Ex* 98-00; P-in-c Abbots Bickington and Bulkworthy 98-00; R Bradworthy, Sutcombe, Putford etc from 00; RD Holsworthy from 99. *The Rectory,*

St Peterswell Lane, Bradworthy EX22 7TQ Tel (01409) 241411 E-mail therector@bradworthy.co.uk

DORSET, Archdeacon of. *See* MAGOWAN, The Ven Alistair James

DORSETT, Mark Richard. b 63. Univ of Wales (Lamp) BA84 MTh86 Birm Univ PhD90. Ripon Coll Cuddesdon 91. **d** 93 **p** 94. C Yardley St Edburgha *Birm* 93-96; Chapl K Sch Worc from 96; Min Can Worc Cathl *Worc* from 96. *12A College Green, Worcester WR1 2LH* Tel (01905) 25837

DOSSOR, John Haley. b 41. Leeds Univ BA62. EAMTC 87. **d** 90 **p** 91. NSM Hadleigh *St E* 90-01; P-in-c Ipswich St Mary at the Elms from 01. *The Vicarage, 68 Black Horse Lane, Ipswich IP1 2EF* Tel (01473) 216484 Mobile 07876-126676 E-mail haley@dossor.org

DOSSOR, Timothy Charles. b 70. Birm Univ BEng94. Ridley Hall Cam BTh99. **d** 99 **p** 00. C Ipswich St Jo *St E* 99-03; Asst Ldr Iwerne Holidays Titus Trust from 03. *c/o The Revd P E Bolton, 93 Morrell Avenue, Oxford OX4 1NQ* Tel 07748-184503 (mobile) E-mail tim@dossor.org

DOTCHIN, Andrew Steward. b 56. Federal Th Coll S Africa DipTh84. **d** 84 **p** 85. S Africa 84-01; C Standerton w Evender 84-87; Asst P St Martin's-in-the-Veld 87-89; R Belgravia St Jo the Divine 89-94; Chapl St Martin's Sch Rosettenville 94-01; TV Blyth Valley *St E* from 01. *The Vicarage, Beccles Road, Holton St Peter, Halesworth IP19 8NG* Tel and fax (01986) 874548 Mobile 07769-786152 E-mail andrew.dotchin@ntlworld.com

DOTCHIN, Canon Joan Marie. b 47. NEOC 84. **d** 87 **p** 94. C Newc St Gabr *Newc* 87-92; TD Willington Team 92-94; TV 94-95; TR from 95; Hon Can Newc Cathl from 01. *St Mary's Vicarage, 67 Churchill Street, Wallsend NE28 7TE* Tel 0191-262 8208 Fax 287 3178 E-mail revj.dotchin@goldserve.net

DOTY, Joseph Bonn. b 27. Woodstock Coll PhL51 STL58 Fordham Univ MA63. **d** 57 **p** 57. In RC Ch 57-70; USA 57-85; Prec St Ninian's Cathl Perth *St And* 85-88; R Church Brampton, Chapel Brampton, Harleston etc *Pet* 88-93; rtd 93; Perm to Offic *Sarum* from 93. *9 Kingsbury Square, Wilton, Salisbury SP2 0BA* Tel (01722) 744197

DOUBLE, Richard Sydney (Brother Samuel). b 47. K Coll Lon BD69 AKC69. St Aug Coll Cant 69. **d** 70 **p** 71. C Walton St Mary *Liv* 70-74; SSF from 75; Guardian Hilfield Friary Dorchester 92-01; Can and Preb Sarum Cathl *Sarum* 95-01; V Cambridge St Benedict *Ely* from 01. *St Francis House, 14 Botolph Lane, Cambridge CB2 3RD* Tel (01223) 353903 E-mail thebrothers@sstfrancis.freeserve.co.uk

DOUBTFIRE, Canon Barbara. b 39. LMH Ox BA61 MA65. **d** 91 **p** 94. Par Development Adv *Ox* from 88; NSM Kidlington w Hampton Poyle from 91; Hon Can Ch Ch from 98. *6 Meadow Walk, Woodstock OX20 1NR* Tel (01993) 810005 E-mail pdaoxf@oxford.anglican.org

DOUBTFIRE, Samuel. b 33. Edin Th Coll 63. **d** 66 **p** 66. C Knottingley *Wakef* 66-68; V Ripponden 68-76; V Crosthwaite Keswick *Carl* 76-81; V Barrow St Matt 81-87; R N Reddish *Man* 87-92; rtd 92; Perm to Offic *Bradf* from 92. *Greenacre, Station Road, Threshfield, Skipton BD23 5EP* Tel (01756) 752260

DOUGALL, David Brian. b 23. CBE. Oak Hill Th Coll. **d** 81 **p** 82. C Sandringham w W Newton *Nor* 81-83; P-in-c Fritton St Edm 83-84; R Somerleyton w Ashby 83-84; R Somerleyton w Ashby, Fritton and Herringfleet 84-92; rtd 92; Perm to Offic *Bris* from 92. *Somerley, The Green, Dauntsey, Chippenham SN15 4HY* Tel (01666) 510759

DOUGHTY, Andrew William. b 56. K Coll Lon BD AKC. Westcott Ho Cam 80. **d** 82 **p** 83. C Alton St Lawr *Win* 82-85; TV Basingstoke 85-91; V Chilworth w N Baddesley 91-95; R St Mary the Virgin Warwick Bermuda from 95. *PO Box WK 530, Warwick WK BX, Bermuda* Tel (001441) 236 5744 Fax 236 3667 E-mail adoughty@ibl.bm

DOUGLAS, Canon Alexander Joseph. b 18. TCD BA45 MA61. CITC 45. **d** 45 **p** 46. C Belfast St Mary *Conn* 45-49; I Connor St Sav 49-51; I Magheralin *D & D* 51-63; I Orangefield w Moneyreagh 63-86; rtd 86. *6 Rannoch Road, Holywood BT18 0NA* Tel (028) 9042 3661

DOUGLAS, Ann Patricia. b 49. Lon Univ CertEd71. Oak Hill NSM Course 85. **d** 88 **p** 94. Par Dn Chorleywood Ch Ch *St Alb* 88-94; V Oxhey All SS 94-02; TR Woodley *Ox* from 02. *The Rectory, 36 Church Road, Woodley, Reading RG5 4QJ* Tel 0118-969 2316 *or* 969 7956 Mobile 07885-022155 E-mail annidouglas@btopenworld.com

DOUGLAS, Anthony Victor. b 51. St Jo Coll Nottm 74. **d** 76 **p** 77. C Gt Crosby St Luke *Liv* 76-79; TV Fazakerley Em 79-84; TR Speke St Aid 84-90; TR Gt and Lt Coates w Bradley *Linc* 90-97; TR E Ham w Upton Park St Alb *Chelmsf* 97-02; R Holkham w Egmere w Warham, Wells and Wighton *Nor* from 02. *The Rectory, Church Street, Wells-next-the-Sea NR23 1JB* Tel (01328) 710107

DOUGLAS, Canon Archibald Sholto. b 14. TD50. Selw Coll Cam BA37 MA46. Wells Th Coll 38. **d** 47 **p** 48. C Macclesfield St Mich *Ches* 47-51; CF (TA) 49-64; C Ashton-upon-Mersey St Mary *Ches* 51-52; V Wharton 52-55; V Capesthorne w Siddington 55-69; P-in-c Marton 65-69; V Capesthorne w Siddington and

Marton 69-82; Hon Can Ches Cathl 78-82; rtd 82; Perm to Offic *Ches* from 82. *Monks Heath Hall Farm, Chelford, Macclesfield SK10 4SY* Tel (01625) 861154

DOUGLAS, Charles David. b 29. Leeds Univ BSc50. Linc Th Coll 68. **d 70 p** 71. C Royton St Anne *Man* 70-73; V Edenfield 73-83; V Spotland 83-88; P-in-c Calderbrook 88-95; P-in-c Shore 92-95; rtd 95; Perm to Offic *Man* from 95 and *Liv* from 00. *11 Harrison Crescent, Blackrod, Bolton BL6 5EX* Tel (01204) 667595

DOUGLAS, Ian Alexander. b 11. St Aug Coll Cant 71. **d 71 p** 72. C Palmers Green St Jo *Lon* 71-81; rtd 81; Perm to Offic *Lon* from 82. *105 The Chine, London N21 2EG* Tel (020) 8360 3472

DOUGLAS, Miss Janet Elizabeth. b 60. SS Paul & Mary Coll Cheltenham BEd83. Cranmer Hall Dur 88. **d 90 p** 94. Par Dn Yardley St Edburgha *Birm* 90-93; Par Dn Hamstead St Paul 93-94; C 94-00; Perm to Offic from 00. *14 Yateley Avenue, Birmingham B42 1JN* Tel 0121-358 0351

DOUGLAS, John Howard Barclay. b 23. St Jo Coll Dur BA48. Bps' Coll Cheshunt 48. **d 50 p** 51. C Hartlepool St Hilda *Dur* 50-53; C Woodhouse *Wakef* 53-55; PC Gateshead St Edm *Dur* 55-60; V Thirkleby w Kilburn and Bagby *York* 60-88; rtd 88; Perm to Offic *York* from 88. *6 St Giles Close, York Road, Thirsk YO7 3BU* Tel (01845) 524573

DOUGLAS, Martyn Graham. b 59. St Steph Ho Ox 85. **d 88 p** 89. C Stanmore *Win* 88-91; TV Basingstoke 91-94; USA from 94. *2509 Reabok Circle, Huntsville, AL 35803, USA* Tel (001) (205) 881 7041 *or* 534 7733 Fax 534 7733

DOUGLAS, Michael Williamson. b 51. Birm Univ BSc72 Liv Univ PGCE74. Trin Coll Bris 00. **d 02 p** 03. C Macclesfield Team Par *Ches* from 02. *7 Brackelehurst Way, Macclesfield SK10 2HY* Tel (01625) 617680 Mobile 07801-817061 E-mail mikedougie@yahoo.co.uk

DOUGLAS, Pamela Jean. *See* WELCH, Mrs Pamela Jean

DOUGLAS, Peter Melvyn. b 47. **d 96 p** 97. NSM Prestwick *Glas* 96-01; Chapl HM Pris Dovegate 01-03. *Address temp unknown*

DOUGLAS, Richard Norman Henry. b 37. St Alb and Ox Min Course 94. **d 97 p** 98. NSM Watercombe *Sarum* 97-02; rtd 02; Perm to Offic *Sarum* from 02. *15 Conway Drive, Broadmayne, Dorchester DT2 8EF* Tel (01305) 852574 E-mail douglasdn@ddougmail.freeserve.co.uk

DOUGLAS LANE, Charles Simon Pellew. b 47. BNC Ox MA71 Brooklands Tech Coll MCIPD79. Oak Hill Th Coll 91. **d 94 p** 95. C Whitton St Aug *Lon* 94-97; P-in-c Hounslow W Gd Shep 97-02; V from 02. *Good Shepherd House, 360 Beavers Lane, Hounslow TW4 6HJ* Tel (020) 8570 4035 E-mail goodshepherd5@thefreeinternet.co.uk

DOUGLASS, Preb Philip. b 48. Open Univ BA88. St Steph Ho Ox 87. **d 89 p** 90. C Peterlee *Dur* 89-92; V Crowan w Godolphin *Truro* 92-97; V Crowan w Treslothan from 98; P-in-c Penponds from 01; Preb St Endellion from 02. *Crowan Vicarage, 37 Trethannas Gardens, Praze, Camborne TR14 9NB* Tel (01209) 831009 Fax as telephone E-mail philip@thedouglasses.freeserve.co.uk

DOULIN, Patrick Brian Harry. b 36. Linc Th Coll 67. **d 70 p** 71. C Hurstpierpoint *Chich* 70-73; C Albourne 71-73; Australia 73-00; Papua New Guinea from 00. *PO Box 5845, Boroka, Papua New Guinea*

DOULL, Iain Sinclair. b 43. Univ of Wales (Cardiff) DPS88. St Mich Coll Llan 86. **d 88 p** 89. C Malpas *Mon* 88-91; P-in-c Newport All SS 91-98; V 98-02; V Newport Ch Ch from 02. *The Vicarage, Christchurch, Newport NP18 1JJ* Tel (01633) 420701

DOULTON, Dick. b 32. St Cath Coll Cam BA60 MA64. Ridley Hall Cam 61. **d 63 p** 64. C Gedling *S'well* 63-65; C Danbury *Chelmsf* 65; Lic to Offic *Ox* 89-90; Lic to Offic *L & K* from 90. *Ballygriffin, Kenmare, Killarney, Co Kerry, Irish Republic* Tel (00353) (64) 41743

DOULTON, Roderick John. b 55. Oak Hill Th Coll DipHE93. **d 93 p** 94. C Hoddesdon *St Alb* 93-96; P-in-c Caldecote All SS 96-98; P-in-c Old Warden 97-98; V Caldecote, Northill and Old Warden 98-99; TV Macclesfield Team Par *Ches* from 99; Chapl W Park Hosp Macclesfield from 99. *261 Oxford Road, Macclesfield SK11 8JY* Tel (01625) 423851 E-mail roddoulton@aol.com

DOVE, Canon Reginald George James Thomas. b 16. Leeds Univ BA38. Coll of Resurr Mirfield 38. **d 40 p** 41. C Blyth St Mary *Newc* 40-43; S Africa 43-52 and from 72; C Orlando and Pimville 43-47; P-in-c Pimville Miss Distr 47-52; Basutoland 52-66; Lesotho 66-72; R Leribe and Dir Hlotse Miss 52-72; Can Maseru 59-72; Asst P Kimberley Cathl 72-74; R Edenvale St Chad 74-88; rtd 88. *PO Box 2263, Edenvale, 1610 South Africa* Tel (0027) (11) 609 4257

DOVE, Richard. b 54. EMMTC DipHE99. **d 99 p** 00. NSM Dronfield w Holmesfield *Derby* from 99. *29 Hollins Spring Avenue, Dronfield S18 1RN* Tel (01246) 412502 E-mail rdove1553@aol.com

DOVER, Suffragan Bishop of. *See* VENNER, The Rt Revd Stephen Squires

DOW, Andrew John Morrison. b 46. Univ Coll Ox BA67 MA71. Oak Hill Th Coll 69. **d 71 p** 72. C Watford St Luke *St Alb* 71-74;

C Chadderton Ch Ch *Man* 75-78; V Leamington Priors St Paul *Cov* 78-88; V Knowle *Birm* 88-97; RD Solihull 95-97; V Clifton Ch Ch w Em *Bris* from 97. *16 Mortimer Road, Clifton, Bristol BS8 4EY* Tel 0117-974 3404 *or* 973 6524 E-mail andrew@christchurchclifton.org.uk

✠**DOW, The Rt Revd Geoffrey Graham.** b 42. Qu Coll Ox BA63 BSc65 MA68 MSc81 Birm Univ DPS74 Nottm Univ MPhil82. Clifton Th Coll 66. **d 67 p 68 c** 92. C Tonbridge SS Pet and Paul *Roch* 67-72; Chapl St Jo Coll Ox 72-75; Lect St Jo Coll Nottm 75-81; V Cov H Trin *Cov* 81-92; Can Th Cov Cathl 88-92; Area Bp Willesden *Lon* 92-00; Bp Carl from 00. *Rose Castle, Dalston, Carlisle CA5 7BZ* Tel (01697) 476274 Fax 476550 E-mail bishop.carlisle@carlislediocese.org.uk

DOWD, Canon Garfield George. b 60. QUB BSc TCD DipTh83. **d 86 p** 87. C Monkstown *D & G* 86-90; I Carlow w Urglin and Staplestown *C & O* from 90; Can Ossory Cathl from 96. *The Rectory, Green Road, Carlow, Irish Republic* Tel (00353) (59) 913 2565 E-mail garydowd@eircom.net *or* carlow@leighlin.anglican.org

DOWDEN, Gordon Frederick. b 25. Selw Coll Cam BA51 MA55. Chich Th Coll 51. **d 53 p** 54. C Salisbury St Mich *Sarum* 53-56; C St Neots *Ely* 56-58; C Gt w Lt Paxton and Toseland 56-58; R Hulme St Phil *Man* 58-70; R Hulme Ascension 70-78; RD Hulme 73-78; P-in-c Holybourne cum Neatham *Win* 78-82; RD Alton 79-82; C Man Resurr *Man* 82; AD Ardwick 82-90; C Man Gd Shep 82-91; Chapl Ancoats Hosp Man 85-90; rtd 91; Perm to Offic *Man* from 91. *41 Rozel Square, Manchester M3 4FQ* Tel 0161-832 5592

DOWDING, Clare. **d** 03. USA from 03. *240 Jennings Road, Cold Spring Harbor, NY 11724, USA* E-mail caedowding@hotmail.com

DOWDING, Edward Brinley. b 47. St Mich Coll Llan 70 St D Coll Lamp BA71. **d 72 p** 73. C Canton St Cath *Llan* 72-75; C Aberdare 75-78; V Aberavon H Trin 78-85; R Sully from 85; RD Penarth and Barry from 98. *The Rectory, 26 South Road, Sully, Penarth CF64 5TG* Tel (029) 2053 0221

DOWDING, Jeremy Charles. b 51. RMN72. St Steph Ho Ox 89. **d 91 p** 92. C Newport St Steph and H Trin *Mon* 91-94; C Risca 94-96; P-in-c Whitleigh *Ex* from 96. *The Vicarage, 17 Whitleigh Green, Plymouth PL5 4DD* Tel (01752) 773547

DOWDING, Stanley Frederick. b 10. ALCD32 St Jo Coll Dur BA33 LTh33. **d 34 p** 35. C Bris St Silas *Bris* 34-37; C Downend 37-39; C Portland All SS w St Pet *Sarum* 39-42; OCF 39-42; P-in-c Weston Mill *Ex* 42-46; V Preston St Luke *Blackb* 46-55; Chapl HM Pris Preston 51-52; V Nelson in Lt Marsden *Blackb* 55-75; Chapl Reedyford Hosp 64; RD Burnley 68-70; RD Pendle 70-75; rtd 75; Lic to Offic *Blackb* 76-93; Perm to Offic from 93. *4 Hillside Avenue, Reedley, Burnley BB10 2NF* Tel (01282) 693030

DOWDLE, Canon Cynthia. b 48. Cranmer Hall Dur 88. **d 90 p** 94. C Allerton *Liv* 90-94; TR Halewood 94-00; V Knowsley from 00; Dean of Women's Min from 01; Hon Can Liv Cathl from 01. *The Vicarage, Tithebarn Road, Prescot L34 0JA* Tel 0151-546 4266 E-mail cynthiadowdle@hotmail.com

DOWDY, Simon Mark Christopher. b 67. Trin Hall Cam BA89 MA93. Wycliffe Hall Ox 93. **d 96 p** 97. C Beckenham Ch Ch *Roch* 96-00; C St Helen Bishopsgate w St Andr Undershaft etc *Lon* from 00; P-in-c St Botolph without Aldersgate from 02. *22 Chisenhale Road, London E3 5QZ* Tel (020) 8981 6360

DOWIE, Canon Winifred Brenda McIntosh. b 57. Callendar Park Coll of Educn Falkirk DipEd78 Trin Coll Bris ADPS96. BA91. **d 92 p** 94. Par Dn Downend *Bris* 92-94; C 94-95; Chapl Asst Southmead Health Services NHS Trust 95-98; Chapl St Pet Hospice Bris from 98; Hon Can Bris Cathl *Bris* from 02. *St Peter's Hospice, St Agnes Avenue, Knowle, Bristol BS4 2DU* Tel 0117-977 4605 *or* 915 9462 Fax 915 9473

DOWLAND, Martin John. b 48. Lon Univ BD70 Southn Univ PGCE71. Wycliffe Hall Ox 75. **d 77 p** 78. C Jesmond Clayton Memorial *Newc* 77-80; C Chadderton Ch Ch *Man* 80-85; R Haughton St Mary from 85. *Haughton Green Rectory, Meadow Lane, Denton, Manchester M34 1GD* Tel 0161-336 4529 Fax as telephone E-mail mdowland@aol.com

DOWLEN, Edward Mark. b 25. DLC47 Cranfield Inst of Tech MSc49. St Jo Coll Dur 79. **d 79 p** 80. C Rhyl w St Ann *St As* 79-82; C Warton St Paul *Blackb* 83-90; rtd 90; Lic to Offic *Sarum* from 90; Lic to Offic *Mor* from 93. *33 Hythe Road, Poole BH15 3NN* Tel (01202) 737699 *or* 770636

DOWLEN, Isabella McBeath. b 45. Man Univ CertEd86 Bournemouth Univ DMS91. STETS DipTh99. **d 99 p** 01. NSM Branksome St Aldhelm *Sarum* from 99. *33 Hythe Road, Poole BH15 3NN* Tel (01202) 737699 *or* 770636

DOWLER, Robert Edward Mackenzie. b 67. Ch Ch Ox BA89 Selw Coll Cam BA93. Westcott Ho Cam 91. **d 94 p** 95. C Southgate Ch Ch *Lon* 94-97; C Somers Town 97-01; Tutor and Dir Past Th St Steph Ho Ox from 01; Vice Prin from 03. *St Stephen's House, 16 Marston Street, Oxford OX4 1JX* Tel (01865) 247874 Fax 794338

DOWLING, Donald Edward. b 43. St Jo Coll Dur DipTh74 St Andr Univ MA66. **d 74 p** 75. C Thame w Towersey *Ox* 74-77; C Norton *St Alb* 77-80; V Wilbury 81-99; V Stevenage St Nic and

Graveley from 99. *St Nicholas House, 2A North Road, Stevenage SG1 4AT* Tel (01438) 354355
E-mail dondowling@strayduck.com

DOWLING, Kingsley Avery Paul. b 60. Open Univ BA Leeds Univ DipM91. Aston Tr Scheme 93 Ripon Coll Cuddesdon DipMin97. d 97 p 98. C Headingley *Ripon* 97-99; C Far Headingley St Chad 99-01; V Wortley de Leeds from 01. *Wortley Vicarage, Dixon Lane Road, Leeds LS12 4RU* Tel 0113-263 8867
E-mail kd@homeuser1.freeserve.co.uk

DOWLING, Paul Martin. b 55. ACA G&C Coll Cam MA79. Cranmer Hall Dur 88. d 90 p 91. C Redhill St Jo *S'wark* 90-94; V Wakef St Jo *Wakef* from 94. *St John's Vicarage, 65 Bradford Road, Wakefield WF1 2AA* Tel (01924) 371029 Fax as telephone

DOWMAN, Peter Robert. b 52. City Univ BSc76. Wycliffe Hall Ox 82. d 84 p 85. C Cheltenham Ch Ch *Glouc* 84-87; C Danbury *Chelmsf* 87-90; R Woodham Ferrers and Bicknacre 90-95; Consultant E England CPAS 95-03; R Warboys w Broughton and Bury w Wistow *Ely* from 03. *The Rectory, 15 Church Road, Warboys, Huntingdon PE28 2RJ* Tel (01487) 824612
E-mail pdowman@bigfoot.com

DOWN, Martin John. b 40. Jes Coll Cam BA62 MA68. Westcott Ho Cam 63. d 65 p 66. C Bury St Mary *Man* 65-68; C Leigh St Mary 68-70; R Fiskerton *Linc* 70-75; V Irnham w Corby 75-79; RD Beltisloe 76-84; P-in-c Creeton w Swinstead 78-79; P-in-c Swayfield 78-79; V Corby Glen 79-84; Good News Trust 84-88; Perm to Offic *Linc* 84-88; *Pet* 86-88; P-in-c Ashill w Saham Toney *Nor* 88-94; R 94-00; C Watton w Carbrooke and Ovington from 00. *43 Cressingham Road, Ashill, Thetford IP25 7DG* Tel (01760) 440363 Fax as telephone

DOWN, Peter Michael. b 54. K Coll Lon BD78 AKC. Coll of Resurr Mirfield 78. d 79 p 80. C Swindon Ch Ch *Bris* 79-82; C Southmead 82-84; TV Cannock *Lich* 84-92; V Coleford w Holcombe *B & W* 92-01; Hon C Westfield from 01. *19 Wesley Avenue, Radstock, Bath BA3 3XA* Tel (01761) 436774

DOWN, The Ven Philip Roy. b 53. R Melbourne Inst of Tech Dip Applied Science 76 Hull Univ MA93. Melbourne Coll of Div BTh82 MTh88. d 89 p 89. C Gt Grimsby St Mary and St Jas *Linc* 89-91; TV 91-95; R Hackington *Cant* 95-02; AD Cant 99-02; Adn Maidstone from 02. *The Old Rectory, The Street, Pluckley, Ashford TN27 0QT* Tel (01233) 840291 Fax 840759
E-mail pdown@archdeacmaid.org

✠**DOWN, The Rt Revd William John Denbigh.** b 34. St Jo Coll Cam BA57 MA61 FNI91. Ridley Hall Cam 57. d 59 p 60 c 90. C Fisherton Anger *Sarum* 59-63; Miss to Seamen 63-90; Australia 71-74; Dep Gen Sec Miss to Seamen 75; Gen Sec 76-90; Hon C Gt Stanmore *Lon* 75-90; Chapl St Mich Paternoster Royal 76-90; Perm to Offic *St Alb* 78-90; Hon Can Gib Cathl *Eur* 85-90; Hon Can Kobe Japan from 87; Bp Bermuda 90-95; Asst Bp Leic 95-01; P-in-c Humberstone 95-01; P-in-c Thurnby Lodge 01; rtd 01; Hon Asst Bp Ox from 01. *54 Dark Lane, Witney OX28 6LX* Tel (01993) 706615

DOWN AND DROMORE, Bishop of. *See* MILLER, The Rt Revd Harold Creeth

DOWN, Archdeacon of. *See* McCAMLEY, The Ven Gregor Alexander

DOWN, Dean of. *See* DINNEN, The Very Revd John Frederick

DOWNER, Barry Michael. b 58. STETS 99. d 02. NSM Shanklin St Sav *Portsm* from 02; NSM Lake from 02. *3 Yarborough Terrace, St John's Road, Wroxall, Ventnor PO38 3ED* Tel (01983) 855970 Fax as telephone

DOWNER, Cuthbert John. b 18. S'wark Ord Course 60. d 74 p 75. Hon C Kirdford *Chich* 74-76; C Halesworth w Linstead and Chediston *St E* 76-79; P-in-c Knodishall w Buxlow 79-80; P-in-c Friston 79-80; R Bacton w Wyverstone 80-83; P-in-c Cotton and Wickham Skeith 80-83; R Bacton w Wyverstone and Cotton 83-84; rtd 84; Perm to Offic *St Alb* 84-87; *B & W* 88-95 and 97-98. *6 The Maples, Princes Road, Shepton Mallet BA4 5HL* Tel (01749) 344102

DOWNES, Gregory Charles. b 69. Roehampton Inst BSc91 Hughes Hall Cam PGCE92. Wycliffe Hall Ox BA95. d 96 p 97. C Hazlemere *Ox* 96-99; Chapl HM Pris Ashfield 99-01; Lect Lon Bible Coll from 01; Perm to Offic *St Alb* from 01. *London Bible College, Green Lane, Northwood HA6 2UW* Tel (01923) 456000 Fax 456001 E-mail gregdownes@email.com

DOWNES, Richard John. b 63. Cranmer Hall Dur CTM94. d 94 p 95. C Bishopwearmouth St Gabr *Dur* 94-97; CF from 97. *c/o MOD Chaplains (Army)* Tel (01980) 615804 Fax 615800

DOWNEY, Canon John Stewart. b 38. QUB CertEd60 Open Univ BA76. Oak Hill Th Coll 63. d 66 p 67. C Londonderry St Aug *D & R* 66-71; I Dungiven w Bovevagh 71-82; Bp's Dom Chapl 75-82; V Bishopwearmouth St Gabr *Dur* 82-91; V New Malden and Coombe *S'wark* from 91; Hon Can S'wark Cathl from 97; RD Kingston from 00. *The Vicarage, 93 Coombe Road, New Malden KT3 4RE* Tel (020) 8942 0915

DOWNHAM, Canon Peter Norwell. b 31. Man Univ BA52. Ridley Hall Cam 54. d 56 p 57. C Cheadle *Ches* 56-62; V Rawtenstall St Mary *Man* 62-68; Chapl Rossendale Gen Hosp 62-68; V Denton Holme *Carl* 68-79; V Reading Greyfriars *Ox* 79-95; Hon Can Ch Ch 90-95; rtd 95; Hon C Cotehill w

Cumwhinton *Carl* 95-00; Perm to Offic from 98. *19 The Green, Dalston, Carlisle CA5 7QB* Tel (01228) 711850

DOWNHAM, Simon Garrod. b 61. Solicitor 87 K Coll Lon LLB84. Wycliffe Hall Ox BA93 DipMin94. d 94 p 95. C Brompton H Trin w Onslow Square St Paul *Lon* 94-99; P-in-c Hammersmith St Paul from 00. *14 Lena Gardens, London W6 7PZ* Tel 020-7603 9662 *or* 8748 3855
E-mail simon.downham@stph.org.uk

DOWNIE, James Hubert. b 23. DL. Barrister 58 FRSA70. d 92 p 93. NSM Stornoway *Arg* 92-94; C Leverburgh 92-94; P-in-c from 94. *Dunarin, Strond, Isle of Harris HS5 3UD* Tel (01859) 520247 E-mail rosechess@clara.net

DOWNING, Francis Gerald. b 35. Qu Coll Ox BA56 MA60. Linc Th Coll. d 58 p 59. C Filwood Park CD *Bris* 58-60; Tutor Linc Th Coll 60-64; V Unsworth *Man* 64-80; Tutor N Ord Course 80-82; Vice-Prin 82-90; V Bolton SS Simon and Jude *Man* 90-97; rtd 97; Perm to Offic *Blackb* from 97. *33 Westhoughton Road, Chorley PR7 4EU* Tel (01257) 474240

DOWNS, Caroline Rebecca. b 58. UWIST BA80 Univ of Wales (Cardiff) PGCE81. St Mich Coll Llan 98. d 02 p 03. C Roath *Llan* from 02. *6 Newminster Road, Roath, Cardiff CF23 5AP* Tel (029) 2049 5699 E-mail carolinerebecca.downs@btinternet.com

DOWNS, Miss Geinor. b 47. UEA BA72 Southn Univ BTh89. Chich Th Coll 85. d 87 p 94. Par Dn Wellingborough All SS *Pet* 87-89; Development Officer Chich Th Coll 89-92; C Durrington *Chich* 92-95; Chapl City Hosp NHS Trust Birm from 95. *Chaplaincy Department, City Hospital NHS Trust, Dudley Road, Birmingham B18 7QH* Tel 0121-554 3801 ext 4055 Fax 523 0951

DOWNS, Ivan Frederick. b 26. Chich Th Coll 65. d 66 p 67. C Corbridge w Halton *Newc* 66-70; C Tynemouth Ch Ch 70-74; V Walker 74-79; V Dudley 79-89; V Weetslade 90-91; rtd 91; Perm to Offic *Newc* from 91. *East Cottage, Stannersburn, Hexham NE48 1DD* Tel (01434) 240471

DOWNS, John Alfred. b 58. MIBiol80 CBiol80 Leic Univ BSc79 PGCE80. EMMTC 90. d 93 p 94. NSM Barlestone *Leic* 93-96; NSM Markfield 96-99; NSM Thornton, Bagworth and Stanton 96-99; NSM Markfield, Thornton, Bagworth and Stanton etc from 99. *29 Meadow Road, Barlestone, Nuneaton CV13 0JG* Tel (01455) 290195

DOWSE, Edgar. b 10. Dur Univ LTh35 Lon Univ BD37 Fitzw Coll Cam BA72 MA74 Lon Univ MPhil90. Clifton Th Coll 32 Cen Sch of Religion MA ThD. d 36. Asst Chapl and Tutor Clifton Th Coll 35-36; C Chippenham St Andr w Tytherton Lucas *Bris* 36-40; Tutor St Andr Th Coll Whittlesford 40-41; C Bournemouth St Mich *Win* 41-45; P-in-c Bournemouth H Epiphany 45-51; R Freemantle 51-57; V Bethnal Green St Bart *Lon* 57-71; Lect Lon Bible Coll 60-61; Lect St Mich Cornhill 60-63; St Steph Walbrook 65-68; P-in-c Acton Green St Alb *Lon* 71-72; V 72-75; rtd 75; Perm to Offic *Lon* 75-96. *87 College Road, Isleworth TW7 5DP* Tel (020) 8568 2548

DOWSE, Ivor Roy. b 35. ARHistS MRSL. St Deiniol's Hawarden 66. d 68 p 70. C Harrow St Pet *Lon* 68-69; C Sudbury St Andr 69-71; C Weeke *Win* 71-73; Min Can Ban Cathl *Ban* 73-78; V Hollym w Welwick and Holmpton *York* 78-81; R Bearwood *Ox* 81-82; P-in-c Rothesay *Arg* 83-86; C Boxmoor St Jo *St Alb* 86-92; Hon C Cowes H Trin and St Mary *Portsm* 92-94; Perm to Offic 94-98; P-in-c St Hilary w Perranuthnoe *Truro* 98-00; rtd 01. *14 Close Famman, Port Erin, Isle of Man IM9 6BJ* Tel (01624) 837392

DOWSETT, Alan Charles. b 27. Selw Coll Cam BA51 MA55 Bris Poly CQSW76. Cuddesdon Coll 51. d 53 p 54. C Portsea St Mary *Portsm* 53-57; C Wokingham All SS *Ox* 57-60; V Water Orton *Birm* 60-64; Chapl Colston's Sch Bris 64-65; C Stoke Bishop *Bris* 65-68; Lic to Offic 69-89; rtd 89. *23 Upper Cranbrook Road, Bristol BS6 7UW* Tel 0117-924 3227

DOWSETT, Ian Peter. b 71. Liv Univ BA95 Lon Inst of Educn PGCE96. Wycliffe Hall Ox BA01. d 02. C Kensington St Helen w H Trin *Lon* from 02. *St Francis House, Dalgarno Way, London W10 5EL* Tel (020) 8968 4733 Mobile 07985-726465
E-mail irdowsett@talk21.com

DOWSETT, Marian Ivy Rose. b 40. d 88 p 97. NSM Rumney *Mon* 88-94; C St Mellons and Michaelston-y-Fedw 94-96; C St Mellons from 96. *114 Ridgeway Road, Rumney, Cardiff CF3 4AB* Tel (029) 2079 2635

DOWSON, Roger Christopher. b 32. Clifton Th Coll 60. d 63 p 64. C Virginia Water *Guildf* 63-66; C Darfield *Sheff* 66-68; V Thorpe Edge *Bradf* 68-80; V Wyke 80-91; rtd 91; Hon C Coley *Wakef* from 91; Perm to Offic *Bradf* 93-99. *1 Windsor Villas, Norwood Green, Halifax HX3 8QS* Tel (01274) 674557

DOWSON, Simon Paul. b 63. Bris Univ BSc85 Cam Univ PGCE89. Cranmer Hall Dur 95. d 97 p 98. C Bradf St Aug Undercliffe *Bradf* 97-99; C Werrington *Pet* from 99. *44 Woodhall Rise, Peterborough PE4 5BU* Tel (01733) 323146
E-mail sifi@dowzim.fsnet.co.uk

DOXSEY, Roy Desmond. b 41. St D Coll Lamp 64. d 67 p 68. C Pembroke St Mary w St Mich *St D* 67-70; C Milford Haven 70-73; C Loughton *Ox* 73-75; Chapl Llandovery Coll 75-81 and 92-96; Zambia 81-86; Chapl Epsom Coll 86-92; V Roath

St German *Llan* from 96. *St Germans Vicarage, Metal Street, Roath, Cardiff CF24 0LA* Tel (029) 2049 4488

DOYE, Andrew Peter Charles. b 64. BNC Ox BA85. Trin Coll Bris BA93. **d** 93 **p** 94. C Surbiton St Matt *S'wark* 93-96; C Bourne *Guildf* 96-99; C The Bourne and Tilford 99-00; R Wheathampstead *St Alb* from 00. *The Rectory, Old Rectory Gardens, Wheathampstead, St Albans AL4 8AD* Tel (01582) 833144 E-mail andrewdoye@hotmail.com

DOYLE, Canon Alan Holland. b 22. JP72. Lon Univ BD55 Birm Univ MA86 Buckingham Univ DPhil93. Wycliffe Hall Ox 52. **d** 52 **p** 53. C Braddan *S & M* 52-54; C Douglas St Geo 54-55; R Oldham St Andr *Man* 55-59; Chapl Ruzawi Prep Sch S Rhodesia 59-62; V Chaddesley Corbett *Worc* 62-66; CF (TA) 63-67; V Kidderminster St Jo *Worc* 66-67; R Salwarpe 67-74; RD Droitwich 69-78; P-in-c Himbleton w Huddington 74-78; Hon Can Worc Cathl 74-87; P-in-c Ombersley w Doverdale 78-83; R 83-87; rtd 87; Perm to Offic *Worc* from 87. *3 Graham Court, Graham Road, Malvern WR14 2HX* Tel (01684) 891816

DOYLE, Andrew Michael. b 63. K Coll Lon BD85 AKC85. Ripon Coll Cuddesdon 86. **d** 88 **p** 89. C Lytchett Minster *Sarum* 88-92; TV Kirkby *Liv* 92-97; V Rotherhithe H Trin *S'wark* from 97; RD Bermondsey from 00. *Holy Trinity Vicarage, Bryan Road, London SE16 1HE* Tel (020) 7237 3963

DOYLE, Brian William. b 31. FRSH. Sarum Th Coll 87. **d** 87 **p** 88. NSM Heene *Chich* 87-91; Chapl Qu Alexandra's Hosp Worthing 89-91; C W Tarring *Chich* 91-93; C Hangleton 93-95; rtd 95; Perm to Offic *Chich* from 96. *56A Langdale Gardens, Hove BN3 4HH* Tel (01273) 727910

DOYLE, Edward Michael. b 70. Univ of Wales (Cardiff) DipTh91. St Mich Coll Llan BTh93. **d** 94 **p** 95. C Sketty *S & B* 94-96; C Llwynderw 96-00; R Rogate w Terwick and Trotton w Chithurst *Chich* from 00. *The Vicarage, Fyning Lane, Rogate, Petersfield GU31 5EE* Tel (01730) 821576

DOYLE, Graham Thomas. b 48. St Barn Coll Adelaide ThL73 ThSchol77 Worc Coll Ox BA85 MA90. **d** 73 **p** 74. Australia 73-83; Perm to Offic *Ox* 83-85; C Cobbold Road St Sav w St Mary *Lon* 86; P-in-c Bradf St Oswald Chapel Green *Bradf* 86-91; Chapl Belgrade w Zagreb *Eur* 91-93; Chapl Belgrade 93-97; Taiwan 97-00; I Killeshandra w Killegar and Derrylane *K, E & A* from 00. *The Rectory, Killeshandra, Co Cavan, Irish Republic* Tel (00353) (49) 433 4098 E-mail gtdoylekilleshandra@kilmore.anglican.org

DOYLE, Nigel Paul. b 55. MHort(RHS)82. St Mich Coll Llan 00. **d** 03. NSM Treboeth *S & B* from 03; NSM Landore from 03. *3 Ael-y-Bryn, Penclawdd, Swansea SA4 3LF* Tel (01792) 850659 E-mail tadnigel@yahoo.co.uk

DOYLE, Robin Alfred. b 43. Dur Univ BA65. Westcott Ho Cam 66. **d** 68 **p** 69. C Edgbaston St Geo *Birm* 68-70; C Erdington St Barn 70-73; P-in-c Oldbury 73-81; R Maker w Rame *Truro* from 81. *The Vicarage, Fore Street, Torpoint PL10 1NB* Tel (01752) 822302

DOYLE, Mrs Tracey Elizabeth. b 58. Open Univ BA00. St Alb and Ox Min Course 94. **d** 97 **p** 98. OLM Winslow w Gt Horwood and Addington *Ox* 97-99; C from 00. *53 Spring Lane, Great Horwood, Milton Keynes MK17 0QP* Tel (01296) 714319 Mobile 07976-980093

DRACKLEY, John Oldham. b 36. Em Coll Cam BA57 MA61. Wells Th Coll 57. **d** 59 **p** 60. C Eckington *Derby* 59-62; C Lee Gd Shep w St Pet *S'wark* 62-63; C Derby St Thos *Derby* 63-67; C Matlock and Tansley 67-77; P-in-c Radbourne 77-82; P-in-c Dalbury, Long Lane and Trusley 77-82; P-in-c Longford 77-82; Sec Dioc Cttee for Care of Chs 82-98; rtd 95; Perm to Offic *Derby* from 98. *26 Highfield Drive, Matlock DE4 3FZ* Tel (01629) 55902

DRAFFAN, Prof Ian William. b 42. FBCS77 CEng88 Aston Univ BSc65 MSc66. N Ord Course 83. **d** 86 **p** 87. NSM Millhouses H Trin *Sheff* from 86. *8 Silverdale Crescent, Sheffield S11 9JH* Tel 0114-236 4523

DRAIN, Walter. b 39. JP75. Open Univ BA76 ACP66. NW Ord Course 76. **d** 79 **p** 80. NSM Cheadle *Ches* 79-81; C 81-84; V Chatburn *Blackb* 84-02; Sub Chapl HM Pris Preston 94-02; rtd 02; Perm to Offic *Blackb* from 02. *Angels, 28 The Croft, Euxton, Chorley PR7 6LH* Tel (01257) 249646

DRAKE, Frances. b 43. Brentwood Coll of Educn TCert67 Sussex Univ BEd74 Birkbeck Coll Lon DipRS93. S'wark Ord Course 90. **d** 93 **p** 94. NSM Fryerning w Margaretting *Chelmsf* 93-01; P-in-c Mountnessing St Giles from 01; P-in-c Margaretting St Marg from 01; P-in-c Buttsbury St Mary from 01. *Little Pump House, Ongar Road, Kelvedon Hatch, Brentwood CM15 0LA* Tel (01277) 364383 Fax as telephone E-mail revfrances.drake@tiscali.co.uk

DRAKE, Graham. b 46. Linc Th Coll 81. **d** 83 **p** 85. C Alford w Rigsby *Linc* 83-84; Perm to Offic *Wakef* 84-85; Hon C Purston cum S Featherstone 85-89; NSM Castleford All SS 89-92; C Cudworth 92-95. *Flat 3, Woodland House, 5 Mill Hill, Pontefract WF8 4HR* Tel (01977) 708713 or 683324

DRAKE, Canon Graham Rae. b 45. Fitzw Coll Cam BA68 MA72. Qu Coll Birm 70. **d** 73 **p** 74. C New Windsor *Ox* 73-77; TV 77-78; P-in-c Bath Ascension *B & W* 78-81; TV Bath Twerton-on-Avon 81-86; P-in-c Buxton w Oxnead *Nor* 86-90; P-in-c Lammas w Lt Hautbois 86-90; RD Ingworth 88-94; R Buxton w Oxnead, Lammas and Brampton 90-95; P-in-c Cockley Cley w Gooderstone 95-01; P-in-c Gt and Lt Cressingham w Threxton 95-01; P-in-c Didlington 95-01; P-in-c Hilborough w Bodney 95-01; P-in-c Oxborough w Foulden and Caldecote 95-01; P-in-c Mundford w Lynford 99-01; P-in-c Ickburgh w Langford 99-01; P-in-c Cranwich 99-01; Hon Can Nor Cathl from 99; V Thorpe St Matt from 01. *St Matthew's Vicarage, Albert Place, Norwich NR1 4JL* Tel (01603) 620820 E-mail gdrake@freeuk.com

DRAKE, John Paul. b 19. Qu Coll Ox BA41 MA44. Cuddesdon Coll 46. **d** 47 **p** 48. C Stepney St Dunstan and All SS *Lon* 47-54; V Brighton All So *Chich* 54-59; Chapl St Edw Sch Ox 59-69; V Stewkley *Ox* 69-75; V Stewkley w Soulbury and Drayton Parslow 75-85; RD Mursley 77-83; rtd 85; Perm to Offic *St Alb* from 85. *3 The Cloisters, Welwyn Garden City AL8 6DU* Tel (01707) 325379

DRAKE, Leslie Sargent. b 47. Boston Univ BA69 MTh72 Hull Univ BPhil74 Anglia Poly Univ MSc93. Coll of Resurr Mirfield 78. **d** 78 **p** 79. C Oldham *Man* 78-81; TV Rochdale 81-83; V Palmers Green St Jo *Lon* 83-89; St Mary's Sch Cheshunt 89-91; Hd RE St Mary's Sch Hendon 91-99; TV Wimbledon *S'wark* 99-03; V Clay Hill St Jo and St Luke *Lon* from 03. *St Luke's Vicarage, 92 Browning Road, Enfield EN2 0HG* Tel (020) 8363 6055

DRAKELEY, Stephen Richard Francis. b 51. Aston Univ BSc73. Chich Th Coll 76. **d** 76 **p** 77. C Yardley Wood *Birm* 76-79; V Rednal 79-89; TV Bodmin w Lanhydrock and Lanivet *Truro* 89-99; P-in-c Falmouth All SS from 99. *All Saints' Vicarage, 72 Dracaena Avenue, Falmouth TR11 2EN* Tel and fax (01326) 317474 E-mail srfd@compuserve.com

DRAPER, The Ven Alfred James. b 23. Natal Univ BA50. St Aug Coll Cant DipTh59 St Paul's Coll Grahamstown LTh54. **d** 54 **p** 54. S Africa 54-63 and 75-87; V Tile Cross *Birm* 63-72; V Olton 72-75; Adn Durban 79-87; R S Ferriby *Linc* 87-93; V Horkstow 87-93; R Saxby All Saints 87-93; rtd 93; Perm to Offic *Ches* from 93. *4 Rugby Close, Macclesfield SK10 2HW* Tel (01625) 619033

DRAPER, Charles James. b 59. Dur Univ BSc80 Cam Univ BA86. Ridley Hall Cam 84. **d** 87 **p** 88. C Wareham *Sarum* 87-90; C Maltby *Sheff* 90-93; R The Claydons *Ox* 93-99; R Chinnor w Emmington and Sydenham etc 99-02; P-in-c Gt Faringdon w Lt Coxwell from 02. *The Vicarage, Coach Lane, Faringdon SN7 8AB* Tel (01367) 240106 E-mail 6drapers@cdraper.fslife.co.uk

DRAPER, Derek Vincent. b 38. Linc Th Coll 65. **d** 68 **p** 69. C Orpington All SS *Roch* 68-72; C Bramley *Guildf* 72-74; P-in-c Kempston *St Alb* 74-76; Min Kempston Transfiguration CD 77-79; V Kempston Transfiguration 79-84; RD Bedford 79-84; V Bromham w Oakley 84-88; P-in-c Stagsden 84-88; V Bromham w Oakley and Stagsden 88-03; RD Elstow 00-02; Chapl Bromham Hosp 84-03; rtd 03. *24 Wilkinson Close, Eaton Socon, St Neots PE19 8HJ* Tel (01480) 384031

DRAPER, Elizabeth Ann. See BRADLEY, Mrs Elizabeth Ann

DRAPER, Ivan Thomas. b 32. FRCP FRCPGlas Aber Univ MB, ChB56. St Jo Coll Nottm 87. **d** 90 **p** 91. NSM Glas St Bride *Glas* from 90; P-in-c 96-97. *1311 Whistlefield Court, 2 Canniesburn Road, Bearsden, Glasgow G61 1PX* Tel 0141-943 0954 E-mail murieldra@clara.net

DRAPER, Jean Margaret. b 31. **d** 80 **p** 97. NSM Pontnewydd *Mon* 80-83; BRF 82-83; NSM Llantilio Pertholey w Bettws Chpl etc *Mon* 83-94; NSM Newport St Andr 94-03. *Govilon House, Merthyr Road, Govilon, Abergavenny NP7 9PT* Tel (01873) 830380

DRAPER, John William. b 54. Aston Tr Scheme 86 Qu Coll Birm 88. **d** 90 **p** 91. C Stepney St Dunstan and All SS *Lon* 90-94; C Leigh Park *Portsm* 94-96; C Warren Park 94-96; R Rowner from 96. *The Rectory, 174 Rowner Lane, Gosport PO13 9SU* Tel and fax (023) 9258 1834 *or* 9258 7934 Mobile 07802-730742 E-mail smrowner@netscapeonline.co.uk

DRAPER, Canon Jonathan Lee. b 52. Gordon Coll Mass BA76 St Jo Coll Dur BA78 PhD84. Ripon Coll Cuddesdon 83. **d** 83 **p** 84. C Baguley *Man* 83-85; Dir Academic Studies Ripon Coll Cuddesdon 85-92; V Putney St Mary *S'wark* 92-00; Can Res York Minster *York* from 00. *3 Minster Court, York YO1 7JJ* Tel (01904) 625599 E-mail jonathan@draperyork.fsnet.co.uk

DRAPER, Canon Martin Paul. b 50. OBE98. Birm Univ BA72 Southn Univ BTh79. Chich Th Coll 72. **d** 75 **p** 76. C Primrose Hill St Mary w Avenue Road St Paul *Lon* 75-78; C Westmr St Matt 79-84; Chapl Paris St Geo *Eur* 84-02; Adn France 94-02; Can Gib Cathl 94-02. *25 rue Vicq D'azir, 75010 Paris, France*

DRAPER, Patrick Hugh. b 43. S Dios Minl Tr Scheme 91. **d** 94 **p** 95. NSM Boscombe St Jo *Win* 94-99; P-in-c Southbourne St Chris 99-02; rtd 02. *82 Tuckton Road, Bournemouth BH6 3HT* Tel (01202) 420190

DRAPER, Canon Paul Richard. b 64. Glas Univ MA87 TCD BTh90. **d** 90 **p** 91. C Drumragh w Mountfield *D & R* 90-94; I Ballydehob w Aghadown *C, C & R* from 94; Can Cork and Ross

Cathls from 98; Bp's Dom Chapl from 99. *The Rectory, Ballydehob, Co Cork, Irish Republic* Tel (00353) (28) 37117

DRAPER, Raymond James. b 48. Ex Coll Ox BA70 MA75 Em Coll Cam BA73 MA78. Ridley Hall Cam 71. **d** 74 **p** 75. C Sheff Manor *Sheff* 74-78; Ind Chapl 78-82; R Wickersley 82-00; V Leytonstone St Jo *Chelmsf* from 00. *St John's Vicarage, 44 Hartley Road, London E11 3BL* Tel (020) 8257 2792

DRAPER, Mrs Sylvia Edith. b 39. ARCM60. N Ord Course 86. **d** 89 **p** 94. C Aughton St Mich *Liv* 89-92; Par Dn Wigan St Jas w St Thos 92-94; Asst Chapl Wigan and Leigh Health Services NHS Trust 92-97; C Wigan St Jas w St Thos *Liv* 94-97; TV Walton-on-the-Hill 97-02; rtd 02. *6 Brookfield Lane, Aughton, Ormskirk L39 6SP* Tel (01695) 422138

DRAX, Elizabeth Margaret. *See* ANSON, Mrs Elizabeth Margaret

DRAY, John. b 66. St Chad's Coll Dur BSc87. St Steph Ho Ox BTh95. **d** 95 **p** 96. C Byker St Ant *Newc* 95-98; C Cullercoats St Geo 98-01; P-in-c Platt *Roch* from 01; Chapl to the Deaf from 01. *The Vicarage, Comp Lane, Platt, Sevenoaks TN15 8NR* Tel and fax (01732) 885482 Mobile 07931-514834 E-mail john.dray@bigfoot.com

DRAYCOTT, John. b 53. Sheff Univ BA84 Dip Community Educn 82. Br Isles Nazarene Coll DipTh77 Linc Th Coll 85. **d** 85 **p** 86. In Wesleyan Reform Union 77-82; C Wombwell *Sheff* 85-87; V W Bessacarr 87-92; V Erith Ch Ch *Roch* from 92; P-in-c Erith St Jo 92-95. *Christ Church Vicarage, Victoria Road, Erith DA8 3AN* Tel (01322) 334729 Fax as telephone

DRAYCOTT, John Edward. b 54. EMMTC 99. **d** 01 **p** 02. C Calverton *S'well* from 01; C Epperstone from 01; C Gonalston from 01; C Oxton from 01. *21 Dunhelm Avenue, Calverton, Nottingham NG14 6NN* Tel 0115-910 3675

DRAYCOTT, Philip John. b 27. Sarum & Wells Th Coll. **d** 83 **p** 84. C Bishop's Cleeve *Glouc* 83-86; V Chedworth, Yanworth and Stowell, Coln Rogers etc 86-93; rtd 94; Perm to Offic *B & W* from 94. *April Cottage, Newton Road, North Petherton, Bridgwater TA6 6NA* Tel (01278) 662487

DRAYSON, Nicholas James Quested. b 53. Keble Coll Ox BA75 MA83. Wycliffe Hall Ox DipTh83. **d** 79 **p** 79. SAMS Argentina 79-82 and 92-00; Pastor Tartacal and Chapl to Chorote Indians 79-82; P-in-c Seville Ascension Spain 83-91; Adn Andalucia 89-91; Translations Co-ord 92-98; Pastor Salta St Andr 92-98; C Beverley Minster *York* from 00. *38 Highgate, Beverley HU17 0DN* Tel (01482) 862656 E-mail nickd@fish.co.uk

DRAYTON, James Edward. b 30. St Deiniol's Hawarden 81. **d** 84 **p** 86. Hon C Heald Green St Cath *Ches* 84-88; C Bollington St Jo 88-92; P-in-c Lt Leigh and Lower Whitley 92-96; P-in-c Aston by Sutton 92-96; P-in-c Antrobus 92-96; rtd 96; Perm to Offic *York* from 96. *87 Wharfedale, Filey YO14 0DP*

DREDGE, David John. b 32. Cranmer Hall Dur 69. **d** 71 **p** 72. C Goole *Sheff* 71-74; P-in-c Eastoft 74-77; V Whitgift w Adlingfleet 74-77; V Whitgift w Adlingfleet and Eastoft 77-78; V Walkley 78-81; TV Bicester w Bucknell, Caversfield and Launton *Ox* 81-86; V N Brickhill and Putnoe *St Alb* 86-90; P-in-c Sarratt 90-95; rtd 95; Perm to Offic *Lich* from 95. *19 Waterdale, Wombourne, Wolverhampton WV5 0DH* Tel (01902) 897467

DREDGE, David Julian. b 36. ALA74 Sheff Univ BA59. Cranmer Hall Dur 61 Ban Ord Course 85. **d** 87 **p** 88. NSM Dwygyfylchi *Ban* 87-92; R Llanllechid 92-97; rtd 97; Perm to Offic *Ban* from 97. *Westfield, Treforris Road, Penmaenmawr LL34 6RH* Tel (01492) 623439 Mobile 07721-941861 Fax 0870-056 7258 E-mail djd-emd-chrstn.demon.co.uk

DREW, Gerald Arthur. b 36. Bps' Coll Cheshunt 59. **d** 61 **p** 62. C Lyonsdown H Trin *St Alb* 61-67; C Tring 67-71; R Bramfield w Stapleford and Waterford 71-78; V Lashleybury St Paul 78-90; P-in-c Hormead, Wyddial, Anstey, Brent Pelham etc 90-95; V 95-01; rtd 01; Perm to Offic *St Alb* and *St E* from 01. *33 The Glebe, Lavenham, Sudbury CO10 9SN* Tel (01787) 248133

DREW, Joseph Harold. b 09. St D Coll Lamp BA30. St Mich Coll Llan 30. **d** 32 **p** 33. C Blaenavon w Capel Newydd *Mon* 32-35; C Roath St Sav *Llan* 35-38; C Newport St Jo Bapt *Mon* 38-39; V 39-50; Chapl HM Borstal Feltham 50-55; Chapl HM Pris Man 55-58; Chapl HM Pris Pentonville 58-64; Chapl and Sec Pris Chapl Coun 64-74; Asst Chapl Gen of Pris 64-74; rtd 74; Perm to Offic *S'wark* from 82. *50 Kingsley Court, Pincott Road, Bexleyheath DA6 7LA* Tel (020) 8298 1216

DREW, Michael Edgar Cecil. b 31. Oriel Coll Ox BA55 MA59. St Steph Ho Ox 55. **d** 57 **p** 58. C Plymouth St Pet *Ex* 57-63; Missr Pemb Coll Cam Miss Walworth 63-67; Asst Chapl All Hallows Sch Rousdon 67-75; Chapl 80-81; Chapl Ex Sch 81-83; V Scraptoft *Leic* 83-97; V Hungarton 83-87; P-in-c Leic St Eliz Nether Hall 87-97; rtd 97. *28 St Mary's Paddock, Wellingborough NN8 1HJ* Tel (01933) 277407

DREW, Canon Rosemary. b 43. SRN64. EAMTC 90. **d** 93 **p** 94. NSM Gt Dunmow *Chelmsf* 93-96; NSM Gt Dunmow and Barnston from 96; Hon Can Chelmsf Cathl from 01. *The Bowling Green, 8 The Downs, Dunmow CM6 1DT* Tel (01371) 872662 Fax as telephone E-mail bruce.drew@btinternet.com

DREW, Simon Mark. b 68. Liv Univ BEng89 CEng94 MICE94. St Jo Coll Nottm MA98 DipMM99. **d** 99 **p** 00. C Torquay St Matthias, St Mark and H Trin *Ex* 99-03; V Marshfield w Cold Ashton and Tormarton etc *Bris* from 03. *The Vicarage, Church Lane, Marshfield, Chippenham SN14 8NT* Tel (01225) 891850 E-mail simon@smdrew.freeserve.co.uk

DREWERY, Graeme Robert. b 66. FRCO89 St Jo Coll Cam BA88 MA92 PhD94. Linc Th Coll MDiv94. **d** 94 **p** 95. C Paston *Pet* 94-97; C Cottingham *York* 97-00; V Middlesbrough St Jo the Ev from 00. *St John's Vicarage, 45 Lothian Road, Middlesbrough TS4 2HS* Tel (01642) 242926

DREWETT, Canon Mervyn Henry. b 27. Wadh Coll Ox BA50 MA53. Linc Th Coll 52. **d** 54 **p** 55. C Filwood Park CD *Bris* 54-58; C Bishopston 58-61; V Brislington St Chris 61-67; V Henbury 67-80; RD Westbury and Severnside 79-80; TR Gtr Corsham 80-94; Hon Can Bris Cathl 80-94; RD Chippenham 82-88; rtd 94; Perm to Offic *Bris* and *Sarum* from 94. *14 The Beeches, Shaw, Melksham SN12 8EP* Tel (01225) 702726

DREYER, Rodney Granville. b 55. Lon Univ MPhil91 AKC91. St Paul's Coll Grahamstown DipTh81. **d** 81 **p** 82. S Africa 81-84 and 94-98; NSM Headstone St Geo *Lon* 84-86; NSM Northolt St Mary 86-87; C Portsea St Mary *Portsm* 87-90; V Sudbury St Andr *Lon* 90-94; Adn W and S Free State 94-95; V Hawkhurst *Cant* from 98. *The Vicarage, Hawkhurst, Cranbrook TN18 4QB* Tel (01580) 753397 E-mail rodneydreyer@onetel.net.uk

DRISCOLL, Canon David. b 42. Lon Univ BSc64 Nottm Univ DipTh69. Linc Th Coll 68. **d** 71 **p** 72. C Walthamstow St Jo *Chelmsf* 71-76; Chapl NE Lon Poly 71-79; C-in-c Plaistow St Mary 76-79; P-in-c Stratford St Jo and Ch Ch w Forest Gate St Jas 79-89; V Theydon Bois 89-01; RD Epping Forest 92-01; Hon Can Chelmsf Cathl 01; C All Hallows by the Tower etc *Lon* from 01. *159 Wapping High Street, London E1W 3NQ* Tel (020) 7481 0901

DRIVER, Arthur John Roberts. b 44. FCIPA73 SS Coll Cam MA70 Nottm Univ DipTh75. Linc Th Coll 73. **d** 76 **p** 77. C S'wark H Trin w St Matt *S'wark* 76-80; TV N Lambeth 80-85; CMS 85-92; Sri Lanka 86-92; V Putney St Marg *S'wark* 92-97; V Streatham St Paul from 97. *St Paul's Vicarage, 63 Chillerton Road, London SW17 9BE* Tel (020) 8672 5536 E-mail ajrdriver@btinternet.com

DRIVER, Bruce Leslie. b 42. Lon Univ LLB73 Nottm Univ DipTh77. Linc Th Coll 76. **d** 78 **p** 79. C Dunstable *St Alb* 78-81; TV 81-86; V Rickmansworth 86-98; RD Rickmansworth 91-98; V Northwood Hills St Edm *Lon* from 98. *St Edmund's Vicarage, 2 Pinner Road, Northwood HA6 1QS* Tel (020) 8866 9230

DRIVER, Geoffrey. b 41. Chich Th Coll 86. **d** 88 **p** 89. C Pontefract St Giles *Wakef* 88-91; V Glass Houghton 91-97; Chapl Pontefract Hosps NHS Trust 97-99; R Southwick H Trin *Dur* from 99. *St Cuthbert's Vicarage, 28 Rotherham Road, Sunderland SR5 5QS* Tel 0191-549 1261 E-mail fathergeoff@lineone.net

DRIVER, Geoffrey Lester. b 59. Liv Poly BA83. Chich Th Coll 86. **d** 89 **p** 90. C Walton St Mary *Liv* 89-92; C Walton-on-the-Hill 92; C Selsey *Chich* 92-95; V Cowfold from 95. *The Vicarage, Cowfold, Horsham RH13 8AH* Tel (01403) 864296

DRIVER, Gordon Geoffrey. b 32. Garnett Coll Lon Dip Teaching59. Trin Coll Bris. **d** 95 **p** 96. NSM Radipole and Melcombe Regis *Sarum* 95-03; rtd 03; Perm to Offic *Sarum* from 03. *11 Greenway Close, Weymouth DT3 5BQ* Tel (01305) 812784

DRIVER (née FRENCH), Janet Mary. b 43. Leeds Univ BA65 PGCE66 Surrey Univ BA98 Lon Univ DipArch99. Linc Th Coll 74. **dss** 78 **d** 92 **p** 94. Hon C N Lambeth *S'wark* 80-85; St Paul's Cathl *Lon* 80-82; Miss Partner CMS 86-92; Sri Lanka 86-92; NSM Putney St Marg *S'wark* 92-97; Hon C Streatham St Paul from 97. *St Paul's Vicarage, 63 Chillerton Road, London SW17 9BE* Tel (020) 8672 5536

DRIVER, Canon Penelope May. b 52. N Ord Course. **d** 87 **p** 94. Dioc Youth Adv *Newc* 86-88; C Cullercoats St Geo 87-88; Youth Chapl *Ripon* 88-96; Dioc Adv Women's Min from 91; Asst Dir of Ords 96-98; Dioc Dir of Ords from 98; Min Can Ripon Cathl from 96; Hon Can from 98. *The Parish House, 16 Orchard Close, Sharow, Ripon HG4 5BE* Tel (01765) 607017 E-mail pdrvr@globalnet.co.uk

DRIVER, Roger John. b 64. Trin Coll Bris BA88. **d** 90 **p** 91. C Much Woolton *Liv* 90-93; C Fazakerley Em 93-94; TV 94-00; P-in-c Bootle St Matt from 00; P-in-c Litherland St Andr from 00; P-in-c Bootle St Leon from 00. *The Vicarage, 70 Merton Road, Bootle L20 7AT* Tel 0151-922 1315

DROMORE, Archdeacon of. *See* CHILLINGWORTH, The Ven David Robert

DROMORE, Dean of. *See* LOWRY, The Very Revd Stephen Harold

DROWLEY, Arthur. b 28. Oak Hill Th Coll 54. **d** 56 **p** 57. C Longfleet *Sarum* 56-59; C Wallington H Trin *S'wark* 59-62; V Taunton St Jas *B & W* 62-73; RD Taunton N 72-73; V Rodbourne Cheney *Bris* 73-87; R Bigbury, Ringmore and Kingston *Ex* 87-94; rtd 94; Perm to Offic *Ex* 94-02 and *Man* from 03. *166 Platt Lane, Manchester M14 7PY* Tel 0161-224 6776

DROWN, Richard. b 19. BNC Ox BA41 MA43. Wycliffe Hall Ox 41. **d** 42 **p** 43. C St Helens St Helen *Liv* 42-45; Chapl K Coll Budo Uganda 46-65; Hd Master St Andr Sch Turi Kenya 65-73; Hd Master Edin Ho Sch New Milton 73-84; rtd 84; Hon C Brockenhurst *Win* from 85. *3 Waters Green Court, Brockenhurst SO42 7QR* Tel (01590) 624038

DRUCE, Brian Lemuel. b 31. ARICS55 MRICS01. Bps' Coll Cheshunt 58. **d** 60 **p** 61. C Whitton St Aug *Lon* 60-63; C Minehead *B & W* 63-66; R Birch St Agnes *Man* 66-70; V Overbury w Alstone, Teddington and Lt Washbourne *Worc* 70-81; Ind Chapl 81-91; rtd 91; Perm to Offic *Worc* from 91. *Park Cottage, Elmley Castle, Pershore WR10 3HU* Tel (01386) 710577 E-mail brian.druce@talk21.com

DRUCE, John Perry. b 34. ALCM86 Em Coll Cam BA57 MA61 Lambeth STh97. Wycliffe Hall Ox 57. **d** 59 **p** 60. C Wednesbury St Bart *Lich* 59-62; C Bushbury 62-64; C Walsall Wood 64-74; R Farnborough *Roch* 74-87; R E Bergholt *St E* 87-99; P-in-c Bentley w Tattingstone 95-99; rtd 99. *9 Fullers Close, Hadleigh, Ipswich IP7 5AS* Tel (01473) 827242

DRUMMOND, Canon Christopher John Vaughan. b 26. Magd Coll Ox MA51 Magd Coll Cam MA56. Ridley Hall Cam 51. **d** 53 **p** 54. C Barking St Marg *Chelmsf* 53-56; Tutor Ridley Hall Cam 56-59; Lic to Offic *Ely* 57-62; Chapl Clare Coll Cam 59-62; Nigeria 63-69; V Walthamstow St Jo *Chelmsf* 69-74; P-in-c Stantonbury *Ox* 74-75; R 75-84; P-in-c Ducklington 84-88; Dioc Ecum Officer 84-88; Can Ibadan from 87; Home Sec Gen Syn Bd for Miss and Unity 88-91; rtd 91; P-in-c Colton *Lich* 91-94; Perm to Offic 94-99; *Guildf* from 97. *77 Markham Road, Capel, Dorking RH5 5JT* Tel (01306) 712637 Mobile 07966-518681

DRUMMOND, John Malcolm. b 44. Nottm Univ CertEd65. Edin Th Coll 68. **d** 71 **p** 72. C Kirkholt *Man* 71-74; C Westleigh St Pet 74-76; Hd of RE Leigh High Sch from 76; Lic Preacher from 76; Hon C Leigh St Jo 84-90; Hon C Tonge Moor from 90. *14 Bull's Head Cottages, Turton, Bolton BL7 0HS* Tel (01204) 852232 E-mail sdrummond@deanery.wigan.sch.uk

DRUMMOND, Josceline Maurice Vaughan. b 29. Lon Univ DipTh59 BD70. Wycliffe Hall Ox 55. **d** 58 **p** 59. C Tunbridge Wells St Jo *Roch* 58-60; C Walthamstow St Mary *Chelmsf* 60-62; V Oulton *Lich* 62-68; V Leyton St Cath *Chelmsf* 71-85; Gen Dir CMJ 85-94; Public Preacher *St Alb* 88-94; rtd 94; Perm to Offic *St Alb* from 94. *3 Fryth Mead, St Albans AL3 4TN* Tel (01727) 857620

DRURY, Anthony Desmond. b 42. Liv Poly FTC63. Nor Ord Course. **d** 99 **p** 00. NSM New Ferry *Ches* from 99. *61 Church Road, Bebington, Wirral CH63 3DZ* Tel 0151-334 4797

DRURY, Mrs Carol. b 61. SRN83. Trin Coll Bris 00. **d** 01 **p** 02. NSM Soundwell *Bris* from 01. *33 Syston Way, Bristol BS15 1UE* Tel 0117-961 1890 E-mail its-mrs-d@drury28@freeserve.co.uk

DRURY, Mrs Caroline. b 60. St Alb and Ox Min Course 00. **d** 03. C Leavesden All SS *St Alb* from 03. *44 Haydon Road, Watford WD19 4DD* Tel (01923) 236894 E-mail caroline.drury@btinternet.com

DRURY, The Very Revd John Henry. b 36. Trin Hall Cam MA66. Westcott Ho Cam 61. **d** 63 **p** 64. C St John's Wood *Lon* 63-66; Chapl Down Coll Cam 66-69; Chapl Ex Coll Ox 69-73; Can Res Nor Cathl *Nor* 73-79; Vice-Dean 78-79; Lect Sussex Univ 79-81; Dean and Chapl K Coll Cam 81-91; Dean Ch Ch *Ox* from 91. *The Deanery, Christ Church, Oxford OX1 1DP* Tel (01865) 276161 E-mail jan.bolongaro@christ-church.ox.ac.uk

DRURY, Michael Dru. b 31. Trin Coll Ox BA55 MA59. Wycliffe Hall Ox DipTh57. **d** 58 **p** 59. C Fulham St Mary N End *Lon* 58-62; C Blackheath St Jo *S'wark* 62-64; Chapl and Asst Master Canford Sch Wimborne 64-80; Chapl and Teacher Fernhill Manor Sch New Milton 80-81; P-in-c Stowe *Ox* 82-92; Asst Master Stowe Sch Bucks 82-92; R Rampton w Laneham, Treswell, Cottam and Stokeham *S'well* 92-96; rtd 96; Perm to Offic *Sarum* from 96. *Tanfield, Giddylake, Wimborne BH21 2QT* Tel (01202) 881246

DRURY, Richard Alexander. b 63. Lon Univ BD85 Avery Hill Coll PGCE86 ACII91. Trin Coll Bris MA00. **d** 00 **p** 01. C Kingswood *Bris* from 00. *33 Syston Way, Bristol BS15 1UE* Tel 0117-961 1890 E-mail richard@drury86.freeserve.co.uk

DRURY, Valerie Doreen. b 40. MBATOD80 Univ of Wales (Cardiff) BA62 K Coll Lon PGCE63 Lon Inst of Educn ADEDC80. Oak Hill Th Coll 85. **d** 87 **p** 94. NSM Becontree St Alb *Chelmsf* 87-89; NSM Becontree S from 89. *63 Tilney Road, Dagenham RM9 6HL* Tel (020) 8592 7285

DRYDEN, Barry Frederick. b 44. Chester Coll of HE BTh00. N Ord Course 97. **d** 00 **p** 01. C Formby St Pet *Liv* 00-03; V Woolston from 03. *The Vicarage, 20 Warren Lane, Woolston, Warrington WA1 4ES* Tel (01925) 813083 E-mail barjan@fish.co.uk

DRYDEN, Canon Leonard. b 29. MIEE59 MIMechE59 Lon Univ BD64 Bath Univ MSc73. Ridley Hall Cam. **d** 61 **p** 62. C Luton w E Hyde *St Alb* 61-65; C-in-c Bedminster *Bris* 65-74; Bp's Soc and Ind Adv 65-74; Chapl Bris Cathl 66-70; Hon Can Bris Cathl 70-74; Dir CORAT 74-76; Sec from 76; Team Ldr and Convener Lon Ind Chapl *Lon* 77-85; V Frindsbury w Upnor *Roch* 85-91; rtd 91; P-in-c Sevenoaks Weald *Roch* 91-95; Perm to

Offic *Win* from 95. *1 King Alfred Terrace, Winchester SO23 7DE* Tel (01962) 852170

DRYE, Douglas John. b 37. Man Univ BSc61. Clifton Th Coll. **d** 63 **p** 64. C Whalley Range St Edm *Man* 63-66; C Drypool St Columba w St Andr and St Pet *York* 66-68; V Worsbrough Common *Sheff* 68-86; R Armthorpe 86-92; rtd 92; Perm to Offic *Pet* from 92. *25 Willow Crescent, Oakham LE15 6EQ* Tel (01572) 770429

DUBLIN (Christ Church), Dean of. See PATERSON, The Very Revd John Thomas Farquhar

DUBLIN (St Patrick's), Dean of. See MacCARTHY, The Very Revd Robert Brian

DUBLIN, Archbishop of, and Bishop of Glendalough. See NEILL, The Most Revd John Robert Winder

DUBLIN, Archdeacon of. See LINNEY, The Ven Gordon Charles Scott

DUCE, Canon Alan Richard. b 41. St Pet Coll Ox BA65 MA68 Enfield Poly CQSW75. Cuddesdon Coll 65. **d** 67 **p** 68. C Boston *Linc* 67-71; Chapl St Geo Hosp Lon 71-73; Hon C Harringay St Paul *Lon* 73-75; Chapl HM Pris Pentonville 75-76; Chapl HM Pris The Verne 76-81; Chapl HM Pris Linc 81-03; Gen Preacher *Linc* 81; rtd 03; Can and Preb Linc Cathl *Linc* from 02; Ed *Justice Reflections* from 02; Perm to Offic from 03. *2 Temple Gardens, Lincoln LN2 1NP* Tel (01522) 529468 Fax 514831 E-mail alanduce@hotmail.com

DUCK, Mrs Jacqueline. b 44. Chester Coll of HE BTh00 ACMA70. N Ord Course 97. **d** 00 **p** 01. NSM Ormskirk *Liv* from 00. *17 Westhaven Crescent, Aughton, Ormskirk L39 5EN* Tel and fax (01695) 423436 Mobile 07811-938441 E-mail jackie@17westhaven.freeserve.co.uk

DUCKETT, Canon Brian John. b 45. ALCD70. **d** 70 **p** 71. C S Lambeth St Steph *S'wark* 70-73; C Norwood St Luke 73-75; C Bushbury *Lich* 75-77; TV 77-79; V Dover St Martin *Cant* 79-92; TR Swindon Dorcan *Bris* 92-00; RD Highworth 95-99; Hon Can Bris Cathl from 98; V Clifton H Trin, St Andr and St Pet from 00. *Holy Trinity Vicarage, 6 Goldney Avenue, Bristol BS8 4RA* Tel 0117-973 4751

DUCKETT, Ms Helen Lorraine. b 71. Keble Coll Ox BA92 Sheff Univ MA94 Birm Univ MPhil98. Qu Coll Birm 95. **d** 98 **p** 99. C Cannock *Lich* 98-01; TV Wednesfield from 01. *St Chad's Vicarage, 157 Stubby Lane, Wolverhampton WV11 3NE* Tel (01902) 732763 E-mail duckett.h@tinyworld.co.uk

DUCKETT, John Dollings. b 41. Nottm Univ BA62 BTh81. Linc Th Coll 79. **d** 81 **p** 82. C Boston *Linc* 81-84; V Baston 84-86; V Langtoft Gp 86-88; V Sutterton and Wigtoft 88-89; R Sutterton w Fosdyke and Algarkirk 89-92; P-in-c Chapel St Leonards w Hogsthorpe 92-97; V 97-00; V Bracebridge from 00. *The Vicarage, 60 Chiltern Road, Lincoln LN5 8SE* Tel (01522) 532636

DUCKETT, Keith Alexander. b 69. Worc Coll of Educn BA93 Birm Univ BD97 MA98. Qu Coll Birm 95. **d** 98 **p** 99. C Willenhall H Trin *Lich* 98-01; TV Blakenall Heath 01-03; Asst Chapl Sandwell Health Care NHS Trust from 03. *Sandwell General Hospital, Lyndon, West Bromwich B71 4HJ* Tel 0121-553 1831 *or* (01902) 732763 E-mail keith.duckett@swbh.nhs.uk *or* duckettk@fish.co.uk

DUCKETT, Raphael Thomas Marie James. b 65. N Staffs Poly BA87. Cranmer Hall Dur 01. **d** 03. C Madeley *Heref* from 03. *7 Mellor Close, Madeley, Telford TF7 5SS* Tel (01952) 413674 E-mail raphael@fish.co.uk

DUCKWORTH, Mrs Annette Jacqueline. b 54. **d** 00 **p** 01. OLM Moxley *Lich* from 00. *1 Sutton Road, Wednesbury WS10 8SG* Tel (01902) 650656

DUCKWORTH, Brian George. b 47. Edin Th Coll 85. **d** 87 **p** 88. C Sutton in Ashfield St Mary *S'well* 87-95; C Sutton in Ashfield St Mich 89-95; P-in-c 95-98; TV Hucknall Torkard 98-03; R S Ockendon and Belhus Park *Chelmsf* from 03. *The Vicarage, 121 Foyle Drive, South Ockendon RM15 5HF* Tel (01708) 853246 Fax as telephone E-mail bduck@fish.co.uk

DUCKWORTH, Derek. b 29. Fitzw Ho Cam BA52 MA58 Lon Univ PGCE66 Lanc Univ PhD72. Oak Hill Th Coll 52. **d** 54 **p** 55. C Preston All SS *Blackb* 54-57; C Sutton *Liv* 57-58; Hon C Wakef St Jo *Wakef* 58-60; Public Preacher *Blackb* 60-64; C Whalley 64-73; Hon C Newbury *Ox* 73-80; Perm to Offic *Ox* 80-81; *Cant* 81-84 and 85-86; P-in-c Dymchurch w Burmarsh and Newchurch *Cant* 84-85; Chapl Leybourne Grange Hosp W Malling 85-86; P-in-c Rampton w Laneham, Treswell, Cottam and Stokeham *S'well* 86-89; R 89-91; rtd 91; Perm to Offic *Cant* from 91. *Glebe Cottage, 11 Church Walk, Headcorn, Ashford TN27 9NP* Tel (01622) 890143

DUDDING, Edward Leslie (Father Gregory). b 30. Auckland Univ MSc52 St Jo Coll Auckland LTh56. **d** 57 **p** 57. New Zealand 57-60; Lic to Offic *Chich* from 62; CSWG from 62; Father Superior from 73. *Monastery of The Holy Trinity, Crawley Down, Crawley RH10 4LH* Tel (01342) 712074

DUDLEY, Harold George. b 14. St Mich Coll Llan 68. **d** 70 **p** 70. C Fleur-de-Lis *Mon* 70-73; V Goldcliffe and Whitson and Nash 73-83; rtd 83; Lic to Offic *Mon* from 83. *59 Oakfield Road, Newport NP20 4LX* Tel (01633) 661281

DUDLEY, Mrs Janet Carr. b 36. EMMTC 86. **d** 89 **p** 94. NSM Countesthorpe w Foston *Leic* 89-94; NSM Arnesby w Shearsby and Bruntingthorpe 94-01; rtd 01; Perm to Offic *Leic* 01-02; NSM Market Harborough and The Transfiguration etc from 02. *13 The Broadway, Market Harborough LE16 7LZ* Tel (01858) 467619

DUDLEY, John Donald Swanborough. b 34. Edin Univ DipAgr53 Ox Univ BTh95. St Alb and Ox Min Course 96. **d** 97 **p** 98. NSM Emmer Green *Ox* 97-02; Perm to Offic from 02. *26 Russet Glade, Caversham, Reading RG4 8UJ* Tel 0118-954 6664 Fax as telephone

DUDLEY, John Rea. b 31. Pemb Coll Cam BA54 MA58. St Steph Ho Ox. **d** 57 **p** 58. C Kennington St Jo *S'wark* 57-61; C Merstham and Gatton 61-68; V N Gosforth *Newc* 68-79; RD Newc Cen 77-82; V Newc St Jo 79-91; V Sunbury *Lon* 91-98; rtd 98; Perm to Offic *Bris* from 99. *2 Hay Street, Marshfield, Chippenham SN14 8NJ* Tel (01225) 891128

DUDLEY, Martin Raymond. b 53. K Coll Lon BD77 AKC77 MTh78 PhD94 Univ of Wales (Cardiff) DPS79 FRHistS95 FSA97 SBStJ98. St Mich Coll Llan 78. **d** 79 **p** 80. C Whitchurch *Llan* 79-83; V Weston *St Alb* 83-88; P-in-c Ardeley 97-88; V Owlsmoor *Ox* 88-95; Lect Simon of Cyrene Th Inst 92-95; R Smithfield St Bart Gt *Lon* from 95. *Church House, Cloth Fair, London EC1A 7JQ* Tel (020) 7606 5171 or 7628 3644 Fax 7600 6909 E-mail st.bartholomew@btinternet.com

DUDLEY, Miss Wendy Elizabeth. b 46. City of Sheff Coll CertEd68. Cranmer Hall Dur 79. **dss** 81 **d** 87 **p** 94. Cumnor *Ox* 81-87; Par Dn 87-89; Par Dn Hodge Hill *Birm* 89-94; C 94-95; TV 95-98; TV Bucknall and Bagnall *Lich* from 98. *The Vicarage, Dawlish Drive, Stoke-on-Trent ST2 0ET* Tel (01782) 260876 *or* 279300 E-mail wed.btm@tinyworld.co.uk

DUDLEY-SMITH, James. b 66. Fitzw Coll Cam BA89 MA92. Wycliffe Hall Ox BTh94. **d** 97 **p** 98. C New Borough and Leigh *Sarum* 97-01; C Hove Bp Hannington Memorial Ch *Chich* from 01. *43 Hogarth Road, Hove BN3 5RH* Tel (01273) 725642

✠**DUDLEY-SMITH, The Rt Revd Timothy.** b 26. OBE03. Pemb Coll Cam BA47 MA51 Lambeth MLitt91. Ridley Hall Cam 48. **d** 50 **p** 51 **c** 81. C Erith St Paul *Roch* 50-53; Lic to Offic *S'wark* 53-62; Hd of Cam Univ Miss Bermondsey 53-55; Chapl 55-60; Ed Sec Evang Alliance and Ed *Crusade* 55-59; Asst Sec CPAS 59-65; Gen Sec 65-73; adn Nor 73-81; Suff Bp Thetford 81-91; rtd 92. *9 Ashlands, Ford, Salisbury SP4 6DY* Tel (01722) 326417

DUDLEY, Archdeacon of. *See* TRETHEWEY, The Ven Frederick Martyn

DUDLEY, Suffragan Bishop of. *See* WALKER, The Rt Revd David Stuart

DUERDEN, Martin James. b 55. Liv Poly BA77. Oak Hill Th Coll 86. **d** 88 **p** 89. C Tunbridge Wells St Jas *Roch* 88-92; V Southport SS Simon and Jude *Liv* 92-98; P-in-c Maghull 98-02; TR from 02. *The Rectory, 20 Damfield Lane, Liverpool L31 6DD* Tel 0151-526 5017

DUFF, Alison. *See* FINCH, Mrs Alison

DUFF, Andrew John. b 57. MIOT. Sarum & Wells Th Coll 92. **d** 92 **p** 93. C Banbury *Ox* 92-95; C Bracknell 95-96; TV 96-98; CF from 98. *c/o MOD Chaplains (Army)* Tel (01980) 615804 Fax 615800

DUFF, Garden Ian. b 34. ACGI56 Imp Coll Lon BScEng56. Sarum & Wells Th Coll 92. **d** 93 **p** 94. NSM Ashton Gifford *Sarum* 93-97; TV Upper Wylye Valley from 97. *Trinity Trees Cottage, 58 Upton Lovell, Warminster BA12 0JP* Tel (01985) 850291 Fax as telephone

DUFF, Jillian Louise Calland. b 72. Ch Coll Cam BA93 MA97 Worc Coll Ox DPhil96. Wycliffe Hall Ox BA02. **d** 03. C Litherland St Phil *Liv* from 03. *3 Harrington Road, Litherland, Liverpool L21 7NA* Tel 0151-222 5819 E-mail jilldluff@fish.co.uk

DUFF, John Alexander. b 57. York Univ BA78. EMMTC DTPS94. **d** 94 **p** 95. NSM Linc St Geo Swallowbeck *Linc* 94-00. *37 Mornington Crescent, Harrogate HG1 5DL*

DUFF, Michael Ian. b 63. Ox Univ BA85. Trin Coll Bris BA98 MA99. **d** 99 **p** 00. C Southsea St Jude *Portsm* 99-03; CMS Bandung Indonesia from 03. *Gang Kencana II No 180B, Jalan Gunung Mas, Bandung, West Java, Indonesia* E-mail all@theduffs.me.uk

DUFF, Timothy Cameron. b 40. G&C Coll Cam BA62 LLM63 MA66 Solicitor 65. NEOC 90. **d** 93 **p** 94. NSM Tynemouth Priory *Newc* 93-96; NSM N Shields 96-00; then TV from 00. *26 The Drive, North Shields NE30 4JW* Tel 0191-257 1463 Fax 296 1904 E-mail timothy@dufftyne.freeserve.co.uk

DUFFETT, Canon Paul Stanton. b 33. Keble Coll Ox BA55 MA59. Ripon Hall Ox DipTh58. **d** 59 **p** 60. C Portsea St Cuth *Portsm* 59-63; S Africa 63-80; Hon Can Zululand from 87; Accredited Rep Zululand and Swaziland Assn from 89; P-in-c Greatham w Empshott *Portsm* 80-85; R 85-88; R Papworth Everard *Ely* 88-98; Chapl Papworth Hosps 88-98; rtd 98; Hon Chapl Mother's Union from 97; Perm to Offic *Ely* from 99. *11 Roman Hill, Barton, Cambridge CB3 7AX* Tel (01223) 262831

DUFFETT-SMITH (née RUSHTON), Ms Patricia Mary. b 54. Lon Univ BPharm76 Anglia Poly Univ MA99 MRPharmS77

Cam Univ CTM97. EAMTC 94. **d** 97 **p** 98. NSM Haddenham *Ely* 97-99; NSM Wilburton from 97; Chapl Asst Hinchingbrooke Health Care NHS Trust from 99. *41 Denmark Road, Cottenham, Cambridge CB4 8QS* Tel (01954) 201276 E-mail pmd23@hermes.cam.ac.uk

DUFFIELD, Ian Keith. b 47. K Coll Lon BD71 AKC71 MTh73. NY Th Sem DMin84. **d** 73 **p** 74. C Broxbourne *St Alb* 73-77; C Harpenden St Nic 77-81; TV Sheff Manor *Sheff* 81-87; V Walkley 87-02; V Sheff Norwood St Leon from 02. *St Leonard's Vicarage, Everingham Road, Sheffield S5 7LE* Tel 0114-243 6689

DUFFIELD, John Ernest. b 55. BA86. Oak Hill Th Coll 83. **d** 86 **p** 87. C Walton Breck Ch Ch *Liv* 86-89; TV Fazakerley Em 89-00; Chapl N Cheshire Hosps NHS Trust from 00. *Warrington Hospital, Lovely Lane, Warrington WA5 1QG* Tel (01925) 662146 Fax 662048 E-mail john.duffield@nch.nhs.uk

DUFFIELD, Ronald Bertram Charles. b 26. Hull Univ Coll BA49 TCert50. Sarum & Wells Th Coll 91. **d** 92 **p** 93. NSM E Knoyle, Semley and Sedgehill *Sarum* 92-94; P-in-c 94-95; rtd 95; Perm to Offic *York* 95-99 and from 01; P-in-c Isfield *Chich* 99-01. *35 Sackville Close, Beverley HU17 8XF* Tel (01482) 880983

DUFFUS, Mrs Barbara Rose. b 51. EMMTC DipTh98. **d** 98 **p** 99. C Linc St Faith and St Martin w St Pet *Linc* 98-00; C Grantham 00-02; P-in-c Brothertoft Gp from 02; Mental Health Chapl SE Lincs from 02. *The Vicarage, Main Road, Brothertoft, Boston PE20 3SW* Tel (01205) 280267 E-mail bduffus@fish.co.uk

DUFOUR, Prudence Elaine. b 42. MBE82. Middx Hosp SRN64. St Alb and Ox Min Course 97. **d** 00 **p** 01. NSM Old Windsor *Ox* 00-03; NSM Blackdown *B & W* from 03. *3 Fairfield Green, Churchinford, Taunton TA3 7RR* Tel (01823) 601594 Fax as telephone E-mail pruedufour@globalnet.co.uk

DUFTON, Francis Trevor. b 29. Trin Coll Cam BA51 MA55. Ridley Hall Cam 51. **d** 53 **p** 54. C Ware Ch Ch *St Alb* 53-56; V Bengeo Ch Ch 56-67; R Elmdon and Wendon Lofts *Chelmsf* 67-80; R Strethall 67-80; P-in-c Bottisham *Ely* 80-85; P-in-c Swaffham Bulbeck 80-85; rtd 85; Perm to Offic *Ely* 85-91. *23 Hyde Road, Eastbourne BN21 4SX* Tel (01323) 416659

DUGDALE, Angela Marion. b 33. DL92. ARCM52 GRSM54 UEA Hon MA89. LNSM course 96. **d** 97 **p** 98. OLM Weybourne Gp *Nor* 97-03; rtd 03; Perm to Offic *Nor* from 03. *Beck House, Kelling, Holt NR25 7EL* Tel (01263) 588389 Fax 588594

DUGMORE, Barry John. b 61. STETS. **d** 01 **p** 02. C Cowplain *Portsm* from 01. *24 Wincanton Way, Cowplain, Waterlooville PO7 8NW* Tel (023) 9225 9129 E-mail b.dugmore@ukgateway.net

DUGUID, Ms Alison Audrey. b 52. STETS 99. **d** 02 **p** 03. C Appledore w Brookland, Fairfield, Brenzett etc *Cant* from 02. *Puddleglum, Appledore Road, Brenzett, Romney Marsh TN29 9UG* Tel (01797) 344125 Mobile 07870-988507 E-mail ali@dogooders.co.uk

DUGUID, Reginald Erskine. b 29. S'wark Ord Course. **d** 88 **p** 89. NSM Notting Hill All SS w St Columb *Lon* from 88. *53 Sandbourne, Dartmouth Close, London W11 1DA* Tel (020) 7221 4436

DUKE, Canon Alan Arthur. b 38. Tyndale Hall Bris 59. **d** 64 **p** 65. C Whalley Range St Marg *Man* 64-67; C Folkestone H Trin w Ch Ch *Cant* 67-71; V Queenborough 71-76; V Bearsted w Thurnham 76-86; P-in-c Torquay St Luke *Ex* 86-91; R Barham w Bishopsbourne and Kingston *Cant* 91-00; Dioc Communications Officer 91-95; Hon Can Cant Cathl from 99; Chapl to Bp Dover from 00; Bp's Media Link Officer from 00. *Roundways, Derringstone Hill, Barham, Canterbury CT4 6QD* Tel (01227) 831817 *or* 459382 E-mail alan.duke@bishcant.org

DUKE, David Malcolm. b 40. Ch Ch Ox BA61 DipTh64 MA65 Newc Poly MPhil80 CQSW81. Cuddesdon Coll 63. **d** 65 **p** 66. C Sunderland Pennywell St Thos *Dur* 65-68; C Dur St Oswald 68-70; C Harton 70-74; Perm to Offic 85-96; Hon C Hedworth from 96. *43 Coquet Street, Jarrow NE32 5SW* Tel 0191-430 1200 Mobile 07979-036977 Fax 0191-537 4409

DULFER, John Guidi. b 37. Lich Th Coll 62. **d** 64 **p** 65. C Fenny Stratford and Water Eaton *Ox* 64-67; C Cheshunt *St Alb* 67-68; C Kennington Cross St Anselm *S'wark* 68-74; C N Lambeth 74-76; P-in-c Kensington St Phil Earl's Court *Lon* 76-79; V 79-84; Chapl Odstock Hosp Salisbury 84; USA from 84; rtd 02. *135 West 22 Street #2, New York, NY 10011, USA* Tel (001)(212) 604 9040 E-mail johndulfer@hotmail.com

DULLEY, Arthur John Franklyn. b 32. Mert Coll Ox BA54 MA57. St Jo Coll Nottm 69. **d** 71 **p** 72. Lect St Jo Coll Nottm 71-96; Hon C Attenborough w Chilwell *S'well* 71-73; C Penn Fields *Lich* 73-74; Chapl Aldenham Sch Herts 74-79; Chapl HM Pris Ashwell 79-87; V Langham *Pet* 79-96; rtd 96; Perm to Offic *Ely* 96-98. *8 Prickwillow Road, Ely CB7 4QP* Tel (01353) 664381

DUMAT, Mrs Jennifer. b 42. ARCM62. Qu Coll Birm 80 EMMTC 82. **dss** 83 **d** 87 **p** 94. Chapl Asst Pilgrim Hosp Boston 83-94; P-in-c Friskney *Linc* from 94. *The Vicarage, Yawling Road, Friskney, Boston PE22 8NA* Tel (01754) 820418

✠**DUMPER, The Rt Revd Anthony Charles.** b 23. Ch Coll Cam BA45 MA48. Westcott Ho Cam. **d** 47 **p** 48 **c** 77. C E Greenwich Ch Ch w St Andr and St Mich *S'wark* 47-49; Malaya 49-63;

Malaysia 63-64; Dean Singapore 64-70; V Stockton St Pet *Dur* 70-77; P-in-c Stockton H Trin 76-77; RD Stockton 70-77; Suff Bp Dudley *Worc* 77-93; rtd 93; Asst Bp Birm from 93. *117 Burberry Close, Birmingham B30 1TB* Tel 0121-458 3011

DUNBAR, Peter Lamb. b 46. Bede Coll Dur DipEd68. Lambeth STh77 N Ord Course 78. d 81 p 82. NSM Knaresborough *Ripon* 81-82; C Knaresborough 82-84; R Farnham w Scotton, Staveley, Copgrove etc 84-92; V Upper Nidderdale from 92; Chapl St Aid Sch Harrogate 86-94. *The Vicarage, Pateley Bridge, Harrogate HG3 5LQ* Tel (01423) 711414 E-mail lionlamb@dircon.co.uk

DUNCAN, Canon Bruce. b 38. MBE93. Leeds Univ BA60 FRSA. Cuddesdon Coll 65. d 67 p 68. C Armley St Bart *Ripon* 67-69; Dir Children's Relief Internat 69-71; Chapl Vienna w Budapest and Prague *Eur* 71-75; V Crediton *Ex* 75-82; R Crediton and Shobrooke 82-86; RD Cadbury 76-81 and 84-86; Can Res Man Cathl *Man* 86-95; Prin Sarum Coll 95-02; Can and Preb Sarum Cathl *Sarum* 95-02; rtd 02; Perm to Offic *Sarum* from 02. *Church Path Cottage, St David's Hill, Exeter EX4 4DU* Tel and fax (01392) 420988 Mobile 07949-268541 E-mail churchpath@fsmail.net

DUNCAN, Christopher Robin. b 41. AKC71. d 72 p 73. C Allington *Cant* 72-77; P-in-c Wittersham 77-82; R Wittersham w Stone-in-Oxney and Ebony 82-85; V Chilham 85-92; P-in-c Challock w Molash 87-92; RD W Bridge 92-95 and 02-03; V Chilham w Challock and Molash from 92. *The Vicarage, 3 Hambrook Close, Chilham, Canterbury CT4 8EJ* Tel (01227) 730235 E-mail chris.duncan@chil-vic.co.uk

DUNCAN, Colin Richard. b 34. SS Coll Cam BA58 MA60. Ripon Coll Cuddesdon 83. d 85 p 86. C Stafford *Lich* 85-89; C Wednesfield 89-90; TV 90-99; rtd 99; Perm to Offic *Glouc* from 99. *Fir Tree Cottage, Union Road, Bakers Hill, Coleford GL16 7QB*

DUNCAN, Graham Charles Dewar. b 65. Sheff Univ BSc87. NTMTC AdDipTh98. d 98 p 99. NSM Dawley St Jerome *Lon* 98-00; Manager St Mary's Ch Community Cen from 00; NSM Sheff St Mary Bramall Lane *Sheff* from 00. *St Mary's Community Centre, Bramall Lane, Sheffield S2 4QZ* Tel 0114-272 5596 Fax 275 3892

DUNCAN, The Very Revd Gregor Duthie. b 50. Glas Univ MA72 Clare Coll Cam PhD77 Oriel Coll Ox BA83. Ripon Coll Cuddesdon 81. d 83 p 84. C Oakham, Hambleton, Egleton, Braunston and Brooke *Pet* 83-86; Edin Th Coll 87-89; R Largs *Glas* 89-99; Dean Glas from 96; R Glas St Ninian from 99. *St Ninian's Rectory, 32 Glencairn Drive, Glasgow G41 4PW* Tel 0141-423 1247 Fax 424 3332 E-mail dean@glasgow.anglican.org

DUNCAN, James Montgomerie. b 29. Edin Th Coll 53. d 56 p 57. C Edin St Pet *Edin* 56-59; C Edin Old St Paul 59-60; S Africa 60-65; Prov Youth Org Scotland 65-69; R Edin St Salvador *Edin* 69-86; Chapl HM Pris Saughton 69-86; R Aberlour *Mor* 86-98; R Fochabers 86-98; rtd 98. *East Scores House, 24 East Scores, St Andrews KY16 9BE* Tel (01334) 472295 E-mail h-eduncan@excite.com

DUNCAN, John. b 22. Open Univ BA. Roch Th Coll 64. d 66 p 67. C Gainsborough All SS *Linc* 66-68; C Boultham 68-71; V W Pinchbeck 72-76; Canada 76-81; R Ridgewell w Ashen, Birdbrook and Sturmer *Chelmsf* 81-88; rtd 88; Perm to Offic *Pet* from 91. *20 Westcott Way, Northampton NN3 3BE* Tel (01604) 30797

DUNCAN, The Ven John Finch. b 33. Univ Coll Ox BA57 MA63. Cuddesdon Coll 57. d 59 p 60. C S Bank *York* 59-61; SSF 61-62; C Birm St Pet *Birm* 62-65; Chapl Birm Univ 65-76; V Kings Heath 76-85; Hon Can Birm Cathl 83-85; Adn Birm 85-01; rtd 01; Perm to Offic *Birm* from 01. *66 Glebe Rise, King's Sutton, Banbury OX17 3PH* Tel (01295) 812641

DUNCAN, Peter Harold Furlong. b 25. AKC52 Lon Univ BA68 Goldsmiths' Coll Lon BA71 MPhil79. d 53 p 54. C Sheff St Geo and St Steph *Sheff* 53-56; C Wealdstone H Trin *Lon* 56-57; V Battersea St Pet *S'wark* 57-60; Nigeria 64-66; Hon C All Hallows by the Tower etc *Lon* 67-73; Ind Chapl Lon Docks 67-73; Sen Lect in Sociology City of Lon Poly 73-87; Hon C Gt Ilford St Andr *Chelmsf* 73-80; P-in-c Gt Canfield 80-87; P-in-c N Woolwich w Silvertown 87-93; rtd 93; Perm to Offic *York* from 93. *179 Windsor Drive, Haxby, York YO32 2YD* Tel (01904) 769888

DUNCAN, Tom. b 37. d 97 p 98. NSM Poplar *Lon* from 97. *1 Chardwell Close, Northumberland Road, London E6 5RR*

DUNCAN, The Ven William Albert. b 30. TCD BA53 MA61 BD66. CITC 54. d 54 p 55. C Bangor Abbey *D & D* 54-57; C Larne and Inver *Conn* 57-61; Hd of Trin Coll Miss Belf 61-66; I Rasharkin w Finvoy 66-78; I Ramoan w Ballycastle and Culfeightrin 78-96; Adn Dalriada 93-96; rtd 96. *8 Beech Hill, Ballymoney BT53 6DB* Tel (028) 7066 4285

DUNCANSON, Derek James. b 47. TD93. AKC69 Open Univ BA80 Lon Univ MA(Ed)93 FCollP94. St Aug Coll Cant 69. d 70 p 71. C Norbury St Oswald *Cant* 70-72; CF (TAVR) 71-76 and 79-95; C Woodham *Guildf* 72-76; CF 76-79; V Burneside *Carl* 79-84; R Coppull St Jo *Blackb* 84-86; Chapl Bloxham Sch 86-99; V Pet St Mary Boongate *Pet* from 99; Chapl Pet Regional Coll

from 00; RD Pet from 01. *St Mary's Vicarage, 214 Eastfield Road, Peterborough PE1 4BD* Tel (01733) 343418 E-mail duncansonderek@hotmail.com

DUNCOMBE, Maureen Barbara. See WHITE, Mrs Maureen Barbara

DUNDAS, Edward Paul. b 67. NUU BSc88. TCD Div Sch BTh91. d 91 p 92. C Portadown St Mark *Arm* 91-95; I Ardtrea w Desertcreat 95-00; Dioc Youth Adv to Abp Armagh 99-00; I Belfast St Aid *Conn* from 00. *12 Royal Lodge Mews, Belfast BT8 7YT* Tel (028) 9079 0977 Mobile 07718-890368 Fax 9079 0977 E-mail paul_dundas@yahoo.com

DUNDAS, Edward Thompson. b 36. TCD BA63. d 64 p 65. C Conwall *D & R* 64-67; I Kilbarron 67-78; I Donaghady 78-84; I Kilmore St Aid w St Sav *Arm* from 84. *38 Vicarage Road, Portadown, Craigavon BT62 4HF* Tel (028) 3833 2664

DUNDEE, Provost of. See BYRNE, The Very Revd Miriam Alexandra Frances

DUNFORD, Malcolm. b 34. FCA74. EMMTC 73. d 76 p 77. NSM Frodingham *Linc* from 76. *57 Rowland Road, Scunthorpe DN16 1SP* Tel (01724) 840879

DUNGAN, Hilary Anne. b 46. TCD BA98 ARCM68. CITC 98. d 00 p 01. C Arm St Mark *Arm* 00-03; I Maryborough w Dysart Enos and Ballyfin *C & O* from 03. *The Rectory, Coote Street, Porlaoise, Co Laois, Irish Republic* Tel (00353) (502) 21154

DUNHILL, Robin Arnold. b 15. BNC Ox BA38 MA46. Cuddesdon Coll. d 46 p 47. C Pet All SS *Pet* 46-53; V Wellingborough All SS 53-63; V Hampstead Garden Suburb *Lon* 63-73; RD W Barnet 70-73; Perm to Offic *Pet* from 74; rtd 80. *Abbeyfield, 86 Rockingham Road, Kettering NN16 9AD* Tel (01536) 482902

DUNK, Michael Robin. b 43. Oak Hill Th Coll BA82. d 82 p 83. C Northampton All SS w St Kath *Pet* 82-86; Ind Chapl *Birm* 86-96; P-in-c Warley Woods 96; V from 96; AD Warley from 01. *St Hilda's Vicarage, Abbey Road, Smethwick, Warley B67 5NQ* Tel 0121-429 1384

DUNK, Peter Norman. b 43. Sarum Th Coll 67. d 69 p 70. C Sheff St Mary w St Simon w St Matthias *Sheff* 69-71; C Margate St Jo *Cant* 71-74; Dioc Youth Officer *Birm* 74-78; R Hulme Ascension *Man* 78-83; V E Farleigh and Coxheath *Roch* 83; P-in-c Linton w Hunton 83; R Coxheath w E Farleigh, Hunton and Linton 83-88; Australia from 88; R Swanbourne 88-99; rtd 00. *7 Raffan View, Gwelup, W Australia 6018* Tel (0061) (8) 9447 8877 Fax as telephone

DUNKERLEY, James Hobson. b 39. Seabury-Western Th Sem BD69 STh70. d 64 p 65. C Stirchley *Birm* 64-66; C Perry Barr 66-70; R Chicago St Pet USA from 70. *621 Belmont Avenue, Chicago, IL 60657, USA*

DUNKLEY, Christopher. b 52. Edin Univ MA74 Ox Univ BA77 MA81. St Steph Ho Ox 75. d 78 p 79. C Newbold w Dunston *Derby* 78-82; C Chesterfield St Mary and All SS 82; Chapl Leic Univ *Leic* 82-85; TV Leic Ascension 85-92; Chapl Leics Hospice 85-87; V Leic St Aid 92-97; V Holbrooks *Cov* from 97. *St Luke's Vicarage, Rotherham Road, Coventry CV6 4FE* Tel (024) 7668 8604 E-mail kitdunkley@tiscali.co.uk

DUNKLEY, Reginald Alfred Lorenz. b 13. Clifton Th Coll 56. d 58 p 59. C Meopham *Roch* 59-60; C Belvedere All SS 60-64; R Longfield 64-78; rtd 78. *33 Sheriff Drive, Chatham ME5 9PU* Tel (01634) 862143

DUNLOP, Canon Arthur John. b 27. AKC52. d 53 p 54. C Loughton St Jo *Chelmsf* 53-57; C-in-c Chelmsf All SS CD 57-65; R Laindon w Basildon 65-72; RD Basildon 65-72; V Maldon All SS w St Pet 72-92; RD Maldon 73-82; Hon Can Chelmsf Cathl 80-92; RD Maldon and Dengie 89-92; rtd 92; Perm to Offic *Chelmsf* from 92; Perm to Offic *St E* from 92. *Maeldune, 64 Highfield Road, Sudbury CO10 2QJ* Tel (01787) 881699

DUNLOP, Canon Ian Geoffrey David. b 25. FSA New Coll Ox BA48 MA56. Linc Th Coll 54. d 56 p 57. C Bp's Hatfield *St Alb* 56-60; Chapl Westmr Sch 60-62; C Bures *St E* 62-72; Can Res and Chan Sarum Cathl *Sarum* 72-92; Dir Post-Ord Tr 72-92; Dir of Ords 73-92; Lect Sarum & Wells Th Coll 76-92; rtd 92. *Gowanbrae, The Glebe, Selkirk TD7 5AB* Tel (01750) 20706

DUNLOP, Peter John. b 44. TCD BA68 MA72 Dur Univ DipPH70 CertEd71. Cranmer Hall Dur. d 71 p 72. C Barking St Marg w St Patr *Chelmsf* 71-75; C Gt Malvern Ch Ch *Worc* 75-78; Chapl K Sch Tynemouth 78-89; V Monkseaton St Pet *Newc* 90-96; rtd 96; Perm to Offic *Newc* from 96. *19 Cliftonville Gardens, Whitley Bay NE26 1QJ* Tel 0191-251 0983

DUNN, Alastair Matthew Crusoe. b 40. Lon Univ LLB64 AKC64. Wycliffe Hall Ox 78. d 80 p 81. C Yardley St Edburgha *Birm* 80-83; R Bishop's Sutton and Ropley and W Tisted *Win* 83-90; V Milford from 90. *The Vicarage, Lymington Road, Milford on Sea, Lymington SO41 0QN* Tel (01590) 643289

DUNN, Mrs Barbara Anne. b 42. Man Univ BA72 Sheff Univ CQSW76. N Ord Course 92. d 95 p 96. NSM Stretford St Matt *Man* 95-02; Perm to Offic from 02. *71 Manley Road, Whalley Range, Manchester M16 8WF* Tel 0161-881 6929 E-mail bnsdunn@btinternet.com

DUNN, Brian. b 40. St Aid Birkenhead 66. d 69 p 70. C Over Darwen H Trin *Blackb* 69-71; C Burnley St Pet 71-74; V Darwen

St Barn 74-84; V S Shore H Trin 84-02; Chapl Arnold Sch Blackpool 84-02; rtd 02; Perm to Offic *Blackb* from 02. *11 Kingsway, Blackpool FY4 2DF*

DUNN, Christopher George Hunter. b 28. Pemb Coll Cam BA49 MA53. Oak Hill Th Coll 51. **d** 53 **p** 54. C Tunbridge Wells H Trin *Roch* 53-54; C Broadwater St Mary *Chich* 54-58; R Garsdon w Lea and Cleverton *Bris* 58-74; Chapl Marie Curie Foundn (Tidcombe Hall) 74-95; V Tiverton St Geo *Ex* 74-01; RD Tiverton 84-91; C Tiverton St Geo and St Paul 01; rtd 01. *8 Counter Close, Blandford Forum, Dorset DT11 7XJ* Tel (01258) 456843

DUNN, David James. b 47. Leeds Univ CertEd79 BA82 Bris Univ DipHE90. Trin Coll Bris 88. **d** 90 **p** 91. C Magor w Redwick and Undy *Mon* 90-92; Chapl Toc H from 90; C St Mellons and Michaelston-y-Fedw *Mon* 92-93; V Pontnewydd from 93. *The Vicarage, 44 Church Road, Pontnewydd, Cwmbran NP44 1AT* Tel (01633) 482300

DUNN, David Michael. b 47. AKC70. St Aug Coll Cant 70. **d** 71 **p** 72. C Padgate *Liv* 71-74; C Halliwell St Marg *Man* 74-76; V Lever Bridge 76-84; V Bradshaw 84-01; TR Turton Moorland Min from 01. *St Maxentius Rectory, Bolton Road, Bolton BL2 3EU* Tel (01204) 304240 Fax as telephone

DUNN, David Whitelaw Thomas. b 34. Trin Coll Carmarthen CertEd54. St Mich Coll Llan 87 St Deiniol's Hawarden 83. **d** 83 **p** 85. NSM Brecon St Mary and Battle w Llanddew *S & B* 83-87; Min Can Brecon Cathl 87-88; V Llanfihangel Crucorney w Oldcastle etc *Mon* 88-98; rtd 98. *The Craig, Cwmyoy, Abergavenny NP7 7NF* Tel (01873) 890092

DUNN, Derek William Robert. b 48. AMusTCL74 LTCL75 Stranmillis Coll CertEd70 Open Univ BA80 DASE86 MA01. **d** 85 **p** 87. NSM Carnalea *D & D* 85-97; NSM Bangor Abbey from 97. *13 Wandsworth Park, Carnalea, Bangor BT19 1BD* Tel (028) 9145 6898 E-mail derek@mambolo.freeserve.co.uk

DUNN, John Frederick. b 44. Trin Coll Bris 71. **d** 74 **p** 75. C Carl St Jo *Carl* 74-77; C Tooting Graveney St Nic *S'wark* 77-82; V Attleborough *Cov* 85; Perm to Offic *Cant* 86-02; V Tipton St Martin and St Paul *Lich* from 02. *St Martin's Vicarage, 1 Dudley Port, Tipton DY4 7PR* Tel 0121-557 1902

DUNN, Julian. b 46. Open Univ BA84. K Coll Lon 67 St Aug Coll Cant 70. **d** 71 **p** 72. C Hanworth All SS *Lon* 71-74; C Kidlington *Ox* 74-76; C-in-c Cleethorpes St Fran CD *Linc* 76-77; TV Cleethorpes 77-85; Chapl Friarage and Distr Hosp Northallerton 85-88; Chapl Broadmoor Hosp Crowthorne 88; Ind Chapl *York* 88-89; P-in-c Micklefield 88-89; Perm to Offic *Ox* from 91. *timbles brewery* [sic], *1 Lewington Close, Great Haseley, Oxford OX44 7LS* Tel (01844) 279687 E-mail eisendora@compuserve.com

DUNN, Kevin Lancelot. b 62. Newc Univ BSc83. St Steph Ho Ox 89. **d** 92 **p** 93. C Tynemouth Cullercoats St Paul *Newc* 92-95; C Newc St Matt w St Mary 95-97; P-in-c Kirkholt *Man* 97-00; Chapl Rochdale Healthcare NHS Trust from 00. *17 Rochester Avenue, Prestwich, Manchester M25 0LF* Tel 0161-772 0717

DUNN, Kevin Samuel. b 31. Toronto Univ MDiv74. **d** 73 **p** 74. USA 73-90 and from 92; I Rathkeale w Askeaton and Kilcornan *L & K* 90-92. *20683 Waalew Road #118, Apple Valley, CA 92307, USA*

DUNN, Michael Henry James. b 34. Em Coll Cam BA56 MA62. Cuddesdon Coll 57 and 62. **d** 62 **p** 63. C Chatham St Steph *Roch* 62-66; C Bromley SS Pet and Paul 66-70; V Rock St Justus 70-83; P-in-c Malvern Wells and Wyche *Worc* 83-85; P-in-c Lt Malvern, Malvern Wells and Wyche 85-97; rtd 97; Perm to Offic *Worc* from 97. *253 Oldbury Road, Worcester WR2 6JT* Tel (01905) 429938

DUNN, Paul James Hugh. b 55. Dur Univ PhD93. Ripon Coll Cuddesdon. **d** 83 **p** 84. C Wandsworth St Paul *S'wark* 83-87; C Richmond St Mary w St Matthias and St Jo 88-92; TV Wimbledon 92-98; V Ham St Rich from 98. *The Vicarage, Ashburnham Road, Ham, Richmond TW10 7NL* Tel (020) 8948 3758 E-mail revpdunn@aol.com

DUNN, Reginald Hallam. b 31. Oak Hill NSM Course 79. **d** 82 **p** 83. NSM Enfield St Andr *Lon* 82-88; NSM Forty Hill Jes Ch 88-92; NSM Enfield Chase St Mary 92-97; rtd 97; Perm to Offic *Lon* from 97. *3 Conway Gardens, Enfield EN2 9AD* Tel (020) 8366 3982

DUNN, Sharon Louise. See GOBLE, Mrs Sharon Louise

DUNN, Canon Struan Huthwaite. b 43. Ch Coll Hobart 66 Moore Th Coll Sydney ThL68 Clifton Th Coll. **d** 70 **p** 71. C Orpington Ch Ch *Roch* 70-74; C Cheltenham St Mary *Glouc* 74-76; C Cheltenham St Mary, St Matt, St Paul and H Trin 76; C Welling *Roch* 76-79; Chapl Barcelona w Casteldefels *Eur* 79-83; R Addington w Trottiscliffe *Roch* 83-89; P-in-c Ryarsh w Birling 83-89; P-in-c S Gillingham 89-90; TR 90-96; RD Gillingham 91-96; R Meopham w Nurstead from 96; Hon Can Roch Cathl from 97. *The Rectory, Shipley Hills Road, Meopham, Gravesend DA13 0AD* Tel (01474) 815259

DUNN, Thomas. See DUNN, David Whitelaw Thomas

DUNNAN, Donald Stuart. b 59. Harvard Univ AB80 AM81 Ch Ch Ox BA85 MA90 DPhil91. Gen Th Sem (NY) 86. **d** 86

p 87. USA 86-87 and from 92; Lib Pusey Ho 87-89; Lic to Offic *Ox* 87-92; Perm to Offic *Cant* 87-92; Chapl Linc Coll Ox 90-92. *St James School, St James, MD 21781, USA* E-mail dsdunnan@stjames.edu

DUNNE, Dermot Patrick Martin. b 59. Pontifical Univ Maynooth DipPhil80 DipTh83 Chiron Cen for Holistic Psychotherapy Cert Psychotherapy 95. CITC 98. **d** 83 **p** 84. In RC Ch 83-95; Dean's V Ch Ch Cathl Dublin *D & G* 99-01; I Crosspatrick Gp *C & O* from 01. *The Rectory, Tinahely, Arklow, Co Wicklow, Irish Republic* Tel (00353) (402) 34948 Mobile 87-826 4316 E-mail crosspatrick@ferns.anglican.org

DUNNE, Kevin Headley. b 43. Cranmer Hall Dur 85. **d** 87 **p** 88. C Chester le Street *Dur* 87-90; V S Hetton w Haswell 90-94; P-in-c Oxclose 94-02; AD Chester-le-Street 97-02; R Chester le Street from 02. *The Rectory, Lindisfarne Avenue, Chester le Street DH3 3PT* Tel 0191-388 4027 E-mail revdunne@aol.com

DUNNE, Nigel Kenneth. BA BTh. **d** 90 **p** 91. C Dublin St Bart w Leeson Park *D & G* 90-93; C Taney 93-95; I Blessington w Kilbride, Ballymore Eustace etc 95-03; Can Ch Ch Cathl Dublin 01-03; I Bandon Union *C, C & R* from 03. *The Rectory, Castle Road, Bandon, Cork, Irish Republic* Tel (00353) (23) 41259 E-mail nidunne@oceanfree.net

DUNNETT, John Frederick. b 58. CQSW82 SS Coll Cam MA84 Worc Coll Ox MSc83. Trin Coll Bris BA87. **d** 88 **p** 89. C Kirkheaton *Wakef* 88-93; V Cranham Park *Chelmsf* from 93. *St Luke's Vicarage, 201 Front Lane, Upminster RM14 1LD* Tel (01708) 222122 E-mail jd@johndunnett.co.uk

DUNNETT, Keith Owen. b 66. Cranfield Inst of Tech BSc87. Trin Coll Bris BA00. **d** 00 **p** 01. C Walton and Trimley *St E* from 00; V Clayton *Bradf* from 03. *The Vicarage, Clayton Lane, Clayton, Bradford BD14 6AX* Tel (01274) 880373 Mobile 07779-832286 E-mail keith.dunnett@virgin.net

DUNNETT, Robert Curtis. b 31. SS Coll Cam BA54 MA58. Oak Hill Th Coll 56. **d** 58 **p** 59. C Markfield *Leic* 58-60; C Bucknall and Bagnall *Lich* 60-73; Perm to Offic *Birm* from 72; Chapl and Tutor Birm Bible Inst 72-79; Vice-Prin 84-92; Hon Vice-Prin from 92; rtd 96. *30 Station Road, Harborne, Birmingham B17 9LY* Tel 0121-428 3945 Fax 428 3370

DUNNILL, Canon John David Stewart. b 50. UEA BA72 Ox Univ CertEd76 Birm Univ DipTh82 PhD88. Ripon Coll Cuddesdon 86. **d** 88 **p** 89. C Tupsley *Heref* 88-92; Lect Glouc Sch for Min 89-91; Sen Lect Murdoch Univ Australia from 92; Dir Bibl and Th Studies Angl Inst of Th from 92; Can Perth from 99. *School of Social Inquiry, Murdoch University, Murdoch, W Australia 6150* Tel (0061) (8) 9360 6369 *or* 9383 4403 Fax 9360 6480 E-mail dunnill@socs.murdoch.edu.au

DUNNING, Adam Jonathan. b 73. Regent's Park Coll Ox BA95 MA99 Birm Univ PhD00. Westcott Ho Cam. **d** 99 **p** 00. C Evesham w Norton and Lenchwick *Worc* 99-02; C Hamstead St Paul *Birm* from 02. *97 Institute Road, Birmingham B14 7EU* Tel 0121-444 5551 E-mail a.dunning@ukonline.co.uk

DUNNING, David John. b 52. Liv Univ BA73 Ox Univ CertEd76 Open Univ BA96. Ripon Coll Cuddesdon 79. **d** 82 **p** 84. C N Gosforth *Newc* 82-83; C Willington Team 83-85; C Bellingham/Otterburn Gp 85-86; Chapl Magd Coll Sch Ox 86-94; Hd of Theol Sherborne Sch from 94; Perm to Offic *Sarum* 94-99; NSM Sherborne w Castleton and Lillington from 99. *10 St Aldhelm's Road, Sherborne DT9 4EB* Tel (01935) 810432 E-mail david.dunning@ukgateway.net

DUNNING, John Stanley. b 19. Lon Univ BSc41. EMMTC 78. **d** 81 **p** 82. NSM Nottingham St Pet and St Jas *S'well* 81-85; rtd 85; Perm to Offic *S'well* from 85. *12 Brookhill Drive, Wollaton, Nottingham NG8 2PS* Tel 0115-928 3357

DUNNING, Martyn Philip. b 51. Reading Univ MSc79 Dur Univ MA95 MRTPI77. St Jo Coll Dur 89. **d** 92 **p** 93. C Beverley Minster *York* 92-96; P-in-c Leven w Catwick 96-97; P-in-c Brandesburton 96-97; R Brandesburton and Leven w Catwick 97-02; RD N Holderness 97-02; P-in-c Scarborough St Mary w Ch Ch and H Apostles from 02. *St Mary's Vicarage, 1 North Cliff Gardens, Scarborough YO12 6PR* Tel (01723) 371354

DUNNINGS, Reuben Edward. b 36. Clifton Th Coll 62. **d** 66 **p** 67. C Longfleet *Sarum* 66-70; C Melksham 70-73; TV 73-78; R Broughton Gifford w Gt Chalfield 78-84; V Holt St Kath 78-84; R Broughton Gifford, Gt Chalfield and Holt 85-86; V Salisbury St Fran 86-99; P-in-c Stratford sub Castle 98-99; V Salisbury St Fran and Stratford sub Castle 99-01; rtd 01. *11 Cornbrash Rise, Hilperton, Trowbridge BA14 7TS* Tel (01225) 768834

DUNSETH, George William. b 52. Multnomah Sch of the Bible Oregon BRE79. Oak Hill Th Coll BA85. **d** 85 **p** 86. C Cheadle All Hallows *Ches* 85-88; C New Borough and Leigh *Sarum* 88-91; V Thurnby w Stoughton *Leic* from 91. *The Vicarage, Thurnby, Leicester LE7 9PN* Tel 0116-241 2263 E-mail george.dunseth@btinternet.com

DUNSTAN, Canon Alan Leonard. b 28. Wadh Coll Ox BA49 MA52. Ripon Hall Ox 50. **d** 52 **p** 53. C Barford *Cov* 52-55; C Brompton H Trin Lon 55-57; V Gravesend St Mary *Roch* 57-63; Chapl Wycliffe Hall Ox 63-66; Vice-Prin 66-70; Hon C Ox St Mary V w St Cross and St Pet *Ox* 70-78; Chapl Keble Coll Ox 70-71; Vice-Prin Ripon Hall Ox 71-74; Acting Prin 74-75; Vice-

Prin Ripon Coll Cuddesdon 75-78; Can Res Glouc Cathl *Glouc* 78-93; rtd 93; Perm to Offic *Truro* from 93. *7 The Crescent, Truro TR1 3ES* Tel (01872) 279604

DUNSTAN, Prof Gordon Reginald. b 17. CBE89. Leeds Univ BA38 MA39 Ex Univ Hon DD73 Leic Univ Hon LLD86 Hon MRCP87 FRCOG90 Hon FRCGP93 Hon FRCP95 Hon FRCPCH96. Coll of Resurr Mirfield 39. **d** 41 **p** 42. C King Cross *Wakef* 41-45; C Huddersfield St Pet 45-46; Subwarden St Deiniol's Lib Hawarden 46-49; Lect Wm Temple Coll 46-49; V Sutton Courtenay w Appleford *Ox* 49-55; Lect Ripon Hall Ox 53-55; Clerical Sec C of E Coun for Soc Work 55-63; Sec Ch Assembly Jt Bd of Studies 63-66; Ed *Theology* 65-75; Min Can Windsor 55-59; Min Can Westmr Abbey 59-67; Dep P in O 59-64; P in O 64-76; Select Preacher Cam Univ 60 and 77; Can Th Leic Cathl *Leic* 66-82; Prof Moral and Soc Th K Coll Lon 67-82; Chapl to The Queen 76-87; rtd 82; Perm to Offic *Ex* from 82. *33 Maple Dene, 10-14 St Agnes Road, Moseley, Birmingham B13 9PW* Tel 0121-449 7486

DUNSTAN, Gregory John Orchard. b 50. Cam Univ MA75 TCD BTh90. CITC 87. **d** 90 **p** 91. C Ballymena w Ballyclug *Conn* 90-93; I Belfast St Matt from 93. *Shankill Rectory, 51 Ballygomartin Road, Belfast BT13 3LA* Tel (028) 9071 4325 Fax as telephone

DUNSTAN, Kenneth Ian. b 40. ACP Goldsmiths' Coll Lon BEd71. Oak Hill NSM Course 86. **d** 88 **p** 89. NSM Creeksea w Althorne, Latchingdon and N Fambridge *Chelmsf* 88-94; P-in-c Woodham Mortimer w Hazeleigh 94-98; P-in-c Woodham Walter 94-98; NSM Bradwell on Sea from 99. *35 Ely Close, Southminster CM0 7AQ* Tel (01621) 772199
E-mail ken@kdunstan.go-plus.net

DUNSTAN, Mark Philip. b 70. Middx Univ BSc93. Oak Hill Th Coll BA03. **d** 03. C Stranton *Dur* from 03. *41 Arncliffe Gardens, Hartlepool TS26 9JG* Tel (01429) 277591
E-mail dunstan_mark@hotmail.com

DUNSTAN-MEADOWS, Victor Richard. b 63. Chich Th Coll BTh90. **d** 90 **p** 91. C Clacton St Jas *Chelmsf* 90-93; C Stansted Mountfitchet 93-95; CF 95-00; Chapl RAF from 00. *Chaplaincy Services (RAF), HQ, Personnel and Training Command, RAF Innsworth, Gloucester GL3V 1EZ* Tel (01452) 712612 ext 5164 Fax 510828

DUNTHORNE, Paul. b 63. K Coll Lon LLB85 Paris Sorbonne 85 St Jo Coll Dur BA90 Dur Univ MA98. Cranmer Hall Dur 88. **d** 91 **p** 92. C Heacham and Sedgeford *Nor* 91-95; C Eastbourne H Trin *Chich* 95-98; P-in-c Preston and Ridlington w Wing and Pilton *Pet* 98-00; Local Min Officer 98-00; CME Officer *Heref* from 00. *7 Devereux Close, Hereford HR1 1QR* Tel (01432) 267918 E-mail paul@dunthorne55.freeserve.co.uk

DUNWICH, Suffragan Bishop of. *See* YOUNG, The Rt Revd Clive

DUNWOODY, Stephen John Herbert. b 71. Glam Univ BA92. St Steph Ho Ox BTh96. **d** 96 **p** 97. C Skewen *Llan* 96-98; C Roath 98-99; C Stanley *Liv* 99-02; TV Colyton, Southleigh, Offwell, Widworthy etc *Ex* 02-03; V Offwell, Northleigh, Farway, Cotleigh etc from 03. *The Rectory, Offwell, Honiton EX14 9SB* Tel (01404) 831480

DUNWOODY, Thomas Herbert Williamson. b 35. TCD BA58 MA64. TCD Div Sch Div Test59. **d** 59 **p** 60. C Newcastle *D & D* 59-61; Asst Missr Ballymacarrett St Martin 61-63; C Lurgan Ch the Redeemer 63-66; I Ardglass w Dunsford 66-74; Offg Chapl RAF 66-74; V Urmston *Man* 74-85; I Wexford w Ardcolm and Killurin *C & O* 85-93; Can Ferns Cathl 88-93; I Newry *D & D* 93-02; rtd 02. *3 Eden Court, Markethill, Co Armagh BT60 1LH* Tel (028) 3755 2893 E-mail thw_dunwoody@tiscali.co.uk

DUPLOCK, Canon Peter Montgomery. b 16. OBE76. Qu Coll Cam BA38 MA42. Ridley Hall Cam 38. **d** 40 **p** 41. C Morden *S'wark* 40-43; CF (EC) 43-47; R Nottingham St Nic *S'well* 47-52; R Loddington w Harrington *Pet* 52-55; V Kettering St Andr 55-64; Chapl Geneva *Eur* 64-71; Chapl Brussels w Charleroi, Liege and Waterloo 71-81; Chan Brussels Cathl 81; Adn NW Eur 81; rtd 81; Hon Can Brussels Cathl *Eur* from 81; R Breamore *Win* 81-86; Perm to Offic 86-95; Perm to Offic *Sarum* 86-98. *9 Capel Court, The Burgage, Prestbury, Cheltenham GL52 3EL* Tel (01242) 580518

DUPREE, Hugh Douglas. b 50. Univ of the South (USA) BA72 Virginia Th Sem MDiv75 Ch Ch Ox MA86 Ball Coll Ox DPhil88. **d** 75 **p** 76. USA 75-80; Hon C Ox St Mich w St Martin and All SS *Ox* 80-87; Asst Chapl Ball Coll Ox 84-87; Chapl from 87; Chapl HM Pris Ox 88-97. *Balliol College, Oxford OX1 3BJ* Tel (01865) 277777 *or* 721261

DUPUY, Alan Douglas William. b 48. Kent Univ Dip Chr Th 00. SEITE 98. **d** 00 **p** 01. NSM Forest Hill St Aug *S'wark* 00-01; NSM S Dulwich St Steph from 01. *16 Dominic Court, 43 The Gardens, London SE22 9QR* Tel (020) 8695 5769 Mobile 07960-226518 Fax 8693 4175
E-mail alandupuy@compuserve.com

DURAND, Noel Douglas. b 33. Jes Coll Cam BA57 MA61 BD76. Westcott Ho Cam 72. **d** 74 **p** 75. C Eaton *Nor* 74-78; V Cumnor *Ox* 78-01; rtd 01; Perm to Offic *Nor* from 01. *21 Nelson Road, Sheringham NR26 8BU* Tel (01263) 822388

DURAND, Stella Evelyn Brigid, Lady. b 42. TCD BA64 Sorbonne Univ Paris DèS65 St Jo Coll Dur DipTh70. CITC BTh99. **d** 00. C Kiltegan w Hacketstown, Clonmore and Moyne *C & O* from 00. *The Rectory, Kiltegan, Co Wicklow, Irish Republic* Tel (00353) (059) 647 3368

DURANT, Robert-Ashton. b 23. OSB St D Coll Lamp BA47. Bp Burgess Hall Lamp. **d** 48 **p** 49. C Brynmawr *S & B* 48-49; C Fleur-de-Lis *Mon* 49-51; C Bassaleg 51-56; CF (TA) 53-55; V Trellech and Cwmcarvan *Mon* 56-69; Priest Tymawr Convent 56-69; V Slapton *Ex* 69-81; V Strete 69-81; R E Allington, Slapton and Strete 81-92; rtd 92; Perm to Offic *Ex* from 92. *18 Grosvenor Avenue, Torquay TQ2 7LA* Tel (01803) 613710

DURANT, William John Nicholls. b 55. K Coll Lon BA76 DipTh DPS. St Jo Coll Nottm 77. **d** 80 **p** 81. C Norwood St Luke *S'wark* 80-83; C Morden 83-88; TV 88-92; V Frindsbury w Upnor *Roch* 92-00; CF from 00. *c/o MOD Chaplains (Army)* Tel (01980) 615804 Fax 615800

DURBIN, Roger. b 41. Bris Sch of Min 83. **d** 85 **p** 86. NSM Bedminster *Bris* 85-91; NSM Henbury 91-94; NSM Clifton All SS w St Jo from 94. *13 Charbury Walk, Bristol BS11 9UU* Tel 0117-985 8404

DURELL, Miss Jane Vavasor. b 32. Bedf Coll Lon BSc55. Gilmore Ho 61 Lambeth STh64. **dss** 86 **d** 87 **p** 94. Banbury *Ox* 86-87; Par Dn 87-92; rtd 92; Perm to Offic *Nor* 92-94 and from 02; NSM Norwich St Mary Magd w St Jas 94-02. *51 Branford Road, Norwich NR3 4QD* Tel (01603) 486084

DURHAM, Mrs Eleanore Jane. b 62. St Andr Univ MTheol84. Trin Coll Bris MA01. **d** 01 **p** 02. C Childwall All SS *Liv* from 01. *80 Green Lane North, Childwall, Liverpool L16 8NL* Tel 0151-737 2214 E-mail janedurham@onetel.net.uk

DURHAM, Archdeacon of. *See* CONWAY, The Ven Stephen David

DURHAM, Bishop of. *See* WRIGHT, The Rt Revd Nicholas Thomas

DURHAM, Dean of. *See* SADGROVE, The Very Revd Michael

DURIE, David James. b 63. Cen Lancs Univ BA93 St Martin's Coll Lanc MA99. Carl and Blackb Dioc Tr Inst 97. **d** 99 **p** 00. C Briercliffe *Blackb* 99-01. *Address temp unknown* E-mail david.durie@talk21.com

DURIE, Ian Geoffrey Campbell. b 44. CBE91. St Jo Coll Cam BA69 MA75. St Jo Coll Nottm MA98. **d** 98 **p** 99. NSM Battersea Rise St Mark *S'wark* from 98. *24 Parma Crescent, London SW11 1LT* Tel (020) 7978 7650 *or* 7223 6188 Fax 7978 7651 E-mail ianduriе@surfaid.org

DURING, Arthur Christopher. b 59. Sierra Leone Th Hall 80. **d** 83 **p** 85. Sierra Leone 83-86; Perm to Offic *S'wark* from 00. *23 Kynaston House, Challice Way, London SW2 3ER* Tel (020) 8671 9762

DURKAN, Miss Barbara Isobel Mary. b 43. Kent Univ BSc71 MPhil00 Ch Ch Coll Cant MA95 Sarum Dioc Tr Coll CertEd65. SEITE 99. **d** 01 **p** 02. Aux Chapl HM Pris Standford Hill from 01; NSM Newington w Hartlip and Stockbury *Cant* from 01. *HM Prison Standford Hill, Church Road, Eastchurch, Sheerness ME12 4AA* Tel (01795) 880441 Fax 880267

DURKIN, Anthony Michael. b 45. Sarum & Wells Th Coll 87. **d** 89 **p** 90. C Faversham *Cant* 89-92; V St Margarets-at-Cliffe w Westcliffe etc from 92. *The Vicarage, Sea Street, St Margarets-at-Cliffe, Dover CT15 6AR* Tel (01304) 852179 Fax 853898 E-mail anthony-durkin@care4free.net

DURNDELL, Miss Irene Frances. b 43. Nottm Univ DipRE78. Trin Coll Bris DipHE86. **dss** 86 **d** 87 **p** 94. Erith Ch Ch *Roch* 86-93; Par Dn 87-93; Par Dn Erith St Paul 93-94; C 94-98; Asst Dir of Tr 93-98; V Falconwood from 98. *The Vicarage, The Green, Welling DA16 2PD* Tel (020) 8298 0065 Fax as telephone

DURNELL, John. b 32. St Aid Birkenhead 64. **d** 66 **p** 67. C Newport w Longford *Lich* 66-69; P-in-c Church Aston 69-72; R 72-77; V Weston Rhyn 77-82; P-in-c Petton w Cockshutt and Weston Lullingfield etc 82-83; R Petton w Cockshutt, Welshampton and Lyneal etc 83-97; rtd 97; Perm to Offic *Lich* from 97. *Fronlwyd, Hirnant, Penybontfawr, Oswestry SY10 0HP* Tel (01691) 870686

DURNFORD, Canon Catherine Margaret. b 36. St Mary's Coll Dur BA57 DipEd58. Gilmore Course 78 NW Ord Course 77. **d** 87 **p** 94. Area Sec USPG *York* and *Ripon* 82-89; Par Dn Whitby *York* 89-92; Par Dn Redcar 92-94; C 94; C Selby Abbey 94-97; V New Marske from 97; V Wilton from 97; Can and Preb York Minster from 01; rtd 03; Perm to Offic *York* from 03. *18 Canongate, Cottingham HU16 4DG* Tel (01482) 844868

DURNFORD, John Edward. b 30. CCC Cam BA53 MA61. Linc Th Coll 53. **d** 55 **p** 56. C Selby Abbey *York* 55-58; C Newland St Jo 58-62; S Rhodesia 62-65; Rhodesia 65-76; V Hebden Bridge *Wakef* 76-84; RD Calder Valley 82-84; P-in-c Blanchland w Hunstanworth *Newc* 84-90; P-in-c Edmundbyers w Muggleswick *Dur* 84-90; RD Corbridge *Newc* 88-93; R Blanchland w Hunstanworth and Edmundbyers etc 90-94; rtd 94; Perm to Offic *Newc* from 94. *7 Islestone Drive, Seahouses NE68 7XB* Tel (01665) 721032

DURNFORD, Comdr Peter Jeffrey. b 20. Bps' Coll Cheshunt 63. **d** 65 **p** 66. C Edmonton St Alphege *Lon* 65-67; Chapl Bonn w

Cologne *Eur* 67-69; R St Just in Roseland *Truro* 70-82; P-in-c Ruan Lanihorne w Philleigh 70-82; P-in-c St Mewan 82-85; Chapl Mount Edgcumbe Hospice 82-88; rtd 85; Perm to Offic *Truro* from 85. *8 Tredenham Road, St Mawes, Truro TR2 5AN* Tel (01326) 270793

DURRAN, Ms Margaret. b 47. Lady Spencer Chu Coll of Educn CertEd70 Surrey Univ MSc96. S'wark Ord Course 88. **d** 91 **p** 94. Par Dn Brixton St Matt *S'wark* 91-94; C 94; C Streatham St Leon 94-95; V Walworth St Chris 95-99; Hist Churches Project Officer *Lon* from 99; Hon C S'wark St Geo the Martyr w St Alphege & St Jude *S'wark* from 99. *Ground Floor Flat, 2 St Alphege House, Pocock Street, London SE1 0BJ* Tel and fax (020) 7401 8808 Mobile 07711-906442 E-mail maggie.durran@virgin.net

DURRANS, Canon Anthony. b 37. Leeds Univ BA59. Linc Th Coll 60. **d** 62 **p** 63. C Stanningley St Thos *Ripon* 62-64; C Chorlton upon Medlock *Man* 64-69; SCM Field Sec Man 64-66; NW Sec 66-68; Asst Gen Sec 68-69; R Old Trafford St Jo *Man* 69-80; V Langley All SS and Martyrs 80-82; TR Langley and Parkfield 82-85; R Man Miles Platting 85-87; P-in-c Man Apostles 85-87; R Man Apostles w Miles Platting 87-97; Hon Can Man Cathl from 86; AD Ardwick 91-96; P-in-c Stretford All SS from 97. *The Rectory, 233 Barton Road, Stretford, Manchester M32 9RB* Tel 0161-865 1350

DURRANT, Melvyn. b 59. Leeds Univ BA82 St Luke's Coll Ex PGCE86. Trin Coll Bris 01. **d** 03. C Watercombe *Sarum* from 03. *51 Binghams Road, Crossways, Dorchester DT2 8BW* E-mail mel@durranthome.freeserve.co.uk

DURRANT, Reginald Patrick Bickersteth. b 37. AKC64. **d** 65 **p** 66. C Summertown *Ox* 65-68; C Ascot Heath 68-71; C Heene *Chich* 71-76; R Burwash 76-94; rtd 94. *17 Glebeland Close, West Stafford, Dorchester DT2 8AE*

DURSTON, Canon David Michael Karl. b 36. Em Coll Cam BA60 MA64. Clifton Th Coll 61. **d** 63 **p** 64. C Wednesfield Heath *Lich* 63-66; Project Officer Grubb Inst 67-78; Ind Chapl *Lich* 78-84; P-in-c W Bromwich St Paul 78-82; V 82-84; Adult Educn Officer 84-92; Preb Lich Cathl 89-92; Can Res and Chan Sarum Cathl *Sarum* from 92; TR Wylye and Till Valley from 03; Can and Preb Sarum Cathl from 03. *The Rectory, Duck Street, Steeple Langford, Salisbury SP3 4NH* Tel (01722) 792832

DUSSEK, Jeremy Neil James Christopher. b 70. St Jo Coll Dur BA92 DipTh. Westcott Ho Cam 96. **d** 97 **p** 98. C Whickham *Dur* 97-00; C Fareham H Trin *Portsm* 00-01; TV from 01. *The Vicarage, Hillson Drive, Fareham PO15 6PF* Tel (01329) 843705 or 232688 E-mail jeremy@dussek.fsnet.co.uk

DUST, Simon Philip. b 63. Oak Hill Th Coll BA95. **d** 95 **p** 96. C Chesham Bois *Ox* 95-00; C-in-c Bushmead CD *St Alb* from 00. *73 Hawkfields, Luton LU2 7NW* Tel (01582) 487327 E-mail simondust@ntlworld.com

DUTFIELD, Canon Alan. b 20. Linc Th Coll 54. **d** 55 **p** 56. C Kimberworth *Sheff* 55-60; V New Rossington 60-71; R Old Brumby *Linc* 71-77; TR 77-86; Can and Preb Linc Cathl 81-86; RD Manlake 82-86; rtd 86; Perm to Offic *Linc* 89-94 and from 01. *30 Barnes Green, Scotter, Gainsborough DN21 3RW* Tel (01724) 764220

DUTHIE, Elliot Malcolm. b 31. Clifton Th Coll 63. **d** 66 **p** 67. C Eccleston St Luke *Liv* 66-69; Malaysia 70-75; P-in-c Bootle St Leon *Liv* 76-78; V 78-81; V Charlton Kings H Apostles *Glouc* 81-94; rtd 94; Perm to Offic *Glouc* 94-00. *13 Veitch Gardens, Alphington, Exeter EX2 8AB* Tel (01392) 254787

DUTTON, Andrew Rivers George. b 49. Bris Univ BSc71 PGCE72 Reading Univ MSc79 Open Univ DMEd92. EAMTC 98. **d** 98 **p** 99. NSM Kettering SS Pet and Paul *Pet* from 98; Chapl Bp Stopford Sch from 99. *10 Beardsley Gardens, Kettering NN15 5UB* Tel (01536) 392401

DUTTON, Leonard Arthur. b 35. Bps' Coll Cheshunt 63. **d** 66 **p** 67. C Knighton St Jo *Leic* 66-70; C Chilvers Coton w Astley Cov 70-73; R Hathern *Leic* 73-79; V Ashby-de-la-Zouch H Trin from 79. *Holy Trinity Vicarage, 1 Trinity Close, Ashby-de-la-Zouch LE65 2GQ* Tel (01530) 412339

DUVAL, Canon Philip Ernest. b 18. MBE45. Mert Coll Ox BA45 MA45. Westcott Ho Cam 47. **d** 47 **p** 48. C Tooting All SS *S'wark* 47-51; C Raynes Park St Sav 51-55; V Balham St Mary 55-66; R Merstham and Gatton 66-86; Hon Can S'wark Cathl 78-86; rtd 86; Perm to Offic *Cant* from 88. *2 The Holt, Frogs Hill, Newenden, Hawkhurst TN18 5PX* Tel (01797) 252578

DUVALL, Michael James. b 31. **d** 79 **p** 80. Hon C Kings Langley *St Alb* 79-89; Hon C Selworthy and Timberscombe and Wootton Courtenay *B & W* 89-95; Hon C Luccombe 89-95; Hon C Selworthy, Timberscombe, Wootton Courtenay etc 95-97; rtd 97; Perm to Offic *B & W* from 97. *Dovery Edge, 19 Hawkcombe View, Porlock, Minehead TA24 8NB* Tel (01643) 862834

DUXBURY, Clive Robert. b 49. St Jo Coll Nottm DCM92. **d** 92 **p** 93. C Horwich *Man* 92-93; C Horwich and Rivington 93-96; P-in-c Bury St Paul 96-00; P-in-c Bury Ch King 98-00; P-in-c Freethorpe, Wickhampton, Halvergate w Tunstall *Nor* 00-02; P-in-c Reedham w Cantley w Limpenhoe and Southwood 00-02; R Freethorpe, Wickhampton, Halvergate etc from 02. *The Rectory, Church Road, Reedham, Norwich NR13 3TZ* Tel (01493) 700268 E-mail clive@cduxbury.freeserve.co.uk

DUXBURY, Canon James Campbell. b 33. Tyndale Hall Bris 58. **d** 61 **p** 62. C Southport SS Simon and Jude *Liv* 61-65; V Tittensor *Lich* 65-70; V W Bromwich Gd Shep w St Jo 70-75; P-in-c Wellington w Eyton 75-80; V 80-85; V Padiham *Blackb* 85-01; Hon Can Blackb Cathl 97-01; rtd 01; Can Emer Blackb Cathl *Blackb* from 01; Perm to Offic from 01. *1 Gills Croft, Clitheroe BB7 1LJ* Tel (01200) 429261

DUXBURY, Miss Margaret Joan. b 30. JP81. DipEd52. St Jo Coll Nottm 83. **dss** 84 **d** 87 **p** 94. Thornthwaite w Thruscross and Darley *Ripon* 84-86; Middleton St Cross 86-90; C 87-90; Par Dn Dacre w Hartwith and Darley w Thornthwaite 90-94; C 94-96; rtd 97; NSM Bishop Monkton and Burton Leonard *Ripon* 97-01. *Scot Beck House, Darley, Harrogate HG3 2QN* Tel (01423) 780451

DYALL, Henry. b 19. ARICS51 Lon Univ BSc51 LLB58 MRICS01. S'wark Ord Course 81. **d** 82 **p** 83. Hon C St Mary Cray and St Paul's Cray *Roch* 82-84; Perm to Offic 84-86; Hon C Sidcup Ch Ch 86-02; rtd 02; Perm to Offic *Roch* from 02. *2 Hillsley Court, 8 Elm Road, Sidcup DA14 6AB* Tel (020) 8308 0769

DYAS, Stuart Edwin. b 46. Lon Univ BSc67. Ridley Hall Cam 78. **d** 80 **p** 81. C Bath Weston St Jo *B & W* 80; C Bath Weston St Jo w Kelston 81-83; C Tunbridge Wells St Jas *Roch* 83-90; V Nottingham St Jude *S'well* 90-99; AD Nottingham Cen 93-98; V Long Eaton St Jo *Derby* from 99. *St John's Vicarage, 59 Trowell Grove, Long Eaton, Nottingham NG10 4AY* Tel 0115-973 4819

DYAS, Sylvia Denise (Dee). b 51. Bedf Coll Lon BA72 Nottm Univ PhD99. St Jo Coll Nottm 98. **d** 00 **p** 01. Tutor St Jo Coll Nottm from 00; Perm to Offic *Derby* from 00. *St John's Vicarage, 59 Trowell Grove, Long Eaton, Nottingham NG10 4AY* Tel 0115-973 4819 or 925 5388 E-mail dyas@globalnet.co.uk

DYE, Mrs Margaret Mary. b 48. N Ord Course 95. **d** 98 **p** 99. C Morley St Pet w Churwell *Wakef* 98-02; TV Morley from 02. *The Vicarage, 4 Lewisham Street, Morley, Leeds LS27 0LA* Tel 0113-252 3783 E-mail s.m.dye@btinternet.com

DYER, Canon Anne Catherine. b 57. St Anne's Coll Ox MA80 Lon Univ MTh89. Wycliffe Hall Ox 84. **d** 87 **p** 94. NSM Beckenham St Jo *Roch* 87-88; NSM Beckenham St Geo 88-89; Hon Par Dn Luton Ch 89-94; Chapl for Evang 93-98; NSM Istead Rise 94-98; Min Development Officer from 98; Hon Can Roch Cathl from 00. *Frindsbury Vicarage, 4 Parsonage Lane, Rochester ME2 4UR* Tel (01634) 714301 E-mail adyer82120@aol.com

DYER, Ms Catherine Jane. b 46. Westf Coll Lon BA68. Ox NSM Course 85. **d** 88 **p** 94. NSM Wokingham All SS *Ox* 88-90; C 90-95; TV W Slough 95-01; P-in-c Linslade from 01; AD Mursley from 03. *Linslade Vicarage, Vicarage Road, Leighton Buzzard LU7 2LP* Tel (01525) 372149 E-mail cdyer@fish.co.uk

DYER, Canon Christine Anne. b 53. Nottm Univ BEd75. EMMTC 81. **dss** 84 **d** 87 **p** 94. Mickleover St Jo *Derby* 85-87; Par Dn 87-90; Dioc Youth Adv 86-90; Par Educn Adv 90-98; Dioc Youth Officer from 91; P-in-c Morton and Stonebroom 98-99; P-in-c Shirland 98-99; R Morton and Stonebroom w Shirland from 99; Hon Can Derby Cathl from 02. *The Rectory, Main Road, Shirland, Alfreton DE55 6BB* Tel (01773) 836003 E-mail c.a.dyer@talk21.com

DYER, Mrs Gillian Marie. b 50. Sheff Univ BA71 Leic Univ CertEd72 Dip Counselling 99. S Dios Minl Tr Scheme 81. **dss** 84 **d** 87 **p** 94. Witney *Ox* 84-85; Carl St Cuth w St Mary *Carl* 86-89; Par Dn 87-89; Dioc Communications Officer 86-89; Par Dn Kirkbride w Newton Arlosh 89-91; Par Dn Carl H Trin and St Barn 91-94; TV 94-97; P-in-c Arbroath *Bre* 01-03; P-in-c Lower Darwen St Jas *Blackb* from 03. *The Vicarage, Stopes Brow, Lower Darwen, Darwen BB3 0QP* Tel (01254) 677903 E-mail tergill@aol.com

DYER, Canon James Henry. b 14. ALCD39. **d** 39 **p** 40. C S Hackney St Jo w Ch Ch *Lon* 39-43; C New Malden and Coombe *S'wark* 43-50; New Zealand from 50; V Murchison 50-56; V Collingwood 56-59; V Spring Creek 59-67; V Amuri 67-70; V Motupiko 70-77; Hon Can Nelson Cathl 85. *7 Talbot Street, Richmond, Nelson, New Zealand* Tel (0064) (3) 554 8638 E-mail james.dyer@xtra.co.nz

DYER, Janet. b 35. LNSM course 77. **dss** 85 **d** 86 **p** 94. Balerno *Edin* 85-86; NSM 86-93; Chapl Edin R Infirmary 88-93; Dn-in-c Roslin (Rosslyn Chpl) *Edin* 93-94; P-in-c 94-97; C Livingston LEP from 97. *499 Lanark Road West, Balerno EH14 7AL* Tel 0131-449 3767 E-mail adrian@dyer499.freeserve.co.uk

DYER, John Alan. b 31. Linc Coll Ox BA53 MA57 Lon Univ BD58. Tyndale Hall Bris 53. **d** 56 **p** 57. C Weston-super-Mare Ch Ch *B & W* 56-60; V Battersea St Geo w St Andr *S'wark* 60-69; Australia from 69; C-in-c Narraweena 69-74; R 74-96; AD Warringah 85-92; rtd 96. *5 Crisallen Street, Port Macquarie, NSW, Australia 2444* Tel (0061) (2) 6584 2868 E-mail johndy@ozemail.com.au

DYER, Ronald Whitfield. b 29. Solicitor 51. Guildf Dioc Min Course 91. **d** 95 **p** 96. NSM Fleet *Guildf* 95-99; rtd 99; Perm to Offic *Guildf* from 99. *7 Dukes Mead, Fleet GU13 8HA* Tel (01252) 621457

DYER, Stephen Roger. b 57. Brunel Univ BSc. Wycliffe Hall Ox 83. **d** 86 **p** 87. C Beckenham St Jo *Roch* 86-89; C Luton Ch Ch 89-94; V Istead Rise 94-01; V Frindsbury w Upnor from 01. *Frindsbury Vicarage, 4 Parsonage Lane, Rochester ME2 4UR* Tel (01634) 717580

DYER, Miss Sylvia Mary. b 30. Westf Coll Lon BA66. Ab Dioc Tr Course 90. **d** 95 **p** 98. *The Sheiling, Westfield Road, Turriff AB53 4AF* Tel (01888) 562530

DYER, Terence Neville. b 50. Sheff Univ BEng71 Leic Univ PGCE72. Carl Dioc Tr Course 86. **d** 89 **p** 90. NSM Kirkbride w Newton Arlosh *Carl* 89-91; NSM Carl H Trin and St Barn 91-97; NSM Arbroath *Bre* 01; P-in-c Monifieth 01-03; P-in-c Over Darwen St Jas *Blackb* from 03. *The Vicarage, Stopes Brow, Lower Darwen, Darwen BB3 0QP* Tel (01254) 677903
E-mail tergill@aol.com

DYKE, Mrs Elizabeth Muriel. b 55. St Mary's Coll Dur BSc77 St Martin's Coll Lanc PGCE78. Oak Hill Th Coll 92. **d** 94 **p** 95. C High Wycombe *Ox* 94-95; C W Wycombe w Bledlow Ridge, Bradenham and Radnage 95-97; TV Bedworth *Cov* 97-02; V Dunchurch from 02. *The Vicarage, 11 Critchley Drive, Dunchurch, Rugby CV22 6PJ* Tel (01788) 810274

DYKE, George Edward. b 22. TCD BA65 BCom65 MA80. CITC. **d** 79 **p** 80. NSM Dublin St Geo *D & G* 79-82; NSM Tallaght 83-89; NSM Killiney Ballybrack 89-90; Bp's C Dublin St Geo and St Thos and Finglas 90-95; Bp's C Dublin St Geo and St Thos 95-96; Chapl Mountjoy Pris 90-96; Chapl Arbour Hill Pris 90-96; rtd 96. *45 Thornhill Road, Mount Merrion, Co Dublin, Irish Republic* Tel (00353) (1) 288 9376

DYKES, John Edward. b 33. DipHE84. Trin Coll Bris 82. **d** 84 **p** 85. C Rushden w Newton Bromswold *Pet* 84-87; R Heanton Punchardon w Marwood *Ex* 87-97; rtd 97. Perm to Offic *Guildf* 98-01. *42 Ashley Road, Taunton TA1 5BP* Tel (01823) 282507

DYKES, Michael David Allan. b 42. Chich Th Coll 68. **d** 71 **p** 72. C Pocklington w Yapham-cum-Meltonby, Owsthorpe etc *York* 72-75; C Howden 75-77; V Eskdaleside w Ugglebarnby and Sneaton 77-85; R Stokesley from 85; P-in-c Hilton in Cleveland 85-95; P-in-c Seamer in Cleveland from 85. *The Rectory, Leven Close, Stokesley, Middlesbrough TS9 5AP* Tel (01642) 710405
E-mail mdykes@fish.co.uk

DYKES, Philip John. b 61. Loughb Univ BSc83 DIS83. Trin Coll Bris Dip Th Studies 90 ADPS91. **d** 91 **p** 92. C Morden *S'wark* 91-95; C St Helier 95-98; TV Camberley St Paul *Guildf* 98-99; Chapl Elmhurst Ballet Sch from 98; V Camberley Heatherside *Guildf* from 99. *61 Goldney Road, Camberley GU15 1DW* Tel (01276) 514451 E-mail jehu@bigfoot.com

DYMOCK, Michael James Paul. b 45. AKC69. St Aug Coll Cant 70. **d** 70 **p** 71. C Benhilton *S'wark* 70-73; V Clapham St Jo 73-77; P-in-c Clapham Ch Ch 76-77; V Clapham Ch Ch and St Jo 77-80; V Hackbridge and N Beddington 80-84; V Plumstead St Nic 84-92; Sub-Dean Woolwich 87-91; Sub-Dean Greenwich 91-92; V Elham w Denton and Wootton *Cant* 92-95; Perm to Offic *Chich* from 98. *12 West Hill Street, Brighton BN1 3RR* Tel (01273) 325498

DYMOND, Rosie. d 03. C The Hague *Eur* from 03. *Address temp unknown*

DYSON, Frank. b 28. Open Univ BA. Oak Hill Th Coll 60. **d** 62 **p** 63. C Parr *Liv* 62-65; V Newchapel *Lich* 65-77; R Bunwell w Carleton Rode *Nor* 77-79; P-in-c Tibenham 78-80; R Bunwell w Carleton Rode and Tibenham 80-81; R Pakefield 81-93; rtd 93; Perm to Offic *Nor* from 93. *12 Viburnum Green, Lowestoft NR32 2SN* Tel (01502) 574898

DYSON, Peter Whiteley. b 51. Man Univ BA73 LLB75. Qu Coll Birm DipTh80. **d** 81 **p** 82. C Swindon Ch Ch *Bris* 81-84; P-in-c Brislington St Luke 84-91; V Bourne *Guildf* 91-92; Perm to Offic from 02. *10 The Fairfield, Farnham GU9 8AH* Tel (01252) 728361

E

EADE, John Christopher. b 45. Ch Coll Cam BA68 MA72. Linc Th Coll 68. **d** 70 **p** 71. C Portsea N End St Mark *Portsm* 70-73; C Henleaze *Bris* 73-77; V Slad *Glouc* 77-82; V N Bradley, Southwick and Heywood *Sarum* 82-91; R Fovant, Sutton Mandeville and Teffont Evias etc from 91. *The Rectory, Brookwood House, Fovant, Salisbury SP3 5JA* Tel (01722) 714826

EADES, David Julian John. b 74. Univ of Wales BA95 Birm Univ DipTh97. St Jo Coll Dur BA99 Cranmer Hall Dur. **d** 00 **p** 01. C Walbrook Epiphany *Derby* from 00. *70 Violet Street, Derby DE23 8SQ* Tel (01332) 762821

EADES, Jonathan Peter. b 51. Dundee Univ MA74 Edin Univ BD77. Coates Hall Edin 74. **d** 77 **p** 78. Chapl St Paul's Cathl Dundee *Bre* 77-88; Chapl Dundee Univ 79-88; TV Leek and Meerbrook *Lich* 88-96; RD Leek 93-96; TR Wolstanton from 96. *Wolstanton Rectory, Knutton Road, Newcastle ST5 0HU* Tel (01782) 717561

EADY, David Robert. b 43. Salford Univ BSc Birm Univ DSS. Glouc Th Course 82. **d** 85 **p** 86. NSM Highnam, Lassington, Rudford, Tibberton etc *Glouc* 85-95; NSM Stratton, N Cerney, Baunton and Bagendon 95-99; P-in-c Swindon w Uckington and Elmstone Hardwicke from 99. *The Rectory, Rectory Lane, Swindon, Cheltenham GL51 9RD* Tel (01242) 239069
E-mail davideady@hotmail.com

EADY, Timothy William. b 57. Open Univ BA. Cranmer Hall Dur 82. **d** 85 **p** 86. C Boulton *Derby* 85-88; C Portchester *Portsm* 88-92; Relig Progr Adv Ocean Sound Radio from 88; R Brighstone and Brooke w Mottistone *Portsm* from 92. *The Rectory, Rectory Lane, Brighstone, Newport PO30 4QH* Tel (01983) 740267 E-mail timothy_eady@yahoo.co.uk

EAGER, Ms Rosemary Anne McDowall. b 65. St Andr Univ MA87 Strathclyde Univ 88. Ridley Hall Cam CTM95. **d** 95 **p** 96. C Walthamstow St Mary w St Steph *Chelmsf* 95-98; C Walthamstow 98-01; TV Bushbury *Lich* from 01. *The Good Shepherd Vicarage, 17 Goodyear Avenue, Wolverhampton WV10 9JX* Tel (01902) 353546 or 731963

EAGGER, Mrs Christine Mary. b 32. **d** 94 **p** 95. NSM Upper w Lower Gravenhurst *St Alb* 94-03; NSM Gravenhurst, Shillington and Stondon from 03. *43 Cainhoe Road, Clophill, Bedford MK43 4AQ* Tel (01525) 860973
E-mail eagger@fish.co.uk

EAGLE, Canon Julian Charles. b 32. Qu Coll Cam BA56 MA60. Westcott Ho Cam. **d** 58 **p** 59. C Billingham St Aid *Dur* 58-61; C Eastleigh *Win* 61-65; Ind Chapl 65-97; Hon Can Win Cathl 83-97; rtd 97; Perm to Offic *Win* from 97. *123 Cranleigh Road, Bournemouth BH6 5JY* Tel (01202) 429639

EAGLES, Peter Andrew. b 59. K Coll Lon BA82 AKC82 Ox Univ BA88. St Steph Ho Ox 86. **d** 89 **p** 90. C Ruislip St Martin *Lon* 89-92; CF from 92; Perm to Offic *Ripon* from 92. *c/o MOD Chaplains (Army)* Tel (01980) 615804 Fax 615800

EALES, Geoffrey Pellew. b 50. Trin Coll Bris 95. **d** 97 **p** 98. C Uphill *B & W* 97-00; C Weston super Mare Em from 00; Chapl Weston Area Health Trust from 00. *16 The Drive, Weston-super-Mare BS23 2SR* Tel (01934) 612534
E-mail geoffeales@aol.com

EALES, Howard Bernard. b 46. Sarum & Wells Th Coll 73. **d** 76 **p** 77. C Timperley *Ches* 76-78; C Stockport St Thos 78-82; V Wythenshawe Wm Temple Ch *Man* 82-95; V Cheadle Hulme All SS *Ches* from 95; RD Cheadle from 02. *All Saints' Vicarage, 27 Church Road, Cheadle Hulme, Cheadle SK8 7JL* Tel 0161-485 3455

EAMAN, Michael Leslie. b 47. Ridley Hall Cam 87. **d** 89 **p** 90. C Wharton *Ches* 89-93; V Buglawton 93-98; TV Congleton from 98. *St John's Vicarage, Buxton Road, Congleton CW12 2DT* Tel (01260) 273294 E-mail revmike@btopenworld.com

✠**EAMES, The Most Revd and Rt Hon Lord (Robert Henry Alexander).** b 37. QUB LLB60 PhD63 Hon LLD89 TCD Hon LLD92 Cam Univ Hon DD94 Lanc Univ Hon LLD94 Aber Univ Hon DD97 Ex Univ Hon DD99 Hon FGMS88. TCD Div Sch Div Test 60. **d** 63 **p** 64 **c** 75. C Bangor St Comgall *D & D* 63-66; I Gilnahirk 66-74; Bp's Dom Chapl 70-72; I Dundela St Mark 74-75; Bp D & R 75-80; Bp D & D 80-86; Abp Arm from 86. *The See House, Cathedral Close, Armagh BT61 7EE* Tel (028) 3752 7144 Fax 3752 7823
E-mail archbishop@armagh.anglican.org

EARDLEY, John. b 38. Ch Coll Cam BA61. Ridley Hall Cam 60. **d** 62 **p** 63. C Barnston *Ches* 62-65; C Wilmslow 65-67; V Hollingworth 67-75; V Leasowe 75-91; RD Wallasey 86-91; V Church Hulme 91-03; Chapl Cranage Hall Hosp 91-03; rtd 03. *7 Rhodes Road, Heswall, Wirral CH60 9JS* Tel 0151-342 9537

EARDLEY, Canon John Barry. b 35. MBE97. MEd87. AKC62. **d** 63 **p** 64. C Merton St Jas *S'wark* 63-66; C St Helier 66-69; C Bilton *Cov* 69-70; C Canley CD 70-74; P-in-c Church Lawford w Newnham Regis 74-80; P-in-c Leamington Hastings and Birdingbury 82-88; Dioc Educn Officer 83-00; Hon Can Cov Cathl 87-00; rtd 01; Perm to Offic *Cov* from 01. *8 Margaret's Close, Kenilworth CV8 1EN* Tel 024-7630 2345 or 7667 3467
E-mail johnbarry.eardley@ntlworld.com

EARDLEY, Robert Bradford. b 44. St Alb Minl Tr Scheme 90. **d** 93 **p** 94. NSM Digswell and Panshanger *St Alb* 93-96; NSM Wheathampstead 97-98; P-in-c Tewin from 98. *16 Coneydale, Welwyn Garden City AL8 7RZ* Tel (01707) 332609
E-mail stpeter.tewin@virgin.net

EARDLEY, William Robert. b 56. Oak Hill Th Coll DipHE96. **d** 96 **p** 97. C Whitfield *Derby* 96-99; TV Dronfield w Holmesfield from 99. *The Vicarage, Vicarage Close, Holmesfield, Dronfield S18 7WZ* Tel 0114-289 1425
E-mail william@wildenear.freeserve.co.uk

EAREY, Mark Robert. b 65. Loughb Univ BSc87 St Jo Coll Dur BA91. Cranmer Hall Dur 88. **d** 91 **p** 92. C Glen Parva and S

Wigston *Leic* 91-94; C Luton Ch Ch *Roch* 94-97; Praxis Nat Educn Officer Sarum Coll 97-02; TR Morley *Wakef* from 02. *St Peter's Vicarage, Rooms Lane, Morley, Leeds LS27 9PA* Tel 0113-253 2052 E-mail earey@fish.co.uk

EARIS, Stanley Derek. b 50. Univ Coll Dur BA71 BCL80. Ripon Hall Ox BA73 MA80. **d** 74 **p** 75. C Sutton St Jas and Wawne *York* 74-77; C Acomb St Steph 77-81; V Skelmanthorpe *Wakef* 81-87; R Market Deeping *Linc* 87-02; V N Walsham w Antingham *Nor* from 02. *The Vicarage, 28A Yarmouth Road, North Walsham NR28 9AT* Tel (01692) 406380
E-mail derek.earis@ntlworld.com

EARL, David Arthur. b 34. Hartley Victoria Coll 63 Coll of Resurr Mirfield. **d** 83 **p** 83. In Meth Ch 67-83; P-in-c Paddock *Wakef* 83-84; C Huddersfield St Pet and All SS 84-99; rtd 99. *2 Clifton Court, Cleveland Road, Huddersfield HD1 4PU* Tel (01484) 535608

EARL, The Very Revd David Kaye Lee. b 28. TCD BA54. **d** 55 **p** 56. C Chapelizod *D & G* 55-58; I Rathkeale *L & K* 58-65; I Killarney 65-79; Prec Limerick Cathl 77-79; Dean Ferns *C & O* 79-94; I Ferns w Kilbride, Toombe, Kilcormack etc 79-94; rtd 94. *Random, Seafield, Tramore, Co Waterford, Irish Republic* Tel (00353) (51) 390503

EARL, Simon Robert. b 50. Culham Coll of Educn CertEd71 Open Univ BA82. Linc Th Coll 94. **d** 96 **p** 97. C Bexhill St Aug *Chich* 96-99; R Ninfield from 99; V Hooe from 99. *The Rectory, Church Lane, Ninfield, Battle TN33 9JW* Tel (01424) 892308 Fax as telephone E-mail srearl@btopenworld.com

EARL, Stephen Geoffrey Franklyn. b 53. Univ Coll Lon BA76 Goldsmiths' Coll Lon PGCE77. Ridley Hall Cam 91. **d** 93 **p** 94. C Sawston *Ely* 93-96; V Burwell from 96; RD Fordham and Quy from 02. *The Vicarage, High Street, Burwell, Cambridge CB5 0HB* Tel (01638) 741262 Fax as telephone
E-mail earls@fish.co.uk

EARLEY, Stephen John. b 48. Trin Coll Bris DipHE93. **d** 93 **p** 94. C Stroud H Trin *Glouc* 93-98; C Leckhampton SS Phil and Jas w Cheltenham St Jas 98-02; V Nailsworth w Shortwood, Horsley etc from 02. *The Vicarage, Avening Road, Nailsworth, Stroud GL6 0BS* Tel (01453) 832181 E-mail stevearl@ukonline.co.uk

EARNEY, Preb Graham Howard. b 45. AKC67. **d** 68 **p** 69. C Auckland St Helen *Dur* 68-72; C Corsenside *Newc* 72-76; P-in-c 76-79; TV Willington Team 79-83; TR 83-87; Dioc Soc Resp Officer *B & W* 87-95; Dir Bp Mascall Cen *Heref* 95-02; Hon TV Ludlow, Ludford, Ashford Carbonell etc 95-02; Dioc Development Rep 96-02; Local Min Officer from 02; Preb Heref Cathl from 02; RD Condover from 03. *The Rectory, Wistanstow, Craven Arms SY7 8DG* Tel (01588) 672067

EARNSHAW, Alan Mark. b 36. Jes Coll Cam BA42 MA45. Ridley Hall Cam 42. **d** 43 **p** 44. C Portman Square St Paul *Lon* 43-46; Tutor Ridley Hall Cam 46-48; Chapl 48-51; Vice-Prin 51-56; Chapl Eton Coll 56-62; V Hartley Wintney and Elvetham *Win* 62-77; RD Odiham 76-83; V Hartley Wintney, Elvetham, Winchfield etc 77-88; rtd 88; Perm to Offic *Nor* from 89. *3 The Driftway, Sheringham NR26 8LD* Tel (01263) 827497

EARWAKER, John Clifford. b 36. Keble Coll Ox BA59 MA63 Man Univ MEd71. Linc Th Coll 59. **d** 61 **p** 62. C Ecclesall *Sheff* 61-64; Succ St Mary's Cathl *Edin* 64-65; Lic to Offic *Man* 65-69; Lic to Offic *Sheff* from 69; Chapl and Lect Sheff Poly 81-92; Chapl and Lect Sheff Hallam Univ 92-93; rtd 93; Perm to Offic *Sheff* from 93. *89 Dransfield Road, Crosspool, Sheffield S10 5RP* Tel 0114-230 3487

EASEMAN, Robert Leslie. **d** 00 **p** 01. NSM Hunstanton St Edm w Ringstead *Nor* from 00. *5 Lighthouse Close, Hunstanton PE36 6EL* Tel and fax (01485) 535258 Mobile 07941-323218 E-mail robert.easeman@virgin.net

EASON, Canon Cyril Edward. b 21. Leeds Univ BA43 MA67. Coll of Resurr Mirfield 43. **d** 45 **p** 46. C Tonge Moor *Man* 45-51; C Blackpool H Cross *Blackb* 51-53; V Lever Bridge *Man* 53-65; Area Sec USPG *B & W* 65-86; Area Sec USPG *Ex* and *Truro* 75-86; Perm to Offic *Truro* 75-86; Hon Can Mufulira from 85; rtd 86; P-in-c Tilshead, Orcheston and Chitterne *Sarum* 86-92; Perm to Offic *Truro* from 92 and *Ripon* from 95. *11 Bishop's Court, Williamson Drive, Ripon HG4 1AY* Tel (01765) 608300

EAST, Bryan Victor. b 46. Oak Hill Th Coll DipHE93. **d** 93 **p** 94. C Waltham Cross *St Alb* 93-96; C Wotton St Mary *Glouc* 96-99;

V Humberston *Linc* from 99. *The Vicarage, 34 Tetney Road, Humberston, Grimsby DN36 4JF* Tel (01472) 813158

EAST, Mark Richard. b 57. Trin Coll Bris BA89. **d** 89 **p** 90. C Dalton-in-Furness *Carl* 89-93; TV Bucknall and Bagnall *Lich* 93-00; P-in-c Church Coniston *Carl* from 00; P-in-c Torver from 00. *St Andrew's Vicarage, Yewdale Road, Coniston LA21 8DX* Tel (01539) 441262 E-mail mark.east@lineone.net

EAST, Peter Alan. b 61. ACIB89 Southn Univ LLB82. Cranmer Hall Dur 90. **d** 93 **p** 94. C Combe Down w Monkton Combe and S Stoke *B & W* 93-97. *Address withheld by request*

EAST, Reginald Walter. b 16. St Jo Coll Dur BA49 DipTh50. **d** 50 **p** 51. C Loughton St Mary *Chelmsf* 50-52; Youth Chapl 52-57; V W Mersea 57-71; R E Mersea 57-71; C Winterborne Whitechurch w Clenston *Sarum* 71-75; Warden Barn Fellowship Whatcombe Ho 75-80; Lic to Offic 80-85; rtd 85. *Shepherds, 68 Pendre Gardens, Brecon LD3 9EQ* Tel (01874) 624507

EAST, Richard Kenneth. b 47. Oak Hill Th Coll 86. **d** 88 **p** 89. C Necton w Holme Hale *Nor* 88-92; R Garsdon, Lea and Cleverton and Charlton *Bris* from 92; RD Malmesbury 93-99. *The Rectory, Lea, Malmesbury SN16 9PG* Tel (01666) 823861

EAST, Stuart Michael. b 50. Chich Th Coll 86. **d** 88 **p** 89. C Middlesbrough St Martin *York* 88-92; R Upper Ryedale 92-97; V Macclesfield St Paul *Ches* 97-01; C Maidstone St Luke *Cant* 01-03; R Peopleton and White Ladies Aston w Churchill etc *Worc* from 03. *The Rectory, Peopleton, Pershore WR10 2EE* Tel (01905) 840243

EAST KERALA, Bishop of. See SAMUEL, The Most Revd Kunnumpurathu Joseph

EAST RIDING, Archdeacon of. See HARRISON, The Ven Peter Reginald Wallace

EASTELL, Jane Rosamund. b 47. Sheff Univ BA68 DipArch71 RIBA73 Bris Univ BA99. Trin Coll Bris 97. **d** 99 **p** 00. C Backwell w Chelvey and Brockley *B & W* from 99; NSM 99-00; C Chew Stoke w Nempnett Thrubwell from 03. *The Rectory, Pilgrims Way, Chew Stoke, Bristol BS40 8TX*
E-mail jane.eastell@btclick.com

EASTER, Canon Ann Rosemarie. SRN68 Cam Univ DipRS80 Univ of E Lon MBA94. Gilmore Ho 78. **dss** 80 **d** 87 **p** 94. Chapl Asst Newham Gen Hosp 80-89; Stratford St Jo and Ch w Forest Gate St Jas *Chelmsf* 80-89; Par Dn 87-89; Perm to Offic from 89; Chief Exec The Renewal Programme from 95; AD Newham from 97; Hon Can Chelmsf Cathl from 99. *The Vicarage, Larkswood Road, London E4 9DS* Tel (020) 8524 1201 Mobile 07889-799290 Fax (020) 8529 5226
E-mail ann@renewalprogramme.freeserve.co.uk

EASTER, Brian James Bert. b 33. Lon Univ DipTh55 Birm Univ DPS75 PhD83. Tyndale Hall Bris 53 St Aug Coll Cant 56. **d** 57 **p** 58. C Tipton St Martin *Lich* 57-59; Midl Area Sec BCMS 59-64; V Bastard *Birm* 64-72; Chapl Mentally Handicapped S Birm HA 72-94; Chapl Monyhull Hosp Birm 72-94; Lect Birm Univ 86-98; Chapl S Birm Mental Health NHS Trust 94-98; rtd 98; Perm to Offic *Birm* from 98. *24 Dingle Lane, Solihull B91 3NG* Tel 0121-705 8342

EASTER, Stephen Talbot. b 22. St Cath Coll Cam BA47 MA53. Ely Th Coll. **d** 50 **p** 51. C Whitstable All SS *Cant* 50-53; S Rhodesia 53-56; V Womenswold *Cant* 56-61; C-in-c Aylesham CD 56-61; V St Margarets-at-Cliffe w Westcliffe etc 61-85; rtd 85; Perm to Offic *Cant* 85-02. *9-11 Blenheim Road, Deal CT14 7AJ* Tel (01304) 368021

EASTERN ARCHDEACONRY, Archdeacon of the. See CURRAN, The Ven Patrick Martin Stanley

EASTERN ZAMBIA, Bishop of. See OSMERS, The Rt Revd John Robert

EASTGATE, Canon John. b 30. Kelham Th Coll 47. **d** 54 **p** 55. C Ealing St Pet Mt Park *Lon* 54-58; C-in-c Leic St Gabr CD *Leic* 58-64; V Leic St Gabr 64-69; Asst RD Christianity 64-69; V Glen Parva and S Wigston 69-74; V Woodley St Jo the Ev *Ox* 74-83; V Hughenden 83-94; RD Wycombe 87-90; Hon Can Ch Ch 90-94; rtd 94. *11 Orchard Park, Holmer Green, High Wycombe HP15 6QY* Tel (01494) 713761
E-mail john@eastgate1702.fsnet.co.uk

EASTOE, Robin Howard Spenser. b 53. Lon Univ BD75 AKC75. Coll of Resurr Mirfield 77. **d** 78 **p** 79. C Gt Ilford St Mary *Chelmsf* 78-81; C Walthamstow St Sav 81-84; V Barkingside St Fran 84-92; V Leigh-on-Sea St Marg from 92; Chapl Southend Health Care NHS Trust from 96; RD Hadleigh *Chelmsf* from 00. *St Margaret's Vicarage, 1465 London Road, Leigh-on-Sea SS9 2SB* Tel (01702) 471773 E-mail eastoe@dialstart.net

EASTON, Christopher Richard Alexander. b 60. TCD BA81 DipTh84. **d** 84 **p** 85. C Belfast St Donard *D & D* 84-89; I Inishmacsaint *Clogh* 89-95; I Magheralin w Dollingstown *D & D* 95-01; I Coleraine *Conn* from 01. *St Patrick's Rectory, Mountsandel Road, Coleraine BT52 1JE* Tel (028) 7034 3429 or 7034 4213 E-mail chriseaston@talk21.com

EASTON, Donald Fyfe. b 48. St Edm Hall Ox BA69 MA85 Nottm Univ CertEd70 Univ Coll Lon MA76 PhD90 Clare Hall Cam MA85. Westcott Ho Cam 89. **d** 90 **p** 91. NSM Fulham St Andr Fulham Fields *Lon* 90-97; Lic Preacher from 97. *12 Weltje Road, London W6 9TG* Tel (020) 8741 0233

EASTON, John. b 34. St Cath Soc Ox BA59 MA63. Chich Th Coll 59. **d** 61 **p** 62. C Rugeley *Lich* 61-64; TR 72-87; C Shrewsbury All SS 64-66; Ind Chapl *Sheff* 66-72; V Bolsover *Derby* 87-99; RD Bolsover and Staveley 93-98; rtd 99; Perm to Offic *Derby* from 99. *71 Wythburn Road, Chesterfield S41 8DP* Tel (01246) 555610

EASTON, John. b 41. Nor City Coll 71. LNSM course 95. **d** 97. OLM New Catton Ch Ch *Nor* from 97. *14 Carteford Drive, Norwich NR3 4DW* Tel (01603) 412589

EASTON, Richard Huntingford. b 26. Oriel Coll Ox BA51 MA51. Westcott Ho Cam 53. **d** 54 **p** 55. C Bris St Ambrose Whitehall *Bris* 54-57; New Zealand from 57. *271 Muriwai Road, RD1, Waimauku, Auckland 1250, New Zealand* Tel (0064) (9) 411 8320

EASTON, Robert Paul Stephen. b 62. Bris Univ BA84 Univ of Wales (Cardiff) Dip Journalism 85. St Steph Ho Ox BTh00. **d** 00 **p** 01. C Stoke Newington St Mary *Lon* from 00. *The Flat, St Mary's Rectory, Stoke Newington Church Street, London N16 9ES* Tel (020) 7249 6138 E-mail easton@britishlibrary.net

EASTON-CROUCH, Jonathan Brian. b 65. Univ Coll Lon DipHE96. SEITE 96. **d** 99 **p** 00. C Mitcham SS Pet and Paul *S'wark* 99-02; Chapl Kingston Hosp NHS Trust 02. *19 Charminster Avenue, London SW19 3EL* Tel (020) 8544 0205

EASTWOOD, Colin Foster. b 34. Leeds Univ BA56 MA66. Linc Th Coll 65. **d** 67 **p** 68. C Cottingham *York* 67-70; C Darlington St Cuth *Dur* 70-75; V Eighton Banks 75-81; V Sutton St Jas *Ches* 81-99; rtd 99; Perm to Offic *Glouc* from 00. *14 Ross Close, Chipping Sodbury, Bristol BS37 6RS* Tel (01454) 317594

EASTWOOD, Harry. b 26. Man Univ BSc48. Ridley Hall Cam 81. **d** 82 **p** 83. NSM Barton Seagrave w Warkton *Pet* 82-00; Perm to Offic from 00. *22 Poplars Farm Road, Kettering NN15 5AF* Tel (01536) 513271

EASTWOOD, Miss Janet. b 54. Wycliffe Hall Ox 83. dss 86 **d** 87 **p** 94. Ainsdale *Liv* 86-87; Par Dn 87-90; TD Kirkby Lonsdale *Carl* 90-94; TV 94-95; Dioc Youth Officer 90-94; R Wavertree H Trin *Liv* from 95; P-in-c Wavertree St Thos 95-97. *Wavertree Rectory, Hunters Lane, Liverpool L15 8HL* Tel 0151-733 2172

EASTWOOD, Martin Russell. b 66. Edin Univ BMus88 LRSM02. Ripon Coll Cuddesdon 01. **d** 03. C Wymondham *Nor* from 03. *118 Tuttles Lane West, Wymondham NR18 0JJ* Tel (01953) 606775 Mobile 07967-501102 E-mail wymondhamcurate@hotmail.com

EATOCK, John. b 45. Lanc Univ MA82. Lich Th Coll 67. **d** 70 **p** 71. C Crumpsall St Mary *Man* 70-73; C Atherton 73-74; C Ribbleton *Blackb* 74-77; V Ingol 77-83; V Laneside 83-92; RD Accrington 90-92; Perm to Offic from 92. *57 Heys Avenue, Haslingden, Rossendale BB4 5EE* Tel (01706) 222531 E-mail john@jeatock.freeserve.co.uk

EATON, Barry Anthony. b 50. St Martin's Coll Lanc MA98. Wilson Carlile Coll Dip Evang79 Carl and Blackb Dioc Tr Inst 94. **d** 97 **p** 98. C W Burnley *Blackb* 97-99; Dep Chapl HM Pris Leeds 99-00; Chapl HM Pris Buckley Hall from 00. *HM Prison, Buckley Hall, Buckley Road, Rochdale OL12 9DP* Tel (01706) 8861610

EATON, David Andrew. b 58. ACA83 Man Univ BSc79. Trin Coll Bris BA89. **d** 89 **p** 90. C Barking St Marg w St Patr *Chelmsf* 89-92; C Billericay and Lt Burstead 92-95; P-in-c Vange from 95. *Vange Rectory, 782 Clay Hill Road, Basildon SS16 4NG* Tel (01268) 581574 Fax as telephone E-mail davidaeaton@lineone.net

EATON, Canon David John. b 45. Nottm Univ LTh BTh74. St Jo Coll Nottm 70. **d** 74 **p** 75. C Headley All SS *Guildf* 74-77; Ind Chapl *Worc* 77-82; TV Halesowen 80-82; V Rowledge *Guildf* 82-89; V Leatherhead 89-01; R Leatherhead and Mickleham from 01; RD Leatherhead 93-98; Hon Can Guildf Cathl from 02. *The Vicarage, 3 St Mary's Road, Leatherhead KT22 8EZ* Tel (01372) 372313

✠**EATON, The Rt Revd Derek Lionel.** b 41. QSM85. Cert Français 69 Internat Inst Chr Communication Nairobi 74 Univ of Tunis CertFAI70 MA78. Trin Coll Bris DipTh66 WEC Miss Tr Coll DipTh66. **d** 71 **p** 71 **c** 90. C Barton Hill St Luke w Ch Ch *Bris* 71-72; Chapl Br Emb Tunisia 72-78; Provost All SS Cathl Cairo and Chapl Br Emb 78-83; Hon Can 85; New Zealand from 84; Assoc P Papanui St Paul 84; V Sumner-Redcliffs 85-90; Bp Nelson from 90. *PO Box 100, Nelson, New Zealand* Tel and fax (0064) (3) 548 8991 *or* tel 548 3124 Fax 548 2125 E-mail +derek@nn.ang.org.nz

EATON (née CRAIG), Mrs Julie Elizabeth. b 57. SEN81. Trin Coll Bris DipHE89. **d** 89 **p** 94. Par Dn Gt Ilford St Andr *Chelmsf* 89-92; NSM Billericay and Lt Burstead 92-95; C 95-96; TV 96-01; Chapl Thameside Community Healthcare NHS Trust from 92; Perm to Offic *Chelmsf* from 01. *Vange Rectory, 782 Clay Hill Road, Basildon SS16 4NG* Tel (01268) 557332 Fax 581574 E-mail julie@eatoncraig.freeserve.co.uk

EATON, Mrs Margaret Anne. b 44. Ab Dioc Tr Course 82. dss 84 **d** 86 **p** 94. NSM Ellon *Ab* 84-95; Nottm Cruden Bay 84-95; C Bridge of Don from 95. *12 McDonald Gardens, Ellon AB41 8BT* Tel (01358) 729250 E-mail eeatonnhrf@netscapeonline.co.uk

EATON, Canon Oscar Benjamin (Ben). b 67. Puerto Rico Th Coll STB66. **d** 66 **p** 67. Ecuador 66-69; C Wandsworth St Anne *S'wark* 69-71; C Aldrington *Chich* 71-73; TV Littleham w Exmouth *Ex* 74-79; R Alphington 79-84; Chapl Barcelona w Casteldefels *Eur*

84-88; Chapl Maisons-Laffitte 88-02; Can Malta Cathl from 96; rtd 02; P-in-c St Raphaël *Eur* from 02. *62 Hameau de Valescure, 83600 Fréjus, France* Tel (0033) (4) 94 40 48 61 E-mail htcml@aol.com

EATON, The Very Revd Peter David. b 58. K Coll Lon BA82 AKC82 Qu Coll Cam BA85 MA89 Magd Coll Ox MA90. Westcott Ho Cam 83. **d** 86 **p** 87. C Maidstone All SS and St Phil w Tovil *Cant* 86-89; Fells' Chapl Magd Coll Ox 89-91; Lic to Offic *Ox* from 89; USA from 91; Assoc R Salt Lake City St Paul 91-95; Hon Can Th Utah 91-01; R Lancaster St Jas Penn 95-01; Dean St Jo Cathl Denver from 02. *St John's Cathedral, 1350 Washington Street, Denver, CO 80203-2008, USA* Tel (001) (303) 831 7115 *or* 295 0956 Fax 831 7119 E-mail deansadmin@sjc-den.org

EATON, Miss Phyllis Mary. b 42. SRD Qu Eliz Coll Lon BSc63 Univ of S Africa BA79. WMMTC 87. **d** 90 **p** 94. NSM Washwood Heath *Birm* 90-91; NSM Edgbaston SS Mary and Ambrose 91-95; Perm to Offic from 95. *26 Blackthorne Road, Smethwick, Warley B67 6PZ* Tel 0121-552 4904 *or* 507 4085

EAVES, Alan Charles. b 37. Lon Univ DipTh64. Tyndale Hall Bris 62. **d** 65 **p** 66. C Southport SS Simon and Jude *Liv* 65-66; C Eccleston Ch Ch 66-70; V Earlestown 70-79; V Orpington Ch Ch *Roch* 79-02; rtd 02. *4 Chervil Close, Folksworth, Peterborough PE7 3SZ* Tel (01733) 241644 Mobile 07904-357476

EAVES, Brian Maxwell. b 40. Tyndale Hall Bris 66. **d** 69 **p** 70. C Wolverhampton St Jude *Lich* 69-72; C Fazeley 72-75; TV Ipsley *Worc* 75-79; Chapl Amsterdam *Eur* 79-86; Chapl Bordeaux w Riberac, Cahors, Duras etc 86-91; Monaco 91-93; TV Buckhurst Hill *Chelmsf* 93-96; R Culworth w Sulgrave and Thorpe Mandeville etc *Pet* from 96. *The Rectory, Culworth, Banbury OX17 2AT* Tel (01295) 760383

EBBITT, Francis Simon. b 20. TCD BA42 MA49 BD56. TCD Div Sch 40. **d** 43 **p** 44. C Belfast St Mary Magd *Conn* 43-46; C Lurgan Ch the Redeemer *D & D* 46-48; C Bangor St Comgall 48-50; I Ballee 50-53; I Aghalee 53-59; V Stanwix *Carl* 59-65; V Rainhill *Liv* 65-74; V Stanford in the Vale w Goosey and Hatford *Ox* 74-80; RD Vale of White Horse 75-80; V Furze Platt 80-87; Chapl St Mark's and Clarefield Hosps 80-87; rtd 87; Asst Chapl Malaga *Eur* 87-90. *229A Courthouse Road, Maidenhead SL6 6HF* Tel (01628) 22418

EBBSFLEET, Suffragan Bishop of (Provincial Episcopal Visitor). See BURNHAM, The Rt Revd Andrew

EBELING, Mrs Barbara. b 44. Hull Univ BA67. St Alb Minl Tr Scheme 87. **d** 94 **p** 95. C Stevenage St Hugh and St Jo *St Alb* 94-99; R Blunham, Gt Barford, Roxton and Tempsford etc from 99. *The Vicarage, High Street, Great Barford, Bedford MK44 3JJ* Tel (01234) 870363

ECCLES, Ernest Pattison. b 23. Kelham Th Coll 46. **d** 50 **p** 51. C Sheff Norwood St Leon *Sheff* 50-54; P-in-c Elsecar 54; P-in-c Thorpe Salvin 55-56; R Braithwell w Bramley 56-88; P-in-c Hooton Roberts w Ravenfield 62-75; rtd 88; Perm to Offic *Sheff* from 88. *Stonegates, Back Lane, Clifton, Maltby, Rotherham S66 7RA* Tel (01709) 867910

ECCLES, James Henry. b 30. DLC64 Lon Univ Cert Psychology 70 DipEd. Wycliffe Hall Ox 86. **d** 87 **p** 88. NSM Llandudno *Ban* 87-91; rtd 91; NSM Llanrhos *St As* 94-00; Perm to Offic *Ban* from 99. *Lowlands, 7 St Seiriol's Road, Llandudno LL30 2YY* Tel (01492) 878524

ECCLES, Mrs Vivien Madeline. LNSM course. **d** 92 **p** 94. OLM Stretford St Bride *Man* from 92. *479 Barton Road, Stretford, Manchester M32 9TA* Tel 0161-748 9795

ECCLESTON, Mrs Frances Mary. b 61. Jes Coll Cam BA83 Sheff Univ CQSW88. N Ord Course 00. **d** 03. C Ranmoor *Sheff* from 03. *Flat 1, 5 Ranmoor Park Road, Sheffield S10 3GX* Tel 0114-230 5204 E-mail eccleston@clara.co.uk

ECCLESTONE, Gary Edward. b 73. Ex Univ BA95 PGCE96. Cuddesdon Coll BTh99. **d** 99 **p** 00. C Salisbury St Martin and Laverstock *Sarum* 99-03; P-in-c Hanslope w Castlethorpe *Ox* from 03. *The Vicarage, Park Road, Hanslope, Milton Keynes MK19 7LT* Tel (01908) 510542

ECHOLS, Mrs Janet Lyn Roberts. b 58. Coll of Charleston (USA) BA. Trin Episc Sch for Min Penn MDiv. **d** 95 **p** 96. Asst R Mt Pleasant Ch Ch USA 95-02; P-in-c Stapleford *Ely* from 02. *The Vicarage, Mingle Lane, Stapleford, Cambridge CB2 5BG* Tel (01223) 842150

ECKERSLEY, Mrs Nancy Elizabeth. b 50. York Univ BA72 Leeds Univ CertEd73. NEOC 86. **d** 89 **p** 94. C Clifton *York* 89-00; Chapl York Distr Hosp 90-93; Lay Tr Officer *York* 93-00; V Heslington from 00. *The Vicarage, School Lane, Heslington, York YO10 5EE* Tel (01904) 410389

ECKERSLEY, Canon Richard Hugh. b 25. Trin Coll Cam BA48 MA50. Chich Th Coll 49. **d** 51 **p** 52. C Portsea St Jo Rudmore *Portsm* 51-57; C Portsea N End St Mark 57-62; V Paulsgrove 62-73; V Brighton St Nic *Chich* 73-84; Can Res Portsm Cathl *Portsm* 84-92; rtd 92; Perm to Offic *Portsm* from 92. *136 Kensington Road, Portsmouth PO2 0QY* Tel (023) 9265 3512

EDDISON, Frederick Donald Buchanan. b 19. Trin Coll Cam BA41 MA46. Ridley Hall Cam 47. **d** 48 **p** 49. C Fulham St Matt *Lon* 48-51; C St Marylebone All So w SS Pet and Jo 51-53; Asst

Chapl and Asst Master Forres Sch Swanage 53-56; Chapl CSSM 56-65; V Tunbridge Wells St Jo *Roch* 65-80; rtd 80; Perm to Offic *Roch* from 81; Perm to Offic *Chich* 81-99. *c/o J M B Eddison Esq, 31 Hillside Road, Harpenden AL5 4BS* Tel (01582) 621180

EDDISON, Robert John Buchanan. b 16. Trin Coll Cam BA38 MA42. Ridley Hall Cam 38. **d** 39 **p** 40. C Tunbridge Wells St Jo *Roch* 39-43; Travelling Sec Scripture Union 42-80; rtd 81; Perm to Offic *Chich* from 81. *Durham Lodge, Gordon Road, Crowborough TN6 1EW* Tel (01892) 652606

EDE, The Ven Dennis. b 31. Nottm Univ BA55 Birm Univ MSocSc73. Ripon Hall Ox 55. **d** 57 **p** 58. C Sheldon *Birm* 57-60; C Castle Bromwich SS Mary and Marg 60-64; Chapl E Birm Hosp 60-76; C-in-c Hodge Hill CD *Birm* 64-70; V Hodge Hill 70-72; TR 72-76; Chapl Sandwell Distr Gen Hosp 76-90; V W Bromwich All SS *Lich* 76-90; P-in-c W Bromwich Ch Ch 76-79; RD W Bromwich 76-90; Preb Lich Cathl 83-90; Adn Stoke 90-97; rtd 97; Hon C Tilford *Guildf* 97-99; Hon C The Bourne and Tilford 99-02; Perm to Offic *Guildf* s'wark from 03. *Tilford, 13 Park Close, Carshalton SM5 3EU* Tel (020) 8647 5891
E-mail dennisangelaede@aol.co.uk

EDEBOHLS, Canon William Ernest. b 54. Trin Coll Melbourne BTh80. **d** 78 **p** 79. Australia 78-98 and from 00; C S Ballarat 78-80; C Ballarat St Pet 80; C Terang w Timboon 80-81; V Timboon 81-87; Prec Ballarat 87; Dean 87-98; Adn Italy and Malta *Eur* 98-00; Can Malta Cathl 98-00; Chapl Milan w Genoa and Varese 98-00. *807 Barkly Street, Ballarat, Vic, Australia 3350* Tel (0061) (3) 5333 7907 Mobile 427-879733
E-mail edebohls@cbl.com.au

EDEN, Grenville Mervyn. b 37. Bris Univ BA58 Lon Univ MPhil78. Ox Min Course 88. **d** 95 **p** 96. NSM Burnham w Dropmore, Hitcham and Taplow *Ox* from 95. *Langdale, Grays Park Road, Stoke Poges, Slough SL2 4JG* Tel (01753) 525962

EDEN, Henry. b 36. G&C Coll Cam BA59 MA64. Ox NSM Course. **d** 87 **p** 88. NSM Abingdon w Shippon *Ox* 87-88; Chapl Brentwood Sch Essex 88-95; TV Beaconsfield *Ox* 95-00; Perm to Offic *St E* from 01. *Ely Cottage, Denham, Bury St Edmunds IP29 5EQ* Tel (01284) 811884

EDEN, Mrs Lesley Patricia. b 54. Liv Univ MTh99. Nor Ord Course 93. **d** 96 **p** 97. C Wallasey St Hilary *Ches* 96-98; C Oxton 98-01; V Whitegate w Lt Budworth from 01; Min Review Officer from 01. *The Vicarage, Cinder Hill, Whitegate, Northwich CW8 2BH* Tel (01606) 882151 Fax as telephone
E-mail lesley_eden88@hotmail.com

EDEN, Leslie Thomas Ernest. b 19. ACII55. S'wark Ord Course. **d** 69 **p** 70. NSM Kidbrooke St Jas *S'wark* 69-94; rtd 94; Perm to Offic *S'wark* from 94. *47 Begbie Road, London SE3 8DA* Tel (020) 8856 3088

EDEN, Michael William. b 57. Nottm Univ BTh86. Linc Th Coll 83. **d** 86 **p** 87. C Daventry *Pet* 86-89; TV Northampton Em 89-92; V Corby St Columba 92-03; P-in-c Stowmarket *St E* from 03. *The Vicarage, 2 Lockington Road, Stowmarket IP14 1BQ* Tel (01449) 678623 *or* 774652 Fax 774652
E-mail theedens@talk21.com

EDGAR, David. b 59. Newc Univ BA81. Linc Th Coll BTh86. **d** 86 **p** 87. C Wednesbury St Paul Wood Green *Lich* 86-91; V Winterton Gp *Linc* 91-00; C Linc St Swithin 00-01; P-in-c from 01; Chapl N Lincs Coll from 00. *1 St Giles Avenue, Lincoln LN2 4PE* Tel (01522) 528199

EDGCUMBE, Irena Christine. *See* CZERNIAWSKA EDGCUMBE, Mrs Irena Christine

EDGE, Canon John Francis. b 32. Ex Coll Ox BA54 MA56. St Steph Ho Ox 54. **d** 58 **p** 59. C Oswestry H Trin *Lich* 58-62; V 64-79; Tutor Lich Th Coll 62-64; Malaysia 79-87; Hon Can Kuching from 88; TV Wolverhampton *Lich* 88-91; Chapl R Hosp Wolv 88-91; Subwarden St Deiniol's Lib Hawarden 91-93; C Briercliffe *Blackb* 93-96; C W Felton *Lich* 96-97; Res Min 97-01; rtd 97; Perm to Offic *Blackb* from 01. *24 Talbot Street, Briercliffe, Burnley BB10 2HW* Tel (01282) 429287

EDGE, John Nicholson. b 53. ONC73 HNC75. OLM course 96. **d** 99 **p** 00. OLM Flixton St Jo *Man* from 99. *5 Devon Road, Flixton, Manchester M41 6PN* Tel 0161-748 4736

EDGE, Michael MacLeod. b 45. St Andr Univ BSc68 Qu Coll Cam BA70 MA74. Westcott Ho Cam 68. **d** 72 **p** 73. C Allerton *Liv* 72-76; R Bretherton *Blackb* 76-82; P-in-c Kilpeck *Heref* 82-84; P-in-c St Devereux w Wormbridge 82-84; TR Ewyas Harold w Dulas, Kenderchurch etc 82-93; RD Abbeydore 84-90; V Enfield St Andr *Lon* from 93. *The Vicarage, Silver Street, Enfield EN1 3EG* Tel (020) 8363 8676
E-mail michaeledge@freeuk.com

EDGE, Philip John. b 54. Ripon Coll Cuddesdon 77. **d** 80 **p** 81. C N Harrow St Alb *Lon* 80-83; C St Giles Cripplegate w St Bart Moor Lane etc 83-86; P-in-c Belmont *Blackb* 86-92; V 92-97; V Ellesmere and Welsh Frankton *Lich* 92-97; V Ellesmere from 97. *The Vicarage, Church Hill, Ellesmere SY12 0HB* Tel (01691) 622571

EDGE, Ms Renate Erika. b 50. Bonn Chamber of Commerce Translator's Dip 75 DIL77. Cranmer Hall Dur 86. **d** 88. Par Dn Leic H Spirit *Leic* 88-89; Asst Chapl Leic and Co Miss for the Deaf 88-89; Par Dn Leic H Apostles *Leic* 89-94. *6 Tideswell Bank, Glossop SK13 6HQ* Tel (01457) 855928

EDGE, Timothy Peter. b 55. Brighton Poly BSc80 CEng85 MIEE85 FRAS80. Westcott Ho Cam 85. **d** 88 **p** 89. C Norton *Ches* 88-91; C Bedworth *Cov* 91-96; TV Witney *Ox* 96-02; Asst Chapl HM Pris Bullingdon from 02; NSM Cogges and S Leigh *Ox* from 03. *HM Prison Bullingdon, Patrick Haugh Road, Arncott, Bicester OX25 1PZ* Tel (01869) 353100
E-mail tim.edge@talk21.com

EDGELL, Hugh Anthony Richard. b 31. ARHistS84. AKC57. **d** 58 **p** 59. C N Lynn w St Marg and St Nic *Nor* 58-64; R S Walsham 64-74; V Upton w Fishley 64-74; R Hingham 74-81; R Hingham w Woodrising w Scoulton 81-85; OStJ 79-88; SBStJ from 88; V Horning *Nor* 85-89; P-in-c Beeston St Laurence w Ashmanhaugh 85-89; R Horning w Beeston St Laurence and Ashmanhaugh 89-95; Prior St Benet's Abbey Horning 87-95; rtd 95; Perm to Offic *Nor* from 95. *Brambles, Brimbelow Road, Hoveton, Norwich NR12 8UJ* Tel (01604) 782206

EDGELL, William John Raymond. b 15. St Aid Birkenhead 63. **d** 65 **p** 66. C Sutton *Liv* 65-68; V Bury St Paul *Man* 68-77; rtd 80; Perm to Offic *Man* from 80. *20 Chilton Drive, Walshaw Park, Bury BL8 1QY* Tel 0161-764 7237

EDGERTON, Ms Hilary Ann. b 66. R Holloway & Bedf New Coll Lon BSc88. Wycliffe Hall Ox BTh93. **d** 93 **p** 94. Par Dn S Cave and Ellerker w Broomfleet *York* 93-94; C 94-97; TV Howden 97-00; V Hayfield and Chinley w Buxworth *Derby* from 00. *8 Bluebell Close, Hayfield, High Peak SK22 2PG* Tel (01663) 743350 E-mail hilary@philippians3.totalserve.co.uk

EDINBOROUGH, David. b 36. Nottm Univ BA58 MEd74. EMMTC 79. **d** 82 **p** 83. NSM Bramcote *S'well* 82-01; P-in-c 94-01; Dioc Officer for NSMs 89-94; rtd 01; Perm to Offic *S'well* 01-02; P-in-c Radford St Pet from 02. *105A Derby Road, Beeston, Nottingham NG9 3GZ* Tel 0115-925 1066
E-mail david.edinborough@btopenworld.com

EDINBURGH, Bishop of. *See* SMITH, The Rt Revd Brian Arthur

EDINBURGH, Dean of. *See* MEIN, The Very Revd James Adlington

EDINBURGH, Provost of. *See* FORBES, The Very Revd Graham John Thompson

EDIS, John Oram. b 26. ACIS50 ACP52 CDipAF78 FCollP89 Open Univ BA81. Ox NSM Course 85. **d** 88 **p** 89. Hon Warden and Chapl E Ivor Hughes Educn Foundn from 88; NSM Gt Chesham *Ox* 88-96; Perm to Offic *Lon* and *Ox* from 96. *21 Greenway, Chesham HP5 2BW* Tel (01494) 785815

EDMEADS, Andrew. b 53. Linc Th Coll 84. **d** 86 **p** 87. C Sholing *Win* 86-89; R Knights Enham 89-97; rtd 97; Perm to Offic *Win* 97-99; Chapl St Mich Hospice Basingstoke from 00. *10 Altona Gardens, Andover SP10 4LG* Tel (01264) 391464

EDMONDS (née HARRIS), Mrs Catherine Elizabeth. b 52. Leic Coll of Educn CertEd73 ACP79 K Alfred's Coll Win 86 Basingstoke Coll of Tech 87. S Dios Minl Tr Scheme 91. **d** 95 **p** 96. NSM Basing *Win* 95-99; C Yeovil H Trin w Barwick *B & W* 99-01; Chapl Coll of SS Mark and Jo Plymouth *Ex* from 01. *Chaplain's House, College of St Mark and St John, Derriford Road, Plymouth PL6 8BH* Tel (01752) 789910 *or* 777188 ext 2047
E-mail pauledmonds@lineone.net

EDMONDS, Clive Alway. b 42. ACII. S'wark Ord Course 78. **d** 81 **p** 82. C Horsell *Guildf* 81-85; R Bisley and W End 85-92; RD Surrey Heath 90-92; R Haslemere 92-00; Chapl Wispers Sch Haslemere 92-00; P-in-c Westbury-on-Severn w Flaxley and Blaisdon *Glouc* 00-02; V Westbury-on-Severn w Flaxley, Blaisdon etc from 03. *The Vicarage, Westbury-on-Severn GL14 1LW* Tel (01452) 760592

EDMONDS, Canon Joseph William. b 12. Bps' Coll Cheshunt 46. **d** 49 **p** 50. C Tottenham St Paul *Lon* 49-54; V Edmonton St Alphege 54-66; R Dickleburgh *Nor* 66-69; P-in-c Thelveton w Frenze 66-69; R Dickleburgh w Thelveton and Frenze 69-80; R Dickleburgh w Thelveton w Frenze and Shimpling 80-81; RD Redenhall 73-88; rtd 81; Perm to Offic *Nor* from 81; Hon Can Nor Cathl 84-89. *Cliff House, 114 Beach Road, Scratby, Great Yarmouth NR29 3PG* Tel (01493) 720578

EDMONDS (née MAGUIRE), Mrs Sarah Alison. b 65. Univ Coll Lon BSc87 Southn Univ MSc93. STETS 95. **d** 98 **p** 99. C Warwick St Paul *Cov* 98-02; P-in-c Hampton Lucy w Charlecote and Loxley from 02. *The Vicarage, Charlecote, Warwick CV35 9EW* Tel (01789) 840244
E-mail sedmonds@informs.co.uk

EDMONDS, Sidney. b 20. Oak Hill Th Coll. **d** 58 **p** 59. C Holborn St Geo w H Trin and St Bart *Lon* 58-61; Chapl HM Pris Liv 61-63; Dur 63-69; Parkhurst 69-74; Reading 74-85; V Aldworth and Ashampstead *Ox* 74-85; rtd 85. *22 Sandlea Park, Wirral CH48 0QF* Tel 0151-625 6147

EDMONDS-SEAL, John. b 34. FFARCS61 Lon Univ MB, BS58. Ox NSM Course DipTh90. **d** 90 **p** 91. NSM Ox St Aldate w St Matt *Ox* 90-94; NSM Wheatley from 95. *Otway, Woodperry Road, Oxford OX3 9UY* Tel (01865) 351582
E-mail edmondsseal@doctors.org.uk

EDMONDSON, Christopher Paul. b 50. Dur Univ BA71 MA81 St Jo Coll Dur DipTh72. **d** 73 **p** 74. C Kirkheaton *Wakef* 73-79; V Ovenden 79-86; Bp's Adv on Evang 81-86; P-in-c Bampton w

Mardale *Carl* 86-92; Dioc Officer for Evang 86-92; V Shipley St Pet *Bradf* 92-02; Warden Lee Abbey from 02. *Garden Lodge, Lee Abbey, Lynton EX35 6JJ* Tel (01598) 752621 *or* 754204 Fax 752619 E-mail warden@leeabbey.org.uk

EDMONDSON, John James William. b 55. St Jo Coll Dur BA83 MA91. Cranmer Hall Dur 80. **d** 83 **p** 84. C Gee Cross *Ches* 83-86; C Camberley St Paul *Guildf* 86-88; TV 88-90; V Foxton w Gumley and Laughton and Lubenham *Leic* 90-94; R Bexhill St Mark *Chich* from 94. *St Mark's Rectory, 11 Coverdale Avenue, Bexhill-on-Sea TN39 4TY* Tel (01424) 843733

EDMONTON, Area Bishop of. *See* WHEATLEY, The Rt Revd Peter William

EDMUND, Brother. *See* BLACKIE, Richard Footner

EDMUNDS, Andrew Charles. b 57. Whitelands Coll Lon BEd80 Croydon Coll DASS83 CQSW83. Oak Hill NSM Course 87. **d** 89 **p** 90. NSM Hawkwell *Chelmsf* 89-95; C Torquay St Matthias, St Mark and H Trin *Ex* 95-97; V Ripley *Derby* from 97. *The Vicarage, 26 Mount Pleasant, Ripley DE5 3DX* Tel (01773) 749641
E-mail acedmunds@allsaintsripley.freeserve.co.uk

EDMUNDS, Eric John. b 39. Univ of Wales TCert60. WMMTC 87. **d** 90 **p** 91. NSM Brewood *Lich* 90-93; Chapl St Pet Colleg Sch Wolv 91-93; R Llanerch Aeron w Ciliau Aeron and Dihewyd etc *St D* 93-97; R Aberporth w Tremain w Blaenporth and Betws Ifan 97-02; Bp's Adv on Tourism 95-02; Asst Dioc Dir of Educn 95-97 and 97-02; rtd 02. *15 Cwrt y Gloch, Peniel, Carmarthen SA32 7HW* Tel (01267) 221426

EDSON, The Ven Michael. b 42. Birm Univ BSc64 Leeds Univ BA71. Coll of Resurr Mirfield 69. **d** 72 **p** 73. C Barnstaple St Pet w H Trin *Ex* 72-77; TV Barnstaple and Goodleigh 77-79; TV Barnstaple, Goodleigh and Landkey 79-82; V Roxbourne St Andr *Lon* 82-89; AD Harrow 85-89; P-in-c S Harrow St Paul 86-89; Warden Lee Abbey 89-94; Lic to Offic *Ex* 89-94; Adn Leic 94-02; Bp's Insp of Par Registers and Records 94-02; TR Bideford, Northam, Westward Ho, Appledore etc *Ex* from 02. *The Rectory, Abbotsham Road, Bideford EX39 3AB* Tel (01237) 470228 *or* 474078

EDWARD, Brother. *See* LEES-SMITH, Christopher John

EDWARDS, Preb Albert. b 20. Univ of Wales (Lamp) BA48. St Mich Coll Llan 48. **d** 50 **p** 51. C Welshpool *St As* 50-54; V Stanton on Hine Heath *Lich* 54-58; R Hanley w Hope 58-64; RD Stoke N 63-64; V Tamworth 65-86; RD Tamworth 69-81; Preb Lich Cathl 73-86; rtd 86; Perm to Offic *Lich* from 86; Perm to Offic *Heref* from 89. *Broom Cottage, Mount Street, Welshpool SY21 7LW* Tel (01938) 554008

EDWARDS, Aled. b 55. Univ of Wales (Lamp) BA77. Trin Coll Bris 77. **d** 79 **p** 80. C Glanogwen *Ban* 79-82; V Llandinorwig w Penisa'r-waen 82-85; R Botwnnog 85-93; V Cardiff Dewi Sant *Llan* 93-99; Nat Assembly Liaison Officer from 99; Hon Chapl Llan Cathl from 99. *2 Maple Tree Close, Radyr, Cardiff CF15 8RU* Tel (029) 2070 5278 E-mail aled@globalnet.co.uk

EDWARDS, Allen John. b 50. Univ of Wales (Cardiff) BSc72 Imp Coll Lon DIC81 PhD81 CEng81 EurIng88 FIMechE93 FINucE95 MIMgt95. St Alb and Ox Min Course 00. **d** 02. NSM Didcot All SS *Ox* from 02. *23 North Bush Furlong, Didcot OX11 9DY* Tel (01235) 519090

EDWARDS, Andrew Colin. b 55. ACA81 Pemb Coll Cam BA77 MA80. St Mich Coll Llan BD89. **d** 89 **p** 90. C Newport St Paul *Mon* 89-91; C Newport St Woolos 91-93; Min Can St Woolos Cathl 91-93; P-in-c Ynysddu 93-95; TV Mynyddislwyn 95-97; rtd 97. *197 Heritage Park, St Mellons, Cardiff CF3 0DU* Tel (029) 2079 2715

EDWARDS, Andrew David. b 42. Tyndale Hall Bris 67. **d** 70 **p** 71. C Blackpool Ch Ch *Blackb* 70-73; C W Teignmouth *Ex* 73-76; P-in-c Ilfracombe SS Phil and Jas 76-85; C-in-c Lundy Is 79-89; V Ilfracombe SS Phil and Jas w W Down 85-89; TV Canford Magna *Sarum* 89-98; R Moresby *Carl* from 98; RD Calder from 02. *The Rectory, Low Moresby, Whitehaven CA28 6RR* Tel (01946) 693970 Fax 599501

EDWARDS, Andrew James. b 54. York Univ BA76. Wycliffe Hall Ox 77. **d** 80 **p** 81. C Beckenham St Jo *Roch* 80-83; C Luton Ch Ch 83-87; V Skelmersdale Ch at Cen *Liv* 87-95; V Netherton 95-02; V Southport St Phil and St Paul from 02; P-in-c Southport All SS and All So from 03. *63 Belmont Street, Southport PR8 1JH* Tel (01704) 531615

EDWARDS, Andrew Jonathan Hugo. b 56. Ex Univ BA78. Sarum & Wells Th Coll BTh93. **d** 93 **p** 94. C Honiton, Gittisham, Combe Raleigh, Monkton etc *Ex* 93-97; P-in-c Queen Thorne *Sarum* 97-01; Chapl Clayesmore Sch Blandford from 01. *Hambledon, Clayesmore School, Iwerne Minster, Blandford Forum DT11 8LJ* Tel (01747) 813064

EDWARDS, Miss Anita Carolyn. b 71. Trin Coll Bris 01. **d** 03. C Notting Hill St Pet *Lon* from 03. *7 The Lodge, Kensington Park Gardens, London W11 3HA* Tel (020) 7792 8527

EDWARDS, Mrs Anne Joan. b 67. Lanc Univ BA89. N Ord Course 97. **d** 00 **p** 01. C Elton All SS *Man* from 00; Chapl Bolton Hosps NHS Trust from 02. *St James's Vicarage, Roscow Avenue, Bolton BL2 6HU* Tel (01204) 525640 Fax as telephone
E-mail anna.edwards@dsl.pipex.com

EDWARDS, Canon Arthur John. b 42. Qu Mary Coll Lon BA64 MPhil66. St Mich Coll Llan 66. **d** 68 **p** 69. C Newport St Woolos *Mon* 68-71; V Llantarnam 71-74; Chapl Bp of Llan High Sch 74-78; V Griffithstown *Mon* 78-86; Dioc Dir RE 86-91; TR Cwmbran 86-95; Hon Can St Woolos Cathl 88-91; Can from 91; V Caerleon 95-02; V Caerleon w Llanhennock from 02; RD Newport from 98. *The Vicarage, Caerleon, Newport NP18 1AZ* Tel (01633) 420248

EDWARDS, Miss Carol Rosemary. b 46. Lon Univ DipTh76. Trin Coll Bris 74. **dss** 81 **d** 87 **p** 94. Hengrove *Bris* 81-82; Trin 82-85; Brislington St Chris 85-99; Dn-in-c 87-94; P-in-c 94-99; P-in-c Brislington St Chris and St Cuth 99-00; Hon Can Bris Cathl 93-00; P-in-c California *Ox* from 00. *California Vicarage, Vicarage Close, Finchampstead, Wokingham RG11 4JW* Tel 0118-973 0030

EDWARDS, Charles Grayson. b 37. Macalester Coll (USA) BSc59. Ripon Hall Ox 64. **d** 66 **p** 67. C Bletchley *Ox* 66-68; C Ware St Mary *St Alb* 68-73; TV Basingstoke *Win* 73-80; P-in-c Sandford w Upton Hellions *Ex* 80-82; R 82-94; Perm to Offic from 95; rtd 97. *The Peak, Higher Road, Crediton EX17 2EU* Tel (01363) 772530

EDWARDS, Christopher Alban. b 27. Hertf Coll Ox. Th Ext Educn Coll. **d** 89 **p** 92. S Africa 89-96; Pietersburg Ch Ch 89; Montagu 90-96; Harare Cathl Zimbabwe 96-01; Perm to Offic *Ripon* 01; *York* from 01. *1 Hastings House, Holyrood Lane, Ledsham, South Milford, Leeds LS25 5LL* Tel (01977) 682117 Mobile 07780-543114 E-mail chrisalban@btopenworld.com

EDWARDS, David Arthur. b 26. Wadh Coll Ox BA50 MA51. Wycliffe Hall Ox 50. **d** 52 **p** 53. C Didsbury St Jas and Em *Man* 52-55; Liv Sec SCM 55-58; Chapl Liv Univ *Liv* 55-58; C St Martin-in-the-Fields 58-66; Ed SCM Press 59-66; Gen Sec SCM 65-66; Dean K Coll Cam 66-70; Six Preacher Cant Cathl *Cant* 69-76; Can Westmr Abbey 70-78; R Westmr St Marg 70-78; Chapl to Speaker of Ho of Commons 72-78; Sub-Dean Westmr 74-78; Chmn Chr Aid 71-78; Dean Nor 78-83; Provost S'wark 83-94; rtd 94; Perm to Offic *Win* from 95; Hon Chapl Win Cathl from 95. *19 Crispstead Lane, Winchester SO23 9SF* Tel (01962) 862597

EDWARDS, Canon Diana Clare. b 56. SRN77 RSCN81 Nottm Univ BTh86. Linc Th Coll 83. **dss** 86 **d** 87 **p** 94. S Wimbledon H Trin and St Pet *S'wark* 86-87; Par Dn 87-90; Par Dn Lingfield and Crowhurst 90-94; C 94-95; Chapl St Piers Hosp Sch Lingfield 90-95; R Bletchingley *S'wark* from 95; RD Godstone from 98; Hon Can S'wark Cathl from 01; Dean of Women's Min from 03. *The Rectory, Out Wood Lane, Bletchingley, Redhill RH1 4LR* Tel (01883) 743252

EDWARDS, Dudley James Milne. b 15. AKC38. **d** 38 **p** 39. C Beeston *S'well* 38-42; C N Hinksey *Ox* 42-44; C Maidenhead St Luke 44-46; S Africa 46-49; V Wigan St Andr *Liv* 49-51; S Rhodesia 51-63; R Barlborough *Derby* 63-68; V Mackworth St Fran 68-75; R Ashwick w Oakhill and Binegar *B & W* 75-81; rtd 80; Perm to Offic *B & W* 81-98. *Trefechan, The Street, Draycott, Cheddar BS27 3TH* Tel (01934) 743573

EDWARDS, Erwyd. *See* EDWARDS, The Very Revd Thomas Erwyd Pryse

EDWARDS (née DALLISON), Canon Frances Mary. b 39. RSCN61 SRN64. St Mich Ho Ox CertRK68 Cranmer Hall Dur IDC71. **d** 92 **p** 94. NSM Skerton St Chad *Blackb* 92-97; Asst Chapl R Albert Hosp Lanc 92-94; Chapl 94-96; Regional Co-ord (NW) Ch Action on Disability from 96; Hon Can Blackb Cathl *Blackb* from 00. *9 Rochester Avenue, Morecambe LA4 4RH* Tel (01524) 421224 Fax 413661 E-mail frances@floray.fsnet.co.uk

EDWARDS, Canon Geoffrey Lewis. b 14. Lon Univ BD39 AKC39. **d** 39 **p** 40. C Twickenham All Hallows *Lon* 39-44; C Bushey *St Alb* 44-47; V Mill End 47-72; V W Hyde St Thos 47-72; RD Watford 68-70; RD Rickmansworth 70-72; V Hockerill 72-84; RD Bishop's Stortford 74-84; Hon Can St Alb 76-84; rtd 84; Perm to Offic *Ox* from 89. *91 Early Road, Witney OX8 6ET* Tel (01993) 704342

EDWARDS, Canon Geraint Wyn. b 47. Univ of Wales (Ban) BTh93. St D Coll Lamp DipTh70. **d** 71 **p** 72. C Llandudno *Ban* 71-73; C Ban St Mary 73-74; V Penisarwaen and Llanddeiniolen 74-77; V Llandinorwig w Penisarwaen and Llanddeiniolen 77-78; R Llanfechell w Bodewryd w Rhosbeirio etc from 78; RD

Twrcelyn 94-01; AD from 01; Hon Can Ban Cathl 97-99; Prec from 99. *The Rectory, Penbodeistedd Estate, Llanfechell, Amlwch LL68 0RE* Tel (01407) 710356
E-mail geraint@rheithordy.fsnet.co.uk

EDWARDS, Canon Gerald Lalande. b 30. Bris Univ MEd72. Glouc Th Course 75. **d** 76 **p** 76. NSM Pittville All SS *Glouc* 76-79; NSM Cheltenham St Mich 79-96; Hon Can Glouc Cathl 91-96; rtd 96; Perm to Offic *Glouc* 96-97. *26 Monica Drive, Cheltenham GL50 4NQ* Tel (01242) 516863

EDWARDS, Gordon Henry. b 33. FRICS62 FCILA67 FCIArb72 Reading Univ PhD87. Ripon Coll Cuddesdon 89. **d** 90 **p** 91. NSM Sherston Magna, Easton Grey, Luckington etc *Bris* 90-92; NSM Yatton Keynell 92-96; NSM Chippenham St Paul w Hardenhuish etc 96-00; NSM Kington St Michael 96-00; Perm to Offic *Glouc* 00-01; NSM Badminton w Lt Badminton, Acton Turville etc from 01. *The Old Vicarage, Sherston, Malmesbury SN16 0LR* Tel (01666) 840405 Mobile 07889-132046 Fax (01666) 840683 E-mail gordonh.edwards@virgin.net

EDWARDS, Canon Graham Arthur. b 32. HNC53. St D Coll Lamp 56. **d** 61 **p** 62. C Betws w Ammanford *St D* 61-65; V Castlemartin and Warren 65-69; R Castlemartin w Warren and Angle etc 69-77; V St Clears w Llangynin and Llanddowror 77-83; CF (TAVR) 78-96; V St Clears w Llangynin and Llanddowror etc *St D* 83-94; Can St D Cathl 90-94; rtd 94. *Caswell, Station Road, St Clears, Carmarthen SA33 4BX* Tel (01994) 230342

EDWARDS, Graham Charles. b 40. Qu Coll Birm 80. **d** 82 **p** 83. C Baswich *Lich* 82-86; C Tamworth 86-88; R Hertford St Andr *St Alb* from 88; RD Hertford and Ware 96-99. *St Andrew's Rectory, 43 North Road, Hertford SG14 1LZ* Tel (01992) 582726

EDWARDS, Guy. *See* EDWARDS, Jonathan Guy

EDWARDS, Harold James. b 50. Lon Univ CertEd72. Ridley Hall Cam 84 Qu Coll Birm 78. **d** 81 **p** 82. NSM The Quinton *Birm* 81-84; C Highters Heath 84-85; V Llanwddyn and Llanfihangel-yng-Nghwynfa etc *St As* 85-88; V Ford *Heref* 88-97; V Alberbury w Cardeston 88-97; Chapl Shropshire and Mid-Wales Hospice from 96. *Shropshire and Mid-Wales Hospice, Bicton Heath, Shrewsbury SY3 8HS* Tel (01743) 236565 Mobile 07074-236236

EDWARDS, Harry Steadman. b 37. St Aid Birkenhead 64. **d** 66 **p** 67. Hon C Handsworth St Jas *Birm* 66-83; Hon C Curdworth w Castle Vale 83-85; P-in-c Small Heath St Greg 85-88; V High Crompton *Man* 88-98; rtd 98; Perm to Offic *Man* from 99. *42 Manor Road, Shaw, Oldham OL2 7JJ* Tel (01706) 672820

EDWARDS, Helen. *See* HINGLEY, Ms Helen

EDWARDS, Helen Glynne. *See* WEBB, Mrs Helen Glynne

EDWARDS, The Ven Henry St John. b 30. Southn Univ DipEd. Ripon Hall Ox. **d** 59 **p** 60. C Wickford *Chelmsf* 59-62; Australia from 62; R Woodburn 62-65; Educn Officer Dio Grafton 65-69; Dean Grafton 69-78; V Mt Waverley St Steph 78-83; R Chelmer 83-89; Adn Moreton 85-89; Abp's Chapl 89-90; R Tamborine Mountain 90-95; Adn W Moreton 91-93; Adn Gold Coast 93-95; rtd 95. *PO Box 26, Wooli, NSW, Australia 2462* Tel (0061) (2) 6649 7626 E-mail stjohn@midcoast.com.au

EDWARDS, Canon Henry Victor. b 48. AKC71 Open Univ BA85 Middx Univ MSc00. St Aug Coll Cant 72. **d** 73 **p** 74. C W Leigh CD *Portsm* 73-77; V Cosham 77-84; V Reydon *St E* 84-96; V Blythburgh w Reydon 86-96; Chapl St Felix Sch Southwold 86-96; Chapl Blythburgh Hosp 86-96; Dioc Adv for Counselling and Past Care *St E* from 96; P-in-c Campsea Ashe w Marlesford, Parham and Hacheston 96-00; R from 00; Hon Can St E Cathl from 00. *The Rectory, Marlesford, Woodbridge IP13 0AT* Tel (01728) 746747 Mobile 07710-417071 Fax 748175
E-mail harry@psalm23.demon.co.uk

EDWARDS, Herbert Joseph. b 29. Nottm Univ BA51. Wells Th Coll 54. **d** 56 **p** 57. C Leic St Pet *Leic* 56-61; C-in-c Broom Leys CD 61-65; V Broom Leys 65-68; Lect Lich Th Coll 68-71; Rhodesia 71-79; Botswana 74-75; V Bloxwich *Lich* 80-84; R Asfordby *Leic* 84-92; R N w S Kilworth and Misterton 92-96; rtd 96; Perm to Offic *Leic* from 97; *Lich* from 00. *St John's Hospital, St John Street, Lichfield WS13 6PB* Tel (01543) 416620

EDWARDS, Canon James Frederick. b 28. ALCD62. **d** 62 **p** 63. C Kenwyn *Truro* 62-68; V Tuckingmill 68-76; V St Columb Minor and St Colan 76-01; RD Pydar 84-93; Hon Can Truro Cathl 92-01; rtd 01; Perm to Offic *Truro* from 01. *45 Tretherras Road, Newquay TR7 2TF* Tel (01637) 870967

EDWARDS, Janet Margaret. b 41. TCert62 Lon Bible Coll BD73. WEMTC 98. **d** 01 **p** 02. NSM Coalbrookdale, Iron-Bridge and Lt Wenlock *Heref* from 01. *2 Madeley Wood View, Madeley, Telford TF7 5TF* Tel (01952) 583254

EDWARDS, Mrs Jill Kathleen. b 48. Man Univ BA69 Goldsmiths' Coll Lon CQSW72 Lon Univ DipRS85. S'wark Ord Course 90. **d** 93 **p** 95. NSM Grays Thurrock *Chelmsf* from 93; Ind Chapl from 93. *The Old Tennis Court, Allenby Crescent, Grays RM17 6DH* Tel (01375) 372887
E-mail jill.edwards@mailbox.ulcc.ac.uk

EDWARDS, John Gregory. b 29. Univ of Wales BA49 MA53. St Steph Ho Ox 64. **d** 66 **p** 67. C Ealing Ch the Sav *Lon* 66-70; C Greenford H Cross 70-75; P-in-c Poundstock *Truro* 75-82; R

Week St Mary w Poundstock and Whitstone 82-94; rtd 94. *8 Vestry Drive, Exeter EX2 8FG* Tel (01392) 432603

EDWARDS, John Ralph. b 50. Bris Univ BSc71 FCA74. St Alb and Ox Min Course 98. **d** 01 **p** 02. NSM California *Ox* from 01. *Green Hedges, 25 St John's Street, Crowthorne RG45 7NJ* Tel (01344) 774586 Mobile 07850-602488 Fax (01344) 774056 E-mail john.edwards@fish.co.uk

EDWARDS, Jonathan. *See* EDWARDS, Andrew Jonathan Hugo

EDWARDS, Jonathan Guy. b 63. Bris Univ BA85. Ridley Hall Cam BA93 MA96. **d** 94 **p** 95. C Preston Plucknett *B & W* 94-98; C Clevedon St Andr and Ch Ch 98-02; V Farrington Gurney from 02; V Paulton from 02. *The Vicarage, Church Street, Paulton, Bristol BS39 7LG* Tel (01761) 416581
E-mail guy.edwards1@tesco.net

EDWARDS, Judith Sarah. *See* McARTHUR-EDWARDS, Mrs Judith Sarah

EDWARDS (née EVANS), Mrs Linda Mary. b 49. Univ of Wales (Cardiff) BA71 K Coll Lon BD74 AKC74. Yale Div Sch STM76. **dss** 76 **d** 80 **p** 99. Llanishen and Lisvane *Llan* 76-78; Wrexham *St As* 78-80; C 80-82; Chapl Maudsley Hosp Lon 82-84; Chapl Bethlem R Hosp Beckenham 82-84; Chapl Lon Univ *Lon* 84-87; NSM Llanfair-pwll and Llanddaniel-fab etc *Ban* from 99. *Cefn-y-Cerrig, Nant-y-Felin Road, Llanfairfechan LL33 0TB* Tel (01248) 681462 E-mail lme@mcmail.com

EDWARDS, Malcolm Ralph. b 27. Man Univ 49. Cranmer Hall Dur 57. **d** 59 **p** 60. C Withington St Paul *Man* 59-62; C Chadderton Em 62-64; R Longsight St Jo 64-70; V Halliwell St Thos 70-81; V Milnrow 81-92; rtd 92; Perm to Offic *Man* from 92. *20 Upper Lees Drive, Westhoughton, Bolton BL5 3UE* Tel (01942) 813279

EDWARDS, Mark Anthony. b 61. Moorlands Bible Coll Dip Th & Min 86 St Jo Coll Dur Cert Th & Min 95. **d** 95 **p** 97. C Ulverston St Mary w H Trin *Carl* 95-97; C Barrow St Jo 97-00; TV Barrow St Matt from 00. *St Francis House, 158 Schneider Road, Barrow-in-Furness LA14 5ER* Tel (01229) 839686 E-mail mark@edwards3016.freeserve.co.uk

EDWARDS, Mrs Mary. b 47. St Jo Coll York CertEd69 Birkbeck Coll Lon BSc74 New Coll Edin BD93. S Dios Minl Tr Scheme 96. **d** 96 **p** 97. NSM Avon Valley *Sarum* 96-00; TV Wexcombe 00-02; TV Savernake from 02. *The Vicarage, Collingbourne Ducis, Marlborough SN8 3EL* Tel (01264) 852502

EDWARDS, Michael Norman William. b 34. Bp Gray Coll Cape Town 61 St Paul's Coll Grahamstown 62. **d** 63 **p** 65. S Africa 63-81; C Woodstock 63-66; C Plumstead 66-69; P-in-c Lansdowne All SS 69-72; R Hoetjes Bay 73-78; R Parow St Marg 78-80; Chaplain Tristan da Cunha 81-83; R Aston-on-Trent and Weston-on-Trent *Derby* 84-87; V Derby St Thos 87-95; P-in-c Blackwell 95-01; rtd 01. *16 Ridley Close, Holbury, Southampton SO45 2NR* Tel (023) 8089 2924

EDWARDS, Nicholas John. b 53. UEA BA75 Fitzw Coll Cam BA77 MA80. Westcott Ho Cam 75. **d** 78 **p** 79. C Kirkby *Liv* 78-81; V Cantril Farm 81-87; V Hale 87-94; R Chingford SS Pet and Paul *Chelmsf* from 94; Asst RD Waltham Forest from 94. *The Rectory, 2 The Green Walk, London E4 7ER* Tel (020) 8529 1291 E-mail nicholasjedwards@lineone.net

EDWARDS, Mrs Nita Mary. b 50. Univ of Wales (Ban) BD72 Nottm Univ PGCE73. Cranmer Hall Dur 93. **d** 93 **p** 94. C Ormesby *York* 93-95; C Billingham St Aid *Dur* 95-97; V 97-02; V Clayton *Lich* from 02. *The Vicarage, Clayton Lane, Newcastle ST5 3DW* Tel (01782) 614500 Fax as telephone E-mail nita.edwards@ntlworld.com

EDWARDS, Mrs Patricia Anne. b 52. EMMTC 76. **dss** 79 **d** 87 **p** 94. Hon Par Dn Clifton *S'well* 87-91; NSM Edwalton from 91. *Le Petit Champ, Widmerpool Road, Wysall, Nottingham NE12 6QW* Tel (0509) 880385

EDWARDS, Peter Clive. b 50. Lon Univ BA72. St Steph Ho Ox 83. **d** 85 **p** 86. C Lee St Aug *S'wark* 85-90; V Salfords 90-97; R Newington St Mary 97-03. *Apdo Correos 158, 03420 Castalla, Alicante, Spain* Tel (0034) (96) 656 0716
E-mail pce11@yahoo.com

EDWARDS, Canon Philip John. b 28. Lon Univ MRCS51 LRCP51. Chich Th Coll 58. **d** 60 **p** 61. C Orpington St Andr *Roch* 60-67; C Mayfield *Chich* 67-71; V Haywards Heath St Rich 71-91; Can and Preb Chich Cathl 84-91; rtd 91; Perm to Offic *Chich* from 91. *22 Hamsey Road, Sharpthorne, East Grinstead RH19 4PA* Tel (01342) 810210

EDWARDS, Philip Osbert Clifford. b 11. St Jo Coll Ox BA33 MA47. Wycliffe Hall Ox 33. **d** 35 **p** 36. C Bayswater *Lon* 35-38; C Chelsea St Luke 38-39; C Woburn Square Ch Ch 39-41; Chapl RAFVR 41-47; New Zealand 47-54; Chapl Oundle Sch 54-69; P-in-c Stoke Doyle *Pet* 60-63; Chapl St Chris Hospice Sydenham 69-74; Chapl Algarve *Eur* 74-77; rtd 77; Perm to Offic *Heref* 86-92. *8 The Old Orchard, Nash Meadows, South Warnborough, Hook RG29 1TR* Tel (01256) 862960

EDWARDS, Phillip Gregory. b 52. Lon Univ BSc73 Imp Coll Lon ARCS73 Birm Univ DipTh80 MSOSc90. Qu Coll Birm 78. **d** 81 **p** 82. C Lillington *Cov* 81-85; P-in-c Cov St Alb 85-86; TV Cov E 86-01; C Bury St Paul *Man* 01-03; C Bury Ch King 01-03; Chapl Bolton Inst of F&HE from 03. *St James's Vicarage, 280 Walshaw*

Road, Bury BL8 1PY Tel 0161-764 6217 Fax 762 5219
E-mail phil@edwards.clara.co.uk

EDWARDS, Raymond Lewis. Keble Coll Ox BA46 MA47 TCert48. St Deiniol's Hawarden 69. **d** 70 **p** 71. Prin Educn Cen Penmaenmawr 56-81; Hon C Dwygyfylchi *Ban* 70-81; P-in-c Llandwrog 81-82; R 82-90; Dioc Dir of Educn 84-92; rtd 90; Perm to Offic *Ban* from 90. *Bryn Llwyd, St Davids Road, Caernarfon LL55 1EL* Tel 07789-566370 (mobile)

EDWARDS, Richard John. b 47. Queensland Univ BA85. St Fran Coll Brisbane 83 McAuley Coll Brisbane DipRE85. **d** 85 **p** 85. Australia 85-87 and 88-96; C Olveston *Bris* 87-88; R Kingston St Mary w Broomfield etc *B & W* from 96. *The Rectory, Kingston St Mary, Taunton TA2 8HW* Tel (01823) 451257 Fax 451933 E-mail redwards@ukonline.co.uk

EDWARDS, Robert James. b 52. Cranmer Hall Dur 01. **d** 03. C Broadwater St Mary *Chich* from 03. *115 Shandon Road, Worthing BN14 9EA* E-mail roberted@supanet.com

EDWARDS, Roger Brian. b 41. Sarum & Wells Th Coll 87. **d** 89 **p** 90. C Wellington and Distr *B & W* 89-92; V Hursley and Ampfield *Win* from 92. *The Vicarage, Knapp Lane, Ampfield, Romsey SO5 9BT* Tel (01794) 368291

EDWARDS, Rowland Thomas. b 62. Univ of Wales DipTh88 BTh91. St Mich Coll Llan 85. **d** 88 **p** 89. C Llangiwg *S & B* 88-90; C Morriston 90-91; V Llangorse, Cathedine, Llanfihangel Talyllyn etc 91-01; V Llyn Safaddan from 01; RD Hay from 02. *The Vicarage, Llangorse, Brecon LD3 7UG* Tel (01874) 658298

EDWARDS, Rupert Quintin. b 67. Bris Univ LLB83. Wycliffe Hall Ox BTh94. **d** 97 **p** 98. C Brompton Ch Ch *Roch* 97-00; C Hammersmith St Paul *Lon* 00-02. *342 Bluewater House, Smugglers Way, London SW18 1ED*

EDWARDS, Canon Ruth Blanche. b 39. Girton Coll Cam BA61 MA65 PhD68 Aber Coll of Educn PGCE75. Ab Dioc Tr Course 77. **d** 87 **p** 94. Lect Aber Univ *Ab* 77-90; Sen Lect 90-96; Nsm Aberdeen St Jas 87-88; NSM Aberdeen St Jo 88-96; Lect Ripon Coll Cuddesdon 96-99; Hon Can St Andr Cathl *Ab* from 97; rtd 00; NSM Aberdeen St Jas *Ab* from 00. *99 Queen's Den, Aberdeen AB15 8BN* Tel (01224) 312688

EDWARDS, Mrs Sandra May. b 48. STETS 96. **d** 99 **p** 01. NSM Denmead *Portsm* from 99. *82 Drift Road, Clanfield, Waterlooville PO8 0NX* Tel (023) 9236 7228 *or* 9259 4968
E-mail sandra@pinoy.fsnet.co.uk

EDWARDS, Scott. b 71. Wolv Univ LLB93 St Jo Coll Dur BA00. Cranmer Hall Dur 97. **d** 00 **p** 01. C Halas *Worc* from 00. *9 Carpenter Glade, Halesowen B63 2BG* Tel (01384) 567601 E-mail stuartedwded@supanet.com

EDWARDS, Stephen. b 44. S'wark Ord Course. **d** 82 **p** 83. C Benhilton *S'wark* 82-86; P-in-c Clapham Ch Ch and St Jo 86-87; TV Clapham TM 87-94; Chapl HM Pris Wormwood Scrubs 94-96; Chapl HM Pris Maidstone 96-01; Chapl HM Pris Wandsworth from 01. *HM Prison Wandsworth, PO Box 757, Heathfield Road, London SW18 3HS* Tel (020) 8874 7292 Fax 8877 0358

EDWARDS, Stephen Michael. b 72. Lanc Univ BSc93 Anglia Poly Univ MA99. Westcott Ho Cam 93. **d** 96 **p** 97. C Colwyn Bay *St As* 96-99; C Colwyn Bay w Brynymaen 99-02; P-in-c Birch-in-Rusholme St Agnes w Longsight St Jo etc *Man* from 02. *St Agnes's Rectory, Slade Lane, Manchester M13 0GN* Tel 0161-224 2596 E-mail frsme@btinternet.com

EDWARDS, Steven Charles. b 54. Sheff Poly HND80 Lanc Univ BSc82 PhD86. Linc Th Coll 94. **d** 94 **p** 95. C Bradshaw *Man* 94-98; P-in-c Bolton Breightmet St Jas from 98. *St James's Vicarage, Roscow Avenue, Bolton BL2 6HU* Tel (01204) 525640 Fax as telephone E-mail steve.edwards@dsl.pipex.com

EDWARDS, Stuart. b 46. Lon Univ DipTh70 Lanc Univ BA73. Kelham Th Coll 66. **d** 71 **p** 72. C Skerton St Luke *Blackb* 71-76; C Ribbleton 76-80; TV 80-82; V Blackb St Mich w St Jo and H Trin 82-91; V Blackpool H Cross from 91; RD Blackpool 93-94; P-in-c S Shore St Pet from 00. *Holy Cross Vicarage, Central Drive, Blackpool FY1 6LA* Tel (01253) 341263

EDWARDS, Mrs Susan. b 54. R Holloway Coll Lon BSc75 SS Hild & Bede Coll Dur PGCE76. Qu Coll Birm 78. **dss** 81 **d** 87 **p** 94. Lillington *Cov* 81-85; Cov E 85-01; Par Dn 87-94; C 94-01; P-in-c Woolfold *Man* from 01. *St James's Vicarage, 280 Walshaw Road, Bury BL8 1PY* Tel 0161-764 6217 Fax 762 5219 E-mail sue@edwards.clara.co.uk

EDWARDS, Mrs Susan Diane. b 48. St Alb Minl Tr Scheme 86 Cranmer Hall Dur 91. **d** 92 **p** 94. Par Dn Borehamwood *St Alb* 92-94; C 94-96; V Arlesey w Astwick from 96. *The Vicarage, 77 Church Lane, Arlesey SG15 6UX* Tel (01462) 731227 E-mail susan.d.edwards@ntlworld.com

EDWARDS, The Very Revd Thomas Erwyd Pryse. b 33. Univ of Wales (Lamp) BA56. St Mich Coll Llan 56. **d** 58 **p** 59. C Llanbeblig w Caernarfon *Ban* 58-63; Chapl Asst St Geo Hosp Lon 63-66; Lic to Offic *S'wark* 63-72; Chapl K Coll Hosp Lon 66-72; R Penmon and Llangoed w Llanfihangel Dinsylwy *Ban* 72-75; V Llandysilio 75-81; V Glanadda 81-85; Chapl St D Hosp Ban 81-84; Chapl Gwynedd Hosp Ban 84-86; V Ban St D and St Jas 86-88; Dean Ban 88-98; Hon Can Ban Cathl from 88; R

Bangor 88-93; rtd 98; Perm to Offic *Ban* from 98. *61 Ffriddoedd Road, Bangor LL57 2TT* Tel (01248) 362108

EDWARDS, Thomas Harold David. b 16. Jes Coll Ox BA38 MA46. Westmr Coll Cam 38 St Aug Coll Cant 58. **d** 58 **p** 59. C Southbroom *Sarum* 58-61; V Upper Tooting H Trin *S'wark* 61-64; V Bledlow *Ox* 64-73; RD Aylesbury 72-77; R Bledlow w Saunderton and Horsenden 73-89; rtd 89; Perm to Offic *Heref* from 89. *22 St Anne's Grove, Knowle, Solihull B93 9JB* Tel (01564) 772593

EDWARDS, Thomas Victor. b 22. Univ of Wales (Lamp) BA52 LTh54 Birm Univ MA57. **d** 54 **p** 55. C Griffithstown *Mon* 54-56; Special Service Clergyman *Lich* 56-57; C Kingswinford St Mary 57-59; V Tipton St Jo 59-65; V Oxley 65-71; R Kingsley 71-90; rtd 90; Perm to Offic *Lich* from 90. *26 Pennymore Close, Trentham, Stoke-on-Trent ST4 8YQ* Tel (01782) 644073

EDWARDSON, David Roger Hately. b 54. Stirling Univ BSc79 DipEd79 Edin Univ BD91. Edin Th Coll 88. **d** 91 **p** 92. C Edin St Jo *Edin* 91-93; R Kelso 93-98; Asst Chapl Oundle Sch from 98. *46A West Street, Oundle, Peterborough PE8 4EF* Tel (01832) 274405 Fax as telephone E-mail david.edwardson@lineone.net

EDWARDSON, Joseph Philip. b 28. Dur Univ BA52 Leeds Univ PGCE53. Wells Th Coll 61. **d** 63 **p** 64. C Macclesfield St Mich *Ches* 63-66; V Egremont St Jo 66-72; V Eastham 72-81; V Poulton 81-94; rtd 94; Perm to Offic *Ches* from 94. *Keppler, 38 Hazel Grove, Irby, Wirral CH61 4UZ* Tel 0151-648 2661

EDY, Robert James. b 48. Southn Univ BA70 CertEd71. Ox Min Course CBTS93. **d** 93 **p** 94. Dep Hd Master Henry Box Sch Witney from 90; NSM Ducklington *Ox* 93-99; P-in-c from 99. *The Rectory, 6 Standlake Road, Ducklington, Witney OX8 7XG* Tel (01993) 776625 E-mail bobedy21@hotmail.com

EDYE, Ian Murray. b 21. K Coll Lon BD AKC. S'wark Ord Course 66. **d** 69 **p** 70. NSM E Grinstead St Swithun *Chich* 69-00; Perm to Offic 00-02. *12 The Chancery, Bramcote, Nottingham NG9 3AJ* Tel 0115-943 6343

EFEMEY, Raymond Frederick. b 28. Ball Coll Ox BA51 MA64. Cuddesdon Coll 51. **d** 53 **p** 54. C Croydon St Mich *Cant* 53-57; C Hendford *B & W* 57-60; V Upper Arley *Worc* 60-66; Ind Chapl 60-66; P-in-c Dudley St Jas 66-69; V Dudley St Thos 66-69; V Dudley St Thos and St Luke 69-75; Hon C Stretford All SS *Man* 76-82; SSF from 81; P-in-c Weaste *Man* 82-87; V 87-93; rtd 93. *20 Groby Road, Chorlton-cum-Hardy, Manchester M21 1DD* Tel 0161-860 5416

EGERTON, George. b 28. S'wark Ord Course 70. **d** 73 **p** 74. NSM Shere *Guildf* 73-94; Perm to Offic from 94. *Weyside, Lower Street, Shere, Guildford GU5 9HX* Tel (01483) 202549

EGGERT, Max Alexander. b 43. AKC67 Birkbeck Coll Lon BSc74 Poly Cen Lon MA87 CPsychol90. **d** 67 **p** 68. C Whitton St Aug *Lon* 67-69; Hon C Hackney 72-74; Hon C Llantwit Major *Llan* 74-76; NSM Haywards Heath St Rich *Chich* 78-93; Lic to Offic from 93. *94 High Street, Lindfield, Haywards Heath RH16 2HP* Tel (01444) 483057

EGLIN, Ian Charles. b 55. St Jo Coll Dur BA76. Coll of Resurr Mirfield 77. **d** 79 **p** 80. C Cov St Mary *Cov* 79-83; TV Kingsthorpe w Northampton St Dav *Pet* 83-87; P-in-c Pitsford w Boughton 85-87; Chapl RN 87-03; V Ipplepen, Torbryan and Denbury *Ex* from 03. *The Rectory, Paternoster Lane, Ipplepen, Newton Abbot TQ12 5RY* Tel (01803) 812215 E-mail ianeglin@btopenworld.com

EICHELMAN, Canon George Charles. b 14. Roch Univ NY BA37. **d** 40 **p** 40. USA 40-78; rtd 79; Hon C Costa Blanca *Eur* 83-86; Hon Can Gib Cathl 85-86. *6C Marisol Park, Calpe, Alicante, Spain*

EKE, Canon Robert Foord Stansfield. b 17. K Coll Lon BD39 AKC39. Ely Th Coll 40. **d** 40 **p** 41. C Carl St Aid and Ch Ch *Carl* 40-43; C Bournemouth St Clem *Win* 43-46; C Wimbledon *S'wark* 46-54; V Clapham Ch Ch 54-62; St Kitts-Nevis 62-72; V Alton St Lawr *Win* 72-89; Bp's Ecum Officer 80-82; Hon Can Win Cathl 82-89; RD Alton 82-89; rtd 89; Perm to Offic *Chich* from 89; Hon Can Antigua from 95. *77 Hangleton Way, Hove BN3 8AF* Tel (01273) 421443 Fax as telephone

EKIN, Tom Croker. b 29. Linc Th Coll 59. **d** 60 **p** 61. C Leamington Priors All SS *Cov* 60-63; R Ilmington w Stretton-on-Fosse 63-72; S Africa 72-77; R Moreton-in-Marsh w Batsford *Glouc* 77-83; R Moreton-in-Marsh w Batsford, Todenham etc 83-94; rtd 95; Hon C Theale and Englefield *Ox* from 96. *St Mark's House, Englefield, Reading RG7 5EP* Tel 0118-930 2227

ELBOURNE, Keith Marshall. b 46. Nottm Univ BTh74 Lon Univ BD76. Westmr Past Foundn DAPC89 St Jo Coll Nottm 70. **d** 74 **p** 75. C Romford Gd Shep Collier Row *Chelmsf* 74-78; C Victoria Docks St Luke 78-81; P-in-c 81-92; V Walthamstow St Pet 92-02; TR Tettenhall Wood and Perton *Lich* from 02. *Christ Church Rectory, 7 Broxwood Park, Tettenhall Wood, Wolverhampton WV6 8LZ* Tel (01902) 751116 E-mail petros2@surfaid.org

ELBOURNE, Canon Raymond Nigel Wilson. b 43. Dur Univ BA66. Linc Th Coll 67. **d** 69 **p** 70. C Liscard St Mary *Ches* 69-72; V Hattersley 72-77; R Odd Rode 77-02; P-in-c Congleton St Jas from 02; RD Congleton from 97; Hon Can Ches Cathl from 99. *St James's Vicarage, 116 Holmes Chapel Road, Congleton CW12 4NX* Tel (01260) 273722 E-mail elbourne@europe.com

ELBOURNE, Canon Timothy. b 60. Selw Coll Cam BA81 MA85 PGCE82. Westcott Ho Cam 84. **d** 86 **p** 87. C Tottenham H Trin *Lon* 86-88; Chapl York Univ *York* 88-94; P-in-c Thorp Arch w Walton 94-98; Dir of Educn *Ely* from 98; Hon Can Ely Cathl from 99. *19 The Oaks, Soham, Ely CB7 5FF* Tel and fax (01353) 723867 Pager (04325) 320796
E-mail tim.elbourne@ely.anglican.org

ELCOAT, Canon George Alastair. b 22. Qu Coll Birm. **d** 51 **p** 52. C Corbridge w Halton *Newc* 51-55; V Spittal 55-62; V Chatton w Chillingham 62-70; V Sugley 70-81; RD Newc W 77-81; Hon Can Newc Cathl 79-91; P-in-c Tweedmouth 81-87; V 87-91; RD Norham 82-91; Miss to Seamen 81-91; Chapl to The Queen 82-93; rtd 91; Perm to Offic *Newc* from 91. *42 Windsor Crescent, Berwick-upon-Tweed TD15 1NT* Tel (01289) 331936

ELDER, Andrew John. b 49. Sunderland Poly BSc72 MSc76. NEOC 91. **d** 94 **p** 95. NSM Wallsend St Luke *Newc* 94-02; NSM Wallsend St Pet and St Luke from 02. *51 Rowantree Road, Newcastle upon Tyne NE6 4TE* Tel 0191-262 8795
E-mail andy.elder@btinternet.com

ELDER, David. b 28. Brechin NSM Ord Course 75. **d** 79 **p** 80. NSM Dundee St Salvador *Bre* 79-93; rtd 93; P-in-c Dundee St Martin *Bre* from 93. *Thistlemount, 21 Law Road, Dundee DD3 6PZ* Tel (01382) 827844

ELDER, Nicholas John. b 51. Hatf Poly BA73. Cuddesdon Coll 73. **d** 76 **p** 77. C Mill End *St Alb* 76-77; C Mill End and Heronsgate w W Hyde 77-79; TV Borehamwood 79-85; V Bedford St Mich 85-90; V Bedford All SS 90-00; V Camberwell St Geo *S'wark* from 00; Warden Trin Coll Cen Camberwell from 00. *St George's Vicarage, 115 Wells Way, London SE5 7SZ* Tel (020) 7703 2895

ELDRID, John Gisborne Charteris. b 25. OBE97. AKC52. **d** 53 **p** 54. C St Geo-in-the-East w Ch Ch w St Jo *Lon* 53-56; C E Grinstead St Mary *Chich* 56-58; C St Steph Walbrook and St Swithun etc *Lon* 58-64 and 72-81; V Portsea All SS *Portsm* 64-71; P-in-c Portsea St Jo Rudmore 69-71; V Portsea All SS w St Jo Rudmore 71-72; Gen Consultant Cen Lon Samaritans 72-74; Dir The Samaritans 74-87; Gen Consultant-Dir from 87; Lic to Offic *Lon* from 82; rtd 90; Perm to Offic *Portsm* from 90. *46 Marshall Street, London W1V 1LR* Tel (020) 7439 1406

ELDRIDGE, John Frederick. b 48. Lough Univ BSc70 Golden Gate Sem (USA) MDiv83 Fuller Th Sem California DMin96. Oak Hill Th Coll 90. **d** 92 **p** 93. C Maidstone St Luke *Cant* 92-97; Min Prince's Park CD *Roch* 97-02; P-in-c Wickham Market w Pettistree *St E* from 02. *The Vicarage, Crown Lane, Wickham Market, Woodbridge IP13 0SA* Tel (01728) 746026
E-mail jeldridge@supanet.com

ELDRIDGE, John Kenneth Tristan. b 59. St Steph Ho Ox 90. **d** 92 **p** 93. C Brighton Resurr *Chich* 92-96; C Hangleton 96-98; TR Moulsecoomb from 98; Chapl Sussex Beacon Hospice from 00. *St Andrew's Rectory, Hillside, Brighton BN2 4TA* Tel (01273) 680680 Fax as telephone

ELDRIDGE, Stephen William. b 50. Open Univ DipEurHum97 BA98. Chich Th Coll 87. **d** 89 **p** 90. C Stroud and Uplands w Slad *Glouc* 89-92; C Glouc St Mary de Crypt w St Jo and Ch Ch 92-95; C Glouc St Mary de Lode and St Nic 92-95; Bp's Chapl 92-93; P-in-c Kingswood w Alderley and Hillesley 95-00; P-in-c Cheltenham St Pet from 00. *St Peter's Vicarage, 375 Swindon Road, Cheltenham GL51 9LB* Tel (01242) 524369 Fax as telephone

ELEY, John Edward. b 49. Sarum & Wells Th Coll 74. **d** 77 **p** 78. C Sherborne w Castleton and Lillington *Sarum* 77-80; Min Can Carl Cathl *Carl* 80-84; V Bromsgrove All SS *Worc* 84-88; Perm to Offic *St E* 90-98; V Stourhead from 98. *The Rectory, Mill Road, Kedington, Haverhill CB9 7NN* Tel and fax (01440) 710216 Mobile 07785-575230 E-mail johneley@btinternet.com

ELFORD, Keith Anthony. b 59. Em Coll Cam BA80 MA84. Wycliffe Hall Ox 87. **d** 90 **p** 91. C Chertsey *Guildf* 90-94; P-in-c Ockham w Hatchford 94-98; Bp's Chapl 94-98; Perm to Offic 98-00; Lic to Offic from 01. *15 Canford Drive, Addlestone KT15 2HH* Tel (01932) 885137 E-mail keith.elford@lineone.net

ELFORD, Canon Robert John. b 39. Man Univ MA71 Ex Univ PhD74. Brasted Th Coll 64 Ridley Hall Cam 66. **d** 68 **p** 69. C Denton St Lawr *Man* 68-71; P-in-c Gwinear *Truro* 71-74; R Phillack w Gwithian and Gwinear 74-78; Lect Man Univ 78-87; Hon C Withington St Paul *Man* 79-83; Warden St Anselm Hall 82-87; Lic to Offic 84-87; Pro-R Liv Inst of HE 88-99; Lic to Offic *Liv* from 88; Can Th Liv Cathl from 92. *Howarden, 90 Beech Lane, Liverpool L18 3ER* Tel 0151-724 1622

ELFRED, Michael William. b 48. BA76 MPhil. Linc Th Coll 77. **d** 79 **p** 80. C Boultham *Linc* 79-82; C Croydon H Sav *Cant* 82-84; C Upper Norwood All SS *S'wark* 84-88; V Sanderstead St Mary 88-01; P-in-c Tadworth from 01. *The Vicarage, 1 The Avenue, Tadworth KT20 5AS* Tel (01737) 813152 Mobile 07931-463661 E-mail michael.elfred@talk21.com

ELGAR, Richard John. b 50. MRCGP80 Charing Cross Hosp Medical Sch MB, BS73 LRCP73 MRCS73. St Jo Coll Nottm 92. **d** 92 **p** 93. NSM Derby St Alkmund and St Werburgh *Derby*

92-96; P-in-c Derby St Barn 96-01; V from 01. *St Barnabas' Vicarage, 122 Radbourne Street, Derby DE22 3BU* Tel (01332) 342553 E-mail relgar1015@aol.com

ELIOT, Whately Ian. b 12. **d** 39 **p** 40. C Wolborough w Newton Abbot *Ex* 39-48; V Thorverton 48-55; C-in-c Burnt Ho Lane CD 55-64; Min 64-69; R Ex St Paul 69-77; RD Christianity 68-70; rtd 77; Perm to Offic *Ex* from 77. *c/o Messrs Foot, Anstey and Sargent, Unit D1, Pynes Hill, Exeter EX2 5AZ* Tel (01392) 218554

ELIZABETH CSF, Sister. *See* WEBB, Marjorie Valentine

ELIZABETH MARY CSD, Sister. *See* NOLLER, Hilda Elizabeth Mary

ELKINGTON, Mrs Audrey Anne. b 57. St Cath Coll Ox BA80 UEA PhD83 Nottm Univ DipTh86. St Jo Coll Nottm 85 EAMTC 86. **dss** 88 **d** 92 **p** 94. Monkseaton St Mary *Newc* 88-91; Ponteland 91-93; Par Dn 92-93; C Prudhoe 93-02; RD Corbridge 99-02; Bp's Adv for Women in Min from 01; Bp's Chapl from 02; Dir of Ords from 02. *16 Towers Avenue, Jesmond, Newcastle upon Tyne NE2 3QE* Tel 0191-281 0714
E-mail rev-elk@lineone.net

ELKINGTON, Canon David John. b 51. Nottm Univ BTh76 Leic Univ MEd81. St Jo Coll Nottm 73. **d** 76 **p** 77. C Leic Martyrs *Leic* 76-78; C Kirby Muxloe 78-80; Asst Chapl Leic Univ 80-82; Hon C Leic H Spirit 82; Chapl UEA *Nor* 82-88; TV Newc Epiphany *Newc* 88-91; TR 91-93; P-in-c Prudhoe 93-98; V 98-02; Can Res Newc Cathl from 02. *16 Towers Avenue, Jesmond, Newcastle upon Tyne NE2 3QE* Tel 0191-281 0714
E-mail rev-elk@lineone.net

ELKINS, Alan Bernard. b 47. Sarum & Wells Th Coll 70. **d** 73 **p** 74. C Wareham *Sarum* 73-77; P-in-c Codford, Upton Lovell and Stockton 77-79; P-in-c Boyton w Sherrington 77-79; C Ashton Gifford 79; R Bishopstrow and Boreham 79-92; R Corfe Mullen 92-03; V W Byfleet *Guildf* from 03. *The Vicarage, 5 Dartnell Avenue, West Byfleet KT14 6PJ* Tel (01932) 345270

ELKINS, Mrs Joy Kathleen. b 45. Sarum Th Coll 93. **d** 96 **p** 97. NSM Corfe Mullen *Sarum* 96-03; NSM W Byfleet *Guildf* from 03. *The Vicarage, 5 Dartnell Avenue, West Byfleet KT14 6PJ* Tel (01932) 345270 E-mail joy-elkins@lineone.net

ELKINS, Canon Patrick Charles. b 34. St Chad's Coll Dur BA57 DipTh60 DipEd. **d** 60 **p** 61. C Moordown *Win* 60-63; C Basingstoke 64-67; V Bransgore from 67; Hon Can Win Cathl from 89. *The Vicarage, Ringwood Road, Bransgore, Christchurch BH23 8JH* Tel (01425) 672327 Fax 674190

ELKS, Roger Mark. b 60. ACGI83 Imp Coll Lon BSc83. Wycliffe Hall Ox 89. **d** 92 **p** 93. C St Austell *Truro* 92-95; V Carbis Bay w Lelant 95-01; I Holywood *D & D* from 01. *The Parish Centre, 71 Church Road, Holywood BT18 9BZ* Tel (028) 9042 3622 E-mail vicarroger@ntlworld.com

ELLACOTT, David Alfred. b 35. SW Minl Tr Course 95. **d** 97 **p** 98. NSM Fremington *Ex* from 97. *2 Coppice Close, Fremington, Barnstaple EX31 2QE* Tel (01271) 373270

ELLAM, Stuart William. b 53. Westcott Ho Cam. **d** 85 **p** 86. C Ditton St Mich *Liv* 85-88; C Greenford H Cross *Lon* 88-91; Perm to Offic 91-94. *26 Church Road, Cowley, Uxbridge UB8 3NA* Tel (01895) 238815

ELLEANOR, David John. b 48. Leic Univ LLB70 St Jo Coll Dur BA88. Cranmer Hall Dur 85. **d** 88 **p** 89. C Consett *Dur* 88-90; P-in-c Ingleton from 96. *The Old Vicarage, Front Street, Ingleton, Darlington DL2 3JG* Tel (01325) 730928

ELLEM, Peter Keith. b 58. Nottm Univ BTh90 Leeds Univ MA99 CQSW. St Jo Coll Nottm 87. **d** 90 **p** 91. C Islington St Mary *Lon* 90-94; C Leeds St Geo *Ripon* 94-99; Australia from 99; R Yagoona from 00. *211 Auburn Road, Yagoona, NSW, Australia 2199* Tel (0061) (2) 9790 6281 Fax 9796 6201
E-mail prellen@smartchat.net.au

ELLENS, Gordon Frederick Stewart. b 26. FRAS Columbia Univ (NY) MPhil62 PhD68. Wycliffe Coll BD52 AKC52 St Boniface Warminster 52. **d** 53 **p** 54. C Old Street St Luke w St Mary Charterhouse etc *Lon* 53-55; C Chiswick St Mich 55-57; Canada 57-60; USA 62-66 and from 88; Japan 70-88; Asst Prof Relig St Sophia Univ Tokyo 70-75; Rikkyo Women's Univ 75-84; Prof Humanities Ueno Gakuen 84-88; rtd 92. *PO Box 1578, Santa Monica, CA 90406, USA* Tel (001) (310) 396 2062 Fax 396 5543

ELLERTON, Mrs Mary Diane. b 45. RGN67 RHV68 Huddersfield Poly Cert Health Educn 89. N Ord Course 90. **d** 93 **p** 94. NSM Upper Holme Valley *Wakef* from 93; Chapl Calderdale and Huddersfield NHS Trust from 01. *13 Liphill Bank Road, Holmfirth, Huddersfield HD9 2LQ* Tel (01484) 684207

ELLERY, Arthur James Gabriel. b 28. St Jo Coll Dur BSc49. Linc Th Coll 51. **d** 53 **p** 54. C Milton next Sittingbourne *Cant* 53-56; C St Laur in Thanet 56-58; C Darlington St Cuth *Dur* 58-62; V Tanfield 62-70; Chapl St Olave's Sch York 70-78; V Gt Ayton w Easby and Newton in Cleveland *York* 78-81; Chapl Bancroft's Sch Woodford Green 81-86; V Chipperfield St Paul *St Alb* 86-93; rtd 93; Perm to Offic *Ely* 93-00; Perm to Offic *Pet* from 93. *7 Church Drive, Orton Waterville, Peterborough PE2 5EX* Tel (01733) 231800

ELLERY, Ian Martyn William. b 56. K Coll Lon BD AKC. Chich Th Coll. **d** 82 **p** 83. C Hornsey St Mary w St Geo *Lon* 82-85; V Choral York Minster *York* 85-89; Subchanter York Minster 86-89; R Patrington w Hollym, Welwick and Winestead 89-97; TR Howden from 97; RD Howden 97-02. *The Minster Rectory, Market Place, Howden, Goole DN14 7BL* Tel (01430) 430332 E-mail jeimwe@aol.com

ELLIN, Lindsey Jane. *See* GOODHEW, Mrs Lindsey Jane Ellin

ELLINGTON, David John. b 39. Oriel Coll Ox BA63 MA. Cuddesdon Coll 63. **d** 65 **p** 66. C Sheff St Mark Broomhall *Sheff* 65-68; C Timperley *Ches* 68-72; P-in-c Altrincham St Jo 72-74; V 74-80; P-in-c Ashley 82-86; rtd 86; Perm to Offic *Ches* 87-00. *6 Hough Green, Ashley, Altrincham WA15 0QS* Tel 0161-928 2173

ELLIOT, Hugh Riversdale. b 25. Bps' Coll Cheshunt. **d** 62 **p** 65. C Swaffham *Nor* 62-64; C Kessingland 64-67; C Mutford w Rushmere 65-67; P-in-c 67-68; P-in-c Gisleham 67-68; P-in-c Welborne 68-72; P-in-c Yaxham 68-80; P-in-c N Tuddenham 72-80; R E w W Harling 80-90; R Bridgham and Roudham 81-90; R E w W Harling and Bridgham w Roudham 90-92; rtd 92; Perm to Offic *Nor* from 93. *Berryfields, 27 The Street, Alburgh, Harleston IP20 0DJ* Tel (01986) 86498

ELLIOT, Neil Robert Minto. b 63. Hatfield Poly BEng87 Herts Univ CertEd93. St Jo Coll Nottm 94. **d** 96 **p** 97. C Walbrook Epiphany *Derby* 96-00; Chapl Univ of Cen England in Birm from 00. *4 Inverclyde Road, Birmingham B20 2LJ* Tel 0121-554 4579 Mobile 07974 150364 E-mail rev.nelli@virginnet

ELLIOT, William. b 33. Glouc Sch of Min 84. **d** 87 **p** 88. C Kington w Huntington, Old Radnor, Kinnerton etc *Heref* 87-90; C Heref H Trin 90-92; Chapl Corfu *Eur* 92-98; rtd 98; P-in-c Barlavington, Burton w Coates, Sutton and Bignor *Chich* from 98. *The Rectory, The Street, Sutton, Pulborough RH20 1PS* Tel (01798) 869220

ELLIOT, William Brunton. b 41. Edin Th Coll 90 Edin Dioc NSM Course 81. **d** 84 **p** 85. NSM Lasswade *Edin* 84-92; NSM Dalkeith 84-92; Assoc P Edin St Pet 92-94; R Selkirk from 94. *St John's Rectory, 23 Viewfield Park, Selkirk TD7 4LH* Tel (01750) 21364

ELLIOT-NEWMAN, Christopher Guy. b 43. Bede Coll Dur TCert67 Hull Univ BTh83 MEd87. Westcott Ho Cam 67. **d** 70 **p** 71. C Ditton St Mich *Liv* 70-73; C Hazlemere *Ox* 73-77; R Stockton-on-the-Forest w Holtby and Warthill *York* 77-87; Dir of Educn *Cant* 87-94; Perm to Offic *Newc* 95-99; P-in-c Warden w Newbrough 99-01. *15 Hextol Terrace, Hexham NE46 2DF* Tel (01434) 609612

ELLIOTT, Ben. *See* ELLIOTT, William Henry Venn

ELLIOTT, Brian. b 49. Dur Univ BA73. Coll of Resurr Mirfield 73. **d** 75 **p** 76. C Nunthorpe *York* 75-77; CF from 77. *c/o MOD Chaplains (Army)* Tel (01980) 615804 Fax 615800 E-mail brian@newpost.com

ELLIOTT, Charles Middleton. b 39. Linc Coll Ox BA60 Nuff Coll Ox DPhil62. Linc Th Coll 62. **d** 64 **p** 65. Lect Nottm Univ 63-65; C Wilford S'well 64-65; Zambia 65-69; Chapl Lusaka Cath 65-69; Asst Gen Sec Jt Cttee WCC 69-72; Asst Gen Sec Pontifical Commn Justice and Peace 69-72; Sen Lect UEA 72-77; Hon Min Can Nor Cathl *Nor* 73-77; Prof Development Studies Univ of Wales (Swansea) 77-82; Dir Chr Aid 82-84; Asst Gen Sec BCC 82-84; Prof Bris Univ 85-87; Australia 87-88; Visiting Prof K Coll Lon 88-89; Preb Lich Cathl *Lich* 88-97; Dean and Chapl Trin Hall Cam from 90. *Trinity Hall, Cambridge CB2 1TJ* Tel (01223) 332525 or 69233 Fax 332537 E-mail cme13@hermes.cam.ac.uk

ELLIOTT, Christopher. b 44. Sarum Th Coll 66. **d** 69 **p** 70. C Walthamstow St Pet *Chelmsf* 69-71; C Witham 71-74; P-in-c Gt and Lt Bentley 74-80; R Colchester Ch Ch w St Mary V 80-85; R Sible Hedingham 85-93; V Leigh-on-Sea St Aid 93-98; P-in-c Thornton Gp *Linc* 98-01; RD Horncastle 98-01; P-in-c Lt Waltham *Chelmsf* from 01; P-in-c Lt Leighs from 01; P-in-c Gt Leighs from 01. *The Rectory, Brook Hill, Little Waltham, Chelmsford CM3 3LJ* Tel (01245) 360241 E-mail christopher.elliott@care4free.net

ELLIOTT, Christopher John. b 67. Southn Univ 93. Chich Th Coll 94. **d** 94 **p** 95. C Alton St Lawr *Win* 94-97; Perm to Offic *Guildf* from 99. *72 Woodlands, Fleet GU51 4NU* Tel 07788-195548 (Mobile)

ELLIOTT, Colin David. b 32. AKC55. **d** 56 **p** 57. C W Wickham St Jo *Cant* 56-59; C Dover St Mary 59-64; V Linton 64-66; V Gillingham H Trin *Roch* 66-81; V Belvedere All SS 81-88; V Bromley St Jo 88-97; rtd 97; Perm to Offic S'wark from 98; *Roch* from 99. *Flat 3, 160 George Lane, London SE13 6JF* Tel (020) 8698 4901

ELLIOTT, David Reed. b 62. Lon Bible Coll BA91. Oak Hill Th Coll 91. **d** 93 **p** 94. C Luton Lewsey St Hugh *St Alb* 93-98; Dioc Communications Dept 98-00. *21 Elm Close, Weston Turville, Aylesbury HP22 5SS* Tel (01296) 614597

ELLIOTT, Derek John. b 26. Pemb Coll Cam BA50 MA55. Oak Hill Th Coll 48. **d** 51 **p** 53. C Ealing Dean St Jo *Lon* 51-53; C New Milverton *Cov* 53-55; C Boscombe St Jo *Win* 55-57; V Biddulph *Lich* 57-63; R Rushden w Newton Bromswold *Pet* 63-68; RD Higham 66-68; Chapl Bedford Modern Sch 68-83; V Potten End w Nettleden *St Alb* 83-91; rtd 91; Hon C Twickenham St Mary *Lon* from 91; Perm to Offic *Guildf* from 99. *Westwinds, Ridgeway Road, Dorking RH4 3AT* Tel (01306) 876655

ELLIOTT, Miss Eveline Mary. b 39. ALA63 Bedf Coll Lon BA60 Cam Univ DipRS92. EAMTC 92. **d** 95 **p** 96. NSM Bury St Edmunds St Mary *St E* 95-97; NSM Lark Valley from 97. *4 St Michael's Close, Northgate Street, Bury St Edmunds IP33 1HT* Tel (01284) 753592

ELLIOTT, George Evan. b 17. Sarum Th Coll. **d** 58 **p** 59. C Padiham *Blackb* 58-61; C Cleveleys 61-63; V Kimblesworth *Dur* 63-71; V Sutton St James *Linc* 71-77; V Sutton St Edmund 71-77; P-in-c Bishop Norton 77-80; R Wadingham w Snitterby 77-80; R Bishop Norton, Wadingham and Snitterby 80-82; rtd 82; Perm to Offic *Nor* 82-98. *23 Ramsay Hall, 11-13 Byron Road, Worthing BN11 3HN* Tel (01903) 215480

ELLIOTT, Gordon. b 25. St Aid Birkenhead 63. **d** 65 **p** 66. C Latchford St Jas *Ches* 65-68; C Bollington St Jo 68-70; V Dukingfield St Mark 70-73; TV Tenbury *Heref* 74-78; V Bromfield 78-82; R Culmington w Onibury 78-82; V Stanton Lacy 78-82; P-in-c Withybrook w Copston Magna *Cov* 82-83; P-in-c Wolvey, Burton Hastings and Stretton Baskerville 82-83; V Wolvey w Burton Hastings, Copston Magna etc 83-90; rtd 90; Perm to Offic *Worc* from 90; Perm to Offic *Heref* 90-95. *12 Handbury Road, Malvern WR14 1NN* Tel (01684) 569388

ELLIOTT, Ian David. b 40. Qu Coll Cam BA61 MA65. Tyndale Hall Bris 64. **d** 66 **p** 67. C Halewood *Liv* 66-71; C Gt Crosby St Luke 71-74; C-in-c Dallam CD 74-80; V Dallam 80-83; TV Fazakerley Em 83-92; V Warrington H Trin from 92. *Holy Trinity Vicarage, 6 Palmyra Square North, Warrington WA1 1JQ* Tel (01925) 630057 E-mail rev-elliott@hotmail.com

ELLIOTT, John Andrew. b 44. ACIB68. St Alb and Ox Min Course 95. **d** 98 **p** 99. NSM Bedgrove *Ox* 98-01; C Modbury, Bigbury, Ringmore w Kingston etc *Ex* from 01. *The Church House, Ringmore, Kingsbridge TQ7 4HR* Tel (01548) 810565 E-mail johnaelliott@compuserve.com

ELLIOTT, John George. b 15. Qu Coll Ox BA37 MA46. Westcott Ho Cam 46. **d** 47 **p** 48. C Oxton *Ches* 47-51; Ceylon 51-61; Chapl Loughborough Gr Sch 61-80; rtd 80; Perm to Offic *Leic* from 80. *2 Quorn Court, 26 High Street, Quorn, Loughborough LE12 8DT* Tel (01509) 415207

ELLIOTT, John Philip. b 37. MIChemE61 MBIM Salford Univ CEng. Glouc Th Course 79. **d** 80 **p** 80. NSM Brimscombe *Glouc* 80-86; C Caverswall *Lich* 86-91; R Tredington and Darlingscott w Newbold on Stour *Cov* 91-97; rtd 97; Perm to Offic *Glouc* from 97. *Pipers Barn, 69 Bownham Park, Stroud GL5 5BZ*

ELLIOTT, Joseph William. b 37. Chich Th Coll. **d** 66 **p** 67. C Whickham *Dur* 66-72; V Lamesley 72-78; TR Usworth 78-93; P-in-c Belmont 93-95; V 95-98; rtd 98; Perm to Offic *Newc* from 01. *12 Harriot Drive, West Moor, Newcastle upon Tyne NE12 7EU* Tel 0191-256 6471

ELLIOTT, Capt Keith Alcock. b 51. St Jo Coll Dur 95 CA Tr Coll 83. **d** 95 **p** 96. C Chulmleigh, Chawleigh w Cheldon, Wembworthy etc *Ex* 95-99; TV Barnstaple from 99; C-in-c Roundswell CD from 99. *16 Mulberry Way, Roundswell, Barnstaple EX31 3QZ* Tel (01271) 375877

ELLIOTT (née JUTSUM), Mrs Linda Mary. b 56. St Pet Coll Birm CertEd77. WMMTC 92. **d** 95 **p** 96. NSM Longthorpe *Pet* 95-99; P-in-c Etton w Helpston and Maxey from 99. *The Rectory, Golden Drop Lane, Helpston, Peterborough PE6 7DW* Tel (01733) 253456 E-mail rev_linda@lycos.co.uk

ELLIOTT, Mary. *See* ELLIOTT, Miss Eveline Mary

ELLIOTT, Maurice John. b 65. St Andr Univ MA87 TCD BTh92 MPhil93. CITC 89. **d** 93 **p** 94. C Coleraine *Conn* 93-98; I Greenisland 98-02; I Lurgan Ch the Redeemer *D & D* from 02. *Shankill Rectory, 62 Banbridge Road, Lurgan, Craigavon BT66 7HG* Tel (028) 3832 3341 E-mail maurice.elliott@lineone.net

ELLIOTT, Canon Michael Cowan. b 38. Auckland Univ BA63 Episc Th Sch Mass MDiv66 Massey Univ (NZ) MPhil82. St Jo Coll Auckland LTh61. **d** 61 **p** 62. New Zealand 61-65; C New Lynn 61-64; C Thames 65; USA 65-66; Warden Pemb Coll Miss Walworth S'wark 66-70; Dir St Luke's Cen Haifa Jerusalem 70-74; BCC 74-75; C Amersham *Ox* 74-75; Ecum Secretariat on Development NZ 76-84; Dir Chr Action NZ 84-87; Chapl City of Lon Poly *Lon* 87-89; Dir Inner City Aid 89-91; Tutor Westmr Coll Ox 91-98; Dir Ox Educn Trust 99-02; Dir Taught Progr Ox Cen for Miss Studies 00-02; Dir Min and Can Res Brecon Cathl *S & B* 02-03; rtd 03; Lect Univ of Wales (Lamp) *St D* from 03. *Orchard House, Chapel Road, Llanfihangel Talyllyn, Brecon LD3 7TH* Tel (01874) 658194 E-mail canonmelliott@aol.com

ELLIOTT, Michael James. b 58. LTh. St Jo Coll Nottm 80. **d** 83 **p** 84. C Pontypridd St Cath *Llan* 83-86; C Leamington Priors St Paul *Cov* 86-89; Chapl RAF from 89; Perm to Offic *Ely* from 01. *Chaplaincy Services (RAF), HQ, Personnel and Training Command, RAF Innsworth, Gloucester GL3 1EZ* Tel (01452) 712612 ext 5164 Fax 510828

ELLIOTT, Nigel Harvey. b 55. St Jo Coll Nottm DCM92. **d** 92 **p** 93. C Radcliffe *Man* 92-95; V Kilnhurst *Sheff* from 95. *The Vicarage, Highthorne Road, Kilnhurst, Rotherham S64 5UU* Tel (01709) 589674 E-mail neii199076@aol.com

ELLIOTT, Norman. *See* ELLIOTT, William Norman

ELLIOTT, The Ven Peter. b 41. Hertf Coll Ox BA63 MA68. Linc Th Coll 63. **d** 65 **p** 66. C Gosforth All SS *Newc* 65-68; C Balkwell 68-72; V High Elswick St Phil 72-80; V N Gosforth 80-87; V Embleton w Rennington and Rock 87-93; RD Alnwick 89-93; Hon Can Newc Cathl 90-93; Adn Northd and Can Res Newc Cathl from 93. *80 Moorside North, Newcastle upon Tyne NE4 9DU* Tel 0191-273 8245 Fax 226 0286 E-mail p.elliott@newcastle.anglican.org

ELLIOTT, Peter Wolstenholme. b 31. CChem MRSC. NEOC 78. **d** 81 **p** 82. NSM Yarm *York* 81-02; Perm to Offic from 02. *48 Butterfield Drive, Eaglescliffe, Stockton-on-Tees TS16 0EZ* Tel (01642) 652698 E-mail revdpeter@hotmail.com

ELLIOTT, Philip. *See* ELLIOTT, John Philip

ELLIOTT, Simon Richard James. b 66. Lon Univ BSc88. Cranmer Hall Dur BA95. **d** 95 **p** 96. C Hendon St Paul Mill Hill *Lon* 95-99; V Hull St Martin w Transfiguration *York* from 99. *St Martin's Vicarage, 942 Anlaby Road, Hull HU4 6AH* Tel (01482) 352995

ELLIOTT, Stanley Griffin. b 19. Lon Univ BA50. Ridley Hall Cam 50. **d** 52 **p** 53. C Astley Bridge *Man* 52-54; C Bedford Leigh 54-56; R Ordsall in Salford St Cypr 56-59; R Ashton-upon-Mersey St Martin *Ches* 59-80; V Tile Hill *Cov* 80-85; rtd 85; Perm to Offic *Win* 85-97; Perm to Offic *Sarum* from 85. *38 Melton Court, 37 Lindsay Road, Poole BH13 6BH* Tel (01202) 766080

ELLIOTT, William. *See* ELLIOTT, Joseph William

ELLIOTT, William. b 20. Lon Univ BA56. Ripon Hall Ox 60. **d** 61 **p** 62. C Kidderminster St Mary *Worc* 61-70; V Bewdley Far Forest 70-78; V Rock w Heightington w Far Forest 78-82; V Mamble w Bayton, Rock w Heightington etc 82-85; rtd 85; Perm to Offic *Heref* from 85; Perm to Offic *Worc* from 85. *8 Lea View, Cleobury Mortimer, Kidderminster DY14 8EE* Tel (01299) 270993 E-mail welliott@fish.co.uk

ELLIOTT, William Henry Venn (Ben). b 34. K Coll Cam BA55 MA59. Wells Th Coll 59. **d** 61 **p** 62. C Almondbury *Wakef* 61-66; V Bramshaw *Sarum* 66-81; P-in-c Landford w Plaitford 77-81; V Mere w W Knoyle and Maiden Bradley 81-99; rtd 99. *3 St George's Close, Salisbury SP2 8HA* Tel (01722) 338409

ELLIOTT, William James. b 38. Jes Coll Cam BA62 MA66 Birm Univ MA69 PhD74. Qu Coll Birm 62. **d** 64 **p** 65. C Hendon St Paul Mill Hill *Lon* 64-67; C St Pancras w St Jas and Ch Ch 67-69; P-in-c Preston St Paul *Blackb* 69-74; R Elstree *St Alb* 74-00; Research Assoc Th Birm Univ *Birm* 00-03; Perm to Offic *Nor* from 01. *Idolvestre, 30B New Street, Holt NR25 6JH* Tel (01263) 713853 Fax 710215

ELLIOTT, William Norman. b 20. Kelham Th Coll 37. **d** 43 **p** 44. C Tividale *Lich* 43-50; C Barnsley St Mary *Wakef* 50-55; V Smawthorpe St Mich 55-63; V S Crosland 64-85; rtd 85; Chapl Community of St Peter Horbury from 85; Perm to Offic *Wakef* from 85. *18 Woodlands, Horbury, Wakefield WF4 5HH* Tel (01924) 265547

ELLIOTT SMITH, Mark Charles. b 59. LRAM85 GRSM86 DipRAM87 ARCO88 Lon Univ MA96. St Steph Ho Ox 92. **d** 94 **p** 97. C W Hampstead St Jas *Lon* 94-95; In RC Ch 95-96; C Tottenham St Paul 96-01; P-in-c New Southgate St Paul 01-03; V from 03. *St Paul's Vicarage, 11 Woodland Road, London N11 1PN* Tel (020) 8361 1946 E-mail frmark_elliottsmith@talk21.com

ELLIS, Anthony. *See* ELLIS, John Anthony

ELLIS, Anthony Colin. b 56. Keble Coll Ox BA77 Man Univ PhD80. Linc Th Coll 80. **d** 81 **p** 82. C Mill Hill Jo Keble Ch *Lon* 81-83; Staff Tutor in RS Man Univ from 83; Dir of Centre for Continuing Educn from 99; C Stretford St Pet *Man* 83-87; NSM Shore 87-89; Lic Preacher from 89. *2 Crowther Terrace, Blackshaw, Hebden Bridge HX7 6DE* Tel (01422) 844242 or 0161-275 3302

ELLIS, Canon Bryan Stuart. b 31. Qu Coll Cam BA54 MA58. Ridley Hall Cam 55. **d** 57 **p** 58. C Ramsgate St Luke *Cant* 57-59; C Herne Bay Ch Ch 59-62; V Burmantofts St Steph and St Agnes *Ripon* 62-81; RD Wakef 81-96; V Wakef St Andr and St Mary 81-00; Hon Can Wakef Cathl 89-00; rtd 00. *302 Oakwood Lane, Leeds LS8 3LE*

ELLIS, Charles Harold. b 50. N Ord Course 78. **d** 81 **p** 82. C Davyhulme St Mary *Man* 81-85; V Tonge w Alkrington 85-91; P-in-c Radcliffe St Thos and St Jo 91; P-in-c Radcliffe St Mary 91; TR Radcliffe 91-99; AD Radcliffe and Prestwich 96-99; P-in-c Newchurch 99-00; TR Rossendale Middle Valley from 00; AD Rossendale from 00. *The Rectory, 539 Newchurch Road, Newchurch, Rossendale BB4 9HH* Tel (01706) 215098 E-mail charlesandsue@compuserve.com

ELLIS, Christopher Charles. b 55. Societas Oecumenica 90 Edin Univ BD78 Hull Univ MA80. Edin Th Coll 76 Irish Sch of Ecum 78. **d** 79 **p** 80. C Selby Abbey *York* 79-82; C Fulford 82-85;

Dioc Ecum Officer 81-98; Dioc Ecum Adv 90-98; Lect Ecum Th Hull Univ from 84; P-in-c Kexby w Wilberfoss *York* 85-90; Ecum Officer S Cleveland and N Yorks Ecum Coun 88-98; P-in-c Bulmer w Dalby, Terrington and Welburn 98-01; R Howardian Gp from 01. *The Rectory, Terrington, York YO60 6PU* Tel (01653) 648226

ELLIS, Canon David Craven. b 34. Man Univ BA56 MA57. St Aid Birkenhead 59. **d** 61 **p** 62. C Gt Crosby St Luke *Liv* 61-65; Hong Kong 65-69; P-in-c Sawrey *Carl* 69-74; Dioc Youth Officer 69-74; V Halifax St Aug *Wakef* 74-84; R Greystoke, Matterdale and Mungrisdale *Carl* 84-87; R Watermillock 84-87; TR Greystoke, Matterdale, Mungrisdale etc 88-91; RD Penrith 87-91; TR Carl H Trin and St Barn 91-96; Hon Can Carl Cathl 91-96; rtd 96; Perm to Offic *Carl* 97-02; NSM Cartmel Peninsula from 02. *Calderstones, 5 Fellside, Allithwaite, Grange-over-Sands LA11 7RN* Tel (01539) 533974

ELLIS, Gay Winifred. b 48. Oak Hill Th Coll DipTh96. **d** 96 **p** 97. NSM Nazeing *Chelmsf* 96-99; C 99-00; P-in-c Chingford St Anne 00-02; V from 02. *St Anne's Vicarage, 200A Larkhall Road, London E4 6NP* Tel (020) 8529 4740 E-mail gayellis@cs.com

ELLIS, Gillian Patricia. b 99 **p** 00. OLM Blymhill w Weston-under-Lizard *Lich* 99-00; OLM Lapley w Wheaton Aston from 00. *18 Ashleigh Crescent, Wheaton, Aston ST19 9PN* Tel (01785) 840925

ELLIS, Hugh William. b 54. Sussex Univ BSc76. Ridley Hall Cam 88. **d** 90 **p** 91. C Reading St Jo *Ox* 90-93; P-in-c Bradfield and Stanford Dingley 93-97; R from 97. *The Rectory, Southend Road, Bradfield, Reading RG7 6EU* Tel 0118-974 4333 E-mail hughellis@compuserve.com

ELLIS, Canon Ian Morton. b 52. QUB BD75 MTh82 TCD PhD89. CITC. **d** 77 **p** 78. C Portadown St Columba *Arm* 77-79; C Arm St Mark 79-85; Chapl Arm R Sch 79-85; Hon V Choral Arm Cathl 82-93; I Mullavilly 85-93; Dom Chapl to Abp Arm 86-93; Tutor for Aux Min (Arm) 90-93; Dioc Adv on Ecum 92-93; I Newcastle *D & D* from 93; Can Belf Cathl from 00; Ed *The Church of Ireland Gazette* from 01; Preb Newcastle St Patr Cathl Dublin from 01. *The Rectory, 1 King Street, Newcastle BT33 0HD* Tel (028) 4372 2439 E-mail ian.m.ellis@btinternet.com

ELLIS, Ian William. b 57. QUB BSc78 CertEd79 TCD BTh89. CITC 86. **d** 89 **p** 90. C Arm St Mark w Aghavilly *Arm* 89-91; I Loughgall w Grange 91-02; Sec Gen Syn Bd of Educn from 02. *Church of Ireland House, 61-67 Donegall Street, Belfast BT1 2QH* Tel (028) 9023 1202 Fax 9023 7802 E-mail edunorth@ireland.anglican.org

ELLIS, Jean Miriam. b 35. St Mich Coll Llan DipMin92. **d** 95 **p** 97. NSM Llanelli *S & B* 95-98; NSM Rockfield and St Maughen's w Llangattock etc *Mon* from 99. *Rockfield Vicarage, Rockfield, Monmouth NP25 5QB* Tel (01600) 712003

ELLIS, John Anthony (Tony). b 47. Univ of Wales (Lamp) DipTh70 Open Univ BA80. Coll of Resurr Mirfield 70. **d** 72 **p** 73. C Sketty *S & B* 72-75; C Duston *Pet* 75-80; R Lichborough w Maidford and Farthingstone 80-85; V Stratfield Mortimer *Ox* 85-98; P-in-c Mortimer W End w Padworth 85-98; TR Kidlington w Hampton Poyle from 98. *St Mary's Rectory, 19 Mill Street, Kidlington OX5 2EE* Tel (01865) 372230 Fax as telephone E-mail churchkid@tesco.net

ELLIS, John Beaumont. b 45. Univ of Wales (Lamp) BA67 LTh69. Bp Burgess Hall Lamp. **d** 69 **p** 70. C Abergavenny St Mary w Llanwenarth Citra *Mon* 69-72; C Swansea St Gabr *S & B* 72-75; V Llanbister and Llanbadarn Fynydd w Llananno 75-77; V Newport St Andr *Mon* 77-80; V Risca 80-84; V Cheadle Heath *Ches* 84-94. *12 Upper Hibbert Lane, Marple, Stockport SK6 7HX* Tel 0161-427 1963

ELLIS, John Franklyn. b 34. Leeds Univ BA58. Linc Th Coll 58. **d** 60 **p** 61. C Ladybarn *Man* 60-63; C Stockport St Geo *Ches* 63-66; V High Lane 66-81; V Chelford w Lower Withington 81-99; rtd 99; Perm to Offic *Ches* from 00. *3 Millers Croft, Adlington Street, Macclesfield SK10 1BD*

ELLIS, John Raymond. b 63. St Steph Ho Ox 95. **d** 97 **p** 98. C Clare w Poslingford, Cavendish etc *St E* 97-00; P-in-c Bury St Edmunds St Jo 00-02; P-in-c Bury St Edmunds St Geo 00-02; TV Bury St Edmunds All SS w St Jo and St Geo from 02. *2 Fen Way, Bury St Edmunds IP33 3ZA* Tel (01284) 752906 E-mail john.ellis@stedmundsbury.anglican.org

ELLIS, John Roland. b 32. Wells Th Coll 67. **d** 69 **p** 70. C Kettering St Pet and Paul *Pet* 69-71; C Kingsthorpe 71-73; TV 73-74; TV Ebbw Vale *Mon* 74-76; V Llanddewi Rhydderch w Llanvapley etc 76-83; Miss to Seamen 79-86; V New Tredegar *Mon* 83-86; V Llanelli *S & B* 86-98; RD Crickhowell 91-98; rtd 98; P-in-c Rockfield and St Maughen's w Llangattock etc *Mon* from 99. *Rockfield Vicarage, Rockfield, Monmouth NP25 5QB* Tel (01600) 712003

ELLIS, Canon John Wadsworth. b 42. MBE98. TCD BA64. **d** 66 **p** 67. C Lisburn Ch Ch Cathl *Conn* 66-69; C Norbiton *S'wark* 69-72; C New Clee *Linc* 72-85; V from 85; RD Grimsby and Cleethorpes 94-99; Can and Preb Linc Cathl from 98. *120 Queen*

Mary Avenue, Cleethorpes DN35 7SZ Tel and fax (01472) 696521 *or* 329922 E-mail jellis1098@aol.com

ELLIS, Keith. b 39. Univ of Wales (Swansea) BSc60 Birm Poly BSc(Econ)74 Liv Univ CertEd61. St Jo Coll Nottm 95. **d** 96 **p** 97. NSM Marple All SS *Ches* 96-99; NSM Camelot Par *B & W* 99-03. *5 Lavender Close, Melksham SN12 6FW*

ELLIS, Kevin Stuart. b 67. Newc Univ BA91 Lon Bible Coll PhD97. Qu Coll Birm 99. **d** 01 **p** 02. C Matson *Glouc* from 01. *58 Haycroft Drive, Matson, Gloucester GL4 6XX* Tel (01452) 311041 E-mail kevinellis@fish.co.uk

ELLIS, Sister Lilian. b 44. Keswick Hall Coll TCert66. Wilson Carlile Coll Dip Evang90 Oak Hill Th Coll 95. **d** 96 **p** 97. C Vange *Chelmsf* 96-00; C Pitsea w Nevendon 00-02; rtd 02. *31 Sparkbridge, Laindon, Basildon SS15 6QJ* Tel (01268) 419391 E-mail lilian.ellis@tesco.net

ELLIS, Malcolm Railton. b 35. LTCL71 Univ of Wales (Lamp) BA56. Sarum Th Coll 56. **d** 58 **p** 59. C Llangynwyd w Maesteg *Llan* 58-61; C Llantrisant 61-67; V Troedrhiwgarth 67-70; PV Truro Cathl *Truro* 70-73; V Eglwyshayle 73-81; V Margam *Llan* 81-87; V Cardiff St Jo 87-00; TR Cen Cardiff 00-02; Prec and Can Llan Cathl 96-02; Offg Chapl OStJ 87-02; rtd 02. *41 Wendron Street, Helston TR13 8PT* Tel (01326) 574000

ELLIS, Preb Mark Durant. b 39. Ex Univ BA62. Cuddesdon Coll 62. **d** 64 **p** 65. C Lyngford *B & W* 64-67; V Weston-super-Mare St Andr Bournville 67-76; TV Yeovil 76-88; V Yeovil St Mich from 88; Preb Wells Cathl from 90; RD Merston from 94. *St Michael's Vicarage, St Michael's Avenue, Yeovil BA21 4LH* Tel (01935) 475752 Fax as telephone

ELLIS, Paul. b 56. Man Poly HNC79. Aston Tr Scheme 88 Trin Coll Bris DipHE92. **d** 92 **p** 93. C Pennington *Man* 92-96; TV Deane from 96. *St Andrew's Vicarage, Over Hulton, Bolton BL5 1EN* Tel (01204) 651851 E-mail paul.ellis@stabolton.freeserve.co.uk

ELLIS, Peter Andrew. b 46. St D Coll Lamp 65. **d** 69 **p** 70. C Milford Haven *St D* 69-71; R Walwyn's Castle w Robeston W 71-74; Miss to Seafarers from 74; Hong Kong 74-75 and from 92; Singapore 75-82; The Tees and Hartlepool 82-92. *The Mariner's Club, 11 Middle Road, Kowloon, Hong Kong* Tel (00852) 2368 8261 Fax 2366 0928

ELLIS, Randolph John Keith. b 44. Univ of Wales MEd Man Univ CertEd. Westcott Ho Cam 98. **d** 01 **p** 02. C Glanogwen w St Ann's w Llanllechid *Ban* from 01. *Glan Arthur, Penisarwaun, Caernarfon LL55 3PW* Tel (01286) 873623 E-mail randolph@afoncfeim.freeserve.co.uk

ELLIS, Richard. b 47. **d** 02. OLM Leiston *St E* from 02. *9 Kings Road, Leiston IP16 4DA* Tel (01728) 832168

ELLIS, Robert Albert. b 48. Roch Coll Lon BD70 AKC70. St Aug Coll Cant 70. **d** 72 **p** 73. C Liv Our Lady and St Nic w St Anne *Liv* 72-76; P-in-c Meerbrook *Lich* 76-80; Producer Relig Progr BBC Radio Stoke 76-80; V Highgate All SS *Lon* 80-81; P-in-c Longdon *Lich* 81-87; Dioc Communications Officer 81-01; Chapl Palma de Mallorca *Eur* from 01. *Nunez de Balboa 6, Son Armadans, 07014 Palma de Mallorca, Spain* Tel (0034) (971) 737279 Fax 454492 E-mail anglicanpalma@terra.es

ELLIS, The Ven Robin Gareth. b 35. Pemb Coll Ox BA57 BCL58 MA62. Chich Th Coll 58. **d** 60 **p** 61. C Swinton St Pet *Man* 60-63; Asst Chapl Worksop Coll Notts 63-66; V Swaffham Prior *Ely* 66-74; Asst Dir Educn 66-74; V Wisbech St Aug 74-82; V Yelverton *Ex* 82-86; Adn Plymouth 82-00; rtd 00. *24 Lyndhurst Road, Exmouth EX8 3DT* Tel (01395) 272891

ELLIS, Roger Henry. b 40. Natal Univ BA60 Selw Coll Cam BA64 MA68 Linacre Coll Ox BLitt69. **d** 66 **p** 67. C Ox St Mich *Ox* 66-68; S Africa 68-76; P-in-c Wortham *St E* 77; V Wheatley Hills *Sheff* 77-84; Chapl St Edm Sch Cant 84-00; P-in-c Dymchurch w Burmarsh and Newchurch *Cant* from 00; AD Romney from 01. *The New Rectory, 135 High Street, Dymchurch, Romney Marsh TN29 0LD* Tel (01303) 872150

ELLIS, Simon David. b 68. Univ of Wales (Cardiff) BSc89 Bris Univ PGCE90. St Steph Ho Ox BTh94. **d** 97 **p** 98. C Knowle H Nativity *Bris* 97-01; V Long Eaton St Laur *Derby* from 01. *The Vicarage, Regent Street, Long Eaton, Nottingham NG10 1JX* Tel 0115-973 3154 E-mail ellis.family@ukgateway.net

ELLIS, Susannah Margaret. b 44. Open Univ BA82 New Coll Dur CertEd88. EAMTC 93. **d** 96 **p** 97. NSM S Elmham and Ilketshall *St E* 96-98; Warden Quiet Waters Chr Retreat Ho 96-98; C Worlingham w Barnby and N Cove *St E* 98-01; C Beccles St Mich 98-01; P-in-c Worlingham w Barnby and N Cove 01-03; R from 03. *27 Lowestoft Road, Worlingham, Beccles NR34 7DZ* Tel (01502) 715403

ELLIS, The Ven Timothy William. b 53. AKC75. St Aug Coll Cant 75. **d** 76 **p** 77. C Old Trafford St Jo *Man* 76-80; V Pendleton St Thos 80-87; Chapl Salford Coll of Tech 80-87; V Sheff Norwood St Leon *Sheff* 87-01; P-in-c Shiregreen St Hilda 94-01; RD Ecclesfield 94-99; Hon Can Sheff Cathl 00-01; Adn Stow *Linc* from 01; Can and Preb Linc Cathl from 01. *The Archdeacon's House, Main Street, Hackthorn, Lincoln LN2 3PF* Tel (01673) 860382 Fax 860015 E-mail arch.stowlind@virgin.net

ELLISDON, Patrick Leon Shane. b 61. St Jo Coll Nottm 99. **d** 01 **p** 02. C Margate St Phil *Cant* from 01. *4 Sandhurst Road, Margate CT9 3HR* Tel (01843) 226832 Mobile 07932-734932 E-mail panddellisdon@aol.com

✠**ELLISON, The Rt Revd John Alexander.** b 40. ALCD67. **d** 67 **p** 68 **c** 88. C Woking St Paul *Guildf* 67-70; SAMS from 71; Argentina 80-83; R Aldridge *Lich* 83-88; Bp Paraguay from 88. *Iglesia Anglicana Paraguaya, Casilla 1124, Asunción, Paraguay* Tel (00595) (21) 224028

ELLISON, Simon John. b 51. SEITE 99. **d** 02. NSM Caterham Valley *S'wark* from 02. *30 Whyteleafe Road, Caterham CR3 5EF* Tel (01883) 345951 E-mail simon.ellison@quista.net

ELLISTON, John Ernest Nicholas. b 37. ALCD61. **d** 61 **p** 62. C Gipsy Hill Ch Ch *S'wark* 61-64; C Whitton and Thurleston w Akenham *St E* 64-68; P-in-c New Clee *Linc* 68-71; V 75-76; V Grimsby St Steph 71-75; P-in-c Mildenhall *St E* 77-79; RD Mildenhall 81-84; R Barton Mills, Beck Row w Kenny Hill etc 80-84; V Ipswich St Aug 84-96; R Guernsey St Peter Port *Win* 96-02; Chapl Princess Eliz Hosp Guernsey 96-02; rtd 02; Perm to Offic *St E* from 03. *27 Wyvern Road, Ipswich IP3 9TJ* Tel (01473) 726617 *or* 720036

ELLMORE, Geoffrey Richard. b 36. CEng68 MIMechE68 Leic Coll of Art & Tech BScEng57. S'wark Ord Course 86. **d** 87 **p** 88. NSM Coxheath w E Farleigh, Hunton and Linton *Roch* 87-01. *5 Shelden Drive, Rainham, Gillingham ME8 8JX* Tel (01634) 386645

ELLMORE, Peter Robert. b 44. Portsm Univ MA. Sarum & Wells Th Coll 84. **d** 86 **p** 87. C Bridgemary *Portsm* 86-89; C Portsea N End St Mark 89-91; Asst Chapl St Mary's Hosp Portsm 91-92; Chapl Qu Alexandra Hosp Portsm 91-93; Chapl Team Ldr Portsm Hosps NHS Trust 93-97; P-in-c Cosham *Portsm* 97-99; Angl Chapl Univ Coll Lon Hosps NHS Trust 99-01; Chapl Team Ldr United Bris Healthcare NHS Trust from 01. *United Bristol Healthcare NHS Trust, Marlborough Street, Bristol BS1 3NU* Tel 0117-928 3600 E-mail peter.ellmore@lineone.net

ELLOR, Michael Keith. b 52. St Jo Coll Nottm 92. **d** 94 **p** 95. C Stafford St Jo and Tixall w Ingestre *Lich* 94-97; TV Bucknall and Bagnall 97-03; TR from 03; RD Stoke from 02. *12 Tansey Close, Stoke-on-Trent ST2 9QX* Tel (01782) 280667 *or* 279300 E-mail ellors@bucknall12.fsnet.co.uk

ELLSLEY, Howard. b 23. Roch Th Coll 65. **d** 67 **p** 68. C Glas St Marg *Glas* 67-71; R Dalbeattie 71-77; TV Melton Mowbray w Thorpe Arnold *Leic* 77-78; R Balcombe *Chich* 78-83; R Airdrie *Glas* 83-88; R Gartcosh 83-88; rtd 88. *Auchencraig, Lower Barcaple, Ringford, Castle Douglas DG7 2AP* Tel (01557) 820228

ELLSON, Sister Deborah Louise. b 61. Chelmer Inst of HE BEd84 Univ of Wales (Ban) MA00. EAMTC 98. **d** 00 **p** 01. NSM Lowestoft St Marg *Nor* from 00. *8 Oulton Street, Oulton, Lowestoft NR32 3BB* Tel (01502) 564651 E-mail callme@revsislou.free-online.co.uk

ELLSON, Montague Edward. b 33. Birm Univ BA56 Cam Univ AdCertEd67. EAMTC 84. **d** 87 **p** 88. Hon C Freethorpe w Wickhampton, Halvergate etc *Nor* 87-90; C Gaywood, Bawsey and Mintlyn 90-92; Miss to Seafarers from 90; R Pulham *Nor* 92-94; P-in-c Starston 93-94; Dioc NSM Officer 94-97; R Pulham Market, Pulham St Mary and Starston 94-97; RD Redenhall 95-97; rtd 97; Perm to Offic *Nor* from 97. *Barn Cottage, Neatishead Road, Horning NR12 8LB*

ELLSWORTH, Lida Elizabeth. b 48. Columbia Univ (NY) BA70 Girton Coll Cam PhD76. EMMTC 85. **d** 88 **p** 94. NSM Bakewell *Derby* from 88. *Apple Croft, Granby Gardens, Bakewell DE45 1ET* Tel (01629) 814255 Fax as telephone

ELLWOOD, Keith Brian. b 36. AIGCM58 FRSA65 DipRIPH&H65 ACP66 FCollP83 Curwen Coll Lon BA58 MMus65 Bede Coll Dur CertEd59 Hon DD99. Bps' Coll Cheshunt 64. **d** 64 **p** 65. Asst Master R Wanstead Sch 60-66; Chapl 64-66; C Wanstead St Mary *Chelmsf* 64-66; CF 66-70; OCF 70-71 and 76-79; Hong Kong 70-71; P-in-c Bicknoller *B & W* 71-73; Chapl Roedean Sch Brighton 73-76; Perm to Offic *B & W* 74-79; W Germany 76-79; Chapl Trin Coll Glenalmond 79-81; Hd Master St Chris Sch Burnham-on-Sea 82-86; Hon C Burnham *B & W* 82-86; R Staple Fitzpaine, Orchard Portman, Thurlbear etc 86-89; P-in-c Hugill *Carl* 89-93; Educn Adv 89-93; P-in-c Coldwaltham and Hardham *Chich* 93-95; rtd 96; Perm to Offic *Chich* from 96. *21 Fiddlers Drive, Armthorpe, Doncaster DN3 3TS* Tel (01302) 834031 E-mail k.b.e@btinternet.com

ELMAN, Simon Laurie. b 57. NTMTC DipTh99. **d** 99 **p** 00. C Loughton St Jo *Chelmsf* from 99. *86 Theydon Grove, Epping CM16 4QA* Tel (01992) 579532 E-mail simon@elman42.freeserve.co.uk

ELMES, Sister Evelyn Sandra. b 61. **d** 97 **p** 98. CA from 89; C Southchurch H Trin *Chelmsf* 97-00. *18 Chawton Close, Winchester SO22 6HY* Tel (01926) 880928

ELMORE, Graeme Martin. b 47. Sarum & Wells Th Coll 71. **d** 74 **p** 75. C Norbury St Oswald *Cant* 74-77; P-in-c St Allen *Truro*

77-79; P-in-c St Erme 77-79; V Newlyn St Pet 79-85; CF (TA) 80-86; R Redruth w Lanner *Truro* 85-86; Chapl RN from 86. *Royal Naval Chaplaincy Service, Room 203, Victory Building, HM Naval Base, Portsmouth PO1 3LS* Tel (023) 9272 7903 Fax 9272 7111

ELPHICK, Robin Howard. b 37. ALCD63. **d** 64 **p** 65. C Clapham Common St Barn *S'wark* 64-67; C Woking St Pet *Guildf* 67-71; R Rollesby w Burgh w Billockby *Nor* 71-80; P-in-c Ashby w Oby, Thurne and Clippesby 79-80; R Rollesby w Burgh w Billockby w Ashby w Oby etc 80-84; R Frinton *Chelmsf* 84-94; P-in-c W w E Mersea and Peldon w Gt and Lt Wigborough 94-02; rtd 02; Perm to Offic *Nor* from 02. *1 Barn Cottages, Dodma Road, Weasenham, King's Lynn PE32 2TJ* Tel (01328) 838340 E-mail robin@relphick.fsnet.co.uk

ELPHICK, Miss Vivien Margaret. b 53. Solicitor 77 Kent Univ BA74. Trin Coll Bris BA90. **d** 90 **p** 94. C Oulton Broad *Nor* 90-94; P-in-c Burlingham St Edmund w Lingwood, Strumpshaw etc from 94; RD Blofield from 98. *The Rectory, Barn Close, Lingwood, Norwich NR13 4TS* Tel (01603) 713880

ELPHIN AND ARDAGH, Archdeacon of. *See* FORSTER, The Ven Andrew James

ELPHIN AND ARDAGH, Dean of. *See* GRISCOME, The Very Revd David

ELSDON, Bernard Robert. b 29. Roch Th Coll 65. **d** 67 **p** 68. C Wallasey St Hilary *Ches* 67-71; C Liv Our Lady and St Nic w St Anne *Liv* 71-72; V Anfield St Marg 73-89; Dioc Exec Dir for Chr Resp 80-83; rtd 89; Perm to Offic *Man* and *Ches* from 89. *31 Douglas Road, Hazel Grove, Stockport SK7 4JE* Tel 0161-292 1858 E-mail hillcrest@hzgrove.freeserve.co.uk

ELSDON, Mrs Janice Margaret. b 49. CITC 92. **d** 95 **p** 96. NSM Cloughfern *Conn* 95-99; NSM Ahoghill w Portglenone 99-02; NSM Belfast St Thos from 02. *St Bartholomew's Rectory, 16 Mount Pleasant, Belfast BT9 5DS* Tel (028) 9066 9995 E-mail jelsdon@madasafish.com

ELSDON, Ronald. b 44. St Jo Coll Cam BA66 Trin Hall Cam PhD69 K Coll Lon BD86 Milltown Inst Dub PhD. CITC 97. **d** 99 **p** 00. C Ballymena w Ballyclug *Conn* 99-02; I Belfast St Bart from 02. *St Bartholomew's Rectory, 16 Mount Pleasant, Belfast BT9 5DS* Tel (028) 9066 9995 E-mail elsdon.rj@nireland.com

ELSEY, Cyril. b 08. Ridley Hall Cam 65. **d** 66 **p** 67. C Rolleston *Lich* 66-69; C Anslow 66-69; R Petton w Cockshutt 69-75; rtd 75; Perm to Offic *Ex* from 82. *9 Raleigh Court, Raleigh Road, Budleigh Salterton EX9 6HR* Tel (01395) 445504

ELSMORE, Canon Guy Charles. b 66. Edin Univ BSc88. Ridley Hall Cam 93. **d** 93 **p** 94. C Huyton St Mich *Liv* 93-98; V Hough Green St Basil and All SS from 98; P-in-c Widnes St Mary from 03; P-in-c Widnes St Paul from 03; Hon Can Liv Cathl from 03; AD Widnes from 03. *All Saints' Vicarage, Hough Green Road, Widnes WA8 9SZ* Tel 0151-420 4963

ELSON, Christopher John. b 52. K Coll Lon BD75 AKC75. St Aug Coll Cant. **d** 76 **p** 77. C New Haw *Guildf* 76-79; C Guildf H Trin w St Mary 79-82; C Hale 85-87; V Ripley from 87; Sub-Chapl HM Pris Send from 88. *The Vicarage, High Street, Ripley, Woking GU23 6AE* Tel (01483) 211460 Mobile 07956-103289 E-mail celson@fish.co.uk

ELSON, John Frederick. Roch Th Coll 62. **d** 64 **p** 65. C Tenterden St Mildred w Smallhythe *Cant* 64-68; P-in-c Chart next Sutton Valence 68-71; V Fletching *Chich* 71-93; Chapl Wivelsfield Green Hospice 91-93; rtd 93; Perm to Offic *Chich* from 93. *Fernbank, 36 Olive Meadow, Uckfield TN22 1QY* Tel (01825) 760663

ELSON, Sharon Anne. b 50. WEMTC 99. **d** 00 **p** 01. OLM Heref St Pet w St Owen and St Jas *Heref* from 00. *26 Craig House, Sudbury Avenue, Hereford HR1 1XU* Tel (01432) 370417 Mobile 07718-481318

ELSTOB, Stephen William. b 57. Sarum & Wells Th Coll. **d** 86 **p** 87. C Sunderland Springwell w Thorney Close *Dur* 86-88; C Upholland *Liv* 88-89; TV 89-96; V Cinnamon Brow from 96. *The Vicarage, 1 Briers Close, Fearnhead, Warrington WA2 0DN* Tel (01925) 823108

ELSTON, Philip Herbert. b 35. RD80 and Bar 90. Leeds Univ MA76 K Coll Lon AKC63 Leic Coll of Educn CertEd67. St Boniface Warminster 63. **d** 64 **p** 65. C Thurnby Lodge *Leic* 64-66; Hon C 66-67; Chapl RNR 67-90; Chapl Malosa Sch Malawi 68-75; Hon C Far Headingley St Chad *Ripon* 75-79; V Knowl Hill w Littlewick *Ox* 79-84; Chapl RN Sch Haslemere 85-89; C Felpham w Middleton *Chich* 89-90; Asst S Regional Dir Miss to Seamen 91-93; Dep S Regional Dir 93-97; S Regional Dir 97-00; Perm to Offic *Win* from 93; *Cant* 94-00; *Chich* from 97; rtd 00; Hon C Witchampton, Stanbridge and Long Crichel etc *Sarum* from 00; Hon Chapl Miss to Seafarers from 00. *The Vicarage, Witchampton, Wimbourne BH21 5AP* Tel (01258) 840422

ELTON, Canon Derek Hurley. b 31. Lon Univ BSc52. Wycliffe Hall Ox 53. **d** 55 **p** 56. C Ashton-on-Ribble St Andr *Blackb* 55-57; India 58-70; C R Wickmere w Lt Barningham and Itteringham *Nor* 71-79; R Lt w Gt Ellingham 79-83; P-in-c Rockland All SS and St Andr w St Pet 81-83; R Lt w Gt Ellingham w Rockland 83-88; Chapl Wayland Hosp Norfolk 84-88; Perm to Offic 88-97; Miss to Seamen 89-98; Algeria

89-94; Eritrea 94-98; rtd 96; Perm to Offic *Nor* from 00. *22 Alfred Road, Cromer NR27 9AN* Tel (01263) 511730 E-mail jedclef@paston.co.uk

ELTRINGHAM, Mrs Fiona Ann. b 48. CertEd69. NEOC 86. **d** 89 **p** 94. Par Dn Willington Team *Newc* 89-92; Chapl HM YOI Castington 92-97; Chapl HM Pris Dur from 97. *HM Prison Durham, Old Elvet, Durham DH1 3HU* Tel 0191-386 2621 Fax 386 2524

ELVERSON, Ronald Peter Charles. b 50. St Edm Hall Ox BA73 MA86. St Jo Coll Nottm LTh84. **d** 86 **p** 87. C Whitnash *Cov* 86-90; V Dunchurch 90-01; R Dersingham w Anmer and Shernborne *Nor* from 01. *The Vicarage, Sherborne Road, Dersingham, King's Lynn PE31 6JA* Tel (01485) 540214 E-mail ronelverson@theelversons.fsnet.co.uk

ELVEY, Ms Charlotte Evanthia. b 44. St Anne's Coll Ox BA66 Bris Univ CertEd67 Open Univ Dip Reading Development 86. S'wark Ord Course 91. **d** 94 **p** 95. NSM Sydenham St Bart *S'wark* 94-95; C 95-98; P-in-c Worcester Park Ch Ch w St Phil from 98. *The Vicarage, 1E Lindsay Road, Worcester Park KT4 8LF* Tel (020) 8337 1327

ELVIN, Jonathan Paul Alistair. b 65. Bris Univ BSc90 Fitzw Coll Cam BA94. Ridley Hall Cam CTM95. **d** 95 **p** 96. C Gravesend St Geo *Roch* 95-98; C Ex St Leon w H Trin *Ex* from 98. *63 Cedars Road, Exeter EX2 4NB* Tel (01392) 432607 Fax as telephone E-mail jonelvin@aol.com

ELVY, Canon Peter David. b 38. Lon Univ BA62 Fitzw Ho Cam BA64 MA68 Edin Univ PhD95. Ridley Hall Cam. **d** 65 **p** 66. C Herne *Cant* 65-66; C New Addington 66-68; C Addiscombe St Mildred 69-71; Youth Chapl *Chelmsf* 71-80; V Gt Burstead 75-92; Can Chelmsf Cathl 80-92; V Chelsea All SS *Lon* from 92; Can Ughelli from 98. *2 Old Church Street, London SW3 5DQ* Tel (020) 7352 5627 Fax 7352 5467 E-mail peterelvy@compuserve.com

ELWIN, Ernest John. b 31. Selw Coll Cam BA54 MA58. Ridley Hall Cam 54. **d** 56 **p** 57. C Wandsworth All SS *S'wark* 56-59; C Harlow New Town w Lt Parndon *Chelmsf* 59-61; Asst Teacher Tidworth Down Sch Dorset 61-63; V Soundwell *Bris* 63-66; Asst Teacher Seldown Sch Dorset 66-68; Wareham Modern Sch 68-69; Perm to Offic *Sarum* from 67; Lect S Dorset Tech Coll Weymouth 70-85; Weymouth Coll 85-88; Sub Chapl HM Youth Cust Cen Portland from 93. *4 Portesham Hill, Portesham, Weymouth DT3 4EU* Tel (01305) 871358

ELWIS, Malcolm John. b 42. Melbourne Univ DipEd74. St Jo Coll Morpeth 69 ACT LTh73. **d** 70 **p** 72. Australia 70-80; Perm to Offic *Chich* from 80; Chapl Hellingly and Amberstone Hosps 88-93; Chapl Eastbourne and Co Healthcare NHS Trust from 93; Sub Chapl HM Prison Lewes from 92. *Puddledock, Boreham Lane, Wartling, Hailsham BN27 1RS* Tel (01323) 833233

ELWOOD, Alan Roy. b 54. Sarum & Wells Th Coll 90. **d** 92 **p** 93. C Street w Walton *B & W* 92-96; V Kingsbury Episcopi w E Lambrook, Hambridge etc from 96. *The Vicarage, Folly Road, Kingsbury Episcopi, Martock TA12 6BH* Tel (01935) 824605

ELY, Nigel Patrick. b 62. Thames Poly BA83 Southn Univ BTh92. Chich Th Coll 89. **d** 92 **p** 93. C Rustington *Chich* 92-93; C Bexhill St Pet 93-96; Chapl Post 16 Cen *Birm* 96-99; NSM Lozells St Paul and St Silas from 99. *57 Cherry Orchard Road, Birmingham B20 2LD* Tel 0121-554 6340

ELY, Archdeacon of. *See* WATSON, The Ven Jeffrey John Seagrief

ELY, Bishop of. *See* RUSSELL, The Rt Revd Anthony John

ELY, Dean of. Vacant

EMBERTON, John Nicholas. b 45. FCA69. Oak Hill NSM Course 85. **d** 88 **p** 89. NSM Purley Ch Ch *S'wark* 88-94; Vineyard Min Internat (UK) from 96. *49 Oakwood Avenue, Purley CR8 1AR* Tel (020) 8668 2684

EMBLETON, Harold. b 21. Ch Coll Cam BA47 MA52. Qu Coll Birm 47. **d** 49 **p** 50. C Kidderminster St Mary *Worc* 49-52; CF (TA) 50-52; C Wimbledon *S'wark* 52-53; Chapl RN 53-76; QHC 74-76; V Bognor *Chich* 76-84; RD Arundel and Bognor 77-82; V Skirwith, Ousby and Melmerby w Kirkland *Carl* 84-87; rtd 87; Perm to Offic *Carl* 87-93; Perm to Offic *Chich* from 93. *Flat 3, 7 Chatsworth Gardens, Eastbourne BN20 7JP* Tel (01323) 411426

EMBLIN, Richard John. b 48. BEd71 MA81. S Dios Minl Tr Scheme 83. **d** 86 **p** 87. C S w N Hayling *Portsm* 86-89; P-in-c Wootton 89-95; V Cowes H Trin and St Mary from 95; RD W Wight from 01. *The Vicarage, Church Road, Cowes PO31 8HA* Tel (01983) 292509 E-mail cowesvic@yahoo.com

EMBRY, Miss Eileen Margaret. b 38. Westf Coll Lon BA60 Bris Univ DipSS62 Lon Univ BD71. Lon Bible Coll DipTh67. **dss** 81 **d** 87 **p** 94. Lect Trin Coll Bris 71-83; Bishopsworth *Bris* 83-89; Par Dn 87-89; Tutor Trin Coll Bris 91-95; Perm to Offic *Bris* 91-98; rtd 95; Perm to Offic *B & W* from 98. *14 Saxby Close, Clevedon BS21 7YF* Tel (01275) 343533

EMERSON, Arthur Edward Richard. b 24. Lich Th Coll 69. **d** 72 **p** 73. C Barton upon Humber *Linc* 72-74; V Chapel St Leonards 75-88; P-in-c Hogsthorpe 77-88; V Chapel St Leonards w Hogsthorpe 88-91; rtd 91; Perm to Offic *Linc* from 91. *47 Highfields, Nettleham, Lincoln LN2 2SZ* Tel (01522) 754175

EMERSON, Mrs Jan Vivien. b 44. S Dios Minl Tr Scheme 89. **d** 92 **p** 95. NSM Chich St Paul and St Pet *Chich* 92-94; NSM

Bosham from 94. *Spindrift, Crede Lane, Bosham, Chichester PO18 8NX* Tel (01243) 574948

EMERTON, Prof John Adney. b 28. CCC Ox BA50 MA54 CCC Cam MA55 BD60 St Jo Coll Cam DD73 Edin Univ Hon DD77 FBA79. Wycliffe Hall Ox 50. **d** 52 **p** 53. C Birm Cathl *Birm* 52-53; Asst Lect Th Birm Univ 52-53; Lect Hebrew and Aramaic Dur Univ 53-55; Lect Div Cam Univ 55-62; Fell St Pet Coll Ox 62-68; Reader in Semitic Philology Ox Univ 62-68; Regius Prof Hebrew Cam Univ 68-95; Fell St Jo Coll Cam from 70; Hon Can Jerusalem from 84; Perm to Offic *Ely* from 98. *34 Gough Way, Cambridge CB3 9LN* Tel (01223) 363219

EMERY, Ms Karen Maureen. b 53. R Holloway Coll Lon BA74. St Alb Minl Tr Scheme 88. **d** 92 **p** 94. Par Dn Royston *St Alb* 92-94; C 94-96; TV Chipping Barnet w Arkley 96-02; P-in-c Heddon-on-the-Wall *Newc* from 02; Chapl Northumbria Police from 02. *St Andrew's Vicarage,The Towne Gate, Heddon-on-the-Wall, Newcastle upon Tyne NE15 0DT* Tel (01661) 853142

EMM, Robert Kenneth. b 46. K Coll Lon BD68 AKC68. **d** 69 **p** 70. C Hammersmith SS Mich and Geo White City Estate CD *Lon* 69-72; C Keynsham *B & W* 72-75; C Yeovil 75-80; TV Gt Grimsby St Mary and St Jas *Linc* 80-85; R N Thoresby 85-94; R Grainsby 85-94; V Waithe 85-94; R The North-Chapel Parishes from 94. *The Rectory, Church Lane, North Thoresby, Grimsby DN36 5QG* Tel (01472) 840029 Fax as telephone
E-mail bob@bobemm.demon.co.uk

EMMEL, Canon Malcolm David. b 32. Qu Coll Birm DipTh58. **d** 58 **p** 59. C Hessle *York* 58-62; Canada 62-66; V Catterick *Ripon* 66-73; V Pateley Bridge and Greenhow Hill 73-77; P-in-c Middlesmoor w Ramsgill 76-77; V Upper Nidderdale 77-88; RD Ripon 79-86; Hon Can Ripon Cathl 84-97; R Bedale 88-97; P-in-c Leeming 88-97; rtd 97; Perm to Offic *Bradf* from 98. *29 Greystone Close, Burley in Wharfedale, Ilkley LS29 7RS* Tel (01943) 865047

EMMERSON, Peter Barrett. b 29. Fitzw Ho Cam BA54 MA58. Tyndale Hall Bris 50. **d** 54 **p** 57. Canada 54-58; V Fazakerley St Nath *Liv* 59-64; Distr Sec BFBS (Northd and Dur) 64-70; Distr Sec BFBS (Warks, Staffs and Birm) 70-74; W Midl Regional Sec BFBS 72-74; Hon C Boldmere *Birm* 71-74; C-in-c Crown E CD *Worc* 74-77; P-in-c Crown E and Rushwick 77-81; R Stoke Prior, Wychbold and Upton Warren 81-93; rtd 93; Perm to Offic *Worc* from 93. *Fir Tree Cottage, Ivy Lane, Fernhill Heath, Worcester WR3 8RW* Tel (01905) 456416

✠**EMMERSON, The Rt Revd Ralph.** b 13. AKC38 Lon Univ BD38. Westcott Ho Cam 38. **d** 38 **p** 39 **c** 72. C Leeds St Geo *Ripon* 38-41; C-in-c Seacroft CD 41-48; C Methley 48-49; P-in-c 49-52; R 52-56; P-in-c Mickletown 49-52; R 52-56; V Headingley 56-66; Hon Can Ripon Cathl 64-66; Can Res Ripon Cathl 66-72; Suff Bp Knaresborough 72-79; rtd 79; Asst Bp Ripon and Leeds *Ripon* from 86. *Flat 1, 15 High St Agnes Gate, Ripon HG4 1QR* Tel (01765) 701626

EMMET, Herbert Gerald. b 18. Trin Coll Cam BA40. Linc Th Coll 40. **d** 42 **p** 43. C Leic St Pet *Leic* 42-44; C Melksham *Sarum* 44-48; C St Alb St Sav *St Alb* 48-51; V Leic St Nic *Leic* 51-56; Ind Chapl 51-53; V Hatfield Hyde *St Alb* 56-64; V Harpenden St Jo 64-73; V Kings Langley 73-80; RD Wheathampstead 70-72; rtd 80; Perm to Offic *St Alb* 80-00. *39 Linwood Grove, Leighton Buzzard LU7 8RP* Tel (01525) 377360

EMMETT, Kerry Charles. b 46. St Jo Coll Dur BA68. St Jo Coll Nottm 71. **d** 73 **p** 74. C Attenborough w Chilwell *S'well* 73-75; C Chilwell 75-76; C Wembley St Jo *Lon* 76-79; V Nuneaton St Rich 79-89; R Ravenstone and Swannington *Leic* from 89; RD Akeley S 97-03. *The Rectory, 9 Orchard Close, Ravenstone, Coalville LE67 2JW* Tel (01530) 839802

EMMETT, Thomas. b 40. Chich Th Coll 67. **d** 70 **p** 71. C Shiremoor *Newc* 70-73; C Haltwhistle 73-75; V Newc Ch Ch 75-80; P-in-c Newc St Anne 77-80; V Newc Ch Ch w St Ann 81-87; V Bywell from 87; P-in-c Mickley from 97. *Bywell Vicarage, Meadowfield Road, Stocksfield NE43 7PY* Tel (01661) 842272 Fax as telephone
E-mail tomemmett@toon99.fsnet.co.uk

EMMOTT, David Eugene. b 41. St Chad's Coll Dur BA63 DipTh66. **d** 66 **p** 67. C Bingley H Trin *Bradf* 66-69; C Anfield St Marg *Liv* 69-70; C Kirkby 70-75; Chapl Newc Poly *Newc* 75-78; Hon C Toxteth Park St Marg *Liv* 78-80; TV Upholland 80-88; V Southfields St Barn *S'wark* 88-99; TV Liv Our Lady and St Nic w St Anne *Liv* from 99. *6A Eastern Drive, Liverpool L19 0NB* Tel 0151-281 5493 *or* 236 5387 Fax 236 4118
E-mail davidemmott@livpc.co.uk

EMMOTT, Douglas Brenton. b 45. K Coll Lon BD78 AKC78 York Univ MA97. Linc Th Coll 79. **d** 80 **p** 81. C Kingston upon Hull St Alb *York* 80-83; V Scarborough St Sav w All SS 83-91; V York St Chad 91-99; V Leeds All So *Ripon* from 99; Racial Justice Officer from 99. *All Souls' Vicarage, Blackman Lane, Leeds LS2 9EY* Tel 0113-245 3078 Mobile 07812-852667
E-mail allsouls.leeds@virgin.net

EMMOTT, John Charles Lionel. b 32. SEITE 96. **d** 96 **p** 97. NSM Tenterden St Mich *Cant* 96-02; rtd 02; Perm to Offic *Cant* from 02. *58 Grange Crescent, St Michaels, Tenterden TN30 6DZ* Tel (01580) 762092

EMPEY, Canon Clement Adrian. b 42. TCD BA64 MA68 PhD71. CITC. **d** 74 **p** 75. C Dublin St Ann *D & G* 75-76; I Kells-Inistioge Gp *C & O* 76-84; Preb Tassagard St Patr Cathl Dublin from 82; I Clane w Donadea and Coolcarrigan *M & K* 84-88; Hon Chapl Miss to Seafarers from 88; Sen Chapl Miss to Seamen (Irish Republic) from 97; I Dublin St Ann and St Steph *D & G* 88-01; Treas St Patr Cathl Dublin 89-91; Chan 91-96; Prec 96-01; Chapl Rotunda Hosp from 98; Prin CITC from 01; Prec Ch Ch Cathl Dublin *D & G* from 01. *CITC, Braemor Park, Rathgar, Dublin 14, Irish Republic* Tel (00353) (1) 492 3506 *or* 492 4828 Fax 492 3082 *or* 492 405 5025
E-mail adrian.emp@eircom.net

✠**EMPEY, The Rt Revd Walton Newcome Francis.** b 34. TCD BA57. K Coll (NS) BD68. **d** 58 **p** 59 **c** 81. C Glenageary *D & G* 58-60; Canada 60-66; Bp's C Grand Falls New Brunswick 60-63; I Madawaska 63-66; I Stradbally *C & O* 66-71; Dean Limerick *L & K* 71-81; I Limerick St Mich 71-81; Preb Taney St Patr Cathl Dublin 73-81; Bp L & K 81-85; Bp M & K 85-96; Abp Dublin *D & G* 96-02; Preb Cualaun St Patr Cathl Dublin 96-02; rtd 02. *Rathmore Lodge, Rathmore, Tullow, Co Carlow, Irish Republic* Tel (00353) (59) 916 1891 E-mail lempey@iol.ie

EMSLEY, John Stobart. b 13. Qu Coll Birm 39. **d** 41 **p** 41. C Norwood St Luke *S'wark* 41-44; C Charlton St Luke w St Paul 44-46; C Ilkley St Marg *Bradf* 46-51; V Bradf St Oswald Chapel Green 51-71; V Yeadon St Andr 71-79; rtd 79. *11 Bishop Garth, Pateley Bridge, Harrogate HG3 5LL* Tel (01423) 711835

EMSON, Stanley George. b 26. Glouc Sch of Min. **d** 89 **p** 90. NSM Cirencester *Glouc* 89-92; NSM Coates, Rodmarton and Sapperton etc 92-96; Perm to Offic from 96. *The School House, Rodmarton, Cirencester GL7 6PE* Tel (01285) 841348

EMTAGE, Miss Susan Raymond. b 34. St Mich Ho Ox 63. **dss** 79 **d** 87 **p** 94. SW Area Sec CPAS Women's Action 75-82; Leic St Chris *Leic* 82-86; Bramerton w Surlingham *Nor* 86-87; C 87-88; C Rockland St Mary w Hellington, Bramerton etc 88-89; Par Dn W Bromwich St Jas *Lich* 89-94; C 94; Par Dn W Bromwich St Paul 89-94; C 94; rtd 94; Hon C Stapleton *Bris* from 96. *55 Sheldrake Drive, Bristol BS16 1UE* Tel 0117-965 7188

ENDALL, Peter John. b 38. Linc Th Coll 83. **d** 85 **p** 86. C Burley in Wharfedale *Bradf* 85-88; V Thwaites Brow 88-03; RD S Craven 96-02; rtd 03. *The Parsonage, Church Drive, Hopwas, Tamworth B78 3AL* Tel (01827) 54599

ENDEAN, Michael George Devereux. b 33. Ox NSM Course. **d** 84 **p** 85. NSM Wantage Downs *Ox* 84-93. *87 Brookmead Drive, Wallingford OX10 9BH* Tel (01491) 824231

ENDICOTT, Michael John. b 45. **d** 97. NSM Pontnewydd *Mon* 97; NSM The Well Cen from 97. *The Well Centre, Station Road, Pontnewydd, Cwmbran NP44 1NZ* Tel (01633) 483660

ENEVER, John William. b 44. MBE92. Open Univ BA80. NTMTC AdDipPTS97. **d** 97 **p** 98. NSM Waltham H Cross *Chelmsf* 97-02; NSM Gt Ilford St Andr from 02. *The Vicarage, St Andrew's Road, Ilford IG1 3PE* Tel (020) 8554 3858
E-mail rosemaryenever@onetel.net.uk

ENEVER, Mrs Rosemary Alice Delande. b 45. Oak Hill Th Coll 86. **d** 88 **p** 94. NSM Gt Ilford St Jo *Chelmsf* 88-94; TV Waltham H Cross 94-02; Asst Area Dean Epping Forest from 00; V Gt Ilford St Andr from 02. *The Vicarage, St Andrew's Road, Ilford IG1 3PE* Tel (020) 8554 3858
E-mail rosemaryenever@onetel.net.uk

ENEVER, Mrs Susan Elizabeth. b 33. WMMTC 87. **d** 92 **p** 94. NSM Rugby St Andr *Cov* 92-97; Perm to Offic *Cov* from 97; *Pet* from 98. *7 Rocheberie Way, Rugby CV22 6EG* Tel (01788) 813135

ENEVER, Vivian John. b 61. Collingwood Coll Dur BA82 Cam Univ PGCE85 Man Univ BPhil97. Westcott Ho Cam 88. **d** 91 **p** 92. C Gt Crosby St Faith *Liv* 91-95; C Cantril Farm 95-97; TV Halas *Worc* 97-03; TR Newark *S'well* from 03. *The Rectory, 6 Bede House Lane, Newark NG24 1PY* Tel (01636) 704513

ENGEL, Jeffrey Davis. b 38. Man Univ BA59 Liv Univ PGCE60 Keele Univ ADC69 Aston Univ MSc82 FCP83. St Deiniol's Hawarden 86. **d** 89 **p** 90. NSM Formby St Pet *Liv* 89-92; C Prescot 92-94; Dioc Adv for Past Care and Counselling from 94; P-in-c Hale from 94. *The Vicarage, Hale, Liverpool L24 4AX* Tel 0151-425 3195

ENGELSEN, Christopher James. b 57. Nottm Univ BTh86. Linc Th Coll 83. **d** 86 **p** 87. C Sprowston *Nor* 86-89; C High Harrogate Ch Ch *Ripon* 89-92; TV Seacroft 92-95; P-in-c Foulsham w Hindolveston and Guestwick *Nor* 95-01; P-in-c Hevingham w Hainford and Stratton Strawless from 01. *The Rectory, Westgate Green, Hevingham, Norwich NR10 5RF* Tel (01603) 754643

ENGLAND, Robert Gordon. b 39. TCD BA62 QUB MTh76. TCD Div Sch Div Test65. **d** 66 **p** 67. C Raheny w Coolock *D & G* 66-69; C Lisburn Ch Ch *Conn* 72-73; Lic to Offic *D & D* from 74; Hd RE Regent Ho Sch Newtownards from 74. *20 Lowry Court, 27 Hampton Park, Belfast BT7 3JY*

ENGLAND, Tarie. See CARLYON, Mrs Jessie Marguerite Tarie

ENGLAND-SIMON, Haydn Henry. b 57. Llan Dioc Tr Scheme 92. **d** 96 **p** 97. NSM Penydarren *Llan* 96-97; C Caerphilly 97-01; V Pentre from 01. *The Vicarage, 7 Llewellyn Street, Pentre CF41 7BY* Tel (01443) 433651

ENGLER, Mrs Margaret Dorothy. b 44. Lon Univ TCert77. S'wark Ord Course 90. **d** 93 **p** 94. NSM Harlesden All So *Lon* 93-97; Dep Chapl HM Pris Wandsworth 97; Acting Chapl HM Pris Wormwood Scrubs 97-98; Chapl HM Pris High Down from 98. *HM Prison High Down, Sutton Lane, Sutton SM2 5PJ* Tel (020) 8643 0063

ENGLISH, Peter Gordon. b 31. Edin Univ MA55. Ripon Hall Ox 59. **d** 61 **p** 62. C Bingley All SS *Bradf* 61-64; V Cottingley 64-66; Uganda 66-72; rtd 86. *9 Carlton Row, Trowbridge BA14 0RJ* Tel (01225) 752243

ENGLISH, Peter Redford. b 26. Ridley Hall Cam 70. **d** 72 **p** 73. C Tyldesley w Shakerley *Man* 72-74; C Worsley 74-76; R Levenshulme St Mark 76-81; R Heytesbury and Sutton Veny *Sarum* 81-91; rtd 91; NSM Redmarley D'Abitot, Bromesberrow w Pauntley etc *Glouc* 91-97; Perm to Offic *Sarum* from 95. *69 Tyrrell Mead, Sidmouth EX10 9TR* Tel (01395) 513578

ENGLISH, Philip Trevor. b 37. Dur Univ BSc60 DipTh62 FLIA81 MITPA84. Cranmer Hall Dur 60. **d** 62 **p** 63. C Hall Green Ascension *Birm* 62-66; Chapl St Jo Cathl Hong Kong 66-67; V Dorridge *Birm* 67-72. *Churchlands, Appletree Road, Chipping Warden, Banbury OX17 1LN* Tel (01295) 660222 Mobile 07831-446421 Fax (01295) 660725 E-mail pteifs@aol.com

ENNION, Peter. b 56. Aston Tr Scheme 85 Coll of Resurr Mirfield 87. **d** 89 **p** 90. C Middlewich w Byley *Ches* 89-91; C Aylestone St Andr w St Jas *Leic* 91-92; C Coppenhall *Ches* 92-94; P-in-c Newton in Mottram 94-99; P-in-c Tranmere St Paul w St Luke from 99. *St Paul's Vicarage, Old Chester Road, Birkenhead CH42 3XD* Tel 0151-645 3547

ENNIS, Mrs Lesley. b 47. Bp Lonsdale Coll CertEd68 Open Univ BA84. OLM course 97. **d** 99 **p** 00. NSM Sowerby Bridge w Norland *Wakef* from 99. *26 Springfield, Sowerby Bridge HX6 1AD* Tel (01422) 832747 Mobile 07703-628897 Fax 842747 E-mail lesley.ennis@ennis26.freeserve.co.uk

ENNIS, Martin Michael. b 58. MCollP84 Man Univ BSc80. Sarum & Wells Th Coll 87. **d** 89 **p** 90. C Newquay *Truro* 89-92; C Tewkesbury w Walton Cardiff *Glouc* 92-95; P-in-c Brockworth 95-96; V from 96. *The Vicarage, 42 Court Road, Gloucester GL3 4ET* Tel (01452) 553192 E-mail vicar@st-george.org.uk

ENOCH, William Frederick Palmer. b 30. EMMTC 76. **d** 79 **p** 80. NSM Ilkeston St Mary *Derby* 79-85; P-in-c Ilkeston H Trin 85-95; rtd 95; Perm to Offic *Derby* from 95. *82 Derby Road, Ilkeston DE7 5EZ* Tel 0115-944 3003

ENSOR, Paul George. b 56. Ripon Coll Cuddesdon. **d** 82 **p** 83. C Newington St Mary *S'wark* 82-87; TV Croydon St Jo 87-91; P-in-c Brandon and Santon Downham *St E* 91-92; R Brandon and Santon Downham w Elveden 92-95; V Mitcham St Olave *S'wark* from 95. *St Olave's Vicarage, 22 Church Walk, London SW16 5JH* Tel (020) 8764 2048 E-mail pedrazzini@ukgateway.net

ENSOR, Canon Terence Bryan. b 45. K Coll Lon BD78 AKC78. Westcott Ho Cam 78. **d** 79 **p** 80. C Bermondsey St Hugh CD *S'wark* 79-82; Seychelles 82-85; V Northampton St Benedict *Pet* 85-90; Uruguay 90-93; Fieldworker USPG *Blackb, Bradf, Carl* and *Wakef* 93-96; V Blackb St Jas *Blackb* 96-02; Assoc P Caracas Venezuela from 02; Hon Can Venezuela and Curazao from 02. *Apartado 49-143, Avenida Caroni 100, Colinas de Bello Monte, Caracas 1042-A, Venezuela* Tel (0058) 212) 753 0723 Fax 751 3180

ENTICOTT, Ian Peter. b 59. Sheff Univ BA82 St Jo Coll Dur MA00. All Nations Chr Coll DipM87 Cranmer Hall Dur DMS99. **d** 99 **p** 00. C Higher Bebington *Ches* 99-02; P-in-c Kelsall from 02. *St Philip's Vicarage, Chester Road, Kelsall, Tarporley CW6 0SA* Tel (01829) 751472 E-mail ian_enticott@clergy.net

ENTWISTLE, Christopher John. b 47. N Ord Course 79. **d** 82 **p** 83. NSM Colne H Trin *Blackb* 82-84; C Poulton-le-Fylde 84-87; V Blackpool St Paul 87-96; RD Blackpool 94-96; P-in-c Overton 96-01; V Ashton-on-Ribble St Andr from 01. *The Vicarage, 240 Tulketh Road, Ashton-on-Ribble, Preston PR2 1ES* Tel (01772) 726848

ENTWISTLE, Frank Roland. b 37. Dur Univ BA59 DipTh60. Cranmer Hall Dur 59. **d** 61 **p** 62. C Harborne Heath *Birm* 61-65; S Area Sec BCMS 65-66; Educn Sec 66-73; Hon C Wallington H Trin *S'wark* 68-73; UCCF 73-02; Hon C Ware Ch Ch *St Alb* 73-76; Hon C Leic H Trin w St Jo *Leic* 76-02; rtd 02. *Three Gables, Tews Lane, Bickington, Barnstaple EX31 2JU* Tel (01271) 321861 E-mail entwistles@cwcom.net

ENTWISTLE, The Ven Harry. b 40. St Chad's Coll Dur BSc61 DipTh63. **d** 63 **p** 64. C Fleetwood *Blackb* 63-69; P-in-c Aston Abbots w Cublington *Ox* 69-74; P-in-c Hardwick St Mary 69-74; Chapl HM Pris Aylesbury 69-74; Chapl HM Pris Lewes 74-77; Chapl HM Rem Cen Risley 77-81; Chapl HM Pris Wandsworth 81-88; Australia from 88; Adn Northam 92-99; R Mount Lawley from 99. *731 Beaufort Street, Mount Lawley, W Australia 6050* Tel (0061) (8) 9271 1654 *or* 9271 1654 Mobile 417-180145 Fax 9271 1654 E-mail venharry@iinet.net.au

ENTWISTLE, Howard Rodney. b 36. Ball Coll Ox BA61. Linc Th Coll 61. **d** 63 **p** 64. C Langley St Aid CD *Man* 63-64; C Langley All SS and Martyrs 64-66; V Wythenshawe St Martin 66-73; R Stretford St Matt 73-99; rtd 99. *3 Coombes Avenue, Marple, Stockport SK6 7BW* Tel 0161-427-6294

ENWUCHOLA, Benjamin Ameh. b 56. HND82. Lon Bible Coll BA94 DPS94. **d** 95 **p** 98. NSM S Tottenham St Ann *Lon* 96-99; Chapl Nigerian Community from 99. *82 Keslake Road, London NW6 6DG* Tel (020) 8969 2379 Fax as telephone E-mail benewuchola7@yahoo.com

EPPS, Christopher Derek. b 54. ACII79. Linc Th Coll 95. **d** 95 **p** 96. C Clevedon St Jo *B & W* 95-98; R St John w Millbrook *Truro* from 98. *The Vicarage, Millbrook, Torpoint PL10 1BW* Tel (01752) 822264 Fax 823559 E-mail frcdepps@ntlworld.com

EPPS, Gerald Ralph. b 31. Open Univ BA79. Oak Hill Th Coll 52 K Coll Lon 54. **d** 57 **p** 58. C Slade Green *Roch* 57-60; V Freethorpe w Wickhampton *Nor* 60-70; P-in-c Halvergate w Tunstall 62-67; V 67-70; R Pulham St Mary Magd 70-80; P-in-c Alburgh 76-77; P-in-c Denton 76-77; P-in-c Pulham St Mary V 76-80; R Pulham 80-91; rtd 91; Perm to Offic *Nor* from 91. *10 Lime Close, Harleston IP20 9DG* Tel (01379) 854532

EQUEALL, Canon David Edward Royston. b 41. Open Univ BA. St Mich Coll Llan 68. **d** 71 **p** 72. C Mountain Ash *Llan* 71-74; C Gabalfa 74-77; Chapl Asst Univ Hosp of Wales Cardiff 74-77; Chapl 77-79; Chapl N Gen Hosp Sheff 79-94; Chapl N Gen Hosp NHS Trust Sheff from 94; Hon Can Sheff Cathl *Sheff* from 98. *Northern General Hospital, Herries Road, Sheffield S5 7AU* Tel 0114-271 5056 *or* 243 4343

ERRIDGE, David John. b 45. Lon Univ DipTh68. Tyndale Hall Bris 66. **d** 69 **p** 70. C Bootle St Matt *Liv* 69-72; C Horwich H Trin *Man* 72-77; R Blackley St Andr 77-00; AD N Man 85-94; V Acomb St Steph *York* from 00. *The Vicarage, 32 Carr Lane, York YO26 5HX* Tel (01904) 798106

ERRINGTON, Mrs Sarah. b 67. UEA BA90. Wycliffe Hall Ox BTh94. **d** 97 **p** 98. C Gateacre *Liv* 97-02; TV Halewood from 02. *22 Kenton Road, Liverpool L26 9TS* Tel 0151-486 1159

ESAU, John Owen. b 39. St Mich Coll Llan Dip Practical Th 95. **d** 95 **p** 96. Min Can St D Cathl *St D* 95-97; V Llanpumsaint w Llanllawddog 97-01; V Cydweli and Llandyfaelog 01-03; R Aberporth w Tremain w Blaenporth and Betws Ifan from 03. *The Rectory, Aberporth, Cardigan SA43 2BX* Tel (01239) 810556

ESCOLME, Miss Doreen. b 29. St Jo Coll Nottm 82. **dss** 83 **d** 87 **p** 94. Hunslet Moor St Pet and St Cuth *Ripon* 83-87; C 87-88; Par Dn Wyther Ven Bede 88-94; C 94; rtd 94; Perm to Offic *Ripon* from 94. *6 Heather Gardens, Leeds LS13 4LF* Tel 0113-257 9055

ESCRITT, Canon Margaret Ruth. b 37. Selly Oak Coll IDC62. **d** 87 **p** 94. Dioc Adv for Diaconal Mins *York* 85-91; Hon C Selby Abbey 87-90; Asst Chapl HM Pris Full Sutton 92-94; C Kexby w Wilberfoss *York* 93-94; Chapl HM Pris Everthorpe 95-98; Can and Preb York Minster *York* 95-01; rtd 97; Perm to Offic *York* from 01. *73 Heslington Lane, Fulford, York YO10 4HN* Tel (01904) 639444

ESCRITT, Michael William. b 35. Birm Univ DipTh67. Qu Coll Birm 64. **d** 67 **p** 68. C Huntington *York* 67-69; Abp's Dom Chapl 69-72; V Bishopthorpe 72-83; V Acaster Malbis 73-83; V Selby Abbey 83-90; TR Haxby w Wigginton 90-98; rtd 98; Perm to Offic *York* from 98. *73 Heslington Lane, Fulford, York YO10 4HN* Tel (01904) 639444

ESDAILE, Canon Adrian George Kennedy. b 35. Mert Coll Ox BA57 MA61. Wells Th Coll 59. **d** 61 **p** 62. C St Helier *S'wark* 61-64; C Wimbledon 64-68; V Hackbridge and N Beddington 68-80; RD Sutton 76-80; TR Chipping Barnet w Arkley *St Alb* 80-01; RD Barnet 84-90; Hon Can St Alb 94-01; rtd 01; Perm to Offic *S'wark* from 01. *29 Hereford Close, Epsom KT18 5DZ* Tel (01372) 723770

ESHUN, Daniel Justice. b 69. Cape Coast Univ Ghana BA93 DipEd93 K Coll Lon MA97 PhD00 St Jo Coll Dur MA03. Cranmer Hall Dur 00. **d** 03. C Staines St Mary and St Pet *Lon* from 03. *Peterhouse, 14 Thames Side, Staines TW18 2HA* Tel (01784) 450861 *or* 469155 Mobile 07743-923846 E-mail daniel.j.eshun@talk21.com

ESPIN-BRADLEY, Richard John. b 61. Lanc Univ BSc84. Oak Hill Th Coll DipHE95. **d** 95 **p** 96. C Brundall w Braydeston and Postwick *Nor* 95-98; C St Helier *S'wark* 98-02; V Wolverhampton St Luke *Lich* from 02. *St Luke's Vicarage, 122 Goldthorn Hill, Wolverhampton WV2 3HU* Tel (01902) 340261 E-mail richard.eb@clara.net

ESSER, Lindsay Percy David. b 53. BA. Oak Hill Th Coll. **d** 84 **p** 85. C Barnsbury St Andr and H Trin w All SS *Lon* 84-87; Chapl Paris St Mich *Eur* 87-90; C Spring Grove St Mary *Lon* 90-95; Mauritius from 95. *The Rectory, St Barnabas Church, Royal Road, Pamplemousses, Mauritius* Tel (00230) 243 3549 E-mail st.barnabas@intnet.mu

ESSEX, Mary Rose. b 50. **d** 02 **p** 03. NSM E and W Leake, Stanford-on-Soar, Rempstone etc *S'well* from 02. *The Rectory, Main Street, Stanford on Soar, Loughborough LE12 5PY* Tel (01509) 215191

ESTABROOK, Wendy Elizabeth. b 58. K Coll Lon LLB80 AKC80 ACA83. EAMTC 96. **d** 99. NSM Ely 99-00. *8 Broad Street, Ely CB7 4AH* Tel (01353) 610775

ESTDALE, Canon Francis Albert. b 26. ALCD53. **d** 53 **p** 54. C Penn *Lich* 53-56; C Watford Ch Ch *St Alb* 56-61; V Stopsley

61-94; Hon Can St Alb Abbey 90-94; rtd 94; Perm to Offic *Ely* and *Pet* from 94. *4 Peacock Way, South Bretton, Peterborough PE3 9AA* Tel (01733) 261048

ETCHELLS, Peter. b 26. Kelham Th Coll 48. **d** 52 **p** 53. C Chesterton St Geo *Ely* 52-55; C Leic St Marg *Leic* 55-58; R Willoughby Waterleys, Peatling Magna etc 58-96; rtd 96. *29 Upperfield Drive, Felixstowe IP11 9LS*

ETCHES, Haigh David. b 45. St Jo Coll Dur BA71 DipTh72. **d** 73 **p** 74. C Whitnash *Cov* 73-77; C Wallingford *Ox* 77-79; C Wallingford w Crowmarsh Gifford etc 79-83; P-in-c Bearwood 83-86; R from 86. *The Rectory, 6 St Catherine's Close, Sindlesham, Wokingham RG41 5BZ* Tel 0118-979 4364

ETHERIDGE, Mrs Marjorie. b 18. Univ of Wales (Ban) BA38 Open Univ BA84 CertEd39. St Alb Minl Tr Scheme 80. **dss** 83 **d** 87 **p** 94. Hitchin *St Alb* 83-94; Hon Par Dn 87-94; Perm to Offic from 94. *23 Stormont Road, Hitchin SG5 1SH* Tel (01462) 450496

ETHERIDGE, Canon Richard Thomas. b 32. Lon Univ BD62. ALCD61. **d** 62 **p** 63. C Wilmington *Roch* 62-65; C Rainham 65-69; V Langley St Jo *Birm* 69-01; P-in-c Oldbury 83-01; P-in-c Langley St Mich 95-01; Hon Can Birm Cathl 97-01; rtd 01; Perm to Offic *Birm* from 01. *23 Scobell Close, Pershore, Worcester WR10 1QJ* Tel (01386) 547545

ETHERIDGE, Terry. b 44. Wells Th Coll 68. **d** 70 **p** 71. C Barrow St Jo *Carl* 70-73; C Wilmslow *Ches* 73-76; V Knutsford St Cross 76-85; R Malpas and Threapwood from 85. *The Rectory, Church Street, Malpas SY14 8PP* Tel (01948) 860209

ETHERINGTON, Mrs Ferial Mary Gould. b 44. FILEx83. St Alb Minl Tr Scheme 86. **d** 93 **p** 94. NSM Luton St Chris Round Green *St Alb* from 93; Selection Sec and Co-ord for OLM Min Division from 97. *St Christopher's Vicarage, 33 Felix Avenue, Luton LU2 7LE* Tel and fax (01582) 724754 *or* tel (020) 7898 1395 E-mail ferial.etherington@virgin.net

ETHERINGTON, Robert Barry. b 37. Man Univ BA62. Linc Th Coll 62. **d** 64 **p** 65. C Linc St Jo *Linc* 64-67; C Frodingham 67-69; V Reepham 69-78; Ind Chapl 70-78; Ind Chapl *St Alb* 78-88; V Luton St Chris Round Green from 88; RD Luton 98-02. *St Christopher's Vicarage, 33 Felix Avenue, Luton LU2 7LE* Tel (01582) 724754 Fax as telephone

ETHERTON, Geoffrey Robert. b 74. Birm Univ BMus96. Trin Coll Bris BA01. **d** 02 **p** 03. C Hanford *Lich* 02-03; C Trentham 02-03; C Hanley H Ev from 03. *45 The Parkway, Hanley, Stoke-on-Trent ST1 3BB* Tel (01782) 641721

ETTERLEY, Peter Anthony Gordon. b 39. Kelham Th Coll 63 Wells Th Coll 66. **d** 68 **p** 69. C Gillingham St Aug *Roch* 68-71; Papua New Guinea 71-80; V Cleeve w Chelvey and Brockley *B & W* 80-84; V Seaton Hirst *Newc* 84-86; TR 86-96; P-in-c Longframlington w Brinkburn 96-00; V from 00; P-in-c Felton 96-00; V from 00. *The Vicarage, 1 Benlaw Grove, Felton, Morpeth NE65 9NG* Tel (01670) 787263 E-mail peter.etterley@boltblue.com

ETTLINGER, Max Brian. b 28. Open Univ BA01. Sarum & Wells Th Coll 70. **d** 72 **p** 73. C Mill Hill Jo Keble Ch *Lon* 72-74; Min Cricklewood St Pet CD 74-78; R Monken Hadley 78-88; Bp's Dom Chapl *St E* 88-91; Dioc Communications Officer 88-91; P-in-c Stratford St Mary 91-93; P-in-c Raydon 91-93; P-in-c Holton St Mary w Gt Wenham 91-93; P-in-c Higham 92-93; rtd 93; Perm to Offic *St E* from 93. *11 Bowthorpe Close, Ipswich IP1 3PZ* Tel (01473) 214362 E-mail maxett@btinternet.com

ETTRICK, Peter Alured. b 14. OBE67 TD56 and Bars. Ch Coll Cam BA36 MA41. Qu Coll Birm 36. **d** 37 **p** 38. C Werneth *Man* 37-39; P-in-c Blackley St Pet 39-40; P-in-c Ashton Ch Ch 40-42; CF (EC) 42-47; R Heaton Norris Ch w All SS *Man* 47-52; Sen CF (TA) 48-62; Dep Asst Chapl Gen 62-66; R Flixton St Mich *Man* 52-61; V Gaydon w Chadshunt *Cov* 61-65; Asst Dir RE 61-65; V Radford 65-70; V Bisley *Glouc* 70-79; rtd 79; Perm to Offic *Glouc* from 80. *Meiktila, The Ridge, Bussage, Stroud GL6 8BB* Tel (01453) 883272

EUROPE, Bishop of Gibraltar in. *See* ROWELL, The Rt Revd Douglas Geoffrey

EUROPE, Suffragan Bishop in. *See* HAMID, The Rt Revd David

EUSTICE, Peter Lafevre. b 32. AKC56. **d** 57 **p** 58. C Finsbury Park St Thos *Lon* 57-60; C Redruth *Truro* 60-63; V Treslothan 63-71; V Falmouth All SS 71-76; R St Stephen in Brannel 76-97; rtd 97; Perm to Offic *Truro* from 97. *21 Gloucester Avenue, Carlyon Bay, St Austell PL25 3PT* Tel (01726) 817343

EVA, Canon Owen Vyvyan. b 17. AKC41. Selw Coll Cam BA39 MA43. Ridley Hall Cam 46. **d** 47 **p** 48. C Garston *Liv* 47-51; V Edge Hill St Cath 51-57; Hong Kong 57-61; P-in-c Warrington H Trin *Liv* 61-62; R Halewood 62-83; TR 83-86; RD Farnworth 71-81; Hon Can Liv Cathl 74-86; rtd 86; Perm to Offic *Ches* and *Liv* from 87. *10 Saddler's Rise, Norton, Runcorn WA7 6PG* Tel (01928) 717119

EVANS, Canon Alun Wyn. b 47. Down Coll Cam BA70 MA73. Cuddesdon Coll 70. **d** 72 **p** 73. C Bargoed w Brithdir *Llan* 72-74; C Bargoed and Deri w Brithdir 74-75; C Coity w Nolton 75-77;

V Cwmavon 77-81; Warden of Ords 80-81; V Llangynwyd w Maesteg 81-86; Prov Officer for Soc Resp 86-93; V Cardiff Ch Ch 93-99; V Swansea St Mary w H Trin *S & B* 99-00; TR Cen Swansea from 00; Can Res Brecon Cathl from 00. *St Mary's Vicarage, 7 Eden Avenue, Uplands, Swansea SA2 0PS* Tel (01792) 298616

EVANS, Mrs Amanda Jane. b 49. Lon Univ CertEd70 W Sussex Inst of HE DAES86. STETS Dip Chr Th and Min 97. **d** 97 **p** 98. C Faversham *Cant* 97-01; TV Whitstable from 01. *The Rectory, 69 Swalecliffe Court Drive, Whitstable CT5 2NF* Tel (01227) 792826 E-mail amanda@a-j-evans.fsnet.co.uk

EVANS, Andrew. *See* EVANS, John Andrew

EVANS, Andrew. b 57. Southn Univ BA80. S Dios Minl Tr Scheme 88. **d** 91 **p** 92. NSM Cricklade w Latton *Bris* 91-97; C Yatton Keynell 97-99; TV By Brook 99-00; R Hullavington, Norton and Stanton St Quintin from 00; Bp's Adv for Rural Min from 00; OCF from 00. *The Rectory, 1 Rectory Close, Stanton St Quintin, Chippenham SN14 6DT* Tel and fax (01666) 837187 Mobile 07931-616331
E-mail andrew@evansa63.fsnet.co.uk

EVANS, Andrew Eric. b 58. Sheff Univ LLB80 Solicitor 83. Trin Coll Bris 01. **d** 03. C Gt Bookham *Guildf* from 03. *19 The Lane, Great Bookham, Leatherhead KT23 4JY* Tel (01372) 453729 E-mail andrew@evansabove.supanet.com

EVANS, Anthony Nigel. b 53. Nottm Univ BA74 Fitzw Coll Cam BA76. Westcott Ho Cam 74. **d** 77 **p** 78. C Sneinton St Cypr *S'well* 77-80; C Worksop Priory 80-83; V Nottingham St Geo w St Jo 83-88; R Broxtoll 88-95; P-in-c Sutton in Ashfield St Mary from 95; AD Newstead from 01. *St Mary's Vicarage, Church Avenue, Sutton-in-Ashfield NG17 2EB* Tel (01623) 554509
E-mail frtony@care4free.net

EVANS, Ashley Francis. b 58. Birm Univ BA79. WEMTC 00. **d** 03. C Kington w Huntington, Old Radnor, Kinnerton etc *Heref* from 03. *5 Gravel Hill Drive, Kington HR5 3AE* Tel (01544) 231821 Mobile 07763-070177
E-mail ashley@castlefrome.freeserve.co.uk

EVANS, Aylmer. *See* EVANS, David Aylmer

EVANS, Barrie. *See* EVANS, The Ven John Barrie

EVANS, Brian. b 34. Univ of Wales (Cardiff) DipTh58 Open Univ BA86. St Deiniol's Hawarden 70. **d** 71 **p** 72. C Porthkerry *Llan* 71-72; C Barry All SS 72-75; V Abercynon 75-82; V Pendoylan w Welsh St Donats 82-87; R Maentwrog w Trawsfynydd *Ban* 87-99; rtd 99; Perm to Offic *Ban* from 99. *Madryn, 46 Glan Ysgethin, Talybont LL43 2BB* Tel (01341) 247965

EVANS, Caroline Mary. b 46. Ban Coll CertEd69 Liv Univ Dip Counselling 96. St Jo Coll Nottm DipTh86 Selly Oak Coll 72. **d** 86 **p** 97. C Llanbeblig w Caernarfon and Betws Garmon etc *Ban* 86-88; Dn-in-c Bodedern w Llechgynfarwy and Llechylched etc 88-97; V 97; RD Llifon and Talybolion 96-97; R Llanfairfechan w Aber from 97. *The Rectory, Aber Road, Llanfairfechan LL33 0HN* Tel (01248) 680591

EVANS, Charles Wyndham. b 28. Univ of Wales (Ban) BA49 St Cath Soc Ox BA51 MA55. St Steph Ho Ox 49. **d** 52 **p** 53. C Denbigh *St As* 52-56; Lic to Offic *St D* 56-57; Chapl Llandovery Coll 56-67; Chapl and Sen Lect Trin Coll Carmarthen 67-79; V Llanrhaeadr-yng-Nghinmeirch and Prion *St As* 79-98; Chapl Ruthin Sch 79-86; Dioc RE Adv *St As* 84-98; Tutor St Deiniol's Lib Hawarden 84-86; RD Denbigh *St As* 84-98; rtd 98. *Parciau, 12 The Close, Llanfairfechan, Conwy LL33 0AG* Tel (01248) 681766

EVANS, Prof Christopher Francis. b 09. CCC Cam BA32 MA38 Ox Univ MA48 Southn Univ Hon DLitt77 Glas Univ Hon DD85 FBA91 FKC70. Linc Th Coll 33. **d** 34 **p** 35. C Southampton St Barn *Win* 34-38; Tutor Linc Th Coll 38-44; Chapl and Lect Linc Dioc Tr Coll 44-48; Chapl and Fell CCC Ox 48-58; Select Preacher Ox Univ 55-57; Select Preacher Cam Univ 59-60; Lightfoot Prof Div Dur Univ 58-62; Can Res Dur Cathl *Dur* 58-62; Prof NT Studies K Coll Lon 62-77; rtd 77. *4 Church Close, Cuddesdon, Oxford OX44 9EX* Tel (01865) 874406

EVANS, Christopher Idris. b 51. Chich Th Coll 74. **d** 77 **p** 78. C Gelligaer *Llan* 77-80; C St Andrews Major w Michaelston-le-Pit 80-81; V Llangeinor 81-87; V Watlington w Pyrton and Shirburn *Ox* 87-97; R Icknield from 97. *The Vicarage, Hill Road, Watlington OX49 5AD* Tel (01491) 612494
E-mail icknield@aol.com

EVANS, Christopher Jonathan. b 43. AKC67 AKC88. **d** 68 **p** 69. C Wednesfield St Thos *Lich* 68-71; C Dorridge *Birm* 71-74; V Marston Green 74-81; V Acocks Green 81-86; RD Yardley 84-86; V Hill 86-88; Area Officer COPEC Housing Trust 88-91; V Harborne St Pet from 91. *St Peter's Vicarage, Old Church Road, Birmingham B17 0BB* Tel 0121-681 5446 *or* 681 1940

EVANS, Claire Elizabeth Phoebe. b 78. St Steph Ho Ox BTh02. **d** 02. C Whitchurch *Llan* from 02. *160 Pantbach Road, Cardiff CF14 1UF* Tel (029) 2052 9830 Mobile 07813-767956 E-mail claireevans2k@hotmail.com

EVANS, Clive Richard. b 49. WEMTC 99. **d** 00 **p** 01. OLM Heref S Wye *Heref* from 00. *14 St Vincents Cross, Lower Bullingham, Hereford HR2 6EL* Tel (01432) 270838 *or* 353717
E-mail s.wye.team.ministry@talk21.com

EVANS, Clive Roger. b 59. Worc Coll Ox BA80 MA84. St Jo Coll Nottm 94. **d** 94 **p** 95. C Barton Seagrave w Warkton *Pet* 94-97; V Long Buckby w Watford from 97; P-in-c W Haddon w Winwick and Ravensthorpe from 03; RD Brixworth from 01. *The Vicarage, 10 Hall Drive, Long Buckby, Northampton NN6 7QU* Tel (01327) 842909 Fax as telephone
E-mail clive@evans1359.freeserve.co.uk

EVANS, Canon Colin Rex. b 24. Reading Univ BA49. Linc Th Coll. **d** 57 **p** 58. C Boultham *Linc* 57-59; C Linc St Nic w St Jo Newport 59-62; V Linc St Mary-le-Wigford w St Martin 62-66; P-in-c Linc St Faith 63-66; R Bassingham 66-74; V Aubourn w Haddington 66-74; V Carlton-le-Moorland w Stapleford 66-74; R Skinnand 66-74; R Thurlby w Norton Disney 66-74; RD Graffoe 69-74; RD Elloe E 74-89; Can and Preb Linc Cathl 74-89; V Holbeach 74-89; rtd 90; Hon C Dawlish *Ex* 90-97; RD Kenn 95-97; Perm to Offic from 97. *87 West Cliff Park Drive, Dawlish EX7 9EL* Tel (01626) 865191

EVANS, Daniel Barri. b 70. St Steph Ho Ox 01. **d** 03. C Weymouth H Trin *Sarum* from 03. *Weldon Lodge, 65 Rodwell Road, Weymouth DT4 8QX* Tel (01305) 779088 Mobile 07952-679760
E-mail mary-dan.evans@virgin.net

EVANS, Miss Daphne Gillian. b 41. Bible Tr Inst Glas 67 Trin Coll Bris IDC75. **dss** 83 **d** 87. Wenlock *Heref* 83-88; TD 87-88; rtd 88. *19 Glenwood Close, Newcastle ST5 6LA* Tel (01782) 624354

EVANS, David. *See* EVANS, Alan David Carter

EVANS, Canon David. b 37. Keble Coll Ox BA60 MA65 Lon Univ BD64. Wells Th Coll 62. **d** 64 **p** 65. Min Can Brecon Cathl *S & B* 64-68; C Brecon w Battle 64-68; C Swansea St Mary and H Trin 68-71; Chapl Univ of Wales (Swansea) 68-71; Bp's Chapl for Samaritan and Soc Work *Birm* 71-75; Jt Gen Sec Samaritans 75-84; Gen Sec 84-89; R Heyford w Stowe Nine Churches *Pet* 89-96; R Heyford w Stowe Nine Churches and Flore etc 96-01; Chapl Northants Police 89-01; RD Daventry 96-00; Can Pet Cathl 97-01; rtd 01; Perm to Offic *Ex* from 01. *Curlew River, The Strand, Starcross, Exeter EX6 8PA* Tel (01626) 891712

EVANS, David. b 37. Open Univ BA73 FRSA95. St Mich Coll Llan 65. **d** 67 **p** 68. C Swansea St Pet *S & B* 67-70; C St Austell *Truro* 70-75; R Purley *Ox* 75-90; RD Bradfield 85-90; R Bryanston Square St Mary w St Marylebone St Mark *Lon* 90-99; P-in-c St Marylebone Ch Ch 90-91; R Nuthurst *Chich* from 99. *The Rectory, Nuthurst Street, Nuthurst, Horsham RH13 6LH* Tel (01403) 891449

EVANS, David Aylmer. b 28. Lon Univ CertEd62 Reading Univ DipC&G73. St D Coll Lamp BA49 LTh51. **d** 51 **p** 52. C Brecon St David w Llanspyddid and Llanilltyd *S & B* 51-53; C Colwyn Bay *St As* 53-54; C Macclesfield St Mich *Ches* 54-56; V Lostock Gralam 56-59; Perm to Offic *Chelmsf* 58-65; Perm to Offic *Ox* 65-73; Chapl Endsleigh Sch 59-65; Wokingham Gr Sch 65-72; Counsellor S Molton Sch and Community Coll 73-87; V Middlezoy and Othery and Moorlinch *B & W* 87-93; rtd 93; Perm to Offic *Ex* from 94; Perm to Offic *B & W* from 94. *2 Higher Mead, Hemyock, Cullompton EX15 3QH* Tel (01823) 680974

EVANS (or BURTON EVANS), David Burton. b 35. Open Univ BA87 Goldsmiths' Coll Lon BMus93. K Coll Lon 58 Edin Th Coll 60. **d** 62 **p** 63. C Leeds St Hilda *Ripon* 62-63; C Cross Green St Sav and St Hilda 63-67; Min Can Dur Cathl *Dur* 67-71; Chapl Prebendal Sch Chich 71-74; PV Chich Cathl *Chich* 71-74; R Lynch w Iping Marsh 74-79; Chapl K Edw VII Hosp Midhurst 77-86; V Easebourne *Chich* 79-86; R St Mich Cornhill w St Pet le Poer etc *Lon* 86-96; rtd 96; Chapl Pau Eur 96-01. *rue Biscarse, 64490 Bedous, France* Tel (0033) (5) 59 34 58 12 Fax 59 34 58 25
E-mail evtherev@club-internet.fr

EVANS, David Elwyn. b 43. St Mich Coll Llan 71. **d** 73 **p** 74. C Llandybie *St D* 73-75; C Llanelli 75-78; V Tre-lech a'r Betws w Abernant and Llanwinio 78-02; rtd 02. *8 Ger y Llan, The Parade, Carmarthen SA31 1LY*

EVANS, David Frederick Francis. b 35. Univ of Wales BSc59. Wells Th Coll 59. **d** 61 **p** 62. C Eltham St Jo *S'wark* 61-64; C Banbury *Ox* 64-69; V Brize Norton and Carterton 69-73; V Tilehurst St Geo 73-84; V Lydney w Aylburton *Glouc* 84-95; V Lydney 95-02; RD Forest S 90-95; Chapl Severn NHS Trust 94-02; rtd 02. *2 Bodforis, Bethesda, Bangor LL57 3PU* Tel (01248) 601994

EVANS, David John. b 49. Univ of Wales (Ban) BSc72 Bath Univ CertEd73 Leeds Univ DipTh77. Coll of Resurr Mirfield 75. **d** 78 **p** 79. C Wandsworth St Anne *S'wark* 78-81; C Angell Town St Jo 81-82; TV Catford (Southend) and Downham 82-90; P-in-c Broughton *Ely* 90-91; P-in-c Somersham w Pidley and Oldhurst 90-91; R 91-98; R Hilgay from 98. *The Rectory, Hilgay, Downham Market PE38 0JL* Tel (01366) 384418
E-mail g4ynd@aol.com *or* david.evans@ely.anglican.org

EVANS, David Leslie Bowen. b 28. Univ of Wales (Lamp) BA52 LTh54. **d** 54 **p** 55. C Cardigan *St D* 54-57; C Llangathen w Llanfihangel Cilfargen 57-58; C Betws w Ammanford 58-60; V

Betws Ifan 60-64; V Burry Port and Pwll 64-76; V Cardiff Dewi Sant *Llan* 76-86; Asst Chapl HM Pris Cardiff 76-86; V Llan-llwch w Llangain and Llangynog *St D* 86-95; Can St D Cathl 89-90; rtd 95. *35 Ger y Capel, Llangain, Carmarthen SA33 5AQ* Tel (01267) 241916

EVANS, David Richard. b 47. St Steph Ho Ox 68. **d** 72 **p** 73. C Cardiff St Jo *Llan* 72-76; PV Llan Cathl 76-80; V Cleeve Prior and The Littletons *Worc* from 80. *The Vicarage, South Littleton, Evesham WR11 8TJ* Tel (01386) 830397
E-mail father.evans@tesco.net

✠**EVANS, The Rt Revd David Richard John.** b 38. G&C Coll Cam BA63 MA66. Clifton Th Coll 63. **d** 65 **p** 66 **c** 78. C Enfield Ch Ch Trent Park *Lon* 65-68; SAMS Argentina 69-77; Peru 77-88; Bp Peru 78-88; Bp Bolivia 82-88; Asst Bp Bradf 88-93; Gen Sec SAMS 93-03; Hon Asst Bp Chich 94-97; Hon Asst Bp Roch 95-97; Hon Asst Bp Birm 97-03; rtd 03; Hon Asst Bp Cov from 03; Hon C Alderminster and Halford from 03; Hon C Butlers Marston and the Pillertons w Ettington from 03. *The Vicarage, Alderminster, Stratford-upon-Avon CV37 8PE* Tel (01789) 450198 E-mail bishop.drjevans@virgin.net

EVANS, David Russell. b 36. Liv Univ BA57. Ripon Hall Ox 59. **d** 61 **p** 62. C Netherton CD *Liv* 61-65; Chapl Canon Slade Sch Bolton 65-93; Lic Preacher *Man* from 65; Perm to Offic *Liv* from 76; rtd 00. *2 Rushford Grove, Bolton BL1 8TD* Tel (01204) 592981

EVANS, David Victor (formerly David John Parker Smith). b 47. Bris Univ Dip Counselling 97. S'wark Ord Course 83. **d** 86 **p** 95. SSF 71-94; Hon C Stepney St Dunstan and All SS *Lon* 86-89; Adult Educn Development Officer 86-89; Guardian Hilfield Friary Dorchester 89-91; Novice Guardian Liv 91-93; Birm 93-94; NSM Southmead *Bris* 94-98; TR Uttoxeter Area *Lich* from 98; RD Uttoxeter from 02. *The Vicarage, 12 Orchard Close, Uttoxeter ST14 7DZ* Tel (01889) 563651 *or* 562915
E-mail dvictorevans@aol.com

EVANS, Derek. b 38. St As Minl Tr Course 93. **d** 97 **p** 98. NSM Llangollen w Trevor and Llantysilio *St As* 97-00; NSM Corwen and Llangar w Gwyddelwern and Llawrybetws 00-02; NSM Betws Gwerful Goch w Llangwm, Gwyddelwern etc from 02. *Fern Mount, 68 Berwyn Street, Llangollen LL20 8NA* Tel (01978) 861893

EVANS, Canon Derek. b 45. St D Coll Lamp DipTh68. **d** 68 **p** 69. C Pembroke Dock *St D* 68-74; V Ambleston, St Dogwells, Walton E and Llysyfran 74-78; V Wiston w Ambleston, St Dogwells, Walton E etc 81-85; R Haverfordwest St Mary and St Thos w Haroldston from 85; Dep Dioc Dir of Educn 92-97; Dir from 97; Can St D Cathl from 99; RD Roose from 00. *The Rectory, Scarrowscant Lane, Haverfordwest SA61 1EP* Tel (01437) 763170 Fax as telephone
E-mail derek.evans0@talk21.com

EVANS, Preb Derek Courtenay. b 29. Down Coll Cam BA52 MA56. St Aid Birkenhead 55. **d** 57 **p** 58. C Taunton St Mary *B & W* 57-61; V Trull 61-77; RD Taunton S 72-77; P-in-c Walton 77; R Street 77; Preb Wells Cathl 77-94; R Street w Walton 78-94; RD Glastonbury 79-82; R Greinton 81-93; rtd 94; Perm to Offic *B & W* from 94. *41 Moorham Road, Winscombe BS25 1HS* Tel (01934) 843150

EVANS, Desmond. b 26. Univ of Wales (Lamp) BA48 St Cath Soc Ox BA50 MA54. St Steph Ho Ox 48. **d** 51 **p** 52. C Clydach *S & B* 51-54; V 82-87; Chapl Cranleigh Sch Surrey 54-59; Lic to Offic *Ban* 59-78; St Mary's Coll Ban 59-78; V Llanwrtyd w Llanddulas in Tir Abad etc *S & B* 78-82; RD Builth 79-82; V Abercraf and Callwen 87-95; rtd 95. *26 Palleg Road, Lower Cwmtwrch, Swansea SA9 2QE* Tel (01639) 845389

EVANS, Donald Henry. b 13. St D Coll Lamp BA35. **d** 36 **p** 37. C Wrexham *St As* 36-48; R Worthenbury w Tallarn Green 48-61; V Towyn 61-64; V Seighford, Derrington and Cresswell *Lich* 64-78; rtd 78; Perm to Offic *Ches* 80-01. *3 Highfield Avenue, Audlem, Crewe CW3 0HW* Tel (01270) 811165

EVANS, Edward John. b 47. Univ of Wales (Cardiff) DipTh71. St Mich Coll Llan 67. **d** 71 **p** 72. C Llantwit Fardre *Llan* 71-77; R Eglwysilan 77-88; V Laleston w Tythegston and Merthyr Mawr from 88; RD Bridgend from 94. *The Vicarage, Rogers Lane, Laleston, Bridgend CF32 0LB* Tel and fax (01656) 654254 Mobile 07968-044583
E-mail edward@lal-vicarage.freeserve.co.uk

EVANS, Elaine. *See* EVANS, Jennifer Elaine

EVANS, Ms Elaine. b 63. St Mich Coll Llan BTh02. **d** 02 **p** 03. C Llantwit Major *Llan* from 02. *8 Illtyd Avenue, Llantwit Major CF61 1TG* Tel (01446) 792476

EVANS, Elwyn David. b 36. Keble Coll Ox BA58 MA62. St Steph Ho Ox 58 St Mich Coll Llan 60. **d** 61 **p** 62. C Aberystwyth H Trin *St D* 61-63; C Llanelli St Paul 63-66; C Roath St German *Llan* 66-69; V Crynant 69-78; R Llanilid w Pencoed 79-95; rtd 95; Perm to Offic *Llan* and *S & B* from 95. *23 Christopher Rise, Pontlliw, Swansea SA4 9EN* Tel (01792) 891961

EVANS, Ernest Maurice. b 28. JP70. MIMechE66. St As Minl Tr Course 84. **d** 86 **p** 87. NSM Hope *St As* 86-89; P-in-c Corwen and Llangar w Gwyddelwern and Llawrybetws 89-90; R 90-95;

rtd 95; Perm to Offic *Ban* from 97. *43 Cil-y-Graig, Llanfairpwllgwyngyll LL61 5NZ* Tel (01248) 712169
E-mail e.mauriceevans@btinternet.com

EVANS, Evan Walter. b 16. MBE66. St D Coll Lamp BA36. **d** 39 **p** 40. C Narberth *St D* 39-40; C Cardigan 40-42; CF (EC) 42-47; R Didmarton w Oldbury-on-the-Hill and Sopworth *Glouc* 47-52; CF 52-72; Chapl R Hosp Chelsea 72-81; Perm to Offic *St D* from 85. *3 Cilgwyn Row, Llandysul SA44 4BD* Tel (01559) 362275

EVANS, Frank Owen. b 23. Univ of Wales BA44. St D Coll Lamp 44. **d** 46 **p** 63. C Hubberston *St D* 46; C Llanelli 63-81; Hd Master Coleshill Secondary Sch Dyfed 74-82; Hon C Cydweli and Llandyfaelog *St D* 81-82; V Martletwy w Lawrenny and Minwear and Yerbeston 82-87; rtd 87. *35 Stradey Park Avenue, Llanelli SA15 3EG* Tel (01554) 777149

EVANS, Ms Freda Christine. b 48. MBE89. NTMTC 96. **d** 99 **p** 00. C Hampton Hill *Lon* 99-02; V Kingshurst *Birm* from 02. *St Barnabas' Vicarage, 51 Overgreen Drive, Birmingham B37 6EY* Tel 0121-770 3972 Fax as telephone E-mail freda@fish.co.uk

EVANS, Mrs Freda Mary Ann (Frieda). b 54. St D Coll Lamp DipTh96. **d** 00. OLM Malpas *Mon* from 00. *3 The Firs, Malpas, Newport NP20 6YD* Tel (01633) 850600 Mobile 0411-650088 E-mail frieda@evafirs.freeserve.co.uk

EVANS, Frederick Albert. b 29. **d** 83 **p** 84. NSM Maisemore *Glouc* 83-94; NSM Glouc St Geo w Whaddon 86-94; Perm to Offic from 94. *10 Hillborough Road, Gloucester GL4 0JQ* Tel (01452) 526034 E-mail fevans8533@aol.com

EVANS, Frederick James Stephens. b 21. Qu Coll Cam BA42 MA46. St D Coll Lamp LTh44. **d** 44 **p** 45. C Shirley *Birm* 44-47; R Scotter w E Ferry *Linc* 47-65; CF (TA) 48-51; R Chalfont St Peter *Ox* 65-78; V Rustington *Chich* 78-86; rtd 86; Perm to Offic *Chich* from 86. *45 Falmer Avenue, Goring-by-Sea, Worthing BN12 4SY* Tel (01903) 503905

EVANS, Canon Frederick John Margam. b 31. Magd Coll Ox BA53 MA57. St Mich Coll Llan 53. **d** 54 **p** 55. C New Tredegar *Mon* 54-58; C Chepstow 58-60; Asst Chapl United Sheff Hosps 60-62; Chapl Brookwood Hosp Woking 62-70; V Crookham *Guildf* 70-98; RD Aldershot 78-83; Hon Can Guildf Cathl 89-98; rtd 98; Perm to Offic *Guildf* from 98. *4 Radford Close, Farnham GU9 9AB* Tel (01252) 710594 Fax as telephone E-mail johnjunee@aol.com

EVANS, Gareth Clive. b 68. Univ of Wales (Cardiff) DipTh91. Ripon Coll Cuddesdon BTh96. **d** 96 **p** 97. C Gosforth All SS *Newc* 96-00; USA from 00. *HDS Student, Harvard Divinity School, 45 Francis Avenue, Cambridge, MA 02138, USA* Tel (001) (617) 495 4518

EVANS, Gareth Milton. b 39. Bris Univ LLB60 St Cath Coll Ox BA62 MA66. Ripon Hall Ox 60. **d** 63 **p** 64. C Hengrove *Bris* 63-65; Min Can Bris Cathl 65-68; C Bishopston 68-71; C Notting Hill *Lon* 71-83; V Bayswater from 83. *St Matthew's Vicarage, 27 St Petersburgh Place, London W2 4LA* Tel (020) 7229 2192

EVANS, Gareth Rae. b 48. MIPD. Ripon Coll Cuddesdon DipMin98. **d** 98 **p** 99. C Chepstow *Mon* 98-00; TV Cwmbran from 00. *The Vicarage, 292 Llantarnam Road, Llantarnam, Cwmbran NP44 3BW* Tel (01633) 489280

EVANS, Canon Geoffrey Bainbridge. b 34. St Mich Coll Llan 56 Lambeth MA94. **d** 58 **p** 59. C Llan All SS CD *Llan* 58-60; C Llandaff N 60-67; Guyana 67-73; Chapl Izmir (Smyrna) w Bornova *Eur* 73-94; Adn Aegean 78-94; Can Malta Cathl 78-00; Chapl Ankara 85-91; Chapl Istanbul 87-89; Chapl Rome 94-99; Chapl Moscow 99; P-in-c Ankara from 00. *Sehit Ersan Caddesi 32/12, Cankaya, Ankara 06680, Turkey* Tel (0090) (312) 467 8276 E-mail gb_evans@hotmail.com

EVANS, Geoffrey David. b 44. Ex Univ PGCE74. K Coll Lon BD69 AKC69 St Aug Coll Cant 69. **d** 70 **p** 71. C Lawrence Weston *Bris* 70-73; Chapl Grenville Coll Bideford 74-79; Chapl Eastbourne Coll 79-82; Chapl Taunton and Somerset Sch from 92. *Hele Manor, Bradford on Tone, Taunton TA4 1AH* Tel (01823) 461561

EVANS, Gerald Arthur. b 35. Univ of Wales (Swansea) BA57 Lon Univ DipRS77. S'wark Ord Course 74. **d** 77 **p** 78. NSM Balcombe *Chich* 77-81; NSM Cuckfield 81-87; R Tillington 87-93; R Duncton 87-93; R Up Waltham 87-93; R W Chiltington 93-98; Dioc Ecum Officer 93-98; RD Storrington 93-98; rtd 98; Perm to Offic *Chich* 98-00. *Lindens, Kithurst Park, Storrington, Pulborough RH20 4JH* Tel (01903) 742206

EVANS, Mrs Gillian. b 39. Imp Coll Lon BSc61 Univ of Wales (Cardiff) DPS88. Mon Dioc Tr Scheme 84. **d** 88 **p** 94. NSM Penallt and Trellech *Mon* 88-89; NSM Overmonnow w Wonastow and Michel Troy 89-92; C Ludlow *Heref* 92-93; C Ludlow, Ludford, Ashford Carbonell etc 93-95; Dioc Ecum Officer 92-95; Pakistan 95-96; Perm to Offic *Heref* from 96; Hon C Dawlish *Ex* 97-98; TV Golden Cap Team *Sarum* 98-01; rtd 01. *Great Hillshone Barn, Ganarew, Monmouth NP25 3SS* Tel (01600) 891351

EVANS, Canon Glyn. b 10. Univ of Wales BA33. St Steph Ho Ox 33. **d** 34 **p** 35. C Dolgellau *Ban* 34-39; C Llanfairfechan 39-43; R Llanallgo w Llaneugrad 43-55; V St Issells *St D* 55-80; RD

Narberth 65-80; Can St D Cathl 69-80; Treas 77-80; rtd 80. *3 Flemish Close, St Florence, Tenby SA70 8LT* Tel (01834) 871434

EVANS, Glyn. b 59. Nene Coll Northampton BA80 Leic Univ BA80 Ch Ch Coll Cant CertEd82 Kent Univ PGCE82 Birm Univ DipTh87. Qu Coll Birm 85. **d** 88 **p** 89. C Denton *Newc* 88-92; V Choppington 92-97; P-in-c Longhorsley and Hebron 97-01; Chapl HM Pris Acklington 97-01; P-in-c Newc St Andr and Newc St Luke *Newc* from 01; City Cen Chapl from 01. *12 The Glebe, Stannington, Morpeth NE61 6HW* Tel (01670) 789481

EVANS, Glyn Peter. b 54. Leeds Univ BA75. Ripon Coll Cuddesdon 76. **d** 77 **p** 78. C Binley *Cov* 77-80; C Clifton upon Dunsmore w Brownsover 80-84; P-in-c Lacock w Bowden Hill *Bris* 84-89; P-in-c Lt Compton w Chastleton, Cornwell etc *Ox* 89-00; Agric Chapl 89-00; Dioc Rural Officer from 00. *Juxon House, Little Compton, Moreton-in-Marsh GL56 0SE* Tel (01608) 674567 Mobile 07870-405241 Fax (01608) 674805 E-mail glynevansrro@tiscali.co.uk *or* glynevans@goldserve.net

EVANS, Godfrey. *See* EVANS, Joseph Henry Godfrey

EVANS, Canon Gwyneth Mary. b 43. Gilmore Ho 69 Linc Th Coll 70. **dss** 74 **d** 87 **p** 94. Stamford Hill St Thos *Lon* 74-79; Chapl Asst R Free Hosp Lon 79-89; Chapl Salisbury Health Care NHS Trust 89-01; Can and Preb Sarum Cathl *Sarum* 96-01; rtd 01; Perm to Offic *Sarum* from 01. *37 Sarum Close, Salisbury SP2 7LE* Tel (01722) 412546

EVANS, Canon Henry Thomas Platt. b 28. Selw Coll Cam BA51 MA55. Linc Th Coll 51. **d** 53 **p** 54. C Lt Ilford St Barn *Chelmsf* 55-56; C-in-c Stocking Farm CD *Leic* 56-58; V Stocking Farm 58-67; R Stretford St Matt *Man* 67-73; V Knighton St Mary Magd *Leic* 73-83; Hon Can Leic Cathl 76-93; RD Christianity 81-83; Warden Launde Abbey 83-93; P-in-c Loddington *Leic* 83-92; rtd 93; Perm to Offic *Leic* from 93. *16 Central Avenue, Leicester LE2 1TB* Tel 0116-270 2169

EVANS (née TAYLOR), Mrs Hilary Elizabeth. b 57. Man OLM Scheme 00. **d** 03. OLM Reddish *Man* from 03. *13 Lindfield Road, Stockport SK5 6SD* Tel 0161-442 3023
E-mail hilary@mojomusica.freeserve.co.uk

EVANS, Hilary Margaret. b 49. Redland Coll of Educn TDip71 Chester Coll 92. N Ord Course BTh97. **d** 97 **p** 98. NSM Heald Green St Cath *Ches* 97-98; C 98-00; P-in-c Davyhulme Ch Ch *Man* from 00. *Christ Church Vicarage, 14 Welbeck Avenue, Urmston, Manchester M41 0GJ* Tel 0161-748 2018
E-mail hmevans@mcmail.com

EVANS, Huw David. b 68. Sheff Univ BEng90 PGCE91. Trin Coll Bris BA98. **d** 98. C Sherborne w Castleton and Lillington *Sarum* 98-99; Hon Par Dn Martock w Ash *B & W* from 01. *5 Silver Street, Stoford, Yeovil BA22 9UF* Tel (01935) 429263

EVANS, Mrs Jane. b 59. **d** 03. OLM Lilleshall, Muxton and Sheriffhales *Lich* from 03. *5 Collett Way, Priorslee, Telford TF2 9SL* Tel (01952) 291340 E-mail eeyore@rmplc.co.uk

EVANS, Mrs Jennifer. b 41. Ilkley Coll DipEd62. Sarum Th Coll 88. **d** 88. Par Dn Bramshott *Portsm* 88-91; C Bramshott and Liphook 91-92; Par Dn Whippingham w E Cowes 92-95; Par Dn Sarisbury from 95; rtd 01. *Honeycombs, 1A Addison Road, Sarisbury Green, Southampton SO31 7ER* Tel (01489) 572129
E-mail jennie.honeycombs@virgin.net

EVANS, Mrs Jennifer. b 43. **d** 01. Par Dn New Tredegar *Mon* from 01. *Chapel House, 95 Ruperra Street, New Tredegar NP2 6AG* Tel (01443) 836798

EVANS, Jennifer Elaine. b 59. Wolv Univ BA92. Qu Coll Birm 00. **d** 02. C Stafford St Jo and Tixall w Ingestre *Lich* from 02. *42 Longhurst Drive, Stafford ST16 3RG* Tel (01785) 213196

EVANS, Jill. *See* EVANS, Mrs Gillian

EVANS, John. *See* EVANS, Canon Frederick John Margam

EVANS, John Andrew. b 53. Hull Univ BSc74 Univ of Wales MSc75 Bris Univ BA96. Trin Coll Bris 94. **d** 96 **p** 97. C Walton H Trin *Ox* 96-98; C Caversham St Pet and Mapledurham etc 98-01; R Bradford Abbas and Thornford w Beer Hackett *Sarum* from 01. *The Rectory, Church Road, Thornford, Sherborne DT9 6QE* Tel (01935) 872382
E-mail rectorbradfordabbas@supaworld.com

EVANS, The Ven John Barrie. b 23. Univ of Wales (Lamp) BA47 St Edm Hall Ox BA49 MA54. St Mich Coll Llan 50. **d** 51 **p** 52. C Trevethin *Mon* 51-57; V Caerwent w Dinham and Llanfair Discoed 57-64; V Chepstow 64-79; Can St Woolos Cathl 71-77; Adn Mon 77-86; R Llanmartin w Wilcrick and Langstone 79-83; R Llanmartin 83-86; Adn Newport 86-93; rtd 93; Lic to Offic *Mon* from 93; Perm to Offic *Glouc* from 93. *Rockfield, Coleford Road, Tutshill, Chepstow NP16 7BU* Tel (01291) 626147

EVANS, John David Vincent. b 41. CQSW78. Lich Th Coll 66. **d** 68 **p** 70. C Kingsthorpe *Pet* 68-69; C Corby Epiphany w St Jo 69-72; Bp's Adv in Children's Work 72-74; Perm to Offic 88-90; R Green's Norton w Bradden 90-91; R Greens Norton w Bradden and Lichborough 91-96; V Northampton Ch Ch from 96. *Christ Church Vicarage, 3 Christ Church Road, Northampton NN1 5LL* Tel (01604) 633254
E-mail revjohnevans@mgownersclub.net

EVANS, Canon John Griffiths. b 37. Glouc Th Course 76. **d** 77 **p** 77. Hd Master Corse Sch Glos from 70; C Hartpury w Corse and Staunton *Glouc* 77-79; P-in-c from 79; Hon Can Glouc

Cathl from 96; P-in-c Maisemore from 01. *Elm House, Gadfield Elms, Staunton, Gloucester GL19 3PA* Tel (01452) 840302

EVANS, John Laurie. b 34. Pretoria Univ BSc54 Imp Coll Lon BSc55 Rhodes Univ BA59. Ripon Coll Cuddesdon 84. **d** 86 **p** 87. C Bruton and Distr *B & W* 86-89; P-in-c Ambrosden w Merton and Piddington *Ox* 89-91; C Pet St Mary Boongate *Pet* 91-93; V Michael *S & M* 93-96; R Ballaugh 93-96; rtd 96; Chapl Goring Heath Almshouses 96-99; P-in-c Fochabers *Mor* 99-00; P-in-c Strathnairn St Paul 00-03; TV Langtree *Ox* from 03. *The Vicarage, Crabtree Corner, Ipsden, Wallingford OX10 6BN* Tel and fax (01491) 682832 Mobile 07909-986369
E-mail jonevans@fish.co.uk

EVANS, John Miles. b 39. Yale Univ BA61 JD67 St Cath Coll Cam BA64 MA68. NY Th Sem MDiv93. **d** 95 **p** 95. Chapl St Jo Cathl Oban *Arg* 95-97; USA from 97; Interim R Lynbrook Ch Ch 98-99; R Davidsonville All Hallows from 99. *809 West Central Avenue, PO Box 103, Davidsonville, MD 21035, USA* Tel (001) (410) 798 1900 Fax as telephone
E-mail 76765.633@compuserve.com

EVANS, John Rhys. b 45. Hull Univ BSc66. Sarum & Wells Th Coll 77. **d** 79 **p** 80. C Alton St Lawr *Win* 79-82; C Tadley St Pet 82-85; V Colden 85-91; V Bitterne Park 91-01; C Ringwood from 01; Chapl R Bournemouth and Christchurch Hosps NHS Trust from 01. *3 Waterside Close, Poulner, Ringwood BH24 1SB* Tel (01425) 483370

EVANS, John Ronald. b 16. Univ of Wales BA40. St Mich Coll Llan 41. **d** 42 **p** 44. C Rhosllannerchrugog *St As* 42-45; C Holywell 45-54; V Glyndyfrdwy 54-81; RD Edeyrnion 64-81; Dioc Sec SPCK 66-81; rtd 81. *21 Bryn Hyfryd, Johnstown, Wrexham LL14 1PR* Tel (01978) 842300

EVANS, John Stuart. b 57. Univ of Wales (Abth) BA78 Bretton Hall Coll PGCE81. Trin Coll Bris BA98. **d** 98 **p** 99. C Connah's Quay *St As* 98-02; V Rhosllannerchrugog from 02. *16 Delyn, Johnstown, Wrexham LL14 1UY* Tel (01978) 840809
E-mail jsevans@surfaid.org

EVANS, Canon John Thomas. b 43. Univ of Wales DipTh66 DPS67. St Mich Coll Llan 66. **d** 67 **p** 68. C Connah's Quay *St As* 67-71; C Llanrhos 71-74; Chapl Rainhill Hosp Liv 74-78; TV Wrexham *St As* 78-83; V Holywell 83-96; RD Holywell 95-96; V Colwyn Bay 96-99; V Colwyn Bay w Brynymaen 99-02; RD Rhos 00-02; R Caerwys and Bodfari from 02; Can Cursal St As Cathl from 96. *The Rectory, Pen-y-Cefn Road, Caerwys, Mold CH7 5AQ* Tel (01352) 720223
E-mail johnevans@jtevans.freeserve.co.uk

EVANS, The Very Revd John Wyn. b 46. FSA88 FRHistS94 Univ of Wales (Cardiff) BA68 BD71. St Mich Coll Llan 68. **d** 71 **p** 72. C St D Cathl *St D* 71-72; Min Can St D Cathl 72-75; Perm to Offic *Ox* 75-77; Dioc Archivist *St D* 76-82; R Llanfallteg w Clunderwen and Castell Dwyran etc 77-82; Warden of Ords 78-83; Dioc Dir of Educn 82-92; Chapl Trin Coll Carmarthen 82-90; Dean of Chpl 90-94; Hd Th and RS 91-94; Hon Can St D Cathl *St D* 88-90; Can St D Cathl 90-94; Dean St D from 94; V St D Cathl 94-01; TR Dewisland from 01. *The Deanery, St Davids, Haverfordwest SA62 6RH* Tel (01437) 720202 Fax 721885

EVANS, Jonathan Alan. b 53. Fitzw Coll Cam BA75 PGCE77 MA79. St Jo Coll Nottm MA95. **d** 95 **p** 96. C Drypool *York* 95-98; V Beverley St Nic from 98. *St Nicholas' Vicarage, 72 Grovehill Road, Beverley HU17 0ER* Tel (01482) 881458
E-mail evansfamily@macunlimited.net

EVANS, Joseph Henry Godfrey. b 31. Univ of Wales (Lamp) BA50 St Mary's Coll Cheltenham CertEd75 Kingston Poly 89. Qu Coll Birm 53. **d** 55 **p** 56. C Hackney St Jo *Lon* 55-58; C Stonehouse *Glouc* 58-60; V Selsley 60-65; V Cheltenham St Pet 65-74; R Willersey w Saintbury 74-77; Chapl Tiffin Sch Kingston 77-94; rtd 95; Perm to Offic *S'wark* from 01. *300 Raeburn Avenue, Surbiton KT5 9EF* Tel (020) 8390 0936

EVANS, Mrs Judith Ann. b 55. DipN79. SEITE 99. **d** 02 **p** 03. C Crayford *Roch* from 02. *1A Iron Mill Place, Dartford DA1 4RT* Tel (01322) 552884 Mobile 07929-978523

EVANS, Keith. b 57. Trin Coll Carmarthen CertEd81 BEd82. St D Coll Lamp BA84 Sarum & Wells Th Coll 84. **d** 85 **p** 86. C Swansea St Thos and Kilvey *S & B* 85-87; C Gorseinon 87-89; V Oxwich w Penmaen and Nicholaston 89-94; Dir Post-Ord Tr from 93; R Ystradgynlais 94-98; V Oystermouth from 98. *The Vicarage, 9 Western Close, Mumbles, Swansea SA3 4HF* Tel (01792) 369971

EVANS, Kenneth. b 50. Bp Burgess Hall Lamp DipTh74. **d** 74 **p** 75. C Llanaber w Caerdeon *Ban* 74-79; C Upper Clapton St Matt *Lon* 79-82; P-in-c Tottenham St Phil from 82. *St Philip's Vicarage, 226 Philip Lane, London N15 4HH* Tel (020) 8808 4235

✠**EVANS, The Rt Revd Kenneth Dawson.** b 15. Clare Coll Cam BA37 MA41. Ripon Hall Ox 37. **d** 38 **p** 39 **c** 68. C Northampton St Mary *Pet* 38-41; C Northampton All SS w St Kath 41-45; R Ockley *Guildf* 45-49; V Ranmore 49-57; R Dorking 49-57; R Dorking w Ranmore 57-63; RD Dorking 57-63; Hon Can Guildf Cathl 55-63 and 79-85; Can Res Guildf Cathl 63-68; Adn Dorking 63-68; Suff Bp Dorking 68-85; rtd 85. *3 New Inn Lane, Guildford GU4 7HN* Tel (01483) 567978

EVANS, Kenneth Roy. b 47. Lon Univ BSc FRSA96. Ridley Hall Cam 79. **d** 81 **p** 81. C Stratford-on-Avon w Bishopton *Cov* 81-82; C Trunch *Nor* 82-85; Chapl Mapperley Hosp Nottm 85-91; Chapl Nottm Mental Illness and Psychiatric Unit 85-94; Chapl Notts Healthcare NHS Trust from 94; Lic to Offic *S'well* from 85; Dir Sherwood Psychotherapy Tr Inst from 87. *31 Foxhill Road, Burton Joyce, Nottingham NG14 5DR* Tel 0115-931 4081
E-mail ken.evans@btinternet.com

EVANS, Kevin Stuart. b 56. Bris Poly CQSW80. Qu Coll Birm DipTh95. **d** 95 **p** 96. C Madeley *Heref* 95-98; P-in-c Wombridge *Lich* from 98. *Wombridge Vicarage, Wombridge Road, Telford TF2 6HT* Tel (01952) 613334

EVANS, Lewys Thomas Gareth. b 29. St Mich Coll Llan. **d** 58 **p** 59. C Clydach *S & B* 58-65; R Vaynor and Capel Taffechan 65-80; V Defynnog w Rhydybriw, Llandeilo'r Fan etc 80-83; V Defynnog w Rhydybriw and Llandeilo'r-fan 83-87; V Ystalyfera 87-95; rtd 95. *15 Beech Grove, Brecon LD3 9ET* Tel (01874) 622480

EVANS, Linda Mary. *See* EDWARDS, Mrs Linda Mary

EVANS, Miss Madeleine Thelma Bodenham. b 30. K Coll Lon BD76 AKC76. Gilmore Course 80. **dss** 85 **d** 87 **p** 94. Chapl Pipers Corner Sch 85-91; Par Dn Calne and Blackland *Sarum* 91-94; C 94-00; Chapl St Mary's Sch Calne 91-99; rtd 00; Perm to Offic *Sarum* from 00. *11 Fairway, Rookery Park, Calne SN11 0LB* Tel (01249) 814755 Fax as telephone

EVANS, Ms Margaret Elizabeth. b 48. Leeds Univ BA69 Lon Inst of Educn CertEd70. Oak Hill Th Coll 91. **d** 94 **p** 95. NSM Canonbury St Steph *Lon* from 94. *St Stephen's Canonbury, 17 Canonbury Road, London N1 2DF* Tel (020) 7226 7526 *or* 7359 4343

EVANS, Martin Lonsdale. b 69. Man Univ BA91. Ripon Coll Cuddesdon DipMin95. **d** 95 **p** 96. C Morpeth *Newc* 95-98; Chapl RN from 98. *Royal Naval Chaplaincy Service, Room 203, Victory Building, HM Naval Base, Portsmouth PO1 3LS* Tel (023) 9272 7903 Fax 9272 7111 E-mail ml.evans@virgin.com

EVANS, Matthew Scott. b 72. Grey Coll Dur BA93. Cranmer Hall Dur DMS98. **d** 98 **p** 99. C Fountains Gp *Ripon* 98-03; P-in-c Dacre w Hartwith and Darley w Thornthwaite from 03. *The Vicarage, Dacre Banks, Harrogate HG3 4ED* Tel (01423) 780262

EVANS, Michael. b 49. St Jo Coll Nottm 88. **d** 90 **p** 91. C Beeston *S'well* 90-93; P-in-c Kirkby in Ashfield St Thos 93-97; V from 97; Chapl Notts Healthcare NHS Trust from 93. *The Vicarage, 109 Diamond Avenue, Kirkby-in-Ashfield, Nottingham NG17 7LX* Tel (01623) 755131

EVANS, Michael John. b 53. **d** 00 **p** 01. OLM Longnor, Quarnford and Sheen *Lich* from 00. *Lower Marnshaw Head, Barrowmoor, Longnor, Buxton SK17 0QR* Tel (01298) 83293

EVANS, Neil Robert. b 54. Lon Univ MA93. Coll of Resurr Mirfield. **d** 84 **p** 85. C Bethnal Green St Jo w St Bart *Lon* 84-86; C St Jo on Bethnal Green 87-88; P-in-c Stoke Newington Common St Mich 88-95; V 95-98; V Twickenham All Hallows from 98; Kensington Area CME Officer from 98. *All Hallows' Vicarage, 138 Chertsey Road, Twickenham TW1 1EW* Tel (020) 8892 1322 Fax 8241 2346 E-mail neil.evans@allhallowstwick.org.uk

EVANS, Nicholas Anthony Paul. b 60. Sheff Univ BA81 Liv Univ PGCE86. Qu Coll Birm 81. **d** 84 **p** 87. C Ludlow *Heref* 84-85; C Sunbury *Lon* 86-92; Hd RE Guildf Co Sch 93-99; NSM Crookham *Guildf* 94-99; CF 99-02; V Shenley Green *Birm* from 02. *St David's Vicarage, 49 Shenley Green, Birmingham B29 4HH* Tel 0121-475 4874 Mobile 07769-550204
E-mail evnsnick@aol.com

EVANS, Nigel William Reid. b 70. Sheff Hallam Univ BEd96. Ridley Hall Cam BTh01. **d** 01 **p** 02. C Gawthorpe and Chickenley Heath *Wakef* 01-02; C Ossett and Gawthorpe from 02. *73A Chickenley Lane, Dewsbury WF12 8QD* Tel (01924) 437232

EVANS, Norman Cassienet. b 30. Keble Coll Ox MA54. Guildf Dioc Min Course 91. **d** 95 **p** 96. OLM Seale, Puttenham and Wanborough *Guildf* 95-00; Perm to Offic from 00. *Tree Tops, Seale Lane, Puttenham, Guildford GU3 1AX* Tel (01483) 810677 E-mail norman@thereverend.fsnet.co.uk

EVANS, Patricia. **d** 02. OLM Panteg *Mon* from 02. *Pentwyn Farm, Glascoed, Pontypool NP4 0TX* Tel (01495) 785285

EVANS, The Ven Patrick Alexander Sidney. b 43. Linc Th Coll 70. **d** 73 **p** 74. C Lyonsdown H Trin *St Alb* 73-76; C Royston 76-78; V Gt Gaddesden 78-82; V Tenterden St Mildred w Smallhythe *Cant* 82-89; Adn Maidstone 89-02; Hon Can Cant Cathl 89-02; Dir of Ords 89-93; Adn Cant and Can Res Cant Cathl from 02. *Chillenden Chambers, 29 The Precincts, Canterbury CT1 2EP* Tel (01227) 463036 Fax 785209 E-mail pevans@diocant.clara.co.uk

EVANS, Peter. b 35. St Aid Birkenhead 57. **d** 60 **p** 61. C Higher Bebington *Ches* 60-63; C W Kirby St Bridget 63-66; P-in-c Lower Tranmere 66-68; V Flimby *Carl* 68-74; V Kirkby Ireleth 74-79; P-in-c Kirkbride w Newton Arlosh 79-80; R 80-85; V Beckermet St Jo and St Bridget w Ponsonby 85-97; rtd 97; Perm to Offic *Carl* from 98. *26 Gelt Close, Carlisle CA3 0HJ*

EVANS, Peter. b 40. S'wark Ord Course 75. **d** 75 **p** 76. C Welling *S'wark* 75-78; C Sutton New Town St Barn 78-81; C Kingston All

SS w St Jo 81-87; V Croydon Woodside 87-99; TV Sanderstead All SS from 99. *35 Audley Drive, Warlingham CR6 9AH* Tel (020) 8657 5505

EVANS, Peter Anthony. b 36. Imp Coll Lon BScEng57 St Cath Coll Ox DipTh59. St Steph Ho Ox 58. **d** 60 **p** 61. C Surbiton St Mark *S'wark* 60-63; Asst Chapl Lon Univ *Lon* 63-64; C S Kensington St Luke 64-68; C Surbiton St Andr and St Mark *S'wark* 68-69; C Loughton St Jo *Chelmsf* 69-74; P-in-c Becontree St Geo 74-82; Perm to Offic 82-89; NSM Romford St Alb 89-93; NSM Coopersale 93-95; NSM Epping Distr 95-96; rtd 97; Perm to Offic *Chelmsf* from 97. *6 Woodhall Crescent, Hornchurch RM11 3NN* Tel (01708) 509399

EVANS, Peter Gerald. b 41. Man Univ BA71. AKC65. **d** 65 **p** 66. C Kidbrooke St Jas *S'wark* 65-68; C Fallowfield *Man* 68-71; C Brockley Hill St Sav *S'wark* 71-73; P-in-c Colchester St Botolph w H Trin and St Giles *Chelmsf* 74-79; V 79-92; Perm to Offic from 93. *97 Northgate Street, Colchester CO1 1EY* Tel (01206) 543297

EVANS, Peter Kenneth Dunlop. b 38. Ch Coll Cam BA60. St D Coll Lamp 72. **d** 74 **p** 75. C Roath *Llan* 74-77; V Buttington and Pool Quay *St As* 77-87; V Llanfair Caereinion w Llanllugan from 87. *The Vicarage, Llanfair Caereinion, Welshpool SY21 0RR* Tel (01938) 810146

EVANS, Philip Ronald. b 55. Qu Coll Cam BA77 MA81 Dur Univ Cert Counselling 90. Cranmer Hall Dur 88. **d** 90 **p** 91. C Devonport St Budeaux *Ex* 90-92; C Torquay St Matthias, St Mark and H Trin 92-94; Chapl St Jas Univ Hosp NHS Trust Leeds 94-99; V Wetherby *Ripon* from 99. *3 Lazenby Drive, Wetherby LS22 6WL*

EVANS, Richard. *See* EVANS, David Richard

EVANS, Richard Edward Hughes. b 14. Univ of Wales BA44. St Mich Coll Llan. **d** 45 **p** 46. C Nantymoel *Llan* 45-48; C Pontyberem *St D* 48-50; C Llandeilo Fawr 50-53; V Ysbyty Cynfyn 53-64; V Llanybydder and Llanwenog w Llanwnnen 64-72; V Llanychaiarn 72-79; rtd 79. *23 Gwarfelin, Llanilar, Aberystwyth SY23 4PE* Tel (01974) 241357

EVANS, Richard Edward Victor. b 21. Linc Th Coll 66. **d** 68 **p** 69. C Aston cum Aughton *Sheff* 68-71; C Prestwich St Mary *Man* 71-74; R Moston St Jo 74-83; R Failsworth H Family 83-91; rtd 91; Perm to Offic *Man* from 91. *508 Edge Lane, Droylesden, Manchester M35 6JW* Tel 0161-370 1947

EVANS, Richard Gregory. b 50. Univ of Wales (Cardiff) DipTh72. St Mich Coll Llan 69. **d** 73 **p** 74. C Oystermouth *S & B* 73-76; C Clydach 76-79; CF 78-81; V Llanddew and Talachddu *S & B* 79-83; Youth Chapl 79-83; Hon Min Can Brecon Cathl 79-83; New Zealand from 83. *Wanganui Collegiate School, Wanganui, New Zealand* Tel (0064) (6) 349 0281 ext 8750 Fax 348 8302 E-mail rgevans@collegiate.school.nz

EVANS, Richard Neville. b 15. Qu Coll Cam BA36 MA44. Ripon Hall Ox 36. **d** 38 **p** 39. C E Wickham *S'wark* 38-43; Chapl RNVR 43-46; C Surbiton St Andr *S'wark* 46-47; R Southacre *Nor* 47-55; V Westacre 47-55; V Castle Acre w Newton 49-55; Chapl R Free Hosp Lon 55-60; V Cambridge St Andr Gt *Ely* 60-72; V Waterbeach 72-74; Perm to Offic 75-86; rtd 84; Perm to Offic *Truro* 86-95. *2 Hounster Drive, Millbrook, Torpoint PL10 1BZ* Tel (01752) 822811

EVANS, Richard Trevor. b 33. Jes Coll Ox MA58 DipEd58. St And Dioc Tr Course 73. **d** 76 **p** 76. NSM Leven *St And* 76-95; NSM St Andrews St Andr from 95. *33 Huntingtower Park, Whinnyknowe, Glenrothes KY6 3QF* Tel (01592) 741670 E-mail revans9973@aol.com

EVANS, Robert. *See* EVANS, Simon Robert

EVANS, Canon Robert Arthur. b 24. Univ of Wales (Cardiff) BA48. St Mich Coll Llan 48. **d** 50 **p** 51. C Aberdare St Fagan *Llan* 50-52; C Roath 52-57; C Llandaff w Capel Llanilltern 57-61; Asst Chapl Mersey Miss to Seamen 61-62; Chapl Supt Mersey Miss to Seamen 62-74 and 79-89; Chapl RNR 67-89; V Rainhill *Liv* 74-79; Perm to Offic *Ches* 79-91; Hon Can Liv Cathl *Liv* 88-89; rtd 89; Perm to Offic *Liv* from 89. *1 Floral Wood, Riverside Gardens, Liverpool L17 7HR* Tel 0151-727 3608

EVANS, Robert Charles. b 55. K Coll Lon BA77 AKC77 MA78 MTh89 Qu Coll Cam BA80 MA83 CertEd85. Westcott Ho Cam 79. **d** 81 **p** 82. C St Breoke *Truro* 81-83; C St Columb Minor and St Colan 83-84; Chapl Rob Coll Cam 87-92; Lect Ches Coll *Ches* from 92. *Chester College, Parkgate Road, Chester CH1 4BJ* Tel (01244) 375444

EVANS, Robert George Roger. b 49. Cam Univ MA. Trin Coll Bris 74 St Jo Coll Nottm 94. **d** 77 **p** 78. C Bispham *Blackb* 77-80; C Chadwell *Chelmsf* 80-84; V Ardsley *Sheff* from 84; Chapl Barnsley Community & Priority Services NHS Trust 98-00. *The Vicarage, Doncaster Road, Barnsley S71 5EF* Tel (01226) 203784 E-mail rgrevans@compuserve.com

EVANS, Robert Stanley. b 51. Univ of Wales (Lamp) BA72 Univ of Wales (Cardiff) PGCE73. St Mich Coll Llan DPS92. **d** 92 **p** 93. C Penarth All SS *Llan* 92-95; R Gelligaer 95-99; V Roath from 99. *Roath Vicarage, Waterloo Road, Cardiff CF23 5AD* Tel (029) 2048 4808

EVANS, Ronald. b 47. Univ of Wales (Cardiff) DipTh87. St Mich Coll Llan 85. **d** 87 **p** 88. C Flint *St As* 87-91; TV Wrexham 91-97; V Rhosymedre 97-99; V Rhosymedre w Penycae from 99. *The*

Vicarage, Church Street, Rhosymedre, Wrexham LL14 3EA Tel (01978) 810786 E-mail ronarthosymedre@compuserve.com

EVANS, Ronald Wilson. b 47. Windsor Univ Ontario BA69 Dalhousie Univ MA83. Trin Coll Toronto MDiv73. **d** 72 **p** 73. Canada 72-98; R Springhill 73-76; Chapl Univ of Prince Edw Is 76-79; Lect 82-85; Chapl King's-Edgehill Sch 85-87; R Clements 87-98; Lect Bilgi Univ Istanbul 98-00; Asst Chapl Izmir (Smyrna) w Bornova *Eur* 00-03; P-in-c from 03. *PK 1005, Pasaport, Izmir 35120, Turkey* Tel and fax (0090) (232) 464 5753 Mobile 535-734 1051 E-mail seljuk85@hotmail.com

EVANS, Mrs Sheila Jean. b 40. **d** 99 **p** 01. OLM Tollard Royal w Farnham, Gussage St Michael etc *Sarum* 99-01; OLM Chase from 01. *Church Mead, Harley Lane, Gussage All Saints, Wimborne BH21 5HD* Tel (01258) 840182

EVANS, Simon. b 55. Newc Univ BA77. St Steph Ho Ox 78. **d** 80 **p** 81. C Pet St Jude *Pet* 80-84; C Wantage *Ox* 84-87; V W Leigh *Portsm* 87-96; V Ruislip St Martin *Lon* from 96. *The Vicarage, 13 Eastcote Road, Ruislip HA4 8BE* Tel (01895) 633040

EVANS, Simon Andrew. b 59. Sarum & Wells Th Coll 81. **d** 84 **p** 85. C Norbury St Steph and Thornton Heath *Cant* 84; C Norbury St Steph and Thornton Heath *S'wark* 85-88; C Putney St Mary 88-92; P-in-c Telford Park St Thos 92-94; V from 94. *The Vicarage, 12A Salford Road, London SW2 4BH* Tel (020) 8674 1466 Fax 8674 2881 E-mail vicar@st-thomas.fsnet.co.uk

EVANS, Simon Robert (Bob). b 58. Reading Univ BSc79. N Ord Course 99. **d** 02 **p** 03. C Pudsey St Lawr and St Paul *Bradf* from 02. *18 West Park, Pudsey LS28 7SN* Tel 0113-257 4582 E-mail bob@becs2000.freeserve.co.uk

EVANS, Stanley. **d** 03. NSM Killaloe w Stradbally *L & K* from 03. *Killernan, Miltown Malbay, Co Clare, Irish Republic* Tel (00353) (65) 708 4970 Mobile 87-919 4331 Fax (65) 708 4983 E-mail sevans@indigo.ie

EVANS, Stanley Munro. b 30. AKC53. **d** 54 **p** 55. C Norbury St Oswald *Cant* 54-57; C St Laur in Thanet 57-63; V Bredgar 63-71; V Bredgar w Bicknor and Huckinge 71-72; V Westgate St Sav 72-01; rtd 01; Perm to Offic *Cant* from 01. *40 Queen Bertha Road, Ramsgate CT11 0ED* Tel (01843) 594459

EVANS, Canon Stephen John. b 60. Dartmouth RN Coll 81 St Steph Ho Ox BA86 MA89 Aber Univ MPhil94. **d** 86 **p** 87. Prec St Andr Cathl Inverness *Mor* 86-89; R Montrose *Bre* 89-91; P-in-c Inverbervie 89-91; Miss to Seamen 89-91; V Northampton St Paul *Pet* 91-98; Continuing Minl Educn Officer 94-00; Liturg Officer 96-03; P-in-c Ecton 98-00; Warden Ecton Ho 98-00; R Uppingham w Ayston and Wardley w Belton *Pet* from 00; Can Pet Cathl from 03. *The Rectory, London Road, Uppingham, Oakham LE15 9TJ* Tel (01572) 823381 Fax as telephone E-mail evanssj@globalnet.co.uk *or* stephen.evans@rutnet.co.uk

EVANS, Steven Edward. b 52. Carl and Blackb Dioc Tr Inst 97. **d** 00 **p** 01. NSM Caton w Littledale *Blackb* from 00. *Swallow Nest Cottage, Melling, Carnforth LA6 2RA* Tel (01524) 222124 E-mail se_emh@hotmail.com

EVANS, Ms Susan Mary. b 55. St Jo Coll Dur BA76 CertEd77 Nottm Univ BCombStuds84. Linc Th Coll 81. **dss** 84 **d** 87 **p** 94. Weaste *Man* 84-88; Par Dn 87-88; Par Dn Longsight St Luke 88-92; Par Dn Claydon and Barham *St E* 92-94; C 94-99; P-in-c Henley 98-99; Chapl HM YOI Hollesley Bay Colony 99-02; NSM Henley, Claydon and Barham *St E* from 02. *The Rectory, 7 Back Lane, Claydon, Ipswich IP6 0EB* Tel (01473) 830362

EVANS, Tenniel. *See* EVANS, Walter Tenniel

EVANS, Terence. b 35. St Mich Coll Llan 67. **d** 69 **p** 70. C Loughor *S & B* 69-73; C Gowerton w Waunarlwydd 73-77; V Llanbister and Llanbadarn Fynydd w Llananno 77-82; V Llanyrnewydd 82-01; rtd 01. *28 Orchard Court, New Orchard Street, Swansea SA1 5EN*

EVANS, Terence Robert. b 45. N Ord Course 82. **d** 85 **p** 86. C Warrington St Elphin *Liv* 85-88; V Cantril Farm 88-94; V Rainhill 94-03; R Odd Rode *Ches* from 03. *Odd Rode Rectory, Church Lane, Scholar Green, Stoke-on-Trent ST7 3QN* Tel (01270) 882195 Fax as telephone

EVANS, Thomas Norman. b 30. K Coll Lon BA51 BD53 AKC56. **d** 56 **p** 57. C Handsworth *Sheff* 56-59; C Mexborough 59-61; V Denaby Main 61-65; V Wythenshawe Wm Temple Ch *Man* 65-78; RD Withington 72-78; R Prestwich St Mary 78-85; RD Radcliffe and Prestwich 78-85; Hon Can Man Cathl 79-85; R Skelton w Upleatham *York* 87-99; RD Guisborough 91-99; rtd 99; Perm to Offic *York* from 00. *4 Castelo Grove, Pickering YO18 7JV* Tel (01751) 476628

EVANS, Canon Timothy Simon. b 57. York Univ BA79 Sussex Univ MA81 Fitzw Coll Cam BA85 MA88. Ridley Hall Cam 83. **d** 87 **p** 88. C Whitton St Aug *Lon* 87-90; C Ealing St Steph Castle Hill 90-93; P-in-c Shireshead *Blackb* 93-97; Asst Chapl Lanc Univ 93-97; Dep Prin Carl and Blackb Dioc Tr Inst from 97; P-in-c Natland *Carl* from 97; RD Kendal from 00; Hon Can Carl Cathl from 00. *The Vicarage, Natland, Kendal LA9 7QQ* Tel (01539) 560355 E-mail evansosmaston@clara.co.uk

EVANS, Trefor Rhys. b 06. Univ of Wales BA32. St Mich Coll Llan 33. **d** 33 **p** 34. C Llantrisant *Llan* 33-35; Chapl St D Cathl *St D* 35-38; R Llangeitho 38-43; V Llandysul 43-56; V Lampeter

Pont Steffan 56-74; rtd 74. *60 Penbryn, Lampeter SA48 7EU* Tel (01570) 422060

EVANS, The Very Revd Trevor Owen. b 37. Univ of Wales BSc59. Coll of Resurr Mirfield 59. **d** 61 **p** 62. C Llanaber w Caerdeon *Ban* 61-64; C Llandudno 64-70; TV 70-75; V Llanidloes w Llangurig 75-89; RD Arwystli 75-89; Can and Preb Ban Cathl 82-98; Dioc Adv on Spirituality from 84; R Trefdraeth 89-90; Dir of Min 89-98; R Llanfairpwll w Penmynydd 90-98; Dean Ban from 98; RD Ogwen 99-00. *The Deanery, Cathedral Close, Bangor LL57 1LH* Tel (01248) 370693 Fax 352466
E-mail revtrev@fish.co.uk

EVANS, Walter James. b 29. Huron Coll Ontario LTh58. **d** 58 **p** 59. Canada 58-63; C Wolborough w Newton Abbot *Ex* 63-65; R Chilthorne Domer, Yeovil Marsh and Thorne Coffin *B & W* 65-70; V Chalford *Glouc* 70-91; rtd 91; Perm to Offic *Glouc* 91-97. *67 Mandara Grove, Gloucester GL4 9XT* Tel (01452) 385157

EVANS, Walter Tenniel. b 26. Ox NSM Course. **d** 84 **p** 85. NSM Beaconsfield *Ox* from 84. *Candlemas, Jordans, Beaconsfield HP9 2ST* Tel (01494) 873165

EVANS, William James Lynn. b 30. St D Coll Lamp 73. **d** 75 **p** 76. P-in-c Penbryn and Blaenporth *St D* 75-77; V Penbryn and Betws Ifan w Bryngwyn 77-79; V Penrhyncoch and Elerch 79-83; V Cynwil Elfed and Newchurch 83-87; V Llandybie 87-95; rtd 95. *5 Dolau Tywi, Manordeilo, Llandeilo SA19 7BL* Tel (01550) 777944

EVANS, Wyn. *See* EVANS, The Very Revd John Wyn

EVANS-PUGHE, Thomas Goronwy. b 29. TCD. Wycliffe Hall Ox 59. **d** 61 **p** 62. C Grassendale *Liv* 61-63; P-in-c Mossley Hill St Matt and St Jas 63-64; C Irlam 65-69; Prec Chelmsf Cathl *Chelmsf* 65-69; R Birchanger 69-94; rtd 94; Perm to Offic *Glouc* from 94. *Bath Orchard, Blockley, Moreton-in-Marsh GL56 9HU* Tel (01386) 701223

EVANS-SMITH, Brian. **d** 02. OLM S Ramsey St Paul *S & M* from 02. *707 King's Court, Isle of Man IM8 1LN* Tel (01624) 817322

EVASON, Stuart Anthony. b 44. Salford Univ BSc. Chich Th Coll 79. **d** 81 **p** 82. C Heref St Martin *Heref* 81-85; TV Cleethorpes *Linc* 85-87; TV Howden *York* 87-92; V Heywood St Jas *Man* from 92. *St James's Vicarage, 46 Bury Old Road, Heywood OL10 3JD* Tel (01706) 369745

EVE, Cedric Robert Sutcliff. b 18. Lon Coll of Div 63. **d** 65 **p** 66. C Plumstead St Jas w St Jo *S'wark* 65-68; C Plumstead St Jo w St Jas and St Paul 68-69; C Ipsley *Worc* 69-73; TV 73-78; P-in-c Harvington and Norton and Lenchwick 78-84; rtd 84; Perm to Offic *Chich* from 85; *Guild* 93-99. *Manormead Residential Home, Tilford Road, Hindhead GU26 6RA* Tel (01428) 604107

EVE, David Charles Leonard. b 45. AKC74 St Aug Coll Cant 74. **d** 75 **p** 76. C Hall Green Ascension *Birm* 75-79; TV Kings Norton 79-84; V Rowley Regis 84-93; Perm to Offic *Heref* 94-98 and from 01; NSM Hallow and Grimley w Holt *Worc* from 98. *Cleanlyseat Farm, Neen Savage, Cleobury Mortimer, Kidderminster DY14 8EN* Tel (01299) 270510
E-mail d.eve@virgin.net

EVE, Hilary Anne. *See* FIFE, Hilary Anne

EVE, Canon Ian Halliday. b 33. St Paul's Coll Grahamstown LTh59. **d** 59 **p** 60. S Africa 59-80 and from 81; P-in-c Salcombe *Ex* 80-81; Can Cape Town from 86. *Christ Church Rectory, Main Road, Constantia, 7800 South Africa* Tel (0027) (21) 794 6352 *or* 794 5051 Fax 794 1065

EVELEIGH, Raymond. b 36. Univ of Wales (Cardiff) BSc58. NW Ord Course 73. **d** 76 **p** 77. NSM S Cave and Ellerker w Broomfleet *York* 76-79; P-in-c Kingston upon Hull St Mary 79-82; Chapl Hull Coll of FE 79-01; V Anlaby Common St Mark *York* 82-94; V Langtoft w Foxholes, Butterwick, Cottam etc 94-01; rtd 01; Perm to Offic *York* from 01. *Pasture Lodge, West End, Kilham, Driffield YO25 4RR* Tel (01262) 420060
E-mail rev@raybren.demon.co.uk

EVENS, Jonathan Adrian Harvey. b 63. Middx Poly BA84 Middx Univ BA03 ACIPD90. NTMTC 00. **d** 03. C Barking St Marg w St Patr *Chelmsf* from 03. *48 Sunningdale Avenue, Barking IG11 7QF* E-mail jon.evens@ntlworld.com

EVENS, Philip Alistair. b 36. Leic Univ BA61. Trin Coll Bris 84. **d** 86 **p** 87. C Aston SS Pet and Paul *Birm* 86-89; V Tyseley 89-99; rtd 99; Perm to Offic *Birm* from 99. *39 Douglas Road, Acocks Green, Birmingham B27 6HH* Tel 0121-708 1686

EVENS, Robert Alan. b 51. **d** 00 **p** 01. NSM Sharnbrook and Knotting w Souldrop *St Alb* 00-03; P-in-c Wymington w Podington from 03. *The Rectory, Manor Lane, Wymington, Rushden NN10 9LL* Tel (01933) 313069
E-mail robert.evens@lineone.net

EVENS, The Ven Robert John Scott. b 47. ACIB74 DipTh. Trin Coll Bris 74. **d** 77 **p** 78. C Southsea St Simon *Portsm* 77-79; C Portchester 79-83; V Locks Heath 83-96; RD Fareham 93-96; Adn Bath and Preb Wells Cathl *B & W* from 96. *56 Grange Road, Saltford, Bristol BS31 3AG* Tel (01225) 873609 Fax 874110
E-mail adbath@bathwells.anglican.org

EVENSON, Bruce John. b 46. Wittenberg Univ Ohio BA68. Lutheran Sch of Th Chicago MDiv72. **d** 98 **p** 98. C Charleston

Grace Ch USA 98-02; Chapl Porter-Gaud Sch Charleston 01-02; Chapl Stockholm w Gävle and Västerås *Eur* from 02. *The English Church of Stockholm, Styrmansgatan 1, SE-114 54 Stockholm, Sweden* Tel (0046) (8) 663 8248 Fax 663 8911
E-mail anglican.church@chello.se

EVEREST, Harold William. b 26. Lon Univ BD54. Tyndale Hall Bris 51. **d** 54 **p** 55. C Crookes St Thos *Sheff* 54-57; C Leyland St Andr *Blackb* 57-59; V Darwen St Barn 59-67; V Sheff St Jo *Sheff* 67-78; V Tinsley 78-91; Ind Chapl 78-91; rtd 91. *34 Oakdale Road, Bakersfield, Nottingham NG3 7EE* Tel 0115-987 6155

EVEREST, Canon John Cleland. b 45. Sarum Th Coll 66. **d** 68 **p** 69. C Moulsecoomb *Chich* 68-71; C Easthampstead *Ox* 71-74; C Southwick St Mich *Chich* 74-77; Dioc Soc Services Adv *Worc* 77-84; Ind Chapl 84-93; R Worc City St Paul and Old St Martin etc 84-93; RD Worc E 89-93; Hon Can Worc Cathl from 90; TR Halas from 93; RD Dudley 95-98. *The Rectory, Bundle Hill, Halesowen B63 4AR* Tel 0121-550 1158 Fax as telephone
E-mail halasoffice@ic24.net

EVERETT, Alan Neil. b 57. St Cath Coll Ox BA79 DPhil96 SS Coll Cam BA84. Westcott Ho Cam 82. **d** 85 **p** 86. C Hindley All SS *Liv* 85-88; Chapl Qu Mary Coll *Lon* 88-91; V S Hackney St Mich w Haggerston St Paul from 94. *97 Lavender Grove, London E8 3LR* Tel (020) 7249 4440 *or* 7249 2627
E-mail alan@n16.org.uk

EVERETT, Anthony William. b 60. S Bank Poly BA82. Oak Hill Th Coll BA89. **d** 89 **p** 90. C Hailsham *Chich* 89-92; C New Malden and Coombe *S'wark* 92-97; V Streatham Park St Alb 97-02; V Herne Bay Ch Ch *Cant* from 02. *Christ Church Vicarage, 38 Beltinge Road, Herne Bay CT6 6BU* Tel (01227) 374906 *or* 366640 E-mail anthony@fayland.freeserve.co.uk

EVERETT, Mrs Christine Mary. b 46. St Osyth Coll of Educn CertEd67. Westcott Ho Cam 90. **d** 92 **p** 94. Par Dn Ipswich St Fran *St E* 92-94; C 94-95; C Gt and Lt Bealings w Playford and Culpho 96; P-in-c 96-02; P-in-c Creeting St Mary, Creeting St Peter etc from 02. *190 Hawthorne Drive, Ipswich IP2 0QQ* Tel (01473) 688339 Mobile 07980-023236

EVERETT, Colin Gerald Grant. b 44. Open Univ BA77 Keswick Hall Coll CertEd. Ripon Coll Cuddesdon 79. **d** 81 **p** 82. C Aston cum Aughton *Sheff* 81-84; R Fornham All SS and Fornham St Martin w Timworth *St E* 84-92; P-in-c Old Newton w Stowupland 92-94; C Ipswich All Hallows 94-95; TV Ipswich St Fran 95-97; TV Ipswich St Mary at Stoke w St Pet and St Fran from 97. *190 Hawthorne Drive, Ipswich IP2 0QQ* Tel (01473) 688339

EVERETT, David Gordon. b 45. Pemb Coll Ox BA67 MA. Lon Coll of Div LTh68. **d** 70 **p** 71. C Hatcham St Jas *S'wark* 70-73; C Reading St Jo *Ox* 73-77; TV Fenny Stratford and Water Eaton 77-82; Hon C Bletchley 82-87; C Loughton 84-85; NSM Stantonbury and Willen 87-92; Chapl Ox Brookes Univ 92-96; NSM Iffley 93-96; C Treslothan *Truro* 96-97; C Crowan and Treslothan 98-02; Chapl Camborne Pool Redruth Coll 98-02; P-in-c Ketton w Tinwell *Pet* 02; P-in-c Easton on the Hill, Collyweston w Duddington etc 02; R Ketton, Collyweston, Easton-on-the-Hill etc from 03. *The Vicarage, 4 Edmonds Drive, Ketton, Stamford PE9 3TH* Tel (01780) 720228

EVERETT, Canon John Wilfred. b 37. Qu Coll Cam BA61 MA65. Cuddesdon Coll 64. **d** 66 **p** 67. C St Helier *S'wark* 66-69; C Yeovil St Jo w Preston Plucknett *B & W* 69-73; R Wincanton 73-82; R Pen Selwood 80-82; V Ashford *Cant* 82-02; Hon Can Cant Cathl 90-02; rtd 02; Perm to Offic *Cant* from 02. *Stream Cottage, 17 Gladstone Road, Willesborough, Ashford TN24 0BY* Tel (01233) 640736

EVERETT, Robert Henry. b 60. Em Coll Cam BA82 MA86 Ox Univ BA85 MA90 Ex Univ MPhil95. St Steph Ho Ox 83. **d** 86 **p** 87. C Ex St Thos and Em *Ex* 86-88; C Plymstock 88-91; R St Dominic, Landulph and St Mellion w Pillaton *Truro* 91-96; P-in-c Reading All SS *Ox* 96-98; V from 98. *All Saints' Vicarage, 14 Downshire Square, Reading RG1 6NH* Tel 0118-957 2000
E-mail frhenry@allsaints.fsnet.co.uk

EVERETT, Robin Nigel. b 34. Dur Univ BA55 DipTh59. Cranmer Hall Dur 57. **d** 59 **p** 60. C New Humberstone *Leic* 59-62; C Humberstone 62-66; V Quorndon 66-74; V Castle Donington 74-82; P-in-c Lockington w Hemington 81-82; V Castle Donington and Lockington cum Hemington 82-86; Antigua 86-87; R Ibstock w Heather *Leic* 87-98; rtd 98; Perm to Offic *Derby* from 98. *90 Sevenlands Drive, Boulton Moor, Derby DE24 5AQ* Tel (01332) 751879

EVERETT, Simon Francis. b 58. Oak Hill Th Coll BA89. **d** 89 **p** 90. C Wroughton *Bris* 89-93; TV Wexcombe *Sarum* 93-98; P-in-c The Iwernes, Sutton Waldron and Fontmell Magna 98-01; V Iwerne Valley from 01; RD Milton and Blandford from 01. *The Vicarage, Iwerne Minster, Blandford Forum DT11 8NF* Tel (01747) 811291

EVERETT-ALLEN, Canon Clive. b 47. AKC70. St Aug Coll Cant 69. **d** 70 **p** 71. C Minera *St As* 70-72; C Hatcham St Cath *S'wark* 72-75; C Beaconsfield *Ox* 75; TV 75-83; R Southwick St Mich *Chich* 83-98; V E Grinstead St Swithun from 98; Can and Preb Chich Cathl from 98; Chapl Qu Victoria Hosp NHS Trust East

Grinstead from 98. *St Swithun's Vicarage, Church Lane, East Grinstead RH19 3AZ* Tel (01342) 323307 E-mail revclive@telinco.co.uk

EVERINGHAM, Georgina Wendy (formerly WALLACE, Godfrey Everingham). b 32. Tyndale Hall Bris BA57. **d** 58 **p** 59. C Broadwater St Mary *Chich* 58-61; V Shipton Bellinger w S Tidworth *Win* 61-70; V Bournemouth St Paul 70-84; V Throop 84-95; rtd 95; Perm to Offic *Worc* from 96. *3 Harlech Close, Berkeley Alford, Worcester WR4 0JU* Tel (01905) 754394

EVERITT, Mark. b 34. Linc Coll Ox BA58 MA62. Wells Th Coll. **d** 60 **p** 61. C Hangleton *Chich* 60-63; Chapl Mert Coll Ox 63-02; rtd 02. *48 Annandale Avenue, Bognor Regis PO21 2EX* Tel (01243) 823852

EVERITT, Michael John. b 68. K Coll Lon BD90 AKC90. Qu Coll Birm DipTh90 English Coll Rome 91. **d** 92 **p** 93. C Cleveleys *Blackb* 92-95; S Africa 95-98; Succ Bloemfontein Cathl 95-98; Prec 96-98; Chapl and Asst Lect Univ of Orange Free State 96-98; Sen Chapl St Martin's Coll *Blackb* 98-02; Asst Dir of Ords 00-02; R Standish from 02. *The Rectory, 13 Rectory Lane, Standish, Wigan WN6 0XA* Tel (01257) 421396 E-mail rector@standish.org.uk

EVERITT, William Frank James. b 38. FCA63 Dur Univ BA68 DipTh69. Cranmer Hall Dur 65. **d** 69 **p** 70. C Leic St Phil *Leic* 69-73; P-in-c Prestwold w Hoton 73-77; R Settrington w N Grimston and Wharram *York* 77-84; RD Buckrose 80-84; V Cheltenham St Pet *Glouc* 84-99; rtd 99. *27 Lark Hill Crescent, Ripon HG4 2HN* Tel (01765) 603683

EVERSON, Canon Owen Neville. b 32. St Jo Coll Cam BA56 MA61. Wycliffe Hall Ox 56. **d** 58 **p** 59. C Edgbaston St Aug *Birm* 58-63; Tutor Wycliffe Hall Ox 63-66; Chapl 66-67; V Lee Gd Shep w St Pet *S'wark* 67-85; Hon Can S'wark Cathl from 83; V W Wickham St Fran 85-98; rtd 98; Perm to Offic *Chich* and *S'wark* from 98. *1 Lewis Road, Chichester PO19 7LZ*

EVERY, Canon Edward. b 09. Mert Coll Ox BA30 MA46. Linc Th Coll 36. **d** 36 **p** 37. C Caistor w Holton le Moor and Clixby *Linc* 36-38; C Burnley St Pet *Blackb* 38-40; C Glouc St Paul *Glouc* 40-41; Chapl RAFVR 41-46; Field Officer Chr Reconstruction in Eur Greece 46-47; C St Helier *S'wark* 48-49; Jerusalem 50-79; Can Res 52-79; Acting Dean 78-79; rtd 79; Perm to Offic *Lon* 82-86; *S'wark* 86-91. *College of St Barnabas, Blackberry Lane, Lingfield RH7 6NJ* Tel (01342) 870806

EVES, Barry. b 51. Sunderland Poly Dip Humanities 86. Cranmer Hall Dur 86. **d** 88 **p** 89. C Tadcaster w Newton Kyme *York* 88-91; C York St Paul 91-93; V Bubwith w Skipwith from 93. *The Vicarage, North Duffield, Selby YO8 5RR* Tel (01757) 288613

EWART, John. b 66. QUB BA89. CITC BTh02. **d** 02 **p** 03. C Derryloran *Arm* from 02. *51 Oldtown Street, Cookstown BT80 8EE* Tel (028) 8676 6046 E-mail johnewart@eircom.net

EWBANK, Mark Robert. b 59. Qu Coll Ox MA86. Westcott Ho Cam 84. **d** 86 **p** 87. Zimbabwe 86-00; Asst P N End St Marg Bulawayo 87-88; P-in-c Pumula St Luke 88-96; R Famona St Mary 96-00; C Chalfont St Peter *Ox* from 00. *All Saints' Parsonage, Oval Way, Chalfont St Peter SL9 8PZ* Tel (01753) 883839 E-mail mre.vre@virginnet.co.uk

EWBANK, The Very Revd Robert Arthur Benson. b 22. Ox Univ MA48. Cuddesdon Coll 46. **d** 48 **p** 49. C Boston *Linc* 48-52; Chapl Uppingham Sch Pet 52-56; S Rhodesia 57-65; Rhodesia 65-80; Zimbabwe 80-00; Dean Bulawayo 82-90; rtd 97; Perm to Offic *Ely* from 01. *15 Egremont Street, Ely CB6 1AE* Tel (01353) 654981

EWBANK, Canon Robin Alan. b 42. Ex Coll Ox BA64 MA88 Lon Univ BD68. Clifton Th Coll 66. **d** 69 **p** 70. C Woodford Wells *Chelmsf* 69-72; Warden Cam Univ Miss Bermondsey 72-76; TV Sutton St Jas and Wawne *York* 76-82; R Bramshott *Portsm* 82-91; R Bramshott and Liphook 91-99; Chmn IDWAL *Chich, Guildf* and *Portsm* 90-99; Hon Can Koforidua from 96; P-in-c Hartley Wintney, Elvetham, Winchfield etc *Win* 99-02; V from 02. *The Vicarage, Church Lane, Hartley Wintney, Basingstoke RG27 8DZ* Tel (01252) 842670 Fax 842215 E-mail robin_ewbank@lineone.net *or* stjohns_hw@talk21.com

EWBANK, The Ven Walter Frederick. b 18. Ball Coll Ox BA45 MA45 BD52. Bps' Coll Cheshunt. **d** 46 **p** 47. C Windermere St Martin *Carl* 46-49; V Hugill 49-52; V Casterton H Trin 52-62; V Raughton Head w Gatesgill 62-66; Hon Can Carl Cathl 66-78 and 83-84; V Carl St Cuth 66-71; Adn Westmorland and Furness 71-77; V Winster 71-78; Adn Carl 78-84; Can Res Carl Cathl 78-82; rtd 84; Perm to Offic *Carl* 84-94. *7 Castle Court, Castle Street, Carlisle CA3 8TP* Tel (01228) 810293

EWEN, Keith John McGregor. b 43. Sarum & Wells Th Coll 77. **d** 79 **p** 80. C Kington w Huntington *Heref* 79-82; C Kington w Huntington, Old Radnor, Kinnerton etc 82-83; P-in-c Culmington w Onibury 83-89; P-in-c Bromfield 83-89; P-in-c Stanton Lacy 83-89; R Culmington w Onibury, Bromfield etc 90-01; R Llangenni and Llanbedr Ystrad Yw w Patricio *S & B* from 01. *The Rectory, Llangenny, Crickhowell NP8 1HD* Tel (01873) 812557

EWER, Edward Sydney John (Jonathan). b 36. Univ of New England BA69 Lanc Univ MPhil91. St Mich Th Coll Crafers ThL63. **d** 62 **p** 63. Australia 62-83; SSM from 68; Perm to Offic *Blackb* 83-84; Lic to Offic *Dur* 84-98; Prior SSM Priory Dur 85-98; Dioc Dir of Ords 94-98; Perm to Offic *S'wark* from 00. *SSM Priory, 90 Vassall Road, London SW9 6JA* Tel (020) 7582 2040 Fax 7582 6640 E-mail j ewer@yahoo.com

EWINGTON, John. b 43. ARICS65 MRICS01. Chich Th Coll 74. **d** 78 **p** 79. C Walthamstow St Jo *Chelmsf* 78-81; Papua New Guinea 81-87; V Southend St Sav Westcliff *Chelmsf* 87-96; TV Bideford, Northam, Westward Ho, Appledore etc *Ex* from 96. *The Vicarage, Meeting Street, Appledore, Bideford EX39 1RJ* Tel (01237) 470469

EXALL, John Aubrey. b 20. Univ Coll Lon BSc41. Cuddesdon Coll 46. **d** 48 **p** 49. C Bitterne Park *Win* 48-53; C Romsey 53-56; P-in-c Southampton St Barn 56-57; V 57-85; rtd 86; Perm to Offic *Win* from 86. *Delve Cottage, 36 Church Lane, Romsey SO51 8EP* Tel (01794) 522928

EXCELL, Robin Stanley. b 41. AKC64. St Boniface Warminster 64. **d** 65 **p** 66. C Ipswich St Mary Stoke *St E* 65-68; C Melton Mowbray w Thorpe Arnold *Leic* 68-70; TV 70-71; R Gt and Lt Blakenham w Baylham *St E* 71-76; R Gt and Lt Blakenham w Baylham and Nettlestead 76-86; RD Bosmere 84-86; NSM Sproughton w Burstall 91-94; R Rattlesden w Thorpe Morieux, Brettenham etc from 94. *The Rectory, High Street, Rattlesden, Bury St Edmunds IP30 0RA* Tel (01449) 737993

EXELL, Ernest William Carter. b 28. Qu Coll Cam BA52 MA53. Tyndale Hall Bris 49. **d** 52 **p** 53. C Sydenham H Trin *S'wark* 52-54; C E Ham St Paul *Chelmsf* 54-57; Uganda 57-65; Tanzania 66-70; R Abbess and Beauchamp Roding *Chelmsf* 70-71; P-in-c White Roding w Morrell Roding 70-71; R Abbess Roding, Beauchamp Roding and White Roding 71-94; RD Roding 75-79; rtd 94; Perm to Offic *St E* from 94. *8 Ickworth Drive, Bury St Edmunds IP33 3PX* Tel (01284) 724726

EXELL, Michael Andrew John. b 45. FHCIMA MRIPHH67 MICA70. Sarum & Wells Th Coll 87. **d** 89 **p** 90. C Ryde H Trin *Portsm* 89-93; C Swanmore St Mich w Havenstreet 89-92; C Swanmore St Mich 92-93; P-in-c Carisbrooke St Mary 93-99; V from 99; P-in-c Carisbrooke St Nic 93-99; V from 99. *The Vicarage, 56 Castle Road, Carisbrooke, Newport PO30 1DT* Tel (01983) 522205

EXETER, Archdeacon of. *See* GARDNER, The Ven Paul Douglas

EXETER, Bishop of. *See* LANGRISH, The Rt Revd Michael Laurence

EXETER, Dean of. *See* JONES, The Very Revd Keith Brynmor

EXLEY, Malcolm. b 33. Cranmer Hall Dur. **d** 67 **p** 68. C Sutton St Jas *York* 67-73; V Mappleton w Goxhill 73-77; V Market Weighton 77-90; P-in-c Goodmanham 77-78; R 78-90; V Bridlington Em 90-98; rtd 98; Perm to Offic *York* from 00. *11 The Chase, Driffield YO25 7FJ* Tel (01377) 272312

EXLEY-STIEGLER, Canon George Ebdon. b 16. Syracuse Univ BS51. Berkeley Div Sch STM53. **d** 53 **p** 54. USA 53-79 and from 89; R Camden Trin NY 53-57; R Brockport St Luke NY 57-64; R Rochester Calvary-St Andr NY 64-79; rtd 79; Hon C Knowsley *Liv* 80-81; Hon C Upholland 81-89; Lect Upholland N Inst 80-84. *1471 Long Pond Road #247, Rochester, NY 14626, USA* Tel (001) (716) 723 4367 E-mail geoes@frontiernet.net

EXON, Helier John Philip. b 44. MBE87. BSc70 CEng87 MIEE87. STETS 96. **d** 99 **p** 00. NSM Milton Abbas, Hilton w Cheselbourne etc *Sarum* from 99; NSM Piddletrenthide w Plush, Alton Pancras etc from 02. *The Monk's House, Hilton, Blandford Forum DT11 0DG* Tel (01258) 880396 *or* (01242) 870253 E-mail helier@exon.demon.co.uk

EYDEN, Christopher David. b 59. DipRSAMDA81. St Steph Ho Ox 88. **d** 91 **p** 92. C Tottenham St Paul *Lon* 91-93; C Ealing St Pet Mt Park 93-96; TV Wimbledon *S'wark* from 96. *55 Alwyne Road, London SW19 7AE* Tel (020) 8946 4175

EYEONS, Keith James. b 70. Clare Coll Cam BA92 MA96 Lon Inst of Educn PGCE95. St Jo Coll Nottm MA(MM)03. **d** 01 **p** 02. C Iffley *Ox* from 01; Chapl Down Coll Cam from 03. *Downing College, Cambridge CB2 1DQ* Tel (01223) 334800 E-mail eyeons@hotmail.com

EYERS, Frederick Thomas Laurence. b 12. Ridley Coll Melbourne LTh39. **d** 39 **p** 40. Australia 39-46, 50-73 and from 82; Perm to Offic *York* 46-50; SSM from 50. *Seniors House, 18 Victoria Street, Camberwell, Vic, Australia 3124* Tel (0061) (3) 9882 9597

EYLES, Anthony John. b 34. Bris Univ BSc57. Sarum Th Coll 61. **d** 63 **p** 64. C Wellington w W Buckland *B & W* 63-67; C Wilton 67-74; Ind Chapl *Dur* 74-85; Ind Chapl *Worc* 85-90; P-in-c Bickenhill w Elmdon *Birm* 90; P-in-c Bickenhill St Pet 90-00; Chapl Birm Airport 90-00; rtd 00; Perm to Offic *Ex* from 00. *5 Kersbrook Lane, Kersbrook, Budleigh Salterton EX9 7AD* Tel (01395) 446084

EYLES, David William. b 45. Sarum & Wells Th Coll 75. **d** 77 **p** 78. C Knaresborough *Ripon* 77-80; C Chapel Allerton 80-82; P-in-c W Tanfield and Well w Snape and N Stainley 82-83; R 83-91; P-in-c Middleham w Coverdale and E Witton 93-94; R 94-01; P-in-c Thornton Watlass w Thornton Steward 94-01; P-in-c Markington w S Stainley and Bishop Thornton from 01. *The Vicarage, Westerns Lane, Markington, Harrogate HG3 3PB* Tel (01765) 677123

EYNON, John Kenneth. b 56. Nottm Univ BA77 BArch80. LNSM course 93. **d** 96 **p** 97. OLM Croydon Ch Ch *S'wark* from 96. *33 Fairlands Avenue, Thornton Heath CR7 6HD* Tel (020) 8684 9866 Mobile 0956-640328 Fax 8665 9871 E-mail johneynon@btinternet.com

EYRE, The Very Revd Richard Montague Stephens. b 29. Oriel Coll Ox BA53 MA56. St Steph Ho Ox 53. **d** 56 **p** 57. C Portsea N End St Mark *Portsm* 56-59; Tutor Chich Th Coll 59-61; Chapl 61-62; Chapl Eastbourne Coll 62-65; V Arundel w Tortington and S Stoke *Chich* 65-73; V Brighton Gd Shep Preston 73-75; Dir of Ords 75-79; Adn Chich 75-81; Can Res and Treas Chich Cathl 78-81; Dean Ex 81-95; rtd 95; Perm to Offic *B & W* 95-00; P-in-c Pau *Eur* 01-03. *Hathersage, Enmore, Bridgwater TA5 2DP* Tel (01278) 671790

EYRE, Richard Stuart. b 48. Bris Univ BEd81 Nottm Univ MTh86. Linc Th Coll 74. **d** 77 **p** 78. C Henbury *Bris* 77-81; C Bedminster 81-82; TV 82-84; Chapl Bp Grosseteste Coll Linc 84-95; Sen Tutor 89-95; P-in-c Long Bennington w Foston *Linc* 95; P-in-c Saxonwell 95-97; R 97-01; RD Grantham 96-01; TR Hykeham from 01; RD Graffoe from 02. *The Rectory, Mill Lane, North Hykeham, Lincoln LN6 9PA* Tel (01522) 882880 E-mail richard@saxonwell.freeserve.co.uk

F

FACER, Miss Rosemary Jane. b 44. Hull Univ BA65 Reading Univ CertEd66 LTCL72. Trin Coll Bris DipHE80. **dss** 80 **d** 87 **p** 98. St Paul's Cray St Barn *Roch* 80-88; Par Dn 87-88; C Cheltenham St Mark *Glouc* 88-01; C Clifton *York* from 01. *2 Doe Park, Clifton Moor, York YO30 4UQ* Tel (01904) 691474 E-mail r.rj.facer@talk21.com

FACEY, Andrew John. b 57. Trin Coll Cam BA79 MA83 Barrister-at-Law 80. Trin Coll Bris BA92. **d** 92 **p** 93. C Egham *Guildf* 92-96; P-in-c E Molesey St Paul 96-01; Dioc Inter Faith Adv from 96; P-in-c Epsom Common Ch Ch 01-02; V from 02. *Christ Church Vicarage, 20 Christ Church Road, Epsom KT19 8NE* Tel (01372) 720302 Fax as telephone E-mail andrew.facey@virgin.net

FADUGBA, David. b 65. Ibadan Univ Nigeria BA89. Immanuel Coll Ibadan DipTh93. **d** 93 **p** 94. Nigeria 93-99; V Igboglia St Pet 93-95; V Oba St Jo 95-99; C Earlestown *Liv* from 99. *St John's Vicarage, 63 Market Street, Newton-le-Willows WA12 9BS* Tel (01925) 224771

FAGAN, Jeremy David. b 75. Qu Coll Ox BA98 Wycliffe Hall Ox 99. **d** 01. C Chell *Lich* from 01. *2 Silverstone Crescent, Stoke-on-Trent ST6 6JQ* Tel (01782) 834479 E-mail faganj@yahoo.com

FAGAN, John Raymond. b 32. Lon Univ BD69. Ripon Hall Ox 71. **d** 72 **p** 73. C Stalybridge *Man* 72-74; C Madeley *Heref* 74-79; V Amington *Birm* 79-91; P-in-c Stonnall *Lich* 91-97; Chapl HM YOI Swinfen Hall 91-97; rtd 97; C Stonnall *Lich* 97; Res Min Elford from 98. *The Rectory, Church Road, Elford, Tamworth B79 9DA* Tel (01827) 383212

FAGAN, Thomas. b 27. MCIOB67 Man Univ CertEd70. NW Ord Course 78. **d** 81 **p** 82. NSM Rainhill *Liv* 81-90; NSM Prescot 90-97; rtd 97; Perm to Offic *Liv* from 97. *4 Wensleydale Avenue, Prescot L35 4NR* Tel 0151-426 4788

FAGBEMI, Olubunmi Ayobami (Bunmi). b 57. Lagos Univ LLB78 LSE LLM81 Qu Mary Coll Lon PhD91 Solicitor 79. Ripon Coll Cuddesdon 95. **d** 97 **p** 98. C Enfield St Andr *Lon* 97-01; V Tottenham H Trin from 01. *Holy Trinity Vicarage, Philip Lane, London N15 4GZ* Tel (020) 8801 3021 E-mail bunmif@aol.com

FAGBEMI, Canon Stephen Ayodeji Akinwale. b 67. Nottm Univ BTh96. Immanuel Coll Ibadan 87. **d** 90 **p** 91. C Iyere St Jo Nigeria 90-91; C Owo St Patr 91-92; P-in-c Wakajaye-Etile Ch Ch 92-93; V Emure-Ile St Sav 96-00; Can Owo from 99; Perm to Offic *Cant* 00-03; Hon C Murston w Bapchild and Tonge from 03. *The Rectory, Portland Avenue, Sittingbourne ME10 3QY* Tel (01795) 437643 Mobile 07796-643468 E-mail saaf@kent.ac.uk *or* saaf90@yahoo.co.uk

FAGERSON, Joseph Leonard Ladd. b 35. Harvard Univ BA57 Lon Univ DipTh62. Ridley Hall Cam 61. **d** 63 **p** 64. C Tonbridge SS Pet and Paul *Roch* 63-67; Afghanistan 67-74; P-in-c Marbury *Ches* 74-75; P-in-c Kinloch Rannoch *St And* 75-00; Chapl Rannoch Sch Perthshire 75-00; rtd 00. *Westgarth, Tomnacroich, Fortingall, Aberfeldy PH15 2LJ* Tel (01887) 830569

FAHIE, Mrs Stephanie Bridget. b 48. St Jo Coll Nottm 85. **d** 87 **p** 94. Par Dn Leic St Chris *Leic* 87-90; Chapl Scargill Ho 90-95; P-in-c Hickling w Kinoulton and Broughton Sulney *S'well* 95-00; R from 00. *The Rectory, 41 Main Street, Kinoulton, Nottingham NG12 3EA* Tel (01949) 81657 E-mail kinoulton.rectory@virgin.net

FAINT, Paul Edward. b 38. Qu Coll Birm 85. **d** 87 **p** 88. C Cradley *Worc* 87-90; V Hanley Castle, Hanley Swan and Welland 90-94; V Northwood H Trin *Lon* 94-97; Miss to Seafarers from 97; Chapl Larnaca Cyprus 97-01; rtd 01; Perm to Offic *Ox* from 01; Hon Chapl Miss to Seafarers from 02. *17 Priory Orchard, Wantage OX12 9EL* Tel (01235) 772297 E-mail thefaints@lineone.net

FAIR, Richard Francis. b 64. Ex Univ BEd88. Cranmer Hall Dur 97. **d** 99 **p** 00. C Old Hill H Trin *Worc* 99-03; C Thorpe Acre w Dishley *Leic* from 03. *13 Burbage Close, Loughborough LE11 5UL* Tel (01509) 212029

FAIRALL, Michael John. b 45. SW Minl Tr Course 88. **d** 90 **p** 91. NSM Southway *Ex* from 90. *132 Lakeview Close, Tamerton Foliot, Plymouth PL5 4LX* Tel (01752) 707694 E-mail m.j.fairall@talk21.com

FAIRBAIRN, Francis Stephen. b 41. LNSM course 94. **d** 98 **p** 99. Hon C Orrell *Liv* from 98. *27 Greenslate Road, Billinge, Wigan WN5 7BQ* Tel (01695) 623127 *or* (01722) 812176 Fax (01722) 815398

FAIRBAIRN, John Alan. b 46. Trin Coll Cam BA67 MA72. Wycliffe Hall Ox 84. **d** 86 **p** 87. C Boscombe St Jo *Win* 86-89; C Edgware *Lon* 89-95; R Gunton St Pet *Nor* from 95; Chapl Jas Paget Healthcare NHS Trust from 96. *The Rectory, 36 Gunton Church Lane, Lowestoft NR32 4LF* Tel (01502) 580707

FAIRBAIRN, Stella Rosamund. **d** 87 **p** 94. NSM Banbury *Ox* 87-99; Perm to Offic *Pet* 88-94. *Hillside, Overthorpe, Banbury OX17 2AF* Tel (01295) 710648

FAIRBANK, Brian Douglas Seeley. b 53. AKC75. St Steph Ho Ox 77. **d** 78 **p** 79. C Newton Aycliffe *Dur* 78-81; C Stocking Farm *Leic* 81-84; TV Ratby cum Groby 84-91; Chapl RN from 91. *Royal Naval Chaplaincy Service, Room 203, Victory Building, HM Naval Base, Portsmouth PO1 3LS* Tel (023) 9272 7903 Fax 9272 7111

FAIRBROTHER, Robin Harry. b 44. Univ of Wales DipTh68. Ho of Resurr Mirfield 64 Wells Th Coll 68. **d** 69 **p** 70. C Wrexham *St As* 69-74; C Welshpool w Castle Caereinion 74-77; V Bettws Cedewain and Tregynon 77-80; V Betws Cedewain and Tregynon and Llanwyddelan 80-92; TR Marshwood Vale *Sarum* 92-98; TR Golden Cap Team from 98. *The Rectory, Whitchurch Canonicorum, Bridport DT6 6RQ* Tel (01297) 489223 E-mail robin.fairbrother@talk21.com

FAIRBROTHER, Ronald Peter. b 20. St Steph Ho Ox 59. **d** 61 **p** 62. C Dawlish *Ex* 61-69; R Newton Ferrers w Revelstoke 69-83; V Abbotskerswell 83-89; rtd 90. *3 Chestnut Court, Alphington, Exeter EX2 8XY*

FAIRCLOUGH, John Frederick. b 40. St Jo Coll Dur BA63 MA68 MBIM DMS78. Coll of Resurr Mirfield 81. **d** 83 **p** 84. C Horninglow *Lich* 83-87; V Skerton St Luke *Blackb* 87-94; V Thornton-le-Fylde 94-00; rtd 00; Perm to Offic *Blackb* from 01. *18 Crossfield Avenue, Bury BL9 5NX* Tel (01706) 825664

FAIRHURST, Canon Alan Marshall. b 30. Clare Coll Cam BA52 MA56 Lon Univ BD56. Tyndale Hall Bris 53 Hask's Th Academy Istanbul 54 Wycliffe Hall Ox 55. **d** 56 **p** 57. Tutor St Jo Coll Dur 56-60; C Stockport St Geo *Ches* 60-62; Ceylon 62-66; R Ashley w Silverley *Ely* 67-71; R Stockport St Mary *Ches* 71-95; Chapl Stockport Acute Services NHS Trust 76-95; Hon Can Ches Cathl *Ches* 81-95; RD Stockport 86-95; rtd 95; Perm to Offic *Ches* from 95. *50 Ridge Park, Bramhall, Stockport SK7 2BL* Tel 0161-439 3126

FAIRHURST, John Graham. b 39. Linc Th Coll 86. **d** 88 **p** 89. C Whiston *Sheff* 88-91; V Elsecar from 91; AD Tankersley from 01; Chapl Barnsley Community & Priority Services NHS Trust from 98. *The Vicarage, Wath Road, Elsecar, Barnsley S74 8HJ* Tel (01226) 742149

FAIRHURST, Ms Rosemary Anne. b 63. Newnham Coll Cam BA85 MA85 Lon Inst of Educn PGCE86. Wycliffe Hall Ox BA92. **d** 93 **p** 94. C Hackney Marsh *Lon* 93-97; C Islington St Mary 97-02; Dir Miss and Min Ripon Coll Cuddesdon from 02. *Ripon College, Cuddesdon, Oxford OX44 9EX* Tel (01865) 874404 Fax 875431 E-mail rosyfairhurst@ripon-cuddesdon.ac.uk

FAIRLAMB, Neil. b 49. Univ of Wales (Ban) BA71 Jes Coll Ox BPhil73 Pemb Coll Cam CertEd74. S'wark Ord Course 90. **d** 93 **p** 94. Hon C Dulwich St Barn *S'wark* 93-95; P-in-c Elerch w Penrhyncoch w Capel Bangor and Goginan *St D* 95-96; V 96-98; R Arthog w Fairbourne w Llangelynnin w Rhoslefain *Ban* from

98. *The Rectory, Llwyngwril LL37 2JB* Tel (01341) 250919 Fax as telephone E-mail fairlamb57@hotmail.com

FAIRLESS (née CARTER), Mrs Elizabeth Jane. b 57. Derby Univ BSc00. St Jo Coll Nottm MTh02. **d** 02. C Leek and Meerbrook *Lich* from 02. *Old Timbers, 5 Stockwell Street, Leek ST13 6DH* Tel (01538) 383590 Mobile 07968-033489 E-mail lizfairless@hotmail.com

FAIRWEATHER, David James. b 35. Keele Univ BEd79. Wycliffe Hall Ox 70. **d** 72 **p** 73. C Trentham *Lich* 72-76; C Cheddleton 76; C Hanley H Ev 77-79; C Rugeley 79-86; V Brown Edge 86-03; rtd 03. *St Anne's Vicarage, Church Road, Brown Edge, Stoke-on-Trent ST6 8TD* Tel (01782) 502134

FAIRWEATHER, John. b 39. K Coll Lon AKC66 BD72. **d** 67 **p** 68. C Plymouth St Jas Ham *Ex* 67-69; C Townstal w St Sav and St Petrox w St Barn 69-73; R Corringham w Springthorpe *Linc* 73-78; P-in-c Blyborough 76-78; P-in-c Heapham 76-78; P-in-c Willoughton 76-78; V Pinchbeck 78-82; V Exwick *Ex* from 82. *Exwick Vicarage, Exwick Road, Exeter EX4 2AT* Tel (01392) 255500

FAIRWEATHER, Miss Sally Helen. b 69. St Hilda's Coll Ox BA91. Cranmer Hall Dur 94. **d** 97 **p** 98. C Illingworth *Wakef* 97-01; Warden H Rood Ho *York* 01-02; C Thirsk 01-02; Chapl Northallerton Health Services NHS Trust 01-02; C Sheff St Mark Broomhill *Sheff* from 02. *9 Betjeman Gardens, Sheffield S10 3FW* Tel 0114-266 4343

FALCONER, Ian Geoffrey. b 40. BNC Ox BA62 Newc Univ MA93. Cuddesdon Coll 62. **d** 64 **p** 65. C Chiswick St Nic w St Mary *Lon* 64-68; C-in-c Hounslow Gd Shep Beavers Lane CD 68-76; P-in-c Hammersmith St Matt 76-84; P-in-c Byker St Silas *Newc* 84-93; V 93-95; P-in-c Newc St Phil and St Aug 95-98; P-in-c Newc St Matt w St Mary 95-98; P-in-c Newc St Phil and St Aug and St Matt w St Mary 98-00; V Seghill from 00. *Seghill Vicarage, Mares Close, Seghill, Cramlington NE23 7EA* Tel 0191-237 1228

FALKNER, Jonathan Michael Shepherd. b 47. Open Univ BA74 St Jo Coll Dur DipTh78. **d** 79 **p** 80. C Penrith w Newton Reigny *Carl* 79-81; C Penrith w Newton Reigny and Plumpton Wall 81-82; C Dalton-in-Furness 82-84; V Clifton 84-90; P-in-c Dean 85-89; R 89-90; P-in-c Rumburgh w S Elmham w the Ilketshalls *St E* 90-92; R S Elmham and Ilketshall 92-99; RD Beccles and S Elmham 94-99; Hon Can St E Cathl 98-99; P-in-c Bromfield w Waverton *Carl* 99-02; P-in-c W Newton 99-02; P-in-c Holme Cultram St Mary 00-02; P-in-c Holme Cultram St Cuth 00-02; TR Solway Plain from 02. *The Vicarage, Langrigg, Wigton CA7 3NA* Tel (01697) 320261 E-mail jonathan.falkner@talk21.com *or* falcon.langrigg@talk21.com

FALL, Harry. b 17. Leeds Univ BA40 BD51 Dur Univ BA42 MA48. **d** 42 **p** 43. C Eccles St Mary *Man* 42-44; C Heaton Norris Ch 44-45; C Linthorpe *York* 45-49; V Danby 49-54; V Harden *Bradf* 54-57; R Scrayingham *York* 57-71; R York H Trin w St Jo Micklegate and St Martin 71-84; rtd 84; Perm to Offic *York* from 84. *20 Weaponness Valley Road, Scarborough YO11 2JF* Tel (01723) 361822

FALLA, Miles. b 43. DipM74 MCIM. EAMTC 93. **d** 96 **p** 97. NSM Buckden *Ely* 96-98; P-in-c Gretton w Rockingham *Pet* 98-99; V Gretton w Rockingham and Cottingham w E Carlton from 99; RD Corby 01-02. *The Vicarage, Station Road, Gretton, Corby NN17 3BY* Tel (01536) 770237 E-mail gretton@mfalla.fsnet.co.uk

FALLONE, Christopher. b 55. Aston Tr Scheme 85 Oak Hill Th Coll 87. **d** 90 **p** 91. C Rochdale *Man* 90-93; P-in-c Thornham w Gravel Hole 93-94; TV Middleton w Thornham from 94. *St John's Vicarage, 1177 Manchester Road, Rochdale OL11 2XZ* Tel (01706) 631825 Mobile 07976-624124 Fax 631645 E-mail chrisfallone@bigfoot.com

FALLOWS, Stuart Adrian. b 50. Moray Ho Edin 75. **d** 78 **p** 79. Hon C Forres w Nairn *Mor* 78-81; Hon C Elgin w Lossiemouth 81-86; Hon Dioc Chapl 86; C Brighton St Geo w St Anne and St Mark *Chich* 86-89; V Wivelsfield 89-98; P-in-c Kieth, Huntly and Aberchirder *Mor* 98-02; P-in-c Ringwould w Kingsdown *Cant* from 02. *The Rectory, Upper Street, Kingsdown, Deal CT14 8BJ* Tel (01304) 373951 E-mail fallows@beeb.net

FALSHAW, Simon Meriadoc. b 60. Leeds Univ BSc82. Oak Hill Th Coll BA93. **d** 93 **p** 94. C Stapleford *S'well* 93-99; Crosslinks Missn Partner Zimbabwe 99-01; P-in-c The Lye and Stambermill *Worc* from 01; Perm to Offic *Sheff* 01-02. *Christ Church Vicarage, High Street, Lye, Stourbridge DY9 8LF* Tel (01384) 423142

FANE, Clifford Charles. b 39. Kelham Th Coll 62. **d** 67 **p** 68. C Heston *Lon* 67-73; C Bedminster St Mich *Bris* 73-76; P-in-c 76-77; C Gaywood, Bawsey and Mintlyn *Nor* 77-81; V Bolton St Jo *Man* 81-90; rtd 90. *10 Booth Road, Little Lever, Bolton BL3 1JY* Tel (01204) 709420

FANTHORPE, Robert Lionel. b 35. FCMI81 FCP90 CertEd63 Open Univ BA80. Llan Dioc Tr Scheme. **d** 87 **p** 88. NSM Roath St German *Llan* 87-00; Lic to Offic from 00. *Rivendell, 48 Claude Road, Roath, Cardiff CF24 3QA* Tel (029) 2049 8368 Mobile 07767-207289 Fax 2049 6832 E-mail fanthorpe@aol.com

FARADAY, John. b 49. Leeds Univ BSc71 MICE78. Oak Hill Coll 81. **d** 83 **p** 84. C Sutton *Liv* 83-86; C Rainhill 86-89; Chapl Whiston Hosp 86-89; V Over Darwen St Jas *Blackb* 89-02; TR S Rochdale *Man* from 02. *St Mary's Vicarage, The Sett, Badger Lane, Rochdale OL16 4RQ* Tel (01706) 649886 E-mail vicarj@btinternet.com

FARAH, Mones Anton. b 64. Trin Coll Bris BA88. **d** 88 **p** 89. C Aberystwyth *St D* 88-91; Chapl St D Coll Lamp 91-98; TV Gt Baddow *Chelmsf* from 98. *The Vicarage, 42 Riffhams Drive, Great Baddow, Chelmsford CM2 7DD* Tel (01245) 471516 E-mail monesf@yahoo.com

FARAH, The Ven Rafiq Amin. b 21. Beirut Univ BA45. Near E Sch of Th 45. **d** 46 **p** 48. Jerusalem 46-86; Adn and Can Res 74-86; Min to Arab Angl and Evang in Lon 86-92; Hon C Herne Hill *S'wark* 86-92; Canada 92-95. *Address temp unknown*

FARBRIDGE, Nicholas Brisco. b 33. FCA. Sarum & Wells Th Coll 75. **d** 77 **p** 78. C Gt Bookham *Guildf* 77-80; C Ewell 80-83; V Addlestone 83-89; R Shere 89-95; rtd 96; Perm to Offic *Guildf* from 96. *55 Curling Vale, Guildford GU2 7PH* Tel (01483) 531140 E-mail nickfarbridge@beeb.net

FARDON, Jean Audrey May. b 24. Westf Coll Lon BA45 Lon Inst of Educn DipEd46. Gilmore Ho DipTh69. **dss** 79 **d** 87 **p** 94. St Alb St Pet *St Alb* 79-92; Hon Par Dn 87-92; NSM Powick *Worc* 92-94; Perm to Offic from 94. *17 The Greenway, Powick, Worcester WR2 4RZ* Tel (01905) 830472

FARDON, Raymond George Warren. b 30. St Pet Hall Ox BA52 MA56. Ridley Hall Cam 54. **d** 59 **p** 60. C High Wycombe All SS *Ox* 59-63; Chapl Bedford Secondary Modern Sch 63-68; Hd Master K Sch Grantham 72-82; Travelling Ev 82-95; Hon C Longfleet *Sarum* 82-83; Perm to Offic from 83; rtd 95. *26 Kingland Road, Poole BH15 1TP* Tel (01202) 773226

FAREY, David Mark. b 56. St Jo Coll Dur BA85. Cranmer Hall Dur 82. **d** 86 **p** 87. C Brackley St Pet w St Jas *Pet* 86-89; TV Kingsthorpe w Northampton St Dav 89-96; R Laughton w Ripe and Chalvington *Chich* from 96; Chapl to Bp Lewes from 96. *The Rectory, Church Lane, Laughton, Lewes BN8 6AH* Tel (01323) 811642 Fax as telephone

FARGUS, Gavin James Frederick. b 30. AKC54. K Coll Lon. **d** 55 **p** 57. C Salisbury St Mark *Sarum* 55-57; C Wareham w Arne 57-60; C Marlborough 60-63; P-in-c Davidstow w Otterham *Truro* 63-65; R Nether Lochaber *Arg* 65-81; R Kinlochleven 65-81; rtd 81; Lic to Offic *Arg* 82-94. *61 Loan Fearn, Ballachulish, Argyll PA39 4JB* Tel (01855) 811851

FARGUS, Maxwell Stuart. b 34. Linc Coll Ox BA57 MA61 Leeds Univ DipAdEd79. Cuddesdon Coll 57. **d** 59 **p** 60. C Newc St Fran *Newc* 59-62; C Rothbury 62-64; Dioc Youth Officer *Ripon* 64-76; R Kirkby Wiske 64-76; Community Educn Officer Barnsley MBC 76-88; Perm to Offic *Sheff, Wakef* and *York* 77-88; V Rudston w Boynton and Kilham *York* 88-93; rtd 93; Perm to Offic *York* from 93. *56 Fir Tree Drive, Filey YO14 9NR* Tel (01723) 513511 Fax as telephone

FARISH, Alan John. b 58. Lanc Univ BA. St Jo Coll Nottm LTh86 DPS86. **d** 86 **p** 87. C Bishopwearmouth St Gabr *Dur* 86-89; C Fatfield 89-98; P-in-c Preston on Tees from 98. *The Vicarage, Quarry Road, Eaglescliffe, Stockton-on-Tees TS16 9BD* Tel (01642) 789814

FARLEY, Ms Claire Louise. b 69. Man Univ BA91 Heythrop Coll Lon MTh99. Westcott Ho Cam 96. **d** 99 **p** 00. C Sherborne w Castleton and Lillington *Sarum* 99-00; C Weymouth H Trin 00-02. *1 St James's House, 2 Sherriff Road, London NW6 2AP* Tel (020) 7372 6441 E-mail clairefarley@waitrose.com

FARLEY, David Stuart. b 53. Univ Coll Dur BA75 Westmr Coll Ox MTh00 Nottm Univ DipTh82 Dip Counselling 99. St Jo Coll Nottm. **d** 84 **p** 85. C Bath Weston All SS w N Stoke *B & W* 84-87; Chapl Scargill Ho 87-90; Min Hedge End N CD *Win* 90-94; V Hedge End St Luke 94-00; Dep Chapl HM Pris Belmarsh 00-01; Chapl HM Pris Shrewsbury from 01. *HM Prison, The Dana, Shrewsbury SY1 2HR* Tel (01743) 352511 ext 325

FARLEY, Ian David. b 56. Linc Coll Ox BA78 MA87 Dur Univ PhD88. Cranmer Hall Dur 84. **d** 87 **p** 88. C Thorpe Acre w Dishley *Leic* 87-92; V S Lambeth St Steph *S'wark* 92-99; V Bacton w Edingthorpe w Witton and Ridlington *Nor* from 99; Ind Chapl 99-03; TR Buckhurst Hill *Chelmsf* from 03. *St John's Rectory, High Road, Buckhurst Hill IG9 5RX* Tel (020) 8504 1931

FARLEY, James Trevor. b 37. IEng MIEE FRSA. EMMTC 80. **d** 82 **p** 83. NSM Grantham *Linc* from 82. *Highfield Cottage, Station Road, Bottesford, Nottingham NG13 0EN* Tel (01949) 843646 Fax 843860 E-mail jimandroma@highfield40.fsnet.co.uk

FARLEY, Ronald Alexander. b 30. Oak Hill NSM Course. **d** 79 **p** 80. NSM Stoke Newington St Faith, St Matthias and All SS *Lon* 79-97; NSM Upper Clapton St Matt from 99. *St Matthew's Vicarage, 20 Moresby Road, London E5 9LF* Tel (020) 8806 2430

FARLEY-MOORE, Peter James. b 72. Sheff Univ BA94. Ridley Hall Cam MA00. **d** 00 **p** 01. C Chapeltown *Sheff* 00-03; CMS from 03. *Church Mission Society, Partnership House, 157 Waterloo Road, London SE1 8UU* Tel (020) 7928 8681 E-mail farley-moore@tinyworld.co.uk

FARMAN, Joanne Margaret. b 46. Birkbeck Coll Lon BA81 Southlands Coll Lon PGCE82. SEITE 97. **d** 00 **p** 01. Chapl St Geo Healthcare NHS Trust Lon from 00; NSM Limpsfield and Titsey *S'wark* from 00. *10 Detillens Lane, Limpsfield, Oxted RH8 0DJ* Tel (01883) 713086 *or* (020) 8725 3070

FARMAN, Robert Joseph. b 54. Ridley Hall Cam 86. **d** 88 **p** 89. C Sutton St Nic *S'wark* 88-90; C Cheam Common St Phil 90-92; R Wootton w Glympton and Kiddington *Ox* 92-00; TV Kings Norton *Birm* from 00. *53 Wychall Park Grove, Birmingham B38 8AG* Tel 0121-451 3268 E-mail robfarman@robfarman.demon.uk

FARMAN, Mrs Roberta. b 48. Aber Univ MA70 Cam Univ CertEd72. Qu Coll Birm 78. **dss** 82 **d** 87 **p** 01. Ovenden *Wakef* 80-82; Scargill Ho 83-84; Coulsdon St Jo *S'wark* 85-86; Hon Par Dn Cambridge St Mark *Ely* 86-88; Hon Par Dn Sutton St Nic *S'wark* 88-92; Hon Par Dn Wootton w Glympton and Kiddington *Ox* 92-00; NSM Kings Norton *Birm* from 01; Chapl Univ Hosp Birm NHS Trust from 01. *53 Wychall Park Grove, Birmingham B38 8AG* Tel 0121-451 3268

FARMBOROUGH, James Laird McLelland (Mac). b 22. MBE90. Magd Coll Cam BA49 MA54. Tyndale Hall Bris. **d** 52 **p** 53. C Wolverhampton St Luke *Lich* 52-55; C Holloway St Mary w St Jas *Lon* 55-56; C Broadwater St Mary *Chich* 56-58; Brazil 58-64; Org Sec SAMS 65-70; V Marple All SS *Ches* 70-80; Chile 80-92; Miss to Seamen 80-92; rtd 92. *11 Manormead, Tilford Road, Hindhead GU26 6RA* Tel (01428) 602562

✠**FARMBROUGH, The Rt Revd David John.** b 29. Linc Coll Ox BA51 MA53. Westcott Ho Cam 51. **d** 53 **p** 54 **c** 81. C Bp's Hatfield *St Alb* 53-57; P-in-c 57-63; V Bishop's Stortford St Mich 63-74; RD Bishop's Stortford 73-74; Adn St Alb 74-81; Suff Bp Bedford 81-93; rtd 94; Hon Asst Bp St Alb from 94. *St Michael Mead, 110 Village Road, Bromham, Bedford MK43 8HU* Tel (01234) 825042

FARMER, Diane Marcia (Diana). b 61. Warwick Univ BSc82 PGCE83. WMMTC 97 Cranmer Hall Dur. **d** 01 **p** 02. C Allesley Park and Whoberley *Cov* from 01. *14 Harewood Road, Coventry CV5 8BQ* Tel (024) 7667 6839 E-mail diana@whoberley.org.uk

FARMER, George Wilson. b 37. Lich Th Coll 61. **d** 65 **p** 66. C Kingston All SS *S'wark* 65-69; C Heston *Lon* 69-74; C Southmead *Bris* 74-75; C Bedminster 75-80; TV Langley Marish *Ox* 80-86; R Wexham 86-03; rtd 03. *Address temp unknown*

FARMER, Lorelie Joy. b 43. Southn Univ BA65 MA68 Mass Univ EdD88. Cranmer Hall Dur DTM99. **d** 99 **p** 00. C Newbury *Ox* 99-03; C Stratford-upon-Avon, Luddington etc *Cov* from 03. *St James's House, 61 Maidenhead Road, Stratford-upon-Avon CV37 6XU* Tel (01789) 415868 E-mail lpor9146@aol.com

FARMER, Robert John Thayer. b 62. Kent Univ BA84 SSC. St Steph Ho Ox 91. **d** 93 **p** 94. C Leigh St Clem *Chelmsf* 93-96; P-in-c Wellingborough St Mary *Pet* 96-00; V from 00; Chapl Northants Healthcare NHS Trust from 99. *St Mary's Vicarage, 193 Midland Road, Wellingborough NN8 1NG* Tel (01933) 225626 E-mail vicar@stmarywellingborough.org.uk

FARMER, Simon John. b 60. Birm Univ BSc82. St Jo Coll Nottm 86. **d** 89 **p** 90. C Ulverston St Mary w H Trin *Carl* 89-92; CF 92-97; Chapl HM Pris Lowdham Grange 97-00; CF (TA) from 99; Perm to Offic *S'well* from 00; Operations Dir (Africa) ACCTS Mil Min Internat from 00. *26 Halloughton Road, Southwell NG25 0LR* Tel (01636) 813599

FARMER, Canon William John Cotton. b 19. St Jo Coll Dur LTh42 BA43. St Aid Birkenhead. **d** 43 **p** 44. C Ipswich St Aug *St E* 43-45; C Warwick St Mary *Cov* 45-49; C Solihull *Birm* 49-54; V Blackheath 54-64; V Packwood w Hockley Heath 64-81; Hon Can Birm Cathl 80-81; rtd 84. *12 Bowling Green Court, Hospital Road, Moreton-in-Marsh GL56 0BX* Tel (01608) 651082

FARMILOE, Preb Trevor James. b 42. Sarum & Wells Th Coll. **d** 82 **p** 82. C S Petherton w the Seavingtons *B & W* 82-85; R Norton St Philip w Hemington, Hardington etc 85-93; Chapl Rural Affairs Wells Adnry 87-92; RD Frome 89-93; V Martock w Ash from 93; RD Ivelchester 95-01; Preb Wells Cathl from 96. *The Vicarage, 10 Water Street, Martock TA12 6JN* Tel (01935) 826113 Fax as telephone E-mail revtrev.martock@virgin.net

FARNHAM, Barry. b 30. SS Mark & Jo Coll Plymouth TCert52 Ex Univ AdDipEd66 MEd75. S Dios Minl Tr Scheme 80. **d** 83 **p** 84. Lect Bp Otter Coll Chich 70-78; Sen Lect W Sussex Inst of HE 78-92; NSM Barnham and Eastergate *Chich* 83-85; NSM Aldingbourne, Barnham and Eastergate 85-92; R 92-96; rtd 96; Perm to Offic *Chich* from 96. *16 Henty Close, Walberton, Arundel BN18 0PW* Tel (01243) 555992

FARNWORTH, Ms Joanna Helen. b 66. Jes Coll Cam BA88 MA92. St Jo Coll Nottm BTh98 MA99. **d** 99 **p** 00. C Middleton w Thornham *Man* 99-03. *St James's Vicarage, Union Street, Ashton-under-Lyne OL6 9NQ* Tel 0161-330 4925 E-mail joannafarnworth@aol.com

FARNWORTH, Michael Godfrey Frankland. b 18. Selw Coll Cam BA40 MA46. Westcott Ho Cam 40. **d** 42 **p** 43. C Horsham *Chich* 42-47; C Storrington 47-50; CF 50-72; P-in-c Hindringham and Binham *Nor* 72-77; R 77-84; rtd 84; Perm to Offic *Nor* 85-00. *15 Sheldrake Close, Fakenham NR21 8ND* Tel (01328) 855211

FARNWORTH, Roger. b 60. Man Univ BSc81. St Jo Coll Nottm MA99. **d** 99 **p** 00. C Tonge w Alkrington *Man* 99-03; TV Ashton from 03. *St James's Vicarage, Union Street, Ashton-under-Lyne OL6 9NQ* Tel 0161-330 2771 E-mail rogerfarnworth@aol.com

FARNWORTH, Russell. b 60. Lon Bible Coll BA82 Nottm Univ MTh85. St Jo Coll Nottm DPS84. **d** 84 **p** 85. C Blackpool St Jo *Blackb* 84-87; TV Darwen St Pet w Hoddlesden 87-91; V Kidsgrove *Lich* 91-02; Chief Exec Officer Trans World Radio UK from 03. *28 Kingsway East, Newcastle ST5 3PZ* Tel (01782) 637130 E-mail rfarnworth@twr.org.uk

FARQUHAR, Preb Patricia Ann. b 42. **dss** 78 **d** 87 **p** 94. S Hackney St Jo w Ch Ch *Lon* 80-01; Par Dn 87-94; C 94-01; Preb St Paul's Cathl 97-01; rtd 01. *5A Coronation Close, Norwich NR6 5HF* Tel (01603) 417554

FARQUHARSON, The Very Revd Hunter Buchanan. b 58. ALAM LLAM. Edin Th Coll 85. **d** 88 **p** 89. C Dunfermline *St And* 88-91; R Glenrothes 91-97; R Leven 95-97; R Dunfermline 97-99; Provost St Ninian's Cathl Perth from 99. *St Ninian's House, 40 Hay Street, Perth PH1 5HS* Tel (01738) 626874 E-mail hbfi@compuserve.com

FARR, Arthur Ronald. b 24. JP77. Llan Dioc Tr Scheme 77. **d** 80 **p** 81. NSM Penarth All SS *Llan* 80-90; rtd 90; Perm to Offic *Llan* from 90. *3 Cymric Close, Ely, Cardiff CF5 4GR* Tel (029) 2056 1765

FARR (née ROSE), Margaret. b 37. Man Univ BDS, LDS60 Birm Univ MB, ChB69 MD85. WMMTC 99. **d** 02 **p** 03. NSM Handsworth St Jas *Birm* from 02. *35 West Drive, Handsworth, Birmingham B20 3ST* Tel 0121-554 0909

FARR, Mark Julian Richard. b 60. **d** 87 **p** 88. C Clapham TM *S'wark* 87-91; TV Wimbledon 91-95; USA from 96. *Sojourners, 2401 15th Street NW, Washington, DC 20009, USA*

FARR, Richard William. b 55. Ridley Hall Cam. **d** 83 **p** 84. C Enfield Ch Ch Trent Park *Lon* 83-87; C Eastbourne H Trin *Chich* 87-90; P-in-c Henham and Elsenham w Ugley *Chelmsf* from 90. *The Vicarage, Carters Lane, Henham, Bishop's Stortford CM22 6AQ* Tel (01279) 850281 E-mail dickthevic@netscapeonline.co.uk

FARRAN, Canon George Orman. b 35. Worc Coll Ox BA58 MA62. Wycliffe Hall Ox 58. **d** 60 **p** 61. C Tyldesley w Shakerley *Man* 60-62; Tutor Wycliffe Hall Ox 62-64; V Netherton *Liv* 64-73; R Sefton 69-73; R Credenhill w Brinsop, Mansel Lacey, Yazor etc *Heref* 73-83; RD Heref Rural 81-83; R Ditcheat w E Pennard and Pylle *B & W* 83-94; Dir of Ords 86-89; Can and Chan Wells Cathl 85-97; rtd 97; Perm to Offic *B & W* 97-00. *Bethany, Ashton Hill, Corston, Bath BA2 9EY* Tel (01225) 872348

FARRANCE, William Kenneth. b 22. Univ of Wales (Ban) 46. Bps' Coll Cheshunt 49. **d** 52 **p** 53. C Newc St Gabr *Newc* 52-58; V Newsham 58-63; V Heddon-on-the-Wall 63-78; Chapl Tynemouth Hosps 79-82; AP Tynemouth Ch 79-82; rtd 82; Perm to Offic *Newc* from 82. *32 Garden Terrace, Earsdon, Whitley Bay NE25 9LQ* Tel 0191-251 1599

FARRANT, David Stuart. b 38. Ripon Coll Cuddesdon 82. **d** 84 **p** 85. C Woodford St Mary w St Phil and St Jas *Chelmsf* 84-87; P-in-c Clymping *Chich* 87; R Clymping and Yapton w Ford 87-92; Dioc Schs Admin Officer 92-95; Chapl Qu Alexandra Hosp Home Worthing from 95; Lic to Offic *Chich* from 92. *101 Nutley Crescent, Goring-by-Sea, Worthing BN12 4LB* Tel (01903) 507458 *or* 213458

FARRANT, Canon John Frederick Ames. b 30. Aber Univ MA51 BD58 MTh80. Edin Th Coll 51. **d** 53 **p** 54. C Dundee St Mary Magd *Bre* 53-58; R Clydebank *Glas* 58-65; R Motherwell 65-70; Papua New Guinea 70-73 and 81-84; R Glas St Bride *Glas* 73-81; Can St Mary's Cathl 77-81; Provost Rabaul 81-84; R Penicuik *Edin* 85-96; R W Linton 85-96; Can St Mary's Cathl 92-96; Chapl Madeira *Eur* 96-98; rtd 98; Hon Asst P St Mary le Strand w St Clem Danes *Lon* from 98; Perm to Offic from 01. *20 Defoe House, London EC2Y 8DN* Tel (020) 7638 3963

FARRANT, Canon Martyn John. b 38. AKC61. **d** 62 **p** 63. C Hampton St Mary *Lon* 62-65; C Shere *Guildf* 65-67; V Stoneleigh 67-75; V Addlestone 75-83; V Dorking w Ranmore 83-98; RD Dorking 89-94; Hon Can Guildf Cathl 94-98; rtd 98; Perm to Offic *Guildf* from 98; Chapl Phyllis Tuckwell Hospice Farnham from 98. *42 Hampstead Road, Dorking RH4 3AE* Tel (01306) 740916

FARRAR, Canon James Albert. b 27. TCD BA55 MA57. CITC 56. **d** 56 **p** 57. C Dublin Drumcondra w N Strand *D & G* 56-59; C Dublin Rathmines 59-61; I Ballinaclash 61-72; I Dunganstown w Redcross 72-79; Warden Ch Min of Healing 79-95; Hon Clerical V Ch Ch Cathl Dublin 79-92; Can Ch Ch Cathl Dublin from 92; rtd 95. *15 Hillside, Greystones, Co Wicklow, Irish Republic* Tel (00353) (1) 287 2706

FARRAR, Prof Roy Alfred. b 39. Imp Coll Lon BSc60 PhD67 FWeldI85 DIC60. Wycliffe Hall Ox 99. **d** 00 **p** 01. NSM Portswood St Denys *Win* from 00. *The Coach House, 11B Thorold Road, Southampton SO18 1HZ* Tel (023) 8055 8440

FARRELL, Miss Katherine Lucy Anne. b 61. Westcott Ho Cam 00. **d** 02. C Forest Gate Em w Upton Cross *Chelmsf* 02-03; C Lt Ilford St Mich from 03. *52 Bolton Road, London E15 4JY*

FARRELL, Ms Margaret Ruth. b 57. Linc Inst Melbourne BAppSc(OT)78. **d** 02 **p** 03. C Bury St Edmunds All SS w St Jo and St Geo *St E* from 02. *140 Abbot Road, Bury St Edmunds IP33 3UW* Tel (01284) 768317 Mobile 07855-996831 E-mail farrell@fish.co.uk

FARRELL, Peter Godfrey Paul. b 39. Sarum & Wells Th Coll 72. **d** 74 **p** 75. C St Just in Roseland *Truro* 74-77; C Kenwyn 77-80; V Knighton St Jo *Leic* 80-86; TR Clarendon Park St Jo w Knighton St Mich 86-89; V Woodham *Guildf* 89-99; V Wells St Cuth w Wookey Hole *B & W* from 99. *The Vicarage, 1 St Cuthbert Street, Wells BA5 2AW* Tel (01749) 673136 Fax as telephone

FARRELL, Robert Edward. b 54. Univ of Wales (Abth) BA74 Jes Coll Ox BA77 MA81. Qu Coll Birm 85. **d** 86 **p** 87. C Llanrhos *St As* 86-88; C Prestwich St Marg *Man* 89-91; V Moulsham St Luke *Chelmsf* 91-98; V Thorpe Bay from 98. *The Vicarage, 86 Tyrone Road, Southend-on-Sea SS1 3HB* Tel (01702) 587597 E-mail robert_farrell21@hotmail.com

FARRELL, Ronald Anthony. b 57. Edin Univ BD84 Birm Univ MA86. Qu Coll Birm 84. **d** 86 **p** 87. C Shard End *Birm* 86-87; C Shirley 87-89; Bp's Officer for Schs and Young People 89-93; V Kingstanding St Mark 93-01; TR Swinton and Pendlebury *Man* from 01; P-in-c Lower Broughton Ascension from 02. *St Peter's Rectory, Vicarage Road, Swinton, Manchester M27 3WA* Tel 0161-794 1578

FARRELL, Thomas Stanley. b 32. Lon Univ BD71. Ridley Hall Cam 69. **d** 71 **p** 72. C Much Woolton *Liv* 71-73; C Gt Sankey 73-74; Asst Chapl Dulwich Coll 74-76; Chapl 76-81; P-in-c Wonersh *Guildf* 81-86; V 86-90; RD Cranleigh 87-90; R St Marg Lothbury and St Steph Coleman Street etc *Lon* 90-00; P-in-c St Botolph without Aldersgate 90-97; rtd 00; Hon C Burford w Fulbrook, Taynton, Asthall etc *Ox* from 00. *West Farthing Cottage, 1 Lawrence Lane, Burford OX18 4RP* Tel (01993) 823951

FARRER, Canon Carol Elizabeth. b 47. Open Univ BA88. Cranmer Hall Dur 81. **dss** 83 **d** 87 **p** 94. Newbarns w Hawcoat *Carl* 83-86; Egremont and Haile 86-91; Par Dn 87-91; TD Penrith w Newton Reigny and Plumpton Wall 91-94; TV 94-01; Dioc Lay Min Adv 87-88; Assoc Dir of Ords 88-97; Dir of Ords 97-00; Dioc OLM Officer from 00; Hon Can Carl Cathl from 01; TV Barrow St Geo w St Luke from 01. *The Vicarage, 98A Roose Road, Barrow-in-Furness LA13 9RL* Tel (01229) 826489 Fax as telephone E-mail carolfarrer@hotmail.com

FARRER, Canon Michael Robert Wedlake. b 22. St Pet Hall Ox BA52 MA57. Tyndale Hall Bris 47. **d** 52 **p** 53. C St Ebbe *Ox* 52-56; Tutor Clifton Th Coll 56-65; R Barton Seagrave *Pet* 65-73; R Barton Seagrave w Warkton 73-78; V Cambridge St Paul *Ely* 78-92; RD Cambridge 84-89; Hon Can Ely Cathl 88-92; rtd 92; Bp's Sen Chapl *Ely* 92-95; Perm to Offic from 92. *2 Houghton Gardens, Ely CB7 4JN* Tel (01353) 665654

FARRER, Simon James Anthony. b 52. St Cath Coll Cam MA77 K Coll Lon BD78 MTh92. AKC78 Coll of Resurr Mirfield 78. **d** 79 **p** 80. C St John's Wood *Lon* 79-84; C N Harrow St Alb 84-87; P-in-c Hammersmith St Luke 87-93; USPG 93-99; Zambia 94-99; P-in-c Stoke Newington Common St Mich *Lon* 99-02; V from 02. *St Michael's Vicarage, 55 Fountayne Road, London N16 7ED* Tel (020) 8806 4225

FARRINGTON, Canon Christine Marion. b 42. Birkbeck Coll Lon BA65 Nottm Univ DASS66 Middx Poly MA75. St Alb Min Tr Scheme 79. **dss** 82 **d** 87 **p** 94. Redbourn *St Alb* 82-87; Dir Past Studies Linc Th Coll 86-87; HM Pris Linc 86-87; Dir Sarum Chr Cen 87-93; Dn Sarum Cathl *Sarum* 87-93; Co-Dir of Ords and Dir of Women's Min *Ely* 93-02; Hon Can Ely Cathl 93-02; C Cambridge Gt St Mary w St Mich 93-96; V Cambridge St Mark 96-02; Chapl Wolfs Coll Cam 97-02; Perm to Offic *St Alb* from 97; Chapl to The Queen from 98; rtd 02. *30 Lybury Lane, Redbourn, St Albans AL3 7HY* Tel (01582) 793409

FARRINGTON, Lynda. d 01. NSM Cannock *Lich* from 01. *Blithford Farm, Blithbury, Rugeley WS15 3JB* Tel (01283) 840253 or 502131 E-mail farringtontowers@compuserve.com

FARROW, Edward. b 38. Sarum Th Coll 69. **d** 71 **p** 72. C Parkstone St Pet w Branksea *Sarum* 71-74; R Tidworth 74-79; P-in-c W and E Lulworth 79-80; P-in-c Winfrith Newburgh w Chaldon Herring 79-80; R The Lulworths, Winfrith Newburgh and Chaldon 80-83; V Ensbury Park from 83; Chapl Talbot Heath Sch Bournemouth 83-97. *The Vicarage, 42 Coombe Avenue, Bournemouth BH10 5AE* Tel (01202) 514286

FARROW, Elizabeth Maura. b 43. Edin Th Coll 93. **d** 91 **p** 96. NSM Knightswood H Cross Miss *Glas* 91-96; TV Bearsden from 96. *5 Campsie Road, Strathblane G63 9AB* Tel (01360) 770936

FARROW, Ian Edmund Dennett. b 38. S'wark Ord Course 70. **d** 72 **p** 73. C Tunbridge Wells St Jo *Roch* 72-78; Chapl N Cambs Gen Hosp Gp 78-92; P-in-c Walsoken *Ely* 78-80; R 80-92; V Bisley, Oakridge, Miserden and Edgeworth *Glouc* from 92. *The Vicarage, Cheltenham Road, Bisley, Stroud GL6 7BJ* Tel (01452) 770056

FARROW, Peter Maurice. b 44. St Chad's Coll Dur BSc65 DipTh68. **d** 68 **p** 69. C Gt Yarmouth *Nor* 68-71; C N Lynn w St Marg and St Nic 71-75; P-in-c Sculthorpe w Dunton and Doughton 75-77; Perm to Offic 78-89; TV Lowestoft and Kirkley 89-94; Ind Miss 89-94; Sen Ind Chapl 94-99; TV Gaywood 95-02; P-in-c Mundford w Lynford from 02; P-in-c Ickburgh w Langford from 02; P-in-c Cranwich from 02. *The Rectory, St Leonard's Street, Mundford, Thetford IP26 5HG* Tel (01842) 878220 E-mail farrpm@dialstart.net

FARROW, Robin Thomas Adrian. b 72. K Coll Lon BA93 AKC93. St Steph Ho Ox 94. **d** 96 **p** 97. C Lancing w Coombes *Chich* 96-00; R W Blatchington from 00. *St Peter's Rectory, 23 Windmill Close, Hove BN3 7LJ* Tel (01273) 732459

FARTHING, Michael Thomas. b 28. St Cuth Soc Dur 48. Lambeth STh81 St Steph Ho Ox. **d** 58 **p** 59. C St Marylebone St Mark w St Luke *Lon* 58-63; C Newport Pagnell *Ox* 63-69; R Standlake 69-76; R Yelford 69-76; R Lower Windrush 76-82; V Wheatley w Forest Hill and Stanton St John 82-95; rtd 95; Perm to Offic *Ox* from 95. *32 Falstaff Close, Eynsham, Oxford OX29 4QA* Tel (01865) 883805

FARTHING, Paul Andrew. b 58. McGill Univ Montreal BA80 STM82. Montreal Dioc Th Coll DipMin83. **d** 83 **p** 84. Canada 83-99; C Montreal W St Phil 83-85; R Montreal St Jo Divine 85-96; R Montreal St Jo Ev 96-99; P-in-c Burton from 99. *The Vicarage, Rangemore Street, Burton-on-Trent DE14 2ED* Tel (01283) 544054 E-mail paul@pafarthing.clara.co.uk

FARTHING, Ronald Edward. b 27. Oak Hill Th Coll. **d** 58 **p** 59. C Tollington Park St Anne *Lon* 58-61; C Tollington Park St Mark 58-61; V Clodock and Longtown w Craswell and Llanveyno *Heref* 61-67; R Langley *Cant* 67-72; V Bapchild w Tonge and Rodmersham 72-80; TV Widecombe, Leusden and Princetown etc *Ex* 80-84; P-in-c Riddlesworth w Gasthorpe and Knettishall *Nor* 84-87; P-in-c Garboldisham w Blo' Norton 84-87; P-in-c Brettenham w Rushford 84-87; R Garboldisham w Blo' Norton, Riddlesworth etc 88-92; rtd 92; Perm to Offic *Nor* from 92. *23 Home Close, Great Ellingham, Attleborough NR17 1HW* Tel (01953) 456750

FASS, Michael John. b 44. Trin Coll Cam MA75. Edin Dioc NSM Course 89. **d** 95 **p** 95. NSM Penicuik *Edin* 95-97; NSM W Linton 95-97; NSM Roslin (Rosslyn Chpl) from 97. *60 Braid Road, Edinburgh EH10 6AL* Tel 0131-447 8106 Fax 447 7367 E-mail fass@dial.pipex.com

FATHERS, Canon Derek Esmond. b 27. Magd Coll Ox MA50 DipEd52. St Aid Birkenhead DipTh56. **d** 56 **p** 57. Tutor St Aid Birkenhead 56-59; C W Kirby St Bridget *Ches* 59-63; V Thornton Hough 63-86; RD Wirral S 78-86; Hon Can Ches Cathl 82-92; C Woodchurch 86-89; Chapl Arrowe Park Hosp Wirral 86-92; rtd 92; Perm to Offic *Ches* from 92. *6 Ashton Drive, West Kirby, Wirral CH48 0RQ* Tel 0151-625 1181

FATHERS, Jeremy Mark. b 54. Crewe & Alsager Coll BEd78. WMMTC 93. **d** 96 **p** 97. NSM Baxterley w Hurley and Wood End and Merevale etc *Birm* 96-00; C Sheldon 00-03; Chapl N Warks NHS Trust 00-02; R Chelmsley Wood *Birm* from 03. *The Vicarage, Pike Drive, Birmingham B37 7US* Tel 0121-770 5155 or 770 1511 Fax 743 2033 E-mail j.fathers@virgin.net

FAULDS, John Parker. b 33. Edin Th Coll 55. **d** 57 **p** 58. C Edin St Dav *Edin* 57-58; C Edin St Jo 58-60; Chapl Dundee Hosps 60-63; Chapl Qu Coll Dundee 60-63; Dioc Supernumerary *Bre* 60-63; Lic to Offic *Birm* 65-66; P-in-c Aston Brook 66-69; V Handsworth St Pet 69-87; Perm to Offic 87-98; rtd 99. *Address withheld by request*

FAULKES, Edmund Marquis. See MARQUIS-FAULKES, Edmund

FAULKNER, Mrs Anne Elizabeth. b 38. **d** 00 **p** 01. NSM Aylesbury w Bierton and Hulcott *Ox* from 00; Chapl to Bp Buckingham from 02. *The Vicarage, St James's Way, Bierton, Aylesbury HP22 5ED* Tel (01296) 331090 Fax as telephone E-mail aefpcf@aol.com

FAULKNER, Brian Thomas. b 48. S Dios Minl Tr Scheme. **d** 84 **p** 85. C W Leigh *Portsm* 84-88; R Foulsham w Hindolveston and Guestwick *Nor* 88-93; P-in-c Erpingham w Calthorpe, Ingworth, Aldborough etc 93-94; R from 94. *The Rectory, School Road, Erpingham, Norwich NR11 7QX* Tel (01263) 768073 E-mail brian-faulkner@lineone.net

FAULKNER, Mrs Catherine Evelyn. b 43. Man Poly RHV82. Dioc OLM tr scheme 98. **d** 01 **p** 02. OLM Urmston *Man* from 01. *5 Barnfield, Urmston, Manchester M41 9EW* Tel 0161-748 3226 E-mail cath@northwood1.freeserve.co.uk

FAULKNER, David Ernest. b 43. Univ of Wales (Lamp) DipTh65. St Mich Coll Llan 65. **d** 66 **p** 67. C Aberystwyth St Mich *St D* 66-68; C Tenby and Gumfreston 68-69; C Burry Port and Pwll 69-73; R Jeffreyston w Reynalton and E Williamston 73-79; R Jeffreyston w Reynoldston and E Williamston etc 79-89; V Whitland w Cyffig and Henllan Amgoed etc 89-96; V Llawhaden w Bletherston and Llanycefn from 96. *The Vicarage, Rock Road, Llawhaden, Narberth SA67 8HL* Tel (01437) 541225

FAULKNER, Henry Odin. b 35. G&C Coll Cam BA56 MA59. St Jo Coll Nottm DipTh74. **d** 74 **p** 75. C Heigham H Trin *Nor* 74-76; C Heeley *Sheff* 76-80; TV Netherthorpe 80-84; Perm to Offic *St Alb* from 84; rtd 00. *69 Holywell Hill, St Albans AL1 1HF* Tel (01727) 854177 Mobile 07719-642479

FAULKNER, Mrs Margaret Evelyn. b 54. Goldsmiths' Coll Lon BEd77. EAMTC 98. **d** 01 **p** 02. C Grays Thurrock *Chelmsf* from 01. *48 Parker Road, Grays RM17 5YN* Tel (01375) 379309 E-mail mrgrtfaulkner@aol.com

FAULKNER, Peter Charles. b 37. Chich Th Coll 72. **d** 74 **p** 75. C Armley w New Wortley *Ripon* 74-76; C Tilehurst St Mich *Ox* 76-80; V Calcot 80-82; V Hagbourne 82-88; TV W Slough 88-95; TV Aylesbury w Bierton and Hulcott from 95. *The Vicarage, St James's Way, Bierton, Aylesbury HP22 5ED* Tel (01296) 423920 E-mail aefpcf@aol.com

FAULKNER, Peter Graham. b 47. Lon Univ CertEd69. Oak Hill Th Coll BA87. **d** 82 **p** 83. C Crofton *Portsm* 87-89; R Mid Marsh Gp *Linc* 89-98; V S Cave and Ellerker w Broomfleet *York* from 98. *The Vicarage, 10 Station Road, South Cave, Brough HU15 2AA* Tel (01430) 423693 E-mail peter@faulknerzp.karoo.co.uk

FAULKNER, Canon Roger Kearton. b 36. AKC62. **d** 63 **p** 64. C Oxton *Ches* 63-67; C Ellesmere Port 67-69; V Runcorn H Trin 69-73; TV E Runcorn w Halton 73-76; V Altrincham St Geo 76-90; Chapl Altrincham Gen Hosp 80-96; Hon Can Ches Cathl *Ches* 88-96; V Higher Bebington 90-96; rtd 96; Perm to Offic *Ches* 96-98. *58 Albermarle Road, Wallasey, Wirral CH44 6LX*

FAULKNER, Ms Susan Ann. b 70. Lanc Univ BA96. Ripon Coll Cuddesdon 97. **d** 99 **p** 00. C Scotswood *Newc* 99-03; P-in-c Byker St Silas from 03. *St Wilfrid's House, Trevelyan Drive, Newcastle upon Tyne NE5 4DA* Tel 07899-796895 (mobile) E-mail sue@faulkner20.fsnet.co.uk

FAULKS, David William. b 45. EMMTC 82. **d** 86 **p** 87. C Market Harborough *Leic* 86-88; C Wootton Bassett *Sarum* 88-90; R Clipston w Naseby and Haselbech w Kelmarsh *Pet* from 90. *The Rectory, 18 Church Lane, Clipston, Market Harborough LE16 9RW* Tel (01858) 525342 Fax as telephone E-mail david.faulks@btinternet.com

FAULL, The Very Revd Cecil Albert. b 30. TCD BA52 MA87. **d** 54 **p** 55. C Dublin Zion Ch *D & G* 54-57; C Dublin St Geo 57-59; Hon Clerical V Ch Ch Cathl Dublin 58-63; C Dun Laoghaire 59-63; I Portarlington w Cloneyhurke and Lea *M & K* 63-71; I Dublin St Geo and St Thos *D & G* 71-80; I Clondalkin w Rathcoole 81-91; Can Ch Ch Cathl Dublin 90-91; I Dunleckney w Nurney, Lorum and Kiltennel *C & O* 91-96; Dean Leighlin from 91; P-in-c Leighlin w Grange Sylvae, Shankill etc from 91. *136 Beech Park, Lucan, Co Dublin, Irish Republic* Tel (00353) (1) 628 0593

FAULL, The Very Revd Vivienne Frances. b 55. St Hilda's Coll Ox BA77 MA82 Clare Coll Cam MA90. St Jo Coll Nottm BA81 DPS82. **dss** 82 **d** 87 **p** 94. Mossley Hill St Matt and St Jas *Liv* 82-85; Chapl Clare Coll Cam 85-90; Chapl Glouc Cathl *Glouc* 90-94; Can Res Cov Cathl *Cov* 94-00; Vice-Provost 95-00; Provost Leic 00-02; Dean Leic from 02. *The Cathedral Centre, 21 St Martin's, Leicester LE1 5DE* Tel 0116-262 5294 Fax 262 5295 E-mail dean@leicester.anglican.org

FAULL, William Baines. b 29. FRCVS70 Lon Univ BSc51. NW Ord Course 77. **d** 79 **p** 80. NSM Willaston *Ches* 79-80; NSM Neston 80-82; P-in-c Harthill and Burwardsley 82-86; Perm to Offic 87-91; from 96; Sen Fell Liv Univ from 89; V Ashton Hayes *Ches* 91-96; Chapl Hospice of the Good Shepherd Backford from 99. *Tioman, Briardale Road, Willaston, Neston CH64 1TD* Tel 0151-327 4424

FAVELL, Brian Jeffrey. b 23. Cuddesdon Coll 64. **d** 66 **p** 67. C Rubery *Birm* 66-69; Lic to Offic 70-76; V Cwmtillery *Mon* 76-86; P-in-c Six Bells 77-86; RD Blaenau Gwent 83-86; V Cwmcarn 86-88; rtd 88; Perm to Offic *Worc* from 88. *3 Church Street, Fladbury, Pershore WR10 2QB* Tel (01386) 860585

FAWCETT, Canon Frederick William. TCD BA49 MA52. CITC 50. **d** 50 **p** 51. C Belfast St Aid *Conn* 50-52; C-in-c Draperstown *D & R* 52-59; I 59-60; I Cumber Upper w Learmount 60-87; Can Derry Cathl 86-99; I Camus-juxta-Mourne 87-99; rtd 99. *Springbank, 73 Moneysallin Road, Kilrea, Coleraine BT51 5SR* Tel (028) 2954 1744

FAWCETT, Canon Pamela Margaret. b 29. Univ Coll Lon BA51 DipEd75. EAMTC 83. **dss** 86 **d** 87 **p** 94. Stiffkey and Cockthorpe w Morston, Langham etc *Nor* 86-90; Hon C 87-90; Hon Asst Min Repps Deanery 91-92; Hon C Trunch 92-01; Asst Dir of Ords 93-99; Bp's Consultant for Women's Min 93-01; Hon Can Nor Cathl 94-01; Perm to Offic from 01. *Seekings, 47A High Street, Mundesley, Norwich NR11 8JL* Tel (01263) 721752

FAWCETT, Timothy John. b 44. K Coll Lon BD66 AKC67 PhD71. **d** 67 **p** 68. C Blackpool St Steph *Blackb* 67-70; Hon C St Marylebone All SS *Lon* 68-70; C Southgate St Mich 70-72; Sacr Dur Cathl *Dur* 72-75; V Wheatley Hill 75-77; V Torrisholme *Blackb* 79-84; V Thaxted *Chelmsf* 84-89; Perm to Offic *Nor* 89-94; NSM Holt Deanery from 94. *Dowitchers, 14 The Cornfield, Langham, Holt NR25 7DQ* Tel (01328) 830415

FAWNS, Lynne. b 56. Thames Valley Univ BA95. NTMTC 97. **d** 00 **p** 01. C Hillingdon All SS *Lon* from 00. *Glebe House, Royal Lane, Hillingdon UB8 3QR* Tel (01895) 256427 E-mail lynne.ffamily@tesco.net

FAYERS, Robert Stanley. b 48. DipFD SSC. St Steph Ho Ox 82. **d** 84 **p** 85. C Deptford St Paul *S'wark* 84-88; V Beckenham St Mich w St Aug *Roch* 88-00; V Brighton St Mich *Chich* from 00. *St Michael's Vicarage, 6 Montpelier Villas, Brighton BN1 3DH* Tel (01273) 727362 E-mail smb@supanet.com

FAYLE, David Charles Wilfred. b 51. Sarum & Wells Th Coll. **d** 83 **p** 84. C Parkstone St Pet w Branksea and St Osmund *Sarum* 83-87; TV Dorchester 87-96; P-in-c Taunton All SS *B & W* 96-97; V from 97. *All Saints' Vicarage, Roman Road, Taunton TA1 2DE* Tel (01823) 324730 E-mail dfayle@freeserve.co.uk

FAZZANI, Keith. b 47. Portsm Poly BSc70. Cant Sch of Min 93. **d** 96 **p** 97. NSM Appledore w Brookland, Fairfield, Brenzett etc *Cant* 96-01; Asst Chapl E Kent Hosps NHS Trust from 01. *Oakhouse Farm, Appledore, Ashford TN26 2BB* Tel (01233) 758322 E-mail kfazzani@btinternet.com

FEAK, Christopher Martin. b 52. Keele Univ BA75 Trent Poly DCG76. Trin Coll Bris DipHE94. **d** 94 **p** 95. C Handsworth St Mary *Birm* 94-97; P-in-c Perry Common 97-00; V from 00; AD Aston from 01. *St Martin's Vicarage, 148 Witton Lodge Road, Birmingham B23 5AP* Tel 0121-382 7666

FEARN, Anthony John. b 34. Lich Th Coll 58. **d** 61 **p** 62. C Redditch St Steph *Worc* 61-64; C Bladon w Woodstock *Ox* 64-66; V Ruscombe and Twyford 67-85; P-in-c Westmill w Gt Munden *St Alb* 85-87; Asst Dioc Stewardship Adv 85-87; Chr Giving Adv *Heref* 87-99; rtd 99. *49 Centurion Way, Credenhill, Hereford HR4 7FF* Tel (01432) 760060 Fax as telephone E-mail john_fearn@bigfoot.com

FEARN, Michael Wilfrid. b 47. MBIM MIHT Plymouth Poly 70. Sarum & Wells Th Coll DipTh94. **d** 94 **p** 95. C Blandford Forum and Langton Long *Sarum* 94-98; TV Wylye and Till Valley from 98. *The Vicarage, Chapel Lane, Shrewton, Salisbury SP3 4BX* Tel (01980) 620580

FEARNLEY, Jeffrey Malcolm. b 46. Newc Univ BSc69. St Jo Coll Nottm DCM92. **d** 92 **p** 93. C Bispham *Blackb* 92-95; C Bolton w Ireby and Uldale *Carl* 95-00; TV Binsey 00-02; C from 02. *The Vicarage, Ireby, Wigton CA7 1EX* Tel (01697) 371307

FEARNSIDE, Mary Ingrid. b 44. OLM course 98. **d** 98 **p** 99. OLM Shelton and Oxon *Lich* from 98; Chapl R Shrewsbury Hosps NHS Trust from 98. *23 Eastwood Road, Shrewsbury SY3 8YJ* Tel (01743) 353290 Pager 01743-261000 E-mail mary.fearnside@fsmail.net

FEARON, Mrs Doris Ethel Elizabeth. b 26. Gilmore Ho 66. **dss** 72 **d** 87. Lingfield *S'wark* 68-75; Farnborough *Roch* 75-77; Bitterne *Win* 78-86; rtd 86; Bexhill St Pet *Chich* 86-87; Hon Par Dn 87-89; Perm to Offic 89-95; New Zealand from 96; Hon Asst Dn One Tree Hill St Oswald from 99. *The Haven, 2/66 Moana Avenue, One Tree Hill, Auckland 6, New Zealand* Tel (0064) (9) 636 6147

FEATHERSTON, Margery. *See* GRANGE, Mrs Alice Margery

FEATHERSTONE, Andrew. b 53. St Chad's Coll Dur BA74 MA93. Sarum & Wells Th Coll 78. **d** 80 **p** 81. C Newc H Cross *Newc* 80-83; C Seaton Hirst 83-86; TV 86-87; R Crook *Dur* 87-99; V Stanley 87-99; AD Stanhope 94-99; V Stockton from 99. *61 Bishopton Road, Stockton-on-Tees TS18 4PD* Tel (01642) 617420 or tel and fax 611734 E-mail andrew.featherstone@durham.anglican.org

FEATHERSTONE, Gray. b 42. Stellenbosch Univ BA62 LLB64. Cuddesdon Coll 65. **d** 67 **p** 68. C Woodstock S Africa 67-70; Asst Master Waterford Sch Swaziland 70-72; P-in-c Maputo St Steph and St Lawr Mozambique 73-76; Miss to Seamen 73-80; V Upper Clapton St Matt *Lon* 80-83; V Stamford Hill St Thos 80-89; Chr Aid Area Sec (N & W Lon) from 89; Perm to Offic *Lon* 90-97. *137 Leslie Road, London N2 8BH* Tel (020) 8444 1975 *or* 7496 1690 E-mail gfeatherstone@christian-aid.org

FEATHERSTONE, John. b 32. Man Univ BA53 St Cath Soc Ox MTh59 Dur Univ DipEd66. Wycliffe Hall Ox 57. **d** 60 **p** 61. C Newland St Aug *York* 60-62; C Kidderminster St Jo and H Innocents *Worc* 62-65; Hd RE Co Gr Sch Pet 66-70; Hd RE Qu Anne Gr Sch York 70-85; Chapl Tangier *Eur* 86-87 and 90-93; Chapl Pau w Biarritz 87-88; C Mexborough *Sheff* 88-90; rtd 93; Perm to Offic *York* from 93. *39 Cambridge Avenue, Marton-in-Cleveland, Middlesbrough TS7 8EH* Tel (01642) 318181

FEATHERSTONE, Robert Leslie. b 54. LLCM74 Lon Univ CertEd75. Chich Th Coll 84. **d** 86 **p** 87. C Crayford *Roch* 86-89; V Belvedere St Aug 89-94; V Crowborough St Jo *Chich* 94-01; P-in-c New Brompton St Luke *Roch* from 01. *St Luke's Vicarage, Sidney Road, Gillingham ME7 1PA* Tel (01634) 853060 Mobile 07702-062296 E-mail frrobertf@hotmail.com

FEENEY, Damian Prescott Anthony. b 62. Grey Coll Dur BA83 PGCE84 ALCM81. Chich Th Coll BTh94. **d** 94 **p** 95. C Harrogate St Wilfrid *Ripon* 94-96; C Preston St Jo and St Geo *Blackb* 96-99; Bp's Miss P to Longsands 99-01; TR Ribbleton from 01. *The Rectory, 238 Ribbleton Avenue, Ribbleton, Preston PR2 6QP* Tel (01772) 791747 Fax as telephone E-mail frdfeeney@aol.com

FEHRENBACH, Donald Joseph. b 17. Selw Coll Cam BA49 MA53. Qu Coll Birm 49. **d** 51 **p** 52. C Beverley Minster *York* 51-54; Man Sarum Cathl *Sarum* 54-59; Man Windsor 59-65; V Sandford-on-Thames *Ox* 65-84; rtd 84; Perm to Offic *Ox* from 84. *2 Walbury, Bracknell RG12 9JB* Tel (01344) 640062

FEIST, Canon Nicholas James. b 45. Solicitor 70. St Jo Coll Nottm LTh76. **d** 76 **p** 77. C Didsbury St Jas *Man* 76-80; TV Didsbury St Jas and Em 80; V Friarmere 80-88; R Middleton 88-94; TR Middleton w Thornham from 94; Hon Can Man Cathl from 98;

AD Heywood and Middleton from 99. *St Leonard's Rectory, Mellalieu Street, Middleton, Manchester M24 3DN* Tel 0161-643 2693

FEIT, Michael John. b 24. FICE68 FIStructE68. S'wark Ord Course. **d** 69 **p** 71. C Feltham *Lon* 69-76; C Ashford St Matt 76-78; C Hykeham *Linc* 78-81; V Cranwell 81-85; R Leasingham 81-85; R Bishop Norton, Wadingham and Snitterby 85-90; rtd 90; Hon C Surrey Epiphany Canada from 91. *14717-109A Avenue, Surrey BC, Canada, V3R 1Y7* Tel (001) (604) 582 5889

FELCE, Brian George. b 30. Jes Coll Ox BA54 MA57. Oak Hill Th Coll. **d** 58 **p** 59. C E Twickenham St Steph *Lon* 58-60; C Ramsgate St Luke *Cant* 60-64; R Bedingfield w Southolt *St E* 64-73; V Preston All SS *Blackb* 73-86; rtd 86. *11 St Barnabas Road, Sutton SM1 4NL* Tel (020) 8642 7885

FELIX, David Rhys. b 55. Univ of Wales (Cardiff) LLB76 Solicitor 81. Ripon Coll Cuddesdon 83. **d** 86 **p** 87. C Bromborough *Ches* 86-89; V Grange St Andr 89-99; Chapl Halton Gen Hosp NHS Trust 95-99; P-in-c Runcorn H Trin *Ches* 96-99; RD Frodsham 98-99; V Daresbury from 99; Sen Ind Chapl from 00. *All Saints' Vicarage, Daresbury Lane, Daresbury, Warrington WA4 4AE* Tel (01925) 740348 Fax 740799 E-mail david.felix@btinternet.com

FELIX, Donald Cameron. b 24. St Aid Birkenhead 64. **d** 65 **p** 66. C Walsall *Lich* 65-68; V Pype Hayes *Birm* 68-73; V Burslem St Paul *Lich* 73-76; V Bloxwich 76-79; P-in-c Seighford, Derrington and Cresswell 79-81; V 81-86; V Hanbury w Newborough 86-94; P-in-c 94-97; P-in-c Hanbury w Newborough and Rangemore 97-98; rtd 94; Perm to Offic *Lich* from 00. *12 Liberty Park, Stafford ST17 9QF*

FELL, Canon Alan William. b 46. Ball Coll Ox BA69 Leeds Univ DipTh70. Coll of Resurr Mirfield 68. **d** 71 **p** 72. C Woodchurch *Ches* 71-74; C Man Clayton St Cross w St Paul *Man* 74-75; C Prestwich St Marg 75-77; V Hyde St Thos *Ches* 77-80; R Tattenhall and Handley 80-86; V Sedbergh, Cautley and Garsdale *Brad* from 86; Hon C Firbank, Howgill and Killington from 86; Hon Can Bradf Cathl from 96; RD Ewecross from 00. *The Vicarage, Loftus Hill, Sedbergh LA10 5SQ* Tel (01539) 620283

FELL, Stephen. b 18. St Jo Coll Dur LTh41 BA42. Oak Hill Th Coll 38. **d** 42 **p** 43. C Preston Em *Blackb* 42-45; C Tottenham All Hallows *Lon* 45-49; C Luton St Mary *St Alb* 49-52; R Toddington 52-58; R Castleford All SS *Wakef* 58-83; rtd 83; Perm to Offic *Ripon* from 83. *255 Lower Mickletown, Methley, Leeds LS26 9AN* Tel (01977) 515530

FELLOWS, Grant. b 56. K Coll Lon BD77 AKC77. Coll of Resurr Mirfield 79. **d** 80 **p** 81. C Addington *Cant* 80-84; C S Gillingham *Roch* 84-86; V Heath and Reach *St Alb* 86-94; V Radlett from 94; RD Aldenham from 98. *The Vicarage, Church Field, Christchurch Crescent, Radlett WD7 8EE* Tel (01923) 856606 E-mail grant@gfellows.f9.co.uk

FELLOWS, Ian Christopher. b 73. Univ Coll Ox BA94 MA98 St Jo Coll Dur BA99. Cranmer Hall Dur 96. **d** 99 **p** 00. C Bucknall and Bagnall *Lich* 99-03; TV Broughton *Man* from 03. *St John's Vicarage, 237 Great Clowes Street, Salford M7 2DZ* Tel 0161-792 9161 E-mail ianfellows@yahoo.co.uk

FELLOWS, John Lambert. b 35. LTCL67 SS Mark & Jo Coll Chelsea CertEd58. Portsm Dioc Tr Course 86. **d** 88. NSM Portsea St Cuth *Portsm* 88-94; NSM Farlington from 94. *7 Court Lane, Portsmouth PO6 2LG* Tel (023) 9237 7270

FELLOWS, John Michael. b 46. Oriel Coll Ox MA77. Coll of Resurr Mirfield 74. **d** 77 **p** 78. C Kings Heath *Birm* 77-80; TV E Ham w Upton Park St Alb *Chelmsf* 80-85; P-in-c Wormingford 85-90; P-in-c Mt Bures 85-90; P-in-c Lt Horkesley 85-90; V Wormingford, Mt Bures and Lt Horkesley 90; R Compton w Shackleford and Peper Harow *Guildf* from 90; Chapl Prior's Field Sch from 90. *The Rectory, The Street, Compton, Guildford GU3 1ED* Tel (01483) 810328

FELLOWS, Peter William. b 48. CertEd70 DipEd79. Chich Th Coll 86. **d** 88 **p** 89. C Westmr St Steph w St Jo *Lon* 88-93; R Deptford St Paul *S'wark* from 93. *The Rectory, Mary Anne Gardens, London SE8 3DP* Tel (020) 8692 0989

FELLOWS, Mrs Susan Elizabeth. b 46. ATCL65 LTCL66 GTCL67. St Alb and Ox Min Course 99. **d** 02. NSM Weston Turville *Ox* from 02. *65 Craigwell Avenue, Aylesbury HP21 7AG* Tel (01296) 424982 Mobile 07712-226999 E-mail susan@sefellows.freeserve.co.uk

FELTHAM, Keith. b 40. Lon Univ DipTh66. **d** 75 **p** 76. In Bapt Ch 66-75; C Plympton St Mary *Ex* 75-79; TV Northam w Westward Ho! and Appledore 79-82; TR Lynton, Brendon, Countisbury, Lynmouth etc 82-85; P-in-c Bickleigh (Plymouth) 85-86; TR 86-91; Chapl R Bournemouth Gen Hosp 91-95; P-in-c Whimple, Talaton and Clyst St Lawr *Ex* 95-00; rtd 00; Perm to Offic *Ex* from 00. *6 The Heathers, Woolwell, Plymouth PL6 7QT* Tel (01792) 774447

FELTHAM-WHITE, Antony James. b 67. Ox Brookes Univ BSc92 Reading Univ MA94. Wycliffe Hall Ox 99. **d** 01 **p** 02. C Bernwode *Ox* from 01. *Westfields, Church Lane, Ludgershall, Aylesbury HP18 9NU* Tel (01844) 239335 Mobile 07720-527405 E-mail antony@revelation-racing.org.uk

FENBY, Mrs Sarah Louise. b 66. Kent Univ BA88 Lon Bible Coll BA96. Trin Coll Bris MA00. **d** 00 **p** 01. C Stoke Gifford *Bris* from 00. *56 Simmonds View, Stoke Gifford, Bristol BS34 8HL* Tel (01454) 776662

FENN, Norman Alexander. b 20. Kelham Th Coll 37. **d** 43 **p** 44. C Tunstall Ch Ch *Lich* 43-47; C Leek St Edw 47-51; V Tilstock 51-55; V Milton 55-61; V Ellesmere 61-85; V Welsh Frankton 62-85; RD Ellesmere 70-85; rtd 85; Perm to Offic *Lich* from 85. *1 Larkhill Road, Oswestry SY11 4AW* Tel (01691) 659411

FENN, Roy William Dearnley. b 33. FRHistS70 FCP86 FSA88 Jes Coll Ox BA54 MA59 BD68. St Mich Coll Llan 54. **d** 56 **p** 57. C Swansea St Mary and H Trin *S & B* 57-59; C Cardiff St Jo *Llan* 59-60; C Coity w Nolton 60-63; V Glascombe w Rhulen and Gregrina *S & B* 63-68; V Glascwm and Rhulen 68-74; P-in-c Letton w Staunton, Byford, Mansel Gamage etc *Heref* 75-79; Perm to Offic *S & B* 80-85; Perm to Offic *Heref* 85-95; rtd 98. *9 Victoria Road, Kington HR5 3BX* Tel (01544) 230018

FENNELL, Canon Alfred Charles Dennis. b 15. Bp's Coll Calcutta 35. **d** 38 **p** 39. India 38-48; C Kensington St Helen w H Trin *Lon* 48-50; Min Queensbury All SS 50-54; V 54-62; Prec Birm Cathl *Birm* 62-65; V Yardley St Cypr Hay Mill 65-80; Hon Can Birm Cathl 78-80; rtd 80; Perm to Offic *Birm* and *Worc* from 80. *6 Merrievale Court, Barnards Green Road, Malvern WR14 3NE* Tel (01684) 560613

FENNELL, Anthony Frederick Rivers. b 26. Pemb Coll Cam BA50 MA55 York Univ BPhil76. Ab Dioc Tr Course 90. **d** 90 **p** 91. NSM Braemar *Ab* 90-96; NSM Ballater 90-96; NSM Aboyne 90-96; rtd 96. *19 Craigendarroch Circle, Ballater AB35 5ZA* Tel (01339) 755048

FENNEMORE, Canon Nicholas Paul. b 53. Wycliffe Hall Ox 76. **d** 79 **p** 80. C N Mymms *St Alb* 79-82; C Chipping Barnet w Arkley 82-83; TV Preston w Sutton Poyntz and Osmington w Poxwell *Sarum* 84-86; Chapl St Helier Hosp Carshalton 86-90; Chapl Jo Radcliffe Hosp Ox 90-94; Chapl Ox Radcliffe Hosp NHS Trust 94-96; Sen Chapl Ox Radcliffe Hosps NHS Trust from 96; Hon Can Ch Ch *Ox* from 03. *John Radcliffe Hospital, Headington, Oxford OX3 9DU* Tel (01865) 741166 or 221732

FENNING, John Edward. b 32. CITC 86. **d** 88 **p** 89. NSM Douglas Union w Frankfield *C, C & R* 88-89; Chapl Ashton Sch Cork 88-96; NSM Moviddy Union *C, C & R* 89-99; rtd 99. *1 Kingston College, Mitchelstown, Co Cork, Irish Republic* Tel (00353) (25) 85587 E-mail revdjohne@eircom.net

FENSOME, Canon Anthony David. b 49. DipYL74 Open Univ BA89. Sarum & Wells Th Coll 82. **d** 84 **p** 85. C Gtr Corsham *Bris* 84-88; P-in-c Lyddington w Wanborough 88-91; P-in-c Bishopstone w Hinton Parva 88-91; V Lyddington and Wanborough and Bishopstone etc 91-93; V Chippenham St Pet from 93; RD Chippenham 94-99; Hon Can Bris Cathl from 98. *St Peter's Vicarage, Lords Mead, Chippenham SN14 0LL* Tel (01249) 654835 Fax as telephone E-mail tonyfens@aol.com

FENTIMAN, David Frank. b 40. RIBA74 Poly Cen Lon DipArch72 Roehampton Inst PGCE94. S Dios Minl Tr Scheme 90. **d** 93 **p** 94. NSM Hastings St Clem and All SS *Chich* 93-98; P-in-c Blacklands Hastings Ch Ch and St Andr 98-01; V from 01. *4 Barnfield Close, Hastings TN34 1TS* Tel (01424) 421821

FENTON, Barry Dominic. b 59. Leeds Univ BA85. Coll of Resurr Mirfield 85. **d** 87 **p** 88. C Leigh Park *Portsm* 87-90; Chapl and Prec Portsm Cathl 90-95; Min Can and Prec Westmr Abbey 95-02; Chapl N Middx Hosp NHS Trust from 02. *North Middlesex Hospital, Sterling Way, London N18 1QX* Tel (020) 8887 2000

FENTON, Christopher Miles Tempest. b 28. Qu Coll Cam BA50 LLB51 MA53 LLM. Ridley Hall Cam 52. **d** 54 **p** 55. C Welling *Roch* 54-57; Chapl Malsis Prep Sch Keighley 57-63; C Hove Bp Hannington Memorial Ch *Chich* 63-65; V Ramsgate Ch Ch *Cant* 65-71; Hd Dept of Gp Studies Westmr Past Foundn 71-83; P-in-c Mottingham St Andr *S'wark* 71-73; Sen Tutor Cambs Consultancy in Counselling 73-85; Co-ord of Tr St Alb Past Foundn 80-88; Dir St Anne's Trust for Psychotherapy Ledbury from 85; Perm to Offic *Heref* from 85; rtd 93. *The Leys, Aston, Kingsland, Leominster HR6 9PU* Tel (01568) 708632

FENTON, Geoffrey. b 54. St Jo Coll Ox BA75 MSc76. WEMTC 98. **d** 01. NSM Wedmore w Theale and Blackford *B & W* from 01. *Grove Cottage, Redmans Hill, Blackford, Wedmore BS28 4NG* Tel (01934) 710224 E-mail geoffrey.fenton@ukonline.co.uk

FENTON, Heather. b 48. Trin Coll Bris. **d** 87 **p** 97. C Corwen and Llangar *St As* 87-89; C Corwen and Llangar w Gwyddelwern and Llawrybetws 89-98; Dioc Rural Min Co-ord *St As* 98; Perm to Offic from 98; Asst P Penllyn Deanery from 01. *Coleg y Groes, The College, Corwen LL21 0AU* Tel (01490) 412169

FENTON, Ian Christopher Stuart. b 40. AKC62. **d** 63 **p** 64. C Banstead *Guildf* 63-67; V N Holmwood 67-84; RD Dorking 80-84; V Witley 84-00; Perm to Offic *Ex* from 00. *Sweet Coppin Cottage, Lemonford Lane, Bickington, Newton Abbot TQ12 6JR* Tel (01626) 821880

FENTON, Canon John Charles. b 21. Qu Coll Ox BA43 MA47 BD53 Lambeth DD01. Linc Th Coll 43. **d** 44 **p** 45. C Hindley All

SS *Liv* 44-47; Chapl Linc Th Coll 47-51; Sub-Warden 51-54; Prin Lich Th Coll 58-65; V Wentworth *Sheff* 54-58; Prin St Chad's Coll Dur 65-78; Can Res Ch Ch *Ox* 78-91; Hon Can 91-92; rtd 91. *8 Rowland Close, Oxford OX2 8PW* Tel (01865) 554099

FENTON, Keith John. b 54. Coll of Resurr Mirfield 01. **d** 03. C Heyhouses on Sea *Blackb* from 03. *2 Vicarage Close, Lytham St Annes FY8 3BQ* Tel 07773-630784 (mobile)

FENTON, Michael John. b 42. Linc Th Coll 67. **d** 69 **p** 70. C Guiseley *Bradf* 69-72; C Heswall *Ches* 72-75; TV Birkenhead Priory 75-81; V Alvanley 81-91; Chapl Crossley Hosp Cheshire 82-91; V Holbrook and Lt Eaton *Derby* 91-03; V Allenton and Shelton Lock from 03. *St Edmund's Vicarage, Sinfin Avenue, Allenton, Derby DE24 9JA* Tel (01332) 701194

FENTON, Miss Penelope Ann. b 41. Leic Univ BSc64. Cant Sch of Min 92. **d** 95 **p** 96. NSM Eastling w Ospringe and Stalisfield w Otterden *Cant* 95-00; P-in-c from 00; Asst to Bp's Officer for NSM from 99. *9 Brogdale Road, Faversham ME13 8SX* Tel (01795) 536366 E-mail penny.fenton@lineone.net

FENTON, Vincent Thompson. b 52. 94. **d** 96 **p** 97. C Heworth St Mary *Dur* 96-99; C-in-c Bishop Auckland Woodhouse Close CD from 99; Chapl S Durham Healthcare NHS Trust from 01. *18 Watling Road, Bishop Auckland DL14 6RP* Tel (01388) 604086 E-mail vincent.fenton@durham.anglican.org

FENTON, Canon Wallace. b 32. TCD. **d** 64 **p** 65. C Glenavy *Conn* 64-67; I Tullaniskin w Clonoe *Arm* 67-87; Bp's C Sallaghy *Clogh* 87-96; Warden of Readers 91-96; Preb Clogh Cathl 95-96; I Kilwarlin Upper w Kilwarlin Lower *D & D* 96-99; rtd 99. *2 Beech Green, Doagh, Ballyclare BT39 0QB* Tel (028) 9334 0576

FENWICK, Canon Jeffrey Robert. b 30. Pemb Coll Cam BA53 MA57. Linc Th Coll 53. **d** 55 **p** 56. C Upholland *Liv* 55-58; S Rhodesia 58-64; Area Sec USPG *Ox* 64-65; Rhodesia 65-78; Adn Charter 73-75; Dean Bulawayo 75-78; Adn Bulawayo 75-78; Can Res Worc Cathl *Worc* 78-89; R Guernsey St Peter Port *Win* 89-95; Dean Guernsey 89-95; Hon Can Win Cathl 89-95; Pres Guernsey Miss to Seamen 89-95; rtd 95; Zimbabwe from 95. *4 Moffat Avenue, Hillside, Bulawayo, Zimbabwe* Tel (00263) (9) 286240 E-mail pembroke@mweb.co.zw

FENWICK, John Robert Kipling. b 51. Van Mildert Coll Dur BSc72 Nottm Univ BA74 MTh78 K Coll Lon PhD85 Lambeth STh84. St Jo Coll Nottm 72. **d** 77 **p** 78. C Dalton-in-Furness *Carl* 77-80; Lect Trin Coll Bris 80-88; Chapl 80-87; Abp Cant's Asst Sec for Ecum Affairs 88-92; NSM Purley Ch Ch *S'wark* 88-92; Asst ChStJ from 89; R Chorley St Laur *Blackb* 92-01; Perm to Offic *Carl* from 02. *16 Windsor Crescent, Ulverston LA12 9NP* Tel (01229) 584997 E-mail phoenix51@tiscali.co.uk

FENWICK, Canon Malcolm Frank. b 38. Cranmer Hall Dur 62. **d** 65 **p** 66. C Tynemouth Cullercoats St Paul *Newc* 65-68; C Bywell 68-73; V Alnmouth 73-75; CF (TAVR) 75-83; V Lesbury w Alnmouth *Newc* 75-80; V Delaval 80-91; RD Bedlington 83-88; V Riding Mill 91-01; P-in-c Whittonstall 91-01; Chapl Shepherd's Dene Retreat Ho from 91; RD Corbridge 93-99; P-in-c Slaley 97-99; P-in-c Healey 99-01; Hon Can Newc Cathl 97-01; rtd 01; Perm to Offic *Newc* from 01. *21 Welburn Close, Ovingham, Prudhoe NE42 6BD* Tel (01661) 835565

FENWICK, The Very Revd Richard David. b 43. FLCM68 FTCL76 Univ of Wales (Lamp) BA66 MA86 TCD MusB79 MA92 Univ of Wales (Lamp) PhD95. Ridley Hall Cam 66. **d** 68 **p** 69. C Skewen *Llan* 68-72; C Penarth w Lavernock 72-74; PV, Succ and Sacr Roch Cathl *Roch* 74-78; Min Can St Paul's Cathl *Lon* 78-79; Min Can and Succ 79-83; Warden Coll Min Cans 81-83; PV Westmr Abbey 83-90; V Ruislip St Martin *Lon* 83-90; Can Res and Prec Guildf Cathl *Guildf* 90-97; Sub-Dean 96-97; Dean Mon from 97; V Newport St Woolos from 97; Warden Guild of Ch Musicians from 98; OStJ from 01. *The Deanery, Stow Hill, Newport NP20 4ED* Tel (01633) 263338 Fax as telephone

FEREDAY, Adrian Paul. b 57. Huddersfield Poly CQSW88 DipSW88. Coll of Resurr Mirfield 92. **d** 94 **p** 95. C Gleadless *Sheff* 94-96; TV Aston cum Aughton w Swallownest, Todwick etc 96-01; R Firbeck w Letwell from 01; V Woodsetts from 01. *The Rectory, 44A Barkers Hades Road, Letwell, Worksop S81 8DF* Tel (01909) 730346 E-mail adie@globalnet.co.uk

FEREDAY, Harold James Rodney. b 46. Sheff Univ CEIR76. St Jo Coll Nottm 87. **d** 89 **p** 90. C Rastrick St Matt *Wakef* 89-92; V Siddal 92-99; Dir Chr Care from 99; rtd 01; Perm to Offic *Wakef* and *York* from 01. *311 Filey Road, Scarborough YO11 3AF*

FERGUS, David. b 52. Imp Coll Lon BSc74. St Jo Coll Nottm 00. **d** 02 **p** 03. C Ilkeston St Mary *Derby* from 02. *1 Sparrow Close, Ilkeston DE7 4PW* Tel 0115-930 1978 E-mail fergii95@aol.com

FERGUSON, Aean Michael O'Shaun. b 39. CITC 87. **d** 90 **p** 91. NSM Kilmallock w Kilfynn, Kilfinane, Knockaney etc *L & K* 90; NSM Killaloe w Stradbally 90-94; NSM Adare w Kilmallock w Kilpeacon, Croom etc 94-97; C Killala w Dunfeeny, Crossmolina, Kilmoremoy etc *T, K & A* 97-00; I 00; I Skreen w Kilmacshalgan and Dromard from 00. *The Rectory, Skreen, Co Sligo, Irish Republic* Tel (00353) (71) 916 6941 Mobile 87-812 1020 Fax (71) 916 6989

FERGUSON, Alastair Stuart. b 45. Lon Univ MB, BS69 Ball Coll Ox BA78 MA82 LRCP69 MRCS69. St Steph Ho Ox 80. **d** 82 **p** 83. NSM Dengie w Asheldham *Chelmsf* 82-86; NSM Mayland 86-89; NSM Steeple 86-89; Perm to Offic 89-91; R Mvurwi St Andr Zimbabwe 91-00; V Lastingham w Appleton-le-Moors, Rosedale etc *York* from 00. *The Vicarage, Lastingham, York YO62 6TN* Tel (01751) 417344 Mobile 07967-588776 E-mail vicarage@lastinghamchurch.org.uk

FERGUSON, Anthony David Norman. b 51. Wycliffe Hall Ox 75. **d** 78 **p** 79. C Tipton St Matt *Lich* 78-79; USA from 79; Chapl SAMS 79-80; R Marion St Jo 80-84; P-in-c Charlotte St Marg 84-89; R 89-93; R Jacksonville St Pet from 93. *5042 Timuquana Road, Jacksonville, FL 32210, USA* Tel (001) (904) 778 1436 Fax 778 1437 E-mail adnfs51@hotmail.com

FERGUSON, Edith Constance May (Joy). b 37. Ch of Ireland Tr Coll DipEd60. CITC 99. **d** 02. Lic to Offic *C, C & R* from 02. *Telkador, Kinure, Oysterhaven, Co Cork, Irish Republic* Tel (00353) (21) 770663 Mobile 86-350 3138

FERGUSON, Canon Ian John. b 51. Aber Univ BD77. Trin Coll Bris 77. **d** 78 **p** 79. C Foord St Jo *Cant* 78-82; C Bieldside *Ab* 82-86; Dioc Youth Chapl 82-86; P-in-c Westhill 86-96; R from 96; Can St Andr Cathl from 01. *1 Westwood Drive, Westhill, Skeene AB32 6WW* Tel (01224) 740007

FERGUSON, John Aitken. b 40. Glas Univ BSc64 Strathclyde Univ PhD74 CEng MICE ARCST64. Linc Th Coll 79. **d** 81 **p** 82. C Morpeth *Newc* 81-85; V Whittingham and Edlingham w Bolton Chapel 85-96; rtd 00. *Cold Harbour Cottage, Cold Harbour, Berwick-upon-Tweed TD15 2TQ*

FERGUSON, John Richard Preston. b 34. CITC 63. **d** 65 **p** 66. C Dundela St Mark *D & D* 65-70; I Annahilt 70-76; I Belfast St Brendan 76-94; rtd 94. *49 Kinedale Park, Ballynahinch BT24 8YS* Tel (028) 9756 2599

FERGUSON, Mrs Kathleen. b 46. LMH Ox BA68 MA72 ALA76. St As Minl Tr Course 86. **d** 88 **p** 97. NSM Llanidloes w Llangurig *Ban* 88-01; P-in-c Llandinam w Trefeglwys w Penstrowed 01-02; V from 02; RD Arwystli from 02. *The Vicarage, Llandinam SY17 5BS* Tel (01686) 688341 Fax as telephone E-mail kathy.ferguson@ntlworld.com

FERGUSON (née BOIVIN), Michelle Dorothy Marie. b 58. Ottawa Univ BA78. Cranmer Hall Dur CTM93. **d** 95 **p** 96. NSM Gt Aycliffe *Dur* 95-97; Chapl Asst HM Pris Holme Ho 97-98; NSM Heighington *Dur* from 99. *4 Highside Road, Heighington Village, Newton Aycliffe DL5 6PG* Tel (01325) 320860

FERGUSON, The Ven Paul John. b 55. New Coll Ox BA76 MA80 K Coll Cam BA88 MA88 FRCO75. Westcott Ho Cam 82. **d** 85 **p** 86. C Ches St Mary *Ches* 85-88; Sacr and Chapl Westmr Abbey 88-92; Prec 92-95; Can Res and Prec York Minster *York* 95-01; Adn Cleveland from 01; Can and Preb York Minster from 01. *2 Langbaurgh Road, Hutton Rudby, Yarm TS15 0HL* Tel (01642) 706095 Fax 706097 E-mail ppmja@btinternet.com

FERGUSON, Richard Archie. b 39. Dur Univ BA62. Linc Th Coll 62. **d** 64 **p** 65. C Stretford St Matt *Man* 64-68; Bp's Dom Chapl *Dur* 68-69; C Newc St Geo *Newc* 69-71; V Glodwick *Man* 71-77; V Tynemouth Ch Ch *Newc* 77-82; P-in-c Tynemouth St Aug 82-87; V Tynemouth Ch Ch w H Trin 82-87; TR N Shields 87-90; TR Upton cum Chalvey *Ox* 90-95; V Kirkwhelpington, Kirkharle, Kirkheaton and Cambo *Newc* from 95; AD Morpeth from 95. *The Vicarage, Kirkwhelpington, Newcastle upon Tyne NE19 2RT* Tel (01830) 540260

FERGUSON, Robert Garnett Allen. b 48. Leeds Univ LLB70 Clare Coll Cam. Cuddesdon Coll 71. **d** 73 **p** 74. C Wakef Cathl *Wakef* 73-76; V Lupset 76-83; Chapl Cheltenham Coll 83-87; Sen Chapl Win Coll from 87. *Winchester College, Winchester SO23 9NA* Tel (01962) 884056 or 840592

FERGUSON, Robin Sinclair. b 31. Worc Coll Ox BA53 MA57 Lon Univ CertEd63. ALCD55 Wycliffe Coll Toronto 55. **d** 57 **p** 58. C Brompton H Trin *Lon* 57-60; C Brixton St Matt *S'wark* 60-63; Hon C Framlingham w Saxtead *St E* 63-65; Hon C Haverhill 65-67; Chapl St Mary's Sch Richmond 67-75; C Richmond St Mary *S'wark* 68-76; P-in-c Shilling Okeford *Sarum* 76-87; Chapl Croft Ho Sch Shillingstone 76-87; R Milton Abbas, Hilton w Cheselbourne etc *Sarum* 87-96; rtd 96; Perm to Offic *Sarum* from 98. *11 Stowell Crescent, Wareham BH20 4PT* Tel (01929) 551340

FERGUSON, Ronald Leslie. b 36. Open Univ BA86 BA89 Newc Poly CertFT90. Chich Th Coll 65. **d** 68 **p** 69. C Toxteth Park St Marg *Liv* 68-72; C Oakham w Hambleton and Egleton *Pet* 72-74; Asst Chapl The Dorothy Kerin Trust Burrswood 74-76; V Castleside *Dur* 76-96; C Washington 96-99; Chapl Gateshead Healthcare NHS Trust 96-98; Chapl Gateshead Health NHS Trust from 98; P-in-c Eighton Banks *Dur* from 99. *St Thomas's Vicarage, 8 Norwood Court, Gateshead NE9 7XF* Tel 0191-487 6927 or 416 2895

FERGUSON, Wallace Raymond. b 47. Qu Coll Birm BTheol CITC 76. **d** 78 **p** 79. C Lurgan Ch the Redeemer *D & D* 78-80; I Newtownards w Movilla Abbey 80-84; I Mullabrack w Markethill and Kilcluney *Arm* 84-00; Hon V Choral Arm Cathl from 86; Dioc Chapl to Rtd Clergy from 92; I Carnteel and Crilly from 00. *St James's Rectory, 22 Carnteel Road, Aughnacloy BT69 6DU* Tel (028) 8555 7682

FERGUSON-STUART, Hamish. b 51. Open Univ BA92 RGN. OLM course 97. **d** 99 **p** 00. OLM Burton St Chad *Lich* from 99. *210 Derby Road, Burton-on-Trent DE14 1RN* Tel (01283) 510447

FERGUSSON, Miss Catherine Margaret. b 28. MCIPD Birm Univ CertSS50. Linc Th Coll 77. **dss** 79 **d** 87 **p** 94. Watford St Pet *St Alb* 79-82; Prestwood *Ox* 82-86; Gt Horwood 86-87; Par Dn 87-89; Dir Cottesloe Chr Tr Progr 86-89; rtd 89; Perm to Offic *Sarum* from 89. *Checkmate, Middle Ground, Fovant, Salisbury SP3 5LP* Tel (01722) 720314

FERMER, Michael Thorpe. b 30. Lon Univ BSc52 ARCS52 St Cath Soc Ox BA54. Wycliffe Hall Ox 52. **d** 54 **p** 55. C Upper Holloway All SS *Lon* 54-57; C Plymouth St Andr *Ex* 57-59; V Tamerton Foliot 59-63; Asst Chapl United Sheff Hosps 63-64; Chapl 64-66; Lic to Offic *Sheff* 66-73; V Holmesfield *Derby* 73-79; TR Old Brampton and Loundsley Green 79-83; V Brightside St Thos and St Marg *Sheff* 83; V Brightside w Wincobank 83-89; V Loscoe *Derby* 89-94; rtd 94; Perm to Offic *Derby* from 94. *123 Bacons Lane, Chesterfield S40 2TN* Tel (01246) 555793

FERMER, Richard Malcolm. b 71. St Pet Coll Ox BA94 K Coll Lon MA95 PhD02 Surrey Univ PGCE96. Coll of Resurr Mirfield 00. **d** 02 **p** 03. C Palmers Green St Jo *Lon* from 02. *6 Park Avenue, London N13 5PF*

FERN, John. b 36. Nottm Univ BA57 DipRE64 MA88. Coll of Resurr Mirfield 57. **d** 59 **p** 60. C Carlton *S'wark* 59-61; C Hucknall Torkard 61-68; V Rainworth 68-97; rtd 97. *17 Wharfdale Gardens, Mansfield NG18 3GZ* Tel (01623) 420165

FERNANDO, Percy Sriyananda. b 49. Dundee Coll Dip Community Educn 81. Univ And Dioc Tr Course 85. **d** 88 **p** 89. NSM Blairgowrie *St And* from 88; NSM Coupar Angus from 89; NSM Alyth from 89. *Gowrie Cottage, Perth Road, Blairgowrie PH10 6QB*

FERNELEY, Alastair John. b 69. Roehampton Inst BA93 K Coll Lon MA94 Birm Univ MPhil98 St Jo Coll Dur MA02. Cranmer Hall Dur 00. **d** 02 **p** 03. C Skipton Ch Ch *Bradf* from 02. *61 Roughaw Road, Skipton BD23 2QA* Tel (01756) 798927

FERNS, Stephen Antony Dunbar. b 61. St Chad's Coll Dur BA84 MA94. Ripon Coll Cuddesdon BA87 MA91. **d** 88 **p** 89. C Billingham St Cuth *Dur* 88-90; Chapl Dur Univ 91; Chapl Van Mildert and Trevelyan Colls Dur 91-95; V Norton St Mary 95-97; Bp's Dom Chapl *Blackb* 97-01; Voc Officer and Selection Sec Min Division from 01. *Ministry Division, Church House, Great Smith Street, London SW1P 3NZ* Tel (020) 7898 1399 Fax 7898 1421 E-mail stephen.ferns@c-of-e.org.uk

FERNS, Archdeacon of. *See* MOONEY, The Ven Paul Gerard

FERNS, Dean of. *See* FORREST, The Very Revd Leslie David Arthur

FERNYHOUGH, Timothy John Edward. b 60. Leeds Univ BA81. Linc Th Coll 81. **d** 83 **p** 84. C Daventry *Pet* 83-86; Chapl Tonbridge Sch 86-92; Chapl Dur Sch 92-02; Hd RS and Asst Chapl Radley Coll from 02. *Radley College, Radley, Abingdon OX14 2HR* Tel (01235) 543000 Fax 543106

FERRIDAY, Donald Martin. b 30. Univ of Wales (Lamp) BA55. Qu Coll Birm 55. **d** 57 **p** 58. C Stockport St Sav *Ches* 57-59; C Heswall 59-64; V Cheadle Hulme All SS 64-72; V Ches 72-76; TR Ches Team 76-77; R W Kirby St Bridget 77-98; rtd 98; Perm to Offic *Ches* from 98. *9 Bodnant Road, Llandudno LL30 1LH* Tel (01492) 872374

FERRIER, Malcolm. b 38. Brasted Th Coll 65 St Mich Coll Llan 67. **d** 69 **p** 70. C Solihull *Birm* 69-73; C E Grinstead St Swithun *Chich* 73-75; V Saltley *Birm* 75-82; V Waterlooville *Portsm* from 82; rtd 03. *44 Woodcock Gardens, Warminster BA12 9JG* Tel (01985) 211344

FERRIS, Amanda Jane. b 61. RGN83. St Alb and Ox Min Course 00. **d** 03. NSM Letchworth St Paul w Willian *St Alb* from 03. *Rivendell, 33B Stotfold Road, Arlesey SG15 6XL* Tel (01462) 834627 Mobile 07780-670651
E-mail amanda@rivendell.freeserve.co.uk

FERRIS, Samuel Albert. b 41. Open Univ BA80. S & M Dioc Tr Inst 98. **d** 99 **p** 00. OLM Douglas All SS and St Thos *S & M* from 99. *27 Hillberry Meadows, Governors Hill, Douglas, Isle Of Man IM2 7BJ* Tel (01624) 619631 Fax as telephone

FERRITER, Felicity Eunicé Myfanwy. b 54. Sheff Univ BA76 Nottm Univ MA98. EMMTC 95. **d** 98 **p** 99. Hon C Retford *S'well* 98-03; Asst Chapl Rampton Hosp Retford 99-01; Asst Chapl Notts Healthcare NHS Trust 01-02; Chapl 02-03; Asst to Area Dean Retford from 03. *The Gables, Treswell Road, Rampton, Retford DN22 0HU* Tel (01777) 248580

FERRY, David Henry John. b 53. TCD BTh88. **d** 88 **p** 89. C Enniskillen *Clogh* 88-90; I Leckpatrick w Dunnalong *D & R* 90-01; Bp's Dom Chapl from 96; I Donagheady from 01. *Earlsgift Rectory, 33 Longland Road, Dunamanagh, Strabane BT82 0PH* Tel (028) 7139 8017

FERRY, Malcolm Ronald Keith. b 66. QUB BEd88. CITC BTh96. **d** 96 **p** 97. C Agherton *Conn* 96-99; I Kilwaughter w Cairncastle and Craigy Hill 99-03; I Castlerock w Dunboe and Fermoyle *D & R* from 03. *The Rectory, 52 Main Street, Castlerock, Coleraine BT51 4RA* Tel (028) 7084 8242

FESSEY, Mrs Annis Irene. b 40. St Mary's Coll Cheltenham CertEd60. Ripon Coll Cuddesdon 88. **d** 90 **p** 94. Par Dn Bris St Andr Hartcliffe *Bris* 90-94; C The Lydiards 94-95; C Penhill 95-00; rtd 00; Perm to Offic *Bris* from 00. *The Vicarage, 4 Church Street, Purton, Swindon SN5 4DS* Tel (01793) 770210 or 490975

FESSEY, Canon Brian Alan. b 39. Bris Univ CertEd61 Leeds Univ DipEd71. Ripon Coll Cuddesdon 88. **d** 90 **p** 91. Hon C Bishopsworth *Bris* 90; C Withywood CD 91-94; V Purton from 94; Hon Can Bris Cathl from 01. *The Vicarage, 4 Church Street, Purton, Swindon SN5 4DS* Tel (01793) 770210

FEWKES, Jeffrey Preston. b 47. Derby Univ MA99. Wycliffe Hall Ox 72. **d** 75 **p** 76. C Chester le Street *Dur* 75-78; C Kennington St Mark *S'wark* 78-81; V Bulwell St Jo *S'well* 81-98; V Stapleford 98-02; Dep Co-ord Victim Support Nottm City N from 02. *3 Monks Close, Ilkeston DE7 5EY* Tel 0115-844 5093 E-mail jeffrey.fewkes@ntlworld.com

FFRENCH (née WILLIAMS), Mrs Janet Patricia (Trish). b 59. Bradf Univ BTech81. Trin Coll Bris BA02. **d** 02. C Quinton Road W St Boniface *Birm* from 02. *1 Four Acres, Quinton, Birmingham B32 1RY* Tel 0121-421 3530 Mobile 07801-257959 E-mail jtrishw@blueyonder.co.uk

FFRENCH, Timothy Edward. b 58. Ball Coll Ox MA86. Trin Coll Bris BA01 MA03. **d** 03. C Pedmore *Worc* from 03. *1 Four Acres, Birmingham B32 1RY* Tel 0121-421 3530 Mobile 07801-492126 E-mail timffrench@yahoo.co.uk

FICKE, Michael John. b 46. LNSM course 96. **d** 97 **p** 98. OLM Marnhull *Sarum* from 97. *13 Plowman Close, Marnhull, Sturminster Newton DT10 1LB* Tel (01258) 820509

FIDDYMENT, Alan John. b 40. Cant Sch of Min 91. **d** 94 **p** 95. NSM Chatham St Wm *Roch* 94-96; NSM Spalding *Linc* 96-99; R Barkston and Hough Gp from 99. *The Rectory, Barkston Road, Marston, Grantham NG32 2HN* Tel (01400) 250875 Mobile 07930-434126 Fax 250875 E-mail alanfid@hotmail.com

✠**FIDÈLE, The Most Revd Dirokpa Balufuga.** Bp Bukavu; Abp Congo from 02. *BP 134, Cyangugu, Rwanda* Tel (00250) 841 7697
E-mail anglicandiobkv@yahoo.com *or* dirokpa1@hotmail.com

FIDLER, John Harvey. b 49. Hatf Poly BSc72. St Alb Minl Tr Scheme 84. **d** 87 **p** 88. NSM Royston *St Alb* from 87; Perm to Offic *Ely* from 00. *8 Stamford Avenue, Royston SG8 7DD* Tel (01763) 241886

FIELD, Brian Hedley. b 31. St Jo Coll York CertEd53 DipPE53 ACP66 FCP84. **d** 99 **p** 00. NSM Maidstone St Luke *Cant* from 99. *Shebri, 21 Fauchons Close, Bearsted, Maidstone ME14 4BB* Tel (01622) 730117 Mobile 07785-156606

FIELD, David Hibberd. b 36. K Coll Cam BA58. Oak Hill Th Coll 58. **d** 60 **p** 61. C Aldershot H Trin *Guildf* 60-63; C Margate H Trin *Cant* 63-66; Sec Th Students Fellowship 66-68; Tutor Oak Hill Th Coll 68-93; Vice Prin 79-93; Dean Minl Tr Course 88-93; Dir Professional Min Div CPAS 94-00; Patr Sec CPAS 94-00; Perm to Offic *Cov* from 94; rtd 02. *25 Field Barn Road, Hampton Magna, Warwick CV35 8RX* Tel (01926) 410291

FIELD, Geoffrey Alder. b 13. Ely Th Coll. **d** 47 **p** 48. C King Cross *Wakef* 47-50; C Ely 50-54; V Whittlesey St Andr 54-75; V Foxton 75-80; rtd 81; Perm to Offic *Ely* 81-02. *14 Poplar Close, Great Shelford, Cambridge CB2 5LX* Tel (01223) 842099

FIELD, Gerald Gordon. b 54. K Coll Lon BD75 AKC75. Coll of Resurr Mirfield 76. **d** 77 **p** 78. C Broughton *Blackb* 77-79; C Blackpool St Steph 79-82; V Skerton St Luke 82-86; NSM Westleigh St Pet *Man* 92-93; V Shap w Swindale and Bampton w Mardale *Carl* 93-97; P-in-c Netherton 97; V 98-01; I Tullamore w Durrow, Newtownfertullagh, Rahan etc *M & K* from 01. *St Catherine's Rectory, Church Avenue, Tullamore, Co Offaly, Irish Republic* Tel and fax (00353) (506) 21731 Mobile 87-956 9188 E-mail gerald_field@bigfoot.com *or* tullamore@meath.anglican.org

FIELD, James Lewis. b 46. Open Univ BSc96 DMS79 HNC70 Kent Univ DipTh97. SEITE 94. **d** 97 **p** 98. NSM Chatham St Mary w St Jo *Roch* 97-00; R Gravesend H Family w Ifield from 00. *The Rectory, 2 Wilberforce Way, Gravesend DA12 5DQ* Tel (01474) 363038

FIELD, Martin Richard. b 55. Keswick Hall Coll CertEd76 Leic Univ MA87. St Jo Coll Nottm BTh82 LTh. **d** 82 **p** 83. C Gaywood, Bawsey and Mintlyn *Nor* 82-85; Perm to Offic *Leic* 85-87; Hon C S'well Minster *S'well* 87-88; Hon C Stand *Man* 88-89; Dioc Press and Communications Officer 88-91; CUF 91-95; Perm to Offic *Cant* 96-99. *7 Fosbrook House, Davidson Gardens, London SW8 2XH* Tel (020) 7627 1640

FIELD, Miss Olwen Joyce. b 53. St Jo Coll Nottm 86. **d** 88 **p** 94. Par Dn Kensal Rise St Mark and St Martin *Lon* 88-91; Par Dn Northwood H Trin 91-94; C 94-95; Chapl Mt Vernon Hosp 91-99; P-in-c W Drayton 99-03; V from 03; Dean of Women's Min Willesden Area from 01; AD Hillingdon from 03. *The Vicarage, 4 Beaudesert Mews, West Drayton UB7 7PE* Tel (01895) 442194 E-mail olwen@swanroad.fsnet.co.uk

FIELD, Richard Colin. b 33. St Cath Soc Ox BA54 MA63. Clifton Th Coll 63. **d** 65 **p** 66. C Highbury Ch Ch *Lon* 65-70; V Hanger Lane St Ann 70-85; V Leytonstone St Jo *Chelmsf* 85-98; rtd 98; Perm to Offic *Chich* from 99. *21 Rufus Close, Lewes BN7 1BG* Tel (01273) 472884

FIELD, Miss Susan Elizabeth. b 59. York Univ BA80 Birm Univ CertEd81 Ox Univ MTh98. Qu Coll Birm 84. **d** 87 **p** 94. C Coleshill *Birm* 87-90; Chapl Loughb Univ *Leic* 91-98; Dir Post-Ord Tr from 95; Bp's Adv for Women's Min from 97; TV Loughborough Em and St Mary in Charnwood from 98. *134 Valley Road, Loughborough LE11 3QA* Tel (01509) 234472 E-mail sue.field1@tesco.net

FIELD, William Jenkin. b 25. St Deiniol's Hawarden. **d** 66 **p** 67. C Cardiff St Jo *Llan* 66-72; V Llancarfan w Llantrithyd 72-94; rtd 94; Perm to Offic *Llan* from 94. *20 Whitmore Park Drive, Barry CF62 8JL* Tel (01446) 701027

FIELDEN, Elizabeth Ann. b 42. TCert63. LNSM course 98. **d** 99 **p** 00. OLM Broughton Gifford, Gt Chalfield and Holt *Sarum* from 99. *393 Ham Green, Holt, Trowbridge BA14 6PX* Tel (01255) 782509 Fax 783152

FIELDEN, Hugh. b 66. BNC Ox BA88 Birm Univ PGCE90. Qu Coll Birm 91. **d** 93 **p** 94. C Sholing *Win* 93-97; TV Bramley *Ripon* 97-02; TV Bingley All SS *Bradf* from 02. *Winston Grange, Otley Road, Bingley BD16 3EQ* Tel (01274) 568266

FIELDEN, Mrs Janice. b 46. Warwick Univ BEd82 MEd89. St Alb and Ox Min Course 99. **d** 02. NSM Chipping Norton *Ox* from 02. *The Vicarage, Church Lane, Charlbury OX7 3PX* Tel (01608) 810286 Fax as telephone E-mail parishoff@aol.com

FIELDEN, Robert. b 32. Linc Th Coll 65. **d** 67 **p** 68. C Bassingham *Linc* 67-72; R Anderby w Cumberworth 72-88; P-in-c Huttoft 72-88; P-in-c Mumby 77-88; R Fiskerton 88-90; rtd 90; Perm to Offic *Carl* 91-99; *Linc* from 91. *Woodlands, 8 Fiskerton Road, Reepham, Lincoln LN3 4EB* Tel (01522) 750480 E-mail robert@rfielden.freeserve.co.uk

FIELDER, Canon Arthur John. b 14. Lon Univ DipTh48. Bps' Coll Cheshunt 46. **d** 47 **p** 50. C Luton All SS *St Alb* 47-48; C Taunton St Mary *B & W* 48-50; C Bexhill St Pet *Chich* 50-56; V Luton All SS *St Alb* 56-61; Youth Chapl *Leic* 61-67; Hon Can Leic Cathl 67-77; Dioc Dir of Educn 67-77; Master Wyggeston's Hosp Leic 68-78; rtd 78; Perm to Offic *St Alb* 78-93; Perm to Offic *Chich* 92-98. *3 Morley House, College of St Barnabas, Lingfield RH7 6NJ* Tel (01342) 870407

FIELDER, Joseph Neil. b 67. Univ of Wales BSc89. Wycliffe Hall Ox 93. **d** 96 **p** 97. C Cheadle All Hallows *Ches* 96-00; V Preston St Steph *Blackb* from 00. *St Stephen's Vicarage, 60 Broadgate, Preston PR1 8DU* Tel (01772) 555762 E-mail the.fielders@lineone.net

FIELDGATE, John William Sheridan. b 44. St Jo Coll Dur BA68. Ox NSM Course 75. **d** 79 **p** 80. NSM Haddenham w Cuddington, Kingsey etc *Ox* 79-90; C Northleach w Hampnett and Farmington *Glouc* 90-92; C Cold Aston w Notgrove and Turkdean 90-92; P-in-c Upper and Lower Slaughter w Eyford and Naunton 92-01; P-in-c The Guitings, Cutsdean and Farmcote 92-01; V Acton w Gt Waldingfield *St E* from 01. *The Vicarage, Melford Road, Acton, Sudbury CO10 0BA* Tel (01787) 377287 Fax as telephone E-mail jandjfieldgate@ukonline.co.uk

FIELDING, John Joseph. b 29. TCD BA53 MA65 QUB DipEd57. **d** 54 **p** 55. C Belfast St Luke *Conn* 54-57; C Belfast St Mary Magd 57-60; W Germany 61-69; Chapl St Edw Sch Ox 69-73; V Highgate St Mich *Lon* 73-95; rtd 95; Perm to Offic *Guildf* from 95; *S'wark* from 99. *30 Sackville Mews, Sackville Road, Sutton SM2 6HS* E-mail j.j.fielding@btinternet.com

FIELDING, Stephen Aubrey. b 67. Ulster Univ BSc89 TCD BTh93. CITC 90. **d** 93 **p** 94. C Bangor Abbey *D & D* 93-97; I Templepatrick w Donegore *Conn* from 97. *926 Antrim Road, Templepatrick, Ballyclare BT39 0AT* Tel (028) 9443 2300 E-mail templepatrick@connor.anglican.org

FIELDSEND, John Henry. b 31. Nottm Univ BSc54 Lon Univ BD61. Lon Coll of Div ALCD59. **d** 61 **p** 62. C Pennington *Man* 61-64; C Didsbury Ch Ch 64-66; P-in-c Bayston Hill *Lich* 66-67; V 67-88; UK Dir CMJ 89-91; Dir and Min at Large CMJ 91-96; rtd 96; Perm to Offic *St Alb* 96-00; Hon C Thame *Ox* from 01. *58 Cedar Crescent, Thame OX9 2AU* Tel (01844) 212559 E-mail john@tehillah.freeserve.co.uk

FIELDSON, Robert Steven. b 56. Qu Coll Cam BA78 MA81 Wye Coll Lon MSc79 Nottm Univ BA86. St Jo Coll Nottm 84. **d** 87 **p** 88. C Walmley *Birm* 87-90; Chapl Protestant Ch in Oman 90-95; P-in-c Cofton Hackett w Barnt Green *Birm* 95-98; V from 98; AD Kings Norton from 00. *The Vicarage, 8 Cofton Church Lane, Barnt Green, Birmingham B45 8PT* Tel 0121-445 1269 E-mail rob@fieldson.co.uk

FIENNES, The Very Revd the Hon Oliver William. b 26. New Coll Ox BA54 MA55. Cuddesdon Coll 52. **d** 54 **p** 55. C Milton *Win* 54-58; Chapl Clifton Coll Bris 58-63; R St Mary-at-Lambeth *S'wark* 63-68; RD Lambeth 68; Can and Preb Linc Cathl *Linc* 69-97; Dean Linc 69-89; rtd 89; Perm to Offic *Pet* and *St E* from 89; *Linc* 99-02. *Home Farm House, Colsterworth, Grantham NG33 5HZ* Tel (01476) 860811

FIFE (née EVE), Hilary Anne. b 57. Lon Univ BEd80. Ripon Coll Cuddesdon 89. **d** 91 **p** 94. Par Dn Coulsdon St Andr *S'wark* 91-94; C 94-95; Chapl Croydon Coll 92-94; Asst Chapl Mayday Healthcare NHS Trust Thornton Heath 94-02; Sen Chapl from 02; Chapl Harestone Marie Curie Cen Caterham 94-98. *19 Greenview Avenue, Croydon CR0 7QW* Tel (020) 8654 8685 *or* 8401 3105

FIFE, Miss Janet Heather. b 53. Sussex Univ BA77. Wycliffe Hall Ox 84. **d** 87 **p** 94. Chapl Bradf Cathl *Bradf* 87-89; Par Dn York St Mich-le-Belfrey *York* 89-92; Chapl Salford Univ *Man* 92-00; Hon C Pendleton St Thos w Charlestown 92-95; Hon C Pendleton 95-96; V Upton Priory *Ches* from 00. *The Vicarage, Church Way, Macclesfield SK10 3HT* Tel (01625) 827761 E-mail jhfife@nildram.co.uk

FIGG, Robin Arthur Rex. b 62. RN Eng Coll Plymouth BScEng84. Westcott Ho Cam CTM94. **d** 94 **p** 95. C Old Cleeve, Leighland and Treborough *B & W* 94-97; C Gt Berkhamsted *St Alb* 97-01; V Kildwick *Bradf* from 01. *The Vicarage, Kildwick, Keighley BD20 9BB* Tel (01535) 633307 E-mail vicar@kildwick.org.uk

FILBERT-ULLMANN, Mrs Clair. b 44. Leuven Univ Belgium BTh94 MA94. Virginia Th Sem 95. **d** 94 **p** 96. USA 94-95; Asst Chapl Charleroi *Eur* 95-00; P-in-c Leuven 99-02; Asst Chapl Tervuren w Liège 99-01; Perm to Offic from 02. *Muhlbach am Hochkonig 437, A-5505, Austria* Tel (0043) (6467) 20107 E-mail crullmann2001@yahoo.com

FILBY, The Ven William Charles Leonard. b 33. Lon Univ BA58. Oak Hill Th Coll 53. **d** 59 **p** 60. C Eastbourne All SS *Chich* 59-62; C Woking St Jo *Guildf* 62-65; V Richmond H Trin *S'wark* 65-71; V Hove Bp Hannington Memorial Ch *Chich* 71-79; R Broadwater St Mary 79-83; RD Worthing 80-83; Can and Preb Chich Cathl 81-83; Adn Horsham 83-02; rtd 02. *The Archdeaconry, Itchingfield, Horsham RH13 0NX* Tel (01403) 790315 Fax 791153

FILER, Victor John. b 43. Sheff Univ MMin95. Sarum Th Coll 66. **d** 69 **p** 70. C Mortlake w E Sheen *S'wark* 69-74; SSF 75-82; P-in-c Plaistow SS Phil and Jas w St Andr *Chelmsf* 80-83; Chapl Plaistow Hosp 81-83; TV Plaistow 83; TV Beaconsfield *Ox* 84-90; TR Maltby *Sheff* 90-98; V Abbeydale St Jo from 98. *The Vicarage, 6 Kenwell Drive, Bradway, Sheffield S17 4PJ* Tel 0114-236 0786

FILLERY, William Robert. b 42. Univ of Wales (Swansea) BA65 Surrey Univ MA96. St D Coll Lamp CPS68 BD69 PGCE72. **d** 68 **p** 69. C Llangyfelach and Morriston *S & B* 68-71; C Morriston 71-72; Lic to Offic *Ox* 73-76; Chapl Windsor Girls' Sch Hamm W Germany 76-81; OCF 79-81; Chapl Reed's Sch Cobham 81-86; V Oxshott *Guildf* 86-89; P-in-c Seale 89-91; P-in-c Puttenham and Wanborough 89-91; Hd of RE Streatham Hill & Clapham Sch for Girls 91-03; V Llanybydder and Llanwenog w Llanllwni *St D* from 03. *The Vicarage, Llanllwni, Pencader SA39 9DR* Tel (01559) 395413

FILLINGHAM, Richard James. b 58. Man Univ BA80 ACA83. All Nations Chr Coll Wycliffe Hall 84. **d** 98 **p** 99. C Brinsworth w Catcliffe and Treeton *Sheff* 98-01; C Ecclesall from 01. *48 Renshaw Road, Sheffield S11 7PD* Tel 0114-266 2313 E-mail rickfillingham@ecclesall.parishchurch.com

FILMER, Paul James. b 58. Open Univ BA88. Aston Tr Scheme 95 Oak Hill Th Coll DipHE95. **d** 97 **p** 98. C Petham and Waltham w Lower Hardres etc *Cant* 97-00; P-in-c Patrixbourne w Bridge and Bekesbourne from 00. *The Vicarage, 23 High Street, Bridge, Canterbury CT4 5JZ* Tel (01227) 830250 E-mail revpfilmer@btinternet.com

FINCH, Mrs Alison. b 59. SEN79. Sarum & Wells Th Coll 92. **d** 92 **p** 94. Par Dn Banbury *Ox* 92-94; C 94-95; C Wokingham All SS 95-98; C Binfield 98-99; C St Peter-in-Thanet *Cant* 99-02; R Kirkwall *Ab* from 02; P-in-c Stromness from 02. *St Olaf's Rectory, Dundas Crescent, Kirkwall KW15 1JQ* Tel (01856) 872024

FINCH, Barry Marshall. *See* PALMER-PALMER-FFYNCHE, Barry Marshall

FINCH, Christopher. b 41. Lon Univ BA63 AKC63 BD69. Sarum Th Coll 63. **d** 65 **p** 66. C High Wycombe *Ox* 65-69; Prec Leic Cathl *Leic* 69-73; R Lt Bowden St Nic 73-81; V Evington 81-99; P-in-c Leic St Phil 95-99; P-in-c Lower Dever Valley *Win* 99-00; R from 00. *The Rectory, 10 Pigeon House Field, Sutton Scotney, Winchester SO21 3NY* Tel (01962) 760240

FINCH, David Walter. b 40. Cam Univ MA74 FIBMS69. Ridley Hall Cam. **d** 91 **p** 92. C Ixworth and Bardwell *St E* 91-92; C Blackbourne 92-94; P-in-c Stoke by Nayland w Leavenheath 94-00; P-in-c Polstead 95-00; P-in-c Fressingfield, Mendham etc from 00; RD Hoxne from 00. *The Vicarage, Christmas Lane, Metfield, Harleston IP20 0JY* Tel (01379) 586488

FINCH, Canon Edward Alfred. b 23. Lon Univ BSc50. Sarum Th Coll 50. **d** 52 **p** 53. C Wealdstone H Trin *Lon* 52-55; C E Grinstead St Swithun *Chich* 55-59; V Walthamstow St Pet *Chelmsf* 59-70; Can Res Chelmsf Cathl 70-85; Dir Interface Assn 85-90; rtd 90; Perm to Offic *Chelmsf* from 90 and *St E* from 91. *St Clare, The Street, Pakenham, Bury St Edmunds IP31 2JU* Tel (01359) 230949 Fax as telephone E-mail finch-travelfriends@talk21.com

FINCH, Frank. b 33. Qu Coll Birm 72. **d** 74 **p** 75. C Bilston St Leon *Lich* 74-78; R Sudbury and Somersal Herbert *Derby* 78-87; Chapl HM Pris Sudbury 78-87; HM Det Cen Foston Hall 80-87; V Lilleshall and Sheriffhales *Lich* 87-90; R The Ridwares and Kings Bromley 90-98; rtd 98; Perm to Offic *Lich* from 00. *11 Ferrers Road, Yoxall, Burton-on-Trent DE13 8PS* Tel (01543) 472065

FINCH, Jeffrey Walter. b 45. Man Univ BA(Econ)66 Liv Univ DASE80. Linc Th Coll 82. **d** 84 **p** 85. C Briercliffe *Blackb* 84-87;

P-in-c Brindle 87-93; Asst Dir of Educn 87-93; V Laneside 93-00; TV Fellside Team from 00. *The Vicarage, Church Lane, Bilsborrow, Preston PR3 0RL* Tel (01995) 640269

FINCH, John. b 20. Bps' Coll Cheshunt 59. **d** 61 **p** 62. C Middlesbrough St Paul *York* 61-64; V Easington w Skeffling and Kilnsea 64-68; V Habergham Eaves St Matt *Blackb* 68-75; V Garstang St Helen Churchtown 75-86; rtd 86; Perm to Offic *Blackb* from 86. *55 Worcester Avenue, Garstang, Preston PR3 1FJ* Tel (01995) 602386

FINCH, Morag Anne Hamilton. b 64. EAMTC 97. **d** 00 **p** 01. C Cranham *Chelmsf* from 00. *The Vicarage, 17 St Nicholas Avenue, Elm Park, Hornchurch RM12 4PT* Tel (01708) 451451

FINCH, Paul William. b 50. Oak Hill Th Coll DipTh73 Lon Bible Coll. **d** 75 **p** 76. C Hoole *Ches* 75-78; C Charlesworth *Derby* 78-87; C Charlesworth and Dinting Vale 87-88; TV Radipole and Melcombe Regis *Sarum* 88-01; V Malvern St Andr and Malvern Wells and Wyche *Worc* from 01. *St Andrew's Vicarage, 48 Longridge Road, Malvern WR14 3JB* Tel (01684) 573912

FINCH, Richard William. b 62. Westcott Ho Cam 95. **d** 97 **p** 98. C Saffron Walden w Wendens Ambo and Littlebury *Chelmsf* 97-00; C Elm Park St Nic Hornchurch 00-01; V from 01. *The Vicarage, 17 St Nicholas Avenue, Elm Park, Hornchurch RM12 4PT* Tel (01708) 451451 E-mail finches@aic.co.uk

FINCH, Ronald. b 15. Qu Coll Birm 79. **d** 80 **p** 80. Hon C Welford w Weston and Clifford Chambers *Glouc* 80-85; Perm to Offic *Ches* from 85. *Cornerstone, 1 Penrhyd Road, Irby, Wirral CH61 2XJ* Tel 0151-648 1559

FINCH, Miss Rosemary Ann. b 39. Leeds Univ CertEd60. LNSM course 91. **d** 93 **p** 94. OLM S Elmham and Ilketshall *St E* from 93; Asst Chapl Ipswich Hosp NHS Trust from 00. *Grace Farmhouse, St Michael, South Elmham, Bungay NR35 1ND* Tel (01986) 782342 Fax as telephone E-mail rosiestmse@aol.com

FINCH, Canon Stanley James. b 31. Mert Coll Ox BA55 MA58. Wells Th Coll 55. **d** 57 **p** 58. C Lancaster St Mary *Blackb* 57-61; C Leeds St Pet *Ripon* 61-65; V Habergham All SS *Blackb* 65-73; V S Shore H Trin 73-84; V Broughton 84-98; RD Preston 86-92; Hon Can Blackb Cathl 91-98; rtd 98; P-in-c Alderton, Gt Washbourne, Dumbleton etc *Glouc* 98-02; Perm to Offic from 02. *14 Bellflower Road, Walton Cardiff, Tewkesbury GL20 7SB* Tel (01684) 850544

FINCH, Thomas. b 20. Lon Univ BD57. Edin Th Coll 48. **d** 51 **p** 51. Chapl St Andr Cathl *Ab* 51-55; C St Marylebone St Cypr *Lon* 55-58; V Warmington *Pet* 58-67; RD Oundle 62-67; V Wellingborough St Mary 67-88; rtd 88; Perm to Offic *Blackb* from 88. *18 Royal Avenue, Leyland, Preston PR5 1BQ* Tel (01772) 433780

FINCHAM, Nicholas Charles. b 56. St Jo Coll Dur BA78 MA80. Westcott Ho Cam 80 Bossey Ecum Inst Geneva 81. **d** 82 **p** 83. C Seaham w Seaham Harbour *Dur* 82-85; C Lydney w Aylburton *Glouc* 85-87; C Isleworth All SS *Lon* 87-95; P-in-c Chiswick St Mich from 95. *St Michael's Vicarage, 60 Elmwood Road, London W4 3DZ* Tel (020) 8994 3173 E-mail nicholas.fincham@talk21.com

FINDLAY, Canon Brian James. b 42. Wellington Univ (NZ) BA62 MA63 BMus66 Magd Coll Ox MA75. Qu Coll Birm DipTh71. **d** 72 **p** 73. C Deptford St Paul *S'wark* 72-75; Chapl and Dean of Div Magd Coll Ox 75-84; V Tonge Moor *Man* 84-02; Hon Can Man Cathl from 00; rtd 02. *The Bull Pen, Hallthwaites, Millom LA18 5HP* Tel (01229) 770049

FINDLAYSON, Roy. b 44. Man Univ CQSW69 MA89. Sarum & Wells Th Coll 80. **d** 82 **p** 83. C Benwell St Jas *Newc* 82-83; Hon C 83-85; C Morpeth 85-88; C N Gosforth 88; TV Ch the King 88-94; V Newc St Fran 94-98; Asst Chapl Newcastle upon Tyne Hosps NHS Trust from 98; Chapl Marie Curie Cen Newc from 98. *Marie Curie Centre, Marie Curie Drive, Newcastle upon Tyne NE4 6SS* Tel 0191-219 5560

FINDLEY, Peter. b 55. Trin Coll Ox BA77 MA80 Barrister-at-Law (Gray's Inn) 78. Trin Coll Bris DipHE92. **d** 92 **p** 93. C Yateley *Win* 92-97; V Westwood *Cov* from 97. *St John's Vicarage, Featherbed Lane, Coventry CV4 7DD* Tel (024) 7647 0515 or 7669 5026 E-mail peterfindley@stjohnswestwood.freeserve.co.uk

FINDON, John Charles. b 50. Keble Coll Ox BA71 MA75 DPhil79. Ripon Coll Cuddesdon DipTh76. **d** 77 **p** 78. C Middleton *Man* 77-80; Lect Bolton St Pet 80-83; V Astley 83-91; V Baguley 91-98; P-in-c Bury St Mary from 98. *St Mary's Rectory, Tithebarn Street, Bury BL9 0JR* Tel 0161-764 2452

FINKENSTAEDT, Harry Seymour. b 23. Yale Univ BA49 Mass Univ MA68. Episc Th Sch Cam Mass BD50. **d** 53 **p** 54. USA 53-71; C Hazlemere *Ox* 71-73; C Huntingdon St Mary w St Benedict *Ely* 73-75; R Castle Camps 75-84; R Shudy Camps 75-84; P-in-c W Wickham 79-84; P-in-c Horseheath 79-81; P-in-c Gt w Lt Stukeley 84-88; rtd 88; Perm to Offic *Ely* 88-01. *13761 Charismatic Way, Gainesville, VA 20155, USA* Tel (001) (703) 743 5787

FINLAY, Alison Mary. See CAW, Alison Mary

FINLAY, Christopher John. b 46. FCII71. WMMTC 95. **d** 98 **p** 99. NSM Coln St Aldwyns, Hatherop, Quenington etc *Glouc*

from 98. *Coombe House, Calcot, Cheltenham GL54 3JZ* Tel (01285) 720806

FINLAY, Hueston Edward. b 64. TCD BA85 BAI85 BTh89 MA92 Kent Univ MA98 Lon Univ PhD98. CITC 86. **d** 89 **p** 90. C Kilkenny w Aghour and Kilmanagh *C & O* 89-92; Bp Ossory Dom Chapl 89-92; Lib and Registrar Kilkenny Cathl 89-92; Bp's V Ossory Cathl 90-92; Chapl Girton Coll Cam 92-95; C Cambridge St Mary w St Mich *Ely* 92-95; Chapl and Fell Magd Coll Cam 95-99; Dean of Chpl from 99. *9 Hertford Street, Cambridge CB4 3AE,* or *Magdalene College, Cambridge CB3 0AG* Tel (01223) 332129

FINLAY, Michael Stanley. b 45. N Ord Course 78. **d** 81 **p** 82. C Padgate *Liv* 81-85; V Newton-le-Willows 85-90; V Orford St Marg 90-98; P-in-c Warrington St Elphin 98-00; R from 00. *The Rectory, Church Street, Warrington WA1 2TL* Tel (01925) 635020

FINLAY, Nicholas. b 47. Regent Coll Vancouver MCS00. St Jo Coll Nottm LTh02. **d** 02. C Haydock St Mark *Liv* 02-03; C Seaforth from 03. *St Thomas's Vicarage, Elm Road, Liverpool L21 1BH* Tel (0151) 920771 E-mail nickfinlay@aol.com

FINLAYSON, Duncan. b 24. LNSM course 73. **d** 76 **p** 76. NSM Bridge of Allan *St And* 76-94; NSM Alloa 77-94; NSM Dollar 77-94; Hon AP Hillfoots Team 80-87; rtd 94. *29 Cawder Road, Bridge of Allan, Stirling FK9 4JJ* Tel (01786) 833074

FINLAYSON, Grantley Adrian. b 55. Wilson Carlile Coll 74 Chich Th Coll 87. **d** 89 **p** 90. C Watford St Mich *St Alb* 89-92; TV W Slough *Ox* 92-97; Dioc Officer for Race Relations *Glouc* 97-02; V Luton St Andr *St Alb* from 02. *St Andrew's Vicarage, 11 Blenheim Crescent, Luton LU3 1HA* Tel (01582) 732380

FINLINSON, Paul. b 58. St Chad's Coll Dur BA79 St Martin's Coll Lanc PGCE81. Carl Dioc Tr Course 86. **d** 89 **p** 90. NSM Kirkby Lonsdale *Carl* 89-99; Perm to Offic *Blackb* from 95; Chapl Worksop Coll Notts from 99. *Worksop College, Worksop S80 3AP* Tel (01909) 537109 or (01524) 69652

FINN, Gordon Frederick. b 33. Dur Univ BA60. Ely Th Coll 60. **d** 62 **p** 63. C Kingswinford St Mary *Lich* 62-65; C Northampton St Mary *Pet* 65-67; Chapl Barnsley Hall Hosp Bromsgrove 67-71; Chapl Lea Hosp Bromsgrove 67-71; C Swanage *Sarum* 71-73; P-in-c Ford End *Chelmsf* 73-79; V S Shields St Oswin *Dur* 79-98; rtd 98. *8 Windsor Drive, Lingdale, Saltburn-by-the-Sea TS12 3HR* Tel (01287) 653638

FINN, Ian Michael. b 58. AKC. Chich Th Coll 81. **d** 82 **p** 83. C Habergham All SS *Blackb* 82-83; C W Burnley 83-85; C Torrisholme 85-87; V Lancaster Ch Ch w St Jo and St Anne 87-91; P-in-c Tillingham and Dengie w Asheldham *Chelmsf* 91-97; Chapl R Gr Sch Worc 97-99; P-in-c Denston w Stradishall and Stansfield *St E* 99-01; P-in-c Wickhambrook w Lydgate, Ousden and Cowlinge 00-01; R Bansfield from 02. *The Vicarage, Church Road, Wickhambrook, Newmarket CB8 8XH* Tel (01440) 820288 E-mail ifinn@ifinn98.freeserve.co.uk

FINN, Miss Sheila. b 30. LMH Ox BA68 MA69. Gilmore Ho 68. **dss** 78 **d** 87 **p** 94. Tettenhall Wood *Lich* 78-86; Dioc Ecum Officer 86-95; The Ridwares and Kings Bromley 86-87; Par Dn 87-94; C 94-95; rtd 95; Perm to Offic *Lich* from 97. *15 Leacroft Road, Penkridge, Stafford ST19 5BU* Tel (01785) 716018

FINNEMORE, Ernest Harold. b 28. Keble Coll Ox BA49 MA53. St Steph Ho Ox 51. **d** 53 **p** 54. C Almondbury *Wakef* 53-55; C Talke *Lich* 55-57; V Longnor 57-64; V Hanford 64-90; rtd 90; Perm to Offic *Lich* from 90. *24 Belgrave Road, Newcastle ST5 1LR* Tel (01782) 638179

FINNEMORE, James Christopher. b 59. Pemb Coll Cam BA81 MA85. Coll of Resurr Mirfield. **d** 85 **p** 86. C Manston *Ripon* 85-88; C Hessle *York* 88-92; R Bishop Wilton w Full Sutton, Kirby Underdale etc 92-99; R Garrowby Hill from 99. *The Rectory, Bishop Wilton, York YO42 1SA* Tel (01759) 368230

FINNEY, David. b 41. St Mich Coll Llan 68. **d** 70 **p** 71. C Wythenshawe Wm Temple Ch *Man* 70-73; C Bedford Leigh 73-75; V Royton St Anne 75-81; V Dearnley 81-94; TV Rochdale from 94. *The Vicarage, 39 Clement Royds Street, Rochdale OL12 6PL* Tel (01706) 646272 Fax as telephone E-mail davidfinney@tinyworld.co.uk

FINNEY, Canon Fred. b 17. Bris Univ BA38 DipEd39. Wycliffe Hall Ox 61. **d** 62 **p** 63. C Gt Crosby St Luke *Liv* 62-66; V Ashton-in-Makerfield St Thos 66-86; Hon Can Liv Cathl 83-86; rtd 86; Perm to Offic *Blackb* from 86; Perm to Offic *Liv* from 86. *1 Howard Drive, Tarleton, Preston PR4 6DA* Tel (01772) 812598

FINNEY, Canon John Thomas. b 27. Sheff Univ BA51 DipEd52. Ripon Hall Ox 60. **d** 62 **p** 63. C Leigh St Mary *Man* 62-65; V 83-97; V Peel 65-69; Chapl Hockerill Coll Bishop's Stortford 69-74; V Astley *Man* 74-83; AD Leigh 83-93; Hon Can Man Cathl 87-97; rtd 97; Perm to Offic *Man* from 97. *36 Station Road, Blackrod, Bolton BL6 5BW* Tel (01204) 698010

✠**FINNEY, The Rt Revd John Thornley.** b 32. Hertf Coll Ox BA55. Wycliffe Hall Ox DipTh58. **d** 58 **p** 59 **c** 93. C Highfield *Ox* 58-61; C Weston Turville 61-65; R Tollerton *S'well* 65-71; V Aspley 71-80; Bp's Adv on Evang 80-89; Bp's Research Officer 88-89; Hon Can S'well Minster 84-89; Officer for Decade of Evang in C of E 90-93; Suff Bp Pontefract *Wakef* 93-98; rtd 98; Hon Asst Bp S'well from 98. *Greenacre, Crow Lane, South*

Muskham, Newark NG23 6DZ Tel (01636) 679791 Fax as telephone E-mail john.finney2@ntlworld.com

FINNEY, Ms Melva Kathleen. b 24. LTh76. St Jo Coll Auckland 47 Gilmore Ho 56. **dss** 57 **d** 78. E Dulwich St Jo *S'wark* 56-59; Community of Sisters of the Love of God Ox 59-61; New Zealand from 61; Asst Chapl Christchurch 61-62; Fendalton St Barn 62-63; Asst Chapl Womens and Templeton Hosp 63-72; Asst Chapl Princess Marg Hosp Christchurch 63-72; Chapl 72-86; rtd 86. *22 Gunns Crescent, Cashmere, Christchurch 8002, New Zealand* Tel (0064) (3) 332 7100

FINNIE, Canon Robert. b 20. **d** 84 **p** 84. NSM Aberdeen St Andr *Ab* from 84; NSM Aberdeen St Ninian 84-97; Hon Can St Andr Cathl from 97. *10 Cairngorm Crescent, Aberdeen AB1 5BL* Tel (01224) 874669

FINNIMORE, Keith Anthony. b 36. AKC59. **d** 60 **p** 61. C Wanstead H Trin Hermon Hill *Chelmsf* 60-63; C Kingswood *S'wark* 63-65; V Bolney *Chich* 65-67; V Elmstead *Chelmsf* 67-73; R Pentlow, Foxearth, Liston and Borley 73-77; NSM Cockfield w Bradfield St Clare, Felsham etc *St E* 89-91; R Hawstead and Nowton w Stanningfield etc 91-96; P-in-c 96-01; rtd 96; Perm to Offic *St E* from 01. *Larkhill, Rede Road, Whepstead, Bury St Edmunds IP29 4SS* Tel (01284) 735291

FIRMIN, Canon Dorrie Eleanor Frances. b 19. LNSM course. **d** 88 **p** 94. NSM Cruden Bay 88-99; Hon Can St Andr Cathl from 97. *Minas Tirith, 7 Slains Avenue, Ellon AB41 9ZA* Tel (01358) 721623

FIRMIN, Paul Gregory. b 57. ACIB80. Trin Coll Bris BA87. **d** 87 **p** 88. C Swindon Ch Ch *Bris* 87-91; V Shrewsbury H Trin w St Julian *Lich* 91-99; V Astley, Clive, Grinshill and Hadnall 99-01; V Southampton St Mary Extra *Win* from 01. *The Vicarage, 65 Peartree Avenue, Bitterne, Southampton SO19 7JN* Tel (023) 8043 7192 E-mail revpaulf@nimrifs.freeserve.co.uk

FIRMSTONE, Ian Harry. b 44. Qu Coll Birm. **d** 82 **p** 83. C Warminster St Denys *Sarum* 82-84; C N Stoneham *Win* 84-88; R Freemantle 88-90; V Littleport *Ely* 90-91; TV Stanground and Farcet 91-97; P-in-c Holme w Conington 95-96; rtd 97. *29 Garfield Road, Southampton SO19 4DA* Tel (02380) 224809

FIRTH, Mrs Ann Neswyn. b 40. St As Minl Tr Course 95. **d** 98 **p** 99. NSM Llanidloes w Llangurig *Ban* from 98. *Springfield, Westgate Street, Llanidloes SY18 6HJ* Tel (01686) 413098 E-mail davidandneswyn@firth19.freeserve.co.uk

FIRTH, Barry. b 37. ACA60 FCA71. NW Ord Course 74. **d** 77 **p** 78. NSM Brighouse *Wakef* 77-81; P-in-c Batley St Thos 81-85; V 85-88; V Rastrick St Matt 88-95; RD Brighouse and Elland 92-96; TV Brighouse and Clifton 95-97; rtd 97; Perm to Offic *Wakef* from 97. *51 Bolehill Park, Hove Edge, Brighouse HD6 2RS* Tel (01484) 710227

FIRTH, Christopher John Kingsley. b 37. St Mich Coll Llan DipTh66. **d** 66 **p** 67. C Sutton in Ashfield St Mary *S'well* 66-70; V Langold 70-74; C Falmouth K Chas *Truro* 74-77; P-in-c Mabe 77-81; V 81-95; RD Carnmarth S 90-94; rtd 99. *The Gables, Trewin Road, Budock Water, Falmouth TR11 5EA* Tel (01326) 377539

✠FIRTH, the Rt Revd Peter James. b 29. Em Coll Cam BA52 MA63. St Steph Ho Ox 53. **d** 55 **p** 56 **c** 83. C Barbourne *Worc* 55-58; C Malvern Link St Matthias 58-62; R Abbey Hey *Man* 62-66; Asst Network Relig Broadcasting BBC Man 66-67; Sen Producer/Org Relig Progr TV w Radio BBC Bris 67-83; Hon Can Bris Cathl *Bris* 74-83; Suff Bp Malmesbury 83-94; Angl Adv HTV West 84-96; rtd 94. *Mill House, Silknill Lane, Winchcombe, Cheltenham GL54 5HZ* Tel (01242) 603669

FIRTH, Ronald Mahlon. b 22. Linc Th Coll 60. **d** 61 **p** 62. C Marske in Cleveland *York* 61-64; C Thornaby on Tees St Paul 64-66; V York St Thos w St Maurice 66-73; V Marton-in-Cleveland 73-87; rtd 87; Perm to Offic *York* from 87. *24 Whenby Grove, Huntington, York YO31 9DS* Tel (01904) 634531

FISH, Winthrop. b 40. Dalhousie Univ Canada BA63 BEd Birm Univ BPhil76 MEd78. K Coll (NS) 62. **d** 64 **p** 65. Canada 64-74; Perm to Offic *Birm* 74-77; Asst Chapl Solihull Sch 77-79; Chapl Wroxall Abbey Sch 79-82; C Newquay *Truro* 82-84; V Highertown and Baldhu 84-89; P-in-c Newlyn St Newlyn 89-97; Dioc Children's Adv 89-97; Dioc Adv in RE 95-97; rtd 98; Perm to Offic *Ex* from 98. *2 Vicarage Road, East Budleigh, Budleigh Salterton EX9 7EF* Tel (01395) 445371

FISHER, Adrian Charles Proctor. b 24. TCD BA48 MA62. TCD Div Sch Div Test47. **d** 49 **p** 50. C Carlow *C & O* 49-52; C Tintern 49-52; C Killesk 49-52; CF 52-57 and 62-69; I Fethard w Killesk, Tintern and Templetown *C & O* 57-62; P-in-c N Stoke w Mongewell and Ipsden *Ox* 70-83; V 83-92; Chapl Oratory Prep Sch 73-80; rtd 92; Perm to Offic *Ox* from 99. *Aldermaston Soke, Silchester, Reading RG7 2PB* Tel 0118-970 0246

FISHER, Andrew John. b 72. St Jo Coll Nottm BA02. **d** 02 **p** 03. C Ilkeston St Jo *Derby* from 02. *51 Doris Road, Ilkeston DE7 5DP* Tel 0115-852 9138

FISHER, Brian Robert. b 36. Dioc OLM tr scheme 99. **d** 02. OLM Sole Bay *St E* from 02. *Greengates, Main Street, Walberswick, Southwold IP18 6UH* Tel (01502) 723023 Mobile 07766-216111 E-mail emite99660@aol.com

FISHER, David Stephen. b 66. Cuddesdon Coll BTh98. **d** 98 **p** 99. C Stockport SW *Ches* 98-01; V Gatley from 01. *St James's Vicarage, 11 Northenden Road, Cheadle SK8 4EN* Tel 0161-428 4764 E-mail daifisher@aol.com

FISHER, Mrs Diana Margaret. b 44. EMMTC DipTh94. **d** 94 **p** 95. NSM E and W Leake, Stanford-on-Soar, Rempstone etc *S'well* 94-97; NSM W Bridgford 97-98; NSM Aberfoyle and Callander *St And* 99; C Spalding St Jo w Deeping St Nicholas *Linc* 99-01; R Hallaton w Horninghold and Allexton, Tugby etc *Leic* from 01. *The Rectory, Churchgate, Hallaton, Market Harborough LE16 8TY* Tel (01858) 555363

FISHER, Eric Henry George. b 48. NTMTC 94. **d** 97 **p** 98. NSM Heydon, Gt and Lt Chishill, Chrishall etc *Chelmsf* from 97. *5 Elm Court, Elmdon, Saffron Walden CB11 4NP* Tel (01763) 838716 *or* (020) 7448 2625 E-mail eric.fisher@ukgateway.net

FISHER, Eric William. b 30. Birm Univ BA53. Coll of Resurr Mirfield 70. **d** 72 **p** 73. C Styvechale *Cov* 72-75; C Chesterfield St Mary and All SS *Derby* 75-78; Chapl Buxton Hosps 78-84; TV Buxton w Burbage and King Sterndale *Derby* 78-84; R Shirland 84-89; V Sheff St Matt *Sheff* 89-95; rtd 95; Perm to Offic *Lich* 95-02. *6 Wickstead Row, Main Road, Betley, Crewe CW3 9AB*

FISHER, Frank. *See* FISHER, Canon Kenneth Francis McConnell

FISHER, George Arnold. b 54. Lon Univ BD75. N Ord Course 81. **d** 84 **p** 85. C Conisbrough *Sheff* 84-92; V Blackpool St Thos *Blackb* from 92. *St Thomas's Vicarage, 80 Devonshire Road, Blackpool FY3 8AE* Tel (01253) 392544 *or* 399276 Fax as telephone E-mail george@stthomaschurch.co.uk

FISHER, Gordon. b 44. NW Ord Course 74. **d** 77 **p** 78. NSM Airedale w Fryston *Wakef* 77-81; C Barkisland w W Scammonden 81-84; C Ripponden 81-84; V Sutton St Mich *York* 84-87; V Marton-in-Cleveland 87-96; R Kettering SS Pet and Paul *Pet* 96-02; rtd 02. *8 Mount Pleasant Avenue, Marske-by-the-Sea, Redcar TS11 7BW* Tel (01642) 489489 E-mail rector@sspp.co.uk

FISHER, Henry John. b 25. Lich Th Coll 64. **d** 66 **p** 67. C Kings Norton *Birm* 66-70; C Weston-super-Mare St Jo *B & W* 70-75; C Weston-super-Mare H Trin 72-75; P-in-c Leigh upon Mendip 75-78; P-in-c Stoke St Michael 75-78; P-in-c Leigh upon Mendip w Stoke St Michael 78-80; C Wilton 80-88; C Street w Walton 88-90; rtd 90; Perm to Offic *B & W* from 90. *18 Hawker's Lane, Wells BA5 3JL* Tel (01749) 677092

FISHER, Humphrey John. b 33. Harvard Univ AB55 Ox Univ DPhil59. Heythrop Coll Lon MA. **d** 91 **p** 92. NSM Bryngwyn and Newchurch and Llanbedr etc *S & B* from 91. *Rose Cottage, Newchurch, Kington, Hereford HR5 3QF* Tel (01544) 370632

FISHER, Ian St John. b 59. Down Coll Cam BA80 MA84 Leic Univ PhD84. St Steph Ho Ox BA88. **d** 88 **p** 89. C Colwall w Upper Colwall and Coddington *Heref* 88-91; Chapl Surrey Univ *Guildf* 92-97; V Hurst *Man* from 97. *St John's Vicarage, 155 Kings Road, Ashton-under-Lyne OL6 8EZ* Tel 0161-330 1935

FISHER, Mrs Joan. b 52. **d** 00 **p** 01. NSM Blackpool St Mark *Blackb* from 00. *St Thomas's Vicarage, 80 Devonshire Road, Blackpool FY3 8AE* Tel (01253) 392544 Fax as telephone E-mail joan@stthomas.church.co.uk

FISHER, John Andrew. b 63. Bath Univ BSc85 MA97. Wycliffe Hall Ox BA93 DipMin94. **d** 94 **p** 95. C Rayleigh *Chelmsf* 94-98; V Burton Joyce w Bulcote and Stoke Bardolph *S'well* from 98; AD Gedling from 00. *The Vicarage, 9 Chestnut Grove, Burton Joyce, Nottingham NG14 5DP* Tel 0115-931 2109 E-mail john.a.fisher@btinternet.com

FISHER, Canon Kenneth Francis McConnell (Frank). b 36. K Coll Lon 57. **d** 61 **p** 62. C Sheff St Geo and St Steph *Sheff* 61-63; Chapl Sheff Univ 64-69; Chapl Lon Univ 69-75; P-in-c Dean *Carl* 75-80; Soc Resp Officer 75-80; TR Melksham *Sarum* 80-90; P-in-c Stapleford *Ely* 90-01; Dioc Ecum Officer 90-01; RD Shelford from 94; Hon Can Ely Cathl from 98; rtd 01; P-in-c Grantchester *Ely* from 01. *The Vicarage, 44 High Street, Grantchester, Cambridge CB3 9NF* Tel (01223) 840460 E-mail malfisher@waitrose.com

FISHER, Mark Simon. b 52. K Coll Lon BD76 AKC76 Trin Coll Ox MA82 DPhil83 BAC Acc 92 Dip Psychotherapy 92. Kelham Th Coll 70 Perkins Sch of Th (USA) 76. **d** 78 **p** 78. SSF 78-80; Hon C Victoria Docks Ascension *Chelmsf* 78-79; Lic to Offic *Eur* 78-80; Lic to Offic *Lon* 78-80; Lic to Offic *Ox* 78-87; Chapl LMH Ox 80-86; R Glas St Matt *Glas* 87-89; Hon Asst P W Derby St Jo *Liv* from 97. *29A Rodney Street, Liverpool L1 9EH* Tel 0151-707 9748

FISHER, Canon Michael Harry. b 39. Ex Univ BA61. St Steph Ho Ox 61. **d** 63 **p** 64. C Wolverhampton St Pet *Lich* 63-67; C Newquay *Truro* 67-70; V Newlyn St Pet 70-75; P-in-c Launceston St Steph w St Thos 75-82; V Carbis Bay w Lelant 82-95; V

Newquay 95-99; Hon Can Truro Cathl 85-99; RD Penwith 88-93; Chapl Costa del Sol W *Eur* 99-00; rtd 00; Perm to Offic *Truro* from 00. *Chymedda, Southway, Windmill, Padstow PL28 8RN* Tel (01841) 521544 Mobile 07970-865049 E-mail mfisher39@aol.com

FISHER, Michael John. b 43. Leic Univ BA64 Keele Univ MA67. Qu Coll Birm 75. **d** 78 **p** 79. NSM Stafford St Mary and St Chad *Lich* 78-79; NSM Stafford from 79. *35 Newland Avenue, Stafford ST16 1NL* Tel (01785) 245069

FISHER, Paul Vincent. b 43. Worc Coll Ox BA66 MA70 ARCM73. Qu Coll Birm DipTh68. **d** 70 **p** 71. C Redditch St Steph *Worc* 70-73; C Chorlton upon Medlock *Man* 73-79; Chapl Man Univ 73-79; Exec Sec Community Affairs Division BCC 79-81; Asst Dir of Tr and Dir of Lay Tr *Carl* 81-86; P-in-c Raughton Head w Gatesgill 81-85; Lay Tr Team Ldr *S'wark* 86-90; Dir of Tr 90-94; V Kingswood 94-00; rtd 00; Perm to Offic *Bradf* from 01. *3 Buxton Park, Langcliffe, Settle BD24 9NQ* Tel (01729) 824058 E-mail paul.fisher@ukonline.co.uk

FISHER, Peter Francis Templar. b 36. CCC Cam BA60 MA. Wells Th Coll 62. **d** 63 **p** 64. C Gt Ilford St Mary *Chelmsf* 63-67; C Colchester St Mary V 67-70; C-in-c Basildon St Andr CD 70-72; P-in-c Edstaston *Lich* 83-87; P-in-c Whixall 83-87; P-in-c Tilstock 84-87; V Shelton and Oxon 87-97; rtd 97. *8 Cecil Road, Dronfield S18 2GU* Tel 0114-258 1455

FISHER, Canon Peter Timothy. b 44. Dur Univ BA68 MA75. Cuddesdon Coll 68. **d** 70 **p** 71. C Bedford St Andr *St Alb* 70-74; Chapl Surrey Univ *Guildf* 74-78; Sub-Warden Linc Th Coll 78-83; R Houghton le Spring *Dur* 83-94; RD Houghton 87-92; Prin Qu Coll Birm 94-02; V Maney *Birm* from 02; Hon Can Birm Cathl from 00. *The Vicarage, Maney Hill Road, Sutton Coldfield B72 1JJ* Tel 0121-354 2426 E-mail pfisher@fish.co.uk

✠**FISHER, The Rt Revd Reginald Lindsay (Brother Michael).** b 18. Lambeth MA78 Westcott Ho Cam 51. **d** 53 **p** 54 **c** 79. SSF from 42; Lic to Offic *Ely* 53-62; Lic to Offic *Newc* 62-67; Lic to Offic *Germany* 67-79; Suff Bp St Germans *Truro* 79-85; Bp HM Pris 85; Min Gen SSF 85-91; rtd 85; Asst Bp Ely from 85. *St Francis House, 15 Botolph Lane, Cambridge CB2 3RD* Tel (01223) 353903

FISHER, Richard John. b 60. K Coll Lon BA82 AKC82 Selw Coll Cam BA87 Cam Univ MA95. Ridley Hall Cam 85. **d** 88 **p** 89. C Woodley St Jo the Ev *Ox* 88-91; C Acomb St Steph *York* 91-95; Chapl Preston Acute Hosps NHS Trust 98-02; Chapl Lanc Teaching Hosps NHS Trust from 02. *Royal Preston Hospital, Sharoe Green Lane North, Fulwood, Preston PR2 4HT* Tel (01772) 523730 *or* 716565 Fax 522447 E-mail richard.fisher@lthtr.nhs.uk

FISHER, Roy Percy. b 22. Lon Univ TCert50 Univ of Wales MTh00. Linc Th Coll 51. **d** 53 **p** 54. C Lewisham St Jo Southend *S'wark* 53-56; Clare Coll Miss Rotherhithe 56-59; V Boughton under Blean *Cant* 59-66; V Westgate St Sav 66-71; R Staplegrove *B & W* 71-79; TR Eckington w Handley and Ridgeway *Derby* 79-87; rtd 87; Perm to Offic *Llan* from 87. *258 New Road, Porthcawl CF36 5BA* Tel (01656) 788682

FISHER, Stephen Newson. b 46. CEng82 MIEE82 Univ of Wales (Swansea) BSc67. Linc Th Coll 84. **d** 86 **p** 87. C Nunthorpe *York* 86-89; P-in-c Middlesbrough St Oswald 89-90; V 90-94; V Redcar 94-02; P-in-c The Thorntons and The Otteringtons from 02. *The Vicarage, 4 Endican Lane, Thornton le Moor, Northallerton DL7 9FB* Tel (01609) 761806 Fax 08701-634640 E-mail stephen@thefishers.vnet.co.uk

FISHER, Thomas Andrew. b 35. Southn Univ HNC57. Sarum & Wells Th Coll 84. **d** 86 **p** 87. C Win Ch Ch *Win* 86-89; Chapl Salisbury Coll of Tech *Sarum* 89-94; Chapl Salisbury Coll of FE 89-94; Perm to Offic *Sarum* 94-99; rtd 00; NSM Salisbury St Mark *Sarum* from 99. *Mombasa, Manor Farm Road, Salisbury SP1 2RR* Tel (01722) 335155

FISHER, Thomas Ruggles. b 20. Cranmer Hall Dur 58. **d** 60 **p** 61. C Melton Mowbray w Thorpe Arnold *Leic* 60-63; R Husbands Bosworth 63-74; R Husbands Bosworth w Mowsley and Knaptoft 74-79; R Husbands Bosworth w Mowsley and Knaptoft etc 79-82; Perm to Offic 82-96; Perm to Offic *Pet* from 83; rtd 85. *12 The Dell, Oakham LE15 6JG* Tel (01572) 757630

FISHER-BAILEY, Mrs Carol. b 56. **d** 96 **p** 97. C Eccleshill *Bradf* 96-99; TV Sutton St Jas and Wawne *York* from 99. *Wawne Vicarage, 50 Main Street, Wawne, Hull HU7 5XH*

FISHLOCK, Mrs Margaret Winifred (Peggy). b 28. Cant Sch of Min 87. **d** 97 **p** 98. NSM Deal St Leon and St Rich and Sholden *Cant* from 97. *58 Gilford Road, Deal CT14 7DQ* Tel (01304) 365841

FISHWICK, Alan. b 48. Chich Th Coll 87. **d** 89 **p** 90. C Laneside *Blackb* 89-92; C Accrington 92-93; TV 93-96; V Blackb St Aid 96-02; V Scorton and Barnacre and Calder Vale from 02. *St Peter's Vicarage, Snow Hill Lane, Scorton, Preston PR3 1AY* Tel (01524) 791229

FISHWICK, Mrs Ann. b 40. St Barn Coll Adelaide 91 Trin Coll Melbourne 93. **d** 91 **p** 94. Australia 91-97 and from 02; Chapl Charters Towers Hosp and Home 91-94; Dn Charters Towers St Paul 91-94; Asst P 94-97; Perm to Offic *Heref* 98-99; NSM Worthen 99-02; NSM Hope w Shelve 98-02; NSM Middleton

99-02. *PO Box 544, Weipa, Qld, Australia 4874* Tel (0061) (7) 4069 7228 E-mail capeyorkp@bigpond.com.au

FISHWICK, Ian Norman. b 54. Lanc Univ BEd E Lon Univ MA99. St Jo Coll Nottm DipTh. **d** 82 **p** 83. C High Wycombe *Ox* 82-87; V Walshaw Ch Ch *Man* 87-93; Area Voc Adv 88-93; V W Ealing St Jo w St Jas *Lon* 93-98; Dir of Ords Willesden Area 94-98; E Region Area Co-ord for CA 98-99; Operations Dir from 99. *24 Avenue Road, Isleworth TW7 4JN* Tel (020) 8560 2574 Fax as telephone E-mail i.fishwick@churcharmy.org.uk

FISHWICK, Raymond Allen. b 42. St Fran Coll Brisbane 93 N Queensland Coll of Min ACP96. **d** 91 **p** 92. Australia 91-97 and from 02; R Charters Towers St Paul 91-97; P-in-c Worthen *Heref* 98-02; P-in-c Hope w Shelve 98-02; P-in-c Middleton 98-02; P-in-c Weipa St Luke from 02; CF from 02. *PO Box 544, Weipa, Qld, Australia 4874* Tel (0061) (7) 4069 7228 E-mail capeyorkp@bigpond.com.au

FISKE, Paul Francis Brading. b 45. St Jo Coll Dur BA68 PhD72. Wycliffe Hall Ox DipTh72. **d** 73 **p** 74. C Sutton *Liv* 73-76; TV Cheltenham St Mary, St Matt, St Paul and H Trin *Glouc* 76-80; C-in-c Hartplain CD *Portsm* 80-84; Hd of Miss UK CMJ 84-86; Hon C Edgware *Lon* 84-86; R Broughton Gifford, Gt Chalfield and Holt *Sarum* 86-95; TV Bourne Valley 95-97; Adv Chr Action 95-97; P-in-c Princes Risborough w Ilmer *Ox* 97-98; TR Risborough from 98. *The Rectory, Church Lane, Princes Risborough HP27 9AW* Tel (01844) 344784 Fax as telephone E-mail fiske@tiscali.co.uk

FISON, Geoffrey Robert Martius. b 34. Dur Univ BA59. Ely Th Coll 59. **d** 61 **p** 62. C Heavitree *Ex* 61-64; Australia 64-69; BSB 64-69; C Southampton Maybush St Pet *Win* 70-73; TV Strood *Roch* 73-79; TV Swindon Dorcan *Bris* 79-83; P-in-c Brislington St Cuth 83-99; rtd 99; Perm to Offic *Glouc* and *Bris* from 99. *88 Oakleaze Road, Thornbury, Bristol BS35 2LP* Tel (01454) 850678

FITCH, Capt Alan John. b 45. Open Univ BA82 Warwick Univ MA84. Wilson Carlile Coll 64 Qu Coll Birm 92. **d** 92 **p** 93. CA from 66; C Glouc St Jas and All SS *Glouc* 92-97; NSM Wotton St Mary 93-97; V Douglas All SS and St Thos *S & M* 97-02; Chapl HM Pris Is of Man 97-02; TR Walbrook Epiphany *Derby* from 02; Dioc Adv on Racial Justice from 02. *St Augustine's Rectory, 155 Almond Street, Derby DE23 6LY* Tel (01332) 766603 E-mail a.fitch@virgin.net

FITCH, Canon John Ambrose. b 22. CCC Cam BA44 MA48. Wells Th Coll 45. **d** 47 **p** 48. C Newmarket All SS *St E* 47-50; Chapl St Felix Sch Southwold 51-69; V Reydon *St E* 51-70; R Brandon and Santon Downham 70-80; Hon Can St E Cathl 75-87; RD Mildenhall 78-80; R Monks Eleigh w Chelsworth and Brent Eleigh etc 80-87; rtd 87; Perm to Offic *St E* from 87; Perm to Offic *Chelmsf* from 87. *The Oak House, High Street, Great Yeldham, Halstead CO9 4EX* Tel (01787) 237053

FITTER, Matthew Douglas. b 59. City of Lon Poly BSc81. Trin Coll Bris MA03. **d** 03. C Purley Ch Ch *S'wark* from 03. *132 Whytecliffe Road, Purley CR8 2YU* Tel (020) 8763 8505 E-mail matthewfitter@hotmail.com

FITZ, Lionel Alfred. b 24. **d** 87 **p** 88. NSM Cheltenham St Mary, St Matt, St Paul and H Trin *Glouc* 87-04; Perm to Offic from 04. *9 Foxgrove Drive, Cheltenham GL52 6TQ* Tel (01242) 243405

FITZGERALD, Gerald. b 26. **d** 54 **p** 55. C Salford St Phil *Man* 54-57; New Zealand from 57. *8 Searidge Lane, Scarborough, Christchurch, New Zealand* Tel (0064) (3) 326 6112 Fax 326 6186

FITZGERALD, John Edward. b 44. Leic Univ MSc98 Dip Counselling. Oak Hill Th Coll DPS74. **d** 76 **p** 77. C Rainham *Chelmsf* 76-79; C Cambridge St Andr Less *Ely* 79-86; V Holmesfield *Derby* 86-88; Chapl HM Pris Wakef 88-90; Chapl HM Pris Whatton 90-93; Chapl HM Pris Nottm 90-98; Chapl HM YOI Glen Parva from 98. *HM Young Offender Institution, Glen Parva, Tiger's Road, Wigston LE18 4TN* Tel 0116-264 3100 ext 3339

FITZGERALD, Miss Melanie Anne. b 52. Sheff Univ BMus75. Westcott Ho Cam 96. **d** 98 **p** 99. C Rotherham *Sheff* 98-01; C Stannington 01-02; P-in-c Walkley from 02. *St Mary's Vicarage, 150 Walkley Road, Sheffield S6 2XQ* Tel 0114-234 5029 E-mail mfitzg@tesco.net

FITZGERALD CLARK, Mrs Diane Catherine. b 54. Rhode Is Univ BA76. Gen Th Sem NY MDiv86. **d** 86 **p** 95. USA 86-95; NSM Hampstead Em W End *Lon* 96-99; Chapl St Alb High Sch for Girls from 98; Assoc Min St Alb Abbey *St Alb* from 98; Perm to Offic *Lon* from 00. *13 Eleanor Avenue, St Albans AL3 5TA* Tel (01727) 860099

FITZGIBBON, Kevin Peter. b 49. St Jo Coll Nottm BTh81. **d** 81 **p** 82. C Corby St Columba *Pet* 81-85; V Newborough 85-99; V Eaton Socon *St Alb* from 99. *St Mary's Vicarage, 34 Drake Road, Eaton Socon, St Neots PE19 8HS* Tel (01480) 212219 E-mail k.fitzgibbon@care4free.net

FITZHARRIS, Barry. b 47. Lon Univ BA69 W Ontario Univ MA70 K Coll Lon BD72 AKC72. St Aug Coll Cant 72. **d** 73 **p** 74. C Whitstable All SS *Cant* 73-75; C Whitstable All SS w St Pet 75-76; Hon C Clapham Old Town *S'wark* 77-79; Asst Chapl Abp Tenison's Sch Kennington 78-84; Chapl and Hd RS 87-89; Hon C Streatham Ch Ch *S'wark* 80-84; R Radwinter w

Hempstead *Chelmsf* 84-87; Hon C Streatham St Pet *S'wark* 87-89 and 97-98. *196 Davidson Road, Croydon CR0 6DP*

FITZHARRIS, The Ven Robert Aidan. b 46. Sheff Univ BDS71. Linc Th Coll 87. **d** 89 **p** 90. C Dinnington *Sheff* 89-92; V Bentley 92-01; RD Adwick 95-01; Hon Can Sheff Cathl 98-01; Adn Doncaster from 01. *Fairview House, 14 Armthorpe Lane, Doncaster DN2 5LZ* Tel (01302) 325787 *or* (01709) 309110 Fax (01709) 309107
E-mail archdeacon.of.doncaster@sheffield-diocese.org.uk

FITZMAURICE, Arthur William John. b 65. AGSM89 Lon Inst of Educn PGCE92 Leeds Univ BA. Coll of Resurr Mirfield 97. **d** 99 **p** 00. C Spondon *Derby* 99-02; P-in-c Emscote *Cov* 02-03; TV Warwick from 03. *All Saints' Vicarage, Vicarage Fields, Warwick CV34 5NJ* Tel (01926) 492073
E-mail john@fmaurice.freeserve.co.uk

FITZPATRICK, Paul Kevin. b 60. Open Univ BA99. Cuddesdon Coll DipMin98. **d** 98 **p** 99. C Okehampton w Inwardleigh, Bratton Clovelly etc *Ex* 98-02; P-in-c Whipton from 02. *The Vicarage, 9 Summer Lane, Exeter EX4 8BY* Tel (01392) 462206

FITZSIMONS, Mrs Kathryn Anne. b 57. Bedf Coll of Educn CertEd78. NEOC 87. **d** 90. NSM Bilton *Ripon* from 90; Soc Resp Development Officer Richmond Adnry 92-99; Urban Min Officer from 99. *52 Newton Court, Leeds LS8 2PM* Tel 0113-248 5011 E-mail kathrynfitzsimons@hotmail.com

FITZWILLIAMS, Canon Mark Morshead. b 36. Trin Coll Cam BA59 MA64. Westcott Ho Cam 59. **d** 61 **p** 62. C St John's Wood *Lon* 61-64; C Hempnall *Nor* 64-70; R Lathbury *Ox* 70-78; R Newport Pagnell 70-78; RD Newport 73-78; TR Beaconsfield 78-94; RD Amersham 82-86; Hon Can Ch Ch 88-01; P-in-c Hambleden Valley 94-01; rtd 01. *24 Gorwell, Watlington OX49 5QD* Tel (01491) 613085
E-mail mark.fitzwilliams@lineone.net

FLACH (née ROLLINS), Mrs Deborah Mary Rollins. b 54. Trin Coll Bris DipHE81 Sarum & Wells Th Coll 88. **d** 94 **p** 97. Asst Chapl Chantilly *Eur* 94-96; Asst Chapl Maisons-Laffitte from 96. *63 rue de Boissy, 60340 St Leu d'Esserent, France* Tel (0033) (3) 44 56 76 08 Fax 44 56 64 24 E-mail debjerflach@wanadoo.fr

FLACK, Miss Heather Margaret. b 47. **d** 95 **p** 96. C Shenley Green *Birm* 95-00; TV Kings Norton from 00. *195 Monyhull Hall Road, Birmingham B30 3QN* Tel 0121-458 3483 Fax 486 2825

✠**FLACK, The Rt Revd John Robert.** b 42. Leeds Univ BA64. Coll of Resurr Mirfield 64. **d** 66 **p** 67 **c** 97. C Armley St Bart *Ripon* 66-69; C Northampton St Mary *Pet* 69-72; V Chapelthorpe *Wakef* 72-81; V Ripponden 81-85; V Barkisland w W Scammonden 81-85; V Brighouse 85-88; TR Brighouse St Martin 88-92; RD Brighouse and Elland 86-92; Hon Can Wakef Cathl 89-92; Adn Pontefract 92-97; Suff Bp Huntingdon *Ely* 97-03; Hon Can Ely Cathl 97-03; Abp's Rep H See and Dir Angl Cen Rome from 03; Hon Asst Bp Pet from 03. *Anglican Centre, Palazzo Doria Pamphilj, Piazza del Collegio Romano 2, 00186 Rome, Italy* Tel (0039) (06) 678 0302 Fax 678 0674
E-mail anglican.centre@flashnet.it

FLAGG, David Michael. b 50. CCC Cam BA71 MA75. St Jo Coll Nottm BA76 Dip Past Counselling 94. **d** 77 **p** 78. C Hollington St Leon *Chich* 77-80; C Woodley St Jo the Ev *Ox* 80-86; Chapl The Dorothy Kerin Trust Burrswood 86-94; R Knockholt w Halstead *Roch* 94-99; Dir Chapl Services Mildmay UK 99-03; Hd Chapl Services Qu Eliz Hosp NHS Trust from 03. *Queen Elizabeth Hospital, Stadium Road, London SE18 4QH* Tel (020) 8836 6831 E-mail david.flagg@nhs.net

✠**FLAGG, The Rt Revd John William Hawkins (Bill).** b 29. **d** 59 **p** 61 **c** 69. Paraguay 59-63; Argentina 64-73; Adn N Argentina 65-69; Bp Paraguay and N Argentina 69-73; Asst Bp Chile 73-77; Bp Peru 73-77; Asst Bp Liv 78-86; V Toxteth St Cypr w Ch Ch 78-85; P-in-c Litherland Ch Ch 85-86; Gen Sec SAMS 86-93; Asst Bp Roch 87-92; Asst Bp S'well 92-96; Dioc Stewardship Adv 93-96; Dioc Adv in Rural Affairs 93-96; Dioc Adv for Overseas Affairs 94-96; rtd 97; Hon Asst Bp S'well from 97. *c/o A J Flagg Esq, 1 Denshaw, Up Holland, Wigan WN8 0AY* E-mail bill@southwell.anglican.org

FLAHERTY, Jane Venitia. *See* ANDERSON, Mrs Jane Venitia

FLANAGAN, Miss Vivienne Lesley. b 66. Liv Poly BA89 Nottm Univ PGCE90. St Jo Coll Nottm MA98. **d** 98 **p** 99. C Huthwaite *S'well* 98-02; P-in-c Lenton Abbey from 02. *St Barnabas' Vicarage, Derby Road, Beeston, Nottingham NG9 2SN* Tel 0115-925 5488

FLATHER, Peter George. b 29. Sarum Th Coll. **d** 59 **p** 60. C Fordingbridge w Ibsley *Win* 59-63; C Lyndhurst 63-65; R E w W Bradenham *Nor* 65-72; P-in-c Speke All SS *Liv* 72-73; P-in-c Sharrington *Nor* 73-87; R Gunthorpe w Bale 73-87; P-in-c Gt w Lt Snoring 77-83; R Gunthorpe w Bale w Field Dalling, Saxlingham etc 87-89; rtd 89; Perm to Offic Nor 89-99. *29 Jannys Close, Aylsham, Norwich NR11 6DL* Tel (01263) 733548

FLATT, Donald Clifford. b 15. Worc Ord Coll 63. **d** 65 **p** 66. C Tring *St Alb* 65-67; V Wigginton 67-75; Chapl HM Pris Bedf 75-80; V Biddenham *St Alb* 75-02; rtd 83; P-in-c Oare w Culbone B & W 83-86; Perm to Offic 86-01. *The Stables Cottage, Lamb Court, Dulverton TA22 9HB* Tel (01398) 323088

FLATT, The Very Revd Roy Francis Ferguson. b 47. Edin Th Coll 78. **d** 80 **p** 81. C St Andrews St Andr *St And* 80-82; C Elie w

Earlsferry 80-82; C Pittenweem 80-82; Dioc Supernumerary 82-83; Dioc Sec *Arg* 83-87; Dioc Youth Chapl 83-94; R Lochgilphead from 83; R Kilmartin from 83; P-in-c Inveraray from 83; Dean Arg from 99. *Bishopton House, Bishopton Road, Lochgilpead PA31 8PY* Tel (01546) 602315 Mobile 0777-5852115 Fax 602519 E-mail lochgilphead@argyll.anglican.org

FLATT, Stephen Joseph. b 57. SRN79 RSCN81 NDN83. Sarum & Wells Th Coll 92. **d** 92 **p** 93. C Limpsfield and Titsey *S'wark* 92-96; TV Pewsey *Sarum* 96-97; Staff Nurse R Free Hampstead NHS Trust 97-99; Charge Nurse from 99; Perm to Offic *S'wark* 98-99; Lic to Offic from 99; Asst Chapl Univ Coll Lon Hosps NHS Trust 00-01; Chapl from 01. *4 Highwood House, 148 New Cavendish Street, London W1W 6YH* Tel (020) 7637 8249

FLATTERS, Clive Andrew. b 56. Sarum & Wells Th Coll 83. **d** 86 **p** 88. C Weston Favell *Pet* 86-87; C Old Brumby *Linc* 88-91; C Syston *Leic* 91-93; TV 93-99; V Knottingley *Wakef* 99-02; TR Knottingley and Kellington w Whitley from 02. *The Vicarage, Chapel Street, Knottingley WF11 9AN* Tel (01977) 672267

FLAVELL, Paul William Deran. b 44. Univ of Wales (Ban) DipTh66. St Mich Coll Llan DPS68. **d** 68 **p** 69. Australia 68-71; C Blaenavon w Capel Newydd *Mon* 71-74; V Ynysddu 74-84; R Llanaber w Caerdeon *Ban* 84-00; V Llanstadwel *St D* from 00. *The Vicarage, 68 Church Road, Llanstadwel, Milford Haven SA73 1EB* Tel (01646) 600227

FLEET, Daniel James Russell. b 60. Wye Coll Lon BSc84 Keele Univ PGCE02. St Jo Coll Nottm LTh88 DPS89. **d** 89 **p** 90. C Boldmere *Birm* 89-92; C Caverswall and Weston Coyney w Dilhorne *Lich* 92-95; V Alton w Bradley-le-Moors and Oakamoor w Cotton 95-01; rtd 01; Perm to Offic *Lich* from 01. *124 Byrds Lane, Uttoxeter ST14 7RD* Tel (01889) 560214
E-mail dan.fleet@lineone.net

FLEMING, The Ven David. b 37. Kelham Th Coll 58. **d** 63 **p** 64. C Walton St Marg Belmont Road *Liv* 63-67; Chapl HM Borstal Gaynes Hall 68-76; V Gt Staughton *Ely* 68-76; RD St Neots 72-76; V Whittlesey 76-85; RD March 77-82; Hon Can Ely Cathl 82-01; P-in-c Ponds Bridge 83-85; Adn Wisbech 84-93; V Wisbech St Mary 85-89; Chapl Gen of Pris 93-01; Chapl to The Queen from 95; Perm to Offic *Ely* from 01. *Fair Haven, 123 Wisbech Road, Littleport, Ely CB6 1JJ* Tel (01353) 862498

FLEMING, Elizabeth Julie. b 57. Westhill Coll Birm CertEd79 Chester Coll of HE BTh00. N Ord Course 97. **d** 00 **p** 01. C Widnes St Jo *Liv* 00-03; P-in-c Walton Breck Ch Ch from 03. *Christ Church Vicarage, 157 Hartnup Street, Liverpool L5 1UW* Tel 0151-263 2518 E-mail joolz@merseymail.com

FLEMING, George. b 39. IDC. CITC. **d** 78 **p** 79. C Donaghcloney w Waringstown *D & D* 78-80; C Newtownards 80; I Movilla 80; C Heref St Pet w St Owen and St Jas *Heref* 80-85; V Holmer w Huntington 85-96; P-in-c Worfield 96-98; V from 98. *The Vicarage, Worfield, Bridgnorth WV15 5JZ* Tel (01746) 716698

FLEMING, Mrs Penelope Rawling. b 43. Glas Univ MA63. Westcott Ho Cam 87. **d** 89 **p** 94. C Bourne *Guildf* 89-94; R Wotton and Holmbury St Mary 94-01; Dioc Voc Adv from 94; RD Dorking 99-01; R Gt Bookham from 01. *The Rectory, 2A Fife Way, Bookham, Leatherhead KT23 3PH* Tel (01372) 452405 E-mail pennyflem@aol.com

FLEMING, Ronald Thorpe. b 29. Codrington Coll Barbados 52. **d** 56 **p** 57. Barbados 56-61; C Delaval *Newc* 61-64; V Cambois 64-69; V Ancroft w Scremerston 69-81; V Longhirst 81-84; Lic to Offic 84-94; Chapl Preston Hosp N Shields 84-94; Chapl N Tyneside Hosps 84-94; rtd 94; Perm to Offic *Newc* from 94. *18 Holly Avenue, Whitley Bay NE26 1ED* Tel 0191-252 7414

FLEMING, William Edward Charlton. b 29. TCD BA51 MA65. CITC 52. **d** 52 **p** 53. C Dublin Santry *D & G* 52-56; C Arm St Mark *Arm* 56-61; I Tartaraghan 61-80; Prov Registrar 79-96; I Tartaraghan w Diamond 80-96; Can Arm Cathl 86-96; Treas Arm Cathl 88-92; Chan Arm Cathl 92-96; rtd 96. *65 Annareagh Road, Drumorgan, Richhill, Armagh BT61 9JT* Tel (028) 3887 9612

FLENLEY, Benjamin Robert Glanville. b 50. Sarum & Wells Th Coll 86. **d** 88 **p** 89. C Eastleigh *Win* 88-92; V Micheldever and E Stratton, Woodmancote etc from 92. *The Vicarage, Micheldever, Winchester SO21 3DA* Tel (01962) 774233 Fax as telephone E-mail flenbenley@aol.com

FLETCHER, Anthony. *See* FLETCHER, James Anthony

FLETCHER, Anthony Peter Reeves. b 46. Bede Coll Dur CertEd Nottm Univ BTh78. Kelham Th Coll 63 Ridley Hall Cam Dip Past Th. **d** 74 **p** 75. C Luton St Mary *St Alb* 74-78; Chapl RAF 78-00; P-in-c Lyneham w Bradenstoke *Sarum* 98-99; rtd 00; P-in-c Kyrenia St Andr and Chapl N Cyprus from 00. *PO Box 22075, 1517 Nicosia, Cyprus* Tel (0090) (392) 815 4329 Fax 815 4486 E-mail standrews@iecnc.org

FLETCHER, Arthur William George. b 24. Leeds Univ BA50. Coll of Resurr Mirfield 50. **d** 52 **p** 53. C Bush Hill Park St Mark *Lon* 52-55; Chapl RAF 55-58 and 61-72; V Topcliffe *York* 58-61; R Challoch w Newton Stewart *Glas* 73-75; R Kilmacolm 75-82; R Bridge of Weir 75-82; R Largs 82-89; rtd 89; Perm to Offic *Glas* from 89. *Westhaven, Main Road, Inverkip, Greenock PA16 0EA* Tel (01475) 521611

FLETCHER, Miss Barbara. b 41. ALAM79. WMMTC 93. **d** 96 **p** 97. NSM Smethwick *Birm* 96-97; C 97-02; Perm to Offic from 02. *231 Abbey Road, Smethwick, Warley B67 5NN* Tel 0121-429 9354 E-mail bfletcher@warleywoods.fsnet.co.uk

FLETCHER, Christopher Ian. b 43. BSc PhD. Glouc Sch of Min. **d** 89 **p** 90. C Tenbury *Heref* 89-93; R Bredenbury w Grendon Bishop and Wacton etc from 93; RD Bromyard from 99. *The Rectory, Bredenbury, Bromyard HR7 4TF* Tel (01885) 482236 E-mail fletcherc.m@talk21.com

FLETCHER, Colin John. b 46. Chich Th Coll. **d** 83 **p** 84. C Lt Ilford St Mich *Chelmsf* 83-86; C Hockerill *St Alb* 86-89; V New Cantley *Sheff* 89-95; C Kenton *Lon* 95-01; C Heavitree w Ex St Paul *Ex* 01-02; C Heavitree and St Mary Steps from 02. *10 Sherwood Close, Heavitree, Exeter EX2 5DX* Tel (01392) 677153

✠**FLETCHER, The Rt Revd Colin William.** b 50. OBE00. Trin Coll Ox BA72 MA76. Wycliffe Hall Ox 72. **d** 75 **p** 76 **c** 00. C Shipley St Pet *Bradf* 75-79; Tutor Wycliffe Hall Ox 79-84; Hon C Ox St Andr *Ox* 79-84; V Margate H Trin *Cant* 84-93; RD Thanet 88-93; Abp's Chapl 93-00; Hon Can Dallas from 93; Area Bp Dorchester *Ox* from 00. *Arran House, Sandy Lane, Yarnton, Kidlington OX5 1PB* Tel (01865) 375541 Fax 379890 E-mail bishopdorchester@oxford.anglican.org

FLETCHER, David Clare Molyneux. b 32. Worc Coll Ox BA55 MA59 DipTh56. Wycliffe Hall Ox 56. **d** 58 **p** 59. C Islington St Mary *Lon* 58-62; Hon C 62-83; Field Worker Scripture Union 62-86; R Ox St Ebbe w H Trin and St Pet *Ox* 86-98; rtd 98. *51 Charlbury Road, Oxford OX2 6UX* Tel (01865) 552420

FLETCHER, David Ernest. b 53. Worc Coll of Educn BEd76 Open Univ MTh01. St Jo Coll Nottm 99. **d** 01 **p** 02. C Mixenden *Wakef* from 01. *The Old Sweet Factory, 1 Wheatley City, Halifax HX3 5LG* Tel (01422) 367713

FLETCHER, David Mark. b 56. Chich Th Coll 84. **d** 87 **p** 88. C Taunton St Andr *B & W* 87-91; P-in-c Chard, Furnham w Chaffcombe, Knowle St Giles etc 91-95; P-in-c Tiverton St Andr *Ex* from 95; RD Tiverton from 02; Chapl Mid Devon Primary Care Trust from 95. *St Andrew's Vicarage, Blackmore Road, Tiverton EX16 4AR* Tel (01884) 257865 E-mail dmfletcher@standrewstiv.fsnet.co.uk

FLETCHER, Douglas. b 40. Coll of Resurr Mirfield 67. **d** 68 **p** 69. C Notting Hill St Jo *Lon* 68-73; C Cambridge St Mary Less *Ely* 73-74; C Fulham St Jo Walham Green *Lon* 74-76; C Walham Green St Jo w St Jas 76-84; P-in-c Kensal Town St Thos w St Andr and St Phil 84-92; V from 92. *St Thomas's Vicarage, 231 Kensal Road, London W10 5DB* Tel (020) 8969 2810

FLETCHER, Francis Cecil. b 12. Clifton Th Coll 33. **d** 36 **p** 38. C Burton Ch Ch *Lich* 36-39; C Chasetown 39-44; C Gresley *Derby* 44-46; V Shrewsbury St Julian *Lich* 46-49; V Darlaston All SS 49-54; V Hammerwich 54-66; V Weston upon Trent 66-75; rtd 77. *243 Congleton Road, Biddulph, Stoke-on-Trent ST8 7RQ*

FLETCHER, Capt Frank. b 40. Wilson Carlile Coll 71 EAMTC 94. **d** 96 **p** 96. Asst Chapl HM Pris Highpoint 90-97; Chapl HM Pris Wealstun from 97. *The Chaplain's Office, HM Prison Wealstun, Thorp Arch, Wetherby L23 7AZ* Tel (01937) 844844

FLETCHER, George Henry Yorke. b 11. Wycliffe Hall Ox 58. **d** 59 **p** 60. C Yardley Wood *Birm* 59-62; V Hursley *Win* 62-67; V Hall Green St Pet *Birm* 67-75; V Clive w Grinshill *Lich* 75-80; rtd 80; Perm to Offic *Lich* from 80. *4 Croft Close, Bomere Heath, Shrewsbury SY4 3PZ* Tel (01939) 290337

FLETCHER, Gordon Wolfe Robin. b 31. Edin Th Coll. **d** 62 **p** 63. C Eston *York* 62-65; C Harton Colliery *Dur* 65-68; V Pelton 68-81; V Ryhope 81-96; rtd 96. *23 Swinburne Road, Darlington DL3 7TD* Tel (01325) 265994 E-mail gordon.fletcher@btinternet.com

FLETCHER, James Anthony. b 36. St Edm Hall Ox BA60 DipTh61 MA66. St Steph Ho Ox 60. **d** 62 **p** 63. C Streatham St Pet *S'wark* 62-65; C Hobs Moat CD *Birm* 65-68; C Cowley St Jo *Ox* 68-77; V Hanworth All SS *Lon* 77-02; P-in-c Hanworth St Geo 89-91; rtd 02; Perm to Offic *Cant* from 02. *19 Strand Street, Sandwich, Kent CT13 9OX* Tel (01304) 620506

FLETCHER, Miss Janet. b 59. Cranmer Hall Dur. **d** 00 **p** 01. C Ainsdale *Liv* from 00. *St John's House, 23 Pinfold Lane, Ainsdale, Southport PR8 3QH* Tel and fax (01704) 571520

FLETCHER, Canon Jeremy James. b 60. Dur Univ BA81. St Jo Coll Nottm DipTh86. **d** 88 **p** 89. C Stranton *Dur* 88-91; C Nottingham St Nic *S'well* 91-94; P-in-c Skegby 94-00; P-in-c Teversal 96-00; Bp's Dom Chapl 00-02; Can Res and Prec York Minster *York* from 02. *2 Minster Court, York YO1 7JJ* Tel (01904) 624965 *or* 557205 E-mail jeremyf@tiscali.co.uk *or* precentor@yorkminster.org

FLETCHER, Canon John Alan Alfred. b 33. Oak Hill Th Coll 58. **d** 61 **p** 62. C Erith St Paul *Roch* 61-64; C Rushden *Pet* 64-67; R Hollington St Leon *Chich* 67-86; V Chadwell Heath *Chelmsf* 86-00; RD Barking and Dagenham 91-00; Chapl Chadwell Heath Hosp Romford 86-93; Chapl Redbridge Health Care NHS Trust 93-00; Hon Can Chelmsf Cathl *Chelmsf* 99-00; rtd 00; Perm to Offic *Chich* from 01. *87 Hoads Wood Road, Hastings TN34 2BB* Tel (01424) 712345 Mobile 07860-128912 E-mail john/pam@fletchers17.freeserve.co.uk

FLETCHER, Jonathan James Molyneux. b 42. Hertf Coll Ox BA66 MA68. Wycliffe Hall Ox 66. **d** 68 **p** 69. C Enfield Ch Ch Trent Park *Lon* 68-72; C Cambridge St Sepulchre *Ely* 72-76; C St Helen Bishopsgate w St Martin Outwich *Lon* 76-81; Min Wimbledon Em Ridgway Prop Chpl *S'wark* from 82. *Emmanuel Parsonage, 8 Sheep Walk Mews, London SW19 4QL* Tel (020) 8946 4728

FLETCHER, Keith. b 47. Man Univ DipTh72. Chich Th Coll 79. **d** 80 **p** 81. C Hartlepool St Paul *Dur* 80-82; V Eighton Banks 82-85; V Haydon Bridge *Newc* 85-96; RD Hexham 93-96; P-in-c Beltingham w Henshaw 93-96; R Ashmanhaugh, Barton Turf etc *Nor* 96-99; rtd 99. *2 Churchill Terrace, Sherburn Hill, Durham DH6 1PF* Tel 0191-372 0362

FLETCHER, Miss Linden Elisabeth. b 50. Lon Univ BEd73 MA80. St Jo Coll Nottm 87. **d** 89 **p** 94. C Fakenham w Alethorpe *Nor* 89-93; C Cumnor *Ox* 93-02; P-in-c Ringshall w Battisford, Barking w Darmsden etc *St E* from 02. *The Rectory, Main Road, Willisham, Ipswich IP8 4SP* Tel (01473) 657768 Fax as telephone

FLETCHER, Mark. b 72. Staffs Poly BSc93. Oak Hill Th Coll BA00. **d** 00 **p** 01. C Paddington Em Harrow Road *Lon* 00-03. *Address temp unknown* E-mail mark@midwinter.org.uk

FLETCHER, Martin. b 60. Bradf Univ BEng83. Ripon Coll Cuddesdon. **d** 00 **p** 01. C Oatlands *Guildf* from 00. *6 Oatlands Court, St Mary's Road, Weybridge KT13 9QE* Tel (01932) 829622

FLETCHER, Martin James. b 48. FSAScot MIFA. SW Minl Tr Course 99. **d** 02 **p** 03. NSM Wolborough and Ogwell *Ex* from 02. *11 Troarn Way, Chudleigh, Newton Abbot TQ13 0PP* Tel (01626) 853998 E-mail martin.fletcher@rchme.co.uk

FLETCHER, Maurice. *See* FLETCHER, Ralph Henry Maurice

FLETCHER, Mrs Patricia. b 34. K Alfred's Coll Win CertEd74. Chich Th Coll 94. **d** 94. NSM Droxford *Portsm* 94-97; NSM Meonstoke w Corhampton cum Exton 94-97; rtd 97; Perm to Offic *Portsm* 97-00; NSM Blendworth w Chalton w Idsworth from 00. *17 Maylings Farm Road, Fareham PO16 7QU* Tel (01329) 311489

FLETCHER, Paul Gordon MacGregor. b 61. St Andr Univ MTh84. Edin Th Coll 84. **d** 86 **p** 87. C Cumbernauld *Glas* 86-89; C-in-c Glas H Cross 89-93; P-in-c Milngavie 93-99; R Clarkston from 99. *73 Finlay Rise, Milngavie, Glasgow G62 6QL* Tel 0141-956 2363 E-mail paul@staidans.freeserve.co.uk

FLETCHER, Ralph Henry Maurice. b 43. St Steph Ho Ox 71. **d** 74 **p** 75. C Chislehurst Annunciation *Roch* 74-77; Chapl Quainton Hall Sch Harrow 77-87 and 94-00; Hon C Hillingdon All SS *Lon* 87-94; Perm to Offic *Lon* 94-00 and *Roch* 00-02. *7 Park View, Kingstone, Barnsley S70 6NB* Tel (01226) 779928

FLETCHER, Robert Alexander. b 52. Ridley Hall Cam. **d** 84 **p** 85. C Chalfont St Peter *Ox* 84-88; C Bushey *St Alb* 88-93; TV Digswell and Panshanger 93-00; P-in-c Aldenham from 00. *The Vicarage, Church Lane, Aldenham, Watford WD2 8BE* Tel (01923) 855905

FLETCHER, Canon Robin Geoffrey. b 32. Nottm Univ BA57. Ridley Hall Cam 57. **d** 59 **p** 60. C S Mimms Ch Ch *Lon* 59-64; V Wollaton Park *S'well* 64-71; V Clifton *York* 71-97; Chapl Clifton Hosp York 71-88; RD City of York 86-97; Can and Preb York Minster 89-00; rtd 98; Perm to Offic *York* from 00. *68 Huntsman's Walk, York YO24 3LA* Tel (01904) 796876 E-mail rgeoff@soo.co.uk

FLETCHER, Mrs Sheila Elizabeth. b 35. Nottm Univ BA52 CertEd58. NEOC 84. **d** 87 **p** 94. NSM Dringhouses *York* 87-90; Par Dn 90-94; C 94-97; P-in-c Sutton on the Forest 97-02; rtd 02; Perm to Offic *York* from 02. *68 Huntsman's Walk, York YO24 3LA* Tel (01904) 796876 E-mail rgeoff@soo.co.uk

FLETCHER, Stephen. b 57. Man Univ BA79 MA84. St Jo Coll Nottm 82. **d** 84 **p** 85. C Didsbury St Jas and Em *Man* 84-88; C Kersal Moor 88-01; TR Horwich and Rivington from 01. *The Rectory, Chorley Old Road, Horwich, Bolton BL6 6AX* Tel (01204) 468263 Fax as telephone E-mail stephen@fletchers.freeserve.co.uk

FLETCHER, Stephen William. b 62. Wolv Poly BA84 Birm Univ DipTh87. Qu Coll Birm 85. **d** 88 **p** 89. C Rainham *Roch* 88-91; C Shottery St Andr *Cov* 91-97; Min Bishopton St Pet 91-97; V Llanrumney *Mon* 97-02; V Adderbury w Milton *Ox* from 02. *The Vicarage, Dog Close, Adderbury, Banbury OX17 3EF* Tel (01295) 810309

FLETCHER, Steven John Carylon. b 60. NCTJ83. Aston Tr Scheme 89 Ripon Coll Cuddesdon 89. **d** 92. C Newquay *Truro* 92-93. *Address temp unknown*

FLETCHER, Timothy John. b 63. Sheff Univ BA88. Cranmer Hall Dur 01. **d** 03. C Four Marks *Win* from 03. *25 Badger Close, Four Marks, Alton GU34 6HB* Tel (01420) 568277 E-mail tim@fletcherchester.fsnet.co.uk

FLETCHER-CAMPBELL, Walter John Fletcher. b 12. Magd Coll Ox BA33 BSc38 MA44. Wells Th Coll 37. **d** 38 **p** 39. C Portsea St Mary *Portsm* 38-45; V Sarisbury 45-47; V Milton 47-60; RD Portsm 55-60; Metrop Sec USPG (Lon and Chelmsf) 60-66; Promotion and Tr Sec 66-68; Dep Home Sec 68-70; V Stanton Harcourt w Northmoor *Ox* 70-75; RD Witney 71-76; P-in-c Bampton Aston w Shifford 75-76; P-in-c Bampton Proper w Bampton Lew 75-76; rtd 77; RD Abingdon *Ox* 80-87; C

Radley and Sunningwell 89-93. *153 Upper Road, Kennington, Oxford OX1 5LR* Tel (01865) 730467

FLEWKER, David William. b 53. Birm Univ BA75. Wycliffe Hall Ox 76. **d** 78 **p** 79. C Netherton *Liv* 78-82; C Prescot 82-84; V Seaforth 84-88; TV Whitstable *Cant* 88-96; Miss to Seamen 88-96; V Bethersden w High Halden *Cant* from 96; Asst Dir of Ords from 02. *The Vicarage, Bull Lane, Bethersden, Ashford TN26 3HA* Tel (01233) 820266

FLIGHT, Michael John. b 41. Sarum Th Coll 68. **d** 71 **p** 72. C Wimborne Minster *Sarum* 71-75; R Tarrant Gunville, Tarrant Hinton etc 75-78; P-in-c Tarrant Rushton, Tarrant Rawston etc 77-78; R Tarrant Valley 78-80; V Westbury 80-00; RD Heytesbury 83-87 and 96-00; R Broad Town, Clyffe Pypard, Hilmarton etc from 00. *The Rectory, Wood Lane, Clyffe Pypard, Swindon SN4 7PY* Tel (01793) 731623

FLINDALL, Roy Philip. b 39. K Coll Lon AKC61 BD64 MPhil71 Keswick Hall Coll PGCE71. St Boniface Warminster 62. **d** 63 **p** 64. C Gt Yarmouth *Nor* 63-68; V Nor St Sav w St Paul 68-70; C-in-c Nor St Clem and St Geo 68-70; Lic to Offic *Ely* 90-92; *S'wark* 92-95; Chapl Pet High Sch 95-03; P-in-c Thorney Abbey *Ely* from 03. *The Vicarage, The Green, Thorney, Peterborough PE6 0QD* Tel (01733) 270388

FLINN, Canon John Robert Patrick. b 30. CITC. **d** 65 **p** 66. C Dublin Rathfarnham *D & G* 65-67; I Baltinglass w Ballynure etc *C & O* 67-76; I Castlepollard and Oldcastle w Loughcrew etc *M & K* 76-84; rtd 84; Treas Ossory and Leighlin Cathls *C & O* 90-92; Chan Ossory and Leighlin Cathls 96-01. *The Old School House, Kells, Kilkenny, Irish Republic* Tel (00353) (56) 772 8297

FLINT, Howard Michael. b 59. Edge Hill Coll of HE BEd81. Cranmer Hall Dur 95. **d** 97 **p** 98. C Chipping Campden w Ebrington *Glouc* 97-00; V Upper Wreake *Leic* from 00; RD Framland from 02. *The Vicarage, 2 Carrfields Lane, Frisby on the Wreake, Melton Mowbray LE14 2NT* Tel (01664) 434878 E-mail howard.flint@btopenworld.com

FLINT, Nicholas Angus. b 60. Chich Th Coll 84. **d** 87 **p** 88. C Aldwick *Chich* 87-91; Bp's Asst Chapl for the Homeless *Lon* 91-92; TV Ifield *Chich* 92-96; R Rusper w Colgate from 96. *The Rectory, High Street, Rusper, Horsham RH12 4PX* Tel (01293) 871251

FLINTHAM, Alan Jenkinson. b 45. Leeds Univ BSc66 PGCE67 MEd74. EMMTC 98. **d** 00 **p** 01. NSM Melbourne *Derby* from 00. *50 Burlington Way, Mickleover, Derby DE3 9BD* Tel (01332) 512293 E-mail flintham@flinthams.org.uk

FLIPPANCE, Miss Kim Sheelagh May. b 64. RGN85 RM88. Trin Coll Bris 97. **d** 99 **p** 00. C Alderbury Team *Sarum* 99-01; C Clarendon 01-02; Asst Chapl Salisbury Health Care NHS Trust from 02. *The Chaplain's Office, Salisbury District Hospital, Salisbury SP2 8BJ* Tel (01722) 336262

FLOATE, Herbert Frederick Giraud. b 25. Keble Coll Ox BA50 MA54. Qu Coll Birm 50. **d** 61 **p** 62. Seychelles 61; Hon C Quarrington w Old Sleaford *Linc* 63-65; P-in-c Mareham le Fen 65-66; Australia 66-72; R Stroxton *Linc* 72-74; R Harlaxton w Wyville and Hungerton 72-74; Lect Shenston New Coll Worcs 74-78; P-in-c Redditch St Geo *Worc* 78-79; Lic to Offic 80-84; R Upton Snodsbury and Broughton Hackett etc 84-89; Chapl Mojacar *Eur* 89-91; rtd 91; Perm to Offic *Heref* from 97. *15 Progress Close, Ledbury HR8 2QZ* Tel (01531) 635509

FLOATE, Miss Rhona Cameron. b 59. Univ of Wales (Cardiff) BA80. Trin Coll Bris 01. **d** 03. C Lighthorne *Cov* from 03; C Chesterton from 03; C Newbold Pacey w Moreton Morrell from 03. *5 Chestnut Grove, Moreton Morrell, Warwick CV35 9DG* Tel (01926) 650093 E-mail rhonafloate@hotmail.com

FLOCKHART, Mrs Ruth. b 56. TISEC 96. **d** 99 **p** 00. NSM Strathpeffer *Mor* from 99; NSM Dingwall from 99. *Ancarraig House, Bunloit, Drumnadrochit, Inverness IV3 6XG* Tel (01456) 450633 E-mail ruth@ancarraig.clara.co.uk

FLOOD, Kenneth. b 75. St Chad's Coll Dur BSc96 St Steph Ho Ox BTh01. **d** 01 **p** 02. C Hulme Ascension *Man* from 01. *35 Millington Walk, Hulme, Manchester M15 4DF* Tel 0161-226 4199 E-mail kenneth.flood@usa.net

FLOOD, Nicholas Roger. b 42. FCA. Ripon Hall Ox 71. **d** 92 **p** 93. NSM Romsey *Win* 92-94; Chapl Win and Eastleigh Healthcare NHS Trust from 94. *Royal Hampshire County Hospital, Romsey Road, Winchester SO22 5DG* Tel (01962) 824906 *or* 863535

FLORANCE, James Andrew Vernon. b 44. MCIOB. Linc Th Coll 84. **d** 86 **p** 87. C Lt Ilford St Mich *Chelmsf* 86-90; TV Becontree S 90-93; R Orsett and Bulphan and Horndon on the Hill 93-97; P-in-c Liscard St Mary w St Columba *Ches* 97-02; RD Wallasey 99-02; Chapl St D Foundn Hospice Care Newport 02-03; P-in-c Abersychan and Garndiffaith *Mon* from 03. *The Vicarage, Abersychan, Pontypool NP4 8PX* Tel (01495) 772213

FLORY, John Richard. b 35. Clare Coll Cam BA59 MA63. Westcott Ho Cam 69. **d** 71 **p** 72. C Shirehampton *Bris* 71-74; V Patchway 74-82; R Lydiard Millicent w Lydiard Tregoz 82-86; TR The Lydiards 93-95; R Box w Hazlebury and Ditteridge 93-01; rtd 01; Perm to Offic *Derby* from 02. *Beechbank, 3 Ivonbrook Close, Darley Bridge, Matlock DE4 2JX* Tel (01629) 734707

FLOWER, David. b 48. IPFA75. EMMTC DTPS95. **d** 95 **p** 99. NSM Ashby-de-la-Zouch H Trin *Leic* from 95. *29 Money Hill, Ashby-de-la-Zouch LE65 1JA* Tel (01530) 414939 E-mail david.flower@tesco.net

FLOWER, Roger Edward. b 45. AKC68. **d** 69 **p** 70. C Gt Stanmore *Lon* 69-72; C Wells St Cuth w Coxley and Wookey Hole *B & W* 72-77; V Tatworth 77-82; P-in-c Taunton St Andr 82-84; V 84-96; RD Taunton 90-96; Preb Wells Cathl 92-96; V Dartmouth *Ex* 96-99. *Address temp unknown*

FLOWERDAY, Andrew Leslie. b 53. Imp Coll Lon BSc75. St Jo Coll Nottm DipTh. **d** 90 **p** 91. C Farnborough *Guildf* 90-95; TV Morden *S'wark* from 95. *140 Stonecot Hill, Sutton SM3 9HQ* Tel (020) 8330 6566 *or* 8337 6421

FLOWERDEW, Martin James. b 56. Herts Coll CertEd78 Pemb Coll Cam BEd79 UEA CertCS82. Sarum & Wells Th Coll 89. **d** 91 **p** 92. C Leagrave *St Alb* 91-95; C Radlett 95-99; TV Wilford Peninsula *St E* 99-01; V St Osyth *Chelmsf* from 01. *The Vicarage, The Bury, St Osyth, Clacton-on-Sea CO16 8NX* Tel (01255) 820348 E-mail theblacksheep@tinyworld.co.uk

FLOWERS, John Henry. b 33. Qu Coll Birm 63. **d** 65 **p** 66. C Aberdare St Fagan *Llan* 65-68; C Llantrisant 68-72; V Nantymoel w Wyndham 72-76; Asst Chapl HM Pris Wormwood Scrubs 76-78; Chapl HM Pris Birm 78-80; Chapl HM Pris Albany 80-93; rtd 93; Perm to Offic *Portsm* from 93. *1 Ulster Crescent, Newport PO30 5RU* Tel (01983) 525493

FLUX, Brian George. b 39. Oak Hill Th Coll 68. **d** 71 **p** 72. C Chadderton Ch Ch *Man* 71-74; C Preston All SS *Blackb* 74-76; Min Preston St Luke 76-81; CF (TA) from 78; R Higher Openshaw *Man* 81-88; Chapl HM Pris Haverigg 88-92; rtd 92. *65 Crosby Street, Maryport CA15 6DR* Tel (01900) 810635

FLYNN, Alexander Victor George. b 45. DTh. **d** 90 **p** 91. C Kilsaran w Drumcar, Dunleer and Dunany *Arm* 90-91; P-in-c 91-94; I 94-98; I Clonenagh w Offerlane, Borris-in-Ossory etc *C & O* 98-00. *Shalom, Ridge Road, Portlaoise, Co Laois, Irish Republic*

FLYNN, Peter Murray. b 35. Oak Hill Th Coll 76. **d** 79 **p** 80. Hon C Finchley St Mary *Lon* 79-83; Hon C Mill Hill Jo Keble Ch 84-86; C Mill End and Heronsgate w W Hyde *St Alb* 86-92; V Chessington *Guildf* from 92. *The Vicarage, Garrison Lane, Chessington KT9 2LB* Tel (020) 8397 3016

FOALE, Rosemary. b 41. **d** 01 **p** 02. NSM Shebbear, Buckland Filleigh, Sheepwash etc *Ex* from 01. *16 J H Taylor Drive, Northam, Bideford EX39 1TU* Tel (01237) 421366

FODEN, Eric. Local Minl Tr Course. **d** 93 **p** 94. OLM New Bury *Man* 93-96. *45 Stetchworth Drive, Worsley, Manchester M28 1FU* Tel 0161-790 4627

FODEN, Mrs Janice Margaret. b 54. Sheff Univ BA76 Sheff City Poly PGCE77. N Ord Course 98. **d** 01 **p** 02. NSM Kimberworth *Sheff* from 01. *10 Chapelfield Way, Thorpe Hesley, Rotherham S61 2TL* Tel 0114-221 3934 E-mail kf@kfoden.free-online.co.uk

FODEN-CURRIE, Mary Agnes. b 43. Bp Grosseteste Coll BEd64. St Jo Coll Nottm MA97. **d** 98 **p** 99. NSM Skegby *S'well* 98-02; NSM Skegby w Teversal 02-03; rtd 03; Perm to Offic *S'well* from 03. *40 Harvey Road, Mansfield NG18 4ES* Tel (01623) 479838

FOGDEN, Canon Elizabeth Sally. b 40. MCSP61 DipRS77. Qu Coll Birm 76. **dss** 78 **d** 87 **p** 94. Chevington w Hargrave and Whepstead w Brockley *St E* 78-84; Honington w Sapiston and Troston 84-87; Par Dn 87-92; Par Dn Euston w Barnham, Elvedon and Fakenham Magna 90-92; TD Blackbourne 92-94; Chapl Center Parc Elvedon from 90; Dioc Adv Women's Min from 90; Hon Can St E Cathl from 92; TV Blackbourne from 94. *The Rectory, Church Road, Honington, Bury St Edmunds IP31 1RG* Tel (01359) 269265 Mobile 07860-101980 Fax as telephone E-mail honingtonrectory@freeserve.co.uk

FOGDEN, Patricia. b 40. **d** 03. OLM Orlestone w Snave and Ruckinge w Warehorne etc *Cant* from 03. *Address temp unknown*

FOGG, Sister Cynthia Mary (Sister Mary Clare). b 34. Bp Grosseteste Coll TCert54 CertRK54. LNSM course 94. **d** 95 **p** 96. NSM Westgate Common *Wakef* from 95. *St Peter's Convent, Dovecote Lane, Horbury, Wakefield WF4 6BD* Tel (01924) 272181 Fax 261225

FOIZEY, Michael John. b 24. Trin Coll Cam BA45 MA65. Westcott Ho Cam 45. **d** 47 **p** 48. C Munster Square St Mary Magd *Lon* 47-53; V Willesden St Matt 53-60; R Lon Docks St Pet w Wapping St Jo 60-82; V Ealing Ch the Sav 82-89; Perm to Offic *Worc* from 89. *157 Birmingham Road, Kidderminster DY10 2SL* Tel (01562) 823277

FOLEY, Geoffrey Evan. b 30. Univ of New England BA71 DipEd73 MEd79. St Jo Coll Morpeth 51 ACT ThL54. **d** 53 **p** 54. Australia 53-90 and from 91; Perm to Offic *S'wark* 90-91; Chapl Hamburg w Kiel *Eur* 91; C Stoke-upon-Trent *Lich* 91; rtd 93; Dioc Archivist *Grafton* from 97. *198 Dawson Street, Lismore, NSW, Australia 2480* Tel (0061) (2) 6621 4684 E-mail gefoley@nor.com.au

FOLEY, James Frank. b 50. MBE91. Reading Univ BSc72 Edin Univ DMS83. STETS DTM98. **d** 99 **p** 00. C St Illogan *Truro* 99-03; P-in-c Droxford *Portsm* from 03; P-in-c Meonstoke w

Corhampton cum Exton from 03. *The Rectory, Rectory Lane, Meonstoke, Southampton SO32 3NF* Tel (01489) 877512

✠**FOLEY, The Rt Revd Ronald Graham Gregory.** b 23. St Jo Coll Dur BA49 DipTh50. **d** 50 **p** 51 **c** 82. C S Shore H Trin *Blackb* 50-54; V Blackb St Luke 54-60; Dir RE *Dur* 60-71; V Brancepeth 60-71; Hon Can Dur Cathl 65-71; Hon Can Ripon Cathl *Ripon* 71-82; V Leeds St Pet 71-82; Chapl to The Queen 77-82; Suff Bp Reading *Ox* 82-87; Area Bp Reading 87-89; rtd 89; Hon Asst Bp York from 95. *3 Poplar Avenue, Kirkbymoorside, York YO62 6ES* Tel (01751) 432439

FOLKARD, Oliver Goring. b 41. Nottm Univ BA63. Lich Th Coll 64. **d** 66 **p** 67. C Carlton *S'well* 66-67; C Worksop Priory 67-68; C Brewood *Lich* 68-71; C Folkingham w Laughton *Linc* 72-75; P-in-c Gedney Hill 76-77; V 77-84; V Whaplode Drove 76-84; V Sutton St Mary 84-94; RD Elloe E 89-94; P-in-c Scotter w E Ferry 94-99; R from 99; R Scotton w Northorpe from 99. *The Rectory, Church Lane, Scotter, Gainsborough DN21 3RZ* Tel (01724) 762951

FOLKS, Andrew John. b 42. St Jo Coll Dur BA65 DipTh69. **d** 69 **p** 70. C Stranton *Dur* 69-72; Chapl Sandbach Sch 73-80; Lic to Offic *Carl* 80-85; Chapl Casterton Sch Lancs 80-85; Hd Master Fernhill Manor Sch New Milton 85-97; Perm to Offic *Win* 85-97; NSM Langdale *Carl* from 97. *Langdale Vicarage, Chapel Stile, Ambleside LA22 9JG* Tel (01539) 437267

FOLKS, Peter William John. b 30. FRCO56 ARCM. Launde Abbey 72. **d** 72 **p** 73. C Leic St Aid *Leic* 72-76; V Newfoundpool 76-84; V Whetstone 84-94; rtd 94; Perm to Offic *Leic* from 94. *34 Triumph Road, Glenfield, Leicester LE3 8FR* Tel 0116-287 3177

FOLLAND, Mark Wilkins. b 59. Univ of Wales (Cardiff) DipTh86 Southn Univ BTh88. Sarum & Wells Th Coll 86. **d** 88 **p** 00. C Kirkby *Liv* 88-91; Chapl Asst Man R Infirmary 91-93; Chapl Cen Man Healthcare NHS Trust 93-00; Trust Chapl Team Ldr Cen Man/Man Children's Univ Hosp NHS Trust from 00. *Manchester Royal Infirmary, Oxford Road, Manchester M13 9WL* Tel 0161-276 4582 Fax 276 5156 E-mail mfolland@central.cmht.nwest.nhs.uk

FOLLETT, Jeremy Mark. b 66. Jes Coll Cam BA82. St Jo Coll Nottm 90. **d** 91 **p** 92. C Newark *S'well* 91-95; C Hellesdon *Nor* 95-01; V St Alb Ch Ch *St Alb* from 01. *Christ Church Vicarage, 5 High Oaks, St Albans AL3 6DJ* Tel (01727) 857592

FOLLETT, Neil Robert Thomas. b 50. RMCS BSc75 Open Univ BA85. EAMTC 86. **d** 89 **p** 90. C Godmanchester *Ely* 89-92; V 92-00; V Wilton Place St Paul *Lon* 00; rtd 00. *Address withheld by request*

FOLLIN, Michael Stuart. b 62. UMIST BSc84. St Jo Coll Nottm MTh02. **d** 02. C Aughton Ch Ch *Liv* from 02. *25 Peet Avenue, Ormskirk L39 4SH* Tel (01695) 577958 Mobile 07813-794252 E-mail michael.follin@tiscali.co.uk

FOLLIS, Bryan Andrew. b 61. Ulster Poly BA83 QUB PhD90 TCD BA98. CITC 95. **d** 98 **p** 99. C Portadown St Mark *Arm* 98-01; I Belfast All SS *Conn* from 01. *All Saints Rectory, 25 Rugby Road, Belfast BT7 1PT* Tel (028) 9032 3327

FOLLIS, Raymond George Carlile. b 23. DFC45. Lich Th Coll 63. **d** 65 **p** 66. C Walsall Wood *Lich* 65-69; R New Fishbourne *Chich* 69-88; P-in-c Appledram 84-88; rtd 88; Perm to Offic *Chich* from 88. *8 Old Rectory Gardens, Felpham, Bognor Regis PO22 7EP* Tel (01243) 825388

FONTAINE, Mrs Marion Elizabeth. b 39. RM61 RM62. St Alb and Ox Min Course 96. **d** 99 **p** 00. OLM Thatcham *Ox* from 99. *33 Druce Way, Thatcham RG19 3PF* Tel (01635) 827746

FOOKES, Roger Mortimer. b 24. VRD63 and Bars 73. Ch Ch Ox BA49 MA53. Wells Th Coll 48. **d** 50 **p** 51. C Westbury-on-Trym H Trin *Bris* 50-53; Chapl RNVR 51-58; Chapl RNR 58-74; C Frome St Jo *B & W* 53-55; R Barwick 55-62; R Closworth 55-62; V Midsomer Norton 62-78; RD Midsomer Norton 72-78; P-in-c Stratton on the Fosse 74-78; P-in-c Clandown 75-78; V Wotton-under-Edge w Ozleworth and N Nibley *Glouc* 78-89; RD Dursley 85-89; rtd 89; Perm to Offic *B & W* 90-99 and *Ex* from 90. *5 Gracey Court, Woodland Road, Broadclyst, Exeter EX5 3LP* Tel (01392) 461109

FOOKS, George Edwin. b 25. Trin Hall Cam BA49 MA52 Reading Univ AdDipEd70. Linc Th Coll 49. **d** 51 **p** 52. C Portsea St Cuth *Portsm* 51-53; C Fareham SS Pet and Paul 53-55; Chapl Earnseat Sch Carl 55-59; V Sheff St Cuth *Sheff* 59-64; Hd Careers Fairfax Gr Sch Bradf 64-66; Hd RE/Careers Buttershaw Comp Sch Bradf 66-70; Counsellor Ifield Sch Crawley 70-73; Hd Guidance Hengrove Sch Bris 73-78; Counsellor w Hearing Impaired Children (Avon) 78-89; Perm to Offic *Bris* from 83; Chapl Southmead Hosp Bris 89-90; Chapl Qu Eliz Hosp Bris 90-96; Chapl Thornbury Hosp from 90; rtd 90; Perm to Offic *Glouc* 90-97. *26 Rudgeway Park, Rudgeway, Bristol BS35 3RU* Tel (01454) 614072

FOOT, Adam Julian David. b 58. Thames Poly BSc80 Garnett Coll Lon CertEd87. Trin Coll Bris DipHE95. **d** 97 **p** 98. C Luton Ch Ch *Roch* 97-00; V Welling from 00. *St John's Vicarage, Danson Lane, Welling DA16 2BQ* Tel (020) 8303 1107 E-mail adam.foot@lineone.net

FOOT, Daniel Henry Paris. b 46. Peterho Cam BA67 MA74. Ridley Hall Cam 77. **d** 79 **p** 80. C Werrington *Pet* 79-82; P-in-c

Cranford w Grafton Underwood 82; R Cranford w Grafton Underwood and Twywell from 83; P-in-c Slipton from 94. *The Rectory, Rectory Hill, Cranford, Kettering NN14 4AH* Tel (01536) 330231

FOOT, Keith George. b 45. Surrey Univ BSc70 Lon Univ PhD73 MRSC CChem. NTMTC 96. **d** 99 **p** 00. C New Thundersley *Chelmsf* 99-03; Min Prince's Park CD *Roch* from 03. *6 Thrush Close, Chatham ME5 7TG* Tel (01634) 685828 E-mail keith.foot@ukgateway.net

FOOT, Leslie Robert James. b 33. Bris Univ BSc54. Wells Th Coll 67. **d** 69 **p** 70. Hon C Yeovil *B & W* 69-76; Lic to Offic from 76. *45 The Roman Way, Glastonbury BA6 8AB* Tel (01458) 832247

FOOT, Lynda. b 43. EMMTC 00. **d** 00 **p** 01. NSM Coalville and Bardon Hill *Leic* from 00. *78 Willesley Gardens, Ashby-de-la-Zouch LE65 2QF* Tel (01530) 414190

FOOT, Paul. b 41. Lon Univ BA64. Chich Th Coll 65. **d** 67 **p** 68. C Portsea N End St Mark *Portsm* 67-72; C Grimsborough *Ox* 72-74; V Cury w Gunwalloe *Truro* 74-80; P-in-c Port Isaac 80-83; P-in-c St Kew 80-83; V St Day 83-91; rtd 95. *Aeaea, 39 New Road, Llandovery SA20 0EA* Tel (01550) 720140

FOOTE, Desmond. b 46. S Dios Minl Tr Scheme. **d** 82 **p** 83. NSM Furze Platt *Ox* 82-88; NSM Ruscombe and Twyford from 88. *52 Broadwater Road, Twyford, Reading RG10 0EU* Tel 0118-934 2603

FOOTE, John Bruce. b 18. FRCPath G&C Coll Cam BA39 MA43 MD51. St Jo Coll Nottm 78. **d** 79 **p** 80. NSM Crookes St Thos *Sheff* 79-88; Perm to Offic *Derby* from 79; rtd 88; Perm to Offic *Sheff* from 88. *67 St Thomas Road, Sheffield S10 1UW* Tel 0114-266 5021

✠**FOOTTIT, The Rt Revd Anthony Charles.** b 35. K Coll Cam BA57 MA70. Cuddesdon Coll 59. **d** 61 **p** 62 **c** 99. C Wymondham *Nor* 61-64; C Blakeney w Lt Langham 64-67; P-in-c Hindringham w Binham and Cockthorpe 67-71; P-in-c Yarlington *B & W* 71-76; R N Cadbury 71-75; P-in-c S Cadbury w Sutton Montis 75-76; TR Camelot Par 76-81; RD Cary 79-81; Dioc Missr *Linc* 81-87; Can and Preb Linc Cathl 86-87; Dioc Rural Officer *Nor* 87; Adn Lynn 87-99; Suff Bp Lynn from 99. *The Old Vicarage, Castle Acre, King's Lynn PE32 2AA* Tel (01760) 755553 Fax 755085

FORAN, Andrew John. b 55. Aston Tr Scheme 84 Linc Th Coll 86. **d** 88 **p** 89. C Epping St Jo *Chelmsf* 88-92; TV Canvey Is 92-97; C Dorking w Ranmore *Guildf* 97-99; Chapl HM Pris Send from 97. *HM Prison, Ripley Road, Send, Woking GU23 7LJ* Tel (01483) 223048 Fax 223173

FORBES, Mrs Angela Laura. b 47. Ox Min Course 91. **d** 94 **p** 96. NSM Cowley St Jo *Ox* from 94. *80 Southfield Road, Oxford OX4 1PA* Tel (01865) 242697

FORBES, The Very Revd Graham John Thompson. b 51. Aber Univ MA73 Edin Univ BD76. Edin Th Coll 73. **d** 76 **p** 77. C Edin Old St Paul *Edin* 76-82; Can St Ninian's Cathl Perth *St And* 82-90; R Stanley 82-88; Provost St Ninian's Cathl Perth 82-90; R Perth St Ninian 82-90; Provost St Mary's Cathl *Edin* from 90; R Edin St Mary from 90. *8 Lansdowne Crescent, Edinburgh EH12 5EQ* Tel 0131-225 2978 or 225 6293 Fax 226 1482 or 225 3181 E-mail provost@cathedral.net

FORBES, Iain William. b 56. Ex Univ BA81. Chich Th Coll 83. **d** 85 **p** 86. C Upper Norwood St Jo *S'wark* 85-88; C Lewisham St Mary 88-90; Chapl St Martin's Coll of Educn *Blackb* 90-94; P-in-c Woodplumpton 94-99; Dioc Voc Adv 94-99; V Woodham *Guildf* from 99. *The Vicarage, 25 Woodham Waye, Woking GU21 5SW* Tel (01483) 762857

FORBES, Canon John Francis. b 29. CITC Dip Ecum 85. **d** 88 **p** 90. C Ferns w Kilbride, Toombe, Kilcormack etc *C & O* 88-90; NSM Gorey w Kilnahue, Leskinfere and Ballycanew from 90; Treas Ferns Cathl 98-03; Chan Ferns Cathl from 03. *Ballinabarna House, Enniscorthy, Co Wexford, Irish Republic* Tel (00353) (54) 33353 Mobile 87-2379319

FORBES, The Very Revd John Franey. b 33. AKC57. **d** 58 **p** 59. C Darlington H Trin *Dur* 58-62; S Africa from 62; Dean Pietermaritzburg from 76. *The Deanery, PO Box 1639, Pietermaritzburg, 3200 South Africa* Tel (0027) (331) 425848 or 941567 Fax 948785

FORBES, Joyce Brinella. b 52. Dioc OLM tr scheme 00. **d** 03. OLM Norbury St Steph and Thornton Heath *S'wark* from 03. *36 Dalmeny Avenue, London SW16 4RT* Tel (020) 8240 0283 E-mail petnard36@aol.com

FORBES, Patrick. b 38. Lon Univ Dip Sociology 74 Open Univ BA82. Linc Th Coll 64. **d** 66 **p** 67. C Yeovil *B & W* 66-69; C Plumstead Wm Temple Ch Abbey Wood CD *S'wark* 69-70; Thamesmead Ecum Gp 70-73; TV Thamesmead 73-78; Dioc Communications Officer *St Alb* 78-90; P-in-c Offley w Lilley 78-82; Lic to Offic 91-95; Info Officer Communications Dept Ch Ho Lon 91-95; Press Officer Miss to Seamen 95-99; rtd 99. *18 Francis Road, Hinxworth, Baldock SG7 5HL* Tel (01462) 742015 Fax as telephone E-mail patrickforbes@waitrose.com

FORBES, Raymond John. b 34. ALCD58. **d** 58 **p** 59. C Wandsworth St Steph *S'wark* 58-61; C Kewstoke *B & W* 61-63; V Fordcombe *Roch* 63-73; R Ashurst 64-73; P-in-c Morden w Almer and Charborough *Sarum* 73-76; P-in-c Bloxworth 73-76; V Red Post 76-84; P-in-c Hamworthy 84-92; P-in-c

Symondsbury and Chideock 92-96; rtd 96; Perm to Offic *Sarum* from 96. *65A Millhams Road, Bournemouth BH10 7LJ*

FORBES, Stuart. b 33. Lon Univ BD59. Oak Hill Th Coll 56. **d** 61 **p** 62. C Halliwell St Pet *Man* 61-64; P-in-c Wicker w Neepsend *Sheff* 64-69; V Stainforth 69-77; V Salterhebble All SS *Wakef* 77-89; V Toxteth Park St Mich w St Andr *Liv* 89-98; rtd 98; Perm to Offic *Lich* from 00. *29 Firbeck Gardens, Wildwood, Stafford ST17 4QR* Tel (01785) 663658

FORBES ADAM, Stephen Timothy Beilby. b 23. Ball Coll Ox. Chich Th Coll 59. **d** 61 **p** 62. C Guisborough *York* 61-64; R Barton in Fabis *S'well* 64-70; V Thrumpton 65-70; P-in-c S Stoke *B & W* 74-81; C Combe Down w Monkton Combe and S Stoke 81-83; Perm to Offic 83-86; Perm to Offic *Ox* 86-87; NSM Epwell w Sibford, Swalcliffe and Tadmarton 87-92; rtd 88; Perm to Offic *York* from 88. *Woodhouse Farm, Escrick, York YO19 6HT* Tel (01904) 878827

FORBES STONE, Elizabeth Karen. b 61. Birm Univ MB, BCh85 MRCGP89. Ridley Hall Cam BA99. **d** 00 **p** 01. C Brentford *Lon* 00-02; C Shaw cum Donnington *Ox* from 02. *The Rectory, 64 Northcroft Lane, Newbury RG14 1BN* Tel (01635) 35320 Mobile 07980-431710 E-mail buff@dandb.org.uk

FORCE-JONES, Graham Roland John. b 41. Sarum Th Coll 65. **d** 68 **p** 69. C Calne and Blackland *Sarum* 68-73; TV Oldbury 73-78; R Bubb 80-82; TR Upper Kennet 80-94; RD Marlborough 90-94; P-in-c Atworth w Shaw and Whitley from 94. *The Vicarage, Corsham Road, Shaw, Melksham SN12 8EH* Tel (01706) 703335

FORD, Adam. b 40. Lanc Univ MA72 K Coll Lon BD63 AKC63. **d** 65 **p** 65. C Cirencester *Glouc* 65-70; V Hebden Bridge *Wakef* 70-76; Chapl St Paul's Girls' Sch Hammersmith 77-01; Lic to Offic *Lon* 77-98; P in O 84-91. *55 Bolingbroke Road, London W14 0AH* Tel (020) 7602 5902

FORD, Ms Amanda Kirstine. b 61. Middx Univ BA83 Open Univ MA97. St Steph Ho Ox 98. **d** 00 **p** 01. C Leic Resurr *Leic* from 00. *St Matthew's House, 25 Kamloops Crescent, Leicester LE1 2HX* Tel 0116-253 9158
E-mail aford@leicester.anglican.org

FORD, Mrs Avril Celia. b 43. St Mary's Coll Dur BSc64 Chelsea Coll Lon PGCE65. LNSM course 85. **d** 92 **p** 94. OLM Horncastle w Low Toynton *Linc* 92-98; NSM from 98; OLM High Toynton 92-98; NSM from 98; OLM Greetham w Ashby Puerorum 92-98; NSM from 98. *Frolic, Reindeer Close, Horncastle LN9 5AA* Tel (01507) 526234

FORD, Benjamin Pierson. b 22. Princeton Univ AB48. Gen Th Sem (NY) MDiv51. **d** 51 **p** 52. USA 51-85 and from 87; C Gt Grimsby St Mary and St Jas *Linc* 85-87. *1544 Union Road, Waldoboro, ME 04572, USA* Tel (001) (207) 832 7219

FORD, Brian. b 40. OBE89. Imp Coll Lon BSc62 Nottm Univ MSc66 PhD74 Ox Univ MA74 CMathFIMA ARCS. St Alb and Ox Min Course 96. **d** 99 **p** 00. NSM Witney *Ox* 99-02; NSM Ramsden, Finstock and Fawler, Leafield etc from 02. *Ramsden Farmhouse, Ramsden, Oxford OX7 3AU* Tel (01993) 868343 Fax 868322 E-mail brian@nag.co.uk

FORD (née HARRISON-WATSON), Mrs Carole. b 44. Reading Univ ASc64 St Martin's Coll Lanc PGCE79 Cam Univ DipRS91. Carl Dioc Tr Inst 92. **d** 95 **p** 96. NSM Windermere *Carl* 95-98; NSM Borrowdale 98-01; NSM Thornthwaite cum Braithwaite, Newlands etc from 01. *The Vicarage, Borrowdale, Keswick CA12 5XQ* Tel (01768) 777238

FORD, Christopher Simon. b 51. AKC74 Leeds Univ MPhil86 PhD91. **d** 75 **p** 76. C Wythenshawe Wm Temple *Man* 75-77; C New Bury 77-80; R Old Trafford St Jo 80-94; Bp's Adv on Archives from 93; R Moston St Jo from 94; AD N Man 94-00. *St John's Rectory, Railton Terrace, Manchester M9 1WW* Tel 0161-205 4967

FORD, David John. b 38. Lon Coll of Div BD68. **d** 69 **p** 70. C Blackheath St Jo *S'wark* 69-71; C Westlands St Andr *Lich* 71-75; V Sheff St Steph w St Phil and St Ann *Sheff* 75-77; R Netherthorpe 77-80; TR 80-84; R Thrybergh 82-84; R Thrybergh w Hooton Roberts 84-94; Ind Chapl 86-87; TV Parkham, Alwington, Buckland Brewer etc *Ex* 94-01; rtd 03; Hon C Knaresborough *Ripon* from 01. *39 Birkdale Avenue, Knaresborough HG5 0LS* Tel (01423) 864484
E-mail revdford@fish.co.uk

FORD, Mrs Deborah Perrin. b 59. Leeds Univ BA81 Birm Univ MSocSc85 Univ of Wales (Ban) BTh CQSW85. EAMTC 00. **d** 03. NSM Cambridge St Benedict *Ely* from 03. *102 Millington Lane, Cambridge CB3 9HA* Tel (01223) 329321

FORD, Derek Ernest. b 32. St Mich Coll Llan 56. **d** 58 **p** 59. C Roath St Martin *Llan* 58-61; C Newport St Julian 61-67; V Abercanaid 67-70; Perm to Offic *Win* 70-80; SSF from 72; Lic to Offic *Sarum* 73-80; Lic to Offic *Newc* 75-80; USA from 80; OStJ from 94; Chapl from 01; Min Prov American Province SSF from 02. *St Elizabeth's Friary, 1474 Bushwick Avenue, Brooklyn, NY 11207, USA* Tel (001) (718) 455 5963 Fax 443 3437
E-mail broderekssf@aol.com

FORD, Eric Charles. b 31. Ely Th Coll 56. **d** 59 **p** 60. C Kettering St Mary *Pet* 59-65; R Bowers Gifford *Chelmsf* 65-69; V Walthamstow St Barn and St Jas Gt 69-76; V Chingford St Edm

76-97; rtd 97. *32 Hookstone Way, Woodford Green IG8 7LF* Tel (020) 8504 6226

FORD, Eric Copeland. b 20. Linc Th Coll 68. **d** 70 **p** 71. C Lupset *Wakef* 70-73; V Cornholme 73-78; V Sharlston 78; V Wragby w Sharlston 78-85; P-in-c Highfown 85-87; V 87-88; V Hartshead and Hightown 88-90; rtd 90; P-in-c Halifax St Jo *Wakef* 90-91; Chapl Las Palmas *Eur* 91-97; Perm to Offic *Blackb* from 98. *28 Monkswood Avenue, Morecambe LA4 6TW* Tel (01524) 412140

FORD, Canon Henry Malcolm. b 33. Em Coll Cam BA54 MA58. Ely Th Coll 58. **d** 59 **p** 69. C Ipswich St Matt *St E* 59-61; Hon C Bury St Edmunds St Jo 66-76; Hon C Hawstead and Nowton w Stanningfield etc 76-89; Hon Can St E Cathl 86-97; NSM Cockfield w Bradfield St Clare, Felsham etc 89-98. *Thatch on the Green, Cross Green, Cockfield, Bury St Edmunds IP30 0LG* Tel (01284) 828479

FORD, John. *See* FORD, William John

FORD, John. b 31. Sarum Th Coll 58. **d** 61 **p** 62. C Saffron Walden *Chelmsf* 61-64; C Chingford SS Pet and Paul 64-67; V Choral S'well Minster *S'well* 67-72; R N and S Wheatley w W Burton 72-78; P-in-c Sturton w Littleborough 72-78; P-in-c Bole w Saundby 72-78; V Edwinstowe 78-95; rtd 95; Perm to Offic *S'well* from 95. *Sidings, 21 The Lawns, Collingham, Newark NG23 7NT* Tel (01636) 892588

FORD, Canon John Albert. b 13. TCD BA35 MA38. CITC 36. **d** 36 **p** 37. C Derryloran *Arm* 36-39; C Arm St Mark 39-44; I Portadown St Sav 44-61; I Drumcree 61-83; Can Arm Cathl 75-83; rtd 83. *84 Bleary Road, Portadown BT63 5NF* Tel (028) 3834 5484

FORD, Canon John Frank. b 52. Chich Th Coll 76. **d** 79 **p** 80. C Forest Hill Ch Ch *S'wark* 79-82; V Lee St Aug 82-91; V Lower Beeding *Chich* 91-94; Dom Chapl to Bp Horsham 91-94; Dioc Missr 94-00; Can and Preb Chich Cathl 97-00; Prec and Can Res Chich Cathl from 00. *4 Vicars' Close, Canon Lane, Chichester PO19 1PT* Tel and fax (01444) 414658

FORD, Jonathan Laurence. *See* ALDERTON-FORD, Jonathan Laurence

FORD, Joyce. b 42. Qu Coll Birm 97. **d** 00 **p** 01. NSM Bentley *Lich* from 00. *33 Bowness Grove, Willenhall WV12 5DB* Tel (01922) 408420 E-mail joyce.ford@bigfoot.com

FORD, Lionel Peter. b 32. St Mich Coll Llan 57. **d** 60 **p** 61. C Ribbesford w Bewdley and Dowles *Worc* 60-63; C St Mary in the Marsh *Cant* 63-67; P-in-c 76-78; V Elmsted w Hastingleigh 67-71; V New Romney w Hope 71-78; RD S Lympne 75-81; V New Romney w Hope and St Mary's Bay etc 78-82; Hon Can Cant Cathl 82-94; V New Romney w Old Romney and Midley 82-94; Asst Chapl Oslo w Bergen, Trondheim, Stavanger etc *Eur* 94-97; rtd 97; Perm to Offic *Heref* from 97. *9 Mayfields, Fishmore, Ludlow SY8 2QB* Tel (01584) 876832 Fax as telephone

FORD, Mrs Nancy Celia. b 48. FCIPD00 Open Univ BA02. STETS 98. **d** 01 **p** 02. NSM Crookham *Guildf* from 01. *34 Rowhill Avenue, Aldershot GU11 3LS* Tel (01252) 677995
E-mail sidnancy.ford@ntlworld.com

FORD, Peter. b 46. Bede Coll Dur TCert72 ACP75 York Univ MA96. Linc Th Coll 76. **d** 78 **p** 79. OGS from 72; C Hartlepool H Trin *Dur* 78-81; Dioc Youth Officer *Wakef* 81-84; C Mirfield Eastthorpe St Paul 82-84; C Upper Hopton 82-84; V Dodworth 84-88; Chapl and Hd RS Rishworth Sch W Yorks 88-97; Ho Master 94-97; P-in-c Accrington St Mary *Blackb* 97-99; C Torrisholme 99-01; V Warton St Paul from 01; Dioc Ecum Officer from 01. *The Vicarage, Church Road, Warton, Preston PR4 1BD* Tel (01772) 632227 Fax 632351
E-mail pford@ogs.net

FORD, Canon Peter Hugh. b 43. St Cath Coll Cam BA65 MA69. Cuddesdon Coll 65. **d** 67 **p** 68. C Is of Dogs Ch Ch and St Jo w St Luke *Lon* 67-70; Canada 70-91; C Tillsonburg St Jo 71-73; St Catharine's St Thos 71-73; P-in-c Thorold 71-73; R Port Colborne St Brendan 73-78; R Milton 78-80; Can Pastor Ch Ch Cathl Hamilton 80-86; Adn Lincoln 86-91; R Niagara-on-the-Lake St Mark 86-91; Montserrat 91; Saba 92-98; Perm to Offic *Chich* 98-99; and from 01; V Newchurch *Portsm* from 99; V Arreton from 99. *The Vicarage, Newchurch, Sandown PO36 0NN* Tel (01983) 865504 E-mail ph.ford@virgin.net

FORD, Richard Graham. b 39. AKC65 Open Univ BA96. **d** 66 **p** 67. C Morpeth *Newc* 66-71; C Fordingbridge w Ibsley *Win* 71-73; TV Whorlton *Newc* 73-80; Chapl RNR 75-92; V Choppington *Newc* 80-92; V Tynemouth Priory from 92. *Holy Saviour Vicarage, 1 Crossway, North Shields NE30 2LB* Tel 0191-257 1636 *or* 257 0660

FORD, Roger James. b 33. Sarum & Wells Th Coll 81. **d** 83 **p** 84. C Sidcup St Jo *Roch* 83-86; V Darenth 86-98; rtd 98; Perm to Offic *Cov* from 02. *21 Hawthorn Way, Shipston-on-Stour CV36 4FD* Tel (01608) 664875 E-mail margaretandroger@hotmail.com

FORD, Roger Lindsay. b 47. Ex Univ LLB68. Llan Dioc Tr Scheme 87. **d** 91 **p** 92. NSM Fairwater *Llan* 91-96; NSM Llandaff 96-01. *93 Cardiff Road, Caerphilly CF83 1WS* Tel (029) 2088 2441

FORD, Mrs Shirley Elsworth. b 40. Open Univ BA88. Sarum & Wells Th Coll 89. **d** 91 **p** 94. C Farnham *Guildf* 91-96; V

Wrecclesham from 96. *The Vicarage, 2 King's Lane, Wrecclesham, Farnham GU10 4QB* Tel (01252) 716431

FORD, Simone Louise. *See* BENNETT, Ms Simone Louise

FORD, William John. b 50. Linc Th Coll 89. **d** 91 **p** 92. C Marton-in-Cleveland *York* 91-94; V Whorlton w Carlton and Faceby 94-02; P-in-c Stainton w Hilton from 02; RD Stokesley from 03. *The Vicarage, 21 Thornton Road, Stainton, Middlesbrough TS8 9DS* Tel (01642) 288131
E-mail revjohn.ford@ntlworld.com

FORDE, Stephen Bernard. b 61. Edin Univ BSc TCD DipTh. **d** 86 **p** 87. C Belfast St Mary *Conn* 86-89; Chapl QUB 89-95; Min Can Belf Cathl 89-91; Bp's Dom Chapl *Conn* 90-95; I Dublin Booterstown *D & G* 95-99; Dean of Res UCD 95-99; I Larne and Inver *Conn* from 99; I Glynn w Raloo from 99. *The Rectory, Lower Cairncastle Road, Larne BT40 1PQ* Tel (028) 2827 2788 *or* 2827 4633

FORDER, The Ven Charles Robert. b 07. Ch Coll Cam BA28 MA32. Ridley Hall Cam 28. **d** 30 **p** 31. C Hunslet Moor St Pet *Ripon* 30-33; C Burley 33-34; V Wibsey *Bradf* 34-40; V Bradf St Clem 40-47; V Drypool St Andr and St Pet *York* 47-55; Chapl HM Pris Hull 49-51; Chapl HM Borstal Hull 51-52; R Routh *York* 55-57; V Wawne 55-57; Adn York 57-72; Can and Preb York Minster 57-76; R Sutton upon Derwent 57-63; R York H Trin w St Jo Micklegate and St Martin 63-66; rtd 72; Perm to Offic *York* from 76. *Dulverton Hall, Esplanade, Scarborough YO11 2AR* Tel (01723) 340112

FORDHAM, Mrs June Erica. b 28. DCR52. Oak Hill Th Coll 83. **dss** 86 **d** 87 **p** 94. Digswell and Panshanger *St Alb* 86-87; Par Dn 87-90; TD 91-93; rtd 93; NSM Lemsford *St Alb* 93-01; Perm to Offic from 01. *22 Crossway, Welwyn Garden City AL8 7EE* Tel (01707) 326997

FORDHAM, Richard George. b 34. AIMarE60 LicIM&C67 TEng71 FBIM74 SBStJ84 ONC62. **d** 91 **p** 92. NSM Cookham *Ox* 91-94; NSM Hedsor and Bourne End 94-01; Perm to Offic from 01. *Address temp unknown*

FORDYCE, Andrew Ian. b 70. K Alfred's Coll Win BA94 Southn Univ PGCE96. Trin Coll Bris BA03. **d** 03. C Bramshott and Liphook *Portsm* from 03. *2 Meadow End, Liphook GU30 7UA* Tel (01428) 722142 Mobile 07884-010376
E-mail fordyce@fsmail.net

FOREMAN, Joseph Arthur. b 26. AIB. S Dios Minl Tr Scheme 83. **d** 86 **p** 87. NSM Win St Bart *Win* 86-96; Perm to Offic from 96. *4 Denham Close, Winchester SO23 7BL* Tel (01962) 852138

FOREMAN, Patrick Brian. b 41. CertEd. St Jo Coll Nottm 77. **d** 79 **p** 80. C Gainsborough All SS *Linc* 79-83; V Thornton St Jas *Bradf* 83-91; R Hevingham w Hainford and Stratton Strawless *Nor* 91-99; RD Ingworth 94-99; V Heacham from 99. *The Vicarage, Church Lane, Heacham, King's Lynn PE31 7HJ* Tel (01485) 570268

FOREMAN, Roy Geoffrey Victor. b 31. Oak Hill Th Coll 62. **d** 64 **p** 65. C Chitts Hill St Cuth *Lon* 64-67; C Rodbourne Cheney *Bris* 67-70; C Walthamstow St Mary w St Steph *Chelmsf* 71-92; TV 92-96; rtd 96; Perm to Offic *S'wark* from 97. *1 Vicarage Road, Croydon CR0 4JS* Tel (020) 8681 3303

FOREMAN, Timothy. b 56. K Coll Lon BD77. SEITE 97. **d** 99 **p** 00. C Camberwell St Giles w St Matt *S'wark* 99-02; R Buckland in Dover w Buckland Valley *Cant* from 02. *St Andrew's Rectory, London Road, Dover CT17 0TF* Tel (01304) 201324
E-mail fr.tim@ntlworld.com

FOREMAN, Vanessa Jane. *See* LAWRENCE, Mrs Vanessa Jane

FORGAN, Eleanor. b 44. St Andr Univ MA66 Aber Univ DipEd67. St Andr and Dioc Tr Course. **d** 89 **p** 95. NSM Alloa *St And* from 89. *18 Alexandra Drive, Alloa FK10 2DQ* Tel (01259) 212836 *or* 724550 E-mail eforgan@surfaid.org

FORMAN, Alastair Gordon. b 48. St Jo Coll Nottm 78. **d** 80 **p** 81. C Pennycross *Ex* 80-83; C Woking St Jo *Guildf* 83-88; V Luton Lewsey St Hugh *St Alb* 88-95; P-in-c Jersey Millbrook St Matt *Win* 95-01; P-in-c Jersey St Lawr 95-01. *Farnham Vineyard, 1 The Borough, Farnham GU9 7NA* Tel (01252) 737586
E-mail onformok@super.net.uk

FORMAN, Miss Diana Blanche Grant. b 19. DCR51. Edin Dioc NSM Course 79. **dss** 83 **d** 86 **p** 94. Edin St Jo *Edin* 83-86; NSM 86-91; rtd 91. *7/3 Myreside Court, Edinburgh EH10 5LX* Tel 0131-447 4463

FORRER, Michael Dennett Cuthbert. b 34. St Pet Hall Ox BA59 MA63. Wycliffe Hall Ox 59. **d** 60 **p** 61. C Westwood *Cov* 60-63; C Cov Cathl 63-71; Ind Chapl 63-69; Sen Ind Chapl 69-71; Hon C All Hallows by the Tower etc *Lon* 76-99; Perm to Offic *Sarum* from 99; *Ox* 01-02; Hon C Sonning *Ox* from 02. *6 Park View Drive South, Charvil, Reading RG10 9QX* Tel 0118-934 1989

FORREST, Canon Kenneth Malcolm. b 38. Linc Coll Ox BA61 MA65. Wells Th Coll 60. **d** 62 **p** 63. C Walton St Mary *Liv* 62-65; Asst Chapl Liv Univ 65-67; Chapl Blue Coat Sch *Liv* 67-75; R Wavertree H Trin 67-75; R Wigan All SS from 75; Hon Can Liv Cathl from 87; AD Wigan E 89-02. *The Hall, New Market Street, Wigan WN1 1HN* Tel (01942) 244459

FORREST, The Very Revd Leslie David Arthur. b 46. TCD BA68 MA86. CITC 70. **d** 70 **p** 71. C Conwall *D & R* 70-73; I Tullyaughnish 73-80; I Galway w Kilcummin *T, K & A* 80-95; Dir of Ords 84-95; Can Tuam Cathl 86-95; Provost Tuam 91-95;

Preb Tassagard St Patr Cathl Dublin from 91; Dean Ferns *C & O* from 95; I Ferns w Kilbride, Toombe, Kilcormack etc from 95. *The Deanery, Ferns, Enniscorthy, Co Wexford, Irish Republic* Tel (00353) (54) 66124 Fax 66985

FORREST, Michael Barry Eric. b 38. Lon Univ BA87 MA89. NZ Bd of Th Studies LTh62 Chich Th Coll 64. **d** 66 **p** 67. C Beckenham St Jas *Roch* 66-70; Papua New Guinea 70-76; C Altarnon and Bolventor *Truro* 76-78; TV N Hill w Altarnon, Bolventor and Lewannick 78-79; R St Martin w E and W Looe 79-84; V Kensington St Phil Earl's Court *Lon* from 84. *St Philip's Vicarage, 46 Pembroke Road, London W8 6NU* Tel (020) 7602 5025 *or* 7373 4847

FORREST, Canon Robin Whyte. b 33. Edin Th Coll 58. **d** 61 **p** 62. C Glas St Mary *Glas* 61-66; R Renfrew 66-70; R Motherwell 70-79; R Wishaw 75-79; R Forres *Mor* 79-98; R Nairn 79-92; Can St Andr Cathl Inverness 88-98; Hon Can from 98; Syn Clerk 91-92; Dean Mor 92-98; rtd 98. *Landeck, Cummingston, Elgin IU30 2XY* Tel (01343) 835539 Fax as telephone

FORREST-REDFERN, Mrs Susan Michèle. b 57. S Bank Poly BEd86. St Jo Coll Nottm 01. **d** 03. C Lostock St Thos and St Jo *Man* from 03. *12 Salterton Drive, Bolton BL3 3RG* Tel (01204) 652977 E-mail s.forrest-redfern@lineone.net

FORRESTER, Herbert Howarth. b 19. Liv Univ LLB46. Wycliffe Hall Ox 65. **d** 67 **p** 68. C Blundellsands St Nic *Liv* 67-70; V Liv St Phil 70-76; V Liv St Phil w St Dav 76-85; rtd 85; Perm to Offic *Liv* from 85. *5 Kenilworth Road, Liverpool L16 7PS* Tel 0151-722 1365

FORRESTER, Ian Michael. b 56. Chich Th Coll. **d** 82 **p** 83. C Leigh-on-Sea St Marg *Chelmsf* 82-84; Min Can, Succ and Dean's V Windsor 84-86; Perm to Offic *Ox* 84-86; Chapl Distinguished Conduct Medal League 86-95; Chapl Gallantry Medallists' League from 95; Prec and Chapl Chelmsf Cathl *Chelmsf* 86-91; Perm to Offic 91-99; Chapl Lancing Coll 91-99; P-in-c Boxgrove *Chich* from 99. *The Vicarage, Boxgrove, Chichester PO18 0ED* Tel (01243) 774045 E-mail iforrester@hotmail.com

FORRESTER, James Oliphant. b 50. SS Coll Cam BA72 MA76. Wycliffe Hall Ox 73. **d** 76 **p** 77. C Hull Newland St Jo *York* 76-80; C Fulwood *Sheff* 80-87; V Lodge Moor St Luke 87-90; V Ecclesfield 90-01; AD Ecclesfield 99-01; P-in-c Kingston upon Hull H Trin *York* 01-02; V and Lect from 02. *Holy Trinity Vicarage, 66 Pearson Park, Hull HU5 2TQ* Tel (01482) 342292

FORRESTER, Mrs Joyce. b 33. Thornbridge Hall Coll of Educn TCert53 ACP84 DACE85 Crewe & Alsager Coll MSc88. St Jo Coll Nottm 94. **d** 94 **p** 95. NSM Endon w Stanley *Lich* 94-00; Assoc Min Stonnall from 00. *The Vicarage, 3 St Peter's Close, Stonall, Walsall WS9 9EN* Tel (01543) 360395

FORRESTER, Matthew Agnew. b 31. Univ of Wales (Cardiff) BA64 Lon Univ DipTh72. Trin Coll Bris 70. **d** 72 **p** 73. C Tonbridge SS Pet and Paul *Roch* 72-77; Chapl Elstree Sch Woolhampton 77-78; Chapl Duke of York's R Mil Sch Dover 78-96; rtd 96; Perm to Offic *Cant* from 96. *4 Abbots Place, Canterbury CT1 2AH* Tel (01304) 823758

FORRYAN, Canon John Edward. b 31. Wells Th Coll 58. **d** 60 **p** 61. C Leckhampton SS Phil and Jas *Glouc* 60-63; C Cirencester 63-68; V Glouc St Paul 68-78; R Rodborough 78-91; P-in-c Deerhurst, Apperley w Forthampton and Chaceley 91-95; V 95-97; Hon Can Glouc Cathl 94-97; rtd 97; Perm to Offic *Glouc* from 97. *26 Wye Road, Brockworth, Gloucester GL5 4PP* Tel (01452) 863578

FORRYAN, Thomas Quested. b 64. Pemb Coll Cam BA85 DipTh86. Wycliffe Hall Ox 87. **d** 90 **p** 91. C Cheadle Hulme St Andr *Ches* 90-93; C Aberavon *Llan* 93-94; UCCF 94-98. *1 Grosvenor Road, Watford WD1 2QS*

FORSE, Reginald Austin. b 43. Oak Hill Th Coll 77. **d** 79 **p** 80. C Crofton *Portsm* 79-84; NSM Gosport Ch Ch 91-96; NSM Alverstoke from 96. *40 Osprey Gardens, Lee-on-the-Solent PO13 8LJ* Tel (023) 9255 3395 E-mail regforse@yahoo.co.uk

FORSHAW, David Oliver. b 27. Trin Coll Cam BA50 MA52. Qu Coll Birm. **d** 53 **p** 54. C Glen Parva and S Wigston *Leic* 53-55; Singapore 55-59; V Heptonstall *Wakef* 59-66; V Whitehaven St Nic *Carl* 66-76; P-in-c Whitehaven Ch Ch w H Trin 73-76; V Benchill *Man* 76-89; C Elton All SS 89-92; rtd 92; Perm to Offic *Carl* from 92. *Tynashee, Church Street, Broughton-in-Furness LA20 6HJ* Tel (01229) 716068

FORSHAW, Canon Eric Paul. b 42. Lon Univ BSc63 Birm Univ MA78 Zürich Univ ThD90. Ridley Hall Cam 67 Gossner Inst Mainz 73. **d** 70 **p** 71. C Yardley St Edburgha *Birm* 70-72; Hon Chapl 72-78; Hon C Edgbaston St Geo 72-78; Bp's Adv on Ind Soc *S'well* 78-90; Perm to Offic 78-82; Assoc Min Nottm St Pet and St Jas 82-94; Hon Can S'well Minster from 86; Bp's Research Officer 90-92; Progr Dir Nottm Common Purpose 92-94; TR Clifton from 94. *The Rectory, 569 Farnborough Road, Clifton, Nottingham NG11 9DG* Tel 0115-974 9388 Fax as telephone
E-mail eric@forshaw.surfaid.org

FORSHAW, Mrs Frances. b 52. Edin Univ BSc74. **d** 98 **p** 02. NSM Elgin w Lossiemouth *Mor* 98-01; NSM Perth St Jo *St And* from 01. *1 Cairnies House, Glenalmond College, Glenalmond, Perth PH1 3RY* Tel (01738) 880777

FORSTER, The Ven Andrew James. QUB BA89. CITC BTh92. **d** 92 **p** 93. C Willowfield *D & D* 92-95; Dean of Res QUB 95-02; C of I Adv Downtown Radio Newtownards 96-02; I Drumcliffe w Lissadell and Munninane *K, E & A* from 02; Adn Elphin and Ardagh from 02. *The Rectory, Drumcliffe, Co Sligo, Irish Republic* Tel (00353) (71) 916 3125
E-mail andrew@theforsters.org

FORSTER, Bennet Fermor. b 21. BNC Ox BA48 MA53. Cuddesdon Coll. **d** 51 **p** 52. C Stepney St Dunstan and All SS *Lon* 51-53; C Petersfield w Sheet *Portsm* 53-57; V Portsea St Cuth 57-65; Chapl Bedford Sch 65-72; C Bedford St Pet *St Alb* 72-73; Lic to Offic 73-78; P-in-c Froxfield w Privett *Portsm* 78-81; V 81-88; P-in-c Hawkley w Prior's Dean 78-81; V 81-88; rtd 88; Perm to Offic *Worc* from 88. *39 Parkview, Abbey Road, Malvern WR14 3HG* Tel (01684) 567915

FORSTER, Gregory Stuart. b 47. Worc Coll Ox BA69 MA73 Dip Soc Anthropology 70. Wycliffe Hall Ox 69. **d** 72 **p** 73. C Bath Walcot *B & W* 72-74; C Bolton Em *Man* 74-76; C Bolton St Paul w Em 77-79; R Northenden from 79. *The Rectory, Ford Lane, Northenden, Manchester M22 4NQ* Tel 0161-998 2615

FORSTER, Ian Duncan. b 51. St Mich Coll Llan 95. **d** 97 **p** 98. C Lampeter Pont Steffan w Silian *St D* 97-00; C Llandysul w Bangor Teifi w Henllan etc from 00. *Dolawelon, Seion Hill, Llandysul SA44 4BX* Tel (01559) 362193

FORSTER, Kenneth. b 27. St Jo Coll Cam BA50 MA52 Salford Univ MSc77 PhD80. NEOC 83. **d** 86 **p** 87. NSM Hessle *York* 86-92; Chapl Humberside Poly 87-91; Chapl Humberside Univ 92; rtd 92; NSM Hull St Mary Sculcoates *York* 92-95; Perm to Offic from 95. *1 Peel Court, Longwick Road, Princes Risborough HP27 9EZ* Tel (01844) 343050

✠**FORSTER, The Rt Revd Peter Robert.** b 50. Mert Coll Ox MA73 Edin Univ BD77 PhD85. Edin Th Coll 78. **d** 80 **p** 81 **c** 96. C Mossley Hill St Matt and St Jas *Liv* 80-82; Sen Tutor St Jo Coll Dur 83-91; V Beverley Minster *York* 91-96; C Routh 91-96; Bp Ches from 96. *Bishop's House, Abbey Square, Chester CH1 2JD* Tel (01244) 350864 Fax 314187
E-mail bpchester@chester.anglican.org

FORSTER, Thomas Shane. b 72. QUB BA93. CITC BTh93. **d** 96 **p** 97. C Drumglass w Moygashel *Arm* 96-99; Hon V Choral Arm Cathl 97-99; I Donaghmore w Upper Donaghmore from 99; Dioc Communications Officer from 02. *St Michael's Rectory, 66 Main Street, Castlecaulfield, Dungannon BT70 3NP* Tel (028) 8776 1214 Fax 8776 9095
E-mail donaghmore@armagh.anglican.org

FORSTER, The Ven Victor Henry. b 17. TCD BA45 MA49. **d** 45 **p** 46. C Magheralin *D & D* 45-47; C-in-c Garrison w Slavin *Clogh* 47-51; Bp's C Ballybay 51-52; I Killeevan 52-59; I Rathgraffe *M & K* 59-67; I Aghalurcher w Tattykeeran, Cooneen etc *Clogh* 67-89; Preb Clogh Cathl 80-83; Adn Clogh 83-89; rtd 89; Lic to Offic *D & D* from 90. *4 Ard-Na-Ree, Groomsport, Bangor BT19 2JL* Tel (028) 9146 4548

FORSTER, William. b 50. Liv Poly HNC71. N Ord Course 92. **d** 95 **p** 96. C Ashton-in-Makerfield St Thos *Liv* 95-00; TR Fazakerley Em from 00. *Emmanuel Rectory, Higher Lane, Liverpool L9 9DJ* Tel 0151-525 2689

FORSYTH, Jeanette Mary Shaw. b 48. Aber Coll of Educn ACE78. Moray Ho Edin Dip Primary Educn 67 Ab Dioc Tr Course 83 St Jo Coll Nottm CertCS89. **d** 89. NSM Old Deer *Ab* 89-92; NSM Longside 89-92; NSM Strichen 89-92; NSM Fraserburgh 92-94; Tanzania 95-96, 97-98 and 99-00. *Moss-side of Strichen, Bogensourie, Strichen AB43 7TU* Tel (01771) 637230
E-mail jeanetteforsyth@hotmail.com

FORSYTH, John Warren. b 38. Edin Univ DPS76 Univ of W Aus BA62. Princeton Th Sem DMin98. **d** 65 **p** 66. Australia 65-74 and from 76; C Edin St Pet *Edin* 74-76; C Busselton 65-68; R Kondinin 68-72; C Warw 72-74; R E Fremantle and Palmyra 76-79; R Midland 82-89. *40B Cookham Road, Lathlain, W Australia 6100* Tel (0061) (8) 9472 1893 *or* 9224 2482 Fax 9472 1893 *or* 9224 3511 E-mail john.forsyth@rph.health.wa.gov.aau

FORSYTH, William. b 10. Lich Th Coll 55. **d** 56 **p** 57. C Fenham St Jas and St Basil *Newc* 56-59; V Cleator *Carl* 59-65; V Netherton 65-70; V Levens 70-77; rtd 77; Perm to Offic *Carl* from 77. *2 Vicarage Road, Levens, Kendal LA8 8PY* Tel (01539) 560926

FORSYTHE, John Leslie. b 27. CITC. **d** 65 **p** 66. C Cloughfern *Conn* 65-67; C Carnmoney 67-71; I Mossley 71-80; I Antrim All SS 80-95; Preb Conn Cathl 94-95; rtd 95. *96 Hopefield Road, Portrush BT56 8HF* Tel (028) 7082 2623

FORTNUM, Brian Charles Henry. b 48. Hertf Coll Ox MA Imp Coll Lon MSc. Wycliffe Hall Ox 82. **d** 84 **p** 85. C Tonbridge St Steph *Roch* 84-87; V Shorne 87-94; P-in-c Speldhurst w Groombridge and Ashurst 94-98; R 98-01; V Tunbridge Wells St Mark from 01. *The Vicarage, 1 St Mark's Road, Tunbridge Wells TN2 5LT* Tel (01892) 526069 Fax as telephone
E-mail brian.fortnum@btinternet.com

FORTUNE-WOOD, Janet. b 61. Selw Coll Cam BA82 MA88 CertEd83. Trin Coll Bris 86. **d** 88 **p** 94. Par Dn Rotherhithe H Trin *S'wark* 88-92; TD Swindon St Jo and St Andr *Bris* 92-94; TV 94-95; P-in-c Kingshurst *Birm* 95-01; V 01-02; rtd 02. *Meirion*

House, Tanygrisiau, Blaenau Ffestiniog LL41 3SU Tel (01766) 832112

FORWARD, Eric Toby. b 50. Nottm Univ BEd72 Hull Univ MA93. Cuddesdon Coll 74. **d** 77 **p** 78. C Forest Hill Ch Ch *S'wark* 77-80; Chapl Goldsmiths' Coll Lon 80-84; Chapl Westwood Ho Sch Pet 84-86; V Brighton St Aug and St Sav *Chich* 86-90; Perm to Offic *York* 90-95; V Kingston upon Hull St Alb from 95. *St Alban's Vicarage, 62 Hall Road, Hull HU6 8SA* Tel (01482) 446639 Fax as telephone

FORWARD, Miss Frances Mary. b 43. Bp Otter Coll Chich TCert64. SEITE DipTM99. **d** 99 **p** 00. NSM Ham St Andr *S'wark* from 99. *66 Tudor Drive, Kingston on Thames KT2 5QF* Tel (020) 8546 1833

FORWARD, Canon Ronald George. b 25. Selw Coll Cam BA50 MA54. Ridley Hall Cam 50. **d** 52 **p** 53. C Denton Holme *Carl* 52-55; C-in-c Mirehouse St Andr CD 55-61; V Mirehouse 61-66; V Kendal St Thos 66-90; V Crook 78-90; Hon Can Carl Cathl 79-90; rtd 90; Perm to Offic *Carl* from 90. *51 Mayo Park, Cockermouth CA13 0BJ* Tel (01900) 824359

FOSBUARY, David Frank. b 32. Leeds Univ BA63. Coll of Resurr Mirfield 63. **d** 65 **p** 66. C Fleetwood *Blackb* 65-68; Lesotho 69-76; C Dovercourt *Chelmsf* 76-78; TV 78-79; TV Basildon St Martin w H Cross and Laindon etc 79-82; R Colsterworth *Linc* 82-84; R Colsterworth Gp 84-90; RD Beltisloe 89-90; R Lawshall w Shimplingthorne and Alpheton *St E* 90-96; rtd 96; Perm to Offic *St E* from 96. *56 Lindisfarne Road, Bury St Edmunds IP33 2EH* Tel (01284) 767687

FOSDIKE, Lewis Bertram. b 23. Keble Coll Ox BA52 MA56. Wells Th Coll 52. **d** 54 **p** 55. C Westbury-on-Trym H Trin *Bris* 54-58; V Bedminster St Fran 58-64; V Summertown *Ox* 64-76; TR Wolvercote w Summertown 76-89; rtd 89; Chapl St Hugh's Coll Ox 89-97. *18 Osberton Road, Oxford OX2 7NU* Tel (01865) 515817

FOSKETT, Eric William. b 29. Qu Coll Birm 75. **d** 78 **p** 79. NSM Billesley Common *Birm* 78-82; V Allens Cross 82-95; Chapl Hollymoor Hosp Birm 90-95; rtd 95; Perm to Offic *Birm* from 95. *1 Warmington Road, Hollywood, Birmingham B47 5PE* Tel (01564) 526181

FOSKETT, Canon John Herbert. b 39. St Cath Coll Cam BA62. Chich Th Coll 62. **d** 64 **p** 65. C Malden St Jo *S'wark* 64-70; P-in-c Kingston St Jo 70-76; Chapl Maudsley Hosp Lon 76-94; Chapl Bethlem R Hosp Beckenham 76-94; Hon Can S'wark Cathl *S'wark* 88-94; rtd 94; Perm to Offic *B & W* 95-01. *Victoria Cottage, 8 Cornwall Road, Dorchester DT1 1RT* Tel (01305) 751572

FOSS, David Blair. b 44. Bris Univ BA65 Dur Univ MA66 Fitzw Coll Cam BA68 MA72 K Coll Lon PhD86. St Chad's Coll Dur 68. **d** 69 **p** 70. C Barnard Castle *Dur* 69-72; Sierra Leone 72-74; Chapl St Jo Coll York 74-75; Chapl Ch Ch Coll of HE Cant 75-80; Chapl Elmslie Girls' Sch Blackpool 80-83; Tutor Coll of Resurr Mirfield 83-88; V Battyeford *Wakef* 88-99; V Ryde All SS *Portsm* 99-01; TR Rochdale *Man* from 01. *The Vicarage, Sparrow Hill, Rochdale OL16 1QT* Tel (01706) 645014

FOSS, William Cecil Winn. b 40. Man Univ BA68 MA87 Lon Univ DipTh66 CertEd72 BD76. Ely Th Coll 64. **d** 68 **p** 69. C S'wark St Geo *S'wark* 68-73; Perm to Offic *Ches* 73-79; V Crewe Ch Ch 79-83; V Crewe Ch Ch and St Pet from 83. *Christ Church Vicarage, 3 Heathfield Avenue, Crewe CW1 3BA* Tel (01270) 213148

FOSSETT, Michael Charles Sinclair. b 30. Dur Univ BSc54 CEng57 MIMechE59. NEOC 82. **d** 90 **p** 91. NSM Nether w Upper Poppleton *York* from 90. *20 Fairway Drive, Upper Poppleton, York YO26 6HE* Tel (01904) 794712

FOSTEKEW, Dean James Benedict. b 63. Bulmershe Coll of HE BEd86. Chich Th Coll 89. **d** 92 **p** 93. C Boyne Hill *Ox* 92-95; P-in-c Lockerbie *Glas* 95-97; P-in-c Annan 95-97; P-in-c Dalmahoy *Edin* 97-02; Miss Co-ord from 98; TV Edin St Mary from 02. *7/6 Hermand Terrace, Edinburgh EH11 1QZ, or St Mary's Church Centre, Dalmahoy, Kirknewton EH27 8EB* Tel and fax 0131-346 2748 *or* 333 1683 Mobile 07702-924586
E-mail mission21@edinburgh.anglican.org

FOSTER, Antony John. b 39. Down Coll Cam BA61 MA65. Ridley Hall Cam 65. **d** 66 **p** 67. C Sandal St Helen *Wakef* 66-69; Uganda 69-74; V Mount Pellon *Wakef* 74-92; rtd 92; Perm to Offic *Wakef* from 92. *32 Savile Drive, Halifax HX1 2EU* Tel (01422) 344152

FOSTER, Basil. See FOSTER, William Basil

✠**FOSTER, The Rt Revd Christopher Richard James.** b 53. Univ Coll Dur BA75 Man Univ MA77 Trin Hall Cam BA79 MA83 Wadh Coll Ox MA83. Westcott Ho Cam 78. **d** 80 **p** 81 **c** 01. C Tettenhall Regis *Lich* 80-82; Chapl Wadh Coll Ox 82-86; C Ox St Mary V w St Cross and St Pet *Ox* 82-86; V Southgate Ch Ch *Lon* 86-94; CME Officer 88-94; Can Res and Sub-Dean St Alb 94-01; Suff Bp Hertford from 01. *Hertford House, Abbey Mill Lane, St Albans AL3 4HE* Tel (01727) 866420 Fax 811426
E-mail bishophertford@stalbans.anglican.org

FOSTER, David Brereton. b 55. Selw Coll Cam BA77 MA81 Ox Univ BA80. Wycliffe Hall Ox 78. **d** 81 **p** 82. C Luton St Mary

St Alb 81-84; C Douglas St Geo and St Barn *S & M* 84-87; V S Ramsey St Paul 87-91; Dir Dioc Tr Inst 88-91; Asst Dir Buckingham Adnry Chr Tr Scheme *Ox* 91-95; Dir Buckingham Adnry Chr Tr Sch 95-97; C W Wycombe w Bledlow Ridge, Bradenham and Radnage 91-97; TV High Wycombe from 97. *15 The Brackens, High Wycombe HP11 1EB* Tel (01494) 451762 or 529686
E-mail david.foster@st-andrews.wycombechurches.org.uk

FOSTER, Donald Wolfe. b 24. St Cath Coll Cam BA48 MA50 TCD BD56. **d** 50 **p** 51. C Dunleckney *C & O* 50-52; C Coseley Ch Ch *Lich* 52-54; C Newland St Aug *York* 54-58; Chapl HM Borstal Hull 58-62; V Kingston upon Hull St Mary *York* 58-62; V Osbaldwick w Murton 62-67; Asst Chapl Loughborough Gr Sch 67-80; Chapl 80-87; Perm to Offic *Leic* from 81; rtd 87. *73 Park Road, Loughborough LE11 2HD* Tel (01509) 212782

FOSTER, Edward James Graham. b 12. St Jo Coll Cam BA34 MusBac35 MA38. Wells Th Coll 35. **d** 37 **p** 38. C Kidderminster St Mary *Worc* 37-43; C Feckenham w Astwood Bank 43-45; Chapl and Lect Dioc Tr Coll Chester 45-51; V Balby w Hexthorpe *Sheff* 51-67; V Ashford w Sheldon *Derby* 67-78; rtd 78; Perm to Offic *Derby* from 78. *Beckside, Baslow Road, Ashford-in-the-Water, Bakewell DE45 1QA* Tel (01629) 812868

FOSTER, Edward Philip John. b 49. Trin Hall Cam BA70 MA74. Ridley Hall Cam 76. **d** 79 **p** 80. C Finchley Ch Ch *Lon* 79-82; C Marple All SS *Ches* 82-86; P-in-c Cambridge St Matt *Ely* 86-90; V from 90. *St Matthew's Vicarage, 24 Geldart Street, Cambridge CB1 2LX* Tel (01223) 363545 Fax 512304
E-mail pf.smp@dial.pipex.com

FOSTER, Frances Elizabeth. *See* TYLER, Mrs Frances Elizabeth

FOSTER, Francis Desmond. b 11. ALCD33. **d** 34 **p** 35. C Norbury St Phil *S'wark* 34-39; C Faversham *Cant* 39-48; V Throwley 48-75; P-in-c Stalisfield w Otterden 73-75; V Throwley w Stalisfield and Otterden 75-77; rtd 77; Perm to Offic *Chich* from 78. *43 Milton Road, Eastbourne BN21 1SH* Tel (01323) 639430

FOSTER, Canon Gareth Glynne. b 44. Open Univ BA. Chich Th Coll 66. **d** 69 **p** 70. C Fairwater *Llan* 69-71; C Merthyr Tydfil 71-72; C Merthyr Tydfil and Cyfarthfa 72-76; TV 76-87; Dioc Soc Resp Officer from 87; P-in-c Abercanaid from 87; Exec Officer Dioc Bd Soc Resp from 95; Can Llan Cathl from 00. *19 The Walk, Merthyr Tydfil CF47 8RU, or Diocesan Office, Heol Fair, Llandaff, Cardiff CF5 2EE* Tel (029) 2057 8899 Mobile 07850-823038
E-mail garethfoster.dbf.llandaff@churchinwales.org.uk

FOSTER, Mrs Geraldine. b 55. RGN77. St Alb and Ox Min Course 00. **d** 03. NSM Flackwell Heath *Ox* from 03. *15 The Brackens, High Wycombe HP11 1EB* Tel (01494) 444995 Fax 451762

FOSTER, James. b 29. Man Univ BA52 MA55 Lon Univ CertEd53 Leeds Univ MEd74. NEOC 82. **d** 85 **p** 86. NSM Aldborough w Boroughbridge and Roecliffe *Ripon* 85-91; P-in-c Kirby-on-the-Moor, Cundall w Norton-le-Clay etc 91-97; rtd 97; Perm to Offic *Ripon* from 97. *Lylands Farm, Ouseburn, York YO26 9TU* Tel (01423) 330276

FOSTER, Mrs Joan Alison. b 46. ARMCM67. Nor Ord Course 95. **d** 98 **p** 99. NSM Blundellsands St Nic *Liv* 98-02; Asst Chapl Southport and Ormskirk NHS Trust 98-02; V N Harrow St Alb *Lon* from 02. *St Alban's Vicarage, Church Drive, Harrow HA2 7NS* Tel (020) 8868 6567 Mobile 07713-819012
E-mail revjoan@fish.co.uk

FOSTER, Jonathan Guy Vere. b 56. Goldsmiths' Coll Lon BA78. Wycliffe Hall Ox 83. **d** 86 **p** 87. C Hampreston *Sarum* 86-90; Chapl Chantilly *Eur* 90-97; V Branksome St Clem *Sarum* from 97. *The Vicarage, 3 Parkstone Heights, Branksome, Poole BH14 0QE* Tel (01202) 748058

FOSTER, Joseph James Frederick. b 22. SS Paul & Mary Coll Cheltenham CertEd42 Birm Univ DipEd59. **d** 88 **p** 88. NSM Elstead *Guildf* 88-94; Perm to Offic from 94. *Wodenscroft, Thursley Road, Elstead, Godalming GU8 6DH* Tel (01252) 703198

FOSTER, Leslie. b 49. Linc Th Coll 89. **d** 91 **p** 92. C Coseley Ch Ch *Lich* 91-93; C Coseley Ch Ch *Worc* 93-95; V Firbank, Howgill and Killington *Bradf* 95-00; Hon C Sedbergh, Cautley and Garsdale 95-00; Dioc Rural Adv 96-00; P-in-c Ruyton XI Towns w St and Lt Ness *Lich* from 00. *The Vicarage, The Village, Ruyton Eleven Towns, Shrewsbury SY4 1LQ* Tel (01939) 261234 E-mail lesfoster@lunevic.freeserve.co.uk

FOSTER, Michael John. b 52. St Steph Ho Ox 76. **d** 79 **p** 80. C Wood Green St Mich *Lon* 79-82; C Wood Green St Mich w Bounds Green St Gabr etc 82; TV Clifton *S'well* 82-85; P-in-c Aylesbury *Ox* 85-87; Dep Warden Durning Hall Chr Community Cen 87-89; V Lydbrook *Glouc* 89-97; R Hemsby, Winterton, E and W Somerton and Horsey *Nor* 97-99; P-in-c Tarrant Valley *Sarum* 99-01; P-in-c Tollard Royal w Farnham, Gussage St Michael etc 99-01; R Chase from 01. *The Rectory, Church Hill, Tarrant Hinton, Blandford Forum DT11 8JB* Tel (01258) 830764

FOSTER, Paul. b 60. MAAT80. Oak Hill Th Coll DipHE93. **d** 93 **p** 94. C New Clee *Linc* 93-96; P-in-c Aldington w Bonnington and Bilsington *Cant* 96-02; P-in-c Lympne w W Hythe 00-02;

Chapl HM Pris Aldington 96-02; Chapl HM YOI Feltham from 02. *HM Young Offender Institution, Bedfont Road, Feltham TW13 4ND* Tel (020) 8890 0061 ext 325
E-mail pfozzy@hotmail.com

FOSTER, Ronald George. b 25. Bris Univ BSc51 AKC51. **d** 52 **p** 53. C Lydney w Aylburton *Glouc* 52-54; C Leighton Buzzard *St Alb* 54-60; Chapl Bearwood Coll Wokingham 61-83; R Wantage Downs *Ox* 83-91; rtd 91; RD Wantage *Ox* 92-95; Perm to Offic from 92. *Ascension Cottage, Horn Lane, East Hendred, Wantage OX12 8LD* Tel (01235) 820790

FOSTER, Simon John Darby. b 57. Qu Mary Coll Lon BSc78. Wycliffe Hall Ox 85. **d** 88 **p** 89. C Bedgrove *Ox* 88-92; C Glyncorrwg w Afan Vale and Cymmer Afan *Llan* 92-94; R Breedon cum Isley Walton and Worthington *Leic* 94-98; R Anstey from 98. *The Rectory, 1 Hurd's Close, Anstey, Leicester LE7 7GH* Tel 0116-236 2176
E-mail sfoster@leicester.anglican.org

FOSTER, Stephen. b 47. Leeds Univ CertEd69. NEOC 83. **d** 86 **p** 87. NSM Kingston upon Hull St Nic *York* 86-87; NSM Aldbrough, Mappleton w Goxhill and Withernwick 87-98; TV Howden from 98; RD Howden from 02; Chapl HM Pris Wolds from 03. *The Vicarage, 3 Thimblehall Lane, Newport, Brough HU15 2PX* Tel (01430) 440546
E-mail sf@howdendeanery.karoo.co.uk

FOSTER, Stephen Arthur. b 54. Lon Univ BMus75 BA78 Potchefstroom Univ PhD98. Coll of Resurr Mirfield 75. **d** 78 **p** 79. C Ches H Trin *Ches* 78-82; C Tranmere St Paul w St Luke 82-83; V Grange St Andr 83-88; V Cheadle Hulme All SS 88-94; P-in-c Stockport St Matt 94-00; Asst Dir of Ords from 96; V Sale St Anne from 00. *St Anne's Vicarage, Church Road, Sale M33 3HB* Tel and fax 0161-973 4145 Mobile 07715-560669
E-mail fatherstephen@supanet.com

FOSTER, Steven. b 52. Wadh Coll Ox BA75 MA80. Ridley Hall Cam 76. **d** 79 **p** 80. C Ipsley *Worc* 79-83; TV Woughton *Ox* 83-94; V Walshaw Ch Ch *Man* from 94. *Christ Church Vicarage, 37 Gisburn Drive, Walshaw, Bury BL8 3DH* Tel 0161-763 1193

FOSTER, Steven Francis. b 55. Lon Univ BD76 AKC76 Open Univ BA91 FRSA90. Coll of Resurr Mirfield 77. **d** 78 **p** 79. C Romford St Edw *Chelmsf* 78-80; C Leigh St Clem 80-83; Ed Mayhew McCrimmon Publishers 84-86; Hon C Southend 85-86; P-in-c Sandon 86-90; R 90-91; R Wanstead St Mary 91-93; R Wanstead St Mary w Ch Ch 93-00; Perm to Offic from 00; Asst to Master R Foundn of St Kath in Ratcliffe from 00. *The Royal Foundation of St Katharine, 2 Butcher Row, London E14 8DS* Tel (020) 7265 9082 Fax 08701-269648
E-mail stevenffoster@aol.com

FOSTER, Stuart Jack. b 47. Oak Hill Th Coll DipHE79 BA80 Lambeth STh86. **d** 80 **p** 81. C Worting *Win* 80-84; C-in-c Kempshott CD 84-88; R Hook 88-95; Chapl and Warden Bp Grosseteste Coll Linc 95-99; R Kirton in Lindsey w Manton *Linc* from 99; R Grayingham from 99; OCF from 99. *The Vicarage, 28 Southcliffe Road, Kirton Lindsey, Gainsborough DN21 4NR* Tel and fax (01652) 648009 Mobile 07885-701876
E-mail sjfoster.standrew@virgin.net

FOSTER, Susan. b 58. Nottm Univ BMedSci80 BM, BS82. WEMTC 00. **d** 03. NSM Tenbury *Heref* from 03. *Little Oaks Cottage, Hope Bagot, Ludlow SY8 3AE* Tel (01584) 891092
E-mail thefosters@littleoakshb.fsnet.uk

FOSTER, Susan Anne. b 53. Trin Coll Bris BA97. **d** 98 **p** 99. C Watton w Carbrooke and Ovington *Nor* 98-02; Min S Wonston CD *Win* from 02. *6 Green Close, South Wonston, Winchester SO21 3EE* Tel (01962) 880650

FOSTER, Thomas Arthur. b 23. St D Coll Lamp BA47. Cuddesdon Coll 47. **d** 49 **p** 50. C Risca *Mon* 49-52; C Win H Trin *Win* 52-55; C Rumney *Mon* 55-56; V Cwmtillery 56-59; R Llanfoist and Llanellen 59-92; rtd 92; Perm to Offic *Mon* from 98. *The Bungalow, 5 The Bryn, Llangattock-juxta-Usk, Abergavenny NP7 9AG* Tel (01873) 840516

FOSTER, William Basil. b 23. Worc Ord Coll 65. **d** 67 **p** 68. C Folkingham w Laughton *Linc* 67-71; P-in-c Gedney Hill 71-75; V Whaplode Drove 71-75; R Heydour w Culverthorpe, Welby and Londonthorpe 75-77; P-in-c Ropsley 75-79; R 79-93; R Sapperton w Braceby 79-93; R Old Somerby 82-93; rtd 93. *31 Hedgefield Road, Barrowby, Grantham NG32 1TA* Tel (01476) 575925

FOSTER-CLARK, Mrs Sarah Hazel. b 75. Man Univ BA97 Heythrop Coll Lon MA99. Wycliffe Hall Ox 98. **d** 00 **p** 01. C Walmsley *Man* 00-01; C Turton Moorland Min 01; C Horwich and Rivington from 01. *27 Brownlow Road, Bolton BL6 7DW* Tel (01204) 696923 Mobile 07909-916741
E-mail revdf-c@xalt.co.uk

FOTHERGILL, Anthony Page. b 36. Dur Univ BA60. Cranmer Hall Dur DipTh62. **d** 62 **p** 63. C Wolverhampton St Mark *Lich* 62-66; C Chasetown 66-69; V Wellington St Luke 69-77; TV Hanley H Ev 77-78; V Rocester 78-87; P-in-c Croxden 85-87; RD Uttoxeter 87; rtd 87; Hon C Basildon w Aldworth and Ashampstead *Ox* from 97. *Bowerleigh, 24 Purley Rise, Purley-on-Thames, Reading RG8 8AE* Tel 0118-984 2984

FOTHERGILL, Richard Patrick. b 61. Newc Univ BA83. Trin Coll Bris DipHE93. **d** 95 **p** 96. C E Twickenham St Steph *Lon* 95-97; Asst P Kenilworth All SS S Africa from 97. *The Rectory, 16 Waterloo Road, Wynberg, Cape Town, 7824 South Africa*

FOULDS, John Stuart. b 64. Lanc Univ BA87 Southn Univ BTh91. Chich Th Coll 88. **d** 91 **p** 92. C Eastcote St Lawr *Lon* 91-95; C Wembley Park 95-99; P-in-c Meir *Lich* from 99. *The Vicarage, 715 Uttoxeter Road, Stoke-on-Trent ST3 5PY* Tel (01782) 313347

FOULGER, Bernard Darwin. b 28. Cant Sch of Min 86. **d** 89 **p** 90. OLM Sittingbourne H Trin w Bobbing *Cant* 89-97; rtd 97; Perm to Offic *Cant* from 97. *30 Frederick Street, Sittingbourne ME10 1AU* Tel (01795) 422724

FOULIS BROWN, Graham Douglas. b 50. JP87. St Steph Ho Ox 80. **d** 82 **p** 83. C Hungerford and Denford *Ox* 82-84; Chapl Hungerford Hosp 83-84; C Bicester w Bucknell, Caversfield and Launton *Ox* 84-85; TV 85-90; V Kidmore End and Sonning Common 90-03; P-in-c Rotherfield Peppard 02-03; R Rotherfield Peppard and Kidmore End etc from 03. *The Rectory, Kidmore End, Reading RG4 9AY* Tel 0118-972 3987 Fax 972 4202
E-mail gdfb.vicarage@lineone.net

FOULKES, Chan Meurig. b 21. St D Coll Lamp BA46. St Mich Coll Llan 46. **d** 47 **p** 48. C Llanbeblig w Caernarfon *Ban* 47-55; Bp's Private Chapl 54-58; V Harlech and Llanfair juxta Harlech 58-66; RD Ardudwy 64-76; R Llanaber w Caerdeon 66-76; Can Ban Cathl 71-89; Treas 74-83; Chan 83-89; R Llandegfan and Beaumaris w Llanfaes w Penmon etc 76-89; rtd 90; Perm to Offic *Ban* from 90. *Llanaber, 11 Gogarth Avenue, Penmaenmawr LL34 6PY* Tel (01492) 623011

FOULKES, Simon. b 58. Ox Poly BA81. Oak Hill Th Coll BA89. **d** 89 **p** 90. C St Austell *Truro* 89-92; C Boscombe St Jo *Win* 92-94; P-in-c Portswood St Denys 94-99; Par Evang Adv *Wakef* from 99; TR Almondbury w Farnley Tyas from 02. *The Rectory, 2 Westgate, Almondbury, Huddersfield HD5 8XE* Tel (01484) 421753 Fax as telephone E-mail teamrector@simonfoulkes.net *or* peadviser@atlas.co.uk

FOUNTAIN, David Roy (Brother Malcolm). b 48. Qu Coll Birm 85. **d** 87 **p** 88. SSF from 72; NSM Handsworth St Mich *Birm* 87-92; Lic to Offic *Sarum* 92-95; Perm to Offic *Worc* 95-00, Newc 00-02, *Lon* 02-03; V Bentley *Sheff* from 03. *The Vicarage, 3A High Street, Bentley, Doncaster DN5 0AA* Tel (01302) 876272

FOUNTAIN, John Stephen. b 43. RAF Coll Cranwell 65 Solicitor 80. LNSM course 91. **d** 93 **p** 94. NSM Nacton and Levington w Bucklesham and Foxhall *St E* from 93. *High Trees, Bridge Road, Levington, Ipswich IP10 0LZ* Tel (01473) 659908

FOUNTAIN, Miss Stephanie Ann Cecilia. b 58. Lon Univ BMus81 Roehampton Inst PGCE88. Westcott Ho Cam 00. **d** 02 **p** 03. C Tadworth *S'wark* from 02. *22 Station Approach Road, Tadworth KT20 5AD* Tel (01737) 817872
E-mail stephaniefountain@yahoo.co.uk

FOUTS, Arthur Guy. b 44. Washington Univ BA72 DMin98. Ridley Hall Cam 78. **d** 81 **p** 82. C Alperton *Lon* 81-84; R Pinxton *Derby* 84-87; USA from 88; R Dublin St Patr Ohio 88-89; Pastor Warren St Mark Rhode Is 90-91; R Wheaton St Mary Magd Washington DC from 91. *19520 Darnestown Road, Beallsville, MD 20839, USA* Tel (001) (301) 407 0661
E-mail artie301@aol.com

FOWELL, Graham Charles. b 48. Southn Univ BTh85. Chich Th Coll. **d** 82 **p** 83. C Clayton *Lich* 82-86; C Uttoxeter w Bramshall 86-90; V Oxley 90-95; P-in-c Shifnal from 95. *St Andrew's Vicarage, Manor Close, Shifnal TF11 9AJ* Tel (01952) 463694
E-mail graham@shifvic.fsnet.co.uk

FOWKE, Thomas Randall. b 07. **d** 54 **p** 55. *Address withheld by request*

FOWLER, Anthony Lewis. b 57. Oak Hill Th Coll BA93. **d** 93 **p** 94. C Walton *St E* 93-96; P-in-c Combs 96-00; P-in-c Hitcham w Lt Finborough 98-00; R Combs and Lt Finborough from 00; Chapl Suffolk Coll from 00. *The Rectory, 135 Poplar Hill, Combs, Stowmarket IP14 2AY* Tel (01449) 612076
E-mail tonyfowler@ukonline.co.uk

FOWLER, Canon Colin. b 40. DCMus83. Linc Th Coll 80. **d** 82 **p** 83. C Barbourne *Worc* 82-85; TV Worc St Martin w St Pet, St Mark etc 85-86; TV Worc SE 86-92; P-in-c Moulton *Linc* 92-95; Chapl Puerto de la Cruz Tenerife *Eur* 95-01; Hon Can Madrid Cathl from 99; R Tangmere and Oving *Chich* from 01. *St Andrew's Vicarage, 21 Gibson Road, Tangmere, Chichester PO20 2JA* Tel (01243) 785089

FOWLER, Canon David Mallory. b 51. Lancs Coll of Agric OND72. Brasted Th Coll 74 Trin Coll Bris 75. **d** 78 **p** 79. C Rainhill *Liv* 78-81; C Houghton *Carl* 81-84; P-in-c Grayrigg 84-89; P-in-c Old Hutton w New Hutton 84-89; V Kirkoswald, Renwick and Ainstable 89-99; P-in-c Gt Salkeld w Lazonby 98-99; R Kirkoswald, Renwick, Gt Salkeld and Lazonby from 00; RD Penrith from 99; Hon Can Carl Cathl from 99. *The Vicarage, Kirkoswald, Penrith CA10 1DQ* Tel (01768) 898176
E-mail revdmf@aol.com

FOWLER, Mrs Janice Karen Brenda. b 56. Middx Univ BA97. Oak Hill Th Coll DipHE93. **d** 93 **p** 94. NSM Walton *St E* 93-96; Chapl Ipswich Hosp NHS Trust 94-00; NSM Combs *St E* 96-00;

NSM Hitcham w Lt Finborough 98-00; C Combs and Lt Finborough from 00. *The Rectory, 135 Poplar Hill, Combs, Stowmarket IP14 2AY* Tel (01449) 612076 Mobile 07720-262201

FOWLER, John Ronald. b 30. Ely Th Coll 55. **d** 58 **p** 59. C Surbiton St Andr *S'wark* 58-61; Guyana 61-70 and 83-89; V Sydenham All SS *S'wark* 70-81; V Wood End *Cov* 81-83; Can St Geo Cathl 86-89; Adn Demerara 86-89; V Bedford St Mich *St Alb* 90-95; rtd 95. *21 Painters Lane, Sutton, Ely CB6 2NS* Tel (01353) 776268

FOWLER, John Thomas. b 42. EAMTC. **d** 01 **p** 02. NSM Stoke by Nayland w Leavenheath and Polstead *St E* from 01. *Warners, Thorington Street, Stoke by Nayland, Colchester CO6 4SP* Tel (01206) 337229 Fax as telephone
E-mail john@albys.freeserve.co.uk

FOWLER, Miss Morag Margaret. b 45. CertEd67 DipRE67 Dip Librarianship 76 St Andr Univ MA66. St Jo Coll Nottm 84. **dss** 85 **d** 87 **p** 94. Skipton H Trin *Bradf* 85-87; Par Dn 87-89; Par Dn Market Bosworth, Cadeby w Sutton Cheney etc *Leic* 90-94; C 94; TV 94-96; rtd 96. *25 Springfield Avenue, Market Bosworth, Nuneaton CV13 0NS* Tel (01455) 292275

FOWLES, Canon Christopher John. b 31. Lich Th Coll 54. **d** 58 **p** 59. C Englefield Green *Guildf* 58-63; C Worplesdon 63-69; V Chessington 69-77; V Horsell 77-95; RD Woking 92-94; Hon Can Guildf Cathl 94-95; rtd 95; Perm to Offic *Guildf* from 95. *78 St Jude's Road, Egham TW20 0DF* Tel (01784) 439457

FOX, Albert. b 06. MBE. **d** 73 **p** 74. C Bris St Ambrose Whitehall *Bris* 73-75; C Bris St Pet *Bris* 75-79; rtd 79. *20 New Brunswick Avenue, Bristol BS5 8PW* Tel 0117-967 2632

FOX, Mrs Carole Ann. b 36. TISEC 98. **d** 99 **p** 00. NSM Ellon *Ab* from 99. *4 Mavis Bank, Newburgh, Ellon AB41 6FB* Tel (01358) 789693 E-mail thefoxes@ythan1.demon.co.uk

FOX, Charles Edward. b 36. Lich Th Coll 62. **d** 66 **p** 67. C S Bank *York* 66-69; C Stokesley 69-72; P-in-c Ugthorpe 72-82; V Egton w Grosmont 72-82; P-in-c Newbold Verdon *Leic* 82-83; R Newbold de Verdun and Kirkby Mallory from 84. *The Rectory, Main Street, Newbold Verdon, Leicester LE9 9NN* Tel (01455) 822528

FOX, Colin George. b 46. TD. Southn Univ DipTh75. Sarum & Wells Th Coll 73. **d** 75 **p** 76. C N Hammersmith St Kath *Lon* 75-79; CF (TA) 76-90; C Heston *Lon* 79-81; TV Marlborough *Sarum* 81-90; P-in-c Pewsey 90-91; TR 91-98; TR Pewsey and Swanborough 98-03; Chapl Pewsey Hosp 90-95; P-in-c Avon Valley *Sarum* from 03. *The Vicarage, High Street, Netheravon, Salisbury SP4 9QP* Tel (01980) 670326
E-mail foxy.col@talk21.com

FOX, Harvey Harold. b 27. Lich Th Coll 58. **d** 60 **p** 61. C Birchfield *Birm* 60-62; C Boldmere 62-65; V Sparkbrook Em 65-71; V Dordon 71-77; V Four Oaks 77-82; V Packwood w Hockley Heath 82-90; rtd 90; Perm to Offic *Cov* from 90. *37 Meadow Road, Henley-in-Arden B95 5LB* Tel (01564) 795302

FOX, Canon Herbert Frederick. b 26. Leeds Univ BA50. Coll of Resurr Mirfield 50. **d** 52 **p** 53. C Bury St Thos *Man* 52-55; V Unsworth 55-61; V Turton 61-72; V Farnworth and Kearsley 72-78; RD Farnworth 77-84; TR E Farnworth and Kearsley 78-84; Hon Can Man Cathl 81-84; V Ashford Hill w Headley Win 84-91; rtd 91; Perm to Offic *Man* from 91. *9 Highfield Road, Blackrod, Bolton BL6 5BP* Tel (01204) 670326

FOX, Canon Ian James. b 44. Selw Coll Cam BA66 MA70. Linc Th Coll 66. **d** 68 **p** 69. C Salford St Phil w St Steph *Man* 68-71; C Kirkleatham *York* 71-73; TV Redcar w Kirkleatham 73-77; V Bury St Pet *Man* 77-85; V Northallerton w Kirby Sigston *York* 85-03; RD Northallerton 85-91; Chapl Friarage and Distr Hosp Northallerton 88-92; Chapl Northallerton Health Services NHS Trust 92-03; V Barlby w Riccall *York* from 03; Can and Preb York Minster from 95. *The Vicarage, York Road, Barlby, Selby YO8 5JP* Tel (01757) 702384

FOX, Preb Jacqueline Frederica. b 43. Ripon Coll of Educn CertEd66 Leeds Univ BEd74 MEd84 HonRCM85. S Dios Minl Tr Scheme 83. **dss** 85 **d** 87 **p** 94. RCM *Lon* 85-86; Dioc FE Officer 87-96; Hon C Acton St Mary 87-96; R from 96; Dean of Women's Min from 96; Dir of Ords Willesden Area from 01; Preb St Paul's Cathl from 01. *The Rectory, 14 Cumberland Park, London W3 6SX* Tel (020) 8992 8876 *or* 8993 0422 Fax 8896 3754
E-mail jackie.fox@london.anglican.org

FOX, Mrs Jane. b 47. Open Univ BA91 Bp Otter Coll Chich CertEd75 ALA70. S Dios Minl Tr Scheme 92. **d** 95 **p** 96. NSM W Blatchington *Chich* 95-98; C Peacehaven and Telscombe Cliffs 98-01; C Telscombe w Piddinghoe and Southease 98-01; TV Hitchin *St Alb* from 01. *Holy Saviour Vicarage, St Anne's Road, Hitchin SG5 1QB* Tel (01462) 456140

FOX (née COULDRIDGE), Mrs Janice Evelyn. b 49. Bognor Regis Coll of Educn CertEd71. Glouc Sch of Min 89. **d** 92 **p** 94. C Tupsley w Hampton Bishop *Heref* 92-96; P-in-c Orleton w Brimfield 96-01; Dioc Ecum Officer 96-01; TV Worc SE *Worc* from 01. *The Vicarage, 160 Bath Road, Worcester WR5 3EP* Tel (01905) 358010 *or* 356499 E-mail janfox@orleton.fsnet.co.uk

FOX, Jeremy Robin. b 68. St Chad's Coll Dur BA89 MA92 Leeds Univ BA94. Coll of Resurr Mirfield 92. **d** 95 **p** 96. C S Shields All SS *Dur* 95-99; C Tottenham St Paul *Lon* from 99; C Edmonton

St Mary w St Jo from 99. *St John's Vicarage, Dyson Road, London N18 2DS* Tel (020) 8807 2767

FOX, John Brian. b 38. **d** 94 **p** 95. NSM Phillack w Gwithian and Gwinear *Truro* 94-96; NSM Godrevy from 96. *Abbeydale, 26 Tresdale Parc, Connor Downs, Hayle TR27 5DX* Tel (01736) 753935

FOX, Jonathan Alexander. b 56. St Jo Coll Nottm LTh77 BTh78. **d** 81 **p** 82. C Chasetown *Lich* 81-85; TV Fazakerley Em *Liv* 85-89; TV Madeley *Heref* 97-02. *Bridge House, Chirbury, Montgomery SY15 6BQ* Tel (01938) 561462

FOX, Leonard. b 41. AKC66. **d** 67 **p** 68. C Salford Stowell Memorial *Man* 67-68; C Hulme St Phil 68-72; C Portsea All SS w St Jo Rudmore *Portsm* 72-75; V Oakfield St Jo 75-92; P-in-c Portsea All SS from 92; Dir All SS Urban Miss Cen from 92. *All Saints' Vicarage, 51 Staunton Street, Portsmouth PO1 4EJ* Tel (023) 9287 2815 *or* 9282 9119 Fax 9283 8116 E-mail lf.rjf@virgin.net

FOX, Mrs Lynn. b 51. EMMTC 92. **d** 92 **p** 94. Assoc P Clifton *S'well* 92-96; TV 96-98. *Address temp unknown*

FOX, Maurice Henry George. b 24. Lon Univ BD58. St Aid Birkenhead 47. **d** 49 **p** 50. C Eccleshill *Bradf* 49-52; C Bingley All SS 52-56; V Cross Roads cum Lees 56-62; V Sutton 62-79; V Grange-over-Sands *Carl* 79-88; rtd 89. *7 Manor Close, Topcliffe, Thirsk YO7 3RH* Tel (01845) 578322

FOX, The Ven Michael John. b 42. Hull Univ BSc63. Coll of Resurr Mirfield 64. **d** 66 **p** 67. C Becontree St Elisabeth *Chelmsf* 66-70; C Wanstead H Trin Hermon Hill 70-72; V Victoria Docks Ascension 72-76; V Chelmsf All SS 76-88; P-in-c Chelmsf Ascension 85-88; RD Chelmsf 86-88; R Colchester St Jas, All SS, St Nic and St Runwald 88-93; Hon Can Chelmsf Cathl 91-93; Adn Harlow 93-95; Adn W Ham from 95. *86 Aldersbrook Road, London E12 5DH* Tel (020) 8989 8557 Fax 8530 1311 E-mail a.westham@chelmsford.anglican.org

FOX, John Holland. b 41. Lon Univ BD68. Oak Hill Th Coll 64. **d** 69 **p** 70. C Reigate St Mary *S'wark* 69-73; NSM 76-01; C Guildf St Sav *Guildf* 73-76; Asst Chapl Reigate Gr Sch 76-81; Chapl from 81; NSM Reigate St Pet CD *S'wark* 96-01; P-in-c Reigate St Luke S Park from 01. *St Luke's Vicarage, Church Road, Reigate RH2 8HY* Tel (01737) 246302 E-mail mikejh.fox@virgin.net

FOX, Nigel Stephen. b 35. Sarum Th Coll 59. **d** 62 **p** 63. C Rainbow Hill St Barn *Worc* 62-65; C Kidderminster St Geo 65-67; C-in-c Warndon CD 67-69; V Warndon 69-74; R S Hill w Callington *Truro* 74-85; RD E Wivelshire 78-81; R St Martin w E and W Looe 85-95; rtd 95; Perm to Offic *Truro* from 95. *Newlair, 4 Bindown Court, Nomansland, Widegates, Looe PL13 1PX* Tel (01503) 240584

FOX, Norman Stanley. b 39. Wolv Univ LLB97 Univ of Wales DipTh64. St Mich Coll Llan 61. **d** 64 **p** 65. C Brierley Hill *Lich* 64-67; C Tettenhall Regis 67-70; V Cradley *Worc* 70-73; Asst Chapl HM Pris Wakef 73-74; Chapl HM Pris The Verne 74-76; R Clayton W w High Hoyland *Wakef* 76-81; R Cumberworth 81-84; C Tettenhall Wood *Lich* 85-89; TV 89-91; V Pennsett 91-93; rtd 93. *54 Lyndon Road, Solihull B92 7RQ* Tel 0121-707 8216 E-mail norman@nsfox.evesham.net

✠**FOX, The Rt Revd Peter John.** b 52. AKC74. St Aug Coll Cant 74. **d** 75 **p** 76 **c** 02. C Wymondham *Nor* 75-79; Papua New Guinea 79-85 and from 02; P-in-c Tattersett *Nor* 85-88; P-in-c Houghton 85-88; P-in-c Syderstone w Barmer and Bagthorpe 85-88; P-in-c Tatterford 85-88; P-in-c E w W Rudham 85-88; R Coxford Gp 88-89; TR Lynton, Brendon, Countisbury, Lynmouth etc *Ex* 89-95; RD Shirwell 93-95; P-in-c Harpsden *Ox* 95-02; Gen Sec Melanesian Miss 95-02; Bp Port Moresby from 02. *PO Box 6491, Boroko, NCD, Port Moresby, Papua New Guinea* Tel (00675) 323 2489 Fax 326 2493 E-mail acpngpom@global.net.pg *or* foxfamily@daltron.com.pg

FOX, Canon Raymond. b 46. QUB BSc69. CITC 71. **d** 71 **p** 72. C Holywood *D & D* 71-75; C Min Can Down Cathl 75-78; I Killinchy w Kilmood and Tullynakill 78-81; I Belfast St Mary *Conn* 81-88; I Killaney w Carryduff *D & D* 88-02; Can Down Cathl 98-02; Chapter Clerk and V Choral Belf Cathl 00-02; I Donegal w Killymard, Lough Eske and Laghey *D & R* from 02. *The Rectory, Ballyshannon Road, Donegal, Irish Republic* Tel (00353) (74) 972 1075 E-mail donegal@raphoe.anglican.org

FOX, Robert. b 54. Man Univ BEd76. N Ord Course 89. **d** 91 **p** 92. NSM Stalybridge *Man* 91; NSM Ashton St Mich 91-96; NSM Stalybridge from 96. *36 Norman Road, Stalybridge SK15 1LY* Tel 0161-338 8481 E-mail rob@foxesbrige.freeserve.co.uk

FOX, Robin. *See* FOX, Jeremy Robin

FOX, Canon Sidney. b 47. Nottm Univ BTh79 PhD93. Linc Th Coll 75. **d** 79 **p** 80. C Middlesbrough St Oswald *York* 79-81; P-in-c 81-86; V 86-87; V Newby 87-92; R Brechin *Bre* from 92; R Tarfside from 92; P-in-c Auchmithie from 92; Can St Paul's Cathl Dundee from 98. *St Andrew's Rectory, 9 Castle Street, Brechin DD9 6JW* Tel (01356) 622708 Fax 0870-7348008 E-mail revsfox@compuserve.com

FOX, Timothy William Bertram. b 37. CCC Cam BA61. Qu Coll Birm 66. **d** 68 **p** 69. C Cannock *Lich* 68-72; C Bilston St Leon 72-75; V Essington 75-81; R Buildwas and Leighton w Eaton Constantine etc 81-92; RD Wrockwardine 88-92; P-in-c

Moreton and Church Eaton 92; P-in-c Bradeley St Mary and All SS 92; R Bradeley, Church Eaton and Moreton from 92. *The Rectory, High Street, Church Eaton, Stafford ST20 0AG* Tel (01785) 823091

FOX-WILSON, Francis James. b 46. Nottm Univ BTh73. Linc Th Coll 69. **d** 73 **p** 74. C Eastbourne St Eliz *Chich* 73-76; C Seaford w Sutton 76-78; P-in-c Hellingly 78-79; P-in-c Upper Dicker 78-79; V Hellingly and Upper Dicker 79-85; V Goring-by-Sea 85-93; R Alfriston w Lullington, Litlington and W Dean from 93. *The Rectory, Sloe Lane, Alfriston, Polegate BN26 5UY* Tel (01323) 870376

FOXWELL, Rupert Edward Theodore. b 54. Magd Coll Cam BA76 MA80 Solicitor 79. Wycliffe Hall Ox 91. **d** 93 **p** 94. C Tonbridge SS Pet and Paul *Roch* 93-98. *24 Cheviot Close, Tonbridge TN9 1NH* Tel (01732) 358535 Fax as telephone E-mail foxwell@harvester.org.uk

FOY, Malcolm Stuart. b 48. ACP80 FCollP FRSA Univ of Wales (Lamp) BA71 Magd Coll Cam CertEd72 K Coll Lon MA89. Ox NSM Course 84. **d** 87 **p** 88. NSM Tilehurst St Mich *Ox* 87-90; C Ireland Wood *Ripon* 90-96; Adv RE Leeds Adnry 90-96; Dir Educn *Bradf* 96-99; C Otley 99; Perm to Offic from 00. *45 The Chase, Keighley BD20 6HU* Tel (01535) 665112

FRAIS, Jonathan Jeremy. b 65. Kingston Poly LLB87. Oak Hill Th Coll BA92. **d** 92 **p** 93. C Orpington Ch Ch *Roch* 92-96; Asst Chapl Moscow *Eur* 96-99; Chapl Kiev from 99. *clo BCFO (Kiev), King Charles Street, London SW1A 2AH* Tel (0038) (44) 229 7458 Fax as telephone E-mail frais@public.icyb.kiev.ua

FRAMPTON, Miss Marcia Ellen. b 36. SRN65 SCM66. Ripon Coll Cuddesdon 86. **d** 88 **p** 95. Par Dn Paston *Pet* 88-89; Par Dn Burford w Fulbrook and Taynton *Ox* 90-92; Par Dn Witney 92-93; NSM Heref S Wye *Heref* 94-01; rtd 01; Perm to Offic *Heref* from 02. *15 Waterfield Road, Hereford HR2 7DD* Tel (01432) 278955 E-mail ellenkate@beeb.net

FRAMPTON-MORGAN, Anthony Paul George. *See* MORGAN, Anthony Paul George

FRANCE, Charles Malcolm. b 48. ACA71 FCA76. EAMTC 94. **d** 97 **p** 98. C Gt Grimsby St Mary and St Jas *Linc* 97-02; P-in-c Skegness and Winthorpe from 02; P-in-c Ingoldmells w Addlethorpe from 02. *20 Drake Road, Skegness PE25 3BH* Tel (01754) 612079 E-mail malcolmfrance@aol.com

FRANCE, Elizabeth Claire. *See* PIERCY, Miss Elizabeth Claire

FRANCE, Evan Norman Lougher. b 52. Jes Coll Cam BA74 MA78. Wycliffe Hall Ox 76. **d** 79 **p** 80. C Hall Green Ascension *Birm* 79-82; CMS 82-84; C Bexhill St Pet *Chich* 84-87; V Westfield from 87. *The Vicarage, Vicarage Lane, Westfield, Hastings TN35 4SD* Tel (01424) 751029

FRANCE, Geoffrey. b 37. S Dios Minl Tr Scheme 87. **d** 90 **p** 91. NSM Uckfield *Chich* 90-92; C 92-94; R Warbleton and Bodle Street Green 94-02; rtd 02. *Little Croft, 19 James Avenue, Herstmonceux, Hailsham BN27 4PB* Tel (01323) 831840

FRANCE, Canon Geoffrey Charles. b 23. Ripon Hall Ox 57. **d** 59 **p** 60. C Mansfield St Mark *S'well* 59-61; V Rainworth 61-68; V Sneinton St Cypr 68-90; Hon Can S'well Minster 87-90; rtd 90; Perm to Offic *S'well* from 90. Nor 90-00. *11 Elsden Close, Holt NR25 6JW* Tel (01263) 711210

FRANCE, John Andrew. b 68. Edin Univ MA90 Leeds Univ BA00. Coll of Resurr Mirfield 98. **d** 00 **p** 01. C Hartlepool H Trin *Dur* from 00. *43 Alderwood Close, Hartlepool TS27 3QR* Tel (01429) 894013 E-mail andrew.france1@ntlworld.com

FRANCE, Malcolm Norris. b 28. Ch Ch Ox BA53 MA57 Essex Univ PhD75. Westcott Ho Cam 53. **d** 55 **p** 56. C Ipswich St Mary le Tower *St E* 55-58; V Esholt *Bradf* 58-64; Chapl Essex Univ *Chelmsf* 64-73; Perm to Offic *Chich* 77-87; P-in-c Starston *Nor* 87-93; rtd 93; Perm to Offic *Nor* from 93. *The Old Rectory, Starston, Harleston IP20 9NG* Tel (01379) 854326

FRANCE, Canon Richard Thomas. b 38. Ball Coll Ox BA60 MA63 Lon Univ BD62 Bris Univ PhD67. Tyndale Hall Bris 60. **d** 66 **p** 67. C Cambridge St Matt *Ely* 66-69; Nigeria 69-73 and 76-77; Hon Can Ibadan from 94; Lib Tyndale Ho Cam 73-76; Warden 78-81; Vice-Prin Lon Bible Coll 81-88; Prin Wycliffe Hall Ox 89-95; R Wentnor w Ratlinghope, Myndtown, Norbury etc *Heref* 95-99; rtd 99. *T'yn-y-Twll, Langelynin, Llwyngwril LL37 2QL* Tel (01341) 250596 E-mail rtfrance@lineone.net

FRANCE, Robert Alistair. b 71. Ox Poly BA92. Oak Hill Th Coll BA94. **d** 97 **p** 98. C Hartford *Ches* 97-02; P-in-c Stokenchurch and Ibstone *Ox* from 02. *The Vicarage, Wycombe Road, Stokenchurch, High Wycombe HP14 3RG* Tel (01494) 483384 Mobile 07929-147552 E-mail revalistair@aol.com

FRANCE, Robert Lyle. b 47. Univ of Mississippi BS69 Univ of Cincinnati MD73. Trin Coll Bris BA03. **d** 03. C Mangotsfield *Bris* from 03. *19 Hicks Avenue, Emersons Green, Bristol BS16 7HA* Tel 0117-957 5025 Mobile 07786-641751 E-mail fbobinengland@aol.com

FRANCE, Stephen Mark. b 66. Wycliffe Hall Ox BTh00. **d** 00 **p** 01. C Newbold w Dunston *Derby* from 00; P-in-c Darley Abbey from 03; Dioc Duty Press Officer from 03. *St Edmund's Vicarage, Kingscroft, Allestree, Derby DE22 2FN* Tel (01332) 557396 *or* (01246) 292775 Mobile 07041-484212 E-mail revfrance@hotmail.com

FRANCE, William Michael. b 43. Sydney Univ BA68 Lon Univ BD72 Chas Sturt Univ NSW MEd96. Moore Th Coll Sydney LTh70. d 73 p 73. Australia 73-76 and from 78; C Barton Seagrave w Warkton Pet 76-78. 6 Wesson Road, West Pennant Hills, NSW, Australia 2125 Tel (0061) (2) 9875 2987 or 9286 9605 Mobile 411-276050 Fax 9286 9632 E-mail b.j.b@optusnet.com.au or wfrance@sacs.nsw.edu.au

FRANCE, Archdeacon of. See WELLS, The Ven Anthony Martin Giffard

FRANCES, Nicolas Francis. b 61. MBE98. Portsm Poly HND82. N Ord Course 92. d 95 p 96. NSM Anfield St Columba Liv 95-98; Australia from 98; Acting Dir Health and Welfare Chapls Melbourne 98-99; Exec Dir Brotherhood of St Laur from 99. 15 Traill Street, Northcote, Vic, Australia 3070 Tel (0061) (3) 9481 7373 or 9483 1347 Fax 9486 9724 E-mail nic@bsl.org.au

FRANCES ANNE CSD, Mother. See COCKER, Mrs Frances Rymer

FRANCIS, Miss Annette. b 44. DCR66. Trin Coll Bris DipHE93. d 93 p 94. NSM Belmont Lon 93; C 94-97; C Swansea St Pet S & B 97-99; V Llanelli from 99. Llanelly Rectory, Abergavenny Road, Gilwern, Abergavenny NP7 0AD Tel (01873) 830280

FRANCIS, Brother. See TYNDALE-BISCOE, William Francis

FRANCIS, Claude Vernon Eastwood. b 15. Univ of Wales BA38. Ripon Hall Ox 38. d 40 p 41. C Cilybebyll Llan 40-44; C Treorchy 44-46; C Whitchurch 46-49; C Winscombe B & W 49-55; R E Pennard w Pylle 55-75; R Ditcheat w E Pennard and Pylle 75-81; rtd 81; Perm to Offic B & W from 81. Millbank, Mill Lane, Alhampton, Shepton Mallet BA4 6PX Tel (01749) 860225

FRANCIS, David Carpenter. b 45. Southn Univ BSc66 Loughb Univ MSc71 Sussex Univ MA83. Westcott Ho Cam 85. d 87 p 88. C Ealing St Mary Lon 87-90; Chapl Ealing Coll of HE 87-90; Chapl Clayponds Hosp Ealing 88-90; P-in-c Wembley St Jo Lon 90-93; Chapl Wembley Hosp 90-93; V Platt Roch 93-01; Post Ord Tr Officer 93-98; RD Shoreham 99-01; R Stow on the Wold, Condicote and The Swells Glouc from 01. The Rectory, Sheep Street, Stow on the Wold, Cheltenham GL54 1AA Tel (01451) 830607 Mobile 07799-410370 Fax (01451) 830903 E-mail david@francisatthevicarage.freeserve.co.uk

FRANCIS, David Everton Reginald. b 29. Roch Th Coll 59. d 61 p 62. Chapl TS Arethusa 61-64; C Frindsbury Roch 61-64; C-in-c Chatham St Wm CD 64-71; V Chatham St Wm 71-73; RD Roch 73-78; V Roch 73-78; Hon Can Roch Cathl 79-94; Ind Chapl 79-89; Dir Continuing Minl Educn 89-94; Adn Bromley 79-94; rtd 94; Perm to Offic Roch 94-97. 3 Powell Close, Aylesford ME20 7BW

FRANCIS, The Ven Edward Reginald. b 29. Roch Th Coll 59. d 61 p 62. Chapl TS Arethusa 61-64; C Frindsbury Roch 61-64; C-in-c Chatham St Wm CD 64-71; V Chatham St Wm 71-73; RD Roch 73-78; V Roch 73-78; Hon Can Roch Cathl 79-94; Ind Chapl 79-89; Dir Continuing Minl Educn 89-94; Adn Bromley 79-94; rtd 94; Perm to Offic Roch 94-97. 3 Powell Close, Aylesford ME20 7BW

FRANCIS, Donald. b 31. Bris Univ BA52. St Mich Coll Llan 52. d 54 p 55. C Newport St Julian Mon 54-59; C Pokesdown St Jas Win 59-61; R Wolvesnewton w Kilgwrrwg and Devauden Mon 61-74; V Llantilio Pertholey w Bettws Chpl 74-83; V Llantilio Pertholey w Bettws Chpl etc 83-93; RD Abergavenny 87-93; rtd 93; Perm to Offic Heref from 93. 114 Park Street, Hereford HR1 2RE Tel (01432) 269674

FRANCIS, Canon Ernest Walter. b 08. MBE45. Bible Churchmen's Coll Bris 29. d 36 p 37. BCMS Burma 32-67; CF 43-46; Area Sec BCMS 67-76; rtd 76; Hon Can Sittwe Burma from 82. Kenilworth Manor, Thickthorn Close, Kenilworth CV8 2AF

FRANCIS, Miss Gillian Cartwright. b 40. CertEd61. Dalton Ho Bris Trin Coll Bris DipTh71. dss 85 d 87 p 94. Blackheath Birm 86-94; Par Dn 87-94; P-in-c Stechford 94-03; rtd 03. 22 Ince Castle Way, Gloucester GL1 4DT Tel (01452) 503059

FRANCIS, Canon Graham John. b 45. Univ of Wales (Cardiff) DipTh70. St Mich Coll Llan 66. d 70 p 71. C Llanblethian w Cowbridge and Llandough etc Llan 70-76; V Penrhiwceiber w Matthewstown and Ynysboeth 76-02; V Cardiff St Mary and St Steph w St Dyfrig etc from 02; Can Llan Cathl from 02. 43 Pentre Street, Grangetown, Cardiff CF11 6QX Tel (029) 2038 9384 E-mail francisgj@aol.com

FRANCIS, Canon James More MacLeod. b 44. Edin Univ MA65 BD68 PhD74 Yale Univ STM69. New Coll Edin 65. d 87 p 87. Sen Lect RS Sunderland Univ Dur from 82; NSM Sunderland St Chad 87-98; TV Sunderland from 98; Tutor NEOC 89-98; Bp's Adv for NSM Dur from 99; Prin Dioc OLM Course from 02; Hon Can Dur Cathl from 00. 8 Cooke's Wood, Broompark, Durham DH7 7RL Tel 0191-384 9638 E-mail jamesfrancis@mac.com

FRANCIS, James Stephen. b 66. Univ of Wales (Ban) DipTh85. SEITE DipTM99. d 99. NSM St Botolph Aldgate w H Trin Minories Lon 99-02; NSM Brixton Road Ch Ch S'wark 99-01; Perm to Offic Derby and S'wark from 01; NSM Soho St Anne w St Thos and St Pet Lon from 02. 26 Rosewood House, Vauxhall Grove, London SW8 1TB Tel (020) 7587 0562 or 7702 5629 E-mail jamesfrancis@trb.info

FRANCIS, Canon James Woodcock. b 28. OBE97. Wilberforce Univ Ohio AB57 Payne Th Sem Ohio BD58. Bexley Hall Div Sch Ohio 59. d 59 p 60. USA 59-84; Bermuda from 85; Can Res Bermuda 85-99; R Devonshire Ch Ch from 99. PO Box HM 627, Hamilton HM CX, Bermuda Tel (001809) 295 1125 Fax 292 5421

FRANCIS, Jeffrey Merrick. b 46. Bris Univ BSc69. Qu Coll Birm 72. d 76 p 77. C Bris Ch the Servant Stockwood Bris 76-79; C Bishopston 79-82; V Bris St Andr Hartcliffe 82-93; TV Bris St Paul's 93-00; P-in-c Barton Hill St Luke w Ch Ch and Moorfields 00-02; Perm to Offic from 02. 32 Burfoot Gardens, Stockwood, Bristol BS14 8TE Tel (01275) 831020

FRANCIS, Jeremy Montgomery. b 31. BNC Ox BA53 MA56. Glouc Sch of Min 84. d 87 p 88. NSM Chedworth, Yanworth and Stowell, Coln Rogers etc Glouc 87-90; NSM Coates, Rodmarton and Sapperton etc 90-01; NSM Daglingworth w the Duntisbournes and Winstone 95-97; NSM Brimpsfield w Birdlip, Syde, Daglingworth etc 97-00; Perm to Offic from 01. Old Barnfield, Duntisbourne Leer, Cirencester GL7 7AS Tel (01285) 821370

FRANCIS, John. b 56. Bris Poly BA78 MCIH81. LNSM course 95. d 98 p 99. OLM Hatcham Park All SS S'wark from 98. Flat 2, 133 Deptford High Street, London SE8 4NS Tel (020) 8691 3145 or 8875 5942 E-mail franci@threshold.org.uk

FRANCIS, John Sims. b 25. Fitzw Ho Cam BA54 MA58. St D Coll Lamp BA47 LTh49. d 49 p 50. C Swansea St Barn S & B 49-52; C Chesterton St Andr Ely 52-54; C Swansea St Mary and H Trin S & B 54-58; V Newbridge-on-Wye and Llanfihangel Brynpabuan 58-65; R Willingham Ely 65-82; RD N Stowe 78-82; R Rampton 82; P-in-c Buckden 82-85; V 85-91; rtd 91; Perm to Offic Linc 92-01. 3 The Brambles, Bourne PE10 9TF Tel (01778) 426396

FRANCIS, Julian Montgomery. b 60. Selw Coll Cam BA83 MA83. S'wark Ord Course 88. d 91 p 92. C S Wimbledon H Trin and St Pet S'wark 91-95; V Cottingley Bradf 95-99; Minority Ethnic Angl Concerns Officer Lich 99-02; Assoc Min W Bromwich St Andr w Ch Ch 99-02; TR Coventry Caludon Cov from 02. Stoke Rectory, 365A Walsgrave Road, Coventry CV2 4BG Tel (024) 7663 5731 or 7644 3691 E-mail stoke.st.michael@fish.co.uk

FRANCIS, Kenneth. b 30. Em Coll Cam BA56 MA60. Coll of Resurr Mirfield. d 58 p 59. C De Beauvoir Town St Pet Lon 58-61; Zambia 62-70; V Harlow St Mary Magd Chelmsf 70-76; V Felixstowe St Jo St E 76-97; rtd 98. 33 Cordy's Lane, Trimley, Felixstowe IP10 0UD

FRANCIS, Kenneth Charles. b 22. Oak Hill Th Coll 46. d 50 p 51. C Wandsworth All SS S'wark 50-53; V Deptford St Nic w Ch Ch 53-61; V Summerstown 61-77; R Cratfield w Heveningham and Ubbeston etc St E 77-87; rtd 87; Perm to Offic Truro from 87. Wheal Alfred, Chapel Hill, Bolingey, Perranporth TR6 0DQ Tel (01872) 571317

FRANCIS (or ROOSE FRANCIS), Leslie. b 18. Magd Coll Ox BA48 MA52. Westcott Ho Cam 48. d 49 p 50. C Rochdale Man 49-52; C Odiham w S Warnborough Win 52-54; V Awbridge w Mottisfont 54-60; V Bournemouth H Epiphany 60-68; R Compton Bassett Sarum 68; V Hilmarton and Highway 68-78; rtd 78. Flat 1, Robartes Court, Radnor Place, Exeter EX2 4EH Tel (01392) 412771

FRANCIS, Canon Leslie John. b 47. Pemb Coll Ox BA70 MA74 BD90 Nottm Univ MTh76 Qu Coll Cam PhD76 ScD97 Lon Univ MSc77 FBPsS88 FCP94. Westcott Ho Cam 70. d 73 p 74. C Haverhill St E 73-77; P-in-c Gt Bradley 78-82; P-in-c Lt Wratting 79-82; Research Officer Culham Coll Inst 82-88; P-in-c N Cerney w Bagendon Glouc 82-85; Perm to Offic 85-95; Fell Trin Coll Carmarthen 89-99; Dean of Chpl 95-99; Prof Th Univ of Wales (Lamp) 92-99; Prof Th Univ of Wales (Ban) from 99; Perm to Offic Ox 95-01; Hon Can St D Cathl St D from 98. University of Wales, Neuadd Ardudwy, Holyhead Road, Bangor LL57 2PX Tel (01248) 382566 Fax 383954 E-mail l.j.francis@bangor.ac.uk

FRANCIS, Martin Rufus. b 37. Pemb Coll Ox BA60 MA64. Linc Th Coll 60. d 63 p 64. C W Hartlepool St Paul Dur 63-67; C Yeovil St Jo w Preston Plucknett B & W 67-69; Chapl Tonbridge Sch 69-83; Chapl and Dep Hd St Jo Sch Leatherhead 83-94; R Herstmonceux and Wartling Chich 94-01; rtd 01. 50 Lower Bryanston, Blandford Forum DT11 0DR Tel (01258) 488619

FRANCIS, Paul Edward. b 52. Southn Univ BTh84. Sarum & Wells Th Coll 78. d 81 p 82. C Biggin Hill Roch 81-85; R Fawkham and Hartley 85-90; V Aylesford 90-99; V Riverhead w Dunton Green from 99; Chapl Dioc Assn of Readers from 01. The Vicarage, Riverhead, Sevenoaks TN13 3BS Tel (01732) 455736

FRANCIS, Peter Brereton. b 53. St Andr Univ MTh77. Qu Coll Birm 77. d 78 p 79. C Hagley Worc 78-81; Chapl Qu Mary Coll Lon 81-87; R Ayr Glas 87-92; Miss to Seamen 87-92; Provost St Mary's Cathl Glas 92-96; R Glas St Mary 92-96; Warden and Lib St Deiniol's Lib Hawarden from 97. St Deiniol's Library,

Church Lane, Hawarden, Deeside CH5 3LT Tel (01244) 532350
E-mail deiniol.visitors@btinternet.com

FRANCIS, Peter Philip. b 48. St Jo Coll Dur BA73. Wycliffe Hall
Ox 73. **d** 75 **p** 76. C Foord St Jo *Cant* 75-78; C Morden *S'wark*
78-83; P-in-c Barford St Martin, Dinton, Baverstock etc *Sarum*
83-88; P-in-c Fovant, Sutton Mandeville and Teffont Evias etc
83-86; R Newick *Chich* from 88. *The Rectory, Church Road,
Newick, Lewes BN8 4JX* Tel (01825) 722692

FRANCIS, Philip Thomas. b 58. TD03. St D Coll Lamp BA81
Regent's Park Coll Ox MTh99. Chich Th Coll 81. **d** 82 **p** 83. C
Llanelli St Paul *St D* 82-84; C Barnsley St Mary *Wakef* 84-87; V
Burton Dassett *Cov* from 87; V Gaydon w Chadshunt from 87;
CF (TA) from 88. *Burton Dassett Vicarage, Northend, Southam
CV47 2TH* Tel (01295) 770400
E-mail philip.francis@regents.ox.ac.uk

FRANCIS-DEHQANI, Gulnar Eleanor (Guli). b 66. Nottm Univ
BA89 Bris Univ MA94 PhD99. SEITE 95. **d** 98 **p** 99. C
Mortlake w E Sheen *S'wark* 98-02; Chapl R Academy of Music
Lon from 02; Chapl St Marylebone C of E Sch from 02.
St Matthias's House, 22 Cambrian Road, Richmond TW10 6JQ
Tel (020) 8948 7217 *or* 7563 1386 Mobile 07771-948190 Fax
(020) 8948 7217 *or* 7563 1387
E-mail guli@francis-dehqani.freeserve.co.uk *or*
chaplain@ram.ac.uk

FRANCIS-DEHQANI, Lee Thomas. b 67. Nottm Univ BA89.
Sarum & Wells Th Coll 92 Trin Coll Bris BA95. **d** 95 **p** 96. C
Putney St Mary *S'wark* 95-98; TV Richmond St Mary w
St Matthias and St Jo from 98. *St Matthias's House, 22 Cambrian
Road, Richmond TW10 6JQ* Tel (020) 8948 7217 Fax as tele-
phone E-mail lee@matthias-house.freeserve.co.uk

FRANK, Derek John. b 49. ACGI70 Imp Coll Lon BScEng70
Warwick Univ MSc71. Cranmer Hall Dur 83. **d** 85 **p** 86. C Clay
Cross *Derby* 85-87; C Crookes St Thos *Sheff* 87-90; TV 90-93;
Chapl Vevey w Château d'Oex and Villars *Eur* 93-02. *Address
temp unknown*

FRANK, Penelope Edith. b 45. WMMTC 96. **d** 99 **p** 00. NSM
Edgbaston St Geo *Birm* 99-02; Perm to Offic *Cov* from 03; CPAS
from 87. *CPAS, Athena Drive, Tachbrook Park, Warwick
CV3 6NG* Tel (01926) 458446

FRANK, Canon Richard Patrick Harry. b 40. St Chad's Coll Dur
BA66 DipTh68. **d** 68 **p** 69. C Darlington H Trin *Dur* 68-72; C
Monkwearmouth St Andr 72-74; C-in-c Harlow Green CD
74-79; R Skelton and Hutton-in-the-Forest w Ivegill *Carl* 79-86;
V Carl St Luke Morton 86-92; RD Carl 88-89; P-in-c Thursby
89-90; P-in-c Kirkbride w Newton Arlosh 89-92; TR Greystoke,
Matterdale, Mungrisdale etc 92-98; P-in-c Patterdale 95-98; TR
Gd Shep TM 98-99; RD Penrith 96-99; Hon Can Carl Cathl
97-99; rtd 99; Perm to Offic *Carl* 00-02; *York* from 02. *11 Risby
Place, Beverley HU17 8NT* Tel (01482) 679540
E-mail richardandann.frank@virgin.net

FRANK, Richard Stephen. b 70. Keble Coll Ox MEng93 Fitzw
Coll Cam BA98. Ridley Hall Cam 96. **d** 99 **p** 00. C Cranham
Park *Chelmsf* from 99. *72 Marlborough Gardens, Upminster
RM14 1SG* Tel (01708) 225604 E-mail richardfrank@mail.com

FRANKLAND, Angela Tara. b 69. Lon Bible Coll BA96 MA98.
EAMTC 97. **d** 99 **p** 00. C Hornchurch St Andr *Chelmsf* 99-03;
TV Wickford and Runwell from 03. *8 Friern Walk, Wickford
SS12 0HZ* Tel (01268) 734077
E-mail tfrankland@btinternet.com

FRANKLIN, Hector Aloysius. b 32. Sheff Univ Dip Tech79 Coll
of Ripon & York St Jo DipTh98. N Ord Course 94. **d** 97 **p** 98.
NSM Chapeltown *Sheff* 97-99; P-in-c Sheff St Paul 99-02; rtd 02.
108 Mackenzie Crescent, Burncross, Sheffield S35 1US Tel 0114-
245 7160

FRANKLIN, Joan Mary. b 20. St Andr Ho Portsm 47. **dss** 61 **d** 87.
Scunthorpe St Jo *Linc* 66-70; Gt Grimsby St Mary and St Jas
70-86; rtd 86. *41 Ferry Road, Scunthorpe DN15 8QF* Tel (01724)
846685

FRANKLIN, Canon Lewis Owen. b 46. Natal Univ BSc67. S'wark
Ord Course 68 DipTh73. **d** 73 **p** 74. S Africa 73-99; C Durban
St Paul 74-75; R Newcastle H Trin 76-79; Dir St Geo Cathl Cen
Cape Town 80-83; Chapl St Geo Gr Sch 84-86; R Sea Pt H
Redeemer 87-89; R Cape Town St Paul 89-90; Subdean and Prec
Kimberley Cathl 91-94 and 96-99; Hon Can from 93; Dioc Sec
Kimberley and Kuruman 94-96; C Altrincham St Geo *Ches*
99-00; P-in-c Newcastle St Paul *Lich* from 00. *St Paul's Vicarage,
Hawkstone Close, Newcastle ST5 1HT* Tel (01782) 617913
E-mail owenf@4u2give.com

FRANKLIN, Richard Charles Henry. b 48. Ch Ch Coll Cant
CertEd70. Sarum & Wells Th Coll 75. **d** 78 **p** 79. C Pershore w
Pinvin, Wick and Birlingham *Worc* 78-80; Educn Chapl 80-85; V
Wollescote 85-92; V Fareham SS Pet and Paul *Portsm* 92-98; V
Luton All SS w St Pet *St Alb* from 98; RD Luton from 02. *All
Saints' Vicarage, Shaftesbury Road, Luton LU4 8AH* Tel (01582)
720129 E-mail richard.franklin@which.net

FRANKLIN, Canon Richard Heighway. b 54. Southn Univ BA75
MPhil83. Sarum & Wells Th Coll 75. **d** 78 **p** 79. C Thame w
Towersey *Ox* 78-81; Asst Chapl Southn Univ *Win* 81-83; Dir of
Studies Chich Th Coll 83-89; P-in-c Stalbridge *Sarum* 89-94; V

Weymouth H Trin from 94; Can and Preb Sarum Cathl from 02.
Holy Trinity Vicarage, 7 Glebe Close, Weymouth DT4 9RL Tel
(01305) 760354 *or* 774597 E-mail richardfranklin@iname.com

FRANKLIN, Simon George. b 54. Bris Univ BA75. Ridley Hall
Cam 77. **d** 79 **p** 80. C Woodmansterne *S'wark* 79-83; C St Peter-
in-Thanet *Cant* 83-86; R Woodchurch 86-96; P-in-c Ottery
St Mary, Alfington, W Hill, Tipton etc *Ex* 96-99; TR from 99.
The Vicar's House, 7 College Road, Ottery St Mary EX11 1DQ
Tel (01404) 812062 E-mail stpaul_church@lineone.net

FRANKLIN, Stephen Alaric. b 58. Lon Univ BD87. Sarum &
Wells Th Coll 87. **d** 89 **p** 90. C Chenies and Lt Chalfont, Latimer
and Flaunden *Ox* 89-93; CF from 93. *c/o MOD Chaplains
(Army)* Tel (01980) 615804 Fax 615800

FRANKLIN, William Henry. b 50. Macquarie Univ (NSW) BA78
Birkbeck Coll Lon MA82. Moore Th Coll Sydney 76 Melbourne
Coll of Div 83 Chich Th Coll 85. **d** 86 **p** 87. C S Leamington St Jo
Cov 86-89; Chapl RN from 89. *Royal Naval Chaplaincy Service,
Room 203, Victory Building, HM Naval Base, Portsmouth
PO1 3LS* Tel (023) 9272 7903 Fax 9272 7111

FRANKS, John Edward. b 29. **d** 61 **p** 62. C Plymouth St Matthias
Ex 61-66; V Upton Grey w Weston Patrick and Tunworth *Win*
66-77; V Upton Grey, Weston Patrick, Tunworth etc 77-79;
P-in-c Wolverton cum Ewhurst and Hannington 79-80; R
Baughurst, Ramsdell, Wolverton w Ewhurst etc 81-94; rtd 94.
57 Victoria, Santa Lucija, Naxxar, NXR 02, Malta Tel (00356)
2143 7006

FRANKS, John William. b 45. K Alfred's Coll Win BEd87
DAES94 MISM89. STETS 97. **d** 00 **p** 01. NSM Fareham H Trin
Portsm 00-03; Hon Chapl Pitmore Sch Chandler's Ford 00-01;
Hon Chapl Fareham Coll of F&HE 01-03; C Rowner *Portsm*
from 03. *21 Oxford Close, Fareham PO16 7PA* Tel (01329)
232150

FRANKUM, Matthew David Hyatt. b 65. Leic Poly BSc87. Trin
Coll Bris DipHE99. **d** 99 **p** 00. C Bath St Luke *B & W* 99-03; TV
Worle from 03. *The Vicarage, 21 Westmarch Way, Weston-super-
Mare BS22 7JY* Tel (01934) 513294

FRANSELLA, Cortland Lucas. b 48. Trin Hall Cam BA70 MA74
Heythrop Coll Lon MA00. NTMTC AdDipTh98 ADPS98.
d 98 **p** 99. NSM Palmers Green St Jo *Lon* 98-03; NSM Hornsey
St Mary w St Geo from 03. *17 Warner Road, London N8 7HB* Tel
(020) 8340 7706 Fax as telephone
E-mail fransella@btinternet.com

FRANZ, Kevin Gerhard. b 53. Edin Univ MA74 BD79 PhD92.
Edin Th Coll 76. **d** 79 **p** 80. C Edin St Martin *Edin* 79-83; R
Selkirk 83-90; Provost St Ninian's Cathl Perth *St And* 90-99; R
Perth St Ninian 90-99; Gen Sec Action of Churches Together in
Scotland from 99. *Scottish Churches House, Kirk Street,
Dunblane FK15 0AJ* Tel (01786) 823588 Fax 825844
E-mail acts.ecum@dial.pipex.com

FRASER, Alister Douglas. b 26. Qu Coll Cam BA49 MA55.
Tyndale Hall Bris 50. **d** 68 **p** 69. C Weymouth St Jo *Sarum* 68-72;
R Kingswood *Glouc* 72-80; V Woodside St Steph 80-84; RD
Forest S 84-88; V Cinderford St Steph w Littledean 84-90; rtd 90;
Perm to Offic *Ex* from 91. *4 Stevens Cross Close, Sidmouth
EX10 9QJ* Tel (01395) 579568

FRASER, Andrew Thomas. b 52. Newc Univ Aus BA81. St Jo
Coll (NSW) ThL79. **d** 81 **p** 82. Australia 81-87; C Prestbury
Glouc 87-91; C Wotton St Mary 91-92. *79 Victoria Street,
Gloucester GL1 4EP* Tel (01452) 381082

FRASER, David Ian. b 32. Em Coll Cam BA54 MA58. Oak Hill
Th Coll 56. **d** 58 **p** 59. C Bedford St Jo *St Alb* 58-61; C Cheadle
Hulme St Andr *Ches* 61-64; R Fringford w Hethe and Newton
Purcell *Ox* 64-67; V Preston St Luke *Blackb* 67-71; V Surbiton
Hill Ch Ch *S'wark* 71-91; rtd 91; Perm to Offic *Ox* from 97.
7 Godwyn Close, Abingdon OX14 1BU Tel (01235) 532049

FRASER, Geoffrey Michael. b 29. Sarum Th Coll. **d** 59 **p** 60. C
Thames Ditton *Guildf* 59-63; C Shere 63-65; C Dunsford and
Doddiscombsleigh *Ex* 65-70; V Uffculme 70-92; rtd 92; Perm to
Offic *Worc* from 92. *46 Priory Road, Malvern WR14 3DB* Tel
(01684) 576302

FRASER, Giles Anthony. b 64. Newc Univ BA84 Ox Univ BA92
MA97 Lanc Univ PhD99. Ripon Coll Cuddesdon. **d** 93 **p** 94. C
Streetly *Lich* 93-97; C Ox St Mary V w St Cross and St Pet *Ox*
97-00; Chapl Wadh Coll Ox 97-00; V Putney St Mary *S'wark*
from 00. *The Vicarage, 45 St John's Avenue, London SW15 6AL*
Tel (020) 8788 4575

FRASER, Jane Alicia. b 44. Man Univ BA. Glouc Sch of Min 86.
d 89 **p** 94. NSM Upton on Severn *Worc* 89-00; NSM Ripple,
Earls Croome w Hill Croome and Strensham 97-00; NSM
Upton-on-Severn, Ripple, Earls Croome etc from 00; Faith Adv
Dept of Health's Adv Gp on Teenage Pregnancy from 00.
*Sunnybank House, Holly Green, Upton-upon-Severn, Worcester
WR8 0PG* Tel (01684) 594715
E-mail brook@revjane.demon.co.uk

FRASER, Leslie. b 34. ALCD62. **d** 62 **p** 63. C St Helens St Matt
Thatto Heath *Liv* 62-64; C Fazakerley Em 64-67; R Collyhurst
St Oswald and St Cath *Man* 67-72; P-in-c Collyhurst St Jas 67-72;
R Collyhurst 72-74; RNLI 75-92; rtd 95; Hon C Bispham *Blackb*

95-98; Perm to Offic 98-00; P-in-c Bridekirk *Carl* from 99. *The Vicarage, Bridekirk, Cockermouth CA13 0PE* Tel (01253) 592538

FRASER, Leslie John. b 60. OLM course 96. **d** 99 **p** 00. OLM Thamesmead *S'wark* from 99. *4 Goldcrest Close, London SE28 8JA* Tel (020) 8473 4736 E-mail les.fraser@lineone.net

FRASER-SMITH, Keith Montague. b 48. St Jo Coll Dur BA70. Trin Coll Bris DipTh72. **d** 73 **p** 74. C Bishopsworth *Bris* 73-75; CMS 76-84; Egypt 76-80; Jerusalem 80-84; Asst Chapl Marseille w St Raphaël, Aix-en-Provence etc *Eur* 84-90; Media Dir Arab World Min 84-92; E Area Dir 92-97; Dep to Internat Dir 97-98; NSM Worthing Ch the King *Chich* 90-93; Cyprus 93-97; NSM Tranmere St Cath *Ches* 97-98; P-in-c Barnton from 98. *The Vicarage, Church Road, Barnton, Northwich CW8 4JH* Tel (01606) 74358
E-mail keith@barntonv1.freeserve.co.uk

FRAY, Bernard Herbert. b 44. Worc Coll of Educn CertEd65 Open Univ BA73 LTCL67. Cranmer Hall Dur 02. **d** 03. NSM Long Marston *York* from 03; NSM Rufforth w Moor Monkton and Hessay from 03; NSM Healaugh w Wighill, Bilbrough and Askham Richard from 03; NSM Tockwith and Bilton w Bickerton from 03. *The Vicarage, 32 Westfield Road, Tockwith, York YO26 7PY* Tel (01423) 358338
E-mail bernardfray@hotmail.com

FRAY, Roger William. b 43. Philippa Fawcett Coll TCert69 Reading Univ BEd76. St Jo Coll Nottm MA95. **d** 95 **p** 96. C Grove *Ox* 95-99; P-in-c Brittany *Eur* from 99. *14A Le Lesnot, 56460 La Chapelle-Caro, France* Tel (0033) (2) 97 74 97 93
E-mail fraylesnot@aol.com

FRAY, Vernon Francis. b 41. Southn Coll of Tech HNC62 FCIOB79. S'wark Ord Course 91. **d** 94 **p** 95. NSM Heston *Lon* 94-96; NSM Twickenham All Hallows 96-02; NSM Teddington St Mark and Hampton Wick St Jo from 02. *198 Broom Road, Teddington TW11 9PQ* Tel (020) 8977 2068

FRAY, Vivienne Jane. *See* KERNER, Vivienne Jane

FRAYLING, The Very Revd Nicholas Arthur. b 44. Ex Univ BA69 Liv Univ Hon LLD01. Cuddesdon Coll 69. **d** 71 **p** 72. C Peckham St Jo *S'wark* 71-74; V Tooting All SS 74-83; Can Res and Prec Liv Cathl *Liv* 83-87; R Liv Our Lady and St Nic w St Anne 87-90; TR 90-02; Hon Can Liv Cathl 89-02; Dean Chich from 02. *The Deanery, Canon Lane, Chichester PO19 1PX* Tel (01243) 812485 *or* 812494
E-mail dean@chichestercathedral.org.uk

FRAYNE, The Very Revd David. b 34. St Edm Hall Ox BA58 MA62 Birm Univ DipTh60. Qu Coll Birm 58. **d** 60 **p** 61. C E Wickham *S'wark* 60-63; C Lewisham St Jo Southend 63-67; V N Sheen St Phil and All SS 67-73; R Caterham 73-83; RD Caterham 80-83; Hon Can S'wark Cathl 82-83; V Bris St Mary Redcliffe w Temple etc *Bris* 83-92; RD Bedminster 86-92; Hon Can Bris Cathl 91-92; Provost Blackb 92-00; Dean Blackb 00-01; rtd 01. *Newlands Cottage, Peacemarsh, Gillingham SP8 4HD* Tel (01747) 824065

FRAZER, David. b 60. QUB BSSc TCD DipTh84. TCD Div Sch. **d** 84 **p** 85. C Taney *D & G* 84-87; C Dublin Ch Ch Cathl Gp 87-88; I Clane w Donadea and Coolcarrigan *M & K* from 88. *St Michael's Vicarage, Sallins, Naas, Co Kildare, Irish Republic* Tel and fax (00353) (45) 868276 Mobile 087-2661587
E-mail dfrazer@eircom.net

FRAZER, Ian Martin. b 44. QUB BTh. **d** 91 **p** 93. Lic to Offic *D & D* 91-98; NSM Orangefield w Moneyreagh from 98. *The Stacks, Deramore Park South, Belfast BT9 5JY* Tel (028) 9066 7100

FRAZER, Canon James Stewart. b 27. TCD Dip Bibl Studies. TCD Div Sch. **d** 57 **p** 58. C Belfast Whiterock *Conn* 57-59; C Belfast St Matt 59-61; I Lack *Clogh* 61-64; I Mullaglass *Arm* 64-65; I Milltown 65-70; Australia 70-72; I Heathcote w Axedale 70-72; I Kangaroo Par w Marong, Lockwood and Ravenswood 72-74; I Dromore *Clogh* 74-82; Bp Dom Chapl 82; I Derryvullen S w Garvary 82-90; Can Clogh Cathl 83-85; Preb 85-94; I Clogh w Errigal Portclare 90-94; Glebes Sec 91-94; Chan Clogh Cathl 93-94; rtd 94. *8 Carsons Avenue, Ballygowan, Newtownards BT23 5GD* Tel (028) 9752 1562

FREAR, Philip Scott. b 45. Univ of Wales (Lamp) BA66. Bris & Glouc Tr Course 77. **d** 80 **p** 81. Hon C Purton *Bris* 80-81; C Rodbourne Cheney 81-85; V Hengrove 85-95; V Braddan *S & M* from 95; Perm to Offic *B & W* from 95; Chapl Isle of Man Dept of Health and Social Security from 95. *The Vicarage, Saddle Road, Braddan, Isle of Man IM4 4LB* Tel (01624) 675523

FREARSON, Andrew Richard. b 57. BA. Wycliffe Hall Ox. **d** 83 **p** 84. C Acocks Green *Birm* 83-86; C Moseley St Mary 86-89; P-in-c Holme *Blackb* 89-96; USA from 96. *3136 Lynnray Drive, Doraville, GA 30340, USA*

FREATHY, Nigel Howard. b 46. Lon Univ BA68 CertEd. Sarum & Wells Th Coll 79. **d** 81 **p** 82. C Crediton *Ex* 81-82; C Crediton and Shobrooke 82-84; TV Ex St Thos and Em 84-86; V Beer and Branscombe 86-01; P-in-c Stockland, Dalwood, Kilmington and Shute 01-03; V Kilmington, Stockland, Dalwood, Yarcombe etc from 03; RD Honiton 96-99. *The Vicarage, Kilmington, Axminster EX13 7RF* Tel (01297) 33156

FREDERICK, John Bassett Moore. b 30. Princeton Univ BA51 Birm Univ PhD73. Gen Th Sem (NY) MDiv54. **d** 54 **p** 55. USA 54-56 and 61-71; C All Hallows Barking *Lon* 56-58; C Ox SS Phil and Jas *Ox* 58-60; R Bletchingley *S'wark* 74-95; Reigate Adnry Ecum Officer 90-95; RD Godstone 92-95; rtd 95. *32 Chestnut Street, Princeton, NJ 08542, USA* Tel (001) (609) 924 7590 Fax 924 1694 E-mail jf9642@netscape.net

FREDERICK, Warren Charles. b 47. Illinois Univ BSc. Qu Coll Birm 86. **d** 88 **p** 89. C W Leigh *Portsm* 88-91; V N Holmwood *Guildf* 91-00; R Cumberland H Cross USA from 00. *612 Brookfield Avenue, Cumberland, MD 21502, USA* Tel (001) (301) 759 2688

FREDRIKSEN, Martin. b 47. St Chad's Coll Dur BA69 DipTh70 Univ of Wales (Lamp) MA03. **d** 70 **p** 71. C Bideford *Ex* 70-73; C Guildf St Nic *Guildf* 73-76; R Cossington *B & W* 76-82; V Woolavington 76-82; Asst Chapl K Coll Taunton 82-84; C Bp's Hatfield *St Alb* 84-94; P-in-c Broadstone *Sarum* 94; V from 94. *St John's Vicarage, Macaulay Road, Broadstone BH18 8AR* Tel (01202) 694109
E-mail fr.martin1@eggconnect.net

FREE, Canon James Michael. b 25. K Coll Lon BD50 AKC50. **d** 51 **p** 52. C Corsham *Bris* 51-54; Trinidad and Tobago 54-62; PC Knowle St Barn *Bris* 62-67; V Pilning 67-75; P-in-c Lydiard Millicent w Lydiard Tregoz 75-82; Hon Can Bris Cathl 76-82; Can Res, Prec and Sacr Bris Cathl 82-83; Can Treas 83-90; Bp's Adv for Miss 82-87; Bp's Officer for Miss and Evang 87-89; rtd 90; Perm to Offic *B & W* 90-03 and *Bris* from 90; P-in-c Haselbury Plucknett, Misterton and N Perrott *B & W* from 03. *The Rectory, New Street, North Perrott, Crewkerne TA18 7ST* Tel (01460) 271489

FREEBAIRN-SMITH, Canon Jane. b 36. K Coll Lon DipTh59. St Chris Coll Blackheath IDC60. **d** 88 **p** 94. NSM Uddingston *Glas* 88-91; NSM Cambuslang 88-91; Dioc Missr 88-92; Dioc Past Counsellor 92-95; NSM Baillieston 91-92; C St Mary's Cathl 92-95; TV Hykeham *Linc* from 95; Can and Preb Linc Cathl from 02. *23 Baildon Crescent, North Hykeham, Lincoln LN6 8HS* Tel (01522) 690885

FREEBORN, John Charles Kingon. b 30. G&C Coll Cam BA52 MA56. Ridley Hall Cam 53. **d** 55 **p** 56. C Doncaster St Geo *Sheff* 55-57; Tutor Wycliffe Hall Ox 57-61; R Flixton St Mich *Man* 61-72; C Leic H Apostles *Leic* 72-73; Teacher Greenacres Sch Oldham 73-75; C E Crompton *Man* 73-74; Hon C Ashton St Mich 74-76; Teacher St Jo Sch Ellesmere 75-79; Perm to Offic 77-80; Hd Master H Trin Sch Halifax 80-88; Teacher St Chad's Sch Hove Edge Wakef 88-91; Lic to Offic *Wakef* 80-83; Hon C Sowerby 83-94; NSM Halifax All SS from 94; rtd 95; Perm to Offic *Bradf* from 01. *27 Crossley Hill, Halifax HX3 0PL* Tel (01422) 342489

FREEMAN, Canon Alan John Samuel. b 27. SS Coll Cam BA48 MA52. Sarum Th Coll 50. **d** 52 **p** 53. C Tottenham Ch W Green *Lon* 52-55; C Harpenden St Nic *St Alb* 55-60; R Aspley Guise 60-75; RD Fleete 67-70; RD Ampthill 70-75; Hon Can St Alb 74-92; V Boxmoor St Jo 75-92; Chapl Hemel Hempstead Gen Hosp (W Herts Wing) 75-92; RD Berkhamsted *St Alb* 85-92; rtd 92; Perm to Offic *St Alb* from 00. *3A Queen Street, Leighton Buzzard LU7 1BZ* Tel (01525) 384799

FREEMAN, Anthony John Curtis. b 46. Ex Coll Ox BA68 MA72. Cuddesdon Coll 70. **d** 72 **p** 73. C Worc St Martin *Worc* 72-74; C Worc St Martin w St Pet 74-75; Bp's Dom Chapl *Chich* 75-78; C-in-c Parklands St Wilfrid CD 78-82; V Durrington 82-89; P-in-c Staplefield Common 89-94; Bp's Adv on CME 89-93; Asst Dir of Ords 89-93. *4 Godolphin Close, Newton St Cyres, Exeter EX5 5BZ* Tel (01392) 851453 Fax as telephone
E-mail anthony@imprint.co.uk

FREEMAN, Douglas James. b 20. Ox NSM Course 80. **d** 83 **p** 84. NSM Ellesborough *Ox* 83-91; NSM Ellesborough, The Kimbles and Stoke Mandeville 91-00. *29 Chadley, Chalkshire Road, Butlers Cross, Aylesbury HP17 0TS* Tel (01296) 623240

FREEMAN, Gordon Bertie. b 37. CITC DipTh95. **d** 95 **p** 96. C Lecale Gp *D & D* 95-98; I Ardara w Glencolumbkille, Inniskeel etc *D & R* from 98. *The Rectory, Ardara, Lifford, Co Donegal, Irish Republic* Tel (00353) (74) 954 1124
E-mail ardara@raphoe.anglican.org

FREEMAN, James Henry. b 14. **d** 79 **p** 80. Hon C Wandsworth St Steph *S'wark* 79-97. *53 Coombe Gardens, New Malden KT3 4AB*

FREEMAN, Jane. b 54. Dur Univ BA75 PhD80 Birm Univ BD00. Qu Coll Birm 98. **d** 00 **p** 01. C Waterloo St Jo w St Andr *S'wark* from 00. *1 Cranfield Row, Gerridge Street, London SE1 7QN* Tel (020) 7928 2259 Mobile 07702-922818
E-mail freemanj@ukonline.co.uk

FREEMAN, Karl Fredrick. b 57. St Luke's Coll Ex BEd80. **d** 90 **p** 91. C Plymouth St Andr w St Paul and St Geo *Ex* 90-95; TV Plymouth St Andr and St Paul Stonehouse 95-96; Chapl Coll of SS Mark and Jo Plymouth 96-01; TR Plymouth Em, St Paul Efford and St Aug from 01. *The Rectory, 9 Seymour Drive, Plymouth PL3 5BG* Tel (01752) 248601

FREEMAN, Malcolm Robin. b 48. Master Mariner 78. St And NSM Tr Scheme 85. **d** 88 **p** 89. NSM Kirkcaldy *St And* 88-94; NSM Westbury *Sarum* 99-02; R Tidworth, Ludgershall and Faberstown from 02. *The Rectory, 10 St James's Street, Ludgershall, Andover SP11 9QF* Tel (01264) 791202 Mobile 07810-862740 E-mail fgmastermariner@aol.com

FREEMAN (née ADAMS), Mrs Margaret Anne. b 27. AKC48. Gilmore Ho. **dss** 82 **d** 87 **p** 94. C Gt Yarmouth *Nor* 80-87; rtd 87; Hon Par Dn Malborough w S Huish, W Alvington and Churchstow *Ex* 87-94; Hon C 94-96; Perm to Offic *Nor* from 97. *9 Barton Way, Ormesby, Great Yarmouth NR29 5SD* Tel (01493) 730101

FREEMAN, Michael Charles. b 36. Magd Coll Cam BA61 MA68 Lon Univ BD69 PhD93. Clifton Th Coll 67. **d** 69 **p** 70. C Bedworth *Cov* 69-72; C Morden *S'wark* 72-77; P-in-c Westcombe Park St Geo 77-85; V Kingston Vale St Jo 85-94; rtd 99. *6 Wristland Road, Watchet TA23 0DH* Tel (01984) 634378 E-mail FreemMic@aol.com

FREEMAN, Michael Curtis. b 51. Lanc Univ BA72. Cuddesdon Coll 72. **d** 75 **p** 76. C Walton St Mary *Liv* 75-78; C Hednesford *Lich* 78-81; TV Solihull *Birm* 81-86; V Yardley Wood 86-90; V Farnworth *Liv* 90-03; AD Widnes 01-03; P-in-c Blundellsands St Mich from 03. *St Michael's Vicarage, 41 Dowhills Road, Liverpool L23 8SJ* Tel 0151-924 3424

FREEMAN, Michael Raymond. b 58. Chu Coll Cam BA80 MA84 Ox Univ BA87. St Steph Ho Ox 85. **d** 88 **p** 89. C Clifton All SS w St Jo *Bris* 88-92; TV Elland *Wakef* 92-01; V Horninglow *Lich* from 01. *Horninglow Vicarage, 14 Rolleston Road, Burton-on-Trent DE13 0JZ* Tel (01283) 568613 E-mail cft-rfreeman@supanet.com

FREEMAN, Mrs Pamela Mary. b 45. WMMTC 83. **dss** 86 **d** 87 **p** 94. Cannock *Lich* 86-88; Par Dn 87-88; Min for Deaf (Salop Adnry) 88-95; Par Dn Shelton and Oxon 88-94; C 94-95; TV Stafford 95-00; P-in-c High Offley and Norbury 00-02; R Adbaston, High Offley, Knightley, Norbury etc from 02. *The Rectory, Newport Road, Woodseaves, Stafford ST20 0NP* Tel (01785) 284747 E-mail pmfreeman@bigfoot.com

FREEMAN, Philip Martin (Brother Martin Philip). b 54. Westcott Ho Cam 76. **d** 79 **p** 80. C Stanley *Liv* 79-82; C Bromborough *Ches* 82-84; Chapl Halton Gen Hosp 84-91; V Runcorn H Trin *Ches* 84-91; R Ashton-upon-Mersey St Martin 91-96; SSF from 96; Perm to Offic *Sarum* 96-99; *Birm* from 98. *10 Halcron Street, London E1 2EP* Tel (020) 7247 6233

FREEMAN, Philip Michael. b 25. Jes Coll Cam BA50 MA54. Qu Coll Birm 50. **d** 52 **p** 53. C Gainsborough All SS *Linc* 52-58; V Messingham 58-65; V Goxhill 65-66; P-in-c Bottesford w Ashby 66-73; TR 73-75; P-in-c Warwick St Nic *Cov* 75-76; TV Warwick 77-87; P-in-c Claverdon w Preston Bagot 87-90; rtd 90; Perm to Offic *Cov* from 90. *38 Cocksparrow Street, Warwick CV34 4ED* Tel (01926) 411431

FREEMAN, Richard Alan. b 52. Ripon Coll Cuddesdon. **d** 83 **p** 84. C Crayford *Roch* 83-86; V Slade Green 86-94; R Eynsford w Farningham and Lullingstone 94-01; P-in-c Shoreham from 01; Chapl St Mich Sch Otford from 01. *The Vicarage, Station Road, Shoreham, Sevenoaks TN14 7SA* Tel (01959) 522363 E-mail ricktherec@aol.com

FREEMAN, The Ven Robert John. b 52. St Jo Coll Dur BSc74 Fitzw Coll Cam BA76 MA. Ridley Hall Cam 74. **d** 77 **p** 78. C Blackpool St Jo *Blackb* 77-81; TV Chigwell *Chelmsf* 81-85; V Leic Martyrs *Leic* 85-99; Hon Can Leic Cathl 94-03; RD Christianity 95-98; Nat Adv in Evang 99-03; Lic to Offic *Leic* 99-03; Adn Halifax *Wakef* from 03. *2 Vicarage Gardens, Brighouse HD6 3HD* Tel (01484) 714553 Fax 711897 E-mail robert@frmn.com

FREEMAN, Rosemary. b 47. **d** 03. NSM Madeley *Heref* from 03. *5 Rowley Close, Madeley, Telford TF7 5RR*

FREEMAN, Terence. b 40. Wells Th Coll 67. **d** 70 **p** 71. C Hanham *Bris* 70-75; C Cockington *Ex* 75-77; R Sampford Spiney w Horrabridge 77-89; V Wembury from 89; Hon Chapl RN from 89. *The Vicarage, 63 Church Road, Wembury, Plymouth PL9 0JJ* Tel (01752) 862319 E-mail revkarl.freeman@lineone.net

FREEMAN, William Rodney. b 35. MA FCA. **d** 95 **p** 96. NSM Chelmondiston and Erwarton w Harkstead *St E* from 95. *Lavender Cottage, Harkstead, Ipswich IP9 1BN* Tel (01473) 328381 E-mail revrod@lavcot.freeserve.co.uk

FREER, Andrew Selwyn Bruce. b 26. Wells Th Coll 55. **d** 57 **p** 58. C Yardley St Edburgha *Birm* 57-62; R Byfield *Pet* 62-71; V Brackley St Pet w St Jas 71-81; R Bincombe w Broadwey, Upwey and Buckland Ripers *Sarum* 81-91; rtd 91; Perm to Offic *Sarum* 91-02. *Appletree Cottage, High Street, Walsham-le-Willows, Bury St Edmunds IP31 3AA* Tel (01359) 259819

FREETH, Barry James. b 35. Birm Univ BA60. Tyndale Hall Bris 60. **d** 62 **p** 64. C Selly Hill St Steph *Birm* 62-63; C Birm St Jo Ladywood 63-71; Chapl RAF 71-75; P-in-c Crudwell w Ashley *Bris* 75-81; P-in-c Lanreath *Truro* 81-84; R 84-87; P-in-c Pelynt 81-84; V 84-87; R Harvington and Norton and Lenchwick *Worc* 87-93; V Ramsden, Finstock and Fawler, Leafield etc *Ox*

93-99; rtd 99; Perm to Offic *Derby* from 99. *St Mary's House, 2A New Market Street, Buxton SK17 6LP* Tel (01298) 22433 or 77401

FREETH, John Stanton. b 40. Selw Coll Cam BA62 MA66. Ridley Hall Cam 64. **d** 66 **p** 67. C Gillingham St Mark *Roch* 66-72; TV Heslington *York* 72-80; Chapl York Univ 72-80; TR Wynberg St Jo S Africa from 80; Adn Athlone 88-93. *15 Wellington Road, Wynberg, 7800 South Africa* Tel (0027) (21) 761 0908

FREETH, Patricia. b 48. Wycliffe Hall Ox BTh95. **d** 95 **p** 96. NSM Ramsden, Finstock and Fawler, Leafield etc *Ox* 95-99; TV Buxton w Burbage and King Sterndale *Derby* from 99. *St Mary's House, 2A New Market Street, Buxton SK17 6LP* Tel (01298) 22433

FRENCH, Basil Charles Elwell. b 19. Edin Th Coll LTh44. **d** 45 **p** 46. C Falkirk *Edin* 45-46; C Bris St Aid *Bris* 46-49; C Hendford *B & W* 49-51; V Ash 51-58; P-in-c Long Load 57-58; S Rhodesia 59-65; Rhodesia 65-80; Zimbabwe 80-85; rtd 85; Hon C Wrington w Butcombe *B & W* 85-88; Perm to Offic 88-92; Perm to Offic *Ex* from 92. *9 Elmbridge Gardens, Exeter EX4 4AE* Tel (01392) 215933

FRENCH, Clive Anthony. b 43. AKC70. St Aug Coll Cant 70. **d** 71 **p** 72. C Monkseaton St Mary *Newc* 71-73; Dioc Youth Adv 73-76; Chapl RN 76-97; Chapl RN Coll Greenwich 75-97; Dir of Ords RN 85-90; R Cheam *S'wark* from 97. *The Rectory, 33 Mickleham Gardens, Cheam, Sutton SM3 8QJ* Tel (020) 8641 4664

FRENCH, Canon Dendle Charles. b 29. Lon Univ BD56. ALCD55. **d** 56 **p** 57. C Gt Yarmouth *Nor* 56-63; Jamaica 63-66; V Sedgeford w Southmere *Nor* 66-71; P-in-c Gt Ringstead 66-67; V Sedgeford w Southmere *Nor* 66-71; P-in-c Gt Ringstead 66-67; R 67-71; TV Thetford 71-74; Chapl Hockerill Coll Bishop's Stortford 74-78; P-in-c St Paul's Walden *St Alb* 78-85; V 85-94; RD Hitchin 84-89; Hon Can St Alb 91-94; rtd 94; Chapl Glamis Castle from 94. *Woodfaulds, 7 Braehead Road, Glamis, Angus DD8 1RW* Tel (01307) 840485 Fax as telephone E-mail dendle.french@talk21.com

FRENCH, Derek John. b 47. Man Univ BA03. Ripon Coll Cuddesdon DipMin95. **d** 95 **p** 96. C Stand *Man* 95-98; TV E Farnworth and Kearsley 98-00; P-in-c Halliwell St Marg from 00. *St Margaret's Vicarage, 1 Somerset Road, Bolton BL1 4NE* Tel (01204) 840850 E-mail rev.djf@btinternet.com

FRENCH, George Leslie. b 47. AIFST NE Lon Poly BSc70. S'wark Ord Course 86. **d** 89 **p** 90. NSM Reading St Barn *Ox* 89-99. *Hawthorne House, 2 Cutbush Close, Lower Earley, Reading RG6 4XA* Tel 0118-986 1886

FRENCH, Janet. b 54. EAMTC 99. **d** 02 **p** 03. C Thetford *Nor* from 02. *44 Monksgate, Thetford IP24 1BY* Tel (01842) 753818 Mobile 07762-708818 Fax as telephone E-mail frenchrevj@hotmail.com

FRENCH, Janet Mary. See DRIVER, Janet Mary

FRENCH, Jonathan David Seabrook. b 60. Westcott Ho Cam 84. **d** 87 **p** 88. C Loughton St Jo *Chelmsf* 87-90; Chapl St Bede's Ch for the Deaf Clapham 90-92; C Richmond St Mary w St Matthias and St Jo *S'wark* 92-95; TV from 96; Chapl amongst the Deaf from 92. *19 Old Deer Park Gardens, Richmond TW9 2TN* Tel (020) 8940 8359 E-mail seabrook.french@virgin.net

FRENCH, Ms Judith Karen. b 60. St D Coll Lamp BA89. St Steph Ho Ox 89. **d** 91 **p** 94. Par Dn Botley *Portsm* 91-94; C Bilton *Cov* 94-97; V Charlbury w Shorthampton *Ox* from 97. *The Vicarage, Church Lane, Charlbury, Chipping Norton OX7 3PX* Tel (01608) 810286 Fax as telephone E-mail judyvicar@aol.com

FRENCH, Michael Anders. b 61. Ch Coll Cam BA83 MA87 Ridley Hall Cam BA91 Man Univ MA(Econ)96. **d** 92 **p** 93. C Norbury *Ches* 92-96; Chapl Ches Coll 96-01; Chapl Geneva *Eur* from 01. *105 route du Bois des Iles, La Bâtie, 1290 Versoix, Switzerland* Tel (0041) (22) 779 0465 E-mail frenchgeneva@hotmail.com or m.french@anglican.ch

FRENCH, Michael John. b 37. WEMTC 92. **d** 95 **p** 96. OLM Cheltenham St Pet *Glouc* 95-01; NSM from 01. *8 Alexandria Walk, Cheltenham GL52 5LG* Tel (01242) 236661

FRENCH, Peter Robert. b 65. Man Univ BTh87. Qu Coll Birm 88. **d** 90 **p** 91. C Unsworth *Man* 90-93; C Bury Ch King w H Trin 93-95; V Bury Ch King 95-98; V Handsworth St Andr *Birm* from 98. *St Andrew's Vicarage, 55 Laurel Road, Birmingham B21 9PB* Tel 0121-551 2097 Fax 554 1084 E-mail peter@frenchp.swinternet.co.uk

FRENCH, Philip Colin. b 50. Sarum & Wells Th Coll 81. **d** 83 **p** 84. C Llansamlet *S & B* 83-86; P-in-c Waunarllwydd 86-87; V 87-97; P-in-c Swansea St Jas *S & B* 97-98; V from 98. *St Barnabas' Vicarage, 57 Sketty Road, Swansea SA2 0EN* Tel (01792) 298601

FRENCH, Richard John. b 34. Open Univ BA82. Tyndale Hall Bris 62. **d** 64 **p** 65. C Rustington *Chich* 64-68; C Walton H Trin *Ox* 68-72; V Grove 72-99; rtd 99; Perm to Offic *Chich* from 01. *5 Green Meadows, The Welkin, Haywards Heath RH16 2PE* Tel (01444) 487842

FRENCH, Stephen Robert James. b 52. St Jo Coll Nottm. **d** 87 **p** 88. C Chell *Lich* 87-91; TV 91-94; V Wednesfield Heath 94-01; TV Hemel Hempstead *St Alb* from 01. *The Vicarage,*

436 Warners End Road, Hemel Hempstead HP1 3QF Tel (01442) 251897

FREND, Prof William Hugh Clifford. b 16. TD59. FSA54 FRHistS54 FRSE79 FBA83 Keble Coll Ox BA37 DPhil40 MA51 DD66 Cam Univ BD64 Edin Univ Hon DD74. **d** 82 **p** 83. Prof Ecclesiastical Hist Glas Univ 69-84; NSM Aberfoyle *St And* 82-84; P-in-c Barnwell w Thurning and Luddington *Pet* 84-90; rtd 90; Perm to Offic *Ely* from 90. *The Clerk's Cottage, Little Wilbraham, Cambridge CB1 5CB* Tel (01223) 811731

FRERE, Christopher Michael Hanbury. b 21. Roch Th Coll 65. **d** 67 **p** 68. C Spilsby w Hundleby *Linc* 67-71; V N Kelsey 71-76; V Cadney 71-76; P-in-c Aisthorpe w W Thorpe and Scampton 75-79; P-in-c Brattleby 75-79; R Fillingham 76-78; V Ingham w Cammeringham 76-78; RD Lawres 78-84; V Ingham w Cammeringham w Fillingham 79-86; R Aisthorpe w Scampton w Thorpe le Fallows etc 79-86; rtd 86; Perm to Offic *Linc* 86-01. *164 Newark Road, North Hykeham, Lincoln LN6 8LZ* Tel (01522) 806326 E-mail cmh.frere@ntlworld.com

FRESHNEY, June. b 46. EMMTC 95. **d** 98 **p** 99. NSM Washingborough w Heighington and Canwick *Linc* from 98. *4 Raynton Close, Washingborough, Lincoln LN4 1HD* Tel (01522) 800905 Mobile 07798-840015 E-mail revjune@supanet.com

FRESTON, John Samuel Kern. b 28. Lich Th Coll 70. **d** 72 **p** 73. C Walsall *Lich* 72-75; TV Trunch w Swafield *Nor* 75-77; TV Trunch 77-82; R W Winch 82-91; Chapl St Jas Hosp King's Lynn 82-85; Chapl Qu Eliz Hosp King's Lynn 85-90; rtd 91; Perm to Offic *Ely* and *Nor* from 91. *71 Howdale Road, Downham Market PE38 9AH* Tel (01366) 385936

FRETT, Daniel Calvin. b 60. Univ of S Carolina 85. NTMTC 95 Oak Hill Th Coll BA99. **d** 98 **p** 99. NSM Clerkenwell St Jas and St Jo w St Pet *Lon* 98-00; NSM Chelsea St Jo w St Andr from 00. *3 Patience Road, London SW11 2PY* Tel (020) 7652 2243 E-mail frettd@netscape.net

FRETWELL, Brian George. b 34. TD. CEng MIMechE. Chich Th Coll 79. **d** 81 **p** 82. C Bude Haven *Truro* 81-82; C Saltash 82-85; C Walthamstow St Sav *Chelmsf* 85-87; V Doncaster Intake *Sheff* 87-97; rtd 99. *65 Little Breach, Chichester PO19 5TY* Tel (01243) 775980

FRETWELL, Cynthia Mary. b 37. EMMTC 90. **d** 91 **p** 94. Chapl Asst Doncaster R Infirmary 91-92; Chapl Asst Tickhill Road and St Cath Hosps 91-92; Chapl Asst Doncaster R Infirmary and Montagu Hosp NHS Trust 92-95; Chapl 95-96; rtd 96. *65 Little Breach, Chichester PO19 5TY* Tel (01243) 775980

FREWIN, William Charles. b 46. Trin Coll Bris 84. **d** 86 **p** 87. C Southchurch H Trin *Chelmsf* 86-89; C Shrub End 89-91; R W Bergholt 91-00; P-in-c Gt Wakering w Foulness from 00. *The Vicarage, 2 New Road, Great Wakering, Southend-on-Sea SS3 0AH* Tel (01702) 217493

FREY, Christopher Ronald. b 44. AKC69 Uppsala Univ BD73 MTh77. St Aug Coll Cant 69. **d** 70 **p** 71. C Addington *Ox* 70-72; Lic to Offic *Eur* 73-78; Chapl Stockholm w Uppsala 78-85; Can Brussels Cathl 81-85; Chapl Casterton Sch Lancs 85-89; Chapl Epsom Coll 89-91; Chapl Worksop Coll Notts 91-94; rtd 96. *Koriandergaten 42, 261 61 Landskrona, Sweden* Tel (0046) (418) 20953

FRIARS, Ian Malcolm George. b 50. Sarum & Wells Th Coll 83. **d** 85 **p** 86. C Norton *St Alb* 85-88; C Ramsey *Ely* 88-90; TV The Ramseys and Upwood 90-93; P-in-c Cottenham 93-94; R 94-01; P-in-c Long Melford *St E* 01-02; R Chadbrook from 02. *The Rectory, The Green, Long Melford, Sudbury CO10 9DT* Tel (01787) 310845 Fax 313767 E-mail ian.friars@stedmundsbury.anglican.org

FRIARS, Robert John. b 32. Trin Coll Cam BA55 MA59. Wells Th Coll 55. **d** 57 **p** 58. C Hackney St Jo *Lon* 57-62; Youth Tr Officer 62-65; C St Andr Holborn 62-70; Sen Youth Chapl 65-70; TV Hackney 70-79; V Sompting *Chich* 79-91; rtd 92. *47 Cowslip Close, Cansbrook Green, Gosport PO13 0BQ* Tel (01329) 282658

FRICKER, Canon David Duncan. b 27. Lon Univ BA53. Ridley Hall Cam 53. **d** 55 **p** 56. C Ecclesfield *Sheff* 55-58; C Luton St Mary *St Alb* 58-61; V Luton St Paul 61-64; R Bedford St Pet 64-75; RD Bedford 69-79; Hon Can St Alb 74-88; P-in-c Bedford St Paul 75-79; R Bedford St Pet w St Cuth 75-88; R Brightling, Dallington, Mountfield etc *Chich* 88-97; RD Dallington 88-95; rtd 97; Perm to Offic *Chich* from 97. *Merton, Langham Road, Robertsbridge TN32 5EP* Tel (01580) 880064

FRIEND, Adam Lyndon David. b 76. St Martin's Coll Lanc BA98. Cranmer Hall Dur 99. **d** 02 **p** 03. C Witton *Ches* from 02. *162 Middlewich Road, Northwich CW9 7DX* Tel (01606) 41965 E-mail fr.friend@btopenworld.co.uk

FRIEND, Frederick James. b 41. BA. Oak Hill NSM Course. **d** 82 **p** 83. NSM Hughenden *Ox* from 82. *The Chimes, Cryers Hill Road, High Wycombe HP15 6JS* Tel (01494) 563168

FRIENDSHIP, Roger Geoffrey (John-Francis). b 46. ACII72. WMMTC 90. **d** 93 **p** 94. SSF 76-02; NSM Harborne St Faith and St Laur *Birm* 93-94; Asst Novice Guardian Hilfield Friary 94-97; Novice Guardian 97-99; Gen Sec SSF 99-01; C Clerkenwell H Redeemer and St Mark *Lon* 00-01; R Romford St Andr *Chelmsf*

from 01. *The Rectory, 119 London Road, Romford RM7 9QD* Tel and fax (01708) 741256 Mobile 07808-500717 E-mail francis.jon@btopenworld.com

FRIGGENS, Canon Maurice Anthony. b 40. Sheff Univ BA65. Westcott Ho Cam 65. **d** 67 **p** 68. C Stocksbridge *Sheff* 67-70; C St Buryan, St Levan and Sennen *Truro* 70-72; R 72-84; RD Penwith 82-84; R St Columb Major w St Wenn 84-91; Dioc Dir of Ords 87-93; Hon Can Truro Cathl 87-00; V St Clear 91-00; rtd 00; Perm to Offic *Ban* from 00; *Eur* from 01. *Tŷ Cernyw, Rhiw, Pwllheli LL53 8AF* Tel (01758) 780365

FRITH, Canon Christopher John Cokayne. b 44. Ex Coll Ox BA65 MA69. Ridley Hall Cam 66. **d** 68 **p** 69. C Crookes St Thos *Sheff* 68-71; C Rusholme H Trin *Man* 71-74; R Haughton St Mary 74-85; R Brampton St Thos *Derby* 85-02; V Alvaston from 02; Hon Can Derby Cathl from 99. *The Vicarage, 8 Church Street, Alvaston, Derby DE24 0PR* Tel (01332) 571143

FRITH, David William. b 65. K Coll Lon BD87 PGCE88 MA96 Lambeth STh90. Westcott Ho Cam 88. **d** 90 **p** 91. C St John's Wood *Lon* 90-93; C Maidstone All SS and St Phil w Tovil *Cant* 93-95; V E Wickham *S'wark* 96-03; Local Min Adv 98-00; RD Plumstead 01-03; TR Cen Wolverhampton *Lich* from 03. *St Peter's House, 4 Exchange Street, Wolverhampton WV1 1TS* Tel (01902) 428491 Fax 420014 E-mail centralparish@wolves94.fsnet.co.uk

FRITH, Mrs Gillian. b 43. EAMTC 99. **d** 02 **p** 03. NSM Chipping Ongar w Shelley *Chelmsf* from 02. *82 Upper Park, Harlow CM20 1TW* Tel (01279) 301400 Mobile 07890-376779 E-mail g.frith@ntlworld.com

FRITH, Canon Ivy Florence. b 24. CertEd56. Lambeth DipTh93 St Chris Coll Blackheath 48. **dss** 79 **d** 87 **p** 94. St Alb Abbey *St Alb* 79-82; Truro St Paul and St Clem *Truro* 82-84; Truro St Mary 84-87; Hon Par Dn 87-94; Dioc Lay Min Adv 85-95; Asst Dioc Dir of Ords 87-95; MU Chapl 91-94; Hon Can Truro Cathl 93-94; Hon C Feock 94-96; Perm to Offic *S'wark* from 96. *4 Wordsworth Road, Welling DA16 3NU* Tel (020) 8855 4083

FRITH, Jonathan Paul (Jonty). b 72. Jes Coll Cam BA94 MA97. Wycliffe Hall Ox 95. **d** 97 **p** 98. C Houghton *Carl* 97-00; Chapl Cranleigh Sch Surrey from 00. *Cranleigh School, Horseshoe Lane, Cranleigh GU6 8QQ* Tel (01483) 542121, 542028 or 272510 E-mail jpf@cranleigh.org *or* jp@jpfrith.freeserve.co.uk

✠**FRITH, The Rt Revd Richard Michael Cokayne.** b 49. Fitzw Coll Cam BA72 MA76. St Jo Coll Nottm 72. **d** 74 **p** 75 **c** 98. C Mortlake w E Sheen *S'wark* 74-78; TV Thamesmead 78-83; TR Keynsham *B & W* 83-92; Preb Wells Cathl 91-98; Adn Taunton 92-98; Suff Bp Hull *York* from 98. *Hullen House, Woodfield Lane, Hessle HU13 0ES* Tel (01482) 649019 Fax 647449 E-mail richard@bishop.karoo.co.uk

FROGGATT, Mrs Alison. b 35. Dur Univ BA56 Bradf Univ MA79. N Ord Course 96. **d** 98 **p** 98. NSM Bingley H Trin *Bradf* 98-02; rtd 02; Perm to Offic *Bradf* from 02. *2 Gilstead Hall, Bingley BD16 3NP* Tel (01274) 511596

FROGGATT, Mrs Elaine Muriel. b 43. Dioc OLM tr scheme 97. **d** 00 **p** 01. OLM Skirwith, Ousby and Melmerby w Kirkland *Carl* from 00. *The Old Corn Mill, Blencarn, Penrith CA10 1TX* Tel (01768) 88757 Fax as telephone

FROGGATT, Jeffrey. b 27. Ch Coll Cam BA48 MA52. Ridley Hall Cam 49. **d** 51 **p** 52. C Scunthorpe St Jo *Linc* 51-53; C Doncaster St Jas *Sheff* 53-56; V New Edlington 56-62; V Malin Bridge 62-73; Ind Chapl 73-79; V Wortley 73-79; R Todwick 79-85; V Dore 85-92; rtd 92; Perm to Offic *Sheff* from 92; Perm to Offic *Derby* 92-00. *20 Bocking Lane, Sheffield S8 7BH* Tel 0114-262 0914

FROGGATT, Peter Michael. b 65. St Hild Coll Dur BA86 PGCE88. Wycliffe Hall Ox BTh95. **d** 95 **p** 96. C Bebington *Ches* 95-00; V New Ferry from 00. *The Vicarage, St Peter's Road, Birkenhead CH42 1PY* Tel 0151-645 1622 or 643 1042 E-mail prfroggatt@talk21.com

FROOM, Ian Leonard John. b 42. Sarum Th Coll 69. **d** 71 **p** 72. C Gillingham and Fifehead Magdalen *Sarum* 71-75; C Parkstone St Pet w Branksea and St Osmund 75-78; V Sedgley St Mary *Lich* 78-85; TV Weston-super-Mare Cen Par *B & W* 85-94; Perm to Offic 94-97; V Truro St Geo and St Ju *Truro* 97-03; rtd 03. *11 Marlborough Crescent, Falmouth TR11 2RJ* Tel (01326) 311760

FROST, Alan Sydney. b 26. K Coll Lon BD50 AKC50. **d** 51 **p** 52. C Folkestone St Sav *Cant* 51-56; C Sneinton St Steph *S'well* 56-59; C Croydon Woodside *Cant* 60-63; Asst Chapl Mersey Miss to Seamen 63-66; rtd 91. *Address excluded by request*

FROST, David J. b 48. **d** 86 **p** 87. Hon C Upper Norwood All SS *S'wark* 86-89; C Battersea St Luke 90-94; V Shirley St Geo from 94. *St George's Vicarage, The Glade, Croydon CR0 7QJ* Tel (020) 8654 8747 Fax 8654 1102 E-mail revdavid@stgeorgeschurch.co.uk

FROST, David Richard. b 54. Ridley Hall Cam 84. **d** 86 **p** 87. C Burgess Hill St Andr *Chich* 86-90; TV Rye 90-94; V Bexhill St Steph from 94. *The Vicarage, 67 Woodsgate Park, Bexhill-on-Sea TN39 4DL* Tel (01424) 211186 Fax as telephone E-mail david@drfrost.worldonline.co.uk

FROST, Derek Charles. b 47. Lich Th Coll 69. **d** 71 **p** 72. C Woodley St Jo the Ev *Ox* 71-76; V Bampton w Clanfield 76-81; V Minster Lovell and Brize Norton 81-88; TV Upper Kennet *Sarum* 88-92; P-in-c Seend and Bulkington 92-97; P-in-c Poulshot 95-97; V Seend, Bulkington and Poulshot 97-01; V Derry Hill w Bremhill and Foxham from 01. *The Vicarage, Church Road, Derry Hill, Calne SN11 9NN* Tel (01249) 812172

FROST, The Ven George. b 35. Dur Univ BA56 MA61. Linc Th Coll 57. **d** 60 **p** 61. C Barking St Marg *Chelmsf* 60-64; C-in-c Marks Gate CD 64-70; V Tipton St Matt *Lich* 70-77; V Penn 77-87; RD Trysull 84-87; Preb Lich Cathl 85-87; Adn Salop 87-98; V Tong 87-98; P-in-c Donington 97-98; Adn Lich and Can Res and Treas Lich Cathl 98-00; rtd 00; Perm to Offic *Lich* from 00. *23 Darnford Lane, Lichfield WS14 9RW* Tel (01543) 415109 E-mail gfrost@fish.co.uk

FROST, Jeremy James. b 74. New Coll Ox BA96 MA99. Wycliffe Hall Ox BA99. **d** 00 **p** 01. C Wellington, All SS w Eyton *Lich* from 00. *1 Stile Rise, Telford TF5 0LR* Tel (01952) 641229 E-mail jeremy@jamesfrost.fsnet.co.uk

FROST, Canon Jonathan Hugh. b 64. Aber Univ BD88 Nottm Univ MTh99 MSSTh91. Ridley Hall Cam 91. **d** 93 **p** 94. C W Bridgford *S'well* 93-97; Police Chapl Trent Division 94-97; R Ash *Guildf* 97-02; Tutor Dioc Min Course from 99; Chapl Surrey Univ from 02; Can Res Guildf Cathl from 02. *6 Cathedral Close, Guildford GU2 7TL* Tel (01483) 576380 Mobile 07870-277709 E-mail j.frost@surrey.ac.uk

FROST, Canon Julian. b 36. Bris Univ BA61 MA65 Lon Univ CertEd70 Solicitor 57. Clifton Th Coll 64. **d** 65 **p** 66. C Welling *Roch* 65-69; Hon C 70-73; Dep Dir Schs Coun RE Project Lanc Univ 73-78; V New Beckenham St Paul 78-01; Hon Can Roch Cathl 00-01; rtd 01; Perm to Offic *Blackb* from 01. *93 Scotforth Road, Lancaster LA1 4JN* Tel (01524) 841967

FROST, Michael John. b 42. Westmr Coll Ox TCert64. LNSM course 92. **d** 95 **p** 96. OLM Harwood *Man* from 95. *86 Harden Drive, Harwood, Bolton BL2 5BX* Tel (01204) 418596

FROST, Richard John. b 49. Ch Ch Coll Cant CertEd71 BA00. SW Minl Tr Course 95. **d** 97 **p** 98. NSM Bideford, Northam, Westward Ho, Appledore etc *Ex* 97-00; C 00-03; TV from 03. *The Rectory, Northam, Bideford EX39 1AW* Tel (01237) 476749

FROST, Ronald Andrew. b 48. Cam Univ DipRS77 Univ of S Carolina BTh81. Ridley Hall Cam 86. **d** 87 **p** 88. C Gt Wilbraham *Ely* 87-89; P-in-c Stow Longa 89-91; V from 91; P-in-c Kimbolton 89-91; V from 91. *The Vicarage, Kimbolton, Huntingdon PE28 0HB* Tel (01480) 860279

FROST, Stanley. b 37. Univ of Wales BSc Liv Univ MSc PhD MIBiol CBiol FAEB. N Ord Course 79. **d** 82 **p** 83. NSM Lower Kersal *Man* 82-87; NSM Patricroft 87-89; NSM Convenor (Dio Man) 87-95; Lic Preacher from 89. *5 Moorside Road, Kersal, Salford M7 0PJ* Tel 0161-792 3107

FROST, Preb William Selwyn. b 29. Wells Th Coll 61. **d** 62 **p** 63. C Cheddleton *Lich* 62-67; V Longdon-upon-Tern 67-81; R Rodington 67-81; RD Wrockwardine 77-84; Preb Lich Cathl 81-96; R Longdon-upon-Tern, Rodington, Uppington etc 81-84; R Whittington St Jo 84-86; C Trysull 86-89; TV Wombourne w Trysull and Bobbington 89-96; rtd 96; Perm to Offic *Heref* from 96. *Ty Ffos, Dilwyn, Hereford HR4 8HZ* Tel (01544) 318703

FROSTICK, Alan Norman. b 25. Ripon Hall Ox 74. **d** 75 **p** 76. C Crewkerne w Wayford *B & W* 75-78; P-in-c Brompton Regis w Upton and Skilgate 78-80; V Buttershaw St Aid *Bradf* 80-83; V Aylesham *Cant* 83-85; P-in-c Adisham 84-85; R Aylesham w Adisham 85-90; rtd 90; Perm to Offic *Cant* from 90. *18 Hawthorn Close, St Marys Bay, Romney Marsh TN29 0SZ* Tel (01303) 875158

FROSTICK, Canon John George. b 23. Wells Th Coll 52. **d** 54 **p** 55. C Loughborough St Pet *Leic* 54-57; C Knighton St Mary Magd 57-58; V Frisby-on-the-Wreake w Kirby Bellars 58-71; V Shepshed 71-83; Hon Can Leic Cathl 80-83; R Kirton w Falkenham *St E* 83-90; rtd 90; Perm to Offic *Leic* from 91. *68 Melton Road, Barrow-upon-Soar, Loughborough LE12 8NX* Tel (01509) 620110

FROSTICK, Paul Andrew. b 52. Stockwell Coll of Educn CertEd73. Ripon Hall Ox 74. **d** 77 **p** 78. C Shepton Mallet *B & W* 77-80; TV Barton Mills, Beck Row w Kenny Hill etc *St E* 80-85; TV Mildenhall 85-86; TV Raveningham *Nor* 86-89; V Bottisham and P-in-c Lode and Longmeadow *Ely* 89-90; V Bottisham and Lode w Long Meadow 90-94; Hd RE Brittons Sch Romford 94-97; Hd RE The Grove Sch St Leonards 97-00; rtd 00; Assoc P Bexhill St Aug *Chich* from 99. *18 The Ridings, Bexhill-on-Sea TN39 5HU* Tel (01424) 218126 E-mail paul@frostickrev.freeserve.co.uk

FROUD, Andrew William. b 65. Mansf Coll Ox BA87 St Cath Coll Cam MPhil92. Westcott Ho Cam 90. **d** 93 **p** 94. C Almondbury w Farnley Tyas *Wakef* 93-96; P-in-c Wootton *Portsm* 96-00; R 00-01; V Thornton-le-Fylde *Blackb* from 01. *The Vicarage, Meadows Avenue, Thornton-Cleveleys FY5 2TW* Tel (01253) 855099 E-mail froud.family@virgin.net

FROUD, James George. b 23. MBE89. **d** 54 **p** 55. Hong Kong 54-58; C All Hallows by the Tower etc *Lon* 58-61; Chapl Durning Hall Chr Community Cen Forest Gate 61-82; P-in-c Forest Gate St Jas *Chelmsf* 61-66; Chapl Forest Gate Hosp Lon 61-69; Chapl

Aston Charities Trust from 82; NSM Barking St Marg w St Patr *Chelmsf* 91-94; Perm to Offic from 94. *37 The Drive, Loughton IG10 1HB* Tel (020) 8508 6479

FROUDE (née WOOLCOCK), Canon Christine Ann. b 47. ACIB73 Southn Univ DipTh96. S Dios Minl Tr Scheme 92. **d** 95 **p** 96. NSM Stoke Bishop *Bris* 95-99; Asst Chapl United Bris Healthcare NHS Trust 99-01; Dean Women's Min *Bris* from 00; Hon Can Bris Cathl from 01; P-in-c Shirehampton from 01. *St Mary's Vicarage, 8 Priory Gardens, Bristol BS11 0BZ* Tel 0117-985 5450 Fax as telephone E-mail christinefroude@lineone.net

FROWLEY, Peter Austin. b 32. CEng61 MIMechE61. WMMTC 82. **d** 84 **p** 85. NSM Tardebigge *Worc* 84-87; P-in-c 87-88; NSM Redditch St Steph 84-87; Hong Kong 88-92; V St Minver *Truro* 92-96; rtd 96; Perm to Offic *Ex* from 96. *Bramblecrest, Fortescue Road, Salcombe TQ8 8AP* Tel (01548) 842515

FRY, Alison Jacquelyn. b 65. Newnham Coll Cam BA86 MA90 Hertf Coll Ox DPhil90. Cranmer Hall Dur BA95 Dip Minl Studies 96. **d** 96 **p** 97. C Milton *B & W* 96-00; V Batheaston w St Cath from 00. *Batheaston Vicarage, Bannerdown Road, Batheaston, Bath BA1 7ND* Tel (01225) 858192 E-mail ajfry@fish.co.uk

FRY, Canon Barry James. b 49. ACIB. Ripon Coll Cuddesdon 81. **d** 83 **p** 84. C Highcliffe w Hinton Admiral *Win* 83-87; V Southampton St Barn from 87; Hon Can Ruvuma Cathl Tanzania from 02. *St Barnabas' Vicarage, 12 Rose Road, Southampton SO14 6TE* Tel (023) 8022 3107

FRY, Mrs Florence Marion. b 24. WMMTC 87. **d** 88 **p** 94. Chapl and Welfare Officer to the Deaf 70-94; Chapl Cov Cathl *Cov* 88-94; Chmn Cov Coun of Chs 88-91; rtd 94; Perm to Offic *St Alb* from 96. *37 Grace Gardens, Bishop's Stortford CM23 3EU* Tel (01279) 652315

FRY, Canon James Reinhold. b 30. St Cuth Soc Dur BSc53 MA70. Oak Hill Th Coll 55. **d** 57 **p** 58. C Bromley St Jo *Roch* 57-60; V Deptford St Luke *S'wark* 60-66; V Chalk *Roch* 66-97; RD Gravesend 81-91; Hon Can Roch Cathl 87-97; rtd 97; Perm to Offic *Roch* from 99; *Cant* from 00. *67 Park Lane, Birchington CT7 0AU* Tel (01843) 843423 Mobile 07721-375096 E-mail jrfry@globalnet.co.uk

FRY, Miss Joan Aileen. b 29. Bedf Coll Lon BA50. Qu Coll Birm 79. dss 82 **d** 87 **p** 94. Colindale St Matthias *Lon* 82-87; Hendon St Mary 84-87; Hon Par Dn Swanage and Studland *Sarum* 87-95; Hon C Bridport 95-99; rtd 99; Perm to Offic *Sarum* from 00. *21 St James's Park, Bridport DT6 3UR* Tel (01308) 458614

FRY, Lynn. b 60. **d** 03. OLM E w W Harling, Bridgham w Roudham, Larling etc *Nor* from 03. *40 White Hart Street, East Harling, Norwich NR16 2NE* Tel (01953) 717423 E-mail fryfam@fish.co.uk

FRY, Michael John. b 59. Nottm Univ BA80 Sheff Univ CQSW83 Cam Univ BA85. Westcott Ho Cam 83. **d** 86 **p** 87. C Upholland *Liv* 86-89; C Dovecot 89-91; TV St Luke in the City from 91. *2 Minster Court, Crown Street, Liverpool L7 3QB* Tel 0151-709 9665

FRY, Nigel. b 49. Kent Univ BA95. SEITE 97. **d** 00 **p** 01. NSM Lenham w Boughton Malherbe *Cant* 00-02; NSM Len Valley 02-03; NSM Hollingbourne and Hucking w Leeds and Broomfield from 03; Chapl HM Pris E Sutton Park from 02. *The Vicarage, Upper Street, Hollingbourne, Maidstone ME17 1UJ* Tel (01622) 880243 Mobile 07768-053400 E-mail nfry@supanet.com

FRY, Nigel Edward. b 57. E Warks Coll DipGD78. St Jo Coll Nottm DCM93. **d** 93 **p** 94. C Wellingborough All Hallows *Pet* 93-96; R Peakirk w Glinton and Northborough from 96. *The Rectory, 11 Lincoln Road, Glinton, Peterborough PE6 7JR* Tel (01733) 252265 E-mail enfry@romans5.fsnet.co.uk

FRY, Roger Joseph Hamilton. b 29. Em Coll Cam BA52 MA56. Clifton Th Coll 52. **d** 54 **p** 55. C Walcot *B & W* 54-57; C Gresley *Derby* 57-61; P-in-c Bowling St Bart and St Luke *Bradf* 61-65; V Bowling St Jo 61-87; V Ingleton w Chapel le Dale 87-95; rtd 95; Perm to Offic *Bradf* from 95. *5 Margerison Crescent, Ilkley LS29 8QZ* Tel (01943) 608738

FRY, Roger Owen. b 30. Sarum Th Coll 58. **d** 60 **p** 61. C Yeovil St Mich *B & W* 60-63; P-in-c Weston-in-Gordano 64-70; R Clapton-in-Gordano 64-70; R Portishead 64-80; V Weston Zoyland w Chedzoy 80-94; rtd 94; Perm to Offic *B & W* from 95. *14 Lewmond Avenue, Wells BA5 2TS*

FRYDAY, Mrs Barbara Yvonne. b 47. Ch of Ireland Tr Coll TCert67. CITC 90. **d** 92 **p** 93. NSM Cashel w Magorban, Tipperary, Clonbeg etc *C & O* 93-96; C Kilcooley w Littleton, Crohane and Fertagh 96-99; 1 from 99. *The Rectory, Grange Barna, Thurles, Co Tipperary, Irish Republic* Tel and fax (00353) (56) 883 4147 *or* tel (88) 2750735 E-mail frydayb@eircom.net *or* kilcooley@cashel.anglican.org

FRYER, Anthony Charles. b 18. RMA. Wycliffe Hall Ox 58. **d** 60 **p** 60. C Furze Platt *Ox* 60-62; V Shinfield 62-73; Perm to Offic *Pet* 85-86 and from 91; P-in-c Charwelton w Fawsley and Preston Capes 86-91. *Glebe House, Byfield, Daventry NN11 6XN* Tel (01327) 260244

FRYER, Charles Eric John. b 14. Lon Univ BA54 PhD84. Linc Th Coll 62. **d** 63 **p** 64. C Finham *Cov* 63-66; Perm to Offic *S'well* 66-75; Lic to Offic 75-79; R Killin *St And* 79-94; R

Lochearnhead 79-89; Min Can Cork Cathl *C, C & R* from 97. *25 Vicar Street, Cork, Irish Republic* Tel (00353) (21) 316397
FRYER, George. b 33. St Jo Coll Cam BA57 MA61. Ox NSM Course 73. **d** 76 **p** 77. NSM Wallingford *Ox* 76-79; C Wokingham St Paul 79-83; V Linc St Swithin *Linc* 83-88; P-in-c Walsden *Wakef* 88-97; P-in-c Cornholme 96-97; rtd 97; Hon C Aynho and Croughton w Evenley etc *Pet* 97-00. *7 Spencer Court, Britannia Road, Banbury OX16 5EY* Tel (01295) 262909
FRYER, Mrs Ida Doris. b 31. Lon Univ BA53. **d** 95 **p** 96. OLM Brantham w Stutton *St E* 95-00; OLM Holbrook, Stutton, Freston, Woolverstone etc 00-01; rtd 01; Perm to Offic *St E* from 01. *The Grove, Church Field Road, Stutton, Ipswich IP9 2SE* Tel (01473) 328230
FRYER, Mrs Jenifer Anne. b 43. N Ord Course 89. **d** 92 **p** 94. Par Dn Ecclesfield *Sheff* 92-94; C 94-95; Chapl R Hallamshire Hosp Sheff 92-96; Chapl Weston Park Hosp Sheff 94-96; Chapl Asst N Gen Hosp NHS Trust Sheff from 96. *Northern General Hospital, Herries Road, Sheffield S5 7AU* Tel 0114-243 4343 ext 5056 *or* 246 1027
FRYER, Michael Andrew. b 56. St Jo Coll Nottm 88. **d** 90 **p** 91. C Hull St Martin w Transfiguration *York* 90-95; V Kingston upon Hull St Aid Southcoates from 95. *St Aidan's Vicarage, 139 Southcoates Avenue, Hull HU9 3HF* Tel (01482) 374403 E-mail mick@fryerm.fsnet.co.uk
FRYER, Preb Peter Hugh. b 25. Linc Th Coll 58. **d** 60 **p** 61. C Tavistock and Gulworthy *Ex* 60-64; R St Buryan *Truro* 64-72; R St Levan 66-72; R St Sennen 70-72; R Lanivet *Mor* 72-76; Chapl RAF 72-76; P-in-c Lewannick *Truro* 76-78; P-in-c Altarnon and Bolventor 76-78; P-in-c N Hill 76-78; TR N Hill w Altarnon, Bolventor and Lewannick 78-84; P-in-c Laneast w St Clether and Tresmere 80-84; Preb St Endellion 84-90; R St Endellion w Port Isaac and St Kew 84-90; rtd 90; Perm to Offic *Truro* from 90. *Blythswood, Fore Street, Marazion TR17 0AS* Tel (01736) 711857
FUDGE, Prof Erik Charles. b 33. Ch Coll Cam BA55 MA59 Southn Univ CertEd58 Cam Univ PhD68. Ox Min Course 91. **d** 93 **p** 94. NSM Wokingham St Sebastian *Ox* from 93. *4 South Close, Wokingham RG11 2DJ* Tel 0118-978 6081
FUDGER, David John. b 53. K Coll Lon 76 Sheff Univ MMin96. Coll of Resurr Mirfield 76. **d** 77 **p** 78. C Sutton in Ashfield St Mary *S'well* 77-80; P-in-c Duston *Pet* 80-82; V Radford All So w Ch Ch and St Mich *S'well* 82-91; Min Bermondsey St Hugh CD *S'well* 91-97; Hon Chapl S'wark Cathl from 91; P-in-c Blackheath Ascension from 97; Woolwich Area Miss Team from 97. *Ascension Vicarage, 40 Dartmouth Row, London SE10 8AP* Tel (020) 8691 8884 E-mail revfudger@mistral.co.uk
FUDGER, Canon Michael Lloyd. b 55. K Coll Lon BD77 AKC77. Coll of Resurr Mirfield 77. **d** 78 **p** 79. C Weston Favell *Pet* 78-82; C Pet H Spirit Bretton 82-84; V Irchester 84-90; TV Darnall-cum-Attercliffe *Sheff* 90-96; RD Attercliffe 91-96; TV Attercliffe, Darnall and Tinsley 96-97; TR from 97; Hon Can Sheff Cathl from 00. *The Vicarage, 66 Mather Road, Sheffield S9 4GQ* Tel 0114-244 0167
FUGGLE, Francis Alfred. b 13. Selw Coll Cam BA34 MA38. Wells Th Coll 35. **d** 36 **p** 37. C Kingsbury St Andr *Lon* 36-38; S Africa from 38. *360A Florida Road, Durban, 4001 South Africa* Tel (0027) (31) 238923
FULFORD, Susan. **d** 03. OLM Pemberton St Mark Newtown *Liv* from 03. *Address temp unknown*
FULHAM, Suffragan Bishop of. *See* BROADHURST, The Rt Revd John Charles
FULLAGAR, Michael Nelson. b 35. SS Coll Cam BA57 MA61. Chich Th Coll 57. **d** 59 **p** 60. C Camberwell St Giles *S'wark* 59-61; C Northolt Park St Barn *Lon* 61-64; C Hythe *Cant* 64-66; Zambia 66-78; R Freemantle *Win* 78-87; P-in-c Westbury w Turweston, Shalstone and Biddlesden *Ox* 87-94; Chapl S Bucks NHS Trust 94-96; rtd 96; P-in-c Burwash Weald *Chich* from 97. *The Vicarage, Burwash Common, Etchingham TN19 7NA* Tel (01435) 883287 Fax as telephone
FULLALOVE, Brenda Hurst. *See* CRASTON, Mrs Brenda Hurst
FULLARD, Craig William. b 73. BA97. Westcott Ho Cam 97. **d** 99 **p** 00. C Tipton St Jo *Lich* 99-01; C Tividale from 01. *26 View Point, Tividale, Oldbury B69 1UU* Tel (01384) 243611 E-mail fullard@ukonline.co.uk
FULLARTON, Mrs Heather Mary. b 42. Whitelands Coll Lon TCert63. Qu Coll Birm 90. **d** 92 **p** 94. Par Dn Colwich w Gt Haywood *Lich* 92-94; C 94-97; P-in-c Swindon and Himley 97-01; V Prees and Fauls 01-02; rtd 02. *3 Rivers Arms Close, Sturminster Newton DT10 1DL* Tel 07703-379684 (mobile) E-mail hfullarton@aol.com
FULLER, Alison Jane. b 61. St Andr Univ MTheol84. Edin Th Coll 85. **d** 87 **p** 88. C Selkirk *Edin* 87-89; C Melrose 87-89; C Galashiels 87-89; C Edin H Cross 89-92; Dn-in-c Edin St Columba 92-94; R from 94; Chapl Edin Univ from 96. *28 Castle Terrace, Edinburgh EH1 2EL* Tel 0131-228 6470 Fax as telephone E-mail incumbent@edsstcolumba.freeserve.co.uk
FULLER, Alistair James. b 66. Univ of Wales (Lamp) BA87. Ripon Coll Cuddesdon 88. **d** 90 **p** 91. C Thornton-le-Fylde *Blackb* 90-95; V Skerton St Luke 95-01; R Bowbrook N *Worc*

from 01. *The Rectory, Droitwich Road, Hanbury, Bromsgrove B60 4DB* Tel (01527) 821826
FULLER, Christopher John. b 53. Chich Th Coll 85. **d** 87 **p** 88. C Swinton and Pendlebury *Man* 87-90; C Chiswick St Nic w St Mary *Lon* 90-92; V Hounslow W Gd Shep 92-96; V Stoke Newington St Faith, St Matthias and All SS from 96. *St Matthias Vicarage, Wordsworth Road, London N16 8DD* Tel (020) 7254 5063
FULLER, Canon Frank William. b 22. Chich Th Coll 53. **d** 54 **p** 55. C Risby *St E* 54-55; P-in-c W Stow w Wordwell 55-57; P-in-c Lackford 55-59; R Culford, W Stow and Wordwell 58-61; R Cockfield 61-72; RD Lavenham 64-72; Hon Can St E Cathl 67-87; V Bungay H Trin w St Mary 73-87; RD Beccles and S Elmham 76-83; rtd 87; Perm to Offic *B & W* from 87. *23 Middle Street, Puriton, Bridgwater TA7 8AU* Tel (01278) 684131
FULLER, Frederick Walter Tom. b 17. St Cath Coll Cam BA48 MA53 Bris Univ MLitt72 Ex Univ PhD74. Union Th Sem (NY) STM54 Cuddesdon Coll 49. **d** 51 **p** 52. C Helmsley *York* 51-53; Lect and Chapl St Luke's Coll Ex 59-78; Dep PV Ex Cathl *Ex* from 62; Hon C Swindon New Town *Bris* 79-82; rtd 82; Perm to Offic *Bris* from 89. *29 Oxford Road, Swindon SN3 4HP* Tel (01793) 824980
FULLER, Canon Graham Drowley. b 33. AKC58. **d** 59 **p** 60. C E Grinstead St Swithun *Chich* 59-62; C Coulsdon St Andr *S'wark* 62-64; Chapl RN 64-68; V Battersea St Luke *S'wark* 68-75; V S Stoneham *Win* 75-90; Bp's Ecum Officer 84-90; R Eversley 90-96; Hon Can Win Cathl 93-96; rtd 96. *Brookside Dairy, Nunnery Lane, Newport PO30 1YR* Tel (01983) 525976
FULLER, Canon John James. b 38. SS Coll Cam BA63 SS Coll Cam MA66. Chich Th Coll 63 Union Th Sem (NY) STM64. **d** 65 **p** 66. C Westmr St Steph w St Jo *Lon* 65-71; Tutor Cuddesdon Coll 71-75; Tutor Ripon Coll Cuddesdon 75-77; Prin S Dios Minl Tr Scheme 77-96; Can and Preb Sarum Cathl *Sarum* 83-96; V Wheatley w Forest Hill and Stanton St John *Ox* 96-97; TR Wheatley from 97; rtd 03. *11 Ratcliffs Gardens, Shaftesbury SP7 8HJ*
FULLER, Michael George. b 46. Chich Th Coll 90. **d** 92 **p** 93. C Fulham All SS *Lon* 92-94; C Kensington St Mary Abbots w St Geo from 94; Dir Post-Ord Tr Kensington Area 94-99; Bp Kensington's Liaison Officer to Metrop Police from 99. *32A Campden Hill Gardens, London W8 7AZ* Tel (020) 7727 9486 Mobile 07733-010935 Fax (020) 7460 8566 E-mail fathermichael@btopenworld.com
FULLER, Canon Michael Jeremy. b 63. Worc Coll Ox BA85 MA89 DPhil89 Qu Coll Cam BA91. Westcott Ho Cam CTM92. **d** 92 **p** 93. C High Wycombe *Ox* 92-95; C Edin St Jo *Edin* 95-00; Prin TISEC from 00; Can St Mary's Cathl *Edin* from 00. *28 Blackford Avenue, Edinburgh EH9 2PH* Tel 0131-667 7273 *or* 220 2272 Fax 220 2294 E-mail michael@fuller78.freeserve.co.uk
FULLER, Canon Reginald Horace. b 15. Cam Univ BA37 MA41. Qu Coll Birm 39. **d** 40 **p** 41. C Bakewell *Derby* 40-43; C Ashbourne w Mapleton 43-46; C Edgbaston St Bart *Birm* 46-50; Prof Th St D Coll Lamp 50-55; USA from 55; Lic to Offic *Derby* from 64; rtd 80; Hon Can St Paul's Cathl Burlington from 88. *Westminster-Canterbury House, Apt 320, 1600 Westbrook Avenue, Richmond, VA 23227, USA*
FULLER, Robert James. b 10. Lon Univ BD53. **d** 55 **p** 56. C Nottingham St Andr *S'well* 55; R Exford w Exmoor *B & W* 61-75; rtd 75. *c/o Messrs Longueville Gittens, DX 26603, Oswestry* Tel (01691) 652241 Fax 670074
FULLER, Robert Peter. b 49. Bernard Gilpin Soc Dur 71 Trin Coll Bris 72. **d** 75 **p** 76. C Tonbridge SS Pet and Paul *Roch* 75-79; C Welling 79-83; V Nottingham St Sav *S'well* 83-89; V Ripley *Derby* 89-97; Chapl Ripley Hosp 89-97; Chapl S Derbyshire Community Health Services NHS Trust 93-97; V Colchester St Jo *Chelmsf* from 97. *St John's Vicarage, Evergreen Drive, Colchester CO4 4HU* Tel (01206) 843232 E-mail stjohnschurch.col@talk21.com
FULLER, Canon Terence James. b 30. Bris Univ BA55. Clifton Th Coll 55. **d** 56 **p** 57. C Uphill *B & W* 56-60; V Islington St Jude Mildmay Park *Lon* 60-67; V Southgate *Chich* 67-80; R Stoke Climsland *Truro* 80-95; RD Trigg Major 85-91; P-in-c Lezant w Lawhitton and S Petherwin w Trewen 93-95; Hon Can Truro Cathl 94-96; rtd 96; Perm to Offic *Truro* from 96. *9 Westover Road, Callington PL17 7EW* Tel (01579) 384958
FULLERTON, Hamish John Neville. b 45. Ball Coll Ox BA68 MA73. S'wark Ord Course 76. **d** 79 **p** 80. NSM Clapham Old Town *S'wark* 79-82; Abp Tenison's Sch Kennington 79-88; Hon C Brixton Road Ch Ch *S'wark* 89-91; C Streatham Ch Ch 91-96; C Purley St Mark 96-98; Asst P Tooting St Aug 98-01; Perm to Offic from 01. *Flat 4, 21 Offerton Road, London SW4 0DJ* Tel (020) 7622 7890
FULLJAMES, Mrs Janet Kathleen Doris. b 43. Open Univ BA79 Birm Univ MA93. Qu Coll Birm 85. **d** 87 **p** 94. Par Dn Harborne St Pet *Birm* 87-93; Par Dn Smethwick SS Steph and Mich 93-94; C 94-95; C Smethwick Resurr 95-98; P-in-c Dudley St Thos and St Luke *Worc* from 98; P-in-c Dudley St Jo from 98. *The Vicarage, King Street, Dudley DY2 8QB* Tel (01384) 252015 Fax 231686 E-mail janet@fullj.freeserve.co.uk
FULLJAMES, Michael William. b 36. OBE94. K Coll Lon AKC60. St Boniface Warminster 60. **d** 61 **p** 62. C Armley St Bart

Ripon 61-64; C E Wells *B & W* 64-67; Chapl Mendip Hosp Wells 64-67; R Stanningley St Thos *Ripon* 67-73; Chapl St Aug Hosp Cant 73-88; St Martin's Hosp 82-88; RD W Bridge *Cant* 87-88; Chapl Rotterdam *Eur* 88-94; Sen Chapl Rotterdam Miss to Seamen 88-94; Sen Chapl Burrswood Chr Cen *Roch* 94-01; rtd 01; Perm to Office *Cant* and *Roch* from 01. *40 Somner Close, Canterbury CT2 8LJ* Tel (01227) 766950
E-mail michaelfulljames@onetel.net.uk

FULLJAMES, Peter Godfrey. b 38. BNC Ox BA60 MA64 Birm Univ PhD91. Qu Coll Birm DipTh62. **d** 62 **p** 63. C Mexborough *Sheff* 62-65; Chapl Union Chr Coll India 65-69; Asst Master Wednesfield High Sch Wolverhampton 69-71; Asst Master Moorside High Sch Werrington 71-79; NSM Nairobi St Mark Kenya 80-85; Asst Master Nairobi High Sch 80-85; Research Fell Qu Coll Birm 85-87; Tutor WMMTC 87-90; Vice-Prin 90-93; Tutor Qu Coll Birm 93-94; Tutor Crowther Hall CMS Tr Coll Selly Oak 94-00; Hon Lect Th Birm Univ 97-03; rtd 00; Perm to Offic *Birm* from 00. *The Vicarage, King Street, Dudley DY2 8QB* Tel (01384) 252015 E-mail peter@fullj.freeserve.co.uk

FULLWOOD, William. b 11. St Aid Birkenhead 45. **d** 48 **p** 49. C Horton *Bradf* 48-51; C Shipley St Pet 51-53; V Earby 53-64; V Blacktoft *York* 64-68; V Laxton 64-68; V Laxton w Blacktoft 68-74; V Rudston w Boynton 74-77; rtd 77; Perm to Offic *York* from 77. *11 Ambrey Close, Hunmanby, Filey YO14 0LZ* Tel (01723) 891027

FULTON, John William. b 49. Ex Coll Ox BA71 BPhil72 MA75 MPhil79. Wycliffe Hall Ox 72. **d** 76 **p** 77. C Bexleyheath Ch Ch *Roch* 76-79; C Ealing Dean St Jo *Lon* 79-83; V Aldborough Hatch *Chelmsf* 83-87; Chapl Chantilly *Eur* 87-90; R Hepworth, Hinderclay, Wattisfield and Thelnetham *St E* from 90. *The Rectory, Church Lane, Hepworth, Diss IP22 2PU* Tel (01359) 250285 Fax as telephone

FUNNELL, Norman Richard James. b 40. Univ of Wales (Lamp) BA64. Ripon Hall Ox 64. **d** 66 **p** 67. C Hackney *Lon* 66-70; Hon C 71-85; TV 85-93; R S Hackney St Jo w Ch Ch from 93. *The Rectory, Church Crescent, London E9 7DH* Tel (020) 8985 5145 E-mail nrjf@tesco.net

FURBER, Mrs Jennifer Margaret. b 50. WEMTC 98. **d** 01 **p** 02. NSM Malvern Link w Cowleigh *Worc* from 01. *The Vicarage, 8 Christchurch Road, Malvern WR14 3BE* Tel (01684) 574106 E-mail jfurber@classicfm.net

FURBER, Peter. b 43. Ex Univ BA. Sarum & Wells Th Coll 83. **d** 85 **p** 86. C Stanmore *Win* 85-88; TV Basingstoke 88-95; C Ringwood 95-98; P-in-c Gt Malvern Ch Ch *Worc* 98-99; V from 99. *The Vicarage, 8 Christchurch Road, Malvern WR14 3BE* Tel (01684) 574106 E-mail pfurber@classicfm.net

FURBEY, Mrs Linda Alice. b 49. Hockerill Coll of Educn CertEd70 Wolfs Coll Cam BEd71 Coll of Ripon & York St Jo MA03. N Ord Course 00. **d** 03. NSM Crosspool *Sheff* from 03. *20 Crimicar Avenue, Sheffield S10 4EQ* Tel 0114-230 6356

FURLONG, Andrew William Ussher. b 47. TCD BA69 Jes Coll Cam BA71. Westcott Ho Cam 70 CITC 72. **d** 72 **p** 73. C Dundela St Mark *D & D* 72-76; C Dublin St Ann w St Mark and St Steph *D & G* 76-83; Zimbabwe 83-94; Adn W Harare 88-89; Can Harare 89-94; Asst Chapl Leeds Teaching Hosps NHS Trust 94-97; Dean Clonmacnoise *M & K* 97-02; I Trim and Athboy Gp 97-02; Prec Kildare Cathl 98-02. *12 Tubbermore Road, Dalkey, Co Dublin, Irish Republic* Tel (00353) (1) 285 9817 E-mail tiripo@gofree.indigo.ie

FURLONG (née DAVIES), Mrs Catharine Mary. b 48. Philippa Fawcett Coll CertEd73. EMMTC 85. **d** 88 **p** 95. C Spalding *Linc* 88-92; Zimbabwe 92-94; C Gt w Lt Gidding and Steeple Gidding *Ely* 94-96; P-in-c from 96; P-in-c Brington w Molesworth and Old Weston from 96; P-in-c Leighton Bromswold from 96; P-in-c Winwick from 96. *The Rectory, 6 Luddington Road, Great Gidding, Huntingdon PE28 5PA* Tel (01832) 293587

FURNELL, The Very Revd Raymond. b 35. Linc Th Coll 63. **d** 65 **p** 66. C Cannock *Lich* 65-69; V Clayton 69-75; RD Stoke N 75-81; R Shelton 75-77; TR Hanley H Ev 77-81; Provost St E 81-94; V St E Cathl Distr 81-94; Dean York from 94. *The Deanery, York YO1 7JQ* Tel (01904) 623618 *or* 557202 E-mail rfurnell@compuserve.com

FURNESS, Colin. b 43. Lich Th Coll 65. **d** 68 **p** 69. C New Bentley *Sheff* 68; C Sheff Parson Cross St Cecilia 68-74; V Edlington 74-78; C Heavitree w Ex St Paul *Ex* 78-81; TV 81-89; R Sampford Spiney w Horrabridge 89-03; TV Chard and Distr *B & W* from 03. *The Rectory, Furnham Road, Chard TA20 1AE* Tel (01460) 61012 E-mail furness@fish.co.uk

FURNESS, Dominic John. b 53. Bris Univ BA76. Ridley Hall Cam 82. **d** 84 **p** 85. C Downend *Bris* 84-88; V Stoke Hill *Guildf* from 88. *St Peter's House, 37 Hazel Avenue, Guildford GU1 1NP* Tel (01483) 572078 E-mail furness@ntlworld.com

FURNESS, Edward Joseph. b 41. S'wark Ord Course 74. **d** 77 **p** 78. NSM S Lambeth St Steph *S'wark* 77-81; Warden Mayflower Family Cen Canning Town *Chelmsf* 82-96; P-in-c Aston St Jas *Birm* 96-00; V from 00. *The Vicarage, 215 Albert Road, Aston, Birmingham B6 5NA* Tel 0121-327 3230

FURNESS, Edward Peter Alexander. b 29. St Edm Hall Ox BA52 MA56. St Aid Birkenhead 52. **d** 54 **p** 55. C Ashton-on-Ribble St Andr *Blackb* 54-57; C Storrington *Chich* 57-59; C Sullington

57-59; V Worsthorne *Blackb* 59-64 and 88-94; V Longridge 64-88; rtd 94; Perm to Offic *Blackb* from 94. *26 Severn Street, Longridge, Preston PR3 3ND* Tel (01772) 784092

FURNESS, John Alfred. b 31. Chich Th Coll 60. **d** 62 **p** 63. C Leeds St Aid *Ripon* 62-66; C Rickmansworth *St Alb* 66-73; R Wymington 73-75; P-in-c Podington w Farndish 74-75; R Wymington w Podington 75-79; V Waltham Cross 79-89; RD Cheshunt 84-89; R Swyncombe w Britwell Salome *Ox* 89-97; rtd 97; Perm to Offic *St Alb* from 97; Perm to Offic *S'wark* from 00. *9 The Quadrangle, Morden College, London SE3 0PW* Tel (020) 8858 2838

FURST, John William. b 41. Bris Sch of Min Ripon Coll Cuddesdon. **d** 84 **p** 85. C Bris Ch the Servant Stockwood *Bris* 84-88; V Hanham 88-94; Perm to Offic *Llan* from 98; V Gosberton, Gosberton Clough and Quadring *Linc* from 99. *The Vicarage, 6 Wargate Way, Gosberton, Spalding PE11 4NH* Tel (01775) 840694

✠**FURUMOTO, The Rt Revd John Junichiro.** b 33. Tokushima Univ BEd56 Wycliffe Coll Toronto LTh BTh Hon DD97. Cen Th Coll Tokyo 62. **d** 63 **p** 64 **c** 92. R Kobe Ascension 63-91; Bp Kobe from 92; Primate of Nippon Seikokai 00-02. *65-3 Yaraicho, Shinjuku-ku, Tokyo, 162-0805, Japan* Tel (0081) (3) 5228 3171 Fax 5228 3175

FUTCHER, Christopher David. b 58. Edin Univ BD80. Westcott Ho Cam 80. **d** 82 **p** 83. C Borehamwood *St Alb* 82-85; C Stevenage All SS Pin Green 85-88; V 88-96; V St Alb St Steph 96-00; R Harpenden St Nic from 00. *The Rectory, 9 Rothamsted Avenue, Harpenden AL5 2DD* Tel (01582) 712202 *or* 765524 Fax 713646 E-mail cdfutcher@goldserve.net

FUTERS, Michael Roger. b 58. Trin & All SS Coll Leeds BEd80. St Jo Coll Nottm 82. **d** 85 **p** 86. C Narborough and Huncote *Leic* 85-87; C Spondon *Derby* 87-90; P-in-c Derby St Jas 90-95; TV Walbrook Epiphany 95-99; Community Development Officer Home Housing from 99; Hon C Derby St Mark from 99. *3 St Pancras Way, Derby DE1 3TH* Tel (01332) 203075

FYFE, Gordon Boyd. b 63. Edin Univ BD93 Edin Univ MTh95. TISEC 94. **d** 96 **p** 97. C Ayr *Glas* 96-99; C Maybole 96-99; C Girvan 96-99; R Airdrie from 99; R Coatbridge from 99. *The Rectory, 24 Etive Drive, Airdrie ML6 9QQ* Tel (01236) 756550 Fax as telephone

FYFFE, Canon Robert Clark. b 56. Edin Univ BD78 Bris Poly Dip Audio Visual Media 87 Napier Univ Edin MBA98. Edin Th Coll 74. **d** 79 **p** 80. C Edin St Jo *Edin* 79-83; Youth Chapl *B & W* 83-87; Prov Youth Officer Scottish Episc Ch 87-92; Co-ord Internat Angl Youth Network from 88; R Perth St Jo *St And* from 93; Can St Ninian's Cathl Perth from 96. *23 Comley Bank, Perth PH2 7HU* Tel (01738) 625394 Fax 443053 E-mail hostmaster@scotland.anglican.org

FYFFE, Timothy Bruce. b 25. New Coll Ox MA54. Westcott Ho Cam 54. **d** 56 **p** 57. C Lewisham St Mary *S'wark* 56-60; Nigeria 60-68; TV Lowestoft St Marg *Nor* 69-80; Chapl HM Pris Blundeston 70-78; TV Tettenhall Regis *Lich* 80-85; Chapl Compton Hall Hospice Wolv 85-87; NSM Wolverhampton St Andr *Lich* from 88; rtd 90. *40 Glentworth Gardens, Wolverhampton WV6 0SG* Tel (01902) 716510

FYLES, Gordon. b 39. Trin Coll Bris 76. **d** 77 **p** 78. C Islington St Mary *Lon* 77-81; Ext Sec BCMS 81-88; Hon C Kingston Hill St Paul *S'wark* 82-88; C Wimbledon Em Ridgway Prop Chpl 88-97; I Crinken *D & G* from 97. *Crinken Parsonage, Bray, Co Wicklow, Irish Republic* Tel (00353) (1) 282 2048 E-mail gfyles@iol.ie

FYSH, Leslie David. b 35. Glouc Sch of Min 88. **d** 91 **p** 92. NSM Stonehouse *Glouc* 91-95; Asst Chapl Wycliffe Coll Glos 91-95; NSM W Walton *Ely* 95-00; Perm to Offic from 00. *16 Tower Court, Tower Road, Ely CB7 4XS* Tel (01353) 659776

G

GABB-JONES, Adrian William Douglas. b 43. ARICS MRICS01. Ripon Coll Cuddesdon 79. **d** 81 **p** 82. C Northolt Park St Barn *Lon* 81-84; C Ruislip St Martin 84-89; V Minster Lovell and Brize Norton *Ox* 89-03; V Minster Lovell from 03. *The Vicarage, Burford Road, Minster Lovell, Oxford OX8 5RA* Tel (01993) 776492

GABBADON, Kenneth Fitz Arthur. b 53. N Man Coll Cert Counselling 89. N Ord Course 97. **d** 99 **p** 00. C Burnage St Marg *Man* 99-01; C Bury St Jo w St Mark from 01. *St Mark's House, 150 Walmersley Road, Bury BL9 6LL* Tel 0161-764 6928 E-mail kgabba7036@bigfoot.com

GABE, Eric Sigurd. b 15. Lon Univ BA52 PhD94. St Aid Birkenhead 54. **d** 55 **p** 55. C W Kirby St Andr *Ches* 55-57; C Hoylake 57-60; V Cricklewood St Mich *Lon* 60-72; V Brondesbury St Anne w Kilburn H Trin 72-80; rtd 80; Perm to Offic *St Alb* from 80; Perm to Offic *Lon* from 81. *21 Cromer Road, Barnet EN5 5HT* Tel (020) 8449 6779

GABLE, Michael David. b 70. Poly of Wales BEng92. St Mich Coll Llan DipTh94 BTh95. **d** 95 **p** 96. C Newton Nottage *Llan* 95-99; V Aberavon H Trin 99-01; TV Aberavon from 01. *Holy Trinity Vicarage, Fairway, Port Talbot SA12 7HG* Tel (01639) 790407 Fax as telephone E-mail michaelgable@hotmail.com

GABRIEL, Michael Hunt. b 29. BA. **d** 57 **p** 58. C Waterford Ch Ch *C & O* 57-60; C New Windsor H Trin *Ox* 60-62; C Albany Street Ch Ch *Lon* 62-63; R W and E Shefford *Ox* 63-67; C Hillingdon St Jo *Lon* 67-86; C Kingston Buci *Chich* 86-94; rtd 94. *Flat 1, 6 Dittons Road, Eastbourne BN21 1DN*

GADD, Alan John. b 44. FRMetS67 Imp Coll Lon BSc65 PhD69. S'wark Ord Course 68. **d** 71 **p** 72. Asst Chapl Lon Univ *Lon* 71-72; Perm to Offic *S'wark* 73-91; C Battersea Park All SS 91-95; P-in-c 95-96; C Battersea Fields from 96. *100 Prince of Wales Drive, London SW11 4BD* Tel (020) 7622 3809

GADD, Brian Hayward. b 33. Hatf Coll Dur BA54 DipEd55. Glouc Sch of Min 82. **d** 85 **p** 87. NSM Cleobury Mortimer w Hopton Wafers etc *Heref* 85-98; rtd 98; Perm to Offic *Heref* from 99. *34 Lower Street, Cleobury Mortimer, Kidderminster DY14 8AB* Tel (01299) 270758

GADD, Bryan Stephen Andrew. b 56. Dur Univ BA Ox Univ CertEd. Chich Th Coll. **d** 81 **p** 82. C Newlyn St Pet *Truro* 81-86; R St Mawgan w St Ervan and St Eval 86-90; Chapl Summer Fields Sch Ox from 90; Perm to Offic *Truro* from 90. *Meadow Barn, Summer Fields, Summertown, Oxford OX2 7EH* Tel (01865) 516047 E-mail bryan.gadd@lineone.net

GADEN, Timothy John. b 64. Melbourne Univ BA86 Monash Univ Aus PhD96. Melbourne Coll of Div BD90. **d** 91 **p** 91. Australia 91-96 and from 01; C Battersea St Mary *S'wark* 97; V 97-01; Dir Post-Ord Tr Kingston Area 99-01; R Camberwell St Jo from 01. *15 The Grove, Camberwell, Vic, Australia 3124* Tel (0061) (3) 9889 6456 *or* 9882 4851 Mobile 419-114697 Fax (3) 9882 0086 E-mail gaden@stjohnscamberwell.org.au

GAGE, Alan William. b 52. Univ of Wales (Cardiff) BMus72 PGCE73 Bris Univ MEd90. WEMTC 98. **d** 00 **p** 01. NSM Tuffley *Glouc* from 00. *Chadburn, 83 Dinglewell, Hucclecote, Gloucester GL3 3HT* Tel (01452) 614892 E-mail alan@leapyear.demon.co.uk

GAGE, Aëlla Rupert Fitzehardinge Berkeley. b 66. Reading Univ BEd92. Oak Hill Th Coll 98. **d** 00. C Muswell Hill St Jas w St Matt *Lon* from 00. *67 St James Lane, London N10 3QY* Tel (020) 8365 3194

GAGE, Canon Robert Edward. b 47. Whitman Coll Washington BA69. Cuddesdon Coll BA75 MA81. **d** 76 **p** 77. C Cheshunt *St Alb* 76-79; C Harpenden St Nic 79-81; V S Mymms 81-82; P-in-c Ridge 81-82; V S Mymms and Ridge 82-97; Prec and Can Res Wakef Cathl *Wakef* from 96. *4 Cathedral Close, Wakefield WF1 2DP* Tel (01924) 210008 E-mail gage@tromba.freeserve.co.uk

GAINER, Jeffrey. b 51. Jes Coll Ox BA73 MA77 Univ of Wales LLM94. Wycliffe Hall Ox 74. **d** 77 **p** 78. C Baglan *Llan* 77-81; V Cwmbach 81-85; V Tonyrefail w Gilfach Goch and Llandyfodwg 85-87; Dir NT Studies and Dir Past Studies St Mich Coll Llan 87-92; V Meidrim and Llanboidy and Merthyr *St D* from 92. *The Vicarage, Meidrim, Carmarthen SA33 5QF* Tel (01994) 231378

GAIR, Andrew Kennon. b 62. Westcott Ho Cam 88. **d** 91 **p** 92. C Clare w Poslingford, Cavendish etc *St E* 91-95; R Debden and Wimbish w Thunderley *Chelmsf* from 95. *The Rectory, Mill Road, Debden, Saffron Walden CB11 3LB* Tel (01799) 540285 E-mail andrew.gair@btinternet.com

✠**GAISFORD, The Rt Revd John Scott.** b 34. St Chad's Coll Dur BA59 MA76 DipTh60. **d** 60 **p** 61 **c** 94. C Audenshaw St Hilda *Man* 60-62; C Bramhall *Ches* 62-65; V Crewe St Andr 65-86; RD Nantwich 74-85; Hon Can Ches Cathl 80-86; Adn Macclesfield 86-94; Suff Bp Beverley (PEV) *York* 94-00; Asst Bp Ripon and Leeds *Ripon* 96-00; rtd 00; Perm to Offic from 00. *5 Trevone Close, Knutsford WA16 9EJ* Tel (01565) 633531 Mobile 07855-615469 E-mail jandg.gaisford@tiscali.co.uk

GAIT, David James. b 48. BNC Ox BA71 BSc72 MA77 MSc83. Ridley Hall Cam 71. **d** 74 **p** 75. C Litherland St Paul Hatton Hill *Liv* 74-77; C Farnworth 77-80; V Widnes St Jo from 80; Chapl Widnes Maternity Hosp 86-90. *St John's House, Greenway Road, Widnes WA8 6HA* Tel 0151-424 3134

GAKURU, Griphus Stephen. Makerere Univ Kampala BSc81 PGDE83 Selw Coll Cam MPhil92 PhD. Bp Tucker Coll Mukono BD88. **d** 88 **p** 91. Uganda 89-91; Hon C Cambridge H Trin w St Andr Gt *Ely* 91-92; Hon C Cambridge H Trin 92-95; Chapl Selw Coll Cam 95-98; C Small Heath *Birm* 95-98; C Huyton St Mich *Liv* 98-01; P-in-c Brownswood Park *Lon* from 01. *St John's Vicarage, 2A Gloucester Drive, London N4 2LW* Tel (020) 8211 0729

GALBRAITH, Alexander Peter James. b 65. Qu Coll Ox BA86 MA90. Wycliffe Hall Ox 87. **d** 90 **p** 91. C Southport Em *Liv* 90-94; C Mossley Hill St Matt and St Jas 94-97; V Kew from 97; Chapl Southport and Ormskirk NHS Trust from 97. *20 Markham Drive, Kew, Southport PR8 6XR* Tel (01704) 547758

GALBRAITH, Jane. b 95. **p** 96. NSM Kildare w Kilmeague and Curragh *M & K* 95-97; NSM Newbridge w Carnalway and Kilcullen 97-99; C Limerick *L & K* from 03. *50 Ballinvoher, Father Russell Road, Dooradoyle, Limerick, Republic of Ireland* Tel (00353) (61) 302038 Fax as telephone

GALBRAITH, John Angus Frame. b 44. Sarum Th Coll 68. **d** 71 **p** 72. C Richmond St Mary *S'wark* 71-74; Chapl W Lon Colls 74-79; R S'wark H Trin w St Matt 79-95; V New Addington 95-02; Asst Chapl HM Pris Wandsworth from 02. *HM Prison Wandsworth, PO Box 757, Heathfield Road, London SW18 3HS* Tel (020) 8874 7292 ext 327

GALBRAITH, John Watson Joseph Denham. b 19. Glas Univ MA41. Bps' Coll Cheshunt 45. **d** 48 **p** 49. C Biggleswade *St Alb* 48-49; C Tring 49-51; C Challoch w Newton Stewart *Glas* 51-53; CF 53-67; Dep Asst Chapl Gen 67-72; R Hodnet w Weston under Redcastle *Lich* 72-77; V Deeping St James *Linc* 77-81; Chapl Oporto *Eur* 81-85; rtd 85; Perm to Offic *B & W* from 86. *64 High Street, Rode, Frome BA11 6PB* Tel (01373) 830077

GALBRAITH, Peter John. b 59. QUB BA MTh TCD DipTh. **d** 85 **p** 86. C Knockbreda *D & D* 85-88; C Ballynafeigh St Jude 88-91; I Broomhedge *Conn* from 91. *Broomhedge Rectory, 30 Lurganure Road, Broughmore, Lisburn BT28 2TR* Tel (028) 9262 1229

GALE, Ms Charlotte. b 70. Leeds Univ BEng92 Nottm Univ MA00. St Jo Coll Nottm 98. **d** 01 **p** 02. C Whitnash *Cov* from 01. *13 Palmer Road, Whitnash, Leamington Spa CV31 2HP* Tel (01926) 425366 E-mail cgale@fish.co.uk

GALE, Canon Christopher. b 44. ALCD67. **d** 68 **p** 69. C Balderton S'well 68-72; C Bilborough St Jo 72-75; P-in-c Colwick 75-78; V Radford St Pet 78-84; V Sherwood 84-98; AD Nottingham N 90-98; P-in-c Bulwell St Mary 98-02; R from 02; Hon Can S'well Minster from 03. *Bulwell Rectory, Station Road, Nottingham NG6 9AA* Tel 0115-927 8468 E-mail rev.chris@bulwell75.fsnet.co.uk

GALE, Colin Edward. b 49. Lon Univ PGCE74. St Jo Coll Nottm LTh BTh73. **d** 79 **p** 80. C Hoole *Ches* 79-82; C Woodley St Jo the Ev *Ox* 82-87; V Clapham St Jas *S'wark* 87-96; V Sutton Ch Ch from 96. *Christ Church Vicarage, 14C Christchurch Park, Sutton SM2 5TN* Tel (020) 8642 2757 Fax as telephone E-mail galeforce4@tinyworld.co.uk

GALE, The Ven John. b 34. Univ of Wales (Lamp) 67. **d** 69 **p** 70. C Aberdare *Llan* 69-71; C Merthyr Dyfan 71-74; S Africa 74-00; R Walmer St Sav 74-82; R Knysna St Geo 82-00; Adn Knysna 93-00; Lic to Offic *St D* from 00. *3 Connacht Way, Pembroke Dock SA72 6FB* Tel (01946) 622219 Fax as telephone

GALE, Keith George. b 44. St Jo Coll Lusaka 68 Sarum Th Coll 69. **d** 70 **p** 71. C Sheff St Cuth *Sheff* 70-77; P-in-c Brightside All SS 72-77; C Birm St Martin *Birm* 77-81; USPG 81-94; Malawi 81-94; Adn Lilongwe Lake Malawi 89-92; TV Sampford Peverell, Uplowman, Holcombe Rogus etc *Ex* from 94. *The Rectory, Blackdown View, Sampford Peverell, Tiverton EX16 7BE* Tel (01884) 821879

GALE, Ms Lucille Catherine. b 67. Sarum & Wells Th Coll 92. **d** 94 **p** 95. C Welling *S'wark* 94-97; Chapl Univ of Greenwich 97-00; V Welling from 00. *St Mary's Vicarage, Sandringham Drive, Welling DA16 3QU* Tel (020) 8856 0684

GALE, Peter Simon. b 56. Welsh Coll of Music & Drama 73 K Alfred's Coll Win PGCE78. St Mich Coll Llan BD83. **d** 83 **p** 84. C Caerphilly *Llan* 83-89; Chapl RN 89-93; V Ystrad Rhondda w Ynyscynon *Llan* from 93. *St Stephen's Vicarage, Ystrad, Pentre CF41 7RR* Tel (01443) 434426

GALES, Alan. b 29. Sarum Th Coll 56. **d** 59 **p** 60. C Greenside *Dur* 59-60; C Peterlee 60-63; Ind Chapl 60-70; V Marley Hill 63-94; Asst Chapl HM Pris Dur 74-81; rtd 94. *46 Corsair, Whickham, Newcastle upon Tyne NE16 5YA* Tel 0191-488 7352

GALES, Bernard Henry. b 27. Lon Univ BSc(Econ)51 Open Univ BA02. Wells Th Coll 62. **d** 64 **p** 65. C Sholing *Win* 64-67; C Fordingbridge w Ibsley 67-71; C S Molton w Nymet St George *Ex* 71-73; C Thelbridge 73-77; P-in-c 77-78; P-in-c Creacombe 77-78; P-in-c W w E Worlington 77-78; P-in-c Meshaw 77-78; P-in-c Witheridge 77-78; C Witheridge, Thelbridge, Creacombe, Meshaw etc 79-80; R Bow w Broad Nymet 80-93; V Colebrooke 80-93; R Zeal Monachorum 80-93; RD Cadbury 90-93; rtd 93; Perm to Offic *Ex* from 93. *8 Old Rectory Gardens, Morchard Bishop, Crediton EX17 6PF* Tel (01363) 877601

GALES, Simon Richard. b 59. CEng87 MICE87 Jes Coll Cam BA81 MA84. Wycliffe Hall Ox 91. **d** 93 **p** 94. C Houghton *Carl* 93-97; V Lindow *Ches* from 97. *St John's Vicarage, 137 Knutsford Road, Wilmslow SK9 6EL* Tel (01625) 583251 *or* 586329 E-mail simon@srgales.freeserve.co.uk

GALILEE, Canon George David Surtees. b 37. Oriel Coll Ox BA60 MA64. Westcott Ho Cam 61. **d** 62 **p** 63. C Knighton St Mary Magd *Leic* 62-67; V Stocking Farm 67-69; Tutor

Westcott Ho Cam and Homerton Coll 69-71; V Sutton *Ely* 71-80; P-in-c Addiscombe St Mildred *Cant* 80-81; V 81-84; V Addiscombe St Mildred *S'wark* 85-95; Can Res and Chan Blackb Cathl *Blackb* from 95. *Ivy Hatch, 25 Ryburn Avenue, Blackburn BB2 7AU* Tel (01254) 671540 *or* 51491 Fax 689666

GALLAGHER, Adrian Ian. b 43. CITC 89. **d** 92 **p** 93. C Drumachose *D & R* 92-96; I Camus-juxta-Bann 96-00; TV Langley and Parkfield *Man* from 00. *The Vicarage, 5 Wentworth Close, Middleton, Manchester M24 4BD* Tel 0161-643 8701 Mobile 07796-022473

GALLAGHER, Hubert. b 31. Linc Th Coll 78. **d** 80 **p** 81. C Lupset *Wakef* 80-82; C Badsworth 82-86; V Kinsley 86-88; V Kinsley w Wragby 88-91; rtd 91; Perm to Offic *Wakef* 91-98; NSM Is of Arran *Arg* 97-98. *Ivy Cottage, Brodick, Isle of Arran KA27 8DD* Tel and fax (01770) 700225 Mobile 07774-971310 E-mail hugal@supanet.com *or* arran@argyll.anglican.org

GALLAGHER, Canon Ian. BTh. **d** 90 **p** 91. C Annagh w Drumgoon, Ashfield etc *K, E & A* 90-93; I Drumcliffe w Lissadell and Munninane 93-01; Can Elphin Cathl 97-01; Dioc Sec (Elphin and Ardagh) 97-01; Preb Mulhuddart St Patr Cathl Dublin 98-01; I Stillorgan w Blackrock *D & G* from 01. *The Rectory, St Brigid's Church Road, Stillorgan, Blackrock, Co Dublin, Irish Republic* Tel (00353) (1) 288 1091 Mobile 86-811 9544 Fax (1) 278 1833 E-mail stillorgan@dublin.anglican.org

GALLAGHER, Matthew Edward. b 51. Glas Univ BSc75. EAMTC. **d** 00 **p** 01. NSM Northampton St Jas *Pet* 00-02. *11 Penfold Gardens, Great Billing, Northampton NN3 9PG* Tel (01604) 416972 E-mail me.gallagher@virgin.net

GALLAGHER, Michael Collins. b 48. Dur Univ BA. Sarum Th Coll. **d** 82 **p** 83. C Bridport *Sarum* 82-86; V Downton 86-01; RD Alderbury 93-99; R Crewkerne w Wayford *B & W* from 01. *The Rectory, Gouldsbrook Terrace, Crewkerne TA18 7JA* Tel (01460) 271188 Fax 271194 E-mail m.gallagher@mail.com

GALLAGHER, Neville Roy. b 45. Birm Univ CertEd66 K Coll Lon AKC70 BD76 Open Univ BA97. **d** 71 **p** 72. C Folkestone St Mary and St Eanswythe *Cant* 71-74; Hon C Sutton Valence w E Sutton and Chart Sutton 74-76; TV Cen Telford *Lich* 76-78; P-in-c Gt Mongeham *Cant* 78-80; P-in-c Ripple 78-80; R Gt Mongeham w Ripple and Sutton by Dover 80-83; V Kennington 83-88; Chapl Bedgebury Sch Kent from 88. *3 Beech Drive, Bedgebury Park, Goudhurst, Cranbrook TN17 2SJ* Tel (01580) 211989 *or* 211221 E-mail ngallagher@bedgebury.ndirect.co.uk

GALLAGHER, Robert. b 43. St Chad's Coll Dur BSc65 DipTh67. **d** 67 **p** 68. C Crosland Moor *Wakef* 67-69; C Huddersfield St Pet and St Paul 69-71; Chapl Huddersfield Poly 72-79; Min Coulby Newham Ecum Project *York* 79-90; V Toxteth St Marg *Liv* from 90. *St Margaret's Vicarage, 3 Princes Road, Liverpool L8 1TG* Tel 0151-709 1526

GALLAGHER, Stephen. b 58. Southn Univ BTh89. Chich Th Coll 86. **d** 89 **p** 90. C S Shields All SS *Dur* 89-92; C Hartlepool St Paul 92-94; Chapl Hartlepool Gen Hosp 92-94; R Loftus and Carlin How w Skinningrove *York* 94-97; P-in-c Lower Beeding *Chich* from 97; Dioc Youth Officer from 97. *The Vicarage, Plummers Plain, Lower Beeding, Horsham RH13 6NU* Tel (01403) 891367
E-mail fatherstephen@plummersplain.freeserve.co.uk

GALLANT, Mrs Joanna-Sue Sheena. b 62. St Alb and Ox Min Course 99. **d** 02. C Amersham on the Hill *Ox* from 02. *8 Woodside Close, Amersham HP6 5EG* Tel (01494) 580077 Mobile 07813-886805 E-mail gallant.family@zoom.co.uk

GALLETLY, Thomas. b 23. St Chad's Coll Dur BA50 DipTh52. **d** 52 **p** 53. C Woodhorn w Newbiggin *Newc* 52-55; Chapl Aycliffe Approved Sch Co Dur 56-57; Chapl Chailey Heritage Hosp and Sch Lewes 57-88; Lic to Offic *Chich* 59-88; rtd 88; Perm to Offic *Chich* from 88. *The Glen, Lewes Road, Scaynes Hill, Haywards Heath RH17 7PG* Tel (01444) 831510

GALLEY, Giles Christopher. b 32. Qu Coll Cam BA56 MA60. Linc Th Coll 56. **d** 58 **p** 59. C Gt Yarmouth *Nor* 58-62; C N Lynn w St Marg and St Nic 62-66; C Leeds St Pet *Ripon* 66-69; V N Hull St Mich *York* 70-79; V Strensall 79-00; RD Easingwold 82-97; rtd 00; Perm to Offic *York* from 00. *19 St John's Road, Stamford Bridge, York YO41 1PH* Tel (01759) 371592

GALLICHAN, Henry Ernest. b 45. Sarum Th Coll 70. **d** 72 **p** 73. C Kenton Ascension *Newc* 72-76; Tanzania 76-80; Lic to Offic *Truro* 80-83; Public Preacher from 83. *Karibu, Trevelmond, Liskeard PL14 4LZ* Tel (01579) 320530
E-mail karibu@iname.com

✠**GALLIFORD, The Rt Revd David George.** b 25. Clare Coll Cam BA49 MA51. Westcott Ho Cam. **d** 51 **p** 52 **c** 75. C Newland St Jo *York* 51-54; C Eton w Boveney *Ox* 54-56; Min Can Windsor 54-56; V Middlesbrough St Oswald *York* 56-61; R Bolton Percy 61-71; Dioc Adult Tr Officer 61-71; Can and Preb York Minster 69-70; Can Res and Treas 70-75; Suff Bp Hulme *Man* 75-84; Suff Bp Bolton 84-91; rtd 91; Hon Asst Bp York from 95. *Bishopgarth, Maltongate, Thornton Dale, Pickering YO18 7SA* Tel (01751) 474605

GALLIGAN, Adrienne. **d** 03. C Seapatrick *D & D* from 03. *26 Larchwood Avenue, Banbridge BT32 3XH* Tel (028) 4066 9086

GALLON, Mrs Audrey Kay. b 41. SEITE 94. **d** 97 **p** 98. NSM Gt Mongeham w Ripple and Sutton by Dover *Cant* 97-98; NSM Eastry and Northbourne w Tilmanstone etc 97-98; NSM Walmer from 98. *Hove-To, Collingwood Road, St Margaret's-at-Cliffe, Dover CT15 6EX* Tel (01304) 853946
E-mail dibly@talk21.com

GALLOWAY, Canon Charles Bertram. b 41. Lon Univ BA62 Birm Univ DipTh64. Qu Coll Birm 64. **d** 64 **p** 65. C Darlington H Trin *Dur* 64-68; Ind Chapl Teesside 68-77; Sen Ind Chapl *Liv* 77-87; Team Ldr and Convener Lon Ind Chapl *Lon* 87-93; P-in-c Gosforth w Nether Wasdale and Wasdale Head *Carl* 93-98; R from 98; Chapl Sellafield from 94; Hon Can Carl Cathl from 03. *The Rectory, Gosforth, Seascale CA20 1AZ* Tel (01946) 725251 E-mail bert.galloway@btinternet.com

GALLOWAY, Michael Edward. b 41. Chich Th Coll 72. **d** 74 **p** 75. C Aldwick *Chich* 74-77; C Bournemouth St Clem w St Mary *Win* 78-82; V S Benfleet *Chelmsf* from 83. *St Mary's Vicarage, 105 Vicarage Hill, Benfleet SS7 1PD* Tel (01268) 792294 E-mail ceag@dialstart.net

GALLOWAY, Peter John. b 54. OBE96 JP89. Goldsmiths' Coll Lon BA76 K Coll Lon PhD87 FRSA88 FSA00. St Steph Ho Ox 80. **d** 83 **p** 84. C St John's Wood *Lon* 83-86; C St Giles-in-the-Fields 86-90; Warden of Readers (Lon Episc Area) 87-92; OStJ 86-92; ChStJ 92-97; KStJ from 97; P-in-c Hampstead Em W End *Lon* 90-95; V from 95; Hon Fell Goldsmiths' Coll Lon from 99; AD N Camden *Lon* from 02. *Emmanuel Vicarage, Lyncroft Gardens, London NW6 1JU* Tel (020) 7435 1911 Fax 7431 5521

GALSWORTHY, Colin. b 44. St Mich Coll Llan 95. **d** 00 **p** 01. NSM Skewen *Llan* 00-01; NSM Resolven w Tonna from 01. *29 Woodlands Park Drive, Cadoxton, Neath SA10 8DE* Tel (01639) 636128

GALT, Ian Ross. b 34. Leeds Univ BSc56. **d** 76 **p** 77. NSM Newport St Julian *Mon* 76-87; NSM Newport St Teilo 87-98. *47 Brynglas Avenue, Newport NP20 5LR* Tel (01633) 821499

GAMBLE, David Lawrence. b 34. AKC61. **d** 62 **p** 63. C-in-c Shrub End All SS CD *Chelmsf* 62-65; C Colchester St Jas, All SS, St Nic and St Runwald 65-69; V Chelmsf St Andr 69-73; P-in-c Hatfield Heath 69-73; C 74-77; TV Hemel Hempstead *St Alb* 77-82; P-in-c Renhold 82-90; Chapl HM Pris Bedf 82-90; P-in-c Petersham *S'wark* 90-96; Chapl HM Pris Latchmere Ho 90-96; P-in-c Portsea St Geo *Portsm* 96-99; rtd 99; Hon C Yarmouth *Portsm* from 99; Hon C Freshwater from 99. *Easterholme, Tennyson Road, Yarmouth PO41 0PR* Tel (01983) 761360

GAMBLE, Diane Mary. BSc. **d** 00 **p** 01. NSM Sanderstead All SS *S'wark* from 00. *14 Barnfield Road, Sanderstead CR2 0EY*

GAMBLE, Donald William. b 67. NUU BSc88. TCD Div Sch BTh91. **d** 91 **p** 92. C Belfast St Mich *Conn* 91-95; I Dromore Clogh 95-00; P-in-c Renewal and Outreach in the City *Conn* from 00. *35 Knockview Road, Carnmoney, Newtonabbey BT36 6TT* Tel (028) 9083 0427 E-mail roc@nireland.com

GAMBLE, Mrs Edana Bronwen. b 56. Hull Univ BSc(Econ)78 FCA82 Nottm Univ MA02. EMMTC 99. **d** 02 **p** 03. NSM Nuthall *S'wark* from 02. *8 Turner Close, Stapleford, Nottingham NG9 7HQ* Tel 0115-939 3062
E-mail brongamble@hotmail.com

GAMBLE, Ian Robert. b 66. Ulster Univ BA90 MA98 TCD BTh93. CITC 90. **d** 93 **p** 94. C Bangor St Comgall *D & D* 93-96; C Bangor Primacy 93-96; Bp's C Belfast Whiterock *Conn* 96-99; R Donaghadee *D & D* from 99. *3 The Trees, New Road, Donaghadee BT21 0EJ* Tel (028) 9188 2594

GAMBLE, Norman Edward Charles. b 50. TCD BA72 HDipEd73 PhD78. CITC 76. **d** 79 **p** 80. C Bangor St Comgall *D & D* 79-83; I Dunleckney w Nurney, Lorum and Kiltennel *C & O* 83-90; Warden of Readers 84-90; P-in-c Leighlin w Grange Sylvae, Shankill etc 89-90; Can Leighlin Cathl 89-90; Preb Ossory Cathl 89-90; I Malahide w Balgriffin *D & G* from 90; Abp's Dom Chapl 95-03. *The Rectory, Church Road, Malahide, Co Dublin, Irish Republic* Tel (00353) (1) 845 4770 Fax as telephone E-mail norman_gamble@hotmail.com

GAMBLE, Canon Robin Philip. b 53. Oak Hill Th Coll 74. **d** 77 **p** 78. C Kildwick *Bradf* 77-78; C Laisterdyke 78-80; C York St Paul *York* 80-80; V Bradf St Aug Undercliffe *Bradf* 82-95; Dioc Adv in Evang 93-01; Can Ev Man Cathl *Man* from 01. *30 Rathen Road, Manchester M20 4GH* Tel 0161-446 1099 *or* 438 2834 E-mail robin.gamble1@virgin.net

GAMBLE, Ronald George. b 41. Cant Sch of Min 92. **d** 95 **p** 96. NSM Loose *Cant* 95-00; P-in-c Boxley w Detling from 00; Chapl NHS Ambulance Trust from 99. *The Vicarage, The Street, Boxley, Maidstone ME14 3DX* Tel (01622) 758606 Mobile 07712-562491 E-mail ron.gamble@talk21.com

GAMBLES, Una Beryl. b 33. Man Univ BEd78. St Chris Coll Blackheath 59. **d** 87 **p** 94. NSM Upton Priory *Ches* 87-01; Chapl Parkside Hosp *Ches* 87-93; Chapl E Cheshire NHS Trust 93-01; Chapl HM Pris Styal 94-98; Perm to Offic *Ches* from 01. *23 Grangelands, Upton, Macclesfield SK10 4AB* Tel (01625) 421691

GAMESTER, Sidney Peter. b 27. SS Coll Cam BA51 MA55. Oak Hill Th Coll 56. **d** 58 **p** 59. C Surbiton Hill Ch Ch *S'wark* 58-61; C Worthing H Trin *Chich* 61-69; R Silverhill St Matt 69-86; R

Bexhill St Mark 86-93; rtd 93; Perm to Offic *Chich* from 93. *18 Crofton Park Avenue, Bexhill-on-Sea TN39 3SE* Tel (01424) 842276

GAMMON, William Paul Lachlan. b 60. SS Hild & Bede Coll Dur BA82. St Steph Ho Ox 89. **d** 91 **p** 92. C Chalfont St Peter *Ox* 91-94; Lect Bolton St Pet *Man* 94-98; R Woodston *Ely* from 98; P-in-c Fletton from 98. *The Rectory, 2 Rectory Gardens, Peterborough PE2 8HN* Tel (01733) 562786

GANDIYA, Chad Nicholas. b 53. Nottm Univ BTh80 Univ of Zimbabwe MA84 Michigan State Univ MA95. St Jo Coll Nottm 77. **d** 80 **p** 81. C Avondale Zimbabwe 80-83; R Mabelreigh St Pet 83-85; Chapl Michigan Univ USA 86-87; Asst P Harare Cathl 88; Warden Bp Gaul Coll 88-91; USA 92-95; R Marlborough St Paul 95-96; Prin Bp Gaul Coll 96-01; Tutor United Coll of Ascension Selly Oak from 01. *1 Huddleston Way, Selly Oak, Birmingham B29 5AJ* Tel 0121-415 6829
E-mail c.gandiya@bham.ac.uk

GANDIYA, Leonard Farirayi (Lee). b 64. Colorado Coll 87 Boston Univ 90 MA92. Ridley Hall Cam 92. **d** 94 **p** 95. NSM Camberwell St Luke *S'wark* 94-95; C Lowestoft St Marg *Nor* 95-98; Dioc Rep for Black Anglican Concerns 96-98; CF from 98. *c/o MOD Chaplains (Army)* Tel (01980) 615804 Fax 615800

GANDON, Andrew James Robson. b 54. St Jo Coll Dur BA76. Ridley Hall Cam 76. **d** 78 **p** 79. C Aston SS Pet and Paul *Birm* 78-82; CMS 82-95; Zaïre 82-88; Kenya 89-94; V Harefield *Lon* from 95; Chapl R Brompton and Harefield NHS Trust from 95. *28 Countess Close, Harefield, Uxbridge UB9 6DL* Tel (01895) 825960 Fax 820705
E-mail andrew.gandon@london.anglican.org

GANDON, James Philip. b 31. ALCD56. **d** 56 **p** 57. C Westcliff St Mich *Chelmsf* 56-58; Canada from 58; rtd 92. *185 Jones Street, Goderich ON, Canada, N7A 3B5* Tel (001) (519) 524 9718
E-mail phil.gandon@odyssey.on.ca

GANDON, Percy James. b 22. ALCD53. **d** 53 **p** 54. C New Humberstone *Leic* 53-56; C Leic H Trin 56-57; Uganda 57-63; V Hoddesdon *St Alb* 63-83; RD Cheshunt 81-83; Perm to Offic *Nor* 83-85 and from 86; P-in-c Lyng w Sparham 85-86; rtd 87. *The Old Bakery, Hindolveston, Dereham NR20 5DF* Tel (01263) 861325

GANDY, Nicholas John. b 53. Westf Coll Lon BSc75 Reading Univ MSc76 Ex Coll Ox CertEd78 CBiol79 MIBiol. St Steph Ho Ox 86. **d** 88 **p** 89. C Crowthorne *Ox* 88-89; C Tilehurst St Mary 89-93; P-in-c Didcot St Pet 93-97; V from 97; V Brackley St Pet w St Jas *Pet* from 03; OGS from 96. *The Vicarage, Old Town, Brackley NN13 7BZ* Tel (01280) 702767
E-mail nicholas@ngandy.fsnet.co.uk

GANE, Canon Christopher Paul. b 33. Qu Coll Cam BA57 MA61. Ridley Hall Cam 57. **d** 59 **p** 60. C Rainham *Chelmsf* 59-62; C Farnborough *Guildf* 62-64; V Erith St Paul *Roch* 64-71; V Ipswich St Marg *St E* 71-88; Hon Can St E Cathl 82-98; R Hopton, Market Weston, Barningham etc 88-98; rtd 98. *25 The Croft, Bardwell, Bury St Edmunds IP31 1AN* Tel (01359) 251868

GANE, Nicholas. b 57. St Jo Coll Nottm 93. **d** 95 **p** 96. C Keynsham *B & W* 95-99; TV 99-02. *10 Ludlow Court, Willsbridge, Bristol BS30 6HB* E-mail nick.gane@virgin.net

GANGA, Jeremy Franklin. b 62. Cape Town Univ BSocSc86 Lon Bible Coll BA92 St Jo Coll Nottm MA93. Ridley Hall Cam 93. **d** 95 **p** 96. C St Peter-in-Thanet *Cant* 95-98; Chapl Felsted Sch 98-00; Past Chapl St Paul's Sch Barnes 00-02; NSM Fulham St Pet *Lon* 00-02; P-in-c from 02. *St Peter's Vicarage, St Peter's Terrace, London SW6 7JS* Tel (020) 7385 2045
E-mail jfg@ukgateway.net

GANJAVI, John Farhad. b 57. ACGI79 Imp Coll Lon BSc79. Ridley Hall Cam 79. **d** 82 **p** 83. C Yardley St Edburgha *Birm* 82-85; C Knowle 85-89; P-in-c Beaudesert and Henley-in-Arden w Ullenhall *Cov* 89-92; R from 92; RD Alcester 92-99. *The Rectory, Beaudesert Lane, Henley-in-Arden B95 5JY* Tel (01564) 792570

GANN, Canon Anthony Michael. b 37. TCD BA60 MA64 BD64. **d** 62 **p** 63. V Choral Derry Cathl *D & R* 62-66; Lesotho 66-74; Dioc Officer for Miss and Unity *Carl* 75-80; P-in-c Bampton and Mardale 75-80; TV Cen Telford *Lich* 80-89; P-in-c Wolvercote w Summertown *Ox* 89-02; RD Ox 95-99; rtd 02. *Avalon, 84 Pickersleigh Road, Malvern WR14 2RS* Tel (01684) 568114

GANN, John West. b 29. Ex Coll Ox BA55 MA59. Wells Th Coll 55. **d** 57 **p** 58. C Wendover *Ox* 57-59; C Walton St Mary *Liv* 59-62; R Didcot *Ox* 62-70; R Newbury St Nic 70-78; TR Newbury 73-78; V Twickenham St Mary *Lon* 78-87; Dir of Ords 81-87; TR Bridport *Sarum* 87-94; RD Lyme Bay 89-92; rtd 94; Perm to Offic *Glouc* from 94; *Bris* from 96. *Three Gables, Charlton Road, Tetbury GL8 8DX* Tel (01666) 503965
E-mail gann.jh@btopenworld.com

GANT, Canon Brian Leonard. b 45. Ox Univ MTh01. K Coll Lon 72. **d** 73 **p** 74. C Hillmorton *Cov* 73-75; C Cov St Geo 76; P-in-c Maldon St Mary *Chelmsf* 76-79; R Muthill *St And* 79-81; R Crieff 79-81; R Comrie 79-81; V Walsall St Paul *Lich* 81-84; Min Can Worc Cathl *Worc* 84-89; Chapl K Sch Worc 84-89; V Tunbridge Wells K Chas *Roch* 89-95; Hon Can Kumasi from 94; V Wymondham *Nor* 95-01; P-in-c York All SS N Street *York*

from 01; CME Officer York Adnry from 01. *1 Love Lane, York YO24 1FE* Tel (01904) 641729 E-mail brianlgant@aol.com

GANT, Peter Robert. b 38. BNC Ox BA60 MA64 G&C Coll Cam BA62 MA67. Ridley Hall Cam 61. **d** 63 **p** 64. C Portsea St Mary *Portsm* 63-67; V Blackheath *Birm* 67-73; Asst Master Harold Malley Gr Sch Solihull 73-75; Perm to Offic 73-75; Perm to Offic *Guildf* from 75; rtd 93. *8 Sandon Close, Esher KT10 8JE* Tel (020) 8398 5107

GANZ, Timothy Jon. b 36. ARCM63 Univ Coll Ox BA58 MA62. St Steph Ho Ox 58. **d** 61 **p** 62. C Shrewsbury H Cross *Lich* 61-65; Asst Chapl Hurstpierpoint Coll 65-69; Chapl 69-73; Chapl Univ of Wales (Swansea) *S & B* 74-75; P-in-c Hanley All SS *Lich* 75-80; TV Stoke-upon-Trent 80-81; V Tutbury from 81. *The Vicarage, Tutbury, Burton-on-Trent DE13 9JF* Tel (01283) 813127

GARBETT, Capt Phillip Ronald. b 52. CA Tr Coll CertRS80 EAMTC 95. **d** 97 **p** 98. CA from 80; C Ipswich St Mary at Stoke w St Pet and St Fran *St E* 97-00; TV Walton and Trimley from 00. *2 Blyford Way, Felixstowe IP11 2FW* Tel (01394) 213992 Mobile 07884-212218 E-mail philip.garbett@ntlworld.com

GARBUTT, Gerald. b 41. St Aid Birkenhead 65. **d** 67 **p** 68. C Stretford All SS *Man* 67-70; Lic to Offic 70-72; R Salford St Bart 72-74; V Lower Kersal 74-79; TR Bethnal Green St Jo w St Bart *Lon* 79-90; P-in-c Stepney St Pet w St Benet 85-87; Chapl Furness Gen Hosp 90-94; Chapl S Cumbria HA 90-94; Hosp Services Chapl Furness Hosps NHS Trust 94-98; Chapl Westmorland Hosps NHS Trust 94-98; Chapl Morecambe Bay Hosps NHS Trust from 98; rtd 03. *6 Dale Garth, Leece, Ulverston LA12 0QU* Tel (01229) 823852

GARBUTT, Mrs Mary Yvonne. b 45. Ripon Coll Cuddesdon 00. **d** 02 **p** 03. C Desborough, Brampton Ash, Dingley and Braybrooke *Pet* from 02. *134 Pioneer Avenue, Desborough, Kettering NN14 2PB* Tel (01536) 760651
E-mail revmgarbutt@aol.com

✠**GARCIA-MONTIEL, The Rt Revd Martiniano.** Bp Cuernavaca; Acting Primate of Mexico from 03. *Apartado Postal 538, Admon 4, CP 62431 Cuernavaca, Morelos, Mexico* Tel (0052) (73) 152870 Fax as telephone
E-mail diovca@giga.com.mx

GARDEN, Robert Andrew (Robin). b 26. MInstP58 FIMA72 Edin Univ BSc49 Kent Univ MA95. Cant Sch of Min 87. **d** 90 **p** 91. NSM Sandwich *Cant* 90-97; Chapl St Bart Hosp Sandwich 91-00; Perm to Offic *Cant* from 97. *Naini, 164 St George's Road, Sandwich CT13 9LD* Tel (01304) 612116

GARDINER, Anthony Reade. b 35. Univ of NZ BA59. Cuddesdon Coll 60. **d** 62 **p** 63. C Gosforth All SS *Newc* 62-65; New Zealand 65-93 and from 00; V Waikohu 65-69; V Edgecumbe 69-74; V Eltham 74-78; V Trentham 78-81; V Waipukurau 81-88; Chapl Nelson Cathl 88-92; C Highcliffe w Hinton Admiral *Win* 93-94; TV N Creedy *Ex* 94-00; rtd 00. *1 Puriri Street, Eastbourne, Wellington 6008, New Zealand* E-mail nantony2@paradise.net.nz

GARDINER, Charles Graham. b 18. AKC49. St Boniface Warminster. **d** 50 **p** 51. C Clapham H Trin *S'wark* 50-54; S Africa from 54. *55 Weltevreden Avenue, Rondebosch, 7700 South Africa* Tel (0027) (21) 689 1111

GARDINER, James Carlisle. b 18. St Jo Coll Dur LTh48. Tyndale Hall Bris. **d** 49 **p** 50. C Blackpool Ch Ch *Blackb* 49-52; C Rushen *S & M* 52-56; R Ditton *Roch* 56-83; rtd 83; Perm to Offic *Roch* from 83. *5 Larch Crescent, Tonbridge TN10 3NN* Tel (01732) 362323

GARDINER, Canon Kenneth Ashton. b 27. S'wark Ord Course 60. **d** 63 **p** 64. C Sydenham H Trin *S'wark* 63-67; C Macclesfield St Mich *Ches* 67-70; V Chatham St Phil and St Jas *Roch* 70-93; RD Roch 88-93; Hon Can Roch Cathl 88-93; Perm to Offic *Roch* from 93. *44 Trevale Road, Rochester ME1 3PA* Tel (01634) 844524 E-mail ken.gardiner@blueyonder.co.uk

GARDINER, Thomas Alfred. b 29. Chich Th Coll Dur BA52 MA56. Ridley Hall Cam 54. **d** 56 **p** 57. C Stockport St Geo *Ches* 56-60; Asst Chapl Brentwood Sch Essex 60-62; Chapl 62-88; R Greensted-juxta-Ongar w Stanford Rivers *Chelmsf* 88-00; rtd 00; Perm to Offic *St E* from 00. *Oakwood Cottage, The Street, Wenhaston, Halesworth IP19 9DP* Tel (01502) 478367

GARDINER, William Gerald Henry. b 46. Lon Univ BD72. Oak Hill Th Coll 68. **d** 72 **p** 73. C Beckenham St Jo *Roch* 72-75; C Cheadle *Ches* 75-81; P-in-c Swynnerton *Lich* 81-83; P-in-c Tittensor 81-83; R Swynnerton and Tittensor 83-86; V Westlands St Andr from 86; RD Newcastle from 97. *St Andrew's Vicarage, 50 Kingsway West, Westlands, Newcastle ST5 3PU* Tel (01782) 619594

GARDNER, Canon Anthony Brian. b 32. Lon Coll of Div 62. **d** 64 **p** 65. C Stoke *Cov* 64-68; R Whitnash 68-98; RD Leamington 78-79; RD Warwick and Leamington 79-87; Hon Can Cov Cathl 83-98; rtd 98; Perm to Offic *Cov* from 99. *4 Mark Antony Drive, Heathcote, Warwick CV34 6XA* Tel (01926) 832690

GARDNER, Christine. See GARDNER, Mary Christine

GARDNER, The Ven Clifton Gordon. b 15. Toronto Univ BA36 Lon Univ BD39 AKC39. **d** 39 **p** 40. C Maidenhead St Luke *Ox* 39-41 and 46-47; Chapl RNVR 41-46; V Furze Platt *Ox* 47-52; Canada 52-76; Can St Paul's Cathl Lon Ontario 64-74; Adn

Middx Ontario 74-76; Perm to Offic *Chelmsf* from 77. *1 Shepherd's Way, Saffron Walden CB10 2AH* Tel (01799) 527890

GARDNER, Clive Bruce. b 67. Selw Coll Cam BA89 MA92 Wycliffe Hall Ox BA93. **d** 96 **p** 97. C Beverley Minster *York* 96-98; Bp's Dom Chapl *Liv* 98-01; V Cumnor *Ox* from 01. *The Vicarage, 1 Abingdon Road, Cumnor, Oxford OX2 9QN* Tel (01865) 865402 Fax as telephone E-mail vicarofcumnor@tesco.net

GARDNER, David. b 57. Oak Hill Th Coll BA87. **d** 87 **p** 88. C Ogley Hay *Lich* 87-91; TV Mildenhall *St E* 91-98; P-in-c Woodbridge St Jo 98-00; V 00-03; P-in-c Bredfield 01-03; V Woodbridge St Jo and Bredfield from 03. *St John's Vicarage, St John's Hill, Woodbridge IP12 1HS* Tel (01394) 382083 *or* tel and fax 383162 E-mail stjohns.woodbridge@btinternet.com

GARDNER, Elizabeth Mary. b 47. Nottm Univ BA01. Trin Coll Bris 72 St Jo Coll Nottm 00. **d** 01 **p** 02. C Swindon Dorcan *Bris* from 01. *19 Nyland Road, Swindon SN3 3RJ* Tel (01793) 485287

GARDNER, Geoffrey Maurice. b 28. K Coll Lon BA51 Lon Inst of Educn PGCE52 Bris Univ DipEd74. Cranmer Hall Dur DipTh59. **d** 59 **p** 60. C Bowling St Jo *Bradf* 59-62; Nigeria 62-72; Hon C Bath St Luke *B & W* 72-73; Perm to Offic 73-90; and 94-99; NSM Bath Widcombe 90-94; rtd 94. *15 Bramley Gardens, Whimple, Exeter EX5 2SJ*

GARDNER, Helen Jane. b 39. Man Univ BSc61 PGCE62. WMMTC 93. **d** 96 **p** 97. NSM Stow on the Wold *Glouc* 96-00; NSM Stow on the Wold, Condicote and The Swells 00-03; NSM The Guitings, Cutsdean, Farmcote etc from 03. *6 St Marys Close, Lower Swell, Cheltenham GL54 1LJ* Tel (01451) 832553

GARDNER, Ian Douglas. b 34. St Pet Hall Ox BA58 MA62. Oak Hill Th Coll 58. **d** 60 **p** 61. C Biddulph *Lich* 60-63; C Weston St Jo *B & W* 64; Nigeria 65-76; P-in-c Hurstbourne Tarrant and Faccombe *Win* 77-79; V Hurstbourne Tarrant, Faccombe, Vernham Dean etc 79-85; R Nursling and Rownhams 85-99; rtd 99. *Wilderness Cottage, Haroldston Hill, Broad Haven, Haverfordwest SA62 3JP* Tel (01437) 781592

GARDNER, Mrs Jacqueline Anne. b 49. Cheltenham & Glouc Coll of HE DipApTh98. WEMTC 95. **d** 98 **p** 99. NSM Fairford and Kempsford w Whelford *Glouc* 98-02; NSM Cirencester from 02. *10 Park Street, Cirencester GL7 2BN* Tel (01285) 655505

GARDNER, Canon John Phillip Backhouse. b 21. St Aid Birkenhead 49. **d** 52 **p** 53. C Ashtead *Guildf* 52-55; C Bromley SS Pet and Paul *Roch* 55-57; V New Hythe 57-63; V Roch St Justus 63-69; R Wisley w Pyrford *Guildf* 70-87; RD Woking 82-87; Hon Can Guildf Cathl 86-87; rtd 87; Perm to Offic *Pet* from 87; *Guildf* from 98. *42 Godley Road, Byfleet, West Byfleet KT14 7ER* Tel (01932) 347431

GARDNER, Mrs Marian Elizabeth. b 50. Ripon Coll of Educn DipEd71. WMMTC 00. **d** 03. NSM Kirkleatham *York* from 03. *The Willows, 29 Newcomen Terrace, Redcar TS10 1DD* Tel (01642) 756933 Mobile 07736-350643 E-mail marian@thegardners.org.uk

GARDNER, Mark Douglas. b 58. TCD BA80 MA83 DipTh83. **d** 83 **p** 84. C Ballymacarrett St Patr *D & D* 83-87; C Belfast St Steph w St Luke *Conn* 87-89; C Hendon and Sunderland *Dur* 89-90; TV Sunderland 90-95; I Dublin Santry w Glasnevin and Finglas *D & G* 95-01; PV and Chapter Clerk Ch Ch Cathl Dublin from 96; Min Can St Patr Cathl Dublin 96; Treas V 96-01; Dean's V from 01. *24 Wainsfort Manor Crescent, Terenure, Dublin 6W, Irish Republic* Tel (00353) (1) 499 1571 Mobile 87-266 0228 E-mail markgardner@eircom.net

GARDNER, Mary Christine. b 42. SRN64 SCM66 Liv Univ HVCert71. St Jo Coll Nottm 80. **dss** 82 **d** 85 **p** 94. Ches St Paul *Ches* 82-84; Macclesfield St Mich 84-85; Macclesfield Team Par 85-87; Par Dn 87; Chapl Asst Nottm City Hosp 87-93; Chapl St Chris Hospice Lon 93-01; V Over St Jo *Ches* from 01. *St John's Vicarage, Delamere Street, Winsford CW7 2LY* Tel (01606) 594651

GARDNER, Michael Ronald. b 53. Wilson Carlile Coll Dip Evang86 Trin Coll Bris 95. **d** 97 **p** 98. CA 86-00; C Stanmore *Win* 97-01; V from 01. *St Luke's Vicarage, Mildmay Street, Winchester SO22 4BX* Tel (01962) 865240

GARDNER, Neil Kenneth. Univ of Wales (Swansea) BA92 Peterho Cam BA00 Univ of Wales (Cardiff) PhD01. Westcott Ho Cam 98. **d** 01 **p** 02. C Wisbech SS Pet and Paul *Ely* from 01; C Wisbech St Aug from 03. *The Rectory, Gorefield Road, Leverington, Wisbech PE13 5AS* Tel (01945) 581486 Mobile 07855-111794 E-mail neil@hmpleasure.freeserve.co.uk

GARDNER, The Ven Paul Douglas. b 50. K Coll Lon BA72 AKC72 Reformed Th Sem Mississippi MDiv79 SS Coll Cam PhD89. Ridley Hall Cam 79. **d** 80 **p** 81. C Cambridge St Martin *Ely* 80-83; Lect Oak Hill Th Coll 83-90; V Hartford *Ches* 90-03; RD Middlewich 94-99; Adn Ex from 03. *St Matthew's House, 45 Spicer Road, Exeter EX1 1TA* Tel (01392) 425432 Fax 425783 E-mail archdeacon.of.exeter@exeter.anglican.org

GARDNER, Richard Beverley Twynam. b 11. Chich Th Coll 33. **d** 36 **p** 37. C Gainsborough St Jo *Linc* 36-38; C Linc St Giles 38-39; C Horsell *Guildf* 39-42; Chapl RNVR 42-47; C York Town St Mich *Guildf* 47-48; V E Molesey St Paul 48-54; V Botleys and Lyne 54-71; V Long Cross 56-71; V Ewshott 71-76; rtd 76;

Perm to Offic *Guildf* 81-93. *16 Palace Gate, Odiham, Hook, Basingstoke RG29 1JZ* Tel (01256) 704563

GARDNER (née JAMES), Mrs Sandra Kay. b 66. Aston Tr Scheme 97 Westcott Ho Cam CTM99. **d** 99 **p** 00. C Whittlesey, Pondersbridge and Coates *Ely* 99-02; R Leverington from 02; V Southea w Murrow and Parson Drove from 02. *The Rectory, Gorefield Road, Leverington, Wisbech PE13 5AS* Tel (01945) 581486 E-mail sandra.gardner@ely.anglican.org

GARDNER, Stephen John. b 70. Southn Univ MEng92. St Jo Coll Nottm 00. **d** 02 **p** 03. C Brinsworth w Catcliffe and Treeton *Sheff* from 02. *58 Kynance Crescent, Brinsworth, Rotherham S60 5EW* Tel and fax (01709) 361901 Mobile 07740-200942 E-mail stephen@gardnerfamily.co.uk

GARDOM, Francis Douglas. b 34. Trin Coll Ox BA55 MA59. Wells Th Coll 58. **d** 60 **p** 61. C Greenwich St Alfege w St Pet *S'wark* 60-68; C Lewisham St Steph and St Mark 68-76; Hon C from 76. *79 Maze Hill, London SE10 8XQ* Tel (020) 8858 7052 *or* 8852 1474 E-mail francis_gardom@compuserve.com

GARDOM, James Theodore Douglas. b 61. St Anne's Coll Ox BA83 K Coll Lon PhD92. Ripon Coll Cuddesdon 88. **d** 90 **p** 91. C Witney *Ox* 90-92; Zimbabwe 92-97; Dean of Studies Bp Gaul Coll Harare 93-97; V Chesterton St Andr *Ely* from 97. *10 Lynfield Lane, Chesterton, Cambridge CB4 1DR* Tel (01223) 303469 Fax as telephone E-mail james.gardom@ely.anglican.org

GARLAND, Christopher John. b 47. Ex Univ BA69 PhD72. Qu Coll Birm 78. **d** 80 **p** 81. C Beckenham St Jas *Roch* 80-82; C Roch 82-84; Papua New Guinea 85-93; Australia 94-95; R Copford w Easthorpe and Messing w Inworth *Chelmsf* from 95. *The Vicarage, Kelvedon Road, Messing, Colchester CO5 9TN* Tel (01621) 815434 E-mail cngarland@fish.co.uk

GARLAND, Michael. b 50. St D Coll Lamp DipTh72 Sarum & Wells Th Coll 72. **d** 73 **p** 74. C Swansea St Thos and Kilvey *S & B* 73-76; C Boldmere *Birm* 76-79; V Kingshurst 79-88; P-in-c Curdworth w Castle Vale 88-90; R Curdworth 90-03; P-in-c Wishaw 99-00; V Charlton Kings St Mary *Glouc* from 03. *The Vicarage, 63 Church Street, Charlton Kings, Cheltenham GL53 8AT* Tel (01242) 253402 Mobile 07974-066929 E-mail michaelgarland@compuserve.com

GARLAND, Peter Stephen John. b 52. N Lon Poly Dip Librarianship 77 ALA79 Univ Coll Lon BA73 Univ of W Ontario MA74 Dur Univ PGCE75. Ripon Coll Cuddesdon 88. **d** 90 **p** 91. C Crookham *Guildf* 90-94; V Tongham 94-99; Chapl Farnborough Coll of Tech 94-99; V Spalding St Jo w Deeping St Nicholas *Linc* from 99. *St John's Vicarage, 66A Hawthorn Bank, Spalding PE11 1JQ* Tel (01775) 722816 Fax as telephone E-mail peter-garland@hotmail.com

GARLICK, Canon David. b 37. Nottm Univ BA62 Ox Univ DipPSA63. St Steph Ho Ox 62. **d** 64 **p** 65. C Kennington St Jo *S'wark* 64-66; Hon C Newington St Paul 66-68; P-in-c Vauxhall St Pet 68-79; V Lewisham St Mary from 79; RD E Lewisham 92-99; Hon Can S'wark Cathl from 93. *Lewisham Vicarage, 48 Lewisham Park, London SE13 6QZ* Tel and fax (020) 8690 2682 *or* 8690 1585 E-mail davidgarlick@smarysl.fsnet.co.uk

GARLICK, Dennis. b 26. ACIS. Qu Coll Birm. **d** 84 **p** 85. NSM Dronfield *Derby* 84-88; C 88-89; C-in-c Holmesfield 89-90; TV Dronfield w Holmesfield 90-93; rtd 93; Perm to Offic *Derby* from 93. *51 Holmesdale Road, Dronfield S18 2FA* Tel (01246) 418792

GARLICK, Preb Kathleen Beatrice. b 49. Leeds Univ BA71 Birm Univ PGCE72. Glouc Sch of Min 87. **d** 90 **p** 94. NSM Much Birch w Lt Birch, Much Dewchurch etc *Heref* 90-03; P-in-c from 03; Chapl Heref Sixth Form Coll 96-03; Preb Heref Cathl *Heref* from 99. *The Rectory, Birch Lodge, Much Birch, Hereford HR2 8HT* Tel (01981) 540666 Mobile 07812-995442 E-mail kaygarlick@hotmail.com

GARLICK, Canon Peter. b 34. AKC57. **d** 58 **p** 59. C Swindon All SS *Bris* 58-63; St Kitts-Nevis 63-66; V Heyside *Man* 66-73; R Stretford All SS 73-79; RD Wootton *Pet* 79-88; V Duston 79-91; TR Duston Team 91-94; Can Pet Cathl 85-94; rtd 94; Perm to Offic *Pet* from 94. *120 Worcester Close, Northampton NN3 9GD* Tel (01604) 416511

GARLICK, William Frederick. b 51. LNSM course 95. **d** 98 **p** 99. OLM Bermondsey St Jas w Ch Ch and St Crispin *S'wark* from 98. *6 Hannah Mary Way, London SE1 5QG* Tel (020) 7237 8326

GARNER, Alistair Ross. b 58. Pemb Coll Ox BA81 MA86. St Jo Coll Nottm Dip Th Studies 92. **d** 92 **p** 93. C Ashton-upon-Mersey St Mary *Ches* 92-96; P-in-c Bredbury St Mark 96-01; V from 01. *St Mark's Vicarage, 61 George Lane, Bredbury, Stockport SK6 1AT* Tel 0161-406 6552 E-mail revrossgarner@hotmail.com

GARNER, Canon Carl. b 42. Rhodes Univ BA62 Keble Coll Ox BA65 MA70. St Paul's Coll Grahamstown 66. **d** 67 **p** 68. S Africa 67-84; Dioc Missr *St Alb* 84-98; Can Res St Alb 84-98; P-in-c Digswell and Panshanger from 98; Hon Can St Alb from 99; RD Welwyn Hatfield from 01. *354 Knightsfield, Welwyn Garden City AL8 7NG* Tel (01707) 326677 E-mail carl@stjohnsdigswell.freeserve.co.uk

GARNER, David Henry. b 40. Trin Coll Bris 70. **d** 73 **p** 74. C Tunstead *Man* 73-75; C Fazeley *Lich* 76-78; V Sparkhill St Jo *Birm* 78-85; V Blackheath 85-01; Deanery P Warley Deanery from 01. *94 Honeybourne Road, Halesowen B63 3HD* Tel 0121-550 2498 E-mail david.h.garner@btinternet.com

GARNER, Geoffrey Walter. b 40. Ripon Hall Ox 69. **d** 71 **p** 72. C Stoke *Cov* 71-76; V Tile Hill 76-80; TV Hackney *Lon* 80-89; R Bow w Bromley St Leon from 89. *16 Tomlins Grove, London E3 4NX* Tel (020) 8981 6710

GARNER, John. d 03. OLM Kirkdale St Lawr *Liv* from 03. *Address temp unknown*

GARNER, John Howard. b 45. Univ of Wales (Swansea) BSc67 Univ of Wales (Ban) PhD75. Moorlands Bible Coll DPS91 SW Minl Tr Course 95. **d** 98 **p** 99. NSM Upton *Ex* from 98. *Highgrove Lodge, Sunbury Hill, Upton, Torquay TQ1 3ED* Tel (01803) 293640 E-mail johngarner@onetel.net.uk

GARNER, Martin Wyatt. b 39. Lon Coll of Div 60 Tyndale Hall Bris 63 Sarum Th Coll 66. **d** 66 **p** 67. C Coleraine *Conn* 66-70; C Cambridge St Martin *Ely* 70-72; V Edge Hill St Nath *Liv* 72-80; P-in-c Burton in Kendal *Carl* 80-87; R Burghclere w Newtown and Ecchinswell w Sydmonton *Win* 87-93; R Ewelme, Brightwell Baldwin, Cuxham w Easington *Ox* from 93. *The Rectory, Ewelme, Wallingford OX10 6HP* Tel (01491) 837823

GARNER, Canon Peter. b 35. Lon Univ BSc56 Leeds Univ MEd91. Wycliffe Hall Ox 56. **d** 58 **p** 59. C Walthamstow St Jo *Chelmsf* 58-61; V Hainault 61-70; R Theydon Garnon 70-73; P-in-c Kirby-le-Soken 73-74; V 74-82; P-in-c Fountains *Ripon* 82-88; P-in-c Kirkby Malzeard w Grewelthorpe and Mickley etc 82-88; Par Development Adv 88-93; P-in-c Birstwith 91-93; R Walkingham Hill 93-01; Hon Can Ripon Cathl 99-01; rtd 01. *Laver House, 29 Hell Wath Grove, Ripon HG4 2JT* Tel (01765) 601543 E-mail petergarner@laverhouse.sagehost.co.uk

GARNER, Roderick George. b 48. Lon Univ BA87 Hull Univ MPhil96 Man Univ PhD01 Birm Univ DipTh77 MCIPD75. Qu Coll Birm 75. **d** 78 **p** 79. C Tranmere St Paul w St Luke *Ches* 78-81; V Eccleston St Thos *Liv* 81-90; P-in-c Sculcoates St Paul w Ch Ch and St Silas *York* 90-95; Lay Tr Officer (E Riding Adnry) 90-95; P-in-c Southport H Trin *Liv* 95-96; V from 96; Dioc Th Consultant from 95. *24 Roe Lane, Southport PR9 9DX* Tel (01704) 538560 Fax and telephone E-mail anglican@garner.freeserve.co.uk

GARNER, Ross. See CASTLER, Alistair Ross

GARNER, Canon Thomas Richard. b 43. K Coll Lon. **d** 69 **p** 70. C Tynemouth Ch Ch *Newc* 69-73; C Fenham St Jas and St Basil 73-76; V Hamstead St Bernard *Birm* 76-80; New Zealand from 80; Can Wellington from 96. *1/109 Hill Street, Thorndon, Wellington, New Zealand* Tel (0064) (4) 473 3511 *or* 472 0286

GARNETT, The Ven David Christopher. b 45. Nottm Univ BA67 Fitzw Coll Cam BA69 MA73. Westcott Ho Cam 67. **d** 69 **p** 70. C Cottingham *York* 69-72; Chapl Selw Coll Cam 72-77; P-in-c Patterdale *Carl* 77-80; Dir of Ords 78-80; V Heald Green St Cath *Ches* 80-87; R Christleton 87-92; TR Ellesmere Port 92-96; Adn Chesterfield *Derby* from 96; Hon Can Derby Cathl from 96. *The Old Parsonage, Church Street, Baslow, Bakewell DE45 1RY* Tel (01246) 583928 Fax 583949 E-mail davidcgarnett@yahoo.co.uk

GARNETT, James Arthur. b 42. N Ord Course 77. **d** 80 **p** 81. C Kirkby *Liv* 80-91; P-in-c Liv St Phil w St Dav from 91. *The Vicarage, 55 Sheil Road, Liverpool L6 3AD* Tel 0151-263 6202

GARNETT, Preb Ralph Henry. b 28. Cuddesdon Coll 58. **d** 60 **p** 61. C Broseley w Benthall *Heref* 60-64; V Leintwardine 64-69; P-in-c Downton w Burrington and Aston and Elton 66-69; RD Ludlow 72-75; R Burford II w Greete and Hope Bagot 69-87; R Burford III w Lt Heref 69-87; P-in-c Burford I 72-74; R 74-87; V Tenbury 69-74; TR 74-87; Preb Heref Cathl 82-93; P-in-c Fownhope 87-93; P-in-c Brockhampton w Fawley 87-93; RD Heref Rural 92-93; rtd 93; Perm to Offic *Heref* from 93. *5 Hampton Manor Close, Hereford HR1 1TG* Tel (01432) 274985

GARNETT, Roger James. b 58. Dur Univ BA79. Wycliffe Hall Ox 89. **d** 91 **p** 92. C Forest Gate St Sav w W Ham St Matt *Chelmsf* 91-94; C Collier Row St Jas and Havering-atte-Bower 94-02; V from 02. *St James Vicarage, 24 Lower Bedfords Road, Romford RM1 4DG* Tel (01708) 749891 E-mail rogergarnett@hotmail.com

GARNSEY, George Christopher. b 36. Qu Coll Ox BA63. **d** 60 **p** 60. Lic to Offic *Wakef* 78-79; C Lupset 80; Australia from 80; Prin St Jo Coll Morpeth 80-91; R Gresford w Paterson 93-01; rtd 01; Lect St Jo Coll Morpeth from 01. *17 James Street, Morpeth, NSW, Australia 2321* Tel (0061) (2) 4934 2658 Fax 4921 6898 E-mail jan@arch.newcastle.edu.au

GARRARD, Mrs Christine Ann. b 51. LCST75 Open Univ BA86. EAMTC 87. **d** 90 **p** 94. Par Dn Kesgrave *St E* 90-94; C 94-96; V Ipswich All Hallows 96-02; R Higham, Holton St Mary, Raydon and Stratford from 02; Asst Dioc Dir of Ords from 03. *The Rectory, School Lane, Stratford St Mary, Colchester CO7 6LZ* Tel (01206) 322537 E-mail revdchris@aol.com

GARRARD, James Richard. b 65. Dur Univ BA88 Keble Coll Ox DPhil92 Leeds Univ MA01. Westcott Ho Cam CTM94. **d** 94 **p** 95. C Elland *Wakef* 94-97; TV Brighouse and Clifton 98-01; P-in-c Balderstone *Blackb* from 01; Warden of Readers from 01. *The Vicarage, Commons Lane, Balderstone, Blackburn BB2 7LL* Tel (01254) 812232 E-mail jamesgarrard@4-mat.net

GARRARD, Nicholas James Havelock. b 62. Leeds Univ BA83. Westcott Ho Cam 86. **d** 88 **p** 89. C Scotforth *Blackb* 88-91; C Eaton *Nor* 91-95; V Heigham St Thos from 95; RD Nor S from 03. *St Thomas's Vicarage, 77 Edinburgh Road, Norwich NR2 3RL* Tel (01603) 624390 E-mail nickgarr39@aol.com

✠**GARRARD, The Rt Revd Richard.** b 37. K Coll Lon BD60 AKC60. **d** 61 **p** 62 **c** 94. C Woolwich St Mary w H Trin *S'wark* 61-66; C Cambridge Gt St Mary w St Mich *Ely* 66-68; Chapl Keswick Hall Coll of Educn 68-74; Prin Wilson Carlile Coll of Evang 74-79; Can Res and Chan S'wark Cathl *S'wark* 79-87; Dir of Tr 79-87; Can Res St E Cathl *St E* 87-94; Dioc Adv for CME 87-91; Adn Sudbury 91-94; Suff Bp Penrith *Carl* 94-01; Hon Can Carl Cathl 94-01; Abp's Rep H See and Dir Angl Cen Rome 01-03; Hon Asst Bp Eur from 01; rtd 03. *26 Carol Close, Stoke Holy Cross, Norwich NR14 8NN* Tel (01508) 494165

GARRATT, Bernard John. b 43. Lon Univ BA65 Linacre Coll Ox BA67 MA71. St Steph Ho Ox 65. **d** 68 **p** 69. C Notting Hill St Jo *Lon* 68-71; C Fareham SS Pet and Paul *Portsm* 71-73; Chapl City of Lon Poly *Lon* 73-79; R Trowbridge H Trin *Sarum* 79-81; TR 81-87; V Wootton Bassett from 87; RD Calne 88-90. *The Vicarage, Glebe Road, Wootton Bassett, Swindon SN4 7DU* Tel (01793) 854302 *or* tel and fax 853272 E-mail st-barts@telinco.co.uk

GARRATT, David. b 43. AKC68. **d** 69 **p** 70. C Nottingham St Andr *S'well* 69-71; C Boughton 71-75; C Esh *Dur* 75-79; V Hamsteels 75-79; V Woodborough *S'well* 79-90; C Daybrook 90-91; Perm to Offic *Dur* from 92. *7 Thomas Street, Sacriston, Durham DH7 6NG* Tel 0191-371 1695

GARRATT, John William. b 11. **d** 78 **p** 78. Hon C Hounslow H Trin *Lon* 78-88; Hon C Hounslow H Trin w St Paul 88-94; Perm to Offic 94-99. *Flat 25, Smoothfield, 130 Hibernia Road, Hounslow TW3 3RJ* Tel (020) 8570 6009

GARRATT, Malcolm John. b 52. Nottm Univ BSc73. Trin Coll Bris DipHE99. **d** 99 **p** 00. C Bawtry w Austerfield and Misson *S'well* 99-00; C Hucknall Torkard 00-03; P-in-c Clipstone from 03. *The Vicarage, Church Road, Clipstone, Mansfield NG21 9DG* Tel (01623) 623916 Fax as telephone E-mail malcolm@2garratts.freeserve.co.uk

GARRATT, Peter James. b 37. ALCD64. **d** 64 **p** 65. C Bingham *S'well* 64-67; C Mansfield St Pet 67-69; V Purlwell *Wakef* 69-73; R Kirk Sandall and Edenthorpe *Sheff* 73-82; R Whippingham w E Cowes *Portsm* 82-87; V Soberton w Newtown 87-01; rtd 02; Perm to Offic *Portsm* from 02. *35 Fair Isle Close, Fareham PO14 3RT* Tel (01329) 661162

GARRATT, Roger Charles. b 50. St Jo Coll Dur BA72. Cranmer Hall Dur 72. **d** 74 **p** 75. C Leamington Priors St Paul *Cov* 74-77; Chapl Emscote Lawn Sch Warw 77-00; Chapl and Dep Hd Arden Lawn Sch 77-00; TV Warwick *Cov* 02-03; TV Warwick from 03. *St Nicholas' Vicarage, 184 Myton Road, Warwick CV34 6PS* Tel (01926) 492997 E-mail roger.garratt@btopenworld.com

GARRATT, Ms Celia Joy. b 60. RGN81 RM85. Cant Sch of Min 92. **d** 95. C S Ashford St Fran *Cant* 95-98; NSM from 98. *Address withheld by request*

GARRETT, Christopher Hugh Ahlan. b 35. Sarum & Wells Th Coll 72. **d** 75 **p** 76. C Addiscombe St Mildred *Cant* 75-81; V Thornton Heath St Jude w St Aid *S'wark* 81-00; rtd 00; Perm to Offic *Glouc* from 01. *Edge View, 18 Gloucester Road, Painswick GL6 6RA* Tel (01452) 813688

GARRETT, Clive Robert. b 54. Sheff Univ BA75 PhD80 Ex Univ PGCE88. St Jo Coll Nottm MA98. **d** 98 **p** 99. C Bath Weston St Jo w Kelston *B & W* 98-02; R from 02. *The Rectory, 8 Ashley Avenue, Bath BA1 3DR* Tel (01225) 427206 E-mail crg@cix.co.uk

GARRETT, Miss Elizabeth Clare. b 46. Trin Coll Bris. **d** 94 **p** 95. C Ewyas Harold w Dulas, Kenderchurch etc *Heref* 94-96; C Tupsley w Hampton Bishop 96-00; TV Uttoxeter Area *Lich* from 00. *The New Vicarage, Uttoxeter Road, Checkley, Stoke-on-Trent ST10 4NB* Tel (01538) 722732 E-mail claregarrett@aol.com

GARRETT, Geoffrey David. b 57. Oak Hill Th Coll 83. **d** 86 **p** 87. C Trentham *Lich* 86-90; V Rhodes *Man* 90-00; P-in-c Bardsley from 00. *The Vicarage, Byrth Road, Oldham OL8 2TJ* Tel 0161-624 9004 E-mail garretts@tinyworld.co.uk

GARRETT, Ian Lee. b 60. MCSP Dip Physiotherapy 81. Sarum & Wells Th Coll 86. **d** 89 **p** 90. C Maidstone St Martin *Cant* 89-95; P-in-c S Ashford St Fran from 95. *St Francis House, Cryol Road, Ashford TN23 5AS* Tel (01233) 625555

GARRETT, John Watkins. b 09. St Chad's Coll Dur BA35 LTh36. **d** 36 **p** 37. C Leic St Mary *Leic* 36-38; C Win H Trin *Win* 38-42; C Staveley *Derby* 42-44; C Derby St Barn 44-48; R Aylestone Park *Leic* 48-59; Chapl Carlton Hayes Psychiatric Hosp Narborough 54-90; R Narborough 75; rtd 75; Lic to Offic *Leic* 75-81; Perm to Offic 81-95. *4 Walcot Lane, Folkingham, Sleaford NG34 0TP* Tel (01529) 497385

GARRETT, Kevin George. b 48. Oak Hill Th Coll BA86. **d** 86 **p** 87. C Hoddesdon *St Alb* 86-89; C Loughton St Mary and St Mich *Chelmsf* 89-90; TV 90-95; P-in-c Loughton St Mich 95-96; Public Preacher 97; V Dover St Martin *Cant* from 97.

St Martin's Vicarage, 339 Folkestone Road, Dover CT17 9JG Tel (01304) 205391 E-mail k.garrett@tesco.net

GARRETT, Timothy Michael. b 70. Univ of Wales (Abth) BA91. Wycliffe Hall Ox BA01. d 02. C Ox St Andr *Ox* from 02. *5 Squitchey Lane, Oxford OX2 7LD* Tel (01865) 553944 E-mail tim.garrett@standrewsoxford.org.uk

GARROD, Mrs Christine Anne. b 49. EAMTC. d 00 p 01. C N w S Wootton *Nor* from 00. *Ambleside, 34 Castle Rising Road, South Wootton, King's Lynn PE30 3JB* Tel (01553) 674632

GARROW, Alan John Philip. b 67. Lon Bible Coll BA90 Wycliffe Hall Ox MPhil94 Jes Coll Ox DPhil00. d 93 p 94. C Waltham H Cross *Chelmsf* 93-97; C Akeman *Ox* from 00; Tutor St Alb and Ox Min Course from 00. *The Rectory, Troy Lane, Kirtlington OX5 3HA* Tel (01869) 350224 E-mail alan_garrow@lineone.net

GARRUD, Christopher Charles. b 54. Cranmer Hall Dur DipTh84. d 85 p 86. C Watford *St Alb* 85-89; C Ireland Wood *Ripon* 89-95; Chapl Cookridge Hosp Leeds 93-95; R Farnley 95-02. *Address temp unknown*

GARSIDE, Canon Howard. b 24. Leeds Univ BA49. Coll of Resurr Mirfield 49. d 51 p 52. C Barnsley St Pet *Wakef* 51-53; C Linthorpe *York* 53-56; V Middlesbrough St Aid 56-64; V Manston *Ripon* 64-78; RD Whitkirk 70-78; Hon Can Ripon Cathl 78-89; V Harrogate St Wilfrid 78-80; P-in-c Harrogate St Luke 78-80; V Harrogate St Wilfrid and St Luke 80-89; RD Harrogate 83-88; rtd 89; Perm to Offic *Ripon* from 89. *73 Kirkby Road, Ripon HG4 2HH* Tel (01765) 690625

GARSIDE, Melvin. b 42. N Ord Course 85. d 88 p 89. C Lindley *Wakef* 88-91; C Shelf *Bradf* 91-93; V Lundwood *Wakef* 93-97; V Hanging Heaton 97-01; V Woodhouse from 01; Bp's Adv in Racial Justice from 01. *The Vicarage, 43 Ashbrow Road, Huddersfield HD2 1DX* Tel and fax (01484) 424669 Mobile 07803-250258 E-mail melgarside@melgarside.demon.co.uk

GARTLAND, Christopher Michael. b 49. Man Univ BA78 Sheff Univ Dip Psychotherapy 92 Leeds Univ MEd99. Coll of Resurr Mirfield 82. d 84 p 85. C Almondbury w Farnley Tyas *Wakef* 84-87; P-in-c Upperthong 87-89; TV Upper Holme Valley 89-91; Chapl Stanley Royd Hosp Wakef 91-94; Chapl Wakef HA (Mental Health Services) 91-95; Chapl Wakef and Pontefract Community NHS Trust from 95. *Fieldhead Hospital, Ouchthorpe Lane, Wakefield WF1 3SP* Tel (01924) 327498

GARTON, Mrs Anne-Marie. b 48. BA MSW CQSW. d 02. NSM Caterham *S'wark* from 02. *51 Crescent Road, Caterham CR3 6LH* Tel (01883) 343188 E-mail anne-marie@garton.com *or* anne-marie.garton@dswark.org.uk

GARTON, Derek John. b 33. ALCD59. d 59 p 60. C Bromley Common St Aug *Roch* 59-62; C Gravesend St Aid 62-64; Chapl Gordon High Sch Gravesend 64-73; Lic to Offic *Roch* 73-74; Chapl Plymouth Coll 74-82; Australia from 83; R Cann River 89-92; R Boolara w Yinnar 92-94; rtd 98. *PO Box 12, L/48 Baillieu Street, Wonthaggi, Vic, Australia 3995* Tel (0061) (3) 5672 1746

GARTON, Capt Jeremy. b 56. Wilson Carlile Coll 78 SEITE 94. d 96 p 97. C Clapham TM *S'wark* 96-00; P-in-c Caterham Valley from 00. *St John's Vicarage, 51 Crescent Road, Caterham CR3 6LH* Tel (01883) 343188 Fax (020) 7544 7320 E-mail jerry@garton.com

✠**GARTON, The Rt Revd John Henry.** b 41. Worc Coll Ox BA67 MA DipTh67. Cuddesdon Coll 67. d 69 p 70 c 96. CF 69-73; Lect Linc Th Coll 73-78; TR Cov E *Cov* 78-86; Prin Ripon Coll Cuddesdon 86-96; V Cuddesdon *Ox* 86-96; Hon Can Worc Cathl *Worc* 87-96; Suff Bp Plymouth *Ex* from 96. *31 Riverside Walk, Tamerton Foliot, Plymouth PL5 4AQ* Tel (01752) 769836 Fax 769818 E-mail bishopofplymouth@aol.com

GARTSIDE, Philip Oswin. b 60. Pemb Coll Ox BA82 MA86 Leeds Univ BA92. Coll of Resurr Mirfield 93. d 93 p 94. C Walton-on-the-Hill *Liv* 93-97; CR from 97. *House of the Resurrection, Stocks Bank Road, Mirfield WF14 0BN* Tel (01924) 483327

GARVIE, Mrs Anna-Lisa Karen. b 48. Luton Univ BA96. St Alb Minl Tr Scheme 89. d 96 p 97. NSM Caddington *St Alb* 96-99; NSM St Paul's Walden 99-01; Chapl Chelsea and Westmr Healthcare NHS Trust 98-01; Co-ord Chapl Hinchingbrooke Health Care NHS Trust from 01. *Hinchingbrooke Hospital, Hinchingbrooke Park, Huntingdon PE18 8NT* Tel (01480) 416416 E-mail anna.garvie@hinchingbrooke.nhs.uk

GARWOOD, Simon Frederick. b 62. Reading Univ BA85 Lon Univ PGCE93 Birm Univ BD99. Qu Coll Birm MA00. d 00 p 01. C Chelmsf All SS *Chelmsf* from 00. *80 Swiss Avenue, Chelmsford CM1 2AE* Tel (01245) 494145 E-mail simonliz@fish.co.uk

GASCOIGNE, Philip. b 27. Oak Hill Th Coll. d 62 p 63. C Blackpool Ch Ch *Blackb* 62-65; V Bootle St Leon *Liv* 65-71; Staff Evang CPAS 71-74; V St Helens St Mark *Liv* 74-77; V Blackpool Ch Ch *Blackb* 77-81; V Blackpool Ch Ch w All SS 81-97; rtd 98; Perm to Offic *Blackb* from 98. *6 King's Close, Staining, Blackpool FY3 0EJ* Tel (01253) 890045

GASH, Christopher Alan Ronald. b 39. St Andr Univ 57 Nottm Univ CPTS. EMMTC 83. d 86 p 87. C Thurmaston *Leic* 86-89; P-in-c Stoke Golding w Dadlington 89-01; rtd 01; Perm to Offic

Cov 01-03 and *Sarum* from 03. *The Vicarage, High Street, Seend, Melksham SN12 6NR*

GASH, Canon Wilfred John. b 31. Lon Univ DipTh62. St Aid Birkenhead 60. d 62 p 63. C St Mary Cray and St Paul's Cray *Roch* 62-65; C Bexley St Jo 65-67; R Levenshulme St Pet *Man* 67-72; V Clifton 72-94; AD Eccles 81-87; Hon Can Man Cathl 86-97; P-in-c Pendlebury Ch Ch 86-87; P-in-c Pendlebury St Aug 86-87; Dioc Adv on Evang 89-97; TR Bolton St Paul w Em 94-96; C Urmston 96-97; rtd 98; Perm to Offic *Ches* from 98. *79 Birkenhead, Meols, Wirral CH47 5AG* Tel 0151-632 2506

GASKELL, David. b 48. Lon Univ BD76. Trin Coll Bris 72. d 76 p 77. C Eccleston Ch Ch *Liv* 76-80; C Rainhill 80-83; V Over Darwen St Jas *Blackb* 83-88; V Livesey 88-95; V Preston St Cuth 95-01; V Copp w Inskip from 01. *St Peter's Vicarage, Preston Road, Inskip, Preston PR4 0TT* Tel (01772) 690316

GASKELL, Canon Ian Michael. b 51. Nottm Univ BTh81. Linc Th Coll 77. d 81 p 82. C Wakef St Jo *Wakef* 81-83; Ind Chapl *Sheff* 83-86; V Cleckheaton St Luke and Whitechapel *Wakef* 86-93; V Birkenshaw w Hunsworth 93-98; RD Birstall 96-98; Can Res Wakef Cathl from 98; Dioc Soc Resp Adv from 98. *2 Elm Grove, Horbury, Wakefield WF4 5EP* Tel (01924) 315110 *or* 371802 Fax 315114 *or* 364834 E-mail ian.gaskell@wakefield.anglican.org

GASKELL, Preb John Bernard. b 28. Jes Coll Ox BA52 MA58. Chich Th Coll 59. d 60 p 61. C Beckenham St Jas *Roch* 60-64; C St Marylebone All SS *Lon* 64-68; C-in-c Grosvenor Chpl 68-79; Warden Liddon Ho Lon 68-79; V Holborn St Alb w Saffron Hill St Pet *Lon* 79-93; AD S Camden 81-86; Preb St Paul's Cathl 85-93; rtd 93; Perm to Offic *Lon* 93-96. *8 Margaret Street, London W1N 7LG* Tel (020) 7436 3287

GASKELL, Marion Ingrid. b 52. Wilson Carlile Coll 74 N Ord Course 96. d 99 p 00. C Thorpe Edge *Bradf* 99-02; TV Shelf St Mich w Buttershaw St Aid from 02. *8 Redwing Drive, Bradford BD6 3YD* Tel (01274) 817978

GASKELL, Mary. b 50. Nottm Univ BTh81 Bradf and Ilkley Coll CertEd89. Linc Th Coll 77. dss 81 d 89 p 94. Wakef St Jo *Wakef* 81-83; NSM Cleckheaton St Luke and Whitechapel 89-93; NSM Birkenshaw w Hunsworth 93-95; Asst Chapl St Jas Univ Hosp NHS Trust Leeds 95-97; Chapl Rishworth Sch Ripponden 97-99; P-in-c Purlwell *Wakef* 00-01; Chapl Dewsbury Health Care NHS Trust 01-02; Chapl Mid Yorks Hosps NHS Trust from 02. *2 Elm Grove, Horbury, Wakefield WF4 5EP* Tel (01924) 315110 Fax 315114

GASKELL, Peter John. b 70. d 03. NSM Poulton Lancelyn H Trin *Ches* from 03. *Address temp unknown*

GASPER (née COHEN), Mrs Janet Elizabeth. b 47. Birm Univ CertEd70. WMMTC 93. d 96 p 97. NSM Leominster *Heref* 96-99; Hon Chapl RAF 97-01; C Letton w Staunton, Byford, Mansel Gamage etc *Heref* 99-01; R Baxterley w Hurley and Wood End and Merevale etc from 01. *The Rectory, Dexter Lane, Hurley, Atherstone CV9 2JQ* Tel (01827) 874252 E-mail mgasper1@hotmail.com

GASTON, Raymond Gordon. b 62. Leeds Univ BA94. Linc Th Coll MTh94. d 96 p 97. C Leeds Gipton Epiphany *Ripon* 96-99; V Leeds St Marg and All Hallows from 99. *All Hallows Vicarage, 24 Regent Terrace, Leeds LS6 1NP* Tel 0113-242 2205 E-mail raymoira@gn.apc.org

GATENBY, Canon Denis William. b 31. Ex Coll Ox BA54 DipTh55 MA58 Man Univ DSPT82. Wycliffe Hall Ox 54. d 56 p 57. C Deane *Man* 56-60; C Bradf Cathl *Bradf* 60-63; V Bootle St Matt *Liv* 63-72; V Horwich H Trin *Man* 72-84; TR Horwich 84-93; TR Horwich and Rivington 93-99; Hon Can Man Cathl 91-99; AD Deane 87-98; rtd 99; Perm to Offic *Man* from 00. *10 Parkgate Drive, Bolton BL1 8SD* Tel (01204) 592290

GATENBY, Paul Richard. b 32. Dur Univ BA55. Qu Coll Birm DipTh64. d 64 p 65. C Wellingborough St Barn *Pet* 64-68; V Braunston w Brooke 68-71; C Langley Marish *Ox* 71-72; TV Basildon St Martin w H Cross and Laindon *Chelmsf* 73-76; R Isham w Pytchley *Pet* 77-97; rtd 97; Perm to Offic *Pet* from 98. *8 Ivy Lane, Finedon, Wellingborough NN9 5NE* Tel (01933) 398819 E-mail paul.gatenby@ntlworld.com

GATENBY, Simon John Taylor. b 62. Nottm Univ BA83. St Jo Coll Nottm 84. d 87 p 88. C Haughton St Mary *Man* 87-90; C Newburn *Newc* 90-93; P-in-c Brunswick *Man* 93-96; R from 96; AD Hulme from 99. *The Rectory, Hartfield Close, Brunswick, Manchester M13 9YX* Tel 0161-273 2470 E-mail simon@brunswickchurch.freeserve.co.uk

GATES, Alan Raymond. b 46. EAMTC 98. d 01 p 02. NSM W w E Mersea *Chelmsf* from 01; NSM Peldon w Gt and Lt Wigborough from 01. *Levade, 121 High Road, Layer-de-la-Haye, Colchester CO2 0EA* Tel (01206) 734338 Mobile 07974-020379 E-mail agates@messages.co.uk

GATES, John Michael. b 35. Dur Univ BA56 DipTh60. Cranmer Hall Dur 58. d 60 p 61. C Felixstowe St Jo *St E* 60-67; R Boyton w Capel St Andrew and Hollesley 67-98; P-in-c Shottisham w Sutton 87-92; rtd 98. *9 Foxgrove Lane, Felixstowe IP11 7JS* Tel (01394) 276886

GATES, Richard James. b 46. BA85. Oak Hill Th Coll 82. d 85 p 86. C Heald Green St Cath *Ches* 85-89; V Norton 89-98; V

Bunbury and Tilstone Fearnall from 98. *The Vicarage, Vicarage Lane, Bunbury, Tarporley CW6 9PE* Tel (01829) 260991 Mobile 07715-178750 E-mail rick@prayer.fsnet.co.uk

GATES, Simon Philip. b 60. St Andr Univ MA82. Cranmer Hall Dur BA86. **d** 87 **p** 88. C Southall Green St Jo *Lon* 87-91; Hong Kong 91-95; V Clapham Park St Steph *S'wark* from 96. *The Vicarage, 2 Thornton Road, London SW12 0JU* Tel (020) 8671 8276 E-mail sgates2207@aol.com

GATFORD, The Ven Ian. b 40. AKC65. **d** 67 **p** 68. C Clifton w Glapton *S'well* 67-71; R 71-75; V Sherwood 75-84; Can Res Derby Cathl *Derby* 84-93; Adn Derby from 93; Hon Can Derby Cathl from 93. *1 Thatch Close, Derby DE22 1EA* Tel (01332) 553455 *or* 382233 Fax 552322 *or* 292969 E-mail archderby@talk21.com

GATHERCOLE, The Ven John Robert. b 37. Fitzw Ho Cam BA59 MA63. Ridley Hall Cam 59. **d** 62 **p** 63. C Dur St Nic *Dur* 62-66; C Croxdale 66-69; Bp's Soc and Ind Adv 66-69; Ind Chapl *Worc* 69-87; RD Bromsgrove 77-85; Sen Chapl Worcs Ind Miss 85-01; Hon Can Worc Cathl 80-01; Adn Dudley 87-01; rtd 01; Perm to Offic *Worc* from 01. *Wisteria Cottage, Main Road, Ombersley, Droitwich WR9 0EL* Tel (01905) 620263

GATISS, Lee. b 72. New Coll Ox BA96. Oak Hill Th Coll BA00. **d** 01 **p** 02. C Barton Seagrave w Warkton *Pet* from 01. *Rectory Cottage, St Botolph's Road, Barton Seagrave, Kettering NN15 6SR* Tel (01536) 517760 Fax telephone E-mail lee@gatiss.net

GATLIFFE, David Spenser. b 45. Keble Coll Ox BA67 Fitzw Coll Cam BA69. Westcott Ho Cam 67. **d** 69 **p** 70. C Oxted *S'wark* 69-72; C Roehampton H Trin 72-75; C S Beddington St Mich 76-77; TV Clapham Old Town 78-87; P-in-c Clapham Ch Ch and St Jo 81-87; TV Clapham TM 87-89; V S Wimbledon H Trin and St Pet 89-01; R Lee St Marg from 01. *The Rectory, Brandram Road, London SE13 5EA* Tel (020) 8297 1181 *or* 8318 9643 E-mail stmargarets-lee@fish.co.uk

GATRILL, Adrian Colin. b 60. Southn Univ BTh82. Linc Th Coll 83. **d** 85 **p** 86. C W Bromwich St Andr *Lich* 85-88; C W Bromwich St Andr w Ch Ch 88-89; Chapl RAF from 89; Perm to Offic *St D* 90-95. *Chaplaincy Services (RAF), HQ, Personnel and Training Command, RAF Innsworth, Gloucester GL3 1EZ* Tel (01452) 712612 ext 5164 Fax 510828

GAUGE, Canon Barrie Victor. b 41. St D Coll Lamp BA62 Selw Coll Cam BA64 MA74 Liv Univ CQSW81 DipSocSc81. Bp Burgess Hall Lamp DPS65. **d** 65 **p** 66. C Newtown w Llanllwchaiarn w Aberhafesp *St As* 65-68; C Prestatyn 68-73; R Bodfari 73-76; Dioc RE Adv 73-76; Perm to Offic *Ches* 76-84; V Birkenhead St Jas w St Bede 84-90; Dir of Resources 90-98; Hon Can Ches Cathl 94-98; C Lache cum Saltney 95-98; Par Development Adv *Derby* from 98; Can Res Derby Cathl from 99; Miss Adv from 01. *The Vicarage, 2 Glebe Crescent, Stanley, Ilkeston DE7 6FL* Tel 0115-932 2267 E-mail barrie.gauge@talk21.com

GAUNT, Arthur Raymond. b 15. St Aid Birkenhead 47. **d** 49 **p** 50. C Thornbury *Bradf* 49-51; C Skipton Ch Ch 51-52; C-in-c Pudsey St Jas CD 52-55; V Bingley H Trin 55-58; V Glaisdale *York* 58-63; V York H Trin Goodramgate w St Maurice 63-66; V Kexby w Wilberfoss 66-71; Rtd Clergy and Widows Officer (E Riding) 67-85; V Scarborough St Columba 71-78; rtd 78; Perm to Offic *Bradf* 80-84. *20 Grantley Drive, Harrogate HG3 2ST* Tel (01423) 504998

GAUNT (née COTTELL), Mrs Avril Jane. b 50. SRN72 SCM74 Lon Univ Dip Nursing 81 Southn Univ DipTh97. S Dios Minl Tr Scheme 92. **d** 95 **p** 97. NSM Yatton Moor *B & W* 95-96 and 97-02; NSM Bourne *Guildf* 96-97; Asst Chapl N Bris NHS Trust from 02. *Myrtle Cottage, Ham Lane, Kingston Seymour, Clevedon BS21 6XE* Tel (01934) 832029

GAUNT, Eric Emmerson. b 33. Sarum Th Coll 65. **d** 67 **p** 68. C Hatch End St Anselm *Lon* 67-74; V Neasden cum Kingsbury St Cath 74-80; V Neasden St Cath w St Paul from 80. *St Catherine's Vicarage, Tanfield Avenue, London NW2 7RX* Tel (020) 8452 7322

GAUSDEN, Canon Peter James. b 32. Qu Coll Birm 57. **d** 60 **p** 61. C Battersea St Pet *S'wark* 60-63; C St Peter-in-Thanet *Cant* 63-68; V Sturry 68-74; R Sturry w Fordwich and Westbere w Hersden 74-97; Dioc Ecum Officer 91-97; Hon Can Cant Cathl 96-97; rtd 97; Perm to Offic *Cant* 97-99; Hon C St Nicholas at Wade w Sarre and Chislet w Hoath 99-01. *The Vicarage, The Length, St Nicholas at Wade, Birchington CT7 9PW* Tel (01843) 847200

GAVED, Kenneth John Drew. b 31. LNSM course 92. **d** 95 **p** 96. OLM W Wickham St Jo *S'wark* from 95. *42 Queensway, West Wickham BR4 9ER* Tel (020) 8462 4326

GAVIGAN, Josephine Katherine. b 49. Univ Coll Chich BA00. Sarum Th Coll 93. **d** 96. NSM Boxgrove *Chich* 96-00; C 00-03; Dn-in-c Maybridge from 03. *56 The Boulevard, Worthing BN13 1LA* Tel (01903) 249463 Mobile 07760-277262 E-mail deaconjo@hotmail.com

GAVIN, David Guy. b 63. Birm Univ BA85 Dur Univ BA90. Cranmer Hall Dur 88. **d** 91 **p** 92. C Parr *Liv* 91-95; TV Toxteth St Philemon w St Gabr and St Cleopas 95-02; P-in-c from 02. *St Cleopas Vicarage, Beresford Road, Liverpool L8 4SG* Tel 0151-727 0633

GAVIN (née GREGORY), Mrs Judith Rosalind. b 61. Open Univ BA97. St Jo Coll Nottm 99. **d** 01 **p** 02. C Moss Side St Jas w St Clem *Man* from 01; C Whalley Range St Edm from 01. *68 Dudley Road, Whalley Range, Manchester M16 8DE* Tel 0161-226 8502 E-mail judith.gregory@custard-computers.co.uk

GAWITH, Canon Alan Ruthven. b 24. Man Univ Soc Admin Cert 47. Lich Th Coll 54. **d** 56 **p** 57. C Appleby and Murton cum Hilton *Carl* 56-59; C Newton Aycliffe *Dur* 59-61; C-in-c Owton Manor CD 61-67; V Kendal St Geo *Carl* 67-74; Soc Resp Officer *Man* 74-89; Hon Can Man Cathl 82-89; Bp's Adv on AIDS 88-92; rtd 90; Perm to Offic *Man* from 90. *7 Redwaters, Leigh WN7 1JD* Tel (01942) 676641

GAWNE-CAIN, John. b 38. CEng MICE &GC Coll Cam BA61 MA66. Cuddesdon Coll 74. **d** 76 **p** 77. C Cowley St Jas *Ox* 76-80; P-in-c Ox St Giles 80-85; V Ox St Giles and SS Phil and Jas w St Marg 85-92; P-in-c Uffington w Woolstone and Baulking 92-93; P-in-c Shellingford 92-93; R Uffington, Shellingford, Woolstone and Baulking from 93. *St Mary's Vicarage, Uffington, Faringdon SN7 7RA* Tel (01367) 820633 Fax 820617 E-mail j.gawne-cain@ruralnet.org.uk

GAWTHROP-DORAN, Mrs Sheila Mary. b 37. Birm Univ CertEd. Dalton Ho Bris 68. **dss** 79 **d** 87. Halliwell St Paul *Man* 79-82; New Bury 82-89; Par Dn 87-89; Par Dn Tonge w Alkrington 89-94; rtd 94; Perm to Offic *York* from 95. *35 Swarthdale, Haxby, York YO32 3NZ* Tel (01904) 761247

GAY, Colin James. b 37. Univ of Wales (Lamp) BA63. Chich Th Coll 63. **d** 65 **p** 66. C W Hackney St Barn *Lon* 65-69; C Hitchin *St Alb* 69-74; P-in-c Apsley End 74-80; TV Chambersbury 80-85; V Barnet Vale St Mark 85-03; rtd 03. *14 Barleyfield Way, Houghton Regis, Dunstable LU5 5ER* Tel (01582) 862309

GAY, David Charles. b 46. CCC Cam BA68 MA72 PhD71. Coll of Resurr Mirfield DipTh74. **d** 75 **p** 76. C Sheff St Mark Broomhall *Sheff* 75-78; Bp's Chapl for Graduates 78-80; Lib Pusey Ho 78-80; Lic to Offic *Sheff* 80-82; C Warmsworth 82-84; V Worsbrough St Thos and St Jas 84-98. *87 Park Road, Worsbrough, Barnsley S70 5DD*

GAY, John Dennis. b 43. St Pet Coll Ox BA64 DipTh65 MA68 DPhil69 MSc78. Ripon Hall Ox 64. **d** 67 **p** 68. C Paddington St Jas *Lon* 67-71; P-in-c 71-72; Lic to Offic *Ox* from 72; Chapl Culham Coll Abingdon 72-79; Lect Ox Univ 78-80; Dir Culham Coll Inst from 80; Perm to Offic *Chich* 87-89. *Culham College Institute, 60 East St Helen Street, Abingdon OX14 5EB* Tel (01235) 520458 Fax 535421 E-mail john.gay@culham.ac.uk

GAY, Canon Perran Russell. b 59. St Cath Coll Cam BA81 MA85 Ex Univ CertEd82. Ripon Coll Cuddesdon BA86. **d** 87 **p** 88. C Bodmin w Lanhydrock and Lanivet *Truro* 87-90; Bp's Dom Chapl 90-94; Dioc Officer for Unity 90-94; Can Res and Chan Truro Cathl from 94; Prec from 01; Dir of Tr 94-99. *52 Daniell Road, Truro TR1 2DA* Tel (01872) 276491 *or* 276782 Fax 277788 E-mail perrangay@aol.com

GAY, Stuart. b 66. Oak Hill Th Coll BA94. **d** 00 **p** 01. C Sunningdale *Ox* from 00. *62 Park Crescent, Sunningdale, Ascot SL5 0AY* Tel (01344) 638771 E-mail stuart.gay@virgin.net

GAYLER, Roger Kenneth. b 44. Lich Th Coll 68. **d** 70 **p** 71. C Chingford St Anne *Chelmsf* 70-75; P-in-c Marks Gate 75-81; V from 81. *The Vicarage, 187 Rose Lane, Romford RM6 5NR* Tel (020) 8599 0415 E-mail rev@r-gayler.fsnet.co.uk

GAYNOR, Mrs Mieke Aaltjen Cornelia. b 43. UEA BA79. St Jo Coll Nottm 02. **d** 03. NSM Hambleden Valley *Ox* from 03. *5 Lodge Close, Marlow SL7 1RB* Tel (01628) 481704 E-mail mieke.gaynor@btopenworld.com

GAZE, Mrs Sally Ann. b 69. SS Coll Cam BA91 MA95 Birm Univ PGCE92 MPhil98. Qu Coll Birm 94. **d** 96 **p** 97. C Martley and Wichenford, Knightwick etc *Worc* 96-00; C Crickhowell w Cwmdu and Tretower *S & B* 00-02; TR Newton Flotman, Swainsthorpe, Tasburgh, etc *Nor* from 02. *The Rectory, Church Road, Newton Flotman, Norwich NR15 1QB* Tel (01508) 470762 E-mail sally@tasvalley.org

GEACH, Canon Michael Bernard. b 26. Qu Coll Cam BA51 MA56. Westcott Ho Cam 51. **d** 53 **p** 54. C Kenwyn *Truro* 53-56; C Bodmin 56-59; C Helland 56-59; R St Dominic 59-65; Chapl Cotehele Ho Chapl Cornwall 60-65; V Linkinhorne 65-84; R Veryan w Ruan Lanihorne 84-96; Hon Can Truro Cathl 92-96; rtd 96; Perm to Offic *Truro* from 96. *17 Paul's Row, Truro TR1 1HH* Tel (01872) 262927

GEACH, Mrs Sarah Jane. b 50. Trin Coll Carmarthen CertEd73 CertRS94. WEMTC DipHE99. **d** 99 **p** 00. C Pill w Easton in Gordano and Portbury *B & W* 99-02; TV Ross *Heref* from 02. *The Rectory, Brampton Abbotts, Ross-on-Wye HR9 7JD* Tel (01989) 562010 E-mail sarah.geach@rtm.org.uk

GEAKE, Peter Henry. b 17. Trin Hall Cam BA39 MA46. Cuddesdon Coll 45. **d** 47 **p** 48. C Portsea St Mary *Portsm* 47-50; C Southbroom *Sarum* 50-52; R Clovelly *Ex* 52-55; Chapl Canford Sch Wimborne 55-62; V Tattenham Corner and Burgh Heath *Guildf* 62-72; R Hungerford *Linc* 72-82; P-in-c Caistor Scroop w Normanton 72-82; rtd 82; Perm to Offic *Ox* 94-95; Perm to Offic *Sarum* from 98. *33 Abbey Mews, Amesbury, Salisbury SP4 7EX* Tel (01980) 624815

GEAR, John Arthur. b 37. St Aid Birkenhead 62. **d** 64 **p** 66. C Attleborough *Cov* 64-66; C Attercliffe *Sheff* 66-68; C Sheerness

H Trin w St Paul *Cant* 68-73; Asst Youth Adv *S'wark* 73-78; Youth Chapl *Lich* 78-88; V Stafford St Jo and Tixall w Ingestre 88-92; Gen Sec NCEC 92-97; rtd 97; Perm to Offic *Lich* 01-02; P-in-c Shrewsbury H Cross from 02. *Greenside, Lime Kiln Bank, Telford TF2 9NU* Tel (01952) 613487 *or* (01743) 232723

✠**GEAR, The Rt Revd Michael Frederick.** b 34. Dur Univ BA59 DipTh61. Cranmer Hall Dur 59. **d** 61 **p** 62 **c** 93. C Bexleyheath Ch Ch *Roch* 61-64; C Ox St Aldate w H Trin *Ox* 64-67; V Clubmoor *Liv* 67-71; Rhodesia 71-76; Tutor Wycliffe Hall Ox 76-80; V Macclesfield St Mich *Ches* 80-85; RD Macclesfield 84-88; TR Macclesfield Team Par 85-88; Hon Can Ches Cathl 86-88; Adn Ches 88-93; Suff Bp Doncaster *Sheff* 93-99; rtd 99; Hon Asst Bp Roch from 99; Hon Asst Bp Cant from 00. *10 Acott Fields, Yalding, Maidstone ME18 6DQ* Tel (01622) 817388 E-mail mike.gear@rochester.anglican.org

GEBAUER, George Gerhart. b 25. Sarum & Wells Th Coll 71. **d** 73 **p** 74. C Portsdown *Portsm* 73-78; V Purbrook 78-91; rtd 91; Perm to Offic *Portsm* from 91. *52 St John's Road, Locks Heath, Southampton SO31 6NF* Tel (01489) 575172

GEDDES, Gordon David. b 38. St Chad's Coll Dur BA59 DipTh60. **d** 61 **p** 62. C Bishopwearmouth St Mary V w St Pet CD *Dur* 61-65; P-in-c Jarrow 65-68; Teacher Crewe Boys' Gr Sch 68-71; Hd of RS 71-78; Hd of RE Ruskin Sch Crewe 78-90; Lic to Offic *Ches* 68-90; P-in-c Church Minshull w Leighton and Minshull Vernon 90-91; V Leighton-cum-Minshull Vernon from 91; RD Nantwich from 01; Chapl Mid Cheshire Hosps Trust from 91. *The Vicarage, Minshull Vernon, Crewe CW1 4RD* Tel (01270) 522213 Fax 522694 E-mail revggeddes@aol.com

GEDDES, Peter Henry. b 51. DipHE86. Trin Coll Bris 84. **d** 86 **p** 87. C Blackpool St Mark *Blackb* 86-88; C Barnston *Ches* 88-92; V Haslington w Crewe Green from 92. *The Vicarage, 163 Crewe Road, Haslington, Crewe CW1 5RL* Tel (01270) 582388

GEDDES, Roderick Charles. b 47. Man Univ DipEd78 MPhil85. N Ord Course 88. **d** 91 **p** 93. C Alverthorpe *Wakef* 91-92; C S Ossett 92-94; P-in-c Gargrave *Bradf* from 03. *The Vicarage, Gargrave, Skipton BD23 3NQ* Tel (01756) 748548 E-mail geddes@mcb.net

GEDGE, Lloyd Victor. b 23. Cuddesdon Coll 54. **d** 57 **p** 58. C Headington *Ox* 57-60; Canada 60-63 and 66-82 and from 86; New Zealand 63-66; P-in-c N Creake *Nor* 82-83; P-in-c S Creake 82-83; R N and S Creake w Waterden 84-86; rtd 88. *PO Box 61, Bruce, Alberta, Canada, T0B 0R0*

GEDGE, Simon John Francis. b 44. Keble Coll Ox BA67 MA73. Cuddesdon Coll 67. **d** 69 **p** 70. C Perry Barr *Birm* 69-73; C Handsworth St Andr 73-75; V Birm St Pet 75-81; Perm to Offic *Lon* 81-85; Hon C Croydon St Jo *S'wark* 85-87. *121 Albyn Road, London SE14 4EB* Tel (020) 8692 7328

GEE, Anne Alison. b 43. **d** 01 **p** 02. NSM Canford Magna *Sarum* from 01. *37 Floral Farm, Wimborne BH21 3AT* Tel (01202) 887078

GEE, Mrs Dorothy Mary. b 33. St Jo Coll Nottm 88. **d** 89 **p** 94. Chapl Asst Univ Hosp Nottm 89-95; NSM Plumtree *S'well* 95-97; P-in-c 97-01; rtd 01. *16 The Leys, Normanton-on-the-Wolds, Keyworth, Nottingham NG12 5NU* Tel 0115-937 4927

GEE, Canon Edward. b 28. St Deiniol's Hawarden 59. **d** 61 **p** 62. C Hanging Heaton *Wakef* 61-65; V Brownhill 65-75; V Alverthorpe 75-84; R Castleford All SS 84-92; Hon Can Wakef Cathl 87-92; rtd 92; Perm to Offic *Bradf* and *Wakef* from 92. *1 Holme Ghyll, Colne Road, Glusburn, Keighley BD20 8RG* Tel (01535) 630060

GEE, Norman. b 11. Lon Univ BA33 St Cath Soc Ox BA35 MA42. Wycliffe Hall Ox 33. **d** 35 **p** 36. C Kilburn St Mary *Lon* 35-38; Youth Sec CMJ 38-41; P-in-c Woodside Park St Barn *Lon* 40-41; V 41-49; V Oakwood St Thos 49-58; V Bath St Bart *B & W* 58-73; V Curry Rivel 73-78; rtd 78; Perm to Offic *B & W* 79-97. *5 Barn Close, Nether Stowey, Bridgwater TA5 1PA* Tel (01278) 732317

GEEN, James William. b 50. Chich Th Coll 76. **d** 79 **p** 80. C Brandon *Dur* 79-84; C Sunderland Red Ho 84-86; P-in-c N Hylton St Marg Castletown w S Hylton 86-89; V Dep Chapl HM Pris Dur 91-92; Chapl HM YOI Lanc Farms 92-95; Chapl HM Pris Long Lartin 95-01; Chapl HM Pris Blakenhurst from 01. *HM Prison Blakenhurst, Hewell Lane, Redditch B97 6QS* Tel (01527) 543348 E-mail jacobus@fsmail.net

GEERING, Preb Anthony Ernest. b 43. Lon Univ DipTh66 Columbia Pacific Univ BSc. Kelham Th Coll 62. **d** 68 **p** 69. C Cov St Mary *Cov* 68-71; New Zealand 71-75; P-in-c Brinklow *Cov* 75-77; R 77-81; V Monks Kirby w Pailton and Stretton-under-Fosse 77-81; R Harborough Magna 77-81; V Pilton w Ashford *Ex* 81-86; P-in-c Shirwell w Loxhore 83-86; R Crediton and Shobrooke 86-01; P-in-c Sandford w Upton Hellions 00-01; R Crediton, Shobrooke and Sandford etc 01; RD Cadbury 93-97; R Chagford, Drewsteignton, Hittisleigh etc from 01; RD Okehampton from 02; Preb Ex Cathl from 02. *The Rectory, Chagford, Newton Abbot TQ13 8BW* Tel (01647) 433014

GEESON, Brian Alfred. b 30. Qu Coll Ox BA51 Trin & All SS Coll Leeds PGCE76. Qu Coll Birm 54. **d** 56 **p** 57. C Newbold w Dunston *Derby* 55-59; PC Calow 59-64; R Broughton *Bradf* 64-71; TV Seacroft *Ripon* 71-77; Hon C Hanging Heaton *Wakef*

77-87; Hon C Purlwell 87-94; rtd 94; Perm to Offic *Wakef* from 94. *30 Ullswater Avenue, Dewsbury WF12 7PL* Tel (01924) 465621

GEILINGER, John Edward. b 27. Lon Univ BSc53 BD58 BA76 MPhil79. Tyndale Hall Bris. **d** 59 **p** 60. C Plymouth St Jude *Ex* 59-61; Nigeria 63-77; Perm to Offic *Portsm* from 79; rtd 92. *Emmaus House, Colwell Road, Freshwater PO40 9LY* Tel (01983) 753030

GEISOW, Hilary Patricia. b 46. Salford Univ BSc67 Warwick Univ PhD71 Nottm Univ PGCE74. St Jo Coll Nottm 01. **d** 03. C Linc St Faith and St Martin w St Pet *Linc* from 03. *74 Roman Wharf, Lincoln LN1 1SR* Tel (01522) 546022 E-mail hilary@geisow.freeserve.co.uk

GELDARD, Preb Mark Dundas. b 50. Liv Univ BA71 Bris Univ MA75. Trin Coll Bris 73. **d** 75 **p** 76. C Aughton Ch Ch *Liv* 75-78; Tutor Trin Coll Bris 78-84; V Fairfield *Liv* 84-88; Dir of Ords *Lich* from 88; C Lich St Mary w St Mich 95-96; C Lich St Mich w St Mary and Wall from 96; Preb Lich Cathl from 00. *10 The Brambles, Lichfield WS14 9SE* Tel (01543) 306192 *or* 306220 Fax 306229 E-mail sue.jackson@lichfield.anglican.org

GELL, Anne Elizabeth. b 63. St Hugh's Coll Ox BA85 R Free Hosp Sch of Medicine MB, BS90 Surrey Univ BA01. STETS 98. **d** 01 **p** 02. C Headley All SS *Guildf* from 01. *7 Windmill Drive, Headley Down, Bordon GU35 8AL* Tel (01428) 714565 E-mail annegell@lineone.net

GELL, Miss Margaret Florence. b 30. **d** 00 **p** 01. NSM Madeley *Lich* from 00. *19 Pear Tree Drive, Madeley, Crewe CW3 9EN* Tel (01782) 750569

GELLI, Frank Julian. b 43. Birkbeck Coll Lon BA78 K Coll Lon MTh82. Ripon Coll Cuddesdon 84. **d** 86 **p** 87. C Chiswick St Nic w St Mary *Lon* 86-89; Chapl Ankara *Eur* 89-91; C Kensington St Mary Abbots w St Geo *Lon* 91-99. *58 Boston Gardens, Brentford TW8 9LP* Tel (020) 8847 4533 E-mail numapomp@talk21.com

GELLING, Canon John Drury. b 22. Pemb Coll Ox BA44 DipTh45 MA48. Wycliffe Hall Ox 44. **d** 54 **p** 55. Hd Master Eccles High Sch 50-64; C Irlam *Man* 54-59; V Rushen *S & M* 64-77; RD Castletown 71-77; R Ballaugh 77-92; P-in-c Michael 77-78; V 78-92; Can St German's Cathl 80-92; rtd 92; Perm to Offic *S & M* from 93. *Uplands, Ballavitchell Road, Crosby, Isle of Man IM4 2DN* Tel (01624) 851223

GELSTON, Anthony. b 35. Keble Coll Ox BA57 MA60 DD85. Ridley Hall Cam 59. **d** 60 **p** 61. C Chipping Norton *Ox* 60-62; Lect Th Dur Univ *Dur* 62-76; Sen Lect 76-88; Dean Div Faculty 77-79; Reader 89-95; Lic to Offic 62-95; rtd 95. *Lesbury, Hetton Road, Houghton le Spring DH5 8JW* Tel 0191-584 2256 E-mail anthony.gelston@durham.ac.uk

GEMMELL, Canon Ian William Young. b 52. ALAM. St Jo Coll Nottm LTh77. **d** 77 **p** 78. C Old Hill H Trin *Worc* 77-81; C Selly Hill St Steph *Birm* 81; C Selly Park St Steph and St Wulstan 81-83; V Leic St Chris *Leic* 83-93; RD Christianity S 92-93; P-in-c Gt Bowden w Welham, Glooston and Cranoe 93-02; P-in-c Church Langton w Tur Langton, Thorpe Langton etc 93-99; P-in-c Church Langton cum Tur Langton etc 99-02; R Gt Bowden w Welham, Glooston and Cranoe etc from 02; RD Gartree I from 97; Hon Can Leic Cathl from 03. *The Rectory, Dingley Road, Great Bowden, Market Harborough LE16 7ET* Tel (01858) 462032 E-mail budgem@leicester.anglican.org

GENDALL, Stephen Mark. b 63. Univ of Zimbabwe DipRS90. **d** 89 **p** 90. Lundi St Apollos Zimbabwe 89-01; Youth Chapl 93-01; Can Cen Zimbabwe 00-01; V Lingfield and Crowhurst *S'wark* from 02. *The Vicarage, Vicarage Road, Lingfield RH7 6HA* Tel (01342) 832021 Mobile 07752-063150 E-mail steve@thegendalls.freeserve.co.uk

GENDERS, Nigel Mark. b 65. Oak Hill Th Coll BA92. **d** 92 **p** 93. C New Malden and Coombe *S'wark* 92-96; C Enfield Ch Ch Trent Park *Lon* 96-98; P-in-c Eastry and Northbourne w Tilmanstone etc *Cant* from 98. *The Vicarage, Brook Street, Eastry, Sandwich CT13 0HR* Tel (01304) 611323 E-mail nigel@genders.freeserve.co.uk

✠**GENDERS, The Rt Revd Roger Alban Marson (Anselm).** b 19. BNC Ox BA47 MA47. Coll of Resurr Mirfield 48. **d** 52 **p** 52 **c** 77. Lic to Offic *Wakef* 52-55; CR from 52; Barbados 55-65; Rhodesia 66-75; Adn E Distr 70-75; Bp Bermuda 77-82; Asst Bp Wakef from 83; rtd 84. *House of the Resurrection, Stocks Bank Road, Mirfield WF14 0BN* Tel (01924) 494318

GENEREUX, Patrick Edward. b 47. William Carey Coll BSc73 Univ of the South (USA) MDiv78. **d** 78 **p** 79. USA 78-81 and from 82; C Spalding *Linc* 81-82. *621 North 5th Street, Burlington, IA 52601-0608, USA* Tel (001) (319) 754 6420 E-mail pgenereux@aol.com

GENT, David Robert. b 71. Surrey Univ BSc94. Qu Coll Birm BD97. **d** 98 **p** 99. C Wotton-under-Edge w Ozleworth and N Nibley *Glouc* 98-02; C Yeovil H Trin w Barwick *B & W* from 02; Chapl Yeovil Coll from 02. *The Vicarage, Church Lane, Barwick, Yeovil BA22 9TE* Tel (01935) 426866 E-mail rev_d_gent@hotmail.com

GENT, Mrs Miriam. b 29. Leeds Univ BA51. SW Minl Tr Course 84. **d** 87 **p** 94. NSM Pinhoe and Broadclyst *Ex* 87-02; Dioc Adv in Adult Tr 96-99; Perm to Offic from 02. *Moss Hayne Cottage, West Clyst, Exeter EX1 3TR* Tel (01392) 467288 Fax 462980

GENT, Miss Susan Elizabeth. SSC81 K Coll Lon LLB78 Brunel Univ BA95 Wycliffe Hall Ox MPhil96 DipMin97. **d** 97 **p** 98. C Notting Hill St Jo and St Pet *Lon* 97-00; Chapl to City law firms from 00; Hon Assoc P St Paul's Cathl from 00; Dioc Visitor from 01. *3B Amen Court, London EC4M 7BU* Tel (020) 7329 2702 E-mail susangent@compuserve.com

GENTRY, Michael John. b 66. St Steph Ho Ox BTh95. **d** 98 **p** 99. C Bromley SS Pet and Paul *Roch* 98-02; V Langton Green from 02. *The Vicarage, The Green, Langton Green, Tunbridge Wells TN3 0JB* Tel (01892) 862072 E-mail frmichael@beeb.net

GEOFFREY, Brother. *See* PEARSON, Canon Harold

GEOGHEGAN, Prof Luke. b 62. SS Hild & Bede Coll Dur BA83 Bedf Coll Lon MSc87 CQSW87 FRSA93. St Alb and Ox Min Course87. **d** 00 **p** 01. NSM Spitalfields Ch Ch w All SS *Lon* 00-- 03; NSM Gt Berkhamsted *St Alb* from 03; Warden Toynbee Hall from 98. *16 Gravel Path, Berkhamsted HP4 2EF* E-mail luke.geoghegan@virgin.net

GEORGE, Canon Alec. b 29. Lich Th Coll 56. **d** 59 **p** 60. C Holbrooks *Cov* 59-65; R Lower Broughton Ascension *Man* 65-71; V Hollinwood 71-96; Hon Can Man Cathl 94-96; rtd 96; Perm to Offic *Blackb* from 98. *107 Fairway, Fleetwood FY7 8RA* Tel (01253) 771758

GEORGE, Alexander Robert. b 46. K Coll Lon BD69 AKC69. St Aug Coll Cant. **d** 70 **p** 71. C Newmarket St Mary w Exning St Agnes *St E* 70-74; C Swindon Ch Ch *Bris* 74-76; C Henbury 76-79; Lic to Offic 79-80; TV Oldland 80-88; C Ipswich St Aug *St E* 89; C Hadleigh w Layham and Shelley 89-90; P-in-c Assington 90-91; R Assington w Newton Green and Lt Cornard 91-00; Dioc Moderator for Reader Tr from 95; P-in-c Hundon from 00; Asst Liturg Officer (Formation and Educn) from 00. *The Vicarage, 5 Armstrong Close, Hundon, Sudbury CO10 8HD* Tel (01440) 786617

GEORGE, Charles Roy. b 32. St Edm Hall Ox BA55 MA59. Cuddesdon Coll 55. **d** 57 **p** 58. C Chorley St Laur *Blackb* 57-60; C Norton *Derby* 60-64; V Eltham St Barn *S'wark* 64-74; V Milton *Portsm* 74-90; R Rowner 90-96; rtd 96; Perm to Offic *Portsm* from 96. *46 The Thicket, Fareham PO16 8PZ* Tel (01329) 288185

GEORGE, David. b 64. Wycliffe Hall Ox 01. **d** 03. C Inkberrow w Cookhill and Kington w Dormston *Worc* from 03. *3 The Pleck, Inkberrow, Worcester WR7 4JB* Tel (01386) 791369 E-mail revdavegeorge@lineone.net

GEORGE, The Ven David Michael. b 45. Selw Coll Cam BA66 MA70. Chich Th Coll 70. **d** 73 **p** 74. C Chiswick St Nic w St Mary *Lon* 73-76; C Kensington St Mary Abbots w St Geo 76-78; C Northolt Park St Barn 78-81; Argentina from 81; Adn River Plate from 84. *San Lorenzo 2274, 1640 Martinez, Buenos Aires, Argentina* Tel (0054) (1) 4798 0078 E-mail smtla@cvtci.com.ar

GEORGE, Mrs Elizabeth Ann. b 33. Westf Coll Lon BA56. S Dios Minl Tr Scheme 84. **d** 87 **p** 94. NSM Basingstoke *Win* from 87. *71 Camrose Way, Basingstoke RG21 3AW* Tel (01256) 464763 E-mail elizabethgeorge@compuserve.com

GEORGE, The Ven Frederick. b 39. St Luke's Coll Ex CertEd61. Chich Th Coll 82 ACT DipTh91. **d** 72 **p** 83. Australia 72-75; Brunei 75-80; The Gambia 80-82 and 83-88; C Hellingly and Upper Dicker *Chich* 83; P-in-c Ringsfield w Redisham, Barsham, Shipmeadow etc *St E* 89-92; R Wainford 92-97; St Helena from 97; Adn St Helena from 99. *St James's Vicarage, Napoleon Street, Jamestown, St Helena* Tel (00290) 2663 Fax as telephone

GEORGE, Preb John Thomas. b 17. St D Coll Lamp BA42 Selw Coll Cam BA44 MA47. Westcott Ho Cam 44. **d** 45 **p** 46. C Llanstadwel *St D* 45-48; C Eastville St Thos *Bris* 48-50; C Wells St Cuth *B & W* 50-52; PV Wells Cathl 50-52; Teacher Wells Cathl Sch 50-52; V Cheddar 52-57; P-in-c Priddy 55-57; CF 57-60; V Thornton w Allerthorpe *York* 60-62; R Backwell *B & W* 62-72; RD Portishead 68-72; V Wellington w W Buckland and Nynehead 72-76; TR Wellington and Distr 76-82; Preb Wells Cathl 78-86; rtd 82; Hon C Diptford, N Huish, Harberton and Harbertonford *Ex* 85-97; Perm to Offic from 97. *12 Woolcombe Lane, Ivybridge PL21 0UA* Tel (01752) 698284

GEORGE, Nicholas Paul. b 58. St Steph Ho Ox 86. **d** 89 **p** 90. C Leeds St Aid *Ripon* 89-92; C Leeds Richmond Hill 92-96; Chapl Agnes Stewart C of E High Sch Leeds 93-96; V Leeds Halton St Wilfrid *Ripon* 96-02; V Camberwell St Giles w St Matt *S'wark* from 02. *St Giles's Vicarage, 200 Benhill Road, London SE5 7LL* Tel (020) 7703 4504 E-mail nick.george@care4free.net

✠**GEORGE, The Rt Revd Randolph Oswald.** b 24. Codrington Coll Barbados 46. **d** 50 **p** 51 **c** 76. Barbados 50-53; C Leigh *Lich* 53-55; C Ardwick St Benedict *Man* 55-57; C Bedford Park *Lon* 57-58; C Lavender Hill Ascension *S'wark* 58-60; Trinidad and Tobago 60-71; Hon Can Trinidad 68-71; Guyana from 71; Dean Georgetown 71-76; Suff Bp Stabroek 76-80; Bp Guyana from 80. *Austin House, Kingston, Georgetown 1, Guyana* Tel (00592) (2) 63862 Fax 64183

GEORGE, Robert Henry. b 45. FCCA73. WEMTC 99. **d** 01 **p** 02. OLM S Cerney w Cerney Wick and Down Ampney *Glouc* from

01. *Jedems, Berkeley Close, South Cerney, Cirencester GL7 5UN* Tel (01285) 860973 E-mail jedems@fish.co.uk

GEORGE, Roy. *See* GEORGE, Charles Roy

GEORGE-JONES, Canon Gwilym Ifor. b 26. K Coll (NS) 56. **d** 57 **p** 57. Canada 57-61; V Kirton in Lindsey *Linc* 61-71; R Grayingham 61-71; R Manton 61-71; V Alford w Rigsby 71-92; R Maltby 71-92; R Well 71-92; V Bilsby w Farlesthorpe 71-92; R Hannah cum Hagnaby w Markby 71-92; R Saleby w Beesby 71-92; RD Calcewaithe and Candleshoe 77-85 and 87-89; Can and Preb Linc Cathl 81-01; rtd 92. *42 Kelstern Road, Doddington Park, Lincoln LN6 3NJ* Tel (01522) 691896

GEORGE-ROGERS, Gillian Jean Richeldis. **d** 99. C Llanishen *Llan* from 99. *100 Templeton Avenue, Llanishen, Cardiff CF14 5JH* Tel (029) 2075 8413

GERARD, John William. b 23. BNC Ox BA47 MA52. Trin Coll Toronto LTh50. **d** 51 **p** 51. Canada 51-61; Jamaica 62; Perm to Offic *Sheff* 62-64; Perm to Offic *Chelmsf* 64-89. *Oak Tree Cottage, 31 Wycke Lane, Tollesbury, Maldon CM9 8ST*

GERD, Sister. *See* SWENSSON, Sister Gerd Inger

GERRARD, The Ven David Keith Robin. b 39. St Edm Hall Ox BA61. Linc Th Coll 61. **d** 63 **p** 64. C Stoke Newington St Olave *Lon* 63-66; C Primrose Hill St Mary w Avenue Road St Paul 66-69; V Newington St Paul *S'wark* 69-79; V Surbiton St Andr and St Mark 79-89; RD Kingston 84-88; Hon Can S'wark Cathl 85-89; Adn Wandsworth from 89. *68 North Side, London SW18 2QX* Tel (020) 8874 5766 *or* 8392 3742 Fax 8392 3743 E-mail david.gerrard@dswark.org.uk

GERRARD, George Ernest. b 16. TEM. FCIS60 DD94. Ridley Hall Cam 66. **d** 68 **p** 69. OStJ from 65; C Hilborough w Bodney *Nor* 68-70; C Ramsey *Ely* 70-75; rtd 81; Perm to Offic *Nor* 86-98. *46 Cornwallis Court, Hospital Road, Bury St Edmunds IP33 3NH* Tel (01284) 756900

GERRARD, Paul Christian Francis. b 58. St Steph Ho Ox 92. **d** 94 **p** 01. C Longton *Lich* 94-95; NSM New Radnor and Llanfihangel Nantmelan etc *S & B* from 01. *The Old Vicarage, Norton, Presteigne LD8 2EN* Tel (01544) 260038

GERRISH, David Victor. b 38. St Jo Coll Dur BSc61 MA65. Oak Hill Th Coll 61. **d** 64 **p** 65. C Fareham St Jo *Portsm* 64-66; Asst Chapl K Sch Roch 67-71; Asst Chapl Bryanston Sch 71-73; Chapl 73-77; Chapl Mon Sch 77-86; Chapl Warminster Sch 86-89; R Portland All SS w St Pet *Sarum* 89-96; Chapl Aquitaine *Eur* 96-00; rtd 00; Perm to Offic *Sarum* from 01. *Scribbage House, 1 Herbert Place, Weymouth DT4 8LR* Tel (01305) 789319

GERRY, Brian John Rowland. b 38. Oak Hill Th Coll 69. **d** 71 **p** 72. C Hawkwell *Chelmsf* 71-74; C Battersea Park St Sav *S'wark* 74-77; C Battersea St Geo w St Andr 74-77; V Axmouth w Musbury *Ex* 77-86; R Upton from 86. *Upton Rectory, Furzehill Road, Torquay TQ1 3JG* Tel (01803) 211572

GERRY, Ulric James. b 67. Bris Univ BEng89. Wycliffe Hall Ox BA96 DipMin97. **d** 97 **p** 98. C Hemel Hempstead *St Alb* 97-00; Perm to Offic from 01. *3 Trinity Road, Ware SG12 7DB* Tel (01920) 467901 E-mail ulric@nildram.co.uk

GHEST, Richard William Iliffe. b 31. Em Coll Cam BA53 MA57 Lon Univ BA66. Wells Th Coll 53. **d** 55 **p** 56. C Weston-super-Mare St Jo *B & W* 55-57; India 58-63; C Holborn St Geo w H Trin and St Bart *Lon* 63-67; Ceylon 67-68; C Combe Down *B & W* 68-73; C Combe Down w Monkton Combe 73-74; R Tickenham 74-96; rtd 96. *120 Cottrell Road, Roath, Cardiff CF24 3EX* Tel (029) 2048 1597

GHINN, Edward. b 45. Oak Hill Th Coll 71. **d** 74 **p** 75. C Purley Ch Ch *S'wark* 74-77; Chile 77-82; V Sevenoaks Weald *Roch* 82-86; Chapl HM Pris Hull 86-89; Chapl HM Pris Pentonville 89-91; Chapl HM Pris Maidstone 91-96; Brazil 96-98; Min Parkwood CD *Cant* 98-01; Chapl HM Pris Grendon and Spring Hill 01-03; Chapl HM Pris Stocken from 03. *HM Prison Stocken, Stocken Hall Road, Stretton, Oakham LE15 7RD* Tel (01780) 485281 Fax 410681 E-mail e.ghinn@virgin.net

GHOSH, Dipen. b 43. St Jo Coll Nottm 71. **d** 74 **p** 75. C Bushbury *Lich* 74-77; Hon C 86-89; C Wednesfield Heath 89-91; TV Wolverhampton 91-98; TV Bushbury 98-02; Chapl Compton Hall Hospice Wolv 98-02; V Wolverhampton St Matt *Lich* from 02. *St Matthew's Vicarage, 14 Sydenham Road, Wolverhampton WV1 2NY* Tel (01902) 453056

GIBB, David Richard Albert. b 68. Lon Bible Coll BA90 Cov Univ MPhil95 Wycliffe Hall Ox DipMin95. **d** 95 **p** 96. C Ox St Ebbe w H Trin and St Pet *Ox* 95-01; V Leyland St Andr *Blackb* from 01. *St Andrew's Vicarage, 1 Crocus Field, Leyland PR25 3DY* Tel (01772) 621645 E-mail david.gibb7@ntlworld.com

GIBBARD, Roger. b 48. Southn Univ BA73. Cuddesdon Coll 73. **d** 75 **p** 76. C Portsea St Mary *Portsm* 75-79; P-in-c New Addington *Cant* 79-81; C Ditton St Mich *Liv* 81-82; TV 82-88; Asst Chapl HM Pris Liv 88-89; Chapl HM YOI Hindley 89-92; Chapl HM Pris Risley 92-00; V Wigan St Mich *Liv* from 01. *St Michael's Vicarage, 1 Duke Street, Wigan WN1 2DN* Tel (01942) 233465

GIBBINS, John Grenville. b 53. Aston Tr Scheme 89 Linc Th Coll 89. **d** 91 **p** 92. C Market Harborough *Leic* 91-95; P-in-c Blaby from 95. *The Rectory, Wigston Road, Blaby, Leicester LE8 4FU* Tel 0116-277 2588 E-mail ggibbins@leicester.anglican.org

GIBBON, Matthew. b 79. Trin Coll Carmarthen BA00. St Steph Ho Ox BTh03. **d** 03. C Caerau w Ely *Llan* from 03. *79 Heol y Castell, Ely, Cardiff CF5 5LR* Tel (029) 2067 0096 E-mail gibbmatt23@hotmail.com

GIBBONS, David Austen. b 63. York Univ BSc84. Ch Div Sch of Pacific 93 Ripon Coll Cuddesdon BA94. **d** 94 **p** 95. C Ryde H Trin *Portsm* 94-97; C Swanmore St Mich 94-97; C Gosport Ch Ch 97-01; R Havant from 01. *St Faith's Rectory, 5 Meadowlands, Havant PO9 2RP* Tel (023) 9248 3485 E-mail d_gibbons@talk21.com

GIBBONS, David Robert Christian. b 36. Chich Th Coll 82. **d** 84 **p** 85. C Seaford w Sutton *Chich* 84-87; R Harting 87-93; R Harting w Elsted and Treyford cum Didling from 93. *The Rectory, South Harting, Petersfield GU31 5QB* Tel (01730) 825234

GIBBONS, Eric. b 47. Sarum & Wells Th Coll 69. **d** 72 **p** 73. C New Haw *Guildf* 72-76; C Hawley H Trin 76-79; P-in-c Blackheath and Chilworth 79-90; V 90-98; C Shere, Albury and Chilworth 98-99; P-in-c Tongham from 99. *The Vicarage, Poyle Road, Tongham, Farnham GU10 1DU* Tel (01252) 782224

GIBBONS, Harvey Lloyd. b 62. Harper Adams Agric Coll HND84. Ripon Coll Cuddesdon DipMin99. **d** 99 **p** 00. C Verwood *Sarum* 99-00; C Gillingham 00-02; P-in-c Upavon w Rushall and Charlton from 02; Dioc Voc Adv from 02. *The Vicarage, 5A Vicarage Lane, Upavon, Pewsey SN9 6AA* Tel (01980) 630248 E-mail gibonzfamly@freeuk.com

GIBBONS, The Ven Kenneth Harry. b 31. Man Univ BSc52. Cuddesdon Coll 54. **d** 56 **p** 57. C Fleetwood *Blackb* 56-60; NE Sch Sec SCM 60-62; Hon C Leeds St Pet *Ripon* 60-62; C St Martin-in-the-Fields *Lon* 62-65; V New Addington *Cant* 65-70; V Portsea St Mary *Portsm* 70-81; RD Portsm 73-79; Hon Can Portsm Cathl 76-81; Dir Post-Ord Tr *Blackb* 81-83; Acting Chapl HM Forces Weeton 81-85; Dir of Ords 82-90; Adn Lancaster 81-97; P-in-c Weeton 81-85; V St Michaels-on-Wyre 85-97; rtd 97; Perm to Offic *S'wark* from 97; P-in-c St Magnus the Martyr w St Marg New Fish Street *Lon* from 97; P-in-c St Clem Eastcheap w St Martin Orgar from 99. *112 Valley Road, Kenley CR8 5BU* Tel (020) 7633 8022

GIBBONS, Paul James. b 37. JP. Chich Th Coll 63. **d** 65 **p** 66. C Croydon St Mich *Cant* 65-72; V Maidstone St Mich from 72. *The Vicarage, 109 Tonbridge Road, Maidstone ME16 8JS* Tel (01622) 752710

GIBBONS, Mrs Susan Janet. b 51. St Mary's Coll Dur BA73 Birm Univ PGCE74. WMMTC 89. **d** 92 **p** 94. NSM Fladbury w Wyre Piddle and Moor etc *Worc* 92-00; Perm to Offic from 00. *The Old School, Bricklehampton, Pershore WR10 3HJ* Tel (01386) 710475

GIBBONS, Thomas Patrick. b 59. St Jo Coll Dur BA82. St Steph Ho Ox 88. **d** 90 **p** 91. C Whorlton *Newc* 90-94; C Gosforth St Nic 94-96; R Radley and Sunningwell *Ox* from 96. *The Vicarage, Kennington Road, Radley, Abingdon OX14 2JN* Tel (01235) 554739

GIBBONS, Canon William Simpson. b 32. TCD BA60 MA64. **d** 61 **p** 62. C Londonderry Ch Ch *D & R* 61-65; I Drumholm and Rossnowlagh 65-70; C Dublin St Ann w St Steph *D & G* 70-72; I Kill 72-95; Can Ch Ch Cathl Dublin 91-95; rtd 95. *Muthaiga, 8 Mount Bernard Drive, Castlederg BT81 7JA* Tel (028) 8267 0691 E-mail williamgibbons@hotmail.com

GIBBS, Colin Hugh. b 35. St Mich Coll Llan 82. **d** 84 **p** 85. C Bistre *St As* 84-87; V Penycae 87-92; rtd 92. *Asaph, 26 Cil y Coed, Ruabon, Wrexham LL14 6TA* Tel (01978) 823550

GIBBS, Colin Wilfred. b 39. Man Univ BA62 Birm Univ CertEd63. St Jo Coll Nottm 71. **d** 73 **p** 74. C Crowborough *Chich* 73-76; C Rodbourne Cheney *Bris* 76-77; C Bickenhill w Elmdon *Birm* 77-80; CF 80-96; Dir Ichthus Ho Homestay from 96; Perm to Offic *Ex* from 96; Chapl Grenville Coll Bideford 99-02. *132 Bay View Road, Bideford EX39 1BJ* Tel (01237) 425348 Fax as telephone E-mail colin@thenet.co.uk

GIBBS, Darryl. b 73. Trin Coll Carmarthen BEd95. Cuddesdon Coll BTh98. **d** 98 **p** 99. C Llandysul w Bangor Teifi w Henllan etc *St D* 98-99; C Carmarthen St Pet 99-01; C Llanelli 01-03; V Llanwynno *Llan* from 03. *The Vicarage, 40 Heol-y-Plwyf, Ynysybwl, Pontypridd CF37 3HU* Tel (01443) 790340 Mobile 07775-805919 E-mail darrylgibbs@easynet.co.uk

GIBBS, David Norman. b 65. Cam Univ BA87 MA90. Oak Hill Th Coll BA98. **d** 99 **p** 00. C Virginia Water *Guildf* 99-02; C Leyton Ch Ch *Chelmsf* from 02. *37 Norlington Road, London E11 4BE* Tel (020) 8556 3295 E-mail davidgibbs@x5g.com

GIBBS, Edmund. b 38. Fuller Th Sem California DMin81. Oak Hill Th Coll BD62. **d** 63 **p** 64. C Wandsworth All SS *S'wark* 63-66; SAMS Chile 66-70; Educn Sec SAMS 70-77; Ch Progr Manager Bible Soc 77-84; USA from 84; Assoc Prof Evang and Ch Renewal Fuller Th Sem 84-93; Prof Ch Growth from 96; Assoc R Beverly Hills All SS 93-96. *1136 Crowne Drive, Pasadena, CA 91107, USA* Tel (001) (626) 794 6393 E-mail eddgibbs@fuller.edu

GIBBS, Mrs Fiorenza Silvia Elisabetta. b 49. SRN71 Surrey Univ DipHV72. St Alb Minl Tr Scheme 90. **d** 93 **p** 99. NSM Hitchin *St Alb* 93-96; NSM Pirton 97-99; Asst Chapl N Herts NHS Trust 99-00; Asst Chapl E and N Herts NHS Trust from 00. *12 Bunyon Close, Pirton, Hitchin SG5 3RE* Tel (01462) 711846

GIBBS, Ian Edmund. b 47. Lon Univ BEd69. St Steph Ho Ox 72. **d** 75 **p** 76. C Stony Stratford *Ox* 75-79; V Forest Town *S'well* 79-83; R Diddlebury w Munslow, Holdgate and Tugford *Heref* from 83; R Abdon from 83. *The Rectory, Munslow, Craven Arms SY7 9ET* Tel (01584) 841688

GIBBS, James Millard. b 28. Univ of Michigan BSE51 Nottm Univ PhD68. Seabury-Western Th Sem BD57. **d** 57 **p** 57. USA 57-60; Lic to Offic *S'well* 61-62 and 65-66; C Brandon *Dur* 62-64; Vice-Prin Lich Th Coll 66-71; Lic to Offic *Lich* 66-71; India 72-77; Tutor Qu Coll Birm 78-84; V Stechford *Birm* 84-93; rtd 93; Perm to Offic *Birm* from 93. *13 Lingfield Court, 60 High Street, Harbourne, Birmingham B17 9NE* Tel 0121-426 2108

✠**GIBBS, The Rt Revd John.** b 17. Bris Univ BA42 Lon Univ BD48. Linc Th Coll 55. **d** 55 **p** 56 c 73. C Brislington St Luke *Bris* 55-57; Chapl St Matthias's Coll Bris 57-64; Vice-Prin 61-64; Prin Keswick Hall Coll of Educn 64-73; Lic to Offic *Nor* 64-73; Hon Can Nor Cathl 68-73; Suff Bp Bradwell *Chelmsf* 73-76; Bp Cov 76-85; rtd 85; Hon Asst Bp Bris and Glouc from 85. *Farthingloe, Southfield, Minchinhampton, Stroud GL6 9DY* Tel (01453) 886211

GIBBS, Jonathan Robert. b 61. Jes Coll Ox MA89 Jes Coll Cam PhD90. Ridley Hall Cam 84. **d** 89 **p** 90. C Stalybridge H Trin and Ch Ch *Chester* 89-92; Chapl Basle w Freiburg-im-Breisgau *Eur* 92-98; R Heswall *Chester* from 98. *The Rectory, Village Road, Heswall, Wirral CH60 0DZ* Tel 0151-342 3471 E-mail jgibbs@fish.co.uk

GIBBS, Mrs Patricia Louise. b 39. S'wark Ord Course 91. **d** 94 **p** 95. NSM Croydon H Sav *S'wark* from 94; Chapl Asst Mayday Healthcare NHS Trust Thornton Heath from 94. *41 Sandringham Road, Thornton Heath CR7 7AX* Tel (020) 8684 9720

GIBBS, Peter Winston. b 50. Ex Univ BA72 CQSW75. St Jo Coll Nottm DipTh. **d** 90 **p** 91. C Hampreston *Sarum* 90-94; P-in-c Ipswich St Matt *St E* 94-99; Assoc P Attenborough *S'well* 99-01; V Toton from 01. *95 Stapleford Lane, Toton, Beeston, Nottingham NG9 6FZ* Tel 0115-877 4771 E-mail ladybird1@ntlworld.com

GIBBS, Canon Philip Roscoe. b 33. Codrington Coll Barbados 57. **d** 60 **p** 61. Br Honduras 60-73; Belize 73-74; Hon Can Br Honduras 71-73; Hon Can Belize from 73; V Stoke Newington Common St Mich *Lon* 74-87; New Zealand from 87; rtd 93. *10 Gardener Street, Levin 5500, New Zealand* Tel (0064) (6) 367 9884

GIBBS, Raymond George. b 55. NTMTC 94. **d** 97 **p** 98. NSM Becontree S *Chelmsf* 97-99; C Dedham from 99. *84 Titus Way, Colchester CO4 5GB* Tel (01206) 502165 E-mail raymond.gibbs@ntlworld.com

GIBBS, Richard James. b 68. St Paul's Cheltenham BSc90 Nottm Univ MTh01. St Jo Coll Nottm 99. **d** 01 **p** 02. C Southport Ch Ch *Liv* from 01. *10 Sefton Street, Southport PR8 6SL* Tel (01704) 546294

GIBBS, Canon William Gilbert. b 31. Bps' Coll Cheshunt 55. **d** 58 **p** 59. C Wellington w W Buckland *B & W* 58-61; C Kensington St Mary Abbots w St Geo *Lon* 61-68; V Guilsborough *Pet* 68; V Guilsborough w Hollowell 68-74; V Guilsborough w Hollowell and Cold Ashby 74-98; Jt P-in-c Cottesbrooke w Gt Creaton and Thornby 83-98; Jt P-in-c Maidwell w Draughton, Lamport w Faxton 88-98; Can Pet Cathl 88-98; rtd 98; Perm to Offic *Pet* 98-01 and from 03; P-in-c W Haddon w Winwick and Ravensthorpe 01-03. *Paines Close, Maidwell, Northampton NN6 9JB* Tel (01604) 686424

GIBBS, William John Morris. b 71. Birm Univ BSc94. Ripon Coll Cuddesdon BTh00. **d** 00 **p** 01. C Staines St Mary and St Pet *Lon* 00-03; C Kensington St Mary Abbots w St Geo from 03. *Vicarage Cottage, Vicarage Gate, London W8 4HN* Tel (020) 7937 2364

GIBBY, Thomas Rees. b 12. St D Coll Lamp BA33 BD42. St Mich Coll Llan 33. **d** 35 **p** 36. C Llangeinor *Llan* 35-39; C Llantrisant 39-44; C Bideford *Ex* 44-45; R Langtree 45-58; P-in-c Lt Torrington 49-55; R 55-58; V Bradworthy 58-62; P-in-c W w E Putford 59-62; V Ivybridge 62-75; R Harford 63-75; RD Plympton 66-71; rtd 75; Perm to Offic *St D* from 75. *Penlon, Cwmann, Lampeter SA48 8DU* Tel (01570) 422100

GIBLIN, Brendan Anthony. b 64. K Coll Lon BD86 AKC93 Leeds Univ MA95. Wycliffe Hall Ox 90. **d** 92 **p** 93. C Tadcaster w Newton Kyme *York* 92-96; R Stockton-on-the-Forest w Holtby and Warthill 96-02; P-in-c Middleham w Coverdale and E Witton etc *Ripon* 02-03; R from 03. *The Rectory, The Springs, Middleham, Leyburn DL8 4RB* Tel (01969) 622276 E-mail rev.brendan@virgin.net

GIBLING, Derek Vivian. b 31. Wadh Coll Ox BA56 MA63. Wycliffe Hall Ox 70. **d** 72 **p** 73. C Fisherton Anger *Sarum* 72-74; C Yatton Keynell *Bris* 74-77; C Castle Combe 74-77; C Biddestone w Slaughterford 74-77; P-in-c Youlgreave *Derby* 77-82; P-in-c Stanton-in-Peak 77-82; V Youlgreave, Middleton, Stanton-in-Peak etc 82-88; P-in-c Hartington and Biggin 88-90; V Hartington, Biggin and Earl Sterndale 90-96; rtd 96; Perm to Offic *Linc* 96-02; RD Bolingbroke 00-02. *The Hawthorns, Church Lane, West Keal, Spilsby PE23 4BG* Tel (01790) 754762

GIBRALTAR IN EUROPE, Bishop of. *See* ROWELL, The Rt Revd Douglas Geoffrey

GIBRALTAR, Archdeacon of. *See* SASSER, Col the Ven Howell Crawford

GIBRALTAR, Dean of. *See* WOODS, The Very Revd Alan Geoffrey

GIBSON, Alan. b 35. Birm Univ BSc56 Man Univ MSc72. NW Ord Course 71. **d** 74 **p** 75. C Sale St Anne *Ches* 74-77; V Runcorn St Mich 77-82; Educn Adv *Carl* 82-88; P-in-c Hugill 82-88; V Grange-over-Sands 88-97; rtd 97; Perm to Offic *Derby* from 01. *11 Ecclesbourne Drive, Buxton SK17 9BX* Tel (01298) 22621

GIBSON, Alexander Douglas. b 21. Wycliffe Hall Ox 60. **d** 62 **p** 63. C St Helens St Helen *Liv* 62-65; V Gresley *Derby* 65-77; V Hartington 77-78; V Biggin 77-78; V Hartington and Biggin 78-88; rtd 88; Perm to Offic *Derby* from 88. *Westmead, Aldern Way, Baslow Road, Bakewell DE45 1AJ* Tel (01629) 812723 E-mail doug.gibson2@virgin.net

GIBSON, Anthony Richard. b 43. Ridley Hall Cam 83. **d** 85 **p** 86. C Rushmere *St E* 85-88; P-in-c N Tawton and Bondleigh *Ex* 88; P-in-c Sampford Courtenay w Honeychurch 88; R N Tawton, Bondleigh, Sampford Courtenay etc 88-93; RD Okehampton 92-93; P-in-c Tiverton St Pet 93-95; P-in-c Tiverton St Pet and Chevithorne w Cove from 95. *St Peter's Rectory, 32 The Avenue, Tiverton EX16 4HW* Tel (01884) 254079

GIBSON, Catherine Snyder. b 39. Parson's Sch of Design (NY) 57. Ab Dioc Tr Course 82 Edin Th Coll 92. **d** 86 **p** 94. Colombia 86-87; NSM Aberdeen St Marg *Ab* 87-88; Dioc Hosp Chapl 89-92; C Aberdeen St Mary 93-94; Bp's Chapl for Tr and Educn 93-94; P-in-c Ballater 95-96; R 96-98; P-in-c Aboyne 95-96; R 96-98; P-in-c Braemar 95-97; USA from 98; Assoc P Fort Lauderdale from 98. *1250 South East 2nd Street, Fort Lauderdale, FL 33301, USA* Tel (001) (561) 524 3977 *or* 467 6496 E-mail ksgib@mindspring.com

GIBSON, Charles Daniel. b 48. **d** 03. OLM Wisley w Pyrford *Guildf* from 03. *The Corner Cottage, Send Marsh Road, Ripley, Woking GU23 6JN* Tel (01483) 225317 Fax 223681 E-mail charles@chas01.freeserve.co.uk

GIBSON, Colin Taylor. b 54. Trin Coll Cam BA77. Oak Hill Th Coll DipHE88. **d** 88 **p** 89. C Thrybergh w Hooton Roberts *Sheff* 88-91; P-in-c Tinsley 91-96; TV Attercliffe, Darnall and Tinsley 96-02; TR Walsall *Lich* from 02. *St Matthew's Rectory, 48 Jesson Road, Walsall WS1 3AX* Tel (01922) 624012 E-mail c.t.gibson@btinternet.com

GIBSON, David Francis. b 36. Magd Coll Cam BA57 BChir60 MB61. SW Minl Tr Course 84. **d** 90 **p** 91. NSM Newport, Bishops Tawton and Tawstock *Ex* 90-95; Chapl N Devon Healthcare NHS Trust 95-96; Perm to Offic *Ex* from 96. *Little Beara, Marwood, Barnstaple EX31 4EH* Tel (01271) 814876

GIBSON, David Innes. b 31. NDD53. Oak Hill Th Coll 56. **d** 59 **p** 60. C S Croydon Em *Cant* 59-62; C Washfield *Ex* 62-63; Asst Master and Chapl Blundells Sch Tiverton 63-64; Chapl Sutton Valence Sch Maidstone 64-68; Chapl Dean Close Sch Cheltenham 68-75; Asst Chapl and Ho Master 75-85; Asst Master Brightlands Sch Newnham-on-Severn 85-90; C Cheltenham St Mary, St Matt, St Paul and H Trin *Glouc* 91-96; rtd 96; Perm to Offic *Glouc* 96-97; and from 01. *2 Withyholt Park, Charlton Kings, Cheltenham GL53 9BP* Tel (01242) 511612

GIBSON, Douglas. *See* GIBSON, Alexander Douglas

GIBSON, Douglas Harold. b 20. Portsm Dioc Tr Course. **d** 87. NSM Portsea St Luke *Portsm* 87-92; Perm to Offic from 92. *83 Middle Street, Southsea PO5 4BW* Tel (023) 9282 9769

GIBSON, Garry Stuart. b 36. Univ Coll Lon BA62 PhD75 Birkbeck Coll Lon BA79. Oak Hill Th Coll. **d** 64 **p** 65. C Watford St Mary *St Alb* 64-67; Lect Cambridgeshire Coll of Arts and Tech 67-69; Government of Israel Scholar Hebrew Univ 69-70; Asst Master Angl Sch Jerusalem 69-70; Sen Lect RS and Philosophy Middx Univ 70-97; Perm to Offic *Lon* 91-93 and *Ex* 94-96; Hon C Sidmouth, Woolbrook, Salcombe Regis, Sidbury etc *Ex* 96-99; C Stockland, Dalwood, Kilmington and Shute 99-03; C Kilmington, Stockland, Dalwood, Yarcombe etc from 03; rtd 03; rtd 01. *The Vicarage, Dalwood, Honiton EX14 9EF* Tel (01404) 881401 E-mail garrygib@yahoo.co.uk

GIBSON, The Ven George Granville. b 36. Cuddesdon Coll 69. **d** 71 **p** 72. C Tynemouth Cullercoats St Paul *Newc* 71-73; TV Cramlington 73-77; V Newton Aycliffe *Dur* 77-85; R Bishopwearmouth St Mich w St Hilda 85-90; TR Sunderland 90-93; RD Wearmouth 85-93; Hon Can Dur Cathl 88-01; Adn Auckland 93-01; rtd 01. *12 West Crescent, Darlington DL3 7PR* Tel (01325) 462526 E-mail granville.gibson@durham.anglican.org

GIBSON, Henry Edward. b 15. Keble Coll Ox BA41 DipTh42 MA46. St Steph Ho Ox 41. **d** 43 **p** 44. C Summertown *Ox* 43-49; Warden Youth Ho and Youth Org Scottish Episc Ch 49-51; C Farlington *Portsm* 51-56; V Ryde H Trin 56-63; V Waterlooville 63-81; rtd 81; Perm to Offic *Portsm* 81-96; *Chich* from 81. *8 Worcester Road, Chichester PO19 5DJ* Tel (01243) 779194

GIBSON, Ian. b 48. Open Univ BA85 MSc MCIPD MCMI. S Dios Minl Tr Scheme 82. **d** 85 **p** 86. NSM Uckfield *Chich* 85-88; NSM Lt Horsted 85-88; NSM Isfield 85-88; V Fairwarp 88-93; P-in-c 94-00; V High Hurstwood 88-93; P-in-c 94-00; NSM Fairwarp from 00. *The Vicarage, Fairwarp, Uckfield TN29 3BL* Tel (01825) 712277 Fax 713557 E-mail tigtrain@cs.com

GIBSON, John Murray Hope. b 35. Dur Univ BA58 DipTh60. Cranmer Hall Dur 58. **d** 60 **p** 61. C Chester le Street *Dur* 60-63; C Stockton 63-68; V Denton and Ingleton 68-75; V Swalwell 75-00; Chapl Dunston Hill Hosp Gateshead 80-99; rtd 00; Perm to Offic *Dur* and *Newc* from 01. *50 Church Road, Gosforth, Newcastle upon Tyne NE3 1BJ* Tel 0191-285 2942

GIBSON, Canon John Noel Keith. b 22. MBE89. Ch Coll Cam MA48 Lon Univ BD59. Coll of Resurr Mirfield 45. **d** 47 **p** 48. C S Elmsall *Wakef* 47-51; Antigua 51-56; Virgin Is from 56; Can All SS Cath Wakef 92. PO Box 65, Valley, Virgin Gorda, British Virgin Islands* Tel (001284) 495 5587

GIBSON, Kenneth George Goudie. b 54. Glas Univ MA83 Edin Univ BD87 Strathclyde Univ PGCE95. Edin Th Coll 83. **d** 88 **p** 89. C Glas St Marg *Glas* 88-90; R E Kilbride 90-98; R Carnoustie *Bre* from 98. *Holy Rood Rectory, 58 Maule Street, Carnoustie DD7 6AB* Tel (01241) 852202 E-mail revkgibson@ukonline.co.uk

GIBSON, Laura Mary. *See* WILFORD, Laura Mary

GIBSON, Mark. b 48. OSB from 67; Abbot of Alton 82-90; Perm to Offic *Win* 84-95; NSM Paddington St Sav *Lon* from 90; Acting Bp's Chapl 90-91; Perm to Offic 91-94; NSM Paddington St Mary from 95; NSM Paddington St Mary Magd from 98. *6 Park Place Villas, London W2 1SP* Tel (020) 7262 3787 *or* 7724 7444

GIBSON, Nigel Stephen David. b 53. St Barn Coll Adelaide DipMin87. **d** 87 **p** 87. Australia 87-89; Lect Boston *Linc* 90-91; P-in-c Stamford St Mary and St Mich 91-92; P-in-c Stamford Baron 91-92; R Stamford St Mary and St Martin 92-98; Perm to Offic 98-00; V Kempston Transfiguration *St Alb* from 00. *The Vicarage, Cleveland Street, Kempston, Bedford MK42 8DW* Tel (01234) 854788 E-mail frnigel@boxingkangaroo.org.uk

GIBSON, Mrs Patricia Elizabeth. b 57. EAMTC MA02. **d** 02 **p** 03. C Wigston Magna *Leic* from 02. *163 Little Glen Road, Leicester LE2 9TX* Tel 0116-277 4275 E-mail tgibson@leicester.anglican.org

GIBSON, Paul Saison. b 32. BA LTh Huron Coll Ontario Hon DD90. Coll of Em and St Chad Hon DD88 Vancouver Sch of Th Hon DD95 Montreal Dioc Th Coll Hon DD98 Trin Coll Toronto Hon DD99. **d** 56 **p** 57. C Bloomsbury St Geo w St Jo *Lon* 56-59; R Homer St Geo Canada 59-60; Chapl McGill Univ Montreal 60-66; Prin Hong Kong Union Th Coll 66-72; Consultant Angl Ch of Canada 72-82; Liturg Officer 82-98. *588 Millwood Road, Toronto ON, Canada, M4S 1K8* Tel (001) (416) 487 2008

GIBSON, Philip Nigel Scott. b 53. St Jo Coll Dur BA78. Cranmer Hall Dur DipTh79. **d** 79 **p** 80. C Yardley St Edburgha *Birm* 79-82; C Stratford-on-Avon w Bishopton *Cov* 82-84; Chapl SW Hosp Lon 84-91; Chapl St Thos Hosp Lon 84-91; Assoc P Newington St Paul *S'wark* 91-92; Chapl Charing Cross Hosp Lon 92-93; Chapl R Lon Hosp (Whitechapel) 93-94; Chapl Bedford Hosp NHS Trust from 95; Lic to Offic *St Alb* from 95. *Chaplain's Office, Bedford Hospital, South Wing, Kempston Road, Bedford MK42 9DJ* Tel (01234) 355122

GIBSON, Raymond. b 23. Ely Th Coll 60. **d** 62 **p** 63. C Leic St Jas *Leic* 62-67; Succ Leic Cathl 67-68; Chapl Leic R Infirmary 67-68; Chapl Nottm City Hosp 68-84; V Barlings *Linc* 84-88; rtd 88. *11 Cornell Drive, Nottingham NG5 8RF*

GIBSON, Raymond Frank. b 34. Toronto Bible Coll BTh61 Tyndale Hall Bris 62. **d** 64 **p** 65. C Gt Horton *Bradf* 64-67; C Otley 67-72; V Fairlight *Chich* 72-83; V Hallwood *Ches* 83-85; R Freethorpe, Wickhampton, Halvergate w Tunstall *Nor* 85-99; P-in-c Reedham w Cantley w Limpenhoe and Southwood 94-99; rtd 99; Perm to Offic *Nor* from 99. *8 Waters Avenue, Carlton Colville, Lowestoft NR33 8BJ* Tel (01502) 537522

GIBSON, Canon Robert Swinton. b 26. Wadh Coll Ox BA50 MA55. Wells Th Coll 50. **d** 53 **p** 54. C Greenwich St Alfege w St Pet *S'wark* 53-61; Ind Missr 55-62; Hon Chapl to Bp S'wark 56-67; Sen Chapl S Lon Ind Miss 62-67; Nigeria 67-69; R Guisborough *York* 69-83; RD Guisborough 73-83; TR Halifax *Wakef* 83-94; Hon Can Wakef Cathl 85-94; RD Halifax 86-92; rtd 94; Perm to Offic *Wakef* and *York* from 94. *The Cottage, Main Street, Hutton Buscel, Scarborough YO13 9LL* Tel (01723) 862133

GIBSON, The Ven Terence Allen. b 37. Jes Coll Cam BA61 MA65. Cuddesdon Coll 61. **d** 63 **p** 64. C Kirkby *Liv* 63-66; TV 72-75; TR 75-84; Warden Cen 63 66-75; Youth Chapl 66-72; RD Walton 79-84; Adn Suffolk *St E* 84-87; Adn Ipswich from 87. *99 Valley Road, Ipswich IP1 4NF* Tel (01473) 250333 Fax 286877 E-mail archdeacon.terry@stedmundsbury.anglican.org

GIBSON, Thomas Thomson. b 23. Sarum Th Coll 62. **d** 63 **p** 64. C E w W Harnham *Sarum* 63-66; V Rowde 66-74; R Poulshot 67-74; V Badminton w Acton Turville *Glouc* 74-84; P-in-c

Hawkesbury 81-84; V Badminton w Lt Badminton, Acton Turville etc 84-93; rtd 93; Perm to Offic *Glouc* 93-96 and from 01; *B & W* and *Sarum* from 95; *Eur* from 99. *9 Lansdown Place West, Bath BA1 5EZ* Tel (01225) 337903 Fax 483676

GIDDENS, Leslie Vernon. b 29. Bps' Coll Cheshunt 54. **d** 56 **p** 57. C Harrow St Pet *Lon* 56-58; C Tottenham St Benet Fink 58-63; C-in-c Hayes St Nic CD 63-94; rtd 94; Perm to Offic *Lon* from 94. *6 Ashdown Road, Uxbridge UB10 0HY* Tel (01895) 232406

GIDDEY, Canon William Denys. b 17. Leeds Univ BA39. Coll of Resurr Mirfield 39. **d** 41 **p** 42. C Weymouth St Paul *Sarum* 41-43; C St Geo-in-the-East St Mary *Lon* 43-48; R Binbrook *Linc* 48-61; R Swinhope w Thorganby 48-61; Chapl Eastbourne Hosp Gp 61-83; Can and Preb Chich Cathl *Chich* 78-90; rtd 82; Perm to Offic *Chich* from 90. *c/o S C Giddey Esq, 21 Grange Road, Lewes BN7 1TS*

GIDDINGS, Mrs Jaqueline Mary. b 44. St Aid Coll Dur BA67. SW Minl Tr Course 91. **d** 94 **p** 95. C Plympton St Mary *Ex* 94-02; rtd 02. *Grange End, Harrowbeer Lane, Yelverton PL20 6EA* Tel (01822) 854825

GIDDINGS, John Norton Cornock. b 22. **d** 86 **p** 87. NSM Cromhall w Tortworth and Tytherington *Glouc* 86-90; Hon C Stockland w Dalwood *Ex* 90-95; Perm to Offic from 95. *22 Scalwell Lane, Seaton EX12 2JP*

GIFFORD-COLE, David Henry. b 30. San Francisco Th Sem DMin87 ALCD56. **d** 56 **p** 57. C Ashtead *Guildf* 56-59; C Farnham 59-60; Canada from 60. *225 Hoylake Road West, Qualicum Beach BC, Canada, V9K 1K5*

✠**GILBERD, The Rt Revd Bruce Carlyle.** b 38. Auckland Univ BSc59. St Jo Coll Auckland LTh64 STh74. **d** 62 **p** 64 **c** 85. New Zealand 62-71 and from 73; C Devonport 62-64; C Ponsony and Grey Lynn 65; P Asst Panmure 66-68; V Avondale 68-71; Ind Chapl and C Eaglescliffe *Dur* 71-73; Dir Ind Miss Wellington 73-79; Dir Th Educn by Ext 80-85; Bp Auckland 85-94; P-in-c Albany Greenhithe 95-00; P-in-c Tamaki St Thos 96-00; Chapl K Sch 97-00; rtd 00. *81 Manaia Road, Tairua, via Thames, New Zealand* Tel (0064) (7) 864 8727

GILBERT, Anthony John David. b 54. LRSC83 Open Univ BA91. Ripon Coll Cuddesdon 83. **d** 86 **p** 87. C Exning St Martin w Landwade *St E* 86-89; Chapl RAF from 89. *Chaplaincy Services (RAF), HQ, Personnel and Training Command, RAF Innsworth, Gloucester GL3 1EZ* Tel (01452) 712612 ext 5164 Fax 510828

GILBERT, Arthur John. b 57. LTCL76 GBSM79 Reading Univ PGCE80. Coll of Resurr Mirfield 88. **d** 91 **p** 92. C Uppingham w Ayston and Wardley w Belton *Pet* 91-94; C Armley w New Wortley *Ripon* 94-96; V Doncaster St Jude *Sheff* from 96; AD W Doncaster from 00. *St Jude's Vicarage, 2 Riverside Close, Doncaster DN4 0HW* Tel (01302) 852057 Fax 310716 E-mail posaune@ic24.net

GILBERT, Barry. b 46. Leeds Univ BA67. Coll of Resurr Mirfield 67. **d** 69 **p** 70. C Malvern Link w Cowleigh *Worc* 69-73; P-in-c Bromsgrove All SS 73-81; V 81-83; P-in-c Lower Mitton 83-88; V 88-92; V Stourport and Wilden from 92; RD Stourport 93-00 and from 02. *The Vicarage, Church Avenue, Stourport-on-Severn DY13 9DD* Tel (01299) 822041 E-mail barry_gilbert@talk21.com

GILBERT, Caroline Margaret. b 62. Nottm Univ BTh90. St Jo Coll Nottm 87. **d** 90. Hon C Aston SS Pet and Paul *Birm* 90-93. *Address temp unknown*

GILBERT, Miss Christine Lesley. b 44. DipHE. Trin Coll Bris 79. **dss** 85 **d** 86 **p** 94. Par Dn Bilston *Lich* 87-94; TV Penkridge Team 94-98; Bp's Soc and Ind Adv *Bris* 98-03; Hon C Swindon All SS w St Barn 98-03; rtd 03. *15 Ridgeway Court, East Street, Warminster BA12 9AT* Tel (01985) 216770 Mobile 07759-977794 E-mail chrisgilb@aol.com

GILBERT, Christopher Anthony. b 60. Aston Univ BSc82. St Jo Coll Nottm 86. **d** 89 **p** 90. C Aston SS Pet and Paul *Birm* 89-93; TV Parr *Liv* 93-97; TV Cannock *Lich* 97-01. *Address temp unknown*

GILBERT, Clive Franklyn. b 55. City of Liv Coll of HE CertEd76 BEd77. SEITE 01. **d** 02 **p** 03. C Paddock Wood *Roch* from 02. *3 Ashcroft Road, Paddock Wood, Tonbridge TN12 6LG* Tel (01892) 833194 Mobile 07752-676663 E-mail gilbert_clive@hotmail.com

GILBERT, Frederick Herbert. b 14. Worc Ord Coll 64. **d** 66 **p** 67. C Ex St Paul *Ex* 66-69; C Paignton Ch Ch 69-73; TV Offwell, Widworthy, Cotleigh, Farway etc 73-79; rtd 80; Lic to Offic *Ex* 80-95; Perm to Offic from 95. *17 Hoskings Court, Strode Road, Buckfastleigh TQ11 0PF* Tel (01364) 643321

GILBERT, Frederick Joseph. b 29. Lich Th Coll 58. **d** 59 **p** 60. C Westhoughton *Man* 59-62; V Goodshaw 62-68; R Crumpsall St Matt 68-75; RD Cheetham 70-74; RD N Man 74-75; V Rochdale St Aid 75-78; TV Rochdale 78-80; V Westhoughton 80-84; TR 84-87; AD Deane 85-87; R W Bowbrook *Worc* 87-89; R Bowbrook N 89-93; rtd 93; Perm to Offic *Worc* from 93. *Freshways, Main Road, Peopleton, Pershore WR10 2EG* Tel (01905) 841629

GILBERT, John. See GILBERT, Arthur John

GILBERT, John Edwin. b 28. FCA62. Bps' Coll Cheshunt 54. **d** 57 **p** 58. C Luton Ch Ch *St Alb* 57-60; C Gt Berkhamsted 60-64; P-in-c Kemptee India 65-68; Hon Chapl Nagpur Cathl 68-70; Dioc Treas Nagpur 65-70; Perm to Offic *St Alb* 71-77; Lic to Offic 77-86; Hon C Sunnyside w Bourne End 86-89; TV Padgate *Liv* 89-94; rtd 94; Perm to Offic *Heref* from 94. *4 Westgate Drive, Bridgnorth WV16 4QF* Tel (01746) 762611

GILBERT, Joseph. b 12. Chich Th Coll 33. **d** 36 **p** 37. C Bolton St Mark *Man* 36-39; C Withington St Crispin 39-43; R Ardwick St Matt 43-49; V Heyside 49-65; V Lever Bridge 65-76; rtd 77; Perm to Offic *Man* from 77. *159 Bolton Road, Turton, Bolton BL7 0AF* Tel (01204) 852736

GILBERT, Mrs Margaret Ann. b 39. Dub Inst of Adult Educn Dip Past Min 89 TCD DipTh91. CITC 89. **d** 92 **p** 93. NSM Dublin Clontarf *D & G* 92-96; NSM Dublin Santry w Glasnevin and Finglas from 96. *67 Grange Park Road, Raheny, Dublin 5, Irish Republic* Tel (00353) (1) 848 1340

GILBERT, Ms Mary Rose. b 63. Ridley Hall Cam 94. **d** 97 **p** 97. C Walsall Wood *Lich* 97-00; TV Bilston from 00; AD Wolverhampton from 03. *St Chad's Vicarage, 8 Cumberland Road, Bilston WV14 6LT* Tel (01902) 497794 E-mail mgdartford@aol.com

GILBERT, Michael Victor. b 61. Dur Univ BA84 Westhill Coll Birm CYCW86. Trin Coll Bris DipTh94. **d** 94 **p** 95. C Chapeltown *Sheff* 94-97; V Brightside w Wincobank from 97. *The Vicarage, 24 Beacon Road, Sheffield S9 1AD* Tel 0114-281 9360 E-mail mike@thegilberts.f9.co.uk

GILBERT, Philip Mark. b 62. Liv Univ BA84 SSC. Coll of Resurr Mirfield 84. **d** 87 **p** 88. C Frodsham *Ches* 87-89; C Stockton Heath 89-92; R Tangmere and Oving *Chich* 92-01; P-in-c Graffham w Woolavington from 01; Chapl Seaford Coll Petworth from 01. *The Rectory, Graffham, Petworth GU28 0NL* Tel (01798) 867247 *or* 867851 Mobile 07810-004062 E-mail frmark@mgilbert.clara.co.uk

GILBERT, Raymond. b 34. AKC61. **d** 62 **p** 63. C Newbold w Dunston *Derby* 62-66; PV and Succ S'wark Cathl *S'wark* 66-68; P-in-c Stuntney *Ely* 68-74; Prec and Sacr Ely Cathl 68-74; Min Can Cant Cathl *Cant* 74-79; Hon Min Can 79-00; P-in-c Patrixbourne w Bridge and Bekesbourne 79-81; V 81-00; RD E Bridge 92-98; rtd 00. *16 Green Acres, Eythorne, Dover CT15 4LX* Tel (01304) 831485

GILBERT, Raymond Frederick. b 44. LNSM course 91. **d** 93 **p** 94. OLM Stowmarket *St E* from 93. *3 Violet Hill Road, Stowmarket IP14 1NE* Tel (01449) 677700

GILBERT, Roger Charles. b 46. Ex Coll Ox BA69 MA74 Nottm Univ MEd81. St Steph Ho Ox 69. **d** 71 **p** 72. NSM Bridgwater St Mary w Chilton Trinity *B & W* 71-74; NSM Rugeley *Lich* 74-81; NSM Cannock 81-83; NSM Wednesbury St Jas and St Jo from 83. *41 Stafford Road, Cannock WS11 4AF* Tel (01543) 570531 *or* 0121-505 1188

GILBERT, Canon Roger Geoffrey. b 37. K Coll Lon BD69 AKC69. **d** 70 **p** 71. C Walton-on-Thames *Guildf* 70-74; R St Mabyn *Truro* 74-81; P-in-c Helland 74-81; P-in-c Madron 81-86; R Falmouth K Chas 86-02; Hon Can Truro Cathl 94-02; RD Carnmarth S 94-00; Chapl to The Queen from 95; rtd 02. *2 rue de Plouzon, 22690 Pleudihen-sur-Rance, France* Tel (0033) (2) 96 88 28 69

GILBERT, Roy Alan. b 48. Birm Univ BEd70 Lon Univ DipTh79. Ripon Coll Cuddesdon 74. **d** 76 **p** 77. C Moseley St Mary *Birm* 76-82; Australia from 82. *Guildford Grammar School, 11 Terrace Road, Guildford, W Australia 6055* Tel (0061) (8) 9377 9245, 9377 9222 *or* 9279 1135 Fax 9377 3140 E-mail rgilbert@ggs.wa.edu.au

GILBERT, Sidney Horace. b 34. Dur Univ BA58 MA69 Univ of Wales BD62 CertEd83. St Mich Coll Llan 58. **d** 61 **p** 62. C Colwyn Bay *St As* 61-63; C Llanrhos 63-69; R Penley and Bettisfield 69-78; V Brymbo and Bwlchgwyn 78-82; Univ of Wales (Swansea) *S & B* 82-83; R Beeston Regis *Nor* 84-97; Holiday Chapl 84-91; Sen Chapl 91-97; V Llanwddyn and Llanfihangel-yng-Nghwynfa etc *St As* 97-99; rtd 99; Perm to Offic *Ches* from 01. *Mountain View, 23 Holyrood Crescent, Wrexham LL11 2EN* Tel (01978) 352707

GILBERTSON, Michael Robert. b 61. New Coll Ox BA82 MA92 Dur Univ PhD97. St Jo Coll Dur BA91. **d** 97 **p** 98. C Surbiton St Matt *S'wark* 97-00; V Stranton *Dur* from 00; AD Hartlepool from 02. *The Vicarage, 34 Westbourne Road, Hartlepool TS25 5RE* Tel (01429) 263190 Fax 400118 E-mail mikegilbertson@supanet.com

GILCHRIST, David John. b 51. Mert Coll Ox BA75 MA79 Nottm Univ DipTh77. St Jo Coll Nottm DPS79. **d** 79 **p** 80. C Gt Ilford St Andr *Chelmsf* 79-81; C Buckhurst Hill 81-84; Chapl Dover Coll 84-95; Chapl Brentwood Sch Essex from 95; Perm to Offic *Chelmsf* from 96. *Brentwood School, Brentwood CM15 8AS* Tel (01277) 214580 E-mail djgilchrist@brentwood.essex.sch.uk

GILCHRIST, Gavin Frank. b 53. AKC74. Coll of Resurr Mirfield 76. **d** 77 **p** 78. C Newbold w Dunston *Derby* 77-80; C Addlestone

Guildf 80-84; V Blackpool St Mary *Blackb* 84-92; P-in-c Carl St Herbert w St Steph *Carl* 92-97; V 97-01; V Tynemouth Cullercoats St Paul *Newc* from 01. *The Vicarage, 53 Grosvenor Drive, Whitley Bay NE26 2JR* Tel 0191-252 4916 Fax as telephone E-mail fr.gavin.gilchrist@virgin.net

GILCHRIST, Lawrence Edward. b 29. Liv Univ BSc52. NW Ord Course 74. **d** 76 **p** 77. NSM Buxton w Burbage and King Sterndale *Derby* 76-83; V Chinley w Buxworth 83-94; rtd 94; Perm to Offic *St E* 94-03. *9 Santingley Lane, New Crofton, Wakefield WF4 1LG* Tel (01924) 860262

GILCHRIST, Spencer. b 66. QUB BA88 BTh. **d** 91 **p** 92. C Ballynafeigh St Jude *D & D* 91-97; I Connor w Antrim St Patr *Conn* from 97. *Connor Rectory, Church Road, Kells, Ballymena BT42 3JU* Tel (028) 2589 1254

GILDING, James <u>Peter</u>. b 33. Leeds Univ BA64. Ely Th Coll 61. **d** 63 **p** 64. C Chorley St Pet *Blackb* 63-66; C Pemberton St Fran Kitt Green *Liv* 66-69; P-in-c Terrington St John *Ely* 69-74; P-in-c Walpole St Andrew 69-74; V Elm 74-81; TR Stanground and Farcet 81-89; V Haslingfield 89-95; R Harlton 89-95; R Haslingfield w Harlton and Gt and L Eversden 95-96; rtd 96; Perm to Offic *York* from 98. *14 Main Street, Bishop Wilton, York YO42 1RX* Tel (01759) 368510

GILES, Anthony Richard. b 68. Nottm Univ BA00. St Jo Coll Nottm 98. **d** 01 **p** 02. C Chellaston *Derby* from 01. *30 Acrefield Way, Chellaston, Derby DE73 1PN* Tel (01332) 705504 E-mail argiles@isaiah53.freeserve.uk

GILES, Canon Barry James. b 35. Kelham Th Coll 54. **d** 59 **p** 60. C Leytonstone St Marg w St Columba *Chelmsf* 59-62; Prec Gib Cathl *Eur* 62-66; V Darwen St Geo *Blackb* 66-69; V Forest Gate St Edm *Chelmsf* 69-73; R Jersey St Pet *Win* 73-00; Vice-Dean Jersey 84-00; Hon Can Win Cathl 93-00; rtd 00; Perm to Offic *Chich* from 00. *St Pierre, 5 Bracken Road, Eastbourne BN20 8SH* Tel (01323) 439240 E-mail beejaygee.giles@btopenworld.com

GILES, Brother. See SPRENT, Michael Francis

GILES, Edward Alban. b 34. Bps' Coll Cheshunt. **d** 58 **p** 59. C Colne St Bart *Blackb* 58-61; C Warrington St Paul *Liv* 61-63; S Africa 63-70; Chapl HM Pris Camp Hill 70-75; Chapl HM Pris Stafford 75-83; Chapl HM YOI Hollesley Bay Colony 83-94; rtd 94; Sub-Chapl HM Pris Blundeston from 94; Perm to Offic *Nor* 94-00; Perm to Offic *St E* from 94. *The Hollies, Ferry Farm Drive, Sutton Hoo, Woodbridge IP12 3DR* Tel (01394) 387486 E-mail eag1@onetel.net.uk

GILES, Canon Eric Francis. b 34. Sarum Th Coll 61. **d** 63 **p** 64. C Plympton St Mary *Ex* 63-71; R Dumbleton w Wormington *Glouc* 71-77; P-in-c Toddington w Stanley Pontlarge 71-77; R Dumbleton w Wormington and Toddington 77-79; V Churchdown St Jo 79-99; Hon Can Glouc Cathl 95-99; rtd 99; Perm to Offic *Glouc* from 99. *25 Station Road, Pershore WR10 1PN* Tel (01386) 554246

GILES, Gordon John. b 66. Lanc Univ BA88 Magd Coll Cam MLitt95. Ridley Hall Cam BA95 CTM95. **d** 95 **p** 96. C Chesterton Gd Shep *Ely* 95-98; Min Can and Succ St Paul's Cathl *Lon* 98-03; V Enfield Chase St Mary from 03. *St Mary Magdalene Vicarage, 30 The Ridgeway, Enfield EN2 8QH* Tel (020) 8363 1875 E-mail vicar@saintmarymagdalene.org.uk

GILES, Graeme John. b 56. Linc Th Coll 82. **d** 85 **p** 86. C Prestbury *Glouc* 85-88; C Paulsgrove *Portsm* 88-96; V Friern Barnet St Pet le Poer *Lon* from 96. *St Peter's Presbytery, 163 Colney Hatch Lane, London N10 1HA* Tel (020) 8883 1526 Mobile 07973-892861 E-mail graeme@priest.com

GILES (née WILLIAMS), Mrs Gwenllian. b 34. RSCN55 SRN58 SCM60. WMMTC 88. **d** 92 **p** 94. NSM Bromsgrove St Jo *Worc* 92-00; Perm to Offic 00-03; P-in-c Clifton-on-Teme, Lower Sapey and the Shelsleys from 03. *The Rectory, Church Road, Clifton-on-Teme, Worcester WR6 6DJ* Tel (01886) 812483

GILES, Canon John Robert. b 36. Em Coll Cam BA60 MA65. Ripon Hall Ox 60. **d** 61 **p** 62. C Lowestoft St Marg *Nor* 61-65; Chapl UEA 65-72; R Kidbrooke St Jas *S'wark* 72-79; Sub-Dean Greenwich 74-79; V Sheff St Mark Broomhall *Sheff* 79-87; Ind Chapl 79-92; Can Res Sheff Cathl 87-92; V Ken and Rep St Pet *S'wark* 92-98; rtd 98. *25 The Terrace, Aldeburgh IP15 5HJ* Tel (01728) 452319

GILES, Kevin Norman. b 40. Lon Univ BD69 DipRE69 Dur Univ MA74 ACT ThD90. ThL67 MTh78. **d** 68 **p** 69. Australia 69-72 and from 75; TV Chester le Street *Dur* 73-74; Chapl Tubingen Univ W Germany 75; Chapl Armidale Univ 75-80; R Kensington 81-95; I N Carlton St Mich from 96. *44 Arnold Street, North Carlton, Vic, Australia 3054* Tel (0061) (3) 9387 7214 *or* 9380 6387 Fax 9388 9050 E-mail k.giles@melbpc.org.au

GILES, Peter Michael Osmaston. b 40. Solicitor 65. S Dios Minl Tr Scheme 85. **d** 88 **p** 89. Hon C Wootton Bassett *Sarum* 88-90; Lic to RD Calne from 91; RD Calne from 98; Chapl St Mary's Sch Calne from 00. *The Old Vicarage, Honeyhill, Wootton Bassett, Swindon SN4 7DY* Tel (01793) 852643 Fax 853191

GILES, The Very Revd Richard Stephen. b 40. Newc Univ BA63 MLitt88 MRTPI71. Cuddesdon Coll 64. **d** 65 **p** 66. C Higham Ferrers w Chelveston *Pet* 65-68; Perm to Offic *Ox* 69; C Oakengates *Lich* 70; C Stevenage St Geo *St Alb* 71-75; P-in-c

---

Howdon Panns *Newc* 75-76; TV Willington Team 76-79; Bp's Adv for Planning *Pet* 79-87; V Pet St Jude 79-87; Par Development Officer *Wakef* 87-99; P-in-c Huddersfield St Thos 87-93; V 93-99; Hon Can Wakef Cathl 94-99; Can Th Wakef Cathl 98-99; Dean Philadelphia USA from 99. *3723 Chestnut Street, Philadelphia, PA 19104-3189, USA* Tel (001) (215) 386 0234 Fax 386 5009 E-mail philadean@aol.com

GILES, Robert Medwin. b 37. Man Univ BA(Econ)58 PGCE59. Ripon Hall Ox 64. **d** 66 **p** 67. C Peel *Man* 66-69; C Alverstoke *Portsm* 69-71; P-in-c Edale *Derby* 71-79; Warden Champion Ho Youth Tr Cen 71-79; Sen Youth Officer *York* 79-86; P-in-c Shipley *Chich* 86-87; V 87-91; Area Sec USPG *Pet* and *St Alb* 91-92; R Broughton w Loddington and Cransley etc *Pet* 92-02; RD Kettering 99-02; rtd 02. *Stone Cottage, Croft Lane, Staverton, Daventry NN11 6JE* Tel (01327) 705193 E-mail bobgiles@bgiles.demon.co.uk *or* bobandjoan@talk21.com

GILES, Susan Jane. b 58. BSc. dss 83 **d** 92 **p** 94. Balsall Heath St Paul *Birm* 83-85; Asst Chapl Southmead Hosp Bris 86-90; Asst Chapl HM Rem Cen Pucklechurch 90-96; Asst Chapl HM Pris Bris 92-98; Chapl HM Pris Shepton Mallet 98-01; P-in-c Stockton H Trin *Dur* from 01; Chapl Ian Ramsey Sch Stockton from 01. *4 Greymouth Close, Stockton-on-Tees TS18 5LF* Tel (01642) 585749

GILES, Timothy David. b 46. FCA69. Oak Hill Th Coll DipTh90. **d** 90 **p** 91. C Ipswich St Marg *St E* 90-94; C Reigate St Mary *S'wark* 94-99; P-in-c W Wickham St Jo 99-03; V from 03. *The Rectory, 30 Coney Hill Road, West Wickham BR4 9BX* Tel (020) 8462 4001

GILFORD, George. b 49. St Kath Coll Liv CertEd72 LTCL86. N Ord Course 88. **d** 91 **p** 92. NSM Gt Crosby St Faith *Liv* 91-98; NSM Gt Crosby St Faith and Waterloo Park St Mary 98-01. *Flat 2, 17 Alexandra Road, Waterloo, Liverpool L22 1RJ* Tel 0151-920 5744

GILKES, Donald Martin. b 47. St Jo Coll Nottm 78. **d** 80 **p** 81. C Conisbrough *Sheff* 80-84; P-in-c Balne 84-86; P-in-c Hensall 84-86; TV Gt Snaith 86-88; V Whittle-le-Woods *Blackb* 88-02; V Normanton *Wakef* from 02. *The Vicarage, High Street, Normanton WF6 1NR* Tel (01924) 893100 Fax as telephone E-mail don.gilkes@charis.co.uk

GILKS, Peter Martin. b 51. SRN77 Nottm Univ BMus72. Ripon Coll Cuddesdon 82. **d** 84 **p** 85. C Bitterne Park *Win* 84-87; TV Basingstoke 87-93; R Abbotts Ann and Upper and Goodworth Clatford 93-98; V Boyatt Wood from 98. *St Peter's Church House, 53 Sovereign Way, Eastleigh SO50 4SA* Tel (023) 8064 2188 E-mail pgilks@aol.com

GILL, Canon Alan Gordon. b 42. Sarum & Wells Th Coll 73. **d** 75 **p** 76. C Wimborne Minster *Sarum* 75-78; R Winterbourne Stickland and Turnworth etc 78-86; V Verwood 86-00; Can and Preb Sarum Cathl from 99; TR Gillingham from 00. *The Rectory, High Street, Gillingham SP8 4AH* Tel (01747) 822435

GILL, Mrs Carol Ann. b 42. Lady Mabel Coll TCert71. Nor Ord Course 96. **d** 99 **p** 00. NSM Hanging Heaton *Wakef* 99-02; P-in-c from 02. *The Vicarage, 150 High Street, Hanging Heaton, Batley WF17 6DW* Tel (01924) 461917 Mobile 07946-038562 E-mail rev@cgill2.fsnet.co.uk

GILL, Christopher John Sutherland. b 28. Selw Coll Cam BA52 MA70. Ely Th Coll 52. **d** 54 **p** 55. C Portslade St Nic *Chich* 54-58; C Goring-by-Sea 58-60; Chapl St Edm Sch Cant 60-76; Chapl Bennett Memorial Dioc Sch Tunbridge Wells from 76; Hon C Tunbridge Wells K Chas *Roch* 77-93; rtd 93; Perm to Offic *Roch* from 93. *Flat 1, Hurstleigh, Hurstwood Lane, Tunbridge Wells TN4 8YA* Tel (01892) 528409

GILL, David Alan. b 64. Coll of Resurr Mirfield 98. **d** 00 **p** 01. C Devizes St Jo w St Mary *Sarum* from 00. *52 Queens Road, Devizes SN10 5HW* Tel (01380) 727826 E-mail frdavid@houseofgill.org

GILL, David Brian Michael. b 55. Southn Univ BTh88. Sarum & Wells Th Coll 83. **d** 86 **p** 87. C Honiton, Gittisham, Combe Raleigh, Monkton etc *Ex* 86-89; C E Teignmouth 89; C W Teignmouth 89; C Teignmouth, Ideford w Luton, Ashcombe etc 90-91; TV Ex St Thos and Em from 91. *Emmanuel Vicarage, 49 Okehampton Road, Exeter EX4 1EL* Tel (01392) 435840 E-mail david@dbmg.freeserve.co.uk

GILL, Donald Maule Harvell. b 08. Keble Coll Ox BA33 MA39. Wells Th Coll 34. **d** 35 **p** 36. C Bournemouth St Andr *Win* 35-38; C-in-c Bournemouth H Epiphany 38-45; V Micheldever 45-70; R Minstead 71-80; rtd 80; Perm to Offic *Win* 80-95. *Edwina Mountbatten House, Broadwater Road, Romsey SO51 8GH* Tel (01794) 518317

GILL, Capt Frank Emmanuel. b 34. Oak Hill Th Coll 73. **d** 75 **p** 76. Chapl Race Relns *Lon* 75-78; C Shepherd's Bush St Steph w St Thos 76-77; P-in-c Kensal Town St Thos w St Andr and St Phil 79-82; Barbados from 82; rtd 96. *# 4 Friendly Hall, Hothersal, St Michael, Barbados* Tel (001246) 228 0698 E-mail fegill@caribsurf.com

GILL, Mrs Gabrielle Mary (<u>Gay</u>). **d** 90 **p** 94. NSM Timperley *Ches* 90-96; rtd 96; Perm to Offic *Ches* from 97. *The Croft, 3 Harrop Road, Hale, Altrincham WA15 9BU* Tel 0161-928 1800

GILL, Miss Helen Barbara. b 61. K Alfred's Coll Win BEd87. Cranmer Hall Dur DipTM99. **d** 99 **p** 00. C Newc St Gabr *Newc* from 99. *33 Swindon Terrace, Newcastle upon Tyne NE6 5RB* Tel 0191-224 1596

GILL, James Joseph. b 45. Pontifical Univ Maynooth BD78. **d** 77 **p** 78. In RC Ch 77-82; C Howden *York* 82-83; TV 83-86; P-in-c Wragby w Sharlston *Wakef* 86-88; V Sharlston 88-91; V Tilehurst St Geo *Ox* 91-98; P-in-c Eastney *Portsm* from 98. *St Margaret's Vicarage, 13 Cousins Grove, Southsea PO4 9RP* Tel (023) 9273 1316

✠**GILL, The Rt Revd Kenneth Edward.** b 32. Hartley Victoria Coll. **d** 58 **p** 60 **c** 72. In Ch of S India 58-80; Bp Karnataka Cen 72-80; Asst Bp Newc 80-98; rtd 99; Hon Asst Bp Newc from 99. *54 Merley Gate, Morpeth NE61 2EP* Tel (01670) 510194 Fax 518357 E-mail k.gill@newcastle.anglican.org

GILL, Mrs Mary. b 20. Nottm Univ BA42. St Jo Coll Nottm CertCS43. **d** 88 **p** 96. NSM Alston Team *Newc* 88-90; rtd 90; Perm to Offic *Newc* from 90. *Old School, Garrigill, Alston CA9 3DP* Tel (01434) 381594

GILL, Michael John. b 59. SSC K Coll Lon BA81 AKC81 Univ of Wales (Cardiff) BD85. St Mich Coll Llan 82. **d** 85 **p** 86. Min Can St Woolos Cathl *Mon* 85-90; Chapl St Woolos Hosp Newport 87-90; Succ Heref Cathl *Heref* 90-93; C Heref St Jo 90-93; TV Ebbw Vale *Mon* 93-96; V Tonypandy w Clydach Vale *Llan* from 96. *The Vicarage, Richards Terrace, Tonypandy CF40 2LD* Tel (01443) 437759

GILL, Paul Joseph. b 45. Ridley Coll Melbourne 73. Melbourne Coll of Div DipRE76. **d** 74 **p** 74. Australia 74-76 and from 89; C Perth St Dav 74-76; C Birm St Martin *Birm* 77-79; V Pype Hayes 79-89; Perm to Offic *Perth* 89-93; R Perth St Paul 93-00; Sen Chapl HM Min of Justice from 00. *118 Waddell Road, Bicton, W Australia 6157* Tel (0061) (8) 9317 3912 *or* 9411 5476 Mobile 416-021945 Fax 9411 5542 E-mail pgill@global.com.au

GILL, Prof Robin Morton. b 44. K Coll Lon BD66 AKC66 Lon Univ PhD69 Birm Univ MSocSc72. **d** 68 **p** 69. C Rugby St Andr *Cov* 68-71; Papua New Guinea 71-72; Lect Th Edin Univ 72-86; Sen Lect 86-88; Assoc Dean Faculty of Div 85-88; P-in-c Edin SS Phil and Jas *Edin* 73-75; P-in-c Ford *Newc* 75-87; P-in-c Coldstream *Edin* 87-92; Perm to Offic *Newc* from 92; Wm Leech Prof Applied Th Newc Univ 88-92; Mich Ramsey Prof Modern Th Kent Univ from 92; Hon Prov Can Cant Cathl *Cant* from 92; AD N Downs from 02; P-in-c Hollingbourne and Hucking w Leeds and Broomfield from 03. *University of Kent, Cornwallis, Canterbury CT2 7NF* Tel (01227) 764000 Fax 823641 E-mail r.gill@ukc.ac.uk

GILL, Simon David. b 66. Southn Univ BSc87 PhD91. St Jo Coll Nottm BTh00. **d** 01 **p** 02. C Frinton *Chelmsf* from 01. *38 St Mary's Road, Frinton-on-Sea CO13 9HS* Tel (01255) 674688 E-mail sallie.simon@tinyworld.co.uk

GILL, Stanley. b 11. Clifton Th Coll 37. **d** 39 **p** 40. C Scotswood *Newc* 39-40; CF 40-46; Hon CF from 46; C Woodhorn w Newbiggin *Newc* 46-49; C Hornsea and Goxhill *York* 49-50; V Chatton w Chillingham *Newc* 50-60; V Alston cum Garrigill w Nenthead and Kirkhaugh 60-67; V Cornhill w Carham 67-74; V Branxton 71-74; rtd 76. *Dulverton Hall, Esplanade, Scarborough YO11 2AR* Tel (01723) 340121

GILL, Stanley. b 34. Sarum Th Coll 66. **d** 68 **p** 69. C Ipswich St Mary at Stoke w St Pet & St Mary Quay *St E* 68-73 and 78-80; TV 80-82; V Bury St Edmunds St Geo 73-78; P-in-c Childe Okeford, Manston, Hammoon and Hanford *Sarum* 82-89; R The Lulworths, Winfrith Newburgh and Chaldon 89-94; R Hazelbury Bryan and the Hillside Par 94-99; rtd 99; Perm to Offic *Ex* 99-02; *Sarum* 00-02. *28 Old School Court, Violet Hill Road, Stowmarket IP14 1NB* Tel (01449) 614581

GILL, Thomas. b 21. St Aid Birkenhead 62. **d** 63 **p** 64. C Newland St Aug *York* 63-67; V Burstwick w Thorngumbald 67-78; RD S Holderness 74-78; R Brandesburton 78-86; RD N Holderness 80-86; rtd 87; Perm to Offic *York* from 87. *Bellfield, Arnold Lane, Arnold, Hull HU11 5HP* Tel (01964) 562282

GILL, Timothy Charles. b 66. Newc Univ BA88 Jes Coll Cam MPhil93. Westcott Ho Cam 89. **d** 92 **p** 93. C N Hull St Mich *York* 92-96; P-in-c Sculcoates St Paul w Ch Ch and St Silas 96-98; P-in-c Hull St Mary Sculcoates 96-98; V York St Luke 98-02; R Adel *Ripon* from 02. *The Rectory, 25 Church Lane, Adel, Leeds LS16 8DQ* Tel 0113-267 3676 E-mail ttimgill@aol.com

GILLARD, David John. b 66. Ridley Hall Cam CTM98. **d** 98 **p** 99. C Seaford w Sutton *Chich* 98-02; P-in-c Eastbourne St Eliz from 02. *The Vicarage, 11 Baldwin Avenue, Eastbourne BN21 1UJ* Tel (01323) 694728

GILLESPIE, David Ivan. b 68. TCD BTh01. CITC 98. **d** 01 **p** 02. C Agherton *Conn* from 01. *10 Morelli Plaza, The Promenade, Portstewart, Co Londonderry, Irish Republic BT55 7AH* Tel (028) 7083 5527 *or* 7083 3277 E-mail digillespie15@aol.com

GILLESPIE, George Henry. b 20. SS Coll Cam BA46 MA55. Cuddesdon Coll 46. **d** 48 **p** 49. C Wigan All SS *Liv* 48-53; C Ashbourne w Mapleton and Clifton *Derby* 53-55; V Allenton and Shelton Lock 56-71; Chapl Derby High Sch for Girls 58-71; V Bath Ascension *B & W* 71-78; P-in-c Norton St Philip w Hemington, Hardington etc 78-81; R 81-85; rtd 85; Perm to Offic

B & W 86-02. *50 Wilton Way, Abbotskerswell, Newton Abbot TQ12 5PG* Tel (01626) 367386

GILLESPIE, Michael David. b 41. EMMTC 86. **d** 89 **p** 90. NSM Countesthorpe w Foston *Leic* from 89. *3 Penfold Drive, Countesthorpe, Leicester LE8 3TP* Tel 0116-278 1130

GILLESPIE, Nancy Gillian. b 41. TCD MA68 NUI DipBS84. DipTh97. **d** 97 **p** 98. Lib Ossory Cathl *C & O* 97-00; C Kilkenny w Aghour and Kilmanagh 97-00; I Stradbally w Ballintubbert, Coraclone etc from 00; P-in-c Maryborough w Dysart Enos and Ballyfin from 02. *The Rectory, Church Lane, Co Laois, Irish Republic* Tel (00353) (502) 25173 Mobile 087-2322574 E-mail ngilles@iol.ie

GILLETT, Brian Alan Michael. b 42. ARICS73 MRICS01. Chich Th Coll. **d** 82 **p** 83. C Tupsley *Heref* 82-86; R Kingstone w Clehonger, Eaton Bishop etc 86-97; V Baltonsborough w Butleigh, W Bradley etc *B & W* from 97; Sub-Warden of Readers Wells Adnry 00-02. *The Vicarage, Church Close, Butleigh, Glastonbury BA6 8SH* Tel (01458) 850409

✠**GILLETT, The Rt Revd David Keith.** b 45. Leeds Univ BA65 MPhil68. Oak Hill Th Coll 66. **d** 68 **p** 69 **c** 99. C Watford St Luke *St Alb* 68-71; Sec Pathfinders and CYFA N Area 71-74; Lect St Jo Coll Nottm 74-79; Ch of Ireland Renewal Cen 80-82; V Luton Lewsey St Hugh *St Alb* 82-88; Prin Trin Coll Bris 88-99; Hon Can Bris Cathl *Bris* 91-99; Suff Bp Bolton *Man* from 99. *Bishop's Lodge, Bolton Road, Hawkshaw, Bury BL8 4JN* Tel (01204) 882955 Fax 882988 E-mail david.gillett@ukgateway.net

GILLETT, Victor Henry John. b 31. Open Univ BA83 BTh87 MTh94. Clifton Th Coll 59. **d** 62 **p** 63. C Walton Breck *Liv* 62-65; C Wednesfield Heath *Lich* 65-68; V Tipton St Paul 68-76; V Moulton *Pet* 76-92; TV Worthing Ch the King *Chich* 92-98; Chapl Ramsay Hall 92-98; rtd 98; Perm to Offic *Leic* from 98. *Manoah, 50 Stoneygate Drive, Hinckley LE10 1TD* Tel (01455) 239082 E-mail vgillett@manoah.freeserve.co.uk

GILLETT, Vincent. b 30. FCollP81 Lon Univ BSc55 UEA MSc72. Chich Th Coll 59. **d** 61 **p** 62. C Blackpool St Mich *Blackb* 61-63; Ghana 63-72; Lic to Offic *Liv* 72-79; Lic to Offic *Ex* 79-84; Hd Master St Wilfrid's Sch Ex 79-84; R Atherington and High Bickington 84-94; V Burrington 84-94; rtd 95. *Birchy Barton Lodge, 2 Honiton Road, Heavitree, Exeter EX1 3EA* Tel (01392) 436393

GILLEY, Margaret. b 54. St Andr Univ MTheol76 Dur Univ PhD97. NEOC 97. **d** 00 **p** 01. C Birtley *Dur* 00-03; P-in-c Stockton St Mark from 03. *The Vicarage, 76 Fairfield Road, Stockton-on-Tees TS19 7BP* Tel (01642) 586179 E-mail meg.gilley@durham.anglican.org

GILLHAM, Martin John. b 45. Wilson Carlile Coll IDC66 Qu Coll Birm 72. **d** 75 **p** 76. C Whitley Ch Ch *Ox* 75-78; TV Crowmarsh Gifford w Newnham Murren 78-79; TV Wallingford w Crowmarsh Gifford etc 79-83; V Kintbury w Avington 83-94; Dioc Lay Min Adv and Warden of Readers 89-97; P-in-c W Wycombe w Bledlow Ridge, Bradenham and Radnage 94-00; R 00; Prov Chapl Third Order SSF 95-99; P-in-c Norham and Duddo *Newc* from 00; P-in-c Cornhill w Carham from 00; P-in-c Branxton from 00. *The Vicarage, Church Lane, Norham, Berwick-upon-Tweed TD15 2LF* Tel (01289) 382325

GILLHAM, Mrs Patricia Anne. b 40. Wilson Carlile Coll IDC66 Ox Min Course CBTS93. **d** 93 **p** 94. Par Dn Kintbury w Avington *Ox* 93-94; C 94-95; C W Wycombe w Bledlow Ridge, Bradenham and Radnage 95-00; rtd 00; Perm to Offic *Newc* from 00. *The Vicarage, Church Lane, Norham, Berwick-upon-Tweed TD15 2LF* Tel (01289) 382325

GILLHESPEY, Canon Clive. b 28. Lon Univ DipTh66 BD73. Cranmer Hall Dur 63. **d** 65 **p** 66. C Barrow St Geo w St Luke *Carl* 65-69; V Flookburgh 69-74; R Barrow St Geo w St Luke 74-81; TR 81-92; Hon Can Carl Cathl 84-92; rtd 92; Perm to Offic *Carl* from 92. *Canon's Court, 43 Holyoake Avenue, Barrow-in-Furness LA13 9LH* Tel (01229) 839041

GILLIAN, Ronald Trevor. b 57. Ulster Univ Dip Music77 MTD78 QUB BEd89 TCD BTh93. CITC 90. **d** 93 **p** 94. C Belfast St Donard *D & D* 93-96; I Aghalurcher w Tattykeeran, Cooneen etc *Clogh* from 96. *St Ronan's Rectory, Owenskerry Lane, Killarbran, Fivemiletown BT75 0SR* Tel and fax (028) 8953 1822 Mobile 07866-681247 E-mail colebrooke@clogher.anglican.org

GILLIBRAND, John Nigel. b 60. Ox Univ BA82 MA86 Lon Univ PGCE83. St Steph Ho Ox BTh97. **d** 88 **p** 89. C Dolgellau w Llanfachreth and Brithdir etc *Ban* 88-90; C Llanbeblig w Caernarfon and Betws Garmon etc 90-91; V Ffestiniog w Blaenau Ffestiniog 91-97; V Llandegfan w Llandysilio 97-02; Nat Co-ord (Wales) Nat Autistic Soc from 02; Lic to Offic *Llan* from 02. *National Autistic Society, Suite C1, William Knox House, Britannic Way, Llandarcy, Neath SA10 6EL* Tel (01792) 815915

GILLIBRAND, Margaret Ann Jane. b 43. **d** 01 **p** 02. OLM Deal St Leon and St Rich and Sholden *Cant* from 01. *Cornerstone, 161 Church Path, Deal CT14 9UD* Tel (01304) 380333 E-mail gillibrand@onetel.com.uk

GILLIES, Canon Robert Arthur. b 51. Edin Univ BD77 St Andr Univ PhD91. Edin Th Coll 73. **d** 77 **p** 78. C Falkirk *Edin* 77-80; C

Edin Ch Ch 80-84; Chapl Napier Coll 80-84; Chapl Dundee Univ *Bre* 84-90; R St Andrews St Andr *St And* from 91; Dioc Dir of Ords from 96; Can St Ninian's Cathl Perth from 97. *St Andrew's Rectory, Queen's Terrace, St Andrews KY16 9QF* Tel (01334) 473344

GILLING, John Reginald. b 25. Cam Univ BA49 MA51 MLitt55. Cuddesdon Coll 53. **d** 55 **p** 56. C Romford St Alb *Chelmsf* 55-58; C Cambridge St Mary Less *Ely* 58-62; Chapl Ch Ch Ox 62-71; V Pimlico St Mary Graham-street *Lon* 71-90; AD Westmr St Marg 79-85; rtd 90; Perm to Offic *Chich* from 90. *49 Westgate, Chichester PO19 3EZ* Tel (01243) 775169

GILLINGHAM, John Bruce. b 48. Ch Ch Ox BA69 MA74. St Jo Coll Nottm BA73. **d** 73 **p** 74. C Plymouth St Andr w St Paul and St Geo *Ex* 73-77; C Ox St Aldate w H Trin *Ox* 78; Chapl Jes Coll Ox 78-88; Chapl Ox Pastorate 79-88; Dioc Missr *Birm* 88-92; R Ox St Clem *Ox* from 92. *St Clement's Rectory, 58 Rectory Road, Oxford OX4 1BW* Tel (01865) 248735

GILLINGHAM, Michael John. b 46. Univ of Wales (Swansea) DSCE80 Hull Univ MA90. Chich Th Coll 68. **d** 71 **p** 72. C Llanharan w Peterston-super-Montem *Llan* 71-73; C Skewen 73-76; Neath Deanery Youth Chapl 74-76; Perm to Offic 79-80; TV Valley Youth Chapl *Ches* 77-79; Perm to Offic *St Alb* 80-83; Sen Youth Worker 80-83; TV Sheff Manor *Sheff* 83-88; Chapl Sheff Sea Cadets from 87; R Frecheville from 88. *Frecheville Rectory, Brackenfield Grove, Sheffield S12 4XS* Tel 0114-239 9555 Mobile 07702-133809 E-mail mgillingham@mcmail.com

GILLINGS, The Ven Richard John. b 45. St Chad's Coll Dur BA67. Linc Th Coll 68. **d** 70 **p** 71. C Altrincham St Geo *Ches* 70-75; P-in-c Stockport St Thos 75-77; R 77-83; P-in-c Stockport St Pet 78-83; TR Birkenhead Priory 83-93; RD Birkenhead 85-93; Hon Can Ches Cathl 92-94; V Bramhall 93-94; Adn Macclesfield from 94. *The Vicarage, Robin's Lane, Bramhall, Stockport SK7 2PE* Tel 0161-439 2254 Fax 439 0878 E-mail richard.gillings@chester.anglican.org

GILLION, Robert Alan. b 51. LRAM. Sarum & Wells Th Coll 81. **d** 83 **p** 84. C E Dereham *Nor* 83-86; C Richmond St Mary w St Matthias and St Jo *S'wark* 86-90; P-in-c Discovery Bay Ch Hong Kong 90-98; Chapl Shek Pik Pris 90-98; Bp Kensington's Adv for Evang *Lon* from 98; P-in-c Upper Chelsea 01-02; V from 02. *St Simon Zelotes Vicarage, 34 Milner Street, London SW3 2QF* Tel (020) 7589 5747 E-mail rob.gillion@london.anglican.org

GILLIONS, Michael George. b 37. Ch Ch Ox MA65 Keele Univ PGCE74. WEMTC 93. **d** 96 **p** 97. NSM Dorrington w Leebotwood, Longnor, Stapleton etc *Heref* 96-00; NSM Condover w Frodesley, Acton Burnell etc from 00. *The Maltsters, Dorrington, Shrewsbury SY5 7JD* Tel (01743) 718550

GILLMAN, Noel Francis. b 26. St D Dioc Tr Course St D Coll Lamp St Mich Coll Llan. **d** 79 **p** 80. NSM Llanelli *St D* 79-83; C 83-85; TV Tenby 85-91; rtd 91. *4 Oaklands, Swiss Valley, Llanelli SA14 8DA* Tel (01554) 772663

GILLMOR, Canon Samuel Frederick. b 29. St Aid Birkenhead. **d** 62 **p** 63. C Carlow Union *C & O* 62-64; I Fenagh Union 64-68; I Maryborough w Dysart Enos 68-79; Can Ossory Cathl 78-79; Can Leighlin Cathl 78-79; I Clane w Donadea *M & K* 79-84; I Mullingar, Portnashangan, Moyliscar, Kilbixy etc 84-93; Can Meath 92-93; I Achonry w Tubbercurry and Killoran *T, K & A* from 93; Can Achonry Cathl from 93. *Back Acre, Carrowdubh, Strandhill, Co Sligo, Irish Republic* Tel (00353) (71) 916 8571

GILLUM, Thomas Alan. b 55. Ex Univ BSc76. Cranmer Hall Dur 87. **d** 89 **p** 90. C Brompton H Trin w Onslow Square St Paul *Lon* 89-94; P-in-c Paddington St Steph w St Luke from 94. *St Stephen's Vicarage, 25 Talbot Road, London W2 5JF* Tel (020) 7792 2283 *or* 7221 9329

GILMAN, Charles Philip. b 12. Tyndale Hall Bris 39. **d** 41 **p** 42. C Kirkdale St Mary *Liv* 41-43; C Wellington w Eyton *Lich* 43-46; Perm to Offic *Mon* 47-50; V Leyton St Cath *Chelmsf* 50-64; R Marks Tey 64-74; V Leigh *S'wark* 74-81; rtd 81; Perm to Offic *Win* 81-95 and 97-00. *c/o David Gilman Esq, 35 Sackville Street, Hebden Bridge HX7 7DJ*

GILMAN, Michael. b 35. Man Univ BA57 Sheff Univ PhD99. Ripon Hall Ox 59. **d** 61 **p** 62. C Old Trafford St Jo *Man* 61-64; C Englefield Green *Guildf* 64-69; Historic Buildings Division Gtr Lon Coun 66-86; English Heritage 86-89; rtd 00. *6 Osborne Road, Egham TW20 9PN* Tel (01784) 437106

GILMORE, David Samuel. b 70. Univ of Ulster BSc92 CQSW92 QUB MSSc95. EAMTC 01. **d** 03. C Basildon St Martin *Chelmsf* from 03. *7 Botelers, Basildon SS16 5SE* Tel (01268) 411875 Fax as telephone E-mail davidgilmore@btinternet.com

GILMORE, Canon Henry. b 51. Man Univ BA72 TCD BD82. CITC 75. **d** 75 **p** 76. C Arm St Mark w Aghavilly *Arm* 75-78; C Dublin St Patr Cathl Gp *D & G* 78-81; I Stranorlar w Meenglas and Kilteevogue *D & R* 81-84; I Achill w Dugort, Castlebar and Turlough *T, K & A* 84-91; I Newbrin w Greencastle, Donagh, Cloncha etc *D & R* from 91; Can Raphoe Cathl from 01. *The Rectory, Moville, Co Donegal, Irish Republic* Tel (00353) (74) 938 2572 E-mail hgilmore@eircom.net

GILMOUR, Ian Hedley. b 57. Ex Univ LLB Lon Univ BD. Wycliffe Hall Ox 80. **d** 83 **p** 84. C Harold Wood *Chelmsf* 83-86; C Thame w Towersey *Ox* 86-91; V Streatham Vale H Redeemer *S'wark* from 91. *The Vicarage, Churchmore Road, London SW16 5UZ* Tel (020) 8764 5808

GILMOUR, John Logan. b 14. Cuddesdon Coll 46. **d** 48 **p** 49. C Reading St Mary V *Ox* 48-51; Min St Barn CD Reading 51-55; Thailand 55-58; V Ellel *Blackb* 58-60; S Africa from 60. *2 Russell Lodge, Main Road, Constantia, 7800 South Africa* Tel (0027) (21) 794 1523

GILPIN, Jeremy David. b 59. Pemb Coll Ox BA80 CertEd82. Trin Coll Bris BA88. **d** 88 **p** 89. C Southsea St Jude *Portsm* 88-92; R Itchingfield w Slinfold *Chich* 92-96; Chapl St Hugh's Coll Ox from 97. *12 Bay Tree Close, Iffley, Oxford OX4 4DT* Tel (01865) 770471 Fax as telephone E-mail gilpins@compuserve.com

GILPIN, Richard John. b 45. Lon Univ BSc66 Bris Univ DipTh69. Wells Th Coll 67. **d** 70 **p** 71. C Davyhulme Ch Ch *Man* 70-74; Pastor Gustav Adolf Berlin EKD 74-77; R Heaton Norris Ch w All SS 77-83; R Chorlton-cum-Hardy St Clem 83-99; AD Hulme 95-99; V Norley, Crowton and Kingsley *Ches* from 99; RD Frodsham from 03. *The Vicarage, Station Road, Crowton, Northwich CW8 2RQ* Tel (01928) 788310 *or* 788933 E-mail dick@crowton.f9.co.uk

GILPIN, The Ven Richard Thomas. b 39. Lich Th Coll 60. **d** 63 **p** 64. C Whipton *Ex* 63-66; C Tavistock and Gulworthy 66-69; V 73-91; C Swimbridge 69-73; Preb Ex Cathl from 82; RD Tavistock 87-90; Dioc Dir of Ords 90-91; Adv for Voc and Dioc Dir of Ords 91-96; Sub Dean Ex Cathl 92-96; Adn Totnes from 96. *Blue Hills, Bradley Road, Bovey Tracey, Newton Abbot TQ13 9EU* Tel (01626) 832064 Fax 834947 E-mail archdeacon.of.totnes@exeter.anglican.org

GIMSON, Francis Herbert. b 54. Reading Univ BSc79 LTh. St Jo Coll Nottm 83. **d** 86 **p** 87. C Menston w Woodhead *Brad* 86-89; C Barnoldswick w Bracewell 89-91; V Langleybury St Paul *St Alb* 91-02; P-in-c Downton *Sarum* from 02. *The Vicarage, Barford Lane, Downton, Salisbury SP5 3QA* Tel (01725) 510326 E-mail fgimson@nildram.co.uk

GINEVER, Paul Michael John. b 49. AKC71. **d** 72 **p** 73. C Davyhulme Ch Ch *Man* 72-75; Australia 76-77; C Tettenhall Wood *Lich* 77-80; C Halesowen *Worc* 80; TV 80-86; P-in-c Gt Malvern Ch Ch *Worc* 86-98; V S Hayling *Portsm* from 98. *The Vicarage, 34 Church Road, Hayling Island PO11 0NT* Tel (023) 9246 2914 *or* 9263 7649 E-mail parishoffice@haylinganglicans.freeserve.co.uk

GINGELL, John Lawrence. b 27. Lon Univ BD55. ALCD53. **d** 55 **p** 56. C Normanton *Derby* 55-58; C Ilkeston St Bart CD 58-61; Toc H Staff Padre 61-70; Asst Chapl S Lon Ind Miss 61-64; Lic to Offic *S'wark* 61-66; Lic to Offic *Liv* 67-70; V Somercotes *Derby* 70-72; Bp's Ind Adv 72-80; rtd 92. *18 Bournville Road, London SE6 4RN* Tel (020) 8690 0148

GINN, Daniel Vivian. b 33. Univ of Wales (Cardiff) BSc55 DipEd56. Llan Dioc Tr Scheme 79. **d** 82 **p** 83. NSM Llantwit Major and St Donat's *Llan* 82-83; NSM Llantwit Major 83-02; TV 88-02; RD Llantwit Major and Cowbridge 94-02; Perm to Offic from 02. *Chenet, 24 Voss Park Drive, Llantwit Major CF61 1YE* Tel (01446) 792774

GINN, Canon Richard John. b 51. Lon Univ BD77 St Jo Coll Dur DipTh78 Lambeth STh85 ACIB73. Oak Hill Th Coll 75 Cranmer Hall Dur 77. **d** 79 **p** 80. C Hornsey Ch Ch *Lon* 79-82; C Highgate St Mich 82-85; V Westleton w Dunwich *St E* from 85; V Darsham from 85; P-in-c Yoxford and Peasenhall w Sibton from 01; Hon Can St E Cathl from 01. *The Vicarage, Westleton, Saxmundham IP17 3AQ* Tel (01728) 648271 E-mail r.ginn@btinternet.com

GINNO, Albert Charles. b 31. CA Tr Coll 51 Lon Coll of Div 66. **d** 68 **p** 69. C Kemp Town St Mark and St Matt *Chich* 68-72; P-in-c E Hoathly 72-83; V Westham 83-96; rtd 96; Perm to Offic *Chich* from 96. *106 Sorrel Drive, Eastbourne BN23 8BJ* Tel (01323) 761479 Fax 768920

GIRARD, Canon William Nicholas Charles. b 35. Coll of Resurr Mirfield 65. **d** 67 **p** 68. C Yate *Glouc* 67-70; C Westbury-on-Trym St Alb *Bris* 70-73; Chapl K Sch Ely 73-76; V Fenstanton *Ely* 76-85; V Hilton 76-85; R Balsham 85-99; P-in-c W Wickham 85-99; P-in-c Horseheath 85-96; RD Linton 93-94 and 96-99; Hon Can Ely Cathl from 97; C Alconbury w Alconbury Weston 99-00; Hon C from 00; C Buckworth 99-00; Hon C from 00; C Gt w Lt Stukeley 99-00; RD Leightonstone 00-02; Hon C Gt w Lt Stukeley from 00; rtd 00. *The Rectory, 29 Church Road, Great Stukeley, Huntingdon PE28 4AL* Tel (01480) 453016

GIRLING, Andrew Martin. b 40. Em Coll Cam BA63 MA67. Wycliffe Hall Ox 63. **d** 65 **p** 66. C Luton w E Hyde *St Alb* 65-69; Chapl Hull Univ *York* 69-75; V Dringhouses 75-00; Can and Preb York Minster 97-00; P-in-c Thurlestone w S Milton *Ex* 00-02; R Thurlestone, S Milton, W Alvington etc from 02. *The Rectory, Homefield, Thurlestone, Kingsbridge TQ7 3LF* Tel (01548) 562219

GIRLING, David Frederick Charles. b 33. Kelham Th Coll 49 Edin Th Coll 58. **d** 61 **p** 62. C Caister *Nor* 61-65; C Leigh St Clem *Chelmsf* 65-66; CF 66-83; V Prittlewell St Luke *Chelmsf* 83-98;

rtd 98; Perm to Offic *Nor* from 98. *37 Dell Road East, Lowestoft NR33 9LA* Tel (01502) 567426

GIRLING, Francis Richard (Vincent). b 28. Worc Coll Ox BA52 MA56 Lon Univ BD65. Coll of Resurr Mirfield 55. **d** 57 **p** 59. CR from 57; rtd 98; Lic to Offic *Wakef* from 98. *House of the Resurrection, Stocks Bank Road, Mirfield WF14 0BN* Tel (01924) 494318

GIRLING, Stephen Paul. b 61. Southn Univ BSc83. Trin Coll Bris BA91. **d** 91 **p** 92. C Ogley Hay *Lich* 91-95; TV S Molton w Nymet St George, High Bray etc *Ex* 95-01; RD S Molton 97-01; V Crofton *Portsm* from 01. *The Vicarage, 40 Vicarage Lane, Stubbington, Fareham PO14 2JX* Tel (01329) 662007 Fax as telephone E-mail girlingsp@aol.com

GIRLING, Canon Timothy Havelock. b 43. St Aid Birkenhead 63. **d** 67 **p** 68. C Wickford *Chelmsf* 67-70; C Luton w E Hyde *St Alb* 70-74; Chapl Luton and Dunstable Hosp 74-80; C Luton All SS w St Pet *St Alb* 74-80; R Northill w Moggerhanger 80-89; Chapl Glenfield Hosp NHS Trust Leic 89-00; Chapl Glenfrith Hosp 89-93; Chapl Univ Hosps Leic NHS Trust from 00; Hon Can Leic Cathl *Leic* from 97. *36 Winton Avenue, Leicester LE3 1DH, or Chaplain's Office, Glenfield Hospital, Groby Road, Leicester LE3 9QP* Tel 0116-291 3795 or 287 1471
E-mail timothy.girling@glenfield-tr.trent.nhs.uk

GIRTCHEN, John Christopher. b 54. Linc Th Coll 94. **d** 96 **p** 97. C Bourne *Linc* 96-00; V Barrow and Goxhill from 00. *The Vicarage, Thornton Street, Barrow-upon-Humber DN19 7DG* Tel (01469) 530357 E-mail jcgirtchen@lineone.net

GISBOURNE, Michael Andrew. b 65. Leeds Univ BA87. St Jo Coll Nottm BTh91 DipMM91. **d** 92 **p** 93. C Gateacre *Liv* 92-95; C Marton *Blackb* 95-98; V Freckleton 98-03; V Garstang St Thos from 03. *St Thomas's Vicarage, Church Street, Garstang, Preston PR3 1PA* Tel (01995) 602162 Fax as telephone
E-mail revgis@fish.co.uk

✠**GITARI, The Most Revd David Mukuba.** b 37. K Coll Lon BA64 BD71 Ashland Univ (USA) Hon DD83 Kent Univ Hon DD98. Tyndale Hall Bris 68. **d** 71 **p** 72 **c** 75. Gen Sec Bible Soc Kenya 71-75; Bp Mt Kenya E 75-90; Bp Kirinyaga 90-97; Dean of Angl Ch of Kenya 94-97; Abp Kenya 96-02. *PO Box 607, 60100 Embu, Kenya* Tel (00254) (0161) 30832 Fax (0161) 30824
E-mail davidgitari@insightkenya.com

GITTINGS, Graham. b 46. Qu Coll Birm 75. **d** 78 **p** 79. C Caverswall *Lich* 78-81; C Wolverhampton St Matt 81-82; C Walthamstow St Mary w St Steph *Chelmsf* 82-83; C Dagenham 83-89; V Earl Shilton w Elmesthorpe *Leic* from 89. *The Vicarage, Maughan Street, Earl Shilton, Leicester LE9 7BA* Tel (01455) 843961 E-mail ggvicar@aol.com

GITTOES, Miss Julie Anne. b 76. Trevelyan Coll Dur BA98 Graduate Soc Dur MA99. Westcott Ho Cam 99. **d** 03. C Hampton Hill *Lon* from 03. *82 Pigeon Lane, Hampton TW12 1AF* Tel (020) 8941 4424 Mobile 07941-871570 E-mail jag46@cam.ac.uk

GIVEN, Harold Richard. b 54. Oak Hill Th Coll 75. **d** 78 **p** 79. C Belfast St Clem *D & D* 78-80; C Belfast St Donard 80-83; I Tamlaght O'Crilly Upper w Lower *D & R* 83-92; I Tamlaghtfinlagan w Myroe from 92. *Finlagan Rectory, 77 Ballykelly Road, Limavady BT49 9DS* Tel (028) 7176 2743

GLADSTONE, Robert Michael. b 60. Ch Ch Ox BA82 MA86. Wycliffe Hall Ox DipMin94. **d** 94 **p** 95. C Trentham *Lich* 94-97; C Heigham H Trin *Nor* 97-01; V Rothley *Leic* from 01. *The Vicarage, 128 Hallfields Lane, Rothley, Leicester LE7 7NG* Tel 0116-230 2241 E-mail gladrob@clara.net

✠**GLADWIN, The Rt Revd John Warren.** b 42. Chu Coll Cam BA65 MA68. Cranmer Hall Dur DipTh66. **d** 67 **p** 68 **c** 94. C Kirkheaton *Wakef* 67-71; Tutor St Jo Coll Dur 71-77; Dir Shaftesbury Project 77-82; Sec Gen Syn Bd for Soc Resp 82-88; Preb St Paul's Cathl *Lon* 84-88; Provost Sheff 88-94; Angl Adv Yorkshire TV 88-94; Bp Guildf 94-03; Bp Chelmsf from 03. *Bishopscourt, Main Road, Margaretting, Ingatestone CM4 0HD* Tel (01277) 352001 Fax 355374

GLADWIN, Thomas William. b 35. St Alb Minl Tr Scheme 78. **d** 81 **p** 82. NSM Hertford St Andr *St Alb* 81-82; NSM Digswell and Panshanger 82-86; C 86-96; rtd 96; Perm to Offic *St Alb* from 96. *99 Warren Way, Welwyn AL6 0DL* Tel (01438) 714700

GLAISTER, James Richard. b 30. Oak Hill Th Coll 81. **d** 83 **p** 84. NSM Shrub End *Chelmsf* 83-85; NSM Lawshall w Shimplingthorne and Alpheton *St E* 85-87; NSM Lavenham 87-88; C Felixstowe St Jo 88-95; rtd 95; Perm to Offic *St E* 95-01; *Carl* 00-02 and *Blackb* from 02. *11 Tranmere Avenue, Heysham, Morecambe LA3 2BB* Tel (01524) 859364

GLAISYER, The Ven Hugh. b 30. Oriel Coll Ox BA51 MA55. St Steph Ho Ox 51. **d** 56 **p** 56. C Tonge Moor *Man* 56-62; C Sidcup St Jo *Roch* 62-64; V Milton next Gravesend Ch Ch 64-81; RD Gravesend 74-81; V Hove All SS *Chich* 81-91; Can and Preb Chich Cathl 82-91; RD Hove 82-91; P-in-c Hove St Jo 87-91; Adn Lewes and Hastings 91-97; rtd 97; Perm to Offic *Chich* from 97. *Florence Villa, Hangleton Lane, Ferring, Worthing BN12 6PP* Tel and fax (01903) 244688 Mobile 07712-317118
E-mail h.glaisyer@virgin.net

GLANVILLE-SMITH, Canon Michael Raymond. b 38. Leeds Univ MA95. AKC61. **d** 62 **p** 63. C St Marylebone St Mark w St Luke *Lon* 62-64; C Penzance St Mary *Truro* 64-68; R Worc St Andr and All SS w St Helen *Worc* 68-74; Dioc Youth Chapl 68-74; V Catshill 74-80; P-in-c Worc St Martin w St Pet 80-81; TR Worc St Martin w St Pet, St Mark etc 81-86; TR Worc SE 86-90; Hon Can Worc Cathl 83-90; Can Res Ripon Cathl *Ripon* from 90; RD Ripon 96-97. *St Wilfrid's House, Minster Close, Ripon HG4 1QP* Tel (01765) 700211

GLARE, Michael Francis. b 28. Southn Univ BA54. St Steph Ho Ox 56. **d** 57 **p** 58. C Withycombe Raleigh *Ex* 57-62; C-in-c Goodrington CD 62-65; C Tamerton Foliot 65-70; R Weare Giffard w Landcross 70-76; RD Hartland 74-76; P-in-c Babbacombe 76-80; V 80-87; V Ilsington 87-93; rtd 93; Perm to Offic *Ex* from 94. *Poplar Lodge, 23 Albion Street, Shaldon, Teignmouth TQ14 0DF* Tel (01626) 872679

GLASBY, Alan Langland. b 46. Nottm Univ LTh77. Linc Th Coll DipMin89 St Jo Coll Nottm 74. **d** 77 **p** 78. C Erith St Paul *Roch* 77-80; C Moor Allerton *Ripon* 80-81; TV 81-87; V Middleton St Mary 87-92; V Bilton 92-00; V Barton and Manfield and Cleasby w Stapleton from 00. *The Vicarage, Silver Street, Barton, Richmond DL10 6JJ* Tel (01325) 377274 Mobile 07889-192832
E-mail bartonvic@aol.com

GLASGOW AND GALLOWAY, Bishop of. See JONES, The Rt Revd Idris

GLASGOW AND GALLOWAY, Dean of. See DUNCAN, The Very Revd Gregor Duthie

GLASGOW, Provost of. See DINES, The Very Revd Philip Joseph

GLASS, Edward Eric Ivor. b 25. Rhodes Univ BA56 Natal Univ BA62. St Aug Coll Cant 62. **d** 63 **p** 63. S Africa 63-75 and from 77; C Maidstone St Martin *Cant* 75-76. *c/o Parish of St Paul, PO Box 2849, Durban, 4001 South Africa* Tel (0027) (31) 306 3880

GLASS, Kenneth William. b 23. FRSA68. **d** 57 **p** 58. C Ipswich St Matt *St E* 57-59; R Glemsford 59-63; P-in-c Somerton 59-63; V Ipswich St Nic 63-73; P-in-c Ipswich St Helen 73; R Sproughton w Burstall 74-76; rtd 83; Perm to Offic *St E* from 01. *19 Chalkeith Road, Needham Market, Ipswich IP6 8HA* Tel (01449) 720393

GLASS, Mrs Yvonne Elizabeth. b 58. EMMTC 94. **d** 97 **p** 98. NSM Bingham *S'well* 97-00; Asst Chapl Nottm City Hosp NHS Trust from 00. *30 Willoughby Road, West Bridgford, Nottingham NG2 6EZ* Tel 0115-846 2125

GLASSPOOL, John Martin. b 59. RGN87 Kent Univ BA83 Heythrop Coll Lon MTh95. Westcott Ho Cam 88. **d** 90 **p** 91. C Forest Gate Em w Upton Cross *Chelmsf* 90-93; P-in-c Theydon Garnon 93-95; Chapl St Marg Hosp Epping 93-99; TV Epping Distr *Chelmsf* 95-99; Asst Chapl R Free Hampstead NHS Trust 99-02; Chapl Surrey and Sussex Healthcare NHS Trust from 02. *Chaplaincy Department, East Surrey Hospital, Canada Avenue, Redhill RH1 5RH* Tel (01737) 768511
E-mail jglasspool@aol.com

GLAZEBROOK, William Leng. b 29. Edin Th Coll 76. **d** 76 **p** 77. C Dollar *St And* 76-82; Dioc Supernumerary 83; Chapl Trin Coll Glenalmond 84; P-in-c Glencarse *Bre* 84-87; Dioc Sec 84-87; Chapl HM Pris Perth 85-87; V Broughton Poggs w Filkins, Broadwell etc *Ox* 87-94; rtd 94; Perm to Offic *Bre* from 94; Hon C Perth St Jo *St And* from 98. *10 Rose Terrace, Perth PH1 5HA* Tel (01738) 624913

GLEADALL, John Frederick. b 39. Ripon Hall Ox 66 Sarum Th Coll 69. **d** 70 **p** 71. C S Ashford Ch Ch *Cant* 70-76; P-in-c Hothfield 76-83; P-in-c Eastwell w Boughton Aluph 81-83; P-in-c Westwell 81-83; V Westwell, Hothfield, Eastwell and Boughton Aluph 84-03; rtd 03; Hon C Old Leake w Wrangle *Linc* from 03; Chapl HM Pris N Sea Camp from 03. *Field House, Walcot Road, Billinghay, Lincoln LN4 4EG*

GLEAVES, John. b 39. Alsager Coll of Educn CertEd60 Westmr Coll Ox CertRE61. N Ord Course 99. **d** 00 **p** 01. NSM Alsager St Mary *Ches* from 00. *46 Linley Grove, Alsager, Stoke-on-Trent ST7 2PS* Tel (01270) 878169

GLEDHILL, Alan. b 43. Lon Univ BSc(Econ). N Ord Course 81. **d** 84 **p** 85. C Knaresborough *Ripon* 84-87; P-in-c Easby 87-88; P-in-c Bolton on Swale 87-88; V Easby w Brompton on Swale and Bolton on Swale 88-96; Teacher St Fran Xavier Sch Richmond from 96; Perm to Offic *Ripon* from 96. *15 White Lands, Richmond DL10 7DR* Tel (01748) 826973 *or* 823414

GLEDHILL, Canon James William. b 27. Dur Univ BA52. Westcott Ho Cam 52. **d** 56 **p** 57. C Mexborough *Sheff* 56-59; CF 59-61; C Bywell *Newc* 61-65; V Warden w Newbrough 65-98; RD Hexham 78-88; Hon Can Newc Cathl 88-98; rtd 98; Perm to Offic *Newc* from 98. *Castleview, Castlegate, Jedburgh TD8 6BD* Tel (01835) 862834

✠**GLEDHILL, The Rt Revd Jonathan Michael.** b 49. Keele Univ BA72 Bris Univ MA75. Trin Coll Bris 72. **d** 75 **p** 76 **c** 96. C Marple All SS *Ches* 75-78; C Folkestone H Trin w Ch Ch *Cant* 78-83; V Cant St Mary Bredin 83-96; Tutor Cant Sch of Min 83-96; RD Cant 88-94; Hon Can Cant Cathl 92-96; Suff Bp Southampton *Win* 96-03; Bp Lich from 03. *Bishop's House, 22 The Close, Lichfield WS13 7LG* Tel (01543) 306000 Fax 306009 E-mail jonathan.gledhill@dial.pipex.com

GLEDHILL, Peter. b 29. Ball Coll Ox BA53 MA54. Cuddesdon Coll 54. **d** 56 **p** 57. C Balham St Mary *S'wark* 56-58; C Loughton St Jo *Chelmsf* 58-63; Jamaica 63-66; Barbados 66-67; Asst Master Cheadle Gr Sch 68-70; Lic to Offic *Lich* 70-71; P-in-c Kingstone w Gratwich 71-83; P-in-c Llanyblodwel and Trefonen 83-84; R 84-89; C Menai and Malltraeth Deanery *Ban* 90-94; NSM 95-96; rtd 94; Perm to Offic *Ban* from 96. *Yr Hen Felin, Pwllfanogl, Llanfairpwllgwyngyll LL61 6PD* Tel (01248) 714434

GLEESON, Robert Godfrey. b 49. Man Univ CQSW74. Qu Coll Birm 83. **d** 85 **p** 86. C Hall Green St Pet *Birm* 85-88; Asst Chapl Mental Health & Elderly Care Services Birm HA 88-90; Chapl 90-94; Chapl Moseley Hall Hosp Birm 90-94; Chapl S Birm Mental Health NHS Trust from 94. *180 Pineapple Road, Birmingham, B30 2TY, or Queen Elizabeth Hospital, Mindelsohn Way, Birmingham B15 2QZ* Tel 0121-444 2793 *or* 627 2885

GLEN, Robert Sawers. b 25. Qu Coll Cam BA49 MA56. Sarum & Wells Th Coll 79. **d** 81 **p** 82. Chapl Sherborne Sch 81-86; C Yetminster w Ryme Intrinseca and High Stoy *Sarum* 86-95; RD Sherborne 92-95; rtd 95; Perm to Offic *Sarum* from 95. *Devan Haye, North Road, Sherborne DT9 3BJ* Tel (01935) 812018

GLENDALOUGH, Archdeacon of. *See* SWANN, The Ven Edgar John

GLENDINING, Canon Alan. b 24. LVO79. Westcott Ho Cam 58. **d** 60 **p** 61. C S Ormsby w Ketsby, Calceby and Driby *Linc* 60-63; V Raveningham *Nor* 63-70; P-in-c Hales w Heckingham 63-70; R Thurlton w Thorpe next Haddiscoe 63-70; V Norton Subcourse 63-70; P-in-c Aldeby w Wheatacre w Burgh St Peter 66-70; P-in-c Haddiscoe w Toft Monks 68-70; Dom Chapl to The Queen 70-79; Chapl to The Queen 79-94; R Sandringham w W Newton *Nor* 70-79; RD Heacham and Rising 72-76; Hon Can Nor Cathl 77-89; TR Lowestoft and Kirkley 79-85; Sen Chapl to Holidaymakers 85-89; V Ranworth w Panxworth and Woodbastwick 85-89; RD Blofield 87-89; rtd 90; Perm to Offic *Nor* from 90. *7 Bellfosters, Kings Staithe Lane, King's Lynn PE30 1LZ* Tel (01553) 760113

GLENFIELD, Samuel Ferran. b 54. QUB BA76 TCD MLitt90 MA94 Ox Univ MTh99. Wycliffe Hall Ox 88. **d** 91 **p** 92. C Douglas Union w Frankfield *C, C & R* 91-94; I Rathcooney Union 94-96; I Kill *D & G* from 96. *The Rectory, Kill o' the Grange, Blackrock, Co Dublin, Irish Republic* Tel (00353) (1) 280 1721 *or* 289 6442 Fax 289 6442

GLENN, Michael David. b 37. Lich Th Coll 67. **d** 70 **p** 71. C Denton Ch Ch *Man* 70-74; Chapl Oldham Hosps 74-77; P-in-c Moss Side Ch Ch *Man* 77-78; Hon C Drayton Bassett *Lich* 78-82; Hon C Hints 78-82; Perm to Offic *Man* 82-90; TV Corby SS Pet and Andr w Gt and Lt Oakley *Pet* 90-97; Perm to Offic from 97; rtd 01. *83A Main Road, Collyweston, Stamford PE9 3PQ* Tel (01780) 444757

GLENNON, James Joseph. b 37. St Mary's Coll Strawberry Hill TCert69 BA70. Franciscan Ho of Studies. **d** 62 **p** 63. C S Woodford *Chelmsf* 64-65; NSM Hadleigh w Layham and Shelley *St E* 88-95; C Hadleigh 95-02; rtd 02; Perm to Offic *St E* from 02. *11 Sycamore Close, Ipswich IP8 3RL* Tel (01473) 680915

GLOUCESTER, Archdeacon of. *See* SIDAWAY, The Ven Geoffrey Harold

GLOUCESTER, Bishop of. *See* BENTLEY, The Rt Revd David Edward

GLOUCESTER, Dean of. *See* BURY, The Very Revd Nicholas Ayles Stillingfleet

GLOVER, Alan. b 47. SW Minl Tr Course DTPS99. **d** 99 **p** 00. NSM Bideford, Northam, Westward Ho, Appledore etc *Ex* from 99. *West Fordlands, Heywood Road, Northam, Bideford EX39 3QA* Tel (01237) 479542

GLOVER, David Charles. b 66. St Jo Coll Dur BA87 St Jo Coll Cam MPhil91. Ridley Hall Cam 87. **d** 90 **p** 91. C Wath-upon-Dearne w Adwick-upon-Dearne *Sheff* 90-92; Chapl Hatf Coll Dur 92-00; P-in-c Dur St Marg *Dur* 95-00; R Dur St Marg and Neville's Cross St Jo from 00. *St Margaret's Rectory, South Street, Durham DH1 4QP* Tel 0191-384 3623 Mobile 07932-683745 E-mail david@glover.u-net.com *or* david.glover@durham.anglican.org

GLOVER, Mrs Diana Mary. b 50. Kent Univ BA73 MA75. St Alb and Ox Min Course. **d** 01 **p** 02. C Aylesbury w Bierton and Hulcott *Ox* from 01. *9 Purbeck Close, Aylesbury HP21 9UU* Tel (01296) 487501 E-mail diana.glover@btinternet.com

GLOVER, Elisabeth Ann. b 53. Univ Coll Ches BTh99. **d** 98 **p** 99. NSM Thurstaston *Ches* 98-99; C Stockton Heath from 00. *8 St Monica's Close, Appleton, Warrington WA4 3AW* Tel (01925) 210726 E-mail glover01@btinternet.com

GLOVER, Henry Arthur. b 32. Lon Univ BSc58. Wycliffe Hall Ox 59. **d** 61 **p** 62. C Fareham St De *Portsm* 61-63; C Liv Our Lady and St Nic *Liv* 63-64. *15 Thorncliffe Road, Wallasey CH44 3AA* Tel 0151-638 6018

GLOVER, Janet Mary. b 58. Natal Univ BSc79 UED80. EAMTC 98. **d** 01 **p** 02. NSM Cambridge St Phil *Ely* from 01. *35 Garlic Row, Cambridge CB5 8HW* Tel (01223) 563585 E-mail janet.glover@ntlworld.com

GLOVER, John. b 48. Kelham Th Coll 67. **d** 71 **p** 72. C Foley Park *Worc* 71-75; TV Sutton *Liv* 75-79; P-in-c Churchill w Blakedown

Worc 79-84; R 84-87; R Belbroughton w Fairfield and Clent 87-91; Chapl Children's Family Trust from 91; NSM Flint *St As* 92-93; R Halkyn w Caerfallwch w Rhesycae 93-97; V Rhyl w St Ann from 97. *The Vicarage, 31 Bath Street, Rhyl LL18 3LU* Tel (01745) 353732

GLOVER, Mrs Judith Rosalind. b 53. NEOC DipHE95. **d** 95 **p** 96. C Glendale Gp *Newc* 95-99; P-in-c Alwinton w Holystone and Alnham from 99. *The Vicarage, Alwinton, Morpeth NE65 7BE* Tel (01669) 650203

GLOVER, Michael John Myers. b 28. CEng MICE MSAICE Bradf Tech Coll Dip Civil Engineering 48 Lon Univ BSc48. Cuddesdon Coll 54. **d** 56 **p** 57. C Leic St Pet *Leic* 56-60; S Africa 60-73 and from 86; TR Northampton Em *Pet* 74-86; Bp's Chapl E Area North 73-74; rtd 93. *PO Box 447, Nongoma, 3950 South Africa* Tel (0027) (358) 310044 Fax 310457

GLOVER, Richard John. b 47. Nottm Univ BTh77. Linc Th Coll 73. **d** 77 **p** 78. C Barrow St Geo w St Luke *Carl* 77-79; C Netherton 79-80; P-in-c Addingham 80-83; P-in-c Edenhall w Langwathby and Culgaith 80-83; V Addingham, Edenhall, Langwathby and Culgaith 83-84; V Bishops Hull *B & W* 84-89; V Shilbottle *Newc* 89-96; V Whittingham and Edlingham w Bolton Chapel 96-00; P-in-c Barton, Pooley Bridge and Martindale *Carl* from 00; Dioc Adv for Spiritual Direction and Healing from 00. *The Vicarage, Pooley Bridge, Penrith CA10 2LT* Tel (01768) 486220 E-mail richard@glov.fsnet.co.uk

GLYN-JONES, Alun. b 38. JP. CCC Cam BA59 MA63. Bps' Coll Cheshunt 60. **d** 61 **p** 62. C Portsea St Mary *Portsm* 61-65; Chapl Hampton Sch Middx 65-76; Hd Master Abp Tenison Sch Croydon 76-88; V Twickenham St Mary *Lon* 88-01; rtd 01. *10 Fitzmaurice Close, Bradford-on-Avon BA15 1UE* Tel (01225) 866874

GLYNN, Simon Adrian. b 59. Dur Univ BSc80. Nor Ord Course 96. **d** 99 **p** 00. NSM Carr Mill *Liv* from 99. *238 Elmers Green Lane, Skelmersdale WN8 6SJ* Tel (01695) 732775 E-mail glynnd@pilkington.com

GOALBY, George Christian. b 55. Leeds Univ BA77. St Jo Coll Nottm DPS81. **d** 81 **p** 82. C Wakef St Andr and St Mary *Wakef* 81-84; Asst Chapl HM Pris Wakef 84-85; Chapl HM Youth Cust Cen Deerbolt 85-87; Chapl HM Pris Frankland 87-89; V Swinderby *Linc* from 89. *All Saints' Vicarage, 27 Station Road, Swinderby, Lincoln LN6 9LY* Tel (01522) 868430 Fax as telephone E-mail family.goalby@virgin.net

GOATCHER, Mrs Sara Jacoba Helena. b 46. Oak Hill NSM Course 86. **d** 89 **p** 94. NSM S Croydon Em *S'wark* 89-95; C 95-96; R Sutton St Nic from 96. *The Rectory, 34 Robin Hood Lane, Sutton SM1 2RG* Tel (020) 8642 3499 E-mail sara@richardandsara.demon.co.uk

GOATER, Charles Frederick. b 16. **d** 82 **p** 82. NSM Fishponds St Mary *Bris* 82-89; Perm to Offic 89-00. *72 Queensholme Crescent, Downend, Bristol BS16 6LH* Tel 0117-956 1147

GOATER, Michael Robert. b 46. York Univ BA MA. N Ord Course 89. **d** 92 **p** 93. C Norton *Sheff* 92-94; V Endcliffe 94-99; Chapl Sheff Ind Miss 94-95; Assoc Chapl Hallam Univ 95-99; Asst Post-Ord Tr Officer 95-99; Dioc Voc Officer 96-99; C Stratford-upon-Avon, Luddington etc *Cov* 99-02; P-in-c Gt Shelford *Ely* from 02. *The Vicarage, 12 Church Street, Great Shelford, Cambridge CB2 5EL* Tel (01223) 843274 E-mail mickthevic@btopenworld.com

GOBBETT, Michael George Timothy. b 64. St Chad's Coll Dur BSc86. St Steph Ho Ox BA89 MA98. **d** 90 **p** 91. C Hartlepool St Aid *Dur* 90-94; P-in-c Norton St Mich 94-95; V from 95. *St Michael's Vicarage, 13 Imperial Avenue, Norton, Stockton-on-Tees TS20 2EW* Tel (01642) 553984 E-mail michael@mgobbett.freeserve.co.uk

GOBEY, Ian Clifford. b 48. WEMTC 94. **d** 96 **p** 97. NSM Whiteshill and Randwick *Glouc* 96-00; NSM The Edge, Pitchcombe, Harescombe and Brookthorpe 00-01; NSM Painswick, Sheepscombe, Cranham, The Edge etc from 01. *The Rectory, Edge, Stroud GL6 6PF* Tel (01452) 812319 E-mail ian.gobey@tesco.net

GOBLE, Christopher. b 75. Univ of Wales (Lamp) BA96. Trin Coll Bris 96. **d** 98 **p** 99. C St Jo in Bedwardine *Worc* 98-01; P-in-c Worc St Clem 01-02; R Brington w Whilton and Norton etc *Pet* from 02. *The Rectory, Church Lane, Nether Heyford, Northampton NN7 3LQ* Tel (01327) 342201

GOBLE, Canon Clifford David. b 41. Oak Hill Th Coll 69. **d** 72 **p** 73. C Erith St Paul *Roch* 72-76; C Tunbridge Wells St Jas 76-79; R Southfleet from 79; RD Gravesend from 94; Hon Can Roch Cathl from 99. *The Rectory, Hook Green Road, Southfleet, Gravesend DA13 9NQ* Tel (01474) 833252

GOBLE (née DUNN), Mrs Sharon Louise. b 71. Univ of Wales (Swansea) BA93 Fitzw Coll Cam BA97. Ridley Hall Cam CTM98. **d** 98 **p** 99. C Malpas *Mon* 98-01; C Cyncoed 01-02; R Heyford w Stowe Nine Churches and Flore etc *Pet* from 02. *The Rectory, Church Lane, Nether Heyford, Northampton NN7 3LQ* Tel (01327) 342201 E-mail rev@dunnsl.freeserve.co.uk

GODBER, Canon Francis Giles. b 48. Open Univ BA88. Ridley Hall Cam 74. **d** 75 **p** 76. C Blackheath *Birm* 75-78; C Wolverhampton St Matt *Lich* 78-80; TV Washfield, Stoodleigh,

Withleigh etc *Ex* 80-85; R Shenley and Loughton *Ox* 85-88; TR Watling Valley 88-96; Chapl Heatherwood and Wexham Park Hosp NHS Trust 96-00; P-in-c Geddington w Weekley *Pet* from 00; Dioc Ecum Officer from 00; Can Pet Cathl from 03. *The Vicarage, 25 West Street, Geddington, Kettering NN14 1BD* Tel (01536) 742200 E-mail gilbar@telco4u.net

GODDARD, Andrew John. b 67. St Jo Coll Ox BA88 MA93 DipTh89 DPhil96. Cranmer Hall Dur 94. **d** 96 **p** 97. C Cogges and S Leigh *Ox* 96-99; Tutor Wycliffe Hall Ox from 99. *Wycliffe Hall, 54 Banbury Road, Oxford OX2 6PW* Tel (01865) 274200 E-mail andrew.goddard@wycliffe.ox.ac.uk

GODDARD, Charles Douglas James. b 47. CITC 67. **d** 70 **p** 71. C Orangefield *D & D* 70-73; C Stormont 73-75; Miss to Seafarers from 75; Sen Chapl and Sec N Ireland from 77. *7 Abercorn Drive, Carnreagh Road, Hillsborough BT26 6LB* Tel (028) 9268 3592 E-mail flying@angel.dnet.co.uk

GODDARD, Christopher. b 45. Sarum & Wells Th Coll 79. **d** 81 **p** 82. C Whitehaven *Carl* 81-83; C Barrow St Geo w St Luke 83-85; P-in-c Hayton St Mary 85-90; V Brigham 90-98; V Mosser 90-98; rtd 98; Perm to Offic *Carl* from 00. *High Garth, Lorton Road, Cockermouth CA13 9DF* Tel (01900) 821743 E-mail chris.goddard@virgin.net

GODDARD, Derek George. b 38. St Martin's Coll Lanc BA97 CEng FIMechE FIMarE FCMI. Cranmer Hall Dur 94 Carl and Blackb Dioc Tr Inst DipTh95. **d** 97 **p** 98. NSM Windermere St Mary and Troutbeck *Carl* 97-01; P-in-c Leven Valley from 01. *The Vicarage, Haverthwaite, Ulverston LA12 8AJ* Tel (01539) 531476 E-mail d.d.goddard@talk21.com

GODDARD, Mrs Doris. b 48. St Mary's Coll Twickenham CertEd70 Open Univ BA80. S'wark Ord Course 93. **d** 96 **p** 97. Chapl John Nightingale Sch W Molesley from 96; NSM Addlestone *Guildf* 96-98; NSM Botleys and Lyne from 98; NSM Long Cross from 98; Perm to Offic *B & W* from 00. *25 Albert Road, Addlestone KT15 2PX* Tel (01932) 849505 E-mail jimgd@strodes.edx.co.uk

GODDARD, Mrs Elaine Clare. b 53. K Alfred's Coll Win CertEd78. WEMTC DipApTh99. **d** 99 **p** 00. C Leominster *Heref* from 99. *Cuckoo's Nest Cottage, 1 Park Terrace, Kingsland, Leominster HR6 9SQ* Tel (01568) 708577

GODDARD, Elisabeth Ann. b 64. St Hugh's Coll Ox BA89 MA99. Cranmer Hall Dur 94. **d** 96 **p** 97. C Cogges and S Leigh *Ox* 96-99; Chapl Jes Coll Ox from 99. *Jesus College, Oxford OX1 3DW* Tel (01865) 279757 Fax 274215

GODDARD, Canon Frederick Paul Preston. b 24. Jes Coll Cam BA49 MA51. Westcott Ho Cam 49. **d** 51 **p** 52. C Bp's Hatfield *St Alb* 51-57; New Zealand 57-61; V Abbots Langley *St Alb* 61-68; Chapl Yeatman and Coldharbour Hosp Dorset 69-87; V Sherborne w Castleton and Lillington *Sarum* 69-87; RD Sherborne 73-77; Can and Preb Sarum Cathl 75-87; rtd 87; Perm to Offic *Truro* from 92. *56 West Street, Polruan, Fowey PL23 1PL* Tel (01726) 870339

GODDARD, Giles William. b 62. Clare Coll Cam MA84. S'wark Ord Course 92. **d** 95 **p** 96. C N Dulwich St Faith *S'wark* 95-98; TR Walworth St Pet from 98; RD S'wark and Newington from 02. *St Peter's Rectory, Liverpool Grove, London SE17 2HH* Tel (020) 7703 3139 E-mail giles.goddard@virgin.net

GODDARD, Canon Harold Frederick. b 42. Keble Coll Ox BA63 MA69 DipTh65. Cuddesdon Coll 64. **d** 66 **p** 67. C Birm St Pet *Birm* 66-70; Chapl Dudley Road Hosp Birm 66-70; C Alverstoke *Portsm* 70-72; Chapl Gosport Cottage Hosp' Portsm 70-72; P-in-c Portsea St Geo CD 72-76; Chapl Portsm Cathl 73-76; P-in-c Stoke Prior *Worc* 76-78; P-in-c Wychbold and Upton Warren 77-78; R Stoke Prior, Wychbold and Upton Warren 78-80; Chapl Forelands Orthopaedic Hosp Worc 77-80; Chapl R Marsden Hosp Lon and Surrey 80-83; P-in-c Knightwick w Doddenham, Broadwas and Cotheridge 85-88; R Martley and Wichenford, Knightwick etc 89-90; Bp's Adv on Min of Healing 84-99; Chapl St Rich Hospice Worc 87-94; RD Martley and Worc W *Worc* 88-90; Chapl Kidderminster Gen Hosp 90-92; P-in-c Hallow *Worc* 91-92; P-in-c Sedgeberrow w Hinton-on-the-Green 92-00; Chapl Evesham Community Hosp Worc 93-00; Co-ord Chapl Worcs Community Healthcare NHS Trust 97-00; Co-ord W Midl Healing Advisers 94-99; RD Evesham *Worc* 97-00; TR Kidderminster St Jo and H Innocents from 00; Hon Can Worc Cathl from 03. *The Vicarage, 9 Sutton Park Road, Kidderminster DY11 6LE* Tel and fax (01562) 822186 *or* 751914 Mobile 07768-106287 E-mail h.goddard@easicom.com

GODDARD, John David. b 42. Dioc OLM tr scheme 00. **d** 03. OLM Morden S'wark from 03. *58 Queen Mary Avenue, Morden SM4 4JR* Tel (020) 8540 5082 E-mail jdg13@blueyonder.co.uk

✠**GODDARD, The Rt Revd John William.** b 47. St Chad's Coll Dur BA69 DipTh70. **d** 70 **p** 71 **c** 00. C S Bank *York* 70-74; C Cayton w Eastfield 74-75; V Middlesbrough Ascension 75-82; RD Middlesbrough 81-87; V Middlesbrough All SS 82-88; Can and Preb York Minster 87-88; Vice-Prin Edin Th Coll 88-92; TR Ribbleton *Blackb* 92-00; Suff Bp Burnley from 00. *Dean House, 449 Padiham Road, Burnley BB12 6TE* Tel (01282) 470360 Fax 470361 E-mail bishop.burnley@ukonline.co.uk

GODDARD, Mrs Margaret. **d** 01 **p** 02. NSM Cockermouth w Embleton and Wythop *Carl* from 01. *Highgarth, Lorton Road, Cockermouth CA13 9DF* Tel (01900) 821743 *or* 826151

GODDARD, Ms Marion. b 54. Sarum & Wells Th Coll 87. **d** 89 **p** 94. Par Dn Lewisham St Swithun *S'wark* 89-94; C 94-95; Chapl Brook Gen Hosp Lon 95-96; TV Thamesmead *S'wark* from 96. *5 Finchdale Road, London SE2 9PG* Tel (020) 8310 5614

GODDARD, Matthew Francis. b 45. Lon Univ DipTh69. Kelham Th Coll 65. **d** 69 **p** 70. C Mansfield St Mark *S'well* 69-72; C Northolt Park St Barn *Lon* 72-78; P-in-c Acton Green St Pet 78-87; R Norwood St Mary 87-96. *27 Hounslow Avenue, Hounslow TW3 2DZ* Tel (020) 8230 6591

GODDARD, Mrs Pamela Gay. b 53. LSE BSc(Econ)74 CQSW77. St Alb and Ox Min Course 95 EAMTC 97. **d** 98 **p** 99. C New Catton St Luke w St Aug *Nor* from 98. *Church House, Bowthorpe Hall Road, Norwich NR5 9AA* Tel (01603) 747871 E-mail pamgoddard@ic24.net

GODDARD, Mrs Rosemary Joy. b 48. Philippa Fawcett Coll CertEd69. EAMTC 00. **d** 03. C Linc St Nic w St Jo Newport *Linc* from 03. *14 Nettleham Close, Lincoln LN2 1SJ* Tel 07740-203149 (mobile) E-mail rosemaryjg@aol.com

GODDARD, Stuart David. b 53. Cen Sch of Art Lon BA76 Middx Poly PGCE82. Trin Coll Bris DipHE93. **d** 93 **p** 94. C Watling Valley *Ox* 93-97; P-in-c Bowthorpe *Nor* 97-00; TV from 00. *Church House, Bowthorpe Hall Road, Norwich NR5 9AA* Tel (01603) 747871 E-mail stuart@goddard7.fsbusiness.co.uk

GODDARD, Canon Sydney Thomas. b 16. St Aid Birkenhead 46. **d** 49 **p** 50. C Ravenhead *Liv* 49-52; C St Helens St Helen 52-55; V Widnes St Ambrose 55-59; Warden World Friendship Ho 59-83; Chapl Liv Maternity Hosp 59-81; V Liv St Sav *Liv* 59-71; Hon Can Liv Cathl 69-83; rtd 83; Perm to Offic *Ban* from 84. *Ynys Thomas, Bronaber, Trawsfynydd, Blaenau Ffestiniog LL41 4UR* Tel (01766) 540413

GODDEN, Peter David. b 47. ARCO70 Leeds Univ BA69. Linc Th Coll 85. **d** 87 **p** 88. C Bearsted w Thurnham *Cant* 87-90; C Hykeham *Linc* 90-91; Hon PV Linc Cathl 90-99; TV Hykeham 91-95; P-in-c Linc St Pet-at-Gowts and St Andr 95-99; R Armthorpe *Sheff* 99-00; R Owmby Gp *Linc* from 00. *The Rectory, Owmby Cliff Road, Owmby-by-Spital, Market Rasen LN8 2HL* Tel (01673) 878275

GODDEN, Timothy Richard James. b 62. Univ Coll Lon BA84. St Jo Coll Nottm 89. **d** 89 **p** 90. C Tulse Hill H Trin and St Matthias *S'wark* 89-93; TV Horsham *Chich* 93-01; TR Bishopsworth and Bedminster Down *Bris* from 01. *St Peter's Vicarage, 61 Fernsteed Road, Bristol BS13 8HE* Tel 0117-964 2734 Fax as telephone E-mail tim@godden.fsnet.co.uk

GODECK, John William George. b 30. Chich Th Coll 57. **d** 60 **p** 61. C Wadhurst *Chich* 60-62; C Tidebrook 60-62; C Eastbourne 62-63; R Bondleigh *Ex* 63-78; R Zeal Monachorum 63-78; P-in-c Broadwoodkelly 65-67; R 68-78; R Dunchideock and Shillingford St George w Ide 78-96; RD Kenn 83-89; rtd 96; Perm to Offic *Ex* from 96. *Boxgrove, 6 Barley Lane, Exeter EX4 1TE* Tel (01392) 424224

GODFREY, Ann Veronica. See MacKEITH, Mrs Ann Veronica

GODFREY, Canon Brian Ernest Searles. b 37. Lon Univ BSc60 MSc63 PhD72. S'wark Ord Course 78. **d** 81 **p** 82. NSM Hayes *Roch* 81-86; C 86-88; R Kingsdown 88-93; R Sundridge w Ide Hill 93-02; RD Sevenoaks 95-00; Hon Can Roch Cathl from 99; rtd 02. *Rowans, Kingcombe Road, Toller Porcorum, Dorchester DT2 0DG* Tel (01300) 320833 E-mail godfrey@centrenet.co.uk

GODFREY, The Very Revd David Samuel George. b 35. CITC 64. **d** 66 **p** 67. C Londonderry Ch Ch *D & R* 66-68; I Tomregan w Drumlane *K, E & A* 68-71; I Cloonclare 71-79; I Templebreedy *C, C & R* 79-85; I Bray *D & G* 85-97; Can Ch Ch Cathl Dublin from 95; Dean Kilmore *K, E & A* from 97; I Kilmore w Ballintemple, Kildallon etc from 97; Preb Mulhuddart St Patr Cathl Dublin from 01. *The Deanery, Danesfort, Kilmore, Cavan, Irish Republic* Tel (00353) (49) 4331918 Fax as telephone E-mail dean@kilmore.anglican.org

GODFREY, Edward Colin. b 30. Wells Th Coll 63 ADipR62. **d** 65 **p** 66. C Lyndhurst and Emery Down *Win* 65-69; C Paignton Ch Ch *Ex* 69-73; V Stockland w Dalwood 73-77; Chapl HM Pris Man 77-78; Chapl HM Pris Cant 78-83; Chapl HM Pris Highpoint 83-85 and 90-95; Chapl HM YOI Glen Parva 85-90; rtd 95; Perm to Offic *St E* from 95. *11 De Burgh Place, Clare, Sudbury CO10 8QL*

✠**GODFREY, The Rt Revd Harold William.** b 48. AKC71. St Aug Coll Cant 71. **d** 72 **p** 73 **c** 87. C Warsop *S'well* 72-75; TV Hucknall Torkard 75-86; Dioc Ecum Officer 81-82; USPG from 86; R and Adn Montevideo and Can Buenos Aires 86-88; Asst Bp Argentina and Uruguay 87-88; Bp Uruguay 88-98; Bp Peru from 98. *Calle Alcalá 336, Urb la Castellana, Santiago de Surco, Lima 33, Peru* Tel (0051) (1) 422 9160 *or* 448 4855 Fax as telephone E-mail wgodfrey@amauta.rcp.net.pe

GODFREY, Ian. b 56. **d** 01 **p** 02. NSM Mill Hill Jo Keble Ch *Lon* from 01. *Sirocco, 40 Hillside Grove, London NW7 2LR* Tel (020) 8959 5123

GODFREY, Jennifer Olwen. **d** 02. C Lasswade *Edin* from 02; C Dalkeith from 02. *131 Newbattle Abbey Crescent, Dalkeith EH23 3LP* Tel 0131-660 6145

GODFREY, John Frederick. b 31. Solicitor 57 Lon Univ LLB53 AKC54. Cuddesdon Coll 59. **d** 61 **p** 92. C Battersea St Luke *S'wark* 61-65; Min Reigate St Phil CD 65-72; Public Preacher *St Alb* 73-03; Perm to Offic from 03. *3 Davidge Place, Knotty Green, Beaconsfield HP9 2SR* Tel (01494) 689925 Fax 672930

GODFREY, Michael James. b 50. Sheff Univ BEd77. St Jo Coll Nottm DipTh79 CPS79. **d** 82 **p** 83. C Walton H Trin *Ox* 82-86; C Chadderton Ch Ch *Man* 86-91; V Woodlands *Sheff* from 91. *The Vicarage, 9 Great North Road, Woodlands, Doncaster DN6 7RB* Tel (01302) 723268 E-mail mikegodfrey@btinternet.com

GODFREY, Nigel Philip. b 51. Ripon Coll Cuddesdon BA78 MA84 Lon Guildhall Univ MBA00 Bris Poly Dip Town Planning 73 S Bank Univ DMS98 MRTPI76. Ripon Coll Cuddesdon 77. **d** 79 **p** 80. C Kennington St Jo w St Jas *S'wark* 79-89; Community of Ch the Servant 84-93; V Brixton Road Ch Ch *S'wark* 89-01; Prin OLM Scheme from 01; Chapl S'wark Cathl from 02. *47 Curtis Way, London SE1 5XW* Tel (020) 7564 9252 *or* 7378 7506 Fax 7403 6497 E-mail nigel.godfrey@dswark.org.uk

GODFREY (née ROGERS), Mrs Pauline Ann. b 58. LMH Ox BA79 MA83 Ox Univ Inst of Educn PGCE80. S Dios Mnstr Tr Scheme 89. **d** 92 **p** 94. NSM Headley All SS *Guildf* 92-96; C 96-99; Past Tutor Dioc Min Course from 96; P-in-c Wyke 99-01; V from 01. *Wyke Vicarage, Guildford Road, Normandy, Guildford GU3 2DA* Tel (01483) 811332 E-mail pag@yerfdog1.screaming.net

GODFREY, Rumley Myles. b 48. S'wark Ord Course. **d** 83 **p** 84. NSM Dorchester *Ox* from 83. *The Old Malthouse, Warborough OX10 7DY* Tel (01865) 858627 E-mail myles@warborough.fsnet.co.uk

GODFREY, Simon Henry Martin. b 55. TD00. K Coll Lon BD80 AKC80. St Steph Ho Ox 80. **d** 81 **p** 82. C Kettering SS Pet and Paul *Pet* 81-84; R Crick and Yelvertoft w Clay Coton and Lilbourne 84-89; V Northampton All SS w St Kath 89-98; R Northampton All SS w St Kath and St Pet from 98. *All Saints' Rectory, 6 Albion Place, Northampton NN1 1UD* Tel (01604) 621854 *or* tel and fax 632194 E-mail simongodfrey@breathemail.net

GODFREY, Stanley William. b 24. CEng MIEEE67. Qu Coll Birm 71. **d** 74 **p** 74. C Sutton Coldfield St Chad *Birm* 74-78; Hon C Handsworth St Andr 78-86; Hon C Worc City St Paul and Old St Martin etc Worc 86-89; Hon C Droitwich Spa 89-96; Perm to Offic from 96. *2 The Pippins, Eckington, Pershore WR10 3PY* Tel (01386) 751184 Fax 751421

GODIN, Mrs Mary Louise. b 42. Newc64 QN66. Oak Hill NSM Course 89. **d** 92 **p** 94. NSM Surbiton Hill Ch Ch *S'wark* 92-97; Chapl Kingston and Distr Community NHS Trust 97-01; Team Chapl SW Lon and St George's Mental Health NHS Trust from 01. *Tolworth Hospital, Red Lion Road, Surbiton KT6 7QU* Tel and fax (020) 8390 0102 *or* tel 8399 5088 E-mail mary.godin@honeycomb.co.uk

GODSALL, Andrew Paul. b 59. Birm Univ BA81. Ripon Coll Cuddesdon 86. **d** 88 **p** 89. C Gt Stanmore *Lon* 88-91; C Ealing All SS 91-94; V Hillingdon All SS 94-01; Dir of Ords Willesden Area 99-01; Bp's Dom Chapl *Ex* from 01. *2 West Avenue, Pennsylvania, Exeter EX4 4SD* Tel (01392) 676714

GODSALL, Canon Ralph Charles. b 48. Qu Coll Cam BA71 MA75. Cuddesdon Coll 73. **d** 75 **p** 76. C Sprowston *Nor* 75-78; Chapl Trin Coll Cam 78-84; V Hebden Bridge *Wakef* 84-91; V Westmr St Steph w St Jo *Lon* 93-01; Can Res Roch Cathl *Roch* from 01. *Easter Garth, The Precinct, Rochester ME1 1SX* Tel (01634) 405265 *or* 843366 Mobile 07789-542951 Fax 401410 E-mail canonralph@aol.com

GODSELL, David Brian. b 40. Lon Univ BA62. Coll of Resurr Mirfield 65. **d** 67 **p** 68. C Middlesbrough All SS *York* 67-73; C Stainton-in-Cleveland 73-75; V Byker St Ant *Newc* 75-90; P-in-c Brandon *Dur* 90-94; V from 94. *The Vicarage, Sawmill Lane, Brandon, Durham DH7 8NS* Tel 0191-378 0845

GODSELL, Kenneth James Rowland. b 22. Birm Univ DipTh50 Birm Coll of Educn Dip Teaching50. Qu Coll Birm 75. **d** 76 **p** 77. Sen Lect Westhill Coll of HE Birm 74-85; Hon C Selly Hill St Steph Birm 76-81; Hon C Selly Park St Steph and St Wulstan 81-90; rtd 90; Lic to Offic Birm 90-96; Perm to Offic Worc from 96. *The Quest, Dock Lane, Tewkesbury GL20 7LN* Tel (01684) 772469

GODSON, Alan. b 31. Ch Coll Cam BA61 MA65. Clifton Th Coll 61. **d** 63 **p** 64. C Preston All SS *Blackb* 63-66; Lic to Offic *Man* 66-69; Asst Chapl Emb Ch Paris 69; Dioc Ev *Liv* 69-01; P-in-c Edge Hill St Mary 72-78; V 78-01; rtd 01. *28 Handley Court, Aigburth, Liverpool L19 3QS* Tel 0151-427 0255

GODSON, Mark Rowland. b 61. K Coll Lon BD83 AKC83 CertEd84. Linc Th Coll 84. **d** 86 **p** 87. C Hurst Green *S'wark* 86-88; C Fawley *Win* 88-90; TV Wimborne Minster and Holt *Sarum* 90-95; P-in-c Horton and Chalbury 90-95; P-in-c Stalbridge 95-96; Chapl Forest Healthcare NHS Trust Lon 96-00; P-in-c Bicton, Montford w Shrawardine and Fitz *Lich* from 00; Chapl Shropshire's Community NHS Trust from 01. *The Rectory, 15 Brookside, Bicton, Shrewsbury SY3 8EP* Tel (01743) 851306 *or* 261000 E-mail sparky15@ntlworld.com

GODWIN, Canon David Harold. b 45. Lon Univ DipTh71. Kelham Th Coll 67. **d** 71 **p** 72. C Camberwell St Phil and St Mark *S'wark* 71-75; Asst Chapl The Lon Hosp (Whitechapel) 75-79; Chapl R E Sussex Hosp Hastings 79-86; Chapl Over Hosp Glouc 86-92; Chapl Glos R Hosp 86-94; Chapl Glos R Hosp NHS Trust 94-02; Chapl Glos Hosps NHS Trust from 02; Hon Can Glouc Cathl *Glouc* from 03. *Gloucestershire Royal Hospital, Great Western Road, Gloucester GL1 3NN* Tel (01452) 394200 *or* 528555 ext 4200 E-mail godwins@compuserve.com

GODWIN, Canon Michael Francis Harold. b 35. Nottm Univ BSc57. Ely Th Coll 59. **d** 61 **p** 62. C Farnborough *Guildf* 61-65; V Epsom St Barn 66-85; V Bramley and Grafham 85-98; Hon Can Guildf Cathl 89-98; rtd 00. *14 Lemmington Way, Horsham RH12 5JG* Tel (01403) 273411

GOFF, Philip Francis Michael. b 52. K Coll Lon BD73 AKC73 MBAC95 FBS00. **d** 75 **p** 76. C Ruislip St Martin *Lon* 75-79; Chapl Aldenham Sch Herts 79-82; V Tokyngton St Mich *Lon* 82-89; In RC Ch 89-91; Primary Care Cllr NHS 91-98; Perm to Offic *Lon* from 99; Chapl to Bp Edmonton from 00; Lic Preacher from 00. *24 Redhill Street, London NW1 4DQ* Tel (020) 7388 0580 Mobile 07768-920506 E-mail phildress@blueyonder.co.uk

GOFTON, Canon William Alder. b 31. Dur Univ BA54. Coll of Resurr Mirfield 59. **d** 61 **p** 62. C Benwell St Aid *Newc* 61-64; C N Gosforth 64-69; V Seaton Hirst 69-77; V Newc H Cross 77-89; RD Newc W 85-89; Hon Can Newc Cathl 88-96; R Bolam w Whalton and Hartburn w Meldon 89-96; P-in-c Nether Witton 89-95; V 95-96; Chapl Kirkley Hall Coll 90-96; rtd 96; Perm to Offic *Newc* from 96. *4 Crossfell, Ponteland, Newcastle upon Tyne NE20 9EA* Tel (01661) 820344

GOLBOURNE, Winston George. b 30. Univ of W Indies BA53. Virginia Th Sem STM69 Sarum & Wells Th Coll 71. **d** 73 **p** 74. C Bitterne Park *Win* 73-76; Jamaica 76-79; C Handsworth St Andr *Birm* 79-83; V Perry Hill St Geo *S'wark* 83-00; rtd 00; Perm to Offic *Roch* from 00. *42 Myrtle Close, Erith DA8 3PT* Tel (01322) 341798

GOLD, Guy Alastair Whitmore. b 16. TD50. Trin Coll Cam BA38 MA48. Qu Coll Birm 55. **d** 55 **p** 56. C Prittlewell St Pet *Chelmsf* 55-57; Bp's Dom Chapl 58-61; R Wickham Bishops 62-69; R Hasketon *St E* 69-76; rtd 76; Perm to Offic *St E* 76-89. *Bridge House, Great Bealings, Woodbridge IP13 6NW* Tel (01473) 735518

GOLDENBERG, Ralph Maurice. b 45. City Univ FBCO67 FBOA67. Trin Coll Bris DipHE90. **d** 90 **p** 91. C Kinson *Sarum* 90-93; C Edgware *Lon* 93-97; TV Roxeth 97-01; V Bayston Hill *Lich* from 01. *The Vicarage, 42 Eric Lock Road West, Bayston Hill, Shrewsbury SY3 0QA* Tel (01743) 872164 E-mail rgoldenberg@btopenworld.com

GOLDER, Rebecca Marie. *See* ROGERS, Mrs Rebecca Marie

GOLDIE, James Stuart. b 46. Edin Univ BTh73 BEd73. ALCD69. **d** 69 **p** 70. C Blackpool St Paul *Blackb* 69-70; C Gt Sankey *Liv* 70-73; Asst Chapl Greystone Heath Sch 70-73; Chapl Kilmarnock Academy 73-75; V Flixton St Jo *Man* 75-78; Chapl Trin Sch Liv 78-80; Chapl Westbrook Hay Sch Hemel Hempstead 83-89; V Pennington w Lindal and Marton *Carl* 89-90; Chapl Bp Wand Sch *Lon* 90-95; Chapl Queenswood Sch Herts 96-97. *23 Ffordd Naddyn, Glan Conway, Colwyn Bay LL28 4NH* Tel (01924) 892254

GOLDIE, Katrina Ruth. b 76. Fitzw Coll Cam BA97 MPhil00 MA01. Westcott Ho Cam 98. **d** 00 **p** 01. C Cov E *Cov* from 00. *5 Waterloo Street, Coventry CV1 5JS* Tel (024) 7622 2045 E-mail katrinagoldie@hotmail.com

GOLDING, Neil Christopher. b 47. Warwick Univ BA69. S'wark Ord Course 92. **d** 95 **p** 96. C Mitcham Ascension *S'wark* 95-00; P-in-c Croydon Woodside from 00. *St Luke's Vicarage, Portland Road, London SE25 4RB* Tel (020) 8654 9841 Fax as telephone E-mail rev_neil@btopenworld.com

GOLDING, Piers Edwin Hugh. b 26. RD76. St Aug Coll Cant 48 Edin Th Coll 50. **d** 53 **p** 54. C Guildf Ch Ch *Guildf* 53-55; C Enfield St Andr *Lon* 55-58; Chapl RN 58-62; Chapl RNR 62-93; V S Bermondsey St Aug *S'wark* 62-93; rtd 93; Perm to Offic *S'wark* from 93; Perm to Offic *St E* from 93. *6 White Lion House, Broad Street, Eye IP23 7AF* Tel (01379) 871253

GOLDING, The Ven Simon Jefferies. b 46. CBE02. Brasted Place Coll 70. Linc Th Coll 72. **d** 74 **p** 75. C Wilton *York* 74-77; Chapl RN 77-97; Chapl of the Fleet 97-98 and 00-02; Adn for the RN 97-02; Dir Gen Naval Chapl Service 00-02; QHC from 97; Hon Can Gib Cathl *Eur* 98-02; rtd 02. *Arlanza, Hornby Road, Appleton Wiske, Northallerton DL6 2AF* Tel (01609) 881185

GOLDING, Stephen. b 57. Keele Univ BA79 CertEd79 Lon Bible Coll BA86. Cant Sch of Min 93. **d** 95 **p** 96. NSM Ramsgate St Luke *Cant* 95-98; Chapl St Lawr Coll Ramsgate 95-98; Chapl Berkhamsted Colleg Sch Herts from 98; Lic to Offic *St Alb* from 98. *Adelbert House, Mill Street, Berkhamsted HP4 2BA* Tel (01442) 878190

GOLDINGAY, Prof John Edgar. b 42. Keble Coll Ox BA64 Nottm Univ PhD83 Lambeth DD97. Clifton Th Coll 64. **d** 66 **p** 67. C Finchley Ch Ch *Lon* 66-69; Lect St Jo Coll Nottm 70-75; Dir Studies 76-79; Registrar 79-85; Vice-Prin 85-88; Prin 88-97; Prof OT Fuller Th Sem Pasadena from 97. *111 South Orange Grove, Apartment 108, Pasadena, CA 91105, USA* Tel (001) (626) 405 0626 E-mail johngold@fuller.edu

GOLDSMITH, Brian Derek. b 36. Leeds Univ BA64. Coll of Resurr Mirfield 64. **d** 66 **p** 67. C Littlehampton St Mary *Chich* 66-69; C Guildf St Nic *Guildf* 69-73; V Aldershot St Aug 73-81; C-in-c Leigh Park St Clare CD *Portsm* 82-85; C Rowner 85-96; rtd 97; C Catherington and Clanfield *Portsm* 97-01; Perm to Offic *Win* from 98. *27 White Dirt Lane, Catherington, Waterlooville PO8 0NB* Tel (023) 9259 9462

GOLDSMITH, Christopher. b 54. York Univ BA76 DPhil79. NTMTC. **d** 00 **p** 01. NSM Pitsea w Nevendon *Chelmsf* from 00. *21 Pittfields, Langdon Hills, Basildon SS16 6RD* Tel (01268) 414590 E-mail c.goldsmith@btinternet.com

GOLDSMITH, John Oliver. b 46. K Coll Lon BD69 AKC69. St Aug Coll Cant 69. **d** 70 **p** 71. C Dronfield *Derby* 70-73; C Ellesmere Port *Ches* 73-74; TV Ellesmere Port 74-81; P-in-c Pleasley *Derby* 81-87; P-in-c Pleasley Hill *S'well* 83-87; V Matlock Bank *Derby* 87-97; RD Wirksworth 92-97; P-in-c Kirk Hallam 97-01; V 01-02; P-in-c Taddington, Chelmorton and Flagg, and Monyash from 02; P-in-c Hartington, Biggin and Earl Sterndale from 02; RD Buxton from 02. *The Vicarage, Church Street, Monyash, Bakewell DE45 1JH* Tel (01629) 812234

GOLDSMITH, Malcolm Clive. b 39. Birm Univ BSocSc60 Aston Univ MSc01. Ripon Hall Ox 60. **d** 62 **p** 63. C Balsall Heath St Paul *Birm* 62-64; Chapl Aston Univ 64-72; Bp's Adv on Ind Soc *S'well* 72-79; R Nottingham St Pet and St Jas 79-85; Gen Sec IVS 85-88; Bp's Personal Exec Asst *Bradf* 88-91; Research Fell Stirling Univ *St And* 91-94; R Edin St Cuth *Edin* 94-02; Dioc Dir of Ords 95-01; rtd 02. *39 Craigleith View, Station Road, North Berwick EH39 4BF* Tel (01620) 892421 Fax as telephone E-mail malcolm.goldsmith123@btopenworld.com

GOLDSMITH, Mrs Mary Louie. b 48. K Coll Lon BA70 AKC70. Qu Coll Birm 91. **d** 93 **p** 94. NSM Matlock Bank *Derby* 93-97; NSM Kirk Hallam 97-02; NSM Taddington, Chelmorton and Flagg, and Monyash from 00. *The Vicarage, Church Street, Monyash, Bakewell DE45 1JH* Tel (01629) 812234

GOLDSMITH, Mrs Pauline Anne. b 40. Linc Th Coll 82. dss 84 **d** 87 **p** 94. Waddington *Linc* 86-88; Par Dn 87-88; Par Dn Gt and Lt Coates w Bradley 88-94; TV 94-96; TV Kidderminster St Mary and All SS w Trimpley etc *Worc* 96-01; rtd 01; Perm to Offic *Derby* and *Sheff* from 01. *143 Ravencar Road, Eckington, Sheffield S21 4JR* Tel (01246) 430083

GOLDSMITH, Stephen. b 32. Edin Th Coll. **d** 76 **p** 77. SPCK Staff 53-97; Bookshops Regional Manager SPCK 87-97; NSM Penicuik *Edin* 76-81; NSM Linc St Nic w St Jo Newport *Linc* 81-90; NSM Gt and Lt Coates w Bradley 90-96; NSM Kidderminster St Mary and All SS w Trimpley etc *Worc* 96-01; Perm to Offic *Derby* and *Sheff* from 01. *143 Ravencar Road, Eckington, Sheffield S21 4JR* Tel (01246) 430083

GOLDSPINK, David. b 35. Open Univ BA81 BAC Acc 88. Lon Coll of Div 62. **d** 65 **p** 66. C Mile Cross *Nor* 65-68; C St Austell *Truro* 68-70; TV Bramerton w Surlingham *Nor* 70-73; Min Gunton St Pet 73-75; R Mutford w Rushmere w Gisleham w N Cove w Barnby 75-81; Asst Chapl HM Pris Man 81-82; Chapl HM Youth Cust Cen Hollesley Bay Colony 82-84; Chapl HM Pris Blundeston 84-88; Perm to Offic *St E* 87-01; rtd 88; Perm to Offic *Nor* 88-01. *14 Deepdale, Carlton Colville, Lowestoft NR33 8TU*

GOLDSPINK, Canon Robert William. b 23. Fitzw Coll Cam BA52 MA56. Trin Coll Bris 47. **d** 52 **p** 53. C Blackpool St Mark *Blackb* 52-56; V Erith St Paul *Roch* 56-64; V Tunbridge Wells St Jas 64-83; Lect Lon Coll of Div 65-66; Hon Can Roch Cathl *Roch* 83-87; V Seal St Pet 83-87; rtd 87; Perm to Offic *Nor* from 87. *7 Oaklands, Fenstanton, Huntingdon PE28 9LS* Tel (01480) 469352

GOLDSTONE-CREASEY, Graham. b 51. Trent Poly BA. Cranmer Hall Dur 80. **d** 83 **p** 84. C Birstall and Wanlip *Leic* 83-87; C-in-c Wheatley Park St Paul CD *Sheff* 87-92; V Wheatley Park 92-95; P-in-c Gleadless Valley 95-98. *11 Roselands, Walmer, Deal CT14 7QE* Tel (01304) 389880

GOLDSTRAW, William Henry. b 15. Lich Th Coll 40. **d** 61 **p** 62. C Stone St Mich *Lich* 61-68; V Alton 68-82; V Bradley-in-the-Moors 68-82; V Alton w Bradley-le-Moors 82-84; rtd 84; Perm to Offic *Lich* from 84. *36 The Avenue, Cheddleton, Leek ST13 7JB* Tel (01538) 360204

GOLDTHORPE, Peter Martin. b 36. AKC61. **d** 62 **p** 63. C Lt Ilford St Barn *Chelmsf* 62-66; C Wickford 66-68; P-in-c Luton St Anne *St Alb* 68-71; P-in-c Linby w Papplewick *S'well* 78-82; Perm to Offic *Linc* 86-92; V Leaton and Albrighton w Battlefield *Lich* 93-98; rtd 98. *1 Sandhurst Avenue, Ipswich IP3 8DU* Tel (01473) 257988

GOLDTHORPE, Ms Shirley. b 42. Linc Th Coll 70. dss 76 **d** 87 **p** 94. Thornhill Lees *Wakef* 76-78; Birkenshaw w Hunsworth 78-80; Batley St Thos 80-85; Batley All SS 80-85; Purlwell 80-92; Par Dn 87-92; Dn-in-c 88-92; Dn-in-c Horbury Junction 92-94; P-in-c 94-01; rtd 02. *10 Orchid View, Alverthorpe, Wakefield WF2 0FG* Tel 07885-462837 (mobile)

GOLLEDGE, Christopher John. b 66. St Mich Coll Llan DipTh92. **d** 92 **p** 93. C Newton Nottage *Llan* 92-95; Perm to Offic *Chich* from 95. *32 Bennett Road, Brighton BN3 5JL*

GOLLEDGE, Miss Patricia Anne. b 55. Trin Coll Bris BA00. **d** 00 **p** 01. C Pontypool *Mon* 00-03; TV from 03. *St Matthew's House, Victoria Road, Pontypool NP4 5JU* Tel (01495) 752233

GOLLOP, Michael John. b 58. Keble Coll Ox BA81 MA85. St Mich Coll Llan BD85. **d** 85 **p** 86. C Newport St Mark *Mon* 85-87; C Bassaleg 87-91; V St Hilary Greenway 91-93; V Itton and St Arvans w Penterry and Kilgwrrwg etc from 93. *The Vicarage, St Arvans, Chepstow NP16 6EU* Tel (01291) 622064

GOLTON, Alan Victor. b 29. St Jo Coll Ox BA51 MA54 DPhil54. LNSM course 84. **d** 85 **p** 86. P-in-c Barston *Birm* 87-95; Perm to Offic 95-96; Hon C Grenoble *Eur* 97-00. *Chant du Matin, Les Michallons, 38250 St Nizier du Moucherotte, France* Tel (0033) (4) 76 53 43 77 E-mail avgolton@hotmail.com

GOMERSALL, Ian Douglass. b 56. Birm Univ BSc77 Fitzw Coll Cam BA80 MA85 Dur Univ MA94. Westcott Ho Cam 78. **d** 81 **p** 82. C Darlington St Mark w St Paul *Dur* 81-84; C Barnard Castle w Whorlton 84-86; Chapl HM YOI Deerbolt 85-90; P-in-c Cockfield *Dur* 86-88; R 88-90; Dep Chapl HM Pris Wakef 90-91; Chapl HM Pris Full Sutton 91-97; P-in-c Kexby w Wilberfoss *York* 93-97; TV Man Whitworth *Man* from 97; P-in-c Man Victoria Park from 98; Chapl Man Univ 97-03; Hon Chapl from 03; Chapl Man Metrop Univ 97-03; Hon Chapl from 03. *St Chrysostom's Rectory, 38 Park Range, Manchester M14 5HQ* Tel 0161-224 6971 Mobile 07711-670225 E-mail fatherian@priest.com

GOMERSALL, Richard. b 45. FCA68. N Ord Course 90. **d** 93 **p** 94. NSM Thurcroft *Sheff* 93-96; NSM Sheff St Matt 96-03; Ind Chapl 98-03; C-in-c Southey Green St Bernard CD from 03. *Dale View House, 14 Wignall Avenue, Wickersley, Rotherham S66 2AX* Tel (01709) 546441 Fax 701900 E-mail fr.gomersall@btinternet.com

✠**GOMEZ, The Most Revd Drexel Wellington.** b 37. BA59. Codrington Coll Barbados 55. **d** 59 **c** 72. Tutor Codrington Coll Barbados 64-68; Bp Barbados 72-93; Bp Coadjutor Nassau and Bahamas 95-96; Dioc Bp 96-01; Bp Bahamas and Turks and Caicos Is from 01; Abp W Indies from 98. *PO Box N-7107, Nassau, Bahamas* Tel (001242) 322 3015 Fax 322 7943 E-mail primate@batelnet.bs

GOMM, Timothy Frank. b 64. St Jo Coll Nottm 00. **d** 02 **p** 03. C Kinson *Sarum* from 02. *13 Greaves Close, Bournemouth BH10 5EG* Tel (01202) 521480 Fax as telephone E-mail tim.gomm@ntlworld.com

GOMPERTZ, Canon Peter Alan Martin. b 40. ALCD63. **d** 64 **p** 65. C Eccleston St Luke *Liv* 64-69; Scripture Union 69-73; C Yeovil *B & W* 73-75; V Northampton St Giles *Pet* 75-96; Can Pet Cathl from 88; R Aynho and Croughton w Evenley etc from 96. *The Rectory, Croughton Road, Aynho, Banbury OX17 3BG* Tel (01869) 810903 Mobile 07771-615364 Fax (01869) 811240 E-mail canon.gompertz@virgin.net

GONIN, Christopher Willett. b 33. Man Univ DipRS82 DACE87 MBA92. AKC59. **d** 60 **p** 61. C Camberwell St Geo *S'wark* 60-64; C Stevenage H Trin *St Alb* 64-69; C Bletchley *Ox* 70-73; R Newington St Mary *S'wark* 73-76; Perm to Offic *Bris* 76-77; Hon C Horfield H Trin 77-89; Hon C City of Bris 89-91; V Milton Ernest *St Alb* 92-97; V Thurleigh 92-97; rtd 97; Perm to Offic *St E* from 97. *10 Mill Field, Church Farm, Aldeburgh IP15 5LL* Tel (01728) 454308 Fax as telephone E-mail chris@grow.ftech.co.uk

GOOCH, John Ellerton. b 46. Natal Univ BEcon70. Trin Coll Bris 73. **d** 75 **p** 76. Chapl S Africa 75-98; Perm to Offic *Chelmsf* 98-00; Casablanca *Eur* from 98. *Place Leclerc, Angle rue de Vanneaux 1, Oasis 20100, Casablanca, Morocco* Tel (00212) (2) 257120 Fax as telephone E-mail john.gooch@cwcom.net

GOOCH, Michael Anthony. b 44. Nottm Coll of Educn TCert66. Cant Sch of Min 90. **d** 93 **p** 94. NSM New Romney w Old Romney and Midley *Cant* 93-97; P-in-c Teynham w Lynsted and Kingsdown 97-98; P-in-c from 98; Bp's Officer for NSM from 98. *The Vicarage, 76 Station Road, Teynham, Sittingbourne ME9 9SN* Tel (01795) 522510 E-mail mgooch@connectfree.co.uk

GOOD, Alan Raymond. b 39. Bris Sch of Min 83. **d** 85 **p** 86. NSM Horfield St Greg *Bris* 85-97; Chapl Asst Southmead Health Services NHS Trust 97-99; Chapl Asst N Bris NHS Trust from 99. *Southmead Hospital, Westbury-on-Trym, Bristol BS10 5NB* Tel 0117-959 5447, 950 5050 *or* (01454) 415778

GOOD, Andrew Ronald. b 60. Bris Univ BA82. Linc Th Coll 83. **d** 85 **p** 86. C Epping St Jo *Chelmsf* 85-88; C Cheshunt *St Alb* 88-91; R Spixworth w Crostwick *Nor* 91-92; R Frettenham w Stanninghall 91-92; R Spixworth w Crostwick and Frettenham from 92. *The Rectory, Buxton Road, Spixworth, Norwich NR10 3PR* Tel (01603) 898258

GOOD, Anthony Ernest. b 28. ARIBA51 Heriot-Watt Univ MSc73. Wells Th Coll 54. **d** 56 **p** 57. C Maidstone All SS *Cant* 56-60; C Reading St Mary V *Ox* 60-62; R Sandhurst 62-70; Perm to Offic *Ex* 71-82; TR Wallingford w Crowmarsh Gifford etc *Ox* 82-92; RD Wallingford 85-91; rtd 92; Perm to Offic *Ex* from 92. *Cotts Weir Quay, Bere Alston, Yelverton PL20 7BX* Tel (01822) 840524

GOOD, David Howard. b 42. Glouc Sch of Min 84. **d** 87 **p** 88. NSM Bromyard *Heref* 87-92; C Pontesbury I and II 92-95; P-in-c Ditton Priors w Neenton, Burwarton etc 95-98; R Ditton Priors w Neenton, Burwarton etc 98-02; rtd 02. *26 Farjeon Close, Ledbury HR8 2FU* Tel (01531) 636474

GOOD, Geoffrey. b 27. St Aid Birkenhead. **d** 61 **p** 62. C Roby *Liv* 61-65; V Staincliffe *Wakef* 65-79; V Thornes St Jas w Ch Ch 79-93; rtd 93; Perm to Offic *Wakef* from 93. *147 Thornes Road, Wakefield WF2 8QN* Tel (01924) 378273

GOOD, The Very Revd George Fitzgerald. b 19. TCD BA41. CITC 42. **d** 42 **p** 43. C Drumglass *Arm* 42-45; Clerical V Ch Ch Cathl Dublin *D & G* 45-49; I Inniskeel w Lettermacaward *D & R* 49-60; I Raphoe w Raymochy 60-67; Can Raphoe Cathl 60-62; Dean Raphoe 62-67; Dean Derry 67-84; I Templemore 67-84; rtd 84. *Cliff Cottage, Portnoo, Lifford, Co Donegal, Irish Republic* Tel (00353) (74) 954 5268

GOOD, Preb John Hobart. b 43. Bps' Coll Cheshunt 66 Coll of Resurr Mirfield 68. **d** 69 **p** 70. C Ex St Jas *Ex* 69-73; C Cockington 73-75; C Wolborough w Newton Abbot 75-78; P-in-c Exminster 78-80; P-in-c Kenn 78-80; R Exminster and Kenn 80-95; RD Kenn 89-95; TR Axminster, Chardstock, All Saints etc from 95; Preb Ex Cathl from 02; Chapl All Hallows Sch Rousdon from 98. *The Rectory, Church Street, Axminster EX13 5AQ* Tel (01297) 32264
E-mail jhgood_minster@hotmail.com

✠**GOOD, The Rt Revd Kenneth Raymond.** b 52. TCD BA74 Nottm Univ BA76 NUI HDipEd81 MEd84. St Jo Coll Nottm 75. **d** 77 **p** 78 **c** 02. C Willowfield *D & D* 77-79; Chapl Ashton Sch Cork 79-84; I Dunganstown w Redcross and Conary *D & G* 84-90; I Lurgan Ch the Redeemer *D & D* 90-02; Adn Dromore 97-02; Bp *D & R* from 02. *The See House, 112 Culmore Road, Londonderry BT48 8JF* Tel (028) 7135 1206 *or* 7126 2440 Fax 7135 2554 E-mail bishop@derry.anglican.org

GOOD, The Ven Kenneth Roy. b 41. K Coll Lon BD66 AKC66. **d** 67 **p** 68. C Stockton St Pet *Dur* 67-70; Chapl Antwerp Miss to Seamen *Eur* 70-74; Japan 74-79; Hon Can Kobe from 74; Asst Gen Sec Miss to Seamen 79-85; Asst Chapl St Mich Paternoster Royal *Lon* 79-85; V Nunthorpe *York* 85-93; RD Stokesley 90-93; Adn Richmond *Ripon* from 93. *Hoppus House, Smith Lane, Hutton Conyers, Ripon HG4 5DX* Tel (01765) 604342 Fax as telephone E-mail good.richmond@freeuk.com

GOOD, Robert Stanley. b 24. TCD BA45 BD47 Kent Univ MA82. TCD Div Sch Div Test 46. **d** 47 **p** 48. C Lurgan Ch the Redeemer *D & D* 47-49; CMS 50-60; Kenya 50-60; Perm to Offic *Cant* from 61; Sen Div Master Maidstone Gr Sch 62-64; Sen Lect Ch Ch Coll Cant 64-78; Fiji 83-87; Par Educn Officer Herne Bay Ch Ch *Cant* 88-94; rtd 94. *Njiani, 44 Ivanhoe Road, Herne Bay CT6 6EG* Tel (01227) 363561

GOOD, Stuart Eric Clifford. b 37. Wycliffe Hall Ox 63. **d** 64 **p** 65. C Walton H Trin *Ox* 64-67; Australia from 66; Dir Chapl Services Angl Homes Inc from 85. *6 Enright Circuit, Stanford Gardens, Beeliar, W Australia 6164* Tel (0061) 419-145369 (Mobile) Fax (8) 9310 5580 E-mail bargood@webace.com.au

GOOD, Canon William Thomas Raymond. b 13. TCD BA39 MA45. **d** 39 **p** 40. C Castlecomer *C & O* 39-43; Dioc C (Cork) *C, C & R* 43-45; I Kilnagross 45-52; I Castleventry w Kilmean 52-60; I Rathcooney 60-73; Can Cloyne Cathl 67-69; Prec 69-82; I Carrigrohane Union 73-82; Can Cork Cathl 79-82; rtd 82. *Woodley, Main Road, Shankill, Co Dublin, Irish Republic* Tel (00353) (01) 272 0921

GOODACRE, Canon David Leighton. b 36. Birm Univ DPS69. AKC59. **d** 60 **p** 61. C Stockton St Chad *Dur* 60-63; C Birtley 63-68; Chapl Sunderland Gen Hosp 69-74; P-in-c Ryhope *Dur* 75-81; V Ovingham *Newc* 81-01; Hon Can Newc Cathl 92-01; rtd 01; Perm to Offic *Newc* from 01. *9 Wilmington Close, Newcastle upon Tyne NE3 2SF* Tel (0191) 271 4382

GOODAIR, Janet. *See* CHEESEMAN, Ms Janet

GOODALL, George. b 24. LCP. **d** 86 **p** 87. NSM Bretby w Newton Solney *Derby* 86-94; Perm to Offic from 94. *6 Brizlincote Lane, Burton-on-Trent DE15 0PR* Tel (01283) 562467

GOODALL, John William. b 45. Hull Univ BA69. Ripon Hall Ox 69. **d** 71 **p** 72. C Loughborough Em *Leic* 71-74; C Dorchester *Ox* 74-75; TV Dorchester 75-80; Tutor Sarum & Wells Th Coll 80-88; Vice Prin S Dios Minl Tr Scheme 80-88; P-in-c Gt Wishford *Sarum* 80-83; P-in-c Colehill 88-96; V from 96; Dioc Dir of Readers 88-95. *The Vicarage, Smugglers Lane, Colehill, Wimborne BH21 2RY* Tel (01202) 883721

GOODALL, Jonathan Michael. b 61. R Holloway Coll Lon BMus83. Wycliffe Hall Ox 86. **d** 89 **p** 90. C Bicester w Bucknell, Caversfield and Launton *Ox* 89-92; Asst Chapl HM Pris Bullingdon 90-92; Min Can, Chapl, and Sacr Westmr Abbey 92-98; Bp's Chapl and Research Asst *Eur* from 98; Hon C Westmr St Matt *Lon* from 99. *Bishop's Lodge, Worth, Crawley RH10 7RT, or, 14 Tufton Street, London SW1P 3QZ* Tel (01293) 883051 *or* (020) 7898 1155 Fax (01293) 884479 *or* (020) 7898 1166 E-mail chaplain@eurobish.clara.co.uk

GOODALL, Malcolm. b 39. Newc Univ MA93. Carl Dioc Tr Inst 80. **d** 85 **p** 86. NSM Allonby and Cross Canonby *Carl* 85-88; C Auckland St Andr and St Anne *Dur* 88-90; V Grindon and Stillington 90-98; P-in-c Wolsingham and Thornley 98-03; R from 03. *The Rectory, 14 Rectory Lane, Wolsingham, Bishop Auckland DL13 3AJ* Tel (01388) 527340
E-mail malcolm.goodall@durham.anglican.org

GOODBODY, Ruth Vivien. b 68. Wycliffe Hall Ox 96 STETS 00. **d** 02. C Bourne Valley *Sarum* from 02. *26 Winterslow Road, Porton, Salisbury SP4 0LR* Tel (01980) 610838
E-mail the.goodbodies@virgin.net

GOODBODY, Steven John. b 70. Univ of Wales (Cardiff) BD92. Wycliffe Hall Ox 00. **d** 02 **p** 03. C Tunbridge Wells St Jo *Roch* from 02. *112 Stephen's Road, Tunbridge Wells TN4 9QA* Tel (01892) 521767 Mobile 07768-645172
E-mail sjgoodbody@csi.com

GOODBODY, Timothy Edward. b 66. York Univ BA89 Surrey Univ DipTran90. Wycliffe Hall Ox BTh98. **d** 98 **p** 99. C Blandford Forum and Langton Long *Sarum* 98-02; NSM Bourne Valley from 02. *26 Winterslow Road, Porton, Salisbury SP4 0LR* Tel (01980) 610838

GOODBURN, David Henry. b 41. S'wark Ord Course 73. **d** 76 **p** 77. NSM Enfield SS Pet and Paul *Lon* 76-82; Perm to Offic 83-85; NSM Potters Bar *St Alb* 85-88; Chapl RN 88-96; V Luton St Sav *St Alb* from 96. *St Saviour's Vicarage, St Saviour's Crescent, Luton LU1 5HG* Tel (01582) 730445

GOODCHILD, Andrew Philip. b 55. CertEd80. Oak Hill Th Coll BA85. **d** 85 **p** 86. C Barnston *Ches* 85-88; C Hollington St Leon *Chich* 88-89; P-in-c Millbrook *Ches* 89-94; Chapl and Hd RE Kimbolton Sch Cambs from 94. *Kimbolton School, Kimbolton, Huntingdon PE28 0EA* Tel (01480) 862209 Fax 860386
E-mail melandi@talk21.com

GOODCHILD, Canon John McKillip. b 42. Clare Coll Cam BA64 MA68 Oriel Coll Ox CertEd69. Wycliffe Hall Ox 67. **d** 69 **p** 70. C Clubmoor *Liv* 69-72; Nigeria 72-83; Hon Can Aba from 74; V Ainsdale *Liv* 83-89; TR Maghull 89-98; Prin OLM Tr Scheme *Nor* from 98. *Emmaus House, 65 The Close, Norwich NR1 4DH* Tel (01603) 611196 *or* 632041 Fax 766476

GOODCHILD, Roy John. b 30. Wycliffe Hall Ox 60. **d** 61 **p** 62. C Hayes *Roch* 61-64; C S w N Bersted *Chich* 64-68; R Birdham w W Itchenor 68-73; V Saltdean 74-83; V Hollington St Jo 83-90; V Ticehurst and Flimwell 90-97; RD Rotherfield 95-97; rtd 97; Perm to Offic *Chich* from 97. *2 Brewers Row, Fletching, Uckfield TN22 3SJ* Tel (01825) 722160

GOODDEN, John Maurice Phelips. b 34. Sarum & Wells Th Coll 70. **d** 72 **p** 75. C Weymouth H Trin *Sarum* 72-74; C Harlow New Town w Lt Parndon *Chelmsf* 74-78; Ind Chapl 78-82; Chapl Princess Alexandra Hosp Harlow 78-82; V Moulsham St Jo *Chelmsf* 86-90; R Chipstead *S'wark* from 90; Adv Rural Min from 90. *The Rectory, Starrock Lane, Chipstead, Coulsdon CR5 3QD* Tel (01737) 552157 *or* 553527

GOODE, Allan Kenneth. b 37. S'wark Ord Course. **d** 72 **p** 73. C Belmont *Lon* 72-74; V Liv St Bride w St Sav *Liv* 74-78; V Eccleston Park 78-89; C Billinge 89-91; P-in-c Scarisbrick 91-94; V 94-03; rtd 03. *Kincon, Kilfian, Ballina, Co Mayo, Irish Republic*

GOODE, Anthony Thomas Ryall (Tom). b 42. Ex Coll Ox BA64 MA71. Cuddesdon Coll 65. **d** 67 **p** 68. C Wolvercote *Ox* 67-71; P-in-c Edith Weston w Normanton *Pet* 72-74; Chapl RAF 71-91; Asst Chapl-in-Chief 91-97; Chapl to The Queen 95-97; Chapl Abu Dhabi St Andr UAE 97-00; V Hurstbourne Tarrant, Faccombe, Vernham Dean etc *Win* from 00. *The Vicarage, Hurstbourne Tarrant, Andover SP11 0AH* Tel (01264) 736222 Fax 736148 E-mail spetroshbt@aol.com

GOODE, John Laurence. b 48. W Cheshire Coll of Tech TEng70 Federal Univ Minas Gerais Brazil Dip Teaching78. Chich Th Coll 81. **d** 83 **p** 84. C Crewe St Andr *Ches* 83-86; USPG 87-94; Brazil 91-94; TV Ches Team *Ches* 94-00; V Latchford Ch Ch from 00. *Christ Church Vicarage, Wash Lane, Warrington WA4 1HT* Tel (01925) 630846

GOODE, Jonathan. b 67. St Martin's Coll Lanc BA89. Qu Coll Birm. **d** 00 **p** 01. C Middleton St Mary *Ripon* from 00. *1 Gledhow Grange View, Leeds LS8 1PM* Tel 0113-266 8212
E-mail revjgoode@yahoo.com

GOODE, Michael Arthur John. b 40. K Coll Lon BD AKC63. **d** 64 **p** 65. C Sunderland Springwell w Thorney Close *Dur* 64-68; C Solihull *Birm* 68-70; R Fladbury, Wyre Piddle and Moor *Worc* 70-75; P-in-c Foley Park 75-81; V 81-83; RD Kidderminster 81-83; TR Crawley *Chich* 83-93; TR Abingdon *Ox* from 93; V Shippon from 93. *The Rectory, St Helen's Court, Abingdon OX14 5BS* Tel (01235) 520144 E-mail st.helens@tesco.net

GOODE, Canon Peter William Herbert. b 23. Oak Hill Th Coll 60. **d** 62 **p** 63. C Woodford Wells *Chelmsf* 62-65; V Harold Hill St Paul 65-76; V Gt Warley Ch Ch 76-93; RD Brentwood 89-93; Hon Can Chelmsf Cathl 90-93; rtd 93; Perm to Offic *St Alb* from 93. *52 Slimmons Drive, St Albans AL4 9AP* Tel (01727) 852166

GOODER, Canon Martin Lee. b 37. Sheff Univ BSc58. Oak Hill Th Coll 58. **d** 60 **p** 61. C Barrow St Mark *Carl* 60-63; C Halliwell St Pet *Man* 63-66; R Chorlton on Medlock St Sav 66-71; R Brunswick 71-92; P-in-c Bacup Ch Ch 92-02; Hon Can Man Cathl 98-02; rtd 02; Perm to Offic *Man* from 02. *12 Walton Close, Bacup OL13 9RE* Tel (01706) 872418
E-mail gooder@btopenworld.com

GOODERHAM, Daniel Charles. b 24. St Fran Coll Brisbane 49 ACT ThL51. **d** 52 **p** 53. Australia 52-60; C Staveley *Derby* 60-61; C Ipswich St Thos *St E* 61-64; V Ipswich St Bart 64-71; R Drinkstone 71-78; R Rattlesden 71-78; RD Lavenham 75-78; V Beckenham St Mich w St Aug *Roch* 78-87; P-in-c Whiteparish *Sarum* 87-89; rtd 89; Perm to Offic *St E* from 89. *58 Millfield, Eye IP23 7DE* Tel (01379) 871589

GOODERICK, Peter Handley. b 26. Down Coll Cam BA50 MA52. Linc Th Coll 51. **d** 53 **p** 54. C Brighouse *Wakef* 53-56; Prec Gib Cathl *Eur* 56-58; Chapl Izmir 58-59; C Wimbledon *S'wark* 59-63; CF (TAVR) 59-74; V Streatham St Paul *S'wark* 63-68; V Merton St Jas 68-80; P-in-c Baginton *Cov* 80-81; P-in-c Stoneleigh w Ashow 80-81; R Stoneleigh w Ashow and Baginton 81-88; RD Kenilworth 83-90; R Berkswell 88-91; rtd 91; Chapl Malaga w Almunecar and Nerja *Eur* 91-92; Perm to Offic *Cov* from 93. *9 Margetts Close, Barrowfield Lane, Kenilworth CV8 1EN* Tel (01926) 859855

GOODEY, Philip Julian Frank. b 61. Glos Coll of Arts & Tech HND83. Aston Tr Scheme 87 Trin Coll Bris DipTh92. **d** 92 **p** 93. C Iver *Ox* 92-94; C Hornchurch St Andr *Chelmsf* 94-99; V Wickham Market w Pettistree *St E* 99-01; TR Parkham, Alwington, Buckland Brewer etc *Ex* from 01; P-in-c Lundy Is from 01. *The Rectory, Parkham, Bideford EX39 5PL* Tel (01237) 451204 E-mail phil.goodey@zetnet.co.uk

GOODFELLOW, Ian. b 37. St Cath Coll Cam BA61 MA65 Lon Univ PGCE76 Dur Univ PhD83. Wells Th Coll 61. **d** 63 **p** 64. C Dunstable *St Alb* 63-67; Chapl Haileybury Coll 67-71; Asst Chapl St Bede Coll Dur 71-74; Lect and Tutor 71-75; Sen Lect and Tutor SS Hild and Bede Coll Dur 75-78; Sen Counsellor Open Univ (SW Region) 78-97; Perm to Offic *Ex* from 89; rtd 02. *Crosslea, 206 Whitchurch Road, Tavistock PL19 9DQ* Tel (01822) 612069 E-mail goodfellow1@lineone.net

GOODFIELD, Dudley Francis. b 40. AKC65. **d** 66 **p** 67. C Bath Twerton-on-Avon *B & W* 66-69; C Lache cum Saltney *Ches* 69-71; C Portishead *B & W* 71-76; V Weston-super-Mare St Andr Bournville 76-82; V Ruishton w Thornfalcon from 82. *The Vicarage, Church Lane, Ruishton, Taunton TA3 5JW* Tel (01823) 442269

GOODGER, Kenneth Andrew. b 67. Queensland Univ BA96. St Fran Coll Brisbane BTh97. **d** 93 **p** 96. Australia 93-99 and from 02; C Pimlico St Pet w Westmr Ch Ch *Lon* 99-02; R Moorooka and Salisbury from 02. *28 Piers Street, PO Box 104, Moorooka, Qld, Australia 4105* Tel (0061) (7) 3892 2508

GOODHAND, Richard. b 51. Sarum & Wells Th Coll 88. **d** 90 **p** 91. C Wollaton *S'well* 90-93; P-in-c Clarborough w Hayton 93-98; Sub-Chapl HM Pris Ranby 93-96; Asst Chapl 96-98; P-in-c Blidworth *S'well* 98-02; P-in-c Rainworth 98-02; V Blidworth w Rainworth from 02. *The Vicarage, 27 St Peter's Drive, Rainworth, Mansfield NG21 0BE* Tel (01623) 798980

GOODHEW, David John. b 65. Collingwood Coll Dur BA86 CCC Ox DPhil92 St Jo Coll Dur BA92. Cranmer Hall Dur 90. **d** 93 **p** 94. C Bedminster *Bris* 93-96; Chapl and Fell St Cath Coll Cam 96-01; V Fulford *York* from 01; P-in-c York St Denys from 01. *The Vicarage, 1 Fulford Park, Fulford, York YO10 4QE* Tel (01904) 633261

GOODHEW, Mrs Lindsey Jane Ellin. b 66. UEA BA87 St Jo Coll Dur BA92 Dip Minl Studies 93. Cranmer Hall Dur 90. **d** 93 **p** 94. C Bishopsworth *Bris* 93-96; Perm to Offic *Ely* 96-97; NSM Cambridge St Mark 97-01; Perm to Offic *York* from 01. *The Vicarage, 1 Fulford Park, Fulford, York YO10 4QE* Tel (01904) 633261

GOODHEW, Roy William. b 41. Reading Univ BA. S Dios Minl Tr Scheme. **d** 89 **p** 90. C Southampton Maybush St Pet *Win* 89-94; V Hound from 94. *The Vicarage, Grange Road, Netley Abbey, Southampton SO3 5FF* Tel (023) 8045 2209

GOODING, Canon Ian Eric. b 42. Leeds Univ BSc63 BCom65 MIProdE68 CEng69. St Jo Coll Nottm 70 Lon Coll of Div LTh72 DPS73. **d** 73 **p** 74. C Wandsworth All SS *S'wark* 73-77; Bp's Ind Adv *Derby* from 77; P-in-c Stanton-by-Dale w Dale Abbey 77-87; R 87-00; P-in-c Risley 94-00; R Stanton-by-Dale w Dale Abbey and Risley from 00; RD Erewash from 98; Hon Can Derby Cathl from 02. *The Rectory, Stanhope Street, Stanton-by-Dale, Ilkeston DE7 4QA* Tel 0115-932 4584 Mobile 07768-917385 Fax 0115-944 0299 E-mail iangooding@zoom.co.uk

GOODING, Ian Peter Slade. b 56. MBCS88 Imp Coll Lon BScEng77. Qu Coll Birm DipTh92. **d** 92 **p** 93. C Swindon Dorcan *Bris* 92-96; TV Langley Marish *Ox* 96-02. *4 Cubb Field, Aylesbury HP19 7SH*

GOODING, John Henry. b 47. St Jo Coll Nottm. **d** 84 **p** 85. C Charles w Plymouth St Matthias *Ex* 84-88; C Leeds St Geo *Ripon* 88-93; TV Liskeard, St Keyne, St Pinnock, Morval etc *Truro* 93-94; Lon and SE Consultant CPAS from 94; Perm to Offic *Guildf* 94-96; *S'wark* from 00; Cant, Chich, Lon, and Roch from 94; Hon C Egham *Guildf* from 96; Dioc Par Resource Officer 00-03; Dioc Dir Miss, Evang and Par Development from 03. *Diocesan House, Quarry Street, Guildford GU1 3XG* Tel (01483) 571826 ext 206 E-mail john.gooding@cofeguildford.org.uk

GOODLAD, Canon Martin Randall. b 39. Sheff City Coll of Educn TDip60. Linc Th Coll 63. **d** 66 **p** 67. C Bramley *Ripon*

66-69; TV Daventry *Pet* 69-71; Asst Dioc Youth Officer 69-71; Asst Dir of Educn Warwick 71-74; Youth Work Officer Gen Syn Bd of Educn 74-83; P-in-c Cheam Common St Phil *S'wark* 83-85; V 85-97; RD Sutton 90-97; Hon Can S'wark Cathl from 96; V Coulsdon St Andr from 97. *St Andrew's Vicarage, Julien Road, Coulsdon CR5 2DN* Tel (020) 8660 0398 Fax as telephone E-mail canmartin@aol.com

GOODLAND, Michael Eric. b 53. SW Minl Tr Course. **d** 97 **p** 98. NSM Ilminster and Distr *B & W* 97-02; NSM Crewkerne w Wayford from 02. *26 Bincombe Drive, Crewkerne TA18 7BE* Tel (01460) 72363 *or* 76151 E-mail mike07@themail.co.uk

GOODLEY, Christopher Ronald. b 47. K Coll Lon BD72 AKC72. **d** 73 **p** 74. C Shenfield *Chelmsf* 73-77; C Hanley H Ev *Lich* 77-78; TV 78-83; Chapl Whittington Hosp Lon 83-86; Chapl St Crispin's Hosp Northampton 88-94; Chapl Northampton Community Healthcare NHS Trust 94-01; Chapl Northants Healthcare NHS Trust from 01. *Princess Marina Hospital, Duston, Northampton NN5 6UH* Tel (01604) 595087 *or* 752323 Fax 583795 E-mail chris.goodley@nchc-tr.anglox.nhs.uk

GOODMAN, Ms Alice Abigail. b 58. Harvard Univ BA80 Girton Coll Cam BA82 MA86 Boston Univ MDiv97. Ripon Coll Cuddesdon 00. **d** 01 **p** 03. C Redditch, The Ridge *Worc* 01-02; C Kidderminster St Mary and All SS w Trimpley etc from 02. *10 James Road, Kidderminster DY10 2TR* Tel (01562) 748274 E-mail goodhill@appleonline.net

GOODMAN, Andrew Francis. b 56. Lon Univ BA79 Birm Univ MSocSc88 CQSW88. Qu Coll Birm 01. **d** 03. NSM Hamstead St Paul *Birm* from 03. *21 Loxley Road, Smethwick B67 5BL* Tel 0121-420 2063

GOODMAN, Preb Denys Charles. b 24. Selw Coll Cam BA49 MA56. Linc Th Coll 49. **d** 51 **p** 52. C Leigh St Mary *Man* 51-54; C Pendlebury St Aug 54-57; V Hollinwood 57-70; R Bath Bathwick St Mary *B & W* 70-78; P-in-c Bath Bathwick St Jo 76-78; R Bath Bathwick 78-91; RD Bath 81-90; Preb Wells Cathl 82-96; Sub-Dean Wells 82-96; rtd 91; Perm to Offic *B & W* from 96. *Hollinwood, Johnson Close, Wells BA5 3NN* Tel (01749) 675011

GOODMAN, Canon Derek George. b 34. Keble Coll Ox BA57 MA60. Ridley Hall Cam 59. **d** 61 **p** 62. C Attenborough *S'well* 61-65; R Eastwood 65-84; Dioc Insp of Schs 65-89; V Woodthorpe 84-89; Dioc Dir of Educn *Leic* 89-96; Hon Can Leic Cathl 90-96; rtd 96; Perm to Offic *Leic* from 96. *1 Brown Avenue, Quorn, Loughborough LE12 8RH* Tel (01509) 415692

GOODMAN, John. b 20. Selw Coll Cam BA42 MA46. Linc Th Coll 47. **d** 49 **p** 50. C Kidderminster St Jo *Worc* 49-53; C Marlborough *Sarum* 53-56; V Wootton Bassett 56-65; C Broad Town 56-65; C Salisbury St Mark 65-68; V 68-83; R Wool and E Stoke 83-88; rtd 88; Perm to Offic *Sarum* from 88. *141 Avon Road, Devizes SN10 1PY* Tel (01380) 721267

GOODMAN, John Dennis Julian. b 35. Sarum & Wells Th Coll 74. **d** 76 **p** 77. C Cromhall *Derby* 76-79; TV Old Brampton and Loundsley Green 79-86; R Finningley w Auckley *S'well* 86-96; rtd 96; Perm to Offic *Pet* from 96. *6 Mason Close, Thrapston, Kettering NN14 4UQ* Tel (01832) 731194

GOODMAN, Canon Mark Alexander Scott. b 61. Lanc Univ BA84 Nottm Univ BTh90 New Coll Edin MTh97. Linc Th Coll 87. **d** 90 **p** 91. C Denton St Lawr *Man* 90-93; R Dalkeith *Edin* from 93; R Lasswade from 93; Can St Mary's Cathl from 02. *The Rectory, 7 Ancrum Bank, Dalkeith, Midlothian EH22 3AY* Tel and fax 0131-663 7000 Mobile 07711-547927 E-mail markas@goodman24.freeserve.co.uk

GOODMAN, Peter William (Bill). b 59. St Cath Coll Cam BA82. St Jo Coll Nottm 85. **d** 89 **p** 90. C Stapenhill w Cauldwell *Derby* 89-92; C Ovenden *Wakef* 92-94; V Halifax St Aug 94-98; Crosslinks Ethiopia from 98. *c/o Crosslinks, 251 Lewisham Way, London SE4 1XF*

GOODMAN, Canon Sidney William. b 10. Kelham Th Coll 27. **d** 33 **p** 34. C Wigan St Mich *Liv* 33-36; C Gt Grimsby St Mary and St Jas *Linc* 36-39; V Fulstow 39-44; V Habrough 44-55; V Immingham 44-55; V Habrough Gp 55-71; RD Grimsby N 57-64; RD Haverstoe 64-76; Can and Preb Linc Cathl 69-79; P-in-c Wold Newton w Hawerby *Linc* 71-78; rtd 78; Perm to Offic *Linc* from 78. *28 Grosvenor Road, Louth LN11 0BB* Tel (01507) 603798

GOODMAN, Victor Terence. b 46. Liv Univ BSc67 CEng92 MBCS74. EMMTC 82. **d** 85 **p** 86. NSM Barwell w Potters Marston and Stapleton *Leic* 85-89; NSM Croft and Stoney Stanton 89-94; P-in-c Whetstone 94-03; TV Hugglescote w Donington, Ellistown and Snibston from 03. *St James's Vicarage, Highfield Street, Coalville LE67 3BN* Tel (01530) 832679 E-mail vgoodman@leicester.anglican.org

GOODMAN, Mrs Victoria Elizabeth Stuart. b 51. RGN74. Trin Coll Bris DipTS98. **d** 98 **p** 99. C Ilminster and Distr *B & W* 98-02; R Blagdon w Compton Martin and Ubley from 02; Dioc Chapl Mother's Union from 01. *The Rectory, High Street, Blagdon, Bristol BS40 7TA* Tel (01761) 462495

GOODRICH, Derek Hugh. b 27. Selw Coll Cam BA48 MA54. St Steph Ho Ox 50. **d** 52 **p** 53. C Willesden St Andr *Lon* 52-57; Guyana 57-00; Adn Berbice 81-84; V Gen Dio Guyana 82-94; Dean Georgetown 84-93; P-in-c St Aloysius 93-00; rtd 00. *The*

College of St Barnabas, Blackberry Lane, Lingfield RH7 6NJ Tel (01342) 871630

GOODRICH, Canon Peter. b 36. Dur Univ BA58. Cuddesdon Coll 60. **d** 62 **p** 63. C Walton St Jo *Liv* 62-66; C Prescot 66-68; V Anfield St Marg 68-72; V Gt Crosby St Faith 72-83; P-in-c Seaforth 76-80; RD Bootle 78-83; TR Upholland 83-94; R Halsall 94-02; Dir Dioc OLM Scheme 94-02; Hon Can Liv Cathl 89-02; rtd 03; Perm to Offic *Liv* from 03. *Dunelm, 16 Hillside Avenue, Ormskirk L39 4TD* Tel (01695) 573285

GOODRIDGE, Canon Peter David. b 32. Yale Univ STM84 FRSA92. AKC57. **d** 58 **p** 59. C Eastcote St Lawr *Lon* 58-64; V Tottenham St Phil 64-71; V W Drayton 71-85; P-in-c St Michael Penkevil *Truro* 85-88; P-in-c Lamorran and Merther 85-88; Dir of Educn 85-97; Hon Can Truro Cathl 87-96; Can Lib Truro Cathl 96-00; Perm to Offic from 01. *16 Crescent Rise, Truro TR1 3ER* Tel (01872) 270940 *or* 274352 Fax 222510

✠**GOODRIDGE, The Rt Revd Sehon Sylvester.** b 37. K Coll Lon BD66 AKC91 Gen Th Sem NY DD95. Huron Coll Ontario DD77 Codrington Coll Barbados 59. **d** 63 **p** 64 **c** 94. St Lucia 64-66; Chapl Univ of W Indies Jamaica 66-71; Warden and Dep Prin United Th Coll W Indies 69-71; Barbados 71-89; Prin Codrington Coll 71-82; Warden, Cllr and Sen Lect Univ of W Indies 83-89; Hon Can Barbados from 76; Prin Simon of Cyrene Th Inst 89-94; Chapl to The Queen 93-94; Bp Windward Is 94-02; rtd 02. *Bishop's Court, PO Box 502, St Vincent, West Indies* Tel (001) (784) 457 1942 *or* 457 0775

GOODRUM, Mrs Alice. b 30. Lightfoot Ho Dur 58. **dss** 80 **d** 87 **p** 94. Fenham St Jas and St Basil *Newc* 80-91; C 87-91; rtd 91; Perm to Offic *Dur* and *Newc* from 91. *58 West Avenue, South Shields NE34 6BD* Tel 0191-425 3629

GOODSELL, Patrick. b 32. BA88. Linc Th Coll 62. **d** 64 **p** 65. C Thornton Heath St Jude *Cant* 64-65; C Croydon St Jo *S'wark* 65-70; V Tenterden St Mich *Cant* 70-78; P-in-c Sellindge w Monks Horton and Stowting 78-84; P-in-c Lympne w W Hythe 82-84; V Sellindge w Monks Horton and Stowting etc 84-92; V Nonington w Wymynswold and Goodnestone etc 92-98; rtd 98; Perm to Offic *Cant* from 98. *3 James Close, Lyminge, Folkestone CT18 8NL* Tel (01303) 863976

GOODWIN, Barry Frederick John. b 48. Birm Univ BSc69 PhD77. St Jo Coll Nottm LTh88. **d** 88 **p** 89. C Ware Ch Ch *St Alb* 88-91; P-in-c Stanstead Abbots 91-96; P-in-c Gt Amwell w St Marg 95-96; V Gt Amwell w St Margaret's and Stanstead Abbots 96-99; RD Hertford and Ware 96-99; V Clapham Park All SS *S'wark* from 99; RD Clapham from 02. *All Saints' Vicarage, 250 Lyham Road, London SW2 5NP* Tel (020) 8678 6020 E-mail barry.goodwin@ukgateway.net

GOODWIN, Daphne Mary. b 35. Lon Univ MB, BS60. STETS 94. **d** 97 **p** 98. NSM Ifield *Chich* from 97. *150 Buckswood Drive, Gossops Green, Crawley RH11 8JF* Tel (01293) 612906 E-mail dapheter.goodwin@ukgateway.net

GOODWIN, David Wayne. b 71. Univ of Wales BD95. Cranmer Hall Dur 95. **d** 97 **p** 98. C Ches H Trin *Ches* 97-00; Dep Chapl HM Pris Dur 00-01; Chapl HM YOI Thorn Cross from 01. *HM Young Offender Institution, Arley Road, Appleton Thorn, Warrington WA4 4RL* Tel (01925) 605085 Fax 262153

GOODWIN, Mrs Gillian Sheila. b 54. N Ord Course MTh99. **d** 99 **p** 00. C Penkridge Team *Lich* 99-02; TV Wrockwardine Deanery from 02. *The Rectory, Wrockwardine, Telford TF6 5DD* Tel (01902) 240969

GOODWIN, Canon John Fletcher Beckles. b 20. Jes Coll Cam BA43 MA46. Ridley Hall Cam 42. **d** 45 **p** 46. C Southall H Trin *Lon* 45-48; C Drypool *York* 48-49; Niger 50-57; Vice-Prin Ripon Hall Ox 57-62; V Merton *Ox* 62-70; V Heanor *Derby* 70-74; V Hazlewood 74-85; V Turnditch 74-85; Adv for In-Service Tr and Chapl to Bp 74-88; Hon Can Derby Cathl 81-85; rtd 85; Perm to Offic *Derby* 85-99. *1 Kirby Place, Oxford OX4 2RX* Tel (01865) 712356

GOODWIN, Ronald Victor. b 33. S'wark Ord Course. **d** 86 **p** 87. NSM Wickford and Runwell *Chelmsf* 86-98; Perm to Offic 98-01; NSM W Hanningfield 01-03; P-in-c from 03. *164 Southend Road, Wickford SS11 8EH* Tel (01268) 734447

GOODWIN, Stephen. b 58. Sheff Univ BA80. Cranmer Hall Dur 82. **d** 85 **p** 86. C Lytham St Cuth *Blackb* 85-87; C W Burnley 88-90; TV Headley All SS *Guildf* 90-98; NSM Leek and Meerbrook *Lich* from 98. *St Chad's House, 3 Southfields, Leek ST13 5LR* Tel (01538) 382483 Fax 381148 E-mail goodwin@mcmail.com

GOODWIN, Mrs Susan Elizabeth. b 51. Leeds Poly BSc74 Leeds Univ MSc76. St Jo Coll Dur 82. **dss** 84 **d** 87 **p** 94. Norton Woodseats St Chad *Sheff* 84-87; Par Dn 87; Chapl Scargill Ho 87-89; NSM W Burnley *Blackb* 89-90; NSM Headley All SS *Guildf* 90-98; Past Asst Acorn Chr Healing Trust 91-93; P-in-c Wetley Rocks *Lich* from 98. *St Chad's House, 3 Southfields, Leek ST13 5LR* Tel (01538) 382483 Fax 381148

GOODWIN HUDSON, Brainerd Peter de Wirtz. b 34. K Coll Lon BD57 AKC57. Westcott Ho Cam 57. **d** 59 **p** 60. C Morden *S'wark* 59-60; Australia 61-65; Asst Sec CCCS 65-68; Chapl St Lawr Coll Ramsgate 68-74; Chapl Repton Sch Derby 74-94; Chapl Santiago Chile 94-01; rtd 99; Hon C Broadwell, Evenlode,

Oddington, Adlestrop etc *Glouc* from 02. *The Vicarage, Bledington, Chipping Norton OX7 6UR* Tel (01608) 658102 E-mail brainerd@freeuk.com

GOODWINS, Christopher William Hedley. b 36. St Jo Coll Cam BA58 MA62. Linc Th Coll 62. **d** 64 **p** 65. C Lowestoft Ch Ch *Nor* 64-69; V Tamerton Foliot *Ex* 69-98; P-in-c Southway 78-82; rtd 98; P-in-c Isleham *Ely* from 99. *102 The Causeway, Isleham, Ely CB7 5ST* Tel (01638) 780284 E-mail christopher@isleham.freeserve.co.uk

GOODYER, Canon Edward Arthur. b 42. Witwatersrand Univ BA63 SS Coll Cam BA67 MA70 Rhodes Univ MTh91. St Paul's Coll Grahamstown 68. **d** 68 **p** 69. S Africa 69-92; Can Cape Town 80-84; R Alverstoke *Portsm* from 92; P-in-c Gosport Ch Ch 97-01; Hon Can Wusasa Nigeria from 99. *The Rectory, Little Anglesey Road, Alverstoke, Gosport PO12 2JA* Tel and fax (023) 9258 1979 *or* 9258 0551 Mobile 07947-884714 E-mail ego.lizg@virgin.net

GOOLD, Peter John. b 44. Lon Univ BD74. St Steph Ho Ox 71. **d** 70 **p** 71. C Chiswick St Nic w St Mary *Lon* 70-73; Chapl Asst R Masonic Hosp Lon 73-74; Chapl Asst Basingstoke Distr Hosp 74-77; Chapl R Marsden Hosp Lon and Surrey 77-80; Chapl N Hants Hosp 80-94; Chapl N Hants Hosps NHS Trust from 94; Chapl N Hants Loddon Community NHS Trust from 94; Perm to Offic *Guildf* from 94. *The North Hampshire Hospital, Aldermaston Road, Basingstoke RG24 9NA* Tel (01256) 473202 *or* 314901

GORDON, Alan Williamson. b 53. Strathclyde Univ BA75 MCIBS79. Wycliffe Hall Ox 98. **d** 98 **p** 99. C Win Ch Ch *Win* 98-02; R King's Worthy from 02; R Headbourne Worthy from 02. *The Rectory, Campion Lane, King's Worthy, Winchester SO23 7QP* Tel (01962) 882166 E-mail alan.gordon98@ntlworld.com

GORDON, Canon Alexander Ronald. b 49. Nottm Univ BPharm71 Leeds Univ DipTh76. Coll of Resurr Mirfield 74. **d** 77 **p** 78. C Headingley *Ripon* 77-80; C Fareham SS Pet and Paul *Portsm* 80-83; V Cudworth *Wakef* 83-85; P-in-c Tain *Mor* 85-87; P-in-c Laird Miss 87-01; P-in-c Brora 88-01; P-in-c Dornoch 88-01; Dioc Dir of Ords 89-01; Can St Andr Cathl Inverness 95-01; Hon Can from 02; Chapl Strasbourg *Eur* from 02. *Aumônerie Anglicane, 2 quai Mathiss, 67000 Strasbourg, France* Tel (0033) (3) 88 36 93 90 Mobile (6) 24 33 16 16 E-mail 113156.276@compuserve.com

✠**GORDON, The Rt Revd Archibald Ronald McDonald.** b 27. Ball Coll Ox BA50 MA52. Cuddesdon Coll 50. **d** 52 **p** 53 **c** 75. C Stepney St Dunstan and All SS *Lon* 52-55; Chapl Cuddesdon Coll 55-59; Lic to Offic *Ox* 57-59; V Birm St Pet *Birm* 59-68; Lect Qu Coll Birm 60-62; Can Res Birm Cathl *Birm* 67-71; V Ox St Mary V w St Cross and St Pet *Ox* 71-75; Bp Portsm 75-84; Bp at Lambeth (Hd of Staff) *Cant* 84-91; Asst Bp S'wark 84-91; Bp HM Forces 85-90; Can Res and Sub-Dean Ch Ch *Ox* 91-96; Asst Bp *Ox* from 97. rtd 96. *16 East St Helen Street, Abingdon OX14 5EA* Tel (01235) 526956

GORDON, Bruce Harold Clark. b 40. Hull Univ DipMin87 Edin Univ MTh96. Cranmer Hall Dur 85. **d** 65 **p** 66. C Edin St Jas *Edin* 68-71; C Blackheath St Jo *S'wark* 71-74; R Duns *Edin* 74-90; R Lanark *Glas* from 90; R Douglas from 90. *The Rectory, 1 Cleghorn Road, Lanark ML11 7QT* Tel (01555) 663065

GORDON, David John. b 65. Edin Th Coll CECM93. **d** 93 **p** 94. Chapl St Andr Cathl *Ab* 93-95; P-in-c Alexandria *Glas* 95-00; Chapl NE Lincs NHS Trust 00-01; Chapl Tayside Univ Hosps NHS Trust from 01. *Tayside University Hospitals NHS Trust, Ninewells Hospital, Dundee DD1 9SY* Tel (01382) 632755 *or* 660111 E-mail david.gordon@nlg.nhs.uk

GORDON, Donald Ian. b 30. Nottm Univ BA52 PhD64. Westcott Ho Cam 71. **d** 71 **p** 72. NSM Newport *Chelmsf* 71-75; NSM Creeksea w Althorne, Latchingdon and N Fambridge 76-00; rtd 00; Perm to Offic *Chelmsf* from 01. *Holden House, Steeple Road, Latchingdon, Chelmsford CM3 6JX* Tel (01621) 740296

GORDON, Edward John. b 32. Univ of Wales BA52. St Mich Coll Llan 52. **d** 55 **p** 56. C Baglan *Llan* 55-61; C Newcastle w Laleston and Tythegston 61-65; V Ynyshir 65-69; C Bramhall *Ches* 69-72; V Cheadle Hulme All SS 72-79; V Tranmere St Paul w St Luke 79-88; V Sandbach Heath 88-97; Chapl Arclid Hosp 90-93; RD Congleton *Ches* 92-97; P-in-c Wheelock 95-97; rtd 97; Perm to Offic *B & W* from 99. *55 Greenslade Gardens, Nailsea, Bristol BS48 2BJ* Tel (01275) 853404

GORDON, Ms Jennifer Anne. b 60. Hull Univ BSc81. S Dios Minl Tr Scheme 90. **d** 93 **p** 94. C Alverstoke *Portsm* 93-96; C Elson 97-01; P-in-c Gosport Ch Ch from 01; Dioc FE Officer from 01. *6 Carlton Way, Gosport PO12 1LN* Tel (023) 9250 3921 E-mail mum@gordonfam.freeserve.co.uk

GORDON, John Michael. b 30. CITC. **d** 83 **p** 84. NSM Dublin St Geo *D & G* 83-85; NSM Dublin Irishtown w Donnybrook from 85. *Ferndale House, Rathmichael, Shankill, Co Dublin, Irish Republic* Tel (00353) (1) 282 2421 Fax 282 2954

GORDON, Jonathan Andrew. b 61. Keele Univ BA83 MPhil98 Southn Univ BTh88. Sarum & Wells Th Coll. **d** 87 **p** 88. C Wallingford w Crowmarsh Gifford etc *Ox* 87-91; C Tilehurst St Mich 91-93; TV Stoke-upon-Trent *Lich* 93-97; Chapl Southn

Inst of HE *Win* from 98. *24 Butterfield Road, Southampton SO16 7EE* Tel (023) 8079 1097
E-mail jonathan.gordon@solent.ac.uk

GORDON, Canon Kenneth Davidson. b 35. Edin Univ MA57. Tyndale Hall Bris 58. **d** 60 **p** 61. C St Helens St Helen *Liv* 60-66; V Daubhill *Man* 66-71; R Bieldside *Ab* 71-01; Can St Andr Cathl 81-01; Syn Clerk 96-01; rtd 01; Hon Can St Andr Cathl *Ab* from 01; Perm to Offic *Blackb* and *Liv* from 01. *The Old Schoolhouse, Hurst Green, Mawdesley, Ormskirk L40 2QT* Tel (01704) 823084 Mobile 07715-169548 Fax (01704) 821263
E-mail canonken@btopenworld.com

GORDON, Miss Kristy. *See* PATTIMORE, Mrs Kristy

GORDON, Mrs Pamela Anne. b 48. Brighton Coll of Educn CertEd69 BEd70. St Alb and Ox Min Course 99. **d** 02 **p** 03. NSM Wargrave w Knowl Hill *Ox* from 02. *Rebeny, 2A Hawthorn Road, Caversham, Reading RG4 6LY* Tel 0118-947 8676 Fax 954 3076 E-mail pam.gordon@ntlworld.com

GORDON, Sister Patricia Ann. b 44. St Alb and Ox Min Course. **d** 00 **p** 01. Professed CSMV from 80; NSM Didcot St Pet *Ox* from 00. *St Mary's Convent, Challow Road, Wantage OX12 9DJ* Tel and fax (01235) 767122 Mobile 07884-196004
E-mail sisterscsmv@btinternet.com

GORDON, Robert Andrew. b 42. Llan Dioc Tr Scheme 82. **d** 84 **p** 85. C Bargoed and Deri w Brithdir *Llan* 84-87; V Aberpergwm and Blaengwrach 87-94; R Johnston w Steynton *St D* 94-97; R Cosheston w Nash and Upton from 97. *The Rectory, St Michael's House, Cosheston, Pembroke Dock SA72 4UD* Tel (01646) 682477

GORDON, Robert John. b 56. Edin Univ MA81. Wycliffe Hall Ox 87. **d** 89 **p** 90. C Wilnecote *Lich* 89-91; C Bideford *Ex* 91-95; P-in-c Feniton, Buckerell and Escot from 95. *The Rectory, Station Road, Feniton, Honiton EX14 3DF* Tel (01404) 850253
E-mail robert.gordon@care4free.net

GORDON, Ronald. *See* GORDON, The Rt Revd Archibald Ronald McDonald

GORDON, Thomas William. b 57. QUB BEd80 Univ of Ulster MA86 TCD BTh89 DPS89 Dip Counselling 96. CITC 85. **d** 89 **p** 90. C Ballymacash *Conn* 89-91; Min Can Belf Cathl 91-95; Chapl and Tutor CITC 91-96; Dir Extra-Mural Studies from 96; Lect Past Th and Liturgy from 01; PV Ch Ch Cathl Dublin *D & G* from 96; Co-ord Relig Progr RTE from 99. *CITC, Braemar Park, Dublin 14, Irish Republic* Tel (00353) (1) 492 3506 or 492 3695 Fax 492 3082 E-mail tommi@eircom.net or tgordon@tcd.ie

GORDON CLARK, Charles Philip. b 36. Worc Coll Ox BA59 MA61. Cuddesdon Coll 61. **d** 62 **p** 63. C Haslemere *Guildf* 62-65; Chapl Tonbridge Sch 65-68; R Keston *Roch* 68-74; V Tunbridge Wells K Chas 74-86; Perm to Offic *S & B* from 86; rtd 96. *4 Dan yr Allt, Llaneglwys, Builth Wells LD2 3BJ* Tel (01982) 560656

GORDON CLARK, John Vincent Michael. b 29. FCA DipRS. S'wark Ord Course 73. **d** 76 **p** 77. NSM Guildf H Trin w St Mary *Guildf* 76-81; NSM Albury w St Martha 81-91; Dioc Chapl to MU 92-95; Lic to Offic 95-99; Hon C Guildf Cathl 91-99; Perm to Offic from 99. *Hillfield, 8 Little Warren Close, Guildford GU4 8PW* Tel (01483) 569027

GORDON-CUMMING, Henry Ian. b 28. Barrister-at-Law (Gray's Inn) 56. Oak Hill Th Coll 54. **d** 57 **p** 58. C Southsea St Jude *Portsm* 57-60; Uganda 61-68; V Virginia Water *Guildf* 68-78; R Busbridge 78-87; R Lynch w Iping Marsh and Milland *Chich* 87-94; rtd 94; Perm to Offic *Chich* from 94. *Bay Cottage, Brookside, Runcton, Chichester PO20 1PX* Tel (01243) 783395

GORDON-KERR, Canon Francis Alexander. b 39. Hull Univ BA64 MA67 Hull Univ PhD81 DipEd. Wycliffe Hall Ox 65. **d** 67 **p** 68. C Heworth St Mary *Dur* 67-70; Chapl Newc Poly *Newc* 70-75; Chapl Hull Univ *York* 75-82; V Welton w Melton 82-92; Clergy Tr Officer E Riding 82-92; AD W Hull 87-96; RD Hull 89-96; Can and Preb York Minster 89-98; V Anlaby St Pet 92-98; R Crowland *Linc* from 98. *The Abbey Rectory, East Street, Crowland, Peterborough PE6 0EN* Tel (01733) 210499

GORDON-TAYLOR, Benjamin Nicholas. b 69. St Jo Coll Dur BA90 MA92 Leeds Univ BA94 FRSA99. Coll of Resurr Mirfield 92. **d** 95 **p** 96. C Launceston *Truro* 95-97; C Northampton St Matt *Pet* 97-99; Tutor and Chapl Univ Coll Dur from 99. *University College, The Castle, Durham DH1 3RW* Tel 0191-334 3800 or 0191-334 4116
E-mail b.n.gordon-taylor@durham.ac.uk

GORDON-WALKER, Caroline. b 37. LMH Ox BA59. Cranmer Hall Dur 01. **d** 02. NSM Poitou-Charentes *Eur* from 02. *La Grange, Coussot, 16350 Benest, France* Tel (0033) (5) 45 31 38 90
E-mail carolinegw@wanadoo.fr

GORE, Canon John Charles. b 29. Leeds Univ BA52. Coll of Resurr Mirfield 52. **d** 54 **p** 55. C Middlesbrough St Jo the Ev *York* 54-59; N Rhodesia 59-64; Zambia 64-75; Can Lusaka 70-75; R Elland *Wakef* 75-84; TR 84-86; RD Brighouse and Elland 77-86; V Wembley Park St Aug *Lon* 86-95; P-in-c Tokyngton St Mich 89-90; AD Brent 90-95; rtd 95; P-in-c Heptonstall *Wakef* 95-99; Perm to Offic *Bradf* from 99. *3 Navigation Square, Skipton BD23 1XB* Tel (01756) 792297

GORE, Canon John Harrington. b 24. Em Coll Cam BA49 MA52. Westcott Ho Cam 49. **d** 51 **p** 52. C Deane *Man* 51-54; C

Whitstable All SS w St Pet *Cant* 54-59; CF 59-62; V Womenswold *Cant* 62-67; C-in-c Aylesham CD 62-67; R Deal St Leon 67-75; RD Sandwich 70-78; P-in-c Sholden 74-75; R Deal St Leon w Sholden 75-80; R Southchurch H Trin *Chelmsf* 80-90; RD Southend-on-Sea 84-89; Hon Can Chelmsf Cathl 86-90; rtd 90; Perm to Offic *St E* from 90; Perm to Offic *Chelmsf* from 90. *8 De Burgh Place, Clare CO10 8QL* Tel (01787) 278558

GORHAM, Andrew Arthur. b 51. Bris Univ BA73 Birm Univ DipTh78 MA87. Qu Coll Birm 77. **d** 79 **p** 80. C Plaistow St Mary *Roch* 79-82; Chapl Lanchester Poly *Cov* 82-87; TV Warwick 87-95; Chapl Birm Univ *Birm* 95-00; Bp's Dom Chapl from 00. *Bishop's Croft, Old Church Road, Harborne, Birmingham B17 0BE* Tel 0121-427 2295 or 427 1163 Fax 426 1322
E-mail bishopschaplain@birmingham.anglican.org

GORHAM, Miss Karen Marisa. b 64. Trin Coll Bris BA95. **d** 95 **p** 96. C Northallerton w Kirby Sigston *York* 95-99; P-in-c Maidstone St Paul *Cant* from 99; Asst Dir of Ords from 02; AD Maidstone from 03. *St Paul's Vicarage, 130 Boxley Road, Maidstone ME14 2AH* Tel (01622) 691926
E-mail revdkaren@aol.com

GORICK, David Charles. b 32. Reading Univ BA55 Nottm Univ DipEd72. EMMTC 81. **d** 84 **p** 85. NSM W Bridgford *S'well* 84-89; C Gotham 89-97; C Kingston and Ratcliffe-on-Soar 89-97; C Barton in Fabis 89-97; C Thrumpton 89-97; P-in-c Gotham 97-99; rtd 99. *11 Brookfields Way, East Leake, Loughborough LE12 6HD* Tel (01509) 856960

GORICK, Janet Margaret. b 30. Reading Univ BA54. EMMTC 84. **dss** 86 **d** 87 **p** 94. Hon Par Dn W Bridgford *S'well* 87-95; NSM Gotham 95-99; NSM Barton in Fabis 95-99; NSM Kingston and Ratcliffe-on-Soar 95-99; NSM Thrumpton 95-99; rtd 99. *11 Brookfields Way, East Leake, Loughborough LE12 6HD* Tel (01509) 856960

GORICK, Martin Charles William. b 62. Selw Coll Cam BA84 MA88. Ripon Coll Cuddesdon 85. **d** 87 **p** 88. C Birtley *Dur* 87-91; Bp's Dom Chapl *Cov* 91-94; V Smethwick *Birm* 94-01; AD Warley 97-01; R Stratford-upon-Avon, Luddington etc *Cov* from 01. *The Vicarage, 7 Old Town, Stratford-upon-Avon CV37 6BG* Tel (01789) 266022 or 266316
E-mail office@stratford-upon-avon.org

GORING, Charles Robert. b 60. Nottm Univ BA91. Linc Th Coll Cert Min & Miss 93. **d** 93 **p** 94. C Thornbury *Glouc* 93-96; Perm to Offic *Chich* 97-98; Facilitator Demined Trust from 98; C Mayfield 98-00; V The Hydneye from 00. *St Peter's House, The Hydneye, Eastbourne BN22 9BY* Tel (01323) 504392 Fax as telephone E-mail demined@onetel.net.uk

GORRIE, Richard Bingham. b 27. Univ Coll Ox BA49 MA51. Ridley Hall Cam 49. **d** 51 **p** 52. C Ox St Clem *Ox* 51-54; C Morden S'wark 54-56; Scripture Union Rep (Scotland) 56-92; Chapl Fettes Coll Edin 60-74; Dir Inter-Sch Chr Fellowship (Scotland) 74-80; rtd 92; Perm to Offic *Glas* from 92. *17 Auchlochan Courtyard, New Trows Road, Lesmahagow, Lanark ML11 0JS* Tel (01555) 895076

GORRINGE, Prof Timothy Jervis. b 46. St Edm Hall Ox BA69 MPhil75. Sarum Th Coll 69. **d** 72 **p** 73. C Chapel Allerton *Ripon* 72-75; C Ox St Mary V w St Cross and St Pet *Ox* 76-78; India 79-86; Chapl St Jo Coll Ox 86-96; Reader St Andr Univ from 96; Prof Th Ex Univ from 99. *Department of Theology, Exeter University, Queen's Building, The Queen's Drive, Exeter EX4 4QH* Tel (01392) 264242 E-mail t.j.gorringe@exeter.ac.uk

GORTON, Anthony David Trevor. b 39. Lon Univ BSc65. Oak Hill Th Coll 78. **d** 81 **p** 82. NSM Colney Heath St Mark *St Alb* 81-00; NSM Waterdell St Pet from 00. *Waterdell, Lane End, Hatfield AL10 9AG* Tel (01707) 263605

GORTON, Ian Charles Johnson. b 62. Bp Otter Coll BA84 Sarum & Wells Th Coll 86. **d** 89 **p** 90. C Wythenshawe Wm Temple Ch *Man* 89-92; C Man Apostles w Miles Platting 92-95; P-in-c Abbey Hey 95-03; P-in-c Moston St Chad from 03. *St Chad's Rectory, 30 Hawthorn Road, Manchester M40 3RH* Tel 0161-681 3203

GORTON (née CARTER), Sarah Helen Buchanan. b 44. St Andr Univ BSc65 DipEd66. TISEC 93. **d** 96 **p** 98. NSM Lenzie *Glas* from 96. *Northbank Gardens, Northbank Road, Kirkintilloch, Glasgow G66 1EZ* Tel 0141-775 1204
E-mail sally@sgorton.freeserve.co.uk

GOSDEN, Timothy John. b 50. Open Univ BA86. Chich Th Coll 74. **d** 77 **p** 78. C Cant All SS *Cant* 77-81; Asst Chapl Loughb Univ *Leic* 81-85; Lic to Offic *Cant* 85-87; Chapl Ch Ch Coll of HE *Cant* 85-87; Sen Chapl Hull Univ 87-94; V Taunton Lyngford *B & W* 94-98; V Harrow St Mary *Lon* from 98. *St Mary's Vicarage, Church Hill, Harrow HA1 3HL* Tel (020) 8422 2652 E-mail timgos@aol.com

GOSHAI, Miss Veja Helena. b 32. SRN57 SCM59 Midwife Teacher's Dip 66 Plater Coll of FE Ox Special Dip Soc Studies 96 City Univ BSc99. Trin Coll Bris 75. **d** 87 **p** 94. Asst Chapl St Bart Hosp Lon 87-97; rtd 92; Perm to Offic *S'wark* 99-03. *Grace, 26 Bilston Road, Crawford, Cape Town, 7780 South Africa* Tel (0027) (21) 697 2703

GOSLING, David. b 27. St Alb and Ox Min Course 95. **d** 98 **p** 99. OLM High Wycombe *Ox* from 98. *72 Hatters Lane, High Wycombe HP13 7NJ* Tel (01494) 443947

304

GOSLING, David Lagourie. b 39. Man Univ MSc63 Fitzw Coll Cam MA69 Lanc Univ PhD74 MInstP69 CPhys84. Ridley Hall Cam 63. **d** 73 **p** 74. Hon C Lancaster St Mary *Blackb* 73-74; Hon C Kingston upon Hull St Matt w St Barn *York* 74-77; Hon C Cottingham 78-83; Asst Chapl Geneva *Eur* 84-89; C Cambridge Gt St Mary w St Mich *Ely* 89-90; C Dry Drayton 90-94; USPG India 95-99; Perm to Offic *York* from 95 and *Ely* from 01; Clare Hall Cam from 01. *Clare Hall, Herschel Road, Cambridge CB3 9AL* Tel (01223) 352450 Fax 332333

GOSLING, James Albert. b 41. Oak Hill Th Coll 81. **d** 84 **p** 85. NSM Victoria Docks St Luke *Chelmsf* 84-96; Hon C Gt Mongeham w Ripple and Sutton by Dover *Cant* 96-01; Hon C Eastry and Northbourne w Tilmanstone etc 96-01; C Kenton, Mamhead, Powderham, Cofton and Starcross *Ex* 01-02. *2 Wordsworth Close, Exmouth EX8 5SQ* Tel (01395) 225278 E-mail jimandjan@jimandjan.fsnet.co.uk

GOSLING, John William Fraser. b 34. St Jo Coll Dur BA58 DipTh60 MA71 Ex Univ PhD78. Cranmer Hall Dur 58. **d** 60 **p** 61. C Plympton St Mary *Ex* 60-68; V Newport 68-78; Org Sec CECS *St Alb* and *Ox* 78-82; C Stratford sub Castle *Sarum* 83-86; Adv on CME 83-86; Perm to Offic 86-91 and from 95; C Swindon Ch Ch *Bris* 91-95; rtd 95. *1 Wiley Terrace, Wilton, Salisbury SP2 0HN* Tel (01722) 742788 E-mail jgosling@fish.co.uk

GOSNEY, Jeanette Margaret. b 58. Bath Univ BA81 Nottm Univ PGCE82. St Jo Coll Nottm BTh93 MPhil95. **d** 95 **p** 96. C Ipswich St Marg *St E* 95-98; Asst Chapl Loughb Univ *Leic* 98; Sen Chapl 98-01; Tutor Trin Coll Bris from 01. *7 Cranleigh Gardens, Stoke Bishop, Bristol BS9 1HD* Tel 0117-968 4640 *or* 968 2803 E-mail jeanette.gosney@trinity-bris.ac.uk

GOSS, David James. b 52. Nottm Univ BCombStuds. Linc Th Coll. **d** 83 **p** 84. C Wood Green St Mich w Bounds Green St Gabr etc *Lon* 83-86; TV Gleadless Valley *Sheff* 86-89; TR 89-95; V Wheatley Hills from 95. *The Vicarage, 18 Central Boulevard, Doncaster DN2 5PE* Tel (01302) 342047 E-mail geese@talk21.com

GOSS, Kevin Ian. b 56. LRAM75 LTCL76 GRSM77 LGSM80 Hughes Hall Cam PGCE78. S Dios Minl Tr Scheme 89. **d** 92 **p** 93. NSM Ardingly *Chich* 92-98; Asst Chapl Ardingly Coll 92-98; Min Can, Prec and Sacr Cant Cathl *Cant* from 98. *5 The Precincts, Canterbury CT1 2EE* Tel (01227) 765843

GOSS, Michael John. b 37. Chich Th Coll 62. **d** 65 **p** 66. C Angell Town St Jo *S'wark* 65-68; C Catford St Laur 68-71; P-in-c Lewisham St Swithun 71-81; V Redhill St Jo 81-88; V Dudley St Thos and St Luke *Worc* 88-98; C Small Heath *Birm* 98-02; rtd 02; Perm to Offic *Birm* from 02. *8 Mayland Road, Birmingham B16 0NG* Tel 0161-429 6022

GOSSWINN, Nicholas Simon. b 50. Birm Poly FGA80. St D Coll Lamp DipTh73. **d** 73 **p** 77. C Abergavenny St Mary *Mon* 73-74; C-in-c Bassaleg 74-80; TV Barrow St Geo w St Luke *Carl* 81-87; C Usworth *Dur* 89-90; TV 90-96; P-in-c Sunderland Red Ho 96-02; P-in-c Stockport St Matt *Ches* 02-03. *St Matthew's Vicarage, 99 Chatham Street, Stockport SK3 9EG* Tel 0161-480 5515

GOSTELOW (née THOMPSON), Mrs Ruth Jean. b 47. St Alb Minl Tr Scheme 85. **d** 90 **p** 94. Par Dn Stonebridge St Mich *Lon* 90-94; C Ealing St Paul 94-96; TV W Slough *Ox* 96-03; V New Haw *Guildf* from 03. *The Vicarage, 149 Woodham Lane, New Haw, Addlestone KT15 3NJ* Tel (01932) 343187 Fax as telephone E-mail reverendruth@aol.com

GOSWELL, Geoffrey. b 34. SS Paul & Mary Coll Cheltenham CertEd68. Glouc Th Course 70. **d** 71 **p** 72. C Cheltenham Em *Glouc* 71-73; C Lydney w Aylburton 73-76; P-in-c Falfield w Rockhampton 76-79; Chapl HM Det Cen Eastwood Park 76-79; Area Sec CMS *Ely* 79-81; *Linc* and *Pet* 79-86; Dep Regional Sec (UK) CMS 86-97; P-in-c Orton Waterville *Ely* 90-96; TV The Ortons, Alwalton and Chesterton 96-97; rtd 97; Perm to Offic *Pet* from 01. *9 Kimble Close, Northampton NN4 0RF* Tel (01604) 709512

GOTELEE, Peter Douglas. b 28. K Coll Lon 50. **d** 54 **p** 55. C Croydon St Pet S End *Cant* 54-57; C Camberley St Paul *Guildf* 57-65; P-in-c Badshot Lea CD 65-75; P-in-c Bisley 75-76; V W End 75-76; R Bisley and W End 76-85; V Yarcombe w Membury and Upottery *Ex* 85-93; P-in-c Cotleigh 85-93; rtd 93; Perm to Offic *Ex* from 93. *3 Sharpiter Close, Paignton TQ3 1AR* Tel (01803) 559150

GOTHARD, Mrs Anne Marie. b 51. STETS. **d** 00. NSM E Meon *Portsm* from 00; NSM Langrish from 00. *27 Green Lane, Clanfield, Waterlooville PO8 0JU* Tel (023) 9259 6315 Mobile 07939-472796 E-mail anne@gothard.freeserve.co.uk

GOTT, Joseph Desmond. b 26. Ch Ch Ox BA47 MA51 St Chad's Coll Dur DipTh52. **d** 52 **p** 53. C Horden *Dur* 52-55; C Bishopwearmouth St Mich 55-58; R Bishopwearmouth St Mich w St Hilda 58-66; Prin Argyle Ho Sch Sunderland 59-65; V Down Ampney *Glouc* 66-72; PC Poulton 66-69; V 69-72; V Cheltenham St Steph 72-89; rtd 89; Perm to Offic *Chich* from 01. *41 Kirkstall Close, Willingdon Trees, Eastbourne BN22 0UQ*

GOTT, Stephen. b 61. St Jo Coll Nottm Dip Th & Min 94. **d** 94 **p** 95. C Mount Pellon *Wakef* 94-97; V Greetland and W Vale

from 97. *The Vicarage, 2 Goldfields Way, Greetland, Halifax HX4 8LA* Tel (01422) 372802

GOUGH, Andrew Stephen. b 60. Sarum & Wells Th Coll 83. **d** 86 **p** 87. C St Leonards Ch Ch and St Mary *Chich* 86-88; C Broseley w Benthall *Heref* 88-90; V Ketley and Oakengates *Lich* 90-93; TV Bickleigh (Plymouth) *Ex* 93; TV Bickleigh and Shaugh Prior 94; P-in-c St Day *Truro* 94-96; V Chacewater w St Day and Carharrack from 96. *The Vicarage, St Day, Redruth TR16 5LD* Tel (01209) 820275 E-mail stpaulchacewater@churchserve.net

GOUGH, Andrew Walter. b 55. Bris Univ BA78. Trin Coll Bris ADMT92. **d** 92 **p** 93. C Mossley Hill St Matt and St Jas *Liv* 92-94; C Wavertree H Trin 94-96; Chapl Warw Sch from 96. *9 Griffin Road, Warwick CV34 6QX* Tel (01926) 400533 E-mail agough@trinity.u-net.com

GOUGH, Anthony Walter. b 31. Lon Univ DipTh68 Leic Univ MA76. Chicago Th Sem DMin81 Oak Hill Th Coll 57. **d** 60 **p** 61. C Southsea St Simon *Portsm* 60-64; R Peldon *Chelmsf* 64-71; V Rothley *Leic* 71-80; USA 80-81; Chapl St Jo Hosp Aylesbury 81-82; Perm to Offic *Leic* 82-96; rtd 96. *410 Hinckley Road, Leicester LE3 0WA* Tel 0116-285 4284 Fax as telephone E-mail tg1@ntlworld.com

GOUGH, Colin Richard. b 47. St Chad's Coll Dur BA69. Cuddesdon Coll 73. **d** 75 **p** 76. C Lich St Chad *Lich* 75-78; C Codsall 78-84; V Wednesbury St Paul Wood Green 84-92; TR Tettenhall Wood 92-99; TR Tettenhall Wood and Perton 99-01; P-in-c Stannington *Newc* from 01; Dioc Adv for CME from 01. *The Vicarage, Beechlea, Stannington, Morpeth NE61 6HL* Tel (01670) 789122 *or* 0191-270 4153 E-mail colin.gough@talk21.com *or* c.gough@newcastle.anglican.org

GOUGH, David Norman. b 42. Oak Hill Th Coll 70. **d** 70 **p** 71. C Penn Fields *Lich* 70-73; C Stapenhill w Cauldwell *Derby* 73-77; V Heath 77-86; P-in-c Derby St Chad 86-95; TV Walbrook Epiphany from 95. *81 Palmerston Street, Derby DE23 6PF* Tel (01332) 760846 E-mail gough@heyho.fsnet.co.uk

GOUGH, Derek William. b 31. Pemb Coll Cam BA55 MA59. St Steph Ho Ox 55. **d** 57 **p** 58. C E Finchley All SS *Lon* 57-60; C Roxbourne St Andr 60-66; V Edmonton St Mary w St Jo 66-98; rtd 98; Perm to Offic *Chelmsf* from 98; Perm to Offic *St Alb* from 00. *11 Church Lane, Letchworth Garden City SG6 1AJ* Tel (01462) 680683

GOUGH, Mrs Elizabeth. b 54. Carl and Blackb Dioc Tr Inst. **d** 00 **p** 01. OLM Brampton and Farlam and Castle Carrock w Cumrew *Carl* 00-02; OLM Hayton w Cumwhitton 00-02; OLM Irthington, Crosby-on-Eden and Scaleby 00-02; OLM Eden, Gelt and Irthing from 02. *Brackenside Barn, Brampton CA8 2QX* Tel (01697) 746252

GOUGH, Canon Ernest Hubert. b 31. TCD BA53 MA57. TCD Div Sch Div Test 54. **d** 54 **p** 55. C Glenavy *Conn* 54-57; C Lisburn Ch Ch 57-61; P-in-c Belfast St Ninian 61-62; I 62-71; I Belfast St Bart 71-85; I Templepatrick w Donegore 85-97; Can Conn Cathl from 91; rtd 97. *The Caim, 15 Swilly Road, Portstewart BT55 7DJ* Tel (028) 7083 3253 E-mail ehg@thecaim.fsnet.co.uk

GOUGH, Frank Peter. b 32. Lon Coll of Div 66. **d** 68 **p** 69. C Weymouth St Mary *Sarum* 68-70; C Attenborough w Chilwell *S'well* 70-73; R Barrow *Ches* 73-77; P-in-c Summerstown *S'wark* 77-88; RD Tooting 80-88; Dioc Past Sec 88-93; Tutor and Chapl Whittington Coll Felbridge 93-98; rtd 98. *18 Bromley College, London Road, Bromley BR1 1PE* Tel (020) 8290 1090 Mobile 07970-199135

GOUGH, Canon Jonathan Robin Blanning. b 62. Univ of Wales (Lamp) BA83 Westmr Coll Ox MTh96 FRSA03. St Steph Ho Ox 83. **d** 85 **p** 86. C Braunton *Ex* 85-86; C Matson *Glouc* 86-89; CF 89-01; Abp's Officer for Ecum *Cant* from 01; Can Gib Cathl *Eur* from 02; Public Preacher *Win* from 02. *Lambeth Palace, London SE1 7JU* Tel (020) 7898 1218 E-mail jonathan.gough@c-of-e.org.uk

GOUGH, Miss Lynda Elizabeth. b 54. RGN83 SS Hild & Bede Coll Dur BA94. Wycliffe Hall Ox 97. **d** 99 **p** 00. C Stranton *Dur* 99-03; V Spennymoor, Whitworth and Merrington from 03. *10 Merrington Close, Kirk Merrington, Spennymoor DL16 7HU* Tel (01388) 815471

GOUGH, Martyn John. b 66. Univ of Wales (Cardiff) BA. St Steph Ho Ox 88. **d** 90 **p** 91. C Port Talbot St Theodore *Llan* 90-92; C Roath 92-94; Asst Chapl Milan w Genoa and Varese *Eur* 95-98; Chapl RN from 98. *Royal Navy Chaplaincy Service, Room 203, Victory Building, HM Naval Base, Portsmouth PO1 3LS* Tel (023) 9272 7903 Fax 9272 7111

GOUGH, Robert. b 50. S'wark Ord Course 79. **d** 82 **p** 83. C Heston *Lon* 82-83; C Feltham 83-86; TV Hemel Hempstead *St Alb* 86-90; NSM Kingston All SS w St Jo *S'wark* 90-91; Perm to Offic *S'wark* 91-94; St *As* 95-00; P-in-c Corwen and Llangar w Gwyddelwern and Llawrybetws *St As* 00-02; P-in-c Betws Gwerful Goch w Llangwm, Gwyddelwern etc 02-03. *Pen y Gaer Uchaf, Llanfihangel Glyn Myfyr, Corwen LL21 9UH* Tel (01490) 420791

GOUGH, Stephen William Cyprian. b 50. Alberta Univ BSc71. Cuddesdon Coll BA80. **d** 79 **p** 80. C Walton St Mary *Liv* 79-83; V

New Springs 83-87; V Childwall St Dav from 87. *St David's Vicarage, Rocky Lane, Liverpool L16 1JA* Tel 0151-722 4549

GOULD, Alan Charles. b 26. Lon Univ DipTh53. **d** 62 **p** 63. C Bromborough *Ches* 62-67; V Audlem and Burleydam 67-80; P-in-c Coreley and Doddington *Heref* 80-83; V Knowbury 80-83; P-in-c Berrington w Betton Strange 83-91; P-in-c Cound 83-91; rtd 91; Perm to Offic *Heref* from 91; Perm to Offic *Lich* from 91. *32 Mytton Oak Road, Shrewsbury SY3 8UD* Tel (01743) 244820

GOULD, David Robert. b 59. Cov Poly BA81. Cranmer Hall Dur 87. **d** 90 **p** 91. C Rugby St Andr *Cov* 90-93; CF 93-94; Perm to Offic *Cov* from 01. *The Flat, 7 Market Hill, Southam CV47 0HE* Tel (01926) 817517 *or* (01295) 265439

GOULD, Preb Douglas Walter. b 35. St Jo Coll Cam BA59 MA63. Ridley Hall Cam 59. **d** 61 **p** 62. C Clifton *York* 61-64; C Bridgnorth w Tasley *Heref* 64-67; C Astley Abbotts w Linley 64-67; R Acton Burnell w Pitchford 67-73; P-in-c Cound 68-73; Asst Dioc Youth Officer 68-73; P-in-c Frodesley 69-73; V Bromyard 73-00; P-in-c Stanford Bishop 73-00; RD Bromyard 73-99; Chapl Bromyard Community Hosp 73-92; Chapl Herefordshire Community Health NHS Trust 92-00; P-in-c Ocle Pychard *Heref* 76-88; P-in-c Ullingswick 76-88; P-in-c Stoke Lacy, Moreton Jeffries w Much Cowarne etc 76-83; Preb Heref Cathl 83-00; rtd 00; Perm to Offic *Heref* from 00. *Highwood Croft, Marden, Hereford HR1 3EW* Tel (01432) 880084 Fax as telephone E-mail waltergould@waitrose.com

GOULD, Gerald. b 37. Wilson Carlile Coll 60 S Dios Minl Tr Scheme 84. **d** 86 **p** 87. CA from 62; C Hedge End St Jo *Win* 86-89; V St Goran w Caerhays *Truro* 89-93; P-in-c Crook Peak *B & W* 93-94; R 94-99; rtd 99; Perm to Offic *Ex* from 99. *2 Nightingale Lawns, Cullompton EX15 1UB* Tel (01884) 38105

GOULD, John Barry. b 38. MICE68. S'wark Ord Course 77. **d** 77 **p** 78. C Streatham St Leon *S'wark* 77-80; V Upper Tooting H Trin 80-87; P-in-c Brockham Green 87-90; P-in-c Betchworth 87-95; P-in-c Buckland 87-95; C-in-c Roundshaw St Paul CD from 95; RD Sutton from 00. *St Paul's House, 32 Waterer Rise, Wallington SM6 9DN* Tel (020) 8773 2842 E-mail johngould@stpauls.surfaid.org

GOULD, Jonathan George Lillico. b 58. Bris Univ LLB79. Wycliffe Hall Ox 86. **d** 89 **p** 91. Australia 89-93; Schs Worker Scripture Union Independent Schs 93-95; Perm to Offic *S'wark* 93-95; Min Hampstead St Jo Downshire Hill Prop Chpl *Lon* from 95. *The Parsonage, 64 Pilgrim's Lane, London NW3 1SN* Tel (020) 7435 8404 Fax as telephone

GOULD, Mrs Pamela Rosemarie. **d** 01 **p** 02. NSM New Bilton *Cov* from 01; Chapl HM YOI Onley from 01. *HM Young Offender Institution, Onley, Willoughby, Rugby CV23 8AP* Tel (01788) 522022 Fax 522260

GOULD, Peter Richard. b 34. Univ of Wales BA57. Qu Coll Birm DipTh62. **d** 62 **p** 63. C Rothwell *Ripon* 62-68; V Allerton Bywater 68-73; Lic to Offic *S'well* 73-76; Chapl Lic Victuallers' Sch Ascot 76-93; V Aberavon H Trin *Llan* 93-99; rtd 99. *Amber Cottage, 1 Load Lane, Weston Zoyland, Bridgwater TA7 0EQ* Tel (01278) 691029

GOULD, Robert Ozburn. b 38. Williams Coll Mass BA59 St Andr Univ PhD63. **d** 78 **p** 83. NSM Edin St Columba *Edin* 78-80; TV from 83; Hon Dioc Supernumerary 80-83. *33 Charterhall Road, Edinburgh EH9 3HS* Tel 0131-667 7230 E-mail gould@ed.ac.uk

GOULD, Susan Judith. *See* MURRAY, Mrs Susan Judith

GOULD, Walter. *See* GOULD, Preb Douglas Walter

GOULDER, Mrs Catherine Helen. b 44. Hull Univ BA65 MA67 Ox Univ DipEd68 Coll of Ripon & York St Jo DipRE88. NEOC 96. **d** 98 **p** 99. NSM Sutton St Mich *York* 98-02; P-in-c N Cave w Cliffe from 02; P-in-c Hotham from 02. *The Vicarage, Church Lane, Elloughton, Brough HU15 1SP* Tel (01430) 470716

GOULDING, John Gilbert. b 29. Univ Coll Dur BA54 MA59. **d** 88 **p** 89. NSM Kemsing w Woodlands *Roch* 88-91; Hon Nat Moderator for Reader Tr ACCM 90-91; ABM 91-94; NSM Sevenoaks St Luke CD 91-96; Perm to Offic from 97. *Springwood, 50 Copperfields, Kemsing, Sevenoaks TN15 6QG* Tel (01732) 762558

GOULDING, Nicolas John. b 56. Southn Univ BSc78 PhD82. NTMTC 94. **d** 97 **p** 98. NSM St Bart Less *Lon* from 97; Chapl St Bart's and RLSMD Qu Mary and Westf Coll from 97; Perm to Offic *St Alb* from 99. *5 Eastfield Close, Harpenden AL5 3HP* Tel (01582) 461293 Fax (020) 7982 6076 E-mail n.j.goulding@mds.qmw.ac.uk

GOULDSTONE, Canon Timothy Maxwell. b 46. Ex Univ BSc68 MSc76 PhD02 Lon BD94 MSOSc87. Trin Coll Bris 76. **d** 78 **p** 79. C Ware Ch Ch *St Alb* 78-81; P-in-c Ansley *Cov* 81-82; V 82-85; V St Keverne *Truro* 85-95; Preb St Endellion 90-99; P-in-c St Michael Penkevil 95-02; P-in-c Lamorran and Merther 95-02; Dir Lay Tr 95-02; RD Powder 96-01; Hon Can Truro Cathl 99-02; Chapl UEA *Nor* from 02; Dir Nor Cathl Inst from

02. *40 Heigham Road, Norwich NR2 3AU* Tel (01603) 614397 E-mail gouldstone@btinternet.com *or* t.gouldstone@uea.ac.uk

GOULDTHORPE, Rachel Carolyn. b 72. Bp Otter Coll 00. **d** 03. NSM Hove *Chich* from 03. *Flat 6, 7 Albany Villas, Hove BN3 2RS* Tel (01273) 749367 Mobile 07714-727330 E-mail rc@goul.fsnet.co.uk

GOULSTON, Jeremy Hugh. b 68. St Aid Coll Dur BA90. Ripon Coll Cuddesdon 01. **d** 03. C Henfield w Shermanbury and Woodmancote *Chich* from 03. *Glebe House, 41 Furners Mead, Henfield BN5 9JA*

GOULSTONE, The Very Revd Thomas Richard Kerry. b 36. Univ of Wales (Lamp) BA57. St Mich Coll Llan 57. **d** 59 **p** 60. C Llanbadarn Fawr *St D* 59-61; C Carmarthen St Pet 61-64; V 84-93; V Whitchurch w Solva and St Elvis 64-67; V Gors-las 67-76; V Burry Port and Pwll 76-84; Chapl W Wales Gen Hosp Carmarthen 84-93; Can St D Cathl *St D* 86-93; Hon Can St D Cathl from 93; RD Carmarthen 88-92; Adn Carmarthen 91-93; Dean and Lib St As Cathl *St As* 93-01; rtd 01. *80 Sandpiper Road, Llanelli SA15 4SH* Tel (01554) 746117

GOUNDREY-SMITH, Stephen John. b 67. Brighton Poly BSc88 MRPharmS89 City Univ MSc94. Aston Tr Scheme 96 Wycliffe Hall Ox BTh01. **d** 99 **p** 00. C Happisburgh, Walcott, Hempstead w Eccles etc *Nor* 99-01; Perm to Offic *Pet* from 02. *1 The Walnuts, Main Street, Charlton, Banbury OX17 3DR* Tel (01295) 816887 Mobile 07771-741009 E-mail stephen@goundrey-smith.freeserve.co.uk

GOUNDRY, Canon Ralph Walter. b 31. St Chad's Coll Dur BA56 DipTh58. **d** 58 **p** 59. C Harton Colliery *Dur* 58-62; Prec Newc Cathl *Newc* 62-65; V Sighill 65-72; V Long Benton 72-96; Hon Can Newc Cathl 94-96; rtd 96; Perm to Offic *York* 96-98. *16 Old Manor Way, Chislehurst BR27 5SX*

GOUPILLON, Mrs Jane Elizabeth. b 50. Univ of Wales (Lamp) BA92 Trin Coll Carmarthen PGCE94. St Mich Coll Llan. **d** 03. C Carmarthen St Dav *St D* from 03. *26 Knoll Gardens, Carmarthen SA31 3EJ* Tel (01267) 222865

GOURLEY, Malcolm Samuel. b 37. MRPharmS58. NEOC DipHE94. **d** 98 **p** 98. NSM Gt Smeaton w Appleton Wiske and Birkby etc *Ripon* 98-00; NSM Ainderby Steeple w Yafforth and Kirby Wiske etc 00-02; NSM Penshaw *Dur* from 02; NSM Shiney Row from 02; NSM Herrington from 02. *10 Weymouth Drive, Houghton-le-Spring DH4 7TQ* Tel 0191-385 4076

GOURLEY, William Robert Joseph. b 48. K Coll Lon BD74. CITC 68. **d** 75 **p** 76. C Newtownards *D & D* 75-78; I Currin w Drum and Newbliss *Clogh* 78-81; I Dublin St Geo and St Thos, Finglas and Free Ch *D & G* 81-88; I Dublin Zion Ch from 88. *The Rectory, 18 Bushy Park Road, Rathgar, Dublin 6, Irish Republic* Tel (00353) (1) 406 4730 E-mail wilbertgourley@ireland.com

GOVAN, Kesh Rico. b 66. Bolton Inst of HE HND90. St Jo Coll Dur BA96. **d** 96 **p** 97. C Astley Bridge *Man* 96-00; TV Walkden and Lt Hulton from 00. *Peel Rectory, 122 Peel Lane, Little Hulton, Manchester M38 0SD* Tel 0161-799 6300

GOVENDER, Rogers Morgan. b 60. Natal Univ BTh97. St Paul's Coll Grahamstown DipTh85. **d** 85 **p** 86. S Africa 85-00; C Overport Ch Ch 85-87; R Greyville St Mary 88-92; R Hayfields St Matt 93-98; Adn Pietermaritzburg 97-98; R Berea St Thos 99-00; P-in-c Didsbury Ch Ch *Man* from 01; P-in-c Withington St Chris from 03. *Christ Church Rectory, 35 Darley Avenue, Manchester M20 2ZD* Tel 0161-445 4152 E-mail rogersg@darleyave.fsnet.co.uk

GOVER, Michael Sydney Richard. b 41. Culham Coll Ox BA63. Chich Th Coll 68. **d** 71 **p** 72. C Ryde All SS *Portsm* 71-75; C Waterlooville 75-83; Perm to Offic 83-91; NSM Portsea Ascension 91-01. *333 Twyford Avenue, Portsmouth PO2 8PE* Tel (023) 9267 1161

GOW, Iain Douglas. b 60. Denver Univ USA BA83 MIM85. Trin Coll Bris DipHE92 MA94. **d** 94 **p** 95. C Kenilworth St Jo *Cov* 94-97; C Birm St Martin w Bordesley St Andr *Birm* from 97; AD Birm City Cen from 02. *59 Featherstone Road, Kings Heath, Birmingham B14 6BD* Tel 0121-443 1400 *or* 443 4822 E-mail iain@bullring.org

GOW, Peter Draffin. b 52. Bede Coll Dur BEd76. St Jo Coll Nottm 83. **d** 85. C Kingston Hill St Paul *S'wark* 85-86; rtd 86. *Chatsworth Wing, Royal Hospital for Neuro-disability, London SW15 3SW* Tel (020) 8788 5158 E-mail petergow@waacis.edex.co.uk

GOWDEY, Michael Cragg. b 32. Oriel Coll Ox BA56 MA58 Keele Univ CertEd73. Qu Coll Birm DipTh57. **d** 58 **p** 59. C Ashbourne w Mapleton and Clifton *Derby* 58-63; V Chellaston 63-69; Asst Chapl Ellesmere Coll Shropshire 69-74; Chapl Trent Coll Nottm 74-81; Educn Chapl *Worc* 81-97; Chapl K Edw Sixth Form Coll Worc 81-97; rtd 97; P-in-c Beeley and Edensor *Derby* 97-02. *18 Moorhall Estate, Bakewell DE45 1FX*

GOWEN, John Frank. b 30. **d** 87 **p** 89. NSM Lecale Gp *D & D* 87-91; NSM Cregagh 87-91; Lic to Offic 89-99; NSM Stormont 99-01; NSM Knock from 01. *36 Downshire Road, Belfast BT6 9JL* Tel (028) 9070 1640

GOWER, Christopher Raymond. b 45. Nottm Univ BA73 Heythrop Coll Lon MA96 Univ of Wales MTh02 FRSA84. St Jo

Coll Nottm 70. **d** 73 **p** 74. C Hounslow H Trin *Lon* 73-76; Hon C N Greenford All Hallows 76-77; P-in-c Willesden Green St Gabr 77-83; P-in-c Brondesbury St Anne w Kilburn H Trin 81-82; Perm to Offic 82-84; P-in-c Yiewsley 84-96; R St Marylebone w H Trin from 97; P-in-c St Marylebone St Cypr from 99. *21 Beaumont Street, London W1G 6DQ* Tel (020) 7935 8965 *or* 7935 7315
GOWER, Denys Victor. b 33. Cant Sch of Min 85. **d** 87 **p** 88. NSM Gillingham H Trin *Roch* 87-91; NSM Gillingham St Aug 89-91; C Perry Street 91-93; P-in-c Wateringbury w Teston and W Farleigh 93-96; R 96-00; rtd 00; Perm to Offic *Roch* 00-02; Ind Chapl from 02; Perm to Offic *Cant* from 03. *4 Locarno Avenue, Gillingham ME8 6ET* Tel (01634) 375765 Mobile 07930-820441
GOWER, Nigel Plested. b 37. SS Coll Cam BA62 MA65 Lon Univ PGCE68. Ridley Hall Cam 61. **d** 63 **p** 64. C Walthamstow St Jo *Chelmsf* 63-66; CMS Nigeria 67-78; P-in-c Loscoe *Derby* 78-79; V 79-88; RD Heanor 84-88; R Bamford 88-98; Dioc World Development Officer 90-96; P-in-c Bradwell 96-98; Assoc P Alfreton Deanery 98-02; rtd 02. *New Cottage, Llanbister Road, Llandrindod Wells LD1 5UW* Tel (01547) 550318
GOWER, Miss Patricia Ann. b 44. Wilson Carlile Coll IDC79 Sarum & Wells Th Coll 88. **d** 88 **p** 94. Chapl Bris Univ *Bris* 88-91; Hon Par Dn Clifton St Paul 88-91; Par Dn Spondon *Derby* 91-94; C 94-95; P-in-c Hatton 95-98; Asst Chapl HM Pris Sudbury 95-98; Chapl from 98. *Chaplain's Office, HM Prison, Sudbury, Derby DE6 5HW* Tel (01283) 584088
GOWER, Miss Paulette Rose-Mary de Garis. b 70. Plymouth Univ BEd93. Cranmer Hall Dur 01. **d** 03. C Shrewsbury St Geo w Greenfields *Lich* from 03. *5 Bayford Drive, Shrewsbury SY1 3XQ* Tel (01743) 289122
GOWER, Archdeacon of. *See* WILLIAMS, The Ven Robert John
GOWING-CUMBER, Alexander John. b 72. Moorlands Th Coll BA94 Ridley Hall Cam MA00. **d** 00 **p** 03. C Vange *Chelmsf* 00-02; C Rayleigh from 02. *86 Lower Lambricks, Rayleigh SS6 8DB* Tel (01268) 777430 E-mail countdarcy@hotmail.com
GOYMOUR, Mrs Joanna Leigh. b 58. Reading Univ BA79. Dioc OLM tr scheme 99. **d** 02. OLM Bures w Assington and Lt Cornard *St E* from 02. *Dorking Tye House, Dorking Tye, Bures CO8 5JY* Tel (01787) 227494
E-mail jo@acgoymour.freeserve.co.uk
GOYMOUR, Michael Edwyn. b 29. Selw Coll Cam BA51 McGill Univ Montreal BD53. Montreal Dioc Th Coll 51 Wells Th Coll 53. **d** 53 **p** 54. C Bury St Edmunds St Jo *St E* 53-56; C Ipswich St Bart 56-60; R Gamlingay *Ely* 60-68; rtd 92; Perm to Offic *Ely* and *Pet* from 92. *56 Church Drive, Orton Waterville, Peterborough PE2 5HE* Tel (01733) 231535
GRACE, Capt David Leonard. b 55. Wilson Carlile Coll Dip Evang 92 Ripon Coll Cuddesdon DipMin99. **d** 99 **p** 00. CA from 92; C St Leonards and St Ives *Win* from 99. *31 Lions Wood, St Leonards, Ringwood BH24 2LU* Tel (01425) 476198
GRACE, Mrs Irene. b 36. Nottm Univ BSc58. Guildf Dioc Min Course 96. **d** 98 **p** 99. OLM Stoneleigh *Guildf* from 98. *33 Woodhouse Avenue, Stoneleigh, Epsom KT17 2JS* Tel (020) 8393 7280
GRACE, Juliet Christine. b 38. Cam Inst of Educn 60. S Dios Minl Tr Scheme 84. **d** 87 **p** 94. NSM Petersfield *Portsm* 87-93; NSM Steep and Froxfield w Privett 93-97; Community Mental Health Chapl Petersfield from 93; Perm to Offic 97-98; NSM Buriton from 98; NSM Petersfield from 98; NSM Sheet from 98; Chapl Portsm Healthcare NHS Trust from 98; Hon Chapl Miss to Seafarers from 02. *33 Woodbury Avenue, Petersfield GU32 2ED* Tel (01730) 262335 E-mail chris.grace@lineone.net
GRACE, Kenneth. b 24. Leeds Univ BA49. Wycliffe Hall Ox 62. **d** 63 **p** 64. C Tonge w Alkrington *Man* 63-66; R Thwing *York* 66-70; V Wold Newton 66-70; Chapl St Andr Sch Worthing 70-76; R Berwick w Selmeston and Alciston *Chich* 76-81; P-in-c Kingston Buci 81-85; R Westbourne 85-90; rtd 90; Perm to Offic *Chich* from 90. *17 Ramsay Hall, 11-13 Byron Road, Worthing BN11 3HN* Tel (01903) 230611
GRACE, Ms Louise Sarah. b 68. Girton Coll Cam BA89. Ripon Coll Cuddesdon BA97 Ch Div Sch of Pacific 97. **d** 98 **p** 99. C Wordsley *Worc* 98-02; R Teme Valley N from 03. *The Rectory, Lindridge, Tenbury Wells WR15 8JQ* Tel (01584) 881331
E-mail louisegrace@hotmail.com
GRACE, Richard Maurice. b 29. St Chad's Coll Dur BA53. Chich Th Coll 53. **d** 55 **p** 56. C Toxteth Park St Agnes *Liv* 55-58; C Wolverhampton St Pet *Lich* 58-62; V W Bromwich St Fran 62-78; P-in-c Salt 78-84; P-in-c Sandon w Burston 82-84; V Salt and Sandon w Burston 84-93; rtd 94; Perm to Offic *Ches* from 94. *Little Owls, 1 Trinity Close, Crewe CW2 8FD* Tel (01270) 662221
GRACE, Wilfrid Windsor. b 15. ACA39 FCA60. Westcott Ho Cam 52. **d** 53 **p** 54. C Chippenham St Andr w Tytherton Lucas *Bris* 53-57; V Minety w Oaksey 57-71; V Oldland 71-76; V Abbots Leigh w Leigh Woods 76-80; Chapl Ham Green Hosp 79-87; rtd 80; Perm to Offic *B & W* from 81; Hon Chapl Cheshire Home Axbridge from 81. *Hurn Mead, 71 Woodborough Road, Winscombe BS25 1BA* Tel (01934) 843362
GRACIE, Anthony Johnstone. b 25. Ch Coll Cam BA48 MA51. Linc Th Coll 57. **d** 59 **p** 60. C Edgbaston St Geo *Birm* 59-62; R

Lyndon w Manton and Martinsthorpe *Pet* 62-76; R N Luffenham 66-76; V Odiham w S Warnborough and Long Sutton *Win* 76-85; Perm to Offic *Bris* 85-88; rtd 88. *Colt Corner, Horn Lane, East Hendred, Wantage OX12 8LD* Tel (01235) 821509 E-mail a.gracie@btconnect.com
GRACIE, Bryan John. b 45. Open Univ BA81. AKC67. **d** 68 **p** 69. C Whipton *Ex* 68-72; Chapl St Jo Sch Tiffield 72-73; Chapl HM Borstal Stoke Heath 74-78; Asst Chapl HM Pris Liv 74; Chapl HM Youth Cust Cen Feltham 78-85; Chapl HM Pris Birm from 85. *HM Prison, Winson Green Road, Birmingham B18 4AS* Tel 0121-554 3838 Fax 554 7990
GRAEBE, Canon Denys Redford. b 26. Qu Coll Cam BA48 MA51. Westcott Ho Cam 50. **d** 51 **p** 52. C Hitchin St Mary *St Alb* 51-57; R Gt Parndon *Chelmsf* 57-72; V Norton *St Alb* 72-83; R Kimpton w Ayot St Lawrence 83-92; RD Wheathampstead 87-92; Hon Can St Alb Abbey 90-92; rtd 92; Perm to Offic *St E* from 92. *5 Sancroft Way, Fressingfield, Eye IP21 5QN* Tel (01379) 588178
GRAESSER, Adrian Stewart. b 42. Tyndale Hall Bris 63. **d** 67 **p** 68. C Nottingham St Jude *S'well* 67-69; C Slaithwaite w E Scammonden *Wakef* 69-72; CF 72-75; V Earl's Heaton *Wakef* 75-81; R Norton Fitzwarren *B & W* 81-86; R Bickenhill w Elmdon *Birm* 86-90; R Elmdon St Nic 90-00; P-in-c Dolton *Ex* from 00; P-in-c Iddesleigh w Dowland from 00; P-in-c Monkokehampton from 00; RD Torrington from 02. *The Rectory, Rectory Road, Dolton, Winkleigh EX19 8QT* Tel (01805) 804264 E-mail graesser.dolton@tinyworld.co.uk
GRAHAM, Alan Robert. b 44. St Edm Hall Ox BA67 MA71. St Steph Ho Ox 67. **d** 70 **p** 71. C Clifton All SS *Bris* 70-74; C Tadley St Pet *Win* 74-77; P-in-c Upper Clatford w Goodworth Clatford 77-79; R Abbotts Ann and Upper and Goodworth Clatford 79-84; V Lyndhurst and Emery Down 84-92; P-in-c Over Wallop w Nether Wallop 92-02; rtd 02; Perm to Offic *Win* from 02. *4 Sutton Place, Brockenhurst SO42 7TX* Tel (01590) 622324
GRAHAM, Alfred. b 34. Bris Univ BA57. Tyndale Hall Bris. **d** 58 **p** 59. C Chaddesden St Mary *Derby* 58-61; C Bickenhill w Elmdon *Birm* 61-64; V Kirkdale St Lawr *Liv* 64-70; V Stapleford *S'well* 70-83; V Burton Joyce w Bulcote 83-95; V Burton Joyce w Bulcote and Stoke Bardolph 95-97; rtd 97. *2 Hobsons Acre, Gunthorpe, Nottingham NG14 7FF* Tel 0115-966 3912
GRAHAM, Alistair. *See* GRAHAM, Michael Alistair
✠**GRAHAM, The Rt Revd Andrew Alexander Kenny (Alec).** b 29. St Jo Coll Ox BA52 DipTh53 MA57 Lambeth DD95. Ely Th Coll 53. **d** 55 **p** 56 **c** 77. C Hove All SS *Chich* 55-58; Chapl, Lect Th, and Tutor Worc Coll Ox 58-70; Warden Linc Th Coll 70-77; Can and Preb Linc Cathl *Linc* 70-77; Suff Bp Bedford *St Alb* 77-81; Bp Newc 81-97; Chmn ACCM 84-87; Chmn Doctrine Commn 87-95; rtd 97. *Fell End, Butterwick, Penrith CA10 2QQ* Tel (01931) 713147
GRAHAM, Canon Anthony Nigel. b 40. Univ of Wales (Abth) BA62 CertEd70. Ripon Hall Ox 62. **d** 64 **p** 65. C Heref H Trin *Heref* 64-67; C Birm St Martin *Birm* 67-69; C Selly Oak St Mary 71-75; V Edgbaston SS Mary and Ambrose 75-83; CMS Miss Partner Nigeria 84-88; Hon Can Jos from 88; V Highworth w Sevenhampton and Inglesham etc *Bris* 88-95; RD Highworth 93-95; P-in-c Coalpit Heath 95-99; V 99-00; rtd 00. *19 Dormer Road, Cheltenham GL51 0AX*
GRAHAM, Anthony Stanley David. b 34. SS Coll Cam BA56 MA60. Cuddesdon Coll 58. **d** 60 **p** 61. C Welwyn Garden City *St Alb* 60-64; Asst Chapl Ipswich Sch 64-65; C Margate St Jo *Cant* 65-68; Chr Aid Area Sec *Chich* 68-99; Perm to Offic *Cant* from 68; rtd 94. *48 Springfield Road, Crawley RH11 8AH* Tel (01293) 526279 E-mail tonygraham@satyagraha.fsnet.co.uk
GRAHAM, Christopher John. EMMTC. **d** 03. NSM Ripley *Derby* from 03. *41 Lathkill Drive, Ripley DE5 8HW* Tel (01773) 747223
GRAHAM, Clifton Gordon. b 53. ARCM72 GRSM74 FRCO75 Coll of Ripon & York St Jo PGCE76. St Steph Ho Ox 90. **d** 92 **p** 93. C Northfield *Birm* 92-93; C Perry Beeches 93-97; P-in-c S Yardley St Mich 97-00; V from 00. *St Michael's Vicarage, 60 Yew Tree Lane, Birmingham B26 1AP* Tel 0121-706 2563
GRAHAM, Canon Douglas Wrixon. b 13. TCD BA39. Div Test40. **d** 41 **p** 43. C Donaghcloney *D & D* 41-42; C Taney *D & G* 42-43; C New Ross *C & O* 43-50; I Killegney Union 50-66; I Roscommon w Donamon, Rathcline, Kilkeevin etc *K, E & A* 66-88; Preb Elphin Cathl 79-88; rtd 88. *Forest View Nursing Home, Ballymurray, Roscommon, Irish Republic* Tel (00353) (90) 663 0765
GRAHAM, Canon Frederick Lawrence. b 35. TCD BA65 DCCD88. CITC 66. **d** 66 **p** 67. C Belfast St Matt *Conn* 66-69; TV Chelmsley Wood *Birm* 69-73; Ch of Ireland Youth Officer 73-78; Bp's C Stoneyford *Conn* 78-88; Bp's C Fahan Lower and Upper *D & R* 88-91; Can Raphoe Cathl 90-01; I Donagh(eady 91-01; Can Derry Cathl 95-01; rtd 01. *Thuma Mina, 80 Altnahinch Road, Loughguile, Ballymena BT44 9JS* Tel (028) 2764 1016
E-mail freka@thuma.fsnet.co.uk
GRAHAM, Frederick Louis Roth. b 20. Selw Coll Cam BA47 MA49. Ridley Hall Cam 48. **d** 50 **p** 51. C Shirley *Win* 50-53; R

Old Trafford St Jo *Man* 53-61; R Wombwell *Sheff* 61-71; V Thorne 71-77; P-in-c Chilton-super-Polden w Edington *B & W* 77-82; P-in-c Catcott 77-82; V W Poldens 82-86; RD Glastonbury 82-86; rtd 86; Perm to Offic *Win* from 86. *73 Newlands Avenue, Southampton SO15 5EQ* Tel (023) 8078 9353

GRAHAM, George David. b 42. Jes Coll Cam BA64 MA68. St Jo Coll Nottm LTh Lon Coll of Div 66. **d** 71 **p** 72. C Corby St Columba *Pet* 71-74; C Deptford St Jo *S'wark* 74-77; P-in-c Deptford St Pet 77-82; C-in-c Wheatley Park St Paul CD *Sheff* 82-87; TV Dunstable *St Alb* 87-92; V Bromley Common St Luke *Roch* 92-02; R Hayes from 02. *The Rectory, Hayes Street, Bromley BR2 7LH* Tel (020) 8462 1373

GRAHAM, George Edgar. b 55. QUB BA91. Sarum & Wells Th Coll 74 CITC 77. **d** 78 **p** 79. C Lisburn Ch Ch *Conn* 78-81; C Mossley 81-83; I Broomhedge 83-91; I Derriaghy w Colin 91-96; I Ballywillan from 96. *The Rectory, 10 Coleraine Road, Portrush BT56 8EA* Tel (028) 7082 4298

E-mail g.k.graham@btinternet.com

GRAHAM, George Gordon. b 17. OBE96. St Chad's Coll Dur BA48 DipTh50 MSc71. **d** 50 **p** 51. C Luton Ch Ch *St Alb* 50-53; C Bakewell *Derby* 53-56; P-in-c Wheatley Hill *Dur* 56-69; V Hunwick 69-88; Chapl Homelands Hosp Dur 80-94; Chapl Bishop Auckland Hospitals NHS Trust 94-98; Chapl S Durham Healthcare NHS Trust from 98; rtd 88. *3 The Willows, Bishop Auckland DL14 7HH* Tel (01388) 602758

GRAHAM, George Gordon. b 34. Harvard Univ BA55 MDiv JD71. **d** 96 **p** 97. Aux Min Seapatrick *D & D* 97-99; Aux Min Lecale Gp 99-03; NSM Castlewellan w Kilcoo from 03. *Address temp unknown* E-mail gorbargrah@aol.com

GRAHAM, Gordon Cecil. b 31. JP. Cn Coll Cam BA53 MA57. Ripon Hall Ox 53. **d** 55 **p** 56. C Didsbury St Jas and Em *Man* 55-58; C Rochdale 58-60; R Heaton Mersey 60-67; Chapl Hulme Gr Sch Oldham 67-74; Lic to Offic *Ches* 72-92; rtd 92. *21 The Crescent, Davenport, Stockport SK3 8SL* Tel 0161-483 6011

GRAHAM, Harry John. b 52. Magd Coll Cam BA75 MA86. Trin Coll Bris BA94. **d** 96 **p** 97. C Walkden and Lt Hulton *Man* 96-99; Chapl Salford Coll of Tech 96-99; P-in-c Edgeside *Man* 99-00; TV Rossendale Middle Valley 00-02; Gen Sec Miss without Borders (UK) Ltd from 02. *69 Eyre Court, Finchley Road, London NW8 9TX* Tel (020) 7586 8336

GRAHAM, Ian Maxwell. b 50. CertEd76. Chich Th Coll 86. **d** 88 **p** 89. C Middlesbrough St Thos *York* 88-90; C Stainton-in-Cleveland 90-93; V Hemlington 93-00; V Grangetown from 00. *The Vicarage, Clynes Road, Grangetown, Middlesbrough TS6 7LY* Tel (01642) 453704 E-mail casahild@lineone.net

GRAHAM, James Hamilton. b 54. Trin Hall Cam BA76 MA80 Solicitor 78. Ripon Coll Cuddesdon BA83 MA87. **d** 84 **p** 85. C Harlescott *Lich* 84-88; C Adderley 88-93; C Drayton in Hales 88-93; C Moreton Say 88-93; R Hodnet w Weston under Redcastle 93-00; RD Hodnet 97-00; V Eccleshall from 00. *The Vicarage, Church Street, Eccleshall, Stafford ST21 6BY* Tel (01785) 850351

GRAHAM, John Francis Ottiwell Skelton. b 15. G&C Coll Cam BA37 MA48. Wells Th Coll 37. **d** 39 **p** 40. C Walton St Mary *Liv* 39-48; V Speke All SS 48-58; V Winterbourne Earls w Winterbourne Dauntsey etc *Sarum* 58-72; R Bincombe w Broadwey 72-80; R Bincombe w Broadwey, Upwey and Buckland Ripers 80-81; rtd 81; Perm to Offic *Win* 81-95 and from 95. *15A Belmore Lane, Lymington SO41 3NL* Tel (01590) 673256

GRAHAM, John Galbraith. b 21. K Coll Cam BA43 MA46. Ely Th Coll 46. **d** 48 **p** 49. C E Dulwich St Jo *S'wark* 48-49; Chapl St Chad's Coll *Dur* 49-52; C Aldershot St Mich *Guildf* 52-55; C-in-c Beaconsfield St Mich CD *Ox* 55-62; Chapl Reading Univ 62-72; C Pimlico St Pet w Westmr Ch Ch *Lon* 72-74; R Houghton w Wyton *Ely* 74-78; rtd 86; Lic to Offic *St E* from 86; Perm to Offic *Ely* from 93. *31 Rectory Lane, Somersham, Huntingdon PE17 3EL* Tel (01487) 842737

GRAHAM, Kevin. See GRAHAM, Terence Kevin Declan

GRAHAM, Mrs Marian McKenzie. b 39. St As Minl Tr Course. **d** 89 **p** 97. NSM Bagillt *St As* 89-93; NSM Flint 93-99 and from 00; C 99-00. *Sharondale, Bryntirion Road, Bagillt CH6 6BZ* Tel (01352) 734139

GRAHAM, Canon Matthew. b 30. Univ Coll Dur BSc54. K Coll (NS) BD71 Ridley Hall Cam 54. **d** 56 **p** 57. C Littleover *Derby* 56-59; C Fazakerley Em *Liv* 59-61; V Huyton St Geo 61-65; Canada 65-71; V Sutton Coldfield St Columba *Birm* 71-85; V Warley Woods 85-95; RD Warley 87-93; Hon Can Birm Cathl 90-95; rtd 95; Perm to Offic *Worc* from 95. *18 The Drive, Checketts Lane, Worcester WR3 7JS* Tel (01905) 458151

GRAHAM, Michael. b 51. Westcott Ho Cam 61. **d** 61 **p** 62. C Withington St Paul *Man* 61-64; V Lawton Moor 64-87; V Mobberley *Ches* 87-99; rtd 99; Perm to Offic *Ches* from 00. *16 Wood Lane, Timperley, Altrincham WA15 7QB* Tel 0161-904 8335

GRAHAM, Michael. b 51. CITC BTh95. **d** 95 **p** 96. C Cork St Fin Barre's Union *C, C & R* 95-98; Min Can Cork Cathl 97-98; I Drogheda w Ardee, Collon and Termonfeckin *Arm* from 98; Ch of Ireland Internet Co-ord from 99. *St Peter's Rectory, Drogheda, Co Louth, Irish Republic* Tel (00353) (41) 983 9458 Fax 983 9459 *or* 987 0073

E-mail drogheda@armagh.anglican.org

GRAHAM, Michael Alistair. b 47. CITC 67. **d** 70 **p** 71. C Dublin Clontarf *D & G* 71-75; C Ox St Mich w St Martin and All SS *Ox* 76-78; P-in-c Dublin Sandymount *D & G* 80-86; I Stillorgan w Blackrock 86-00; Soc Worker E Health Bd Dub from 00. *Address temp unknown*

GRAHAM, Nigel. See GRAHAM, Canon Anthony Nigel

GRAHAM, Ms Olivia Josephine. b 56. UEA BA84. St Alb and Ox Min Course 94. **d** 97 **p** 98. NSM Wheatley *Ox* 97-98; C Risborough 98-01; TV Burnham w Dropmore, Hitcham and Taplow from 01. *12 Hatchgate Gardens, Burnham, Slough SL1 8DD* Tel (01628) 559992

E-mail graham.glenny@virgin.net

GRAHAM, Peter. b 32. CEng MIMechE. **d** 86 **p** 87. NSM Minchinhampton *Glouc* 86-96; Perm to Offic 96-97; NSM Alderminster and Halford *Cov* 98-02; NSM Butlers Marston and the Pillertons w Ettington 98-02; rtd 02; Perm to Offic *Cov* from 02. *10 Banbury Road, Ettington, Stratford-upon-avon CV37 7TB* Tel (01789) 740335

GRAHAM, Peter Bartlemy. b 23. K Coll Cam BA47 MA52. Ely Th Coll 50. **d** 52 **p** 53. C St Alb Abbey *St Alb* 52-55; V Eaton Bray 55-64; R Harpenden St Nic 64-73; V Aylesbury *Ox* 73-82; Hon Can Ch Ch 79-82; R Elford *Lich* 82-88; Dioc Adv Past Care and Counselling 82-88; rtd 88; Perm to Offic *Sarum* from 88. *Carriers Cottage, Buckland Newton, Dorchester DT2 7DW* Tel (01300) 345287

GRAHAM, Robert John. b 70. Wycliffe Hall Ox BTh99. **d** 99 **p** 00. C Nailsea H Trin *B & W* from 99. *3 Wedmore Road, Nailsea BS48 4PZ* Tel (01275) 790320 Fax as telephone

E-mail revgraham@btinternet.com

GRAHAM, Ronald Fleming. b 33. Edin Th Coll 67. **d** 69 **p** 69. Chapl St Andr Cathl *Ab* 69-73; R Glas Gd Shep *Glas* 73-75; R Glas Gd Shep and Ascension 75-76; CF (TA) 74-76; R Peterhead *Ab* 76-80; Chapl RAF 76-80; Bp's Dom Chapl *Arg* 80-84; Itinerant Priest 80-84; R Lanark *Glas* 84-89; R Douglas 84-89; rtd 89; Hon C Glas St Ninian *Glas* 90-98. *77 Merryvale Avenue, Merrylee Park, Giffnock, Glasgow G46 6DE* Tel 0141-569 5090

GRAHAM, Ronald Gaven. b 27. **d** 90 **p** 91. NSM Adare w Kilpeacon and Croom *L & K* 90-92; Dioc Info Officer (Limerick) 91-95; NSM Rathkeale w Askeaton and Kilcornan 92-96; NSM Wexford w Ardcolm and Killurin *C & O* from 97. *8 Chestnut Grove, Fernyhill, Killinick, Co Wexford, Irish Republic* Tel (00353) (53) 43013 *or* 58369

GRAHAM, Roy Richard Arthur. b 39. Lon Univ BD63 Open Univ BA78. ALCD62. **d** 63 **p** 64. C Southsea St Jude *Portsm* 63-66; C Morden *S'wark* 66-69; V Tittensor *Lich* 70-79; R Hurworth and Dinsdale w Sockburn *Dur* 79-02; rtd 02. *The School House, Eaglesfield, Lockerbie DG11 3PA* Tel (01461) 500499 E-mail rragraham@onenet.co.uk

GRAHAM, Mrs Susan Lochrie. b 46. Sheff Univ PhD01. Yale Div Sch MDiv90. **d** 90 **p** 91. Canada 90-96; Cow Head Par 90-92; P-in-c Kingsway All SS, St Hilary, Bolton etc 92-96; NSM Ilminster and Distr *B & W* 96-97; NSM W Poldens from 97. *The Vicarage, Holy Well Road, Edington, Bridgwater TA7 9LE* Tel (01278) 723055 E-mail s.l.graham@exeter.ac.uk

GRAHAM, Terence Kevin Declan. b 67. NUI BSc89 TCD BTh02. CITC 99. **d** C Knock *D & D* from 02. *3 Sandown Park South, Belfast BT5 1HE* Tel (028) 9065 3370 Mobile 07973-257193 E-mail revkevin@fish.co.uk

GRAHAM, Mrs Wendy. **d** 01 **p** 02. OLM Chalfont St Peter *Ox* from 01. *The Box, Hillfield Road, Chalfont St Peter, Gerrards Cross SL9 0DU* Tel (01753) 885066

GRAHAM, William Bruce. b 37. **d** 90 **p** 91. Canada 90-97; P-in-c W Poldens *B & W* from 97; RD Glastonbury from 03. *The Vicarage, Holy Well Road, Edington, Bridgwater TA7 9LE* Tel (01278) 723055 Fax 722962

GRAHAM, William Stig. b 53. Newc Univ BSc75. NEOC DipHE99. **d** 99 **p** 00. C W Acklam *York* 99-02; Chapl Myton Hamlet Hospice from 02. *2 Winyates Road, Lighthorne Heath, Leamington Spa CV33 9TU* Tel (01926) 640811 *or* 492518

E-mail stiggraham@netscape.net

GRAHAM-BROWN, John George Francis. b 34. CA60. Wycliffe Hall Ox 60. **d** 63 **p** 64. C Darlington St Cuth *Dur* 63-67; C Rufforth w Moor Monkton and Hessay *York* 67-73; Sec York Dioc Redundant Chs Uses Cttee 69-83; Asst Sec DBF 73-84; Dioc Past Cttee 73-89; Hon C York St Barn 73-85; P-in-c 85-92; TV Marfleet 92-99; rtd 99; Perm to Offic *St Alb* from 00. *40 Hunters Oak, Hemel Hempstead HP2 7SW* Tel (01482) 402226 E-mail f.graham-brown@tinyonline.co.uk

GRAHAM-ORLEBAR, Ian Henry Gaunt. b 26. New Coll Ox BA49 MA56. Cuddesdon Coll 60. **d** 62 **p** 63. C Hemel Hempstead *St Alb* 62-70; R Barton-le-Cley w Higham Gobion 70-80; R Barton-le-Cley w Higham Gobion and Hexton 80-92;

rtd 92; Perm to Offic *Ex* from 94. *Hole Farm, Bickington, Newton Abbot TQ12 6PE* Tel (01626) 821298

GRAIN, Anthony Ernest. b 07. CCC Cam BA31 MA35. Ely Th Coll 31. **d** 32 **p** 33. C Fulham St Clem *Lon* 32-34; C Cheshunt *St Alb* 35-41; P-in-c Eversholt 41-43; V Stotfold 43-48; Chapl Control Commn Germany 48-52; Chapl Marseille *Eur* 52-55; P-in-c Edin St Barn *Edin* 55-58; Jamaica 61-62; S Rhodesia 63-65; Rhodesia 65-80; Zimbabwe 80-86; rtd 73; Perm to Offic *Chich* from 86. *College of St Barnabas, Blackberry Lane, Lingfield RH7 6NJ* Tel (01342) 870260

GRAIN, Canon Keith Charles. b 27. St Boniface Warminster 47 AKC51. **d** 52 **p** 53. C Liversedge *Wakef* 52-55; C Barnsley St Mary 55-60; V Hanging Heaton 60-70; V Heckmondwike 70-82; Hon Can Wakef Cathl 74-82; RD Birstall 79-82; V Gargrave *Bradf* 82-92; rtd 92; Perm to Offic *Bradf* from 92. *2 Holme Ghyll, Colne Road, Glusburn, Keighley BD20 8RG* Tel (01535) 630668

GRAINGER, Canon Bruce. b 37. Nottm Univ BA62 Hull Univ MA83. Cuddesdon Coll 62. **d** 64 **p** 65. C Bingley All SS *Bradf* 64-67; Chapl K Sch Cant 67-72; Hon Min Can Cant Cathl *Cant* 69-72; V Baildon *Bradf* 72-88; V Oxenhope from 88; Hon Can Bradf Cathl from 84; Dir of Ords 88-96; Dioc Ecum Officer from 96; Lect Bradf Univ from 99; RD S Craven from 02. *The Vicarage, Gledhow Drive, Oxenhope, Keighley BD22 9SA* Tel (01535) 642529 Fax as telephone E-mail grainger@nildram.co.uk

GRAINGER, Horace. b 34. Carl Dioc Tr Course 82. **d** 85 **p** 86. NSM Barrow St Matt *Carl* 85-89; C Carl St Herbert w St Steph 89-91; TV Penrith w Newton Reigny and Plumpton Wall 91-96; P-in-c Holme Cultram St Mary 96-00; P-in-c Holme Cultram St Cuth 96-00; rtd 00; NSM Barrow St Aid *Carl* from 01. *15 Maylands Avenue, Barrow-in-Furness LA13 0AL* Tel (01229) 828603

GRAINGER, Ian. b 66. Barrow-in-Furness Coll of FE BTEC NC86. Cranmer Hall Dur 89. **d** 92 **p** 93. C Whitehaven *Carl* 92-94; C Walney Is 94-97; P-in-c Barrow St Aid 97-02; V Camerton, Seaton and W Seaton from 02. *The Vicarage, Ling Beck Park, Seaton, Workington CA14 1JQ* Tel (01900) 602162 E-mail revd.ian@grainger89.fsnet.co.uk

GRAINGER, Michael Noel Howard. b 40. Trin Coll Carmarthen. **d** 91 **p** 92. NSM Haverfordwest St Martin w Lambston *St D* 91-95; V Maenclochog and New Moat etc from 95. *The Rectory, New Moat, Clarbeston Road SA63 4RQ* Tel (01437) 532238

GRAINGER, Prof Roger Beckett. b 34. Birm Univ MB70 Leeds Univ PhD79 Lon Univ BA80 DD90 Huddersfield Poly MPhil88 Bris Univ PhD92 Leeds Metrop Univ BSc98 PhD(Educ)01 Lambeth STh83 FRSA85 FRAI85 British Psychological Soc Statement of Equivalence 96 CPsychol96 AFBPsS99. Lich Th Coll 64. **d** 66 **p** 69. C W Bromwich All SS *Lich* 66-68; C Walsall 69-73; Chapl Stanley Royd Hosp Wakef 73-90; rtd 91; Hon C Wakef St Jo *Wakef* from 93; Dioc Drama Adv from 98; Prof Extraordinary Potchefstroom Univ S Africa from 01; Hon Chapl Wakef Cathl from 02. *7 Park Grove, Horbury, Wakefield WF4 6EE* Tel (01924) 272742

GRAINGER-SMITH, James Edward. b 71. Nottm Univ BA92. St Jo Coll Nottm MA02. **d** 02 **p** 03. C Hordle *Win* from 02. *Church Cottage, Sway Road, Tiptoe, Lymington SO41 6FR* Tel (01425) 616670

GRANDELL, Canon Peter Frank. b 59. Wagner Coll NY BS81 Gen Th Sem NY MDiv95. **d** 95 **p** 95. USA 95-96 and from 98; Asst to Dean St Paul's Cathl Burlington VT 95-96; C St John's Wood *Lon* 96-98; Can Prec SS Pet and Paul Cathl Washington DC from 99. *4000 Massachusetts Avenue NW, Washington, DC 20016, USA*

GRANGE (née FEATHERSTON), Mrs Alice Margery. b 55. Teesside Univ BA97. Nor Ord Course DipHE99. **d** 99 **p** 00. C Pickering w Lockton and Levisham *York* 99-02; TV Crosslacon *Carl* from 02. *The Vicarage, Arlecdon, Frizington CA26 3UB* Tel (01946) 861353 Fax as telephone E-mail margerygrange@care4free.net

GRANGER, Canon Ronald Harry. b 22. Selw Coll Cam BA49 MA53. Cuddesdon Coll 49. **d** 51 **p** 52. C Portsea St Mary *Portsm* 51-57; V Lower Sandown St Jo 57-63; V Ryde All SS 63-70; RD E Wight 65-70; Hon Can Portsm Cathl 67-90; V Petersfield 70-90; RD Petersfield 75-80; P-in-c Buriton 79-84; R 84-90; rtd 90; Perm to Offic *Portsm* from 90. *45 Siskin Close, Bishops Waltham SO32 1RP* Tel (01489) 894378

GRANNER, Mrs Linda. b 52. WMMTC. **d** 03. NSM Bearwood *Birm* from 03. *36 Roman Way, Birmingham B15 2SJ* Tel 0121-472 4330

GRANT, Alistair Sims. b 25. SS Coll Cam BA49 MA53. Sarum Th Coll 49. **d** 51 **p** 52. V Haddenham *Ely* 58-65; rtd 90; Perm to Offic *Ely* 90-00. *56 The Causeway, Burwell, Cambridge CB5 0DU* Tel (01638) 741670

GRANT, Andrew Richard. b 40. Univ of Wales BA62. Chich Th Coll 63. **d** 65 **p** 66. C Kennington St Jo *S'wark* 65-68; Hon C 70-72; Hon C Stockwell Green St Andr 68-70; V Nunhead St Antony 72-79; TR N Lambeth 79-92; USPG Ghana 92-99; C Paddington St Jo w St Mich *Lon* 99-01; P-in-c Stockwell Mich

S'wark from 01. *St Michael's Vicarage, 78 Stockwell Park Road, London SW9 0DA* Tel (020) 7274 6357

GRANT, Antony Richard Charles. b 34. Ch Ch Ox BA59 MA64. Coll of Resurr Mirfield 72. **d** 74 **p** 75. C St John's Wood *Lon* 74-77; Novice CR 77-79; CR from 79; Lic to Offic *Wakef* from 80; Perm to Offic *Lon* from 98; rtd 99. *Community of the Resurrection, Stocks Bank Road, Mirfield WF14 0BN* Tel (01924) 494318

GRANT, Arthur Glyndŵr Webber (Glyn). b 28. K Coll Lon RTC47 St Luke's Coll Ex CertEd34. Wells Th Coll 52. **d** 54 **p** 55. C Cannock *Lich* 54-57; S Rhodesia 57-63; C Paignton St Jo *Ex* 63-68; C Brighton Gd Shep Preston *Chich* 68-76; C Moulsecoomb 76-80; Chapl HM Pris Northeye 80-83; P-in-c Wartling *Chich* 80-83; C Seaford w Sutton 83-87; Sub-Chapl HM Pris Lewes 86-92; rtd 92; Perm to Offic *Ex* 93-95 and from 98. *33 Occombe Valley Road, Paignton TQ3 1QX* Tel (01803) 522722

GRANT, David Francis. b 32. Chich Th Coll. **d** 60 **p** 61. C Acton Green St Pet *Lon* 60-63; C Ruislip St Martin 63-68; V Oving w Merston *Chich* 68-75; Bp's Dom Chapl 68-75; R Graffham w Woolavington 75-86; R Hastings St Clem and All SS 86-91; R Petworth 91-94; R Egdean 91-94; RD Petworth 92-94; rtd 97. *Glebeland, Graffham, Petworth GU28 0QE* Tel (01798) 867289

GRANT, Canon Edward Francis. b 14. TCD BA37. TCD Div Sch Div Test. **d** 40 **p** 41. C New Ross *C & O* 40-43; P-in-c Preban w Moyne 43-46; I Fethard w Tintern and Killesk 46-56; P-in-c Ardcolm 56-70; I Wexford w Ardcolm 70-85; Preb Ferns Cathl 57-63; Treas 64-65; Chan 65-69; Prec 69-85; Preb Stagonil St Patr Cathl Dublin 76-85; rtd 85. *9 Kingston College, Mitchelstown, Co Cork, Irish Republic* Tel (00353) (25) 84214

GRANT, Eric. See GRANT, William Frederick

GRANT, Canon Geoffrey. b 27. Lich Th Coll 55. **d** 58 **p** 59. C Swindon New Town *Bris* 58-62; V Eastville St Thos 62-67; V Sherston Magna w Easton Grey 67-75; P-in-c Luckington w Alderton 71-75; P-in-c Woolcott Park 75-78; V Cotham St Mary 76-78; V Cotham St Sav w St Mary 78-81; TR Yate New Town 81-88; Hon Can Bris Cathl 82-92; Dir St Jo Home Bris 89-92; rtd 92; Perm to Offic *Bris* 92-97; Chapl Beaulieu-sur-Mer *Eur* 97-00. *1266 Chemin des Espinets, 06570 St Paul de Vence, France* Tel (00334) (9) 358 7849

GRANT, Canon Geoffrey Leslie. b 33. Trin Coll Cam BA57 MA61. Ridley Hall Cam 57. **d** 59 **p** 60. C Chelsea St Luke *Lon* 59-64; Chapl Orwell Park Sch Nacton from 64; R Nacton w Levington *St E* 64-78; P-in-c Bucklesham w Brightwell and Foxhall 75-76; R Nacton and Levington w Bucklesham and Foxhall from 78; RD Colneys from 86; Hon Can St E Cathl from 94; P-in-c Kirton w Falkenham from 96. *The Rectory, Nacton, Ipswich IP10 0HY* Tel (01473) 659232 E-mail canon@nildram.co.uk

GRANT, James Neil. b 57. Toorak Coll of Educn BEd80. Trin Coll Melbourne BTh84. **d** 85 **p** 86. Australia 85-87 and from 89; C Feltham *Lon* 87-89. *7/858 Hampton Street, Brighton, Vic, Australia 3186* Tel (0061) (3) 9592 2673 *or* 9787 4411 Mobile 419-560230 Fax 9787 7646 E-mail jgrant@tps.vic.edu.au

GRANT, John Brian Frederick. b 47. Bris Univ BSc68 MB, ChB71 MD76 FRCS76. Coll of Resurr Mirfield 91. **d** 93 **p** 94. C Doncaster Ch Ch *Sheff* 93-95; C Doncaster H Trin 95-96; Asst Chapl Salford R Hosps NHS Trust from 96. *Chaplains' Office, Hope Hospital, Stott Lane, Salford M6 8HD* Tel 0161-787 5167 *or* 789 7373

GRANT, Ms Kerry Jean. b 65. SEITE 00. **d** 03. *76 Kinveachy Gardens, London SE7 8EJ* Tel (020) 8473 7676 Mobile 07866-690527 E-mail kes@waitrose.com

GRANT, Canon Malcolm Etheridge. b 44. Edin Univ BSc66 BD69. Edin Th Coll 66. **d** 69 **p** 70. C St Mary's Cathl *Glas* 69-72; C Grantham w Manthorpe *Linc* 72; TV Grantham 72-78; P-in-c Invergordon St Ninian *Mor* 78-81; Provost St Mary's Cathl *Glas* 81-91; R Glas St Mary 81-91; Provost St Andr Cathl Inverness *Mor* 91-02; R Inverness St Andr 91-02; P-in-c Culloden St Mary-in-the-Fields 91-97; R Strathnairn St Paul 91-97; Hon Can St Andr Cathl Inverness from 02; V Eaton Bray w Edlesborough *St Alb* from 02. *The Vicarage, 11 High Street, Eaton Bray, Dunstable LU6 2DN* Tel (01525) 220261

GRANT, Murray William. b 36. Chich Th Coll 64. **d** 66 **p** 67. C Stanley *Liv* 66-70; C Munster Square St Mary Magd *Lon* 70-74; C Westmr St Sav and St Jas Less 74-82; P-in-c Albany Street Ch Ch 82; P-in-c Hammersmith H Innocents 83-94; V 94-99; Chapl Naples w Sorrento, Capri and Bari *Eur* from 99. *via S Pasquala a Chiaia 15B, 80121 Naples, Italy* Tel (0039) (081) 411842 Fax 409789

GRANT, Patrick Iain Douglas. b 67. K Alfred's Coll Win BA88. Cuddesdon Coll BTh93. **d** 96 **p** 97. C Croydon Woodside *S'wark* 96-99; V S Beddington St Mich from 99. *St Michael's Vicarage, Milton Road, Wallington SM6 9RP* Tel (020) 8647 1201 E-mail grant.saintmichael@tesco.net

GRANT, Canon Rodney Arthur. b 26. AKC52. K Coll Lon St Boniface Warminster. **d** 53 **p** 54. C Edin St Jas *Edin* 53-56; C Musselburgh 56-59; P-in-c Prestonpans 59-60; P-in-c Edin St Aid

Miss Niddrie Mains 60-72; R Edin St Jas 72-80; R Edin Ch Ch 72-80; R Edin Ch Ch-St Jas 80-86; R Edin SS Phil and Jas 86-92; Chapl St Columba's Hospice Edin 86-92; Hon Can St Mary's Cathl from 91; rtd 92; P-in-c Edin St Vin *Edin* from 98. *29 Bruntsfield Gardens, Edinburgh EH10 4DY* Tel 0131-229 1857

GRANT, William Frederick (Eric). b 23. Fitzw Ho Cam BA48 MA50 Cam Univ CertEd50. Wycliffe Hall Ox 51. **d** 53 **p** 54. C Islington St Paul Ball's Pond *Lon* 53-57; V Islington All SS 57-60; Head RE Therfield Sch Leatherhead 60-84; Perm to Offic *Guildf* from 66; rtd 88; Perm to Offic *S'wark* from 89. *Kingfishers, 24 The Avenue, Brockham, Betchworth RH3 7EN* Tel (01737) 842551

GRANT, The Very Revd William James. b 29. **d** 58 **p** 59. Asst Missr S Ch Miss Ballymacarrett *D & D* 58-60; C Belfast St Geo *Conn* 60-63; Canada 63-66; Miss to Seamen 66-70; I Fethard w Tintern and Killesk *C & O* 70-77; I Cong, Ballinrobe and Aasleagh *T, K & A* 77-81; Adn Tuam 80-93; I Tuam w Cong and Aasleagh 81-93; Dean Tuam 81-93; rtd 93. *48 Brazabon House, Sandymount, Dublin 4, Irish Republic* Tel (00353) (1) 269 5071

GRANTHAM, Michael Paul. b 47. Linc Th Coll. **d** 84 **p** 85. C Gainsborough All SS *Linc* 84-87; R S Kelsey Gp 87-94; R Dunster, Carhampton and Withycombe w Rodhuish *B & W* from 94; RD Exmoor from 03. *The Rectory, St George's Street, Dunster, Minehead TA24 6RS* Tel (01643) 821812

GRANTHAM, Suffragan Bishop of. See REDFERN, The Rt Revd Alastair Llewellyn John

GRASBY, Derek. b 56. Bris Univ BA80 MA82. Wesley Coll Bris 77 EAMTC 95. **d** 95 **p** 96. C Harlescott *Lich* 95-96; C W Bromwich St Andr w Ch Ch 96-98; R Newton Heath *Man* 98-02; Chapl UWE *Bris* from 02. *1 Saxon Way, Bradley Stoke, Bristol BS32 9AR* Tel (01454) 202483 Mobile 07958-089156 Fax 08701-339312 E-mail graz@clara.co.uk *or* derek.grasby@uwe.ac.uk

GRATTON, Patricia Margaret. See MAGUIRE, Mrs Patricia Margaret

GRATY, Canon John Thomas. b 33. Univ Coll Ox BA58 MA60. Coll of Resurr Mirfield 58. **d** 60 **p** 61. C Cov St Mark *Cov* 60-63; C Hitchin St Mary *St Alb* 63-67; R Cov St Alb *Cov* 67-75; P-in-c Radway w Ratley 75-77; P-in-c Warmington w Shotteswell 75-77; RD Dassett Magna 76-79; R Warmington w Shotteswell and Radway w Ratley 77-84; Hon Can Cov Cathl 80-96; P-in-c Nuneaton St Mary 84-89; V 89-96; rtd 96; Perm to Offic *Cov* from 96. *48 Shakespeare Street, Stratford-upon-Avon CV37 6RN* Tel (01789) 298856

GRAVELL, Canon John Hilary. b 45. Univ of Wales (Abth) BA65 DipEd66. Burgess Hall Lamp 66. **d** 68 **p** 69. C Aberystwyth *St D* 68-72; R Llangeitho w Blaenpennal 72-81; V Betws Leuci 73-81; V Llan-non 81-95; Can St D Cathl from 92; V Llandybie from 95; RD Dyffryn Aman from 01. *The Vicarage, 77 Kings Road, Llandybie, Ammanford SA18 2TL* Tel (01269) 850337

GRAVES, Jonathan Mark. b 57. BEd. St Steph Ho Ox. **d** 84 **p** 85. C St Leonards Ch Ch and St Mary *Chich* 84-88; C-in-c N Langley CD 88-95; V Stone Cross St Luke w N Langney 95-02; Chapl St Wilfrid's Hospice Eastbourne 94-02; Chapl Grenville Coll Bideford from 02. *Grenville College, Belvoir Road, Bideford EX39 3JP* Tel (01237) 472212 *or* 472384 E-mail frjonathan@jgraves.fslife.co.uk

GRAVES, Peter. b 33. RMN STD FInstSMM. EMMTC 78. **d** 81 **p** 82. NSM Roughey *Chich* 81-89; NSM Itchingfield w Slinfold 89-98; Perm to Offic *S'wark* from 98. *5 Fletcher Court, The Woodlands, Farnsfield, Newark NG22 8LY* Tel (01623) 882987 Fax as telephone

GRAY, Alan. b 25. LRAM52 Dip Community Educn 75. Qu Coll Birm 51. **d** 54 **p** 55. C Monkseaton St Pet *Newc* 54-56; C Sighill 56-61; C-in-c Balkwell CD 61-66; R Callander *St And* 66-74; R Killin 66-74; R Lochearnhead 66-74; R Alloa 74-77; Community Educn Officer 76-85; Lic to Offic 77-85; R Alyth 85-90; R Blairgowrie 85-90; R Coupar Angus 85-90; rtd 90. *12B Park Terrace, Stirling FK8 2JT* Tel (01786) 479616

GRAY, Alan Eric. b 18. Lich Th Coll 38. **d** 41 **p** 42. C Sampford Peverell *Ex* 41-44; Africa 47-60; V Lower Breeding Chich 61-70; rtd 83. *Appletree Cottage, 81 Belmont Road, Malvern WR14 1PN* Tel (01684) 572453

GRAY, Canon Angela Margery. b 46. St D Coll Lamp DipTh73. **dss** 73 **d** 80 **p** 97. Aberystwyth *St D* 73-80; C Dafen and Llwynhendy 80-90; C-in-c 90-97; V Llwynhendy from 97; Hon Can St D Cathl from 01. *Clergy House, 10 Bryn Isaf, Llwynhendy, Llanelli SA14 9EX* Tel (01554) 774213

GRAY, Charles Malcolm. b 38. Sheff Univ. Lich Th Coll 67. **d** 69 **p** 70. C St Geo-in-the-East St Mary *Lon* 69-72; C Bush Hill Park St Mark 72-75; V Winchmore Hill H Trin from 75. *Holy Trinity Vicarage, King's Avenue, London N21 3NA* Tel and fax (020) 8360 2947 *or* 8364 2724 Mobile 07721-664178

GRAY, Ms Christine Angela (Kit). b 46. Nottm Univ BA67 CertEd68 Dur Univ DipTh73. Cranmer Hall Dur 71. **dss** 80 **d** 87 **p** 94. Rawthorpe *Wakef* 74-81; Chapl Nottm Univ *S'well* 81-88; C Rushmere *St E* 88-94; Chapl to Ringshall w Battisford, Barking w Darmsden etc 94-00; P-in-c Nayland w Wiston from 00. *The Vicarage, Bear Street, Nayland, Colchester CO6 4LA* Tel (01206) 262316

GRAY, Dale Armitage. b 42. Edin Th Coll 62. **d** 92 **p** 93. Dioc Missr *Arg* 92-98; Chapl St Jo Cathl Oban 92-95; P-in-c Cumbrae (or Millport) 95-98; rtd 98. *Hoggwood Cottage, 11 Nursery Lane, Coldstream TD12 4DE* Tel (01890) 882653

GRAY, David. b 55. Oak Hill Th Coll. **d** 00 **p** 01. C Bestwood Em w St Mark *S'well* from 00. *45 Pine Hill Close, Nottingham NG5 9DA* Tel 0115-927 9547 E-mail davidgray72@hotmail.com

GRAY, David Bryan. b 28. RD77. Roch Th Coll 59. **d** 61 **p** 62. C Linc St Giles *Linc* 61-65; V Thurlby 65-67; P-in-c Ropsley 67-75; P-in-c Sapperton w Braceby 67-75; P-in-c Somerby w Humby 67-75; R Trimley *St E* 75-82; R Orford w Sudbourne, Chillesford, Butley and Iken 82-94; rtd 94; Perm to Offic *St E* from 94. *30 Roman Way, Felixstowe IP11 9NJ* Tel (01394) 285778

GRAY, David Cedric. b 53. RMN77 Hollings Coll Man 79. LNSM course 94. **d** 97 **p** 98. OLM Gorton Em w St Jas *Man* from 97. *39 Jessop Street, Gorton, Manchester M18 8TZ* Tel 0161-355 6605 Pager 017623-725682

GRAY, David Michael. b 57. ACIBS80 St Jo Coll Dur BA99. CA Tr Coll 90 Cranmer Hall Dur 97. **d** 99 **p** 00. C Newc H Cross *Newc* 99-02; V Long Benton St Mary from 02. *St Mary's Vicarage, Blackfriars Way, Newcastle-upon-Tyne NE12 8ST* Tel 0191-266 2326 E-mail revdavegray@aol.com

GRAY, Canon Donald Cecil. b 24. K Coll Lon 46. Linc Th Coll 49. **d** 50 **p** 51. C Abington *Pet* 50-53; C Bedford St Paul *St Alb* 53-56; Chapl Bedf Gen Hosp 53-56; C Wilton Place St Paul *Lon* 56-59; V N Holmwood *Guildf* 59-67; RD Dorking 63-67; Chapl Cobgates Hosp and Farnham Hosp Guildf 67-89; R Farnham 67-89; RD Farnham 69-74; Hon Can Guildf Cathl 71-89; rtd 89; Perm to Offic *Win* from 89. *13 Benenden Green, Alresford SO24 9PE* Tel (01962) 734234

GRAY, Canon Donald Clifford. b 30. CBE98 TD70. Liv Univ MPhil81 Man Univ PhD85 FRHistS88. AKC55. **d** 56 **p** 57. C Leigh St Mary *Man* 56-60; CF (TA) 58-67; V Westleigh St Pet *Man* 60-67; V Elton All SS 67-74; CF (TAVR) 67-77; QHC 74-77; R Liv Our Lady and St Nic w St Anne *Liv* 74-87; RD Liv 75-81; Hon Can Liv Cathl 82-87; Chapl to The Queen 82-00; Can Westmr Abbey 87-98; R Westmr St Marg 87-98; Chapl to Speaker of Ho of Commons 87-98; rtd 98; Perm to Offic *Linc* 98-01. *3 Barn Hill Mews, Stamford PE9 2GN* Tel (01780) 765024 Fax 756183

GRAY, Evan William. b 43. Oak Hill Th Coll 86. **d** 88 **p** 89. C Street w Walton *B & W* 88-92; V Blackpool St Mark *Blackb* 92-03; V Ellel w Shireshead from 03. *The Vicarage, Chapel Lane, Ellel, Lancaster LA2 0PW* Tel (01524) 752017 E-mail sianevan@evan20.freeserve.co.uk

GRAY, Frank Harold Castell. b 14. ALCD41. **d** 41 **p** 42. C Northwood Em *Lon* 41-45; P-in-c Nottingham St Ann *S'well* 45-47; V Gatten St Paul *Portsm* 47-53; V Prestonville St Luke *Chich* 53-66; V Watford St Luke *St Alb* 66-79; rtd 79; Perm to Offic *B & W* 80-98 and from 00. *9 Southwell Close, Trull, Taunton TA3 7EU* Tel (01823) 282567

GRAY, Canon Geoffrey Thomas. b 23. Oak Hill Th Coll 40 and 46. **d** 46 **p** 47. C Havering-atte-Bower *Chelmsf* 46-48; C Dovercourt 48-49; C Ches Square St Mich w St Phil *Lon* 49-51; V Lee Gd Shep *S'wark* 51-56; P-in-c Eltham St Pet 52-56; R Bermondsey St Mary w St Olave and St Jo 56-59; P-in-c Bermondsey St Luke 57-59; V Yalding *Roch* 59-66; RD Malling 64-66; V Gillingham St Mary 66-75; RD Gillingham 66-75; Perm to Offic 75-80; V Strood St Nic w St Mary 80-87; Hon Can Roch Cathl 82-87; Chapl Huggens Coll Northfleet 87-91; rtd 88; Hon Bp's Chapl *Roch* from 90; Hon PV Roch Cathl from 91; Perm to Offic from 00. *Deanery Lodge, The Precinct, Rochester ME1 1TG* Tel (01634) 844165

GRAY, The Ven Hugh Henry James. b 21. TCD BA48 Div Test49 MA64. **d** 49 **p** 50. C Enniscorthy *C & O* 49-51; I Fenagh w Myshall 51-60; I Clonenagh w Roskelton 60-80; Preb Ossory & Leighlin Cathls 70-78; Treas 78-80; Chan 80-83; I Clonenagh w Offerlane, Borris-in-Ossory etc 80-96; Adn Ossory and Leighlin 83-92; rtd 96. *Old Borris Road, Castletown, Mountrath, Co Laois, Irish Republic* Tel (00353) (502) 32196

GRAY (née ROBERTS), Mrs Jennifer. b 55. R Holloway Coll Lon BA76 Ox Univ Inst of Educn PGCE77. St Alb and Ox Min Course 00. **d** 03. NSM Welwyn Garden City *St Alb* from 03. *62 Attimore Road, Welwyn Garden City AL8 6LP* Tel (01707) 321177 E-mail jennygraywgc@aol.com

GRAY, John David Norman. b 38. Oak Hill Th Coll DipHE86. **d** 86 **p** 87. C Portsdown *Portsm* 86-88; C Worthing St Geo *Chich* 88-91; TV Swanborough *Sarum* 91-98; rtd 98; Perm to Offic *Ex* 00-03 and *Portsm* from 03. *15 Charminster Court, 46 Craneswater Park, Southsea PO4 0NU* Tel (023) 9285 1299

GRAY, John Howard. b 39. St Aid Birkenhead 61. **d** 65 **p** 66. C Old Trafford St Cuth *Man* 65-68; C Urmston 68-74; V Oldham Moorside from 74. *The Vicarage, 1 Glebe Lane, Oldham OL1 4SJ* Tel 0161-652 6452

GRAY, Mrs Joy Dora. b 24. SRN46 SCM48 HVCert. Gilmore Ho 79. **dss** 81 **d** 92 **p** 95. Newick *Chich* 81-87; Hon Par Dn 87-94; NSM Fletching 94-98; Perm to Offic from 98. *10 High Hurst Close, Newick, Lewes BN8 4NJ* Tel (01825) 722965

GRAY, Julian Francis. b 64. Univ of Wales (Lamp) BA86. Coll of Resurr Mirfield 86. **d** 88 **p** 89. Min Can St Woolos Cathl *Mon* 88-91; C Newport St Woolos 88-91; C Bassaleg 91-93; V Overmonnow w Wonastow and Michel Troy 93-98; V King's Sutton and Newbottle and Charlton *Pet* 98-00; V Usk and Monkswood w Glascoed Chpl and Gwehelog *Mon* from 00. *The Vicarage, Castle Parade, Usk NP15 1AA* Tel (01291) 672653

GRAY, Malcolm. *See* GRAY, Charles Malcolm

GRAY, The Ven Martin Clifford. b 44. Westcott Ho Cam 78. **d** 80 **p** 81. C Gaywood, Bawsey and Mintlyn *Nor* 80-84; V Sheringham 84-94; P-in-c Lowestoft and Kirkley 94; TR Lowestoft St Marg 94-99; Chapl Lothingland Hosp 95-99; RD Lothingland *Nor* 97-99; Adn Lynn from 99. *Holly Tree House, Whitwell Road, Sparham, Norwich NR9 5PN* Tel (01362) 688032 Fax as telephone E-mail martin.gray@lynnarch.freeserve.co.uk

GRAY, Maurice William Halcro. b 27. Hertf Coll Ox BA48 MA60. Coll of Resurr Mirfield. **d** 60 **p** 61. C Cricklade w Latton *Bris* 60-63; Chapl Ellesmere Coll Shropshire 63-92; Lic to Offic *Lich* 63-93; rtd 92; Hon C Ellesmere *Lich* from 93; RD Ellesmere 95-98. *Finstown, 6 Teal Drive, Ellesmere SY12 9PX* Tel (01691) 623353

GRAY, Melvyn Dixon. b 38. Lon Univ BD86 Dur Univ MA89. NEOC 84. **d** 87 **p** 88. C Richmond w Hudswell *Ripon* 87-90; P-in-c Downholme and Marske 88-90; P-in-c Forcett and Aldbrough and Melsonby 90-91; R 91-00; R Mobberley *Ches* from 00. *The Rectory, Church Lane, Mobberley, Knutsford WA16 7RA* Tel (01565) 873218

GRAY, Neil Kenneth. b 48. Kelham Th Coll 67. **d** 71 **p** 72. C Chorley St Laur *Blackb* 71-74; C S Shore H Trin 74-78; P-in-c Preston St Oswald 78-83; C Blackpool St Steph 83-87; Chapl Bolton HA from 87; Chapl Bolton Hosps NHS Trust from 90; Co-ord Spiritual and Cultural Care from 90. *The Chaplain's Office, Royal Bolton Hospital, Minerva Road, Farnworth, Bolton BL4 0JR* Tel (01204) 390770 *or* 390390 E-mail neil.gray@boltonh-tr.nwest.nhs.uk

GRAY, Neil Ralph. b 53. MA. St Steph Ho Ox. **d** 82 **p** 83. C Kennington St Jo w St Jas *S'wark* 82-85; C Somers Town *Lon* 85-88. *3 Parsonage Close, High Wycombe HP13 6DT* Tel (01494) 531875

GRAY, Mrs Patricia Linda. b 51. Univ of Wales (Swansea) BA73 Chester Coll of HE BTh02. N Ord Course 99. **d** 02. NSM Glazebury w Hollinfare *Liv* from 02. *14 Bollin Close, Culcheth, Warrington WA3 5DU* Tel and fax (01925) 763750 Mobile 07747-772345 E-mail pat.gray@virgin.net

GRAY, Penelope Jane. *See* GRAYSMITH, Mrs Penelope Jane

GRAY, Percy. b 28. OBE94 TD71. Lon Univ BA53 St Cath Soc Ox BA55 MA59. Oak Hill Th Coll. **d** 55 **p** 56. C Sutton *Liv* 55-58; C Chelsea Ch Ch *Lon* 58-59; V Bermondsey St Crispin w Ch Ch *S'wark* 59-99; CF (TA) 59-67; CF (TAVR) from 67; CF (ACF) from 76; rtd 99. *12 King Edward III Mews, Paradise Street, London SE16 4QH*

GRAY, Philip Charles. b 67. Nottm Univ BA91. St Steph Ho Ox 91. **d** 93 **p** 94. C Scarborough St Martin *York* 93-97; TV Leek and Meerbrook *Lich* 97-01; Bp's Dom Chapl *Blackb* from 02. *79 Ribchester Road, Blackburn BB1 9HT* Tel (01254) 248234

GRAY, Philip Thomas. b 41. Lon Univ BA65. Chich Th Coll 66. **d** 68 **p** 69. C Leigh St Clem *Chelmsf* 68-74; P-in-c Wickham Skeith *St E* 86-97; V Mendlesham from 74. *The Vicarage, Old Station Road, Mendlesham, Stowmarket IP14 5RS* Tel (01449) 766359

GRAY, Robert James. b 70. TCD BA92 HDipEd93 MA95 Irish Sch of Ecum MPhil97. CITC 94. **d** 96 **p** 97. C Clooney w Strathfoyle *D & R* 96-99; Hon Sec Gen Synod Cttee for Chr Unity from 98; I Ardamine w Kiltennel, Glascarrig etc *C & O* from 99. *Ardamine Rectory, Courtown Harbour, Gorey, Co Wexford, Irish Republic* Tel and fax (00353) (55) 25423 Mobile 0876-847621 E-mail rjgray@esatclear.ie

GRAY, Sidney Patrick. b 19. Worc Ord Coll. **d** 63 **p** 63. C Skegness *Linc* 63-65; V Dunholme 65-71; R Cliffe at Hoo w Cooling *Roch* 72-75; V Gillingham St Aug 78-84; rtd 84; Perm to Offic *Cant* and *Roch* from 84. *September Cottage, 168 Loose Road, Maidstone ME15 7UD*

GRAY, Stephen James Norman. b 66. Hughes Hall Cam PGCE91. Spurgeon's Coll BA89 Ridley Hall Cam MA00. **d** 00 **p** 01. C Cheltenham Ch Ch *Glouc* from 00; Chapl RN from 03. *Royal Naval Chaplaincy Service, Room 203, Victory Building, HM Naval Base, Portsmouth PO1 3LS* Tel (023) 9272 7903 Fax 9272 7111

GRAY-STACK, Martha Mary Stewart. b 35. QUB BA57. **d** 90 **p** 91. NSM Limerick City *L & K* 90-93; Warden of Readers 90-93; NSM Clara w Liss, Moate and Clonmacnoise *M & K* 93-00; Chapl Kingston Coll Co Cork from 00. *16 Kingston College, Mitchelstown, Co Cork, Irish Republic* Tel (00353) (25) 258 5975 Fax as telephone

GRAYSHON, Matthew Richard. b 47. St Jo Coll Nottm BTh81. **d** 81 **p** 82. C Beverley Minster *York* 81-85; V Hallwood *Ches* 85-93; R Hanwell St Mary w St Chris *Lon* from 93. *The Rectory, 91 Church Road, London W7 3BJ* Tel (020) 8567 6185 Fax 8579 8755 E-mail grayshonstwo@tesco.net

GRAYSHON, Paul Nicholas Walton (Nick). b 50. St Jo Coll Dur 81. **d** 83 **p** 84. C Walkden Moor *Man* 83-87; V Radcliffe St Andr from 87. *St Andrew's Vicarage, St Andrew's View, Radcliffe, Manchester M26 4HE* Tel 0161-723 2427 Fax as telephone E-mail nickgrayshon@btopenworld.com

GRAYSMITH (née GRAY), Mrs Penelope Jane. b 63. SS Hild & Bede Coll Dur BA85 Em Coll Cam MPhil88. Westcott Ho Cam 86. **d** 89 **p** 94. Par Dn Evington *Leic* 89-92; Par Dn Cannock *Lich* 92-94; C 94-96; Chapl Asst Mid Staffs Gen Hosps NHS Trust from 96; Chapl Kath Ho Hospice Stafford from 96. *The Vicarage, 97 Baswich Lane, Stafford ST17 0BN* Tel (01785) 251057 *or* 230930 E-mail graysmit@fish.co.uk

GRAYSMITH, Peter Alexander. b 62. UEA BSc83. Westcott Ho Cam 85. **d** 88 **p** 89. C Tettenhall Regis *Lich* 88-89; C Cannock 89-92; TV 92-99; V Rocester and Croxden w Hollington 99-01; V Baswich from 01. *The Vicarage, 97 Baswich Lane, Stafford ST17 0BN* Tel (01785) 251057 E-mail graysmit@fish.co.uk

GRAYSON, Canon Robert William. b 24. Worc Coll Ox BA48 MA49 DipTh50. Wycliffe Hall Ox 49. **d** 50 **p** 51. C N Meols *Liv* 50-53; India 53-57; P-in-c Litherland St Paul Hatton Hill *Liv* 57-61; V Knowsley 61-66; V Stanwix *Carl* 66-79; RD Carl 71-79; Hon Can Carl Cathl 76-89; V Appleby 79-89; R Ormside 81-89; rtd 89; Perm to Offic *Carl* 89-99; and from 01. *Panorama, North End, Burgh-by-Sands, Carlisle CA5 6BD* Tel (01228) 576863

GRAYSON, Robin John. b 53. Mert Coll Ox BA74 DPhil78. Wycliffe Hall Ox. **d** 02 **p** 03. C Beaconsfield *Ox* from 02. *26 Candlemas Mead, Beaconsfield HP9 1AP* Tel (01494) 675083 Mobile 07801-280475 E-mail r.j.grayson@btinternet.com

GREADY, Andrew John. b 63. Univ Coll Lon BSc84 Newc Univ MA93. St Jo Coll Nottm LTh88 DPS89. **d** 89 **p** 90. C Monkwearmouth St Andr *Dur* 89-92; S Africa 92-99; C Bramley St Cath 92-96; R Sunninghill St Steph 96-99; Chapl St Pet Prep Sch 99; V Shottermill *Guildf* from 00; Chapl Amesbury C of E Jun Sch from 00. *The Vicarage, Vicarage Lane, Shottermill, Haslemere GU27 1LQ* Tel (01428) 645878 Fax 645880 E-mail andrew@greadyfamily.fsnet.co.uk

GREANY, Richard Andrew Hugh. b 44. Qu Coll Ox BA67 MA83. Coll of Resurr Mirfield 67. **d** 69 **p** 70. C Hartlepool St Oswald *Dur* 69-72; C Clifton All SS *Bris* 72-75; Tutor Coll of Resurr Mirfield 75-78; V Whitworth w Spennymoor *Dur* 78-83; P-in-c Byers Green 78-79; Asst Prin St Alb Minl Tr Scheme 83-88; V Flamstead *St Alb* 83-88; V Hessle *York* 88-94; P-in-c Cambridge St Mary Less *Ely* 94-95; V from 95; Dioc Spirituality Officer from 99. *St Mary the Less Vicarage, 4 Newnham Terrace, Cambridge CB3 9EX* Tel (01223) 350733 *or* 366202 E-mail andrew.greany@ely.anglican.org

GREANY, Mrs Virginia Clare. b 52. Bris Univ BA74 PGCE75 Hull Univ Dip Counselling 93 MSc94. Westcott Ho Cam 96 EAMTC 97. **d** 98. Bp's Dn to Local Government *Ely* from 98; Asst to Dean Trin Hall Cam from 98. *St Mary the Less Vicarage, 4 Newnham Terrace, Cambridge CB3 9EX* Tel (01223) 350733 *or* 332500

GREAR, Hugh Massey. b 60. Bris Univ LLB82. SEITE. **d** 00 **p** 01. C Warlingham w Chelsham and Farleigh *S'wark* from 00. *243 Tithe Pit Shaw Lane, Warlingham CR6 9AW* Tel (020) 8949 5654 E-mail hughgrear@x-stream.co.uk

GREASLEY, James Kenneth. b 39. K Coll Lon BD AKC66. **d** 67 **p** 68. C Stoke upon Trent *Lich* 67-70; Zambia 70-76; Chapl HM Borstal Gaynes Hall 76-81; V Gt Staughton *Ely* 76-81; V Melbourn 81-96; V Meldreth 81-96; RD Shingay 82-96; R Chalfont St Peter *Ox* from 96. *The Vicarage, 4 Austenway, Gerrards Cross SL9 8NW* Tel (01753) 882389 E-mail jk.greasley@btinternet.com

GREATBATCH, John Charles. b 56. BA. Coll of Resurr Mirfield. **d** 83 **p** 84. C Wednesbury St Paul Wood Green *Lich* 83-88; C Codsall 88-94; V Tipton St Jo 94-97; V Charlestown *Truro* from 97; Chapl Cornwall Healthcare Trust from 98. *The Vicarage, 19 Appletree Lane, St Austell PL25 3QB* Tel (01726) 812824 Fax 816711 E-mail john@obadiah19.fsnet.co.uk

GREATREX, Richard Quintin. b 65. K Coll Lon BD86 Surrey Univ BA02. STETS 99. **d** 02 **p** 03. NSM Westbury-on-Trym St Alb *Bris* from 02. *The Garden Flat, 97B Pembroke Road, Clifton, Bristol BS8 3EE* Tel 0117-974 3607

GREATREX, Warren Robert. b 20. Qu Univ Kingston Ontario BCom41. Trin Coll Toronto LTh50 BD51. **d** 50 **p** 51. Canada 50-78; Perm to Offic *Heref* 78-98; *Ely* from 99. *16 Westberry Court, Cambridge CB3 9BG* Tel (01223) 369335

GREAVES, Canon John Neville. b 29. Lon Univ DipTh60 Newc Univ MA96 Dur Univ MLitt03 AAAI56. St Aid Birkenhead 58. **d** 61 **p** 62. C Pendleton St Ambrose *Man* 61-62; P-in-c 62-63; C Benchill 63-65; C-in-c Wythenshawe St Rich CD 65-71; V Wythenshawe St Rich 71-73; R Sandbar *Dur* 73-78; V Dur St Cuth 78-94; Chapl New Coll Dur 78-92; Lect NEOC 79-84; Chapl Dur Co Fire Brigade 85-94; RD Dur 80-93; Hon Can Dur Cathl 91-94; rtd 94; Perm to Offic *Ches* 94-97; P-in-c Salt and Sandon w Burston *Lich* 97-00; Past Aux Eccleshall Deanery 00-01; Perm to Offic *Lich* 01-02 and *Heref* from 03. *3 Sitwell Close, Bucknell SY7 0DD* Tel (01547) 530152

GREED, Frederick John. b 44. Trin Coll Bris 79. **d** 81 **p** 82. C Yateley *Win* 81-85; R Ore *Chich* 85-95; R Street w Walton *B & W* from 95. *The Rectory, Vestry Close, Street BA16 0HZ* Tel (01458) 442671 E-mail john.greed@tesco.net

GREEDY, Tegryd Joseph. b 31. St D Coll Lamp 59. **d** 61 **p** 62. C Newbridge *Mon* 61-64; C Bassaleg 64-66; V Newport St Teilo 66-74; Hon C Newport St Mark 80-83; V Goldcliffe and Whitson and Nash 83-90; Ind Chapl 83-90; V Marshfield and Peterstone Wentloog etc 90-96; rtd 96. *42 Churchward Drive, Newport NP19 4SB* Tel (01633) 282159

GREEN, Alan John Enrique. b 56. Worc Coll Ox BA78 MA83. Linc Th Coll 83. **d** 85 **p** 86. C Kirkby *Liv* 85-88; TV 88-94; Chapl Knowsley Community Coll 87-90; Chapl Worc Coll Ox 94-98; C Ox St Giles and SS Phil and Jas w St Marg *Ox* 94-98; TR St Jo on Bethnal Green *Lon* from 98. *St John's Rectory, 30 Victoria Park Square, London E2 9PB* Tel (020) 8980 1742 Fax as telephone E-mail alan.green@virgin.net

GREEN, Canon Alan Thomas. b 21. Launde Abbey. **d** 64 **p** 65. C Loughborough All SS *Leic* 64-67; V Oaks (Charnwood Forest) 67-70; R Braunstone 70-74; P-in-c Loddington 74-83; Hon Can Leic Cathl 78-87; P-in-c Knossington and Cold Overton 81-83; P-in-c Owston and Withcote 81-83; V Enderby w Lubbesthorpe and Thurlaston 83-87; rtd 87; Perm to Offic *Leic* from 87. *22 Main Street, Cold Overton, Oakham LE15 7QA* Tel 0116-445 4345

GREEN, Anthony Brian. b 39. Birm Univ CertEd60 Coll of Preceptors ACP66 Sussex Univ MA88 Brighton Univ DipRE95. Bps' Coll Cheshunt 64. **d** 64 **p** 65. C Batheaston w St Cath *B & W* 64-67; Chapl Aiglon Coll and Villars *Eur* 67-71; Hd Master Battisborough Sch Holbeton 71-81; Perm to Offic *Ex* 71-81; *Worc* 81-83 and *Glouc* 83-96; Chapl R Gr Sch Worc 81-83; Hd Master Frewen Coll Rye 83-96; P-in-c New Groombridge *Chich* from 97. *The Vicarage, Corsley Road, Groombridge, Tunbridge Wells TN3 9SE* Tel (01892) 864265 Fax as telephone E-mail fidgreen@aol.com

GREEN, Arthur Edward. b 27. Chich Th Coll 58. **d** 59 **p** 60. C Malden St Jas *S'wark* 59-62; C Caterham 62-67; R Burgh Parva w Briston *Nor* 67-75; V Middleton 75-76; V Middleton w E Winch 76-84; R Neatishead w Irstead 84-90; V Barton Turf 84-90; R Neatishead, Barton Turf and Irstead 90-92; rtd 92; Perm to Offic *Portsm* from 92. *10 James Butcher Court, 16 Eastern Villas Road, Southsea PO4 0TD* Tel (023) 9275 0701

GREEN, Barrie. b 51. SS Coll Cam BA72 MA76. Wycliffe Hall Ox 75. **d** 78 **p** 79. C Castle Vale *Birm* 78-81; V W Heath 81-96; RD Kings Norton 87-95; TR Dronfield w Holmesfield *Derby* from 96. *The Rectory, Church Street, Dronfield S18 1QB* Tel (01246) 411531 *or* 412328 Fax 08707-065540 E-mail barrie.green@dwhparish.org.uk

GREEN, Benedict. *See* GREEN, Humphrey Christian

GREEN, Brian Robert. b 31. Bris Univ BA55. Tyndale Hall Bris 52. **d** 56 **p** 57. C Toxteth Park St Philemon *Liv* 56-58; V Toxteth Park St Philemon w St Silas 58-69; P-in-c Toxteth Park St Gabr 64-69; P-in-c Toxteth Park St Jo and St Thos 64-69; P-in-c Toxteth Park St Jas and St Matt 68-69; V Elsenham *Chelmsf* 69-85; V Henham 69-85; P-in-c Ugley 84-85; V Henham and Elsenham w Ugley 85-89; RD Newport and Stansted 87-89; Perm to Offic *Ex* 90-91; V Tidenham w Beachley and Lancaut *Glouc* 91-97; RD Forest S 95-97; rtd 97; Perm to Offic *Ex* from 97. *1 The Square, Offwell, Honiton EX14 9SA* Tel (01404) 831795

GREEN, Mrs Catherine Isabel. b 48. Cant Sch of Min 89. **d** 92 **p** 94. C Willesborough *Cant* 92-96; Sen Asst P E Dereham and Scarning *Nor* 96-97; Asst Chapl HM Pris Wayland 96-97; Chapl HM Pris Leic 97-00; Chapl HM YOI Castington 00-02; Chapl HM Pris Cant from 02. *The Chaplain's Office, HM Prison, 46 Longport, Canterbury CT1 1PJ* Tel (01227) 862863

GREEN, Christopher Frederick. b 46. Nottm Univ BTh75 Birm Univ DipEd85 Univ of Wales (Abth) MEd94. Bp Otter Coll CertEd69 Linc Th Coll 71. **d** 75 **p** 76. C Hodge Hill *Birm* 75-77; C S Lafford *Linc* 77-79; P-in-c Worc St Mich *Worc* 79-82; Hd RS and Lib RNIB New Coll Worc 82-96; V Clipstone *S'well* 96-02; rtd 02. *Cobwebs, Middlefarm Lane, Glentham, Market Rasen LN8 2ET* Tel (01673) 878633

GREEN, Christopher Martyn. b 58. New Coll Edin BD80. Cranmer Hall Dur 82. **d** 83 **p** 84. C Virginia Water *Guildf* 83-87; C Bromley Ch Ch *Roch* 87-91; Study Asst the Proclamation Trust 91-92; C Surbiton Hill Ch Ch *S'wark* 92-00; Vice Prin Oak Hill Th Coll from 00. *Oak Hill Theological College, Chase Side, London N14 4PS* Tel (020) 8449 0467 *or* 8441 0315

GREEN, Mrs Clare Noreen. b 30. SW Minl Tr Course 84. **d** 88. NSM Bideford *Ex* 88-90; Perm to Offic from 90. *6 Balmoral Gardens, Topsham, Exeter EX3 0DJ* Tel (01392) 875118

GREEN, Daphne Mary. b 55. K Coll Cam BA77 Bradf Univ MBA91 Leeds Univ PhD01 Lon Inst of Educn PGCE79. N Ord Course 95. **d** 98 **p** 99. C Headingley *Ripon* 98-02; Chapl Leeds Metrop Univ 00-02; R Stanningley St Thos from 02. *50 Lane End, Pudsey LS28 9AD* Tel 0113-255 0909 Mobile 07796-084264 Fax 0113-255 0910 E-mail daphne@stanningleyparish.org.uk

GREEN, David Allen. b 61. Sheff City Poly BA90. Cranmer Hall Dur 00. **d** 02 **p** 03. C Huyton St Geo *Liv* from 02. *31 Endmoor Road, Huyton, Liverpool L36 3UH* Tel 0151-489 4086

GREEN, David John. b 54. DCR, MU. SW Minl Tr Course 82. **d** 85 **p** 86. C St Marychurch *Ex* 85-89; C Laira 89-90; V Maughold *S & M* from 90; RD Ramsey from 98. *The Vicarage, Maughold, Isle of Man IM7 1AS* Tel (01624) 812070 E-mail dgreen@mcb.net

GREEN, David Norman. b 37. Magd Coll Cam BA60. Clifton Th Coll 60. **d** 62 **p** 63. SSF from 55; C Islington St Mary *Lon* 62-65; C Burley *Ripon* 65-68; Kenya 69-80; P-in-c Brimscombe *Glouc* 81-90; R Woodchester and Brimscombe 90-96; P-in-c Coberley w Cowley 96-97; P-in-c Colesborne 96-97; P-in-c Coberley, Cowley, Colesbourne and Elkstone from 97; Dioc Rural Adv from 96. *The Rectory, Cowley, Cheltenham GL53 9NJ* Tel (01242) 870232 E-mail glosrural@star.uk

GREEN, David William. b 53. CertEd75 Nottm Univ BCombStuds84. Linc Th Coll 81. **d** 84 **p** 85. C S Merstham *S'wark* 84-88; C Walton-on-Thames *Guildf* 88-91; V Gillingham H Trin *Roch* 91-99; Chapl Lennox Wood Elderly People's Home 91-99; V Strood St Nic w St Mary from 99. *The Vicarage, 3 Central Road, Strood, Rochester ME2 3HF* Tel (01634) 719052

GREEN, Canon Derek George Wilson. b 27. Bris Univ BA53 MA58. Tyndale Hall Bris 48. **d** 53 **p** 54. C Weymouth St Mary *Sarum* 53-55; Chapl RAF 55-58; R N Pickenham w Houghton on the Hill *Nor* 58-89; R S Pickenham 58-89; R N Pickenham w S Pickenham etc 89-93; Hon Can Nor Cathl 78-93; E Region Co-ord Scripture Union 80-92; rtd 93; Perm to Offic *Sarum* from 93. *5 Hawkins Meadow, College Fields, Marlborough SN8 1UA* Tel (01672) 511713

GREEN, Donald Henry. b 31. Selw Coll Cam BA54 Lon Inst of Educn PGCE55. Qu Coll Birm 81. **d** 83 **p** 84. C Dudley St Aug Holly Hall *Worc* 83-85; V Dudley St Barn 85-90; rtd 96. *The Cuckoo's Nest, 12 Mill Green, Knighton LD7 1EE* Tel (01547) 528289

GREEN, Donald Pentney (Brother Donald). b 25. Leeds Univ BA50. Coll of Resurr Mirfield 50. **d** 52 **p** 53. C Ardwick St Benedict *Man* 52-55; SSF from 55; Sec for Miss SSF 78-96; Lic to Offic *Chelmsf* 58-60 and 69-72; Papua New Guinea 60-63; Chapl HM Pris Kingston (Portsm) 72-76; Lic to Offic *Edin* 76-77; Org Sec Catholic Renewal 77; Lic to Offic *Lich* from 78; rtd 95. *85 Crofton Road, London E13 8QT* Tel (020) 7474 5863

GREEN, Mrs Dorothy Mary. b 36. Westf Coll Lon BA58. Selly Oak Coll 90. **dss** 83 **d** 87 **p** 94. Ryde All SS *Portsm* 83-87; C 87-91; Hon C Hempnall *Nor* 91-96; rtd 96; Perm to Offic *B & W* from 97. *Oneida, Charnwood Drive, Cheddar BS27 3HD* Tel (01934) 742167

GREEN, Douglas Edward. b 17. Sarum Th Coll 47. **d** 50 **p** 51. C Glouc St Paul *Glouc* 50-53; C Malvern Link St Matthias *Worc* 53-56; R Tolladine 56-58; V Bosbury *Heref* 58-78; R Coddington 59-79; V Wellington Heath 59-79; Hon C Minsterley 78-80; rtd 82; Perm to Offic *Worc* from 83. *21 The Quadrangle, Newland, Malvern WR13 5AX*

GREEN, Canon Duncan Jamie. b 52. Sarum & Wells Th Coll 82. **d** 84 **p** 85. C Uckfield *Chich* 84-87; Dioc Youth Officer *Chelmsf* 87-96; Warden and Chapl St Mark's Coll Res Cen 93-96; TR Saffron Walden w Wendens Ambo, Littlebury etc from 96; Hon Can Chelmsf Cathl from 03. *The Rectory, 17 Borough Lane, Saffron Walden CB11 4AG* Tel (01799) 500947 E-mail rector.saffronwalden@ntlworld.com

GREEN, Edward John. b 35. Lich Th Coll. **d** 59 **p** 60. C Longford *Cov* 59-61; C Wigston Magna *Leic* 61-65; V 73-00; V Ellistown 65-73; rtd 00; Perm to Offic *Leic* 00-03. *Holly Mount, 27 Greendale Road, Glen Parva, Leicester LE2 9HD* Tel 0116-277 2479

GREEN, Edward Marcus. b 66. Mert Coll Ox BA88 MA92. Wycliffe Hall Ox 90. **d** 94 **p** 95. C Glyncorrwg w Afan Vale and Cymmer Afan *Llan* 94-96; C Aberystwyth *St D* 96-99; P-in-c Pontypridd St Cath w St Matt *Llan* 00-01; V Pontypridd St Cath from 01. *St Catherine's Vicarage, Gelliwastad Grove, Pontypridd CF37 2BS* Tel (01443) 402021 E-mail marcusgreen@manutd.com

GREEN, Canon Edward Michael Bankes. b 30. Ex Coll Ox BA53 MA56 Qu Coll Cam BA57 MA61 BD66 Toronto Univ DD92 Lambeth DD96. Ridley Hall Cam 55. **d** 57 **p** 58. C Eastbourne H Trin *Chich* 57-60; Tutor Lon Coll of Div 60-69; Prin St Jo Coll Nottm 69-75; Hon Can Cov Cathl *Cov* 70-78; R Ox St Aldate w H Trin *Ox* 75-82; R Ox St Aldate w St Matt 82-86; Canada 87-92; Prof Evang Regent Coll Vancouver 87-92; Abps' Adv Springboard for Decade of Evang 92-96; Six Preacher Cant Cathl *Cant* 93-99; rtd 96; Sen Research Fell Wycliffe Hall Ox from 97; Perm to Offic *Ox* from 99. *7 Little Acreage, Marston, Oxford OX3 0PS* Tel (01865) 248387

GREEN, Mrs Elizabeth Pauline Anne. b 29. Lon Coll of Div DipRK70. **dss** 76 **d** 87 **p** 94. Chorleywood Ch Ch *St Alb* 76-87; Par Dn 87-90; C Chipping Sodbury and Old Sodbury *Glouc* 90-95; Asst Dioc Missr 90-95; rtd 95; NSM Chipping Sodbury and Old Sodbury *Glouc* 95-99; Perm to Offic *Glouc; Bris* from 99. *The Old House, The Common, Chipping Sodbury, Bristol BS37 6PX* Tel (01454) 311936 E-mail p.green@care4free.net

GREEN, Eric Kenneth. b 18. Tyndale Hall Bris 40. **d** 45 **p** 47. C Heatherlands St Jo *Sarum* 45-48; C Radipole 48-49; C Bucknall and Bagnall *Lich* 49-50; V Halwell w Moreleigh *Ex* 50-53; V Wakef St Mary *Wakef* 53-55; R Peldon *Chelmsf* 55-57; P-in-c Leaden Roding 57-58; R 58-63; V Aythorpe Roding and High Roding 60-63; R All Cannings w Etchilhampton *Sarum* 63-75; V Over Kellet *Blackb* 75-83; rtd 83; Perm to Offic *Bradf* 91-98. *1 Capel Court, The Burgage, Prestbury, Cheltenham GL52 3EL*

GREEN, Ernest James. b 31. Pemb Coll Cam BA55 MA62. Linc Th Coll 55. **d** 57 **p** 58. C Rawmarsh *Sheff* 57-60; Sec Th Colls Dept SCM 60-62; Prec and Sacr Bris Cathl *Bris* 62-65; Min Can 62-65; V Churchill *B & W* 65-78; RD Locking 72-78; V Burrington and Churchill 78-82; Preb Wells Cathl 81-82; V Ryde All SS *Portsm* 82-91; P-in-c Ryde H Trin 82-86; RD E Wight 83-88; TR Hempnall *Nor* 91-96; rtd 96; Perm to Offic *B & W* from 97. *Oneida, Charnwood Drive, Cheddar BS27 3HD* Tel (01934) 742167 E-mail egreen@fish.co.uk

GREEN, Fleur Estelle. b 72. Univ of Wales (Ban) BD94. Ripon Coll Cuddesdon DipMin95. **d** 97 **p** 98. C Blackpool St Jo *Blackb* 97-00; C Lancaster St Mary w St John and St Anne from 00. *10 Croasdale Close, Carnforth LA5 9NN* Tel (01524) 730760

GREEN, Frank Gilbert. b 23. Kelham Th Coll 46. **d** 50 **p** 51. C Sheff Parson Cross St Cecilia *Sheff* 50-56; SSM from 52; C Nottingham St Geo w St Jo *S'well* 56-58; Basutoland 59-62; S Africa 62-69 and 84-88; Lesotho 69-84; Lic to Offic *Ox* from 88; rtd 93. *Society of the Sacred Mission, 1 Linford Lane, Willen, Milton Keynes MK15 9DL* Tel (01908) 234546

GREEN, Gareth David. b 60. Worc Coll Ox BA82 MA86 FRCO79 FLCM87 ARCM75 Leeds Univ MA98. N Ord Course 94. **d** 97 **p** 98. NSM Lupset *Wakef* 97-00; V W Ardsley 00-03. *Address temp unknown* E-mail gareth@gareth73.freeserve.co.uk

GREEN, Gary Henry. b 64. Univ of Wales (Cardiff) BD87. St Mich Coll Llan 93. **d** 95 **p** 96. C Baglan *Llan* 95-97; C Neath w Llantwit 97-01; TV Neath 01-02; V Llangiwg *S & B* from 02. *The Vicarage, 10 Uplands Road, Pontardawe, Swansea SA8 4AH* Tel (01792) 862003

GREEN, George James. b 26. Cuddesdon Coll 69. **d** 69 **p** 70. C Handsworth St Mary *Birm* 69-76; R Croughton w Evenley *Pet* 76-88; R Aynho and Croughton w Evenley 88-95; rtd 95; Perm to Offic *Cov* from 95. *Dibbinsdale, Langley Road, Claverdon, Warwick CV35 8PU*

GREEN, Gloria. STETS. **d** 03. NSM Jersey St Brelade *Win* from 03. *29 La Rue Verte, Mont es Croix, St Brelade, Jersey JE3 8EL* Tel (01534) 744804

GREEN, Gordon Sydney. b 33. Ridley Hall Cam 77. **d** 79 **p** 80. C Ipswich St Marg *St E* 79-83; TV Barton Mills, Beck Row w Kenny Hill etc 83-85; TV Mildenhall 85-86; Perm to Offic *Pet* from 87; rtd 88. *65 Orwell View Road, Shotley Street, Ipswich IP9 1NW* Tel (01473) 787303

GREEN, Graham Herbert. b 53. City Univ BSc74. Westcott Ho Cam 75. **d** 78 **p** 79. C Hatcham St Cath *S'wark* 78-82; C S Ashford Ch Ch *Cant* 82-88; V Cheriton All So w Newington 88-97; P-in-c Milton next Sittingbourne 97-02; V from 02. *The Vicarage, Vicarage Road, Milton Regis, Sittingbourne ME10 2BL* Tel (01795) 472016 E-mail graham@green90.fsnet.co.uk

GREEN, Graham Reginald. b 48. Sarum & Wells Th Coll 71. **d** 74 **p** 75. C Chorley St Laur *Blackb* 74-76; C Padiham 76-79; V Osmondthorpe St Phil *Ripon* 79-94. *3 Northwood Gardens, Colton, Leeds LS15 9HH* Tel 0113-264 3558

GREEN, Humphrey Christian (Father Benedict). b 24. Mert Coll Ox BA49 MA52. Cuddesdon Coll 50. **d** 51 **p** 82. C Northolt St Mary *Lon* 51-56; Lect Th K Coll Lon 56-60; Lic to Offic *Wakef* from 61; CR from 62; Vice-Prin Coll of Resurr Mirfield 65-75; Prin 75-84; rtd 94. *House of the Resurrection, Stocks Bank Road, Mirfield WF14 0BN* Tel (01924) 494318

GREEN, Imogen Elizabeth. See VIBERT, Imogen Elizabeth

GREEN, Miss Jennifer Mary. b 55. SEN78 SRN81 RM84. Trin Coll Bris DipHE88 ADPS89. **d** 90 **p** 95. C Tong *Bradf* 90-93; Chapl Bradf Cathl 93; CMS from 94; Uganda from 94. *Muhabura Diocese, PO Box 22, Kisoro, Uganda*

GREEN, Jeremy Nigel. b 52. St Andr Univ MA Nottm Univ DipTh. St Jo Coll Nottm 80. **d** 83 **p** 84. C Dorridge *Birm* 83-86; V Scrooby *S'well* 86-94; V Bawtry w Austerfield and Misson from 94; AD Bawtry from 01. *The Vicarage, Martin Lane, Bawtry, Doncaster DN10 6NJ* Tel (01302) 710298

GREEN, John. See GREEN, William John

GREEN, John. See GREEN, Edward John

GREEN, John. b 28. AKC54. **d** 55 **p** 56. C Poulton-le-Fylde *Blackb* 55-57; C St Annes 57-63; V Inskip 63-75; V Fairhaven 75-87; rtd 87; Perm to Offic *Blackb* from 87. *42 Westwood Road, Lytham, Lytham St Annes FY8 5NX* Tel (01253) 735828

GREEN, John. b 53. Nottm Univ BCombStuds83. Linc Th Coll 80. **d** 83 **p** 84. C Watford St Mich *St Alb* 83-86; C St Alb St Steph 86-91; Chapl RN from 91. *Royal Naval Chaplaincy Service, Room 203, Victory Building, HM Naval Base, Portsmouth PO1 3LS* Tel (023) 9272 7903 Fax 9272 7111

GREEN, John David. b 29. Lon Univ. Roch Th Coll 63. **d** 66 **p** 66. C Roch St Pet w St Marg *Roch* 66-72; V Oxshott *Guildf* 72-85; R Weybridge 85-94; rtd 94; Perm to Offic *Guildf* from 94. *103 Bitterne Drive, Woking GU21 3JX* Tel (01483) 727936

GREEN, John Francis Humphrey. b 44. Ex Univ BA65 Heythrop Coll Lon MA96. Westcott Ho Cam CTM93. **d** 93 **p** 94. C Tadworth *S'wark* 93-96; Chapl St Geo Sch Harpenden 96-01; P-in-c Flamstead *St Alb* from 01; P-in-c Markyate Street from 01. *The Vicarage, 50 Trowley Hill Road, Flamstead, St Albans AL3 8EE* Tel (01582) 842040

GREEN, Canon John Henry. b 44. K Coll Lon BD72 AKC. **d** 73 **p** 74. C Tupsley *Heref* 73-77; Asst Chapl Newc Univ *Newc* 77-79; V Stevenage St Hugh Chells *St Alb* 79-85; V St Jo in Bedwardine *Worc* 85-92; P-in-c Guarlford and Madresfield w Newland 92-99; Dir of Ords from 92; Hon Can Worc Cathl from 94; C Fladbury w Wyre Piddle and Moor etc from 99. *The Vicarage, Main Street, Cropthorne, Pershore WR10 3NB* Tel (01386) 861304

GREEN, John Herbert Gardner-Waterman. b 21. Trin Hall Cam BA48 MA58. Wells Th Coll 58. **d** 59 **p** 60. C New Romney w Hope *Cant* 59-63; V Hartlip 63-68; R Sandhurst w Newenden 68-90; RD W Charing 74-81; rtd 90; Perm to Offic *Cant* from 90 and *Chich* from 98. *Littlefield House, Maytham Road, Rolvenden Layne, Cranbrook TN17 4NS* Tel (01580) 241579

GREEN, Preb John Stanley. b 12. Keble Coll Ox BA33 MA37. Wells Th Coll 33. **d** 35 **p** 36. C Stockport St Matt *Ches* 35-39; C Bournemouth St Mary *Win* 39-46; PV Ex Cathl 46-49; Dep PV 49-77; R Ex St Jas 49-77; Preb Ex Cathl 69-84; rtd 77; Perm to Offic *Ex* from 84. *2 Whiteway Drive, Heavitree, Exeter EX1 3AN* Tel (01392) 437291

GREEN, Joseph Hudson. b 28. TD76. Dur Univ TCert73. Kelham Th Coll 48. **d** 53 **p** 54. C Norton St Mich *Dur* 53-56; C Heworth St Mary 56-62; V Harton Colliery 62-69; Chapl S Shields Gen Hosp 62-69; CF (TA) 63-67; CF (TAVR) 67-77; V Leadgate *Dur* 69-78; V Dudleston *Lich* 78-85; V Criftins 78-85; R Hodnet w Weston under Redcastle 85-93; RD Hodnet 86-93; rtd 93; Perm to Offic *Lich* from 93. *3 The Paddocks, Market Drayton TF9 3UE* Tel (01630) 658887

GREEN, Julia Ann. See CARTWRIGHT, Julia Ann

GREEN, Miss Karina Beverley. b 61. Ripon Coll Cuddesdon 87. **d** 90 **p** 94. C Lee-on-the-Solent *Portsm* 90-93; Dioc Youth Officer *Guildf* 94-99; Youth and Children's Work Adv *Portsm* 99-03; P-in-c Portsea St Geo from 03; CME Officer from 03. *The Vicarage, 8 Queen Street, Portsmouth PO1 3HL* Tel (023) 9283 8713 E-mail youth@portsmouth.anglican.org

✠**GREEN, The Rt Revd Laurence Alexander.** b 45. K Coll Lon BD68 AKC68. DMin82 NY Th Sem STM69 St Aug Coll Cant 70. **d** 70 **p** 71 **c** 93. C Kingstanding St Mark *Birm* 70-73; V Erdington St Chad 73-83; Prin Aston Tr Scheme 83-89; Hon C Birchfield *Birm* 84-89; TR Poplar *Lon* 89-93; Area Bp Bradwell *Chelmsf* from 93. *The Bishop's House, Orsett Road, Horndon-on-the-Hill, Stanford-le-Hope SS17 8NS* Tel (01375) 673806 Fax 674222 E-mail lauriegr@globalnet.co.uk

GREEN, Mrs Linda Anne. b 60. Avery Hill Coll DipHE84. Westcott Ho Cam 84. **dss** 86 **d** 87 **p** 94. Borehamwood *St Alb* 86-89; Par Dn 87-89; Par Dn Sheff St Cuth *Sheff* 89-90; Chapl Asst N Gen Hosp Sheff 89-90; Chapl Qu Mary's Sidcup NHS Trust from 96. *Queen Mary's Hospital, Frognal Avenue, Sidcup DA14 6LT* Tel (020) 8302 2678

GREEN, Marcus. See GREEN, Edward Marcus

GREEN, Mrs Margaret Elizabeth. b 34. DipYL65. St Mich Ho Ox 60. **dss** 84 **d** 87 **p** 94. Ecclesall *Sheff* 84-87; Par Dn 87-90; C Doncaster St Jas 90-94; rtd 95; Perm to Offic *Sheff* from 95. *91 Littemoor Lane, Doncaster DN4 0LQ* Tel (01302) 365884

✠**GREEN, The Rt Revd Mark.** b 17. MC45. Linc Coll Ox BA40 MA44 Aston Univ Hon DSc80. Cuddesdon Coll 40. **d** 40 **p** 41 **c** 72. C Glouc St Cath *Glouc* 40-42; CF (EC) 43-46; V Newland St Jo *York* 48-53; CF 53-56; V S Bank *York* 56-58; R Cottingham 58-64; Can and Preb York Minster 63-72; Hon Chapl to Abp York 64-72; V Bishopthorpe 64-72; V Acaster Malbis 64-72; RD Ainsty 64-72; Suff Bp Aston *Birm* 72-82; Dioc Dir of Ords 80-82; rtd 82; Asst Bp Chich from 82. *27 Selwyn House, Selwyn Road, Eastbourne BN21 2LF* Tel (01323) 642707

GREEN, Martin Charles. b 59. Bris Univ BA81 MPhil86. Wycliffe Hall Ox 82. **d** 84 **p** 85. C Margate H Trin *Cant* 84-88; V Kingston upon Hull St Aid Southcoates *York* 88-94; P-in-c Bishop's Itchington *Cov* from 94; Dioc Children's Officer from 94. *The Vicarage, Bishop's Itchington, Leamington Spa CV47 2QJ* Tel (01926) 613466 E-mail revmcg@aol.com

GREEN, Martyn. b 41. FCA. Ridley Hall Cam 78. **d** 80 **p** 81. C Wetherby *Ripon* 80-83; V Leeds St Cypr Harehills 83-90; V Ossett cum Gawthorpe *Wakef* 90-99; TR Haxby w Wigginton *York* from 99. *The Rectory, 3 Westfield Close, Wigginton, York YO32 2JG* Tel (01904) 760455 Fax as telephone

GREEN, Mrs Maureen. b 49. Avery Hill Coll CertEd70 Lon Univ BEd71. EAMTC 95. **d** 98 **p** 02. NSM Ipswich St Jo *St E* from 98; Asst Chapl Ipswich Hosp NHS Trust from 98; Asst Chapl Local Health Partnerships NHS Trust 98-02; Asst Chapl Cen Suffolk Primary Care Trust from 02. *Rose Cottage, 41 Cowper Street, Ipswich IP4 5JB* Tel (01473) 434330 E-mail maureengreen@talk21.com

GREEN, Canon Maurice Paul. b 34. MCIMA60. Wells Th Coll 68. **d** 70 **p** 71. C Eaton *Nor* 70-74; R N w S Wootton 74-90; RD Lynn 83-89; Hon Can Nor Cathl 88-96; V Swaffham 90-96; rtd

96; Perm to Offic *St E* from 96. *6 Wimborne Avenue, Ipswich IP3 8QW* Tel (01473) 711061

GREEN, Michael. *See* GREEN, Canon Edward Michael Bankes

GREEN, Muriel Hilda. b 38. SEITE 94. **d** 96 **p** 97. NSM Ealing St Barn *Lon* 96-98; C 98-00; rtd 00; Hon C Elmstead *Chelmsf* from 00. *3 Laurence Close, Elmstead Market, Colchester CO7 7EJ* Tel (01206) 825401
E-mail murielgreen@onetel.net.uk

GREEN, Neil Howard. b 57. New Coll Ox BA80 PGCE81. Wycliffe Hall Ox 87. **d** 90 **p** 91. C Finchley St Paul and St Luke *Lon* 90-94; C Muswell Hill St Jas w St Matt 94-98; V Eastbourne All So *Chich* from 98. *The Vicarage, 53 Susan's Road, Eastbourne BN21 3TH* Tel (01323) 731366

GREEN, Norman. b 20. St Pet Hall Ox BA48 BCL50 MA53. Wycliffe Hall Ox 51. **d** 52 **p** 53. C Mossley Hill St Matt and St Jas *Liv* 52-55; Chapl Liv Coll 55-64; Prin Cathl Sch Lahore Pakistan 64-70; Chapl R Masonic Sch for Girls Rickmansworth 70-80; Prin Edwardes Coll Pakistan 80-82; rtd 82; Perm to Offic *B & W* from 82. *Badgers' Way, Holton, Wincanton BA9 8AL* Tel (01963) 33363

GREEN, Paul. b 25. RD. Sarum & Wells Th Coll 72. **d** 74 **p** 75. C Pinhoe *Ex* 74-77; P-in-c 77-79; V 79-85; P-in-c Bishopsteignton 85-88; P-in-c Ideford, Luton and Ashcombe 85-88; rtd 88; Perm to Offic *Ex* from 88. *58 Maudlin Drive, Teignmouth TQ14 8SB* Tel (01626) 777312

GREEN, Paul John. b 48. Sarum & Wells Th Coll 72. **d** 73 **p** 74. C Tuffley *Glouc* 73-76; C Prestbury 76-82; P-in-c Highnam w Lassington and Rudford 82-83; P-in-c Tibberton w Taynton 82-83; R Highnam, Lassington, Rudford, Tibberton etc 84-92; Hon Min Can Glouc Cathl 85-96; V Fairford 92-96; RD Fairford 93-96; rtd 96; Perm to Offic *Glouc* from 98. *19 Prices Road, Abbeymead, Gloucester GL4 4PD* Tel (01452) 614259

GREEN, Pauline. *See* GREEN, Mrs Elizabeth Pauline Anne

GREEN, Peter. b 38. Ex Univ BSc59. Sarum Th Coll 59. **d** 61 **p** 62. C Romford St Edw *Chelmsf* 61-66; Chapl Trin Coll Kandy Ceylon 66-70; V Darnall *Sheff* 71-80; TV Stantonbury *Ox* 80-87; TV Stantonbury and Willen 87-91; Dep Chapl HM Pris Belmarsh 91-92; Chapl HM Pris Woodhill 92-03; rtd 03. *34 North Twelfth Street, Milton Keynes MK9 3BT* Tel (01908) 240634 Mobile 07808-556213 Fax (01908) 240635
E-mail petergspp@aol.com

GREEN, Canon Peter Edwin. b 33. Lich Th Coll. **d** 62 **p** 63. C Sprowston *Nor* 62-65; C-in-c Heartsease St Fran CD 65-73; V Loddon w Sisland 73-91; Hon Can Nor Cathl 86-92; rtd 92; Perm to Offic *Nor* 92-96; Perm to Offic *St E* from 96. *Ambleside, Lowestoft Road, Beccles NR34 7DG* Tel (01502) 717740

GREEN, Peter Geoffrey. b 59. St Andr Univ MA83 Open Univ MA01. Coll of Resurr Mirfield 85. **d** 88 **p** 89. C Pershore w Pinvin, Wick and Birlingham *Worc* 88-91; V Dudley St Barn 91-99; V W Bromwich St Fran *Lich* from 99; RD W Bromwich from 02. *Friar Park Vicarage, Freeman Road, Wednesbury WS10 0HJ* Tel 0121-556 5823
E-mail stfrancis@blueyonder.co.uk

GREEN, Peter Jamie. b 63. Reading Coll of Tech C&G82. Aston Tr Scheme 87 Oak Hill Th Coll BA93. **d** 93 **p** 94. C Brigg *Linc* 93-97; C Brigg, Wrawby and Cadney cum Howsham 97; P-in-c Billinghay 97-01; V Carr Dyke Gp 01-02; R Kelsey Gp from 02. *The Vicarage, Grange Lane, North Kelsey, Market Rasen LN7 6EZ* Tel (01652) 678924

GREEN, Philip Charles. b 53. Wigan Coll of Tech HNC77 Ind Mgt Cert81. Nor Ord Course 91. **d** 94 **p** 95. C Southport Em *Liv* 94-98; P-in-c Crossens from 98. *St John's Vicarage, Rufford Road, Southport PR9 8JH* Tel (01704) 27662
E-mail revphilgreen@crossens1.freeserve.co.uk

GREEN, Canon Philip Harry. b 19. ALCD50. **d** 50 **p** 51. C Keighley *Bradf* 50-53; V Everton St Sav *Liv* 53-57; V Barnoldswick w Bracewell *Bradf* 57-64; V Shipley St Paul 64-77; Hon Can Bradf Cathl 77-82; V Gargrave 77-82; rtd 82; Perm to Offic *Bradf* 82-94 and Carl from 82. *102 Kentsford Road, Grange-over-Sands LA11 7BB* Tel (015395) 532150

GREEN, Richard Alistair. b 76. Ex Univ BA97 St Steph Ho Ox BA01. **d** 01 **p** 02. C Cockerton *Dur* from 01. *213 Brinkburn Road, Darlington DL3 9LE* Tel (01325) 360944

GREEN, Richard Charles. b 49. K Coll Lon 68 St Aug Coll Cant 73. **d** 74 **p** 75. C Broseley w Benthall *Heref* 74-79; TV Heref St Martin w St Fran 80-95; C from 95; rtd 99; Hon Chapl Heref S Wye *Heref* 99-02; C from 02. *5 Bardolph Close, Hereford HR2 7QA* Tel (01432) 354588 *or* 353717 Mobile 07976--910881 E-mail rghswtm@aol.com

GREEN, Robert Henry. b 57. K Coll Lon BD79. Wycliffe Hall Ox 81. **d** 83 **p** 84. C Norbury *Ches* 83-86 and from 91; C Knutsford St Jo and Toft 86-88; rtd 88. *122 Cavendish Road, Hazel Grove, Stockport SK7 6JH* Tel (01625) 858680
E-mail rob.green122@ntlworld.com

GREEN, Robert Leonard. b 44. Sarum & Wells Th Coll. **d** 84 **p** 85. C Battersea St Luke *S'wark* 84-89; CF from 89. *c/o MOD Chaplains (Army)* Tel 01980 615800 Fax 615800

GREEN, Robert Stanley. b 42. Dur Univ BA65. Wells Th Coll 65. **d** 67 **p** 68. C Ashford *Cant* 67-73; R Otham 73-80; V Bethersden w High Halden 80-87; R Winterbourne Stickland and

Turnworth etc *Sarum* 87-99; R Monkton Farleigh, S Wraxall and Winsley from 99. *The Rectory, 6 Millbourn Close, Winsley, Bradford-on-Avon BA15 2NN* Tel (01225) 722230

GREEN, Robin Christopher William. b 43. Leeds Univ BA64 Fitzw Ho Cam BA67. Ridley Hall Cam 65. **d** 68 **p** 69. C S'wark H Trin *S'wark* 68-71; C Englefield Green *Guildf* 71-73; Chapl Whitelands Coll of HE *S'wark* 73-78; Team Ldr Dioc Lay Tr Team 78-84; V W Brompton St Mary w St Pet *Lon* 84-87; USPG 87-90; Perm to Offic *S'wark* 88-90; NSM from 91. *2 Church Path, Mitcham CR4 3BN* Tel (020) 8543 0519

GREEN, Rodney William. b 52. LNSM course 90. **d** 93 **p** 94. OLM Flixton St Jo *Man* from 93. *85 Arundel Avenue, Flixton, Manchester M41 6MG* Tel 0161-748 7238

GREEN, Roger Thomas. b 43. Oak Hill Th Coll DipHE79. **d** 79 **p** 80. C Paddock Wood *Roch* 79-83; R High Halstow w All Hallows and Hoo St Mary 83-89; Chapl HM Pris Brixton 89-90; Chapl HM Pris Standford Hill 90-94; Chapl HM Pris Swaleside 94-00; Chapl HM Pris Roch 99-03; Chapl HM Pris Blantyre Ho from 03. *HM Prison Blantyre House, Goudhurst, Cranbrook TN17 2NH* Tel (01580) 211367

GREEN, Preb Ronald Henry. b 27. Lambeth MA86 Bps' Coll Cheshunt 53. **d** 55 **p** 56. C St Marylebone Ch Ch w St Barn *Lon* 55-58; R 58-62; Dioc Youth Tr Officer 62-64; C St Andr Holborn 62-64; RE Adv 63-73; V Hampstead St Steph 64-73; RD N Camden 67-73; V Heston 73-80; Preb St Paul's Cathl 75-83; Jt Dir Lon and S'wark Bd of Educn 79-83; Dir of Educn *Sarum* 83-86; R Chiddingfold *Guildf* 86-91; rtd 91; Perm to Offic *Sarum* 91-92; Master St Nic Hosp Salisbury 91-97; Perm to Offic *Sarum* from 98. *20 Ayleswade Road, Salisbury SP2 8DR* Tel (01722) 327660

GREEN (née JARMAN), Mrs Rosemary Susan. b 44. St Alb and Ox Min Course 99. **d** 01 **p** 02. OLM Bradfield and Stanford Dingley *Ox* from 01. *1 Buscot Copse, Bradfield, Reading RG7 6JB* Tel 0118-974 4640 Fax 974 4910
E-mail rosemary.s.green@talk21.com

GREEN, Ruth Valerie. *See* JAGGER, Mrs Ruth Valerie

GREEN, Sidney Leonard. b 44. K Coll Lon MTh86 Montessori DipEd84. Oak Hill Th Coll DipTh70 BD72. **d** 72 **p** 73. C Skelmersdale St Paul *Liv* 72-74; C Denton Holme *Carl* 74-76; In Bapt Min 76-85; Chapl Qu Eliz Gr Sch Blackb 85-91; Chapl Epsom Coll 91-01; P-in-c Sway *Win* from 01. *The Vicarage, Station Road, Sway, Lymington SO41 6BA* Tel (01590) 682358
E-mail sidneygreen@onetel.net.uk

GREEN, Ms Stella Louise. b 61. Kent Univ BA84. St Mich Coll Llan 01. **d** 03. C Stamford Hill St Thos *Lon* from 03. *Top Flat, 306 Amhurst Road, London N16 7UE* Tel 07815-089704 (mobile)

GREEN, Stephen Keith. b 48. Ex Coll Ox BA69 Mass Inst of Tech MSc75. N Ord Course 84. **d** 87 **p** 88. Hong Kong 87-93; Perm to Offic *Lon* 93-00. *44 Scarsdale Villas, London W8 6PP* Tel (020) 7937 3290 *or* 7336 3354 Fax 7336 3661
E-mail stephen.green@hsbcgroup.com

GREEN, Steven Douglas. b 57. Univ of Wales (Ban) DipTh81 Dip Counselling 99 Univ of Wales BA97. Sarum & Wells Th Coll 81. **d** 82 **p** 83. C Hawarden *St As* 82-86; V Mostyn 86-93; V Ffynnongroyw 86-93; V Mostyn w Ffynnongroyw 93-99; R Trefnant w Tremeirchion 99-01; R Cefn w Trefnant w Tremeirchion from 01. *The Rectory, Trefnant, Denbigh LL16 5UG* Tel (01745) 730584 E-mail s.d.green@talk21.com

GREEN, Mrs Susan Denise. b 66. TCD BA89 HDipEd90. **d** 92 **p** 93. C Antrim All SS *Conn* 92-95; Dioc Youth Officer (Cashel) *C & O* 95-00; Chapl Adelaide and Meath Hosp Dublin from 00. *Castleknock Rectory, 12 Hawthorn Lawn, Castleknock, Dublin 15, Irish Republic* Tel (00353) (1) 821 3083
E-mail greenorr@esatclear.ie

GREEN, Mrs Susan Margaret. b 54. Univ of Wales (Abth) BSc75. SW Minl Tr Course 92. **d** 95 **p** 96. NSM Wiveliscombe w Chipstable, Huish Champflower etc *B & W* from 95; Sub-Warden of Readers Taunton Adnry from 00. *North Rodden Cottage, Maundown, Wiveliscombe, Taunton TA4 2BU* Tel (01984) 623809 E-mail suegreen@mountain.freeserve.co.uk

GREEN, Miss Sylvia. b 45. Bris Univ LLB66. WEMTC 97. **d** 00 **p** 01. NSM W Heref from 00. *23 Tower Road, Hereford HR4 0LF* Tel (01432) 264599 *or* 353863 Mobile 07970-287394 Fax (01432) 352952 E-mail hereford@diooffice.freeserve.co.uk

GREEN, Trevor Geoffrey Nash. b 45. BA. Oak Hill Th Coll 81. **d** 84 **p** 85. C Stalybridge H Trin and Ch Ch *Ches* 84-89; V 89-96; V Lache cum Saltney from 96. *St Mark's Vicarage, 5 Cliveden Road, Chester CH4 8DR* Tel (01244) 671702 *or* 675372 Fax 677818 E-mail trevoratmarks@aol.com

GREEN, Trevor Howard. b 37. Sarum & Wells Th Coll 72. **d** 74 **p** 75. C Bloxwich *Lich* 74-77; C Willenhall St Steph 77-79; P-in-c 79-80; V 80-82; V Essington 82-90; V Bishopswood and Brewood 90-02; P-in-c Coven 00-02; RD Penkridge 94-01; rtd 02. *113 Stafford Street, Cannock WS12 2EN* Tel (01543) 271159

GREEN, Vivian Hubert Howard. b 15. DD58. **d** 39 **p** 40. Lic to Offic *Cant* 39-47; Perm to Offic *Sarum* 42-51; Chapl Linc Coll Ox 51-79; Rector Linc Coll Ox 83-87; rtd 87. *Calendars, Sheep Street, Burford OX18 4LS* Tel (01993) 823214

GREEN, William. b 44. Newc Univ BA66 DipEd67 MA77. N Ord Course 87. d 90 p 91. NSM Utley *Bradf* 90-97; P-in-c Scarborough St Jas w H Trin *York* 97-00; V Thornton St Jas *Bradf* from 00. *The Vicarage, 300 Thornton Road, Thornton, Bradford BD13 3AB* Tel (01274) 833200
E-mail billgreen@vicarage24.freeserve.co.uk

GREEN, William John. b 23. Birm Univ BSc43. Roch Th Coll 64. d 66 p 67. C Minchinhampton *Glouc* 66-68; C Standish w Hardwicke and Haresfield 68-70; R Eastington and Frocester 70-80; P-in-c S Cerney w Cerney Wick 80-84; V S Cerney w Cerney Wick and Down Ampney 84-87; P-in-c Maisemore 87-90; rtd 90; Perm to Offic *Sarum* from 90. *36 Fairfield, Upavon, Pewsey SN9 6DZ* Tel (01980) 630798

GREEN, William Lewis. b 12. St Cath Coll Cam BA34 MA39. Cuddesdon Coll 34. d 35 p 36. C Hackney Wick St Mary of Eton *Lon* 35-46; C Desborough *Pet* 40-45; Vice-Prin Old Rectory Coll Hawarden 46-47; Chapl and Lect St Mary's Old Ban 47-62; Kenya 62-70; Nigeria 70-78; Perm to Offic *Ches* 78-79 and 82-01; Tanzania 79-82; rtd 82. *20 Dunkirk Drive, Ellesmere Port CH65 6QH* Tel 0151-355 5456

GREENACRE, Canon Roger Tagent. b 30. Ordre national du Merite 98. Clare Coll Cam BA52 MA56 Lambeth DD01. Coll of Resurr Mirfield 52. d 54 p 55. C Hanworth All SS *Lon* 54-59; Chapl Ely Th Coll 59-60; Chapl Summer Fields Sch Ox 60-61; C N Audley Street St Mark *Lon* 62-63; Chapl Liddon Ho Lon 63-65; Chapl Paris St Geo *Eur* 65-75; RD France 70-75; Dioc Ecum Officer *Chich* 75-88; Lect Chich Th Coll 75-89; Can Res Chich Cathl *Chich* 75-00; Chan 75-97; Prec 97-00; Select Preacher Ox Univ 95; Chmn Chich Dioc Eur Ecum Cttee 89-99; rtd 00; Perm to Offic *Eur* from 00. *Le Saint Michel, 9 rue Paul-Doumer, 06310 Beaulieu-sur-Mer, France* Tel (0033) (4) 93 01 45 61 Fax as telephone

GREENALL, Canon Ronald Gilbert. b 41. St Aid Birkenhead 61. d 64 p 65. C Adlington *Blackb* 64-67; C Ribbleton 67-69; R Coppull St Jo 69-84; V Garstang St Thos 84-99; RD Garstang 89-96; Hon Can Blackb Cathl 95-99; rtd 99; Perm to Offic *Blackb* from 99. *40 Duckworth Drive, Catterall, Preston PR3 1YS* Tel (01995) 606135

GREENAWAY-ROBBINS, Mark. b 72. Ox Univ BA95. Qu Coll Birm 96. d 99 p 00. C Redruth w Lanner and Treleigh *Truro* 99-01; Consultant on Other Faiths 00-01; TV Whitchurch *Llan* from 02. *3 Lon Ganol, Cardiff CF14 6EB*

GREENE, Colin John David. b 50. QUB BA73 Fitzw Coll Cam MA75 Nottm Univ PhD. St Jo Coll Nottm 78. d 80 p 81. Hon C Sandiacre *Derby* 80-81; C Loughborough Em *Leic* 81-84; V Thorpe Acre w Dishley 84-89; Evang Tr Consultant Bible Soc 89-91; Tutor Trin Coll Bris 91-95; Th Consultant Bible Soc and Springdale Coll 95-96; Hd Th and Public Policy Bible Soc from 96; Perm to Offic *Bris* from 96. *18 Cross Hayes, Malmesbury SN16 9BG* Tel (01666) 823879

GREENE, David Arthur Kirsopp. b 36. St Pet Coll Ox BA60 MA64 FE TCert81. Tyndale Hall Bris 61. d 63 p 64. C Southgate *Chich* 63-66; C Kirby Grindalythe *York* 66-69; C N Grimston w Wharram Percy and Wharram-le-Street 66-69; R Folke, N Wootton and Haydon w Long Burton *Sarum* 69-75; R Long Burton, Folke, N Wootton, Haydon etc 75-80; P-in-c Thornford w Beer Hackett 80-84; P-in-c High Stoy 81-84; R Bradford Abbas and Thornford w Beer Hackett 84-00; rtd 00. *Little Orchards, Priestlands, Sherborne DT9 4HW* Tel (01935) 813467

GREENE, John Howe. b 22. K Coll Lon AKC48 BD49. d 49 p 50. C Drayton in Hales *Lich* 49-52; C Stoke upon Trent 52-56; V Wilnecote 56-62; V Lodsworth *Chich* 62-69; R Selham 62-69; R Burwash 69-75; R Petworth 75-88; RD Petworth 76-88; P-in-c Egdean 76-80; R 80-88; rtd 88; Perm to Offic *Chich* from 88. *37 Wilderness Road, Hurstpierpoint, Hassocks BN6 9XD* Tel (01273) 833651

GREENE, Paul David O'Dwyer. b 53. Brunel Univ BSc78 Southn Univ DASS81 CQSW81. Oak Hill NSM Course 90. d 93 p 94. NSM Northwood Em *Lon* from 93. *50 The Drive, Northwood HA6 1HP* Tel (01923) 829605

GREENER, Jonathan Desmond Francis. b 61. Trin Coll Cam BA83 MA87. Coll of Resurr Mirfield 89. d 91 p 92. C S'wark H Trin w St Matt S'wark 91-94; Bp's Dom Chapl *Truro* 94-96; V Brighton Gd Shep Preston *Chich* from 96. *The Good Shepherd Vicarage, 272 Dyke Road, Brighton BN1 5AE* Tel (01273) 882987 Fax 386989 E-mail jonathangreener@compuserve.com

GREENFIELD, Canon Martin Richard. b 54. Em Coll Cam MA75. Wycliffe Hall Ox MA78. d 79 p 80. C Enfield Ch Ch Trent Park *Lon* 79-83; CMS from 84; Nigeria 85-94; Hon Can Aba from 89; C Langdon Hills *Chelmsf* 94-95; R Brampton *Ely* from 95; RD Huntingdon from 99. *The Rectory, 15 Church Road, Brampton, Huntingdon PE28 4PF* Tel (01480) 453341
E-mail m.greenfield@ntlworld.com

GREENFIELD, Norman John Charles. b 27. Leeds Univ BA51. Chich Th Coll 51. d 53 p 54. C Portsea St Cuth *Portsm* 53-56; C Whitley Ch Ch *Ox* 56-60; V Moorends *Sheff* 60-65; V Littleworth *Ox* 65-71; Asst Stewardship Adv 65-70; V New Marston 71-79; Dioc Stewardship Adv *Chich* 79-88; P-in-c Amberley w N Stoke 79-83; R Guestling and Pett 88-94; rtd 94;

Perm to Offic *Chich* from 94. *5 Marlborough Close, Eastbourne BN23 8AN* Tel (01323) 769494

GREENHALGH, David Murray. b 13. Jes Coll Cam BA34 MA38 Lon Univ BD47. Ridley Hall Cam 34. d 36 p 37. C Worsley *Man* 36-38; C Pennington 38-43; R Newton Heath St Anne 43-49; V Guilden Morden *Ely* 49-55; V Terrington St Clement 55-59; V Shirley *Win* 59-78; rtd 78. *12 St Christopher's Home, Abington Park Crescent, Northampton NN3 3AD* Tel (01604) 232087

GREENHALGH, Eric. b 20. Tyndale Hall Bris. d 63 p 64. C Preston St Mary *Blackb* 63-66; Perm to Offic 66-68; V 68-72; V Partington and Carrington *Ches* 72-81; V Inskip *Blackb* 81-85; rtd 85; Perm to Offic *Blackb* and *Carl* from 85. *Maranatha, 4 Rydal Close, Millom LA18 4QR* Tel (01229) 770995

GREENHALGH, Ian Frank. b 49. Wycliffe Hall Ox 74. d 77 p 78. C Parr *Liv* 77-80; V Wigan St Barn Marsh Green 80-84; Chapl RAF from 84. *Chaplaincy Services (RAF), HQ, Personnel and Training Command, RAF Innsworth, Gloucester GL3 1EZ* Tel (01452) 712612 ext 5164 Fax 510828

GREENHALGH, Philip Adrian. b 52. Ian Ramsey Coll 75 Wycliffe Hall Ox 76. d 79 p 80. C Gt Clacton *Chelmsf* 79-82; P-in-c Stalmine *Blackb* 82-86; Rep Leprosy Miss E Anglia 86-87; Area Org CECS 88-90; NSM Alston Team *Newc* 90-92; NSM Chulmleigh *Ex* 92-93; NSM Chawleigh w Cheldon 92-93; NSM Wembworthy w Eggesford 92-93; P-in-c Gilsland w Nether Denton *Carl* 93-95; V Millom 95-00; P-in-c Heathercleugh *Dur* from 00; P-in-c Westgate from 00; P-in-c St John in Weardale from 00; AD Stanhope from 00; P-in-c Stanhope w Frosterley from 02; P-in-c Eastgate w Rookhope from 02. *The Rectory, Front Street, Stanhope, Bishop Auckland DL13 2UE* Tel (01388) 528449

GREENHALGH, Stephen. b 53. Dip Counselling 97 Man Univ MA99. Trin Coll Bris 77 Lon Bible Coll BA81. d 81 p 82. C Horwich H Trin *Man* 81-84; C Horwich 84-85; Chapl RAF 85-89; Perm to Offic *Blackb* 96-01 and *Carl* from 01. *75 Archers Meadow, Kendal LA9 7DY* Tel (01539) 737856

GREENHILL, Anthony David. b 30. Bris Univ BSc59. Tyndale Hall Bris 61. d 63 p 64. C Southsea St Jude *Portsm* 63-65; India 65-78; C Kinson *Sarum* 78-81; V Girlington *Bradf* 81-97; C Platt Bridge *Liv* 97-00; rtd 00; Perm to Offic *Bradf* from 01. *12 Monterey Drive, Allerton, Bradford BD15 9LP* Tel (01274) 484074

GREENHOUGH, Alan Kenneth. b 40. St D Coll Lamp DipTh66. d 66 p 67. C Allestree *Derby* 66-70; C Ilkeston St Mary 70-73; V Bradwell 73-85; R Twyford w Guist w Bintry w Themelthorpe etc *Nor* 85-95; P-in-c Stibbard 94-95; R Twyford, Guist, Bintree, Themelthorpe etc from 95. *The Rectory, Guist, Dereham NR20 5LU* Tel (01362) 84255

GREENHOUGH, Andrew Quentin. b 68. E Lon Poly BSc89. Wycliffe Hall Ox BTh94. d 94 p 95. C Partington and Carrington *Ches* 94-98; C Davenham from 98; P-in-c Moulton from 01. *The Vicarage, 66 Jack Lane, Moulton, Northwich CW9 8NR* Tel (01606) 593355 E-mail a.greenhough@virgin.net

GREENHOUGH, Arthur George. b 30. Fitzw Ho Cam BA52 MA56. Tyndale Hall Bris 55. d 57 p 58. C Wakef St Andr *Wakef* 57-63; R Birkin w Haddlesey *York* 63-85; RD Selby 77-84; P-in-c Hambleton 84-85; R Haddlesey w Hambleton and Birkin 85-00; rtd 01; Perm to Offic *York* from 01. *16 Grange Road, Camblesforth, Selby YO8 8HF* Tel (01757) 617347

GREENHOUGH, Geoffrey Herman. b 36. Sheff Univ BA57 Lon Univ BD71. St Jo Coll Nottm 74. d 75 p 76. C Cheadle Hulme St Andr *Ches* 74-78; R Tilston and Shocklach 78-82; V Hyde St Geo 82-87; V Pott Shrigley 87-00; rtd 00; Perm to Offic *Ches* from 00. *3 Spey Close, Winsford CW7 3BP* Tel (01625) 573316

GREENISH, Brian Vivian Isitt. b 20. LRCP MRCS Lon Univ MB BS. d 89 p 89. NSM Bedford St Pet w St Cuth *St Alb* 89-91; Perm to Offic from 91. *69 Chaucer Road, Bedford MK40 2AL* Tel (01234) 352498

GREENLAND, Martin. b 65. Warwick Univ BSc87. Westcott Ho Cam CTM94. d 97 p 98. C Scarborough St Martin *York* 97-00; TV Bramley and Ravenfield w Hooton Roberts etc *Sheff* from 00. *The Rectory, Micklebring Lane, Braithwell, Rotherham S66 7AS* Tel (01709) 812665

GREENLAND, Paul Howard. b 59. Bath Univ BA80 ACA85. Trin Coll Bris. d 00 p 01. C Caverswall and Weston Coyney w Dilhorne *Lich* from 00. *30 Firbank Place, Weston Coyney, Stoke-on-Trent ST3 5RU* Tel and fax (01782) 596783 Pager 07669-017638 E-mail paulhgreenland@care4free.net

GREENLAND, Roy Wilfrid. b 37. St Steph Ho Ox 71. d 73 p 74. C Wanstead St Mary *Chelmsf* 73-76; V Harlow St Mary Magd 76-83; P-in-c Huntingdon All SS w St Jo *Ely* 83-84; P-in-c Huntingdon St Barn 83-84; P-in-c Huntingdon St Mary w St Benedict 83-84; Bermuda 84-89; V Northampton St Alb *Pet* 89-92; R Waldron *Chich* 92-02; rtd 02. *2 The Glebe, Flore, Northampton NN7 4LX* Tel (01327) 349877

GREENMAN, David John. b 35. Lon Univ BA59. Oak Hill Th Coll 57. d 61 p 62. C Wandsworth St Steph *S'wark* 61-63; C Bishopwearmouth St Gabr *Dur* 63-66; C-in-c Bedgrove CD *Ox* 66-74; P-in-c Macclesfield Ch Ch *Ches* 74-77; V 77-81; P-in-c Glouc All SS *Glouc* 81-85; V Glouc St Jas 81-85; V Bare *Blackb*

85-91; V Market Lavington and Easterton *Sarum* 91-99; rtd 99; Perm to Offic *Sarum* and *Win* from 00. *3 Bure Lane, Christchurch BH23 4DJ* Tel (01425) 241034

GREENMAN (née CHESTER), Mrs Irene Mary. b 51. Dioc OLM tr scheme 97. **d** 99 **p** 00. OLM Cornholme *Wakef* 99-00; OLM Cornholme and Walsden from 00. *8 Glenview Street, Cornholme, Todmorden OL14 8LT* Tel (01706) 817296 Fax as telephone E-mail irene@stmicks99.freeserve.co.uk

GREENSLADE, Mrs Gillian Carol. b 43. Leic Univ BA64 Nottm Univ PGCE65 Essex Univ MA78 UEA DipHE97. EAMTC 93. **d** 96 **p** 97. NSM Dovercourt and Parkeston w Harwich *Chelmsf* 96-00; NSM Colchester, New Town and The Hythe 00-02; R Broxted w Chickney and Tilty etc from 02. *The Rectory, Park Road, Little Easton, Dunmow CM6 2JJ* Tel (01371) 872509

GREENSLADE, Keith James Inglis. b 27. St Mich Coll Llan 60. **d** 62 **p** 63. C Bishopsworth *Bris* 62-65; C Chippenham St Paul w Langley Burrell 65-68; V Upper Stratton 68-95; rtd 95; Perm to Offic *Bris* and *Sarum* from 95. *65 Shakespeare Road, Wootton Bassett, Swindon SN4 8HF* Tel (01793) 853253

GREENSLADE, Peter Michael. b 37. Bp Burgess Hall Lamp 69. **d** 71 **p** 72. C Llanwnda w Goodwick and Manorowen *St D* 71-73; C Lydiate *Liv* 73-75; V Wigan St Cath 75-76; Chapl Newsham Gen Hosp Liv 76-78; C Knotty Ash St Jo *Liv* 76-78; C Lache cum Saltney *Ches* 78-80; V Barnton 80-84; C Warburton 85-86; Warden Petroc Chr Guest Ho 86-90; rtd 90. *8 Ash Grove Close, Bodenham, Hereford HR1 3LT* Tel (01658) 797210

GREENSLADE, Timothy Julian. b 63. St Jo Coll Ox BA86. Oak Hill Th Coll BA95. **d** 95 **p** 96. C Broadwater St Mary *Chich* 95-99; TV Radipole and Melcombe Regis *Sarum* from 99. *106 Spa Road, Weymouth DT3 5ER* Tel (01305) 771938

GREENSTREET, Mark George. b 68. St Jo Coll Dur BA94. **d** 98 **p** 98. C St Alb St Pet *St Alb* 97-99; C Stevenage St Hugh and St Jo 99-01; C Dorridge *Birm* from 01. *2 Hurst Green Road, Bentley Heath, Solihull B93 8AE* Tel (01564) 775494
E-mail mark-greenstreet@lineone.net

GREENWAY, John. b 32. Bps' Coll Cheshunt 68 Qu Coll Birm 69. **d** 69 **p** 70. C Luton Ch Ch *St Alb* 69-74; C Pulloxhill w Flitton 75-76; P-in-c Marston Morteyne 76-79; P-in-c Lidlington 77-79; V Marston Morteyne w Lidlington 80-81; R 81-97; rtd 97; Perm to Offic *Portsm* from 98. *73 Northmore Road, Locks Heath, Southampton SO3 6LA* Tel (01489) 886791

GREENWAY, John Michael. b 34. LNSM course 94. **d** 96 **p** 97. OLM Gt Yarmouth *Nor* from 96. *17 Hamilton Road, Great Yarmouth NR30 4ND* Tel (01493) 853558

GREENWAY, Margaret Hester. b 26. **d** 87. Downend *Bris* 75-79; Oldland 79-82; Stratton St Margaret w S Marston etc 82-86; rtd 86; Perm to Offic *B & W* 87-95. *5 Weston Lodge, Lower Bristol Road, Weston-super-Mare BS23 2PJ* Tel (01934) 623561

GREENWELL, Christopher. b 49. Linc Th Coll 79. **d** 81 **p** 82. C Scarborough St Martin *York* 81-84; V S Bank 84-89; R Bolton by Bowland w Grindleton *Bradf* 89-92; V Nether Hoyland St Andr *Sheff* 92-96; V Kirkleatham *York* from 96. *Kirkleatham Vicarage, 130 Mersey Road, Redcar TS10 4DF* Tel (01642) 482073
E-mail chris@greenwell49.freeserve.co.uk

GREENWELL, Paul. b 60. Magd Coll Ox BA81 MA85. St Steph Ho Ox 82. **d** 85 **p** 86. C Hendon and Sunderland *Dur* 85-88; Min Can and Prec Ripon Cathl *Ripon* 88-93; Chapl Univ Coll of Ripon and York St Jo 88-93; V Hunslet St Mary *Ripon* 93-02; Asst Chapl Harrogate Health Care NHS Trust from 02; Convenor Dioc Adv Gp for Chr Healing *Ripon* from 03. *Harrogate District Hospital, Lancaster Park Road, Harrogate HG2 7SX* Tel (01423) 553045
E-mail chaplaincy@hhc-tr.northy.nhs.uk

GREENWOOD, David. *See* GREENWOOD, Norman David

GREENWOOD, Canon Gerald. b 33. Leeds Univ BA57 Sheff Poly MSc81 Surrey Univ Hon MA93. Linc Th Coll 57. **d** 59 **p** 60. C Rotherham *Sheff* 59-62; V Elsecar 62-70; V Wales 70-77; P-in-c Thorpe Salvin 74-77; Dioc Sch Officer 77-84; P-in-c Bramley and Ravenfield 77-78; P-in-c Hooton Roberts 77-78; R 78-84; Hon Can Sheff Cathl 80-84; Dioc Dir of Educn 81-84; Hon Can S'wark Cathl 84-97; Dir of Educn 84-97; rtd 97; Perm to Offic *Cant* from 97. *Home Farm Cottage, Westmarsh, Canterbury CT3 2LW* Tel (01304) 812160

GREENWOOD, Gordon Edwin. b 44. Trin Coll Bris 78. **d** 80 **p** 81. C Bootle St Matt *Liv* 80-83; V Hunts Cross 83-93; V Skelmersdale St Paul from 93; P-in-c Skelmersdale Ch at Cen from 02. *The Vicarage, Church Road, Skelmersdale WN8 8ND* Tel (01695) 722087

GREENWOOD, Hilary Peter Frank. b 29. Nottm Univ BA57. Kelham Th Coll 54. **d** 57 **p** 58. SSM from 54; Tutor Kelham Th Coll 57-59 and 66-70; Warden 70-74; S Africa 59-60; Australia 60-66 and from 97; Asst Chapl Madrid *Eur* 74-75; Perm to Offic *Blackb* 75-80; *Man* 80-82; R Longsight St Jo w St Cypr 82-89; Perm to Offic *Dur* 89-91 and 95-97; Hon Asst Chapl Prague *Eur* 91-95; rtd 98. *St Michael's Priory, 75 Watsons Road, Diggers Rest, Vic, Australia 3427* Tel (0061) (3) 9740 1618 Fax (3) 9740 0007 E-mail ssm.melbourne@bigpond.com

GREENWOOD, James Peter. b 61. Univ Coll Lon BSc83 DipArch86 St Jo Coll Dur BA90 RIBA87. Cranmer Hall Dur 88.

d 91 **p** 92. C Belper *Derby* 91-94; CMS Pakistan 95-01; V Islamabad St Thos 95-00; V Silsden *Bradf* from 01. *The Vicarage, Briggate, Silsden, Keighley BD20 9JS* Tel (01535) 652204
E-mail jpetergreenwood@hotmail.com

GREENWOOD, John Newton. b 44. St Chad's Coll Dur BA69 DipTh70. **d** 70 **p** 71. C Hartlepool H Trin *Dur* 70-72; Lic to Offic from 72; Hd Master Archibald Primary Sch Cleveland 84-97; Asst Chapl HM Pris Holme Ho from 99. *1 Brae Head, Eaglescliffe, Stockton-on-Tees TS16 9HP* Tel (01642) 783200

GREENWOOD, Leslie. b 37. Dur Univ BA59 DipTh61. St Jo Coll Dur. **d** 61 **p** 62. C Birstall *Wakef* 61-63; C Illingworth 64-70; Chapl H Trin Sch Halifax 84-89; V Charlestown 70-91; TV Upper Holme Valley 91-97; Perm to Offic from 97; rtd 00. *2 Trenance Gardens, Greetland, Halifax HX4 8NN* Tel (01422) 373926 E-mail kyandles@aol.com

GREENWOOD, Mrs Margaret Elizabeth. b 34. St Mary's Coll Cheltenham TCert65 Surrey Univ MA93. St Mich Ho Ox 60. **d** 00. NSM Shepperton *Lon* 00-01; NSM Whitton SS Phil and Jas from 01. *Bundoran Cottage, Vicarage Lane, Laleham, Staines TW18 1UE* Tel (01784) 458115
E-mail wedderburn.phoebe@talk21.com

GREENWOOD, Michael Eric. b 44. Oak Hill Th Coll 78. **d** 80 **p** 81. C Clubmoor *Liv* 80-83; V Pemberton St Mark Newtown 83-94; V Grassendale 94-00; V Ashton-in-Makerfield St Thos from 00. *The Vicarage, 18 Warrington Road, Ashton-in-Makerfield, Wigan WN4 9PL* Tel (01942) 727275

GREENWOOD, Norman David. b 52. Edin Univ BMus74 Lon Univ BD78 Nottm Univ MPhil90. Oak Hill Th Coll 76. **d** 78 **p** 79. C Gorleston St Andr *Nor* 78-81; SAMS 81-83; C Cromer *Nor* 83-84; R Appleby Magna and Swepstone w Snarestone *Leic* 84-94; P-in-c Chesterfield H Trin *Derby* 94-95; P-in-c Chesterfield Ch 94-95; R Chesterfield H Trin and Ch Ch 95-99; V S Ramsey St Paul *S & M* from 99; Dir of Ords from 01. *St Paul's Vicarage, Walpole Drive, Ramsey, Isle of Man IM8 1NA* Tel (01624) 812275

GREENWOOD, Canon Robin Patrick. b 47. St Chad's Coll Dur BA68 MA71 DipTh69 Birm Univ PhD92. **d** 70 **p** 71. C Adel *Ripon* 70-73; Min Can and Succ Ripon Cathl 73-78; V Leeds Halton St Wilfrid 78-86; Dioc Can Res Glouc Cathl *Glouc* 86-95; Dioc Missr and Dir Lay and Post-Ord Tr 86-95; Dir of Min *Chelmsf* 95-00; Hon Can Chelmsf Cathl 95-00; Prov Officer for Min Ch in Wales from 01; Hon C Canton St Jo *Llan* from 02. *Prov Council for Mission & Ministry, 39 Cathedral Road, Cardiff CF11 9XF* Tel (029) 2023 1638 Fax 2038 7835

GREENWOOD, Roy Douglas. b 27. Tyndale Hall Bris 58. **d** 60 **p** 61. C Ox St Matt *Ox* 60-62; V Ulpha *Carl* 62-63; V Seathwaite w Ulpha 63-72; P-in-c Haverthwaite 72-74; C Ulverston St Mary w H Trin 74-78; V Egton w Newland 78-86; Assoc Chapl Palma de Mallorca and Balearic Is *Eur* 86-93; Assoc Chapl Palma de Mallorca 93-95; rtd 95. *La Finquita, Apartado 78, Pollensa, Palma de Mallorca 07460, Spain* Tel (0034) (71) 530966

GREER, Eric Gordon. b 52. Pepperdine Univ BA74. Princeton Th Sem MDiv80. **d** 93 **p** 94. C Southgate St Andr *Lon* 93-96; C Camden Square St Paul 96-00; V Grange Park St Pet from 00. *The Vicarage, Langham Gardens, London N21 1DN* Tel (020) 8360 2294 E-mail egreer@talk21.com

GREER, Robert Ferguson. b 34. TCD BA56 MA59. Div Test 60. **d** 60 **p** 61. C Dundela St Mark *D & D* 60-65; I Castlewellan 65-77; I Castlewellan w Kilcoo 77-02; Can Dromore Cathl 90-02; Prec 93-02; rtd 02. *Dromore, Townsend, Harwell, Didcot OX11 0DX* Tel (01235) 835639 Fax 820473
E-mail rfgreer@ukonline.co.uk

GREETHAM, Canon William Frederick. b 40. Bede Coll Dur CertEd. Cranmer Hall Dur 63. **d** 66 **p** 67. C St Annes *Blackb* 66-69; C Ashton-on-Ribble St Andr 69-71; Chapl Aysgarth Sch 71-82; C Bedale *Ripon* 72-75; V Crakehall 75-82; V Hornby 75-82; V Patrick Brompton and Hunton 75-82; V Kirkby Stephen *Carl* 82-90; R Kirkby Stephen w Mallerstang etc 90-96; RD Appleby 86-91; Hon Can Carl Cathl from 89; P-in-c Crosthwaite Kendal from 96; P-in-c Cartmel Fell from 96; P-in-c Winster from 96; P-in-c Witherslack from 96. *The Vicarage, Crosthwaite, Kendal LA8 8HT* Tel (01539) 568276

GREEVES, Roger Derrick. b 43. TCD BA66 MA70 Fitzw Coll Cam BA68 MA73. Wesley Ho Cam 66 Westcott Ho Cam 98. **d** 98 **p** 99. In Methodist Ch 68-98; NSM Cam St Edw *Ely* 98-00; Chapl Oakington Immigration Reception Cen 00-01; Chapl Peterho Cam 00-01; Dean Clare Coll Cam from 01. *28 Bateman Street, Cambridge CB2 1NB* Tel (01223) 571699 *or* 333240 Mobile 07719-863772 Fax 571705 E-mail rdg20@cam.ac.uk

GREG, John Kennedy. b 24. Trin Coll Cam BA46 MA61. Chich Th Coll 46. **d** 49 **p** 50. C Walmsley *Man* 49-51; C Carl H Trin *Carl* 51-55; V Lanercost w Kirkcambeck 55-62; V Cumwhitton 62-75; C Carl St Barn 75; TV 75-80; Chapl Strathclyde Ho Hosp Carl 80-85; TV Carl H Trin and St Barn *Carl* 80-85; rtd 85; Perm to Offic *Carl* 86-93. *113 Wigton Road, Carlisle CA2 7EL* Tel (01228) 538837

GREGG, David William Austin. b 37. Lon Univ BD66 Bris Univ MA69. Tyndale Hall Bris 63. **d** 68 **p** 69. C Barrow St Mark *Carl* 68-71; P-in-c Lindal w Marton 71-75; Communications Sec Gen

Syn Bd for Miss and Unity 76-81; Prin Romsey Ho Coll Cam 81-88; V Haddenham w Cuddington, Kingsey etc *Ox* 88-96; P-in-c Newton Longville w Stoke Hammond and Whaddon 96-02; rtd 03. *Lowick Farm House, Lowick Green, Ulverston LA12 8DX* Tel (01229) 885258

GREGORY, Alan Paul Roy. b 55. K Coll Lon BD77 MTh78 AKC. Ripon Coll Cuddesdon 78. **d** 79 **p** 80. C Walton-on-Thames *Guildf* 79-82; Tutor and Dir Studies Sarum & Wells Th Coll 82-88; USA from 88. *3817 Red River Street, Austin, TX 78751, USA*

GREGORY, Andrew Forsythe. b 71. St Jo Coll Dur BA92. Wycliffe Hall Ox BA96 DipMin97. **d** 97 **p** 98. C E Acton St Dunstan w St Thos *Lon* 97-99; Asst Chapl Keble Coll Ox 97-99; Chapl Linc Coll Ox from 99. *Lincoln College, Oxford OX1 3DR* Tel (01865) 279789
E-mail andrew.gregory@lincoln.ox.ac.uk

GREGORY, Brian. b 43. Trin Coll Bris. **d** 82 **p** 83. C Burscough Bridge *Liv* 82-85; V Platt Bridge 85-92; V Ben Rhydding *Bradf* from 92. *The Vicarage, Ben Rhydding, Ilkley LS29 8PT* Tel (01943) 607363 *or* 601430
E-mail brian@bgregory.freeserve.co.uk

GREGORY, Clive Malcolm. b 61. Lanc Univ BA84 Qu Coll Cam BA87 MA89 Warwick Univ Hon MA99. Westcott Ho Cam 85. **d** 88 **p** 89. C Margate St Jo *Cant* 88-92; Chapl Warw Univ *Cov* 92-98; TR Cov E from 98. *St Peter's Rectory, Charles Street, Coventry CV1 5NP* Tel (024) 7622 5907
E-mail clive@coveastteam.clara.co.uk

GREGORY, Father. See DUDDING, Edward Leslie

GREGORY, Graham. b 36. Open Univ BA78 Lon Univ DipTh65. Tyndale Hall Bris 63. **d** 66 **p** 67. C Wandsworth St Mich *S'wark* 66-71; C Hastings Em and St Mary in the Castle *Chich* 71-75; V Douglas St Ninian *S & M* 75-91; Dioc Youth Officer 78-88; Chapl HM Pris Douglas 82-86; RD Douglas *S & M* 86-91; V Wollaton Park *S'well* 91-95; V Lenton Abbey 91-95; rtd 95; Perm to Offic *York* from 98. *15 Keble Drive, Bishopthorpe, York YO23 2TA* Tel (01904) 701679

GREGORY, Ian Peter. b 45. Open Univ BA82 Plymouth Univ PGCE92. Bernard Gilpin Soc Dur 66 Chich Th Coll 67. **d** 70 **p** 71. C Tettenhall Regis *Lich* 70-73; C Shrewsbury H Cross 73-76; P-in-c Walsall St Mary and All SS Palfrey 76-80; R Petrockstowe, Petersmarland, Merton, Meeth etc *Ex* 80-87; TV Ex St Thos and Em 87-91; Hon C S Wimbledon All SS *S'wark* 94-00. *142 Monkleigh Road, Morden SM4 4ER* Tel (020) 8401 6148

GREGORY, Ivan Henry. b 31. Leeds Univ BA52. Ely Th Coll 58. **d** 60 **p** 60. C Stoke Newington St Faith, St Matthias and All SS *Lon* 60-63; C Withycombe Raleigh *Ex* 63-67; V Braunton 67-77; V Tintagel *Truro* 77-93; RD Trigg Minor 84-86; rtd 93. *20 Greenfields Avenue, Alton GU34 2ED* Tel (01420) 542804

GREGORY, John Frederick. b 33. Glouc Sch of Min 75. **d** 78 **p** 78. NSM S Cerney w Cerney Wick *Glouc* 78-81; NSM Coates, Rodmarton and Sapperton etc 81-88; P-in-c Kempsford w Welford 88-98; rtd 98; Perm to Offic *B & W* from 99. *Mount Cottage, Skilgate, Taunton TA4 2DQ*

GREGORY, Judith Rosalind. See GAVIN, Mrs Judith Rosalind

GREGORY, Peter. b 35. Cranmer Hall Dur 59. **d** 62 **p** 63. C Pennington *Man* 62-65; C N Ferriby *York* 65-68; V Tonge Fold *Man* 68-72; V Hollym w Welwick and Holmpton *York* 72-77; P-in-c Foston w Flaxton 77-80; P-in-c Crambe w Whitwell and Huttons Ambo 77-80; R Whitwell w Crambe, Flaxton, Foston etc 81-94; rtd 94. *6 High Terrace, Northallerton DL6 1BG* Tel (01609) 776956

GREGORY, Richard Branson. b 33. Fitzw Ho Cam BA58 MA62. Sarum Th Coll 58 Ridley Hall Cam 59. **d** 60 **p** 61. C Sheff St Cuth *Sheff* 60-62; Asst Chapl Leeds Univ *Ripon* 62-64; V Yeadon St Jo *Bradf* 64-71; R Keighley 71-74; TR Keighley St Andr 74-82; Hon Can Bradf Cathl 71-82; RD S Craven 71-73 and 78-82; P-in-c Broadmayne, W Knighton, Owermoigne etc *Sarum* 82-85; R 85-98; rtd 98; Perm to Offic *Sarum* from 98. *2 Huish Cottages, Sydling, Dorchester DT2 9NS* Tel (01300) 341835

GREGORY, Canon Stephen Simpson. b 40. Nottm Univ BA62 CertEd63. St Steph Ho Ox. **d** 68 **p** 69. C Aldershot St Mich *Guildf* 68-71; Chapl St Mary's Sch Wantage 71-74; R Edgefield *Nor* 74-88; R Holt 74-94; R Holt w High Kelling 94-95; RD Holt 79-84 and 93-95; Hon Can Nor Cathl 94-95; V Prestbury *Glouc* 95-03; P-in-c Pittville All SS 99-03; TR Prestbury and All SS from 03; RD Cheltenham from 00. *The Vicarage, Tatchley Lane, Prestbury, Cheltenham GL52 3DQ* Tel (01242) 244373
E-mail prestbur@globalnet.co.uk

GREGORY, Timothy Stephen. b 48. Sheff City Coll of Educn CertEd70 Coll of Ripon & York St Jo DipTh99. N Ord Course 96. **d** 99 **p** 00. NSM Deepcar *Sheff* from 99. *33 St Margaret Avenue, Deepcar, Sheffield S36 2TE* Tel 0114-288 4198
E-mail tim.gregory@virgin.net

GREGORY-SMITH, Hew Quentin. b 69. Univ of Wales (Abth) BSc93. St Mich Coll Llan 98. **d** 01 **p** 02. C Pembroke Gp *St D* from 01. *Silva Piana, Woodbine Terrace, Pembroke SA71 4PQ* Tel (01646) 687325

GREGSON, Gillian Amy. b 33. LSE CQSW78 Westmr Coll Ox BTh02. LNSM course 95. **d** 98 **p** 99. OLM Coulsdon St Jo *S'wark* from 98. *3 Coulsdon Road, Coulsdon CR5 2LG* Tel (020) 8660 0304

GREGSON, Peter John. b 36. Univ Coll Dur BSc61. Ripon Hall Ox 61. **d** 63 **p** 64. C Radcliffe St Thos *Man* 63-65; C Baguley 65-67; Chapl RN 68-91; V Ashburton w Buckland in the Moor and Bickington *Ex* 91-01; RD Moreton 95-98; rtd 01. *Beech Tree Cottage, Rectory Road, Broadmayne, Dorchester DT2 8EG* Tel (01305) 852478

GREIG, George Malcolm. b 28. CA53 St Andr Univ BD95. LNSM course 75. **d** 81 **p** 82. NSM Dundee St Mary Magd *Bre* 81-84; NSM Dundee St Jo 82-84; P-in-c Dundee St Ninian 84-85; Chapl St Paul's Cathl Dundee 85-98. *61 Charleston Drive, Dundee DD2 2HE* Tel (01382) 566709

GREIG, John Kenneth. b 38. Natal Univ BA57. St Paul's Coll Grahamstown LTh60. **d** 61 **p** 62. S Africa 61-66 and 71-78; C Friern Barnet St Jas *Lon* 66-69; C Kenton 69-71; Chapl Whitelands Coll of HE *S'wark* 78-84; Area Ecum Officer (Croydon) from 84; V Purley St Swithun from 84. *Windsor Lodge, Purley Rise, Purley CR8 3AW* Tel (020) 8660 3744

GREIG, Martin David Sandford. b 45. Bris Univ BSc67. St Jo Coll Nottm 72. **d** 75 **p** 76. C Keresley and Coundon *Cov* 75-79; C Rugby St Andr 79-83; TV 83-86; V Cov St Geo 86-93; TV Southgate *Chich* 93-01; R Maresfield from 01; P-in-c Nutley from 01. *16 The Paddock, Maresfield, Uckfield TN22 2HQ* Tel (01825) 764536 E-mail martin.greig@ntlworld.com *or* martin.greig@dsl.pipex.com

GREIG, Michael Lawrie Dickson. b 48. Shuttleworth Agric Coll NDA70. All Nations Chr Coll 78 St Jo Coll Nottm 94. **d** 96 **p** 97. C Hunningham *Cov* 96-00; C Wappenbury w Weston under Wetherley 96-00; C Offchurch 96-00; C Long Ichington and Marton 96-00; P-in-c Napton-on-the-Hill, Lower Shuckburgh etc from 00. *The Vicarage, Butt Hill, Napton, Rugby CV47 8NE* Tel (01926) 812383
E-mail mg@biggles99.freeserve.co.uk

GRELLIER, Brian Rudolph. b 34. AKC61. **d** 62 **p** 63. C Wandsworth St Paul *S'wark* 62-66; Japan 66-72; Miss to Seamen 72-76; V Freiston w Butterwick *Linc* 76-97; Chapl HM Pris N Sea Camp 89-96; rtd 97; Perm to Offic *Chich* from 99. *4 Fairfield Crescent, Hurstpierpoint, Hassocks BN6 9SE* Tel (01273) 833437

GRENFELL, James Christopher. b 69. Qu Coll Ox BA93 MA96 MPhil95 Ox Univ DPhil00. Westcott Ho Cam 98. **d** 00 **p** 01. C Kirkby *Liv* 00-03; P-in-c Sheff Manor *Sheff* from 03. *St Aidan's Vicarage, 2 Manor Lane, Sheffield S2 1UF* Tel 0114-272 4676
E-mail james.grenfell@btinternet.com

GRENFELL, Joanne Woolway. b 72. Oriel Coll Ox BA93 DPhil97 Univ of BC MA94. Westcott Ho Cam 98. **d** 00 **p** 01. C Kirkby *Liv* 00-03; C Sheff Manor *Sheff* from 03. *St Aidan's Vicarage, 2 Manor Lane, Sheffield S2 1UF* Tel 0114-272 4676

GRENHAM-TOZE, Mrs Sharon Carmel. b 66. Reading Univ LLB87 Solicitor 92. Trin Coll Bris 94 St Alb and Ox Min Course DipTh98. **d** 98 **p** 00. C Buckingham *Ox* 98-00; C Milton Keynes 00-02; Miss Adv USPG *Lon, Ox* and *St Alb* from 02. *The Vicarage, 15 Vicarage Lane, Wilstead, Bedford MK45 3EU* Tel (01234) 740423 *or* 742550 E-mail violet@ukgateway.net *or* sharong@uspg.org.uk

GRESHAM, Miss Karen Louise. b 75. Hull Univ LLB96. Ripon Coll Cuddesdon BA01. **d** 02 **p** 03. C Leesfield *Man* from 02. *124 Spring Lane, Lees, Oldham OL4 5BD* Tel 0161-652 6398

GRETTON, Tony Butler. b 29. St Jo Coll Dur BA53. **d** 54 **p** 55. C W Teignmouth *Ex* 54-57; R Norton Fitzwarren *B & W* 57-68; rtd 68; Chapl Glouc Docks Mariners' Ch *Glouc* 73-92; P-in-c Brookthorpe w Whaddon 79-82; Hon C The Edge, Pitchcombe, Harescombe and Brookthorpe 82-89; Perm to Offic from 89. *18 Clover Drive, Hardwicke, Gloucester GL2 4TG* Tel (01452) 721505

GREW, Nicholas David. b 52. Surrey Univ BSc74 MSc75. Wycliffe Hall Ox DipMin95. **d** 95 **p** 96. C Biddulph *Lich* 95-99; P-in-c Knaphill *Guildf* 99-00; V Knaphill w Brookwood from 00. *Trinity House, Trinity Road, Knaphill, Woking GU21 2SY* Tel (01483) 473489 E-mail nickthevic@onetel.net.uk

GREW, Richard Lewis. b 32. Clare Coll Cam BA54 MA58. Wycliffe Hall Ox 67. **d** 68 **p** 70. C Repton *Derby* 68-73; Asst Chapl Repton Sch Derby 74-93; Lic to Offic *Derby* 73-93; rtd 93; Perm to Offic *Sarum* from 94. *5 Priory Gardens, Spetisbury, Blandford Forum DT11 9DS* Tel (01258) 857613

GREWCOCK, Peter Joseph. b 28. Sarum Th Coll. **d** 58 **p** 59. C Mitcham St Barn *S'wark* 58-60; C Kingswood 60-62; V Howe Bridge *Man* 62-72; P-in-c Werrington, St Giles in the Heath and Virginstow *Truro* 72-73; V Leic St Chad *Leic* 73-76; P-in-c Trotton w Chithurst *Chich* 76-80; C Broadstone *Sarum* 80-84; TV Gillingham 84-88; P-in-c Milborne St Andrew w Dewlish 88-92; rtd 92; Perm to Offic *Sarum* 92-98. *9 Hambledon Close, Blandford Forum DT11 7SA* Tel (01258) 450893

GREY, Canon Edward Alwyn. b 23. Univ of Wales (Swansea) BA48. St D Coll Lamp. **d** 50 **p** 51. C Wrexham *St As* 50-58; R Llanfynydd 58-69; R Flint 69-89; RD Holywell 73-89; Can St As Cathl 76-89; rtd 89. *60 Gronant Road, Prestatyn LL19 9NE* Tel (01745) 855302

GREY, Richard Thomas. b 50. TD94. St D Coll Lamp BA73 Ripon Hall Ox 73. **d** 75 **p** 76. C Blaenavon w Capel Newydd *Mon* 75-77; Ind Chapl 77-02; C Newport St Paul 77-80; CF (TA) from 78; Chapl Aberbargoed Hosp 80-88; V Bedwellty *Mon* 80-88; R Llanwenarth Ultra 88-92; R Govilon w Llanfoist w Llanelen 92-02; RD Abergavenny 98-02; V Brynmawr *S & B* from 02. *The Vicarage, Dumfries Place, Brynmawr, Ebbw Vale NP23 4RA* Tel (01495) 310405

GREY, Canon Roger Derrick Masson. b 38. AKC61. **d** 62 **p** 63. C Darlington H Trin *Dur* 62-63; C Bishopwearmouth St Mich 63-67; V Mabe *Truro* 67-70; Dioc Youth Chapl 67-70; Youth Chapl *Glouc* 70-77; V Stroud H Trin 77-82; Dioc Can Res Glouc Cathl 82-03; Dir of Educn 82-94; Bp's Chapl from 94; Clergy Widows' Officer (Glouc Adnry) from 03. *12 Buckingham Close, Walton Cardiff, Tewkesbury GL20 7QA* Tel (01684) 275742

GREY, Stephen Bernard. b 56. Linc Th Coll 86. **d** 88 **p** 89. C Worsley *Man* 88-93; V Bamford from 93; P-in-c Rochdale St Geo w St Alb from 99. *St Michael's Vicarage, 389 Bury and Rochdale Old Road, Heywood OL10 4AT* Tel (01706) 369610

GREY, Canon Thomas Hilton. b 18. St D Coll Lamp BA39 Keble Coll Ox BA41 MA46. St Mich Coll Llan 41. **d** 42 **p** 43. C Aberystwyth H Trin *St D* 42-49; R Ludchurch and Templeton 49-64; R Haverfordwest St Thos and Haroldston E St Issell 64-77; Can St D Cathl 72-84; Treas St D Cathl 80-84; RD Roose 74-84; R Haverfordwest St Mary and St Thos w Haroldston 77-84; rtd 85. *3 Gwscwm Park, Burry Port SA16 0DX* Tel (01554) 833629

GREY-SMITH, Donald Edward. b 31. ACT ThL64. **d** 64 **p** 65. Australia 64-68 and from 71; W Germany 68-69; C Weeke *Win* 69-71; rtd 96. *6/317 Military Road, Semaphore Park, S Australia 5019* Tel (0061) (8) 8449 4420

GRIBBEN, John Gibson. b 44. Lon Univ DipTh73 K Coll Lon BD75 QUB MTh81. CITC 73. **d** 75 **p** 76. C Dunmurry *Conn* 75-78; CR from 79; Lic to Offic *Wakef* from 83. *House of the Resurrection, Stocks Bank Road, Mirfield WF14 0BN* Tel (01924) 490441

GRIBBIN, Canon Bernard Byron. b 35. Bradf Univ MPhil84. St Aid Birkenhead 58. **d** 60 **p** 61. C Maghull *Liv* 60-63; C Prescot 63-65; V Denholme Gate *Bradf* 65-71; V Bankfoot 71-79; Dioc Stewardship Adv 79-86; Prec and Chapl Choral Ches Cathl *Ches* 86-91; V Ringway 91-96; Dioc Tourism Officer 91-96; Hon Can Ches Cathl 91-96; rtd 96; Perm to Offic *Bradf* from 96. *Abbey Way, 12 Hodgson Fold, Addingham, Ilkley LS29 0HA* Tel (01943) 831502

GRIBBLE, Howard Frank. b 27. Magd Coll Cam BA50 MA56. Ely Th Coll 50. **d** 52 **p** 53. C Leytonstone St Marg w St Columba *Chelmsf* 52-56; N Rhodesia 56-59; Metrop Area Sec UMCA 59-62; V Harlow St Mary Magd *Chelmsf* 62-70; R Lawhitton *Truro* 70-81; R Lezant 70-81; RD Trigg Major 75-79; P-in-c S Petherwin w Trewen 77-79; Chapl R Cornwall Hosps Trust 81-84; rtd 84; Perm to Offic *Truro* from 84. *Westerlies, Marine Drive, Widemouth Bay, Bude EX23 0AQ* Tel (01288) 361528

GRIBBLE, Malcolm George. b 44. Chu Coll Cam BA67 MA71. Linc Th Coll 79. **d** 81 **p** 82. C Farnborough *Roch* 81-84; V Bostall Heath 84-90; V Bexleyheath Ch Ch 90-02; P-in-c Hever, Four Elms and Mark Beech from 02. *The Rectory, Rectory Lane, Hever, Edenbridge TN8 7LH* Tel (01732) 862249 E-mail malcolm@gribule.net

GRICE, Charles. b 24. MBE83. **d** 58 **p** 59. C Stocksbridge *Sheff* 58-61; R Armthorpe 61-66; Ind Missr 66-69; Ind Chapl 69-76; V Tinsley 69-73; V Oughtibridge 73-76; Gen Sec Ch Lads' and Ch Girls' Brigade 77-91; R Braithwell w Bramley *Sheff* 88-91; rtd 89; Perm to Offic *Sheff* from 89. *57 Deepdale Road, Rotherham S61 2NR* Tel (01709) 557551

GRICE, Canon David Richard. b 32. Keble Coll Ox BA55 MA59. St Steph Ho Ox 55. **d** 57 **p** 58. C Leeds St Aid *Ripon* 57-61; C Middleton St Mary 61-62; V Woodlesford 62-69; V Leeds St Wilfrid 69-78; TR Seacroft 78-93; Hon Can Ripon Cathl 92-99; P-in-c Thorner 93-95; V 95-99; rtd 99. *15 Manor Close, Leeds LS15 9JR* Tel 0113-260 4371 E-mail david@grice12.freeserve.co.uk

GRIDLEY, Miss Susan Mary. b 49. EAMTC 94. **d** 97 **p** 98. NSM Doddinghurst and Mountnessing *Chelmsf* from 97. *11 Worrin Close, Shenfield CM15 8DG* Tel (01277) 210137

GRIER, James Emerson. b 74. St Pet Coll Ox BA95 MA01. Wycliffe Hall Ox 96. **d** 98 **p** 99. C Ox St Andr *Ox* 98-02; C Harborne Heath *Birm* from 02. *33 Margaret Road, Harborne, Birmingham B17 0EU* Tel 07947-834365 (mobile) E-mail jamesgrier@btinternet.com

GRIERSON, Peter Stanley. b 42. Lon Univ BD68 Leeds Univ MPhil74. Linc Th Coll 68. **d** 69 **p** 70. C Clitheroe St Mary *Blackb* 69-71; C Ashton upon Mersey *Sheff* 71-74; V Preston St Jude w St Paul *Blackb* 74-81; V Blackb St Luke w St Phil 89-97; RD Blackb 91-97; V Burnley St Matt w H Trin 97-02. *2 Spindle Mill, Skipton BD23 1NY* Tel (01756) 797175

GRIEVE, David Campbell. b 51. St Jo Coll Dur BA74. Wycliffe Hall Ox 74. **d** 76 **p** 77. C Upton (Overchurch) *Ches* 76-80; C Selston *S'well* 80-82; V Pelton *Dur* 82-89; rtd 89. *17 Mayfield, Barnard Castle DL12 8EA* Tel (01833) 638253 E-mail davidgrieve@cix.co.uk

GRIEVE (née PIERSSENÉ), Frances Jane. b 55. St Jo Coll Dur BA76. Cranmer Hall Dur 99. **d** 01 **p** 02. C Barnard Castle w Whorlton *Dur* from 01. *17 Mayfield, Barnard Castle DL12 8EA* Tel (01833) 638253 E-mail davidgrieve@cix.co.uk

GRIEVE, Mrs Judith Margaret. b 52. Goldsmiths' Coll Lon CertEd73. NEOC 91. **d** 94 **p** 96. NSM Choppington *Newc* 94-99; P-in-c Woodhorn w Newbiggin from 99. *The Vicarage, 34A Front Street, Newbiggin-by-the-Sea NE64 6PS* Tel (01670) 817220

GRIEVES, Anthony Michael. b 47. St Alb Minl Tr Scheme 81. **d** 84 **p** 85. NSM Stevenage St Mary Shephall *St Alb* 84-86; NSM Stevenage St Mary Sheppall w Aston 86-95; Perm to Offic from 95. *27 Falcon Close, Stevenage SG2 9PG* Tel (01438) 727204

GRIEVES, Ian Leslie. b 56. Bede Coll Dur CertEd77 BEd78. Chich Th Coll 82. **d** 84 **p** 85. C Darlington St Mark w St Paul *Dur* 84-87; C Whickham 87-89; V Darlington St Jas from 89. *St James's Vicarage, Vicarage Road, Darlington DL1 1JW* Tel (01325) 465980 E-mail father_grieves@lineone.net

GRIFFIN, Alan Howard Foster. b 44. TCD BA66 MA69 Peterho Cam PhD71. Sarum & Wells Th Coll 75. **d** 78 **p** 79. Lect Ex Univ 78-01; Asst to Lazenby Chapl 78-92; Sub-Warden Duryard Halls 78-81; Warden 81-84; Sen Warden 84-98; Perm to Offic *Ex* 92-98; C Heavitree w Ex St Paul 98-01; Ex Campus Chapl Plymouth Univ 98-01; R St Andr-by-the-Wardrobe w St Ann, Blackfriars *Lon* from 01; R St Jas Garlickhythe w St Mich Queenhithe etc from 01; CME Officer (Two Cities Area) from 01. *St Andrew's House, 35 St Andrew's Hill, London EC4V 5DE* Tel (020) 7248 7546

GRIFFIN, Christopher Donald. b 59. Reading Univ BA80 CertEd81. Wycliffe Hall Ox DipTh85. **d** 85 **p** 86. C Gerrards Cross *Ox* 85-88; Chapl Felsted Sch 88-98; Perm to Offic *Chelmsf* 88-98; Chapl Sedbergh Sch from 98; Lic to Offic *Bradf* from 98. *Sedbergh School, Sedbergh LA10 5HG* Tel (01539) 620535

GRIFFIN, Dennis Gordon. b 24. Worc Ord Coll 66. **d** 68 **p** 69. C Cradley *Worc* 68-69; V Rainbow Hill St Barn 69-74; R Broughton St Jo *Man* 74-79; V Pendlebury Ch Ch 79-86; rtd 89. *20 The Quadrangle, The Beauchamp Community, Newland, Malvern WR13 5AX* Tel (01684) 563371

GRIFFIN, Gerald Albert Francis. b 31. Qu Coll Birm 74. **d** 77 **p** 78. NSM Bushbury *Lich* 77-83; Ind Chapl *Dur* 83-88; Chapl HM Pris Man 88-89; Chapl HM Pris Featherstone 89-93; C Toxteth St Philemon w St Gabr and St Cleopas *Liv* 93-96; rtd 96; NSM W Bromwich Deanery *Lich* from 00. *7 Chartwell Drive, Bushbury, Wolverhampton WV10 8JL* Tel (01902) 836414

GRIFFIN, Harold Rodan Bristow. b 12. Jes Coll Cam BA33 LLB34 MA43. Ridley Hall Cam 43. **d** 45 **p** 46. C Kirby Moorside w Gillamoor *York* 45-49; C Linthorpe 49-52; C Boylestone *Derby* 52; R Hulland, Atlow and Bradley 52-61; V Framsden *St E* 61-71; R Helmingham 61-71; rtd 77; Perm to Offic *Ely* 91-99. *Highlands, Fitzgerald Road, Woodbridge IP12 1EN* Tel (01394) 383090

GRIFFIN, Joan Angela. b 35. Qu Coll Birm 82. **dss** 85 **d** 92 **p** 94. Moseley St Mary *Birm* 85-92; NSM from 92. *389 Wake Green Road, Birmingham B13 0BH* Tel 0121-777 8772 or 449 2243 Fax 449 2243

GRIFFIN, Canon John Henry Hugh. b 13. St Cath Coll Cam BA35 MA39. Linc Th Coll 35. **d** 38 **p** 39. C Bramford w Burstall *St E* 38-42; P-in-c Halesworth 42-46; R Stratford St Mary 46-72; V Higham 46-72; C Hadleigh w Layham and Shelley 72-73; P-in-c Gt and Lt Glemham 73-79; P-in-c Blaxhall w Stratford St Andrew and Farnham 73-79; Hon Can St E Cathl 78-79; rtd 79; Perm to Offic *St E* from 79. *3 Church Street, Hadleigh, Ipswich IP7 5DT* Tel (01473) 823100

GRIFFIN, Canon Joseph William. b 48. Univ of Wales (Cardiff) DipTh73 DPS74. St Mich Coll Llan 70. **d** 74 **p** 75. C Killay *S & B* 74-78; C Swansea St Thos and Kilvey 78-81; V Troedrhiwgarth *Llan* 81-91; V Llanrhidian w Llanmadoc and Cheriton *S & B* 91-99; RD W Gower 94-99; Hon Can Brecon Cathl from 98; V Swansea St Nic from 99; RD Swansea from 02. *St Nicholas' Vicarage, 58A Dyfed Avenue, Townhill, Swansea SA1 6NG* Tel (01792) 547703

GRIFFIN, Keith. b 66. Nottm Trent Univ BA88. Cranmer Hall Dur BA94. **d** 95 **p** 96. C Gedling *S'well* 95-98; V Barkingside St Geo *Chelmsf* 99-02; TV Upper Holme Valley *Wakef* from 02. *The Vicarage, 3 Vicarage Meadows, Holmfirth HD9 1DZ* Tel (01484) 682644 E-mail revdkg@fish.co.uk

GRIFFIN, Kenneth Francis. b 21. Lon Univ BSc64. St Jo Coll Nottm 72. **d** 73 **p** 74. C Bexleyheath Ch Ch *Roch* 73-77; R Kingsdown 77-82; rtd 86. *Woodlands, Palmers Cross Hill, Rough Common, Canterbury CT2 9BL* Tel (01227) 457314

GRIFFIN, Malcolm Roger. b 46. Goldsmiths' Coll Lon TCert67 Open Univ BA73 DipMgt90 Lon Univ DipRS83 MCIPD91. S'wark Ord Course. **d** 83 **p** 84. NSM Romford St Andr *Chelmsf* 83-87; NSM Romford St Jo 87-91; P-in-c 98-00; NSM Gt Ilford

St Alb 91-97; Perm to Offic 97-98; P-in-c Cratfield w Heveningham and Ubbeston etc *St E* 00-02; Perm to Offic *Nor* and *St E* from 02. *4 Old Forge Court, Brockdish, Diss IP21 4JE* Tel (01379) 669252

GRIFFIN, Mark Richard. b 68. Trin Coll Bris BA93. Westcott Ho Cam 94. **d** 96 **p** 97. C Walmer *Cant* 96-00; V Wingham w Elmstone and Preston w Stourmouth from 00. *St Mary's House, 5 St Mary's Meadow, Wingham, Canterbury CT3 1DF* Tel (01227) 721530 E-mail revd.mark.griffin@talk21.com

GRIFFIN, Michael. b 59. **d** 01 **p** 01. C Kirkdale St Lawr *Liv* 01-02; P-in-c from 02. *St Lawrence's Vicarage, 21 Westminster Close, Liverpool L4 1XB* Tel 0151-922 5794

GRIFFIN, Canon Michael Richard. b 19. CD78. Trin Coll Bris 43. **d** 44 **p** 44. C Tonbridge St Steph *Roch* 44-45; C Tunbridge Wells H Trin 45-47; V Hindley St Pet *Liv* 47-51; Canada from 51; Can Huron from 64; CStJ from 78. *68 Caledonia Street, Stratford ON, Canada, N5A 5W6*

GRIFFIN, Niall Paul. b 37. TCD BA61 Div Test61. **d** 61 **p** 62. C Newtownards *D & D* 61-63; C Arm St Mark *Arm* 63-64; Jamaica 64-66; C Lurgan Ch the Redeemer *D & D* 66-69; Chapl RAF 69-84; Missr Chr Renewal Cen *D & D* 84-89; Nat Dir (Ireland) SOMA UK from 89. *7 Cloughmore Park, Rostrevor, Newry BT34 3AX* Tel (028) 4173 8959 Fax as telephone E-mail n&g@griffin.go-plus.net

GRIFFIN, Nigel Robert. b 50. Univ of Wales (Lamp) BA71. Ripon Hall Ox 71. **d** 73 **p** 74. C Burry Port and Pwll *St D* 73-77; C Carmarthen St Pet 77-79; Youth Chapl 79-86; V Whitland and Kiffig 80-89; Warden of Ords 86-91; V Llangunnor w Cwmffrwd 89-92; RD Carmarthen 91-92; R Aberporth w Tremain and Blaenporth 92-95; R Aberporth w Tremain w Blaenporth and Betws Ifan 95-96; Chapl Morriston Hosp/Ysbyty Treforys NHS Trust 96-99; Chapl Swansea NHS Trust from 99. *Morriston Hospital, Heol Maes Eglwys, Cwmrhydyceirw, Swansea SA6 8EL* Tel (01792) 702222

GRIFFIN, Canon Roger Thomas Kynaston. b 14. ALCD41. **d** 41 **p** 42. C Norbiton *S'wark* 41-45; V Gd Easter *Chelmsf* 45-55; R Berners Roding 45-55; R Abbess and Beauchamp Roding 49-55; V Becontree St Alb 55-61; V W Ham 61-82; P-in-c Plaistow St Mary 71-72; Chmn RADD 73-86; Hon Can Chelmsf Cathl 80-82; rtd 82; Perm to Offic *B & W* 83-98. *c/o Mrs M Williams, Lattice House, Short Green, Winfarthing, Diss IP22 2EH*

GRIFFIN, Canon Rutland Basil. b 16. ALCD41. **d** 41 **p** 42. C Aylesbury *Ox* 41-45; C Bp's Hatfield *St Alb* 45-50; V Biggleswade 50-61; V Dartford H Trin *Roch* 61-84; RD Dartford 64-84; Hon Can Roch Cathl 70-84; rtd 84; Perm to Offic *Roch* and *Cant* 84-95; *Cov* 97-00. *10 Upper Stables, Parkfield Way, Haywards Heath RH16 4TA* Tel (01444) 474440

GRIFFIN, The Very Revd Victor Gilbert Benjamin. b 24. MRIA TCD BA46 MA57 Hon DD92. CITC 47. **d** 47 **p** 48. C Londonderry St Aug *D & R* 47-51; C Londonderry Ch 51-57; I 57-68; Preb Howth St Patr Cathl Dublin 62-68; Dean St Patr Cathl Dublin 68-91; rtd 91. *7 Tyler Road, Limavady BT49 0DW* Tel (028) 7176 2093

GRIFFIN, William George. b 13. St Pet Hall Ox BA36 MA45. Wycliffe Hall Ox 36. **d** 37 **p** 38. C Chatham St Paul *Roch* 37-41; P-in-c Strood St Fran 41-45; V Lozells St Paul *Birm* 45-51; V Birm Bp Ryder 51-56; V Burton All SS *Lich* 56-59; V Bretby w Newton Solney *Derby* 59-66; V Church Broughton w Barton and Sutton on the Hill 66-72; R Brington w Whilton *Pet* 72-78; rtd 78; Perm to Offic *Pet* 86-01. *6 Riverside Drive, Weedon, Northampton NN7 4RT* Tel (01327) 41585

GRIFFISS, Mrs Helen Mary. b 48. Univ of Wales (Ban) CertEd69 K Alfred's Coll Win MA98. STETS. **d** 00 **p** 01. NSM Bransgore *Win* from 00; Perm to Offic *Sarum* from 01. *4 Pease Close, Bransgore, Christchurch BH23 8NQ* Tel and fax (01425) 629531 *or* tel 672108 Mobile 07909-536154 E-mail uspgfwhg@dircon.co.uk

GRIFFITH, Brian Vann. b 34. Univ Sch Th Abth & Lamp DipTh82 BTh91 MTh94 St D Dioc Tr Course 81. **d** 82 **p** 83. NSM C Aberystwyth *St D* 82-87; NSM Llanfihangel w Llanafan and Llanwnnws etc 87-88; NSM C Llanbadarn Fawr w Capel Bangor and Goginan 88-93; Public Preacher 93-96; NSM Machynlleth w Llanwrin and Penegoes *Ban* 97-99; rtd 99; Perm to Offic *St D* from 00. *14 Ystwyth Close, Penparcau, Aberystwyth SY23 3RU*

GRIFFITH, The Ven David Vaughan. b 36. St D Coll Lamp BA60. Lich Th Coll 60. **d** 62 **p** 63. C Llanfairfechan *Ban* 62-66; C Dolgellau 66-67; R Llanfair Talhaiarn *St As* 70-82; R Llanfairtalhaiarn and Llansannan 82-85; P-in-c Llangernyw, Gwytherin and Llanddewi 77-85; V Colwyn 85-98; Warden of Readers 91-99; Can Cursal St As Cathl 95-98; P-in-c Berriew and Manafon 98-99; V 99-02; Preb St As Cathl and Adn Montgomery 99-02; rtd 02. *1 Bishop's Walk, St Asaph LL17 0SU* Tel (01745) 582903

GRIFFITH, Donald Bennet. b 17. Dur Univ LTh40. St Aid Birkenhead 36. **d** 40 **p** 41. C Collyhurst St Oswald *Man* 40-43; C Pendlebury St Jo 43-45; P-in-c Pendleton 45-47; V Everton St Cuth *Liv* 47-52; V Lathom 52-58; R Frating w Thorrington *Chelmsf* 58-66; R Lawford 66-73; R Theydon Garnon 73-77;

P-in-c Bradfield 77-82; rtd 82; Perm to Offic *Chelmsf* from 82. *Porto Cristo, Mill Lane, Thorpe-le-Soken, Clacton-on-Sea CO16 0ED* Tel (01255) 861766

GRIFFITH, Frank Michael. b 24. Bris Univ BSc50 Lon Univ DipTh60. St Aid Birkenhead 58. **d** 60 **p** 61. C Leamington Priors H Trin *Cov* 60-63; C Stratford-on-Avon w Bishopton 63-67; V Rounds Green *Birm* 67-70; R Barford *Cov* 70-78; V Wasperton 70-78; RD Stratford-on-Avon 77-79; R Barford w Wasperton and Sherbourne 78-89; RD Fosse 79-87; rtd 90; Perm to Offic *Cov* from 90. *Wusi, Armscote Road, Tredington, Shipston-on-Stour CV36 4NP* Tel (01608) 661621

GRIFFITH, Canon Geoffrey Grenville. b 17. Linc Coll Ox BA48 MA56. Chich Th Coll 48. **d** 50 **p** 51. C Newland St Aug *York* 50-53; R Waddington *Linc* 53-57; Chapl Dur Univ *Dur* 57-66; V Chapel-en-le-Frith *Derby* 66-84; RD Buxton 71-78; Hon Can Derby Cathl 80-84; rtd 84; Perm to Offic *Derby* 84-90; Chapl HM Pris Morton Hall 85-90; Chapl St Barn Hospice Linc 91-94. *292 Hykenham Road, Lincoln LN6 8BJ* Tel (01522) 695683

GRIFFITH, Glyn Keble Gethin. b 37. St D Coll Lamp BA59. Ridley Hall Cam 67. **d** 69 **p** 70. C Derby St Aug *Derby* 69-72; C Coity w Nolton *Llan* 72-75; P-in-c Heage *Derby* 75-81; V Allestree St Nic 81-92; R Wilne and Draycott w Breaston 92-01; rtd 01. *3 Cornford Close, Osbaston, Monmouth NP25 3NT* Tel (01600) 719740

GRIFFITH, Canon Hugh Emrys. b 24. St D Coll Lamp BA53. **d** 54 **p** 55. C Welshpool *St As* 54-56; C Abergele 56-58; R Llanfair Talhaiarn 58-61; R Llangeinwen w Llangaffo and Llanfair-yn-y-Cwmwd *Ban* 61-75; R Llanllyfni 75-81; R Amlwch 81-94; RD Twrcelyn 82-94; Can Ban Cathl from 89; rtd 94; Perm to Offic *Ban* from 94. *Llys Caerwynt, Rhos-y-bol, Amlwch LL68 9PR* Tel (01407) 831917

GRIFFITH, Canon John Vaughan. b 33. LTh73. St D Coll Lamp 53. **d** 58 **p** 59. C Holyhead w Rhoscolyn *Ban* 58-63; R Maentwrog w Trawsfynydd 63-68; Chapl RAF 68-72; V Winnington *Ches* 72-76; V Northwich St Luke and H Trin 76-81; V Sandiway 81-98; Dioc Communications Officer 84-86; Hon Can Ches Cathl 89-98; rtd 98; Perm to Offic *Ches* from 99. *41 Moss Lane, Cuddington, Northwich CW8 2PT*

GRIFFITH, Peter Malcolm. b 43. FRICS71. EAMTC 94. **d** 97 **p** 98. NSM Stilton w Denton and Caldecote etc *Ely* 97-99; R Sawtry and Glatton from 00. *The Rectory, Church Causeway, Sawtry, Huntingdon PE28 5TD* Tel (01487) 830215 E-mail rev.griffith@tiscall.co.uk

GRIFFITH, Steven Ellsworth. b 53. St Steph Ho Ox. **d** 87 **p** 88. C Holyhead w Rhoscolyn w Llanfair-yn-Neubwll *Ban* 87-90; CF from 90. *c/o MOD Chaplains (Army)* Tel (01980) 615804 Fax 615800

GRIFFITH, Mrs Wendy Margaret. b 41. **d** 01 **p** 02. NSM Sixpenny Handley w Gussage St Andrew etc *Sarum* from 01. *Horsehill Cottage, Donhead St Mary, Shaftesbury SP7 9DS* Tel (01747) 828495 Mobile 07720-942996 E-mail wendy@michaelblyth.co.uk

GRIFFITH, William Stephen. b 50. MBE02. Univ of Wales (Ban) BA71 FRAS93. Westcott Ho Cam 71. **d** 73 **p** 74. C Llandudno *Ban* 73-76; C Calne and Blackland *Sarum* 76-78; P-in-c Broadwindsor w Burstock and Seaborough 78-79; TV Beaminster Area 79-81; Lic to Offic 81-83; Chapl St Pet Sch York 83-87; C Leeds St Pet *Ripon* 87; Chapl Bearwood Coll Wokingham 87-92; CMS Jordan 92-95; Chapl Univ of Wales (Cardiff) *Llan* 95-96; Chapl Damascus 96-02; Lic to Offic *Eur* from 98; P-in-c Yerevan from 03; P-in-c Baku from 03; P-in-c Tbilisi from 03. *Apt 13, 190 Antarain, Yerevan, Armenia* Tel (00374) (2) 522409 E-mail apocrisiarios@yahoo.co.uk

GRIFFITH-JONES, Robin Guthrie. b 56. New Coll Ox BA78 Ch Coll Cam BA88. Westcott Ho Cam 86. **d** 89 **p** 90. C Cantril Farm *Liv* 89-92; Chapl Linc Coll Ox 92-99; Master of The Temple from 99. *The Master's House, Temple, London EC4 7BB* Tel (020) 7353 8559 E-mail master@templechurch.com

GRIFFITHS, Ainsley. See GRIFFITHS, John Mark Ainsley

GRIFFITHS, Alan Charles. b 46. Dur Univ BA67 DipTh69. Cranmer Hall Dur 66. **d** 69 **p** 70. C Leic H Apostles *Leic* 69-72; Lic to Offic *York* 73-77; V Lea Hall *Birm* 77-87; Asst Dir of Educn *Sheff* 87-92; V W Bessacarr 92-02; V Conisbrough from 02. *The Vicarage, 8 Castle Avenue, Conisbrough, Doncaster DN12 3BT* Tel (01709) 864695

GRIFFITHS, Alec. b 42. St Chad's Coll Dur BA63 DipTh65. **d** 65 **p** 66. C Glas St Ninian *Glas* 65-68; C Greenock 68-72; R Glas H Cross 72-79; V Birchencliffe *Wakef* 79-83; Chapl Kingston Hosp Surrey 83-99; rtd 99; Perm to Offic *S'wark* 99-00; Hon C W Acton St Martin *Lon* from 00; Hon C Ealing All SS from 00; Perm to Offic *S'wark* from 00. *St Martin's Cottage, Hale Gardens, London W3 9SQ* Tel (020) 8896 9009 Fax as telephone

GRIFFITHS, Andrew Taylor. b 68. Jes Coll Ox BA92 MA96. Cranmer Hall Dur 98. **d** 00 **p** 01. C Paris St Mich *Eur* from 00. *6 rue de Behagle, 92400 Courbevoie, France* Tel (0033) (1) 47 68 76 50 E-mail saintmichaelsparis@free.fr

GRIFFITHS, Arthur Evan. b 27. ACP66. St Deiniol's Hawarden. **d** 69 **p** 70. Hon C Cleobury Mortimer w Hopton Wafers *Heref* 69-83; C 84-86; P-in-c Coreley and Doddington 86-88; P-in-c

Knowbury 86-88; rtd 89; Perm to Offic *Heref* from 93. *Maryn, Catherton Road, Cleobury Mortimer, Kidderminster DY14 8EB* Tel (01299) 270489

GRIFFITHS, Beatrice Mary. b 29. Chelsea Coll Lon DipPE50 CertEd60 Lon Univ CertRK60. Westcott Ho Cam 85. **dss** 86 **d** 87 **p** 94. W Bridgford *S'well* 86-87; NSM Wilford Hill from 87. *7 Stella Avenue, Tollerton, Nottingham NG12 4EX* Tel 0115-937 4155

GRIFFITHS, Caroline. *See* PRINCE, Caroline Heidi Ann

GRIFFITHS, (née MITCHELL), Mrs Clare. d 01 **p** 02. C Caerleon w Llanhennock *Mon* from 01. *28 Roman Reach, Caerleon, Newport NP18 3SN* Tel (01633) 430746

GRIFFITHS, Canon David. b 38. St Mich Coll Llan DipTh67. **d** 67 **p** 68. C Llangollen *St As* 67-71; C Rhyl 71-74; V Kerry 74-77; V Kerry and Llanmerewig 77-82; R Caerwys and Bodfari 82-87; V Gresford from 87; V Holt from 97; RD Wrexham 97-01; RD Gresford from 01; Can St As Cathl from 98. *The Vicarage, Church Green, Gresford, Wrexham LL12 8RG* Tel (01978) 852236 Fax 856630 E-mail allsaintsgresford@btinternet.com

GRIFFITHS, David Bruce. b 44. Sussex Univ BA69 Hull Univ MA83. Linc Th Coll. **d** 82 **p** 83. C Springfield All SS *Chelmsf* 82-84; TV Horwich *Man* 84-92; V Heaton Ch Ch 92-03; P-in-c Ainsworth from 03. *The Vicarage, Ainsworth Hall Road, Ainsworth, Bolton BL2 5RY* Tel (01204) 398567 E-mail dbgriff@fish.co.uk

GRIFFITHS, David John. b 53. Bromsgrove F E Coll HND76. St Jo Coll Nottm BTh93 DipMM94. **d** 94 **p** 95. C Retford St Sav *S'well* 94-96; NSM Thwaites Brow *Bradf* 96-98; P-in-c Oakenshaw cum Woodlands 98-03; Asst Chapl Airedale NHS Trust 96-03; V Buttershaw St Paul *Bradf* from 03. *St Paul's Vicarage, 42A Wibsey Park Avenue, Bradford BD6 3QA* Tel (01274) 676359

GRIFFITHS, David Mark. b 41. Univ of Wales (Cardiff) BA67 CertEd71. St Mich Coll Llan DMS72. **d** 94 **p** 95. C Llwynderw *S & B* 94-96; R Llanbadarn Fawr, Llandegley and Llanfihangel etc 96-02; V Slebech and Uzmaston w Boulston *St D* from 02. *The Vicarage, Uzmaston, Haverfordwest SA62 4AE* Tel (01437) 762325

GRIFFITHS, David Mark. b 59. Kent Univ BA80. Chich Th Coll 81. **d** 83 **p** 84. C Clydach *S & B* 83-84; C Llwynderw 84-88; V Swansea St Nic 88-98; Chapl Swansea Inst of HE 88-98; V Swansea St Gabr from 98; Chapl Swansea NHS Trust from 98. *St Gabriel's Vicarage, Bryn Road, Brynmill, Swansea SA2 0AP* Tel (01792) 464011

GRIFFITHS, The Ven David Nigel. b 27. RD77. Worc Coll Ox BA52 MA56 Reading Univ PhD91 FSA. Linc Th Coll 56. **d** 58 **p** 59. C Northampton St Matt *Pet* 58-61; SPCK HQ Staff 61-67; Chapl RNR 63-77; Hon C Bromley St Andr *Roch* 65-67; V Linc St Mich *Linc* 67-73; R Linc St Mary Magd w St Paul 67-73; Vice Chan and Lib Linc Cathl 67-73; TR New Windsor *Ox* 73-87; RD Maidenhead 77-82 and 84-87; Chapl to The Queen 77-97; Hon Can Ch Ch *Ox* 83-87; Adn Berks 87-92; rtd 92; Chapl St Anne's Bede Houses Linc 93-00; Perm to Offic *Linc* from 00. *2 Middleton's Field, Lincoln LN2 1QP* Tel (01522) 525753

GRIFFITHS, David Percy Douglas. b 25. St Mich Coll Llan. **d** 78 **p** 79. C Betws w Ammanford *St D* 78-80; V Llanarth w Mydroilyn, Capel Cynon, Talgarreg etc 80-84; V Llanarth and Capel Cynon w Talgarreg etc 84-86; V Newcastle Emlyn w Llandyfriog and Troed-yr-aur 86-95; rtd 95. *The Poplars, Ebenezer Street, Newcastle Emlyn SA38 9BS* Tel (01239) 711448

GRIFFITHS, David Rowson Hopkin. b 38. Oak Hill Th Coll 59. **d** 62 **p** 63. C Barrow St Mark *Carl* 62-65; OMF Internat from 66; Japan 66-88; Philippines from 88; rtd 03. *clo Mrs Bronwen Coe, 52 Shepherds Way, Cirencester GL7 2ET* Tel (01285) 885841

GRIFFITHS, David Wynne. b 47. Univ of Wales (Cardiff) BD73. St Mich Coll Llan 69. **d** 73 **p** 74. Hon C Gabalfa *Llan* 73-76; Lic to Offic 77-79; Hon C Tonypandy w Clydach Vale 79-80; Hon C Pontypridd St Cath 80-87; Perm to Offic from 87. *13 Heol Ty'n-y-Cae, Rhiwbina, Cardiff CF14 6DH*

GRIFFITHS, Ms Elizabeth Leigh. b 61. St Hugh's Coll Ox BA83 MA87 Warwick Univ PGCE84. Ripon Coll Cuddesdon 96. **d** 98 **p** 99. C Bettws *Mon* 98-99; C Maindee 99-01; TV Cen Swansea and Dioc Chapl Tertiary Educn *S & B* 01-03; C St Martin-in-the-Fields *Lon* from 03. *6 St Martin's Place, London WC2N 4JJ* Tel (020) 7766 1102 Fax 7839 5163 E-mail lizgriff@fish.co.uk

GRIFFITHS, Eric. b 33. **d** 02. NSM St Andr-by-the-Wardrobe w St Ann, Blackfriars *Lon* from 02. *The Charterhouse, Charterhouse Square, London EC1M 6AN* Tel (020) 7490 1025 E-mail egcharterhouse@yahoo.co.uk

GRIFFITHS, Garrie Charles. b 53. St Jo Coll Nottm LTh77. **d** 77 **p** 78. Canada 77-78; C Stalybridge H Trin and Ch Ch *Ches* 78-81; C Moreton 81-84; V Godley cum Newton Green 84-89; V Bayston Hill *Lich* 89-01; TR Mildenhall *St E* from 01. *The Rectory, The Street, Barton Mills, Bury St Edmunds IP28 6AP* Tel (01638) 716044 Fax 716040 E-mail garriegriff@whsmithnet.co.uk

GRIFFITHS, Gerald Brian. b 44. Open Univ BA88 IEng. SEITE 97. **d** 00 **p** 01. NSM Cliftonville *Cant* from 00. *8 Park Avenue, Birchington CT7 0DJ* Tel (01843) 848424 E-mail griffiths_brian@hotmail.com

GRIFFITHS, Gerald Lewis. b 38. Westmr Coll Ox MTh97. Qu Coll Birm. **d** 88 **p** 89. C Wrexham *St As* 88-91; TV 91-95; R Hope 95-00; rtd 00. *10 Ryder Close, Wrexham LL13 9GS* Tel (01978) 355244

GRIFFITHS, Gordon John. b 31. Univ of Wales (Cardiff) BA53. S'wark Ord Course 72. **d** 75 **p** 76. NSM Sutton St Nic *S'wark* 75-78; Asst Chapl Eastbourne Coll 78-81; Perm to Offic *Chich* from 81. *15 Buckhurst Close, Willingdon, Eastbourne BN20 9EF* Tel (01323) 505547

GRIFFITHS, Griff. *See* GRIFFITHS, Stephen David

GRIFFITHS, Harvey Stephen. b 35. Linc Coll Ox BA58 MA62. Linc Th Coll 62. **d** 62 **p** 63. C Frodingham *Linc* 62-65; C Darlington St Cuth *Dur* 65-70; Chapl RN 70-92; P-in-c Southwick w Boarhunt *Portsm* from 92. *The White House, High Street, Southwick, Fareham PO17 6EB* Tel (023) 9237 7568 Mobile 07747-093365 E-mail harvey@hsgriffiths.fsnet.co.uk

GRIFFITHS, Mrs Jean Rose. b 36. Avery Hill Coll TCert56. S'wark Ord Course 93. **d** 95 **p** 96. NSM Charlton *S'wark* 95-03; Asst Chapl HM Pris Brixton 95-03; Chapl from 03. *HM Prison Brixton, PO Box 369, Jebb Avenue, London SW2 5XF* Tel (020) 8674 9811 Fax 8674 6128

GRIFFITHS, John Alan. b 48. CPsychol AFBPsS Univ of Wales BSc72 Cape Town Univ MSc76. St Mich Coll Llan 87. **d** 89 **p** 90. C Neath w Llantwit *Llan* 89-93; V Roath St German 93-95. *All Pine Grange, Bath Road, Bournemouth BH1 2PF* Tel (01202) 314120

GRIFFITHS, John Gareth. b 44. Lich Th Coll 68. **d** 71 **p** 72. C Shotton *St As* 71-73; C Rhyl w St Ann 73-76; V Llanasa 76-95; RD Holywell 89-95; V Rhuddlan from 95. *The Vicarage, Vicarage Lane, Rhuddlan, Rhyl LL18 2UE* Tel (01745) 591568

GRIFFITHS, John Mark Ainsley. b 68. Man Univ BSc90 MSc91 PGCE92 Ox Univ BA97. Ripon Coll Cuddesdon 95. **d** 98 **p** 99. Min Can Bangor *Ban* 98-01; P-in-c Denio w Abererch 01-02; V from 02. *The Vicarage, Ala Road, Pwllheli LL53 5BL* Tel (01758) 612305 E-mail ainsley@fish.co.uk

GRIFFITHS, Mrs Judith Rosemary. b 47. Wadh Coll Dur TCert68 CertRS95. SEITE 95. **d** 99 **p** 00. C Charing w Charing Heath and Lt Chart *Cant* 99-03; Perm to Offic from 03. *18 Earls Avenue, Willesborough, Ashford TN24 0AB* Tel (01233) 623790

GRIFFITHS, Malcolm. b 47. St Alb Minl Tr Scheme. **d** 82 **p** 83. NSM Hemel Hempstead *St Alb* 82-86; C 86-87; TV Liskeard, St Keyne, St Pinnock, Morval etc *Truro* 87-96; V Landrake w St Erney and Botus Fleming from 96. *The Vicarage, School Road, Landrake, Saltash PL12 5EA* Tel (01752) 851801

GRIFFITHS, Margaret. *See* MacLACHLAN, Mrs Margaret

GRIFFITHS, Mrs Margarett. b 29. ATCL47 LRAM48. CA Tr Coll 50. **dss** 81 **d** 87. Hackington *Cant* 81-83; Ashford 84-89; Par Dn 87-89; rtd 89. *39 Newington Way, Craven Arms SY7 9PS* Tel (01588) 673848

GRIFFITHS, Mark. *See* GRIFFITHS, David Mark

GRIFFITHS, Canon Martyn Robert. b 51. Nottm Univ BTh74 St Martin's Coll Lanc PGCE75. Kelham Th Coll 70. **d** 74 **p** 75. C Kings Heath *Birm* 74-77; C-in-c Elmdon Heath CD 77-79; TV Solihull 79-81; Asst Admin Shrine of Our Lady of Walsingham 81-85; V Oldham St Steph and All Martyrs *Man* 85-89; TR Swinton and Pendlebury 89-98; Hon Can Man Cathl 96-98; R Preston St Jo and St Geo *Blackb* from 98; Hon Can Blackb Cathl from 00. *The Rectory, 13 Ribblesdale Place, Preston PR1 3NA* Tel (01772) 252528 Fax 202769 E-mail martyn.griffiths@tesco.net

GRIFFITHS, Meirion. b 38. Clifton Th Coll 63. **d** 66 **p** 67. C Upper Holloway St Pet *Lon* 66-68; C Taunton St Jas *B & W* 68-70; C Radipole *Sarum* 70-74; R Chich St Pancras and St Jo *Chich* 74-82; R Corwen and Llangar *St As* 82-88; RD Edeyrnion 82-88; Australia from 88; C Albany 88; R Collie 89-93; P-in-c Maddington 97-00; rtd 00. *27 Coachwood Way, Maddington, W Australia 6109* Tel (0061) (8) 9459 2920 Fax 9452 2720

GRIFFITHS, Mervyn Harrington. b 15. Ripon Hall Ox 53. **d** 54 **p** 55. C Aigburth *Liv* 54-56; C Grassendale 56-58; C Findon *Chich* 58-59; R Brighton *Win* 59-78; V Bishop's Sutton 59-78; rtd 80; Perm to Offic *Ex* from 80. *7 Barnards Farm, Beer, Seaton EX12 3NF* Tel (01297) 22382

GRIFFITHS, Morgan Emlyn. b 17. St D Coll Lamp BA38 St Mich Coll Llan 39. **d** 43 **p** 44. C Loughor *S & B* 43-45; C Defynnog w Rhydybriw and Llandeilo'r Fan 45-47; Barbados 47-59; R Cwmdu and Tretower *S & B* 60-78; V Crickhowell w Cwmdu and Tretower 78-83; rtd 83. *10 St John's, Pendre Close, Brecon LD3 9ED* Tel (01874) 611125

GRIFFITHS, Neville. b 39. Univ of Wales BA63. St D Coll Lamp LTh66. **d** 66 **p** 67. C Newport St Mark *Mon* 66-68; C Cardiff St Jo *Llan* 68-70; Chapl Greystoke Coll Carl 70-76; C Greystoke w Matterdale *Carl* 70-75; TV Greystoke, Matterdale and Mungrisdale 75-76; Chapl Grey Coll Dur 76-81; C Croxdale *Dur* 76-81; R Didsbury Ch Ch *Man* 81-83; P-in-c Lowther and Askham *Carl* 83-84; R 84-88; V Guernsey St Matt *Win* 88-93; R Guernsey St Pierre du Bois 93-02; R Guernsey St Philippe de Torteval 93-02; Vice-Dean Guernsey 99-02; rtd 03. *6 Howlcroft Villas, Neville's Cross, Durham DH1 4DU* Tel 0191-386 4778

GRIFFITHS, Paul Edward. b 48. St Jo Coll Nottm 86. **d** 88 **p** 89. C Ipswich St Andr *St E* 88-92; P-in-c Tollerton *S'well* 92-00; P-in-c Plumtree 95-97; Ind Chapl and Dioc Adv on Ind Soc 97-00; V Hellesdon *Nor* from 00. *The Vicarage, Broom Avenue, Hellesdon, Norwich NR6 6LG* Tel (01603) 426902

GRIFFITHS, Percy. *See* GRIFFITHS, David Percy Douglas

GRIFFITHS, Richard Barre Maw. b 43. CCC Ox BA65 MA69. Cranmer Hall Dur DipTh71 BA71. **d** 71 **p** 72. C Fulwood *Sheff* 71-74; Hon C Sheff St Jo 74-76; Fell Dept of Bibl Studies Sheff Univ 74-76; C Fulham St Matt *Lon* 76-78; P-in-c 78-83; R Chich St Pancras and St Jo *Chich* from 83. *St Pancras's Rectory, 9 St John Street, Chichester PO19 1UR* Tel (01243) 536390 *or* 536387 E-mail stpancraschichester@hotmail.com

GRIFFITHS, Prof Richard Mathias. b 35. K Coll Cam BA57 MA61 PhD62 BNC Ox MA66 FIL91 FKC95. Ox Min Course 89 St Alb and Ox Min Course 96. **d** 97 **p** 98. Prof French K Coll Lon 90-00; NSM W Woodhay w Enborne, Hampstead Marshall etc *Ox* 97-00; NSM Llantrisant *Llan* from 01. *Waltham House, Bradford Place, Penarth CF64 1AG* Tel (029) 2070 7828 Fax 2070 9699 E-mail richard.griffiths@newbury.net

GRIFFITHS, Canon Robert Herbert. b 53. Univ of Wales (Ban) DipTh75. Chich Th Coll 75. **d** 76 **p** 77. C Holywell *St As* 76-80; CF (TA) 79-87; P-in-c Gyffylliog *St As* 80-84; V Llanfair Dyffryn Clwyd 80-84; V Llanfair DC, Derwen, Llanelidan and Efenechtyd 84-88; Asst Dioc Youth Chapl 81-86; Dioc Youth Chapl 86-91; PV St As and Tremeirchion w Cefn 88-97; Chapl H M Stanley Hosp 88-97; Bp's Visitor and Dioc RE Adv *St As* 88-93; Chapl Glan Clwyd Distr Gen Hosp 93-97; V Llanrhos *St As* from 97; Chapl Gwynedd Hosp NHS Trust from 97; Can St As Cathl *St As* from 98; RD Llanrwst from 01. *Llanrhos Vicarage, 2 Vicarage Road, Llandudno LL30 1PT* Tel (01492) 876152

GRIFFITHS, Robert James. b 52. Nottm Univ BTh82. St Jo Coll Nottm 79. **d** 82 **p** 83. C Kettering St Andr *Pet* 82-85; C Collier Row St Jas and Havering-atte-Bower *Chelmsf* 86-89; R High Ongar w Norton Mandeville 89-97; R Ilmington w Stretton-on-Fosse etc *Cov* 97-99; V Newport *Chelmsf* from 99. *The Vicarage, 5 Meadowford, Newport, Saffron Walden CB11 3QL* Tel (01799) 540339 E-mail robert.griffiths@btinternet.com

GRIFFITHS, Roger. b 46. Trin Coll Bris 70. **d** 74 **p** 75. C Normanton *Derby* 74-77; C Bucknall and Bagnall *Lich* 77-80; TV 80-83; TV Aberystwyth *St D* 83-86; R Letterston w Llanfair Nant-y-Gof etc from 86; RD Dewisland and Fishguard from 01. *The Rectory, 122 St David's Road, Letterston, Haverfordwest SA62 5SE* Tel (01348) 840336

GRIFFITHS, Roger Michael. b 47. Wycliffe Hall Ox 83. **d** 86 **p** 87. Min Can St D Cathl *St D* 86-88; V Pen-boyr 88-94; V Fishguard w Llanychar and Pontfaen w Morfil etc 94-03. *Address temp unknown*

GRIFFITHS, Russell Howard. b 22. Glouc Th Course 75. **d** 77 **p** 78. NSM Fownhope w Fawley *Heref* 77-80; NSM Brockhampton 77-80; P-in-c Bridstow w Peterstow 80-81; TV Ross w Brampton Abbotts, Bridstow and Peterstow 81-87; rtd 87; Perm to Offic *Heref* 91-01. *Flat 1, Weirside House, 29 Bridge Avenue, Otley LS21 2AA*

GRIFFITHS, Shirley Thelma. b 48. Univ of Wales (Ban) CertEd69 Open Univ BA83 Coll of Ripon & York St Jo MA01. St Deiniol's Hawarden 79. **d** 82 **p** 95. NSM Dyserth and Trelawnyd and Cwm *St As* 82-91; RE Officer 89-95; Min Can St As Cathl 91-95; P-in-c The Cowtons *Ripon* 95-02; RE Adv 95-02; V Abergele *St As* from 02. *The Vicarage, 28 Lon Dirion, Abergele LL22 8PX* Tel (01745) 833112 Fax as telephone E-mail stg@fish.co.uk

GRIFFITHS, Simon Mark. b 62. Ch Ch Coll Cant BA84 Kent Univ MA95. Chich Th Coll. **d** 87 **p** 88. C Cardiff St Jo *Llan* 87-91; Sub-Chapl HM Pris Cardiff 87-91; Chapl and Succ Roch Cath *Roch* 91-96; Chapl Univ Coll Chich 96-01; V Sheff St Matt *Sheff* from 01. *St Matthew's Vicarage, 29 Winchester Road, Sheffield S10 4EE* Tel 0114-230 5641

GRIFFITHS, Canon Stanley Arthur. b 17. Lon Univ BSc38. Cuddesdon Coll 46. **d** 47 **p** 48. C Southsea St Matt *Portsm* 47-48; C Southsea H Spirit 48-51; C Cowley St Jas *Ox* 51-55; V Northbourne 55-65; V St Neots *Ely* 65-77; RD St Neots 76-82; Hon Can Ely Cathl 76-82; V Buckden 77-82; rtd 82; Perm to Offic *Ely* 82-96; Perm to Offic *York* from 82. *17 York Road, Malton YO17 6AX* Tel (01653) 697324

GRIFFITHS, Stephen David (Griff). b 70. Oak Hill Th Coll BA96 Trin Coll Bris. **d** 00 **p** 01. C Cranleigh *Guildf* from 00. *22 Orchard Gardens, Cranleigh GU6 7LG* Tel (01483) 272573 Mobile 07713-498763 E-mail griff@griffsaccount.freeserve.co.uk

GRIFFITHS, Stephen Mark. b 67. Nottm Univ BTh93. St Jo Coll Nottm 90. **d** 93 **p** 94. C Glascote and Stonydelph *Lich* 93-96; P-in-c Stratford New Town St Paul *Chelmsf* 96-02; P-in-c Steeple Bumpstead and Helions Bumpstead from 02; Tutor Ridley Hall Cam from 01. *The Vicarage, North Street, Steeple Bumpstead, Haverhill CB9 7DP* Tel (01440) 730128 Mobile 07905-861234 E-mail revsgriff@aol.com

GRIFFITHS, Mrs Susan Angela. b 61. St Jo Coll Nottm BTh94. **d** 94 **p** 95. C Ingrow cum Hainworth *Bradf* 94-98; V Wyke 98-03;

C ButTershaw St Paul from 03. *St Paul's Vicarage, 42A Wibsey Park Avenue, Bradford BD6 3QA* Tel (01274) 676359

GRIFFITHS, Miss Sylvia Joy. b 50. Gipsy Hill Coll of Educn CertEd71. St Jo Coll Nottm 85. **dss** 86 **d** 87 **p** 94. Woodthorpe *S'well* 86-90; Par Dn 87-90; Min Bestwood/Rise Park LEP 90-94; TD Bestwood 90-94; TR 94-99; P-in-c Sherwood 99-01; V from 01. *St Martin's Vicarage, Trevose Gardens, Sherwood, Nottingham NG5 3FU* Tel 0115-960 7547

GRIFFITHS, Thomas. b 31. AKC57. **d** 58 **p** 59. C Cheadle Hulme All SS *Ches* 58-61; C Oxton 61-63; V Micklehurst 63-72; V Ringway 73-91; V Liscard St Mary w St Columba 91-96; rtd 96; Perm to Offic *Ches* from 96; *Lich* from 01. *14A High Street, Ellesmere SY12 0EP* Tel 0115-960 7547

GRIFFITHS, Tudor Francis Lloyd. b 54. Jes Coll Ox BA76 MA81 Leeds Univ PhD99. Wycliffe Hall Ox 76. **d** 79 **p** 80. C Brecon w Battle *S & B* 79-81; Min Can Brecon Cathl 79-81; C Swansea St Mary w H Trin 81-83; R Llangattock and Llangynidr 83-88; CMS Uganda 89-95; C Newton St Pet *S & B* 96; Dioc Missr *Mon* from 96; V Goldcliffe and Whitson and Nash 96-98; TV Magor 98-03; TR Hawarden *St As* from 03. *The Rectory, 2 Birch Rise, Hawarden CH5 3DD* Tel (01244) 520091

GRIFFITHS, Vyrnach Morgan. b 24. Univ of Wales (Lamp) BA50. St Mich Coll Llan 52. **d** 54 **p** 55. C Llantrisant *Llan* 54-56; C Ystradyfodwg 56-60; C Cwmavon 60-61; V Clydach Vale 61-63; R Llanfair Talhaiarn *St As* 63-70; V Dinas w Penygraig *Llan* 70-74; R Llanddulas *St As* 74-80; R Llanddulas and Llysfaen 80-89; rtd 89. *10 Cilfan, Pensarn, Abergele LL22 7RD*

GRIFFITHS, William Bevan. b 13. AKC37. **d** 37 **p** 38. C Llangyfelach and Morriston *S & B* 37-50; R Llanbadarn Fawr and Llandegley 50-59; R Braunston *Pet* 59-79; rtd 79; Perm to Offic *Llan* from 79. *73 Glannant Way, Cimla, Neath SA11 3YP* Tel (01639) 770527

GRIFFITHS, Canon William David Aled. b 52. Univ of Wales (Abth) BA74 Man Univ AHA77. St Mich Coll Llan DipTh83. **d** 83 **p** 84. C Carmarthen St Pet *St D* 83-87; Asst Warden of Ords 84-91; Warden of Ords from 91; V Llansadwrn w Llanwrda and Manordeilo 87-92; V Llangunnor w Cwmffrwd from 92; Can St D Cathl from 01. *The Vicarage, Llangunnor Road, Carmarthen SA31 2HY* Tel (01267) 236435

GRIFFITHS, William David Maldwyn. b 23. St D Coll Lamp BA47. **d** 50 **p** 51. C Cardigan *St D* 50-54; C Henfynyw w Aberaeron 54-57; P-in-c Llechryd 57-59; V Mathri, St Edrens and Llanrheithan 59-67; V Llanfihangel Genau'r Glyn 67-89; RD Llanbadarn Fawr 87-89; rtd 89. *Bro Enlli, Lower Regent Street, Aberaeron SA46 0HZ* Tel (01545) 570176

GRIFFITHS, William Thomas Gordon. b 48. York Univ BA70 Fitzw Coll Cam BA79. Ridley Hall Cam 78. **d** 80 **p** 81. C Dulwich St Barn *S'wark* 80-83; C Egglescliffe *Dur* 83-85; Ind Chapl 85-90; V Stockton St Jas 90-98; NSM Leamington Hastings and Birdingbury *Cov* 98-03; NSM Grandborough w Willoughby and Flecknoe 98-03; NSM Leam Valley from 03. *The Vicarage, Lower Street, Willoughby, Rugby CV23 8BX* Tel (01788) 890309

GRIGG, Simon James. b 61. Warwick Univ BA82 MA83 Southn Univ BTh90. Chich Th Coll 87. **d** 90 **p** 91. C Cowley St Jas *Ox* 90-94; C W Hampstead St Jas *Lon* 94-95; V Munster Square Ch Ch and St Mary Magd from 95. *8 Laxton Place, London NW1 3PT* Tel (020) 7388 3095 Mobile 07958-472568

GRIGG, Canon Terence George. b 34. Kelham Th Coll 54. **d** 59 **p** 60. C Brookfield St Anne, Highgate Rise *Lon* 59-62; Chapl Lee Abbey 63-66; Chapl and Lect St Luke's Coll Ex 66-70; V Stainton-in-Cleveland *York* 70-83; R Cottingham from 83; Hon Can Koforidua from 84; Can and Preb York Minster *York* from 90. *The Rectory, Hallgate, Cottingham HU16 4DD* Tel (01482) 847668

GRIGG, William John Frank. b 27. SSC. Ripon Hall Ox. **d** 66 **p** 67. C Wigan All SS *Liv* 66-67; C Leek St Luke *Lich* 67-69; C Fenton 69-74; C St Stephen by Saltash *Truro* 74-76; TV Redruth 76-79; TV LanEast w St Clether and Tresmere 79-81; P-in-c Wendron 81-85; TV Helston and Wendron 85-91; rtd 91. *St Germoe, 23 Dunheved Fields, Launceston PL15 7HS* Tel (01566) 772878

GRIGGS, Canon Alan Sheward. b 33. Trin Hall Cam BA56 MA60. Westcott Ho Cam 58. **d** 60 **p** 61. C Arnold *S'well* 60-63; Succ S'wark Cathl *S'wark* 63-66; Ind Chapl 66-71; C Leeds H Trin *Ripon* 71-81; V 81-91; Soc and Ind Adv 71-81; Hon Can Ripon Cathl 84-98; Soc Resp Officer 91-98; rtd 98. *32 St Chad's Avenue, Leeds LS6 3QF* Tel 0113-275 8100

GRIGGS, Mrs Anthea Mary. b 37. Homerton Coll Cam TCert57 New Coll Edin BA86. St Alb and Ox Min Course. **d** 00 **p** 01. NSM Sunningdale *Ox* from 00. *Shrub House, 1 Coworth Road, Sunningdale SL5 0NX* Tel (01344) 623450 E-mail a.m.griggs@talk21.com

GRIGGS, Frederick John. b 20. Peterho Cam BA48 MA53. Linc Th Coll. **d** 50 **p** 51. C Stand *Man* 50-53; C Writtle *Chelmsf* 53-55; P-in-c The Chignals w Mashbury 55-58; V Chelmsf St Andr 58-62; R Colne Engaine 62-80; P-in-c Frating w Thorrington 80-83; rtd 85. *6 Church View, Holton, Halesworth IP19 8PB* Tel (01986) 875298

✠**GRIGGS, The Rt Revd Ian Macdonald.** b 28. Trin Hall Cam BA52 MA56. Westcott Ho Cam. **d** 54 **p** 55 **c** 87. C Portsea St Cuth *Portsm* 54-59; Dioc Youth Chapl *Sheff* 59-64; Bp's Dom Chapl 59-64; V Sheff St Cuth 64-71; V Kidderminster St Mary *Worc* 71-82; Hon Can Worc Cathl 77-84; TR Kidderminster St Mary and All SS, Trimpley etc 82-84; Preb Heref Cathl *Heref* 84-94; Adn Ludlow 84-87; P-in-c Tenbury St Mich 84-87; Suff Bp Ludlow 87-94; rtd 94; Hon Asst Bp Carl from 94. *Rookings, Patterdale, Penrith CA11 0NP* Tel (01768) 482064

GRIGOR, Miss Alice Moira (Trish). b 49. Ripon Coll Cuddesdon 94. **d** 96 **p** 97. C Curry Rivel w Fivehead and Swell *B & W* 96-98; C Nailsea Ch Ch w Tickenham 98-00; TV Ross *Heref* from 00. *The Rectory, Weston under Penyard, Ross-on-Wye HR9 7QA* Tel (01989) 562926

GRIGOR, David Alexander. b 29. Lon Univ DipTh54. St Aid Birkenhead 51. **d** 54 **p** 55. C Hengrove *Bris* 54-57; C Marshfield w Cold Ashton 57-60; V Newport *Ex* 60-67; V Paignton St Paul Preston 67-73; Brazil 73-74; Hon C Heavitree *Ex* 74-77; Chapl Ex Sch 74-77; Chapl Brighton Coll 77-89; Chapl Warminster Sch 89-93; rtd 93; Perm to Offic *Portsm* from 03. *13 College Close, Hamble, Southampton SO41 4QU* Tel (023) 8045 3946

GRIGSBY, Peter Edward. b 31. Magd Coll Cam MA56 CertEd56. NEOC 85. **d** 88 **p** 89. NSM Haxby w Wigginton *York* 88-90; C Brayton 90-92; TV 92-97; rtd 97; Perm to Offic *Chich* 98-01. *4 The Hop Garden, South Harting, Petersfield GU31 5QL* Tel (01730) 825295

GRIGSON, Richard John Stephen. b 60. Man Univ BA83. Qu Coll Birm 86. **d** 88 **p** 89. C W Bromwich St Fran *Lich* 88-92; V Smallthorne from 92. *St Saviour's Vicarage, Ford Green Road, Stoke-on-Trent ST6 1NX* Tel (01782) 835941 Fax (07092) 214726 E-mail richard.grigson@lichfield.anglican.org

GRIMASON, The Very Revd Alistair John. b 57. CITC 76. **d** 79 **p** 80. C Belfast H Trin *Conn* 79-82; C Dublin Drumcondra w N Strand *D & G* 82-84; I Navan w Kentstown, Tara, Slane, Painestown etc *M & K* 84-91; Dioc Youth Officer (Meath) 90-94; Dioc Info Officer (Meath) 90-96; I Tullamore w Durrow, Newtownfertullagh, Rahan etc 91-00; Preb Tipper St Patr Cathl Dublin 92-00; Can Meath *M & K* 92-00; Chan Kildare Cathl 98-00; Dean Tuam *T, K & A* from 00; I Tuam w Cong and Aasleagh from 00. *Deanery Place, Cong, Claremorris, Co Mayo, Irish Republic* Tel (00353) (94) 954 6017 Fax as telephone

GRIME, Arthur Michael. b 28. Kelham Th Coll 48. **d** 52 **p** 53. Basutoland 52-55; C Ealing St Barn *Lon* 55-57; C Pimlico St Gabr 57-59; C Greenford H Cross 59-62; V Fulham St Pet 62-66; V Chiswick St Paul Grove Park 66-88; rtd 89; Perm to Offic *Chich* from 89. *29 Eton Close, Datchet, Slough SL3 9BE* Tel (01753) 545802

GRIME, William John Peter. b 38. St Jo Coll Ox BA60 MA66. Cuddesdon Coll 69. **d** 70 **p** 71. C Blackb St Jas *Blackb* 70-74; Chapl St Martin's Coll of Educn 74-77; V Seascale *Carl* 77-78; P-in-c Irton w Drigg 77-78; V Seascale and Drigg from 78. *The Vicarage, The Banks, Seascale CA20 1QT* Tel (01946) 728217

GRIMLEY, The Very Revd Robert William. b 43. Ch Coll Cam BA66 MA70 Wadh Coll Ox BA68 MA76. Ripon Hall Ox 66. **d** 68 **p** 69. C Radlett *St Alb* 68-72; Hon C Moseley St Mary *Birm* 72-84; Chapl K Edw Sch Birm 72-84; V Edgbaston St Geo *Birm* 84-97; Dean Bris from 97. *The Deanery, 20 Charlotte Street, Bristol BS1 5PZ* Tel 0117-926 2443 or 926 4879 Fax 925 3678 E-mail dean@bristol.anglican.org

GRIMSBY, Suffragan Bishop of. *See* ROSSDALE, The Rt Revd David Douglas James

GRIMSDALE, Mrs Margaret. b 24. Sister-Tutor's Dip 48 Lon Univ STD55. Gilmore Course 80. **dss** 82 **d** 87. Stoke Poges *Ox* 82-87; Hon Par Dn 87-88; Hon Par Dn Burrington and Churchill *B & W* 88-90; rtd 90; Perm to Offic *B & W* 90-94. *Address temp unknown*

GRIMSHAW, Eric Fenton Hall. b 34. Bris Univ BA57. Tyndale Hall Bris 54. **d** 58 **p** 59. C Moss Side St Jas *Man* 58-61; C Leyland St Andr *Blackb* 61-64; V Preston St Mark 64-72; V Mirehouse *Carl* 72-91; Hon Can Carl Cathl 86-91; V Knowsley *Liv* 91-99; rtd 99; Perm to Offic *Liv* from 99. *22 Lynwood Avenue, Aughton, Ormskirk L39 5BB* Tel (01695) 424864

GRIMSTER, Barry John. b 49. Ex Univ BA70. Trin Coll Bris 72. **d** 74 **p** 75. C S Lambeth St Steph *S'wark* 74-77; C New Malden and Coombe 77-82; P-in-c Deptford St Jo 82-84; V Deptford St Jo w H Trin 84-89; V Woking St Pet *Guildf* 89-01; TR from 02. *The Rectory, 28 High Street, Old Woking, Woking GU22 9ER* Tel (01483) 762707

GRIMWADE, Eric Peter. b 14. AKC37. **d** 37 **p** 38. C Nunhead St Silas *S'wark* 37-39; C Camberwell St Mark 39-40; Chapl RAFVR 40-46; C Redruth *Truro* 46-48; R St Enoder 48-52; V St Clement 52-62; Chapl R Cornwall Infirmary 52-62; Chapl St Lawr Hosp Bodmin 62-69; Chapl Cane Hill Hosp Coulsdon 69-78; C Lee-on-the-Solent *Portsm* 78-79; Hon C 79-81; rtd 79; Perm to Offic *Chich* from 82. *Little Compton, 42 Compton Road, Haywards Heath RH16 2JZ* Tel (01444) 487217

GRIMWADE, Canon John Girling. b 20. Keble Coll Ox BA48 MA52. Cuddesdon Coll 48. **d** 50 **p** 51. C Kingston All SS *S'wark* 50-53; C Ox St Mary V *Ox* 53-56; PC Londonderry *Birm* 56-62; R Caversham *Ox* 62-81; Hon Can Ch Ch 73-90; Chapl to The Queen 80-90; R Caversham St Pet and Mapledurham etc *Ox* 81-83; P-in-c Stonesfield 83-89; rtd 89; Perm to Offic *Ox* from 89; Perm to Offic *Glouc* from 89. *88 Alexander Drive, Cirencester GL7 1UJ* Tel (01285) 885767

GRIMWADE, Leslie Frank. b 24. FBIM60. Trin Coll Bris 74. **d** 77 **p** 78. C Taunton St Jas *B & W* 77-80; C Polegate *Chich* 80-83; R Swainsthorpe w Newton Flotman *Nor* 83-90; rtd 90; Hon Min Malmesbury Abbey *Bris* 90-97; Chapl Malmesbury Hosp 90-97; Perm to Offic *Sarum* and *Ex* from 97; Perm to Offic *B & W* from 01. *4 St George's Mews, The Mount, Taunton TA1 3TA* Tel (01823) 254887

GRIMWOOD, Andrew Stuart. b 68. Ex Univ BA89. St Mich Coll Llan BD97. **d** 98 **p** 99. C Llangynwyd w Maesteg *Llan* 98-01; P-in-c Rhyl w St Ann *St As* from 01. *18B Dyserth Road, Rhyl LL18 4DP* Tel (01745) 332224 E-mail andy-fran@grimwood65.freeserve.co.uk

GRIMWOOD, Canon David Walter. b 48. Lon Univ BA70 K Coll Lon BD73 AKC73. **d** 74 **p** 75. C Newc St Geo *Newc* 74-78; C Whorlton 78-80; TV Totton *Win* 80-93; Adv to Coun for Soc Resp *Roch* and *Cant* 93-02; Chief Exec Ch in Soc *Roch* and *Cant* from 02; Hon Can Roch Cathl *Roch* from 97. *56 Postley Road, Maidstone ME15 6TR* Tel (01622) 764625 *or* 755014 Fax 693531 E-mail david@csr.org.uk

GRINDELL, James Mark. b 43. Nottm Univ BA66 Bris Univ MA69. Wells Th Coll 66. **d** 68 **p** 69. C Bushey Heath *St Alb* 68-72; C Ex St Dave *Ex* 72-74; Chapl St Audries Sch W Quantoxhead 74-83; Chapl Berkhamsted Colleg Sch Herts 83-86; Chapl Denstone Coll Uttoxeter 86-91; Chapl Portsm Gr Sch 91-03; rtd 03; Hon Chapl Portsm Cathl *Portsm* from 91. *60 Cottage Grove, Southsea PO5 1EW* Tel (023) 9229 1318

✠**GRINDROD, The Most Revd John Basil Rowland.** b 19. KBE90. Qu Coll Ox BA49 MA54. Linc Th Coll 49 DTh51. **d** 51 **p** 52 **c** 66. C Hulme St Mich *Man* 51-54; R Ancoats All SS 56-60; Australia from 60; Adn Rockhampton 60-65; Bp Riverina 66-71; Bp Rockhampton 71-80; Abp Brisbane 80-90; rtd 90. *14B Thomas Street, Murwillumbah, NSW, Australia 2484* Tel (0061) (2) 6672 6640

GRINHAM, Garth Clews. b 36. Oak Hill Th Coll 61. **d** 64 **p** 65. C Beckenham Ch Ch *Roch* 64-68; C Wallington H Trin *S'wark* 68-71; V Erith St Paul *Roch* 71-76; Asst Sec CPAS 76-81; Hon C Knockholt *Roch* 76-81; V Southport Ch Ch *Liv* 81-94; V Douglas St Ninian *S & M* 94-01; rtd 01; Perm to Offic *Liv* from 01. *8 Ottery Close, Southport PR9 9GE* Tel (01704) 213468

GRINHAM, Julian Clive. b 39. Birkbeck Coll Lon BA65. Oak Hill Th Coll DipTh79. **d** 81 **p** 82. C Blackb Ch Ch w St Matt *Blackb* 81-83; Nat Sec Pathfinders CPAS 83-89; Dir CYPECS 89-94; V Normanton *Derby* 94-00; rtd 00; Perm to Offic *Nor* from 01. *85 Gwyn Crescent, Fakenham NR21 8NE* Tel (01328) 853068

GRINSELL, Robert Paul. b 62. Ch Ch Coll Cant BA86 PGCE89. Trin Coll Bris MA03. **d** 03. C Foord St Jo *Cant* from 03. *2 Chalk Close, Folkestone CT19 5TD* Tel (01303) 245281 E-mail grinsell@btopenworld.com

GRINSTED, Richard Anthony. b 43. Leic Univ BSc65. Oak Hill Th Coll 67. **d** 70 **p** 71. C Egham *Guildf* 70-73; C Woodford Wells *Chelmsf* 73-76; P-in-c Havering-atte-Bower 76-84; R Ditton *Roch* 84-94; R Chulmleigh *Ex* 94-96; R Chawleigh w Cheldon 94-96; R Wembworthy w Eggesford 94-96; R Chulmleigh, Chawleigh w Cheldon, Wembworthy etc 96-00; rtd 00. *Stonehouse, Christow, Exeter EX6 7NE* Tel (01647) 252653

GRISCOME, The Very Revd David. b 47. Oak Hill Th Coll BA88 TCD Div Sch 89. **d** 89 **p** 90. C Glendermott *D & R* 89-91; I Clondehorkey w Cashel 91-95; I Mevagh w Glenalla 91-95; Bp's C Calry *K, E & A* 95-97; I 97-00; Dean Elphin and Ardagh from 99; I Sligo w Knocknarea and Rosses Pt from 99. *The Deanery, Strandhill Road, Sligo, Irish Republic* Tel (00353) (71) 916 2263 E-mail dgriscome@unison.ie

✠**GRISWOLD, The Most Revd Frank Tracy.** b 37. Harvard Univ AB59 Oriel Coll Ox BA62 MA66. Gen Th Sem NY 59 Hon DD85 Seabury-Western Th Sem Hon DD85. **d** 62 **p** 63 **c** 85. C Bryn Mawr Redeemer 63-67; R Yardley St Andr 67-74; R Philadelphia St Martin-in-the-Fields 74-85; Bp Coadjutor Chicago 85-87; Bp Chicago 87-97; Presiding Bp from 98. *Episcopal Church Center, 815 Second Avenue, New York, NY 10017, USA* Tel (001) (212) 716 6276 *or* 867 8400 Fax 490 3298 E-mail pboffice@episcopalchurch.org

GRITTEN, Desmond Digby. b 17. ALCD54. **d** 54 **p** 55. C Blackheath St Jo *S'wark* 54-58; V Kenilworth St Jo *Cov* 58-87; RD Kenilworth 63-73; rtd 87; Perm to Offic *Cant* from 87; Ex from 92 and *Chelmsf* and *Cant* from 97. *54 Claremont Road, London E7 0PZ* Tel (020) 8257 1301

GROARKE, Ms Nicola Jane. b 62. Lanc Univ BA84. Ridley Hall Cam. **d** 00 **p** 01. C Balham Hill Ascension *S'wark* from 00. *22 Rochelle Close, London SW11 2RX* Tel (020) 8871 1118 *or* 8675 8626 E-mail nikki@groarke.fsnet.co.uk

GROEPE, Thomas Matthew Karl. b 51. St Pet Coll Natal 76. **d** 78 **p** 79. S Africa 78-83 and from 88; Hon C Waterloo St Jo w St Andr *S'wark* 83-88. *75 Old Helshoogte Road, Idas Valley, Stellenbosch, 7600 South Africa* Tel (0027) (21) 887 6912 *or* 887 6913 Fax 886 5799

GROOCOCK, Christopher John. b 59. St Jo Coll Nottm LTh92 DCM92. **d** 92 **p** 93. C Shawbury *Lich* 92-95; V Hengoed w Gobowen 95-00; CF from 00. *c/o MOD Chaplains (Army)* Tel (01980) 615804 Fax 615800

GROOM, Mrs Susan Anne. b 63. Univ of Wales BA85 Hughes Hall Cam MPhil86 Lon Bible Coll MA94 Open Univ MPhil00. St Jo Coll Nottm 94. **d** 96 **p** 97. C Harefield *Lon* 96-99; C Eastcote St Lawr 99-01; P-in-c Yiewsley 01-03; V from 03. *The Vicarage, 93 High Street, Yiewsley, West Drayton UB7 7QH* Tel (01895) 442093 E-mail sue.groom@connectfree.co.uk

GROSSCURTH, Stephen. b 55. Sarum & Wells Th Coll 81. **d** 84 **p** 85. C Southport H Trin *Liv* 84-87; C Amblecote *Worc* 87-89; V Walton St Jo *Liv* 89-95; Chapl S Man Univ Hosps NHS Trust from 95. *Wythenshawe Hospital, Southmoor Road, Manchester M23 9LT* Tel 0161-291 2298 *or* (01925) 821124 Fax 0161-946 2603

GROSSE, Anthony Charles Bain. b 30. Oak Hill Th Coll 58. **d** 61 **p** 62. C Chislehurst Ch Ch *Roch* 61-65; C Washfield *Ex* 65-71; TV Washfield, Stoodleigh, Withleigh etc 71-73; R Hemyock 73-86; P-in-c Clayhidon 76-86; R Hemyock w Culm Davy and Clayhidon 87-93; R Hemyock w Culm Davy, Clayhidon and Culmstock 93-96; rtd 96; Perm to Offic *Ex* from 98. *17 Frog Street, Bampton, Tiverton EX16 9NT* Tel (01398) 331981

GROSSE, Peter George. b 43. St Steph Ho Ox 02. **d** 03. NSM Reading St Matt *Ox* from 03. *18 Rangewood Avenue, Reading RG30 3NN* Tel 0118-959 4573 E-mail petergrosse@supanet.com

GROSSE, Richard William. b 52. Solicitor 77 Mid Essex Tech Coll LLB73. Ridley Hall Cam 86. **d** 88 **p** 89. C Soham *Ely* 88-91; C Bedale *Ripon* 91-93; C-in-c Thornton Watlass w Thornton Steward 91-93; V Barton and Manfield w Cleasby 93-95; V Barton and Manfield and Cleasby w Stapleton 95-99; R Keelby Gp *Linc* from 99. *The Vicarage, 24 Victoria Road, Keelby, Grimsby DN41 8EH* Tel (01469) 560251 Fax as telephone E-mail richard-grosse@hotmail.com

GROSU, Iosif. b 60. Iasi Univ BTh92. RC Inst Iasi DipTh89. **d** 89 **p** 89. In RC Ch 89-93; C Darlington St Cuth *Dur* 96-99; C Stockton St Jo and Stockton St Jas 99-02; TV Ch the K from 02. *6 Badgers Wood, Stanley DH9 0HR* Tel (01207) 237732 E-mail i.grosu@ntlworld.com

GROSVENOR, Royston Johannes Martin. b 47. K Coll Lon BD70 AKC. **d** 71 **p** 72. C Pontesbury I and II *Heref* 71-75; C Bishopston *Bris* 75-79; P-in-c Croydon St Pet S End *Cant* 79-81; V Croydon St Pet 81-84; V Croydon St Pet *S'wark* 85-87; R Merstham and Gatton 87-97; V Tidenham w Beachley and Lancaut *Glouc* from 97. *Tidenham Vicarage, Gloucester Road, Tutshill, Chepstow NP16 7DH* Tel (01291) 622442 E-mail roystongrosvenor@tidenham42.freeserve.co.uk

GROVE, Ronald Edward. b 32. Oak Hill Th Coll 60. **d** 63 **p** 64. C Bromley St Jo *Roch* 63-66; V Stratford New Town St Paul *Chelmsf* 66-94; rtd 97; Perm to Offic *Chich* from 97; *Cant* from 00. *Flat 3, Beacon Height, 4 Church Road, Haywards Heath RH16 3PB* Tel (01444) 416892

GROVER, Wilfrid John. b 29. Lich Th Coll 55. **d** 58 **p** 59. C Northampton St Alb *Pet* 58-61; C Boyne Hill *Ox* 61-65; V Cookham 65-85; RD Maidenhead 82-85; Warden Christchurch Retreat Ho *Glouc* 85-93; rtd 89; Hon C Jedburgh *Edin* from 93. *Cairnbrook, Bemersyde, Melrose TD6 9DP* Tel (01835) 822054

GROVES, Elizabeth Ann. Bp Otter Coll 94. **d** 97. NSM Soberton w Newtown *Portsm* from 01; NSM Botley from 01; NSM Curdridge from 01; NSM Durley from 01. *33 Vectis Road, Alverstoke, Gosport PO12 2QD* Tel (023) 9258 2841 *or* (01489) 782445 E-mail akeagroves@aol.com

GROVES, James Alan. b 32. CCC Cam BA58 MA62. Wells Th Coll 58. **d** 60 **p** 61. C Milton next Gravesend Ch Ch *Roch* 60-64; C Beckenham St Jas 64-66; V Orpington St Andr 66-98; rtd 98; Perm to Offic *Chich* from 98. *9 Wykeham Road, Hastings TN34 1UA* Tel (01424) 200839

GROVES, Mrs Jill. b 61. Univ Coll Lon BSc82. St Jo Coll Nottm Dip Th Studies 91 MA93. **d** 93 **p** 94. C Tenbury *Heref* 93-98; P-in-c Hope Bowdler w Eaton-under-Heywood from 98; P-in-c Cardington from 98; P-in-c Rushbury from 98. *The Rectory, Hope Bowdler, Church Stretton SY6 7DD* Tel (01694) 722918 E-mail jill@grovesfamily.org.uk

GROVES, Justin Simon John. b 69. Lon Bible Coll BA93. Ridley Hall Cam 00. **d** 02 **p** 03. C Glouc St Cath *Glouc* from 02. *35 St Mary Square, Gloucester GL1 2QT* Tel (01452) 310810

GROVES, Margaret Ann. b 49. Nottm Univ BEd71 BPhil88. EMMTC 95. **d** 98 **p** 99. NSM Farnsfield *S'well* from 98; NSM Bilsthorpe from 98. *Churchill House, Church Hill, Bilsthorpe, Newark NG22 8RU* Tel (01623) 870679

GROVES, Peter John. b 70. New Coll Ox BA92 MA96 DPhil96. Westcott Ho Cam 95. **d** 97 **p** 98. C Leigh-on-Sea St Marg *Chelmsf* 97-99; P Lib Pusey Ho Ox 99-01; Asst Chapl and Tutor

Keble Coll Ox 01-02; Hon C Ox St Mary Magd *Ox* from 01; Chapl and Fell BNC Ox from 02. *Brasenose College, Oxford OX1 4AJ* Tel (01865) 277833 Fax as telephone E-mail peter.groves@theology.ox.ac.uk

GROVES, Canon Philip Neil. b 62. Man Univ BA84. St Jo Coll Nottm 86. **d** 88 **p** 89. C Holbeck *Ripon* 88-91; CMS 91-99; Tanzania 93-98; Hon Can Mpwampwa from 98; TV Melton Mowbray *Leic* from 99. *1 Palmerston Road, Melton Mowbray LE13 0SS* Tel (01664) 564229 E-mail rev.phil@ntlworld.com

GROVES, Robert John. b 42. Trin Coll Bris 74. **d** 76 **p** 77. C Norwood St Luke *S'wark* 76-79; P-in-c Clapham Park All SS 79-86; V Anerley *Roch* 86-95; TV Canford Magna *Sarum* 95-98; TR Tollington *Lon* 98-02; rtd 02; Perm to Offic *Lon* from 02. *12 Oatfield Close, Cranbrook TN17 3NH* Tel (01580) 715756 E-mail bob_groves@lineone.net

GROWNS, John Huntley. b 28. Chich Th Coll 57. **d** 60 **p** 61. C Hayes St Mary *Lon* 60-64; C Addlestone *Guildf* 64-67; C-in-c Kempston Transfiguration CD *St Alb* 67-74; R Stevenage St Geo 74-82; R Felpham w Middleton *Chich* 82-88; P-in-c Westmill w Gt Munden *St Alb* 88-89; Dioc Stewardship Adv 88-93; P-in-c Westmill 89-93; rtd 93; Perm to Offic *Chich* from 93; Perm to Offic *St Alb* 93-00. *45 Lewes Road, Ditchling, Hassocks BN6 8TU* Tel (01273) 846415

GRUBB, Greville Alexander (Alex). b 36. Saltley Tr Coll Birm CertEd60 Leeds Univ DipPE61 Lon Univ DipRE67. St Jo Coll Nottm 72. **d** 74 **p** 75. C Rushden w Newton Bromswold *Pet* 74-77; Chapl St D Coll Llandudno 77-89; Chapl Casterton Sch Lancs 90-96; Hon C Blackb from 96 and *Bradf* from 02. *Beckstones, 21 Littledale Road, Brookhouse, Lancaster LA2 9PH* Tel (01524) 770512

GRUNDY, Anthony Brian. b 36. Pemb Coll Cam BA62 MA87. Ridley Hall Cam 61. **d** 63 **p** 64. C Hatcham St Jas *S'wark* 63-66; C Margate H Trin *Cant* 66-68; C Brixton Hill St Sav *S'wark* 68-70; V Assington *St E* 70-76; TV Much Wenlock w Bourton *Heref* 76-81; TV Wenlock 81-82; TR 82-88; RD Condover 86-88; R Burghfield *Ox* 88-02; rtd 02. *29 Gerald Road, Worthing BN11 5QQ* Tel (01903) 507213

GRUNDY, Christopher John. b 49. ACA72. Trin Coll Bris 74. **d** 77 **p** 78. C Maidstone St Luke *Cant* 77-81; Argentina 81-82; Chile 82-84; Perm to Offic *Guildf* 84-96; NSM Guildf Ch Ch w St Martha-on-the-Hill 96-99; C Shere, Albury and Chilworth from 99. *The Vicarage, Brook Road, Chilworth, Guildford GU4 8ND* Tel (01483) 454070 E-mail chris@grundy.org.uk

GRUNDY, Jocelyn Pratchitt. b 22. Trin Coll Cam MA. Westcott Ho Cam 64. **d** 66 **p** 67. C Guildf H Trin w St Mary *Guildf* 66-68; R Shere 68-73; V Fleet 73-83; C Aldershot St Mich 83-87; rtd 87; Perm to Offic *Guildf* from 87. *Richmond Cottage, School Hill, Seale, Farnham GU10 1HY* Tel (01252) 782238

GRUNDY, Mrs Judith Michal Towers Mynors. b 54. Lady Spencer Chu Coll of Educn CertEd76 Ox Univ BEd77. Trin Coll Bris DipHE87. **d** 94. NSM Kensal Rise St Mark and St Martin *Lon* 93-95; NSM Snettisham w Ingoldisthorpe and Fring *Nor* from 95. *The Vicarage, 18 Park Lane, Snettisham, King's Lynn PE31 7NW* Tel (01485) 541301

GRUNDY, Julian David. b 60. St Andr Univ MA83. Trin Coll Bris BA88. **d** 89 **p** 90. C Lancaster St Thos *Blackb* 89-92; C Kensal Rise St Mark and St Martin *Lon* 92-95; R Snettisham w Ingoldisthorpe and Fring *Nor* from 95. *The Vicarage, 18 Park Lane, Snettisham, King's Lynn PE31 7NW* Tel (01485) 541301

GRUNDY, The Ven Malcolm Leslie. b 44. AKC68 Open Univ BA76. **d** 69 **p** 70. C Doncaster St Geo *Sheff* 69-72; Ind Chapl 72-80; Dir of Educn *Lon* 80-86; TR Huntingdon *Ely* 86-91; Hon Can Ely Cathl 88-94; Dir Avec 91-94; Adn Craven *Bradf* from 94. *Woodlands, Netherghyll Lane, Cononley, Keighley BD20 8PB* Tel (01535) 635113 E-mail malcolm@adcraven.u-net.com

GRUNDY, Paul. b 55. BD77 AKC. Linc Th Coll 79. **d** 80 **p** 81. C Ryhope *Dur* 80-82; C Ferryhill 82-85; TV Cramlington *Newc* 85-87; TV Swinton and Pendlebury *Man* 87-90; V Wingate Grange *Dur* 90-95; R Willington and Sunnybrow from 95. *The Rectory, Willington, Crook DL15 0DE* Tel (01388) 746242

GRÜNEBERG, Keith Nigel. b 72. CCC Ox BA93 MA96 St Jo Coll Dur BA97. Cranmer Hall Dur 95. **d** 01 **p** 02. C Pangbourne w Tidmarsh and Sulham *Ox* from 01. *51 Reading Road, Pangbourne, Reading RG8 7HY* Tel 0118-984 5870 E-mail keithgruneberg@dunelm.org.uk

GRÜNEWALD, Gottfried Johannes. b 38. Loyola Univ Chicago MPS92. Th Faculty Frankfurt 66. **d** 69 **p** 69. Denmark 70-95; C Dunbar *Edin* 95-97; R Dollar *St And* from 98. *St James's Rectory, 12 Harviestoun Road, Dollar FK14 7HF* Tel (01259) 742494

GRYLLS, Ms Catherine Anne. b 70. Ripon Coll Cuddesdon 97. **d** 00 **p** 01. C Hall Green St Pet *Birm* from 00. *4 Etwall Road, Hall Green, Birmingham B28 0LE* Tel 0121-778 4375

GRYLLS, Canon Michael John. b 38. Qu Coll Cam BA62 MA66. Linc Th Coll 62. **d** 64 **p** 65. C Sheff Gillcar St Silas *Sheff* 64-67; C-in-c Dunscroft CD 67-70; V Herringthorpe 70-78; V Amport, Grateley, Monxton and Quarley *Win* 78-89; RD Andover 85-89; V Whitchurch w Tufton and Litchfield from 89; Hon Can Win

Cathl from 01. *The Vicarage, Church Street, Whitchurch RG28 7AS* Tel (01256) 892535

GUBBINS, Andrew Martin. b 65. York Univ BA86 Keele Univ 93. St Jo Coll Nottm LTh93. **d** 96 **p** 97. C Harrogate St Mark *Ripon* 96-00; P-in-c Osmondthorpe St Phil from 00. *St Philip's Vicarage, 68 Osmondthorpe Lane, Leeds LS9 9EF* Tel 0113-249 7371 E-mail andrew.gubbins@ukgateway.net

GUBBINS (née O'BRIEN), Mrs Mary. b 68. Leeds Univ BSc90. St Jo Coll Nottm BTh93 DipMM94. **d** 94 **p** 95. C Middleton St Mary *Ripon* 94-96; C Bilton 96-99. *St Philip's Vicarage, 68 Osmondthorpe Lane, Leeds LS9 9EF* Tel 0113-249 7371

GUDGEON, Canon Michael John. b 40. Qu Coll Cam BA63 MA67. Chich Th Coll 65. **d** 66 **p** 67. C Kings Heath *Birm* 66-72; Asst Chapl K Edw Sch Birm 69-72; Chapl and Tutor Cuddesdon Coll 72-75; V Hawley H Trin *Guildf* 75-80; V Minley 75-80; Adult Educn Adv *Chich* 80-87; Can Res Portsm Cathl *Portsm* 87-90; Dioc Dir of Educn 87-90; V Hove St Thos *Chich* 90-93; TV Hove 93-94; Perm to Offic 94-98; Bp's Chapl *Eur* 94-98; Dir of Ords 94-97; Can Gib Cathl from 96; P-in-c Worthing St Andr *Chich* from 98. *St Andrew's Vicarage, 21 Victoria Road, Worthing BN11 1XB* Tel (01903) 233442 Fax as telephone E-mail michaelgudgeon@aol.com

GUERNSEY, Dean of. *See* TRICKEY, The Very Revd Frederick Marc

✠**GUERRERO, The Rt Revd Orlando.** b 45. Episc Sem of Ecuador. **p** 80 **c** 95. P Puerto la Cruz H Trin 80-93; Interim P Caracas St Mary 80-84; Bp Venezuela from 95. *Apartado 49-143, Avenida Caroní 100, Colinas de Bello Monte, Caracas 1042-A, Venezuela* Tel (0058) (2) 753 0723 Fax 751 3180

GUEST, David. b 41. Dur Univ BA62. Coll of Resurr Mirfield 70. **d** 72 **p** 73. C Horsforth *Ripon* 72-75; C Richmond 75-76; C Richmond w Hudswell 76-78; R Middleham 78-81; R Middleham and Coverham w Horsehouse 81-86; R W Rainton *Dur* from 86; V E Rainton from 86; RD Houghton 92-94 and 96-97; rtd 03. *Lindisfarne, 3 New Croft, Horsforth, Leeds LS18 4TD* Tel 0113-258 0521

GUEST, David Andrew. b 61. Portsm Coll of Tech NDTJ82. Chich Th Coll BTh92 Cert Minl Th92. **d** 92 **p** 93. C Prenton *Ches* 92-94; C Ches H Trin 94-97; Assoc P Douglas All SS and St Thos *S & M* 97-00; Dioc Communications Officer 97-00; Relig Adv Manx Radio 97-00; Bp's Dom Chapl 98-00; Dioc Communications Officer *Chich* from 00; C Hove from 00; C Southwick St Pet from 03. *St Peter's House, 107A Gardner Road, Portslade, Brighton BN41 1PN* Tel (01273) 592474 *or* 421021 Fax 421041 E-mail david.guest@diochi.org.uk

GUEST, Derek William. b 55. N Ord Course 90. **d** 93 **p** 94. C Cheadle Hulme St Andr *Ches* 93-99; V from 99. *2 Orrishmere Road, Cheadle Hulme, Cheadle SK8 5HP* Tel 0161-486 9306 E-mail revdguest@yahoo.co.uk

GUEST, Ernest Anthony. b 64. NTMTC 99. **d** 02 **p** 03. C Gt Ilford St Jo *Chelmsf* from 02. *25 Valentines Road, Ilford IG1 4RZ* Tel (020) 8518 3982 Mobile 07810-516356 E-mail ernie@eguest.fsnet.co.uk

GUEST, Mrs Helen. b 54. Totley Thornbridge Coll CertEd75. EMMTC 92. **d** 02 **p** 03. NSM Brimington *Derby* from 02. *33 Gloucester Road, Chesterfield S41 7EF* Tel (01246) 230048 E-mail helenmick@btopenworld.com

GUEST, John. b 36. Trin Coll Bris 59. **d** 61 **p** 62. C Barton Hill St Luke w Ch Ch *Bris* 61-64; C Liv St Sav *Liv* 65-66; USA from 66; rtd 01. *30 Myrtle Hill Road, Sewickley, PA 15143, USA*

GUEST, John Andrew Kenneth. b 55. Univ of Wales (Lamp) BA78. Wycliffe Hall Ox 78. **d** 80 **p** 81. C Eastwood *S'well* 80-84; TV Toxteth St Philemon w St Gabr and St Cleopas *Liv* 84-89; C Cranham Park *Chelmsf* 89-93; P-in-c Stanford-le-Hope w Mucking 93-03; R from 03. *The Rectory, The Green, Stanford-le-Hope SS17 0EP* Tel (01375) 672271 E-mail gof4god@aol.com

GUEST, Michael. b 52. FTC73. EMMTC. **d** 99 **p** 00. NSM Heath *Derby* from 99. *33 Gloucester Road, Stonegravels, Chesterfield S41 7EF* Tel (01246) 230048

GUEST, Simon Llewelyn. b 56. Univ of Wales (Lamp) BA78 CertEd79 DipTh85. St Mich Coll Llan 83. **d** 85 **p** 86. C Bassaleg *Mon* 85-88; C Cwmbran 88-89; TV 89-91; V Raglan w Llandenny and Bryngwyn from 91; RD Raglan-Usk from 01. *The Vicarage, Primrose Green, Raglan, Usk NP15 2DU* Tel (01291) 690330

GUEST-BLOFELD, Thomas. b 35. St D Coll Lamp BA59 Cranmer Hall Dur 59. **d** 62 **p** 63. C Maltby *Sheff* 62-63; C Goole 63-66; C Pocklington w Yapham-cum-Meltonby, Owsthorpe etc *York* 67-68; C Ely 68-70; C Pemberton St Jo *Liv* 70-72; V Walton St Jo 72-74; V Barkisland w W Scammonden *Wakef* 74-80; V Smallbridge *Man* 80-82; C Irlam 83-86; rtd 87. *192/351 Mooban Kullaphan, Tambol Mae Hear M004, Amper Muang, Chiang Mai 50000, Thailand* Tel (0066) (53) 838403

GUILDFORD, Bishop of. *Vacant*

GUILDFORD, Dean of. *See* STOCK, The Very Revd Victor Andrew

GUILFORD, John Edward. b 50. S & M Dioc Tr Inst 94. **d** 99 **p** 00. OLM Lonan *S & M* from 99; OLM Laxey from 99.

Tremissary House, Strathallan Road, Douglas IM2 4PN Tel and fax (01624) 672001 Mobile 07624-494274 E-mail j.guilford@adrys.co.uk

GUILLAN, Miss Barbara Doris. b 19. S'wark Ord Course 45. **d** 87. NSM St Stythians w Perranarworthal and Gwennap *Truro* 87-89; rtd 89; Perm to Offic *Truro* 89-94. *Address temp unknown*

GUILLE, The Ven John Arthur. b 49. Southn Univ BTh79. Sarum & Wells Th Coll 73. **d** 76 **p** 77. C Chandler's Ford *Win* 76-80; P-in-c Bournemouth St Jo 80-84; P-in-c Bournemouth St Mich 83-84; V Bournemouth St Jo w St Mich 84-89; R Guernsey St Andr 89-99; Adn Win from 99; Can Res Win Cathl from 99. *6 The Close, Winchester SO23 9LS* Tel (01962) 857263 Fax 857242 E-mail john.guille@winchester-cathedral.org.uk

GUILLEBAUD, Miss Margaret Jean. b 43. Edin Univ BSc66. All Nations Chr Coll DipRS79 Cranmer Hall Dur 79. **dss** 80 **d** 87 **p** 94. New Malden and Coombe *S'wark* 80-84; Carlton Colville w Mutford and Rushmere *Nor* 84-91; Par Dn 87-91; Par Dn Rodbourne Cheney *Bris* 91-94; C 94-95; Rwanda from 95. *BP 426, Kigali, Rwanda*

GUILLOTEAU, Claude. b 32. Ripon Coll Cuddesdon 77. **d** 57 **p** 57. In RC Ch 57-76; C Warmsworth *Sheff* 78-80; C Goole 80-86; C Hatfield 86-88; C Ecclesall 88-94; rtd 94. *Résidence Frédéric Mistral, Escalier A/8, 3 rue Frédéric Mistral, F-81200 Mazamet, France* Tel (0033) (5) 63 98 88 19

GUINNESS, Christopher Paul. b 43. Lon Coll of Div 64. **d** 67 **p** 68. C Farnborough *Guildf* 67-70; C Tulse Hill H Trin *S'wark* 70-74; C Worting *Win* 74-78; P-in-c S Lambeth St Steph *S'wark* 78-89; V 89-91; RD Lambeth 86-90; C Ches Square St Mich w St Phil *Lon* 91-97; Living Waters Trust 98-00; Chapl Ealing Hosp NHS Trust from 00. *Ealing Hospital, Uxbridge Road, Southall UB1 3HW* Tel (020) 8574 2444

GUINNESS, Canon Garry Grattan. b 40. Em Coll Cam BA64 MA68. Ridley Hall Cam 64. **d** 66 **p** 67. C Wallington H Trin *S'wark* 66-69; C St Marylebone All So w SS Pet and Jo *Lon* 69-72; P-in-c Clifton H Trin, St Andr and St Pet *Bris* 72-79; V Watford St Luke *St Alb* 79-90; TR Worthing Ch the King *Chich* from 90; Hon Can Kigeme from 02. *4 Shakespeare Road, Worthing BN11 4AL* Tel (01903) 205185 E-mail gguinness@lineone.net

GUINNESS, Graham Alexander. b 60. Jordan Hill Coll Glas DCE82 Edin Univ LTh85. Edin Th Coll 82. **d** 85 **p** 86. Dioc Youth Chapl *Mor* 85-88; C Elgin w Lossiemouth 85-88; Asst P Glas St Ninian *Glas* 88-90; R Tighnabruaich *Arg* 90-91 and 94-99; R Dunoon 90-99; Miss to Seamen 90-99; R Fort William *Arg* from 99. *St Andrew's Rectory, Parade Road, Fort William PH33 6BA* Tel (01397) 702979 Fax as telephone E-mail ftwilliam@argyll.anglican.org

GUINNESS, Peter Grattan. b 49. Man Univ BSc71 CertEd72 Nottm Univ DipTh81. St Jo Coll Nottm 80. **d** 82 **p** 83. C Normanton *Wakef* 82-87; V Fletchamstead *Cov* 87-91; V Lancaster St Thos *Blackb* from 91. *St Thomas's Vicarage, 33 Belle Vue Terrace, Lancaster LA1 4TY* Tel (01524) 62987 Fax 846895 E-mail peter@st.tees.org.uk

GUINNESS, Canon Robin Gordon. b 38. St Jo Coll Cam MA61. Ridley Hall Cam 63. **d** 63 **p** 64. C Bedworth *Cov* 63-66; CMS 66-68; Canada from 68. *47 Prospect Street, Westmount PQ, Canada, H3Z 1W5* Tel (001) (514) 931 6796

GUISE, John Christopher. b 29. Cheltenham & Glouc Coll of HE MA94 MRPharmS51. WMMTC 80 Dip Miss87. **d** 83 **p** 84. NSM Alfrick, Lulsley, Suckley, Leigh and Bransford *Worc* 83-94; NSM Martley and Wichenford, Knightwick etc 94-00; Perm to Offic from 00. *Marsh Cottage, Leigh, Worcester WR6 5LE* Tel (01886) 832336

GUISE, Stephen. b 48. Win Sch of Art BA75. Chich Th Coll 85. **d** 87 **p** 88. C Bexhill St Pet *Chich* 87-90; TV Haywards Heath St Wilfrid 90-94; V Kirdford 94-97; Chapl Community of Servants of the Cross 97-01; P-in-c Amberley w N Stoke and Parham, Wiggonholt etc *Chich* 99-03; TV Bridport *Sarum* from 03. *Allington Vicarage, Parsonage Road, Bridport DT6 5ET* Tel (01308) 456661 E-mail sguise@supanet.com

GUITE, Ayodeji Malcolm. b 57. Pemb Coll Cam BA80 MA84 Newc Poly PGCE82 Dur Univ PhD93. Ridley Hall Cam 88. **d** 90 **p** 91. C Ely 90-93; TV Huntingdon 93-98; Chapl Anglia Poly Univ 98-03; Chapl Girton Coll Cam from 03. *Girton College, Cambridge CB3 0JG* Tel (01223) 338999 E-mail mg320@cam.ac.uk

GUITE, Mrs Margaret Ann. b 53. Girton Coll Cam BA74 MA78 St Jo Coll Dur DipTh76 PhD81. Cranmer Hall Dur 75. **dss** 79 **d** 87 **p** 94. Warlingham w Chelsham and Farleigh *S'wark* 79-82; Cherry Hinton St Jo *Ely* 82-86; Tutor Westcott Ho Cam 82-90; Tutor Wesley Ho Cam 87-90; NSM Ely 90-93; NSM Chettisham 90-93; NSM Prickwillow 90-93; NSM Huntingdon 93-99; V Fenstanton from 99; V Hilton from 99. *The Vicarage, 16 Church Street, Fenstanton, Huntingdon PE28 9JL* Tel (01480) 463334 E-mail mguite@bigfoot.com

GUIVER, Paul Alfred (George). b 45. St Chad's Coll Dur BA68. Cuddesdon Coll 71. **d** 73 **p** 74. C Mill End and Heronsgate w W

Hyde *St Alb* 73-76; P-in-c Bishop's Frome *Heref* 76-82; P-in-c Castle Frome 76-82; P-in-c Acton Beauchamp and Evesbatch 76-82; CR from 85; Lic to Offic *Wakef* from 85. *House of the Resurrection, Stocks Bank Road, Mirfield WF14 0BN* Tel (01924) 494318

GUIVER, Roger William Antony. b 53. Edin Univ MA75 St Chad's Coll Dur BA78. Coll of Resurr Mirfield. **d** 82 **p** 83. C Rekendyke *Dur* 82-85; Chapl Middlesbrough Gen Hosp 85-93; P-in-c Middlesbrough St Columba w St Paul *York* 85-94; V Acomb *York* 94-97; V Middlesbrough St Thos 97-00. *Swang Farm, Glaisdale, Whitby YO21 2QZ* Tel (01947) 897210

GULL, William John. b 42. Ripon Hall Ox 63. **d** 65 **p** 66. C Worksop Priory *S'well* 65-69; C Newark St Mary 69-71; P-in-c Mansfield St Lawr 71-77; V 77-78; Chapl HM YOI Lowdham Grange 78-90; R Lambley *S'well* 78-91; V Sneinton St Cypr 91-99; rtd 99. *37 Hazel Grove, Mapperley, Nottingham NG3 6DQ* Tel 0115-920 8071 E-mail wjgull@btopenworld.com

GULLAND, John Robertson. b 46. ACIB Avery Hill Coll CertEd70 Open Univ BA76 Chelsea Coll Lon MA82. Oak Hill Th Coll 88. **d** 90 **p** 91. NSM Woodside Park St Barn *Lon* 90-92; Lic to Offic *S & M* from 93; NSM Castletown from 92; Chapl K Wm Coll from 92. *Anchor House, Queens Road, Port St Mary, Isle of Man IM9 5ES* Tel (01624) 834548

GULLIDGE, Philip Michael Nowell. b 60. Univ of Wales (Swansea) BSc82 Univ of Wales (Cardiff) BD93. St Mich Coll Llan 90. **d** 93 **p** 94. C Neath w Llantwit *Llan* 93-97; V Treharris w Bedlinog from 97. *The Vicarage, 13 The Oaks, Pentwyn, Quakers Yard, Treharris CF46 5HQ* Tel (01443) 410280

GULLIFORD, Mrs Susan Diane. b 49. W Midl Coll of Educn BEd86. WMMTC 97. **d** 00 **p** 01. NSM Tettenhall Regis *Lich* 00-02; C Wednesfield from 02. *St Alban's Vicarage, Griffiths Drive, Wolverhampton WV11 2LJ* Tel (01902) 732317 E-mail sue.gulliford@btinternet.com

GULLIFORD, William Douglas FitzGerald. b 69. Selw Coll Cam BA91 MA95. Westcott Ho Cam CTM92. **d** 94 **p** 95. C Banstead *Guildf* 94-97; C Wilton Place St Paul *Lon* 97-00; Chapl Guildhall Sch of Music and Drama 97-01; P-in-c St Dunstan in the West from 00; Gen Sec Angl and E Churches Assn from 00; Bp's Chapl *Lon* 00-02; P-in-c St Mary le Strand w St Clem Danes from 02; Bp's Chapl for E Orthodox Affairs from 02. *184A Fleet Street, London EC4A 2HD* Tel (020) 7405 1929 Fax as telephone E-mail william.gulliford@london.anglican.org

GULLY, Paul David. b 59. Lon Univ BEd81. Trin Coll Bris BA95. **d** 95 **p** 96. C Radcliffe *Man* 95-99; TV New Bury from 99. *New Bury Vicarage, 507 Plodder Lane, Farnworth, Bolton BL4 0JZ* Tel (01204) 791577 E-mail revdpaulgully@aol.com

GULVIN, Philip Christopher. b 53. BSc76. St Jo Coll Nottm 82. **d** 85 **p** 86. C Northwood H Trin *Lon* 85-89; TV Sanderstead All SS *S'wark* 89-96; V Croydon St Matt 96-99; C W Wickham St Fran 99-02; C W Wickham St Fran and St Mary from 02. *The Vicarage, 2 The Grove, West Wickham BR4 9JS* Tel (020) 8777 6010 E-mail gulvip@aol.com

GUMBEL, Nicholas Glyn Paul. b 55. Trin Coll Cam MA76 BA85. Wycliffe Hall Ox 83. **d** 86 **p** 87. C Brompton H Trin w Onslow Square St Paul *Lon* from 86. *13 Macaulay Road, London SW4 0QP* Tel (020) 7498 1472

GUMMER, Dudley Harrison. b 28. Roch Th Coll 61. **d** 63 **p** 64. C Deptford St Paul *S'wark* 63-65; C Melton Mowbray w Thorpe Arnold *Leic* 65-68; C-in-c E Goscote 68-75; V E Goscote 75-78; V Luton St Anne *St Alb* 78-88; R Albury w St Martha *Guildf* 88-95; rtd 95; Perm to Offic *Chich* from 95; *Portms* from 03. *Wyndham House, The Gardens, West Ashling, Chichester PO18 8DX* Tel (01243) 573002

GUNN, The Very Revd Jeffrey Thomas. b 47. St Chad's Coll Dur BA77 Kent Univ MA95. Coll of Resurr Mirfield 77. **d** 79 **p** 80. C Prestbury *Glouc* 79-82; P-in-c Coldham *Ely* 82-87; P-in-c Elm 82-87; P-in-c Friday Bridge 82-87; V Larkfield *Roch* 87-94; P-in-c Leybourne 87-94; V Petts Wood 94-99; Dean Ballarat from 99. *Cathedral Office, PO Box 89, Ballarat, Vic, Australia 3353* Tel (0061) (3) 5331 1183 *or* 5333 4559 Mobile 407-210022 Fax 5333 2982 E-mail jtgunn@cbl.com.au

GUNN, Robert. b 35. Oak Hill Th Coll 59. **d** 62 **p** 63. C Upper Holloway St Jo *Lon* 62-66; C Woking St Jo *Guildf* 66-69; Scripture Union 69-71; R Necton w Holme Hale *Nor* 71-77; V Tottenham St Jo *Lon* 77-81; V Gt Cambridge Road St Jo and St Jas 82-85; V Luton St Fran *St Alb* 85-90; Chapl Luton Airport 90-95; rtd 95; Perm to Offic *St Alb* from 95. *95 Edgewood Drive, Luton LU2 8ER* Tel (01582) 416151

GUNN-JOHNSON, The Ven David Allan. b 49. Lambeth STh85 MA95. St Steph Ho Ox 79. **d** 81 **p** 82. C Oxhey St Matt *St Alb* 81-84; C Cheshunt 84-88; TR Colyton, Southleigh, Offwell, Widworthy etc *Ex* 88-03; RD Honiton 90-96; Preb Ex Cathl 99-03; Adn Barnstaple from 03. *Stage Cross, Sanders Lane, Bishops Tawton, Barnstaple EX32 0BE* Tel (01271) 375475 Fax 377934 E-mail archdeacon.of.barnstaple@exeter.anglican.org

GUNNER, Canon Laurence François Pascal. b 36. Keble Coll Ox BA59 MA63. Wells Th Coll 59. **d** 61 **p** 62. C Charlton Kings St Mary *Glouc* 61-65; C Hemel Hempstead *St Alb* 65-69; Chapl

Bloxham Sch 69-86; Sen Chapl Marlborough Coll 86-96; Can Windsor from 96; Steward from 97. *6 The Cloisters, Windsor Castle, Windsor SL4 1NJ* Tel (01753) 848767 E-mail l.gunner@stgeorges-windsor.org

GUNSTONE, Canon John Thomas Arthur. b 27. St Chad's Coll Dur BA48 MA55. Coll of Resurr Mirfield 50. **d** 52 **p** 53. C Walthamstow St Jas Gt *Chelmsf* 52-53; C Forest Gate St Edm 53-58; C-in-c Rush Green St Aug CD 58-71; Chapl Barn Fellowship Winterborne Whitechurch 71-75; Tutor Sarum & Wells Th Coll 71-75; Sec Gtr Man Co Ecum Coun 75-92; Lic to Offic *Man* 75-80; Hon Can Man Cathl 80-92; rtd 92; Perm to Offic *Man* 03. *12 Deneford Road, Didsbury, Manchester M20 2TD* Tel 0161-434 8351

GUNTER, Timothy Wilson. b 37. Leeds Univ BA59 St Jo Coll Cam BA62 MA66. Ridley Hall Cam 59. **d** 62 **p** 63. C Beverley Minster *York* 62-65; C Hornsea and Goxhill 65-70; V Silsden *Bradf* 70-80; V Sunninghill *Ox* from 80. *Sunninghill Vicarage, Church Lane, Ascot SL5 7DD* Tel (01344) 620727 E-mail rev@t.gunter.freeserve.co.uk

GUNYON, Stephen Francis. b 14. Selw Coll Cam BA38 MA48. Linc Th Coll 38. **d** 40 **p** 41. C Greenhill St Jo *Lon* 40-43; SSF 43-44; CF 44-48; C Westmr St Steph w St Jo 48-50; V Thornaby on Tees St Paul *York* 50-57; Res Chapl Middx Hosp *Lon* 57-66; Gen Sec Hosp Chapl Fellowship 57-66; V Hinchley Wood *Guildf* 66-71; V Hindhead 71-80; rtd 80; Perm to Offic *Pet* 80-94. *c/o Mrs M M Hayns, 4 The Gateway, Sicklesmere Road, Bury St Edmunds IP33 2BN*

GUPPY, Kenneth Henry Stanley. b 29. Univ of Wales (Lamp) BA54. St Mich Coll Llan 54. **d** 56 **p** 57. C Rumney *Mon* 56-61; Chapl Shirley Ho Sch Watford 61-63; V Llangwm Uchaf and Llangwm Isaf w Gwernesney etc *Mon* 63-85; rtd 85; Lic to Offic *Ox* 88-92; Perm to Offic *B & W* 94-00. *11 St Thomas's Court, Woodbury Avenue, Wells BA5 2XY*

GURD, Brian Charles (Simon). b 44. Sarum & Wells Th Coll 72. **d** 74 **p** 75. OSP from 67; Lic to Offic *Win* 74-82; Prior Alton Abbey 79-82; C Shepherd's Bush St Steph w St Thos *Lon* 82-84; NSM Willesborough *Cant* 85-87; V Bethersden w High Halden 87-95; R Etchingham *Chich* 95-97; V Hurst Green 95-97; V Langney 97-01; R Yarm *York* from 01. *The Rectory, 6 Westgate, Yarm TS15 9BU* Tel (01642) 781115

GURDON, Mrs June Mary. b 38. Sarum Th Coll 83. **dss** 86 **d** 87 **p** 94. Jersey St Sav *Win* 85-86; Jersey St Mary 86-88; Par Dn 87-88; Par Dn Jersey St Brelade 88-94 and from 94. *The Glade, La rue des Pres, Jersey JE3 3EH* Tel (01534) 864282

GURNEY, Miss Ann. b 27. Lon Univ DipTh48 STh92. Gilmore Ho 45. **dss** 54 **d** 87 **p** 94. Lewisham St Jo Southend *S'wark* 54-56; Warden Berridge Ho Coll of Educn 56-59; Prin Gilmore Ho 59-70; Bp's Adv for Lay Min *Lon* 70-87; rtd 87; Hon C Eltham H Trin *S'wark* 94-98; Perm to Offic from 98. *3 Brecon Court, Greenacres, London SE9 5BG* Tel (020) 8850 4083

GURNEY, Canon Dennis Albert John. b 31. OBE02. Lon Coll of Div. **d** 67 **p** 68. C Boscombe St Jo *Win* 67-69; V Hurstbourne Tarrant and Faccombe 70-77; R Jersey St Ouen w St Geo 77-84; Hon Chapl Miss to Seafarers from 84; Chapl ICS UAE 84-01; Can Bahrain from 98; rtd 01. *3 Stevens Cross Close, Sidford, Sidmouth EX10 9QJ* Tel (01395) 515362

GURNEY, Canon Richmond Harptree. b 24. Worc Coll Ox BA48 MA48 Open Univ BA97. Cuddesdon Coll 48. **d** 50 **p** 51. C Bishopwearmouth St Mich *Dur* 50-53; C Beamish 53-55; PC Silksworth 55-66; R Gateshead St Mary 66-72; TR Gateshead 72-75; P-in-c Eskdale, Irton, Muncaster and Waberthwaite *Carl* 75-78; V 78-82; Sec Dioc Past and Redundant Chs Uses Cttees 82-87; R Asby 82-89; V Bolton 82-89; V Crosby Ravensworth 82-89; Hon Can Carl Cathl 84-89; rtd 89; Perm to Offic *Carl* 89-98; Perm to Offic *York* from 98. *Ingleby Cottage, 47 South End, Osmotherley, Northallerton DL6 3BN* Tel (01609) 883309

GURR, Mrs Mary Sandra. b 42. St Alb and Ox Min Course 95. **d** 98 **p** 99. C Easthampstead *Ox* 98-02; TV High Wycombe from 02. *The Vicarage, 245 Micklefield Road, High Wycombe HP13 7HU* Tel (01494) 520323 E-mail marygurr@stmichaelshouse.freeserve.co.uk

GURR, Ralph Sydney. b 27. AKC55. **d** 57 **p** 58. C Lewisham St Mary *S'wark* 57-63; Chapl Lewisham Hosp 61-63; C Cheam *S'wark* 63-69; V Wyke *Bradf* 69-72; V Edmonton St Mich *Lon* 72-79; R Fordingbridge w Ibsley *Win* 79-82; V Fordingbridge 82-84; C N Stoneham 84-94; P-in-c 89-90; rtd 94; Perm to Offic *Win* from 94. *1 Grosvenor Mansions, Grosvenor Square, Polygon, Southampton SO15 2GQ* Tel (023) 8033 9243

GURR, Stephen John. b 72. Kent Univ BA94. Trin Coll Bris MLitt94. **d** 97 **p** 98. C Ore *Chich* 97-00; C Goring-by-Sea 00-03; V Findon w Clapham and Patching from 03. *Quince Cottage, Horsham Road, Findon, Worthing BN14 0UY* Tel (01903) 873601

GUSH, Laurence Langley. b 23. Lon Univ BSc44. NW Ord Course 73. **d** 76 **p** 77. NSM Sheff St Matt *Sheff* 76-82; NSM Aston cum Aughton 82-84; NSM Aston cum Aughton and Ulley 84-89; rtd 89. *3 New Court, Eyam, Hope Valley S32 5RL* Tel (01433) 631818

GUSSMAN, Canon Robert William Spencer Lockhart. b 50. Ch Ch Ox BA72 MA76. Coll of Resurr Mirfield BA74. **d** 75 **p** 76. C Pinner *Lon* 75-79; C Northolt W End St Jos 79-81; P-in-c Sutton *Ely* 81-82; V 82-89; P-in-c Witcham w Mepal 81-82; R 82-89; RD Ely 86-89; V Alton St Lawr *Win* 89-02; Hon Can Win Cathl 99-02; rtd 02. *6A Patrick's Close, Liss GU33 7ER* Tel (01730) 893545

GUTHRIE, Adrian Malcolm. b 57. Goldsmiths' Coll Lon BEd80. Wycliffe Hall Ox 01. **d** 03. C Ickenham *Lon* from 03. *6 Broadacre Close, Uxbridge UB10 8BL* Tel (01895) 676092
E-mail am.guthrie@virgin.net

GUTHRIE, Nigel. b 60. LRAM78 ARCO80 ARCM81 Bris Univ BA82 Ox Univ BA87 MA91. Ripon Coll Cuddesdon 85. **d** 88 **p** 89. C Cov St Jo *Cov* 88-91; Chapl Cov Cathl 91-94; V Chellaston *Derby* 94-02; RD Melbourne 99-02; R Crediton, Shobrooke and Sandford etc *Ex* from 02. *The Vicarage, Church Street, Crediton EX17 2AQ* Tel (01363) 772669 *or* 773226

GUTSELL, Canon David Leonard Nicholas. b 35. Sheff Univ BA59 LTh74. ALCD61. **d** 61 **p** 62. C Clapham Common St Barn *S'wark* 61-65; V Upper Tulse Hill St Matthias 65-76; RD Clapham and Brixton 74-75; V Patcham *Chich* 76-93; Can and Preb Chich Cathl 89-00; V Polegate 93-00; rtd 00; C Peacehaven and Telscombe Cliffs *Chich* from 01; C Southease from 01; C Piddinghoe from 01. *30 Balsdean Road, Brighton BN2 6PF* Tel (01273) 301085 E-mail gutselldln@davidln.fsnet.co.uk

GUTSELL, Eric Leslie. b 44. Goldsmiths' Coll Lon TCert65 Ox Univ Special Dip Educn Studies 87. Ox NSM Course 79. **d** 82 **p** 83. NSM Gt Faringdon w Lt Coxwell *Ox* 82-88; NSM Shrivenham w Watchfield and Bourton 82-99; Asst Chapl HM Pris Wormwood Scrubs 99-00; Chapl HM Pris Coldingley from 00. *HM Prison Coldingley, Shaftesbury Road, Bisley, Woking GU24 9EX* Tel (01483) 476721 ext 325 Fax 488586
E-mail ericgutsell@virgin.net

GUTTERIDGE, David Frank. b 39. Man Univ BSc61 Lon Inst of Educn PGCE62 DipEd67 Birkbeck Coll Lon MSc73. WMMTC 82. **d** 85 **p** 87. NSM Droitwich *Worc* 85-87; NSM Droitwich Spa 87-93; C Shrawley, Witley, Astley and Abberley 93-98; Chapl Abberley Hall Sch Worc 93-97; Dioc Tertiary Educn Officer *Worc* 97-99; NSM Ombersley w Doverdale 98-99; TV Malvern Link w Cowleigh 99-02; rtd 02. *79 Tan House Lane, Malvern WR14 1LQ* Tel (01886) 833578
E-mail dgutteridge@cofe-worcester.org.uk

GUTTERIDGE, John. b 34. Oak Hill Th Coll 60. **d** 63 **p** 64. C Deptford St Luke *S'wark* 63-66; C Southgate *Chich* 66-70; P-in-c Brixton Road Ch Ch *S'wark* 70-73; P-in-c Manuden w Berden *Chelmsf* 73-76; Distr Sec (N Lon, Herts and Essex) BFBS 76-82; Hon C Walthamstow St Gabr 79-82; V 82-95; Chapl Thorpe Coombe Psycho-Geriatric Hosp 83-95; rtd 95; Perm to Offic *Chelmsf* from 95. *52 Hatch Road, Pilgrims Hatch, Brentwood CM15 9PX* Tel (01277) 375401
E-mail john.gutteridge@hotmail.com

GUTTERIDGE, John Philip. b 52. QUB BA74. Chich Th Coll 75. **d** 78 **p** 79. C Leeds St Aid *Ripon* 78-82; C Manston 82-85; P-in-c Beeston Hill H Spirit 85-00. *Address temp unknown*

GUTTRIDGE (née EVANS), Mrs Frances Margaret Bethan. b 54. Reading Univ BSc75 Univ of Wales (Cardiff) PGCE76. STETS. **d** 00 **p** 01. C Weston-super-Mare St Andr Bournville *B & W* from 00. *45 Amberey Road, Weston-super-Mare BS23 3QJ* Tel (01934) 632952 Mobile 07778-137454
E-mail bethanguttridge@hotmail.com

GUTTRIDGE, John Arthur. b 26. Trin Hall Cam BA51 MA55. Westcott Ho Cam 51. **d** 53 **p** 54. C Rugby St Andr *Cov* 53-59; Lect Wells Th Coll 59-61; Chapl 61-63; Vice-Prin 63-66; Bp's Dom Chapl *Wakef* 66-68; Dir Post-Ord Tr 66-68; Dir of Further Tr *Dur* 68-74; Dir Studies Sarum & Wells Th Coll 74-78; C Bilston St Leon *Lich* 78-79; TV Bilston 80-84; V Wall 84-90; V Stonnall 84-90; rtd 91. *The Charterhouse, Charterhouse Square, London EC1M 6AN* Tel (020) 7251 6357

GUTWEIN, Martin. b 45. Hobart Coll (NY) BA67. Episc Th Sch Cam Mass MA69 MDiv72. **d** 72 **p** 72. USA 72-78 and from 80; C Toxteth St Marg *Liv* 78-80. *527 North 2nd Street, Camden, NJ 08102, USA* Tel (001) (856) 365 2664 *or* 365 5880

GUY, Mrs Alison. b 43. CQSW69 DATh98. WMMTC 95. **d** 98 **p** 99. NSM Minchinhampton *Glouc* from 98. *7 Tooke Road, Minchinhampton, Stroud GL6 9DA* Tel (01453) 883906

GUY, Ian Towers. b 47. Newc Univ MB, BS70 MSc89 MRCGP. NEOC. **d** 83 **p** 84. NSM Saltburn-by-the-Sea *York* 83-88; NSM Skelton w Upleatham 88-92; Perm to Offic from 92. *14 North Terrace, Skelton-in-Cleveland, Saltburn-by-the-Sea TS12 2ES* Tel (01287) 650309 Mobile 07092-298033
E-mail ian.guy@gp-a81630.nhs.uk

GUY, John Richard. *See* MORGAN-GUY, John Richard

GUY, Kate Anne. b 26. LNSM course 87. **d** 88 **p** 94. OLM Welton *Linc* 88-92; OLM Welton and Dunholme w Scothern 92-96; Perm to Offic 96-02. *2 Eastfield Close, Welton, Lincoln LN2 3NB* Tel (01673) 860285

GUY, Peter-John. b 71. Bournemouth Univ BA93. Oak Hill Th Coll BA03. **d** 03. C Eastbourne All So *Chich* from 03. *Wellesley*

House, Longstone Road, Eastbourne BN21 3SL Tel (01323) 749915 E-mail pjgerdaguy@hotmail.com

GUY, Simon Edward Walrond. b 39. St Andr Univ MA61. St D Coll Lamp LTh67. **d** 67 **p** 68. C Bris St Mary Redcliffe w Temple etc *Bris* 67-68; C Knowle St Martin 68-71; C Bishopston 71-75; V Westwood *Sarum* 75-81; TV Melksham 81-82; TV Wednesfield *Lich* 82-90; R Heaton Moor *Man* 90-02; P-in-c Heaton Norris Ch w All SS 99-01; TV Heatons from 02. *St Paul's Rectory, 42 Lea Road, Stockport SK4 4JU* Tel 0161-432 1227
E-mail sewguy@supanet.com

GUYANA, Bishop of. *See* GEORGE, The Rt Revd Randolph Oswald

GUYMER, Canon Raymond John. b 41. AKC64. **d** 65 **p** 66. C W Bromwich All SS *Lich* 65-70; Chapl HM Pris Wormwood Scrubs 70-71; Chapl HM Borstal Portland 71-78; Chapl HM Youth Cust Cen Hollesley Bay Colony 78-84; Chapl HM Pris Wormwood Scrubs 84-93; Chapl HM Pris Win 93-01; Hon Can Win Cathl *Win* from 99; Hon C Upper Itchen from 02. *24 Arle Close, Alresford SO24 9BG* Tel (01962) 734022

GWILLIAM, Christopher. b 44. St Chad's Coll Dur BA65 DipTh67. **d** 67 **p** 68. C Chepstow *Mon* 67-70; C Risca 70-72; V Cwmtillery 72-75; V Hartlepool St Oswald *Dur* 75-82; Relig Progr Producer Radio Tees 80-87; C Stockton w St Jo 82-83; R Longnewton w Elton 83-87; Relig Progr Producer Radio Nottm *S'well* 87-93; Relig Progr Producer BBC Radio 4 (Man) 93-94. *Address temp unknown*

GWILLIAMS (formerly HARTLEY), Mrs Dianna Lynn. b 57. Santa Ana Community Coll AS76 California Univ BA78 K Coll Lon MA01. S'wark Ord Course DipRS92. **d** 92 **p** 94. NSM Peckham St Sav *S'wark* 92-97; C Dulwich St Barn 97-99; V from 99. *St Barnabas's Vicarage, 38 Calton Avenue, London SE21 7DG* Tel (020) 8693 1524 *or* 8693 2936 Fax (020) 8693 0203
E-mail dgwilliams@stbarnabasdulwich.com

GWILLIM, Allan John. b 51. Coll of Resurr Mirfield 87. **d** 89 **p** 90. C Skerton St Luke *Blackb* 89-94; P-in-c Ellel 94-98; V Fleetwood from 98. *St Peter's Vicarage, 39 Mount Road, Fleetwood FY7 6EX* Tel (01253) 771642

GWILT, Stephen Gary. b 59. **d** 88 **p** 89. S Africa 88-94; Chapl Glouc Docks Mariners' Ch *Glouc* 95-00; C Moreton *Ches* 00-03; R High Halstow w All Hallows and Hoo St Mary *Roch* from 03. *The Rectory, 2 Cooling Road, High Halstow, Rochester ME3 8SA* Tel (01634) 250637

GWINN, Brian Harvey. b 35. MIQA75. St Alb Minl Tr Scheme 83. **d** 86 **p** 87. NSM Wheathampstead *St Alb* 86-88; Ind Chapl 88--95; RD Hatfield 93-95; P-in-c Watton at Stone 95-99; P-in-c Bramfield w Stapleford and Waterford 96-99; R Bramfield, Stapleford, Waterford etc 99-01; rtd 01; Perm to Offic *St Alb* from 01. *32 Wick Avenue, Wheathampstead, St Albans AL4 8QB* Tel (01582) 629903 E-mail gwinns@ntlworld.com

GWYNN, Phillip John. b 57. Univ of Wales BA87 Univ of Wales (Cardiff) DPS89. St Mich Coll Llan 87. **d** 89 **p** 90. C Clydach *S & B* 89-93; V Swansea St Thos and Kilvey 93-00; V Tycoch from 00; Hon Chapl Miss to Seafarers from 93. *The Vicarage, 26 Hendrefoilan Road, Swansea SA2 9LS* Tel and fax (01792) 204476 Mobile 07803-059629 E-mail rev.gwynn@virgin.net

GWYNNE, Robert Durham. b 44. Birm Univ DipTh70. Qu Coll Birm 67. **d** 70 **p** 72. C N Hammersmith St Kath *Lon* 70-75; C Ramsey *Ely* 76-78; TV Old Brumby *Linc* 78-81; P-in-c Goxhill and Thornton Curtis 81-83; C Edmonton All SS w St Mich *Lon* 83-84; rtd 86. *127 Eastfield Road, Louth LN11 7AS* Tel (01507) 600966

GWYTHER, Canon Geoffrey David. b 51. St D Coll Lamp DipTh73. **d** 74 **p** 75. C Pembroke Dock *St D* 74-77; C Milford Haven 77-81; V Llawhaden w Bletherston and Llanycefn 81-88; R Prendergast w Rudbaxton from 88; RD Daugleddau from 01; Can St D Cathl from 01. *Prendergast Rectory, 5 Cherry Grove, Haverfordwest SA61 2NT* Tel (01437) 762625

GWYTHER, Ronald Lloyd. b 23. Lon Univ BA85 Southn Univ MA97. St Fran Coll Brisbane ThL47. **d** 47 **p** 48. Australia 48-50; Perm to Offic *Ox* 50-51; Australia 51-56; C Broadstairs *Cant* 56-60; R Pinxton *Derby* 60-73; CF (TA) 71-88; V Swanley St Mary *Roch* 73-89; rtd 89; Perm to Offic *Portsm* from 89. *St Helen's, 20 Maylings Farm Road, Fareham PO16 7QU* Tel (01329) 230990

GYLE, Alan Gordon. b 65. Aber Univ MA87 Ox Univ BA91 FRSA99. St Steph Ho Ox. **d** 92 **p** 93. C Acton Green *Lon* 92-94; Min Can, Succ and Dean's V Windsor 94-99; Chapl Imp Coll and R Coll of Art 99-01; P-in-c Wilton Place St Paul *Lon* from 01. *St Paul's Vicarage, 32 Wilton Place, London SW1X 8SH* Tel (020) 7235 1810 *or* 235 3460 E-mail a.gyle@ic.ac.uk

GYLES, Ms Sonia. b 76. TCD BTh01. CITC 98. **d** 01 **p** 02. C Taney *D & G* from 01. *Church Lodge, 21 Taney Road, Dundrum, Dublin 14, Irish Republic* Tel (00353) (1) 295 1895 *or* 298 5491 E-mail sgyles@eircom.net

GYTON, Robert Wilfred. b 21. N Ord Course. **d** 78 **p** 79. NSM Repps *Nor* 78-79; C Trunch 79-83; TV 83-88; rtd 88; Perm to Offic *Nor* 88-94; P-in-c Castleacre w Newton, Rougham and Southacre 94-97; Perm to Offic from 97. *Yamato, 47 Fir Park, Ashill, Thetford IP25 7DE* Tel (01760) 440305

H

HAARHOFF, Robert Russell. b 46. St Paul's Coll Grahamstown 89 Th Ext Educn Coll 91. **d** 90 **p** 91. Zimbabwe 91-02; Harare Cathl 91-94; I Makonde 94-02; P-in-c Astley, Clive, Grinshill and Hadnall *Lich* from 02. *The Vicarage, Shrewsbury Road, Hadnall, Shrewsbury SY4 4AG* Tel (01939) 210241
E-mail robhaarhoff@tiscali.co.uk

HABERMEHL, Canon Kenneth Charles. b 22. Em Coll Cam BA46 MA48. Chich Th Coll 47. **d** 49 **p** 50. C Luton St Chris Round Green CD *St Alb* 49-53; C Luton Ch Ch 53-56; V Caddington 56-65; V Kempston 65-87; Hon Can St Alb 81-87; rtd 87; Perm to Offic *St Alb* 87-93 and from 00. *34 Bedford Road, Aspley Guise, Milton Keynes MK17 8DH* Tel (01908) 584710

HABERSHON, Kenneth Willoughby. b 35. MBE01. New Coll Ox BA57 MA60 DipTh58. Wycliffe Hall Ox 57. **d** 59 **p** 60. C Finchley Ch Ch *Lon* 59-66; Sec CYFA 66-74; CPAS Staff 74-90; Hon C Slaugham *Chich* from 84; Ldr Mayfield CYFA 90-00; Sec Ch Patr Trust and Peache Trustees from 90; rtd 00. *Truckers Ghyll, Horsham Road, Handcross, Haywards Heath RH17 6DT* Tel (01444) 400274 Fax 401293

✠**HABGOOD, The Rt Revd and Rt Hon Lord (John Stapylton).** b 27. PC83. K Coll Cam BA48 MA51 PhD52 Dur Univ Hon DD75 Cam Univ Hon DD84 Aber Univ Hon DD88 Huron Coll Hon DD90. Cuddesdon Coll 53. **d** 54 **p** 55 **c** 73. C Kensington St Mary Abbots w St Geo *Lon* 54-56; Vice-Prin Westcott Ho Cam 56-62; R Jedburgh *Edin* 62-67; Prin Qu Coll Birm 67-73; Hon Can Birm Cathl *Birm* 71-73; Bp Dur 73-83; Abp York 83-95; rtd 95. *18 The Mount, Malton YO17 7ND*

HABGOOD, Simon. b 60. Nottm Univ BTh88 MA97 Indiana Univ DMin01. St Jo Coll Nottm 85. **d** 88 **p** 89. C Holbeach *Linc* 88-90; CF (TA) from 89; CF (ACF) from 90; C Alford w Rigsby *Linc* 90-91; R Rattlesden w Thorpe Morieux and Brettenham *St E* 91-93; V Churchdown *Glouc* 93-95; V Maenclochog w Henry's Moat and Mynachlogddu etc *St D* 93-94; R Overstrand, Northrepps, Sidestrand etc *Nor* 95-98; rtd 98; Perm to Offic *Nor* from 02. *5 Bernham Road, Norwich NR6 5QG* Tel (01603) 400081
E-mail silvpug@globalnet.co.uk

HABGOOD, Stephen Roy. b 52. Univ of Wales (Cardiff) DipTh77 Open Univ MBA95 Fitzw Coll Cam MSt01. St Mich Coll Llan 75. **d** 77 **p** 78. C Whitchurch *Llan* 77-80; Perm to Offic *Worc* 85-91. *Yew Tree Cottage, Wharf Road, Gnosall, Stafford ST20 0DA* Tel (01785) 824244

HABIBY, Canon Samir Jamil. b 33. Phillips Univ BA55 MA56. Ch Div Sch of Pacific MDiv58 Episc Th Sem Kentucky DD. **d** 58 **p** 59. USA 58-98; P-in-c Lausanne *Eur* from 98. *Avenue de l'Eglise Anglaise, Case Postale 70, CH 1000 Lausanne 6, Switzerland*

HACK, Ms Alison Ruth. b 53. RGN75 RSCN75 RHV80. Sarum & Wells Th Coll 89. **d** 91. Par Dn St Marylebone St Paul *Lon* 91-94; C from 94. *St Paul's House, 9A Rossmore Road, London NW1 6NJ* Tel (020) 7402 1000

HACK, Canon Rex Hereward. b 28. ACA56 FCA67 Pemb Coll Cam BA50 MA56. Ripon Hall Ox 58. **d** 59 **p** 60. C Ashton-upon-Mersey St Mary *Ches* 59-62; C Ellesmere Port 62-65; V Norton Cuckney *S'well* 65-69; V Bramhall *Ches* 69-93; RD Cheadle 87-92; Hon Can Ches Cathl 90-93; rtd 93; Perm to Offic *Ches* from 93. *The Oaks, 214 Woodford Road, Woodford, Stockport SK7 1QF* Tel 0161-439 0300

✠**HACKER, The Rt Revd George Lanyon.** b 28. Ex Coll Ox BA52 MA56. Cuddesdon Coll 52. **d** 54 **p** 55 **c** 79. C Bris St Mary Redcliffe w Temple *Bris* 54-59; Chapl St Boniface Coll Warminster 59-64; V Bishopwearmouth Gd Shep *Dur* 64-71; R Tilehurst St Mich *Ox* 71-79; Suff Bp Penrith *Carl* 79-94; Hon Can Carl Cathl 79-94; Episc Adv for the Angl Young People's Assn 87-94; rtd 94; Hon Asst Bp Carl from 94. *Keld House, Milburn, Penrith CA10 1TW* Tel (01768) 361506

HACKER HUGHES, Katherine Lucy. b 60. York Univ BA81. Westcott Ho Cam 90. **d** 92 **p** 94. Par Dn S Woodham Ferrers *Chelmsf* 92-94; C 94-95; NSM Maldon All SS w St Pet 95-98; Chapl Chelmsf Cathl 98-01; P-in-c Gt Waltham w Ford End from 01; Adv relationship and family issues (Bradwell Area) 01-03. *The Vicarage, The Village, Great Waltham, Chelmsford CM3 1AR* Tel (01245) 360334 E-mail katyhh@lineone.net

HACKETT, Bryan Malcolm. b 66. Magd Coll Ox BA88 MA93 Cam Univ BA92 MA03. Westcott Ho Cam 89. **d** 93 **p** 94. C Willington Team *Newc* 93-97; TV Radcliffe *Man* 97-03; P-in-c Prestwich St Mary from 03. *The Rectory, Church Lane, Prestwich, Manchester M25 5AN* Tel 0161-773 2912
E-mail bryan.hackett@btinternet.com

HACKETT, Canon Frank James. b 33. AMIMechE68 MBIM72 MIIM79 HNC54 DMS72 Birm Univ MA77. Bps' Coll Cheshunt 62. **d** 64 **p** 65. C Feltham *Lon* 64-69; Ind Chapl *Lich* 69-73; Ind Chapl Port of Lon *Chelmsf* 73-79; Hon C N Ockendon 79-93; Hon Can Chelmsf Cathl 93-98; Ind Chapl 93-98; rtd 98; Perm to Offic *Lon* from 98. *11 Fairfield Avenue, Upminster RM14 3AZ* Tel (01708) 221461

HACKETT, John Nigel. b 32. Trin Hall Cam BA55 MA59. Ely Th Coll. **d** 59 **p** 60. C Handsworth St Mary *Birm* 59-66; V Handsworth St Jas 66-82; P-in-c Balsall Common 82-83; V 83-95; Perm to Offic *B & W* from 96; rtd 97. *Honeymead, Duck Lane, Kenn, Clevedon BS21 6TP* Tel (01275) 876591

HACKETT, Peter Edward. b 25. Magd Coll Ox BA48 MA51 ALCD60. **d** 60 **p** 61. C Lenton *S'well* 60-62; C Attenborough w Bramcote 62-63; V Lenton Abbey 63-67; R Acton Beauchamp and Evesbatch w Stanford Bishop *Heref* 67-71; V Choral Heref Cathl 72-76; P-in-c St Weonards w Orcop 76-79; P-in-c Tretire w Michaelchurch and Pencoyd 76-79; P-in-c Garway 76-79; P-in-c Welsh Newton w Llanrothal 77-79; V Rounds Green *Birm* 79-87; C Sutton Coldfield H Trin 87-90; rtd 90; NSM Shipton Moyne w Westonbirt and Lasborough *Glouc* 91-94; Perm to Offic *Birm* 94-99; Perm to Offic *Worc* 94-99; Perm to Offic *Heref* from 00. *96 The Pastures, Lower Bullingham, Hereford HR2 6EX* Tel (01432) 272462

HACKETT, The Ven Ronald Glyndwr. b 47. Hatf Coll Dur BA70. Cuddesdon Coll 70. **d** 72 **p** 73. C Pembroke St Mary w St Mich *St D* 72-75; C Bassaleg *Mon* 75-78; V Blaenavon w Capel Newydd 78-84; Chapl R Gwent Hosp 84-90; V Newport St Paul *Mon* 84-90; V Newport Ch Ch 90-01; Adn Mon from 01; R Mamhilad and Llanfihangel Pontymoile from 01. *The Rectory, 1 Millbrook Court, Little Mill, Pontypool NP4 0HT* Tel (01495) 785528

HACKETT, Victoria Anne. b 52. St Gabr Coll Lon CertEd73 Open Univ BA91 Surrey Univ DipTh00. SEITE 97. **d** 00 **p** 01. NSM Earlsfield St Andr *S'wark* from 00. *40 Freshford Street, London SW18 3TF* Tel (020) 8947 3755
E-mail v.ah@btopenworld.com

HACKING, Philip Henry. b 31. St Pet Hall Ox BA53 MA57. Oak Hill Th Coll 53. **d** 55 **p** 56. C St Helens St Helen *Liv* 55-58; C-in-c Edin St Thos *Edin* 59-68; V Fulwood *Sheff* 68-97; rtd 97; Perm to Offic *Sheff* from 98. *61 Sefton Court, Sefton Road, Sheffield S10 3TP* Tel 0114-230 4324

HACKING, Stuart Peter. b 60. St Pet Coll Ox BA82 MA. Oak Hill Th Coll 83. **d** 85 **p** 86. C Shipley St Pet *Bradf* 85-88; C Darfield *Sheff* 88-91; V Thornton St Jas *Bradf* 91-00; P-in-c Frizinghall St Marg from 00. *5 Redbeck Vale, Shipley BD18 3BN* Tel (01274) 580166 Fax (07020) 972854
E-mail stuart.hacking@breathemail.net

HACKL, Aileen Patricia. b 41. Wycliffe Hall Ox 00. **d** 01 **p** 02. Hon Asst Chapl Vienna *Eur* from 01. *Hardmuthgasse 25/3/20, A-1100 Vienna, Austria* Tel (0043) (1) 600 3083 Fax as telephone
E-mail aileen_hackl@hotmail.com

HACKNEY, Bryan William George. b 41. Hull Univ MA80. Linc Th Coll 65. **d** 68 **p** 69. C Baildon *Bradf* 68-71; R Gt and Lt Casterton w Pickworth and Tickencote *Pet* 71-74; Lic to Offic *Linc* 74-77; V Barnetby le Wold 77-81; P-in-c Somerby w Humby 77-81; P-in-c Bigby 77-81; Bp's Ind Adv *Derby* 81-85; R Morton and Stonebroom 85-91; V Mackworth St Fran 91-01. *Little Portion, Back Lane, Barnby, Newark NG24 2SD*
E-mail hackneyw@aol.com

HACKNEY, Archdeacon of. See DENNEN, The Ven Lyle

HACKSHALL, Brian Leonard. b 33. K Coll Lon BD53 AKC53. **d** 57 **p** 58. C Portsea St Mary *Portsm* 57-62; C Westbury-on-Trym St Alb *Bris* 62-64; V Avonmouth St Andr 64-71; Miss to Seamen 71-79; C Crawley *Chich* 79; TV 79-98; Ind Chapl 89-98; rtd 98. *5 St Michael Street, Brecon LD3 9AB* Tel (01874) 611319

HACKWOOD, Paul Colin. b 61. Bradf Coll of Educn DSS82 Huddersfield Poly BSc84 Birm Univ DipTh88. Qu Coll Birm 86. **d** 89 **p** 90. C Horton *Bradf* 89-93; Soc Resp Adv *St Alb* 93-97; V Thornbury *Bradf* from 97. *The Cottage, Fagley Croft, Bradford BD2 3JQ* Tel and fax (01274) 632034 or tel 663030 Fax 666911

HADDLETON, Peter Gordon. b 53. UEA BA74 Southn Univ BTh80. Sarum & Wells Th Coll 76. **d** 79 **p** 80. C Thamesmead *S'wark* 79-83; TV Bridgnorth, Tasley, Astley Abbotts, etc *Heref* 83-91; TV Heref S Wye 91-98; TR from 98. *The Rectory, 91 Ross Road, Hereford HR2 7RJ* Tel (01432) 277234 or 353717 Fax 352142 E-mail peter.haddleton@talk21.com

HADDOCK, Malcolm George. b 27. Univ of Wales (Cardiff) DipTh53 BA56 CertEd73. St Deiniol's Hawarden 87. **d** 80 **p** 81. NSM Newport Ch Ch *Mon* 80-85; NSM Risca 85-87; C 87-89; C Caerleon 89-96; rtd 96; Lic to Offic *Mon* from 96. *48 Cambria Close, Caerleon, Newport NP18 1LF* Tel (01633) 422090

HADDON-REECE (née STREETER), Mrs Christine Mary. b 50. St Jo Coll Nottm BTh81 LTh81. **dss** 83 **d** 87 **p** 94. Monkwearmouth St Andr *Dur* 83-85; Stranton 85-87; Par Dn 87-90; Par Dn Lastingham w Appleton-le-Moors, Rosedale etc *York* 90-94; C Wirt 92; V Topcliffe, Baldersby w Dishforth, Dalton etc from 97. *St Columba's Vicarage, Front Street, Topcliffe, Thirsk YO7 3RU* Tel (01845) 577939

HADFIELD, Prof Brigid. b 50. Edin Univ LLB72 QUB LLM77 Essex Univ PhD03. EAMTC 02. **d** 03. NSM Wivenhoe *Chelmsf* from 03. *12 Thornton Drive, Colchester CO4 5WB* Tel (01206) 843426

HADFIELD, Christopher John Andrew Chad. b 39. Jes Coll Cam BA61. Wells Th Coll 63. **d** 65 **p** 66. C Wigton w Waverton *Carl* 65-68; Teacher Newlands Sch 70-99; Lic to Offic *Mor* from 92;

Perm to Offic *Chich* from 96. *15 The Fridays, East Dean, Eastbourne BN20 0DH* Tel (01323) 422050

HADFIELD, Derek. b 34. **d** 01 **p** 02. OLM Folkestone H Trin w Ch Ch *Cant* from 01; OLM Sandgate St Paul w Folkestone St Geo from 01. *49 Collingwood Court, Folkestone CT20 3PX* Tel (01303) 246808 E-mail derekandruth@dhadfield20.freeserve.co

HADFIELD, Douglas. b 22. K Coll Cam BA44 MA49. St Jo Coll Nottm 84. **d** 88 **p** 89. Hon C Lenzie *Glas* 88-92; rtd 92; Perm to Offic *Glas* from 92; Perm to Offic *Pet* from 94. *8 Church Street, Helmdon, Brackley NN13 5QJ* Tel (01295) 760679

HADFIELD, Graham Francis. b 48. Bris Univ BSc69 St Jo Coll Dur DipTh71. **d** 73 **p** 74. C Blackpool St Thos *Blackb* 73-76; CF from 76; Perm to Offic *Lich* from 99. *c/o MOD Chaplains (Army)* Tel (01743) 262215 *or* 262230 Fax 262541

HADFIELD, Jonathan Benedict Philip John. b 43. Lon Univ BA64 Jes Coll Cam BA67 MA72. Edin Th Coll 66. **d** 68 **p** 69. C Fort William *Arg* 68-70; Chapl K Sch Glouc from 70; Hon Min Can Glouc Cathl *Glouc* from 70. *Dulverton House, King's School, Pitt Street, Gloucester GL1 2BG* Tel (01452) 521251

HADFIELD, Norman. b 39. Doncaster Coll of Educn TEng78 Univ of Wales (Cardiff) DPS90. St Mich Coll Llan 89 Llan Dioc Tr Scheme 83. **d** 86 **p** 87. NSM Ferndale w Maerdy *Llan* 86-90; C Llanblethian w Cowbridge and Llandough etc 90-92; V Resolven w Tonna from 92; RD Neath from 01. *The Vicarage, Neath Road, Resolven, Neath SA11 4AN* Tel (01639) 710354

HADJIOANNOU, John. b 56. Ch Coll Cam BA78 MA81. St Alb and Ox Min Course 95. **d** 97 **p** 98. C Linslade *Ox* 97-00; V Kinsley w Wragby *Wakef* from 00. *Kinsley Vicarage, Wakefield Road, Fitzwilliam, Pontefract WF9 5BX* Tel (01977) 610497 E-mail john@minster.co.uk

HADLEY, Charles Adrian. b 50. Trin Coll Cam BA71 MA75. Cuddesdon Coll 73. **d** 75 **p** 76. C Hadleigh w Layham and Shelley *St E* 75-78; C Bracknell *Ox* 78-82; R Blagdon w Compton Martin and Ubley *B & W* 82-92; RD Chew Magna 88-92; R Somerton w Compton Dundon, the Charltons etc from 92. *The Vicarage, Vicarage Lane, Somerton TA11 7NQ* Tel (01458) 272216 Fax as telephone

HADLEY, David Charles. b 42. **d** 02. NSM Kenley *S'wark* from 02. *21 Park Road, Kenley CR8 5AQ* Tel (020) 8763 6206

HADLEY, Donald Thomas. b 30. Lich Th Coll 55. **d** 58 **p** 59. C Saltley *Birm* 58-61; C-in-c S Yardley St Mich CD 61-66; V S Yardley St Mich 66-70; V Tonge Moor *Man* 70-84; C Selly Oak St Mary *Birm* 85-90; rtd 90; Perm to Offic *Birm* from 90; Perm to Offic *Worc* from 00. *175 Studley Road, Redditch B98 7HG* Tel (01527) 522658

HADLEY, John Spencer Fairfax. b 47. Ch Ch Ox BA70 MA73. Coll of Resurr Mirfield BA72. **d** 73 **p** 74. C Stoke Newington St Mary *Lon* 73-77; C High Wycombe *Ox* 77-81; TV 82-87; P-in-c Clifton St Paul *Bris* 87-91; Sen Chapl Bris Univ 87-91; Chapl Hengrave Hall Ecum Cen 91-94; Ecum Assoc Min Chelsea Methodist Ch 94-97; Hon C Chelsea St Luke and Ch Ch *Lon* 94-97; Chapl Westcott Ho Cam 97-02; P-in-c Horfield H Trin *Bris* from 02. *Horfield Rectory, Wellington Hill, Bristol BS7 8ST* Tel 0117-924 6185 E-mail spencer@fairfax2.fsnet.co.uk

HADLEY, Stuart James. b 55. K Coll Lon BD76 AKC76. St Steph Ho Ox 77. **d** 78 **p** 79. C Mansfield St Mark *S'well* 78-82; V Cowbit *Linc* 82-86; Perm to Offic 86-88; NSM W w E Allington and Sedgebrook 88-95; NSM Saxonwell 95-96; NSM Woolsthorpe 88-95; NSM Harlaxton Gp 95-96; Perm to Offic 97-99; NSM Barkston and Hough Gp from 99. *35 Wensleydale Close, Grantham NG31 8FH* Tel (01476) 575854 E-mail hadleystuart@hotmail.com

HADLOW, Mrs Jennifer Lesley. b 48. **d** 01 **p** 02. OLM Herne *Cant* from 01. *2 Hicks Forstal Cottages, Hicks Forstal Road, Hoath, Canterbury CT3 4NA* Tel (01227) 711516 E-mail jennyhadlow@hotmail.com

HAGAN, Canon Kenneth Raymond. b 40. BA97. ACT ThDip64. **d** 64 **p** 65. C Charlestown *Man* 64-69; Australia 69-75 and from 89; C Portsea St Mary *Portsm* 75-78; P-in-c Wolvey, Burton Hastings and Stretton Baskerville *Cov* 78-81; OCF 78-81; P-in-c Withybrook w Copston Magna *Cov* 78-81; P-in-c Shilton w Ansty 78-81; Perm to Offic *Leic* 81-83; Perm to Offic *Lon* 82-89; Can Portland Australia from 00. *57 Julia Street, PO Box 171, Portland, Vic, Australia 3305* Tel (0061) (3) 5521 7938 Fax 5523 7461

HAGGAN, David Anthony. b 25. Barrister-at-Law 70 QUB LLB49. S'wark Ord Course 87. **d** 89 **p** 90. NSM Reigate St Mary *S'wark* from 89. *2 Fairford Close, Brightlands Road, Reigate RH2 0EY* Tel (01737) 246197

HAGGAR, Keith Ivan. b 38. MRPharmS61. Cant Sch of Min 87. **d** 90 **p** 91. NSM Woodnesborough w Worth and Staple *Cant*

90-98; Perm to Offic from 98; Chapl St Bart Hosp Sandwich from 00. *Burtree Cottage, The Street, Worth, Deal CT14 0DE* Tel (01304) 613599

HAGGER, Jonathan Paul. b 59. St Jo Coll Nottm BTh95. **d** 95 **p** 96. C Newsham *Newc* 95-97; C Newc St Gabr 97-00; P-in-c Cresswell and Lynemouth 00-02; C Newc St Fran from 02. *18 Cotswold Gardens, Newcastle upon Tyne NE7 7AE* Tel 0191-281 2147

HAGGIE, Deborah. *See* HOLMYARD, Mrs Deborah

HAGGIS, Richard. b 66. Ch Ch Ox BA88 MA95 Nottm Univ MA95. Linc Th Coll DipMM94. **d** 95 **p** 96. C Romford St Edw *Chelmsf* 95-98; Chapl Trin Coll Cam 98-00; C St Giles-in-the-Fields *Lon* from 00. *Flat 2, 26 West Street, London WC2H 9NA* Tel (020) 7379 5649 E-mail rev.haggis@bigfoot.com

HAGGIS, Timothy Robin. b 52. New Coll Ox BA75 MA79. St Jo Coll Nottm DipTh. **d** 82 **p** 83. C Chilwell *S'well* 82-86; TV Hucknall Torkard 86-94; Chapl Trent Coll Nottm from 94. *Trent College, Long Eaton, Nottingham NG10 4AD* Tel 0115-849 4949

HAGON, Roger Charles. b 58. Nottm Univ BA80. St Steph Ho Ox 82. **d** 85 **p** 86. C Charlton St Luke w H Trin *S'wark* 85-88; C St Helier 88-95; V Kenley from 95; P-in-c Purley St Barn from 01. *The Vicarage, 3 Valley Road, Kenley CR8 5DJ* Tel (020) 8660 3263

HAGUE, David Hallett. b 59. Univ Coll Lon BScEng81 MSc82. Ridley Hall Cam CTM93. **d** 93 **p** 94. C Luton St Mary *St Alb* 93-96; V Stevenage St Pet Broadwater from 96. *St Peter's House, 1 The Willows, Stevenage SG2 8AN* Tel (01438) 238236 E-mail david.stpeter@lineone.net

HAHNEMAN, Geoffrey Mark. b 54. Baylor Univ (USA) BA77 MDiv80 Ox Univ DPhil87. **d** 80 **p** 80. USA 80-84; from 90; Hon C Ox St Mary Magd *Ox* 85-87; Asst Chapl Brussels *Eur* 87-90. *340 Court Street, Portsmouth, VA 23704, USA* E-mail trinity-portsmouth@worldnet.att.net

HAIG, Alistair Matthew. b 39. K Coll Lon BD63 AKC63. **d** 64 **p** 65. C Forest Gate St Edm *Chelmsf* 64-67; C Laindon w Basildon 67-71; V S Woodham Ferrers 71-78; P-in-c Bath H Trin *B & W* 78-83; R 83-89; R Bocking St Mary *Chelmsf* 89-95; Dean Bocking 89-95; rtd 00. *66 Wimpole Road, Colchester CO1 2DN* Tel (01206) 795275

HAIG, Andrew Livingstone. b 45. Keble Coll Ox BA67. Coll of Resurr Mirfield 67. **d** 69 **p** 70. C Elton All SS *Man* 69-75; V R Brantham *St E* 75-76; R Brantham w Stutton 76-82; RD Samford 81-82; P-in-c Haverhill 82; TR Haverhill w Withersfield, the Wrattings etc 82-90; RD Clare 84-87; Chapl Qu Eliz Hosp King's Lynn 90-94; Chapl King's Lynn and Wisbech Hosps NHS Trust from 94. *The Chaplain's Office, Queen Elizabeth Hospital, Gayton Road, King's Lynn PE30 4ET* Tel (01553) 613613 ext 2642

HAIG, Canon Murray Nigel Francis. b 39. Univ of Wales (Lamp) BA62. Kelham Th Coll 62. **d** 66 **p** 67. C Felixstowe St Jo *St E* 66-72; C Morpeth *Newc* 72-74; V Byker St Mich 74-79; V Byker St Mich w St Lawr 79-81; V Benwell St Jas 81-85; TR Benwell Team 85-91; TR Cramlington 91-97; Hon Can Newc Cathl from 95; P-in-c Alnwick 97-98; V from 98. *St Michael's Vicarage, Howling Lane, Alnwick NE66 1DH* Tel (01665) 602184 Fax 606820 E-mail d.haig@abbeyfield.com

HAIGH, Alan Bernard. b 42. NEOC 87. **d** 90 **p** 91. NSM Thorner *Ripon* from 90. *4 The Paddock, Thorner, Leeds LS14 3JB* Tel 0113-289 2870

HAIGH, Colin. b 15. St Chad's Coll Dur BA40 DipTh41 MA43. **d** 41 **p** 42. C Linthwaite *Wakef* 41-44; C Featherstone 44-45; C Streatham St Pet *S'wark* 45-48; C Benhilton 48-50; C Ipswich St Bart *St E* 50-52; C Leigh St Clem *Chelmsf* 52-56; R Fobbing 56-64; P-in-c Rawreth 64-68; V Romford St Alb 68-80; rtd 80; Perm to Offic *Chelmsf* from 80. *159 King's Road, Glemsford, Sudbury CO10 7QX* Tel (01787) 281715

HAIGH, John Gibson. b 47. Chich Th Coll 88. **d** 90 **p** 91. C Swinton and Pendlebury *Man* 90-93; C Richmond w Hudswell *Ripon* 93-96; C Downholme and Marske 93-96; R Nuthurst *Chich* 96-99; V Burnley St Mark *Blackb* from 99. *St Mark's Vicarage, 9 Rossendale Road, Burnley BB11 5DQ* Tel (01282) 428178 Fax as telephone E-mail revjhaigh@hotmail.com

HAIGH, Owen Quentin. b 15. St Chad's Coll Dur BA43 MA46. **d** 43 **p** 44. C Birtley *Dur* 43-47; C Billingham St Cuth 47-50; Min Darlington St Mark CD 50-55; R Wiston *Chich* 55-75; R Ashington 55-75; P-in-c Stedham w Iping 75-83; P-in-c Trotton w Chithurst 80-81; rtd 83; Perm to Offic *Chich* 84-00. *4 Manormead, Tilford Road, Hindhead GU26 6RA* Tel (01428) 602504

HAIGH, Richard Michael Fisher. b 30. Dur Univ BA57 Birm Univ DPS71. Cranmer Hall Dur DipTh59. **d** 59 **p** 60. C Stanwix Carl 59-62; CMS 62-70; India 63-67 and 68-70; R Salford St Clem w St Cypr Ordsall *Man* 71-75; R Holcombe 75-85; V Unsworth 85-93; R Brough w Stainmore, Musgrave and Warcop Carl 93-97; rtd 97; Perm to Offic *Carl* from 98. *21 Templand Park, Allithwaite, Grange-over-Sands LA11 7QS* Tel (01539) 532312 E-mail richard@randshaigh.freeserve.co.uk

HAILES, Derek Arthur. b 38. Coll of Resurr Mirfield. **d** 82 **p** 83. C Sneinton St Cypr *S'well* 82-84; V Kneesall w Laxton 84-85;

P-in-c Wellow 84-85; V Kneesall w Laxton and Wellow 85-88; V Sneinton St Steph w St Alb 88-95; P-in-c Bury H Trin *Man* from 95. *Holy Trinity Vicarage, Spring Street, Bury BL9 0RW* Tel 0161-764 2006

HAILS, Canon Brian. b 33. JP71. ACMA62 FCMA76. NEOC 77. **d** 81 **p** 82. NSM Harton *Dur* 81-87; Ind Chapl 87-99; Hon Can Dur Cathl 93-99; TR Sunderland 96-99; rtd 99. *Inhurst, 5 Hepscott Terrace, South Shields NE33 4TH* Tel 0191-456 3490 E-mail canon-hails@ukonline.co.uk

HAINES, Andrew Philip. b 47. LSE BSc68. Oak Hill Th Coll 84. **d** 87 **p** 88. C Enfield Ch Ch Trent Park *Lon* 87-91; V Hillmorton *Cov* from 91. *The Vicarage, Hoskyn Close, Hillmorton, Rugby CV21 4LA* Tel (01788) 576279 E-mail andrew@cahaines.fsnet.co.uk

HAINES, Daniel Hugo. b 43. TD89. MRCS73 DRCOG78 Lon Univ BDS68 Witwatersrand Univ 78. **d** 79 **p** 84. Swaziland 79-80; Falkland Is 80-82; Hon C Hatcham St Cath *S'wark* 84-99; Perm to Offic from 92. *56 Vesta Road, London SE4 2NH* Tel (020) 7635 0305

HAINES, Canon Robert Melvin. b 31. Coll of Resurr Mirfield 71. **d** 73 **p** 74. C Derringham Bank *York* 73-76; P-in-c Newport St Steph 76-79; TV Howden 80-82; R Turriff *Ab* 82-97; R Cuminestown 82-97; R Banff 82-97; P-in-c Portsoy 94-97; P-in-c Buckie 94-97; rtd 97; NSM Turriff *Ab* from 97; Hon Can St Andr Cathl from 01. *Ceol-na-Mara, 11 Scotstown, Banff AB45 1LA* Tel (01261) 818258

HAINES, Stephen Decatur. b 42. Freiburg Univ MA68 Fitzw Coll Cam BA70 MA74. **d** 71 **p** 72. C Fulham St Dionis Parson's Green *Lon* 71-76; C Finchley St Mary 76-78; Hon C Clapham Old Town *S'wark* 83-87; Hon C Clapham TM 87-88; Hon C Camberwell St Giles w St Matt 88-94; Hon Chapl S'wark Cathl from 92. *3 Lyndhurst Square, London SE15 5AR* Tel (020) 7703 4239

HAIR, James Eric. b 48. Lon Univ BA69 MPhil92. St Steph Ho Ox 69. **d** 72 **p** 73. C Fishponds St Jo *Bris* 72-75; C Bushey *St Alb* 75-79; P-in-c Lake *Portsm* 79-81; V 81-88; P-in-c Shanklin St Sav 79-82; V 82-88; TV Totton *Win* 88-95; C Portchester *Portsm* 96-97; Community Mental Health Chapl Portsm Healthcare NHS Trust from 97; Asst to RD Fareham *Portsm* 97-98 and 99. *St Christopher's Hospital, 53 Wickham Road, Fareham PO16 7JD* Tel (023) 9221 5832 *or* (01329) 822269

HALAHAN, Maxwell Crosby. b 30. Lon Univ BSc52 Southn Univ CertEd78 W Sussex Inst of HE AdCertEd83. Westcott Ho Cam 54. **d** 56 **p** 57. C Forton *Portsm* 56-60; C Liv Our Lady and St Nic *Liv* 60-62; Bahamas 62-64; C Widley w Wymering *Portsm* 64-66; C-in-c Cowes St Faith CD 66-70; V Cowes St Faith 70-77; Hon C Portsea St Sav 77-84; rtd 84; Perm to Offic *Portsm* 84-94. *4 Coach House Mews, Old Canal, Southsea PO4 8HD*

HALE, Antony Jolyon (Jon). b 56. MRTPI82 Newc Univ BA79. Sarum & Wells Th Coll 86. **d** 88 **p** 89. C Monkseaton St Mary *Newc* 88-92; P-in-c Tandridge *S'wark* 92-97; C Oxted 92-97; C Oxted and Tandridge 97-98; V Crawley Down All SS *Chich* from 98. *The Vicarage, Vicarage Road, Crawley Down, Crawley RH10 4JJ* Tel (01342) 714922 E-mail aj@jkcahale.plus.com

HALE, David Nigel James. b 03. NSM Aylesham w Adisham *Cant* from 03; NSM Nonington w Wymynswold and Goodnestone etc from 03. *Chilton House, 43 The Street, Ash, Canterbury CT3 2EN* Tel (01304) 813161 E-mail halenigelval@hotmail.com

HALE, Canon Dennis Ernest (Jim). b 26. MBE02. Southn Univ MA(Ed)66. Sarum & Wells Th Coll 74. **d** 77 **p** 78. NSM N Stoneham *Win* 77-86; Assoc Chapl Southn Univ 86-99; NSM Swaythling 90-99; rtd 99; Hon Can Win Cathl *Win* from 01. *12 Field Close, Southampton SO16 3DY* Tel (023) 8055 4538 Fax as telephone

HALE, Elsie Amelia. Gilmore Ho 53. **dss** 58 **d** 87. R Devon and Ex Hosp 64-84; Heavitree w Ex St Paul *Ex* 84-88; Perm to Offic from 88. *13 Riverside Court, Colleton Crescent, Exeter EX2 4BZ*

HALE, John. b 37. Ban Coll Dip Bibl Studies 60 Trin Coll Carmarthen CertEd59. St D Coll Lamp DipTh66. **d** 66 **p** 67. C Tenby and Gumfreston *St D* 66-71; R Burton 71-78; R Burton and Rosemarket 78-99; rtd 99. *Glantraeth, 5 Heol Emrys, Fishguard SA65 9EB* Tel (01348) 872416

HALE, John Frederick. b 29. Fitzw Ho Cam BA54 MA58. Tyndale Hall Bris. **d** 55 **p** 56. C Heigham H Trin *Nor* 55-58; C Paddington St Jas *Lon* 58-61; V St Leonards St Ethelburga *Chich* 61-79; C Prestonville St Luke 79-90; R Rotherfield w West Cross 90-92; rtd 92; Perm to Offic *Chich* from 92. *51 Brangwyn Drive, Brighton BN1 8XB* Tel (01273) 554944

HALE, Keith John Edward. b 53. Sheff Poly BSc75. St Jo Coll Nottm DipTh91 MA94. **d** 91 **p** 92. C Greasbrough *Sheff* 91-94; P-in-c Tankersley 94-95; R Tankersley, Thurgoland and Wortley from 95. *The Rectory, 9 Chapel Road, Tankersley, Barnsley S75 3AR* Tel (01226) 744140

HALE (née McKAY), Mrs Margaret McLeish (Greta). b 37. RN76. WEMTC 92. **d** 95 **p** 96. OLM Bream *Glouc* 95-01; NSM from 01. *14 Meadow Walk, Sling, Coleford GL16 8LR* Tel (01594) 834919

HALE, Roger Anthony. b 41. MIH85. Brasted Th Coll 68 Oak Hill Th Coll 70. **d** 72 **p** 73. C Blackb Sav *Blackb* 72-75; C Burnley St Pet 75-77; Chapl Burnley Gen Hosp 75-77; V Fence in Pendle *Blackb* 77-82; Chapl Lancs Ind Miss 77-82; NSM Tottenham St Mary *Lon* 88-91; R Cheddington w Mentmore and Marsworth *Ox* from 91. *The Rectory, 29 Mentmore Road, Cheddington, Leighton Buzzard LU7 0SD* Tel (01296) 661358

HALES, Ms Jan. b 65. TCD BEd85. CITC BTh94. **d** 94 **p** 95. C Lisburn Ch Ch Cathl *Conn* 94-99; C Coleraine from 99. *14 Loughanhill Park, Ballysally, Coleraine BT52 2QG* Tel (028) 7035 5148

HALES, Sandra Louise. BTh MSc RGN. **d** 02. C Lucan w Leixlip *D & G* from 02. *280 River Forest, Leixlip, Co Kildare, Irish Republic* E-mail slhales@eircom.net

HALEY, Thomas Arthur. b 52. NTMTC 98. **d** 98 **p** 99. NSM Old Ford St Paul and St Mark *Lon* 98-02; NSM Hackney Marsh from 02. *4 Vivian Road, London E3 5RF* Tel (020) 8981 1656 E-mail tomarcie@aol.com

HALFORD, David John. b 47. JP84. Open Univ DipEd86 Didsbury Coll Man CertEd69 Open Univ BA75 Man Univ MEd79 ACP72. LNSM course 96. **d** 96 **p** 97. OLM Royton St Anne Man from 96. *33 Broadway, Royton, Oldham OL2 5DD* Tel 0161-633 4650 Fax as telephone

HALFPENNY, Brian Norman. b 36. CB90. St Jo Coll Ox BA60 MA64. Wells Th Coll 60. **d** 62 **p** 63. C Melksham *Sarum* 62-65; Chapl RAF 65-83; Sen Chapl RAF Coll Cranwell 82-83; Asst Chapl-in-Chief RAF 83-88; Chapl-in-Chief RAF 88-91; QHC 85-91; Offg Chapl RAF from 91; Can and Preb Linc Cathl *Linc* 89-91; TR Redditch, The Ridge *Worc* 91-01; rtd 01; Perm to Offic *Glouc* from 02. *80 Roman Way, Bourton-on-the-Water, Cheltenham GL54 2EW* Tel (01451) 821589

HALIFAX, Archdeacon of. See FREEMAN, The Ven Robert John

HALKES, Canon John Stanley. b 39. SW Minl Tr Course 87. **d** 90 **p** 91. NSM St Buryan, St Levan and Sennen *Truro* 90-92; P-in-c Lanteglos by Fowey from 92; Hon Can Truro Cathl from 03. *The Vicarage, Battery Lane, Polruan, Fowey PL23 1PR* Tel (01726) 870213 Fax as telephone E-mail skypilot@by-fowey.demon.co.uk

HALL, Alan Maurice Frank. b 28. FCCA. Sarum & Wells Th Coll 86. **d** 89 **p** 90. NSM Winterbourne Stickland and Turnworth etc *Sarum* 89-97; Perm to Offic 97-00; Perm to Offic St Alb from 00. *2 Barnes Road, Wooton, Bedford MK43 9FA* Tel (01234) 764676

✠**HALL, The Rt Revd Albert Peter.** b 30. St Jo Coll Cam BA53 MA56. Ridley Hall Cam 53. **d** 55 **p** 56 **c** 84. C Birm St Martin Birm 55-60; S Rhodesia 60-65; Rhodesia 65-70; R Birm St Martin Birm 70-84; Hon Can Birm Cathl 75-84; Suff Bp Woolwich *S'wark* 84-91; Area Bp Woolwich 91-96; Chmn ACUPA 90-96; rtd 96; Asst Bp Birm from 96. *27 Jacey Road, Birmingham B16 0LL* Tel 0121-455 9240

HALL, Canon Alfred Christopher. b 35. Trin Coll Ox BA58 MA61. Westcott Ho Cam 58. **d** 61 **p** 62. C Frecheville *Derby* 61-64; C Dronfield 64-67; V Smethwick St Matt *Birm* 67-70; V Smethwick St Matt w St Chad 70-75; Can Res Man Cathl *Man* 75-83; Hon Can 83-90; Dioc Adult Educn Officer 75-83; Dioc World Development Officer 84-90; P-in-c Bolton St Pet 83-90; Co-ord Chr Concern for One World 90-00; rtd 96; Hon Can Ch Ch *Ox* 00-01. *The Knowle, Philcote Street, Deddington, Banbury OX15 0TB* Tel (01869) 338225 Fax 337766 E-mail achall@globalnet.co.uk

HALL, Mrs Ann Addington. b 34. Ex Univ CertEd71. SW Minl Tr Course 82. **dss** 85 **d** 87 **p** 94. Ex St Mark *Ex* 85-90; Hon Par Dn 87-90; Perm to Offic 90-92; NSM Cen Ex from 92. *33 Union Road, Exeter EX4 6HU* Tel (01392) 278717

HALL, Arthur John. b 23. Bris Univ BSc48. Sarum & Wells Th Coll 74. **d** 76 **p** 77. Hon C Portishead *B & W* 76-88; Perm to Offic from 88; Chapl St Brandon's Sch Clevedon 86-91. *34 Beechwood Road, Portishead, Bristol BS20 8EP* Tel (01275) 842603

HALL, Barry George. b 38. Solicitor 62. Oak Hill Th Coll 78. **d** 81 **p** 82. NSM Stock Harvard *Chelmsf* 81-90; NSM W Hanningfield 90-02; P-in-c 93-02. *Harvard Cottage, Swan Lane, Stock, Ingatestone CM4 9BQ* Tel (01277) 840387

HALL, Brian. b 59. Aston Tr Scheme 90 Oak Hill Th Coll DipHE94. **d** 94 **p** 95. C Mansfield St Jo *S'well* 94-96; C Skegby 96-99; P-in-c Sutton in Ashfield St Mich from 99. *The Vicarage, 11A Deepdale Gardens, Sutton-in-Ashfield NG17 4ER* Tel (01623) 476358 E-mail brian.hall2@ntlworld.com

HALL, Brian Arthur. b 48. Ex Univ BEd70. Cuddesdon Coll 73. **d** 75 **p** 76. C Hobs Moat *Birm* 75-79; V Smethwick 79-93; R Handsworth St Mary from 93; AD Handsworth from 99. *Handsworth Rectory, 288 Hamstead Road, Birmingham B20 2RB* Tel 0121-554 3407 E-mail b.a.hall@talk21.com

HALL, Charles Bryan. b 37. Liv Univ BA59. St Mich Coll Llan 59. **d** 62 **p** 63. C Prestatyn *St As* 62-64; C Cardiff St Mary *Llan* 64-67; V 73-75; C Hawarden *St As* 67-72; TV 72-73 and 84-86; P-in-c Cardiff St Mary w St Steph *Llan* 73-75; V Cardiff St Mary w St Steph 75-81; V Penycae *St As* 81-84; R Llandegla and Llanarmon yn Ial 86-02; rtd 02. *35 Heenan Road, Old Colwyn, Colwyn Bay LL29 9DP* Tel (01492) 514786

HALL, Charles John. b 40. JP. Lon Coll of Div ALCD68 LTh74. **d** 68 **p** 69. C Upton (Overchurch) *Ches* 68-72; C Morden *S'wark* 72-76; V Hyson Green *S'well* 76-84; V Stapleford 84-97; RD Beeston 90-97; TR Thetford *Nor* from 97; RD Thetford and Rockland from 99. *The Rectory, 6 Redcastle Road, Thetford IP24 3NF* Tel (01842) 762291 Fax as telephone E-mail hallthetrec@tesco.net

HALL, Christine Mary. b 45. K Coll Lon BD67 MPhil86. **d** 87. NSM Bickley *Roch* 87-92; Vice-Prin Chich Th Coll 92-95; Lic to Offic *Chich* from 95. *The Old School, East Marden, Chichester PO18 9JE* Tel (01243) 535244

HALL, Christopher. *See* HALL, Canon Alfred Christopher

HALL, David Anthony. b 43. Reading Univ BA66. Qu Coll Birm 79. **d** 81 **p** 82. C Norton *St Alb* 81-85; TV Hitchin 85-93; P-in-c Bidford-on-Avon *Cov* 93; V from 93. *5 Howard Close, Bidford-on-Avon, Alcester B50 4EL* Tel (01789) 772217 E-mail davidahall@onetel.net.uk

HALL, David Martin. b 66. Greenwich Univ BA89. Oak Hill Th Coll BA00. **d** 00 **p** 01. C Bebington *Ches* from 00. *8 Rolleston Drive, Bebington, Wirral CH63 3DB* Tel 0151-645 5026 Fax 643 9664

HALL, Denis. b 43. Lon Coll of Div 65. **d** 69 **p** 70. C Netherton *Liv* 69-71; C Roby 72-75; V Wigan St Steph 75-90; V Newton-le-Willows from 90. *The Vicarage, 243 Crow Lane East, Newton-le-Willows WA12 9UB* Tel (01925) 290545

HALL, Derek. *See* HALL, Canon John Derek

HALL, Derek Guy. b 26. Tyndale Hall Bris 50. **d** 51 **p** 52. C Preston All SS *Blackb* 51-54; C Halliwell St Pet *Man* 54-56; C-in-c Buxton Trin Prop Chpl *Derby* 56-58; V Blackb St Jude *Blackb* 58-67; R Fazakerley Em *Liv* 67-74; TR 74-81; V Langdale *Carl* 81-86; rtd 86; Perm to Offic *Carl* from 86. *14 Gale Park, Ambleside LA22 0BN* Tel (01539) 433144

HALL, Edwin George. b 40. Sarum & Wells Th Coll 88. **d** 91 **p** 92. NSM Purton *Bris* 91-97; rtd 97; Perm to Offic *Bris* from 97. *Common Farm Cottage, Witts Lane, Purton, Swindon SN5 9ES* Tel 07771-822851 (mobile)

HALL, Elaine Chegwin. b 59. RGN82 Liv Univ MTh01. N Ord Course 94. **d** 97 **p** 98. C Frankby w Greasby *Ches* 97-01; V Stretton and Appleton Thorn from 01. *The Vicarage, Stretton Road, Stretton, Warrington WA4 4NT* Tel (01925) 730276 E-mail petera.hall@care4free.net

HALL, Ernest. b 10. AKC36. **d** 36 **p** 37. C Kingsbury H Innocents *Lon* 36-40; C Highgate St Mich 40-44; V Enfield St Mich 44-49; V Kingsbury H Innocents 49-59; R Clifton *St Alb* 59-69; RD Shefford 66-69; V Osmotherley *York* 69-75; rtd 75; Perm to Offic *York* from 75. *Dulverton Hall, Esplanade, Scarborough YO11 2AR* Tel (01723) 340102

HALL, Frances. *See* HALL, Miss Judith Frances

HALL, Geoffrey Hedley. b 33. Bris Univ BA55. St Steph Ho Ox 63. **d** 65 **p** 66. C Taunton H Trin *B & W* 65-67; CF 67-80; Sen CF 80-86; P-in-c Ambrosden w Arncot and Blackthorn *Ox* 72-75; V Barnsley St Edw *Wakef* 86-98; rtd 98. *39 Heston Crescent, Perth PH2 7XD* Tel (01738) 636802

HALL, George Richard Wyndham. b 49. Ex Univ LLB71. Wycliffe Hall Ox BA74 MA78. **d** 75 **p** 76. C Walton H Trin *Ox* 75-79; C Farnborough *Guildf* 79-84; Bp's Chapl *Nor* 84-87; R Saltford w Corston and Newton St Loe *B & W* from 87; Chapl Bath Coll of HE 88-90; RD Chew Magna *B & W* 97-03. *The Rectory, 12 Beech Road, Saltford, Bristol BS31 3BE* Tel (01225) 872275 Fax as telephone E-mail richardhall@blueyonder.co.uk

HALL, Canon George Rumney. b 37. LVO99 CVO03. Westcott Ho Cam 60. **d** 62 **p** 63. C Camberwell St Phil *S'wark* 62-65; C Waltham Cross *St Alb* 65-67; R Buckenham w Hassingham and Strumpshaw *Nor* 67-74; Chapl St Andr Hosp Thorpe 67-72; Chapl HM Pris Nor 72-74; V Wymondham *Nor* 74-87; RD Humbleyard 86-87; R Sandringham w Newton 87-94; P-in-c Flitcham 87-94; P-in-c Wolferton w Babingley 87-94; R Sandringham w W Newton and Appleton etc 95-03; P-in-c Castle Rising 87-03; P-in-c Hillington 87-03; Hon Can Nor Cathl 87-03; RD Heacham and Rising 89-01; Dom Chapl to The Queen 87-03; Chapl to The Queen from 89; rtd 03; Perm to Offic *Nor* from 03. *Town Farm Cottage, Lynn Road, Bircham, King's Lynn PE31 6RJ* Tel (01485) 576134

HALL, Mrs Gillian Louise. b 45. N Ord Course 87. **d** 90 **p** 94. NSM Earby *Bradf* 90-96; NSM Gisburn 96-01; NSM Hellifield 96-01; Perm to Offic from 01; Chapl Airedale NHS Trust from 02. *244 Colne Road, Barnoldswick, Colne BB18 6TD* Tel (01282) 842593

HALL, Canon Godfrey Charles. b 43. Linc Coll Ox BA66 MA72. Cuddesdon Coll 66. **d** 68 **p** 69. C St Helier *S'wark* 68-72; Asst Chapl Ch Hosp Horsham 72-82; Hd Master Prebendal Sch Chich from 82; Can and Preb Chich Cathl *Chich* from 93. *53 West Street, Chichester PO19 1RT* Tel (01243) 782026

HALL, Harold Henry Stanley Lawson. b 23. Qu Coll Birm 56. **d** 58 **p** 59. C Bishopwearmouth Ch Ch *Dur* 58-61; C Winlaton 61-65; V Cockerton 65-69; V Newton Aycliffe 69-76; R Whitburn 76-89; rtd 89. *9 Balmoral Terrace, East Herrington, Sunderland SR3 3PR* Tel 0191-528 0108

HALL, Harry. b 41. Open Univ BA93. Chich Th Coll 91. **d** 91 **p** 92. C Boston *Linc* 91-92; C Bourne 92-94; P-in-c Sutterton w Fosdyke and Algarkirk 94-97; R Sutterton, Fosdyke, Algarkirk and Wigtoft 97-99; V Barnsley St Edw *Wakef* from 99; Chapl ATC from 99. *St Edward's Vicarage, 186 Racecommon Road, Barnsley S70 6JY* Tel (01226) 201616 E-mail hxh@sandh-barnsley.freeserve.co.uk

HALL, Henry. *See* DEANE-HALL, Henry Michael

HALL, Canon Hubert William Peter. b 35. Ely Th Coll 58. **d** 60 **p** 61. C Louth w Welton-le-Wold *Linc* 60-62; C Gt Grimsby St Jas 62-69; C Gt Grimsby St Mary and St Jas 69-71; Hon Chapl Miss to Seafarers 71-01; V Immingham *Linc* 71-01; RD Haverstoe 86-01; Can and Preb Linc Cathl 89-01; rtd 01; Perm to Offic *Linc* from 01. *6 Abbey Rise, Barrow-upon-Humber DN17 7IF* Tel (01469) 531504 E-mail peterhall@freeuk.com

HALL, Ian Alfred. b 60. Sheff Univ BA96. Ushaw Coll Dur 81 N Ord Course 98. **d** 85 **p** 86. In RC Ch 86-98; C Whitkirk *Ripon* 99-02; TV Swinton and Pendlebury *Man* from 02. *St Augustine's Vicarage, 23 Hospital Road, Pendlebury, Swinton, Manchester M27 4EY* Tel 0161-794 4298 E-mail carolian86@yahoo.co.uk

HALL, Ian Michael. b 48. Mansf Coll Ox MA70 Leeds Univ CertEd71. Carl Dioc Tr Course 85. **d** 88 **p** 89. NSM Eskdale, Irton, Muncaster and Waberthwaite *Carl* from 88. *Fisherground Farm, Boot, Holmrook CA19 1TF* Tel (01946) 723319

HALL, James. b 28. Wollongong Univ BA78. CITC 53. **d** 56 **p** 57. C Belfast St Mich *Conn* 56-59; I Cleenish *Clogh* 59-62; R Openshaw *Man* 63-68; Australia 68-89; R Morley w Deopham, Hackford, Wicklewood etc *Nor* 89-92; R High Oak 92-93; rtd 93. *54 Sunnybank Crescent, Horsley, NSW, Australia 2530* Tel (0061) (2) 4262 7881

HALL, Canon James Robert. b 24. TCD BA48 MA54. **d** 49 **p** 50. C Seagoe *D & D* 49-51; C Lisburn Ch Ch *Conn* 51-59; I Belfast St Mich 59-66; I Finaghy 66-89; Can Belf Cathl 82-89; rtd 89. *3 Coachman's Way, Hillsborough BT26 6HQ* Tel (028) 9268 9678

HALL, Mrs Jean Margaret. b 38. Bris Univ CertEd59 DipRE59 AdCertEd73. Bris Sch of Min 84. **d** 88 **p** 94. NSM Bris St Andr w St Bart *Bris* 88; NSM E Bris 88-91; Par Dn Plympton St Mary *Ex* 91-93; Asst Chapl E Kent Community NHS Trust 93-98; P-in-c Brompton Regis w Upton and Skilgate *B & W* 98-00; rtd 00; Hon C Bratton, Edington and Imber, Erlestoke etc *Sarum* from 00. *The Vicarage, 1A The Weir, Edington, Westbury BA13 4PX* Tel (01380) 830010

HALL, Jeffrey Ernest. b 42. Linc Th Coll 73. **d** 75 **p** 76. C Brampton St Thos *Derby* 75-78; C Whittington and New Whittington 78-81; TV Riverside *Ox* 81-90; R Anstey *Leic* 90-97; TR Hugglescote w Donington, Ellistown and Snibston from 97. *The Rectory, Grange Road, Hugglescote, Coalville LE67 2BQ* Tel (01530) 832557

HALL, The Ven John Barrie. b 41. Sarum & Wells Th Coll 82. **d** 84 **p** 85. Chapl St Edward's Hosp Cheddleton 84-88; C Cheddleton *Lich* 84-88; V Rocester 88-94; V Rocester and Croxden w Hollington 94-98; RD Uttoxeter 91-98; Adn Salop from 98; V Tong from 98; P-in-c Donington from 98. *Tong Vicarage, Shifnal TF11 8PW* Tel (01902) 372622 Fax 374021 E-mail archdeacon.salop@lichfield.anglican.org

HALL, John Bruce. b 33. St Louis Covenant Th Sem MTh80 DMin85 Lon Coll of Div ALCD60 LTh74. **d** 60 **p** 61. C Kingston upon Hull H Trin *York* 60-67; C Beverley Minster 67-68; V Clapham Park St Steph *S'wark* 68-76; R Tooting Graveney St Nic from 76. *The Rectory, 20A Rectory Lane, London SW17 9QJ* Tel (020) 8672 7691

HALL, John Charles. b 46. Hull Univ BA71. Ridley Hall Cam 71. **d** 73 **p** 74. C Bromley Common St Aug *Roch* 73-77; C Westbury-on-Trym St Alb *Bris* 78-80; Oman 80-82; C-in-c Bishop Auckland Woodhouse Close CD *Dur* 82-90; P-in-c Gt and Lt Glemham, Blaxhall etc *St E* 90-91; P-in-c Rodney Stoke w Draycott *B & W* 91-01; Dioc Ecum Officer 91-01; V Southmead *Bris* from 01. *St Stephen's Vicarage, Wigton Crescent, Bristol BS10 6DR* Tel 0117-950 7164 Mobile 07811-316249 E-mail revjon@ukonline.co.uk

HALL, John Curtis. b 39. CEng73 MIMechE73. Coll of Resurr Mirfield 80. **d** 82 **p** 83. C Pet Ch Carpenter *Pet* 82-86; TV Heavitree w Ex St Paul *Ex* 86-93; R Bow w Broad Nymet from 93; V Colebrooke from 93; R Zeal Monachorum from 93; RD Cadbury 97-02. *The Rectory, Bow, Crediton EX17 6HS* Tel (01363) 82566

HALL, Canon John Derek. b 25. St Cuth Soc Dur BA50. Linc Th Coll 50. **d** 52 **p** 53. C Redcar *York* 52-54; C Newland St Jo 54-57; V Boosbeck w Moorsholm 57-61; V Middlesbrough St Oswald 61-68; V York St Chad 68-90; Can and Preb York Minster 85-90; rtd 90; Chapl Castle Howard York 90-02; Perm to Offic *York* from 98. *25 Fairfields Drive, Skelton, York YO30 1YP* Tel (01904) 470978

HALL, John Edmund. b 49. Birm Poly CQSW76 Open Univ BA84. Trin Coll Bris BA89. **d** 89 **p** 90. C Winchmore Hill St Paul *Lon* 89-92; V Edmonton St Aldhelm 92-01; Dir Soc Resp *Cov* from 01. *The Rectory, Spring Hill, Bubbenhall, Coventry CV8 3BD* Tel (024) 7630 2345 *or* 7667 4328 E-mail john.hall@covdioc.org

HALL, Canon John Kenneth. b 32. Qu Coll Birm 61. **d** 63 **p** 64. C Ilminster w Whitelackington *B & W* 63-66; P-in-c Mackworth St Fran *Derby* 66-69; V Blackford *B & W* 69-76; R Chapel Allerton 69-76; New Zealand from 77; Can St Pet Cathl Waikato 85-91; rtd 93. *24 Pohutukawa Drive, Athenree, Katikati RD1, New Zealand* Tel (0064) (7) 863 4465 Fax as telephone

HALL, John MacNicol. b 44. Glas Univ BSc65 MB, ChB69 MRCGP75 St Jo Coll Cam BA73 MA76 Nottm Univ MTh88. Westcott Ho Cam 71. **d** 86 **p** 86. NSM Knighton St Jo *Leic* 86; NSM Clarendon Park St Jo w Knighton St Mich 86-89; Perm to Offic *Ely* 89-91; *St Alb* 90-92; *Birm* 91-00; Lic to Offic *Birm* from 00. *HM Prison, Winson Green Road, Birmingham B18 4AS* Tel 0121-554 3838 Fax 554 7990
E-mail rev.john.hall@tinyworld.co.uk

HALL, John Michael. b 47. BD. Oak Hill Th Coll 68. **d** 73 **p** 74. C Walthamstow St Mary w St Steph *Chelmsf* 73-76; C Rainham 76-79; P-in-c Woodham Mortimer w Hazeleigh 79-93; P-in-c Woodham Walter 79-93; Ind Chapl 79-93; R Fairstead w Terling and White Notley etc from 93; RD Witham from 01. *The Rectory, New Road, Terling, Chelmsford CM3 2PN* Tel (01245) 233256 E-mail revjohnhall@tinyworld.co.uk

HALL, Canon John Michael. b 62. Leeds Univ BA. Coll of Resurr Mirfield 83. **d** 86 **p** 87. C Ribbleton *Blackb* 86-89; C Carnforth 89-92; V Lt Marsden 92-98; V Lt Marsden w Nelson St Mary 98; V Warton St Oswald w Yealand Conyers from 98; Hon Can Bloemfontein Cathl from 01. *St Oswald's Vicarage, Warton, Carnforth LA5 9PG* Tel (01524) 732946 Fax as telephone E-mail johnbloem@aol.com

HALL, John Redvers. b 25. Dur Univ BA59 DipTh62 Man Univ CertEd74. **d** 61 **p** 62. C Lutterworth w Cotesbach *Leic* 61-63; C Loughborough Em 63-66; Lic to Offic 66-70; Lic to Offic *Blackb* 70-81; P-in-c Ingoldmells w Addlethorpe *Linc* 81-83; V Cholsey *Ox* 83-92; rtd 92; Perm to Offic *Chich* from 92. *3 Peak Coach House, Cotmaton Road, Sidmouth EX10 8SY*

HALL, Canon John Robert. b 49. St Chad's Coll Dur BA71. Cuddesdon Coll 73. **d** 75 **p** 76. C Kennington St Jo *S'wark* 75-78; P-in-c S Wimbledon All SS 78-84; V Streatham St Pet 84-92; Dioc Dir of Educn *Blackb* 92-98; Hon Can Blackb Cathl 92-94 and 98-00; Can Res 94-98; Gen Sec Nat Soc from 98; Chief Educn Officer and Gen Sec C of E Bd of Educn 98-02; Hd Educn Division Abps' Coun from 03; Hon C S Norwood St Alb *S'wark* from 03. *25 Goodenough Road, London SW19 3QW* Tel (020) 8543 7428 Fax as telephone
E-mail john@hall50.fsnet.co.uk

HALL, John Terence Peter. b 67. St Jo Coll Dur BA98. Cranmer Hall Dur. **d** 98 **p** 99. C Towcester w Easton Neston *Pet* 98-01; P-in-c Blakesley w Adstone and Maidford etc from 01. *The Vicarage, Collswell Lane, Blakesley, Towcester NN12 8RB* Tel (01327) 860507 E-mail john@beneficeofbamf.f9.co.uk

HALL, Jonathan. b 62. Ch Ch Coll Cant BA83 MIPD94. STETS BTh99. **d** 99 **p** 00. C Weymouth H Trin *Sarum* 99-03; R Whippingham w E Cowes *Portsm* from 03. *The Rectory, 69 Victoria Grove, East Cowes PO32 6DL* Tel (01983) 200107

HALL, Miss Judith Frances. b 64. SS Coll Cam BA85 MEng86 MA89 BTh02 CEng97. Ridley Hall Cam 99. **d** 02. C Drayton in Hales *Lich* from 02. *30 Berrisford Close, Market Drayton TF9 1LG* Tel (01630) 658977
E-mail jfh@franceshall.fsnet.co.uk

HALL, Kenneth Robert James. b 59. St Jo Coll Nottm 95. **d** 98 **p** 99. NSM Derryloran *Arm* 98-02; C Drumglass w Moygashel 02-03; I Brackaville w Donaghendry and Ballyclog from 03. *82 Dungannon Road, Coalisland, Dungannon BT71 4HT* Tel (028) 8774 0243 E-mail krjhall@btinternet.com

HALL, Keven Neil. b 47. Auckland Univ BSc PhD74. K Coll Lon BD AKC79. **d** 79 **p** 80. New Zealand 79-87; NSM Shepherd's Bush St Steph w St Thos *Lon* 91-95 and 98-00; NSM W Acton St Martin 96-98; Chapl Nat Soc for Epilepsy 91-03; Chapl Cem Middx Hosp NHS Trust from 00. *3 Roman Close, London W3 8HE* Tel (020) 8752 0543 *or* 8965 5733
E-mail kevenhall@hotmail.com

HALL, Leslie. b 37. Man Univ BSc59. EMMTC 83. **d** 86 **p** 87. NSM Freiston w Butterwick *Linc* 86-99; NSM Benington w Leverton 86-99; NSM Freiston w Butterwick and Benington from 99; Dioc NSM Officer 94-97. *29 Brand End Road, Butterwick, Boston PE22 0ET* Tel (01205) 760375

HALL, Mrs Linda Charlotte. b 50. Cam Inst of Educn CertEd72. St Alb Minl Tr Scheme 98. Oak Hill Th Coll 91. **d** 92 **p** 94. NSM St Alb St Steph *St Alb* 92-98; NSM Sandridge 98-99; C Ipswich All Hallows *St E* 99-00; Perm to Offic 01; TV Cwmbran *Mon* from 01. *St Mary's Vicarage, 87 Bryn Eglwys, Cwmbran NP44 2LF* Tel (01633) 483945

HALL, Mrs Margaret Mercia. b 39. Bedf Coll Lon BA61 Cam Univ DipRS78. Gilmore Ho 73. dss 80 **d** 87 **p** 94. Gt Chesham *Ox* 81-00; Par Dn 87-94; C 94-00; rtd 00; Perm to Offic *Ox* from 01. *The Elms, 94 Fullers Hill, Chesham HP5 1LR* Tel (01494) 784479

HALL, Mrs Marigold Josephine. b 29. Linc Th Coll 81. dss 85 **d** 87. Chapl Asst Hellesdon Hosp Nor 83-94; Nor St Pet Parmentergate w St Jo *Nor* 83-87; C 87-94; rtd 90; Perm to Offic

---

Nor from 94. *36 Cavendish House, Recorder Road, Norwich NR1 1BW* Tel (01603) 625933

HALL, Ms Melanie Jane. b 55. Ex Univ BA78. Ripon Coll Cuddesdon 01. **d** 03. C Stepney St Dunstan and All SS *Lon* from 03. *6 Arbour Square, London E1 0SH* Tel (020) 7790 9961 Fax as telephone

HALL, Michael Alan. b 76. Univ of Wales (Lamp) BA98. Ripon Coll Cuddesdon 99. **d** 01. C Wellington Ch Ch *Lich* from 01. *180 Holyhead Road, Wellington, Telford TF1 2DW* Tel (01952) 251655 E-mail revd.michael@btinternet.com

HALL, Canon Michael Anthony. b 41. St Paul's Coll Grahamstown LTh64. **d** 64 **p** 65. S Africa 64-01; C E London St Alb 65-67; C Queenstown St Mich 67-69; R Port Elizabeth All SS 70-78; R E London All SS 78-81; R Queenstown St Mich w Tarkastad St Mary 81-91; Adn Aliwal N 81-01; R Barkly E St Steph and P-in-c Dordrecht St Aug 91-01; Hon Can Grahamstown from 01; P-in-c Lapford, Nymet Rowland and Coldridge *Ex* 01-03; TV N Creedy from 03. *The Rectory, Lapford, Crediton EX17 6PX* Tel and fax (01363) 83321 Mobile 07751-798670 E-mail micksandhall@btopenworld.com

HALL, Michael Edward. b 32. Fitzw Ho Cam BA57 MA61. Ridley Hall Cam 68. **d** 69 **p** 70. C Aspley *S'well* 69-73; C Bulwell St Jo 73-75; V 75-81; P-in-c Tylers Green *Ox* 81-90; V 90-00; rtd 00. *The Round House, 107 High Street, Brampton, Huntingdon PE28 4TQ*

HALL, Murray. b 34. K Coll Lon. **d** 61 **p** 62. C Eaton *Nor* 61-64; C Shalford *Guildf* 64-67; V Oxshott 67-72; P-in-c Runham *Nor* 72-80; P-in-c Stokesby w Herringby 72-80; R Filby w Thrigby w Mautby 72-80; R Filby w Thrigby, Mautby, Stokesby, Herringby etc 80-94; rtd 94; Perm to Offic *Nor* from 94. *64 Nursery Close, Acle, Norwich NR13 3EH* Tel (01493) 751287

HALL, Nicholas Charles. b 56. St Jo Coll Dur BA71. **d** 86 **p** 87. C Hyde St Geo *Ches* 86-89; C Cheadle 89-91; NSM from 91. *5 Brooklyn Crescent, Cheadle SK8 1DX* Tel 0161-491 6758 Fax 491 0285
E-mail nick@domini.org

HALL, Canon Nigel David. b 46. Univ of Wales (Cardiff) BA67 BD76 Lon Univ CertEd68. St Mich Coll Llan 73. **d** 76 **p** 77. C Cardiff St Jo *Llan* 76-81; R Llanbadarn Fawr, Llandegley and Llanfihangel etc *S & B* 81-95; RD Maelienydd 89-95; Can Brecon Cathl from 94; Prec 99-00; V Builth and Llanddewi'r Cwm w Llangynog etc from 95; Treas Brecon Cathl from 00. *The Vicarage, 1 North Road, Builth Wells LD2 3BT* Tel (01982) 552355

HALL (née WANSTALL), Canon Noelle Margaret. b 53. Wolfs Coll Cam BEd76. Sarum & Wells Th Coll 84. dss 86 **d** 87 **p** 94. Hythe *Cant* 86-89; Par Dn 87-89; Par Dn Reculver and Herne Bay St Bart 89-94; C 94-95; Dioc Adv in Women's Min 92-99; Asst Dir Post-Ord Tr 94-97; P-in-c Sittingbourne St Mary 95-00; Hon Can Cant Cathl from 96; P-in-c Cant St Martin and St Paul 00-02; R from 02. *The Rectory, 13 Ersham Road, Canterbury CT1 3AR* Tel (01227) 462686
E-mail noelle@thinker117.freeserve.co.uk

HALL, Peter. *See* HALL, Canon Hubert William Peter

HALL, Peter. *See* HALL, The Rt Revd Albert Peter

HALL, Peter Douglas. b 60. Ox Poly HND81. Oak Hill Th Coll BA92. **d** 92 **p** 93. C Bromyard *Heref* 92-96; C Dorridge *Birm* 96-01; V Fareham St Jo *Portsm* from 01. *St John's Vicarage, 3A Upper St Michael's Grove, Fareham PO14 1DN* Tel (01329) 284203 *or* 280762 E-mail peter@revhall.freeserve.co.uk

HALL, Philip Edward Robin. b 36. Oak Hill Th Coll 64. **d** 67 **p** 68. C Ware Ch Ch *St Alb* 67-70; C Rayleigh *Chelmsf* 70-73; R Leven w Catwick *York* 73-85; P-in-c Mayfield *Lich* 85-95; P-in-c Ilam w Blore Ray and Okeover 89-95; Res Min Canwell, Hints and Drayton Bassett 95-01; rtd 01; Perm to Offic *Sheff* from 01. *45 St Alban's Road, Sheffield S10 4DN* Tel 0114-229 5032

HALL, Richard. *See* HALL, George Richard Wyndham

HALL, Richard Alexander Bullock. b 71. Ex Univ BA93 Edin Univ MTh95 BD98. Edin Th Coll 98. **d** 98 **p** 99. C Boxmoor St Jo *St Alb* 98-01; CF from 01. *c/o MOD Chaplains (Army)* Tel (01980) 615804 Fax 615800 E-mail rhall13572@aol.com

HALL, Robert Arthur. b 35. Lon Univ BSc66. NW Ord Course 74. **d** 77 **p** 78. C York St Paul *York* 77-79; R Elvington w Sutton on Derwent and E Cottingwith 79-82; Chapl Tiffield Sch Northants 82-84; V Bessingby *York* 84-88; V Carnaby 84-88; V Fulford 88-00; P-in-c York St Denys 97-00; rtd 00; Perm to Offic *York* from 00. *8 Beech Avenue, York YO24 4JL* Tel (01904) 790579

HALL, Robert Stainburn. b 72. Qu Coll Cam BA93. St Steph Ho Ox 96. **d** 98 **p** 99. C Worc SE *Worc* 98-01; TV Halas from 01. *St Margaret's Vicarage, 55 Quarry Lane, Halesowen B63 4PD* Tel 0121-550 8744

HALL, Roger John. b 53. QCVS95 MBE97. Linc Th Coll. **d** 84 **p** 85. C Shrewsbury St Giles w Sutton and Atcham *Lich* 84-87; CF from 87; Warden Amport Ho from 98; Dir Ord and Warden of Readers from 98. *c/o MOD Chaplains (Army)* Tel (01980) 615804 Fax 615800

HALL, Ronald Cecil. b 20. St Aid Birkenhead 63. **d** 65 **p** 66. C Tamworth *Lich* 65-69; R Talke 69-74; V Birstwith *Ripon* 74-90; P-in-c Thornthwaite w Thruscross and Darley 76-77; rtd 90.

Wickham House, Kingsmead, Farm Road, Bracklesham Bay, Chichester PO20 8JU Tel (01243) 671190

HALL, Mrs Sonia Winifred. b 44. Nottm Univ BSc66 Leeds Univ MSc68. Ox Min Course DipMin94. **d** 94 **p** 95. NSM Ox St Andr *Ox* 94-95; C Buckland 96-98; C Gainfield 98-99. *Alcudia, Bilbrook Lane, Minehead TA24 6HE* Tel 07930-558882 (mobile)

HALL, Stephen Clarence. b 23. Kelham Th Coll 46. **d** 51 **p** 52. C Killingworth *Newc* 51-53; C Newc H Cross 53-56; Rhodesia 56-77; S Africa from 77; R Makoni 56-69; P-in-c Bonda 59-62; R Mabelreign 62-68; Chapl Univ Coll of Rhodesia 68-77; Chapl Michaelhouse Sch 77-86; R Richard's Bay St Andr 86-97; rtd 97. *PO Box 102124, Meer-en-See, Zululand, 3901 South Africa* Tel (0027) (351) 32293

HALL, Stephen Philip. b 56. Ripon Coll Cuddesdon. **d** 84 **p** 85. C Camberwell St Giles *S'wark* 84-88; Chapl Brighton Poly *Chich* 88-92; TV Bicester w Bucknell, Caversfield and Launton *Ox* 92-02; Sub Chapl HM Pris Bullingdon 92-02; TV Southampton (City Cen) *Win* from 02. *The Deanery, 100 Chapel Road, Southampton SO14 5GL* Tel (023) 8063 3134

HALL, Prof Stuart George. b 28. New Coll Ox BA52 MA55 BD72. Ripon Hall Ox 53. **d** 54 **p** 55. C Newark w Coddington *S'well* 54-58; Tutor Qu Coll Birm 58-62; Lect Th Nottm Univ 62-73; Sen Lect 73-78; Prof Ecclesiastical Hist K Coll Lon 78-90; Perm to Offic *St Alb* 80-86; Perm to Offic *S'wark* 86-90; R Pittenweem *St And* 90-98; R Elie and Earlsferry 90-98; rtd 93. *Hopedene, 15 High Street, Elie, Leven KY9 1BY* Tel (01333) 330145 Fax as telephone E-mail sgh1@st-andrews.ac.uk

HALL, Thomas Bartholomew Berners. b 39. St Fran Coll Brisbane 63 ThL65. **d** 65 **p** 66. Australia 65-75 and from 82; P-in-c Whitehawk *Chich* 75-82. *1 Sutherland Drive, PO Box 647, Strathpine, Qld, Australia 4500* Tel (0061) (7) 3881 2090 *or* 3882 0880 Fax 3882 3269

HALL, Timothy Patrick. b 65. Bucks Coll of Educn BSc87 Lon Univ HA93 Bris Univ MA01. Oak Hill Th Coll 90 Trin Coll Bris 99. **d** 01 **p** 02. C Kingsnorth and Shadoxhurst *Cant* from 01. *10 Farrers Walk, Kingsnorth, Ashford TN23 3NL* Tel (01233) 501254

HALL, Timothy Robert. b 52. Dur Univ BA74. St Jo Coll Nottm LTh87. **d** 87 **p** 88. C Hawarden *St As* 87-89; Chapl St D Coll Llandudno from 90. *Woodpecker Cottage, St David's College, Llandudno LL30 1RD* Tel (01492) 581224

HALL, William. b 34. Hull Univ BSc(Econ)56 St Jo Coll Dur CertRS88. NEOC 89. **d** 92 **p** 93. NSM Bishopwearmouth St Nic *Dur* 92-01; rtd 01. *31 Nursery Road, Silksworth Lane, Sunderland SR3 1NT* Tel 0191-528 4843

HALL, Canon William Cameron. b 40. K Coll Lon 60. **d** 65 **p** 66. C Thornaby on Tees St Paul *York* 65-68; Chapl to Arts and Recreation *York* and *Dur* from 68; V Grindon 71-80; Hon Can Dur Cathl from 84; Sen Chapl Actors' Ch Union from 89; Perm to Offic *York* from 89; Hon Sen Research Fell Sunderland Univ *Dur* from 98. *59 Albert Street, Durham DH1 4RJ* Tel 0191-386 3177 Fax as telephone E-mail billhalluk@yahoo.co.uk

HALL, William Nawton Sinclair. b 17. Kelham Th Coll 35. **d** 41 **p** 42. C Gateshead St Cuth *Dur* 41-43; C Notting Hill All SS w St Columb *Lon* 43-46; C Clewer St Andr *Ox* 46-50; PC Gateshead St Aid *Dur* 50-55; R Witton Gilbert 55-61; R Lowther w Askham *Carl* 61-84; rtd 83; Perm to Offic *Carl* 84-99. *1 Ambler Grove, Holmfield Park, Halifax HX2 9TR*

HALL, William Norman. b 30. ARIC74 TCD BA52 MA64 BD65. TCD Div Sch Div Test54. **d** 54 **p** 55. C Dundela St Mark *D & D* 54-58; C Holywood 58-63; I Drumgooland 63-66; Chapl St Jas Choir Sch Grimsby 66-70; Asst Master Hautlieu Sch Jersey 70-73; V Jersey St Mark *Win* 73-92; rtd 92. *La Chansonette, 26 Seafield Avenue, La Route de St Aubin, Jersey JE2 3LZ* Tel (01534) 80221

HALL CARPENTER, Leslie Thomas Frank. b 19. Lich Th Coll 55. **d** 57 **p** 58. C Methley w Mickletown *Ripon* 57-59; V Kirkby Ravensworth w Dalton 59-61; India 61-63; V Ellingham w S Charlton *Newc* 63-67; V Horsford *Nor* 67-69; V Hexham St Faith w Newton St Faith 67-69; R Lochgilphead *Arg* 69-70; Area Sec USPG *York* 70-73; P-in-c Well *Ripon* 73-74; V Kirk Hammerton 74-75; R Hunsingore w Cowthorpe 74-75; V Nun Monkton 74-75; R Kirk Hammerton w Nun Monkton and Hunsingore 75-77; P-in-c Hackness w Harwood Dale *York* 77-79; V Melbecks and Muker *Ripon* 79-82; R Twyford w Guist w Bintry w Themelthorpe etc *Nor* 82-84; rtd 84; Perm to Offic *Nor* 90-96. *Shipdham Manor, Chapel Street, Shipdham, Thetford IP25 7LB* Tel (01362) 820939

HALL-MATTHEWS, Preb John Cuthbert Berners. b 33. Queensland Univ BA55 K Coll Lon PGCE65. Coll of Resurr Mirfield 58. **d** 60 **p** 61. C Woodley St Jo the Ev *Ox* 60-63; C Is of Dogs Ch Ch and St Jo w St Luke *Lon* 63-65; Asst Chapl Ch Hosp Horsham 65-72; Chapl R Hosp Sch Holbrook 72-75; V Tupsley *Heref* 75-90; P-in-c Hampton Bishop and Mordiford w Dormington 77-90; RD Heref City 84-90; Preb Heref Cathl 85-90; TR Wolverhampton *Lich* 90-98; TR Cen Wolverhampton 98-02; Preb Lich Cathl from 01; rtd 02. *Hillcrest, Corvedale Road, Halford, Craven Arms SY7 9BT* Tel (01588) 672706 E-mail jotricia@hall-matthews.freeserve.co.uk

HALL-THOMPSON, Colin Lloyd. b 51. JP. TCD DipTh. **d** 84 **p** 85. C Dublin Rathfarnham *D & G* 84-86; Bp's C Clonmel Union *C, C & R* 86-91; Chapl Fort Mitchel Pris 86-91; Chapl Port of Cork 86-89; I Kilbride *Conn* 91-03; I Ballymacarrett *D & D* from 03; Hon Chapl Miss to Seafarers from 91. *The Vicarage, 155 Upper Newtownards Road, Belfast BT4 3HX* Tel (028) 9065 7180 E-mail hallthompson@rapidial.co.uk

HALLAM, Lawrence Gordon. b 31. Lich Th Coll 61. **d** 63 **p** 64. C Brighton St Martin *Chich* 63-68; R Cocking w Bepton 68-71; V Eastbourne Ch Ch 71-84; V Bexhill St Barn 84-87; rtd 87; Perm to Offic *Chich* 87-92. *18 Eaton Court, Eaton Gardens, Hove BN3 3PL* Tel (01273) 772328

HALLAM, Nicholas Francis. b 48. MRCPath91 Univ Coll Ox BA71 MA81 Glas Univ PhD76 MB, ChB81. Ox NSM Course 84. **d** 87 **p** 88. NSM Ox St Clem *Ox* 87-93; NSM Balerno *Edin* from 93. *11 Ravelrig Park, Edinburgh EH14 7DL* Tel 0131-449 5341 *or* 536 6329

HALLAM, Canon Peter Hubert. b 33. Trin Hall Cam BA56 MA60. Westcott Ho Cam 56. **d** 58 **p** 59. C St Annes *Blackb* 58-62; Asst Chapl and Tutor St Bede Coll Dur 62-67; V Briercliffe *Blackb* 67-98; Hon Can Blackb Cathl 92-98; rtd 98; Perm to Offic *Blackb* from 02. *57 Grassington Drive, Burnley BB10 2SP* Tel (01282) 441070

HALLAM, Stuart Peter. b 66. St Martin's Coll Lanc BA92 Wolfs Coll Cam BTh99. Westcott Ho Cam 96. **d** 99 **p** 00. C Battersea St Mary *S'wark* 99-02; Chapl RN from 02. *Royal Naval Chaplaincy Service, Room 203, Victory Building, HM Naval Base, Portsmouth PO1 3LS* Tel (01705) 727903 E-mail revhallam@aol.com

✠**HALLATT, The Rt Revd David Marrison.** b 37. Southn Univ BA59 St Cath Coll Ox BA62 MA66. Wycliffe Hall Ox 59. **d** 63 **p** 64 **c** 94. C Maghull *Liv* 63-67; PC Totley *Derby* 67-75; R Didsbury St Jas *Man* 75-80; R Barlow Moor 76-80; TR Didsbury St Jas and Em 80-89; Adn Halifax *Wakef* 89-94; Area Bp Shrewsbury *Lich* 94-01; Asst Bp Sheff from 01; rtd 02. *1 Merbeck Grove, High Green, Sheffield S35 4HE* Tel 0114-284 4464 E-mail david.hallatt@sheffield-diocese.org.uk

HALLATT, John Leighton. b 34. St Pet Coll Ox BA58 MA62. Wycliffe Hall Ox 58. **d** 60 **p** 61. C Ipswich St Jo *St E* 60-63; C Warrington St Paul *Liv* 63-66; V Wadsley *Sheff* 66-72; V Hindley St Pet *Liv* 72-75; Area Sec (Scotland and Dios Newc and Dur) CMS 75-83; N Sec CMS 78-83; TR Cramlington *Newc* 83-90; V Monkseaton St Mary 90-99; rtd 99; Perm to Offic *Newc* from 99. *16 Eastfield Avenue, Whitley Bay NE25 8LT* Tel 0191-252 9518

HALLETT, Howard Adrian. b 43. Man Univ MPhil90. Oak Hill Th Coll BA81. **d** 81 **p** 82. C Walshaw Ch Ch *Man* 81-84; V Stoke sub Hamdon *B & W* 84-99; RD Ivelchester 91-95; V Kea *Truro* from 99. *The Vicarage, Kea, Truro TR3 6AE* Tel (01872) 272850 E-mail adrian@stkea.go-plus.net

HALLETT, Miss Jacqueline Victoria. b 54. Ex Univ BA75 PGCE76. Linc Th Coll 94. **d** 94 **p** 95. C Crook and Stanley *Dur* 94-99; P-in-c Crook 99-01; R from 01. *The Rectory, 14 Hartside Close, Crook DL15 9NH* Tel (01388) 764024

HALLETT, Keith Philip. b 37. Tyndale Hall Bris 61. **d** 64 **p** 65. C Higher Openshaw *Man* 64-68; C Bushbury *Lich* 68-71; P-in-c Drayton Bassett 71-72; R 72-90; V Fazeley 71-90; P-in-c Hints 78-83; V 83-90; C-in-c Canwell CD 78-83; V Canwell 83-90; RD Tamworth 81-90; P-in-c Buckhurst Hill *Chelmsf* 90-93; TR 93-02; rtd 02. *46 Balmoral Way, Worle, Weston-super-Mare BS22 9AL* Tel (01934) 413711 E-mail kph@webtribe.net

HALLETT, Peter. b 49. Bath Univ BSc72. Oak Hill Th Coll DPS. **d** 76 **p** 77. C Brinsworth w Catcliffe *Sheff* 76-79; P-in-c Doncaster St Jas 80-81; V 81-86; R Henstridge and Charlton Horethorne w Stowell *B & W* from 86. *The Vicarage, Henstridge, Templecombe BA8 0QE* Tel (01963) 362266 Fax as telephone E-mail halatvic@aol.com

HALLETT, Peter Duncan. b 43. CCC Cam BA66 MA68. Westcott Ho Cam 69. **d** 71 **p** 72. C Sawston *Ely* 71-73; C Lyndhurst and Emery Down *Win* 73-78; C Skegness and Winthorpe *Linc* 78-80; P-in-c Samlesbury *Blackb* 80-91; Asst Dir RE 80-00; C Leyland St Ambrose 91-94; V Lostock Hall from 00; P-in-c Farington Moss from 03. *St James's Vicarage, 76A Brownedge Road, Lostock Hall, Preston PR5 5AD* Tel (01772) 335366 E-mail peter.hallett@blackburn.anglican.org

HALLETT, Raymond. b 44. EMMTC 85. **d** 88 **p** 89. NSM Hucknall Torkard *S'well* 88-01; NSM Basford St Leodegarius from 01. *26 Nursery Close, Hucknall, Nottingham NG15 6DQ* Tel 0115-953 7677

HALLETT, Canon Roy. b 17. St D Coll Lamp BA48. **d** 49 **p** 50. C Llantarnam *Mon* 49-52; C Llanfrechfa All SS 52-58; V Caldicot 58-71; V Rumney 71-87; RD Bassaleg 82-87; Can St Woolos Cathl 86-87; rtd 87; Lic to Offic *Mon* from 87. *247 Llantarnam Road, Cwmbran NP44 3BQ* Tel (01633) 874128

HALLIBURTON, Canon Robert John. b 35. Selw Coll Cam BA56 MA60 Keble Coll Ox BA58 MA71 DPhil61. St Steph Ho Ox 58. **d** 61 **p** 62. C Stepney St Dunstan and All SS *Lon* 61-67; Lect St Steph Ho Ox 67-71; Vice-Prin 71-75; Lect Linc Coll Ox 73-75; Prin Chich Th Coll 75-82; Can and Preb Chich Cathl *Chich* 76-82; Wightring Preb and Th Lect 88-90; P-in-c

St Margaret's-on-Thames *Lon* 82-90; Can Res and Chan St Paul's Cathl 90-03; rtd 03; P-in-c Pau *Eur* from 03. *3 bis rue Pasteur, 64000 Pau, France* Tel (0033) (5) 59 90 09 30 E-mail john.halliburton@dial.pipex.com

HALLIDAY, Christopher Norton Robert. b 48. Bradf Univ PhD99. N Ord Course 82. **d** 85 **p** 86. C Davyhulme St Mary *Man* 85-87; Lect Bolton St Pet 87-90; I Rathdrum w Glenealy, Derralossary and Laragh *D & G* 90-00; R Valley Lee St Geo USA from 00. *St George's Episcopal Rectory, 19165 Poplar Hill Lane, Valley Lee, MD 20692, USA* Tel (001) (301) 994 9122 *or* tel and fax 994 2549 E-mail christopher@olg.com

HALLIDAY, Mrs Diana Patricia. b 40. ALA66. N Ord Course 89. **d** 92 **p** 94. NSM Burley in Wharfedale *Bradf* 92-95; NSM Harden and Wilsden 95-97; P-in-c Cullingworth from 97. *The Vicarage, Halifax Road, Cullingworth, Bradford BD13 5DE* Tel (01535) 272434 Mobile 07774-235844

HALLIDAY, Edwin James. b 35. NW Ord Course 70. **d** 73 **p** 74. C New Bury *Man* 73-76; V Bolton St Phil 76-82; Dioc Communications Officer 82-88; V Radcliffe St Thos and St Jo 82-90; R Gt Lever 90-02; rtd 02; Perm to Offic *Man* from 02. *8 Oxford Close, Farnworth, Bolton BL4 0NF* Tel (01204) 792347

HALLIDAY, Geoffrey Lewis. b 40. Lon Coll of Div ALCD66 LTh74. **d** 66 **p** 67. C W Bridgford *S'well* 66-72; V Woodborough 72-78; Bermuda 78-80; V Rampton *S'well* 80-81; P-in-c Laneham 80-81; P-in-c Treswell and Cottam 80-81; V Rampton w Laneham, Treswell and Cottam 81-85; V Attenborough 85-88; Perm to Offic *Derby* 91-92; NSM Ilkeston St Mary from 92; rtd 03. *Frog Hollow, 323 Heanor Road, Ilkeston DE7 8TN* Tel 0115-930 8607

HALLIDAY, Jean Douglas. b 47. NTMTC 99. **d** 01 **p** 02. NSM Forest Gate Em w Upton Cross *Chelmsf* 01-02; NSM E Ham w Upton Park St Alb from 02. *St John's Flat, 522A Goresbrook Road, Dagenham RM9 4XB* Tel (020) 8593 0616 Fax as telephone

HALLIDAY, Louisa. b 42. Open Univ BA77 BA94. STETS. **d** 00 **p** 01. NSM Wylye and Till Valley *Sarum* from 00. *Station House, Great Wishford, Salisbury SP2 0PA* Tel (01722) 790618

HALLIDAY, Paula Patricia. b 50. Man Univ MEd83 TCD BTh94. **d** 94 **p** 95. C Killala w Dunfeeny, Crossmolina, Kilmoremoy etc *T, K & A* 94-97; I Crosspatrick Gp *C & O* 97-00; R California St Andr USA from 00. *St George's Episcopal Rectory, 19165 Poplar Hill Lane, Valley Lee, MD 20692, USA* Tel (001) (301) 994 9122 E-mail revpaula@olg.com

✠**HALLIDAY, The Rt Revd Robert Taylor.** b 32. Glas Univ MA54 BD57. Edin Th Coll 55. **d** 57 **p** 58 **c** 90. C St Andrews St Andr *St And* 57-60; R 83-90; C Glas St Marg *Glas* 60-63; Lect NT Edin Th Coll 63-74; R Edin H Cross *Edin* 63-83; Tutor Edin Univ 69-71; Can St Mary's Cathl *Edin* 73-83; R St Andrews St Andr *St And* 83-90; Tutor St Andr Univ 84-90; Bp Brn 90-96; rtd 96. *28 Forbes Road, Edinburgh EH10 4ED* Tel 0131-221 1490

HALLIDIE SMITH, Andrew. b 31. Pemb Coll Cam BA54 MA58. Ely Th Coll 55. **d** 56 **p** 57. C Pype Hayes *Birm* 56-58; Sec Albany Trust Lon 58-60; Canada 60-63 and 67-70 and 79-81 and from 91; V Elmstead *Chelmsf* 63-67; R Alresford 70-79; V Elsecar *Sheff* 81-91; rtd 91. *PO Box 765, Big River SK, Canada, S0J 0E0* Tel (001) (306) 469 4417 Fax 469 5662

HALLING, William Laurence. b 43. Linc Coll Ox BA64 DipTh66 MA68 Lon Univ BD68. Tyndale Hall Bris 66. **d** 68 **p** 69. C Beckenham St Jo *Roch* 68-72; C Walton H Trin *Ox* 72-78; V Barrow St Mark *Carl* 78-86; R Kirkheaton *Wakef* from 86; Chapl Mill Hill Hosp Huddersfield from 86. *The New Rectory, Church Lane, Kirkheaton, Huddersfield HD5 0BH* Tel (01484) 532410 E-mail halling@fish.co.uk

HALLIWELL, Christopher Eigil. b 57. Newc Univ BA78. Trin Coll Bris DipHE91. **d** 91 **p** 92. C Mildenhall *St E* 91-94; R Wrentham w Benacre, Covehithe, Frostenden etc 94-97; TV Sileby, Cossington and Seagrave *Leic* 97-01; V Preston St Cuth *Blackb* from 01. *St Cuthbert's Vicarage, 20 Black Bull Lane, Fulwood, Preston PR2 3PX* Tel (01772) 717346 E-mail challiwell@fish.co.uk *or* vicarstcuthberts@fish.co.uk

HALLIWELL, Ivor George. b 33. St Cath Coll Cam BA57 MA60. Wells Th Coll 58. **d** 60 **p** 60. C Hanworth St Geo *Lon* 60-62; C Willenhall *Cov* 62-65; C-in-c Whitley St Jas CD 65-68; V Whitley 68-72; V Corton *Nor* 72-77; P-in-c Hopton 72-74; V 74-77; Asst Chapl HM Pris Pentonville 77; Chapl HM Pris Ex 77-83; Chapl HM Pris Wakef 83-85; P-in-c Bickington *Ex* 85-87; P-in-c Ashburton w Buckland-in-the-Moor 85-87; V Ashburton w Buckland in the Moor and Bickington 87-90; Chapl HM Pris Channings Wood 90-97; Lic to Offic *Ex* 90-97; rtd 97; Perm to Offic *Ex* from 97. *Anastasis, Avenue Road, Bovey Tracey, Newton Abbot TQ13 9BQ* Tel (01626) 834899 E-mail ivorhalliwell@aol.com

HALLIWELL, Canon Michael Arthur. b 28. St Edm Hall Ox BA50 MA53. Ely Th Coll 52. **d** 54 **p** 55. C Welling *S'wark* 54-57; C Bournemouth St Alb *Win* 57-59; Asst Gen Sec C of E Coun on Foreign Relns 59-62; C St Dunstan in the West *Lon* 60-62; Chapl Bonn w Cologne *Eur* 62-67; Chapl RAF 66-67; V Croydon St Andr *Cant* 67-71; R Jersey St Brelade *Win* 71-96; Chapl HM Pris Jersey 75-80; Vice-Dean Jersey *Win* 85-99; Tutor S Dios

Minl Tr Scheme 92-96; rtd 96; Hon C Jersey Grouville *Win* 96-99; Hon Can Win Cathl 98-99. *16 Le Clos du Rivage, Gorey Coast Road, St Martin, Jersey JE3 6EY* Tel (01534) 856506 Fax as telephone E-mail halliwells@jerseymail.co.uk

HALLOWS, John Martin. b 50. Birm Univ BA78 Lon Univ PGCE82 E Lon Univ MSc93. Oak Hill Th Coll 92. **d** 94 **p** 95. C Boxmoor St Jo *St Alb* 94-98; TV Bracknell *Ox* 98-01; V Barrowford and Newchurch-in-Pendle *Blackb* from 01. *St Thomas's Vicarage, Wheatley Lane Road, Barrowford, Nelson BB9 6QS* Tel (01282) 613206 Fax as telephone E-mail jhallows@compuserve.com

HALLS, Canon Peter Ernest. b 38. Bris Univ BA62. Tyndale Hall Bris 59. **d** 64 **p** 65. C Blackb St Barn *Blackb* 64-67; C Bromley Ch Ch *Roch* 67-70; V Halvergate w Tunstall *Nor* 70-79; V Freethorpe w Wickhampton 71-79; P-in-c Beighton and Moulton 77-79; V Tuckswood 79-90; RD Nor S 86-90; R Brooke, Kirstead, Mundham w Seething and Thwaite 90-93; RD Depwade 91-97 and 01-03; Hon Can Nor Cathl 99-03; rtd 03; Perm to Offic *Nor* from 03. *1 Church Farm Close, Weston Longville, Norwich NR9 5JY* Tel (01603) 880835

HALMSHAW, Mrs Stella Mary. b 36. Brighton Coll of Educn TCert57 Westmr Coll Lon CertRE58. St Alb Minl Tr Scheme 81. **dss** 84 **d** 87 **p** 96. Radlett *St Alb* 84-01; Par Dn 87-93; Hon C 93-01; Chapl Herts Univ 93-96; rtd 96; P-in-c Wittersham w Stone-in-Oxney and Ebony *Cant* from 01. *The Rectory, The Street, Wittersham, Tenterden TN30 7EA* Tel (01797) 270142

HALSALL, Graham. b 61. **d** 00 **p** 01. C Preston St Jo and St Geo *Blackb* 00-02; C Torrisholme from 02. *St Martin's House, Braddon Close, Morecambe LA4 4UZ* Tel (01524) 422249 E-mail frgraham@whsmithnet.co.uk

HALSALL, Mrs Isobel Joan. b 47. Liv Univ CertEd71. Local Minl Tr Course 91. **d** 94 **p** 95. OLM Walshaw Ch Ch *Man* from 94. *42 Knowsley Road, Bolton BL2 5PU* Tel (01204) 394171

HALSALL, Michael John. b 61. Salford Univ BSc83. Wycliffe Hall Ox 88. **d** 91 **p** 92. C Cowley St Jo *Ox* 91-93; CF 93-99; P-in-c Prittlewell St Luke *Chelmsf* 99-00; V from 00. *The Vicarage, St Luke's Road, Southend-on-Sea SS2 4AB* Tel (01702) 467620 E-mail m.j.hallsall@talk21.com

HALSE, Raymond Stafford. b 19. Lon Univ BA49. Oak Hill Th Coll 46. **d** 50 **p** 51. C Rodbourne Cheney *Bris* 50-52; C Farnborough *Guildf* 52-54; V Islington St Jude Mildmay Park *Lon* 54-59; V Over Stowey w Aisholt *B & W* 59-68; V Ramsgate St Luke *Cant* 68-85; P-in-c Ramsgate Ch Ch 85; rtd 85; Hon C Hordle *Win* 86-92; Perm to Offic *Sarum* 90-01. *23 Ramsay Hall, 11-13 Byron Road, Worthing BN11 3HN* Tel (01903) 219478

HALSEY, Anthony Michael James. b 35. K Coll Cam BA56 MA62 Solicitor 64. St Jo Coll Nottm 73. **d** 75 **p** 76. C Derby St Werburgh *Derby* 75-77; Chapl Canford Sch Wimborne 78-87; TV Sanderstead All SS *S'wark* 87-89; Perm to Offic *Portsm* from 89; rtd 00. *Woodlands, South Road, Liphook GU30 7HS* Tel (01428) 724459 E-mail halseys@southroad.fsbusiness.co.uk

✠**HALSEY, The Rt Revd Henry David.** b 19. K Coll Cam BA38. Sarum Th Coll 40. **d** 42 **p** 43 **c** 68. C Petersfield w Sheet *Portsm* 42-45; Chapl RN 46-47; C Plymouth St Andr *Ex* 47-50; V Netheravon w Fittleton *Sarum* 50-53; C-in-c Chatham St Steph CD *Roch* 53-59; V Chatham St Steph 59-62; V Bromley SS Pet and Paul 62-68; Chapl Bromley Hosp 62-68; Hon Can Roch Cathl *Roch* 64-68; RD Bromley 65-66; Adm Bromley 66-68; Suff Bp Tonbridge 68-72; Bp Carl 72-89; rtd 89; Hon Asst Bp Portsm from 91. *Bramblecross, Gully Road, Seaview PO34 5BY* Tel (01983) 613583

HALSEY, Brother John Walter Brooke. b 33. Cam Univ BA57 Edin Univ Dip Past Th 67. Westcott Ho Cam 61. **d** 61 **p** 62. C Stocksbridge *Sheff* 61-65; Community of the Transfiguration Midlothian from 65; Ind Chapl Edin 65-69. *Hermitage of the Transfiguration, 23 Manse Road, Roslin EH25 9LF*

HALSON, Bryan Richard. b 32. Jes Coll Cam BA56 MA60 Liv Univ MA72 Geneva Univ 59. Ridley Hall Cam 57. **d** 59 **p** 60. C Coulsdon St Andr *S'wark* 59-62; Lic to Offic *Ches* 63-68; Tutor St Aid Birkenhead 63-65; Sen Tutor 65-68; Vice-Prin 68-69; Lect Alsager Coll of Educn 69-72; Prin Lect Crewe and Alsager Coll of HE 72-90; Perm to Offic *Ches* from 97. *1 Victoria Mill Drive, Willaston, Nantwich CW5 6RR*

✠**HAMBIDGE, The Most Revd Douglas Walter.** b 27. Lon Univ BD58. ALCD62 Angl Th Coll (BC) DD70. **d** 53 **p** 54 **c** 69. C Dalston St Mark w St Bart *Lon* 53-56; Canada 56-93 and from 95; R Cassiar 56-58; R Smithers 58-64; R Fort St John 64-69; Can Caledonia 65-69; Bp Caledonia 69-80; Bp New Westmr 80; Abp New Westmr and Metrop BC 81-93; Prin St Mark's Th Coll Dar es Salaam 93-95; Asst Bp Dar es Salaam 93-95; Chan Vancouver Sch of Th from 95. *1621 Golf Club Drive, Delta BC, Canada, V4M 4E6* Tel (001) (604) 948 1931 E-mail hambidge@vst.edu

HAMBIDGE, John Robert. b 29. Birm Univ MA02. Sarum Th Coll. **d** 55 **p** 56. C Tynemouth H Trin W Town *Newc* 55-57; C Middlesbrough St Jo the Ev *York* 58-63; C Clerkenwell H Redeemer w St Phil *Lon* 63-64; C Richmond St Mary *S'wark* 64-66; V Richmond St Jo 66-76; R Swanscombe *Roch* 76-84; V Aberedw w Llandeilo Graban and Llanbadarn etc *S & B* 84-91; P-in-c Sibson w Sheepy and Ratcliffe Culey *Leic* 91-94; P-in-c

Orton-on-the-Hill w Twycross etc 92-94; R The Sheepy Gp 95-97; rtd 97; Perm to Offic *Lich* from 99. *99 Elizabeth Drive, Tamworth B79 8DE* Tel (01827) 61526
E-mail john@hambidge.org.uk

HAMBLEN, John William Frederick. b 24. Sarum Th Coll 64. **d** 65 **p** 66. C Weymouth H Trin *Sarum* 66-68; C Marlborough 68-70; V Chardstock 70-77; P-in-c Lytchett Matravers 77-83; P-in-c Burpham *Chich* 83-89; Dioc Stewardship Adv 83-89; rtd 89; Perm to Offic *Ex* from 89. *73 West Cliff Road, Dawlish EX7 9QX*

HAMBLETON, Ronald Dalzell. b 27. Ripon Hall Ox 61. **d** 62 **p** 63. C Stokesay *Heref* 62-65; V Knowbury 65-75; P-in-c Weston under Penyard 75-79; P-in-c Hope Mansell 75-79; R Weston-under-Penyard w Hope Mansel and The Lea 79-92; rtd 92; NSM Portree *Arg* 92-95; Perm to Offic *Heref* from 96. *21 Pentaloe Close, Mordiford, Hereford HR1 4LS* Tel (01432) 870622

HAMBLIN, Derek Gordon Hawthorne. b 35. SW Minl Tr Course 94. **d** 96 **p** 97. Hon C S Brent and Rattery *Ex* from 96. *Little Sand Park, Chapel Fields, South Brent TQ10 9BS* Tel (01364) 72388

HAMBLIN, John Talbot. b 38. St Steph Ho Ox 64. **d** 66 **p** 67. C Newc St Jo *Newc* 66-70; C Covent Garden St Paul *Lon* 70-71; C St Marylebone Ch Ch w St Barn 71-72; C St Marylebone Ch Ch w St Paul 72-73; C Hendon St Mary 73-76; P-in-c Hornsey St Pet 76-77; V Tottenham Ch Ch w Green 76-77; V W Green Ch Ch w St Pet 77-96; rtd 98. *Terry's Cross House, Brighton Road, Woodmancote, Henfield BN5 9SX* Tel (01273) 491256

HAMBLIN, Roger Noel. b 42. Ripon Hall Ox 67. **d** 70 **p** 71. C Scotforth *Blackb* 70-73; C Altham w Clayton le Moors 73-76; V Cockerham w Winmarleigh 76-87; V Cockerham w Winmarleigh and Glasson 87-00; P-in-c Wray w Tatham and Tatham Fells 00-03; V E Lonsdale from 03. *The Vicarage, Main Street, Wray, Lancaster LA2 8QF* Tel (01524) 221030

HAMBORG, Graham Richard. b 52. Bris Univ BSc73 Nottm Univ BA76 MTh77. St Jo Coll Nottm 74. **d** 77 **p** 78. C Tile Cross *Birm* 77-80; C Upton cum Chalvey *Ox* 80-82; TV 82-86; V Ruscombe and Twyford from 86; AD Sonning from 03. *Ruscombe and Twyford Church Office, St Mary's Church Centre, Station Road, Twyford, Reading RG10 9NT* Tel 0118-934 4792

HAMBREY, Canon Frank Bernard. b 14. Leeds Univ BA42. Coll of Resurr Mirfield 43. **d** 44 **p** 45. C W Bromwich St Andr *Lich* 44-46; C Edgmond 46-51; V Bury St Thos *Man* 51-57; Area Sec (Dios Man and Liv) SPG 57-64; USPG 65-68; V Colton *Carl* 68-70; Can Res Bermuda 70-75; Perm to Offic *Carl* 77-99; rtd 79. *Bully Cottage, Embleton, Cockermouth CA13 9YA* Tel (01768) 776379

HAMBREY, Frederick Charles. b 19. Leeds Univ BA41. Coll of Resurr Mirfield 41. **d** 43 **p** 45. C Bloxwich *Lich* 43-45; C Willenhall St Giles 45-49; C Hednesford 49-54; V W Bromwich Gd Shep 54-59; V Hanbury 59-70; V Colton *Carl* 70-71; V Satterthwaite and Rusland 70-71; V Colton w Satterthwaite and Rusland 71-84; rtd 84; Perm to Offic *Carl* from 85. *Underknott, Blease Road, Threlkeld, Keswick CA12 4RX* Tel (01768) 779604

HAMBROOK, Peter John. b 37. **d** 01 **p** 02. OLM Gt Mongeham w Ripple and Sutton by Dover *Cant* from 01. *4 Brewery Cottages, Northbourne Road, Great Mongeham, Deal CT14 0HA* Tel (01304) 364457 E-mail peter@4brewerycotts.fsnet.co.uk

HAMEL COOKE, Ian Kirk. b 17. Birm Univ BA39. Chich Th Coll 39. **d** 41 **p** 42. C Bedminster St Fran *Bris* 41-43; C Alton All SS *Win* 43-48; V N Baddesley 48-55; R Hartest w Boxted *St E* 55-63; V Addlestone *Guildf* 63-75; R Tittleshall w Godwick and Wellingham *Nor* 75-76; R Tittleshall w Godwick, Wellingham and Weasenham 76-82; rtd 82; Perm to Offic *Nor* from 82. *Crugmeer, Croft Yard, Wells-next-the-Sea NR23 1JS* Tel (01328) 710358

HAMER, David Handel. b 41. Cape Town Univ BA61 Trin Coll Ox BA66. Coll of Resurr Mirfield 62. **d** 66 **p** 67. S Africa 66-73; C Claremont 66-70; Chapl St Paul's Coll Grahamstown 70-73; Chapl Blundell's Sch Tiverton 73-01; rtd 01. *Jaspers Green, Uplowman, Tiverton EX16 7DP* Tel (01884) 829130

HAMER, Irving David. b 59. **d** 84 **p** 85. C Newton Nottage *Llan* 84-88; C Roath 88-90; V Llansawel, Briton Ferry 90-00; V Roath St Martin from 00; Miss to Seafarers from 90. *St Martin's Vicarage, Strathnairn Street, Roath, Cardiff CF24 3JL* Tel (029) 2048 2295

HAMER, Mrs Penelope Ann. MA FIBMS. **d** 00 **p** 01. NSM Hartpury w Corse and Staunton *Glouc* from 00. *Catsbury Cottage, Corsend Road, Hartpury GL19 3BP* Tel (01425) 700314

HAMER, Canon Val. b 52. Leeds Univ BA74. S'wark Ord Course 83. **dss** 86 **d** 87 **p** 94. Warlingham w Chelsham and Farleigh *S'wark* 86-87; Par Dn 87-88; Par Dn Caterham 88-94; C 94-96; RD Caterham 95-96; V Addiscombe St Mildred 96-02; Can Res and Chan Heref Cathl *Heref* from 02. *2 Cathedral Close, Hereford HR1 2NG* Tel (01432) 278672 Fax as telephone E-mail chancellor@herefordcathedral.co.uk or val_hamer@hotmail.com

HAMERTON, Thomas Patrick. b 13. St Edm Hall Ox BA35 DipTh36 MA50. Cuddesdon Coll 37. **d** 38 **p** 39. C Bury St Mary *Man* 38-40; C Southbourne St Kath *Win* 40-42; India 42-44; C Parkstone St Pet w Branksea *Sarum* 44-52; V Weedon Lois w

Plumpton *Pet* 52-58; R Abthorpe 52-58; R Slapton 52-58; V Weedon Lois w Plumpton and Moreton Pinkney 58-63; R Abington 63-76; V Welton w Ashby St Ledgers 76-83; rtd 83; Perm to Offic *Glouc* 83-95. *15 Langton Road, Rugby CV21 3UA* Tel (01788) 546599

HAMEY, Geoffrey Allan. b 25. Lon Univ BSc47. S'wark Ord Course 75. **d** 78 **p** 79. NSM Pinner *Lon* 78-83; P-in-c Fincham *Ely* 83-84; P-in-c Marham 83-84; P-in-c Shouldham 83-84; P-in-c Shouldham Thorpe 83-84; V 84-88; rtd 88; Hon C Winkleigh *Ex* 88-96; Perm to Offic *Ex* 96-02; *Lich* from 02. *15 Victoria Gardens, Lichfield WS13 8BG* Tel (01543) 416079

✠**HAMID, The Rt Revd David.** b 55. McMaster Univ Ontario BSc78. Trin Coll Toronto MDiv81. **d** 81 **p** 82 **c** 02. Canada 81-96; C Burlington St Chris 81-83; R Burlington St Jo 83-87; Miss Co-ord Gen Syn of Angl Ch of Canada 87-96; Hon Can Santo Domingo 93-02; Dir Ecum Affairs ACC 96-02; Suff Bp Eur from 02. *14 Tufton Street, London SW1P 3QZ* Tel (020) 7898 1160 Fax 7898 1166 E-mail david.hamid@europe.c-of-e.org.uk

HAMIL, Sheila. b 49. TCert71. NEOC DipHE95. **d** 95 **p** 98. NSM Wallsend St Luke *Newc* 95-97; NSM Long Benton St Mary 97-02; NSM Willington Team from 02. *5 Kings Road, Wallsend NE28 7QT* Tel 0191-287 3449

HAMILL-STEWART, Simon Francis. b 32. Pemb Coll Cam BA56. N Ord Course 77. **d** 80 **p** 81. NSM Neston *Ches* 80-83; C 83-86; V Over St Jo 86-00; Dioc Ecum Officer 92-00; rtd 00; Perm to Offic *Ches* 00-01; C Middlewich w Byley from 01. *87 Warmingham Lane, Middlewich CW10 0DJ* Tel (01606) 737329

HAMILTON, Canon Edgar Reid. b 27. TCD BA49 MA52. CITC 51. **d** 51 **p** 52. C Belfast St Donard *D & D* 51-55; Dean's V Belf Cathl 55-59; C-in-c Stormont *D & D* 60-64; I 64-93; Can Belf Cathl 85-91; Preb Wicklow St Patr Cathl Dublin 90-93; rtd 93. *13 Massey Park, Belfast BT4 2JX* Tel (028) 9076 3835

HAMILTON, Gerald Murray Percival. b 14. Ch Coll Cam BA37 MA41. Ridley Hall Cam 37. **d** 39 **p** 40. C Shirley *Win* 39-40; Bp's Dom Chapl 40-41; C Odiham w S Warnborough and Long Sutton 41-44; C Leeds St Pet *Ripon* 44-46; V Ashton-upon-Mersey St Mary *Ches* 46-51; Relig Broadcasting Org BBC N Region 52-65; Lic to Offic *Ches* 51-65; Can Res Newc Cathl *Newc* 65-67; Bp's Ind and Community Adv 65-67; Prin Lect Coll of Ripon & York St Jo 67-79; R Crayke w Brandsby and Yearsley *York* 78-82; rtd 82; Perm to Offic *York* from 82. *31 St Andrewgate, York YO1 7BR* Tel (01904) 632506

HAMILTON, Graham. *See* HAMILTON, William Graham

HAMILTON, Canon James. b 22. Dur Univ LTh48. Tyndale Hall Bris 41. **d** 49 **p** 50. C Carl St Jo *Carl* 49-52; N Area Sec BCMS 52-55; V Southport SS Simon and Jude *Liv* 55-66; V Eccleston Ch Ch 66-87; Hon Can Liv Cathl 76-87; rtd 87; Perm to Offic *Liv* from 87. *6 Freckleton Road, St Helens WA10 3AW* Tel (01744) 57716

HAMILTON, James Davy. b 20. Hatf Coll Dur 38. Edin Th Coll 40. **d** 43 **p** 45. C Kirkcaldy *St And* 43-46; C Wokingham St Paul *Ox* 46-49; Chapl RAF 49-55; C St Athan *Llan* 49-50; C Boscombe Down 50-52; C Amersham *Ox* 55-62; R Sandford w Upton Hellions *Ex* 62-79; P-in-c Ashprington 79-81; P-in-c Cornworthy 79-81; R Ashprington, Cornworthy and Dittisham 81-83; C Weymouth St Paul *Sarum* 83-85; rtd 85; Perm to Offic *Ex* from 85. *21 Langaton Lane, Pinhoe, Exeter EX1 3SP* Tel (01392) 466747

HAMILTON, John Frederick. b 57. Leeds Univ BA78. Edin Th Coll 78. **d** 80 **p** 81. C Whitkirk *Ripon* 80-83; C Leeds Belle Is St Jo and St Barn 83-86; V Oulton w Woodlesford 86-94; V Cookridge H Trin from 94. *Cookridge Vicarage, 53 Green Lane, Cookridge, Leeds LS16 7LW* Tel 0113-267 4921 Mobile 07780-677341 Fax 0113-261 2102 E-mail sulaco57@btopenworld.com

HAMILTON, John Hans Patrick. b 44. BD66 AKC67 DipAdEd76 DMS85 FCMI96. K Coll Lon 66. **d** 67 **p** 68. C Cleobury Mortimer w Hopton Wafers *Heref* 67-69; C Sanderstead All SS *S'wark* 69-73; V Battersea St Mary-le-Park 73-75; Perm to Offic *Ely* 75-90; Dir of Educn *Derby* 90-95; P-in-c Cliddesden and Ellisfield w Farleigh Wallop etc *Win* 95-00; Perm to Offic 00-03; P-in-c Dungeon Hill *Sarum* from 03; P-in-c The Caundles w Folke and Holwell from 03. *The Rectory, Holwell, Sherborne DT9 5LF* Tel (01963) 23035
E-mail john@montoid2.fsnet.co.uk

HAMILTON, John Nicholas. b 49. Trin Coll Cam BA71 MA75. Ridley Hall Cam 72. **d** 75 **p** 76. C Ealing Dean St Jo *Lon* 75-79; C Stoughton *Guildf* 79-83; R Denton St Lawr *Man* 83-88; R The Sherbornes w Pamber *Win* from 88. *The Rectory, Sherborne St John, Basingstoke RG24 9HX* Tel (01256) 850434
E-mail jnh@btinternet.com

HAMILTON, Canon Noble Ridgeway. b 23. TD66. TCD BA45 MA49. **d** 47 **p** 48. C Dundela St Mark *D & D* 47-51; C Holywood 51-55; I Belfast St Clem 55-61; I Seapatrick 61-89; Can Dromore Cathl 66-89; Prec 75-84; Chan 84-89; rtd 89; Lic to Offic *D & D* from 90. *67 Meadowvale, Waringstown, Craigavon BT66 7RL* Tel (028) 3888 2064

HAMILTON, Paul Stuart. b 69. Univ of Wales (Ban) BTh02. EAMTC. **d** 02 **p** 03. C Hawkwell *Chelmsf* from 02. *44 Hawkwell*

Park Drive, Hockley SS5 4HB Tel (01702) 204547
E-mail paulhamilton@fish.co.uk

HAMILTON, Richard Alexander. b 46. Pemb Coll Cam BA67 MA87 Brunel Univ PGCE97. S Dios Minl Tr Scheme 82. **d** 85 **p** 86. NSM Guernsey St Sampson *Win* 85-89; C Highgate St Mich *Lon* 89-91; P-in-c Tottenham H Trin 91-96; Master Denbigh High Sch Luton 96-98; TV The Ortons, Alwalton and Chesterton *Ely* from 98. *The Rectory, 67 Church Drive, Orton Waterville, Peterborough PE2 5HE* Tel (01733) 238877 Mobile 07958-317512 E-mail hamvic@aol.com

HAMILTON, Robert Hair. b 26. Oak Hill Th Coll 75. **d** 76 **p** 77. C Bootle St Matt *Liv* 76-78; C Horwich H Trin *Man* 78-81; R Whalley Range St Marg 81-86; Lect Em Bible Coll Birkenhead 86-97; Perm to Offic *Ches* from 86; rtd 91. *Akolutos, 27 Wimbourne Avenue, Thingwall, Wirral CH61 7UL* Tel 0151-648 4014

HAMILTON, Samuel Derek. b 34. Bris Univ BA58. Tyndale Hall Bris 54. **d** 59 **p** 60. C Dublin St Cath *D & G* 59-61; C Dublin Booterstown 61-63; I Drumcliffe w Lissadell *K, E & A* 63-69; I Cahir *C & O* 69-78; Bp's C Sallaghy *Clogh* 79-83; rtd 83. *12 Cairnshill Court, Saintfield Road, Belfast BT8 6TX*

HAMILTON, William Graham. b 63. New Coll Ox BA86. Wycliffe Hall Ox BA95. **d** 95 **p** 96. C Ivybridge w Harford *Ex* 95-99; V Bovey Tracey SS Pet, Paul and Thos w Hennock from 99. *The Vicarage, Coombe Cross, Bovey Tracey, Newton Abbot TQ13 9EP* Tel (01626) 833813
E-mail graham.hamilton@lineone.net

HAMILTON, William Joseph Taylor. b 40. DMA64 Univ Coll Ches MTh00. **d** 97 **p** 98. NSM Ches Team *Ches* 97-02; C Malborough w S Huish, W Alvington and Churchstow *Ex* 02; C Thurlestone, S Milton, W Alvington etc from 02. *The Vicarage, Townsend Road, West Alvington, Kingsbridge TQ7 3PZ* Tel (01548) 857658 E-mail bill@hamiltonb.freeserve.co.uk

HAMILTON-BROWN, James John. b 35. Lon Univ BSc59. Trin Coll Bris AdDipTh90 Ridley Hall Cam 59. **d** 61 **p** 62. C Attenborough w Bramcote *S'well* 61-67; V Bramcote 67-76; R and D Officer Abps' Coun on Evang 76-79; Lic to Offic *Sarum* 76-81 and 91-95; TR Dorchester 81-91; Sec Par and People 91-95; P-in-c Tarrant Valley 95-99; C Tollard Royal w Farnham, Gussage St Michael etc 99-00; rtd 00. Perm to Offic *Sarum* from 00. *The Old Mill, Spetisbury, Blandford Forum DT11 9DF* Tel (01258) 453939 E-mail jumperhb@aol.com

HAMILTON MANON, Phillip Robert Christian. b 49. BA88. St Steph Ho Ox 89. **d** 90 **p** 91. C Norton St Mary *Dur* 90-94; P-in-c Cleadon Park 94-95; V 95-97; TV Lewes All SS, St Anne, St Mich and St Thos *Chich* 97-00; R Lewes St Anne from 00. *St Anne's Rectory, 57 St Anne's Crescent, Lewes BN7 1SD* Tel (01273) 472545

HAMLET, Paul Manning. b 42. Open Univ BA81 Ex Univ MEd96 Lambeth STh84 FCollP96. Kelham Th Coll 61. **d** 66 **p** 67. C Rumboldswyke *Chich* 66-69; C Ely 69-73; Hon C Ipswich St Bart *St E* 73-84; Chapl Wellington Sch Somerset 84-94; Chapl Ipswich Sch 94-02; CF (TAVR) 88-99; CF (ACF) from 99; Perm to Offic *St E* from 02. *5 Wincanton Close, Ipswich IP4 3EE* Tel (01473) 724413 E-mail paul.hamlet@btopenworld.com

HAMMERSLEY, John Goodwin. b 34. Keble Coll Ox BA57 MA60. Westcott Ho Cam 57. **d** 60 **p** 61. C Sheff St Swithun *Sheff* 60-67; Sec Par and People 67-70; P-in-c Linc St Mary-le-Wigford w St Benedict etc *Linc* 70-78; C Tettenhall Regis *Lich* 78-80; TV 80-87; Preb Lich Cathl 81-87; Chapl Metro Cen Gateshead *Dur* 87-94; RD Gateshead W 88-93; TV Langley Marish *Ox* 94-96; Dir Thamesway Progr 94-96; Co-ord Tr Portfolio (Bucks) 96-99; Perm to Offic *Sheff* from 99; rtd 00. *8 Brincliffe Court, Nether Edge Road, Sheffield S7 1RX* Tel 0114-255 7849

HAMMERSLEY, Peter. b 41. Lon Univ BD78 Birm Univ MEd87 PhD97. Kelham Th Coll 60. **d** 65 **p** 66. C Oadby *Leic* 65-69; Jamaica 70-77; Chapl and Hd RE K Sch Worc 77-84; Min Can Worc Cathl *Worc* 77-84; V Foley Park 84-90; TV Kidderminster St Jo and H Innocents 90-91; Dioc Warden of Readers 91; Vice-Prin Aston Tr Scheme 91-97; Hon Lect Sch of Educn Birm Univ *Birm* from 98; Adult RE Researcher St Pet Saltley Trust 98-99; Chapl HM Pris Hewell Grange from 98. *52 Hanbury Road, Droitwich WR9 8PR* Tel (01905) 798590 Fax 776197 E-mail p_hammersley@hotmail.com

HAMMERSLEY, Peter Angus Ragsdale. b 35. Linc Th Coll 74. **d** 76 **p** 77. C Stafford *Lich* 76-79; P-in-c W Bromwich St Andr 79-83; V 83-88; P-in-c W Bromwich Ch Ch 85-88; V Streetly 88-98; RD Walsall 90-98; C Ledbury *Heref* 98-00; Team Chapl W Heref 98-00; rtd 01; Assoc TV Ledbury *Heref* from 01. *The Rectory, Tarrington, Hereford HR1 4EU* Tel (01432) 890610

HAMMETT, The Ven Barry Keith. b 47. Magd Coll Ox BA71 MA74. St Steph Ho Ox 71. **d** 74 **p** 75. C Plymouth St Pet *Ex* 74-77; Chapl RN 77-02; Chapl of the Fleet and Adn for the RN from 02; Dir Gen Naval Chapl Service from 02; QHC from 99; Hon Can Portsm Cathl *Portsm* from 02; Can Gib Cathl *Eur* from 03. *Royal Naval Chaplaincy Service, Room 203, Victory Building, HM Naval Base, Portsmouth PO1 3LS* Tel (023) 9272 7900 Fax 9272 7111

HAMMON, David Edward. b 48. St Mich Coll Llan 99. **d** 01 **p** 02. C Pembroke Dock *St D* from 01. *22 Glenview Avenue, Pembroke Dock SA72 6EJ* Tel (01646) 686158 Mobile 07779-711239 E-mail davidhammon@lineone.net

HAMMOND, Mrs Barbara Watson. b 33. ACP70 Lanc Univ MA79. Bp Otter Coll TCert53 S'wark Ord Course DipRS92. **d** 92 **p** 94. NSM Upper Norwood St Jo *S'wark* 92-94; Hon C Spring Park All SS 94-97; Perm to Offic *S'wark* from 97; Perm to Offic *Portsm* from 98. *27 Maisemore Gardens, Emsworth PO10 7JU* Tel (01243) 370531
E-mail barbara@br2811.demon.co.uk

HAMMOND, Canon Brian Leonard. b 31. Bris Univ BSc54. Wells Th Coll 56. **d** 58 **p** 59. C Clapham H Trin *S'wark* 58-62; V Walworth All SS and St Steph 62-72; V S Merstham 72-87; RD Reigate 80-86; Hon Can S'wark Cathl 83-97; V Spring Park All SS 87-97; rtd 97; Perm to Offic *S'wark* from 97; Perm to Offic *Portsm* from 98. *27 Maisemore Gardens, Emsworth PO10 7JU* Tel (01243) 370531 Mobile 07802-482974
E-mail brian@br2811.demon.co.uk

HAMMOND, Carolyn John-Baptist. b 64. St Jo Coll Ox MA90 Univ Coll Ox DPhil93 CCC Ox BA97. Westcott Ho Cam CTM98. **d** 98 **p** 99. C Gamlingay w Hatley St Geo and E Hatley *Ely* 98-99; C Gamlingay and Everton 99-01; R from 01. *The Rectory, Stocks Lane, Gamlingay, Sandy SG19 3JP* Tel (01767) 651204 E-mail revcally@ukonline.co.uk

HAMMOND, Charles Kemble. b 10. TCD BA33 MA37. TCD Div Sch Div Test33. **d** 34 **p** 35. C Willowfield *D & D* 35-37; C Belfast St Donard 37; Australia from 37; C Summer Hill 37-38; C-in-c Golden Grove 38-40; Dir Educn *Sydney* 40-49; R Carlingford 49-52; R Heyfield 52-58; Chapl St Vin and Prince Henry Hosps 58-59; Chapl Alfred Hosp 59-64; Chapl Parramatta Psychiatric Hosp 64-66; Dir of Chapl Dio Melbourne 66-78; rtd 78. *69 Courtlands, 15 Gloucester Avenue, North Parramatta, NSW, Australia 2151* Tel (0061) (2) 9360 1064

HAMMOND, Diana Mary. b 46. **d** 99 **p** 00. OLM Bishopstrow and Boreham *Sarum* from 99. *41 Bishopstrow, Warminster BA12 9HN* Tel (01985) 214495

HAMMOND, Frank. b 49. Linc Th Coll 75. **d** 77 **p** 78. C Sutton *Liv* 77-79; C Blundellsands St Nic 80-83. *Address temp unknown*

HAMMOND, Canon Jacob Aryee. b 47. St Nic Th Coll Ghana LTh85. **d** 84 **p** 85. Ghana 84-97; Hon Can Koforidua from 95; RD Larteh 95-97; C Merthyr Tydfil St Dav *Llan* from 97. *4 Lancaster Terrace, Merthyr Tydfil CF47 8SL* Tel (01685) 379718 Fax 722922

HAMMOND, Lindsay John. b 57. Southn Univ BA83. Sarum & Wells Th Coll 84. **d** 86 **p** 87. C Ashford *Cant* 86-90; V Appledore w Brookland, Fairfield, Brenzett etc from 90; Hon Min Can Cant Cathl from 93; P-in-c Stone-in-Oxney from 95; RD S Lympne 95-01. *The Vicarage, Appledore, Ashford TN26 2DB* Tel (01233) 758250 Fax 758066 E-mail applevic@clara.co.uk

HAMMOND, Mary. b 15. Dur Univ BA51 Maria Grey Coll Lon PGCE52. Roch and S'wark Dss Ho 40. **dss** 43 **d** 87. Australia 68-73; Abp Langton Sch Beare Green 73-75; rtd 75; Perm to Offic *Linc* 75-87; *Ox* 87-89; *Ex* from 95. *2 Gracey Court, Woodland Road, Broadclyst, Exeter EX5 3LP*

HAMMOND, Peter Clark. b 27. Linc Coll Ox BA49 MA53. Wells Th Coll 51. **d** 52 **p** 53. C Willesborough *Cant* 52-55; C Croydon 55-59; R Barham 60-66; V Walmer 66-85; V Rolvenden 85-89; rtd 89; Perm to Offic *Ely* from 89. *19 Hardwick Street, Cambridge CB3 9JA* Tel (01223) 467425

HAMNETT, Herbert Arnold. b 22. K Coll Lon BSc49. Qu Coll Birm 49. **d** 51 **p** 52. C Greenhill St Jo *Lon* 51-54; C Horsham *Chich* 55-60; R Yapton w Ford 60-87; rtd 87; Perm to Offic *St E* from 87. *Clarence House, Stradbrooke Road, Fressingfield, Eye IP21 5PP*

HAMPEL, Michael Hans Joachim. b 67. Univ Coll Dur BA89 MA02 FRSA02. Westcott Ho Cam CTM93. **d** 93 **p** 94. C Whitworth w Spennymoor *Dur* 93-97; Min Can, Prec and Sacr Dur Cathl 97-02; Sen Tutor St Chad's Coll Dur from 02. *St Chad's College, 18 North Bailey, Durham DH1 3RH* Tel 0191-334 3358 *or* 3354 Fax 334 3371
E-mail m.h.j.hampel@durham.ac.uk

HAMPSON, Claude Eric. b 25. Rhodes Univ BA49. St Paul's Coll Grahamstown LTh50. **d** 50 **p** 51. S Africa 50-54; C Greenford H Cross *Lon* 54-58; Sec Fellowship of SS Alb and Sergius 58-60; Australia 60-74; Adn of the W 67-74; Vietnam 74-75; V Kilburn St Aug w St Jo *Lon* 75-77; Australia from 77; rtd 85. *Goodwin Village, PO Box 107, Edgecliff, NSW, Australia 2027* Tel (0061) (2) 9327 8215 Fax 9362 4063

HAMPSON, David. b 46. Chich Th Coll 69. **d** 72 **p** 73. C Penrith *Carl* 72-78; V Crosscrake 78-95; V Crosscrake and Preston Patrick 95; P-in-c Arnside 95-97; rtd 97. *81 Rectory Road, North Ashton, Wigan WN4 0QD* Tel (01942) 728760

HAMPSON, Miss Judith Elizabeth. b 50. I M Marsh Coll of Physical Educn Liv BEd72 Open Univ BA89. Ripon Coll Cuddesdon 90. **d** 92 **p** 94. C Alnwick *Newc* 92-96; R Allendale w Whitfield from 96. *Allendale Rectory, 16 Forstersteads, Allendale, Hexham NE47 9AS* Tel (01434) 683336 Fax as telephone E-mail rev.jude@btinternet.com

HAMPSON, Michael John. b 67. Jes Coll Ox BA88. Ripon Coll Cuddesdon 88. **d** 91 **p** 92. C W Burnley *Blackb* 91-93; C Harlow St Mary Magd *Chelmsf* 93-00; V Church Langley from 00. *7 Ashworth Place, Church Langley, Harlow CM17 9PU* Tel (01279) 629950 E-mail michael.hampson@bigfoot.com

HAMPSON, Robert Edward. b 58. LSE BSc80 Heythrop Coll Lon BA91 MTh93. Ridley Hall Cam CTM97. **d** 97 **p** 98. C Chingford SS Pet and Paul *Chelmsf* 97-01; V Wanstead H Trin Hermon Hill from 01. *Holy Trinity Vicarage, 185 Hermon Hill, London E18 1QQ* Tel (020) 8530 3029
E-mail roberthampson@btinternet.com

HAMPSTEAD, Archdeacon of. *See* LAWSON, The Ven Michael Charles

HAMPTON, Alison Jean. b 61. St Mary's Coll Twickenham BA98. SEITE. **d** 01 **p** 02. C Notting Dale St Clem w St Mark and St Jas *Lon* from 01. *95 Sirdar Road, London W11 4EQ* Tel (020) 7243 2091 E-mail alison@clementjames.co.uk

HAMPTON, Carla Irene. b 47. ARCM67 GRSM68. NTMTC 96. **d** 99 **p** 00. Asst Chapl Mid-Essex Hosp Services NHS Trust 98-02; Chapl from 02; NSM Chelmsf St Andr *Chelmsf* from 99. *280 Broomfield Road, Chelmsford CM1 4DY* Tel (01245) 356287 *or* 514069 E-mail carla@hamptonc.freeserve.co.uk

HAMPTON, Canon John Waller. b 28. Linc Coll Ox BA51 MA58. Westcott Ho Cam 51. **d** 53 **p** 54. C Rugby St Andr *Cov* 53-56; Chapl St Paul's Sch Hammersmith 56-65; Chapl St Paul's Girls' Sch Hammersmith 60-65; V Gaydon w Chadshunt *Cov* 65-69; Asst Dir RE 65-70; C-in-c Warwick St Nic 69-75; Fell Qu Coll Birm 75-76; P-in-c Wetton *Lich* 76-82; P-in-c Alstonfield 76-82; P-in-c Sheen 76-80; RD Alstonfield 80-82; P-in-c Butterton 80-82; P-in-c Warslow and Elkstones 80-82; P-in-c Broadway *Worc* 82-91; V 91-93; RD Evesham 87-93; Hon Can Worc Cathl 88-93; rtd 93; Perm to Offic *Ab* from 93. *41 Craigton Terrace, Aberdeen AB15 7RN* Tel (01224) 310074

HAMPTON, Stephen William Peter. b 72. Magd Coll Cam BA93 MA97. Wycliffe Hall Ox BA95 MA98. **d** 96 **p** 97. C St Neots *Ely* 96-98; Chapl Ex Coll Ox 98-03. *Address temp unknown*
E-mail stephen.hampton@exeter.ox.ac.uk

HAMPTON, Terence Alastair Godfrey Macpherson. b 38. Bris Univ PGCE73. Lon Coll of Div ALCD63 BD68. **d** 64 **p** 65. C Clifton Ch Ch w Em *Bris* 64-66; C Ickenham *Lon* 66-67; C Patchway *Bris* 67-73; TV Jersey St Brelade *Win* 73-83; R Jersey Grouville 83-94; rtd 00. *Jersey Cheshire Home, Rope Walk, St Helier, Jersey JE2 4UU* Tel (01534) 285858

HAMPTON-SMITH, David Charles. b 22. Ch Ch Ox BA48 MA48. Cuddesdon Coll 48. **d** 50 **p** 51. C Shrewsbury St Chad *Lich* 50-53; C Kingswood *S'wark* 53-56; V Howe Bridge *Man* 56-62; Chapl Woodbridge Sch 62-65; Australia from 65; rtd 87. *139 Esplanade, Port Noarlunga South, S Australia 5167* Tel (0061) (8) 8386 1284

HANAWAY, Peter Louis. b 47. Open Univ BA85 Middx Univ BA02. NTMTC 99. **d** 02 **p** 03. NSM Westmr St Matt *Lon* from 02. *711 Duncan House, Dolphin Square, London SW1V 3PP* Tel (020) 7798 8478 Mobile 07947-722219
E-mail peter.hanaway@cwctv.com

HANCE, Mrs Joy. b 47. Cam Inst of Educn. St Alb and Ox Min Course 99. **d** 02. NSM Cherbury w Gainfield *Ox* from 02. *The Vicarage, Buckland, Faringdon SN7 8QN* Tel (01367) 870618 Mobile 07752-187014 E-mail joysmail@talk21.com

HANCE, Mrs Marion. **d** 01 **p** 02. OLM Cheddington w Mentmore and Marsworth *Ox* from 01. *20 New Street, Cheddington, Leighton Buzzard LU7 0RL* Tel (01296) 661761

HANCE, Stephen John. b 66. Portsm Poly BSc89 Nottm Univ BTh92 MA93. St Jo Coll Nottm 90. **d** 93 **p** 94. C Southsea St Jude *Portsm* 93-96; TV Tollington *Lon* 96-99; V Balham Hill Ascension *S'wark* from 99. *Ascension Vicarage, 22 Malwood Road, London SW12 8EN* Tel (020) 8673 7666 *or* 8675 8626 Fax 8516 9429 *or* 8673 3796 E-mail stephen.hance@virgin.net

HANCOCK, Mrs Barbara. b 40. TCert60. EMMTC 93. **d** 96. NSM Caythorpe *Linc* from 96. *Fulbeck Cottage, Sudthorpe Hill, Fulbeck, Grantham NG32 3LE* Tel (01400) 272644
E-mail bchancock@lineone.net

HANCOCK, The Very Revd Christopher David. b 54. Qu Coll Ox BA75 MA80 St Jo Coll Dur PhD84. Cranmer Hall Dur BA78. **d** 82 **p** 83. C Leic H Trin w St Jo *Leic* 82-85; Chapl Magd Coll Cam 85-88; USA 88-94; V Cambridge H Trin *Ely* 94-02; Dean Bradf from 02. *The Deanery, Cathedral Close, Bradford BD1 4EG* Tel (01274) 777722 *or* 777727 Fax 777730
E-mail chancock@btinternet.com

HANCOCK, David Richard. b 48. Chich Th Coll. **d** 89 **p** 90. C Maidstone All SS and St Phil w Tovil *Cant* 89-93; CF 90-93; P-in-c Sellindge w Monks Horton and Stowting etc *Cant* 93-99; Perm to Offic from 99; Thailand from 99. *73/5 Moo 2 Patak Road, Karon Subdistrict, Muang District, Phuket 83100, Thailand* Tel (0066) (76) 284163 Fax 284193
E-mail yohan@phuket.ksc.co.th

HANCOCK, Douglas Charles. b 16. Lon Univ BSc39 PhD52. Wycliffe Hall Ox 59. **d** 60 **p** 61. C Bournemouth St Alb *Win* 60-64; R Baughurst w Ramsdale 64-70; V Bournemouth St Andr 70-79; RD Alresford 79-84; R Hinton Ampner w Bramdean and

Kilmeston 79-84; rtd 84; Perm to Offic *Win* from 84; Perm to Offic *Sarum* 86-96. *17 Old Parsonage Court, Otterbourne, Winchester SO21 2EP* Tel (01962) 714941

HANCOCK, Preb Frances Margaret. b 34. LMH Ox BA56 MA94 LSE Dip Personnel Mgt 57. Gilmore Course IDC81. **dss** 81 **d** 87 **p** 94. Isleworth All SS *Lon* 81-87; Team Deacon Ross w Brampton Abbotts, Bridstow and Peterstow *Heref* 87-93; Dioc Adv on Women in Min 93-99; NSM Peterchurch w Vowchurch, Turnastone and Dorstone 93-00; NSM Madley w Tyberton, Peterchurch, Vowchurch etc from 00; Preb Heref Cathl 96-99. *Brockwell, Peterchurch, Hereford HR2 0TE* Tel (01981) 550457

HANCOCK, Ivor Michael. b 31. Lon Univ BD60. Linc Th Coll 65. **d** 66 **p** 67. C Havant *Portsm* 66-69; V Gosport Ch Ch 69-76; P-in-c Southend St Alb *Chelmsf* 76-80; V Hawley H Trin *Guildf* 80-96; V Minley 80-96; RD Aldershot 83-88; rtd 96; Perm to Offic *Ox* from 98. *Assisi, 15 Whaley Road, Wokingham RG40 1QA* Tel 0118-962 9976

HANCOCK, Canon John Clayton. b 36. Dur Univ BA58. Cranmer Hall Dur DipTh60. **d** 60 **p** 61. C Newbarns w Hawcoat *Carl* 60-65; V Church Coniston 65-76; R Torver 66-76; P-in-c Heversham 76-77; V 77-93; V Heversham and Milnthorpe from 93; Hon Can Carl Cathl from 98. *The Vicarage, Woodhouse Lane, Heversham, Milnthorpe LA7 7EW* Tel (01539) 563125

HANCOCK, John Martin. b 55. Ealing Coll of Educn BA78. Wycliffe Hall Ox DipMin99. **d** 99 **p** 00. C Bedford St Jo and St Leon *St Alb* from 99. *53 Hillesden Avenue, Elstow, Bedford MK42 9AJ* Tel (01234) 358307

HANCOCK, Canon John Mervyn. b 38. St Jo Coll Dur BA61 DipTh64 MA70 Hertf Coll Ox BA63 MA66. Cranmer Hall Dur 63. **d** 64 **p** 65. C Bishopwearmouth St Gabr *Dur* 64-67; V Hebburn St Jo 67-87; RD Jarrow 83-92; V S Westoe from 87; Hon Can Dur Cathl from 88; C-in-c S Shields St Aid w St Steph 92-95. *St Michael's Vicarage, Westoe Road, South Shields NE33 3PJ* Tel 0191-425 2074 Fax as telephone
E-mail kda77@dial.pipex.com

HANCOCK, Leonard George Edward. b 28. Open Univ BA81 Leic Univ MEd84. ALCD52. **d** 52 **p** 56. C Bilston St Leon *Lich* 52-53; C Sheff St Swithun *Sheff* 56-58; C Ecclesfield 58; C-in-c Ecclesfield St Paul CD 58-63; V Sheff St Mary w St Simon w St Matthias 63-72; V Michael *S & M* 72-76; R Loughborough All SS *Leic* 76-83; R Loughborough All SS and H Trin 83-93; rtd 93; Perm to Offic *Leic* from 93. *5 Rumsey Close, Quorn, Loughborough LE12 8EZ* Tel (01509) 827258

HANCOCK, Malcolm James. b 50. AGSM73 Leeds Univ MA02. Sarum & Wells Th Coll 85. **d** 87 **p** 88. C Sandhurst *Ox* 87-90; P-in-c Bradbourne and Brassington *Derby* 90-92; TV Wirksworth 92-95; V Tunbridge Wells K Chas *Roch* 95-02; R Beckenham St Geo from 02. *The Rectory, 14 The Knoll, Beckenham BR3 5JW* Tel (020) 8650 0983 *or* 8663 6996 Fax 8658 4914 E-mail malcolmhancock@clara.co.uk

HANCOCK, Ms Mary Joy. b 40. Auckland Univ BA61 Auckland Teachers' Coll PGCE62 Man Univ CQSW69. S'wark Ord Course 91. **d** 94 **p** 95. NSM Merton St Mary *S'wark* 94-01; NSM Colliers Wood Ch Ch from 01. *55 Huntspill Street, London SW17 0AA* Tel (020) 8946 8984

HANCOCK, Nigel John. b 35. K Coll Cam BA63 MA67. EAMTC 86. **d** 89 **p** 91. NSM Cambridge St Mary Less *Ely* 89-00; PV St Jo Coll Cam 95-99; Perm to Offic *Ely* from 00. *5 Atherton Close, Cambridge CB4 2BE* Tel (01223) 355828

HANCOCK, Preb Paul. b 43. AKC66. **d** 67 **p** 68. C Wednesbury St Paul Wood Green *Lich* 67-70; C Rugeley 70-73; V Rickerscote 73-75; R Blisland w St Breward *Truro* 75-78; V Mansfield St Lawr *S'well* 78-82; P-in-c Charleton *Ex* 82-83; P-in-c E Portlemouth, S Pool and Chivelstone 82-83; R Charleton w Buckland Tout Saints etc 83-95; RD Woodleigh 88-95; P-in-c Plymouth Crownhill Ascension 95-99; V from 99; Preb Ex Cathl from 03. *The Vicarage, 33 Tavistock Road, Plymouth PL5 3AF* Tel (01752) 783617

HANCOCK, Paul Byron. b 51. Bris Univ BA71 MA73. Ripon Hall Ox 72. **d** 75 **p** 76. C Croydon *Cant* 75-78; USA from 78. *3200 Woodland Ridge Boulevard, Baton Rouge, LA 70816, USA*
E-mail hancockp@ehsbr.org

HANCOCK, The Ven Peter. b 55. Selw Coll Cam BA76 MA79. Oak Hill Th Coll BA80. **d** 80 **p** 81. C Portsdown *Portsm* 80-83; C Radipole and Melcombe Regis *Sarum* 83-87; V Cowplain *Portsm* 87-99; RD Havant 93-98; Hon Can Portsm Cathl from 97; Adn The Meon from 99; Dioc Dir Miss from 03. *Victoria Lodge, 36 Osborn Road, Fareham PO16 7DS* Tel (01329) 828100 *or* 280101 Mobile 07974-008134 Fax (01329) 281603
E-mail phancock@fish.co.uk

HANCOCK, Peter Ernest. b 33. Man Univ BA54. Qu Coll Birm 54. **d** 56 **p** 57. C Wigston Magna *Leic* 56-59; C Hucknall Torkard *S'well* 59-61; V Sutton in Ashfield St Mich 61-65; Dioc Youth Officer *Portsm* 65-73; R Broughton Astley *Leic* 73-86; Dioc Adv for Min of Health and Healing *B & W* 86-93; rtd 94; Perm to Offic *B & W* from 94. *24 Mulberry Road, Congresbury, Bristol BS49 5HD* Tel (01934) 838920

HANCOCK, Peter Thompson. b 31. G&C Coll Cam BA54 MA58. Ridley Hall Cam 54. **d** 56 **p** 57. C Beckenham Ch Ch

Roch 56-59; Chapl St Lawr Coll Ramsgate 59-62; Chapl Stowe Sch 62-67; Asst Chapl and Lect Br Embassy Ch Paris *Eur* 67-70; V Walton H Trin *Ox* 70-80; Canada 80-84; V Northwood H Trin *Lon* 84-94; rtd 94; Perm to Offic *Ox* from 99. *Roughwood Oak, Deadhearn Lane, Chalfont St Giles HP8 4HG* Tel (01494) 872324

HANCOCK, Reginald Legassicke (Rex). b 28. Trin Coll Cam BA51 MA57. Clifton Th Coll 60. **d** 61 **p** 62. C Finchley Ch Ch *Lon* 61-63; CF 63-82; R Quantoxhead *B & W* 82-93; rtd 93; Perm to Offic *B & W* from 94. *Stowleys, Bossinton Lane, Porlock, Minehead TA24 8HD* Tel (01643) 862327

HANCOCK, Richard Manuel Ashley. b 69. Linc Th Coll 94 Westcott Ho Cam 95. **d** 97 **p** 98. C Didcot St Pet *Ox* 97-00; P-in-c Shrivenham w Watchfield and Bourton 00-03; V Shrivenham and Ashbury from 03. *St Andrew's Vicarage, Shrivenham, Swindon SN6 8AN* Tel (01793) 782243

HANCOCK, Ronald Edward. b 24. MRCS49 LRCP49. **d** 78 **p** 79. Hon C Highbury Ch Ch w St Jo *Lon* 78-82; R Puddletown and Tolpuddle *Sarum* 82-90; rtd 90; Perm to Offic *Sarum* from 90. *27 Clarendon Avenue, Weymouth DT3 5BG* Tel (01305) 812436

HANCOCK, Mrs Vittoria Ruth. b 74. Univ of Wales (Ban) BSc95 BD99. Cranmer Hall Dur 91. **d** 01 **p** 02. C Llanberis w Llanrug *Ban* from 01. *Ty Sant Padarn, The Rectory, Church Road, Llanberis, Caernarfon LL55 4TF* Tel (01286) 872691 Fax as telephone E-mail revvit@fish.co.uk

HANCOCKS, Graeme. b 58. Univ of Wales (Ban) BD79 Oslo Univ 87. Linc Th Coll 79. **d** 81 **p** 82. C Denbigh and Nantglyn *St As* 81-84; Asst Chapl Oslo St Edm *Eur* 84-88; Chapl Stockholm 88-89; Chapl Marseille w St Raphaël, Aix-en-Provence etc 89; Chapl Gothenburg w Halmstad, Jönköping etc 90-93; Chapl Southn Univ Hosps NHS Trust 93-98; Chapl Trafford Healthcare NHS Trust 98-02; Chapl Leeds Teaching Hosps NHS Trust from 02. *St James University Hospital, Beckett Street, Leeds LS9 7TF* Tel 0113-243 3144

HANCOX, Granville Leonard. b 32. Lich Th Coll 67. **d** 70 **p** 71. C Caverswall *Lich* 70-73; C Norton in the Moors 73-76; P-in-c Leek St Luke 76-79; TV Leek 79-83; V Priors Lee and St Georges 83-97; rtd 97; Perm to Offic *Lich* from 00. *4 Cedarwood Drive, Muxton, Telford TF2 8SH* Tel (01952) 604018

✠**HAND, The Rt Revd Geoffrey David.** b 18. CBE75 KBE84. Oriel Coll Ox BA41 MA46. Cuddesdon Coll 40. **d** 42 **p** 43 **c** 50. C Heckmondwike *Wakef* 42-46; Papua New Guinea 46-83; Bp Coadjutor New Guinea 50-63; Adn N New Guinea 50-63; Bp Papua New Guinea 63-77; Abp Papua New Guinea 77-83; Bp Port Moresby 77-83; rtd 83; P-in-c E w W Rudham *Nor* 83-85; P-in-c Houghton 83-85. *121 Brackenbury Road, London W6 0BQ*

HAND, Michael Anthony (Tony). b 63. SROT York Univ BA84 DipCOT88. St Jo Coll Nottm MA95. **d** 95 **p** 96. C Lutterworth w Cotesbach *Leic* 95-98; C Lutterworth w Cotesbach and Bitteswell 99-01; V Acomb H Redeemer *York* from 01; Chapl Manor Sch from 01. *The Vicarage, 108 Boroughbridge Road, York YO26 6AB* Tel (01904) 798593 E-mail holyredeemer01@hotmail.com

HAND, Nigel Arthur. b 54. St Jo Coll Nottm. **d** 84 **p** 85. C Birm St Luke *Birm* 84-88; C Walton H Trin *Ox* 88-89; TV 89-97; C Selly Park St Steph and St Wulstan *Birm* from 97. *927 Pershore Road, Selly Oak, Birmingham B29 7PS* Tel 0121-472 2514

HAND, Peter Michael. b 42. Univ Coll Ox BA63 Lon Univ BSc75. Sarum & Wells Th Coll 77. **d** 80 **p** 81. NSM Shaston *Sarum* 80-81; C Tisbury 81-83; C Glastonbury St Jo w Godney *B & W* 83-84; C Glastonbury w Meare, W Pennard and Godney 84-87; V High Littleton 87-99; RD Midsomer Norton 92-98; R Winford w Felton Common Hill from 99. *The Rectory, 4 Parsonage Lane, Winford, Bristol BS40 8DG* Tel (01275) 474636

✠**HANDFORD, The Most Revd George Clive.** b 37. Hatf Coll Dur BA61. Qu Coll Birm DipTh63. **d** 63 **p** 64 **c** 90. C Mansfield St Pet *S'well* 63-67; Lebanon 67-74; Dean Jerusalem 74-78; UAE 78-83; Adn Gulf 78-83; V Kneesall w Laxton *S'well* 83-84; P-in-c Wellow 83-84; RD Tuxford and Norwell 83-84; Adn Nottingham 84-90; Suff Bp Warw *Cov* 90-96; Bp Cyprus and the Gulf from 96; Pres Bp Episc Ch Jerusalem and Middle E from 02. *PO Box 22075, 1517 Nicosia, Cyprus* Tel (00357) (22) 671220 Fax 674553 E-mail bishop@spidernet.com.cy or cygulf@spidernet.com.cy

HANDFORD, John Richard. b 32. Sydney Univ BSc52 Univ Coll Lon MSc62 Surrey Univ MA84 Lon Univ DipTh67 Heythrop Coll Lon MTh96. Lon Coll of Div 68. **d** 69 **p** 70. Asst Chapl Wellington Coll Berks 69-80; C Hon C Windlesham *Guild* 87-92; Perm to Offic from 92. *Desiderata, 33 Chertsey Road, Windlesham GU20 6EW* Tel (01276) 472397

HANDFORD, Maurice. b 25. Oak Hill Th Coll 48. **d** 52 **p** 53. C Dublin Miss Ch *D & G* 52-55; Org & Deputation Sec ICM (N & Midl) 55-58; C-in-c Buxton Trin Prop Chpl *Derby* 58-87; I Clondevaddock w Portsalon and Leatbeg *D & R* 87-90; Bp's Dom Chapl 88-90; rtd 90; Perm to Offic *Ches* from 90 and *Derby* from 92. *9 Birtlespool Road, Cheadle Hulme, Cheadle SK8 5JZ* Tel 0161-485 3134

HANDFORTH, Canon Richard Brereton. b 31. St Pet Coll Ox BA55 MA60. Westcott Ho Cam 63. **d** 64 **p** 65. C Hornchurch St Andr *Chelmsf* 64-65; Hong Kong 65-73; Chapl CMS

Fellowship Ho Chislehurst 73-75; Hon C Chislehurst St Nic *Roch* 73-75; Home Educn Sec CMS 75-83; V Biggin Hill *Roch* 83-88; Inter-change Adv CMS 88-96; Hon C Plaistow St Mary *Roch* from 95; Hon Can Lagos from 95; rtd 96. *67 Murray Avenue, Bromley BR1 3DJ* Tel (020) 8460 0238

HANDLEY, The Ven Anthony Michael. b 36. Selw Coll Cam BA60 MA64. Chich Th Coll 60. **d** 62 **p** 63. C Thorpe *Nor* 62-66; C Gaywood, Bawsey and Mintlyn 66-72; V Hellesdon 72-80; RD Nor N 80-81; Adn Nor 81-93; Adn Norfolk 93-02; rtd 02; Perm to Offic *Nor* from 02. *25 New Street, Sheringham NR26 8EE*

HANDLEY, Dennis Francis. b 57. MIE79 TEng(CEI)80. Coll of Resurr Mirfield 82. **d** 85 **p** 86. C Headingley *Ripon* 85-88; C Rothwell 88-92; V Liversedge *Wakef* 92-97; V Ripponden from 97; V Barkisland w W Scammonden from 97. *St Bartholomew's Vicarage, Ripponden, Sowerby Bridge HX6 4DF* Tel (01422) 822239

HANDLEY, Harold. b 14. ACIS42 AACCA44 ACWA48. Bps' Coll Cheshunt 62. **d** 63 **p** 64. C Hitchin St Mary *St Alb* 63-65; V Totternhoe 65-79; C Ringwood *Win* 79-80; rtd 79; Perm to Offic *Win* 80-95. *Risdene, 16 Barton Court Avenue, Barton on Sea, New Milton BH25 7HD* Tel (01425) 611771

HANDLEY, John. b 38. Oak Hill Th Coll. **d** 83 **p** 84. C Witton w Brundall and Braydeston *Nor* 83-86; R Reedham w Cantley w Limpenhoe and Southwood 86-93; P-in-c E w W Harling and Bridgham w Roudham 93-95; R E w W Harling, Bridgham w Roudham and Larling 95-96; P-in-c Garboldisham w Blo' Norton, Riddlesworth etc 94-96; RD Thetford and Rockland 95-98; P-in-c E w W Harling, Bridgham w Roudham and Larling 96-97; R E w W Harling, Bridgham w Roudham, Larling etc from 97. *The Rectory, Church Road, East Harling, Norwich NR16 2NB* Tel (01953) 717235

HANDLEY, Neil. b 40. St Aid Birkenhead 64. **d** 67 **p** 68. C Ashton Ch Ch *Man* 67-70; C Stretford All SS 70-73; C Tonge 73; C-in-c Bolton St Jo Breightmet CD 74-79; V Bolton St Jo 79-80; R Broughton St Jo 80-87; Perm to Offic *Eur* from 90. *La Taire du Grel, 24250 Domme, France* Tel (0033) 53 28 23 42

HANDLEY, Terence Anthony. b 55. Trent Poly HNC Open Univ BA89. Trin Coll Bris 85. **d** 87 **p** 88. C Meole Brace *Lich* 87-91; V Stafford St Paul Forebridge 91-94. *Address temp unknown*

HANDLEY MACMATH, Terence. b 59. Goldsmiths' Coll Lon BA80 K Coll Cam MA98. Westcott Ho Cam 91. **d** 94 **p** 95. NSM Southwold *St E* 94-95; Perm to Offic *St Alb* 96-99; C St Alb St Pet from 99. *6 Gombards, St Albans AL3 5NW* Tel (01727) 838359 E-mail terencestalbans@aol.com

HANDS, Graeme. b 35. Cranmer Hall Dur. **d** 61 **p** 62. C Atherstone *Cov* 61-63; Chapl Aldwickbury Sch Harpenden 63-66; C Cov St Alb *Cov* 66-68; P-in-c Warwick St Paul 68-80; V Radford 80-98; RD Cov N 87-93; rtd 98; Perm to Offic *Nor* and *Cov* from 99. *Rose Cottage, The Hill, Walsingham NR22 6DP* Tel (01328) 820288

HANDSCOMBE, Canon Richard John. b 23. Cuddesdon Coll 58. **d** 60 **p** 61. C Shrub End *Chelmsf* 60-63; V Fingringhoe 63-86; P-in-c E Donyland 75-77; R Fingringhoe w E Donyland 86-90; R Fingringhoe w E Donyland and Abberton etc 90-02; Hon Can Chelmsf Cathl 89-02; rtd 02. *The Rectory, Fingringhoe, Colchester CO5 7BN* Tel (01206) 729383

HANFORD, William Richard. b 38. Keble Coll Ox BA60 MA64 Lon Univ BD66 Univ of Wales LLM95. St Steph Ho Ox 60. **d** 63 **p** 64. C Roath St Martin *Llan* 63-66; C Llantwit Major 67-68; PV Llan Cathl 68-72; Chapl RN 72-76; Lic to Offic *Eur* 74-76; Hon C Eastbourne St Sav and St Pet *Chich* 76-77; C Brighton St Pet 77-78; Can Res and Prec Guildf Cathl *Guildf* 78-83; V Ewell from 83. *St Mary's Vicarage, 14 Church Street, Ewell, Epsom KT17 2AQ* Tel (020) 8393 2643

HANKE, Canon Hilary Claire. b 53. Qu Coll Birm BTheol93. **d** 93 **p** 94. C Kempsey and Severn Stoke w Croome d'Abitot *Worc* 93-97; TV Wordsley 97-99; Convenor for Women's Min from 98; Hon Can Worc Cathl from 98; P-in-c Reddal Hill St Luke from 01. *St Luke's Vicarage, Upper High Street, Cradley Heath, Warley B64 5HX* Tel (01384) 569940

HANKEY, Miss Dorothy Mary. b 38. CertEd65. Trin Coll Bris 75. **dss** 78 **d** 87 **p** 94. Wigan St Jas w St Thos *Liv* 78-84; Middleton *Man* 84-85; Litherland Ch Ch *Liv* 85-89; Par Dn 87-89; Par Dn Blackpool St Mark *Blackb* 89-94; C 94-95; C Blackpool St Paul 95-98; rtd 98; Perm to Offic *Blackb* from 98. *89 Rutland Avenue, Poulton-le-Flyde FY6 7RX* Tel (01253) 890635

HANKINS, Clifford James. b 24. Chich Th Coll 70 SSC87. **d** 72 **p** 73. C Henfield *Chich* 72-76; V Fernhurst 76-84; V Mithian w Mount Hawke *Truro* 84-89; rtd 89; Hon C W Wittering and Birdham w Itchenor *Chich* from 90. *2 Kestrel Close, East Wittering, Chichester PO20 8PQ* Tel (01243) 672164

HANLEY, John. **d** 03. NSM Tralee w Kilmoyley, Ballymacelligott etc *L & K* from 03. *20 Cloghar Li, Tralee, Co Kerry, Irish Republic* Tel (00353) 87-619 4733 (mobile)

HANLON, Michael James. b 50. St Jo Coll Nottm 94. **d** 98 **p** 99. C Tamworth *Lich* 98-00; C Melbourne St Jo Australia from 00. *81 Castella Street, Lilydale, Vic, Australia 3140* Tel (0061) (3) 9739 5235 or 9739 3541 E-mail mikeruth90@mail.com

HANLON, Thomas Kyle. b 72. QUB BA94 TCD BTh97. **d** 97 **p** 98. C Bangor *D & D* 97-00; I Dromore *Clogh* from 00; Chairman Clogh Dio Newc from 01; Chapl to Bp Clogh from 03. *The Rectory, 19 Galbally Road, Dromore, Omagh BT78 3EE* Tel (028) 8289 8300 E-mail k.hanlon@tiscali.co.uk

HANMER, Canon Richard John. b 38. Peterho Cam BA61 MA65. Linc Th Coll 62. **d** 64 **p** 65. C Sheff St Swithun *Sheff* 64-69; Bp's Chapl *Nor* 69-73; V Cinderhill *S'well* 73-81; V Eaton *Nor* 81-94; Dioc Chapl MU from 91; Hon Can Nor Cathl 93-94; Can Res Nor Cathl from 94. *52 The Close, Norwich NR1 4EG* Tel (01603) 665210

HANNA, Miss Elizabeth. b 50. QUB BA73 Lon Bible Coll BA79 Milltown Inst Dub MA01. CITC 99. **d** 01 **p** 02. C Bangor Abbey *D & D* from 01. *9 Pinehill Crescent, Bangor BT19 6FS* Tel (028) 9147 7182 Mobile 07801-946909 E-mail bangorabbeyliz@yahoo.co.uk

HANNA, John. b 44. Lon Bible Coll BA83. Westcott Ho Cam 86. **d** 87 **p** 88. C Denton Ch Ch *Man* 87-91; V Higher Walton *Blackb* 91-98; C Marple All SS *Ches* 98-02; TV Burrington, Chawleigh, Cheldon, Chulmleigh etc *Ex* from 02; RD S Molton from 03. *The Vicarage, The Square, Witheridge, Tiverton EX16 8AE* Tel (01884) 860768

HANNA, Patricia Elizabeth. TCD BA HDipEd QUB BD NUU MA. **d** 99 **p** 00. Aux Min Nenagh *L & K* from 99; Aux Min Drumcliffe w Kilnasoolagh from 00. *St Columba's Rectory, Bindon Street, Ennis, Co Clare, Irish Republic* Tel (00353) (65) 20109 Fax as telephone E-mail patriciahanna.ennis@eircom.net

HANNA, Peter Thomas. b 45. ACII66 GIFireE75. CITC 85. **d** 88 **p** 89. NSM Cork St Fin Barre's Union *C, C & R* 88-95; Min Can Cork Cathl from 92; Dioc Info Officer 94-95; Aux Min Cork St Luke Union from 95; Aux Min Kinsale Union from 00. *Mount Windsor, Farnahoe, Inishannon, Co Cork, Irish Republic* Tel (00353) (21) 477 5470 Fax as telephone E-mail hanna7@gofree.indigo.ie

HANNA, Canon Robert Charles. b 49. Oak Hill Th Coll 75. **d** 77 **p** 78. C Coleraine *Conn* 77-82; I Convoy w Monellan and Donaghmore *D & R* 82-94; Can Raphoe Cathl 88-94; I Drumcliffe w Kilnasoolagh *L & K* from 94; Can Limerick, Killaloe and Clonfert Cathls from 00. *St Columba's Rectory, Bindon Street, Ennis, Co Clare, Irish Republic* Tel (00353) (65) 20109 Fax as telephone E-mail rchanna.ennis@eircom.net

HANNA, Steven. b 70. **d** 02. C Dagenham *Chelmsf* from 02. *8 Church Lane, Dagenham RM10 9UL* Tel (020) 8517 2664 E-mail stevenhanna@yahoo.com

HANNAFORD, Prof Robert. b 53. Ex Univ BEd76 MA78 PhD87. St Steph Ho Ox 78. **d** 80 **p** 81. C Ex St Jas *Ex* 80-83; Chapl Ex Univ 83-88; Tutor St Steph Ho Ox 89-92; Sen Lect Ch Ch Coll Cant 92-99; Prof Chr Th Univ Coll Chich 99-01; Hon C Bury w Houghton and Coldwaltham and Hardham *Chich* 99-01; Th Consultant Bp Horsham 99-01; Can and Preb Chich Cathl 00-01; Prof Th St Martin's Coll Lanc from 02; Hon C Tunstall w Melling and Leck *Blackb* 02-03; Hon C E Lonsdale from 03. *The Vicarage, Church Lane, Tunstall, Carnforth LA6 2RQ* Tel (01524) 274376 E-mail robert@hannafor.freeserve.co.uk

HANNAH, Darrell Dale. b 62. Grand Canyon Univ BA85 S Bapt Th Sem MDiv89 Regent Coll Vancouver ThM92 Magd Coll Cam PhD96. WMMTC 00. **d** 03. NSM Edgbaston St Geo *Birm* from 03. *126 Edith Road, Smethwick B66 4QZ* Tel 0121-565 2063 E-mail drddhannah@yahoo.ac.uk

HANNAH, Kimberley Victoria. *See* WILLIAMS, Mrs Kimberley Victoria

HANNAH, Richard. b 24. CCC Ox BA49 MA53. St Mich Coll Llan 49. **d** 51 **p** 52. C Cardiff St Jo *Llan* 51-55; C Usk *Mon* 55-58; V Llanfihangel Crucorney w Oldcastle etc 58-63; R Shenington w Alkerton *Ox* 63-69; R Shenington and Alkerton w Shutford 69-79; P-in-c Deddington w Clifton and Hempton 79-80; V Deddington w Barford, Clifton and Hempton 81-89; RD Deddington 78-84; rtd 89. *3 Craig Walk, Bridgnorth WV15 6BZ* Tel (01746) 763102

HANNEN, Robert John. *See* DAVIES-HANNEN, Robert John

✠**HANNON, The Rt Revd Brian Desmond Anthony.** b 36. TCD BA59 MA62. TCD Div Sch Div Test61. **d** 61 **p** 62 **c** 86. C Clooney *D & R* 61-64; I Desertmartin 64-69; I Londonderry Ch Ch 69-82; I Enniskillen *Clogh* 82-84; Preb Clogh Cathl 82-84; Dean Clogh 85-86; Bp Clogh 86-01; rtd 01. *Drumconnis Top, 202 Mullaghmeen Road, Ballinamallard, Enniskillen BT94 2DZ* Tel (028) 6638 8557 Fax 6638 8086 E-mail bdah@btinternet.com

HANOVA, Ms Petra. b 70. Chas Univ Prague BA97. Ridley Hall Cam 00. **d** 03. C Toxteth St Philemon w St Gabr and St Cleopas *Liv* from 03. *40 Madryn Street, Liverpool L8 3TT* Tel 0151-726 0581

HANSEN, Mrs Moira Jacqueline. b 55. K Coll Lon BSc76. Oak Hill Th Coll BA88. **d** 88 **p** 96. Par Dn Finchley Ch Ch *Lon* 88-91; Par Dn Broadwater St Mary *Chich* 91-94; Chapl Oak Hill Th Coll 94-00; Perm to Offic *St Alb* 96-00; *Lon* 97-00; P-in-c Hopton, Market Weston, Barningham etc *St E* from 00; P-in-c Stanton from 00. *The Rectory, The Street, Stanton, Bury St Edmunds IP31 2DQ* Tel (01359) 250239 E-mail moira@hansenj.fsnet.co.uk

HANSEN, Neil Bertram. b 29. **d** 53 **p** 54. C Plymouth St Pet *Ex* 53-55; New Zealand from 55. *3 Mascot Street, Tawa, Wellington, New Zealand* Tel (0064) (4) 232 9983

HANSFORD, Gordon John. b 40. Southn Univ BSc61. Trin Coll Bris 77. **d** 79 **p** 80. C Ex St Leon w H Trin *Ex* 79-82; C Shirley *Win* 82-87; R Landcross, Littleham, Monkleigh etc *Ex* 87-96; TV Bideford, Northam, Westward Ho!, Appledore etc 96-99; P-in-c Monkleigh 96-99; RD Hartland 96-99; V Paul *Truro* from 99. *The Vicarage, 1 St Pol-de-Leon View, Paul, Penzance TR19 6US* Tel (01736) 731261

HANSFORD, Ruth Patricia. b 68. K Coll Lon BSc90 Surrey Univ MSc96 Sch of Pharmacy Lon PhD00. Trin Coll Bris BA02. **d** 03. C Parkham, Alwington, Buckland Brewer etc *Ex* from 03. *Lupins, 5 Manor Court, Parkham, Bideford EX39 5PG* Tel (01237) 452120 Mobile 07718-765936 E-mail maggiethecat@waitrose.com

HANSON, Christopher. b 48. Ox Univ BA(Theol)02. Birm Bible Inst DipMin75 Wycliffe Hall Ox 87. **d** 89 **p** 90. C Heref St Pet w St Owen and St Jas *Heref* 89-91; C Plymouth St Andr w St Paul and St Geo *Ex* 91-93; C Devonport St Mich 93-94; TV Shebbear, Buckland Filleigh, Sheepwash etc 94-97; TV Langley Marish *Ox* from 97. *The Vicarage, Parlaunt Road, Langley, Slough SL3 8BB* Tel (01753) 545167

HANSON, Dale Robert. b 57. Fitzw Coll Cam BA78 MA81 Univ of BC MA80. Ridley Hall Cam 81. **d** 84 **p** 85. C Much Woolton *Liv* 84-87; Hong Kong 87-91; TV Billingham St Aid *Dur* 91-95; C Dur St Nic 95-98; V from 98. *St Nicholas' Vicarage, Kepier Villas, Durham DH1 1JP* Tel 0191-384 6066 E-mail dale.hanson@virgin.net

HANSON, Edward William. b 51. Salem State Coll (USA) BA73 Tufts Univ (USA) MA78 Boston Coll (USA) PhD92. Episc Div Sch (USA) MDiv00 Ripon Coll Cuddesdon 00. **d** 01 **p** 02. C Linc St Pet-at-Gowts and St Andr from 01; C Linc St Botolph from 01. *69 Western Crescent, Lincoln LN6 7TA* Tel (01522) 514506 E-mail ed.hanson@alumni.tufts.edu

HANSON, Canon John Westland. b 19. OBE74. St Jo Coll Dur BA41 DipTh43 MA44. **d** 43 **p** 44. C Louth w Welton-le-Wold *Linc* 43-50; Chapl and Lect RAF Flying Coll Manby 50-76; R Grimoldby w Manby 50-76; RD E Louthesk 60-68; Chief Examiner Relig Studies Cam Univ 66-82; Can and Preb Linc Cathl 67-02; RD Louthesk 68-77; V Woodhall Spa and Kirkstead 76-88; P-in-c Langton w Woodhall 76-88; rtd 88. *Brookfield, 28 Tor-o-Moor Road, Woodhall Spa LN10 6TD* Tel (01526) 352554

HANSON, Keith. b 59. Cranmer Hall Dur 99. **d** 01 **p** 02. C Armley w New Wortley *Ripon* from 01. *20 Wesley Road, Armley, Leeds LS12 1UN* Tel 0113-279 7377 E-mail khanson@lineone.net

HANSON, Michael Beaumont. b 49. Ox Univ MA. N Ord Course 81. **d** 84 **p** 85. NSM Leeds St Geo *Ripon* 84-98; Chapl Leeds Gr Sch 84-99; rtd 99; Perm to Offic *Carl* from 00. *21 Duke's Meadow, Hutton Roof, Penrith CA11 0XW* Tel (017684) 84692

HANSON, Peter Richard. b 45. ARCM. Chich Th Coll 72. **d** 75 **p** 76. C Forest Gate St Edm *Chelmsf* 75-79; C Chingford SS Pet and Paul 79-81; V Leytonstone H Trin Harrow Green 81-86; Dep Chapl HM Pris Wandsworth 86-88; Chapl HM Pris Lewes 88-91; rtd 91; Perm to Offic *Chich* from 91. *Flat 2, 39 St Anne's Crescent, Lewes BN7 1SB* Tel (01273) 471714

HANSON, Robert Arthur. b 35. Keele Univ BA57. St Steph Ho Ox 57 St Mich Coll Llan 59. **d** 60 **p** 61. C Langton St Mary and St Chad *Lich* 60-65; Chapl St Mary's Cathl *Edin* 65-69; R Glas St Matt *Glas* 69-79; R Paisley H Trin 79-87; V Walsall St Andr *Lich* 87-93; Perm to Offic *Worc* 94-97; C Kentish Town *Lon* 97-01; rtd 02. *St Benet's Church House, Ospringe Road, London NW5 2JB* Tel (020) 7267 4720 Mobile 07951-154384

HANSON, Timothy David. b 68. Oak Hill Th Coll BA95. **d** 95 **p** 96. C Boscombe St Jo *Win* 95-00; V Wharton *Ches* from 00. *The Vicarage, 165 Crook Lane, Winsford CW7 3DR* Tel (01606) 593215 *or* 861860 E-mail tiohanson@aol.com

HANWELL, David John. b 46. Leic Univ CertEd74 UEA BEd94. LNSM course 96. **d** 98 **p** 99. OLM Mundford w Lynford *Nor* from 98. *42 Impson Way, Mundford, Thetford IP26 5JU* Tel (01842) 898989

HAOKIP (formerly YAM), David Tongkhoyam. b 60. Serampore Univ BTh89 Madras Univ MDiv92. H Cross Coll Rangoon. **d** 84 **p** 85. Burma 84-93; India 93-95; Korea 96-97; Perm to Offic *S'wark* 99; TV Southampton (City Cen) *Win* from 00. *12-14 Kings Park Road, Southampton SO15 2AT* Tel (023) 8063 5988 Fax 8033 0760 E-mail haokip@lineone.net

HAPGOOD-STRICKLAND, Peter Russell. b 57. BA. St Steph Ho Ox. **d** 83 **p** 84. C Ashford *Cant* 83-86; C Sheerness H Trin w St Paul 86-90; V Blackb St Thos w St Jude *Blackb* 90-97; P-in-c Burnley St Andr w St Marg 97; V Burnley St Andr w St Marg and St Jas from 98. *St Andrew's Vicarage, 230 Barden Lane, Burnley BB10 1JD* Tel (01282) 423185 E-mail standrews@marsdens.net

HARBIDGE, The Ven Adrian Guy. b 48. St Jo Coll Dur BA70. Cuddesdon Coll 73. **d** 75 **p** 76. C Romsey *Win* 75-80; V Bournemouth St Andr 80-86; V Chandler's Ford 86-99; RD Eastleigh 93-99; Adn Bournemouth from 99. *Glebe House, 22 Bellflower Way, Chandler's Ford, Eastleigh SO53 4HN* Tel (023) 8026 0955 Fax as telephone E-mail adrian.harbidge@dial.pipex.com

HARBORD, Paul Geoffrey. b 56. Keble Coll Ox BA78 MA86. Chich Th Coll 81. **d** 83 **p** 84. C Rawmarsh w Parkgate *Sheff* 83-86; C Doncaster St Geo 86-90; C-in-c St Edm Anchorage Lane CD 90-95; V Masbrough from 95. *St Paul's Vicarage, 256 Kimberworth Road, Rotherham S61 1HG* Tel (01709) 557810 E-mail paulchurch@beeb.net

HARBORD, Philip James. b 56. St Cath Coll Ox BA77. Cranmer Hall Dur 78. **d** 80 **p** 81. C Enfield St Andr *Lon* 80-83; CMS 84-88; Pakistan 84-88; C Clay Hill St Jo and St Luke *Lon* 88-91; Chapl Wexham Park Hosp Slough 91-92; Chapl Upton Hosp Slough 91-92; Chapl Heatherwood and Wexham Park Hosp NHS Trust 92-95; Chapl Leic Gen Hosp NHS Trust 95-98; Chapl Fosse Health NHS Trust 98-99; Chapl Leics and Rutland Healthcare NHS Trust 99-01; P-in-c Cosby *Leic* from 01. *The Vicarage, 15 Starmer Close, Cosby, Leicester LE9 1SL* Tel 0116-286 2313

HARBOTTLE, Anthony Hall Harrison. b 25. LVO79. Ch Coll Cam BA50 MA53. Wycliffe Hall Ox 50. **d** 52 **p** 53. C Boxley *Cant* 52-54; C St Peter-in-Thanet 54-60; R Sandhurst w Newenden 60-68; Chapl in Windsor Gt Park 68-81; Chapl to The Queen 68-95; R E Dean w Friston and Jevington *Chich* 81-95; rtd 95; P-in-c E Dean w Friston and Jevington *Chich* 95-96. *44 Summerdown Road, Eastbourne BN20 8DQ* Tel (01323) 730881

HARBRIDGE, Philip Charles Anthony. b 65. K Coll Lon LLB88 AKC88 Ch Coll Cam BA98 MA02. Westcott Ho Cam. **d** 99 **p** 00. C Hampton All SS *Lon* 99-02; Chapl Ch Coll Cam from 02. *Christ's College, Cambridge CB2 3BU* Tel (01223) 334922 E-mail pcah2@cam.ac.uk

HARCOURT, Canon Giles. b 36. Westcott Ho Cam 68. **d** 71 **p** 72. C Bishopwearmouth St Mich w St Hilda *Dur* 71-73; C Fishponds St Mary *Bris* 73-75; Bp's Dom Chapl *S'wark* 75-78; Lic to Offic 78-79; V S Wimbledon H Trin and St Pet 79-88; V Greenwich St Alfege from 88; Chapl RN Coll Greenwich from 89; RD Greenwich Thameside *S'wark* 94-98; Boro Dean Greenwich 94-98; Hon Can S'wark Cathl from 96. *The Vicarage, Park Vista, London SE10 9LZ* Tel (020) 8858 6828

HARCOURT, Paul George. b 67. Em Coll Cam BA88 MA92. Wycliffe Hall Ox BA91. **d** 92 **p** 93. C Moreton *Ches* 92-95; C Woodford Wells *Chelmsf* 95-00; V from 00. *All Saints' Vicarage, 4 Inmans Row, Woodford Green IG8 0NH* Tel (020) 8504 0266 Fax 8504 9640 E-mail pharcourt@btclick.com

HARCOURT-NORTON, Michael Clive. *See* NORTON, Michael Clive Harcourt

HARCUS, Canon Arthur Reginald (Reg). b 38. Lon Univ BD71 MPhil78. Kelham Th Coll 58. **d** 63 **p** 64. C Charlton St Luke w St Paul *S'wark* 63-69; C Felpham w Middleton *Chich* 78-80; P-in-c Donnington 80-85; V Fernhurst 85-91; V Bolney 91-02; Tutor Lay Educn & Tr 91-02; TV Crawley from 02; Hon Can Koforidua from 91. *Peterhouse, 128 Ifield Road, Crawley RH11 7BW* Tel (01293) 520921

HARDACRE (née BROOKFIELD), Patricia Anne. b 50. St Mary's Coll Dur BA72. Cranmer Hall Dur DipTh73 MA74. **dss** 84 **d** 87 **p** 94. Kingston upon Hull St Nic *York* 84-86; Acomb St Steph 86-87; Par Dn 87-94; C 94-96; TV Preston Risen Lord *Blackb* from 96. *St Mary's Vicarage, St Mary's Close, Preston PR1 4XN* Tel (01772) 794222 E-mail anne@hipporage.fsnet.co.uk

HARDAKER, Canon Ian Alexander. b 32. K Coll Lon BD59 AKC59. **d** 60 **p** 61. C Beckenham St Geo *Roch* 60-65; R Eynsford w Lullingstone 65-70; V Chatham St Steph 70-85; RD Roch 78-85; Hon Can Roch Cathl 83-98; Clergy Appts Adv 86-98; Chapl to The Queen from 94; rtd 99; Perm to Offic *B & W* from 00. *The Old Post Office, Huish Champflower, Taunton TA4 2EY* Tel (01984) 623409

HARDCASTLE, Nigel John. b 47. Reading Univ BSc68. Qu Coll Birm DipTh71. **d** 72 **p** 73. C Weoley Castle *Birm* 72-75; C Handsworth St Andr 75-78; V Garretts Green 78-86; Exec Sec Ch Computer Project BCC 86-89; R Emmer Green *Ox* 89-99; V Reading St Luke w St Bart from 99. *St Luke's Vicarage, 14 Erleigh Road, Reading RG1 5LH* Tel 0118-926 2372 Fax as telephone E-mail nigel@hardcastle33.fsnet.co.uk

HARDCASTLE, Roger Clive. b 52. Southn Univ BSc73. Qu Coll Birm DipTh77. **d** 78 **p** 79. C Walton St Mary *Liv* 78-82; V Pemberton St Fran Kitt Green 82-94; TV Padgate 94-96; V Birchwood from 96. *The Vicarage, Admiral's Road, Birchwood, Warrington WA3 6QG* Tel (01925) 811906

HARDIE, John Blair. b 16. MBE46. LDS FDS MRCS38 MRCSE66. Edin Th Coll 73. **d** 76 **p** 76. Chapl St Paul's Cathl Dundee *Bre* 76-86; rtd 86; Hon C Carnoustie *Bre* from 86. *4 Lammerton Terrace, Dundee DD4 7BW* Tel (01382) 860836

HARDIE, Canon Stephen. b 41. AKC67. **d** 68 **p** 69. C Roxbourne St Andr *Lon* 68-73; C Colchester St Mary V *Chelmsf* 73-76; R

Wivenhoe 76-92; TR Dovercourt and Parkeston 92-96; P-in-c Harwich 92-96; R Dovercourt and Parkeston w Harwich from 96; P-in-c Ramsden Crays w Ramsden Bellhouse from 02; RD Harwich from 97; Hon Can Chelmsf Cathl from 02. *The Rectory, 51 Highfield Avenue, Harwich CO12 4DR* Tel (01255) 552033

HARDING, Alan. b 45. St Jo Coll Ox BA67 MA73 Pemb Coll Ox DPhil92. Oak Hill NSM Course 89. **d** 93 **p** 94. NSM Lt Heath *St Alb* 93-99; P-in-c S Mymms and Ridge from 99. *The Vicarage, 6 Hamilton Close, South Mimms, Potters Bar EN6 3PG* Tel (01707) 643142

HARDING, Alec James. b 61. St Andr Univ MA83 DTh. Cranmer Hall Dur 86. **d** 89 **p** 90. C Thirsk *York* 89-93; TV Heref St Martin w St Fran *Heref* 93-95; TV Heref S Wye 95-00; V Barnard Castle w Whorlton *Dur* from 00. *The Vicarage, Parson's Lonnen, Barnard Castle DL12 8ST* Tel (01833) 637018 E-mail aleckim@barney16.fsnet.co.uk

HARDING, Andrew Barry. b 66. Trent Poly HND88 Birm Univ DipHE97. Westcott Ho Cam CTM99. **d** 99 **p** 00. C Rainham *Roch* 99-03; V Hoo St Werburgh from 03. *The Vicarage, Vicarage Lane, Hoo, Rochester ME3 9BB* Tel (01634) 250291 E-mail ardy@abh123.freeserve.co.uk

HARDING, Brenda Kathleen. b 39. Bedf Coll Lon BA60 K Coll Lon BD62. St Deiniol's Hawarden 91. **d** 92 **p** 94. NSM Lancaster Ch Ch *Blackb* from 92. *14 Ascot Close, Lancaster LA1 4LT* Tel (01524) 66071

HARDING, Canon Brian Edward. b 38. ALCD65. **d** 65 **p** 66. C Chislehurst Ch Ch *Roch* 65-68; P-in-c Baxenden *Blackb* 68-70; V 70-88; V Douglas from 88; Hon Can Blackb Cathl from 96. *The Vicarage, 5 Tan House Lane, Parbold, Wigan WN8 7HG* Tel (01257) 462350 Fax 464827 E-mail brian.hardfam@virgin.net

HARDING, Clifford Maurice. b 22. Leeds Univ BA47. Coll of Resurr Mirfield 46. **d** 48 **p** 49. C Tonge Moor *Man* 48-54; Nyasaland 54-56; CF 56-59; V Oldham St Jo *Man* 59-65; Lic to Offic *Blackb* 65-87; rtd 87; Perm to Offic *Blackb* from 87. *31 Riley Avenue, St Annes, Lytham St Annes FY8 1HZ* Tel (01253) 725138

HARDING, Colin Ronald Stansby. b 32. RGN71 FVCM92 Dip Th & Min. Bp Otter Coll 94. **d** 97. NSM Aldingbourne, Barnham and Eastergate *Chich* from 97. *Spindle Trees, 67 Elm Grove, Barnham, Bognor Regis PO22 0HJ* Tel (01243) 552579

HARDING, David Anthony. b 30. St Edm Hall Ox BA54 MA58 Dur Univ MPhil83. Ely Th Coll 54. **d** 56 **p** 57. C Fulham All SS *Lon* 56-59; Lect Armenian Sem Istanbul 59-62; Chapl K Sch Cant 63-68; Chapl Westmr Sch 68-74; Chapl St Bede Coll Dur 74-75; SS Hild and Bede Coll 75-80; Asst Chapl Worksop Coll Notts 80-82; Chapl 82-91; Chapl St Mary and St Anne's Sch Abbots Bromley 91-95; rtd 95; Perm to Offic *Glouc* from 95. *29 King John's Court, King John's Island, Tewkesbury GL20 6EG* Tel (01684) 291978

HARDING, Derek Gordon Edward. b 50. Open Univ BA89 MIAP95. **d** 01 **p** 02. OLM Godstone and Blindley Heath *S'wark* from 01. *68 Lagham Road, Godstone RH9 8HB* Tel (01342) 893892

HARDING, Frederick Arthur. b 16. S'wark Ord Course 75. **d** 77 **p** 78. NSM Oxted *S'wark* 77-97; NSM Oxted and Tandridge from 97. *19 Crabwood, 13 Blue House Lane, Oxted RH8 0UA* Tel (01883) 716454

HARDING, John Stuart Michael. b 45. St Jo Coll Nottm 79. **d** 81 **p** 82. C Clifton *S'well* 81-87; V Broxtowe 87-98; Consultant to Churches 98-00; Perm to Offic *Chelmsf* 98-01; *M & K* from 01. *Hoylake, Castle Vale, Athlone, Co West Meath* E-mail rflexnserv@aol.com

HARDING, John William Christopher. b 31. St Jo Coll Dur BA55. **d** 58 **p** 59. C Wigan St Cath *Liv* 58-60; C Much Woolton 60-63; V Whiston 63-73; V Birkdale St Jo 73-97; rtd 97; Perm to Offic *Liv* from 98. *17 Baytree Close, Southport PR9 8RE* Tel (01704) 507654

HARDING, Ms Lesley Anne. b 58. Westcott Ho Cam 98 SEITE 99. **d** 01 **p** 02. C Walmer *Cant* from 01. *9 Roselands, Walmer, Deal CT14 7QE* Tel (01304) 368656 E-mail lesley.harding@ukgateway.net

HARDING, Lyndon Albert. b 60. Trin Coll Bris 00. **d** 02 **p** 03. C Hollington St Leon *Chich* from 02. *158 Old Church Road, St Leonards-on-Sea TN38 9HD* Tel (01424) 852496

HARDING, Mrs Marion. b 33. Gilmore Course 75. **dss** 85 **d** 87 **p** 94. Hertford St Andr *St Alb* 85-87; Par Dn 87-93; rtd 93; NSM Lt Amwell *St Alb* 93-97; Perm to Offic from 97. *41 Calton Avenue, Hertford SG14 2ER*

HARDING, Mrs Mary Elizabeth. b 46. Univ Coll Lon SRN67 Dorset Inst of HE DN85. STETS 97. **d** 00 **p** 01. NSM Shaston Sarum from 00. *The Old Mill, Manor Farm, Fontmell Magna, Shaftesbury SP7 0NW* Tel (01747) 811731 E-mail mary@harding6.freeserve.co.uk

HARDING, Michael Anthony John. b 37. Brasted Th Coll 67 Sarum Th Coll 68. **d** 71 **p** 72. C Forest Hill Ch Ch *S'wark* 71-72; C Catford St Laur 72-74; C Leominster *Heref* 74-77; R Neenton and V Ditton Priors 77-86; P-in-c Aston Botterell w Wheathill and Loughton 77-86; P-in-c Burwarton w N Cleobury 77-86; R Ditton Priors w Neenton, Burwarton etc 86-94; V E Budleigh w

Bicton and Otterton *Ex* 94-03; rtd 03. *The Beaches, 22 Middlehill Road, Colehill, Wimborne BH21 2SD* Tel (01202) 884775
E-mail michael.harding@care4free.net

HARDING, Preb Michael David. b 38. Man Univ BA61. Lich Th Coll 61. d 63 p 64. C Hednesford *Lich* 63-67; C Blurton 67-70; V Newcastle St Paul 70-99; RD Newcastle 87-97; Preb Lich Cathl 89-99; rtd 99; Perm to Offic *Lich* from 00. *7 Staines Court, Stone ST15 8XF* Tel (01785) 811737
E-mail mdharding@argonet.co.uk

HARDING, Peter Edward. b 39. Univ Coll Ox BA61 MA69. Wycliffe Hall Ox 62. d 64 p 65. C Westlands St Andr CD *Lich* 64-67; C Hinckley H Trin *Leic* 67-69; R Sutton cum Duckmanton *Derby* 69-75; P-in-c Elvaston and Shardlow 75-96; rtd 02. *40 Denstone Drive, Alvaston, Derby DE24 0HY* Tel (01332) 753569

HARDING, Peter Gordon. b 45. Lon Univ BA70 Open Univ BA88 MA90. Cranmer Hall Dur DipTh79. d 79 p 80. C Kirkheaton *Wakef* 79-82; NSM New Sleaford *Linc* 90-00. *67 The Drove, Sleaford NG34 7AS* Tel (01529) 307231
E-mail pgharding@lineone.net

HARDING, Peter Richard. b 46. AKC69. St Aug Coll Cant 69. d 70 p 71. C Chorley St Pet *Blackb* 70-73; C Ribbleton 73-74; C St Marylebone w H Trin *Lon* 74-80; P-in-c St Marylebone St Cypr 80-82; V 82-98; AD Westmr St Marylebone 83-92; Sub-Warden Guild of St Raphael 88-98; rtd 98; Perm to Offic *Chich* 98-99; Asst to RD Brighton from 00. *27A Chichester Place, Brighton BN2 1FF* Tel (01273) 685323

HARDING, Richard Michael. b 42. St Alb Minl Tr Scheme 80. d 83 p 84. C Pershore w Pinvin, Wick and Birlingham *Worc* 83-86; V Longdon, Castlemorton, Bushley, Queenhill etc 86-95; P-in-c Catshill and Dodford 95-97; V 97-02; P-in-c Stokenham w Sherford and Beesands, and Slapton *Ex* from 02. *The Vicarage, Stokenham, Kingsbridge TQ7 2ST* Tel (01548) 580385

HARDING, Rolf John. b 22. Oak Hill Th Coll 41 Lon Coll of Div 46. d 49 p 50. C Sydenham H Trin *S'wark* 49-52; C Harold Wood *Chelmsf* 52-53; Min Harold Hill St Paul CD 53-61; V Coopersale 61-91; Chapl St Marg Hosp Epping 73-91; Chapl W Essex HA 86-91; rtd 91; Perm to Offic *B & W* from 91. *11 Westbrook Park, Weston, Bath BA1 4DP* Tel (01225) 484968

HARDING, Miss Sylvia. b 23. St Mich Ho Ox 55. dss 64 d 87. Rodbourne Cheney *Bris* 57-66; Midl Area Sec CPAS 66-71; Patchway 71-78; Sec Coun of Women's Min Bris 77-84; rtd 84; Westbury-on-Trym St Alb *Bris* 86-92; Hon Par Dn 87-92; Perm to Offic *Bris* and *B & W* from 92. *53 Brampton Way, Portishead, Bristol BS20 6YW* Tel (01275) 847046 or 848638

HARDINGHAM, Paul David. b 52. Lon Univ BSc74 Fitzw Coll Cam BA77. Ridley Hall Cam 75. d 78 p 79. C Cambridge St Martin *Ely* 78-81; C Jesmond Clayton Memorial *Newc* 81-88; C Harborne Heath *Birm* 88-91; R Ipswich St Matt *St E* from 91. *St Matthew's Rectory, 3 Portman Road, Ipswich IP1 2ES* Tel (01473) 251630 E-mail paul@hardingham60.freeserve.co.uk

HARDMAN, Bryan Edwin. b 29. Lon Univ BD60 Selw Coll Cam PhD64 K Coll Lon MTh75. Moore Th Coll Sydney ThL54. d 55 p 55. Australia 55-60; 68-83; 98-99; from 00; Perm to Offic *Ely* 60-65; V Cambridge St Andr Less 65-68; Bangladesh 83-86; Singapore 87-95; rtd 94; Canada 99-00. *U197/1215 Grand Junction Road, Hope Valley, S Australia 5090*

HARDMAN, The Ven Christine Elizabeth. b 51. Lon Univ BSc(Econ)73. St Alb Minl Tr Scheme 81. dss 84 d 87 p 94. Markyate Street *St Alb* 84-87; Par Dn 87-88; Tutor St Alb Minl Tr Scheme 88-91; Course Dir 91-96; C Markyate Street 94-96; V Stevenage H Trin 96-01; RD Stevenage 99-01; Adn Lewisham *S'wark* from 01. *129A Honor Oak Park, London SE23 3LD* Tel (020) 7939 9408 E-mail christine.hardman@dswark.co.uk

HARDMAN, Geoffrey James. b 41. Birm Univ BA63. N Ord Course 77. d 80 p 81. NSM Latchford St Jas *Ches* 80-93; NSM Haydock St Jas *Liv* from 94. *48 Denbury Avenue, Stockton Heath, Warrington WA4 2BW* Tel (01925) 264064
E-mail geoff@ghardman.freeserve.co.uk

HARDMAN, Mrs Pamela. b 39. d 01 p 02. NSM Bramhall *Ches* from 01. *38 Deva Close, Poynton, Stockport SK12 1HH* Tel (01625) 877936 E-mail pamela_hardman@lineone.net

HARDMAN, Canon Peter George. b 35. Man Univ BSc56. Ridley Hall Cam 58. d 60 p 61. C Oldham St Paul *Man* 60-63; NW England Area Sec SCM 63-64; NW England Area Sec CEM 64-67; Asst Chapl Marlborough Coll 67-72; Chapl 72-79; P-in-c Wareham *Sarum* 79-80; TR 80-00; Chapl Wareham Hosp 80-92; Chapl Dorset Health Care NHS Trust 92-00; Can and Preb Sarum Cathl *Sarum* 87-00; RD Purbeck 89-99; rtd 00; Perm to Offic *Sarum* from 00. *55 Palairet Close, Bradford-on-Avon BA15 1US* Tel (01225) 867198
E-mail peterhardman@onetel.net.uk

HARDWICK, Canon Christopher George. b 57. Open Univ BA94 Birm Univ MA96 PhD00 ACIB79 DASSc94. Ripon Coll Cuddesdon 90. d 92 p 93. C Worc SE *Worc* 92-95; R Ripple, Earls Croome w Hill Croome and Strensham 95-00; R Upton-on-Severn, Ripple, Earls Croome etc from 00; RD Upton from 97; Hon Can Worc Cathl from 03. *The Rectory, Old Street,*

Upton-upon-Severn, Worcester WR8 0JQ* Tel (01684) 591241 Fax as telephone E-mail cghardw@globalnet.co.uk

HARDWICK, Dennis Egerton. b 27. St Deiniol's Hawarden. d 82 p 83. NSM Lache cum Saltney *Ches* 82-85; P-in-c Backford 85-88; P-in-c Capenhurst 87-88; R Backford and Capenhurst 88-93; rtd 93; Perm to Offic *Chich* from 93. *11 Prime Close, Walberton, Arundel BN18 0PL*

HARDWICK, Graham John. b 42. Qu Coll Birm 68. d 70 p 71. C Watford St Mich *St Alb* 70-73; C N Mymms 73-75; Youth Officer Cov Cathl *Cov* 75-81; Chapl Lanchester Poly 76-81; V Nuneaton St Nic 81-95; P-in-c New Bilton from 95; Ind Chapl from 95. *St Oswald's Vicarage, New Street, Rugby CV22 7BE* Tel (01788) 544011 Fax 333256 E-mail revgjh@talk21.com

HARDWICK, John Audley. b 28. Em Coll Cam BA51 MA55. Westcott Ho Cam 51. d 53 p 54. C Selby Abbey *York* 53-56; Chapl St Edm Sch Hindhead 56-60; Chapl Aysgarth Sch 60-62; Chapl St Edm Sch Hindhead 62-86; Asst Hd Master 73-90; Lic to Offic *Guildf* 63-90; rtd 93; Perm to Offic *Ches* from 95. *1 Schoolfield Close, Buerton, Crewe CW3 0DW*

HARDWICK, Robert. b 56. St Jo Coll Nottm DCM93. d 93 p 94. C Beeston *S'well* 93-97; V Scawby, Redbourne and Hibaldstow *Linc* 97-01; RD Yarborough 00-01; R Swift Current St Steph Canada from 01. *108 Second Avenue NE, Swift Current SK, Canada, S9H 2C7* Tel (001) (306) 773 4007 Fax 773 3641 E-mail rob.hardwick@sasktel.net

HARDWICK, Mrs Susan Frances. b 44. Warwick Univ BA81. Qu Coll Birm 82. dss 85 d 87 p 94. Chilvers Coton w Astley *Cov* 85-91; C 87-91; Dioc Disabilities Officer 91-96; Chapl Hereward Coll 91-96; Chapl FE Colls from 94; Hon C New Bilton 96-98; FE Field Officer Team Co-ord (W Midl) from 97; Chapl Rainsbrook Secure Tr Cen from 99. *St Oswald's Vicarage, New Street, Rugby CV22 7BE* Tel (01788) 544011 Fax 333256 E-mail susanhardwick@group4.com

HARDWICKE, Stephen Michael. b 57. Herts Coll BA85 Lon Bible Coll MA87 K Coll Lon MTh92. Westcott Ho Cam 93. d 95 p 96. C Leagrave *St Alb* 95-01; P-in-c Cowley *Lon* 01-03; R from 03. *St Laurence Rectory, Church Road, Cowley, Uxbridge UB8 3NB* Tel (01895) 232728 Fax as telephone

HARDY, Ms Alison Jane. b 61. St Anne's Coll Ox BA82 MA96. Nor Ord Course 92. d 95 p 96. C Flixton St Mich *Man* 95-98; Lect Bolton St Pet 98-00; P-in-c Irlam from 00. *The Vicarage, Vicarage Road, Irlam, Manchester M44 6WA* Tel 0161-775 2461 E-mail alisonhardy@fsmail.net

HARDY, Anthony. b 36. d 86 p 87. NSM Malden St Jas *S'wark* from 86. *48 Blake's Lane, New Malden KT3 6NR* Tel (020) 8949 0703

HARDY, Anthony William. b 56. Man Univ BEd79 MEd86 Open Univ BSc00. St Jo Coll Nottm LTh88. d 88 p 89. C Pennington *Man* 88-91; V Eccleston St Luke *Liv* 91-00; NW Regional Consultant CPAS from 00; Dioc Evang *Liv* from 00; Perm to Offic *Carl* from 00. *52 Swinburne Road, Dentons Green, St Helens WA10 6AN* Tel (01744) 454303 Fax as telephone
E-mail tonyh@cpas.org.uk

HARDY, Canon Brian Albert. b 31. St Jo Coll Ox BA54 DipTh55 MA58. Westcott Ho Cam 55. d 57 p 58. C Rugeley *Lich* 57-62; Chapl Down Coll Cam 62-66; C-in-c Livingston Miss *Edin* 66-74; Preb Heref Cathl *Heref* 74-78; Ch Planning Officer Telford 74-78; RD Telford Severn Gorge 75-78; Chapl Edin Th Coll 78-82; Chapl Edin R Infirmary 82-86; R Edin St Columba *Edin* 82-91; Dean Edin 86-91; Hon Can St Mary's Cathl from 91; R St Andrews All SS *St And* 91-96; rtd 96. *3/3 Starbank Road, Edinburgh EH5 3BN* Tel 0131-551 6783

HARDY, Christopher Richard. b 52. R Holloway Coll Lon BMus77 Southn Univ BTh90. Chich Th Coll 87. d 90 p 91. C Kenton *Lon* 90-95; V E Finchley All SS from 95. *All Saints' Vicarage, Twyford Avenue, London N2 9NH* Tel (020) 8883 9315 Mobile 07785-728272
E-mail christopherhardy@btinternet.com

HARDY, Prof Daniel Wayne. b 30. Haverford Coll (USA) BA52. Gen Th Sem (NY) STB55 STM63. d 55 p 56. USA 55-61 and 90-95; Fell and Tutor Gen Th Sem 59-61; Lic to Offic *Ox* 61-65; Lect Modern Th Thought Birm Univ 65-75; Sen Lect 75-86; Hon C Londonderry *Birm* 67-86; Van Mildert Prof Div Dur Univ 86-90; Can Res Dur Cathl *Dur* 86-90; Dir Cen Th Inquiry 90-95; rtd 96; Perm to Offic *Ely* from 96. *101 Millington Lane, Cambridge CB3 9HA* Tel (01223) 312302 Fax 303609
E-mail dwhardy@compuserve.com

HARDY, Miss Janet Frances. b 59. Newc Univ BA81 CertEd82. Trin Coll Bris 87. d 89 p 94. Par Dn Sheff St Paul *Sheff* 89-92; TD Gt Snaith 92-94; TV 94-96; V Pitsmoor Ch Ch 96-01; V Thorpe Hesley from 01. *The Vicarage, 30 Barnsley Road, Thorpe Hesley, Rotherham S61 2RR* Tel 0114-246 3487

HARDY, John Charles. b 22. Sheff Univ BA48 DipEd49 Lon Univ DipTh53. St Deiniol's Hawarden 66. d 67 p 68. Hon C Chorley St Laur *Blackb* 67-87; rtd 87; Perm to Offic *Blackb* from 87. *4 Glamis Drive, Chorley PR7 1LX* Tel (01257) 265743

HARDY, John Christopher. b 61. St Jo Coll Dur BA83 Dur Univ MA95 New Coll Edin BD92 Ox Univ MLitt00. Coates Hall Edin 89 Aston Tr Scheme 87. d 92 p 93. C Walker *Newc* 92-95;

Fell Chapl Magd Coll Ox 95-98; TV Benwell Team *Newc* from 98; R Alston Moor from 03. *The Parsonage House, Brampton Road, Alston CA9 3AA* Tel (01434) 381458

HARDY, Canon John Lewis Daniel. b 26. St Chad's Coll Dur BA51 DipTh52. **d** 52 **p** 53. C Hucknall Torkard *S'well* 52-58; V Harworth 58-65; V Sutton in Ashfield St Mary 65-85; R Keyworth 85-93; P-in-c Stanton-on-the-Wolds 85-93; RD S Bingham 91-93; Perm to Offic *Leic and Pet* from 99. *14 Dean's Street, Oakham LE15 6AF* Tel (01572) 722591

HARDY, Michael John. b 35. Keble Coll Ox BA58 MA66. Cuddesdon Coll 59. **d** 61 **p** 62. C Dalton-in-Furness *Carl* 61-64; C Harborne St Pet *Birm* 64-68; Min Can Ripon Cathl *Ripon* 68-73; Appt and Tr Sec USPG 73-80; R Stretford St Pet *Man* 80-91; P-in-c Newton Hall *Dur* 91-96; TR Keighley St Andr *Bradf* 96-00; rtd 00. *5 Outlane, Netherthong, Huddersfield HD9 3EQ* Tel (01484) 683655

HARDY, Canon Paul Richard. b 30. K Coll Cam BA52 MA56. St Steph Ho Ox 57. **d** 59 **p** 60. C Corringham *Chelmsf* 59-61; C Prittlewell All SS 61-64; USPG 64-95; Tanzania 64-95; Can Dar-es-Salaam 74-88; Can Zanzibar and Tanga 88-95; Hon Can from 95; rtd 95; Perm to Offic *Roch* from 95. *22 Bromley College, London Road, Bromley BR1 1PE* Tel (020) 8290 1289 E-mail paul@hardy84.fsnet.co.uk

HARDY, Miss Pauline. b 41. CertEd. Linc Th Coll 85. **d** 87 **p** 94. Par Dn Walsall Wood *Lich* 87-89; Par Dn Buckingham *Ox* 89-93; C Buckingham w Radclive cum Chackmore 93-97; C Nash w Thornton, Beachampton and Thornborough 96-97; C Buckingham from 97. *The Rectory, Chapel Lane, Thornborough, Buckingham MK18 2DJ* Tel (01280) 812515

✠**HARDY, The Rt Revd Robert Maynard.** b 36. CBE01. Clare Coll Cam BA60 MA64 Hull Univ Hon DD92. Cuddesdon Coll 60. **d** 62 **p** 63 **c** 80. C Langley St Aid CD *Man* 62-64; C Langley All SS and Martyrs 64-65; Chapl and Lect Th Selw Coll Cam 65-72; V Boreham Wood All SS *St Alb* 72-75; Dir St Alb Minl Tr Scheme 75-80; P-in-c Aspley Guise *St Alb* 75-79; P-in-c Husborne Crawley w Ridgmont 76-79; R Aspley Guise w Husborne Crawley and Ridgmont 80; Suff Bp Maidstone *Cant* 80-87; Bp Linc 87-01; Bp HM Pris 85-01; rtd 01. *Carleton House, Back Lane, Langwathby, Penrith CA10 1NB* Tel (01768) 881210

HARDY, Stephen John Arundell. b 49. Spurgeon's Coll DipTh74. SEITE 95. **d** 97 **p** 98. NSM Marden *Cant* 97-00; P-in-c Lydd from 00. *All Saints' Rectory, Park Street, Lydd, Romney Marsh TN29 9AY* Tel (01797) 320345 E-mail stephenhardy@macmail.com

HARE, Christopher Sumner. b 49. Solicitor 73. WEMTC92. **d** 95 **p** 96. NSM Saltford w Corston and Newton St Loe *B & W* 95-01; P-in-c Timsbury and Priston from 01. *The Rectory, South Road, Timsbury, Bath BA2 0EJ* Tel (01761) 479660

HARE, David. b 46. Qu Coll Birm. **d** 83 **p** 83. SSF 67-96; Bp's Dom Chapl *Birm* 83-87; V Handsworth St Mich 87-97; R Newton Regis w Seckington and Shuttington 97-03; rtd 03; Perm to Offic *Birm* from 03. *118 Southam Road, Birmingham B28 0AD* Tel 0121-777 3493

HARE, Douglas Stewart. b 27. Bris Univ BA51 Lon Inst of Educn PGCE52. Wycliffe Hall Ox 82. **d** 96 **p** 97. NSM Margate H Trin *Cant* 96-99; rtd 99; Perm to Offic *Sarum* from 00. *8 Lady Down View, Tisbury, Salisbury SP3 6LL* Tel (01747) 871544

HARE, Frank Richard Knight. b 22. Trin Hall Cam BA46 MA48. Cuddesdon Coll 46. **d** 48 **p** 49. C Dennington *St E* 48-51; C Eastbourne St Mary *Chich* 51-54; R Rotherfield 54-62; V Steyning 62-70; R Ashurst 62-70; TV Raveningham *Nor* 70-71; TR Barnham Broom 71-79; V Buxton w Oxnead 79-86; R Lammas w Lt Hautbois 79-86; rtd 86; Perm to Offic *St E* from 86. *14 Lee Road, Aldeburgh IP15 5HG* Tel (01728) 453372

HARE, Michael John. b 41. Lon Univ MD71 Cam Univ MA77. EAMTC 00. **d** 02 **p** 03. NSM E Leightonstone *Ely* from 02. *Manor House, 66 Main Street, Hartford, Huntingdon PE29 1YA* Tel (01480) 453172 Mobile 07850-845004 Fax (01480) 451731 E-mail john@hare.waitrose.com

HARE, Richard William. b 66. Bris Univ BSc88 PhD94. Cranmer Hall Dur BA95. **d** 95 **p** 96. C Coulsdon St Jo *S'wark* 95-98; C Coventry Caludon *Cov* 98-99; TV from 99; AD Cov E from 01. *The Vicarage, Wyken Croft, Coventry CV2 3AD* Tel (024) 7660 2332 E-mail thehares@ic24.net

✠**HARE, The Rt Revd Thomas Richard.** b 22. Trin Coll Ox BA48 MA53. Westcott Ho Cam 48. **d** 50 **p** 51 **c** 71. C Haltwhistle *Newc* 50-52; Bp's Dom Chapl *Man* 52-59; Can Res Carl Cathl *Carl*

59-65; R Barrow St Geo w St Luke 65-69; Adn Westmorland and Furness 65-71; Hon Can Carl Cathl 65-71; V Winster 69-71; Suff Bp Pontefract *Wakef* 71-92; rtd 92. *Wood Cottage, Mirehouse, Underskiddaw, Keswick CA12 4QE* Tel (01768) 772996

✠**HARE DUKE, The Rt Revd Michael Geoffrey.** b 25. Trin Coll Ox BA49 MA51 St Andr Univ Hon DD94. Westcott Ho Cam 50. **d** 52 **p** 53 **c** 69. C St John's Wood *Lon* 52-56; V Bury St Mark *Man* 56-62; Past Dir Clinical Th Assn Nottm 62-64; Past Consultant 64-69; V Daybrook *S'well* 64-69; Bp St And 69-94; rtd 94. *2 Balhousie Avenue, Perth PH1 5HN* Tel (01738) 622642 E-mail bishmick@aol.com

HARES, David Ronald Walter. b 40. Qu Coll Cam BA63 MA67 CertEd. Westcott Ho Cam 64. **d** 66 **p** 67. C Cannock *Lich* 66-69; Chapl Peterho Cam 69-72; Asst Master Chesterton Sch Cam 72-74; V Kesgrave *St E* 74-98; R Lt Barningham, Blickling, Edgefield etc *Nor* from 98. *The Rectory, The Street, Itteringham, Norwich NR11 7AX* Tel (01263) 584262

HAREWOOD, John Rupert. b 24. Man Univ BA48. Sarum & Wells Th Coll 76. **d** 79 **p** 80. NSM Taunton St Jas *B & W* 79-82; TV Camelot Par 82-89; rtd 89; Perm to Offic *Ex* from 92. *19 Swains Road, Budleigh Salterton EX9 6HU* Tel (01395) 445802

HARFORD, Julian Gray. b 29. Univ Coll Ox BA52 MA59 Lon Univ PGCE58. Qu Coll Birm DipTh64. **d** 64 **p** 65. C W End *Win* 64-67; C Chearsley w Nether Winchendon *Ox* 67-77; C Chilton All SS 72-77; R Westbury w Turweston, Shalstone and Biddlesden 77-86; C Chenies and Lt Chalfont 86-87; C Chenies and Lt Chalfont, Latimer and Flaunden 87-95; rtd 95; Perm to Offic *Sarum* from 95. *14 Dial Close, Seend, Melksham SN12 6NP* Tel (01380) 828306

HARFORD, The Ven Michael Rivers Dundas. b 26. Trin Coll Cam BA49 MA51. Westcott Ho Cam 50. **d** 52 **p** 53. C Ashton-on-Ribble St Andr *Blackb* 52-55; Perm to Offic *Edin* 55-56; Malaya 56-63; Malaysia 63-66; V Childwall St Dav *Liv* 66-71; Australia from 71; Adn Albany 76-79; Adn Swan 86-89; Adn Mitchell 90-91; rtd 91. *Unit 12, 18 Bridges Road, Melville, W Australia 6157* Tel (0061) (8) 9319 1538 Mobile 410-5668 E-mail michael.harford@perth.anglican.org

HARFORD, Timothy William. b 58. Nottm Univ BTh89. Linc Th Coll 86. **d** 89 **p** 90. C Minehead *B & W* 89-93; R Knebworth *St Alb* 93-03; Children's Soc from 03. *The Children's Society, Edward Rudolf House, Margery Street, London WC1X 0JL* Tel (020) 7841 4400 E-mail tim@harford1.freeserve.co.uk

HARGER, Robin Charles Nicholas. b 49. BTh. Sarum & Wells Th Coll 78. **d** 81 **p** 82. C Charlton Kings St Mary *Glouc* 81-85; C Folkestone St Mary and St Eanswythe *Cant* 85-89; TV Langley and Parkfield *Man* 89-95; TV Bournemouth St Pet w St Swithun, H Trin etc *Win* from 95. *The Vicarage, 2A St Anthony's Road, Bournemouth BH2 6PD* Tel (01202) 554355 E-mail robin.harger2@btopenworld.com

HARGRAVE, Alan Lewis. b 50. Birm Univ BSc73 PhD77. Ridley Hall Cam 87. **d** 89 **p** 90. C Cambridge H Trin w St Andr Gt *Ely* 89-92; C Cambridge H Trin 92-93; C-in-c Fen Ditton 93-94; V Cambridge H Cross from 94. *Holy Cross Vicarage, 192 Peverel Road, Cambridge CB5 8RL* Tel (01223) 413343 E-mail hargraveal@aol.com

HARGREAVE, James David. b 44. ALCM89 LTCL90 Lon Univ BA66 CertEd68. Coll of Resurr Mirfield DipTh72. **d** 73 **p** 74. C Houghton le Spring *Dur* 73-77; C Gateshead St Cuth w St Paul 77-79; V Trimdon 79-87; C-in-c Stockton Green Vale H Trin CD 87-94; V Hedon w Paull *York* 94-02; rtd 02; Perm to Offic *York* from 03. *27 Southwood Avenue, Cottingham HU16 5AD* Tel (01482) 844377

HARGREAVES, Arthur Cecil Monsarrat. b 19. Trin Hall Cam BA42 MA46. Westcott Ho Cam 47. **d** 49 **p** 50. C Wembley St Jo *Lon* 49-52; India 52-61 and 70-76; Asia Sec CMS 61-69; Gen Sec Conf of Br Miss Socs 76-79; Hon C Croydon St Aug *Cant* 79-81; V Marden 81-86; rtd 86; Perm to Offic *S'wark* from 86. *Windrush Cottage, 87 Downscourt Road, Purley CR8 1BJ* Tel (020) 8668 8871

HARGREAVES, Arthur Walsh. b 34. FRCSE FRCS Man Univ MB, ChB FRCSGlas. St Deiniol's Hawarden 89. **d** 90 **p** 91. NSM Baguley *Man* 90-00; Perm to Offic from 00. *Greenaways, Woodbourne Road, Sale M33 3SX* Tel 0161-973 7674

HARGREAVES, John. b 43. St Jo Coll Nottm 86. **d** 88 **p** 89. C Werneth *Man* 88-91; TV Rochdale 91-96; C Man Gd Shep 96-97; Perm to Offic *Liv* 96-97; C Manchester Gd Shep and St Barn *Man* 97-98; rtd 98. *15 Ambleside Avenue, Rawtenstall, Rossendale BB4 6RY*

HARGREAVES, Canon John Henry Monsarrat. b 11. Trin Coll Cam BA33 MA37. Westcott Ho Cam 35. **d** 37 **p** 38. C Bishopwearmouth Ch Ch *Dur* 37-39; C Hunslet St Mary *Ripon* 39-43; C Brompton H Trin *Lon* 57-58; CMS (Nigeria) 43-57 and 59-63; SPCK 65-90; C-in-c Sevenoaks St Luke CD *Roch* 65-83; RD Sevenoaks 74-79; Hon Can Roch Cathl 81-83; rtd 83; Perm to Offic *Guildf* from 91. *20 St Pauls Road West, Dorking RH4 2HU* Tel (01306) 888648

HARGREAVES, John Rodney. b 36. Open Univ BA74. Didsbury Methodist Coll 59 St Deiniol's Hawarden 74. **d** 75 **p** 75. In Methodist Ch 63-74; C Pontypool *Mon* 75-77; C Llanedeyrn

77-79; Chapl HM Pris Aylesbury 79-83; Sen Chapl HM Pris Stafford 83-88; Asst Chapl Gen of Pris (N) 88-90; Asst Chapl Gen of Pris 90-96; R Stone St Mich and St Wulfad w Aston St Sav *Lich* 96-01; rtd 01; Master St Jo Hosp Lich from 01. *The Master's House, St John's Hospital, St John Street, Lichfield WS13 6PB* Tel (01543) 264169 E-mail jrhargreaves@easynet.co.uk

HARGREAVES, John Wilson. b 46. Aber Univ BScFor67 Birm Poly DipVG73. Westcott Ho Cam 84. **d** 86 **p** 87. C Rugby St Andr *Cov* 86-90; TV Daventry, Ashby St Ledgers, Braunston etc *Pet* 90-97; Chapl Daventry Tertiary Coll 94-97; P-in-c Pinxton *Derby* 97-01; R 01-02; TR E Scarsdale from 02. *The Rectory, Rectory Road, Upper Langwith, Mansfield NG20 9RE* Tel (01623) 742413

HARGREAVES, Ms Marise. b 60. Leeds Univ BA81. Cranmer Hall Dur 82. **dss** 85 **d** 94 **p** 95. Yeadon St Jo *Bradf* 85-87; NSM Bradf St Clem 94-96; NSM Buttershaw St Paul 96-00; C Eccleshill from 00. *3 Hall Road, Bradford BD2 2DP* Tel (01274) 634017

HARGREAVES, Mark Kingston. b 63. Oriel Coll Ox BA85 MA89 Rob Coll Cam PhD91 W Lon Inst of HE PGCE86. Ridley Hall Cam 87. **d** 91 **p** 92. C Highbury Ch Ch w St Jo and St Sav Lon 91-94; C Ealing St Steph Castle Hill 94-97; C Notting Hill St Jo and St Pet 97-02; V Notting Hill St Pet from 03. *48 Ladbroke Road, London W11 3NW* Tel (020) 7221 9841

HARGREAVES, Raymond. Open Univ BA79 St Jo Coll York CertEd61. Ripon Hall Ox 72. **d** 73 **p** 74. C Stanwix *Carl* 73-78; Chapl St Olave's Sch York 78-94; Perm to Offic *York* from 94; rtd 96. *21 Oak Tree Lane, Haxby, York YO32 3YL* Tel (01904) 763127

HARGREAVES-STEAD, Terence Desmond. b 32. Edin Th Coll 60. **d** 63 **p** 64. C Walney Is *Carl* 63-66; Chapl Withington Hosp Man 66-72; V Westleigh St Paul *Man* from 72; Chapl Wigan and Leigh Health Services NHS Trust 96-01; Chapl Wrightington Wigan and Leigh NHS Trust from 01. *St Paul's Vicarage, Westleigh Lane, Leigh WN7 5NW* Tel (01942) 882883 *or* 672333

HARINGTON, Roger John Urquhart. b 48. Trin Hall Cam BA70 MA71. Coll of Resurr Mirfield 72. **d** 75 **p** 76. C Liv Our Lady and St Nic w St Anne *Liv* 75-78; Asst Chapl Leeds Univ and Poly *Ripon* 78-81; TV Moor Allerton 81-86; Dioc Drama Adv (Jabbok Theatre Co) 86-95; V Leeds Gipton Epiphany 95-02. *21 Spencer Place, Leeds LS7 4DQ* Tel 0113-240 0769 E-mail jabbok@gn.apc.org

HARKER, Harold Aidan. b 35. **d** 82 **p** 83. OSB from 53; C Reading St Giles *Ox* 82-83; Lic to Offic 83-87; C Halstead St Andr w H Trin and Greenstead Green *Chelmsf* 87-89; P-in-c Belchamp St Paul 89-97; R Belchamp Otten w Belchamp Walter and Bulmer etc 97-00; rtd 00; Lic to Offic *Chelmsf* from 00. *38 Sheppard's College, London Road, Bromley BR1 1PE* Tel (020) 8464 1206

HARKER, Ian. b 39. Dur Univ BA61. Lich Th Coll Moray Ho Edin 66. **d** 63 **p** 64. C Knottingley *Wakef* 63-66; Perm to Offic 66-70; C Notting Hill *Lon* 70-75; Chapl Newc Univ *Newc* 75-83; Master Newc St Thos Prop Chpl 75-83; Perm to Offic *Chelmsf* 99-01; C Plaistow and N Canning Town 01; C Loughton St Jo 01-02; V Leytonstone H Trin Harrow Green from 02. *The Vicarage, 4 Holloway Road, London E11 4LD* Tel (020) 8539 7760 Fax as telephone E-mail harkatvic@aol.com

HARKER, John Hadlett. b 37. Dur Univ BSc59 Newc Univ PhD67 CEng MIChemE64 MInstE64 CChem MRSC65 FIChemE80. NEOC 81. **d** 84 **p** 85. C Earsdon *Newc* 84-87; P-in-c Long Horsley 87-91; V Bassenthwaite, Isel and Setmurthy *Carl* 91-94; TR Howden *York* 94-96; P-in-c Willerby w Ganton and Folkton 96-98; rtd 98; Perm to Offic *Newc* 98-01; Hon C Newc St Andr and Newc St Luke from 01. *The Vicarage, 15 Claremont Street, Newcastle upon Tyne NE2 4AH* Tel 0191-221 1009 E-mail harker@thestell.freeserve.co.uk

HARKER, Stephan John. b 47. Em Coll Cam BA68 MA72. Westcott Ho Cam 70. **d** 72 **p** 73. C Marton *Blackb* 72-76; C Preston St Matt 76-79; C Fleetwood 79-80; Chapl Charterhouse Sch Godalming from 81. *Lower Oakhurst, Frith Hill Road, Godalming GU7 2ED* Tel (01483) 422155

HARKIN, John Patrick. b 53. Open Univ BA92. Oak Hill Th Coll DipHE89. **d** 89 **p** 90. C Wisley w Pyrford *Guildf* 89-93; P-in-c Mickleham 93-98; Chapl Box Hill Sch Surrey 93-98; R Jersey St Ouen w St Geo *Win* from 98; Vice-Dean Jersey from 01; Hon Chapl ATC from 02. *The Rectory, La Route du Marais, St Ouen, Jersey JE3 2GG* Tel (01534) 481800 Fax 484202 E-mail harkin@jerseymail.co.uk

HARKIN, Terence James. b 46. Lon Bible Coll BA82 New Coll Edin MTh94. **d** 95 **p** 96. In Bapt Min 86-95; C Edin H Cross *Edin* 95-96; C S Queensferry 95-96; P-in-c from 96. *12 Springfield Place, South Queensferry, West Lothian EH30 9XE* Tel 0131-319 1099 *or* 331 5540 E-mail tjharkin@nildram.co.uk

HARKINS, James Robert. b 27. Minnesota Univ BA49. Seabury-Western Th Sem MTh53. **d** 52 **p** 52. USA 52-60, 72-79 and 91-93; Colombia 60-72; Dominica 79-85; Venezuela 85-91; Chapl Venice w Trieste *Eur* 94-99; P-in-c Menton 99-01; rtd 01. *Soleil du Menton, 2 Sent Pigautier, 06500 Menton, France* Tel (0033) (4) 9357 2025

HARKNESS, Verney Austin Barnett. b 19. Lon Univ BA40 DipTh63. Ridley Hall Cam 46. **d** 47 **p** 48. C Cockermouth All SS w Ch Ch *Carl* 47-50; R The Shelsleys *Worc* 53-56; Egypt 50-53; V Bris H Trin *Bris* 56-60; R Stoke next Guildf St Jo *Guildf* 63-72; Sri Lanka 73-77; P-in-c Walkington *York* 78-79; P-in-c Bishop Burton 78-79; R Bishop Burton w Walkington 79-84; rtd 85; Perm to Offic *York* 85-98. *St Andrew's Nursing Home, Church Bank, Stanley DH9 0DU* Tel (01207) 290398

HARKNETT, David Philip. b 74. St Pet Coll Ox BA97. Oak Hill Th Coll BA03. **d** 03. C Radipole and Melcombe Regis *Sarum* from 03. *1 Campion Close, Weymouth DT4 7UE* Tel (01305) 788202 E-mail davidharknett@hotmail.com

HARKNETT, Linda. b 48. Open Univ BA81 Croydon Coll CertEd92. SEITE 97. **d** 00 **p** 01. NSM Sutton St Nic *S'wark* 00-03; Chapl Epsom and St Helier NHS Trust 01-03; Chapl Whitelands Coll Roehampton Inst *S'wark* from 03. *Roehampton Institute, Whitelands College, West Hill, London SW15 3SN* Tel (020) 8392 3516

HARLAND, Canon Harold William James. b 35. Hertf Coll Ox BA59 MA63. Clifton Th Coll 59. **d** 61 **p** 62. C Reigate St Mary *S'wark* 61-64; C Farnborough *Guildf* 64-68; V Walmley *Birm* 68-74; V Bromley Ch Ch *Roch* 74-86; V Foord St Jo *Cant* 86-00; Dir Post-Ord Tr 93-97; Hon Can Cant Cathl 94-00; rtd 00; Perm to Offic *Cant* from 00. *121 Station Road West, Canterbury CT2 8DE* Tel (01227) 764699

✠**HARLAND, The Rt Revd Ian.** b 32. Peterho Cam BA56 MA60. Wycliffe Hall Ox 58. **d** 60 **p** 61 **c** 85. C Melton Mowbray w Thorpe Arnold *Leic* 60-63; V Oughtibridge *Sheff* 63-72; V Sheff St Cuth 72-75; P-in-c Brightside All SS 72-75; RD Ecclesfield 73-75; V Rotherham 75-79; RD Rotherham 76-79; Adn Doncaster 79-85; P-in-c Dunscroft Ch Ch 81-83; Hon Can Blackb Cathl *Blackb* 85-89; Suff Bp Lancaster 85-89; Bp Carl 89-00; rtd 00; Hon Asst Bp Eur from 00. *White House, 11 South Street, Gargrave, Skipton BD23 3RT* Tel (01756) 748623 E-mail isharland.gargrave@amserve.net

HARLEY, Brother Brian Mortimer. b 25. K Coll Lon 48. **d** 53 **p** 54. C Bris St Agnes w St Simon *Bris* 53-56; Lic to Offic *Sarum* 56-62; SSF from 56; Chapl St Fran Sch Hooke 58-61; Papua New Guinea 61-79; Australia from 87; Min Gen SSF from 81; rtd 95. *The Hermitage of St Bernadine, PO Box 46, Stroud, NSW, Australia 2425* Tel (0061) (2) 4994 5372 Fax 4994 5527

HARLEY, Canon Brian Nigel. b 30. Clare Coll Cam BA53 MA57. Cuddesdon Coll 53. **d** 55 **p** 56. C Basingstoke *Win* 55-60; TV 71-73; TR 73-80; C W End 60-61; C-in-c Southn St Chris Thornhill CD 61-71; V Eastleigh 80-93; RD Eastleigh 85-93; rtd 93; Perm to Offic *Win* from 93; Bp's Dom Chapl 94-96. *18 Phillimore Road, Southampton SO16 2NR* Tel (023) 8055 1049

HARLEY, Mrs Carol Anne. b 46. **d** 00 **p** 01. OLM Tettenhall Wood and Perton *Lich* from 00. *27 Tyrley Close, Compton, Wolverhampton WV6 8AP* Tel (01902) 755316 E-mail allynharley@lineone.net

HARLEY, Christopher David. b 41. Selw Coll Cam BA63 MA69 Bris Univ PGCE64 Columbia Bible Sem DMin92 Utrecht Univ PhD02. Clifton Th Coll 64. **d** 66 **p** 67. C Finchley Ch Ch *Lon* 66-69; Hon C 75-78; Ethiopia 70-75; Hd of UK Miss CMJ 75-78; Lect All Nations Chr Coll Ware 78-85; Prin 85-93; Chmn Lon Inst of Contemporary Christianity 88-89; Chmn CMJ 89-90; Crosslinks from 93; Gen Dir OMF Internat from 93; NSM Bromley Ch Ch *Roch* 93-96; NSM Singapore from 96. *2 Cluny Road, Singapore 259570* Tel (0065) 473 6180 *or* 473 5755 E-mail harleydavid@omf.net

HARLEY, David Bertram. b 22. Down Coll Cam BA50 MA55. Westcott Ho Cam 55. **d** 56 **p** 58. Asst Master Bedford Sch 50-58; C Biddenham *St Alb* 56-58; Chapl Stamford Sch 58-87; rtd 87; Confrater Browne's Hosp Stamford from 87; Lic to Offic *Linc* 59-94; Perm to Offic from 94. *Beggars' Roost, Priory Road, Stamford PE9 2ES* Tel (01780) 763403

HARLEY, Michael. b 50. AKC73 Ch Ch Coll Cant CertEd74 Lambeth STh92 Kent Univ MPhil95. St Aug Coll Cant 74. **d** 75 **p** 76. C Chatham St Wm *Roch* 75-78; C-in-c Weeke *Win* 78-81; V Southampton St Mary Extra 81-86; V Hurstbourne Tarrant, Faccombe, Vernham Dean etc 86-99; ACORA Link Officer 91-94; Dioc Rural Officer 95-97; RD Andover 95-99; V Chandler's Ford from 99. *The Vicarage, 30 Hursley Road, Chandler's Ford, Eastleigh SO53 2FT* Tel (023) 8025 2597 E-mail michael@st-boniface-church.fsnet.co.uk

HARLEY, Robert Patterson. b 53. St Andr Univ MA75 Cam Univ CertEd76 Glas Univ PhD89 Edin Univ BD97. **d** 97 **p** 98. C Edin St Thos *Edin* 97-00; P-in-c Kirriemuir *St And* from 00. *81 Glasgow Road, Edinburgh EH12 8LJ* Tel 0131-334 4434

HARLEY, Roger Newcomb. b 38. Ely Th Coll 61. **d** 64 **p** 65. C Plymouth St Pet *Ex* 64-66; C Heston *Lon* 66-69; C Maidstone All SS w St Phil and H Trin *Cant* 69-73; R Temple Ewell w Lydden 73-79; P-in-c Shirley St Geo 79-81; V 81-85; V Croydon H Sav *S'wark* 85-95; V Forest Row *Chich* 95-03; rtd 03. *7 Roman Way, St Margarets-at-Cliffe, Dover CT15 6AH* Tel (01304) 851720 E-mail roger.harley@btinternet.com

HARLOW, Antony Francis. b 24. Pemb Coll Cam BA50 MA55 DipTh55. Oak Hill Th Coll 84. **d** 85 **p** 86. NSM Watford St Luke

St Alb 85-86; CMS 86-91; Uganda 86-91; Perm to Offic *St Alb* 90-98; NSM Watford St Pet 92-96; Perm to Offic *B & W* from 98. *1 Jubilee Homes, Langford Road, Langford, Bristol BS40 5HU* Tel (01934) 862605

HARLOW, Canon Derrick Peter. b 30. St Jo Coll Cam BA53 MA57. Ridley Hall Cam 53. **d** 55 **p** 56. C Barking St Marg *Chelmsf* 55-58; V Leyton Em 58-63; V Goodmayes All SS 63-75; R Thundersley 76-83; TR Saffron Walden w Wendens Ambo and Littlebury 83-95; Hon Can Chelmsf Cathl 84-95; rtd 95; Perm to Offic *Ely* from 95 and *Chelmsf* from 98. *26 Kintbury, Duxford, Cambridge CB2 4RR* Tel (01223) 833891

HARLOW, Mrs Elizabeth Gilchrist. b 27. MSc50 DipTh60. Oak Hill Th Coll 85. **d** 91 **p** 94. NSM St Alb St Luke *St Alb* 91-94; NSM Watford St Luke 94-96; Perm to Offic 96-98; Perm to Offic *B & W* from 98. *1 Jubilee Homes, Langford Road, Langford Road, Bristol BS40 5HU* Tel (01934) 862605

HARLOW-TRIGG, Richard John St Clair. b 63. Cam Univ BA85 MA88. Cranmer Hall Dur 87. **d** 89 **p** 90. C Hyson Green *S'well* 89-91; C Basford w Hyson Green 91-94; C Mansfield St Pet 94-97; TV Newark 97-01; Chapl Mid Sussex NHS Trust from 01; St Pet and St Jas Hospice N Chailey from 02. *The Princess Royal Hospital, Lewes Road, Haywards Heath RH16 4EX* Tel (01444) 441881 ext 4232 E-mail richard.harlow-trigg@bsuh.nhs.uk

HARLOW, Archdeacon of. *See* TAYLOR, The Ven Peter Flint

HARMAN, Joyce. d 03. C Llangynwyd w Maesteg *Llan* from 03. *2 Heol Cadrawd, Llangynwyd, Maesteg CF34 9TE* Tel (01656) 731001

HARMAN, Leslie Davies. b 46. Nottm Univ BTh76. St Jo Coll Nottm LTh75. **d** 76 **p** 77. C Wandsworth All SS *S'wark* 76-78; C Godstone 78-82; V Thorncombe w Winsham and Cricket St Thomas *B & W* 82-87; TV Hitchin *St Alb* 87-95; V Royston from 95; RD Buntingford 96-01. *The Vicarage, 31 Baldock Road, Royston SG8 5BJ* Tel (01763) 243145 or 246371 E-mail lesharman@beeb.net

HARMAN, Michael John. b 48. Chich Th Coll 71. **d** 74 **p** 75. C Blackpool St Steph *Blackb* 74-79; Chapl RN from 79. *Royal Naval Chaplaincy Service, Room 203, Victory Building, HM Naval Base, Portsmouth PO1 3LS* Tel (023) 9272 7903 Fax 9272 7111

HARMAN, Canon Robert Desmond. b 41. TCD BA65 MA71. TCD Div Sch 67. **d** 67 **p** 68. C Taney Ch Ch *D & G* 67-73; I Dublin Santry w Glasnevin 73-86; I Dublin Sandford w Milltown from 86; Can Ch Ch Cathl Dublin from 91; Treas from 02; Hon Sec Gen Syn from 99. *The Rectory, Sandford Close, Ranelagh, Dublin 6, Irish Republic* Tel (00353) (1) 497 2983 Fax 496 4789 E-mail sandford@dublin.anglican.org

HARMAN, Theodore Allan. b 27. Linc Coll Ox BA52 MA56 Hatf Coll Dur MA90. Wells Th Coll 52. **d** 54 **p** 55. C Hawkshead and Low Wray *Carl* 54-55; C Kirkby Stephen w Mallerstang 55-57; Asst Chapl Sedbergh Sch 57-84; Sen Chapl 84-87; Tutor Hatf Coll Dur from 88; Admissions Tutor 89-90; Lib and Coll Officer 91-02; Acting Chapl 99-00; Fell from 00; Perm to Offic *Dur* from 88. *Flat D1, Hatfield College, North Bailey, Durham DH1 3RQ* Tel 0191-334 2626 Fax 334 3101 E-mail t.a.harman@durham.ac.uk

HARMER, Timothy James. b 47. Birm Univ CertEd68. St Jo Coll Nottm BA95. **d** 95 **p** 96. C Studley *Cov* 95-98; V Tanworth *Birm* from 98. *The Vicarage, Tanworth-in-Arden, Solihull B94 5EB* Tel (01564) 742565

HARMSWORTH, Roger James. b 46. Univ of W Ontario BA87. Huron Coll Ontario MDiv90. **d** 90 **p** 90. Canada 90-96; I Maryborough w Dysart Enos and Ballyfin *C & O* 96-01; I Killanne w Killegney, Rossdroit and Templeshanbo from 01; Treas Ferns Cathl from 03. *The Rectory, Clonroche, Enniscorthy, Co Wexford, Irish Republic* Tel (00353) (54) 44180 Fax as telephone E-mail therev@iol.ie

HARNDEN, Peter John. b 63. Coll of Resurr Mirfield 96. **d** 98 **p** 99. C Staplehurst *Cant* 98-02; V Tokyngton St Mich *Lon* from 02. *The Vicarage, St Michael's Avenue, Wembley HA9 6SL* Tel (020) 8902 3290 E-mail harny@cwcom.net

HARNEY, Janice. b 56. Man OLM Scheme 99. **d** 02 **p** 03. OLM Pennington *Man* from 02. *29 Green Lane, Leigh WN7 2TL* Tel and fax (01942) 671481 Mobile 07811-764355 E-mail jan.harney@btinternet.com

HARNISH, Robert George. b 64. Univ of Ottawa BSc87 Worc Coll Ox DPhil90 MA92. Wycliffe Hall Ox 90. **d** 93 **p** 94. C Chinnor w Emmington and Sydenham etc *Ox* 93-95; Chapl and Dean of Div New Coll Ox 96-01; Chapl Eliz Coll Guernsey from 01. *11 Saumarez Street, St Peter Port, Guernsey GY1 2PT* Tel (01481) 713298 or 726544

HARONSKI, Boleslaw. b 46. Pemb Coll Ox BA68 MA72 DPhil73. St Mich Coll Llan 80 Westcott Ho Cam 82. **d** 82 **p** 83. C Maindee *Mon* 82-85; V Llanishen w Trelleck Grange and Llanfihangel etc 85-89; V Blackwood 89-92. *45 St Julian's Road, Newport NP9 7GN*

✠**HARPER, The Rt Revd Alan Edwin Thomas.** b 44. OBE96. Leeds Univ BA65. CITC 75. **d** 78 **p** 79 **c** 02. C Ballywillan *Conn* 78-80; I Moville w Greencastle, Upper Moville etc *D & R* 80-82; I Londonderry Ch Ch 82-86; I Belfast Malone St Jo *Conn* 86-02;

Preb St Audoen St Patr Cathl Dublin 90-01; Adn Conn 96-02; Prec Belf Cathl 96-02; Bp Conn from 02. *Bishop's House, 113 Upper Road, Greenisland, Carrickfergus BT38 8RR* Tel (028) 9086 3165 Fax 9036 4266 E-mail aharper@fish.co.uk

HARPER, Preb Alan Peter. b 50. FCA83 Man Univ BA73. Ripon Coll Cuddesdon 86. **d** 88 **p** 89. C Newport w Longford and Chetwynd *Lich* 88-91; P-in-c Wilnecote 91-94; V 94-98; V Codsall from 98; Preb Lich Cathl from 02. *The Vicarage, 48 Church Road, Codsall, Wolverhampton WV8 1EH* Tel (01902) 842168 E-mail rev.alan.harper@lineone.net

HARPER, Barry. *See* HARPER, Canon Malcolm Barry

HARPER, Brian John. b 61. Liv Univ BA82 TCD DipTh85. **d** 85 **p** 86. C Portadown St Columba *Arm* 85-88; C Drumglass 88-89; I Errigle Keerogue w Ballygawley and Killeshil 89-93; I Mullavilly from 93. *89 Mullavilly Road, Tandragee, Craigavon BT62 2LX* Tel (028) 3884 0221 or 3884 1918 E-mail mullavilly@btinternet.com

HARPER, Clive Stewart. b 35. FCIS71. Ridley Hall Cam 80. **d** 82 **p** 83. C Bromyard *Heref* 82-85; P-in-c Bredenbury and Wacton w Grendon Bishop 85-89; P-in-c Edwyn Ralph and Collington w Thornbury 85-89; P-in-c Pencombe w Marston Stannett and Lt Cowarne 85-89; R Bredenbury w Grendon Bishop and Wacton etc 89-92; R Bilton *Cov* 92-02; rtd 02; Hon C Churchover w Willey *Cov* from 02. *9 Fieldfare Close, Rugby CV23 0WS* Tel (01788) 541041

HARPER, David Laurence. b 51. Qu Coll Cam BA73 MA77 PhD78. Wycliffe Hall Ox BA80. **d** 80 **p** 81. C Mansfield St Pet *S'well* 80-84; C Wollaton 84-87; V Brinsley w Underwood 87-94; R Bingham from 94; AD Bingham 00-03; AD E Bingham from 03. *The Rectory, Bingham, Nottingham NG13 8DR* Tel (01949) 837335 E-mail dlharper@cix.co.uk

HARPER, Geoffrey. b 32. Hertf Coll Ox BA55 MA59. Coll of Resurr Mirfield. **d** 57 **p** 58. C Cov St Pet *Cov* 57-60; C Handsworth St Mich *Birm* 60-62; C-in-c Kingstanding St Mark CD 62-71; V Kingstanding St Mark 71-73; R Sheviock *Truro* 73-80; R Antony w Sheviock 80-82; V Paul 82-98; Dioc Development Rep 86-98; rtd 98; Perm to Offic *Truro* from 99. *Carennac House, Polbreen Lane, St Agnes TR5 0UL* Tel (01872) 554056

HARPER, Geoffrey Roger. b 57. Jes Coll Cam BA MA DipTh. St Jo Coll Nottm 81. **d** 84 **p** 85. C Belper *Derby* 84-87; C Birstall and Wanlip *Leic* 87-90; TV Tettenhall Regis *Lich* 90-97; C Aldridge 97-02; Perm to Offic from 02. *16 Valleyside, Pelsall, Walsall WS3 4LL* Tel (01922) 685678 E-mail roger.harper@virgin.net

HARPER, Gordon. b 32. Oak Hill Th Coll 64. **d** 66 **p** 67. C Halliwell St Pet *Man* 66-71 and 84-99; P-in-c Brinsworth *Sheff* 71-75; V Brinsworth w Catcliffe 76-84; rtd 99. *15 New Church Road, Bolton BL1 5QP* Tel (01204) 849413

HARPER, Gordon William Robert. b 48. Wellington Univ (NZ) BA70 St Chad's Coll Dur BA74 Nottm Univ PhD89. Coll of Resurr Mirfield 74. **d** 75 **p** 76. C Battyeford *Wakef* 75-76; New Zealand 76-80; P-in-c Byers Green *Dur* 80-83; V Evenwood 83-89; R Wolviston 89-00; V Billingham St Mary 97-01; P-in-c Winlaton from 01. *The Rectory, Winlaton, Blaydon-on-Tyne NE21 6PL* Tel 0191-414 3165 Fax as telephone E-mail drgwr&jharper@westbill.freeserve.co.uk

HARPER, Preb Horace Frederic. b 37. Lich Th Coll 58. **d** 60 **p** 61. C Stoke upon Trent 60-65; C Fenton 65-66; V Coseley Ch Ch 66-75; V Trent Vale 75-88; P-in-c Dresden 88-89; V 89-03; P-in-c Normacot 94-03; Preb Lich Cathl 96-03; rtd 03. *3 Mahogany Drive, Stafford ST16 2TS* Tel (01785) 251284

HARPER, Ian. b 54. AKC78. Oak Hill Coll Nottm 79. **d** 80 **p** 81. C Sidcup St Jo *Roch* 80-83; C Bushey *St Alb* 83-87; TV Thamesmead *S'wark* 87-92; TR N Lambeth 92-00; V Homerton St Luke *Lon* from 00. *St Luke's Vicarage, 23 Cassland Road, London E9 7AL* Tel (020) 8985 2263 E-mail sluke.hackney@london.anglican.org

HARPER, James. b 35. St Luke's Coll Ex TDip57. SW Minl Tr Course DipTh89. **d** 90 **p** 91. NSM Pendeen w Morvah *Truro* 90-97; Perm to Offic *Win* from 01. *1 Millstream Mews, 50 Beaconsfield Road, Christchurch BH23 1QT* Tel (01202) 477138

HARPER, John Anthony. b 46. AKC69. **d** 70 **p** 71. C Pet St Mary Boongate *Pet* 70-73; C Abington 73-75; V Grendon w Castle Ashby 75-82; Asst Dioc Youth Chapl 75-82; R Castor w Sutton and Upton 82-94; TV Riverside *Ox* from 94. *St Andrew's Vicarage, 55 Welley Road, Wraysbury, Staines TW19 5ER* Tel (01784) 481258 E-mail j.harper@ukgateway.net

HARPER, John Hugh. b 34. ALAM62 Hertf Coll Ox BA57 MA61. Wells Th Coll 57. **d** 59 **p** 60. C Twerton *B & W* 59-62; R Chapel Allerton 62-69; V Blackford 62-69; V Halsetown *Truro* 69-91; RD Penwith 84-88; P-in-c S Brent *Ex* 91; V S Brent and Rattery 91-99; rtd 99; Perm to Offic *Chelmsf* from 00. *63 Queen Anne Road, West Mersea, Colchester CO5 8BA* Tel (01206) 385848

HARPER, Joseph Frank. b 38. Hull Univ BA60 MA86 MPhil98. Linc Th Coll 80. **d** 81 **p** 82. C Preston St Cuth *Blackb* 81-83; C Lancaster St Mary 83-87; V Bamber Bridge St Aid 87-92; V Kinsley w Wragby *Wakef* 92-99; R Newhaven *Chich* from 99.

The Rectory, 36 Second Avenue, Newhaven BN9 9HN Tel (01273) 515251

HARPER, Canon Malcolm Barry. b 37. Dur Univ BSc59. Wycliffe Hall Ox 59. **d** 61 **p** 62. C Harold Wood *Chelmsf* 61-65; C Madeley *Heref* 65-68; V Slaithwaite w E Scammonden *Wakef* 68-75; V Walmley *Birm* 75-03; Hon Can Birm Cathl 96-03; rtd 03. *1 Welcombe Drive, Sutton Coldfield B76 1ND* Tel 0121-351 3990 E-mail barryharper@clara.net

HARPER, Mrs Margaret. b 51. Nottm Coll of Educn TCert73 Nottm Univ BEd74. St Alb and Ox Min Course 98. **d** 01 **p** 02. C Slough *Ox* from 01. *209 Stoke Road, Slough SL2 5AX* Tel (01753) 528672

HARPER, Martin Nigel. b 48. FRICS88 PGCE95. S Dios Minl Tr Scheme. **d** 85 **p** 86. NSM St Leonards Ch Ch and St Mary *Chich* 85-93; NSM Rye 94-95. *Bexhill High School, Down Road, Bexhill-on-Sea TN39 4HT*

HARPER, Canon Maurice. b 20. St Steph Ho Ox 60. **d** 62 **p** 63. C Upminster *Chelmsf* 62-67; V Gt Ilford St Mary 67-71; R Upminster 71-85; RD Havering 80-85; Hon Can Chelmsf Cathl 84-85; rtd 85; Perm to Offic *Chelmsf* and *Nor* from 85; Perm to Offic *St E* from 87. *30 Cookham Dene, Buckhurst Road, Bexhill-on-Sea TN40 1RU* Tel (01424) 222189 E-mail mauriceh@fish.co.uk

HARPER, Michael Sydney. b 36. Portsm Dioc Tr Course 86. **d** 87. NSM Leigh Park St Clare CD *Portsm* 87-88; NSM Warren Park from 88; NSM Leigh Park from 96. *17 Hampage Green, Warren Park, Havant PO9 4HJ* Tel (023) 9245 4275

HARPER, Richard Michael. b 53. Lon Univ BSc75 Univ of Wales PhD78. St Steph Ho Ox BA80 MA87. **d** 81 **p** 82. C Holt *Nor* 81-84; C-in-c Grahame Park St Aug CD *Lon* 84-88; Sub-Warden and Dir Studies St Mich Coll Llan 88-93; Lect Ch Hist Univ of Wales (Cardiff) 88-93; R St Leonards Ch Ch and St Mary *Chich* from 94; RD Hastings 02-03; V Weymouth St Paul *Sarum* from 03. *St Paul's Vicarage, 58 Abbotsbury Road, Weymouth DT4 0BJ* Tel (01305) 771217

HARPER, Roger. b 43. FCA Man Univ BSc. **d** 87 **p** 88. NSM Onchan *S & M* 87-97; NSM Douglas St Geo from 97. *Ballahowin House, St Mark's, Ballasalla, Isle of Man IM9 3AS* Tel (01624) 851251

HARPER, Rosemary Elizabeth. b 55. Birm Univ BA76 ARCM75 DipRAM78. NTMTC 96. **d** 99 **p** 00. C Amersham *Ox* 99-03; P-in-c Gt Missenden w Ballinger and Lt Hampden from 03. *The Rectory, Church Street, Amersham HP7 0BD* Tel (01494) 728988 E-mail rosie51619@aol.com

HARPER, Thomas Reginald. b 31. Dur Univ BA57 MA67. **d** 58 **p** 59. C Corbridge w Halton *Newc* 58-60; C Byker St Mich 60-62; V Ushaw Moor *Dur* 62-67; Asst Chapl HM Pris Dur 62-67; N Sec CMS 67-74; V Thornthwaite *Carl* 74-75; V Thornthwaite cum Braithwaite and Newlands 76-90; TV Bellingham/ Otterburn Gp *Newc* 90-91; TV N Tyne and Redesdale Team 91-92; TR 92-98; RD Bellingham 93-98; rtd 98; Perm to Offic *Carl* from 98. *Dunelm, Old Lake Road, Ambleside LA22 0DH* Tel (01539) 433556

HARPER, Timothy James Lincoln. b 54. LRAM Lon Univ BMus76 CertEd DipP&C MA96. Wycliffe Hall Ox 84. **d** 86 **p** 87. C Morden *S'wark* 86-90; V Deptford St Pet 90-97; R Amersham *Ox* from 97. *The Rectory, Church Street, Amersham HP7 0DB* Tel (01494) 724426 or 729380 Fax 08701-639596 E-mail tjlharper@aol.com

HARPHAM, Mrs Diana Joan. b 44. MCSP66. St Alb Minl Tr Scheme 94. **d** 98 **p** 99. NSM Harrold and Carlton w Chellington *St Alb* 98-01; NSM Bromham w Oakley and Stagsden from 01. *The Old Police House, 40 Stagsden Road, Bromham, Bedford MK43 8PT* Tel (01234) 823222

HARRAP, William Charles. b 32. BEM86. **d** 72 **p** 74. Hon C Bethnal Green St Jas Less *Lon* 72-00. *12 Wedgewood House, Morpeth Street, London E2 0PZ* Tel (020) 8980 6887

HARRATT, Preb Philip David. b 56. Magd Coll Ox BA79 MA83. Ripon Coll Cuddesdon 82. **d** 85 **p** 86. C Ewyas Harold w Dulas, Kenderchurch etc *Heref* 85-88; V Chirbury from 88; V Marton from 88; V Trelystan from 88; RD Pontesbury from 01; P-in-c Middleton from 02; Preb Heref Cathl from 03. *The Vicarage, Chirbury, Montgomery SY15 6BN* Tel (01938) 561218 Fax as telephone E-mail philip@chirvic.freeserve.co.uk

HARREX, David Brian. b 54. DipHE85. Trin Coll Bris 87. **d** 89 **p** 90. C Bedminster St Mich *Bris* 89-93; V Pilning w Compton Greenfield 93-00; RD Westbury and Severnside 97-99; AD Bris W 99-00; TR Yate New Town from 00. *The Rectory, 97 Canterbury Close, Yate, Bristol BS37 5TU* Tel (01454) 311483 E-mail 101352.2157@compuserve.com

HARRIES, Canon Gwilym David. b 41. Univ of Wales (Lamp) BA63. St Mich Coll Llan 63. **d** 65 **p** 66. C Llangiwg *S & B* 65-68; C Llangyfelach and Morriston 68-71; TV Aberystwyth *St D* 71-76; R Hubberston 76-82; R Hubberston w Herbrandston and Hasguard etc 82-84; V Burry Port and Pwll from 84; Hon Can St D Cathl from 00. *The Vicarage, 134 Pencoed Road, Burry Port SA16 0PS* Tel (01554) 832936

HARRIES, Henry Rayner Mackintosh. b 30. MBE67. Chich Th Coll 53. **d** 55 **p** 56. C Hastings H Trin *Chich* 55-58; Chapl RAF 58-79; Asst Chapl-in-Chief RAF 79-84; QHC 83-84; P-in-c Gt

Brickhill w Bow Brickhill and Lt Brickhill *Ox* 84-86; R 86-94; RD Mursley 91-94; rtd 95; Perm to Offic *Chelmsf* from 94. *2 Fyfield Road, Ongar CM5 0AH* Tel (01277) 363741

HARRIES, John Edward. b 60. Bris Univ BSc81 PhD84. Wycliffe Hall Ox 94. **d** 96 **p** 97. C Hyde St Geo *Ches* 96-00; P-in-c Walton from 00; C Latchford St Jas from 00; Chapl Sir Thos Boteler High Sch from 03. *St John's Vicarage, Chester Road, Higher Walton, Warrington WA4 6TJ* Tel (01925) 662939

HARRIES, Mrs Judith Janice. b 43. SRN67 Trin Coll Bris BA93 Bris Univ PGCE94. WEMTC 99. **d** 01 **p** 02. NSM Bath St Sav w Swainswick and Woolley *B & W* 01-03; Hon C Farmborough, Marksbury and Stanton Prior from 03. *19 Victoria Buildings, Bath BA2 3EH* Tel (01225) 332418 E-mail judithharries@hotmail.com

HARRIES, Malcolm David. b 44. BA99. Oak Hill Th Coll 94. **d** 96 **p** 97. C Rock Ferry *Ches* 96-00; P-in-c Godley cum Newton Green from 00. *The Vicarage, 43 Sheffield Road, Hyde SK14 2PR* Tel 0161-368 2159

✠**HARRIES, The Rt Revd Richard Douglas.** b 36. Selw Coll Cam BA61 MA65 Lon Univ Hon DD94 FKC83 FRSL96. Cuddesdon Coll 61. **d** 63 **p** 64 **c** 87. C Hampstead St Jo *Lon* 63-69; Chapl Westf Coll Lon 67-69; Tutor Wells Th Coll 69-71; Warden Sarum & Wells Th Coll 71-72; V Fulham All SS *Lon* 72-81; Dean K Coll Lon 81-87; Consultant to Abps Cant and York on Inter-Faith Relns from 86; Bp Ox from 87. *Bishop's House, 27 Linton Road, Oxford OX2 6UL* Tel (01865) 208222 Fax 790470 E-mail bishopoxon@dch.oxford.anglican.org

HARRINGTON, John Christopher Henry. b 43. Conf Catholic Colls CertRE63. Qu Coll Birm 71. **d** 74 **p** 75. C Northampton St Mich *Pet* 74-76; CF (TA) 75-85; C Paston *Pet* 76-79; Chapl Doddington Co Hosp 79-83; R Benwick St Mary *Ely* 79-82; R Doddington 79-82; R Doddington w Benwick 82-83; V Eastbourne St Mich *Chich* 83-02; R Selsey from 02. *The Rectory, 75 St Peter's Crescent, Selsey, Chichester PO20 0NA* Tel (01243) 601984 E-mail harrington@fastnet.co.uk

HARRINGTON, William Harry. b 33. AKC57. **d** 58 **p** 59. C Childwall All SS *Liv* 58-60; C Sutton 60-64; V Ditton St Mich 64-76; V Mossley Hill St Barn 76-83; V Highfield 83-01; rtd 01. *4 Crowther Drive, Winstanley, Wigan WN3 6LY* Tel (01942) 225021

HARRIS, Arthur Emlyn Dawson. b 27. Ex Univ BSc47 Lon Univ DipRS86. S'wark Ord Course 83. **d** 86 **p** 87. NSM Frant w Eridge *Chich* 86-87; P-in-c Withyham St Mich 87-95; rtd 95. *53A The Close, Salisbury SP1 2EL* Tel (01722) 339886 E-mail closecelts@aol.com

HARRIS, Bernard Malcolm. b 29. Leeds Univ BA54. Coll of Resurr Mirfield 54. **d** 56 **p** 57. C Shrewsbury St Chad *Lich* 56-60; C Porthill 60-61; V Birches Head 61-66; V W Bromwich St Jas 66-78; V Sedgley All SS 78-93; rtd 93; Perm to Offic *Worc* from 93. *6 Beacon Lane, Sedgley, Dudley DY3 1NB* Tel (01902) 663134

HARRIS, Brian. *See* HARRIS, The Ven Reginald Brian

HARRIS, Brian. b 33. Man Univ BSc. Qu Coll Birm 79. **d** 80 **p** 81. C Lich St Chad *Lich* 80-81; Perm to Offic *Ches* 82-87; NSM Warburton 87-88; P-in-c 88-92; R Gt and Lt Casterton w Pickworth and Tickencote *Pet* 92-98; RD Barnack 96-98; rtd 98; Perm to Offic *Pet* from 99. *Meadowbrook, Carlby Road, Greatford, Stamford PE9 4PR* Tel (01778) 560978

HARRIS, Brian William. b 38. K Coll Lon BD61 AKC61. St Boniface Warminster 61. **d** 62 **p** 63. C Liversedge *Wakef* 62-65; C Kirkby *Liv* 65-70; V Dalton 70-79; V Aberford w Saxton *York* 79-91; V Hemingbrough 91-95; rtd 95; Perm to Offic *York* from 95; Dom Chapl to Bp Selby 95-03; Rtd Clergy and Widows Officer (York Adnry) from 99. *2 Furness Drive, Rawcliffe, York YO30 5TD* Tel (01904) 638214 E-mail harrischap@tiscali.co.uk

HARRIS, Catherine Elizabeth. *See* EDMONDS, Mrs Catherine Elizabeth

HARRIS, Charles Edward. b 20. Roch Th Coll 63. **d** 65 **p** 66. C Hertford St Andr *St Alb* 65-71; R Sywell w Overstone *Pet* 71-90; rtd 90; Perm to Offic *Chich* from 92; *St Alb* from 00. *College of St Barnabas, Blackberry Lane, Lingfield RH7 6NJ* Tel (01342) 870607

HARRIS, Cyril Evans. b 30. Linc Th Coll 61. **d** 63 **p** 64. C Beaconsfield *Ox* 63-68; V Stoke Poges 68-98; rtd 98; Perm to Offic *Ox* from 99. *The Gables, 8 De Parys Avenue, Bedford MK40 2TW* Tel (01234) 344927

HARRIS, David. b 52. AKC76. St Steph Ho Ox 76. **d** 77 **p** 79. C Wimbledon *S'wark* 77-80; C Coalbrookdale, Iron-Bridge and Lt Wenlock *Heref* 80-82; V Highters Heath *Birm* 82-84; Perm to Offic *Lon* from 85. *35 Paddonswick Road, London W6 0UA* Tel (020) 8748 5195

HARRIS, David Rowland. b 46. Ch Ch Ox BA69 DipTh71 MA72. Wycliffe Hall Ox 70. **d** 73 **p** 74. C Virginia Water *Guildf* 73-76; C Clifton Ch Ch w Em *Bris* 76-79; Scripture Union 79-85; V Bedford Ch Ch *St Alb* 85-99; R Ex St Leon w H Trin *Ex* from 99. *St Leonard's Rectory, 27 St Leonard's Road, Exeter EX2 4LA* Tel (01392) 255681 E-mail dandsharris@hotmail.com

HARRIS, Derrick William. b 21. **d** 63 **p** 64. C Birkdale St Jo *Liv* 63-67; V Billinge 67-81; V Walton *Ches* 81-87; rtd 88; Perm to

Offic *Ches* and *Liv* from 88. *3 Melrose Avenue, Southport PR9 9UY* Tel (01704) 213828

HARRIS, Duncan Roy. b 46. **d** 89 **p** 90. Chapl Miss to Seamen 89-98; UAE 89-92; Cyprus 92-97; P-in-c Patrington w Hollym, Welwick and Winestead *York* from 98. *The Rectory, Northside, Patrington, Hull HU12 0PA* Tel (01964) 630327 Fax 630366 E-mail fr.duncan@tiscali.co.uk

HARRIS, Elaine. **d** 03. NSM Dyffryn Llan from 03. *15 Fforest Goch, Rhos, Pontardawe SA8 3JB*

HARRIS, Ernest John. b 46. Lon Univ DipTh74 QUB BD75. **d** 75 **p** 76. C Lisburn Ch Ch *Conn* 75-78; C Coleraine 78-83; I Belfast St Kath 83-90; I Ballinderry from 90. *The Rectory, 124 Ballinderry Road, Ballinderry Upper, Lisburn BT28 2NL* Tel (028) 9265 1310

HARRIS, Frank Edward. b 33. ACT ThL69 St Fran Coll Brisbane 65. **d** 68 **p** 69. Australia 68-71 and 73-76; C Plymstock *Ex* 71-72; C E Acton St Dunstan w St Thos *Lon* 72-73; C Bodmin *Truro* 76-77; P-in-c Menheniot 77-79; V Winton *Man* 79-87; Guinea 87-89; R Blisland w St Breward *Truro* 90-96; rtd 98. *4 Gwel Marten, Headland Road, Carbis Bay, St Ives TR26 2PB* Tel (01736) 793280

HARRIS, Geoffrey Daryl. b 39. Lon Univ DipTh66 Open Univ BA83. St Aid Birkenhead 63. **d** 66 **p** 67. C Eston *York* 66-70; C Iffley *Ox* 70-75; V Bubwith *York* 75-78; V Bubwith w Ellerton and Aughton 78-79; P-in-c Stillingfleet w Naburn 79-80; R Escrick and Stillingfleet w Naburn 80-95; Chapl Qu Marg Sch York 83-94; Hon C Okehampton w Inwardleigh, Bratton Clovelly etc *Ex* 96-99; P-in-c Ashwater, Halwill, Beaworthy, Clawton etc 99-01; R 01-03; rtd 03. *Beggars Roost, 2 Hillside, Ashwater, Beaworthy EX21 5EJ* Tel (01409) 211220 E-mail the.harrisclan1@tinyonline.co.uk

HARRIS, George. b 36. Sarum Th Coll 66. **d** 68 **p** 69. C Shildon *Dur* 68-70; CF 70-74; P-in-c Doddington *Ely* 74-75; R 75-78; R Benwick St Mary 74-78; V Shotton *Dur* 78-86; V Stockton St Mark 86-87; V Chilton Moor 87-94; P-in-c Lyons 96; R 96-99; rtd 99. *49 Dunelm Drive, Houghton le Spring DH4 5QQ* Tel 0191-584 7119

HARRIS, Harriet Anne. b 68. Oriel Coll Ox BA90 New Coll Ox DPhil94. St Steph Ho Ox. **d** 00 **p** 01. C Ox St Mary V w St Cross and St Pet *Ox* from 00; Chapl Wadh Coll Ox from 00. *24 Beauchamp Lane, Oxford OX4 3LF* Tel (01865) 775098 *or* 277905 E-mail harriet.harris@wadh.ox.ac.uk

HARRIS, Jack Peter Francis. b 49. Barrister-at-Law (Lincoln's Inn) 72 St Cath Coll Ox BA70 MA74 Fitzw Coll Cam BA85 MA89. Westcott Ho Cam 83. **d** 86 **p** 87. C Doncaster Ch Ch *Sheff* 86-91; P-in-c 91-92; V 92-95; V Doncaster H Trin 95-96; V Belsize Park *Lon* from 96. *St Peter's Vicarage, Belsize Square, London NW3 4HY* Tel (020) 7794 4020

HARRIS, James. b 54. CITC 99. **d** 02. NSM Ballybeen *D & D* from 02. *8 Grangewood Avenue, Dundondald, Belfast BT16 1GA* Tel (028) 9050 6074 Mobile 07761-066421 E-mail harrisj639@aol.com

HARRIS, Canon James Nigel Kingsley. b 37. St D Coll Lamp BA60. Sarum Th Coll. **d** 62 **p** 63. C Painswick *Glouc* 62-65; C Glouc St Paul 65-67; V Slad 67-77; V Cam 77-78; P-in-c Stinchcombe 77-78; V Cam w Stinchcombe 78-82; V Stonehouse 82-02; Chapl Glos R Hosp NHS Trust 92-02; rtd 02; Hon Can Antsiranana Madagascar from 00; Perm to Offic *Glouc* from 03. *14 Shalford Close, Cirencester GL7 1WG* Tel (01285) 885641

HARRIS, James Philip. b 59. Westf Coll Lon BA82 Univ of Wales PGCE97. St Mich Coll Llan BD86. **d** 86 **p** 87. C Newport St Paul *Mon* 86-89; C Bedwellty 89-91; V Newport St Matt 91-96; Chapl Univ of Wales Inst Cardiff *Llan* 97-99; Glam Univ from 99. *10 Llantwit Road, Treforest, Pontypridd CF37 1TR* Tel (01443) 491294 *or* 482080 Pager 04325-214017 Fax 482084 E-mail jharris3@glam.ac.uk

HARRIS, Jeremy Michael. b 64. Gwent Coll of HE HNC86. St Steph Ho Ox BTh93. **d** 93 **p** 94. C Newport St Julian *Mon* 93-95; C Ebbw Vale 95-97; Dioc Youth Chapl 96-98; TV Ebbw Vale 97-98; TV Bracknell *Ox* from 98. *St Andrew's Vicarage, 25 Stoney Road, Bracknell RG42 1XY* Tel (01344) 425229 E-mail jeremy_m_harris@compuserve.com

HARRIS, The Very Revd John. b 32. Univ of Wales (Lamp) BA55. Sarum Th Coll 55. **d** 57 **p** 58. V Pontnewynydd *Mon* 57-60; C Bassaleg 60-63; V Penmaen 63-69; V Newport St Paul 69-84; RD Newport 77-93; V Maindee 84-93; Can St Woolos Cathl 84-93; Dean Brecon *S & B* 93-98; V Brecon St Mary and Battle w Llanddew 93-98; rtd 98; Lic to Offic *Mon* from 98. *40 Mounton Drive, Chepstow NP16 5EH* Tel (01291) 621233

HARRIS, Canon John. b 45. St Steph Ho Ox 72. **d** 75 **p** 76. C Wanstead St Mary *Chelmsf* 75-84; V Penponds *Truro* 84-91; V St Gluvias from 91; RD Carnmarth S from 00; Hon Can Truro Cathl from 01. *The Vicarage, St Gluvias, Penryn TR10 9LQ* Tel (01326) 373356

HARRIS, John. b 54. Leeds Univ BSc75. St Jo Coll Nottm LTh86. **d** 86 **p** 87. C S Ossett *Wakef* 86-90; V Moldgreen 90-97; P-in-c S Ossett from 97. *36 Manor Road, Ossett, Wakefield WF5 0AU* Tel (01924) 263311 *or* 281732

HARRIS, John Brian. b 53. Hertf Coll Ox BA76. Ripon Coll Cuddesdon 87. **d** 89 **p** 90. C Witton *Ches* 89-93; R Thurstaston 93-99; V Stockton Heath from 99. *The Vicarage, 91 Walton Road, Stockton Heath, Warrington WA4 6NR* Tel (01925) 261396 E-mail brian@jbharris.fsnet.co.uk

HARRIS, Canon John Peter. b 33. St D Coll Lamp BA57. **d** 58 **p** 59. Chapl St Woolos Hosp Newport 58-63; C Newport St Woolos *Mon* 58-60; Chapl St Woolos Cathl 60-63; CF (TA) 59-63; CF 63-82; V Chepstow *Mon* 82-98; RD Chepstow 85-97; Can St Woolos Cathl 93-98; rtd 98; Lic to Offic *Mon* from 98. *7 Victoria Way, Undy, Magor, Newport NP26 3NW* Tel (01633) 882423

HARRIS, John Stuart. b 29. Hertf Coll Ox BA52 MA56. Wells Th Coll 52. **d** 54 **p** 55. C Epsom St Martin *Guildf* 54-58; C Guildf H Trin w St Mary 58-63; R Bentley 63-72; V Milford 72-87; R Walton-on-the-Hill 87-98; Dioc Ecum Officer 87-92; rtd 98; Perm to Offic *Roch* from 00. *6 Pearse Place, Lamberhurst, Tunbridge Wells TN3 8EJ* Tel (01892) 890582

HARRIS, Mrs Judith Helen. b 42. Chelsea Coll Lon TCert64 Westmr Coll Ox MTh03. St Alb Minl Tr Scheme 83. **dss** 86 **d** 87 **p** 94. Leagrave *St Alb* 86-87; Hon Par Dn 87-91; TD Dunstable 91-94; TV 94-03; rtd 03. *Belmont, Fore Street, Porthleven, Helston TR13 9HN* Tel (01326) 563090 E-mail revdjhharris@ntlworld.com

HARRIS, Canon Kenneth. b 28. NW Ord Course 70. **d** 72 **p** 73. NSM Upton Ascension *Ches* 72-77; NSM Eccleston and Pulford 77-80; P-in-c Hargrave 80-81; V 81-94; Exec Officer Dioc Bd for Soc Resp 84-94; Hon Can Ches Cathl 91-94; rtd 94; Perm to Offic *Ches* from 94; P-in-c Ashton Hayes 96-98; P-in-c Alvanley 98-99. *Delsa, Willington Road, Willington, Tarporley CW6 0ND* Tel (01829) 751880

HARRIS, Lawrence Rex Rowland. b 35. St Cath Coll Cam BA59 MA63. Ely Th Coll. **d** 61 **p** 62. C Carrington *S'well* 61-63; Chapl Rampton Hosp Retford 63-66; V Sturton w Littleborough *S'well* 66-71; V Bole w Saundby 66-71; R Clowne *Derby* from 71; RD Bolsover and Staveley 81-86. *The Rectory, Rectory Road, Clowne, Chesterfield S43 4BH* Tel (01246) 810387

HARRIS, Leslie Gerald Conley Eyre. b 44. Culham Coll of Educn CertEd66 St Jo Coll Nottm LTh00 FRGS83. Wycliffe Hall Ox 71. **d** 75 **p** 76. Kenya 75-99; Chapl Banda Sch Nairobi 75-99; NSM Karen St Fran 75-99; NSM Kiambu St Paul 84-99; NSM Limuru All SS 90-99; C Sawley *Derby* from 00. *7 Sovereign Grove, Long Eaton, Nottingham NG10 3QL* Tel 0115-946 8862

HARRIS, Margaret Claire (Novice Sister Margaret Joy). b 53. RGN85 Homerton Coll Cam BEd78. Ridley Hall Cam CTM92. **d** 92. Par Dn Stevenage All SS Pin Green *St Alb* 92-93; 92-93; CSMV 95-99; OSB from 99. *St Mary's Abbey, 52 Swan Street, West Malling ME19 6JX*

HARRIS, Mark Jonathan. b 66. St Cath Coll Cam BA88 MA92 PhD92. Ripon Coll Cuddesdon BA01. **d** 02 **p** 03. C Cowley St Jas *Ox* from 02. *24 Beauchamp Lane, Oxford OX4 3LF* Tel (01865) 775098 E-mail mark.harris@rl.ac.uk

HARRIS, Martin John. b 54. Trin Coll Cam BA76 MA. Wycliffe Hall Ox 82. **d** 85 **p** 86. C Lindfield *Chich* 85-88; C Galleywood Common *Chelmsf* 88-91; V Southchurch Ch Ch from 91; RD Southend-on-Sea from 00. *Christ Church Vicarage, 58 Colbert Road, Southend-on-Sea SS1 3BP* Tel (01702) 582585 E-mail martin.harris@messages.co.uk

HARRIS, Michael. b 34. ACP65 MIL76 St Mark & St Jo Coll Lon CertEd56. Qu Coll Birm. **d** 83 **p** 84. NSM Bournville *Birm* 83-90; NSM Stirchley 90-96; Chapl Univ of Cen England in Birm 92-99; Dean NSMs 96-99; rtd 00; Perm to Offic *Birm* and *Cov* from 00. *West Wing, The Old Council House, West Street, Shipston-on-Stour CV36 4GA* Tel and fax (01608) 661672 Mobile 07811-489713 E-mail revmichael@harrisann.fsnet.co.uk

HARRIS, Michael Andrew. b 53. Ian Ramsey Coll 74 Trin Coll Bris 75. **d** 78 **p** 79. C St Paul's Cray St Barn *Roch* 78-82; C Church Stretton *Heref* 82-87; Res Min Penkridge w Stretton *Lich* 87-90; Res Min Penkridge Team 90-92; V Amington *Birm* from 92. *The Vicarage, 224 Tamworth Road, Amington, Tamworth B77 3DE* Tel (01827) 62573 E-mail mike.harris26@ntlworld.com

HARRIS, Nicholas Bryan. b 60. Down Coll Cam BA81 MA85. Ridley Hall Cam 82. **d** 85 **p** 86. C Walney Is *Carl* 85-88; C S'wark Ch Ch *S'wark* 88-92; Perm to Offic *Chich* from 92. *82 Hurst Road, Eastbourne BN21 2PW* Tel (01323) 731922

HARRIS, Owen. b 50. Univ of Wales (Swansea) BSc(Econ)71 PGCE72. St Mich Coll Llan DipTh94. **d** 94 **p** 95. C Bassaleg *Mon* 94-98; TV Cwmbran 98-01; V Maindee 01-02; rtd 02. *2 Marine Cottages, Ferryside SA17 5SB* Tel (01267) 267095

✠**HARRIS, The Rt Revd Patrick Burnet.** b 34. Keble Coll Ox BA58 MA63. Clifton Th Coll 58. **d** 60 **p** 61 **c** 73. C Ox St Ebbe w St Pet *Ox* 60-63; SAMS 63-81; Adn N Argentina 70-73; Bp 73-80; R Kirkheaton *Wakef* 81-85; Asst Bp Wakef 81-85; Sec C of E Partnership for World Miss 86-88; Asst Bp Ox 86-88; Bp S'well 88-99; rtd 99; Hon Asst Bp Eur from 99; Asst Bp Linc from 99. *Meadow Cottage, 17 Dykes End, Collingham, Newark NG23 7LD* Tel (01636) 892395

HARRIS, Paul. b 55. St Paul's Cheltenham BEd79. Oak Hill Th Coll DipHE84. **d** 84 **p** 85. C Billericay and Lt Burstead *Chelmsf*

84-87; TV Cheltenham St Mary, St Matt, St Paul and H Trin *Glouc* 87-93; V Bitterne *Win* 93-97; UK Evang Co-ord Evang Alliance 97-02; C Portswood Ch Ch *Win* from 02. *Gull's Cry, 113 Peartree Avenue, Southampton SO19 7JJ* Tel (023) 8043 8687 E-mail associate@highfield.org.uk

HARRIS, Paul Ian. b 45. MSc. Qu Coll Birm. **d** 82 **p** 83. C The Quinton *Birm* 82-86; V Atherstone *Cov* from 86. *40 Holte Road, Atherstone CV9 1HN* Tel (01827) 713200
E-mail paulih@ntlworld.com

HARRIS, Paul Michael. b 58. Chelsea Coll Lon BSc79 Oak Hill Th Coll BA89 Bath Coll of HE CertEd82. **d** 89. C Finchley Ch Ch *Lon* 89-90; Asst Master St Luke's Sch W Norwood 90-91; Master and Asst Chapl Brent Internat Sch Manila 91-92; Volunteer Miss Movement Sunningdale 93-94; Past Asst St Joseph's RC Ch Dorking 94-95; Form Master Merton Court Prep Sch Sidcup 95-97; Asst Master Clewborough Ho Prep Sch Camberley 98-01; Asst Master St Nic Sch for Girls Church Crookham from 01. *66 Horsham Road, Owlsmoor, Sandhurst GU47 0YZ* Tel (01344) 771376

HARRIS, Peter Frank. b 43. WMMTC 89. **d** 92 **p** 93. NSM Lich Ch Ch *Lich* 92-96; NSM Ogley Hay 96-00; NSM Rushall from 00. *94 Ogley Hay Road, Boney Hay, Walsall WS7 2HU* Tel (01543) 319163

HARRIS, Peter Malcolm. b 52. Em Coll Cam BA74 MA79. Trin Coll Bris DipHE80. **d** 80 **p** 81. C Upton (Overchurch) *Ches* 80-83; BCMS 83-93; Crosslinks from 93; Portugal from 83. *clo A Rocha Trust, Connansknowe, Kirkton, Dumfries DG1 1SX* Tel (01387) 710286 E-mail peterharris@compuserve.com

HARRIS, Raymond. b 36. Nottm Univ BA58. Lich Th Coll 58. **d** 60 **p** 61. C Clifton St Fran *S'well* 60-63; C Davyhulme St Mary *Man* 63-66; V Bacup Ch Ch 66-82; R Dunsby w Dowsby *Linc* 82-87; R Rippingale 82-87; R Rippingale Gp 87-94; rtd 94. *2 The Bungalow, High Street, Swaton, Sleaford NG34 0JU* Tel (01529) 421343

HARRIS, Canon Raymond John. b 29. Leeds Univ BA51. Coll of Resurr Mirfield 51. **d** 53 **p** 54. C Workington St Mich *Carl* 53-59; V New Swindon St Barn Gorse Hill *Bris* 59-94; Hon Can Bris Cathl 80-94; RD Cricklade 82-88; rtd 94; Perm to Offic *Glouc* from 94. *46 Courtbrook, Fairford GL7 4BE* Tel (01285) 713965

HARRIS, Rebecca Jane. *See* SWYER, Mrs Rebecca Jane

HARRIS (née LEE), Mrs Rebecca Susan. b 62. Man Univ BA85 S Glam Inst HE 86. Trin Coll Bris DipHE95. **d** 95 **p** 96. C Cirencester *Glouc* 95-99; TV Gt Chesham *Ox* from 99. *Christ Church Vicarage, 55 Latimer Road, Chesham HP5 1QQ* Tel (01494) 773318 Fax as telephone

HARRIS, The Ven Reginald Brian. b 34. Ch Coll Cam BA58 MA61. Ridley Hall Cam. **d** 59 **p** 60. C Wednesbury St Bart *Lich* 59-61; C Uttoxeter w Bramshall 61-64; V Bury St Pet *Man* 64-70; V Walmsley 70-80; RD Walmsley 70-80; Adn Man 80-98; Can Res Man Cathl 80-98; rtd 98; Perm to Offic *Derby* from 98. *9 Cote Lane, Hayfield, Stockport SK22 2HL* Tel (01663) 746321

HARRIS, Robert Douglas. b 57. BEd. Chich Th Coll 80. **d** 82 **p** 83. C Portsea St Mary *Portsm* 82-87; V Clevedon St Jo *B & W* 87-92; R Felpham w Middleton *Chich* 92-99; R Felpham from 99; RD Arundel and Bognor from 98. *The Rectory, 24 Limmer Lane, Felpham, Bognor Regis PO22 7ET* Tel (01243) 842522 *or* 826886 E-mail robertharris@stmaryscentre.freeserve.co.uk

HARRIS, Robert James. b 45. Nottm Univ MA02 ALCD73. St Jo Coll Nottm 69. **d** 72 **p** 73. C Sheff St Jo *Sheff* 72-76; C Goole 76-78; V Bramley and Ravenfield 78-91; P-in-c Boulton *Derby* 91-99; RD Melbourne 96-99; P-in-c Hazlewood 99-02; P-in-c Hazlewood and Milford from 02. *The Vicarage, Hob Hill, Hazlewood, Belper DE56 4AL* Tel (01332) 840161
E-mail robert@kneetinnit.fsnet.co.uk

HARRIS, Thomas William. b 54. AKC76. Linc Th Coll 77. **d** 78 **p** 79. C Norton Woodseats St Chad *Sheff* 78-81; V Barnby Dun 81-91; P-in-c Kirk Bramwith and Fenwick 81-85; Chapl RN 91-94; R Draycot *Bris* 94-02; P-in-c Cawston w Booton and Brandiston etc *Nor* from 02; Chapl Norfolk and Nor Univ Hosp NHS Trust from 02. *The Rectory, Ames Court, Cawston, Norwich NR10 4AN* Tel (01603) 871282 E-mail tom@twharris.com

HARRIS, William Edric Mackenzie. b 46. Sarum & Wells Th Coll 72. **d** 75 **p** 76. C Langney *Chich* 75-79; C Moulsecoomb 80-81; TV 81-85; R W Grinstead from 85. *The Rectory, Steyning Road, West Grinstead, Horsham RH13 8LR* Tel (01403) 710339 E-mail williamem.harris@virgin.net

HARRIS, William Fergus. b 36. CCC Cam BA59 MA63 Edin Univ DipEd70. Yale Div Sch 59 Westcott Ho Cam 60. **d** 62 **p** 63. C St Andrews St Andr *St And* 62-64; Chapl Edin Univ *Edin* 64-71; R Edin St Pet 71-83; R Perth St Jo *St And* 83-90; Hon C from 90; rtd 90; Prov Archivist from 91. *35 St Mary's Drive, Perth PH2 7BY* Tel (01738) 621379

HARRIS-DOUGLAS, John Douglas. b 34. Ripon Hall Ox 65. **d** 66 **p** 67. C Ringwood *Win* 66-67; C Baswich *Lich* 67-71; R St Tudy *Truro* 71-74; R St Tudy w Michaelstow 74-76; Adv in Children's Work and Asst Dir Educn 71-76; R Fiskerton *Linc* 76-79; Dir of Educn and Adv RE 76-79; P-in-c Thormanby *York* 79-84; V Brafferton w Pilmoor and Myton on Swale 79-84; V Brafferton w Pilmoor, Myton-on-Swale etc 84-97; rtd 97; Perm

to Offic *York* from 97. *Tanglewood Cottage, Newton-upon-Ouse, York YO30 2BN* Tel (01347) 848219

HARRIS-EVANS, William Giles. b 46. AKC68. Bangalore Th Coll DipTh70. **d** 70 **p** 71. C Clapham H Trin *S'wark* 70-74; Sri Lanka 75-78; V Benhilton *S'wark* 78-86; TR Cov E *Cov* 86-93; TR Brighouse and Clifton *Wakef* 93-99; V Petersfield *Portsm* from 99; R Buriton from 99. *The Vicarage, Shackleford House, 12 Dragon Street, Petersfield GU31 4AB* Tel and fax (01730) 264138 *or* 260213 E-mail petersfield@stpeters.fsbusiness.co.uk

HARRIS-WHITE, John Emlyn. b 34. St Aid Birkenhead 59. **d** 62 **p** 63. C Cricklade w Latton *Bris* 62-63; C Kingswood 63-66; C Ashton-on-Ribble St Andr *Blackb* 66-69; V Heyhouses 69-71; Chapl Roundway Hosp Devizes 71-77; Chapl R Variety Children's Hosp 77-89; Chapl K Coll and Belgrave Hosps Lon 77-89; Regional Community Relns Co-ord 89-93; rtd 94; Hon C Folkestone St Pet *Cant* 97-01. *40 Tippet Knowes Road, Winchburgh, Broxburn EH52 6UL*

HARRISON, Alan George. b 20. Leeds Univ BA49. Coll of Resurr Mirfield 49. **d** 51 **p** 52. C Wellingborough St Mary *Pet* 51-55; Br Honduras 55-61; V Bournemouth St Fran *Win* 61-68; V Eastleigh 68-72; Chapl Guild of Health Lon 72-76; Chapl St Mich Convent Ham 73-86; Sec Coun for Relig Communities 76-86; rtd 86; Perm to Offic *S'wark* from 86. *10 The Quadrangle, Morden College, London SE3 0PW* Tel (020) 8858 5134

HARRISON, Alan William. b 16. Lich Th Coll 38. **d** 41 **p** 42. C Norbury St Oswald *Cant* 41-43; C Sheff St Cuth *Sheff* 43-49; V Orton-on-the-Hill w Twycross etc *Leic* 49-55; V Somerby, Burrough on the Hill and Pickwell 55-72; R Boxford *St E* 72-82; rtd 82; Perm to Offic *St E* 82-03. *Manormead, Tilford Road, Hindhead GU26 6RA* Tel (01428) 602500 Fax 602550

HARRISON, Alastair Lee. b 22. ALCD51. **d** 51 **p** 52. C Stoke Damerel *Ex* 51-54; Chapl RAF 54-67; Chapl Miss to Seamen 67-77; Lic to Offic *D & G* 77-83; Lic to Offic *M & K* 77-83; C Dublin St Ann w St Mark and St Steph *D & G* 83-92; rtd 92. *8 Grosvenor Place, Rathgar, Dublin 6, Irish Republic* Tel (00353) (1) 497 6053

HARRISON, Mrs Alison Edwina. b 53. Newc Univ BEd75. Linc Th Coll 84. **dss** 86 **d** 87 **p** 94. Loughborough Em *Leic* 86-87; Par Dn 87-89; C Stockton *Dur* 89-92; P-in-c Lynesack 92-95; P-in-c Cockfield 92-95; P-in-c Ebchester 95-96; R 96-97; V Medomsley 96-97; V Newc H Cross *Newc* 97-01; P-in-c Ulgham from 01; P-in-c Widdrington from 01. *The Vicarage, Grangemoor Road, Widdrington, Morpeth NE61 5PU* Tel (01670) 790389

HARRISON, Mrs Barbara Ann. b 41. Man Univ BA63 Leic Univ CertEd64. EMMTC 85. **d** 88 **p** 94. C Immingham *Linc* 88-94; P-in-c Habrough Gp 94-99; V 99-01; rtd 02. *3 Windsor Mews, Louth LN11 9AY* Tel (01507) 610015

HARRISON, Canon Barbara Anne. b 34. Westf Coll Lon BA56 CertEd57 Hull Univ MA85. Linc Th Coll 76. **dss** 79 **d** 87 **p** 94. Lakenham St Jo *Nor* 79-80; Chapl York Univ *York* 80-88; TD Sheff Manor *Sheff* 88-93; Par Dn Holts CD *Man* 93-94; C-in-c 94-98; Dioc UPA Officer 93-98; Chapl Rochdale Healthcare NHS Trust from 98; NSM Bury Ch King *Man* 98-99; C 00-01; NSM Bury St Paul 98-99; C from 00; P-in-c Kirkholt from 01; Hon Can Man Cathl from 02. *St Thomas's Vicarage, Cavendish Road, Rochdale OL11 2QX* Tel (01706) 45962

HARRISON, Bernard Charles. b 37. St Mich Coll Llan 61. **d** 64 **p** 65. C Toxteth Park St Marg *Liv* 64-69; C Hindley All SS 69-71; V Wigan St Geo 71-02; rtd 02. *66 Brookhouse Street, Wigan WN1 3EY*

HARRISON, Brian John. b 35. FCP. Glouc Sch of Min 83. **d** 86 **p** 89. NSM Broseley w Benthall *Heref* 86-93; Perm to Offic 94-97. *17 Hafren Road, Little Dawley, Telford TF4 3HJ* Tel (01952) 591891

HARRISON, Bruce. b 49. Linc Th Coll 86. **d** 88 **p** 89. C Syston *Leic* 88-90; C Whitby *York* 90-93; V Glaisdale 93-99; R Brotton Parva from 99. *St Margaret's Rectory, 9 Crispin Court, Brotton, Saltburn-by-the-Sea TS12 2XL* Tel (01287) 676275
E-mail br218@hotmail.com

HARRISON, Bruce Mountford. b 49. AKC71. **d** 72 **p** 73. C Hebburn St Cuth *Dur* 72-75; C Bethnal Green St Jo w St Simon *Lon* 75-77; P-in-c Bethnal Green St Bart 77-78; TV Bethnal Green St Jo w St Bart 78-80; C-in-c Pennywell St Thos and Grindon St Oswald CD *Dur* 80-85; V Sunderland Pennywell St Thos 85-90; V Gateshead St Helen from 90. *The Vicarage, 7 Carlton Terrace, Gateshead NE9 6DE* Tel 0191-487 6510

HARRISON, Christine Amelia. b 47. Southn Univ DipHE97. STETS 94. **d** 98 **p** 99. NSM Goldsworth Park *Guildf* from 98. *Ravenscroft, Fernhill Lane, St John's, Woking GU22 0DR* Tel (01483) 750645 E-mail christine@revharrison.freeserve.co.uk

HARRISON, Christopher Dennis. b 57. Clare Coll Cam BA79 BA86. Westcott Ho Cam 84. **d** 87 **p** 88. C Camberwell St Geo *S'wark* 87-92; V Forest Hill 92-96; P-in-c Fenny Bentley, Kniveton, Thorpe and Tissington *Derby* 96-98; P-in-c Parwich w Alsop-en-le-Dale 96-98; R Fenny Bentley, Thorpe, Tissington, Parwich etc from 98; RD Ashbourne from 98. *The Vicarage, Parwich, Ashbourne DE6 1QD* Tel (01335) 390226
E-mail christopherharrison@ntlworld.com

HARRISON, Christopher Joseph. b 38. AKC61 Hull Univ CertEd68 Bris Univ BEd75. **d** 62 **p** 63. C Bottesford *Linc* 62-67;

C Elloughton *York* 67-68; P-in-c Farmington *Glouc* 69-74; C Tredington w Stoke Orchard and Hardwicke 74-86; Perm to Offic from 87. *Appledore, 93 Stoke Road, Bishops Cleeve, Cheltenham GL52 4RP* Tel (01242) 673452

HARRISON, Colin Charles. b 32. Nottm Univ BA59. Ripon Hall Ox 59. **d** 61 **p** 62. C Everton St Chad w Ch Ch *Liv* 61-64; Japan 64-66; P-in-c Glas St Gabr *Glas* 66-71; R Clarkston 70-74; Area Sec (Inner Lon) Chr Aid 74-84; Hon C St Nic Cole Abbey *Lon* 74-78; Hon C St Botolph without Bishopgate 78-84; Miss to Seamen 85-97; Nigeria 85-86; S Africa 87-88; Korea 88-91; Trinidad and Tobago 91-92; Singapore 92-97; rtd 97. *92 Towngate Wood Park, Tonbridge TN10 3RT* Tel (01732) 770604

HARRISON, Crispin. *See* HARRISON, Michael Burt

HARRISON, Sister Cécile. b 29. Bp Lonsdale Coll TCert51 Lon Univ DBRS73. St Steph Ho Ox 97. **d** 97 **p** 97. CGA from 66; Lic to Offic *Eur* from 97. *Prasada, Quartier Subrane, Montauroux, 83440 Fayence, France* Tel (0033) (4) 94 47 74 26 Fax as telephone E-mail cga.prasada@wanadoo.fr

HARRISON, David Henry. b 40. Lon Univ DipTh67. Tyndale Hall Bris 65. **d** 68 **p** 69. C Bolton St Paul *Man* 68-72; V Bircle 72-83; V Southport SS Simon and Jude *Liv* 83-91; TR Fazakerley Em 91-99; V Toxteth Park Ch Ch and St Mich w St Andr from 99. *St Michael's Vicarage, 6 St Michael's Church Road, Liverpool L17 7BD* Tel 0151-727 2601 Fax as telephone E-mail getrevdake@hotmail.com

HARRISON, David Robert. b 31. Bris Univ BSc52 CertEd55. Oak Hill Th Coll 56. **d** 58 **p** 59. C Brixton Hill St Sav *S'wark* 58-60; C Harpurhey Ch Ch *Man* 60-62; Singapore 62-67; V Greenfield *Man* 67-78; V Tonge Fold 78-90; R Tasburgh w Tharston, Forncett and Flordon *Nor* 90-93; C Gorleston St Andr 93-96; rtd 96. *7 The Close, Brixham TQ5 8RE* Tel (01803) 854627

HARRISON, David Samuel. b 44. Univ of Wales (Ban) BSc67. St Mich Coll Llan 67. **d** 70 **p** 71. C Canton St Jo *Llan* 70-74; C Witton *Ches* 74-78; V Sutton St Geo 78-96; P-in-c Henbury 96-01; V from 01. *The Vicarage, Church Lane, Henbury, Macclesfield SK11 9NN* Tel (01625) 424113

HARRISON, Miss Doreen. b 32. Leeds Univ BA53 PGCE54 DipRE57 Lanc Univ MLitt78 MA(Ed)79. **d** 92 **p** 94. C Ambleside w Brathay Car 92-96; Asst P Colton 96-01; P-in-c 01-02; Asst P Rusland 96-01; P-in-c 01-02; Asst P Satterthwaite 96-01; P-in-c 01-02; rtd 02. *Fox How, Ambleside LA22 9LL* Tel (01539) 433021

HARRISON, Ernest Wilfrid. b 17. Ox Univ MA Toronto Univ MA. Sarum Th Coll. **d** 40 **p** 41. C Roby *Liv* 40-43; C-in-c St D Huyton w Roby 43-45; C Coulsdon St Jo *S'wark* 45-47; Asst Dioc Missr 48-52; Canada from 52. *Address temp unknown*

HARRISON, Francis Russell. b 20. EAMTC. **d** 82 **p** 83. NSM Felixstowe St Jo *St E* 82-85; Asst Chapl Ipswich Hosp 85-87; rtd 87; Perm to Offic *St E* from 87. *The Strands, London Road, Copdock, Ipswich IP8 3JF* Tel (01473) 730292

HARRISON, Fred Graham. b 41. Lon Univ BSc62. Ridley Hall Cam 80. **d** 82 **p** 83. C Lenton *S'well* 82-85; V Ruddington from 85. *The Vicarage, 62 Musters Road, Ruddington, Nottingham NG11 6HW* Tel 0115-921 1505 E-mail graham@fgharrison.freeserve.co.uk

HARRISON, Guy Patrick. b 58. Dip Counselling 91 Ox Univ MTh99. Sarum & Wells Th Coll 92. **d** 94 **p** 95. C Wimborne Minster and Holt *Sarum* 94-96; C Wimborne Minster 96-97; Chapl Dorothy House Hospice Winsley 97-01; Chapl Stoke Mandeville Hosp NHS Trust from 01. *Stoke Mandeville Hospital NHS Trust, Mandeville Road, Aylesbury HP21 8AL* Tel (01296) 316677 Fax 316604 E-mail guy.harrison@smh.nhs.uk

HARRISON, Herbert Gerald. b 29. Oak Hill Th Coll 53. **d** 56 **p** 57. C Chesterfield H Trin *Derby* 56-59; C Cambridge St Andr Less *Ely* 59-64; Miss to Seamen 64-74; Kenya 64-68; Port Chapl Ipswich 68-74; V Ipswich All SS *St E* 74-81; P-in-c Elmsett w Aldham 81-88; P-in-c Kersey w Lindsey 81-88; R Horringer cum Ickworth 88-94; rtd 94; Perm to Offic *St E* from 94. *15 Lynwood Avenue, Felixstowe IP11 9HS* Tel (01394) 283764

HARRISON, Ian David. b 45. Imp Coll Lon BSc66. Oak Hill Th Coll 93. **d** 96 **p** 97. NSM Tunbridge Wells St Jo *Roch* 96-99; P-in-c Chiddingstone w Chiddingstone Causeway from 99. *The Rectory, Chiddingstone, Edenbridge TN8 7AH* Tel (01892) 870478 Fax as telephone

HARRISON, Ian Wetherby. b 39. Kelham Th Coll 59. **d** 64 **p** 65. C Kennington Park St Agnes *S'wark* 64-67; C E Ham w Upton Park *Chelmsf* 67-71; V Walthamstow St Mich 71-78; Dioc Ecum Officer *Wakef* 78-87; P-in-c Upper Hopton 78-87; P-in-c Mirfield Eastthorpe St Paul 82-87; Min St D Cathl *St D* 87-90; Succ St D Cathl 87-90; P-in-c Leic Ascension *Leic* 90-92; V Leic St Anne from 92. *St Anne's Vicarage, 76 Letchworth Road, Leicester LE3 6FH* Tel 0116-285 8452 E-mail iwharri@aol.com

HARRISON (née HOLLINRAKE), Mrs Jean Margaret. b 28. Leeds Univ DSS51 Bolton Teacher Tr Coll TCert64. Wakef Dioc Reader Tr 82. **d** 93 **p** 96. NSM Perth St Ninian *St And* 93-96; NSM Stanley 96-98; Bp's Chapl 95-99. *14 Valley View, Heptonstall, Hebden Bridge HX7 7LP* Tel (01442) 845822

HARRISON, John. b 49. Fitzw Coll Cam BA71 MA74. Westcott Ho Cam 74. **d** 77 **p** 78. C Nunthorpe *York* 77-81; C Acomb

St Steph 81-83; C-in-c St Aid 81-83; V Heptonstall *Wakef* 83-91; R Stamford Bridge Gp of Par *York* 91-02; V Easingwold w Raskelfe from 02. *The Vicarage, Churchhill, Easingwold, York YO61 3JT* Tel (01347) 821394

HARRISON, John Northcott. b 31. St Jo Coll Cam BA54. Westcott Ho Cam 54. **d** 56 **p** 57. C Moor Allerton *Ripon* 56-59; C Bedale 59-61; V Hudswell w Downholme 61-64; Youth Chapl *Dur* 64-68; V Auckland St Andr and St Anne 68-76; Community Chapl Stockton-on-Tees 76-83; TR Southampton (City Cen) *Win* 83-88; V Bris Ch the Servant Stockwood *Bris* 88-96; RD Brislington 89-95; Chapl St Brendan's Sixth Form Coll 90-96; rtd 96; Perm to Offic *B & W* and *Bris* from 96. *8 Moorham Road, Winscombe BS25 1HS* Tel (01934) 844403

HARRISON, Josephine Mary. b 42. Southn Univ DTM97. **d** 97 **p** 98. NSM Yatton Keynell *Bris* 97-99; NSM By Brook 99-01; Perm to Offic *B & W* 01-02; NSM Wellington and Distr from 02. *Pippins, 18 Cox Road, Wellington TA21 9RD* Tel (01823) 669525 Fax as telephone

HARRISON, Keith. *See* HARRISON, Peter Keith

HARRISON, Lyndon. b 47. St D Coll Lamp DipTh91 St Mich Coll Llan Dip Minl Studies 93. **d** 93 **p** 94. C Ebbw Vale *Mon* 93-96; TV 96-01; TV Caldicot from 01. *The Vicarage, 19 Main Road, Portskewett, Caldicot NP26 5SG* Tel (01291) 420313

HARRISON, Martin. b 58. Bris Univ BA89 DCR78. Trin Coll Bris 86. **d** 89 **p** 90. C Heworth H Trin *York* 89-94; Chapl York Distr Hosp 89-94; P-in-c Skelton w Shipton and Newton on Ouse *York* 94-95; R 95-01; V Strensall from 01; RD Easingwold from 00. *The Vicarage, 10 York Road, Strensall, York YO32 5UN* Tel (01904) 490683 E-mail martin.harrison1@tesco.net

HARRISON, Mary Furley. b 21. MBE63. Westf Coll Lon BA42. Moray Ho Edin CertEd43 Edin Dioc NSM Course 79. **dss** 83 **d** 86. Edin H Cross *Edin* 83-86; NSM from 86; rtd 89. *Barnhill, 33 Barnton Avenue, Edinburgh EH4 6JJ* Tel 0131-336 2226

HARRISON, Matthew Henry. b 64. Univ Coll Dur BA85. St Steph Ho Ox BA88 MA92 Union Th Sem (NY) STM93. **d** 89 **p** 90. C Whickham *Dur* 89-92; USA 92-93; C Owton Manor *Dur* 93-95; Asst Chapl Paris St Geo *Eur* 95-02; Perm to Offic from 02. *136 rue Amelot, 75011 Paris, France*

HARRISON, Michael Anthony. b 48. Westhill Coll Birm CertCYW72 Huddersfield Poly CertEd88 Leeds Poly BA91 Leeds Univ MA98. N Ord Course 94. **d** 97 **p** 98. NSM Thornhill and Whitley Lower *Wakef* 97-99; TV Wrexham *St As* from 99. *St Mark's Vicarage, Menai Road, Wrexham LL13 9LB* Tel (01978) 356647 E-mail whernside@aol.com

HARRISON, Michael Burt (Crispin). b 36. Leeds Univ BA59 Trin Coll Ox BA62 MA66. Coll of Resurr Mirfield 59. **d** 63 **p** 64. C W Hartlepool St Aid *Dur* 63-64; C Middlesbrough All SS *York* 64-66; Lic to Offic *Wakef* 67-69 and 78-87; CR from 68; S Africa 69-77 and 87-97; Registrar Coll of the Resurr Mirfield 78-84; Vice-Prin 84-87; Superior CR from 97. *House of the Resurrection, Stocks Bank Road, Mirfield WF14 0BN* Tel (01924) 483301 Fax 490489 E-mail charrison@mirfield.org.uk

HARRISON, Michael Robert. b 63. Selw Coll Cam BA84 K Coll Lon PhD97 Bradf Univ MA99. Ripon Coll Cuddesdon BA89 Union Th Sem (NY) STM90. **d** 90 **p** 91. C S Lambeth St Anne and All SS *S'wark* 90-94; Chapl Bp's Chapl to Students *Bradf* 94-98; Chapl Bradf Univ 94-98; Chapl Bradf and Ilkley Community Coll 94-98; P-in-c Eltham H Trin *S'wark* 98; V from 98. *Holy Trinity Vicarage, 59 Southend Crescent, London SE9 2SD* Tel (020) 8850 1246 E-mail mikeharrison7@hotmail.com

HARRISON, Canon Noel Milburn. b 27. Lon Univ DipTh56 Leeds Univ MPhil75 PhD80. St Aid Birkenhead 54. **d** 57 **p** 58. C Doncaster St Jas *Sheff* 57-60; Chapl Yorkshire Res Sch for Deaf Doncaster 60-68; C Woodlands *Sheff* 60-62; Chapl to the Deaf 60-68; Hd Master Elmete Hall Sch Leeds 68-84; Hon C Whitgift w Adlingfleet and Eastoft 83-84; Hon C Abbeydale St Jo 84-86; Dioc Dir of Educn 84-94; R Tankersley 86-94; Hon Can Sheff Cathl 88-94; rtd 94; Perm to Offic *Sheff* from 94; *Linc* 95-99. *Aidan House, 118 High Street, Crowle, Scunthorpe DN17 4DR*

HARRISON, Mrs Nona Margaret. b 50. Open Univ BA80. S Dios Minl Tr Scheme 92. **d** 95 **p** 96. NSM E w Wellow and Sherfield English *Win* 95-99; NSM Barton Stacey and Bullington etc 99; NSM Hurstbourne Priors, Longparish etc from 00. *The Rectory, Longparish, Andover SP11 6PG* Tel (01264) 720215

HARRISON, Oliver. b 71. SS Paul & Mary Coll Cheltenham BA93. St Jo Coll Nottm MA95. **d** 97 **p** 98. Asst Chapl The Hague *Eur* 97-00; C Walmley *Birm* from 00. *90 Walmley Ash Road, Sutton Coldfield B76 1JB* Tel 0121-351 1245 E-mail ollieharrison@clara.co.uk

HARRISON, Miss Patricia Mary. b 35. St Kath Coll Lon CertEd65 Dip Primary Educn 70 Open Univ BA74. St Mich Ho Ox IDC59. **dss** 85 **d** 87 **p** 94. Nunthorpe *York* 85-87; NSM 87-98; rtd 95; Perm to Offic *York* from 98. *22 Lamonby Close, Nunthorpe, Middlesbrough TS7 0QG* Tel (01642) 313524

HARRISON, Paul Graham. b 53. Sarum & Wells Th Coll 76. **d** 79 **p** 80. C Brixham w Churston Ferrers *Ex* 79-82; C Portsea N End St Mark *Portsm* 82-87; V Tiverton St Andr *Ex* 87-94; Chapl

Tiverton and Distr Hosp 90-94; P-in-c Astwood Bank *Worc* from 94; Chapl to the Deaf from 94; Perm to Offic *Cov* from 94. *The Vicarage, 16 Church Road, Astwood Bank, Redditch B96 6EH* Tel (01527) 892489

HARRISON, Paul Thomas. b 57. Nor Sch of Art BA80 Leic Poly PGCE88 Coll of Ripon & York St Jo MA99. Qu Coll Birm 95. **d** 97 **p** 98. C Northallerton w Kirby Sigston *York* 97-01; TV Usworth *Dur* from 01. *14 Prestwick Close, Washington NE37 2LP* Tel 0191-416 7604

HARRISON, Peter. *See* HARRISON, Robert Peter

HARRISON, Peter Keith. b 44. Open Univ BA85. St Aid Birkenhead. **d** 68 **p** 69. C Higher Bebington *Ches* 68-71; C Walmsley *Man* 71-74; V Lumb in Rossendale 74-79; V Heywood St Marg 79-87; V Hey 87-95; AD Saddleworth 93-95; Chapl Athens w Kifissia *Eur* 95-98; V Aston Cantlow and Wilmcote w Billesley *Cov* 98-02; V W Burnley *Blackb* from 02. *All Saints' Vicarage, Padiham Road, Burnley BB12 6PA* Tel (01282) 775629 Fax as telephone E-mail harrison.ssc@virgin.net

HARRISON, The Ven Peter Reginald Wallace. b 39. Selw Coll Cam BA62. Ridley Hall Cam 62. **d** 64 **p** 65. C Barton Hill St Luke w Ch Ch *Bris* 64-69; Chapl Greenhouse Trust 69-77; Dir Northorpe Hall Trust 77-84; Lic to Offic *Wakef* 77-84; TR Drypool *York* 84-98; AD E Hull 88-98; Can and Preb York Minster from 94; Adn E Riding from 98. *Brimley Lodge, 27 Molescroft Road, Beverley HU17 7DX* Tel (01482) 881659 Fax as telephone E-mail peterrwharrison@breathemail.net

HARRISON, Canon Philip Hubert. b 37. Sarum & Wells Th Coll 77. **d** 79 **p** 80. C Wymondham *Nor* 79-83; V Watton w Carbrooke and Ovington 83-92; R Drayton w Felthorpe 92-02; Hon Can Nor Cathl 99-02; rtd 02; Perm to Offic *Nor* from 02. *The Fairstead, 1 Back Street, Horsham St Faith, Norwich NR10 3JP*

HARRISON, Mrs Rachel Elizabeth. b 53. NEOC 98. **d** 01 **p** 02. C Skelton w Upleatham *York* from 01. *St Margaret's Rectory, 9 Crispin Court, Brotton, Saltburn-by-the-Sea TS12 2XL* Tel (01287) 676275 E-mail rachelhere@hotmail.com

HARRISON, Richard Crispin. b 57. Plymouth Poly BSc79. Trin Coll Bris 82. **d** 85 **p** 86. C Southway *Ex* 85-89; TV Kinson *Sarum* 89-96; C Prestefield *Portsm* 96-99; Asst Regional Dir Miss to Seafarers from 99; Perm to Offic *Guildf* from 01. *Flying Angel House, Arundel Road, Littlehampton BN17 7BY* Tel (01903) 726969 or (023) 9245 5226 Fax (01903) 734455 E-mail m2ssr@fsmail.net

HARRISON, Richard Kingswood. b 61. Linc Coll Ox BA83 MA88 Leeds Univ BA90. Coll of Resurr Mirfield 88. **d** 91 **p** 92. C Reading St Giles *Ox* 91-93; Asst Chapl Merchant Taylors' Sch Northwood 93-96; Chapl Ardingly Coll 96-02; R Shill Valley and Broadshire *Ox* from 02. *The Rectory, Church Lane, Shilton, Burford OX18 4AE* Tel (01993) 845954

HARRISON, Robert Peter. b 28. Chich Th Coll. **d** 60 **p** 61. C Ealing Ch the Sav *Lon* 60-64; C Hammersmith SS Mich and Geo White City Estate CD 64-66; P-in-c Fulham St Pet 66-73; V 73-94; rtd 94; Perm to Offic *Chich* from 94. *8 Broadwater Way, Worthing BN14 9LP* Tel (01903) 217073

HARRISON, Robert William. b 62. Mansf Coll Ox BA84. Qu Coll Birm 87. **d** 89 **p** 90. C Sholing *Win* 89-93; Communications Adv to Bp Willesden *Lon* 93-97; C Cricklewood St Gabr and St Mich 93-97; V Hillingdon St Jo from 97. *St John's Vicarage, Royal Lane, Uxbridge UB8 3QR* Tel (01895) 461945 E-mail rob.harrison@london.anglican.org

HARRISON, Rodney Lovel Neal. b 46. MBE87. Dur Univ BA67. Ripon Coll Cuddesdon DipMin95. **d** 95 **p** 96. C N w S Wootton *Nor* 95-98; P-in-c Gt and Lt Bedwyn and Savernake Forest *Sarum* 98-02; TV Savernake from 02. *The Vicarage, Church Street, Great Bedwyn, Marlborough SN8 3PF* Tel (01672) 870779 E-mail rodney@rlnh-ejhh.demon.co.uk

HARRISON, Rosemary Jane. b 53. Bradf Coll of Educn CertEd76. Trin Coll Bris DipHE85. **d** 87 **p** 94. NSM Southway *Ex* 87-89; NSM Kinson *Sarum* 89-96. *41 North Lane, Buriton, Petersfield GU31 5RS* Tel (01730) 269390

HARRISON, Russell. *See* HARRISON, Francis Russell

HARRISON, Miss Ruth Margaret. b 33. BEM85. FRSA94. Ripon Coll Cuddesdon 02. **d** 02 **p** 03. NSM Baddiley and Wrenbury w Burleydam *Ches* from 02. *2 Heywood Cottages, Heywood Lane, Audlem, Crewe CW3 0EX* Tel (01270) 812010

HARRISON, Steven John. b 47. Univ of Wales (Abth) BSc68 PhD74 FRMetS74. St And Dioc Tr Course 87. **d** 90 **p** 91. NSM Alloa *St And* 90-94; NSM Bridge of Allan 94-02; NSM Spittal *Newc* from 02; NSM Scremerston from 02. *St John's Vicarage, 129 Main Street, Spittal, Berwick-upon-Tweed TD15 1RP* Tel (01289) 307342 E-mail sjhl@stir.ac.uk

HARRISON, Walter William. b 28. St Jo Coll Nottm. **d** 71 **p** 72. C Lenton *S'well* 71-74; R Carlton-in-the-Willows 74-93; rtd 93. *20 Conway Gardens, Nottingham NG5 6LR* Tel 0115-920 0766

HARRISON, Canon William Roy. b 34. Dur Univ BA58 DipTh59. Cranmer Hall Dur 57. **d** 59 **p** 60. C Kingswood *Bris* 59-62; Kenya 62-65; P-in-c Gt Somerford *Bris* 66; V Soundwell 66-99; Hon Can Bris Cathl 92-99; rtd 99; Perm to Offic *Bris* from 99. *20 Pool Road, Bristol BS15 1XL* Tel 0117-967 9802

HARRISON-WATSON, Carole. *See* FORD, Mrs Carole

HARRISON, John Anthony Lomax. b 47. Ex Univ BA72 DipTh85. Qu Coll Birm 72. **d** 74 **p** 75. C Loughton St Jo *Chelmsf* 74-81; V Chingford St Anne 81-98; TV Aldrington *Chich* from 98. *18 Amesbury Crescent, Hove BN3 5RD* Tel (01273) 207281

HARROLD, Canon Jeremy Robin. b 31. Hertf Coll Ox BA54 BSc56 MA58 DipTh59. Wycliffe Hall Ox. **d** 59 **p** 60. C Rushden *Pet* 59-61; Bp's Chapl *Lon* 61-64; Australia 64-67; V Harlesden St Mark *Lon* 67-72; V Hendon St Paul Mill Hill 72-84; V Stowmarket *St E* 84-96; RD Stowmarket 90-96; Hon Can St E Cathl 94-96; rtd 96; Perm to Offic *St E* from 96. *18 Wilkinson Way, Woodbridge IP12 1SS* Tel (01394) 380127

HARRON, Gareth Andrew. b 71. QUB BA92. CITC BTh95. **d** 95 **p** 96. C Willowfield *D & D* 95-98; C Dromore Cathl 98-02; I Magheralin w Dollingstown from 02. *The Rectory, 12 New Forge Road, Magheralin, Craigavon BT67 0QJ* Tel (028) 9261 1273 E-mail gareth@gharron.freeserve.co.uk

HARRON, James Alexander. b 37. GIMechE61 HNC59. St Aid Birkenhead 63. **d** 65 **p** 66. C Willowfield *D & D* 65-69; I Desertmartin *D & R* 69-80; Dep Sec BCMS (Ireland) 80-84; I Aghalee *D & D* 84-03; Preb Dromore Cathl 02-03; Chapl HM Pris Maghaberry 86-03; rtd 03. *The Sanctuary, 8 Churchill Avenue, Lurgan, Craigavon, Co Armagh BT66 7BW* Tel (028) 3834 6543

HARROP, Preb Joseph Blakemore (Blake). b 17. Saltley Tr Coll Birm TCert39. Qu Coll Birm 51. **d** 53 **p** 56. CMS Sudan 48-55; C Stoke upon Trent *Lich* 56-58; V Foxt w Whiston 58-93; Hon P-in-c 93-00; P-in-c Oakamoor w Cotton 78-85; Hon C Kingsley 93-00; Preb Lich Cathl 93-00; rtd 93; Perm to Offic *Lich* from 01. *6 New Cottages, Foxt, Stoke-on-Trent ST10 2HL* Tel (01538) 266656

HARROP, Stephen Douglas. b 48. St Jo Coll York CertEd74 Man Univ DSPT85 DipAdEd90. Edin Th Coll 77. **d** 79 **p** 82. C Middlesbrough St Martin *York* 79-80; C N Hull St Mich 80; C Cayton w Eastfield 80-81; C Oldham *Man* 82-84; V Oldham St Barn 84-89; Hong Kong 89-93; TV Kidderminster St Mary and All SS w Trimpley etc *Worc* 93-95; Ind Chapl 93-95; Chapl Kidderminster Coll 93-95; Sandwell Chs Link Officer *Birm* 95-96; Dep Chapl HM Pris Brixton 96-97; Taiwan 97-98; USA from 98. *16 W Third Street, Essington, PA 19029, USA* E-mail harropsd@aol.com

HARRY, Bruce David. b 40. JP77. Culham Coll Ox CertEd60. N Ord Course 83. **d** 86 **p** 87. NSM Liscard St Thos *Ches* 86-91; NSM Eastham 91-94; C New Brighton St Jas 94-96; C New Brighton Em 94-96; C New Brighton St Jas w Em 96-98; NSM 98-02; NSM New Brighton All SS 98-02; P-in-c 02-03. *21 Sandymount Drive, Wallasey CH45 0LJ* Tel 0151-639 7232

HART, Allen Sydney George. b 38. Chich Th Coll 64. **d** 67 **p** 68. C N Wembley St Cuth *Lon* 67-71; C W Bromwich All SS *Lich* 71-74; TV Hucknall Torkard *S'well* 74-80; V Annesley Our Lady and All SS 80-86; V Bilborough St Jo 86-99; RD Nottingham W 94-99; P-in-c Clarborough w Hayton 99-03; Asst Chapl HM Pris Ranby 99-03; rtd 03. *3 Castleton Close, Hucknall, Nottingham NG15 6TD* Tel 0115-955 2067

HART, André Hendrik. b 62. Cape Town Univ BA86. St Steph Ho Ox 89. **d** 91 **p** 92. C Newbold w Dunston *Derby* 91-95; P-in-c Clifton and Norbury w Snelston 95-02; Chapl S Derbyshire Community Health Services NHS Trust 95-02; V Westbury-on-Trym H Trin *Bris* from 02. *Holy Trinity Vicarage, 44 Eastfield Road, Westbury-on-Trym, Bristol BS9 4AG* Tel 0117-962 1536 or 950 8644 E-mail ahart001@fish.co.uk

HART, Anthony. b 35. St Mich Coll Llan 77. **d** 79 **p** 80. NSM Jersey St Helier *Win* 79-81; C Heref All SS *Heref* 81-82; C Kingstone 82-84; C Eaton Bishop 82-84; C Clehonger 82-84; R Sutton St Nicholas w Sutton St Michael 84-88; R Withington w Westhide 84-88; R Jersey St Mary *Win* 88-01; rtd 01. *Villa Rapallo, Mont de la Trinite, St Helier, Jersey JE2 4NJ* Tel (01534) 739146 Mobile 07797-750435 E-mail hart@localdial.com

HART, Colin Edwin. b 45. Leeds Univ BA66 PGCE67 MPhil89 Fitzw Coll Cam BA73 MA77 K Coll Lon MTh76 Man Univ PhD98. Trin Coll Bris 74. **d** 74 **p** 75. C Ware Ch Ch *St Alb* 74-78; TV Sheff Manor *Sheff* 78-80; V Wombridge *Lich* 80-87; Lect St Jo Coll Nottm 87-01; Public Preacher *S'well* 87-01; Hon C Chilwell 87-91; Hon C Trowell 91-01. *Address temp unknown*

HART, Dagogo. b 50. Birm Bible Inst Dip Systematic Th 79 LicTh81. **d** 82 **p** 83. Nigeria 82-01; C Niger Delta St Cypr 82-88; V 93-96; Bp's Chapl *Niger Delta* 83-88; Res Min Niger Delta Ch Ch 89-92; Can Res St Steph Cathl 97-00; C W Bromwich St Jas w St Paul *Lich* from 01. *3 Tiverton Drive, West Bromwich B71 1DA* Tel 0121-553 0601

HART, David. b 48. Edge Hill Coll of HE BEd80 Liv Inst of Educn AdDipEd84 Liv Univ MEd87 Chester Coll of HE BPhil94. N Ord Course 91. **d** 94 **p** 95. NSM Ashton-in-Makerfield St Thos *Liv* 94-02; NSM Wigan W Deanery from 02. *12 Ratcliffe Road, Aspull, Wigan WN2 1YE* Tel (01942) 832918

HART, David Alan. b 54. Keble Coll Ox BA75 MPhil78. Union Th Sem (NY) STM79 Westcott Ho Cam 83. **d** 83 **p** 84. Asst Chapl Gresham's Sch Holt 83-84; Chapl Nor Sch 84-85; Chapl

Shrewsbury Sch 85-87; Chapl St Jo Coll Sch Cam 87-88; C Camberwell St Giles w St Matt *S'wark* 88-90; Chapl Loughb Univ *Leic* 90-97; Perm to Offic *Ely* from 95; Relig and Roehampton Inst *S'wark* 97-98; Past Services Development Co-ord Derby Univ *Derby* 98-02; Perm to Offic from 98. *Address temp unknown* E-mail d.hart@derby.ac.uk

HART, David Alan. b 54. Rhodes Univ BTh86 MTh89 PhD92. **d** 81 **p** 82. S Africa 81-99; Chapl Bournemouth and Poole Coll of FE *Sarum* from 99. *21B Laidlaw Close, Poole BH12 5EW* Tel (01202) 595383 E-mail dhart@bournemouth.ac.uk

HART, David John. b 58. K Coll Lon BD80 Univ of Wales (Cardiff) DPS86. St Mich Coll Llan 83. **d** 85 **p** 86. C Denbigh and Nantglyn *St As* 85-88; Chapl RAF 88-89; C Llanrhos *St As* 89-91; V Rhosllannerchrugog 91-01. *Address temp unknown*

HART, David Leonard. b 42. Ripon Hall Ox 68. **d** 71 **p** 72. C Castle Vale *Birm* 71-73; Chapl All SS Hosp Birm 73-94; Chapl Services Manager N Birm Mental Health Trust from 94. *12 Dorchester Drive, Birmingham, B17 0SW, or All Saints' Hospital, Lodge Road, Birmingham B18 5SD* Tel 0121-427 7828 *or* 523 5151 ext 6236

HART, David Maurice. b 35. Univ Coll Dur BSc57. Clifton Th Coll 59. **d** 61 **p** 62. C Bolton St Paul *Man* 61-64; C Hamworthy *Sarum* 64-70; R W Dean w E Grimstead 70-81; R Farley w Pitton and W Dean w E Grimstead 81-90; V Steeple Ashton w Semington and Keevil from 90. *The Vicarage, Vicarage Lane, Steeple Ashton, Trowbridge BA14 6HH* Tel (01380) 870344

HART, Canon Dennis Daniel. b 22. Linc Th Coll 45. **d** 48 **p** 49. C Abbots Langley *St Alb* 48-49; C Bedford St Paul 49-53; CF 53-55; V St Alb St Sav *St Alb* 55-92; Hon Can St Alb 74-92; RD St Alb 84-90; rtd 92. *7 Bassett Close, Redbourn AL3 7JY* Tel (01582) 794464

HART, Dennis William. b 30. JP. Open Univ BA. Oak Hill Th Coll 75. **d** 78 **p** 79. NSM Clacton St Paul *Chelmsf* from 78. *15 Albert Gardens, Clacton-on-Sea CO15 6QN* Tel (01255) 431794

HART, Edwin Joseph. b 21. Oak Hill Th Coll 56. **d** 58 **p** 59. C Harlow New Town w Lt Parndon *Chelmsf* 58-60; C Leyton 60-61; C-in-c Cranham Park St Luke CD 61-69; V Cranham Park 69-71; R Markfield *Leic* 71-89; rtd 89; Perm to Offic *Leic* from 89. *135 Grace Dieu Road, Thringstone, Coalville LE67 5AP* Tel (01530) 222767

HART, Geoffrey Robert. b 49. **d** 95 **p** 96. P-in-c Edin St Salvador *Edin* 96-98; C Edin St Cuth 96-98; Lic to Offic from 98. *27 Links View, Port Seton, Prestonpans EH32 0EZ*

HART, Canon Geoffrey William. b 27. Ex Coll Ox BA51 MA55. Ridley Hall Cam 51. **d** 54 **p** 55. C Islington St Mary *Lon* 54-58; C Leeds St Geo *Ripon* 58-59; V Harold Wood *Chelmsf* 59-65; V Southport Ch Ch *Liv* 65-73; R Cheltenham St Mary *Glouc* 73-76; TR Cheltenham St Mary, St Matt, St Paul and H Trin 76-93; Hon Can Glouc Cathl 78-93; rtd 93; Chapl All Hallows Sch Rousdon 94-96; Perm to Offic *Ex* 94-02. *2 Little Lane, Eynsham, Witney OX29 4LG* Tel (01865) 884055

HART, Mrs Gillian Mary. b 57. Sheff City Poly BA79. Carl Dioc Tr Inst 92. **d** 95 **p** 96. C Burgh-by-Sands and Kirkbampton w Kirkandrews etc *Carl* 95-99; C Aikton 95-99; C Orton St Giles 95-99; Dioc Youth Officer 99-03; Chapl St Martin's Coll Carl 99-03; R Barony of Burgh *Carl* from 03. *The Rectory, Burgh-by-Sands, Carlisle CA5 6AW* Tel (01228) 576324 E-mail hart.david@btopenworld.com

HART, Graham Cooper. b 36. S Dios Minl Tr Scheme 88. **d** 91 **p** 92. NSM Filton *Bris* 91-93; NSM Downend 93-01. *11 West Hill, Portishead, Bristol BS20 6LQ* Tel (01275) 840363

HART, Canon Graham Merril (Merry). b 23. Ridley Coll Melbourne 65. **d** 77 **p** 77. Tanzania 69-84; CMS 72-83; Can Musoma from 85; Chapl Ostend w Knokke and Bruges *Eur* 84-93; Miss to Seamen 84-93; rtd 93; Perm to Offic *S'wark* from 93. *Morden College, 7 Alexander Court, Kidbrook Grove, London SE3 0LH* Tel (020) 8858 3731

HART, Henry St John. b 12. St Jo Coll Cam BA34 Qu Coll Cam MA38 BD54. **d** 36 **p** 37. Chapl Qu Coll Cam 36-50; Dean 40-50 and 55-72; Fell from 36; Vice Pres 78-79; Reader in Hebrew Cam Univ 72-79; rtd 80; Lic to Offic *Nor* 80-86. *The Retreat, Felbrigg Hall, Norwich NR11 8PR* Tel (01263) 837451

HART, James. b 53. MIL84 Dur BA75 DipEd76 DipHE85 Lon Univ BD98. Oak Hill Th Coll 86. **d** 88 **p** 89. C Starbeck *Ripon* 88-90; SAMS Argentina 90-96; Chapl Bishop's Stortford Coll 96-00; Chapl Felsted Sch from 00; Dioc FE Officer *Chelmsf* from 00. *Austens, Bury Chase, Felsted, Great Dunmow CM6 3DQ* Tel (01371) 820414 E-mail james@hart1234.freeserve.co.uk

HART, John Peter. b 39. Bris Sch of Min 80. **d** 84 **p** 85. NSM Malmesbury w Westport and Brokenborough *Bris* 84-88; C Yatton Moor *B & W* 89-90; V Bridgwater H Trin 90-96; Chapl HM Pris The Mount 96-01; P-in-c Sarratt *St Alb* from 96; P-in-c Chipperfield St Paul from 01. *The Rectory, The Green, Sarratt, Rickmansworth WD3 6BP* Tel (01923) 264377

HART, Mark. b 61. Chu Coll Cam BA82 Cam Univ MA86 PhD86. Trin Coll Bris BA98. **d** 98 **p** 99. C Bromborough Ches 98-02; V Plemstall w Guilden Sutton from 02. *The Vicarage, Wicker Lane, Guilden Sutton, Chester CH3 7EL* Tel (01244) 300306 E-mail hart@mkgfr.freeserve.co.uk

HART, Canon Michael Anthony. b 50. AKC71. St Aug Coll Cant 72. **d** 73 **p** 74. C Southwick St Columba *Dur* 73-76; C Hendon St Alphage *Lon* 76-78; P-in-c Eltham Park St Luke *S'wark* 78-83; V 83-85; R Newington St Mary 85-96; P-in-c Camberwell St Mich w All So w Em 85-96; RD S'wark and Newington 93-96; P-in-c Caterham 96-97; P-in-c Chaldon 96-97; TR Caterham from 98; RD Caterham from 98; Hon Can S'wark Cathl from 01. *The Rectory, 5 Whyteleafe Road, Caterham CR3 5EG* Tel (01883) 342062 E-mail father@mhart.freeserve.co.uk

HART, Preb Michael Stuart. b 39. Univ of Wales (Lamp) BA61 Lanc Univ MA72. Wycliffe Hall Ox 61. **d** 63 **p** 64. C W Bromwich St Jas *Lich* 63-66; C Tarrington w Stoke Edith *Heref* 66-67; C Putney St Mary *S'wark* 67-70; V Accrington St Mary *Blackb* 70-82; RD Accrington 76-82; Hon Can Blackb Cathl 81-91; V Walton-le-Dale 82-91; P-in-c Samlesbury 91; TR Heavitree w Ex St Paul *Ex* 91-02; P-in-c Ex St Mary Steps 01-02; TR Heavitree and St Mary Steps from 02; Preb Ex Cathl from 92. *St Mary Steps Rectory, 10 Victoria Park Road, Exeter EX2 4NT* Tel (01392) 677150

HART, Peter Osborne. b 57. St Jo Coll Nottm DCM92. **d** 92 **p** 93. C Shipley St Pet *Bradf* 92-97; TV Walsall *Lich* from 97. *St Martin's House, 17 Daffodil Road, Walsall WS5 3DQ* Tel (01922) 623216

HART, Peter William. b 60. Liv Univ BA82 Université de Haute Normandie MèsL84 Univ of Wales (Swansea) MPhil92. Sarum & Wells Th Coll 86. **d** 88 **p** 89. C Llansamlet *S & B* 88-89; C Sketty 89-92; P-in-c Warndon St Nic *Worc* 92-97; R Berkhamsted St Mary *St Alb* from 97. *St Mary's Rectory, 80 High Street, Northchurch, Berkhamsted HP4 3QW* Tel (01442) 865312 E-mail pwhart1@aol.com

HART, Richard. b 49. St D Coll Lamp BA82 Oriel Coll Ox MPhil84. Qu Coll Birm 84. **d** 85 **p** 86. C Sketty *S & B* 85-87; P-in-c Llanbister w Llanbadarn Fynydd w Llananno 87-88; V 88-92; P-in-c Preston and Dymock w Donnington and Kempley *Glouc* 92-00; P-in-c Beguildy and Heyope and Llangynllo and Bleddfa *S & B* from 01. *The Vicarage, Beguildy, Knighton LD7 1YE* Tel (01547) 510252

HART, Robert William. b 76. R Holloway & Bedf New Coll Lon BSc97 Leeds Univ BA01. Coll of Resurr Mirfield 99. **d** 02. C Haydock St Jas *Liv* from 02. *27 Homestead Avenue, Haydock, St Helens WA11 0ND* Tel (01744) 633312 Mobile 07970-229469 E-mail rwhart@orange.net

HART, Ronald George. b 46. BSc Lon Univ DASS77 CQSW77. Sarum & Wells Th Coll. **d** 85 **p** 86. C Sittingbourne St Mich *Cant* 85-88; C Walton H Trin *Ox* 88-89; TV 89-96; R Broughton Gifford, Gt Chalfield and Holt *Sarum* from 96. *The Rectory, Ham Green, Holt, Trowbridge BA14 7PZ* Tel (01225) 782289

HART, Tony. b 36. CCC Cam BA59 MA63. Cuddesdon Coll 59. **d** 61 **p** 62. C Middlesbrough All SS *York* 61-64; Bp's Dom Chapl *Dur* 64-67; Hon Chapl 67-72; C Owton Manor CD 67-70; V Harton College Hartlepool *Dur* 75; TR S Shields All SS 71-83; RD Jarrow 77-83; Can Res Dur Cathl 83-92; V Easingwold w Raskelfe *York* 92-97; V 97-01; RD Easingwold 97-00; rtd 01. *13 Stobhill Villas, Morpeth NE61 2SH* Tel (01670) 519017

HART, Prof Trevor Andrew. b 61. St Jo Coll Dur BA82 Aber Univ PhD89. **d** 88 **p** 88. NSM Bieldside *Ab* 88-95; NSM St Andrews St Andr *St And* from 95; Prof Div St Mary's Coll St Andrews Univ from 95. *St Mary's College, South Street, St Andrews KY16 9JU* Tel (01334) 462864 *or* (01224) 273380 E-mail tah@st-andrews.ac.uk

HARTE, Frederick George. b 25. AKC53. **d** 54 **p** 55. C Lewisham St Jo Southend *S'wark* 54-57; C Eltham H Trin 57-60; V Bellingham St Dunstan 60-73; V Plumstead St Nic 73-84; V Sutton Bridge *Linc* 84-90; rtd 90; Master St Jo Hosp Bath and P-in-c of Chpl 90-00; Perm to Offic *Guildf* from 00. *Heartsease, 5 Vale Road, Claygate, Esher KT10 0NJ* Tel (01372) 802548 Fax as telephone E-mail hartefamily1@cwctv.net

HARTE, The Ven Matthew Scott. b 46. TCD BA70 MA74. CITC 71. **d** 71 **p** 72. C Bangor Abbey *D & D* 71-74; C Ballynafeigh St Jude 74-76; I Ardara w Glencolumbkille, Inniskeel etc *D & R* 76-98; I Dunfanaghy, Raymunterdoney and Tullaghbegley from 98; Adn Raphoe from 83. *The Rectory, Horn Head Road, Dunfanaghy, Letterkenny, Co Donegal, Irish Republic* Tel (00353) (74) 913 6187 Fax 913 6651 E-mail archdeacon@raphoe.anglican.org

HARTERINK, Mrs Joy Frances. b 49. DCEG82 Essex Univ BA71 Hughes Hall Cam CertEd72 Lon Univ MSc87. Oak Hill NSM Course 89. **d** 92 **p** 94. NSM Richmond H Trin and Ch Ch *S'wark* from 92; Chapl Richmond Coll from 97. *9 Sandringham House, Courtlands, Sheen Road, Richmond TW10 5BG* Tel (020) 8948 7579

HARTLAND, David Robson. b 33. Qu Coll Birm 64. **d** 66 **p** 67. C Brierley Hill *Lich* 66-71; V Hartshill 71-76; V Moxley 76-85; V Willenhall St Steph 85-99; rtd 99; Perm to Offic *Lich* from 01. *80 Clifton Street, Bilston WV14 9HB* Tel (01902) 563262

HARTLAND, Ian Charles. b 49. K Coll Lon BD72 AKC72 PGCE73 MTh76. Sarum & Wells Th Coll 83. **d** 84 **p** 85. C Orpington All SS *Roch* 84-87; Sen Lect Ch Ch Coll Cant 87-95;

Adv for RE Kent Co Coun from 96. *Ivy Lodge, 4 The Terrace, Canterbury CT2 7AJ* Tel (01227) 760789 Fax 768978
E-mail ian.hartland@kent.gov.uk

HARTLESS, Mrs Berengaria Isabella de la Tour. b 52. Univ of Wales (Cardiff) BSc74 Goldsmiths' Coll Lon PGCE76 Liv Univ MA03. Ox Min Course CBTS93. **d** 93 **p** 94. Par Dn High Wycombe *Ox* 93-94; C 94-97; P-in-c Seer Green and Jordans 97-00; OLM Tr Officer (Bucks) 97-00; Dioc Prin of OLM from 00. *27 Don Bosco Close, Oxford OX4 2LD* Tel (01865) 717986
E-mail beren.hartless@oxford.anglican.org

HARTLEY, Brian. b 41. N Ord Course 82. **d** 85 **p** 86. NSM Royton St Paul *Man* 85-91; NSM Oldham St Steph and All Martyrs 91-94; TV E Farnworth and Kearsley 94-97; TR New Bury from 97; AD Farnworth from 98. *New Bury Rectory, 130A Highfield Road, Farnworth, Bolton BL4 0AJ* Tel (01204) 572334
E-mail brian.hartley2@tesco.net

HARTLEY, Daniel George. b 73. Leeds Univ BA95. Coll of Resurr Mirfield 96. **d** 99 **p** 00. C Richmond w Hudswell *Ripon* 99-03; Chapl HM YOI Deerbolt from 03. *HM YOI Deerbolt, Bowes Road, Barnard Castle DL12 9BG* Tel (01833) 637561 Fax 631736 E-mail daniel@danielhartley.fsnet.co.uk

HARTLEY, Diann Lynn. *See* GWILLIAMS, Mrs Dianna Lynn

HARTLEY, Graham William Harrington. b 21. Ripon Hall Ox 61. **d** 62 **p** 63. C N Meols *Liv* 62-65; Nigeria 65-66; V Knowsley *Liv* 66-72; V Langdale *Carl* 72-81; V Egremont and Haile 81-85; TV Whitehaven 85-88; rtd 88; Perm to Offic *Carl* from 88. *6 Meadowside, Chapel Stile, Ambleside LA22 9JE* Tel (01539) 437322

HARTLEY, Harold Aitken. b 21. Whitaker Sch of Th. **d** 84 **p** 85. USA 84-89; from 92; NSM Fulford *York* 89-92; Perm to Offic from 92. *1106 Riverview, Rogers City, MI 49779, USA*

HARTLEY, Herbert. b 28. AKC52. **d** 53 **p** 54. C Blackpool H Cross *Blackb* 53-55; C Reading St Giles *Ox* 55-58; V Ruscombe and Twyford 58-66; Chapl RN 66-73; C Langley Marish *Ox* 73-77; R Hedsor and Bourne End 77-93; rtd 93. *The College of St Barnabas, Blackberry Lane, Lingfield RH7 6NJ* Tel (01342) 870260

HARTLEY, John Peter. b 56. Cam Univ BA78 Leeds Univ PhD82 Dur Univ BA84. Cranmer Hall Dur 82. **d** 85 **p** 86. C Spring Grove St Mary *Lon* 85-88; C Bexleyheath St Pet *Roch* 88-91; P-in-c Hanford *Lich* 91-00; Faith in the City Officer (Potteries) 91-00; V Eccleshill *Bradf* from 00. *The Vicarage, 2 Fagley Lane, Bradford BD2 3NS* Tel (01274) 636403 Mobile 07811-915320 E-mail vicar@stluke-eccleshill.org.uk

HARTLEY, John William. b 47. St Jo Coll Dur BA69. Linc Th Coll 70. **d** 72 **p** 73. C Poulton-le-Fylde *Blackb* 72-76; C Lancaster St Mary 76-79; V Barrowford 79-87; V Salesbury from 87; AD Whalley from 01. *St Peter's Vicarage, 49A Ribchester Road, Blackburn BB1 9HU* Tel (01254) 248072
E-mail john@salesbury49a.freeserve.co.uk

HARTLEY, Julian John. b 57. Oak Hill Th Coll BA85. **d** 85 **p** 86. C Eccleston Ch Ch *Liv* 85-89; V Goose Green 89-00; P-in-c Mosley Common *Man* from 00. *St John's Vicarage, Mosley Common Road, Worsley, Manchester M28 4AN* Tel 0161-790 2957 Fax 799 0314 E-mail j.hartley@btinternet.com

HARTLEY, Michael Leslie. b 56. Leeds Univ BSc77. Ripon Coll Cuddesdon 87. **d** 89 **p** 90. C Standish *Blackb* 89-93; V Bamber Bridge St Aid 93-98; TR Colne and Villages from 98. *The Vicarage, Keighley Road, Colne BB8 7HF* Tel (01282) 83511
E-mail mike@hartley00.freeserve.co.uk

HARTLEY, Nigel John. b 48. Portsm Poly BA. St Jo Coll Nottm. **d** 83 **p** 84. C Ipswich St Marg *St E* 83-86; P-in-c Hintlesham w Chattisham 86-95; Dioc Radio Officer 86-95; P-in-c Gt Finborough w Onehouse, Harleston, Buxhall etc from 95; RD Stowmarket 96-99; Millennium Info Officer from 98. *The Rectory, Woodland Close, Onehouse, Stowmarket IP14 3HL* Tel (01449) 614378
E-mail nigel.hartley@stedmundsbury.anglican.org

HARTLEY, Paul. b 51. Nottm Univ BTh88. Linc Th Coll 85. **d** 88 **p** 89. C Clitheroe St Mary *Blackb* 88-91; TV Guiseley w Esholt *Bradf* 91-97; R Ackworth *Wakef* from 97. *The Rectory, Cross Hill, Ackworth, Pontefract WF7 7EJ* Tel (01977) 602751

HARTLEY, Canon Peter. b 44. Avery Hill Coll PGCE67 Ox Univ DipRE74 St Cath Coll Cam BA66 MA69. Sarum & Wells Th Coll 77. **d** 78 **p** 79. Hon C Freemantle *Win* 78-79; Chr Educn Officer *Pet* 79-81; Dir of Educn 81-90; Dir Coun of Educn and Tr *Chelmsf* from 90; Hon Can Chelmsf Cathl from 92. *St Clare, Links Drive, Chelmsford CM2 9AW* Tel (01245) 251461
E-mail hartleyp@chelmsford.anglican.org

HARTLEY, Peter Mellodew. b 41. Qu Coll Cam BA63 MA66 Lon Univ MSc71 DipTh83 FICE. S'wark Ord Course 80. **d** 83 **p** 84. NSM Salfords *S'wark* 83-97; Chapl Surrey and Sussex Healthcare NHS Trust 97-02; rtd 02; Perm to Offic *Chich* from 00; *S'wark* from 02. *Old Timbers, North Lane, West Hoathly RH19 4QF* Tel (01342) 811238

HARTLEY, Stephen William Mark. b 50. St Chad's Coll Dur BA71. Westcott Ho Cam 72. **d** 74 **p** 75. C Holbrooks *Cov* 74-76; C Styvechale 76-79; P-in-c Snitterfield w Bearley 79-81; V 81-83; V Exhall 83-88; V Tilehurst St Cath *Ox* 88-95; TR Cowley St Jas

from 95. *Cowley Rectory, St James House, Beauchamp Lane, Cowley, Oxford OX4 3LF* Tel (01865) 747680 Fax 395896
E-mail stephen.hartley@btinternet.com

HARTLEY, Stewart John Ridley. b 47. St Jo Coll Nottm 78. **d** 80 **p** 81. C Altham w Clayton le Moors *Blackb* 80-84; P-in-c Nelson St Phil 84-91; V 91-98; V Gt Marsden w Nelson St Phil 99-03; Hon Can Blackb Cathl 99-03; V Bermondsey St Anne and St Aug *S'wark* from 03; V Bermondsey St Jas w Ch Ch and St Crispin from 03. *St Anne's Vicarage, 10 Thorburn Square, London SE1 5QH* Tel (020) 7237 3950
E-mail stewarthartley@btinternet.com

HARTLEY, Susan Mary. b 49. Newc Univ MB, BS73 MRCGP77. SEITE 99. **d** 02. NSM Spitalfields Ch Ch w All SS *Lon* from 02. *35 Buxton Street, London E1 5EH* Tel (020) 7247 1344 Mobile 07890-901249

HARTLEY, Canon William Reginald (Rex). b 19. CCC Cam BA41 MA45. Linc Th Coll 41. **d** 42 **p** 43. C Stourbridge St Thos *Worc* 42-46; Lic to Offic *Ox* 46-47; Tutor CA Tr Coll 46-47; C Tardebigge *Worc* 47-50; V White Ladies Aston w Spetchley and Churchill 50-53; V Pendleton St Barn *Man* 53-59; R Birch St Jas 59-74; V Atherton 74-86; Hon Can Man Cathl 76-86; AD Leigh 79-85; rtd 86; Perm to Offic *Bradf* from 86. *21 Easby Close, Ilkley LS29 9DJ* Tel (01943) 609005

HARTNELL, Canon Bruce John. b 42. Ex Univ BA64 Linacre Coll Ox BA66 MA. Ripon Hall Ox 64. **d** 66 **p** 67. C S Stoneham *Win* 66-69; Chapl and Tutor Ripon Hall Ox 69-74; V Knowl Hill w Littlewick *Ox* 74-78; Chapl Southn Univ *Win* 78-83; V Sholing from 83; AD Southn 93-01; Hon Can Win Cathl from 93. *The Vicarage, 41 Station Road, Southampton SO19 8FN* Tel (023) 8044 8337 E-mail bruce.hartnell@ukgateway.net

HARTOPP, Mrs Penelope Faye. b 55. Ripon Coll Cuddesdon. **d** 03. C Studley *Cov* from 03. *3 Westmeade Avenue, Studley B80 7NB* Tel (01527) 857463

HARTREE, Steven John. b 45. FFA78 CertRS94. WMMTC 96. **d** 99 **p** 00. NSM Highbridge *B & W* from 99. *54 Palmers Close, Burnham-on-Sea TA8 2SS* Tel (01278) 780435

HARTROPP, Andrew James. b 59. Southn Univ BSc80 PhD85. Oak Hill Th Coll BA95. **d** 98 **p** 99. C Watford *St Alb* 98-01; C Watford Ch Ch from 01; Teacher Henrietta Barnett Sch from 01. *77 Northfield Gardens, Watford WD24 7RF* Tel (01923) 225411 E-mail a.hartropp@clara.net

HARVEY, Alan Douglas. b 25. FRSH82. Melbourne Coll of Div 78. **d** 79 **p** 81. Australia 79-86; Perm to Offic *Ely* 86-87; V Wiggenhall St Germans and Islington 88-95; V Wiggenhall St Mary Magd 88-95; rtd 95; Perm to Offic *Cant* from 95. *17 Day View Road, Broadstairs CT10 2EA* Tel (01843) 862794

HARVEY, Alison Christine Vera. b 57. Open Univ BA97 Nottm Univ MA03. EMMTC 01. **d** 03. C Horncastle w Low Toynton *Linc* from 03; C High Toynton from 03; C Greetham w Ashby Puerorum from 03. *St Mary's House, 6 Park Road, Horncastle LN9 5EF* Tel (01507) 527312 Mobile 07789-835039
E-mail alison@harvey8086.freeserve.co.uk

HARVEY, Canon Anthony Ernest. b 30. Worc Coll Ox BA53 MA56 DD83. Westcott Ho Cam 56. **d** 58 **p** 59. C Chelsea Ch Ch *Lon* 58-62; Ch Ch Ox 62-69; Warden St Aug Coll Cant 69-75; Lect Th Ox Univ 76-82; Chapl Qu Coll Ox 77-82; Can and Lib Westmr Abbey 82-99; Sub-Dean and Adn Westmr 87-99; rtd 99; Perm to Offic *Glouc* from 00. *Mendelssohn Cottage, Broadway Road, Willersey, Broadway WR12 7BH* Tel (01386) 859260

HARVEY, Anthony Peter. b 42. Birm Univ BSc63 MSc64. Wycliffe Hall Ox 79. **d** 81 **p** 82. C Stoke Damerel *Ex* 81-84; Canada 84-90; Chapl HM YOI Deerbolt 91-92; Chapl HM Pris Wakef 92-95; Chapl HM Pris Kirkham 95-01. *Address temp unknown*

HARVEY, Arthur Ernest. b 30. Lon Univ DipTh58 MSc80. Oak Hill Th Coll 54. **d** 57 **p** 58. C Rayleigh *Chelmsf* 57-60; C Morpeth *Newc* 60-63; R Pitsea *Chelmsf* 63-74; Bp's Ind Officer 73-80; R Bobbingworth 74-81; Chapl Bordeaux w Riberac, Cahors, Duras etc *Eur* 82-86; V Barnsbury St Andr and H Trin w All SS *Lon* 86-90; TR Barnsbury 90-97; rtd 97; Perm to Offic *Chich* from 01. *Prompt Corner, 4A Arundel Road, Eastbourne BN21 2EL* Tel (01323) 642982

HARVEY, The Very Revd Brian. b 16. TCD BA38 BD41. TCD Div Sch Div Test39. **d** 40 **p** 41. C Dublin St Geo *D & G* 40-45; Min Can St Patr Cathl Dublin 42-45; Sec SCM (Ireland) 45-48; Dean of Res QUB 45-48; Min Can Belf Cathl 45-48; India 48-63; Adn Hazaribagh 60-63; Can Th Belf Cathl 63-70; I Kilkenny w Aghour and Kilmanagh *C & O* 70-91; Can Leighlin Cathl from 70; Dean Ossory 70-91; rtd 91. *Alton, Kilbrittain, Co Cork, Irish Republic* Tel (00353) (23) 49686

HARVEY, Christopher John Alfred. b 41. S'wark Ord Course 66. **d** 69 **p** 70. C Grays Thurrock *Chelmsf* 69-73; C Gt Baddow 73-75; V Berechurch St Marg w St Mich 75-94; R Tendring and Lt Bentley w Beaumont cum Moze 94-00; P-in-c Alresford from 00. *The Rectory, St Andrew's Close, Alresford, Colchester CO7 8BL* Tel (01206) 823163 E-mail cjharvey@ukonline.co.uk

HARVEY, The Ven Cyril John. b 30. Univ of Wales (Lamp) BA51. Coll of Resurr Mirfield 51. **d** 53 **p** 54. C Caerau w Ely *Llan* 53-57; C Milford Haven *St D* 57-61; V Castlemartin and

Warren 61-65; R Begelly w Kilgetty 65-73; V Haverfordwest St Martin w Lambston 73-88; Can St D Cathl from 85; R Tenby 88-96; Adn St D 91-96; rtd 96. *10 Oakwood Grove, Slade Lane, Haverfordwest SA61 2HF* Tel (01437) 768036

HARVEY, Canon Debra Eileen. b 54. SW Minl Tr Course. **d** 94 **p** 95. NSM Camborne *Truro* from 94; Chapl w Deaf People from 94; Hon Can Truro Cathl from 03. *Ankorva Salow, Tehidy Road, Camborne TR14 0NA* Tel (01209) 716282 Mobile 07774-975268 Fax and minicom as telephone
E-mail hippo@ankorva.freeserve.co.uk

HARVEY, Desmond Victor Ross. b 37. QUB BA59 Princeton Th Sem ThM63 Fuller Th Sem California DMin93. St Mich Coll Llan 95. **d** 95 **p** 96. C Cwmbran *Mon* 95-97; TV 97; Perm to Offic from 97; Offg Chapl RAF from 98. *Mallory, Llanmaes, Llantwit Major CF61 2XR* Tel (01446) 792753 Fax as telephone

HARVEY, John. b 30. S'wark Ord Course. **d** 65 **p** 66. C Lewisham St Jo Southend *S'wark* 65-73; V Bellingham St Dunstan 73-78; TV Bourne Valley *Sarum* 78-81; TR 81-87; R Kilkhampton w Morwenstow *Truro* 87-90; rtd 90; Perm to Offic *Roch* 90-99. *18 Ramsay Hall, 11-13 Byron Road, Worthing BN11 3HN*

HARVEY, John Christopher. b 65. Univ of Wales (Lamp) BA86 Nottm Univ BTh89. Linc Th Coll 86. **d** 89 **p** 90. C Dwygyfylchi *Ban* 89-93; V Llangrannog w Llandysiliogogo w Penbryn *St D* 93-02; RD Glyn Aeron 99-02; P-in-c Llangystennin *St As* from 02. *The Rectory, Glyn y Marl Road, Llandudno Junction LL31 9NS* Tel (01492) 583579

HARVEY, John Mark. b 64. QUB BEd87 TCD BTh93. CITC 90. **d** 93 **p** 94. C Portadown St Columba *Arm* 93-96; I Monaghan w Tydavnet and Kilmore *Clogh* 96-01; Dioc Communications Officer 97-00; Miss Officer (Ireland) CMS from 01. *Church Missionary Society (Ireland), Church of Ireland House, 61 Donegal Street, Belfast BT1 2QH* Tel (028) 9047 3934
E-mail dco@clogher.anglican.org

HARVEY, Lt Col John William Arthur. b 43. Guildf Dioc Min Course 98. **d** 01 **p** 02. OLM Aldershot St Aug *Guildf* from 01. *59 Knoll Road, Fleet GU51 4PT* Tel (01252) 622793
E-mail john@harvey59.freeserve.co.uk

HARVEY, Lance Sydney Crockford. b 25. Ridley Hall Cam 67. **d** 69 **p** 70. C Mortlake w E Sheen *S'wark* 69-74; P-in-c Woolwich St Thos 75-86; V Lee Gd Shep w St Pet 86-92; RD E Lewisham 87-91; rtd 92; Perm to Offic *Truro* from 92. *17 Lariggan Road, Penzance TR18 4NJ*

HARVEY, Margaret Claire. b 41. Univ of Wales (Abth) BA62 DipEd63 Lon Univ BD68. Dalton Ho Bris 66. **dss** 68 **d** 80 **p** 97. Flint *St As* 68-74; Lect Trin Coll Bris 74-80; Connah's Quay *St As* 79-80; C 80-86; Bp's Adv for Continuing Clerical Educn 86-98; Hon C Corwen and Llangar 86-87; Dn-in-c Bryneglwys 87-97; P-in-c *St As* 97-02; rtd 02. *Coleg y Groes, The College, Corwen LL21 0AU* Tel (01490) 412169 E-mail colegygroes@talk21.com

HARVEY, Maurice. b 31. CITC 70. **d** 70 **p** 71. C Lisburn St Paul *Conn* 70-72; C Ballymacarrett St Patr *D & D* 72-77; I Ballyphilip w Ardquin 77-79; I Ardmore w Craigavon 79-87; I Killyman *Arm* 87-94; Bp's C Acton and Drumbanagher 94-97; rtd 97. *Flat 1, 16 Cathedral Close, Armagh BT61 7EE* Tel (028) 3752 3971

HARVEY, Murray Alexander. b 63. Univ of Qld BA85 MAPsS87. St Fran Coll Brisbane BTh91. **d** 91 **p** 92. Australia 91-02; C Milton 92-93; C Stafford 94-95; P-in-c Tamborine Mt St Geo 95-02; V Glen Gp *Linc* from 02. *The Vicarage, 19 Spalding Road, Pinchbeck, Spalding PE11 3UD* Tel (01775) 725698 Fax as telephone E-mail murray.harvey@spaldingchurches.org

HARVEY, Canon Norman Roy. b 43. Nottm Univ DipAE86. Wycliffe Hall Ox 66. **d** 69 **p** 70. C Clay Cross *Derby* 69-72; C Dronfield 72-76; TV 76-79; P-in-c Rowsley 79-89; Dioc Youth Officer 79-83; Dioc Adv in Adult and Youth Educn 83-89; TR Eckington w Handley and Ridgeway 89-01; R Eckington and Ridgeway from 01; RD Bolsover and Staveley from 00; Hon Can Derby Cathl from 00. *The Rectory, 17 Church Street, Eckington, Sheffield S21 4BG* Tel (01246) 432196 Fax as telephone
E-mail nrharvey@talk21.com

HARVEY, Oliver Paul. b 33. Magd Coll Ox BA55 MA59. Cuddesdon Coll 57. **d** 59 **p** 60. C S Norwood St Mark *Cant* 59-61; C Hythe 61-64; Zambia 64-71; Chapl Cant Coll of Tech 71-77; Hon C Cant St Martin and St Paul *Cant* 73-77; Chapl K Sch Roch 77-88; C Roch 88-90; V Gillingham St Mary 90-00; RD Gillingham 98-00; rtd 00; Perm to Offic *Roch* from 00. *140 Maidstone Road, Rochester ME1 3EA* Tel (01634) 845693

HARVEY, Miss Pamela Betty. b 33. Dalton Ho Bris IDC59 CertRK59. **dss** 68 **d** 87 **p** 95. Nottingham St Ann *S'well* 68-72; Bestwood St Matt 72-76; CPAS Staff 76-93; Dir Consultants Division CPAS 93-99; Hon C Glenfield *Leic* from 95; rtd 99. *72 Chestnut Road, Glenfield, Leicester LE3 8DB* Tel 0116-232 2959

HARVEY, Mrs Patricia Ann. b 45. Qu Coll Birm. **dss** 82 **d** 87 **p** 94. Gospel Lane St Mich *Birm* 82-85; Exhall *Cov* 85-89; C 87-89; TD Droitwich Spa *Worc* 89-94; TV 94-97; P-in-c Finstall 97-00; V 00-02; rtd 02. *15 Mount Orchard, Tenbury Wells WR15 8DW* Tel (01584) 819444
E-mail patst.godwalds@tesco.net

HARVEY, Canon Patrick Arnold. b 58. TCD BA DipTh MA. CITC 82. **d** 85 **p** 86. C Bandon Union *C, C & R* 85-88; Dean's V Limerick St Mich *L & K* 88-91; Dioc Info Officer 88-91; I Abbeyleix w Old Church, Ballyroan etc *C & O* from 91; Can Ossory Cathl from 97. *The Rectory, Abbeyleix, Portlaoise, Co Laois, Irish Republic* Tel (00353) (502) 31243 Fax as telephone E-mail abbeyleix@leighlin.anglican.org

HARVEY, Robert Martin. b 30. S'wark Ord Course 69. **d** 70 **p** 71. C Sutton New Town St Barn *S'wark* 70-75; C Leatherhead *Guildf* 76-78; V Wadworth w Loversall *Sheff* 78-96; RD W Doncaster 94-97; rtd 96; Perm to Offic *Sheff* from 96. *44 Castlegate, Tickhill, Doncaster DN11 9QU* Tel (01302) 746532

HARVEY, Robin Grant. b 43. Clare Coll Cam BA64 MA68 Univ of NSW PhD74. Tyndale Hall Bris 67. **d** 87 **p** 88. C Keynsham *B & W* 87-91; R E w W Harptree and Hinton Blewett 91-97; Chapl Surrey Univ *Guildf* 98-02; P-in-c Cuddington from 02. *St Mary's Vicarage, St Mary's Road, Worcester Park KT4 7JL* Tel (020) 8337 5025 *or* 8337 4026 Fax 8337 6680

HARVEY, Roland. b 68. St Jo Coll Nottm 99. **d** 01 **p** 02. C Skelmersdale St Paul *Liv* from 01. *6 Wilcove, Skelmersdale WN8 8NF* Tel (01695) 726491 Mobile 07817-901455
E-mail revdrol@fish.co.uk

HARVEY, Simon John. b 63. Trin Coll Bris BA00. **d** 00 **p** 01. C Walsall St Paul *Lich* from 00. *11 The Cloisters, Walsall WS4 2AJ* Tel (01922) 721144 *or* 620669 Fax 724897
E-mail simon@sjharvey.freeserve.co.uk

HARVEY, Steven Charles. b 58. Reading Univ BA79 Ox Univ BA83 MA88 FRSA03. Ripon Coll Cuddesdon 81. **d** 84 **p** 85. C Oldham *Man* 84-87; Chapl and Hd RS St Pet Sch York 87-96; Sen Dep Hd Kingswood Sch Bath 96-03; Sen Provost Woodard Corp from 03; Perm to Offic *Lich* from 03. *The Provost's Lodging, High Street, Abbots Bromley, Rugeley WS15 3BW* Tel (01283) 840670 *or* 840120 E-mail scharvey@surfaid.org

HARVEY, Trevor John. b 43. Sheff Univ BA64 K Coll Lon MA94. Coll of Resurr Mirfield 64. **d** 66 **p** 67. C Kingswinford St Mary *Lich* 66-72; V Upper Gornal 72-77; V Meir 77-86; Chapl St Geo Sch Windsor 86-99; Min Can Windsor 86-99; Chapl Ellesmere Coll Shropshire 99-03; rtd 03. *Address temp unknown*

HARVEY, Mrs Verity Margaret. b 48. Bris Univ BA69 Saltley Tr Coll Birm DipEd70. St Alb and Ox Min Course 99. **d** 02. NSM Radlett *St Alb* from 02. *28 Field Road, Watford WD19 4DR* Tel (01923) 492863

HARVEY-COOK, Ann. See SMITHAM, Mrs Elizabeth Ann

HARVEY-NEILL, Nicola Lisa Jane. b 69. QUB BD91 TCD MPhil95. CITC BTh94. **d** 95 **p** 96. Dioc C *T, K & A* 95-96; C Galway w Kilcummin 96-97; Dioc Youth Adv (Limerick) *L & K* 97-01; Chapl Villier's Sch Limerick 98-01; Chapl Limerick Univ 98-01; Perm to Offic from 01. *Modreeny Rectory, Cloughjordan, Co Tipperary, Irish Republic* Tel (00353) (505) 42183 *or* (61) 202225 Mobile 87-250 0570 Fax (505) 42183
E-mail nickihn@eircom.net

HARWOOD, Frederick Ronald. b 21. Wells Th Coll 61. **d** 63 **p** 64. C Devonport St Mark Ford *Ex* 63-66; V Hessenford *Truro* 66-71; V Hayle 71-87; rtd 87; Hon C Madron *Truro* 88-92; Prec Gib Cathl and Port Chapl *Eur* 92-95; Perm to Offic *Truro* from 95. *Ferncliffe, 5 Harbour View, Hayle TR27 4LB*

HARWOOD (formerly SOUTH), Mrs Gillian. b 51. NEOC 87. **d** 90 **p** 94. C Rothbury *Newc* 90-93; C Morpeth 93-97; V Amble from 97. *The Vicarage, Straffen Court, Amble, Morpeth NE65 0HA* Tel (01665) 710273

HARWOOD, Canon John Rossiter. b 26. Selw Coll Cam BA51 MA55. Wycliffe Hall Ox 51. **d** 53 **p** 54. C Handsworth St Mary *Birm* 53-55; Nigeria 55-64; Sierra Leone 64-67; Home Educn Sec CMS 67-75; V Cheltenham Ch Ch *Glouc* 75-91; RD Cheltenham 84-89; Hon Can Glouc Cathl 85-91; rtd 91; Perm to Offic *Ex* 91-99; Chich from 00. *8 Kingsey Avenue, Emsworth PO10 7HP* Tel (01243) 372215 E-mail john-harwood@intelynx.net

HARWOOD, Peter James. b 64. Birm Univ MB88 ChB88. Wycliffe Hall Ox BA93. **d** 94 **p** 95. C Cov H Trin *Cov* 94-97; C Kensington St Barn *Lon* 97-02; V Woking Ch Ch *Guildf* from 02. *Christ Church Vicarage, 10 Russetts Close, Woking GU21 4BH* Tel (01483) 762100 E-mail peterandclare@ntlworld.com

HASELHURST (née STERLING), Mrs Anne. b 51. Macalester Coll (USA) BA73. EAMTC 89. **d** 92 **p** 94. Par Dn Bury St Edmunds St Jo *St E* 92-94; C 94-95; V Fordham St Pet *Ely* from 95; P-in-c Kennett from 95. *The Vicarage, 24 Mildenhall Road, Fordham, Ely CB7 5NR* Tel (01638) 720266
E-mail annehaselhurst@compuserve.com

HASELOCK, Canon Jeremy Matthew. b 51. York Univ BA73 BPhil74. St Steph Ho Ox BA82 MA86. **d** 83 **p** 84. C Pimlico St Gabr *Lon* 83-86; C Paddington St Jas 86-88; Bp's Dom Chapl *Chich* 88-91; P-in-c Boxgrove 91-94; V 94-98; Dioc Adv on Liturgy 91-98; Can and Preb Chich Cathl 94-98; Can Res and Prec Nor Cathl *Nor* from 98. *34 The Close, Norwich NR1 4DZ* Tel (01603) 619169 Fax 766032

HASKINS, Canon Thomas. b 41. TCD BA72. CITC 71. **d** 73 **p** 74. C Larne and Inver *Conn* 73-78; C Antrim All SS 78-83; I Belfast

St Mark 83-90; I Dublin Clontarf *D & G* 90-02; I Dublin St Ann and St Steph from 02; Can Ch Ch Cathl Dublin from 99. *St Ann's Vicarage, 88 Mount Anville Wood, Dublin 14, Irish Republic* Tel (00353) (1) 288 0663

HASLAM, Andrew James. b 57. Univ Coll Dur BSc78 Coll of Ripon & York St Jo PGCE79. Lambeth STh84 Trin Coll Bris 80. **d** 83 **p** 84. C Leyland St Andr *Blackb* 83-86; C Hartford *Ches* 86-88; V Grimsargh *Blackb* 88-98; V St Helens St Mark *Liv* from 98. *St Mark's Vicarage, 160 North Road, St Helens WA10 2TZ* Tel (01744) 23806
E-mail andrewhaslam@st-h.freeserve.co.uk

HASLAM, Canon Frank. b 26. Bris Univ BA50. Tyndale Hall Bris 49. **d** 51 **p** 52. C Halliwell St Paul *Man* 51-55; Uganda 56-60; C Wednesfield Heath *Lich* 60-61; V Wolverhampton St Matt 61-65; V Blackpool Ch Ch *Blackb* 65-70; V Macclesfield St Mich *Ches* 71-80; Dir of Resources 80-91; Hon Can Ches Cathl 81-91; rtd 91; Perm to Offic *Ches* from 91; P-in-c Bistre *St As* 99-00. *Brackendale, Chester Road, Buckley CH7 3AH* Tel (01244) 294544

HASLAM, James Robert. b 31. Open Univ BA74. Bps' Coll Cheshunt 55. **d** 57 **p** 58. C Penwortham St Mary *Blackb* 57-63; V Cockerham 63-74; V Cockerham w Winmarleigh 74-76; V Gt Harwood St Bart 76-88; V Fairhaven 88-95; rtd 95; Perm to Offic *Blackb* from 95. *5 Willow Trees Drive, Blackburn BB1 8LB* Tel (01254) 697092

HASLAM, Mrs Jane. b 70. Leeds Poly BA92. Trin Coll Bris 94. **d** 97 **p** 98. C Minehead *B & W* 97-00; Perm to Offic *Newc* from 00. *52 Fern Avenue, Jesmond, Newcastle upon Tyne NE2 2QX* Tel 0191-281 5166

HASLAM, John Gordon. b 32. Birm Univ LLB53. Qu Coll Birm 75. **d** 77 **p** 77. Hon C Bartley Green *Birm* 77-79; Hon C Moseley St Mary 79-96; Chapl to The Queen from 89; Perm to Offic *Heref* from 99. *16 Mill Street, Ludlow SY8 1BE* Tel (01584) 876663 Fax as telephone

HASLAM, Michael Henry. b 72. Buckingham Univ BA93. Trin Coll Bris BA94 MA94. **d** 97 **p** 98. C Minehead *B & W* 97-00; Chapl Newc Univ *Newc* from 00. *52 Fern Avenue, Jesmond, Newcastle upon Tyne NE2 2QX* Tel 0191-281 5166 *or* 222 6341 E-mail jama.haslam@virgin.net

HASLAM, Robert John Alexander. b 34. CCC Cam BA58. Coll of Resurr Mirfield 58. **d** 60 **p** 61. C Rawmarsh w Parkgate *Sheff* 60-66; Perm to Offic *Edin* 66-73; Perm to Offic *Carl* 73-77; P-in-c Peebles *Edin* 77-81; V Darnall *Sheff* 81-85; Hon C Bermondsey St Hugh CD *S'wark* 86-88; R Clydebank *Glas* 88-98; Chapl Malaga *Eur* from 98. *Paseo de Reding 21 2-D, 29016 Malaga, Spain* Tel (0034) (95) 221 9396 Fax as telephone

HASLAM-JONES, Christopher John. b 28. AKC53. **d** 53 **p** 54. C Walthamstow St Jo *Chelmsf* 53-57; C High Wycombe All SS *Ox* 57-62; V Parkfield in Middleton *Man* 62-68; V Radcliffe St Andr 68-86; R Colchester Ch Ch w St Mary V *Chelmsf* 86-93; rtd 93; Perm to Offic *Sarum* from 93. *Ramla, 4A Belle Vue Road, Poole BH14 8TW* Tel (01202) 717674 Fax as telephone E-mail c.jhaslamjones@tiscali.co.uk

HASLER, John Joseph (Joe). b 45. Univ of Wales (Cardiff) MPhil99. Qu Coll Birm 89. **d** 90 **p** 91. C Horfield H Trin *Bris* 90-93; V Bris St Andr Hartcliffe 93-01; V Bris Lockleaze St Mary Magd w St Fran from 01. *The Vicarage, Copley Gardens, Bristol BS7 9YE* Tel 0117-951 2516

HASSALL, William Edwin. b 41. St Jo Coll Nottm 75. **d** 77 **p** 78. C Wellington w Eyton *Lich* 77-80; C Farewell 80-82; V 82-93; C Gentleshaw 80-82; V 82-93; P-in-c Cheddleton 93-94; Perm to Offic *Lich* from 97; Chapl Asst Birm Heartlands and Solihull NHS Trust 98-01; Chapl Team Ldr from 01. *Birmingham Heartlands Hospital, Bordesley Green East, Birmingham B9 5SS* Tel 0121-424 1369 *or* (01543) 275087

HASSELL, David Edwin. b 38. WMMTC 87. **d** 90 **p** 91. NSM Worc SE *Worc* 90-93; C Abberton, Naunton Beauchamp and Bishampton etc 93-94; P-in-c 94; R Abberton, The Flyfords, Naunton Beauchamp etc from 94. *The Rectory, Bishampton, Pershore WR10 2LT* Tel (01386) 462648

HASSELL, John Charles. b 44. FCA. Sarum & Wells Th Coll 81. **d** 83 **p** 84. C Tottenham St Paul *Lon* 83-86; C Fingringhoe w E Donyland *Chelmsf* 86-90; V Moulsham St Jo 90-00; TR Grays Thurrock from 00; RD Thurrock 01-03. *The Rectory, 10 High View Avenue, Grays RM17 6RU* Tel (01375) 377379 E-mail john@hassell2000.fsnet.co.uk

HASTE, James Victor William. b 36. St Mich Th Coll Crafers LTh69. **d** 68 **p** 70. Australia 68-69 and from 76; C Ormond 68-69; C Roehampton H Trin *S'wark* 70-72; P-in-c Boroko Papua New Guinea 72-76; Sec ABM Vic 76-81; I Armadale w Hawksburn 81-86; I Vermont S 86-89; Inter-Ch Trade and Ind Chapl 89-99; rtd 01; Lic to Offic *The Murray* from 99. *Lot 4, Nitschke Road, PO Box 119, Littlehampton, S Australia 5250* Tel (0061) (8) 8391 0286 Mobile 407-044086 E-mail maha@picknoal.com.au

HASTED, Marcus Arthur David. b 35. Qu Coll Birm 63. **d** 66 **p** 67. C Woodchurch *Ches* 66-69; C W Kirby St Bridget 69-72; V Farndon 72-76; V Farndon and Coddington 76-79; Perm to Offic 98-00; NSM Liscard St Mary w St Columba from 00.

62 South Road, West Kirby, Wirral CH48 3HQ Tel 0151-625 0428

HASTEY, Erle. b 44. St Mich Coll Llan 66. **d** 68 **p** 69. C Pontefract St Giles *Wakef* 68-71; C Almondbury 71-74; V Purlwell 74-79; P-in-c Batley Carr 76-79; V Ynyshir *Llan* 79-86; V Tylorstown w Ynyshir 86-87; V Tonyrefail w Gilfach Goch 87-97; P-in-c Llandyfodwg 87-97; V Tonyrefail w Gilfach Goch and Llandyfodwg 97-99; V Pyle w Kenfig from 99. *The Vicarage, Pyle Road, Pyle, Bridgend CF33 6PG* Tel (01656) 740500 Fax as telephone

HASTIE-SMITH, Timothy Maybury. b 62. Magd Coll Cam MA84. Wycliffe Hall Ox 85. **d** 88 **p** 89. C Ox St Ebbe w H Trin and St Pet *Ox* 88-91; Chapl Stowe Sch 91-98; Hd Master Dean Close Sch Cheltenham from 98; Perm to Offic *Glouc* from 99. *Dean Close House, Landsdown Road, Cheltenham GL51 6QD* Tel (01242) 512537 *or* 522640 Fax 258003

HASTINGS, David Kerr. b 40. St Luke's Coll Ex CertEd63. Ox NSM Course 84. **d** 87 **p** 88. Hd Master St Edburg's Sch Bicester 82-89; Asst Chapl HM Pris Grendon and Spring Hill 87-89; NSM Bicester w Bucknell, Caversfield and Launton *Ox* 87-89; Chapl HM Pris Reading 90-92; P-in-c Gt Wishford *Sarum* 92; P-in-c S Newton 92; P-in-c Stapleford w Berwick St James 92; P-in-c Winterbourne Stoke 92; R Lower Wylye and Till Valley 92-95; Chapl HM Pris Ex 96-01; Perm to Offic *Ex* from 01; rtd 01. *26 Hoopern Street, Exeter EX4 4LY* Tel (01392) 498233

HASTINGS, Canon Gary Lea. b 56. New Univ of Ulster BA82 MA87 TCD BTh93. CITC 90. **d** 93 **p** 94. C Galway w Kilcummin *T, K & A* 93-95; Dom Chapl to Bp Tuam from 94; I Aughaval w Achill, Knappagh, Dugort etc from 95; Can Tuam Cathl from 00. *The Rectory, Newport Road, Westport, Co Mayo, Irish Republic* Tel (00353) (98) 25127 E-mail gary@anu.ie

HASTINGS, Patrick John Alan. b 45. ACIB68 CertEd75 Sussex Univ BEd82. S Dios Minl Tr Scheme 83. **d** 86 **p** 87. NSM Whyke w Rumboldswhyke and Portfield *Chich* 86-87; C Weybridge *Guildf* 87-89; C Verwood *Sarum* 89-93; P-in-c Lytchett Matravers from 93. *The Rectory, Jenny's Lane, Lytchett Matravers, Poole BH16 6BP* Tel (01929) 459200

HASTROP, Paul. b 39. Wells Th Coll 70. **d** 72 **p** 73. C Parkstone St Osmund *Sarum* 72-76; C Penzance St Mary w St Paul *Truro* 76-79; V St Blazey 79-87; TV Bournemouth St Pet w St Swithun, H Trin etc *Win* 87-94; TV Thornaby on Tees *York* 94-96; P-in-c Portsea St Sav *Portsm* 96-03; rtd 03. *14 Mannington Way, West Moors, Ferndown BH22 0JE*

HASTWELL, James Sydney. b 37. Roch Th Coll 67. **d** 69 **p** 70. C Croydon St Aug *Cant* 69-73; C Hurstpierpoint *Chich* 73-75; P-in-c Twineham 75; P-in-c Sayers Common 76; P-in-c Albourne 76; R Albourne w Sayers Common and Twineham 76-88; V Forest Row 88-94; rtd 97; Perm to Offic *Chich* from 97. *54 Ridgewood Gardens, Bexhill-on-Sea TN40 1TS*

HATCH, Canon George Andrew. b 29. Leeds Univ BA. Coll of Resurr Mirfield 51. **d** 53 **p** 54. C S Farnborough *Guildf* 53-55; Windward Is 55-63; Barbados from 63; R St Mary Barbados 63-73; Assoc Dir Chr Action Development in Caribbean 73-83; R St Jas Barbados 83-94; rtd 94. *St James, Barbados* Tel (001809) 432 0700

HATCH, Richard Francis. b 36. Qu Coll Cam BA60 MA64. Cuddesdon Coll 60. **d** 62 **p** 63. C Leigh St Mary *Man* 62-66; PC Peel Green 66-71; V Barton w Peel Green 71-75; Dioc Broadcasting Officer 73-85; R Birch St Jas and Fallowfield 75-78; Lic Preacher from 78; rtd 01. *24 Denison Road, Manchester M14 5SQ* Tel 0161-225 0799

HATCHETT, Michael John. b 49. Enfield Coll BSc72 K Coll Lon BD77 AKC77. Linc Th Coll 77. **d** 78 **p** 79. C Halstead St Andr *Chelmsf* 78-79; C Halstead St Andr w H Trin and Greenstead Green 79-81; C Greenstead 81-85; V Gt Totham 85-01; R Gt and Lt Totham w Goldhanger from 01; RD Witham 96-01. *The Vicarage, 1 Hall Road, Great Totham, Maldon CM9 8NN* Tel (01621) 893150 E-mail michael.hatchett@virgin.net

HATCHLEY, Canon Walter John. b 24. Lon Univ BA65. Coll of Resurr Mirfield 64. **d** 66 **p** 67. C Monkseaton St Pet *Newc* 66-69; C Gosforth All SS 69-72; C Cullercoats St Geo 72; TV 72-78; V Newc St Fran 78-93; RD Newc E 83-92; Hon Can Newc Cathl 90-93; rtd 93; Perm to Offic *Newc* from 93. *4 Woodthorne Road, Jesmond, Newcastle upon Tyne NE2 3PB*

HATCHMAN, Ms Elizabeth Mary. b 63. St Andr Univ MA85 Kent Coll for Careers DCG87. Selly Oak Coll Qu Coll Birm BD92. **d** 93 **p** 94. C Aston SS Pet and Paul *Birm* 93-96; C Rowley Regis 96-00; Chapl Post 16 Cen from 00. *21 Westfield Road, Birmingham B14 7SX*

HATCHMAN, Hugh Alleyne. b 28. Qu Coll Cam BA52 MA56. Ridley Hall Cam 52. **d** 54 **p** 55. C E Twickenham St Steph *Lon* 54-56; C Morden *S'wark* 56-59; E Midl Area Sec CPAS 59-63; V New Catton St Luke *Nor* 63-79; Chapl Bexley Hosp Kent 79-93; rtd 93. *Braemar, North Lyminge, Lyminge, Folkestone CT18 8EF* Tel (01303) 862369

HATHAWAY, Canon David Alfred Gerald. b 48. St Mich Coll Llan DipTh72. **d** 72 **p** 73. C Newport St Julian *Mon* 72-74; P-in-c Oakham w Hambleton and Egleton *Pet* 74-77; V Newport St Matt *Mon* 77-83; CF (TA) from 78; V Abertillery *Mon* 83-88; V Rumney from 88; Hon Can St Woolos Cathl from 91. *The Vicarage, 702 Newport Road, Rumney, Cardiff CF3 4DF* Tel (029) 2079 7882

HATHAWAY, John Albert. b 24. Sarum Th Coll 59. **d** 60 **p** 61. C Fleet *Guildf* 60-64; C Cowley St Jas *Ox* 64-66; V Holmwood *Guildf* 66-71; R Westborough 71-74; V Newmarket All SS *St E* 74-82; V Acton w Gt Waldingfield 82-85; R W Downland *Sarum* 85-90; rtd 90; Perm to Offic *Sarum* from 94. *12 St Edwards Court, Shaftesbury SP7 8LZ* Tel (01747) 851950

HATHAWAY, Martin Charles. b 48. St Jo Coll Nottm LTh95. **d** 95 **p** 96. C Weddington and Caldecote *Cov* 95-99; V Potters Green from 99. *St Philip's Vicarage, Ringwood Highway, Coventry CV2 2GF* Tel (024) 7661 7706

E-mail martin hathaway@lineone.net

HATHAWAY, Vivienne Ann. b 57. Bucks Chilterns Univ Coll BSc96. Westcott Ho Cam 00. **d** 02 **p** 03. C Bp's Hatfield *St Alb* from 02. *Church Cottage, 2 Church Street, Hatfield AL9 5AP* Tel (01707) 261949 E-mail vivienne@vhathaway.freeserve.co.uk

HATHERLEY, Peter Graham. b 46. Univ of Wales (Cardiff) BSc67 PhD70. St Mich Coll Llan 70. **d** 72 **p** 73. C Ystrad Mynach *Llan* 72-75; Hon C Tonyrefail 75-88; Perm to Offic from 88. *Treetops, The Derwen, Bridgend CF35 6HD* Tel (01656) 662196

HATHERLEY, Victor Charles. b 17. St Aug Coll Cant 63. **d** 64 **p** 64. C Crewkerne *B & W* 64-68; R E Harptree 68-73; R E w W Harptree 73-76; R E w W Harptree and Hinton Blewett 76-82; rtd 82; Perm to Offic *B & W* 83-91; Perm to Offic *Sarum* from 91. *10 Fairview Road, Broadstone BH18 9AX* Tel (01202) 699371

HATHORNE (née MARSH), Mrs Carol Ann. b 44. W Midl Coll of Educn BA83. WMMTC 88. **d** 91 **p** 94. Par Dn Wednesbury St Paul Wood Green *Lich* 91-93; NSM Pensnett *Worc* 93-97; TV Cannock *Lich* 97-01. *The Vicarage, 129 Essington Road, Willenhall WV12 5DT*

HATHORNE, Mark Stephen. b 51. Boston Univ MDiv76. **d** 00 **p** 00. C Willenhall H Trin *Lich* 00-01; TV from 01. *The Vicarage, 129 Essington Road, Willenhall WV12 5DT* Tel (01922) 409460 E-mail m.s.hathorne@virgin.net

HATHWAY, Ross Arthur. b 56. DATh87. Moore Th Coll Sydney BTh86. **d** 86 **p** 87. C Tamworth St Pet Australia 87-88; C Corby St Columba *Pet* 89-92; R Trull w Angersleigh *B & W* 92-02; R Kellyville St Steph Australia from 03. *12 Falkirk Court, Kellyville, NSW, Australia 2155*

HATREY, David Nigel. b 57. SS Mark & Jo Coll Plymouth CertEd79 Cert Science 87 BEd90 Ex Univ MA01. SW Minl Tr Course 90. **d** 93 **p** 94. NSM S Hill w Callington *Truro* 93-01; Hon C Street w Walton *B & W* from 01. *Pilgrims Way, Chilton Polden Hill, Edington, Bridgwater TA7 9AL* Tel (01278) 723616 E-mail hatreys@micehouse.fsnet.co.uk

HATTAN, Jeffrey William Rowland. b 49. Cranmer Hall Dur 83. **d** 85 **p** 86. C Eston w Normanby *York* 85-89; TV 89-95; V Hunmanby w Muston from 95. *The Vicarage, 6 Northgate, Hunmanby, Filey YO14 0NT* Tel (01723) 890294 E-mail jeff@all-saints.freeserve.co.uk

HATTER, Canon David George. b 21. Lich Th Coll. **d** 57 **p** 58. C Carrington *S'well* 57-61; V Clipstone 61-67; V Mansfield St Mark 67-81; V Sutton w Carlton and Normanton upon Trent etc 81-86; P-in-c Caunton 84-86; Hon Can S'well Minster 84-86; RD Tuxford and Norwell 84-86; rtd 86; Perm to Offic *S'well* 86-00. *1 North End, Farndon, Newark NG24 3SX* Tel (01636) 76960

HATTON, Jane Elizabeth. b 53. St Alb and Ox Min Course CBTS98. **d** 98 **p** 99. NSM Stevenage St Pet Broadwater *St Alb* from 98. *2 Dancote, Park Lane, Knebworth SG3 6PB* Tel (01438) 811039 E-mail janehatton@dial.pipex.com

HATTON, Jeffrey Charles. b 49. K Coll Lon BD70 Bris Univ MA72. Westcott Ho Cam 73 Episc Th Sch Cam Mass 74. **d** 74 **p** 75. C Nor St Pet Mancroft *Nor* 74-78; C Earlham St Anne 78-79; Relig Broadcasting Asst IBA 79-82; Hon C Kensington St Barn *Lon* 79-84; Hon C Fulham All SS 85-89; R Win All SS w Chilcomb and Chesil *Win* 89-94; Dioc Communications Officer 89-94; P-in-c Salisbury St Thos and St Edm *Sarum* 94-99; R from 99. *Little Bower, Campbell Road, Salisbury SP1 3BG* Tel (01722) 501344 *or* 322537 E-mail charlesh@cix.co.uk

HATTON, Michael Samuel. b 44. St Jo Coll Dur BA72 DipTh74. **d** 74 **p** 75. C Dudley St Jas *Worc* 74-75; C N Lynn w St Marg and St Nic *Nor* 75-77; C Walsall Wood *Lich* 78-79; Min Shelfield St Mark CD 79-89; V Middleton St Cross *Ripon* 89-97; V Ingol *Blackb* from 97. *St Margaret's Vicarage, 1A St Margaret's Close, Ingol, Preston PR2 3ZU* Tel (01772) 727208 E-mail spike.ingol@virgin.net

HATTON, Trevor. b 55. Oak Hill Th Coll BA86. **d** 86 **p** 87. C Chilwell *S'well* 86-90; R Trowell 90-95; Chapl Nottm Trent Univ 95-99; P-in-c Nottingham St Nic 99-02; R from 02. *37 Lyme Park, West Bridgford, Nottingham NG2 7TR* Tel 0115-982 0407 E-mail office@stnics.org

HATWELL, Timothy Rex. b 53. Oak Hill Th Coll BA85. **d** 85 **p** 86. C Tonbridge St Steph *Roch* 85-90; V Cudham and Downe from 90. *The Vicarage, Cudham Lane South, Cudham, Sevenoaks TN14 7QA* Tel (01959) 572445 Fax as telephone E-mail tim@hatwell.net

HAUGHAN, John Francis (Frank). b 28. Tyndale Hall Bris 56. **d** 60 **p** 61. C Tonbridge St Steph *Roch* 60-63; C Cheltenham St Mark *Glouc* 63-67; V Tewkesbury H Trin 67-92; rtd 92; Perm to Offic *Glouc* from 92. *1 Farmers Lane, Childswickham, Broadway WR12 7HN* Tel (01386) 852268

HAUGHTON, Peter Steele. b 57. K Coll Lon BD84 MA90 Fitzw Coll Cam DipTh85. Westcott Ho Cam 84. **d** 86 **p** 87. C Cheam Common St Phil *S'wark* 86-90; Chapl Lon Univ Medical Schs 90-94; Educn Adv Lon Univ Medical Schs 94-95; P-in-c Kingston Vale St Jo 95-03; Lect K Coll Lon from 03. *95 Bullar Road, Southampton SO18 1GT* Tel 07815-803920 (mobile) E-mail peter.haughton@btinternet.com

HAVARD, Alan Ernest. b 27. Qu Coll Birm 79. **d** 81 **p** 82. NSM Rugby St Matt *Cov* 81-84; C Portishead *B & W* 84-86; V Mickleover All SS *Derby* 86-96; rtd 96; Perm to Offic *Derby* from 96. *7 Headingley Court, Littleover, Derby DE3 6XS*

HAVARD, David William. b 56. Man Univ BA84. Qu Coll Birm 84. **d** 85. C Man Clayton St Cross w St Paul *Man* 85-88; Canada from 88. *Address temp unknown*

HAVELL, Edward Michael. b 38. Dur Univ BA65. Ridley Hall Cam 66. **d** 68 **p** 69. C Ecclesall *Sheff* 68-71; C Roch St Justus *Roch* 71-74; P-in-c Holbeach Hurn *Linc* 74-75; C Hollington St Jo *Chich* 75-85; TV Rye 85-92; C E Dereham and Scarning *Nor* 92; rtd 93; Perm to Offic *Chich* from 99. *4 Gammons Way, Sedlescombe, Battle TN33 0RQ* Tel (01424) 870864

HAVENS, Mrs Anita Sue. b 44. Mass Univ BSEd67 Clark Univ (USA) MA72 Hughes Hall Cam BA79. Cranmer Hall Dur MA83. **dss** 84 **d** 92 **p** 94. Gateshead Hosps 84-87; Par Dn Cen Telford *Lich* 87-90; Ind Chapl 87-90; Ind Chapl *Liv* 90-96; TV Man Whitworth *Man* 96-99; Chapl Man Univ 96-99; R Birch St Agnes w Longsight St Jo w St Cypr 99-01; rtd 01. *Stone Cottage, Kirkby Thore, Penrith CA10 1UE* Tel (01768) 362682 E-mail sue.havens@lineone.net

HAVEY, Kenneth Richard. b 61. St Steph Ho Ox 95. **d** 97 **p** 98. C Corringham *Chelmsf* 97-98; C Leigh St Clem 98-02; R from 02. *St Clement's Rectory, 80 Leigh Hill, Leigh-on-Sea SS9 1AR* Tel (01702) 475305 E-mail frkenneth@stclement.plus.com

HAVILAND, Edmund Selwyn. b 24. K Coll Cam BA49 MA51. Wells Th Coll 49. **d** 51 **p** 52. C St Helier *S'wark* 51-55; C-in-c Bermondsey St Hugh CD 55-58; V Ockbrook *Derby* 58-68; V E Peckham *Roch* 68-78; R E Peckham and Nettlestead 78-84; S Africa 84-85; Chapl HM Pris Brixton 85-89; rtd 89; Perm to Offic *Guildf* from 89. *Hill Farm, Thursley, Godalming GU8 6QQ* Tel (01252) 702115

HAWES, Andrew Thomas. b 54. Sheff Univ BA77 Em Coll Cam MA79. Westcott Ho Cam 77. **d** 80 **p** 81. C Gt Grimsby St Mary and St Jas *Linc* 80-84; P-in-c Gedney Drove End 84-86; P-in-c Sutton St Nicholas 84-86; V Lutton w Gedney Drove End, Dawsmere 86-89; V Edenham w Witham on the Hill 89-00; V Edenham w Witham on the Hill and Swinstead from 00; RD Beltisloe from 97. *The Vicarage, Church Lane, Edenham, Bourne PE10 0LS* Tel (01778) 591358 Fax as telephone

HAWES, The Ven Arthur John. b 43. UEA BA86 Birm Univ DPS72 DLA75. Chich Th Coll 65. **d** 68 **p** 69. C Kidderminster St Jo *Worc* 68-72; P-in-c Droitwich 72-76; R Alderford w Attlebridge and Swannington *Nor* 76-92; Chapl Hellesdon and David Rice Hosps and Yare Clinic 76-92; RD Sparham *Nor* 81-91; Mental Health Act Commr 86-94; Hon Can Nor Cathl *Nor* 88-95; TR Gaywood 92-95; Adn Linc from 95; Can and Preb Linc Cathl from 95. *Archdeacon's House, Northfield Road, Quarrington, Sleaford NG34 8RT* Tel (01529) 304348 *or* (07803) 249834 Fax 304354 E-mail ad.oflincoln@virgin.net

HAWES, Clive. b 37. Univ of Wales BSc59. Coll of Resurr Mirfield 61. **d** 63 **p** 64. C Ynyshir *Llan* 63-65; C Roath 65-72; V Llanddewi Rhondda w Bryn Eirw 72-75; Chapl Ch Coll Brecon 75-92; V Llantilio Crossenny w Penrhos, Llanvetherine etc *Mon* 92-97; rtd 97. *Caeredin, 1 College Lane, Trefecca, Brecon LD3 0PP* Tel (01874) 711999

HAWES, George Walter. b 10. Lon Coll of Div 39. **d** 41 **p** 42. C Woodford Wells *Chelmsf* 41-48; Chapl Herts Sanatorium 43-46; V E Ham St Paul 48-56; Adn W Kenya 56-60; R Rowner *Portsm* 60-78; rtd 78. *12 Funtley Lane, Fareham PO17 5EQ* Tel (01329) 286309

HAWES, Joseph Patricius. b 65. St Chad's Coll Dur BA87. St Steph Ho Ox 88. **d** 91 **p** 92. C Clapham TM *S'wark* 91-96; P-in-c Barnes St Mich 96-97; TV Barnes 97-03; V Fulham All SS *Lon* from 03. *All Saints' Vicarage, 70 Fulham High Street, London SW6 3LG* Tel (020) 7736 6301 E-mail angelos@surfaid.org

HAWES, Mary Elizabeth. b 56. SEITE 94. **d** 00 **p** 01. Dioc Children's Adv *Lon* from 98; NSM Streatham St Leon *S'wark* from 00. *9 Roman Rise, London SE19 1JG* Tel (020) 8761 0231 E-mail therevs@fish.co.uk

HAWES, Michael Rowell. b 31. AKC61. **d** 62 **p** 63. C Epsom St Martin *Guildf* 62-65; Chapl RAF 65-86; R Newnham w Nately

Scures w Mapledurwell etc *Win* 86-97; rtd 97; Perm to Offic *Win* from 97. *7 Holly Lane, Ashley, New Milton BH25 5RF* Tel (01425) 620698

HAWKEN, Andrew Robert. b 58. K Coll Lon BD81 AKC81. St Steph Ho Ox 83. **d** 85 **p** 86. C Ex St Dav *Ex* 85-88; TV Witney *Ox* 88-93; V Benson from 93; AD Aston and Cuddesdon from 02. *The Vicarage, Church Road, Benson, Wallingford OX10 6SF* Tel and fax (01491) 201668 Mobile 07711-664877
E-mail andrew.hawken@ntlworld.com

HAWKEN, Rosalind Mary. b 56. York Univ BA77 Univ of Wales (Cardiff) BTh02. St Mich Coll Llan 99. **d** 02 **p** 03. C Swansea St Thos and Kilvey *S & B* from 02. *76 Danygraig Road, Port Tennant, Swansea SA1 8NA* Tel (01792) 480952

HAWKER, The Ven Alan Fort. b 44. Hull Univ BA65 Lon Univ DipTh68. Clifton Th Coll 65. **d** 68 **p** 69. C Bootle St Leon *Liv* 68-71; C Fazakerley Em 71-73; V Goose Green 73-81; TR Southgate *Chich* 81-98; Can and Preb Chich Cathl 91-98; RD E Grinstead 94-98; Hon Can Bris Cathl *Bris* from 98; Adn Swindon 98-99; Adn Malmesbury from 99. *Church Paddock, Church Lane, Kington Langley, Chippenham SN15 5NR* Tel (01249) 750085 Fax 750086 E-mail alan@venjen.fsnet.co.uk

HAWKER, Brian Henry. b 34. AKC61 St Boniface Warminster 61. **d** 62 **p** 63. C Hemel Hempstead *St Alb* 62-66; R Stone w Hartwell w Bishopstone *Ox* 66-69; Chapl St Jo Hosp Stone 66-69; V W Wycombe 69-72; Past Consultant Clinical Th Assn 72-83; Past Consultant 83-94; Public Preacher *S'well* 72-76; Perm to Offic *B & W* 76-83; Perm to Offic *Truro* 83-90; rtd 94; Perm to Offic *Leic* from 99. *12 Burfield Avenue, Loughborough LE11 3AZ* Tel (01509) 261439

HAWKER, The Ven Peter John. b 37. OBE96. Ex Univ BA59. Wycliffe Hall Ox 69. **d** 70 **p** 71. Asst Chapl Berne *Eur* 70-76; Chapl Berne w Neuchâtel 76-89; Adn Switzerland from 86; Can Brussels Cathl from 86; Chapl Zürich w St Gallen, Baden and Zug 90-00. *Schulgasse 10, 3280 Murten, Switzerland* Tel (0041) (26) 670 6221 Fax 670 6219 E-mail phawker@anglican.ch

HAWKES, Mrs Cecilia (Cilla). b 48. Reading Univ BSc69 Canley Coll of Educn DipEd71. EAMTC 99. **d** 02 **p** 03. NSM Takeley w Lt Canfield *Chelmsf* from 02. *Greenfields, Felsted, Dunmow CM6 3LF* Tel (01341) 856480 Fax as telephone
E-mail pandchawkes@aol.com

HAWKES, Mrs Elisabeth Anne. b 56. GRNCM78 PGCE80 Kent Univ MA97. Linc Th Coll 86. **d** 88 **p** 97. Hon Par Dn Finham *Cov* 88-90; Hon Par Dn Bexhill St Pet *Chich* 90-97; Asst to RD Oundle *Pet* 97-98; NSM Oundle 98-00; NSM Benefield and Southwick w Glapthorn 99-00; Perm to Offic *Cant* from 00. *The Vicarage, 25 Dence Park, Herne Bay CT6 6BQ* Tel (01227) 360948

HAWKES, The Ven Francis George. b 23. LTh50. St Barn Coll Adelaide ACT 50. **d** 51 **p** 51. Australia 51-65 and from 83; Adn Marsden 87-89; CF 65-83; rtd 89. *PO Box 62, Kurrajong, NSW, Australia 2758* Tel (0061) (2) 4573 1617

HAWKES, Mrs Helen Vanda. b 50. Surrey Univ BA01. STETS 98. **d** 01 **p** 02. NSM N Hayling St Pet *Portsm* from 01; NSM Hayling Is St Andr from 01. *67 East Lodge Park, Farlington, Portsmouth PO16 1BZ* Tel (023) 9221 9005 Mobile 07719-828113 E-mail vanda.hawkes@btinternet.com

HAWKES, Keith Andrew. b 28. Oak Hill Th Coll 72. **d** 74 **p** 75. C Gt Yarmouth *Nor* 74-77; C-in-c Bowthorpe CD 77; Chapl Düsseldorf *Eur* 77-83; TV Quidenham *Nor* 83-88; TR 88-90; RD Thetford and Rockland 86-90; R Wickmere w Lt Barningham, Itteringham etc 90-96; Dioc Rural Officer 90-94; P-in-c Saxthorpe w Corpusty, Blickling, Oulton etc 94-96; R Lt Barningham, Blickling, Edgefield etc 96-98; Bp's Chapl 98; rtd 98; Perm to Offic *Nor* 98-00; P-in-c Guiltcross from 00; Chapl Norwich Primary Care Trust 00-02. *The Rectory, Back Street, Garboldisham, Diss IP22 2SD* Tel (01953) 688347
E-mail revkahawkes@aol.com

HAWKES, Martyn John. b 71. Nottm Univ BA94 St Jo Coll Dur BA01. Cranmer Hall Dur 99. **d** 02. C Is of Dogs Ch Ch and St Jo w St Luke *Lon* from 02. *Flat 2, St Mildred's House, Roserton Street, London E14 3PG*

HAWKES, Nigel Anthony Robert. b 59. UEA BSc80 Edin Univ MSc82. Ripon Coll Cuddesdon 00. **d** 02 **p** 03. C Chase *Ox* from 02. *The Vicarage, Little Tew Road, Church Enstone, Chipping Norton OX7 4NL* Tel (01608) 678424
E-mail revnige@fish.co.uk

HAWKES, Ronald Linton. b 54. Leeds Univ CertEd75 BEd76 Kent Univ MA96. Linc Th Coll 85. **d** 87 **p** 88. C Finham *Cov* 87-90; C Bexhill St Pet *Chich* 90; TV 91-97; V Oundle *Pet* 97-00; Dir Post-Ord Tr 98-00; P-in-c Benefield and Southwick w Glapthorn 99-00; Chapl and Hd RE St Edm Sch Cant 00-03; Hon Min Can Cant Cathl *Cant* 01-03; V Reculver and Herne Bay St Bart from 03. *The Vicarage, 25 Dence Park, Herne Bay CT6 6BQ* Tel (01227) 360948

HAWKETT, Graham Kenneth. b 20. Bps' Coll Cheshunt 61. **d** 63 **p** 64. C Farncombe *Guildf* 63-67; V Wyke 67-85; rtd 85; Perm to Offic *Guildf* from 85. *Bede House, Beech Road, Haslemere GU27 2BX* Tel (01428) 656430

HAWKINGS, Timothy Denison. b 55. Ex Univ BA78 Nottm Univ BA80. St Jo Coll Nottm 78. **d** 81 **p** 82. C Penn *Lich* 81-85; C Stafford 85; TV 85-94; TR Stratton St Margaret w S Marston etc *Bris* from 94. *The Rectory, Kenwin Close, Swindon SN3 4NY* Tel (01793) 822793

HAWKINS, The Ven Alun John. b 44. K Coll Lon BA66 AKC66 Univ of Wales (Ban) BD81. St Deiniol's Hawarden 78. **d** 81 **p** 82. C Dwygyfylchi *Ban* 81-84; R Llanberis 84-89; Tutor Ban Dioc NSM Course 85-90; Dir of Ords *Ban* 86-90; V Knighton and Norton *S & B* 89-93; Chapl Knighton Hosp 89-93; R Bangor *Ban* from 93; Can Res and Can Missr Ban Cathl 93-00; Adult Educn Officer from 93; Sec Dioc Bd of Miss from 93; Adn Ban from 00. *The Archdeaconry, 1 Belmont Road, Bangor LL57 2LL* Tel (01248) 362840 Fax as telephone

HAWKINS, Andrew Robert. b 40. St Andr Univ BSc64. St Chad's Coll Dur BA68 DipTh69. **d** 69 **p** 70. C Sutton St Nic *S'wark* 69-73; C Wimbledon 73-77; TV Cramlington *Newc* 77-81; R Clutton w Cameley *B & W* 81-89; Chapl City of Bath Coll of FE from 89; Perm to Offic *B & W* from 90. *18 Wally Court Road, Chew Stoke, Bristol BS40 8XN* Tel (01275) 332422
E-mail andrewr.hawkins@virgin.net

HAWKINS, Canon Bruce Alexander. b 44. Qu Coll Ox BA66 MA71. Sarum Th Coll 66. **d** 68 **p** 69. C Epsom St Martin *Guildf* 68-71; Dioc Youth Chapl *Cant* 72-81; Hon Min Can Cant Cathl 75-99; Dep Dir of Educn 81-86; V Walmer from 86; RD Sandwich 94-00; Hon Can Cant Cathl from 99. *The Vicarage, St Mary's Road, Deal CT14 7NQ* Tel (01304) 374645 Fax as telephone

HAWKINS, Mrs Christine Ann. b 56. SEITE. **d** 01 **p** 02. NSM Epping Distr *Chelmsf* 01-02; C Woodford St Mary w St Phil and St Jas from 02. *33 Elmhurst Drive, London E18 1BP* Tel (020) 8530 4492 Mobile 07944-431794
E-mail christine.hawkins@unisonfree.net

HAWKINS, Clive Ladbrook. b 53. DHSA79 St Pet Coll Ox BA76 MA79 DipTh82. Trin Coll Bris 80. **d** 82 **p** 83. C Win Ch Ch *Win* 82-86; R Eastrop from 86; AD Basingstoke from 00. *Eastrop Rectory, 2A Wallis Road, Basingstoke RG21 3DW* Tel (01256) 355507 E-mail clive.hawkins@stmarys-basingstoke.org.uk

✠**HAWKINS, The Rt Revd David John Leader.** b 49. Nottm Univ BTh73 LTh. St Jo Coll Nottm 69 ALCD73. **d** 73 **p** 74 **c** 02. C Bebington *Ches* 73-76; Nigeria 76-82; C Ox St Aldate w St Matt *Ox* 83-86; V Leeds St Geo *Ripon* 86-99; TR 99-02; Area Bp Barking *Chelmsf* from 02. *Barking Lodge, 35A Verulam Avenue, London E17 8ES* Tel (020) 8509 7377
E-mail b.barking@chelmsford.anglican.org

HAWKINS, David Kenneth Beaumont. b 36. Em Coll Saskatoon LTh63. **d** 63 **p** 64. Canada 63-85; C St Alb St Paul *St Alb* 85-87; C Hednesford *Lich* 87-92; R Buildwas and Leighton w Eaton Constantine etc 92-95; TV Wrockwardine Deanery 95-01; rtd 01. *PO Box 454, 131 Westward Crescent, Wellington ON, Canada, K0K 3L0*

HAWKINS, David Sewell. b 33. Bps' Coll Cheshunt. **d** 58 **p** 59. C Chingford St Anne *Chelmsf* 58-59; C Bridlington Quay Ch Ch *York* 59-63; V Rudston, Grindale and Ergham w Boynton 63-64; P-in-c Boynton 63-64; V Rudston w Boynton 64-68; Chapl RADD 68-77; R Burton Agnes w Harpham *York* 77-80; P-in-c Lowthorpe w Ruston Parva 77-80; P-in-c Kilham 77-80; R Burton Agnes w Harpham, Kilham, Lowthorpe etc 80-85; R Burton Agnes w Harpham and Lowthorpe etc 85-97; rtd 97; Perm to Offic *York* from 99. *71A St James Road, Bridlington YO15 3PQ* Tel (01262) 672817

HAWKINS, Donald John. b 39. K Coll Lon BD62 AKC62. St Boniface Warminster 62. **d** 63 **p** 64. C Winlaton *Dur* 63-66; C Gateshead St Mary 66-69; C Ryhope 69-71; R Cockfield 71-79; Chapl N Staffs R Infirmary Stoke-on-Trent 79-89; Chapl Stoke-on-Trent City Gen Hosp 89-93; Chapl N Staffs Hosp NHS Trust 93-99; Chapl Co-ord 94-99; rtd 99; Perm to Offic *Lich* from 99. *12 The Avenue, Hartshill, Stoke-on-Trent ST4 6BJ* Tel (01782) 620691 Fax as telephone E-mail hawkins@12ave.freeserve.co.uk

HAWKINS, Canon Francis John. b 36. Ex Coll Ox BA61 MA63. Chich Th Coll 59. **d** 61 **p** 62. C Tavistock and Gulworthy *Ex* 61-64; Lect Chich Th Coll 64-73; Vice-Prin 73-75; V E Grinstead St Mary *Chich* 75-81; Can Res and Treas Chich Cathl 81-01; V Sidlesham 81-89; Dir of Ords 89-01; rtd 01. *6 Priory Road, Chichester PO19 1NS* Tel (01243) 771921

HAWKINS, Ian Clinton. b 27. Roch Th Coll 63. **d** 65 **p** 66. C Boulton *Derby* 65-68; V Cotmanhay 68-77; V Ospringe *Cant* 77-85; P-in-c Eastling 77-85; P-in-c Goodnestone H Cross w Chillenden and Knowlton 85; P-in-c Womenswold 85; V Nonington w Wymynswold and Goodnestone etc 85-92; rtd 92; Perm to Offic *Derby* from 92. *7 Main Road, Bradwell, Hope Valley S33 9JG* Tel (01433) 621360
E-mail ian.hawkins4@virgin.net

HAWKINS, James Reginald. b 39. Ex Univ BA61 Hull Univ MA00. Westcott Ho Cam 61. **d** 63 **p** 64. C Cannock *Lich* 63-66; C Wem 66-67; C Cheddleton 67-69; R Yoxall 69-77; R The Quinton *Birm* 77-84; V Bosbury w Wellington Heath etc *Heref* 84-96; P-in-c Ancaster Wilsford Gp *Linc* 96-99; R from 99; RD Loveden from 97. *The Rectory, 117 Ermine Street, Ancaster,*

HAWKINS, John. b 27. Ox Poly DipArch52 Lon Univ DipRS87. S'wark Ord Course 84. **d** 87 **p** 88. Hon C Carshalton Beeches *S'wark* 87-89; Perm to Offic from 89. *44 Castlemaine Avenue, South Croydon CR2 7HR* Tel (020) 8688 9685

HAWKINS, John Arthur. b 45. Lon Univ DipTh69. Kelham Th Coll 64. **d** 69 **p** 70. C Cov St Alb *Cov* 70-73; C Fletchamstead 73-77; V Whitley 77-81; TV Northampton Em *Pet* 81-90; TV Gt Chesham *Ox* 90-98; C Thorpe *Nor* from 98. *8 Hampton Drive, Thorpe St Andrew, Norwich NR7 0UT* Tel (01603) 431868

HAWKINS, John Charles Lacey. b 18. Linc Th Coll 40. **d** 42 **p** 43. C Dalton-in-Furness *Carl* 42-44; C Workington St Micah 44-48; V Allonby w W Newton 48-53; V Thornton w Allerthorpe *York* 53-60; R Stockton-on-the-Forest w Holtby and Warthill 60-77; R Sigglesthorne and Rise w Nunkeeling and Bewholme 77-83; rtd 83; Perm to Offic *York* 83-96. *Flat 4, Sheppards College, London Road, Bromley BR1 1PE* Tel (020) 8460 1469

HAWKINS, John Colin. b 50. Birkbeck Coll Lon DipRS96. SEITE 97. **d** 00 **p** 01. NSM W Wickham St Jo *S'wark* from 00. *198 Pickhurst Rise, West Wickham BR4 0AU* Tel (020) 8289 7608 E-mail john.hawkins@classicfm.net

HAWKINS, John Edward Inskipp. b 63. K Coll Lon BD85. Qu Coll Birm 86. **d** 88 **p** 89. C Birchfield *Birm* 88-92; C Poplar *Lon* 92-93; TV 93-99; V W Hendon St Jo from 99. *St John's Vicarage, Vicarage Road, London NW4 3PX* Tel (020) 8202 8606

HAWKINS, Canon John Henry. b 13. TCD BA35 MA BD52. TCD Div Sch 37. **d** 37 **p** 38. C Ballymacarrett St Patr *D & D* 37-39; Min Can Down Cathl 39-44; I Ballee w Bright 44-50; I Antrim All SS w Connor St Sav *Conn* 50-55; I Antrim All SS w Muckamore 57-63; I Antrim All SS 63-67; I Agherton 67-78; Can Conn Cathl 76-78; rtd 78. *11 Carnreagh Avenue, Hillsborough BT26 6LL* Tel (028) 9268 2565

HAWKINS, Nicholas Milner. b 45. Univ of Wales (Swansea) BA MSc. **d** 01. Par Dn Dingestow and Llangovan w Penyclawdd etc *Mon* 01-02; Perm to Offic *Ban* 02-03; NSM Nefyn w Tudweiliog w Llandudwen w Edern from 03. *Bryn Mor, Llangwnadl, Pwllheli LL53 8NS* Tel (01758) 770582 Mobile 07870-264385 Fax (01758) 770228 E-mail nick.hawkins@btinternet.com

HAWKINS, Noel. b 46. St Jo Coll Nottm 82. **d** 84 **p** 85. C Worksop St Jo *S'well* 84-86; C Wollaton Park 86-89; TV Billericay and Lt Burstead *Chelmsf* 89-95; TV Keynsham *B & W* 95-00; V Brislington St Chris and St Cuth *Bris* from 00. *St Cuthbert's Vicarage, 35 Wick Crescent, Bristol BS4 4HG* Tel 0117-977 6351

HAWKINS, Miss Patricia Sally. b 59. LMH Ox BA80 MA84 Ex Univ BPhil85 CQSW85. St Steph Ho Ox 99. **d** 01. C Stafford *Lich* from 01. *9 Brunswick Terrace, Stafford ST16 1BB* Tel (01785) 243995 Mobile 07929-975651

HAWKINS, Paul Henry Whishaw. b 46. Ex Coll Ox BA68 MA74 SS Coll Cam MA84. St Steph Ho Ox 70. **d** 72 **p** 73. C Fawley *Win* 72-75; C Ealing St Steph Castle Hill *Lon* 75-77; P-in-c Dorney *Ox* 77-78; TV Riverside 78-81; Chapl SS Coll Cam 82-87; V Plymstock *Ex* 87-97; RD Plymouth Sutton 91-96; TR Plymstock and Hooe 97-00; Preb Ex Cathl 98-00; P-in-c St Pancras w St Jas and Ch Ch *Lon* 00-02; V from 02. *6 Sandwich Street, London WC1H 9PL* Tel (020) 7388 1630 Fax 7388 1461

HAWKINS, Peter Edward. b 35. Leeds Univ BA60. Coll of Resurr Mirfield 60. **d** 62 **p** 63. C Forest Gate St Edm *Chelmsf* 62-65; C Sevenoaks St Jo *Roch* 65-68; Chapl Metrop Police Cadet Corps Tr Sch 68-73; P-in-c Knowle H Nativity *Bris* 73; TV Knowle 73-79; V Westbury-on-Trym H Trin 79-87; TR Solihull *Birm* 87-96; Hon Can Birm Cathl 92-96; rtd 00. *Back Street Cottage, 15 St Andrew's Road, Stogursey, Bridgwater TA5 1TE* Tel (01278) 733635 Fax as telephone E-mail peh.stogursey@tiscali.net

HAWKINS, Peter Michael. b 38. Kelham Th Coll 58. **d** 63 **p** 64. India 63-69; C Manningham St Paul and St Jude *Bradf* 70-72; C Bradf Cathl 72-75; V Allerton 75-90; V Pet H Spirit Bretton *Pet* from 90; P-in-c Marholm 90-95. *23 Westhawe, Bretton, Peterborough PE3 8BE* Tel (01733) 264418 *or* 842508 Mobile 07952-805657 Fax (01733) 332544 E-mail holyspiritchurch@fish.co.uk *or* hawkinspp@aol.com

HAWKINS, Richard Randal. b 39. **d** 65 **p** 66. C Bushbury *Lich* 65-68; C Woodford St Mary *Chelmsf* 68-71; S Africa from 71. *PO Box 100282, Scottsville, 3209 South Africa* Tel (0027) (331) 420262 *or* 453336

✠**HAWKINS, The Rt Revd Richard Stephen.** b 39. Ex Coll Ox BA61 MA65 Ex Univ BPhil76. St Steph Ho Ox 61. **d** 63 **p** 64 **c** 88. C Ex St Thos *Ex* 63-66; C Clyst St Mary 66-75; TV Clyst St George, Aylesbeare, Clyst Honiton etc 75-78; Bp's Officer for Min 78-81; Jt Dir Ex and Truro NSM Scheme 78-81; TV Cen Ex 78-81; Dioc Dir of Ords 79-81; Adn Totnes 81-88; P-in-c Oldridge 81-87; P-in-c Whitestone 81-87; Suff Bp Plymouth 88-96; Suff Bp Crediton from 96. *10 Cathedral Close, Exeter EX1 1EZ* Tel (01392) 273509 Fax 431266 E-mail bishop.of.crediton@exeter.anglican.org

HAWKINS, Richard Whishaw. b 51. Coll of Resurr Mirfield 93. **d** 95 **p** 96. C Weymouth H Trin *Sarum* 95-99; P-in-c Hey *Man* from 99; AD Saddleworth from 03. *St John's Vicarage, 1 Owen*

Fold, Oldham OL4 3DT Tel 0161-626 3630 E-mail richard.hawkins107@ntlworld.com

HAWKINS, Roger David William. b 33. K Coll Lon BD58 AKC58. **d** 59 **p** 60. C Twickenham St Mary *Lon* 59-61; C Heston 61-64; C Dorking w Ranmore *Guildf* 64-65; V Mitcham St Mark *S'wark* 65-74; V Redhill St Matt 74-91; P-in-c Warlingham w Chelsham and Farleigh 91-97; TR 97-98; rtd 98. *2 Grove Court, Falkland Grove, Dorking RH4 3DL* Tel (01306) 885817

HAWKINS, Roger Julian. b 32. Ripon Hall Ox 59. **d** 61 **p** 62. C-in-c Newall Green CD *Man* 61-63; Chapl RAF 63-67; R Mawgan in Pyder *Truro* 67-75; R Lanteglos by Camelford w Advent 75-78; R Newmarket St Mary w Exning St Agnes *St E* 78-85; P-in-c Coltishall w Gt Hautbois *Nor* 87; R Coltishall w Gt Hautbois and Horstead 87-90; Chapl Whiteley Village *Guildf* 90-94; rtd 97; Perm to Offic *Win* from 01. *42 St Anne's Place, Salisbury SP1 2SU* Tel (01722) 415979

HAWKINS, Steven Andrew. b 51. Nottm Univ BEd75 Open Univ BSc91 Bris Poly ADEd90. STETS 95. **d** 98 **p** 99. C Horfield H Trin *Bris* 98-02; V Brislington St Anne from 02. *The Vicarage, 23 First Avenue, Bristol BS4 4DU* Tel 0117-983 0283 Mobile 07900-242443 E-mail steven@hawkins96.freeserve.co.uk

HAWKINS, Susan. b 47. Doncaster Coll of Educn CertEd69 Chester Coll of HE BTh99. N Ord Course 95. **d** 99 **p** 00. NSM Prestbury *Ches* 99-02; P-in-c Marthall from 02; Chapl David Lewis Cen for Epilepsy from 02. *The Vicarage, Sandlebridge Lane, Marthall, Knutsford WA16 7SB* Tel (01625) 860981 E-mail dvs.hawkins@btinternet.com

HAWKINS, Timothy St John. b 59. CCC Ox BA82. Trin Coll Bris BA87. **d** 87 **p** 88. C Cheltenham St Mary, St Matt, St Paul and H Trin *Glouc* 87-90; C Cowplain *Portsm* 90-94; V Pennycross *Ex* 94-96; P-in-c St Keverne *Truro* from 96. *The Vicarage, St Keverne, Helston TR12 6NG* Tel (01326) 280227 E-mail helen.hawkins@tesco.net

HAWKINS, William Arthur. b 18. Clifton Th Coll 50. **d** 53 **p** 54. C Ellacombe *Ex* 53-54; C Totnes 54-58; R Ashill w Broadway *B & W* 58-74; R Herstmonceux *Chich* 74-83; rtd 83; Perm to Offic *Chich* from 84. *Three Gables, 17 Heighton Road, Newhaven BN9 0RB* Tel (01273) 513694

HAWKSBEE, Canon Derek John. b 28. Lon Univ BSc49. S'wark Ord Course 70. **d** 71 **p** 72. C Norbiton *S'wark* 71-75; Cand and SAMS 71-79; Overseas Sec 73-79; Hon Can Paraguay from 73; Hon C Tunbridge Wells St Jo *Roch* 75-79; USA 79-87; R Ravendale Gp *Linc* 88-96; rtd 96; Perm to Offic *Roch* from 99. *205 Upper Grosvenor Road, Tunbridge Wells TN1 2EG* Tel (01892) 533485

HAWKSWORTH, Maldwyn Harry. b 45. Aston Univ CertEd74. St Jo Coll Nottm 87. **d** 89 **p** 90. C Penn *Lich* 89-94; TV Bloxwich from 94. *6 Cresswell Crescent, Bloxwich, Walsall WS3 2UW* Tel (01922) 476647

HAWKSWORTH, Peter John Dallas. b 54. Solicitor 79 St Jo Coll Ox BA75 MA79. Sarum & Wells Th Coll 89. **d** 91 **p** 92. C Warminster St Denys, Upton Scudamore etc *Sarum* 91-95; P-in-c Salisbury St Mark 95-99; V from 99. *St Mark's Vicarage, 62 Barrington Road, Salisbury SP1 3JD* Tel (01722) 323767 E-mail sarumark@hxwf.surfaid.org

HAWLEY, Canon Anthony Broughton. b 41. St Pet Coll Ox BA67 MA71 Kent Univ DMS96. Westcott Ho Cam 67. **d** 69 **p** 70. C Wolverhampton St Pet *Lich* 69-72; C-in-c Bermondsey St Hugh CD *S'wark* 73-84; Hon PV S'wark Cathl 83-84; TR Kirkby *Liv* 84-02; AD Walton 93-02; Hon Can Liv Cathl 96-02; Can Res Liv Cathl from 02. *2 Cathedral Close, Liverpool L1 7BR* Tel 0151-708 0932 E-mail canon.hawley@liverpoolcathedral.org.uk

HAWLEY, Georgina. b 45. **d** 01 **p** 02. Australia 01-02; NSM Chippenham St Pet *Bris* 02-03; Perm to Offic from 03. *2 Coopers Meadow, Yatton Keynell, Chippenham SN14 7PZ* Tel (01249) 782858 Fax as telephone E-mail ghawley@brookes.ac.uk

HAWLEY, The Ven John Andrew. b 50. K Coll Lon BD71 AKC71. Wycliffe Hall Ox 72. **d** 74 **p** 75. C Kingston upon Hull H Trin *York* 74-77; C Bradf Cathl Par *Bradf* 77-80; V Woodlands *Sheff* 80-91; TR Dewsbury *Wakef* 91-02; Hon Can Wakef Cathl 98-02; Adn Blackb from 02. *19 Clarence Park, Blackburn BB2 7FA* Tel (01254) 262571 Pager 07623-110608 Fax (01254) 263394 E-mail archdeacon.blackburn@milestonenet.co.uk

HAWLEY, Nigel David. b 51. Coll of Resurr Mirfield 77. **d** 80 **p** 81. C Birch w Fallowfield *Man* 80-84; P-in-c Moston St Jo 84-85; R 85-93; R Reddish from 93. *St Elisabeth's Rectory, Bedford Street, Stockport SK5 6DJ* Tel 0161-432 3033 E-mail frnigel@stelisabeths.fsnet.co.uk

HAWLEY, William David Llewellyn. b 41. Univ of W Aus BCom77 Curtin Univ Aus DPA88 Murdoch Univ Aus BD94. **d** 92 **p** 95. Australia 92-00; Hon C Bullcreek w Bateman 92-94; Hon C Kwinana 94-95; Dioc Registrar 95-97; Assoc P Spearwood w Hilton 95-98; R Hilton 98-00; TV Br Brook *Bris* from 01. *2 Coopers Meadow, Yatton Keynell, Chippenham SN14 7PZ* Tel (01249) 782858 Fax as telephone

HAWNT, John Charles Frederick. b 30. St Paul's Cheltenham. Selly Oak Coll 52 Westwood Cen Zimbabwe 72. **d** 75 **p** 76. Rhodesia 75-80; Zimbabwe 80-81; C Rugby St Andr *Cov* 81-85; R Lydeard St Lawrence w Brompton Ralph etc *B & W* 85-00; rtd

00; S Africa from 00. *39 St Andrew Road, Houghton, Johannesburg, 2198 South Africa*

HAWORTH, Mrs Betsy Ellen. b 24. Wm Temple Coll Hawarden 50. **dss** 80 **d** 89. Walkden Moor *Man* 80-81; Third Ch Estates Commr 81-88; Lic to Offic 88-89; NSM Astley Bridge 89-99. *14 Sharples Hall Fold, Bolton BL1 7EH* Tel (01204) 591588

HAWORTH (née ARMSTRONG), Fiona Heather. b 65. Reading Univ BSc86 Nottm Univ PhD90. St Jo Coll Nottm BTh94. **d** 97 **p** 98. C Sutton in Ashfield St Mary *S'well* 97-02; TV Kidderminster St Mary and All SS w Trimpley etc *Worc* from 02. *The Vicarage, 50 Nursery Grove, Kidderminster DY11 5BG* Tel (01562) 748016

HAWORTH, John Luttrell. b 28. CITC 67. **d** 67 **p** 68. C Kilcommick *K, E & A* 67-70; C Ballymacelligott *L & K* 70-71; TV Tralee w Kilmoyley, Ballymacelligott etc 71-72; I Kinneigh w Ballymoney *C, C & R* 72-76; I Easkey w Kilglass *T, K & A* 77-83; I Monasterevan w Nurney and Rathdaire *M & K* 83-87; I Kiltegan w Hacketstown, Clonmore and Moyne *C & O* 87-92; I Fermoy Union *C, C & R* 92-96; rtd 96. *Shane Cottage, Fennells Bay, Myrtleville, Co Cork, Irish Republic* Tel (00353) (21) 483 1157

HAWORTH, Mark Newby. b 50. Aber Univ BSc73 MICFor81. Westcott Ho Cam 88. **d** 90 **p** 91. C Cherry Hinton St Andr *Ely* 90-93; C Teversham 90-93; P-in-c Swaffham Bulbeck and Swaffham Prior w Reach 93-94; V 94-02; RD Fordham 96-02; Chapl Framlingham Coll 03; Chapl to Bp Pet from 03. *Coach House, The Palace, Peterborough PE1 1XZ* Tel (01733) 342055 *or* 562492 Mobile 07932-160009 Fax (01733) 890077 E-mail mark.haworth@peterborough-diocese.org.uk

HAWORTH, Paul. b 47. G&C Coll Cam BA68 MA72. Westcott Ho Cam 75. **d** 78 **p** 79. C Hornchurch St Andr *Chelmsf* 78-81; C Loughton St Mary and St Mich 81-88; TV Waltham H Cross 88-92; TR Becontree S 92-00; P-in-c S Woodham Ferrers from 00. *The Vicarage, 10 Victoria Road, South Woodham Ferrers, Chelmsford CM3 5LR* Tel (01245) 322134 E-mail preacherman@pewend.org

HAWORTH, Stanley Robert. b 48. St Jo Coll Dur BA69. Sarum & Wells Th Coll 71. **d** 73 **p** 74. C Skipton H Trin *Bradf* 73-76; C Bradf Cathl 76-78; C Grantham *Linc* 78; TV 78-82; V Deeping St James 82-96; V Middlewich w Byley *Ches* 96-01; P-in-c Forcett and Aldbrough and Melsonby *Ripon* from 01. *The Vicarage, 1 Appleby Close, Aldbrough St John, Richmond DL11 7TT* Tel (01325) 374634 E-mail stantheroman@hotmail.com

HAWORTH, Stuart. b 43. Local Minl Tr Course 91. **d** 94 **p** 95. OLM Bradshaw *Man* 94-01; OLM Turton Moorland Min from 01. *178 Turton Road, Bolton BL2 3EE* Tel (01204) 594506

HAWTHORN, The Ven Christopher John. b 36. Qu Coll Cam BA60 MA64. Ripon Hall Ox 60. **d** 62 **p** 63. C Sutton St Jas *York* 62-66; V Kingston upon Hull St Nic 66-72; V E Coatham 72-79; V Scarborough St Martin 79-91; RD Scarborough 82-91; Can and Preb York Minster 87-01; Adn Cleveland 91-01; rtd 01; Perm to Offic *York* from 01. *43 Barley Rise, Strensall, York YO32 5AB* Tel (01904) 492060

HAWTHORN, David. b 63. Chich Th Coll 87. **d** 90 **p** 91. C Hartlepool H Trin *Dur* 90-94; C Middlesbrough All SS *York* 94-95; P-in-c Thornaby on Tees 95-96; V S Thornaby 96-02; P-in-c Brighton Annunciation *Chich* from 02. *Annunciation Vicarage, 89 Washington Street, Brighton BN2 2SR* Tel (01273) 681341 E-mail hawthorn@supanet.com

HAWTHORN, Thomas Russell. b 18. MBE90. Imp Coll Lon BSc48 Lon Univ ACGI48. **d** 82 **p** 82. Mexico 82-84; Perm to Offic *Nor* from 84; Sub Chapl HM Pris Blundeston 86-94. *82 Wollaston Road, Lowestoft NR32 2PF* Tel (01502) 518741

HAWTHORNE, Andrew. b 68. Jes Coll Ox BA89 MA93. Chich Th Coll BTh93. **d** 93 **p** 94. C Christchurch *Win* 93-97; TV Dorchester *Sarum* 97-00; rtd 00. *68 Arnewood Road, Southbourne, Bournemouth BH6 5DN* Tel (01202) 569163

HAWTHORNE, John William. b 32. St Aug Coll Cant 74. **d** 77 **p** 78. C Boxley *Cant* 77-80; P-in-c Langley 80-82; P-in-c Otham 80-82; R Otham w Langley 82-83; TR Preston w Sutton Poyntz and Osmington w Poxwell *Sarum* 83-87; R Tetbury w Beverston *Glouc* 87-01; rtd 01. *200 High Street, Honiton EX14 1AJ* Tel (01404) 46388 Fax 46468 E-mail honitonhawthorne@aol.com

HAWTHORNE, Canon William James (Jim). b 46. MBE01. TCD 66 Ch of Ireland Tr Coll 66. **d** 69 **p** 70. C Gilnahirk *D & D* 69-72; Asst Chapl Miss to Seamen 72-76; C Boultham *Linc* 76-78; C Bracebridge Heath 78-90; Dioc Adv for Relig Broadcasting 80-90; Chapl Palma de Mallorca and Balearic Is *Eur* 90-93; Chapl Palma de Mallorca 93-01; P-in-c Menorca 97-98; Can Gib Cathl 97-01; rtd 01. *16-08 Victoria Centre, Milton Street, Nottingham NG1 3PL* Tel 0115-840 7913 E-mail williamjameshawthorne@hotmail.com

✠**HAWTIN, The Rt Revd David Christopher.** b 43. Keble Coll Ox BA65 MA70. Wm Temple Coll Rugby 65 Cuddesdon Coll 66. **d** 67 **p** 68 **c** 99. C Pennywell St Thos and Grindon St Oswald CD *Dur* 67-71; C Stockton St Pet 71-74; C-in-c Leam Lane CD 74-79; R Washington 79-88; Dioc Ecum Officer 88-91; Adn Newark *S'well* 92-99; Suff Bp Repton *Derby* from 99. *Repton House, Lea, Matlock DE4 5JP* Tel (01629) 534644 Fax 534003 E-mail bishop.repton@btinternet.com

HAY, David Frederick. b 38. MA67. Qu Coll Birm 82. **d** 84 **p** 85. C Prenton *Ches* 84-88; V Stockport St Sav 88-96; P-in-c Gt Saughall from 96. *The Vicarage, Church Road, Saughall, Chester CH1 6EN* Tel (01244) 880213

HAY, Ian Gordon. b 52. Dundee Univ MA73 Edin Univ BD76 CertEd84. Edin Th Coll 73. **d** 76 **p** 77. C Dumfries *Glas* 76-79; Dioc Chapl *Bre* 79-81; R Brechin 81-85; Asst Chapl H Trin Sch Halifax 85-88; Dioc Youth Officer *Carl* 89-98; Sen Development Worker Youth Link Scotland from 98. *The Ross House, Pittendreich, Kinross KY13 9HD* Tel (01592) 840820 E-mail youthlink-scot@sol.co.uk

HAY, Jack Barr. b 31. Bps' Coll Cheshunt 57. **d** 60 **p** 61. C Byker St Ant *Newc* 60-63; C Killingworth 63-68; V Cowgate 68-77; V Woodhorn w Newbiggin 77-96; rtd 96; Perm to Offic *Newc* from 96. *7 Glebelands, Corbridge NE45 5DS* Tel (01434) 632979

HAY, Mrs Joanna Jane Louise. b 61. Coll of Ripon & York St Jo BEd83. NEOC 98. **d** 01 **p** 02. NSM Scalby *York* from 01. *19 Stepney Grove, Scarborough YO12 5DF* Tel (01723) 364336 E-mail jjlhay@fish.co.uk

HAY, John. b 43. St D Coll Lamp 63. **d** 67 **p** 68. C Ynyshir *Llan* 67-70; C Cardiff St Mary and St Steph w St Dyfrig etc 70-74; V Llanwynno 74-78; P-in-c Weston-super-Mare All SS *B & W* 78-80; TV Weston-super-Mare Cen Par 80-85; P-in-c Handsworth St Mich *Birm* 85-86; NSM Eastbourne St Sav and St Pet *Chich* 88-91; V Buckley *St As* 91-96; P-in-c Ardwick St Benedict *Man* 96-99; C Hollinwood and Oldham St Chad Limeside 99-01; rtd 01. *11 Mayfair Court, 357 Park Road, Blackpool FY1 6QR*

HAY, The Very Revd John. b 45. CITC 77. **d** 79 **p** 80. C Newtownards *D & D* 79-81; I Galloon w Drummully *Clogh* 81-89; I Donacavey w Barr 89-03; Can Clogh Cathl 91-03; Dean Raphoe *D & R* from 03; I Raphoe w Raymochy and Clonleigh from 03. *The Deanery, Raphoe, Lifford, Co Donegal, Irish Republic* Tel (00353) (74) 914 5226 E-mail john@johnhay.freeserve.co.uk

HAY, Nicholas John. b 56. Sheff Poly BSc85 DPS88. St Jo Coll Nottm 85. **d** 88 **p** 89. C Blackb Redeemer *Blackb* 88-91; C Hellesdon *Nor* 91-95; R Widford *Chelmsf* 95-01; Sen Chapl HM Pris Ashfield from 01. *HM Prison and YOI Ashfield, Shortwood Road, Pucklechurch, Bristol BS16 9QJ* Tel 0117-303 8128 *or* 303 8000 E-mail chaplaincy@premiercustodial.com

HAY, Richard. b 42. CMG92. Ball Coll Ox BA63. Cranmer Hall Dur 94. **d** 96 **p** 97. C Hastings St Clem and All SS *Chich* 96-99; V Addlestone *Guildf* from 99; RD Runnymede from 02. *The Vicarage, 140 Church Road, Addlestone KT15 1SJ* Tel (01932) 842879 E-mail randmhay@compuserve.com

HAYBALL, Douglas Reginald. b 18. Oak Hill Th Coll 66. **d** 68 **p** 69. C Ilkley All SS *Bradf* 68-72; V Parr Mt *Liv* 72-75; P-in-c Sheepy w Ratcliffe Culey *Leic* 75-76; R Sibson w Sheepy and Ratcliffe Culey 76-86; rtd 86; Perm to Offic *B & W* from 86. *57 Parklands Way, Somerton TA11 6JG* Tel (01458) 273312

HAYCRAFT, Roger Brian Norman. b 43. Oak Hill Th Coll 69. **d** 73 **p** 74. C Belsize Park *Lon* 73-76; C Yardley St Edburgha *Birm* 76-79; V Hornchurch H Cross *Chelmsf* from 79. *The Vicarage, 260 Hornchurch Road, Hornchurch RM11 1PX* Tel (01708) 447976

HAYDAY, The Very Revd Alan Geoffrey David. b 46. Kelham Th Coll 65. **d** 69 **p** 70. C Evington *Leic* 69-72; C Spalding *Linc* 72-78; V Cherry Willingham w Greetwell 78-86; RD Lawres 84-86; TR Brumby 86-02; RD Manlake 93-99; Can and Preb Linc Cathl 00-02; Dean St Chris Cathl Bahrain from 02. *St Christopher's Cathedral, PO Box 36, Manama, Bahrain* Tel (00973) 253 3866 E-mail alan.hayday@ntlworld.com *or* decani@batelco.com.bh

HAYDEN, The Very Revd David Frank. b 47. Lon Univ DipTh69 BD71. Tyndale Hall Bris 67. **d** 71 **p** 72. C Silverhill St Matt *Chich* 71-75; C Galleywood Common *Chelmsf* 75-79; R Redgrave cum Botesdale w Rickinghall *St E* 79-84; RD Hartismere 81-84; V Cromer *Nor* 84-98; P-in-c Gresham 84-98; Chapl Cromer and Distr Hosp Norfolk 84-94; Chapl Norfolk and Nor Health Care NHS Trust 94-00; Chapl Fletcher Hosp Norfolk 85-00; RD Repps *Nor* 95-02; Hon Can Nor Cathl from 96; Adn Norfolk from 02. *8 Boulton Road, Thorpe St Andrew, Norwich NR17 0DF* Tel (01603) 702477 Fax as telephone E-mail david_hayden@lineone.net

HAYDEN, Eric Henry Ashmore. b 26. ACII65. Sarum & Wells Th Coll 71. **d** 73 **p** 74. C Horsham *Chich* 73-78; V Cuckfield 78-92; rtd 92; P-in-c Tilshead, Orcheston and Chitterne *Sarum* 92-97; Perm to Offic *Ex* from 98; *Sarum* from 98. *2 Parsonage Lane, Hungerford RG17 0JB* Tel (01488) 686584

HAYDEN, Canon John Donald. b 40. Lon Univ BD62. Tyndale Hall Bris 63. **d** 65 **p** 66. C Macclesfield Ch Ch *Ches* 65-68; Tanzania 68-77; Home Sec USCL 77-83; TV Ipswich St Mary at Stoke w St Pet & St Mary Quay *St E* 83-85; TV Ipswich St Mary at Stoke w St Pet 85-94; P-in-c Bury St Edmunds St Mary 94-99; V from 99. *St Mary with St Peter Vicarage, 78 Hardwick Lane, Bury St Edmunds IP33 2PA* Tel (01284) 754680 Mobile 07973-737682 Fax 725910 E-mail hr50@dial.pipex.com

HAYDEN, Mark Joseph James. b 68. St Thos Aquinas Pontifical Univ Rome BD93 Clonliffe Coll Dip Humanities 89. H Cross

Coll Clonliffe 86. **d** 92 **p** 93. In RC Ch 92-99; C Monkstown *D & G* 99-01; I Gorey w Kilnahue, Leskinfere and Ballycanew *C & O* from 01. *The Rectory, The Avenue, Gorey, Co Wexford, Irish Republic* Tel and fax (00353) (55) 21383 Mobile 86-817 3888 E-mail markhayden@oceanfree.net

HAYDOCK, Canon Alan. b 41. Kelham Th Coll 60. **d** 65 **p** 66. C Rainworth *S'well* 65-68; C Hucknall Torkard 68-71; TV 71-74; V Bilborough St Jo 74-80; R E Bridgford 80-82; R E Bridgford and Kneeton from 82; RD Bingham 84-94; Hon Can S'well Minster from 86. *The Rectory, Kirk Hill, East Bridgford, Nottingham NG13 8PE* Tel (01949) 20218

HAYDON, Mrs Christine Mary. b 45. K Alfred's Coll Win CertEd66. NTMTC 93. **d** 96 **p** 97. NSM Aylesford *Roch* from 96. *44 Bramley Road, Snodland ME6 5DY* Tel (01634) 241821

HAYDON, Keith Frank. b 46. Cuddesdon Coll 73. **d** 75 **p** 76. C De Beauvoir Town St Pet *Lon* 75-77; C Wells St Thos w Horrington *B & W* 77-80; TV Weston-super-Mare Cen Par 80-84; TV Cowley St Jas *Ox* 84-87; TR 87-95; V Walsingham, Houghton and Barsham *Nor* 95-96; P-in-c 96-99; rtd 01. *Address withheld by request*

HAYES, Brian Richard Walker. b 33. Qu Coll Birm 81. **d** 83 **p** 84. C Cheadle Hulme All SS *Ches* 83-87; C Sheff Parson Cross St Cecilia *Sheff* 87-88; C Sheff Norwood St Leon 88-91; V Gazeley w Dalham, Moulton and Kentford *St E* 91-02; P-in-c Higham Green 98-02; rtd 02; Perm to Offic *St E* from 02. *The Rectory, Fox Lane, West Felton, Oswestry SY11 4EN* Tel (01691) 610228 E-mail brianhayes@cwcom.net

HAYES, Bruce John. b 75. UCD BA97 TCD BTh01. CITC 98. **d** 01 **p** 02. C Cregagh *D & D* from 01. *St Finnian's Curatage, 54 Rochester Avenue, Belfast BT6 9JW* Tel (028) 9079 6193

HAYES, Christopher John. b 64. Univ of Wales BN RGN Leeds Univ MA. Cranmer Hall Dur. **d** 96 **p** 97. C Burton Fleming w Fordon, Grindale etc *York* 96-99; R Buckrose Carrs from 99; P-in-c Weaverthorpe w Helperthorpe, Luttons Ambo etc from 03. *The Vicarage, Low Moorgate, Rillington, Malton YO17 8JW* Tel (01944) 758891 E-mail chris@buckrose.org.uk

HAYES, David Malcolm Hollingworth. b 42. K Coll Lon BD68 AKC68 MPhil97. **d** 69 **p** 70. C Upper Teddington SS Pet and Paul *Lon* 69-70; C Ruislip St Martin 70-75; P-in-c Ludford *Heref* 75-80; P-in-c Ashford Carbonell w Ashford Bowdler 75-80; V Eastcote St Lawr *Lon* 80-90; R Cant St Pet w St Alphege and St Marg etc *Cant* from 90; P-in-c Blean from 03; Master Eastbridge Hosp from 90; Guardian of the Greyfriars from 97. *The Master's Lodge, 58 St Peter's Street, Canterbury CT1 2BE* Tel (01227) 462395 E-mail davmon@eastbridge.co.uk

HAYES, David Roland Payton. b 37. Hertf Coll Ox BA62 MA66. Coll of Resurr Mirfield 62. **d** 64 **p** 65. C Woodley St Jo the Ev *Ox* 64-67; C Emscote *Cov* 67-69; C Farnham Royal *Ox* 69-75; P-in-c 75-78; P-in-c Lathbury 78-79; P-in-c Newport Pagnell 78-79; R Newport Pagnell w Lathbury 79-85; RD Newport 80-85; Chapl Renny Lodge Hosp 85-87; R Newport Pagnell w Lathbury and Moulsoe *Ox* 85-86; P-in-c 86-87; P-in-c Bucknell w Buckton, Llanfair Waterdine and Stowe *Heref* 87-91; V Bucknell w Chapel Lawn, Llanfair Waterdine etc 91-94; R Clun Forest 91-94; P-in-c Presteigne w Discoed, Kinsham and Lingen 94-00; P-in-c Knill 97-00; R Presteigne w Discoed, Kinsham, Lingen and Knill 00-01; rtd 01. *3 Redcar Avenue, Hereford HR4 9TJ* Tel (01432) 261466

HAYES, John Henry Andrew. b 52. BSc. Wycliffe Hall Ox 82. **d** 84 **p** 85. C Moreton *Ches* 84-87; R Barrow 87-94; Bp's Chapl 87-94; P-in-c Runcorn St Mich from 94; P-in-c Runcorn All SS from 94. *The Vicarage, 1 Highlands Road, Runcorn WA7 4PS* Tel (01928) 572417 E-mail john@hayesruncorn.freeserve.co.uk

HAYES, Kenneth Richard. b 50. Cen Sch of Art London DipAD72 RCA(Lon). Qu Coll Birm 95. **d** 97 **p** 98. C Gravesend H Family w Ifield *Roch* 97-01; V Gillingham St Mary from 01. *The Vicarage, 27 Gillingham Green, Gillingham ME7 1SS* Tel (01634) 850529

HAYES, Michael Gordon William. b 48. St Cath Coll Cam BA69 MA73 PhD73. Ridley Hall Cam 73. **d** 75 **p** 76. C Combe Down w Monkton Combe *B & W* 75-78; C Cambridge H Trin *Ely* 78-81; V Bathampton *B & W* 81-88; V Clevedon St Andr and Ch Ch 88-95; C Belper *Derby* 95-00; P-in-c Drayton in Hales *Lich* from 00; RD Hodnet from 01. *The Vicarage, Mount Lane, Market Drayton TF9 1AW* Tel (01630) 652527 E-mail mhhayes@freeuk.com

HAYES, Michael John. b 52. Lanc Univ BA73 Leeds Univ DipTh77. Coll of Resurr Mirfield 75. **d** 78 **p** 79. C Notting Hill *Lon* 78-81; C Hammersmith SS Mich and Geo White City Estate CD 81-88; Perm to Offic 98-00; NSM Norwood St Mary 00-03. *49 Lea Road, Southall UB2 5QA* Tel (020) 8574 7005

HAYES, Richard. b 39. K Coll Lon BD68 AKC68. **d** 69 **p** 70. C Dartford H Trin *Roch* 69-72; C S Kensington St Steph *Lon* 72-76; V Ruislip Manor St Paul 76-82; V Ealing St Pet Mt Park 82-91; R St Edm the King and St Mary Woolnoth etc 91-99; rtd 99; Perm to Offic *Lich* from 99; *Heref* from 00. *26 St John's Hill, Shrewsbury SY1 1JJ* Tel (01743) 244668 E-mail rhayes@beeb.net

HAYES, Richard Henry. b 65. Bp Otter Coll St Jo Coll Nottm 89. **d** 92 **p** 93. C Southborough St Pet w Ch Ch and St Matt *Roch* 92-95; C Downend *Bris* 95-97; V Gravesend St Mary *Roch* 97-02; R Clymping and Yapton w Ford *Chich* from 02. *The Rectory, St Mary's Meadow, Yapton, Arundel BN18 0EE* Tel (01243) 552962 Mobile 07944-804933 E-mail hayesrev@supanet.com

HAYES, Mrs Rosemarie Eveline. b 51. Brighton Coll of Educn CertEd72. N Ord Course 88. **d** 91 **p** 94. Par Dn Manston *Ripon* 91-94; C 94-95; C Beeston 95-00; V Horsforth from 00. *St Margaret's Vicarage, Church Lane, Horsforth, Leeds LS18 5LA* Tel 0113-258 2481

HAYES, Stephen Anthony. b 57. St Jo Coll Dur BA80 S Bank Univ PGCE96. St Alb and Ox Min Course DipMin99. **d** 99 **p** 00. NSM Kingham w Churchill, Daylesford and Sarsden *Ox* 99-01; NSM Chipping Norton from 01; Chapl Kingham Hill Sch from 99. *Severn House, Kingham Hill School, Kingham, Chipping Norton OX7 6TW* Tel (01608) 658341 Fax as telephone E-mail steve@hayesfamily.freeuk.com

HAYES, Timothy James. b 62. **d** 89 **p** 90. C Lache cum Saltney *Ches* 89-94; P-in-c Dukinfield St Jo 94-99; V from 99. *37 Harald Avenue, Dukinfield SK16 5NH* Tel 0161-308 4708

HAYHOE, Geoffrey John Stephen. b 57. Portsm Univ BSc00. Qu Coll Birm 01. **d** 03. C Felixstowe St Jo *St E* from 03. *20 Russell Road, Felixstowe IP11 2BD* Tel (01394) 278592 Mobile 07946-379678 E-mail john@hayhoe.net

HAYLER, Peter John. b 65. R Holloway Coll Lon BSc87 Univ of Wales MPhil02. Wilson Carlile Coll 89 St Mich Coll Llan 99. **d** 00. Ind Chapl *Mon* from 95; C Pontnewydd from 00. *16 Steynton Path, Fairwater, Cwmbran NP44 4QJ* Tel (01633) 862414 E-mail haylers@dialstart.net

HAYLES, Graham David. b 39. Lon Univ DipTh66. Clifton Th Coll 64. **d** 67 **p** 68. C Gipsy Hill Ch Ch *S'wark* 67-70; C Heatherlands St Jo *Sarum* 70-74; V W Streatham St Jas *S'wark* 74-90; TR Hinckley H Trin *Leic* from 90; rtd 03. *Address temp unknown* E-mail holytrinityhinckley@bigfoot.com

HAYLLAR, Bruce Sherwill. b 23. Trin Hall Cam BA47 MA53. Cuddesdon Coll 48. **d** 50 **p** 51. C Almondbury *Wakef* 50-53; India 53-63; V Peacehaven *Chich* 63-72; Zambia 72-75; V Moulsecoomb *Chich* 76-81; TR 81-83; R Rotherfield w Mark Cross 83-90; RD Rotherfield 87-90; rtd 90; Perm to Offic *Chich* from 90. *Moses Farm Cottage, Piltdown, Uckfield TN22 3XN* Tel (01825) 722006

HAYMAN, Mrs Audrey Doris. b 41. St Mary's Coll Cheltenham 61 Bris Univ CertEd61 Cov Coll of Educn 65. Glouc Sch of Min 88. **d** 91 **p** 94. NSM Matson *Glouc* 91-98; P-in-c Falfield w Rockhampton 98-02; P-in-c Oldbury-on-Severn 98-02; Perm to Offic from 02. *32 Corncroft Lane, Matson, Gloucester GL7 2BN* Tel (01452) 411786 E-mail audrey.hayman@hotmail.com

HAYMAN, Canon Robert Fleming. b 31. Princeton Univ BA53. Gen Th Sem (NY) MDiv56. **d** 56 **p** 56. USA 56-88; I Drumcliffe w Lissadell and Munninane *K, E & A* 88-92; Preb Elphin Cathl 88-92; rtd 92. *1102 East Boston Street, Seattle, WA 98102, USA* Tel (001) (206) 860 7565

HAYNES, Miss Catherine Mary. b 68. Man Univ BA90. St Mich Coll Llan BD95 Dip Past Th 96. **d** 96 **p** 97. C Llantwit Major *Llan* 96-99; C Coity w Nolton 99-01; P-in-c Llangammarch w Llanganten and Llanlleonfel etc *S & B* 01-03; P-in-c Irfon Valley from 03. *The Rectory, Maesglas, Llangammarch Wells LD4 4EE* Tel (01591) 620482 E-mail cmhaynes@compuserve.com

HAYNES, Clifford. b 33. Cam Univ MA60. Linc Th Coll 80. **d** 82 **p** 83. C Lightcliffe *Wakef* 82-84; V Bradshaw 85-98; rtd 98; Perm to Offic *Carl* from 98. *East Lyn, Lazonby, Penrith CA10 1BX* Tel (01768) 897018

HAYNES, Cyril Michael. b 26. Univ of Wales BEd64. **d** 84 **p** 85. NSM Wenlock *Heref* 84-96; Perm to Offic 96-99. *Address temp unknown*

HAYNES, Canon John Richard. b 35. Ely Th Coll 60. **d** 63 **p** 64. C Bollington St Jo *Ches* 63-67; C Ches St Jo 67-68; C Davenham 68-70; Rhodesia 70-80; Zimbabwe 80-90; Sub-Dean Bulawayo Cathl 78-83; Hon Can Matabeleland from 90; V Bishop's Stortford *St Alb* 90-00; rtd 00; Perm to Offic *B & W* from 01. *53 Stag Way, Glastonbury BA6 9PR* Tel (01458) 830686

HAYNES, John Stanley. b 30. WMMTC. **d** 82 **p** 83. NSM Westwood *Cov* 82-84; C Radford Semele and Ufton 84-85; V 85-95; rtd 95; Perm to Offic *Cov* from 95. *64 Rugby Road, Cubbington, Leamington Spa CV32 7JF* Tel (01926) 330016

HAYNES, Leonard Thomas. b 17. **d** 69 **p** 70. C Lutterworth w Cotesbach *Leic* 69-73; C-in-c Swinford w Catthorpe, Shawell and Stanford 73-74; V 74-83; rtd 83; Perm to Offic *Leic* 83-02; *Birm* 95-97. *Seale Pastures House, Burton Road, Acresford, Swadlincote DE12 8AP* Tel (01283) 761024

HAYNES, Michael Anthony Ricado (Tony). b 47. MA LLB. **d** 00 **p** 01. NSM Tottenham St Paul *Lon* from 00; Perm to Offic *S'wark* from 02. *51 Lorraine Court, Clarence Way, London NW1 8SG*

HAYNES, Canon Michael Thomas Avery. b 32. AKC61. St Boniface Warminster 61. **d** 62 **p** 63. C Hebden Bridge *Wakef* 62-64; C Elland 64-68; V Thornhill Lees 68-82; V Lindley 82-97; Hon Can Wakef Cathl 82-97; rtd 97. *Longwood Edge Cottage, 86 Lamb Hall Road, Huddersfield HD3 3TJ*

HAYNES, The Very Revd Peter. b 25. Selw Coll Cam BA49 MA54. Cuddesdon Coll 50. **d** 52 **p** 53. C Stokesley *York* 52-54; C Hessle 54-58; V Drypool St Jo 58-63; Asst Dir RE *B & W* 63-70; Youth Chapl 63-70; V Glastonbury St Jo 70-72; V Glastonbury St Jo w Godney 72-74; Adn Wells, Can Res and Preb Wells Cathl 74-82; Dean Heref 82-92; V Heref St Jo 82-92; rtd 92; Perm to Offic *B & W* from 92. *23 Conway Crescent, Burnham-on-Sea TA8 2SL* Tel (01278) 789048
HAYNES, Peter Nigel Stafford. b 39. Hertf Coll Ox BA62 MA66. Cuddesdon Coll 62. **d** 64 **p** 65. C Norwood All SS *Cant* 64-68; C Portsea N End St Mark *Portsm* 68-72; Asst Chapl Brussels *Eur* 72-76; TV Banbury *Ox* 76-80; Asst Sec (Internat Affairs) Gen Syn Bd Soc Resp 80-85; P-in-c E Peckham and Nettlestead *Roch* 85-92; R Bredgar w Bicknor and Frinsted w Wormshill etc *Cant* 92-99; rtd 99. *1 Vesper Cottage, Cage Lane, Smarden, Ashford TN27 8QD* Tel (01233) 770367
HAYSMORE, Geoffrey Frederick. b 39. Bps' Coll Cheshunt 63. **d** 66 **p** 67. C St Marylebone St Mark w St Luke *Lon* 66-69; C Stockton St Chad *Dur* 69-72; C-in-c Town End Farm CD 72-77; Perm to Offic *York* from 95; rtd 10. *139 Lambton Road, Middlesbrough TS4 2ST* Tel (01642) 275259
HAYTER, Mary Elizabeth. *See* BARR, Mary Elizabeth
HAYTER, Canon Michael George. b 18. Ch Ch Ox BA39 MA43. Cuddesdon Coll 40. **d** 41 **p** 42. C Scarborough St Mary *York* 41-46; R Steeple Aston *Ox* 46-77; P-in-c Tackley 76-77; R Steeple Aston w N Aston and Tackley 77-83; RD Woodstock 64-74; Hon Can Ch Ch 75-83; rtd 83; Perm to Offic *Pet* 84-94. *Felden House, Charlton, Banbury OX17 3DL* Tel (01295) 811426
HAYTER, Raymond William. b 48. Oak Hill Th Coll 74. **d** 77 **p** 78. C Bermondsey St Jas w Ch Ch *S'wark* 77-80; C Sydenham H Trin 81-83; Asst Chapl HM Pris Brixton 83-84; Chapl HM Youth Cust Cen Stoke Heath 84-88; Chapl HM Pris Maidstone 88-91; CF from 91. *c/o MOD Chaplains (Army)* Tel (01980) 615804 Fax 615800
HAYTER, Ronald William Joseph. b 19. Keble Coll Ox BA40 MA44. Wells Th Coll 40. **d** 42 **p** 43. C Honiton *Ex* 42-45; C Ex St Mark 45-47; C Ex St Thos 47-51; C Paignton St Jo 51-55; V Countess Wear 55-87; rtd 87; Perm to Offic *Ex* 92-98. *32 Brookmill Close, Colwall, Malvern WR13 6HY*
HAYTER, Sandra. *See* RAILTON, Sandra
HAYTHORNTHWAITE, Robert Brendan. b 31. Solicitor 59 TCD BA53 LLB56 MA64 QUB DipEd71. Edin Th Coll 63. **d** 64 **p** 65. C Belfast St Jo Laganbank w Orangefield *D & D* 64-66; C Belfast St Thos *Conn* 66-68; Lic to Offic 68-75; C Belfast Malone St Jo 75-89; I Shinrone w Aghancon etc *L & K* 89-98; Dom Chapl to Bp of Killaloe and Clonfert 89-98; rtd 98. *La Nauvrasse, 17270 St Pierre du Palais, Montguyon, Charente-Maritime, France* Tel (0033) (5) 46 04 56 58
HAYTON, John Anthony. b 45. TD81. Heythrop Coll Lon MA00 ACII70. Oak Hill Th Coll 93. **d** 96 **p** 97. NSM St Alb St Mich *St Alb* from 96; OCF from 02. *89 Harpenden Road, St Albans AL3 6BY* Tel (01727) 761719 Fax 765832
E-mail john.hayton@ntlworld.com
HAYTON, Mark William. b 59. St Steph Ho Ox 85. **d** 88 **p** 89. C Sittingbourne St Mich *Cant* 88-91; C Kennington 91-94; R Broadstairs from 94; RD Thanet 96-01. *The Rectory, Nelson Place, Broadstairs CT10 1HQ* Tel (01843) 862921
E-mail markhayton@supanet.com
HAYTON, Norman Joseph Patrick. b 32. ARICS57 MRICS01. Sarum Th Coll 69. **d** 71 **p** 72. C Lytham St Cuth *Blackb* 71-74; V Wesham 74-79; V Chorley St Geo 79-80; NSM Kells *Carl* 84-85; P-in-c Flimby 85-90; V Barrow St Jas 90-94; TV Egremont and Haile 94-97; P-in-c Distington 97-00; rtd 00; P-in-c Charnock Richard *Blackb* from 01. *The Vicarage, 132 Church Lane, Charnock Richard, Chorley PR7 5NA* Tel (01257) 791385
E-mail normanhayton@hotmail.com
HAYWARD, Canon Alan Richard. b 25. Open Univ BA72. Wycliffe Hall Ox 54. **d** 56 **p** 57. C Dudley St Fran *Worc* 56-59; C-in-c Wollescote CD 59-65; V Wollescote 65-85; Hon Can Worc Cathl 85-91; R Alvechurch 85-91; rtd 91; Perm to Offic *Worc* from 91. *2 St Kenelm's Court, St Kenelm's Road, Romsley, Halesowen B62 0NF* Tel (01562) 710749
HAYWARD, Alfred Ross. b 20. Clifton Th Coll 52. **d** 54 **p** 55. C Attenborough w Bramcote *S'well* 54-56; V Snape w Friston *St E* 56-60; V Willoughby-on-the-Wolds w Wysall *S'well* 60-65; V Woodborough 65-70; Warden Braithwaite Gospel Tr Stathern 73-77; V Tugby and E Norton w Skeffington *Leic* 77-81; R Beeston Regis *Nor* 81-83; rtd 83; Perm to Offic *S'well* from 96. *4 Somersby Road, Nottingham NG3 5QY* Tel 0115-920 1406
HAYWARD, Canon Christopher Joseph. b 38. TCD BA63 MA67. Ridley Hall Cam 63. **d** 65 **p** 66. C Hatcham St Jas *S'wark* 65-69; Warden Lee Abbey Internat Students' Club Kensington 69-74; Chapl Chelmsf Cathl *Chelmsf* 74-77; P-in-c Darlaston All SS *Lich* 77-83; Ind Chapl 77-83; Can Res Bradf Cathl *Bradf* 83-92; Sec Bd Miss 83-92; R Linton in Craven from 92; P-in-c Burnsall w Rylstone from 97; RD Skipton 93-98; Hon Can Bradf Cathl from 92. *The Rectory, Hebden Road, Grassington, Skipton BD23 5LA* Tel (01756) 752575 Fax 722898

HAYWARD, Canon Jeffrey Kenneth. b 47. Nottm Univ BTh74. St Jo Coll Nottm LTh74. **d** 74 **p** 75. C Stambermill *Worc* 74-77; C Woking St Jo *Guildf* 77-83; V Springfield H Trin *Chelmsf* 83-98; Chapl HM Pris Chelmsf 86-00; Area RD Chelmsf 86-88; RD Chelmsf 88-93; RD Chelmsf N 93-95; Hon Can Chelmsf Cathl 93-98; Chapl HM Pris Wakef from 00. *HM Prison, Love Lane, Wakefield WF2 8AG* Tel (01924) 378282 Fax 384391
HAYWARD, Mrs Jennifer Dawn. b 38. WMMTC 85. **d** 88 **p** 94. NSM Gt Malvern St Mary *Worc* 88-90; NSM Gt Malvern Ch Ch 88-90; Par Dn 90-94; C 94-96; TV Wirksworth *Derby* from 96. *58 Yokecliffe Drive, Wirksworth, Matlock DE4 4EX* Tel (01629) 822896
HAYWARD, John Andrew. b 63. MHCIMA83 Nottm Univ BTh89. Linc Th Coll 86. **d** 89 **p** 90. C Seaford w Sutton *Chich* 89-92; C St Pancras H Cross w St Jude and St Pet *Lon* 92-95; V Kentish Town St Martin w St Andr from 95. *St Martin's Vicarage, 26 Vicar's Road, London NW5 4NL* Tel (020) 7485 3807 Fax as telephone E-mail smartingospeloak@aol.com
HAYWARD, The Ven John Derek Risdon. b 23. OBE00. Trin Coll Cam BA56 MA54. Westcott Ho Cam 56. **d** 57 **p** 58. C Sheff St Mary w St Simon w St Matthias *Sheff* 57-59; V Sheff Gillcar St Silas 59-63; V Isleworth All SS *Lon* 64-94; Adn Middx 74-75; Gen Sec Lon Dio 75-93; rtd 94; Perm to Offic *B & W* from 94. *5 Sion Hill Place, Lansdown, Bath BA1 5SJ* Tel (01225) 336305
HAYWARD, Preb John Talbot. b 28. Selw Coll Cam BA52 MA56. Wells Th Coll 52. **d** 54 **p** 55. C S Lyncombe *B & W* 54-58; R Lamyatt 58-71; V Bruton w Wyke Champflower and Redlynch 58-71; RD Bruton 62-71; R Weston-super-Mare St Jo 71-75; Preb Wells Cathl from 73; TR Weston-super-Mare Cen Par 75-92; rtd 92; Perm to Offic *B & W* from 92. *5 Chelswood Avenue, Weston-super-Mare BS22 8QP* Tel (01934) 628431
HAYWARD, Ms Pamela Jane. b 52. RGN82. Westcott Ho Cam 84. **d** 87 **p** 94. Par Dn Northampton St Mary *Pet* 87-90; Par Dn Bris St Mary Redcliffe w Temple etc *Bris* 90-94; C 94-96; V Eastville St Anne w St Mark and St Thos from 96. *St Anne's Vicarage, 75 Greenbank Road, Bristol BS5 6HD* Tel 0117-952 0202 Fax as telephone
HAYWARD, Peter Noel. b 26. Leeds Univ BA48 BD78. Coll of Resurr Mirfield 48. **d** 50 **p** 51. C S Elmsall *Wakef* 50-56; C Sheldon *Birm* 56-60; C-in-c Garretts Green CD 60-69; V Garretts Green 69-70; V N Cave w Cliffe *York* 70-00; R Hotham 70-00; RD Howden 78-86; P-in-c Newbald 97-00; rtd 00; Perm to Offic *Carl* from 00; Hon C Solway Plain from 02. *The Old Chapel, Allonby, Maryport CA15 6QH* Tel (01900) 881466
HAYWARD, Roynon Albert Oscar James. b 25. **d** 67 **p** 68. Hon C Glouc St Paul *Glouc* 67-89; rtd 89; Perm to Offic *Glouc* 89-92. *37 Forest View Road, Gloucester GL4 0BX* Tel (01452) 521164
HAYWARD, William Richmond. b 42. JP98. NY Th Sem BA90 NY Th Sem MPS91. Chich Th Coll 88. **d** 88 **p** 90. Bermuda from 88; Miss to Seafarers from 91. *8 Seabright Avenue, Paget DV 04, Bermuda* Tel (001441) 236 3221 Fax as telephone
HAYWOOD, James William. b 36. Chich Th Coll 69. **d** 73 **p** 74. C Leeds Halton St Wilfrid *Ripon* 73-76; C Workington St Jo *Carl* 76-78; V Clifton 78-84; P-in-c Barrow St Jas 84-85; V 85-89; V Crosby Ravensworth 89-94; R Asby 89-94; V Bolton 89-94; rtd 98. *19 Bramham Road, Whitwood, Castleford WF10 5PA*
HAYWOOD, Keith Roderick. b 48. Oak Hill Th Coll 84. **d** 86 **p** 87. C Fazeley *Lich* 86-90; TV Leek and Meerbrook 90-01; Acting TR Hanley H Ev 01-03; TR from 03. *45 The Parkway, Stoke-on-Trent ST11 3BB* Tel (01782) 266066
E-mail krhaywood@xalt.co.uk
HAZEL, Sister. *See* SMITH, Sister Hazel Ferguson Waide
HAZELL, The Ven Frederick Roy. b 30. Fitzw Ho Cam BA53 MA59. Cuddesdon Coll 54. **d** 56 **p** 57. C Ilkeston St Mary *Derby* 56-59; C Heanor 59-62; V Marlpool 62-63; Chapl Univ of W Indies 63-66; C St Martin-in-the-Fields *Lon* 66-68; V Croydon H Sav *Cant* 68-84; RD Croydon 72-78; Hon Can Cant Cathl 73-84; P-in-c Croydon H Trin 77-80; Adn Croydon *S'wark* 84-93; rtd 93; P-in-c Chard, Furnham w Chaffcombe, Knowle St Giles etc *B & W* 95-99; P-in-c Tardebigge *Worc* from 00. *Cotswold Cottage, School Lane, Alvechurch, Birmingham B48 7SA* Tel 0121-445 1318
HAZELL, Thomas Jeremy. b 35. Bris Univ LLB56 PhD01. St D Coll Lamp 56. **d** 58 **p** 59. C Newport St Paul *Mon* 58-61; C Derby St Jo *Derby* 61-64; V Arksey *Sheff* 64-69; Sen Student Cllr Univ of Wales (Cardiff) *Llan* 69-89; rtd 95. *Castlewood Barn, Ponde, Llandefalle, Brecon LD3 0NR* Tel (01874) 754030
HAZELTON, John. b 35. St Cath Coll Cam BA56 MA60 Bris Univ MLitt74 Newc Univ BPhil80. Wells Th Coll 59. **d** 61 **p** 62. C Twerton *B & W* 61-65; V Pittcombe w Shepton Montague 65-72; Lect SS Hild and Bede Dur 72-79; Asst Master Dame Allan's Schs Newc 79-88; Chapl 88-95; rtd 95; Perm to Offic *Dur* from 97. *36 Orchard Drive, Durham DH1 1LA* Tel 0191-384 6606
HAZELTON, Michael John. b 53. UEA BA76 Bedf Coll Lon PhD81 Heythrop Coll Lon BD89. **d** 90 **p** 91. Asst Chapl Helsinki *Eur* 94-95; Asst Chapl Zürich w Winterthur 95-98; R Mablethorpe w Trusthorpe *Linc* 98-02; R Saxonwell from 02. *Saxonwell Vicarage, Church Street, Long Bennington, Newark NG23 5ES* Tel (01400) 282545

HAZELTON, Robert Henry Peter. b 22. Wells Th Coll 65. d 67 p 68. C Eastover *B & W* 67-69; C Milton 69-76; V Peasedown St John 76-80; V Peasedown St John w Wellow 80-89; rtd 90; Perm to Offic *B & W* from 90. *37 High Meadows, Midsomer Norton, Bath BA3 2RY* Tel (01761) 419675

HAZELWOOD, Ms Jillian. b 32. Bp Otter Coll CertEd52 St Alb Minl Tr Scheme 82. d 87 p 94. NSM Wheathampstead *St Alb* from 87. *14 Butterfield Road, Wheathampstead, St Albans AL4 8PU* Tel (01582) 833146

HAZLEDINE, Basil William. b 18. St Pet Hall Ox BA42 MA45. Wycliffe Hall Ox 42. d 43 p 44. C Highfield *Ox* 43-46; C Gerrards Cross 46-51; V Barking St Patr *Chelmsf* 51-55; V Sayers Common *Chich* 55-60; R Twineham 55-60; V Stoughton *Guildf* 60-70; V Westlands St Andr *Lich* 70-77; P-in-c Whatfield w Semer *St E* 77-78; R 78-81; P-in-c Nedging w Naughton 77-81; R Whatfield w Semer, Nedging and Naughton 81-84; rtd 84; Perm to Offic *Guildf* 91-99. *14 Willis Close, Epsom KT18 7SS* Tel (01372) 726615

HAZLEHURST, Anthony **Robin**. b 43. Man Univ BSc64. Tyndale Hall Bris 65. d 68 p 69. C Macclesfield Ch Ch *Ches* 68-71; C Bushbury *Lich* 71-75; P-in-c New Clee *Linc* 75-85; TV Deane *Man* 85-96; V Harwood from 96. *The Vicarage, Stitch mi Lane, Bolton BL2 4HU* Tel (01204) 525196 E-mail robinhaz@fish.co.uk

HAZLEHURST, David. b 32. Liv Univ BSc54. St Steph Ho Ox 55. d 57 p 58. C Sheff Arbourthorne *Sheff* 57-59; C Doncaster Ch Ch 59-61; C W Wycombe *Ox* 61-63; P-in-c Collyhurst St Jas *Man* 66-67; V Blackrod 67-79; V Halliwell St Marg 79-84; R Sutton St Nic *S'wark* 84-94; rtd 94; Perm to Offic *S'wark* from 95; Perm to Offic *Guildf* 95-99. *3 Up The Quadrangle, Morden College, 19 St Germans Place, London SE3 0PW* Tel (020) 8853 1180

HAZLEHURST, David John Benedict (**Benny**). b 63. Trin Coll Bris 88. d 91 p 92. C Plumstead St Jo w St Jas and St Paul *S'wark* 91-98; Estates Outreach Worker (S'wark Adnry) 98-02; V Brixton Road Ch Ch from 02. *The Vicarage, 96 Brixton Road, London SW9 6BE* Tel (020) 7793 0621 Mobile 07973-498590 E-mail christchurchnb@tiscali.co.uk

HAZLETT, Stephen David. b 56. TCD BTh88. CITC. d 88 p 89. C Ballywillan *Conn* 88-90; I Rathcoole 90-95; I Dunluce 95-00; TV Sunderland *Dur* from 00; Ind Chapl from 00. *14 The Oaks West, Sunderland SR2 8HZ* Tel 0191-565 4121 E-mail stephen.hazlett@lineone.net

HAZLEWOOD, Andrew Lord. b 54. BSc. Wycliffe Hall Ox. d 82 p 83. C Leamington SS Phil and Jas w Cheltenham St Jas *Glouc* 82-85; C Waltham H Cross *Chelmsf* 85-89; R Pedmore *Worc* from 89. *The Rectory, Pedmore Lane, Stourbridge DY9 0SW* Tel (01562) 884856 E-mail andrew@hazlewood.fsnet.co.uk

HAZLEWOOD, David Paul. b 47. Sheff Univ MB, ChB70 Campion Hall Ox BA72 MA77. Wycliffe Hall Ox 70. d 73 p 74. C Chapeltown *Sheff* 73-75; Singapore 76; Indonesia 76-88; R Ipswich St Helen *St E* 88-97; V Shirley *Win* from 97. *The Vicarage, 2B Wordsworth Road, Southampton SO15 5LX* Tel (023) 8077 4329 E-mail david.hazlewood@ukgateway.net

HAZLEWOOD, William Peter Guy. b 71. De Montfort Univ BA97 St Steph Ho Ox BTh01. d 01 p 02. C Knowle H Nativity *Bris* from 01; C Easton All Hallows from 01. *12 Woodbridge Road, Bristol BS4 2EU* Tel 0117-977 2918 Fax as telephone E-mail frwill@onetel.net.uk

HEAD, David Nicholas. b 55. Pemb Coll Cam BA77 MA81. Westcott Ho Cam 78. d 81 p 82. C Surbiton St Andr and St Mark *S'wark* 81-84; C St Marylebone w H Trin *Lon* 84-89; TV Clapham TM *S'wark* 89-96; Chapl Trin Hospice Clapham 90-96; Chapl Princess Alice Hospice Esher 96-03; R Lyng, Sparham, Elsing, Bylaugh, Bawdeswell etc *Nor* from 03. *The Rectory, Rectory Road, Lyng, Norwich NR9 5SU* Tel (01603) 872381

HEAD, Canon Derek Leonard Hamilton. b 34. ALCD58. d 58 p 59. C Bexleyheath Ch Ch *Roch* 58-61; C Wisley w Pyrford *Guildf* 61-66; C-in-c Ewell St Paul Howell Hill CD 66-73; R Headley All SS 73-81; TR 81-82; RD Farnham 80-82; V Chertsey 82-99; Hon Can Guildf Cathl 83-99; RD Runnymede 88-93; Dir Post-Ord Tr 90-94; rtd 99; Perm to Offic *Win* from 00. *9 Tangmere Close, Mudeford, Christchurch BH23 4LZ* Tel (01425) 276545

HEAD, Canon Ivan Francis. b 53. Univ of W Aus BA75 Glas Univ PhD75. Melbourne Coll of Div BD78. d 79 p 79. Australia 79-81 and from 85; C Uddingston *Glas* 81-85; C Cambuslang 81-85; Dir Angl Inst Theol Perth 85-91; Warden Ch Coll Tasmania Univ 91-94; Warden St Paul's Coll Sydney Univ from 95. *St Paul's College, University of Sydney, NSW, Australia 2006* Tel (0061) (2) 9550 7444 or 9557 1447 Fax 9519 7246 E-mail ihead@mail.usyd.edu.au

HEAD, Peter Ernest. b 38. Lon Univ BSc59. Ridley Hall Cam 61. d 63 p 64. C Fulwood *Sheff* 63-66; C Belper *Derby* 66-68; Hd RE Shoeburyness Sch Southend-on-Sea 69-74; Hd RE Bilborough Coll 74-79; Public Preacher *S'well* 74-79; NSM Bramcote 74-79; Vice-Prin Totton Coll Southn 79-93; rtd 93; Hon C Hordle *Win*

94-02; rtd 03. *44 Lentune Way, Lymington SO41 3PF* Tel (01590) 678097 Fax as telephone E-mail peter_head@bigfoot.com

HEAD, William Peter. b 18. St Edm Hall Ox BA46 MA51. Cuddesdon Coll 46. d 48 p 49. C Beeston *S'well* 48-52; CF 52-56; V Wellingborough St Barn *Pet* 56-61; Chapl Highfield Sch Liphook 61-74; rtd 83; Perm to Offic *Chich* from 83. *3 Ferndale Road, Chichester PO19 6QJ* Tel (01243) 527075

HEADING, Margaret **Anne**. b 66. Leeds Univ BSc88 Man Univ PhD91 Aston Univ PGCE99. Wycliffe Hall Ox BA01. d 02 p 03. C Fletchamstead *Cov* from 02. *466 Tile Hill Lane, Coventry CV4 9DY* Tel (024) 7647 3281 E-mail heading@fish.co.uk

HEADING, Canon Richard Vaughan. b 43. ARCS65 Lon Univ BSc65. Coll of Resurr Mirfield 66. d 68 p 69. C Heref St Martin *Heref* 68-75; P-in-c Birches Head *Lich* 75-77; P-in-c Northwood 75-77; TV Hanley H Ev 77-82; V Heref H Trin *Heref* 82-92; TR Bedminster *Bris* from 92; Hon Can Bris Cathl from 00; RD Bris S from 01. *Bedminster Rectory, 287 North Street, Bristol BS3 1JP* Tel 0117-966 4025 Fax 963 1209 E-mail heading@surfaid.org

HEADLAND, James Frederick. b 20. Clifton Th Coll 51. d 53 p 54. C Barnsbury St Andr *Lon* 53-55; C Spitalfields Ch Ch w All SS 55-57; V Upper Tulse Hill St Matthias *S'wark* 57-65; P-in-c Smethcott w Woolstaston *Heref* 65-81; R Church Pulverbatch 65-81; P-in-c Cantley w Limpenhoe and Southwood *Nor* 81; R Reedham 81; R Reedham w Cantley w Limpenhoe and Southwood 81-86; rtd 86; Perm to Offic *Heref* from 86; Lich 88-00. *3 Ashford Avenue, Pontesbury, Shrewsbury SY5 0QN* Tel (01743) 790565

HEADLEY, Miss Carolyn Jane. b 50. MCSP71 Grad Dip Physiotherapy 71 K Coll Lon MA94. Lon Bible Coll DipTh76 Oak Hill Th Coll BA83. dss 83 d 87 p 94. Harlesden St Mark *Lon* 83-86; Kensal Rise St Mark and St Martin 86-87; Par Dn 87; Par Dn Uxbridge St Andr w St Jo 87-88; Par Dn Uxbridge 88-90; TD 90-92; Warden of Readers (Willesden Episc Area) 88-92; Tutor Wycliffe Hall Ox from 94. *6 Tanners Court, Dancers Hill, Charlbury, Chipping Norton OX7 3RP* Tel (01608) 810799 E-mail carolyn.headley@wycliffe.ox.ac.uk

HEADS, John. b 27. Bps' Coll Cheshunt 60. d 62 p 63. C Beamish *Dur* 61-64; C Monkwearmouth St Andr 64-65; C Stockton St Chad 65-70; rtd 94. *18 Green Crescent, Golcar, Huddersfield HD7 4RF* Tel (01484) 651232

HEAGERTY, Alistair John. b 42. MBE86. Oriel Coll Ox BA63 MA67. Lon Coll of Div BD68. d 68 p 69. C Margate H Trin *Cant* 68-72; CF 72-97; Chapl R Memorial Chpl Sandhurst 92-97; TV Kingswood *Bris* from 97. *60 Lavers Close, Kingswood, Bristol BS15 9ZG* Tel 0117-935 2658 E-mail alistair@heagerty.freeserve.co.uk

HEAK, Philip George. b 70. QUB BA92. CITC BTh95. d 95 p 96. C Ballymacash *Conn* 95-98; C Galway w Kilcummin *T, K & A* 98-00; Dioc Youth Officer (Cashel) *C & O* from 00. *2 Colonnade Cottages, St Canice's Cathedral, Co Kilkenny, Irish Republic* Tel (00353) (86) 817 2356 E-mail pheak@eircom.net

HEAL, David Walter. b 37. Ox Univ MA63. Trin Coll Carmarthen 87. d 90 p 91. NSM Henfynyw w Aberaeron and Llanddewi Aberarth *St D* 90-96; Hon Asst Chapl Algarve *Eur* 96-98; Chapl Madeira 98-03; rtd 03. *Cae Gwair Bach, Llanon SY23 5LZ* Tel (01974) 202596

HEAL, Miss Felicity Joan. b 42. Brighton Poly Dip Counselling 88. Portsm Dioc Tr Course 89. d 92. NSM Bramshott and Liphook *Portsm* 92-95; NSM Blendworth w Chalton w Idsworth 95-97; Perm to Offic from 97. *40 Rushes Road, Petersfield GU32 3BW* Tel (01730) 260410 Mobile 07712-249608 E-mail felicity@felicityheal.fsnet.co.uk

HEAL, Geoffrey. b 28. Linc Th Coll 54. d 56 p 57. C Camberwell St Giles *S'wark* 56-59; C Rotherhithe St Mary w All SS 59-62; V Peckham St Jo 62-75; V Southfields St Barn 75-88; rtd 88; Perm to Offic *Ex* 89-98. *Digby Cottage, 5 Hind Street, Ottery St Mary EX11 1BW* Tel (01404) 814729

HEALD, William Roland. b 40. Birm Univ DPS79. St Jo Coll Auckland LTh74. d 74 p 75. New Zealand 74-78 and 79-93; C Bournville *Birm* 78-79; V S Kensington St Luke *Lon* from 93. *St Luke's Vicarage, 1 Cathcart Road, London SW10 9NL* Tel (020) 7352 7553 or 7370 0338 E-mail bill.heald@virgin.net

HEALE, Nicholas James. b 67. St Cath Coll Ox BA89 DPhil95 Leeds Univ BA94. Coll of Resurr Mirfield 95. d 95 p 96. C Syston *Leic* 95-99; V Blackpool St Mich *Blackb* from 99. *St Michael's Vicarage, Calvert Place, Blackpool FY3 7RU* Tel (01253) 397755

HEALE, Walter James Grenville. b 40. Wycliffe Hall Ox 77. d 79 p 80. C Walsall *Lich* 79-82; TV Marfleet *York* 82-89; TR 89-94; R Easington w Skeffling, Kilnsea and Holmpton from 94; P-in-c Owthorne and Rimswell w Withernsea from 00. *The Rectory, Hull Road, Easington, Hull HU12 0TE* Tel (01964) 650203

HEALES, John. b 48. K Coll Lon BD71 AKC71 PGCE72 DPS76. St Mich Coll Llan 75. d 76 p 77. C Cwmbran *Mon* 76-78; Chapl Rendcomb Coll Cirencester 78-82; Chapl Mon Sch 84-88; V Penhow, St Brides Netherwent w Llandavenny etc *Mon* from 88. *Flat 1, The Rectory, Llanfaches, Newport NP26 3AY* Tel (01633) 400901

HEALEY, James Christopher. b 44. Linc Th Coll 84. **d** 86 **p** 87. C Boultham *Linc* 86-90; TV Gt Grimsby St Mary and St Jas 90-91; I Narraghmore and Timolin w Castledermot etc *D & G* 91-93; I New Ross *C & O* 93-97; Dean Lismore 97-99; I Lismore w Cappoquin, Kilwatermoy, Dungarvan etc 97-99; Chan Cashel Cathl 97-99; Prec Waterford Cathl 97-99; Can Ossory Cathl 97-99; I Arvagh w Carrigallen, Gowna and Columbkille *K, E & A* 99-02; P-in-c Winthorpe and Langford w Holme *S'well* 02-03; R Coddington and Winthorpe and Langford w Holme from 03. *All Saints' Vicarage, Newark Road, Coddington, Newark NG24 2QF* Tel (01636) 704768

HEANEY, James Roland. b 59. DipTh85. **d** 85 **p** 86. C Ballynafeigh St Jude *D & D* 85-88; C Lisburn Ch Ch Cathl *Conn* 88-90; I Dunganstown w Redcross and Conary *D & G* from 90. *The Rectory, Redcross, Co Wicklow, Irish Republic* Tel (00353) (404) 41637 Fax as telephone E-mail heaney@indigo.ie

HEANEY, Michael Roger. b 43. TCD BA66 HDipEd67 MA69 DCG83. CITC 74. **d** 76 **p** 77. Chapl St Columba's Coll Dub from 76. *Montana, Scholarstown Road, Dublin 16, Irish Republic* Tel (00353) (1) 493 1167 *or* 493 2219 E-mail mheaney@iol.ie

HEANEY, Robert Stewart. **d** 01 **p** 02. C Dunboyne Union *M & K* from 01. *5 The Coachyard, Enfield, Co Meath, Irish Republic* Tel (00353) (46) 954 9729 E-mail heaney@gofree.indigo.ie

HEANEY, Samuel Stewart. b 44. Open Univ BEd79 Ulster Univ BEd83 Lon Univ BD93 QUB MPhil99. St Deiniol's Hawarden 92. **d** 92 **p** 93. In Presbyterian Ch 85-92; C Knockbreda *D & D* 92-96; I Belfast H Trin and St Silas *Conn* 96-02; I Ballyrashane w Kildollagh from 02. *9 Sandelwood Avenue, Coleraine BT52 1JW* Tel (028) 7034 3061

HEANEY, Wendy Anne. b 42. St Alb Minl Tr Scheme 90. **d** 95 **p** 96. NSM Clifton and Southill *St Alb* 95-99; Asst Chapl HM Pris Bedf 95-99; Chapl 99-02; Lic to Offic *St Alb* 99-02; rtd 02; Perm to Offic *St Alb* from 03. *34 Meadow Way, Letchworth Garden City SG6 3JB* Tel (01462) 641303

HEANS, Simon John. b 56. Peterho Cam BA77 MA81. St Steph Ho Ox 92. **d** 94 **p** 95. Asst Chapl Lancing Coll 94-99; NSM Lancing St Mich *Chich* 94-99; Chapl R Gr Sch Worc 99-00; C Brighton Resurr *Chich* from 00. *107 Hartington Road, Brighton BN2 3PA* Tel (01273) 672358

HEAP, David Leonard. b 58. Man Univ BA79. Cranmer Hall Dur 82. **d** 85 **p** 86. C Clitheroe St Jas *Blackb* 85-88; C Blackb St Gabr 88-92; V Bare from 92. *St Christopher's Vicarage, 12 Elm Grove, Morecambe LA4 6AT* Tel (01524) 411363 E-mail davidheap@readingroom.freeserve.co.uk

HEAPS, Richard Peter. b 35. Bernard Gilpin Soc Dur 58 Qu Coll Birm 58. **d** 61 **p** 62. C Castle Bromwich SS Mary and Marg *Birm* 61-65; C-in-c Erdington St Chad CD 65-70; V Nechells 70-81; RD Aston 75-81; V Marston Green 81-86; P-in-c Shrawley and Witley w Astley *Worc* 86-92; R Shrawley, Witley, Astley and Abberley 92-01; rtd 01. *9 Timberdyne Close, Rock, Kidderminster DY14 9RT* Tel (01299) 832376

HEARD, Charles. b 19. S'wark Ord Course 62. **d** 65 **p** 66. C Plumstead St Nic *S'wark* 65-71; C Blackheath All SS 71-72; V Barnes H Trin 72-84; rtd 84; Hon C E Wickham *S'wark* from 84. *Flat 5, Elmfield Court, Wickham Street, Welling DA16 3DF* Tel (020) 8855 9809

HEARN, John Henry. b 49. Trin Coll Bris. **d** 82 **p** 83. C Epsom Common Ch Ch *Guildf* 82-85; C Ringwood *Win* 85-88; Chapl Basingstoke Distr Hosp 88-91; Chapl Luton and Dunstable Hosp 91-96; C Ampthill w Millbrook and Steppingley *St Alb* 96-99; P-in-c Wymington w Podington 99-03; V W Acklam *York* from 03. *St Mary's Vicarage, 50 Church Lane, Middlesbrough TS5 7EB* Tel (01642) 817150 E-mail john.hearn@tesco.net

HEARN, Jonathan. b 58. Leeds Univ BA81 GradIPM85. Westcott Ho Cam 89. **d** 91 **p** 92. C Tuffley *Glouc* 91-94; C Milton *Win* 94-02; P-in-c Warwick St Paul *Cov* 02-03; TV Warwick from 03. *St Paul's Vicarage, 33 Stratford Road, Warwick CV34 6AS* Tel (01926) 419814

HEARN, Canon Peter Brian. b 31. St Jo Coll Dur 52. **d** 55 **p** 56. C Frodingham *Linc* 55-59; R Belton SS Pet and Paul 59-64; PC Manthorpe w Londonthorpe 59-64; V Billingborough 64-73; V Sempringham w Pointon and Birthorpe 64-73; V Flixborough w Burton upon Stather 73-96; RD Manlake 87-93; Can and Preb Linc Cathl 92-01; rtd 96; Perm to Offic *Linc* from 01. *7 St Andrews Drive, Burton-upon-Stather, Scunthorpe DN15 9BY* Tel (01724) 720510

HEARN, Thomas Peter. b 18. Selw Coll Cam BA40 MA45. Linc Th Coll 40. **d** 42 **p** 43. C Oxhey St Matt *St Alb* 42-45; C Cirencester *Glouc* 45-52; V Childswyckham 52-62; R Aston Somerville 52-62; RD Winchcombe 60-62; R Stratton w Baunton 62-75; V Farnce Lynch 75-83; rtd 84; Perm to Offic *Glouc* from 84. *9 Cotswold Close, Cirencester GL7 1XP* Tel (01285) 655627 E-mail hearn.petvon@amserve.net

HEARN, Trevor. b 36. Sarum Th Coll 61. **d** 64 **p** 65. C Hounslow St Steph *Lon* 64-67; Miss to Seafarers 67-01; Lic to Offic *St E* 74-80; *Bris* 80-92; UAE 92-01; rtd 01; Perm to Offic *Bris* from 01. *37 Elberton Road, Bristol BS9 2PZ* Tel 0117-983 6526 E-mail tandv@hearn3136.fsnet.co.uk

HEARTFIELD, Canon Peter Reginald. b 27. Chich Th Coll 61. **d** 63 **p** 64. C Hurstpierpoint *Chich* 63-67; V Brighton St Alb

Preston 67-73; Chapl Kent and Cant Hosp 73-92; Chapl Nunnery Fields Hosp Cant 73-92; Six Preacher Cant Cathl *Cant* 79-84; Hon Can Cant Cathl 84-92; rtd 92; Perm to Offic *Cant* from 00. *13 Lanfranc Gardens, Harbledown, Canterbury CT2 8NJ* Tel (01227) 451621

HEASLIP, William John (Jack). b 44. TCD BA66. CITC 79. **d** 80 **p** 81. Chapl Mt Temple Sch Dub 80-86; Bp's C Aughaval w Burrishoole, Knappagh and Louisburgh *T, K & A* 86-88; I Aughaval w Achill, Knappagh, Dugort etc 88-95; Radio Officer (Tuam) 90-95; I Cork St Luke Union *C, C & R* 95-98; Colann Renewal Min *T, K & A* from 98. *Cloghadockan, Turlough, Castlebar, Co Mayo, Irish Republic* Tel (00353) (94) 902 5282 E-mail jackheaslip@eircom.net

HEATH, Mrs Cynthia Grace. b 46. ARCM66 GRSM68 St Mark & St Jo Coll Lon TCert68 Open Univ BA85. WMMTC 94. **d** 97 **p** 98. NSM Penkridge Team *Lich* 97-00; TV from 00. *The Vicarage, Top Road, Acton Trussell, Stafford ST17 0RQ* Tel (01785) 711154 Fax as telephone E-mail cheath@fish.co.uk

HEATH, Henry. b 40. FCII77. Oak Hill Th Coll 77. **d** 80 **p** 81. NSM Lexden *Chelmsf* 80-86; C Colne Engaine 86-87; NSM Halstead St Andr w H Trin and Greenstead Green 87-90; NSM W w E Mersea 91-95; R Stanway 95-02; rtd 02. *6 West Quay, Wivenhoe, Colchester CO7 9TF* Tel (01206) 820076

HEATH, Mrs Janet. b 45. EMMTC 89. **d** 91 **p** 94. Par Dn Rainworth *S'well* 91-94; C 94-96; C Mansfield Woodhouse 96-99; rtd 00. Perm to Offic *S'well* from 00. *17 The Hollies, Sherwood Park, Rainworth, Mansfield NG21 0FZ* Tel (01623) 490422

HEATH, John Henry. b 41. Chich Th Coll 69. **d** 71 **p** 72. C Crediton *Ex* 71-74; C Tavistock and Gulworthy 74-76; C Brixham 76-77; C Brixham w Churston Ferrers 77-79; R Bere Ferrers 79-85; P-in-c Moretonhampstead, N Bovey and Manaton 85-88; R 88-93; P-in-c Lifton 93-99; P-in-c Kelly w Bradstone 93-99; P-in-c Broadwoodwidger 93-99; R Lifton, Broadwoodwidger, Coryton, Stowford etc 99-01; V Lifton, Broadwoodwidger, Stowford etc from 01. *The Rectory, Lifton PL16 0BJ* Tel (01566) 784291

HEATH, Canon Peter Henry. b 24. Kelham Th Coll 40. **d** 47 **p** 48. C Derby St Anne *Derby* 47-49; C Staveley 49-52; C Brampton St Thos 52-54; C-in-c Brampton St Mark CD 54-59; V New Whittington 59-66; V Glossop 66-92; RD Glossop 83-89; Hon Can Derby Cathl 84-92; rtd 92; Perm to Offic *Derby* from 92. *Birchinlea, 15 Park Crescent, Glossop SK13 7BQ* Tel (01457) 862047

HEATH, Mrs Wendy Hillary. b 47. WMMTC 95. **d** 98 **p** 99. NSM Rugeley *Lich* 98-99; C 00-01; P-in-c Brereton from 01. *The Vicarage, 72 Main Road, Brereton, Rugeley WS15 1DU* Tel (01889) 582466 E-mail wen_heath@hotmail.com

HEATH, William Walter. b 11. St Jo Coll Ox BA32. **d** 72 **p** 73. Hon C Petworth *Chich* 72-90; Perm to Offic from 90. *Malthouse, Lurgashall, Petworth GU28 9ET* Tel (01428) 707212

HEATH-WHYTE, David Robert. b 68. Fitzw Coll Cam BA89. Wycliffe Hall Ox BTh98. **d** 98 **p** 99. C Gt Chesham *Ox* 98-02; V Frogmore *St Alb* from 02. *Holy Trinity Vicarage, 39 Frogmore, St Albans AL2 2JU* Tel (01727) 872172 E-mail david@hotfrog.info

HEATHCOTE, Warwick. b 46. **d** 03. C Cirencester *Glouc* from 03. *The Parsonage, 32 Watermoor Road, Cirencester GL7 1JR* Tel (01285) 652299 Fax as telephone E-mail warwick@htcw.fsnet.co.uk

HEATHER, Dennis Eric. b 34. LNSM course 95. **d** 98 **p** 99. OLM Hook *S'wark* from 98. *276 Hook Road, Chessington KT9 1PF* Tel (020) 8397 0063

HEATHER, Mark Duncan Grainger. b 62. Leic Poly LLB83 Leeds Univ BA99. Coll of Resurr Mirfield 97. **d** 99 **p** 00. C Leeds St Aid *Ripon* 99-03; V Leeds Halton St Wilfrid from 03. *St Wilfrid's Vicarage, Selby Road, Leeds LS15 7NP* Tel 0113-264 7000 E-mail mark.heather@bigfoot.com

HEATHER, Sally Patricia. b 51. Avery Hill Coll BEd73. STETS 99. **d** 02 **p** 03. NSM Michelmersh and Awbridge and Braishfield etc *Win* from 02. *Narnia, 2 Airlie Road, Winchester SO22 4NQ* Tel (01962) 622305 E-mail spheather@narnians.freeserve.co.uk

HEATHFIELD, Simon David. b 67. Birm Univ BMus88. Ridley Hall Cam BTh99. **d** 99 **p** 00. C Heswall *Ches* 99-02; Voc and Min Adv CPAS from 02. *27 Chestnut Tree Avenue, Coventry CV4 9FZ* Tel (024) 7646 7410 Fax as telephone E-mail srheath@fish.co.uk

HEATLEY, David Henry. b 50. Kent Univ BA72. Qu Coll Birm 86. **d** 88 **p** 89. C Liss *Portsm* 88-91; V Newchurch and Arreton 91-99; R Greatham w Empshott and Hawkley w Prior's Dean from 99; Dioc Rural Officer from 99. *The Vicarage, Hawkley, Liss GU33 6NF* Tel (01730) 827459 E-mail dhheatley@aol.com

HEATLEY, Henry Daniel. b 24. CITC DipTh68. **d** 68 **p** 69. C Belfast St Matt *Conn* 68-72; C-in-c Upper Falls 72-78; C Belfast St Mary 78-80; I Belfast St Barn 80-92; rtd 92. *Ebenezer, 91 Larne Road, Carrickfergus BT38 7NH* Tel (028) 9336 5382

HEATLEY, Canon William Cecil. b 39. QUB BA61. Ridley Hall Cam 62. **d** 64 **p** 65. C Ballymacarrett St Patr *D & D* 64-69; C Herne Hill St Paul *S'wark* 69-74; TV Sanderstead All SS 75-82; P-in-c Peckham St Sav 82-87; V from 87; RD Dulwich 97-02;

Hon Can S'wark Cathl from 01. *173 Choumert Road, London SE15 4AW* Tel (020) 7639 5072 *or* 7732 3435

HEATON, Alan. b 36. K Coll Lon BD64 AKC64 Nottm Univ MTh76. **d** 65 **p** 66. C Stockton St Chad *Dur* 65-68; C Englefield Green *Guildf* 68-70; C Winlaton *Dur* 70-74; Chapl Derby Lonsdale Coll *Derby* 74-79; V Alfreton 79-87; RD Alfreton 81-86; TR Clifton *S'well* 87-93; P-in-c Rolleston w Fiskerton, Morton and Upton 93-96; rtd 97; Perm to Offic *Liv* from 97. *29 The Parchments, Newton-le-Willows WA12 0DX* Tel (01925) 292209

HEATON, Sister Elizabeth Ann. b 65. Bath Coll of HE BSc87. Ripon Coll Cuddesdon. **d** 00 **p** 01. C Lostwithiel, St Winnow w St Nectan's Chpl etc *Truro* 00-03; CSF from 03. *St Francis Convent, Compton Durville, South Petherton TA13 5ES* Tel (01460) 240473 E-mail comptondurvillecsf@franciscans.org.uk

HEATON, Julian Roger. b 62. LSE BSc(Econ)83. St Steph Ho Ox BA86 MA92. **d** 87 **p** 88. C Stockport St Thos w St Pet *Ches* 87-90; Chapl Asst Qu Medical Cen Nottm 90-92; Chapl Asst Univ Hosp Nottm 90-92; V Knutsford St Cross *Ches* 92-01; P-in-c Altrincham St Jo from 01; Voc Officer (Macclesfield Adnry) from 01. *St John's Vicarage, 52 Ashley Road, Altrincham WA14 2LY* Tel 0161-928 3236 E-mail julian@heatonfamily.freeserve.co.uk

✠**HEAVENER, The Rt Revd Robert William.** b 05. TCD BA28. CITC 29. **d** 29 **p** 30 **c** 73. C Clones *Clogh* 29-31; Dioc C 31-32; C-in-c Lack 32-38; I Derryvullen N 38-46; R Monaghan w Tyholland 46-51; R Monaghan w Tydavnet 51-73; Can St Patr Cathl Dublin 62-68; Adn Clogh 68-73; Bp Clogh 73-80; rtd 80. *12 Church Avenue, Jordanstown, Newtonabbey BT37 0PJ* Tel (028) 9086 3242

HEAVER, Derek Cyril. b 47. St Jo Coll Nottm BTh69. **d** 73 **p** 74. C Win Ch Ch *Win* 73-77; CF 77-02; rtd 02. *Orchard Cottage, 2 Myrtle Close, Puncknowle, Dorchester DT2 9EH* Tel (01308) 898466 Fax as telephone E-mail delsaun@eurobell.co.uk

HEAVISIDES, Canon Neil Cameron. b 50. Selw Coll Cam BA72 MA76 Ox Univ BA74 MA85. Ripon Hall Ox 72. **d** 75 **p** 76. C Stockton St Pet *Dur* 75-78; Succ S'wark Cathl *S'wark* 78-81; V Seaham w Seaham Harbour *Dur* 81-88; P-in-c Edington and Imber, Erlestoke and E Coulston *Sarum* 88-89; R 89-93; Can Res Glouc Cathl *Glouc* from 93. *7 College Green, Gloucester GL1 2LX* Tel (01452) 523987

HEAWOOD, Canon Alan Richard. b 32. G&C Coll Cam BA54 MA58. Union Th Sem (NY) BD56 Ripon Hall Ox 56. **d** 57 **p** 58. C Horwich H Trin *Man* 57-59; C Weaste 59-60; C Beverley Minster *York* 60-62; Chapl and Lect St Pet Coll Saltley 62-65; R Hockwold w Wilton *Ely* 65-72; V Weeting 65-72; V Melbourn 72-80; V Meldreth 72-80; P-in-c Teversham 80-89; Adult Educn Sec 80-89; Dir of Educn 80-98; Hon Can Ely Cathl 80-98; rtd 98; Perm to Offic *Ely* from 98. *10 Westberry Court, Grange Road, Cambridge CB3 9BG* Tel (01223) 460088

HEAZELL, Pamela Fletcher. b 50. NTMTC 96. **d** 99 **p** 00. NSM Hayes St Nic CD *Lon* 99-01; NSM N Greenford All Hallows from 01. *72 Horsenden Lane North, Greenford UB6 0PD* Tel (020) 8933 7700 E-mail pfheazell@aol.com

HEBBLETHWAITE, Canon Brian Leslie. b 39. Magd Coll Ox BA61 MA67 Magd Coll Cam BA63 MA68 BD84. Westcott Ho Cam 62. **d** 65 **p** 66. C Elton All SS *Man* 65-68; Chapl Qu Coll Cam 68; Dean of Chpl 69-94; Life Fellow from 94; Asst Lect Cam Univ 73-77; Lect 77-99; Can Th Leic Cathl *Leic* from 82; rtd 99; Perm to Offic *Ely* from 02. *The Old Barn, 32 High Street, Stretham, Ely CB6 3JQ* Tel (01353) 648279 E-mail blh1000@cam.ac.uk

HEBBLETHWAITE, Emma Sian. b 65. CCC Cam BA88 MA91 PhD92. Westcott Ho Cam CTM94. **d** 94 **p** 95. C Framlingham w Saxtead *St E* 94-96; Chapl K Coll Cam 96-01. *c/o The Dean's Secretary, King's College, Cambridge CB2 1ST* Tel (01223) 331100 E-mail esh12@cam.ac.uk

HEBBLEWHITE, David Ernest. b 52. Hull Univ BA81 Nottm Univ MA82 CQSW82. St Jo Coll Nottm MA95. **d** 97 **p** 98. C Melton Mowbray *Leic* 97-00; TV Cannock *Lich* from 00. *226 Hednesford Road, Heath Hayes, Cannock WS12 3DZ* Tel (01543) 450481

HEBBORN, Roy Valentine Charles. S Dios Minl Tr Scheme 83. **d** 86 **p** 87. NSM Lewes All SS, St Anne, St Mich and St Thos Chich 86-00; NSM Lewes St Anne 00-01; rtd 01. *3 St Anne's Terrace, Western Road, Lewes BN7 1RH* Tel (01273) 474063

HEBDEN, Cynthia Margaret. b 47. Univ of Wales (Ban) BTh94. **d** 94 **p** 97. NSM Llanfairpwll w Penmynydd *Ban* 94-95; C Twrcelyn Deanery 95-96; C Knighton St Mary Magd *Leic* 96-99; P-in-c Higham-on-the-Hill w Fenny Drayton and Witherley 99-02; P-in-c Stoke Golding w Dadlington 01-02; R Fenn Lanes Gp from 02. *The Vicarage, High Street, Stoke Golding, Nuneaton CV13 6HE* Tel (01455) 212317 E-mail hebden@lineone.net

HEBDEN, John Percy. b 18. Sheff Univ 46 Lon Univ 67. St Aid Birkenhead 58. **d** 60 **p** 60. C Skipton H Trin *Bradf* 60-62; R Kirby Misperton *York* 63-67; V Laxey *S & M* 70-83; V Lonan 80-83; rtd 84; Hon C Douglas St Geo and St Barn *S & M* 84-95. *Begra, Clayhead Road, Baldrine, Isle of Man IM4 6DN* Tel (01624) 861296

HEBDEN, Peter. b 43. Wigan Coll of Tech MICE67. St As Minl Tr Course 92. **d** 95 **p** 96. NSM Twrcelyn Deanery *Ban* 95-96; NSM Glen Magna cum Stretton Magna etc *Leic* 96-98; Chapl to Asst Bp Leic 98-99; NSM Barwell w Potters Marston and Stapleton from 00. *The Vicarage, High Street, Stoke Golding, Nuneaton CV13 6HE* Tel (01455) 212317 E-mail hebdens@leicester.anglican.org

HEBER, Andrew John. b 63. Nottm Univ BA86 MA89 CQSW89 Dip Counselling 97. Trin Coll Bris BA99. **d** 99 **p** 00. C Parr *Liv* 99-03; TV Kirkby from 03. *St Andrew's Vicarage, 9 Redwood Way, Liverpool L33 4DU* Tel 0151-548 7969

HEBER-PERCY, Christopher John. b 41. St Jo Coll Cam BA64 MA68. Wells Th Coll 66. **d** 68 **p** 69. C Leigh St Mary *Man* 68-71; Asst Ind Chapl 71-80; P-in-c Oldham St Andr 75-78; TV Oldham 78-80; Ind Chapl *Win* 80-90; N Humberside Ind Chapl *York* from 90; AD E Hull from 98. *19 Bellfield Avenue, Hull HU8 9DS* Tel (01482) 702033

HECKINGBOTTOM, John Michael. b 33. Leeds Univ BA55. St Steph Ho Ox 55. **d** 57 **p** 58. C Wigan All SS *Liv* 57-59; Min Can and Succ Ripon Cathl *Ripon* 59-63; P-in-c at Seacroft 63-66; V Menston w Woodhead *Bradf* 66-82; P-in-c Bishop Monkton and Burton Leonard *Ripon* 82-88; Chapl Scotton Banks Hosp Knaresborough 86-88; V Collingham w Harewood *Ripon* 88-94; Perm to Offic from 94; Perm to Offic *York* from 95; Perm to Offic *Eur* from 98; rtd 98. *8 Lawson Road, York YO24 1NE* Tel (01904) 707916

HECTOR, Noel Antony. b 61. Barrister-at-Law 84 Sheff Univ LLB83. Oak Hill Th Coll BA91. **d** 91 **p** 92. C Rodbourne Cheney *Bris* 91-92; C Bris St Mary Redcliffe w Temple etc 92-95; R Wrington w Butcombe *B & W* 95-03; R E Clevedon w Clapton in Gordano etc from 03; Chapl N Bris NHS Trust from 03. *The Rectory, All Saints' Lane, Clevedon BS21 6AU* Tel (01275) 873257 Fax as telephone E-mail noelhector@aol.com

HEDDLE, Duncan. b 34. Wadh Coll Ox BA57 MA61 DPhil64. **d** 86 **p** 86. Chapl Aber Univ *Ab* from 86; P-in-c Bucksburn from 90. *2 Douglas Place, High Street, Aberdeen AB2 3EA* Tel (01224) 485975 *or* 272888

HEDGE, Peter Andrew. b 62. New Coll Ox MA90. Coll of Resurr Mirfield 90. **d** 93 **p** 94. C Thornbury *Bradf* 93-97; V Queensbury from 97. *7 Russell Hall Lane, Queensbury, Bradford BD13 2AJ* Tel (01274) 815516

HEDGER, Graham. b 57. Lon Bible Coll BA79. Ridley Hall Cam 81. **d** 83 **p** 84. C Walton *St E* 83-86; TV Mildenhall 86-91; R Swainsthorpe w Newton Flotman *Nor* 91-94; Dioc Evang Officer 91-94; Perm to Offic *St E* 95-99; Bp's Chapl and Liaison Officer from 99. *14 St Peter's Close, Charsfield, Woodbridge IP13 7RG* Tel (01473) 277042 *or* 252829 Fax 737820 *or* 232552 E-mail graham@stedmundsbury.anglican.org

HEDGES, Mrs Anne Violet. b 53. Ripon Coll Cuddesdon 87. **d** 89 **p** 94. C Thetford *Nor* 89-94; Chapl Riddlesworth Hall Sch *Nor* 93-00; P-in-c Garboldisham w Blo' Norton, Riddlesworth etc *Nor* 94-97; R Guiltcross 97-00; Dep Chapl HM Pris Leeds 00-01; Chapl HM Pris Leic from 01. *HM Prison, Welford Road, Leicester LE2 7AJ* Tel 0116-254 6911 Fax 247 1753

HEDGES, Canon Dennis Walter. b 29. Sarum Th Coll. **d** 62 **p** 63. C Walton-on-Thames *Guildf* 62-66; C Westborough 66-69; V Blackheath and Chilworth 69-79; R Farncombe 79-94; RD Godalming 84-89; Hon Can Guildf Cathl 92-94; rtd 94; Perm to Offic *Guildf* and *Win* from 94; Perm to Offic *Portsm* from 99. *21 Lincoln Green, Alton GU34 1SX* Tel and fax (01420) 542624 Mobile 07989-110454 E-mail dennisw.hedges@lineone.net

HEDGES, Ian Charles. b 55. Sarum & Wells Th Coll 79. **d** 82 **p** 83. C Chessington *Guildf* 82-85; C Fleet 85-90; Dioc Adv on Homelessness from 87; V S Farnborough from 90; Tr Officer for Past Assts 91-00. *The Vicarage, 1 St Mark's Close, Farnborough GU14 6PP* Tel (01252) 544711

HEDGES, Canon Jane Barbara. b 55. St Jo Coll Dur BA78. Cranmer Hall Dur 78. **dss** 80 **d** 87 **p** 94. Fareham H Trin *Portsm* 80-83; Southampton (City Cen) *Win* 83-87; Par Dn 87-88; Dioc Stewardship Adv *Portsm* 88-93; Can Res Portsm Cathl 93-01; P-in-c Honiton, Gittisham, Combe Raleigh, Monkton etc *Ex* 01-03; TR from 03. *The Rectory, Rookwood Close, Honiton EX14 1BH* Tel (01404) 42925

HEDGES, Mrs Jane Rosemary. b 44. RGN65. S Dios Minl Tr Scheme 86. **d** 89 **p** 94. NSM Gillingham *Sarum* from 89. *Dene Hollow, Wyke, Gillingham SP8 4NG* Tel (01747) 822812

HEDGES, John Michael Peter. b 34. Leeds Univ BA60. Ripon Hall Ox 60. **d** 61 **p** 62. C Weaste *Man* 61-65; V Ashton St Pet 65-74; C Easthampstead *Ox* 74-85; V Tilehurst St Geo 85-91; C Thatcham 91-94; TV 94-99; rtd 99; Perm to Offic *Ox* from 99. *39 Mallard Way, Grove, Wantage OX12 0QG* Tel (01235) 766834

HEDGES, Leslie Norman. b 26. Bris Univ BA51 Lon Univ BD56. Clifton Th Coll 48. **d** 53 **p** 54. C Summerstown *S'wark* 53-55; C Wolverhampton St Luke *Lich* 55-56; C Reigate St Mary *S'wark* 56-59; V Clapham Park All SS 59-70; V Findern *Derby* 70-82; V Willington 70-82; V Trowbridge St Thos and W Ashton *Sarum* 82-91; rtd 91; Perm to Offic *Truro* from 91. *16 Penwerris Road, Truro TR1 3QS* Tel (01872) 279858

HEDLEY, Charles John Wykeham. b 47. R Holloway Coll Lon BSc69 PhD73 Fitzw Coll Cam BA75 MA79. Westcott Ho Cam 73. **d** 76 **p** 77. C Chingford St Anne *Chelmsf* 76-79; C St Martin-in-the-Fields *Lon* 79-84 and 85-86; P-in-c 84-85; Chapl Ch Coll Cam 86-90; TR Gleadless *Sheff* 90-99; R Westmr St Jas *Lon* from 99. *St James's Rectory, 197 Piccadilly, London W1J 9LL* Tel (020) 7734 4511

HEDLEY, Mrs Julia Margaret. b 56. Goldsmiths' Coll Lon BA78 Bedf Coll Lon MSc85 SRN80 Lon Univ DipN82. N Ord Course 97. **d** 00 **p** 01. C Altrincham St Geo *Ches* from 00. *26 Wainwright Road, Altrincham WA14 4BW* Tel 0161-941 1355

HEDLEY, Ronald. b 27. Codrington Coll Barbados. **d** 64 **p** 65. Trinidad and Tobago 64-92; rtd 92; Perm to Offic *Dur* from 92. *6 Ludlow Road, Sunderland SR2 9HH*

HEDLEY, William Clifford. b 35. Tyndale Hall Bris 65. **d** 67 **p** 68. C Hensingham *Carl* 67-69; C Rainhill *Liv* 69-71; C St Helens St Helen 71-73; V Low Elswick *Newc* 73-81; V Kingston upon Hull St Aid Southcoates *York* 81-87; TV Heworth H Trin 87-94; V Norton juxta Malton 94-97; C Newburn *Newc* 97-01; rtd 01. *21 Laburnum Grove, Sunniside, Newcastle upon Tyne NE16 5LY* Tel 0191-488 2908

HEELEY, Mrs Janet. b 45. **d** 00 **p** 01. OLM Lich St Chad *Lich* from 00. *43 High Grange, Lichfield WS13 7DU* Tel (01543) 251600 *or* 416595

HEFFER, Thomas Patrick Peter. b 69. K Coll Lon BD90 AKC90 Univ of Wales (Cardiff) LLM03. Ripon Coll Cuddesdon 94. **d** 96 **p** 97. C Sprowston w Beeston *Nor* 96-98; Bp's Chapl and Press Officer 98-01; Min Sec Miss to Seafarers from 01; Lic to Offic *Lon* from 01; Perm to Offic *Ox* and *St Alb* from 01. *The Mission to Seafarers, St Michael Paternoster Royal, College Hill, London EC4R 2RL* Tel (020) 7248 5202 Fax 7248 4761 E-mail ministry@missiontoseafarers.org

HEFFER, William John Gambrell. b 30. AKC55. **d** 56 **p** 57. C Biggleswade *St Alb* 56-59; C Clacton St Jas *Chelmsf* 59-61; V Langford *St Alb* 61-67; V Luton All SS 67-73; P-in-c Eaton Socon 73-75; V 75-77; Lic to Offic 78-81; R Wingrave w Rowsham, Aston Abbotts and Cublington *Ox* 81-88; R Wilden w Colmworth and Ravensden *St Alb* 88-91; C Leighton Buzzard w Eggington, Hockliffe etc 91-94; rtd 94; Perm to Offic *St Alb* from 94 and *Ox* 97-01; P-in-c Empingham and Exton w Horn w Whitwell *Pet* 01. *Domus, 35 Pebblemoor, Edlesborough, Dunstable LU6 2HZ* Tel (01525) 220618

HEFFERNAN, Anna Elizabeth. b 65. Cuddesdon Coll DipMin95. **d** 97 **p** 98. C Limpsfield and Titsey *S'wark* 97-00; C Warlingham w Chelsham and Farleigh 00-03; TV from 03. *St Christopher's Vicarage, Chelsham Road, Warlingham CR6 9EQ* Tel (01883) 624494

HEFFERNAN, Ms May Olive. b 52. Maria Grey Coll Lon CertEd74 Lon Univ BD93. Aston Tr Scheme 88 Westcott Ho Cam 93. **d** 93 **p** 94. C Duddeston w Nechells *Birm* 93-97; P-in-c Ward End 97-03; rtd 03. *c/o Mrs O Heffernan, 1 Horn Park Lane, London SE12 8UX*

HEGARTY, Gerald. b 52. QUB BA74 BD81. Union Th Coll Belf 78. **d** 86 **p** 87. NSM Leic H Trin w St Jo *Leic* 86-87; P-in-c Sibson w Sheepy and Ratcliffe Culey 87-90; Tutor Wycliffe Hall Ox 90-95; Chapl St Edm Hall Ox 90-96; Tutor St Alb and Ox Min Course *Ox* 96-99; Vice Prin from 00. *39 Lakeside, Oxford OX2 8JF* Tel (01865) 557847

HEIDT, John Harrison. b 32. Yale Univ BA54 Ox Univ BLitt67 DPhil75. Nashotah Ho BD57 MDiv69. **d** 56 **p** 57. USA 57-75 and from 96; C Ox St Mary Magd *Ox* 75-80; V Up Hatherley *Glouc* 80-96; P-in-c Cheltenham St Steph 89-95; rtd 97. *204 North Rosemont Avenue, Dallas, TX 75208, USA* Tel (001) (214) 948 3442 Fax 941 0339

HEIGHTON, Miss Janet Elizabeth. b 67. Leeds Poly BSc92. Ripon Coll Cuddesdon. **d** 00 **p** 01. C Leeds Gipton Epiphany *Ripon* from 00. *154 Amberton Road, Leeds LS9 6SP* Tel 0113-249 4356 E-mail jheighton@tesco.net

HEIL, Miss Janet. b 53. Liv Univ BEd75 St Jo Coll Dur BA84. Cranmer Hall Dur. **dss** 85 **d** 87 **p** 94. Ashton Ch Ch *Man* 85-91; Par Dn 87-91; Par Dn Scotforth *Blackb* 91-94; C 94-95; V Gt Harwood St Bart from 95; P-in-c Gt Harwood St Jo from 02. *St Bartholomew's Vicarage, 1 Church Lane, Great Harwood, Blackburn BB6 7PU* Tel (01254) 884039

HEINZE, Canon Rudolph William. b 31. Concordia Coll (USA) BSc56 CertEd56 De Paul Univ (USA) MA59 Univ of Iowa PhD65. **d** 86 **p** 87. NSM London Colney St Pet *St Alb* 86-98; Lect Oak Hill Th Coll 86-98; Sen Tutor 88-94; Vice-Prin 94-97; Visiting Scholar from 99; Hon Can Port Sudan from 94; Hon Prof Middx Univ *Lon* from 98; Perm to Offic *St Alb* from 98. *1714D Lakecliffe Drive, Briarcliffe Lakes, Wheaton, IL 60187, USA* Tel (001) (630) 588 8954 E-mail revrudi@aol.com

HELEY, John. b 28. Lon Univ BD74. Bps' Coll Cheshunt 54. **d** 56 **p** 57. S Africa 57-61; C Wimborne Minster *Sarum* 61-62; V Narborough w Narford *Nor* 62-67; R Pentney St Mary Magd w W Bilney 62-67; V Catton 67-69; Lic to Offic *Ox* 69-72; R E w W Rudham *Nor* 72-75; P-in-c Houghton 72-74; V 74-75; V Hunstanton St Edm 75-82; V Hunstanton St Edm w Ringstead

82-83; rtd 88. *Meadow Cottage, Cradle Hall Farm, Burnham Market, Kings Lynn PE31 8JX* Tel (01485) 518686

HELFT, Gunter. b 23. Lon Univ BA48. Ely Th Coll 46. **d** 48 **p** 49. Chapl Essex Home Sch Chelmsf 48-52; C Chelmsf Ascension *Chelmsf* 48-49; C Billesley Common *Birm* 52-53; Miss to Seamen 53-62; Japan 53-57; Sec HQ 57-62; Sudan 57; Bp's Youth Officer *Ox* 62-65; Tr Officer C of E Youth Coun 65-67; Hd Master Abp Temple's Sch Lambeth 67-71; Hd Master Don Valley High Sch S Yorkshire 71-80; rtd 80; Perm to Offic *Worc* from 87. *19 Kenwood Avenue, Worcester WR4 9BD* Tel (01905) 29797 Fax as telephone E-mail gunterhelft@lineone.net

HELLARD, Dawn Yvonne Lorraine. b 47. St Mich Coll Llan 89. **d** 91 **p** 97. C Llantwit Major *Llan* 91-95; TV Cowbridge from 95. *The Vicarage, St Hilary, Cowbridge CF71 7DP* Tel (01446) 772460

HELLEWELL, John. b 63. **d** 94 **p** 95. C Greasbrough *Sheff* 94-98; P-in-c High Hoyland, Scissett and Clayton W *Wakef* from 98. *The Rectory, Church Lane, Clayton West, Huddersfield HD8 9LY* Tel (01484) 862321 E-mail john@revjhell.freeserve.co.uk

HELLICAR, Hugh Christopher. b 37. Birm Univ DPS70. Qu Coll Birm 69. **d** 70 **p** 71. C Bromyard *Heref* 70-73; C Bishop's Castle w Mainstone 73-75; Perm to Offic *S'wark* 77-85 and *Chich* 83-93; NSM Hove *Chich* 93-98; rtd 02. *74 Marina, St Leonards-on-Sea TN38 0BJ*

HELLIER, Jeremy Peter. b 53. K Coll Lon BD75 AKC75 Westmr Coll Ox DipRE98. St Aug Coll Cant 75. **d** 76 **p** 77. C Walton *St E* 76-79; C Ipswich St Fran 79-80; C Wolborough w Newton Abbot *Ex* 80-82; C Pendine w Llanmiloe and Eglwys Gymyn w Marros *St D* 84-89; TR Widecombe-in-the-Moor, Leusdon, Princetown etc *Ex* 89-94; CF (TAVR) from 90; RD Moreton *Ex* 91-94; Chapl and Hd RE Wellington Sch Somerset from 94. *Wellington School, Wellington TA21 8NT* Tel (01823) 668827 *or* 668837 Fax 668844 E-mail jph@wellington-school.org.uk

HELLIWELL (née SWALLOW), Mrs Judith Hazel. b 46. Dioc OLM tr scheme 99. **d** 01 **p** 02. OLM Meltham *Wakef* from 01. *3 Upper Wilshaw, Meltham, Huddersfield HD7 3EA* Tel (01484) 851158

HELLIWELL, Zena Mary. b 43. Lon Univ BD71 Bris Poly PGCE80 ALCM. Lon Bible Coll ALBC69 Trin Coll Bris 89. **d** 99 **p** 00. NSM Westbury-on-Trym St Alb *Bris* 99-02; NSM Lawrence Weston and Avonmouth 02-03; rtd 03. *6 Metford Place, Redland, Bristol BS6 7LE* Tel 0117-924 3089

HELLMUTH, Miss Lynn. b 61. Lon Bible Coll BA82 Birm Univ PGCE83. Wycliffe Hall Ox 00. **d** 02 **p** 03. C Twickenham Common H Trin *Lon* from 02. *20 Mereway Road, Twickenham TW2 6RG* Tel (020) 8894 2513 E-mail lynn.hellmuth@lineone.net

HELLYER, Ian Anthony. b 66. Plymouth Poly HNC87 Lanc Univ BSc91 Nottm Univ BTh95. Linc Th Coll 92. **d** 95 **p** 96. C Poulton-le-Fylde *Blackb* 95-01; R Moretonhampstead, Manaton, N Bovey and Lustleigh *Ex* from 01. *The Rectory, 3 Grays Meadow, Moretonhampstead, Newton Abbot TQ13 8NB* Tel (01647) 440977 E-mail hellyer@surfaid.org

HELLYER, Stephen John. b 56. St Cath Coll Cam BA77 MA81. Wycliffe Hall Ox 82. **d** 84 **p** 85. C Plymouth St Andr w St Paul and St Geo *Ex* 84-88; Chapl Lee Abbey 88-89; Lon and SE Consultant CPAS 90-94; C Nottingham St Nic *S'well* 94-98; P-in-c Ox St Matt *Ox* from 98. *St Matthew's Vicarage, Marlborough Road, Oxford OX1 4LW* Tel (01865) 243434

HELM, Alistair Thomas. b 53. Aston Univ BSc75. EAMTC 88. **d** 91 **p** 92. NSM Leic St Jas *Leic* 91-95; NSM Humberstone 95-03; NSM Ascension TM from 03. *20 Stoughton Drive North, Leicester LE5 5UB* Tel 0116-273 0613 E-mail ahelm@leicester.anglican.org

HELM, Nicholas. b 57. Surrey Univ BSc81. St Jo Coll Nottm 85. **d** 88 **p** 89. C Old Ford St Paul w St Steph and St Mark *Lon* 88-92; TV Netherthorpe *Sheff* 92-93; V Sheff St Bart 93-98; Bp's Chapl and Adv in Spirituality from 99; Chapl Whirlow Grange Conf Cen Sheff from 99. *23 Hill Turrets Close, Sheffield S11 9RE* Tel 0114-235 0191 Fax 235 2275 E-mail nick@bishopscroft.idps.co.uk

HELMS, David Clarke. b 50. Boston Univ AB72. Yale Div Sch MDiv77. **d** 77 **p** 77. USA 77-88; Ind Chapl *Worc* 88-97; Ind Chapl Teesside *York* 97-02. *17 Gilesgate, Durham DH1 1QW*

HELYER, Patrick Joseph Peter. b 15. FRGS83. ALCD39 Wycliffe Hall Ox 38. **d** 38 **p** 39. C Maidstone St Paul *Cant* 38-41; Asst Chapl Miss to Seamen 41-42; Chapl RNVR 42-46; V St Nicholas at Wade w Sarre *Cant* 46-50; Australia 51-61; V Rolvenden *Cant* 62-66; R Frome St Quintin w Evershot and Melbury Bubb *Sarum* 66-71; Falkland Is 71-75; Hon Can Port Stanley 72-75; R Streat w Westmeston *Chich* 75-78; Tristan da Cunha 78-81; rtd 81; Perm to Offic *Heref* 84-00; *Glouc* from 84. *Tristan, 4 Gorse Lane, Sling, Coleford GL16 8JH* Tel (01594) 834990

HEMINGWAY, Peter. b 32. S'wark Ord Course 72. **d** 75 **p** 76. NSM Belmont *S'wark* 75-79; C Herne Hill St Paul 79-87; V Headstone St Geo *Lon* 81-92; V N Harrow St Alb 87-02; rtd 02. *Chelmerton, 138 Winthrope Road, Bury St Edmunds IP33 3XW* Tel (01284) 705070

HEMMING, Terry Edward. b 47. S Wales Bible Coll DipTh70 Calvin Coll Michigan MA84 S Dios Minl Tr Scheme 88. **d** 90 **p** 91. NSM Win All SS w Chilcomb and Chesil *Win* from 90; Chapl St Swithun's Sch Win from 95. *15 Gordon Avenue, Winchester SO23 0QE* Tel (01962) 855701 *or* 835717 E-mail revhem@gordave.fsnet.co.uk

HEMMING-CLARK, Stanley Charles. b 29. Peterho Cam BA52 MA56. Ridley Hall Cam 52. **d** 54 **p** 55. C Redhill H Trin *S'wark* 54-56; C Woking St Jo *Guildf* 56-59; V Crockenhill All So *Roch* 59-97; rtd 97; Perm to Offic *Guildf* from 97. *St Anthony's, 22 Ashcroft, Shalford, Guildford GU4 8JT* Tel (01483) 568197

HEMMINGS, Ms Jane Marie. b 68. Lon Univ BD91 AKC91 Heythrop Coll Lon MTh95. NTMTC 01. **d** 03. C Bishop's Waltham *Portsm* from 03; C Upham from 03. *15 Denewulf Close, Bishops Waltham, Southampton SO32 1GZ* Tel (01489) 890530

HEMMINGS, Keith. b 43. **d** 97. Par Dn Bedwellty *Mon* from 97. *Penydarren, Park Drive, Bargoed CF81 8PJ* Tel (01443) 830662

HEMMINGS, Roy Anthony. b 48. Univ of Wales (Cardiff) BD85 MTh00. St Mich Coll Llan 82. **d** 86 **p** 87. C Rhyl w St Ann *St As* 86-90; CF from 90. *c/o MOD Chaplains (Army)* Tel (01980) 615804 Mobile 07710-774431 Fax (01980) 615800 E-mail ryghemm@aol.com

HEMPENSTALL, John Albert. b 43. CITC 64. **d** 67 **p** 68. C Carlow w Urglin and Staplestown *C & O* 67-70; Chapl RN 70-99. *Address temp unknown*

HEMPHILL, John James. b 44. TCD BA68 MA72. Oak Hill Th Coll 71. **d** 73 **p** 74. C Dundonald *D & D* 73-78; I Balteagh w Carrick *D & R* 78-02; I Ballyhalbert w Ardkeen *D & D* from 02. *Ballyeasboro Rectory, 187 Main Road, Portavogie, Newtownards BT22 1DA* Tel (028) 4277 1234

HEMS, Canon Richard Brian. b 30. K Coll Lon BD58. St Aug Coll Cant. **d** 59 **p** 60. C Whitnash *Cov* 59-63; C-in-c Tuckswood CD *Nor* 63-69; V Tuckswood 69-78; R Framingham Earl 78-94; R Gt w Lt Poringland and Howe 78-94; P-in-c Bixley 93-94; R Poringland 94-00; Hon Can Nor Cathl 92-00; rtd 00; Perm to Offic *Nor* from 00 and *St E* from 01. *2 White House Gardens, Poringland, Norwich NR14 7RU* Tel (01508) 491028

HEMSLEY, David Ridgway. b 36. AKC61. **d** 61 **p** 62. C Penhill *Bris* 61-64; C Highworth w Sevenhampton and Inglesham etc 64-66; C Surbiton St Andr *S'wark* 67-70; P-in-c Tingewick w Water Stratford *Ox* 70-75; P-in-c Radclive 72-75; PM N Marston w Granborough etc 75-81; P-in-c Quainton 75-81; TV Schorne 81-90; P-in-c Lt Missenden 90-93; V 93-01; rtd 01. *27 Overn Avenue, Buckingham MK18 1LG* Tel (01280) 814636

HEMSLEY, Susan Mary. b 59. Cranmer Hall Dur 93. **d** 95 **p** 96. C Wilnecote *Lich* 95-00; P-in-c Attenborough *S'well* from 00; Dioc Chapl amongst Deaf People from 00. *Vale Cottage, 2 The Strand, Attenborough, Beeston NG9 6AU* Tel 0115-925 9602

HEMSTOCK, Julian. b 51. Trent Poly BSc74 CEng MIProdE. Sarum & Wells Th Coll 89. **d** 91 **p** 92. C Carrington *S'well* 91-94; C Basford St Aid 94-97; Asst Chapl Qu Medical Cen Nottm Univ Hosp NHS Trust from 97. *Queen's Medical Centre University Hospital, Derby Road, Nottingham NG7 2UH* Tel 0115-924 9924 ext 43799 *or* 985 6980 E-mail chaplaincy@mail.qmcuh-trent.nhs.uk

HEMSTOCK, Mrs Pat. b 51. Sarum & Wells Th Coll 89. **d** 91 **p** 95. Par Dn Carrington *S'well* 91-94; Par Dn Basford St Aid 94-95; C 95-97; P-in-c from 97. *103 Arnold Road, Nottingham NG5 1NG* Tel 0115-985 6980 Fax 962 3989 E-mail pat.hemstock@btinternet.com

HEMSWORTH, John Alan. b 45. FGA67. Man OLM Scheme 99. **d** 02 **p** 03. OLM Droylsden St Andr *Man* from 02. *13 Keston Avenue, Droylsden, Manchester M43 6BL* Tel 0161-292 7356

HENCHER, John Bredon. b 31. Lich Th Coll 58. **d** 60 **p** 61. C Pershore w Wick *Worc* 60-62; Bp's Dom Chapl 63-64; V Amblecote 64-70; Perm to Offic *Glouc* 72-74; Dioc RE Adv *Heref* 74-80; Lic to Offic 80-87; Perm to Offic *Mon* 87-00; Asst Chapl Mon Sch 87-00; Chapl from 00. *The Tank House, Weston, Pembridge, Leominster HR6 9JE* Tel (01544) 388540

HENDERSON, Canon Alastair Roy. b 27. BNC Ox BA51 MA54. Ridley Hall Cam 52. **d** 54 **p** 55. C Ex St Leon w H Trin *Ex* 54-57; Travelling Sec IVF 57-60; C St Mary le Bow w St Pancras Soper Lane etc *Lon* 58-60; V Barton Hill St Luke w Ch Ch *Bris* 60-68; P-in-c Bris St Phil and St Jacob w Em 67-68; V Stoke Bishop 68-92; Lect Clifton Th Coll 69-71; Lect Trin Coll Bris 71-73; RD Westbury and Severnside *Bris* 73-79; Hon Can Bris Cathl 80-92; rtd 92; Perm to Offic *Ex* from 92. *3 Garden Court, Cricketfield Lane, Budleigh Salterton EX9 6PN* Tel (01395) 446147

HENDERSON, Andrew Douglas. b 36. MBASW Trin Coll Cam BA60 MA64 Ox Univ DipPSA63 Liv Univ DASS65. Cuddesdon Coll 60. **d** 62 **p** 63. C Newington St Paul *S'wark* 62-64; Hon C Camberwell St Luke 65-80; Perm to Offic *Lon* from 85. *178 Lancaster Road, London W11 1QU* Tel (020) 7229 6790

HENDERSON, David. b 35. Oak Hill NSM Course. **d** 83 **p** 84. NSM Rush Green *Chelmsf* 83-00; Perm to Offic from 00. *The Vicarage, 4 Church Green, Coggeshall, Colchester CO6 1UD*

HENDERSON, Elizabeth. b 42. Cert Counselling & Learning Support Cert Ecum. **d** 99 **p** 00. C Ballymacash *Conn* from 99; Asst Chapl R Group of Hosps Health and Soc Services Trust from 99; C Finaghy *Conn* from 00. *39 Garvey Court, Lisburn BT27 4DG* Tel (028) 9260 7146

HENDERSON, Francis Colin. b 35. St Cath Coll Cam BA59 MA63. Cuddesdon Coll 60. **d** 62 **p** 63. C Croydon *Cant* 62-67; V Westwood *Cov* 67-75; V Chilvers Coton w Astley 75-80; P-in-c Wolston 80; P-in-c Church Lawford w Newnham Regis 80; V Wolston and Church Lawford 80-85; USA from 85; rtd 00. *1364 Katella Street, Laguna Beach, CA 92651, USA* Tel (001) (949) 497 2239 E-mail echenderson@earthlink.net

HENDERSON, James. b 22. Chich Th Coll 51. **d** 54 **p** 55. C Burnage St Nic *Man* 54-56; C Prestwich St Mary 56-59; V Waterfoot 59-64; P-in-c Rawtenstall St Jo 61-64; V Bolton St Geo 64-70; V Newhey 70-87; rtd 87; Perm to Offic *Man* from 87. *17 Swift Road, Rochdale OL11 5RF* Tel (01706) 522228

HENDERSON, Canon Janet. b 57. St Jo Coll Dur BA88 RGN82. Cranmer Hall Dur 85. **d** 88 **p** 94. Par Dn Wisbech SS Pet and Paul *Ely* 88-90; Par Dn Bestwood *S'well* 90-93; Tutor St Jo Coll Nottm 92-97; Lect Worship 93-97; NSM Bramcote *S'well* 94-97; Lect Worship and Tutor Ridley Hall Cam 97-01; Dir Studies 00-01; P-in-c Nuthall *S'well* from 01; Dean of Women's Min from 01; Hon Can S'well Minster from 03. *24 Watnall Road, Nuthall, Nottingham NG16 1DU* Tel 0115-938 9923 E-mail j.henderson2@btinternet.com

HENDERSON, Judith Ann. b 37. **d** 89 **p** 94. NSM Sheringham *Nor* 89-92; NSM Brampton St Thos *Derby* 92-00; Perm to Offic *Sarum* from 00. *Blackmore House, Stone Lane, Wimborne BH21 2QT* Tel (01202) 881422

HENDERSON, Canon Julian Tudor. b 54. Keble Coll Ox BA76 MA81. Ridley Hall Cam 77. **d** 79 **p** 80. C Islington St Mary *Lon* 79-83; V Hastings Em and St Mary in the Castle *Chich* 83-92; V Claygate *Guildf* from 92; RD Emly 96-01; Hon Can Guildf Cathl from 02. *The Vicarage, Church Road, Claygate, Esher KT10 0JP* Tel (01372) 463603 Fax 464894 E-mail htclaygate@aol.com

HENDERSON, Nicholas Paul. b 48. Selw Coll Cam BA73 MA77. Ripon Hall Ox 73. **d** 75 **p** 76. C St Alb St Steph *St Alb* 75-78; Warden J F Kennedy Ho Cov Cathl 78-79; C Bow w Bromley St Leon *Lon* 79-85; P-in-c W Acton St Martin 85-96; V from 96. *The Parishes Office, 25 Birch Grove, London W3 9SP* Tel (020) 8992 2333 Fax 8932 1951 E-mail nicholashenderson@btinternet.com

HENDERSON, Olive Elizabeth. b 48. St Jo Coll Nottm CertCS. **d** 97 **p** 98. Aux Min Tallaght *D & G* 97-99; P-in-c Moviddy Union *C, C & R* 99-01; P-in-c Rathdrum w Glenealy, Derralossary and Laragh *D & G* from 01. *The Rectory, Rathdrum, Co Wicklow, Irish Republic* Tel (00353) (404) 43814 E-mail oliveernest@hotmail.com

HENDERSON, Patrick James. b 57. R Holloway Coll Lon BA78 Surrey Univ PGCE01. St Steph Ho Ox 83. **d** 86 **p** 87. C Hornsey St Mary w St Geo *Lon* 86-90; V Whetstone St Jo 90-95; In RC Ch 95-01; Perm to Offic 01-02; C Hornsey H Innocents from 02; C Stroud Green H Trin from 02. *Holy Trinity Vicarage, Granville Road, London N4 4EL* Tel (020) 8340 2051 Mobile 07947-714893 E-mail pjhenderson2001@yahoo.co.uk

✠**HENDERSON, The Rt Revd Richard Crosbie Aitken.** b 57. Magd Coll Ox MA84 DPhil84. St Jo Coll Nottm 83. **d** 86 **p** 87 **c** 98. C Chinnor w Emmington and Sydenham etc *Ox* 86-89; I Abbeystrewry Union *C, C & R* 89-95; I Ross Union 95-98; Dean Ross 95-98; Chan Cork Cathl 95-98; Bp T, K & A from 98. *Bishop's House, Knockglass, Crossmolina, Ballina, Co Mayo, Irish Republic* Tel (00353) (96) 31317 Fax 31775 E-mail bishop@tuam.anglican.org

HENDERSON, Robert. b 43. TCD 66 Ulster Univ DipG&C87 Lambeth STh94. **d** 69 **p** 70. C Drumglass *Arm* 69-72; Chapl Miss to Seamen 72-78; Kenya 77-78; I Mostrim w Granard, Clonbroney, Killoe etc *K, E & A* 78-82; I Belfast St Matt *Conn* 82-92; I Kilroot and Templecorran 92-98; rtd 98. *39 Garvey Court, Lisburn BT27 4DG* Tel (028) 9260 7146

HENDERSON, Samuel James Noel. b 16. Hertf Coll Ox BA39 MA42. **d** 42 **p** 43. C Seagoe *D & D* 42-45; C Donaghadee 45-46; P-in-c Clabby *Clogh* 46-47; C Ipswich All SS *St E* 47-48; C Heacham *Nor* 48-49; C Ingoldisthorpe 48-49; R E w W Lexham 49-53; R Gt Dunham 49-53; R Nor St Aug w St Mary 53-56; V Eastbourne Ch Ch *Chich* 56-65; V Hickling *Nor* 65-82; rtd 82; Perm to Offic *Nor* from 82. *96 Church Lane, Beeston Regis, Sheringham NR26 8EY* Tel (01263) 825686

HENDERSON, Mrs Shirley Claire. b 49. Surrey Univ BA02. Bp Otter Coll 94. **d** 96 **p** 02. NSM Gatcombe, Chale and Shorwell w Kingston *Portsm* 96-00; NSM Whitwell, Niton and St Lawrence 00-03; P-in-c Shedfield from 03. *The Vicarage, 52 Brooklynn Close, Waltham Chase, Southampton SO32 2RZ* Tel (01489) 896637 Fax as telephone E-mail rev_shirley@hotmail.com

HENDERSON, Terry James. b 45. Warwick Univ Dip Counselling 97. St Deiniol's Hawarden 76. **d** 77 **p** 77. C Wrexham *St As* 77-79; Wilson Carlile Coll of Evang 79-81; TV Langtree *Ox* 81-87; P-in-c Aston Cantlow and Wilmcote w Billesley *Cov* 87-90; V 90-97; V St Peter-in-Thanet *Cant* 97-02; R Elmley Castle w Bricklehampton and Combertons *Worc* from 02. *The Rectory, 22 Parkwood, Elmley Castle, Pershore WR10 3HT* Tel (01386) 710394 E-mail terry.henderson@talk21.com

HENDERSON, William Desmond. b 27. TCD BA56 Div Test 56 MA64. **d** 56 **p** 57. C Derryloran *Arm* 56-59; C Conwall *D & R* 59-62; I Killoughter *K, E & A* 62-64; I Kilrush *C & O* 64-66; I Tubbercurry w Kilmactigue *T, K & A* 66-75; rtd 75. *8 Kingston College, Mitchelstown, Co Cork, Irish Republic*

HENDERSON, William Ernest. b 53. CEng81 MICE81 Southn Univ BSc75. St Jo Coll Nottm 87. **d** 89 **p** 90. C Win Ch Ch *Win* 89-93; V Stanley *Wakef* from 93. *The Vicarage, 379 Aberford Road, Stanley, Wakefield WF3 4HE* Tel (01924) 822143

HENDERSON, William Ralph. b 32. Oak Hill Th Coll 65. **d** 67 **p** 68. C Littleover *Derby* 67-68; C Nottingham St Sav *S'well* 68-74; V Alkham *York* 75-92; Chapl York Distr Hosp 86-92; rtd 92; Perm to Offic *York* from 92. *15 Drakes Close, Bishop's Manor, Huntington, York YO31 9GN* Tel (01904) 761741

HENDEY, Clifford. b 30. K Coll Lon BD53 AKC53. **d** 54 **p** 55. C S Wimbledon All SS *S'wark* 54-58; Trinidad and Tobago 58-71 and 81-82; V Spratton *Pet* 72-77; V Leeds All So *Ripon* 77-80; R Corringham *Linc* 80-81; V Alkham w Capel le Ferne and Hougham *Cant* 82-95; rtd 95; Perm to Offic *Cant* from 95. *308 Dover Road, Folkestone CT19 6NZ*

HENDRICKSE, Canon Clarence David. b 41. CEng MIMechE71 Nottm Univ PGCE73. St Jo Coll Nottm 71. **d** 74 **p** 75. C St Helens St Helen *Liv* 74-76; C Netherley Ch Ch CD 76-77; TV 78-87; V Liv Ch Ch Norris Green 87-93; V Eccleston Ch Ch from 93; Hon Can Liv Cathl from 96. *The Vicarage, Chapel Lane, Eccleston, St Helens WA10 5DA* Tel (01744) 22698 Fax as telephone

HENDRY, Mrs Helen Clare. b 58. Lanc Univ BA79 Cam Univ PGCE80. Reformed Th Sem Mississippi MA85 Oak Hill Th Coll 94. **d** 95. Lect Oak Hill Th Coll from 86; NSM Muswell Hill St Jas w St Matt *Lon* from 95. *7 Byre Road, Chase Side, London N14 4PQ* Tel (020) 8441 7805

HENDRY, Leonard John. b 34. Univ of Wales Cert Past Th68. St D Coll Lamp DipTh68. **d** 68 **p** 69. C Minchinhampton *Glouc* 68-71; C Bishop's Cleeve 71-74; V Cheltenham St Mich 74-78; V Horsley and Newington Bagpath w Kingscote 78-82; Chapl Salonika *Eur* 82-91; rtd 94. *Stratigi 34, Pilea, Salonika 543 52, Greece* Tel (0030) (31) 281193

HENDY, Canon Graham Alfred. b 45. St Jo Coll Dur BA67 MA75 Fitzw Coll Cam CertEd. Sarum Th Coll 67. **d** 70 **p** 71. C High Wycombe *Ox* 70-75; TV 75-78; R Upton cum Chalvey 78-83; TR 83-90; R S Walsham and Upton *Nor* 90-97; Dioc Lay Tr Officer 90-97; Can Res S'well Minster *S'well* 97-02; R Upper Itchen *Win* from 02. *The Rectory, Cheriton, Alresford SO24 0QH* Tel (01962) 771226 E-mail mail@grahamhendy.fsnet.co.uk

HENEY, William Butler. b 22. Potchefstroom Univ BA99. CITC. **d** 60 **p** 61. C Seagoe *D & D* 60-63; I Carrickmacross *Clogh* 64-73; I Newbridge w Carnalway and Kilcullen *M & K* 73-95; Treas Kildare Cathl 81-86; Can Kildare Cathl 81-95; Adn Kildare 86-94; rtd 95; Chapl Mageough Home *D & G* from 96. *14 Trees Road, Mount Merrion, Blackrock, Co Dublin, Irish Republic* Tel (00353) (1) 288 9773

HENLEY, Claud Michael. b 31. Keble Coll Ox BA55 MA59. Chich Th Coll 55. **d** 57 **p** 58. C Cowley St Jas *Ox* 57-60; C Wetherby *Ripon* 60-63; C Brighton St Pet *Chich* 63-69; V Brighton St Jo 69-75; V New Groombridge 75-96; rtd 96; Perm to Offic *Chich* from 97. *12 Barn Stables, De Montfort Road, Lewes BN7 1ST* Tel (01273) 472467

HENLEY, David Edward. b 44. Sarum & Wells Th Coll 69. **d** 72 **p** 73. C Fareham H Trin *Portsm* 72-76; C-in-c Leigh Park St Clare CD 76-78; R Freshwater 78-87; RD W Wight 83-87; R Meonstoke w Corhampton cum Exton 87-02; R Droxford 87-02; RD Bishop's Waltham 93-98; Hon Can Portsm Cathl 96-02; TR Chalke Valley *Sarum* from 02. *The Vicarage, Newtown, Broad Chalke, Salisbury SP5 5DS* Tel (01722) 780262

HENLEY, Dean. b 64. St Chad's Coll Dur BA93. Westcott Ho Cam 95. **d** 95 **p** 96. C Farncombe *Guildf* 95-99; TV Hale w Badshot Lea from 99. *The Vicarage, 12 Badshot Lea Road, Badshot Lea, Farnham GU9 9LD* Tel (01252) 327044

HENLEY, John Francis Hugh. b 48. SS Mark & Jo Coll Chelsea CertEd69. St Mich Coll Llan DipTh82. **d** 82 **p** 83. C Griffithstown *Mon* 82-85; V St Hilary Greenway 85-90; P-in-c Fulham St Etheldreda w St Clem *Lon* from 90. *St Etheldreda's Vicarage, Doneraile Street, London SW6 6EL* Tel (020) 7736 3809

✠**HENLEY, The Rt Revd Michael Harry George.** b 38. CB91. Lon Coll of Div LTh60. **d** 61 **p** 62 **c** 95. C St Marylebone w H Trin *Lon* 61-64; Chapl RN 64-88; Chapl of the Fleet and Adn for the RN 89-93; Dir Gen Naval Chapl Services 92-93; Chapl St Andr Univ *St And* 68-72; Chapl R Hosp Sch Holbrook 72-74; QHC 89-93; Hon Can Gib Cathl *Eur* 89-93; P-in-c Pitlochry *St And* 94-95; Bp St And from 95. *Afton House, Kennedy Gardens, St Andrews KY16 9DJ* Tel (01334) 479761 or (01738) 443173 Fax (01738) 443174 E-mail bishop@standrews.anglican.org

HENLY, Francis Michael. b 25. Sarum Th Coll. **d** 67 **p** 68. C E w W Harnham *Sarum* 67-70; P-in-c Stour Provost w Todber 70-75; P-in-c Rowde 75-79; V 79-83; R Poulshot 79-83; V Bishop's Cannings, All Cannings etc 83-92; rtd 92; Perm to Offic

Sarum from 92. *Oldbury View, Middle Lane, Cherhill, Calne SN11 8XX* Tel (01249) 815191

HENNING, Mrs Judy. b 49. Portsm Univ MSc99. S Dios Minl Tr Scheme 85. **d** 88 **p** 97. C Catherington and Clanfield *Portsm* 88-91; C Leigh Park 91-92; Perm to Offic 94-96; Min in Whiteley and Asst to RD Fareham 96-99; C-in-c Whiteley CD from 99. *20 Sheridan Gardens, Whiteley, Fareham PO15 7DY* Tel (01489) 881500 E-mail judy.henning@ntlworld.com *or* jhenning@fish.co.uk

HENRY, Miss Jacqueline Margaret. b 40. Open Univ BA82. Trin Coll Bris DipHE79. **dss** 83 **d** 87 **p** 94. Deptford St Jo *S'wark* 79-82; Catshill and Dodford *Worc* 83-86; The Lye and Stambermill 86-87; Par Dn 87-89; Educn Chapl 89-93; C Tolleshunt Knights w Tiptree and Gt Braxted *Chelmsf* 94-97; Chapl amongst Deaf People 94-97; TV Stantonbury and Willen *Ox* 97-02; rtd 02; Perm to Offic *Cant* from 02. *72 St Nicholas Road, Faversham ME13 7PB* Tel (01795) 538785

HENRY, Peter. b 49. BTh. St Jo Coll Nottm. **d** 84 **p** 85. C Sinfin Moor *Derby* 84-89; C Blagreaves St Andr CD 84-89; V Guernsey St Jo *Win* 89-97; P-in-c Sawley *Derby* 97-01; R from 01. *The Rectory, 561 Tamworth Road, Long Eaton, Nottingham NG10 3FB* Tel 0115-973 4900

HENRY, Canon Stephen Kenelm Malim. b 37. Brasted Th Coll 58 Bps' Coll Cheshunt 60. **d** 62 **p** 63. C Leic St Phil *Leic* 62-67; CF 67-70; V Woodhouse *Wakef* 70-01; Hon Can Wakef Cathl 00-01; rtd 01; Perm to Offic *Wakef* from 01. *1 Yorkstone, Crosland Moor, Huddersfield HD4 5NQ* Tel (01484) 644807 Fax as telephone

✠**HENSHALL, The Rt Revd Michael.** b 28. St Chad's Coll Dur BA54 DipTh56. **d** 56 **p** 57 **c** 76. C Sewerby w Marton *York* 56-59; C Bridlington Quay H Trin 56-59; C Micklehurst CD *Ches* 59-62; V Micklehurst 62-63; V Altrincham St Geo 63-76; Hon Can Ches Cathl 72-76; Suff Bp Warrington *Liv* 76-96; rtd 96; Perm to Offic *Liv* from 99 and *York* 96-99; Hon Asst Bp York from 99. *28 Hermitage Way, Sleights, Whitby YO22 5HG* Tel (01947) 811233

HENSHALL, Canon Nicholas James. b 62. Wadh Coll Ox BA84 MA88. Ripon Coll Cuddesdon 85. **d** 88 **p** 89. C Blyth St Mary *Newc* 88-92; V Scotswood 92-02; Can Res Derby Cathl *Derby* from 02. *24 Kedleston Road, Derby DE22 1GU* Tel (01332) 343144 E-mail precentor@derbycathedral.org.uk

HENSHALL, Ronald Keith. b 54. Loughb Coll of Educn CertEd76. Chich Th Coll 87. **d** 89 **p** 90. C Habblesthorpe *Blackb* 89-92; TV 95-98; USPG St Kitts-Nevis 92-95; V Ellel w Shireshead *Blackb* 98-02; Cyprus from 02. *PO Box 61083, 8130 Paphos, Cyprus* Tel (00357) (26) 222108 Fax as telephone E-mail keithofpaphos@msn.com

HENSHAW, Nicholas Newell. b 49. Rhodes Univ BA72. Cuddesdon Coll 73. **d** 75 **p** 76. C Beaconsfield *Ox* 75-78; Chapl Wellington Coll Berks 78-80; C Pimlico St Pet w Westmr Ch Ch *Lon* 80-82; Chapl Sevenoaks Sch from 82; Hon C Sevenoaks St Nic *Roch* from 82. *Orchards, Solefields Road, Sevenoaks TN13 1PF* Tel (01732) 456710

HENSON, Carolyn. b 44. Bedf Coll Lon BA65 Nottm Univ MTh88 PhD97 Solicitor 75. EMMTC 82. **dss** 85 **d** 87 **p** 94. Braunstone *Leic* 85-89; Par Dn 87-89; Adult Educn and Tr Officer *Ely* 89-91; NSM Sutton and Witcham w Mepal 89-95; Chapl Gt Ormond Street Hosp for Children NHS Trust 95-96; NSM Cainscross w Selsley *Glouc* 96-97; Vice Prin EMMTC *S'well* 97-01; R Morley w Smalley and Horsley Woodhouse *Derby* from 02. *The Vicarage, 80 Main Road, Smalley, Ilkeston DE7 6EF* Tel (01332) 880380 E-mail carolyn.henson@virgin.net

HENSON, John David. b 49. EMMTC. **d** 00 **p** 01. NSM Beckingham w Walkeringham *S'well* 00-02; NSM Gringley-on-the-Hill 00-02; NSM Misterton and W Stockwith from 02; Asst Chapl HM Pris Whatton from 00; Sen Police Chapl *S'well* from 03. *The Vicarage, Church Lane, Misterton, Doncaster DN10 4AL* Tel (01427) 890270 E-mail jd.henson@btinternet.com

HENSON, Canon John Richard. b 40. Selw Coll Cam BA62 MA66. Ridley Hall Cam 62. **d** 65 **p** 66. C Ollerton *S'well* 65-68; Univs Sec CMS 68-73; Chapl Scargill Ho 73-78; V Shipley St Paul *Bradf* 78-83; TR Shipley St Paul and Frizinghall 83-91; V Ilkeston St Mary *Derby* 91-99; V Mickleover St Jo from 99; Dioc Ecum Officer from 96; Hon Can Derby Cathl from 00. *St John's Vicarage, 7 Onslow Road, Mickleover, Derby DE3 9JJ* Tel (01332) 516545 Fax as telephone E-mail jrhenson@totalise.co.uk

HENSON, Richard Clive. b 41. Univ of Wales (Cardiff) BSc63 PhD66. S'wark Ord Course 77. **d** 88 **p** 89. NSM Lee St Mildred *S'wark* 88-97; NSM Donington *Lich* 97-99; rtd 99. *Address temp unknown*

HENSTRIDGE, Edward John. b 31. Ex Coll Ox BA55 MA59 FCIPD77. Wells Th Coll 55. **d** 57 **p** 58. C Milton *Portsm* 57-62; V Soberton w Newtown 62-69; Lic to Offic *Derby* 69-71; Perm to Offic *Guildf* 72-84; Lic to Offic from 84; Bp's Officer for NSMs 97-01; Perm to Offic from 02. *The White House, Thursley Road, Elstead, Godalming GU8 6LW* Tel (01252) 702272 Fax 702747 E-mail johnhn@globalnet.co.uk

HENTHORNE, Thomas Roger. b 30. EAMTC. **d** 79 **p** 80. Hd Master St Mary's Sch St Neots 67-93; Hon C St Neots *Ely* from

79. *Stapeley, 45 Berkley Street, Eynesbury, St Neots PE19 2NE* Tel (01480) 472548 E-mail roger.henthorne@tesco.net

HENTON, John Martin. b 48. AKC71 St Luke's Coll Ex DipEd72. St Aug Coll Cant 74. **d** 74 **p** 75. C Woolwich St Mary w H Trin *S'wark* 74-77; C Cotham St Mary *Bris* 77-78; C Cotham St Sav w St Mary 78-80; R Filton 80-87; Chapl Ex Sch 87-91; Chapl St Marg Sch Ex 87-91; V Ex St Dav *Ex* from 91. *St David's Vicarage, 95 Howell Road, Exeter EX4 4LH* Tel (01392) 254396 E-mail j.henton@tesco.net

HENWOOD, Mrs Gillian Kathleen. b 56. ABIPP81. Carl and Blackb Dioc Tr Inst MA97. **d** 97 **p** 98. NSM Whitechapel w Admarsh-in-Bleasdale *Blackb* 97-00; Par Dn 00-01; Rural Chapl 00-03; C Fellside Team 01; Bp's Adv for Leisure and Tourism 01-03; C Westmr St Jas *Lon* from 03. *2 Topiary Square, Stanmore Road, Richmond TW9 2DB* Tel (020) 8948 7033 *or* 7734 4511 Mobile 07712-526719 Fax (020) 7734 7449 E-mail gillhenwood@hotmail.com

HENWOOD, Martin John. b 58. Glas Univ BD81. Ripon Coll Cuddesdon. **d** 85 **p** 86. C Dartford H Trin *Roch* 85-88; C St Martin-in-the-Fields *Lon* 88-93; V Dartford H Trin *Roch* from 93. *The Vicarage, High Street, Dartford DA1 1RX* Tel (01322) 222782

HENWOOD, Canon Peter Richard. b 32. St Edm Hall Ox BA55 MA69. Cuddesdon Coll 56. **d** 57 **p** 58. C Rugby St Andr *Cov* 57-62; C-in-c Gleadless Valley CD *Sheff* 62-71; V Plaistow St Mary *Roch* 71-97; RD Bromley 79-96; Hon Can Roch Cathl 88-97; rtd 97. *Wayside, 1 Highfield Close, Sandling Road, Saltwood, Hythe CT21 4QP* Tel (01303) 230039

HENWOOD (née OAKLEY), Mrs Susan Mary. b 55. Salford Univ BSc76. St Jo Coll Nottm LTh86 DPS87. **d** 87 **p** 94. Par Dn Armthorpe *Sheff* 87-91; C Howell Hill *Guildf* 91-96; Perm to Offic *Cov* from 02. *5 Blenheim Close, Bideford-on-Avon, Alcester B50 4HW* Tel (01789) 490630

HEPPER, Christopher Michael Alan. b 55. St Jo Coll Nottm 90. **d** 92 **p** 93. C High Harrogate Ch Ch *Ripon* 92-95; Bp's Dom Chapl 95-99; Chapl Poitou-Charentes *Eur* from 99. *29 rue Pierre Pestureau, 86400 Civray, France* Tel (0033) (5) 49 97 04 21 Mobile (6) 85 05 34 62 Fax 49 97 04 37 E-mail michael.hepper@wanadoo.fr

HEPPER, William Raymond. b 62. Kingston Poly BA83. Trin Coll Bris BTh98. **d** 98 **p** 99. C Spring Grove St Mary *Lon* 98-01; CMS from 01. *CMS, Partnership House, 157 Waterloo Road, London SE1 8UU* Tel (020) 8560 7141

HEPPLE, Gordon. b 32. Edin Th Coll. **d** 63 **p** 68. C Billingham St Cuth *Dur* 63-64; C Ryhope 64; Perm to Offic 66-68; C Wingate Grange 68-69; C Heworth St Mary 69; C Gateshead St Mary 69-71; P-in-c Low Team 71-72; R Lyons 72-79; V Basford St Aid *S'well* 79-84; V Blackhill *Dur* 84-95; rtd 97; Perm to Offic *Win* from 97. *66B Ringwood Road, Christchurch BH23 5RE* Tel (01425) 279068

HEPTINSTALL, Mrs Lillian. b 49. EMMTC 99. **d** 02 **p** 03. NSM Chilwell *S'well* from 02. *8 Cranston Road, Bramcote, Nottingham NG9 3GU* Tel 0115-916 4588 E-mail heptinstall@ntlworld.com

HEPWORTH, Canon Ernest John Peter. b 42. K Coll Lon BD65 AKC65 Hull Univ MA87. **d** 66 **p** 67. C Headingley *Ripon* 66-69; Asst Chapl St Geo Hosp Lon 69-71; C Gt Grimsby St Mary and St Jas *Linc* 71-72; TV 72-74; V Crosby 74-80; V Barton upon Humber from 80; RD Yarborough 86-92; Can and Preb Linc Cathl from 94. *The Vicarage, Beck Hill, Barton-on-Humber DN18 5EY* Tel (01652) 632202 E-mail ernest@herbert2000.fsnet.co.uk

HEPWORTH, Michael David Albert. b 37. Em Coll Cam BA59 MA63 Lon Inst of Educn PGCE60. Ridley Hall Cam 65. **d** 67 **p** 68. C Eastbourne All SS *Chich* 67-69; Teacher Eastbourne Coll 67-69; Asst Chapl Bedford Sch 69-72; Chapl 72-83; Hd Master Birkdale Sch 83-98; Perm to Offic *Derby* and *Sheff* from 83. *29 Stumperlowe Park Road, Sheffield S10 3QP* Tel 0114-230 6016 Fax 263 0714 E-mail hepworth@onet.co.uk

HEPWORTH, Michael Edward. b 29. Leeds Univ BA51. NW Ord Course 74. **d** 77 **p** 78. Hon C Timperley *Ches* 77-98; Hon Chapl RAF from 77; Perm to Offic *Ches* from 00. *56 Ridgway Road, Timperley, Altrincham WA15 7HD* Tel 0161-980 5104

HERBERT, Alan. b 33. FPhS62 Open Univ BA80. Paton Congr Coll Nottm 54 Coll of Resurr Mirfield 67. **d** 68 **p** 68. C Cockermouth All SS w Ch Ch *Carl* 68-71; V Clifton 71-77; V Westfield St Mary 77-87; R Long Marton w Dufton and w Milburn 87-98; rtd 98; Perm to Offic *Carl* from 00. *5 Spenser Close, Egremont CA22 2HE* Tel (01946) 822556

HERBERT, Anthony. b 19. Bris Univ. Qu Coll Birm 46. **d** 48 **p** 49. C Frodingham *Linc* 48-51; C Liv St Bride *Liv* 51-54; Chapl Liv Univ 51-54; C Liv St Sav 54-55; C Stapleton *Bris* 55-58; V Hamer *Man* 58-64; Chapl HM YOI Buckley Hall 58-64; V Dur St Cuth *Dur* 64-78; Chapl Low Newton Rem Cen 68-77; V Barrow upon Soar *Leic* 78-83; R Barrow upon Soar w Walton le Wolds 83-84; rtd 84; Perm to Offic *B & W* from 85. *12 Valley View, Clutton, Bristol BS39 5SN* Tel (01761) 452494

HERBERT, Christopher John. b 37. Dur Univ BA60 DipTh62. Cranmer Hall Dur 60. **d** 62 **p** 63. C Huyton Quarry *Liv* 62-65; C Rainford 65-68; V Impington *Ely* 68-78; RD N Stowe 76-78; V

Gt Shelford 78-97; RD Shelford 80-85; rtd 97. *North Place, Crown Street, Great Bardfield, Braintree CM7 4ST* Tel (01371) 810516

✠**HERBERT, The Rt Revd Christopher William.** b 44. Univ of Wales (Lamp) BA65. Wells Th Coll 65. **d** 67 **p** 68 c 95. C Tupsley *Heref* 67-71; Dioc RE Adv 71-76; Dioc Dir RE 76-81; Preb Heref Cathl 76-81; V Bourne *Guildf* 81-90; Hon Can Guildf Cathl 85-95; Adn Dorking 90-95; Bp St Alb from 95. *Abbey Gate House, 4 Abbey Mill Lane, St Albans AL3 4HD* Tel (01727) 853305 Fax 846715 E-mail bishop@stalbans.anglican.org

HERBERT, Clair Geoffrey Thomas. b 36. Tyndale Hall Bris 61. **d** 64 **p** 65. C Nottingham St Sav *S'well* 64-67; C Harwell *Ox* 67-70; C Chilton All SS 67-70; V Bucklebury w Marlston 70-80; Chapl Brighton Coll Jun Sch 80-83; Hon C Upton (Overchurch) *Ches* 85-86; C 86-88; V Collier Row St Jas and Havering-atte-Bower *Chelmsf* 88-01; rtd 01. *24 Birstwith Grange, Birstwith, Harrogate HG3 3AH* Tel (01423) 771315

HERBERT, Clare Marguerite. b 54. Bris Univ CASS85 St Hild Coll Dur BA76 New Coll Edin MTh78. Linc Th Coll 79. **dss** 81 **d** 87 **p** 94. Clifton St Paul *Bris* and Asst Chapl Bris Univ 81-84; Hon Par Dn Bris St Mary Redcliffe w Temple etc *Bris* 87-90; Dioc Past Care Adv 92-95; Hon C Clapham TM *S'wark* 94-96; C St Martin-in-the-Fields *Lon* 96-98; R Soho St Anne w St Thos and St Pet from 98; Dean of Women's Min Two Cities Area from 01. *St Anne's Rectory, 55 Dean Street, London W1D 6AF* Tel (020) 7437 5006 Fax 7437 8039 E-mail stannes.soho@virgin.net

HERBERT, Canon David Alexander Sellars. b 39. Bris Univ BA60. St Steph Ho Ox 65. **d** 67 **p** 68. C St Leonards Ch Ch *Chich* 67-80; C St Leonards Ch Ch and St Mary 81; V Bickley *Roch* from 81; Hon Can Roch Cathl from 92. *The Vicarage, Bickley Park Road, Bromley BR1 2BE* Tel (020) 8467 3809 Fax as telephone E-mail david.herbert@lineone.net

HERBERT, David Roy. b 51. K Coll Lon BD73 AKC73. **d** 74 **p** 75. C Sheff St Aid w St Luke *Sheff* 74-76; C Sheff Manor 76-78; TV Gleadless Valley 78-83; TV Ellesmere Port *Ches* 83-93; V Tarvin from 93. *St Andrew's Vicarage, Tarvin, Chester CH3 8EB* Tel (01829) 740354 E-mail davidherbert@lineone.net

HERBERT, Mrs Denise Bridget Helen. b 42. SRN72 SCM74. Ripon Coll Cuddesdon DipMin95. **d** 95 **p** 96. S Africa 95-00; NSM Ocean View 95-97; NSM Grahamstown Cathl 97-99; Sub-Dean 99-00; R Jedburgh *Edin* from 00. *The Rectory, 46 Castlegate, Jedburgh TD8 6BB* Tel (01835) 863892 Fax as telephone

HERBERT, Geoffrey William. b 38. Ox Univ MA62 Birm Univ PhD72. Qu Coll Birm DipTh82. **d** 82 **p** 83. C Hall Green Ascension *Birm* 82-85; R Sheldon 85-95; rtd 95; Perm to Offic *Birm* from 95; Co-ord for Spiritual Direction from 00. *28 Lulworth Road, Birmingham B28 8NS* Tel (0121) 7772684

HERBERT, Graham Paul. b 54. Birm Univ BA75 CertEd76 Ox Univ BA80 MA. Wycliffe Hall Ox 78. **d** 81 **p** 82. C Crowborough *Chich* 81-85; Chapl Monkton Combe Sch Bath 85-98; C Claygate *Guildf* 99-01. *Address temp unknown*

HERBERT, Graham Victor. b 61. Nottm Univ BA02. St Jo Coll Nottm 00. **d** 02 **p** 03. C Strood St Nic w St Mary *Roch* from 02. *12 Cadnam Close, Rochester ME2 3TS* Tel (01634) 321592

HERBERT, Jonathan Patrick. b 62. Bris Univ BA86. Linc Th Coll 86. **d** 88 **p** 89. C Kirkby *Liv* 88-91; TV Blakenall Heath *Lich* 91-96; Pilsdon Community from 96. *Pilsdon Manor, Pilsdon, Bridport DT6 5NZ* Tel (01308) 868308 Fax 868161

HERBERT, Kenneth Cyril. b 20. Univ of Wales (Abth) BA41. St D Coll Lamp LTh43. **d** 43 **p** 44. C Carmarthen St Pet *St D* 43-56; V Llangynwr 56-89; RD Llanbadarn Fawr 80-86; rtd 89. *68 Ger-y-llan, Penrhyncoch, Aberystwyth SY23 3HQ* Tel (01970) 828207

HERBERT, Malcolm Francis. b 53. K Coll Lon BD74 AKC74 St Mary's Coll Cheltenham CertEd75. Trin Coll Bris 76. **d** 77 **p** 78. C Wotton-under-Edge w Ozleworth and N Nibley *Glouc* 77-79; C Milton *B & W* 79-80; C Worle 80-85; V Woking Ch Ch *Guildf* 86-02; RD Woking 94-99; Dioc Dir of Ords *Bris* from 02. *3 Stapleford Close, Chippenham SN15 3FZ* Tel (01249) 765827 E-mail malcolm.herbert2@btopenworld.com

HERBERT, Michael. b 35. Nottm Univ BA57. St D Coll Lamp 59. **d** 61 **p** 62. C Paston *Pet* 61-65; C Northampton All SS w St Kath 65-67; R Sutton w Upton *Pet* 67-72; Asst Youth Chapl 67-72; Ind Chapl 72-84; P-in-c Pitsford 79-84; Ind Chapl *Worc* 84-01; TV Redditch, The Ridge 84-01; Chapl NE Worcs Coll 86-01; rtd 01. *33 Abbey Road, Redditch B97 4BL* Tel (01527) 69975 Fax as telephone

HERBERT, Canon Ronald. b 53. Worc Coll Ox BA75 MA80 Lon Univ BD78 W Kentucky Univ MA79. Oak Hill Th Coll 75. **d** 79 **p** 80. C Welling *Roch* 79-89; V Falconwood 89-90; V Becontree St Mary *Chelmsf* from 90; Hon Can Chelmsf Cathl from 02. *The Vicarage, 191 Valence Wood Road, Dagenham RM8 3AH* Tel (020) 8592 2822 E-mail ronald.herbert@virgin.net

HERBERT, Mrs Rosemary. b 44. Westf Coll Lon BSc65. Qu Coll Birm 81. **dss** 85 **d** 87. Malvern Link w Cowleigh *Worc* 85-87; Hon Par Dn 87-91; Hon Par Dn Malvern H Trin and St Jas from 91. *4 Cedar Avenue, Malvern WR14 2SG* Tel (01684) 572497

HERBERT, Stephen Edward. b 54. Hastings Coll Nebraska BA76 Bemidji State Univ MA81. Seabury-Western Th Sem MDiv87. **d** 87 **p** 87. V Lake City Grace Ch USA 87-90; Asst P Vancouver St Jas Canada 90-00; TV Wythenshawe *Man* from 00. *St Richard's Vicarage, 42 Lomond Road, Manchester M22 5JD* Tel 0161-499 2022 E-mail stephenherbert@supanet.com

HERBERT, Canon Timothy David. b 57. Man Univ BA78 MPhil88. Ridley Hall Cam 79. **d** 81 **p** 82. C Macclesfield St Mich *Ches* 81-85; V Wharton 85-93; Asst CME Officer 90-93; P-in-c Thanington *Cant* 93-98; Dir of Ords 93-98; Dir Dioc Tr Inst *Carl* from 99; C Cotehill and Cumwhinton 99-00; Hon Can Carl Cathl from 99; C Scotby and Cotehill w Cumwhinton from 00. *The Vicarage, Cotehill, Carlisle CA4 0DY* Tel (01228) 561745 Fax 562366 E-mail therbert@globalnet.co.uk

✠**HERD, The Rt Revd William Brian.** b 31. Clifton Th Coll 55. **d** 58 **p** 59 **c** 76. C Wolverhampton St Luke *Lich* 58-61; Uganda 61-77; Adn Karamoja 70-75; Bp Karamoja 76-77; Deputation Sec (Ireland) BCMS 77-89; C Harrow Trin St Mich *Lon* 89-93; V Gresley *Derby* 93-98; rtd 98; Perm to Offic *Sarum* from 98. *Karibu, 13 Ambleside, Weymouth DT3 5HH* Tel (01305) 770257

HEREFORD, Archdeacon of. See TILLER, The Ven John

HEREFORD, Bishop of. See OLIVER, The Rt Revd John Keith

HEREFORD, Dean of. See TAVINOR, The Very Revd Michael Edward

HEREWARD, John Owen. b 53. FRCSE82 Lon Univ MB, BS77. Ridley Hall Cam 89. **d** 91 **p** 92. C W Ealing St Jo w St Jas *Lon* 91-95; P-in-c Hanwell St Mellitus w St Mark from 95; Dir Post-Ord Tr from 97; AD Ealing 98-03. *St Mellitus Vicarage, Church Road, London W7 3BA* Tel (020) 8567 6535 E-mail 100756.2151@compuserve.com

HEREWARD-ROTHWELL, Canon Michael John. b 46. MA. Chich Th Coll 74. **d** 78 **p** 79. C Chelmsf All SS *Chelmsf* 78-82; C Clacton St Jas 82-85; V Thorpe *Guildf* from 85; Hon Can Guildf Cathl from 99. *The Vicarage, Church Approach, Egham TW20 8TQ* Tel (01932) 565986 Fax as telephone E-mail mjh.r@fish.co.uk

HERITAGE, Barry. b 35. Clifton Th Coll 59. **d** 61 **p** 62. C Wolverhampton St Jude *Lich* 61-65; C Chaddesden St Mary *Derby* 65-67; V Kidsgrove *Lich* 67-76; NE Area Sec CPAS 76-89; V Elloughton and Brough w Brantingham *York* 89-93; C York St Paul 93-00; rtd 00; Perm to Offic *York* from 00. *32 St Swithins Walk, York YO26 4UF* Tel (01904) 786077

HERKES, Richard Andrew. b 54. Kent Univ BA75. STETS 99. **d** 02 **p** 03. NSM Polegate *Chich* from 02. *31 Wannock Lane, Eastbourne BN20 9SB* Tel (01323) 488328 E-mail rherkes@hotmail.com

HERKLOTS, Canon John Radu. b 31. Trin Hall Cam BA53 MA61. Westcott Ho Cam 54. **d** 55 **p** 56. C Attercliffe w Carbrook *Sheff* 55-60; C Stoke Damerel *Ex* 60-65; V Devonport St Bart 65-72; V Denmead *Portsm* 72-97; RD Havant 82-87; Hon Can Portsm Cathl 86-97; rtd 97; Perm to Offic *Heref* 97-02 and *Portms* from 03. *14 Derwent Road, Lee-on-the-Solent PO13 8JG* Tel (023) 9255 2652

HERMAN, Jean-Pierre. b 59. Louvain Univ MA83 BPh83. Namur Dioc Sem BTh87. **d** 86 **p** 87. In RC Ch (Belgium) 86-00; Perm to Offic *Eur* 01-02; C Brussels from 02. *10 rue d'Harscamp, B-5380 Noville-les-Bois, Belgium* Tel and fax (0032) (81) 657576 Mobile 475-684665 E-mail jean.pierre.herman@skynet.be

HERON, Alexander Francis. b 28. Univ of BC BA60. Angl Th Coll (BC) LTh53. **d** 52 **p** 53. C Bush Hill Park St Mark *Lon* 52-53; C Beckenham St Barn *Roch* 54-55; Canada 55-62 and from 77; Chapl RAF 62-77. *99 Seagirt Road, East Sooke BC, Canada, V0S 1N0* Tel (001) (250) 642 7480

HERON, David George. b 49. AKC72. **d** 73 **p** 74. C Stockton St Chad *Dur* 73-77; C Beamish 77-81; R Willington and Sunnybrow 81-95; V Dipton and Leadgate from 95. *The Vicarage, St Ives Road, Leadgate, Consett DH8 7SN* Tel (01207) 503918

HERON, George Dobson. b 34. TD. Cranmer Hall Dur 58. **d** 61 **p** 62. C Benfieldside *Dur* 61-65; C Winlaton 65-68; V Dunston St Nic 68-77; P-in-c Dunston Ch Ch 74-77; V Dunston 77-82; V Gateshead St Helen 82-89; rtd 94; Perm to Offic *Dur* 94-96; Perm to Offic *Newc* from 94. *36 Woodlands Road, Shotley Bridge, Consett DH8 0DE* Tel (01207) 507733

HERON, Nicholas Peter. b 60. Man Univ BA81 Southn Univ BTh86. Sarum & Wells Th Coll. **d** 84 **p** 85. C Brinnington w Portwood *Ches* 84-87; Chapl RAF from 87. *Chaplaincy Services (RAF), HQ, Personnel and Training Command, RAF Innsworth, Gloucester GL3 1EZ* Tel (01452) 712612 ext 5164 Fax 510828

HERRICK, Andrew Frederick. b 58. Univ of Wales (Lamp) BA80. Wycliffe Hall Ox 80. **d** 82 **p** 83. C Aberystwyth *St D* 82-85; P-in-c Llangeitho and Blaenpennal w Betws Leucu etc 85-86; R 86-88; Youth Chapl 86-88; R Aberporth w Tremain and Blaenporth 88-91; Succ St D Cathl 91-94; Min St D Cathl 91-94; V Betws w Ammanford 94-00; TV Aberystwyth from 00. *Fenton, Queens Square, Aberystwyth SY23 2HL* Tel (01970) 624537

HERRICK, David William. b 52. Middx Poly BSc73. St Jo Coll Nottm DipTh80. **d** 82 **p** 83. C Ipswich St Matt *St E* 82-85; C Nor St Pet Mancroft w St Jo Maddermarket *Nor* 85-88; V Bury

St Edmunds St Geo *St E* 88-96; P-in-c Gt Barton 96-99; Dir Studies OLM Scheme from 99. *24 Cromwell Road, Ely CB6 1AS* Tel (01353) 662909 Fax 662056

HERRICK (formerly COWLEY), Mrs Jean Louie Cameron. b 39. Sarum Dioc Tr Coll CertEd59. St Alb and Ox Min Course 94. **d** 96 **p** 97. NSM Chorleywood Ch Ch *St Alb* 96-02; NSM Hermitage *Ox* from 02. *The Vicarage, 8 Yew Tree Stables, Compton, Newbury RG20 6NG* Tel (01635) 579242 E-mail jean.herrick@tesco.net

HERRICK (née RENAUT), Canon Vanessa Anne. b 58. York Univ BA80 LTCL75. St Jo Coll Nottm 80 Ridley Hall Cam MA96 CTM96. **d** 96 **p** 97. C St E Cathl Distr *St E* 96-99; Chapl Fitzw Coll Cam 99-02; Fell 01-02; Tutor Ridley Hall Cam 99-02; Dir Min and Vocation *Ely* from 03; Hon Can Ely Cathl from 03. *24 Cromwell Road, Ely CB6 1AS* Tel (01353) 662909 Mobile 07778-496340 Fax (01353) 662056 E-mail vanessa.herrick@ely.anglican.org

HERROD, Mrs Kathryn. b 59. Warwick Univ BSc80 Matlock Coll of Educn PGCE81. St Jo Coll Nottm MA97. **d** 97 **p** 98. C Wollaton *S'well* 97-01; R Warsop from 01. *The Rectory, Church Road, Warsop, Mansfield NG20 0SL* Tel (01623) 843290

HERRON, Robert Gordon John. b 36. MCIPD75 Dip Counselling CPC. Wycliffe Hall Ox 65. **d** 77 **p** 78. C Ditton St Mich *Liv* 77-80; C W Kirby St Bridget *Ches* 80-82; R Gorton St Mary and St Thos *Man* 82-00; rtd 00. *The Gables, 13 West Road, Bowden, Altrincham WA14 2LD*

HERSCHEL, Richard James. b 27. Villanova Univ USA MA72. **d** 57 **p** 57. USA 57-81 and 84-97; TV Cannock *Lich* 82-84; rtd 92. *80B King Street, Norwich NR1 1PG* Tel (01603) 614873

HERTFORD, Archdeacon of. See JONES, The Ven Trevor Pryce

HERTFORD, Suffragan Bishop of. See FOSTER, The Rt Revd Christopher Richard James

HERVE, John Anthony. b 49. TD94. Open Univ BA81 Birm Univ DPS85 Wolv Univ PGCE95. Lich Th Coll 70. **d** 73 **p** 74. C Middlesbrough All SS *York* 73-76; CF 76-81; P-in-c Handsworth St Andr *Birm* 81-86; Hon C Cowley St Jo *Ox* 86-90; Tutor St Steph Ho Ox 86-90; V Sparkbrook St Agatha w Balsall Heath St Barn *Birm* from 90. *The Clergy House, 288A Ladypool Road, Birmingham B12 8JU* Tel 0121-449 2790

HERVEY, Mrs Mary Diana (Di). b 41. St Hugh's Coll Ox BA63. St And Dioc Tr Course 83 TISEC 96. **d** 92 **p** 94. Par Dn Cupar *St And* 92-94; Asst Chapl St Andr Univ 94-97; Asst P Cen Fife Team 94-97; C Ulverston St Mary w H Trin *Carl* 97-00; P-in-c Barrow St Jo from 00. *St John's Vicarage, James Watt Terrace, Barrow-in-Furness LA14 2TS* Tel (01229) 821101 E-mail revdih@aol.com

HERVET, Dudley. b 18. AKC42. **d** 42 **p** 43. C Southampton St Alb *Win* 42-45; C Finsbury Park St Thos *Lon* 45-48; C Hackney Wick St Mary of Eton w St Aug 48-50; C St Geo-in-the-East St Mary 50-53; V 53-58; V Edmonton St Mich 58-62; V Blean *Cant* 62-73; V Kennington 73-83; rtd 83; Perm to Offic *Cant* 83-96. *27 Homespire House, Knotts Lane, Canterbury CT1 2AB* Tel (01227) 451511

HESELTINE, Mrs Barbara Joan. b 42. Keele Univ BA65. S'wark Ord Course 85. **d** 88 **p** 94. NSM Addington *S'wark* 88-98; Perm to Offic *Truro* from 98; NSM Feock from 02. *The Lodge, Penpol, Devoran, Truro TR3 6NA* Tel and fax (01872) 870039 Mobile 07767-264060

HESELWOOD, Eric Harold. b 43. Oak Hill Th Coll 84. **d** 86 **p** 87. C Farnborough *Roch* 86-88; V Biggin Hill 88-96; V Orpington All SS 96-98; V Bromley Common St Aug from 98. *St Augustine's Vicarage, Southborough Lane, Bromley BR2 8AT* Tel (020) 8467 1351 Fax as telephone E-mail eric.heselwood@talk21.com

HESELWOOD, Mrs Hilda. b 39. CA Tr Coll 61. **dss** 85 **d** 87 **p** 94. CA from 63; Bromley Common St Luke *Roch* 85-00; Par Dn 87-94; C 94-00; rtd 00; Perm to Offic *Roch* from 00. *St Augustine's Vicarage, Southborough Lane, Bromley BR2 8AT* Tel (020) 8467 1351 Fax as telephone

HESFORD-LOCKE, Richard Nigel. b 61. Coll of Resurr Mirfield 92. **d** 94 **p** 95. C Middlesbrough Ascension *York* 94-97; C Paignton St Jo *Ex* 97-98; rtd 98. *2 Windyhill Drive, Bolton BL3 4TH*

HESKETH, Philip John. b 64. K Coll Lon BD86 AKC86 PhD94 Richmond Fellowship Coll Dip Human Relns 90. Ripon Coll Cuddesdon DipMin94. **d** 94 **p** 95. C Bearsted w Thurnham *Cant* 94-98; V Chatham St Steph *Roch* from 98. *St Stephen's Vicarage, 55 Pattens Lane, Chatham ME4 6JR* Tel (01634) 849791

HESKETH, Robin Adams Lempriere. b 18. St Cath Soc Ox BA43 MA47. St Steph Ho Ox 43. **d** 45 **p** 46. C Babbacombe *Ex* 45-48; Perm to Offic 48-51; C Dawlish 51-55; C Brixham 55-61; V S Petherwin w Trewen *Truro* 61-72; V Lewannick 62-71; P-in-c Penponds 72-73; V 73-83; rtd 84; Perm to Offic *Truro* from 84. *Camelview, Marshall Road, Nanstallon, Bodmin PL30 5LD* Tel (01208) 831892

HESKETH, The Ven Ronald David. b 47. Bede Coll Dur BA68 Univ of Wales (Cardiff) DPS71. Ridley Hall Cam 69 St Mich Coll Llan 71. **d** 71 **p** 72. C Southport H Trin *Liv* 71-74; Asst Chapl Miss to Seamen 74-75; Chapl RAF 75-98; Command Chapl RAF 98-01; Chapl-in-Chief RAF from 01; QHC from 01;

Can and Preb Linc Cathl *Linc* from 01. *Chaplaincy Services (RAF), HQ, Personnel and Training Command, RAF Innsworth, Gloucester GL3 1EZ* Tel (01452) 712612 ext 5164 Fax 510828 E-mail vera&ron.hesketh@dunelm.org.uk
HESKINS, Georgiana Mary. b 48. K Coll Lon BD81 AKC81 MTh93. Westcott Ho Cam 81. **dss** 83 **d** 87 **p** 94. Cobbold Road St Sav w St Mary *Lon* 83-85; St Botolph Aldgate w H Trin Minories 85-87; Par Dn 87; Perm to Offic *S'wark* 88-93; Par Dn Kidbrooke St Jas 93-95; Tutor S'wark Ord Course 93-94; Tutor SEITE 94-98; Hon Chapl S'wark Cathl *S'wark* from 95; Teacher Eltham Coll 98-02; Asst Chapl Qu Eliz Hosp NHS Trust from 03. *Queen Elizabeth Hospital NHS Trust, Stadium Road, London SE18 4QH* Tel (020) 8836 6831 E-mail georgiana@lineone.net
HESKINS, Jeffrey George. b 55. AKC78 Heythrop Coll Lon MA94 Princeton Th Sem DMin00. Chich Th Coll 80. **d** 81 **p** 82. C Primrose Hill St Mary w Avenue Road St Paul *Lon* 81-85; Enfield Deanery Youth Officer 85-88; C Enfield Chase St Mary 85-88; TV Kidbrooke St Jas *S'wark* 88-95; R Charlton St Luke w H Trin 95-02; P-in-c Old Charlton St Thos 02; R Charlton from 02. *The Rectory, 185 Charlton Church Lane, London SE7 7AA* Tel (020) 8858 0791 Fax 8305 1297 E-mail heskins@lineone.net
HESLAM, Peter Somers. b 63. Hull Univ BA89 Keble Coll Ox DPhil94 Trin Coll Cam BA96 MA01. Ridley Hall Cam 93. **d** 96 **p** 97. C Huntingdon *Ely* 96-99; Min Stukeley Meadows LEP 99; Dir Studies EAMTC 99-00; Dir Capitalism Project Lon Inst of Contemporary Chr from 00; Tutor Ridley Hall Cam from 00; Hon C Cherry Hinton St Jo *Ely* from 00. *Ridley Hall, Ridley Hall Road, Cambridge CB3 9HG* Tel (01223) 722822 E-mail peter.heslam@ntlworld.com
HESLOP, Andrew James. b 66. Man Univ BA87 PGCE88. Man OLM Scheme 00. **d** 03. OLM Turton Moorland Min *Man* from 03. *677 Tonge Moor Road, Bolton BL2 3BW* Tel 07713-695227 (mobile)
HESLOP, David Anthony. b 45. BSc DipEd DipTh MTh Birm Univ MLitt97. St Jo Coll Nottm 81. **d** 83 **p** 84. C Willenhall H Trin *Lich* 83-86; V Gresley *Derby* 86-92; V Marston on Dove w Scropton 92-95; Chapl Derby Univ 95-99; V Castle Donington and Lockington cum Hemington *Leic* 99-03; Chapl E Midl Airport 99-03; Prin OLM and Integrated Tr *Sarum* from 03. *25 Lime Kiln Way, Salisbury SP2 8RN* Tel (01722) 417616 Fax 08701-301824 E-mail revdave@heslops.co.uk
HESLOP, Harold William. b 40. Leeds Univ BA62 Open Univ BA72. Ox NSM Course 75. **d** 78 **p** 79. NSM Stoke Mandeville *Ox* 78-91; NSM Wendover 82-00; NSM Ellesborough, The Kimbles and Stoke Mandeville 91-94. *7 Chiltern Road, Wendover, Aylesbury HP22 6DB* Tel (01296) 624812
HESLOP, James Alan. b 37. Codrington Coll Barbados 61. **d** 64 **p** 65. Br Guiana 64-66; Guyana 66-68; Bahamas 68-72; C Haxby w Wigginton *York* 72-74; TV 74-76; V York St Olave w St Giles 76-87; V Northampton All SS w St Kath *Pet* 87-88; R Felpham w Middleton *Chich* 88-92; TR Howden *York* 92-94; Warden Coll of St Barn Lingfield 94-95; Warden Morley Retreat and Conf Ho Derby 95-98; R Kirkbride *S & M* 98-99; V Lezayre St Olave Ramsey 98-99; P-in-c Woburn w Eversholt, Milton Bryan, Battlesden etc *St Alb* from 99. *The Vicarage, Park Street, Woburn, Milton Keynes MK17 9PG* Tel (01525) 290225
HESLOP, Michael Andrew. b 47. Trin Coll Bris 73. **d** 76 **p** 77. C Burmantofts St Steph and St Agnes *Ripon* 76-80; V Thorpe Edge *Bradf* 80-87; TV Penrith w Newton Reigny and Plumpton Wall *Carl* 87-91; V Silloth 91-01; V Kettlewell w Conistone, Hubberholme etc *Bradf* from 01. *The Vicarage, Westgate, Kettlewell, Skipton BD23 5QU* Tel (01756) 760237
HESS, John. b 44. Liv Poly BSc70 Westmr Coll Ox 95. SEITE 95. **d** 98 **p** 99. NSM Margate All SS *Cant* 98-02; C 02-03; C The Brents and Davington w Oare and Luddenham from 03. *The Vicarage, Brent Hill, Faversham ME13 7EF* Tel (01795) 533272 E-mail john.hess@connectfree.co.uk
HESS, Paul Austin. b 67. Cape Town Univ BA89. St Bede's Coll Umtata DipTh92. **d** 93 **p** 93. S Africa 92-94; NSM Eythorne and Elvington w Waldershare etc *Cant* 95-96; C Storrington *Chich* 96-99; Chapl Hurstpierpoint Coll from 99. *Hurstpierpoint College, Malthouse Lane, Hassocks BN6 9JS* Tel (01273) 833636
HESTER, Canon John Frear. b 27. St Edm Hall Ox BA48 MA52. Cuddesdon Coll 51. **d** 52 **p** 53. C Southall St Geo *Lon* 52-55; C Clerkenwell H Redeemer w St Phil 55-58; Sec Actors' Ch Union 58-63; Sen Chapl 70-75; Chapl Soc of Sisters of Bethany Lloyd Square 59-62; Dep Min Can St Paul's Cathl 62-75; R Soho St Anne w St Thos and St Pet 63-75; P-in-c Covent Garden St Paul 69-75; P-in-c Brighton St Jo *Chich* 75-80; V Brighton St Pet 75-78; Can and Preb Chich Cathl 76-85; Can Res and Prec Chich Cathl 85-97; RD Brighton 76-85; RD Kemp Town 76-83; RD Preston 76-83; P-in-c Brighton Chpl Royal 77-78; V Brighton St Pet w Chpl Royal 78-80; V Brighton St Pet w Chpl Royal and St Jo 80-85; P-in-c Brighton St Nic 84-85; Chapl to The Queen 84-97; rtd 97; Perm to Offic *Chich* from 97. *The Hovel, Church Lane, Oving, Chichester PO20 2DE* Tel (01243) 782071 E-mail thehovel@bigfoot.com
HETHERINGTON, Andrew. b 50. Sheff Univ BSc71. Wycliffe Hall Ox 71. **d** 74 **p** 75. C Leic H Trin w St Jo *Leic* 74-78; C Leic H

Apostles 78-82; V Bootle St Mary w St Paul *Liv* 82-93; TR W Swindon and the Lydiards *Bris* 93-01; P-in-c Chebsey, Ellenhall and Seighford-with-Creswell *Lich* from 01. *The Vicarage, Seighford, Stafford ST18 9PQ* Tel (01785) 282829
HETHERINGTON, Mrs Charlotte Elizabeth. b 52. Girton Coll Cam BA74 Maria Grey Coll Lon PGCE75. St Alb and Ox Min Course CBTS95. **d** 98 **p** 99. NSM Stratfield Mortimer and Mortimer W End etc *Ox* from 98. *Birchwood, 82 The Avenue, Mortimer, Reading RG7 3QX* Tel 0118-933 2429
HETHERINGTON, Dermot Hugh. b 42. SRN63 RMN65 Worc Coll of Educn BSc. **d** 78 **p** 79. Hon C Raveningham *Nor* 78-90; Perm to Offic from 90. *1 Whiteways, Wheatacre, Beccles NR34 0AU* Tel (01502) 677467
HETHERINGTON, Mrs Glynis Catherine. b 48. EMMTC 93. **d** 93 **p** 94. NSM E and W Leake, Stanford-on-Soar, Rempstone etc *S'well* 93-99; R from 99. *The Rectory, 3 Bateman Road, East Leake, Loughborough LE12 6LN* Tel (01509) 852228
HETHERINGTON, John Carl. b 52. Linc Th Coll. **d** 84 **p** 85. C Crosby *Linc* 84-88; TV Cleethorpes 88-93; Chapl RAF from 93. *Chaplaincy Services (RAF), HQ, Personnel and Training Command, RAF Innsworth, Gloucester GL3 1EZ* Tel (01452) 712612 ext 5164 Fax 510828
HETLING, William Maurice. b 37. AKC61. **d** 62 **p** 63. C Eltham St Barn *S'wark* 62-66; C Horley 66-71; Jamaica 71-75; C-in-c Farnham Royal S CD *Ox* 75-78; TV W Slough 78-80 and 88-91; TR 80-88; TV Parkstone St Pet w Branksea and St Osmund *Sarum* 91-96; P-in-c Reading St Barn *Ox* 96-99; rtd 99; Perm to Offic *Chich* from 99. *12 Manor Close, Storrington, Pulborough RH20 4LF*
HEWER, Sidney Eric. b 24. Nor Ord Course. **d** 78 **p** 79. NSM Grimston w Congham *Nor* 78-91; NSM Grimston, Congham and Roydon 91-92; Perm to Offic from 92. *42 Vong Lane, Pott Row, Grimston, King's Lynn PE32 1BW* Tel (01485) 600635
HEWES, John. b 29. Nottm Univ BA50. Chich Th Coll 79. **d** 81 **p** 82. C Buckland in Dover w Buckland Valley *Cant* 81-84; P-in-c Elmsted w Hastingleigh 84-89; P-in-c Crundale w Godmersham 84-89; RD W Bridge 88-89; R Lydd 89-95; RD S Lympne 89-95; rtd 95; Perm to Offic *Cant* from 95. *Brambledown, Tamley Lane, Hastingleigh, Ashford TN25 5HW* Tel (01233) 750214
HEWES, Timothy William. b 50. Sheff Univ BDS74. St Alb and Ox Min Course 98. **d** 01. NSM Abingdon *Ox* from 01. *55 Lower Radley, Abingdon OX14 3AY* Tel (01235) 523963 Mobile 07771-880117 E-mail tim@rdlf.uninet.co.uk
HEWETSON, The Ven Christopher. b 37. Trin Coll Ox BA60 MA64. Chich Th Coll 67. **d** 69 **p** 70. C Leckhampton St Pet *Glouc* 69-71; C Wokingham All SS *Ox* 71-73; V Didcot St Pet 73-82; R Ascot Heath 82-90; RD Bracknell 86-90; P-in-c Headington Quarry 90-94; Hon Can Ch Ch 92-94; RD Cowley 94; Adn Ches 94-02; rtd 02; Bp's Adv for Spirituality *Ex* from 03. *The Old Estate House, The Square, North Molton, South Molton EX36 3HP* Tel (01598) 740573
HEWETSON, David Geoffrey. b 31. S'wark Ord Course 71. **d** 74 **p** 75. NSM Brighton St Mich *Chich* from 74. *Flat 1, 166 Dyke Road, Brighton BN1 5PU* Tel (01273) 275776
HEWETSON, Canon Robin Jervis. b 39. AKC63 K Coll Lon MA93. **d** 64 **p** 65. C Thorpe *Nor* 64-67; C E Dereham w Hoe 67-69; TV Mattishall w Mattishall Burgh 69-72; R Ingham w Sutton 72-78; R Catfield 75-78; R Taverham w Ringland 78-89; P-in-c Marsham 89-92; P-in-c Burgh 89-92; Dioc Ecum Officer from 89; Exec Officer Norfolk Ecum Coun from 89; R Marsham w Burgh-next-Aylsham from 92; Hon Can Nor Cathl from 01. *The Rectory, Marsham, Norwich NR10 5PP* Tel (01263) 733249 Fax 733799
HEWETSON, Canon Valerie Patricia. b 44. St Mary's Coll Dur BSc66 MSc70 Leeds Univ MA75. Linc Th Coll 89. **d** 91 **p** 94. C Kingston upon Hull St Nic *York* 91-94; V Barmby Moor w Allerthorpe, Fangfoss and Yapham 94-98; V Barmby Moor Gp from 98; Can and Preb York Minster from 01; RD S Wold from 01. *The Vicarage, St Helen's Square, Barmby Moor, York YO42 4HF* Tel (01759) 305971
HEWETT, Andrew David. b 63. Univ of Wales (Lamp) BA. Chich Th Coll 84. **d** 86 **p** 87. C Caldicot *Mon* 86-90; Chapl RAF from 90. *Chaplaincy Services (RAF), HQ, Personnel and Training Command, RAF Innsworth, Gloucester GL3 1EZ* Tel (01452) 712612 ext 5164 Fax 510828
HEWETT, Maurice Gordon. b 28. Lon Univ BA53. Oak Hill Th Coll 49. **d** 54 **p** 55. C Gipsy Hill Ch Ch *S'wark* 54-57; C Maidstone St Faith *Cant* 57-60; R Chevening *Roch* 60-95; rtd 95; Perm to Offic *Cant* and *Roch* from 95; Hon Wing Chapl ATC from 96. *Rosings, 12 The Thicketts, Sevenoaks TN13 3SZ* Tel (01732) 464734 Fax as telephone
HEWETT, Roger Leroy. b 45. St Mich Coll Llan DipTh95. **d** 95 **p** 96. C Whitchurch *Llan* 95-98; R Blaina and Nantyglo *Mon* from 98. *The Rectory, Station Road, Blaina NP13 3BW* Tel (01495) 290130
HEWISON, Alan Stuart. b 30. SS Mark & Jo Coll Plymouth BEd82. K Coll Lon. **d** 57 **p** 58. C S Mymms K Chas *Lon* 57-60; C Bourne *Guildf* 60-63; Chapl RN 63-79; Perm to Offic *Ex* from 79; rtd 95. *8 Hazelwood Crescent, Plymouth PL9 8BL*

HEWITSON, Denise Ann. b 52. Liv Univ BEd74. St Jo Coll Nottm MA97. **d** 97 **p** 98. C Bootle St Matt *Liv* 97-01; Chapl Douglas MacMillan Hospice Stoke-on-Trent from 01; Hon C Blurton *Lich* from 02. *Douglas MacMillan Hospice, Barlaston Road, Stoke-on-Trent ST3 3NZ* Tel (01782) 344300 Fax 344301

HEWITSON, John Kenneth. b 48. Curtin Univ Aus BA Flinders Univ Aus MA96 DSS84. Adelaide Coll of Div ThL70 ACT ThSchol83. **d** 71 **p** 72. C Swindon Ch *Bris* 71-74; Australia from 74; C Spearwood 74-76; R Balga 76-77; Chapl Royal Perth Hosp 79-83; R Lockridge 83-86; R Eliz 92-97; Chapl Trin Coll 93-98; Chapl Kormilda Coll Darwin from 99; R Freds Pass from 00. *PO Box 346, Humpty Doo, NT, Australia 0836* Tel (0061) (8) 8983 3947 Fax 8983 3951 E-mail jah@octa4.net.au

HEWITT, Christopher James Chichele (Chich). b 45. Witwatersrand Univ BSc68 UNISA BA78 MTh92 LTCL69. St Paul's Coll Grahamstown DipTh79. **d** 78 **p** 79. S Africa 78-99; Chapl St Paul's Coll Grahamstown 84-86; Warden 86-92; Can Grahamstown Cathl 88-93; Chan 92; Sub-Dean 93; Dean and Adn Grahamstown 93-98; USA 99; TR Radcliffe *Man* from 00; AD Radcliffe and Prestwich from 02. *St Thomas's Vicarage, Heber Street, Radcliffe, Manchester M26 2TG* Tel 0161-723 2123 E-mail gill-chich@heberstreet.freeserve.co.uk

HEWITT, Colin Edward. b 52. Man Poly BA80 Em Coll Cam BA82 MA86. Westcott Ho Cam 80. **d** 83 **p** 84. C Radcliffe St Thos and St Jo *Man* 83-84; C Langley and Parkfield 84-86; R Byfield w Boddington *Pet* 86-89; R Byfield w Boddington and Aston le Walls 89-91; Chapl RAF from 91. *Chaplaincy Services (RAF), HQ, Personnel and Training Command, RAF Innsworth, Gloucester GL3 1EZ* Tel (01452) 712612 ext 5164 *or* (01845) 815387 Fax 510828

HEWITT, David Warner. b 33. Selw Coll Cam BA56 MA60. Wells Th Coll 57. **d** 59 **p** 60. C Longbridge *Birm* 59-61; C Sheldon 61-64; V Smethwick Old Ch 64-70; V Smethwick 70-78; P-in-c Littlehampton St Jas *Chich* 78-85; P-in-c Wick 78-85; V Littlehampton St Mary 78-85; TR Littlehampton and Wick 86-89; Perm to Offic *Eur* from 95; rtd 98; Hon Asst Chapl Gtr Athens *Eur* from 00. *PO Box 1705, 540 06 Thessalonica, Greece* Tel (0030) (2310) 859651 Fax 864292 E-mail tangulls@the.forthnet.gr

HEWITT, Canon Francis John Adam. b 42. St Chad's Coll Dur BA64 DipTh66. **d** 66 **p** 67. C Dewsbury Moor *Wakef* 66-69; C Huddersfield St Jo 69-73; V King Cross 73-81; V Lastingham *York* 81; P-in-c Appleton-le-Moors 81; V Lastingham w Appleton-le-Moors 81-84; P-in-c Rosedale 83-84; V Lastingham w Appleton-le-Moors and Rosedale 84-86; RD Helmsley 85-94; V Lastingham w Appleton-le-Moors, Rosedale etc 86-94; V Pickering 94-95; V Pickering w Lockton and Levisham from 95; RD Pickering from 94; Can and Preb York Minster from 97. *The Vicarage, Hatcase Lane, Whitby Road, Pickering YO18 7HD* Tel (01751) 472983 Fax as telephone E-mail francis.hewitt@btopenworld.com

HEWITT, Garth Bruce. b 46. St Jo Coll Dur BA68. Lon Coll of Div LTh70. **d** 70 **p** 71. C Maidstone St Luke *Cant* 70-73; Staff Evang CPAS 73-79; Hon C W Ealing St Jo w St Jas *Lon* 73-81; Dir Amos Trust 88-96; World Affairs Adv *Guildf* 94-96; Regional Co-ord (Lon and SE) Chr Aid from 96; Perm to Offic *S'wark* from 96; P-in-c All Hallows Lon Wall *Lon* 97-99; V from 99. *Christian Aid, All Hallows on the Wall, 83 London Wall, London EC2M 5ND* Tel (020) 7496 1680 Fax 7496 1684 E-mail ghewitt@christian-aid.org

HEWITT, Geoffrey Williams. b 48. Leeds Univ BA69. Wells Th Coll 70. **d** 72 **p** 73. C Heywood St Luke *Man* 72-74; Ind Chapl 74-77; P-in-c Hulme St Geo 74-77; R Mamhilad and Llanfihangel Pontymoile *Mon* 77-80; Ind Chapl 77-80; V Arthog w Fairbourne *Ban* 80-89; R Llangelynnin w Rhoslefain 87-89; TV Bangor 89-94; Dioc Soc Resp Officer 89-02; P-in-c Pentir 94-02; Hon Can Ban Cathl 99-02; RD Ogwen 00-02; P-in-c Draycot *Bris* from 02. *The Rectory, Church Road, Christian Malford, Chippenham SN15 4BW* Tel and fax (01249) 720070 Mobile 07950-497580 E-mail geoffrey@revhewitt.freeserve.co.uk

HEWITT, Guy Arlington Kenneth. b 67. Univ of W Indies BSc91 MSc93. SEITE 00. **d** 03. *11 Cupar Road, London SW11 4JW* Tel (020) 7622 4925 E-mail gakhewitt@hotmail.com

HEWITT, Harold William. b 12. Fitzw Ho Cam BA35 MA39. Wycliffe Hall Ox 36. **d** 38 **p** 39. C Westhoughton *Man* 38-40; C Kersal Moor 40-43; V Oldham St Paul 43-52; R Droylsden St Mary 52-66; V Gt Bowden w Welham *Leic* 66-77; rtd 77; Perm to Offic *Ches* from 77. *20 Rectory Close, Bowling Green Court, Nantwich CW5 5SW* Tel (01270) 626660

HEWITT, James Herbert. b 17. Ch Coll Cam BA39 MA42. Ridley Hall Cam 40. **d** 41 **p** 42. C Heworth H Trin *York* 41-43; C York St Mary Castlegate w St Mich Spurriergate 41-43; C Tulse Hill H Trin *S'wark* 43-45; CMS India 45-47; Pakistan 47-60; Vice-Prin CMS Tr Coll Chislehurst 61-65; C Spitalfields Ch Ch w All SS *Lon* 64-65; V New Beckenham St Paul *Roch* 65-71; R Mereworth w W Peckham 71-75; V Bradf St Aug Undercliffe *Bradf* 75-82; rtd 82; Perm to Offic *Glas* from 82. *73 Georgetown Road, Dumfries DG1 4DG* Tel (01387) 263973

HEWITT, John Kaffrell. b 34. St Aid Birkenhead 60. **d** 63 **p** 64. C Woking Ch Ch *Guildf* 63-66; P-in-c Sudbury w Ballingdon and Brundon *St E* 66-70; V 70-80; V Portsdown *Portsm* 80-96; rtd 96; Perm to Offic *Win* from 97. *45 Knowland Drive, Milford-on-Sea, Lymington SO41 0RH* Tel (01590) 644473

HEWITT, Kenneth Victor. b 30. Lon Univ BSc49 CertEd51 MSc53. Cuddesdon Coll 60. **d** 62 **p** 63. C Maidstone St Martin *Cant* 62-64; C Croydon St Mich 64-67; P-in-c S Kensington St Aug *Lon* 67-73; V 73-95; Asst Chapl Lon Univ 67-73; rtd 95; Perm to Offic *Roch* from 95. *Lower Treasurer's House, 41 Bromley College, London Road, Bromley BR1 1PE* Tel (020) 8464 0014

HEWITT, Michael David. b 49. K Coll Lon BD79 AKC79 CertEd. Qu Coll Birm 79. **d** 80 **p** 81. C Bexleyheath Ch Ch *Roch* 80-84; C Buckland in Dover w Buckland Valley *Cant* 84-89; R Ridgewell w Ashen, Birdbrook and Sturmer *Chelmsf* from 89. *The Rectory, Church Lane, Ridgewell, Halstead CO9 4SA* Tel (01440) 85355

HEWITT, Paul Stephen Patrick. b 59. BA DipTh. **d** 86 **p** 87. C Ballymacash *Conn* 86-89; Sen C Ballymena w Ballyclug 89-91; I Glencraig *D & D* from 91; Dir of Ords from 98. *Glencraig Vicarage, 3 Seahill Road, Craigavad, Holywood BT18 0DA* Tel (028) 9042 2225 E-mail paul-hewitt@beeb.net

HEWITT, Robert Samuel. b 51. QUB BSc73. CITC 77. **d** 80 **p** 81. C Dundela St Mark *D & D* 80-84; R Donaghadee 84-92. *3 The Trees, New Road, Donaghadee BT21 0EJ* Tel (028) 9188 2594

HEWITT, Simon. b 76. Brunel Univ BSc99. St Steph Ho Ox BA01. **d** 02 **p** 03. C Warren Park *Portsm* from 02; C Leigh Park from 02. *32 Hursley Road, Leigh Park, Havant PO9 4RF* Tel (023) 9247 5746 Mobile 07986-117603 E-mail frsimonhewitt@hotmail.com

HEWITT, Stephen Wilkes. b 49. Fitzw Coll Cam MA71. St Jo Coll Nottm 88. **d** 90 **p** 91. C Eaton *Nor* 90-93; V Warwick St Paul *Cov* 93-01; Perm to Offic *Newc* 01-02; P-in-c High Spen and Rowlands Gill *Dur* from 02. *2 Beechwood, High Spen, Rowlands Gill NE39 2BL* Tel (01207) 542815 E-mail sandshewitt@hotmail.com

HEWITT, Thomas Peter James. b 24. St Andr Univ MA50. St Steph Ho Ox 50. **d** 52 **p** 53. C Ellesmere Port *Ches* 52-56; C Leytonstone St Marg w St Columba *Chelmsf* 56-60; V Barlby *York* 60-65; V Godshill *Portsm* 65-93; rtd 93. *c/o C L Wiggins Esq, Jerome and Co Solicitors, 98 High Street, Newport PO30 1BD*

HEWITT, Timothy James. b 67. St D Coll Lamp BD. Ripon Coll Cuddesdon. **d** 91 **p** 92. C Milford Haven *St D* 91-94; C Llanelli 94-96; P-in-c Llan-non 96-97; V Clydach *S & B* from 98. *The Vicarage, 53 Bryntawe Road, Ynystawe, Swansea SA6 5AD* Tel (01792) 843203

HEWITT, Canon William Patrick. b 48. Nottm Univ BTh79. Linc Th Coll 75. **d** 79 **p** 80. C Workington St Jo *Carl* 79-83; V Flookburgh 83-87; V Barrow St Matt 87-90; V Lowick and Kyloe w Ancroft *Newc* 90-96; R Ford and Etal 90-96; RD Norham 91-96; I Fanlobbus Union *C, C & R* from 96; Can Cork Cathl from 00; Can Cloyne Cathl from 00. *The Rectory, Sackville Street, Dunmanway, Co Cork, Irish Republic* Tel (00353) (23) 45151 Fax as telephone E-mail fanlobbus@cork.anglican.org *or* fanlobbus@eircom.net

HEWLETT, Mrs Caroline. b 68. Coll of Ripon & York St Jo BEd92 St Jo Coll Dur BA01. Cranmer Hall Dur 99. **d** 01 **p** 02. C Leeds St Geo *Ripon* from 01; Chapl Leeds Combined Court Cen from 03. *34 Dennistead Crescent, Headingley, Leeds LS6 3PU* Tel 0113-293 0907 *or* 243 8498 E-mail carolinehewlett@hotmail.com

HEWLETT, David Bryan. b 49. Bris Univ BEd72. Qu Coll Birm 77. **d** 79 **p** 80. C Ludlow *Heref* 79-81; TV 81-84; V Marden w Amberley and Wisteston 84-92; Lect Glouc Sch for Min 84-92; Field Officer for Lay Min *Heref* 84-91; Continuing Minl Educn Adv 86-92; Dir Post-Ord Tr 91-92; Hd Master St Fran Sch Pewsey 92-94; Co-ord Chapl Frenchay Healthcare NHS Trust Bris 94-00; Min Development Officer (South) *Linc* from 00. *The Vicarage, 11 Station Road, Surfleet, Spalding PE11 4DA* Tel and fax (01775) 680050 Mobile 07775-672054 E-mail david.hewlett@btopenworld.com

HEWLETT, David Jonathon Peter. b 57. Dur Univ BA79 PhD83. Ridley Hall Cam 82. **d** 83 **p** 84. C New Barnet St Jas *St Alb* 83-86; Lect CITC 86-90; P-in-c Feock *Truro* 91-95; Jt Dir SW Minl Tr Course 91-95; Prin 95-03; Adny Local Ord Min 91-95; Hon Can Truro Cathl *Truro* 01-03; Prin Qu Coll Birm from 03. *71 Farquhar Road, Edgbaston, Birmingham B15 2QP* Tel 0121-452 2612 *or* 454 1527 E-mail dhewlett@queens.ac.uk

HEWLETT, Guy Edward. b 59. Thames Poly CertEd89 Open Univ BA90. Oak Hill Th Coll 96. **d** 96 **p** 97. NSM Sudbury St Andr *Lon* 96-99; C Harrow Trin St Mich from 99. *74 Bishop Ken Road, Harrow HA3 7HR* Tel (020) 8861 1710 E-mail guyhewlett@lineone.net

HEWLINS, Pauline Elizabeth. See SEAMAN, Mrs Pauline Elizabeth

HEWSON, Mrs Rose Raylene. b 47. St Alb and Ox Min Course 96. **d** 99 **p** 00. OLM High Wycombe *Ox* from 99. *Hitcham Vicarage, 1 The Precincts, Burnham, Slough SL1 7HU* Tel (01628) 602881 E-mail hewson@blue-rose.com

HEWSON, Thomas Robert. b 45. Man Univ BA66. S'wark Ord Course 85. **d** 89 **p** 90. C Chinnor w Emmington and Sydenham etc *Ox* 89-92; TV Burnham w Dropmore, Hitcham and Taplow from 92. *Hitcham Vicarage, 1 The Precinct, Burnham, Slough SL1 7HU* Tel (01628) 602881 Fax as telephone
E-mail tom.hewson@virgin.net

HEYCOCKS, Christian John. b 71. Univ of Wales (Ban) BA93 MA96 Cam Univ CTM97. Westcott Ho Cam 94 CITC 97. **d** 97 **p** 98. C Rhyl w St Ann *St As* 97-00; Chapl RN from 00. *Royal Naval Chaplaincy Service, Room 203, Victory Building, HM Naval Base, Portsmouth PO1 3LS* Tel (023) 9272 7903 Fax 9272 7111

HEYES, Andrew Robin. b 61. Man Univ BA93. St Steph Ho Ox 93. **d** 95 **p** 96. C Tonge Moor *Man* 95-00; V Glodwick from 00. *St Mark's Vicarage, 1 Skipton Street, Oldham OL8 2JF* Tel 0161-624 4964

HEYES, Robert John. b 46. STETS 00. **d** 03. NSM Bramley and Grafham *Guildf* from 03. *Juniper Cottage, Eastwood Road, Bramley, Guildford GU5 0DS* Tel (01483) 893706 Fax 894001
E-mail heyes@tiscali.co.uk

HEYGATE, Stephen Beaumont. b 48. Loughb Univ BSc71 CQSW73 PhD89. St Jo Coll Nottm LTh88. **d** 88 **p** 89. C Aylestone St Andr w St Jas *Leic* 88-90; V Cosby 90-00; V Evington from 00; P-in-c Leic St Phil from 00. *Evington Vicarage, Stoughton Lane, Stoughton, Leicester LE2 2FH* Tel 0116-271 2032 E-mail sheygate@leicester.anglican.org

HEYHOE, Jonathan Peter. b 53. Man Univ BA75. Trin Coll Bris 77. **d** 80 **p** 81. C Woking St Pet *Guildf* 80-83; C Heatherlands St Jo *Sarum* 83-91; Chr Renewal Cen Rostrevor 91-95; Perm to Offic *D & D* 91-97; I Ballybay w Mucknoe and Clontibret *Clogh* from 98. *The Rectory, Knocknamaddy, Ballybay, Co Monaghan, Irish Republic* Tel (00353) (42) 974 1102
E-mail ballybay@clogher.anglican.org *or* jheyhoe@esatclear.ie

✠**HEYWARD, The Rt Revd Oliver Spencer.** b 26. Univ of Tasmania BA49 Oriel Coll Ox BA53 MA56. Cuddesdon Coll 51. **d** 53 **p** 54 **c** 75. C Brighton St Pet *Chich* 53-56; Australia from 56; Bp Bendigo 75-91; rtd 91. *7 Waltham Street, Richmond, Vic, Australia 3121* Tel (0061) (3) 9429 2806 Fax as telephone
E-mail osh@optusnet.com.au

HEYWOOD, Mrs Anne Christine. b 44. Sarum Th Coll. **d** 97 **p** 98. C Talbot Village *Sarum* 97-01; TV Shaston from 01. *St James's Vicarage, 34 Tanyard Lane, Shaftesbury SP7 8HW* Tel (01747) 852193

HEYWOOD, David Stephen. b 55. Selw Coll Cam BA76 MA80 SS Hild & Bede Coll Dur PhD89. St Jo Coll Dur 80. **d** 86 **p** 87. C Cheltenham St Luke and St Jo *Glouc* 86-90; TV Sanderstead All SS *S'wark* 90-98; V Edensor *Lich* from 98. *St Paul's Vicarage, 131 Longton Hall Road, Stoke-on-Trent ST3 2EL* Tel (01782) 319210 *or* 598366 Fax 341114
E-mail david@edensorvicarage.fsnet.co.uk

HEYWOOD, Geoffrey Thomas. b 26. St Mich Coll Llan 60. **d** 62 **p** 63. C Porthmadog *Ban* 62-64; V Llandudno 64-67; V Caerhun w Llangelynin 67-74; Asst Chapl HM Pris Liv 74-75; Chapl HM Pris Ex 75-77; Chapl HM Pris Wakef 77-79; Chapl HM YOI Eastwood Park 79-90; Chapl HM Pris Leyhill 79-90; rtd 90; Perm to Offic *Glouc* from 94. *5 Meadow Road, Leyhill, Wotton-under-Edge GL12 8HW*

HEYWOOD, Michael Herbert. b 41. Liv Univ BSc63. Clifton Th Coll 63. **d** 65 **p** 66. C Low Elswick *Newc* 65-68; C St Helens St Mark *Liv* 68-75; Lic to Offic *Dur* 75-85; Leprosy Miss Area Org NE & Cumbria 75-85; S Lon, Surrey and Berks 85-91; Internat Publicity and Promotional Co-ord from 91; Lic to Offic *S'wark* from 85. *390 Kingston Road, New Malden KT3 3RX* Tel (020) 8287 9192 Fax 8569 7292 E-mail mikeh@temint.org

HEYWOOD, Peter. b 46. Cranmer Hall Dur 72. **d** 75 **p** 76. C Blackley St Andr *Man* 75-78; C Denton Ch Ch 78-80; V Constable Lee 80-01; rtd 01; Perm to Offic *Man* from 01. *12 Heys Close, Cloughfold, Rossendale BB4 7LW* Tel (01706) 222069

HEZEL, Adrian. b 43. Chelsea Coll Lon BSc64 PhD67. N Ord Course 78. **d** 81 **p** 82. NSM Mirfield *Wakef* 81-89; C 89-90; V Shelley and Shepley 90-99; V Hoylake *Ches* from 99. *The Vicarage, 1 Stanley Road, Hoylake, Wirral CH47 1HL* Tel 0151-632 3897

HIBBERD, Brian Jeffery. b 35. Fitzw Coll Cam MA62 Southn Univ MA84. Ridley Hall Cam 58. **d** 60 **p** 61. C Cambridge H Trin *Ely* 60-63; C Doncaster St Mary *Sheff* 63-66; Asst Master Price's Sch Fareham 66-69; Warblington Sch Havant 69-71; Hd Soc and RS Carisbrooke High Sch 71-84; Distr Health Promotion Officer Is of Wight 84-88; SW Herts 88-90; Hd RS Goffs Sch Cheshunt 90-95; rtd 95; Teacher Qu Sch Bushey 95-97; Teacher R Masonic Sch for Girls Rickmansworth 97-00; Hon C Abbots Langley *St Alb* 00-01; Perm to Offic from 01. *50 Rosehill Gardens, Abbots Langley WD5 0HF* Tel (01923) 267391

HIBBERD, Carol Anne. b 59. Kent Univ BA80. S'wark Ord Course 89. **d** 92 **p** 94. NSM Gospel Lane St Mich *Birm* 92-94; C 94-98; C Coleshill 98-02; Chapl Marie Curie Cen Warren Pearl from 02. *Marie Curie Centre Warren Pearl, 911-913 Warwick Road, Solihull B91 3ER* Tel 0121-254 7800 Mobile 07940-562087 E-mail carol.hibberd@mariecurie.org.uk

HIBBERD, John. b 60. Wadh Coll Ox MA82. Trin Coll Bris BA89. **d** 89 **p** 90. C Northolt St Mary *Lon* 89-92; C-in-c Southall Em CD 92-94; Min of Miss Through Faith Miss *Ely* from 95. *Celandine, 1 School Lane, Swavesey, Cambridge CB4 5RL* Tel (01954) 200285 Fax as telephone
E-mail john.hibberd@ntlworld.com

HIBBERD, John Charles. b 38. Bernard Gilpin Soc Dur 62 Chich Th Coll 63. **d** 66 **p** 67. C W Drayton *Lon* 66-70; C Noel Park St Mark 70-72; C Ealing St Steph Castle Hill 72-75; V Gunnersbury St Jas 75-84; V Whitton SS Phil and Jas 84-86; Finance and Trust Sec Lon Dioc Fund 87-98; Perm to Offic 87-98; rtd 98. *18 Pursley Close, Sandown PO36 9QP* Tel (01983) 401036

HIBBERT, Miss Anne Mary Elizabeth. Southn Univ BA81. Trin Coll Bris 81. dss 83 **d** 87 **p** 94. Muswell Hill St Jas w St Matt *Lon* 83-86; Leic H Trin w St Jo *Leic* 86-87; Par Dn 87-90; Perm to Offic *Cov* from 90; Evang Co-ord and Adv CPAS 90-98; Churches Millennium Exec 98-99; Miss & Spirituality Adv BRF 99-03; Dir Well Chr Healing Cen from 03. *The Well Christian Healing Centre, PO Box 3407, Leamington Spa CV32 6ZH* Tel 07973-563667 (mobile)
E-mail anne@thewellhealingcentre.org.uk

HIBBERT, Charles Dennis. b 24. Linc Th Coll 69. **d** 70 **p** 71. C Radcliffe-on-Trent *S'well* 70-73; P-in-c Ladybrook 73-77; V 77-79; V Boughton 79-85; V Ollerton 79-85; R Nuthall 85-89; rtd 89; Perm to Offic *S'well* from 89. *27 Nottingham Road, Kimberley, Nottingham NG16 2NB* Tel 0115-938 6302

HIBBERT, Peter John. b 43. Hull Univ BA71 Lon Univ CertEd72 MA79. Sarum & Wells Th Coll 85. **d** 88 **p** 89. C Newsome and Armitage Bridge *Wakef* 88-92; P-in-c Newton Flowery Field *Ches* 92-00; P-in-c Hyde St Thos 97-00; V Handsworth St Jas *Birm* from 00. *St James's Vicarage, 21 Austin Road, Birmingham B21 8NU* Tel 0121-554 4151

HIBBERT, Prof Peter Rodney. b 53. Man Univ LLB74 Liv Univ DipArch83 Nottm Univ MA99 Solicitor 77. EMMTC 96. **d** 99 **p** 00. C Knighton St Mary Magd *Leic* 99-01; Perm to Offic *Leic* from 01 and *Birm* from 03. *Grange Cottage, 37 Rushes Lane, Lubenham, Market Harborough LE16 9TN* Tel (01858) 433174

HIBBERT, Richard Charles. b 62. Trin Coll Bris BA93. **d** 96 **p** 97. C Luton St Mary *St Alb* 96-00; V Bedford Ch Ch from 00. *Christ Church Vicarage, 115 Denmark Street, Bedford MK40 3TJ* Tel (01234) 359342 Fax as telephone
E-mail vicar@christchurchbedford.org.uk

HIBBINS, Neil Lance. b 60. St Anne's Coll Ox BA82 MA87. St Mich Coll Llan DPS83. **d** 85 **p** 86. C Griffithstown *Mon* 85-87; C Pontypool 87-88; TV Pontypool 88-92; Walsall Hosps NHS Trust 92-96; Chapl Manor Hosp Walsall 92-96; R Norton Canes *Lich* from 96. *The Rectory, 81 Church Road, Norton Canes, Cannock WS11 9PQ* Tel (01543) 278969
E-mail neil_hibbins@lycos.com

HIBBS, Canon Lawrence Winston. b 14. Kelham Th Coll 31. **d** 37 **p** 38. C Walworth St Jo *S'wark* 37-39; C Hendon St Alphage *Lon* 39-46; R Jersey H Trin *Win* 46-55; V Bournemouth St Alb 55-68; V Chandler's Ford 68-75; R Jersey Grouville 75-83; Hon Can Win Cathl 76-83; rtd 83; Perm to Offic *Win* 83-98. *Jeanne Jugan House, St John's Road, St Helier, Jersey JE2 6XZ* Tel (01534) 506963

HICHENS, Anthony. b 29. AKC59. **d** 60 **p** 61. C Ashford St Hilda *Lon* 60-64; C Leeds St Wilfrid *Ripon* 64-66; Guyana 67-75; P-in-c Stratton Audley w Godington *Ox* 76-83; P-in-c Finmere w Mixbury 76-78; P-in-c Fringford w Hethe and Newton Purcell 78-83; R Stratton Audley and Godington, Fringford etc 83-95; rtd 95; Perm to Offic *Pet* from 95. *86 Horton Drive, Middleton Cheney, Banbury OX17 2LL* Tel (01295) 712826

HICKES, Roy Edward. b 31. Lon Univ DipTh60. St Aid Birkenhead 56. **d** 59 **p** 60. C New Bury *Man* 59-63; C Wyther Ven Bede *Ripon* 63-65; R Oldham St Andr *Man* 65-69; V Smallbridge 69-79; R Winford *B & W* 79-81; R Winford w Felton Common Hill 81-88; RD Chew Magna 85-88; Chapl Costa Blanca *Eur* 88-92; rtd 92; Perm to Offic *B & W* and *Bris* from 92; Hon C Wrington w Butcombe *B & W* 97-98. *8 Nelson House, Nelson Place West, Bath BA1 2TL* Tel (01225) 443022
E-mail randw@rhickes.fsnet.co.uk

HICKEY, Canon Francis Joseph (Tony). b 20. AKC49. **d** 50 **p** 51. C Portsea St Mary *Portsm* 50-58; V Tilbury Docks *Chelmsf* 58-87; RD Orsett and Grays 70-83; Hon Can Chelmsf Cathl 79-87; rtd 87; Perm to Offic *Portsm* from 90; *Guildf* 95-00. *202 Parkside House, Malvern Road, Southsea PO5 2LD* Tel (023) 9275 0301

HICKFORD, The Very Revd Michael Francis. b 53. Edin Th Coll 84. **d** 86 **p** 87. Chapl St Jo Cathl Oban *Arg* 86-89; R Alexandria *Glas* 89-95; P-in-c Dingwall *Mor* 95-03; P-in-c Strathpeffer 95-03; Dean Mor 98-03; Provost St Andr Cathl Inverness from 03; R Inverness St Andr from 03. *The Cathedral Rectory, 15 Ardross Street, Inverness IV3 5NS* Tel (01463) 233535 Mobile 07885-424605 E-mail michaelhickford@onet.com *or* michael.hickford@tesco.net

HICKIN, Maurice Whitehouse. b 09. St Cath Coll Cam BA32 MA38 Bonn Univ DPhil33. Ely Th Coll 33. **d** 34 **p** 35. C Fulham

St Andr Fulham Fields *Lon* 34-35; C London Docks St Pet 35-36; Ghana 36-38; C Paddington St Mary *Lon* 40-46; C Beckenham St Mich *Roch* 46-48; C Worthing St Andr *Chich* 48-51; C Clewer St Andr *Ox* 51-55; Perm to Offic 55-58; C Kirkley *Nor* 58-61; R Runwell *Chelmsf* 61-75; rtd 75. *Calle De Murillo 6, Benidoleig, Alicante 03759, Spain* Tel (0034) (6) 558 3266

HICKLEY, Peter Michael. b 28. Ely Th Coll 56. **d** 59 **p** 60. C Shepherd's Bush St Steph *Lon* 59-62; C Lee Gd Shep w St Pet *S'wark* 62-66; V Carlton *Wakef* 66-68; C Is of Dogs Ch Ch and St Jo w St Luke *Lon* 68-70; R S Hackney St Jo w Ch Ch 70-77; R Euston w Barnham and Fakenham *St E* 77-80; TR Fenny Stratford and Water Eaton *Ox* 80-88; R Benington w Walkern *St Alb* 88-91; rtd 91; Perm to Offic *Birm* 91-96; Perm to Offic *Nor* from 96. *12 Newark Road, Lowestoft NR33 0LY* Tel (01502) 514525

HICKLING, Canon Colin John Anderson. b 31. K Coll Lon BA53 MA57. Chich Th Coll 56. **d** 57 **p** 58. C Pallion *Dur* 57-61; Asst Tutor Chich Th Coll 61-65; Asst Lect K Coll Lon 65-68; Lect 68-84; Hon C Munster Square St Mary Magd *Lon* 68-69; Dep Min Can St Paul's Cathl 69-78; Hon C E Dulwich St Jo *S'wark* 70-84; Dep P in O 71-74; P in O 74-84; Can Th Leic Cathl *Leic* 81-96; Tutor Qu Coll Birm 84-85; Lect Linc Th Coll 85-86; V Arksey *Sheff* 86-98; Hon Lect Bibl Studies Sheff Univ from 86; rtd 98; Hon C Sprotbrough *Sheff* from 99. *5 Chestnut Grove, Sprotbrough, Doncaster DN5 7RW* Tel (01302) 852542

HICKLING, John. b 34. Handsworth Coll Birm 56. Launde Abbey 69. **d** 69 **p** 70. In Methodist Ch 59-69; C Melton Mowbray w Thorpe Arnold *Leic* 69-71; TV 71-75; R Waltham on the Wolds w Stonesby and Saltby 75-84; R Aylestone St Andr w St Jas 84-93; R Husbands Bosworth w Mowsley and Knaptoft etc 93-96; rtd 96; Perm to Offic *Leic* from 99. *28 Oxford Drive, Melton Mowbray LE13 0AL* Tel (01664) 560770

HICKMAN, George May. b 11. AKC33. **d** 35 **p** 36. C Hayes St Mary *Lon* 35-36; C Stepney St Aug w St Phil 36-39; C Bray *Ox* 40-41; V Beedon 41-45; V Rotherhithe H Trin *S'wark* 45-50; R Nettlecombe *B & W* 50-68; R Withycombe 68-84; rtd 84; Perm to Offic *B & W* 85-91. *1 The Causeway, Withycombe, Minehead TA24 6PZ* Tel (01984) 640227

HICKMAN, John William. b 38. Barrister-at-Law (Middle Temple) 69 Qu Coll Cam LLM81. Oak Hill Th Coll 92. **d** 95 **p** 96. NSM Sevenoaks St Nic *Roch* 95-98; P-in-c Stedham w Iping *Chich* from 98. *The Rectory, Stedham, Midhurst GU29 0NQ* Tel (01730) 817570

HICKS, Miss Barbara. b 42. Cranmer Hall Dur BA71. **dss** 85 **d** 87 **p** 94. Norton Woodseats St Paul *Sheff* 85-87; Par Dn Sheff St Jo 87-94; C 94-02; Chapl Shrewsbury Hosp 96-02; rtd 02. *87 Underwood Road, Sheffield S8 8TG* Tel 0114-255 8087

HICKS, Ms Eunice. b 41. Trin Coll Bris BA00. WEMTC 01. **d** 01 **p** 02. NSM Chew Magna w Dundry and Norton Malreward *B & W* from 01. *4 The Crescent, Chew Magna, Bristol BS40 8RH* Tel (01275) 331536 E-mail heunice@fish.co.uk

HICKS, Francis Fuller. b 28. Sarum & Wells Th Coll 71. **d** 74 **p** 75. C Broadstone *Sarum* 74-78; P-in-c Kington Magna and Buckhorn Weston 78-79; TV Gillingham 79-86; P-in-c Portland St Jo 86-89; V 89-93; rtd 93; Perm to Offic *B & W* and *Sarum* from 93. *Windyridge, 21 Castle Road, Sherborne DT9 3RW* Tel (01935) 814837

HICKS, Miss Joan Rosemary. b 60. Homerton Coll Cam BEd83. Westcott Ho Cam 87. **d** 90 **p** 94. C Wendover *Ox* 90-95; C Earley St Pet 95-98; P-in-c Beech Hill, Grazeley and Spencers Wood from 98. *The Vicarage, 11 Clares Green Road, Spencers Wood, Reading RG7 1DY* Tel 0118-988 3215 E-mail joanhicks@compuserve.com

HICKS, Richard Barry. b 32. Dur Univ BA55. Sarum Th Coll 59. **d** 61 **p** 62. C Wallsend St Luke *Newc* 61-64; C Tynemouth Ch Ch 64-69; V Tynemouth St Jo 69-75; V Prudhoe 75-82; TV Swanborough *Sarum* 82-86; R Hilperton w Whaddon and Staverton etc 86-97; rtd 97; Perm to Offic *Newc* from 97; *Carl* from 98. *Lane House, Sawmill Lane, Brampton CA8 1DA* Tel (01697) 72156

HICKS, Stuart Knox. b 34. Univ of W Ontario BA56 Huron Coll LTh59 Ox Univ DipEd67. **d** 58 **p** 60. Canada 58-65; C Allerton *Liv* 65-66; Hon C Rye Park St Cuth *St Alb* 68-72; Lic to Offic *B & W* 72-87 and 88-95; Chapl Magdalen Chpl Bath 80-86; Chapl Partis Coll Bath 88-90; rtd 99. *Folly Orchard, The Folly, Saltford, Bristol BS31 3JW* Tel (01225) 873391

HICKS, Mrs Valerie Joy. b 47. SRN69 HVCert70. Cant Sch of Min 82. **dss** 85 **d** 87 **p** 94. Roch 85-89; Hon Par Dn 87-89; Par Dn Thatcham *Ox* 89-93; TD Aylesbury w Bierton and Hulcott 93-94; TV 94-00; P-in-c Dordon *Birm* from 00; Dioc Chapl Mother's Union from 01. *St Leonard's Vicarage, Watling Street, Dordon, Tamworth B78 1TE* Tel (01827) 892194 E-mail val.hicks@tesco.net

HICKS, William Trevor. b 47. Hull Univ BA68 Fitzw Coll Cam BA70 MA74. Westcott Ho Cam 68. **d** 70 **p** 71. C Cottingham *York* 70-73; C Elland *Wakef* 73-76; V Walsden 76-81; V Knottingley 81-92; R Castleford All SS 92-96; RD Pontefract 94-99; P-in-c Womersley and Kirk Smeaton 96-00; V Bolsover *Derby* from 00. *The Vicarage, Church Street, Bolsover, Chesterfield S44 6BG* Tel (01246) 824888

HIDE, Timothy John. b 71. Roehampton Inst BA95. St Steph Ho Ox 97. **d** 99 **p** 00. C Woodford St Mary w St Phil and St Jas *Chelmsf* 99-01; C Upminster from 01. *6 Gaynes Park Road, Upminster RM14 2HH* Tel (01708) 226004 E-mail frtimhide@grenoble.vianw.co.uk

HIDER, David Arthur. b 46. Lon Univ BSc67. Sarum & Wells Th Coll 86. **d** 89 **p** 90. NSM Southbourne w W Thorney *Chich* 89-91; C Goring-by-Sea 91-94; P-in-c Peacehaven and Telscombe Cliffs 94-99; P-in-c Telscombe w Piddinghoe and Southease 94-99; V Peacehaven and Telscombe Cliffs from 99; V Telscombe Village from 99; V Southease from 99; V Piddinghoe from 99. *Vicarage, 41 Bramber Avenue, Peacehaven BN10 8HR* Tel (01273) 583149 Fax as telephone E-mail revd_d_hider@msn.com

HIGDON, Lewis George. b 36. Dur Univ BA58. Cranmer Hall Dur DipTh60. **d** 60 **p** 61. C Leeds St Pet *Ripon* 60-65; C Shipley St Paul *Bradf* 65-66; V Esholt 67-75; V Kirkstall *Ripon* 75-79; V Stanwix *Carl* 79-87; V Ambleside w Brathay 87-95; rtd 95. *Springtime, 19 Priory Crescent, Grange-over-Sands LA11 7BL* Tel (01539) 532864

HIGGINBOTTOM, Richard. b 48. Lon Univ BD74. Oak Hill Th Coll DipTh72. **d** 74 **p** 75. C Kenilworth St Jo *Cov* 74-77; C Finham 77-79; P-in-c Attleborough 79-81; V 81-84; Asst Chapl HM Pris Brixton 84-85; Chapl HM Pris Roch 85-92; Chapl HM Pris Camp Hill 92-00; Chapl HM YOI Dover from 00. *HM Young Offender Institution, The Citadel, Dover CT17 9DR* Tel (01304) 203848 ext 325 Fax 215165

HIGGINBOTTOM, Richard William. b 51. Man Univ BA73 MA75. Edin Th Coll 83. **d** 85 **p** 86. C Knighton St Mary Magd *Leic* 85-87; C Northleach w Hampnett and Farmington *Glouc* 87-89; V Hayfield *Derby* 89-93; Consultant NW England and Scotland CPAS from 93; Perm to Offic *Blackb* from 93. *2 Highfield Place, Bankfoot, Perth PH1 4AX* Tel (01738) 787429 E-mail rhigginbottom@cpas.org.uk

HIGGINS, Anthony Charles. b 46. LNSM course 96. **d** 97 **p** 98. OLM Swanage and Studland *Sarum* from 97. *The Old School House, School Lane, Studland, Swanage BH19 3AJ* Tel (01929) 450691

HIGGINS, Bernard. b 42. Leic Poly BPharm63 PhD66 MRPharmS68. St Jo Coll Nottm 89. **d** 91 **p** 92. C Stockport St Geo *Ches* 91-94; C Stockport SW 94-95; P-in-c Dunham Massey St Marg and St Mark 95-98; V 98-00; rtd 00; Perm to Offic *Blackb* and *Carl* from 01. *Woodbine Cottage, Promenade, Arnside, Carnforth LA5 0HD* Tel (01524) 761000

HIGGINS, Bernard George. b 27. Wycliffe Hall Ox 68. **d** 70 **p** 72. C Surbiton St Matt *S'wark* 70-72; C Battersea St Mary 72-76; C Warblington w Emsworth *Portsm* 76-81; C Milton 81-91; rtd 91; Perm to Offic *Portsm* from 91. *49 Queens Crescent, Stubbington, Fareham PO14 2QG* Tel (01329) 667905

HIGGINS, Frank Roylance. b 28. Open Univ BA74 MEd83. Bps' Coll Cheshunt 59. **d** 62 **p** 63. C Sunderland *Dur* 62-64; C S Westoe 64-66; P-in-c Smethwick St Mich *Birm* 66-67; V 67-70; V Garretts Green 70-75; Lic to Offic *Birm* 76-84; Perm to Offic *Birm* 81-87; Hon C Feckenham w Bradley *Worc* 84-87; R Ripple, Earls Croome w Hill Croome and Strensham 87-95; RD Upton 92-95; rtd 95; P-in-c Church Lench w Rous Lench and Abbots Morton *Worc* 95-00; Perm to Offic from 00. *Verona, Abberton Road, Bishampton, Pershore WR10 2LU* Tel (01386) 462694 Fax as telephone

HIGGINS, Geoffrey Minta. b 27. New Coll Ox BA52 MA56. Cuddesdon Coll 52. **d** 54 **p** 55. C Pet St Mary Boongate *Pet* 54-56; CF 56-77; Hong Kong from 77. *12-C Far East Consortium Building, On Lok Road, Yuen Long, New Territories, Hong Kong* Tel (00852) 479 9374

HIGGINS, Canon Godfrey. b 39. St Chad's Coll Dur BA61 DipTh62 DipEd63. **d** 63 **p** 64. C Brighouse *Wakef* 63-66; C Huddersfield St Jo 66-68; R High Hoyland w Clayton W 68-75; V Marsden 75-83; V Pontefract St Giles from 83; Hon Can Wakef Cathl from 93. *The Vicarage, The Mount, Pontefract WF8 1NE* Tel (01977) 706803

HIGGINS, John. b 44. Lon Bible Coll MTh98. Trin Coll Bris 71. **d** 73 **p** 74. C Clapham St Jas *S'wark* 73-74; C Ruskin Park St Sav and St Matt 74-77; C Hamworthy *Sarum* 77-80; V Bordesley St Andr *Birm* 80-83; V Bishop Sutton and Stanton Drew and Stowey *B & W* from 83. *The Vicarage, Sutton Hill Road, Bishop Sutton, Bristol BS39 5UR* Tel (01275) 333385

HIGGINS, John Leslie. b 43. Open Univ BA79 Birm Univ MEd89 Univ of Cen England in Birm CQSW75. Lich Th Coll 64. **d** 66 **p** 67. C Sale St Anne *Ches* 66-69; C Bredbury St Mark 69-72; V Wharton 72-74; Hon C Annan *Glas* 75-79; Hon C Lockerbie 75-79; V Coseley Ch Ch *Lich* 79-89; R Arthuret *Carl* 89-96; Soc Resp Officer and Child Protection Co-ord 96-00; C Brampton and Farlam and Castle Carrock w Cumrew 96-00; Hon Can Carl Cathl 96-00; rtd 00; Hon C Annan *Glas* from 00; Perm to Offic *Carl* from 01. *Green Croft Cottage, The Haggs, Ecclefechan, Lockerbie DG11 3ED* Tel (01576) 300796 Fax as telephone E-mail john_l_higgins@lineone.net

HIGGINS, Kenneth. b 56. TCD BTh93. CA Tr Coll Dip Evang83 CITC 90. **d** 93 **p** 94. C Cregagh *D & D* 93-96; Bp's C Movilla

96-00; I from 01. *34 Hollymount Road, Newtownards B23 7DL* Tel (028) 9181 0787

HIGGINS, The Very Revd Michael John. b 35. Birm Univ LLB57 G&C Coll Cam LLB59 PhD62. Ridley Hall Cam 63. **d** 65 **p** 65. C Ormskirk *Liv* 65-67; Selection Sec ACCM 67-74; Hon C St Marylebone St Mark w St Luke *Lon* 69-74; P-in-c Woodlands *B & W* 74-80; V Frome St Jo 74-80; TR Preston St Jo *Blackb* 80-91; Dean Ely 91-03; rtd 03. *Twin Cottage, North Street, Great Dunham, King's Lynn PE32 2LR* Tel (01328) 701058

HIGGINS, Richard Ellis. b 63. Univ of Wales BA84. St Mich Coll Llan DipTh88 DPS89. **d** 89 **p** 90. C Bargoed and Deri w Brithdir *Llan* 89-92; Zimbabwe 92-94; V Penmaen and Crumlin *Mon* 94-99; Chapl Glan Hafren NHS Trust 94-99; V Rhymney *Mon* 99-02; Angl Chapl Pet Hosps NHS Trust from 03. *11 Bryniau Cottages, Pant, Merthyr Tydfil CF48 2DW*

HIGGINS, Rupert Anthony. b 59. Man Univ BA80. Wycliffe Hall Ox 82. **d** 85 **p** 86. C Plymouth St Andr w St Paul and St Geo *Ex* 85-90; C-in-c St Paul 88-90; Assoc V Clifton Ch Ch w Em *Bris* 90-95; V S Croydon Em *S'wark* 95-02; C Langham Place All So *Lon* from 02. *2 St Paul's Court, 56 Manchester Street, London W1U 3AF* Tel (020) 7486 0006

HIGGINS, Canon Timothy John. b 45. Bris Univ BEd70 Lanc Univ MA74 St Jo Coll Dur DipTh79. **d** 79 **p** 80. C Northampton All SS w St Kath *Pet* 79-82; V Whitton St Aug *Lon* 82-90; AD Hampton 86-90; TR Aylesbury w Bierton and Hulcott *Ox* from 90; RD Aylesbury from 94; Hon Can Ch Ch from 00. *The Rectory, Parson's Fee, Aylesbury HP20 2QZ* Tel (01296) 24276

HIGGINSON, Gerald Scott. b 29. Keele Univ BA54 Birm Univ PhD57. NW Ord Course 73. **d** 76 **p** 77. NSM York St Mary Bishophill Junior w All SS *York* 76-84; P-in-c Acaster Malbis 76-79; P-in-c York H Trin w St Jo Micklegate and St Martin 84-86; R Micklegate H Trin and Bishophill Junior St Mary 86-99; rtd 00; Perm to Offic *York* from 00. *35 Aldwark, York YO1 7BX* Tel (01904) 635707

HIGGON, David. Univ of Wales (Swansea) BA75 Birm Univ MBA96 Nottm Univ MA99. EMMTC 96. **d** 00 **p** 01. NSM Crich and S Wingfield *Derby* from 00. *67 Main Road, Morton, Alfreton DE55 6HH* Tel (01773) 872332 E-mail dhiggon@btopenworld.com

HIGGS, Andrew Richard Bowen. b 53. Man Univ BSc75. St Jo Coll Nottm 81. **d** 85 **p** 86. C Droylsden St Mary *Man* 85-88; C Harlow Town Cen w Lt Parndon *Chelmsf* 88-95; TV 95-02; Chapl Princess Alexandra Hosp NHS Trust 96-02; R Stifford *Chelmsf* from 02. *The Rectory, High Road, North Stifford, Grays RM16 5UE* Tel (01375) 372733 E-mail andy@higgs4a.fsnet.co.uk

HIGGS, Michael John. b 53. Sarum & Wells Th Coll 76. **d** 80 **p** 81. C Cant St Martin and St Paul *Cant* 80-84; C Maidstone St Martin 84-88; R Egerton w Pluckley from 88. *St James's Vicarage, Glebeland, Egerton, Ashford TN27 9DH* Tel (01233) 756224

HIGGS, Owen Christopher Goodwin. b 63. St Anne's Coll Ox BA84 MA88. St Steph Ho Ox 90. **d** 93 **p** 94. C Teddington St Mark and Hampton Wick St Jo *Lon* 93-96; C Lon Docks St Pet w Wapping St Jo 96-00; V Petts Wood *Roch* from 00. *The Vicarage, Willett Way, Orpington BR5 1QE* Tel (01689) 829971

HIGHAM, Gerald Norman. b 40. St Aid Birkenhead 64. **d** 68 **p** 69. C Garston *Liv* 68-71; C Blundellsands St Nic 71-73; V Bolton All So w St Jas *Man* 73-78; V Tonge w Alkrington 78-84; P-in-c Edenfield 84-86; P-in-c Stubbins 84-86; V Edenfield and Stubbins from 86. *St Philip's Vicarage, Chatterton Road, Ramsbottom, Bury BL0 0PQ* Tel (01706) 822079 Fax as telephone E-mail revg.higham@rotary1280.org

HIGHAM, Canon Jack. b 33. Linc Coll Ox BA56 MA60 Union Th Sem (NY) STM61 Birm Univ DipTh59. Qu Coll Birm 58. **d** 60 **p** 61. C Handsworth *Sheff* 60-64; V Handsworth Woodhouse 64-70; USA 70-78; R Stoke Bruerne w Grafton Regis and Alderton *Pet* 78-83; RD Towcester 82-83; Can Res, Chan and Lib Pet Cathl 83-03; rtd 03. *44 Alma Hill, Kimberley, Nottingham NG16 2JF* Tel 0115-938 6063

HIGHAM, John Leonard. b 39. Liv Univ DipSocSc71. Wycliffe Hall Ox 62. **d** 65 **p** 66. C Prescot *Liv* 65-71; V Hollinfare 71-74; Adult and Youth Service Adv Knowsley 74-76; TV Padgate 76-84; V Farnworth 84-89; TR Sutton 89-02; rtd 02. *86 Ormskirk Road, Rainford, St Helens WA11 8DB*

HIGHAM (née ANNS), Mrs Pauline Mary. b 49. Bris Univ BEd71. EMMTC 87. **d** 90 **p** 94. Par Dn Wirksworth w Alderwasley, Carsington etc *Derby* 90-92; Par Dn Lt Berkhamsted and Bayford, Essendon etc *St Alb* 92-94; C 94-96; P-in-c from 96. *1 Little Berkhamsted Lane, Little Berkhamsted, Hertford SG13 8LU* Tel (01707) 875940 Fax 875289

HIGHTON, William James. b 31. St Deiniol's Hawarden. **d** 82 **p** 83. NSM Thornton Hough *Ches* 82-84; C Cheadle 84-88; V Walton 88-99; rtd 99; Perm to Offic *Carl* from 01. *15 Mowbray Drive, Burton-in-Kendal, Carnforth LA6 1NF* Tel (01524) 782073

HIGTON, Anthony Raymond. b 42. Lon Univ BD65. Oak Hill Th Coll 65. **d** 67 **p** 68. C Newark Ch Ch *S'well* 67-69; C Cheltenham St Mark *Glouc* 70-75; R Hawkwell *Chelmsf* 75-99; Gen Dir CMJ from 99; Public Preacher *St Alb* from 99. *CMJ, 30C Clarence Road, St Albans AL1 4JJ* Tel (01727) 833114 Fax 848312 E-mail tonyh@cmj.org.uk

HILARY, Sister. *See* JORDINSON, Vera

HILBORN, David Henry Kyte. b 64. Nottm Univ BA85 PhD94 Mansf Coll Ox MA88. **d** 02 **p** 02. C Acton St Mary *Lon* from 02. *39 Derwentwater Road, London W3 6DF* Tel (020) 8896 1306 Fax 8896 2944 E-mail dandm.hilborn@virgin.net

HILBORN, Mrs Mia Alison Kyte. b 63. City Univ BSc84 Mansf Coll Ox MA87. **d** 02 **p** 02. Chapl Team Ldr Guy's and St Thos' Hosps NHS Trust *Lon* from 01; NSM N Lambeth *S'wark* from 02; Perm to Offic *Lon* from 02. *39 Derwentwater Road, London W3 6DF* Tel (020) 8896 1306 Mobile 07740-779585 E-mail mia.hilborn@gstt.sthames.nhs.uk

HILDAGE, James Francis. b 18. Univ of Wales BA44. Coll of Resurr Mirfield 44. **d** 46 **p** 47. C Long Eaton St Laur *Derby* 46-51; C Chesterfield St Mary and All SS 51-54; P-in-c Earl Sterndale and Monyash 54-56; V 56-87; Lect Matlock Coll of HE 66-83; P-in-c Taddington, Chelmorton and Flagg, and Monyash 83-87; rtd 87; Perm to Offic *Ban* from 88. *Llangwyfan Isaf, Ty Croes, Anglesey LL63 5YP* Tel (01407) 810756

HILDITCH, Janet. b 59. St Andr Univ MTh81 PhD87. N Ord Course 92. **d** 94 **p** 95. C Kirkholt *Man* 94-98; Chapl Rochdale Healthcare NHS Trust 97-98; Chapl N Man Health Care NHS Trust 98-00; Chapl Tameside and Glossop Acute Services NHS Trust from 00. *Tameside General Hospital, Fountain Street, Ashton-under-Lyne OL6 9EW* Tel 0161-331 6000

HILDRED, David. b 61. Bath Univ BSc83 CertEd83. Wycliffe Hall Ox 86. **d** 89 **p** 90. C Westcliff St Mich *Chelmsf* 89-92; C Rayleigh 92-96; V Sidcup St Andr *Roch* from 96. *The Vicarage, St Andrew's Road, Sidcup DA14 4SA* Tel (020) 8300 4712 E-mail david@hildred.freeserve.co.uk

HILES, Janet Rita. b 39. St Alb and Ox Min Course 96. **d** 98 **p** 99. OLM Dorchester *Ox* from 98. *1 Fane Drive, Berinsfield, Wallingford OX10 7NB* Tel (01865) 341228 Pager 07625-551175 E-mail chrishiles@4thenet.co.uk

HILES, John Michael. b 32. Qu Coll Cam BA57 MA61. Sarum Th Coll 57. **d** 59 **p** 60. C Clifton St Jas *Sheff* 59-62; V Bramley St Fran 62-69; Hon C Holmfirth *Wakef* 69-89; Hon C Upper Holme Valley 89-91; Lic to Offic 91-97; Perm to Offic 97-03. *22 Oldfield Road, Bishopdown, Salisbury SP1 3GQ* Tel (01722) 349951

HILL, Alexander Francis. b 71. St Mary's Coll Twickenham BA(QTS)94 Leeds Univ MA97. Coll of Resurr Mirfield 95. **d** 97 **p** 98. C Notting Hill All SS w St Columb *Lon* 97-02; V Willesden St Matt from 02. *St Matthew's Vicarage, St Mary's Road, London NW10 4AU* Tel (020) 8965 3748

HILL, Mrs Anne Doreen. b 40. **d** 88 **p** 94. Par Dn Bexleyheath St Pet *Roch* 88-90; Sub-Chapl HM Pris Belmarsh 91-96; Dep Chapl 96-99; Hon C Lee St Mildred *S'wark* from 93. *The Vicarage, 1A Helder Grove, London SE12 0RB* Tel (020) 8857 5205

HILL, Mrs Bridget Ann. b 54. Open Univ BA82 CertEd75. EMMTC 83. **dss** 86 **d** 87 **p** 94. Gt and Lt Coates w Bradley *Linc* 86-88; Hon Par Dn 87-88; Par Dn Louth 88-91; TD 91-94; TV 94-98; Chapl Louth Co Hosp 89-98; P-in-c Saltfleetby and Theddlethorpe *Linc* 98-99; R 99-03; TV E Dereham and Scarning *Nor* from 03. *1 De Narde Road, Dereham NR19 1HQ* Tel (01362) 692982 E-mail bridget.hill@ntlworld.com

HILL, Carol Ann. b 48. St Paul's Univ Ottawa BTh94. **d** 95 **p** 95. Canada 95-98; C Westboro Ottawa All SS 95-98; C Altham w Clayton le Moors *Blackb* 98-01; TV Hawarden *St As* from 01. *St Mary's Vicarage, Church Road, Broughton CH4 0QB* Tel (01244) 520148

HILL, Canon Charles Bernard. b 50. Sheff Univ BA71 Qu Coll Ox DPhil76. Cant Sch of Min 91. **d** 94 **p** 95. NSM Sandgate St Paul w Folkestone St Geo *Cant* 94-98; NSM Folkestone H Trin w Ch Ch from 98; Eur Sec Coun for Chr Unity from 99; Can Gib Cathl *Eur* from 03. *18 Audley Road, Folkestone CT20 3QA,* or *Church House, Great Smith Street, London SW1P 3NZ* Tel (01303) 253270 *or* (020) 7898 1474 Fax (020) 7898 1483 E-mail cbh@cbhill.demon.co.uk

HILL, Charles Merrick. b 52. Strathclyde Univ BA74. Qu Coll Birm DipTh79. **d** 80 **p** 81. C Silksworth *Dur* 80-83; C Stockton St Pet 83-85; TV Southampton (City Cen) *Win* 85-87; V Portsea St Geo *Portsm* 87-94; P-in-c Bodenham w Hope-under-Dinmore, Felton etc *Heref* from 94. *The Vicarage, Bodenham, Hereford HR1 3JX* Tel (01568) 797370

HILL, Charles Winston. b 78. Lanc Univ BA99. St Steph Ho Ox 00. **d** 03. C Lt Marsden w Nelson St Mary *Blackb* from 03. *14 Highgate, Nelson BB9 0DU*

✠**HILL, The Rt Revd Christopher John.** b 45. K Coll Lon BD67 AKC67 MTh68. **d** 69 **p** 70 **c** 96. C Tividale *Lich* 69-73; C Codsall 73-74; Abp's Asst Chapl on Foreign Relns *Cant* 74-81; ARCIC from 74; Sec 74-90; Hon Can Cant Cathl *Cant* 82-89; Abp's Sec for Ecum Affairs 82-89; Chapl To The Queen 87-96; Can Res and Prec St Paul's Cathl *Lon* 89-96; Select Preacher Ox Univ 90; Area Bp Stafford *Lich* from 96. *Ash Garth, 6 Broughton Crescent, Barlaston, Stoke-on-Trent ST12 9DD* Tel (01782) 373308 Fax 373705 E-mail bishop.stafford@lichfield.anglican.org

HILL, Canon Colin. b 42. Leic Univ BSc64 Open Univ PhD88. Ripon Hall Ox 64. **d** 66 **p** 67. C Leic Martyrs *Leic* 66-69; C

Braunstone 69-71; Lect Ecum Inst Thornaby Teesside 71-72; V Worsbrough St Thos and St Jas *Sheff* 72-78; Telford Planning Officer *Lich* 78-96; RD Telford 80-96; RD Telford Severn Gorge *Heref* 80-96; Preb Heref Cathl 83-96; Can Res Carl Cathl *Carl* from 96; Dioc Sec from 96. *4 The Abbey, Carlisle CA3 8TZ* Tel (01228) 590778 *or* 522573 Fax 815400
E-mail diocesan.secretary@carlislediocese.org.uk

HILL, Canon Colin Arnold Clifford. b 29. OBE96. Bris Univ 52. Ripon Coll Ox 55. **d** 57 **p** 58. C Rotherham *Sheff* 57-61; V Brightside St Thos 61-64; R Easthampstead *Ox* 64-72; Chapl RAF Coll Bracknell 68-72; V Croydon *Cant* 72-84; Chapl Abp Whitgift Foundn 72-94; Hon Can Cant Cathl 75-84; V Croydon St Jo *S'wark* 85-94; Hon Can S'wark Cathl 85-94; Chapl to The Queen 90-99; rtd 94. *Silver Birches, 70 Preston Crowmarsh, Wallingford OX10 6SL* Tel (01491) 836102 Fax as telephone

HILL, Canon David. b 25. AKC54. **d** 55 **p** 56. C Kingsbury H Innocents *Lon* 55-58; C Putney St Mary *S'wark* 58-62; V Battersea St Mich 62-89; RD Battersea 69-76; Hon Can S'wark Cathl 74-89; rtd 89; Perm to Offic *Chelmsf* 89-98. *70 Gloucester Avenue, Maldon CM9 6LA* Tel (01621) 855384

HILL, David Rowland. b 34. Lon Univ BSc55. Qu Coll Birm. **d** 59 **p** 60. C Upper Tooting H Trin *S'wark* 59-61; C Cheam 61-63; C Richmond St Mary 63-68; V Sutton St Nicholas *Linc* 68-82; V Pinchbeck 82-99; rtd 99; Perm to Offic *Linc* 99-02. *24 London Road, Spalding PE11 2TA* Tel (01775) 768912

HILL, Canon Derek Ingram. b 12. FSA74 Trin Coll Ox BA34 MA38 Kent Univ Hon DD83. Wells Th Coll 34. **d** 35 **p** 36. C Buckland in Dover *Cant* 35-39; C Sturminster St Andr 39-43; P-in-c S Norwood H Innocents 43-49; V 49-57; V Cant St Greg 57-65; Six Preacher Cant Cathl 64-70; R Cant St Pet and St Alphege w St Marg 65-74; P-in-c Cant St Mildred w St Mary de Castro 72-74; R Cant St Pet w St Alphege and St Marg etc 74-76; RD Cant 69-76; Hon Can Cant Cathl 70-75; Can Res 76-83; rtd 83; Perm to Offic *Cant* from 00. *2 St John's House, 40 Northgate, Canterbury CT1 1BE* Tel (01227) 761954

HILL, Derek Stanley. b 28. AKC53. **d** 53 **p** 54. C Rushmere *St E* 53-55; S Africa 55-57; C Boreham Wood All SS *St Alb* 57-59; V Crowfield *St E* 59-67; P-in-c Stonham Aspal 59-61; R 61-67; V Bury St Edmunds St Geo 67-73; P-in-c Ampton w Lt Livermere and Ingham 68-73; V Gazeley w Dalham 73-75; P-in-c Lidgate w Ousden 73-74; P-in-c Gt Bradley 74-78; V Gazeley w Dalham and Moulton 75-78; V Gt Barton 78-86; V Bury St Edmunds All SS 86-93; rtd 93; Perm to Offic *St E* from 93. *Whinwillow, 38 Maltings Garth, Thurston, Bury St Edmunds IP31 3PP* Tel (01359) 230770

HILL, Elizabeth Jayne Louise. *See* DAVENPORT, Ms Elizabeth Jayne Louise

HILL, Eugene Mark. b 48. Univ of Wales (Lamp) BA71. Sarum Th Coll 71. **d** 73 **p** 74. C Sutton St Nic *S'wark* 73-77; Hon C 77-80; Asst Chapl Em Sch Wandsworth 77-87; Chapl from 87; Hon C St Helier *S'wark* 83-84; Hon C Caterham 84-98; Dir Chr Studies Course from 85; Perm to Offic from 98. *22 Bramley Hill, South Croydon CR2 6LT* Tel (020) 8686 1387

HILL, Geoffrey Dennison. b 31. Tyndale Hall Bris DipTh55. **d** 56 **p** 57. C Denton Holme *Carl* 56-59; R Asby w Ormside 59-63; R Arthuret 63-71; V Arnside 71-76; P-in-c Torver 76-79; rtd 91. *Holywath, Coniston LA21 8HN*

HILL, Geoffrey Lionel. b 45. WEMTC 96. **d** 03. OLM Thornbury *Glouc* from 03; OLM Oldbury-on-Severn w Shepperdine from 03. *2 Solent Way, Thornbury, Bristol BS35 2XD* Tel (01454) 416851 Mobile 07968-229912 E-mail gl.hill@bigfoot.com

HILL, George Ernest. b 25. St Jo Coll Nottm. **d** 85 **p** 87. OLM Selston *S'well* 85-95; Perm to Offic from 95. *105 Main Road, Jacksdale, Nottingham NG16 5HR* Tel (01773) 603446

HILL, Mrs Gillian Beryl. b 53. Open Univ BA86. S Dios Minl Tr Scheme 87. **d** 90 **p** 94. NSM Southsea St Jude *Portsm* 90-95; C Southsea St Pet 95-01; V Catherington and Clanfield from 01. *The Vicarage, 330 Catherington Lane, Catherington, Waterlooville PO8 0TD* Tel (023) 9259 3228 *or* 3139
E-mail gillhill@inglisrd.freeserve.co.uk

HILL, Harold Gordon Haynes. b 15. Tyndale Hall Bris 36. **d** 39 **p** 40. C Aldridge *Lich* 39-42; Org Sec (N and Midl) ICM 42-46; Cen Sec S 46-48; R Whinburgh w Westfield *Nor* 48-81; R Reymerston 48-81; P-in-c Cranworth w Letton and Southbergh 78-79; rtd 81. *34 Morley Road, Sheringham NR26 8JE* Tel (01263) 824965

HILL, Ian Maxwell. b 60. Loughb Univ BSc81 MCIT85. EMMTC DipTh95. **d** 95 **p** 96. NSM Thurnby Lodge *Leic* 95-00; NSM Thurmaston from 00. *Shady Ash, 4 Sturrock Close, Thurnby, Leicester LE7 9QP* Tel 0116-243 1609

HILL, James Arthur. b 47. Ulster Univ BEd85. CITC 69. **d** 72 **p** 73. C Ballymena w Ballyclug *Conn* 72-74; C Arm St Mark w Aghavilly *Arm* 74-78; C Derg w Termonamongan *D & R* 78-79; I Inver w Mountcharles, Killaghtee and Killybegs 79-87. *53 Dufferin Avenue, Bangor BT20 3AB* Tel (028) 9146 9090

HILL, Mrs Jennifer Clare. b 50. City Univ BSc71 FBCO72. EAMTC 94. **d** 97 **p** 98. NSM Bottesford and Muston *Leic* 97-98; C Glen Parva and S Wigston 98-01; C Walsall Wood *Lich* from

01. *Church House, 25 Green Lane, Shelfield, Walsall WS4 1RN* Tel (01922) 692550

HILL, John. b 56. S'wark Ord Course. **d** 89 **p** 90. NSM Upper Norwood St Jo *S'wark* 89-94; Chapl RN from 94. *Royal Naval Chaplaincy Service, Room 203, Victory Building, HM Naval Base, Portsmouth PO1 3LS* Tel (023) 9272 7903 Fax 9272 7111

HILL, John Michael. b 34. FCA. Oak Hill NSM Course 81. **d** 85 **p** 86. NSM Rayleigh *Chelmsf* 85-96; Perm to Offic *Lon* 85-92; Chapl Rochford Gen Hosp 93-95; Chapl Southend Health Care NHS Trust 95-99; NSM Rochford *Chelmsf* from 96. *25D Belchamps Way, Hockley SS5 4NT* Tel (01702) 203287

HILL, Kenneth. b 27. Wycliffe Coll Toronto LTh. **d** 58 **p** 59. Canada 58-61; C Newc St Matt w St Mary *Newc* 61-62; SSF 62-64; C Burslem St Werburgh *Lich* 64-67; C Walsall St Gabr Fulbrook 67-70; P-in-c Hanley St Jude 70-79; P-in-c Chacewater *Truro* 79-92; rtd 92; Perm to Offic *Truro* from 92. *Carbis Barn, Church Road, Stithians, Truro TR3 7DH* Tel (01209) 861070

HILL, Kenneth James (Jim). b 43. Leic Univ BA64 Lon Univ BD68. Oak Hill Th Coll 65. **d** 69 **p** 70. C Southall Green St Jo *Lon* 69-72; C Blackheath Park St Mich *S'wark* 72-75; C Bath Abbey w St Jas *B & W* 75-83; P-in-c Bath St Mich w St Paul 75-82; R 82-83; R Huntspill 83-91; Omega Order 91-98; Perm to Offic *B & W* 91-98; Perm to Offic *Bris* 91-98; C Somerton w Compton Dundon, the Charltons etc *B & W* from 98. *The Parsonage, Charlton Adam, Somerton TA11 7AS* Tel (01458) 223061
E-mail kjhill@tiscali.co.uk

HILL, Laurence Bruce. b 43. AKC67. **d** 69 **p** 70. C Feltham *Lon* 69-72; C-in-c Hampstead St Steph 72-77; V Finchley H Trin from 77. *Holy Trinity Vicarage, 91 Church Lane, London N2 0TH* Tel (020) 8883 8720

HILL, Leslie Hugh. b 23. Westcott Ho Cam 73. **d** 73 **p** 74. NSM Holbrook and Lt Eaton *Derby* 73-79; NSM Loscoe 79-85; P-in-c Denby 85-88; P-in-c Horsley Woodhouse 87-88; rtd 88; Perm to Offic *Derby* from 88. *1 Hunter Drive, Kilburn, Derby DE56 0ND* Tel (01332) 881081

HILL, Malcolm Crawford. b 43. Lon Univ DipTh70. Oak Hill Th Coll 68. **d** 71 **p** 72. C Maidstone St Luke *Cant* 71-74; C Longfleet *Sarum* 74-79; V Bexleyheath St Pet *Roch* 79-90; V Lee St Mildred *S'wark* from 90. *The Vicarage, 1A Helder Grove, London SE12 0RB* Tel (020) 8857 5205

HILL, Mrs Marjorie Ann. b 38. MCSP60. St Jo Coll Nottm 92. **d** 94 **p** 95. Par Dn Hull St Martin w Transfiguration *York* 94; C 94-99; P-in-c Willerby w Ganton and Folkton 99-03; rtd 03; Perm to Offic *York* from 03. *16 Autherd Garth, Walkington, Beverley HU17 8RZ* Tel (01482) 865188

HILL, Mark. *See* HILL, Eugene Mark

HILL, Martyn William. b 43. Man Univ BSc64 Univ of Wales (Ban) PhD70 CPhys85 MInstP68. Westcott Ho Cam CTM92. **d** 92 **p** 93. C Horninglow *Lich* 92-95; TV Hawarden *St As* 95-00; V Bistre from 00. *Bistre Vicarage, Mold Road, Buckley CH7 2NH* Tel (01244) 550947

HILL, Matthew Anthony Robert. b 71. Leeds Univ BA93 Univ of Wales (Cardiff) BD96. St Mich Coll Llan 94. **d** 97 **p** 98. C Cardiff St Jo *Llan* 97-00; Min Can Llan Cathl from 00. *2 White House, The Cathedral Green, Llandaff, Cardiff CF5 2EB* Tel (029) 2055 2313

HILL, Michael. *See* HILL, John Michael

HILL, Michael. b 32. TD77. AKC55. **d** 56 **p** 57. C Tynemouth Cullercoats St Paul *Newc* 56-59; C Drayton in Hales *Lich* 59-61; V Milton 61-64; V Preston Gubbals 64-73; V Leaton 64-76; CF (TA) 65-67; CF (TAVR) 67-87; V Oswestry St Oswald *Lich* 76-87; P-in-c Trefonen 80-83; V Sunningdale *Ox* 87-97; rtd 97; Perm to Offic *Lich* from 97. *20 Winterton Way, Montford Grange, Bicton Heath, Shrewsbury SY3 5PA* Tel (01743) 341076

✠**HILL, The Rt Revd Michael Arthur.** b 49. Ridley Hall Cam 74. **d** 77 **p** 78 **c** 98. C Addiscombe St Mary *Cant* 77-81; C Slough *Ox* 81-83; P-in-c Chesham Bois 83-90; RV Amersham 89-92; Adn Berks 92-98; Area Bp Buckm 98-03; Bp Bris from 03. *Address very unknown*

HILL, The Rt Revd Michael John Giles. b 43. S Dios Minl Tr Scheme 82. **d** 84 **p** 86. Community of Our Lady and St John from 67; Abbot from 90; Perm to Offic *Win* 84-92; Lic to Offic from 92. *Alton Abbey, Abbey Road, Beech, Alton GU34 4AP* Tel (01420) 562145 *or* 563575 Fax 561691

HILL, Nora. b 47. Univ of Wales BA95 PGCE97. St Mich Coll Llan 00. **d** 03. NSM Llandogo w Whitebrook Chpl and Tintern Parva *Mon* from 03. *3 Warwick Close, Chepstow NP6 5BU* Tel (01291) 626784

HILL, Norman William. b 14. Ch Coll Cam BA36 MA40. Linc Th Coll 43. **d** 45 **p** 46. C Hitchin St Mary *St Alb* 45-49; C St Alb Abbey 49-60; V Rickmansworth 60-74; P-in-c Northill 74-78; P-in-c Moggerhanger 74-78; P-in-c Northill w Moggerhanger 78-79; RD Biggleswade 75-79; rtd 80; Perm to Offic *Newc* from 80. *4 Overstone Gardens, Elvaston Road, Hexham NE46 2HH* Tel (01434) 609715

HILL, Patricia Francis. b 49. RGN90. SEITE DipTM99. **d** 99 **p** 00. NSM Hythe *Cant* from 99; Asst Chapl E Kent Hosps NHS Trust from 99. *Springville, Sandling Road, Saltwood, Hythe CT21 4QJ* Tel (01303) 266649

HILL, Canon Peter. b 36. AKC60. St Boniface Warminster 60. **d** 61 **p** 62. C Gt Berkhamsted *St Alb* 61-67; R Bedford St Mary 67-69; P-in-c 69-70; V Goldington 69-79; V Biggleswade 79-90; RD Biggleswade 80-85; Hon Can St Alb 85-90; V Holbeach *Linc* 90-01; RD Elloe E 94-99; P-in-c The Suttons w Tydd 99-01; rtd 01; Perm to Offic *Nor* from 01. *Rayner Cottage, Low Street, Sloley, Norwich NR12 8HD* Tel (01692) 538744

HILL, Canon Peter. b 50. Man Univ BSc71 Nottm Univ MTh90. Wycliffe Hall Ox 81. **d** 83 **p** 84. C Porchester *S'well* 83-86; V Huthwaite 86-95; P-in-c Calverton from 95; RD S'well 97-01; Hon Can S'well Minster from 01. *The Vicarage, Crookdale Lane, Calverton, Nottingham NG14 6GF* Tel 0115-965 2552 E-mail peter@stwilfrids.freeserve.co.uk

HILL, Ralph Jasper. b 15. Tyndale Hall Bris 38. **d** 41 **p** 42. C Stambermill *Worc* 41-44; C Harmondsworth *Lon* 44-45; C Wandsworth St Steph *S'wark* 45-48; Org Sec SAMS 49-59; Asst Master Hove Gr Sch 65-78; rtd 80; Perm to Offic *Chich* from 82. *29 Gorham Way, Telscombe Cliffs, Newhaven BN10 7BA* Tel (01273) 583729

HILL, Richard Brian. b 47. Dur Univ BA68 DipTh70. Cranmer Hall Dur 68 Westcott Ho Cam 70. **d** 71 **p** 72. C Cockermouth All SS w Ch Ch *Carl* 71-74; C Barrow St Geo w St Luke 74-76; V Walney Is 76-83; Dir of Clergy Tr 83-90; P-in-c Westward, Rosley-w-Woodside and Welton 83-90; V Gosforth All SS *Newc* from 90. *All Saints' Vicarage, 33 Brackenfield Road, Newcastle upon Tyne NE3 4DX* Tel 0191-285 6345 or 213 0450 Fax 246 2548 E-mail r.b.hill@lineone.net

HILL, Richard James. b 52. CCC Ox BA74 BA77 MA78. Wycliffe Hall Ox 75. **d** 78 **p** 79. C Harold Wood *Chelmsf* 78-81; C Hampreston *Sarum* 81-86; TV N Ferriby *York* 86-97; V Swanland from 97. *The Vicarage, St Barnabas Drive, Swanland, North Ferriby HU14 3RL* Tel (01482) 631271 E-mail stbrhoh@aol.com

HILL, Robert Joseph. b 45. Oak Hill Th Coll BA81. **d** 81 **p** 82. C W Derby St Luke *Liv* 81-84; P-in-c Devonport St Mich *Ex* 84-97; Chapl Morden Coll Blackheath 97-99; TV Manningham *Bradf* from 99. *St Paul's Vicarage, 63 St Paul's Road, Manningham, Bradford BD8 7LS* Tel (01274) 490550 E-mail rjh@credo-ergo-sum.fsnet.co.uk

HILL, Robin. b 35. Cranmer Hall Dur 59. **d** 62 **p** 63. C Aspley *S'well* 62-65; V Mansfield St Aug 65-71; R Hulland, Atlow and Bradley *Derby* 71-76; Australia 76-86; P-in-c Alkmonton, Cubley, Marston, Montgomery etc *Derby* 86-93; P-in-c Ticknall, Smisby and Stanton-by-Bridge 93-99; P-in-c Barrow-on-Trent w Twyford and Swarkestone 94-99; rtd 99. *34 Samson Street, White Gum Valley, W Australia 6162* Tel (0061) (8) 9335 9652

HILL, Canon Roger Anthony John. b 45. Liv Univ BA67 Linacre Coll Ox BA69 MA. Ripon Hall Ox 67. **d** 70 **p** 71. C St Helier *S'wark* 70-74; C Dawley Parva *Lich* 74-75; C Cen Telford 76-77; TV 77-81; TR 81-88; TR Newark w Hawton, Cotham and Shelton *S'well* 88-89; TR Newark 89-02; RD Newark 90-95; Hon Can S'well Minster 98-02; QHC from 01; R Man St Ann *Man* from 02; Hon Can Man Cathl from 02. *The Rectory, 296 Wilbraham Road, Chorlton-cum-Hardy, Manchester M21 0UU* Tel 0161-881 1229

HILL, Simon George. b 53. Reading Univ BSc75 MSc78 Lon Univ DipRS83. S'wark Ord Course 80. **d** 83 **p** 84. NSM Croydon St Aug *Cant* 83-84; Swaziland 84-86; Fiji 86-88; NSM Croydon St Aug *S'wark* 88-90; Tanzania 90-94; Uganda 94-96; Swaziland 96-98; Perm to Offic *Chich* and *S'wark* 99-02; P-in-c Cockfield w Bradfield St Clare, Felsham etc *St E* from 02. *The Rectory, Howe Lane, Cockfield, Bury St Edmunds IP30 0HA* Tel (01284) 828385 Mobile 07747-022903 E-mail revsimon@dial.pipex.com

HILL, Simon James. b 64. Sheff Univ BA85 Ex Univ PGCE88. Ripon Coll Cuddesdon BA84 DipMin95. **d** 95 **p** 96. C Manston *Ripon* 95-98; TV Dorchester *Ox* 98-03; Dir Berinsfield Progr Ripon Coll Cuddesdon 98-03; R Backwell w Chelvey and Brockley *B & W* from 03. *The Rectory, 72 Church Lane, Backwell, Bristol BS48 3JJ* Tel (01275) 462391

HILL, Stuart Graeme. b 64. Ripon Coll Cuddesdon BTh97. **d** 97 **p** 98. C Usworth *Dur* 97-99; C Monkwearmouth 99-01; TV from 01. *St Peter's Vicarage, St Peter's Way, Sunderland SR6 0DY* Tel 0191-567 3726 E-mail stuart.hill@durham.anglican.org

HILL, Trevor Walton. b 30. Leeds Univ BA57. Coll of Resurr Mirfield. **d** 59 **p** 60. C Bollington St Jo *Ches* 59-62; C Woodchurch 62-64; V Addingham *Carl* 64-67; V Carl H Trin 67-71; R Wetheral w Warwick 71-80; P-in-c Doddington w Wychling *Cant* 80-82; P-in-c Newnham 80-82; rtd 95. *59 Medina Avenue, Newport PO30 1HG*

HILL, William. b 44. Man Univ BSc66 Kent Univ DipTh98 CEng73 MICE73. SEITE 95. **d** 98 **p** 99. NSM Farnham *Guildf* 98-01; P-in-c Smallburgh w Dilham w Honing and Crostwight *Nor* from 01. *Grange Farm House, Yarmouth Road, Worstead, North Walsham NR28 9LX* Tel (01692) 403402 E-mail w_hill_ss@hotmail.com

HILL, William Henry George. b 21. S'wark Ord Course 66. **d** 69 **p** 70. C Welling *S'wark* 69-73; C Reigate St Luke S Park 73-76; V Lynsted w Kingsdown *Cant* 76-87; R Norton 76-87; rtd 87; Perm to Offic *Sarum* from 87. *Querida, 22 West Bay, Bridport DT6 4HD* Tel (01308) 423915 Mobile 07974-864656 Fax 422133

HILL-BROWN, Timothy Duncan. b 65. Westmr Coll Ox BA87. Wycliffe Hall Ox DPS92. **d** 93 **p** 94. C Sparkhill w Greet and Sparkbrook *Birm* 93-97; C Sutton Coldfield H Trin 97-99; P-in-c Short Heath 99-00; V from 00. *St Margaret's Vicarage, Somerset Road, Birmingham B23 6NQ* Tel 0121-373 9209 E-mail duncan@ukonline.co.uk

HILL-TOUT, Mark Laurence. b 50. AKC73. **d** 74 **p** 75. C Brighton Resurr *Chich* 74-77; C New Shoreham 77-79; C Old Shoreham 77-79; Dioc Stewardship Adv Lewes and Hastings 79-84; P-in-c Stonegate 79-83; R Horsted Keynes 84-89; V St Helens *Portsm* 89-95; V Sea View 89-95; P-in-c Widley w Wymering 95-99; V from 99. *The Vicarage, Medina Road, Portsmouth PO6 3NH* Tel (023) 9237 6307 E-mail mark.hilltout@tesco.net

HILLARY, Leslie Tyrone James. b 59. Cranmer Hall Dur 84. **d** 87 **p** 88. C Middlesbrough All SS *York* 87-89; C Stainton-in-Cleveland 89-91; CF from 91. *c/o MOD Chaplains (Army)* Tel (01980) 615804 Fax 615800

HILLAS, Ms Patricia Dorothy. b 66. E Lon Univ BA91 Middx Univ BA02. NTMTC 98. **d** 02 **p** 03. C Kensal Rise St Mark and St Martin *Lon* from 02. *82 Herbert Gardens, London NW10 3BU* Tel (020) 8969 2875 E-mail tricia@hillas.freeserve.co.uk

HILLEBRAND, Frank David. b 46. AKC68. St Boniface Warminster 68. **d** 69 **p** 70. C Wood Green St Mich *Lon* 69-72; C Evesham *Worc* 72-75; V Worc H Trin 75-80; V Kidderminster St Jo 80-90; TR Kidderminster St Jo and H Innocents 90-91; TV High Wycombe *Ox* 91-95; TR 95-00; Team Chapl Portsm Hosps NHS Trust from 00. *Chaplaincy Office, Queen Alexandra Hospital, Portsmouth PO6 3LY* Tel (023) 9228 6408 E-mail fhillebrand@sovereign32.freeserve.co.uk

HILLEL, Laurence Christopher Francis. b 54. Bris Univ BA76 Sheff Univ PGCE78 SOAS Lon MA84. Cuddesdon Coll 98. **d** 98 **p** 99. C Pinner *Lon* 98-00; Chapl Bp Ramsey Sch from 01; NSM Eastcote St Lawr *Lon* from 01. *16 Barrow Point Avenue, Pinner HA5 3HF* Tel (020) 8866 9006

HILLIAM, Mrs Cheryl. b 49. EMMTC DipTh94. **d** 94 **p** 95. C Linc St Faith and St Martin w St Pet *Linc* 94-98; P-in-c S Ormsby Gp from 98. *The Rectory, South Ormsby, Louth LN11 8QT* Tel (01507) 480236

HILLIARD, David. b 57. BTh. **d** 91 **p** 92. C Holywood *D & D* 91-94; C Seagoe 94-96; I Tartaraghan w Diamond *Arm* from 96. *Tartaraghan Rectory, 5 Tarthlogue Road, Portadown BT62 1RB* Tel (028) 3885 1289 Fax as telephone

HILLIARD, Canon George Percival St John. b 45. TCD BA67. **d** 69 **p** 70. C Seapatrick *D & D* 69-73; C Carrickfergus *Conn* 73-76; I Fanlobbus Union *C, C & R* 76-85; Dean Cloyne 85-02; Prec Cork Cathl 85-02; I Cloyne Union 85-02; Chapl Univ Coll Cork from 02; Can Cork and Cloyne Cathls from 02. *The Chaplaincy, Iona, College Road, Cork, Irish Republic* E-mail gchilliard@hotmail.com

HILLIARD, Robert Godfrey. b 52. Univ of Wales DipTh75 Portsm Univ BA97 MA02. St Mich Coll Llan. **d** 75 **p** 76. C Whitchurch *Llan* 75-80; Chapl RN from 80. *Royal Naval Chaplaincy Service, Room 203, Victory Building, HM Naval Base, Portsmouth PO1 3LS* Tel (023) 9272 7903 Fax 9272 7111

HILLIARD, Russell. **d** 03. C Zürich *Eur* from 03. *Address temp unknown*

HILLIER, Andrew. b 68. RGN92. SW Minl Tr Course 99. **d** 02 **p** 03. C Castle Cary w Ansford *B & W* from 02. *The Church House, Ansford Road, Castle Cary BA7 7HG* Tel (01963) 350245 Mobile 07980-743799 E-mail andrew@hillier66.fsnet.co.uk

HILLIER, Derek John. b 30. Sarum Th Coll 61. **d** 63 **p** 64. C Salisbury St Mark *Sarum* 63-65; C Weymouth H Trin 65-66; R Caundle Bishop w Caundle Marsh and Holwell 66-75; P-in-c Pulham 70-78; R The Caundles and Holwell 75-81; R The Caundles w Folke and Holwell 81-02; rtd 02; Perm to Offic *Sarum* and *B & W* from 02. *Sarum House, Bishops Caundle, Sherborne DT9 5ND* Tel (01963) 23243 Fax as telephone

HILLIER, John Frederick. b 43. ARIBA67. Dioc OLM tr scheme 98. **d** 01 **p** 02. OLM Merton St Mary *S'wark* from 01. *36 Watery Lane, London SW20 9AD* Tel (020) 8540 4160 Mobile 07802-646374 Fax (020) 8715 8123 E-mail jfhillier@fish.co.uk

HILLIER, The Ven Michael Bruce. b 49. St Barn Coll Adelaide ThD73. **d** 74 **p** 75. Australia 74-80; C Tewkesbury w Walton Cardiff *Glouc* 81-86; Australia from 86; P-in-c Whyalla from 94; Adn Eyre Peninsula from 01. *37 Wood Terrace, PO Box 244, Whyalla, S Australia 5600* Tel (0061) (8) 8644 0391 Fax 8644 0657 E-mail mjhillier@dove.net.au

HILLIER, Timothy John. b 55. Westmr Coll Ox CertEd77. Oak Hill Th Coll DipHE96. **d** 96 **p** 97. C Chertsey *Guildf* 96-00; V from 00. *The Vicarage, London Street, Chertsey KT16 8AA* Tel (01932) 563141 Fax as telephone
E-mail hillier@timp33.freeserve.co.uk

HILLMAN, Clive Ralph. b 71. York Univ BSc92. St Steph Ho Ox BA93. **d** 96 **p** 97. C Kingston upon Hull St Alb *York* 96-00; TV Ifield *Chich* 00-02; Chapl St Jo Coll Cam from 02. *St John's College, Cambridge CB2 1TP* Tel (01223) 338617
E-mail crh41@cam.ac.uk

HILLMAN, Jesse James. b 22. MRSH. S'wark Ord Course 83. **d** 86 **p** 87. Communications Sec CMS 86; NSM Kidbrooke St Jas *S'wark* 86; NSM Peterchurch w Vowchurch, Turnastone and Dorstone *Heref* 86-93; rtd 93; Perm to Offic *Heref* from 93. *Granary Cottage, Chapel Lane, Dorstone HR3 6AP* Tel (01981) 550609 E-mail hillman@easicom.com

HILLMAN, John Anthony. b 32. St Chad's Coll Dur BA53. St Mich Coll Llan 54. **d** 55 **p** 56. C Llangollen *St As* 56-60; S Africa 60-86; TV Wolstanton *Lich* 86-91; P-in-c E Goscote w Ratcliffe and Rearsby *Leic* 91-93; TV Syston 93-98; rtd 98. *7 Hafod Road West, Penrhyn Bay, Llandudno LL30 3PN* Tel (01492) 541374

HILLMAN, Jonathan. b 68. Man Univ BEng90. Ridley Hall Cam. **d** 00 **p** 01. C N Wingfield, Clay Cross and Pilsley *Derby* from 00; TV Cove St Jo *Guildf* from 03. *Fircroft, 21 St John's Road, Farnborough GU14 9RL* Tel (01252) 543502
E-mail j.hillman@fish.co.uk

HILLMAN, Miss Sarah Catherine. b 68. Selw Coll Cam BA90 MA94. St Jo Coll Nottm 01. **d** 03. C Sandy *St Alb* from 03. *14 Pyms Way, Sandy SG19 1BZ* Tel (01767) 683201
E-mail sarah_hillman@ntlworld.com

HILLS, John Bucknell. b 21. Glouc Sch of Min. **d** 89 **p** 89. NSM Moreton-in-Marsh w Batsford, Todenham etc *Glouc* 89-94; Perm to Offic *Cov* and *Glouc* from 94. *3 Bowling Green Court, Hospital Road, Moreton-in-Marsh GL56 0BX* Tel (01608) 651507

HILLS, Kenneth Hugh. b 30. Univ of NZ BCom54. Ripon Hall Ox 55. **d** 57 **p** 58. C Handsworth St Mary *Birm* 57-59; New Zealand 59-67; Ind Chapl *Birm* 67-74; Chapl Aston Univ 74-82; rtd 91; Community Member Cluny Hill Coll 93-00. *14 Station Road, Belfast BT4 1RE* Tel (028) 9047 1963 Fax as telephone
E-mail ken.hills@findhorn.org *or* k h@onetel.net.uk

HILLS, Michael John. b 58. BA82. Westcott Ho Cam 87. **d** 88 **p** 89. C Workington St Jo *Carl* 88-91; C Gosforth All SS *Newc* 91-93; TV Seaton Hirst 93-98; Chapl RN from 98. *Royal Navy Chaplaincy Service, Room 203, Victory Building, HM Naval Base, Portsmouth PO1 3LS* Tel (023) 9272 7903 Fax 9272 7111

HILLS, Michael Rae Buchanan. b 52. CQSW83 Univ of Wales (Lamp) BA81 Ex Univ BPhil83. St Steph Ho Ox DipMin94. **d** 94 **p** 95. C Kingston upon Hull St Nic *York* 94-97; V Newington w Dairycoates from 97. *St John's Vicarage, 203 St George's Road, Hull HU3 3SP* Tel (01482) 214551
E-mail vicar@kanga.karoo.co.uk

HILLS, Michael William John. b 54. Univ of Wales (Lamp) BA84. Westcott Ho Cam 85. **d** 87 **p** 88. C Reddish *Man* 87-91; V Bolton St Phil 91-00; V Northampton St Mich w St Edm *Pet* from 00. *St Michael's House, 631 Wellingborough Road, Northampton NN3 3HR* Tel (01604) 400511 *or* tel and fax 230316 Mobile 07932-141428 E-mail mickkhills@btconnect.com

HILLS, Richard Leslie. b 36. Qu Coll Cam BA60 MA63 DIC64 UMIST PhD68 FMA83. St Deiniol's Hawarden 85. **d** 87 **p** 88. C Urmston *Man* 87-89; C Gt Yarmouth *Nor* 89-90; NSM Mottram in Longdendale *Ches* 90-01; Perm to Offic from 01. *Stamford Cottage, 47 Old Road, Mottram, Hyde SK14 6LW* Tel (01457) 763104

HILLS, Roger Malcolm. b 42. Oak Hill Th Coll 83. **d** 86 **p** 87. Hon C Mill Hill Jo Keble Ch *Lon* 86-98; NSM Mill Hill St Mich 86-98; Perm to Offic 98-00; V Queensbury All SS from 00. *The Vicarage, 24 Waltham Road, Edgware HA8 5PQ* Tel (020) 8952 4536 *or* 8952 0744 E-mail asq@btinternet.com

HILLS, Stephen Alan. b 59. Sheff Univ BA81. Ridley Hall Cam 97. **d** 99 **p** 00. C Southborough St Pet w Ch Ch and St Matt etc *Roch* 99-02; TV from 02. *The Rectory, Rectory Drive, Bidborough, Tunbridge Wells TN3 0UL* Tel (01892) 528081 E-mail stephen.hills5@virgin.net

HILLYER, Charles Norman. b 21. Lon Univ BD48. Lambeth STh67 ALCD48. **d** 48 **p** 49. C Finchley Ch Ch *Lon* 48-51; C New Malden and Coombe *S'wark* 51-54; V Hanley Road St Sav w St Paul *Lon* 54-59; Chapl City of Lon Maternity Hosp 54-59; V Ponsbourne *St Alb* 59-70; Chapl Tolmers Park Hosp 59-70; Lib Tyndale Ho Cam 70-73; Org Ed UCCF 73-79; Sec Tyndale Fellowship Bibl Research Cam 73-75; P-in-c Hatherleigh *Ex* 79-81; V 81-86; rtd 86; Perm to Offic *Sarum* 89-03 and *Leic* from 03. *10 Smyth Close, Market Harborough LE16 7NS* Tel (01858) 432179 E-mail norman.hillyer@btinternet.com

HILTON, Clive. b 30. Kelham Coll 54. **d** 58 **p** 59. C Wythenshawe Wm Temple Ch CD *Man* 58-61; C Newton Heath All SS 61-62; C-in-c Oldham St Chad Limeside CD 62-65; V Oldham St Chad Limeside 65-70; P-in-c Gravesend H Family *Roch* 70-71; R

Killamarsh *Derby* 71-88; R Broughton w Loddington and Cransley etc *Pet* 88-91; rtd 92; Perm to Offic *Man* 92-95; *Ches* 95-99 and *Linc* 98-01. *73A Tattershall Drive, Market Deeping, Peterborough PE6 8BZ* Tel (01778) 346217

HILTON, Ian Anthony. b 57. St Jo Coll Nottm 83. **d** 86 **p** 87. C Nottingham St Sav *S'well* 86-90; C Aspley 90-97; P-in-c Colchester, New Town and The Hythe *Chelmsf* 97-02; R from 02. *The Rectory, 24 New Town Road, Colchester CO1 2EF* Tel (01206) 530320 E-mail ian.hilton@ntlworld.com

HILTON, John. b 49. Ex Univ BA70. Cuddesdon Coll 71. **d** 73 **p** 74. C W Derby St Jo *Liv* 73-79; V Orford St Andr 79-96; V Leeds St Wilfrid *Ripon* from 96. *St Wilfrid's Vicarage, Chatsworth Road, Leeds LS8 3RS* Tel 0113-249 7724
E-mail john@the-oak-403.demon.co.uk

HILTON, John Read. b 41. Lon Univ BD63 AKC65 LSE BSc73. **d** 65 **p** 66. C Cov H Trin *Cov* 65-69; C Hemel Hempstead *St Alb* 69-70; Hon C Catford St Andr *S'wark* 70-81. *275 Folkestone Road, Dover CT17 9LL* Tel (01304) 206794

HILTON-TURVEY, Geoffrey Michael. b 34. Oak Hill Th Coll 80. **d** 81 **p** 82. C Bispham *Blackb* 81-85; V Inskip 85-99; rtd 99; Perm to Offic *Heref* from 00. *20 Cralves Mead, Tenbury Wells WR15 8EX* Tel (01584) 811153
E-mail gmh-t@gmh-t.freeserve.co.uk

HILTON-TURVEY, Keith Geoffrey Michael. b 59. Oak Hill Th Coll BA03. **d** 03. C S Mimms Ch Ch *Lon* from 03. *8 Wentworth Road, Barnet EN5 4NT* Tel (020) 8441 0645

HINA, Christine Magdeleine. b 66. St Alb and Ox Min Course. **d** 01 **p** 02. C Stevenage St Hugh and St Jo *St Alb* from 01. *1 Vallansgate, Stevenage SG2 8PY* Tel (01438) 236536
E-mail christine@hina.refreeserve.co.uk

HINCHCLIFFE, Garry Anthony Frank. b 68. New Coll Edin BD94. Edin Th Coll CECM93. **d** 94 **p** 95. C Dumfries *Glas* 94-97; P-in-c Motherwell and Wishaw 97-00; V Hampsthwaite and Killinghall *Ripon* from 00. *The Vicarage, Church Lane, Hampsthwaite, Harrogate HG3 2HB* Tel (01423) 770337
E-mail gsahinch@compuserve.com

HINCHEY, Peter John. b 30. LTCL53. Chich Th Coll 55. **d** 58 **p** 59. C Malden St Jo *S'wark* 58-61; V Rosherville *Roch* 61-67; V Gillingham St Aug 67-72; V Bromley St Andr 72-74; Hon Chapl to Bp 74-78; Hon C Lamorbey H Redeemer 76-78; R Foots Cray 78-81; Perm to Offic *Chich* 92-94; rtd 94; Hon C Rotherhithe St Mary w All SS *S'wark* 94-98; Perm to Offic *Chelmsf* from 95; *St E* from 97; *Chich* from 03. *16 Collington Grove, Bexhill-on-Sea TN39 3UB* Tel (01424) 846238 E-mail hincheypj@hotmail.com

HINCKLEY, Paul Frederick. b 61. Cranfield Inst of Tech MSc85 Farnborough Tech Coll HND83. Ridley Hall Cam CTM94. **d** 94 **p** 95. C Ovenden *Wakef* 94-99; TV Billericay and Lt Burstead *Chelmsf* from 99. *Christ Church Vicarage, 10 Chestwood Close, Billericay CM12 0PB* Tel (01277) 652659
E-mail paul@billericaychurches.org

✠**HIND, The Rt Revd John William.** b 45. Leeds Univ BA66. Cuddesdon Coll 70. **d** 72 **p** 73 **c** 91. C Catford (Southend) and Downham *S'wark* 72-76; V Forest Hill Ch Ch 76-82; P-in-c Forest Hill St Paul 81-82; Prin Chich Th Coll 82-91; Wiccamical Preb Chich Cathl *Chich* 82-91; Area Bp Horsham 91-93; Bp Eur 93-01; Asst Bp Chich 93-01; Bp Chich from 01. *The Palace, Chichester PO19 1PY* Tel (01243) 782161 Fax 531332
E-mail bishop@diochi.freeserve.co.uk

HIND, Mrs Ruth Elizabeth. b 71. Cen Lancs Univ BA93. St Jo Coll Nottm MTh01. **d** 02 **p** 03. C Caldbeck, Castle Sowerby and Sebergham *Carl* from 02. *Hudscales Cottage, Hudscales Farm, Hesket Newmarket, Wigton CA7 8JZ* Tel (01697) 478725
E-mail ruthehind@supanet.com

HIND, Canon Stanley Maurice. b 29. AKC53. **d** 54 **p** 55. C Haydock St Jas *Liv* 54-57; C Elland *Wakef* 57-60; V Mirfield Eastthorpe St Paul 60-67; V Carleton 67-78; V E Hardwick 72-78; V Morley St Pet w Churwell 78-86; V Womersley 86-87; P-in-c Kirk Smeaton 86-87; V Womersley and Kirk Smeaton 87-94; Hon Can Wakef Cathl 89-94; rtd 94; Perm to Offic *Wakef* from 94. *1 The Lilacs, Carleton Road, Pontefract WF8 3RW* Tel (01977) 700386

HINDER, Deenon Patterson. b 38. Open Univ BA95. Selly Oak Coll 60 Bris Bapt Coll 68. **d** 97 **p** 98. NSM Stanwix *Carl* 97-99; P-in-c Glenurquhart *Mor* from 99. *St Ninian's Cottage, Milton, Drumnadrochit, Inverness IV63 6UA* Tel (01456) 450158

HINDLE, Miss Penelope Jane Bowyn. b 45. Trin Coll Bris 76. **dss** 84 **d** 87 **p** 94. Stoneycroft All SS *Liv* 84-89; Par Dn 87-89; Asst Chapl Broadgreen Hosp *Liv* 87-89; Asst Chapl R Free Hosp Lon 89-93; Chapl N Herts NHS Trust 93-02; rtd 02. *19 Park Lane, Knebworth SG3 6PD* Tel (01438) 811584

HINDLEY, Canon Andrew David. b 54. Univ of Wales (Lamp) BA. Sarum & Wells Th Coll. **d** 82 **p** 83. C Huddersfield St Pet *Wakef* 82-84; C Huddersfield St Pet and All SS 84-86; C P-in-c Holmfield 86-91; R Ribchester w Stidd *Blackb* 91-96; Bp's Adv for Leisure and Tourism 91-96; Chapl Ribchester Hosp from 91; Hon Can Blackb Cathl 96; Can Res Blackb Cathl from 96. *22 Billinge Avenue, Blackburn BB2 6SD* Tel (01254) 261152 *or* 51491 Fax 689666
E-mail andrew.hindley@blackburn.anglican.org

HINDLEY, Anthony Talbot. b 41. Bernard Gilpin Soc Dur 61 Oak Hill Th Coll 62. **d** 66 **p** 67. C Stoke next Guildf St Jo *Guildf* 66-69; Kenya 70-78; C Redhill H Trin *S'wark* 78-79; P-in-c Eastbourne All So *Chich* 79-83; V 83-86; V S Malling 86-98; R Wainford *St E* from 98; RD Beccles and S Elmham 00-03. *The Rectory, 27 School Road, Ringsfield, Beccles NR34 8NZ* Tel (01502) 717862 Mobile 07766-546601
E-mail anthony.hindley@stedmundsbury.anglican.org

HINDLEY, John Philip Talbot. b 76. Ex Univ BA96 Oak Hill Th Coll BA01. **d** 01 **p** 02. C Astley Bridge *Man* from 01. *51 Shoreswood, Bolton BL1 7DD* Tel (01204) 302070
E-mail j_hindley@yahoo.com

HINDLEY, Canon Roger Dennis. b 48. Man Univ BA70 Ox Univ BA77 MA83. Ripon Coll Cuddesdon 75 Qu Coll Birm 77. **d** 78 **p** 79. C Rubery *Birm* 78-81; C Henbury *Bris* 81-83; V Erdington St Chad *Birm* 83-89; V Hill from 89; AD Sutton Coldfield 96-02; Hon Can Birm Cathl from 00. *61 Mere Green Road, Sutton Coldfield B75 5BW* Tel 0121-308 0074

HINDLEY, Thomas Richard. b 31. ARIBA54 Sheff Univ BA53 Lon Univ BD66. Clifton Th Coll 61. **d** 63 **p** 64. C Kenilworth St Jo *Cov* 63-67; C Cheadle *Ches* 67-70; R Harpurhey Ch Ch *Man* 70-95; R Harpurhey St Steph 72-95; rtd 96; Perm to Offic *Man* from 96. *15 Twyford Close, Didsbury, Manchester M20 2YR* Tel 0161-438 0387

HINDS, Kenneth Arthur Lancelot. b 30. Birkbeck Coll Lon DipRS91 K Coll Lon BA00. Bps' Coll Cheshunt. **d** 64 **p** 65. C Sawbridgeworth *St Alb* 64-67; C Gt Berkhamsted 67-71; V Boreham Wood St Mich 71-75; Trinidad and Tobago 75-79; P-in-c Gt Ilford St Luke *Chelmsf* 79-81; V 81-95; rtd 95; Perm to Offic *Chelmsf* from 95. *214 Aldborough Road South, Ilford IG3 8HF* Tel (020) 8598 2963

HINE, John Victor. b 36. Open Univ BA82. Carl Dioc Tr Course 85. **d** 88 **p** 89. NSM Dean *Carl* 88-92; NSM Clifton 88-92; C Millom 92-94; P-in-c Gt Broughton and Broughton Moor 94-02; P-in-c Brigham from 99; rtd 02. *4 The Paddocks, Thursby, Carlisle CA5 6PB* Tel (01228) 712704 E-mail hine.hine@virgin.net

HINE, Keith Ernest. b 50. Bradf Univ BA Leeds Univ CertEd. N Ord Course 89. **d** 89 **p** 90. C Wilmslow *Ches* 89-94; V Bowdon from 94. *The Vicarage, Church Brow, Bowdon, Altrincham WA14 2SG* Tel 0161-928 2468 E-mail keithhine@fish.co.uk

HINES, Richard Arthur. b 49. Imp Coll Lon MSc73 PhD76 K Coll Lon MTh89. Oak Hill Th Coll 82. **d** 84 **p** 85. C Mile Cross *Nor* 84-87; Lect Oak Hill Th Coll 87-97; Vice-Prin NTMTC 94-97; R Happisburgh, Walcott, Hempstead w Eccles etc *Nor* from 97. *The Rectory, The Hill, Happisburgh, Norwich NR12 0PW* Tel (01692) 650313
E-mail hines@norfolkcoast.fsnet.co.uk

HINEY, Thomas Bernard Felix. b 35. MC61. RMA 56 OStJ. Ridley Hall Cam DipTh69. **d** 69 **p** 70. C Edgbaston St Aug *Birm* 69-71; CF 71-91; Chapl R Hosp Chelsea from 91; Chapl Mercers' Coll Holborn from 99. *The Royal Hospital Chelsea, Royal Hospital Road, London SW3 4SL* Tel (020) 7881 5234 Fax 7823 6871 E-mail thiney2199@aol.com

HINGE, Canon David Gerald Francis. b 30. FRSA57. Wells Th Coll 64. **d** 66 **p** 67. C Brookfield St Anne, Highgate Rise *Lon* 66-69; C N Greenford All Hallows 69-71; V Winton *Man* 71-78; R Etherley *Dur* 78-96; Hon Can Dur Cathl 90-00; rtd 96. *9 Hillside, Ingleton, Darlington DL2 3JH* Tel (01325) 732002

HINGE, Derek Colin. b 36. Imp Coll Lon BSc58 CChem60 MRSC60. St Alb Minl Tr Scheme 84. **d** 88 **p** 89. NSM Bishop's Stortford St Mich *St Alb* from 88. *12 Avenue Road, Bishop's Stortford CM23 5NU* Tel (01279) 652173
E-mail dchinge@surfaid.org

HINGLEY, Christopher James Howard. b 48. Trin Coll Ox BA69 MA71. Wycliffe Hall Ox 81. **d** 80 **p** 81. Zimbabwe 80-81 and from 87; Lic to Offic *Ox* 85-87. *Whitestone School, Postbag 4, Hillside, Bulawayo, Zimbabwe*

HINGLEY (née EDWARDS), Ms Helen. b 55. Natal Univ BSW75. St Steph Ho Ox DipMin94. **d** 96 **p** 97. C Gravelly Hill *Birm* 96-01; TV Cen Wolverhampton *Lich* from 01. *All Saints' Vicarage, 2A Vicarage Road, Wolverhampton WV2 1DT* Tel (01902) 352565 E-mail hhingley@fish.co.uk

HINGLEY, Robert Charles. b 46. Ball Coll Ox BA69 MA74 Birm Univ CertEd73. Qu Coll Birm DipTh72. **d** 73 **p** 74. C Charlton St Luke w H Trin *S'wark* 73-76; Asst Warden Iona Abbey 76-77; TV Langley Marish *Ox* 77-83; V Balsall Heath St Paul *Birm* 83-90; Perm to Offic 90-91; V Birm St Luke 91-96; Lic to Offic from 96; Perm to Offic *Cov* from 01. *40 Grove Avenue, Moseley, Birmingham B13 9RY* Tel 0121-449 0624

HINGLEY, Roderick Stanley Plant. b 51. St Chad's Coll Dur BA72. St Steph Ho Ox 74. **d** 75 **p** 76. C Lower Gornal *Lich* 75-79; C Tividale 79-82; C Broseley w Benthall *Heref* 82-84; C Wanstead St Mary *Chelmsf* 84-92; V Romford St Alb from 92. *St Alban's Vicarage, 3 Francombe Gardens, Romford RM1 2TH* Tel (01708) 473580

HINKES, Sidney George Stuart. b 25. Lon Univ BA50 BD70. St Steph Ho Ox 50. **d** 52 **p** 53. C Burton St Paul *Lich* 52-54; C Leigh St Clem *Chelmsf* 54-58; C Upton cum Chalvey *Ox* 58-66; C-in-c Bayswater St Mary CD 66-82; V Headington St Mary

83-90; rtd 90; Perm to Offic *B & W* from 90-91; *Bris* from 92; *Glouc* from 03; Rtd Clergy Officer Malmesbury Adnry *Bris* from 93. *1 The Bungalow, Bremilham Road, Malmesbury SN16 0DQ* Tel (01666) 825249

HINKS (née CHAMBERS), Mrs Marion Patricia. b 48. Univ of Wales BDS72. SW Minl Tr Course 97. **d** 97 **p** 98. NSM Plymstock and Hooe *Ex* from 97. *52 Southland Park Road, Wembury, Plymouth PL9 0HQ* Tel (01752) 862439 Mobile 07889-291228

HINKSMAN, Adrian James Terence. b 43. Open Univ BA76 Lon Inst of Educn DipEd82. St Alb and Ox Min Course CBTS99. **d** 99 **p** 00. NSM Hemel Hempstead *St Alb* 99-02; NSM St Alb St Mary Marshalswick from 02; Dioc CME Officer from 02. *83 The Ridgeway, St Albans AL4 9NU* Tel (01727) 751230
E-mail adrian_hinksman@hotmail.com

HINKSMAN, Barrie Lawrence James. b 41. K Coll Lon BD64 AKC64 Birm Univ PhD02. St Boniface Warminster 61. **d** 65 **p** 66. C Crosby *Linc* 65-67; Ecum Development Officer Scunthorpe Coun of Chs 67-69; C Chelmsley Wood *Birm* 69-72; TV 72-75; P-in-c Offchurch *Cov* 75-79; Bp's Adv for Lay Tr 75-79; Perm to Offic 89-90; Hon Chapl Cov Cathl from 90; Perm to Offic *Birm* from 01; Hon Sen Fell Warw Univ *Cov* from 02. *Needlers End Cottage, 32 Stoneton Crescent, Balsall Common, Coventry CV7 7QG* Tel (01676) 530085 Fax as telephone
E-mail b.hinksman@btopenworld.com

HINTON, Mrs Frances Mary. b 43. EN(G)85. EMMTC 89. **d** 92 **p** 94. Par Dn Hornsey Rise Whitehall Park Team *Lon* 92-94; C 94-97; C Upper Holloway 97; TV Barking St Marg w St Patr *Chelmsf* from 97. *Christchurch Vicarage, Bastable Avenue, Barking IG11 0NG* Tel (020) 8594 1976
E-mail revfran@fish.co.uk

HINTON, Geoffrey. b 34. Bede Coll Dur BA56 Em Coll Cam MA67 Sussex Univ PGCE72. Ridley Hall Cam 58. **d** 60 **p** 61. C Cheltenham St Mary *Glouc* 60-61; C Beverley Minster *York* 61-65; C Newark St Mary *S'well* 70-71; rtd 99. *1 Northmoor Place, Oxford OX2 6XB* Tel (01865) 510267

HINTON, James William. b 63. Cov Poly BSc84 Leeds Univ PGCE86. St Jo Coll Nottm 00. **d** 02 **p** 03. C Thornbury *Bradf* from 02. *20 Sunny Bank Avenue, Thornbury, Bradford BD3 7DH* Tel (01274) 665610

HINTON, Michael Ernest. b 33. K Coll Lon 53 St Boniface Warminster 56. **d** 57 **p** 58. C Babbacombe *Ex* 57-60; S Africa 60-66; P-in-c Limehouse St Pet *Lon* 66-68; R Felmingham *Nor* 68-72; R Suffield 68-72; P-in-c Colby w Banningham and Tuttington 68-72; Bahamas 72-76; P-in-c Mylor w Flushing *Truro* 76-77; V 77-80; R The Deverills *Sarum* 82-87; Bermuda 87-89; Virgin Is 89-91; Chapl Sequoian Retreat and Conf Progr from 91; rtd 98; Perm to Offic *St E* 00-01; *Ex* from 02. *Le Petit Pain, St Ann's Chapel, Kingsbridge TQ7 4HQ* Tel (01548) 810124
E-mail lacton.int@virgin.net

HINTON, Michael George. b 27. Mert Coll Ox BA48 MA51 Reading Univ PhD59. S Dios Minl Tr Scheme 81. **d** 83 **p** 84. NSM Weston-super-Mare St Paul *B & W* 83-85; NSM Sibertswold w Coldred *Cant* 85-87; NSM Eythorne and Elvington w Waldershare etc 87-95; Perm to Offic from 95. *212 The Gateway, Dover CT16 1LL* Tel (01304) 204198 Fax as telephone E-mail michael@hintonm.demon.co.uk

HINTON, Nigel Keith. b 49. Univ Coll Lon BSc70 Worc Coll of Educn PGCE73 Lon Univ MA87. Oak Hill NSM Course 89. **d** 92 **p** 93. NSM Cudham and Downe *Roch* from 92. *2 Runciman Close, Pratts Bottom, Orpington BR6 7SZ* Tel (01689) 855348

HINTON, Robert Matthew. b 69. Lanc Univ BA91. Cranmer Hall Dur BA97. **d** 97 **p** 98. C Lache cum Saltney *Ches* 97-99; C Cheadle Hulme St Andr 99-02; V Ringway from 02. *Ringway Vicarage, Wicker Lane, Halebarns, Altrincham WA15 0HQ* Tel 0161-980 3955 or 980 3234
E-mail robert@matthew-hinton.totalserve.co.uk

HIPKINS, Leslie Michael. b 35. Univ Coll Dur BA57 ACIS60. Oak Hill Th Coll 78 Westcott Ho Cam 89. **d** 81 **p** 82. NSM Halstead St Andr w H Trin and Greenstead Green *Chelmsf* 81-87; C Tolleshunt Knights w Tiptree and Gt Braxted 87-89; P-in-c Cratfield w Heveningham and Ubbeston etc *St E* 89-00; rtd 00; Perm to Offic *St E* from 01. *Laundry Farm, Thorington, Halesworth IP19 9JF* Tel (01502) 478675

HIPPISLEY-COX, Stephen David. b 63. Sheff Univ BSc85 PhD92 Peterho Cam BA98. Westcott Ho Cam 96. **d** 99 **p** 00. C Ollerton w Boughton *S'well* 99-02; NSM Wilford Hill from 02. *43 Willow Road, West Bridgford, Nottingham NG2 7AY* E-mail s.d.hippisley-cox@bigfoot.com

HIPPLE, Mrs Maureen AtLee. b 53. Miami-Dade Community Coll. **d** 94 **p** 94. USA 94-96 and from 97; Asst Min Tunkhannock St Patr 94-95; Asst Min Towanda Ch Ch 95-97 and 97-98; R from 98; NSM Portarlington w Cloneyhurke and Lea *M & K* 96-97. *RR 5, Box 5069-A, Towanda, PA 18848, USA* E-mail christchurch@sosbbs.com

HIRONS, Malcolm Percy. b 36. Oriel Coll Ox BA59 MA62. Wycliffe Hall Ox 59. **d** 61 **p** 62. C Edgbaston St Aug *Birm* 61-64; Chapl Warw Sch 64-65; C Beverley Minster *York* 65-69; V Barnby upon Don *Sheff* 69-80; P-in-c Kirk Bramwith 75-80; P-in-c Fenwick 75-80; V Norton Woodseats St Paul 80-98; rtd 98;

Perm to Offic *Nor* from 98. *Broome Lodge, 8 Lincoln Square, Hunstanton PE36 6DL*

HIRST, Alan. b 44. Leeds Univ CQSW74. Linc Th Coll 79. **d** 81 **p** 82. C Newton Heath All SS *Man* 81-84; Chapl to the Deaf 84-88; V Oldham St Chad Limeside 88-91; Dep Chapl HM Pris Liv 91-92; Chapl HM Pris Ranby 92-96 and from 00; Chapl HM Pris Wakef 96-99. *HM Prison, Ranby, Retford DN22 8EU* Tel (01773) 706721

HIRST, Anthony Melville. b 50. Keele Univ BA73 LRAM69 Ox Univ DipTh77. Cuddesdon Coll 74. **d** 77 **p** 78. C S Gillingham *Roch* 77-80; C Coity w Nolton *Llan* 80-83; OSB from 81; R Hallaton w Horninghold, Allexton, Tugby etc *Leic* 83-90; R Arthog w Fairbourne w Llangelynnin w Rhoslefain *Ban* 90-97; R Montgomery and Forden and Llandyssil *St As* from 97. *The Rectory, Lions Bank, Montgomery SY15 6PT* Tel (01686) 668243 Fax as telephone E-mail ahirst@avnet.co.uk

HIRST, Arnold. *See* HIRST, Reginald Arnold Archer

HIRST, David William. b 37. Man Univ BA78. Brasted Th Coll 59 St Aid Birkenhead 61. **d** 63 **p** 64. C Clayton *Man* 63-64; C Bury St Jo 64-66; C Wythenshawe Wm Temple Ch 67-70; V Oldham St Chad Limeside 70-79; V Friezland 79-91; R Ashton St Mich 91-95; Chapl HM Pris Buckley Hall 95-00; Chapl HM Pris Wolds 00-02; rtd 02. *8 Priory Mews, Lytham St Annes FY8 4FT* Tel 07833-353837 (mobile)

HIRST, Canon Godfrey Ian. b 41. MBIM Univ of Wales (Lamp) BA63. Chich Th Coll 63. **d** 65 **p** 66. C Brierfield *Blackb* 65-68; Ind Chapl *Liv* 68-71; TV Kirkby 71-75; Ind Chapl *Blackb* 75-94; P-in-c Treales 75-87; Hon Can Blackb Cathl from 83; Can Res Blackb Cathl 87-94; V Lytham St Cuth from 94; AD Kirkham from 98. *The Vicarage, Church Road, Lytham St Annes FY8 5PX* Tel and fax (01253) 736168 Mobile 07885-118331 E-mail ghirst1@compuserve.com

HIRST, John Adrian. b 49. St Jo Coll Nottm BTh78. **d** 78 **p** 79. C Cheltenham St Mark *Glouc* 78-84; TV 84-85; TV Swan *Ox* 85-89; R Denham from 89. *The Rectory, Ashmead Lane, Denham, Uxbridge UB9 5BB* Tel (01895) 832771

HIRST, Mrs Judith. b 54. St Mary's Coll Dur BA76 LMH Ox PGCE77 Hull Univ MA86. Cranmer Hall Dur BA94. **d** 94 **p** 95. Bp's Adv in Past Care and Counselling *Dur* 94-00; C Dur St Oswald 94-00; Dir Min Formation Cranmer Hall Dur from 00. *St John's College, 3 South Bailey, Durham DH1 3RJ* Tel 0191-374 3500 Fax 374 3573

HIRST, Malcolm. b 62. Ilkley Coll BA84. Moorlands Bible Coll 86 Trin Coll Bris BA00. **d** 00 **p** 01. C Bromley Common St Aug *Roch* 00-03; C Farnborough from 03. *Church House, Leamington Avenue, Orpington BR6 9QB* Tel (01689) 856931 E-mail malcolm@port-vale.freeserve.co.uk

HIRST, Mrs Rachel Ann. b 58. Portsm Poly BA79 Hull Univ PGCE81. NEOC 99. **d** 02. NSM Clifton *York* from 02. *13 Florence Grove, Rawcliffe, York YO30 5UR* Tel (01904) 340649

HIRST, Reginald Arnold Archer. b 36. St Paul's Coll Grahamstown. **d** 60 **p** 61. S Africa 60-88; R Wickham *Portsm* from 88. *The Rectory, Southwick Road, Wickham, Fareham PO17 6HR* Tel (01329) 832134 Fax 835434 E-mail arnold@wykhirst.demon.co.uk

HIRST, Wilfrid. b 11. Roch Th Coll 65. **d** 66 **p** 67. C Woodmansterne *S'wark* 66-69; C Shere *Guildf* 69-71; R Lifton *Ex* 71-74; R Kelly w Bradstone 71-74; R Exbourne w Jacobstowe 74-77; rtd 77; Perm to Offic *Chich* from 77. *Royal Bay Residential Home, 86 Aldwick Road, Bognor Regis PO21 2PE* Tel (01243) 267717

HISCOCK, Donald Henry. b 26. St Mich Th Coll Crafers 50 ACT ThL56. **d** 53 **p** 54. Australia 53 and from 65; SSM 54-82; C Averham w Kelham *S'well* 56-58; Lic to Offic 58-59; S Africa 59-60; Basutoland 60-61; rtd 92. *12 Charsley Street, Willagee, W Australia 6156* Tel (0061) (8) 9314 5192 *or* 9364 8472

HISCOCK, Gary Edward. b 43. Dip Drama68 Lon Univ DipRS88. Oak Hill Th Coll BA90. **d** 90 **p** 91. C Cheltenham St Luke and St Jo *Glouc* 90-94; C Hardwicke, Quedgeley and Elmore w Longney 95-96; rtd 96. *25 Bournside Road, Cheltenham GL51 3AL* Tel (01242) 513002

HISCOCK, Peter George Harold. b 31. Wadh Coll Ox BA54 MA66. Ely Th Coll 54. **d** 58 **p** 59. C Edgehill St Dunstan *Liv* 58-61; C Kirkby 61-64; C Southport St Luke 64-66; Asst Dean of Residence TCD 66-68; Dean of Res TCD 68-73; India 73-76; TV Jarrow *Dur* 77-82; Chapl Univ Coll Dur 82-87; RD Newc Cen *Newc* 87-94; P-in-c Dinnington 87-88; TV Ch the King 88-94; rtd 94; Perm to Offic *Lon* from 95. *8 Banbury Road, London E9 7DU* Tel (020) 8986 2252

HISCOCK, Phillip George. b 47. Southn Univ MPhil90 CertEd68 DipAdEd84 MIPD83. STETS 95. **d** 98 **p** 99. NSM Portchester and Chapl Portsm Docks *Portsm* 98-02; Chapl Dunkirk Miss to Seafarers *Eur* from 02. *Princess Alice House, 130 rue de l'Ecole Maternelle, 59140 Dunkerque, France* Tel (0033) (3) 28 59 04 36 Fax 28 66 09 05 E-mail phil.hiscock@mtsmail.org

HISCOCKS, Nicholas Robin Thomas. b 75. Keble Coll Ox BA96 MA01 Anglia Poly Univ MA01. Ridley Hall Cam 99. **d** 01 **p** 02. C Bromley Ch Ch *Roch* from 01. *56 Heathfield Road, Bromley BR1 3RW* Tel (020) 8466 9452 E-mail nrth@tinyworld.co.uk

HISCOX, Miss Denise. b 47. Lon Univ TCert68 Lanchester Poly BSc78. WMMTC 98. **d** 01 **p** 02. NSM Cov St Mary *Cov* from 01. *48 Wainbody Avenue North, Coventry CV3 6DB* Tel (024) 7641 1034 E-mail denisehiscox@lineone.net

HISCOX, Jonathan Ronald James. b 64. Univ of Wales (Cardiff) DipTh85. Qu Coll Birm 87. **d** 89 **p** 90. C Wiveliscombe *B & W* 89-93; P-in-c Donyatt w Horton, Broadway and Ashill 93-94; TV Ilminster and Distr 94-02; R Rowde and Bromham *Sarum* from 02. *The Rectory, Bromham, Chippenham SN15 2HA* Tel (01380) 850322

HISLOP, Martin Gregory. b 55. Jas Cook Univ Townsville BA78 Univ of S Aus MEd88. **d** 92 **p** 93. Australia 92-00; C N Mackay St Ambrose 92-93; Dir Studies St Barn Coll of Min 93-94; Chapl Ballarat Univ 95-98; Asst Chapl St Mich Gr Sch and Assoc P E St Kilda 98; C Kingston St Luke *S'wark* 00-01; P-in-c from 01. *St Luke's Vicarage, 4 Burton Road, Kingston upon Thames KT2 5TE* Tel (020) 8546 4064 Fax 8974 8079 E-mail mhislop@btinternet.com

HITCH, Kim William. b 54. Leic Univ BSc75 K Coll Lon MA94. Trin Coll Bris 76. **d** 78 **p** 79. C Becontree St Mary *Chelmsf* 78-80; C Huyton Quarry *Liv* 80-83; V Hatcham St Jas *S'wark* 83-91; TR Kidbrooke 91-02; R Kidbrooke St Jas from 02. *St James's Rectory, 62 Kidbrooke Park Road, London SE3 0DU* Tel (020) 8856 3438 Fax 08701-364983 E-mail hitchoffice@worldonline.co.uk

HITCHCOCK, David. b 37. MCIEH. S'wark Ord Course 70. **d** 73 **p** 74. NSM Milton next Gravesend Ch Ch *Roch* 73-94; NSM Chalk 96-98; CF (ACF) from 79; Perm to Offic *Lon* 93-02; NSM St Andr-by-the-Wardrobe w St Ann, Blackfriars from 02; NSM St Jas Garlickhythe w St Mich Queenhithe etc from 02; Asst ChStJ from 94. *148 Old Road East, Gravesend DA12 1PF* Tel (01474) 361091 E-mail hitch5@btinternet.com

HITCHING, His Honour Judge Alan Norman. b 41. Ch Ch Ox BA62 MA66 BCL63 Barrister-at-Law (Middle Temple) 64. **d** 01 **p** 02. NSM High Ongar w Norton Mandeville *Chelmsf* from 01. *9 Monkhams Drive, Woodford Green IG8 0LG* Tel (020) 8504 4260 E-mail ahitching@lix.compulink.co.uk

HITCHINS, Graham Edward David. b 54. S Dios Minl Tr Scheme 91. **d** 94 **p** 95. C Bishop's Waltham *Portsm* 94-97; C Upham 94-97; C Honiton, Gittisham, Combe Raleigh, Monkton etc *Ex* 97-98; TV 98-03; Chapl RN from 03. *Royal Navy Chaplaincy Service, Room 203, Victory Building, HM Naval Base, Portsmouth PO1 3LS* Tel (023) 9272 7903 Fax 9272 7111

HITCHINSON, Preb William Henry. b 12. Chich Th Coll 51. **d** 53 **p** 54. C Twickenham St Mary *Lon* 53-56; V Eastcote St Lawr 56-80; Preb St Paul's Cathl 76-80; rtd 80. *66 Waller Drive, Northwood HA6 1BW* Tel (01923) 829778

HITCHMAN, Keith John. b 62. Middx Univ BSc90. Trin Coll Bris BA95. **d** 95 **p** 96. C Bestwood *S'well* 95-99; Chapl Glos Univ from 99. *30 Sedgewick Gardens, Up Hatherley, Cheltenham GL51 5QD* Tel (01242) 575246 *or* 543400 E-mail mdhfineart@netscapeonline.co.uk

HITCHMOUGH, William. b 30. N Ord Course. **d** 81 **p** 82. NSM Penketh *Liv* 81-83; Perm to Offic from 83; Chapl Warrington Distr Gen Hosp 83-99; Perm to Offic *Guildf* from 00. *4 Rex Court, Haslemere GU27 1LJ* Tel (01428) 661504

HIZA, Douglas William. b 38. Richmond Univ Virginia BA60 MDiv63 Mankato State Univ MS70. Virginia Th Sem 60. **d** 63 **p** 64. USA 63-79; Chapl Hackney Hosp Gp Lon 80-95; Chapl Homerton Hosp Lon 80-95; Perm to Offic *Lon* from 96. *10 Meynal Crescent, London E9 7AS* Tel (020) 8985 7832

HJORTH, Rolf Gunnar Leer. b 25. St Jo Coll Ox BA46 MA50 AMICE. Wycliffe Hall Ox 61. **d** 62 **p** 63. C Cumnor *Ox* 62-65; V Bramfield and Walpole *St E* 65-69; V Oulton *Lich* 69-78; Chapl Ostend w Knokke and Bruges *Eur* 78-84; Chapl Düsseldorf 85-90; rtd 90; Perm to Offic *Lich* 90-03. *Carrer Dalma i Bernat, Begur, 17255 Girona, Spain*

HOAD, Anne Elizabeth. b 42. Bris Univ BA63. dss 69 **d** 94 **p** 95. Asst Chapl Imp Coll *Lon* 69-74; S'wark Lay Tr Scheme 74-77; Brixton St Matt *S'wark* 77-80; Charlton St Luke w H Trin 80-94; Project Worker Community of Women and Men 88-91; Voc Adv Lewisham from 91; Asst Chapl Lewisham Hosp from 92; Hon C Lee Gd Shep w St Pet from 94. *14 Silk Close, Dorville Road, London SE12 8DL* Tel (020) 8297 8761

HOAD, Miss Rosemary Claire. b 60. Cranmer Hall Dur 92. **d** 94 **p** 95. C Epsom St Martin *Guildf* 94-97; TV Brentford *Lon* from 97. *St Faith's Vicarage, 122 Windmill Road, Brentford TW8 9NA* Tel (020) 8560 3782 E-mail rosemary.hoad@btinternet.com

HOAR, George Stanley. b 20. Chich Th Coll 47. **d** 50 **p** 53. C Cullercoats St Geo *Newc* 50-52; C Old Brumby *Linc* 53-56; V Alvingham w N and S Cockerington 56-60; V Leake 60-71; V Castle Bytham 71-91; R Careby w Holywell and Aunby 73-91; R Lt Bytham 73-91; rtd 91; Perm to Offic *Pet* from 91. *1 Sulthorpe Road, Ketton, Stamford PE9 3SN* Tel (01780) 720817

HOARE, Carol. b 46. Lon Univ BA68 Birm Univ CertEd69. Qu Coll Birm 86 WMMTC 86. **d** 91 **p** 94. NSM Curdworth *Birm* 91-00; Perm to Offic from 00. *14 Elms Road, Sutton Coldfield B72 1JF* Tel 0121-354 1117

HOARE, David Albert Sylvester. b 47. d 95. C Gibraltar Cathl *Eur* 95-00. *3 Governor's Lane, Gibraltar*

HOARE, Canon David Marlyn. b 33. Bps' Coll Cheshunt 60. d 63 **p** 64. C Ampthill w Millbrook and Steppingley *St Alb* 63-67; C Bushey 67-70; V Harlington 70-76; V Oxhey All SS 76-81; V Hellesdon *Nor* 81-98; Hon Can Nor Cathl 95-98; rtd 98; Perm to Offic *Nor* from 98. *42 Starling Close, Aylsham, Norwich NR11 6XG* Tel (01263) 734565

HOARE, (née CULLING), Elizabeth Ann. b 58. St Mary's Coll Dur BA76 St Jo Coll Dur PhD87 Rob Coll Cam BA88 PGCE80. Ridley Hall Cam 86. d 89 **p** 94. Par Dn S Cave and Ellerker w Broomfleet *York* 89-92; Tutor Cranmer Hall Dur 93-95; P-in-c Cherry Burton *York* 95-00; Abp's Sen Adv on Rural Affairs 95-98; Abp's Adv for Spiritual Direction 98-00; Chapl Bp Burton Coll York 95-00; Perm to Offic *York* 01-02; NSM Cowesby from 02; NSM Felixkirk w Boltby from 02; NSM Kirby Knowle from 02; NSM Leake w Over and Nether Silton and Kepwick from 02. *Leake Vicarage, Knayton, Thirsk YO7 4AZ* Tel (01845) 537277
E-mail liz.wildgoose@bigfoot.com

HOARE, Janet Francis Mary. *See* MILES, Ms Janet Francis Mary

HOARE, Patrick Reginald Andrew Reid (Toddy). b 47. TD80 and Bar 88. Hull Univ MA90. Wycliffe Hall Ox 77. d 80 **p** 81. C Guisborough *York* 80-83; CF (TA) from 82; P-in-c Felixkirk w Boltby *York* from 83; P-in-c Kirby Knowle from 83; P-in-c Leake w Over and Nether Silton and Kepwick from 83; P-in-c Cowesby from 83. *Leake Vicarage, Knayton, Thirsk YO7 4AZ* Tel (01845) 537277

HOARE, Patrick Vernon Keymer. b 35. Oak Hill NSM Course 90. d 93 **p** 94. NSM Staines St Mary and St Pet *Lon* 93-96; P-in-c Littleton 95-99; rtd 00. *2 Saxonby Avenue, Sunbury-on-Thames TW16 5HP* Tel (01932) 700379

HOARE, Roger John. b 38. Tyndale Hall Bris 63. d 66 **p** 67. C Stoughton *Guildf* 66-70; C Chesham St Mary *Ox* 70-73; V Bath St Bart *B & W* 73-83; V Gt Faringdon w Lt Coxwell *Ox* 83-89; Deputation Appeals Org (NE Lon) Children's Soc 89-93; P-in-c Lambourne w Abridge and Stapleford Abbotts *Chelmsf* from 93; Ind Chapl from 93; rtd 03. *44 Anchor Road, Tiptree, Colchester CO5 0AP* Tel (01621) 817236 E-mail rogerhoare@aol.com

✠**HOARE, The Rt Revd Rupert William Noel.** b 40. Trin Coll Ox BA61 MA66 Fitzw Ho Cam BA64 MA84 Birm Univ PhD73. Kirchliche Hochschule Berlin 61 Westcott Ho Cam 62. d 64 **p** 65 c 93. C Oldham St Mary w St Pet *Man* 64-67; Lect Qu Coll Birm 68-72; Can Th Cov Cathl *Cov* 70-76; R Man Resurr *Man* 72-78; Can Res Birm Cathl *Birm* 78-81; Prin Westcott Ho Cam 81-93; Area Bp Dudley *Worc* 93-00; Hon Can Worc Cathl 93-00; Dean Liv from 00. *1 Cathedral Close, Liverpool L1 7BR* Tel 0151-708 9024 *or* 709 6271 Fax 702 7292

HOARE, Canon Simon Gerard. b 37. AKC61. d 62 **p** 63. C Headingley *Ripon* 62-65; C Adel 65-68; R Spofforth 68-71; R Spofforth w Kirk Deighton 71-77; V Rawdon *Bradf* 77-85; Hon Can Bradf Cathl 85-02; R Carleton and Lothersdale 85-02; Dioc Ecum Officer 85-94; rtd 02. *Skell Villa, 20 Wellington Street, Ripon HG4 1PH* Tel (01765) 692187 Fax as telephone
E-mail sghoare@freenetname.co.uk

HOBBS, Antony Ewan Talbot. b 25. Ripon Hall Ox 58. d 60 **p** 61. C Cuckfield *Chich* 62-64; V Staplefield Common 64-89; rtd 89; Perm to Offic *Chich* from 89. *Chippers, Chalvington, Hailsham BN27 3TE* Tel (01321) 811243

HOBBS, Basil Ernest William. b 22. St Chad's Coll Dur BA49 DipTh50. d 51 **p** 52. C Mitcham St Mark *S'wark* 51-54; CF 54-68; Hon C Cuddalore H Trin w St Paul Cam 70-72; Asst Chapl St Mary's Hosp Praed Street Lon 69-72; Novice CR 72-74; Past Consultant Clinical Th Assn 74-84; Lic to Offic *S'well* 74-83; Chapl HM Pris Nottm 81-84; Hon C Nottingham St Andr *S'well* 83-84; C 84-86; TV Clifton 86-87; rtd 87; Perm to Offic *S'well* 87-00; *Leic* from 99. *17 Stuart Court, High Street, Kibworth, Leicester LE8 0LR* Tel 0116-279 6367
E-mail bew.hobbs@zoom.co.uk

HOBBS, Christopher Bedo. b 61. Jes Coll Cam BA83 BTh90. Ridley Hall Cam 88. d 91 **p** 92. C Langham Place All So *Lon* 91-95; C Hull Newland St Jo *York* 95-00; V Selly Park St Steph and St Wulstan *Birm* from 00. *18 Sellywick Road, Birmingham B29 7JA* Tel 0121-472 0050 *or* 472 8253
E-mail ststephens@talk21.com

HOBBS, Christopher John Pearson. b 60. Sydney Univ BA82 K Coll Lon BD89 AKC89. Wycliffe Hall Ox 89. d 91 **p** 92. C S Mimms Ch Ch *Lon* 91-94; C Jesmond Clayton Memorial *Newc* 94-97; V Oakwood St Thos *Lon* from 97. *St Thomas's Vicarage, 2 Sheringham Avenue, London N14 4UE* Tel (020) 8360 1749 *or* tel and fax 8245 9152 E-mail stthomas.oakwood@talk21.com

HOBBS, Edward Quincey. b 74. Bris Univ BSc95. Wycliffe Hall Ox BA99. d 00 **p** 01. C Stapenhill w Cauldwell *Derby* from 00. *11 Clematis Crescent, Stapenhill, Burton-on-Trent DE15 9FF* Tel (01283) 543200

HOBBS, James. b 42. K Alfred's Coll Win CertEd64 Relig Teaching Cert 64 Open Univ BA89 Hull Univ MA94 Lincs & Humberside Univ Dip Counselling 97. Linc Th Coll 66. d 68

p 69. C Moseley St Mary *Birm* 68-73; V Kingstanding St Mark 73-77; R Rushbrooke *St E* 77-78; R Bradfield St Geo 77-80; P-in-c Bradfield St Clare 77-80; P-in-c Felsham w Gedding 77-80; R Bradfield St George w Bradfield St Clare etc 80-84; P-in-c Gt and Lt Whelnetham 84-85; R Gt and Lt Whelnetham w Bradfield St George 85-90; Ecum Chapl for F&HE Grimsby *Linc* 90-97; Chapl Humberside Univ (Grimsby Campus) 90-97; Gen Preacher 92-97; V Ingham w Cammeringham w Fillingham 97-01; R Aisthorpe w Scampton w Thorpe le Fallows etc 97-01; P-in-c Burton by Linc 97-01; rtd 01; Perm to Offic *Linc* from 01. *18 The Belfry, Grantham NG31 9QL* Tel (01476) 566470 Fax as telephone E-mail jimhobbs@tiscali.co.uk

HOBBS, Mrs Joan Rosemary. b 39. Chelsea Coll Lon TDip61. WEMTC 97. d 00 **p** 01. NSM Cheltenham St Mary, St Matt, St Paul and H Trin *Glouc* 00-02; Perm to Offic from 02. *Manor Farmhouse, Woodmancote, Cirencester GL7 7EF* Tel (01285) 831244 Fax as telephone E-mail joan@hobbsjr.fsnet.co.uk

HOBBS, John Antony. b 36. S Dios Minl Tr Scheme. d 87 **p** 88. NSM Crowborough *Chich* from 87. *May Cottage, Alice Bright Lane, Crowborough TN6 3SQ* Tel (01892) 653909

HOBBS, Jonathan Noel Alan. b 70. Oak Hill Th Coll BA03. d 03. C Lindfield *Chich* from 03. *32 Noah's Ark Lane, Haywards Heath RH16 2LT* Tel (01444) 482989
E-mail jon@hobbs99.freeserve.co.uk

HOBBS, Kenneth Brian. b 47. Sussex Univ BA68 Lon Inst of Educn PGCE70. NTMTC 98. d 98 **p** 99. NSM Howell Hill *Guildf* 98-01; NSM Shere, Albury and Chilworth from 01. *Yeoman's Acre, Farley Green, Albury, Guildford GU5 9DN* Tel (01483) 202165 E-mail hobbs@glebe0.demon.co.uk

HOBBS, Kenneth Ian. b 50. Oak Hill Th Coll 74. d 77 **p** 78. C Southborough St Pet w Ch Ch and St Matt *Roch* 77-80; C Hoole *Ches* 80-84; V Barnston 84-95; P-in-c Bedworth *Cov* 95; TR 95-01; RD Nuneaton 00-01; TR Radipole and Melcombe Regis *Sarum* from 01. *39 Icen Road, Weymouth DT3 5JL* Tel (01305) 785553 E-mail kih@fish.co.uk

HOBBS, Leslie. b 42. Sussex Univ BA64 Lon Bible Coll BD67. EAMTC. d 02 **p** 03. NSM Somerleyton, Ashby, Fritton, Herringfleet etc *Nor* from 02. *Nether End Cottage, Blacksmiths Loke, Lound, Lowestoft NR32 5LS* Tel (01502) 732536 Mobile 07833-753704

HOBBS, Ms Maureen Patricia. b 54. Surrey Univ BSc76 Warwick Univ 92. Westcott Ho Cam 95. d 97 **p** 98. C Shrewsbury St Chad w St Mary *Lich* 97-01; R Baschurch and Weston Lullingfield w Hordley from 01. *The Rectory, Baschurch, Shrewsbury SY4 2EB* Tel (01939) 260305
E-mail maureenhobbs@hotmail.com

HOBBS, Michael Bede. b 30. Fitzw Ho Cam BA58 MA62. Clifton Th Coll 58. d 60 **p** 61. C Southsea St Jude *Portsm* 60-63; Paraguay 63-65; Argentina 65-67; V Potters Green *Cov* 68-75; Distr Sec BFBS 75-82; R Plaxtol *Roch* 82-96; Dioc Miss Audits Consultant 90-96; rtd 96; Perm to Offic *Sarum* from 96. *Falcons, Barkers Hill, Semley, Shaftesbury SP7 9BH*

HOBBS, Canon Philip Bertram. b 20. MBE81. Wells Th Coll 46. d 48 **p** 49. C Glouc Ch Ch *Glouc* 48-51; R Boxwell w Leighterton 51-60; P-in-c Ozleworth 58-60; P-in-c Newington Bagpath w Kingscote 58-60; V Glouc St Jas 60-74; Chapl HM Pris Glouc 61-82; V Sevenhampton w Charlton Abbots and Hawling *Glouc* 74-75; P-in-c Whittington 74-75; V Sevenhampton w Charlton Abbotts and Hawling etc 75-95; Hon Can Glouc Cathl 77-95; rtd 95; Perm to Offic *Glouc* from 95. *5 Woodlands View, Hobbs Lane, Woodmancote, Cirencester GL7 7EQ* Tel (01285) 831846

HOBBS, Simon John. b 59. Ox Univ MA82. St Steph Ho Ox 80. d 83 **p** 84. C Middlesbrough Ascension *York* 83-85; C Stainton-in-Cleveland 85-88; C St Marylebone All SS *Lon* 88-90; P-in-c Paddington St Pet 90-94; C-in-c Grosvenor Chpl from 94; C Hanover Square St Geo w St Mark from 94. *24 South Audley Street, London W1K 2PA* Tel (020) 7493 2444 Mobile 07980-945822 E-mail grosvenor@chapel60.freeserve.co.uk

HOBDAY, Peter Hugh Francis. b 34. IEng90. Oak Hill NSM Course 99. d 00 **p** 01. NSM Perivale *Lon* from 00. *41 Bilton Road, Greenford UB6 7BA* Tel (020) 8997 1250 Mobile 07778-007370 E-mail petehobday@aol.com

HOBDEN, Brian Charles. b 38. Oak Hill Th Coll 63. d 66 **p** 67. C S Lambeth St Steph *S'wark* 66-70; C Cheadle *Ches* 70-76; USA from 76. *3160 Executive Hills Road, Las Cruces, NM 88011, USA* Tel (001) (505) 521 9435 Fax 526 4821
E-mail hobo2209@roadrunner.com

HOBDEN, Christopher Martin. b 49. Lon Univ BSc71. Oak Hill Th Coll 80. d 87 **p** 88. NSM St Marylebone All So w SS Pet and Jo *Lon* 87-88; NSM Langham Place All So 88-95. *Soldier's Field, Nepcote Lane, Findon, Worthing BN14 0SH* Tel (01903) 872222

HOBDEN, David Nicholas. b 54. K Coll Lon BD76 AKC76 Cam Univ PGCE. Ripon Coll Cuddesdon 77. d 78 **p** 79. C Marlborough *Sarum* 78-80; C Salisbury St Thos and St Edm 81-85; V Shalford *Guildf* 85-99; Asst Chapl R Surrey Co Hosp NHS Trust 99-00; Sen Chapl from 00. *Department of Pastoral Care, Royal Surrey County Hospital, Egerton Road, Guildford GU2 5XX* Tel (01483) 406835 *or* 571122
E-mail cmhobden@aol.com *or* dhobden@royalsurrey.nhs.uk

HOBDEN, Geoffrey William. b 46. DipTh. Trin Coll Bris 80. **d** 82 **p** 83. C Ex St Leon w H Trin *Ex* 82-86; V Weston-super-Mare Ch Ch *B & W* from 86; RD Locking 93-99. *Christ Church Vicarage, 18 Montpelier, Weston-super-Mare BS23 2RH* Tel (01934) 624376 Fax 641016 E-mail geoff@ccwsm.org.uk

HOBLEY, Ms Susan Elizabeth. b 51. Newc Univ BA74 Dur Univ PGCE75. NEOC 98. **d** 01 **p** 02. NSM Millfield St Mark and Pallion St Luke *Dur* from 01. *29 Wroxton, Biddick, Washington NE38 7NU* Tel 0191-419 4279 E-mail sue@makarios.demon.co.uk

HOBROUGH, Mrs Margaret Edith. b 40. OBE97. Man Univ BA63 Newc Univ MEd75 K Coll Lon MTh80 FRSA94. STETS 01. **d** 03. NSM Godalming *Guildf* from 03. *257 Stoughton Road, Guildford GU2 9PQ* Tel (01483) 538390 Fax 568390 E-mail margarethobrough@v21.me.uk

HOBSON, Anthony Peter. b 53. St Jo Coll Cam BA74. St Jo Coll Nottm 75. **d** 77 **p** 78. C Brunswick *Man* 77-82; R Stretford St Bride 82-92; TR Hackney Marsh *Lon* 92-00; V Leic Martyrs *Leic* from 00. *The Vicarage, 17 Westcotes Drive, Leicester LE3 0QT* Tel 0116-254 6162 Fax as telephone E-mail martyrs@btconnect.com

HOBSON, Capt Barry Rodney. b 57. Open Univ BA98. Wilson Carlile Coll 82 EAMTC 97. **d** 98 **p** 99. CA from 85; C Warboys w Broughton and Bury w Wistow *Ely* 98-01; P-in-c Roxwell *Chelmsf* from 01. *The Vicarage, Vicarage Road, Roxwell, Chelmsford CM1 4NB* Tel (01245) 248644 E-mail b.hobson@btinternet.com

HOBSON, Herbert Leslie. b 09. St Aid Birkenhead 37. **d** 39 **p** 40. C Newark Ch Ch *S'well* 39-42; C Bulwell St Mary 42-47; V Awsworth w Cossall 47-59; V Mansfield St Jo 59-68; Chapl Mansfield Gen Hosp 59-68; V Heath *Derby* 68-75; rtd 75; Perm to Offic *S'well* and *Derby* 75-00. *40 High Tor, Skegby, Sutton-in-Ashfield NG17 3EX* Tel (01623) 557083

HOBSON, Jeremy Graeme. b 71. Lon Univ BMedSci95 MB, BS96. Oak Hill Th Coll BA03. **d** 03. C Eastbourne H Trin *Chich* from 03. *20 Chamberlain Road, Eastbourne BN21 1RU* E-mail thehobsons@onetel.net.uk

HOBSON, John Alexander. b 70. LMH Ox BA91 MA02 York Univ MA94. Wycliffe Hall Ox BA01. **d** 02 **p** 03. C Aynho and Croughton w Evenley etc *Pet* from 02. *The Rectory, Queen's Street, Farthinghoe, Brackley NN13 5NY* Tel (01295) 712437 E-mail hobson@oxfree.com

HOBSON, Canon Patrick John Bogan. b 33. MC53. Magd Coll Cam BA56 MA60. S'wark Ord Course 75 Qu Coll Birm 77. **d** 79 **p** 80. C St Jo in Bedwardine *Worc* 79-81; R Clifton-on-Teme, Lower Sapey and the Shelsleys 81-88; TR Waltham H Cross *Chelmsf* 88-98; Hon Can Chelmsf Cathl 95-98; rtd 98. *24 Cunliffe Close, Oxford OX2 7BL* Tel (01865) 556206 Fax as telephone E-mail patrick.hobson@talk21.com

HOCKEN, Glen Rundle. b 59. ACA84 Kent Univ BA80 Southlands Coll Lon PGCE90. Wycliffe Hall Ox 90. **d** 92 **p** 93. C Cogges *Ox* 92-94; C Cogges and S Leigh 94-96; C Boldmere *Birm* 96-99; TV Southgate *Chich* from 99. *Holy Trinity House, Titmus Drive, Crawley RH10 5EU* Tel (01293) 525809

HOCKEY (née LOOMES), Gaenor Mary. b 65. Hull Univ BA92 RGN86. St Jo Coll Nottm MPhil93. **d** 96 **p** 97. C Charles w Plymouth St Matthias *Ex* 96-00; C Devonport St Aubyn from 00. *St Aubyn's Vicarage, Chapel Street, Devonport, Plymouth PL1 4DP* Tel (01752) 565203

HOCKEY, Paul Henry. b 49. Oak Hill Th Coll BA86. **d** 86 **p** 87. C Dalton-in-Furness *Carl* 86-89; R Clifton, Brougham and Cliburn 89-94; V Fremington *Ex* from 94; Chapl Children's Hospice SW from 97. *The Vicarage, Fremington, Barnstaple EX31 2NX* Tel (01271) 373879

HOCKING, Canon Hugh Michael Warwick. b 12. VRD54. Ch Coll Cam BA34 MA38. Westcott Ho Cam 34. **d** 36 **p** 37. C Hackney St Jo *Lon* 36-37; C Stoke Damerel *Ex* 37-39; Chapl RNVR 39-46; V Madron w Morvah *Truro* 46-54; Chapl Poltair Hosp 50-54; V Bris St Ambrose Whitehall *Bris* 54-62; R Guildf H Trin w St Mary *Guildf* 62-77; Chapl St Luke's Hosp Guildf 63-77; Hon Can Guildf Cathl *Guildf* 68-77; rtd 77; Chapl W Cornwall Hosp Penzance 78-97; Perm to Offic *Ex* from 97. *23 Gracey Court, Woodland Road, Broadclyst, Exeter EX5 3GA* Tel (01392) 465170

HOCKING, Paul Frederick. b 43. Chich Th Coll 84. **d** 86 **p** 87. C Whitton and Thurleston w Akenham *St E* 86-89; V Ipswich All Hallows 89-91; P-in-c Gt Cornard 91-98; V 98; P-in-c Woolpit w Drinkstone from 98. *The Rectory, Woolpit, Bury St Edmunds IP30 9QP* Tel (01359) 242244 E-mail mhock33733@aol.com

HOCKLEY, Paul William. b 47. Chu Coll Cam BA68 MA72 Nottm Univ BA73. St Jo Coll Nottm 71. **d** 74 **p** 75. C Chatham St Phil and St Jas *Roch* 74-78; C Tunbridge Wells St Jo 78-81; V Penketh *Liv* from 81. *St Paul's Vicarage, 6 Poplar Avenue, Penketh, Warrington WA5 2EH* Tel (01925) 723492 Fax 486945 E-mail paul.hockley@lineone.net

HOCKLEY, Canon Raymond Alan. b 29. LRAM53 Em Coll Cam MA71. Westcott Ho Cam 56. **d** 58 **p** 59. C Endcliffe *Sheff* 58-61; P-in-c Wicker w Neepsend 61-63; Chapl Westcott Ho Cam 63-68; Chapl Em Coll Cam 68-76; Can Res and Prec York

Minster *York* 76-95; rtd 95; Perm to Offic *York* from 95. *St Clare's Bungalow, Sneaton Castle, Whitby YO21 3QN* Tel (01947) 821856

HOCKNULL, Mark Dennis. b 63. Surrey Univ BSc85 Univ Coll Lon PhD89. Cranmer Hall Dur BA93. **d** 94 **p** 95. C Prenton *Ches* 94-96; C Runcorn All SS 96-99; C Runcorn St Mich 96-99; V Gt Meols from 99. *St John's Vicarage, Birkenhead Road, Meols, Wirral CH47 0LF* Tel 0151-632 1661 E-mail mark.hocknull@btinternet.com

HOCKRIDGE, Joan. b 25. Girton Coll Cam BA47 MA50. St Steph Ho Ox 82. **dss** 83 **d** 87 **p** 94. Ealing Ascension Hanger Hill *Lon* 83-88; Hon C 87-88; Hon C Hanger Hill Ascension and W Twyford St Mary 88-92; Hon C Hillingdon St Jo 92-95; Perm to Offic 95-00. *17 Mead Way, Ruislip HA4 7QW* Tel (01895) 622643

HODDER, Christopher John. b 75. Huddersfield Univ BA96 Nottm Univ BTh00. St Jo Coll Nottm 98. **d** 01 **p** 02. C Loughborough Em and St Mary in Charnwood *Leic* from 01. *47 Brookfield Avenue, Loughborough LE11 3LN* Tel (01509) 237246 E-mail chrisandlou@clhodder.freeserve.co.uk

HODDER, John Kenneth. b 45. Edin Univ MA68. Cuddesdon Coll 71. **d** 73 **p** 74. C Kibworth Beauchamp *Leic* 73-76; C Whittlesey *Ely* 76-80; P-in-c Coveney 80-81; R 81-87; R Downham 80-87; R Nunney and Witham Friary, Marston Bigot etc *B & W* from 87. *The Rectory, High Street, Nunney, Frome BA11 4LZ* Tel (01373) 836732

HODDER, Trevor Valentine. b 31. Bps' Coll Cheshunt 65. **d** 67 **p** 68. C Oxhey All SS *St Alb* 67-70; C Digswell 70-73; V Colchester St Anne *Chelmsf* 74-96; rtd 96; Perm to Offic *Chelmsf* from 00. *30 Drury Road, Colchester CO2 7UX* Tel (01206) 766480

HODGE, Albert. b 40. N Ord Course 84. **d** 87 **p** 88. C Huyton St Geo *Liv* 87-89; P-in-c Widnes St Paul 89-97; Chapl Halton Coll of FE 89-97; C Linton in Craven *Bradf* from 97; C Burnsall w Rylstone from 97. *The Rectory, Burnsall, Skipton BD23 6BP* Tel (01756) 720331

HODGE, Anthony Charles. b 43. AKC66. **d** 67 **p** 68. C Carrington *S'well* 67-69; C Bawtry w Austerfield 69-72; C Misson 69-72; Grenada 72-74; Trinidad and Tobago 74-76; V Tuckingmill *Truro* 76-78; V Worksop St Paul *S'well* 78-81; P-in-c Patrington w Hollym, Welwick and Winestead *York* 81-86; R 86-88; V York St Olave w St Giles from 88; V York St Helen Stonegate w St Martin Coney Street from 97; Chapl York Coll for Girls 88-96. *St Olave's Vicarage, 52 Bootham, York YO30 7BZ* Tel (01904) 625186 Mobile 07803-042987 E-mail anthony.hodge@lineone.net

HODGE, Colin. b 39. Sarum & Wells Th Coll. **d** 83 **p** 84. NSM Wareham *Sarum* 84-87; C Parkstone St Pet w Branksea and St Osmund 87-89; V Lilliput 89-00; rtd 00; Perm to Offic *Sarum* from 01. *35 Stowell Crescent, Wareham BH20 4PT* Tel (01929) 553222

HODGE, Graham Anthony. b 49. Linc Th Coll 79. **d** 80 **p** 81. C Hale *Guildf* 80-82; C Christchurch *Win* 82-86; R Chawton and Farringdon 86-96; rtd 96. *6 Reads Field, Four Marks, Alton GU34 5DS* Tel (01420) 561782

HODGE, Canon Michael Robert. b 34. Pemb Coll Cam BA57 MA61. Ridley Hall Cam 57. **d** 59 **p** 60. C Harpurhey Ch Ch *Man* 59; C Blackpool St Mark *Blackb* 59-62; V Stalybridge Old St Geo *Man* 62-67; R Cobham w Luddesdowne and Dode *Roch* 67-81; Hon Can Roch Cathl 81-99; R Bidborough 81-99; rtd 99; Hon C Chale *Portsm* from 99; Hon C Gatcombe from 99; Hon C Shorwell w Kingston from 99; Asst to RD W Wight from 99. *Braxton Cottage, Halletts Shute, Norton, Yarmouth PO41 0RH* Tel and fax (01983) 761121 Mobile 07941-232983 E-mail michael.hodge.1954@pem.cam.ac.uk

HODGE, Nigel John. b 61. BTh83 Open Univ BSc97 Univ of Wales DPS85 MIBiol98. St Mich Coll Llan 83. **d** 85 **p** 86. C Mynyddislwyn *Mon* 85-87; C Machen 87-89; TV Ebbw Vale 89-91; V Abercarn 91-98; Lic to Offic from 99. *6 Maple Terrace, Abercarn, Newport NP11 5JF* Tel (01495) 249014

HODGES, Francis Reginald. b 26. Selw Coll Cam BA48 MA61. Chich Th Coll 48. **d** 50 **p** 51. C Portsea St Alb *Portsm* 50-56; Prior Ho of the Resurr Mirfield 56-58; C Heref All SS *Heref* 58-61; R St Breoke *Truro* 61-76; rtd 76; C St Kew *Truro* 77-78; P-in-c 78-80. *Tregellist Cottage, St Kew, Bodmin PL30 3HG* Tel (01208) 880083

HODGES, Jasper Tor. b 62. Leeds Univ BSc84 Sheff Univ MEng85 Lon Univ PGCE87. Trin Coll Bris BA94. **d** 94 **p** 95. C Holbeck *Ripon* 94-97; C Ealing St Steph Castle Hill *Lon* from 97. *26 Drayton Gardens, London W13 0LG* Tel (020) 8810 7898 Fax 0870-168 7299 E-mail jasper@live.freeserve.co.uk

HODGES, Keith Michael. b 53. Southn Univ BTh82. Chich Th Coll 77. **d** 80 **p** 81. C Sydenham St Phil *S'wark* 80-84; Perm to Offic 85; C Leatherhead *Guildf* 86-89; V Aldershot St Aug from 89. *St Augustine's Vicarage, Holly Road, Aldershot GU12 4SE* Tel (01252) 320840 E-mail father.keith@ntlworld.com

HODGES, Miss Stefanie Margaret. b 54. Trin Coll Bris DipHE95. **d** 97. C Croydon Ch Ch *S'wark* 97-99; C Sutton St Nic

99-02; TV Mildenhall *St E* from 02. *The Vicarage, 2 Oak Drive, Beck Row, Bury St Edmunds IP28 8UA* Tel (01638) 717331

HODGETTS, Alan Paul. b 54. Birm Poly BSc78 Heythrop Coll Lon MA96. St Steph Ho Ox 79. **d** 82 **p** 83. C Perry Barr *Birm* 82-85; C Broseley w Benthall *Heref* 85-87; V Effingham w Lt Bookham *Guildf* 87-96; R Merrow from 96. *The Rectory, 232 Epsom Road, Guildford GU4 7AA* Tel (01483) 504311
E-mail alan.hodgetts@ntlworld.net

HODGETTS, Colin William John. b 40. St D Coll Lamp BA61 Ripon Hall Ox 61. **d** 63 **p** 64. C Hackney St Jo *Lon* 63-68; Hon C St Martin-in-the-Fields 70-76; C Creeksea w Althorne *Chelmsf* 76-79; Perm to Offic *Ex* 84-03; C Parkham, Alwington, Buckland Brewer etc from 03. *Quincott, Cheristowe, Hartland, Bideford EX39 6DA* Tel (01237) 441426
E-mail colin-julia@hartland.swinternet.co.uk

HODGETTS, Harry Samuel. b 30. Chich Th Coll 63. **d** 65 **p** 66. C Harton Colliery *Dur* 65-68; C Penzance St Mary *Truro* 68-70; V Penwerris 70-79; V Kettering St Mary *Pet* 79-94; rtd 95. *20 Crofton Close, Christchurch BH23 2JN* Tel (01202) 474456

HODGINS, Miss Kylie Anne. b 68. SEITE 98. **d** 02 **p** 03. C Histon *Ely* from 02; C Impington from 02. *60 Impington Lane, Impington, Cambridge CB4 9NJ* Tel (01223) 236887
E-mail kylie.hodgins@dial.pipex.com

HODGINS, Philip Arthur. b 57. Lanc Univ BA78 Nottm Univ DipTh83 Bradf Univ MBA90 MIPD94. Linc Th Coll 82. **d** 85 **p** 86. C Norton *Ches* 85-88; C Whitkirk *Ripon* 88-89; Perm to Offic *Bradf* 89-90; Jo Grooms from 91; P-in-c Chiddingly w E Hoathly *Chich* from 02. *Little Becks, Batts Bridge Road, Maresfield, Uckfield TN22 2HJ* Tel (01825) 762767
E-mail hobson_hodgins@compuserve.com

HODGKINSON, Canon John. b 27. Trin Hall Cam BA51 MA55. Linc Th Coll 51. **d** 53 **p** 54. C Penrith St Andr *Carl* 53-56; C Linc St Nic w St Jo Newport *Linc* 56-58; C-in-c Linc St Jo Bapt CD 58-63; V Linc St Jo 63-66; R Old Brumby 66-71; V Kendal H Trin *Carl* 71-90; Hon Can Carl Cathl 84-90; rtd 90; Perm to Offic *Carl* from 90. *Boxtree Barn, Levens, Kendal LA8 8NZ* Tel (01539) 560806 E-mail boxtreebarn@hotmail.com

HODGKINSON, John David. b 57. Birm Univ BA78 Edin Univ BD89. Edin Th Coll 86. **d** 89 **p** 90. C Briercliffe *Blackb* 89-92; C Darwen St Cuth w Tockholes St Steph 92-94; R Harrington *Carl* 94-00; V Walney Is from 00. *The Vicarage, Promenade, Walney, Barrow-in-Furness LA14 3QU* Tel (01229) 471268

HODGKINSON, Oswald Merchant. b 21. Qu Coll Birm 68. **d** 69 **p** 70. C Shard End *Birm* 69-74; V 74-80; TV Wrexham *St As* 80-86; rtd 86; Perm to Offic *St As* and *Ban* from 86. *Brackenrigg, Bryn Pydew Road, Bryn Pydew, Llandudno Junction LL31 9JH* Tel (01492) 540395

HODGSON, Ms Amanda Jane. b 66. Westmr Coll Ox BA88 St Andr Univ Dip Div 93 Heythrop Coll Lon MA99. Westcott Ho Cam CTM96. **d** 96 **p** 97. C Epping Distr *Chelmsf* 96-01; TV Wythenshawe *Man* from 01. *St Luke's Vicarage, Brownley Road, Wythenshawe, Manchester M22 4PT* Tel 0161-998 2071
E-mail revmand@aol.com

HODGSON, Anthony Owen Langlois. b 35. Ripon Hall Ox 60. **d** 62 **p** 63. C Blakeney w Lt Langham *Nor* 62-65; C Stiffkey w Morston 62-65; C Paddington Ch Ch *Lon* 66-70; Area Sec (Beds & Cambs) Chr Aid 70-74; (Herts & Hunts) 70-73; (Rutland & Northants) 73-74; V Gt w Lt Gidding and Steeple Gidding *Ely* 77-81; Warden Dovedale Ho 81-89; P-in-c Ilam w Blore Ray and Okeover *Lich* 81-89; Dir Chr Rural Cen 89-91; C Checkley 91-97; C Stramshall 91-97; TV Uttoxeter Area 97-00; rtd 00. *65B Ravensdowne, Berwick-upon-Tweed TD15 1DQ* Tel (01289) 302289

HODGSON, Antony Robert. b 66. Westcott Ho Cam 90. **d** 93 **p** 94. C Chorley St Geo *Blackb* 93-96; C Lytham St Cuth 96-99; V St Annes St Marg from 99. *St Margaret's Vicarage, 24 Chatsworth Road, Lytham St Annes FY8 2JN* Tel (01253) 722648

HODGSON, Christopher. b 24. Oriel Coll Ox BA49 MA54. Qu Coll Birm 50. **d** 52 **p** 53. C Cheltenham Ch Ch *Glouc* 52-55; C Liv Our Lady and St Nic *Liv* 55-57; V Anfield St Columba 57-64; V Pembury *Roch* 64-82; Chapl Pembury Hosp Tunbridge Wells 66-82; R Aynho w Newbottle and Charlton *Pet* 82-85; Chapl Burrswood Cen for Divine Healing 85-94; C Castle Bromwich St Clem *Birm* 86-94; rtd 94. *6 The Covers, Seaford BN25 1DF* Tel (01323) 896461

HODGSON, Canon David George. b 54. Coll of Resurr Mirfield. **d** 82 **p** 83. C Stainton-in-Cleveland *York* 82-87; R Loftus 87; P-in-c Carlin How w Skinningrove 87; R Loftus and Carlin How w Skinningrove 87-93; V Middlesbrough Ascension from 93; RD Middlesbrough from 98; Can and Preb York Minster from 01. *The Ascension Vicarage, Penrith Road, Middlesbrough TS3 7JR* Tel (01642) 447067

HODGSON, David Peter. b 56. Fitzw Coll Cam BA77 MA81 Nottm Univ BA82 MTh85. St Jo Coll Nottm 80. **d** 83 **p** 84. C Guiseley w Esholt *Bradf* 83-86; Asst Chapl Loughb Univ *Leic* 86-89; P-in-c Hatfield Broad Oak *Chelmsf* 89-90; P-in-c Bush End 89-90; P-in-c Hatfield Broad Oak and Bush End 90-97; Ind Chapl to Harlow 89-97; R Wokingham All SS *Ox* from 97. *The*

Rectory, 2A Norreys Avenue, Wokingham RG40 1TU Tel 0118-979 2999 E-mail david@allsaints.prestel.co.uk

HODGSON, Derek Cyril. b 29. Hatf Coll Dur BA50 St Chad's Coll Dur DipTh54. **d** 54 **p** 55. C Lindley *Wakef* 54-58; C-in-c Mixenden CD 58-62; V Thurlstone 62-75; V Mytholm Royd 75-97; rtd 97; Perm to Offic *York* from 98. *The Autumn Barn, Bishop Wilton, York YO42 1TF* Tel (01759) 368741

HODGSON, Gary Stuart. b 65. Ridley Hall Cam CTM98. **d** 98 **p** 99. C S Ossett *Wakef* 98-01; V Kirkburton from 01. *The Vicarage, 3B Shelley Lane, Kirkburton, Huddersfield HD8 0SJ* Tel (01484) 602188 E-mail gary@garyhodgson.freeserve.co.uk

HODGSON, George. b 36. Qu Coll Birm 75. **d** 78 **p** 79. NSM Wordsley *Lich* 78-93; NSM Wordsley *Worc* from 93; Perm to Offic 84-93. *1 Newfield Drive, Kingswinford DY6 8HY* Tel (01384) 292543

HODGSON, John. b 35. St Jo Coll Cam MA62 Lon Univ BD61. St Deiniol's Hawarden 80. **d** 81 **p** 82. Hon C Padiham *Blackb* 81-84; C W Burnley 85-87; V 87-95; rtd 95; Perm to Offic *Worc* 95-02; *Glouc* 98-02. *15 Acton Crescent, Felton, Morpeth NE65 9NF* Tel (01670) 787665

HODGSON, The Ven John Derek. b 31. St Jo Coll Dur BA53. Cranmer Hall Dur DipTh59. **d** 59 **p** 60. C Stranton *Dur* 59-62; C Monkwearmouth St Andr 62-64; V Stillington 64-66; V Consett 66-75; TR Gateshead 75-83; RD Gateshead 76-83; Hon Can Dur Cathl 78-83; Can Res Dur Cathl 83-97; Adn Auckland 83-93; Adn Dur 93-97; rtd 97. *45 Woodside, Barnard Castle, Durham DL12 8DZ* Tel (01833) 690557

HODGSON, Kenneth Jonah. b 36. Open Univ BA79 CQSW89. Oak Hill Th Coll. **d** 69 **p** 70. C Rainford *Liv* 69-72; C Fazakerley Em 72-74; TV 74-78; Soc Worker 78-96; CF 79-82; rtd 00; C Wallasey St Hilary *Ches* from 01. *134 Rake Lane, Wallasey, Merseyside CH45 1JW* Tel 0151-639 2980 Fax as telephone

HODGSON, Matthew William. b 13. Lich Th Coll 40. **d** 44 **p** 45. C N Gosforth *Newc* 44-47; C Wallsend St Luke 47-49; C Haltwhistle 49-50; C Winlaton *Dur* 50-51; Chapl Aberlour Orphanage 51-53; R Jarrow Grange *Dur* 54-60; Chapl Palmer Memorial Hosp 54-60; R Nairn *Mor* 60-64; V Byker St Laur *Newc* 64-71; V Woodhorn w Newbiggin 71-77; rtd 77; Lic to Offic *Newc* 77-93. *5 Cumming Street, Nairn IV12 4NQ* Tel (01667) 56719

HODGSON, Roger Vaughan. b 27. Magd Coll Cam BA49 MA54. Cuddesdon Coll 55. **d** 56 **p** 57. C Westmr St Matt *Lon* 56-59; C Pimlico St Pet w Westmr Ch Ch 59-65; R Lt Hadham *St Alb* 65-78; Chapl Oporto *Eur* 78-80; Chapl and Lect St Deiniol's Lib Hawarden 81-82; V Coldwaltham *Chich* 82-92; rtd 92; Asst Chapl Costa Blanca *Eur* 92-94; Perm to Offic *Chich* from 94. *2 Bakers Arms Hill, Arundel BN18 9DA* Tel (01903) 884708

HODGSON, The Ven Thomas Richard Burnham. b 26. FRMetS88. Lon Coll of Div BD52 ALCD52. **d** 52 **p** 53. C Crosthwaite Kendal *Carl* 52-55; C Stanwix 55-59; V Whitehaven St Nic 59-65; R Aikton 65-67; V Raughton Head w Gatesgill 67-73; Bp's Dom Chapl 67-73; Dir of Ords 70-74; Hon Can Carl Cathl 72-91; V Grange-over-Sands 73-79; RD Windermere 76-79; P-in-c Mosser 79; V 79-83; Adn W Cumberland 79-91; rtd 91; Perm to Offic *Carl* from 91. *58 Greenacres, Wetheral, Carlisle CA4 8LD* Tel (01228) 561159

HODGSON, Vernon Charles. b 34. MRPharmS58 Lon Univ BPharm58 Univ of Wales (Cardiff) DPS91. St Mich Coll Llan 90 Llan Dioc Tr Scheme 83. **d** 86 **p** 87. NSM Roath *Llan* 86-91; C Caerphilly 91-92; V Llanbister w Llanbadarn Fynydd w Llananno *S & B* 93-97; V Llanddewi Ystradenni 94-97; V Llanbister w Llanbadarn Fynydd w Llananno etc 97-01; rtd 01. *114 Carisbrooke Way, Cyncoed, Cardiff CF23 9HX* Tel (029) 2045 3403

HODKINSON, George Leslie. b 48. Qu Coll Birm 86. **d** 88 **p** 89. C Hall Green St Pet *Birm* 88-91; TV Solihull 91-96; P-in-c Billesley Common 96-00; V from 00; AD Moseley 01-02. *Holy Cross Vicarage, 29 Beauchamp Road, Birmingham B13 0NS* Tel 0121-444 1737

HODSON, Gordon George. b 35. St Chad's Coll Dur BA59 DipTh60. **d** 60 **p** 61. C Tettenhall Regis *Lich* 60-64; C Rugeley 64-68; V Shrewsbury St Mich 68-74; V Kinnerley w Melverley 74-87; P-in-c Knockin w Maesbrook 75-87; P-in-c Chebsey 87-91; P-in-c Seighford, Derrington and Cresswell 87-91; V Chebsey, Ellenhall and Seighford-with-Creswell 91-00; rtd 00; Perm to Offic *Lich* from 01. *27 Oak Drive, Oswestry SY11 2RU* Tel (01691) 662849

HODSON, Keith. b 53. Hatf Coll Dur BA74. Wycliffe Hall Ox 77. **d** 80 **p** 81. C Ashton-upon-Mersey St Mary *Ches* 80-84; C Polegate *Chich* 84-92; V Baddesley Ensor w Grendon *Birm* from 92. *The Vicarage, Baddesley Ensor, Atherstone CV9 2BY* Tel (01827) 715327

HODSON, Miss Margaret Christina. b 39. Linc Th Coll 88. **d** 90 **p** 94. Par Dn Old Trafford St Jo *Man* 90-94; C 94-95; P-in-c Calderbrook and Shore 95-01; rtd 01. *53 Lon Thelwal, Benllech, Tyn-y-Gongl LL74 8QH* Tel (01248) 852990

HODSON, Mrs Margot Rosemary. b 60. Bris Univ BSc82 PGCE83. All Nations Chr Coll 87 St Alb and Ox Min Course 99.

d 01 **p** 02. C Grove *Ox* from 01. *2 Edington Place, Grove, Wantage OX12 0BX* Tel (01235) 763193 E-mail margot@hodsons.org

HODSON, Canon Raymond Leslie. b 42. St Chad's Coll Dur BSc64 DipTh66. **d** 66 **p** 67. C Adlington *Blackb* 66-68; C Cleveleys 68-72; V Ewood 72-77; V Nazeing *Chelmsf* 77-84; R Ampthill w Millbrook and Steppingley *St Alb* 84-95; Chapl Madrid *Eur* from 95; Can Gib Cathl from 02. *General Oraa 16, escB, 6B, 28006 Madrid, Spain* Tel (0034) (91) 411 0593 E-mail stgeorgemadrid@compuserve.com

HODSON, William. b 42. Man Univ BA. Cranmer Hall Dur 81. **d** 82 **p** 83. C Ashton St Mich *Man* 82-86; V Tintwistle *Ches* 86-93; P-in-c Weston 93-99; rtd 99. *10 St Anne's Road, Horwich, Bolton BL6 7EJ* Tel (01204) 696172
E-mail bill.hodson@btopenworld.com

HOEY, Canon David Paul. b 57. QUB BD79. CITC 79. **d** 81 **p** 82. C Belfast Whiterock *Conn* 81-83; C Portadown St Mark *Arm* 83-84; I Cleenish w Mullaghdun *Clogh* 84-90; I Magheracross from 90; Dir of Ords from 91; Can Clogh Cathl from 95. *The Rectory, 27 Craghan Road, Ballinamallard, Enniskillen BT94 2BT* Tel (028) 6638 8238 Fax as telephone E-mail dphoey@aol.com

HOEY, The Ven Raymond George. b 46. TCD BA70 MA. **d** 72 **p** 73. C Portadown St Mark *Arm* 72-78; I Camlough w Mullaglass from 78; Dom Chapl to Abp Arm from 86; Adn Arm from 92. *2 Maytown Road, Bessbrook, Newry BT35 7LY* Tel (028) 3083 0301 Fax as telephone
E-mail archdeacon@armagh.anglican.org
or rghoey@btinternet.com

HOEY, William Thomas. b 32. CITC 64. **d** 66 **p** 67. C Belfast St Mary *Conn* 66-68; C Lisburn Ch Ch 69-72; I Ballinderry 72-78; I Belfast St Simon w St Phil 78-02; rtd 02. *11 Carnshill Court, Belfast BT8 6TX* Tel (028) 9079 0595

HOFBAUER, Miss Andrea Martina. b 71. Johannes Gutenberg Univ Mainz. St Steph Ho Ox 00. **d** 02 **p** 03. C Teignmouth, Ideford w Luton, Ashcombe etc *Ex* from 02. *51 Higher Coombe Drive, Teignmouth TQ14 9LR* Tel (01626) 772098
E-mail andihof@hotmail.com

HOFFMAN, Canon Stanley Harold. b 17. St Edm Hall Ox BA39 MA43 Kent Univ MA82. Linc Th Coll 40. **d** 41 **p** 42. C New Windsor *Ox* 41-44; C Weston All SS *B & W* 44-47; C Chertsey *Guildf* 47-51; V Shottermill 51-65; Dir of Educn Roch 65-80; Hon Can Roch Cathl 65-80; Warden of Readers 73-80; Chapl to The Queen 76-88; rtd 80. *13 Manormead, Tilford Road, Hindhead GU26 6RA* Tel (01428) 602564

HOFFMANN, Jonathan Mark. b 60. Cranmer Hall Dur Dip Th & Min 95. **d** 97 **p** 99. C Eaton *Nor* 97-98; C Horsell *Guildf* 98-02; TV Aston cum Aughton w Swallownest and Ulley *Sheff* from 02. *The Vicarage, 27 Skipton Road, Swallownest, Sheffield S26 4NQ* Tel 0114-287 9271 E-mail holyhoff@aol.com

HOGAN, Edward James Martin. b 46. Trin Coll Bris. **d** 85 **p** 86. C St Austell *Truro* 85-88; V Gt Broughton and Broughton Moor *Carl* 88-94; V St Stythians w Perranarworthal and Gwennap *Truro* from 94. *The Vicarage, Old Vicarage Close, Stithians, Truro TR3 7DZ* Tel (01209) 860123 Fax 860196
E-mail martin@houseofhogan.co.uk *or* martin@stythian.co.uk

HOGAN, John James. b 24. St Edm Hall Ox BA51 MA56. Wells Th Coll 51. **d** 53 **p** 54. C Cannock *Lich* 53-55; C Drayton in Hales 55-58; V Woore 58-84; P-in-c Norton in Hales 82-84; V Woore and Norton in Hales 84-89; rtd 89; Perm to Offic *Lich* 89-00. *Wrekin Prospect, Audlem Road, Woore, Crewe CW3 9RJ* Tel (01630) 647677

HOGAN, William Riddell. b 22. Qu Coll Birm 48. **d** 51 **p** 52. C Brighouse *Wakef* 51-54; Singapore 55-58; V Greetland *Wakef* 59-73; V Greetland and W Vale 73-80; V Kellington w Whitley 80-87; rtd 87. *15 The Pastures, Carlton, Goole DN14 9QF* Tel (01405) 862233

HOGARTH, Alan Francis. b 58. Oak Hill Th Coll BA89. **d** 89 **p** 90. C Felixstowe SS Pet and Paul *St E* 89-93; R Beckington w Standerwick, Berkley, Rodden etc *B & W* from 93. *8 Church Street, Beckington, Bath BA11 6TG* Tel (01373) 830314
E-mail rector@beckington.org.uk *or* alan@beckington.org.uk

HOGARTH, Foley James Myddelton. b 16. Ch Ch Ox BA38 MA42. Wells Th Coll 38. **d** 39 **p** 40. C Rainbow Hill St Barn *Worc* 39-41; C Charlton Kings H Apostles *Glouc* 41-42; CF 42-46; V Fordcombe *Roch* 47-52; Asst Hd Master Holmewood Ho Sch Kent 52-53; Australia from 53; rtd 81. *3 Chilton Court, 28 Buxton Street, North Adelaide, S Australia 5006* Tel (0061) (8) 8267 1759

HOGARTH, Joseph. b 32. Edin Th Coll 65. **d** 67 **p** 67. C Walney Is *Carl* 67-71; V Whitehaven St Jas 71-76; V Millom H Trin w Thwaites 76-82; V Maryport 82-91; V Consett Dur 91-97; rtd 97; Perm to Offic *Roch* from 99. *81 High Street, Crayford, Dartford DA1 4EJ* Tel (01322) 526733

HOGARTH, Peter Robert. b 61. Bath Univ MSc97 Bris Univ BA01. Trin Coll Bris 99. **d** 01. C Martock w Ash *B & W* from 01. *3 Chestnut Road, Martock TA12 6DP* Tel (01935) 824732
E-mail prhogarth@talk21.com

HOGBEN, The Ven Peter Graham. b 25. Bps' Coll Cheshunt 60. **d** 61 **p** 62. C Hale *Guildf* 61-64; R Westborough 64-71; V Ewell 71-82; Hon Can Guildf Cathl 79-90; RD Epsom 80-82; Adn

---

Dorking 82-90; rtd 90; Perm to Offic *Guildf* from 90. *3 School Road, Rowledge, Farnham GU10 4EJ* Tel (01252) 793533

HOGG, Mrs Ann Grant. b 46. St Andr Univ MA68 Hughes Hall Cam PGCE70. N Ord Course 99. **d** 02 **p** 03. NSM Bromborough *Ches* from 02. *The Rectory, Mark Rake, Bromborough, Wirral CH62 2DH* Tel 0151-334 1466

HOGG, Anthony. b 42. Univ of Wales (Lamp) BA63. Linc Th Coll 64 Chich Th Coll 78. **d** 78 **p** 79. NSM Ridgeway *Ox* 78-86; C 90-91; NSM W w E Hanney 86-88; Hd Master New Coll Sch Ox 88-89; P-in-c Hanney, Denchworth and E Challow *Ox* 91-92; V from 92. *The Vicarage, Winter Lane, West Hanney, Wantage OX12 0LF* Tel (01235) 868863 E-mail victory@ukgateway.net

HOGG, Neil Richard. b 46. BSc69. Ridley Hall Cam 82. **d** 84 **p** 85. C Bingham *S'well* 84-87; TV Bushbury *Lich* 87-00; V Worksop St Jo *S'well* from 00. *St John's Vicarage, 1B Shepherds Avenue, Worksop S81 0JD* Tel (01909) 489868 Mobile 07585-816697

HOGG, William John. b 49. New Coll Ox MA71 Lon Univ CertEd72 Crewe & Alsager Coll MSc88. Edin Th Coll 86. **d** 88 **p** 89. C Oxton *Ches* 88-93; R Bromborough from 93. *The Rectory, Mark Rake, Bromborough, Wirral CH62 2DH* Tel 0151-334 1466

HOGG, William Ritson. b 47. Leeds Univ BSc69. Qu Coll Birm DipTh71. **d** 72 **p** 73. C Bordesley St Oswald *Birm* 72-76; TV Seacroft *Ripon* 76-82; V Hunslet St Mary 82-88; V Catterick 88-97. *Address temp unknown*

HOGGARD, Mrs Jean Margaret. b 36. NW Ord Course 76. **dss** 79 **d** 87 **p** 94. Northowram *Wakef* 79-94; Par Dn 87-94; C Ovenden 94-00; rtd 00. *13 Joseph Avenue, Northowram, Halifax HX3 7HJ* Tel (01422) 201475

HOGWOOD, Brian Roy. b 38. Bps' Coll Cheshunt. **d** 65 **p** 92. NSM Thetford *Nor* 91-93; Hon C from 93; Chapl Addenbrooke's NHS Trust 98-99; Perm to Offic *Ely* from 98. *31 Byron Walk, Thetford IP24 1JX* Tel (01842) 753915

HOLBEN, Bruce Frederick. b 45. STETS 99. **d** 02 **p** 03. NSM W Wittering and Birdham w Itchenor *Chich* from 02. *3 Elmstead Gardens, West Wittering, Chichester PO20 8NG* Tel 07940-759060 (mobile)

HOLBROOK, Colin Eric Basford. *See* BASFORD HOLBROOK, Colin Eric

HOLBROOK, John Edward. b 62. St Pet Coll Ox BA83 MA87. Ridley Hall Cam 82. **d** 86 **p** 87. C Barnes St Mary *S'wark* 86-89; C Bletchley *Ox* 89-93; C N Bletchley CD 89-93; V Adderbury w Milton 93-02; RD Deddington 00-02; R Wimborne Minster *Sarum* from 02; P-in-c Witchampton, Stanbridge and Long Crichel etc from 02; Chapl S and E Dorset Primary Care Trust from 02. *The Rectory, 17 King Street, Wimborne BH21 1DZ* Tel (01202) 882340 E-mail john.holbrook@ukonline.co.uk

HOLBROOKE-JONES, Canon Stanley Charles. b 27. Dur Univ BA58 DipTh60 MA77. Cranmer Hall Dur 58. **d** 60 **p** 61. C Gravesend St Jas *Roch* 60-63; C Streatham Immanuel w St Anselm *S'wark* 63-66; V W Bromwich H Trin *Lich* 66-79; V W Exe *Ex* 79-88; R Poole *Sarum* 88-97; Miss to Seafarers from 88; Can and Preb Sarum Cathl *Sarum* 96-97; rtd 97; Perm to Offic *Sarum* from 97. *27 Clarendon Road, Broadstone BH18 9HT* Tel (01202) 460433

HOLCOMBE, Graham William Arthur. b 50. Open Univ BA99. St Mich Coll Llan DipTh80. **d** 80 **p** 81. C Neath w Llantwit *Llan* 80-84; Asst Youth Chapl 81-84; PV Llan Cathl 84-86; V Pentyrch 86-00; V Pentyrch w Capel Llanillterne 00-02; Min Can Llan Cathl from 02. *1 White House, Cathedral Green, Llandaff, Cardiff CF5 2EB* Tel (029) 2056 9521

HOLDAWAY, Graham Michael. b 51. Southn Univ BSc73. Sarum & Wells Th Coll 74. **d** 77 **p** 78. C Walton-on-Thames *Guildf* 77-81; TV Westborough 81-86; Perm to Offic 86-01; NSM Walton-on-Thames from 01. *5 Cardinal Drive, Walton-on-Thames KT12 3AX* Tel (01932) 269293

HOLDAWAY, Simon Douglas. b 47. Lanc Univ BA73 Sheff Univ PhD81. N Ord Course 78. **d** 81 **p** 82. NSM Gleadless *Sheff* from 81; Sen Lect in Sociology Sheff Univ from 81. *136 Totley Brook Road, Sheffield S17 3QU* Tel 0114-236 3711

HOLDAWAY, Canon Stephen Douglas. b 45. Hull Univ BA67. Ridley Hall Cam 67. **d** 70 **p** 71. C Southampton Thornhill St Chris *Win* 70-73; C Tardebigge *Worc* 73-78; Ind Chapl 73-78; Ind Chapl *Linc* 78-93; Co-ord City Cen Group Min 81-93; TR Louth from 93; RD Louthesk from 95; Can and Preb Linc Cathl from 00. *The Rectory, 49 Westgate, Louth LN11 9YE* Tel (01507) 603213 Fax 602991 E-mail stephen.holdaway@btinternet.com

HOLDCROFT, Ian Thomas. b 46. St Jo Coll Cam BA68 MA71. Westcott Ho Cam 72. **d** 73 **p** 74. C Bris St Mary Redcliffe w Temple etc *Bris* 73-76; Th Educn Sec Chr Aid 76-80; Exec Sec 80-82; Hon C Battersea St Mary *S'wark* 81-86; Dep Sec Gen Syn Bd for Miss and Unity 82-86; V Whitchurch *Bris* 86-92; V Almondsbury 92-96; P-in-c Olveston 92-95; P-in-c Littleton on Severn w Elberton 92-96. *9 Russell Road, Westbury Park, Bristol BS6 7UB* Tel 0117-942 2539
E-mail all@theholdcrofts47.freeserve.co.uk

HOLDEN, Canon Arthur Stuart James. b 23. ALCD51. **d** 51 **p** 52. C Barking St Marg *Chelmsf* 51-54; P-in-c Berechurch 54-55; V 55-61; V Earls Colne 61-82; P-in-c White Colne 66-67; V

68-82; V Earls Colne and White Colne 82-88; Hon Can Chelmsf Cathl 80-88; rtd 88; Perm to Offic *Chelmsf* from 88. *10 Wroxham Close, Colchester CO3 3RQ* Tel (01206) 560845

HOLDEN, Geoffrey. b 26. FCII54. Oak Hill Th Coll 57. **d** 59 **p** 60. C Crookes St Thos *Sheff* 59-61; C Belper *Derby* 61-63; C Woking St Jo *Guildf* 63-66; R Bath St Mich w St Paul *B & W* 66-73; Chapl Bath Gp Hosps 73-91; rtd 91; Perm to Offic *B & W* from 91. *32 Crescent Gardens, Bath BA1 2NB* Tel (01225) 427933

HOLDEN, Geoffrey Ralph. b 25. Ripon Hall Ox 64. **d** 65 **p** 66. C Sparkhill St Jo *Birm* 65-68; C Walsall *Lich* 68-71; R Longton St Jas 71-75; rtd 90. *Aberscethin, Talybont LL43 2AR* Tel (01341) 247538

HOLDEN, Jack Crawford (Simon). b 30. Leeds Univ BA59. Coll of Resurr Mirfield 59. **d** 61 **p** 61. C Middlesbrough All SS *York* 61-64; Lic to Offic *Wakef* 65-69; CR from 67; Asst Chapl Univ Coll *Lon* 69-74; Lic to Offic 70-74; rtd 98; Lic to Offic *Wakef* from 98. *House of the Resurrection, Stocks Bank Road, Mirfield WF14 0BN* Tel (01924) 494318

HOLDEN, Canon John. b 33. MBE76. Sheff Univ MA02 ACMA62. Ridley Hall Cam 65 Selly Oak Coll 71. **d** 67 **p** 68. C Flixton St Jo CD *Man* 67-71; Uganda 71-75; V Aston SS Pet and Paul *Birm* 75-87; RD Aston 86-87; Hon Can Birm Cathl 86-87; R Ulverston St Mary w H Trin *Carl* 87-98; RD Furness 90-94; Hon Can Carl Cathl 91-94; rtd 98; Perm to Offic *Carl* from 98 and *Heref* from 99. *3 Alison Road, Church Stretton SY6 7AT* Tel (01694) 724167

HOLDEN, John Norman. b 35. Heythrop Coll Lon MA97. Oak Hill Th Coll 91. **d** 95 **p** 96. NSM Codicote St Alb 95-96; Perm to Offic *St Alb* from 96 and *Ely* from 00. *4 Chapel Row, Shay Lane, Upper Dean, Huntingdon PE28 0LU* Tel (01234) 708928 E-mail jnholden@ndirect.co.uk

HOLDEN, John Worrall. b 44. K Coll Lon AKC67 DPS. **d** 70 **p** 71. C Derby St Bart *Derby* 70-72; Lic to Offic 72-74; Hon C St Helier *S'wark* 74-77; Hon C St Marylebone All SS *Lon* 80-83; Hon C St Botolph Aldgate w H Trin Minories 84-95. *4 Foster Lane, London EC2V 6HH*

HOLDEN, Mark Noel. b 61. Collingwood Coll Dur BA82 Edin Univ CQSW85 Warwick Univ TCert93 Birm Univ MA95. Qu Coll Birm 93. **d** 95 **p** 96. C Brumby *Linc* 95-99; P-in-c Wragby 99-00; R Wragby Gp from 00. *The Vicarage, Church Street, Wragby, Lincoln LN8 5RA* Tel (01673) 857825

HOLDEN, Paul Edward. b 53. CEng79 MIM MIBF BSc75 DipHE84. Trin Coll Bris 82. **d** 86 **p** 87. C Harpurhey Ch Ch *Man* 86-88; C Harpurhey St Steph 88-93; Sen Min Harpurhey LEP 88-93. *2 Baywood Street, Harpurhey, Manchester M9 5XJ* Tel 0161-205 2938

HOLDEN, Mrs Rita. b 45. St Alb and Ox Min Course 98. **d** 01 **p** 03. OLM Burghfield *Ox* 01-02; NSM Droitwich Spa *Worc* from 02. *40 Nightingale Close, Droitwich WR9 7HB* Tel (01905) 772787 E-mail rita@openv.clara.co.uk

HOLDEN, Stuart. *See* HOLDEN, Canon Arthur Stuart James

HOLDER, Canon John William. b 41. Chester Coll CertEd61 Open Univ BA73 Bath Univ MEd85. Trin Coll Bris MA94. **d** 87 **p** 88. C Brockworth *Glouc* 87-91; P-in-c Avening w Cherington 91-95; V Cinderford St Jo from 95; P-in-c Lydbrook 99-03; Hon Can Glouc Cathl from 03. *St John's Vicarage, 1 Abbots View, Cinderford GL14 3EG* Tel (01594) 825446 E-mail vicar@churchstjohn.org

HOLDER, Kenneth William. b 29. Sarum Th Coll 60. **d** 61 **p** 62. C Crawley *Chich* 61-65; C-in-c Wick CD 65-73; V Hangleton 73-79; R Rotherfield 79-81; R Rotherfield w Mark Cross 81-83; Chapl Eastbourne Coll 83-84; C Farnborough *Roch* 85; TV Mildenhall *St E* 87-92; R Redgrave cum Botesdale w Rickinghall 92-99; rtd 99; Perm to Offic *Chich* from 01. *Flat 3, 13 Granville Road, Eastbourne BN20 7HE* Tel (01323) 410868

HOLDER, Rodney Dennis. b 50. Trin Coll Cam BA71 MA75 Ch Ch Ox MA75 DPhil78 FRAS75 CPhys91 MInstP91 CMath95 FIMA95. Wycliffe Hall Ox BA96. **d** 97 **p** 98. C Long Compton, Whichford and Barton-on-the-Heath *Cov* 97-01; C Wolford w Burmington 97-01; C Cherington w Stourton 97-01; C Barcheston 97-01; Perm to Offic 01-02; P-in-c The Claydons *Ox* from 02. *The Rectory, Queen Catherine Road, Steeple Claydon, Buckingham MK18 2PY* Tel (01296) 738055 Fax as telephone E-mail rodney.holder@virgin.net

HOLDING, Kenneth George Frank. b 27. Sarum & Wells Th Coll 75. **d** 77 **p** 78. C Bexley St Mary *Roch* 77-80; Min Joydens Wood St Barn CD 80-85; R Mereworth w W Peckham 85-92; rtd 92; Perm to Offic *York* from 92. *121 Burden Road, Beverley HU17 9LW* Tel (01482) 872609

HOLDRIDGE, The Ven Bernard Lee. b 35. Lich Th Coll 64. **d** 67 **p** 68. C Swinton *Sheff* 67-71; V Doncaster St Jude 71-81; R Rawmarsh w Parkgate 81-88; RD Rotherham 86-88; V Worksop Priory *S'well* 88-94; Adn Doncaster *Sheff* 94-01; rtd 01; Perm to Offic *Sheff* from 01. *354 Thorne Road, Doncaster DN2 5AN* Tel (01302) 341331

HOLDSTOCK, Adrian Charles. b 51. BA MA. EMMTC. **d** 03. NSM Bosworth and Sheepy Gp *Leic* from 03. *34 Herald Way, Burbage, Hinckley LE10 2NX* Tel (01455) 251066

HOLDSTOCK, Godfrey. b 48. St Jo Coll Cam BA69 MA72 Ox Univ MA77 MA81. St Steph Ho Ox 76. **d** 78 **p** 79. C Chislehurst Annunciation *Roch* 78-81; Hon C Richmond St Mary w St Matthias and St Jo *S'wark* 82-85; V Billesdon and Skeffington *Leic* 85-89; TV High Wycombe *Ox* 89-91; Chapl St Paul's Prep Sch Barnes from 91; NSM Terriers *Ox* 92-93; P-in-c Barnes H Trin *S'wark* 93-97; TV Barnes from 97. *Holy Trinity Vicarage, 162 Castelnau, London SW13 9ET* Tel (020) 8748 5744

HOLDSWORTH, Ian Scott. b 52. Sheff Poly BA75. Oak Hill Th Coll BA81. **d** 81 **p** 82. C Denham *Ox* 81-84; P-in-c S Leigh 84-89; P-in-c Cogges 84-88; V 88-89; Perm to Offic *Pet* 95; NSM Brackley St Pet w St Jas 96-99; P-in-c Northampton St Mary from 99. *44 Barn Owl Close, Northampton NN1 4JQ* Tel (01604) 761104

HOLDSWORTH, The Ven John Ivor. b 49. Univ of Wales (Abth) BA70 Univ of Wales (Cardiff) BD73 MTh75. St Mich Coll Llan 70. **d** 73 **p** 74. C Newport St Paul *Mon* 73-77; CF (TAVR) 75-90; V Abercraf and Callwen *S & B* 77-86; Bp's Chapl for Th Educn 80-97; V Gorseinon 86-97; Hon Lect Th Univ of Wales (Swansea) 88-96; Prin and Warden St Mich Coll Llan 97-03; Lect Th Univ of Wales (Cardiff) 97-03; Adn St D from 03; V Steynton from 03. *The New Vicarage, Steynton, Milford haven SA73 1AW* Tel (01646) 692867

HOLDSWORTH, Kelvin. b 66. Man Poly BSc89 St Andr Univ BD92 Edin Univ MTh96. TISEC 95. **d** 97 **p** 98. C Perth St Ninian *St And* from 97; Prec St Ninian's Cathl Perth 97-00; R Bridge of Allan from 00; Chapl Stirling Univ from 00. *21 Fountain Road, Bridge of Allan FK9 4AT* Tel (01786) 832368 Fax 831223 E-mail k.holdsworth@btinternet.com

HOLDSWORTH, Michael Andrew. b 65. Univ Coll Dur BA88. Ripon Coll Cuddesdon BA92 MA96. **d** 93 **p** 94. C Cannock *Lich* 93-97; TV Sheff Manor *Sheff* 97-99; Tutor Ripon Coll Cuddesdon 97-99. *39 Calcott Road, Knowle, Bristol BS4 2HB* Tel 0117-977 5769

HOLE, The Very Revd Derek Norman. b 33. Linc Th Coll 57. **d** 60 **p** 61. C Knighton St Mary Magd *Leic* 60-62; S Africa 62-64; C Kenilworth St Nic *Cov* 64-67; R Burton Latimer *Pet* 67-73; V Leic St Jas *Leic* 73-92; Hon Can Leic Cathl 83-92; RD Christianity S 83-92; Provost Leic 92-99; Chapl to The Queen 85-93; rtd 99; Perm to Offic *Leic* from 00. *25 Southernhay Close, Leicester LE2 3TW* Tel 0116-270 9988 E-mail dnhole@leicester.anglican.org

HOLFORD, Andrew Peter. b 62. Nottm Univ BSc84. Cranmer Hall Dur 87. **d** 90 **p** 91. C Waltham Cross *St Alb* 90-93; C Northampton St Benedict *Pet* 93-95; V Pet Ch Carpenter from 95. *The Vicarage, Chestnut Avenue, Peterborough PE1 4PE* Tel (01733) 567140 E-mail andrewholford@ukonline.co.uk

HOLFORD, John Alexander. b 40. Chich Th Coll 65. **d** 67 **p** 68. C Cottingley *Bradf* 67-71; C Baildon 71-73; P-in-c Bingley H Trin 73-74; V 74-86; V Woodhall 86-93; C Shelf 93-94; TV Shelf St Mich w Buttershaw St Aid 94-99; P-in-c Embsay w Eastby from 99. *The Vicarage, 21 Shires Lane, Embsay, Skipton BD23 6SB* Tel (01756) 798057 Fax as telephone

HOLFORD, Margaret Sophia. b 39. St Alb and Ox Min Course 95. **d** 98 **p** 99. NSM Stevenage St Andr and St Geo *St Alb* from 98. *Icknield House, Westmill Lane, Ickleford, Hitchin SG5 3RN* Tel (01462) 432794 Fax 436618

HOLGATE, David Andrew. b 54. Cape Town Univ BA77 Port Eliz Univ BA89 Rhodes Univ MTh90 PhD94. All Nations Chr Coll DipTh82. **d** 82 **p** 84. S Africa 82-93; C Uitenhage St Kath 82-84; Asst P Port Elizabeth St Hugh 84-87; P-in-c Somerset E All SS 88-89; St Paul's Coll Grahamstown 90-93; CME Officer *Chelmsf* 93-96; P-in-c Felsted 93-96; V Felsted and Lt Dunmow 96-97; Dean of Studies STETS from 97; Dep Dir from 01. *19 The Close, Salisbury SP1 2EE*, or *74 Hamilton Road, Salisbury SP1 3TQ* Tel (01722) 424820 or 323740 Fax 424811 E-mail daholgate@stets.ac.uk

✠**HOLLAND, The Rt Revd Alfred Charles.** b 27. St Chad's Coll Dur BA50 DipTh52. **d** 52 **p** 53 **c** 70. C W Hackney St Barn *Lon* 52-54; Australia 55-78 and from 94; R Scarborough 55-70; Asst Bp Perth 70-77; Bp Newcastle 78-92; rtd 92; Chapl St Geo Coll Jerusalem 93-94. *21 Sullivan Crescent, Wanniassa, ACT, Australia 2903* Tel (0061) (2) 6231 8368 E-mail acjmholland@bigpond.com

✠**HOLLAND, The Rt Revd Edward.** b 36. AKC64. **d** 65 **p** 66 **c** 86. C Dartford H Trin *Roch* 65-69; C Mill Hill Jo Keble Ch *Lon* 69-72; Prec Gib Cathl *Eur* 72-74; Chapl Naples Ch Ch 74-79; Chapl Bromley Hosp 79-86; V Bromley St Mark *Roch* 79-86; Suff Bp Eur 86-95; Dean Brussels 86-95; Area Bp Colchester *Chelmsf* 95-01; rtd 01; Hon Asst Bp Lon from 02; Hon Asst Bp Eur from 02. *37 Parfrey Street, London W6 9EW* Tel (020) 8746 3636

HOLLAND, Glyn. b 59. Hull Univ BA Bris Univ CertEd. Coll of Resurr Mirfield 83. **d** 85 **p** 86. C Brighouse St Martin *Wakef* 85-89; V Ferrybridge 89-96; Chapl Pontefract Gen Infirmary Wakef 89-96; V Middlesbrough All SS *York* from 96. *All Saints' Vicarage, Grange Road, Middlesbrough TS1 2LR* Tel (01642) 245035

HOLLAND, Jesse Marvin Sean. b 66. Westmr Coll Ox MTh03. Oak Hill Th Coll BA97. **d** 98 **p** 99. C Thundersley *Chelmsf* 98-02;

P-in-c Tedburn St Mary, Whitestone, Oldridge etc *Ex* from 02. *The Rectory, Church Lane, Whitestone, Exeter EX4 2JT* Tel (01392) 811406 E-mail northkennteam@aol.com

HOLLAND, John Stuart. b 52. Sarum & Wells Th Coll 77. **d** 80 **p** 81. C Wylde Green *Birm* 80-83; C Swanage and Studland *Sarum* 83-85; P-in-c Handley w Pentridge 85-88; TV Preston w Sutton Poyntz and Osmington w Poxwell 88-95; P-in-c Failsworth St Jo *Man* 95-01; V Ashton Ch Ch from 01. *Christ Church Vicarage, Vicarage Road, Ashton-under-Lyne OL7 9QY* Tel and fax 0161-330 1601 Mobile 07718-483817 E-mail john@holland245.freeserve.co.uk

HOLLAND, Laurence Frederick Alfred (Fred). b 21. Sarum & Wells Th Coll. **d** 87 **p** 88. NSM Beaminster Area *Sarum* 87-92; Perm to Offic from 94. *18 St Mary Well Street, Beaminster DT8 3BB* Tel (01308) 862426

HOLLAND, Mrs Linda. b 48. Sarum & Wells Th Coll DCM93. **d** 93 **p** 94. Par Dn Queensbury All SS *Lon* 93-94; C 94-96; C Enfield St Jas 96-01; V Coney Hill *Glouc* from 01. *St Oswald's Vicarage, Coney Hill, Gloucester GL4 7LX* Tel (01452) 523618 E-mail revlynne@batzion.fsnet.co.uk

HOLLAND, Matthew Francis. b 52. Lon Univ BA73. Qu Coll Birm DipTh78. **d** 79 **p** 80. C Ecclesall *Sheff* 79-83; TV Gleadless Valley 83-86; TR 86-88; V Sheff Gillcar St Silas 88-92; V Sheff St Silas Broomhall 92-98; V Southsea St Simon *Portsm* from 98. *St Simon's Vicarage, 6 Trafalgar Road, Southsea PO4 0NG* Tel (023) 9273 3068 E-mail matts@fish.co.uk

HOLLAND, Paul William. b 55. Coll of Resurr Mirfield 78. **d** 80 **p** 81. C Parkstone St Pet w Branksea and St Osmund *Sarum* 80-83; CR 85-93; Asst Chapl Musgrove Park Hosp 93; Asst Chapl St Helier Hosp Carshalton 93-96; C Croydon St Jo *S'wark* from 96. *37 Alton Road, Croydon CR0 4LZ* Tel (020) 8760 9629

HOLLAND, Peter Christie. b 36. St Andr Univ BSc60 Dur Univ DipTh62. Cranmer Hall Dur 60. **d** 62 **p** 63. C Darlington St Jo *Dur* 62-64; C Bishopwearmouth Ch Ch 64-69; V Tudhoe 69-77; V New Seaham 77-89; V Totternhoe, Stanbridge and Tilsworth *St Alb* 89-01; rtd 02; Perm to Offic *Dur* from 02. *Bracken Ridge, Woodland, Bishop Auckland DL13 5RH* Tel (01388) 718881 E-mail hollandpeter90@supanet.com

HOLLAND, Simon Geoffrey. b 63. MHCIMA83 Dorset Inst of HE OND81. Trin Coll Bris DipHE90 BA. **d** 91 **p** 92. C Reigate St Mary *S'wark* 91-95; Chapl Lee Abbey 95-99; Lic to Offic *Ex* 95-99; C Guildf St Sav *Guildf* from 99. *16 Cunningham Avenue, Guildford GU1 2PE* Tel (01483) 562732

HOLLAND, Simon Paul. b 56. Univ Coll Lon LLB77 Qu Coll Cam BA80 MA84 Edin Univ MTh94. Westcott Ho Cam 79. **d** 81 **p** 82. C Uckfield *Chich* 81-84; TV Lewes All SS, St Anne, St Mich and St Thos 84-88; TR 88-91; R Glas St Matt *Glas* 91-95; P-in-c Glas St Kentigern 95-96; R Aldingbourne, Barnham and Eastergate *Chich* from 96. *The Rectory, 97 Barnham Road, Barnham, Bognor Regis PO22 0EQ* Tel (01243) 554077 *or* 553955 Fax 554677 E-mail parishofabe@pavilion.co.uk

HOLLAND, Mrs Teresa Christine. b 59. Hull Univ BA81. STETS 00. **d** 03. NSM Storrington *Chich* from 03. *Wild Fortune, Sandgate Lane, Storrington, Pulborough RH20 3HJ* Tel (01903) 740487

HOLLAND, William Geoffrey Bretton. b 36. Magd Coll Cam BA59 MA63. Westcott Ho Cam 61. **d** 63 **p** 64. C Cannock *Lich* 63-66; C Paddington Ch Ch *Lon* 66-69; Chapl Magd Coll Cam 69-73; V Twyford *Win* 74-78; V Twyford and Owslebury and Morestead 78-84; Chapl Twyford Sch Win 84-90; rtd 01. *68A Warwick Way, London SW1V 1RZ*

HOLLANDS, Albert William. b 17. Roch Th Coll 60. **d** 62 **p** 63. C Aylsham *Nor* 62-66; R Syderstone 66-77; R Tattersett 67-83; P-in-c Tatterford 76-83; R Syderstone w Barmer 77-79; R Syderstone w Barmer and Bagthorpe 79-83; rtd 83; Perm to Offic *Nor* from 84. *25 Renwick Park East, West Runton, Cromer NR27 9LY* Tel (01263) 837352

HOLLANDS, Derek Gordon. b 45. Southn Univ DipTh. Brasted Th Coll Chich Th Coll 72. **d** 74 **p** 75. C Banstead *Guildf* 74-77; C Cranleigh 77-79; C Haywards Heath St Wilfrid *Chich* 79-80; TV 80-82; Chapl Hillingdon Area HA 82-86; Chapl W Suffolk Hosp Bury St Edm 86-95; Pres Coll Health Care Chapls 92-94; Sen Chapl R Cornwall Hosps Trust 95-98; rtd 99. *Oaklands Lodge, Lawshall Road, Hawstead, Bury St Edmunds IP29 5NR* Tel (01284) 386196 E-mail derek.hollands@tesco.net

HOLLANDS, Percival Edwin Macaulay. b 36. Edin Th Coll 57. **d** 60 **p** 61. C Greenock *Glas* 60-64; C Aberdeen St Mary *Ab* 64-65; P-in-c Aberdeen St Clem 65-68; R Cruden Bay 68-70; CF 70-82; C Ribbleton *Blackb* 82-83; TV 83-88; C Longton 88; C Penwortham St Mary 88-92; V Farington 92-98; rtd 98; Perm to Offic *Nor* from 00. *30 Teasel Road, Attleborough NR17 1XX* Tel (01953) 457372

HOLLANDS, Ray Leonard. b 42. AMASI AMRSH. S'wark Ord Course 68. **d** 71 **p** 72. NSM Hanworth All SS *Lon* 71-77 and 85-91 and from 95; NSM Hanworth St Geo 77-85; NSM Marshwood Vale *Sarum* 81-91; NSM Upper Sunbury St Sav *Lon* from 98. *4 Priscilla House, Sunbury Cross Centre, Sunbury-on-Thames TW16 7BE* Tel (01932) 781080

HOLLETT, Catherine Elaine. *See* DAKIN, Mrs Catherine Elaine

HOLLEY, Canon Geoffrey Raymond. b 28. AKC51. **d** 52 **p** 53. C Gt Ilford St Clem *Chelmsf* 52-53; C Gt Burstead 53-56; V 56-75; Bp's Ecum Officer 71-82; R Loughton St Jo 75-91; TR 91-92; Can Chelmsf Cathl 78-92; RD Epping Forest 82-92; rtd 92; Perm to Offic *Chelmsf* from 92. *5 The Maltings, Park Street, Thaxted, Dunmow CM6 2NB* Tel (01371) 830902

HOLLEY, Preb Graham Frank. b 29. Sarum Th Coll 60. **d** 61 **p** 62. C Heref All SS *Heref* 61-63; C W Wycombe *Ox* 63-67; V Much Marcle *Heref* 67-94; P-in-c Lt Marcle 84-86; RD Ledbury 87-90; Preb Heref Cathl 87-94; rtd 94; R Gourock *Glas* from 94. *40 Barrhill Road, Gourock PA19 1LB* Tel (01475) 632487

HOLLEY, Paul Robert. b 65. St Jo Coll Dur 91. **d** 94 **p** 95. C Tonge w Alkrington *Man* 94-98; P-in-c Salford St Phil w St Steph 98-00; P-in-c Salford Sacred Trin 99-00; R Salford Sacred Trin and St Phil from 00. *St Philip's Rectory, 6 Encombe Place, Salford M3 6FJ* Tel 0161-834 2041 E-mail paul.holley@lineone.net

HOLLIDAY, Andrew. b 62. St Steph Ho Ox 89. **d** 92 **p** 93. C Marton *Blackb* 92-95; C Poulton-le-Fylde 95-97; V Leyland St Jas from 97; AD Leyland from 02. *St James's Vicarage, 201 Slater Lane, Leyland, Preston PR5 3SH* Tel (01772) 421034 Fax as telephone

HOLLIDAY, Arthur. b 22. St Jo Coll Dur 80. **d** 81 **p** 82. Hon C Allerton *Bradf* 81-84; Hon C Thornton St Jas 84-91; Perm to Offic from 91. *9 Alston Close, Bradford BD9 6AN* Tel (01274) 487331

HOLLIDAY, Peter Leslie. b 48. FCA79 Birm Univ BCom70 MA92. Qu Coll Birm 81. **d** 83 **p** 84. C Burton *Lich* 83-87; P-in-c Longdon 87-93; PV and Subchanter Lich Cathl 87-93; R Stratford-on-Avon w Bishopton *Cov* 93-00; Dir St Giles Hospice Lich from 00; Chan's V Lich Cathl *Lich* from 02. *St Giles Hospice, Fisherwick Road, Lichfield WS14 9LH* Tel (01543) 432031 E-mail plh@clara.net

HOLLIDAY, William. b 33. Qu Coll Cam BA56 MA60 McGill Univ Montreal BD58 LTh58. Montreal Dioc Th Coll 56 Trin Coll 58. **d** 58 **p** 59. C Stanningley St Thos *Ripon* 58-63; C Romaldkirk 63-64; India 64-77; V Thwaites Brow *Bradf* 77-86; RD S Craven 82-86; P-in-c Horton 86-98; P-in-c Bradf St Oswald Chapel Green 91-98; RD Bowling and Horton 95-98; rtd 98; Perm to Offic *Bradf* from 99. *61 Woodside Crescent, Bingley BD16 1RE* Tel (01274) 568413

HOLLIMAN, The Ven John James. b 44. St D Coll Lamp BA66. **d** 67 **p** 68. C Tidswell *Derby* 67-71; CF 71-99; QHC 94-99; Dep Chapl Gen 96-99; Adn for the Army 96-99; V Funtington and Sennicotts *Chich* from 99; R W Stoke from 99. *The Vicarage, Church Lane, Funtington, Chichester PO18 9LH* Tel (01243) 575257 Fax 572303 E-mail venjjh@aol.com

HOLLIN, Ian. b 40. Open Univ BA76 DCC91. Sarum Th Coll 67. **d** 70 **p** 71. C Lancaster Ch Ch *Blackb* 70-72; C S Shore H Trin 72-75; C Marton Moss 72-75; V Morecambe St Lawr 75-78; V Blackpool St Mary 78-83; PV and Succ Ex Cathl *Ex* 83-87; Counsellor Coun for Chr Care and Sr 87-91; Admin Boniface Cen Ex 91-93; TV Maltby *Sheff* 93-96; R Handsworth from 96. *The Rectory, Handsworth Road, Handsworth, Sheffield S13 9BZ* Tel 0114-269 2403 E-mail ian.hollin@handsworth.org.uk

HOLLINGHURST, Mrs Anne Elizabeth. b 64. Trin Coll Bris BA96. **d** 96 **p** 97. C Nottingham St Sav *S'well* 96-99; Chapl Derby Univ Derby from 99; Chapl Derby Cathl from 99. *1 Peet Street, Derby DE22 3RF* Tel (01332) 206393 E-mail a.e.hollinghurst@derby.ac.uk

HOLLINGHURST, Stephen. b 59. Univ of Wales DipTh. St Jo Coll Nottm 81. **d** 83 **p** 84. C Hyde St Geo *Ches* 83-86; C Cropwell Bishop w Colston Bassett, Granby etc *S'well* 86-90; R Pembridge w Moor Court, Shobdon, Staunton etc *Heref* 90-02; R Presteigne w Discoed, Kinsham, Lingen and Knill from 02; RD Kington and Weobley 95-02. *The Rectory, St David's Street, Presteigne LD8 2BP* Tel (01544) 267777 E-mail steve.hollinghurst@lineone.net

HOLLINGHURST, Stephen Patrick. b 63. Hull Univ BA84. Trin Coll Bris BA93 MA93. **d** 96 **p** 97. C Nottingham St Sav *S'well* 96-99; Chapl Nottm Trent Univ 99-03; Perm to Offic *Derby* from 00. *1 Peet Street, Derby DE22 3RF* Tel (01332) 206393 *or* 0115-848 2305 E-mail stephen.hollinghurst@ntu.ac.uk

HOLLINGS, Miss Patricia Mary. b 39. CertEd59. S'wark Ord Course 84. **d** 87. Par Dn Wyke *Bradf* 87-94; C 94-96; rtd 96; Perm to Offic *Bradf* from 96. *1 Greenacre Way, Wyke, Bradford BD12 9DJ* Tel (01274) 677439

HOLLINGS, Robert George. b 48. St Jo Coll Nottm. **d** 94 **p** 95. C Cotmanhay *Derby* 94-97; TV Godrevy *Truro* 97-02; V Newhall *Derby* from 02. *St John's Vicarage, Church Street, Newhall, Swadlincote DE11 0HY* Tel (01283) 214685

HOLLINGSHEAD, Miss Pauline Carol. b 49. Local Minl Tr Course. **d** 94 **p** 95. OLM Colsterworth Gp *Linc* from 94. *The Lodge, Little Ponton, Grantham NG33 5BS* Tel (01476) 530382 Fax as telephone E-mail thelodge@madasafish.com

HOLLINGSHURST, Christopher Paul. b 63. St Chad's Coll Dur BA85 Westmr Coll Ox PGCE86. Ridley Hall Cam CTM98. **d** 98 **p** 00. C Bourn and Kingston w Caxton and Longstowe *Ely*

99-00; C Papworth from 00. *The Rectory, 2 Short Street, Bourn, Cambridge CB3 7SG* Tel (01954) 719728
E-mail chris.hollingshurst@ely.anglican.org
HOLLINGSHURST, Robert Peter. b 38. Ridley Hall Cam 64. **d** 67 **p** 68. C Roxeth Ch Ch *Lon* 67-70; C Attenborough w Chilwell *S'well* 70-73; C Ramsgate St Luke *Cant* 74-75; Chapl to the Deaf 78-80; TV Louth *Linc* 80-84; Chapl to the Deaf *Sarum* 84-87; P-in-c Odstock w Nunton and Bodenham 84-96; P-in-c Britford 89-96; P-in-c Charlton All Saints 89-96; R Gt and Lt Gaddesden *St Alb* from 96. *The Vicarage, Piper's Hill, Great Gaddesden, Hemel Hempstead HP1 3BY* Tel (01442) 252672
E-mail rpholl38@aol.com
HOLLINGSWORTH, Geoffrey. b 53. MCIPD85 Leeds Poly 74. N Ord Course 86. **d** 86 **p** 87. C Thorne *Sheff* 86-89; V Rawcliffe 89-96; V Airmyn, Hook and Rawcliffe from 96. *The Vicarage, 12 Church Lane, Hook, Goole DN14 5PN* Tel (01405) 763654
HOLLINGSWORTH, James William. b 69. Southn Univ BA91 SS Coll Cam BA96. Aston Tr Scheme 92 Ridley Hall Cam 94. **d** 97 **p** 98. C Mildenhall *St E* 97-01; R Barcombe *Chich* from 01. *The Rectory, 1 The Grange, Barcombe, Lewes BN8 5AT* Tel (01273) 400260 E-mail james@barcombe.net
HOLLINGSWORTH, Miss Paula Marion. b 62. Van Mildert Coll Dur BSc83. Trin Coll Bris BA91. **d** 91 **p** 94. C Keynsham *B & W* 91-95; C Balsall Heath St Paul *Birm* 95-98; Tutor Crowther Hall CMS Tr Coll Selly Oak 95-01; P-in-c Houghton-on-the-Hill, Keyham and Hungarton *Leic* from 01; Bp's Adv for CME from 01. *The Rectory, 16 Main Street, Houghton-on-the-Hill, Leicester LE7 9GD* Tel 0116-241 5828
E-mail phollingsworth@leicester.anglican.org
HOLLINGTON, David Mark. b 61. DipEH83 MIEH83. Trin Coll Bris BA94. **d** 94. C Wednesbury St Paul Wood Green *Lich* 94-95; C Cannock 95-96. *19 Rylands Drive, Wolverhampton WV4 5SQ*
HOLLINRAKE, Jean Margaret. *See* HARRISON, Mrs Jean Margaret
HOLLINS, Mrs Beverley Jayne. b 68. Univ of Wales (Abth) BLib90. St Alb and Ox Min Course 00. **d** 03. C Milton Keynes *Ox* from 03. *2 Symington Court, Shenley Lodge, Milton Keynes MK5 7AN* Tel (01908) 237777 Fax 200216
E-mail beverley.hollins@ukf.net
HOLLINS, John Edgar. b 35. St Jo Coll Cam BA58 MA62. Oak Hill Th Coll 58. **d** 60 **p** 61. C Whalley Range St Edm *Man* 60-63; C Highbury Ch Ch *Lon* 63-66; C St Alb St Paul *St Alb* 66-71; Hon C Halliwell St Paul *Man* 71-72; C Ravenhill St Jo 72-73; Perm to Offic *Birm* 79-81; V Millbrook *Ches* 81-89; rtd 89; Perm to Offic *Truro* from 89. *Tresuan, Meadway, Looe PL13 1JT* Tel (01503) 264062
HOLLINS (formerly SHIPP), Patricia Susan. b 54. Univ of Wales BA76. St Paul's Coll Grahamstown 77 Linc Th Coll 81. **d** 83 **p** 94. C Cyncoed *Mon* 83-87; Par Dn Lawrence Weston *Bris* 89-91; Par Dn Henbury 91-94; P-in-c Longwell Green 94; V 94-99; Hon Can Bris Cathl 97-99; Chapl Mt Vernon and Watford Hosps NHS Trust 99-00; Sen Co-ord Chapl W Herts Hosps NHS Trust from 00. *The Chaplaincy Office, W Hertfordshire Hospitals NHS Trust, Vicarage Road, Watford WD18 0HB* Tel (01923) 244366 ext 3134
E-mail susan.hollins@whht.nhs.uk
HOLLIS, Anthony Wolcott Linsley. b 40. McGill Univ Montreal BA61 Long Is Univ MA76. Gen Th Sem NY MDiv64. **d** 64 **p** 65. USA 64-92; Bermuda from 92. *PO Box GE 85, St George's GE BX, Bermuda* Tel (001441) 297 0216 Fax 297 8256
HOLLIS, The Ven Arnold Thaddeus. b 33. JP87. Stockton State Coll New Jersey BA74 NY Th Sem MDiv74 STM76 DMin78. Codrington Coll Barbados 56. **d** 59 **p** 60. C Wakef St Jo *Wakef* 60-62; Br Guiana 62-64; P-in-c Horbury Bridge *Wakef* 64-66; C Loughton St Jo *Chelmsf* 66-69; USA 69-77; Bermuda from 77; Hon Chapl RN from 77; Chapl HM Pris from 77; Chapl Miss to Seafarers from 90; Hon Can Bermuda Cathl from 87; Adn Bermuda from 96. *3 Middle Road, Sandys, Bermuda 5B 0Z* Tel (001441) 234 0834 *or* 234 2025 Fax 234 2723
E-mail athol@ibl.bm
HOLLIS, Christopher Barnsley. b 28. Clare Coll Cam BA52 MA59. Wells Th Coll 60. **d** 62 **p** 63. C Baildon *Bradf* 62-64; V Esholt 64-66; V Heaton St Barn 66-85; RD Airedale 73-82; Hon Can Bradf Cathl 77-85; Chapl HM YOI Wedmesley 85-90; V Wedmesley *Dur* 85-90; P-in-c Denholme Gate *Bradf* 90-95; rtd 95; Perm to Offic *Bradf* from 95. *52 Wilmer Drive, Bradford BD9 4AS* Tel (01274) 546722
HOLLIS, Derek. b 60. Lough Univ BA82. Cranmer Hall Dur 83. **d** 86 **p** 87. C Evington *Leic* 86-89; C Arnold *S'well* 89-93; V Beckingham w Walkeringham 93-03; P-in-c Gringley-on-the-Hill 95-03; V Beckingham w Walkeringham and Gringley from 03; Hon Chapl Miss to Seafarers from 03. *The Vicarage, Low Street, Beckingham, Doncaster DN10 4PW* Tel (01427) 848266
HOLLIS, Douglas John. b 32. S Dios Minl Tr Scheme. **d** 84 **p** 95. NSM Haywards Heath St Wilfrid *Chich* 84-98; Perm to Offic from 98. *2 Northlands Avenue, Haywards Heath RH16 3RT* Tel (01444) 453688
HOLLIS, Canon Gerald. b 19. Ch Ch Ox BA42 MA45. Wells Th Coll 45. **d** 47 **p** 48. C Stepney St Dunstan and All SS *Lon* 47-50; C

Rossington *Sheff* 50-54; R Armthorpe 54-60; V Rotherham 60-74; Hon Can Sheff Cathl 70-74; Adn Birm 74-84; Hon Can Birm Cathl 74-84; rtd 84; Perm to Offic *Sarum* from 87. *68 Britford Lane, Salisbury SP2 8AH* Tel (01722) 338154
HOLLIS, Howard Charles. b 16. Melbourne Univ MusBac40. Trin Coll Melbourne ThL43. **d** 45 **p** 46. Australia 45-47; C Croydon Woodside *Cant* 47-49; C S Kensington St Steph *Lon* 49-51; Min Can Westmr Abbey 51-59; Dep P in O 54-59; Chapl Westmr Sch 57-59; Australia 59-65 and from 76; V Primrose Hill St Mary w Avenue Road St Paul *Lon* 65-76; rtd 83. *18 Maud Street, North Balwyn, Vic, Australia 3104* Tel (0061) (3) 9859 3213
HOLLIS, Miss Rebecca Catherine. b 78. St Martin's Coll Lanc BA99. Ripon Coll Cuddesdon BTh03. **d** 03. C Broughton *Blackb* from 03. *25 Northway, Fulwood, Preston PR2 9TP* Tel (01772) 717072
HOLLIS, Timothy Knowles. b 28. RN Coll Dartmouth 45. St Steph Ho Ox 54. **d** 58 **p** 59. C Oatlands *Guildf* 58-60; C Crawley *Chich* 60-63; C Sotterley w Willingham *St E* 63-69; R Sotterley, Willingham, Shadingfield, Ellough etc 69-76; Gen Sec L'Arche UK 77-93; rtd 93; Perm to Offic *Chich* 93-02 and *Glouc* from 03. *9 Abbots Court Drive, Twyning, Tewkesbury GL20 6JJ* Tel (01684) 274903
HOLLIS, Mrs Valerie Elizabeth. b 40. **d** 92 **p** 94. NSM Kempston Transfiguration *St Alb* from 92. *33 Silverdale Street, Kempston, Bedford MK42 8BE* Tel (01234) 853397
HOLLOWAY, Canon David Dennis. b 43. Lich Th Coll 65. **d** 68 **p** 69. C Cricklade w Latton *Bris* 68-71; C Bris St Agnes w St Simon 71-72; C Bris St Agnes and St Simon w St Werburgh 72-74; V Bitton 74-78; TV E Bris 78-80; P-in-c Tormarton w W Littleton 80-83; Sub Chapl HM Pris Bris 80-92; Dioc Ecum Officer *Bris* 83-93; Hon C Bris St Mich 89-93; Hon Can Bris Cathl from 92; V Horfield St Greg 93-00; RD Horfield 97-99; Chapl St Monica Home Westbury-on-Trym from 00. *Gate Lodge, St Monica Home, Cote Lane, Bristol BS9 3UN* Tel 0117-949 4000
HOLLOWAY, David Ronald James. b 39. Univ Coll Ox BA62 MA66. Ridley Hall Cam 65. **d** 67 **p** 68. C Leeds St Geo *Ripon* 67-71; Tutor Wycliffe Hall Ox 71-72; V Jesmond Clayton Memorial *Newc* from 73. *The Vicarage, 7 Otterburn Terrace, Jesmond, Newcastle upon Tyne NE2 3AP* Tel 0191-281 2001
HOLLOWAY, Graham Edward. b 45. Chich Th Coll 69. **d** 72 **p** 73. C W Drayton *Lon* 72-75; P-in-c Hawton *S'well* 75-80; TV Newark w Hawton, Cotham and Shelton 80; V Ladybrook 80-85; P-in-c Babworth 85-87; R Babworth w Sutton-cum-Lound 87-97; RD Retford 88-93; C Mansfield Woodhouse from 97. *55 Arun Dale, Mansfield Woodhouse, Mansfield NG19 9RE* Tel (01623) 620803 Fax as telephone
HOLLOWAY, Keith Graham. b 45. Linc Coll Ox BA67 St Jo Coll Dur DipTh72. **d** 73 **p** 74. C Gt Ilford St Andr *Chelmsf* 73-78; Hon C Squirrels Heath 78-80; Min Chelmer Village CD 80-87; V E Springfield 87-89; P-in-c Gt Dunmow 89-96; R Gt Dunmow and Barnston 96-02; R Upper Colne from 02. *The Rectory, Church Road, Great Yeldham, Halstead CO9 4PT* Tel (01787) 236055 Fax as telephone E-mail kanddway@aol.com
HOLLOWAY, Michael Sinclair. b 50. UEA BSc74 Southn Univ PGCE75. STETS 99. **d** 02 **p** 03. NSM Catherington and Clanfield *Portsm* from 02. *15 Rosewood Gardens, Clanfield, Waterlooville PO8 0LT* Tel (023) 9259 9848
E-mail mike@thewolery.freeserve.co.uk
✠**HOLLOWAY, The Rt Revd Prof Richard Frederick.** b 33. Lon Univ BD63 NY Th Sem STM68 Strathclyde Univ DUniv94 Aber Univ Hon DD95 Napier Univ Edin DLitt00 Glas Univ DD01 FRSE95. Edin Th Coll 58. **d** 59 **p** 60 **c** 86. C Glas St Ninian *Glas* 59-63; P-in-c Glas St Marg 63-68; R Edin Old St Paul *Edin* 68-80; R Boston The Advent MA USA 80-84; V Ox St Mary Magd *Ox* 84-86; Bp Edin 86-00; Primus 92-00; rtd 00; Gresham Prof of Div 97-01. *6 Blantyre Crescent, Edinburgh EH10 5AE* Tel 0131-446 0696 E-mail doc.holloway@virgin.net
HOLLOWAY, Roger Graham. b 33. OBE92. Selw Coll Cam BA58 MA61. S'wark Ord Course 75. **d** 78 **p** 80. Hong Kong 78-80 and 85-88; Japan 80-84; PV Westmr Abbey from 88; Nat Dir ICF 91-96; Lic to Offic *Lon* from 94; Preacher Gray's Inn from 97; Lic Preacher *Lon* from 97. *Flat 6, 2 Porchester Gardens, London W2 6JL* Tel (020) 7402 4937 Fax 7402 4683
HOLLOWAY, Simon Anthony. b 50. S'wark Univ BSc72. Trin Coll Bris 76. **d** 79 **p** 81. C Bushbury *Lich* 79-81; C Castle Church 81-84; P-in-c Sparkbrook Ch Ch *Birm* 84-91; V 91-02; AD Bordesley 92-02; TV Horley *S'wark* from 02. *St Wilfrid's Vicarage, Horley Row, Horley RH6 8DF* Tel (01293) 771869 Mobile 07986-274393
E-mail holloway.sparkbrook@charis.co.uk
HOLLOWOOD, Christopher George. b 54. K Alfred's Coll Win BEd76 Open Univ MA97. Ripon Coll Cuddesdon 83. **d** 86 **p** 87. C Tupsley *Heref* 86-89; R Much Birch w Lt Birch, Much Dewchurch etc 89-92; Hd RS Haywood High Sch Heref 92-97; Sen Teacher St Aug Upper Sch 97-00; Dep Hd N Bromsgrove High Sch 00-02; Headmaster Bp Llan Ch in Wales High Sch Cardiff from 02. *170 Kings Road, Cardiff CF11 9DG* Tel (029) 2056 2485 E-mail c.hollowood@ntlworld.com

HOLLOWOOD, Graham. b 56. St Steph Ho Ox DipMin99. **d** 99 **p** 00. C Newport St Julian *Mon* 99-02; V Newport All SS from 02. *The Vicarage, Brynglas Road, Newport NP20 5QY* Tel (01633) 854657

HOLLOWOOD, Lewis William Rye. b 17. Dur Univ 37. Edin Th Coll 37. **d** 40 **p** 41. C St Paul's Cathl Dundee *Bre* 40-41; Chapl 41-43; C Ches St Jo *Ches* 43-44; R Fortrose *Mor* 44-46; R Cromarty 44-46; R Paisley H Trin *Glas* 46-47; R Renfrew 46-47; R Carnoustie *Bre* 47-49; Chapl K Coll Hosp Lon 49-50; V Mark Beech *Roch* 50-59; V New Groombridge *Chich* 59-67; V Hadlow Down 67-74; R Buxted and Hadlow Down 72-74; V Bexhill St Barn 75-81; Chapl Community Servants of the Cross Lindfield 81-97; rtd 82. *Holy Rood Cottage, Park Lane, Lindfield, Haywards Heath RH16 2QY* Tel (01444) 482090

HOLMAN, Francis Noel. b 37. DSPT90. Sarum Th Coll 62. **d** 65 **p** 66. C Weston Favell *Pet* 65-68; C Eckington *Derby* 68-71; Asst Chapl St Thos Hosp Lon 72-77; Chapl Hope Hosp Salford 77-02; Chapl Salford R Hosp 77-93; Chapl Ladywell Hosp 77-99; Chapl Man and Salford Skin Hosp 88-94; rtd 02; Perm to Offic *Man* from 03. *90 Rocky Lane, Eccles, Manchester M30 9LY* Tel 0161-707 1180

HOLMAN, Geoffrey Gladstone. b 32. AKC56. **d** 57 **p** 58. C Eltham St Barn *S'wark* 57-60; CF 60-73; Dep Asst Chapl Gen 73-80; Asst Chapl Gen 80-84; QHC 82-84; V Wetwang and Garton-on-the-Wolds w Kirkburn *York* 84-92; RD Harthill 87-92; rtd 92; P-in-c Askham Bryan *York* 93-01; Perm to Offic from 01. *20 North Parade, Bootham, York YO30 7AB* Tel (01904) 624419 E-mail samegus@samegus.plus.com

HOLMDEN, Miss Maria Irene. b 50. Trent Poly TCert72 BEd73 Goldsmiths' Coll Lon Dip Primary Educn 84. Oak Hill Th Coll DipHE92. **d** 92 **p** 94. Par Dn Stratford St Jo and Ch Ch w Forest Gate St Jas *Chelmsf* 92-94; C 94-96; P-in-c Leyton All SS 96-01; V from 01. *All Saints' Vicarage, 47 Melbourne Road, London E10 7HF* Tel (020) 8558 8139 E-mail mholmden@fish.co.uk

HOLME, Thomas Edmund. b 49. Selw Coll Cam BA71 MA75. Coll of Resurr Mirfield 71. **d** 73 **p** 74. C Wyther Ven Bede *Ripon* 73-76; C Wimbledon *S'wark* 76-78; TV 78-79; V Bermondsey St Anne 79-81; V Stamford Baron *Pet* 83-89; P-in-c Tinwell 83-89; Hon Min Can Pet Cathl 84-89; Prec Worc Cathl *Worc* 89-95; P-in-c Penshurst and Fordcombe *Roch* from 95. *The Rectory, Penshurst, Tonbridge TN11 8BN* Tel (01892) 870316

HOLMES, Alan Stewart. b 57. MInstPkg88 St Andr Univ BSc80. Ox NSM Course 85. **d** 88 **p** 89. NSM Shinfield *Ox* 88-95; NSM Beech Hill, Grazeley and Spencers Wood 95-98. *The Cottage, Church Lane, Three Mile Cross, Reading RG7 1HB* Tel 0118-988 2436

HOLMES, Andrew Keith. b 69. Univ of Wales BEng93. St Mich Coll Llan BTh96. **d** 96 **p** 97. C Clydach *S & B* 96-98; C Swansea St Thos and Kilvey 98-00; P-in-c New Radnor and Llanfihangel Nantmelan etc 00-03; V Penrhiwceiber w Matthewstown and Ynysboeth *Llan* from 03. *The Vicarage, Penrhiwceiber, Mountain Ash CF45 3YF* Tel (01443) 473716 E-mail andrew@akholmes.freeserve.co.uk

HOLMES (née PLATT), Mrs Anne Cecilia. b 46. Birm Univ BA67 Ox Univ DipEd68 MInstGA96. St Alb and Ox Min Course 99. **d** 02. NSM Marston w Elsfield *Ox* from 02; Chapl Headington Sch from 02. *59 Oxford Road, Old Marston, Oxford OX3 0PH* Tel (01865) 794916 Mobile 07831-254727 E-mail anne@acholmes.demon.co.uk

HOLMES, Anthony David Robert. b 38. Oak Hill Th Coll 75. **d** 77 **p** 78. C Iver *Ox* 77-81 and from 00; V Bucklebury w Marlston 81-00. *St Peter's House, Delaford Close, Iver SL0 9JX* Tel (01753) 632846 Fax as telephone E-mail tonyholmes@iver.nildram.co.uk

HOLMES, Brian. b 41. Sunderland Univ DipHE95. NEOC 92. **d** 95 **p** 96. NSM Darlington St Matt and St Luke *Dur* 95-98; V from 98. *The Vicarage, 32 Skeldale Grove, Darlington DL3 0GW* Tel (01325) 354669 E-mail brian.holmes@durham.anglican.org

HOLMES, Clive Horace. b 31. Ox NSM Course. **d** 83 **p** 84. NSM Cumnor *Ox* 83-98; Perm to Offic from 98. *62 Westminster Way, Oxford OX2 0LW* Tel (01865) 249640

HOLMES, David Roy. b 34. FCIPD75. Ox NSM Course 81. **d** 84 **p** 85. NSM Ox SS Phil and Jas w St Marg *Ox* 84-85; NSM Ox St Giles and SS Phil and Jas w St Marg 85-99; Lic to Offic from 99; Perm to Offic *St Alb* from 00. *26 Midway, St Albans AL3 4BQ* Tel (01727) 857442

HOLMES, Frank. b 22. NW Ord Course 75. **d** 78 **p** 79. NSM Hyde St Geo *Ches* 78-81; C Poynton 81-87; rtd 87; Perm to Offic *Ches* from 87. *277 Stockport Road, Marple, Stockport SK6 6ES* Tel 0161-449 9289

HOLMES, Geoffrey. *See* HOLMES, Robert John Geoffrey

HOLMES, Geoffrey Robert. b 67. Nottm Univ BSc89. Ridley Hall Cam BA92. **d** 93 **p** 94. C Clifton St Jas *Sheff* 93-98; V Worsbrough St Thos and St Jas from 98. *80 Kingwell Road, Worsbrough, Barnsley S70 4HG* Tel (01226) 286505 E-mail geoffrey.r.holmes@tesco.net

HOLMES, Grant Wenlock. b 54. St Steph Ho Ox BA78 MA83. **d** 79 **p** 80. C Benhilton *S'wark* 79-82; C-in-c S Kenton Annunciation CD *Lon* 82-86; Tutor Chich Th Coll 86-87; Bp's

Dom Chapl *Chich* 86-88; V Mayfield 88-99; P-in-c Mark Cross 97-99; Asst Chapl Lewisham Hosp NHS Trust from 99; Hon C Barnes *S'wark* from 01. *The Chaplain's Office, University Hospital Lewisham, High Street, London SE13 6LH* Tel (020) 8333 3299 E-mail grant.holmes@uhl.nhs.uk

HOLMES, Canon John Robin. b 42. Leeds Univ BA64. Linc Th Coll 64. **d** 66 **p** 67. C Wyther Ven Bede *Ripon* 66-69; C Adel 69-73; V Beeston Hill St Luke 73-76; V Holbeck 76-86; RD Armley 82-86; V Manston 86-93; Hon Can Ripon Cathl 89-98; Dioc Missr 93-98; Can Missr *Wakef* from 98. *5 Kingfisher Grove, Sandal, Wakefield WF2 6SD* Tel (01924) 255832 Mobile 07712-044364 Fax 258761 E-mail john@holmes1.co.uk

HOLMES, Jonathan Michael. b 49. Qu Coll Cam BA70 MA74 VetMB73 PhD78 MRCVS73. Ridley Hall Cam 87. **d** 88 **p** 89. Chapl Qu Coll Cam from 88; Dean of Chpl from 94. *Queens' College, Cambridge CB3 9ET* Tel (01223) 335545 Fax 335522 E-mail jmh38@cam.ac.uk

HOLMES, Judith Ella. b 38. Edin Univ MA62 Dur Univ PhD75 Goldsmiths' Coll Lon PGCE77. Dioc OLM tr scheme 98. **d** 00 **p** 01. OLM Redenhall, Harleston, Wortwell and Needham *Nor* from 00. *Mill Cottage, Mill Lane, Needham, Harleston IP20 9LE* Tel (01379) 854535

HOLMES, Nigel Peter. b 48. Nottm Univ BTh72 Lanc Univ CertEd72 Lon Univ BD76 Sheff Univ MEd84. Kelham Th Coll. **d** 72 **p** 73. C Barrow St Matt *Carl* 72-75; C Derby St Barn *Derby* 75-78; P-in-c Gt Barlow 78-84; V Carl St Herbert w St Steph *Carl* 84-91; V Keswick St Jo 91-94; V Mexborough *Sheff* 94-97; P-in-c Nether Hoyland St Pet 97-98; P-in-c Nether Hoyland St Andr 97-98; V Hoyland from 98. *The Vicarage, 104 Hawshaw Lane, Hoyland, Barnsley S74 0HH* Tel (01226) 749231

HOLMES, Noel Edwin. b 26. Massey Univ (NZ) BA72. St Jo Coll Auckland 48 NZ Bd of Th Studies LTh65. **d** 51 **p** 52. New Zealand 51-56, 58-89 and from 90; C Lewisham St Mary *S'wark* 56-57; C Pallion *Dur* 57; Lisbon *Eur* 89-90. *Unit 4, Bambury Close, Point Chevalier, Auckland 1002, New Zealand* Tel (0064) (9) 846 0574

HOLMES, Mrs Patricia Ann. b 52. N Ord Course 96. **d** 97 **p** 98. C Almondbury w Farnley Tyas *Wakef* 97-00; V Northowram from 00. *The Vicarage, Church Walk, Northowram, Halifax HX3 7HF* Tel (01422) 202551 E-mail standort@surfaid.org

HOLMES, Peter Anthony. b 55. Univ of Wales (Ban) BA77 Brighton Poly CertEd78. Trin Coll Bris DipHE. **d** 88 **p** 89. C Croydon Ch Ch *S'wark* 88-93; V Norbiton from 93; RD Kingston from 97. *The Vicarage, 21 Wolsey Close, Kingston upon Thames KT2 7ER* Tel (020) 8942 8330

HOLMES, Prof Peter Geoffrey. b 32. Bris Univ BSc59 MSc69 Leic Univ PhD74 CEng FIEE. St Deiniol's Hawarden 74. **d** 76 **p** 77. NSM Glen Parva and S Wigston *Leic* 76-02; Prof Nottm Poly 85-92; Prof Nottm Trent Univ 92-96; rtd 02; Perm to Offic *Leic* from 02. *19 Windsor Avenue, Glen Parva, Leicester LE2 9TQ* Tel 0116-277 4534 E-mail peterholmes@iee.org

HOLMES, Robert John Geoffrey. b 28. TCD BA53 MA57. Ely Th Coll 56. **d** 57 **p** 58. C Whitton St Aug CD *Lon* 57-59; C St Pancras w St Jas and Ch Ch 59-63; C Stepney St Dunstan and All SS 63-66; Chapl The Lon Hosp (Whitechapel) 63-68; C Stepney St Aug w St Phil *Lon* 66-68; S Africa 68-74; Perm to Offic *Ely* 74; Perm to Offic *Chich* 74-76; R Telscombe w Piddinghoe and Southease 76-93; P-in-c Barlavington, Burton w Coates, Sutton and Bignor 93-96; rtd 95; Perm to Offic *Chich* 95-01. *7 Buckhurst Road, Telscombe Cliffs, Peacehaven BN10 7AH*

HOLMES, Roger Cockburn. b 46. Jes Coll Ox BA70 MA74 Edin Univ BD76. Edin Th Coll 73. **d** 84 **p** 85. Canada 84-88; R Ditchingham w Pirnough *Nor* 88-90; R Hedenham 88-90; R Broome 88-90; R Ditchingham, Hedenham and Broome 90-93; V Helmsley *York* 93-97. *16 Heslington Road, York YO10 5AT* Tel (01904) 629640 E-mail fatherholmes@hotmail.com

HOLMES, Roy Grant. b 37. Ox NSM Course 83. **d** 86 **p** 87. NSM Wokingham St Paul *Ox* from 86. *58 Copse Drive, Wokingham RG41 1LX* Tel 0118-978 4141

HOLMES, Stanley Thomas. b 11. Selw Coll Cam BA34 MA46. St Steph Ho Ox 34. **d** 36 **p** 37. C Headington *Ox* 36-48; V Goring 48-84; rtd 84; Perm to Offic *Ox* from 84. *30 London Court, London Road, Headington, Oxford OX3 7SL* Tel (01865) 762657

HOLMES, Stephen. b 54. St Andr Univ MTheol84. Chich Th Coll 84. **d** 86 **p** 87. C Croydon St Jo *S'wark* 86-89; C Tewkesbury w Walton Cardiff *Glouc* 89-92; P-in-c Bournemouth St Luke *Win* 92-94; V from 94. *St Luke's Vicarage, 31 Lonsdale Road, Bournemouth BH3 7LY* Tel (01202) 516653

HOLMES, Stephen John. b 50. CertEd72 DipHE83. Trin Coll Bris 81 Sarum & Wells Th Coll 88. **d** 89 **p** 90. C Skegness and Winthorpe *Linc* 89-93; P-in-c Mablethorpe w Trusthorpe 93-97; V Hadleigh St Barn *Chelmsf* from 97. *St Barnabas' Vicarage, 169 Church Road, Hadleigh, Benfleet SS7 2EJ* Tel (01702) 554658

HOLMES, William John. b 49. **d** 97 **p** 98. Aux Min Billy w Derrykeighan *Conn* 97-02; Aux Min Ballymoney w Finvoy and Rasharkin from 02. *14 Glenlough Park, Coleraine BT52 1TY* Tel (028) 7035 5993

HOLMYARD, Mrs Deborah. b 58. Open Univ BA90 PGCE96. Th Ext Educn Coll 89. **d** 92 **p** 95. C Pretoria St Fran S Africa

92-93; Perm to Offic *S'wark* 93-94; NSM Merton St Mary 94-96; Asst Chapl HM Pris Brixton 96-97; P-in-c Barton Hill St Luke w Ch Ch and Moorfields *Bris* from 02. *St Luke's Vicarage, 60 Barton Hill Road, Bristol BS5 0AW* Tel 0117-955 5947 Mobile 07766-035131 E-mail dholmyard@yahoo.co.uk

HOLNESS, Edwin Geoffrey Nicholas. b 39. RGN. Sarum Th Coll 68. **d** 71 **p** 72. C Upper Beeding *Chich* 71-74; C Bramber w Botolphs 71-74; C Munster Square St Mary Magd *Lon* 74-75; Perm to Offic *Chich* 75-76; C Brighton Annunciation 76-77; Chapl Brighton Hosp Gp 77-94; Chapl R Sussex Co Hosp Brighton 77-94; Perm to Offic *Chich* 77-99; P-in-c Southwick St Pet 99-02; rtd 02. *15 Roedean Court, Brighton BN2 5RT* Tel (01273) 620333

HOLROYD, John Richard. b 54. Liv Univ BA75 PGCE77. Wycliffe Hall Ox 78. **d** 81 **p** 82. C Gt Stanmore *Lon* 81-84; Min Can, V Choral and Prec St E Cathl *St E* 84-89; TV Wolverton *Ox* 89-96; P-in-c Maidenhead St Luke from 96. *St Luke's Vicarage, 26 Norfolk Road, Maidenhead SL6 7AX* Tel (01628) 783033 E-mail rholroyd@dircon.co.uk

HOLROYD, Stephen Charles. b 56. UEA BA79. St Jo Coll Nottm 84. **d** 87 **p** 88. C Barton Seagrave w Warkton *Pet* 87-91; V Eye 91-97; V Silsoe, Pulloxhill and Flitton *St Alb* from 97. *The Vicarage, Firtree Road, Silsoe, Bedford MK45 4DU* Tel (01525) 862380 E-mail silsoe.vicarage@tesco.net

HOLT, Canon David. b 44. St Jo Coll Dur BSc67 DipTh69. **d** 70 **p** 71. C Blackley St Pet *Man* 70-73; C Radcliffe St Thos 73-74; C Radcliffe St Thos and St Jo 74-75; V Ashton St Pet 75-79; Dioc Youth Officer *Guildf* 80-85; V Bagshot 85-97; RD Surrey Heath 92-97; V Fleet from 97; RD Aldershot from 98; Hon Can Guildf Cathl from 99. *The Vicarage, Branksomewood Road, Fleet GU51 4JU* Tel (01252) 616361 Fax 819771 E-mail dholt55075@aol.com

HOLT, Canon Douglas Robert. b 49. MA. Ridley Hall Cam. **d** 82 **p** 83. C Cambridge St Barn *Ely* 82-84; P-in-c 84-86; V 86-91; V Ealing St Mary *Lon* 91-98; Can Res Bris Cathl *Bris* from 98; Dir Par Development Team from 98. *9 Leigh Road, Clifton, Bristol BS8 2DA* Tel 0117-973 7427

HOLT, Francis Thomas. b 38. Edin Th Coll 79. **d** 81 **p** 82. C Cullercoats St Geo *Newc* 81-83; C Ponteland 83-86; Chapl Worc Coll of HE 86-89; R Worc St Clem *Worc* 86-93; V Finstall 93-96; Chapl Menorca *Eur* 96-97; Perm to Offic *Worc* from 97; rtd 98. *10 Ash Close, Malvern WR14 2WF* Tel (01684) 575507

HOLT, Harold. b 20. **d** 52 **p** 52. Dioc Supernumerary *Ab* 52; P-in-c Burravoe 52-56; R Strichen 56-60; V Haslingden St Jo Stonefold *Blackb* 60-72; V Blackb St Aid 72-85; rtd 85; Perm to Offic *Blackb* from 85. *24 Scott Avenue, Baxenden, Accrington BB5 2XA* Tel (01254) 396474

HOLT, Jack Derek. b 38. Trin Coll Bris 71. **d** 73 **p** 74. C Daubhill *Man* 73-76; P-in-c Thornham w Gravel Hole 76-79; V 79-83; R Talke *Lich* 83-93; V Cotmanhay *Derby* 93-03; Chapl S Derbyshire Community and Mental Health Trust 93-03; rtd 03. *31 Hatherton Close, Newcastle ST5 7SN* Tel (01782) 560845

HOLT, James Edward. b 49. St Martin's Coll Lanc BA94 PGCE95. N Ord Course 99. **d** 02 **p** 03. NSM Holme-in-Cliviger w Worsthorne *Blackb* from 02. *5 Graham Street, Padiham, Burnley BB12 8RW* Tel (01282) 778319

HOLT, Keith. b 37. CPFA62. S'wark Ord Course. **d** 82 **p** 83. NSM Selsdon St Jo w St Fran *Cant* 82-84; NSM Selsdon St Jo w St Fran *S'wark* from 85. *12 Ridge Langley, South Croydon CR2 0AR* Tel (020) 8651 1815

HOLT, Mrs Lucinda Jane. b 65. Open Univ BSc00. Wycliffe Hall Ox 01. **d** 03. C Newton Longville and Mursley w Swanbourne etc *Ox* from 03. *The Rectory, Drayton Road, Newton Longville, Milton Keynes MK17 0BH* Tel (01908) 377847 E-mail andrew-lucy@tinyworld.co.uk

HOLT, Michael. b 38. Univ of Wales (Lamp) BA61 DipTh63. **d** 63 **p** 64. C Stand *Man* 63-69; V Bacup St Jo from 69; AD Rossendale 98-00. *St John's Vicarage, Bankside Lane, Bacup OL13 8HG* Tel (01706) 873275

HOLT, Shirley Ann. LNSM course 97. **d** 98 **p** 99. OLM High Oak, Hingham and Scoulton w Wood Rising *Nor* from 98. *Westfields, Church Lane, Wicklewood, Wymondham NR18 9QH* Tel (01953) 603668 E-mail saholt@talk21.com

HOLT, Stuart Henry. b 52. Bath Univ BEd78. Ridley Hall Cam 84. **d** 87 **p** 88. C Locks Heath *Portsm* 87-90; Chapl RAF 89-91; C Worthing St Geo *Chich* 91-93; C Portchester *Portsm* 93-95; Perm to Offic 02-03; P-in-c Soberton w Newtown from 03. *The Vicarage, School Hill, Soberton, Southampton SO32 3PF* Tel (01489) 877400

HOLT, Susan Mary. b 45. Coll of Ripon & York St Jo MA98. Nor Ord Course 97. **d** 97 **p** 98. NSM Longwood *Wakef* 97-00; NSM Liversedge w Hightown from 00. *229/231 Stainland Road, Holywell Green, Halifax HX4 9AJ* Tel (01422) 376481

HOLTAM, Nicholas Roderick. b 54. Collingwood Coll Dur BA75 K Coll Lon BD78 AKC78 Dur Univ MA86. Westcott Ho Cam 78. **d** 79 **p** 80. C Stepney St Dunstan and All SS *Lon* 79-83; Tutor Linc Th Coll 83-88; V Is of Dogs Ch Ch and St Jo w St Luke *Lon* 88-95; V St Martin-in-the-Fields from 95. *6 St Martin's*

Place, London WC2N 4JH Tel (020) 7766 1100 Fax 7839 5163 E-mail clergyoffice@stmartininthefields.freeserve

HOLTH, Oystein Johan. b 31. Open Univ BA75. AKC54. **d** 54 **p** 55. C Greenford H Cross *Lon* 54-56; Br N Borneo and Sarawak 56-63; E Malaysia 63-67; Chapl OHP 67-75; Chapl St Hilda's Sch Whitby 67-75; P-in-c Pimlico St Barn *Lon* 75-97; Ind Chapl 75-97; rtd 97; Perm to Offic *Lon* from 97. *13 Dollis Park, London N3 1HJ* Tel (020) 8346 8131

HOLYER, Vincent Alfred Douglas. b 28. Ex Univ BA54. Oak Hill Th Coll 54. **d** 56 **p** 57. C Bethnal Green St Jas Less *Lon* 56-58; C Braintree *Chelmsf* 58-61; V Islington All SS *Lon* 61-65; R St Ruan w St Grade *Truro* 65-85; V Constantine 85-91; rtd 91; Perm to Offic *Truro* from 91. *22 Warwick Avenue, Illogan, Redruth TR16 4DZ*

HOLZAPFEL, Peter Rudolph. b 51. St Jo Coll Nottm 84. **d** 86 **p** 87. C St Jo in Bedwardine *Worc* 86-89; R Kempsey and Severn Stoke w Croome d'Abitot from 99. *The Rectory, 3 Oakfield Drive, Kempsey, Worcester WR5 3PP* Tel (01905) 820202

HOMER, Alan Fellows. b 30. Ridley Hall Cam 61. **d** 63 **p** 64. C Heref St Jas *Heref* 63-66; V Brixton Hill St Sav *S'wark* 66-73; Dep Chapl HM Pris Brixton 66-70; CF (TA) 70-73; CF 73-76; V Heeley *Sheff* 75-87; R Cheveley *Ely* 87-95; R Ashley w Silverley 87-95; V Wood Ditton w Saxon Street 87-95; V Kirtling 87-95; RD Linton 94-95; rtd 95; Perm to Offic *Bris* from 95; *Ox* 95-01. *62 The Willows, Highworth, Swindon SN6 7PH* Tel (01793) 764023 Fax as telephone

HOMER, Antony James. b 72. La Sainte Union Coll BTh95 Leeds Univ MA02 Southn Univ PGCE96. Coll of Resurr Mirfield 00. **d** 02 **p** 03. C St Leonards Ch Ch and St Mary *Chich* from 02. *17 Alfred Street, St Leonards-on-Sea TN38 0HD* Tel (01424) 433614 E-mail frantonyh@hotmail.com

HOMEWOOD, Michael John. b 33. Wells Th Coll 69. **d** 71 **p** 72. C Ilfracombe H Trin *Ex* 71-72; C Ilfracombe, Lee and W Down 72-75; P-in-c Woolacombe 76-78; TV Ilfracombe, Lee, W Down, Woolacombe and Bittadon 78-82; TR S Molton w Nymet St George, High Bray etc 82-97; RD S Molton 93-95; rtd 97; Perm to Offic *Sarum* from 97. *5 Avon Drive, Wareham BH20 4EL* Tel (01929) 556216

HOMEWOOD, Peter Laurence de Silvie. b 58. Oriel Coll Ox BA80 MA84. St Steph Ho Ox 90. **d** 92 **p** 93. C Ruislip St Martin *Lon* 92-96; R Hayes St Mary from 96; P-in-c Hayes St Anselm from 03. *The Rectory, 170 Church Road, Hayes UB3 2LR* Tel (020) 8573 2470 E-mail peter@hayes-rectory.demon.co.uk

HOMFRAY, John Bax Tayler. b 29. Keble Coll Ox BA52 MA. Ridley Hall Cam 52. **d** 54 **p** 55. C Kingswood *Bris* 54-57; C Leckhampton St Pet *Glouc* 57-64; V Staverton w Boddington 64-86; V Staverton w Boddington and Tredington etc 87-95; rtd 95; Perm to Offic *Glouc* from 95. *Nazareth House, London Road, Cheltenham GL52 6YJ* Tel (01242) 516361

HOMFRAY, Kenyon Lee James. b 55. TCD BTh99 Univ of Wales (Cardiff) LLM02. CITC 96. **d** 99 **p** 00. C Convoy w Monellan and Donaghmore *D & R* 99-02; I from 02. *The Rectory, Convoy, Lifford, Co Donegal, Irish Republic* Tel (00353) (74) 914 7164

HONE, Canon Frank Leslie. b 11. Kelham Th Coll 32. **d** 38 **p** 39. C Sheff Arbourthorne *Sheff* 38-40; CF (EC) 40-45; C Sheff St Anne and St Phil *Sheff* 45-46; C Rotherham 46-49; V Brightside St Thos 49-53; R Attercliffe w Carbrook 53-60; P-in-c Sheff St Swithun 60-66; V Frodingham *Linc* 66-78; RD Manlake 69-76; Can and Preb Linc Cathl 72-78; rtd 78; Perm to Offic *Linc* from 78. *Morcote, 13 Roselea Avenue, Welton, Lincoln LN2 3RT* Tel (01673) 861548

HONES, Simon Anthony. b 54. Sussex Univ BSc75. Qu Coll Birm DipTh78. **d** 79 **p** 80. C Win Ch Ch *Win* 79-82; C Basing 82-88; Min Chineham CD 88-90; V Surbiton St Matt *S'wark* from 90. *St Matthew's Vicarage, 20 Kingsdowne Road, Surbiton KT6 6JZ* Tel (020) 8399 4853 E-mail shones@netcomuk.co.uk

HONEY, Canon Frederick Bernard. b 22. Selw Coll Cam BA48 MA72. Wells Th Coll 48. **d** 50 **p** 51. C S'wark St Geo *S'wark* 50-52; C Claines St Jo *Worc* 52-55; V Wollaston 55-87; RD Stourbridge 72-83; Hon Can Worc Cathl 75-87; rtd 87. *38 Park Farm, Bourton-on-the-Water, Cheltenham GL54 2HF* Tel (01451) 822218

HONEY, Thomas David. b 56. Lon Univ BA78. Ripon Coll Cuddesdon 80. **d** 83 **p** 84. C Mill End and Heronsgate w W Hyde *St Alb* 83-86; C Stepney St Dunstan and All SS *Lon* 86-89; TV High Wycombe *Ox* 89-95; P-in-c Headington Quarry from 95. *The Vicarage, Quarry Road, Headington, Oxford OX3 8NU* Tel (01865) 762931 E-mail tom.honey@ukonline.co.uk

HONG KONG, Dean of. See PHILLIPS, The Very Revd Christopher John

HONG KONG ISLAND, Bishop of. See KWONG KONG KIT, The Most Revd Peter

HONG KONG SHENG KUNG HUI, Archbishop of. See KWONG KONG KIT, The Most Revd Peter

HONNER, Canon Robert Ralph. b 15. St Chad's Coll Dur BA37 DipTh38 MA40. **d** 38 **p** 39. C Gt Crosby St Faith *Liv* 38-41; P-in-c Wigan St Andr 41-44; C Rugby St Andr *Cov* 44-49; V Derby St Barn *Derby* 49-53; V Melbourne 54-72; RD Melbourne

54-67; Hon Can Derby Cathl 58-80; V Beeley and Edensor 72-80; RD Bakewell and Eyam 73-78; rtd 80; Perm to Offic *Derby* from 80. *5 Castle Mews, Blackwell Lane, Melbourne, Derby DE73 1LW* Tel (01332) 864356

HONNOR, Jonathan Michael Bellamy. b 62. Leeds Univ BA84 Kent Univ PGCE89. Stavanger Sch of Miss and Th 98. **d** 00. Norway 00-03; C Warren Park *Portsm* from 03; C Leigh Park from 03. *St Clare's House, Strouden Court Precinct, Havant PO9 4JX* Tel (023) 9245 1762 Mobile 07729-837753
E-mail mikehonnor@netscape.net

HONNOR, Mrs Marjorie Rochefort. b 27. Birm Univ BA48. Cranmer Hall Dur 79. **dss** 81 **d** 87 **p** 94. Church Oakley and Wootton St Lawrence *Win* 81-87; Par Dn 87-89; rtd 89; Perm to Offic *Win* from 98. *33C Surrey Road, Bournemouth BH4 9BJ* Tel (01202) 761021

HONOR MARGARET, Sister. *See* McILROY, Sister Honor Margaret

HONOUR, Colin Reginald. b 44. Lanc Univ CertEd69 Man Univ AdDipEd75 Newc Univ MEd80. N Ord Course 88. **d** 91 **p** 92. NSM Walmsley *Man* 91; C Middleton 92-94; R Holcombe 94-01; P-in-c Hawkshaw Lane 99-01; P-in-c Aldingham, Dendron, Rampside and Urswick *Carl* 01-03; R from 03. *The Vicarage, Church Road, Great Urswick, Ulverston LA12 0TA* Tel (01229) 581383 E-mail cnchonour@btinternet.com

HONOUR, Derek Gordon. b 59. Bath Univ BSc84. St Jo Coll Nottm. **d** 89 **p** 90. C High Wycombe *Ox* 89-91; C Brightside w Wincobank *Sheff* 91-94; P-in-c Dawley St Jerome *Lon* 94-01; C Derby St Alkmund and St Werburgh *Derby* from 01. *54 Park Grove, Derby DE22 1HF* Tel (01332) 331927
E-mail derekhonour@compuserve.com

HONOUR, Mrs Joanna Clare. b 61. Westmr Coll Ox BEd83. St Jo Coll Nottm LTh88 DPS89. **d** 89 **p** 94. Par Dn High Wycombe *Ox* 89-91; Par Dn Brightside w Wincobank *Sheff* 91-94; C 94; Perm to Offic *Lon* 94-96; Dep Chapl HM Pris Wandsworth 95-97; NSM Dawley St Jerome *Lon* 96-01; Chapl HM Pris The Mount 97; Perm to Offic *Derby* from 01; Chapl HM Pris Foston Hall from 01. *Foston Hall, Foston, Derby DE65 5DN* Tel (01283) 584325 *or* (01332) 331927
E-mail derekhonour@compuserve.com

HONOUR, Jonathan Paul. b 68. Ox Brookes Univ BSc90 Greenwich Univ PGCE91. St Jo Coll Nottm MA98 DipMM99. **d** 99 **p** 00. C Tonbridge St Steph *Roch* 99-03; TV Woodley *Ox* from 03. *171 Hurricane Way, Woodley, Reading RG5 4UH* Tel 0118-969 2981 Mobile 07752-241255
E-mail jon.honour@ntlworld.com

HOOD, Mrs Doreen. b 38. Open Univ BA90 SRN59 RFN61. NEOC 90. **d** 93 **p** 94. NSM Cullercoats St Geo *Newc* 93-99; NSM Monkseaton St Pet 99-00; P-in-c Newc St Hilda from 00. *24 Keswick Drive, North Shields NE30 3EW* Tel 0191-253 1762

HOOD, Leslie. b 23. NEOC. **d** 85 **p** 85. NSM Seaham w Seaham Harbour *Dur* 85-90; NSM Dalton le Dale 90-93; NSM Hawthorn 90-93; rtd 93; Perm to Offic *Dur* from 93. *3 Queen Street, Seaham SR7 7SR* Tel 0191-581 2658
E-mail leslie@hood71.freeserve.co.uk

HOOD, Peter Michael. b 47. Sheff Univ BSc68 St Pet Coll Ox DipTh72. Wycliffe Hall Ox 70. **d** 73 **p** 74. C Soundwell *Bris* 73-76; P-in-c Walcot St Andr CD 76-77; TV Swindon St Jo and St Andr 77-80; V Esh *Dur* 80-88; V Hamsteels 80-88; V Stockton St Paul 88-00; P-in-c Penshaw from 00; P-in-c Shiney Row from 00; P-in-c Herrington from 00. *All Saints' Rectory, Old Penshaw, Houghton le Spring DH4 7ER* Tel 0191-584 2631
E-mail peter.hood@rohlfing-hood.freeserve.co.uk

HOOD, Canon Thomas Henry Havelock. b 24. Chich Th Coll 51. **d** 54 **p** 55. C Stella *Dur* 54-57; Australia from 57; Hon Can Brisbane from 88; rtd 93. *18 Moonyean Street, Bellbird Park, Qld, Australia 4300* Tel (0061) (7) 3288 5106
E-mail havelock@gil.com.au

HOOGERWERF, John Constant. b 50. MIH86 Bris Poly BA85. Oscott Coll (RC) 68. **d** 73 **p** 74. In RC Ch 73-84; Hon C Davyhulme Ch Ch *Man* 84-93; Perm to Offic *Heref* from 93. *14 Foster Road, Bridgnorth WV16 4LS* Tel (01746) 766328

HOOK, Ian Kevin. b 57. Trin Coll Bris DipHE95. **d** 95 **p** 96. C Dalton-in-Furness *Carl* 95-98; C Newbarns w Hawcoat 98-01; V Barrow St Mark from 01. *St Mark's Vicarage, Rawlinson Street, Barrow-in-Furness LA14 1BX* Tel (01229) 820405

HOOK, Neil. b 73. Univ of Wales (Swansea) BA94 Univ of Wales (Cardiff) BD96. St Mich Coll Llan 94. **d** 97 **p** 98. C Brecon St Mary and Battle w Llanddew *S & B* 97-99; Min Can Brecon Cathl 97-99; P-in-c Llanllyr-yn-Rhos w Llanfihangel Helygen 99-00; V Upper Wye from 00. *The Vicarage, Highbury, Llanyre, Llandrindod Wells LD1 6NF* Tel (01597) 822472

HOOKER, Richard Malcolm Neil. b 38. Lon Univ BDS63 LDS63. Guildf Dioc Min Course. **d** 98 **p** 99. OLM Ashtead *Guildf* from 98. *Lanacre Cottage, 4 Farm Close, Fetcham KT22 9BJ* Tel (01372) 372446 Mobile 07802-961686

HOOLE, Charles. b 33. St Aid Birkenhead 61. **d** 63 **p** 64. C Skerton St Luke *Blackb* 63-65; P-in-c Preston St Jas 65-69; V Lostock Hall 69-73; Chapl HM Pris Eastchurch 74-75; V St Annes St Marg *Blackb* 75-81; V S Shore St Pet 81-92; C

Laneside 92-94; rtd 95; Perm to Offic *Blackb* from 95. *32 Hanover Crescent, Blackpool FY2 9DL* Tel (01253) 353564

HOOPER, Preb Derek Royston. b 33. St Edm Hall Ox BA57 MA65. Cuddesdon Coll 57. **d** 59 **p** 60. C Gt Walsingham *Nor* 59-62; C Townstall w Dartmouth *Ex* 62-65; V Lynton and Brendon 65-69; C Littleham w Exmouth 70-72; TV 72-79; R Wrington w Butcombe *B & W* 79-94; Preb Wells Cathl 93-94; rtd 94; Perm to Offic *Ex* 95; B & W 95-00. *23 Dagmar Road, Exmouth EX8 2AN* Tel (01395) 272831

HOOPER, Geoffrey Michael. b 39. MBE00. K Coll Lon 61. **d** 66 **p** 67. C Chesterfield St Mary and All SS *Derby* 66-69; Chapl RAF 69-74; P-in-c Hook Norton w Swerford and Wigginton *Ox* 74-80; P-in-c Gt Rollright 75-80; R Hook Norton w Gt Rollright, Swerford etc 80-82; Warden Mansf Ho Univ Settlement Plaistow 82-00; Dir 86-00; rtd 03. *Ty'n Twil, Penbodias, Llaniestyn, Pwllheli LL53 8SD* Tel (01758) 730526
E-mail geoffreyhooper@lineone.net

HOOPER, Ian. b 44. St Jo Coll York CertEd67. Trin Coll Bris DipHE88. **d** 88 **p** 89. C Martlesham w Brightwell *St E* 88-92; R Pakenham w Norton and Tostock from 92; RD Ixworth from 03. *The Vicarage, Church Hill, Pakenham, Bury St Edmunds IP31 2LN* Tel (01359) 230287
E-mail hooper@pakvic.freeserve.co.uk

✠**HOOPER, The Rt Revd Michael Wrenford.** b 41. Univ of Wales (Lamp) BA63. St Steph Ho Ox 63. **d** 65 **p** 66 **c** 02. C Bridgnorth St Mary *Heref* 65-70; P-in-c Habberley 70-78; 78-81; V Minsterley 70-81; RD Pontesbury 75-80; Preb Heref Cathl 81-02; V Leominster 81-85; TR Leominster 85-97; P-in-c Eyton 81-85; RD Leominster 81-97; P-in-c Eye, Croft w Yarpole and Lucton 91-97; Adn Heref 97-02; Suff Bp Ludlow from 02; Adn Ludlow from 02. *Bishop's House, Corvedale Road, Craven Arms SY7 9BT* Tel (01588) 673571 Fax 673585
E-mail bishopofludlow@ukf.net

HOOPER, Paul Denis Gregory. b 52. Man Univ BA75 Ox Univ BA80 MA87. Wycliffe Hall Ox 78. **d** 81 **p** 82. C Leeds St Geo *Ripon* 81-84; Dioc Youth Officer 84-87; Bp's Dom Chapl 87-95; Dioc Communications Officer 87-95; V Harrogate St Mark from 95. *The Vicarage, 15 Wheatlands Road, Harrogate HG2 8BB* Tel (01423) 504959 E-mail stmarks@hgate.totalserve.co.uk

HOOPER, Peter Guy. b 30. St Coll Lon 51. **d** 55 **p** 56. C Huddersfield St Pet *Wakef* 55-60; C Brompton H Trin *Lon* 60-67; R Hazelbury Bryan w Stoke Wake etc *Sarum* 72-84; R Yetminster w Ryme Intrinseca and High Stoy 84-93; RD Sherborne 87-91; rtd 93; Perm to Offic *B & W* and *Sarum* from 93. *Rose Villa, Long Street, Sherborne DT9 3DD* Tel (01935) 816819

HOOPER, Sydney Paul. b 46. QUB BA68 Lanc Univ CertEd69. **d** 85 **p** 87. NSM Killaney w Carryduff *D & D* 85-91; Lic to Offic from 91; NSM Belfast St Chris 01-03; NSM Ballymacarrett from 03. *26 Manse Park, Carryduff, Belfast BT8 8RX* Tel (028) 9081 5607 *or* 9056 6289

HOOPER, William Gilbert. b 38. Ex Univ BA60. St Mich Coll Llan DipTh82. **d** 82 **p** 83. C Hubberston w Herbrandston and Hasguard etc *St D* 82-85; R Llangwm and Freystrop 85-97; R Llangwm w Freystrop and Johnston from 97. *The Rectory, Four Winds, Llangwm, Haverfordwest SA62 4NG* Tel (01437) 891317

HOOTON, David James. b 50. St Kath Coll Liv CertEd72 DipRE81. N Ord Course 83. **d** 86 **p** 87. NSM Pemberton St Mark Newtown *Liv* 86-89; C Ashton-in-Makerfield St Thos 89-92; V Bryn from 92. *The Vicarage, 12 Bryn Road, Ashton-in-Makerfield, Wigan WN4 0AA* Tel (01942) 727114

HOPCRAFT, Jonathan Richard. b 34. Oriel Coll Ox BA55 DipEd66 MA66. Westcott Ho Cam 57. **d** 59 **p** 60. C Cannock *Lich* 59-63; N Rhodesia 63-64; S Rhodesia 64-65; Hon C Olton *Birm* 66-68; Antigua 68-72; C Gt Grimsby St Mary and St Jas *Linc* 72; TV 72-76; P-in-c E Stockwith 76-84; V Blyton w Pilham 76-84; P-in-c Laughton w Wildsworth 76-84; TV Bilston *Lich* 84-90; P-in-c Wolverhampton St Jo 90-98; C Wolverhampton 97-98; TV Cen Wolverhampton 98-00; rtd 00; Perm to Offic *Chelmsf* from 01. *13 Nabbott Road, Chelmsford CM1 2SW* Tel (01245) 263983 E-mail jonhopcraft@supanet.com

HOPE, Charles Henry. b 64. Regent's Park Coll Ox BA87 MA90. St Jo Coll Dur BA90. **d** 90 **p** 91. C Tynemouth St Jo *Newc* 90-94; V 94-03; P-in-c Prudhoe from 03. *The Vicarage, 5 Kepwell Court, Prudhoe NE42 5PE* Tel (01661) 836059 Mobile 07884-070619
E-mail charleshope@lineone.net

HOPE, Colin Frederick. b 49. St Mich Coll Llan 73. **d** 76 **p** 77. C Warrington St Elphin *Liv* 76-80; V Newton-le-Willows 80-84; CSWG from 84; Lic to Offic *Chich* from 88. *The Monastery, Crawley Down, Crawley RH10 4LH* Tel (01342) 712074

✠**HOPE, The Most Revd and Rt Hon David Michael.** b 40. KCVO95 PC91. Nottm Univ BA62 Linacre Ho Ox DPhil65 Hon FGMS94. St Steph Ho Ox 62. **d** 65 **p** 66 **c** 85. C W Derby St Jo *Liv* 65-67 and 68-70; Chapl Bucharest *Eur* 67-68; V Orford St Andr *Liv* 70-74; Prin St Steph Ho Ox 74-82; V St Marylebone All SS *Lon* 82-85; Master of Guardians Shrine of Our Lady of Walsingham 82-93; Bp Wakef 85-91; Bp Lon 91-95; Dean of HM Chpls Royal and Prelate of OBE 91-95; Abp York from 95.

The Palace, Bishopthorpe, York YO23 2QE Tel (01904) 707021 *or* 707022 Fax 709204 E-mail office@bishopthorpepalace.co.uk

HOPE, Miss Edith. b 43. SRN64 SCM66 HVCert72 Lanc Univ MA86. Wycliffe Hall Ox 89. **d** 91 **p** 94. Par Dn Droylsden St Mary *Man* 91-94; Par Dn Ecclesall *Sheff* 94; C 94-01; V Crosspool from 01. *The Vicarage, 1 Barnfield Road, Sheffield S10 5TD* Tel 0114-230 2531 E-mail edith.hope@btclick.com

HOPE, Robert. b 36. Dur Univ BSc61. Clifton Th Coll 61. **d** 63 **p** 64. C Woking St Mary *Guildf* 63-66; C Surbiton Hill Ch Ch *S'wark* 66-68; Th Students' Sec IVF 68-71; Hon C Wallington H Trin *S'wark* 69-71; C Ox St Ebbe w St Pet *Ox* 71-74; V Walshaw Ch Ch *Man* 74-87; TR Radipole and Melcombe Regis *Sarum* 87-93; rtd 93; Perm to Offic *St D* from 93. *1A Swiss Valley, Felinfael, Llanelli SA14 8BS* Tel (01554) 759199

HOPE, Canon Susan. b 49. St Jo Coll Dur BA83. Cranmer Hall Dur 80. dss 83 **d** 87 **p** 94. Boston Spa *York* 83-86; Brightside w Wincobank *Sheff* 86-97; Par Dn 87-89; Dn-in-c 89-94; V 94-97; V Chapeltown 97-02; Dioc Missr from 02; RD Tankersley 00-02; Hon Can Sheff Cathl from 00; Six Preacher Cant Cathl *Cant* from 99. *42 Oswin Avenue, Balby, Doncaster DN4 0PA* Tel (01302) 858225 E-mail shope12443@aol.com

HOPEWELL, Jeffery Stewart. b 52. ACA79 Leic Univ BA75. EMMTC 82. **d** 85 **p** 86. NSM Houghton on the Hill w Keyham *Leic* 85-88; NSM Houghton-on-the-Hill, Keyham and Hungarton 88-91; C Syston 91-93; TV Syston 93-97; Bp's Ecum Adv 91-97; P-in-c Wymeswold and Prestwold w Hoton from 97. *The Vicarage, 5 The Stockwell, Wymeswold, Loughborough LE12 6UF* Tel (01509) 880275
E-mail jhopewell@leicester.anglican.org

HOPKIN, David James. b 67. Qu Coll Birm BTh94 Ripon Coll Cuddesdon DipMin99. **d** 99 **p** 00. C Wickford and Runwell *Chelmsf* 99-02; TV Penistone and Thurlstone *Wakef* from 02. *The Vicarage, Manchester Road, Thurlstone, Sheffield S36 9QS* E-mail hopkin@tesco.net

HOPKIN, Gerallt. b 12. Univ of Wales BA36. Sarum Th Coll 37. **d** 38 **p** 39. C Aberdare St Fagan *Llan* 38-40; C Caerau St Cynfelin 40-44; C Gelligaer 44-50; V Penrhiwceiber 50-55; V Penrhiwceiber and Tyntetown w Ynysboeth 55-68; R St Fagans w Michaelston-super-Ely 68-77; rtd 77; Perm to Offic *Llan* from 79. *25B Tangmere Drive, Fairwood Chase, Cardiff CF5 2PP* Tel (029) 2055 3985

HOPKIN, Neil Richard. b 67. Nottm Univ BTh95 Brunel Univ PGCE97 Lon Univ MA99. St Jo Coll Nottm. **d** 95. C Easton H Trin w St Gabr and St Lawr and St Jude *Bris* 95. *Address temp unknown* E-mail neilhopkin@cyberdude.com

HOPKINS, Mrs Angela Joan. b 42. Bp Otter Coll Chich CertEd64. S Dios Minl Tr Scheme 92. **d** 95 **p** 96. NSM Kingsbury H Innocents *Lon* from 95. *3 Regal Way, Harrow HA3 0RZ* Tel (020) 8907 1045

HOPKINS, Miss Barbara Agnes. b 28. Lon Univ BSc60 Imp Coll Lon DIC66 MPhil67 DipRS80. St Alb Minl Tr Scheme 82. dss 85 **d** 87. Bedford All SS *St Alb* 85-86; Chapl Asst Bedf Gen Hosp 86-88; Bedford St Mich *St Alb* 88-98; Hon Par Dn 87-88; Chapl Asst N Lincs Mental Health Unit 89-91; rtd 91; Perm to Offic *Linc* 93-95. *1 St Anne's Bedehouses, Sewell Road, Lincoln LN2 5QS* Tel (01522) 513359

HOPKINS, Brenda Alison. b 63. St Martin's Coll Lanc BA95 Anglia Poly Univ MA97. Westcott Ho Cam 95. **d** 97 **p** 98. C Camberwell St Geo *S'wark* 97-00; Chapl Nor City Coll of F&HE *Nor* from 00. *Student Services Department, City College, Ipswich Road, Norwich NR2 2LJ* Tel (01603) 773538 *or* 773064 E-mail bhopkins@ccn.ac.uk

HOPKINS, Christopher Freeman. b 41. Dur Univ BA63. Wells Th Coll 63. **d** 65 **p** 66. C Spring Park *Cant* 65-69; S Africa 69-78; Botswana 78-81; R Beckley and Peasmarsh *Chich* from 81. *The Rectory, School Lane, Peasmarsh, Rye TN31 6UW* Tel (01797) 230255 Fax as telephone

HOPKINS, Ernest. b 16. Tyndale Hall Bris 68. **d** 69 **p** 70. C Walton Breck *Liv* 69-70; P-in-c Everton St Chrys 70-74; P-in-c Everton St Jo 70-74; P-in-c Everton Em 70-74; V Everton St Chrys 74-79; RD Walton 76-79; V Eccleston St Luke 79-83; rtd 83; Perm to Offic *St A* from 84 and *Ches* from 88. *12 Shetland Drive, Bromborough, Wirral CH62 7JZ* Tel 0151-334 4044

HOPKINS, Henry Charles. b 46. RD87. Edin Th Coll 65. **d** 71 **p** 72. C Dundee St Salvador *Bre* 71-74; C Dundee St Martin 71-74; Chapl RNVR from 72; R Monifieth *Bre* 74-78; Chapl Miss to Seamen Kenya 78-85; Singapore 85-92; Offg Chapl NZ Defence Force 89-92; Chapl Miss to Seamen Teesside 92-94; V N Thornaby from 94. *St Paul's Vicarage, 60 Lanehouse Road, Thornaby, Stockton-on-Tees TS17 8EA* Tel and fax (01642) 868086
E-mail harry.hopkins@ntlworld.com

HOPKINS, Hugh. b 33. TCD BA. **d** 62 **p** 63. C Ballymena *Conn* 62-64; C Belfast Ch Ch 64-67; I Ballintoy 67-72; I Belfast St Ninian 72-81; I Mossley 81-86; I Ballywillan 86-96; Can Belf Cathl 94-96; rtd 96. *2 Bush Gardens, Ballyness, Bushmills BT57 8AE* Tel (028) 7073 2981

HOPKINS, Ian Richard. b 70. Dur Univ BA92 Ox Univ BTh00. **d** 00. C Edin St Thos *Edin* from 00. *81 Glasgow Road, Edinburgh EH12 8LJ* Tel 0131-334 4434 *or* 316 4292

HOPKINS, John Dawson. b 39. Chich Th Coll 85. **d** 87 **p** 88. C Walker *Newc* 87-89; C Newc St Fran 89-92; V Horton 92-00; rtd 00; Perm to Offic *Newc* from 01. *Amen Cottage, 31 High Fair, Wooler NE71 6PA* Tel (07790) 915763

HOPKINS, John Edgar Alexander. b 19. TD65. Jes Coll Cam BA46 MA48. Wells Th Coll 46. **d** 48 **p** 49. C Forest Gate Em *Chelmsf* 48-50; P-in-c Nursling and Rownhams *Win* 50-55; Min Maybush St Pet CD 50-59; V Southampton Maybush St Pet 59-65; V Holdenhurst 65-71; C-in-c Holdenhurst St Barn CD 65-71; Chapl Stonar Sch Melksham 71-80; P-in-c Broad Town *Sarum* 80-81; P-in-c Clyffe Pypard and Tockenham 80-81; R Broad Town, Clyffe Pypard and Tockenham 81-85; rtd 85; Perm to Offic *Sarum* from 98. *17 Curzon Close, Calne SN11 0EU* Tel (01249) 819563

HOPKINS, Kenneth Victor John. b 45. Univ Coll Lon BA66 Lon Univ BD69 Hull Univ PhD84. Tyndale Hall Bris 66. **d** 69 **p** 70. C S Mimms Ch Ch *Lon* 69-72; C Branksome St Clem *Sarum* 72-75; P-in-c Trowbridge St Thos 75-76; V 76-81; R Wingfield w Rowley 76-81; Chapl and Lect NE Surrey Coll of Tech Ewell 81-84; Hd Student Services Essex Inst of HE 84-88; Kingston Poly 88-92; Kingston Univ 92-98; Dean of Students from 98. *Kingston University, Penrhyn Road, Kingston-upon-Thames KT1 2EE* Tel (020) 8547 7401

HOPKINS, Lionel. b 48. Open Univ BA82. St D Coll Lamp DipTh70. **d** 71 **p** 72. C Llandeilo Tal-y-bont *S & B* 71-74; C Morriston 74-78; P-in-c Waunarllwydd 78-80; V 80-86; Youth Chapl 84-86; V Llangyfelach 86-96; P-in-c Swansea Ch Ch 96-00; Chapl HM Pris Swansea from 96. *HM Prison, 200 Oystermouth Road, Swansea SA1 3SR* Tel (01792) 464030

HOPKINS, Miss Patricia Mary. b 46. Kingston Poly BEd78. Trin Coll Bris 83. dss 85 **d** 87 **p** 94. Gorleston St Andr *Nor* 85-87; C 87-88; C Woking St Jo *Guildf* 88-90; TD Barnham Broom *Nor* 90-94; TV 94-97; V Otford *Roch* from 97. *The Vicarage, The Green, Otford, Sevenoaks TN14 5PD* Tel (01959) 523185

HOPKINS, Peter. b 54. Nottm Univ BSc75 Imp Coll Lon MSc79. Oak Hill Th Coll BA86. **d** 86 **p** 87. C Gee Cross *Ches* 86-90; R Gt Gonerby *Linc* 90-95; R Barrowby and Gt Gonerby from 95; RD Grantham from 01. *The Rectory, 7 Long Street, Great Gonerby, Grantham NG31 8LN* Tel (01476) 565737 Fax as telephone E-mail peterhoppy@worldonline.co.uk

HOPKINS, Richard Clive John. b 74. Nottm Univ BA95 Ex Univ PGCE97. Wycliffe Hall Ox BTh02. **d** 02 **p** 03. C Duffield *Derby* from 02. *2 Mayfair Court, Milford Road, Duffield, Belper DE56 4EL* Tel (01332) 843169
E-mail hopkins@richardcj.fsnet.co.uk

HOPKINS, Robert James Gardner. b 42. Bris Univ BSc64 ACA76 FCA81. St Alb Minl Tr Scheme. **d** 79 **p** 80. NSM Chorleywood Ch Ch *St Alb* 79-83; NSM Parr Mt *Liv* 83-97; NSM Crookes St Thos *Sheff* from 97. *Crookes Endowed Centre, Crookes, Sheffield S10 1UB* Tel 0114-267 8447 Fax 266 9123 E-mail admin@acpi.org.uk

HOPKINSON, Preb Alfred Stephan. b 08. Wadh Coll Ox BA30 MA35. Linc Th Coll 34. **d** 35 **p** 36. C Putney St Mary *S'wark* 35-39; V Barrow St Jo *Carl* 39-43; V Battersea St Mary *S'wark* 43-52; RD Battersea 48-52; P-in-c St Mary Woolnoth *Lon* 52-54; V 54-59; P-in-c Tollington Park St Anne 55-56; Gen Dir ICF 58-63; V St Kath Cree 59-63; Preb St Paul's Cathl 60-63; Angl Adv ATV 60-68; Ind Adv to Bp Chelmsf 63-73; R Bobbingworth *Chelmsf* 63-73; rtd 73; Asst Chapl Win Coll 73-90; Hon C Cambridge Gt St Mary w St Mich *Ely* 90-93; Perm to Offic *Chich* from 93. *c/o Mrs S Thistleton-Smith, Down Place, South Harting, Petersfield GU31 5PN* Tel (01730) 825374

HOPKINSON, The Ven Barnabas John. b 39. Trin Coll Cam BA63 MA67. Linc Th Coll 63. **d** 65 **p** 66. C Langley All SS and Martyrs *Man* 65-67; C Cambridge Gt St Mary w St Mich *Ely* 67-71; Asst Chapl Charterhouse Sch Godalming 71-75; P-in-c Preshute *Sarum* 75-76; TV Marlborough 76-81; RD Marlborough 77-81; TR Wimborne Minster and Holt 81-86; Can and Preb Sarum Cathl from 83; RD Wimborne 85-86; Adn Sarum 86-98; P-in-c Stratford sub Castle 87-98; Adn Wilts from 98. *Sarum House, High Street, Urchfont, Devizes SN10 4QH* Tel (01380) 840373 Fax 848247
E-mail adwilts@salisbury.anglican.org

HOPKINSON, Benjamin Alaric. b 36. Trin Coll Ox BA59. Chich Th Coll 59. **d** 61 **p** 62. C Pallion *Dur* 61-66; Rhodesia 66-67; Botswana 67-74; Hon C Sherwood *S'well* 74-77; Hon C Carrington 74-77; V Lowdham 77-85; R Whitby *York* 85-95; Miss to Seafarers from 85; V Stainton w Hilton *York* 95-01; Chapl Cleveland Constabulary 95-01; rtd 01; Perm to Offic *Newc* from 01. *11 Watershaugh Road, Warkworth, Morpeth NE65 0TT* Tel (01665) 714213 Fax as telephone
E-mail dumela@dial.pipex.com

HOPKINSON, Colin Edward. b 57. BA LLB. Ridley Hall Cam. **d** 84 **p** 85. C Chadwell *Chelmsf* 84-87; C Canvey Is 87-90; P-in-c E Springfield 90-98; RD Chelmsf N 95-99; R Langdon Hills from 98. *The Rectory, 105A Berry Lane, Basildon SS16 6AP* Tel (01268) 542156 E-mail cchopkinson@aol.com

HOPKINSON, David John. b 47. Ox NSM Course. **d** 79 **p** 80. NSM Wardington *Ox* 79-80; Hon C Didcot St Pet 80-83; C

Headingley *Ripon* 83-87; P-in-c Leeds All So 87-91; R Middleton Tyas w Croft and Eryholme 91-95; V Leeds Belle Is St Jo and St Barn 95-98; rtd 98. *17 Sheldrake Drive, Leeds LS10 3NB* Tel 0113-276 2798

HOPKINSON, Canon William Humphrey. b 48. Lon Univ BSc69 Dur Univ MA78 Nottm Univ MPhil84 Man Poly MSc90 ARIC73. St Jo Coll Dur DipTh76. **d** 77 **p** 78. C Normanton *Derby* 77-80; C Sawley 80-82; V Birtles *Ches* 82-87; Dir Past Studies N Ord Course 82-94; Dir of Course Development 90-94; CME Officer *Ches* 87-94; P-in-c Tenterden St Mich *Cant* 94-96; Dir Min and Tr 94-02; Hon Can Cant Cathl from 01; Perm to Offic from 03. *3 Goldings Court, Nineacres, Ashford TN24 9JR* Tel 07710-033575 (mobile)
E-mail bhopkinson@diocant.clara.co.uk

HOPLEY, David. b 37. Wells Th Coll 62. **d** 65 **p** 66. C Frome St Mary *B & W* 65-68; R Staunton-on-Arrow w Byton and Kinsham *Heref* 68-81; P-in-c Lingen 68-81; P-in-c Aymestrey and Leinthall Earles w Wigmore etc 72-81; R Dungeon Hill *Sarum* 81-02; rtd 02. *Sunnyside, Clatworthy, Taunton TA4 2EH* Tel (01984) 623842

HOPLEY, Gilbert. b 40. Univ of Wales (Ban) BA62. St D Coll Lamp LTh65. **d** 65 **p** 66. C St As and Tremeirchion *St As* 65-73; Warden Ch Hostel Ban 73-76; Chapl Univ of Wales (Ban) Ban 73-76; V Meifod and Llangynyw *St As* 76-79; Chapl St Marg Sch Bushey 79-87; Hd Master St Paul's Cathl Choir Sch 87-97. *Plas Afon, Pentrefelin, Criccieth LL52 0PT* Tel (01766) 523588

HOPLEY, William James Christopher. b 50. AKC74. St Aug Coll Cant 74. **d** 75 **p** 76. C Kidderminster St Jo *Worc* 75-78; Ind Chapl 78-85; Co-ord Ind Chapl 85-94; TV Worc St Martin w St Pet, St Mark etc 85-86; TV Worc SE 86-94; Sen Chapl W Midl Police *Birm* from 94. *PO Box 52, Lloyd House, Colmore Circus Queensway, Birmingham B4 6NQ* Tel 0121-626 5071 Fax 626 5064 E-mail b.hopley@west-midlands.police.uk

HOPPER, Peter Edward. b 60. OLM course 96. **d** 99 **p** 00. OLM Bermondsey St Mary w St Olave, St Jo etc *S'wark* from 99. *56 Reverdy Road, London SE1 5QD* Tel (020) 7237 1543 *or* 7525 1831 E-mail phopper@phopper.screaming.net

HOPPER, Peter John. b 37. Univ Coll Dur BSc59 Lon Univ PGCE60. N Ord Course 89. **d** 90 **p** 91. C Aston cum Aughton and Ulley *Sheff* 91-93; C Aston cum Aughton w Swallownest, Todwick etc 93-94; P-in-c Braithwell w Bramley 94-95; TV Bramley and Ravenfield w Hooton Roberts etc 95-00; rtd 00. *21 Hornsby Avenue, Worcester WR4 0PN* Tel (01905) 731618 E-mail peterjhopper@msn.com

HOPPER, Robert Keith. b 45. St Jo Coll Dur 74. **d** 77 **p** 78. C Oxclose *Dur* 77-80; C Hebburn St Jo 80-82; V Lobley Hill from 82; P-in-c Marley Hill from 02. *All Saints' Vicarage, Rowanwood Gardens, Gateshead NE11 0DP* Tel and fax 0191-460 4409 Mobile 07960-754744
E-mail bob.hopper@durham.anglican.org

HOPPERTON, Thomas. b 33. SSC. Chich Th Coll 71. **d** 73 **p** 74. C Cheam *S'wark* 73-89; P-in-c St Alb Ch 76-89; P-in-c Rotherhithe St Kath w St Barn 89-92; P-in-c S Bermondsey St Bart 91-92; V Bermondsey St Kath w St Bart 92-01; rtd 01; Perm to Offic *York* from 03. *8 Croft Heads, Sowerby, Thirsk YO7 1ND* Tel (01845) 524210 E-mail fathert@nildram.co.uk

HOPTHROW, Mrs Elizabeth Rosemary Gladys. b 45. **d** 01 **p** 02. NSM Aylesham w Adisham *Cant* from 01; NSM Nonington w Wymynswold and Goodnestone etc from 01; Chapl Pilgrim's Hospice Cant from 01. *146 The Street, Kingston, Canterbury CT4 6JQ* Tel (01227) 830070 *or* 812610
E-mail lizziehopthrow@quista.net

HOPWOOD, Adrian Patrick. b 37. CBiol MIBiol MCIWEM N Lon Poly BSc61. Ox Min Course 87. **d** 90 **p** 91. NSM Chesham Bois *Ox* 90-93; NSM Amersham 93-95; NSM Ridgeway from 95. *The Glebe House, Childrey, Wantage OX12 9UP* Tel (01235) 751518

HOPWOOD OWEN, Mrs Karen. b 58. Padgate Coll of Educn CertEd79 St Martin's Coll Lanc DASE90. LNSM course 92. **d** 95 **p** 96. OLM Peel *Man* 95-99; OLM Walkden and Lt Hulton from 99. *168 Manchester Road, Tyldesley, Manchester M29 8WY* Tel (01942) 894850

HORAN, John Champain. b 52. WMMTC 95. **d** 98 **p** 99. NSM Leckhampton SS Phil and Jas w Cheltenham St Jas *Glouc* 98-02; Dioc Communications Officer 01-02. *Fairways, Moorend Road, Leckhampton, Cheltenham GL53 0MB* Tel (01242) 235370

HORBURY, Prof William. b 42. Oriel Coll Ox BA64 MA67 Clare Coll Cam BA66 PhD71 DD00 FBA97. Westcott Ho Cam 64. **d** 69 **p** 70. Fell Clare Coll Cam 68-72; CCC Cam from 78; R Gt w Lt Gransden *Ely* 72-78; Lect Div Cam Univ 84-98; Prof Jewish and Early Chr Studies from 98; P-in-c Cambridge St Botolph *Ely* from 90. *5 Grange Road, Cambridge CB3 9AS* Tel (01223) 363529 Fax 462751

HORDER, Mrs Catharine Joy. b 51. Battersea Coll of Educn CertEd72 UWE BA98. S Dios Minl Tr Scheme 92. **d** 95 **p** 96. C Burrington and Churchill *B & W* 95-00; TV Yatton Moor from 00. *1 Miller Road, Cleeve, Bristol BS49 4NL* Tel (01934) 833152

HORDER, Peter Alan Trahair. b 43. LNSM course 93. **d** 97 **p** 98. OLM Madron *Truro* 97-01; OLM Gulval 99-01; OLM Gulval

and Madron from 01. *Kourion, 38 Boscathnoe Way, Heamoor, Penzance TR18 3JS* Tel (01736) 360813

HORDERN, Peter John Calveley. b 35. Jes Coll Cam BA59 MA64 McMaster Univ Ontario PhD72. Linc Th Coll 59. **d** 61 **p** 62. C Billingham St Aid *Dur* 61-65; Canada from 65; rtd 00. *346 Aberdeen Avenue, Brandon MB, Canada, R7A 1N4* Tel (001) (204) 727 3324

HORE, Leslie Nicholas Peter. b 40. SW Minl Tr Course 99. **d** 02 **p** 03. OLM Treverbyn *Truro* from 02. *Tremore, Hallaze Road, Penwithick, St Austell PL26 8YW* Tel (01726) 851750
E-mail hore1@freeuk.com

HORE, Michael John. b 50. Man Univ BSc71. Linc Th Coll 75. **d** 78 **p** 79. C Maidstone St Martin *Cant* 78-81; C St Peter-in-Thanet 81-83; R Storrington *Chich* 83-93; RD Storrington 90-93; V Goring-by-Sea 93-02; R Cottenham *Ely* from 02. *The Rectory, 6 High Street, Cottenham, Cambridge CB4 8SA* Tel (01954) 250454

HORLESTON, Kenneth William. b 50. BA86. Oak Hill Th Coll 84. **d** 86 **p** 87. C Wednesfield Heath *Lich* 86-89; V Blagreaves *Derby* 89-00; P-in-c Horsley 00-02; P-in-c Denby 00-02; V Horsley and Denby from 02. *The Vicarage, Church Street, Horsley, Derby DE21 5BR* Tel (01332) 880284
E-mail ken@horleston.freesrve.co.uk

HORLOCK, The Very Revd Brian William. b 31. OBE78. Univ of Wales (Lamp) BA55. Chich Th Coll 55. **d** 57 **p** 58. C Chiswick St Nic w St Mary *Lon* 57-61; C Witney *Ox* 61-62; V N Acton St Gabr *Lon* 62-68; Chapl Oslo w Bergen, Trondheim and Stavanger *Eur* 68-89; RD Scandinavia 75-79; acdn 80-89; Hon Can Brussels Cathl 80-89; Dean Gib 89-98; Chapl Gib 89-98; rtd 98; Perm to Offic *Eur* from 98; Hon C Wootton Bassett *Sarum* from 98. *1 Richard's Close, Wootton Bassett, Swindon SN4 7LE* Tel (01793) 848344 Fax 848378

HORN, Colin Clive. b 39. CEng MIMechE. Cant Sch of Min. **d** 83 **p** 84. NSM Yalding w Collier Street *Roch* 83-91; V Kemsing w Woodlands 91-98; RD Shoreham 94-98; rtd 99; Perm to Offic *B & W* from 00. *Roundhill Cottage, Tadhill, Leigh upon Mendip, Bath BA3 5QT* Tel and fax (01373) 812736 Mobile 07885-523190

HORNBY (née CHRISTIAN), Mrs Helen. b 47. K Coll Lon BA68 AKC68 Lon Inst of Educn PGCE69. Cranmer Hall Dur 00. **d** 02 **p** 03. C Briercliffe *Blackb* from 02. *16 Oakwood Close, Burnley BB10 2DY* Tel (01282) 452376

HORNE, Brian Edward. b 37. CEng68 MRAeS68 MIEE68 EurIng92 Lon Univ BSc62 PhD78. WEMTC 92. **d** 95 **p** 96. OLM Cheltenham St Mark *Glouc* from 95. *87A Rowanfield Road, Cheltenham GL51 8AF* Tel (01242) 236786

HORNE, Jack Kenneth. b 20. Linc Th Coll 68. **d** 70 **p** 71. C Danbury *Chelmsf* 70-75; V Frampton *Linc* 75-85; rtd 85; Perm to Offic *Linc* from 02. *154 Kenilworth Road, Grantham NG31 9UH* Tel (01476) 578867

HORNE, Mona Lyn Denison. b 38. Gipsy Hill Coll of Educn TCert58. WEMTC 98. **d** 99 **p** 00. OLM Cheltenham St Mark *Glouc* from 99. *87A Rowanfield Road, Cheltenham GL51 8AF* Tel (01242) 236786 Fax 691869

HORNE, Simon Timothy. b 62. Ball Coll Ox BA86 MA90 Southn Univ RN(MH)89 Birm Univ PhD99. Qu Coll Birm BD94. **d** 95 **p** 96. C Basingstoke *Win* 95-99; C Fordingbridge 99-01; TV Fordingbridge and Breamore and Hale etc from 01. *19 Falconwood Close, Fordingbridge SP6 1TB* Tel (01425) 650563 Fax as telephone E-mail simon.horne@fordingbridge.com

HORNER, Eric. b 43. EMMTC 87. **d** 90 **p** 91. C Boultham *Linc* 90-93; P-in-c Kirton in Holland 93-95; P-in-c Frampton 93-95; P-in-c Frampton w Kirton in Holland 95-97; V Kirton in Holland from 97. *The Vicarage, Penny Gardens, Kirton, Boston PE20 1HN* Tel (01205) 722380 E-mail eric.horner@virgin.net

HORNER, Graham. b 57. ACA81 Grey Coll Dur BSc78. St Jo Coll Nottm 93. **d** 93 **p** 94. C Longdon-upon-Tern, Rodington, Uppington etc *Lich* 93-95; C Wrockwardine Deanery 95-96; TV 96-02; TR from 02; RD Wrockwardine from 02. *The Vicarage, Church Road, High Ercall, Telford TF6 6BE* Tel (01952) 770206 E-mail g.horner@ntlworld.com

HORNER, John Henry. b 40. Leeds Univ BA62 Lon Univ DipRS74 Middx Poly MA87. Oak Hill Th Coll 76. **d** 79 **p** 80. Hon C Datchworth w Tewin *St Alb* 79-85; Hon C Ware St Mary 85-91; C S Ashford Ch Ch *Cant* 91-94; C Bp's Hatfield *St Alb* 94-99; V Sandridge 99-02; rtd 02; P-in-c Broxbourne w Wormley *St Alb* from 03. *41 St Leonard's Road, Hertford SG14 3JW* Tel (01992) 423725 E-mail john.horner1@ntlworld.com

HORNER, Peter Francis. b 27. Jes Coll Ox BA51 MA55. Kelham Th Coll 52. **d** 54 **p** 55. Tutor Kelham Th Coll 54-73; Chapl 58-73; C Averham w Kelham *S'well* 54-56; Lic to Offic 56-73; SSM 58-87; Lic to Offic *Ox* 74-87; Australia 87-97; rtd 97. *St Antony's Priory, 77 Claypath, Durham DH1 1QT* Tel 0191-384 3747

HORNER, Philip David Forster. b 30. Tyndale Hall Bris 67. **d** 67 **p** 68. C Ulverston St Mary w H Trin *Carl* 67-71; C Princes Risborough w Ilmer *Ox* 71-76; C Wendover 76-89; P-in-c Ellesborough 76-89; P-in-c Gt and Lt Kimble 82-89; C Walton St Trin 89-92; TV 92-95; rtd 95; P-in-c Cowden w Hammerwood

Chich from 95. *The Rectory, Cowden, Edenbridge TN8 7JE* Tel (01342) 850221

HORNER, Richard Murray. b 61. Dur Univ BSc83. NTMTC 93. **d** 96 **p** 97. C Sherborne w Castleton and Lillington *Sarum* 96-99; Chapl Rugby Sch from 99. *11 Horton Crescent, Rugby CV22 5DJ* Tel (01788) 544939

HORNSBY, Edgar. b 23. AKC50. **d** 51 **p** 52. C Portsea St Mary *Portsm* 51-55; Chapl RAF 55-69; St Mary's Hall and Brighton Coll 69-74; Chapl St Swithun's Sch Win 74-88; rtd 88; Perm to Offic *B & W* from 88; Perm to Offic *Sarum* from 01. *The Manor Farmhouse, Littlewindsor, Beaminster DT8 3QU*

HORNSBY, William John. b 49. RIBA79. SEITE 98. **d** 01 **p** 02. C Faversham *Cant* from 01; C Preston next Faversham, Goodnestone and Graveney from 02. *78 Cyprus Road, Faversham ME13 8HD* Tel (01795) 538334
E-mail billhornsby@smoc.freeserve.co.uk

HOROBIN, Hector Stanley. b 09. Kelham Th Coll 30 Edin Th Coll 46. **d** 46 **p** 47. C Burntisland *St And* 46-47; C Winlaton *Dur* 47-50; V Coundon 50-57; V Birtley 57-62; V Petts Wood Roch 62-88; rtd 88; Perm to Offic *Cant* from 89. *c/o Mrs S B Donkin, Jarvis House, Jarvis Lane, Goudhurst, Cranbrook TN17 2NP*

HOROBIN, Timothy John. b 60. St Jo Coll Nottm Dip Th & Min 94. **d** 94 **p** 95. C Nelson St Phil *Blackb* 94-98; P-in-c Blackpool St Paul 98-00. *75 Main Street, Warton, Carnforth LA5 9PJ* Tel (01524) 733037 Mobile 07811-074063

HORREX, Mrs Gay Lesley. b 42. Guildf Dioc Min Course 90. **d** 96 **p** 97. OLM Walton-on-Thames *Guildf* from 96. *173 Sidney Road, Walton-on-Thames KT12 3SB* Tel (01932) 225742

HORROCKS, Canon Judith Anne. b 53. Univ of Calgary BSc76 Keele Univ MA99. St Jo Coll Nottm DPS82. dss 82 **d** 87 **p** 94. Denton Ch Ch *Man* 82-85; Whalley Range St Edm 85-97; Par Dn 87-94; C 94-97; Chapl Man R Infirmary 88-90; Chapl Christie Hosp NHS Trust Man from 95; Chapl S Man Univ Hosps NHS Trust from 98; Lic Preacher *Man* from 97; Hon Can Man Cathl from 02. *Emmanuel Vicarage, Edward Street, Bolton BL3 5LQ* Tel (01204) 393282
E-mail judie.horrocks@christie-tr.nwest.nhs.uk

HORROCKS, Oliver John. b 30. Clare Coll Cam BA53 MA57. Westcott Ho Cam 53. **d** 55 **p** 56. C Moss Side Ch Ch *Man* 55-58; C Arnold *S'well* 58-60; R Ancoats *Man* 60-67; R Barthomley *Ches* 67-96; rtd 96; Perm to Offic *Ches* from 98. *36 Station Road, Alsager, Stoke-on-Trent ST7 2PD* Tel (01270) 877284

HORROCKS, Robert James. b 56. Grey Coll Dur BSc78. St Jo Coll Nottm DipTh80 DPS82. **d** 82 **p** 83. C Denton Ch Ch *Man* 82-85; R Whalley Range St Edm 85-97; P-in-c Bolton St Paul w Em from 97. *Emmanuel Vicarage, Edward Street, Bolton BL3 5LQ* Tel (01204) 393282 Fax 0870-1247270
E-mail bob@horrocks.org

HORROCKS, Stanley. b 22. Man Univ BA76. Coll of Resurr Mirfield 77. **d** 78 **p** 79. Hon C Man Miles Platting *Man* 78-81; Hon C Lower Broughton St Clem w St Matthias 81-87; rtd 87; NSM Higher Broughton *Man* 87-92; NSM Broughton St Jas w St Clem and St Matthias 92-93; Perm to Offic from 93. *80 Northumberland Street, Salford M7 4DG* Tel 0161-792 1037

HORSEMAN, Christopher Michael. b 54. Bris Sch of Min 84 Trin Coll Bris 87. **d** 88 **p** 89. C Weston-super-Mare Cen Par *B & W* 88-92; TV Yatton Moor 92-02; NSM from 02. *6 Westaway Park, Yatton, Bristol BS49 4JU* Tel (01934) 834537
E-mail cfhors@globalnet.co.uk

HORSEMAN, Colin. b 46. Lon Coll of Div ALCD69 BD70 STh75. **d** 70 **p** 71. C Higher Openshaw *Man* 70-74; C Darfield *Sheff* 75-78; V Stainforth 78-88; V Heeley 88-95; P-in-c Ducklington *Ox* 95-99; P-in-c Gt Horkesley *Chelmsf* 99-02; P-in-c w Bergholt 00-02; R W Bergholt and Gt Horkesley from 02; RD Dedham and Tey from 03. *The Rectory, Ivy Lodge Road, Great Horkesley, Colchester CO6 4EN* Tel (01206) 271242
E-mail revcolin@tiscali.co.uk

HORSEY, Maurice Alfred. b 30. AIB. S'wark Ord Course 61. **d** 64 **p** 65. C Oxhey All SS *St Alb* 64-67; C Coulsdon St Jo *S'wark* 67-71; P-in-c Champion Hill St Sav 71-76; Hon C Lewisham St Swithun 84-86; P-in-c Woolwich St Thos 86-90; R 90-94; rtd 94; Chapl Costa del Sol W Eur 94-98. *6/47 Marina de Casares, 29690 Casares, Malaga, Spain* Tel (0034) (95) 289 2166

HORSEY, Stanley Desmond. b 20. Ely Th Coll 46. **d** 49 **p** 50. C S Clevedon B & W 49-51; C Leigh-on-Sea St Marg *Chelmsf* 51-53; C Barbourne *Worc* 53-55; V Edgbaston St Jas *Birm* 55-60; V Brighton St Martin *Chich* 60-67; V Hove St Barn 67-77; V Hove St Barn and St Agnes 77-85; rtd 85; Perm to Offic *Chich* from 85. *27A Amesbury Crescent, Hove BN3 5RD* Tel (01273) 732081

HORSFALL, David John. b 55. Bris Poly BA77. Trin Coll Bris DipHE82 St Jo Coll Nottm DPS89. **d** 89 **p** 90. C Chaddesden St Mary *Derby* 89-92; V Swadlincote from 92; RD Repton from 99. *The Vicarage, Church Street, Swadlincote DE11 8LF* Tel (01283) 217756

HORSFALL, Keith. b 39. Tyndale Hall Bris 62. **d** 65 **p** 66. C Walton Breck Liv 65-68; C Fazakerley Em 68-70; C Mile Cross *Nor* 70-73; V Gayton 73-80; TR Parr *Liv* 80-90; V Leyland St Andr *Blackb* 90-00; P-in-c Willand *Ex* 00-01; TV Cullompton, Willand, Uffculme, Kentisbeare etc from 01. *The Rectory, Old*

Village, Willand, Cullompton EX15 2RH Tel (01884) 32247
E-mail horsfall@xalt.co.uk

HORSHAM, Archdeacon of. *See* COMBES, The Ven Roger Matthew

HORSHAM, Area Bishop of. *See* URWIN, The Rt Revd Lindsay Goodall

HORSINGTON, Timothy Frederick. b 44. Dur Univ BA66. Wycliffe Hall Ox 67. **d** 69 **p** 70. C Halewood *Liv* 69-72; C Farnworth 72-75; P-in-c Llangarron w Llangrove *Heref* 75-82; P-in-c Whitchurch w Ganarew 77-82; R Llangarron w Llangrove, Whitchurch and Ganarew 83-84; R Highclere and Ashmansworth w Crux Easton *Win* from 84. *The Rectory, 2 Flexford Close, Highclere, Newbury RG20 9PE* Tel (01635) 253991

HORSLEY, Canon Alan Avery. b 36. St Chad's Coll Dur BA58 Pacific States Univ MA84 PhD85. Qu Coll Birm 58. **d** 60 **p** 61. C Daventry *Pet* 60-63; C Reading St Giles *Ox* 63-64; C Wokingham St Paul 64-66; V Yeadon St Andr *Bradf* 66-71; R Heyford w Stowe Nine Churches *Pet* 71-78; RD Daventry 76-78; V Oakham w Hambleton and Egleton 78-81; V Oakham, Hambleton, Egleton, Braunston and Brooke 81-86; Can Pet Cathl 79-86; V Lanteglos by Fowey *Truro* 86-88; Provost St Andr Cathl Inverness *Mor* 88-91; R Inverness St Andr 88-91; P-in-c Culloden St Mary-in-the-Fields 88-91; P-in-c Strathnairn St Paul 88-91; V Mill End and Heronsgate w W Hyde *St Alb* 91-01; RD Rickmansworth 00-01; Perm to Offic *Truro* from 98; rtd 01; Perm to Offic *Pet* from 02. *44 Furnace Drive, Daventry NN11 5FU* Tel (01327) 312550

HORSLEY, Amelia Mary Elizabeth. b 69. K Alfred's Coll Win BEd91. St Jo Coll Nottm MA97 DipMM98. **d** 98 **p** 99. C Southampton Maybush St Pet *Win* 98-01; Teacher Mansel Infant Sch Southampton from 01. *Mansel Infant School, Colver Close, Southampton SO16 9HZ* Tel (023) 8077 6162 Fax 8078 5014
E-mail amehorsley@aol.com

HORSLEY, Peter Alec. b 56. Leeds Metrop Univ CertEd98. Cranmer Hall Dur 99. **d** 01 **p** 02. C Acomb St Steph *York* from 01. *36 Fellbrook Avenue, Acomb, York YO26 5PS* Tel (01904) 793240

HORSMAN, Andrew Alan. b 49. Otago Univ BA70 Man Univ MA72 PhD75. St Steph Ho Ox BA80 MA87. **d** 81 **p** 82. C Hillingdon All SS *Lon* 81-84; C Lt Stanmore St Lawr 84-87; TV Haxby w Wigginton *York* 87-98; V Acomb Moor from 98. *2 Sherringham Drive, York YO24 2SE* Tel (01904) 706047
E-mail andrew@jasdn.freeserve.co.uk

HORSWELL, Kevin George. b 55. Jes Coll Cam BA77 MA81 Nottm Univ BA81. St Jo Coll Nottm 79. **d** 82 **p** 83. C Bootle Ch Ch *Liv* 82-86; Chapl LMH Ox 86-91; C Ox St Giles and SS Phil and Jas w St Marg *Ox* 86-91; R Dodleston *Ches* 91-00; R Llanaber w Caerdeon *Ban* from 00. *The Rectory, Mynach Road, Barmouth LL42 1RL* Tel (01341) 280516

HORTA, Nelson Pinto. b 40. Lisbon Univ Lic80 Cath Univ of Portugal LicTh92. **d** 65 **p** 69. Portugal from 65; V Setúbal H Spirit 69-71; V Lisbon St Paul 71-96; Asst Chapl Gtr Lisbon *Eur* 97-00. *Quinta da Cerieira, rua C, Lote 261, Vale de Figueira-Sobreda, 2800 Almada, Portugal* Tel (00351) (1) 295 7943

HORTON, Alan Michael. b 47. Univ of Wales BScTech71. Linc Th Coll 92. **d** 92 **p** 93. C Bexleyheath Ch Ch *Roch* 92-95; P-in-c Slade Green 95-99; V 99-03; P-in-c Southborough St Thos from 03. *The Vicarage, 28 Pennington Road, Southborough, Tunbridge Wells TN4 0SL* Tel (01892) 529624 *or* 617398
E-mail alanhorton@easynet.co.uk

HORTON, Andrew Charles. b 50. Ex Univ BA71. Sarum Th Coll 71. **d** 73 **p** 74. C Westbury-on-Trym St Alb *Bris* 73-76; USA 76-90; P-in-c Battersea St Mich *S'wark* 90-92; V 92-98; Local Min Officer Kingston Episc Area 94-98; TR Selsdon St Jo w St Fran from 98. *St John's Rectory, Upper Selsdon Road, South Croydon CR2 8DD* Tel (020) 8657 2343

HORTON, Anne. *See* HORTON, Canon Roberta Anne

HORTON, Cathy Lynne Bosworth. b 62. BA JD. SEITE. **d** 99 **p** 00. NSM Warlingham w Chelsham and Farleigh *S'wark* 99-03; USA from 03. *Address temp unknown*

HORTON, Canon Christopher Peter. b 26. Leeds Univ BA49. Coll of Resurr Mirfield 49. **d** 51 **p** 52. C Blyth St Mary *Newc* 51-55; C Delaval 55-59; V Grangetown *York* 59-91; Can and Preb York Minster 85-91; rtd 91; Perm to Offic *Newc* from 91. *51 Well Ridge Close, Seaton Grange, Whitley Bay NE25 9PN* Tel 0191-251 0742

HORTON, David Harold. b 49. St Jo Coll Dur BA72. NEOC 82. **d** 86 **p** 87. C Enfield St Jas *Lon* 86-90; Min Joydens Wood St Barn CD *Roch* 90-93; V Joydens Wood St Barn 93-99; P-in-c Rosherville from 99. *St Mark's Vicarage, 123 London Road, Northfleet, Gravesend DA11 9NH* Tel (01474) 534430
E-mail davidhhorton@yahoo.com

HORTON, Canon Jeremy Nicholas Orkney. b 44. Cranmer Hall Dur 64. **d** 68 **p** 69. C Dalton-in-Furness *Carl* 68-70; C Penrith 70-73; V Hudswell w Downholme and Marske *Ripon* 73-75; R Middleton Tyas and Melsonby 75-81; P-in-c Croft 78-81; P-in-c Eryholme 78-81; V Wortley de Leeds 81-93; V Middleton St Mary 93-98; RD Armley 96-98; V Kirby-on-the-Moor,

Cundall w Norton-le-Clay etc from 98; Hon Can Ripon Cathl from 01. *The Vicarage, 13 The Croft, Kirby Hill, Boroughbridge, York YO51 9YA* Tel (01423) 326284
E-mail horton@kirbyhill.fsnet.co.uk

HORTON, John Ward. b 27. Leeds Univ BA50. Coll of Resurr Mirfield 50. **d** 52 **p** 53. C Balkwell CD *Newc* 52-55; C E Coatham *York* 55-58; C-in-c Acomb Moor CD 58-71; V Acomb Moor 71-93; rtd 93; Perm to Offic *Newc* from 93. *39 Billy Mill Lane, North Shields NE26 8BZ* Tel 0191-296 4082

HORTON, Mrs Joy. b 52. CertEd73 Kent Univ MA98. SEITE 94. **d** 97 **p** 98. C Dartford St Edm *Roch* 97-01; Chapl Bromley Hosps NHS Trust 01-02; C Erith St Jo *Roch* 02-03; Perm to Offic from 03. *The Vicarage, 28 Pennington Road, Southborough, Tunbridge Wells TN4 0SL* Tel (01892) 529624
E-mail hjoy@fish.co.uk

HORTON, Melanie Jane. b 64. Univ of Cen England in Birm LLB85 Solicitor 88. Ripon Coll Cuddesdon BA96. **d** 96 **p** 97. C Lich St Chad *Lich* 96-00; Chapl R Masonic Sch for Girls Rickmansworth 00-03; Chapl St Edm Sch Cant from 03. *St Edmund's School, Canterbury CT2 8HU* Tel (01227) 454575

HORTON, Michael John. b 56. St Jo Coll Cam BA80 MA83 Univ of Wales (Swansea) PGCE83 Ox Univ BA88 MA92. Wycliffe Hall Ox 86. **d** 89 **p** 90. C Northallerton w Kirby Sigston *York* 89-92; C Ulverston St Mary w H Trin *Carl* 92-94; V Lightwater *Guildf* from 94. *The Vicarage, 28 Broadway Road, Lightwater GU18 5SJ* Tel (01276) 472270

HORTON, Ralph Edward. b 41. S'wark Ord Course 75. **d** 78 **p** 79. C Streatham St Leon *S'wark* 78-81; TV Catford (Southend) and Downham 81-88; V Ashford St Matt *Lon* from 88. *The Vicarage, 99 Church Road, Ashford TW15 2NY* Tel (01784) 252459

HORTON, Canon Roberta *Anne*. b 44. Leic Univ BSc66 CertEd67 Nottm Univ BCombStuds82. Linc Th Coll 79. **dss** 82 **d** 87 **p** 94. Cambridge St Jas *Ely* 82-86; Beaumont Leys *Leic* 86-87; Par Dn 87-91; Dioc Dir of Tr 91-00; P-in-c Swithland 94-99; R Woodhouse, Woodhouse Eaves and Swithland from 00; Hon Can Leic Cathl from 94. *The Rectory, 157 Main Street, Swithland, Loughborough LE12 8TQ* Tel (01509) 891163 Fax as telephone E-mail rahorton@leicester.anglican.org

HORWOOD, Graham Frederick. b 34. Univ of Wales (Cardiff) BA55. Coll of Resurr Mirfield 55. **d** 57 **p** 58. C Llantrisant *Llan* 57-61; C Roath St Sav 61-62; C Roath 62-66; V Clydach *S & B* 66-77; V Canton St Luke *Llan* 77-99; rtd 99. *26 Heol-yr-Onnen, Llanharry, Pontyclun CF72 9NJ* Tel (01443) 225777
E-mail ghorwood@freeuk.com

HOSKIN, David James. b 63. Hull Univ BA86. Trin Coll Bris BA94. **d** 94 **p** 95. C Southway *Ex* 94-98; TV Kingswinford St Mary *Worc* from 98. *28 Foundry Road, Kingswinford DY6 9BD* Tel (01384) 273961 E-mail davidhoskin@supanet.com

HOSKIN, David William. b 49. Hatf Coll Dur BSc71. Wycliffe Hall Ox 72. **d** 75 **p** 76. C Bridlington Priory *York* 75-78; C Rodbourne Cheney *Bris* 78-79; C Bebington *Ches* 79-82; R Lockington and Lund and Scarborough w Leconfield *York* 82-88; V Beverley St Mary from 88; RD Beverley from 97. *St Mary's Vicarage, 15 Molescroft Road, Beverley HU17 7DX* Tel (01482) 881437 E-mail office@hoskin.demon.co.uk

HOSKIN, Canon Eric James. b 28. St Chad's Coll Dur BA50 DipTh52. **d** 52 **p** 53. C Coney Hill *Glouc* 52-54; C Stroud 54-57; R Ruardean 57-63; P-in-c Lydbrook 61-63; V Cheltenham Em 63-70; R Dursley 70-86; RD Dursley 77-85; Hon Can Glouc Cathl 81-86; R Easington w Liverton *York* 86-96; rtd 96; Perm to Offic from 96. *37A Algarth Rise, Pocklington, York YO42 2HX* Tel (01759) 305798

HOSKIN, Henry Brian. b 32. NW Ord Course 72. **d** 75 **p** 76. NSM Chesterfield St Aug *Derby* 75-79; NSM Bolsover 79-83; NSM Old Brampton and Loundsley Green 83-88; P-in-c Gt Barlow 88-94; rtd 97; Perm to Offic *Derby* from 97. *25 Barn Close, Chesterfield S41 8BD* Tel (01246) 201550

HOSKING, Canon Harold Ernest. b 19. Lich Th Coll 51. **d** 53 **p** 54. C Penwerris *Truro* 53-56; R Mawgan in Pyder 56-61; V Newlyn St Pet 61-69; V Newquay 69-74; TR Redruth 74-80; R Redruth w Lanner 80-84; Hon Can Truro Cathl 78-84; rtd 84; Perm to Offic *Ex* and *Truro* 84-03. *11 Greenfield Close, Stapleford, Cambridge CB2 5BT*

HOSKINS, Hugh George. b 46. S Dios Minl Tr Scheme. **d** 84 **p** 85. NSM Hilperton w Whaddon and Staverton etc *Sarum* 84-87; C Calne and Blackland 87-90; R W Lavington and the Cheverells 90-97; P-in-c Heytesbury and Sutton Veny 97; TR Upper Wylye Valley from 97; RD Heytesbury from 00. *The Rectory, Bests Lane, Sutton Veny, Warminster BA12 7AU* Tel (01985) 840014 Fax as telephone E-mail h241047@aol.com

HOSKINS, Mrs Rosemary Anne. b 56. Wesley Coll Bris 99 STETS 01. **d** 02 **p** 03. NSM Camelot Par *B & W* from 02. *Springfields, Weston Bampfylde, Yeovil BA22 7HZ* Tel (01963) 440026

HOSKYNS, John Algernon Peyton. b 20. Pemb Coll Cam BA41 MA45. Westcott Ho Cam 47. **d** 49 **p** 50. C Eastleigh *Win* 49-52; C Brompton H Trin *Lon* 52-54; V Hartley Wintney and Elvetham *Win* 54-62; R Worplesdon *Guildf* 62-72; V St Weonards w Orcop *Heref* 73-76; P-in-c Linton w Upton Bishop 76-78;

P-in-c How Caple w Sollers Hope 76-85; P-in-c Sellack and King's Caple w Foy 81-85; rtd 85; Perm to Offic *Truro* from 03. *Dinham House, St Minver, Wadebridge PL27 6RH* Tel (01208) 812516

HOST, Mrs Charmaine Anne. b 54. WMMTC 87. **d** 90 **p** 94. C Westwood *Cov* 90-94; C Whitnash 94-96; V Kineton from 96; V Combroke w Compton Verney from 96. *The Vicarage, Southam Street, Kineton, Warwick CV35 0LL* Tel (01926) 640248

HOTCHEN, Stephen Jeffrie. b 50. Bradf Coll of Educn. Linc Th Coll 85. **d** 87 **p** 88. C Morpeth *Newc* 87-90; TV High Wycombe *Ox* 90-91; R Dingwall *Mor* 91-94; R Strathpeffer 91-94; V Rickerscote *Lich* from 94. *St Peter's Vicarage, 16 Chestnut Drive, Stafford ST17 9WE* Tel and fax (01785) 252878 Mobile 07976-387199 E-mail sjhotchen@aol.com

HOTCHIN, Mrs Hilary Moya. b 52. Birm Univ CertEd73. WMMTC 85. **d** 88 **p** 94. NSM Redditch St Steph *Worc* 88-91; Par Dn Handsworth *Sheff* 91-94; C 94-96; TV Maltby 96-98. *St George's Rectory, 33 Carden Avenue, Hull HU9 4RT* Tel (01482) 791291

HOUGH, Adrian Michael. b 59. MRSC CChem ACIPD Hertf Coll Ox BA81 MA84 DPhil84. Ripon Coll Cuddesdon BA91. **d** 92 **p** 93. C Martley and Wichenford, Knightwick etc *Worc* 92-96; AP Evesham Deanery 96-97; V Badsey w Aldington and Offenham and Bretforton from 97. *The Vicarage, High Street, Badsey, Evesham WR11 7EW* Tel (01386) 830343
E-mail badseyvc@surfaid.org

HOUGH, Miss Carole Elizabeth. b 59. Lon Hosp SRN81. St Jo Coll Nottm DipMin91. **d** 91 **p** 94. C Beoley *Worc* 91-95; Asst Chapl Addenbrooke's NHS Trust 95-98; Chapl Milton Keynes Gen NHS Trust from 98; Chapl Milton Keynes Community NHS Trust from 98. *Milton Keynes General Hospital, Standing Way, Milton Keynes MK6 5LD* Tel (01908) 660033 ext 2215

HOUGH, Edward Lewis. b 38. Univ of Wales (Lamp) BA60. St Mich Coll Llan 60. **d** 62 **p** 63. C Baglan *Llan* 62-69; Ind Chapl *York* 69-72; R Cilybebyll *Llan* 72-93; RD Neath 84-89; Ind Chapl Port Talbot 92-95; V Cadoxton-juxta-Neath 93-95; rtd 95; Perm to Offic *Llan* from 95. *14 Alderwood Close, Crynant, Neath SA10 8PY* Tel (01639) 750006

HOUGH, Michael Jeremy. b 61. Wilson Carlile Coll Oak Hill Th Coll. **d** 02 **p** 03. *3 Ringwood Avenue, Redhill RH1 2DY* Tel (01737) 762593 Mobile 07939-088867
E-mail mickhough@hotmail.com

HOUGH, Peter George. b 40. Dur Univ BA62. Wells Th Coll 62. **d** 64 **p** 65. C Stocking Farm CD *Leic* 64-68; V Leic St Aid 68-76; V Knutton *Lich* from 76; P-in-c Silverdale and Alsagers Bank 93-94; V Alsagers Bank from 01. *The Vicarage, Church Lane, Newcastle ST5 6DU* Tel (01782) 624282

HOUGH, Sharron. d 01. OLM Short Heath *Birm* from 01. *10 Pineneedle Croft, Willenhall WV12 4BY* Tel (03950) 410458

HOUGH, Sidney Stephen Valentine. b 27. G&C Coll Cam BA50 MA54. Ripon Hall Ox 55. **d** 57 **p** 58. C Goodmayes All SS *Chelmsf* 57-60; C Warwick St Mary *Cov* 60-62; V Messing *Chelmsf* 62-72; R Inworth 62-72; V Messing w Inworth 72-77; Chapl Warley Hosp Brentwood 78-79; R Alphamstone w Lamarsh and Pebmarsh *Chelmsf* 79-88; rtd 88. *27 Weavers Court, Weavers Lane, Sudbury CO10 1HY* Tel (01787) 374812

HOUGHTON, Christopher Guy. b 64. W Surrey Coll of Art & Design BA86. Oak Hill Th Coll DipHE88 BA89. **d** 89 **p** 90. C Mossley Hill St Matt and St Jas *Liv* 89-92; C Ashton-in-Makerfield St Thos 92-95; C Southport St Phil and St Paul 95-96; Chapl Chorley and S Ribble NHS Trust 96-01; rtd 01. *35 Deerfold, Chorley PR7 1UD*

HOUGHTON, David John. b 47. Edin Univ BSc(Econ)68. Cuddesdon Coll 69. **d** 71 **p** 72. C Prestbury *Glouc* 71-74; Prec Gib Cathl *Eur* 74-76; Chapl Madrid 76-78; C Croydon *Cant* 78-80; Chapl Warw Sch 80-85; P-in-c Isleworth St Fran *Lon* 85-90; USA 90-91; V Clapham H Spirit 02; Chapl Paris St Geo *Eur* from 02. *7 rue Auguste Vacquerie, 75116 Paris, France* (0033) (1) 47 23 37 27 E-mail davidhoughton@wanadoo.fr

HOUGHTON, Edward Johnson. b 23. Keble Coll Ox BA48 MA48. Linc Th Coll 48. **d** 50 **p** 51. C Nelson in Lt Marsden *Blackb* 50-52; C Lancaster St Mary 52-55; Chapl R Albert Hosp Lanc 52-61; Chapl Ripley Sch Lanc 52-56; R Quernmore *Blackb* 55-61; CF (TA) 56-62; Chapl Hellingly and Amberstone Hosps 61-90; rtd 88; Perm to Offic *Chich* from 88. *1 Nursery Close, Osborne Park, Hailsham BN27 2PX* Tel (01323) 442126

HOUGHTON, Mrs Evelyn Mabel. b 44. Stockwell Coll of Educn TCert65. Oak Hill NSM Course 92. **d** 94 **p** 95. NSM Bedford St Jo and St Leon *St Alb* 94-98; C Reading St Agnes w St Paul *Ox* from 98. *The Vicarage, 290 Northumberland Avenue, Reading RG2 8DE* Tel 0118-987 4448

HOUGHTON, Geoffrey John. b 59. Ridley Hall Cam 87. **d** 90 **p** 91. C Sholing *Win* 90-94; P-in-c Jersey All SS 94-99; V from 99; P-in-c Jersey St Simon 94-99; V from 99; Vice-Dean Jersey from 99; Hon Chapl Jersey Hospice from 96. *All Saints' Vicarage, Savile Street, St Helier, Jersey JE2 3XF* Tel (01534) 768538 E-mail geoff@virtualvicar.org.uk

HOUGHTON, Hugh Alexander Gervase. b 76. St Jo Coll Cam MPhil98 MA01 Leeds Univ BA02. Coll of Resurr Mirfield 00. **d** 03. NSM Weoley Castle *Birm* from 03. *St Gabriels' Church, 34 Shenley Lane, Birmingham B29 5PL* Tel 0121-475 4283 E-mail ssm@hagh.co.uk

HOUGHTON, Ian David. b 50. Lanc Univ BA71 Newc Univ CertEd74 Man Univ CertRS90. Sarum & Wells Th Coll 80. **d** 82 **p** 83. C Newc St Geo *Newc* 82-85; Chapl Newc Poly 85-92; Chapl Univ of Northumbria at Newc 92-95; Master Newc St Thos Prop Chpl 90-95; Black Country Urban Ind Miss *Lich* from 95; Res Min Bilston from 95. *9 Grafton Place, Bilston WV14 6LH* Tel (01902) 408153 *or* 710407 E-mail idh_bcuim@hotmail.com

HOUGHTON, James Robert. b 44. AKC67 St Luke's Coll Ex 73. St Boniface Warminster 67. **d** 68 **p** 69. C Herrington *Dur* 68-70; Asst Dioc Youth Chapl *Bris* 70-72; Perm to Offic *Ex* 73-74; C Heavitree 74-77; C Heavitree w Ex St Paul 78; Perm to Offic *Lon* 78-80 and 83-88; Hon C W Drayton 80-83; Chapl Greycoat Hosp Sch 83-88; Chapl Stonar Sch Melksham 88-95; Chapl St Mary and St Anne's Sch Abbots Bromley 95-99; R Buxted and Hadlow Down *Chich* 99-02; V Eastbourne St Mich from 02. *The Vicarage, 15 Long Acre Close, Eastbourne BN21 1UF* Tel (01323) 645740

HOUGHTON, Canon John Caswell. b 16. Dur Univ BA38 LTh38. St Boniface Warminster 34. **d** 39 **p** 40. C Wolverton St Geo *Ox* 39-42; Zambia 42-74; Warden Dioc Th Sem N Rhodesia 47-52; Can N Rhodesia 60-62; Adn N Rhodesia 62-64; Adn S Zambia 64-70; Can Lusaka 71-74; Promotions Sec Feed the Minds 74-81; rtd 81; Perm to Offic *Ox* from 82. *18 Cornelia Close, Bletchley, Milton Keynes MK2 3LX* Tel (01908) 370526

HOUGHTON, Michael Richard. b 29. CCC Cam BA52 MA56. Cuddesdon Coll 52. **d** 54 **p** 55. C Portsea N End St Mark *Portsm* 54-57; New Zealand from 57; Adn Tamaki 77-81. *Private Bag 12, Papakura, New Zealand* Tel (0064) (9) 292 2432

HOUGHTON, Peter Graham. b 51. St Jo Coll Nottm 85. **d** 87 **p** 88. C Toxteth Park St Clem *Liv* 87-91; Chapl Winwick Hosp Warrington 91-94; Chapl Warrington Community Health Care NHS Trust 94-98; Chapl HM Pris Styal 98-01. *PO Box 68, Frodsham WA6 6XZ* Tel (01928) 734372

HOUGHTON, Robert Sherwood. b 26. LLB59 Clare Coll Cam BA51 MA56 Mercer Ho Melbourne DipEd62. Trin Coll Melbourne BA48 Wells Th Coll 52. **d** 52 **p** 53. C Howe Bridge *Man* 52-54; Australia from 54; rtd 95. *40 Canning Street, North Melbourne, Vic, Australia 3051* Tel (0061) (3) 9328 1419

HOUGHTON, Mrs Rosemary Margaret Anne. b 46. Dioc OLM tr scheme 98. **d** 00 **p** 01. OLM Earlham St Eliz *Nor* from 00. *74 St Mildred's Road, West Earlham, Norwich NR5 8RS* Tel (01603) 502752 Mobile 07808-774811 E-mail user@houghtonfamily.in2home.co.uk

HOUGHTON, Mrs Susan Jeanette. b 39. Qu Mary Coll Lon BSc61 Nottm Univ PGCE62. WMMTC 98. **d** 99 **p** 00. OLM Dursley *Glouc* 99-02; rtd 02; NSM Offwell, Northleigh, Farway, Cotleigh etc *Ex* from 02. *2 Combewater Cottages, Wilmington, Honiton EX14 9SQ* Tel (01404) 831887 E-mail susanhoughton@lineone.net

HOUGHTON, Thomas. b 17. NW Ord Course 71. **d** 74 **p** 75. NSM Newcastle w Butterton *Lich* 74-82; Perm to Offic from 82. *Fernyhough, Little Madeley, Crewe CW3 9JT* Tel (01782) 750275

HOUGHTON, Timothy John. b 56. Kingston Poly BSc88. Oak Hill Th Coll BA93. **d** 97 **p** 98. C Normanton *Derby* from 97. *211 Village Street, Normanton, Derby DE23 8DE* Tel (01332) 767407 E-mail timhough@ntlworld.com

HOULDEN, Prof James Leslie. b 29. Qu Coll Ox BA52 MA56. Cuddesdon Coll 53. **d** 55 **p** 56. C Hunslet St Mary and Stourton *Ripon* 55-58; Tutor Chich Th Coll 58-59; Chapl 59-60; Chapl Trin Coll Ox 60-70; Prin Cuddesdon Coll 70-75; Prin Ripon Coll Cuddesdon 75-77; V Cuddesdon *Ox* 70-77; Hon Can Ch Ch 76-77; Sen Lect NT Studies K Coll Lon 77-87; Prof Th 87-94; rtd 94; Perm to Offic *S'wark* 94-99. *Flat 5, The Court, Fen End Road, West Knowle, Solihull B93 0AN* Tel (01564) 777138 E-mail leslie.houlden@btopenworld.com

HOULDING, David Nigel Christopher. b 53. AKC76 SSC. **d** 77 **p** 78. C Hillingdon All SS *Lon* 77-81; C Holborn St Alb w Saffron Hill St Pet 81-85; V Hampstead St Steph w All Hallows from 85; AD N Camden 01-02. *All Hallows' House, 52 Courthope Road, London NW3 2LD* Tel (020) 7267 7833 *or* 7267 6317 Mobile 07710-403294 Fax 7267 6317

HOULDSWORTH, Raymond Clifford. b 30. Bps' Coll Cheshunt 64. **d** 66 **p** 67. C Egham Hythe *Guildf* 66-70; C Cranbrook *Cant* 70-76; V Hernhill 76-82; V Minster w Monkton 82-95; rtd 95; Perm to Offic *Mon* from 95. *11 Craig Road, Six Bells, Abertillery NP13 2LR* Tel (01495) 321934

HOULT, Roy Anthony. b 35. AKC58. **d** 59 **p** 60. C Walton St Mary *Liv* 59-63; Canada from 63; Hon Can Kootenay 75-79. *381 Huron Street, Toronto ON, Canada, M5S 2G5*

HOUNSFIELD, Thomas Paul. b 15. Lon Coll of Div 46. **d** 47 **p** 48. C Penn Fields *Lich* 47-50; R Treeton *Sheff* 50-61; V Donington *Lich* 61-80; rtd 80; Perm to Offic *Win* from 81. *10 Widden Close, Sway, Lymington SO41 6AX* Tel (01590) 682399

HOUSE, The Ven Francis Harry. b 08. OBE55. Wadh Coll Ox BA30 MA34. Cuddesdon Coll 34. **d** 35 **p** 36. Pemb Coll Miss Walworth *S'wark* 35-37; Sec World Student Chr Federation Geneva 38-40; Lic to Offic *Eur* 38-40; C Leeds St Pet *Ripon* 40-42; Overseas Relig Broadcasting Org BBC 42-44; Rep World Student Relief (Greece) 44-46; Lic to Offic *Eur* 44-46; Hd of Relig Broadcasting BBC 47-55; Sec Youth Dept WCC Geneva 46-47; Hon C Hampstead Garden Suburb *Lon* 47-55; Select Preacher Cam Univ 49; Assoc Gen Sec WCC Geneva 55-62; V Pontefract St Giles *Wakef* 62-67; R Gawsworth *Ches* 67-78; Adn Macclesfield 67-78; rtd 78. *The College of St Barnabas, Blackberry Lane, Lingfield RH7 6NJ* Tel (01342) 870186

HOUSE, Graham Ivor. b 44. BA80. Oak Hill Th Coll 77. **d** 80 **p** 81. C Ipswich St Jo *St E* 80-84; V Ipswich St Andr 84-00; R Monks Eleigh w Chelsworth and Brent Eleigh etc 00-03; rtd 03. *1 Scott Lane, Melton, Woodbridge IP12 1TJ* Tel (01394) 615710 Mobile 07966-169372

HOUSE, Jack Francis. b 35. Bris Univ BEd70 Lon Univ MA80 Univ of Wales MTh94. Bris & Glouc Tr Course 79. **d** 80 **p** 81. NSM Bedminster *Bris* 80-92; Perm to Offic 92-94; NSM Knowle H Nativity from 94; NSM Easton All Hallows from 98. *48 Hendre Road, Bristol BS3 2LR* Tel 0117-966 1144 E-mail rhouse3766@aol.com

HOUSE, Mrs Janet. b 45. UEA BA67 Keswick Hall Coll PGCE68 Sussex Univ MA80. Ripon Coll Cuddesdon 93. **d** 95 **p** 96. C Swindon Ch Ch *Bris* 95-99; TV Worc SE *Worc* from 99. *The Vicarage, 4 Silverdale Avenue, Worcester WR5 1PY* Tel (01905) 353432 Fax as telephone E-mail jhouse@waitrose.com

HOUSE, Miss Maureen Ruth (Mo). b 33. St Mich Ho Ox 56 LNSM course 95. **d** 98 **p** 99. NSM Charlton *S'wark* from 98. *88 Speedwell Street, London SE8 4AT* Tel (020) 8691 1637

HOUSE, Simon Hutchinson. b 30. Peterho Cam BA65 MA67. Cuddesdon Coll 61. **d** 64 **p** 65. C Sutton St Jas *York* 64-67; C Acomb St Steph 67-69; V Allestree St Nic *Derby* 69-81; RD Duffield 74-81; V Bitterne Park *Win* 81-91; rtd 91; Perm to Offic *Win* from 91. *22 Stanley Street, Southsea PO5 2DS* Tel (023) 9283 8592

HOUSE, Vickery Willis. b 45. MA. Kelham Th Coll. **d** 69 **p** 70. C Crediton *Ex* 69-76; TV Sampford Peverell, Uplowman, Holcombe Rogus etc 76-81; R Berwick w Selmeston and Alciston *Chich* 81-90; Chapl Ardingly Coll 90-94; V Brighton St Bart *Chich* from 94. *16 Richmond Terrace, Brighton BN2 9SA* Tel (01273) 685142 *or* 620491 Fax 572215 E-mail stbarts@fastnet.co.uk

HOUSEMAN, Patricia Adele. *See* CAMPION, Mrs Patricia Adele

HOUSLEY, Andrew Arthur. b 67. Wilson Carlile Coll 91 Ridley Hall Cam 00. **d** 02. C Ormskirk *Liv* from 02. *18 Lea Crescent, Ormskirk L39 1PQ* Tel (01695) 570876 E-mail andrewjahousley@ukonline.co.uk

HOUSMAN, Arthur Martin Rowand. b 53. MA CertEd DipTh. Trin Coll Bris 81. **d** 83 **p** 84. C Croydon Ch Ch Broad Green *Cant* 83-84; C Croydon Ch Ch *S'wark* 85-87; TV Stratton St Margaret w S Marston etc *Bris* 87-93; Chapl Peterhouse Sch Zimbabwe 93-98; Chapl Nor Sch from 98; Hon PV Nor Cathl *Nor* from 98. *Cottage Farm Cottage, Beccles Road, Raveningham, Norwich NR14 6NW* Tel (01508) 548991

HOUSTON, Arthur James. b 54. Trin Coll Bris BA87. **d** 87 **p** 88. C Chatham St Phil and St Jas *Roch* 87-91; I Carrigaline Union C, C & R 91-99; Can Cork Cathl 95-99; Can Ross Cathl 95-99; Dir of Ords 96-99; V Margate H Trin *Cant* from 99; AD Thanet from 02. *The Vicarage, 5 Devonshire Gardens, Cliftonville, Margate CT9 3AF* Tel (01843) 294129 E-mail htmargate@freeserve.co.uk

HOUSTON, David Wiliam James. b 52. DipTh98. **d** 93 **p** 95. S Africa 93-00; Lyttelton St Steph 93-96; R Sabie w Lydenburg 96-00; P-in-c Elmsted w Hastingleigh *Cant* from 00; P-in-c Petham and Waltham w Lower Hardres etc from 00. *The Rectory, Curtis Lane, Stelling Minnis, Canterbury CT4 6BT* Tel (01227) 709318 Fax as telephone E-mail davidwjhouston@ssgchurches.fsnet.co.uk

HOUSTON, Edward Davison. b 31. TCD BA56. **d** 57 **p** 58. C Conwall Union *D & R* 57-59; India 59-88; V Whittlebury w Paulerspury *Pet* 89-01; P-in-c Wicken 89-01; Perm to Offic from 01; rtd 01. *38 Meadow Street, Market Harborough LE16 7JZ*

HOUSTON, Helen Sarah. b 70. Bris Univ BA91. St Jo Coll Nottm MA95. **d** 95 **p** 96. C Bourne *Guildf* 95-98; Perm to Offic Bris 98-99; Hon C Chippenham St Pet 99-00. *33 Dunkeld Park, Bangor BT20 0AA*

HOUSTON, Maurice Iain. **d** 02. C Edin Old St Paul *Edin* from 02. *41 Jeffrey Street, Edinburgh EH1 1DH* Tel 0131-556 9035

HOUSTON, Michael Alexander. b 46. Lanc Univ MA92. Linc Th Coll 86. **d** 88 **p** 89. C Longton *Blackb* 88-91; C Woughton *Ox* 91-92; TV 92-98; TR 98-99; TR Gd Shep TM *Carl* from 99. *The Rectory, Greystoke, Penrith CA11 0TJ* Tel (01768) 483293 E-mail michael.houston1@virgin.net

HOUSTON, Michael James. b 41. Dub Bible Coll St Jo Coll Nottm. **d** 95 **p** 97. Aux Min *D & D* 95-99; P-in-c Ballyphilip w

Ardquin from 99. *2 Rectory Wood Road, Cloughey Road, Portaferry BT22 1LJ* Tel (028) 4272 9997

HOUSTON, Prof Samuel Kenneth (Ken). b 43. FIMA73 QUB BSc64 PhD67 MILT. CITC 81. **d** 85 **p** 86. NSM Belfast St Jas w St Silas *Conn* 85-91; NSM Belfast St Andr from 91; Prof Mathematical Studies Ulster Univ from 96. *29 North Circular Road, Belfast BT15 5HB* Tel (028) 9077 1830 *or* 9036 6953 Fax 9036 6859 E-mail sk.houston@north-circular.demon.co.uk

HOUSTON, William Paul. b 54. QUB BSSc76 TCD BTh78. CITC 78. **d** 81 **p** 82. C Carrickfergus *Conn* 81-83; C Bangor St Comgall *D & D* 83-86; I Gilford 86-90; I Carnalea 90-99; I Clondalkin w Rathcoole *D & G* from 99; Min Can St Patr Cathl Dublin from 00. *The Rectory, Monastery Road, Clondalkin, Dublin 22, Irish Republic* Tel (00353) (1) 459 2160

HOVENDEN, Gerald Eric. b 53. York Univ BA75 Ox Univ MA85. Wycliffe Hall Ox 78. **d** 81 **p** 82. C Pitsmoor w Ellesmere *Sheff* 81-85; Chapl Lyon w Grenoble and St Etienne *Eur* 85-90; TV S Gillingham *Roch* 90-98; TR Southborough St Pet w Ch Ch and St Matt 98-02; TR Southborough St Pet w Ch Ch and St Matt etc from 02. *The Vicarage, 86 Prospect Road, Southborough, Tunbridge Wells TN4 0EG* Tel (01892) 528534
E-mail geh@hovendens.freeserve.co.uk

HOVEY, Richard Michael. b 58. Imp Coll Lon BScEng79 ACGI79 Cranfield Inst of Tech MBA84 CEng83 MIEE83. Cranmer Hall Dur CTM95. **d** 95 **p** 96. C Cheddar *B & W* 95-99; TV Gtr Corsham *Bris* 99-01; TV Gtr Corsham and Lacock from 01. *The Vicarage, Wadswick Lane, Neston, Corsham SN13 9TA* Tel (01225) 810572 E-mail rmh@dawntreader.freeserve.co.uk

HOVIL, Jeremy Richard Guy. b 65. K Coll Lon BSc86 Spurgeon's Coll Lon MTh99. Wycliffe Hall Ox BTh95. **d** 95 **p** 96. C Kensington St Barn *Lon* 95-99; Crosslinks Uganda from 00. *PO Box 6016, Kampala, Uganda* Tel (00256) (41) 501972 *or* (77) 612230 E-mail hovils@spacenetuganda.com

HOVIL, Richard Guy. b 29. Ex Coll Ox BA51 MA57. Ridley Hall Cam. **d** 55 **p** 56. C Finchley Ch Ch *Lon* 55-58; Staff Worker Scripture Union 58-71; Chapl Monkton Combe Sch Bath 71-83; V Fremington *Ex* 83-94; rtd 94; Perm to Offic *Sarum* from 94. *37 Upper Marsh Road, Warminster BA12 9PN* Tel (01985) 214337 E-mail richard@hovil.fsnet.co.uk

HOW, Canon John Maxloe. b 15. Magd Coll Cam BA37 MA49. Westcott Ho Cam 39. **d** 39 **p** 40. C Norton St Mary *Dur* 39-44; P-in-c W Pelton 44-45; P-in-c Stella 46-47; V Thornley 47-51; V Monkwearmouth St Andr 51-59; V Barton w Pooley Bridge *Carl* 59-73; RD Penrith 61-73; Hon Can Carl Cathl 72-81; V Kirkby Lonsdale w Mansergh 73-76; TR Kirkby Lonsdale 76-81; rtd 81; Perm to Offic *Carl* from 81. *4 Kilmidyke Drive, Grange-over-Sands LA11 7AL* Tel (01539) 534117

HOWARD, Alan James. b 45. Bris Univ BA69. Clifton Th Coll. **d** 71 **p** 72. C Welling *Roch* 71-74; C Cromer *Nor* 74-78; V Sidcup St Andr *Roch* 78-86; V Leyton St Cath *Chelmsf* 86-93; V Leyton St Cath and St Paul 93-00. *4 Bower Close, Romford RM5 3SR* Tel (01708) 754052

HOWARD, Andrew. b 63. Man Univ BA95 Leeds Univ MA97. Coll of Resurr Mirfield 95. **d** 97 **p** 98. C Worksop Priory *S'well* 97-01; V Hemlington *York* from 01. *St Timothy's House, 31 Coatham Close, Hemlington, Middlesbrough TS8 9JW* Tel (01642) 590496

HOWARD, Arthur Calvin. b 60. Leeds Univ LLB82 Barrister 83. Wycliffe Hall Ox 00. **d** 03. C Heswall *Ches* from 03. *The Croft, Croftsway, Heswall, Wirral CH60 9JP* Tel 0151-348 4146

HOWARD, Charles William Wykeham. b 52. Southn Univ BTh81. Sarum & Wells Th Coll 76. **d** 79 **p** 80. C St Mary-at-Latton *Chelmsf* 79-82; Chapl RN from 82. *Royal Naval Chaplaincy Service, Room 203, Victory Building, HM Naval Base, Portsmouth PO1 3LS* Tel (023) 9272 7903 Fax 9272 7111

HOWARD, Clive Eric. b 65. Oak Hill Th Coll BA99. **d** 99 **p** 00. C Chipping Sodbury and Old Sodbury *Glouc* 99-03; V Tipton St Matt *Lich* from 03. *St Matthew's Vicarage, Dudley Road, Tipton DY4 8DJ* Tel 0121-557 1929
E-mail clive-howard@rev65.fsnet.co.uk

HOWARD, David John. b 47. Brasted Th Coll 68 Ripon Hall Ox 70. **d** 72 **p** 73. C Benchill *Man* 72-75; C Sedgley All SS *Lich* 75-77; C-in-c Lostock CD *Man* 77-85; V Lt Hulton 85-88; Perm to Offic 90-91; C E Leake *S'well* 91-92; C Costock 91-92; C Rempstone 91-92; C Stanford on Soar 91-92; C W Leake w Kingston-on-Soar and Ratcliffe-on-Soar 91-92; C E and W Leake, Stanford-on-Soar, Rempstone etc 92-94; P-in-c Bilborough w Strelley 94-98; Chapl HM YOI Werrington Ho 98-03; Chapl HM Pris Drake Hall from 03. *HM Prison and YOI Drake Hall, Eccleshall, Stafford ST21 6LQ* Tel (01785) 773000 E-mail davaid.howard@hmps.gsi.gov.uk

HOWARD, David John. b 51. Lon Univ BSc73. Oak Hill Th Coll 74. **d** 77 **p** 78. C Radipole and Melcombe Regis *Sarum* 77-83; R Tredington and Darlingscott w Newbold on Stour *Cov* 83-90; P-in-c Binley 90-94; V from 94; RD Cov E 95-99. *Binley Vicarage, 68 Brandon Road, Coventry CV3 2JF* Tel (024) 7663 6334

HOWARD, Canon Donald. b 27. K Coll Lon BD58 AKC58. **d** 59 **p** 60. C Saltburn-by-the-Sea *York* 59-62; S Africa 62-72; R

Haddington *Edin* 72-78; Can St Andr Cathl *Ab* 78-91; Provost St Andr Cathl 78-91; R Aberdeen St Andr 78-91; Chapl Aber Univ 78-82; P-in-c Aberdeen St Ninian 80-91; Angl Adv Grampian TV 84-88; rtd 91; Hon Can St Andr Cathl *Ab* from 91; Perm to Offic *Ripon* from 91. *42 Waterside, Ripon HG4 1RA* Tel (01765) 692144

HOWARD, Mrs Erika Kathryn. b 49. SRN70 SCM72. S Dios Minl Tr Scheme 88. **d** 91 **p** 94. NSM New Shoreham and Old Shoreham *Chich* 91-94; C Kingston Buci 94-03; V Sompting from 03. *The Vicarage, West Street, Sompting, Lancing BN15 0AX* Tel (01903) 234511
E-mail erikahoward@supanet.com

HOWARD, Canon Francis Curzon. b 27. Lon Univ DipTh57. St Aid Birkenhead 54. **d** 57 **p** 58. C Claughton cum Grange *Ches* 57-60; C Cheltenham St Paul *Glouc* 60-62; V Sheff St Barn *Sheff* 62-65; Bermuda 65-71; USA from 71; Asst Atone Westfield Massachusetts 71-76; R Tariffville Tin Connecticut 76-98; rtd 98; Can Kaduna from 95. *PO Box 423, 116 Terry's Plain Road, Simsbury, CT 06070, USA* Tel (001) (860) 658 1897

HOWARD, Frank Thomas. b 36. Lon Univ BSc57. Bps' Coll Cheshunt 59. **d** 61 **p** 62. C Macclesfield St Mich *Ches* 61-64; C Claughton cum Grange 64-66; V Lache cum Saltney 66-76; R Stanton *St E* 76-97; RD Ixworth 79-85; P-in-c Hempnall *Nor* 97-01; rtd 01; Perm to Offic *Nor* from 01. *55 Heywood Avenue, Diss IP22 4DN* Tel (01379) 640819

HOWARD, Geoffrey. b 30. Barrister-at-Law 83 Lon Univ LLB77. EMMTC. **d** 85 **p** 86. NSM Barton *Ely* 85-87; NSM Coton 85-87; C W Walton 87-92; TV Daventry, Ashby St Ledgers, Braunston etc *Pet* 92-97; rtd 97; Perm to Offic *Ely* 97-00. *11 Porson Court, Porson Road, Cambridge CB2 2ER* Tel (01223) 300738

HOWARD, George Granville. b 47. Trin Coll Bris. **d** 88 **p** 89. C Downend *Bris* 88-92; V Clifton H Trin, St Andr and St Pet 92-99; Bp's Officer for Miss and Evang 92-99; V W Streatham St Jas *S'wark* from 99; RD Tooting from 02. *St James's Vicarage, 236 Mitcham Lane, London SW16 6NT* Tel (020) 8664 6059 *or* 8677 3947

HOWARD, John. *See* HOWARD, Nicolas John

HOWARD, John Alexander. b 27. Wesley Coll Leeds 48 Coll of Resurr Mirfield 66. **d** 67 **p** 68. C Almondbury *Wakef* 67-71; V Skelmanthorpe 71-81; R Fortrose *Mor* 81-94; R Cromarty 81-94; R Arpafeelie 81-94; rtd 94; Perm to Offic *Glouc* from 94. *2 Webbs Cottages, Stratford Road, Mickleton, Chipping Campden GL55 6SW* Tel (01386) 438787

HOWARD, John Robert. b 60. NUI BA HDipEd TCD DipTh. **d** 84 **p** 85. C Donaghcloney w Waringstown *D & D* 84-88; I Belfast St Ninian *Conn* 88-94; Bp's Dom Chapl 88-94; Chapl Ulster Univ 88-94; I Annahilt w Magherahamlet *D & D* from 94; Chapl HM Pris Maghaberry from 96. *Annahilt Rectory, 15 Ballykeel Road, Hillsborough BT26 6NW* Tel (028) 9263 8218

HOWARD, Mrs Judith Marion. WEMTC 98. **d** 01 **p** 02. NSM Glouc St Jas and All SS *Glouc* from 01. *Paulmead, Wells Road, Bisley, Stroud GL6 7AG* Tel (01452) 770776

HOWARD, Keith. b 55. Univ of Wales (Ban) DipTh81. St Jo Coll Nottm 81. **d** 84 **p** 85. C Llanidloes w Llangurig *Ban* 84-87; R Llansantffraid Glan Conwy and Eglwysbach *St As* 87-00; V Heapey St Barnabas and Withnell St Paul *Blackb* from 00. *1 Balmoral Drive, Brinscall, Chorley PR6 8ST* Tel (01254) 832017

HOWARD, Martin John Aidan. b 68. Lon Univ BA90 Open Univ MA96. St Jo Coll Nottm MA97. **d** 97 **p** 98. C Billericay and Lt Burstead *Chelmsf* 97-01; TV Kinson *Sarum* from 01. *The Rectory, 51 Millhams Road, Bournemouth BH10 7LJ* Tel (01202) 571996

HOWARD, Canon Michael Charles. b 35. Selw Coll Cam BA58 MA63 CQSW72. Wycliffe Hall Ox 58. **d** 60 **p** 61. C Stowmarket *St E* 60-64; CMS Nigeria 64-71; Hon Can Ondo 70-71; Hon C Southborough St Pet w Ch Ch and St Matt *Roch* 72-73; Perm to Offic *Ox* from 73; rtd 00. *17 Milton Road, Bloxham, Banbury OX15 4HD* Tel (01295) 720470

HOWARD, Canon Michael Paul Penrose. b 40. Keele Univ BA62 Lon Univ BD69. Lon Coll of Div 66. **d** 69 **p** 70. C Nottingham St Nic *S'well* 69-72; C Ox St Aldate w H Trin *Ox* 72-77; Chapl CCC Ox 75-77; V Dartford Ch Ch *Roch* 77-90; Chapl W Hill Hosp Dartford 77-90; P-in-c Cobham w Luddesdowne and Dode *Roch* 90-96; Dioc Adv on Evang from 90; Hon Can Roch Cathl from 92; P-in-c Sevenoaks Weald from 96. *St George's Vicarage, Church Road, Weald, Sevenoaks TN14 6LT* Tel (01732) 463291 Fax as telephone
E-mail michael.howard@rochester.anglican.org

HOWARD, Natalie Delia. b 51. St Mich Coll Llan 99. **d** 02 **p** 03. NSM Magor *Mon* from 02. *8 The Meadows, Magor, Caldicot NP26 3LA* Tel (01633) 881714

HOWARD, Nicolas John. b 61. Nottm Univ BTh90. Aston Tr Scheme 85 Linc Th Coll 87. **d** 90 **p** 91. C Bracknell *Ox* 90-94; P-in-c Oldham St Chad Limeside *Man* 94-96; Perm to Offic *Birm* 96-99. *11 Chesterfield Court, Middleton Hall Road, Birmingham B30 1AF* Tel 0121-459 4975

HOWARD, Norman. b 26. AKC57. St Boniface Warminster 57. **d** 58 **p** 59. C Friern Barnet St Jas *Lon* 58-62; Jamaica 62-69; USA from 69; rtd 91. *766 Lake Forest Road, Clearwater, FL 33765, USA* Tel (001) (813) 799 3929

HOWARD, Paul David. b 47. Lanchester Poly BA69. St Jo Coll Nottm 74. **d** 77 **p** 78. C Bedworth *Cov* 77-83; V Newchapel *Lich* 83-93; V Stretton w Claymills from 93. *The Vicarage, Church Road, Stretton, Burton-on-Trent DE13 0HD* Tel (01283) 565141 E-mail paul@howard510.freeserve.co.uk

HOWARD, Peter Leslie. b 48. Nottm Univ BTh77 Birm Univ MA80 Leeds Univ MEd91. St Jo Coll Nottm LTh77. **d** 77 **p** 78. C Gospel Lane St Mich *Birm* 77-81; P-in-c Nechells 81-85; V Stanley *Wakef* 85-92; P-in-c Nor Heartsease St Fran *Nor* from 92; Dioc UPA/CUF Link Officer from 02. *St Francis's Vicarage, 100 Rider Haggard Road, Norwich NR7 9UQ* Tel (01603) 702799 E-mail plhoward.stfrancis@tinyworld.co.uk

HOWARD, Reginald James. b 33. AKC60. **d** 61 **p** 62. C Shildon *Dur* 61-64; C Hurworth 64-66; V Morley St Paul *Wakef* 66-75; V Westgate Common 75-93; rtd 93; Perm to Offic *Wakef* from 98. *41 Oakleigh Avenue, Wakefield WF2 9DF* Tel (01924) 373020

HOWARD, Canon Robert Weston. b 28. Pemb Coll Cam BA49 MA53. Westcott Ho Cam 51. **d** 53 **p** 54. C Bishopwearmouth St Mich *Dur* 53-56; C Cambridge Gt St Mary w St Mich *Ely* 56-60; Hong Kong 60-66; V Prenton *Ches* 66-75; RD Frodsham 74-82; P-in-c Dunham-on-the-Hill 75-77; V Helsby and Ince 75-77; V Helsby and Dunham-on-the-Hill 77-82; Hon Can Ches Cathl 78-82; V Moseley St Mary *Birm* 82-88; V Chalke Valley W *Sarum* 88-93; rtd 93; Perm to Offic *St D* from 93; Perm to Offic *Heref* from 93. *The Coach House, 13 Clun Road, Aston-on-Clun, Craven Arms SY7 8EW* Tel (01588) 660630

HOWARD, Ronald. b 40. AMIBF65 AMICME01 EngTech91. Cranmer Hall Dur 86. **d** 88 **p** 89. C Baildon *Bradf* 88-92; P-in-c Sutton 92-96; P-in-c St Tudy w St Mabyn and Michaelstow *Truro* 96-00; P-in-c Keyingham w Ottringham, Halsham and Sunk Is *York* 00-03; R from 03. *The Rectory, Ottringham Road, Keyingham, Hull HU12 9RX* Tel (01964) 622171 Fax 622907 E-mail fatherronald@btinternet.com

HOWARD, Simon Charles. b 60. Birm Univ BA81 Westhill Coll Birm CYCW86. Ridley Hall Cam CTM92. **d** 92 **p** 93. C Cambridge St Martin *Ely* 92-96; Chapl St Bede's Sch Cam 92-96; P-in-c Earley Trinity *Ox* from 96. *15 Caraway Road, Reading RG6 5XR* Tel 0118-986 8615 E-mail revsimon@lineone.net

HOWARD, Stanley Reginald Kekewich. b 10. St Pet Hall Ox BA31 MA35. Ridley Hall Cam 31. **d** 33 **p** 34. C Battersea St Mich *S'wark* 33-36; C Watford St Andr *St Alb* 36-39; C Margate H Trin *Cant* 39-40; R Cuxton *Roch* 40-51; V Cheltenham St Paul *Glouc* 51-76; Chapl St Cath Ho 51-68; Chapl Cheltenham Boys' Home 51-56; Chapl Cheltenham Maternity and St Paul's Hosps 61-76; rtd 76; Perm to Offic *Win* from 81. *Grimston Rectory, Watery Lane, Grimston, King's Lynn PE32 1BQ* Tel (01485) 600353 E-mail srkh@grimston-rectory.freeserve.co.uk

HOWARD, Ms Susan. b 65. Lanc Univ BA86. Ripon Coll Cuddesdon 88. **d** 91 **p** 94. C Ditton St Mich *Liv* 91-94; C Kirkby 94-97; Adv for Youth and Young Adults *Man* 97-00; Governor HM Pris Styal from 01. *HM Prison, Styal, Wilmslow SK9 4HR* Tel (01625) 532141

HOWARD, Thomas Norman. b 40. St Aid Birkenhead 64. **d** 67 **p** 68. C Farnworth and Kearsley *Man* 67-70; C Prestwich St Marg 70-73; V Heyside 73-85; Warden Lamplugh Ho Angl Conf Cen 85-90; Hon C Langtoft w Foxholes, Butterwick, Cottam etc *York* 85-87; C 87-90; V Fence and Newchurch-in-Pendle *Blackb* 90-00; Dioc Ecum Officer 90-95; rtd 00; Hon C Stalybridge H Trin and Ch Ch *Ches* from 01. *Bethel Barn, Main Road, Nether Kellet, Carnforth LA6 1EF* Tel (01524) 736552

HOWARD, William Alfred. b 47. St Jo Coll Dur BA69. Wycliffe Hall Ox 74. **d** 77 **p** 79. C Norbiton *S'wark* 77-80; C Mile Cross *Nor* 80-84; R Grimston, Congham and Roydon from 84; Chapl Norfolk Constabulary from 00. *The Rectory, Watery Lane, Grimston, King's Lynn PE32 1BQ* Tel (01485) 600335 E-mail william.howard@dunelm.org.uk

HOWARD-COWLEY, Joseph Charles. b 27. Trin Coll Cam BA53 MA56. Wells Th Coll 53. **d** 55 **p** 56. C Newmarket All SS *St E* 55-58; Chapl Aycliffe Approved Sch Co Dur 58-61; V Aldringham *St E* 61-86; rtd 86; Perm to Offic *St E* 86-93 and *Truro* from 93. *Lower Penquite, St Ive, Liskeard PL14 3NE* Tel (01579) 383469

HOWARD JONES, Preb Raymond Vernon. b 31. AKC54. **d** 55 **p** 56. C Hutton *Chelmsf* 55-58; CF 58-62; V Walpole St Andrew *Ely* 62-64; Chapl St Crispin's Hosp Northampton 64-70; V Brockhampton w Fawley *Heref* 70-86; V Fownhope 70-86; RD Heref Rural 77-81; Preb Heref Cathl 81-97; Communications Adv and Bp's Staff Officer 86-97; rtd 97; Perm to Offic *Heref* from 97. *Kingfishers, Breinton, Hereford HR4 7PP* Tel (01432) 279371

HOWARTH, Arthur. b 14. Dur Univ 36. **d** 37 **p** 38. C Aylesbury *Ox* 37-40; C W Wycombe 41-42; C Acton Vale St Thos *Lon* 42-43; C Fulham All SS 43-44; C Hornsey St Mary 44-46; St Vincent 46-51; Perm to Offic *Ox* 51-54; Perm to Offic *Guildf* 54; Nigeria from 55. *Bishop Lasbrey College Irete, PO Box 68, Owerri, Nigeria*

HOWARTH, Christopher. b 47. Ch Ch Coll Cant CertEd69 Open Univ BA76. S Dios Minl Tr Scheme. **d** 83 **p** 84. NSM Uckfield

Chich from 83; NSM Lt Horsted from 83; NSM Isfield from 83. *137 Rocks Park Road, Uckfield TN22 2BD* Tel (01825) 765352

HOWARTH, Jack Raymond. b 13. Leeds Univ BSc34. Coll of Resurr Mirfield 34. **d** 36 **p** 37. C Anfield St Columba *Liv* 36-39 and 46-47; C Illingworth *Wakef* 39-43; Chapl RAFVR 43-46; C Birstall *Wakef* 47-48; V Harley Wood 48-52; V Manningham St Jude *Bradf* 52-63; RD Bradf 58-63; R Elland *Wakef* 63-75; RD Brighouse and Elland 70-73; V Halifax St Jo 75-78; rtd 78; Hon C Haydock St Jas *Liv* 78-86; Chapl Wigan R Infirmary 86-88; Perm to Offic *Edin* from 88. *13/4 Ladywell Road, Edinburgh EH12 7TA* Tel 0131-334 0594

HOWARTH, Robert Francis Harvey. b 31. S'wark Ord Course 71. **d** 72 **p** 73. C St Marylebone All So w SS Pet and Jo *Lon* 72-73; C St Helen Bishopsgate w St Martin Outwich 73-78; V Harlow St Mary and St Hugh w St Jo the Bapt *Chelmsf* 78-88; P-in-c Victoria Docks Ascension 88-96; rtd 96. *Lochhill, Palnackie, Castle Douglas DG7 1PW* Tel (01556) 600363

HOWARTH, Canon Ronald. b 26. TCD BA51 MA54. Linc Th Coll 50. **d** 52 **p** 53. C Gannow *Blackb* 52-55; Nigeria 55-89; rtd 91. *4 Kingston Court, Walton Street, Oxford OX2 6ES* Tel (01865) 553046

HOWARTH, Toby Matthew. b 62. Yale Univ BA86 Birm Univ MA91 Free Univ of Amsterdam PhD01. Wycliffe Hall Ox 89 Qu Coll Birm 90. **d** 92 **p** 93. C Derby St Aug *Derby* 92-95; Crosslinks India 95-00; The Netherlands 00-02; Tutor Crowther Hall CMS Tr Coll Selly Oak from 02. *Christ Church Vicarage, 34 Grantham Road, Birmingham B11 1LU* Tel 0121-753 4541 E-mail hentob@aya.yale.edu

HOWAT, Jeremy Noel Thomas. b 35. Em Coll Cam BA59 MA62. Ridley Hall Cam 59. **d** 63 **p** 64. C Sutton *Liv* 63-65; C Kirk Ella *York* 65-66; C Bridlington Quay Ch Ch 66-69; R Wheldrake 69-78; Dioc Youth Officer 69-74; SAMS Argentina 78-81 and 90-97; P-in-c Newton upon Ouse *York* 81-82; V Shipton w Overton 81-82; P-in-c Skelton by York 81-82; R Skelton w Shipton and Newton on Ouse 82-89; C Elloughton and Brough w Brantingham 97-99; rtd 99; Perm to Offic *York* from 00. *18 Petersway, York YO30 6AR* Tel (01904) 628946 E-mail jeremy@howat.karoo.co.uk

HOWDEN, Frank Newton. b 16. Connecticut Univ MS68 Univ of the South (USA) AB40. Gen Th Sem NY MDiv43. **d** 43 **p** 43. USA 43-85; Adn New Haven Co Connecticut 65-69; rtd 85; Lic to Offic *Roch* 85-99; Perm to Offic from 99. *9 Argyle Road, Southborough, Tunbridge Wells TN4 0SU* Tel (01892) 528838 E-mail fnhowden@aol.com

HOWDEN, Canon John Travis. b 40. RIBA62. Sarum Th Coll 66. **d** 69 **p** 70. C S Gillingham *Roch* 69-72; C Banbury *Ox* 72-73; Lic to Offic *York* 73-74; Hon C Hull Newland St Jo 74-81; Hon C Stock Harvard *Chelmsf* 82-86; R Doddinghurst and Mountnessing 86-91; P-in-c Pleshey 91-00; Warden Pleshey Retreat Ho 91-00; Hon Can Chelmsf Cathl from 97; R Wickham Bishops w Lt Braxted from 00. *The Rectory, 1 Church Road, Wickham Bishops, Witham CM8 3LA* Tel (01621) 891360 E-mail john.howden@virgin.net

HOWDLE, Glyn. b 50. Bp Lonsdale Coll BEd72 Birm Univ DPSE84. St Alb Minl Tr Scheme 90. **d** 91 **p** 02. NSM Aspenden, Buntingford and Westmill *St Alb* from 01. *58 Ermine Street, Thundridge, Ware SG12 0SY* Tel and fax (01920) 469632 Mobile 07909-920437 E-mail glynjosealicia@howdle.fslife.co.uk

HOWE, Alan Raymond. b 52. Nottm Univ BTh79. St Jo Coll Nottm 76. **d** 80 **p** 81. C Southsea St Simon *Portsm* 80-83; C Bexleyheath St Pet *Roch* 83-86; TV Camberley St Paul *Guildf* 86-93; P-in-c Mansfield St Jo *S'well* 93-96; P-in-c Wollaton Park 96-02; AD Nottingham W from 99; V Wollaton Park from 02. *St Mary's Vicarage, Wollaton Hall Drive, Nottingham NG8 1AF* Tel 0115-978 6988 E-mail howefamilystmary@compuserve.com

HOWE, Anthony Graham. b 72. Qu Coll Ox BA99 MA99 St Steph Ho Ox BA00. **d** 01 **p** 02. C Newbury *Ox* from 01. *37 Newtown Road, Newbury RG14 7BS* Tel (01635) 841668 E-mail father-howe@oratorium.zzn.com

HOWE, Charles. b 30. Lon Univ BD65 Open Univ BA79. Tyndale Hall Bris 55. **d** 58 **p** 59. C Willowfield *D & D* 58-60; C Derryloran *Arm* 60-64; C Belfast St Bart *Conn* 64-65; I Tullyaughnish w Kilmacrennan and Killygarvan *D & R* 65-72; I Londonderry St Aug 73-95; Can Derry Cathl 85-95; Dioc Org and Tutor for Aux Min 93-95; rtd 95. *2 Dunnwood Park, Londonderry BT47 2NN* Tel (028) 7131 2305 E-mail charleshowe1@hotmail.com

HOWE, Canon David Randall. b 24. St Jo Coll Cam BA51 MA55. Wells Th Coll 51. **d** 53 **p** 54. C Basingstoke *Win* 53-59; V Rotherwick, Hook and Greywell 59-70; R Bossington w Broughton 70-81; R Broughton w Bossington and Mottisfont 81-86; R Broughton, Bossington, Houghton and Mottisfont 86--89; Hon Can Win Cathl 83-89; rtd 89; Perm to Offic *Sarum* and *Win* from 89. *Little Orchard, Hilldrop Lane, Ramsbury, Marlborough SN8 2RB* Tel (01672) 20326

HOWE, Miss Frances Ruth. b 28. ACIB67. Cranmer Hall Dur IDC80. **dss** 80 **d** 87 **p** 94. Newc St Andr *Newc* 80-82; Chapl Asst R Victoria Infirmary Newc 80-87; Chapl Wylam and Fleming Ch Hosp 82-87; Chapl St Oswald's Hospice Newc 86-92; C Newc

Epiphany *Newc* 87-90; rtd 92; Hon C Delaval *Newc* 92-98; Perm to Offic from 98. *18 Mason Avenue, Whitley Bay NE26 1AQ* Tel 0191-252 5163

HOWE, The Ven George Alexander. b 52. St Jo Coll Dur BA73. Westcott Ho Cam 73. **d** 75 **p** 76. C Peterlee *Dur* 75-79; C Norton St Mary 79-81; V Hart w Elwick Hall 81-85; R Sedgefield 85-91; RD Sedgefield 89-91; V Kendal H Trin *Carl* 91-00; RD Kendal 94-00; Hon Can Carl Cathl from 94; Adn Westmorland and Furness from 00; Bp's Adv for Ecum Affairs from 01. *The Vicarage, Windermere Road, Lindale, Grange-over-Sands LA11 6LB* Tel (01539) 534717 Fax 535090 E-mail archdeacon.south@carlislediocese.org.uk

HOWE, Harry Norman. b 10. United Th Coll Limuru. **d** 73 **p** 74. Kenya 73-75; C Fringford w Hethe and Newton Purcell *Ox* 75-76; Perm to Offic *York* 76-80; Perm to Offic *Lich* 80-93; Perm to Offic *Wakef* 84-98; rtd 92. *Address temp unknown*

HOWE, Canon John. b 36. Ex Coll Ox BA58 MA63. St Steph Ho Ox 58. **d** 61 **p** 62. C Horninglow *Lich* 61-64; C Sedgley All SS 64-66; V Ocker Hill 66-73; V Gnosall 73-79; P-in-c Hoar Cross 79-82; Preb Lich Cathl 83-88; V Hoar Cross w Newchurch 83-88; Can Res Lich Cathl 88-96; Master St Jo Hosp Lich 96-00; rtd 00; Perm to Offic *Lich* from 01. *9 Cherry Street, The Leys, Tamworth B79 7ED* Tel (01827) 57817

HOWE, Canon Nicholas Simon. b 60. Man Univ BA81 K Coll Lon MTh85. Ridley Hall Cam 86. **d** 88 **p** 89. C Lich St Chad *Lich* 88-92; TV Leeds City *Ripon* 92-01; Dioc Dir of Ords and Post-Ord Tr *Sheff* from 01; Chapl Sheff Cathl from 01; Can Res Sheff Cathl from 03. *47 Firth Park Avenue, Sheffield S5 6HF* Tel 0114-243 6013 E-mail holytrinity@boarlane.freeserve.co.uk

HOWE, Canon Rex Alan. b 29. Ch Coll Cam BA53 MA57. Coll of Resurr Mirfield 53. **d** 55 **p** 56. C Barnsley St Pet *Wakef* 55-57; C Helmsley *York* 57-60; V Middlesbrough St Martin 60-67; V Redcar 67-73; V Kirkleatham 67-73; RD Guisborough 67-73; Dean Hong Kong 73-76; Adn 75-76; TR Grantham *Linc* 77-85; RD Grantham 78-85; Can and Preb Linc Cathl 81-85; V Canford Cliffs and Sandbanks *Sarum* 85-94; RD Poole 92-94; rtd 94; Perm to Offic *Sarum* from 94. *Little Over, Mead Road, Corfe Castle, Wareham BH20 5EW* Tel (01929) 480528

HOWE, Roy William. b 38. ALCD67. **d** 66 **p** 67. C Bradf Cathl *Bradf* 66-70; C Barnoldswick w Bracewell 70-72; V Yeadon St Jo 72-79; P-in-c Bainton *York* 79-86; P-in-c Middleton-on-the-Wolds 79-86; P-in-c N Dalton 79-86; RD Harthill 81-87; C Watton w Beswick and Kilnwick 82-86; R Bainton w N Dalton, Middleton-on-the-Wolds etc 86-87; TV Penrith w Newton Reigny and Plumpton Wall *Carl* 87-92; Dioc Chapl to Agric and Rural Life 87-92; V Cornhill w Carham *Newc* 92-98; V Branxton 92-98; P-in-c Coddenham w Gosbeck and Hemingstone w Henley *St E* from 98; rtd 03. *Ballaclague, 2 Halvasso Vean, Longdowns, Penryn TR10 9DN* Tel (01209) 860552

HOWE, Ruth. *See* HOWE, Miss Frances Ruth

HOWE, William Ernest. b 25. ARICS51 MRICS01. Westcott Ho Cam 68. **d** 70 **p** 71. C Anston *Sheff* 70-73; V 84-92; C Woodsetts 70-73; V Greasbrough 73-84; rtd 92; Perm to Offic *Sheff* from 92; Perm to Offic *S'well* from 97. *18 New Cottages, Worksop S80 3PE* Tel (01909) 479618

HOWELL, Alfred. b 32. Wells Th Coll 57. **d** 59 **p** 60. C Ferryhill *Dur* 59-61; C Tankersley *Sheff* 61-63; V New Edlington 63-66; V Sparkbrook Ch Ch *Birm* 66-73; Lic to Offic *Chelmsf* 73-83; P-in-c Brentwood St Geo 83-88; rtd 88; Perm to Offic *Chich* from 88. *Windy Corner, Grove Lane, Iden, Rye TN31 7QA* Tel (01797) 280564

HOWELL, Andrew John. b 44. Clifton Th Coll 68. **d** 71 **p** 72. C Halliwell St Pet *Man* 71-77; V Facit 77-95; P-in-c Smallbridge and Wardle from 95. *The Vicarage, 151 Wardle Road, Rochdale OL12 9JA* Tel (01706) 713529

HOWELL, Canon Basil Rayson. b 20. St Pet Hall Ox BA49 MA53. Wycliffe Hall Ox 49. **d** 51 **p** 52. C Worksop St Jo *S'well* 51-54; C-in-c Worksop St Paul CD 54-61; V Blundellsands St Nic *Liv* 61-81; RD Bootle 69-78; Hon Can Liv Cathl 78-81; rtd 81; Perm to Offic *Cov* from 81. *9 Arlington Court, Arlington Avenue, Leamington Spa CV32 5HR* Tel (01926) 314746

HOWELL, David. b 29. Clifton Th Coll 56. **d** 59 **p** 60. C Tipton St Martin *Lich* 59-62; V W Bromwich St Paul 62-71; V Deptford St Jo *S'wark* 71-81; Dir and Chapl Home of Divine Healing Crowhurst 81-89; rtd 90; Dir Ch Coun for Health and Healing 91-93; Hon Dioc Adv on Health and Healing *B & W* 93-00; Perm to Offic from 01. *60 Andrew Allan Road, Rockwell Green, Wellington TA21 9DY* Tel (01823) 664529

HOWELL (formerly WILLIAMS), David Paul. b 61. Coll of Resurr Mirfield 91. **d** 93 **p** 94. C Leic St Aid *Leic* 93-97; P-in-c Edvin Loach w Tedstone Delamere etc *Heref* from 97. *The Rectory, Whitbourne, Worcester WR6 5RP* Tel (01886) 821285

HOWELL, Donald Martin. b 32. Lon Univ BD56. **d** 95 **p** 96. NSM Aylmerton w Runton *Nor* 95-96; NSM Holt w High Kelling 96-99; rtd 00; Perm to Offic *Nor* from 00. *8 The Beeches, Station Road, Holt NR25 6AU* Tel (01263) 713397

HOWELL, Geoffrey Peter. b 52. LTCL82 Selw Coll Cam BA75 MA78. Cranmer Hall Dur 85. **d** 87 **p** 88. C Hartlepool St Luke *Dur* 87-90; TV Burford I *Heref* 90-94; TV Burford II w Greete

and Hope Bagot 90-94; TV Burford III w Lt Heref 90-94; TV Tenbury 90-94; TV Tenbury St Mich 94; P-in-c Cradley w Mathon and Storridge 94-97; Succ Heref Cathl 97-99; Chapl Heref Cathl Jun Sch 97-99; Perm to Offic *Heref* from 99; Min Can St Woolos Cathl *Mon* from 02; C Newport St Woolos from 02. *10 Clifton Road, Newport NP20 4EW* Tel (01633) 264805

HOWELL, Mrs Heather Ellen. b 40. Bp Otter Coll Chich TCert60 Sussex Univ BA83. Ripon Coll Cuddesdon 00. **d** 01. NSM Newhaven *Chich* from 01. *1 Rookery Way, Bishopstone, Seaford BN25 2SA* Tel (01323) 898167

HOWELL, Martin John Hope. b 38. Bris Univ BA62. Tyndale Hall Bris 59. **d** 64 **p** 65. C Bolton St Paul *Man* 64-67; C Bishopsworth *Bris* 67-70; V Swindon St Aug 70-81; TR Stratton St Margaret w S Marston etc 81-93; RD Cricklade 88; RD Highworth 88-93; Chapl Lee Abbey 93-98; Chapl St Pet Viña del Mar Chile 99-03; rtd 03. *26 Weymouth Park, Hope Cove, Kingsbridge TQ7 3HD*

HOWELL, Ralph. **d** 01. OLM Langley Marish *Ox* from 01. *26 Mulberry Drive, Slough SL3 7JU* Tel (01753) 542745

HOWELL, Roger Brian. b 43. ALCD67. **d** 67 **p** 68. C Battersea Park St Sav *S'wark* 67-71; C Southgate *Chich* 71-76; V Pendeen *Truro* 76-81; P-in-c Sancreed 76-81; V Bedgrove *Ox* 81-91; R Purley from 91; RD Bradfield from 94. *The Rectory, 1 Westridge Avenue, Purley, Reading RG8 8DE* Tel 0118-941 7727 E-mail rbh@bradean.fsnet.co.uk

HOWELL, Ronald William Fullerton. b 51. Man Univ BA72 CertEd Ox Univ BA78 MA. Ripon Coll Cuddesdon 76. **d** 79 **p** 80. C Newc St Fran *Newc* 79-81; C Warmsworth *Sheff* 81-82; Dioc Educn Officer 82-85; V Millhouses H Trin 85-93; R Thornhill and Whitley Lower *Wakef* 93-96. *East House, 10 Woodbridge Road East, Ipswich IP4 5PA* Tel (01473) 727309

HOWELL, Simon Gordon. b 63. Sheff Univ BMus84 Bath Coll of HE PGCE85 ACII90. Ridley Hall Cam 00. **d** 03. C Northwood Em *Lon* from 03. *10 Northwood Way, Northwood HA6 1AT* Tel (01923) 845200 Fax 845209

HOWELL, Preb Walter Ernest. b 17. St D Coll Lamp BA49. **d** 50 **p** 51. C Bromley St Mich *Lon* 50-56; V Somers Town 56-68; V Kentish Town St Benet and All SS 68-79; Preb St Paul's Cathl 78-84; V Alexandra Park St Sav 79-84; rtd 84; Perm to Offic *York* from 90. *6 Wattlers Close, Copmanthorpe, York YO23 3XR* Tel (01904) 702615

HOWELL-JONES, Peter. b 62. Huddersfield Poly BMus84 Bretton Hall Coll PGCE85. St Jo Coll Nottm Dip Th Studies 92 DipMM93 MA96. **d** 93 **p** 94. C Walsall *Lich* 93-98; V Boldmere *Birm* from 98. *St Michael's Vicarage, Church Road, Sutton Coldfield B73 5RX* Tel 0121-373 3355 Fax as telephone E-mail peter@stmichaels.org.uk

HOWELLS, Chan Arthur Glyn. b 32. Univ of Wales (Lamp) BA54. St Mich Coll Llan 54. **d** 56 **p** 57. C Oystermouth *S & B* 56-58; C Llangyfelach and Morriston 58-64; R Llandefalle and Llyswen w Boughrood etc 64-69; Youth Chapl 67-71; V Landore 70-80; Dioc Missr 80-89; Can Brecon Cathl 80-89; Can Treas 89-94; Dir St Mary's Coll Swansea 82-89; V Swansea St Jas *S & B* 89-98; Chan Brecon Cathl from 94; RD Swansea 96-98; rtd 98. *2 Lilliput Lane, West Cross, Swansea SA3 5AQ* Tel (01792) 402123

HOWELLS, David. b 55. Grey Coll Dur BA78. Ripon Coll Cuddesdon 79. **d** 81 **p** 82. C Birtley *Dur* 81-84; Canada from 84. *127 Glasgow Street North, Guelph ON, Canada, N1H 4W5* Tel (001) (519) 821 7419

HOWELLS, David Morgan. b 24. Qu Coll Birm 72. **d** 75 **p** 76. NSM Radford *Cov* 75-87; rtd 87; Perm to Offic *Cov* from 87; P-in-c Roch from 98. *14 St Werburgh's Court, Pottery Road, Rochester ME3 9AP* Tel (01634) 251544

HOWELLS, Canon Donald Lockwood. b 20. Lon Univ BA43. Oak Hill Th Coll 39. **d** 43 **p** 44. C Wandsworth St Mich *S'wark* 43-45; C Foord St Jo *Cant* 45-48; C Watford St Mary *St Alb* 48-49; V Weston 49-54; C Stevenage 54-57; R Knebworth 57-66; R Tring 66-80; P-in-c Aldbury 78-80; P-in-c Puttenham w Long Marston 79-80; Hon Can St Alb 80-85; RD Berkhamsted 80-85; TR Tring 80-85; rtd 85; Perm to Offic *Cant* 85-03. *4 Thetford Close, Macclesfield SK10 2TP* Tel (01625) 615004

HOWELLS, Euryl. b 60. Univ of Wales (Cardiff) BD93. St Mich Coll Llan 90. **d** 93 **p** 94. C Deanery of Emlyn *St D* 93-97; V Llangeler w Pen-Boyr from 97. *The Vicarage, Llangeler, Llandysul SA44 5EX* Tel (01559) 371170

HOWELLS, Garfield Edwin. b 18. K Coll Lon 53 St Boniface Warminster 53. **d** 54 **p** 55. C Sanderstead All SS *S'wark* 54-57; CF 57-60; R Kingsdown *Roch* 60-64; Australia from 64; rtd 83. *301/17 Hefron Street, Rockingham, W Australia 6168* Tel (0061) (8) 9592 8337

HOWELLS, Gordon. b 39. Univ of Wales (Cardiff) BSc61 DipEd62. Ripon Coll Cuddesdon 86. **d** 88 **p** 89. C Atherstone *Cov* 88-89; C Lillington 89-92; R Clymping and Yapton w Ford *Chich* 92-97; P-in-c Rackheath and Salhouse *Nor* from 97; Chapl to the Deaf from 97. *The Rectory, 56 Green Lane West, Rackheath, Norwich NR13 6PG* Tel and minicom (01603) 720097 Fax 722247 E-mail g.howells.norwich@virgin.net

HOWELLS, Neil. b 23. Qu Mary Coll Lon BSc48. Bps' Coll Cheshunt 48. **d** 50 **p** 51. C Cowley St Jas *Ox* 50-54; C Forest Hill 54-56; Min Headington St Mary 56-60; V Maidenhead St Luke 60-68; Chapl Maidenhead Gen Hosp 60-68; R Welford w Wickham Ha 68-73; R Welford w Wickham and Gt Shefford 73-77; RD Newbury 73-77; V Bray and Braywood 77-84; rtd 84; Perm to Offic *Sarum* from 85. *19 Loders, Bridport DT6 3SA* Tel (01308) 456490

HOWELLS, Richard Grant. b 62. Univ of Wales (Lamp) BA83. Westcott Ho Cam 83 and 92. **d** 93 **p** 94. NSM Harston w Hauxton and Newton *Ely* from 93. *The Old School House, 8 High Street, Harston, Cambridge CB2 5PX* Tel (01223) 871902 E-mail richard@oldschoolhouse.demon.co.uk

HOWELLS, Mrs Sandra Jane. b 52. FBDO77 Univ of Wales (Cardiff) DipRS97. LNSM course 90. **d** 93 **p** 97. NSM Caerwent w Dinham and Llanfair Discoed etc *Mon* 93-97; C Griffithstown 97-00; V Penallt and Trellech from 00. *The Vicarage, Penallt, Monmouth NP25 4SE* Tel (01600) 716622

HOWELLS, William Gordon. b 26. **d** 61 **p** 62. C Aberdare *Llan* 61-64; C Coity w Nolton 64-67; C Northam *Ex* 67-71; V Bishops Tawton 71-76; V Cofton w Starcross 76-80; R Aveton Gifford 80-86; V Modbury 80-86; TV Lynton, Brendon, Countisbury, Lynmouth etc 86-91; rtd 91; Perm to Offic *Ex* from 91; *Linc* from 01. *3 St Nicholas Way, Lutton, Spalding PE12 9HR* Tel (01406) 363466

HOWES, Alan. b 49. Chich Th Coll 76. **d** 79 **p** 80. C Bilborough St Jo *S'well* 79-82; TV Newark w Hawton, Cotham and Shelton 82-89; TV Newark 89-94; P-in-c Coseley St Chad *Worc* 94-96; V from 96. *St Chad's Vicarage, 3 Oak Street, Coseley, Bilston WV14 9TA* Tel (01902) 882285 Mobile 07941-284048 E-mail alan@heavensdoor.co.uk

HOWES, David. b 30. Open Univ BA75. Roch Th Coll 62. **d** 64 **p** 65. C Highweek *Ex* 64-67; C Clyst St George 67-71; P-in-c Woolfardisworthy w Kennerleigh 71-72; P-in-c Washford Pyne w Puddington 71-72; TR N Creedy 72-73; Perm to Offic 74-77; C Walworth *S'wark* 77-78; C-in-c Roundshaw St Paul CD 78-83; R S'wark St Geo 83-90; P-in-c S'wark St Jude 84-90; P-in-c Risley *Derby* 90-93; Bp's Ind Adv 90-93; rtd 93; Perm to Offic *Derby* 93-00; *S'well* 95-00. *Drokensford, Chapel Road, Meonstoke, Southampton SO32 3NJ* Tel (01489) 878174

HOWES, Miss Judith Elizabeth. b 44. SRN RSCN. Ripon Coll Cuddesdon 83. **d** 89 **p** 94. Par Dn Ex St Sidwell and St Matt *Ex* 89-92; Par Dn Brixham w Churston Ferrers and Kingswear 92-94; C 94-95; TV E Darlington *Dur* 95-97; TR 97-02; P-in-c Washington from 02. *47 Ovingham Close, Washington NE38 8NP* Tel 0191-419 4047 E-mail judith.howes@durham.anglican.org

HOWES, Michael John Norton. b 43. Hull Univ BA66. Linc Th Coll 66. **d** 68 **p** 69. C Gt Berkhamsted *St Alb* 68-71; C Ampthill w Millbrook and Steppingley 71-72; Chapl RAF 72-88; V Thurlby w Carlby *Linc* 88-95; V Ness Gp 95-97; R Bassingham 97-00; V Aubourn w Haddington 97-00; V Carlton-le-Moorland w Stapleford 97-00; R Thurlby w Norton Disney 97-00; P-in-c Ashill w Saham Toney *Nor* 01-03; rtd 03. *182 Rookery Lane, Lincoln LN6 7PH* Tel (01522) 801514 E-mail mike.howes5@ntlworld.com

HOWES, Canon Norman Vincent. b 36. AKC61. **d** 62 **p** 63. C Radford *Cov* 62-66; V Napton on the Hill 66-72; V Exhall 72-83; R Walton d'Eiville and V Wellesbourne 83-03; RD Fosse 87-93; Hon Can Cov Cathl 89-03; rtd 03. *Harwood Cottage, Bottom Street, North End, Southam CV47 2TH* Tel (01295) 770303 E-mail norman@nhowes.freeserve.co.uk

HOWES, William John Lawrence. b 46. EAMTC. **d** 00 **p** 01. NSM Lexden *Chelmsf* from 00. *26 Westfield Drive, Coggeshall, Colchester CO6 1PU* Tel and fax (01376) 561826 Mobile 07718-048574 E-mail billh@pgen.net

HOWITT, Barbara Gillian. b 39. K Coll Lon BD60 PGCE61 MA95. EAMTC 99. **d** 00 **p** 01. NSM Longthorpe *Pet* from 00. *8 Wakerley Drive, Orton Longueville, Peterborough PE2 7WF* Tel (01733) 391092

HOWITT, Ivan Richard. b 56. Kent Univ BA81. Sarum & Wells Th Coll 83. **d** 85 **p** 86. C Herne Bay Ch Ch *Cant* 85-87; C St Laur in Thanet 87-90; R Owmby and Normanby w Glentham *Linc* 90-91; P-in-c Spridlington w Saxby and Firsby 90-91; R Owmby Gp 91-99; RD Lawres 96-99; Chapl Hull Miss to Seafarers 99-03; V Hedon w Paull *York* from 03. *The Vicarage, 44 New Road, Hedon, Hull HU12 8BS* Tel (01482) 897693 Mobile 07739-316019 E-mail ivanhowitt@ivanhowitt.karoo.co.uk

HOWITT, John Leslie. b 28. Lon Coll of Div 60. **d** 62 **p** 63. C Attenborough w Bramcote *S'well* 62-66; Chapl Rampton Hosp Retford 66-71; P-in-c Treswell and Cottam *S'well* 68-71; Chapl HM Pris Cardiff 71-75; Chapl HM Youth Cust Cen Dover 75-79; Chapl HM Pris Dartmoor 79-83; Chapl HM Pris Cant 83-87; Chapl HM Det Cen Aldington 83-87; Perm to Offic *Cant* 87-88; V Shobnall *Lich* 88-94; rtd 94; Perm to Offic *Chich* from 94. *6 Park View Road, Hove BN3 7BF*

HOWITZ (formerly TEDD), Christopher Jonathan Richard. b 74. Ch Ch Ox MEng90. Oak Hill Th Coll BA00. **d** 00 **p** 01. C Harpurhey Ch Ch *Man* from 00. *31 Whiteway Street, Harpurhey, Manchester M9 5PN* Tel 0161-205 4479

HOWLDEN, Paul Wilfrid. b 41. Trin Coll Cam BA63 MA67. Cuddesdon Coll 64. **d** 66 **p** 67. C Paulsgrove *Portsm* 66-73; Hon C Ealing Ascension Hanger Hill *Lon* 75-87; R Bishop's Waltham *Portsm* 87-88; Perm to Offic *Chich* from 96; rtd 99. *9 Chichester Court, Osbern Close, Bexhill-on-Sea TN39 4TL* Tel (01424) 843210

HOWLES, Kenneth. b 56. Oak Hill Th Coll DipHE93. **d** 93 **p** 94. C Leyland St Andr *Blackb* 93-96; C Livesey 96-97; C Ewood 96-97; P-in-c 97-99; V 99-03; P-in-c Blackb Sav 01-03; V Chorley St Jas from 03. *St James's Vicarage, St James's Place, Chorley PR6 0NA* Tel (01257) 263153 E-mail kenhowles@btinternet.com

HOWLETT, Mrs Elizabeth Mary. b 58. Southn Univ BA80. WMMTC 99. **d** 01 **p** 02. C Salter Street and Shirley *Birm* from 01. *6 Greenside, Shirley, Solihull B90 4HH* Tel (01564) 702233

HOWLETT, Richard Laurence. b 56. Kent Univ BA79. Trin Coll Bris DipTh94. **d** 94 **p** 95. C Louth *Linc* 94-98; R Marston Morteyne w Lidlington *St Alb* from 98. *The Vicarage, High Street, Lidlington, Bedford MK43 0RN* Tel (01525) 403687 E-mail revrichardhowlett@marld.freeserve.co.uk

HOWLETT, Victor John. b 43. S Dios Minl Tr Scheme 90. **d** 93 **p** 94. NSM Bris St Andr w St Bart *Bris* 93-95; Hon C Bris St Matt and St Nath 95-96; Hon C Bishopston 95-96; C Gtr Corsham 96-99; V Wick w Doynton and Dyrham from 99; AD Kingswood and S Glos from 02. *The Vicarage, 57 High Street, Wick, Bristol BS30 5QQ* Tel 0117-937 3581 E-mail victorhowlett@charis.co.uk

HOWMAN, Anne Louise. b 43. Lon Univ Dip Sociology 81 Ex Univ BA97. SW Minl Tr Course 97. **d** 99 **p** 00. NSM Ex St Dav *Ex* 99-02; C Salcombe and Malborough w S Huish from 02. *The Vicarage, Malborough, Kingsbridge TQ7 3RR* Tel (01548) 561234 E-mail alhow@btinternet.com

HOWORTH, Sister Rosemary. Newnham Coll Cam MA. Westcott Ho Cam. **d** 98 **p** 99. NSM Derby St Andr w St Osmund *Derby* from 98. *The Convent of the Holy Name, Morley Road, Oakwood, Derby DE21 6HP* Tel (01332) 671716

HOWSE, Elizabeth Ann. *See* SMITH, Mrs Elizabeth Ann

HOWSE, Martin David. b 58. St Steph Ho Ox 97. **d** 99 **p** 00. C Colchester St Jas and St Paul w All SS etc *Chelmsf* 99-03; V Rush Green from 03. *St Augustine's Vicarage, 78 Birkbeck Road, Romford RM7 0QP* Tel (01708) 741460 Mobile 07770-928167 Fax (01708) 732093 E-mail martin.howse@virgin.net

HOWSON, Christopher Stewart. b 69. Bradf Univ BA94 CQSW94 St Jo Coll Dur BA02. Cranmer Hall Dur 99. **d** 02 **p** 03. C Tong *Bradf* from 02. *St Christopher's Vicarage, 207 Broadstone Way, Bradford BD4 9BT* Tel (01274) 605256 E-mail chrishowson@yahoo.com

HOWSON, James Edward. b 62. Ridley Hall Cam 97 EAMTC 98. **d** 00 **p** 01. C Cogges and S Leigh *Ox* from 00. *1 Eton Close, Witney OX8 6GA* Tel (01993) 703665

HOY, Michael John. b 30. Reading Univ BSc52. Oak Hill Th Coll 57. **d** 59 **p** 60. C Worthing St Geo *Chich* 59-62; C Tulse Hill H Trin *S'wark* 62-66; R Danby Wiske w Yafforth and Hutton Bonville *Ripon* 66-76; V Camelsdale *Chich* 76-87; V Gt Marsden *Blackb* 87-96; rtd 96. *35 Hardwick Park, Banbury OX16 1YF* Tel (01295) 268744

HOY, Stephen Anthony. b 55. Leeds Poly BA76. Linc Th Coll 92. **d** 94 **p** 95. C Glen Parva and S Wigston *Leic* 94-98; V Linc St Jo *Linc* from 98. *St John's Vicarage, 102 Sudbrooke Drive, Lincoln LN2 2EF* Tel (01522) 525621 E-mail stephen@hoy997.freeserve.co.uk

HOYAL, Richard Dunstan. b 47. Ch Ch Ox BA67 MA71 BA78. Ripon Coll Cuddesdon 76. **d** 79 **p** 80. C Stevenage St Geo *St Alb* 79-83; V Monk Bretton *Wakef* 83-89; V Ilkley St Marg *Bradf* from 89; Dir of Ords from 96. *St Margaret's Vicarage, The Lodge, Wells Road, Ilkley LS29 9JH* Tel (01943) 607015 E-mail richard@rdhoyal.fsnet.co.uk

HOYE, Reginald George. b 16. Tyndale Hall Bris 58. **d** 60 **p** 61. C Penn Fields *Lich* 60-62; V Nottingham St Sav *S'well* 62-82; rtd 82; Perm to Offic *S'well* from 82. *1 White Acre, Burton Joyce, Nottingham NG14 5BU* Tel 0115-931 2485

HOYLAND, John Gregory. b 50. Sussex Univ BEd73. Wycliffe Hall Ox 75. **d** 78 **p** 79. C Pudsey St Lawr *Bradf* 78-81; P-in-c Long Preston 81-84; V Long Preston w Tosside 84; CPAS Staff 85-87; Chapl Univ Coll of Ripon and York St Jo 87-01; Lect from 01; Perm to Offic *York* from 01. *5 White Cross Road, York YO31 8JR* Tel (01904) 632368

HOYLE, David Fredric. b 46. Lon Bible Coll. **d** 02 **p** 03. NSM Northwood Em *Lon* from 02. *154 Hilliard Road, Northwood HA6 1SP* Tel (01923) 840678 E-mail david.f.hoyle@lineone.net

HOYLE, Canon David Michael. b 57. CCC Cam BA80 MA83 PhD91. Ripon Coll Cuddesdon 84. **d** 86 **p** 87. C Chesterton Gd Shep *Ely* 86-88; Chapl and Fell Magd Coll Cam 88-91; Dean and Fell 91-95; V Southgate Ch Ch *Lon* 95-02; Dir Post-Ord Tr (Edmonton) 00-02; Dioc Officer for Min *Glouc* from 02; Dioc Can Res Glouc Cathl from 02. *4 College Green, Gloucester GL1 2LR* Tel (01452) 410022 ext 231 E-mail dhoyle@glosdioc.org.uk

HOYLE, Lawrence. b 27. St Aid Birkenhead 52. **d** 55 **p** 56. C Haley Hill *Wakef* 55-57; C Bromley SS Pet and Paul *Roch* 57-59; V Widnes St Ambrose *Liv* 59-61; R Lanteglos by Camelford w Advent *Truro* 61-66; V Wrose *Bradf* 66-70; R Thwing *York* 70-81; V Wold Newton 71-81; Warden Lamplugh Ho Angl Conf Cen 72-85; Dir Angl Renewal Min 81-89; Hon C Starbeck *Ripon* 87-89; rtd 89; Perm to Offic *Ex* 92-02 and *York* from 02. *2 Wheatcroft Court, Sea Cliff Road, Scarborough YO11 2XT* Tel (01723) 353919 Mobile 07817-256529 E-mail lawrencehoyle@onetel.com

HOYLE, Pamela Margaret. *See* CLOCKSIN, Mrs Pamela Margaret

HOYLE, Stephen Jonathan. b 64. Leeds Univ BA87. Ripon Coll Cuddesdon 88. **d** 90 **p** 91. C Lt Stanmore St Lawr *Lon* 90-93; C Lon Docks St Pet w Wapping St Jo 93-96; Perm to Offic 01-02; TV Withycombe Raleigh *Ex* from 02. *St John's Vicarage, 3 Diane Close, Exmouth EX8 5QG* Tel (01395) 270094

HRYZIUK, Petro. b 57. Lanc Univ BEd80. St Jo Coll Nottm DipTh89. **d** 90 **p** 91. C Huyton St Geo *Liv* 90-93; C Goose Green 93-96; C Wavertree H Trin 96-98; TV Maghull from 98. *St Peter's Vicarage, 1 St Peter's Row, Moorhey Road, Liverpool L31 5LU* Tel 0151-526 3434

HUARD, The Ven Geoffrey Robert. b 43. Lon Univ DipTh71 DMin95. Clifton Th Coll 64 69. **d** 70 **p** 71. C Barking St Marg *Chelmsf* 70-73; C Everton St Ambrose w St Tim *Liv* 73-74; C Everton St Pet 74-76; Australia from 76; Adn Sydney and Cumberland 89-93; Adn Liverpool from 93. *PO Box Q190, QVB, Sydney, NSW, Australia 1230* Tel (0061) (2) 9558 5986 or 9265 1571 Fax 9265 1543 E-mail gchuard@dingoblue.net.au

HUBAND, Eric Bob. b 27. Bris Univ BSc50. Sarum Th Coll 50. **d** 52 **p** 53. C Lockleaze St Fran CD *Bris* 52-56; C Bishopsworth 56-60; V Greenbank 60-67; V Hengrove 67-77; R E Horsley *Guildf* 77-92; rtd 92; Perm to Offic *Bris* from 92; and *Sarum* from 98. *23 Hardens Mead, Chippenham SN15 3AE* Tel (01249) 661219

HUBAND, Richard William. b 39. Trin Coll Cam BA62 MA66. Qu Coll Birm 76. **d** 78 **p** 79. C Norton *St Alb* 78-81; R Aspley Guise w Husborne Crawley and Ridgmont 81-91; V Elstow from 91. *The Abbey Vicarage, Church End, Elstow, Bedford MK42 9XT* Tel (01234) 261477

HUBBARD, David Harris. b 33. St Pet Hall Ox BA57 MA61 K Coll Lon MTh88. Ridley Hall Cam 59. **d** 60 **p** 61. C Dalston St Mark w St Bart *Lon* 60-63; C Stoke Newington St Olave 63-67; Hon C 67-68; Asst Master Dalston Sch 67-75; Hon C Hornsey Ch Ch 69-70; V 70-82; AD W Haringey 78-85; V Highgate All SS 82-02; rtd 02; Hon C W Hampstead St Cuth *Lon* from 02. *13 Kingscroft Road, London NW2 3QE* Tel (020) 8452 1913

HUBBARD, Mrs Elisabeth Ann. b 41. EAMTC 82. **dss** 85 **d** 87 **p** 94. Cambridge H Trin w St Andr Gt *Ely* 85-86; Cherry Hinton St Jo 86-92; Par Dn 87-92; Par Dn Milton 92-94; C 94-95; R Willingham and Rampton 95-00; rtd 00; NSM Ely from 01. *3 Lodge Gardens, Haddenham, Ely CB6 3TR* Tel (01353) 741472 E-mail geolis@fish.co.uk

HUBBARD, Ian Maxwell. b 43. FCollP83 ACP83 Surrey Univ BEd84 Goldsmiths' Coll Lon MA86. Sarum & Wells Th Coll 69. **d** 73 **p** 74. Hon C S'wark H Trin w St Matt *S'wark* 73-78; Hon C Camberwell St Mich w All So w Em 78-87; Hon C Dulwich St Barn 87-90; C Battersea St Mary 90-92; V Winscombe *B & W* 92-98; TR Yatton Moor from 98; RD Portishead from 02. *The Rectory, 1 Well Lane, Yatton, Bristol BS49 4HT* Tel (01934) 832184 E-mail ian@hubbardi.freeserve.co.uk

HUBBARD, Canon Julian Richard Hawes. b 55. Em Coll Cam BA76 MA81. Wycliffe Hall Ox BA80 MA85. **d** 81 **p** 82. C Fulham St Dionis Parson's Green *Lon* 81-84; Tutor Wycliffe Hall Ox 84-89; Chapl Jes Coll Ox 84-89; Selection Sec ACCM 89-91; Sen Selection Sec ABM 91-93; V Bourne *Guildf* 93-99; P-in-c Tilford 97-99; RD Farnham 96-99; Can Res Guildf Cathl from 99; Dir Minl Tr from 99. *4 Cathedral Close, Guildford GU2 7TZ* Tel (01483) 566362 or 790307 Fax 790333 E-mail julian.hubbard@cofeguildford.org.uk

HUBBARD, Laurence Arthur. b 36. Qu Coll Cam BA60 MA64. Wycliffe Hall Ox 60 CMS Tr Coll Chislehurst 65 CMS Tr Coll Selly Oak 93. **d** 62 **p** 63. C Widcombe *B & W* 62-65; CMS Kenya 66-73; V Pype Hayes *Birm* 73-79; P-in-c Norwich-over-the-Water Colegate St Geo *Nor* 79-85; P-in-c Nor St Aug w St Mary 79-85; CMS 85-97; Area Sec *Cant* and *Roch* 85-93; Chapl Damascus, Syria 93-97; Miss to Seamen Aqaba, Jordan 97-00; rtd 00; Perm to Offic *Glouc* from 01. *31 Saddlers Road, Quedgeley, Gloucester GL2 4SY* Tel (01452) 728061

HUBBARD, Roy Oswald. b 32. Lich Th Coll 62. **d** 64 **p** 65. C Baswich *Lich* 64-68; P-in-c Ash 68-70; V Stevenage St Pet Broadwater *St Alb* 71-78; V Flitwick 78-90; RD Ampthill 87-90; R Sharnbrook and Knotting w Souldrop 90-96; rtd 96; Perm to Offic *St Alb* from 96; Perm to Offic *Pet* from 96. *11 Cowslip Close, Rushden NN10 0UD* Tel (01933) 419210

HUBBARD-JONES, Ms Judith Frances. b 49. St Alb Minl Tr Scheme 79. **dss** 82 **d** 87 **p** 94. Hemel Hempstead *St Alb* 82-86; Longden and Annscroft w Pulverbatch *Heref* 86-87; Hon C 87-91; Vice Prin WEMTC 91-97; Acting Prin 94-95; Hon C

Leominster *Heref* 94-97; Cathl Chapl and Visitors' Officer *Glouc* 97-02; I Kinneigh Union *C, C & R* from 02. *The Rectory, Ballineen, Co Cork, Irish Republic* Tel (00353) (23) 47047 E-mail jfhubbard@eircom.net

HUBBLE, Canon Raymond Carr. b 30. Wm Temple Coll Rugby 60. **d** 61 **p** 62. C Newbold w Dunston *Derby* 61-64; Chapl RAF 64-80; Asst Chapl-in-Chief RAF 80-85; QHC 84-85; P-in-c Odiham w S Warnborough and Long Sutton *Win* 85; P-in-c Odiham 85-86; V 86-95; RD Odiham 88-95; Hon Can Win Cathl 94-95; rtd 95; Perm to Offic *Win* from 95. *Dormers, Centre Lane, Everton, Lymington SO41 0JP*

HUBBLE, Canon Trevor Ernest. b 46. Bernard Gilpin Soc Dur 69 Chich Th Coll 70. **d** 76 **p** 77. C Eltham St Barn *S'wark* 76-79; Lesotho 80-87; C St Agnes Mission Teyateyameng 80-81; R Quthing H Trin 81-85; Adn S Lesotho 84-87; Warden Ang Tr Cen and Dir Chr Educ 85-87; S Africa 87-00; Co-ord of Tr for Lay Min 87-89; R Matatiele St Steph 89-00; Adn Matatiele 91-00; V Gen Umzimvubu 95-00; Shared Min Tr Officer *Dur* from 00; C Esh from 00; C Hamsteels from 00; C Langley Park from 00; C Waterhouses from 00. *St Paul's Vicarage, 21 The Wynds, Esh Winning, Durham DH7 9DT* Tel 0191-373 4273 Mobile 07759-310524 E-mail tshubble@freenetname.co.uk

HUCKETT, Andrew William. b 50. AKC72. St Aug Coll Cant 72. **d** 73 **p** 74. C Chipping Sodbury and Old Sodbury *Glouc* 73-76; Miss to Seafarers from 76; Chapl Flushing 76-79; Chapl Teesside 79-82; Chapl Lagos Nigeria 82-85; Chapl Mombasa Kenya 85-86; Chapl Milford Haven 86-92; Chapl Medway Ports 92-03; Staff Chapl and Chapl Thames/Medway from 03. *27 The Finches, Sittingbourne ME10 4PY* Tel (01795) 472851 Fax as telephone

HUCKLE, John Walford (Wally). b 39. EMMTC. **d** 89 **p** 90. C Nottingham St Pet and St Jas *S'well* 89-00; Commercial Chapl Nottingham City Cen 89-00; Dioc Adv on Ind Soc 96-97; rtd 00; Perm to Offic *S'well* from 00. *43 Bingham Road, Radcliffe-on-Trent, Nottingham NG12 2FY* Tel 0115-933 2278 E-mail wally.huckle@ntlworld.com

HUCKLE, Peter. b 46. Ox Univ Inst of Educn CertEd69 Auckland Univ DipPE71 DipEd71. Educn for Min (NZ). **d** 90 **p** 91. New Zealand 90-91; Hon C N Walsham w Antingham *Nor* 91-92; C Gt Yarmouth 92-94; TV 94-96; Min Can and Chapl St Paul's Cathl Lon 96-97; Asst Chapl Athens and Perm to Offic *Eur* 97; SSJE from 97. *St Edward's House, 22 Great College Street, London SW1P 3QA* Tel (020) 7222 9234 Fax 7799 2641

HUCKLE, Stephen Leslie. b 48. Ch Ch Ox BA70 BA72 MA74. Coll of Resurr Mirfield 73. **d** 75 **p** 76. C Wednesbury St Paul Wood Green *Lich* 75-78; C Aylesbury *Ox* 78-85; C Farnham Royal w Hedgerley 85-88; V Fenny Stratford 88-98; V Stirchley *Birm* from 98. *The Vicarage, 18 Pineapple Grove, Birmingham B30 2TJ* Tel 0121-443 1371 E-mail stephen@ascension.fsbusiness.co.uk

HUDD, Philip Simon Gorman. b 68. Westmr Coll Ox BA90. Westcott Ho Cam 91. **d** 93 **p** 94. C Kirkby *Liv* 93-97; TV 97-99; V Lancaster Ch Ch *Blackb* from 99. *Christ Church Vicarage, 1 East Road, Lancaster LA1 3EE* Tel (01524) 34430 E-mail phil@gorhudd.freeserve.co.uk

HUDDLESON, Robert Roulston. b 32. QUB BA55 TCD Div Test57. **d** 57 **p** 58. C Ballymena *Conn* 57-59; C Belfast St Jas 59-63; Ethiopia 65-69; Exec Asst WCC Geneva 69-75; Dep Sec Gen Syn Bd for Miss and Unity 75-81; Admin Sec *Dur* 81-86; Dioc Sec *Ex* 86-97; rtd 97; Perm to Offic *Ex* from 97. *Mount Pleasant, Tiverton Road, Bampton, Tiverton EX16 9DX* Tel (01398) 331412

HUDDLESTON, Geoffrey Roger. b 36. TCD BA63 MA67. Ridley Hall Cam 63. **d** 65 **p** 66. C Tonbridge SS Pet and Paul *Roch* 65-69; Chapl RAF 69-85; V Lyonsdown H Trin *St Alb* 85-00; RD Barnet 94-99; rtd 00; Perm to Offic *Lich* from 01. *The Granary, Bellamour Lodge Farm, Colton Road, Colton, Rugeley WS15 3NZ* Tel (01889) 574052 E-mail rogerandvicky@hotmail.com

HUDGHTON, John Francis. b 56. BA. Cranmer Hall Dur 81. **d** 83 **p** 84. C Stockport St Geo *Ches* 83-85; C Witton 85-87; C Stockport St Alb Hall Street 87-90; V Thornton-le-Moors w Ince and Elton 90-95; Chapl RAF 95-01; P-in-c Burnby *York* from 01; P-in-c Londesborough from 01; P-in-c Nunburnholme and Warter and Huggate from 01; P-in-c Shiptonthorpe and Hayton from 01. *The Vicarage, Town Street, Shiptonthorpe, York YO43 3PE* Tel (01430) 872513

HUDSON, Andrew Julian. b 57. Cranmer Hall Dur 93. **d** 93 **p** 94. C Moldgreen *Wakef* 93-97; P-in-c Lundwood 97-01; V Dodworth from 01. *The Vicarage, Green Road, Dodworth, Barnsley S75 3RT* Tel and fax (01226) 203838 Mobile 07711-498959

HUDSON, Anthony George. b 39. N Ord Course. **d** 84 **p** 85. C Harrogate St Mark *Ripon* 84-87; P-in-c Hampsthwaite 87-96; P-in-c Killinghall 87-94; V Hampsthwaite and Killinghall 96-99; rtd 99. *26 Beckwith Crescent, Harrogate HG2 0BQ* Tel (01423) 858740

HUDSON, Brainerd Peter de Wirtz Goodwin. *See* GOODWIN HUDSON, Brainerd Peter de Wirtz

HUDSON, Christopher John. b 45. Bedf Coll Lon BSc68 MIH73. Cranmer Hall Dur DipTh77. **d** 77 **p** 78. C Bath Weston St Jo *B & W* 77-80; Youth Chapl 77-80; P-in-c Baltonsborough w Butleigh and W Bradley 80-84; V 84-87; P-in-c Shirwell w Loxhore *Ex* 87-89; P-in-c Kentisbury, Trentishoe, E Down and Arlington 88-89; RD Shirwell 88-91; TR Shirwell, Loxhore, Kentisbury, Arlington, etc 90-91; P-in-c Trentishoe 90-91; R Huntspill *B & W* 91-94; rtd 01; Perm to Offic *B & W* from 98. *62B Deane Drive, Taunton TA1 5PQ* Tel (01823) 324615 E-mail christopher.hudson@rdplus.net

HUDSON, Clive. b 42. **d** 02. OLM Redenhall, Harleston, Wortwell and Needham *Nor* from 03. *9 Shotford Road, Harleston IP20 9JH* Tel (01379) 853284 E-mail hudson.harleston@virgin.net

HUDSON, Canon Gerald Ernest. b 20. Ex Coll Ox BA42 MA46. Westcott Ho Cam 42. **d** 43 **p** 44. C Deptford St Paul *S'wark* 43-47; C Raynes Park St Sav 47-51; V Catford St Laur 51-60; V Roehampton H Trin 60-71; Hon Can S'wark Cathl 68-80; Prin S'wark Ord Course 71-80; R St Mary le Bow w St Pancras Soper Lane etc *Lon* 80-85; rtd 85; Perm to Offic *Cant* 85-99; Dir Post-Ord Tr 86-88. *10 Medina Avenue, Whitstable CT5 4EN* Tel (01227) 276548

HUDSON, John. b 47. FRSA CertSS. Linc Th Coll. **d** 83 **p** 84. C Merton St Mary *S'wark* 83-86; C Kirk Ella *York* 86-88; P-in-c Lenborough *Ox* 88-93; V Lenborough 93-03; P-in-c Tingewick w Water Stratford, Radclive etc 89-93; P-in-c Water Stratford 93-00; P-in-c Reading St Matt from 03. *The Vicarage, 205 Southcote Lane, Reading RG30 3AX* Tel 0118-957 3755

HUDSON, John. b 51. Oak Hill Th Coll 84. **d** 86 **p** 87. C Leyland St Andr *Blackb* 86-89; V Coppull from 89. *The Vicarage, Chapel Lane, Coppull, Chorley PR7 4NA* Tel (01257) 791218

HUDSON, Canon John Cecil. b 22. Selw Coll Cam BA46 MA48. Qu Coll Birm BD51. **d** 48 **p** 49. C Darlington St Cuth *Dur* 48-53; CF (TA) 50-57; TR Usworth *Dur* 53-57; V Padiham *Blackb* 57-68; RD Burnley 65-68; RD Whalley 68-83; V Clitheroe St Mary 68-85; Hon Can Blackb Cathl 79-85; rtd 85; Perm to Offic *Blackb* and *Bradf* from 85. *29 Eastfield Drive, West Bradford, Clitheroe BB7 4TQ* Tel (01200) 423531

HUDSON, Canon John Leonard. b 44. AKC66. **d** 67 **p** 68. C Dodworth *Wakef* 67-70; Prec Wakef Cathl 70-73; V Ravensthorpe 73-80; V Royston from 80; P-in-c Carlton from 90; RD Barnsley from 93; Hon Can Wakef Cathl from 98. *The Clergy House, Church Street, Royston, Barnsley S71 4QZ* Tel (01226) 722410

HUDSON, John Peter. b 42. AKC64. St Boniface Warminster 64. **d** 65 **p** 66. C S Shields St Hilda w St Thos *Dur* 65-68; Chapl RN 68-84; V Mellor *Blackb* from 84. *The Vicarage, Church Lane, Mellor, Blackburn BB2 7JL* Tel (01254) 812324 Fax 814567 E-mail jpeterhudson@aol.com

HUDSON, Prof John Richard Keith. b 35. St Pet Coll Ox BA60 MA64 State Univ NY PhD83. Linc Th Coll 60. **d** 62 **p** 63. C Tettenhall Wood *Lich* 62-65; Chapl and Lect Bp Grosseteste Coll Linc 65-71; Staff Officer Gen Syn Bd of Educn 72-73; Australia 73-79; Lect Riverina Coll of Advanced Educn Wagga 73-74; Lect Mt Gravatt Coll of Advanced Educn Brisbane 74-79; Master and Chapl Yardley Court Sch Tonbridge 79-82; USA from 82; Teaching Asst State Univ NY 82-83; Asst Prof Louisiana State Univ Alexandria 83-85; Asst R Alexandria St Jas 84-85; R Camden St Paul Delaware from 85; Prof Wesley Coll Dover 85-92; Chapl Delaware Hospice 92-96; rtd 01. *1300 Morris Avenue, Villanova, PA 19085, USA* Tel (001) (610) 525 3131 E-mail jrkh65@msn.com

HUDSON, John Stephen Anthony. b 49. S Dios Minl Tr Scheme 85 Chich Th Coll 86. **d** 88 **p** 89. C Horsham *Chich* 88-91; TV Littlehampton and Wick from 91. *The Vicarage, 40 Beaconsfield Road, Wick, Littlehampton BN17 6LN* Tel (01903) 724990

HUDSON, Mrs Mary Gertrude. b 29. Univ Coll Lon BA51 CertEd52. Qu Coll Birm 82. dss 85 **d** 87 **p** 94. Kings Norton *Birm* 85-87; NSM 87-97; rtd 97. *1 Wentworth Way, Edwalton, Nottingham NG12 4DJ* Tel 0115-923 5891

HUDSON, Peter John. b 66. Dioc OLM tr scheme 00. **d** 03. OLM Deptford St Paul *S'wark* from 03. *The New Rectory, Mary Ann Gardens, London SE8 3DP* Tel (020) 8692 0989 E-mail curate@paulsdeptford.org.uk

HUDSON, Philip Howard. b 50. St Steph Ho Ox 89. **d** 91 **p** 92. C Poulton-le-Fylde *Blackb* 91-95; V Blackpool St Wilfrid from 95. *St Wilfrid's Vicarage, 8 Langdale Road, Blackpool FY4 4RT* Tel (01253) 761532

HUDSON, Thomas George. b 32. TCD BA54. CITC Div Test54. **d** 55 **p** 56. C Belfast St Matt *Conn* 55-58; C Belfast Ch Ch 58-60; C Carlow *C & O* 60-61; I Hacketstown 61-69; I Kinneigh Union *C, C & R* 69-72; I Monasterevan *M & K* 72-83; I Mostrim w Granard, Clonbroney, Killoe etc *K, E & A* 83-97; Can Elphin Cathl 86-97; rtd 97. *34 Oak Court Grove, Palmerstown, Dublin 20, Irish Republic* Tel (00353) (1) 626 9854

HUDSON, Trevor. b 32. Dur Univ BA56. Cranmer Hall Dur DipTh. **d** 58 **p** 59. C Doncaster St Mary *Sheff* 58-62; C Attercliffe 62-64; V Stannington 64-79; V Abbeydale St Jo 79-88; V Worsbrough 88-95; rtd 95; Perm to Offic *Sheff* from 95. *Spring Villa Garden, 136A Langsett Road South, Oughtibridge, Sheffield S35 0HA* Tel 0114-286 3559

HUDSON, Walter Gerald. b 29. **d** 95 **p** 96. Hon C Eccleston Park *Liv* 95-99; Perm to Offic from 99. *31 Springfield Lane, Eccleston, St Helens WA10 5EW* Tel (01744) 24919

HUDSON, Wilfred. b 23. St Jo Coll Dur BA49 DipTh. **d** 51 **p** 52. C Doncaster St Mary *Sheff* 51-56; V Brampton Bierlow 56-64; V Anston 64-74; V Woodsetts 64-74; V Sharrow St Andr 74-88; rtd 88; Perm to Offic *Sheff* from 88. *128 Totley Brook Road, Sheffield S17 3QU* Tel 0114-236 5558

HUDSON-WILKIN, Mrs Rose Josephine. b 61. WMMTC 89. **d** 91 **p** 94. Par Dn Wolverhampton St Matt *Lich* 91-94; C 94-95; C W Bromwich Gd Shep w St Jo 95-98; Black Anglican Concern 95-98; V Dalston H Trin w St Phil and Haggerston All SS *Lon* from 98. *The Vicarage, Livermere Road, London E8 4EZ* Tel (020) 7254 5062 E-mail rosehud@globalnet.co.uk

HUDSPITH, Colin John. b 46. Nottm Univ BA67. SW Minl Tr Course 93. **d** 96 **p** 97. C Pilton w Ashford *Ex* 96-97; C Barnstaple 97-99; C Shirwell, Loxhore, Kentisbury, Arlington, etc 99-00; TV from 00. *The Rectory, Shirwell, Barnstaple EX31 4JU* Tel (01271) 850436 E-mail chudsp@netcomuk.co.uk

HUDSPITH, Ernest. b 26. Open Univ BA73 Birm Univ DipTh64. Qu Coll Birm 61. **d** 64 **p** 65. PV S'well Minster *S'well* 64-67; Prec Gib Cathl *Eur* 67-68; NSM Twickenham St Mary *Lon* 69-74; rtd 94; Perm to Offic *Chich* from 01. *Flat 3, 68 Warrior Square, St Leonards-on-Sea TN37 6BP* Tel (01424) 441760

HUDSPITH, Mrs Susan Mary. b 49. St Alb Minl Tr Scheme 79. dss 82 **d** 87 **p** 94. Luton St Chris Round Green *St Alb* 82-92; Par Dn 87-88; NSM 88-92; Perm to Offic 92-94; NSM Luton St Mary 94-00; Perm to Offic from 00. *171 Hart Lane, Luton LU2 0JH* Tel (01582) 734948

HUGGETT, Christopher Roy. b 49. Hull Univ BA72 CertEd73. Linc Th Coll 79. **d** 93 **p** 94. C Accrington St Jo w Huncoat *Blackb* 93-95; C Cleveleys 95-97; P-in-c Scorton 97-99; V Scorton and Barnacre and Calder Vale 99-02; P-in-c Leyburn w Bellerby *Ripon* from 02. *The Vicarage, 20 Bellerby Road, Leyburn DL8 5JF* Tel (01969) 622251

HUGGETT, David John. b 34. Lon Univ BSc56 Southn Univ PhD59. Clifton Th Coll 64. **d** 67 **p** 68. C Heatherlands St Jo *Sarum* 67-70; C Cambridge St Sepulchre *Ely* 70-73; R Nottingham St Nic *S'well* 73-92; Cyprus 93-99; rtd 99. *Barn Close Cottage, Bracken Lane, Holloway, Matlock DE4 5AS* Tel (01629) 534213

HUGGETT, John Victor James. b 39. Dur Univ BA64. Tyndale Hall Bris 64. **d** 66 **p** 67. C Hailsham *Chich* 66-69; C Worthing St Geo 69-71; C Woking St Pet *Guildf* 71-73; C Buckhurst Hill *Chelmsf* 73-76; V Meltham Mills *Wakef* 76-78; V Wilshaw 76-78; rtd 79; Jt Ldr Breath Fellowship from 79; Perm to Offic *Wakef* 79-84 and *Roch* 84-97. *Breath Ministries Healing Centre, Weald House, 10A High Street, Tunbridge Wells TN1 1UX* Tel (01892) 514112

HUGGETT, Kevin John. b 62. St Jo Coll Dur BA83. Trin Coll Bris DipHE90 ADPS91. **d** 91 **p** 92. C Gt Ilford St Andr *Chelmsf* 91-94; Regional Manager for Uganda and Sudan CMS 94-01; Hon C Tonbridge SS Pet and Paul *Roch* 98-01; Chapl Lanc Univ *Blackb* from 01. *11 Alderman Road, Lancaster LA1 5FW* Tel (01524) 843091 or 594082/71 E-mail k.huggett@lancaster.ac.uk

HUGGETT, Michael George. b 38. Bris Univ BA60 Birm Univ CertEd61 Nottm Univ DCE83. EMMTC 85. **d** 88 **p** 89. C Sawley *Derby* 88-92; C Chaddesden St Phil 92-93; P-in-c Alkmonton, Cubley, Marston, Montgomery etc 93-99; V from 99. *The Rectory, Cubley, Ashbourne DE6 2EY* Tel (01335) 330680

HUGGINS, Stephen David. b 53. Sussex Univ BEd75 Leic Univ DipEd79 K Coll Lon MA80. STETS. **d** 01 **p** 02. NSM Bexhill St Aug *Chich* 01-02; NSM Sedlescombe w Whatlington from 02. *The Rectory, Church Hill, Sedlescombe, Battle TN33 0QP* Tel (01424) 870233

HUGHES, Adrian John. b 57. Newc Univ BA78 Dur Univ BA82. Cranmer Hall Dur 80. **d** 83 **p** 84. C Shard End *Birm* 83-86; TV Solihull 86-90; TV Glendale Gp *Newc* 90-94; P-in-c Belford 94-95; V Belford and Lucker from 95; V Ellingham 95-02; AD Bamburgh and Glendale from 97; Asst Dioc Dir of Ords from 98. *The Vicarage, North Bank, Belford NE70 7LY* Tel (01668) 213545 Fax as telephone E-mail revdajh@aol.com

HUGHES, Alan. b 34. St D Coll Lamp BA54 St Mich Coll Llan 58. **d** 60 **p** 61. C Aberavon *Llan* 60-62; Chapl RAF 62-66; CF 66-76; USA from 76. *1408 South West 20th Street, Gresham, OR 97030, USA*

HUGHES, Alan. b 46. TD. Edin Th Coll 71. **d** 74 **p** 75. C Edin St Cuth *Edin* 74-76; P-in-c Edin St Luke 76-78; C Marske in Cleveland *York* 78-81; V New Marske 81-84; V Kirkbymoorside w Gillamoor, Farndale etc 84-94; CF 84-94; V Berwick H Trin and St Mary Newc from 94. *The Vicarage, Parade, Berwick-upon-Tweed TD15 1DF* Tel and fax (01289) 306136 Mobile 07941-757412 E-mail berwick.church@bigwig.net

HUGHES, Albert Ashbden. b 10. Univ of Wales BA37. St Mich Coll Llan 38. **d** 39 **p** 40. C Llangeinwen *Ban* 39-42; CF 43-44; C Llanfachraeth *Ban* 42-45; C Llandegai 45-49; R Blaina *Mon* 49-55; V Harlech and Llanfair juxta Harlech *Ban* 55-58; V Coldhurst *Man* 58-64; Chapl Oldham and Distr Gen Hosp 57-64; V Goostrey *Ches* 64-76; rtd 76; Perm to Offic *Ches* from

76. *50 Preston Road, Lytham, Lytham St Annes FY8 5AA* Tel (01253) 795108

HUGHES, Albert William. b 48. S Dios Minl Tr Scheme 90. **d** 92 **p** 93. Community of Our Lady and St John from 70; Prior from 90; Perm to Offic *Win* from 96. *Alton Abbey, Abbey Road, Beech, Alton GU34 4AP* Tel (01420) 562145 *or* 563575 Fax 561691

HUGHES, Alexander James. b 75. Greyfriars Ox BA97 St Edm Coll Cam MPhil99. Westcott Ho Cam 98. **d** 00 **p** 01. C Headington Quarry *Ox* 00-03; Bp's Dom Chapl *Portsm* from 03. *11 Burnham Wood, Fareham PO16 7UD* Tel (01329) 280247 Fax 231538 E-mail bouverie@lineone.net

HUGHES, Allan Paul. b 45. Glam Coll of Educn CertEd69 Open Univ BA91. Abp's Sch of Min 01. **d** 02 **p** 03. NSM Skelton w Shipton and Newton on Ouse *York* from 02; Chapl St Olave's Sch York from 02. *2 Burtree Avenue, Skelton, York YO30 1YT* Tel (01904) 470627 Fax 640975

HUGHES, Andrew Terrell. b 29. Bris Univ BA56 DipEd. Coll of Resurr Mirfield 64. **d** 66 **p** 67. C Weston-super-Mare St Sav *B & W* 66-70; C Yeovil St Jo w Preston Plucknett 70-73; TV Yeovil 73-83; R Wincanton 83-88; rtd 89; Perm to Offic *Sarum* from 89. *2 Cove Street, Weymouth DT4 8TS* Tel (01305) 778639

HUGHES, Miss Angela Mary. b 52. Avery Hill Coll CertEd75. St Steph Ho Ox 90. **d** 92 **p** 94. Par Dn Kidderminster St Mary and All SS w Trimpley etc *Worc* 92-94; C 94-96; P-in-c Gilmorton w Peatling Parva and Kimcote etc *Leic* 96-01; RD Guthlaxton II 99-01; R Wyberton *Linc* from 01; V Frampton from 01. *The Rectory, Church Lane, Wyberton, Boston PE21 7AF* Tel (01205) 353593 E-mail ahughes@webleicester.org.uk

HUGHES, Arthur Lewis. b 36. St Deiniol's Hawarden 65 CA Tr Coll 61. **d** 68 **p** 69. C Holywell *St As* 68-71; Lect Watford St Mary *St Alb* 71-75; V Thornton in Lonsdale w Burton in Lonsdale *Bradf* 75-84; V Daubhill *Man* 84-89; V Castle Town *Lich* 89-00; Chapl Staffs Univ 91-00; rtd 00; Perm to Offic *Ches* from 00. *100 Rhuddlan Road, Buckley CH7 3QA* Tel (01244) 547599

HUGHES, Arthur William Ronald. b 14. Ch Coll Cam BA36 MA40. St Mich Coll Llan 37. **d** 39 **p** 41. C Rhosddu *St As* 39-40; C Minera 40-42; C Wrexham 42-49; R Llangynyw 49-53; R Moston St Jo *Man* 53-57; V Coalbrookdale *Heref* 57-67; V Arthog w Fairbourne *Ban* 67-74; R Machynlleth and Llanwrin 74-77; rtd 77; Perm to Offic *St D* 77-01. *4 Millgate Street, Methwold, Thetford IP26 4NY*

HUGHES, Benjamin John. b 65. Golds Coll Lon BEd91. Cranmer Hall Dur BTh97. **d** 99 **p** 00. NSM Fulham St Matt *Lon* 99-03; Chapl RN from 03. *Royal Naval Chaplaincy Service, Room 203, Victory Building, HM Naval Base, Portsmouth PO1 3LS* Tel (023) 9272 7903 Fax 9272 7111

HUGHES, Bernard Patrick. b 35. Oak Hill Th Coll DipTh64. **d** 65 **p** 66. C Fulham St Matt *Lon* 65-69; Chapl St Steph Hosp Lon 69-89; Chapl St Mary Abbots Hosp Lon 69-97; Chapl Westmr Hosp Lon 89-94; Chapl Westmr Children's Hosp Lon 89-94; Sen Chapl Chelsea and Westmr Healthcare NHS Trust 94-97; rtd 97; Perm to Offic *Bris* and *Sarum* from 97. *Charis, 6 Priory Park, Bradford-on-Avon BA15 1QU* Tel (01225) 868679

HUGHES, Bertram Arthur Edwin. b 23. Clifton Th Coll 64. **d** 66 **p** 67. C Taunton St Jas *B & W* 66-68; C Ramsgate St Luke *Cant* 68-70; Australia 70-76; P-in-c Swanton Abbott w Skeyton *Nor* 76-80; P-in-c Scottow 76-80; Australia 80-83; R Reymerston w Cranworth, Letton, Southburgh etc *Nor* 83-84; rtd 84; Perm to Offic *Ex* from 90. *88 Winslade Road, Sidmouth EX10 9EZ* Tel (01395) 512452

HUGHES, Miss Carol Lindsay. b 51. Cam Inst of Educn CertEd72 Nottm Univ BEd86. Trin Coll Bris DipHE93. **d** 93 **p** 94. C Ilkeston St Mary *Derby* 93-97; P-in-c Langley Mill from 97; RD Heanor from 99. *The Vicarage, 214 Cromford Road, Langley Mill, Nottingham NG16 4HB* Tel (01773) 712441 E-mail lindsay@hugheshouse.freeserve.co.uk

HUGHES, Christopher Clarke. b 40. Lon Coll of Div ALCD65 LTh. **d** 65 **p** 66. C Broadclyst *Ex* 65-68; C Chenies and Lt Chalfont *Ox* 68-70; TV Lydford w Bridestowe and Sourton *Ex* 70-72; TV Lydford, Brent Tor, Bridestowe and Sourton 72-74; V Buckland Monachorum 74-83; R Ashtead *Guildf* 83-98; R Aboyne *Ab* from 98; R Ballater from 98. *The Rectory, 7 Invercauld Road, Ballater AB35 5RP* Tel (01339) 755726 E-mail chrishughes@ballater37.freeserve.co.uk

HUGHES, Clive. b 54. Univ of Wales BA77 MA82. St Mich Coll Llan BD95. **d** 95 **p** 96. C Carmarthen St Dav *St D* 95-97; TV Aberystwyth from 97. *St Anne's Vicarage, Penparcau, Aberystwyth SY23 1RZ* Tel (01970) 617819

HUGHES, David Anthony. b 25. Trin Coll Cam BA48 MA55. Linc Th Coll 74. **d** 76 **p** 77. C Boston *Linc* 76-78; V Graffoe 78-90; rtd 90; Perm to Offic *Linc* from 91. *27 St Clement's Road, Ruskington, Sleaford NG34 9AF* Tel (01526) 832618

HUGHES, David Howard. b 55. Univ of Wales (Ban). St Mich Coll Llan. **d** 79 **p** 80. C Llanrhos *St As* 79-82; C Eckington w Handley and Ridgeway *Derby* 82-83; C Staveley and Barrow Hill 83-85; TV 85-89; V Whitworth St Bart *Man* 89-00. *2 Cromwell Road, Chesterfield S40 4TH* Tel (01246) 277361

HUGHES, David Michael. b 41. Oak Hill Th Coll BD67. **d** 68 **p** 69. C Tunbridge Wells St Jo *Roch* 68-73; C Crookes St Thos

Sheff 73-81; V Normanton *Wakef* 81-90; TR Didsbury St Jas and Em *Man* from 90; AD Withington from 00. *St James's Rectory, 9 Didsbury Park, Manchester M20 5LH* Tel 0161-434 2178 Fax 445 1388 E-mail davidhughes@stj-emm.org

HUGHES, Debbie Ann. *See* PEATMAN, Mrs Debbie Ann

HUGHES, Denis Charles. b 27. LNSM course 92. **d** 95 **p** 96. OLM S Merstham *S'wark* 95-02; rtd 02; Perm to Offic *S'wark* from 02. *1 South Close Green, Merstham, Redhill RH1 3DU* Tel (01737) 642652

HUGHES, Elfed. b 53. St Mich Coll Llan BD75. **d** 77 **p** 78. C Skewen *Llan* 77-80; TV Ystradyfodwg w Gelli, Rhigos and Tonpentre 80-81; P-in-c Pentre CD 81-85; V Pentre 85-87; Chapl Wales Poly 87-91; V Llantrisant 91-97; rtd 97. *19 Heol Brynteg, Tonyrefail, Porth CF39 8DL*

HUGHES, Mrs Elizabeth Jane. b 58. K Coll Lon BD81 AKC81. Ripon Coll Cuddesdon 81. **dss** 83 **d** 87 **p** 94. Chipping Barnet w Arkley *St Alb* 83-86; Dunstable 86-87; Hon Par Dn 87-93; NSM Boxmoor St Jo 93-03; Chapl Hospice of St Fran Berkhamsted from 99. *17 Lansdowne Road, Luton LU3 1EE* Tel (01582) 730722 E-mail liz.hughes@stfrancis.org.uk

HUGHES, Ms Eunice Nesta. b 14. K Coll Lon 38 CertEd51. Lambeth DipTh40 St Chris Coll Blackheath 34. **dss** 61 **d** 87. RE Teacher Darley Gate 62-64; Cheltenham Ladies' Coll 65-74; Cant St Martin and St Paul *Cant* 76-80; Westgate St Sav 80-87; Hon Par Dn 87; Perm to Offic 87-97. *Flat 1, 4 Cedric Road, Westgate-on-Sea CT8 8NZ* Tel (01843) 831746

HUGHES, The Ven Evan Arthur Bertram. b 25. St D Coll Lamp BA48 LTh50. **d** 50 **p** 51. C Abergwili w Llanfihangel-uwch-Gwili *St D* 50-53; C Llanelli 53-58; India 59-69; Adn Bhagalpur 65-66; C Llanstadwel *St D* 70-73; Pakistan 73-74; R Johnston w Steynton *St D* 74-80; Can St D Cathl 80-85; V Newcastle Emlyn 80-81; V Newcastle Emlyn w Llandyfriog and Troed-yr-aur 81-86; Adn Carmarthen 85-91; V Llanegwad w Llanfynydd 86-88; V Cynwil Elfed and Newchurch 88-91; rtd 91. *104 Bronwydd Road, Carmarthen SA31 2AW* Tel (01267) 237155

HUGHES, Canon Evelyn. b 31. Gilmore Ho 73. **dss** 79 **d** 87 **p** 94. Fetcham *Guildf* 79-82; Dioc Adv Lay Min 82-86; Farnborough 83-87; C 87-92; Bp's Adv for Women's Min 87-94; Dn-in-c Badshot Lea CD 92-94; C-in-c 94-96; Hon Can Guildf Cathl 94-96; rtd 96; Perm to Offic *Guildf* from 96. *4 Oaklands, Haslemere GU27 3RQ* Tel (01428) 651576

HUGHES, Gareth Francis. b 73. St Jo Coll Dur MSc94 GInstP94. St Mich Coll Llan BD98. **d** 98 **p** 99. C Haughton le Skerne *Dur* 98-02; TV White Horse *Sarum* from 02. *The Vicarage, The Hollow, Dilton Marsh, Westbury BA13 4BU* Tel (01373) 822560

HUGHES, The Very Revd Geraint Morgan Hugh. b 34. Keble Coll Ox BA58 MA63. St Mich Coll Llan 58. **d** 59 **p** 60. C Gorseinon *S & B* 59-63; C Oystermouth 63-68; R Llanbadarn Fawr, Llandegley and Llanfihangel etc 68-76; R Llandrindod w Cefnllys 76-87; R Llandrindod w Cefnllys and Disserth 87-98; Can Brecon Cathl 89-98; Prec Brecon Cathl 95-98; RD Maelienydd 95-98; Dean Brecon 98-00; rtd 00. *Hafod, Cefnllys Lane, Penybont, Llandrindod Wells LD1 5SW* Tel (01597) 851830

HUGHES, Canon Gerald Thomas. b 30. Lon Univ BD63 MTh. Qu Coll Birm 72. **d** 72 **p** 73. Lic to Offic *Cov* 72-80; P-in-c Birdingbury 80-81; P-in-c Leamington Hastings 80-81; V Leamington Hastings and Birdingbury 81-82; V Dunchurch 82-89; RD Rugby 85-89; Can Res Cov Cathl 89-94; rtd 94; Perm to Offic *Cov* and *Worc* from 94. *Loafers' Cottage, Lazy Lane, Fladbury, Pershore WR10 2QL* Tel (01386) 860650

HUGHES, Gwilym Berw. b 42. St Mich Coll Llan DipTh68. **d** 68 **p** 69. C Conwy w Gyffin *Ban* 68-71; V Llandinorwig 71-75; TV Llandudno 75-80; V Dwygyfylchi 80-96; RD Arllechwedd 88-96; V Bodelwyddan *St As* from 96. *The Vicarage, Bodelwyddan, Rhyl LL18 5UR* Tel (01745) 583034

HUGHES, Gwilym Lloyd. b 48. Univ of Wales (Cardiff) BD76 MA79 DipTh74 Univ of Wales (Ban) CertEd84. St Mich Coll Llan 71. **d** 99 **p** 00. NSM Caerwys and Bodfari *St As* from 99; Warden of Readers 99-02. *Adlonfa, Bodfari, Denbigh LL16 4DA* Tel (01745) 710385

HUGHES, Canon Gwyndaf Morris. b 36. Univ of Wales (Lamp) BA57 St Cath Soc Ox 57. St Steph Ho Ox 58 St Mich Coll Llan 59. **d** 59 **p** 60. C Glanogwen *Ban* 59-62; Chapl RN 62-78; R Llanfairpwll w Penmynydd *Ban* 78-90; R Beaumaris 90-03; RD Tindaethwy 88-01; AD 01-03; Can Ban Cathl 95-99; Prec 97-99; Preb 99-03; rtd 03. *Cae Pysgodlyn, Waterloo Port, Caernarfon LL55 1LW* Tel (01286) 677461

HUGHES, Canon Hazel. b 45. St Jo Coll Dur 75. **dss** 78 **d** 87 **p** 94. Lower Mitton *Worc* 78-81; Worc St Martin w St Pet, St Mark etc 82-87; Par Dn Worc SE 87-88; Dn-in-c Wribbenhall 88-94; V 94; P-in-c from 94; Chapl to Mentally Handicapped from 94; Hon Can Worc Cathl from 95. *Wribbenhall Vicarage, Trimpley Lane, Bewdley DY12 1JJ* Tel (01299) 402196

HUGHES, Heather Alice. b 48. Open Univ BA91 Kent Univ 97. SEITE DipTM99. **d** 99 **p** 00. NSM Pembury *Roch* from 99. *7 Henwoods Crescent, Pembury TN2 4LJ* Tel (01892) 822764 E-mail hughes@heather39.freeserve.co.uk

HUGHES, Hugh. b 13. St D Coll Lamp BA35 St Mich Coll Llan 35. **d** 36 **p** 37. C Llanfaethlu w Llanfwrog *Ban* 36-41; C Holyhead 41-45; V Dolwyddelan 45-56; R Llanbeulan w Llanfaelog and Tal-y-Llyn 56-69; R Llaneugrad w Llanallgo and Penrhoslugwy etc 73-82; RD Twrcelyn 80-82; rtd 82; Perm to Offic *Ban* from 86. *50 Craig-y-Don, Benllech, Tyn-y-Gongl LL74 8TB* Tel (01248) 853500

HUGHES, Canon Hywel Maldwyn. b 20. Univ of Wales (Swansea) BA42. St Mich Coll Llan 42. **d** 44 **p** 45. C Llangyfelach and Morriston *S & B* 44-47; C Builth w Alltmawr and Llanynys 46-48; Min Can Brecon Cathl 48-53; R Llanfeugan w Llanddetty and Glyncollwg 53-59; R Ystradgynlais 59-68; V Killay 68-87; RD Clyne 79; Can Brecon Cathl from 81; Treas Brecon Cathl 81; Chan 83-87; rtd 88; Canada from 95; Perm to Offic Toronto from 95. *142 Three Valleys Drive, Don Mills ON, Canada, M3A 3B9* Tel (001) (416) 445 8571

HUGHES, Ian. b 67. Aston Tr Scheme Trin Coll Bris BA00. **d** 00 **p** 01. C Halton *Ches* from 00. *9 Coppice Close, Castlefields, Runcorn WA7 2HX* Tel (01928) 564726 E-mail ihughes@hotmail.com

HUGHES, Preb Ivor Gordon. b 45. Culham Coll of Educn CertEd68 Westmr Coll Ox MTh94. Ripon Coll Cuddesdon 75. **d** 77 **p** 78. C Newport w Longford *Lich* 77-79; Children's Work Officer CMS 79-82; V Gt and Lt Bedwyn and Savernake Forest *Sarum* 82-86; P-in-c Urchfont w Stert 86-90; TR Redhorn 90-92; Nat Children's Officer Gen Syn Bd of Educn 92-95; R Yeovil w Kingston Pitney *B & W* from 95; Preb Wells Cathl from 02. *The Rectory, 5 West Park, Yeovil BA20 1DE* Tel (01935) 475396 Fax as telephone

HUGHES, Mrs Jackie Louise. b 50. ACP81 Birm Poly BEd86. WMMTC 89. **d** 92. NSM Edgbaston St Geo *Birm* 92-95; Tutor Qu Coll Birm from 96. *267 Stoney Lane, Yardley, Birmingham B25 8YG* Tel 0121-628 4184 or 454 8597

HUGHES, Miss Jacqueline Monica. b 36. Lon Univ TCert56. Dalton Ho Bris 59. **dss** 77 **d** 88. Redditch St Steph *Worc* 77-79; Worc H Trin 79-82; Chapl Asst Worc R Infirmary 82-94; Asst Chapl Worc R Infirmary NHS Trust 94-00. *38 Cockshute Hill, Droitwich WR9 7QP* Tel (01905) 775153 or 763333

HUGHES, James Thomas. b 74. St Anne's Coll Ox BA95 Liv Hope PGCE97. Oak Hill Th Coll BA02. **d** 03. C Virginia Water *Guildf* from 03. *6 Beechmont Avenue, Virginia Water GU25 4EY* Tel (01344) 849172

HUGHES, John Chester. b 24. St Jo Coll Dur BA48 DipTh50 MA51. **d** 50 **p** 51. C Southend St Sav Westcliff *Chelmsf* 50-53; Succ Chelmsf Cathl 53-55; V New Humberstone *Leic* 55-61; V Croxton Kerrial w Branston by Belvoir 61-63; Provost Leic 63-78; ChStJ from 74; V Bringhurst w Gt Easton *Leic* 78-87; rtd 87; Perm to Offic *Leic* 87-99. *29 High Street, Hallaton, Market Harborough LE16 8UD* Tel (01858) 89622

HUGHES, John David. b 58. Leeds Univ BA79 Man Univ PGCE82. Ripon Coll Cuddesdon 97. **d** 99 **p** 00. C Wythenshawe Man from 99. *St Francis's Vicarage, Chalford Road, Manchester M23 8RD* Tel 0161-437 4605

HUGHES, Canon John Herbert Vivian. b 28. St D Coll Lamp BA51 LTh53. **d** 53 **p** 54. C Abergwili w Llanfihangel-uwch-Gwili *St D* 53-58; C Llanelli 58-62; V Newchurch and Merthyr 62-71; V Abergwili w Llanfihangel-uwch-Gwili etc 71-89; RD Carmarthen 82-88; Can St D Cathl 87-89; rtd 89. *104 Bronwydd Road, Carmarthen SA31 2AR* Tel (01267) 237155

HUGHES, John Malcolm. b 47. Man Univ BSc68 Leeds Univ DipTh70. Coll of Resurr Mirfield 68. **d** 71 **p** 72. C Newton Nottage *Llan* 71-78; V Llanwynno 78-92; R Cadoxton-juxta-Barry from 92. *The Rectory, 21 Rectory Road, Cadoxton, Barry CF63 3QB* Tel (01446) 406690 Fax as telephone E-mail cjb@johnmhughes.free-online.co.uk

HUGHES, Canon John Patrick. b 41. Sheff Univ Dip Leadership Renewal & Miss 98. Oak Hill Th Coll DipTh66. **d** 67 **p** 68. C Chorleywood St Andr *St Alb* 67-71; C E Twickenham St Steph *Lon* 71-76; TV High Wycombe *Ox* 77-92; Chapl Wycombe Hosp 77-83; V Harborne Heath *Birm* from 92; Hon Can Birm Cathl from 99. *St John's Vicarage, 99 Wentworth Road, Birmingham B17 9ST* Tel 0121-428 2093 *or* 427 4601 Fax 428 1934 E-mail jphughes@charis.co.uk

HUGHES, John Tudor. b 59. Nottm Univ BSc81 Univ of Wales (Cardiff) DipTh. St Mich Coll Llan 81. **d** 84 **p** 85. C Mold *St As* 84-88; Asst Dioc Youth Chapl 86-90; Dioc Youth Chapl 90-97; Min Can St As Cathl 88-90; Min St As and Tremeirchion 88-90; V Holt 90-96; V Buckley from 96; RD Mold from 00. *St Matthew's Vicarage, 114 Church Road, Buckley CH7 3JN* Tel (01244) 550645

HUGHES, John William George. b 48. MBE93. St Mich Coll Llan DipTh72. **d** 72 **p** 73. C Swansea St Pet *S & B* 72-76; V Cwmddauddwr w St Harmon's and Llanwrthwl 76-79; P-in-c Caereithin 79; V 80-86; Chapl RAF 86-02. *Address temp unknown*

HUGHES, Leonard Mordecai. b 50. St Jo Coll Nottm 95. **d** 97 **p** 98. NSM N Evington *Leic* from 97. *68 Trevino Drive, Leicester LE4 7PH* Tel 0116-266 9979

HUGHES, Lindsay. *See* HUGHES, Miss Carol Lindsay

HUGHES, Martin Conway. b 40. Ex Coll Ox BA61 MA67. Chich Th Coll. **d** 63 **p** 64. C Roehampton H Trin *S'wark* 63-67; C Addlestone *Guildf* 67-71; V Burpham 71-88; V Shamley Green from 88; RD Cranleigh 90-95. *The Vicarage, Church Hill, Shamley Green, Guildford GU5 0UD* Tel (01483) 892030

HUGHES, Martyn Lawrence. b 19. Magd Coll Ox BA42 MA46 K Coll Cam BA43 MA52. Westcott Ho Cam. **d** 44 **p** 45. V Eltham St Jo *S'wark* 44-46; China 47-53; Chapl K Coll Cam 53-56; Asst Chapl Uppingham Sch Leics 56-61; Chapl Harrow Sch 61-73; Perm to Offic *Chich* 73-87; Hd Relig Studies Rich Collyer Coll Horsham 73-84; Chapl St Mich Sch Petworth 85-87; rtd 87. *137 Evergreen Way SW, Calgary, AB, Canada T2Y 3KB*

HUGHES, Matthew James. b 66. K Coll Lon BD88. Westcott Ho Cam 89. **d** 91 **p** 92. C Heston *Lon* 91-94; C Fulham All SS 94-96; TV St Laur in Thanet *Cant* 96-01; R Farnborough *Roch* from 01. *The Rectory, Farnborough Hill, Orpington BR6 7EQ* Tel (01689) 856931 E-mail jmath@btinternet.com

HUGHES, Michael John Minto. b 50. Liv Univ MB, ChB74 DRCOG87 DGM88 Westmr Coll Ox MTh94. Wycliffe Hall Ox 76. **d** 79 **p** 80. C Stranton *Dur* 79-82; Chapl Intercon Ch Soc Peru 82-86; Perm to Offic *Dur* 86-87; Perm to Offic *Carl* 87-89; TV Thetford *Nor* 89-97; P-in-c Downham *Ely* from 97. *The Rectory, Main Street, Little Downham, Ely CB6 2ST* Tel (01353) 699237

HUGHES, Nesta. *See* HUGHES, Ms Eunice Nesta

HUGHES, Neville Joseph. b 52. NUU BA79 MBIM93. CITC 97. **d** 91 **p** 92. NSM Mullabrack w Markethill and Kilcluney *Arm* 91-98; I from 00; C Portadown St Mark 98-00. *The Rectory, 6 Mullurg Road, Markethill BT60 1QN* Tel (028) 3884 1500

HUGHES, The Ven Paul Vernon. b 53. Ripon Coll Cuddesdon 79. **d** 82 **p** 83. C Chipping Barnet w Arkley *St Alb* 82-86; TV Dunstable 86-93; P-in-c Boxmoor St Jo 93-98; V from 98; RD Hemel Hempstead 96-03; Adn Bedford from 03. *17 Lansdowne Road, Luton LU3 1EE* Tel (01582) 730722 Fax 877354 E-mail archbedf@stalbansdioc.org.uk

HUGHES, Mrs Penelope Patricia. b 47. Sheff Univ LLB. WMMTC 95. **d** 98 **p** 99. NSM Whitley *Cov* 98-01; NSM Leamington Spa H Trin and Old Milverton 01-03; P-in-c Berkswell from 03. *The Rectory, Meriden Road, Berkswell, Coventry CV7 7BE* Tel (01676) 533605 E-mail penhughes@aol.com

HUGHES, Peter John. b 43. Melbourne Univ BA67 Ch Ch Ox BPhil77. Trin Coll Melbourne 64 ACT 69. **d** 70 **p** 70. Australia 70-74 and 84-97; Perm to Offic *Ox* 75-77; Lic to Offic 77-79; Chapl Lon Univ *Lon* 79-84. *PO Box 626, North Sydney, NSW, Australia 2059*

HUGHES, Peter John. b 59. Wolv Poly BA83 Lon Univ PGCE85 DipM. Wycliffe Hall Ox 90. **d** 92 **p** 93. C Ecclesall *Sheff* 92-96; V Kimberworth from 96. *The Vicarage, 331 Kimberworth Road, Rotherham S61 1HD* Tel (01709) 554441

HUGHES, Peter Knowles. b 61. Sarum & Wells Th Coll 87. **d** 90 **p** 91. C Whitchurch *Bris* 90-93; Perm to Offic *Worc* 93-97; Lic to Offic from 97; Chapl Worc Coll of HE from 97. *Woodside Farmhouse, Blakes Lane, Guarlford, Malvern WR13 6NZ* Tel (01684) 311308

HUGHES, Philip. b 47. St Jo Coll Nottm 79. **d** 81 **p** 82. C Dolgellau w Llanfachreth and Brithdir etc *Ban* 81-83; Asst Youth Chapl 82-83; R Llaneugrad w Llanallgo and Penrhoslugwy 83-95; V Llanberis w Llanrug 95-03; Dioc Youth Chapl 93-98; RD Arfon 00-02; R Llanfair-pwll and Llanddaniel-fab etc from 03. *The Rectory, Ffordd Caergybi, Llanfairpwllgwyngyll LL61 5SX* Tel (01248) 713746 Fax as telephone E-mail revphilip@aol.com

HUGHES, Philip Geoffrey John. b 60. Nottm Univ BCombStuds82 Birm Univ DipTh88. Aston Tr Scheme 84 Qu Coll Birm 86. **d** 89 **p** 90. C Sedgley All SS *Worc* 89-94; V Boscoppa *Truro* 94-96; Chapl Gatwick Airport *Chich* 96-02; Chapl Sussex Police 96-02; C Crawley 96-02; Heathrow Airport *Lon* from 02; C Harmondsworth from 02. *St Mary's Vicarage, High Street, Harmondsworth, West Drayton UB7 0AQ* Tel (020) 8897 2385 *or* 8745 4261

HUGHES, Philip Stephen. b 34. Dur Univ BA59. Coll of Resurr Mirfield 59. **d** 62 **p** 63. C Horfield St Greg *Bris* 62-66; C Bedminster St Mich 66-69; P-in-c Chippenham St Pet 69-71; V 71-83; TR Bedminster 83-91; V Ashton Keynes, Leigh and Minety 91-00; rtd 00; Perm to Offic *Worc* from 00. *19 Fairways, Pershore WR10 1HA* Tel (01386) 552375

HUGHES, Richard Clifford. b 24. Pemb Coll Cam BA57 MA59. Ely Th Coll 48. **d** 50 **p** 51. C Wandsworth St Anne *S'wark* 50-53; S Rhodesia 53-65; S Africa 65-86; Adn Pinetown 75-80; Australia from 86; rtd 89. *1/184 Springfield Road, Blackburn North, Vic, Australia 3130* Tel (0061) (3) 9894 4889 E-mail cherryh@smart.net.au

HUGHES, Richard Jeffrey. b 47. Trin Coll Carmarthen CertEd68. St Mich Coll Llan 74. **d** 76 **p** 77. C Llanbeblig w Caernarfon and Betws Garmon etc *Ban* 76-78; Dioc Youth Chapl 78-82; TV Holyhead w Rhoscolyn w Llanfair-yn-Neubwll 78-83; R Llanfachraeth 83-92; R Llangefni w Tregaean and Llangristiolus etc 92-95; R Llanbeblig w Caernarfon and Betws Garmon etc from 95. *Hafoty, 30 Bryn Rhos, Rhosbodrual, Caernarfon LL55 2BT* Tel (01286) 674181

HUGHES, Richard Millree. b 33. Univ of Wales BA56 MA79. St Mich Coll Llan 56. **d** 58 **p** 59. C Mold *St As* 58-61; V Choral St As Cathl 61-64; V Towyn 64-67; Asst Master Marlborough Sch Woodstock 77-79; R Whitchurch St Mary *Ox* 79-00; rtd 00. *Cae Canol Mawr, Cwm Teigl, Blaenau Ffestiniog LL41 4RS* Tel 07798-790369 (mobile) E-mail rmillree@aol.com

HUGHES, Robert Elistan-Glodrydd. b 32. Trin Coll Ox BA54 MA58 Birm Univ MLitt85. Westcott Ho Cam 55. **d** 57 **p** 58. C Stoke *Cov* 57-61; Ind Chapl *S'wark* 61-64; Birm Univ *Birm* 64-87; Chapl 64-69; Lodgings Warden and Student Welfare Adv 69-87; Dir Housing Study Overseas Students Trust 88-91; Perm to Offic *Ban* 88-94; V Harlech and Llanfair-juxta-Harlech etc 94-99; rtd 97. *Clogwyn Melyn, Talsarnau LL47 6TP* Tel (01766) 780257 E-mail shebob.clog@virgin.net

HUGHES, Robert Guy. b 64. York Univ BSc86 Reading Univ PhD89 Ox Univ BA92 MA96. Ripon Coll Cuddesdon 90. **d** 93 **p** 94. C Sandhurst *Ox* 93-95; Asst Chapl K Sch Ely 95-96; Chapl 96-99; Min Can Ely Cathl *Ely* 96-99. *59 Silver Street, Ely CB7 4JB* Tel (01353) 668691 E-mail robert.g.hughes@dial.pipex.com

HUGHES, Robert Leslie. b 52. Qu Coll Birm 98. **d** 00 **p** 01. C The Quinton *Birm* from 00. *111 Glyn Farm Road, Quinton, Birmingham B32 1NJ* Tel 0121-422 3596 E-mail roberthughes@fish.co.uk

HUGHES, Rodney Thomas. b 39. Dur Univ BA60 St Cath Coll Ox DipTh61. Wycliffe Hall Ox 60. **d** 62 **p** 63. C Edin St Thos *Edin* 62-65; C Harlow New Town w Lt Parndon *Chelmsf* 65-67; R Haworth *Bradf* 67-74; R W Knighton w Broadmayne *Sarum* 74-77; R Broadmayne, W Knighton, Owermoigne etc 77-82; V Crosthwaite Keswick *Carl* 82-02; rtd 02. *2 Bewcastle Close, Carlisle CA3 0PU* Tel (01228) 401680

HUGHES, Ronald. See HUGHES, Arthur William Ronald

HUGHES, Mrs Sally Lorraine. b 59. Open Univ BA98. EAMTC 99. **d** 02 **p** 03. NSM Gretton w Rockingham and Cottingham w E Carlton *Pet* from 02. *28 Rushton Road, Wilbarston, Market Harborough LE16 8QL* Tel (01536) 770998 Mobile 07740-171139 Fax (01536) 770779 E-mail sally@hughes.uk.com

HUGHES, Mrs Sheila. b 52. Chester Coll of HE DipApTh96. N Ord Course 92. **d** 95 **p** 96. NSM Birkenhead Priory *Ches* 95-97; C 97-99; P-in-c Northwich St Luke and H Trin 99-01; V from 01; Bp's Adv for Women in Min from 00; Chapl Mid Cheshire Hosps Trust from 99. *St Luke's Vicarage, Dyar Terrace, Northwich CW8 4DN* Tel (01606) 74632 E-mail sheila@hughes1051.freeserve.co.uk

HUGHES, Steven Philip. b 52. MBE01. St Jo Coll Dur BA80. Ridley Hall Cam 80. **d** 82 **p** 83. C Chilvers Coton w Astley *Cov* 82-86; TV Kings Norton *Birm* 86-91; Perm to Offic *Eur* 92-96; Asst Chapl Bucharest 96-98; P-in-c Bucharest w Sofia 98-01; P-in-c Belgrade 98-00; P-in-c Hoole *Blackb* from 02. *The Rectory, 69 Liverpool Old Road, Much Hoole, Preston PR4 4GA* Tel (01772) 612267 E-mail stevenhughes@tiscali.co.uk

HUGHES, Ms Valerie Elizabeth. b 53. Birm Univ BA75 CertEd76. Wycliffe Hall Ox DipTh86. **d** 87 **p** 94. C Hallwood *Ches* 87-90; Par Dn Garston *Liv* 90-93; Asst Chapl Liv Univ 93; TD Gateacre 93-94; TV 94-00; C St Helens St Helen from 00. *75 King Edward Road, St Helens WA10 6LE*

HUGHES, William. See HUGHES, Albert William

HUGHES, William Piers Maximillian. b 76. Ex Univ BA99. Ripon Coll Cuddesdon 99. **d** 01 **p** 02. C Cley Hill Warminster *Sarum* from 01. *39 Manor Gardens, Warminster BA12 8PN* Tel (01985) 214953 E-mail will-hattie@lineone.net

HUGHES, William Roger. b 47. ACCA MCIPD MBIM. Trin Coll Carmarthen. **d** 91 **p** 92. NSM Llan-non *St D* 91-93; Dio Officer for Soc Resp from 93; V Llangathen w Llanfihangel Cilfargen etc from 93. *The Vicarage, Llangathen, Carmarthen SA32 8QD* Tel (01558) 668455

HUGHMAN, June Alison. b 58. Kingston Poly BSc81 Southn Univ PhD84. Trin Coll Bris DipHE88. **d** 89 **p** 94. Par Dn Penge St Jo *Roch* 89-93; C Woking Ch Ch *Guildf* 93-98; V Croydon Ch Ch *S'wark* 98-00; C Uxbridge *Lon* from 00; Town Cen Min from 00. *84 Harefield Road, Uxbridge UB8 1PN* Tel (01895) 254121

HUGO, Canon Keith Alan. b 41. Nottm Univ BA62. Chich Th Coll 62. **d** 64 **p** 65. C Pontefract St Giles *Wakef* 64-68; C Chesterfield St Mary and All SS *Derby* 68-71; V Allenton and Shelton Lock 71-77; Dioc Communications Officer *Sarum* 77-89; V Worton 77-84; V Potterne 77-84; Can and Preb Sarum Cathl from 84; V Potterne w Worton and Marston 84-89; R Wyke Regis from 89; RD Weymouth from 94. *The Rectory, 1 Portland Road, Weymouth DT4 9ES* Tel (01305) 784649 Fax as telephone E-mail keith.hugo@talk21.com

HUISH, Barnaby Thomas. b 71. St Chad's Coll Dur BA94 MA95. Cuddesdon Coll BA98. **d** 99 **p** 00. C Darlington H Trin *Dur* 99-02; Prec and Min Can Sac St Alb Abbey *St Alb* from 02. *Flat 1, The Deanery, Sumpter Yard, St Albans AL1 1BY* Tel (01727) 890207

HUITSON, Christopher Philip. b 45. Keble Coll Ox BA66 MA70. Cuddesdon Coll 67. **d** 69 **p** 70. C Croydon St Sav *Cant* 69-73; Soc Service Unit St Martin-in-the-Fields Lon 71-73; C St Alb St Pet *St Alb* 73-77; V Cople 77-78; P-in-c Willington 77-78; V Cople w Willington 78-89; V Leavesden All SS 89-96; V Totteridge from

96; RD Barnet from 99. *The Vicarage, 44 Totteridge Village, London N20 8PR* Tel (020) 8445 6787 E-mail c.huitson@btinternet.com

HULBERT, Hugh Forfar. b 22. Bris Univ BA49. Bible Churchmen's Coll Bris 46. **d** 50 **p** 51. C Summerstown *S'wark* 50-53; C Felixstowe SS Pet and Paul *St E* 53-55; Min Collier Row St Jas CD *Chelmsf* 55-59; SW Area Sec CPAS 59-63; V Portsea St Luke *Portsm* 63-75; V Worthing H Trin *Chich* 75-81; C-in-c Hove H Trin CD 81-85; C Hailsham 86-87; rtd 87; Perm to Offic *Chich* from 87. *8 Ramsay Hall, 11-13 Byron Road, Worthing BN11 3HN* Tel (01903) 209594

HULBERT, John Anthony Lovett. b 40. Trin Coll Cam BA63 MA67. Wells Th Coll 64. **d** 66 **p** 67. C Fareham H Trin *Portsm* 66-70; R Wickham 70-79; RD Bishop's Waltham 74-79; V Bedford St Andr *St Alb* 79-92; RD Bedford 87-92; V Leighton Buzzard w Eggington, Hockliffe etc 92-03; Hon Can St Alb 91-03; C Stansted *Chich* from 03. *Forestside Vicarage, Stansted Estate, Rowland's Castle PO9 6EE* Tel (023) 9263 1371 Fax as telephone E-mail anthony.hulbert@allsaintslb.org.uk

HULBERT, Canon Martin Francis Harrington. b 37. Dur Univ BSc58 MA62. Ripon Hall Ox 58. **d** 60 **p** 61. C Buxton *Derby* 60-63; C Eglingham *Newc* 63-67; C-in-c Loundsley Green Ascension CD *Derby* 67-71; P-in-c Frecheville 71-73; R Frecheville and Hackenthorpe *Sheff* 73-77; P-in-c Hathersage *Derby* 77-83; V 83-90; RD Bakewell and Eyam 81-90; Hon Can Derby Cathl 89-02; R Brailsford w Shirley and Osmaston w Edlaston 90-93; V Tideswell 93-02; RD Buxton 96-99; rtd 02. *16 Lismore Road, Buxton SK17 9AN* Tel (01298) 79566

HULETT, Mrs Janet Elizabeth Mary. b 48. **d** 91 **p** 96. NSM Broadwater St Mary *Chich* 91-95; NSM Thame *Ox* from 96. *24 Clarendon Drive, Thame OX9 3XP* Tel (01844) 216457 E-mail janethulett@onet.co.uk

HULETT, Peter. b 31. CEng MIMechE62 Leeds Univ CertEd74. Wycliffe Hall Ox 75. **d** 77 **p** 78. C Eastwood *S'well* 77-80; C Granby w Elton 80-83; V Gilling and Kirkby Ravensworth *Ripon* 83-90; P-in-c Bishop Monkton and Burton Leonard 90-96; rtd 96; Perm to Offic *Bradf* from 96. *2 Cardan Drive, Ilkley LS29 8PH* Tel (01943) 604202

HULL, Mrs Bernadette Mary. b 46. E Lon Univ BA92 PGCE93. NTMTC 99. **d** 02 **p** 03. NSM Becontree S *Chelmsf* from 02. *46 Hall Road, Chadwell Heath, Romford RM6 4LJ* Tel (020) 8252 3540 or 8491 8765 Mobile 07990-730293 E-mail bmhull@ntlworld.com

HULL, David John. b 44. Linc Th Coll 88. **d** 90 **p** 91. C Mansfield Woodhouse *S'well* 90-93; P-in-c Mansfield St Lawr 93-00; V Mosbrough *Sheff* from 00; V Elmton *Derby* from 03. *The Vicarage, 1 Elmton Road, Creswell, Worksop S80 4HD* Tel (01909) 721264

HULL, John Hammond. b 36. Brasted Th Coll 58 Sarum Th Coll 60. **d** 61 **p** 62. C Gt Clacton *Chelmsf* 61-66; Area Chapl (E Anglia) Toc H 66-70; (Midl Region) 70-75; Lic to Offic *Chelmsf* 66-75; Chapl Toc H HQ 75-82; Lic to Offic *Ox* from 75. *66 Grenville Avenue, Wendover, Aylesbury HP22 6AL* Tel (01296) 624487

HULL, Thomas Henry. b 55. QUB BD79. NTMTC 94. **d** 97 **p** 98. C Kidbrooke *S'wark* 97-99; TV 99-01; I Lecale Gp *D & D* from 01. *Lecale Rectory, 9 Quoile Road, Downpatrick BT30 6SE* Tel (028) 4461 3101 or 4461 4922 Fax 4461 4456 E-mail lecale@down.anglican.org

HULL, Timothy David. b 60. Lon Bible Coll 87 K Coll Lon PhD97. St Jo Coll Nottm BTh90. **d** 90 **p** 91. C Leyton St Mary w St Edw *Chelmsf* 90-95; Chapl Havering Coll of F&HE 94-98; C Harold Hill St Geo *Chelmsf* 95-98; Co-ord NTMTC 98-01; TV Becontree W from 98. *St Peter's Vicarage, 29 Warrington Road, Dagenham RM3 3JH* Tel (020) 8983 8198 E-mail tim_hull@lineone.net

HULL, Suffragan Bishop of. See FRITH, The Rt Revd Richard Michael Cokayne

✠**HULLAH, The Rt Revd Peter Fearnley.** b 49. K Coll Lon BD71 AKC71 FRSA93. Cuddesdon Coll 73. **d** 74 **p** 75 **c** 99. Asst Chapl St Edw Sch Ox 74-77; C Summertown *Ox* 74-76; C Wolvercote w Summertown 76-77; Chapl Sevenoaks Sch 77-82; Hon C Sevenoaks St Nic *Roch* 77-82; Ho Master Internat Cen Sevenoaks Sch 82-87; Hon C Kippington 82-87; Sen Chapl K Sch Cant 87-92; Hon Min Can Cant Cathl *Cant* 87-92; Hd Master Chetham's Sch of Music 92-99; Lic Preacher *Man* 93-99; Perm to Offic *Carl* 87-99; Hon Can Man Cathl *Man* 96-99; Area Bp Ramsbury *Sarum* from 99. *Bishop's Croft, Winterbourne Earls, Salisbury SP4 6HJ,* or *Sarum House, High Street, Urchfont, Devizes SN10 4QH* Tel (01380) 840373 Mobile 07831-896779 Fax (01980) 619128 *or* (01380) 848247 E-mail hullahp@aol.com *or* peter.ramsbury@salisbury.anglican.org

HULLETT, Frederick Graham. b 32. St Jo Coll York CertEd53 Leeds Univ BA58. Coll of Resurr Mirfield 58. **d** 60 **p** 61. C Acton Green St Pet *Lon* 60-61; C W Hackney St Barn 61-64; C Paddington St Mary 64-67; Hon C 67-69; P-in-c Haggerston St Aug w St Steph 69-73; Lic to Offic 73-84; Perm to Offic *Linc* from 84; rtd 91. *2 Ryland Road, Welton, Lincoln LN2 3LU* Tel (01673) 860839

HULLYER, Paul Charles. b 68. Anglia Poly Univ MA98 Lambeth MA04. Aston Tr Scheme 92 Westcott Ho Cam 94. **d** 97 **p** 98. C Stoke Newington St Mary *Lon* 97-00; C Addlestone *Guildf* 00-03; V Hillingdon All SS *Lon* from 03. *All Saints' Vicarage, Ryefield Avenue, Uxbridge UB10 9BT* Tel (01895) 234947 E-mail hullyer@fish.co.uk

HULME, Alan John. b 60. Birm Univ BSc81. Wycliffe Hall Ox BA90. **d** 91 **p** 92. C Chilwell *S'well* 91-96; TV Roxeth *Lon* 96-02; V S Harrow St Paul from 02. *St Paul's Vicarage, Findon Close, Corbins Lane, Harrow HA2 8NJ* Tel (020) 8864 0362 Fax as telephone E-mail alanjhulme@aol.com

HULME, Ms Juliette Mary. b 57. Whitelands Coll Lon BEd81. Cranmer Hall Dur 94. **d** 94 **p** 95. C Crayford *Roch* 94-98; C Leatherhead *Guildf* 98-01; CF from 02. *c/o MOD Chaplains (Army)* Tel (01980) 615804 Fax 615800 E-mail juliette.hulme@hotmail.com

HULME, Norman. b 31. Kelham Th Coll 50. **d** 54 **p** 55. C Blackb St Pet *Blackb* 54-57; C Blakenall Heath *Lich* 57-59; V Gannow *Blackb* 59-64; V Anwick *Linc* 64-74; V S Kyme 64-74; V Moulton 74-83; V Earl Shilton w Elmesthorpe *Leic* 83-88; Chapl Harperbury Hosp Radlett 88-96; rtd 96. *Moorcroft, 9 Birch Grove, Spalding PE11 2HL* Tel (01775) 710127 E-mail norjoan@yahoo.co.uk

HULME, Suffragan Bishop of. *See* LOWE, The Rt Revd Stephen Richard

HULSE, William John. b 42. Dur Univ BA65. Linc Th Coll 65. **d** 67 **p** 68. C S Westoe *Dur* 67-70; Lic to Offic *Newc* 70-72; C Far Headingley St Chad *Ripon* 72-76; R Swillington 76-88; V Shadwell 88-95; V Oulton w Woodlesford 95-02; P-in-c Spennithorne w Finghall and Hauxwell from 02. *The Rectory, Spennithorne, Leyburn DL8 5PR* Tel (01969) 623010

HULT, Mrs Anna Eva Hildegard. b 73. Lund Univ Sweden MTh. Past Inst Uppsala 97. **p** 98. Sweden 98-02; Perm to Offic *Ely* 02-03; P-in-c Witchford w Wentworth from 03. *The Vicarage, 75 Main Street, Witchford, Ely CB6 2HQ* Tel (01353) 669420

HUME, Miss Clephane Arrol. b 46. Edin Occupational Therapy Tr Cen DipOT46 Jordanhill Coll Glas CertFE83 Open Univ BA87 Edin Univ MTh98. Edin Dioc NSM Course 88. **d** 92 **p** 94. NSM Edin St Jo *Edin* from 92. *30 Findhorn Place, Edinburgh EH9 2JP* Tel 0131-667 2996 Fax 668 3568 E-mail clephanehume@compuserve.com

HUME, Ernest. b 45. Linc Th Coll 77. **d** 79 **p** 80. C Ilkeston St Mary *Derby* 79-81; C Sheff Manor *Sheff* 81-82; TV 82-88; V Norton Woodseats St Chad 88-99; V Woodhouse St Jas 99-rtd 02. *Shadwell, 6 Canal Bridge, Killamarsh, Sheffield S21 1DJ* Tel 0114-248 1769 E-mail ehume@vicarage51.freeserve.co.uk

HUME, Martin. b 54. Grimsby Coll of Tech HND75. Coll of Resurr Mirfield 89. **d** 91 **p** 92. C Brentwood St Thos *Chelmsf* 91-94; P-in-c Corringham from 94. *The Rectory, Church Road, Corringham, Stanford-le-Hope SS17 9AP* Tel (01375) 673074 E-mail martinhume@aol.com

HUMMERSTONE, Jeremy David. Mert Coll Ox BA65 MA70. Wells Th Coll 70. **d** 72 **p** 73. C Helmsley *York* 72-75; C Pockley cum E Moors 72-75; P-in-c Manningford Bruce w Manningford Abbots *Sarum* 75-81; TV Swanborough 75-80; P-in-c Frithelstock *Ex* 80-81; P-in-c Gt Torrington 80-81; P-in-c Lt Torrington 80-81; V Gt and Lt Torrington and Frithelstock from 81. *The Vicarage, Calf Street, Torrington EX38 8EA* Tel (01805) 622166 E-mail hummerstone@bigfoot.com

HUMPHREY, Mrs Betty. b 37. St Mich Ho Ox 59. **d** 90 **p** 94. C Hardwicke, Quedgeley and Elmore w Longney *Glouc* 90-93; Dn-in-c Swindon w Uckington and Elmstone Hardwicke 93-94; P-in-c 94-96; R 96-98; rtd 98; Perm to Offic *Glouc* from 00. *11 Lower Orchard, Tibberton, Gloucester GL19 3AX* Tel (01452) 790790

HUMPHREY, David Lane. b 57. Maine Univ BA79. St Jo Coll Nottm 84. **d** 88 **p** 89. C Springfield All SS *Chelmsf* 88-91; C Thundersley 91-96; V Standon *St Alb* from 96; RD Bishop's Stortford from 01. *The Vicarage, Kents Lane, Standon, Ware SG11 1PJ* Tel (01920) 821390 E-mail d.l.humphrey@btinternet.com

HUMPHREY, Derek Hollis. b 37. Chich Th Coll 69. **d** 72 **p** 73. C Havant *Portsm* 72-75; C Southsea H Spirit 75-78; V Finsbury Park St Thos *Lon* 78-88; V S Patcham *Chich* from 88. *10 Church Close, Brighton BN1 8HS* Tel (01273) 502385

HUMPHREY, Canon George William. b 38. Lon Bible Coll BD61 Lon Univ CertEd74 Man Univ Dip Educn Guidance 75. Oak Hill Th Coll 61. **d** 62 **p** 63. C Heigham H Trin *Nor* 62-64; P-in-c Buckenham w Hassingham and Strumpshaw 64-67; Chapl St Andr Hosp Norwich 64-67; Asst Master Mexborough Gr Sch 67-69; Hd RE Cheadle Gr Sch 69-76; Hon C Cheadle Hulme St Andr *Ches* 70-76; P-in-c Kellington w Whitley *Wakef* 76-80; Teacher Thurnscoe Comp Sch 76-80; RE Insp Glos Co Coun and Dioc *Glouc* 80-93; Dioc RE Adv 93-99; Hon Can Glouc Cathl 95-99; rtd 00; Perm to Offic *Glouc* from 00. *11 Lower Orchard, Tibberton, Gloucester GL19 3AX* Tel (01452) 790790

HUMPHREY, Heather Mary. b 46. CertEd68. WMMTC 87. **d** 90 **p** 94. NSM Overbury w Teddington, Alstone etc *Worc* 90-96; NSM Berrow w Pendock, Eldersfield, Hollybush etc

96-98; C Coseley Ch Ch 98-00; V from 00. *The Vicarage, Church Road, Coseley, Bilston WV14 8YB* Tel (01902) 353551

HUMPHREY, Timothy Martin. b 62. Ex Univ BA83. St Jo Coll Nottm DipTh87. **d** 89 **p** 90. C Wallington H Trin *S'wark* 89-92; P-in-c 92-97; C Oakley w Wootton St Lawrence *Win* 97-02; Faith Development Field Officer 97-02; V Kensington St Barn *Lon* from 02. *St Barnabas's Vicarage, 23 Addison Road, London W14 8LH* Tel (020) 7471 7000 Fax 7471 7001 E-mail tim@stbk.org.uk

HUMPHREYS, Mrs Anne-Marie (Anna). b 44. SRN67 K Coll Lon BD92 AKC92 Man Univ MA96 Cert Counselling 99. N Ord Course 92. **d** 95 **p** 96. NSM Manchester Gd Shep and St Barn *Man* 95-98; NSM Burnage St Nic from 98; Chapl Cen Man Healthcare NHS Trust 96-01; Chapl Cen Man/Man Children's Univ Hosp NHS Trust from 01. *16 Clothorn Road, Manchester M20 6BQ* Tel 0161-434 2164

HUMPHREYS, Brian Leonard. b 29. MChS51 SRCh. Bp Attwell Tr Inst. **d** 87 **p** 88. NSM Maughold *S & M* 87-91; NSM S Ramsey St Paul 91-92; NSM Andreas 92-94; Perm to Offic from 94. *Thie Cassan Yack, Jack's Lane, Port E Vullen, Ramsey, Isle of Man IM7 1AW* Tel (01624) 813694

HUMPHREYS, Daniel Robert. b 74. K Coll Lon BA95 AKC95 Leeds Univ BA99. Coll of Resurr Mirfield 97. **d** 00 **p** 01. C Scarborough St Martin *York* 00-02; C Kilburn St Aug w St Jo *Lon* from 02. *122 Dibdin House, Maida Vale, London W9 1QG* Tel (020) 7328 9301

HUMPHREYS, George Bernard. b 10. AKC36. **d** 36 **p** 37. C Leigh St Mary *Man* 36-38; C Streatham St Pet *S'wark* 38-41; C Tarporley *Ches* 42-48; R Moreton Corbet *Lich* 48-53; V Dawley Parva 53-65; R Fobbing *Chelmsf* 65-78; rtd 78; Perm to Offic *Ex* from 78. *Prestercot, Butts Lane, Christow, Exeter EX6 7NN* Tel (01647) 52595

HUMPHREYS, James Graham. b 36. Liv Univ BEng57 PhD60. Trin Coll Bris 61. **d** 63 **p** 64. C Denton Holme *Carl* 63-66; C St Helens St Mark *Liv* 66-68; V Houghton *Carl* 68-79; V Bramcote *S'well* 79-93; RD Beeston 85-90; rtd 93; Perm to Offic *S'well* 93-01. *383 London Road, Carlisle CA1 3HA* Tel (01228) 597108

HUMPHREYS, Canon John Elwyn Price. b 15. OBE77 Portuguese Order of Merit 94. Univ of Wales BA37. St Mich Coll Llan 38. **d** 39 **p** 41. C Newtown *St As* 39-42; C Rhosymedre 42-43; Chapl RNVR 43-46; Chapl RN 46-51; Chapl Santa Cruz *Eur* 51-52; Chapl and Asst Master Reed's Sch Cobham 53-57; Lic to Offic *Guildf* 53-57; Chapl Estoril *Eur* 57-80; Can Gib Cathl 67-80; rtd 80. *Casa Contente, Av Sra do Monte da Saúde 341, 2765-452 Estoril, Portugal* Tel (00351) (21) 468 3238

HUMPHREYS, John Louis. b 51. Jes Coll Cam BA72 MA76 Nottm Univ BA75. St Jo Coll Nottm 73. **d** 76 **p** 77. C W Bromwich Gd Shep w St Jo *Lich* 76-79; C Woodford Wells *Chelmsf* 79-83; V Werrington *Lich* from 83; Chapl HM YOI Werrington Ho 83-98. *The Vicarage, 360 Ash Bank Road, Werrington, Stoke-on-Trent ST9 0JS* Tel (01782) 302441 Fax as telephone E-mail jlhumphreys@lineone.net

HUMPHREYS, Canon Kenneth Glyn. b 28. Bps' Coll Cheshunt 64. **d** 66 **p** 67. C New Windsor St Jo *Ox* 66-67; C Whitley Ch Ch 67-70; V Compton 70-74; V Compton w E Ilsley 74-75; R E Ilsley 74; C Wokingham All SS 75-77; Chapl Lucas Hosp Wokingham (Almshouses) 77-81; V California *Ox* 81-94; RD Sonning 86-88; Hon Can Ch Ch *Ox* 94; rtd 95; Perm to Offic *Ox* from 96. *17 Snowberry Close, Wokingham RG41 4AQ* Tel 0118-977 2096

HUMPHREYS, Mrs Lydia Ann. b 60. CCSk90. Sarum & Wells Th Coll DCM93. **d** 93 **p** 94. C Gaywood *Nor* 93-95 and 95-97; TV Cov E *Cov* from 97. *St Margaret's Vicarage, 18 South Avenue, Coventry CV2 4DR* Tel (024) 7645 7344 Fax as telephone E-mail lydia@humphreys.clara.co.uk

HUMPHREYS, Canon Philip Noel. b 34. Bps' Coll Cheshunt 62. **d** 64 **p** 65. C Plymouth St Andr *Ex* 64-68; Chapl Lee Abbey 68-73; V Porchester *S'well* 73-82; RD W Bingham 82-87; P-in-c W Leake w Kingston-on-Soar and Ratcliffe-on-Soar 82-87; R W Bridgford 82-00; Hon Can S'well Minster 93-00; rtd 00. *48 Windsor Avenue, Newark, Nottingham NG24 4JA* Tel (01636) 705317

HUMPHREYS, Roger John. b 45. CertEd66 Open Univ BA76. Wycliffe Hall Ox 81. **d** 83 **p** 84. Chapl Dragon Sch Ox 83-87; C Ox St Andr *Ox* 83-87; V Carterton 87-94; R Bladon w Woodstock from 94; AD Woodstock from 01. *The Rectory, Rectory Lane, Woodstock OX20 1UQ* Tel (01993) 811415 Fax as telephone E-mail rectorrog@aol.com

HUMPHREYS, Stephen Robert Beresford. b 52. K Coll Lon 74 BA98. **d** 76 **p** 77. C Northwood Hills St Edm *Lon* 76-79; C Manningham St Mary and Bradf St Mich *Bradf* 79-81; C Manningham St Paul and St Jude 82; Chapl Bradf R Infirmary 82-86; C Leeds St Pet *Ripon* 87-90; Perm to Offic *B & W* 94-99; Hon C Selworthy, Timberscombe, Wootton Courtenay etc from 02. *Stowey Farm, Timberscombe, Minehead TA24 7BW* Tel (01643) 841265

HUMPHREYS, William Alfred. b 18. Lich Th Coll 54. **d** 56 **p** 57. C Stone St Mich *Lich* 56-60; V Fazeley 60-65; V Prees 65-83; P-in-c Fauls 66-70; V 70-83; RD Wem and Whitchurch 80-83; rtd

83; Perm to Offic *Heref* 83-97. *Bryncroft, 4 Seabridge Meadow, Bucknell SY7 0AP* Tel (01547) 530597

HUMPHREYS, William Haydn. b 09. AKC36. St D Coll Lamp 29. **d** 36 **p** 37. C Kirkheaton *Wakef* 36-43; CF (EC) 43-47; V Dewsbury St Mark *Wakef* 48-78; Chapl Dewsbury Gen Hosp 50-78; rtd 78. *Flat 24, Marion Court, Lisvane Road, Cardiff CF14 0RZ* Tel (029) 2075 7158

HUMPHREYS, Anthony Roy. b 49. Lon Univ BSc73. Wycliffe Hall Ox DipMin94. **d** 94 **p** 95. C Worksop St Jo *S'well* 94-96; C Retford St Sav 96-98; TV Grantham *Linc* 98-00; TV Bestwood *S'well* 00-03; V Bestwood St Matt w St Phil from 03. *St Matthew's Vicarage, Padstow Road, Nottingham NG5 5GH* Tel 0115-927 7229 E-mail revtonyhumphries@hotmail.com

HUMPHREYS, Benjamin Paul. b 56. Man Univ BA77 Birm Univ DipTh84 FRGS85. Qu Coll Birm 82. **d** 85 **p** 86. C Hall Green Ascension *Birm* 85-88; P-in-c Belmont *Man* 88-96; Fieldworker USPG *Blackb, Bradf, Carl* and *Wakef* 96-98; Perm to Offic *Carl* 96-99; Area Co-ord Lic to Offic *Blackb* from 97; Chr Aid (Cumbria, Lancs and Isle of Man) from 98; Perm to Offic *Carl* from 02. *4 Tinniswood, Ashton-on-Ribble, Preston PR2 1EL* Tel (01772) 768694 *or* 726770 Fax as telephone E-mail bhumphries@christian-aid.org

HUMPHREYS, Catherine Elizabeth. *See* NICHOLLS, Mrs Catherine Elizabeth

HUMPHREYS, Christopher William. b 52. St Jo Coll Cam BA73 MA77 Lon Inst of Educn CertEd74. St Jo Coll Nottm DipTh77 DPS79. **d** 79 **p** 80. C Eccleshill *Bradf* 79-82; Chapl Scargill Ho 82-86; TV Guiseley w Esholt *Bradf* 86-91; V Filey *York* from 91; RD Scarborough from 98. *The Vicarage, 5 Belle Vue Crescent, Filey YO14 9AD* Tel (01723) 512745 Fax as telephone E-mail vicarage@fileypcc.fsnet.co.uk

HUMPHREYS, David. *See* HUMPHRIES, William David

HUMPHREYS, David Graham. b 48. Univ of Wales (Cardiff) DipTh70. St Mich Coll Llan 67. **d** 71 **p** 72. C Neath w Llantwit *Llan* 71-72; C Bishop's Cleeve *Glouc* 81-83; C Cirencester 83-87; V Glouc St Steph 87-96; P-in-c Micklinch 96-03; Assoc P Up Hatherley from 03. *28 Davallia Drive, Up Hatherley, Cheltenham GL51 5XG* Tel (01242) 861261

HUMPHREYS, David John. b 51. BSc CertEd BD. Edin Th Coll. **d** 84 **p** 85. C Styvechale *Cov* 84-88; V Greetland and W Vale *Wakef* 88-96; V Shawbury *Lich* from 96; V Stanton on Hine Heath from 96; R Moreton Corbet from 96. *The Vicarage, Church Road, Shawbury, Shrewsbury SY4 4NH* Tel (01939) 250419

HUMPHREYS, Donald. b 43. Bris Univ BA66. Clifton Th Coll 66. **d** 68 **p** 69. C Selly Hill St Steph *Birm* 68-74; Chapl Warw Univ *Cov* 74-79; V Bedford Ch Ch St Alb 79-85; V Cambridge H Trin w St Andr Gt *Ely* 85-92; V Cambridge H Trin 92-94; rtd 94; Perm to Offic *Ely* from 94. *56 The Rowans, Milton, Cambridge CB4 6YU*

HUMPHREYS, Miss Dorothy Maud. b 22. Bedf Coll Lon BA44 Lon Univ DipEd45 Cam Univ DipTh50. Gilmore Course 85. **dss** 79 **d** 87 **p** 94. Kidderminster Deanery *Worc* 79-97; NSM 87-97; Perm to Offic from 98. *16 George Law Court, Anchorfields, Kidderminster DY10 1PZ* Tel (01562) 824459

HUMPHREYS, Frank Charles. b 40. St Chad's Coll Dur BA61 DipTh63. **d** 63 **p** 64. C Tottenham All Hallows *Lon* 63-66; C S Harrow St Paul 66-71; V Hillingdon All SS 71-80; V Preston Ascension 80-97; Dir of Ords 86-97; rtd 97; Perm to Offic *Lon* from 97. *1 Chantry Place, Headstone Lane, Harrow HA3 6NY* Tel (020) 8428 9944

HUMPHREYS, Grahame Leslie. b 44. Lon Coll of Div ALCD70 LTh. **d** 71 **p** 72. C Wandsworth St Mich *S'wark* 71-74; C Slough *Ox* 74-77; P-in-c Arley *Cov* 77-82; R 82-84; Norfolk Churches' Radio Officer *Nor* 84-96; P-in-c Bawdeswell w Foxley 84-96; P-in-c Mayfield *Lich* 96-02; Local Min Adv (Stafford) 96-02; RD Uttoxeter 98-02; P-in-c Blockley w Aston Magna and Bourton on the Hill *Glouc* from 02; Local Min Officer from 02. *The Vicarage, The Square, Blockley, Moreton-in-Marsh GL56 9ES* Tel (01386) 700283

HUMPHREYS, Harold Joseph. b 14. MIEE52. S'wark Ord Course 70. **d** 70 **p** 71. C Merton St Mary *S'wark* 70-71; C Glouc All SS *Glouc* 71-75; Hon C 78-82; C Glouc St Jas 75-77; Hon Min Can Glouc Cathl 77-01; Perm to Offic from 77. *Flat 6, St Margaret's, London Road, Gloucester GL1 3PH* Tel (01452) 520449

HUMPHREYS, John. b 49. Univ of Wales (Cardiff) DipTh76. St Mich Coll Llan 73. **d** 76 **p** 77. C Pontnewynydd *Mon* 76-78; C Ebbw Vale 78-81; V Pet Ch Carpenter *Pet* 81-86; P-in-c King's Cliffe 86-87; R King's Cliffe w Apethorpe 87-93; R King's Cliffe 93-97; V Finedon from 97. *The Vicarage, Finedon, Wellingborough NN9 5NR* Tel (01933) 680285 Mobile 07976-370434 E-mail frjohn13@aol.com

HUMPHREYS, Miss Marion Betty. b 29. K Coll Lon DipTh50 Open Univ BA84. Selly Oak Coll 51. **dss** 80 **d** 87 **p** 94. Newmarket St Mary w Exning St Agnes *St E* 80-82; Acomb St Steph *York* 83-86; Scarborough St Martin 86-93; Par Dn 87-93; C Cayton w Eastfield 94; rtd 94; Perm to Offic *Nor* from 95. *27 Wells Road, Walsingham NR22 6DL* Tel (01328) 820489

HUMPHRIES, Richard James Robert. b 44. EAMTC 99. **d** 01 **p** 02. NSM Heybridge w Langford *Chelmsf* 01-02; NSM Maldon All SS w St Pet from 02; Assoc Chapl Mid-Essex Hosp Services NHS Trust from 02. *1 Prince of Wales Road, Great Totham, Maldon CM9 8PX* Tel (01621) 892822 Mobile 07803-281036 E-mail richard.humphries1@btopenworld.com

HUMPHRIES, Robert William. b 36. Open Univ BA87. SW Minl Tr Course 96. **d** 99 **p** 00. OLM Kenwyn w St Allen *Truro* from 99. *27 Penhalls Way, Truro TR3 6EX* Tel (01872) 862827

HUMPHRIES, William David. b 57. QUB BEd DipTh LTCL. CITC. **d** 86 **p** 87. C Ballyholme *D & D* 86-90; Min Can Belf Cathl from 89; V Choral 90-93; C Belfast St Anne *Conn* 90-93; I Stormont *D & D* from 93. *3 Rosepark, Belfast BT5 7RG* Tel (028) 9048 2292 *or* 9041 9171 E-mail stormont@down.anglican.org

HUMPHRIS, Richard. b 44. N Glos Tech Coll OND69. Sarum & Wells Th Coll 69. **d** 72 **p** 73. C Cheltenham St Luke and St Jo *Glouc* 72-77; C Lydney w Aylburton 77-82; Chapl RAF 82-85; TV Kippax w Allerton Bywater *Ripon* 85-92; RSPCA 92-95; rtd 95; Perm to Offic *York* from 98. *33 Cliff Terrace, Micklefield, Leeds LS25 4DF* Tel 0113-287 4446

HUMPHRISS, Canon Reginald George. b 36. Kelham Th Coll 56. **d** 61 **p** 62. C Londonderry *Birm* 61-63; Asst Dir RE *Cant* 63-66; Dioc Youth Chapl 63-66; V Preston next Faversham 66-72; P-in-c Goodnestone St Bart and Graveney 71-72; V Spring Park 72-76; R Cant St Martin and St Paul 76-90; RD Cant 82-88; Hon Can Cant Cathl 85-01; R Saltwood 90-01; RD Elham 93-00; rtd 01; Perm to Offic *Cant* from 01. *Winsole, Faussett, Lower Hardres, Canterbury CT4 7AH* Tel (01227) 765264

HUMPHRY, Toby Peter. b 66. Man Univ BA88. Ripon Coll Cuddesdon BA90 Qu Coll Birm 92. **d** 93 **p** 94. C Westhoughton *Man* 93-96; C Westhoughton and Wingates 97; TV Atherton 97-99; TV Atherton and Hindsford 99-02; TV Atherton and Hindsford w Howe Bridge from 02. *21 Greenfield Road, Atherton, Manchester M46 9LW* Tel (01942) 888406

HUMPHRYES, Garry James. b 62. Coll of Resurr Mirfield 92. **d** 95 **p** 96. C Lt Marsden *Blackb* 95-98; C Darwen St Cuth w Tockholes St Steph 98-00; V Nelson St Bede 00-03; V Morecambe St Barn from 03; Dioc Race and Community Relns Officer from 98. *St Barnabas' Vicarage, 101 Regent Road, Morecambe LA3 1AG* Tel (01524) 411283 E-mail blackburn_race_relations@hotmail.com

HUMPHRYS, Kevin Luke. b 73. Surrey Univ BA97. St Steph Ho Ox. **d** 99 **p** 00. C Moulsecoomb *Chich* 99-03. *148 Lyndhurst Road, Worthing BN11 2DW* Tel (01903) 230336 E-mail kevin.humphrys@bigfoot.com

HUMPHRYS, Laura Frances. b 53. STETS. **d** 03. NSM Shorwell w Kingston *Portsm* from 03. *Mallards, Walkers Lane, Shorwell, Newport PO30 3JZ* Tel (01983) 741010

HUMPLEBY, Peter. b 40. Open Univ BA76 Hull Univ DipTh82. Linc Th Coll 75. **d** 77 **p** 78. C Todmorden *Wakef* 77-80; V Bruntcliffe 80-88; R Aldingham and Dendron and Rampside *Carl* 88-92; V Dodworth *Wakef* 92-00; rtd 00; Perm to Offic *York* from 00. *Church Mouse Cottage, 31 Staithes Lane, Staithes, Saltburn-by-the-Sea TS13 5AH* Tel (01947) 840314

HUNDLEBY, Alan. b 41. LNSM course 86. **d** 86 **p** 87. OLM Fotherby *Linc* 86-02; NSM Barnoldby le Beck from 02. *35 Cheapside, Waltham, Grimsby DN37 0HE* Tel (01472) 827159

HUNG, Frank Yu-Chi. b 45. Birm Univ BSc68 BA75 Liv Univ MSc71 Lon Univ DipTh77. Wycliffe Hall Ox 76. **d** 78 **p** 79. C Walton H Trin *Ox* 78-82; C Spring Grove St Mary *Lon* 82-85; TV Wexcombe *Sarum* 85-92; V Hatcham St Jas *S'wark* 92-98; Chapl Goldsmiths' Coll Lon 95-98; Chapl S Bank Univ from 98. *1 St Alphege Clergy House, Pocock Street, London SE1 0BJ* Tel (020) 7928 8912

HUNGERFORD, Robin Nicholas. b 47. Redland Coll of Educn CertEd74. Trin Coll Bris DipHE88. **d** 88 **p** 89. C Swindon Dorcan *Bris* 88-92; TV Melbury *Sarum* 92-01; P-in-c Winterbourne Stickland and Turnworth etc from 01. *The Rectory, Winterbourne Stickland, Blandford Forum DT11 0NL* Tel (01258) 880482 Fax as telephone E-mail rjnk@rhungerford.freeserve.co.uk

HUNNISETT, John Bernard. b 47. AKC73. **d** 73 **p** 74. C Charlton Kings St Mary *Glouc* 73-77; C Portsea St Mary *Portsm* 77-80; V Badgeworth w Shurdington *Glouc* 80-87; R Dursley 87-99; TR Ross *Heref* from 99; RD Ross and Archenfield from 02. *The Rectory, 4 Church Street, Ross-on-Wye HR9 5HN* Tel (01989) 562175 Fax 564387 E-mail team.rector@rtm.org.uk

HUNNYBUN, Martin Wilfrid. b 44. Oak Hill Th Coll 67. **d** 70 **p** 71. C Ware Ch Ch *St Alb* 70-74; C Washfield, Stoodleigh, Withleigh etc *Ex* 74-75; TV 75-80; R Braunston *Pet* 80-85; Asst Chapl HM Pris Onley 80-85; Australia 83 and 85-98 and from 00; Min Flinders Melbourne 83; R Berry and Kangaroo Valley Sydney 85-94; Sen Chapl Ang Retirement Villages 94-98; TV Parkham, Alwington, Buckland Brewer etc *Ex* 98-00; Dioc Ecum Adv 98-00; R Glebe Sydney from 00. *138A Glebe Point Road, PO Box 353, Glebe, NSW, Australia 2037* Tel (0061) (2) 9518 4063 *or* 9660 1818 Fax 9660 5696 E-mail mhunnybun@ozemail.com.au

HUNT, Alan. b 31. GIMechE51 GIPE51. St Mich Coll Llan 65. **d** 67 **p** 68. C Standish *Blackb* 67-72; V Clitheroe St Paul Low Moor 72-76; Lic to Offic 76-85; rtd 85; Perm to Offic *Blackb* from 85. *68 Coniston Drive, Walton-le-Dale, Preston PR5 4RQ* Tel (01772) 339554

HUNT, Andrew Collins. b 54. Reading Univ BA77 Hull Univ PGCE79. St Alb Minl Tr Scheme 82 Sarum & Wells Th Coll 89 WEMTC 99. **d** 00 **p** 01. NSM Cainscross w Selsley *Glouc* 00-02. *Address temp unknown*

HUNT, Ashley Stephen. b 50. St Jo Coll Nottm 81. **d** 83 **p** 84. C Southchurch H Trin *Chelmsf* 83-86; TV Droitwich *Worc* 86-87; USA 88-91; TV Melton Gt Framland *Leic* 92-93; TV Melton Mowbray 93-98; TV Grantham *Linc* 98-00; Chapl Mental Health 98-01; C Stamford All SS w St Jo 00-01; TV Mynyddislwyn *Mon* from 02. *The Vicarage, Commercial Road, Cwmfelinfach, Ynysddu, Newport NP11 7HW* Tel (01495) 200257 E-mail louhunt3@aol.com

HUNT, Mrs Christina. b 24. Qu Mary Coll Lon BSc45. S Dios Minl Tr Scheme 78. **dss** 81 **d** 87 **p** 94. Alderbury and W Grimstead *Sarum* 81-87; Hon Par Dn 87-91; Hon Par Dn Alderbury Team 91-94; rtd 94; Perm to Offic *Sarum* from 94. *The Heather, Southampton Road, Alderbury, Salisbury SP5 3AF* Tel (01722) 710601

HUNT, Christopher Paul Colin. b 38. Ch Coll Cam BA62 MA62. Clifton Th Coll 63. **d** 65 **p** 66. C Widnes St Paul *Liv* 65-68; Singapore 68-70; Malaysia 70-71; Hon C Foord St Jo *Cant* 72-73; Iran 74-80; Overseas Service Adv CMS 81-91; P-in-c Claverdon w Preston Bagot *Cov* 91-02; rtd 02. *Birchfield House, 18 Oaklands, Malvern WR14 4JE* Tel (01684) 578803

HUNT, David John. b 35. Kelham Th Coll 60. **d** 65 **p** 66. C Bethnal Green St Jo w St Simon *Lon* 65-69; C Mill Hill St Mich 69-73; R Staple Fitzpaine, Orchard Portman, Thurlbear etc *B & W* 73-79; P-in-c E Coker w Sutton Bingham 79-88; V E Coker w Sutton Bingham and Closworth 88-00; RD Merston 85-94; rtd 00; Perm to Offic *B & W* from 01. *Meadowside, Head Street, Tintinhull, Yeovil BA22 8QH* Tel (01935) 824554

HUNT, Derek Henry. b 38. ALCD61. **d** 62 **p** 63. C Roxeth Ch Ch *Lon* 62-66; C Radipole *Sarum* 66-70; P-in-c Shalbourne w Ham 70-72; V Burbage 72-73; V Burbage and Savernake Ch Ch 73-78; P-in-c Hulcote w Salford *St Alb* 78-88; R Cranfield 78-88; R Cranfield and Hulcote w Salford 88-95; rtd 95; Perm to Offic *St Alb* 95-98. *26 Jowitt Avenue, Kempston, Bedford MK42 8NW*

HUNT, Ernest Gary. b 36. Univ Coll Dur BA57 DipEd58. Carl Dioc Tr Inst 90. **d** 93 **p** 94. NSM Salesbury *Blackb* 93-95; NSM Blackb St Mich w St Jo and H Trin 95-98; NSM Balderstone 98-01; rtd 01; Perm to Offic *Blackb* from 01. *Dunelm, 10 Pleckgate Road, Blackburn BB1 8NN* Tel (01254) 52531

HUNT, Ernest William. b 09. St Jo Coll Dur BA31 MA34 Birm Univ BD46 St Cath Soc Ox BLitt51 Ox Univ MLitt90. St Jo Coll Dur DipTh32. **d** 32 **p** 33. C Gateshead Fell *Dur* 32-37; V Dunston Ch Ch 37-43; Succ Birm Cathl *Birm* 43-51; Lect Qu Coll Birm 46-51; Vice-Prin Lich Th Coll 51-57; Prof St D Coll Lamp 57-69; rtd 76. *16 Peachcroft Road, Abingdon OX14 2NA* Tel (01235) 521549

HUNT, Giles Butler. b 28. Trin Hall Cam BA51 MA55. Cuddesdon Coll 51. **d** 53 **p** 54. C N Evington *Leic* 53-56; C Northolt St Mary *Lon* 56-58; Bp's Dom Chapl *Portsm* 58-59; Bp's Chapl *Nor* 59-62; R Holt 62-67; R Kelling w Salthouse 63-67; C Pimlico St Pet w Westmr Ch Ch *Lon* 67-72; V Barkway w Reed and Buckland *St Alb* 72-79; V Preston next Faversham, Goodnestone and Graveney *Cant* 79-92; rtd 92; Perm to Offic *Nor* from 92. *The Cottage, The Fairstead, Cley-next-the-Sea, Holt NR25 7RJ* Tel (01263) 740471

HUNT, Canon Ian Carter. b 34. Chich Th Coll 61. **d** 64 **p** 65. C Plymouth St Pet *Ex* 64-67; C Daventry *Pet* 67-70; V Northampton St Paul 70-91; Can Pet Cathl 81-99; V Wellingborough All Hallows 91-99; rtd 99; Chapl Allnutt's Hosp Goring Heath from 99. *The Chaplaincy, Almshouses, Goring Heath, Reading RG8 7RS* Tel (01491) 680261

HUNT, James Allen. b 49. Linc Th Coll 92. **d** 92 **p** 93. C Huddersfield St Pet and All SS *Wakef* 92-95; V Longwood from 95. *St Mark's Vicarage, 313 Vicarage Road, Huddersfield HD3 4HJ* Tel (01484) 314163 Fax as telephone

HUNT, Jeremy Mark Nicholas. b 46. FRGS70 Open Univ BA73 Bris Univ DipEd. Ridley Hall Cam 83. **d** 85 **p** 86. C Leckhampton SS Phil and Jas w Cheltenham St Jas *Glouc* 85-87; Asst Chapl Vevey w Château d'Oex and Villars *Eur* 87-89; Chapl Berne w Neuchâtel 89-90; Dep Chapl HM Pris Pentonville 94-95; Chapl HM Pris Highpoint from 95. *The Chaplain's Office, HM Prison, Highpoint, Stradishall, Newmarket CB8 9YG* Tel (01440) 823301 or 823302 Fax 823097

HUNT, John Barry. b 46. Lich Th Coll 70 Qu Coll Birm 72. **d** 73 **p** 74. C Auckland St Andr and St Anne *Dur* 73-77; C Consett 77-79; R Lyons 79-89; P-in-c Hebburn St Cuth from 89; P-in-c Hebburn St Oswald from 01. *St Cuthbert's Vicarage, Cosserat Place, Hebburn NE31 1RD* Tel 0191-483 2354

HUNT, John Edwin. b 38. ARCO Dur Univ BA60 DipEd. EMMTC 78. **d** 81 **p** 82. NSM Newbold w Dunston *Derby* 81-92; NSM Chesterfield St Mary and All SS 92-02. *4 Ardsley Road,*

Ashgate, Chesterfield S40 4DG Tel (01246) 275141 E-mail fredwin@cwcom.net

HUNT, John Stewart. b 37. Nor Ord Course 75. **d** 78 **p** 79. NSM Hunstanton St Edm *Nor* 78-81; NSM Hunstanton St Mary w Ringstead Parva, Holme etc 81-86; NSM Sedgeford w Southmere 84-86; C Lowestoft and Kirkley 86-89; R Blundeston w Flixton and Lound 89-93; P-in-c Kessingland w Gisleham 93-99; R Kessingland, Gisleham and Rushmere 99-00; rtd 00; Perm to Offic *Nor* from 00. *10 Peddars Drive, Hunstanton PE36 6HF* Tel (01485) 533424

HUNT, Canon Judith Mary. b 57. MRCVS80 Bris Univ BVSc80 Lon Univ PhD85 Fitzw Coll Cam BA90. Ridley Hall Cam 88. **d** 91 **p** 94. Par Dn Heswall *Ches* 91-94; C 94-95; P-in-c Tilston and Shocklach 95-03; Bp's Adv for Women in Min 95-00; Can Res Ches Cathl from 03; Dioc Dir of Min from 03. *5 Abbey Street, Chester CH1 2JF* Tel (01244) 346893 *or* 620444 E-mail hunt@chestercathedral.com

HUNT, Kevin. b 59. St Jo Coll Dur BA80 Ox Univ BA84 MA88. St Steph Ho Ox 81. **d** 84 **p** 85. C Mansfield St Mark *S'well* 84-85; C Hendon and Sunderland *Dur* 85-88; V Sunderland St Mary and St Pet 88-95; TR Jarrow 95-02; V Walker *Newc* from 02. *Walker Vicarage, Middle Street, Newcastle upon Tyne NE6 4DB* Tel 0191-262 3666 E-mail kevinht10@hotmail.com

HUNT, Miss Nicola Mary. b 54. SRN77 RSCN77 RHV87. Ripon Coll Cuddesdon DipMin95. **d** 95 **p** 96. C Broughton Astley and Croft w Stoney Stanton *Leic* 95-98; C Plymouth Em, St Paul Efford and St Aug *Ex* 98-01; V Ermington and Ugborough from 01. *The Vicarage, Lutterburn Street, Ugborough, Ivybridge PL21 0NG* Tel (01752) 897360

HUNT, Paul. *See* HUNT, Christopher Paul Colin

HUNT, Paul Edwin. b 47. Ripon Coll Cuddesdon DipMin95. **d** 95 **p** 96. C Cleobury Mortimer w Hopton Wafers etc *Heref* 95-98; P-in-c Fritwell w Souldern and Ardley w Fewcott *Ox* from 98. *The Vicarage, 44 Forge Place, Fritwell, Bicester OX6 9QQ* Tel (01869) 346739 E-mail paul.hunt@breathemail.net

HUNT, Paul Firth. b 62. Ox Univ MA89 Edin Univ BD89. Edin Th Coll 86. **d** 89 **p** 90. C Leeds Halton St Wilfrid *Ripon* 89-92; C Leeds City 92-95; V Leeds Richmond Hill 95-01. *Address temp unknown* E-mail paul@phunt.fsnet.co.uk

HUNT, Paul Michael. b 57. St Chad's Coll Dur BA79 K Coll Lon PGCE80 K Coll Lon MA96. Chich Th Coll 91. **d** 92 **p** 93. Chapl Brighton Coll 92-93; NSM St Leonards SS Pet and Paul *Chich* 92-93; Chapl Mill Hill Sch Lon 93-98; Hon C Hendon St Paul Mill Hill *Lon* 95-98; P in O 96-98; V Southgate St Andr *Lon* from 98; Warden of Readers (Edmonton) from 01. *St Andrew's Vicarage, 184 Chase Side, London N14 5HN* Tel (020) 8886 7523

HUNT, Canon Peter John. b 35. AKC58. St Boniface Warminster. **d** 59 **p** 60. C Chesterfield St Mary and All SS *Derby* 59-61; C Matlock and Tansley 61-63; Chapl Matlock Hosp 61-63; Lect Matlock Teacher Tr Coll 61-63; V Tottington *Man* 63-69; CF (TA) 65-67 and from 75; V Bollington St Jo *Ches* 69-76; R Wilmslow 76-98; Hon Can Ches Cathl 94-02; P-in-c Brereton w Swettenham 98-02; rtd 02; Perm to Offic *Ches* from 02. *1 Varden Town Cottages, Birtles Lane, Over Alderley, Macclesfield SK10 4RZ* Tel (01265) 829593 E-mail canonhari@aol.com

HUNT, Richard William. b 46. G&C Coll Cam BA67 MA71. Westcott Ho Cam 68. **d** 72 **p** 73. C Bris St Agnes and St Simon w St Werburgh *Bris* 72-77; Chapl Selw Coll Cam 77-84; V Birchfield *Birm* 84-01; R Chich St Paul and Westhampnett *Chich* from 01. *The Rectory, Tower Close, Chichester PO19 1QN* Tel (01243) 531624 E-mail richard@hunts.fsnet.co.uk

HUNT, Ms Rosalind Edna Mary. b 55. Man Univ BA76. St Steph Ho Ox 86. **d** 88 **p** 94. Chapl Jes Coll Cam 88-92; Hon Chapl to the Deaf *Ely* 92-00; C Cambridge St Jas 00-. *107 Hemingford Road, Cambridge CB1 3BY* Tel (01223) 575778 *or* 568801 Fax 565390 E-mail ros.hunt@virgin.net

HUNT, Canon Russell Barrett. b 35. NY Univ Virginia Univ Fitzw Ho Cam. Westcott Ho Cam 73. **d** 75 **p** 76. C Leic St Mary *Leic* 75-78; V Leic St Gabr 78-82; Chapl Leic Gen Hosp 82-95; Hon Can Leic Cathl *Leic* 88-95; rtd 95. *33 Braunstone Avenue, Leicester LE3 0JH* Tel 0116-254 9101

HUNT, Simon John. b 60. Pemb Coll Ox BA81 MA85. St Jo Coll Nottm 82. **d** 90 **p** 91. C Stalybridge St Paul *Ches* 90-93; C Heysham *Blackb* 93-99; V Higher Walton from 99. *The Vicarage, Blackburn Road, Higher Walton, Preston PR5 4EA* Tel (01772) 335406 E-mail shunt@aschurchhw.co.uk

HUNT, Stephen. b 38. Man Univ BSc61 MSc62 PhD64 DSc80. Carl Dioc Tr Inst 88. **d** 91 **p** 92. C Broughton *Blackb* 91-95; Chapl Preston Acute Hosps NHS Trust 94-95; V Preston Em *Blackb* from 95. *Emmanuel Vicarage, 2 Cornthwaite Road, Preston PR2 3DA* Tel (01772) 717136 *or* 824972

HUNT, Timothy Collinson. b 65. ASVA91 Univ of Wales (Cardiff) BD95 Ox Univ MTh98. Ripon Coll Cuddesdon 95. **d** 97 **p** 98. C Ex St Dav *Ex* 97-01; Chapl Blundell's Sch Tiverton from 01. *1B Hillands, 39 Tidcombe Lane, Tiverton EX16 4EA* Tel (01884) 242343 E-mail tc@collhunt.fsnet.co.uk

HUNT, Vera Susan Henrietta. b 33. S Dios Minl Tr Scheme 88. **d** 91 **p** 94. Hon Chapl RAD from 91. *27 Redriff Close, Maidenhead SL6 4DJ* Tel (01628) 23909

HUNTER, Allan Davies. b 36. Univ of Wales (Lamp) BA57. Coll of Resurr Mirfield 57. **d** 59 **p** 60. C Cardiff St Jo *Llan* 59-68; V Llansawel 68-76; Youth Chapl 71-77; V Llansawel w Briton Ferry 76-79; V Canton St Cath 79-01; rtd 01. *9 Avonridge, Thornhill, Cardiff CF14 9AU* Tel (029) 2069 3054
E-mail allanhunter@talk21.com

HUNTER, David. b 30. Edin Th Coll 60. **d** 64 **p** 65. C Glas Ch Ch *Glas* 64-67; R 67-70 and 75-78; R Coatbridge 70-73; Chapl HM Pris Glas (Barlinnie) 72-84; P-in-c Glas H Trin *Glas* 73-84; R Glas All SS 84-95; rtd 95. *5/12 Anniesland Court, 843 Crow Road, Glasgow G13 1LG* Tel 0141-959 4943

HUNTER, David Matheson. b 46. K Coll Lon BD69 AKC69. **d** 76 **p** 77. C Paignton St Jo *Ex* 76-80; C Plymstock 80-82; Jerusalem 82-84; P-in-c Brinkley, Burrough Green and Carlton *Ely* 84-86; P-in-c Westley Waterless 84-86; R Bressingham w N and S Lopham and Fersfield *Nor* 87-96; rtd 96; Chapl and Lect Wymondham Coll *Nor* 96-02; Perm to Offic from 03. *2 Cavick Cottages, Cavick Road, Wymondham NR18 9PJ* Tel (01953) 605672

HUNTER, Edwin Wallace. b 43. FCIM NUI BA83 Dip Catechism. CITC 91. **d** 94 **p** 95. NSM Cork St Fin Barre's Union *C, C & R* from 94; Min Can Cork Cathl from 95. *Cedar Lodge, Church Road, Carrigaline, Co Cork, Irish Republic* Tel (00353) (21) 437 2338

HUNTER, Canon Frank Geoffrey. b 34. Keble Coll Ox BA56 MA60 Fitzw Coll Cam BA58 MA62. Ridley Hall Cam 57. **d** 59 **p** 60. C Bircle *Man* 59-62; C Jarrow Grange *Dur* 62-65; V Kingston upon Hull St Martin *York* 65-72; V Linthorpe 72-76; V Heslington 76-99; RD Derwent 78-98; Can and Preb York Minster 85-99; rtd 99. *2 Flexbury Avenue, Morley, Leeds LS27 0RG* Tel 0113-253 9213 Fax as telephone

HUNTER, Ian Paton. b 20. Em Coll Cam BA46 MA50. Tyndale Hall Bris 40. **d** 43 **p** 47. C Harrington *Pet* 43-47; C Portman Square St Paul *Lon* 47-50; V Furneux Pelham w Stocking Pelham *St Alb* 50-54; V Moulton *Pet* 54-60; V Danehill *Chich* 60-67; R Plumpton w E Chiltington 67-77; V Burwash Weald 77-83; P-in-c Stonegate 83-85; rtd 85; Perm to Offic *Chich* from 86. *Edzell, 15 Harrow Close, Seaford BN25 3PE* Tel (01323) 899871

HUNTER, James. b 38. Bible Tr Inst Glas DipTh65 Union Th Coll Belf BD90. **d** 92 **p** 92. In Pb Ch of Ireland 82-92; V Werneth *Man* 92-98; V Woking St Paul *Guildf* from 98; Asst Chapl HM Pris Coldingley from 01. *St Paul's Vicarage, Pembroke Road, Woking GU22 7ED* Tel (01483) 772081

HUNTER, John Crichton. b 38. Univ of Wales (Cardiff) BA59 DipEd60 LTCL. St Steph Ho Ox 98. **d** 99 **p** 00. NSM Walham Green St Jo w St Jas *Lon* from 99. *The Vicarage Flat, 40 Racton Road, London SW6 1LP* Tel (020) 7381 3368 Fax 7386 5004

HUNTER, Canon John Gaunt. b 21. St Jo Coll Dur BA49 Leeds Univ MA94. Ridley Hall Cam 49. **d** 51 **p** 52. C Bradf Cathl *Bradf* 51-54; C Compton Gifford *Ex* 54-56; V Bootle St Matt *Liv* 56-62; Uganda 62-65; Prin Bp Tucker Coll 62-65; Dioc Missr *Liv* 65-71; V Altcar 65-78; Abp York's Adv in Miss 71-78; Hon Can Liv Cathl 71-78; R Buckhurst Hill *Chelmsf* 78-79; TR 79-89; Dioc Adv in Evang *Bradf* 89-92; rtd 92; Perm to Offic *Bradf* from 92. *Westhouse Lodge, Westhouse, Ingleton LA6 3NZ* Tel (01524) 241305

HUNTER, Mrs Linda Margaret. b 47. Southn Univ DipHE98. STETS 95. **d** 98. NSM Wootton *Portsm* 98-02; NSM Chale from 02; NSM Gatcombe from 02; NSM Shorwell w Kingston from 02. *100 Caesars Road, Newport PO30 5EA* Tel (01983) 529529

HUNTER, Lionel Lawledge Gleave. b 24. Liv Coll of Art NDD50. ALCD53. **d** 53 **p** 54. C Leic H Trin *Leic* 53-56; C Northampton St Giles *Pet* 56-58; C Everton St Chrys *Liv* 58-59; P-in-c Liv St Mich 59-61; Chile 61-72; R Diddlebury w Bouldon and Munslow *Heref* 72-75; P-in-c Abdon w Clee St Margaret 73-75; P-in-c Holdgate w Tugford 73-75; Canada 75-85; V N Elmham w Billingford *Nor* 85-89; R N Elmham w Billingford and Worthing 89-90; rtd 90; Perm to Offic *Heref* from 93. *Araucana, Wyson Lane, Brimfield, Ludlow SY8 4AN* Tel (01584) 711463

HUNTER, Michael John. b 45. CCC Cam BA67 MA71 PhD71 Ox Univ BA75. Wycliffe Hall Ox 73. **d** 76 **p** 77. C Partington and Carrington *Ches* 76-79; CMS 80-90; Uganda 80-89; C Penn Fields *Lich* 90-02; RD Trysull 97-02; V Dore *Sheff* from 02. *The Vicarage, 51 Vicarage Lane, Dore, Sheffield S17 3GY* Tel 0114-236 3335 E-mail dorevicar@aol.com

HUNTER, Canon Michael Oram. b 40. K Coll Lon BD64 AKC64. **d** 65 **p** 66. C Tividale *Lich* 65-68; C Harrogate St Wilfrid *Ripon* 68-70; V Hawksworth Wood 70-78; V Whitkirk 78-86; TR Gt Grimsby St Mary and St Jas *Linc* from 86; Can and Preb Linc Cathl from 89. *49 Park Drive, Grimsby DN32 0EG* Tel (01472) 342933 *or* 358610 Fax 250751 E-mail mo.hunter@virgin.net

HUNTER, Paul. b 55. Huddersfield Poly BEd82. Chich Th Coll 86. **d** 88 **p** 90. C Weymouth H Trin *Sarum* 88-92; P-in-c Hucknall Torkard *S'well* 92; TV 92-96; V Thurcroft *Sheff* from 96. *The Vicarage, 122 Green Arbour Road, Thurcroft, Rotherham S66 9ED* Tel (01709) 542261

HUNTER, Peter Wells. b 52. Bris Univ BSc73. Trin Coll Bris BA91. **d** 91 **p** 92. C New Borough and Leigh *Sarum* 91-97; P-in-c

Warminster Ch Ch from 97. *The Vicarage, 13 Avon Road, Warminster BA12 9PR* Tel (01985) 212219

HUNTER, Robert. b 36. Man Univ BSc60. Clifton Th Coll. **d** 63 **p** 64. C Chadderton Ch Ch *Man* 63-65; C Balderstone 65-69; C Newburn *Newc* 69-73; TV Sutton St Jas and Wawne *York* 73-81; V Bilton St Pet 81-82; Hon C N Hull St Mich 82-91; TV Howden 91-97; P-in-c Ashton St Pet *Man* 97-99; TV Ashton 00-01; rtd 01. *50 Kendall Avenue, Shipley BD18 4DY* Tel (01274) 584884

HUNTER, Canon Rodney Squire. b 33. Ex Coll Ox BA56 MA61. Coll of Resurr Mirfield 56. **d** 58 **p** 59. C Forest Gate St Edm *Chelmsf* 58-61; Lib Pusey Ho Ox 61-65; Zambia 65-74; Malawi from 74; rtd 01. *Matamangwe House, Private Bag 17, Nkhotakota, Malawi*

HUNTER-BAILEY, James Ralph. b 11. Ripon Hall Ox 55. **d** 56 **p** 57. C St Jo in Bedwardine *Worc* 56-58; C Ealing St Pet Mt Park *Lon* 58-59; C Pershore w Wick *Worc* 59-61; V Skegby *S'well* 61-64; R Wychbold and Upton Warren *Worc* 64-71; Lic to Offic *Sarum* 71-78; rtd 76; Perm to Offic *Win* 78-95. *46 Erica Drive, Corfe Mullen, Wimborne BH21 3TQ* Tel (01202) 602260

HUNTER SMART, Ian Douglas. b 60. St Jo Coll Dur BA83 MA99. Edin Th Coll 83. **d** 85 **p** 86. C Cockerton *Dur* 85-89; TV Jarrow 89-92; TV Sunderland 92-98; Chapl Sunderland Univ 92-98; Ecum Chapl Newcastle Coll of H&FE 98-00; Perm to Offic *Dur* from 98. *33 Barbary Drive, Sunderland SR6 0RB* Tel 0191-567 1966 E-mail ihs@dunelm.org.uk

HUNTER SMART, William David. b 75. Bris Univ BSc97. Wycliffe Hall Ox BA01. **d** 02. C Watford *St Alb* from 02. *8A Lammas Road, Watford WD18 0BA* Tel (01923) 232979
E-mail williamhuntersmart@tiscali.co.uk

HUNTINGDON, Archdeacon of. *See* BEER, The Ven John Stuart

HUNTINGDON, Suffragan Bishop of. *See* INGE, The Rt Revd John Geoffrey

HUNTLEY, David Anthony. b 32. AMInstT56 MRTvS78 MILT98. Lon Bible Coll BA60 Fuller Sch of World Miss MTh81 Trin Coll Singapore 65. **d** 64 **p** 65. OMF Internat from 61; Singapore 61-71; Indonesia 72-73; Philippines 74-75; Hong Kong 77-81; Seychelles 82-87; Thailand 88-97; NSM S Croydon Em 76-77, 81-82, 87-88, 91-92 and from 98. *42 Farnborough Avenue, South Croydon CR2 8HD* Tel (020) 8657 5673
E-mail dh@clara.net

HUNTLEY, Denis Anthony. b 56. Saltley Tr Coll Birm CertEd77. Qu Coll Birm 77. **d** 80 **p** 81. C Llanblethian w Cowbridge and Llandough etc *Llan* 80-83; TV Glyncorrwg w Afan Vale and Cymmer Afan 83-86; R 86-89; Chapl Asst Walsgrave Hosp Cov 89-92; Chapl Halifax Gen Hosp 92-94; Chapl Calderdale Healthcare NHS Trust 94-97; C Leeds City *Ripon* 97-02; Chapl to the Deaf 97-02; Chapl amongst Deaf People and Adv for Deaf Min from 02. *11 Bedford View, Leeds LS16 6DL* Tel 0113-267 2599 E-mail dhuntley56@hotmail.com

HUNTRESS, Franklin Elias. b 33. Berkeley Div Sch STM62. **d** 62 **p** 63. USA 62-65, 73-77, 81-91 and from 98; C Ches St Mary *Ches* 65-68; C Waltham Abbey *Chelmsf* 68-73; V Leic St Gabr *Leic* 77-81; C Skegness and Winthorpe *Linc* 91-93; P-in-c Long Bennington w Foston 93-94; rtd 98. *5C Independence Way, Glover Landing, Marble Head, MA 01945, USA* Tel (001) (781) 631 4785

HUNWICKE, John William. b 41. Hertf Coll Ox BA64 MA67. St Steph Ho Ox. **d** 67 **p** 68. C Beaconsfield *Ox* 67-70; C Newington St Paul *S'wark* 70-73; Hd of Th Lancing Coll 73-01; rtd 01; C Lifton, Broadwoodwidger, Stowford etc *Ex* from 01. *The Rectory, Lewdown, Okehampton EX20 4DN* Tel (01566) 783493

HURCOMBE, Thomas William. b 45. BD74 AKC76. **d** 76 **p** 77. C Hampstead All So *Lon* 76-79; C Is of Dogs Ch Ch and St Jo w St Luke 79-83; C Bromley All Hallows 83-89; C E Greenwich Ch Ch w St Andr and St Mich *S'wark* 89-96; Ind Chapl 89-96; Dioc Urban Missr 90-96; Greenwich Waterfront Chapl 96-98; C Charlton St Luke w H Trin 97-98; P-in-c S Norwood St Mark from 98. *St Mark's Vicarage, 101 Albert Road, London SE25 4JE* Tel (020) 8656 6329 E-mail 100613.1505@compuserve.com

HURD, Alun John. b 52. Avery Hill Coll DipHE83 Edin Univ MTh97. Trin Coll Bris BA86. **d** 86 **p** 87. C Chertsey *Guildf* 86-90; Chapl St Pet Hosp Chertsey 86-90; V W Ewell *Guildf* from 90; Chapl NE Surrey Coll Ewell from 01. *All Saints' Vicarage, 7 Church Road, West Ewell, Epsom KT19 9QY* Tel (020) 8393 4357 E-mail alun@hurdbass.fsnet.co.uk

HURD, Mrs Brenda Edith. b 44. Sittingbourne Coll DipEd75. Cant Sch of Min 87. **d** 92 **p** 94. NSM Birling, Addington, Ryarsh and Trottiscliffe *Roch* 92-02; P-in-c Wrotham from 02. *The Rectory, Borough Green Road, Wrotham, Sevenoaks TN15 7RA* Tel (01732) 882211 E-mail b.hurd@virgin.net

HURD, John Patrick. b 37. CertEd65 Open Univ BA73 Kent Univ MA92. S Dios Minl Tr Scheme 77. **d** 80 **p** 81. NSM Billingshurst *Chich* 80-82 and 89-94; NSM Itchingfield w Slinfold 82-89. *Groomsland Cottage, Parbrook, Billingshurst RH14 9EU* Tel (01403) 782167

HURFORD, Colin Osborne. b 33. Qu Coll Ox BA55 MA59. Wells Th Coll 55. **d** 57 **p** 58. C Barnoldswick w Bracewell *Bradf* 57-61; C Warrington St Elphin *Liv* 61-63; Malaysia 63-70; P-in-c Annscroft *Heref* 71-79; P-in-c Longden 71-79; P-in-c Pontesbury III 71-79; R Longden and Annscroft 79-85; P-in-c Church Pulverbatch 81-85; R Longden and Annscroft w Pulverbatch 85-86; Tanzania 86-87; TR Billingham St Aid *Dur* 87-96; rtd 96; Perm to Offic *Heref* from 96; *Lich* from 01. *14 Station Road, Pontesbury, Shrewsbury SY5 0QY* Tel (01743) 792605

✠**HURFORD, The Rt Revd Richard Warwick.** b 44. OAM99. Trin Coll Bris BA96 ACertCM71 Hon FGCM96 MACE81 Univ of Wales MTh02. St Jo Coll Morpeth ACT DipTh69 Sarum Th Coll DipTh71 Melbourne Coll of Div DipRE74. **d** 69 **p** 70 **c** 01. Australia 69-71 and from 78; Prec Grafton Cathl 69-70; P-in-c Tisbury *Sarum* 71-73; R 73-75; R Tisbury and Swallowcliffe w Ansty 75-76; P-in-c Chilmark 76-78; TR Tisbury 76-78; TR Coffs Harbour 78-83; Dean Grafton 83-97; Adn The Clarence and Hastings 85-87; Adn Grafton 87-92; R Sydney St Jas 97-01; Bp Bathurst from 01. *Bishopscourt, 288 William Street, PO Box 23, Bathurst, NSW, Australia 2795* Tel (0061) (2) 6331 3550 *or* 6331 1722 Fax 6331 3660 *or* 6332 2772 E-mail bxbishop@ix.net.au

HURLE, Anthony Rowland. b 54. Lon Univ BSc Em Coll Cam PGCE. Wycliffe Hall Ox 80. **d** 83 **p** 84. C Ipswich St Mary at Stoke w St Pet *St E* 83-87; TV Barking St Marg w St Patr *Chelmsf* 87-92; V St Alb St Paul *St Alb* from 92; RD St Alb from 95. *St Paul's Vicarage, 7 Brampton Road, St Albans AL1 4PN* Tel and fax (01727) 836810 *or* tel 846281 E-mail hurle@ntlworld.com

HURLE (née POWNALL), Mrs Lydia Margaret. b 53. SRN SCM. Wycliffe Hall Ox 78. **dss** 81 **d** 94 **p** 95. Ipswich St Mary at Stoke w St Pet & St Mary Quay *St E* 81-83; NSM St Alb St Paul *St Alb* from 93. *St Paul's Vicarage, 7 Brampton Road, St Albans AL1 4PN* Tel (01727) 836810 Fax as telephone E-mail hurle@ntlworld.com

HURLEY, Daniel Timothy. b 37. St Mich Coll Llan 68. **d** 70 **p** 71. C Llanfabon *Llan* 70-73; CF 73-79; R W Walton *Ely* 79-86; V Cwmddauddwr w St Harmon's and Llanwrthwl *S & B* 86-02; rtd 02. *39 Ellesmere Orchard, Emsworth PO10 8TP* Tel (01243) 376923

HURLEY, Mark Tristan. b 57. Trin Coll Bris BA89. Sarum & Wells Th Coll 89. **d** 91 **p** 92. C Gainsborough All SS *Linc* 91-94; TV Grantham 94-00; V Donington and Bicker 00-02. *Address temp unknown*

HURLEY, Robert. b 64. Univ of Wales (Cardiff) BD86. Ridley Hall Cam 88. **d** 90 **p** 91. C Dagenham *Chelmsf* 90-93; C Egg Buckland *Ex* 93-96; C Devonport St Budeaux 96; P-in-c Camberwell All SS *S'wark* 96-99; V 99-02; Camberwell Deanery Missr 96-02; R Oldbury *Sarum* from 02. *The Rectory, Heddington, Calne SN11 0PR* Tel (01380) 850640

HURLOCK, Ronald James. b 31. BSc PhD. St Deiniol's Hawarden. **d** 83 **p** 84. C Oxton *Ches* 83-87; Chapl Asst Man R Infirmary 87-91; rtd 91. *78 Garwood Close, Westbrook, Warrington WA5 5TF* Tel (01925) 444583

HURLSTON, Ronald Wilcox. b 30. St Deiniol's Hawarden 84. **d** 86 **p** 87. NSM Timperley *Ches* 86-90; C 90-95; rtd 95; Perm to Offic *Ches* from 95. *1 Heath Road, Timperley, Altrincham WA15 6BH* Tel 0161-973 9205

HURN, Mrs June Barbara. b 32. Birm Univ CertEd53. Cant Sch of Min 87. **d** 90 **p** 94. NSM Chislehurst St Nic *Roch* from 90. *Hawkswing, Hawkwood Lane, Chislehurst BR7 5PW* Tel (020) 8467 2320

HURRELL, John William. b 25. Ripon Hall Ox 65. **d** 66 **p** 67. C Painswick *Glouc* 66-68; C Glouc St Geo 68-70; C Thornbury 70-73; V Glouc St Steph 73-86; V Deerhurst, Apperley w Forthampton and Chaceley 86-90; rtd 90; Perm to Offic *B & W* from 90. *1 Church View, Porlock, Minehead TA24 8NA* Tel (01643) 862488

HURRELL, Lionel Rex. b 41. Southn Univ BA64. Coll of Resurr Mirfield 64. **d** 66 **p** 67. C St Marychurch *Ex* 66-69; C Dawlish 69-71; Dioc Youth Officer *Cov* 71-75; V Porthleven *Truro* 75-80; RD Kerrier 78-80; P-in-c Sithney 78-80; V Swindon New Town *Bris* 80-88; TR 88-97; RD Wroughton 93-97; Hon Can Bris Cathl 94-97; rtd 97. *331 Seaside, Eastbourne BN22 7PA* Tel (01323) 649597

HURREN, Timothy John. b 46. York Univ BA74 AIB69. NEOC 99. **d** 02 **p** 03. NSM High Harrogate St Pet *Ripon* from 02. *1 South Park Road, Harrogate HG1 5QU* Tel (01423) 541696 E-mail timhurren@fish.co.uk

HURST, Alaric Desmond St John. b 24. New Coll Ox BA50 MA70. Wells Th Coll 48. **d** 51 **p** 53. C Huddersfield H Trin *Wakef* 51-52; C Leeds St Geo *Ripon* 52-54; Bp's Chapl for Rehabilitation *Roch* 55-56; C St Steph Walbrook and St Swithun etc *Lon* 57-59; V Pudsey St Paul *Bradf* 59-63; V Writtle *Chelmsf* 63-69; rtd 89. *9 Ganderton Court, Pershore WR10 1AW* Tel (01905) 840939

HURST, Antony. b 38. MA MSc. S'wark Ord Course 79. **d** 83 **p** 84. NSM S'wark H Trin w St Matt *S'wark* 83-89; NSM S'wark Ch Ch 89-96; NSM St Martin-in-the-Fields *Lon* from 96; Perm to Offic *S'wark* from 96. *33 Hugh Street, London SW1V 1QJ* Tel (020) 7828 2844

HURST, Brian Charles. b 58. Nottm Univ BA. Ripon Coll Cuddesdon 82. **d** 84 **p** 85. C Cullercoats St Geo *Newc* 84-87; C Prudhoe 87-88; TV Willington Team 88-95; V Denton 95-03; RD Newc W 97-98; TV Glendale Gp from 03. *2 Queens Road, Wooler NE71 6DR* Tel (01668) 281468

HURST, Colin. b 49. Linc Th Coll 88. **d** 90 **p** 91. C Wavertree H Trin *Liv* 90-93; C Croft and Stoney Stanton *Leic* 93-95; TV Broughton Astley and Croft w Stoney Stanton 95-97; V Wigan St Andr *Liv* from 97. *St Andrew's Vicarage, 3A Mort Street, Wigan WN6 7AU* Tel (01942) 243514

HURST, Colin. b 58. Westmr Coll Ox BA90. St Jo Coll Nottm MA95. **d** 95 **p** 96. C Warboys w Broughton and Bury w Wistow *Ely* 95-98; P-in-c Wisbech St Mary from 98; P-in-c Guyhirn w Ring's End from 98. *The Vicarage, Church Road, Wisbech St Mary, Wisbech PE13 4RN* Tel (01945) 410814 Fax as telephone E-mail cehurst@globalnet.co.uk

HURST, Geoffrey. b 30. St Aid Birkenhead 59. **d** 64 **p** 65. C Sheff Parson Cross St Cecilia *Sheff* 64-69; V Wellingborough St Mark *Pet* 69-77; P-in-c Leic St Mark *Leic* 77-82; TV Leic Resurr 82-83; V Willenhall St Steph *Lich* 83-85; V Nether Hoyland St Andr *Sheff* 85-91; V Moorends 91-94; rtd 95. *80 Sunnyvale Road, Sheffield S17 4FB* Tel 0114-236 1407

HURST, Jeremy Richard. b 40. FCP Trin Coll Cam BA61 MA MPhil. Linc Th Coll 62. **d** 64 **p** 65. C Woolwich St Mary w H Trin *S'wark* 64-69; Perm to Offic *Ex* 69-76; Perm to Offic *Ox* 76-84; TV Langley Marish 84-85; TR from 85; Chapl Thames Valley Univ *Lon* 92-98. *The Rectory, 3 St Mary's Road, Langley SL3 7EN* Tel (01753) 542068

HURST, John. b 31. NW Ord Course 76. **d** 79 **p** 80. C Flixton St Jo *Man* 79-82; P-in-c Hindsford 82-86; V 86-88; V Halliwell St Paul 88-93; rtd 93; Perm to Offic *Man* from 99. *26 Cornwall Avenue, Bolton BL5 1DZ* Tel (01204) 659233

HURT, Mrs Grenda Mary. b 36. JP91. LSE BSc63. STETS DipTh99. **d** 99 **p** 01. NSM Freshwater *Portsm* from 99; NSM Yarmouth from 99; Asst Chapl Isle of Wight Healthcare NHS Trust from 03; Chapl Earl Mountbatten Hospice from 03. *Sutton House, Madeira Lane, Freshwater PO40 9SP* Tel and fax (01983) 752335 Mobile 0797-9803127 E-mail grenda@lineone.net

✠**HURTADO, The Rt Revd Jorge A Perera.** b 34. **d** 57 **p** 58 **c** 94. Bp Cuba from 94. *Calle 6 No 273, Vedado, Plaza de la Revolución, Havana 4, 10400, Cuba* Tel (0053) (7) 35655, 38003, 321120 *or* 312436 Fax 333293 E-mail episcopal@ip.etecsa.cu

HUSSEY, Martin John. b 46. STETS 96. **d** 99 **p** 00. NSM Thames Ditton *Guildf* from 99. *94 Wellington Close, Walton-on-Thames KT12 1BE* Tel (01932) 221914

HUSSEY, William Kenneth Alfred. b 27. St Jo Coll Ox BA48 DipEd49 MA52. Wycliffe Hall Ox 51. **d** 52 **p** 53. Asst Chapl Wrekin Coll Telford 55-60; Chapl Ipswich Sch 60-72; Hd Master Ches Cathl Choir Sch 72-74; Chapl Rendcomb Coll Cirencester 74-78; P-in-c Rendcomb *Glouc* 74-78; Chapl Berkhamsted Colleg Sch Herts 78-83; TV Rendcomb w Lanner Truro 83-84; V St Goran w Caerhays 84-89; rtd 89; Perm to Offic *Truro* from 89. *20 Albany Road, Falmouth TR11 3RW* Tel (01326) 312343

HUSTON, Mary Brigid. b 59. Hull Univ BA80 K Coll Lon MA98 RGN84 RM86. SEITE 95. **d** 98 **p** 99. C S Dulwich St Steph *S'wark* 98-02; TV Catford (Southend) and Downham from 02. *233 Bellingham Road, London SE6 1EH* Tel (020) 8695 6376 E-mail mary.huston@ukgateway.net

HUTCHEON, Mrs Elsie. b 39. RGN63 CertEd UEA MEd98. EAMTC 89. **d** 92 **p** 94. NSM Heigham St Thos *Nor* 92-02; P-in-c Heigham St Barn w St Bart from 02. *1 St Barnabas's Vicarage, Russell Street, Norwich NR2 4QT* Tel (01603) 627859

HUTCHIN, David William. b 37. Man Univ MusB58 CertEd59 DipEd59 LRAM ARCM LTCL. Glouc Sch of Min 85. **d** 88 **p** 89. NSM Northleach w Hampnett and Farmington *Glouc* 88-94; NSM Cold Aston w Notgrove and Turkdean 88-94; NSM Chedworth, Yanworth and Stowell, Coln Rogers etc 94-01; RD Northleach 96-99. *44 Spinney Hill, Melbourne DE73 1LX* Tel (01332) 865134

HUTCHINGS, Colin Michael. b 36. Clifton Th Coll 66. **d** 68 **p** 69. C Worksop St Anne *S'well* 68-71; C Hampreston *Sarum* 71-76; TV Tisbury 76-82; R Waddesdon w Over Winchendon and Fleet Marston *Ox* 82-00; rtd 00; Perm to Offic *Pet* from 01. *Nimrod, 4 The Beeches, Pattishall, Towcester NN12 8LT* Tel (01327) 830563

HUTCHINGS, Ian James. b 49. Lon Univ DipTh72 Chester Coll of HE MA03. Clifton Th Coll 69 Trin Coll Bris 72. **d** 73 **p** 74. C Parr *Liv* 73-77; C Timperley *Ches* 77-81; V Partington and Carrington 81-96; V Huntington from 96; Chapl Bp's Blue Coat C of E High Sch from 96. *St Luke's Vicarage, 14 Celandine Close, Huntington, Chester CH3 6DT* Tel (01244) 347345 Fax as telephone E-mail ihutchings@aol.com

HUTCHINGS, John Denis Arthur. b 29. Keble Coll Ox BA53 MA59 MSc59. Chich Th Coll 58. **d** 60 **p** 61. C St Pancras w St Jas and Ch Ch *Lon* 60-63; Asst Chapl Denstone Coll Uttoxeter

63-67 and 79-83; C Stepney St Dunstan and All SS *Lon* 67-78; V Devonport St Boniface *Ex* 83-86; TR Devonport St Boniface and St Phil 86-93; P-in-c Lydford and Brent Tor 93-95; rtd 96; Perm to Offic *Ex* from 96. *Maisonette, 40 Brook Street, Tavistock PL19 0HE* Tel (01822) 616946

HUTCHINSON, Alison Joyce. b 62. Leeds Univ BA84 RMN90. Aston Tr Scheme 92 Ripon Coll Cuddesdon 94. **d** 97 **p** 98. C Benfieldside *Dur* 97-00; C Bishopwearmouth St Nic 00-02; Perm to Offic *Carl* from 02. *7 Park Close, Penrith CA11 8ND* Tel (01768) 867053 E-mail alison.hutchinson@btopenworld.com

HUTCHINSON, Canon Andrew Charles. b 63. Univ of Wales (Ban) BA84 MEd96. Aston Tr Scheme 85 Chich Th Coll 87. **d** 89 **p** 90. C Burnley St Cath w St Alb and St Paul *Blackb* 89-92; C Shrewsbury St Chad w St Mary *Lich* 92-94; Chapl Heref Cathl Sch 94-97; Succ Heref Cathl *Heref* 94-97; Chapl Solihull Sch from 97; Can St Jo Pro-Cathl Katakwa from 00. *2 St Alphege Close, Church Hill Road, Solihull B91 3RQ* Tel 0121-704 3708

HUTCHINSON, Andrew Paul. b 65. Trin Hall Cam BA87 MA91 Solicitor 90. Aston Tr Scheme 92 Ripon Coll Cuddesdon BTh97. **d** 97 **p** 98. C Stanley *Dur* 97-99; C Sunderland 99-01; TV 01-02; Chapl Sunderland Univ 99-02; TV Penrith w Newton Reigny and Plumpton Wall *Carl* from 02; Chapl Cumbria Campus Cen Lancs Univ from 02. *7 Park Close, Penrith CA11 8ND* Tel (01768) 867053 E-mail paul.hutchinson5@btopenworld.com

HUTCHINSON, Canon Cyril Peter. b 37. Dur Univ BA61. Wm Temple Coll Rugby 61. **d** 63 **p** 64. C Birm St Paul *Birm* 63-67; Prin Community Relns Officer 66-69; Perm to Offic 67-69; Dir Bradf SHARE 69-76; Perm to Offic *Bradf* 69-75; Hon C Manningham 75-76; V Clayton 76-83; RD Bowling and Horton 80-83; TR Keighley St Andr 83-94; Hon Can Bradf Cathl from 84; rtd 94; Hon C Keighley All SS *Bradf* from 94. *Wellcroft, Laycock Lane, Laycock, Keighley BD22 0PN* Tel (01535) 606145

HUTCHINSON, David. *See* HUTCHINSON, Canon William David

HUTCHINSON, David Bamford. b 29. QUB BSc53 TCD Div Test55 QUB DipEd57. **d** 55 **p** 56. C Lisburn Ch Ch *Conn* 55-57; Uganda 57-65; I Kilkeel *D & D* 66-75; I Willowfield 75-82; V Longfleet *Sarum* 82-94; rtd 94; Perm to Offic *Sarum* 94-99. *Bethany, 3 Panorama Road, Poole BH13 7RA* Tel (01202) 664964

HUTCHINSON, Harold. b 36. NEOC. **d** 84 **p** 85. C Auckland St Andr and St Anne *Dur* 84-87; V Coundon 87-99; rtd 99. *clo S Hutchinson Esq, 6 West Park, Condon, Bishop Auckland DL14 8QR*

HUTCHINSON, Hugh Edward. b 27. FICE CEng. Bps' Coll Cheshunt. **d** 61 **p** 62. C Limehouse St Anne *Lon* 61-64; C Townstall w Dartmouth *Ex* 64-67; V Ex St Mark 67-75; P-in-c Foston on the Wolds *York* 75-77; P-in-c N Frodingham 75-77; R Beeford w Lissett 75-77; R Beeford w Frodingham and Foston 77-80; RD N Holderness 79-80; P-in-c Appleton Roebuck w Acaster Selby 80-84; P-in-c Etton w Dalton Holme 84-91; rtd 91; Perm to Offic *York* from 91. *33 Limestone Grove, Burniston, Scarborough YO13 0DH* Tel (01723) 871116

HUTCHINSON, Jeremy Olpherts. b 32. Oriel Coll Ox BA55 MA60 St Jo Coll Dur DipTh57. **d** 57 **p** 58. C Shoreditch St Leon *Lon* 57-60; V Hoxton St Jo w Ch 60-78; Hon C Hackney 78-85; C Highbury Ch Ch w St Jo and St Sav Lon 85-91; P-in-c Hanley Road St Sav w St Paul 91-92; TV Tollington 92-96; rtd 96; Perm to Offic *Lon* from 96. *8 Casimir Road, London E5 9NU* Tel (020) 8806 6492

HUTCHINSON, John Charles. b 44. K Coll Lon 64. **d** 69 **p** 70. C Portsea All SS *Portsm* 69-73; TV Fareham H Trin 73-78; P-in-c Pangbourne *Ox* 78-86; P-in-c Tidmarsh w Sulham 84-86; R Pangbourne w Tidmarsh and Sulham 86-96. *The Coombe House, Streatley, Reading RG8 9QL* Tel (01491) 875258

HUTCHINSON, Jonathan Graham. b 62. Bris Univ BA01. Trin Coll Bris 98. **d** 01 **p** 02. C Church Stretton *Heref* from 01. *The School House, 23 Church Street, Church Stretton SY6 6DQ* Tel (01694) 723215 E-mail jghutchinson@onetel.net.uk

HUTCHINSON, Jonathan Mark. b 45. Univ of Sth C of Min 85. **d** 89 **p** 90. NSM Wickham Market w Pettistree and Easton *St E* 89-93; V Thorington w Wenhaston, Bramfield etc 94-97; TV Ipswich St Mary at Stoke w St Pet and St Fran 97-02. *27 Milton Lane, Wells BA5 2QS* Tel (01749) 676096

HUTCHINSON, Julie Lorraine. b 55. WMMTC 90. **d** 93 **p** 94. C Northampton St Mary *Pet* 93-95; P-in-c Morcott w Glaston and Bisbrooke 95-97; P-in-c Lyddington w Stoke Dry and Seaton w Caldecott 97-02; V 03; Dir of Ords from 03. *The Rectory, Stanwick, Wellingborough NN9 6PP* Tel (01933) 622318 E-mail lydding@fish.co.uk

HUTCHINSON, Mrs Karen Elizabeth. b 64. LMH Ox BA85 MA89 Solicitor 89. Wycliffe Hall Ox. **d** 01 **p** 02. C Alton St Lawr *Win* from 01. *13 Walnut Close, Alton GU34 2BA* Tel (01420) 542288 E-mail karen@hutches.freewire.co.uk

HUTCHINSON, Moreen Anne. b 46. Ulster Univ BA84. CITC 98. **d** 01 **p** 02. NSM Larne and Inver *Conn* from 01. *Robmorden, 4 Duneira Park, Larne BT40 1PF* Tel (028) 2827 5577 E-mail moreenhutchinson@talk21.com

HUTCHINSON, Paul. *See* HUTCHINSON, Andrew Paul

HUTCHINSON, Paul Edward. b 33. K Coll Lon. **d** 59 **p** 60. C Bromley St Mich *Lon* 59-63; C Mill Hill St Mich 63-66; C Sandridge *St Alb* 66-73; V St Alb St Mary Marshalswick 73-80; V Tunstall *Lich* 80-91; RD Stoke N 82-91; V Lower Gornal 91-93; V Lower Gornal *Worc* 93-98; rtd 98; Perm to Offic *Lich* from 98. *55 Mill Hayes Road, Burslem, Stoke-on-Trent ST6 4JB* Tel (01782) 813361

HUTCHINSON, Miss Pauline. b 49. St Jo Coll Nottm 88. **d** 90 **p** 94. Par Dn Sherwood *S'well* 90-94; C 94-95; TV Newark from 95; Chapl Newark Hosp NHS Trust from 95. *St Leonard's Vicarage, Lincoln Road, Newark NG24 2DQ* Tel (01636) 703691

HUTCHINSON, Peter. *See* HUTCHINSON, Canon Cyril Peter

HUTCHINSON, Peter Francis. b 52. Portsm Poly HND74. Sarum & Wells Th Coll 87. **d** 89 **p** 90. C Honiton, Gittisham, Combe Raleigh, Monkton etc *Ex* 89-93; V Valley Park *Win* from 93. *35 Raglan Close, Eastleigh SO53 4NH* Tel (023) 8025 5749

HUTCHINSON, Philip Sheldon. b 32. Pemb Coll Cam BA56 MA59. Chich Th Coll 56. **d** 58 **p** 59. C Plumstead St Nic *S'wark* 58-60; C Roehampton H Trin 60-64; R Washington DC St Tim USA 64-65; R Charlton St Luke w St Paul *S'wark* 65-69; Australia from 69; P-in-c Marysville 69-70; R Alexandra 70-73; I Leopold 73-77; I St Kilda Ch Ch 77-97; rtd 97. *clo Mrs S D Cohen, 64 Gordon Street, Naracoorte, S Australia 5271* Tel (0061) (8) 8762 0029

HUTCHINSON, Raymond John. b 51. Liv Univ BSc73. Westcott Ho Cam 73. **d** 76 **p** 77. C Peckham St Jo *S'wark* 76-78; C Peckham St Jo w St Andr 78-79; C Prescot *Liv* 79-81; V Edgehill St Dunstan 81-87; P-in-c Waterloo Park 87-89; P-in-c Litherland Ch Ch 87-89; V Waterloo Ch Ch and St Mary 90-97; Chapl Wigan and Leigh Health Services NHS Trust 97-01; Chapl Wrightington Wigan and Leigh NHS Trust from 01. *St Elizabeth's Vicarage, Bolton Road, Aspull, Wigan WN2 1PR* Tel (01942) 244000 E-mail hutchinsons@glebehouse.fslife.co.uk

HUTCHINSON, The Very Revd Roland Louis. b 29. TCD BA51 MA61. **d** 52 **p** 53. C Mullabrack w Kilcluney *Arm* 52-54; C Dromore Cathl *D & D* 54-62; C-in-c Rathmullan w Tyrella 62-65; I 65-74; I Magheralin w Dollingstown 74-95; Treas Dromore Cathl 86-90; Prec 90-93; Dean Dromore 93-95; rtd 95. *Summerhill Lodge, 22 Summerhill, Lurgan, Craigavon BT66 7AW* Tel (028) 3888 1789

HUTCHINSON, Canon Stephen. b 38. St Chad's Coll Dur BA60 DipTh62. **d** 62 **p** 63. C Tividale *Lich* 62-68; V Walsall St Andr 68-73; R Headless Cross *Worc* 73-81; TR Redditch, The Ridge 81-91; RD Bromsgrove 85-91; V Stourbridge St Thos 91-03; Hon Can Worc Cathl 88-03; rtd 03. *251 Stourbridge Road, Kidderminster DY10 2XJ* Tel (01562) 631658

HUTCHINSON, Canon William David. b 27. Wycliffe Hall Ox 55. **d** 57 **p** 58. C Ipswich St Jo *St E* 57-60; R Combs 60-65; V Ipswich St Aug 65-76; R Ewhurst *Guildf* 76-81; V Aldeburgh w Hazlewood *St E* 81-92; RD Saxmundham 83-88; Hon Can St E Cathl 87-92; rtd 92. *Hazlewood, 3 Birch Close, Woodbridge IP12 4UA* Tel (01394) 383760

HUTCHINSON-CERVANTES, Ian Charles. b 62. Cant Univ (NZ) BSc84 Reading Univ MSc86 Jes Coll Cam BA88. Westcott Ho Cam 86. **d** 89 **p** 90. C Iffley *Ox* 89-92; USPG from 92; Venezuela 93; P-in-c El Cayo St Andr Belize 94-97; Perm to Offic *S'wark* from 97 and *Chelmsf* 98-01. *clo USPG, Partnership House, 157 Waterloo Road, London SE1 8XA* Tel (020) 7928 8681 Fax 7928 2371 E-mail ianhc@uspg.org.uk

HUTCHINSON, Geoffrey John. b 44. Trin Hall Cam MA76 Lon Univ CertEd76. Ridley Hall Cam 77. **d** 79 **p** 80. C Harold Wood *Chelmsf* 79-83; CF 83-89; Warden Viney Hill Chr Adventure Cen 89-96; P-in-c Viney Hill *Glouc* 89-96; V Wadsley *Sheff* from 96. *The Vicarage, 91 Airedale Road, Sheffield S6 4AW* Tel 0114-234 8481 E-mail johnhutch@classicfm.net

HUTT, Colin Villette. b 32. FCA. Glouc Sch of Min 87. **d** 89 **p** 90. NSM Ludlow *Heref* 89-93; C Ludlow, Ludford, Ashford Carbonell etc 93-94; TV Tenbury 94-01; rtd 01. *Broxwell, Livesey Road, Ludlow SY8 1EX* Tel (01584) 877959 Fax 831659 E-mail broxwell@hotmail.com

HUTT, The Ven David Handley. b 38. AKC68. **d** 69 **p** 70. C Bedford Park *Lon* 69-70; C Westmr St Matt 70-73; PV and Succ S'wark Cathl *S'wark* 73-78; Chapl K Coll Taunton 78-82; V Bordesley St Alb and Patr *Birm* 82-86; V St Marylebone All SS *Lon* 86-95; Can Steward Westmr Abbey from 95; Sub-Dean and Adn Westmr from 99. *5 Little Cloister, London SW1P 3PL* Tel (020) 7654 4815 Fax 7654 4825 E-mail david.hutt@westminster-abbey.org

HUTTON, Brian Allan. b 40. Bps' Coll Cheshunt. **d** 69 **p** 70. C Newc St Matt w St Mary *Newc* 69-72; C Blyth St Mary 72-75; V Sheff St Cath Richmond Road *Sheff* 75-85; R Paisley St Barn *Glas* 85-00; R Paisley H Trin 87-00; rtd 01. *9B Heriot Avenue, Paisley PA2 0DN* Tel (01505) 810362

HUTTON, Griffith Arthur Jeremy. b 31. Trin Hall Cam BA56 MA59. Linc Th Coll 56. **d** 58 **p** 59. C Hexham *Newc* 58-60; C Gosforth All SS 60-65; V Whitegate *Ches* 65-71; V Whitegate w Lt Budworth 71-78; R Dowdeswell and Andoversford w the Shiptons etc *Glouc* 78-91; V Newnham w Awre and Blakeney

91-96; rtd 96; Perm to Offic *Heref* from 99. *Hill House, Stoke Lacy, Bromyard HR7 4RE* Tel (01432) 820423

HUTTON, Joseph Charles. b 21. DFC41. Westcott Ho Cam 63. **d** 65 **p** 66. C St Marychurch *Ex* 65-67; V Warborough *Ox* 67-70; V Earley St Pet 70-75; R Ludgvan *Truro* 75-79; rtd 79. *2 Baines Close, Bourton-on-the-Water, Cheltenham GL54 2PU*

HUTTON, Patrick George. b 41. Open Univ BA87. Chich Th Coll 65. **d** 68 **p** 69. C Palmers Green St Jo *Lon* 68-71; Guyana 71-80; P-in-c Stow Bardolph w Wimbotsham and Stow Bridge *Ely* 80-88; P-in-c Nordelph 80-88; V E Bedfont *Lon* from 88; AD Hounslow 93-97. *St Mary's Vicarage, 9 Hatton Road, Feltham TW14 8JR* Tel (020) 8751 0088

HUTTON, Mrs Serena Quartermaine. b 35. Nottm Univ BA57 Lon Univ BA73 Stranmillis Coll PGCE68 FRSA87. St Alb and Ox Min Course 95. **d** 98 **p** 99. OLM Chinnor w Emmington and Sydenham etc *Ox* from 98. *Elma Cottage, The Green, Kingston Blount, Chinnor OX9 4SE* Tel (01844) 354173

HUTTON, Susan Elizabeth. b 70. Univ of Wales (Cardiff) BD91. Ripon Coll Cuddesdon 93. **d** 95 **p** 96. C W Parley *Sarum* 95-99; C Trowbridge H Trin from 99. *The Vicarage, 67A Drynham Road, Trowbridge BA14 0PF* Tel (01225) 751275 E-mail rev.beth@virgin.net

HUTTON-BURY, David. b 44. BA. **d** 94 **p** 95. NSM Geashill w Killeigh and Ballycommon *M & K* 94-97; NSM Clane w Donadea and Coolcarrigan 97-00; NSM Mullingar, Portnashangan, Moyliscar, Kilbixy etc from 00. *Chorleyville Farm, Tullamore, Co Offaly, Irish Republic* Tel (00353) (506) 21813

HUXHAM, Hector Hubert. b 29. Bris Univ BA55. Tyndale Hall Bris 52. **d** 56 **p** 57. C Eccleston St Luke *Liv* 56-58; C Heworth H Trin *York* 59-60; V Burley *Ripon* 61-66; Chapl St Jas Univ Hosp Leeds 67-94; rtd 94; Perm to Offic *Bradf* 94-98 and *Ripon* from 94. *3 Oakwell Oval, Leeds LS8 4AL* Tel 0113-266 8851

HUXHAM, Canon Peter Richard. b 38. Worc Coll Ox BA61 MA74. St Steph Ho Ox 61. **d** 63 **p** 64. C Gillingham *Sarum* 63-67; C Osmondthorpe St Phil *Ripon* 67-70; V Parkstone St Osmund *Sarum* 70-75; TR Parkstone St Pet w Branksea and St Osmund 75-92; RD Poole 85-92; Can and Preb Sarum Cathl 85-92; Chapl Taunton and Somerset NHS Trust 92-93; rtd 03. *Salterns House, 34 Brownsea View Avenue, Poole BH14 8LQ* Tel (01202) 707431

HUXLEY, Canon Stephen Scott. b 30. Linc Th Coll 53. **d** 56 **p** 57. C Cullercoats St Geo *Newc* 56-59; C Eglingham 59-60; C N Gosforth 60-63; V Hartburn and Meldon 63-65; V Nether Witton 63-65; V Tynemouth Priory 65-74; V Warkworth and Acklington 74-78; P-in-c Tynemouth St Jo 78-81; V 81-87; Hon Can Newc Cathl 82-92; V Wylam 87-92; rtd 92; Perm to Offic *Newc* from 92. *35 Castle Street, Norham, Berwick-upon-Tweed TD15 2LQ* Tel (01289) 382356

HUXTABLE, Christopher Michael Barclay. b 61. Ex Univ BA83 Qu Coll Cam PGCE84. St Steph Ho Ox DipMin95. **d** 95 **p** 96. C Chich 95-98; C Haywards Heath St Wilfrid 98-99; TV 99-01; Chapl Geelong Gr Sch Australia from 01. *Geelong Grammar School, Timbertop, Private Mail Bag, Mansfield, Vic, Australia 3722* Tel (0061) (3) 5777 5503 Fax 5777 5772 E-mail chrishux@bigpond.com

HUXTABLE, Michael George. b 29. St Jo Coll Cam BA50 MA54. S Dios Minl Tr Scheme 87. **d** 90 **p** 91. NSM Fisherton Anger *Sarum* 90-01; Perm to Offic from 01. *10 Trews Weir Reach, Exeter EX2 4EG* Tel (01392) 277332

HUXTABLE, Peter Alexander. b 68. Southn Univ BEng90 Nottm Univ MTh01. St Jo Coll Nottm 99. **d** 01 **p** 02. C Kidderminster St Geo *Worc* from 01. *4 Little Grebe Road, Kidderminster DY10 4AF* Tel (01562) 60182 E-mail huxbox@freeuk.com

HUYTON, Stuart. b 37. St D Coll Lamp BA62 DipTh63. **d** 63 **p** 64. C Kingswinford H Trin *Lich* 63-66; C Leek St Edw 66-69; V Wigginton 69-76; V Wombourne 76-89; RD Trysull 79-84; P-in-c Bobbington 85-89; TR Wombourne w Trysull and Bobbington 89-95; V Lt Aston from 95. *The Vicarage, 3 Walsall Road, Sutton Coldfield B74 3BD* Tel 0121-353 0798

HUYTON, Susan Mary. b 57. Birm Univ BA79 DipTh86. Qu Coll Birm 83. **d** 86 **p** 97. C Connah's Quay *St As* 86-89; C Wrexham 89-90; Dn-in-c 90-91; TV 91-99; V Gwersyllt from 99. *The Vicarage, Old Mold Road, Gwersyllt, Wrexham LL11 4SB* Tel (01978) 756391 E-mail suehyton@aol.com

HUZZEY, Peter George. b 48. Trin Coll Bris 74. **d** 76 **p** 77. C Bishopsworth *Bris* 76-79; V 86-96; C Downend 79-80; TV Kings Norton *Birm* 80-86; TR Bishopsworth and Bedminster Down *Bris* 97-00; RD Bedminster 98-99; TR Kingswood from 00. *Holy Trinity Vicarage, High Street, Kingswood, Bristol BS15 4AD* Tel 0117-967 3627 Fax as telephone

HYATT, Robert Keith. b 34. Em Coll Cam BA59 MA63. Ridley Hall Cam 58. **d** 60 **p** 61. C Cheltenham St Mary *Glouc* 60-63; Asst Chapl K Edw Sch Witley 63-65; C Godalming *Guildf* 65-69; Hong Kong 69-78; V Claygate *Guildf* 78-91; TV Whitton *Sarum* 91-96 and 99-00; TR 96-99; rtd 00; Perm to Offic *B & W* from 00. *22 Pooles Close, Nether Stowey, Bridgwater TA5 1LZ* Tel (01278) 733411

HYDE, Dennis Hugh. b 23. Leeds Univ BA56. Sarum Th Coll 60. **d** 60 **p** 61. C Farncombe *Guildf* 60-62; C Burgh Heath 62-65; V Shottermill 65-74; Past Consultant Clinical Th Assn 74-80; rtd

88. *32 Amis Avenue, New Haw, Addlestone KT15 3ET* Tel (01932) 345526

HYDE, Edgar Bonsor. b 29. Clifton Th Coll 59. **d** 61 **p** 62. C Weston-super-Mare Ch Ch *B & W* 61-66; C Chipping Campden *Glouc* 66-70; R Longborough w Condicote and Sezincote 70-78; R Longborough, Sezincote, Condicote and the Swells 78-99; rtd 99; Perm to Offic *Glouc* from 99. *1 Turnpike Close, Primrose Court, Moreton-in-Marsh GL56 0JJ* Tel (01608) 652456

HYDE-DUNN, Keith Frederick. b 43. Sarum Th Coll. **d** 69 **p** 70. Rhodesia 69-72; C Horsham *Chich* 73-77; P-in-c Fittleworth 77-86; P-in-c Graffham w Woolavington 86-00; Perm to Offic from 01. *The Hermitage, Church Place, Pulborough RH20 1AF* Tel (01798) 873892

HYDER, Geoffrey Frank. b 28. St Jo Coll Dur 49. **d** 53 **p** 54. C Kingston upon Hull H Trin *York* 53-56; C Southend St Sav Westcliff *Chelmsf* 56-59; V Haggerston All SS *Lon* 59-65; V Southwick St Pet *Chich* 65-68; Regional Org (Gtr Lon) Chr Aid 68-74; R Keston *Roch* 74-83; R Speldhurst w Groombridge and Ashurst 83-93; RD Tunbridge Wells 86-91; rtd 93; Perm to Offic *Chich* from 93; Perm to Offic *Roch* from 93. *2 Holland House, 16 Pevensey Road, St Leonards-on-Sea TN38 0LF* Tel (01424) 715350

HYDER-SMITH, Brian John. b 45. FInstAM MCMI MBIM. EAMTC 84. **d** 87 **p** 88. NSM Huntingdon *Ely* 87-90; P-in-c Abbots Ripton w Wood Walton 90-98; P-in-c Kings Ripton 90-98; C Whittlesey, Pondersbridge and Coates 98-99; TV from 99. *The Rectory, 17 North Green, Whittlesey, Peterborough PE7 2BQ* Tel (01733) 840932 E-mail brian.hyder-smith@ely.anglican.org

HYDON, Ms Veronica Weldon. b 52. N Lon Poly BA73 Maria Grey Coll Lon CertEd74. Aston Tr Scheme 87 Westcott Ho Cam 89. **d** 91 **p** 94. Par Dn Poplar *Lon* 91-94; C 94-95; P-in-c Roxwell *Chelmsf* 95-00; Lay Development Officer 95-00; V Forest Gate Em w Upton Cross from 00; Hon C Timperley *Ches* from 03. *97 Park Road, Timperley, Altrincham WA15 6QG* E-mail vhydon@hotmail.com

HYETT, Dawn Barbara. b 53. Cyncoed Coll CertEd74 Open Univ BA79. WEMTC 99. **d** 02. NSM Bromyard *Heref* from 02. *Roberts Hill, Norton, Bromyard HR7 4PB* Tel (01885) 483747

HYLAND, Canon Cecil George. b 38. TCD BA62 MA78. CITC Div Test. **d** 63 **p** 64. C Belfast St Nic *Conn* 63-66; C Monkstown *D & G* 66-68; Ch of Ireland Youth Officer 68-73; Chapl TCD 73-79; I Tullow *D & G* 79-90; I Howth from 90; Dir of Ords (Dub) 91-98; Can Ch Ch Cathl Dublin from 91; Cen Dir of Ords from 98. *The Rectory, Howth Road, Dublin 13, Irish Republic* Tel (00353) (1) 832 3019 Fax as telephone E-mail cecilhyland@hotmail.com

HYNDMAN, David Jonathan. b 65. Man Univ BA95. Wycliffe Hall Ox MTh95. **d** 97 **p** 98. C Cockermouth w Embleton and Wythop *Carl* 97-00; TV Congleton *Ches* from 00. *The Vicarage, 79 Leek Road, Congleton CW12 3HX* Tel (01260) 273182 E-mail dhyndman@bun.com

HYSLOP, Mrs Catherine Graham Young. b 53. St Andr Univ CPSS75. Carl Dioc Tr Inst 90. **d** 92 **p** 94. NSM St Bees *Carl* 92-95; NSM Upperby St Jo 95-98; C 98-03; C S Carl TM from 03. *St John's Vicarage, Manor Road, Upperby, Carlisle CA2 4LH* Tel (01228) 523380 E-mail jim.hyslop@talk21.com

HYSLOP, Thomas James (Jim). b 54. St Andr Univ BD76. Edin Th Coll 76. **d** 78 **p** 79. C Whitehaven *Carl* 78-81; C Walney Is 81-83; P-in-c Gt Broughton and Broughton Moor 83-85; V 85-88; V Kells 88-95; P-in-c Upperby St Jo 95-97; V 97-03; TR S Carl TM from 03. *St John's Vicarage, Manor Road, Upperby, Carlisle CA2 4LH* Tel (01228) 523380 E-mail jim.hyslop@talk21.com

HYSON, Peter Raymond. b 51. Open Univ BA80 BA87. Oak Hill Th Coll 85. **d** 87 **p** 88. C Billericay and Lt Burstead *Chelmsf* 87-92; TV Whitton *Sarum* 92-99. *Address temp unknown*

I

I'ANSON, Frederic Mark. b 43. R Agric Coll Cirencester MRAC68. Carl Dioc Tr Inst 89. **d** 92 **p** 93. NSM Sedbergh, Cautley and Garsdale *Bradf* 92-98; P-in-c Kirkby-in-Malhamdale w Coniston Cold from 98. *The Vicarage, Kirkby Malham, Skipton BD23 4BS* Tel (01729) 830215 E-mail mark@mmia.demon.co.uk

IBADAN SOUTH, Bishop of. See AJETUNMOBI, The Rt Revd Jacob Ademola

IBALL, Charles Martin John. b 40. Lich Th Coll 67. **d** 69 **p** 70. C Dudley St Edm *Worc* 69-73; C W Bromwich St Jas *Lich* 73-76; V Oxley 76-80; Hon C Whittington w Weeford from 86; Hon C

Clifton Campville w Edingale and Harlaston from 96. *75 Carlcroft, Stoneydelph, Tamworth B77 4DW* Tel (01827) 896644

IBBOTSON, Miss Tracy Alexandra. b 63. Cranmer Hall Dur 01. **d** 03. C Todmorden *Wakef* from 03. *12 Phoenix Court, Todmorden OL14 5SJ* Tel (01706) 816716

IDDON, Roy Edward. b 40. TCert61 Lanc Univ MA88. N Ord Course 83. **d** 83 **p** 84. Hd Teacher St Andr Primary Sch Blackb from 83; NSM Bolton St Matt w St Barn *Man* 83-88; Lic to AD Walmsley 88-93; NSM Walmsley 93-01; NSM Turton Moorland Min from 01. *28 New Briggs Fold, Egerton, Bolton BL7 9UL* Tel (01204) 306589

IDLE, Christopher Martin. b 38. St Pet Coll Ox BA62. Clifton Th Coll 62. **d** 65 **p** 66. C Barrow St Mark *Carl* 65-68; C Camberwell Ch Ch *S'wark* 68-71; P-in-c Poplar St Matthias *Lon* 71-76; R Limehouse 76-89; P-in-c Palgrave w Wortham and Burgate *St E* 89; P-in-c Thrandeston, Stuston and Brome w Oakley 89; R N Hartismere 89-95; Perm to Offic *S'wark* from 95; *St E* from 01. *13 Unwin Close, Haymerle Road, London SE15 6SH* Tel (020) 7732 8584

IEVINS, Mrs Catherine Ruth. b 54. LMH Ox BA77 MA80 Solicitor 81. EAMTC 98. **d** 01 **p** 02. C Pet Ch Carpenter *Pet* from 01. *32 Ledbury Road, Peterborough PE3 9RH* Tel (01733) 269029

IEVINS, Peter Valdis. b 54. St Jo Coll Ox BA75 MA81 Solicitor 79. Westcott Ho Cam 86. **d** 88 **p** 89. C Sawston *Ely* 88-91; C Babraham 88-91; NSM Pet Ch Carpenter *Pet* from 01. *32 Ledbury Road, Peterborough PE3 9RH* Tel (01733) 269029

IGENOZA, Andrew Olu. b 50. Ife Univ Nigeria BA75 Man Univ PhD82. Immanuel Coll Ibadan 87. **d** 88 **p** 89. Nigeria 88-99; C Gorton St Phil *Man* 00-01. *17 Northmoor Road, Longsight, Manchester M12 4NF* Tel 0161-248 8758

IKIN, Gordon Mitchell. b 30. AKC57. **d** 58 **p** 59. C Leigh St Mary *Man* 58-61; V Westleigh St Paul 61-72; V Thornham St Jas 72-95; rtd 95; Perm to Offic *Man* from 95. *3 Thornham Old Road, Royton, Oldham OL2 5UN* Tel 0161-624 2428

ILES, Canon Paul Robert. b 37. FRCO65 Fitzw Coll Cam BA59 MA64 St Edm Hall Ox MA80. Sarum Th Coll 59. **d** 61 **p** 62. Chapl Bp Wordsworth Sch Salisbury 61-67; C Salisbury St Mich *Sarum* 61-64; Min Can Sarum Cathl 64-67; C Bournemouth St Pet *Win* 67-72; R Filton *Bris* 72-79; V Ox SS Phil and Jas w St Marg *Ox* 79-83; Can Res and Prec Heref Cathl *Heref* 83-03; rtd 03; Hon C Prestbury and All SS *Glouc* from 03. *24 Willowherb Close, Prestbury, Cheltenham GL52 5LP* Tel (01242) 579456

ILLING, Eric James. b 33. Kelham Th Coll 54 Chich Th Coll 55. **d** 57 **p** 58. C Leeds St Aid *Ripon* 57-60; C Leeds All SS 60-62; C E Grinstead St Swithun *Chich* 62-65; V Middleton St Mary *Ripon* 65-74; R Felpham w Middleton *Chich* 74-81; Chapl R Devon and Ex Hosp (Wonford) 81-91; TR Heavitree w Ex St Paul *Ex* 81-91; R Bradninch and Clyst Hydon 91-94; rtd 94; Perm to Offic *B & W* from 94 and *Eur* from 98. *25 Pikes Crescent, Taunton TA1 4HS* Tel (01823) 289203

ILLINGWORTH, John Patrick Paul. b 34. New Coll Ox BA59 DipTh61 MA63. Chich Th Coll 61. **d** 63 **p** 64. C Brighouse *Wakef* 63-66; C Willesden St Andr *Lon* 66-70; Chapl Gothenburg w Halmstad and Jönköping *Eur* 70-74; Perm to Offic *Chich* 74; V Ryhill *Wakef* 74-82; R Weston Longville w Morton and the Witchinghams *Nor* from 82; P-in-c Alderford w Attlebridge and Swannington from 94; RD Sparham 95-00. *The Rectory, Ringland Lane, Weston Longville, Norwich NR9 5JU* Tel (01603) 880163

ILOTT, Philip Edwin. b 36. Roch Th Coll 66. **d** 68 **p** 69. C Leavesden All SS *St Alb* 68-71; C-in-c Godshill CD *Portsm* 71-77; V Mayfield *Chich* 77-81; V Bexhill St Barn 81-84; rtd 84; Perm to Offic *Chich* 85-97. *Durlock, 15 Shining Cliff, Hastings TN34 2GT*

ILSLEY (née ROGERS), Mrs Anne Frances. b 50. Guy's Hosp Medical Sch RGN72 Poly Cen Lon HDipHV78 Heythrop Coll Lon BA00. Wycliffe Hall Ox 00. **d** 02 **p** 03. NSM Harefield *Lon* from 02. *36 Kewferry Road, Northwood HA6 2PB* Tel (01923) 840871 Fax 09356-374624 E-mail annefi36@aol.com

ILSON, John Robert. b 37. Leeds Univ BSc59 Lon Univ BD64 CertEd65. ALCD63. **d** 64 **p** 65. C Kennington St Mark *S'wark* 64-67; C Sydenham H Trin 67-70; Asst Dir RE *Sheff* 70-77; R Hooton Roberts 70-75; R Hooton Roberts w Ravenfield 75-77; P-in-c Kidderminster St Geo *Worc* 77-81; TR 81-85; P-in-c Powick 85-96; Chapl N Devon Healthcare NHS Trust from 97; Lic to Offic *Ex* from 97. *88 Chanters Hill, Barnstaple EX32 8DG* Tel (01271) 379163 or 322577

ILTON, Mrs Jennifer Jane. b 38. S Dios Minl Tr Scheme 92. **d** 95 **p** 96. NSM Jersey St Sav *Win* from 95. *38 Maison St Louis, St Saviour, Jersey JE2 7LX* Tel (01534) 22327

ILYAS, Marilyn. b 51. Oak Hill Th Coll 92. **d** 95 **p** 96. C Roch 95-98; TV S Chatham H Trin 98-01; TR from 01. *26 Mayford Road, Chatham ME5 8SZ* Tel (01634) 660922 E-mail milyas@btinternet.com

IMPEY, Miss Joan Mary. b 35. Lon Univ CertRK69. Dalton Ho Bris 65. dss 74 **d** 87 **p** 94. Kennington St Mark *S'wark* 67-75; Barking St Marg w St Patr *Chelmsf* 75-81; Harwell w Chilton *Ox* 81-87; Par Dn 87-92; Par Dn Didcot All SS 92-94; C 94-97; rtd 98; Perm to Offic *Ox* from 99. *15 Loder Road, Harwell, Didcot OX11 0HR* Tel (01235) 820346

IMPEY, Mrs Patricia Irene. b 45. Birm Univ BA67 Lanc Univ MPhil01. Carl Dioc Tr Course 88. **d** 90 **p** 94. Par Dn Blackpool St Paul *Blackb* 90-94; C 94-95; Chapl Asst Victoria Hosp Blackpool 94-95; Asst Chapl Norfolk and Nor Hosp 95-96; Hon C Sprowston w Beeston *Nor* 96; R King's Beck 96-02; V Ecclesfield *Sheff* from 02. *The Vicarage, 230 The Wheel, Ecclesfield, Sheffield S35 9ZB* Tel 0114-257 0002

IMPEY, Richard. b 41. Em Coll Cam BA63 MA67 Harvard Univ ThM67. Ridley Hall Cam 67. **d** 68 **p** 69. C Birm St Martin *Birm* 68-72; Dir of Tr *B & W* 72-79; Dir of Ords 76-79; V Blackpool St Jo *Blackb* 79-95; RD Blackpool 84-90; Hon Can Blackb Cathl 89-95; Dioc Dir of Tr *Nor* 95-00; P-in-c Heigham St Barn w St Bart 00-02; V Wentworth *Sheff* from 02. *The Vicarage, 230 The Wheel, Ecclesfield, Sheffield S35 9ZB* Tel 0114-257 0002

INALL, Mrs Elizabeth Freda. b 47. MCSP69. St Alb Minl Tr Scheme 88. **d** 92 **p** 94. NSM Tring *St Alb* 92-01; C Harpenden St Nic from 01. *10 Cross Way, Harpenden AL5 4RA* Tel (01582) 713007 E-mail elizabeth.inall@ukf.net

INCE, Peter Reginald. b 26. Bp's Coll Calcutta 48. **d** 51 **p** 52. India 51-55; C Leek St Luke *Lich* 55-57; C Milton 57-59; C Lewisham St Jo Southend *S'wark* 59-62; R Loddington w Cransley *Pet* 62-75; V Snibston *Leic* 75-79; R Mickleham *Guildf* 79-92; rtd 92; Perm to Offic *Guildf* from 92. *Bickerton, 8 Rockdale, Headley Road, Grayshott, Hindhead GU26 6TU* Tel (01428) 604694

IND, Dominic Mark. b 63. Lanc Univ BA87. Ridley Hall Cam 87. **d** 90 **p** 91. C Birch w Fallowfield *Man* 90-93; SSF 93-95; Perm to Offic *Glas* 95-96; C Byker St Martin *Newc* 96-98; C Walker 96-98; P-in-c Cambuslang *Glas* from 98; P-in-c Uddingston from 98. *The Rectory, 5 Brownside Road, Cambuslang, Glasgow G72 8NL* Tel 0141-641 1173 Fax as telephone E-mail dom@alba9.fsnet.co.uk

IND, Philip William David. b 35. K Coll Lon BD82. Wycliffe Hall Ox 74 Cranmer Hall Dur 59. **d** 65 **p** 66. C Ipswich St Jo *St E* 65-67; C Charlton Kings St Mary *Glouc* 67-71; R Woolstone w Gotherington and Oxenton 71-74; Chapl Alleyn's Sch Dulwich 76-81; C Beckenham St Geo *Roch* 83-85; V Bromley St Jo 85-87; Perm to Offic *Ox* 88-91; P-in-c Hurley 91-92; P-in-c Stubbings 91-92; rtd 92. *Stilegate, Tugwood Common, Cookham, Maidenhead SL6 9TT* Tel (01628) 477425 E-mail mtpipind@aol.com

✠**IND, The Rt Revd William.** b 42. Leeds Univ BA64. Coll of Resurr Mirfield 64. **d** 66 **p** 67 **c** 87. C Feltham *Lon* 66-71; C Northolt St Mary 71-73; TV Basingstoke *Win* 73-87; Vice-Prin Aston Tr Scheme 79-82; Dioc Dir of Ords *Win* 82-87; Hon Can Win Cathl 84-87; Suff Bp Grantham *Linc* 87-97; Dean Stamford 87-97; Can and Preb Linc Cathl 87-97; Bp Truro from 97. *Lis Escop, Feock, Truro TR3 6QQ* Tel (01872) 862657 Fax 862037 E-mail bishop@truro.anglican.org

INDER, Patrick John. b 30. K Coll Lon BD54 AKC54 Huddersfield Univ MA98. St Boniface Warminster. **d** 55 **p** 56. C St Margaret's-on-Thames *Lon* 55-57; C Golders Green 57-61; V Hanwell St Mellitus 61-77; R Rawmarsh w Parkgate *Sheff* 77-80; rtd 80; Hon C Sheff St Matt *Sheff* 82-88; Perm to Offic *Wakef* from 98 and *Win* from 02. *Roucoulement, rue de la Brigade, St Andrews, Guernsey GY6 8RQ* Tel (01481) 234343 E-mail roucoulement@cwgsy.net

INDIAN OCEAN, Archbishop of the Province of the. See RABENIRINA, The Most Revd Remi Joseph

INESON, David Antony. b 36. DPS. ALCD62. **d** 62 **p** 63. C Sandal St Helen *Wakef* 62-65; C Birm St Geo *Birm* 66-71; V Horton *Bradf* 71-80; RD Bowling and Horton 78-80; V Sedbergh, Cautley and Garsdale 80-86; C Firbank, Howgill and Killington 81-86; TV Langley and Parkfield *Man* 86-88; TR Banbury *Ox* 92-98; R 98-01; rtd 01. *11 Church Close, Redmire, Leyburn DL8 4HF* Tel (01969) 624631 E-mail hdi@redmire.fslife.co.uk

INESON, Emma Gwynneth. b 69. Birm Univ BA92 MPhil93 PhD98. Trin Coll Bris BA99. **d** 00 **p** 01. C Dore *Sheff* 00-03; Chapl Lee Abbey from 03. *Lee Abbey Fellowship, Lee Abbey, Lynton EX35 6JJ* Tel (01598) 752621 E-mail revsineson@aol.com

INESON, Mathew David. b 69. Birm Univ BEng91. Trin Coll Bris BA99 MA00. **d** 00 **p** 01. NSM Dore *Sheff* 00-03; Chapl Lee Abbey from 03. *Lee Abbey Fellowship, Lee Abbey, Lynton EX35 6JJ* Tel (01598) 752621 E-mail revsineson@aol.com

INESON, Matthew. b 69. Leeds Univ BA00. Coll of Resurr Mirfield 97. **d** 00. C Owton Manor *Dur* from 00. *40 Wisbech Close, Hartlepool TS25 2LW* Tel (01429) 871522 Mobile 07780-686310 or 07625-385261 (pager) E-mail frmatt@excite.com

INGAMELLS, Ronald Sidney. b 32. FCIPD92. AKC56. **d** 57 **p** 58. C Leeds Gipton Epiphany *Ripon* 57-59; C Gt Yarmouth

Nor 59-64; Dioc Youth Officer 64-79; Hon C Nor St Pet Mancroft 64-79; P-in-c Lemsford *St Alb* 79-02; Sec Tr Development and Chr Educn Nat Coun YMCAs 79-92; Consultant to Romania Euro Alliance YMCAs 93-97; rtd 02. *2 Aragon Close, Buckden, St Neots PE19 5TY* Tel (01480) 811608
E-mail ingamells@fish.co.uk

✠INGE, The Rt Revd John Geoffrey. b 55. St Chad's Coll Dur BSc77 MA94 PhD02 Keble Coll Ox PGCE79. Coll of Resurr Mirfield. d 84 p 85 c 03. Asst Chapl Lancing Coll 84-86; Jun Chapl Harrow Sch 86-89; Sen Chapl 89-90; V Wallsend St Luke *Newc* 90-96; Can Res Ely Cathl *Ely* from 96; Vice-Dean 99-03; Suff Bp Huntingdon from 03. *14 Lynn Road, Ely CB6 1DA* Tel (01353) 662137 Fax 669357
E-mail suffragan@ely.anglican.org

INGHAM, Anthony William. b 55. Ven English Coll Rome PhB75 STB78 N Ord Course 98. d 78 p 79. In RC Ch 78-98; NSM Tottington *Man* from 99. *8 Holcombe Road, Tottington, Bury BL8 4AR* Tel (01204) 887528

INGHAM, John Edmund. b 34. Reading Univ BA56. Clifton Th Coll 58. d 60 p 61. C Rodbourne Cheney *Bris* 60-63; C Tunbridge Wells St Jo *Roch* 63-67; V Sevenoaks Weald 67-82; V Farrington Gurney *B & W* 82-92; V Paulton 82-92; RD Midsomer Norton 88-91; R Aspley Guise w Husborne Crawley and Ridgmont *St Alb* 92-99; rtd 99; Perm to Offic *B & W* from 00. *10 Milton Lane, Wookey Hole, Wells BA5 1DG* Tel (01749) 677529

INGHAM, Malcolm John. b 68. Wigan Coll of Tech OND87 Somerset Coll of Arts & Tech HND89. Wycliffe Hall Ox BTh99. d 99 p 00. C Moreton-in-Marsh w Batsford, Todenham etc *Glouc* 99-03; C Leckhampton SS Phil and Jas w Cheltenham St Jas from 03. *72 Salisbury Avenue, Cheltenham GL51 3BU* Tel (01242) 517057
E-mail rev@malcolm-ingham.fsnet.co.uk

INGHAM, Mrs Carol Helen. *See* PHARAOH, Carol Helen

INGHAM, Mrs Pamela. b 47. MBE96. NEOC 93. d 96 p 97. C Newc Epiphany *Newc* 96-99; C Fawdon 99-00; P-in-c from 00. *St Mary's Vicarage, 7 Fawdon Lane, Newcastle upon Tyne NE3 2RR* Tel 0191-285 5403 E-mail pimbe@aol.com

INGHAM, Russell Edward. b 39. Glas Univ MA61 Keble Coll Ox BA63 MA67. Cuddesdon Coll 63. d 64 p 65. Chapl St Mary's Cathl *Glas* 64-69; Warden St John's Youth Cen Tuebrook Liv 69-71; R Port Glas 71-77; R St Andrews All SS *St And* 77-91; V Ruislip St Martin *Lon* 91-94; Chapl Ankara *Eur* 96-00. *Address temp unknown*

INGLEBY, Anthony Richard. b 48. Keele Univ BA72. Trin Coll Bris. d 83 p 84. C Plymouth St Jude *Ex* 83-88; R Lanreath *Truro* 88-97; V Pelynt 88-97; RD W Wivelshire 96-97; P-in-c Stoke Climsland from 97; P-in-c Linkinhorne from 03. *The Rectory, Stoke Climsland, Callington PL17 8NZ* Tel (01579) 370501
E-mail tony@ingleby100.freeserve.co.uk

INGLEDEW, Peter David Gordon. b 48. AKC77 Jo Dalton Coll Man CertEd73 Croydon Coll DASS92 CQSW92 Univ Coll Chich BA03. St Steph Ho Ox 77. d 78 p 79. C Whorlton *Newc* 78-81; C Poplar *Lon* 81-83; TV 83-85; V Tottenham H Trin 85-90; Perm to Offic *Chich* from 90. *11 St Luke's Terrace, Brighton BN2 2ZE* Tel (01273) 689765 Fax 389115

INGLESBY, Eric Vredenburg (Paul). b 15. Qu Coll Ox BA46 MA63. Wycliffe Hall Ox 63. d 64 p 66. C Plymouth Crownhill Ascension *Ex* 64-66; R Caythorpe *Linc* 66-70; C Scilly Is *Truro* 70-73; C Plymouth St Andr w St Paul and St Geo *Ex* 73-76; rtd 76. *43 Palmers Road, Glastonbury BA6 9PB* Tel (01458) 833591

INGLESBY, Richard John. b 47. Birm Univ BSc69 Bris Univ CertEd74. Wycliffe Hall Ox 85. d 87 p 88. C Cheltenham Ch Ch *Glouc* 87-92; P-in-c Paulton *B & W* 92-94; V 94-01; P-in-c Farrington Gurney 92-94; V 94-01; P-in-c Moxley *Lich* from 01; C Darlaston All SS from 01; C Darlaston St Lawr from 01. *The Vicarage, 5 Sutton Road, Moxley, Wednesbury WS10 8SG* Tel (01902) 653084

INGLIS, Kelvin John. b 62. Coll of Ripon & York St Jo DipTh98 Ripon Coll Cuddesdon MTh00. d 00 p 01. C Southampton Maybush St Pet *Win* from 00. *All Saints' House, 60 Brookwood Road, Southampton SO16 9AJ* Tel (023) 8078 1228

INGRAM, Canon Bernard Richard. b 40. Lon Coll of Div 66. d 66 p 67. C Bromley Common St Aug *Roch* 66-70; C Gravesend St Geo 70-74; Chapl Joyce Green Hosp Dartford 75-83; V Dartford St Edm *Roch* 75-83; V Strood St Fran from 83; RD Strood 91-97; Hon Can Roch Cathl from 00. *St Francis's Vicarage, Galahad Avenue, Strood, Rochester ME2 2YS* Tel (01634) 717162 Fax as telephone
E-mail st.francisstrood@cableinet.co.uk

INGRAM, Miss Emmeline Jessica Anne. b 26. Gilmore Ho 53. dss 54 d 87. Ind Chapl Chelmsf 68-82; Leigh-on-Sea St Jas *Chelmsf* 86-87; Hon Par Dn from 87. *73 Bohemia Chase, Leigh-on-Sea SS9 4PW* Tel (01702) 520276

INGRAM, Gary Simon. b 58. K Coll Lon BD AKC. Ripon Coll Cuddesdon. d 83 p 84. Chapl Nelson and Colne Coll 92-98; C Spalding *Linc* 83-87; C Heaton Ch Ch *Man* 87-89; V Colne H Trin *Blackb* 89-98; RD Pendle 96-98; R Poulton-le-Sands w

Morecambe St Laur from 98; AD Lancaster from 98. *The Rectory, Church Walk, Morecambe LA4 5PR* Tel (01524) 410941 Fax as telephone E-mail garyingram@care4free.net

INGRAM, Michael. b 28. St Jo Coll Dur 49. d 53 p 54. C Southend St Sav Westcliff *Chelmsf* 53-56; C Stoke Damerel *Ex* 56-60; Chapl RAF 60-76; P-in-c St Enoder *Truro* 76-79; rtd 90. *2 Cedar Drive, Shanklin PO37 7ED* Tel (01983) 868925

INGRAM, Peter Anthony. b 53. N Ord Course 83. d 86 p 87. C Maltby *Sheff* 86-89; TV Gt Snaith 89-92; R Adwick-le-Street w Skelbrooke from 92; AD Adwick from 01. *The Rectory, Village Street, Adwick-le-Street, Doncaster DN6 7AD* Tel (01302) 723224 Fax as telephone E-mail revingram@lineone.net

INGRAMS, Peter Douglas. b 56. Wheaton Coll Illinois BA77 Ox Univ BA80. Wycliffe Hall Ox 78. d 83 p 84. C Rowner *Portsm* 83-86; C Petersfield w Sheet 86-90; V Sheet 90-96; V Locks Heath from 96. *The Vicarage, 125 Locks Heath Park Road, Locks Heath SO31 6LY* Tel (01489) 572497

INKPEN, Richard John. b 28. AKC56. d 58 p 59. C Willesden St Mary *Lon* 58-61; C Hendon St Mary 61-66; C-in-c S Kenton Annunciation CD 66-69; Chapl Montreux w Gstaad *Eur* 69-70; V Blackmoor *Portsm* 70-93; RD Petersfield 80-85; rtd 94; Perm to Offic *Ex* from 94. *63 St Luke's Road, Newton Abbot TQ12 4ND* Tel (01626) 204231

INKPIN, David Leonard. b 32. CChem MRSC55 Liv Univ BSc54. EMMTC 83. d 86 p 87. NSM Market Rasen *Linc* from 86; NSM Legsby from 86; NSM Linwood from 86. *Weelsby House, Legsby Road, Market Rasen LN8 3DY* Tel (01673) 843360 E-mail inkpens@yahoo.co.uk

INKPIN, Jonathan David Francis. b 60. Mert Coll Ox MA81 Dur Univ PhD96. Ripon Coll Cuddesdon BA85. d 86 p 87. C Hackney *Lon* 86-88; Tutor Ripon Coll Cuddesdon 88-90; C Cuddesdon *Ox* 88-90; TV Gateshead *Dur* 90-95; C Stanhope w Frosterley 95-01; C Eastgate w Rookhope 95-01; Dioc Rural Development Officer 95-01; Australia from 01. *78 Henry Parry Drive, PO Box 4255, Gosford East, NSW, Australia 2250* Tel (0061) (2) 4324 2630

INMAN, John Phillip. b 12. St Jo Coll Dur BA35 DipTh36 MA38. d 36 p 37. C Crook *Dur* 36-39; C Monkwearmouth St Andr 39-40; C Esh 40-43; V Cleadon 43-50; V St John in Weardale 50-56; P-in-c Westgate 50-56; V Grindon 56-60; Lect Charlotte Mason Coll Ambleside 60-73; rtd 77; Perm to Offic *Carl* 77-95. *c/o Mrs K Shepherd, Gill Croft, Haws Bank, Coniston LA21 8AP* Tel (01539) 441559

INMAN, Malcolm Gordon. b 33. Edin Th Coll 58. d 60 p 61. C Lundwood *Wakef* 60-63; C Heckmondwike 63-70; V Wrenthorpe 70-75; Chapl Cardigan Hosp 70-73; Asst Chapl Pinderfields Gen Hosp Wakef 72-73; V Cleckheaton St Jo *Wakef* 75-98; rtd 98; Perm to Offic *Wakef* from 98. *14 Briestfield Road, Thornhill Edge, Dewsbury WF12 0PW* Tel (01924) 437171

INMAN, Mark Henry. b 31. Lon Univ BSc53. EAMTC 80. d 83 p 84. Hon C Orford w Sudbourne, Chillesford, Butley and Iken *St E* 83-85; Chapl HM YOI Hollesley Bay Colony 85-91; Hon C Alderton w Ramsholt and Bawdsey *St E* 85-92; P-in-c 92-00; P-in-c Shottisham w Sutton 92-00; TV Wilford Peninsula 00-01; rtd 01; Perm to Offic *Nor* from 01. *Mill Farm House, Newton Road, Sporle, King's Lynn PE32 2DB* Tel (01760) 722544

INMAN, Martin. b 50. K Coll Lon BD72 AKC73. St Aug Coll Cant 72. d 73 p 74. C Bridgnorth St Mary *Heref* 73-77; C Parkstone St Pet w Branksea and St Osmund *Sarum* 77-79; V Willenhall St Anne *Lich* 79-85; Chapl Yeovil Distr Gen Hosp 85-91; TV Yeovil *B & W* 85-88; R Barwick 88-91; Chapl St Helier Gen Hosp 91-99; Chapl Whittington Hosp NHS Trust 99-03; TV Smestow Vale *Lich* from 03. *The Vicarage, School Road, Trysull, Wolverhampton WV5 7HR* Tel (01902) 324537

INMAN, Paul Stuart. b 60. R Agric Coll Cirencester HND82 DipAI83 Nottm Univ BTh90 Man Univ MA94. Linc Th Coll 87. d 90 p 91. C Hulme Ascension *Man* 90-94; CMS 94-98; Dioc Missr (Owerri) Nigeria 94-98; V in charge Cathl of Transfiguration 95-98; P-in-c Colkirk w Oxwick w Pattesley, Whissonsett etc *Nor* from 98. *The Rectory, Market Hill, Colkirk, Fakenham NR21 7NU* Tel (01328) 863890

INMAN, Canon Thomas Jeremy. b 45. Rhodes Univ BA67. St Steph Ho Ox 67. d 69 p 70. C Deptford St Paul *S'wark* 69-72; S Africa 72-76; P-in-c Donnington *Chich* 80-86; V Hangleton 80-86; V Bosham from 86; RD Westbourne 91-99; Can and Preb Chich Cathl from 00. *The Vicarage, Bosham, Chichester PO18 8HX* Tel (01243) 573228 E-mail tjinman@waitrose.com

INNES, Donald John. b 32. St Jo Coll Ox BA54 MA. Westcott Ho Cam 56. d 56 p 57. C St Marylebone St Mark Hamilton Terrace *Lon* 56-58; C Walton-on-Thames *Guildf* 58-67; Chapl Moor Park Coll Farnham 67-76; P-in-c Tilford *Guildf* 76-97; rtd 97; Perm to Offic *Guildf* from 97. *Watchetts, 67A Upper Hale Road, Farnham GU9 0PA* Tel (01252) 734597

INNES, Donald Keith. b 33. St Jo Coll Ox BA56 MA60 Lon Univ BD58 Bris Univ MPhil01. Clifton Th Coll 56. d 58 p 59. C Harold Hill St Paul *Chelmsf* 58-61; C Ealing Dean St Jo *Lon* 61-65; V Westacre *Nor* 65-70; R Gayton Thorpe w E Walton 65-70; V Woking St Paul *Guildf* 70-78; R Alfold and Loxwood

78-88; V Doddington w Wychling *Cant* 88-90; V Newnham 88-90; V Doddington, Newnham and Wychling 90-97; rtd 97; Perm to Offic *Chich* from 98. *High Elms, Lewes Road, Ringmer, Lewes BN8 5NE* Tel (01273) 814995

INNES, James Michael. b 32. Lon Univ BA56 BD59. Clifton Th Coll 59. **d** 59 **p** 60. C Blackpool St Thos *Blackb* 59-62; Tutor Clifton Th Coll 62-65; V Burton All SS *Lich* 65-73; V Ashton-upon-Mersey St Mary *Ches* 73-90; P-in-c Brereton w Swettenham 90-91; R 91-97; Dioc Clergy Widows and Retirement Officer 93-97; rtd 97; Perm to Offic *Derby* from 97. *22 Sandown Avenue, Mickleover, Derby DE3 0QQ* Tel (01332) 516691 E-mail jminnes@lineone.net

INNES, Robert Neil. b 59. K Coll Cam BA82 MA85 Dur Univ PhD95. Cranmer Hall Dur 89 St Jo Coll Dur BA91 Dip Minl Studies 92. **d** 95 **p** 96. C Dur St Cuth *Dur* 95-97; Lect St Jo Coll Dur 95-99; C Sherburn w Pittington *Dur* 97-99; C Shadforth 97-99; P-in-c Belmont 99-00; V from 00. *Belmont Vicarage, Broomside Lane, Durham DH1 2QW* Tel 0191-386 1545

INSLEY, Michael George Pitron. b 47. Trin Coll Ox BA69 MA70 Nottm Univ MPhil85. Wycliffe Hall Ox 69. **d** 72 **p** 73. C Beckenham Ch Ch *Roch* 72-76; P-in-c Cowden 76-79; Lect St Jo Coll Nottm 79-85; V Tidebrook and Wadhurst *Chich* 85-98; P-in-c Stonegate 95-98; Can and Preb Chich Cathl 94-98; P-in-c Horsmonden and Dioc Rural Officer *Roch* 98-03; V Bromley Common St Luke from 03. *St Luke's Vicarage, 20 Bromley Common, Bromley BR2 9PD* Tel (020) 8464 2076 E-mail michaelinsley@compuserve.com

INSTON, Brian John. b 47. St Alb and Ox Min Course 95. **d** 98 **p** 99. C Bentley *Sheff* 98-01; V Balby from 01. *St John's Vicarage, 6 Greenfield Lane, Doncaster DN4 0PT* Tel (01302) 853278 Mobile 07990-513120

INVERNESS, Provost of. See HICKFORD, The Very Revd Michael Francis

✠**INWOOD, The Rt Revd Richard Neil.** b 46. Univ Coll Ox BSc70 MA73 Nottm Univ BA73. St Jo Coll Nottm 71. **d** 74 **p** 75 **c** 03. C Fulwood *Sheff* 74-78; C St Marylebone All So w SS Pet and Jo *Lon* 78-81; V Bath St Luke *B & W* 81-89; R Yeovil w Kingston Pitney 89-95; Preb Wells Cathl 90-95; Adn Halifax *Wakef* 95-03; Suff Bp Bedford *St Alb* from 03. *168 Kimbolton Road, Bedford MK41 8DN* Tel (01234) 357551 Fax 218134 E-mail bishopbedford@stalbans.anglican.org

IORNS, Derrick John. b 11. AKC33. **d** 34 **p** 35. C Rainham *Roch* 34-38; C-in-c Bentley Common CD *Chelmsf* 38-51; V Bentley Common 51-53; V Maldon All SS w St Pet 53-71; RD Maldon 56-70; R Gt Warley St Mary 71-72; P-in-c Childerditch w Lt Warley 71-72; R Gt Warley w Childerditch 72-81; P-in-c Ingrave 79-81; rtd 81; Perm to Offic *Chelmsf* from 91. *45 South Drive, Brentwood CM1 4DL* Tel (01277) 220777

IPGRAVE, Canon Michael Geoffrey. b 58. Oriel Coll Ox BA78 MA94. Ripon Coll Cuddesdon 79. **d** 82 **p** 83. C Oakham, Hambleton, Egleton, Braunston and Brooke *Pet* 82-85; Japan 85-87; TV Leic Ascension *Leic* 87-90; Asst P Leic H Spirit 91-94; TV 94-95; TR 95-99; Dioc Chapl Relns w People of Other Faiths 91-99; Bp's Dom Chapl 92-99; P-in-c Leic St Mary 93-94; Hon Can Leic Cathl from 94; Adv Inter-Faith Relns Abp's Coun from 99; Sec Ch's Commission Inter-Faith Relns from 99; Hon C Leic Presentation *Leic* from 02. *27 Tudor Road, Leicester LE3 5JF* Tel 0116-262 2628 or (020) 7898 1477 Fax 0116-291 0631 E-mail mipgrave@leicester.anglican.org

IPSWICH, Archdeacon of. See GIBSON, The Ven Terence Allen

IRAN, Bishop in. See MOTTAHEDEH, The Most Revd Iraj

IREDALE, Simon Peter. b 56. Cam Univ BA78 MPhil80. Wycliffe Hall Ox 83. **d** 86 **p** 87. C Thirsk *York* 86-89; Asst Chapl Norfolk and Nor Hosp 89-90; P-in-c Kexby w Wilberfoss *York* 90-93; Sub-Chapl HM Pris Full Sutton 90-93; Chapl RAF from 93. *Chaplaincy Services (RAF), HQ, Personnel and Training Command, RAF Innsworth, Gloucester GL3 1EZ* Tel (01452) 712612 ext 5164 Fax 510828

IRELAND, David Arthur. b 45. MICFM87 Mert Coll Ox BA67 MA71. Cuddesdon Coll 67. **d** 69 **p** 70. C Chapel Allerton *Ripon* 69-72; C Harpenden St Nic *St Alb* 72-76; R Clifton 76-84; Perm to Offic *Guildf* 91-00; NSM Leatherhead and Mickleham from 01. *43 Harefield Avenue, Cheam SM2 7ND* Tel (020) 8224 7821

IRELAND, Leslie Sydney. b 55. York Univ BA76. St Jo Coll Nottm 83. **d** 86 **p** 87. C Harwood *Man* 86-89; C Davyhulme St Mary 89-90; V Bardsley 90-99; R Levenshulme St Andr and St Pet from 99. *The Rectory, 27 Errwood Road, Levenshulme, Manchester M19 2PN* Tel 0161-224 5877 E-mail lesireland@compuserve.com

IRELAND, Mrs Lucy Annabel. b 53. Univ of Zimbabwe BSc74. St Jo Coll Nottm DPS85. **dss** 85 **d** 87 **p** 95. Mansfield St Jo *S'well* 85-87; Hon Par Dn Harwood *Man* 87-89; NSM Bardsley 90-99; C Levenshulme St Andr and St Pet from 99. *The Rectory, 27 Errwood Road, Levenshulme, Manchester M19 2PN* Tel 0161-224 5877 E-mail lesireland@compuserve.com

IRELAND, Mark Campbell. b 60. St Andr Univ MTh81 Sheff Univ MA01. Wycliffe Hall Ox 82. **d** 84 **p** 85. C Blackb St Gabr *Blackb* 84-87; C Lancaster St Mary 87-89; Chapl HM Pris Lanc 87-89; V Baxenden *Blackb* 89-97; Team Ldr Miss Division *Lich*

from 98; TV Walsall from 98. *14 Gorway Gardens, Walsall WS1 3BJ* Tel (01922) 626010 Fax 625924 E-mail mark.ireland@lichfield.anglican.org

IRELAND, Mrs Mary Janet. b 52. EMMTC 96. **d** 99 **p** 00. NSM Kibworth and Smeeton Westerby and Saddington *Leic* 99-02; C Lutterworth w Cotesbach and Bitteswell from 02. *The Vicarage, Lutterworth Road, Bitteswell, Lutterworth LE17 4RX* Tel (01455) 552443

IRELAND, Mrs Sharran. b 49. SEITE 95. **d** 98 **p** 99. C Appledore w Brookland, Fairfield, Brenzett etc *Cant* 98-01; TV St Laur in Thanet from 01. *St Christopher House, Newington, Ramsgate CT12 6HH* Tel (01843) 594160

IRESON, David Christopher. b 45. Man Univ TCert67 Birm Univ BEd80. St Steph Ho Ox DipTh93. **d** 93 **p** 94. C Minehead *B & W* 93-97; V St Decumans from 97. *St Decuman's Vicarage, 47A Brendon Road, Watchet TA23 0HU* Tel (01984) 631228 E-mail david.ireson@btinternet.com

IRESON, Ms Gillian Dorothy. b 39. Gilmore Ho 67. **dss** 72 **d** 87 **p** 94. Stepney St Dunstan and All SS *Lon* 72-99; Par Dn 87-94; C 94-99; rtd 99; Perm to Offic *Nor* from 00. *67 Glebe Road, Norwich NR2 3JH* Tel (01603) 451969

IRESON, Philip. b 52. Newc Univ BSc73. St Jo Coll Nottm LTh84. **d** 84 **p** 85. C Owlerton *Sheff* 84-87; V The Marshland 87-94; Perm to Offic *Linc* 90-93; Chapl HM YOI Hatfield 91-92; R Firbeck w Letwell *Sheff* 94-01; V Woodsetts 94-01; Chapl HM Pris and YOI Doncaster from 01. *HM Prison Doncaster, Marshgate, Doncaster DN5 8UX* Tel (01302) 760870 Fax 760861 E-mail philip@iresonr.freeserve.co.uk

IRESON, Richard Henry. b 46. Linc Th Coll 69. **d** 71 **p** 72. C Spilsby w Hundleby *Linc* 71-74; TV Grantham w Manthorpe 74-76; R Claypole 76-79; P-in-c Westborough w Dry Doddington and Stubton 76-77; R 77-79; R Bratoft w Irby-in-the-Marsh 79-86; V Burgh le Marsh 79-86; V Orby 79-86; R Welton-le-Marsh w Gunby 79-86; R Wyberton 86-01; RD Holland W 95-97; V Frampton 97-01; V Alford w Rigsby from 01; R Well from 01; R Saleby w Beesby and Maltby from 01; V Bilsby w Farlesthorpe from 01; R Hannah cum Hagnaby w Markby from 01. *The Vicarage, 15 Bilsby Road, Alford LN13 9EW* Tel (01507) 462448

IRETON, Paul. b 65. Cranmer Hall Dur 99. **d** 01 **p** 02. C Southway *Ex* from 01. *5 Treago Gardens, Plymouth PL6 7EJ* Tel (01752) 511481 E-mail paulireton@lineone.net

IRETON, Robert John. b 56. Bris Univ BEd. Oak Hill Th Coll BA. **d** 84 **p** 85. C Bromley Ch Ch *Roch* 84-87; TV Greystoke, Matterdale, Mungrisdale etc *Carl* 87-90; V Falconwood *Roch* 90-97; V Stanwix *Carl* from 97. *Stanwix Vicarage, Dykes Terrace, Carlisle CA3 9AS* Tel (01228) 514600 or 511430

IRONS, Barry. b 39. Wilson Carlile Coll 57 Coll of Resurr Mirfield 82. **d** 83 **p** 84. CA from 57; C Willersey, Saintbury, Weston-sub-Edge etc *Glouc* 83-85; R Scalford w Goadby Marwood and Wycombe etc *Leic* 85-88; P-in-c Clun w Chapel Lawn, Bettws-y-Crwyn and Newcastle *Heref* 88-91; Bp's Officer for Evang 91-94; P-in-c Breinton 91-94; P-in-c Weston-super-Mare Cen Par *B & W* 94-95; R Weston super Mare St John from 96. *The Rectory, 24 All Saints Road, Weston-super-Mare BS23 2NN* Tel (01934) 621958

IRONS, Nigel Richard. b 55. Aston Univ BSc77. St Jo Coll Nottm MA95. **d** 97 **p** 98. C Newchapel *Lich* 97-00; V Burton All SS w Ch Ch from 00. *All Saints' Vicarage, 242 Blackpool Street, Burton-on-Trent DE14 3AU* Tel (01283) 565134 E-mail mail@nigelirons.co.uk

IRONSIDE, John Edmund. b 31. Peterho Cam BA55 MA59. Qu Coll Birm 55. **d** 57 **p** 58. C Spring Park *Cant* 57-60; C Guernsey St Sampson *Win* 60-63; Thailand 63-66; V Guernsey St Jo *Win* 66-72; V Sholing 72-82; R Guernsey St Sampson 82-98; Miss to Seamen 82-98; rtd 98; Perm to Offic *Win* from 98. *Vice-Dean Guernsey 99. Le Petit Creux, Les Landes, Vale, Guernsey GY3 5JQ* Tel (01481) 249209 Fax 242776

IRVINE, Mrs Andrea Mary. b 49. Sussex Univ BA70 Ox Univ PGCE71. NTMTC 99. **d** 02. NSM Cov H Trin *Cov* from 02. *The Deanery, 11 Priory Row, Coventry CV1 5EX* Tel (024) 7663 1448 or 7626 7047 E-mail amirvine@lineone.net

IRVINE, Barry. See IRVINE, William Barry

IRVINE, Mrs Catherine Frances. b 70. K Coll Lon BA97. Ripon Coll Cuddesdon 99. **d** 01 **p** 02. C Romsey *Win* from 01. *15 Mount Temple, Romsey SO51 5UW* Tel (01794) 502021 E-mail cateirvine@hotmail.com

IRVINE, Christopher Paul. b 51. Nottm Univ BTh75 Lanc Univ MA76 St Martin's Coll Lanc PGCE77. Kelham Th Coll 73. **d** 76 **p** 76. Chapl Lanc Univ *Blackb* 76-77; C Stoke Newington St Mary *Lon* 77-80; Chapl Sheff Univ *Sheff* 80-85; Chapl St Edm Hall Ox 85-90; Tutor St Steph Ho Ox 85-90; Vice-Prin 91-94; V Cowley St Jo *Ox* 94-98; Prin Coll of Resurr Mirfield from 98. *College of the Resurrection, Stocks Bank Road, Mirfield WF14 0BW* Tel (01924) 481908 Fax 492738 E-mail cirvine@mirfield.org.uk

IRVINE, David John. b 50. Trin Coll Cam BA72 MA75. N Ord Course 91. **d** 94 **p** 95. C Hexham *Newc* 94-99; P-in-c Blanchland w Hunstanworth and Edmundbyers etc from 99; P-in-c Slaley from 99; P-in-c Healey from 03; P-in-c Whittonstall from 03. *The Vicarage, Slaley, Hexham NE47 0AA* Tel (01434) 673609

IRVINE, Donald Andrew. b 45. Trin Coll Bris DipHE94. **d** 96 **p** 97. C Allington and Maidstone St Pet *Cant* 96-99; P-in-c Harrietsham w Ulcombe 99-02; P-in-c Lenham w Boughton Malherbe 00-02; R Len Valley from 02. *The Rectory, Church Road, Harrietsham, Maidstone ME17 1AP* Tel (01622) 859466 Fax as telephone E-mail revirvine@aol.com

IRVINE, Gerard Philip. b 30. QUB BA52. Edin Th Coll 56. **d** 56 **p** 57. Chapl St Andr Cathl *Ab* 56-58; Prec St Andr Cathl 58-59; C Belfast Malone St Jo *Conn* 61-66; Chapl Community of St Jo Ev Dublin 67-77; C Dublin Sandymount *D & G* 77-97; rtd 97. *12A Carraig na Greine House, Coliemore Road, Dalkey, Co Dublin, Irish Republic* Tel (00353) (1) 230 1430

IRVINE, James Clyde. b 35. QUB BA57 NUU BPhil(Ed)83. CITC 59. **d** 59 **p** 60. C Belfast St Luke *Conn* 59-62; C Lisburn Ch Ch Cathl 62-65; R Duneane w Ballyscullion 65-69; I Kilbride 69-74; Hd of RE Ballyclare High Sch 73-98; Bp's C Killead w Gartree from 98. *Killead Rectory, 61 Crumlin Road, Aldergrove, Crumlin BT29 4AQ* Tel (028) 9445 3532

IRVINE, The Very Revd John Dudley. b 49. Sussex Univ BA70. Wycliffe Hall Ox BA80. **d** 81 **p** 82. C Brompton H Trin w Onslow Square St Paul *Lon* 81-85; P-in-c Kensington St Barn 85-94; V 94-01; Dean Cov from 01. *The Deanery, 11 Priory Row, Coventry CV1 5EX* Tel and fax (01203) 76463 1448 *or* tel 7626 7045 E-mail dean@coventrycathedral.org *or* jdirvine@lineone.net

IRVINE, Preb John Graham Gerard Charles. b 20. Mert Coll Ox BA42 MA46. St Steph Ho Ox 42. **d** 45 **p** 46. C Knowle H Nativity *Bris* 45-48; C Longton St Mary and St Chad *Lich* 48-51; C Soho St Anne w St Thos and St Pet *Lon* 51-53; Lon Dioc Home Missr Cranford 53-61; V Earl's Court St Cuth w St Matthias 61-69; V Westmr St Matt 69-86; Preb St Paul's Cathl 82-86; rtd 86; Perm to Offic *Chich* from 86. *42 Montpelier Road, Brighton BN1 3BA* Tel (01273) 730039

IRVINE, The Very Revd John Murray. b 24. Magd Coll Cam BA45 MA49. Ely Th Coll 46. **d** 48 **p** 49. C Poplar All SS w St Frideswide *Lon* 48-53; Chapl SS Coll Cam 53-60; Selection Sec CACTM 60-65; Can Res and Chan Heref Cathl *Heref* 65-78; Dir of Ords 65-78; Provost S'well 78-91; P-in-c Edingley w Halam 78-91; P-in-c Rolleston w Fiskerton, Morton and Upton 90-91; rtd 91; Perm to Offic *Ex* from 92. *9 Salston Barton, Strawberry Lane, Ottery St Mary EX11 1RG* Tel (01404) 815901

IRVINE, Canon Stanley. b 35. TCD DipTh83. **d** 83 **p** 84. C Arm St Mark w Aghavilly *Arm* 83-85; I Kilmoremoy w Castleconnor, Easkey, Kilglass etc *T, K & A* 85-94; Dom Chapl to Bp Tuam 88-94; I Stranorlar w Meenglas and Kilteevogue *D & R* from 94; Bp's Dom Chapl from 01; Can Raphoe Cathl from 02. *The Rectory, Stranorlar, Co Donegal, Irish Republic* Tel (00353) (74) 913 1081

IRVINE, Mrs Suzanne. b 74. Huddersfield Univ BA96. St Jo Coll Nottm 99. **d** 03. C Wrose *Bradf* from 03. *24 Wrose Avenue, Bradford BD2 1HP* Tel (01274) 642883 E-mail chocsxxx@hotmail.com

IRVINE, Timothy. d 03. C Dublin Ch Ch Cathl Gp *D & G* from 03. *32 Shandon Drive, Phibsborough, Dublin 7, Irish Republic*

IRVINE, William Barry. b 48. QUB BD75 Cheltenham & Glouc Coll of HE Dip Palliative Care 99. St Jo Coll Nottm 75. **d** 76 **p** 77. C Belfast St Mich *Conn* 76-80; C Mansfield St Pet *S'well* 80-84; V Chapel-en-le-Frith *Derby* 84-90; Chapl Cheltenham Gen and Delancey Hosps 90-94; Chapl E Glos NHS Trust 94-02; Chapl Glos Hosps NHS Trust from 02. *Cheltenham General Hospital, Sandford Road, Cheltenham GL53 7AN* Tel (01242) 222222 ext 4286 *or* 274286

IRVINE-CAPEL, Luke Thomas. b 75. Greyfriars Ox BA97 MA01 Leeds Univ MA99 SSC. Coll of Resurr Mirfield 97. **d** 99 **p** 00. C Abertillery w Cwmtillery w Six Bells *Mon* 99-01; Min Can St Woolos Cathl from 01; Sub-Chapl HM Pris Cardiff from 02. *Hebron, 9 Clifton Road, Newport NP20 4EW* Tel (01633) 267191 Fax as telephone E-mail frluke.capel@ntlworld.com

IRVING, Canon Andrew. b 27. St Deiniol's Hawarden 62. **d** 65 **p** 66. C Benwell St Jas *Newc* 65-69; C Langley Marish *Ox* 69-73; V Moulsford 73-81; Canada from 81; rtd 92. *204-4630 Ponderosa Drive, Peachland BC, Canada, V0H 1X5* Tel (001) (604) 767 9582

IRVING, Canon Donald Richard. b 31. Lon Univ BSc56. Lon Coll of Div 66. **d** 68 **p** 69. C Leic H Trin *Leic* 68-71; Asst Chapl HM Pris Leic 70-71; Chapl to Leic Students 70-71; E Regional Co-ord CPAS 71-76; Dir Ch Soc 76-82; Gen Sec ICS 82-92; Hon Can Brussels Cathl *Eur* from 83; rtd 92. *The Old Orchard, Manor House Gardens, Edenbridge TN8 5EG*

IRVING, Canon Michael John Derek. b 43. BEd80. Qu Coll Birm 80. **d** 81 **p** 82. C Coleford w Staunton *Glouc* 81-84; V Dean Forest H Trin 84-91; RD Forest S 88-91; P-in-c Hempsted 91-96; Dir of Ords 91-96; Hon Can Glouc Cathl from 94; R Minchinhampton from 96. *The Rectory, Butt Street, Minchinhampton, Stroud GL6 9JP* Tel (01453) 882289 E-mail irvings@enterprise.net

IRWIN, Albert Samuel. b 14. TCD BA38 MA44. CITC 38. **d** 38 **p** 39. C Bury St Pet *Man* 38-42; C Bolton St Pet 42-45; Lect 45-47; Chapl RNVR 47-48; C Gillingham *Sarum* 48-49; Argentina

49-54; V Apethorpe w Woodnewton *Pet* 54-59; R Clyst St Mary *Ex* 59-61; R Clyst St George 59-61; V Stamford Baron *Pet* 61-81; P-in-c Tinwell 77-81; rtd 81; Lic to Offic *Pet* 81-85; Perm to Offic from 85; *Linc* 91-00. *19 Water Street, Stamford PE9 2NJ*

IRWIN, John Nesbitt Cottier. b 27. SEN79 Mert Coll Ox BA50 MA53. SW Minl Tr Course 86. **d** 87 **p** 88. NSM Buckfastleigh w Dean Prior *Ex* from 87. *56 Plymouth Road, Buckfastleigh TQ11 0DH* Tel (01364) 643044

IRWIN, Patrick Alexander. b 55. BNC Ox BA77 MA81 Edin Univ BD81. Edin Th Coll 77 Liturgisches Inst Trier 79. **d** 81 **p** 82. Hon C Cambridge St Botolph *Ely* 81-84; Chapl BNC Ox 84-92; Lect Th 86-92; Lic to Offic *Ox* 85-92; *B & W* 87-92; Perm to Offic *D & G* from 87; *Arm* from 96; CF from 92; Chapl Udruga Hrvata Sv Dominik Gorazde 94-95; Perm to Offic *Guild* from 99-02; *Ripon* 00-03; Hon V Choral Arm Cathl *Arm* from 02. *c/o MOD Chaplains (Army)* Tel (01980) 615804 Fax 615800 E-mail patalexirwin@yahoo.co.uk

IRWIN, Stewart. b 53. Sarum & Wells Th Coll 80. **d** 83 **p** 84. C Brighouse *Wakef* 83-87; V Stockton St Jo *Dur* 87-95; V Howden-le-Wear and Hunwick from 95. *The Vicarage, Hunwick, Crook DL15 0JU* Tel (01388) 604456

IRWIN, Miss Susan Elizabeth. b 47. Cam Univ DipRS79. St Jo Coll Dur 77. **dss** 79 **d** 87 **p** 94. Harborne St Faith and St Laur *Birm* 79-82; Caterham *S'wark* 82-88; Par Dn 87-88; Par Dn Kidlington w Hampton Poyle *Ox* 88-94; C 94-95; TV Gt Marlow w Marlow Bottom, Lt Marlow and Bisham from 95. *18 Oak Tree Road, Marlow SL7 3EE* Tel (01628) 481722 E-mail sue.irwin@btopenworld.com

IRWIN, Victor. b 32. Lon Coll of Div 64. **d** 66 **p** 67. C Leic H Trin *Leic* 66-68; CF 68-72; V Quarry Bank *Lich* 72-81; P-in-c Hopesay w Edgton *Heref* 81-85; V Lydbury N 81-85; R Wickenby Gp *Linc* 85-88; R Gartcosh *Glas* 88-91; R Airdrie 88-91; I Garrison w Slavin and Belleek *Clogh* 91-97; rtd 97. *7 Cowan Heron House, Dromara Road, Dromore BT25 1DW* Tel (028) 9269 8086

IRWIN, William George. b 53. QUB BSc77. CITC 80. **d** 80 **p** 81. C Lisburn St Paul *Conn* 80-83; C Seagoe *D & D* 83-85; C Newtownards w Movilla Abbey 85-88; I Ballymacash *Conn* from 88. *St Mark's Rectory, 49 Antrim Road, Lisburn BT28 3EA* Tel (028) 9266 2393 E-mail wg1@btopenworld.com

IRWIN-CLARK, Peter Elliot. b 49. Univ Coll Lon LLB71 Barrister 72. Cranmer Hall Dur BA80. **d** 81 **p** 82. C Kirkheaton *Wakef* 81-86; V Shirley *Win* 86-96; Perm to Office *Chich* 96-97 and *S'wark* 97; V Prestonville St Luke *Chich* 97-03; Missr Warham Trust and Faith Development Officer (Basingstoke Adnry) *Win* from 03. *Home Farm House, Malshanger, Basingstoke RG23 7ET* Tel (01256) 781860 Fax as telephone E-mail panddic@surfaid.org

ISAAC, Canon David Thomas. b 43. Univ of Wales BA65. Cuddesdon Coll 65. **d** 67 **p** 68. C Llandaff w Capel Llanilltern *Llan* 67-71; P-in-c Swansea St Jas *S & B* 71-73; Chapl Ch in Wales Youth Coun 73-77; V Llangiwg *S & B* 77-79; Dioc Youth Officer *Ripon* 79-83; Nat Officer for Youth Work Gen Syn Bd of Educn 83-90; Dioc Dir of Educn *Portsm* from 90; Can Res Portsm Cathl from 90. *1 Pembroke Close, Portsmouth PO1 2NX* Tel (023) 9281 8107 *or* 9282 2053 Mobile 07768-997220 Fax 9229 5081 E-mail dde@portsmouth.anglican.org

ISAAC, Edward Henry. b 20. Qu Coll Cam BA42 MA46. Ridley Hall Cam 45. **d** 47 **p** 48. C Wednesbury St Bart *Lich* 47-51; V Liv St Phil *Liv* 51-56; V Knowsley 56-61; V Garston 61-66; V Millom St Geo *Carl* 66-85; rtd 85; Perm to Offic *Carl* from 86. *31 Lowther Road, Millom LA18 4PE* Tel (01229) 772332

ISAACS, John Kenneth. b 36. Cam Univ MA. EAMTC. **d** 82 **p** 83. NSM Ely 82-85; Chapl K Sch Ely 85-94; Lic to Offic *Ely* 85-94; P-in-c Denver 94-02; P-in-c Ryston w Roxham 94-02; P-in-c W Dereham 94-02; R Denver and Ryston w Roxham and W Dereham etc from 02. *The Rectory, Ryston Road, Denver, Downham Market PE38 0DP* Tel (01366) 387727 E-mail john.isaacs@ely.anglican.org

ISAACSON, Alan Timothy. b 55. York Univ BA77 Sheff Univ PGCE84 Leeds Univ MA97. N Ord Course 94. **d** 96 **p** 97. C Kimberworth *Sheff* 96-99; TV Brinsworth w Catcliffe and Treeton from 99. *The Rectory, Church Lane, Treeton, Rotherham S60 5PZ* Tel 0114-269 6542

ISABEL, Sister. *See* KEEGAN, Frances Ann

ISAM, Miss Margaret Myra Elizabeth (Wendy). b 35. Nottm Univ BEd73. EMMTC 78. **dss** 81 **d** 87 **p** 94. Humberston *Linc* 81-84; Gt Grimsby St Andr and St Luke 85-93; Dn-in-c 87-93; P-in-c Gt Grimsby St Andr w St Luke and All SS 94-97; V 97-00; rtd 00; Perm to Offic *Linc* from 00. *18 Grainsby Avenue, Cleethorpes DN35 9PA* Tel (01472) 699821 Mobile 07950-464542

ISBISTER, Charles. b 27. Chich Th Coll 58. **d** 60 **p** 61. C Tynemouth Ch Ch *Newc* 60-64; C Boyne Hill *Ox* 64-67; V Cookridge H Trin *Ripon* 67-93; rtd 93. *2 Church Mount, Horsforth, Leeds LS18 5LE* Tel 0113-239 0813

ISHERWOOD, David Owen. b 46. BA68 Lon Univ MA95 MPhil87. Ridley Hall Cam 76. **d** 78 **p** 79. C Sanderstead All SS *S'wark* 78-82; C Horley 82-84; TV 84-88; P-in-c Streatham

Immanuel and St Andr 88-89; V 89-95; TR Clapham TM 95-01; V Clapham H Trin and St Pet from 02. *25 The Chase, London SW4 0NP* Tel (020) 7498 6879 *or* 7627 0941 Fax 7627 5065 E-mail david.htc@lineone.net

ISHERWOOD, Robin James. b 56. Hull Univ BA78 Uppsala Univ MDiv92. Ripon Coll Cuddesdon DipMin94. **d** 94 **p** 95. C Bramhall *Ches* 94-98; V Alsager St Mary from 98; Hon Chapl ATC from 99. *St Mary's Vicarage, 37 Eaton Road, Alsager, Stoke-on-Trent ST7 2BQ* Tel (01270) 875748 E-mail vicar@pit6.fsnet.co.uk

ISHERWOOD, Samuel Peter. b 34. Lon Coll of Div ALCD62 LTh74. **d** 62 **p** 63. C Bacup St Sav *Man* 62-65; C Man Albert Memorial Ch 65-67; V Livesey *Blackb* 67-79; V Handforth *Ches* 79-99; RD Cheadle 92-99; rtd 99; Perm to Offic *York* from 00. *1 Andrew Drive, Huntington, York YO32 9YF* Tel (01904) 438116

ISIORHO, David John Phillip. b 58. Liv Poly BA80 Warwick Univ MA93 Bradf Univ PhD98 Wolv Poly Dip Psychology 89. Westcott Ho Cam 87. **d** 90 **p** 91. C Nuneaton St Mary *Cov* 90-93; P-in-c Bradf St Oswald Chapel Green *Bradf* 93-96; P-in-c Brereton *Lich* 96-00; P-in-c Arthingworth, Harrington w Oxendon and E Farndon *Pet* from 00; P-in-c Maidwell w Draughton, Lamport w Faxton from 01. *The Rectory, 35 Main Street, Great Oxendon, Market Harborough LE16 8NE* Tel (01858) 461992 E-mail davidisiorho@catholic.org

ISIORHO (née NORTHALL), Mrs Linda Barbara. b 50. Birm Univ BA72 Worc Coll of Educn PGCE75 Birm Univ DipTh90. Qu Coll Birm 88. **d** 90 **p** 94. C Wood End *Cov* 90-91; Perm to Offic 91-93; Perm to Offic *Bradf* 93-94; NSM Low Moor St Mark 94-96; Perm to Offic *Lich* 96-97; NSM Alrewas 97-00; Perm to Offic *Pet* from 01. *The Rectory, 35 Main Street, Great Oxendon, Market Harborough LE16 8NE* Tel (01858) 432166

ISITT, Canon David Edgar Reid. b 28. K Coll Cam BA49 MA53. Wells Th Coll 51. **d** 53 **p** 54. C Westbury-on-Trym H Trin *Bris* 53-56; Chapl K Coll Cam 56-60; V Haslingfield *Ely* 60-68; R Harlton 60-68; Chapl St Edw K and Martyr Cam 68-77; Asst Chapl Trin Hall Cam 68-77; Can Res Bris Cathl *Bris* 77-86; Dir Dioc Sch of Min 77-86; P-in-c Bris Ch Ch w St Ewen and All SS 80-82; Dioc Dir of Ords 81-86; Lic to Offic *Ely* 87-93; Acting Dean Trin Hall Cam 89; Tutor Westcott Ho 90; Chapl Fitzw Coll Cam 90-93; rtd 93; Perm to Offic *Ely* from 99. *41 Fulbrooke Road, Cambridge CB3 9EE* Tel (01223) 571763

ISITT, Norman. b 34. St Jo Coll Dur BA56. Cranmer Hall Dur DipTh59. **d** 59 **p** 60. C Loughton St Mary *Chelmsf* 59-62; C Moulsham St Jo 62-64; Billericay Co Sch 64-90; Squirrels Heath Sch Romford 64-90; Althorpe and Keadby Co Sch 66-95; rtd 95. *21 Cambridge Avenue, Bottesford, Scunthorpe DN16 3LT* Tel (01724) 851489

ISLE OF WIGHT, Archdeacon of. Vacant

ISON, Andrew Phillip. b 60. Imp Coll Lon BEng82 Penn Univ MSE83 Univ Coll Lon PhD87 Bris Univ BA01 CEng92 MIChemE92. Trin Coll Bris 99. **d** 01 **p** 02. C Cleethorpes *Linc* from 01. *3 Taylors Avenue, Cleethorpes DN35 0LF* Tel (01472) 598450 E-mail isonandrew@aol.com

ISON, Canon David John. b 54. Leic Univ BA76 Nottm Univ BA78 K Coll Lon PhD85. St Jo Coll Nottm 76. **d** 79 **p** 80. C Deptford St Nic and St Luke *S'wark* 79-85; Lect CA Tr Coll Blackheath 85-88; V Potters Green *Cov* 88-93; Jt Dir SW Minl Tr Course *Ex* 93-95; Dioc Officer for CME from 93; Bp's Officer for NSMs from 97; Can Res Ex Cathl from 95; Chan from 97. *12 Cathedral Close, Exeter EX1 1EZ* Tel and fax (01392) 499710 *or* tel 275745 E-mail ison@exeter-cathedral.org.uk *or* david.ison@talk21.com

ISON, Mrs Hilary Margaret. b 55. Leic Univ BA76 Nottm Univ DipTh78 E Lon Univ MA02. Gilmore Course 77 St Jo Coll Nottm DPS79. **d** 87 **p** 94. NSM Deptford St Nic and St Luke *S'wark* 87-88; NSM Potters Green *Cov* 88-90; C Rugby St Andr 90-93; Chapl Ex Hospiscare 93-00; C Ex St Mark, St Sidwell and St Matt *Ex* 99-02; Bp's Adv for Women in Min from 02; Area Tutor SW Minl Tr Course from 03. *12 Cathedral Close, Exeter EX1 1EZ* Tel (01392) 275745

ISRAEL, Martin Spencer. b 27. Witwatersrand Univ MB49 MRCP52. **d** 74 **p** 75. Hon C St Mich Cornhill w St Pet le Poer etc *Lon* 74-77; Hon C S Kensington H Trin w All SS 77-82; P-in-c 83-96; rtd 96. *21 Soudan Road, London SW11 4HH* Tel (020) 7622 5756

ISSBERNER, Norman Gunther Erich. b 34. Fitzw Ho Cam BA58 MA61. Clifton Th Coll 57. **d** 59 **p** 60. C Cheadle *Ches* 59-61; C Broad Green *Cant* 59-61; C Surbiton Hill Ch Ch *S'wark* 61-66; V Egham *Guildf* 66-75; V Wallington H Trin *S'wark* 75-86; UK Chmn Africa Inland Miss from 77; Adv on Miss and Evang *Chelmsf* 86-91; P-in-c Castle Hedingham 91-93; V Clacton St Paul 93-99; RD St Osyth 94-99; rtd 99; Perm to Offic *Chelmsf* from 99. *14 Darcy Close, Frinton-on-Sea CO13 0RR* Tel (01255) 673548

ITALY AND MALTA, Archdeacon of. See REID, The Ven William Gordon

ITUMU, John Murithi. b 65. Lon Bible Coll 01. **d** 02 **p** 03. C Cricklewood St Gabr and St Mich *Lon* from 02. *London Bible College, Green Lane, Northwood HA6 2UW* Tel (01923) 456417 Mobile 07946-000364 E-mail john.itumu@londonbiblecollege.ac.uk

IVE, Jeremy George Augustus. b 57. Rhodes Univ BA81 Ch Coll Cam PhD86 K Coll Lon MPhil95. Wycliffe Hall Ox DipTh91. **d** 91 **p** 92. NSM Ivybridge w Harford *Ex* 91-95; P-in-c Abbotskerswell 95-99; P-in-c Tudeley cum Capel w Five Oak Green *Roch* from 99; Dioc Lay Min Adv 99-01. *The Vicarage, Sychem Lane, Five Oak Green, Tonbridge TN12 6TL* Tel and fax (01892) 836653 Mobile 07720-841169 E-mail jgaive@btinternet.com

IVE (née KNOTT), Mrs Pamela Frances. b 58. Bedf Coll of Educn BEd79. Wycliffe Hall Ox 88. **d** 90. Par Dn Ivybridge w Harford *Ex* 90-95; Par Dn Abbotskerswell 95-99; Par Dn Tudeley cum Capel w Five Oak Green *Roch* from 99. *The Vicarage, Sychem Lane, Five Oak Green, Tonbridge TN12 6TL* Tel and fax (01892) 836653 *or* tel 835548 E-mail pfive@btinternet.com

IVELL, Robert William. b 45. Lon Univ BSc71 Liv Univ CertEd Sheff Univ Dip Bibl Studies 83. Ridley Hall Cam 83. **d** 85 **p** 86. C Wadsley *Sheff* 85-88; V Laughton w Throapham 88-96; V Wadworth w Loversall from 96. *The Vicarage, Vicarage Drive, Wadworth, Doncaster DN11 9BW* Tel (01302) 851974

IVES, Raymond Charles. b 27. St Mark & St Jo Coll Lon CertEd50. LNSM course 92. **d** 95 **p** 96. OLM Croydon St Pet *S'wark* from 95. *60 Windermere Road, West Wickham BR4 9AW* Tel (020) 8777 4956

IVES, Mrs Susan Ethel. b 48. EAMTC. **d** 01 **p** 02. NSM Moulsham St Luke *Chelmsf* from 01. *47 Long Brandocks, Writtle, Chelmsford CM1 3JL* Tel (01245) 420325 E-mail sives@fish.co.uk

IVESON, Mrs Patricia Jill. b 35. Cam Univ CertEd55 Lon Univ DipTh70 K Coll Lon BD76 AKC76. **dss** 81 **d** 87 **p** 94. Wilmington *Roch* 81-87; Hon Par Dn 87-94; Hon C from 94; Chapl Dartford and Gravesham NHS Trust from 87. *The Birches, 15 Wallis Close, Wilmington, Dartford DA2 7BE* Tel (01322) 279100

IVESON, Robert George. b 70. Oak Hill Th Coll BA01. **d** 01 **p** 02. C Cheadle All Hallows *Ches* from 01. *26 Kelsall Road, Cheadle SK8 2NE* Tel 0161-491 2204 E-mail robiveson@yahoo.co.uk

IVESON, Ronald Edward. b 68. Chester Coll of HE RMN92. Aston Tr Scheme 95 Oak Hill Th Coll BA00. **d** 00 **p** 01. C Lache cum Saltney *Ches* from 00. *69 Sandy Lane, Saltney, Chester CH4 8YB* Tel (01244) 693225

IVIN, Miss Maureen. b 34. Gilmore Ho 60. **dss** 85 **d** 87 **p** 94. Grays Thurrock *Chelmsf* 85-87; Par Dn 87-94; TV 94-99; rtd 99; Perm to Offic *Chelmsf* from 00. *40 Cleveland Drive, Westcliff-on-Sea SS0 0SU* Tel (01702) 346664

IVISON, Norman William. b 54. Hull Univ BA75 DipEd76. Trin Coll Bris DipHE81 DipTh82. **d** 82 **p** 83. Ecum Liaison Officer BBC Radio Furness 82-85; C Barrow St Mark *Carl* 82-85; Chapl Barrow Sixth Form Coll 83-85; Dioc Broadcasting Officer *Lich* 85-91; Relig Progr Producer BBC Radio Stoke 85-91; Hon Chapl Bucknall and Bagnall *Lich* 85-91; Asst Producer Relig Progr BBC TV Man 91-93; Producer Relig Progr BBC TV Man from 93; Perm to Offic *Man* 92-95; Lic to Offic 95-98; Perm to Offic *Blackb* from 98. *44 Peel Park Avenue, Clitheroe BB7 1JR* Tel (01200) 429306 *or* 0161-244 3238 Mobile 0585-866317 Fax 0161-244 3232 E-mail norman.ivison@bbc.co.uk

IVORY, Christopher James. b 54. Reading Univ BSc76. Qu Coll Birm DipTh80. **d** 81 **p** 82. C Waltham Cross *St Alb* 81-84; C Is of Dogs Ch Ch and St Jo w St Luke *Lon* 84-88; V Streatham Ch Ch *S'wark* 88-03; Lambeth Adnry Ecum Officer 90-95; RD Streatham 00-03; R King's Lynn St Marg w St Nic *Nor* from 03. *St Margaret's Vicarage, St Margaret's Place, King's Lynn PE30 5DL* Tel (01553) 772858 E-mail christophers@supanet.com

IWANUSCHAK, Victor. b 51. Coll of Ripon & York St Jo MA00. N Ord Course 97. **d** 00 **p** 01. C Pontefract All SS *Wakef* 00-03; P-in-c from 03. *All Saints' Vicarage, Grenton, South Baileygate, Pontefract WF8 2JL* Tel (01977) 695590 Mobile 07734-710254 E-mail iwanuschak@triom.com

IZOD, Mrs Wendy Janet. b 47. Sheff Univ BSc(Econ)68. SEITE 98. **d** 01 **p** 02. NSM Hever, Four Elms and Mark Beech *Roch* from 01; Chapl ATC from 01. *West Lodge, Stick Hill, Edenbridge TN8 5NJ* Tel (01342) 850738 Mobile 07703-107496 Fax (01342) 850077 E-mail izod.calligraphy@btinternet.com

IZZARD, David Antony. b 55. Trin Coll Bris DipHE94. **d** 94 **p** 95. C E Bris 94-98; V Sea Mills from 98. *St Edyth's Vicarage, Avon Leaze, Bristol BS9 2HV* Tel 0117-968 1912 *or* 968 6965 E-mail clan.izzard@ukgateway.net

IZZARD, Ms Susannah Amanda. b 59. Hatf Poly BA82 Birm Univ MEd93 Wolv Univ PGCE92. Trin Coll Bris BA86. **dss** 86 **d** 87 **p** 01. Birm St Martin w Bordesley St Andr *Birm* 86-89; Par Dn 87-89; C Handsworth St Jas 89-91; Asst Chapl Qu Eliz Hosp Birm 90-91; Lect Birm Univ 93-02; NSM Selly Oak St Mary from 01. *2 Hemyock Road, Birmingham B29 4DG* Tel 0121-243 3745 Fax as telephone E-mail susannah.izzard@virgin.net

J

JACK, Alexander Richard. b 30. Leeds Univ BSc55 MSc66. Oak Hill Th Coll 69. **d** 71 **p** 72. C Penn Fields *Lich* 71-78; P-in-c 78-83; R Barnston and Lt Dunmow *Chelmsf* 83-95; RD Dunmow 88-95; rtd 95; Perm to Offic *Lich* from 95. *30 Bellencroft Gardens, Wolverhampton WV3 8DT* Tel (01902) 763481

JACK, Canon Henry Graham. b 21. K Coll Lon AKC48 BD49. **d** 49 **p** 50. C Hornsey Ch Ch *Lon* 49-50; C Steyning *Chich* 52-56; R Warbleton 56-61; V Alfriston and Lullington 61-65; RD Seaford 64-65; Chile 65-74; Hon Can Chile 66-74; R Trowbridge St Jas *Sarum* 74-87; Can and Preb Sarum Cathl 83-87; rtd 87; Perm to Offic *Sarum* from 87. *285A The Common, Holt, Trowbridge BA14 6QJ* Tel (01225) 782776

JACK, Paul. b 65. QUB BSc92 Univ Coll Galway MSc94 TCD BTh99. CITC 96. **d** 99 **p** 00. C Jordanstown *Conn* 99-01; C Seagoe *D & D* from 01. *39 Seagoe Road, Portadown, Craigavon BT63 5HW* Tel (028) 3839 4315

JACK, Robin Watson. b 43. Westcott Ho Cam. **d** 90 **p** 91. C Debenham w Aspall and Kenton *St E* 90-93; P-in-c Bacton w Wyverstone and Cotton 93-00; R Bacton w Wyverstone, Cotton and Old Newton etc from 00. *The Rectory, Church Road, Bacton, Stowmarket IP14 4LJ* Tel (01449) 781245

JACKLIN, John Frederick. b 30. Oak Hill Th Coll 72. **d** 72 **p** 72. Chile 72-75; C Roxeth Ch Ch *Lon* 75-78; V Selston *S'well* 78-95; rtd 95; Perm to Offic *Derby* from 97. *5 Rose Avenue, Borrowash, Derby DE7 3GA* Tel (01332) 669670

JACKS, David. b 59. Nottm Univ BTh87 Birm Univ MA95. Linc Th Coll 84. **d** 87 **p** 88. C Oakham, Hambleton, Egleton, Braunston and Brooke *Pet* 87-90; V Weedon Bec w Everdon 90-98; P-in-c Dodford 96-98; V Weedon Bec w Everdon and Dodford 98-01; V Llandrillo-yn-Rhos *St As* from 01. *Llandrillo Vicarage, 36 Llandudno Road, Colwyn Bay LL28 4UD* Tel (01492) 548878 Mobile 07850-597891 E-mail david@llandrillo.fsbusiness.co.uk

JACKSON, Alan. b 44. Newc Univ BA67 DipEd68 MEd79. NEOC 79. **d** 81 **p** 82. NSM Jesmond H Trin *Newc* 81-82; Chapl Bp Wand Sch Sunbury-on-Thames 82-89; V Hanworth St Rich *Lon* from 89. *St Richard's Vicarage, 35 Forge Lane, Hanworth TW13 6UN* Tel (020) 8898 0241 E-mail alan.jackson@london.anglican.org

JACKSON, Canon Arthur Malcolm. b 31. TCD BA54 MA60. TCD Div Sch Div Test 54. **d** 54 **p** 55. C Templecorran Union *Conn* 54-57; C Dublin Santry Union *D & G* 57-58; Bp's V and Registrar *C & O* 58-61; I Monasterevan *M & K* 61-68; I Narraghmore w Fontstown and Timolin *D & G* 68-88; I Narraghmore and Timolin w Castledermot etc 88-91; I Killanne w Killegney, Rossdroit and Templeshanbo *C & O* 91-00; Preb Ferns Cathl 93-96; Bp's Dom Chapl 93-97; Chan Ferns Cathl 96-98; Prec Ferns Cathl 98-00; rtd 00. *2 Church Road, Bunclody, Enniscorthy, Co Wexford, Irish Republic* Tel (00353) (54) 496 4742

JACKSON, Barry. b 30. St Jo Coll Cam BA53 DipEd54 MA57. Westcott Ho Cam 63. **d** 65 **p** 66. C Stockport St Geo *Ches* 65-68; C Bridgwater St Mary, Chilton Trinity and Durleigh *B & W* 68-70; P-in-c Thurloxton 70-75; Chapl Wycliffe Coll Glos 75-88; V Hatherfield *Chich* 88-97; rtd 97; Perm to Offic *Chich* from 98. *11 Glenleigh Walk, Robertsbridge TN32 5DQ* Tel (01580) 880067

JACKSON, The Very Revd Brandon Donald. b 34. Liv Univ LLB56 Bradf Univ Hon DLitt90. Wycliffe Hall Ox DipTh59. **d** 58 **p** 59. C New Malden and Coombe *S'wark* 58-61; C Leeds St Geo *Ripon* 61-65; V Shipley St Pet *Bradf* 65-77; Relig Adv Yorkshire TV 69-79; Provost Bradf 77-89; Dean Linc 89-97; rtd 97; Perm to Offic *Ripon* from 98. *Little Spigot, West Witton, Leyburn DL8 4LP* Tel (01969) 624589 E-mail bdj1@mlj2.freeserve.co.uk

JACKSON, Christopher John Wilson. b 45. St Pet Coll Ox BA67 MA87. Ridley Hall Cam 69. **d** 72 **p** 73. C Putney St Marg *S'wark* 72-76; C Battersea St Pet and St Paul 76-79; TV Preston St Jo *Blackb* 79-87; P-in-c Sandal St Cath *Wakef* 87-90; V Shenley Green *Birm* 90-01; AD Kings Norton 95-99; P-in-c Chesterfield H Trin and Ch Ch *Derby* from 01. *31 Newbold Road, Chesterfield S41 7PG* Tel (01246) 273508 E-mail jacks49@tiscali.co.uk

JACKSON, Miss Cynthia. b 42. CertMS90. S'wark Ord Course 93. **d** 96 **p** 97. NSM Wimbledon *S'wark* from 96. *39 Panmuir Road, London SW20 0PZ* Tel (020) 8947 5940 or 7361 2396

JACKSON, Canon David. b 33. Leeds Univ BA60. Coll of Resurr Mirfield 60. **d** 62 **p** 63. C Lewisham St Steph *S'wark* 62-65; P-in-c New Charlton H Trin 65-69; C Charlton St Luke w St Paul 69-72; Sen Tutor Coll of the Resurr Mirfield 72-75; R Clapham H Trin 75-78; P-in-c Clapham St Pet 76-78; TR Clapham Old Town 78-84; Hon Can S'wark Cathl 80-96; V Battersea St Mary-le-Park 84-89; V Surbiton St Andr and St Mark 89-96; rtd 96; Chapl St Mich Convent Ham 96-03. *18 Tower Lane, Bearsted, Maidstone ME14 4JJ* Tel (01622) 730041

JACKSON, David. b 48. Open Univ BA85. Nazarene Th Coll Man DipTh73 St Deiniol's Hawarden 91. **d** 91 **p** 92. C Scotforth *Blackb* 91-95; C Banbury *Ox* 95-98; Chapl Ox Radcliffe Hosps NHS Trust 95-00; V Banbury St Hugh *Ox* from 98. *St Hugh's Vicarage, 4 Longfellow Road, Banbury OX16 9LB* Tel (01295) 264961 E-mail sthughban@aol.com

JACKSON, David Hilton. b 62. Stanford Univ BA84 Princeton Th Sem MDiv90 Ox Univ MSt94 Wycliffe Hall Ox DipTh95. **d** 95 **p** 96. C Ox St Andr *Ox* 95-98; TV Thame 98-00; USA from 00; Assoc R and Chapl Upland St Mark 01-03; Sen Assoc for Par Life Pasadena All SS from 03. *614 Occidental Drive, Claremont, CA 91711, USA* E-mail david.jackson@cgu.edu

JACKSON, David Reginald Estcourt. b 25. OBE. Qu Coll Cam BA45 MA49. St Jo Coll Dur 80. **d** 81 **p** 82. Hon C Douglas *Blackb* 81-82; C 82-87; rtd 90. *64 The Common, Parbold, Wigan WN8 7EA* Tel (01257) 462671

JACKSON, David Robert. b 51. Lon Univ BDS. Linc Th Coll 81. **d** 83 **p** 84. C Hatcham St Cath *S'wark* 83-87; V Sydenham St Bart 87-93; Perm to Offic *Lon* from 93. *168 Manor Park, London SE13 5RH* Tel (020) 8297 9132 E-mail djsaab@aol.com

JACKSON, David William. b 53. Goldsmiths' Coll Lon BA75 PGCE76. Cranmer Hall Dur 90. **d** 92 **p** 93. C Desborough *Pet* 92-95; C Eastham *Ches* 95-98; P-in-c Taverham w Ringland *Nor* from 98. *The Rectory, 173 Taverham Road, Taverham, Norwich NR8 6SG* Tel (01603) 868217

JACKSON, Canon Derek. b 26. Ex Coll Ox BA51 MA55. Westcott Ho Cam 51. **d** 53 **p** 54. C Radcliffe-on-Trent *S'well* 53-56; C Frome St Jo *B & W* 56-57; V Eaton Socon *St Alb* 57-63; V Boxmoor St Jo 63-74; V Bishop's Stortford St Mich 74-85; Hon Can St Alb 82-85; Bermuda 85-89; P-in-c Cerne Abbas w Godmanstone and Minterne Magna *Sarum* 89-95; rtd 95; Chapl Menorca *Eur* 95-96; Perm to Offic *Chelmsf* from 97. *88 Stansted Road, Bishop's Stortford CM23 2DZ* Tel (01279) 652664

JACKSON, Canon Derek Reginald. b 49. K Coll Lon BD72 AKC72. **d** 73 **p** 74. C Westhoughton *Man* 73-75; C Kendal H Trin *Carl* 75-78; V Pennington w Lindal and Marton 78-83; Warden of Readers 82-92; V Kendal St Geo 83-94; Hon Can Carl Cathl 89-00; V Applethwaite 94-96; P-in-c Troutbeck 94-96; V Windermere St Mary and Troutbeck 96-00; RD Windermere 98-00; Can Res Bradf Cathl *Bradf* from 00. *3 Cathedral Close, Bradford BD1 4EG* Tel (01274) 737354 or 777729 Fax 777730

JACKSON, Derrick Raymond. b 20. ALAM. Worc Ord Coll 63. **d** 65 **p** 66. C Old Swinford *Worc* 65-68; C Headless Cross 68-70; R Mamble w Bayton 70; TV Steeple Morden *Ely* 71-80; V Hunningham *Cov* 80-85; V Wappenbury w Weston under Wetherley 80-85; rtd 85; Perm to Offic *Ex* from 85. *9 Caulston Close, Exmouth EX8 3LU* Tel (01395) 266615

JACKSON, Doreen May. b 35. SRN. S Dios Minl Tr Scheme. **d** 88 **p** 94. NSM Fareham H Trin *Portsm* from 88. *134 Oak Road, Fareham PO15 5HR* Tel (01329) 841429

JACKSON, Mrs Elizabeth Mary. b 41. Man Univ BA67. Ox Min Course 90. **d** 92 **p** 94. Chapl Asst Reading Hosps 86-95; NSM Reading St Mary w St Laur *Ox* 92-94; Chapl R Berks and Battle Hosps NHS Trust 95-02; NSM Reading Deanery *Ox* from 02. *2 Belle Avenue, Reading RG6 2BL* Tel 0118-926 4149

JACKSON, Canon Frances Anne (Peggy). b 51. Somerville Coll Ox BA74 MA76 ACA76 FCA81. Ripon Coll Cuddesdon 85. **d** 87 **p** 94. C Ilkeston St Mary *Derby* 87-90; TM Hemel Hempstead *St Alb* 90-94; TV 94-98; TR Mortlake w E Sheen *S'wark* from 98; RD Richmond and Barnes from 00; Hon Can S'wark Cathl from 03. *The Rectory, 170 Sheen Lane, London SW14 8LZ* Tel (020) 8876 4816 E-mail pjackson@all-in.co.uk

JACKSON, Miss Freda. b 41. Bp Otter Coll TCert61 LNSM course 89. **d** 92 **p** 94. OLM Middleton *Man* 92-94; OLM Middleton w Thornham from 94. *783 Manchester Old Road, Middleton, Manchester M24 4RE* Tel 0161-653 5876

JACKSON, George. b 10. St Jo Coll Dur LTh33 BA35 MA39. St Aid Birkenhead 30. **d** 35 **p** 36. C Preston St Cuth *Blackb* 35-37; C Accrington St Jas 38-40; V Haslingden St Jo Stonefold 40-43; V Blackb St Mich 43-53; V Woodplumpton 53-74; C Broughton 74-77; rtd 77; Perm to Offic *Blackb* from 75. *Starr Hills Methodist Home, Ansdell Road South, Lytham St Annes FY8 5PQ* Tel (01253) 735037

JACKSON, Harry Francis. b 30. K Coll Lon BD61 AKC61 FBOA FBCO. Sarum Th Coll 61. **d** 62 **p** 62. Bermuda 62-65; C Cobham *Guildf* 65-69; R Ash 69-96; Chapl RAF Farnborough 80-96; rtd 96; P-in-c Mawnan *Truro* 96-01; Perm to Offic from 02. *Rosnython, Treliever Road, Mabe Burnthouse, Penryn TR10 9EX* Tel (01326) 372532 E-mail rev.harry@pgen.net

JACKSON, Hilary Walton. b 17. St Chad's Coll Dur BA40 MA48. **d** 46 **p** 47. C Selby Abbey *York* 46-49; C Middlesbrough All SS 49-51; V Thornley *Dur* 51-56; V Beamish 56-66; V Heighington 66-82; rtd 82. *127 Bates Avenue, Darlington DL3 0UE* Tel (01325) 243794 E-mail hilary.jackson@durham.anglican.org

JACKSON, Ian. b 53. Jes Coll Ox BA75. Linc Th Coll 76. **d** 78 **p** 79. C Holbeach *Linc* 78-82; V Newsome *Wakef* 82-85; V Newsome and Armitage Bridge 85-03; TR Em TM from 03. *The Vicarage, Jackroyd Lane, Newsome, Huddersfield HD4 6QU* Tel (01484) 308664

JACKSON, Mrs Janet Lesley. b 45. Newc Poly CQSW78 ACertC93. NEOC 93. d 96 p 97. NSM Whorlton Newc 96-98; Chapl St Oswald's Hospice Newc from 98. The Vicarage, Thornhill Road, Ponteland, Newcastle upon Tyne NE20 9PZ Tel (01661) 822140

JACKSON, Mrs Joan. b 44. Bolton Coll of Educn CertEd71 Lanc Univ MA98. Carl and Blackb Dioc Tr Inst 95. d 98 p 99. NSM Staveley, Ings and Kentmere Carl 98-00; Chapl Furness Hosps NHS Trust 98-00; Asst Chapl Bradf Hosps NHS Trust from 00; NSM Bingley H Trin Bradf from 03. 3 Cathedral Close, Bradford BD1 4EG Tel (01274) 737354

JACKSON, John Edward. b 29. K Coll Lon BD57 AKC57. St Boniface Warminster 57. d 58 p 59. C Crofton Park St Hilda w St Cypr S'wark 58-61; V Bremhill w Foxham Sarum 61-69; V Netheravon w Fittleton 69-73; V Netheravon w Fittleton and Enford 73-85; OCF 69-85; V Salisbury St Mark Sarum 85-92; P-in-c Bryngwyn and Newchurch and Llanbedr etc S & B 92-96; rtd 96. The Cloister, 1 Hermon Villas, Rhosgoch, Builth Wells LD2 3JY Tel (01497) 851660

JACKSON, John Frazier. b 52. Cedarville Coll Ohio BA79 Capital Univ Ohio JD83 Reformed Th Sem Mississippi MA96 Worc Coll Ox DPhil01. St Alb and Ox Min Course 99. d 00 p 01. C Kidlington w Hampton Poyle Ox from 00. 33 Hampden Drive, Kidlington OX5 2LR Tel (01865) 424620 Mobile 07980-045276 E-mail john.jackson@worcester.ac.uk

JACKSON, John Reginald. b 25. Selw Coll Cam BA45 MA49. Ridley Hall Cam 45. d 48 p 49. C Doncaster St Jas Sheff 48-50; C Walcot B & W 50-53; C Cheltenham St Mark Glouc 53-56; R Down Ex 56-67; R Georgeham 67-73; V Abbotsley Ely 73-79; V Everton w Tetworth 73-79; V Waresley 73-79; P-in-c Garway Heref 79-85; P-in-c St Weonards w Orcop 79-85; P-in-c Tretire w Michaelchurch and Pencoyd 79-85; P-in-c Welsh Newton w Llanrothal 79-85; rtd 85; Perm to Offic Heref 85-97. 4 Rosemary Gardens, Hereford HR1 1UP Tel (01432) 270271

JACKSON, Preb John Wilson. b 14. St Jo Coll Dur BA38. Wycliffe Hall Ox 38. d 40 p 41. C Bordesley H Trin Birm 40-41; C Sparkhill St Jo 41-44; C Walsall St Matt Lich 44-46; R Birm All SS Birm 46-50; V Bromley Common St Aug Roch 50-52; V Sparkhill St Jo Birm 52-64; Chapl Birm Women's Hosp 52-64; Hon Can Birm Cathl Birm 61-64; V Swindon Ch Ch Bris 64-68; Chapl Swindon Hosps 64-68; V Walsall Lich 68-81; RD Walsall 68-81; Preb Lich Cathl 72-81; rtd 81; Perm to Offic Birm from 82. 6 St Margaret's Court, Kineton Green Road, Solihull B92 7DZ Tel 0121-707 5748 Mobile 07812-913328

JACKSON, Miss Kathryn Dianne. b 64. Leeds Univ BA87 MA01. St Steph Ho Ox 87. d 90 p 94. Par Dn Headingley Ripon 90-94; C Hawksworth Wood 94-00; P-in-c Scarborough St Columba York from 00; Chapl St Cath Hospice Scarborough from 00. 160 Dean Road, Scarborough YO12 7JH Tel (01723) 375070

JACKSON, Kenneth Evans. b 30. Kelham Th Coll 50. d 54 p 55. C Coppenhall Ches 54-57; C Stockport St Alb Hall Street 57-60; CF 60-67; R Lewtrenchard w Thrushelton Ex 67-77; P-in-c Stowford 73-77; P-in-c Malborough w S Huish 77-83; P-in-c W Alvington w S Milton 83-83; V Malborough w S Huish, W Alvington and Churchstow 83-86; P-in-c Lustleigh 86-95; NSM 95-96; rtd 95; Perm to Offic Ex 96-99. 28 Staddons View, Bovey Tracey, Newton Abbot TQ13 9HN Tel (01626) 832736

JACKSON, Kenneth William. b 30. MCSP53. Chich Th Coll 70. d 72 p 73. C Eastney Portsm 72-74; C Portchester 75-79; V Elson 79-95; rtd 95. 13 Jellicoe Avenue, Gosport PO12 2PA Tel (023) 9258 7089

JACKSON, Margaret Elizabeth. b 47. Lon Univ BSc68 MSc95 FCIPD91. S'wark Ord Course DipRS83. dss 83 d 92 p 94. Surbiton Hill Ch Ch S'wark 83-84; Saffron Walden w Wendens Ambo and Littlebury Chelmsf 84-85; Dulwich St Barn S'wark 86-97; Hon C 92-97; Personal Asst to Bp S'wark 92-94; Selection Sec Min Division 96-00; NSM Churt Guildf 98-01; NSM The Bourne and Tilford from 01. Rise Cottage, Hale House Lane, Churt, Farnham GU10 2JG Tel (01428) 714411 or (01722) 413386 Fax (01428) 714426
E-mail k.m.jackson@btinternet.com

JACKSON, Mrs Margaret Elizabeth. b 47. Mon Dioc Tr Scheme. d 87 p 94. C Chepstow Mon 87-90; C Exhall Cov 90-92; C Leamington Priors All SS 92-96; R Hulme Ascension Man 96-99; V Alstonfield, Butterton, Ilam etc Lich from 99; RD Alstonfield 00-03. The Vicarage, Alstonefield, Ashbourne DE6 2FX Tel (01335) 310216 E-mail maggie.walton@virgin.net

JACKSON, Canon Margaret Jane. b 50. RGN72 S Bank Poly HDipHV75. S'wark Ord Course 89. d 92 p 94. Par Dn Hatcham St Cath S'wark 92-94; C 94-98; V Mottingham St Edw from 98; Hon Can S'wark Cathl from 03. St Edward's Vicarage, St Keverne Road, London SE9 4AQ Tel (020) 8857 6278
E-mail margaretjjackson@compuserve.com

JACKSON, Ms Marie Ann. b 45. Nottm Univ BSc66. St Alb and Ox Min Course 98. d 98 p 99. OLM High Wycombe Ox from 98. 19 New Road, Sands, High Wycombe HP12 4LH Tel (01494) 530728

JACKSON, Mark Harding. b 51. Open Univ BA87. Sarum & Wells Th Coll 76. d 79 p 80. C Hobs Moat Birm 79-83; Chapl RN from 83. Royal Naval Chaplaincy Service, Room 203, Victory Building, HM Naval Base, Portsmouth PO1 3LS Tel (023) 9272 7903 Fax 9272 7111

JACKSON, Martin. b 56. Clare Coll Cam BA77 MA81 Dur Univ MA97. Cranmer Hall Dur BA80. d 81 p 82. C Houghton le Spring Dur 81-84; C Bishopwearmouth St Mich w St Hilda 84-86; TV Winlaton 86; V High Spen and Rowlands Gill 86-94; P-in-c Benfieldside 94-97; V from 97; AD Lanchester from 00. St Cuthbert's Vicarage, Church Bank, Consett DH8 0NW Tel (01207) 503019 Fax 588399
E-mail martin.jackson@durham.anglican.org

JACKSON, Matthew Christopher. b 75. Univ of Wales (Abth) BD96 MTh98. Ripon Coll Cuddesdon. d 01 p 02. C King's Lynn St Marg w St Nic Nor from 01. 29 Goodwins Road, King's Lynn PE30 5QX Tel (01553) 692904
E-mail matthew-jackson@talk21.com

JACKSON, Mrs Melanie Jane Susann. b 60. Univ of W of England BA83 Leic Univ MA94. SW Minl Tr Course 97. d 00 p 01. C Ottery St Mary, Alfington, W Hill, Tipton etc Ex from 00. Garden Close, 121 Yonder Street, Ottery St Mary EX11 1HH Tel (01404) 814078 E-mail melaniejackson@cwcom.net

✠JACKSON, The Rt Revd Michael Geoffrey St Aubyn. b 56. TCD BA79 MA82 St Jo Coll Cam BA81 MA85 PhD86 Ch Ch Ox MA89 DPhil89. CITC 86. d 86 p 87 c 02. C Dublin Zion Ch D & G 86-89; Chapl Ch Ch Ox 89-97; Student 93-97; Dean Cork C, C & R 97-02; I Cork St Fin Barre's Union 97-02; Chapl and Asst Lect Univ Coll Cork 98-02; Chapl Cork Inst of Tech 98-02; Bp Clogh from 02. The See House, Ballagh Road, Fivemiletown BT75 0QP Tel (028) 8952 1265 Fax 8952 2299
E-mail jacksmic@indigo.ie

JACKSON, Michael Ian. Southn Univ BA. STETS. d 03. NSM Twyford and Owslebury and Morestead Win from 03. Hill Farm Lodge, Morestead, Winchester SO21 1LZ Tel (01962) 777277

JACKSON, Michael James. b 44. Liv Univ BEng65 Newc Univ PhD84 CEng69 MICE69. NEOC 82. d 84 p 85. C Houghton le Spring Dur 84-87; V Millfield St Mark 87-95; V Ponteland Newc from 95; AD Newc W from 03. The Vicarage, Thornhill Road, Ponteland, Newcastle upon Tyne NE20 9PZ Tel (01661) 822140

JACKSON, Michael Richard. b 31. Selw Coll Cam BA54 MA58. Westcott Ho Cam 54. d 56 p 57. C Gosforth All SS Newc 56-62; R Dinnington Sheff 62-76; V Swinton 76-97; rtd 97; Perm to Offic Sheff from 97. 10 Elmhirst Drive, Rotherham S65 3ED

JACKSON, Norman. b 14. St Jo Coll Dur BA39 DipTh40 MA42. d 40 p 41. C Chorley St Geo Blackb 40-42; C Poulton-le-Fylde 42-45; Distr Sec (Man Area) BFBS 45-49; V Bolton H Trin Man 49-53; V Norden w Ashworth 53-69; R St Mewan Truro 69-79; rtd 80; Perm to Offic Carl 82-93. 23 Riverbank Road, Kendal LA9 5JS

JACKSON, Norman. b 20. CEng MIMechE53. S'wark Ord Course 74. d 77 p 78. NSM Erith Ch Ch Roch 77-82; NSM Bishopstoke Win 82-95; rtd 95; Perm to Offic Win from 95. 7 Otter Close, Eastleigh SO50 8NF Tel (023) 8069 5045

JACKSON, Peggy. See JACKSON, Canon Frances Anne

JACKSON, Peter. See JACKSON, Thomas Peter

JACKSON, Peter. b 39. Open Univ BA81. St Jo Coll Nottm LTh85. d 85 p 86. C Clifton York 85-88; Chapl Clifton Hosp York 85-88; TV Moor Allerton Ripon 88-98; V Holbeck from 98. St Luke's Vicarage, Malvern View, Leeds LS11 8SG Tel 0113-271 7996 E-mail pandarjackson@email.msn.com

JACKSON, Peter Charles. b 71. Univ of Northumbria at Newc BA95. Oak Hill Th Coll BA01. d 02. C Lowestoft Ch Ch Nor from 02. 10 Station Road, Lowestoft NR32 4QF Tel (01502) 508695

JACKSON, Peter Jonathan Edward. b 53. St Pet Coll Ox BA74 MA78 PGCE78. St Steph Ho Ox 79. d 79 p 80. Lect Westmr Coll Ox 79-80; Hon C Ox St Mich w St Martin and All SS Ox 79-80; C Malvern Link w Cowleigh Worc 79-82; Chapl Aldenham Sch Herts 82-89; Chapl and Hd RE Harrow Sch 89-01; Lect K Coll Lon 92-99; Dir Chr Educn and Assoc R Washington St Patr USA 01-03; V Southgate Ch Ch Lon from 03. The Vicarage, 1 The Green, London N14 7EG Tel (020) 8886 0384
E-mail peter.jackson@london.anglican.org

JACKSON, Peter Lewis. b 34. Bps' Coll Cheshunt 63. d 66 p 67. C Stockingford Cov 66-67; C Kenilworth St Nic 67-72; P-in-c Napton on the Hill 72-75; V 75-89; V Lower Shuckburgh 75-89; R Napton-on-the-Hill, Lower Shuckburgh etc 89-99; rtd 99; Perm to Offic Cov from 99. 66 Arthur Street, Kenilworth CV8 2HE Tel (01926) 864234

JACKSON, Rachel Anne. b 57. d 03. OLM Barnham Broom and Upper Yare Nor from 03. Red Hall, Red Hall Lane, Southburgh, Thetford IP25 7TG Tel (01362) 821032

JACKSON, Richard Charles. b 61. Ch Ch Ox BA83 Cranfield Inst of Tech MSc85. Trin Coll Bris DipHE94. d 94 p 95. C Lindfield Chich 94-98; V Rudgwick from 98. The Vicarage, Rudgwick, Horsham RH12 3DD Tel (01403) 822127
E-mail rjac187233@aol.com

JACKSON, Richard Hugh. b 44. St Jo Coll York CertEd66 UEA MA84. LNSM course 96. **d** 98 **p** 99. OLM Stalham and E Ruston w Brunstead *Nor* 98-00; OLM Stalham, E Ruston, Brunstead, Sutton and Ingham from 00. *5 Rivermead, Stalham, Norwich NR12 9PH* Tel (01692) 581389

JACKSON, Robert. b 69. Nottm Univ BA01. St Jo Coll Nottm 98. **d** 01 **p** 02. C Altham w Clayton le Moors *Blackb* 01-03; C Blackb St Gabr from 03. *St Gabriel's House, 1 Chatsworth Close, Blackburn BB1 8QH* Tel (01254) 697632 Mobile 07703-824849 E-mail jacksonsrt@aol.com

JACKSON, Robert Brandon. b 61. Lanchester Poly BA86 Ox Univ BA88 MA95. Wycliffe Hall Ox 86. **d** 89 **p** 90. C Bromley Common St Aug *Roch* 89-92; P-in-c Stowe *Ox* 92-97; Asst Chapl Stowe Sch 92-97; Chapl Ld Wandsworth Coll Basingstoke 97-02; Chapl Stowe Sch from 02. *Stowe School, Buckingham MK18 5EH* Tel (01280) 818000

JACKSON, Robert Fielden. b 35. St D Coll Lamp BA57. Sarum Th Coll 57. **d** 59 **p** 60. C Altham w Clayton le Moors *Blackb* 59-62; C Lytham St Cuth 62-64; V Skerton St Chad 64-69; V Preesall 69-90; RD Garstang 85-89; V Wray w Tatham and Tatham Fells 90-00; rtd 00; Perm to Offic *Blackb* from 01. *8 Squirrel's Chase, Lostock Hall, Preston PR5 5NE* Tel (01772) 338756

JACKSON, Robert William. b 49. K Coll Cam MA73 Man Univ MA. St Jo Coll Nottm 78. **d** 81 **p** 82. C Fulwood *Sheff* 81-84; V Grenoside 84-92; Chapl Grenoside Hosp Sheff 84-92; V Scarborough St Mary w Ch Ch and H Apostles *York* 92-01; Springboard Missr from 01; Perm to Offic from 01. *1 Wilkinson's Close, West Ayton, Scarborough YO13 9LQ* Tel (01723) 863088 E-mail bobjackson@springboard.uk.net

JACKSON, Roger. b 57. Chich Th Coll 85. **d** 88 **p** 89. C Hale *Guildf* 88-92; V Barton w Peel Green *Man* 92-95; P-in-c Long Crendon w Chearsley and Nether Winchendon *Ox* 95-00; V from 00. *The Vicarage, 84A High Street, Long Crendon, Aylesbury HP18 9AL* Tel (01844) 208363 Fax as telephone E-mail vicarlc@supanet.com

JACKSON, Canon Roger Brumby. b 31. Dur Univ BSc53 DipEd54. Ridley Hall Cam 57. **d** 59 **p** 60. C Rowner *Portsm* 59-61; C Drypool St Columba w St Andr and St Pet *York* 61-64; Asst Chapl HM Pris Hull 61-64; V Plumstead St Jas w St Jo *S'wark* 65-68; P-in-c Plumstead St Paul 65-68; V Plumstead St Jo w St Jas and St Paul 68-74; Sub-Dean Woolwich 71-74; Chapl Hulton Hosp Bolton 74-94; Chapl Bolton Hosp NHS Trust 94-01; V Deane *Man* 74-80; RD Bolton 80-85; AD Deane 80-85; Hon Can Man Cathl 90-01; rtd 01; Perm to Offic *Man* from 01. *17 Bentworth Close, Westhoughton, Bolton BL5 2GN* Tel (01942) 813209

JACKSON, Preb Roland Francis. b 20. Univ of Wales (Lamp) BA42. St Mich Coll Llan 42. **d** 44 **p** 45. C Risca *Mon* 44-49; C Chepstow St Arvan's w Penterry 49-54; R Haughton *Lich* 54-61; V Stafford St Paul Forebridge 61-72; RD Eccleshall 72-82; Chapl HM Pris Drake Hall 75-85; V Eccleshall *Lich* 72-85; Preb Lich Cathl 82-85; rtd 85; Perm to Offic *Lich* from 85. *Treginnis, 29 Meadow Drive, Haughton, Stafford ST18 9HQ* Tel (01785) 780571

JACKSON, Canon Ronald William. b 37. ALCD. **d** 69 **p** 70. C Crofton *Portsm* 69-74; V Wolverhampton St Matt *Lich* 74-85; V Bloxwich 85-89; C Tamworth 89-92; Bp's Officer for Par Miss and Development *Bradf* 92-98; Hon Can Bradf Cathl 94-98; rtd 98; Perm to Offic *Bradf* from 98. *94 Primrose Lane, Bingley BD16 4QP* Tel and fax (01274) 510642 E-mail rjackson@bingley.u-net.com

JACKSON, Ruth Ellen. b 69. Dub City Univ BBS91. CITC BTh02. **d** 02 **p** 03. C Portadown St Mark *Arm* from 02. *115 Brownstown Road, Portadown BT62 3PZ* Tel (028) 3833 5562

JACKSON, Miss Ruth Victoria. b 78. Univ Coll Dur BA99 Fitzw Coll Cam BA01. Ridley Hall Cam 99. **d** 02. C York St Mich-le-Belfrey *York* from 02. *11 Rydal Avenue, Burnholme, York YO31 0LS* Tel (01904) 423910

JACKSON, Canon Stanley. b 21. St Cath Soc Ox BA48 MA52. Linc Th Coll 48. **d** 50 **p** 51. C Swinton St Pet *Man* 50-52; C Skegness *Linc* 52-56; CF 56-68; R Lt Coates *Linc* 68-77; R Bradley 75-77; TR Gt and Lt Coates w Bradley 78; C Ruskington 78-86; V Dorrington 78-82; Can and Preb Linc Cathl 79-97; rtd 86; Perm to Offic *Linc* from 97. *73A Lincoln Road, Ruskington, Sleaford NG34 9AR* Tel (01526) 832821

JACKSON (née STAFF), Mrs Susan. b 59. Leeds Univ BA82. Ridley Hall Cam 88. **d** 90 **p** 94. Par Dn Mickleover All SS *Derby* 90-93; Par Dn Chatham St Wm *Roch* 93-94; C 94-97; TV Walton Milton Keynes *Ox* from 97. *The Rectory, London Road, Broughton, Milton Keynes MK10 9AA* Tel (01908) 667846

JACKSON, Thomas Peter. b 27. Univ of Wales (Lamp) BA50. St Mich Coll Llan 50. **d** 52 **p** 53. C Swansea St Mary and H Trin *S & B* 52-58; Area Sec (S Midl and S Wales) UMCA 58-60; V Glouc St Steph *Glouc* 60-73; R Upton St Leonards 73-92; RD Glouc N 82-91; rtd 92; Perm to Offic *Glouc* from 92. *44 Grebe Close, Gloucester GL4 9XL* Tel (01452) 533769

JACKSON, Wendy Pamela. b 45. Th Ext Educn Coll 99. **d** 00 **p** 02. S Africa 00-03; Community P Woodlands 02-03; C

Crediton, Shobrooke and Sandford etc *Ex* from 03. *14 Linhay Park, Sandford, Crediton EX17 4LL* Tel (01363) 776342 E-mail wendy@davwen.freeserve.co.uk

JACKSON, Canon William Stanley Peter. b 39. Univ of Wales DipTh66. St Mich Coll Llan 63. **d** 66 **p** 67. C Llandrindod w Cefnllys *S & B* 66-69; C Gowerton w Waunarlwydd 69-73; V Crickadarn w Gwenddwr and Alltmawr 73-79; R Llanfeugan w Llanthetty etc from 79; Dioc GFS Chapl 84-92; Can Res Brecon Cathl from 90; Prec 98-99; Treas 99-00; Chan from 00; Dioc Communications Officer 92-94; RD Crickhowell 98-02. *The Rectory, Talybont-on-Usk, Brecon LD3 7UX* Tel (01874) 676243 Fax 676499 E-mail canonjacko@aol.com

JACKSON-STEVENS, Preb Nigel. b 42. St Steph Ho Ox. **d** 68 **p** 69. C Babbacombe *Ex* 68-73; P-in-c W Buckland 73-75; V Swimbridge 73-75; V Swimbridge and W Buckland 75-84; P-in-c Mortehoe 84-85; P-in-c Ilfracombe, Lee, W Down, Woolacombe and Bittadon 84-85; TR Ilfracombe, Lee, Woolacombe, Bittadon etc from 85; RD Barnstaple 93-97; Preb Ex Cathl from 95. *The Vicarage, St Brannock's Road, Ilfracombe EX34 8EG* Tel (01271) 863467

JACOB, Mrs Amelia Stanley. b 52. Punjab Univ BA73. Oak Hill Th Coll. **d** 90 **p** 94. NSM Asian Chr Congregation All SS Tufnell Park *Lon* 90-92; NSM Alperton from 92. *62 Clifford Road, Wembley HA0 1AE* Tel (020) 8902 4592

JACOB, John Lionel Andrew. b 26. Selw Coll Cam BA50 MA54. Westcott Ho Cam 50. **d** 52 **p** 53. C Brightside St Thos *Sheff* 52-55; C Maltby 55-58; V Doncaster Intake 58-67; V Sheff St Aid w St Luke 67-75; TR Sheff Manor 75-82; R Waddington *Linc* 82-91; rtd 91; Perm to Offic *Linc* 91-00. *1 Woburn Avenue, Lincoln LN1 3HJ* Tel (01522) 513772

JACOB, Canon Joseph. b 38. CITC 65. **d** 68 **p** 69. C Belfast St Aid *Conn* 68-70; Bp's Dom Chapl 70-71; I Kilscoran *C & O* 71-80; I Geashill *M & K* 80-83; Asst Warden Ch's Min of Healing 83-86; Gen Sec (Ireland) CMJ 87-91; I Ardamine, Kilnamanagh w Monamolin *C & O* 91-98; Preb Ferns Cathl 96-98; rtd 98. *Crannaulin, Clonmullen, Bunclody, Co Wexford, Irish Republic* Tel (00353) (54) 77532

JACOB, Neville Peter. b 60. Kent Univ BA82 Leeds Metrop Univ PGCE86. Ripon Coll Cuddesdon 94. **d** 96 **p** 97. C Market Harborough *Leic* 96-97; C Market Harborough Transfiguration 96-97; C Market Harborough and The Transfiguration etc 97-99; Chapl Miss to Seafarers 99-03; P-in-c Copythorne *Win* from 03; Chapl Ibex from 03. *The Vicarage, Pine Ridge, Romsey Road, Cadnam, Southampton SO40 2NN* Tel (023) 8081 4769 Fax as telephone E-mail raveknave@tinyworld.co.uk

JACOB, The Ven William Mungo. b 44. Hull Univ LLB66 Linacre Coll Ox BA69 MA73 Ex Univ PhD. St Steph Ho Ox 70. **d** 70 **p** 71. C Wymondham *Nor* 70-73; Asst Chapl Ex Univ *Ex* 73-75; Dir Past Studies Sarum & Wells Th Coll 75-80; Vice-Prin 77-80; Selection Sec and Sec Cttee for Th Educn ACCM 80-86; Warden Linc Th Coll 85-96; Can and Preb Linc Cathl *Linc* 86-96; Hon C Linc Minster Gp 88-96; Adn Charing Cross *Lon* from 96; Bp's Sen Chapl 96-00; R St Giles-in-the-Fields from 00. *15A Gower Street, London WC1E 6HW* Tel (020) 7636 4646 Fax 7937 2560 E-mail archdeacon.charingcross@london.anglican.org

JACOBS, Michael David. b 41. Ex Coll Ox BA63 MA67. Chich Th Coll 63. **d** 65 **p** 66. C Walthamstow St Pet *Chelmsf* 65-68; Chapl Sussex Univ *Chich* 68-72; Student Cllr Leic Univ *Leic* 72-84; Sen Lect from 84; Dir Cen for Past Care and Counselling 84-91. *Vaughan College, St Nicholas' Circle, Leicester LE1 4LB* Tel 0116-251 7368 E-mail mdj2u@aol.com

JACOBS, Neville Robertson Eynesford. b 32. Lon Coll of Div ALCD59 LTh74. **d** 59 **p** 60. C Chesham St Mary *Ox* 59-62; CMS 62-67; C Keynsham *B & W* 67-71; R Croscombe and Dinder 72-80; R Pilton w Croscombe, N Wootton and Dinder 80-83; V Biddenham *St Alb* 83-89; V Chipping Sodbury and Old Sodbury *Glouc* 89-97; RD Hawkesbury 91-94; rtd 97; Perm to Offic *S'wark* from 98. *22 Comforts Farm Avenue, Hurst Green, Oxted RH8 9DH* Tel (01883) 714127

JACOBS, Peter John. b 33. JP. CMIWSc MICFM. SEITE 96. **d** 96 **p** 97. NSM Boughton under Blean w Dunkirk and Hernhill *Cant* 96-99; NSM Murston w Bapchild and Tonge 99-02; rtd 02; Perm to Offic *Cant* from 02. *13 Crown Gardens, Canterbury CT2 8LQ* Tel (01227) 455733 E-mail peter@pjacobs72.freeserve.co.uk

JACQUES, Barry John. b 52. Open Univ BSc95. Wycliffe Hall Ox 00. **d** 02 **p** 03. NSM Attleborough *Cov* from 02. *6 Easedale Close, Nuneaton CV11 6EX* Tel (024) 7638 1107 E-mail bjjacques@screaming.net

JACQUES, Mrs Margaret Irene. b 53. St Jo Coll Nottm BA03. **d** 03. C W Hallam and Mapperley w Stanley *Derby* from 03. *8 The Crescent, Stanley Common, Ilkeston DE7 6GH* Tel 0115-944 1811 Mobile 07866-415116 E-mail jacamk@ajacques.fsworld.co.uk

JACQUES, Martin. b 62. Coll of Resurr Mirfield 00. **d** 02 **p** 03. C Margate St Jo *Cant* from 02. *173 Ramsgate Road, Margate CT9 4EY* Tel (01843) 293209 E-mail martin@jacques1078.freeserve.co.uk

JACQUET, Trevor Graham. b 56. Man Univ BSc77. Oak Hill Th Coll BA88. **d** 88 **p** 89. C Deptford St Nic and St Luke *S'wark* 88-92; Chapl HM Pris Brixton 92-95; Chapl HM Pris Elmley from 95; Perm to Offic *S'wark* from 96. *HM Prison Elmley, Eastchurch, Sheerness ME12 4DZ* Tel (01795) 880808 Fax 880118 E-mail trevor@jacquet2.freeserve.co.uk

JACSON, Edward Shallcross Owen. b 38. St Steph Ho Ox 61. **d** 64 **p** 65. C Yate *Glouc* 64-67; C Churchdown 67-71; P-in-c Sandhurst 71-75; V Sherborne w Windrush and the Barringtons 75-76; V Sherborne, Windrush, the Barringtons etc 76-80; TV Shaston *Sarum* 80-87; Perm to Offic 88-90; Lic to Offic from 90. *Grove Farm House, Melbury Abbas, Shaftesbury SP7 0DE* Tel (01747) 853688

JAGE-BOWLER, Christopher William. b 61. Nottm Univ BA83 Ch Ch Ox PGCE84 Down Coll Cam BA89 MA95. Ridley Hall Cam 87. **d** 90 **p** 91. C Downend *Bris* 90-94; Chapl Bris Univ 94-96; C Bris St Mich and St Paul 94-96; Asst Chapl Berlin *Eur* 96-97; Chapl from 97. *Goethestrasse 31, 13158 Berlin, Germany* Tel (0049) (30) 917 2248 Fax as telephone E-mail office@stgeorges.de

JAGGER, The Ven Ian. b 55. K Coll Cam BA77 MA81 St Jo Coll Dur BA80 MA87. Cranmer Hall Dur 78. **d** 82 **p** 83. C Twickenham St Mary *Lon* 82-85; P-in-c Willen *Ox* 85-87; TV Stantonbury and Willen 87-94; TR Fareham H Trin *Portsm* 94-98; Dioc Ecum Officer 94-96; RD Fareham 96-98; Can Missr 98-01; Adn Auckland *Dur* from 01; Dioc Rural Development Officer from 01. *2 Etherley Lane, Bishop Auckland DL14 7QR* Tel (01388) 451635 Fax 607502 E-mail archdeacon.of.auckland@durham.anglican.org

JAGGER, Peter John. b 38. Lambeth MA71 Leeds Univ MPhil76 PhD87 FRHistS78. Wesley Coll Leeds 62 Coll of Resurr Mirfield 67. **d** 68 **p** 69. C Leeds All SS *Ripon* 68-71; V Bolton w Redmire 71-77; Warden and Chief Lib St Deiniol's Lib Hawarden 77-97; Dir of Self Supporting Min 77-97; Lic to Offic *St As* 77-02; rtd 97; Perm to Offic *St E* from 03. *12 Eastlands, Stradbroke, Eye IP21 5JA* Tel (01379) 384292

JAGGER (née GREEN), Mrs Ruth Valerie. b 56. Ex Univ CertEd77. Ox NSM Course 87. **d** 90 **p** 94. NSM Stantonbury and Willen *Ox* 90-94; NSM Fareham H Trin *Portsm* 94-98; NSM Portsm Deanery 98-01; Perm to Offic *Dur* from 02. *2 Etherly Lane, Bishop Auckland DL14 7QR* Tel (01388) 451635 Fax 607502

JAGGS, Michael Richard Moore. b 37. Toronto Univ PhD67 FADO61 FBDO85. S Dios Minl Tr Scheme DipHE95. **d** 95 **p** 96. NSM Hook *Win* 95-99; NSM Basing 99; C Newnham w Nately Scures w Mapledurwell etc from 99. *Turnpike Field, London Road, Hartley Wintney, Hook RG27 8HY* Tel (01252) 842658 Mobile 07973-384777 Fax (01252) 845658

JAGO, Alfred Douglas James. b 28. Leeds Univ BA30. Coll of Resurr Mirfield 30. **d** 32 **p** 33. C Plymouth St Pet *Ex* 32-42; C-in-c Honicknowle CD 42-57; V Honicknowle 57; V Penwerris *Truro* 57-65; RD Carnmarth S 63-65; R St Stephen in Brannel 65-76; RD St Austell 71-76; rtd 76; Hon C Charlestown *Truro* from 77. *22 Fairbourne Road, St Austell PL25 4NR* Tel (01726) 75208

JAGO, Christine May. b 52. SRN73. OLM course 92. **d** 94 **p** 95. OLM St Buryan, St Levan and Sennen *Truro* from 94. *Boscarne House, St Buryan, Penzance TR19 6HR* Tel (01736) 810374 Fax 810070 E-mail w-cjago@supanet.com

JAGO, David. b 48. Shoreditch Coll Lon CertEd69 Birm Univ BPhil77 Hull Univ Dip Counselling 93. St Steph Ho Ox DipMin95. **d** 97 **p** 98. C S Bank *York* 97-00; V Middlesbrough St Martin w St Cuth from 00. *St Martin's Vicarage, Kirby Avenue, Middlesbrough TS5 4LA* Tel (01642) 819634

JAKEMAN, Francis David. b 47. Leeds Univ BSc69 Ealing Coll of Educn DMS81. Cuddesdon Coll 71. **d** 74 **p** 75. C G Grinstead St Mary and St Jas *Linc* 74-77; Ind Chapl *Lon* 77-88; V Harrow Weald All SS from 88; Chapl Weald Coll from 88. *The Vicarage, 175 Uxbridge Road, Harrow HA3 6TP* Tel (020) 8954 0247 *or* 8954 8865 E-mail f.jakeman@themail.co.uk

JALLAND, Hilary Gervase Alexander. b 50. Ex Univ BA72. Coll of Resurr Mirfield 74. **d** 76 **p** 77. C Ex St Thos *Ex* 76-80; C Ex St Thos and Em 80; C Portsea St Mary *Portsm* 80-86; V Hempton and Pudding Norton *Nor* 86-90; TV Hawarden *St As* 90-93; R Llandysilio and Penrhos and Llandrinio etc 93-03; V Towyn and St George from 03. *7 Parc Gwellyn, Kinmel Bay, Rhyl LL18 5HN* Tel (01745) 356362 E-mail hgajalland@talk21.com

JAMES, Andrew Nicholas. b 54. BSc76. Trin Coll Bris 77. **d** 80 **p** 81. C Prescot *Liv* 80-83; C Upholland 83-85; V Hindley Green 85-91; V Dean Forest H Trin *Glouc* from 91; RD Forest S from 97. *Holy Trinity Vicarage, Oakland Road, Harrow Hill, Drybrook GL17 9JX* Tel (01594) 542232 E-mail andrew@dean-net.co.uk

JAMES, Andrew Peter. b 69. Glam Univ BSc96 Univ of Wales (Cardiff) BTh99. St Mich Coll Llan 96. **d** 99 **p** 00. C Roath *Llan* 99-01; C Radyr from 01. *32 Glyn Simon Close, Cardiff CF5 2RZ* Tel (029) 2069 3054 E-mail jamesfra@hotmail.com

JAMES, Anne Loraine. b 45. St Jo Coll Nottm CertCS TISEC Cert Miss Studies97. **d** 90 **p** 94. NSM Ellon *Ab* 90-99; NSM Cruden Bay 90-99; NSM Alford 99-02; P-in-c from 02. *St Andrew's House, 53 Main Street, Alford AB33 8PX* Tel (01975) 564006 E-mail revanne.alford@virgin.net

JAMES, Barry Paul. b 49. BSc. Sarum & Wells Th Coll. **d** 82 **p** 83. C Bitterne Park *Win* 82-86; V Southampton St Mary Extra 86-00; R Fawley from 00. *The Rectory, 1 Sheringham Close, Southampton SO45 1SQ* Tel (023) 8089 3552

JAMES, Brian. *See* JAMES, The Ven David Brian

JAMES, Brother. *See* PICKEN, James Hugh

JAMES, Brunel Hugh Grayburn. b 70. Selw Coll Cam BA93 MA93. Wycliffe Hall Ox BA97 DipMin98. **d** 98 **p** 99. C Thornbury *Bradf* 98-02; R Barwick in Elmet *Ripon* from 02. *The Rectory, Main Street, Barwick in Elmet, Leeds LS15 4JQ* Tel 0113-281 2218 Mobile 07790-880220 E-mail brunel@fish.co.uk

JAMES, Miss Carolyn Anne. b 65. Coll of Ripon & York St Jo BA87 Nottm Univ BTh91. Linc Th Coll 88. **d** 91 **p** 94. Par Dn Middleton St Mary *Ripon* 91-94; C Wetherby 94-97; V Kirkstall from 97. *Kirkstall Vicarage, Vicarage View, Leeds LS5 3HF* Tel 0113-278 1007

✠**JAMES, The Rt Revd Colin Clement Walter.** b 26. K Coll Cam BA49 MA51. Cuddesdon Coll 50. **d** 52 **p** 53 **c** 73. C Stepney St Dunstan and All SS *Lon* 52-55; Asst Chapl Stowe Sch 55-56; Chapl 56-59; Asst in Relig Broadcasting BBC 59-60; Relig Broadcasting Org W Region BBC 60-67; V Bournemouth St Pet *Win* 67-73; P-in-c Bournemouth St Steph 70-73; Dir of Tr 72-77; Can Res Win Cathl 73-77; Suff Bp Basingstoke 73-77; Bp Wakef 77-85; Bp Win 85-95; rtd 95; Hon Asst Bp B & W 95-01. *35 Christchurch Road, Winchester SO23 9SY* Tel (01962) 868874 Fax as telephone

JAMES, Colin Robert. b 34. CPFA. St Deiniol's Hawarden 84. **d** 87 **p** 88. NSM Llanwnda w Llanfaglan *Ban* 87-88; NSM Arfon Deanery 88-90; NSM Bistre *St As* 90-97; rtd 97; Perm to Offic *Ches* from 97. *1 Lea Drive, Buckley CH7 2BQ* Tel (01244) 544392

JAMES, Colin Robert. b 39. Magd Coll Ox BA61 MA65 DipEd62. St Alb and Ox Min Course 93. **d** 96 **p** 97. NSM Wokingham All SS *Ox* from 96. *7 Sewell Avenue, Wokingham RG41 1NT* Tel 0118-978 1515

JAMES, David. *See* JAMES, Richard David

JAMES, The Ven David Brian. b 30. FCA52 Univ of Wales (Swansea) BA63. St Mich Coll Llan 55. **d** 57 **p** 58. C Llandeilo Tal-y-bont *S & B* 57-59; C Swansea Ch Ch 59-63; V Bryngwyn and Newchurch and Llanbedr etc 63-70; R Llanfeugan w Llanthetty and Glyncollwng etc 70-79; V Ilston w Pennard 79-94; Hon Can Brecon Cathl 87-89; RD Gower 89-94; Can Brecon Cathl 89-94; Chan Brecon Cathl 93-94; Adn Brecon 94-99; P-in-c Llanllyr-yn-Rhos w Llanfihangel Helygen 94-99; Adn Gower 99-00; rtd 00. *1 Llys Ger-y-Llan, Pontarddulais, Swansea SA4 8HJ* Tel (01792) 881323 Fax as telephone

✠**JAMES, The Rt Revd David Charles.** b 45. Ex Univ BSc66 PhD71. St Jo Coll Nottm BA73. **d** 73 **p** 74 **c** 98. C Portswood Ch Ch *Win* 73-76; C Goring-by-Sea *Chich* 76-78; Chapl UEA *Nor* 78-82; V Ecclesfield *Sheff* 82-90; RD Ecclesfield 87-90; V Portswood Ch Ch *Win* 90-98; Hon Can Win Cathl 98; Suff Bp Pontefract *Wakef* 98-02; Bp Bradf from 02. *Bishopscroft, Ashwell Road, Heaton, Bradford BD9 4AU* Tel (01274) 545414 Fax 544831 E-mail bishop@bradford.anglican.org

JAMES, David Clive. b 40. Bris Univ BA61 K Coll Lon DipEd87. St Steph Ho Ox 64. **d** 65 **p** 66. C Portslade St Nic *Chich* 65-68; C Haywards Heath St Wilfrid 68-71; Chapl Brighton Poly 71-76; Perm to Offic from 76. *22 Bradford Road, Lewes BN7 1RB* Tel (01273) 471851 Fax as telephone E-mail david@c-james.freeserve.co.uk

JAMES, David Henry. b 45. Univ of Wales MB, BCh68 Univ of Wales (Swansea) MA92 MRCPsych75 DPM74. SW Minl Tr Course 95. **d** 98. NSM Truro Cathl *Truro* 98-00; rtd 00; Perm to Offic *Truro* from 00. *Dreaparc, Green Lane West, Marazion TR17 0HH* Tel (01736) 710854

JAMES, Preb David Howard. b 47. Ex Univ BA70 MA73 Nadn Coll Cam CertEd72. Linc Th Coll 81. **d** 83 **p** 84. C Tavistock and Gulworthy *Ex* 83-86; C E Teignmouth 86-88; C W Teignmouth 86-88; P-in-c Bishopsteignton 88-89; P-in-c Ideford, Luton and Ashcombe 88-89; TV Teignmouth, Ideford w Luton, Ashcombe etc 90-95; P-in-c Sidmouth, Woolbrook, Salcombe Regis, Sidbury etc 95-97; TR from 97; Preb Ex Cathl from 99. *The Rectory, Glen Road, Sidmouth EX10 8RW* Tel (01395) 514223 E-mail dhj@sidvt.freeserve.co.uk

JAMES, Canon David Walter Skyrme. b 36. Nottm Univ BA61. Wells Th Coll 61. **d** 63 **p** 64. C Sneinton St Cypr *S'well* 63-66; C Newark St Mary 66-69; V Kirkby in Ashfield St Thos 69-77; P-in-c Rempstone 76-84; P-in-c Costock 76-84; P-in-c Stanford on Soar 76-84; R E Leake 77-84; R Wollaton 84-01; Hon Can S'well Minster 88-01; AD Nottingham W 90-91; rtd 01. *16 De Ferrers Close, East Leake, Loughborough LE12 6QD* Tel (01509) 853126 E-mail dwsjames@btopenworld.com

JAMES, David William. b 55. Birm Univ BA99. CA Tr Coll CertRS77 Coll of Resurr Mirfield 86. **d** 88 **p** 88. C New Rossington *Sheff* 88-90; V Yardley Wood *Birm* 90-95; P-in-c Allens Cross 95-96; V from 96. *St Bartholomew's Vicarage, 148 Frankley Beeches Road, Birmingham B31 5LW* Tel 0121-475 8329

JAMES, Derek George. b 27. Sarum & Wells Th Coll 72. **d** 74 **p** 75. C Petersfield w Sheet *Portsm* 74-77; P-in-c Gosport Ch Ch 77-81; V 81-96; RD Gosport 90-96; rtd 96; Perm to Offic *Portsm*

from 96. *2 Pyrford Close, Alverstoke, Gosport PO12 2RP* Tel (023) 9258 4753

JAMES, Dewi Hirwaun. b 41. St Mich Coll Llan 66 Lich Th Coll 67. **d** 70 **p** 72. C Porthmadog St Jo w Borth-y-Gest and Tremadog *Ban* 70-73; C Llanbeblig w Caernarfon and Betws Garmon etc 83-85; C Bangor 88-89 and 90-94; C Sheff Parson Cross St Cecilia *Sheff* 89-90; Min Can Ban Cathl *Ban* 94-95; C Holyhead w Rhoscolyn w Llanfair-yn-Neubwll 94-95; C Holyhead 95-96; rtd 02. *30 Ambrose Street, Bangor LL57 1BH* Tel (01248) 354910

JAMES, Canon Eric Arthur. b 25. K Coll Lon AKC50 BD51 FKC78 Trin Coll Cam MA55 Lambeth DD93 FRSA92. **d** 51 **p** 52. C Westmr St Steph w St Jo *Lon* 51-55; Warden Trin Coll Miss Camberwell 59-64; V Camberwell St Geo *S'wark* 59-64; Dir Par and People 64-69; Can Res and Prec S'wark Cathl 66-73; Dioc Missr *St Alb* 73-83; Can Res St Alb 73-83; Hon Can 83-90; Preacher Gray's Inn 78-97; Dir Chr Action 79-90; Hon Dir from 90; Chapl to The Queen 84-95; Extra Chapl to The Queen from 95; rtd 90; Perm to Offic *S'wark* from 90. *11 Denny Crescent, London SE11 4UY,* or *125 Kennington Road, London SE11 6SF* Tel (020) 7582 3068 *or* 7735 2372

JAMES, Frank. *See* JAMES, Idris Frank

JAMES, Gerwyn. *See* JAMES, Joshua John Gerwyn

JAMES, Gillian Mary. b 49. **d** 99. OLM Bassaleg *Mon* from 99. *69 Hollybush Road, Cyncoed, Cardiff CF2 4SZ*

JAMES, Canon Godfrey Walter. b 36. Univ of Wales (Lamp) BA58 Univ of Wales (Cardiff) MA60 St Pet Coll Ox DipEd61 BA63 MA67. St Mich Coll Llan 63. **d** 64 **p** 65. C Canton St Jo *Llan* 64-71; V Williamstown 71-83; V Kenfig Hill 85-01; Hon Can Llan Cathl 96-01; rtd 01. *23 Crossfield Avenue, Porthcawl CF36 3LA*

JAMES, Gordon Cecil (Jimmy). b 35. Sarum Th Coll 66. **d** 67 **p** 68. C Kew *S'wark* 67-72; P-in-c Weston Longville w Morton and the Witchinghams *Nor* 72-81; R Diss 81-01; rtd 01; Perm to Offic *Nor* from 01. *21 St Leonards Close, Scole, Diss IP21 4DW* Tel (01379) 240416

✠**JAMES, The Rt Revd Graham Richard.** b 51. Lanc Univ BA72 Ox Univ DipH74 Hon FGMS92. Cuddesdon Coll 72. **d** 75 **p** 76 **c** 93. C Pet Ch Carpenter *Pet* 75-79; C Digswell *St Alb* 79-82; TV Digswell and Panshanger 82-83; Sen Selection Sec and Sec Cand Cttee ACCM 83-87; Abp's Chapl *Cant* 87-93; Hon Can Dallas from 89; Suff Bp St Germans *Truro* 93-99; Bp Nor from 99. *The Bishop's House, Norwich NR3 1SB* Tel (01603) 629001 Fax 761613 E-mail bishop@bishopofnorwich.org

JAMES, Henley George. b 31. Sarum & Wells Th Coll 79. **d** 81 **p** 82. C Tottenham H Trin *Lon* 81-85; C Cricklewood St Pet 85-88; P-in-c 88-89; V Bearwood *Birm* 89-97; rtd 97. *51 Cedar Gardens Road, PO Box 1401, Mandeville PO, Manchester, Jamaica*

JAMES, Henry Glyn. b 26. Keble Coll Ox BA50 DipTh51 MA58 Toronto Univ MEd74. Wycliffe Hall Ox 50. **d** 52 **p** 53. C Edgbaston St Aug *Birm* 52-54; C Surbiton St Matt *S'wark* 54-57; Housemaster Kingham Hill Sch 57-62; Chapl St Lawr Coll Ramsgate 62-68; Canada 68-73; Hon C Kidmore End *Ox* 74-77; K Jas Coll of Henley 74-87; Hon C Remenham *Ox* 77-88; Chapl The Henley Coll 87-88; Chapl Toulouse *Eur* 88-91; rtd 91; Perm to Offic *Win* from 93. *13 Harbour Road, Bournemouth BH6 4DD* Tel (01202) 427697 E-mail glyn.james1@ntlworld.com

JAMES, Herbert Royston Joseph. b 22. Sarum Th Coll 65. **d** 67 **p** 68. C Whipton *Ex* 67-75; V Shaugh Prior 75-83; V Ipplepen w Torbryan 83-87; rtd 87; Perm to Offic *Ex* from 90. *188 Hamlin Lane, Exeter EX1 2SH*

JAMES, Prof Ian Nigel. b 48. Leeds Univ BSc69 Man Univ PhD74. St Alb and Ox Min Course 99. **d** 02. NSM Bracknell *Ox* from 02. *2 Kyle Close, Bracknell RG12 7DF* Tel (01344) 451155 Mobile 07808-207422 E-mail dr.i.n.james@btinternet.com

JAMES, Idris Frank. b 20. MISM69 AMBIM70. St D Coll Lamp 52. **d** 58 **p** 59. C Llangynwyd w Maesteg *Llan* 55-59; C Plaistow St Andr *Chelmsf* 59-61; C Chadwell Heath 61-62; V Dunton 62-79; P-in-c Bulphan 62-64; R 64-77; rtd 85. *7 Allerdene Walk, Whickham, Newcastle upon Tyne NE16 4LL* E-mail rev.ifj@clara.co.uk

JAMES, Jeffrey Aneurin. b 53. Univ of Wales (Cardiff) BScEcon80 Bris Univ MSc83 MHSM83. WEMTC 98. **d** 01 **p** 02. NSM Minchinhampton *Glouc* from 01. *Jays Cottage, Keble Road, France Lynch, Stroud GL6 8LW* Tel (01453) 882481 E-mail jeff@jayscott.globalnet.co.uk

JAMES, Jeremy Richard. b 52. Jes Coll Cam BA73 MA77 York Univ CertEd77. St Jo Coll Dur 86. **d** 88 **p** 89. C Broxbourne w Wormley *St Alb* 88-91; C Hailsham *Chich* 91-99; V Wadhurst from 99; V Tidebrook from 99; V Stonegate from 99. *The Vicarage, High Street, Wadhurst TN5 6AA* Tel (01892) 782083 E-mail jeremy@jrjames.freeserve.co.uk

JAMES, John Charles. b 37. Keble Coll Ox BA59. Linc Th Coll 67. **d** 70 **p** 71. C S Shields St Hilda w St Thos *Dur* 70-77; P-in-c Jarrow Docks 77-78; Adn Seychelles 78-92; V Mylor w Flushing *Truro* from 92. *The Vicarage, Mylor, Falmouth TR11 5UD* Tel (01326) 374408

JAMES, John David. b 23. CCC Cam MA. Wells Th Coll. **d** 50 **p** 51. C Romford St Edw *Chelmsf* 50-54; C Cannock *Lich* 54-56; R Wickham Bishops *Chelmsf* 56-61; V Stansted Mountfitchet 61-71; V Clacton St Jas 71-84; R Poulshot *Sarum* 84; V Rowde 84; R Rowde and Poulshot 84-88; rtd 88; Perm to Offic *Heref* from 92. *15 Beaconsfield Park, Ludlow SY8 4LY* Tel (01584) 873754

JAMES, John Hugh Alexander. b 56. St Jo Coll Dur BA78 Univ of Wales DipTh81. St Mich Coll Llan. **d** 81 **p** 82. C Newton Nottage *Llan* 81-84; Prov Youth and Children's Officer in Wales 84-92; V Llanfihangel-ar-arth *St D* 92-97; V Llanfihangel-ar-arth w Capel Dewi from 97; RD Emlyn from 01. *The Vicarage, Llanfihangel-ar-arth, Pencader SA39 9HU* Tel (01559) 384858 E-mail hugh@ficerdy.freeserve.co.uk

JAMES, John Morgan. b 21. Lon Univ BD43 MTh45. ALCD43. **d** 44 **p** 45. C Leyton St Mary w St Edw *Chelmsf* 44-47; C Southend St Sav Westcliff 47-50; Prec Chelmsf Cathl 50-53; V Kemp Town St Mark *Chich* 53-65; R Balcombe 65-67; V Sunbury *Lon* 67-77; RD Kemp Town *Chich* 55-65; Dir Coll of Preachers 77-85; Lic to Offic *Guildf* 77-86; rtd 85. *Fair Winds, 126 Pagham Road, Pagham, Bognor Regis PO21 4NN* Tel (01243) 264542

JAMES, John Paul. b 30. Sarum Th Coll 58. **d** 60 **p** 61. C Milton *Portsm* 60-65; C Stanmer w Falmer and Moulsecoomb *Chich* 65-69; PC Brighton H Trin 69-71; Canada from 71; R Saguenay St Jean 71; Dean Quebec 77-87; R Westmount St Matthias 87-96; rtd 96. *Little Portion, 51 rue Principale, Stanstead PQ, Canada, J0B 3E5* Tel (001) (819) 876 2147 Fax 876 5088

JAMES, Joshua John Gerwyn. b 31. St D Coll Lamp BA52. **d** 54 **p** 55. C Haverfordwest St Mary w St Thos *St D* 54-56; C Llanaber w Caerdeon *Ban* 56-57; CF 57-76; V Tidenham w Beachley and Lancaut *Glouc* 76-80; R Aberdovey *Ban* 80-82; V Quinton w Marston Sicca *Glouc* 82-90; RD Campden 88-90; P-in-c Upper Chelsea St Simon *Lon* 90-96; rtd 96; Perm to Offic *S'wark* from 97. *Updown, 31 The Downs, London SW20 8HG* Tel (020) 8946 3720

JAMES, Keith Edwin Arthur. b 38. Sarum & Wells Th Coll 85. **d** 87 **p** 88. C Hempnall *Nor* 87-91; R Roughton and Felbrigg, Metton, Sustead etc 91-98; Ascension 1s 98-01; rtd 02; Chapl Laslett's *Worc* from 02. *The Chaplain's House, Laslett's Almshouses, Union Street, Worcester WR1 2AS* Tel (01905) 24743

JAMES, Keith Nicholas. b 69. Leeds Univ BA91 Nottm Univ MA93. St Jo Coll Nottm 91. **d** 93 **p** 94. C Crosby *Linc* 93-96; P-in-c Cherry Willingham w Greetwell 96-00; R S Lawres Gp from 00; RD Lawres from 01. *The Vicarage, 14 Church Lane, Cherry Willingham, Lincoln LN3 4AB* Tel (01522) 750356

JAMES, Lewis John. b 20. St D Coll Lamp BA42. **d** 48 **p** 49. C Llangiwg *S & B* 48-55; C Clydach 55-57; R Whitton w Pilleth 57-60; V Swansea *Derby* 60-85; P-in-c Morley 72-81; rtd 85; Perm to Offic *Derby* 85-87. *Cartref Annwyl Fan, Colonel Road, Betws, Ammanford SA18 2HW* Tel (01269) 596 630

JAMES, Malcolm. b 37. CEng MICE MIStructE. N Ord Course 80. **d** 83 **p** 84. NSM Ripponden *Wakef* from 83. *Lower Stones, Bar Lane, Rishworth, Sowerby Bridge HX6 4EY* Tel (01422) 822483 Fax 825992 E-mail malcolm@mjconsultancy.demon.co.uk

JAMES, Martin. b 40. ACII. **d** 94 **p** 95. OLM N Farnborough *Guildf* from 94. *43 Ashley Road, Farnborough GU14 7HB* Tel (01252) 544698 E-mail m.andj.james@classicfm.net

JAMES, Michael John. b 29. ALA53 Strathclyde Univ CYCW74 Heriot-Watt Univ CQSW81. Ho of Resurr Mirfield 57. **d** 59 **p** 60. C Applethwaite *Carl* 59-61; C Carl H Trin 61-63; C-in-c Carl St Luke Morton CD 63-67; R Lambley w Knaresdale *Newc* 67-72; Rossie Sch Montrose 75-83; Prin Redding Ho Falkirk 83-86; rtd 93. *28 Windsor Street, Edinburgh EH7 5JR* Tel 0131-556 4935

JAMES, Noel Beddoe Walters. b 39. St Mich Coll Llan DipTh68. **d** 68 **p** 69. C Swansea St Nic *S & B* 68-70; C Swansea St Pet 70-72; Chapl RAF 72-93; P-in-c The Heyfords w Rousham and Somerton *Ox* 93-00; R 00-02; rtd 02. *Ivy-Lee, Llanfihangel-ar-Arth, Pencader SA39 9HX* Tel (01559) 384176

JAMES, Paul Maynard. b 31. Univ of Wales (Ban) BA52 Fitzw Ho Cam BA54 MA58. Ridley Hall Cam 56. **d** 57 **p** 58. C Newhaven *Chich* 57-60; Kenya 60-65; SW Area Sec CCCS 65-68; V Shrewsbury St Julian *Lich* 68-76; V Shrewsbury H Trin w St Julian 76-90; P-in-c Woore and Norton in Hales 90-98; Adn Salop's Adv on Evang 90-98; RD Hodnet 93-97; rtd 98; Perm to Offic *Heref* and *Lich* from 00. *Nettledene, Elms Lane, Little Stretton, Church Stretton SY6 6RD* Tel (01694) 722559

JAMES, Canon Peter David. b 42. Keble Coll Ox BA63 Lon Univ BD67. Tyndale Hall Bris 64. **d** 67 **p** 68. C Haydock St Mark *Liv* 67-69; C Ashton-in-Makerfield St Thos 69-74; V Whiston 74-80; V Harlech and Llanfair-juxta-Harlech etc *Ban* 80-94; R Botwnnog w Bryncroes from 94; R Aberdaron w Rhiw and Llanfaelrhys etc from 00; Hon Can Ban Cathl from 02. *The Rectory, Botwnnog, Pwllheli LL53 8PY* Tel (01758) 730450 E-mail peterjames@botwnnog.fsnet.co.uk

JAMES, Peter Heppell. b 19. Tyndale Hall Bris 39. **d** 42 **p** 43. C Castle Town *Lich* 42-44; Chapl RAFVR 44-47; C Bucknall and Bagnall *Lich* 47-49; C Watford St Mary *St Alb* 49-51; V Braintree *Chelmsf* 51-60; R Lt Leighs 60-70; rtd 84. *57 Tynedale Road, Loughborough LE11 3TA* Tel (01509) 266940

JAMES, Raymond John. b 36. Linc Th Coll 85. **d** 87 **p** 88. C Cov E *Cov* 87-91; V Wolvey w Burton Hastings, Copston Magna etc 91-01; rtd 01. *46 Cornmore, Pershore WR10 1HX* Tel (01336) 556537

JAMES, Richard Andrew. b 44. Mert Coll Ox BA67 MA70. Tyndale Hall Bris DipTh69. **d** 70 **p** 71. C Bebington *Ches* 70-73; C Histon *Ely* 73-77; Chapl Guildf Coll of Tech 77-80; C Guildf St Sav w Stoke-next-Guildford *Guildf* 77-80; Ecum Chapl Bedf Coll of HE *St Alb* 81-83; TV Ipsley *Worc* 84-89; R Mulbarton w Kenningham *Nor* 89-92; rtd 93. *5 Kirkby Close, Ripon HG4 2DS* Tel (01765) 604511

JAMES, Richard David. b 45. DipTh93 Cheltenham & Glouc Coll of HE MA97. Lon Coll of Div 66. **d** 70 **p** 71. C Boultham *Linc* 70-74; C New Waltham 74-77; TV Cleethorpes 77-87; TR E Bris 87-99; V E Bris St Ambrose and St Leon from 99. *St Matthew's Vicarage, Victoria Avenue, Redfield, Bristol BS5 9NH* Tel 0117-955 7350

JAMES, Richard David. b 65. Clare Coll Cam MA88 Lon Hosp MB, BChir90. Ridley Hall Cam CTM95. **d** 95 **p** 96. C Clifton Ch Ch w Em *Bris* 95-98; C Enfield Ch Ch Trent Park *Lon* 98-00; V from 00. *The Vicarage, 2A Chalk Lane, Cockfosters, Barnet EN4 9JQ* Tel (020) 8441 1230 or tel and fax 8449 0556 E-mail richard@ccc1.fsnet.co.uk

JAMES, Richard William. b 47. St D Coll Lamp DipTh75. **d** 75 **p** 76. C Hubberston *St D* 75-78; R Pendine w Llanmiloe and Eglwys Gymyn w Marros 78-83; V Caerwent w Dinham and Llanfair Discoed etc *Mon* 83-84; Chapl Gothenburg w Halmstad, Jönköping etc *Eur* 84-89; P-in-c Shooters Hill Ch Ch *S'wark* 89-97; V Plumstead St Mark and St Marg from 97. *St Mark's Vicarage, 11 Old Mill Road, London SE18 1QE* Tel (020) 8854 2973

JAMES, Roger Michael. b 44. K Coll Lon BD66 AKC66. **d** 69 **p** 70. C Frindsbury w Upnor *Roch* 69-72; Lic to Offic *St Alb* 73-78; C Digswell 78-81; R Knebworth 81-92; P-in-c Upper Tean and Local Min Adv (Stafford) *Lich* 92-99; Dir Cottesloe Chr Tr Progr *Ox* 99-03; R Cusop w Blakemere, Bredwardine w Brobury etc *Heref* from 03. *The Vicarage, Cusop, Hay-on-Wye, Hereford HR3 5RF* Tel (01497) 820634

JAMES, Sandra Kay. *See* GARDNER, Mrs Sandra Kay

JAMES, Stephen Lynn. b 53. Middx Poly DipHCM74 Dip Personnel Mgt 75. Oak Hill Th Coll BA86. **d** 86 **p** 87. C Abraham H Trin *Nor* 86-89; Canada 89-93; R Bebington *Ches* from 93. *The Rectory, Church Road, Bebington, Wirral CH63 3EX* Tel 0151-645 6478 Fax 643 9664 E-mail standrews@bebingtonparishchurchsupanet.com

JAMES, Mrs Veronica Norma. b 59. STETS 99. **d** 02 **p** 03. NSM Ashton Keynes, Leigh and Minety *Bris* from 02. *The Old Toll House, Upper Minety, Malmesbury SN16 9PR* Tel (01666) 860138 E-mail flojoefred@aol.com

JAMES, William Arthur. b 10. Univ of Wales BA40. St Mich Coll Llan 40. **d** 42 **p** 43. C Johnston w Steynton *St D* 42-44; C Llanstephan *S & B* 44-45; C Llangynin w Llandilo Abercowin *St D* 45-46; C Maindee *Mon* 46-54; R Bedwas 54-77; rtd 77. *15 Beaconsfield Park, Ludlow SY8 4LY*

JAMES, William George. b 22. Trin Coll Carmarthen 82. **d** 85 **p** 86. NSM Gorseinon *S & B* from 85. *23 Cecil Road, Gowerton, Swansea SA4 3DF* Tel (01792) 872363

JAMES EDWARD, Brother. *See* ALLEN, Brother James Blaine

JAMESON, David Kingsbury. b 28. Mert Coll Ox BA50 MA55. Qu Coll Birm 50. **d** 53 **p** 54. C Leominster *Heref* 53-56; C Portsm Castle Town *Portsm* 56-60; Dioc Youth Officer 58-61; V Gosport Ch Ch 60-65; V Portsea St Cuth 65-70; V Enfield Jes Chpl *Lon* 70-74; RD Nuneaton *Cov* 74-79; V Nuneaton Nic 74-80; Org Sec (Leics and Northants) CECS 80-82; P-in-c Forty Hill Jes Ch *Lon* 82-87; V 87-91; rtd 91; Hon C Okehampton w Inwardleigh, Bratton Clovelly etc *Ex* 94-96; Hon C St Giles-in-the-Fields *Lon* 96-99; Perm to Offic *Chelmsf* 99-00; *Cov* from 01. *20 Grasmere Crescent, Nuneaton CV11 6ED* Tel (024) 7674 6957

JAMESON, Canon Dermot Christopher Ledgard. b 27. TCD BA49 MA54. CITC 49. **d** 50 **p** 51. C Seagoe *D & D* 50-53; C Holywood 53-57; I Kilkeel 57-62; I Donaghcloney w Waringstown 62-79; Can Dromore Cathl 77-93; I Kilbroney 79-93; Treas Dromore Cathl 81-83; Prec Dromore Cathl 83-90; Chan Dromore Cathl 90-93; rtd 93. *Concord, 10B Kilbroney Road, Rostrevor, Newry BT34 3BH* Tel (028) 3073 9728

JAMESON, Geoffrey Vaughan. b 27. Culham Coll Ox CertEd51 St Luke's Coll Ex AdCertEd52. Wycliffe Hall Ox 68. **d** 70 **p** 71. C Buckingham *Ox* 70-73; R Exton w Whitwell *Pet* 73-86; V Marystowe, Coryton, Stowford, Lewtrenchard etc *Ex* 86-90; rtd 90; Perm to Offic *Portsm* from 91 and *Win* from 03. *18 Eglantine Walk, Cowplain, Waterlooville PO8 9BG* Tel (023) 9257 1112

JAMESON, Howard Kingsley. b 63. Warwick Univ BSc84. Trin Coll Bris 99. **d** 02 **p** 03. C Wareham *Sarum* from 02. *110 Northmoor Way, Wareham BH20 4ET* Tel (01929) 551494 E-mail howard.jameson@virgin.net

JAMESON, Peter. b 31. Trin Coll Cam BA54 MA60. Linc Th Coll. **d** 62 **p** 63. C Earl's Court St Cuth w St Matthias *Lon* 62-68; C Notting Hill St Clem 68-72; C Notting Hill St Clem and St Mark 72-74; TV Notting Hill 74-77; V Stoke Newington St Olave 77-95; rtd 95; Perm to Offic *Chich* from 95. *Colemans, Warren Lane, Cross in Hand, Heathfield TN21 0TB* Tel (01435) 863414

JAMIESON, Douglas. *See* JAMIESON, William Douglas

JAMIESON, Guy Stuart. b 66. Leeds Univ BA98. Ripon Coll Cuddesdon. **d** 00 **p** 01. C Woodhall *Bradf* from 00. *8 Chatsworth Road, Pudsey LS28 8JS* Tel (01274) 662264

JAMIESON, Hugh Gollan. b 20. TCD BA49. CITC 49. **d** 49 **p** 50. C Limerick St Lawr w H Trin and St Jo *L & K* 49-51; I Ballynaclough Union 51-53; Sec BCMS 53-56; I Murragh Union *C, C & R* 56-60; R Birkin w Haddlesey *York* 60-63; I Derralossary *D & G* 63-69; I Mothel *C & O* 69-76; I Badoney Lower *D & R* 76-78; I Donagh w Tyholland and Errigal Truagh *Clogh* 78-82; I Killeshandra w Killegar and Derrylane *K, E & A* 82-87; rtd 87. *Rose Cottage, Killyboley, Glaslough, Monaghan, Irish Republic* Tel (00353) (47) 88231

JAMIESON, Kenneth Euan Oram. b 24. Lon Univ DipTh68. Roch Th Coll 60. **d** 62 **p** 63. C Bromley SS Pet and Paul *Roch* 62-66; R Colchester St Mary Magd *Chelmsf* 66-71; V Bexleyheath St Pet *Roch* 71-78; P-in-c Maidstone St Faith *Cant* 78-83; P-in-c Maidstone St Paul 78-83; Ind Chapl *St Alb* 83-89; rtd 89; Perm to Offic *B & W* from 89. *4 Ashley Road, Taunton TA1 5BP* Tel (01823) 289367

JAMIESON, Canon Marilyn. b 52. Cranmer Hall Dur IDC80. **d** 91 **p** 94. Par Dn Bensham *Dur* 91-93; Par Dn Ryton w Hedgefield 93-94; Chapl Metro Cen Gateshead 94-02; Hon Can Dur Cathl from 97; Adv for Women's Min from 00; Bp's Sen Chapl from 02. *The Rectory, Barmoor House, Main Road, Ryton NE40 3AJ* Tel 0191-413 4592

JAMIESON, Peter Grant. b 64. Liv Univ BA87. Coll of Resurr Mirfield 93. **d** 93 **p** 94. C Charlton Kings St Mary *Glouc* 93-96. *3 Belmont Mews, Upper High Street, Thame OX9 3EJ* Tel (01844) 212895

JAMIESON, Miss Rosalind Heather. b 49. CertEd71. St Jo Coll Dur 79. **dss** 81 **d** 87 **p** 94. Queensbury All SS *Lon* 81-85; Richmond H Trin and Ch Ch *S'wark* 85-87; Par Dn 87-91; Par Dn Burmantofts St Steph and St Agnes *Ripon* 91-94; C 94-99; TV Seacroft from 99. *St Richard's Vicarage, Ramshead Hill, Leeds LS14 1BX* Tel 0113-265 6388

JAMIESON, Mrs Susan Jennifer. b 49. Liv Univ SRN71. Dioc OLM tr scheme 97. **d** 00 **p** 01. OLM Clubmoor *Liv* from 00. *15 Winsford Road, Liverpool L13 0BJ* Tel 0151-475 7562 Mobile 07879-425277 E-mail sujamo@cableinet.co.uk

JAMIESON, Thomas Lindsay. b 53. N Lon Poly BSc74. Cranmer Hall Dur DipTh76. **d** 77 **p** 78. C Gateshead Fell *Dur* 77-80; C Gateshead 80-84; TV 84-90; P-in-c Gateshead St Cuth w St Paul 90-91; TV Bensham 91-93; P-in-c Ryton w Hedgefield 93-95; R from 95; AD Gateshead W 94-98. *The Rectory, Barmoor House, Main Road, Ryton NE40 3AJ* Tel 0191-413 4592 E-mail atl.jamieson@talk21.com

JAMIESON, William Douglas. b 38. Oak Hill Th Coll 63. **d** 66 **p** 67. C Shrewsbury St Julian *Lich* 66-68; C Bucknall and Bagnall 68-70; C Otley *Bradf* 70-74; TV Keighley 74-81; V Utley 81-00; rtd 00; Perm to Offic *Ches* from 00. *11 The Quay, Frodsham, Warrington WA6 7JG* Tel (01928) 731085 Mobile 07974-947838 E-mail douglasjamieson@lineone.net

JAMIESON-HARVEY, Neil Benedict. b 44. Chich Th Coll 89. **d** 91 **p** 92. Bahamas 91-95; C Meir Heath *Lich* 95-96; P-in-c Cross Heath from 96. *St Michael's Presbytery, Linden Grove, Newcastle ST5 9LJ* Tel (01782) 617241 E-mail frneil@crossheath.co.uk

JANES, David Edward. b 40. Lon Univ BSc67. Glouc Sch of Min 86. **d** 89 **p** 90. NSM Church Stretton *Heref* 89-00; rtd 00; Perm to Offic *Heref* from 00. *15 Watling Street South, Church Stretton SY6 7BG* Tel (01694) 722253

JANICKER, Laurence Norman. b 47. SS Mark & Jo Coll Chelsea DipEd69. Ridley Coll Melbourne 77 St Jo Coll Nottm 83. **d** 85 **p** 86. C Beverley Minster *York* 85-89; R Lockington and Lund and Scorborough w Leconfield 89-94; V Cov St Geo *Cov* from 94. *St George's Vicarage, 101 Moseley Avenue, Coventry CV6 1HR* Tel (024) 7659 1994

JANSMA, Henry Peter. b 57. NE Bible Coll (USA) BA79 Westmr Th Sem (USA) MA85 St Jo Coll Dur PhD91. Linc Th Coll 89. **d** 91 **p** 92. C Spalding *Linc* 91-96; P-in-c Cleethorpes St Aid 96-97; V 97-01; R Haddon Heights St Mary USA from 01. *501 Green Street, Haddon Heights, NJ 08035, USA* Tel (001) (856) 547 0565 or 547 3240 Fax 310 0565 E-mail stmaryshh@juno.com

JANSSON, Maria Patricia. b 55. Milltown Inst Dub DipRE75 MRelSc92. CITC 00. **d** 01 **p** 02. C Galway w Kilcummin *T, K & A* 01-02; C Wexford w Ardcolm and Killurin *C & O* from 02; C Kilscoran w Killinick and Mulrankin from 02. *The Rectory, Killinick, Wexford, Irish Republic* E-mail miajansson@eircom.net

JANVIER, Philip Harold. b 57. Trin Coll Bris BA87. **d** 87 **p** 88. C Much Woolton *Liv* 87-90; TV Toxteth St Philemon w St Gabr and

St Cleopas 90-97; TR Gateacre from 97. *St Stephen's Rectory, Belle Vale Road, Gateacre, Liverpool L25 2PQ* Tel 0151-487 9338

JAONA, Ramahalefitra Hyacinthe Arsène. b 70. St Paul's Th Coll Ambatoharanana Madagascar CAP90. **d** 94 **p** 96. Madagascar 94-97 and from 98; C Caldicot *Mon* 97-98. *Mission Angelican, BP 126, 206 Antalaha, Antsiranana, Madagascar*

JAPAN, Primate of. *See* UNO, The Most Revd James Toru

JAQUES, Geoffrey Sanderson. b 48. Man Univ BSc. NEOC 94. **d** 97 **p** 98. NSM Gt Ayton w Easby and Newton in Cleveland *York* from 97. *132 Roseberry Crescent, Great Ayton, Middlesbrough TS9 6EW* Tel (01642) 722979
E-mail geoff.jaques@onyxnet.co.uk

JARAM, Peter Ellis. b 45. Lon Univ BSc70 CEng77 MIEE77 MBIM88. Linc Th Coll 94. **d** 94 **p** 95. C Bridlington Priory *York* 94-96; C Rufforth w Moor Monkton and Hessay 96-97; C Healaugh w Wighill, Bilbrough and Askham Richard 96-97; P-in-c 97-01; Chapl Askham Bryan Coll 97-01; V Brompton by Sawdon w Hutton Buscel, Snainton etc *York* from 01. *The Vicarage, 4 Cayley Lane, Brompton-by-Sawdon, Scarborough YO13 9DL* Tel (01723) 862061 E-mail pej.parish@virgin.net

JARDIN, Kenneth. b 35. TCD 67. **d** 69 **p** 70. Chapl R Sch Arm 69-72; C Arm St Mark *Arm* 69-72; Chapl RAF 72-78; V Barlings *Linc* 78-83; P-in-c Stainton-by-Langworth 78; P-in-c Scothern w Sudbrooke 78; Chapl Monte Carlo *Eur* 83-87; P-in-c Sudbury and Somersal Herbert *Derby* 87-92; Dep Chapl HM Open Pris Foston Hall and Sudbury 87-92; P-in-c Kirk Langley 92-03; P-in-c Mackworth All SS 92-03; P-in-c Mugginton and Kedleston 92-03; rtd 03. *1608 Victoria Centre, Nottingham NG1 3PQ* Tel 0115-840 7913

JARDINE, Canon Anthony. b 38. Lon Univ DipTh70. Qu Coll Birm 64. **d** 67 **p** 68. C Baldock w Bygrave and Clothall *St Alb* 67-71; C N Stoneham *Win* 71-73; P-in-c Ecchinswell cum Sydmonton 73-79; P-in-c Burghclere w Newtown 78-79; R Burghclere w Newtown and Ecchinswell w Sydmonton 79-87; P-in-c Wonston 87; R Wonston and Stoke Charity w Hunton 87-97; P-in-c Chawton and Farringdon from 97; Dioc Rural Officer from 97; Hon Can Win Cathl from 99. *The Rectory, Farringdon, Alton GU34 3EE* Tel (01420) 588398 Fax as telephone

JARDINE, David Eric Cranswick. b 30. CCC Ox BA53 DipTh54 MA57. Wycliffe Hall Ox 53. **d** 55 **p** 56. C Wavertree St Mary *Liv* 55-58; C Liv All So Springwood 58-62; C Horley *S'wark* 62-65; V Mitcham Ch Ch 65-72; V Iford *Win* 72-89; R Smannell w Enham Alamein 89-96; rtd 96; Perm to Offic *Sheff* from 96. *387 Redmires Road, Sheffield S10 4LE* Tel 0114-230 8721
E-mail ema98dej@sheffield.ac.uk

JARDINE, David John (Brother David). b 42. QUB BA65. CITC 67. **d** 67 **p** 68. C Ballymacarrett St Patr *D & D* 67-70; Asst Chapl QUB 70-73; SSF from 73; Asst Chapl HM Pris Belf 75-79; Chapl 79-85; USA 85-88; Sen Asst Warden Ch of Ireland Min of Healing 89-92; Dir Divine Healing Min 92-99. *3 Richmond Park, Stranmillis, Belfast BT9 5EF* Tel (028) 9068 7692 *or* 9031 1532

JARDINE, Canon Norman. b 47. QUB BSc72. Trin Coll Bris 74. **d** 76 **p** 77. C Magheralin *D & D* 76-78; C Dundonald 78-80; Bp's C Ballybeen 80-88; I Willowfield 88-00; Dir Think Again from 00; Can Belf Cathl from 03. *237 Orby Drive, Belfast BT5 6BE* Tel (028) 9050 4976

JARDINE, Thomas Parker. b 44. Oak Hill Th Coll BA87. **d** 87 **p** 88. C Crowborough *Chich* 87-91; R Dersingham w Anmer and Shernborne *Nor* 91-00; V Southport SS Simon and Jude *Liv* from 00; V Southport All SS and All So from 03. *The Vicarage, 128 Roe Lane, Southport PR9 7PJ* Tel (01704) 227095

JARMAN, Christopher (Kit). b 38. QUB BA63. Wells Th Coll 69. **d** 71 **p** 72. C Leckhampton SS Phil and Jas *Glouc* 71-73; Chapl RN 73-93; R Stirling *St And* from 94; Hon Chapl ATC from 97. *29 Parkdyke, Stirling FK7 9LS* Tel (01786) 471755 Fax as telephone

JARMAN, John Geoffrey. b 31. IEng. S'wark Ord Course 75. **d** 78 **p** 79. NSM Chigwell *Chelmsf* 78-81; NSM Leytonstone St Marg w St Columba 81-87; C Walthamstow St Sav 87-89; V Gt Bentley 89-92; P-in-c Frating w Thorrington 89-92; C Wanstead St Mary 92-93; C Wanstead St Mary w Ch Ch 93-95; rtd 95; Perm to Offic *Chelmsf* from 95. *20 Stevens Way, Chigwell IG7 6HR* Tel (020) 8500 2161

JARMAN, Robert Joseph. b 59. Van Mildert Coll Dur BA90 Univ of Wales (Cardiff) DPS91. **d** 92 **p** 93. C Llanishen and Lisvane *Llan* 92-93; C Whitchurch 93-94. *47 Penydre, Rhiwbina, Cardiff CF14 6EJ*

JARMY, David Michael. b 49. Hughes Hall Cam PGCE90. Chich Th Coll 76. **d** 79 **p** 80. C St Leonards Ch Ch *Chich* 79-80; C St Leonards Ch Ch and St Mary 81-82; C St Leonards SS Pet and Paul 82-85; V Sidley 85-89; Lt Gidding Community 89-90; NSM Oundle *Pet* 90-98; Chapl Bp Stopford Sch Kettering 90-98; P-in-c Turners Hill *Chich* from 98; Angl Chapl Worth Sch from 98. *The Vicarage, Church Road, Turners Hill, Crawley RH10 4PB* Tel (01342) 715278 E-mail jarmy@tesco.net

JARRATT, Canon Robert Michael. b 39. K Coll Lon BD62 AKC62. NY Th Sem DMin85. **d** 63 **p** 64. C Corby St Columba *Pet* 63-67; Lay Tr Officer *Sheff* 67-71; Ind Chapl *S'wark* 72-80; P-in-c Betchworth 76-80; V Ranmoor *Sheff* 80-01; RD Hallam

87-94; Hon Can Sheff Cathl from 95; P-in-c Worsbrough from 01; Dir Post-Ord Tr from 01. *St Mary's Vicarage, 1 Church Lane, Worsbrough, Barnsley S70 5LQ* Tel (01226) 203113 Fax as telephone E-mail revmjarratt@hotmail.com

JARRATT, Stephen. b 51. Edin Univ BD76 St Kath Coll Liv CertEd77. **d** 78 **p** 79. C Horsforth *Ripon* 78-81; C Stanningley St Thos 81-84; P-in-c Fishponds St Jo *Bris* 84-85; V 85-92; V Chapel Allerton *Ripon* from 92; AD Allerton from 97. *The Vicarage, Wood Lane, Chapel Allerton, Leeds LS7 3QF* Tel 0113-268 3072

✠**JARRETT, The Rt Revd Martyn William.** b 44. K Coll Lon BD67 AKC67 Hull Univ MPhil91. **d** 68 **p** 69 **c** 94. C Bris St Geo *Bris* 68-70; C Swindon New Town 70-74; C Northolt St Mary *Lon* 74-76; V Northolt W End St Jos 76-81; V Hillingdon St Andr 81-83; P-in-c Uxbridge Moor 82-83; V Uxbridge St Andr w St Jo 83-85; Selection Sec ACCM 85-88; Sen Selection Sec 89-91; V Chesterfield St Mary and All SS *Derby* 91-94; Suff Bp Burnley *Blackb* 94-00; Hon Can Blackb Cathl 94-00; Suff Bp Beverley (PEV) *York* from 00; Hon Asst Bp Dur, Ripon and Sheff from 00; Hon Asst Bp Man, S'well and Wakef from 01; Hon Asst Bp Bradf from 02; Hon Can Wakef Cathl *Wakef* from 01. *3 North Lane, Roundhay, Leeds LS8 2QJ* Tel 0113-265 4280 Fax 265 4281 E-mail bishop-of-beverley@3-north-lane.fsnet.co.uk

JARRETT, Rene Leazar Taiwo. b 49. TCert79 Lon Inst of Educn BEd94. Sierra Leone Th Hall CPS83. **d** 83 **p** 85. Sierra Leone 83-89; Hon C St Pancras w St Jas and Ch Ch *Lon* from 89; Hon C Bloomsbury St Geo w Woburn Square Ch Ch from 95. *2 Woburn Mansions, Torrington Place, London WC1E 7HL* Tel (020) 7580 5165

JARROW, Suffragan Bishop of. *See* PRITCHARD, The Rt Revd John Lawrence

JARVIS, Canon Eric Thomas Noel. b 24. Qu Coll Cam BA52 MA54. Ridley Hall Cam 52. **d** 54 **p** 55. C Stratford St Jo *Chelmsf* 54-57; V Ansley *Cov* 57-64; V Woodbridge St Jo *St E* 64-68; V Roundhay St Edm *Ripon* 68-86; RD Allerton 79-84; Hon Can Ripon Cathl 81-86; R St Olave Hart Street w All Hallows Staining etc *Lon* 86-90; V St Marg Pattens 86-90; rtd 90; Perm to Offic *Ely* from 90. *38 Doggett Road, Cherry Hinton, Cambridge CB1 9LF* Tel (01223) 213387

JARVIS, Ian Frederick Rodger. b 38. Bris Univ BA60. Tyndale Hall Bris 61. **d** 63 **p** 64. C Penge Ch Ch w H Trin *Roch* 63-67; C Bilston St Leon *Lich* 67-71; V Lozells St Silas *Birm* 71-76; V Chaddesden St Mary *Derby* 76-95; V Newhall 95-02; rtd 02; Perm to Offic *Derby* from 02. *29 Springfield Road, Midway, Swadlincote DE11 0BZ* Tel (01283) 551589

JARVIS, Jeffrey Wallace. b 45. Queensland Univ BEd96. Sarum & Wells Th Coll ThL73. **d** 75 **p** 76. C Cherry Hinton St Andr *Ely* 75-77; C Nottingham St Mary *S'well* 77-78; Australia from 78; R Greenwood 78-80; Chapl Ch Gr Sch 80-84; R Edgehill Cairns Gd Shep 84-86; Chapl Brisbane Boys' Coll 86-91; Chapl St Marg Angl Girls' Sch 91-94; Chapl RAN 94-96; Chapl Fraser Coast Angl Coll from 96. *14 Spence Street, Point Vernon, Qld, Australia 4655* Tel (0061) (7) 4124 4506 *or* 4124 5411 Fax 4124 5833 E-mail jjarvis@fcac.qld.edu.au

JARVIS, Mrs Lynda Claire. b 46. Southn Univ CQSW87. STETS 95. **d** 98 **p** 99. C Chandler's Ford *Win* 98-01; rtd 01. *56 Stoney Lane, Winchester SO22 6DP*

JARVIS, Miss Mary. b 35. Leeds Univ BA57 Lon Univ CertEd59. Cranmer Hall Dur 78. **dss** 80 **d** 87 **p** 94. Low Harrogate St Mary *Ripon* 80-84; Wortley de Leeds 84-87; C 87-88; C Upper Armley 88-94; C Holbeck 94-95; rtd 95. *71 Burnsall Croft, Leeds LS12 3LH* Tel 0113-279 7832

JARVIS, Mrs Pamela Ann. b 51. Sussex Univ BEd74. SW Minl Tr Course 97. **d** 00 **p** 01. C Braunton *Ex* from 00. *11 Hazel Avenue, Braunton EX33 2EZ* Tel (01271) 816918 Mobile 07773-900523 E-mail pajarvis@ntlworld.com

JARVIS, Rupert Charles Melbourn. b 69. St Andr Univ MA92 Univ of Wales (Swansea) MPhil96. Cuddesdon Coll 96. **d** 98 **p** 99. C Swansea St Mary w H Trin *S & B* 98-99; Min Can Brecon Cathl 99-01; CF from 01. *c/o MOD Chaplains (Army)* Tel (01980) 615804 Fax 615800

JASPER, Prof David. b 51. Jes Coll Cam BA72 MA76 Keble Coll Ox BD80 Dur Univ PhD83. St Steph Ho Ox BA75 MA79. **d** 76 **p** 77. C Buckingham *Ox* 76-79; C Dur St Oswald *Dur* 80; Chapl Hatf Coll Dur 81-88; Dir Cen Study of Lit and Th Dur 88-91; Prin St Chad's Coll Dur 88-91; Reader and Dir Cen Study of Lit and Th Glas Univ from 91; Vice-Dean of Div 95-98; Dean of Div from 98; Lic to Offic *Glas* from 91. *Netherwood, 124 Old Manse Road, Wishaw ML2 0EP* Tel (01698) 373286 Fax as telephone

JASPER, David Julian McLean. b 44. Dur Univ BA66 Nottm Univ DipTh67. Linc Th Coll 66. **d** 68 **p** 69. C Redruth *Truro* 68-72; TV 72-75; V St Just in Penwith 75-86; P-in-c Sancreed 82-86; C Reading St Matt *Ox* 96-00; P-in-c 00-02; R S Petherton w the Seavingtons *B & W* from 02. *The Rectory, Hele Lane, South Petherton TA13 5DY* Tel (01460) 249443 Mobile 07767-814533 E-mail david.jasper@virgin.net

JASPER, James Roland. b 32. CA Tr Coll 56 NEOC 82. **d** 84 **p** 84. C Newburn *Newc* 84-86; V Ansley *Cov* 86-97; rtd 97; Perm to

Offic *Leic* from 97. *69 Desford Road, Newbold Verdon, Leicester LE9 9LG* Tel (024) 7639 6403

JASPER, Jonathan Ernest Farley. b 50. AKC72 DPMSA85. St Aug Coll Cant 73. **d** 73 **p** 74. C Cheshunt *St Alb* 73-75; C Bedford St Paul 75-77; C Bedford St Pet w St Cuth 75-77; Chapl Southn Univ *Win* 77-80; Chapl Lon Univ Medical Students *Lon* 80-86; PV Chich Cathl *Chich* 86-89; P-in-c Earls Colne and White Colne *Chelmsf* 89-94; P-in-c Colne Engaine 89-94; R Earls Colne w White Colne and Colne Engaine 95-02; C Christchurch *Win* from 02. *49 Brabazon Drive, Christchurch BH23 4TL* Tel (01425) 280831

JAUNDRILL, John Warwick. b 47. MInstM81. Qu Coll Birm 86. **d** 88 **p** 89. C Bistre *St As* 88-91; P-in-c Towyn and St George 91-92; V 92-02. *Address temp unknown*

JAY, Colin. b 62. Keble Coll Ox BA85 St Jo Coll Dur BA89. Cranmer Hall Dur 87. **d** 90 **p** 91. C Bishopwearmouth St Gabr *Dur* 90-94; C Newton Aycliffe 94; TV 94-96; TV Gt Aycliffe 96-03; AD Sedgefield 99-03; Chapl Co Dur & Darlington Priority Services NHS Trust from 03. *Earls House Hospital, Lanchester Road, Durham DH1 5RD* Tel 0191-333 6262
E-mail colsar@netscapeonline.co.uk

JAY, Edmund Arthur. b 41. St Chad's Coll Dur BA63. **d** 65 **p** 66. C Bishopwearmouth Gd Shep *Dur* 65-69; C Southwick St Columba 69-70; Hon C Westbury-on-Trym H Trin *Bris* 72-73; P-in-c S Shields St Francis *Dur* 73-76; C S Shields St Hilda w St Thos 76-79; Chapl S Shields Gen Hosp 79-85; rtd 88. *14 Charter Drive, East Herrington, Sunderland SR3 3PG* Tel 0191-522 6938

JAY, Ms Nicola Mary. b 37. SRN58. NEOC 88. **d** 91 **p** 94. Par Dn Whitburn *Dur* 91-94; C 94-95; P-in-c Sacriston and Kimblesworth 95-00; rtd 00. *29 Church Street, Sacriston, Durham DH7 6JL* Tel 0191-371 0152

JAY, Richard Hylton Michael. b 31. Bris Univ BEd75. Sarum & Wells Th Coll 77. **d** 79 **p** 80. NSM Bath St Barn w Englishcombe *B & W* 79-81; NSM Saltford w Corston and Newton St Loe 81-88; R Hatch Beauchamp w Beercrocombe, Curry Mallet etc 89-97; rtd 97; Perm to Offic *B & W* from 97. *Stableside, 5 Princess Road, Taunton TA1 4SY* Tel (01823) 335531

JAYNE, Martin Philip. b 49. MRTPI73 Man Univ BA71 Preston Poly DMS80. Carl Dioc Tr Course 87. **d** 90 **p** 91. NSM Natland *Carl* from 90. *12 Longmeadow Lane, Natland, Kendal LA9 7QZ* Tel (01539) 560942 E-mail jayne@which.net

JEANES, Gordon Paul. b 55. Ox Univ BA79 MA82 BD90 Univ of Wales (Lamp) PhD99. St Steph Ho Ox 80. **d** 82 **p** 83. C S Wimbledon H Trin and St Pet *S'wark* 82-85; C Surbiton St Andr and St Mark 85-90; Chapl St Chad's Coll Dur 90-93; Sub-Warden St Mich Coll Llan 94-98; Lect Th Univ of Wales (Cardiff) 94-98; V Wandsworth St Anne *S'wark* from 98; Dioc Voc Adv from 99. *St Anne's Vicarage, 182 St Ann's Hill, London SW18 2RS* Tel (020) 8874 2809 E-mail gordon.jeanes@virgin.net

JEANS, The Ven Alan Paul. b 58. MIAAS84 MIBCO84 Southn Univ BTh89 Univ of Wales (Lamp) MA03. Sarum & Wells Th Coll 86. **d** 89 **p** 90. C Parkstone St Pet w Branksea and St Osmund *Sarum* 89-93; P-in-c Bishop's Cannings, All Cannings etc 93-98; Par Development Adv from 98; Can and Preb Sarum Cathl from 02; Adn Sarum from 03. *118 Lower Road, Salisbury SP2 9NW* Tel (01722) 336290 or 411955
E-mail adsarum@salisbury.anglican.org

JEANS, David Bockley. b 48. Mert Coll Ox BA71 MA80 PGCE73 Man Univ MPhil98. Trin Coll Bris DipHE85. **d** 85 **p** 86. C Clevedon St Andr and Ch Ch *B & W* 85-88; V Wadsley *Sheff* 88-96; Dir of Studies Wilson Carlile Coll of Evang 96; Prin from 97. *Wilson Carlile College of Evangelism, 50 Cavendish Street, Sheffield S3 7RZ* Tel 0114-278 7020
E-mail d.jeans@sheffieldcentre.org.uk

JEAPES (née PORTER), Mrs Barbara Judith. b 47. Cam Inst of Educn TCert68. Carl Dioc Tr Inst 91. **d** 94 **p** 95. NSM Egremont and Haile *Carl* from 94. *15 Millfields, Beckermet CA21 2YY* Tel (01946) 841489 E-mail barbara@jeapesb.fsnet.co.uk

JEAVONS, Mrs Margaret Anne. b 51. Liv Poly BA72 Bris Univ BA01 St Kath Coll Liv PGCE74. Trin Coll Bris 99. **d** 01 **p** 02. C Totnes w Bridgetown, Berry Pomeroy etc *Ex* from 01. *The Vales, 3 Weston Road, Totnes TQ9 5AH* Tel (01803) 840990

JEAVONS, Maurice. b 32. Ely Th Coll 60. **d** 62 **p** 63. C Longton St Jo *Lich* 62-68; V Wednesfield St Greg 68-81; V Lower Gornal 81-90; NSM Willenhall St Anne 92-93; C Tunstall 93-99; rtd 99; Hon C Wolverhampton St Steph *Lich* from 99. *17 Colaton Close, Wolverhampton WV10 9BB* Tel (01902) 351118

JEE, Colin Scott. b 32. Worc Coll Ox BA55 MA59. Clifton Th Coll 55. **d** 57 **p** 58. C Spitalfields Ch Ch w All SS *Lon* 57-62; C New Malden and Coombe *S'wark* 62-66; R Ludgershall *Ox* 66-78; P-in-c Oakley 73-82; RD Waddesdon 73-78; R Ludgershall w Wotton Underwood and Ashendon 78-98; rtd 98; Perm to Offic *Ox* from 99. *Robinia, 16 Stokes End, Haddenham, Aylesbury HP17 8DX* Tel (01844) 291045

JEE, Jonathan Noel. b 63. BNC Ox BA84 MA88. Wycliffe Hall Ox 85. **d** 88 **p** 89. C Brampton St Thos *Derby* 88-92; TV Hinckley H Trin *Leic* 92-00; V Leamington Priors St Paul *Cov* from 00. *The Vicarage, 15 Lillington Road, Leamington Spa CV32 5YS* Tel (01926) 772132 or 427149 E-mail jonathan.jee@ntlworld.com

JEFF, Canon Gordon Henry. b 32. St Edm Hall Ox BA56 MA60. Wells Th Coll 59. **d** 61 **p** 62. C Sydenham St Bart *S'wark* 61-64; C Kidbrooke St Jas 64-66; V Clapham St Paul 66-72; V Raynes Park St Sav 73-79; RD Merton 77-79; V Carshalton Beeches 79-86; P-in-c Petersham 86-90; Chapl St Mich Convent 90-96; Hon Can S'wark Cathl 93-96; rtd 96. *9 Barnetts Well, Draycott, Cheddar BS27 3TF* Tel (01934) 744943

JEFFERIES, Michael Lewis. b 45. St Jo Coll Nottm. **d** 87 **p** 88. C Pudsey St Lawr and St Paul *Bradf* 87-93; V Beckenham St Jo *Roch* 93-00; TV Modbury, Bigbury, Ringmore w Kingston etc *Ex* from 00. *The Vicarage, 3 Little Gate, Loddiswell, Kingsbridge TQ7 4RB* Tel (01548) 550841

JEFFERIES, Preb Phillip John. b 42. St Chad's Coll Dur BA65 DipTh67 MA91. **d** 67 **p** 68. C Tunstall Ch Ch *Lich* 67-71; C Wolverhampton St Pet 71-74; P-in-c Oakengates 74-80; V 80-82; P-in-c Ketley 78-82; V Horninglow 82-00; Bp's Adv on Hosp Chapl from 82; RD Tutbury 97-00; Preb Lich Cathl from 99; TR Stafford from 00. *The Rectory, 32 Rowley Avenue, Stafford ST17 9AG* Tel (01785) 258511
E-mail phillipjefferies@stmarysstafford.fsnet.co.uk

JEFFERS, Cliff Peter. b 69. CITC BTh98. **d** 98 **p** 99. C Limerick City L & K 98-01; I Clonenagh w Offerlane, Borris-in-Ossory etc C & O from 01. *The Rectory, Portlaoise Road, Mountrath, Co Laois, Irish Republic* Tel and fax (00353) (502) 32146 Mobile 87-239 0849 E-mail cjeffers@eircom.net

JEFFERSON, Charles Dudley. b 53. St Pet Coll Ox BA78 MA81. Ridley Hall Cam 79. **d** 81 **p** 82. C Chadkirk *Ches* 81-84; C Macclesfield St Pet 84-85; C Macclesfield Team Par 85-89; R Elworth and Warmingham 89-99; Chapl Framlingham Coll 99-01; Chapl Rendcomb Coll Cirencester from 01; P-in-c Rendcomb *Glouc* from 01. *The Rectory, Rendcomb, Cirencester GL7 7EZ* Tel (01285) 831319

JEFFERSON, David Charles. b 33. Leeds Univ BA57. Coll of Resurr Mirfield 57. **d** 59 **p** 60. C Kennington Cross St Anselm *S'wark* 59-62; C Richmond St Mary 62-64; Public Preacher from 64; Chapl Wilson's Sch Camberwell 64-93; Hon C Carshalton Beeches *S'wark* from 74; Chapl Wilson's Sch Wallington 75-99; rtd 93. *15 Sandown Drive, Carshalton SM5 4LN* Tel (020) 8669 0640

JEFFERSON, Michael William. b 41. K Coll Lon AKC64. WMMTC 96. **d** 98 **p** 99. C Four Oaks *Birm* 98-02; P-in-c Longdon *Lich* from 02; Local Min Adv (Wolverhampton) from 02. *The Vicarage, Longdon, Rugeley WS15 4PS* Tel (01543) 492871

JEFFERY, Graham. b 35. Qu Coll Cam BA58. Wells Th Coll 58. **d** 60 **p** 61. C Southampton Maybush St Pet *Win* 60-63; Australia 63-66; C E Grinstead St Swithun *Chich* 66-68; C-in-c The Hydneye CD 68-74; V Wick 74-76; C Hove 76-78; P-in-c Newtimber w Pyecombe 78-82; R Poynings w Edburton, Newtimber and Pyecombe 82-92; P-in-c Pullington and Thakeham w Warminghurst 92-95; rtd 96; NSM Poynings w Edburton, Newtimber and Pyecombe *Chich* 97-99; Perm to Offic from 00. *St Andrews, Rock Road, Ashington, Pulborough RH20 3AG* Tel (01903) 741268

JEFFERY (née CAW), Mrs Hannah Mary. b 69. Birm Univ BMus91. St Jo Coll Nottm Dip Th Studies 94 MA95 LTh95. **d** 95 **p** 96. C Northampton St Giles *Pet* 95-99; Hon C Hanger Hill Ascension and W Twyford St Mary *Lon* from 99. *48 Brentmead Gardens, London NW10 7ED* Tel (020) 8838 2542
E-mail hjeffery@compuserve.com

JEFFERY, Mrs Jennifer Ann. b 45. Philippa Fawcett Coll CertEd66. STETS. **d** 02 **p** 03. NSM Wilton *B & W* from 02. *4 Southwell, Trull, Taunton TA3 7HU* Tel (01823) 286589
E-mail jenny@jajeffery.freeserve.co.uk

JEFFERY, Jonathan George Piers. b 63. Man Univ LLB84. Ripon Coll Cuddesdon 95. **d** 97 **p** 98. C Lee-on-the-Solent *Portsm* 97-01; V Leigh Park from 01; V Warren Park from 01. *The Vicarage, Riders Lane, Havant PO9 4QT* Tel (023) 9247 5276

JEFFERY, Kenneth Charles. b 40. Univ of Wales BA64 Linacre Coll Ox BA67 MA70. St Steph Ho Ox 64. **d** 67 **p** 68. C Swindon New Town *Bris* 67-68; C Summertown *Ox* 68-71; C Brighton St Pet *Chich* 71-77; V Ditchling 77-00. *Sparlings, Leysbourne, Chipping Campden GL55 6HL* Tel (01386) 840505 Fax 841676
E-mail kenneth@jeffery333.fslife.co.uk

JEFFERY, Michael Frank. b 48. Linc Th Coll 74. **d** 76 **p** 77. C Caterham Valley *S'wark* 76-79; C Tupsley *Heref* 79-82; P-in-c Stretton Sugwas 82-84; P-in-c Bishopstone 83-84; P-in-c Kenchester and Bridge Sollers 83-84; V Whiteshill *Glouc* 84-92; P-in-c Randwick 92; V Whiteshill and Randwick 93-02; TV Bedminster *Bris* from 02. *St Paul's Vicarage, 2 Southville Road, Bristol BS3 1DG* Tel (0117) 908 6996

JEFFERY, Norman. b 42. Bps' Coll Cheshunt. **d** 67 **p** 68. C Putney St Marg *S'wark* 67-71; C Hoddesdon *St Alb* 71-74; P-in-c Roxton w Gt Barford 74-79; V 79-86; V Woburn Sands from 86; RD Ampthill from 96. *The Vicarage, Church Road, Woburn Sands, Milton Keynes MK17 8TR* Tel (01908) 582581

JEFFERY, Peter James. b 41. Leeds Univ BSc63. Oak Hill Th Coll 64. **d** 66 **p** 67. C Streatham Park St Alb *S'wark* 66-70; C Northampton St Giles *Pet* 70-73; C Rushden St Pet 73-76; C

Rushden w Newton Bromswold 77-78; V Siddal *Wakef* 78-85; V Sowerby Bridge w Norland 85-98; P-in-c Cornholme 98-00; P-in-c Walsden 98-00; V Cornholme and Walsden from 00. *The Vicarage, 30 Cross Lee Road, Todmorden OL14 8EH* Tel (01706) 813604

JEFFERY, Peter Noel. b 37. Pemb Coll Ox BA60 MA64. Linc Th Coll 66. **d** 62 **p** 63. C W Smethwick *Birm* 62-64; P-in-c Bordesley St Andr 64-69; R Turvey *St Alb* 69-98; P-in-c Stevington 79-98; rtd 98. *Franconia Cottage, The Gardens, Adstock, Buckingham MK18 2JF* Tel (01296) 715770

JEFFERY, Richard William Christopher. b 43. Ex Univ BA65. Coll of Resurr Mirfield 66. **d** 68 **p** 69. C Widley w Wymering *Portsm* 68-71; C Salisbury St Mich *Sarum* 71-74; TV Ridgeway 74-80; V Stanford in the Vale w Goosey and Hatford *Ox* 80-89; V Topsham *Ex* from 89; RD Aylesbeare from 01. *The Vicarage, Globefields, Topsham, Exeter EX3 0EZ* Tel (01392) 876120

JEFFERY, The Very Revd Robert Martin Colquhoun. b 35. K Coll Lon BD58 AKC58 Birm Univ Hon DD99 FRSA91. **d** 59 **p** 60. C Grangetown *Dur* 59-61; C Barnes St Mary *S'wark* 61-63; Asst Sec Miss and Ecum Coun Ch Assembly 64-68; Sec Dept Miss and Unity BCC 68-71; V Headington *Ox* 71-78; RD Cowley 73-78; P-in-c Tong *Lich* 78-83; V 83-87; Dioc Missr 78-80; Adn Salop 80-87; Dean Worc 87-96; Can Res and Sub-Dean Ch Ch Ox 96-02; Select Preacher Ox Univ 91, 97, 98 and 02; rtd 02. *47 The Manor House, Bennett Crescent, Cowley, Oxford OX4 2UG* Tel (01865) 749706
E-mail rmcj@btopenworld.com

JEFFERYES, June Ann. b 37. Dur Univ BA58. WMMTC 87. **d** 90 **p** 94. NSM Caverswall *Lich* 90-92; NSM Caverswall and Weston Coyney w Dilhorne 92-02; rtd 02. *24 Glen Drive, Alton, Stoke-on-Trent ST10 4DJ* Tel (01538) 702150

JEFFERYES, Preb Neil. b 37. St Andr Univ BSc60 Lon Univ BD62. Tyndale Hall Bris 60. **d** 63 **p** 64. C St Helens St Helen *Liv* 63-68; V Barrow St Mark *Carl* 68-77; RD Furness 74-77; P-in-c Tetsworth *Ox* 77-81; P-in-c Adwell w S Weston 77-81; P-in-c Stoke Talmage w Wheatfield 77-81; RD Aston 81-85; R Tetsworth, Adwell w S Weston, Lewknor etc 81-86; V Caverswall *Lich* 86-92; P-in-c Dilhorne 86-92; RD Cheadle 91-98; V Caverswall and Weston Coyney w Dilhorne 92-02; Preb Lich Cathl 97-02; rtd 02. *24 Glen Drive, Alton, Stoke-on-Trent ST10 4DJ* Tel (01538) 702150
E-mail neil@jefferyes.freeserve.co.uk

JEFFORD, Mrs Margaret June. b 50. Univ of Wales RGN81. St Mich Coll Llan 94. **d** 96 **p** 97. C Risca *Mon* 96-98; C Pontypool 98-00; TV 00-02; V Newbridge w Crumlin from 02. *St Paul's Vicarage, High Street, Newbridge, Newport NP11 4FW* Tel (01495) 243975

JEFFORD, Peter Ernest. b 29. AKC53. **d** 54 **p** 55. C Berkeley *Glouc* 54-57; C Petersfield w Sheet *Portsm* 57-61; Chapl Churcher's Coll 57-61; R Rollesby w Burgh w Billockby *Nor* 62-71; V Watton 71-81; V Watton w Carbrooke and Ovington 81-82; Offg Chapl RAF 71-82; P-in-c Brampford Speke *Ex* 82-83; P-in-c Cadbury 82-83; P-in-c Thorverton 82-83; P-in-c Upton Pyne 82-83; TR Thorverton, Cadbury, Upton Pyne etc 83-92; rtd 92; Perm to Offic *Ox* 92-96; Hon C Ox St Mary V w St Cross and St Pet 96-99; Chapl Plater Coll from 96; P-in-c Whitchurch St Mary *Ox* 00-03. *27 Ashlong Road, Headington, Oxford OX3 0NH* Tel (01865) 760593

JEFFORD, Ronald. b 46. Univ of Wales (Lamp) Univ of Wales (Cardiff) DPS. St Mich Coll Llan Dip Minl Studies. **d** 91 **p** 92. C Ebbw Vale *Mon* 91-94; TV 94-95; R Bedwas and Rudry 95-98; V Abersychan and Garndiffaith 98-03; TV Mynyddislwyn from 03. *The Vicarage, Central Avenue, Oakdale, Blackwood NP2 0JS* Tel (01495) 223043

JEFFREE, Robin. b 29. AKC54. **d** 55 **p** 56. C N Harrow St Alb *Lon* 55-59; C Hendon St Mary 59-62; V Manea *Ely* 62-67; V Hartford 67-83; P-in-c Denver 83; R 83-94; P-in-c Ryston w Roxham 83; V W Dereham 83-94; rtd 94; Perm to Offic *Nor* from 94. *3 Church Lane, Hindolveston, Dereham NR20 5BT* Tel (01263) 861857

JEFFREY, Katrina. *See* METZNER, Mrs Katrina

JEFFREYS, David John. b 45. S Dios Minl Tr Scheme 89. **d** 92 **p** 93. NSM Bexhill St Barn *Chich* 92-95; Chapl Hastings and Rother NHS Trust from 95. *The Conquest Hospital, The Ridge, St Leonards-on-Sea TN37 7RD* Tel (01424) 755255 ext 8311 *or* 843672 E-mail chaplaincy@mail.har-tr.sthames.nhs.uk

JEFFREYS (née DESHPANDE), Mrs Lakshmi Anant. b 64. Liv Univ BSc86 Ex Univ PGCE87. Wycliffe Hall Ox BTh94. **d** 94 **p** 95. C Long Eaton St Jo *Derby* 94-97; Chapl Nottm Trent Univ *S'well* from 98. *151 Balfour Road, Derby DE22 8UR* Tel (01332) 770398 E-mail lakshmi.deshpande@ntu.ac.uk

JEFFREYS, Timothy John. b 58. Man Univ BSc79. Cranmer Hall Dur 83. **d** 86 **p** 87. C Goodmayes All SS *Chelmsf* 86-88; Perm to Offic *S'wark* 92-93; Hon C S Lambeth St Anne and All SS 93-96; C Croydon St Jo from 96. *Church House, Barrow Road, Croydon CR0 4EZ* Tel (020) 8688 7006

JEFFRIES, Keith. b 48. St Steph Ho Ox DipMin93. **d** 93 **p** 94. C St Marychurch *Ex* 93-96; TV Wood Green St Mich w Bounds Green St Gabr etc *Lon* 96-98; V The Hydneye *Chich* 98-02; Chapl Univ of Greenwich *Roch* 00-02; Chapl Kent Inst of Art and

Design 00-02; Chapl Tenerife Sur *Eur* 02-03. *Address temp unknown* E-mail fatherkeithjeffries@hotmail.com

JELF, Miss Pauline Margaret. b 55. Chich Th Coll 88. **d** 90 **p** 94. Par Dn Clayton *Lich* 90-94; C Knutton 94-98; P-in-c Silverdale and Alsagers Bank 94-98; Perm to Offic 98-02; C Clayton 02; C Betley and Madeley from 02. *11 Stafford Avenue, Newcastle ST5 3BN* Tel (01785) 639545

JELLEY, David. b 25. St Deiniol's Hawarden 86. **d** 87 **p** 88. NSM Evington *Leic* 87-93; P-in-c New Galloway *Glas* 93-97; rtd 97; Perm to Offic *Leic* from 00. *117A Gartree Road, Oadby, Leicester LE2 2FF* Tel 0116-270 3759

JELLEY, Ian. b 54. Newc Univ MA94 Cert Counselling 97. NEOC 89. **d** 91 **p** 92. C Jarrow *Dur* 91-95; P-in-c Leam Lane 95-96; Chapl HM Pris Holme Ho 96-01; R Grindon, Stillington and Wolviston *Dur* 01-03; rtd 03. *8 Beverley Road, Billingham TS23 3RE*

JELLEY, James Dudley. b 46. Linc Th Coll 78. **d** 80 **p** 81. C Stockwell Green St Andr *S'wark* 80-85; V Camberwell St Phil and St Mark 85-93; Perm to Offic 93-96; V Camberwell St Luke from 96; RD Camberwell from 00. *St Luke's Vicarage, 30 Commercial Way, London SE15 5JQ* Tel (020) 7703 5587 Fax as telephone

JELLEY (née CAPITANCHIK), Mrs Sophie Rebecca. b 72. Leeds Univ BA93. Wycliffe Hall Ox MPhil97. **d** 97 **p** 98. C Shipley St Pet *Bradf* 97-00; Miss Partner CMS 00-03; Hon C Churt and Hindhead *Guildf* from 03. *St John's Vicarage, Old Kiln Lane, Churt, Farnham GU10 2HX* Tel (01428) 713368 Mobile 07985-083429 E-mail baildon@globalnet.co.uk

JENKIN, The Hon Charles Alexander Graham. b 54. BScEng. Westcott Ho Cam 81. **d** 84 **p** 85. C Binley *Cov* 84-88; TV Canvey Is *Chelmsf* 88-94; TR Melton Mowbray *Leic* from 94; RD Framland 98-02. *The Rectory, 67 Dalby Road, Melton Mowbray LE13 0BQ* Tel (01664) 480923
E-mail cjenkin@leicester.anglican.org

JENKIN, Christopher Cameron. b 36. BNC Ox BA61 MA64. Clifton Th Coll 61. **d** 63 **p** 64. C Walthamstow St Mary *Chelmsf* 63-68; C Surbiton Hill Ch Ch *S'wark* 68-78; V Newport St Jo *Portsm* 78-88; R Newbarns w Hawcoat *Carl* 88-01; rtd 01; Perm to Offic *Carl* from 01. *Beckside, Orton, Penrith CA10 3RX* Tel (01539) 624410

JENKINS, Alan David. b 60. Bris Poly BA83 Wolv Poly DipTM87 DipM90 Spurgeon's Coll MTh02. All So Coll of Applied Th DipApTh85 Wycliffe Hall Ox 93. **d** 95 **p** 96. C Tunbridge Wells St Jas w St Phil *Roch* 95-01; TV S Gillingham from 01. *58 Parkwood Green, Gillingham ME8 9PP* Tel (01634) 300883 E-mail suzieandalan.jenkins@virgin.net

JENKINS, Allan Kenneth. b 40. Lon Univ BD63 AKC63 MTh69 PhD85. St Mich Coll Llan 63. **d** 64 **p** 65. C Llanblethian w Cowbridge *Llan* 64-70; India 70-76; V Llanarth w Clytha, Llansantffraed and Bryngwyn *Mon* 76-78; Dir of Studies Chich Th Coll 78-83; P-in-c Fowlmere *Ely* 83-87; P-in-c Thriplow 83-87; Sen Tutor EAMTC 84-87; Sen Chapl Coll 87-95; Dioc Dir Post-Ord Tr *Llan* 88-95; P-in-c Sidlesham *Chich* from 95; Tutor Univ Coll Chich from 95. *The Vicarage, Church Farm Lane, Sidlesham, Chichester PO20 7RE* Tel (01243) 641237
E-mail a.jenkins@ucc.ac.uk

JENKINS, Miss Anne Christina. b 47. Birm Univ BA70 Hull Univ CertEd71 St Jo Coll Dur BA77 DipTh78. Cranmer Hall Dur 75. **dss** 78 **d** 87 **p** 94. E Coatham *York* 78-81; OHP 81-87; Perm to Offic *York* 81-87; Ghana 87-88; Par Dn Beeston *Ripon* 88-93; Par Dn Leeds Gipton Epiphany 93-94; V Leeds St Marg and All Hallows 94-99; rtd 99; Perm to Offic *York* from 00. *28 Hill Cottages, Rosedale East, Pickering YO28 8RG* Tel (01751) 417130

JENKINS, Audrey Joan. b 36. TCert61. St D Coll Lamp. **d** 01. Par Dn Marshfield and Peterstone Wentloog etc *Mon* from 01. *10 Lytham Grove, St Mellons, Cardiff CF3 0LU* Tel (029) 2036 0574 E-mail audrey@stmellons.co.uk

JENKINS, Clifford Thomas. b 38. Westmr Coll Ox MTh02 IEng MIElecIE. Sarum & Wells Th Coll 74. **d** 77 **p** 78. Chapl Yeovil Coll 77-86; Hon C Yeovil w Kingston Pitney *B & W* 77-80; P-in-c 80-86; Chs FE Liaison Officer *B & W, Bris* and *Glouc* 87-90; Perm to Offic *B & W* 87-92 and from 93; FE Adv Gen Syn Bd of Educn and Meth Ch 90-98; rtd 98. *Bethany, 10 Grove Avenue, Yeovil BA20 2BB* Tel (01935) 475043
E-mail clifford.jenkins@virgin.net

JENKINS, Clive Ronald. b 57. Ripon Coll Cuddesdon 81. **d** 84 **p** 85. C E Grinstead St Swithun *Chich* 84-87; C Horsham 87-88; TV 88-90; Dioc Youth Chapl 90-96; P-in-c Amberley w N Stoke and Parham, Wiggonholt etc 93-96; V Southbourne w W Thorney from 96. *The Vicarage, 271 Main Road, Southbourne, Emsworth PO10 8JE* Tel (01243) 372436

JENKINS, Cyril. b 27. Univ of Wales (Lamp) BA53. Wells Th Coll 53. **d** 55 **p** 56. C Uttoxeter w Bramshall *Lich* 55-57; C Shrewsbury St Alkmund 57-60; V Essington 60-69; V Gnosall 69-72; Chapl St Alb Sch Chorley 72-79; Lic to Offic *Blackb* 73-86; Hd of Relig Studies Runshaw Coll 74-84; Lect Runshaw Tertiary Coll 84-86; rtd 86; Perm to Offic *Blackb* from 86. *55 Church Walk, Euxton, Chorley PR7 6HL* Tel (01257) 263973

JENKINS, David. *See* JENKINS, Canon William David

JENKINS, David. *See* JENKINS, Preb Richard David

✠**JENKINS, The Rt Revd David Edward.** b 25. Qu Coll Ox BA51 MA54 Dur Theol DD87. Linc Th Coll 52. **d** 53 **p** 54 **c** 84. C Birm Cathl *Birm* 53-54; Lect Qu Coll Birm 53-54; Chapl Qu Coll Ox 54-69; Lect Th Ox Univ 55-69; Can Th Leic Cathl *Leic* 66-82; Dir WCC Humanum Studies 69-73; Dir Wm Temple Foundn Man 73-78; Jt Dir 79-94; Prof Th and RS Leeds Univ 79-84; Bp Dur 84-94; rtd 94; Hon Asst Bp Ripon and Leeds *Ripon* from 94. *Ashbourne, Cotherstone, Barnard Castle DL12 9PR* Tel (01833) 650804 Fax 650714

JENKINS, David Harold. b 61. SS Coll Cam BA84 MA87 Ox Univ BA88 MA94. Ripon Coll Cuddesdon 86. **d** 89 **p** 90. C Chesterton Gd Shep *Ely* 89-91; C Earley St Pet *Ox* 91-94; V Blackpool St Mich *Blackb* 94-99; V Broughton from 99; AD Preston from 04. *The Vicarage, 410 Garstang Road, Broughton, Preston PR3 5JB* Tel (01772) 862330 E-mail dsn.jenks@virgin.net

JENKINS, David Noble. b 25. CCC Cam BA47 MA50. Cuddesdon Coll 48. **d** 50 **p** 51. C Northampton St Matt *Pet* 50-54; Chapl Hurstpierpoint Coll 54-59; USPG 60-65; Chapl Eastbourne Coll 66-74; V Jarvis Brook *Chich* 75-90; rtd 90; USA 90-92; Perm to Offic *Chich* from 92. *2 Littlebourne Cottages, London Road, Crowborough TN6 1SR* Tel (01892) 661179

JENKINS, David Roland. b 32. Keble Coll Ox BA55 MA58. Wells Th Coll 55. **d** 59 **p** 60. C Middlesbrough St Jo the Ev *York* 59-60; C Kingston upon Hull St Alb 60-64; C Roehampton H Trin *S'wark* 64-68; V Dawley St Jerome *Lon* 68-73; R Harlington 73-98; rtd 98. *21F Cleveland Road, Cowley, Uxbridge UB8 2DR* Tel (01895) 253761

JENKINS, David Thomas. b 43. Ox Univ MA94 RIBA70 Lon Univ DipTh79. S'wark Ord Course 76 Ripon Coll Cuddesdon 86. **d** 79 **p** 80. NSM Merthyr Tydfil and Cyfarthfa *Llan* 79-86; NSM Brecon St David w Llanspyddid and Llanilltyd *S & B* 86-91; P-in-c Llangiwg 91-92; V 92-01; Chapl Puerto de la Cruz Tenerife *Eur* from 02. *Apartado 68, Parque Taoro, Puerto de la Cruz, 38400 Tenerife, Canary Islands* Tel (0034) (922) 384038 Fax 388285

JENKINS, The Ven David Thomas Ivor. b 29. K Coll Lon BD52 AKC52 Birm Univ MA63. **d** 53 **p** 54. C Bilton *Cov* 53-56; V Wolston 56-61; Asst Dir RE *Carl* 61-63; V Carl St Barn 63-72; V Carl St Cuth 72-76; P-in-c Carl St Mary w St Paul 72-76; V Carl St Cuth w St Mary 76-91; Dioc Sec 84-95; Hon Can Carl Cathl 76-91; Can Res 91-95; Adn Westmorland and Furness 95-99; rtd 99; Perm to Offic *Carl* from 00. *Irvings House, Sleagill, Penrith CA10 3HD* Tel (01931) 714400

JENKINS, Canon Eric Neil. b 23. Univ of Wales BSc43 MSc47. Wycliffe Hall Ox 60. **d** 62 **p** 63. C Allerton *Liv* 62-65; V Hale 65-73; Bp's Adv on Soc and Scientific Affairs 73-88; V Hightown 73-88; Hon Can Liv Cathl 83-89; rtd 89; Perm to Offic *Liv* from 89. *51 Oulton Road, Liverpool L16 8NP* Tel 0151-722 5515

JENKINS, Eric Robert. b 52. Poly Cen Lon BSc74. STETS 97. **d** 00 **p** 01. C Weybridge *Guildf* from 00. *Drivers, Elgin Road, Weybridge KT13 8DS* Tel (01932) 844273

JENKINS, Ernest Dennis. b 28. S Dios Minl Tr Scheme 80. **d** 83 **p** 84. NSM Lancing St Mich *Chich* 83-86; C E Grinstead St Swithun 86-89; C Portslade St Nic and St Andr 89-94; rtd 94; Perm to Offic *Chich* from 94. *61A Upton Road, Worthing BN13 1BY* Tel (01903) 263911

JENKINS, The Very Revd Frank Graham. b 23. St D Coll Lamp BA47 Jes Coll Ox BA49 MA53. St Mich Coll Llan 49. **d** 50 **p** 51. C Llangeinor *Llan* 50-53; Min Can Llan Cathl 53-60; CF (TA) 56-61; V Abertillery *Mon* 60-64; V Risca 64-75; Can St Woolos Cathl 67-76; V Caerleon 75-76; Dean Mon 76-90; rtd 90; Lic to Offic *Mon* from 90. *Rivendell, 209 Christchurch Road, Newport NP9 7QL* Tel (01633) 255278

JENKINS, Frederick Llewellyn. b 14. St D Coll Lamp BA35 St Mich Coll Llan 36. **d** 37 **p** 38. C Gilfach Goch w Llandyfodwg *Llan* 37-40; C Bishop's Castle w Mainstone *Heref* 40-45; CF 45-64; CF (R of O) 64-69; Chapl R Masonic Sch Bushey 64-77; rtd 77; Perm to Offic *Lich* 77-95. *Plas Uchaf, Trefonen, Oswestry SY10 9DT* Tel (01691) 653918

JENKINS, Garry Frederick. b 48. Southn Univ BTh79. Chich Th Coll 75. **d** 79 **p** 80. C Kingsbury St Andr *Lon* 79-84; C Leigh St Clem *Chelmsf* 84-88; P-in-c Brentwood St Geo 88-94; V from 94. *The Vicarage, 28 Robin Hood Road, Brentwood CM15 9EN* Tel (01277) 213618 E-mail g.f.jenkins@amserve.net

JENKINS, Gary John. b 59. York Univ BA80 CertEd81. Oak Hill Th Coll BA89. **d** 89 **p** 90. C Norwood St Luke *S'wark* 89-94; P-in-c St Helier 94-95; V 95-01; V Redhill H Trin from 01. *28 Lynwood Road, Redhill RH1 1JS* Tel (01737) 213500 E-mail garyjjenkins@hotmail.com

JENKINS, Canon George Patrick. b 36. Univ of Wales (Lamp) BA61. Lich Th Coll 61. **d** 63 **p** 64. C Dursley *Glouc* 63-66; C Stroud H Trin 66-69; V Churcham w Bulley 69-81; V Churcham w Bulley and Minsterworth 81-02; RD Forest N 79-95; Hon Can Glouc Cathl 90-02; rtd 02. *Meadow Bank, Cefnllys Lane, Penybont, Llandrindod Wells LD1 5TY* Tel (01597) 850027

JENKINS, Canon Jeanette. b 42. St Jo Coll Nottm 83. **dss** 84 **d** 86 **p** 94. NSM Kilmarnock *Glas* 84-94; NSM Irvine St Andr LEP 84-94; NSM Ardrossan 84-94; Asst Chapl Crosshouse Hosp 86-94; Chapl Ayrshire Hospice from 90; Can St Mary's Cathl *Glas* from 99. *4 Gleneagles Avenue, Kilwinning KA13 6RD* Tel (01294) 553383 *or* 269200 Mobile 0777-5595901 Fax (01292) 294401 E-mail ivanjen@lineone.com

JENKINS, John Francis. b 46. Ripon Hall Ox 77 Ripon Coll Cuddesdon 75. **d** 77 **p** 78. C Filton *Bris* 77-79; C Bris St Andr Hartcliffe 79-84; P-in-c Bris H Cross Inns Court 84-85; V 85-95; R Odcombe, Brympton, Lufton and Montacute *B & W* from 95. *The Rectory, Street Lane, Higher Odcombe, Yeovil BA22 8UP* Tel (01935) 863034

JENKINS, John Howard David. b 51. Birm Univ BA72. St Steph Ho Ox 72. **d** 74 **p** 75. C Milford Haven *St D* 74-77; PV Llan Cathl *Llan* 77-81; Chapl Lowther Coll St As 81-84; V Choral St As Cathl *St As* 81-84; C Neath w Llantwit *Llan* 84-86; Chapl Colston's Sch Bris 86-91; Chapl Blue Coat Sch Birm from 91. *Blue Coat School, Metchley Lane, Birmingham B17 0HR* Tel 0121-454 1425

JENKINS, John Morgan. b 33. Open Univ BA96. Mon Dioc Tr Scheme 82. **d** 85 **p** 86. NSM Cwmbran *Mon* 85-02; rtd 02. *5 Ridgeway Avenue, Newport NP9 5AF* Tel (01633) 662231

JENKINS, John Raymond. b 26. K Coll Lon 52. **d** 53 **p** 54. C Wrexham *St As* 53-56; Hon C 77-82; C Welshpool 56-57; V Mochdre 57-65; V Llandysul *St D* 65-67; V Llanfair Caereinion w Llanllugan *St As* 67-70; V Llanychaearn w Llanddeiniol *St D* 82-91; rtd 91; Chapl Lanzarote *Eur* 95-97. *Manorawon, Main Street, Llanon SY23 5HJ* Tel (01974) 202212

JENKINS, John Richard. b 68. Dundee Univ LLB90. St Steph Ho Ox BA94 DipMin94. **d** 94 **p** 95. C Brighouse and Clifton *Wakef* 94-97; C Barnsley St Mary 97-99. *Address withheld by request*

JENKINS, Julian James. b 56. Bris Poly HND76 Univ of Wales (Cardiff) DMS98. St Mich Coll Llan 97. **d** 99 **p** 00. C Whitchurch *Llan* 99-01; TV Aberavon from 01. *77 Victoria Road, Aberavon, Port Talbot SA12 6QQ* Tel (01639) 892306

JENKINS, Lawrence Clifford. b 45. AKC70 Open Univ BA77. St Aug Coll Cant. **d** 71 **p** 72. C Osmondthorpe St Phil *Ripon* 71-74; C Monkseaton St Mary *Newc* 75-84; V Shiremoor 78-84; V Wheatley Hills *Sheff* 84-95; RD Doncaster 92-95; V Greenhill from 95. *St Peter's Vicarage, Reney Avenue, Sheffield S8 7FN* Tel 0114-237 7422 E-mail lawrie.jenkins@ukgateway.net

JENKINS, Patrick. *See* JENKINS, Canon George Patrick

JENKINS, Paul Morgan. b 44. Sussex Univ BEd68 Fitzw Coll Cam BA73 MA76. Westcott Ho Cam 71. **d** 74 **p** 75. C Forest Gate St Edm *Chelmsf* 74-77; Chapl Bryanston Sch 77-85; P-in-c Stourpaine, Durweston and Bryanston *Sarum* 77-83; Asst Chapl and Housemaster Repton Sch Derby 84-89; Dean of Chpl 89-91; R Singleton *Chich* 91-97; V E Dean 91-97; V W Dean 91-97; Dir St Columba's Retreat and Conf Cen from 97; Chapl Community of St Pet Woking from 03. *St Columba's House, Maybury Hill, Woking GU22 8AB* Tel (01483) 766498 Fax 740441 E-mail retreats@st.columba.org.uk

JENKINS (née RICHARDSON), Pauline Kate. b 41. RGN62 Nottm Univ CertEd80 RNT83. St Jo Coll Nottm 91. **d** 94 **p** 98. Uganda 94-96; Perm to Offic *S'well* 96-98; NSM Selston 98-01; NSM Annesley w Newstead 01-03; rtd 03. *The Rookery, 130 Church Street, Eastwood, Nottingham NG16 3HT* Tel 07976-716955 (mobile)

JENKINS, Preb Richard David. b 33. Magd Coll Cam BA58 MA. Westcott Ho Cam 59. **d** 61 **p** 62. C Staveley *Derby* 61-64; C Billingham St Aid *Dur* 64-68; V Walsall Pleck and Bescot *Lich* 68-73; R Whitchurch 73-97; RD Wem and Whitchurch 85-95; P-in-c Tilstock and Whixall 92-95; Preb Lich Cathl 93-97; Perm to Offic *Lich* from 99. *The Council House, Council House Court, Castle Street, Shrewsbury SY1 2AU* Tel (01743) 270051

JENKINS, Richard Morvan. b 44. St Mich Coll Llan DipTh68 DPS69. **d** 69 **p** 70. C Tenby *St D* 69-73; V Llanrhian w Llanhywel and Carnhedryn 73-77; V Llanrhian w Llanhywel and Carnhedryn etc 77-80; R Johnston w Steynton 80-93; V St Ishmael's w Llan-saint and Ferryside from 93. *The Vicarage, Water Street, Ferryside SA17 5RT* Tel (01267) 267288

JENKINS, Robert. *See* JENKINS, Eric Robert

JENKINS, Canon Robert Francis. b 33. BNC Ox BA57 MA59. Wycliffe Hall Ox 57. **d** 59 **p** 60. C Hall Green Ascension *Birm* 59-63; V Dosthill and Wood End 63-71; V Brandwood 71-85; V Sutton Coldfield St Columba 85-97; Hon Can S Malawi from 87; rtd 97; Perm to Offic *Birm* from 97; *Lich* from 00. *4 The Pines, Lichfield WS14 9XA* Tel (01543) 252176

JENKINS, Tanya Louise. b 66. Univ of Wales BD87 MPhil89 PhD93 PGCE94. Westcott Ho Cam 95. **d** 98 **p** 99. C Malltraeth Deanery Ban 98-01; P-in-c Llangefni w Tregaean Ban from 01. *50 Bro Ednyfed, Llangefni LL77 7WB* Tel (01248) 723138 E-mail tanyacwmtawe@cyngar.fsnet.co.uk

JENKINS, Thomas Glennard Owen. b 22. St Jo Coll Ox BA48 MA52. Wells Th Coll 49 Wycliffe Hall Ox 50. **d** 50 **p** 51. Min Can St D Cathl *St D* 50-54; Chapl RN 54-58; Prec and Sacr Worc Cathl *Worc* 58-60; V Hailey w Crawley *Ox* 60-79; V Penbryn and Betws Ifan w Bryngwyn *St D* 79-87; rtd 87. *c/o Mrs R Jenkins, Coed-y-Wern, Sarnau, Llandysul SA44 6PX*

JENKINS, Thomas William. b 14. Univ of Wales BA40. St Mich Coll Llan 40. d 42 p 43. C Newport St Mark *Mon* 42-46; C Kidderminster St Mary and All SS, Trimpley etc *Worc* 46-48; V Walsall Pleck and Bescot *Lich* 48-67; V Shrewsbury H Trin w St Julian 67-75; Chapl Manor Hosp and St Jo Hosp 48-67; V Ruyton 75-80; rtd 80; Perm to Offic *Lich* 80-00. *4 Larkhill Road, Park Hall, Oswestry SY11 4AW* Tel (01691) 659304

JENKINS, Timothy David. b 52. Pemb Coll Ox BA73 MLitt77 MA82 St Edm Ho Cam BA84. Ridley Hall Cam 82. d 85 p 86. C Kingswood *Bris* 85-87; Sen Chapl Nottm Univ *S'well* 88-92; Dean Jes Coll Cam from 92. *50 Stanley Road, Cambridge CB5 8BL* Tel (01223) 363185 *or* 339339
E-mail tdj22@jesus.cam.ac.uk

JENKINS, Canon William David. b 42. Birm Univ BA63. St D Coll Lamp LTh65. d 65 p 66. C Gorseinon *S & B* 65-67; C Llanelli *St D* 67-72; V Clydach *S & B* 72-82; Chapl Gwynedd Hosp NHS Trust 82-97; V Llanrhos *St As* 82-97; RD Llanrwst 84-96; Can Cursal St As Cathl from 93; TR Tenby *St D* from 97. *The Rectory, Church Park, Tenby SA70 7EE* Tel (01834) 842068

JENKINSON, Margaret. b 40. MCSP62. Carl Dioc Tr Inst 89. d 92 p 94. NSM Preesall *Blackb* 92-96; NSM Lanercost w Kirkcambeck and Walton *Carl* 96-99; NSM Gilsland w Nether Denton 96-99; NSM Lanercost, Walton, Gilsland and Nether Denton from 99. *6 Irthing Park, Gilsland, Carlisle CA8 7DL* Tel (01697) 747652 Fax 747712
E-mail margaret.jenkinson@lineone.net

JENKYNS, Preb Henry Derrik George. b 30. Sarum Th Coll 57. d 60 p 61. C Kettering SS Pet and Paul *Pet* 60-64; V Shrewsbury St Geo *Lich* 64-71; V Wednesbury St Paul Wood Green 71-76; V Stokesay *Heref* 76-86; P-in-c Acton Scott 76-86; RD Condover 80-86; Preb Heref Cathl 83-96; R Kington w Huntington, Old Radnor, Kinnerton etc 86-96; rtd 96; Perm to Offic *Heref* from 96. *Llantroft, Newcastle, Craven Arms SY7 8PD* Tel (01588) 640314

JENKYNS, John Thomas William Basil. b 30. Univ of Wales (Lamp) BA54 St Cath Coll Ox BA57 MA62. Wycliffe Hall Ox 54. d 57 p 58. C Neasden cum Kingsbury St Cath *Lon* 57-60; C S Lyncombe *B & W* 60-64; V Gt Harwood St Bart *Blackb* 64-66; R Colne St Bart 66-69; V Chard St Mary *B & W* 69-87; Preb Wells Cathl 87; V Swaffham *Nor* 87-89; V Overbury w Teddington, Alstone etc *Worc* 89-95; rtd 95. *2 Clos y Fran, Glais, Swansea SA7 9TH*

JENKYNS, Stephen. b 60. Univ of Wales (Cardiff) BTh02. St Mich Coll Llan 99. d 02 p 03. C Penarth w Lavernock *Llan* from 02. *Church House, 153 Windsor Road, Penarth CF64 1JF* Tel (029) 2070 5485

JENKYNS, Thomas John Blackwell. b 31. Univ of Wales (Lamp) BA52. d 54 p 55. C Llanelli St Paul *St D* 54-58; C New Windsor St Jo *Ox* 58-64; Chapl RAF 64-85; P-in-c Herriard w Winslade and Long Sutton etc *Win* 85-86; V 86-98; rtd 98; Perm to Offic *Ex* from 98. *Mehring, 1 Walker Court, Old Tiverton Road, Crediton EX17 1EE* Tel (01363) 775561

JENNER, Miss Brenda Anne. b 54. Culham Coll Ox BEd80. St Jo Coll Nottm DPS88. d 88. Par Dn Leigh St Mary *Man* 88-92; Par Dn Leic Ch Sav *Leic* 92-94; rtd 94. *18 Chatsworth Avenue, Wigston, Leicester LE18 4LF*

JENNER, Michael Albert. b 37. Oak Hill Th Coll 75. d 77 p 78. C Mile Cross *Nor* 77-80; P-in-c Easton *Ely* 80-86; P-in-c Ellington 80-86; P-in-c Grafham 80-86; P-in-c Spaldwick w Barham and Woolley 80-86; Perm to Offic *Roch* from 01; rtd 02. *Heathgate Cottage, Langton Road, Langton Green, Tunbridge Wells TN3 0BA* Tel and fax (01892) 535136 Mobile 07831-826954

JENNER, Peter John. b 56. Chu Coll Cam BA77 PhD80 MA81. St Jo Coll Nottm 82. d 85 p 86. C Upperby St Jo *Carl* 85-88; Chapl Reading Univ Ox 88-96; P-in-c Mellor *Derby* 96-99; V from 99. *The Vicarage, Church Road, Mellor, Stockport SK6 5LX* Tel 0161-427 1203

JENNER, William George. b 37. Nottm Univ BSc59 K Coll Lon PGCE60. LNSM course 95. d 97 p 98. OLM Gillingham w Geldeston, Stockton, Ellingham etc *Nor* from 97. *3 Woodland Drive, Kirby Cane, Bungay NR35 2PT* Tel (01508) 518229

JENNETT, The Ven Maurice Arthur. b 34. St Jo Coll Dur BA60. Cranmer Hall Dur 60. d 62 p 63. C Marple All SS *Ches* 62-67; V Withnell *Blackb* 67-75; V Stranton *Dur* 75-91; Crosslinks Zimbabwe 92-99; Asst P Nyanga St Mary Magd 92-93; R 93-99; Can and Adn Manicaland N 97; rtd 99. *2 Southfield Avenue, Ripon HG4 2NR* Tel (01765) 607842

JENNINGS, Anne. *See* SMITH, Mrs Anne

JENNINGS, Prof Barry Randall. b 39. Southn Univ BSc61 PhD64 DSc76 DEng01 FInstP70 FRSC95. SW Minl Tr Course 96. d 98 p 99. Prof Physics Reading Univ from 94; NSM St Germans *Truro* 98-00; NSM S Hill w Callington from 00. *Pitt Meadow, St Dominic, Saltash PL12 6SX* Tel (01579) 350940 Fax as telephone

JENNINGS, Clive John. b 57. Trin Coll Bris. d 00 p 01. C Milton *B & W* 00-02; C Clevedon St Andr and Ch Ch from 02. *34 Rippleside, Clevedon BS21 7JX* Tel (01275) 872134
E-mail cmj11a@ntlworld.com

✠JENNINGS, The Rt Revd David Willfred Michael. b 44. AKC66. d 67 p 68 c 00. C Walton St Mary *Liv* 67-69; C Christchurch *Win* 69-73; V Hythe 73-80; V Romford St Edw *Chelmsf* 80-92; RD Havering 85-92; Hon Can Chelmsf Cathl 87-92; Adn Southend 92-00; Suff Bp Warrington *Liv* from 00. *34 Central Avenue, Eccleston Park, Prescot L34 2QP* Tel 0151-426 1897 Fax 493 2479 E-mail bw@warrington75.freeserve.co.uk

JENNINGS, Canon Frederick David. b 48. K Coll Lon BD73 AKC73 Loughb Univ MPhil98. St Aug Coll Cant 73. d 74 p 75. C Halesowen *Worc* 74-77; Perm to Offic *Birm* 78-80; Perm to Offic *Leic* 78-80 and 85-87; P-in-c Snibston 80-85; Community Relns Officer 81-84; P-in-c Burbage w Aston Flamville 87-91; R from 91; Hon Can Leic Cathl from 03. *The Rectory, New Road, Burbage, Hinckley LE10 2AW* Tel (01455) 230512 Fax 250833

JENNINGS, George. b 20. Lon Univ BD64. Lambeth STh89 Oak Hill Th Coll 46. d 51 p 52. C Laisterdyke *Bradf* 51-53; C Morden *S'wark* 53-56; V Houghton *Carl* 56-66; V Haydock St Mark *Liv* 66-77; V Newburgh 77-89; rtd 89; Perm to Offic *Liv* from 89; Perm to Offic *Heref* from 90. *Shalom, 97 Watling Street South, Church Stretton SY6 7BH* Tel (01694) 722145

JENNINGS, Harold Andrew. b 15. ATCL35 LTCL36 FTCL37 MRST39 LRAM39. St Deiniol's Hawarden 63. d 63 p 64. C Swansea St Gabr *S & B* 63-67; R Aberedw w Llandeilo Graban etc 67-79; V Knighton and Norton 79-85; Hon C Llanbister and Llanbadarn Fynydd w Llananno 85-87; rtd 87. *Finsbury, Beaufort Road, Llandrindod Wells LD1 5EL* Tel (01597) 824892

JENNINGS, Ian. b 47. Leeds Univ MA98. N Ord Course 95. d 97 p 97. NSM Hackenthorpe *Sheff* 97-01; Asst Chapl HM Pris Doncaster 97-98; Chapl HM Pris and YOI Doncaster 98-01; V Sheff St Cuth *Sheff* from 01. *The Vicarage, 7 Horndean Road, Sheffield S5 6UJ* Tel 0114-243 6506

JENNINGS, Janet. b 38. SCM71 SRN74. Oak Hill Th Coll BA87. d 88 p 97. Par Dn Stevenage St Pet Broadwater *St Alb* 88-90; Perm to Offic *St As* from 92. *Pound House, Forden, Welshpool SY21 8NU* Tel (01938) 580400

JENNINGS, Jonathan Peter. b 61. K Coll Lon BD83. Westcott Ho Cam 84. d 86 p 87. C Peterlee *Dur* 86-89; C Darlington St Cuth 89-92; Dioc Communications Officer *Man* 92-95; Broadcasting Officer Gen Syn 95-01; Perm to Offic *S'wark* 95-98; Hon C Banstead *Guildf* from 98; Abp Cant's Press Sec from 01. *14 Glenfield Road, Banstead SM7 2DG,* or *Lambeth Palace, London SE1 7JU* Tel (01737) 353938 *or* (020) 7898 1224 Fax (020) 7261 9836 *or* 7261 1765 E-mail revjpj@aol.com *or* jonathan.jennings@c-of-e.org.uk

JENNINGS, The Very Revd Kenneth Neal. b 30. CCC Cam BA54 MA58. Cuddesdon Coll 54. d 56 p 57. C Ramsgate H Trin *Cant* 56-59; Asst Master St Geo Sch 59-63; Vice-Prin Cuddesdon Coll 67-73; V Hitchin St Mary *St Alb* 73-76; TR Hitchin 77-83; Dean Glouc 83-96; rtd 96; Perm to Offic *Bradf* from 96. *The School House, Keasden, Clapham, Lancaster LA2 8EY* Tel (01524) 251455

JENNINGS, Mervyn. b 39. Sarum & Wells Th Coll 83. d 85 p 86. C Knowle *Bris* 85-89; P-in-c Cressing *Chelmsf* 89-93; Rural Youth Development Officer from 89; V Barkingside St Fran from 93. *St Francis's Vicarage, 144 Fencepiece Road, Ilford IG6 2LA* Tel (020) 8500 2970 Fax 8270 3205 E-mail frjennings@aol.com

JENNINGS, Peter James. b 28. Univ of Wales (Lamp) BA56. St D Coll Lamp LTh57. d 57 p 58. C Dudley St Jo *Worc* 57-60; C Dudley St Thos 61-64; Chapl HM Borstal Portland 64-66; Chapl HM Pris Wakef 66-70; Chapl HM Pris Liv 75-76; RD Walton *Liv* 75-76; Chapl HM Pris Styal 76-77 and 88-92; N Regional Chapl 76-82; Asst Chapl Gen (N) 82-88; Perm to Offic *Man* 77-89 and from 00; *Ches* from 79; rtd 93. *6 St Ann's Road South, Cheadle SK8 3DZ* Tel 0161-437 8828

JENNINGS, Robert Henry. b 46. St Jo Coll Dur BA69 MA79. Qu Coll Birm DipTh71. d 72 p 73. C Dursley *Glouc* 72-74; C Coleford w Staunton 75-78; TV Bottesford w Ashby *Linc* 78-83; TV Witney *Ox* 83-89; V Lane End w Cadmore End from 89. *The Vicarage, 7 Lammas Way, Lane End, High Wycombe HP14 3EX* Tel (01494) 881913

JENNINGS, Canon Thomas Robert. b 24. TCD BA47 MA51. d 48 p 49. C Drumragh *D & R* 48-51; CF 51-67; I Killeshandra *K, E & A* 67-70; I Newcastle w Newtownmountkennedy and Calary *D & G* 70-92; Can Ch Ch Cathl Dublin from 88; rtd 92. *66 Seacourt, Newcastle, Greystones, Co Wicklow, Irish Republic* Tel (00353) (1) 281 0777

JENNINGS, Walter James. b 37. Birm Univ BMus60 MA90. Qu Coll Birm 77. d 80 p 81. Hon C Hampton in Arden *Birm* 80-84; Chapl St Alb Aided Sch Highgate Birm 84-86; C Wotton-under-Edge w Ozleworth and N Nibley *Glouc* 86-89; V Pittville All SS 89-98; rtd 98; Chapl Beauchamp Community 98-00; Perm to Offic *Worc* from 98. *Flat 7, Leamington Court, Wells Road, Malvern WR14 4HF* Tel (01684) 561513

JENNO, Charles Henry. b 25. Wells Th Coll 65. d 66 p 67. C Shirehampton *Bris* 66-69; C Fishponds St Mary 69-73; V Thornes St Jas w Ch Ch *Wakef* 73-78; V Carleton 78-82; V E Hardwick 78-82; rtd 82; Perm to Offic *Wakef* from 82. *32 Tower Avenue, Upton, Pontefract WF9 1EE* Tel (01977) 640925

JENSEN, Alexander Sönderup. b 68. Tübingen Univ 94 St Jo Coll Dur PhD97 Ox Univ MTh01. St Steph Ho Ox 97. d 99 p 00. C

Norton St Mich *Dur* 99-02; Lect CITC from 02. *CITC, Braemor Park, Dublin 14, Irish Republic* Tel (00353) (1) 492 3506 Fax 492 3082 E-mail alexanderjensen@citc.ie

JENSEN, Erik Henning. b 33. Copenhagen Univ BPhil51 Harvard Univ STM54 Worc Coll Ox BLitt58 DPhil69. Ridley Hall Ox 56. **d** 58 **p** 59. C Highwood *Chelmsf* 58-59; C Simanggang Sarawak 59-61; Borneo 61-62; Malaysia 63-03; rtd 02. *The Rock House, Maugersbury, Stow-on-the-Wold GL54 1HP* Tel (01451) 830171

JENSON, Philip Peter. b 56. Ex Coll Ox BA78 MA82 Down Coll Cam BA80 MA86 PhD88. Ridley Hall Cam 80. **d** 87 **p** 88. C Gt Warley Ch Ch *Chelmsf* 87-89; Lect Trin Coll Bris from 89. *15 Henleaze Road, Henleaze, Bristol BS9 4EX, or Trinity College, Stoke Hill, Bristol BS9 1JP* Tel 0117-962 1861 *or* 968 2803 E-mail philip.jenson@trinity-bris.ac.uk

JEPHSON, Douglas Ronald Shipstone. b 17. St Jo Coll Dur BA38 MA43. **d** 40 **p** 41. C Wortley de Leeds *Ripon* 40-43; C Armley St Bart 43-45; C Woodhouse St Mark 45-47; V Riddings *Derby* 47-54; V Elmton 54-70; R Tysoe w Compton Winyates and Oxhill *Cov* 70-81; R Whatcote 76-81; V Tysoe w Oxhill and Whatcote 81-82; rtd 82; Perm to Offic *York* from 92. *The Old School House, 42 The Village, Thorp Arch, Wetherby LS23 7AG* Tel (01937) 845955

JEPPS, Philip Anthony. b 34. BNC Ox BA58 MA68. Wycliffe Hall Ox 58. **d** 60 **p** 73. C Elton All SS *Man* 60; Perm to Offic *Pet* 70-73; R Church w Chapel Brampton 74-80; P-in-c Harlestone 79-80; V Kettering St Andr 80-94; V Conisbrough *Sheff* 94-01; rtd 01. *2 Eagle Cottages, Church Lane, Orleton, Ludlow SY8 4HT* Tel (01568) 780517

JEPSON, Joanna Elizabeth. b 76. Trin Coll Bris BA99 Cam Univ MA03. Ridley Hall Cam 01. **d** 03. C Plas Newton *Ches* from 03. *13 Mannings Lane South, Chester CH2 3RX* Tel (01244) 313746 E-mail joeyjep@yahoo.com

JERMAN, Edward David. b 40. Trin Coll Carmarthen CertEd61. **d** 87 **p** 88. NSM Llandrygarn w Bodwrog and Heneglwys etc *Ban* from 87. *Tryfan, Trefor, Holyhead LL65 3YT* Tel (01407) 720856

JERMY, Jack. b 22. ACP65. Ripon Hall Ox 64. **d** 65 **p** 66. Hd Master SS Simon and Jude Primary Sch Bolton 62-80; C Bolton SS Simon and Jude *Man* 65-74; P-in-c Rivington 74-93; NSM Horwich and Rivington 93-95; Perm to Offic from 95. *Bent House, Long Lane, Heath Charnock, Chorley PR6 9EW* Tel (01257) 480466

JERMY, Stuart John. b 66. Middx Univ BEd90. Wycliffe Hall Ox 01. **d** 03. C Thundersley *Chelmsf* from 03. *42 Bartley Road, Benfleet SS7 4DB* Tel (01268) 795664 Mobile 07801-071443 E-mail stu-liz@fish.co.uk

JERSEY, Dean of. *See* SEAFORD, The Very Revd John Nicholas

JERUSALEM, Bishop of. *See* KAFITY, The Rt Revd Samir

JERUSALEM AND THE MIDDLE EAST, President Bishop of the Episcopal Church in. *See* HANDFORD, The Most Revd George Clive

JERUSALEM, Bishop of. *See* KAFITY, The Rt Revd Samir

JERVIS, Christopher. b 53. BEd Cam Univ DipTh. Wycliffe Hall Ox. **d** 82 **p** 83. C Woodford Wells *Chelmsf* 82-85; Chapl Felsted Sch 85-87; Chapl Canford Sch Wimborne from 87. *Merryvale, Canford Magna, Wimborne BH21 3AF* Tel (01202) 887722 *or* 841254

JERVIS, William Edward. b 47. ARICS74 MRICS01. Linc Th Coll 74. **d** 77 **p** 78. C W Bromwich All SS *Lich* 77-80; C Horsham *Chich* 80-86; R W Tarring from 86. *West Tarring Rectory, Glebe Road, Worthing BN14 7PF* Tel (01903) 235043

JESSETT, David Charles. b 55. K Coll Lon BD77 AKC77 MTh. Westcott Ho Cam 78. **d** 79 **p** 80. C Aveley *Chelmsf* 79-82; C Walthamstow St Pet 82-85; P-in-c Hunningham *Cov* 85-91; P-in-c Wappenbury w Weston under Wetherley 85-91; Progr Dir Exploring Chr Min Scheme 85-91; Dir CME 87-90; Perm to Offic 90-97; P-in-c Barford w Wasperton and Sherbourne from 97. *The Rectory, Church Lane, Barford, Warwick CV35 8ES* Tel (01926) 624238 E-mail david@jessetts.freeserve.co.uk

JESSIMAN, Timothy Edward. b 58. Oak Hill Th Coll DipHE91. **d** 91 **p** 92. C Baldock w Bygrave *St Alb* 91-95; C Bideford *Ex* 95-96; TV Bideford, Northam, Westward Ho, Appledore etc 96-00; Chapl Grenville Coll Bideford 95-00; Chapl N Devon Healthcare NHS Trust 98-00; P-in-c Hartplain *Portsm* from 00. *The Vicarage, 61 Hart Plain Avenue, Waterlooville PO8 8RG* Tel (023) 9226 4551 E-mail tim.jessiman@ntlworld.com

JESSON, Alan Francis. b 47. TD89. Ealing Coll of Educn 70 Loughb Univ MLS77 Selw Coll Cam MA87 ALA70 FLA91 MBIM82. EAMTC 88. **d** 91 **p** 92. NSM Swavesey *Ely* 91-95; NSM Fen Drayton w Conington and Lolworth etc 95-00; CF (ACF) 92-96; Sen Chapl ACF from 96; R Upwell St Pet *Ely* from 00; R Outwell from 00; Perm to Offic *Nor* from 01. *The Rectory, 5 New Road, Upwell, Wisbech PE14 9AB* Tel (01945) 772213 E-mail alan.jesson@ely.anglican.org

JESSON, George Albert Oswald (Ossie). b 54. NCA73. Trin Coll Bris DipHE92. **d** 92 **p** 93. C Thorpe Acre w Dishley *Leic* 92-01; C Chilwell *S'well* from 01. *Church House, Barn Croft, Chilwell, Beeston, Nottingham NG9 4HU* Tel 0115-922 1879

JESSOP, Mrs Gillian Mary. b 48. Hatf Poly BSc71 Nottm Univ MEd85 Homerton Coll Cam PGCE80. EAMTC 91. **d** 94 **p** 95. C Gt Yarmouth *Nor* 94-97; R Gt w Lt Addington and Woodford *Pet* 97-02; Asst Dir Tr for Readers 00-02; R Paston from 02; Dir Tr for Readers from 02. *The Rectory, 236 Fulbridge Road, Peterborough PE4 6SN* Tel (01733) 578228 E-mail rev.gill@tesco.net

JESSOP, John Edward. b 46. RMCS BSc71 CEng78 MIEE78. S Dios Minl Tr Scheme 87 Ridley Coll Melbourne 89. **d** 90 **p** 90. Australia 90-02; C Mooroolbark 90-91; P-in-c S Yarra 92-93; I Blackburn St Jo 93-98; I Kew H Trin 98-02; P-in-c Brimpsfield w Birdlip, Syde, Daglingworth etc *Glouc* from 02. *The Rectory, Church Lane, Daglingworth, Cirencester GL7 7AG* Tel (01285) 640782 Fax as telephone

JESSUP, William Roy. b 27. Lon Univ BSc48 CertEd. Ridley Hall Cam 59. **d** 61 **p** 62. C Walton St E 61-64; R Tuddenham St Mary w Cavenham 64-83; P-in-c Eriswell 75-78; Assoc Min Ipswich All SS 83-85; R Toppesfield and Stambourne *Chelmsf* 85-92; rtd 92; Perm to Offic *Chelmsf* from 92; Perm to Offic *St E* from 92. *41 Ashpole Road, Braintree CM7 5LW* Tel (01376) 322554

JESTY, Mrs Helen Margaret. b 51. York Univ BA72. Cranmer Hall Dur BA81. **dss** 82 **d** 87. S Lambeth St Steph *S'wark* 82-86; Norbiton 86-93; Par Dn 87-90; Hon Par Dn 91-93. *Fairfield, 1 Downside Road, Winchester SO22 5LT* Tel (01962) 849190

JEVONS, Preb Alan Neil. b 56. Ex Univ BA77 Selw Coll Cam BA80 MA84. Ridley Hall Cam. **d** 81 **p** 82. C Halesowen *Worc* 81-84; C Heywood St Luke w All So *Man* 84-87; TV Heref St Martin w St Fran *Heref* 87-93; P-in-c Much Birch w Lt Birch, Much Dewchurch etc 93-02; RD Ross and Archenfield 98-02; TR Tenbury from 02; Preb Heref Cathl from 02. *The Rectory, Burford, Tenbury Wells WR15 8HG* Tel (01584) 819748

JEWELL, Alan David John. b 59. St Cath Coll Ox MA86. Wycliffe Hall Ox 83. **d** 86 **p** 87. C Walton H Trin *Ox* 86-91; TV Sutton *Liv* 91-97; TV Halewood 97-01; TR from 01. *The Rectory, 3 Rectory Drive, Halewood, Liverpool L26 6LJ* Tel 0151-487 5610 E-mail alan@ajewell.freeserve.co.uk

JEWELL, Charles John. b 15. Bps' Coll Cheshunt 46. **d** 49 **p** 50. C Swindon St Aug *Bris* 49-52; CF 52-58; C-in-c Patchway CD *Bris* 58-61; Tristan da Cunha 61 and 71-74; Area Sec (Ireland) USPG 62-69; Area Sec USPG *Ex* and *Truro* 69-71; S Africa 74-87; rtd 87; Perm to Offic *Ex* from 87. *11 Arundel Close, Alphington, Exeter EX2 8UG* Tel (01392) 426781

JEWELL, Mrs Maureen Ann. b 34. Reading Univ CertEd72. Chich Th Coll 90. **d** 91 **p** 95. NSM Parklands St Wilfrid CD *Chich* 91-94; NSM Storrington 94-97; Perm to Offic from 97. *3 Garden Close, Storrington, Pulborough RH20 4PL* Tel (01903) 742780

JEWITT, Martin Paul Noel. b 44. AKC69. St Aug Coll Cant. **d** 70 **p** 71. C Usworth *Dur* 70-74; TV 77-78; Papua New Guinea 74-77; V Balham Hill Ascension *S'wark* 78-93; R N Reddish *Man* 93-99; V Thornton Heath St Paul *S'wark* from 99. *The Vicarage, 1 Norbury Avenue, Thornton Heath CR7 8AH* Tel (020) 8653 2762

JEYNES, Anthony James. b 44. AKC68. **d** 69 **p** 70. C Ellesmere Port *Ches* 69-73; C Birkenhead St Pet w St Matt 73-75; R Oughtrington 75-80; C Timperley 80-85; C Eastham 85-89; V New Brighton St Jas 89-96; P-in-c New Brighton Em 94-96; R Tarleton *Blackb* from 96. *The Rectory, Blackgate Lane, Tarleton, Preston PR4 6UT* Tel (01772) 812614 Fax as telephone E-mail reverend@holytt.freeserve.co.uk

JIGNASU, Nallinkumar Hiralal. b 28. Bombay Univ BA48. Bp Tucker Coll Mukono 68. **d** 68 **p** 69. Uganda 68-73; C Leamington Priors St Mary *Cov* 73-75; Nigeria 75-79; P-in-c New Humberstone *Leic* 80-94; rtd 94; Perm to Offic *Leic* from 94. *8 Somerby Road, Thurnby, Leicester LE7 9PR* Tel 0116-241 8541

JOACHIM, Margaret Jane. b 49. FGS91 St Hugh's Coll Ox BA70 MA74 W Midl Coll of Educn PGCE71 Birm Univ PhD77. S Dios Minl Tr Scheme 91. **d** 94 **p** 95. NSM Ealing St Barn *Lon* 94-97; NSM Ealing St Pet Mt Park from 97. *8 Newburgh Road, London W3 6DQ* Tel (020) 8723 4514 *or* 8754 4547 E-mail margaret.joachim@dlondon.org.uk

JOAN, Sister. *See* DAVIES, Sister Joan Margaret

JOB, Canon Evan Roger Gould. b 36. Magd Coll Ox BA60 MA64 ARCM57. Cuddesdon Coll 60. **d** 62 **p** 63. C Liv Our Lady and St Nic *Liv* 62-65; V New Springs 65-70; Min Can and Prec Man Cathl *Man* 70-74; Prec and Sacr Westmr Abbey 74-79; Can Res, Prec and Sacr Win Cathl *Win* 79-94; Vice-Dean Win 91-94; Select Preacher Ox Univ 74 and 91; Perm to Offic *Win* from 94; rtd 01. *Kitwood Farmhouse, Kitwood Lane, Ropley, Alresford SO24 0DB* Tel (01962) 772303

JOBBER, Barry William. b 38. N Staffs Poly BA84. Cuddesdon Coll 73. **d** 75 **p** 76. C Fenton *Lich* 76-79; V Goldenhill 79-80; Perm to Offic *Ches* 90-02; NSM Middlewich w Byley from 02. *16 Angus Grove, Middlewich CW10 9GR* Tel (01606) 737386 Mobile 07974-380234 E-mail barry-jobber@supanet.com

JOBSON, Clifford Hedley. b 31. St Jo Coll Dur BA54 DipTh56 MA81. **d** 56 **p** 57. C Hall Green Ascension *Birm* 56-59; C

Ambleside w Rydal *Carl* 59-60; R Arthuret 60-62; CF 62-73; Dep Asst Chapl Gen 73-78; Asst Chapl Gen 78-84; QHC from 80; V Fleet *Guildf* 84-96; rtd 96; Perm to Offic *B & W* from 96. *Vine Cottage, 25 Silver Street, South Petherton TA13 5AL* Tel (01460) 241783

JOBSON, Canon Paul. b 39. Wells Th Coll 62. **d** 65 **p** 66. C Woolwich St Mary w H Trin *S'wark* 65-68; Chapl Culham Coll Abingdon 68-72; P-in-c Walworth St Pet *S'wark* 72-75; P-in-c Walworth All SS and St Steph 73-75; TR Walworth 75-89; Hon Can S'wark Cathl 83-89; RD S'wark and Newington 85-88; V Seaham w Seaham Harbour *Dur* 89-97; Hon Chapl Miss to Seamen 89-97; P-in-c Pimlico St Sav *Lon* from 97. *59 Aylesford Street, London SW1V 3RY* Tel (020) 7834 9520 *or* 7592 9733 Mobile 0771-558598 Fax 7821 9865

JOEL, Mrs Mary Tertia. b 35. OLM course 96. **d** 99 **p** 00. OLM Blyth Valley *St E* from 99. *38 Saxmundham Road, Aldeburgh IP15 5JE* Tel (01728) 454886 Mobile 07790-910554

JOHANSEN, Paul Charles. b 33. Miami Univ BEd61 Univ of California Berkeley STB64. Yale Div Sch 61. **d** 64 **p** 64. USA 64-96 and from 98; rtd 96; P-in-c Adare w Kilpeacon and Croom *L & K* 96-98; P-in-c New Philadelphia Trin Ch from 01. *504 Third Avenue NW, New Philadelphia, OH 44663, USA* E-mail trinity@tusco.net

JOHN, Alexander Dominic. b 26. Madras Univ BA47. Episc Sem Austin Texas MDiv63. **d** 63 **p** 64. C Millhouses H Trin *Sheff* 63-65; Switzerland 65-68; India 68-75; Australia from 78; rtd 85. *12 Bentwood Avenue, Woodlands, W Australia 6018* Tel (0061) (8) 9445 3530 E-mail remo@space.net.au

JOHN, Andrew Thomas Griffith. b 64. Univ of Wales LLB. St Jo Coll Nottm BA DPS. **d** 89 **p** 90. C Cardigan w Mwnt and Y Ferwig *St D* 89-91; C Aberystwyth 91-92; TV 92-99; V Henfynyw w Aberaeron and Llanddewi Aberarth from 99. *The Vicarage, Panteg Road, Aberaeron SA4 0EP* Tel (01545) 570433 E-mail andyjohn@andyjohn.freeserve.co.uk

JOHN, Barbara. b 34. Cam Univ DipTh67. Gilmore Ho. **dss** 67 **d** 80 **p** 97. Merthyr Tydfil *Llan* 67-71; Loughton St Jo *Chelmsf* 71-73; Newport St Woolos *Mon* 73-78; Asst Chapl Univ Hosp of Wales Cardiff 78-85; C Radyr *Llan* 85-00; rtd 00. *14 Pace Close, Cardiff CF5 2QZ* Tel (029) 2055 2989

JOHN, Beverley Hayes. b 49. Qu Coll Birm 83. **d** 85 **p** 86. C Oystermouth *S & B* 85-87; C Morriston 87-88; V Cefn Coed w Vaynor from 88; RD Brecon from 99. *The Vicarage, Somerset Lane, Cefn Coed, Merthyr Tydfil CF48 2PA* Tel (01685) 374253

JOHN, Caroline Victoria. b 64. Cam Univ BA86 MA90. St Jo Coll Nottm DPS90. **d** 90. NSM Cardigan w Mwnt and Y Ferwig *St D* 90-91; NSM Aberystwyth 91-96. *The Vicarage, Panteg Road, Aberaeron SA46 0EP* Tel (01545) 570433

JOHN, Canon David Michael. b 36. Univ of Wales (Lamp) BA57. St Mich Coll Llan 57. **d** 59 **p** 60. C Pontypool *Mon* 59-61; C Roath *Llan* 61-66; Asst Chapl HM Pris Liv 66-67; Chapl HM Pris Ex 67-68; V Ystrad Rhondda *Llan* 68-76; V Pontyclun w Talygarn 76-84; R Newton Nottage 84-91; Can Llan Cathl 85-91; rtd 91; Perm to Offic *Llan* from 91; Perm to Offic *Mon* from 91. *1 Hornbeam Close, St Mellons, Cardiff CF3 0JA* Tel (029) 2079 7496

JOHN, David Wyndham. b 61. Univ Bible Coll. NTMTC. **d** 01 **p** 02. NSM Hampstead Em W End *Lon* from 01. *98 Campbell Garden Way, London NW2 6RW* Tel (020) 8208 4380 Mobile 07719-333389

JOHN, The Ven Elwyn Crebey. b 36. Univ of Wales (Lamp) BA57. St Mich Coll Llan 57. **d** 59 **p** 60. C Llangiwg *S & B* 59-62; C Llandrindod w Cefnllys 62-66; V Beguildy and Heyope 66-79; Youth Chapl 72-79; Chapl Agric and Rural Soc 77-03; V Builth and Llanddewi'r Cwm w Llangynog etc 79-95; Can Brecon Cathl 88-95; Can Res Brecon Cathl 95-03; Prec 94-95; Treas 95-98; Chan 98-03; V Brecon St Mary w Llanddew 95-01; Adn Brecon 99-03; rtd 03. *17 Cae Castell, Builth Wells LD2 3BE* Tel (01982) 551553

JOHN, The Ven Islwyn David. b 33. St D Coll Lamp BA56. **d** 58 **p** 59. C Brynamman *St D* 58-61; C Carmarthen St Dav 61-64; V 83-93; V Penbryn and Blaenporth 64-68; V Llandysul 68-83; Can St D Cathl 88-93; RD Carmarthen 92-93; Adn Carmarthen 93-99; V Cynwil Elfed and Newchurch 93-99; rtd 99. *Brookfield, 106 Bronwydd Road, Carmarthen SA31 2AW* Tel (01267) 237868

JOHN, Canon James Richard. b 21. Ch Coll Cam BA47 MA49. Cuddesdon Coll 47. **d** 49 **p** 50. C Sidcup Ch Ch *Roch* 49-52; V Gillingham St Mary 52-66; RD Gillingham 60-66; V Bolton St Jas w St Chrys *Bradf* 66-78; R Guiseley 78-83; RD Otley 80-86; P-in-c Esholt 82-83; TR Guiseley w Esholt 83-87; Hon Can Bradf Cathl 83-87; rtd 87; Perm to Offic *Bradf* from 87. *37 Croft House Drive, Otley LS21 2ER* Tel (01943) 461998

JOHN, Canon Jeffrey Philip Hywel. b 53. Hertf Coll Ox BA75 Magd Coll Ox DPhil84. St Steph Ho Ox BA77 MA78 CPTS78. **d** 78 **p** 79. C Penarth w Lavernock *Llan* 78-80; Asst Chapl Magd Coll Ox 80-82; Fell and Dean of Div 84-91; Chapl and Lect BNC Ox 82-84; V Eltham H Trin *S'wark* 91-97; Chan and Can Th S'wark Cathl from 97; Bp's Adv for Min from 97. *Trinity House, 4 Chapel Court, Borough High Street, London SE1 1HW* Tel

(020) 7939 9449 *or* 7820 8079 Fax 7939 9469 E-mail jeffrey.john@dswark.org.uk

JOHN, Mark Christopher. b 61. SS Mark & Jo Coll Plymouth BA83. St Steph Ho Ox 84. **d** 87 **p** 88. C Treboeth *S & B* 87-90; V Swansea St Mark and St Jo 90-94; Chapl HM Pris Swansea 91-94; Chapl HM Pris Usk and HM Pris and YOI Prescoed 94-97; Chapl HM Pris Cardiff from 97; Lic to Offic *Mon* from 99. *HM Prison Cardiff, Knox Road, Cardiff CF24 0UG* Tel (029) 2043 3100 ext 3233 Fax 2043 3318

JOHN, Meurig Hywel. b 46. St D Coll Lamp 67. **d** 71 **p** 72. C Llanelli Ch Ch *St D* 71-74; V Penrhyncoch and Elerch 74-79; V Llanfihangel Aberbythych 79-81; R Cilgerran w Bridell and Llantwyd 81-83; V Gwaun-cae-Gurwen 83-89; V Llanfihangel Genau'r-glyn and Llangorwen 89-95; V Newcastle Emlyn w Llandyfriog etc 95-01; Assoc V Lampeter and Llanddewibrefi Gp from 01. *Garthowen, Kingsmead, Lampeter SA48 7AP* Tel (01570) 422777

JOHN, Napoleon. b 55. Punjab Univ BA76. Lahetysteologisen Inst Ryttyla Finland DipHE85 Oak Hill Th Coll BA93. **d** 93 **p** 94. C Leyton St Mary w St Edw *Chelmsf* 93-96; C Leyton St Mary w St Edw and St Luke 96-97; P-in-c Becontree St Elisabeth from 97. *The Vicarage, Hewett Road, Dagenham RM8 2XT* Tel (020) 8517 0355 E-mail napojohn@altavista.co.uk

JOHN, Nigel. b 59. Univ of Wales (Cardiff) BA87 Selw Coll Cam MPhil90. Westcott Ho Cam 88. **d** 91 **p** 92. C Carmarthen St Pet *St D* 91-94; Chapl Roehampton Inst *S'wark* 94-96; V Gors-las *St D* 96-98; V Llanelli Ch Ch 98-02; Chapl Univ of Wales (Swansea) *S & B* from 02. *23 Mayals Avenue, Blackpill, Swansea SA3 5DE* Tel (01792) 401703

JOHN, Robert Michael. b 46. Edin Univ BSc67 Man Univ MSc68 PhD70 Otago Univ BD78. St Jo Coll Auckland 76. **d** 78 **p** 79. New Zealand 78-87 and from 88; C Swansea St Jas *S & B* 87-88. *1 Barrymore Road, Mount Albert, Auckland 1003, New Zealand* Tel (0064) (9) 846 4812 *or* 379 7440

JOHN, Stephen Michael. b 63. Univ of Wales (Lamp) BA85. Coll of Resurr Mirfield 87. **d** 89 **p** 90. C Coity w Nolton *Llan* 89-91; C Merthyr Dyfan 91-94; V Tredegar St Geo *Mon* 94-99; Chapl HM Pris Gartree from 99. *HM Prison Gartree, Gallow Field Road, Market Harborough LE16 7RP* Tel (01858) 410234

JOHN-FRANCIS, Brother. See FRIENDSHIP, Roger Geoffrey

JOHNES, Philip Sydney. b 45. St Mich Coll Llan Dip Minl Studies 92. **d** 92 **p** 93. C Cardigan w Mwnt and Y Ferwig *St D* 92-95; V Llanegwad w Llanfynydd from 95. *Llanegwad Vicarage, Heol Alltyferin, Nantgaredig, Carmarthen SA32 7NE* Tel (01267) 290142 Fax as telephone E-mail pjohnes@aol.com

JOHNES, Adam Aubrey. b 34. TCD BA57 MA76 NUU BA75. CITC Div Test 58. **d** 58 **p** 59. C Aghalee *D & D* 58-61; C Derriaghy *Conn* 61-63; I Billy 63-77; I Billy w Derrykeighan 77-03; Can Conn Cathl 98-03; rtd 03. *26 Chatham Road, Armoy, Ballymoney BT53 8TT*

JOHNES, Canon Bernard Thomas. b 36. Birm Univ BSc58. St Mich Coll Llan 61. **d** 63 **p** 64. C Aberavon *Llan* 63-65; C St Andrews Major w Michaelston-le-Pit 65-70; V Cardiff St Andr and St Teilo 70-76; Asst Dioc Dir of Educn 72-91; V Roath 76-88; R Wenvoe and St Lythans 88-02; Dioc Dir Community Educn 91-02; Can Llan Cathl 96-02; rtd 02. *Bay Tree Cottage, 13 Badgers Meadow, Pwllmeyric, Chepstow NP16 6UE* Tel (01291) 623254 E-mail johnsbtwen@mgom.co.uk

JOHNS, James Dudley. b 09. Selw Coll Cam BA34 MA38. Ridley Hall Cam 34. **d** 36 **p** 37. C Moulsham St Jo *Chelmsf* 36-39; C Grays Thurrock 39-41; V Forest Gate All SS 41-49; Dioc Insp of Schs 46-53; Res Chapl Butlin's Camp Clacton 47-48; Chapl and Dean Selw Coll Cam 49-53; Staff Sec SCM (Cam) 49-51; Chapl Barnard Castle Sch 53-64; Chapl St Geo Sch Harpenden 64-69; Chapl Harpenden St Jo *St Alb* 64-69; R Gt w Lt Wymondley 70-80; R Gt and Lt Wymondley w Graveley and Chivesfield 80-81; rtd 81; Perm to Offic *Nor* 82-94; *Chelmsf* from 95. *25A Beeches Close, Saffron Walden CB11 4BU* Tel (01799) 527119

JOHNS, Mrs Patricia Holly. b 33. Girton Coll Cam BA56 MA60 Hughes Hall Cam PGCE57. Ox NSM Course 87. **d** 90 **p** 94. NSM Wantage *Ox* 90-95; NSM Marlborough *Sarum* 94-95; rtd 95; Perm to Offic *Sarum* from 95. *Flat 1, Priory Lodge, 93 Brown Street, Salisbury SP1 2BX* Tel (01722) 328007

JOHNS, Canon Ronald Charles. b 37. TD. Dur Univ BA59. Wells Th Coll 59. **d** 61 **p** 62. C Wigan All SS *Liv* 61-66; TV Kirkby 66-75; Ho Master Ruffwood Sch Kirkby 70-75; TV Maghull 75-79; Dep Hd Master Maghull Old Hall High Sch 75-79; P-in-c Borrowdale *Carl* 79-84; V 84-89; RD Derwent 81-89; Hon Can Carl Cathl 87-89; Can Res Carl Cathl 89-94; R Caldbeck, Castle Sowerby and Sebergham 94-00; rtd 01; Perm to Offic *Nor* from 01. *3 Kings Road, Coltishall, Norwich NR12 7DX*

JOHNS, Thomas Morton. b 43. Oak Hill Th Coll 67. **d** 70 **p** 71. C N Meols *Liv* 70-73; C Farnborough *Guildf* 73-76; P-in-c Badshot Lea CD 76-83; Dep Chapl HM Pris Man 83; Chapl HM Youth Cust Cen Wellingborough 83-88; Chapl HM YOI Swinfen Hall 88-90; Chapl Tr Officer 88-95; Chapl HM Pris Service Coll 90-95; Asst Chapl Gen of Pris (HQ) 95-01; Acting Chapl Gen

00-01; P-in-c Colbury *Win* from 02; Chapl Hants Constabulary from 02. *The Vicarage, Deerleap Lane, Totton, Southampton SO40 7EH* Tel (023) 8029 2132 Mobile 07974-025478 E-mail tom@johns.evesham.net

JOHNS, Trevor Charles. b 33. St D Coll Lamp BA58. **d** 58 **p** 59. C Pembroke St Mary w St Mich *St D* 58-61; R Walwyn's Castle w Robeston W 61-67; CF 67-75; V Spittal and Treffgarne *St D* 75-79; C Tring St Alb 79-80; TV Tring 80-85; V Knighton and Norton *S & B* 85-86; V Merthyr Cynog and Dyffryn Honddu etc 86-98; rtd 98. *109 Hoel-y-Banc, Bancffosfelen, Llanelli SA15 5DF*

JOHNS, William Price. b 28. Keble Coll Ox BA51 DipTh52 MA56. St Mich Coll Llan 52. **d** 53 **p** 54. C Whitchurch *Llan* 53-56; C Pontypridd St Cath 56-59; Min Can Brecon Cathl *S & B* 59-62; V Wellington *Heref* 62-78; R Wellington w Pipe-cum-Lyde and Moreton-on-Lugg 78-93; P-in-c Ford 63-69; rtd 93; Perm to Offic *Llan* from 93. *12 Deepdale Close, Cardiff CF23 5LR* Tel (029) 2048 3762

JOHNSEN, Edward Andrew. b 67. Birm Univ BTheol89. Qu Coll Birm 95. **d** 97 **p** 98. C Birm St Luke *Birm* 97-01; C Handsworth St Mary from 01. *43 St Christophers, Handsworth Wood, Birmingham B20 1BP*

JOHNSON, Amanda Saffery. b 58. K Alfred's Coll Win BEd83. Wycliffe Hall Ox DipMin97. **d** 97 **p** 98. C Oxhey All SS *St Alb* 97-00; C Bricket Wood 00-02; Teacher Bp Wand Sch Sunbury-on-Thames from 02. *Bishop Wand School, Laytons Lane, Sunbury-on-Thames TW16 6LR* Tel (01932) 787537 *or* 788128 E-mail amandola@tesco.net

JOHNSON, Andrew Paul. b 56. W Surrey Coll of Art & Design BA79 Kent Coll for Careers CertEd82 TCD BTh96. CITC 93. **d** 96 **p** 97. C Penarth w Lavernock *Llan* 96-99; R Walton W w Talbenny and Haroldston W *St D* from 99. *The Rectory, Walton West, Little Haven, Haverfordwest SA62 3UB* Tel (01437) 781279

JOHNSON, Andrew Peter. b 67. Westf Coll Lon BA89 St Jo Coll Nottm MA98 LTh99. Aston Tr Scheme 94. **d** 99 **p** 00. C Hitchin *St Alb* 99-03; V Batley All SS and Purlwell *Wakef* from 03. *The Vicarage, Churchfield Street, Batley WF17 5DL* Tel (01924) 473049 Fax as telephone E-mail johnsons@care4free.net

JOHNSON, Mrs Angela Carolyn Louise. b 52. RGN76. STETS 00. **d** 03. NSM Catherington and Clanfield *Portsm* from 03. *90 Downhouse Road, Waterlooville PO8 0TY* Tel (023) 9264 4595

JOHNSON, Anthony. *See* JOHNSON, Edward Anthony

JOHNSON, Anthony Arthur Derry. b 15. Kelham Th Coll 31. **d** 39 **p** 40. C Pinner *Lon* 39-42; C Willesden St Andr 42-44; C Winchmore Hill H Trin 44-49; V Brookfield St Anne, Highgate Rise 49-60; V Mill Hill St Mich 60-73; R Chalfont St Giles *Ox* 73-80; rtd 80; Perm to Offic *Sarum* from 80. *Garden Close, Long Street, Sherborne DT9 3DD* Tel (01935) 813469

JOHNSON, Anthony Peter. b 45. Lon Univ DipTh71 AKC76 BD76 MTh79. Wells Th Coll 67. **d** 70 **p** 71. C Goldington *St Alb* 70-73; C Hainault *Chelmsf* 73-76; TV Loughton St Mary 76-81; V Scunthorpe All SS *Linc* 81-85; V Alkborough 85-87; Chapl Man Univ *Man* 87-96; TV Man Whitworth 87-96; P-in-c Chorlton-cum-Hardy St Werburgh 96-00; R from 00. *St Werburgh's Rectory, 388 Wilbraham Road, Manchester M21 0UH* Tel 0161-881 1642 Fax as telephone E-mail apjohnson@st-werbs.fsnet.co.uk

JOHNSON, Canon Anthony Trevor. b 27. CCC Ox BA51 MA55. Cuddesdon Coll 51. **d** 53 **p** 54. C Wareham w Arne *Sarum* 53-57; C Melksham 57-60; R Tarrant Gunville, Tarrant Hinton etc 60-67; R Upton Scudamore 67-85; V Warminster St Denys 67-85; RD Heytesbury 71-76; Can and Preb Sarum Cathl 75-92; P-in-c Horningsham 76-85; P-in-c Semley and Sedgehill 85-86; R E Knoyle, Semley and Sedgehill 86-92; rtd 92; Perm to Offic *Sarum* from 92. *Coombe Warren, Hindon Lane, Tisbury, Salisbury SP3 6QQ* Tel (01747) 870130

JOHNSON, Anthony Warrington. b 40. Goldsmiths' Coll Lon CertEd60. St Jo Coll Nottm 86. **d** 88 **p** 89. C Lutterworth w Cotesbach *Leic* 88-92; V Countesthorpe w Foston from 92; P-in-c Arnesby w Shearsby and Bruntingthorpe 94-01. *The Vicarage, 102 Station Road, Countesthorpe, Leicester LE8 5TB* Tel 0116-278 4442 *or* 277 8643

JOHNSON, Barry Charles Richard. b 48. EAMTC 96. **d** 99 **p** 00. NSM Billericay and Lt Burstead *Chelmsf* 99-01; C Gt Burstead 01-02; C Bowers Gifford w N Benfleet from 02. *Lyndon, London Road, Basildon SS13 2HE* Tel (01268) 726318 Fax as telephone E-mail johnson@buers.freeserve.co.uk

JOHNSON, Beverley Charles. b 35. Bp Gray Coll Cape Town 59. **d** 61 **p** 62. S Africa 61-67 and from 91; C Woodstock St Mary 61-64; C Clanwilliam St Jo 64-65; C Plumstead St Mark 65-67; C Southsea St Pet *Portsm* 68-69; C Southwick St Cuth CD *Dur* 70-71; P-in-c Waterhouses 71-80; R Burnmoor 80-85; V Brandon 85-89; Australia 89-91; Asst P Sea Point St Jas 91-01; rtd 01. *43 Oxford Street, Goodwood, 7460 South Africa* Tel and fax (0027) (21) 592 1180 Mobile 82-202 5260

JOHNSON, Mrs Brenda Margaret. b 47. TISEC. **d** 00. NSM Edin St Salvador *Edin* 00-02; NSM Wester Hailes St Luke 00-02; NSM Dalmahoy from 02. *58 Ratho Park Road, Ratho, Newbridge*

EH28 8PQ Tel 0131-333 1742 Mobile 07713-154744 E-mail brenmj@freeuk.com

JOHNSON, Brian. b 42. S'wark Ord Course 84. **d** 87 **p** 88. NSM Dulwich St Barn *S'wark* 87-92; NSM Herne Hill 92-94; Perm to Offic 94-96; Chapl HM Pris Man 96-01; P-in-c Rotterdam *Eur* 01-02; Operations Manager ICS from 03. *Intercontinental Church Society, 1 Athena Drive, Tachbrook Park, Warwick CV34 6NL* Tel (01926) 430347 E-mail bjohnson@ics-uk.org

JOHNSON, Christopher Dudley. b 26. Worc Coll Ox BA44 MA51. Cuddesdon Coll 53. **d** 56 **p** 57. C Basingstoke *Win* 56-61; V Bethnal Green St Barn *Lon* 61-67; V Eton w Eton Wick and Boveney *Ox* 67-88; rtd 91; Perm to Offic *Sarum* from 96. *Lavines Cottage, Netherbury, Bridport DT6 5LL*

JOHNSON, Christopher Frederick. b 43. ARICS67 MRICS01. Ripon Hall Ox 71. **d** 74 **p** 75. C Chatham St Steph *Roch* 74-78; V Slade Green 78-85; V Wilmington 85-95; R Chevening from 95. *Chevening Rectory, Homedean Road, Chipstead, Sevenoaks TN13 2RU* Tel (01732) 453555

JOHNSON, Christopher Paul. b 47. St Jo Coll Nottm BTh74. **d** 74 **p** 75. C Normanton *Wakef* 74-78; P-in-c Dewsbury St Mark 78-82; V Harden and Wilsden *Bradf* 82-88; P-in-c Holbeck *Ripon* 88-94; V 94-97; Asst Chapl Leeds Teaching Hosps NHS Trust 97-01; Chapl Bradf Hosps NHS Trust from 01. *Bradford Royal Infirmary, Duckworth Lane, Bradford BD9 6RJ* Tel (01274) 542200 E-mail c-johnson@ic24.net

JOHNSON, Christopher Robert. b 43. Lon Coll of Div 66. **d** 70 **p** 71. C Eacre St Geo *Liv* 70-71; C Childwall All SS 71-75; TV Gateacre 75-76; TV Bushbury *Lich* 76-87; R Burslem from 87. *The Rectory, 16 Heyburn Crescent, Burslem, Stoke-on-Trent ST6 4DL* Tel (01782) 838932

JOHNSON, Canon Colin Gawman. b 32. Leeds Univ BA59. Coll of Resurr Mirfield 59. **d** 61 **p** 62. C Barrow St Matt *Carl* 61-67; V 90-96; V Addingham 67-71; V Carl H Trin 71-80; V Wigton 80-90; Hon Can Carl Cathl 85-96; rtd 96; Perm to Offic *Carl* from 97. *Hemp Garth, Ireby, Wigton CA7 1EA* Tel (01697) 371578

JOHNSON, Colin Leslie. b 41. Trin Coll Cam MA65. Cheshunt Coll Cam 62. **d** 93 **p** 94. Publications Dir Chr Educn Movement from 89; NSM Brailsford w Shirley and Osmaston w Edlaston *Derby* from 93. *33 The Plain, Brailsford, Ashbourne DE6 3BZ* Tel (01335) 360591 E-mail colin@retoday.org.uk

JOHNSON, Colin Stewart. b 46. SEITE 99. **d** 02. NSM Borden *Cant* from 02. *423 Minster Road, Minster on Sea, Sheerness ME12 3NS* Tel (01795) 875175 Mobile 07740-775277 E-mail colinj@kent119.freeserve.co.uk

JOHNSON, Cyril Francis. b 22. St Cath Coll Cam BA49 MA54. Ely Th Coll 50. **d** 52 **p** 53. C Twickenham All Hallows *Lon* 52-56; C Kingsthorpe *Pet* 56-61; R Harpole 61-87; rtd 87; Perm to Offic *Chich* from 01. *16 Blake's Way, Eastbourne BN23 6EW* Tel (01323) 723491

JOHNSON, David. *See* JOHNSON, John David

JOHNSON, David Alan. b 43. Lon Univ BSc63 PhD67. Trin Coll Bris 78. **d** 80 **p** 81. C Watford *St Alb* 80-85; V Idle H Trin *Bradf* from 85. *The Vicarage, 470 Leeds Road, Thackley, Bradford BD10 9AA* Tel (01274) 613300 *or* 615411 E-mail vicar@htidle.org.uk

JOHNSON, David Bryan Alfred. b 36. Kelham Th Coll 56. **d** 61 **p** 62. C Streatham St Paul *S'wark* 61-63; Malaysia 63-71; V Worc St Mich *Worc* 71-74; Warden Lee Abbey Internat Students' Club Kensington 74-77; V Plumstead St Mark and St Marg *S'wark* 77-86; Chapl W Park Hosp Epsom 86-96; Chapl Laslett's *Worc* 96-01; rtd 96. *3 St Birinus Cottages, Wessex Way, Bicester OX26 6DX* Tel (01869) 320839

JOHNSON, David Clark. b 15. Tyndale Hall Bris 61. **d** 62 **p** 63. C Chippenham St Paul *Bris* 62-64; C Chippenham St Paul w Langley Burrell 64-65; V Bishopsworth 65-74; V Stratton St Margaret 75-78; TR Stratton St Margaret w S Marston etc 78-80; rtd 80; Perm to Offic *Bris* from 80. *13 High Kingsdown, Bristol BS2 8EN* Tel 0117-929 8894

JOHNSON, David Francis. b 32. Univ Coll Ox BA55 MA59. Westcott Ho Cam 55. **d** 57 **p** 58. C Earlsdon *Cov* 57-59; C Willenhall 59-61; C Attenborough w Bramcote *S'well* 61-62; V Ravenstone w Weston Underwood *Ox* 62-66; V Crewe Ch Ch *Ches* 66-70; P-in-c Crewe St Pet 67-70; V Thornton w Allerthorpe *York* 70-79; V N Hull St Mich 79-81; V Leyburn w Bellerby *Ripon* 81-88; V Coxwold and Husthwaite *York* 88-97; rtd 97; Perm to Offic *York* from 98. *Spring Garth, High Street, Husthwaite, York YO61 4PX* Tel (01347) 868273

JOHNSON, David John. b 49. Lanc Univ BA72. Linc Th Coll 78. **d** 81 **p** 82. C Stockport St Thos *Ches* 81-84; OGS from 83; C Stockton Heath *Ches* 84-88; V Tranmere St Paul w St Luke 88-99; P-in-c Antrobus 99-02; P-in-c Aston by Sutton 99-02; P-in-c Lt Leigh and Lower Whitley 99-02; V Antrobus, Aston by Sutton, Lt Leigh etc from 02. *The Vicarage, Street Lane, Lower Whitley, Warrington WA4 4EN* Tel (01925) 730158

JOHNSON, David Richard. b 63. Birm Univ BSc88. Ripon Coll Cuddesdon BA92 MA97. **d** 94 **p** 95. C Horfield H Trin *Bris* 94-97; V Two Mile Hill St Mich 97-01; Asst Chapl Haileybury Coll 01-02; Chapl Dauntsey's Sch Devizes from 02. *20 High*

426

Street, West Lavington, Devizes SN10 4HQ Tel (01380) 814573 E-mail johnsoda@dauntseys.wilts.sch.uk

JOHNSON, David William. b 40. Lon Univ BD64. Oak Hill Th Coll 60. **d** 65 **p** 66. C Tunbridge Wells St Jas *Roch* 65-68; C Kirby Muxloe *Leic* 68-72; V Burton Joyce w Bulcote *S'well* 72-83; Chapl Northgate Mental Handicap Unit Morpeth 83-87; V Mitford *Newc* 83-87; Asst Chapl R Victoria Infirmary Newc 87-89; Chapl R Hosp Shrewsbury 89-94; Chapl R Shrewsbury Hosps NHS Trust from 94. *Royal Shrewsbury Hospital, Mytton Oak Road, Shrewsbury SY3 8XF* Tel (01743) 261000 Pager 07693-938157

JOHNSON, David William. b 53. Selw Coll Cam BA76. Ripon Coll Cuddesdon 76. **d** 78 **p** 79. C Fulham St Etheldreda w St Clem *Lon* 78-82; Communications Sec Gen Syn Bd for Miss and Unity 82-87; PV Westmr Abbey 85-87; R Gilmorton w Peatling Parva and Kimcote etc *Leic* 87-91; R Cogenhoe *Pet* 91-95; R Whiston 93-95; rtd 95; Perm to Offic *Ox* from 00. *Seaview Cottage, 115 Hurst Street, Oxford OX4 1HE* Tel (01865) 793393

JOHNSON, Preb Derek John. b 36. St Aid Birkenhead 65. **d** 68 **p** 69. C Eccleshall *Lich* 68-73; C Stafford St Mary 73-75; Chapl New Cross Hosp Wolv 75-96; Preb Lich Cathl *Lich* 83-96; rtd 96; Perm to Offic *St E* from 96. *6 St Paul's Close, Aldeburgh IP15 5BQ* Tel (01728) 452474

JOHNSON, Miss Diana Margaret. b 46. MCSP68 SRP68 Grad Dip Phsyiotherapy 68. Cranmer Hall Dur CTM94. **d** 94 **p** 95. C Birtley *Dur* 94-99; TV Leadenhead from 99. *Venerable Bede House, 3 Wordsworth Street, Gateshead NE8 3HE* Tel 0191-478 2730

JOHNSON, Mrs Diane Pearl. b 47. Leeds Univ BA68 Cam Univ PGCE69. EAMTC 95. **d** 98 **p** 99. NSM Gt Bowden w Welham, Glooston and Cranoe *Leic* 98-01; C Evington from 01; C Leic St Phil from 01. *St Mary's Vicarage, 56 Vicarage Lane, Humberstone, Leicester LE5 1EE* Tel 0116-276 7281 Fax 276 4504 E-mail grahamanddiane@ntlworld.com

JOHNSON, Canon Donald Arnold. b 28. Linc Coll Ox BA51 MA59. Cuddesdon Coll 51. **d** 53 **p** 54. C Henfield *Chich* 53-55; C Horsham 55-59; V Oving w Merston 59-68; Bp's Dom Chapl 59-68; V Hellingly 68-78; V Upper Dicker 68-78; R W Stoke 78-98; V Funtington and Sennicotts 78-98; Can and Preb Chich Cathl 96-98; rtd 98; Perm to Offic *Chich* from 99. *Vectis, Commonside, Westbourne, Emsworth PO10 8TA* Tel (01243) 371433

JOHNSON, Mrs Dorothy. Leic Univ BSc89 Ox Univ MTh95 RGN NDN80 FRSH91. Qu Coll Birm 77. **dss** 80 **d** 87 **p** 94. Coventry Caludon *Cov* 80-81; Wolston and Church Lawford 81-86; NSM Stoneleigh w Ashow from 87; Bp's Asst Officer for Soc Resp 87-96. *The Firs, Stoneleigh Road, Bubbenhall, Coventry CV8 3BS* Tel (024) 7630 3712 Fax as telephone E-mail firsjohn@supanet.com

JOHNSON, Douglas Leonard. b 45. Trin Coll Bris 70 Lon Bible Coll MA95. **d** 73 **p** 74. C New Malden and Coombe *S'wark* 73-76; P-in-c Upper Tulse Hill St Matthias 76-82; CPAS Staff 82-88; Lect and Tutor CA Coll 88-91; Hon C Wimbledon Em Ridgway Prop Chpl *S'wark* from 83; Dir Crossways Chr Educn Trust from 92; Lect Cornhill Tr Course from 95. *11 Preston Road, London SW20 0SS* Tel (020) 8946 2136 Fax 8947 4146

JOHNSON, Edward Anthony (Tony). b 32. Univ of Wales (Swansea) BSc54. St Steph Ho Ox 79. **d** 81 **p** 82. C Wolvercote w Summertown *Ox* 81-84; P-in-c Ramsden 84-87; P-in-c Finstock and Fawler 84-87; P-in-c Wilcote 84-87; V Ramsden, Finstock and Fawler, Leafield etc 87-92; rtd 92; Hon C Kennington *Ox* from 92. *15 Cranbrook Drive, Kennington, Oxford OX1 5RR* Tel (01865) 739751

JOHNSON, Mrs Elizabeth Jane. b 47. St Hilda's Coll Ox MA69. Wycliffe Hall Ox 84. **dss** 86 **d** 87 **p** 94. NSM Ox St Aldate w St Matt *Ox* 86-91; NSM Marston 91-94; NSM Ox St Clem 94-95; NSM Islip w Charlton on Otmoor, Oddington, Noke etc 95-99; OLM Officer (Dorchester) 99-00; NSM Bladon w Woodstock from 99; Asst Chapl Oxon Mental Healthcare NHS Trust from 00. *6 Crecy Walk, Woodstock OX20 1US* Tel (01993) 813596

JOHNSON, Eric. b 38. Nottm Univ BSc60 Open Univ BA92 SS Paul & Mary Coll Cheltenham MA94 Leeds Univ DipFE72. Qu Coll Birm 74. **d** 77 **p** 78. Sen Lect Cov Tech Coll 66-91; NSM Earlsdon *Cov* 77-81; NSM Wolston and Church Lawford 81-86; NSM Stoneleigh w Ashow and Baginton 90-98; FE Liaison Officer *B & W, Bris* and *Glouc* 91-93; Dioc Dir of Educn *Worc* 93-98; rtd 98; Assoc CME Adv *Cov* from 98. *The Firs, Stoneleigh Road, Bubbenhall, Coventry CV8 3BS* Tel (024) 7630 3712 Fax as telephone E-mail firsjohn@supanet.com

JOHNSON, Geoffrey Kemble. b 22. RD71. Roch Th Coll 62. **d** 64 **p** 65. C Hayes *Roch* 64-68; R Worlingham *St E* 68-84; rtd 84; Perm to Offic *Nor* 84-00; Perm to Offic *St E* from 84. *53 St Walstans Road, Taverham, Norwich NR8 6NG* Tel (01603) 860626

JOHNSON, Geoffrey Stuart. b 39. ALCD65 Wolv Poly DipEd Sussex Univ DPhil01. **d** 65 **p** 66. C Worksop St Jo *S'well* 65-68; Taiwan 68-71; Singapore 71-76; Aber Univ *Ab* 76-78; Perm to Offic *Heref* 78-82; P-in-c Hoarwithy, Hentland and Sellack 82-84; Chapl Horton Hosp Epsom 84-90; Distr Chapl Brighton

HA 90-94; Managing Chapl Brighton Health Care NHS Trust 94-99; Managing Chapl S Downs Health NHS Trust 94-99; Chapl from 99; rtd 99; Perm to Offic *Chich* from 01. *5 Garden Mews, 15 Beachy Head Road, Eastbourne BN20 7QP* Tel (01323) 644083

JOHNSON, Gillian Margaret. b 55. Bretton Hall Coll CertEd76. N Ord Course 00. **d** 03. C Thornhill and Whitley Lower *Wakef* from 03. *5 Wood Mount, Overton, Wakefield WF4 4SB* Tel (01924) 262181 E-mail gilljohnson99@hotmail.com

JOHNSON, Gordon Edward. b 27. Oak Hill Th Coll 76. **d** 77 **p** 78. C Scarborough St Mary w Ch Ch and H Apostles *York* 77-82; V Hutton Cranswick w Skerne 82-86; P-in-c Watton w Beswick and Kilnwick 82-86; V Hutton Cranswick w Skerne, Watton and Beswick 86-88; V Bubwith w Skipwith 88-93; rtd 93; Perm to Offic *York* from 93; Perm to Offic *Ripon* from 93. *Greenacres, Lovesome Hill, Northallerton DL6 2PB* Tel (01609) 881512

JOHNSON, Graham. b 37. Westcott Ho Cam 66. **d** 68 **p** 69. C Stafford St Mary *Lich* 68-71; C Wombourne 71-74; Youth Chapl 74-77; P-in-c Tong 76-77; Res Min Wednesfield St Thos 77-78; TV 79-82; P-in-c Milwich and Weston upon Trent 82-88; P-in-c Gayton w Fradswell 84-88; V Fradswell, Gayton, Milwich and Weston 88-90; TV Wolstanton 90-96; V Oxley 96-02; rtd 03. *Ty Pab, 4 Church Street, Tremadog, Porthmadog LL49 9RA* Tel (01766) 513744 E-mail graham@typab.freeserve.co.uk

JOHNSON, Graham James. b 43. Leeds Univ BA67. Coll of Resurr Mirfield DipTh69. **d** 70 **p** 71. C Heckmondwike *Wakef* 70-73; C Pet St Jude *Pet* 73-76; V Gt w Lt Harrowden and Orlingbury 76-83; R Daventry 83-92; TR Daventry, Ashby St Ledgers, Braunston etc 92; RD Daventry 88-92; Chapl Danetre Hosp 83-93; P-in-c Loddington *Leic* 93-99; Warden Launde Abbey 93-99; RD Framland *Leic* 94-96; Bp's Chapl and Interfaith Adv 00-02; P-in-c Humberstone 02-03; P-in-c Thurnby Lodge 02-03; TR Ascension TM from 03. *St Mary's Vicarage, 56 Vicarage Lane, Humberstone, Leicester LE5 1EE* Tel 0116-276 7281 Fax 276 4504 E-mail grahamanddiane@ntlworld.com

JOHNSON, Harriet Etta. LRAM DipEd40. Trin Coll Bris. **dss** 76 **d** 87. Burundi 76-80; Ipplepen w Torbryan *Ex* 81-87; Hon Par Dn 87-90; Perm to Offic from 90. *10 Fairfield West, Huxtable Hill, Torquay TQ2 6RN* Tel (01803) 690115

JOHNSON, Mrs Hilary Ann. b 51. RGN72 RHV74 DipRS85. S'wark Ord Course 82. **dss** 85 **d** 87 **p** 94. Hon Par Dn Salfords *S'wark* 85-90; Chapl St Geo Hosp Lon 90-94; Chapl St Geo Healthcare NHS Trust Lon from 94; Assoc P Wimbledon *S'wark* from 95. *St George's Hospital, Blackshaw Road, London SW17 0QT* Tel (020) 8725 3070, 8725 3071 or 8397 0952 Fax 8725 1621

JOHNSON, Ian Lawrence. b 44. Wells Th Coll 68. **d** 71 **p** 72. C Benhilton *S'wark* 71-73; C Weymouth H Trin *Sarum* 73-76; R Pewsey 76-81; R Compton Abbas W w Wynford Eagle etc 81; P-in-c Maiden Newton w Frome Vauchurch 81; R Maiden Newton and Valleys 81-83; Sherborne Episc Area Youth Officer 81-83; Dioc Youth Officer 83-88; TR Langley and Parkfield *Man* 88-95; P-in-c Haughton St Anne 95-99; Dioc Adv on Evang 95-99; TR Southampton (City Cen) *Win* from 99. *The Rectory, 32B Morris Road, Southampton SO15 2BR* Tel (023) 8023 5716 Fax 8022 3757 E-mail ianljohnson@zoom.co.uk

JOHNSON, Ian Leslie. b 51. Bede Coll Dur TCert73. Wycliffe Hall Ox DipMin93. **d** 93 **p** 94. C Evington *Leic* 93-96; Sub Chapl HM Pris Gartree 96-97; C Foxton w Gumley and Laughton and Lubenham *Leic* 96-97; C Foxton w Gumley and Laughton 97-00; P-in-c from 00; Sub Chapl HM Pris Gartree from 97. *The Vicarage, Vicarage Drive, Foxton, Market Harborough LE16 7RJ* Tel (01858) 545545 E-mail ijoh297@aol.com

JOHNSON (née SILINS), Ms Jacqueline. b 62. Coll of Ripon & York St Jo BA85. Ripon Coll Cuddesdon 01. **d** 03. C Torpoint *Truro* from 03. *3 Grove Park, Torpoint PL11 2PP* Tel (01752) 812418 Mobile 07905-354723 E-mail jackie@sinl.fsnet.co.uk

✠JOHNSON, The Rt Revd James Nathaniel. b 32. Wells Th Coll 63. **d** 64 **p** 65 **c** 85. C Lawrence Weston *Bris* 64-66; St Helena 66-72; Hon Can from 75; Area Sec USPG *Ex* and *Truro* 72-74; R Combe Martin *Ex* 74-80; V Thorpe Bay *Chelmsf* 80-85; Bp St Helena 85-91; R Byfield w Boddington and Aston le Walls *Pet* 91-92; Asst Bp Pet 91-92; V Hockley *Chelmsf* 92-97; Asst Bp Chelmsf 92-97; Can Chelmsf Cathl 94-97; rtd 97; Hon Asst Bp Chelmsf from 97. *St Helena, 249 Woodgrainge Drive, Southend-on-Sea SS1 2SQ* Tel (01702) 613429

JOHNSON, Canon John Anthony. b 18. Selw Coll Cam BA48 MA53 St Jo Coll Dur DipTh51. **d** 51 **p** 52. C Battersea St Mary *S'wark* 51-54; C Merton St Mary 54-56; V Balderton *S'well* 56-60; V Mansfield Woodhouse 60-70; V Beeston 70-85; RD Beeston 81-85; Hon Can S'well Minster 82-85; rtd 86; Perm to Offic *Blackb* from 90. *Driftwood, Ireleth Road, Askam-in-Furness LA16 7JD* Tel (01229) 462291

JOHNSON, John Cecil. b 23. Peterho Cam BA48. Ely Th Coll 57. **d** 59 **p** 60. C Whitton SS Phil and Jas *Lon* 59-70; P-in-c Fulham St Andr Fulham Fields 70-73; V 73-88; rtd 88; Perm to Offic *Lich* from 88; Perm to Offic *Heref* from 90. *13 Selkirk Drive, Sutton Hill, Telford TF7 4JE* Tel (01952) 588407

JOHNSON, John David. b 38. Handsworth Coll Birm 60 Claremont Sch of Th 65 St Deiniol's Hawarden 71. **d** 71 **p** 72. C Heref St Martin *Heref* 71-73; P-in-c Ewyas Harold w Dulas 73-79; P-in-c Kilpeck 73-79; P-in-c St Devereux w Wormbridge 73-79; P-in-c Kenderchurch 73-79; P-in-c Bacton 78-79; TR Ewyas Harold w Dulas, Kenderchurch etc 79-81; R Kentchurch w Llangua, Rowlestone, Llancillo etc 79-81; Chapl Napsbury Hosp St Alb 81-96; Chapl Horizon NHS Trust Herts 96-00; Chapl Barnet Healthcare NHS Trust 96-00; Chapl Barnet and Chase Farm Hosps NHS Trust 00-03; Chapl Herts Partnerships NHS Trust 02-03; rtd 03. *24 Rushendon Furlong, Pitstone, Leighton Buzzard LU7 9QX* Tel (01296) 661390

JOHNSON, Joseph Clarke. b 10. Bps' Coll Cheshunt 46. **d** 48 **p** 49. C Carl H Trin *Carl* 48-51; V St John's in the Vale w Wythburn 51-57; V Beckermet St Bridget w Ponsonby 57-78; rtd 78; Perm to Offic *Carl* from 78. *High Moss, Calderbridge, Seascale CA20 1DQ* Tel (01946) 841289

JOHNSON, Mrs Julie Margaret. b 47. LNSM course 94. **d** 98 **p** 99. OLM Welton and Dunholme w Scothern *Linc* from 98. *7 St Mary's Avenue, Welton, Lincoln LN2 3LN* Tel (01673) 860650

JOHNSON, Kathryn Ann. b 03. C Wrexham *St As* from 03. *The Vicarage, First Avenue, Llay, Wrexham LL12 0TN* Tel (01978) 852262

JOHNSON, Keith Henry. b 64. Keele Univ BA91 CQSW91. Coll of Resurr Mirfield BA97. **d** 97 **p** 98. C W Bromwich St Fran *Lich* 97-00; P-in-c Willenhall St Giles from 00. *St Giles's Vicarage, Walsall Street, Willenhall WV13 2ER* Tel (01902) 605722 E-mail keith.johnson14@btinternet.com

JOHNSON, Keith Winton Thomas William. b 37. K Coll Lon BD63 AKC63. **d** 64 **p** 65. C Dartford H Trin *Roch* 64-69; Chapl Kuwait 69-73; V Erith St Jo *Roch* 73-80; V Bexley St Jo 80-91; V Royston *St Alb* 91-94; R Sandon, Wallington and Rushden w Clothall 94-97; Dean St Chris Cathl Bahrain 97-02; rtd 02. *The Mews, 26 St Peter's Street, Caxton, Cambridge CB3 8PJ* Tel (01954) 719972 E-mail keith1412@hotmail.com

JOHNSON, Kenneth William George. b 53. Hull Univ BA76 PGCE77. EMMTC 92. **d** 95 **p** 96. NSM Ilkeston H Trin *Derby* 95-99; NSM Sandiacre from 99. *18 Park Avenue, Awsworth, Nottingham NG16 2RA* Tel 0115-930 7830 E-mail kwjohnson@lineone.net

JOHNSON, Miss Lesley Denise. b 47. WMMTC 95. **d** 98 **p** 99. NSM Stockingford *Cov* 98-01; TV Cov E from 01. *St Alban's Vicarage, Mercer Avenue, Coventry CV2 4PQ* Tel (024) 7645 2493 Fax as telephone

JOHNSON, Malcolm Arthur. b 36. Univ Coll Dur BA60 MA64 Lon Metrop Univ Hon MA02. Cuddesdon Coll 60. **d** 62 **p** 63. C Portsea N End St Mark *Portsm* 62-67; Chapl Qu Mary Coll *Lon* 67-74; V St Botolph Aldgate w H Trin Minories 74-92; P-in-c St Ethelburga Bishopgate 85-89; AD The City 85-90; Master R Foundn of St Kath in Ratcliffe 93-97; Bp's Adv for Past Care and Counselling *Lon* 97-01; rtd 02. *Mill Eyot, Chertsey Road, Shepperton TW17 9LA* Tel (01932) 224365 Fax 226428

JOHNSON, Canon Malcolm Stuart. b 35. AKC60. **d** 61 **p** 62. C Catford St Laur *S'wark* 61-64; Hon C Hatcham St Cath 66-76; P-in-c Kingstanding St Luke *Birm* 76-77; V 77-82; P-in-c Peckham St Jo w St Andr *S'wark* 82-92; V from 92; Hon Can Sabongidda-Ora from 98. *St John's Vicarage, 10A Meeting House Lane, London SE15 2UN* Tel (020) 7639 0084

JOHNSON, Ms Margaret Anne Hope. b 52. Homerton Coll Cam Open Univ BA81 Fitzw Coll Cam BA95. Ridley Hall Cam 93. **d** 95 **p** 96. C Northampton Em *Pet* 95-97; P-in-c 97-98; TR from 98. *13 Booth Lane North, Northampton NN3 6JG* Tel (01604) 648974 E-mail revmahj@aol.com

JOHNSON, Margaret Joan (Meg). b 41. S'wark Ord Course 92. **d** 95 **p** 96. NSM Sanderstead St Mary *S'wark* from 95. *73 St Peter's Street, South Croydon CR2 7DG* Tel (020) 8686 1711 E-mail meg.johnson@dswark.org.uk

JOHNSON, Mark. b 62. Leic Poly BSc84 Loughb Univ PhD88. Ripon Coll Cuddesdon 88. **d** 94 **p** 95. C Bishop's Cleeve *Glouc* 94-98; TV Heref S Wye *Heref* from 98. *The Vicarage, 1 Holme Lacy Road, Hereford HR2 6DD* Tel (01432) 353275 *or* 353717 Fax 352412 E-mail revmark.johnson@which.net

JOHNSON, Michael. b 42. Birm Univ BSc63. S'wark Ord Course 68. **d** 71 **p** 72. C Kidbrooke St Jas *S'wark* 71-74; NSM Eynsford w Farningham and Lullingstone *Roch* 74-89; NSM Selling w Throwley, Sheldwich w Badlesmere etc *Cant* from 89. *1 Halke Cottages, North Street, Sheldwich, Faversham ME13 0LR* Tel (01795) 536583

JOHNSON, Canon Michael Anthony. b 51. Ex Univ BA76. Ripon Coll Cuddesdon 76 Ch Div Sch of the Pacific (USA) 77. **d** 78 **p** 79. C Primrose Hill St Mary w Avenue Road St Paul *Lon* 78-81; C Hampstead St Jo 81-85; TV Mortlake w E Sheen *S'wark* 85-93; V Wroughton *Bris* from 93; RD Wroughton 97-99; AD Swindon from 99; Hon Can Bris Cathl from 99. *The Vicarage, Church Hill, Wroughton, Swindon SN4 9JS* Tel (01793) 812301 Fax 814582 E-mail canonmike@aol.com

JOHNSON, Michael Colin. b 37. Lon Univ DipRS80. S'wark Ord Course 77. **d** 80 **p** 81. NSM New Eltham All SS *S'wark* 80-84; NSM Woldingham 84-98; rtd 98; Perm to Offic *Chich*

from 99. *5 The Mount, Meads Road, Eastbourne BN20 7PX* Tel (01323) 730501 E-mail tandem@mountmeads.fsnet.co.uk

JOHNSON, Michael Gordon. b 45. Lon Univ DipTh68. Kelham Th Coll 64. **d** 68 **p** 69. C Holbrooks *Cov* 68-72; C Cannock *Lich* 72-75; V Coseley Ch Ch 75-79; P-in-c Sneyd 79-82; R Longton 82-88; Chapl Pilgrim Hosp Boston 88-96; TV Jarrow *Dur* 96-98; Chapl Monkton and Primrose Hill Hosp 96-98; R Burghwallis and Campsall *Sheff* from 98. *The Vicarage, High Street, Campsall, Doncaster DN6 9AF* Tel (01302) 700286

JOHNSON, Michael Robert. b 68. Aston Business Sch BSc90. Ridley Hall Cam CTM97. **d** 97 **p** 98. C E Greenwich *S'wark* 97-00; C Perry Hill St Geo 00-03; Chapl W Lon YMCA from 03. *YMCA, 25 St Mary's Road, Ealing W5 5RE* Tel (020) 7207 8747 E-mail thebluegnu@yahoo.co.uk

JOHNSON, Mrs Nancy May. b 46. TCert67 Sheff Poly MA86. N Ord Course 00. **d** 02 **p** 03. NSM Sheff Cathl *Sheff* from 02. *121 Rustlings Road, Sheffield S11 7AB* Tel 0114-266 6456 E-mail nancy@121rustlings.freeserve.co.uk

JOHNSON, Nigel Edwin. b 41. AKC64 St Boniface Warminster 64. **d** 65 **p** 66. C Poulton-le-Sands *Blackb* 65-68; Chapl RN 68-93; Perm to Offic *Cant* 93-00 and *Carl* from 00; rtd 99. *Mell View, 9 Thirlmere Park, Penrith CA11 8QS* Tel (01768) 899865

JOHNSON, Nigel Victor. b 48. ARCM68 LTCL75 Cam Univ DipEd69. Linc Th Coll 80. **d** 82 **p** 83. C Lindley *Wakef* 82-85; P-in-c Upperthong 85-87; Perm to Offic *Derby* 88-89; NSM Calow and Sutton cum Duckmanton 89-90; R 90-00; RD Bolsover and Staveley 98-00; V Newbold w Dunston from 00; RD Chesterfield from 02. *Newbold Rectory, St John's Road, Chesterfield S41 8QN* Tel (01246) 450374 E-mail anselard@aol.com

JOHNSON, Peter Colin. b 64. SS Mark & Jo Coll Plymouth BEd87 Univ of Wales (Lamp) PhD00. SW Minl Tr Course 97. **d** 00 **p** 01. NSM Godrevy *Truro* from 00. *Seascape, Trewelloe Road, Praa Sands, Penzance TR20 9SU* Tel (01736) 763407 E-mail revdocpj@btinternet.com

JOHNSON, Canon Peter Frederick. b 41. Melbourne Univ BA63 Ch Ch Ox BA68 MA72. St Steph Ho Ox 68. **d** 69 **p** 70. C Banbury *Ox* 69-71; Tutor St Steph Ho Ox 71-74; Chapl St Chad's Coll Dur 74-80; Vice-Prin 78-80; Chapl K Sch Cant 80-90; Perm to Offic *Cant* 80-81; Hon Min Can Cant Cathl 81-90; Can Res Bris Cathl *Bris* from 90. *41 Salisbury Road, Bristol BS6 7AR* Tel 0117-944 4464

JOHNSON, Prof Peter Stewart. b 44. Nottm Univ BA65 PhD70. Cranmer Hall Dur 01. **d** 03. NSM Dur St Nic *Dur* from 03. *126 Devonshire Road, Durham DH1 2BH* Tel 0191-386 6334 Mobile 07949-680467

JOHNSON, Philip Anthony. b 69. All Nations Chr Coll BA97 MA98 FIBMS94. Ridley Hall Cam 00. **d** 02 **p** 03. C Witham *Chelmsf* from 02. *23 Forest Road, Witham CM8 2PS* Tel (01376) 517170 E-mail revdrphilip@aol.com

JOHNSON (née DAVIES), Rhiannon Mary Morgan. b 69. St Anne's Coll Ox BA90 MA96 Univ of Wales (Cardiff) PhD94 BD96 Dip Past Th 97. St Mich Coll Llan 94. **d** 97 **p** 98. C Whitchurch *Llan* 97-99; NSM Walton W w Talbenny and Haroldston W *St D* 99-00; Chapl Trin Coll Carmarthen 00; NSM Walton W w Talbenny and Haroldston W *St D* from 00. *The Rectory, Walton West, Little Haven, Haverfordwest SA62 3UB* Tel (01437) 781279 E-mail rhiannonmm@tesco.net

JOHNSON, Richard Miles. b 59. Bris Univ BSc82. St Jo Coll Nottm 87. **d** 90 **p** 91. C Bromley SS Pet and Paul *Roch* 90-94; USPG/CMS Philippines 94-97; C Bexleyheath Ch Ch *Roch* from 97; Ind Chapl from 97. *69 Garden Avenue, Bexleyheath DA7 4LE* Tel and fax (020) 8303 9509 *or* tel 8304 6887 E-mail dickim@globalnet.co.uk

JOHNSON, Robert Kenneth. b 48. N Ord Course 83. **d** 86 **p** 87. C Hattersley *Ches* 86-88; C Brinnington w Portwood 88-90; V Gospel Lane St Mich *Birm* 90-97; P-in-c Birm St Geo from 97. *St George's Rectory, 100 Bridge Street West, Birmingham B19 2YX* Tel 0121-359 2000

JOHNSON, Canon Robin Edward Hobbs. b 39. Fitzw Ho Cam BA61 MA65. Ripon Hall Ox 61. **d** 63 **p** 64. C Tyldesley w Shakerley *Man* 63-66; Lic to Offic *Leic* 66-71; V Castleton Moor *Man* 71-77; Dir of Ords 76-81; V Prestwich St Gabr 77-81; V Heaton Ch Ch 81-91; Hon Can Man Cathl 86-91; TR Dorchester *Sarum* 91-00; RD Dorchester 99-00; rtd 00; Chapl Torrevieja *Eur* from 00. *Edificio Torre del More 1B, 03180 Torrevieja, Alicante, Spain* Tel (0034) (96) 692 5205 Fax as telephone

JOHNSON, Ronald. b 40. Sunderland Poly NDD61 Liv Coll of Art ATD62. Wycliffe Hall Ox 69. **d** 72 **p** 73. C Deane *Man* 72-74; C N Meols *Liv* 74-75; Chapl St Sav Tiffield 75-82; TV Riverside *Ox* 82-84; Asst Chapl Eton Coll 82-84; Warden Eton Coll Dorney Project 82-84; Chapl Eastbourne Coll 85-99; rtd 99; Perm to Offic *Dur* from 99. *55 Cutlers Hall Road, Consett DH8 8RE* Tel (01207) 582109

JOHNSON, Ronald George. b 33. Chich Th Coll 75. **d** 76 **p** 77. Hon C Shipley *Chich* 76-79; C Brighton St Matthias 79-82; P-in-c Barlavington 82; P-in-c Burton w Coates 82; P-in-c Sutton w Bignor 82; R Barlavington, Burton w Coates, Sutton and Bignor

82-93; rtd 93; Perm to Offic *Chich* from 93. *1 Highdown Drive, Littlehampton BN17 6HJ* Tel (01903) 732210

JOHNSON, The Very Revd Samuel Hugh Stowell Akinsope. b 30. K Coll Lon BD61. Lich Th Coll 52. **d** 55 **p** 56. C Whitechapel St Paul w St Mark *Lon* 55-58; C Sunbury 58-59; C Lisson Grove w St Marylebone St Matt w Em 59-60; C St Martin-in-the-Fields 60-62; Nigeria from 63; Provost Lagos Cathl 70-95; rtd 95. *1 Oba Nle Aro Crescent, Ilupeju, PO Box 10021, Marina, Lagos, Nigeria*

JOHNSON (née ROWE), Mrs Shiela. b 43. Cert Child Care 66. CITC 93. **d** 96 **p** 97. Aux Min Urney w Denn and Derryheen *K, E & A* 96-97; Aux Min Boyle and Elphin w Aghanagh, Kilbryan etc 97-01; Aux Min Roscommon w Donamon, Rathcline, Kilkeevin etc 97-01; Aux Min Clondevaddock w Portsalon and Leatbeg *D & R* from 02. *Ballymore Rectory, Portna-Blagh, Letterkenny, Co Donegal, Irish Republic* Tel (00353) (74) 913 6185 E-mail clondehorkey@raphoe.anglican.org

JOHNSON, Stanley. b 42. QUB BSc63 TCD BTh89. CITC 86. **d** 89 **p** 90. C Kilmore w Ballintemple, Kildallon etc *K, E & A* 89-97; Adn Elphin and Ardagh 97-01; Can Elphin Cathl 97-01; I Templemichael w Clongish, Clooncumber etc 97-01; I Clondehorkey w Cashel *D & R* from 01. *Ballymore Rectory, Port-na-Blagh, Letterkenny, Co Donegal, Irish Republic* Tel (00353) (74) 913 6185 E-mail clondehorkey@raphoe.anglican.org *or* johnsons@esatclear.ie

JOHNSON, Stephen. b 57. Cranmer Hall Dur. **d** 00 **p** 01. C Longton *Blackb* 00-02; C Longridge from 03. *94 Higher Road, Longridge, Preston PR3 3SY* Tel (01772) 784832 Mobile 07790-917504

JOHNSON, Stuart. *See* JOHNSON, Geoffrey Stuart

JOHNSON, Mrs Susan Constance. b 46. EAMTC 01. **d** 03. NSM Heald Green St Cath *Ches* from 03. *St Catherine's Church Office, 217 Outwood Road, Heald Green, Cheadle SK8 3JS* Tel 0161-485 3489 E-mail bjohnson@ics-uk.org.

JOHNSON, Terence John. b 44. Cov Poly BA89. Lon Coll of Div ALCD70 LTh74. **d** 69 **p** 70. C Woodside *Ripon* 69-72; C Leeds St Geo 72-76; C Heworth H Trin *York* 76-81; V Budbrooke *Cov* 81-97; Chapl Wroxall Abbey Sch 83-93; V Stone Ch Ch and Oulton *Lich* 97-02; P-in-c Collingtree w Courteenhall and Milton Malsor *Pet* from 02. *The Rectory, Barn Corner, Collingtree, Northampton NN4 0NF* Tel (01604) 705620 E-mail terence@johnson7142.fsnet.co.uk

JOHNSON, Thomas Bernard. b 44. BA CertEd. Oak Hill Th Coll. **d** 84 **p** 85. C Birkenhead St Jas w St Bede *Ches* 84-88; R Ashover and Brackenfield *Derby* 88-01; P-in-c Wessington 99-01; R Ashover and Brackenfield w Wessington 01-03; Hon Chapl Derbyshire St Jo Ambulance from 91; RD Chesterfield 97-02; V Swanwick and Pentrich from 03. *The Vicarage, 4 Broom Avenue, Swanwick, Alfreton DE55 1DQ* Tel (01773) 602684

JOHNSON, Victor Edward. b 45. Linc Th Coll 83. **d** 85 **p** 86. C Garforth *Ripon* 85-90; Dioc Video Officer 90-92; V Wyther Ven Bede 92-00; V Shelley and Shepley *Wakef* 00-01; rtd 01; Perm to Offic *Bradf* from 02. *12 Rosie's Brae, Isle of Whithorn, Newton Stewart DG8 8LT* Tel (01988) 500511 E-mail vej@onetel.net.uk

JOHNSON, Walter. b 21. St Aid Birkenhead. **d** 59 **p** 60. C W Bridgford *S'well* 59-62; V Bracebridge *Linc* 62-73; R Weston sub Edge and Aston sub Edge *Glouc* 73-77; R Willersey, Saintbury, Weston-sub-Edge etc 77-86; rtd 86; Perm to Offic *Win* from 87. *15 Beechey Road, Bournemouth BH8 8LL* Tel (01202) 557063

JOHNSTON, Alan Beere. b 14. Leeds Univ BA36. Coll of Resurr Mirfield 36. **d** 38 **p** 39. C Manningham St Chad *Bradf* 38-40; C Middlesbrough St Paul *York* 40-43; Perm to Offic 43-45; C Crawley *Chich* 45-47; C Portsea N End St Mark *Portsm* 47-48; C Marske in Cleveland *York* 48-50; P-in-c Carlin How w Skinningrove 50-52; V 52-57; V Clifton 57-62; V Kingston upon Hull St Mary 62-68; Asst Master Sir Henry Cooper High Sch Hull 68-70; Waltham Toll Bar Sch Waltham 70-71; Tutor Workers' Educn Assn 71-81; rtd 81; Perm to Offic *Eur* from 83; Asst Chapl Istanbul 89-90; Perm to Offic *Chich* from 93. *6 Arlington Close, Goring-by-Sea, Worthing BN12 4ST* Tel (01903) 426590

JOHNSTON, Alexander Irvine. b 47. LRAM Keele Univ BA70. St Alb Minl Tr Scheme 77. **d** 80 **p** 81. NSM Hockerill *St Alb* 80-95; NSM High Wych and Gilston w Eastwick 95-96; TV Bottesford w Ashby *Linc* 96-01; P-in-c St Germans *Truro* from 01. *The Vicarage, Quay Road, St Germans, Saltash PL12 5LY* Tel (01503) 230690 Fax as telephone E-mail alec@johnston2000.fsnet.co.uk

JOHNSTON, Allen Niall. b 61. AMBIM87 MISM87 Southn Univ BTh92 Kent Univ MA97. Sarum & Wells Th Coll 89. **d** 92 **p** 93. C Roehampton H Trin *S'wark* 92-95; Dir Past Services Richmond, Twickenham and Roehampton NHS Trust 95-98; Tutor SEITE 95-97; Advisor P Freetown Sierra Leone from 03. *57 Vestry Court, Monck Street, London SW1P 2BW*

JOHNSTON, Austin. b 50. Huddersfield Poly CertEd76 BEd90. Chich Th Coll Dip Th & Min 94. **d** 94 **p** 95. C Peterlee *Dur* 94-97; C Stockton St Pet 97-00; TR Stanley and Tanfield 00-01; TR Ch the K from 01. *The Rectory, Church Bank, Stanley DH9 0DU* Tel (01207) 233936

JOHNSTON, Charles Walter Barr. b 38. Lon Univ BSc61. Oak Hill Th Coll 62. **d** 64 **p** 65. C Holloway St Mark w Em *Lon* 64-68; Argentina from 68; SAMS 70-03; rtd 03. *Calle Salta s/n, 3636 Ing Jvarez, Formosa, Argentina* Tel (0054) (3711) 420265

JOHNSTON, David. *See* JOHNSTON, Thomas David

JOHNSTON, David George Scott. b 66. Avery Hill Coll BA88. SEITE 00. **d** 03. C Frindsbury w Upnor *Roch* from 03. *18 Honeypot Close, Rochester ME2 3DU* E-mail cathryn.johnston@ntlworld.com

JOHNSTON, Canon Donald Walter. b 28. Trin Coll Melbourne BA51 Lon Univ PGCE52 Em Coll Cam BA63 MA67. Ridley Hall Cam 64. **d** 64 **p** 65. C Cottingham *York* 64-66; Australia from 66; Min Nunawading Melbourne 67-69; Chapl Brighton Gr Sch Melbourne 70-73; Chapl Melbourne C of E Gr Sch 74-84; Angl Bd of Miss 85-90; Chapl H Name Sch Dogura 85; Hd Martyrs' Memorial Sch Popondetta 86-89; Hon Commissary from 91; Can Papua New Guinea from 90; rtd 91. *22 Albert Street, PO Box 114, Point Lonsdale, Vic, Australia 3225* Tel (0061) (3) 5258 2139 *or* 9690 0549 Fax 5258 3994 E-mail dncjohnston@al.com.au

JOHNSTON, Duncan Howard. b 63. Hull Univ BA85 Nottm Univ MA93. St Jo Coll Nottm 91. **d** 93 **p** 94. C Werrington *Pet* 93-96; V Gt Doddington and Wilby 96-01; Dioc Adv in Local Miss *Dur* 02-03; R Fremont St Jo USA from 03. *Address temp unknown*

JOHNSTON, Edith Violet Nicholl. b 28. **d** 87. Par Dn Bentley *Sheff* 87-88; rtd 88; Perm to Offic *Sheff* from 88. *32 Tennyson Avenue, Mexborough S64 0AX* Tel (01709) 570189

JOHNSTON, Elizabeth Margaret. b 37. QUB BA58 DipEd69 Serampore Univ BD87 Lon Univ DipTh62. Dalton Ho Bris. **d** 81 **p** 94. BCMS India 62-92; C Belfast St Chris *D & I* 93-94; Bp's C 94-03; Can Down Cathl 01-03; rtd 03. *103 Ballydorn Road, Killinchy, Newtownards BT23 6QB* Tel (028) 9074 2518 Mobile 07980-123181

JOHNSTON, Frank. *See* JOHNSTON, William Francis

JOHNSTON, The Very Revd Frederick Mervyn Kieran. b 11. TCD BA33 MA52. **d** 34 **p** 36. C Castlecomer *C & O* 34-36; C Cork St Luke *C, C & R* 36-38; I Kilmeen 38-40; I Drimoleague 40-45; I Cork St Mich 45-58; Can Cork and Cloyne Cathls 55-59; I Bandon 56-67; Treas Ross Cathl 59-60; Adn Cork 59-66; Dean Cork 66-71; rtd 71. *24 Lapps Court, Hartlands Avenue, Cork, Irish Republic* Tel (00353) (21) 313264

JOHNSTON, Geoffrey Stanley. b 44. Aston Univ MBA81 Lon Univ DipTh68 Birm Univ CertEd78. Kelham Th Coll 64. **d** 68 **p** 69. C Blakenall Heath *Lich* 68-72 and 73-75; C St Buryan, St Levan and Sennen *Truro* 72-73; P-in-c Willenhall St Steph *Lich* 75-76; C W Bromwich All SS 76-77; Lect W Bromwich Coll of Commerce and Tech 78-82; Ind Chapl *Worc* 82-94; TV Halesowen 82-94; NSM Dudley St Fran 94-99; P-in-c from 99. *St Francis's Vicarage, 50 Laurel Road, Dudley DY1 3EZ* Tel and fax (01384) 350422 Mobile 0771-313 4287 E-mail geoff.johnston@blueyonder.co.uk

JOHNSTON, Mrs Helen Kay. b 48. SRN70. St Alb and Ox Min Course 95. **d** 98 **p** 99. OLM Banbury St Paul *Ox* 98-01; P-in-c Flimby *Carl* 01-03; C Netherton 01-03. *Address temp unknown* E-mail kaybees@supanet.com

JOHNSTON, Miss Henrietta Elizabeth Ann. b 59. St Jo Coll Dur BA03. Cranmer Hall Dur 01. **d** 03. C Cov H Trin *Cov* from 03. *85 Stoney Road, Coventry CV3 6HH* Tel 07796-948904 (mobile) E-mail hennie.johnston@tiscali.co.uk

JOHNSTON, James. b 19. FCIB70. Carl Dioc Tr Course. **d** 82 **p** 83. NSM Kendal St Geo *Carl* 82-89; Perm to Offic from 89. *8 Sedbergh Drive, Kendal LA9 6BJ* Tel (01539) 725422

JOHNSTON, Malcolm. *See* JOHNSTON, William Malcolm

JOHNSTON, Michael David Haigh. b 44. MBCS. S Dios Minl Tr Scheme 88. **d** 91 **p** 92. NSM Wootton *Portsm* 91-95; NSM Ryde H Trin 94-99; NSM Swanmore St Mich 95-99; P-in-c Cowes St Faith from 99; Asst Chapl Isle of Wight Healthcare NHS Trust from 03. *7 Dover Street, Ryde PO33 2AQ* Tel (01983) 611291 E-mail rvdmikej@dircon.co.uk

JOHNSTON, Michael Edward. b 68. TCD BA97. CITC BTh00. **d** 00 **p** 01. Bp's V Kilkenny Cathl *C & O* from 00; C Kilkenny w Aghour and Kilmanagh from 00. *St Canice's Library, Cathedral Close, Kilkenny, Irish Republic* Tel (00353) (56) 777 1998

JOHNSTON, Niall. *See* JOHNSTON, Allen Niall

JOHNSTON, Canon Robert John. b 31. Oak Hill Th Coll 64. **d** 64 **p** 65. C Bebington *Ches* 64-68; I Lack *Clogh* 68-99; Can Clogh Cathl 89-99; rtd 99. *2 Beechcroft, Semicock Road, Ballymoney BT53 6NF* Tel (028) 2766 9317

JOHNSTON, Thomas Cosbey. b 15. Em Coll Cam BA40 MA44. Ridley Hall Cam 40. **d** 42 **p** 43. C Handsworth St Mary *Birm* 42-48; New Zealand from 48. *254 Main Road, Moncks Bay, Christchurch 8008, New Zealand* Tel (0064) (3) 384 1224

JOHNSTON, Thomas David. b 52. Salford Univ BSc. N Ord Course 98. **d** 98 **p** 99. Dioc Communications Officer *Man* 96-00; NSM Bolton St Paul w Em 98-00; I Sixmilecross w Termonmaguirke *Arm* 00-03. *671 Chorley New Road, Horwich, Bolton BL6 6HR* Tel (01204) 698748

JOHNSTON, Trevor Samuel. b 72. Ulster Univ BMus96 TCD BTh01. CITC 98. d 01 p 02. C Carrickfergus Conn from 01. 7 Macroom Gardens, Carrickfergus BT38 8NB Tel (028) 9336 2552 E-mail trevor.j@excite.com

JOHNSTON, Canon Wilfred Brian. b 44. TCD BA67 MA70. Div Test 68. d 68 p 70. C Seagoe D & D 68-73; I Inniskeel D & R 73-82; I Castlerock w Dunboe and Fermoyle 82-02; Dioc Registrar from 89; Can Derry Cathl from 92; Preb from 99; Bp's C Gweedore, Carrickfin and Templecrone from 02. The Rectory, Bunbeg, Letterkenny, Co Donegal, Irish Republic Tel (00353) (74) 953 1043

JOHNSTON, William Derek. b 40. CITC 68. d 68 p 69. V Choral Derry Cathl D & R 68-70; I Swanlinbar w Templeport K, E & A 70-73; I Billis Union 73-84; Glebes Sec (Kilmore) 77-03; I Annagh w Drumaloor and Cloverhill 84-87; Preb Kilmore Cathl 85-89; I Annagh w Drumgoon, Ashfield etc 87-99; Adn Kilmore 89-03; I Lurgan w Billis, Killinkere and Munterconnaught 99-03; rtd 03. Ballaghanea, Mullagh Road, Virginia, Co Cavan, Irish Republic Tel (00353) (49) 854 9960 Mobile 086-832 9911

JOHNSTON, William Francis (Frank). b 30. CB83. TCD BA55 MA69. d 55 p 56. C Orangefield D & D 55-59; CF 59-77; Asst Chapl Gen 77-80; Chapl Gen 80-87; P-in-c Winslow Ox 87-91; RD Claydon 89-94; R Winslow w St Horwood and Addington 91-95; rtd 95. Perm to Offic Ex from 95. Lower Axehill, Chard Road, Axminster EX13 5ED Tel (01297) 33259

JOHNSTON, William John. b 35. Lon Univ DipTh72 BA85 MA90. CITC 67. d 70 p 71. C Belfast St Donard D & D 70-72; C Derg D & R 72-78; I Drumclamph w Lower and Upper Langfield 78-91; I Kilskeery w Trillick Clogh 91-00; Chapl to Bp Clogh from 00. The Rectory, 130 Kilskeery Road, Trillick, Omagh BT78 3RJ Tel (028) 6656 1228

JOHNSTON, William Malcolm. b 48. St Alb and Ox Min Course 92. d 95 p 96. NSM Banbury Ox 95-01; P-in-c Netherton Carl 01-03; C Flimby 01-03. Address temp unknown E-mail kaybees@supanet.com

JOHNSTON-HUBBOLD, Clifford Johnston. b 19. Lon Univ BA76 BD80. St Aid Birkenhead 49. d 52 p 53. C Stanwix Carl 52-55; V Gt Broughton 55-59; R Sedgeberrow Worc 59-73; P-in-c Hinton-on-the-Green 72-73; R Sedgeberrow w Hinton-on-the-Green 73-92; rtd 92; Perm to Offic Worc from 92. 2 Mills Close, Broadway WR12 7RB Tel (01386) 852199

JOHNSTONE, William Henry Green. b 26. d 92 p 94. Belize 92-98; OCF 94-98; Hon C Tollard Royal w Farnham, Gussage St Michael etc Sarum 98-01; Hon C Chase from 01. Church Cottage, Chettle, Blandford Forum DT11 8DB Tel (01258) 830396 E-mail padrewmchettle@aol.com

JOINT, Canon Michael John. b 39. Sarum & Wells Th Coll 79. d 79 p 79. CA from 61; Hon C Chandler's Ford Win 79-83; Youth Chapl 79-83; V Lymington 83-95; Co-ord Chapl R Bournemouth and Christchurch Hosps NHS Trust 96-03; Hon Can Win Cathl 00-03; rtd 03. 21 Wycliffe Road, Winton, Bournemouth BH9 1JP Tel (01202) 528677

JOLLEY, Andrew John. b 61. Nottm Univ BSc83 Warwick Univ MBA88 CEng88 MIMechE88. St Jo Coll Nottm BTh97. d 98 p 99. C Sparkhill w Greet and Sparkbrook Birm 98-02; V Aston SS Pet and Paul from 02. The Vicarage, Sycamore Road, Aston, Birmingham B6 5UH Tel 0121-327 5856 Mobile 09773-458403 E-mail andy.jolley@cwcom.net

JOLLY, Leslie Alfred Walter. b 16. AKC40. d 40 p 41. C Bow w Bromley St Leon Lon 40-42; C Cheam Common St Phil S'wark 42-50; C Mottingham St Andr 50-52; V Newington St Matt 52-57; R Chaldon 57-85; rtd 85; Perm to Offic S'wark 85-94; York 85-02. 12 Roseneath Court, Greenwood Gardens, Caterham CR3 6RX Tel (01883) 332463

JONAS, Alan Charles. b 56. Leeds Univ BA79 Univ of Wales (Abth) PGCE80. Wycliffe Hall Ox DipMin94. d 94 p 95. C Hersham Guildf 94-98; P-in-c Westcott from 98; Chapl Priory Sch from 01. The Vicarage, Guildford Road, Westcott, Dorking RH4 3QB Tel (01306) 885309

JONAS, Ian Robert. b 54. St Jo Coll Nottm BTh80. d 80 p 81. C Portadown St Mark Arm 80-82; C Cregagh D & D 82-85; BCMS Sec D & G 85-90; V Langley Mill Derby 90-97; I Kilgariffe Union C, C & R from 97. The Rectory, Gallanes, Clonakilty, Co Cork, Irish Republic Tel (00353) (23) 33357 Fax as telephone E-mail ianjonas@oceanfree.net or kilgariffe@ross.anglican.org

JONES, Alan. b 28. Man Univ LLB48 LLM50. Coll of Resurr Mirfield 53. d 56 p 57. C Streatham St Pet S'wark 56-59; C Hornsey St Luke Lon 59-60; Miss to Seamen 60-61; Chapl RN 61-65; rtd 94. 73 Mousehole Lane, Southampton SO18 4FB Tel (023) 8055 0008

JONES, Alan David. b 32. Lon Coll of Div ALCD58 DipTh70 LTh74. d 58 p 59. C Ipswich All SS St E 58-60; C Southend St Jo Chelmsf 60-64; CF (TA) 60-62; CF (TA - R of O) 62-67; V Leyton St Cath Chelmsf 64-70; V Hatfield Broad Oak 70-77; P-in-c Bush End 77-79; V Theydon Bois 77-88; P-in-c Finchingfield and Cornish Hall End 88-93; rtd 94; Perm to Offic Chelmsf and St E from 94. 3 Grammar School Place, Sudbury CO10 2GE Tel (01787) 370864

JONES, Alan John. b 47. Nottm Univ BA71. Coll of Resurr Mirfield 71. d 73 p 74. C Sedgley St Mary Lich 73-76; C Cov St Jo Cov 76-78; V Bromwich St Fran Lich 78-94; V Ettingshall from 94; AD Wolverhampton from 03. The Vicarage, Ettingshall, Wolverhampton WV4 6QH Tel (01902) 884616

JONES, Alan Pierce. See PIERCE JONES, Alan

JONES, Alban Vaughan. b 24. St D Coll Lamp BA51. d 52 p 53. C Llandeilo Tal-y-bont S & B 52-55; C Swansea St Pet 55-59; R Llangammarch w Garth, Llanfleonfel etc 59-65; Area Sec (Dios Ches, Ban, St As and S & M) CMS 65-72; V Ventnor H Trin Portsm 72-79; V Ventnor St Cath 72-79; V Marshfield and Peterstone Wentloog etc Mon 79-90; RD Bassaleg 87-90; rtd 90. 40 St Hilary Drive, Killay, Swansea SA2 7EH Tel (01792) 208178

JONES, Albert. b 13. K Coll Lon 37. d 41 p 42. C Farnworth and Kearsley Man 41-46; P-in-c 45-46; C Felixstowe St Jo St E 46-47; C Headstone St Geo Lon 47-49; R Stretford All SS Man 49-52; Trinidad and Tobago 52-56; V Farnworth St Pet Man 56-58; Area Sec USPG York 58-63; V Tillingham Chelmsf 63-66; R Dengie w Asheldham 63-66; R Stifford 66-72; P-in-c Stondon Massey 72-79; R Doddinghurst 72-79; rtd 79; Perm to Offic Chelmsf from 79. 29 Seaview Road, Brightlingsea, Colchester CO7 0PP Tel (01206) 303994

JONES, Alfred Albert. b 36. St D Coll Lamp BA59. d 61 p 62. C Treherbert w Tynewydd and Ynsfeio Llan 61-64; C Horsham Chich 64-82; V Shipley 82-86; Chapl Hillingdon Hosp & Mt Vernon Hosp Uxbridge 86-87. Chantry House, Nuthurst Road, Monks Gate, Horsham RH13 6LG Tel (01403) 891218

JONES, Alison. See JONES, Helen Alison

JONES, Alison. See WAGSTAFF, Ms Alison

JONES, Alun. b 52. Leeds Univ BA96. Cuddesdon Coll DipMin94. d 96 p 97. C Newc St Geo Newc 96-98; C Cowgate 98-99; C Fenham St Jas and St Basil from 99. 32 Auburn Gardens, Fenham, Newcastle upon Tyne NE4 9XP Tel 0191-274 0022

JONES, Alwyn Humphrey Griffith. b 30. Leeds Univ BSc51. Coll of Resurr Mirfield 53. d 55 p 56. C W Hackney St Barn Lon 55-58; E Pakistan 58-64; India 65-73; P-in-c Bedminster St Fran Bris 73-75; TR Bedminster 75-83; TV Langport Area Chs B & W 83-85; Dep Chapl HM Pris Nor 85; Chapl HM Pris Preston 85-89; Chapl HM Pris Ashwell 89-91; C Acton Green Lon 91-93; rtd 93; NSM Langport Area Chs B & W 93-98; Perm to Offic B & W and Bris from 98. 46 Imperial Walk, Bristol BS14 9AE Tel 0117-977 1278 E-mail alwyn@fish.co.uk

✠**JONES, The Rt Revd Alwyn Rice.** b 34. Univ of Wales (Lamp) BA55 Fitzw Ho Cam BA57 MA61. St Mich Coll Llan 57. d 58 p 59 c 82. C Llanfairisgaer Ban 58-62; N Wales Sec SCM 60-62; Staff Sec SCM 62-65; Chapl St Winifred's Sch Llanfairfechan 65-68; Dir RE Ban 65-75; Dioc Youth Officer 66-72; Dir of Ords 70-75; Asst Tutor Univ of Wales (Ban) 73-76; V Porthmadog Ban 75-79; Hon Can Ban Cathl 75-78; Preb 78-79; Dean Brecon S & B 79-82; V Brecon w Battle 79-82; Bp St As 82-99; Abp Wales 91-99; rtd 99. Curig, 7 Llwyn Onn, St Asaph LL17 0SQ Tel (01745) 584621

JONES, Alyson Elizabeth. See DAVIE, Mrs Alyson Elizabeth

JONES, Mrs Andrea Margaret. b 46. Qu Coll Birm 88. d 90 p 94. Par Dn Kidderminster St Geo Worc 90-94; TV 94-95; C Penn Fields Lich 95-00; C Gt Wyrley from 00. 46 Gorsey Lane, Great Wyrley, Walsall WS6 6EX Tel (01922) 418271

JONES, Andrew. See JONES, Ian Andrew

JONES, Andrew. b 61. Univ of Wales (Ban) BD82 PGCE82 TCD BTh85 MA91 Univ of Wales MPhil93. CITC 82 St Geo Coll Jerusalem 84. d 85 p 86. Min Can Ban Cathl Ban 85-88; R Dolgellau 88-92; Dir Past Studies St Mich Coll Llan 92-96; Lect Th Univ of Wales (Cardiff) 92-96; Research Fell from 96; R Llanbedrog w Llannor w Llanfihangel etc Ban 96-01; R Llanbedrog w Llannor and Llangian from 01; Dioc CME Officer from 96; RD Llyn and Eifionydd from 99. Tyn-Llan Rectory, Llanbedrog, Pwllheli LL53 7TU Tel (01758) 740919 Fax as telephone

JONES, Andrew. b 64. York Univ BA85. Westmr Th Sem (USA) MDiv91 St Jo Coll Nottm 92. d 94 p 95. C Win Ch Ch Win 94-98; C St Helen Bishopsgate w St Andr Undershaft etc Lon from 98. 15 Morgan Street, London E3 5AB Tel (020) 8983 1463

JONES, Andrew Christopher. b 47. Southn Univ BA69 PhD75. Ridley Hall Cam 78. d 80 p 81. C Wareham Sarum 80-83; P-in-c Symondsbury 83; P-in-c Chideock 83; R Symondsbury and Chideock 84-91; V Shottermill Guildf 91-99; P-in-c Bishopsnympton, Rose Ash, Mariansleigh etc Ex from 99. The Rectory, Bishops Nympton, South Molton EX36 4NY Tel (01769) 550427

JONES, Andrew Collins. b 62. Univ Coll Dur BA83 MA84 MLitt92. St Steph Ho Ox 88. d 90 p 91. C Llangefni w Tregaean and Llangristiolus etc Ban 90-94; C Hartlepool St Aid Dur 94-98; Chapl Hartlepool Gen Hosp 94-98; R Hendon Dur from 98. St Ignatius' Rectory, Bramwell Road, Sunderland SR2 8BY Tel 0191-567 5575

JONES, Anne. See JONES, Christine Anne

JONES, Anthony. b 43. WEMTC 99. d 01 p 02. OLM Lydney Glouc from 01. 12 Almond Walk, Lydney GL15 5LP Tel (01594) 843192 Mobile 07860-331755

JONES, Canon Anthony Spacie. b 34. AKC58. **d** 59 **p** 60. C Bedford St Martin *St Alb* 59-63; Br Guiana 63-66; Guyana 66-71; V Ipswich All Hallows *St E* 72-80; RD Ipswich 78-86; Bp's Dom Chapl 80-82; V Rushmere 82-91; Hon Can St E Cathl 83-99; R Brantham w Stutton 91-99; P-in-c Bentley w Tattingstone 95-99; rtd 99. *6 Fritillary Close, Pinewood, Ipswich IP8 3QT* Tel (01473) 601848
E-mail tonyjones.pinewood@btopenworld.com
JONES, Anthony Thomas. b 70. Wycliffe Hall Ox. **d** 99 **p** 00. C Ox St Ebbe w H Trin and St Pet *Ox* from 99. *St Ebbe's Church Office, 2 Roger Bacon Lane, Oxford OX1 1QE* Tel (01865) 240438 Fax as telephone
JONES, Barbara Christine. b 48. St Hugh's Coll Ox BA71 MA74 Lady Spencer Chu Coll of Educn PGCE74. Carl and Blackb Dioc Tr Inst 97. **d** 00 **p** 01. NSM Bolton-le-Sands *Blackb* from 00. *11 Sandown Road, Lancaster LA1 4LN* Tel (01524) 65598 E-mail jones@barbara.bbfree.co.uk
JONES, Barry Mervyn. b 46. St Chad's Coll Dur BA68 DipTh69. **d** 70 **p** 71. C Bloxwich *Lich* 70-72; C Norwood All SS *Cant* 72-76; C New Addington 76-78; Chapl Mayday Univ Hosp Thornton Heath 78-86; Chapl Qu and St Mary's Hosps Croydon 78-86; Chapl Bromsgrove and Redditch DHA 86-94; Chapl Alexandra Hosp Redditch 86-94; Chapl Alexandra Healthcare NHS Trust Redditch 94-00; Chapl Worcs Acute Hosps NHS Trust from 00. *The Alexandra Hospital, Woodrow Drive, Redditch B98 7UB* Tel (01527) 503030
JONES, Canon Basil Henry. b 26. Bps' Coll Cheshunt 63. **d** 64 **p** 65. C Gt Berkhamsted *St Alb* 64-67; V Leagrave 68-74; RD Luton 71-74; P-in-c Bedford St Paul 74-75; V Wigginton 75-93; Hon Can St Alb 82-93; rtd 93; Perm to Offic *St Alb* from 00. *17 Lochnell Road, Northchurch, Berkhamsted HP4 3QD* Tel (01442) 864485
JONES, The Ven Benjamin Jenkin Hywel. b 39. Univ of Wales BA61. St Mich Coll Llan 61. **d** 64 **p** 65. C Carmarthen St Pet *St D* 64-70; V Cynwyl Gaeo w Llansawel and Talley 70-79; R Llanbadarn Fawr 79-82; V Llanbadarn Fawr w Capel Bangor and Goginan 82-92; Warden of Readers from 82; Can St D Cathl 86-90; RD Llanbadarn Fawr 89-90; Adn Cardigan from 90; V Llanychaearn w Llanddeiniol from 92. *The Vicarage, Llanfarian, Aberystwyth SY23 4BX* Tel (01970) 617100
JONES, Benjamin Tecwyn. b 17. Univ of Wales BA38. K Coll Lon 38. **d** 40 **p** 41. C Hawarden *St As* 40-45; C Pleasley *Derby* 45-46; C Ormskirk *Liv* 46-49; R Rufford *Blackb* 49-55; V S Shore St Pet 55-65; C Oldham St Mary w St Pet *Man* 65-69; Hd Master and Chapl St Mary's Sch Bexhill-on-Sea 69-71; V Blackb St Luke *Blackb* 71-72; P-in-c Griffin 71-72; V Blackb St Luke w St Phil 72-83; rtd 83; Perm to Offic *Blackb* from 83. *527A Livesey Branch Road, Feniscowles, Blackburn BB2 5DB* Tel (01254) 209206
JONES, Bernard Lewis. b 48. Llan Dioc Tr Scheme 89. **d** 93 **p** 94. NSM Aberaman and Abercwmboi w Cwmaman *Llan* 93-99; V Hirwaun from 99. *The Vicarage, High Steet, Hirwaun, Aberdare CF44 9SL* Tel (01685) 811316
JONES, Brian. **d** 94 **p** 96. Lic to Offic *D & D* from 94. *16 Massey Avenue, Belfast BT4 2JS*
JONES, Canon Brian Howell. b 35. Univ of Wales MPhil96. St Mich Coll Llan DipTh61. **d** 61 **p** 62. C Llangiwg *S & B* 61-63; C Swansea St Mary and H Trin 63-70; R New Radnor w Llanfihangel Nantmelan etc 70-75; V Llansamlet 75-89; Dioc Dir of Stewardship 82-89; P-in-c Capel Coelbren 89-95; Dioc Missr 89-95; Can Res Brecon Cathl 89-00; Can Treas 98-00; Chan 99-00; RD Cwmtawe 89-93; V Killay 95-00; rtd 00. *12 Harlech Crescent, Sketty, Swansea SA2 9LP* Tel (01792) 207159 E-mail canonbrian@compuserve.com
JONES, Canon Brian Michael. b 34. Trin Coll Bris DipHE81 Oak Hill Th Coll BA82. **d** 84 **p** 84. CMS 82-93; Sierra Leone 84-93; Can Bo from 91; C Frimley *Guildf* 93-99; rtd 99; Perm to Offic *Newc* 00-01; Hon C N Tyne and Redesdale Team from 01. *7 Redesmouth Court, Bellingham, Hexham NE48 2ES* Tel (01434) 220430
JONES, Canon Brian Noel. b 32. Edin Th Coll 59. **d** 62 **p** 63. C Monkseaton St Mary *Newc* 62-65; C Saffron Walden *Chelmsf* 65-69; P-in-c Swaffham Bulbeck *Ely* 69-75; Dioc Youth Officer 69-75; RD St Ives 75-83 and 87-89; V Ramsey 75-89; V Upwood w Gt and Lt Raveley 75-89; P-in-c Ramsey St Mary's 82-89; Hon Can Ely Cathl 85-97; V Cherry Hinton St Jo 89-97; RD Cambridge 94-97; rtd 97; Perm to Offic *Nor* from 97. *11 Winns Close, Holt NR25 6MQ* Tel (01263) 713645
JONES, Canon Bryan Maldwyn. b 32. St Mich Coll Llan DipTh62. **d** 62 **p** 63. C Swansea St Barn *S & B* 62-69; V Trallwng and Betws Penpont 69-75; V Trallwng, Bettws Penpont w Aberyskir etc 75-00; RD Brecon II 80-91; RD Brecon 91-99; Hon Can Brecon Cathl 92-00; rtd 00. *Plas Newydd, 8 Camden Crescent, Brecon LD3 7BY* Tel (01874) 625063
JONES, Bryan William. b 30. Selw Coll Cam BA53 MA57. Linc Th Coll 53. **d** 55 **p** 56. C Bedminster Down *Bris* 55-58; C Filton 58-62; P-in-c Bedminster St Mich 62-65; V 65-72; P-in-c Moorfields 72-75; TV E Bris 75-95; rtd 95; Perm to Offic *Bris* from 95. *89 Canterbury Close, Yate, Bristol BS37 5TU* Tel (01454) 316795

JONES, Bryon. b 34. Open Univ BA84. St D Coll Lamp 61. **d** 64 **p** 65. C Port Talbot St Theodore *Llan* 64-67; C Aberdare 68-69; C Up Hatherley *Glouc* 69-71; C Oystermouth *S & B* 71-74; V Camrose *St D* 74-77; V Camrose and St Lawrence w Ford and Haycastle from 77. *The Vicarage, Camrose, Haverfordwest SA62 6JE* Tel (01437) 710501
JONES, Miss Celia Lynn. b 54. Trin Coll Bris. **d** 01. C Bris St Paul's *Bris* from 01. *15 St Werburghs Park, Bristol BS2 9YT* Tel 0117-955 6258 E-mail celialynn@supanet.com
JONES, Charles Derek. b 37. K Coll Lon BD60 AKC60. **d** 61 **p** 62. C Stockton St Chad *Dur* 61-64; C Becontree St Elisabeth *Chelmsf* 64-66; C S Beddington St Mich *S'wark* 66-73; Lic to Offic *Ex* 73-77; Perm to Offic *Liv* 77-99; rtd 02. *4 Bryn Glas, Graigfechan, Ruthin LL15 2EX* Tel (01824) 705015
JONES, Charles Eurwyn. b 27. Univ of Wales BSc48 DipEd51. St Mich Coll Llan 53. **d** 55 **p** 56. C Brecon St Dav *S & B* 55-57; C Carmarthen St Dav *St D* 57-61; Tutor Old Cath Sem Bonn 61-64; Tutor Bps' Coll Cheshunt 64-67; V Carlton *S'well* 67-75; P-in-c Colwick 69-75; V Bunny w Bradmore 75-95; rtd 95; Perm to Offic *S'well* from 95. *9 Wentworth Way, Edwalton, Nottingham NG12 4DJ* Tel 0115-923 4119
JONES, Christine Anne. b 51. Leic Coll of Educn CertEd73 Open Univ BA76 Man Univ DASE79 MEd84 PhD91 Chester Coll of HE MTh02. N Ord Course 99. **d** 02 **p** 03. C Offerton *Ches* from 02. *11 Martham Drive, Stockport SK2 5XZ* Tel 0161-487 1067 Mobile 07771-601615 E-mail c-anne@fish.co.uk
JONES, Christopher Howell. b 50. FCCA BA. Oak Hill Th Coll 80. **d** 83 **p** 84. C Leyton St Mary w St Edw *Chelmsf* 83-86; C Becontree St Mary 86-90; P-in-c Bootle St Matt *Liv* 90-93; V 93-99; AD Bootle 97-99; V Ormskirk from 99; Chapl W Lancashire NHS Trust from 99. *The Vicarage, Park Road, Ormskirk L39 3AJ* Tel (01695) 572143
JONES, Christopher John Stark. b 39. Lon Univ BA60 AKC60. Wells Th Coll 63. **d** 65 **p** 66. C Stanmore *Win* 65-67; C Bournemouth St Pet 67-71; C W Wycombe *Ox* 71-75; TV High Wycombe 75-77; V Wokingham St Sebastian 77-84; R Didsbury Ch Ch *Man* 84-00; rtd 00; Perm to Offic *Ches* from 01. *5 Trueman Close, Prenton CH43 7YR* Tel 0151-513 3436
JONES, Christopher Mark. b 54. St Pet Coll Ox BA75 DipTh77 MA79 Selw Coll Cam MPhil80. Ridley Hall Cam 77. **d** 80 **p** 81. C Putney St Marg *S'wark* 80-83; C Ham St Andr 83-86; Chapl HM Rem Cen Latchmere Ho 83-86; Chapl St Jo Coll Dur 87-93; Tutor Cranmer Hall Dur 87-93; Chapl and Fell St Pet Coll Ox from 93. *St Peter's College, Oxford OX1 2DL* Tel (01865) 278903 Fax 278855 E-mail christopher.jones@spc.ox.ac.uk
JONES, Christopher Mark. b 56. St Jo Coll Cam BA78 MA82 Wycliffe Hall Ox BA81 MA85. **d** 82 **p** 83. C Walsall *Lich* 82-84; Chapl St Jo Coll Cam 84-89; Chapl Eton Coll from 89; Ho Master from 97. *The Hopgarden, Eton College, Windsor SL4 6EQ* Tel (01753) 671065 Fax 671067
E-mail c.m.jones@etoncollege.org.uk
JONES, Christopher Yeates. b 51. STETS 97. **d** 00 **p** 01. NSM Yeovil St Mich *B & W* from 00. *20 Bedford Road, Yeovil BA21 5UQ* Tel (01935) 420886 Mobile 07803-371617 E-mail cyjones@care4free.net
JONES, Clifford Albert. b 20. Edin Th Coll 54. **d** 56 **p** 57. C Dundee St Salvador *Bre* 56-58; C Linc St Swithin *Linc* 58-59; C Grantham St Wulfram 59-60; R Dundee St Salvador *Bre* 60-69; V Bradford *B & W* 69-74; V Bridgwater St Jo 74-78; RD Bridgwater 76-80; R Bridgwater St Jo w Chedzoy 78-80; P-in-c Timsbury 80-85; R Timsbury and Priston 85; rtd 85; P-in-c Nor St Geo Tombland *Nor* 85-90; Perm to Offic 94-99; Hon C St Marylebone All SS Lon 90-94; Perm to Offic from 97. *188 John Aird Court, London W2 1UX* Tel (020) 7262 9295
JONES, Clive. b 51. BA82. Oak Hill Th Coll 79. **d** 82 **p** 83. C Brunswick *Man* 82-85; V Pendlebury St Jo 85-96; V Attleborough *Cov* from 96. *Attleborough Vicarage, 5 Fifield Close, Nuneaton CV11 4TS* Tel (024) 7635 4114
E-mail clivej@hta1.freeserve.co.uk
JONES, Clive Morlais Peter. b 40. LTCL71 Univ of Wales (Cardiff) BA63 CertEd64. Chich Th Coll 64. **d** 66 **p** 67. C Llanfabon *Llan* 66-70; PV Llan Cathl 70-75; R Gelligaer 75-85; Prec and Can Llan Cathl 84-85; R Tilehurst St Mich *Ox* 85-94; Chapl Costa Blanca *Eur* 94-97; V Newton St Pet *S & B* from 97. *The Vicarage, Mary Twill Lane, Newton, Swansea SA3 4RB* Tel (01792) 368348
JONES, Clive Wesley. b 68. SSC. St Steph Ho Ox 95. **d** 98 **p** 99. C Swanley St Mary *Roch* 98-02; P-in-c Belvedere St Aug from 02; Chapl Trin Sch Belvedere from 02. *The Vicarage, St Augustine's Road, Belvedere DA17 5HH* Tel (020) 8311 6307 *or* (01322) 441371 E-mail frclive@fish.co.uk
JONES, Colin Stuart. b 56. Southn Univ LLB77. Coll of Resurr Mirfield 81. **d** 84 **p** 85. C Mountain Ash *Llan* 84-86; C Castle Bromwich SS Mary and Marg *Birm* 86-89; V Kingshurst 89-94; V Perry Barr from 94. *Perry Barr Vicarage, Church Road, Birmingham B42 2LB* Tel 0121-356 7998
JONES, Cyril Ernest. b 29. St D Coll Lamp BA54. **d** 56 **p** 57. C Llanedy *St D* 56-60; C Llanelli 60-63; V Mydroilyn w Dihewyd 63-66; V Llanybydder 66-73; V Llanybydder and Llanwenog w

Llanwnnen 73-78; V Betws w Ammanford 78-81; V Cynwyl Gaeo w Llansawel and Talley 81-94; rtd 94. *21 Pontardulais Road, Tycroes, Ammanford SA18 3QD* Tel (01269) 596421

JONES, David. *See* JONES, Preb Wilfred David

JONES, David. *See* JONES, Canon William David

JONES, David. b 55. CA Tr Coll 74 St Steph Ho Ox 83. **d** 85 **p** 86. C Fleur-de-Lis *Mon* 85-87; V Ynysddu 87-93; V Blackwood from 93. *The Vicarage, South View Road, Blackwood NP12 1HR* Tel (01495) 224214

JONES, David Arthur. b 44. Liv Univ BA66 Sussex Univ MA68. St D Coll Lamp LTh74. **d** 74 **p** 75. C Tenby *St D* 74-76; C Chepstow *Mon* 76-78; P-in-c Teversal *S'well* 78-81; R 81-91; Chapl Sutton Cen 78-89; V Radford All So w Ch Ch and St Mich from 91; Adv to Urban Priority Par 96-01. *All Souls' Vicarage, 164 Lenton Boulevard, Nottingham NG7 2BZ* Tel 0115-978 5364

JONES, David Emrys. b 21. Lon Univ BD69 Univ of Wales MA74. St D Coll Lamp BA42. **d** 47 **p** 48. C Llandinorwig *Ban* 47-50; C Conwy w Gyffin 50-57; V Beddgelert 57-72; R Llangystennin *St As* 72-91; rtd 91. *The Rectory, Llanfor, Bala LL23 7YA* Tel (01678) 520080

JONES, Chan David Frederick Donald. b 19. Univ of Wales (Abth) BA41. Westcott Ho Cam 43. **d** 43 **p** 44. C Henfynyw w Aberaeron *St D* 43-46; C Carmarthen St Pet 46-53; V Pencarreg 53-64; Lect Bp Burgess Th Hall Lamp 59-72; V Betws w Ammanford *St D* 72-88; RD Dyffryn Aman 72-78; Can St D Cathl 75-88; Chan St D Cathl 83-88; V Felin-foel 78-88; rtd 88. *93 Nun Street, St Davids, Haverfordwest SA62 6NU* Tel (01437) 720359

JONES, David Gornal. b 47. **d** 74 **p** 75. S Africa 75-94; Miss to Seafarers from 95; Port Chapl Walvis Bay Namibia 95-00; Port Chapl Vlissingen (Flushing) *Eur* 00-02; R Ayr *Glas* from 02; R Girvan from 02; R Maybole from 02. *12 Barnes Terrace, Ayr KA7 2DB* Tel (01292) 269141

JONES, David Hugh. b 34. St D Coll Lamp BA56. St Mich Coll Llan 58. **d** 58 **p** 59. C Swansea St Mary and H Trin *S & B* 58-61; Inter-Colleg Sec SCM (Liv) 61-63; Hon Chapl Liv Univ 61-63; C Swansea St Pet *S & B* 63-69; V Llanddewi Ystradenni and Abbey Cwmhir 69-75; R Port Eynon w Rhosili and Llanddewi and Knelston 75-83; V Swansea St Barn 83-92; rtd 92. *16 Lon Ger-y-Coed, Cockett, Swansea SA2 0YH*

✠**JONES, The Rt Revd David Huw.** b 34. Univ of Wales (Ban) BA55 Univ Coll Ox BA58 MA62. St Mich Coll Llan 58. **d** 59 **p** 60 **c** 93. C Aberdare *Llan* 59-61; C Neath w Llantwit 61-65; V Crynant 65-69; V Cwmavon 69-74; Lect Th Univ of Wales (Cardiff) 74-78; Sub-Warden St Mich Coll Llan 74-78; V Prestatyn *St As* 78-82; Dioc Ecum Officer 78-82; Dean Brecon *S & B* 82-93; V Brecon w Battle 82-83; V Brecon St Mary and Battle w Llanddew 83-93; Asst Bp St As 93-96; Bp St D 96-01; rtd 02. *31 The Cathedral Green, Llandaff, Cardiff CF5 2EB*

JONES, David Huw. b 49. Univ of Wales MB, BCh72 Chelsea Coll Lon MSc78 Univ of Wales MD79 FRCR83 FRCP96. EAMTC 95. **d** 98 **p** 99. NSM Trumpington *Ely* 98-02; Perm to Offic from 02. *17 Barrow Road, Cambridge CB2 2AP* Tel (01223) 358458 Fax as telephone E-mail drhuw@btopenworld.com

JONES, David Ian Stewart. b 34. Selw Coll Cam BA57 MA61. Westcott Ho Cam 57. **d** 59 **p** 60. C Oldham *Man* 59-63; V Elton All SS 63-66; Chapl Eton Coll 66-70; Sen Chapl 70-74; Hd Master Bryanston Sch 74-82; P-in-c Bris Ch Ch w St Ewen and All SS *Bris* 82-84; P-in-c Bris St Steph w St Nic and St Leon 82-84; Soc Resp Adv 84-85; Dir Lambeth Endowed Charities 85-94; Hon PV S'wark Cathl *S'wark* 85-94; rtd 94. *4 Kensington Park, Milford-on-Sea, Lymington SO41 0WD*

JONES, David James Hammond. b 45. Lon Univ DipTh69. Kelham Th Coll 65. **d** 70 **p** 70. C Cheadle *Lich* 70-73; Hon C W Bromwich All SS 78-83; Hon C Primrose Hill St Mary w Avenue Road St Paul *Lon* from 91. *9 Elliott Square, London NW3 3SU* Tel (020) 7483 3363 Fax 7483 1133 E-mail david@colourwash.co.uk

JONES, David Michael. b 48. Chich Th Coll 75. **d** 78 **p** 79. C Yeovil *B & W* 78-84; C Barwick 81-84; V Cleeve w Chelvey and Brockley 84-92; V Heigham St Barn w St Bart *Nor* 92-00; V Writtle w Highwood *Chelmsf* from 00. *The Vicarage, 19 Lodge Road, Writtle, Chelmsford CM1 3HY* Tel (01245) 421282 E-mail revmjoneswrittle@aol.com

JONES, David Noel. b 29. St Deiniol's Hawarden 69. **d** 71 **p** 72. C Llandegfan w Beaumaris and Llandysilio *Ban* 71-74; TV Amlwch, Rhosybol, Llandyfrydog etc 74-77; R Llanfair Mathafarn Eithaf w Llanbedrgoch 77-82; V Porthmadog 82-84; V Ynyscynhaearn w Penmorfa and Porthmadog 84-86; R Llanllyfni 86-95; RD Arfon 89-92; rtd 95; Perm to Offic *Ban* from 95. *3 Rhosfryn, Penrhosgarnedd, Bangor LL54 2DL* Tel (01248) 354088

JONES, David Ormond. b 46. Llan Dioc Tr Scheme 90. **d** 94 **p** 95. NSM Resolven w Tonna *Llan* 94-01; C Skewen from 01. *30 Henfaes Road, Tonna, Neath SA11 3EX* Tel (01639) 770930 E-mail ormond.jones@ntlworld.com

JONES, David Raymond (Ray). b 34. Univ of Wales (Lamp) BA54 St Cath Coll Ox BA57 MA61. Wycliffe Hall Ox 58. **d** 58 **p** 59. C Ex St Dav *Ex* 58-60; C Bideford 60-63; Chapl Grenville Coll Bideford 63-66; Chapl RN 66-89; Hon Chapl to The Queen 84-89; Warden and Dir Ch Min of Healing Crowhurst 89-97; rtd

97; Perm to Offic *Chich* from 97. *Mill View, North Fields Lane, Westergate, Chichester PO20 3UH* Tel (01243) 543179

JONES, David Robert. b 37. MBIM83 Dur Univ BA59 QUB MA83. Cranmer Hall Dur DipTh69. **d** 69 **p** 70. C Middleton *Man* 69-72; CF 72-92; V Staindrop Dur from 92. *St Mary's Vicarage, 7 Beechside, Staindrop, Darlington DL2 3PE* Tel (01833) 660237

JONES, David Robert Deverell. b 50. Sarum & Wells Th Coll 72. **d** 75 **p** 78. C Altrincham St Geo *Ches* 75-76; C Clayton *Lich* 77-80; Carriacou 80-81; P-in-c Baschurch *Lich* 81-83; R Baschurch and Weston Lullingfield w Hordley 83-96; RD Ellesmere 85-95; P-in-c Criftins 94-96; P-in-c Dudleston 94-96; P-in-c Jersey St Luke *Win* 96-99; V from 99; P-in-c Jersey St Jas 96-99; V from 99; R Jersey St Mary from 02. *The Vicarage, Longueville Farm, Longueville Road, St Saviour, Jersey JE2 7WG* Tel (01534) 251445

JONES, David Roy. b 47. CQSW76 Hull Univ BA74 Man Univ DipAdEd76 Bradf Univ MA85 Leic Univ Dip Ind Relns 91. Bernard Gilpin Soc Dur 69 N Ord Course 77. **d** 80 **p** 81. C New Bury *Man* 80-83; NSM Ringley w Prestolee 92-97; NSM Belmont 97-01; TV Turton Moorland Min from 01. *The Vicarage, High Street, Bemont, Bolton BL7 8AP* Tel (01204) 811221

JONES, David Sebastian. b 43. St Cath Coll Cam BA67 MA73. Linc Th Coll 66. **d** 68 **p** 69. C Baguley *Man* 68-71; C Bray and Braywood *Ox* 71-73; V S Ascot from 73; Chapl Heatherwood Hosp E Berks 81-94; Chapl Heatherwood and Wexham Park Hosp NHS Trust from 94; RD Bracknell *Ox* from 96. *The Vicarage, Vicarage Gardens, South Ascot, Ascot SL5 9DX* Tel (01344) 622388 Fax as telephone E-mail sebjones@aol.com

JONES, David Victor. b 37. St Jo Coll Dur BA59. Cranmer Hall Dur DipTh60 Bossey Ecum Inst Geneva 61. **d** 62 **p** 63. C Farnworth *Liv* 62-65; CF 65-68; Asst Master Hutton Gr Sch Preston 68-97; rtd 02. *10 Houghton Close, Penwortham, Preston PR1 9HT* Tel (01772) 745306 E-mail d.v.jones@btinternet.com

JONES, David William. b 42. St Mark & St Jo Coll Lon CertEd64 Open Univ BA79. SEITE 97. **d** 00 **p** 01. NSM Coxheath w E Farleigh, Hunton and Linton *Roch* from 00. *13 Woodlands, Coxheath, Maidstone ME17 4EE* Tel (01622) 741474 E-mail david w jones@talk21.com

JONES, Denise Gloria. b 56. Cov Univ BA93. WMMTC 95. **d** 98 **p** 99. C Hobs Moat *Birm* 98-02; C Olton from 02; Chapl S Birm Mental Health NHS Trust from 02. *St Margaret's Vicarage, 5 Old Warwick Road, Solihull B92 7JU* Tel 0121-706 2386 E-mail revddee@aol.com

JONES, Canon Derek John. b 43. Kelham Th Coll 59 CA Tr Coll 63 Sarum & Wells Th Coll 82. **d** 83 **p** 84. CA from 66; C Fleur-de-Lis *Mon* 83-85; V Rhymney 85-93; TR Ebbw Vale 93-99; RD Blaenau Gwent 94-99; V Caldicot 99-01; TR Caldicot from 01; Can St Woolos Cathl from 96; RD Netherwent from 00. *The Vicarage, 39 Church Road, Caldicot NP26 4HF* Tel (01291) 420221 Fax as telephone

JONES, Miss Diana. b 46. Qu Coll Birm 89. **d** 91 **p** 94. Par Dn Harnham *Sarum* 91-94; C 94-95; C Tidworth, Ludgershall and Faberstown 95-00; P-in-c Hazelbury Bryan and the Hillside Par from 00. *The Rectory, Hazelbury Bryan, Sturminster Newton DT10 2ED* Tel (01258) 818287

JONES, Canon Dick Heath Remi. b 32. Jes Coll Cam BA56. Linc Th Coll 56. **d** 58 **p** 59. C Ipswich St Thos *St E* 58-61; C Putney St Mary *S'wark* 61-65; P-in-c Dawley Parva *Lich* 65-75; P-in-c Lawley 65-75; RD Wrockwardine 70-72; P-in-c Malins Lee 72-75; RD Telford 72-80; P-in-c Stirchley 74-75; TR Cen Telford 75-80; Preb Lich Cathl 76-80; TR Bournemouth St Pet w St Swithun, H Trin etc *Win* 80-96; RD Bournemouth 90-95; Hon Can Win Cathl 91-96; rtd 96; Perm to Offic *Sarum* from 96. *Maltings, Church Street, Fontmell Magna, Shaftesbury SP7 0NY* Tel (01747) 812071 E-mail dick.jones@talk21.com

JONES, Donald. b 50. BA BSc. St Jo Coll Nottm 79. **d** 82 **p** 83. C Hutton *Chelmsf* 82-86; C E Ham w Upton Park St Alb 86-88; TV 88-96; V Nuneaton St Nic *Cov* from 96; RD Nuneaton from 01. *61 Ambleside Way, Nuneaton CV11 6AU* Tel (024) 7634 6900

JONES, Douglas. *See* JONES, John Douglas Mathias

JONES, Canon Douglas Rawlinson. b 19. St Edm Hall Ox BA41 MA45. Lambeth DD Wycliffe Hall Ox 41. **d** 42 **p** 43. C Windmill Hill *Bris* 42-45; Lect Wycliffe Hall Ox 45-50; Chapl Wadh Coll Ox 45-50; Lect Th Dur Univ 51-64; Prof Div 64-85; Can Res Dur Cathl *Dur* 64-85; rtd 85; Lic to Offic *Edin* from 85. *Whitefriars, King's Road, Longniddry EH32 0NN* Tel (01875) 52149

JONES, Dwyfor. *See* JONES, Canon Robert Dwyfor

JONES, Edgar John. b 32. Univ of Wales (Lamp) BA53 Univ of Wales (Ban) PGCE74. St Mich Coll Llan 53. **d** 55 **p** 56. C Holyhead w Rhoscolyn w Llanfair-yn-Neubwll *Ban* 55-61; R Bodedern and Llechcynfarwy 61-70; V Bodedern w Llechgynfarwy and Llechylched etc 70-73; Perm to Offic 73-96; from 98; P-in-c Llangefni w Tregaean and Llangristiolus etc 96-98; rtd 98. *5 Glan Llyn, Llanfachraeth, Holyhead LL65 4UW* Tel (01407) 742322

JONES, Edward. b 36. Dur Univ BA60. Ely Th Coll 60. **d** 62 **p** 63. C S Shields St Hilda w St Thos *Dur* 62-65; C Cleadon Park 65-68;

V Hebburn St Cuth 68-79; R Winlaton 79-00; rtd 00; Perm to Offic *Dur* from 00; *Newc* from 01. *10 Melkridge Gardens, Benton, Newcastle upon Tyne NE7 7GQ* Tel 0191-266 4388

JONES, Edward Harries. b 16. St D Coll Lamp BA38 Ely Th Coll 38. **d** 39 **p** 40. C Rhyl *St As* 39-52; V Ffynnongroyw 52-81; rtd 81. *16 Coed Pella Road, Colwyn Bay LL29 7BA* Tel (01492) 532997

JONES, Edward Wynne. b 45. OBE93. Univ of Wales (Abth) LLB71. St Mich Coll Llan 72. **d** 74 **p** 75. C Llandegfan w Beaumaris and Llanfaes *Ban* 74-76; V Aberffraw and Llangwyfan w Llangadwaladr 76-78; Chapl RN 78-99; rtd 99. *Glanrafon Bach, Mynydd Llandegai, Bangor LL57 4LQ* Tel 07850-143553 (mobile)

JONES, Miss Elaine Edith. b 58. N Glos Tech Coll HND80. St Jo Coll Nottm BA99. **d** 99 **p** 00. C Gainsborough and Morton *Linc* 99-02; C Netherton *Carl* from 02; Lay Tr Officer from 02. *The Vicarage, Church Road, Flimby, Maryport CA15 8TJ* Tel (01900) 817991 E-mail elainejones@gainsborough.fsnet.co.uk

JONES, Mrs Elaine Joan. b 50. Oak Hill Th Coll. **d** 87 **p** 94. Par Dn Tottenham H Trin *Lon* 87-92; Par Dn Clay Hill St Jo and St Luke 92-94; C St Botolph Aldgate w H Trin Minories 94-96; V Hackney Wick St Mary of Eton w St Aug from 96; AD Hackney from 99. *St Mary's House, Eastway, London E9 5JA* Tel (020) 8986 8159

JONES, Mrs Elizabeth Mary. b 48. QUB BA69. N Ord Course 88. **d** 91 **p** 94. Par Dn Kippax w Allerton Bywater *Ripon* 91-94; C 94-95; R Swillington 95-00; TV Wordsley *Worc* 00-02; rtd 02. *5 Claredge House, 8 Princes Road, Clevedon BS21 7SZ* Tel (01275) 872903

JONES, Mrs Elizabeth Somerset. b 49. Nottm Univ Dip Past Counselling 93 UKRC Reg Ind Cllr 98 BAC Acc98. St Jo Coll Nottm CertCS84. **d** 88 **p** 94. NSM Duns *Edin* from 88; NSM Selkirk 89-90; Dioc Dir of Ords from 95. *Care for Mission, Elphinstone Wing, Carberry, Musselburgh EH21 8PW* Tel 0131-653 6767 or 440 2602 Fax 653 3646
E-mail 100633.2065@compuserve.com

JONES, Emile Conrad Modupe Kojo. b 50. Univ of Sierra Leone BA74 MA BD. Trin Coll Bris 74. **d** 77 **p** 78. Sierra Leone 77-85; C Kissy St Patr 77-78; Freetown H Trin 78-81; Asst Chapl and Lect OT Studies Fourah Bay Coll 81-85; Chapl Heidelberg *Eur* 86-97; Miss Partner CMS from 97; C Holloway St Mary Magd *Lon* from 97. *59 Bride Street, London N7 8RN* Tel (020) 7607 2984

JONES, Emmanuel Thomas (Tom). b 19. S Dios Minl Tr Scheme 79. **d** 81 **p** 82. NSM Fareham H Trin *Portsm* 81-89; rtd 89; Perm to Offic *Portsm* from 89. *24 Maylings Farm Road, Fareham PO16 7QU* Tel (01329) 310137

JONES, Eric Alexander. b 19. TCD BA40 MA45 BD45. **d** 42 **p** 43. C Belfast St Matt *Conn* 42-45 and 48-51; C Belfast St Jas 45-47; C Belfast St Nic 47-48; I Larne and Inver 51-59; I Jordanstown 59-68; I Carnmoney 68-76; V Hensall *Sheff* 76-84; RD Snaith and Hatfield 79-84; rtd 84. *222 Cowper Downs, Rathmines, Dublin 6, Irish Republic* Tel (00353) (1) 498 3233

JONES, Canon Eric Vernon. b 26. Ely Th Coll 57. **d** 59 **p** 60. C S Shore H Trin *Blackb* 59-63; V Preston St Matt 64-77; R Chorley St Laur 77-91; Hon Can Blackb Cathl 81-91; rtd 91; Perm to Offic *Blackb* from 91. *8 Glamis Drive, Chorley PR7 1LX* Tel (01257) 230660

JONES, Canon Eric Wilfred. b 22. Linc Coll Ox BA48 MA53. Cuddesdon Coll 48. **d** 50 **p** 51. C E Dulwich St Jo *S'wark* 50-56; V Cov St Pet *Cov* 56-65; Fiji 65-68; Solomon Is 69-74; V Binley *Cov* 74-82; Hon Can Cov Cathl 80-87; RD Cov E 80-82; V Hatton w Haseley and Rowington w Lowsonford 82-87; P-in-c Honiley 85-87; R Hatton w Haseley, Rowington w Lowsonford etc 87; rtd 87; Perm to Offic *Bradf* from 87. *31 Hall Croft, Skipton BD23 1PG* Tel (01756) 793302

JONES, Ernest Edward Stephen. b 39. Lon Univ BD76. St D Coll Lamp DipTh66. **d** 66 **p** 67. C N Meols *Liv* 66-69; C Kirkby 69-71; V Farnworth All SS *Man* 71-75; P-in-c Bempton *York* 75-78; R Rufford *Blackb* 78-84; V Cropredy w Gt Bourton and Wardington *Ox* 84-90; R York St Clem w St Mary Bishophill Senior *York* 90-98; P-in-c York All SS N Street 90-98; V Northampton St Benedict *Pet* from 98. *The Vicarage, 16 Sentinel Road, Northampton NN4 9UF* Tel (01604) 768624 Fax 660509 E-mail stephen@stbennys.fsnet.co.uk

JONES, Evan Hopkins. b 38. St Mich Coll Llan 65. **d** 67 **p** 68. C Churston Ferrers w Goodrington *Ex* 67-70; C Tavistock and Gulworthy 70-73; R Ashprington 73-78; V Cornworthy 73-78; R S Hackney St Jo w Ch Ch *Lon* 78-92; AD Hackney 84-89; V Islington St Jas w St Pet from 92. *St James's Vicarage, 1 Arlington Square, London N1 7DS* Tel (020) 7226 4108

JONES, Evan Merfyn. b 40. **d** 97 **p** 98. NSM Ystradyfodwg *Llan* from 97. *71 Tyntyla Road, Llwynypia, Tonypandy CF40 2SR* Tel (01443) 436763

JONES, Evan Trefor. b 32. Univ of Wales (Ban) BA54 Cert Hosp Chapl 82. Coll of Resurr Mirfield 54. **d** 56 **p** 57. C Ban St Mary *Ban* 56-62; V Llandinorwig 62-71; TV Llanbeblig w Caernarfon and Betws Garmon etc 71-84; Ed dioc magazine *The Link* 79-89; R Llanfairfechan w Aber 84-97; Can Ban Cathl 95-97; rtd 97.

Flat 19, Marlborough Place, Vaughan Street, Llandudno LL30 1AE Tel (01492) 878411

JONES, Frederick. b 33. FRHistS76 Man Univ BA54 Selw Coll Cam PhD72 LSE MSc82. St Steph Ho Ox 56. **d** 58 **p** 59. C Belfield *Man* 58-59; C Westmr St Matt *Lon* 59-60; Hon C Cambridge St Mary Less *Ely* 71-72; Perm to Offic *Win* 72-74; Lic to Offic 74-89. *Casa Renate, Carrer del Pinsa 86, Port de Pollenca, Mallorca, Spain*

JONES, Frederick John. b 32. Wells Th Coll 57. **d** 60 **p** 61. C Tottington *Man* 60-63; C Horwich H Trin 63-65; R Heaton Norris All SS 65-76; R Heaton Norris Ch w All SS 76-77; V Castleton Moor 77-88; C Greenfield 88-93; rtd 93. *69 Manchester Road, Greenfield, Oldham OL3 7SE* Tel (01457) 873954

JONES, Frederick Morgan. b 19. Univ of Wales (Lamp) BA40 BD49. St Mich Coll Llan 42. **d** 42 **p** 43. C Llanelli St Paul *St D* 42-50; Org Sec (Wales) Ind Chr Fellowship 50-53; C-in-c Llwynhendy CD *St D* 52-56; C Llanelli 56-57; V Penrhyncoch and Elerch 57-61; R Llanbedrog and Penrhos *Ban* 61-74; R Llanbedrog w Llannor w Llanfihangel etc 74-84; C Llangefni w Tregaean and Llangristiolus etc 84-85; rtd 85; Perm to Offic *Ban* from 85. *15 Ponc-y-Fron, Llangefni LL77 7NY* Tel (01248) 722850

JONES, Gareth. b 35. St Aid Birkenhead 58. **d** 61 **p** 62. C Doncaster Ch Ch *Sheff* 61-65; Min Can Ripon Cathl *Ripon* 65-68; Chapl RAF 68-85; St Jo Cathl Hong Kong 85-89; R Spofforth w Kirk Deighton *Ripon* 89-00; rtd 00; Perm to Offic *Ripon* from 00; *Dur* from 02. *36 Whitcliffe Lane, Ripon HG4 2JL* Tel (01765) 601745

JONES, Gareth Lewis. b 42. K Coll Lon BD64 AKC64. **d** 65 **p** 66. C Risca *Mon* 65-70; Perm to Offic *Win* 70-74; *Newc* 74-75; *Sarum* 75; C Pontesbury I and II *Heref* 75-77; P-in-c Presteigne w Discoed 77-79; TV Hemel Hempstead *St Alb* 79-86; R Longden and Annscroft w Pulverbatch *Heref* 86-93; TV Leominster from 93. *118 Buckfield Road, Leominster HR6 8SQ* Tel (01568) 612124

JONES, Prof Gareth Vaughan. b 38. Univ of Wales BA61 Selw Coll Cam BA63 MA67 Yale Univ STM69 TCD BD70 Lon Univ PhD75. Episc Sem Austin Texas Hon DD90 Westcott Ho Cam 62. **d** 65 **p** 66. C Holyhead w Rhoscolyn *Ban* 65-68; USA 68-70; P-in-c Merton *Ox* 70-72; Tutor Ripon Hall Ox 72; Sen Tutor 73-75; Lect Ex Coll Ox 73-77; Tutor and Lib Ripon Coll Cuddesdon 75-77; Lect Th Univ of Wales (Ban) 77-89; Sen Lect 89-95; Reader and Hd of Sch from 95; Prof from 98; Sub-Dean Faculty of Th 80-89; Dean 89-92; Chan Ban Cathl *Ban* from 90; Select Preachor Ox Univ 89. *Craig-lwyd, Lon Ganol, Llandegfan, Menai Bridge LL59 5YA* Tel (01248) 712786

JONES, Glyn Evan. b 44. Lon Coll of Div ALCD67 LTh. **d** 67 **p** 68. C G Horton *Bradf* 67-70; SAMS 71-78; Argentina 71-78; V Idle H Trin *Bradf* 78-84; V Hyson Green *S'well* 84-87; V Nottingham St Steph 84-87; V Hyson Green St Paul w St Steph 87-89; V Hyson Green 89-91; V Basford w Hyson Green 91-92; V Worksop St Jo 92-99; RD Worksop 93-99; V Nottingham St Sav from 99. *St Saviour's Vicarage, Arkwright Walk, The Meadows, Nottingham NG2 2JU* Tel and fax 0115-986 4046 Mobile 07885-816697 E-mail chezjones@ntlworld.com

JONES, Preb Glyn Owen. b 16. St D Coll Lamp BA37 St Mich Coll Llan 38. **d** 39 **p** 40. C Wrexham *St As* 39-47; CF (EC) 44-47; C Connah's Quay *St As* 47-49; V Whixall *Lich* 49-53; V Hengoed 53-75; Preb Lich Cathl 73-81; V Baschurch 75-81; rtd 81; Perm to Offic *Lich* from 81; Min Pradoe 90-02. *6 Larkhill Road, Park Hall, Oswestry SY11 4AW* Tel (01691) 662739

JONES, Canon Glyndwr. b 35. St Mich Coll Llan DipTh62. **d** 62 **p** 63. C Clydach *S & B* 62-64; C Llangyfelach 64-67; C Sketty 67-70; V Bryngwyn and Newchurch and Llanbedr etc 70-72; Miss to Seafarers 72-00; Swansea 72-76; Port of Lon 76-81; Aux Min Sec 81-85; Asst Gen Sec 85-90; Sec Gen 90-00; V St Mich Paternoster Royal *Lon* 91-00; rtd 01; Hon Can Kobe Japan from 88; Chapl to The Queen from 90; Perm to Offic *Chelmsf* from 91; *Lon* from 01. *5 The Close, Grays RM16 2XU*

JONES, Glynn. b 56. NEOC 91. **d** 94 **p** 95. NSM Glendale Gp *Newc* 94-97; Sen Chapl HM Pris Leeds 97-99; Chapl HM Pris *Dur* 99-00; Chapl HM YOI Wetherby from 00. *HM Young Offender Institution, York Road, Wetherby LS22 5ED* Tel (01937) 585141

JONES, Godfrey Caine. b 36. Dur Univ BA59 Lon Univ CertEd60 Birm Univ MEd71. St Deiniol's Hawarden 76. **d** 78 **p** 79. Hd Humanities Denbigh High Sch 75-81; NSM Ruthin w Llanrhydd *St As* 78-81; C 83-84; Sen Lect Matlock Coll 81-83; P-in-c Llanfwrog and Clocaenog and Gyffylliog 84-85; R 85-93; V Ruabon 93-02; RD Llangollen 93-02; rtd 02; Min Pradoe *Lich* from 02. *Idoma, Penylan, Ruabon, Wrexham LL14 6HP* Tel (01978) 812102 E-mail dorothy.e.jones@btopenworld.com

JONES, Gordon Howlett. b 26. G&C Coll Cam BA47 MA51. Westcott Ho Cam 49. **d** 51 **p** 52. C Milton *Win* 51-54; Study Sec SCM 54-58; C St Helen Bishopsgate w St Martin Outwich *Lon* 54-58; V Claremont H Angels *Man* 58-63; R Northenden 63-79; P-in-c Hilmarton and Highway *Sarum* 79-83; V Bremhill w Foxham and Hilmarton 83-92; RD Calne 84-88; rtd 92; Perm to Offic *Sarum* from 92. *63 New Park Street, Devizes SN11 8SB* Tel (01380) 720950

JONES, Gordon Michael Campbell. b 33. St D Coll Lamp BA56 St Jo Coll Dur 56. **d** 58 **p** 59. C Maindee *Mon* 58-60; C Penhow, St Brides Netherwent w Llandavenny etc 60-63; V Magor w Redwick 63-68; Australia 68-71; R Southern Cross 68-70; C Floreat Park 70-71; R Kirkby Thore w Temple Sowerby *Carl* 72-73; R Kirkby Thore w Temple Sowerby and Newbiggin 73-79; P-in-c Accrington St Jas *Blackb* 79-81; P-in-c Accrington St Andr 81-83; V Ahmedi St Paul Kuwait 83-91; R Swardeston w E Carleton, Intwood, Keswick etc *Nor* 91-96; Miss to Seafarers from 96; Chapl Limassol St Barn from 96. *St Barnabas' Church, PO Box 1494, 3506 Limassol, Cyprus* Tel (00357) (5) 362713 Fax 747211

JONES, Graham Frederick. b 37. Leeds Univ BA60 GradIPM63. ALCD66. **d** 66 **p** 67. C Chesterfield H Trin *Derby* 66-70; C Leeds St Geo *Ripon* 70-73; P-in-c Newcastle St Geo *Lich* 73-83; New Zealand 83-87; P-in-c Westcote w Icomb and Bledington *Glouc* 89-94; rtd 94. *7 Keynsham Bank, Cheltenham GL52 6ER* Tel (01242) 238680

JONES, Griffith Bernard. b 20. Univ of Wales (Lamp) BA42. St Mich Coll Llan 42. **d** 44 **p** 45. C Ynyshir *Llan* 44-51; C Handsworth St Jas *Birm* 51-56; V Smethwick St Matt 56-60; V Swalcliffe w E Shutford *Ox* 60-64; Perm to Offic *Pet* 64-82; Perm to Offic *St Alb* 74-82; R Llanfallteg w Clunderwen and Castell Dwyran etc *St D* 82-88; rtd 88. *17 Heol Ceirios, Llandybie, Ammanford SA18 2SR* Tel (01269) 851803

JONES, Griffith Trevor. b 56. BSc MPS Univ of Wales BD. **d** 87 **p** 88. C Llandrygarn w Bodwrog and Heneglwys etc *Ban* 87-89; R Llangefni w Tregaean and Llangristiolus etc 89-91; TV Bangor 91-94; Chapl Ysbyty Gwynedd 91-94; Lic to Offic *Ban* 94-00. *8 Carreg-y-Gad, Llanfairpwllgwyngyll LL61 5QF* Tel (01248) 713094

JONES, Canon Griffith Walter Hywyn. b 24. St Mich Coll Llan 47. **d** 50 **p** 51. C Llanaber *Ban* 50-52; Chapl RAF 52-67; V Betws y Coed *Ban* 67-69; V Betws y Coed and Capel Curig 70-78; R Holyhead w Rhoscolyn w Llanfair-yn-Neubwll 78-87; Can and Preb Ban Cathl 78-90; RD Llifon and Talybolion 80-85; Spiritual Dir Cursillo Cymru 81-90; V Ynyscynhaearn w Penmorfa and Porthmadog *Ban* 87-90; rtd 90; Lic to Offic *Ban* 90-96; *St As* from 90. *The Rectory, 4 Sundorne, Overton, Wrexham LL13 0EB* Tel (01978) 710229

JONES, Canon Griffith William. b 31. St D Coll Lamp BA53 LTh55. **d** 55 **p** 56. C Llanycil w Bala and Frongoch *St As* 55-58; V Llandrillo 58-66; V Llandrillo and Llandderfel 66-96; RD Penllyn 83-96; Can Cursal St As Cathl from 87; rtd 96. *45 Yr Hafan, Bala LL23 7AU* Tel (01678) 520217

JONES, Gwyn Harris. b 19. Univ of Wales (Lamp) BA42. K Coll Lon 42. **d** 43 **p** 44. C Pembroke Dock *St D* 43-44; C Letterston 44-46; Uganda 46-53; C Llanelli *St D* 53-54; V Wolverhampton St Paul *Lich* 54-56; V Burton St Chad 56-79; V Shrewsbury St Geo 79-87; rtd 87; Perm to Offic *Lich* from 87. *18 Kenwood Gardens, Shrewsbury SY3 8AQ* Tel (01743) 351057

JONES, Gwynfryn Lloyd. b 35. Univ of Wales (Lamp) BA59. St Mich Coll Llan 59. **d** 61 **p** 62. C Rhyl w St Ann *St As* 61-64; C Prestatyn 64-67; V Whitford 67-75; V Llay 75-83; V Northop 83-98; rtd 98. *Tryfan, 41 Snowdon Avenue, Bryn-y-Baal, Mold CH7 6SZ*

JONES, Gwynn Rees. b 32. St D Coll Lamp BA55. **d** 57 **p** 58. C Llangystennin *St As* 57-59; C Llanrhos 59-64; R Cefn 64-68; R Llanfyllin 68-80; V Bistre 80-89; R Flint 89-97; rtd 97. *Tan y Coed, 68 Bryn Aber, Bryn Twr, Abergele LL22 8DD* Tel (01745) 825188

JONES, Canon Harold Desmond. b 22. Sarum Th Coll 52. **d** 55 **p** 56. C Bushey Heath *St Alb* 55-58; C Stevenage 58-64; V Thurleigh 64-80; V Milton Ernest 64-80; RD Sharnbrook 70-81; Hon Can St Alb 78-90; P-in-c Knotting w Souldrop 80-82; V Sharnbrook 80-82; R Sharnbrook and Knotting w Souldrop 82-90; P-in-c Felmersham 82-87; RD Sharnbrook 86-90; rtd 90; Perm to Offic *St Alb* from 90. *24 Towns End Road, Sharnbrook, Bedford MK44 1HY* Tel (01234) 782524

JONES, Harold Philip. b 49. Leeds Univ BA72 St Jo Coll Dur BA84. Cranmer Hall Dur 82. **d** 85 **p** 86. C Scartho *Linc* 85-88; V Dodworth *Wakef* 88-91; C Penistone and Thurlstone 91-95; C Scunthorpe All SS *Linc* 95-96; TV Brumby 96-02; Chapl S Derbyshire Acute Hosps NHS Trust from 02. *Derby City General Hospital, Uttoxeter Road, Derby DE22 3NE* Tel (01332) 340131 Fax 290559 E-mail harold.jones@sdah-tr.trent.nhs.uk

JONES, Haydn Llewellyn. b 42. Edin Th Coll 63. **d** 65 **p** 66. C Towcester w Easton Neston *Pet* 65-68; C Northampton St Matt 68-72; CF 72-97; Perm to Offic *Roch* 97-98; *Ex* from 98; rtd 99. *11 Lady Park Road, Livermead, Torquay TQ2 6UA* Tel (01803) 690483

JONES, Helen Alison. b 59. St Andr Univ BSc81. EMMTC 93. **d** 96 **p** 97. C Limber Magna w Brocklesby *Linc* 96-97; C Brocklesby Park 97-98. *Address temp unknown*

JONES, Hilary Christine. b 55. Ch Ch Coll Cant CertEd76 Lon Univ BEd77. SEITE. **d** 99 **p** 00. C Kennington *Cant* 99-02; R Cheriton from 02. *St Martin's Rectory, Horn Street, Folkestone CT20 3JJ* Tel (01303) 238509 E-mail hilaryjones@lycos.co.uk

JONES, Howard. *See* JONES, John Howard
JONES, Hugh Owen. b 14. Coates Hall Edin 45. **d** 47 **p** 48. C Dundee St Mary Magd *Bre* 47-50; P-in-c Airdrie *Glas* 50-52; CF 52-58; R Hope w Shelve *Heref* 58-63; V Bodenham w Hope-under-Dinmore 63-78; R Bodenham w Hope-under-Dinmore, Felton etc 78-80; rtd 80; Perm to Offic *Ban* 96-99. *32 Dulverton Hall, Esplanade, Scarborough YO11 2AR*

JONES, Hughie. *See* JONES, The Ven Thomas Hughie
JONES, Humphrey Ingham. b 20. St Pet Coll Ox BA42 MA46. Cuddesdon Coll 42. **d** 43 **p** 44. C High Elswick St Phil *Newc* 43-47; C Haltwhistle 47-49; C Cullercoats St Geo 49-50; C-in-c Newc St Fran High Heaton CD 50-55; V Newc St Fran 55-61; V Monkseaton St Mary 61-67; Tutor and Registrar Richmond Fellowship 68-85; Hon C Bermondsey St Mary w St Olave, St Jo etc *S'wark* 73-78; Perm to Offic *Lon* 79-96; rtd 85. *1 Emden House, Barton Lane, Headington, Oxford OX3 9JU* Tel (01865) 308180

JONES, Huw. *See* JONES, The Rt Revd David Huw
JONES, Hywyn. *See* JONES, Canon Griffith Walter Hywyn
JONES, Ian. b 63. Trin Coll Carmarthen BEd88. St Mich Coll Llan 95. **d** 97 **p** 98. NSM Tycoch *S & B* 97-01; NSM Swansea St Nic from 01. *15 Lon Masarn, Sketty, Swansea SA2 9EL* Tel (01792) 429511 E-mail ianjones99@yahoo.com

JONES, Ian Andrew. b 65. Lanc Univ BA87. St Mich Coll Llan DPS90. **d** 90 **p** 91. C Caerphilly *Llan* 90-96; Chapl RAF from 96. *Chaplaincy Services (RAF), HQ, Personnel and Training Command, RAF Innsworth, Gloucester GL3 1EZ* Tel (01452) 712612 ext 5164 Fax 510828

JONES, Idris. b 31. **d** 88 **p** 94. NSM Llanfihangel Ysgeifiog and Llanffinan etc *Ban* 88-97; NSM Llangefni w Tregaean and Llangristiolus etc 98-01; NSM Llanfihangel Ysgeifiog w Llangristiolus etc 01-02. *Rhoslyn, Gaerwen LL60 6HQ* Tel (01248) 421797

✠**JONES, The Rt Revd Idris.** b 43. Univ of Wales (Lamp) BA64 Edin Univ LTh67. Edin Th Coll 64 NY Th Sem DMin86. **d** 67 **p** 68 **c** 98. C Stafford St Mary *Lich* 67-70; Prec St Paul's Cathl Dundee *Bre* 70-73; P-in-c Gosforth All SS *Newc* 73-80; R Montrose *Bre* 80-89; R Inverbervie 80-89; Can St Paul's Cathl Dundee 84-92; Chapl Angl Students Dundee Univ 89-92; P-in-c Invergowrie 89-92; TR S Ayrshire TM 92-98; Bp Glas from 98. *Diocesan Centre, 5 St Vincent Place, Glasgow G1 2DH* Tel 0141-221 6911 Fax 221 6490 E-mail bishop@glasgow.anglican.org

JONES, Ivor Wyn. b 56. Trin Coll Bris DipHE94. **d** 94 **p** 95. C Gabalfa *Llan* 94-97; TV Daventry, Ashby St Ledgers, Braunston etc *Pet* 97-01; P-in-c Dawley St Jerome *Lon* from 01; C-in-c Harlington Ch Ch CD from 03. *St Jerome's Lodge, 42 Corwell Lane, Uxbridge UB8 3DE* Tel (020) 8573 1895 E-mail wynjones@jireh.co.uk

✠**JONES, The Rt Revd James Stuart.** b 48. Ex Univ BA70 PGCE71 Hull Univ Hon DD99 Lincs & Humberside Univ Hon DLitt01. Wycliffe Hall Ox 81. **d** 82 **p** 83 **c** 94. C Clifton Ch Ch w Em *Bris* 82-90; V S Croydon Em *S'wark* 90-94; Suff Bp Hull *York* 94-98; Bp Liv from 98. *Bishop's Lodge, Woolton Park, Liverpool L25 6DT* Tel 0151-421 0831 Fax 428 3055 E-mail bishopslodge@liverpool.anglican.org

JONES, Canon Jaqueline Dorian. b 58. K Coll Lon BD80 AKC80 MTh81. Westcott Ho Cam 84. **dss** 86 **d** 87 **p** 94. Epsom St Martin *Guildf* 86-87; C 87-91; Chapl Chelmsf Cathl *Chelmsf* 91-97; V Bridgemary *Portsm* 97-03; Can Res S'well Minster *S'well* from 03. *2 Vicars Court, Southwell NG25 0HP* Tel (01636) 813188

JONES, Jeffrey Lloyd. b 66. Univ of Wales (Abth) BA87 PGCE90. Wycliffe Hall Ox DipMin95. **d** 97 **p** 98. C Lampeter Pont Steffan w Silian *St D* 97; C Carmarthen St Dav 97-00; TV Llantwit Major *Llan* from 00. *The Vicarage, Trepit Road, Wick, Cowbridge CF71 7QL* Tel (01656) 890471

JONES, Jennifer Margaret. b 49. Lon Univ CertEd. Cranmer Hall Dur 87. **d** 89 **p** 94. C Musselburgh *Edin* 89-93; Dn-in-c 93-94; P-in-c 94-95; R 95-02; C Prestonpans 89-93; Dn-in-c 93-94; P-in-c 94-95; R 95-02. *Address temp unknown* E-mail jennifer.jones@lineone.net

JONES, John Bernard. b 49. Qu Coll Birm 86. **d** 88 **p** 89. C Mold *St As* 88-91; P-in-c Treuddyn and Nercwys and Eryrys 91-92; V Treuddyn w Nercwys from 92; RD Mold 95-00. *The Vicarage, Treuddyn, Mold CH7 4LN* Tel (01352) 770919 E-mail jbj.rd@dial.pipex.com

JONES, John David Emrys. b 36. Univ of Wales (Abth). Trin Coll Carmarthen. **d** 96 **p** 97. NSM Llanfihangel Ystrad and Cilcennin w Trefilan etc *St D* 96-97; P-in-c Llangeitho and Blaenpennal w Betws Leucu etc from 97. *Dolfor, Ciliau Aeron, Lampeter SA48 8DE* Tel (01570) 470569

JONES, John Douglas Mathias. b 24. Clare Coll Cam BA49 MA51. Chich Th Coll 49. **d** 51 **p** 52. C Battersea Park All SS *S'wark* 51-54; C Caversham *Ox* 54-59; Chapl RAF 59-66; C Harrogate St Wilfrid *Ripon* 66-67; V Cross Stone *Wakef* 67-76; V Hepworth 76-89; Chapl Storthes Hall Hosp Wakef 81-89; rtd 89; Perm to Offic *Wakef* from 89. *59 Luke Lane, Holmfirth, Huddersfield HD7 2SZ* Tel (01484) 681036

JONES, Canon John Francis Williams. b 26. St D Coll Lamp 48. **d** 52 **p** 53. C Glanadda *Ban* 52-55; C Porthmadog 55-57; V

Llandrygarn w Bodwrog 57-62; V Llandrygarn and Bodwrog w Heneglwys 62-74; V Llandrygarn w Bodwrog and Heneglwys etc 74-96; RD Menai and Malltraeth 75-97; Hon Can Ban Cathl 81-83; Can from 83; Preb from 90; rtd 96. *The Vicarage, Tynlon, Holyhead LL65 3AZ* Tel (01407) 720234

JONES, John Hellyer. b 20. Birm Univ LDS43. Westcott Ho Cam 65. **d** 67 **p** 68. C Haddenham *Ely* 67-70; P-in-c Lolworth 70-79 and 81-85; P-in-c Conington 75-79 and 81-85; R Houghton w Wyton 79; rtd 85; Perm to Offic *Ely* 85-02. *13 High Street, Haddenham, Ely CB6 3XA* Tel (01353) 740530

JONES, John Howard. b 48. New Coll Ox BA69 MA73 K Coll Cam CertEd70. Sarum & Wells Th Coll 76. **d** 77 **p** 78. C Salisbury St Mark *Sarum* 77-78; C Morriston *S & B* 78-80; Dir of Ords 80-83; V Gowerton 80-83; V Swansea St Jas 85-89; Chapl Alleyn's Sch Dulwich from 89; Hon C Dulwich St Barn *S'wark* from 90. *53 Gilkes Crescent, London SE21 7BP* Tel (020) 8299 4826

JONES, John Morgan. b 17. Univ of Wales BA39. Ely Th Coll 39. **d** 40 **p** 41. C Chirk *St As* 40-43; C Colwyn Bay 43-50; C Brymbo 46-50; R Pontfadog 50-59; C Rawmarsh *Sheff* 59-60; R Adwick-le-Street 60-63; Asst Master Bentley Sch 63-65; Hatfield Sch 66-80; rtd 82; Perm to Offic *St As* from 82. *3 Heol Awel, Abergele LL22 7UQ* Tel (01745) 823515

JONES, John Samuel. b 11. Univ of Wales BA36. St D Coll Lamp 36. **d** 38 **p** 40. C Llawr-y-Betws *St As* 38-43; P-in-c Llanarmon Dyffryn Ceiriog 43-57; V Pont Robert and Pont Dolanog 57-66; C Hoylake *Ches* 66-69; R Llwydiarth and Llanfihangel yng Nghwynfa *St As* 69-72; V Llanfair Dyffryn Clwyd 72-79; rtd 79. *51 Snowden Drive, Ty Gwyn, Wrexham LL11 2YD* Tel (01978) 364914

JONES, The Ven John Samuel. b 16. Univ of Wales (Lamp) BA37 BD42. St Mich Coll Llan 38. **d** 39 **p** 40. C Llandysul *St D* 39-42; C Llandybie 42-49; V Llanllwni 49-86; RD Lampeter 64-68; RD Lampeter and Ultra-Aeron 68-82; Can St D Cathl 72-82; Chan 78-82; Adn Cardigan 82-86; rtd 86. *Brynheulwen, Bryn Road, Lampeter SA48 7EE* Tel (01570) 423278

JONES, John Trevor. b 14. St D Coll Lamp BA42. **d** 43 **p** 44. C Rhosddu *St As* 43-52; C Timperley *Ches* 52-53; V Barnton 53-60; V Poulton 60-81; rtd 81; Perm to Offic *Ches* from 82. *21 Sandy Lane, Wallasey CH45 3JY* Tel 0151-639 4794

JONES, Joyce Rosemary. b 54. Newnham Coll Cam BA76 MA82 Coll of Ripon & York St Jo MA97 Solicitor 79. N Ord Course 94. **d** 97 **p** 98. C Pontefract All SS *Wakef* 97-00; NSM Cumberworth, Denby and Denby Dale 00-01; Dioc Voc Adv 00-01; Asst Chapl Kirkwood Hospice Huddersfield 00-01; P-in-c Shelley and Shepley *Wakef* from 01. *Oakfield, 206 Barnsley Road, Denby Dale, Huddersfield HD8 8TS* Tel (01484) 862350 Fax as telephone E-mail joycerjones@aol.com

JONES, Judith Frances. See HUBBARD-JONES, Ms Judith Frances

JONES, Kathryn Mary. See BUCK, Mrs Kathryn Mary

JONES (née SANDELLS-REES), Ms Kathy Louise. b 68. Abth Coll of FE DipBBSS87 Univ of Wales (Cardiff) DipTh90 Univ of Wales (Ban) BTh96 Univ Coll Ches Dip Counselling 99. Qu Coll Birm DipTh92. **d** 92 **p** 97. C Holyhead w Rhoscolyn w Llanfair-yn-Neubwll *Ban* 92-94; C Bangor 94-95; Chapl Gwynedd Hosp Ban 94-99; P-in-c Bangor *Ban* 95-99; P-in-c Betws-y-Coed and Capel Curig w Penmachno etc from 99. *The Vicarage, Betws-y-Coed LL24 0AD* Tel (01690) 710313 Fax as telephone

JONES, Katie. **d** 99 **p** 00. NSM Sutton Courtenay w Appleford *Ox* from 99. *The Tutor's House, Radley College, Chestnut Avenue, Abingdon OX14 2HS* Tel (01235) 543003 E-mail kaj@radley.org.uk

JONES, The Very Revd Keith Brynmor. b 44. Selw Coll Cam BA65 MA69. Cuddesdon Coll 67. **d** 69 **p** 70. C Limpsfield and Titsey *S'wark* 69-72; Dean's V St Alb Abbey *St Alb* 72-76; P-in-c Boreham Wood St Mich 76-79; TV Borehamwood 79-82; V Ipswich St Mary le Tower w St Lawr and St Steph *St E* 82-84; V Ipswich St Mary-le-Tower 84-96; RD Ipswich 92-96; Hon Can St E Cathl 93-96; Dean Ex from 96. *The Deanery, Cathedral Close, Exeter EX1 1HT* Tel (01392) 252891 or 272607 E-mail dean@exeter-cathedral.org.uk

JONES, Keith Bythell. b 35. ACP BA DipHE CertEd. Trin Coll Bris. **d** 83 **p** 84. C Bris St Mary Redcliffe w Temple etc *Bris* 83-86; C Filton 86-88; TV Yate New Town 88-95; rtd 95; Perm to Offic *Mon* from 95. *3 Woodlands Close, St Arvans, Chepstow NP16 6EF* Tel (01291) 622377

JONES, Keith Ellison. b 47. Wycliffe Hall Ox 72. **d** 75 **p** 76. C Everton St Chrys *Liv* 75-79; C Buckhurst Hill *Chelmsf* 79-81; TV 81-88; TR Leek and Meerbrook *Lich* 88-99; V Formby H Trin *Liv* from 99. *Holy Trinity Vicarage, 2A Brows Lane, Formby, Liverpool L37 3HZ* Tel (01704) 386464 Fax as telephone E-mail kejones@classicfm.net

JONES, Kenneth Elwyn. b 32. Nottm Univ BA54 Sheff Univ CertEd55 DipEd55. Linc Th Coll 80. **d** 82 **p** 83. C Rotherham *Sheff* 82-85; R Harthill and Thorpe Salvin 85-93; V Millhouses H Trin 93-97; RD Ecclesall 94-97; rtd 97; Perm to Offic *Sheff*

from 97. *27 Hawthorne Avenue, Sheffield S25 5GR* Tel (01909) 560065

JONES, Kenneth John. b 26. ALCD53. **d** 53 **p** 54. C Roxeth Ch Ch *Lon* 53-57; C Woking St Jo *Guildf* 57-59; R S Normanton *Derby* 59-65; V Creech St Michael *B & W* 65-91; rtd 91; Perm to Offic *B & W* from 91. *43 Wansbeck Green, Taunton TA1 2RE* Tel (01823) 331149

JONES, Canon Kenneth William. b 14. TD61. St D Coll Lamp BA36 St Mich Coll Llan 36. **d** 38 **p** 39. C Oswestry H Trin *Lich* 38-40; CF (EC) 40-47; CF (TA) 49-65; CF (TA - R of O) from 65; R Birdsall w Langton *York* 47-53; R Trowell *S'well* 53-58; Bp's Chapl to Ind *Roch* 58-63; Dir Adult Relig Educn 60-63; Dir Chr Stewardship *Chich* 63-66; V Wilmington 63-66; R Folkington 63-66; V Hove St Jo 66-77; Hon Can Albuquerque from 69; R Buxted St Marg *Chich* 77-81; P-in-c High Hurstwood 78-81; rtd 82; Perm to Offic *Chich* 82-99. *Ashmount Nursing Home, Southey Road, Worthing BN11 3HN*

JONES, Kingsley Charles. b 45. Birm Univ BSc66 Open Univ BA75. Sarum Th Coll 66. **d** 69 **p** 70. C Penwortham St Mary *Blackb* 69-72; C Broughton 72-74; P-in-c Gt Wollaston *Heref* 74-77; Chapl RAF 77-83; V Colwich w Gt Haywood *Lich* 83-94; V Winshill *Derby* 94-01; P-in-c Glouc St Aldate *Glouc* from 01. *St Aldate's Vicarage, Finlay Road, Gloucester GL4 6TN* Tel (01452) 523906

JONES, Leslie Joseph. b 23. Linc Th Coll. **d** 57 **p** 58. C Penhill *Bris* 57-60; C-in-c Lockleaze St Mary CD 60-62; V Bris Lockleaze St Mary Magd w St Fran 62-69; V Bedminster St Aldhelm 69-75; TV Bedminster 75-80; V Abbots Leigh w Leigh Woods 80-88; rtd 88; Perm to Offic *Bris* from 88. *4 Summerleaze, Bristol BS16 4ER* Tel 0117-965 3597

JONES, Lloyd. See JONES, Jeffrey Lloyd

JONES, Lloyd. See JONES, Prof Gareth Lloyd

JONES, Miss Mair. b 41. Cartrefle Coll of Educn TCert61 Dip Special Educn 73. St Mich Coll Llan Dip Practical Th 93. **d** 93 **p** 97. C Llangollen w Trevor and Llantysilio *St As* 93-97; V Llandrillo and Llandderfel 97-00; R Llanelian w Betws-yn-Rhos w Trofarth 00-03; TV Colwyn from 03. *The Rectory, 1 Rhodfa Sant Elian, Colwyn Bay LL29 8PY* Tel (01492) 517274

JONES, Malcolm Francis. b 44. Open Univ BA88 Hull Univ MA96. Chich Th Coll 67. **d** 70 **p** 71. C Prestbury *Ches* 70-73; Chapl RAF 73-81; Perm to Offic *Ox* 75-77; R Heaton Reddish *Man* 81-84; CF (ACF) 82-84 and from 98; CF (TA) 83-84; Perm to Offic *York* 84-93; CF 84-93; CF (R of O) 93-99; Perm to Offic *Guildf* 88-93; TV Cleethorpes *Linc* 93-97; Perm to Offic *York* 94-97; OStJ 84-97; ChStJ from 97; V Ryde H Trin *Portsm* from 97; V Swanmore St Mich from 97. *The Vicarage, 11 Wray Street, Swanmore, Ryde PO33 3ED* Tel and fax (01983) 562984 Mobile 07710-543155 E-mail frmalcolmjones@hotmail.com

JONES, Malcolm Stuart. b 41. Sheff Univ BA62. Linc Th Coll 64. **d** 66 **p** 67. C Monkseaton St Mary *Newc* 66-69; C Ponteland 69-72; Venezuela 73-75; C Hexham *Newc* 75-77; P-in-c Killingworth 77-92; V Delaval 92-01; TV Ch the King from 01. *The Vicarage, 2 East Acres, Dinnington, Newcastle upon Tyne NE13 7NA* Tel (01661) 871377

JONES, Maldwyn Lloyd. b 17. St D Coll Lamp BA39. **d** 40 **p** 41. C Gorseinon *S & B* 40-43; Lic to Offic *Ox* 43-46; Brazil 46-50; Falkland Is 50-51; Chapl RN 52-68; USA 68-70; Chapl Lon Nautical Sch 71-72; Lic to Offic *Ban* 72-82; rtd 82; Perm to Offic *Ban* from 82. *Clover Cottage, Ledbury Road, Tirley, Gloucester GL19 4ES*

JONES, Ms Margaret. b 28. TCD BA53 Man Univ PGCE54 Lon Univ BD66. **d** 87 **p** 94. NSM Stanstead Abbots *St Alb* 87-88; NSM Grappenhall *Ches* 89-98; rtd 98; Perm to Offic *Ches* from 98. *19 Hill Top Road, Grappenhall, Warrington WA4 2ED* Tel (01925) 261992

JONES, Mrs Margaret Angela. b 53. Wolv Univ CertEd91. Qu Coll Birm BA99. **d** 99 **p** 00. C Pershore w Pinvin, Wick and Birlingham *Worc* 99-03; TV Solihull *Birm* from 03. *St Helen's House, 6 St Helen's Road, Solihull B91 2DA* Tel 0121-704 2878 E-mail margaret@mccnjones.fsnet.co.uk

JONES, Margaret Mary. b 47. Oak Hill Th Coll 92. **d** 95 **p** 96. C Sydenham H Trin *S'wark* 95-98; V Anerley St Paul *Roch* from 98. *St Paul's Vicarage, Hamlet Road, London SE19 2AW* Tel (020) 8653 0978

JONES, Mark. See JONES, Christopher Mark

JONES, Mark Andrew. b 60. Southn Univ BSc82 Sussex Univ PGCE83. Oak Hill Th Coll BA91. **d** 91 **p** 92. C Wolverhampton St Luke 91-96; I Inishmacsaint *Clogh* 96-01; V Padiham w Hapton and Padiham Green *Blackb* from 01. *The Vicarage, 1 Arbory Drive, Padiham, Burnley BB12 8JS* Tel (01282) 772442 E-mail jones.rectory@care4free.net

JONES, Mark Vincent. b 60. Univ of Wales (Cardiff) DipTh84. St Mich Coll Llan 81. **d** 84 **p** 85. C Whitchurch *Llan* 84-89; V Pwllgwaun w Llanddewi Rhondda 89-90; CF from 90. *c/o MOD Chaplains (Army)* Tel (01980) 615804 Fax 615800

JONES, Canon Mary Nerissa Anna. b 41. MBE02. Qu Mary Coll Lon BA86 FRSA91. Ripon Coll Cuddesdon 86. **d** 88 **p** 94. Par Dn St Botolph Aldgate w H Trin Minories *Lon* 88-93; P-in-c Wood End *Cov* 93-95; V 95-01; Hon Can Cov Cathl 01; rtd 01;

P-in-c Askerswell, Loders and Powerstock *Sarum* from 01. *The Vicarage, Loders, Bridport DT6 3SA* Tel (01308) 425419
E-mail nerissa@surfaid.org

JONES, Canon Mary Valerie. b 37. Univ of Wales (Ban) BD84. St Deiniol's Hawarden 84. **d** 85 **p** 97. C Holyhead w Rhoscolyn w Llanfair-yn-Neubwll *Ban* 85-87; C Ynyscynhaearn w Penmorfa and Porthmadog 87-90; Dn-in-c Llansantffraid Glyn Ceirog and Llanarmon etc *St As* 90-97; V 97-98; R Overton and Erbistock and Penley from 98; RD Bangor Isycoed from 98; Can Cursal St As Cathl from 01. *The Rectory, 4 Sundorne, Overton, Wrexham LL13 0EB* Tel (01978) 710229
E-mail valerie@hywyn.freeserve.co.uk

JONES, Matthew Christopher Howell. b 74. Leeds Univ BSc95 Cam Univ BTh01. Westcott Ho Cam 98. **d** 01 **p** 02. C Cheshunt *St Alb* from 01. *156 Churchgate, Cheshunt, Waltham Cross EN8 9DX* Tel (01992) 620659 E-mail mchjones@lineone.net

JONES, Maurice Maxwell Hughes. b 32. Lon Univ DipTh58 Univ of Wales (Cardiff) DPS72. Clifton Th Coll 56. **d** 60 **p** 61. C Islington St Andr w St Thos and St Matthias *Lon* 60-63; Argentina 63-71; C Whitchurch *Llan* 72-73; Area Sec (NW England) SAMS 73-77; V Haydock St Mark *Liv* 78-87; V Paddington Em Harrow Road *Lon* 87-97; rtd 98. *Glyn Orig, Cemmaes, Machynlleth SY20 9PR* Tel (01650) 511632 Fax as telephone

JONES, Melville Kenneth. b 40. Open Univ BA82. St D Coll Lamp DipTh66. **d** 66 **p** 67. C Aberdare *Llan* 66-71; C Caerau w Ely 71-72; Chapl Pontypridd Hosps 72-89; V Graig *Llan* 72-89; P-in-c Cilfynydd 86-89; V Llantwit Fardre from 89; Chapl E Glam Hosp 89-99; RD Pontypridd from 99; Chapl Pontypridd and Rhondda NHS Trust 99-01. *The Vicarage, Upper Church Village, Pontypridd CF38 1EP* Tel (01443) 202538 Mobile 07974-120268 Fax (01443) 207278 E-mail melville_k.jones@virgin.net

JONES, Michael. *See* JONES, David Michael

JONES, Michael. *See* JONES, Gordon Michael Campbell

JONES, Michael. b 49. Leeds Univ BA71 Man Univ MA73. Qu Coll Birm 83. **d** 85 **p** 86. C Leigh St Mary *Man* 85-88; C-in-c Holts CD 88-93; V Hamer from 93. *All Saints' Vicarage, Foxholes Road, Rochdale OL12 0EF* Tel (01706) 355591

JONES, Michael Denis Dyson. b 39. CCC Cam BA62 MA66 Lon Univ MSc73. Wycliffe Hall Ox DipTh75. **d** 76 **p** 77. C Plymouth St Andr w St Paul and St Geo *Ex* 76-81; V Devonport St Budeaux 81-00; RD Plymouth Devonport 93-95; TV Barnstaple from 00. *Holy Trinity Vicarage, Victoria Road, Barnstaple EX32 9HP* Tel (01271) 344321

JONES, Michael Emlyn. b 47. Aber Univ MB, ChB72 MRCP75 Edin Univ FRCP95 Nottm Univ Dip Past Counselling 93. **d** 79 **p** 79. Tanzania 79-82; NSM Duns *Edin* from 83. *Care for Mission, Elphinstone Wing, Carberry, Musselburgh EH21 8PW* Tel 0131-653 6767 *or* 440 2602 Mobile 07710-276208 Fax 653 3646 E-mail 100633.2065@compuserve.com

JONES, Michael Kevin. b 57. Llan Ord Course 94. **d** 98 **p** 99. NSM Caerau w Ely *Llan* 98-00; NSM Cen Cardiff 01; P-in-c Tremorfa St Phil CD from 02; Area Fundraising Manager Children's Soc *Llan* and *Mon* 98-00; Ch Strategy Manager Wales 01-02. *4 Glas Canol, Whitchurch, Cardiff CF14 1LA* Tel (029) 2061 1669 Fax as telephone

JONES, Morgan. *See* JONES, Frederick Morgan

JONES, Canon Neil Crawford. b 42. Univ of Wales BA63 K Coll Lon BD66 AKC66. **d** 67 **p** 68. C Holywell *St As* 67-69; C Rhyl w St Ann 69-73; C Christchurch *Win* 73-77; V Stanmore 77-84; RD Win 82-84; V Romsey from 84; RD Romsey 89-94; Hon Can Win Cathl from 93. *The Vicarage, Church Lane, Romsey SO51 8EP* Tel (01794) 513125

JONES, Nerissa. *See* JONES, Canon Mary Nerissa Anna

JONES, Canon Neville George. b 36. Univ of Wales (Ban) BA59. St Mich Coll Llan 59. **d** 61 **p** 62. C Broughton *St As* 61-65; C Newcastle *Llan* 65-68; V Laleston w Tythegston 68-84; V Llanishen and Lisvane 84-93; V Llanishen 93-02; Hon Can Llan Cathl 96-02; rtd 02. *21 Cwm Gwynlais, Tongwynlais, Cardiff CF15 7HU* Tel (029) 2081 1150

JONES, Nicholas Godwin. b 58. St Jo Coll Cam BA81 MA84 Hughes Hall Cam PGCE90. Ridley Hall Cam CTM93. **d** 93 **p** 94. C Cambridge H Trin *Ely* 93-97; Chapl St Bede's Sch Cam 97-00; C Fulbourn w Gt and Lt Wilbraham 97-00; V Harston w Hauxton and Newton 00-03; V Gt Horton *Bradf* from 03. *The Vicarage, 30 Bartle Close, Bradford BD7 4QH* Tel (01274) 521456
E-mail nandjjones@aol.com

JONES, Nicholas Newman. b 51. K Coll Lon 71 St Aug Coll Cant 74. **d** 75 **p** 76. C Derringham Bank *York* 75-78; C Stokesley 78-81; P-in-c Kirby Misperton 81-85; R Normanby w Edston and Salton 83-85; R Kirby Misperton w Normanby, Edston and Salton 85-87; V Eskdaleside w Ugglebarnby and Sneaton 87-98; RD Whitby 92-98; P-in-c Wykeham and Hutton Buscel 98-99; P-in-c New Malton 99-02; V from 02; RD S Ryedale from 02. *The Vicarage, 17 The Mount, Malton YO17 7ND* Tel (01653) 692089 Fax as telephone E-mail vicarage17@hotmail.com

JONES, Nicholas Peter. b 55. St Mich Coll Llan DipTh82. **d** 82 **p** 83. C St Andrews Major w Michaelston-le-Pit *Llan* 82-84; C Aberdare 84-88; Youth Chapl 85-89; V Abercynon 88-96; R

Llanilid w Pencoed from 96. *The Rectory, 60 Coychurch Road, Pencoed, Bridgend CF35 5NA* Tel (01656) 860337

JONES, Nigel David. b 69. Qu Coll Cam MA95. Westcott Ho Cam 97. **d** 00 **p** 01. C Abbots Langley *St Alb* 00-03; TV Dunstable from 03. *St Augustine's Vicarage, 83 Half Moon Lane, Dunstable LU5 4AE* Tel (01582) 703919
E-mail nigel.david.jones@ukgateway.net

JONES, Nigel Ivor. b 54. Birm Univ CPS89. WMMTC 91. **d** 94 **p** 95. C Shirley *Birm* 94-99; TV Salter Street and Shirley 99-01; V Olton from 01. *St Margaret's Vicarage, 5 Old Warwick Road, Solihull B92 7JU* Tel 0121-706 2318 Mobile 07719-951856
E-mail revnigel@aol.com

JONES, Norman. b 50. Oak Hill Th Coll BA83. **d** 83 **p** 84. C Ulverston St Mary w H Trin *Carl* 83-87; Hong Kong 88-92; TR Eccles *Man* 92-01; AD Eccles 95-00; R Haslemere and Grayswood *Guildf* from 01; RD Godalming from 02; Chapl Wispers Sch Haslemere from 01. *The Rectory, 7 Derby Road, Haslemere GU27 1BS* Tel (01428) 658107 *or* tel and fax 644578
E-mail revnjones@aol.com

✠**JONES, The Rt Revd Noël Debroy.** b 32. CB86. Univ of Wales (Lamp) BA53. Wells Th Coll 53. **d** 55 **p** 56 **c** 89. C Tredegar St Jas *Mon* 55-57; C Newport St Mark 57-60; V Kano Nigeria 60-62; Chapl RN 62-84; Chapl of the Fleet and Adn for the RN 84-89; QHC from 83; Hon Can Gib Cathl *Eur* from 86; Bp S & M 89-03; rtd 03; Hon Asst Bp York from 03. *The Sudreys, Pickering Road, Thornton Dale, Pickering YO18 7LH*
E-mail holy.noellee@sagainternet.co.uk

JONES, Ormond. *See* JONES, David Ormond

JONES, Mrs Patricia Ann. b 43. LNSM course 96. **d** 97 **p** 00. OLM Bincombe w Broadwey, Upwey and Buckland Ripers *Sarum* from 97. *23 Camedown Close, Weymouth DT3 5RB* Tel (01305) 813056

JONES, Mrs Patricia Anne. b 55. NNEB75 CSS81. Oak Hill Th Coll 92. **d** 95. NSM Mill Hill Jo Keble Ch *Lon* 95-01; NSM Queensbury All SS from 01. *The Flat, St Paul's School, The Ridgeway, London NW7 1QU* Tel (020) 8201 1583

JONES, Canon Patrick Geoffrey Dickson. b 28. Ch Ch Ox MA55. St Deiniol's Hawarden 79. **d** 82 **p** 83. Hon C Sandbach *Ches* 82-84; R Aboyne *Ab* 84-96; R Ballater 84-96; P-in-c Braemar 84-96; rtd 96; Hon Can St Andr Cathl *Ab* from 01. *Byebush of Fedderate, New Deer, Turiff AB53 6UL* Tel (01771) 644110 E-mail patrickgeoffreydj@hotmail.com

JONES, Patrick George. b 42. Cant Ch Ch Univ Coll MA99. Lich Th Coll 69. **d** 72 **p** 73. C Chesterton St Geo *Ely* 72-75; P-in-c Waterbeach 75-78; P-in-c Landbeach 76-78; R Charlton-in-Dover *Cant* 78-90; Cautley Trust from 90. *Cautley House, 95 Seabrook Road, Seabrook, Hythe CT21 5QY* Tel (01303) 230762 E-mail cautleyhouse@compuserve.com

JONES, Paul Anthony. b 72. Cov Univ BSc95. Ripon Coll Cuddesdon BTh99. **d** 99 **p** 00. C Dolgellau w Llanfachreth and Brithdir etc *Ban* 99-02; P-in-c Ffestiniog w Blaenau Ffestiniog from 02. *The Vicarage, Betws-y-Coed LL24 0AD* Tel and fax (01690) 710313 *or* (01766) 832142 E-mail monty@classicfm.net

JONES, Paul Terence. b 35. Dur Univ BA60. Qu Coll Birm 60. **d** 62 **p** 63. C Rainford *Liv* 62-65; C Skelmersdale St Paul 65-68; V Huyton Quarry 68-78; V Widnes St Ambrose 78-00; rtd 00; Perm to Offic *Liv* from 00. *9 Hunter Court, Prescot L34 2UH* Tel 0151-430 6057

JONES, Penelope Howson. b 58. Girton Coll Cam BA80 MA83 LGSM79. Ripon Coll Cuddesdon BA85 MA88. **dss** 86 **d** 87 **p** 94. Hackney *Lon* 86-87; Par Dn 87-88; Tutor Ripon Coll Cuddesdon 88-90; Par Dn Cuddesdon *Ox* 88-90; Perm to Offic *Dur* 92-95; Dir Practical Th NEOC *Newc* 93-97; Hon C Eastgate w Rookhope *Dur* 93-97; Hon C Stanhope w Frosterley 93-97; Perm to Offic *York* 93-97; P-in-c Stanhope w Frosterley *Dur* 97-01; P-in-c Eastgate w Rookhope 97-01; Woman Adv in Min 97-01; Hon Can Dur Cathl 98-01; Sen Assoc P Gosford Australia from 01. *78 Henry Parry Drive, PO Box 4255, Gosford East, NSW, Australia 2250* Tel (0061) (2) 4324 2630
E-mail redimp@bigpong.com

JONES, Peter Anthony Watson. b 53. AKC75. Sarum & Wells Th Coll 76. **d** 77 **p** 78. C Hessle *York* 77-81; C Stainton-in-Cleveland 81-82; P-in-c Weston Mill *Ex* 82-84; Chapl Plymouth Poly 82-90; V Gt Ayton w Easby and Newton in Cleveland *York* 90-92; C Devonport St Aubyn *Ex* 92-98; P-in-c Yealmpton and Brixton 98-01; Asst Chapl Portsm Hosps NHS Trust from 01. *Queen Alexandra Hospital, Southwick Hill Road, Cosham, Portsmouth PO6 3LY* Tel (01705) 286408

JONES, Peter Charles. b 57. Univ of Wales BA81 MA82 DipTh83 PGCE97. St Mich Coll Llan 80. **d** 83 **p** 84. C Pontnewynydd *Mon* 83-85; C Bassaley 85-87; TV Cwmbran 87-94; V Blaenavon w Capel Newydd 94-01; Chapl CME 00-01; Chapl and Fell Trin Coll Carmarthen from 01. *Trinity College, College Road, Carmarthen SA31 3EP*

JONES, Peter David. b 48. S'wark Ord Course 89. **d** 92 **p** 93. NSM Coulsdon St Andr *S'wark* from 92. *79 Beverley Road, Whyteleafe CR3 0DU* Tel (020) 8668 6398

JONES, Peter Gordon Lewis. b 31. Llan Dioc Tr Scheme. **d** 82 **p** 83. NSM Llangynwyd w Maesteg *Llan* 82-84; Deputation

Appeals Org (S & M Glam) CECS 84-87; Appeals Manager (Wales and Glouc) Children's Soc 87-97; NSM Pyle w Kenfig *Llan* 89-97; rtd 97. *18 Fulmar Road, Porthcawl CF36 3UL* Tel (01656) 785455 Mobile 07785-755399

JONES, Peter Robin. b 42. Open Univ BA75 Bp Otter Coll Chich CertEd68. EMMTC 79. **d** 82 **p** 83. NSM Doveridge *Derby* 82-97; NSM Doveridge, Scropton, Sudbury etc from 98; Bp's Inspector of Th Colls and Courses from 98; Chapl Derby Gr Sch for Boys from 03; Perm to Offic *Lich* from 93. *4 Cross Road, Uttoxeter ST14 7JN* Tel (01889) 565123

JONES, Canon Peter Russell. b 48. St Jo Coll Cam BA71 MA75 Univ of Wales MTh86. Wycliffe Hall Ox DipTh72. **d** 75 **p** 76. C Northampton All SS w St Kath *Pet* 75-79; C Ban Cathl Par *Ban* 79-81; Min Can Ban Cathl 79-81; R Pentraeth and Llanddyfnan 81-85; V Conwy w Gyffin from 85; Lect Univ of Wales (Ban) 89-95; RD Arllechwedd *Ban* 90-01; AD from 01; Can and Treas Ban Cathl from 99. *The Vicarage, Rose Hill Street, Conwy LL32 8LD* Tel (01492) 593402

JONES, Philip Hugh. b 51. Solicitor. Chich Th Coll 92. **d** 94 **p** 95. C Horsham *Chich* 94-97; V Southwater from 97; RD Horsham from 02. *The Vicarage, Church Lane, Southwater, Horsham RH13 7BT* Tel (01403) 730229

JONES, Philip Thomas Henry. b 34. Qu Coll Birm 58. **d** 60 **p** 61. C Castle Bromwich SS Mary and Marg *Birm* 60-67; C Reading St Mary V *Ox* 67-72; C-in-c Reading All SS CD 72-75; V Reading All SS 75-95; Perm to Offic *Portsm* from 97; Hon Chapl Portsm Cathl from 97. *13 Oyster Street, Portsmouth PO1 2HZ* Tel (023) 9275 6676

JONES, Canon Phillip Bryan. b 34. St Mich Coll Llan DipTh61. **d** 61 **p** 62. C Hope *St As* 61-64; C Llanrhos 64-67; V Kerry 67-74; R Newtown w Llanllwchaiarn w Aberhafesp 74-97; RD Cedewain 76-97; Sec Ch in Wales Prov Evang Cttee 80-83; Hon Can St As Cathl *St As* 86-93; Can 93-97; rtd 97. *7 Dalton Drive, Shrewsbury SY3 8DA* Tel (01743) 351426

JONES, Phillip Edmund. b 56. Man Poly BA78 Fitzw Coll Cam BA84 MA88. Westcott Ho Cam 82. **d** 85 **p** 86. C Stafford St Jo and Tixall w Ingestre *Lich* 85-89; TV Redditch, The Ridge *Worc* 89-95; TV Worc SE from 95; Ind Chapl from 89; Team Ldr Worcs Ind Miss from 01. *The Vicarage, Walkers Lane, Whittington, Worcester WR5 2RE* Tel (01905) 355989 Fax 0870-122 7958 E-mail phillip@wimworcester.fsnet.co.uk

JONES, Ray. *See* JONES, David Raymond

JONES, Raymond. b 43. N Ord Course 99. **d** 02. NSM Ashton-in-Makerfield St Thos *Liv* 02-03; C Widnes St Mary from 03; C Widnes St Paul from 03. *1 Lofthouse Gate, Widnes WA8 9GT* Tel 0151-420 6658 Mobile 07770-855898

JONES, Raymond Blake. b 29. K Coll Lon BD54 AKC54. **d** 55 **p** 56. C Fenny Stratford *Ox* 55-58; C Lt Brickhill 55-58; C Wooburn 58-60; C Southbourne St Kath *Win* 60-66; R Braiseworth *St E* 66-76; V Eye 66-76; P-in-c Yaxley 74-77; RD Hartismere 76-77; V Eye w Braiseworth and Yaxley 77; R Ufford 77-82; Chapl St Audry's Hosp Melton 77-82; V Southbourne St Kath *Win* 82-95; rtd 95; Perm to Offic *Win* from 95. *4 Russell Drive, Riverslea, Christchurch BH23 3PA* Tel (01202) 473205

JONES, Raymond Sydney. b 35. MSERT71. Glouc Th Course 85. **d** 87 **p** 88. NSM Madley *Heref* 87-89; NSM Preston-on-Wye w Blakemere 87-89; NSM Madley w Tyberton, Preston-on-Wye and Blakemere 89; Chapl St Math Hospice Bartestree 90-00; Perm to Offic from 00. *The Old Cedars, Much Birch, Hereford HR2 8HR* Tel (01981) 540851

JONES, Raymond Trevor. b 35. Linc Th Coll. **d** 82 **p** 83. C Rushmere *St E* 82-85; Bp's Dom Chapl 85-86; CF 86-91; TV Ridgeway *Sarum* 91-97; Relig Programmes Producer BBC Wiltshire Sound 91-97; Chapl Fuengirola St Andr *Eur* 97-00; P-in-c Ypres from 00. *MLK Haiglaan 12, B 8900, Ypres, Belgium* Tel (0032) (5) 721 5685 Fax 721 5927 E-mail raymondstg@hotmail.com

JONES, Ms Rhiannon Elizabeth. b 72. Ex Univ BA93 Brunel Univ MA95. Ridley Hall Cam 98. **d** 00 **p** 01. C Huntingdon *Ely* from 00. *83 Wertheim Way, Huntingdon PE29 6UH* Tel (01480) 434075 E-mail rhiannon.jones@ely.anglican.org

JONES, Richard. b 23. BEM. St Deiniol's Hawarden 74. **d** 76 **p** 77. NSM Welshpool w Castle Caereinion *St As* 76-94; rtd 94. *Sherwood, Rhos Common, Llandrinio, Llanymynech SY22 6RN* Tel (01691) 830534

JONES, Canon Richard. b 28. St D Coll Lamp 54. **d** 56 **p** 57. C Llanaber w Caerdeon *Ban* 56-61; R Aberffraw w Llangwyfan 61-74; CF (TA) 61-71; V Llanfairisgaer *Ban* 74-79; Bp's Private Chapl 78-82; V Llanfair-is-gaer and Llanddeiniolen 79-89; RD Arfon 82-89; Can Ban Cathl from 86; V Llandegfan w Llandysilio 89-96; Chapl ATC from 90; rtd 96; Perm to Offic *Ban* from 96. *Bryn Hedydd, Cildwrn Road, Llangefni LL77 7NN* Tel (01248) 724609

JONES, Richard. b 36. Ely Th Coll 61. **d** 64 **p** 65. C Blyth St Mary *Newc* 64-67; C Wallsend St Pet 67-69; R Paisley H Trin *Glas* 69-78; R Monkseaton *Bre* 78-99; Hon Can St Paul's Cathl Dundee 93-99; rtd 99; Hon C Kelso *Edin* from 99. *12 Hendersyde Avenue, Kelso TD5 7TZ* Tel (01573) 228644 E-mail skypilot111@hotmail.com

JONES, Richard Eifion. b 23. St D Dioc Tr Course 80 St Mich Coll Llan 84. **d** 82 **p** 83. NSM Llangennech and Hendy *St D* 82-84; C Llanbadarn Fawr w Capel Bangor and Goginan 84-86; V Llangadog and Gwynfe w Llanddeusant 86-91; rtd 91. *Gercoed, 186 St Teilo Street, Pontarddulais, Swansea SA4 8LH* Tel (01792) 882234

JONES, Richard Keith. b 40. Jes Coll Ox BA63. Wycliffe Hall Ox 61. **d** 63 **p** 64. C Blaenavon w Capel Newydd *Mon* 63-67; C Mynyddislwyn 67-71; C Pontypool 71; V Abercarn 71-81; V Penhow, St Brides Netherwent w Llandavenny etc 81-88. *32 Quantock Court, South Esplanade, Burnham-on-Sea TA8 1DL* Tel (01278) 458123

JONES, Robert. b 26. Lon Univ BA52 K Coll Lon BD65 Hull Univ MA82. St Deiniol's Hawarden 79. **d** 80 **p** 81. NSM Doncaster St Mary *Sheff* 80-81; C Halifax St Jo Bapt *Wakef* 81-82; C Halifax St Jo; P-in-c Dewsbury St Mark 83-84; TV Dewsbury 84-92; rtd 92; NSM Halifax St Jo *Wakef* 92-95; Perm to Offic from 95. *4 Lidget Street, Huddersfield HD3 3JB* Tel (01484) 658885

JONES, Robert. b 45. Culham Coll Ox CertEd67. St Steph Ho Ox. **d** 85 **p** 86. C High Wycombe *Ox* 85-89; V Beckenham St Barn *Roch* 89-90; C Swanley St Mary 90-91; C Edenbridge from 91; C Crockham Hill H Trin from 91. *The Vicarage, Oakdale Lane, Crockham Hill, Edenbridge TN8 6RL* Tel (01732) 866515 Fax 864352

JONES, Robert Bernard. b 24. St Jo Coll Dur BA48. Wycliffe Hall Ox. **d** 50 **p** 51. C Ecclesall *Sheff* 50-53; C Apsley End *St Alb* 53-58; C Christchurch *Win* 58-61; V Ringwood 61-75; R N Stoneham 75-89; rtd 89; Perm to Offic *Win* from 89. *4 Rowden Close, West Wellow, Romsey SO51 6RF* Tel (01794) 22966

JONES, Robert Cecil. b 32. Univ of Wales (Abth) BA54 DipEd55. Qu Coll Birm 84. **d** 86 **p** 87. C Llanbadarn Fawr w Capel Bangor and Goginan *St D* 86-88; R Llanllwchaearn and Llanina 88-91; R Newport w Cilgwyn and Dinas w Llanllawer 91-98; rtd 98. *10 Station Road, Hathersage, Hope Valley S32 1DL* Tel (01433) 651060

JONES, Canon Robert Dwyfor. b 20. Univ of Wales (Ban) BA41. St Mich Coll Llan 46. **d** 47 **p** 48. C Llandudno *Ban* 47-55; R Cemmaes 55-58; R Llanenddwyn 58-65; V Glanogwen 65-69; V Conwy w Gyffin 69-85; Can and Treas Ban Cathl 76-85; rtd 85; Perm to Offic *St As* and *Ban* from 85. *Ormlea, 12 Hywel Place, Llandudno LL30 1EF* Tel (01492) 874390

JONES, Robert George. b 42. Univ of Wales (Lamp) 87. St Mich Coll Llan DipMin93. **d** 95 **p** 96. NSM Treboeth *S & B* 95-02; P-in-c Treboeth from 02; P-in-c Landore from 03. *Green Gables, 42 Heol Fach, Treboeth, Swansea SA5 9DE* Tel (01792) 774229

JONES, Canon Robert George. b 55. Hatf Coll Dur BA77 Ox Univ BA79 MA87. Ripon Coll Cuddesdon 77. **d** 80 **p** 81. C Foley Park *Worc* 80-84; V Dudley St Fran 84-92; TR Worc St Barn w Ch Ch from 92; RD Worc E from 99; Hon Can Worc Cathl from 03. *St Barnabas' Vicarage, Church Road, Worcester WR3 8NX* Tel (01905) 23785 Fax as telephone E-mail rob.gjones@lineone.net

JONES, Robert Ivan. b 33. Bede Coll Dur CertEd57 CertRK57. Westcott Ho Cam 85. **d** 85 **p** 86. NSM Wymondham *Nor* 85-86; C Epsom St Martin *Guildf* 87-89; V Hutton Cranswick w Skerne, Watton and Beswick *York* 89-94; RD Harthill 92-97; V Wetwang and Garton-on-the-Wolds w Kirkburn 94-98; V Waggoners 98-00; rtd 00; P-in-c Newbald *York* from 00. *The Vicarage, 7 Dot Hill Close, North Newbald, York YO43 4TS* Tel (01430) 801088 Fax as telephone E-mail beemajo@onetel.net.uk

JONES, The Very Revd Robert William. b 55. Ian Ramsey Coll 75 Chich Th Coll 76 TCD Div Sch 77. **d** 79 **p** 80. C Seapatrick *D & D* 79; C Bangor Abbey 81-83; I Drumgath w Drumgooland and Clonduff 83-89; I Finaghy *Conn* 89-93; I Kilwaughter w Cairncastle and Craigy Hill 94-98; I Athlone w Benown, Kiltoom and Forgney *M & K* 98-02; Dean Clonmacnoise from 02; I Trim and Athboy Gp from 02. *St Patrick's Deanery, Loman Street, Trim, Co Meath, Irish Republic* Tel (00353) (46) 943 6698 Mobile 87-290 8344

JONES, Robert William Aplin. b 32. Univ of Wales (Cardiff) BSc52 MSc65 FRSC71 CChem72. St Deiniol's Hawarden 72. **d** 73 **p** 74. C Bassaleg *Mon* 73-77; V Nantyglo 77-82; Perm to Offic 82-86; R Colwinston w Llandow and Llysworney *Llan* 86-95; rtd 95; Perm to Offic *St D* from 99. *Golwg-y-Lan, Feidr Ganol, Newport SA42 0RR* Tel (01239) 820297 Mobile 07968-173759

JONES, Roderick. b 48. Leeds Univ BA70 PGCE72. Westmr Th Sem (USA) 73 Oak Hill Th Coll 74. **d** 76 **p** 77. C Beckenham Ch Ch *Roch* 76-80; C Uphill *B & W* 80-84; R Springfield All SS *Chelmsf* 84-90; Selection Sec ABM 91-96; V Horsell *Guildf* from 96. *The Vicarage, Wilson Way, Horsell, Woking GU21 4QJ* Tel (01483) 772134 E-mail rjones2558@aol.com

JONES, Roger. b 49. St Mich Coll Llan 84. **d** 86 **p** 87. C Llangynwyd w Maesteg *Llan* 86-90; V Wiston w Walton E and Clarbeston *St D* 90-01; V Pembroke Gp from 01. *The Vicarage, Lower Lamphey Road, Pembroke SA71 4AF* Tel and fax (01646) 682710 Mobile 07971-528933 E-mail roger@revjones.fsnet.co.uk

JONES, Russell Frederick. b 55. Man Univ BA77 Edin Univ BD84. Edin Th Coll 81. **d** 84 **p** 85. C Croxteth *Liv* 84-87; V Edgehill St Dunstan 87-98; R Glas St Bride *Glas* from 98. *St Bride's Rectory, 25 Queensborough Gardens, Glasgow G12 9QP* Tel 0141-334 1401 Fax as telephone

JONES, Samuel. b 44. CITC. **d** 86 **p** 87. C Agherton *Conn* 86-88; I Connor w Antrim St Patr 88-97; I Whitehead and Islandmagee 97-01; Bp's C Kilbroney *D & D* from 01. *The Vicarage, 15 Kilbroney Road, Rostrevor, Newry BT34 3BH* Tel (028) 4173 8293

JONES, Sebastian. *See* JONES, David Sebastian

JONES, Mrs Sharon Ann. b 60. Liv Univ BA82. Cranmer Hall Dur 83. **dss** 85 **d** 87 **p** 94. Rubery *Birm* 85-87; Par Dn 87-89; C-in-c Chelmsley Wood St Aug CD 89-92; Perm to Offic *Newc* 92-93; Chapl HM Pris Acklington 93-97; Chapl HM YOI Castington 97-00; Chapl HM Pris Forest Bank from 00. *HM Prison, Forest Bank, Swinton, Manchester M27 8FB* Tel 0161-925 7000 ext 2066 Fax 925 7001

JONES, Miss Sian Eira. b 63. Univ of Wales (Lamp) BA84 Southn Univ BTh88. Sarum & Wells Th Coll 85. **d** 88 **p** 97. C Llan-llwch w Llangain and Llangunnor *St D* 88-93; Dn-in-c Llansteffan and Llan-y-bri etc 93-97; V from 97; RD Carmarthen from 00. *The Vicarage, Llanstephan, Carmarthen SA33 5JT* Tel (01267) 241807

JONES, Sian Hilary. *See* WIGHT, Mrs Sian Hilary

JONES, Simon. b 63. Trin Coll Bris BA89. **d** 89 **p** 90. C Hildenborough *Roch* 89-93; C Crofton *Portsm* 93-96; C Northwood Em *Lon* 96-01; Min in charge Ignite from 01. *44A Azalea Walk, Eastcote, Pinner HA5 2EH* Tel (020) 8868 4185

JONES, Simon Matthew. b 72. SS Hild & Bede Coll Dur BA93 MA94 Selw Coll Cam PhD00 Ox Univ MA02 DPhil03. Westcott Ho Cam 95. **d** 99 **p** 00. C Tewkesbury w Walton Cardiff and Twyning *Glouc* 99-02; Chapl and Fell Mert Coll Ox from 02. *Merton College, Oxford OX1 4JD* Tel (01865) 276365 *or* 281793 Fax 276361 E-mail simon.jones@merton.ox.ac.uk

JONES, Stephen Frederick. b 53. Magd Coll Ox BA75 MA79 Lon Univ BD89 Leeds Univ MA96. Linc Th Coll BCombStuds84. **d** 84 **p** 85. C Kingswinford St Mary *Lich* 84-87; Min Can, Succ and Dean's V Windsor 87-94; C Howden *York* 94-96; Chapl St Elphin's Sch Matlock 96-01; C Worksop Priory *S'well* from 01. *268 Kilton Road, Worksop S80 2DZ* Tel (01909) 484720

JONES, Stephen Leslie. b 59. Hull Univ BA80. Sarum & Wells Th Coll 82. **d** 85 **p** 86. C Perry Barr *Birm* 85-88; C Blackpool St Steph *Blackb* 88-90; V Greenlands 90-95; V Carnforth from 95. *The Vicarage, North Road, Carnforth LA5 9LJ* Tel (01524) 732948 E-mail stephenjones17@hotmail.com

JONES, Stephen Richard. b 49. Heythrop Coll Lon MA01. Oak Hill Th Coll 72. **d** 75 **p** 76. C Welling *Roch* 75-79; C Cheltenham St Mark *Glouc* 79-82; V Shiregreen St Jas and St Chris *Sheff* 82-86; P-in-c Harold Hill St Geo *Chelmsf* 86-88; V 88-97; P-in-c Harold Hill St Paul 94-95; V Kippington *Roch* from 97; RD Sevenoaks from 00. *The Vicarage, 59 Kippington Road, Sevenoaks TN13 2LL* Tel (01732) 452112 E-mail srjones49@hotmail.com

JONES, Stephen William. b 46. K Coll Lon BD70 AKC70. **d** 71 **p** 72. C Streatham St Pet *S'wark* 71-76; C Leeds St Pet *Ripon* 76-79; C Leeds Richmond Hill 79-85; R Gourock *Glas* 85-88; V Porthleven w Sithney *Truro* 88-94; Miss to Seamen 88-94; P-in-c Portsea Ascension *Portsm* 96-00; V Grimsby St Aug *Linc* from 00. *St Augustine's Vicarage, 145 Legsby Avenue, Grimsby DN32 0LA* Tel (01472) 877109

JONES, Canon Stewart William. b 57. Heriot-Watt Univ BA79 Bris Univ BA88 DipHE87. Trin Coll Bris 86. **d** 88 **p** 89. C Stoke Bishop *Bris* 88-92; P-in-c Brislington St Luke 92-97; Abp's Chapl and Dioc Missr *Cant* 97-03; P-in-c Cant All SS from 01; AD Cant from 02; Hon Prov Can Cant Cathl from 02. *All Saints' Vicarage, Military Road, Canterbury CT1 1PA* Tel (01227) 463505 E-mail sjones@canterbury.clara.net *or* stewart@perkin-jones.com

JONES, Susan Helen. b 60. Trin Coll Carmarthen BEd92 MPhil94 Univ of Wales (Ban) PhD. Ripon Coll Cuddesdon DipMin95. **d** 95 **p** 97. Chapl Univ of Wales (Swansea) *S & B* 95-98; Hon C Sketty 95-98; Dir Past Studies St Mich Coll Llan 98-00; TV Bangor *Ban* from 00. *Deiniol, 31 Trefonwys, Bangor LL57 2HU* Tel (01248) 355530 E-mail suejone@netscapeonline.co.uk

JONES, Mrs Susan Jean. b 47. Bp Grosseteste Coll CertEd69. St Alb and Ox Min Course 93. **d** 96 **p** 97. C S Ascot *Ox* 96-01; NSM from 01. *The Vicarage, Vicarage Gardens, South Ascot, Ascot SL5 9DX* Tel (01344) 622388 Fax as telephone

JONES, Tegid Owen. b 27. Univ of Wales (Abth) LLB47. St Deiniol's Hawarden. **d** 68 **p** 69. C Rhosddu *St As* 68-71; C Wrexham 71-75; R Marchwiel 75-83; R Marchwiel and Isycoed 83-92; RD Bangor Isycoed 86-92; rtd 92. *Teglys, 2 Bungalow, Pentre, Chirk, Wrexham LL14 5AW*

JONES, Thomas. *See* JONES, Emmanuel Thomas

JONES, Thomas Glyndwr. b 41. Clifton Th Coll 65. **d** 65 **p** 66. C Islington St Mary *Lon* 65-69; USA from 69. *4425 Colchester Court, Columbus, GA 31907, USA*

JONES, Canon Thomas Graham. b 33. St D Coll Lamp BA57. **d** 59 **p** 60. C Llanelli *St D* 59-64; V Ysbyty Cynfyn 64-69; V Ysbyty Cynfyn w Llantrisant 69-72; V Llanelli Ch Ch 72-94; RD Cydweli 89-93; V Carmarthen St Dav 94-00; Hon Can St D Cathl 93-99; Can from 99; RD Carmarthen 98-00; rtd 00. *32 Pen y Morfa, Llangunnor, Carmarthen SA31 2NP* Tel (01267) 231846

JONES, The Ven Thomas Hughie. b 27. Univ of Wales BA49 LLM94 Lon Univ BD53 Leic Univ MA72 FRSA. St Deiniol's Hawarden. **d** 66 **p** 67. Hon C Evington *Leic* 66-76; Hon C Kirby Muxloe 76-81; Dioc Adult Educn Officer 81-85; R Church Langton w Thorpe Langton and Tur Langton 81-85; Hon Can Leic Cathl 83-86; R Church Langton w Tur Langton, Thorpe Langton etc 85-86; Adn Loughborough 86-92; rtd 92; Perm to Offic *Leic* from 92. *Four Trees, 68 Main Street, Thorpe Satchville, Melton Mowbray LE14 2DQ* Tel (01664) 840262 E-mail thj@connectfree.co.uk

JONES, Thomas Percy Norman Devonshire. b 34. St Jo Coll Ox BA58 MA61 Lambeth MLitt02. Cuddesdon Coll 58. **d** 60 **p** 61. C Portsea S Cuth *Portsm* 60-61; C Portsea N End St Mark 61-67; Asst Chapl Portsm Tech Coll 67-70; Chapl Portsm Poly *Portsm* 70-73; USA 73-74; V Folkestone St Sav *Cant* 75-81; V Regent's Park St Mark *Lon* 81-00; rtd 00; Dir Art and Chr Enquiry Trust from 94. *ACE, 107 Crundale Avenue, London NW9 9PS* Tel (020) 8206 2253 Fax as telephone E-mail tom@devonshirejones.fsnet.co.uk

JONES, Canon Thomas Peter. b 20. Ex Coll Ox BA43 MA46. St Mich Coll Llan 43. **d** 45 **p** 46. C Wrexham *St As* 45-48; C Llandrillo-yn-Rhos 48-57; R Erbistock and Overton 57-83; Can St As Cathl 78-84; Preb and Prec St As Cathl 84-86; RD Bangor Isycoed 80-86; R Overton and Erbistock and Penley 83-86; rtd 86; Perm to Offic *Cov* 86-98; *St As* from 98. *18 All Hallows Close, Retford DN22 7UP* Tel (01777) 700481

JONES, Timothy Llewellyn. b 67. York Univ BA90. Ripon Coll Cuddesdon BA94. **d** 94 **p** 95. C Middlesbrough St Martin *York* 94-96; Chapl HM YOI Northallerton 96-99; P-in-c Rounton w Welbury *York* 96-02; Adv for Young Adults and Yth (Cleveland) 99-02; R Corinth St Paul USA from 02. *St Paul's Episcopal Church, PO Box 1225, Corinth, Mississippi, MS 38834, USA* Tel (001) (662) 286 2922

JONES, Timothy Richard Nigel. b 54. Collingwood Coll Dur BSc75 Birm Univ MSc76 FGS. Trin Coll Bris DipHE86. **d** 86 **p** 87. C Hailsham *Chich* 86-91; V Madley w Tyberton, Preston-on-Wye and Blakemere *Heref* 91-00; R Madley w Tyberton, Peterchurch, Vowchurch etc from 00. *The Vicarage, Madley, Hereford HR2 9LP* Tel (01981) 250245

JONES, Trevor Blandon. b 43. Oak Hill Th Coll 77. **d** 80 **p** 81. NSM Homerton St Barn w St Paul *Lon* 80-83; NSM Harlow New Town w Lt Parndon *Chelmsf* 83-90; C 90-92; V Leyton Em 92-01; rtd 02. *5 Wheatley Close, Sawbridgeworth CM21 0HS* Tel (01279) 600248 E-mail rev.trev@lineone.net

JONES, Trevor Charles. b 50. Trin Hall Th Coll DipHE91. **d** 91 **p** 92. C Goodmayes All SS *Chelmsf* 91-93; C Widford 93-96; V Stowmarket *St E* 96-01. *Address temp unknown*

JONES, Trevor Edwin. b 49. SSC79. Ripon Coll Cuddesdon 74. **d** 76 **p** 77. C Cannock *Lich* 76-79; C Middlesbrough Ascension *York* 79-81; V Oldham St Steph and All Martyrs *Man* 81-84; V Perry Beeches *Birm* 84-90; P-in-c Saltley 90-93; P-in-c Shaw Hill 90-93; V Saltley and Shaw Hill 93-97; R Lon Docks St Pet w Wapping St Jo *Lon* from 97. *St Peter's Clergy House, Wapping Lane, London E1W 2RW* Tel (020) 7481 2985 E-mail fatherjones@stpeterslondondocks.org.uk *or* frtejones@aol.com

JONES, The Ven Trevor Pryce. b 48. Southn Univ BEd76 BTh79. Sarum & Wells Th Coll 73. **d** 76 **p** 77. C Glouc St Geo *Glouc* 76-79; Warden Bp Mascall Cen *Heref* 79-84; Dioc Communications Officer 81-86; TR Heref St Martin w St Fran 84-95; R Dewsall w Callow 84-95; V Holme Lacy w Dinedor 84-95; V Lt Dewchurch, Aconbury w Ballingham and Bolstone 84-95; V Upper and Lower Bullinghope w Grafton 84-95; TR Heref S Wye 95-97; Preb Heref Cathl 93-97; OCF 85-97; Adn Hertford and Hon Can St Alb from 97. *St Mary's House, Church Lane, Stapleford, Hertford SG14 3NB* Tel (01992) 581629 Fax 558745 E-mail archdhert@stalbans.anglican.org

JONES, Canon Tudor Howell. b 39. Univ of Wales (Cardiff) BD91. St Mich Coll Llan DipTh67 DPS68. **d** 68 **p** 69. C Clydach *S & B* 68-72; C Swansea St Pet 72-75; V Ystradfellte 75-79; V Llangiwg 79-91; V Manselton from 91; RD Penderi from 98; Can Res Brecon Cathl from 00. *The Vicarage, Manor Road, Manselton, Swansea SA5 9PA* Tel (01792) 654848

JONES, Victor Harvey. b 25. St D Coll Lamp BA53 Coll of Resurr Mirfield. **d** 55 **p** 56. C Canton St Luke *Llan* 55-57; C Caerau w Ely 57-61; Chapl RN 62-76; Perm to Offic *Truro* 77-80; C Portishead *B & W* 80-83; rtd 83; Perm to Offic *Ex* 92-98. *17 Beech Road, Findon, Worthing BN14 0UR*

JONES, Preb Wilfred David. b 22. Keble Coll Ox BA47 MA48. St Mich Coll Llan 47. **d** 48 **p** 49. C Aberaman *Llan* 48-50; C Cardiff St Jo 50-55; Chapl Kelly Coll Tavistock 55-62; V St Decumans *B & W* 62-76; V Ilminster w Whitelackington 76-92; RD Ilminster 78-87; Preb Wells Cathl from 81; rtd 92;

Perm to Offic *B & W* from 92. *Dragons, Lambrook Road, Shepton Beauchamp, Ilminster TA19 0NA* Tel (01460) 240967

JONES, Wilfred Lovell. b 39. Lon Univ BD71 Cam Univ CertEd. St D Coll Lamp DipTh63. **d** 63 **p** 64. C Llanllyfni *Ban* 63-65; C Llanbeblig w Caernarfon 65-68; V Llanwnog w Penstrowed 68-73; V Llanwnnog and Caersws w Carno 73-75; Asst Chapl Dover Coll 77-90; Chapl Wrekin Coll Telford 91-94; V Llangollen w Trevor and Llantysilio *St As* from 94; AD Llangollen from 03. *The Vicarage, Abbey Road, Llangollen LL20 8SN* Tel (01978) 860231
E-mail vicar@stcollen.freeserve.co.uk

JONES, Canon William. b 30. Univ of Wales (Ban) DipTh54. St Mich Coll Llan 54 BTh92. **d** 55 **p** 56. C Denio w Abererch *Ban* 55-60; V Aberdaron and Bodferin 60-66; R Llandwrog 66-71; R Llanstumdwy, Llangybi w Llanarmon 71-74; R Dolbenmaen w Llanystymdwy w Llangybi etc 74-99; RD Eifionydd 75-99; Can Ban Cathl 84-93; Can and Treas Ban Cathl 93-99; rtd 99; Perm to Offic *Ban* from 99. *Y Fachwen, Rhoshirwaun, Pwllheli LL53 8LB* Tel (01758) 760262

JONES, William Alexander. b 13. Univ of Wales BA35. **d** 69 **p** 70. Hon C Llandegfan w Beaumaris and Llanfaes *Ban* 69-75; C 75-76; P-in-c Penmon and Llangoed w Llanfihangel Dinsylwy 76-77; TV Llandegfan and Beaumaris w Llanfaes w Penmon etc 77-81; rtd 81; Perm to Offic *Ban* from 81. *23 Pont y Brenin, Llangoed, Beaumaris LL58 8JS*

JONES, Canon William David. b 28. St D Coll Lamp BA48 Lon Univ BD57 Leeds Univ MA73. St Mich Coll Llan 48. **d** 51 **p** 52. C Risca *Mon* 51-54; C Chepstow St Arvan's w Penterry 54-55; C St Geo-in-the-East w Ch Ch w St Jo *Lon* 55-59; C Farnham Royal *Ox* 59-64; Lect Div Culham Coll 65-67; Hd of Relig Studies Doncaster Coll of Educn 67-74; Lic to Offic *Sheff* 67-74; Vice-Prin St Bede Coll Dur 74; Vice-Prin SS Hild and Bede Coll Dur 75-89; Lect Th Dur Univ 75-89; Lic to Offic *Dur* 80-85; Dir of Miss Ch in Wales 89-93; Metropolitical and Hon Can St D Cathl *St D* 90-93; rtd 93; Perm to Offic *Glouc* from 93. *Hatfield Cottage, 14 Bath Road, Tetbury GL8 8EF* Tel (01666) 504050 E-mail wdjones@talk21.com

JONES, William Douglas. b 28. St Fran Coll Brisbane ThL56. **d** 56 **p** 58. Australia 56-58; Papua New Guinea 58-72; C Manston *Ripon* 72-75; V Middleton St Mary 75-87; V Ireland Wood 87-94; rtd 94; Perm to Offic *Ripon* from 94. *6 Willow Court, Pool in Wharfedale, Otley LS21 1RX* Tel 0113-284 2028

JONES, William Edward Benjamin. b 19. TCD BA43 MA53. TCD Div Sch Div Test44. **d** 44 **p** 45. C Belfast St Thos *Conn* 44-47; C Sudbury St Andr *Lon* 47-50; CF 50-54; V Endmonton St Pet w St Martin *Lon* 54-59; V N Wembley St Cuth 59-81; V Ripley *Guildf* 81-87; Chapl HM Pris Send 81-87; rtd 87; Perm to Offic *Nor* from 87. *37 Bircham Road, Reepham, Norwich NR10 4NG* Tel (01603) 870738

JONES, Canon William Glyndwr. b 17. St D Coll Lamp BA39. **d** 42 **p** 43. C Monkton *St D* 42-48; C Betws w Ammanford 48-51; R Granston w St Nic 51-86; V Mathry w St Edrens 69-86; R Jordanston 78-86; Hon Can St D Cathl from 84; rtd 86. *Pencraig, Sladeway, Fishguard SA65 9NY* Tel (01348) 874673

JONES, William John. b 59. St Mich Coll Llan Dip Minl Studies 93. **d** 93 **p** 94. C Pembroke Dock w Cosheston w Nash and Upton *St D* 93-96; C Tenby 96; TV 96-99; V Llanrhian w Llanhywel and Carnhedryn etc 99-00; rtd 00. *13 George Street, Milford Haven SA73 2AY* Tel (01646) 697094

JONES, William Lincoln. b 19. St D Coll Lamp BA41 St Mich Coll Llan 41. **d** 43 **p** 44. C Roath *Llan* 43-47; C Wooburn *Ox* 47-50; C Bridgwater w Chilton *B & W* 50-55; V Langford Budville w Runnington 55-60; V Winscombe 60-71; V Bishops Lydeard 71-73; V Bishops Lydeard w Cothelstone 73-80; P-in-c Bagborough 78-80; R Bishops Lydeard w Bagborough and Cothelstone 80-84; rtd 84; Perm to Offic *Ex* from 86. *Holme Lea, Well Mead, Kilmington, Axminster EX13 7SQ* Tel (01297) 32744

JONES, Canon William Lloyd. b 36. Univ of Wales (Lamp) BA59. Wycliffe Hall Ox 59. **d** 61 **p** 62. C Holyhead w Rhoscolyn *Ban* 61-65; C Porthmadog 65-67; R Llanfaethlu w Llanfwrog and Llanrhuddlad etc 67-74; R Llanengan and Llangian 74-99; RD Llyn 90-99; Can Ban Cathl from 97; rtd 99. *Ty Gwair, Llangwnadl, Pwllheli LL53 8NY* Tel (01758) 770430

JONES, Mrs Wyn. **d** 01 **p** 02. OLM Linslade *Ox* from 01. *2 Woodside Way, Linslade, Leighton Buzzard LU7 7PN* Tel (01525) 373638

JONES, Wyn. *See* JONES, Ivor Wyn

JONES-BLACKETT, Enid Olive. b 40. Reading Univ BA61. LNSM course 95. **d** 97 **p** 98. OLM Hellesdon *Nor* from 97. *8 Fastolf Close, Hellesdon, Norwich NR6 5RE* Tel (01603) 414895

JONES-CRABTREE, Stephen. b 56. Nottm Univ BTh80. Linc Th Coll 76. **d** 80 **p** 81. C Chorley St Pet *Blackb* 80-83; C Blackpool St Steph 83-84; C Penwortham St Mary 84-88; R Mareham-le-Fen and Revesby *Linc* 88-02; R Hameringham w Scrafield and Winceby 98-02; V Mareham on the Hill 98-02; R Washingborough w Heighington and Canwick from 02. *The Rectory, Church Hill, Washingborough, Lincoln LN4 1EJ* Tel (01522) 800240 E-mail stephen.jones-crabtree@ukonline.co.uk

JONGMAN, Kären Anngel Irene. b 43. EMMTC 97. **d** 01 **p** 02. NSM Northampton St Mary *Pet* from 01. *Brookhill Cottage, Ravensthorpe Road, East Haddon, Northampton NN6 8BY* Tel (01604) 770617 Mobile 07980-881252
E-mail jongman@nccnet.co.uk

JORDAN, Anne. b 42. RGN66 DipN77. Dioc OLM tr scheme 00. **d** 02 **p** 03. OLM Crofton *Wakef* from 02. *95 Ashdene Avenue, Crofton, Wakefield WF4 1LY* Tel (01924) 865527 Mobile 07450-475184

JORDAN, Anthony John. b 50. Birm Univ BEd73. LNSM course. **d** 83 **p** 84. Asst Chapl Uppingham Sch Leics 83-86; Hon C Uppingham w Ayston and Wardley w Belton *Pet* 83-86; Asst Chapl Sherborne Sch 86-87; NSM Bournemouth St Fran *Win* from 88. *64 Watcombe Road, Bournemouth BH6 3LU* Tel (01202) 511845 Fax as telephone E-mail anthonyjordan1@aol.com

JORDAN, Mrs Elizabeth Ann. b 58. New Hall Cam MA82. St Jo Coll Nottm DipTh84. **d** 87 **p** 94. Par Dn Blackpool St Jo *Blackb* 87-90; Par Dn Ewood 90-94; C 94-95; Asst Dir of Ords 90-95; Min Shelfield St Mark CD *Lich* 95-00; Local Min Adv (Wolverhampton) from 95; OLM Course Dir and Team Ldr Min Division from 03. *17 Blackberry Lane, Shire Oak, Walsall WS9 9RQ* Tel (01543) 820352
E-mail elizabeth.jordan@lichfield.anglican.org

JORDAN, John Charles. b 37. CQSW81. N Ord Course 84. **d** 87 **p** 88. C Southport Em *Liv* 87-90; V Abram and Bickershaw 90-95; V Bempton w Flamborough, Reighton w Speeton *York* 95-00; rtd 00. *35 Hollycroft, Barnston, Driffield YO25 8PP* Tel (01262) 468925 E-mail john@jordan55.freeserve.co.uk

JORDAN, Kenneth John. b 31. K Coll Lon. **d** 69 **p** 70. Guyana 69-74; C Roath *Llan* 74-76; V Nantymoel w Wyndham 76-81; V Cardiff St Mary w St Steph 81-83; V Cardiff St Mary and St Steph w St Dyfrig etc 83-01; Miss to Seafarers 83-01; rtd 01. *45 Kimberley Road, Cardiff CF23 5DL*

JORDAN, Peter Harry. b 42. Leeds Univ BA64. Cranmer Hall Dur 70. **d** 73 **p** 74. C Nottingham St Ann w Em *S'well* 73-77; C Edgware Lon 77-82; V Everton St Chrys *Liv* 82-94; Dioc Ev and V Bootle St Mary w St Paul 94-02; Chapl Barcelona *Eur* from 02. *St George's Church, C/ Horacio 38, 08022 Barcelona, Spain* Tel (0034) (93) 417 8867 E-mail stgeorges@wanadoo.es

JORDAN, Richard William. b 56. Lanchester Poly BSc78. St Jo Coll Nottm DipTh84 St Jo Coll Nottm DPS87. **d** 87 **p** 88. C Blackpool St Jo *Blackb* 87-90; V Ewood 90-95; Perm to Offic *Lich* 95-97; Co-ord Walsall Town Cen Min from 97; Asst Min Walsall St Paul from 97. *17 Blackberry Lane, Walsall Wood, Walsall WS9 9RQ* Tel (01922) 614159 Mobile 07773-340207
E-mail richard@church-links.org.uk *or* wbcclp@beep.net

JORDAN, Robert Brian. b 43. Qu Coll Birm 68. **d** 69 **p** 70. C Norton St Mich *Dur* 69-73; C Hastings St Clem and All SS *Chich* 73-74; C Carshalton *S'wark* 74-81; V Catford St Andr from 81. *The Vicarage, 135 Wellmeadow Road, London SE6 1HP* Tel (020) 8697 2600

JORDAN, Ronald Henry. b 30. K Coll Lon. **d** 57 **p** 58. C Clerkenwell H Redeemer w St Phil *Lon* 57-58; C Southgate Ch Ch 58-59; C Edmonton St Mary w St Jo 62-69; Hon C 86-94; V Wood Green St Mich 69-73; Hon C Finchley H Trin 80-86; Perm to Offic from 94; rtd 95. *120 Church Lane, London N2 0TB* Tel (020) 8883 7828

JORDAN, Thomas. b 36. Man Univ DSPT91. NW Ord Course 76. **d** 79 **p** 80. NSM Prenton *Ches* 79-84; NSM Egremont St Jo 84-91; C 91-96; Ind Chapl 91-96; TV Birkenhead Priory 96-01; rtd 01; Perm to Offic *Ches* from 02. *31 Willowbank Road, Birkenhead CH42 7JU* Tel 0151-652 4212
E-mail jordan@farndene.freeserve.co.uk

JORDAN, Trevor. b 44. Lon Hosp MB, BS67 LRCP68 MRCS68. St Jo Coll Nottm MA99. **d** 03. NSM Seamer *York* from 03. *8 Alderson Crescent, Scarborough YO12 4JT* Tel (01723) 865777 Mobile 07887-537244 E-mail trevor@trevorsweb.net

JORDINSON, Vera (Sister Hilary). b 37. Liv Univ BA60 CertEd61. Westcott Ho Cam 88. **d** 89 **p** 94. CSF from 74; Prov Sec 90-01; Gen Sec 96-02; Sec for Miss SSF 96-99; Gift Aid Sec from 01; Lic to Offic *Heref* 89-92; Perm to Offic *Lich* 90-92; *Birm* 92-94 and from 97; NSM Birchfield *Birm* 94-96. *St Francis House, 113 Gillott Road, Birmingham B16 0ET* Tel 0121-454 8302 Fax 455 9784 E-mail hilcsf@fish.co.uk

JORYSZ, Ian Herbert. b 62. Van Mildert Coll Dur BSc84 MA95 Liv Univ PhD87. Ripon Coll Cuddesdon BA89 MA95. **d** 90 **p** 91. C Houghton le Spring *Dur* 90-93; C Ferryhill 93-95; Research Officer to Bp of Bradwell from 95; P-in-c S Weald *Chelmsf* 95-00; V from 00. *The Vicarage, Wigley Bush Lane, South Weald, Brentwood CM14 5QP* Tel (01277) 212054 Fax 262388 E-mail jorysz@primex.co.uk

JOSS, Martin James Torquil. b 60. Univ of Wales (Lamp) BA79. EAMTC 03. C Harlow Town Cen w Lt Parndon *Chelmsf* from 03. *92 Ram Gorse, Harlow CM20 1PZ* Tel (01279) 863074 Mobile 07816-042476 E-mail martin.joss@ntlworld.com

JOWETT, The Very Revd Alfred. b 14. CBE72. St Cath Coll Cam BA35 MA59 Sheff Univ Hon DLitt82. Linc Th Coll 43. **d** 44 **p** 45. C Goole *Sheff* 44-47; Sec Sheff Coun of Chs and Marriage Guidance Coun 47-51; V Sheff St Geo and St Steph 51-60; V

Doncaster St Geo 60-64; Hon Can Sheff Cathl 60-64; Select Preacher Ox Univ 64 and 79; Dean Man 64-83; rtd 83; Perm to Offic *Sheff* from 84. *37 Stone Delf, Sheffield S10 3QX* Tel 0114-230 5455

JOWETT, Ms Hilary Anne. b 54. Hull Univ BA75. Cranmer Hall Dur IDC80. **dss** 82 **d** 87 **p** 94. Sheff St Jo *Sheff* 82-83; Brampton Bierlow 83-87; Par Dn 87-89; Hon Par Dn Sharrow St Andr 89-95; Chapl Nether Edge Hosp Sheff 89-95; C Sheff St Mark Broomhill *Sheff* 95-97; C Mosbrough 97-00; TR Gleadless from 00. *The Rectory, 243 Hollinsend Road, Sheffield S12 2EE* Tel 0114-239 0757 E-mail hajowett@gleadless243.freeserve.co.uk

JOWETT, Nicholas Peter Alfred. b 44. St Cath Coll Cam BA66 MA Bris Univ CertEd67 Birm Univ DipTh74. Qu Coll Birm 72. **d** 75 **p** 76. C Wales *Sheff* 75-78; TV Sheff Manor 78-83; V Brampton Bierlow 83-89; V Psalter Lane St Andr from 89; Dioc Ecum Adv from 01. *The Rectory, 243 Hollinsend Road, Sheffield S12 2EE* Tel 0114-239 0757 *or* 258 6550 E-mail njowett@fish.co.uk

JOWITT, Andrew Robert Benson. b 56. Down Coll Cam BA78 PGCE79 MA81. Wycliffe Hall Ox 88. **d** 90 **p** 91. C Northampton Em *Pet* 90-94; C Barking St Marg w St Patr *Chelmsf* 94-98; TV 98-00; TV Stantonbury and Willen *Ox* from 00; Bp's Officer for Evang from 00. *Church House, 1A Atterbrook, Bradwell Abbey, Milton Keynes MK13 9EY* Tel (01908) 320850

JOWITT, David Arthur Benson. b 25. St Jo Coll Ox BA49 MA53. Sarum Th Coll 49. **d** 51 **p** 52. C Heckmondwike *Wakef* 51-56; C Harrogate St Wilfrid *Ripon* 56-59; V Kirkby Fleetham 60-69; R Langton on Swale 60-69; OGS from 65; Superior 75-81; P-in-c Edin St Ninian *Edin* 69-77; Dioc Supernumerary 77-80; Chapl Edin R Infirmary 77-80; Syn Clerk *Edin* 77-90; Can St Mary's Cathl 77-90; Vice-Provost 81-86; P-in-c S Queensferry 86-90; rtd 90; Hon C Edin Old St Paul *Edin* 91-99; Perm to Offic *S'wark* from 01. *16 The Quadrangle, Morden College, 19 St German's Place, London SE3 0PW* Tel (020) 8305 0811

JOWITT, John Frederick Benson. b 23. Selw Hall Th Coll 57. **d** 59 **p** 59. Uganda 59-63; CF 63-73; R Thrandeston, Stuston and Brome w Oakley *St E* 73-82; V Docking *Nor* 82-83; P-in-c Gt Bircham 82-83; R Docking w the Birchams 83-88; P-in-c Stanhoe w Barwick 85-88; R Docking w The Birchams and Stanhoe w Barwick 88; rtd 88; Perm to Offic *Nor* from 88; *St E* from 90. *White Lodge, The Street, North Cove, Beccles NR34 7PN* Tel (01502) 76404

JOY, Bernard David. b 50. Sarum & Wells Th Coll 90. **d** 92 **p** 93. C Shortlands *Roch* 92-94; C Henbury *Bris* 94-96; V Bristol St Aid w St Geo 96-03; P-in-c Bridgwater St Fran *B & W* from 03. *The Vicarage, Saxon Green, Bridgwater TA6 4HZ* Tel (01278) 422744 Mobile 07796-678478 E-mail bj00764884@blueyonder.co.uk

JOY, Canon Leslie John Clifton. b 09. AKC33. St Steph Ho Ox 33. **d** 33 **p** 34. C Byker St Laur *Newc* 33-40; C-in-c Balkwell CD 40-48; V Newc St Matt 48-61; V Newc St Matt w St Mary 61-64; V Blyth St Mary 64-83; RD Bedlington 69-83; Hon Can Newc Cathl 70-83; rtd 83; Perm to Offic *Newc* 86-94; Perm to Offic *Ox* 94; Hon C Reading St Giles from 94. *31 Emmbrook Court, Reading RG6 2TZ* Tel 0118-987 3855

JOY, Canon Matthew Osmund Clifton. b 40. St Edm Hall Ox BA62 MA66. St Steph Ho Ox 62. **d** 64 **p** 65. C Brinksway *Ches* 64-66; C Southwick St Columba *Dur* 66-69; V Hartlepool H Trin 69-85; V Rotherham St Paul, St Mich and St Jo Ferham Park *Sheff* 85-88; V Masbrough 88-95; RD Rotherham 88-93; P-in-c Bordesley St Benedict *Birm* 95-01; V from 01; Bp's Adv on Chr/Muslim Relns from 95. *St Benedict's Vicarage, 55 Hob Moor Road, Birmingham B10 9AY* Tel 0121-772 2726 Fax as telephone

JOYCE, Alison Jane. b 59. Univ of Wales (Swansea) BA81 SS Coll Cam PGCE84 Bris Univ MLitt87 Ox Univ BA87 MA94 Birm Univ PhD00. Ripon Coll Cuddesdon 86. **d** 88 **p** 94. Par Dn Chalgrove w Berrick Salome *Ox* 88-90; Tutor WMMTC 90-95; Tutor Qu Coll Birm 95-96; NSM Moseley St Anne *Birm* from 96; Dean NSMs from 00. *88 Willows Road, Balsall Heath, Birmingham B12 9QD* Tel 0121-440 5171

JOYCE, Anthony Owen. b 35. Selw Coll Cam BA60 MA64. Wycliffe Hall Ox 60. **d** 62 **p** 63. C Birm St Martin *Birm* 62-67; Rhodesia 67-70; V Birm St Luke *Birm* 70-79; V Downend *Bris* 79-01; RD Stapleton 83-89; rtd 01; Perm to Offic *Bris* from 01. *116 Jellicoe Avenue, Stapleton, Bristol BS16 1WJ* Tel 0117-956 2510 E-mail tony@joycet.freeserve.co.uk

JOYCE, Ernest Thomas Chancellor. b 16. Lon Univ LLB67. Chich Th Coll 68. **d** 70 **p** 71. C Southsea H Spirit *Portsm* 70-75; V New Southgate St Paul *Lon* 75-77; Chantry Priest Chpl St Mich and H So Walsingham 77-81; Perm to Offic *Nor* from 77; rtd 81. *St Benedict, 16 Cleaves Drive, Walsingham NR22 6EQ* Tel (01328) 820612

JOYCE, Gordon Franklin. b 51. Birm Univ BA72. St Jo Coll Nottm 86. **d** 88 **p** 89. C Didsbury St Jas and Em *Man* 88-92; V Tonge w Alkrington from 92. *St Michael's Vicarage, 184 Kirkway, Middleton, Manchester M24 1LN* Tel 0161-643 2891

JOYCE, Graham Leslie. b 49. Lon Univ CertEd71. Trin Coll Bris DipHE89. **d** 89 **p** 90. C Heald Green St Cath *Ches* 89-93; R Church Lawton from 93. *The Rectory, 1 Liverpool Road West, Church Lawton, Stoke-on-Trent ST7 3DE* Tel (01270) 882103 Fax as telephone E-mail grahamljoyce@aol.com

JOYCE, John Barnabas Altham. b 47. St Chad's Coll Dur BA69 Lon Univ DipEd86. St Steph Ho Ox 72. **d** 74 **p** 75. C Reading St Giles *Ox* 74-77; C Cowley St Jo 77-80; Dioc Youth and Community Officer 80-87; V Hangleton *Chich* 87-94; Dioc Adv for Schs and Dir Educn 94-99; R Hurstpierpoint from 99. *The Rectory, 21 Cuckfield Road, Hurstpierpoint, Hassocks BN6 9RP* Tel (01273) 832203 E-mail rectorhurst@aol.com

JOYCE, Kingsley Reginald. b 49. MBE00 TD91. Man Univ BSc70. Cuddesdon Coll 70. **d** 73 **p** 74. C High Wycombe *Ox* 73-76; C Fingest 76-79; C Hambleden 76-79; C Medmenham 76-79; C Fawley (Bucks) 76-79; C Turville 76-79; P-in-c Hambleden Valley 79-80; R 80-87; R Friern Barnet St Jas *Lon* 87-91; CF from 91. *c/o MOD Chaplains (Army)* Tel (01980) 615804 Fax 615800

JOYCE, Margaret. b 47. Oak Hill NSM Course 86. **d** 89 **p** 94. NSM Chadwell Heath *Chelmsf* 89-92; NSM Bath Odd Down w Combe Hay *B & W* from 92; Chapl Bath and West Community NHS Trust from 95. *69 Bloomfield Rise, Bath BA2 2BN* Tel (01225) 840864 E-mail margaretjoyce@stphilipstjames.org

JOYCE, Martin Ernest Chancellor. b 50. K Coll Lon 69. **d** 73 **p** 74. C Leigh Park *Portsm* 73-77; C Milton 77-83; TV Cambridge Ascension *Ely* 83-85; V Blackpool St Mich *Blackb* 85-87; Perm to Offic *Glas* from 94. *13 Teasdale Road, Carlisle CA3 0HF* Tel (01228) 538767 E-mail martin.joyce3@virgin.net

JOYCE, Canon Norman. b 14. St Jo Coll Dur BA35 MA38 DipTh38. **d** 37 **p** 38. C Monkwearmouth All SS *Dur* 37-40; C W Hartlepool St Paul 40-43; V Monkwearmouth All SS 43-53; R Bowness *Carl* 53-57; R N Wingfield *Derby* 57-73; TR N Wingfield, Pilsley and Tupton 73-80; Hon Can Derby Cathl 77-80; rtd 80; Perm to Offic *Carl* from 80. *Fell View, Thurstonfield, Carlisle CA7 6HG* Tel (01228) 576471

JOYCE, Paul David. b 70. Qu Coll Birm 00. **d** 02 **p** 03. C Perry Beeches Birm from 02. *St Matthew's House, 45 Epwell Road, Perry Barr, Birmingham B44 8DH* Tel 0121-356 3036 Fax as telephone

JOYCE, Miss Penelope Anne. b 53. St Mary's Coll Cheltenham CertEd74. Wycliffe Hall Ox. **d** 00 **p** 01. C Ox St Clem *Ox* from 00. *Paradigm Shift, 12A Morrell Avenue, Oxford OX4 1NE* Tel and fax (01865) 790837 Mobile 07808-181885 E-mail penny@stclements.org.uk *or* pennyre.joyce@virgin.net

JOYCE, Philip Rupert. b 38. Selw Coll Cam BA68 MA72. Cranmer Hall Dur 68. **d** 70 **p** 71. C Newland St Jo *York* 70-73; C Woolwich St Mary w H Trin *S'wark* 73-77; Chapl Thames Poly 73-77; Chapl S Bank Poly 77-79; rtd 03. *49 Ashton Gardens, Chadwell Heath, Romford RM6 6RT* Tel (020) 8491 5427 E-mail philipjoyce@ntlworld.com

JOYCE, Raymond. b 37. Keele Univ BA60 MA67 Linc Coll Ox BA62 MA68 Leic Univ MA97. St Steph Ho Ox 78. **d** 80 **p** 81. NSM Normanton *Derby* 80-83; NSM Derby St Alkmund and St Werburgh 83-87; Lic to Offic 87-97; NSM Mickleover All SS 97-00; Perm to Offic from 01. *23 Hindscarth Crescent, Mickleover, Derby DE3 9NN* Tel (01332) 519001

JOYCE, Sister. See CROSSLAND, Sister Joyce

JOYCE, Canon Terence Alan. b 57. St Jo Coll Nottm BTh84. **d** 84 **p** 85. C Mansfield St Pet *S'well* 84-88; V Greasley 88-00; Dioc Dir of Ords from 99; Dir Post-Ord Support and Tr from 01; Hon Can S'well Minster from 02. *86 Main Road, Ravenshead, Nottingham NG15 9GW* Tel (01623) 489819 E-mail tjoyce@southwell.anglican.org

JUBA, Bishop of. See MARONA, The Most Revd Joseph Biringi Hassan

JUCKES, Jonathan Sydney. b 61. St Andr Univ MA83. Ridley Hall Cam BA87. **d** 88 **p** 89. C Sevenoaks St Nic *Roch* 88-92; Proclamation Trust 92-95; C St Helen Bishopsgate w St Andr Undershaft etc *Lon* 95-98; TR Kirk Ella *York* from 98. *The Rectory, 2 School Lane, Kirk Ella, Hull HU10 7NR* Tel (01482) 653040 E-mail juckes@juckes.karoo.co.uk

JUDD, Adrian Timothy. b 67. Lanc Univ BA88. Cranmer Hall Dur BA92 Trin Coll Singapore 92 St Jo Coll Dur Dip Minl Studies 93. **d** 93 **p** 94. C Dudley St Aug Holly Hall *Worc* 93-97; V Stockbridge Village *Liv* 97-99; V Went Valley *Wakef* from 00. *The Vicarage, Marlpit Lane, Darrington, Pontefract WF8 3AB* Tel (01977) 704744

JUDD, Colin Ivor. b 35. Dur Univ BA61. Ridley Hall Cam 61. **d** 63 **p** 64. C Stratford St Jo w Ch Ch *Chelmsf* 63-66; C Kimberworth *Sheff* 66-68; Area Sec CMS *Bradf* and *Wakef* 68-80; V Bradf St Columba w St Andr *Bradf* 80-00; rtd 00; Perm to Offic *Bradf* from 01. *57 Grosvenor Road, Shipley BD18 4RB* Tel (01274) 584775

JUDD, Mrs Nicola Jane. b 51. Birm Coll of Educn CertEd72. S Dios Minl Tr Scheme 87. **d** 90 **p** 94. NSM Abbotts Ann and Upper and Goodworth Clatford *Win* from 90; Adv for NSM from 01. *13 Belmont Close, Andover SP10 2DE* Tel (01264) 363364

JUDD, The Very Revd Peter Somerset Margesson. b 49. Trin Hall Cam BA71. Cuddesdon Coll 71. **d** 74 **p** 75. C Salford St Phil w St Steph *Man* 74-76; Chapl Clare Coll Cam 76-81; C Burnham *Ox* 81-82; TV Burnham w Dropmore, Hitcham and Taplow 82-88; V Iffley 88-97; RD Cowley 94-97; Provost Chelmsf 97-00;

Dean Chelmsf from 00. *The Deanery, 3 Harlings Grove, Chelmsford CM1 1YQ* Tel (01245) 354318 or 294480
E-mail dean@chelmsfordcathedral.org.uk

JUDGE, Andrew Duncan. b 50. Cape Town Univ BCom72 Keble Coll Ox MA81. Pietermaritzburg Th Sem 82. **d** 83 **p** 84. S Africa 83-01; C Westville 84-87; R Prestbury 88-94; R Westville 94-01; TV Keynsham *B & W* from 01. *St Francis's Vicarage, Warwick Road, Keynsham, Bristol BS31 2PW* Tel 0117-373 7478
E-mail revjudge@blueyonder.co.uk

JUDGE, James Arthur. b 20. Lon Univ BD50. ALCD50. **d** 50 **p** 51. C Southsea St Jude *Portsm* 50-52; Australia 52-62; R Street *B & W* 62-77; V Banwell 77-88; rtd 88. *512 Gipps House, 270 Jersey Road, Woollahra, NSW, Australia 2025* Tel (0061) (2) 9363 0833

JUDGE, Mark Rollo. b 60. Chich Th Coll BTh92. **d** 92 **p** 93. C Forest Gate St Edm *Chelmsf* 92-96; V Gt Ilford St Luke 96-01; Chapl H L Hawes Funeral Dirs 99-01; Asst Chapl Havering Hosps NHS Trust from 01. *Harold Wood Hospital, Gubbins Lane, Harold Wood, Romford RM3 0BE* Tel (017708) 345533
E-mail markjudge_new.uk@excite.co.uk

JUDSON, Mrs Mary Ruth. b 47. Bretton Hall Coll DipEd68. NEOC 89. **d** 92 **p** 94. Par Dn Chester le Street *Dur* 92-94; C 94-96; V Millfield St Mark and Pallion St Luke from 96. *The Vicarage, St Mark's Terrace, Sunderland SR4 7BN* Tel 0191-565 6372 Fax as telephone
E-mail mary.judson@durham.anglican.org

JUDSON, Paul Wesley. b 46. Leic Poly DipAD69 ATD71. Cranmer Hall Dur 87. **d** 89 **p** 90. C Lobley Hill *Dur* 89-92; C Chester le Street 92-96; Ed Dioc Publications and Sec Dioc Bd of Soc Resp 96-98; C Millfield St Mark and Pallion St Luke from 96; Dioc Publications Officer from 98; Dioc Dir of Communications from 02. *The Vicarage, St Mark's Terrace, Sunderland SR4 7BN* Tel 0191-514 7872 Fax as telephone
E-mail director.of.communications@durham.anglican.org

JUDSON, Peter. b 39. Lon Univ BSc61 Plymouth Univ PGCE87. SW Minl Tr Course 99. **d** 02 **p** 03. OLM Bude Haven and Marhamchurch *Truro* from 02. *Meadowcroft, Bagbury Road, Bude EX23 8QJ* Tel and fax (01288) 356597 Mobile 07970-115538

JUKES, Keith Michael. b 54. Leeds Univ BA76. Linc Th Coll 77. **d** 78 **p** 79. C Wordsley *Lich* 78-81; C Wolverhampton 81-83; C-in-c Stoneydelph St Martin CD 83-90; TR Glascote and Stonydelph 90-91; RD Tamworth 90-91; TR Cannock 91-97; V Hatherton 91-97; Preb Lich Cathl 96-97; P-in-c Selby Abbey *York* 97-99; V from 99. *The Abbey Vicarage, 32A Leeds Road, Selby YO8 4HX* Tel (01757) 709218 or 703123
E-mail kmjukes@aol.com

JUKES (née WEATHERHOGG), Mrs Susanne. b 56. Leeds Univ BA77 Sunderland Univ CertHE01 Coll of Ripon & York St Jo PGCE78. NEOC 98. **d** 01 **p** 02. C Monk Fryston and S Milford *York* from 01. *The Abbey Vicarage, 32A Leeds Road, Selby YO8 4HX* Tel (01757) 706719 Mobile 07764-375430
E-mail susanne_jukes@hotmail.com

JUMP, Elizabeth Anne. b 63. Liv Inst of Educn BA95. N Ord Course 97. **d** 00 **p** 01. C Walkden and Lt Hulton *Man* 00-03; P-in-c Elton St Steph from 03. *St Stephen's Vicarage, 44 Peers Street, Bury BL9 2QF* Tel 0161-764 1775
E-mail revlizjump@hotmail.com

JUNG, Mrs Jennifer Margaret. b 61. STETS DipTh95. **d** 98 **p** 99. NSM Fareham H Trin *Portsm* 98-02. *5 Lower Spinney, Warsash, Southampton SO31 9NL* Tel (01489) 578758

JUPE, Canon Derek Robert. b 26. TCD BA53 Div Test54 MA67. **d** 54 **p** 55. C Lurgan Ch the Redeemer *D & D* 54-57; C Dublin Harold's Cross *D & G* 57-60; I Easkey w Kilglass *T, K & A* 60-65; Deputation Sec (Ireland) BCMS 65-72; R Man St Jerome w Ardwick St Silas *Man* 72-78; V Ardsley *Sheff* 78-83; I Tempo and Clabby *Clogh* 83-92; Can Clogh Cathl 89-92; rtd 92; Perm to Offic *Cov* from 92. *29 St Andrew's Drive, Whitstone, Nuneaton CV11 6NQ* Tel (024) 7668 8488

JUPE, Martin Roy. b 27. Lon Univ BD63. St Deiniol's Hawarden. **d** 61 **p** 62. C Camborne *Truro* 61-64; V Penzance St Jo 64-92; RD Penwith 73-76; rtd 92; Perm to Offic *Truro* from 92. *25 Nancherrow Terrace, St Just, Penzance TR19 7LA* Tel (01736) 788320

✠**JUPP, The Rt Revd Roger Alan.** b 56. St Edm Hall Ox BA78 MA82 Surrey Univ PGCE96. Chich Th Coll 79. **d** 80 **p** 81 **c** 03. C Newbold w Dunston *Derby* 80-83; C Cowley St Jo *Ox* 83-85; C Islington St Jas w St Phil *Lon* 85-86; V Lower Beeding *Chich* 86-90; Dom Chapl to Bp Horsham 86-91; V Burgess Hill St Jo 90-93; TR Burgess Hill St Jo w St Edw 93-94; Perm to Offic 97-98; C Aldwick 98-00; Papua New Guinea from 00; Prin Newton Th Coll 00-03; Bp Popondota from 03. *Anglican Diocese of Popondota, PO Box 26, Popondetta, Papua New Guinea* Tel (00675) 329 7194, 329 7073 or 329 7440 Fax 329 7194
E-mail acpngpop@global.net.pg

JUPP, Vincent John. b 64. Leic Poly BTEC HNC87. St Jo Coll Nottm Dip Th & Min 00. **d** 00 **p** 01. C Evington *Leic* from 00. *14 Fallowfield Road, Evington, Leicester LE5 6LQ* Tel 0116-241 2833 Fax as telephone E-mail vjupp@leicester.anglican.org

JUSTICE, Keith Leonard. b 42. Wolv Univ BSc68 CEng83 MIMechE83 Wycliffe Hall Ox DipMin93. **d** 93 **p** 94. C Penwortham St Mary *Blackb* 93-96; C Dovercourt and Parkeston w Harwich *Chelmsf* 96-98; V Wentworth *Sheff* 98-01; Chapl Rotherham Gen Hosps NHS Trust 98-01; R Melrose *Edin* from 01. *The Rectory, 20 High Cross Avenue, Melrose TD6 9SU* Tel (01896) 822626 Fax as telephone E-mail kjustice01@aol.com

JUSTICE, Peter John Michael. b 37. Bernard Gilpin Soc Dur 59 Chich Th Coll 60. **d** 63 **p** 64. C Digswell *St Alb* 63-67; C Guildf St Nic *Guildf* 67-68; C Mill End *St Alb* 68-70; V Eaton Bray 70-73; Hon C Prestwood *Ox* 73-84; Chapl to the Deaf 84-90; rtd 90; Perm to Offic *Ox* 90-93; *Ex* 94-95; *St E* from 95. *8 Theatre Street, Woodbridge IP12 4NE* Tel (01394) 380899

JUSTICE, Canon Simon Charles. b 66. Univ of Wales (Lamp) BD88 Edin Univ MTh90. Cranmer Hall Dur 90. **d** 92 **p** 93. C Tilehurst St Nich *Ox* 92-95; USA from 95; R Troy NY St Paul from 95; Can All SS Cathl Albany from 98. *58 3rd Street, Troy, NY 12180, USA* Tel (001) (518) 273 7351
E-mail justicemm@aol.com

JUTSUM, Linda Mary. See ELLIOTT, Mrs Linda Mary

K

KABOLEH, David Reardon. b 64. Westmr Coll Ox MTh01. Trin Coll Nairobi BD88. **d** 90 **p** 91. Kenya 90-95; C-in-c Nairobi St Phil 90-92; TV Nairobi St Luke and Immanuel 93-95; NSM Hoddesdon *St Alb* 95-97; NSM Ox St Matt *Ox* from 97; NSM Blackbird Leys from 97; Hon C Ox St Aldate from 03. *32 Acacia Avenue, Oxford OX4 7GY* Tel (01865) 433736
E-mail kaboleh@aol.com

✠**KAFITY, The Rt Revd Samir.** Beirut Univ BA57. Near E Sch of Th 57. **d** 57 **p** 58 **c** 86. Jerusalem 57-59; Jordan 59-75; Adn Beirut 74-77; Gen Sec Cen Syn of Episc Ch in JEM 77-86; Adn Jerusalem 77-86; Bp Jerusalem from 86. *St George's Close, PO Box 1248, Jerusalem 91109, Israel* Fax (00972) (2) 27 3847

KAGGWA, Nelson Sonny. b 58. E Lon Univ BA91. Bible Tr Inst Tennessee DipTh84 Bp Tucker Coll Mukono 77. **d** 80 **p** 80. Kenya 80-83; USA 83; Hon C Ox SS Phil and Jas w St Marg *Ox* 84-85; C W Ham *Chelmsf* 86-87; TV Walthamstow St Mary w St Steph 87-92; Perm to Offic *Sheff* 92-95; V Sheff St Paul 96-97; rtd 98. *Al-Salam, 36 Standish Gardens, Sheffield S5 8YD* Tel 0114-273 1428 Mobile 07989-261278 Fax 0114-273 1348
E-mail kaggwanelsonibrahim@msn.com

KAJUMBA, The Ven Daniel Steven Kimbugwe. b 52. S'wark Ord Course. **d** 85 **p** 86. C Goldington *St Alb* 85-87; Uganda 87-99; TV Horley *S'wark* 99-01; Adn Reigate from 01. *84 Higher Drive, Purley CR8 2HJ* Tel (020) 8660 9276
E-mail daniel@kajumba.freeserve.co.uk

KALUS, Rupert. b 61. St Jo Coll Dur BA85 MA93 BA01 W Sussex Inst of HE PGCE87. Cranmer Hall Dur 99. **d** 02 **p** 03. C Dur St Cuth *Dur* 02; C Dur N from 02. *112 Moor Crescent, Durham DH1 1DL* Tel 0191-386 3644

KAMEGERI, Stephen. See NSHIMYE, Stephen Kamegeri

KAMPALA, Bishop of. See MPALANYI-NKOYOYO, The Most Revd Livingstone

KAMRAN, Ernest P. b 58. **d** 90 **p** 90. C Shoreditch St Leon and Hoxton St Jo *Lon* 94-97. *58 Priestman Point, Rainhill Way, London E3 3EZ* Tel (020) 8983 4730

KANERIA, Rajni. b 57. Bath Univ BPharm82. Wycliffe Hall Ox 83. **d** 86 **p** 87. C Hyson Green *S'well* 86-87; C Hyson Green St Paul w St Steph 87-89; C Harold Hill St Geo *Chelmsf* 91-97; TV Oadby *Leic* 91-97. *32 Rendall Road, Leicester LE4 6LE* Tel 0116-266 6613

KARAMURA, Grace Patrick. b 62. Nat Teachers' Coll Uganda DipEd89 Rob Coll Cam MPhil95 Leeds Univ PhD98. Bp Tucker Coll Mukono BD92. **d** 92 **p** 93. C All SS Cathl Kampala Uganda 92-93; C Ebbw Vale *Mon* 98-01; TV 01-03; V Pontyclun w Talygarn *Llan* from 03. *The Vicarage, Heol Miskin, Pontyclun CF72 9AJ* Tel (01443) 225477 Fax as telephone
E-mail gracekaramu@hotmail.com

KARRACH, Herbert Adolf. b 24. TCD BA46 MB48 BCh48 BAO48 LSHTM DTM&H55. EAMTC 85. **d** 88 **p** 89. Hon C Snettisham w Ingoldisthorpe and Fring *Nor* 88-95; Perm to Offic from 95. *Narnia, 5 Docking Road, Fring, King's Lynn PE31 6SQ* Tel (01485) 518346

KASHOURIS, Peter Zacharias. b 66. Peterho Cam BA89 MA93. St Steph Ho Ox 92. **d** 94 **p** 95. C Hampstead St Jo *Lon* 94-97; R Hartlepool St Hilda *Dur* from 97; Dioc Ecum Officer from 03.

The Rectory, Church Close, Hartlepool TS24 0PW Tel (01429) 267030 E-mail p.j.kashouris@durham.anglican.org

KASIBANTE, Amos Sebadduka. b 54. Trin Coll Cam BA83 MA87 Yale Univ STM89. Bp Tucker Coll Mukono DipTh80 Berkeley Div Sch 88. **d** 79 **p** 80. Uganda 79-92; C Lyantonde 79--80; Tutor Bp Tucker Coll Mukono 83-92; Tutor Coll of Ascension Selly Oak 93-95; Prin Simon of Cyrene Th Inst 95-97; Vice-Prin St Mich Coll Llan 97-02; Chapl Leic Univ *Leic* from 02. *290 Victoria Park Road, Leicester LE2 1XE* Tel 0116-270 1900 Fax 255 6318 E-mail amos.kasibante@virgin.net *or* ask11@le.ac.uk

KASOZI NSAMBA, Jackson. b 50. Bp Tucker Coll Mukono BD91 Birm Univ MPhil94. **d** 83 **p** 84. Uganda 84-92 and 96-99; V St Andr Cathl Mityana 84-88; Chapl to Bp W Buganda 91-92; Perm to Offic *Cov* 93-94; Adn W Buganda 96-99; Acting Dean St Paul's Cathl 98-99; NSM Limehouse *Lon* 00-01; NSM Old Ford St Paul and St Mark from 02. *c/o The Vicarage, St Stephen's Road, London E3 5JL* Tel (020) 7515 1928

KASSELL, Colin George Henry. b 42. DCC90. Valladolid Spain 63 Ripon Coll Cuddesdon 76. **d** 68 **p** 69. In RC Ch 69-75; Perm to Offic *Ox* 76-77; C Denham 77-80; V Brotherton *Wakef* 80-84; Chapl and Past Ldr St Cath Hospice Crawley 84-91; R Rogate w Terwick and Trotton w Chithurst *Chich* 91-94; C Heene from 94; Chapl Worthing Hosp from 94. *Park House, 3 Madeira Avenue, Worthing BN11 2AT* Tel (01903) 526571 Mobile 07802-259310

KATE, Sister. *See* BURGESS, Sister Kate Lamorna

KATO, Satoru John Stephen. b 54. Tokyo Union Th Sem BA83 MDiv85 St Steph Ho Ox 97. **d** 00 **p** 01. C Broughton *Blackb* from 00. *60 Lansdown Hill, Fulwood, Preston PR2 3UX* Tel (01772) 861809 E-mail satoru@kato.fsnet.co.uk

KAUNHOVEN, Anthony Peter. b 55. Leeds Univ BA78 Coll of Ripon & York St Jo PGCE79 Edin Univ DipMin80. Edin Th Coll 79. **d** 81 **p** 82. C Leeds St Aid *Ripon* 81-84; C Hawksworth Wood 84-89; V Upper Nidderdale 89-91; Hon C Rawdon *Bradf* 96-99; P-in-c Old Brampton *Derby* from 99; Jt Dioc Ecum Officer from 01. *The Rectory, 25 Oldridge Close, Chesterfield S40 4UF* Tel (01246) 558112 E-mail jazzyrector@aol.com

KAVANAGH, Michael Lowther. b 58. CPsychol90 MBPsS90 York Univ BA80 Newc Univ MSc82 Leeds Univ BA86. Coll of Resurr Mirfield 84. **d** 87 **p** 88. C Boston Spa *York* 87-91; V Beverley St Nic 91-97; RD Beverley 95-97; Abp's Dom Chapl from 97; Dir of Ords from 97. *Brew House Cottage, The Palace, Bishopthorpe, York YO23 2QE* Tel (01904) 706822 E-mail chaplain@bishopthorpepalace.co.uk

KAY, Dennis. b 57. St As Minl Tr Course 96. **d** 99 **p** 00. NSM Llangystennin *St As* from 99. *22 Upper Promenade, Colwyn Bay LL28 4BS* Tel (01492) 531750 Fax as telephone

KAY, George Ronald. b 24. Sarum & Wells Th Coll 74. **d** 77 **p** 78. NSM Bemerton *Sarum* 77-87; rtd 87; Perm to Offic *Sarum* 89-00. *The Lodge, 157 Wilton Road, Salisbury SP2 7JH* Tel (01722) 338326

KAY, Ian Geoffrey. Nor Ord Course. **d** 89 **p** 90. NSM Rochdale *Man* 89-91 and from 95; NSM Heywood St Luke w All So 91-95. *161 Norden Road, Rochdale OL11 5PT* Tel (01706) 639497

KAY, Marjory Marianne Kate. b 61. Melba Memorial Conservatorium Dip Music82 Melbourne Univ Dip Bibl Studies 86 Chich Inst of HE 94. **d** 97. NSM Godshill *Portsm* from 97. *c/o The Revd John Ryder, The Vicarage, Church Hill, Godshill, Ventnor PO38 3HY*

KAY, Ronald William. b 28. Liv Univ BEng49 MEng51. Tyndale Hall Bris 59. **d** 61 **p** 62. C Sparkbrook Ch Ch *Birm* 61-65; V Westcombe Park St Geo *S'wark* 65-76; R Doddington *Linc* 76-78; V Skellingthorpe 76-78; R Skellingthorpe w Doddington 78-91; rtd 91; Perm to Offic *Linc* 91-00. *18 Abingdon Avenue, Lincoln LN6 3LE* Tel (01522) 696275

KAYE, Alistair Geoffrey. b 62. Reading Univ BSc85. St Jo Coll Nottm DPS90 Dip Th Studies 90. **d** 90 **p** 91. C Gt Horton *Bradf* 90-94; C Rushden w Newton Bromswold *Pet* 94-98; V Upper Armley *Ripon* from 98; Asst AD Armley from 02. *22 Hill End Crescent, Leeds LS12 3PW* Tel 0113-263 8788

KAYE, Bruce Norman. b 39. Lon Univ BD64 Sydney Univ BA66 Basel Univ DrTheol75. Moore Th Coll Sydney ThL64. **d** 64 **p** 65. Australia 64-66 and from 83; Perm to Offic *Dur* 67-69; Tutor St Jo Coll Dur 68-75; Sen Tutor 75-83; Vice Prin 79-83. *General Synod Office, PO Box Q190, Queen Victoria Buildings, Sydney, NSW, Australia 1230* Tel (0061) (2) 9265 1525 Fax 9264 6552 E-mail gsoffice@anglican.org.au

KAYE, Canon Gerald Trevor. b 32. Man Univ BSc54. Oak Hill Th Coll. **d** 56 **p** 57. C Widnes St Ambrose *Liv* 56-58; C St Helens St Mark 58-62; V Brixton Hill St Sav *S'wark* 62-65; Canada 65-85; Hon Can Keewatin 70-75; Adn Patricia 75-78; V Slough *Ox* 85-97; rtd 97. *Craiguanach, Torlundy, Fort William PH33 6SW* Tel (01397) 705395

KAYE, Norman. b 15. St Chad's Coll Dur BA47. **d** 49 **p** 50. C Morley St Paul *Wakef* 49-51; C Mexborough *Sheff* 51-54; V Dalton 54-59; V Liv St Paul Stanley *Liv* 59-68; R Leighton w Eaton Constantine *Lich* 68-80; P-in-c Wroxeter 68-80; rtd 80. *7 Rope Lane, Shavington, Crewe CW2 5DT* Tel (01270) 664170

KAYE, Peter Alan. b 47. K Coll Lon BD71 AKC71 Birm Univ DPS80 Leic Univ MA82 CQSW82. St Aug Coll Cant 71. **d** 72 **p** 73. C Fulham All SS *Lon* 72-74; Chapl Jo Conolly Hosp Birm 74-80; Rubery Hill and Jos Sheldon Hosps 74-80; Hon C Northfield *Birm* 80-83; Perm to Offic from 00. *Hildegarden, 99 Bunbury Road, Northfield, Birmingham B31 2ND* Tel 0121-624 8399 E-mail peter.a2030797@infotrade.co.uk

KAYE, Timothy Henry. b 52. Linc Th Coll 77. **d** 80 **p** 81. C Warsop S'well 80-83; C Far Headingley St Chad *Ripon* 83-86; P-in-c Birkby *Wakef* 86; TV N Huddersfield 86-91; R Stone St Mich w Aston St Sav *Lich* 91-95; V S Kirkby *Wakef* from 95. *The Vicarage, Bull Lane, South Kirkby, Pontefract WF9 3QD* Tel (01977) 642795

KAZIRO, Godfrey Sam. b 48. BDSc Lon Univ MSc FDSRCPSGlas FFDRCSI. **d** 02. OLM Waterloo St Jo w St Andr *S'wark* from 02. *19 Hampshire Road, Hornchurch RM11 3EU* Tel (01708) 441609

KEANE, Chan James Goldsworthy. b 23. OBE84 JP71. Selw Coll Cam BA47 MA49. Cuddesdon Coll 47. **d** 49 **p** 50. C Penarth w Lavernock *Llan* 49-56; Org Sec Ch in Wales Prov Youth Coun 56-65; Dir Ch in Wales Publications 65-79; Gen Sec Ch in Wales Prov Educn Coun 65-79; Hon Can Llan Cathl *Llan* 73-90; R St Andrews Major w Michaelston-le-Pit 79-92; Chan Llan Cathl 90-92; rtd 92; Perm to Offic *Llan* from 92. *3 Tudor Close, Westbourne Road, Penarth CF64 5BR*

KEARNS, Mrs Mary Leah. b 38. **d** 87 **p** 94. Par Dn Morden *S'wark* 87-88; Asst Chapl HM Pris Holloway 88-98; rtd 99; Perm to Offic *Guildf* from 01. *48 The Orchard, North Holmwood, Dorking RH5 4JT* Tel (01306) 886858

KEARNS, Philip Gillin. b 59. Ripon Coll Cuddesdon 90. **d** 92 **p** 93. C Winchmore Hill St Paul *Lon* 92-97; V N Shoebury *Chelmsf* 97-02; TR Wickford and Runwell from 02. *The Rectory, 120 Southend Road, Wickford SS11 8EB* Tel (01268) 733147 Mobile 07747-826066 E-mail philip@pkearns.fsnet.co.uk

KEARON, Canon Kenneth Arthur. b 53. TCD BA76 MA79 MPhil91. CITC 78. **d** 81 **p** 82. C Rahny w Coolock *D & G* 81-84; Lect TCD 82-90; Dean of Res TCD 84-90; I Tullow *D & G* 91-99; Can Ch Ch Cathl Dublin from 95; Dir Irish Sch Ecum from 99. *The Irish School of Ecumenics, Bea House, Milltown Park, Milltown, Dublin 6, Irish Republic* Tel (00353) (1) 260 1144 *or* 296 6049 Fax 260 1158 E-mail ise4@indigo.ie

KEAST, William. b 43. Univ Coll Ox BA65 DipEd66. LNSM course 86. **d** 88 **p** 89. OLM Scotton w Northorpe *Linc* from 88. *4 Crapple Lane, Scotton, Gainsborough DN21 3QT* Tel (01724) 763190 E-mail wkeast@hotmail.com

KEATING, Christopher Robin. b 39. K Coll Lon BD AKC84. Sarum Th Coll 62. **d** 65 **p** 66. C Baildon *Bradf* 65-67; CF 67-72; V Thornton Heath St Paul *Cant* 72-79; C Harold Hill St Geo *Chelmsf* 85-89; V Goodmayes All SS from 89. *All Saints' Vicarage, Broomhill Road, Ilford IG3 9SJ* Tel (020) 8590 1476

KEATING, Geoffrey John. b 52. Liv Poly HND79 Open Univ BA94. St Steph Ho Ox 81. **d** 84 **p** 85. C Lancaster Ch Ch w St Jo and St Anne *Blackb* 84-85; C Rotherham *Sheff* 85-87; C Mexborough 87; V Bentley 87-91; V Penponds *Truro* 91-96; V Pet St Jude *Pet* from 96. *St Jude's Vicarage, 49 Atherstone Avenue, Peterborough PE3 9TZ* Tel (01733) 264169 *or* 268816 Fax as telephone E-mail geoffkeatg@aol.com

KEAY, Alfred David. b 26. Aston Univ MSc72. Qu Coll Birm 76. **d** 79 **p** 80. Hon C Penkridge w Stretton *Lich* 79-82; C Rugeley 82-85; V Cheswardine 85-95; V Hales 85-95; rtd 95. *2 The Coppice, Farcroft Gardens, Market Drayton TF9 3UA* Tel (01630) 657924

KEAY, Charles Edward. b 70. Glos Univ BA94. St Steph Ho Ox 01. **d** 03. C Havant *Portsm* from 03. *1 Churchfields, South Street, Havant PO9 1BY* Tel (023) 9247 0817

KEDDIE, Canon Tony. b 37. Qu Coll Birm 63. **d** 66 **p** 67. C Barnoldswick w Bracewell *Bradf* 66-69; C New Bentley *Sheff* 69-71; TV Seacroft *Ripon* 71-79; V Kippax 79-85; TR Kippax w Allerton Bywater 85-92; R Fountains Gp 92-02; Hon Can Ripon Cathl from 94; rtd 02. *2 Westcroft, Station Road, Otley LS21 3HX* Tel (01943) 461565

KEEBLE, Dorothy Deborah. b 20. **d** 87. NSM Glas H Cross *Glas* from 87. *12 Housel Avenue, Glasgow G13 3UR* Tel 0141-959 3102

KEEBLE, Stephen Robert. b 56. K Coll Lon BD84 AKC84 MA98 Selw Coll Cam DipTh86. Westcott Ho Cam 85. **d** 87 **p** 88. C Lt Stanmore St Lawr *Lon* 87-90; C Headstone St Geo 90-93; P-in-c 93-98; V from 98. *St George's Vicarage, 96 Pinner View, Harrow HA1 4RJ* Tel (020) 8427 1253

KEECH, Canon April Irene. b 52. Penn State Univ BA76. Trin Coll Bris BA89. **d** 89 **p** 92. C Walthamstow St Luke *Chelmsf* 89-92; USA 92-95; V Deptford St Jo w H Trin *S'wark* 95-02; Asst Dioc Dir of Ords 96-00; Hon Can S'wark Cathl from 99; V Hoxton St Jo w St Jas from 02. *St John's Vicarage, Crondall Street, London N1 6PT* Tel (020) 7739 9823 *or* 7739 9302 E-mail aikeech@aol.com

KEEGAN, Donald Leslie. b 37. ACII. CITC 65. **d** 68 **p** 69. C Drumragh w Mountfield *D & R* 68-72; I Birr w Lorrha, Dorrha and Lockeen *L & K* 72-02; Can Killaloe Cathl 80-82; Treas Killaloe Cathl 82-87; Prec Limerick and Killaloe Cathls 87-89;

Adn Killaloe, Kilfenora, Clonfert etc 89-02; rtd 02. *279 Redford Park, Greystones, Co Wicklow, Irish Republic* Tel (00353) (1) 201 7259 E-mail donkee@eircom.net

KEEGAN, Frances Ann (Sister Isabel). b 44. SEN74. Franciscan Study Cen 87. **d** 99 **p** 00. NSM Sherborne w Castleton and Lillington *Sarum* 99-01; NSM Golden Cap Team from 01. *The Vicarage, 5 St George's Close, Charmouth, Bridport DT6 6RU* Tel (01935) 817582

KEEGAN, Graham Brownell. b 40. Nottm Univ CertEd68. N Ord Course 81. **d** 84 **p** 85. C Highfield *Liv* 84-87; V Ince St Mary 87-95; V Newton in Makerfield St Pet from 95. *St Peter's Vicarage, Church Street, Newton-le-Willows WA12 9SR* Tel (01925) 224815

KEELER, Alan. b 58. City Univ BSc81. St Jo Coll Nottm MA01. **d** 90 **p** 91. C Paddock Wood *Roch* 90-94; V Blendon from 94. *The Vicarage, 37 Bladindon Drive, Bexley DA5 3BS* Tel (020) 8301 5387 E-mail agkeeler@talk21.com

KEELEY, John Robin. b 38. G&C Coll Cam BA62. Clifton Th Coll 62. **d** 64 **p** 65. C Onslow Square St Paul *Lon* 64-66; C Hove Bp Hannington Memorial Ch *Chich* 66-69; C Harborne Heath *Birm* 69-72; V Leic H Trin *Leic* 72-74; V Leic H Trin w St Jo 74-80; Perm to Offic *St Alb* 81-86; NSM Carterton *Ox* 89-95; Tutor EAMTC *Ely* 95-99; TV Bishopsnympton, Rose Ash, Mariansleigh etc *Ex* from 99; RD S Molton 01-03. *The Vicarage, Molland, South Molton EX36 3NG* Tel (01769) 550551 E-mail rkeeley@spck.co.uk

KEELEY, Keith Morgan. b 12. Man Univ BA33 MA36. **d** 49 **p** 50. C Shipley St Paul *Bradf* 49-52; C Gt Barr *Lich* 52-53; C Blakenall Heath 53-55; V Tipton St Jo 55-59; R Hinstock 59-64; rtd 77. *22A Kingsley Avenue, Whitley Bay NE25 8RX*

KEELING, Michael John. b 28. Chich Th Coll 57. **d** 60 **p** 61. C Hurstpierpoint *Chich* 60-63; C Southwick St Mich 63-64; Australia 64-73; Hon C Hammersmith St Pet *Lon* 74-75; Hon C S Lambeth St Anne and All SS *S'wark* 75-76; Perm to Offic 75-84; Perm to Offic *Chich* 79-82; P-in-c Kensington St Barn *Lon* 84-85; Perm to Offic 85-92; Perm to Offic *Glas* from 92. *17 Cowgate, Garlieston, Newton Stewart DG8 8BW* Tel (01988) 600629

KEELING, Peter Frank. b 34. Kelham Th Coll. **d** 58 **p** 59. C S Elmsall *Wakef* 58-63; C Barnsley St Mary 63-67; V Ravensthorpe 67-73; V Cudworth 73-83; R Downham Market w Bexwell *Ely* 83-00; RD Fincham 83-94; V Crimplesham w Stradsett 85-00; rtd 00; P-in-c Hempton and Pudding Norton *Nor* from 00. *23 Cleaves Drive, Walsingham NR22 6EQ* Tel (01328) 820310

KEEN, David Mark. b 69. Oriel Coll Ox BA91. St Jo Coll Nottm BTh96 MPhil98. **d** 98 **p** 99. C Yeovil w Kingston Pitney *B & W* 98-02; C Haughton le Skerne *Dur* from 02. *57 Rivergarth, Darlington DL1 3SJ* Tel (01325) 243381 E-mail david.keen@ukonline.co.uk

KEEN, Michael Spencer. b 41. GRSM62 ARCM St Pet Coll Ox BA68 MA72 Reading Univ CertEd. Westcott Ho Cam 68. **d** 73 **p** 74. Hon C W Derby St Jo *Liv* 73-74; Hon C Stanley 74-76; Chs Youth and Community Officer Telford *Lich* 77-82; Dioc Unemployment Officer *Sheff* 82-89; Hon C Brixton Road Ch Ch *S'wark* 89-92; Employment Development Officer 89-92; Perm to Offic 92-99; Hon C Camberwell St Giles w St Matt from 99. *114 Lowden Road, London SE24 0BQ* Tel (020) 7274 2206

KEENAN, Leslie Herbert (Bertie). b 32. Cranmer Hall Dur. **d** 66 **p** 67. C Anston *Sheff* 66-70; C Woodsetts 66-70; Chapl HM Borstal Pollington 70-78; V Balne *Sheff* 70-78; V Poughill *Truro* 78-99; rtd 99; Perm to Offic *Chich* from 01. *177 Lyndhurst Road, Worthing BN11 2GU* Tel (01903) 200387

KEENE, Canon David Peter. b 32. Trin Hall Cam BA56 MA60. Westcott Ho Cam. **d** 58 **p** 59. C Radcliffe-on-Trent *S'well* 58-61; C Mansfield St Pet 61-64; V Nottingham St Cath 64-71; R Bingham 71-81; Dioc Dir of Ords 81-90; Can Res S'well Minster 81-97; rtd 97. *Averham Cottage, Church Lane, Averham, Newark NG23 5RB* Tel (01636) 708601

KEENE, Mrs Muriel Ada. b 35. dss 83 **d** 87 **p** 94. Dioc Lay Min Adv *S'well* 87-88; Asst Dir of Ords 88-90; Dn-in-c Oxton 90-93; Dn-in-c Epperstone 90-94; Dn-in-c Gonalston 90-94; NSM Lowdham w Caythorpe, and Gunthorpe from 94; rtd 95. *Averham Cottage, Church Lane, Averham, Newark NG23 5RB* Tel (01636) 708601

KEEP, Andrew James. b 55. Collingwood Coll Dur BA77 Yale Univ STM84. Sarum & Wells Th Coll 78. **d** 80 **p** 81. C Banstead *Guildf* 80-83; Chapl Qu Eliz Hosp Banstead 80-83; USA 83-84; Chapl Cranleigh Sch Surrey 84-98; Chapl Wells Cathl Sch from 98; PV Wells Cathl *B & W* from 01. *18 Vicars Close, Wells BA5 2UJ* Tel (01749) 834207 E-mail andrew.keep@lineone.net

KEEP, Hugh Charles John Martin. b 45. Qu Coll Birm 90. **d** 92 **p** 93. C Aston Cantlow and Wilmcote w Billesley *Cov* 92-95; P-in-c Hampton Lucy w Charlecote and Loxley 95-02; Chapl Rainsbrook Secure Tr Cen from 02. *4 Old Town, Stratford-upon-Avon CV37 6BG* Tel (01789) 414142 E-mail hrkeepnet@aol.com

KEETON, Barry. b 40. Dur Univ BA61 MA69 MLitt78 K Coll Lon BD63 AKC63. **d** 64 **p** 65. C S Bank *York* 64-67; C Middlesbrough St Cuth 67-69; C Kingston upon Hull St Alb 70-71; V Appleton-le-Street w Amotherby 71-74; Dioc Ecum

Adv 74-81; R Ampleforth w Oswaldkirk 74-78; V Howden 78-79; P-in-c Barmby on the Marsh 78-79; P-in-c Laxton w Blacktoft 78-79; P-in-c Wressell 78-79; TR Howden 80-91; Can and Preb York Minster 85-91; RD Howden 86-91; TR Lewes All SS, St Anne, St Mich and St Thos *Chich* 91-96; R Cov St Jo *Cov* 96-01; RD Cov N 97-01; rtd 01. *19 Shardlow Gardens, Bessacarr, Doncaster DN4 6UB* Tel (01302) 532045 E-mail barry.k3@ukonline.co.uk

KEFFORD, Canon Peter Charles. b 44. Nottm Univ BTh74. Linc Th Coll 70. **d** 74 **p** 75. C W Wimbledon Ch Ch *S'wark* 74-77; C All Hallows by the Tower etc *Lon* 77-81; C-in-c Pound Hill CD *Chich* 81; TV Worth 82-83; TR 83-92; V Henfield w Shermanbury and Woodmancote 92-01; Can Res and Treas Chich Cathl from 01; Adv for Ord Min and Dioc Dir of Ords from 01. *12 St Martin's Square, Chichester PO19 1NR* Tel (01243) 783509 E-mail peter_kefford@hotmail.com

KEGG, Gordon Rutherford. b 45. Reading Univ BSc66 Imp Coll Lon PhD71 DIC71 Lon Univ CertEd74. Oak Hill Th Coll DipHE90. **d** 90 **p** 91. C Luton Lewsey St Hugh *St Alb* 90-94; TV Hemel Hempstead 94-01; P-in-c Mattishall w Mattishall Burgh, Welborne etc *Nor* from 01. *The Vicarage, Back Lane, Mattishall, Dereham NR20 3PU* Tel (01362) 850243

KEIGHLEY, Andrew. b 62. Nottm Univ LLB84 Solicitor 85. Wycliffe Hall Ox DipMin96. **d** 97 **p** 98. C Westminster St Jas the Less *Lon* 97-00; NSM from 00. *90 Abercrombie Street, London SW11 2JD* Tel (020) 7924 5951 E-mail andy.keighley@lineone.net

KEIGHLEY, David John. b 48. CertEd Open Univ BA88. Sarum & Wells Th Coll 82. **d** 83 **p** 84. C Sawbridgeworth *St Alb* 83-86; TV Saltash *Truro* 86-89; V Lanlivery w Luxulyan 89-00; P-in-c The Candover Valley *Win* from 00. *The Rectory, Alresford Road, Preston Candover, Basingstoke RG25 2EE* Tel and fax (01256) 389245 Mobile 07736-799262 E-mail davidkeighley@hotmail.com

KEIGHLEY, Martin Philip. b 61. Edin Univ MA83. Westcott Ho Cam 86. **d** 88 **p** 89. C Lytham St Cuth *Blackb* 88-91; C Lancaster St Mary 91-93; R Halton w Aughton 93-00; V Poulton-le-Fylde from 00. *The Vicarage, 7 Vicarage Road, Poulton-le-Fylde, Blackpool FY6 7BE* Tel (01253) 883086 E-mail martin@contact.plus.com

KEIGHLEY, Thomas Christopher. b 51. DipN81 Open Univ BA85. NEOC 00. **d** 03. NSM Upper Nidderdale *Ripon* from 03. *The Old Chapel, Middlesmoor, Harrogate HG3 5ST* Tel and fax (01423) 755344 Mobile 07740-721032 E-mail nurprc@nursing.u-net.com

KEIGHTLEY, Canon Peter Edward. b 17. Leeds Univ BA41. Coll of Resurr Mirfield 41. **d** 43 **p** 44. C Wellingborough All Hallows *Pet* 43-45; C Solihull *Birm* 45-49; C Cirencester *Glouc* 50-53; V Glouc St Paul 53-59; V Widley w Wymering *Portsm* 59-67; V Southsea H Spirit 67-76; Chapl St Mary's Hosp Portsm 76-82; Hon Can Portsm Cathl *Portsm* 81-82; rtd 82; Perm to Offic *Portsm* from 83. *11 Dolphin Court, St Helen's Parade, Southsea PO4 0QL* Tel (023) 9281 6697

KEIGHTLEY, Canon Thomas. b 44. CITC 79. **d** 79 **p** 80. C Seagoe *D & D* 79-83; I Belvoir from 83; Can Down Cathl from 95; Treas 00-01; Prec from 01. *The Rectory, 86B Beechill Road, Belfast BT8 6QN* Tel (028) 9064 3777

KEIGHTLEY, Trevor Charles. b 54. St Jo Coll Nottm. **d** 03. C Wombwell *Sheff* from 03. *202 Summer Lane, Wombwell, Barnsley S73 8QH* Tel (01226) 211102 E-mail trevorkeightley@aol.com

KEILLER, Mrs Jane Elizabeth. b 52. Westmr Coll Ox BEd74 St Jo Coll Dur DipTh78 Bangalore Univ DipTh79. Cranmer Hall Dur 76. dss 80 **d** 87 **p** 94. C Cambridge H Trin w St Andr Gt *Ely* 80-86; NSM Cambridge St Barn 86-88 and 90-94; NSM Cambridge H Cross from 95; Chapl and Tutor Ridley Hall Cam from 96. *68 Pierce Lane, Cambridge CB1 5DL* Tel (01223) 575776 or tel and fax 741076 E-mail jk271@cam.ac.uk

KEIR, Mrs Gillian Irene. b 44. Westf Coll Lon BA66 Somerville Coll Ox BLitt70 Lon Univ MA95. St Alb and Ox Min Course CBTS95. **d** 98 **p** 99. NSM St Alb St Steph *St Alb* from 98. *17 Battlefield Road, St Albans AL1 4DA* Tel (01727) 839392

KEIRLE, Michael Robert. b 62. Trin Coll Bris BA89. **d** 99 **p** 00. C Orpington Ch Ch *Roch* 89-92; Zimbabwe 92-95; R Keston *Roch* 95-03; R Guernsey St Martin *Win* from 03. *St Martin's Rectory, La Grande Rue, St Martin, Guernsey GY4 6RR* Tel (01481) 238303 Fax 237710 E-mail mrkeirle@cwgsy.net

KEITH, Andrew James Buchanan. b 47. Qu Coll Cam BA69 MA73. Wycliffe Hall Ox 71. **d** 74 **p** 75. C Warrington St Elphin *Liv* 74-77; C Southgate *Chich* 77-80; C-in-c Broadfield CD 80-82; P-in-c Walberton w Binsted 82-85; P-in-c Aldingbourne 83-85; Chapl Oswestry Sch 85-95; Chapl HM Pris Liv 95-96; Chapl HM Pris Preston 96-01; Chapl HM Pris Garth from 01. *HM Prison Garth, Ulnes Walton Lane, Leyland PR26 8NE* Tel (01772) 622722 E-mail andrewandjudi@keith20.freeserve.co.uk

KEITH, Gary Mark Wayne. b 71. Ripon Coll Cuddesdon 01. **d** 03. C Botley *Portsm* from 03; C Curdridge from 03; C Durley from 03. *1 Rectory Court, Botley, Southampton SO30 2SJ* Tel (01865) 787715 Mobile 07976-244615 E-mail gazzaloulou@gkeith.fsnet.co.uk

KEITH, John. b 25. LRAM50 LGSM50 AGSM51. Cuddesdon Coll 60. **d** 62 **p** 63. C Lee-on-the-Solent *Portsm* 62-65; C Raynes Park St Sav *S'wark* 65-68; rtd 90. *Leaning Tree, Inchlaggan, Invergarry PH35 4HR*

KELHAM, Adèle. b 46. St Andr Univ BSc69. Cranmer Hall Dur DMS98. **d** 98 **p** 99. Asst Chapl Zürich *Eur* 98-01; P-in-c Bishop Middleham *Dur* from 01; AD Sedgefield from 03. *1 Broad Oaks, Bishop Middleham, Ferryhill DL17 9BW* Tel (01740) 654591 E-mail kelham@swissonline.ch

KELK, Michael Anthony. b 48. Sarum & Wells Th Coll. **d** 83 **p** 84. C Ross w Brampton Abbotts, Bridstow and Peterstow *Heref* 83-86; P-in-c Burghill 86-97; P-in-c Stretton Sugwas 86-97; P-in-c Walford and St John w Bishopswood, Goodrich etc 97-02; P-in-c Llangarron w Llangrove, Whitchurch and Ganarew from 02. *The Vicarage, Llangrove, Ross-on-Wye HR9 6EZ* Tel (01989) 770341

KELLAND, Kenneth William Jerome. b 16. S'wark Ord Course 63. **d** 66 **p** 67. C Addlestone *Guildf* 66-69; C Sholing *Win* 69-74; C Weston 74-82; rtd 82; Hon C Odiham w S Warnborough and Long Sutton *Win* 82-85; Hon C Herriard w Winslade and Long Sutton etc 85-86. *50 Wooteys Way, Alton GU34 2JZ* Tel (01420) 85325

KELLEHER, Mrs Cheryl. b 56. Sheff Univ BA97. N Ord Course 98. **d** 01 **p** 02. NSM Worsbrough *Sheff* from 01. *10 Fieldsend, Oxspring, Sheffield S36 8WH*

KELLEN, David. b 52. Univ of Wales (Cardiff) DipTh73. St Mich Coll Llan 70. **d** 75 **p** 76. C Mynyddislwyn *Mon* 75-77; C Risca 77-78; C Malpas 78-81; V Newport All SS 81-88; V St Mellons from 88; R Michaelston-y-Fedw 89-96. *The Vicarage, Ty'r Winch Road, St Mellons, Cardiff CF3 5UP* Tel (029) 2079 6560

KELLETT, Colin. b 25. Worc Ord Coll 65. **d** 67 **p** 68. C E Ardsley *Wakef* 67-69; C Dewsbury Moor 69-72; V Lundwood 72-77; V Gawber 77-88; rtd 88; Perm to Offic *Wakef* 88-96; *York* from 96. *30 Dulverton Hall, Esplanade, Scarborough YO11 2AR* Tel (01723) 340130

KELLETT, Neil. b 41. Bps' Coll Cheshunt 64. **d** 66 **p** 67. C Ex St Thos *Ex* 66-72; C Win H Trin *Win* 72-74; P-in-c Redditch St Geo *Worc* 74-77; Canada from 77. *39 Fox Avenue, St John's NF, Canada, A1B 2H8* Tel (001) (709) 726 2883

KELLETT, Richard. b 64. Leeds Univ BSc85 PhD89. St Jo Coll Nottm BTh95 MA96. **d** 96 **p** 97. C Nottingham St Jude *S'well* 96-00; P-in-c Skegby 00-02; P-in-c Teversal 00-02; R Skegby w Teversal from 02. *The Vicarage, Mansfield Road, Skegby, Sutton-in-Ashfield NG17 3ED* Tel (01623) 558800 Fax as telephone E-mail richard@kellett.com

KELLEY, Neil George. b 64. ARCM85 DipRCM87. Westcott Ho Cam 88. **d** 91 **p** 92. C E Bedfont *Lon* 91-93; C Chiswick St Nic w St Mary 93-97; C Kirkby *Liv* 97-99; V Gt Crosby St Faith and Waterloo Park St Mary from 99. *The Vicarage, Milton Road, Waterloo, Liverpool L22 4RE* Tel and Fax 0151-928 3342 Mobile 07980-872203 E-mail frneilkelley@tiscali.co.uk

KELLY, Canon Albert Norman. b 21. TCD BA43 MA63. **d** 44 **p** 45. C Donaghcloney *D & D* 44-46; C Belfast Malone St Jo *Conn* 46-55; I Billy 55-63; C Dorking w Ranmore *Guildf* 63-66; C-in-c New Haw CD 66-72; V New Haw 72-78; RD Chertsey 73-75; RD Runnymede 75-78; V Egham Hythe 78-86; Hon Can Guildf Cathl 80-86; rtd 86; USPG Area Sec 88-93. *21 Rosetta Road, Belfast BT6 0LQ* Tel (028) 9069 3921 E-mail knorman@fish.co.uk

KELLY, Brian Eugene. b 56. Otago Univ BA77 Dunedin Coll PGCE79 Bris Univ PhD93. Trin Coll Bris BA89. **d** 90 **p** 91. NSM Redland *Bris* 90-93; C Scarborough St Mary w Ch Ch and H Apostles *York* 93-96; Dean Chpl Cant Ch Ch Univ Coll from 96. *Canterbury Christ Church University College, North Holmes Road, Canterbury CT1 1QU* Tel (01227) 767700 E-mail bek1@cant.ac.uk

KELLY, Canon Brian Horace. b 34. St Jo Coll Dur BA57 MA69 DipTh58. **d** 58 **p** 59. C Douglas St Geo and St Barn *S & M* 58-61; V Foxdale 61-64; V Bolton All So w St Jas *Man* 64-73; V Maughold *S & M* 73-77; Dir of Ords 76-93; V German from 77; Can and Prec St German's Cathl from 80; RD Castletown and Peel from 97. *The Cathedral Vicarage, Albany Road, Peel, Isle of Man IM5 1JS* Tel (01624) 842608

KELLY, Christopher Augustine (Kit). b 15. 45 TD65. Keble Coll Ox BA37. Ripon Hall Ox 37. **d** 45 **p** 46. C Aston SS Pet and Paul *Birm* 45-51; V Habergham Eaves H Trin *Blackb* 51-57; V Knuzden 57-67; V Bolton Breightmet St Jas *Man* 67-76; V Nelson in Lt Marsden *Blackb* 76-83; rtd 83; Perm to Offic *Bradf* from 83. *Gargrave House, West Street, Gargrave, Skipton BD23 3PH* Tel (01756) 748358

KELLY, Canon Dennis Charles. b 31. Liv Univ BA52. Lich Th Coll 54. **d** 56 **p** 57. C Tranmere St Paul *Ches* 56-59; C-in-c Grange St Andr CD 59-63; P-in-c Grange St Andr 63-65; V 65-67; R Coppenhall 67-82; V W Kirby St Andr 82-01; Hon Can Ches Cathl 86-01; rtd 01; Perm to Offic *Ches* from 01. *26 Lyndhurst Road, Hoylake, Wirral CH47 7BP* Tel 0151-632 0335

KELLY, Desmond Norman. b 42. Oak Hill Th Coll DipHE90. **d** 90 **p** 91. C Braintree *Chelmsf* 90-94; P-in-c Castle Hedingham 94-95; P-in-c Sible Hedingham 94-95; R Sible Hedingham w

Castle Hedingham from 95. *The Vicarage, Queen Street, Castle Hedingham, Halstead CO9 3EZ* Tel (01787) 460274 E-mail des.kelly@virgin.net

KELLY, Canon Edward William Moncrieff. b 28. AKC57. **d** 57 **p** 58. C Petersfield w Sheet *Portsm* 57-60; Papua New Guinea 60-65; Dioc Sec Samarai and Hon Chapl Miss to Seamen 61; V Gosport Ch Ch *Portsm* 65-69; Hon C Eltham St Jo *S'wark* 69-87; Org Sec New Guinea Miss 69-77; Org Sec Papua New Guinea Ch Partnership 77-87; Hon Can Papua New Guinea from 78; TR Trowbridge H Trin *Sarum* 87-94; Chapl St Jo Hosp Trowbridge 87-94; Acting RD Bradford 91-92; rtd 94; Perm to Offic *Portsm* from 94. *133 Borough Road, Petersfield GU32 3LP* Tel (01730) 260399

KELLY, Canon John Dickinson. b 42. Nottm Univ BA63. Ripon Hall Ox 63. **d** 65 **p** 66. C Egremont *Carl* 65-67; C Upperby St Jo 67-70; V Arlecdon 70-73; V Barrow St Aid 73-79; V Milnthorpe 79-83; V Beetham and Milnthorpe 83-85; V Camerton St Pet 85-88; P-in-c Camerton H Trin W Seaton 86-88; V Camerton, Seaton and W Seaton 88-01; Hon Can Carl Cathl from 00; P-in-c Kells from 01. *St Peter's Vicarage, Cliff Road, Whitehaven CA28 9ET* Tel (01946) 692496

KELLY, John Graham. b 60. Lanc Univ LLB82 Man Poly Solicitor 84. St Jo Coll Nottm BTh91. **d** 94 **p** 95. C Normanton *Derby* 94-97; P-in-c Ockbrook 97-01; Tutor St Jo Coll Nottm from 01. *St John's College, Chilwell Lane, Bramcote, Nottingham NG9 3DS* Tel 0115-925 1114

KELLY, John Rowe. b 32. Edin Th Coll. **d** 85 **p** 86. C Blyth St Mary *Newc* 85-88; C Slaley 88-91; C Healey 88-91; TV Alston Team 91-96; P-in-c 96-00; R Alston Moor 00-02; Chapl Alston Cottage Hosp 91-02; rtd 02. *The Nook, Brampton Road, Alston CA9 3AA* Tel (01434) 382952 E-mail alstonvicar@aol.com

KELLY, Malcolm Bernard. b 46. St Mich Coll Llan 72. **d** 74 **p** 75. C Tranmere St Paul w St Luke *Ches* 74-77; Chapl Bebington Hosp from 76; C Barnston *Ches* 77-80; R Thurstaston 80-92; R Grappenhall from 92. *The Rectory, 17 Hill Top Road, Stockton Heath, Warrington WA4 2ED* Tel (01925) 261546

KELLY, Martin Herbert. b 55. Selw Coll Cam MA90. Aston Tr Scheme 78 Ripon Coll Cuddesdon 80. **d** 83 **p** 84. C Clapham Old Town *S'wark* 83-87; Chapl and Fell Selw Coll Cam 87-92; Chapl Newnham Coll Cam 87-92; Chapl St Piers Hosp Sch Lingfield *S'wark* 95-01; C Limpsfield and Titsey 95-01. *4 New Street, Westerham TN16 1RN* Tel (01959) 565330

KELLY, Nigel James (Ned). b 60. N Staffs Poly BSc83. Ripon Coll Cuddesdon 83. **d** 86 **p** 87. C Cen Telford *Lich* 86-90; TV 90-92; Chapl RN from 92. *Royal Naval Chaplaincy Service, Room 203, Victory Building, HM Naval Base, Portsmouth PO1 3LS* Tel (023) 9272 7903 Fax 9272 7111

KELLY, Paul Maitland Hillyard. b 24. Ball Coll Ox BA50 MA54. Wells Th Coll 50. **d** 52 **p** 53. C Epsom St Martin *Guildf* 52-57; C-in-c New Cathl CD 57-61; R Abinger cum Coldharbour 61-67; P-in-c Preston St Pet *Blackb* 67-70; V Ottershaw *Guildf* 70-77; R Ickenham *Lon* 77-94; rtd 94; Perm to Offic *B & W* from 94. *37 Dodd Avenue, Wells BA5 3JU* Tel (01749) 673334

KELLY, Peter Hugh. b 46. Sarum & Wells Th Coll 81. **d** 84 **p** 85. C Fareham H Trin *Portsm* 84-87; Chapl and Prec Portsm Cathl 87-90; V Eastney 90-97; P-in-c Swanmore St Barn from 97; RD Bishop's Waltham from 03. *The Vicarage, Church Road, Swanmore, Southampton SO32 2PA* Tel (01489) 892105 E-mail peterkelly@swanmore.net

KELLY, Stephen Paul. b 55. Keble Coll Ox BA77. Linc Th Coll 77. **d** 79 **p** 80. C Illingworth *Wakef* 79-82; C Knottingley 82-84; V Alverthorpe 84-93; Dioc Ecum Officer 88-93; TR Bingley All SS *Bradf* 93-03; P-in-c Woolley *Wakef* from 03. *The Vicarage, Church Street, Woolley, Wakefield WF4 2JU* Tel (01226) 382550 E-mail stephen@kellys4.freeserve.co.uk

KELLY, Canon William. b 35. Dur Univ BA58 St Cath Coll Ox DipTh59. Lambeth STh75 Wycliffe Hall Ox 58. **d** 60 **p** 61. C Walney Is *Carl* 60-66; R Distington 66-71; V Barrow St Matt 71-81; RD Furness 77-81; Hon Can Carl Cathl 79-00; Dir of Ords 81-97; V Dalston 81-92; RD Carl 83-88; P-in-c Raughton Head w Gatesgill 86-92; P-in-c Maryport 92-97; P-in-c Flimby 93-96; P-in-c Arthuret and Nicholforest and Kirkandrews on Esk 97-00; rtd 00; Perm to Offic *Carl* from 00. *73 Upperby Road, Carlisle CA2 4JE* Tel (01228) 511535

KELLY, William Edward. b 31. Univ of Wales (Lamp) BA57 St Cath Soc Ox BA59 MA63. St Steph Ho Ox 57. **d** 60 **p** 61. C S Bank *York* 60-63; C Ingoldisthorpe *Nor* 63-66; C Heacham 63-66; Chapl RAF 66-87; Chapl Woodbridge Sch 82-90; V Newport St Paul *Mon* 90-99; Perm to Offic *Sarum* from 00. *3 Drew Close, Bridport DT6 3JG* Tel (01308) 456954

KELLY, William Norman. b 21. St Aid Birkenhead. **d** 64 **p** 65. Miss to Seamen 64-66; C Douglas St Geo and St Barn *S & M* 66-69; V Wingates *Man* 69-75; Perm to Offic 76-84; Chapl HM Pris Liv 77-78; Chapl HM Borstal Stoke Heath 78-84; V Castletown *S & M* 84-92; rtd 92; Perm to Offic *S & M* from 92. *Crossaq Villa, St Mark's Road, Ballasalla, Isle of Man IM9 3EF* Tel (01624) 825582

KELLY, Canon William Robert. b 28. QUB BSc57. CITC 62. **d** 62 **p** 63. C Lurgan Ch the Redeemer *D & D* 62-66; I Clondehorkey

D & R 66-70; I Raheny w Coolock *D & G* 70-75; Peru 75-83; Hon Can Peru 83; I Ballinderry *Conn* 83-89; I Belfast St Aid 89-96; Can Belf Cathl 94-96; rtd 96. *17 College Avenue, Bangor BT20 5HJ* Tel (028) 9147 3679

KELMAN, Gordon. b 00. C Strichen *Ab* from 00. *12 Church Lane, Longside, Peterhead AB42 7XJ* Tel (01779) 821450
E-mail saintjohnls@aol.com

KELSEY, George Robert. b 61. Imp Coll Lon BSc83 Newc Univ MSc84 PhD92. Cranmer Hall Dur 95. **d** 97 **p** 98. C Denton *Newc* 97-01; TV Glendale Gp from 01. *Eglingham Vicarage, The Village, Eglingham, Alnwick NE66 2TX* Tel (01665) 578250
E-mail robert@josephkelsey.fsnet.co.uk

KELSEY, Michael Ray. b 22. FEPA57. Wycliffe Hall Ox 60. **d** 62 **p** 63. C Lower Broughton St Clem *Man* 62-64; V Ingleby Greenhow *York* 64-68; V Scarborough St Jas 68-71; Asst to the Gen Sec USCL 71-74; V Blackheath St Jo *S'wark* 74-87; rtd 87; Perm to Offic *St E* from 88. *25 Prospect Place, Leiston IP16 4AL* Tel (01728) 830975

✠**KELSHAW, The Rt Revd Terence.** b 36. Lon Univ DipTh67 Pittsburgh Th Sem DMin86. Oak Hill Th Coll. **d** 67 **p** 68 **c** 89. C Clifton Ch Ch w Em *Bris* 67-71; C Woking St Jo *Guildf* 71-73; V Bris H Trin *Bris* 73-75; P-in-c Easton St Gabr w St Laur 73-75; V Easton H Trin w St Gabr and St Lawr 75-80; P-in-c Barton Hill St Luke w Ch Ch 76-80; USA from 80; Bp Rio Grande from 89. *4304 Carlisle Boulevard NE, Albuquerque, NM 87107-4811, USA* Tel (001) (505) 881 0636 Fax 883 9048
E-mail tkelshaw@aol.com

KELSO, Andrew John. b 47. LRAM73 Lon Univ BA70. St Jo Coll Nottm 83. **d** 85 **p** 86. C Gorleston St Mary *Nor* 85-87; C Hellesdon 87-90; TV Ipsley *Worc* from 90. *Matchborough Vicarage, Winward Road, Redditch B98 0SX* Tel (01527) 529098
E-mail andykelso@madasafish.com

KEMM, William St John. b 39. Birm Univ BA62 MA65. Ridley Hall Cam 62. **d** 64 **p** 65. C Kingswinford H Trin *Lich* 64-68; C Hednesford 68-71; V Hanbury 71-76; R Berrow and Breane *B & W* 76-92; V Hertford All SS *St Alb* from 92. *All Saints' Vicarage, Churchfields, Hertford SG13 8AE* Tel (01992) 582096

KEMP, Canon Allan. b 43. Bps' Coll Cheshunt 65 Oak Hill Th Coll 67. **d** 68 **p** 69. C Tunbridge Wells St Jas *Roch* 68-76; V Becontree St Mary *Chelmsf* 76-90; RD Barking and Dagenham 81-86; V Gt w Lt Chesterford from 90; Hon Can Chelmsf Cathl from 99. *The Vicarage, Church Street, Great Chesterford, Saffron Walden CB10 1NP* Tel (01799) 530317

KEMP, Prof Anthony Eric. b 34. St Mark & St Jo Coll Lon CertEd57 LTCL63 FTCL63 Lon Inst of Educn DipEd70 Sussex Univ MA71 DPhil79 Hon FLCM83 CPsychol89 FBPsS97 Helsinki Univ MusDoc03. St Alb and Ox Min Course 96. **d** 98 **p** 99. NSM Wokingham All SS *Ox* from 98. *18 Blagrove Lane, Wokingham RG41 4BA* Tel (0118) 978 2586 Fax as telephone
E-mail a.e.kemp@blagrovelane.freeserve.co.uk

KEMP, Ms Audrey. b 26. MSR49. Gilmore Ho 62. **dss** 69 **d** 87 **p** 94. Cranford *Lon* 67-70; S Ockendon Hosp 70-71; N Greenford All Hallows *Lon* 71-72; Feltham 72-80; Brentford St Faith 80-83; Hanworth All SS 83-85; Hanworth St Geo 85-87; Par Dn 87-88; Hon Par Dn 88-89 and from 99; Hon Par Dn Ditcheat w E Pennard and Pylle 89-94; P-in-c 94-95; Perm to Offic *Win* 95-98. *28 Queen Elizabeth Court, Blake Place, Bridgwater TA6 5QN* Tel (01278) 451348

KEMP, Barry. b 48. St Edm Hall Ox BA70 MA75 Nottm Univ DipTh73 Newc Univ CertEd82. Linc Th Coll 71. **d** 74 **p** 75. C Ashton Ch Ch *Man* 74-77; C Dunston *Dur* 81-83; Perm to Offic *Newc* 83-87; C Monkseaton St Mary 88; Chapl Ld Wandsworth Coll Basingstoke from 92. *Kimbers, Lord Wandsworth College, Long Sutton, Basingstoke RG25 1TB* Tel (01256) 862201 *or* 862206

KEMP, Christopher Michael. b 48. K Coll Lon BD71 AKC71. St Aug Coll Cant 75. **d** 76 **p** 77. C Weaverham *Ches* 76-79; C Latchford St Jas 79-82; P-in-c Sandbach Heath 82-88; V Macclesfield St Paul 88-89; C Cheadle Hulme All SS 89-93; C Oxton 93-98; P-in-c Seacombe 98-02; P-in-c Brereton w Swettenham from 02. *The Rectory, Brereton Park, Brereton, Sandbach CW11 1RY* Tel (01477) 533263

✠**KEMP, The Rt Revd Eric Waldram.** b 15. Ex Coll Ox BA36 MA40 BD44 DD61 Sussex Univ Hon DLitt FRHistS51 DLitt01. St Steph Ho Ox 36. **d** 39 **p** 40 **c** 74. C Newtown St Luke *Win* 39-41; Lib Pusey Ho 41-46; Chapl Ch Ch Ox 43-46; Tutor and Chapl Ex Coll Ox 46-69; Can and Preb Linc Cathl *Linc* 52-01; Chapl to The Queen 67-69; Dean Worc 69-74; Bp Chich 74-01; rtd 01. *5 Alexandra Road, Chichester PO19 7LX* Tel (01243) 780647

KEMP, Geoffrey Bernard. b 20. Lon Univ BD43. ALCD42. **d** 43 **p** 44. C Leyton All SS *Chelmsf* 43-46; C Woodford St Mary 46-49; V Barkingside St Laur 49-60; V Hadleigh St Barn 60-79; R Kelvedon Hatch 79-86; V Navestock 79-86; rtd 86; Perm to Offic *Chelmsf* and *St E* from 86. *24 Roman Way, Felixstowe IP11 9NJ* Tel (01394) 276691

KEMP, Jack Noel. b 14. Univ Coll Lon BA36 MA38. Wycliffe Hall Ox 55. **d** 55 **p** 56. C Harborne Heath *Birm* 55-58; PC Tyseley 58-64; V St Mary Cray and St Paul's Cray *Roch* 64-68;

Lect Brasted 67-74; V Four Elms 68-80; rtd 80; Perm to Offic *Cant* 81-01. *L'Ancresse, 16 Church Street, Whitstable CT5 1PJ* Tel (01227) 265379

KEMP, John Graham Edwin. b 29. Bris Univ BA51 PGCE52 Lon Univ BD65. Wells Th Coll 63. **d** 65 **p** 66. C Maidenhead St Luke *Ox* 65-70; R Rotherfield Greys 70-78; V Highmore 70-78; Dep Dir Tr Scheme for NSM 78-84; P-in-c Taplow 78-82; TV Burnham w Dropmore, Hitcham and Taplow 82-84; Prin EAMTC 84-92; rtd 92; Perm to Offic *St E* from 92. *Lea Cottage, The Street, Middleton, Saxmundham IP17 3NJ* Tel (01728) 648324

KEMP, John Robert Deverall. b 42. City Univ BSc65 BD69. Oak Hill Th Coll 66. **d** 70 **p** 71. C Fulham Ch Ch *Lon* 71-73; C Widford *Chelmsf* 73-79; P-in-c New Thundersley 79-84; V 84-98; Chapl HM Pris Bullwood Hall 79-98; R S Shoebury *Chelmsf* from 98. *The Rectory, 42 Church Road, Shoeburyness, Southend-on-Sea SS3 9EU* Tel (01702) 292778

KEMP, Mrs Pamela Ann. b 52. Coll of St Matthias Bris CertEd73 RMN98. Ripon Coll Cuddesdon 00. **d** 02 **p** 03. C Portland All SS w St Pet *Sarum* from 02. *53 Weston Street, Portland DT5 2DF* Tel (01305) 824953 Mobile 07989-604543
E-mail pam.kemp@cuddesdon47.fsnet.co.uk

KEMP, Trevor George. b 62. Trin Coll Bris 98. **d** 00 **p** 01. C Old Catton *Nor* from 00. *45 Garrick Green, Old Catton, Norwich NR6 7AN* Tel (01603) 424684
E-mail trevor.kemp@ukgateway.net

KEMP, William. b 67. St Anne's Coll Ox BA91 Brunel Univ PGCE92. Ridley Hall Cam BTh99. **d** 99 **p** 00. C Kensington St Barn *Lon* from 99. *17 Devonport Road, London W12 8NZ* Tel (020) 8743 2784 E-mail will@stbk.org.uk

KEMPSTER, Miss Helen Edith. b 49. Guildf Dioc Min Course 98. **d** 00 **p** 01. OLM Weybridge *Guildf* from 00. *28 Dorchester Road, Weybridge KT13 8PE* Tel (01932) 845583

KEMPSTER, Robert Alec. b 29. Selw Coll Cam MA53. Coll of Resurr Mirfield 53. **d** 55 **p** 56. C W Hackney St Barn *Lon* 55-57; C-in-c S'wark All Hallows CD *S'wark* 57-60; PV S'wark Cathl 57-60; Chapl Evelina Children's Hosp 57-70; Chapl Guy's Hosp Lon 70-81; Chapl Nat Hosp for Nervous Diseases Lon 81-89; Chapl Convent Companions Jes Gd Shep W Ogwell 89; rtd 90; Perm to Offic *Ex* from 90. *15A Seymour Road, Newton Abbot TQ12 2PT* Tel (01626) 61720

KEMPTHORNE, Renatus. b 39. Wadh Coll Ox BA60 DipTh61 MA64. Wycliffe Hall Ox 60. **d** 62 **p** 63. C Stoke *Cov* 62-65; New Zealand 65-68 and from 83; R Wytham *Ox* 68-75; Chapl Bp Grosseteste Coll Linc 75-83. *140 Nile Street, Nelson, New Zealand* Tel (0064) (3) 546 7447 E-mail kempthorne@xtra.co.nz

KENCHINGTON (née BALLANTYNE), Mrs Jane Elizabeth Ballantyne. b 58. Hull Univ BSc79 Cam Univ PGCE83. Westcott Ho Cam 88. **d** 90 **p** 94. C Winchcombe, Gretton, Sudeley Manor etc *Glouc* 90-96; Perm to Offic 96-99; NSM Dursley 99-02; Dir Reader Tr from 01. *7 Warren Croft, North Nibley, Dursley GL11 6EN* Tel (01453) 546509
E-mail janeeb.kenchington@virgin.net

KENCHINGTON, Paul Henry. b 54. Worc Coll Ox MA76. St Jo Coll Nottm BA81. **d** 82 **p** 83. C Scarborough St Mary w Ch Ch and H Apostles *York* 82-85; C Caversham St Pet and Mapledurham etc *Ox* 85-89; V Hucclecote *Glouc* 89-00; Hong Kong from 00. *St Andrew's Church, 138 Nathan Road, Tsin Sha Tsui, Kowloon, Hong Kong* Tel (00852) 2367 1478

KENDAL, Gordon McGregor. b 46. Dundee Univ MA70 Mansf Coll Ox BA72 MA76 Lon Univ BA73 PhD79. Edin Th Coll 72. **d** 74 **p** 75. C Bracknell *Ox* 74-77; C Wokingham All SS 77-79; Chapl and Fell Linc Coll Ox 79-83; R Edin St Pet *Edin* 83-87; Man Gr Sch 88-92; Gen Sec Fellowship of St Alb and St Sergius 92-96; V St Andrew St Anne and All SS *S'wark* 96-00. *10 Banff Road, Alyth, Blairgowrie PH11 8DT* Tel (01828) 633400

KENDAL, Henry David. b 59. Bris Poly Dip Valuation & Estate Mgt 80 ASVA83. Lon Bible Coll 90 Oak Hill NSM Course 92. **d** 94 **p** 95. NSM Roxeth *Lon* 94-95; C 95-99; C Woodside Park St Barn from 99. *78 Woodside Avenue, London N12 8TB* Tel (020) 8343 7776 Mobile 07977-521656 Fax 8446 7492
E-mail henrykendal@compuserve.com

KENDAL, Canon Stephen. b 35. Leeds Univ BA59. Coll of Resurr Mirfield 59. **d** 61 **p** 62. C Seaton Hirst *Newc* 61-63; C Newc St Geo 63-66; C Gosforth All SS 66-70; Ind Chapl *Llan* 70-78; Ind Chapl *Dur* 78-91; Hon C Houghton le Spring 78-90; Ind Chapl *Worc* 91-00; Hon Can Worc Cathl 98-00; rtd 00. *15 Coneybury View, Broseley TF12 5AX* Tel (01952) 882447
E-mail wimkiddy@aol.com

KENDALL, Alastair Geoffrey. b 55. BSc DipTh. St Jo Coll Nottm DPS. **d** 84 **p** 85. C Glouc St Aldate *Glouc* 84-87; C Sheff St Jo *Sheff* 87-92; V Bream *Glouc* from 92. *The Vicarage, Bream, Lydney GL15 6ES* Tel (01594) 562376
E-mail breamchurch@btinternet.com

KENDALL, Edward Oliver Vaughan. b 33. Dur Univ BA59. Ridley Hall Cam 59. **d** 61 **p** 62. C Corsham *Bris* 61-64; C Portsea St Mary *Portsm* 64-67; Asst Chapl HM Pris Pentonville 67-68; Chapl HM Borstal Portland 68-71; Lic to Offic *Bradf* from 71;

rtd 94. *10 Halsteads Cottages, Settle BD24 9QJ* Tel (01729) 822860

KENDALL, Frank. b 40. CCC Cam BA62 MA68 FRSA90. S'wark Ord Course 74. **d** 74 **p** 75. NSM Lingfield *S'wark* 74-75 and 78-82; NSM Sketty *S & B* 75-78; NSM Limpsfield and Titsey *S'wark* 82-84; Lic to Offic *Man* 84-89 and *Liv* 89-96; NSM Adnry St Helens *Liv* 96-00; Perm to Offic from 01; NSM Farington Moss *Blackb* from 03; NSM Lostock Hall from 03. *52 Kingsway, Penwortham, Preston PR1 0ED* Tel (01772) 748021

KENDALL, Giles. b 57. Lon Univ BA80 Univ Coll Lon BSc86 Lon Univ PhD90. STETS BTh98. **d** 98 **p** 99. C Wareham *Sarum* 98-01; V Sawston *Ely* from 01; P-in-c Babraham from 01. *The Vicarage, Church Lane, Sawston, Cambridge CB2 4JR* Tel (01223) 832248 E-mail stm_stp@fish.co.uk

KENDALL, Gordon Sydney. b 41. **d** 72 **p** 74. Hon C Old Ford St Paul w St Steph and St Mark *Lon* 72-82; Hon C Homerton St Luke 86-92; Asst Chapl Hackney and Homerton Hosp Lon 87-92; Chapl S Devon Healthcare NHS Trust from 92; Lic to Offic *Ex* from 92. *Torbay Hospital, Lawes Bridge, Newton Road, Torquay TQ2 7AA* Tel (01803) 614567 or 814054

KENDALL, Miss Jacqueline Ann. b 63. Univ of Wales (Abth) BA85. Cranmer Hall Dur 88. **d** 91 **p** 94. Par Dn Stockport St Sav *Ches* 91-94; C 94-95; C Acton and Worleston, Church Minshull etc 95-96; C Helsby and Dunham-on-the-Hill 96-97; C Alvanley 96-97; C Timperley 97-01; P-in-c Dodleston from 01. *St Mary's Rectory, Pulford Lane, Dodleston, Chester CH4 9NN* Tel (01244) 660257

KENDALL, Michael Peter. b 71. St Jo Coll Dur BTh92 Oak Hill Th Coll MPhil94. **d** 96 **p** 97. C Stapenhill w Cauldwell *Derby* 96-00; C Houghton *Carl* from 00. *167 Kingstown Road, Carlisle CA3 0AX* Tel (01228) 591600 E-mail mikekendall@arsenalfc.net

KENDRA, Kenneth Ernest. b 13. OBE66. Leeds Univ BA41 MA48. Linc Th Coll 40. **d** 42 **p** 43. C Pocklington and Kilnwick Percy *York* 42-46; CF 46-71; QHC 70-71; V Lee-on-the-Solent *Portsm* 71-80; RD Alverstoke 77-79; rtd 80. *Bookers Barn, Bolney, Haywards Heath RH17 5NB* Tel (01444) 881064

KENDRA, Neil Stuart. b 46. JP96. FCIPD84 Leeds Univ BA67 Univ of Wales (Swansea) DipAD72 Bradf Univ MSc80 PhD84. Linc Th Coll 67. **d** 69 **p** 70. C Allerton *Liv* 69-72; Ldr Leeds City Cen Detached Youth Work Project 73-75; Dioc Youth Officer *Ripon* 75-77; Lect Ilkley Coll 77-78; Sen Lect Bradf and Ilkley Community Coll 78-88; Hd Community and Youth Studies St Martin's Coll 88-94; Hd Applied Soc Sciences from 94. *St Martin's College, Lancaster LA1 3JD* Tel (01524) 384350

KENDREW, Geoffrey David. b 42. K Coll Lon BD66 AKC66. **d** 67 **p** 68. C Bourne *Guildf* 67-70; C Haslemere 70-76; V Derby St Barn *Derby* 76-95; R Deal St Leon and St Rich and Sholden *Cant* from 95; Chapl E Kent Community NHS Trust from 00. *St Leonard's Rectory, Addelam Road, Deal CT14 9BZ* Tel (01304) 374076

KENDRICK, Dale Evans. b 62. Ch Ch Coll Cant BA86 Nottm Univ MA87 Leeds Univ MA95. Coll of Resurr Mirfield 94. **d** 95 **p** 96. C Tividale *Lich* 95-96; C Blakenall Heath 96-97; C Stafford 97-98; Dep Chapl HM Pris Birm 98-01; Chapl HM Pris Drake Hall 01-03; Chapl RAF from 03. *Chaplaincy Services (RAF), HQ, Personnel and Training Command, RAF Innsworth, Gloucester GL3 1EZ* Tel (01452) 712612 ext 5164 Fax 615800

KENDRICK, Canon Desmond Max. b 22. Leeds Univ BA41. Wycliffe Hall Ox 50. **d** 52 **p** 53. C Glodwick St Mark *Man* 52-54; Chapl Leeds Road Hosp Bradf 54-77; V Bradf St Clem *Bradf* 54-77; RD Bradf 63-73; Hon Can Bradf Cathl 64-89; V Otley 77-89; Chapl Wharfdale Gen Hosp 77-90; rtd 89; Perm to Offic *Bradf* from 89. *26 Ashtofts Mount, Guiseley LS20 9DB* Tel (01943) 870430

KENDRICK, Mrs Helen Grace. b 66. Bris Univ BA88. St Alb and Ox Min Course 96. **d** 99 **p** 00. C Ickenield *Ox* 99-03; P-in-c Sutton Courtenay w Appleford from 03. *The Vicarage, 3 Tullis Close, Sutton Courtenay, Abingdon OX14 4BD* Tel (01235) 848297 E-mail helen@kendricks.fsnet.co.uk

KENDRICK, Ronald Horace. b 35. Univ of Wales (Ban) BD78 DPS79. **d** 82 **p** 83. C Wrexham *St As* 82-85; R Llanelian and Betws-yn-Rhos 85-99; rtd 99. *2 Chapelfield, Marl Lane, Deganwy, Conwy LL31 9BF* Tel (01492) 582522

KENNARD, Ms Alice Marina. b 36. **d** 00. NSM Mynyddislwyn *Mon* 00-02. *21 Trostrey, Hollybush, Cwmbran NP44 7JD* Tel (01633) 482812

KENNARD, Mark Philip Donald. b 60. Man Univ BSc82. Cranmer Hall Dur 85. **d** 88 **p** 89. C Newark w Hawton, Cotham and Shelton *S'well* 88-89; C Newark 89-91; C Cropwell Bishop w Colston Bassett, Granby etc 91-93; P-in-c Shireoaks 93-99; Chapl Bassetlaw Hosp and Community Services NHS Trust 93-96; Chapl RAF from 99. *Chaplaincy Services (RAF), HQ, Personnel and Training Command, RAF Innsworth, Gloucester GL3 1EZ* Tel (01452) 712612 ext 5164 Fax 510828

KENNEDY, Alan. b 52. Liv Univ BSc95. N Ord Course 01. **d** 03. C Westbrook St Phil *Liv* from 03. *16 Ridgebourne Close, Callands, Warrington WA5 4YB*

KENNEDY, Ms Alison Mary. b 66. K Coll Lon BMus87 Roehampton Inst 88 LTCL90 Heythrop Coll Lon MA95. NTMTC DipTh99. **d** 99 **p** 00. C De Beauvoir Town St Pet *Lon* 99-02; TV Walthamstow *Chelmsf* from 02. *St Gabriel's Vicarage, 17 Shernhall Street, London E17 3EU* Tel (020) 8509 1135 E-mail alison_m_kennedy@hotmail.com

KENNEDY, Anthony Reeves. b 32. Lon Univ DipTh67. Roch Th Coll 64. **d** 67 **p** 68. C Ross *Heref* 67-69; C Marfleet *York* 69-71; TV 72-76; V Lightwater *Guildf* 76-83; V W Ham *Chelmsf* 83-89; V Lutton w Gedney Drove End, Dawsmere *Linc* 89-94; Perm to Offic *Chich* from 94; rtd 97. *40 Haydock Close, Alton GU34 2TL* Tel (01420) 549860

KENNEDY, Arthur. b 57. St Pet Coll Ox BA79 MA83. St Jo Coll Nottm 83. **d** 85 **p** 86. C Nor Heartsease St Fran *Nor* 85-89; C Tadley St Pet *Win* 89-91; R Farmborough, Marksbury and Stanton Prior *B & W* 91-98; C Stanton St Jas 99-00; rtd 01. *11 Park View, Buxted, Uckfield TN22 4LS* Tel (01825) 733475

KENNEDY, Miss Carolyn Ruth. b 59. Univ of Wales (Ban) BA81 GradCertEd(FE)85. Ripon Coll Cuddesdon BA90. **d** 91 **p** 94. C Frodingham *Linc* 91-95; Chapl Cov Univ *Cov* 95-00; R Uffington Gp *Linc* from 00. *The Rectory, 67 Main Road, Uffington, Stamford PE9 4SN* Tel (01780) 481786 E-mail crkennedy@clara.co.uk

KENNEDY, David George. b 46. Hull Univ BEd71 MA76. Linc Th Coll 77. **d** 79 **p** 80. C Linc St Faith and St Martin w St Pet *Linc* 79-82; V Bilton St Pet *York* 82-90; V New Seaham *Dur* 90-92; Chapl Lincs and Humberside Univ *York* 92-97; P-in-c Barrow St Matt *Carl* 97-99; TR from 99; Chapl Furness Coll from 97. *The Vicarage, Highfield Road, Barrow-in-Furness LA14 5NZ* Tel (01229) 823569

KENNEDY, Canon David John. b 57. St Jo Coll Dur BA78 Nottm Univ MTh81 Birm Univ PhD96. St Jo Coll Nottm 79. **d** 81 **p** 82. C Tudhoe Grange *Dur* 81-87; C Merrington 84-87; Tutor Qu Coll Birm 88-96; R Haughton le Skerne *Dur* 96-01; Can Res Dur Cathl from 01; Chapl Grey Coll Dur from 01. *7 The College, Durham DH1 3EQ* Tel 0191-375 0242 Fax 386 4267 E-mail david.kennedy@durham.anglican.org

KENNEDY, Gary. b 63. Qu Coll Birm BA02. **d** 03. C New Bury *Man* from 03. *The Vicarage, 15 Lowick Avenue, Bolton BL3 2DS* E-mail garynbogusia@screaming.net

KENNEDY, James Ernest. b 20. TCD BA46 MA51. CITC 46. **d** 46 **p** 47. C Kilnamanagh w Kilcormack, Castle Ellis etc *C & O* 46-48; C Ahoghill *Conn* 48; P-in-c Portglenone 48-51; I 51-60; I Agherton 60-67; I Errigal w Desertoghill *D & R* 67-81; rtd 81. *38 Prospect Road, Portstewart BT55 7LQ* Tel (028) 7083 2052

KENNEDY, Jason Grant. b 68. Oak Hill Th Coll BA95. **d** 98 **p** 99. C Beccles St Mich *St E* 98-01; R Hollington St Leon *Chich* from 01. *The Rectory, Tile Barn Road, St Leonards-on-Sea TN38 9PA* Tel (01424) 852257 Fax 853896 E-mail jason.kennedy@hollingtonpc.org.uk

KENNEDY, Joseph. b 69. Edin Univ BSc91 BD94 St Hugh's Coll Ox MSt00 PGCE97. St Steph Ho Ox 98. **d** 02. C Stratfield Mortimer and Mortimer W End etc *Ox* from 02. *23 The Crescent, Mortimer Common, Reading RG7 3RX* Tel 0118-933 2000 Mobile 07790-610769 E-mail joseph.kennedy@talk21.com

KENNEDY, Canon Michael Charles. b 39. TCD BA63 MA79 BD79 Open Univ PhD87. TCD Div Sch 61. **d** 63 **p** 64. C Drumglass *Arm* 63-66; I Lisnadill w Kildarton from 66; Warden Dioc Guild of Lay Readers from 74; Hon V Choral Arm Cathl from 75; Tutor for Aux Min (Arm) from 82; Preb Yagoe St Patr Cathl Dublin from 92. *Lisnadill Rectory, 60 Newtownhamilton Road, Armagh BT60 2PW* Tel (028) 3752 3630 E-mail lisnadill@armagh.anglican.org

KENNEDY, Paul Alan. b 67. ACA92 Brighton Poly. St Steph Ho Ox BA95. **d** 95 **p** 96. C Romford St Andr *Chelmsf* 95-98; C Cheam *S'wark* 98-01; V Steep and Froxfield w Privett *Portsm* from 01. *The Vicarage, 77 Church Road, Steep, Petersfield GU32 2DF* Tel (01730) 264282 Mobile 07989-255864 E-mail paulak@madasafish.com

KENNEDY, Paul Joseph Alan. b 57. Newc Univ MA93. Sarum & Wells Th Coll 81. **d** 84 **p** 85. C Shildon *Dur* 84-85; C Shildon w Eldon 85-86; C Shotton *St As* 86-88; V Waterhouses *Dur* 88-93; V Denton *Newc* 93-95; CF 95-98; P-in-c Leam Lane *Dur* 98-99; V from 99. *St Andrew's Vicarage, Whinbrooke, Gateshead NE10 8HR* Tel 0191-469 3257

KENNEDY, Brother Philip Bartholomew. b 47. STETS 95. **d** 98 **p** 99. SSF from 77. *The Friary, Hilfield, Dorchester DT2 7BE* Tel (01300) 341345/6 Fax 341293

KENNEDY, Ross Kenneth. b 40. Edin Th Coll 83. **d** 85 **p** 86. C Hexham *Newc* 85-89; TV Glendale Gp 89-93; TR Ch the King from 93. *North Gosforth Vicarage, Wideopen, Newcastle upon Tyne NE13 6NH* Tel 0191-236 2280

KENNEDY, Wendy Patricia. b 58. STETS 00. **d** 03. NSM Warren Park and Leigh Park *Portsm* from 03. *13 Ashcroft Lane, Waterlooville PO8 0AY* Tel (023) 9241 3190 E-mail teamkennedy@lineone.net

KENNEDY, William Edmund. b 20. QUB BA43 TCD BA45 MA48. **d** 45 **p** 46. C Seagoe *D & D* 45-48; C Ballynafeigh St Jude

446

48-57; I Ballyculter w Kilclief 57-85; rtd 85. *Shalom, 8 Dunnanew Road, Seaforde, Downpatrick BT30 8PJ* Tel (028) 4481 1706

KENNERLEY, Canon Katherine Virginia (Ginnie). Somerville Coll Ox BA58 MA65 Irish Sch of Ecum Dip Ecum84 TCD BA86 Princeton Th Sem DMin98. CITC 86. **d** 88 **p** 96. Lect Applied Th CITC 88-93; NSM Bray *D & G* 88-93; I Narraghmore and Timolin w Castledermot etc from 93; Can Ch Ch Cathl Dublin from 96. *The Rectory, Timolin, Co Kildare, Irish Republic* Tel (00353) (59) 862 4278 Mobile 87-647 5092 E-mail kennerley@eircom.net

KENNETT-ORPWOOD, Jason Robert. b 55. St Mich Coll Llan DipTh77 DPS78. **d** 78 **p** 79. Chapl St Woolos Cathl *Mon* 78-82; Chapl St Woolos Hosp Newport 79-82; Dioc Youth Chapl *Mon* 82-85; V Cwmcarn 82-85; TV Wrexham *St As* 85-89; Dioc Ecum Officer 94-99; Chapl Wrexham Maelor Hosp 86-89; V Bistre 89-99. *94 Erddig Road, Wrexham LL13 7DR*

KENNEY, Peter. b 50. Edin Univ BD75. Edin Th Coll 73. **d** 76 **p** 77. C Cullercoats St Geo *Newc* 76-81; TV Whorlton 81-88; P-in-c N Gosforth 88; TR Ch the King 88-93; P-in-c Newc St Jo 93-02; P-in-c Gosforth St Hugh from 02; Dioc Adv in Past Care and Counselling from 02. *The Vicarage, Wansbeck Road, Newcastle upon Tyne NE3 2LR* Tel 0191-285 8792 E-mail kenney@globalnet.co.uk

KENNING, Michael Stephen. b 47. St Chad's Coll Dur BA68. Westcott Ho Cam 69. **d** 71 **p** 72. C Hythe *Cant* 71-75; TV Bow w Bromley St Leon 75-77; C-in-c W Leigh CD *Portsm* 77-81; V Lee-on-the-Solent 81-92; R N Waltham and Steventon, Ashe and Deane *Win* from 92; RD Whitchurch from 03. *The Rectory, North Waltham, Basingstoke RG25 2BQ* Tel (01256) 397256 Fax as telephone E-mail michael.kenning@ukgateway.net

KENNINGTON, John Paul. b 61. Collingwood Coll Dur BA85. St Steph Ho Ox BA87 MA92. **d** 88 **p** 89. C Headington *Ox* 88-91; C Dulwich St Clem w St Pet *S'wark* 91-94; TV Mortlake w E Sheen 94-01; V Battersea St Mary from 01. *St Mary's Vicarage, 32 Vicarage Crescent, London SW11 3LD* Tel (020) 7585 3986 E-mail pkennington@clara.net

KENNY, Canon Charles John. b 39. LGSM74 QUB BA61 MEd78. CITC 69. **d** 69 **p** 70. C Belfast St Paul *Conn* 69-71; Hd of RE Grosvenor High Sch 71-94; V Choral Belf Cathl 94-00; Can Treas 95-00; rtd 00; Lic to Offic *Conn* from 84. *45 Deramore Drive, Belfast BT9 5JS* Tel (028) 9066 9632 *or* 9032 8332 Fax 9023 8855

KENNY, Frederick William Bouvier. b 28. TCD BA53 DipEd54 MA56 LTh. **d** 56 **p** 57. C Ballymacarrett St Patr *D & D* 56-58; C Blackpool St Jo *Blackb* 58-61; Chapl Preston R Infirmary 61-66; V Preston St Paul *Blackb* 61-66; Youth Adv CMS (Lon) 66-70; Youth Sec (Ireland) CMS 70-75; I Belfast St Clem *D & D* 75-80; V Preston St Cuth *Blackb* 80-86; TV Bushbury *Lich* 86-90; P-in-c Stambridge *Chelmsf* 90-97; Chapl Southend Community Care Services NHS Trust 90-97; rtd 97; Perm to Offic *Pet* from 97; Perm to Offic *Chelmsf* from 99. *89 Cavendish Gardens, Westcliff-on-Sea SS0 9XP* Tel (01702) 344791 E-mail c-jkenny@dial.pipex.com

KENNY, Canon Thomas Percival Robert. b 27. TCD BA48 MA51. CITC Div Sch 49. **d** 50 **p** 51. C Drumglass *Arm* 50-53; I Derrynoose w Middletown 53-56; I Aghavilly w Derrynoose 56-62; I Portadown St Sav 62-66; I Magherafelt 66-74; I Derryloran 74-82; CMS 82-88; Nigeria 83-88; Hon Can Owerri from 84; I Cloonclare w Killasnett and Drumlease *K, E & A* 88-90; rtd 90. *26 Clanbrassil Drive, Portadown, Craigavon BT63 5EH* Tel (028) 3833 6479

KENRICK, Kenneth David Norman. b 44. Liv Univ RMN. Ripon Hall Ox 70 NW Ord Course 77. **d** 77 **p** 78. C Stockport St Geo *Ches* 77-83; R Stockport St Thos 83-85; R Stockport St Thos w St Pet from 86; Chapl St Thos and Cheadle Royal Hospitals from 88. *St Thomas's Rectory, 25 Heath Road, Stockport SK2 6JJ* Tel 0161-483 2483 E-mail truefaith_@hotmail.com

KENSINGTON, Area Bishop of. *See* COLCLOUGH, The Rt Revd Michael John

KENT, Barry James. b 41. CPC78. Dioc OLM tr scheme. **d** 02 **p** 03. OLM Kinson *Sarum* from 02. *15 Summers Avenue, Bournemouth BH11 9DQ* Tel (01202) 582484 E-mail barry@kentb60.freeserve.co.uk

KENT, Christopher Alfred. b 48. CEng77 MIChemE77 Birm Univ BSc69 PhD72 Nottm Univ DipTh83. St Jo Coll Nottm 82. **d** 84 **p** 85. C Bucknall and Bagnall *Lich* 84-86; Hon C Halesowen *Worc* 86-96; NSM Reddal Hill St Luke 96-01; NSM The Lye and Stambermill from 01. *40 County Park Avenue, Halesowen B62 8SP* Tel 0121-550 3132 E-mail c.a.kent@bham.ac.uk

KENT, David. b 44. CEng MIMechE. N Ord Course. **d** 83 **p** 84. NSM Huddersfield St Pet and All SS *Wakef* 83-98; NSM Newsome and Armitage Bridge 98-03; NSM Em TM from 03. *118 Woodside Road, Huddersfield HD4 5JW* Tel (01484) 324049 Mobile 07785-386815 E-mail davidk@blinkleeds.co.uk

KENT, Frank. b 44. ARCM76 Open Univ BA82. Ridley Hall Cam. **d** 86 **p** 87. C Faversham *Cant* 86-89; R Lyminge w Paddlesworth, Stanford w Postling etc 89-99; P-in-c Sittingbourne St Mich 99-00; V Sittingbourne St Mary and

St Mich from 01. *St Michael's Vicarage, Valenciennes Road, Sittingbourne ME10 1EN* Tel (01795) 472874

KENT, Keith Meredith. b 32. Lon Univ DipTh57. St Aid Birkenhead 55. **d** 58 **p** 59. C Fulwood Ch Ch *Blackb* 58-60; C Everton St Chrys *Liv* 60-62; C Litherland St Phil 64-68; P-in-c Everton St Polycarp 68-74; V Liv All So Springwood 74-78; V Carr Mill 78-86; V Beddgelert *Ban* 86-91; rtd 91; Perm to Offic *Blackb* from 91. *37 Margaret Road, Penwortham, Preston PR1 9QT* Tel (01772) 746831

KENT, Canon Michael Patrick. b 27. St Edm Hall Ox BA50 MA52. Cuddesdon Coll 50. **d** 52 **p** 53. C W Hartlepool St Aid *Dur* 52-57; C-in-c Pennywell St Thos and Grindon St Oswald CD 57-70; V Cockerton 70-93; RD Darlington 79-84; Hon Can Dur Cathl 83-98; rtd 93; Chapl St Chad's Coll *Dur* 94-95. *5 Ferens Close, Durham DH1 1JX* Tel 0191-386 2835

KENT, Preb Neville. b 40. Sarum & Wells Th Coll 70. **d** 72 **p** 73. C Taunton St Andr *B & W* 72-77; R Bradford w Oake, Hillfarrance and Heathfield 77-89; Adv on Soc Concerns 80-87; RD Tone 87-89; V Worle 89-93; TR from 93; Preb Wells Cathl from 94; Perm to Offic *Bris* from 97. *The Vicarage, 93 Church Road, Worle, Weston-super-Mare BS22 9EA* Tel (01934) 510694 *or* 515922 E-mail worlepo@aol.com

KENT, Richard Hugh. b 38. Worc Coll Ox BA61 MA63. Chich Th Coll 61. **d** 63 **p** 64. C Emscote *Cov* 63-66; C Finham 66-70; V Parkend *Glouc* 70-75; V Glouc St Aldate 75-86; Chapl and Warden Harnhill Healing Cen 86-96; R N Buckingham *Ox* from 96; AD Buckingham from 00. *The Rectory, Main Street, Maids Moreton, Buckingham MK18 1QD* Tel (01280) 813246 E-mail hugh.k@talk21.com

KENT, Roger Anthony Edward. b 56. Kent Univ BA78. St Steph Ho Ox 79. **d** 81 **p** 82. C Ipswich All Hallows *St E* 81-84; C Poplar *Lon* 84-88; V Newington w Hartlip and Stockbury *Cant* 88-95; Chapl Prague *Eur* 95-98; Perm to Offic *Nor* 99; TV Cullercoats St Geo *Newc* from 99. *St Aidan's Vicarage, 29 Billy Mill Lane, North Shields NE29 8BZ* Tel 0191-257 3616

KENT, Ms Susan Elizabeth. b 52. St Aid Coll Dur BA74 St Mary's Coll Newc PGCE77. Ripon Coll Cuddesdon. **d** 00 **p** 01. C Westgate Common *Wakef* from 00. *166 Horbury Road, Wakefield WF2 8BQ* Tel (01924) 383957 Mobile 07884-024202 E-mail revsusan@arken.freeserve.co.uk

KENTIGERN-FOX, Canon William Poyntere Kentigern. b 38. AKC63. **d** 64 **p** 65. C S Mimms St Mary and Potters Bar *Lon* 64-67; C S Tottenham 67-70; P-in-c Duddington w Tixover *Pet* 70-76; R Barrowden and Wakerley 70-76; P-in-c Morcott w S Luffenham 75-77; R Barrowden and Wakerley w S Luffenham 77-79; R Byfield w Boddington 79-86; V Northampton St Mich w St Edm 86-95; V Raunds 95-03; Can Pet Cathl 94-03; RD Higham 97-02; rtd 03. *41 Parkfield Road, Ruskington, Sleaford NG34 9HT* Tel (01526) 830944

KENWARD, Roger Nelson. b 34. Selw Coll Cam BA58 MA62. Ripon Hall Ox 58. **d** 60 **p** 61. C Paddington St Jas *Lon* 60-63; Chapl RAF 64-82; Asst Chapl-in-Chief RAF 82-89; P-in-c Lyneham w Bradenstoke *Sarum* 72-76; Hon Chapl to The Queen 85-89; R Laughton w Ripe and Chalvington *Chich* 90-95; Chapl Laughton Lodge Hosp 90-95; rtd 95; NSM Chiddingly w E Hoathly *Chich* 96; Perm to Offic from 96. *The Coach House, School Hill, Old Heathfield, Heathfield TN21 9AE* Tel (01435) 862618

KENWAY, Ian Michael. b 52. Leeds Univ BA74 Bris Univ PhD86. Coll of Resurr Mirfield 74. **d** 76 **p** 77. C Cov E *Cov* 76-79; C Southmead *Bris* 79-81; P-in-c Shaw Hill *Birm* 82-88; Asst Sec Gen Syn Bd for Soc Resp 88-93; Chapl Essex Univ *Chelmsf* 93-99; Dir Studies Cen for Study of Th *Birm* 99; Perm to Offic *S & B* from 01. *6 Kings Court, Presteigne LD8 2AJ* Tel (01544) 260547 Mobile 07748-223090 Fax 07092-315825 E-mail iank@cischr.org

KENWAY, Robert Andrew. b 56. Bris Univ BA78. Westcott Ho Cam 80. **d** 82 **p** 83. C Birchfield *Birm* 82-85; C Queensbury All SS *Lon* 87-89; R Birm St Geo *Birm* 89-97; V Calne and Blackland *Sarum* from 97. *The Vicarage, Vicarage Close, Calne SN11 8DD* Tel (01249) 812340

KENYA, Archbishop of. *See* NZIMBI, The Most Revd Benjamin

KENYON, Stanley Robert. b 31. Kelham Th Coll 51. **d** 55 **p** 56. C Eckington *Derby* 55-57; C Derby St Andr 57-59; C Lullington 59-61; C Nether and Over Seale 59-61; P-in-c Grimsby St Steph *Linc* 61-71; V Habrough 71-82; V E Halton 73-82; V Killingholme 73-82; V Barnetby le Wold Gp 82-94; rtd 94; Perm to Offic *Linc* from 94. *Machindor, 47 Highfields, Crowle, Scunthorpe DN17 4NP* Tel (01724) 711435

KEOGH, Anthony. b 35. St Mich Coll Llan 63. **d** 66 **p** 67. C Aberaman and Abercwmboi *Llan* 66-70; Hon C Penarth All SS 70-76; R Jersey H Trin *Win* from 76. *Holy Trinity Rectory, La rue du Presbytere, Jersey JE3 5JB* Tel (01534) 861110

KEOGH, Henry James. b 39. TCD BA61 NUI BMus65. **d** 62 **p** 63. C Cork St Fin Barre's Cathl *C, C & R* 62-65; C Belfast St Luke *Conn* 65-66; C Dromore Cathl *D & D* 66-68; I Castlecomer *C & O* 68-85; I Kilscoran w Killinick and Mulrankin 85-02; Hon Chapl Miss to Seafarers 85-02; Preb Ferns Cathl *C & O* 96-02; rtd 02. *5 Ard na Gréine, Dark Road, Midleton, Co Cork, Irish Republic* Tel (00353) (21) 463 0841

KEOGH, Paul Anthony. b 37. Order of Friars Minor 55. **d** 62 **p** 63. In RC Ch 62-66; Hon C Eltham Park St Luke *S'wark* from 00. *78 Greenvale Road, London SE9 1PD* Tel (020) 8850 9958 *or* 8303 4786

KEOGH, Robert Gordon. b 56. TCD DipTh84. **d** 84 **p** 85. C Mossley *Conn* 84-87; I Taunagh w Kilmactranny, Ballysumaghan etc *K, E & A* 87-90; I Swanlinbar w Tomregan, Kinawley, Drumlane etc 90-02; Preb Kilmore Cathl 98-02; I Drumclamph w Lower and Upper Langfield *D & R* from 02. *Drumclamph Rectory, 70 Greenville Road, Castlederg BT81 7NU* Tel (028) 8167 1433 E-mail rgkeogh@eircom.net

KEOWN, Paul. **d** 02 **p** 03. C Llansamlet *S & B* from 02. *2 Monmouth Place, Morriston, Swansea SA6 6RF* Tel (01792) 793197

KER, Desmond Agar-Ellis. b 15. Wells Th Coll 58. **d** 58 **p** 60. C Wyken *Cov* 58-59; C Dawlish *Ex* 60-61; C Cockington 61-69; V Bovey Tracey St Jo 69-80; rtd 80; Perm to Offic *S'wark* 84-92; Perm to Offic *Chich* 92-97. *Flat 36, St Clements Court, Wear Bay Crescent, Folkestone CT19 5AU*

KERLEY, Brian Edwin. b 36. St Jo Coll Cam BA57 MA61. Linc Th Coll 59. **d** 61 **p** 62. C Sheerness H Trin w St Paul *Cant* 61-64; C St Laur in Thanet 64-69; C Coulsdon St Andr *S'wark* 69-76; P-in-c Fulbourn *Ely* 76-77; R 77-03; P-in-c Gt and Lt Wilbraham 86-03; RD Quy 83-93 and 97-00; rtd 03. *The Rectory, 2 Apthorpe Street, Fulbourn, Cambridge CB1 5EY* Tel (01223) 880337 E-mail brian.kerley@ely.anglican.org

KERLEY, Patrick Thomas Stewart. b 42. Linc Th Coll. **d** 85 **p** 86. Hon C Thorpe *Nor* 85-90; C Wymondham 90-94; C Gt Yarmouth 94-95; TV 95-00; TV Wilford Peninsula *St E* from 00. *The Rectory, Eyke, Woodbridge IP12 2QW* Tel (01394) 460289 Mobile 07940-739769

KERNER, Vivienne Jane. b 49. Liv Univ CertEd71 BEd72. WEMTC 91. **d** 94 **p** 95. NSM Glouc St Jas and All SS *Glouc* 94-01; NSM Glouc St Mark and St Mary de Crypt w St Jo etc from 01. *Cornerstone, 10 Arkendale Drive, Hardwicke, Gloucester GL4 2JA* Tel (01452) 883126 E-mail wsm.kerner@tesco.net

KERR, Andrew Harry Mayne. b 41. TCD BA63 Birm Univ DPS72. Melbourne Coll of Div MMin98. **d** 65 **p** 66. C Belfast St Luke *Conn* 65-68; SCM Sec (Ireland) 68-72; C Clooney *D & R* 72-74; Australia from 74; C Swinburne 74-80; I Dallas 80-88; I Mont Albert 88-94; P-in-c W Geelong from 96. *101 Katrina Street, Blackburn North, Vic, Australia 3130* Tel (0061) (3) 5221 6694 *or* 9893 4946 Fax 9893 4946 E-mail ahmkerr@hotmail.com

KERR, Anthony. b 43. Sheff Univ BA64 Man Univ CertEd65. N Ord Course. **d** 85 **p** 86. NSM Greenfield *Man* 85-87; NSM Leesfield 87-97; P-in-c Oldham St Steph and All Martyrs 97-02; NSM Lydgate w Friezland 02-03; NSM Saddleworth from 03. *16 Netherlees, Spring Lane, Oldham OL4 5BA* Tel 0161-620 6512

KERR, Arthur Henry. LRAM47 TCD BA48 DA65. **d** 49 **p** 50. C Templemore *D & R* 49-50; C Dublin Harold's Cross *D & G* 50-57; ICM 57-60; Chapl Rotunda Hosp 60-75; Lic to Offic *Conn* 88-94; P-in-c Clondevaddock w Portsalon and Leatbeg *D & R* 94-01; rtd 01. *Halothane, 172 Mountsandel Road, Coleraine BT52 1JE* Tel (028) 7034 4940

KERR, Bryan Thomas. b 70. QUB BD91 TCD MPhil96. CITC 94. **d** 96 **p** 97. C Enniskillen *Clogh* 96-99; I Garrison w Slavin and Belleek from 99; Dioc Communications Officer from 00. *The Rectory, Knockarevan, Enniskillen BT93 4AE* Tel (028) 6865 8372 E-mail rector@belleek.org *or* dco@clogher.anglican.org

KERR, Charles Alexander Gray. b 33. Open Univ BA75 Birm Univ MA83 MA88. Edin Th Coll 63. **d** 67 **p** 68. C Hawick *Edin* 67-70; C Edgbaston St Geo *Birm* 70-72; Chapl Birm Skin Hosp 70-75; P-in-c Quinton Road W St Boniface *Birm* 72-79; V 79-84; R Musselburgh *Edin* 84-86; P-in-c Prestonpans 84-86; NSM Reighton w Speeton *York* 89-91; P-in-c Burton Pidsea and Humbleton w Elsternwick 91-95; V Anlaby Common St Mark 95; rtd 96; Perm to Offic *York* 96-02. *6A Glebeland Close, West Stafford, Dorchester DT2 8AE*

KERR, David James. b 36. TCD BA58 MA61 BD61 HDipEd66. TCD Div Sch Div Test 59. **d** 60 **p** 61. C Belfast Trin Coll Miss *Conn* 60-63; Dean's V St Patr Cathl Dublin 63-66; Chapl Beechwood Park Sch St Alb 66-01; Hon C Flamstead *St Alb* 74-00; Perm to Offic from 00; rtd 01. *Trumpton Cottage, 12A Pickford Road, Markyate, St Albans AL3 8RU* Tel (01582) 841191 E-mail kerr_david@hotmail.com

KERR, Derek Preston. b 64. TCD BTh90. Oak Hill Th Coll 85. **d** 90 **p** 91. C Belfast St Donard *D & D* 90-93; C Carrickfergus *Conn* 93-96; I Devenish w Boho *Clogh* from 96. *Monea Rectory, Monea, Enniskillen BT74 8GE* Tel (028) 6634 1228

KERR, Miss Dora Elizabeth. b 41. QUB BA65 Southn Univ DipEd66 Nottm Univ DipTh83. St Jo Coll Nottm 82. **dss** 84 **d** 87 **p** 94. Becontree St Mary *Chelmsf* 84-88; Par Dn 87-88; Par Dn Rushden w Newton Bromswold *Pet* 88-93; C Finham *Cov* 94-00; Chapl Walsgrave Hosps NHS Trust Cov 94-00; C Belper *Derby* from 00. *St Mark's House, Openwoodgate, Belper DE56 0SD* Tel (01773) 825727

KERR, Ewan Charles. b 74. Fitzw Coll Cam BA96 MA00. Ripon Coll Cuddesdon MTh01. **d** 01 **p** 02. C Nor St Pet Mancroft w

St Jo Maddermarket *Nor* from 01. *63 Recreation Road, Norwich NR2 3PA* Tel (01603) 451878 Mobile 07967-004121

KERR, George Cecil. b 36. TCD BA60 MA65. CITC 60. **d** 60 **p** 61. C Coleraine *Conn* 60-63; Div Master Annandale Gr Sch Belf 63-65; Dean of Res QUB 65-74; Lic to Offic *D & D* 75-00; rtd 00. *12 Berkeley Grove, Warrenpoint BT34 3TS*

KERR, Mrs Jean. b 46. SS Hild & Bede Coll Dur CertEd69. N Ord Course 84. **d** 87 **p** 94. NSM Peel *Man* 87-93; Par Dn Dixon Green 88-89; Par Dn New Bury 89-93; Par Dn Gillingham St Mark *Roch* 93-94; C 94-98; Warden of Ev from 98; Chapl Medway Secure Tr Cen 98-01; NSM Roch St Justus from 01. *St Justus's Vicarage, 1 Binnacle Road, Rochester ME1 2XR* Tel and fax (01634) 841183 *or* 400673 E-mail jean.kerr@rochester.anglican.org

KERR, John Maxwell. b 43. MSOSc88 Toronto Univ BASc66 Leeds Univ MSc70 Nottm Univ DipTh76. Linc Th Coll 75. **d** 77 **p** 78. C New Windsor *Ox* 77-80; Asst Chapl Cheltenham Coll 80-81; Chapl 81-82; NSM Win St Lawr and St Maurice w St Swithun *Win* 82-94; Chapl Win Coll 82-92; Hd RS 86-97; Visiting Research Fell Mert Coll Ox 90; Visiting Lect Dept of Continuing Educn Ox Univ from 92; rtd 02. *3 School Terrace, Warnford, Southampton SO32 3LE* Tel (01703) 829020 E-mail jmk@kerr.newnet.co.uk

KERR, Canon Nicholas Ian. b 46. Em Coll Cam BA68 MA72. Westcott Ho Cam 74. **d** 77 **p** 78. C Merton St Mary *S'wark* 77-80; C Rainham *Roch* 80-84; Chapl Joyce Green Hosp Dartford 84-90; V Dartford St Edm *Roch* 84-90; V Lamorbey H Redeemer from 90; RD Sidcup from 98; Hon Can Roch Cathl from 02. *The Vicarage, 64 Day's Lane, Sidcup DA15 8JR* Tel (020) 8300 1508 E-mail nik@dircon.co.uk

KERR, Paul Turner. b 47. Cranmer Hall Dur 68. **d** 71 **p** 72. C Kingston upon Hull St Martin *York* 71-72; C Linthorpe 72-76; C Cherry Hinton St Jo *Ely* 76-78; Chapl Addenbrooke's Hosp Cam 76-78; TV Rochdale *Man* 78-84; Chapl Birch Hill Hosp Rochdale 78-84; V New Bury 84-87; TR 87-93; C Gillingham St Mark *Roch* 93-98; RD Gillingham 96-98; V Roch St Justus from 98; RD Roch from 00. *St Justus's Vicarage, 1 Binnacle Road, Rochester ME1 2XR* Tel (01634) 841183 Fax 818353 E-mail kerrevan@global.net

KERR, Canon Stephen Peter. b 46. TCD BA68 Edin Univ BD71 MPhil80. **d** 71 **p** 72. C Belfast H Trin *Conn* 72-76; C Ballywillan 76-78; Lect Linc Th Coll 78-87; Dioc Officer for Adult Educn and Minl Tr *Worc* 87-99; P-in-c Ombersley w Doverdale from 87; Hon Can Worc Cathl from 92; Bp's Th Adv from 99. *The Rectory, Ombersley, Droitwich WR9 0EW* Tel (01905) 620950 E-mail peter.kerr@cofe-worcester.org.uk

KERR, Terence Philip. b 54. QUB BD97. CITC 97. **d** 99 **p** 00. C Antrim All SS *Conn* 99-01; I Drummaul w Duneane and Ballyscullion from 01. *The Vicarage, 1A Glenkeen, Randalstown, Antrim BT41 3JX* Tel (028) 9447 2561 E-mail terry@revkerr99.freeserve.co.uk

KERRIDGE, Donald George. b 32. Bede Coll Dur CertEd72 Hull Univ BA84. Wesley Coll Leeds 57 Bps' Coll Cheshunt 61. **d** 62 **p** 63. C Manston *Ripon* 62-66; C Hawksworth Wood 66-71; Asst Chapl Brentwood Sch Essex 72-74; Lic to Offic *Linc* 81-89; R Tetney, Marshchapel and N Coates 89-91; P-in-c Linc St Swithin 91-95; P-in-c Linc St Swithin w All SS 95-99; Asst Chapl Linc Co Hosp 91-94; rtd 99. *28 Caverleigh Way, Worcester Park KT4 8DG* Tel (020) 8337 3171

KERRIN, Albert Eric. b 26. Aber Univ MA51. Edin Th Coll 51. **d** 53 **p** 54. C Dumfries *Glas* 53-55; P-in-c Cambuslang w Newton Cathl Miss 55-57; I Alford *Ab* 57-69; P-in-c Portpatrick *Glas* 69-98; P-in-c Stranraer 69-98; rtd 91; Perm to Offic *Glas* from 98. *15 London Road, Stranraer DG9 8AF* Tel (01776) 702822

KERRISON, Mrs Anne Edmonstone. b 23. Cranmer Hall Dur 69. **dss** 77 **d** 87 **p** 94. Hellesdon *Nor* 76-78; Ind Miss 78-79; Lic to Offic 79-88; Perm to Offic 88-94; NSM Hevingham w Hainford and Stratton Strawless 94-96; Perm to Offic from 96. *Sloley Lodge, Sloley, Norwich NR12 8HE* Tel (01692) 538253

KERRY, Martin John. b 55. Ox Univ MA78 Nottm Univ BA81 MTh83. St Jo Coll Nottm 79. **d** 82 **p** 83. C Everton St Geo *Liv* 82-85; Lic to Offic *S'well* from 85; Chapl Asst Nottm City Hosp 85-89; Chapl 89-94; Chapl Nottm City Hosp NHS Trust from 94. *Chaplains' Office, City Hospital, Hucknall Road, Nottingham NG5 1BP* Tel 0115-969 1169 *or* 962 7616

KERSHAW, John Harvey. b 51. Coll of Resurr Mirfield 84. **d** 86 **p** 87. C Hollinwood *Man* 86-89; V Audenshaw St Hilda from 89; Chapl Tameside Gen Hosp 90-94; Chapl Tameside and Glossop NHS Trust 94-95. *St Hilda's Vicarage, Denton Road, Audenshaw, Manchester M34 5BL* Tel 0161-336 2310

KERSHAW, Savile. b 37. Bernard Gilpin Soc Dur 60 Chich Th Coll 61. **d** 64 **p** 65. C Staincliffe *Wakef* 64-66; C Saltley *Birm* 66-68; C Birm St Aid Small Heath 68-72; Perm to Offic from 88; rtd 02. *74 Longmore Road, Shirley, Solihull B90 3EE* Tel 0121-744 3470

KERSLEY, Stuart Casburn. b 40. CEng MIEE. Trin Coll Bris. **d** 82 **p** 83. C Lancing w Coombes *Chich* 82-87; TV Littlehampton and Wick 87-90; R Kingston Buci 90-98; V

Kirdford from 98. *The Vicarage, Kirdford, Billingshurst RH14 0LU* Tel (01403) 820605

KERSWILL, Canon Anthony John. b 39. Lambeth STh85 Linc Th Coll 72. **d** 73 **p** 73. C Boultham *Linc* 73-76; P-in-c N Kelsey 76-83; P-in-c Cadney 76-83; V Gainsborough St Geo 83-91; V Bracebridge 91-00; P-in-c Linc St Swithin 00-01; V Linc All SS from 01; RD Christianity 96-02; Can and Preb Linc Cathl from 02. *St Swithin's Vicarage, Croft Street, Lincoln LN2 5AX* Tel (01522) 803572 Fax 856750 E-mail a.kerswill@ntlworld.com

KERTON-JOHNSON, Peter. b 41. St Paul's Coll Grahamstown. **d** 81 **p** 82. S Africa 81-99; Perm to Offic *Sarum* 99-00; P-in-c Stoke sub Hamdon *B & W* from 00. *The Vicarage, 1 Castle Street, Stoke-sub-Hamdon TA14 6RE* Tel (01935) 822529 Fax 818289 E-mail kertonjohnson@btopenworld.com

KESLAKE, Peter Ralegh. b 33. Sarum & Wells Th Coll. **d** 83 **p** 84. C Glouc St Geo w Whaddon *Glouc* 83-86; P-in-c France Lynch 86-91; V Chalford and France Lynch from 91. *The Vicarage, Brantwood Road, Chalford Hill, Stroud GL6 8BS*

KESTER, Jonathan George Frederick. b 66. Ex Univ BA90. Coll of Resurr Mirfield Cert Past Th93. **d** 93 **p** 94. C Cheshunt *St Alb* 93-96; Chapl to Bp Edmonton *Lon* 96-00; Hon C Munster Square Ch and St Mary Magd 96-00; V Gt Ilford St Mary *Chelmsf* from 00. *St Mary's Vicarage, 26 South Park Road, Ilford IG1 1SS* Tel (020) 8478 0546 *or* 8478 0768 E-mail frjonathan.kester@ntlworld.com

KESTON, Marion. b 44. Glas Univ MB, ChB68 Edin Univ MTh95. St And Dioc Tr Course 87 Edin Th Coll 92. **d** 90 **p** 94. NSM W Fife Team Min *St And* 90-93; Priest Livingston LEP *Edin* from 96. *12B Carrick Gardens, Livingston EH54 9ET* Tel (01506) 410668 Fax 416436 E-mail keston@surfaid.org

KETLEY, Christopher Glen. b 62. Aston Tr Scheme 91 Coll of Resurr Mirfield 93. **d** 95 **p** 96. C Gt Crosby St Faith *Liv* 95-98; C Swinton and Pendlebury *Man* 98-00; V Belfield from 00. *St Ann's Vicarage, 310 Milnrow Road, Rochdale OL16 5BT* Tel (01706) 646173

KETLEY, Michael James. b 39. DipHE81. Oak Hill Th Coll 79. **d** 81 **p** 82. C Bedhampton *Portsm* 81-85; R St Ive w Quethiock *Truro* 85-86; Miss Partnership St Andr w H Cross *Chelmsf* 89-90; C Barkingside St Cedd 90-92; P-in-c 92-95; R Hadleigh St Jas from 95. *The Rectory, 50 Rectory Road, Hadleigh, Benfleet SS7 2ND* Tel (01702) 558992 E-mail revmike@stjamesless.freeserve.co.uk

KETTLE, Alan Marshall. b 51. Leeds Univ BA72. Wycliffe Hall Ox MA78. **d** 78 **p** 79. C Llantwit Fardre *Llan* 78-81; Prov RE Adv Ch in Wales 81-84; Chapl Llandovery Coll 84-92; P-in-c Cil-y-Cwm and Ystrad-ffin w Rhandir-mwyn etc *St D* 85-92; Chapl W Buckland Sch Barnstaple from 92; Lic to Offic *Ex* from 92. *2 West Close, West Buckland, Barnstaple EX32 0ST* Tel (01598) 760542

KETTLE, David John. b 47. Bris Univ BSc63 MLitt86 Fitzw Coll Cam BA75 MA79. Westcott Ho Cam 73. **d** 76 **p** 77. C Bris St Andr Hartcliffe *Bris* 76-79; C Fishponds All SS 79-80; P-in-c 81-83; Perm to Offic *St E* 83-91; New Zealand 91-97; NSM Anglesey Gp *Ely* from 99. *11 Redgate Road, Girton, Cambridge CB3 0PP* Tel (01223) 277505 E-mail djk@kettle.force9.co.uk

KETTLE, Martin Drew. b 52. New Coll Ox BA74 Selw Coll Cam BA76 Cam Univ MA85. Ridley Hall Cam 74. **d** 77 **p** 78. C Enfield St Andr *Lon* 77-80; Chapl Ridley Hall Cam 80-84; V Hendon St Paul Mill Hill *Lon* 85-89; AD W Barnet 90-95. *3 Great Northern Street, Huntingdon PE29 7HJ* Tel (01480) 417604 Mobile 07712-977392

KETTLE, Mrs Patricia Mary Carole. b 41. Worc Coll of Educn CertEd61 Lon Univ DipTh68. Dalton Ho Bris 66. **d** 87 **p** 94. C Wonersh *Guildf* 87-98; C Wonersh w Blackheath 98-01; rtd 01; Perm to Offic *Guildf* from 02. *Wakehurst Cottage, Links Road, Bramley GU5 0AL* Tel (01483) 898856

KETTLE, Peter. b 51. K Coll Lon BD74 AKC74. St Aug Coll Cant 74. **d** 75 **p** 76. C Angell Town St Jo *S'wark* 74-78; C Putney St Mary 78-80; V Raynes Park St Sav 80-85; Perm to Offic from 85. *46 Allenswood, Albert Drive, London SW19 6JX* Tel (020) 8785 3797

KEULEMANS, Andrew Francis Charles. b 68. Univ of Wales (Abth) BSc90. St Jo Coll Nottm BTh93. **d** 94 **p** 95. C Mold *St As* 94-97; TV Wrexham 97-02; Chapl Loretto Sch Musselburgh from 02. *The Manse, 4 Eskside East, Musselburgh EH21 7RS* Tel 0131-653 4429

KEVILL-DAVIES, Christopher Charles. b 44. AKC69. St Aug Coll Cant 70. **d** 70 **p** 71. C Folkestone St Sav *Cant* 70-75; V Yaxley *Ely* 75-78; R Chevington w Hargrave and Whepstead w Brockley *St E* 78-86; Perm to Offic *St Alb* 86-89; NSM Stansted Mountfitchet *Chelmsf* 87-89; R Barkway, Reed and Buckland w Barley *St Alb* 89-96; R Chelsea St Luke and Ch Ch *Lon* from 96. *The Rectory, 64A Flood Street, London SW3 5TE* Tel (020) 7352 6331 *or* 7351 7365 E-mail christopher@chelseaparish.demon.co.uk

KEVIS, Lionel William Graham. b 55. York Univ BA. Wycliffe Hall Ox 83. **d** 86 **p** 87. C Plaistow St Mary *Roch* 86-90; R Ash and Ridley 90-00; P-in-c Bidborough 00-02; P-in-c Leigh from 00.

The Vicarage, The Green, Leigh, Tonbridge TN11 8QJ Tel (01732) 833022

KEW, William Richard. b 45. Lon Univ BD69. Lon Coll of Div LTh68. **d** 69 **p** 70. C Finchley St Paul Long Lane *Lon* 69-72; C Stoke Bishop *Bris* 72-76; USA from 76. *1015 Old Lascassas Road, Murfreesboro, TN 37130, USA* E-mail richardkew@aol.com

KEY, Christopher Halstead. b 56. St Jo Coll Dur BA77 K Coll Lon MTh78. Ridley Hall Cam 79. **d** 81 **p** 82. C Balderstone *Man* 81-84; C Wandsworth All SS *S'wark* 84-88; C-in-c W Dulwich Em CD 88-93; V W Dulwich Em 93-95; R Ore *Chich* from 95. *St Helen's Rectory, 266 Elphinstone Road, Hastings TN34 2AG* Tel (01424) 425172 E-mail chriskey@st-helens-ore.freeserve.co.uk

KEY, John Christopher. b 36. Pemb Coll Cam BA60 MA65. Westcott Ho Cam 60. **d** 62 **p** 63. C Rugby St Andr *Cov* 62-67; Papua New Guinea 68-71; V Cov St Geo *Cov* 71-76; RD Cov N 73-76; V Redditch St Steph *Worc* 76-81; Dioc Ecum Officer 80-81; Australia from 81; rtd 96. *74 Purchase Road, Cherrybrook, NSW, Australia 2126* Tel (0061) (2) 9945 1900 Fax 9945 1945 E-mail johnkey@optushome.com.au

KEY, Robert Frederick. b 52. Bris Univ BA73. Oak Hill Th Coll 74. **d** 76 **p** 77. C Ox St Ebbe w St Pet *Ox* 76-80; C Wallington H Trin *S'wark* 80-85; P-in-c Eynsham *Ox* 85; V Eynsham and Cassington 85-91; V Ox St Andr 91-01; Gen Dir CPAS from 01; Perm to Offic *Cov* from 02. *CPAS, Athena Drive, Tachbrook Park, Warwick CV34 6NG* Tel (01926) 458458 *or* (01869) 346476 Fax 458459 E-mail bob@familykey.fsnet.co.uk *or* rkey@cpas.org.uk

KEY, Roderick Charles. b 57. MTh. **d** 84 **p** 85. C Up Hatherley *Glouc* 84-87; V Glouc St Paul from 87. *St Paul's Vicarage, 2 King Edward's Avenue, Gloucester GL1 5DA* Tel (01452) 523732 E-mail key@stpaulsglos.fsnet.co.uk

KEY, Roger Astley. b 49. Coll of Resurr Mirfield 72. **d** 74 **p** 75. Perm to Offic *Wakef* 74-75; Namibia 75-00; P-in-c Khomasdal Grace Ch 75-77; R Luderitz 77-81; Adn The South 77-80; R Walvis Bay 81-85; Personal Asst to Bp Windhoek 85-86; Dean Windhoek 86-00; V Hopton w Corton *Nor* from 00. *The Vicarage, 51 The Street, Corton, Lowestoft NR32 5HT* Tel (01502) 730977 Mobile 07733-028048 E-mail thebunch@uk.packardbell.org *or* rogerkey30@hotmail.com

KEYES, Graham George. b 44. St Cath Coll Cam BA65 MA68 Lanc Univ MA74 Nottm Univ MTh85 MPhil92. EMMTC 82. **d** 84 **p** 85. C Evington *Leic* 84-86; Vice-Prin NEOC 86-89; C Monkseaton St Mary *Newc* 86-89; P-in-c Newc St Hilda 89-94; TV Ch the King *Newc* 94-99. *1 East Avenue, Newcastle upon Tyne NE12 9PH* Tel 0191-259 9024 E-mail simeon.and.anna@talk21.com

KEYES, Mrs Iris Doreen. b 28. SRN. Gilmore Ho 69. **dss** 76 **d** 87 **p** 94. Egham Hythe *Guildf* 76-78; Chapl Asst St Pet Hosp Chertsey 78-82; Addlestone 83-86; Walton-on-Thames 86-87; C 87-89; rtd 89; NSM Addlestone *Guildf* 94-95; Perm to Offic from 95. *36 Finlay Gardens, Addlestone KT15 2XN* Tel (01932) 846912

KEYMER, Philip John. b 72. Bris Univ BSc93. Oak Hill Th Coll 96. **d** 99 **p** 00. C Partington and Carrington *Ches* 99-02; C Cheadle from 02. *1 Warren Avenue, Cheadle SK8 1NB* Tel 0161-428 3001 E-mail keymer@orangenet.co.uk

KEYS, Christopher David. b 56. Southn Univ BTh95. Trin Coll Bris. **d** 02 **p** 03. C Fressingfield, Mendham etc *St E* from 02. *The Lodge, Harleston Road, Weybread, Diss IP21 5TU* Tel (01379) 853249 Mobile 07803-849928 E-mail c1keys@aol.com

KEYT, Fitzroy John. b 34. Linc Th Coll. **d** 67 **p** 68. C Highters Heath *Birm* 67-70; Hon C Sheldon 70-73; Australia from 73; V Miles 73-76; R Rayton 76-86; R Coolangatta 86-98; P-in-c Clayfield 98-01. *58 Thompson Street, Zillmere, Qld, Australia 4034* Tel (0061) (7) 3314 3011 E-mail dskeyt@optusnet.com.au

KEYTE, Douglas Joseph Henry. b 18. St Jo Coll Cam BA40 MA46. Wycliffe Hall Ox 46. **d** 48 **p** 49. C Kersal Moor *Man* 48-51; C Newall Green St Fran 51-54; Chapl K Wm's Coll Is of Man 55-57; Ghana 57-61; Asst Master Co Gr Sch for Girls Sale 61-75; Hon C Charlestown *Man* 75-89; rtd 83; Hon C Pendleton St Thos w Charlestown *Man* 89-95; Hon C Pendleton from 95. *26 Heathfield Close, Sale M33 2PQ* Tel 0161-973 2844

KHAKHRIA, Rohitkumar Prabhulal (Roy). b 60. Sheff Univ BSc82 PGCE82. Oak Hill Th Coll 94. **d** 96 **p** 97. C Muswell Hill St Jas w St Matt *Lon* 96-01; C Stoughton *Guildf* from 01. *12 Grange Close, Guildford GU2 9QJ* Tel (01483) 573154 E-mail khakhria@lineone.net

KHAMBATTA, Neville Holbery. b 48. St Chad's Coll Dur BA74. S'wark Ord Course 81. **d** 84 **p** 85. Asst Chapl Em Sch Wandsworth 84-87; Hon C Thornton Heath St Jude w St Aid *S'wark* 84-87; Asst Warden Horstead Cen 87-01; Hon C Coltishall w Gt Hautbois and Horstead *Nor* 87-01; V Ludham, Potter Heigham, Hickling and Catfield from 01. *The Vicarage, Norwich Road, Ludham, Great Yarmouth NR29 5QA* Tel (01692) 678282 E-mail khambatta@lineone.net

KHOO, Boon-Hor. b 31. FBCO. Llan Dioc Tr Scheme. **d** 87 **p** 88. NSM Llandaff w Capel Llanilltern *Llan* 87-96; Perm to Offic from 96. *38 The Cathedral Green, Llandaff, Cardiff CF5 2EB* Tel (029) 2056 1478

KICHENSIDE, Mark Gregory. b 53. Nottm Univ BTh83. St Jo Coll Nottm 80. **d** 83 **p** 84. C Orpington Ch Ch *Roch* 83-86; C Bexley St Jo 86-90; V Blendon 90-93; V Welling 93-00; R Flegg Coastal Benefice *Nor* from 00; RD Gt Yarmouth from 02. *The Rectory, Somerton Road, Winterton-on-Sea, Great Yarmouth NR29 4AW* Tel (01493) 393227 Fax as telephone
E-mail mark@kiche.enterprise-plc.com

KIDD, Anthony John Eric. b 38. Solicitor. Oak Hill NSM Course. **d** 89 **p** 90. NSM Rawdon *Bradf* 89-91; C Ilkley All SS 91-93; Perm to Offic *Bradf* 93-95; Perm to Offic *York* 95-96 and from 98; Hon C Gt and Lt Driffield 96-98; rtd 00. *22 Maple Road, Bridlington YO16 6TE* Tel (01262) 602834

KIDD, Canon Carol Ivy. b 47. Trent Park Coll of Educn CertEd69. Oak Hill Th Coll DipHE94. **d** 95 **p** 96. C Bootle St Mary w St Paul *Liv* 95-99; TV Speke St Aid from 99; Hon Can Liv Cathl from 03. *All Saints Vicarage, Speke Church Road, Speke, Liverpool L24 3TA* Tel 0151-486 0292

KIDD, John Alan. b 32. Pemb Coll Cam BA58 MA61. Ridley Hall Cam 57. **d** 61 **p** 62. C Onslow Square St Paul *Lon* 61-65; S Africa 65-67; Uganda 67-69; P-in-c Mayfair Ch Ch *Lon* 69-75; V 75-79; V Virginia Water *Guildf* 79-88; Lic to Offic 88-94; rtd 94. *Flat 1, Blayds House, Spring Street, Easingwold, York YO61 3BL* Tel (01347) 823201

KIDD, Maurice Edward. b 26. LTh. **d** 55 **p** 56. C Wembley St Jo *Lon* 55-58; C Middleton *Man* 58-61; Chapl Pastures Hosp Derby 61-69; Chapl Guild of Health Lon 69-72; R Hanworth St Geo *Lon* 72-82; R Chartham *Cant* 82-91; rtd 91; Perm to Offic *Cant* from 91. *Harvest View, The Mint, Harbledown, Canterbury CT2 9AA* Tel (01227) 761655

KIDD, Timothy. b 24. St Chad's Coll Dur BA48 DipTh50 MA53 Nottm Univ MA57 MPhil71 MEd80. Lambeth STh74. **d** 50 **p** 51. C Mexborough *Sheff* 50-52; Lect Boston 52-56; C Boston *Linc* 52-56; Offg Chapl RAF 56-65; V Grantham St Anne *Linc* 56-65; Asst Dioc Youth Chapl 59-65; Prin Lect Kesteven Coll of Educn 65-79; Hon C Harlaxton, Lt Ponton and Stroxton 66-72; Gen Preacher from 73; Visiting Lect Univ Evansville (USA) 79-86; Teacher K Sch Grantham 80-90; Perm to Offic *Leic* from 89; rtd 90. *14 Woodlands Drive, Grantham NG31 9DJ* Tel (01476) 563273

KIDDLE, John. b 58. Qu Coll Cam BA80 MA83. Ridley Hall Cam 79. **d** 82 **p** 83. C Ormskirk *Liv* 82-86; V Huyton Quarry 86-91; V Watford St Luke *St Alb* from 91; RD Watford from 99. *St Luke's Vicarage, Devereux Drive, Watford WD1 3DD* Tel (01923) 242208 E-mail kiddle@lineone.net

KIDDLE, Mark Brydges. b 34. Wycliffe Hall Ox. **d** 63 **p** 64. C Scarborough St Luke *York* 63-66; C Walthamstow St Sav *Chelmsf* 66-71; V Nelson St Bede *Blackb* 71-76; V Perry Common *Birm* 76-79; R Grayingham *Linc* 79-84; V Kirton in Lindsey 79-84; R Manton 79-84; Hon C St Botolph Aldgate w H Trin Minories *Lon* 85-91; Hon C St Clem Eastcheap w St Martin Orgar from 91. *188 Corfield Street, London E2 0DN* Tel (020) 7613 1113

KIDDLE, Martin John. b 42. Lon Univ DipTh75 Open Univ BA80. St Jo Coll Nottm 74. **d** 76 **p** 77. C Gt Parndon *Chelmsf* 76-80; Asst Chapl HM Pris Wakef 80-81; Asst Chapl HM Youth Cust Cen Portland 81-88; Chapl HM Pris Cardiff 88-97; Chapl HM Pris Channings Wood 97-02; rtd 02; Perm to Offic *Ex* from 02. *2 Cricketfield Close, Chudleigh, Newton Abbot TQ13 0GA* Tel (01626) 853980 E-mail mkiddle@btopenworld.com

KIDDLE, Canon Peter. b 22. Fitzw Ho Cam BA50 MA54. Clifton Th Coll 57. **d** 57 **p** 58. Kenya 57-72; Hon Can Nairobi Cathl 72; V Worthing St Paul *Chich* 73-87; rtd 87; Perm to Offic *Sarum* from 87; P-in-c Milton Lilbourne w Easton Royal 87-90. *64 Damask Way, Warminster BA12 9PP* Tel (01985) 214572

KIDDLE, Miss Sarah Elizabeth. b 44. Birm Univ BSc66 Nottm Univ CertEd67. LNSM course 86. **d** 89 **p** 95. OLM Waddington *Linc* 89-97; OLM Bracebridge from 98. *16 Sycamore Drive, Waddington, Lincoln LN5 9DR* Tel (01522) 722010

KIDNER, Frank Derek. b 13. ARCM33 Ch Coll Cam BA40 MA44. Ridley Hall Cam 40. **d** 41 **p** 42. C Sevenoaks St Nic *Roch* 41-47; V Felsted *Chelmsf* 47-51; Sen Tutor Oak Hill Th Coll 51-64; Warden Tyndale Ho Cam 64-78; rtd 78; Perm to Offic *Ely* from 79. *56 Manor Park, Histon, Cambridge CB4 9JT* Tel (01223) 232579

KIGALI, Bishop of. See KOLINI, The Most Revd Emmanuel Musaba

KIGGELL, Mrs Anne. b 36. Liv Univ BA57. St Alb and Ox Min Course 99. **d** 02. OLM Basildon w Aldworth and Ashampstead *Ox* from 02. *Straight Ash, Ashampstead Common, Reading RG8 8QT* Tel (01635) 201385 E-mail anne.kiggell@virgin.net

KIGHTLEY, Canon David John. b 39. AKC67. **d** 68 **p** 69. C Plymouth St Andr *Ex* 68-70; C Ex St Dav 70-73; Chapl Greenwich Distr Hosp & Brook Gen Hosp Lon 73-76; P-in-c Chippenham *Ely* 76-96; P-in-c Snailwell 76-96; P-in-c Isleham 76-96; RD Fordham 95-96; P-in-c Feltwell 96-98; P-in-c Methwold 96-98; R Feltwell and Methwold from 98; RD Feltwell from 96; RD Fincham from 98; Hon Can Ely Cathl

from 00. *The Rectory, 7 Oak Street, Feltwell, Thetford IP26 4DD* Tel (01842) 828104 E-mail davidkightley@aol.com

KILBEY, Mrs Sarah. b 39. MBE98. Edin Univ MA75 Man Poly CETD82. Bp Otter Coll TDip59 Edin Dioc NSM Course 84. **d** 93 **p** 97. NSM Edin St Columba *Edin* 93-96; NSM Edin St Martin from 96. *77 Morningside Park, Edinburgh EH10 5EZ* Tel 0131-447 2378

KILBOURN-MACKIE, Canon Mary Elizabeth. b 26. Toronto Univ BA48 Harvard Univ MA49. Trin Coll Toronto MDiv77. **d** 77 **p** 78. Canada 77-00; Hon Can Toronto from 96; Perm to Offic *Sarum* from 00 and *B W* from 02. *14 Chatham Court, Station Road, Warminster BA12 9LS* Tel (01985) 211049

KILDARE, Archdeacon of. See LAWRENCE, The Ven Patrick Henry Andrew

KILDARE, Dean of. See TOWNLEY, The Very Revd Robert Keith

KILFORD, John Douglas. b 38. Oak Hill Th Coll 73. **d** 75 **p** 76. C Beckenham St Jo *Roch* 75-80; P-in-c Sinfin Moor *Derby* 80-83; V Penge St Jo *Roch* 83-92; Staff Member Ellel Min from 92. *6 Milford Close, Catterall, Preston PR3 0GE* Tel (01995) 604656

KILFORD, William Roy. b 38. Bris Univ BA60. Sarum & Wells Th Coll 82. **d** 84 **p** 85. C Herne Cant 84-87; Chapl Wm Harvey Hosp Ashford 87-93; R Mersham w Hinxhill *Cant* 87-93; P-in-c Sevington 87-93; V Reculver and Herne Bay St Bart 93-95; Chapl Paphos Cyprus 95-98; P-in-c Doddington, Newnham and Wychling *Cant* 98-02; P-in-c Lynsted w Kingsdown 98-02; P-in-c Norton 98-02; AD Ospringe 01-02; rtd 02; Chapl Nord Pas de Calais *Eur* from 02. *56 rue Alexandre Guilmant, 62164 Audresselles, France* Tel (0033) (3) 21 83 26 03
E-mail rev.roy@wanadoo.fr

KILGOUR, The Very Revd Richard Eifl. b 57. Edin Univ BD85. Edin Th Coll 81. **d** 85 **p** 86. C Wrexham *St As* 85-88; V Whitford 88-97; Ind Chapl 89-97; R Newtown w Llanllwchaiarn w Aberhafesp 97-03; RD Cedewain 01-03; Provost St Andr Cathl *Ab* from 03; R Aberdeen St Andr from 03; P-in-c Aberdeen St Ninian from 03. *St Andrew's Cathedral, King Street, Aberdeen AB24 5AX* Tel (01224) 640119
E-mail provost@aberdeen.anglican.org
or newrect@hotmail.com

KILLALA AND ACHONRY, Archdeacon of. *Vacant*

KILLALA, Dean of. *Vacant*

KILLALOE, KILFENORA AND CLONFERT, Dean of. See WHITE, The Very Revd Stephen Ross

KILLALOE, KILFENORA, CLONFERT AND KILMACDUAGH, Archdeacon of. See CARNEY, The Ven Richard Wayne

KILLE, Canon Vivian Edwy. b 30. Tyndale Hall Bris 60. **d** 62 **p** 63. C Dublin Miss Ch *D & G* 62-66; I Emlaghfad *T, K & A* 66-74; I Aghadrumsee w Clogh and Drumsnatt *Clogh* from 74; Can Clogh Cathl from 93. *Sunshine Rectory, 16 Dernawilt Road, Rosslea, Enniskillen BT92 7QY* Tel (028) 6775 1206
E-mail vek@hallelujah.demon.co.uk

KILLINGBACK, Oliver Edwin. b 44. S'wark Ord Course 75. **d** 77 **p** 78. C Kingston All SS w St Jo *S'wark* 77-80; C Horley 80-82; NSM Weston Favell *Pet* 87-93; Perm to Offic from 93. *18 Wansford Walk, Northampton NN3 4YF*
E-mail ollie@areopagus.clara.net

KILLOCK, Alfred Kenneth. b 26. Cranmer Hall Dur 72. **d** 74 **p** 75. C Moor Allerton *Ripon* 74-79; Hon C Bolton St Jas w St Chrys *Bradf* 79-83; P-in-c Oakenshaw cum Woodlands 84-90; P-in-c Allerton 90-91; rtd 91; Perm to Offic *Bradf* from 91. *15 Warwick Road, Bradford BD4 7RA* Tel (01274) 394462

KILLWICK, Simon David Andrew. b 56. K Coll Lon BD80 AKC80. St Steph Ho Ox 80. **d** 81 **p** 82. C Worsley *Man* 81-84; TV 84-97; P-in-c Moss Side Ch Ch from 97. *Christ Church Rectory, Monton Street, Manchester M14 4LT* Tel 0161-226 2476

KILMORE, Archdeacon of. *Vacant*

KILMORE, Dean of. See GODFREY, The Very Revd David Samuel George

KILMORE, ELPHIN AND ARDAGH, Bishop of. See CLARKE, The Rt Revd Kenneth Herbert

KILNER, Canon Frederick James. b 43. Qu Coll Cam BA65 MA69. Ridley Hall Cam 67. **d** 70 **p** 71. C Harlow New Town w Lt Parndon *Chelmsf* 70-74; C Cambridge St Andr Less *Ely* 74-79; P-in-c Milton 79-88; R 88-94; Hon Can Ely Cathl from 88; P-in-c Ely 94-96; P-in-c Chettisham 94-96; P-in-c Prickwillow 94-96; P-in-c Stretham w Thetford 94-96; P-in-c Stuntney 95-96; TR Ely from 96. *St Mary's Vicarage, St Mary's Street, Ely CB7 4ER* Tel (01353) 662308 E-mail kilner@btinternet.com

KILNER, Mrs Valerie June. b 42. MICFM91 Univ of Wales (Abth) BSc64 Hughes Hall Cam PGCE65. EAMTC 98. **d** 98 **p** 99. NSM Ely from 98. *St Mary's Vicarage, St Mary's Street, Ely CB7 4ER* Tel (01353) 662308 Fax as telephone
E-mail kilner@btinternet.com

KILPATRICK, Alan William. b 64. Bournemouth Univ HND85. Birm Bible Inst 94 Oak Hill Th Coll BA94. **d** 96 **p** 97. C Ealing St Paul *Lon* 96-01; Asst R Mt Pleasant USA from 01. *St Andrew's Church, 440 Whilden Street, Mount Pleasant, SC, USA*

KILSBY, Miss Joyce (Jocelyn). b 40. Univ Coll Lon BSc62 Ox Univ DipEd63. N Ord Course 98. **d** 01 **p** 02. NSM Stanley *Wakef* from 01. *18 Hazelwood Court, Outwood, Wakefield WF1 3HP* Tel (01924) 824396 E-mail hilkil.hazco@virgin.net

KIMBALL, Melodie Irene. b 49. **d** 99. USA 99-01; Chapl Asst S Man Univ Hosps NHS Trust 01-02; Asst Chapl Qu Medical Cen Nottm Univ Hosp 02-03; Asst Chapl Leeds Mental Health Teaching NHS Trust from 03. *Meanwood Park, Tongue Lane, Leeds LS6 4QB* Tel 0113-295 2800

KIMBER, Geoffrey Francis. b 46. Univ Coll Lon BA67 PGCE70 DipTh74. St Jo Coll Nottm 86. **d** 88 **p** 89. C Buckhurst Hill *Chelmsf* 88-92; R Arley *Cov* 92-02; P-in-c Ansley 97-02; CMS Romania from 02. *Cross of Nails Reconciliation Centre, Ascensium, Str Ion Slavici nr 7, Sibiu 2400, Romania* Tel (0040) (69) 215181 Fax as telephone
E-mail geoff.kimber@btinternet.com

KIMBER, Mrs Gillian Margaret. b 48. Bedf Coll Lon BA70. Oak Hill Th Coll 89. **d** 91. NSM Buckhurst Hill *Chelmsf* 91-92; C Arley *Cov* 92-97; C Ansley 97-02; CMS Romania from 02. *Cross of Nails Reconciliation Centre, Ascensium, Str Ion Slavici nr 7, Sibiu 2400, Romania* Tel (0040) (69) 215181 Fax as telephone
E-mail gill.kimber@btinternet.com

KIMBER, Mrs Hazel Olive. b 33. Lon Univ CertEd73. LNSM course 92. **d** 95 **p** 96. OLM W Dulwich Em *S'wark* from 95. *18 Michaelson House, Kingswood Estate, London SE21 8PX* Tel (020) 8670 5298

KIMBER, John Keith. b 45. Bris Univ BSc66. St Mich Coll Llan. **d** 69 **p** 70. C Caerphilly *Llan* 69-72; Chapl Birm Univ *Birm* 72-75; TR Bris St Agnes and St Simon w St Werburgh *Bris* 75-82; P-in-c Bris St Paul w St Barn 80-82; Hon C Westbury-on-Trym H Trin 82-83; Area Sec (Wales) USPG 83-89; TR Halesowen *Worc* 89-92; Chapl Geneva *Eur* 92-01; Chapl Monte Carlo 01-02; TR Cen Cardiff *Llan* from 02. *The Vicarage, 16 Queen Anne Square, Cardiff CF10 3ED* Tel (029) 2022 0375
E-mail jkk@ntlworld.com

KIMBER, Jonathan Richard. b 69. K Coll Cam BA91 MA95 St Jo Coll Dur MA02. Cranmer Hall Dur 99. **d** 02 **p** 03. C Weston Favell *Pet* from 02. *5 Kestrel Close, Northampton NN3 3JG* Tel (01604) 403213 E-mail jrkimber@yahoo.co.uk

KIMBER, Stuart Francis. b 53. Qu Eliz Coll Lon BSc74 Fitzw Coll Cam BA79 MA83. Ridley Hall Cam 77. **d** 80 **p** 81. C Edgware *Lon* 80-83; C Cheltenham St Mark *Glouc* 83-84; TV 84-92; C Hawkwell *Chelmsf* 92-01; V Westcliff St Andr from 01. *St Andrew's Vicarage, 65 Electric Avenue, Westcliff-on-Sea SS0 9NN* Tel (01702) 302255
E-mail revskimber@compuserve.com

KIMBERLEY, Countess of (Carol Lylie Wodehouse). b 51. St Hugh's Coll Ox BA73 CertEd74 MA77. Ripon Coll Cuddesdon 87. **d** 89 **p** 94. NSM Hambleden Valley *Ox* 89-02; P-in-c Hormead, Wyddial, Anstey, Brent Pelham etc *St Alb* from 02. *The Vicarage, Great Hormead, Buntingford SG9 0NT* Tel (01763) 289258

KIMBERLEY, John Harry. b 49. Brasted Th Coll 72 St Steph Ho Ox 74. **d** 76 **p** 77. C W Tarring *Chich* 76-79; C Portslade St Nic 79-82; C-in-c Findon Valley CD 82-89; V Findon Valley 89-90; V E Preston w Kingston 90-95; Chapl Eastbourne Hosps NHS Trust from 95. *Eastbourne District General Hospital, King's Drive, Eastbourne BN21 2UD* Tel (01323) 417400 ext 4145

KIMBERLEY, The Ven Owen Charles Lawrence. b 27. Univ of NZ BCom53. Tyndale Hall Bris 57. **d** 59 **p** 60. C Higher Openshaw *Man* 59-62; New Zealand from 62; V Nelson All SS 62-64; V Motupiko 64-69; V Kaikoura 69-76; V Tahunanui 76-85 76-85; Can Nelson Cathl 77-78; Adn Waimea 78-92; V Richmond 85-92; Egypt 94-98; Chapl Port Said 94-98; Adn Egypt 96-98. *11B Gilbert Street, Richmond, Nelson, New Zealand* Tel (0064) (3) 544 2115 Fax as telephone

KIMBERLEY, Canon Wilfred Harry. b 19. St Steph Ho Ox 51. **d** 53 **p** 54. C Wallingford St Mary w All Hallows and St Leon *Ox* 53-55; C Newbury St Jo 55-57; V Highters Heath *Birm* 57-65; V Marsworth *Ox* 65-72; P-in-c Slapton 65-72; P-in-c Cheddington w Mentmore 68-72; V Buckingham 72-78; RD Buckingham 76-78; TR High Wycombe 78-84; Hon Can Ch 79-84; rtd 84; Perm to Offic *Glouc* 85-97; *Ox* 86-98. *Tangle Trees, Springfield, Bourton-on-the-Water, Cheltenham GL54 2DF* Tel (01451) 820779

KIME, Thomas Frederick. b 28. Linc Coll Ox BA50 MA53. Cuddesdon Coll 54. **d** 56 **p** 57. C Forest Gate St Edm *Chelmsf* 56-58; S Africa 58-74; R Ellisfield w Farleigh Wallop and Dummer *Win* 74-83; P-in-c Cliddesden 82-83; R Cliddesden and Ellisfield w Farleigh Wallop etc 83-94; rtd 94; Perm to Offic *Win* from 94. *7 Sparkford Close, Winchester SO22 4NH* Tel (01962) 870240

KINAHAN, Timothy Charles. b 53. Jes Coll Cam BA75. CITC 77. **d** 78 **p** 79. C Carrickfergus *Conn* 78-81; Papua New Guinea 81-84; I Belfast Whiterock *Conn* 84-90; I Gilnahirk *D & D* from 90. *237 Lower Braniel Road, Belfast BT5 7NQ* Tel (028) 9079 1748 Fax 9079 2413

KINCHIN-SMITH, John Michael. b 52. Fitzw Coll Cam MA. Ridley Hall Cam 79. **d** 82 **p** 83. C Sanderstead All SS *S'wark*

82-87; TV Halesworth w Linstead, Chediston, Holton etc *St E* 87-92; R Mursley w Swanbourne and Lt Horwood *Ox* 92-02; R Newton Longville and Mursley w Swanbourne etc from 03. *The Rectory, Main Street, Mursley, Milton Keynes MK17 0RT* Tel (01296) 720056

KINDER, Mark Russell. b 66. Univ of Wales (Swansea) BA(Econ)88. St Jo Coll Nottm 91. **d** 94 **p** 95. C Pheasey *Lich* 94-98; TV Tettenhall Regis from 98. *St Paul's Vicarage, 1 Talaton Close, Pendeford, Wolverhampton WV9 5LS* Tel (01902) 787199

KING, Mrs Angela Margaret. b 45. Bedf Coll Lon BA67 Lon Inst of Educn PGCE68. SEITE 00. **d** 03. NSM Bromley St Andr *Roch* from 03. *4 Avondale Road, Bromley BR1 4EP* Tel (020) 8402 0847 Fax as telephone E-mail angelaking45@hotmail.com

KING, Anthony Richard. b 34. Trin Hall Cam BA58. Ely Th Coll 58 Linc Th Coll 61. **d** 62 **p** 63. C Benwell St Jas *Newc* 62-64; C Thirsk w S Kilvington *York* 64-67; V Halifax St Aug *Wakef* 67-74; R Upton on Severn *Worc* 74-99; RD Upton 86-92; rtd 99; Perm to Offic *Ex* from 99. *4 The Elms, Colyford, Colyton EX24 6QU* Tel (01297) 552666

KING, Benjamin John. b 74. Down Coll Cam BA96 MA00 Peterho Cam 97 Harvard Univ MTh03. Westcott Ho Cam 97. **d** 00 **p** 00. C Eastbourne St Mary *Chich* from 00; C Boston the Advent USA from 00. *30 Brimmer Street, Boston, MA 02108, USA* Tel (001) (617) 523 2377 ext 33 Fax 523 0302
E-mail curate@theadvent.org

✠**KING, The Rt Revd Brian Franklin Vernon.** b 38. ACA59 Univ of NSW BComm61 Lon Univ BD64 Fuller Th Sem California DMin85. Moore Th Coll Sydney. **d** 64 **p** 65 **c** 93. C Manly Australia 64-67; R Dural 67-73; R Wahroonga 73-87; R Manly 87-93; Can Sydney 89-93; Bp W Sydney 93-03; Bp Aus Defence Force 94-01; rtd 03; P-in-c S Malling *Chich* 03. *The Vicarage, Church Lane, Lewes BN7 2JA*

KING, Brian Henry. b 39. Chich Th Coll 63. **d** 65 **p** 66. C Castle Bromwich SS Mary and Marg *Birm* 65-67; C Southwick St Mich *Chich* 68-70; V Southwater 70-73; C Brighton St Alb Preston 73-74; TV Brighton Resurr 74-75; V Eastbourne St Eliz 75-96; rtd 96; Perm to Offic *Chich* from 96. *7 Bracken Road, Eastbourne BN20 8SH* Tel (01323) 431118

KING, Caroline Naomi. b 62. New Coll Edin BD94. Ripon Coll Cuddesdon DipMin94. **d** 97 **p** 98. C Wheatley *Ox* from 97. *92 High Street, Wheatley, Oxford OX33 1XP* Tel (01865) 875625
E-mail caroline.king1@ntlworld.com

KING, Cecil John. b 46. Selw Coll Cam BA67 MA71. Coll of Resurr Mirfield 81. **d** 81 **p** 84. Zambia 81-85; SSF 85-86; Ghana 86-88; C N Harrow St Alb *Lon* 88-89; C Leeds Gipton Epiphany *Ripon* 91-93. *30 Pembroke Grange, Leeds LS9 6RH* Tel 0113-240 2319

KING, Charles John. b 14. Lon Univ BSc39 CEng46 MIEE. Ox NSM Course 73. **d** 76 **p** 77. NSM Cuddesdon *Ox* 76-78; NSM Wantage Downs 78-99. *Address temp unknown*

KING, Christopher John. b 56. Chelsea Coll Lon BSc78 CertEd79. St Jo Coll Nottm LTh87. **d** 88 **p** 89. C Wandsworth All SS *S'wark* 88-92; Canada from 92; R Geraldton w Jellicoe, Longlac, Collins etc 92-97; R Toronto Lt Trin Ch from 97. *425 King Street East, Toronto ON, Canada, M5A 1L3* Tel (001) (416) 367 0272 Fax 367 2074 E-mail chrisking@sympatico.ca

KING, Clare Maria. b 68. St Andr Univ BD91 K Coll Lon MPhil98. Westcott Ho Cam 91. **d** 94. Hon C Norbury St Phil *S'wark* 94-96; Chapl Croydon Coll 95-96; Asst Chapl Cen Sheff Univ Hosps NHS Trust 96-01; C Leic Presentation *Leic* from 02. *The Vicarage, 12 Saddington Road, Fleckney, Leicester LE8 8AW* Tel 0116-240 2215

KING, Mrs Daphne Eileen. b 37. EMMTC 78. **dss** 81 **d** 87 **p** 94. Theddlethorpe *Linc* 84-89; Dn-in-c 87-89; Saltfleetby 84-89; Dn-in-c 87-89; Dn-in-c Healing and Stallingborough 89-94; P-in-c 94-97; rtd 97; Perm to Offic *Linc* 99-02. *28 Charles Street, Louth LN11 0LE* Tel (01507) 606062
E-mail daphneking@lud28.freeserve.co.uk

KING, David Charles. b 52. K Coll Lon 73 Coll of Resurr Mirfield 77. **d** 78 **p** 79. C Saltburn-by-the-Sea *York* 78-81; Youth Officer 81-85; P-in-c Crathorne 81-85; Par Educn Adv *Wakef* 85-91; Min Coulby Newham Ecum Project *York* 91-94; P-in-c Egton w Grosmont 94-00; P-in-c Goathland and Glaisdale 99-00; V Middle Esk Moor from 00. *St Hilda's Vicarage, Egton, Whitby YO21 1UT* Tel (01947) 895315

KING, David Frederick. b 32. Southn Coll of Tech DMA70. Sarum Th Coll 59. **d** 61 **p** 72. C Hanworth All SS *Lon* 61-62; Hon C Andover St Mich *Win* 71-83; P-in-c 83-88; V 88-90; Chapl R S Hants Hosp 90-92; Chapl Countess Mountbatten Hospice 90-92; Chapl Andover District Community Health Care NHS Trust from 92; Perm to Offic *Win* 92-97; rtd 97; P-in-c Smannell w Enham Alamein *Win* from 97. *The Rectory, Dunhills Lane, Andover SP11 6HU* Tel (01264) 352827

KING, David John. b 67. W Sussex Inst of HE BEd91. St Steph Ho Ox 98. **d** 00 **p** 01. C Bexhill St Pet *Chich* 00-03; TV from 03. *The Vicarage, 20 Glassenbury Drive, Bexhill-on-Sea TN40 2NY* Tel (01424) 219937

KING, David Michael. b 73. St Jo Coll Dur BA95 PGCE96 Cam Univ BA02. Ridley Hall Cam 00. **d** 03. C Claygate *Guildf* from

03. *4 Denman Drive, Claygate, Esher KT10 0EA* Tel (01372) 464918 E-mail kanddking@hotmail.com

KING, Canon David Russell. b 42. Univ of Wales (Lamp) BA67. St D Coll Lamp DipTh68. **d** 68 **p** 69. C Barrow St Geo w St Luke *Carl* 68-72; P-in-c Kirkland 72-74; V Edenhall w Langwathby 72-73; P-in-c Culgaith 72-73; V Edenhall w Langwathby and Culgaith 73-74; V Flookburgh 75-79; V Barrow St Jas 79-82; P-in-c Bolton w Ireby and Uldale 82-83; R 83-90; R Burgh-by-Sands and Kirkbampton w Kirkandrews etc 90-00; P-in-c Aikton 95-00; P-in-c Orton St Giles 95-00; R Barony of Burgh 00-02; Hon Can Carl Cathl from 01; P-in-c Gt Broughton and Broughton Moor from 02. *The Vicarage, Little Broughton, Cockermouth CA13 0YG* Tel (01900) 825317

KING, David William Anthony. b 42. Ch Ch Ox BA63 MA68. Westcott Ho Cam 63. **d** 65 **p** 66. C Cayton w Eastfield *York* 65-68; C Southbroom *Sarum* 68-71; R Hinton Parva 71-72; V Holt St Jas 71-72; V Holt St Jas and Hinton Parva 72-75; P-in-c Horton and Chalbury 73-75; R Holt St Jas, Hinton Parva, Horton and Chalbury 75-79; TV Melton Mowbray w Thorpe Arnold *Leic* 79-83; V Foxton w Gumley and Laughton and Lubenham 83-90; P-in-c Boreham *Chelmsf* 90-00; R Tendring and Lt Bentley w Beaumont cum Moze from 00. *The Rectory, The Street, Tendring, Clacton-on-Sea CO16 0BW* Tel (01255) 830586

KING, Dennis. b 31. ACA53 FCA64. EMMTC 73. **d** 76 **p** 77. NSM Chesterfield St Mary and All SS *Derby* 76-00; Perm to Offic from 00. *Hillcrest, Stubben Edge, Ashover, Chesterfield S45 0EU* Tel (01246) 590279

KING, Dennis Charles. b 27. Chich Th Coll 53. **d** 55 **p** 56. C Luton Ch Ch *St Alb* 55-58 and 59-63; USA 58-59; Bahamas 63-66; Jamaica 66-77; V Bromham w Oakley *St Alb* 77-84; TR St Marylebone Ch Ch *Lon* 84-89; V Flamstead *St Alb* 89-93; rtd 93; Perm to Offic *St Alb* from 93. *Te Deum, 36 Manor Road, Toddington, Dunstable LU5 6AH* Tel (01525) 873557

KING, Dennis Keppel. b 33. Lich Th Coll 63. **d** 65 **p** 66. C Eccleston St Thos *Liv* 65-68; C W Derby St Mary 68-71; V Aintree St Giles 71-96; rtd 96; Perm to Offic *York* from 96; Perm to Offic *Liv* from 00. *8 Whiteoak Avenue, Easingwold, York Y06 3GB* Tel (01347) 822625

KING, Derek Edwin Noel. b 31. Qu Mary Coll Lon BSc54 Birkbeck Coll Lon PhD60. LNSM course 91. **d** 93 **p** 94. OLM Nacton and Levington w Bucklesham and Foxhall *St E* from 93. *Vindelis, 1 Eastcliff, Felixstowe IP11 9TA* Tel (01394) 270815 Fax as telephone

KING, Donald. b 32. ISM82. Chich Th Coll. **d** 86. NSM Forton *Portsm* 86-98; Perm to Offic from 98. *8 Burnett Road, Gosport PO12 3AH* Tel (023) 9252 3440

KING, Ernest Cuthbert. b 12. Univ of W Aus BA34. Wells Th Coll 35. **d** 36 **p** 37. C Northampton St Jas *Pet* 36-46; CF (EC) 39-46; V Desborough *Pet* 46-49; Australia from 49; rtd 78. *Cottage 113, Hollywood Village, 31 Williams Road, Nedlands, W Australia 6009* Tel (0061) (8) 9380 5113

KING, Fergus John. b 62. St Andr Univ MA Edin Univ BD89. Edin Th Coll 86. **d** 89 **p** 90. Chapl St Jo Cathl Oban *Arg* 89-92; C Oban St Jo 89-92; Tanzania 92-98; Perm to Offic *S'wark* 99-03; Hon C Thamesmead from 03. *27 Felixstowe Road, London SE2 9QW* Tel (020) 7928 8681 E-mail fergusk@uspg.org.uk

KING, Frederick William. b 24. CertEd74. Richmond Th Coll 46 Qu Coll Birm 49. **d** 50 **p** 51. C Kimberworth *Sheff* 50-52; C Luton St Mary *St Alb* 52-55; Chapl RAF 55-70; Chapl The Leas Sch Hoylake 70-72; Chapl Wirral Gr Sch 74-75; Chapl Summer Fields Sch Ox 75; rtd 89. *31 Saint Yves, 22580 Plouha, France* Tel (0033) (2) 96 22 45 21

KING, George Henry. b 24. MRHS55 NDH55. St Alb Minl Tr Scheme. **d** 79 **p** 80. Hon C Flamstead *St Alb* 79-98; Dioc Agric Chapl 90-98; Perm to Offic from 98. *Chad Lane Farm, Chad Lane, Flamstead, St Albans AL3 8HW* Tel (01582) 841648

KING, Mrs Gillian Daphne. b 38. EMMTC 79. **dss** 83 **d** 87 **p** 94. Knighton St Jo *Leic* 83-85; Clarendon Park St Jo w Knighton St Mich 86-89; Par Dn 87-89; Chapl Kingston and Esher Mental Health Services 89-93; Chapl Kingston and Esher Community Health Unit 93-97; Chapl Long Grove Hosp Epsom 90-92; Chapl Tolworth Hosp Surbiton 91-97; Chapl Kingston and Distr Community NHS Trust 94-97; TV Hale w Badshot Lea *Guildf* 97-99; V Egham Hythe from 99. *St Paul's Vicarage, 214 Wendover Road, Staines TW18 3DF* Tel (01784) 453625 Mobile 0775-724090

KING, James Anthony. b 46. CBE76. K Coll Lon BA69 AKC69 Lon Inst of Educn AcDipEd77. St Alb and Ox Min Course 99. **d** 01 **p** 02. NSM Gerrards Cross and Fulmer *Ox* from 01. *5 Dorchester House, 29 Marsham Lane, Gerrards Cross SL9 8HA* Tel (01753) 893325 Mobile 07785-370803 E-mail jim.king@gs.com

KING, Canon Jeffrey Douglas Wallace. b 43. AKC67. **d** 68 **p** 69. C S Harrow St Paul *Lon* 68-71; C Garforth *Ripon* 71-74; V Potternewton 74-83; TR Moor Allerton 83-99; RD Allerton 85-89; Hon Can Ripon Cathl from 90; R Thorner from 99; Dioc

Ecum Officer from 99. *The Vicarage, Church View, Thorner, Leeds LS14 3ED* Tel 0113-289 2437 E-mail jeffking@thinkdifferent.co.uk

KING, Jennifer Mary. b 41. Lon Univ BDS65 MSc75 PhD Ox Univ DipTh97. Ripon Coll Cuddesdon 86. **d** 88 **p** 94. NSM S Hackney St Mich w Haggerston St Paul *Lon* 88-99; NSM St John-at-Hackney from 99. *83 Victoria Park Road, London E9 7NA* Tel (020) 7377 7000 ext 3069 E-mail jenny.king@mds.qmw.ac.uk

KING, Jeremy Norman. *See* CLARK-KING, Jeremy Norman

KING, John. b 38. S'wark Ord Course DipRS77. **d** 80 **p** 81. C S Gillingham *Roch* 80-85; Min Joydens Wood St Barn CD 85-90; V Borstal 90-98; Chapl HM Pris Cookham Wood 90-98; Chapl The Foord Almshouses 90-98; rtd 98; Perm to Offic *Cant* from 99. *14 Lamberhurst Way, Cliftonville, Margate CT9 3HH* Tel 07889-277195 (mobile)

KING, John Andrew. b 50. Qu Coll Birm 72. **d** 75 **p** 76. C Halesowen *Worc* 75-77; C Belper Ch Ch and Milford *Derby* 78-81; Perm to Offic from 87. *11 Well Lane, Milford, Belper DE56 0QQ* Tel (01332) 841810

KING, John Charles. b 27. St Pet Hall Ox BA51 MA55. Oak Hill Th Coll. **d** 53 **p** 54. C Slough *Ox* 53-57; V Ware Ch Ch *St Alb* 57-60; Ed *C of E Newspaper* 60-68; Lic to Offic *St Alb* 60-70; Teacher St Fran Bacon Sch St Alb 68-71; Boston Gr Sch 71-88; Lic to Offic *Linc* 74-92; rtd 92. *6 Somersby Way, Boston PE21 9PQ* Tel (01205) 363061

KING, John Colin. b 39. Cuddesdon Coll 69. **d** 71 **p** 72. C Cookham *Ox* 71-75; Youth Chapl *B & W* 75-80; P-in-c Merriott 76-80; P-in-c Hinton w Dinnington 79-80; R Merriott w Hinton, Dinnington and Lopen from 80. *The Rectory, Church Street, Merriott TA16 5PS* Tel (01460) 73226

KING, John Michael Stuart. b 22. St Edm Hall Ox BA48 MA52. Cuddesdon Coll 48. **d** 50 **p** 51. C Ryhope *Dur* 50-53; C Guisborough *York* 53-56; V High and Low Worsall 56-60; V Kirklevington 56-60; R Hinderwell w Roxby 60-71; V Hibaldstow *Linc* 71-88; rtd 88; Perm to Offic *Linc* from 88. *Old School House, Church Lane, Saxby-All-Saints, Brigg DN20 0QE* Tel (01652) 618693

KING, Joseph Stephen. b 39. St Chad's Coll Dur BA62 DipTh63 MPhil83. **d** 64 **p** 65. C Lewisham St Mary *S'wark* 64-69; Hon C Milton next Gravesend Ch Ch *Roch* 70-85; V from 85. *The Vicarage, 48 Old Road East, Gravesend DA12 1NR* Tel (01474) 352643

KING, Mrs Katharine Mary. b 63. St Hugh's Coll Ox BA85 MA89 SS Coll Cam BA88. Ridley Hall Cam 86. **d** 89 **p** 94. C Ipswich St Aug *St E* 89-91; NSM Bures 92-02; NSM Bures w Assington and Lt Cornard from 02. *The Vicarage, Church Square, Bures CO8 5AA* Tel (01787) 227315 Mobile 07885-863687 E-mail katharine@ricking.freeserve.co.uk

KING, Malcolm Charles. b 37. Chich Th Coll 67. **d** 70 **p** 71. C Mill End *St Alb* 70-72; Chapl RAF 72-76; R W Lynn *Nor* 76-81; V Croxley Green All SS *St Alb* 81-90; V Grimsby St Aug *Linc* 90-99; Asst Local Min Officer 90-95; OGS 90-02; V Bury w Houghton and Coldwaltham and Hardham *Chich* 99-02; rtd 02; Warden Community of St Pet Woking from 02. *9 Riverside Court, Station Road, Pulborough RH20 1RG* Tel (01798) 875213

KING, Canon Malcolm Stewart. b 56. Sarum & Wells Th Coll 77. **d** 80 **p** 81. C Farnham *Guildf* 80-83; C Chertsey 83-86; Chapl St Pet Hosp Chertsey 83-86; V Egham Hythe *Guildf* 86-91; TR Cove St Jo 91-98; RD Aldershot 93-98; V Dorking w Ranmore from 98; Hon Can Guildf Cathl from 99; RD Dorking from 01. *St Martin's Vicarage, Westcott Road, Dorking RH4 3DP* Tel (01306) 882875 E-mail malcolm.king3@btinternet.com

KING (née COWIE), Mrs Margaret Harriet. b 53. Glas Univ BSc76 FMA97. Edin Th Coll 95. **d** 98 **p** 99. NSM Montrose *Bre* from 98. *97H High Street, Review Close, Montrose DD10 8QR* Tel (01674) 676534

KING, Marie. b 40. Dioc OLM tr scheme 00. **d** 03. OLM Addiscombe St Mildred *S'wark* from 03. *8 Annandale Road, Croydon CR0 7HP* Tel (020) 8654 2651 E-mail marieking@8annan.fsnet.co.uk

KING, Martin Quartermain. b 39. Reading Univ BA61. Cuddesdon Coll 62. **d** 64 **p** 65. C S Shields St Hilda w St Thos *Dur* 64-66; C Newton Aycliffe 66-71; V Chilton Moor 71-78; R Middleton St Geo 78-91; R Sedgefield from 91; RD Sedgefield 91-96; Chapl Co Dur & Darlington Priority Services NHS Trust from 91. *The Rectory, Durham Road, Sedgefield, Stockton-on-Tees TS21 3DW* Tel (01740) 620274 E-mail martin.king@durham.anglican.org

KING, Maurice Charles Francis. b 32. ACP58 Em Coll Cam BA55 MA59. Chich Th Coll 78. **d** 79 **p** 80. C Burnley St Cath *Blackb* 79-81; C Burnley St Cath w St Alb and St Paul 81-83; C Sheff Parson Cross St Cecilia *Sheff* 83-88; V New Bentley 88-94; rtd 94; Perm to Offic *Carl* from 94. *204 Wordsworth Court, Cockermouth CA13 0EB* Tel (01900) 827503

KING, Michael Charles. Worc Coll Ox BA56 MA60. Coll of Resurr Mirfield. **d** 62 **p** 63. Hon C Hampstead All So *Lon* 62-65; Ed Asst SCM Press 62-65; C Thorpe *Nor* 66-69; Ed Sec BRF 69-90; Hon C Queensbury All SS *Lon* 69-79; Hon C Lt Stanmore

St Lawr 80-90; R Cawston w Haveringland, Booton and Brandiston *Nor* 91-96; P-in-c Heydon 94-96; R Cawston w Booton and Brandiston etc 96-01; rtd 01; Perm to Offic *Leic* from 01. *84 Beacon Road, Loughborough LE11 2BH* Tel (01509) 563103

KING, Nathan Richard. b 68. Whitelands Coll Lon BA89 Univ of Wales (Cardiff) BTh94 Man Univ MA00. St Mich Coll Llan 91. d 94 p 95. C Hawarden *St As* 94-99; P-in-c 99-00; P-in-c Coreley and Doddington *Heref* 00-02; P-in-c Knowbury w Clee Hill 00-02; TV Ellesmere Port *Ches* from 02. *4 Deeside Close, Whitby, South Wirral CH65 6TH* Tel 0151-355 3571
E-mail nathanking@onetel.co.uk

KING, Nicholas Bernard Paul. b 46. Wycliffe Hall Ox 72. d 75 p 76. C Pitsmoor w Wicker *Sheff* 75-78; C Erdington St Barn *Birm* 78-80; C Sutton Coldfield H Trin 80-84; V Lynesack *Dur* 84-92; rtd 93. *16 Chatsworth Avenue, Bishop Auckland DL14 6AX* Tel (01388) 605614

KING, Peter Duncan. b 48. TD. K Coll Lon LLB70 AKC70 Fitzw Coll Cam BA72 MA77. Westcott Ho Cam 65. d 80 p 81. Hon C Notting Hill *Lon* 80-84; Hon C Mortlake w E Sheen *S'wark* from 84; Dean MSE from 99. *49 Leinster Avenue, London SW14 7JW* Tel (020) 8876 8997 Fax 8287 9329

KING, Peter William Stephen. b 65. St Steph Ho Ox BTh01. d 01 p 02. C Abertillery w Cwmtillery w Six Bells *Mon* from 01. *St Paul's Vicarage, Church Lane, Cwmtillery, Abertillery NP13 1LS* Tel (01495) 212364 Fax as telephone

KING, Canon Philip David. b 35. Keble Coll Ox BA57 MA61. Tyndale Hall Bris 58. d 60 p 61. C Redhill H Trin *S'wark* 60-63; C Wallington H Trin 63-68; V Fulham Ch Ch *Lon* 68-74; Lic to Offic *S'wark* 74-86; Sec SAMS 74-86; V Roxeth Ch Ch and Harrow St Pet *Lon* 86-89; Gen Sec Gen Syn Bd for Miss 89-00; Perm to Offic *Lon* from 89; Lic to Offic *Cant* and *York* from 98; rtd 00. *31 Myrtle Avenue, Ruislip HA4 8SA* Tel (020) 8429 0636

KING, Miss Philipa Ann. b 65. Heythrop Coll Lon. Westcott Ho Cam CTM95. d 95 p 96. C Cambridge Ascension *Ely* 95-00; TV 00-02; TR from 02. *Ascension Rectory, 95 Richmond Road, Cambridge CB4 3PS* Tel (01223) 361919
E-mail pipking@btinternet.com

KING, Richard Andrew. b 51. Linc Th Coll. d 84 p 85. C Bramhall *Ches* 84-87; V Heald Green St Cath 87-92; P-in-c Ashprington, Cornworthy and Dittisham *Ex* 92-99; R Totnes 97-99; P-in-c Torquay St Jo and Ellacombe 98-02; P-in-c Stoneleigh *Guildf* from 02; Dioc Spirituality Adv from 02. *The Vicarage, 59 Stoneleigh Park Road, Epsom KT19 0QU* Tel (020) 8393 3738 Fax as telephone E-mail rking11@hotmail.com

KING, Richard David. b 63. Oak Hill Th Coll 87. d 90 p 91. C Foord St Jo *Cant* 90-94; P-in-c Orlestone w Snave and Ruckinge w Warehorne 94-02; R Orlestone w Snave and Ruckinge w Warehorne etc 02; Dioc Ecum Officer 97-02; CA Field Officer *Cant, Lon, Roch* and *S'wark* from 02. *38 Rosewood Drive, Ashford TN25 4QF* Tel (01233) 731280
E-mail richard.d.king@tesconet.uk

KING, Robert Dan. b 57. Sarum & Wells Th Coll 92. d 94 p 95. C Heref H Trin *Heref* 94-97; TV W Heref 97-00; V Weobley w Sarnesfield and Norton Canon from 00; P-in-c Letton w Staunton, Byford, Mansel Gamage etc from 00. *The Vicarage, Church Road, Weobley, Hereford HR4 8SD* Tel (01544) 318415
E-mail bobking@wbsnet.co.uk

KING, Robin Lucas Colin. b 59. Dundee Univ MA81. Ridley Hall Cam 87. d 89 p 90. C Ipswich St Aug *St E* 89-92; V Bures 92-02; C Assington w Newton Green and Lt Cornard 00-02; V Bures w Assington and Lt Cornard from 02. *The Vicarage, Church Square, Bures CO8 5AA* Tel (01787) 227315 Mobile 07885-863687 E-mail robin@ricking.freeserve.co.uk

KING, Canon Stuart John Langley. b 33. Selw Coll Cam BA57 MA61. Linc Th Coll 57. d 59 p 60. C Plymouth Crownhill Ascension *Ex* 59-62; C Horsham *Chich* 62-67; V Devonport St Mark Ford *Ex* 67-77; RD Plymouth 74-77; Can Res Cov Cathl *Cov* 77-84; V Tooting All SS *S'wark* 84-96; rtd 96; Perm to Offic *Ex* from 96. *12 Lowertown Close, Landrake, Saltash PL12 5DG* Tel (01752) 851512

KING, Thomas James Richard. b 27. LGSM64 ACP66. St Jo Coll Nottm. d 85 p 86. Hon C Enderby w Lubbesthorpe and Thurlaston *Leic* 85-97; Perm to Offic from 97. *6 Copt Oak Road, Narborough, Leicester LE19 3EF* Tel 0116-286 4250

KING, Timothy William. b 52. CertEd. Ripon Coll Cuddesdon. d 81 p 82. C Ludlow *Heref* 81-83; C Walton-on-Thames *Guildf* 83-86; C Hammersmith St Paul *Lon* 86-88; V Send *Guildf* 88-95; R Farncombe 95-00. *Givendale, St Mary's School, St Mary's Road, Ascot SL5 9JF* Tel (01344) 874425

KING, Tony Christopher. b 62. Lanc Univ BA83. Coll of Resurr Mirfield 83. d 86 p 87. C Stansted Mountfitchet *Chelmsf* 86-89; USPG 89-92; Chaplain SS Pet and Paul *Chelmsf* 92-93. *12 Livingstone Road, London E17 9AX*

KING, Canon Walter Raleigh. b 45. New Coll Ox BA67 MA74. Cuddesdon Coll 71. d 74 p 75. C Wisbech SS Pet and Paul *Ely* 74-77; C Barrow St Geo w St Luke *Carl* 77-79; P-in-c Clifford *Heref* 79-83; P-in-c Cusop 79-83; P-in-c Hardwick 79-83; P-in-c Whitney w Winforton 81-84; R Cusop w Clifford, Hardwicke,

Bredwardine etc 83-86; R Heref St Nic 86-92; Dir of Ords 86-92; Preb Heref Cathl 86-92; TR Huntingdon *Ely* 92-01; RD Huntingdon 94-99; Hon Can Ely Cathl 99-01; Vice Dean and Can Res Chelmsf Cathl *Chelmsf* from 01. *115 Rainsford Road, Chelmsford CM1 2PF* Tel (01245) 267773
E-mail vicedean@chelmsfordcathedral.org.uk

KING-SMITH, Giles Anthony Beaumont. b 53. Univ Coll Ox BA75. Trin Coll Bris DipHE88. d 88 p 89. C Gtr Corsham *Bris* 88-92; V Two Mile Hill St Mich 92-96; TV Ilfracombe, Lee, Woolacombe, Bittadon etc *Ex* from 96. *The Vicarage, Springfield Road, Woolacombe EX34 7BX* Tel (01271) 870467

KING-SMITH, Philip Hugh (Brother Robert Hugh). b 28. CCC Cam BA52 MA56. Cuddesdon Coll 52. d 54 p 55. C Stockton St Pet *Dur* 54-59; V Bishopwearmouth Gd Shep 59-64; SSF from 64; USA from 66; rtd 98. *San Damiano, 573 Dolores, San Francisco, CA 94110, USA* Tel (001) (415) 861 1372 Fax 861 7952

KINGCOME, John Parken. b 18. CEng50 MIMechE50. Sarum Th Coll 65. d 67 p 68. C Melksham *Sarum* 67-70; P-in-c Woodborough w Manningford Bohun etc 70-72; R Swanborough 72-75; TR Swanborough 75-79; RD Pewsey 75-84; Custos St Jo Hosp Heytesbury 79-84; rtd 84; Perm to Offic *B & W* from 85-95 and *Bris* from 92. *Stonecrop, The Butts, Biddestone, Chippenham SN14 7DY* Tel (01249) 713412

KINGDON, Mrs Margaret Victoria. b 44. NNEB. St Alb and Ox Min Course 95. d 98 p 99. OLM Wokingham St Sebastian *Ox* from 98. *60 Pinewood Avenue, Crowthorne RG45 6RP* Tel (01344) 774625

KINGHAM, Derek Henry. b 29. Oak Hill Th Coll 56. d 58 p 59. C Deptford St Jo *S'wark* 58-60; C Normanton *Derby* 60-63; R Gaulby w Kings Norton and Stretton Parva *Leic* 63-73; V Bacup St Sav *Man* 73-95; rtd 95; Perm to Offic *Carl* from 95. *12 Castle Green Close, Kendal LA9 6AT* Tel (01539) 727008

KINGHAM, Mair Josephine. *See* TALBOT, Canon Mair Josephine

KINGMAN, Paul Henry Charles. b 64. Reading Univ BSc86. Wycliffe Hall Ox BTh95. d 95 p 96. C Whitton *Sarum* 95-99; C Harold Wood *Chelmsf* from 99. *48 Harold Court Road, Romford RM3 0YX* Tel (01708) 341348
E-mail paul@stpetersharoldwood.org

KINGS, Mrs Frances Bridget (Biddi). b 48. City Univ BSc70 Birm Univ MSc77. WEMTC 00. d 03. NSM Eckington *Worc* from 03. *Merebrook Farm, Hanley Swan, Worcester WR8 0DX* Tel (01684) 310950 E-mail biddi@btconnect.com

KINGS, Canon Graham Ralph. b 53. Hertf Coll Ox BA77 MA80 Selw Coll Cam DipTh80 Utrecht Univ PhD02. Ridley Hall Cam 78. d 80 p 81. C Harlesden St Mark *Lon* 80-84; CMS 85-91; Kenya 85-91; Dir Studies St Andr Inst Kabare 85-88; Vice Prin 89-91; Lect Miss Studies Cam Th Federation 92-00; Overseas Adv Henry Martyn Trust 92-95; Dir Henry Martyn Cen Westmr Coll Cam 95-00; Hon C Cambridge H Trin *Ely* 92-96; Hon C Chesterton St Andr 96-00; V Islington St Mary *Lon* from 00. *St Mary's Vicarage, Upper Street, London N1 2TX* Tel (020) 7226 8981 *or* tel and fax 7226 3400 E-mail vicar@stmaryislington.org

KINGS, Mrs Jean Alison. *See* THORN, Mrs Jean Alison

KINGS, Peter Robert. b 33. AKC61. d 62 p 63. C Moorfields *Bris* 62-65; Dep Dir of Educn *Lon* and *S'wark* 66-70; Lic to Offic *Nor* 79-95; rtd 86. *113 Gaywood Road, King's Lynn PE30 2PU* Tel (01553) 772404

KINGSBURY, Canon Richard John. b 41. Lon Univ BA63. Linc Th Coll 65. d 67 p 68. C Wallsend St Luke *Newc* 67-69; C Monkseaton St Mary 69-70; Chapl K Coll Lon 70-75; V Hungerford and Denford *Ox* 75-83; R Caversham and Mapledurham from 83; Hon Can Ch Ch from 92. *The Rectory, 20 Church Road, Reading RG4 7AD* Tel 0118-947 9130 *or* 947 1703

KINGSLAND, Desmond George. b 23. Sarum Th Coll 75. d 78 p 79. Hon C Bournemouth H Epiphany *Win* 78-95; rtd 95. *Windy Ridge, 23 Granby Road, Bournemouth BH9 3NZ* Tel (01202) 526011

KINGSLEY, Brian St Clair. b 26. St Steph Ho Ox 56. d 59 p 60. C Tilehurst St Mich *Ox* 59-63; CSWG from 63; Prior from 85; Lic to Offic *Chich* 60-00; rtd 96; Perm to Offic *Chich* from 01. *The Monastery of Christ the Saviour, 23 Cambridge Road, Hove BN3 1DE* Tel (01273) 726698

KINGSLEY-SMITH, John Sydney. b 45. ARCM. Ridley Hall Cam 78. d 80 p 81. C Nailsea H Trin *B & W* 80-84; TV Whitton *Sarum* 84-91; V Chorleywood Ch Ch *St Alb* 91-01; RD Rickmansworth 98-01; rtd 01; Perm to Offic *St Alb* from 01. *29 Lewes Way, Croxley Green, Rickmansworth WD3 3SW* Tel (01923) 249949

KINGSTON, Canon Albert William. b 47. Bernard Gilpin Soc Dur 68 Oak Hill Th Coll 69. d 72 p 73. C Walton Breck *Liv* 72-74; C Templemore *D & R* 74-76; I Kildallon w Newtowngore and Corrawallen *K, E & A* 76-82; Bp's C Ardagh w Tashinny, Shrule and Kilcommick from 82; Can and Preb Elphin Cathl from 95. *Oakhill Lodge, Rathmore, Ballymahon, Co Longford, Irish Republic* Tel (00353) (90) 643 8945

KINGSTON, Mrs Avril Dawson. b 34. Local Minl Tr Course 91. d 94 p 95. Aux Min Douglas Union w Frankfield *C, C & R* from

94. *Ballymartin House, Glencairn, Co Waterford, Irish Republic* Tel (00353) (58) 56227 E-mail am.douglas@cork.anglican.org

KINGSTON, Canon Eric. b 24. **d** 69 **p** 70. C Ballymacarrett St Patr *D & D* 69-72; C Knock 72-76; I Annahilt w Magherahamlet 76-93; rtd 93; Can and Prec Dromore Cathl *D & D* 93. *38 Kinedale Park, Ballynahinch BT24 8YS* Tel (028) 9756 5715

KINGSTON, George Mervyn. b 47. CITC 70. **d** 73 **p** 74. C Comber *D & D* 73-77; C Belfast St Donard 77-80; Min Can Down Cathl 80-84; Bp's C Lecale Gp 82-84; Bp's C Belfast St Andr *Conn* 84-90; I Ballymascanlan w Creggan and Rathcor *Arm* from 90. *1 Whitemill Road, Lower Faughart, Dundalk, Co Louth, Irish Republic* Tel and fax (00353) (42) 937 1921 Mobile 087-272 9892 E-mail creggan@armagh.anglican.org

KINGSTON, John Desmond George. b 40. TCD BA63 MA66. CITC 64. **d** 64 **p** 65. C Arm St Mark *Arm* 64-70; Hon V Choral Arm Cathl 69-70; Chapl Portora R Sch Enniskillen from 70; Lic to Offic *Clogh* from 70; Can Clogh Cathl from 96. *Ambleside, 45 Old Rossory Road, Enniskillen BT74 7LF* Tel (028) 6632 4493

KINGSTON, Canon Kenneth Robert. b 42. TCD BA65 MA69. **d** 66 **p** 67. C Enniscorthy *C & O* 66-69; C Ballymena *Conn* 70-72; C Drumragh w Mountfield *D & R* 72-78; I Badoney Lower w Greenan and Badoney Upper 78-84; I Desertmartin w Termoneeny from 84; Can Derry Cathl from 97. *25 Dromore Road, Desertmartin, Magherafelt BT45 5JZ* Tel (028) 7963 2455

KINGSTON, Michael Joseph. b 51. K Coll Lon BD73 AKC73. St Aug Coll Cant 73. **d** 74 **p** 75. C Reading H Trin *Ox* 74-77; C New Eltham All SS *S'wark* 77-83; V Plumstead Ascension 83-94; Sub-Dean Greenwich N 92-94; V Sydenham St Bart from 94. *St Bartholomew's Vicarage, 4 Westwood Hill, London SE26 6QR* Tel (020) 8778 5290 E-mail michaelkingston@lineone.net

KINGSTON, Michael Marshall. b 54. St Jo Coll Nottm MA94. **d** 96 **p** 97. C Drayton w Felthorpe *Nor* 96-99; R Gt and Lt Plumstead w Thorpe End and Witton from 99; Chapl Norwich Primary Care Trust from 01. *The Rectory, 9 Lawn Crescent, Thorpe End, Norwich NR13 5BP.* Tel (01603) 434778

KINGSTON, Robert George. b 46. TCD BA68 Div Test69. **d** 69 **p** 72. C Belfast St Thos *Conn* 69-72; C Kilkenny St Canice Cathl *C & O* 72-75; I Ballinasloe w Taughmaconnell *L & K* 77-79; I Maryborough w Dysart Enos and Ballyfin *C & O* 79-85; I Lurgan w Billis, Killinkere and Munterconnaught *K, E & A* 85-88; Registrar Kilmore 87-92; I Lurgan etc w Ballymachugh, Kildrumferton etc 88-92; I Tallaght *D & G* 92-98; Warden of Readers 93-98; I Mallow Union *C, C & R* from 98. *The Rectory, Lower Bearforest, Mallow, Co Cork, Irish Republic* Tel (00353) (22) 21473

KINGSTON, Roy William Henry. b 31. Chich Th Coll 60. **d** 62 **p** 63. C Leeds St Aid *Ripon* 62-66; S Africa 66-73; V Bramley *Ripon* 74-81; TR Hemel Hempstead *St Alb* 81-85; TR Fareham H Trin *Portsm* 85-93; RD Alverstoke 89-90; RD Fareham 90-93; P-in-c Hambledon 93-97; rtd 97; Perm to Offic *Guildf, Portsm* and *Win* from 97. *8 Pengilly Road, Farnham GU9 7XQ* Tel (01252) 711371 Mobile 07855-457670 E-mail roykingston@roykingston.plus.com

KINGSTON, Mrs Shirley Alexandra. b 42. Ch of Ireland Tr Coll Dip Primary Educn 61 TCD BA68 HDipEd70. CITC 90. **d** 93 **p** 94. NSM Castlemacadam w Ballinaclash, Aughrim etc *D & G* 93-95; NSM Rathdrum w Glenealy, Derralossary and Laragh 95-97; NSM Bray from 97. *Kilpatrick House, Redcross, Wicklow, Irish Republic* Tel (00353) (404) 47137

KINGSTON-UPON-THAMES, Area Bishop of. *See* CHEETHAM, The Rt Revd Richard Ian

KINGTON, Canon David Bruce. b 45. Trin Coll Bris 72. **d** 72 **p** 73. C Wellington w Eyton *Lich* 72-77; C Boscombe St Jo *Win* 77-81; R Michelmersh, Timsbury, Farley Chamberlayne etc 81-98; R Michelmersh and Awbridge and Braishfield etc from 98; RD Romsey from 95; Hon Can Win Cathl from 02. *The Rectory, Braishfield Road, Braishfield, Romsey SO51 0PR* Tel (01794) 368335 E-mail dbkington@dbkington.worldonline.co.uk

KINNA, Michael Andrew. b 46. Chich Th Coll 84. **d** 86 **p** 87. C Leominster *Heref* 86-90; TV Wenlock 90-93; P-in-c Broseley w Benthall 93; P-in-c Jackfield 93; P-in-c Linley w Willey and Barrow 93; R Broseley w Benthall, Jackfield, Linley etc from 94. *The Rectory, Church Street, Broseley TF12 5DA* Tel (01952) 882647 Fax as telephone E-mail mak@ridewise.fsnet.co.uk

KINNAIRD, Jennifer. b 41. Hull Univ BA62 Ex Univ PGCE63. NEOC DipHE94. **d** 97 **p** 98. NSM Corbridge w Halton and Newton Hall *Newc* from 97. *17 Glebelands, Corbridge NE45 5DS* Tel (01434) 632695

KINNAIRD, Keith. b 42. Chich Th Coll 72. **d** 75 **p** 76. C Didcot St Pet *Ox* 75-78; C Abingdon w Shippon 78-82; Chapl Abingdon Hosp 79-92; P-in-c Sunningwell *Ox* 82-90; P-in-c Radley 88-90; R Radley and Sunningwell 90-95; Chapl and SBStJ from 91; V Old Shoreham *Chich* 95-00; V New Shoreham 95-00; R Caversham St Andr *Ox* from 00; Voc Adv from 00; Adv for Min of Healing from 00. *St Andrew's Vicarage, Harrogate Road, Reading RG4 7PW* Tel 0118-947 2788 Fax as telephone E-mail kinnaird@waitrose.com

KINSELLA, Nigel Paul. b 66. Wolv Univ LLB95. Westcott Ho Cam 00. **d** 02 **p** 03. C Attleborough w Besthorpe *Nor* from 02; C

Quidenham Gp from 03. *The Vicarage, Mill Road, Old Buckenham, Attleborough NR17 1SG*

KINSEY, Bruce Richard Lawrence. b 59. K Coll Lon BD81 AKC81 MTh86 MA94. Wycliffe Hall Ox. **d** 84 **p** 85. C Gt Stanmore *Lon* 84-88; C Shepherd's Bush St Steph w St Thos 88-91; Chapl and Fell Down Coll Cam 91-01; Hd Philolosopy and RS Perse Sch Cam from 01. *The Perse School, Hills Road, Cambridge CB2 2QF* Tel (01223) 3568266 E-mail br@perse.co.uk

KINSEY, Paul. b 56. Nottm Univ BTh89. Linc Th Coll 86. **d** 90. C Connah's Quay *St As* 89-91; Min Can St As Cathl 91-94; Asst Chapl Univ Coll Lon Hosps NHS Trust 94-00; R S Lynn *Nor* from 00; Ind Chapl from 00. *All Saints' Rectory, 33 Goodwins Road, King's Lynn PE30 5QX* Tel (01553) 771779 E-mail therector.allsaints@btinternet.com

KINSEY, Russell Frederick David. b 34. Sarum Th Coll 59. **d** 62 **p** 63. C Twerton *B & W* 62-66; C N Cadbury 66-76; C Yarlington 66-76; P-in-c Compton Pauncefoot w Blackford 66-76; P-in-c Maperton 66-76; P-in-c N Cheriton 66-76; TV Camelot Par 76-79; V Pill 79-82; P-in-c Easton-in-Gordano w Portbury and Clapton 80-82; V Pill w Easton in Gordano and Portbury 82-92; rtd 94. *25 Newbourne Road, Weston-super-Mare BS22 8NF*

KINSMEN, Barry William. b 40. Chan Sch Truro. **d** 74 **p** 75. NSM Padstow *Truro* 74-78; Dioc Adv in RE 79-95; P-in-c St Issey 80-81; P-in-c Lt Petherick 80-81; R St Issey w St Petroc Minor 81-95; rtd 95; Perm to Offic *Truro* from 95. *14 Old School Court, School Hill, Padstow PL28 8ED* Tel (01841) 532507

KIPPAX, Michael John. b 48. Open Univ BA82. SW Minl Tr Course 89. **d** 92 **p** 93. C Camborne *Truro* 92-95; C Woughton *Ox* 95-96; TV 96-98; R St Illogan *Truro* from 98. *The Rectory, Robartes Terrace, Illogan, Redruth TR16 4RX* Tel (01209) 842233 Fax (08707) 051466 E-mail mike@illogan.plus.com

KIRBY, David Anthony. b 42. Dur Univ BA64 PhD68. N Ord Course 84. **d** 87 **p** 88. NSM Crosland Moor *Wakef* 87-00; Asst Chapl Algarve *Eur* from 00. *Casa s'ta Catarina, Parque da Praia, Praia da Luz, 8600 Lagos, Portugal* Tel and fax (00351) (282) 789126 Mobile 91-772 7976 E-mail revdakirby@hotmail.com

KIRBY, David Graham. b 58. Univ of Wales (Cardiff) BA80. Wycliffe Hall Ox BA85 MA92. **d** 86 **p** 87. C Northallerton w Kirby Sigston *York* 86-89; C Southport Ch Ch *Liv* 89-92; R Bishop Burton w Walkington *York* from 92. *The Rectory, Walkington, Beverley HU17 8SP* Tel (01482) 868379

KIRBY, Mrs Joan Florence. b 32. St Hugh's Coll Ox MA57 Lon Univ BA66. St Alb Minl Tr Scheme 79. **d** 87 **p** 94. NSM Hemel Hempstead *St Alb* 87-90; C Blisland w St Breward *Truro* 90-94; NSM Cardynham 94-96; rtd 96; Perm to Offic *Truro* from 96. *Penrose, Tresarrett, Blisland, Bodmin PL30 4QY* Tel (01208) 851003

KIRBY, John Patrick. b 24. Leeds Univ BA50. Coll of Resurr Mirfield 50. **d** 52 **p** 53. C Birm St Aid Small Heath *Birm* 52-55; C Usuthu Miss Swaziland 55-59; C Solihull *Birm* 59-63; St Mary's Th Sch Odibo Namibia 63-68; V Coalbrookdale *Heref* 68-77; P-in-c Lt Wenlock 68-77; P-in-c Buildwas *Lich* 68-77; C S Gillingham *Roch* 77-83; V New Brompton St Luke 83-89; rtd 89; Perm to Offic *Ely* 91-02. *clo Mrs Sarah Turnbull (née Kirby), 7 Abbey Mill View, Knaresborough HG5 8ES* Tel (01423) 866948

KIRBY, Maurice William Herbert. b 31. K Coll Lon DipTh CertEd AKC. **d** 55 **p** 56. C Eltham Park St Luke *S'wark* 55-56; C Horley 56-59; C Westbury *Sarum* 59-62; R Poulshot w Worton 62-66; P-in-c Gt Cheverell 65; P-in-c Burcombe 66-68; V 68-70; V Salisbury St Martin 70-73; Chapl SS Helen and Kath Sch Abingdon 73-79; Chapl and Hd RS Wrekin Coll Telford 79-84; V Frensham *Guildf* 84-93; Dir of Reader Tr 84-93; rtd 93; Perm to Offic *Ex* 93-94; *Chich* 94-97; *York* 01-03. *17 Kingsmark Lane, Chepstow NP16 5LZ* Tel 07866-338314 (mobile)

KIRBY, Paul Michael. b 51. Wycliffe Hall Ox 74 Seabury-Western Th Sem DMin99. **d** 76 **p** 77. C Gateacre *Liv* 76-79; C Barton Seagrave w Warkton *Pet* 79-83; V Bidston *Ches* 83-93; V Ormskirk *Liv* 93-99; Team Ldr Chapl E Kent Hosps NHS Trust 99-00; Sen Team Ldr Chapl from 00; Bp's Adv for Hosp Chapl Cant from 02. *Buckland Hospital, Coombe Valley Road, Dover CT17 0HD* Tel (01304) 201624 ext 43334 Mobile 07811-134383 E-mail paul.kirby@ekht.nhs.uk

KIRBY, Simon Thomas. b 67. Lon Bible Coll BA92 NTMTC 00. **d** 03. C Woodside Park St Barn *Lon* from 03. *63 Brunswick Park Road, London N11 1JH* Tel (020) 8361 1545 Mobile 07967-838272 E-mail simonkirby@stbarnabas.co.uk

KIRBY, Stennett Roger. b 54. St Pet Coll Ox BA75 MA79. Sarum & Wells Th Coll 75. **d** 77 **p** 78. C Belsize Park *Lon* 77-79; NSM Plumstead St Nic *S'wark* 88; C Leic Ch Sav *Leic* 90-91; TV Hanley H Ev *Lich* 91-95; P-in-c Walsall St Pet 95-01; V from 01. *St Peter's Vicarage, 22 Bloxwich Road, Walsall WS2 8DB* Tel (01922) 623995 E-mail church@stpeters22.fsnet.co.uk

KIRK, Clive John Charles. b 37. TD81. FIBMS66. Guildf Dioc Min Course 95. **d** 98 **p** 99. OLM E Molesey St Paul *Guildf* from 98. *9 Fleet Close, West Molesey KT8 2NS* Tel (020) 8979 1227 E-mail candakirk@lineone.net

KIRK, Miss Erika Cottam. b 58. Nottm Univ LLB76 Solicitor 81. St Jo Coll Nottm MA98. **d** 98 **p** 99. NSM Epperstone, Gonalston, Oxton, Calverton etc *S'well* 98-03; NSM Burton Joyce w Bulcote and Stoke Bardolph from 03. *24 St Helen's Crescent, Burton Joyce, Nottingham NG14 5DW* Tel 0115-931 4125

KIRK, Canon Gavin John. b 61. Southn Univ BTh. Chich Th Coll 83. **d** 86 **p** 87. C Seaford w Sutton *Chich* 86-89; Chapl and Succ Roch Cath *Roch* 89-91; Min Can Roch Cathl 89-91; Hon PV Roch Cathl 91-98; Asst Chapl K Sch Roch 91-98; Can Res Portsm Cathl *Portsm* from 98; Can Res and Prec Linc Cathl *Linc* from 03. *The Precentory, 16 Minster Yard, Lincoln LN2 1PX* Tel (01522) 523644 E-mail gjkirk@newnet.co.uk

KIRK, Geoffrey. b 45. Keble Coll Ox BA67. Coll of Resurr Mirfield 71. **d** 72 **p** 73. C Leeds St Aid *Ripon* 72-74; C St Marylebone St Mark w St Luke *Lon* 74-76; C Kennington St Jo *S'wark* 77-79; C Kennington St Jo w St Jas 79-81; P-in-c Lewisham St Steph and St Mark 81-87; V from 87. *St Stephen's Vicarage, Cressingham Road, London SE13 5AG* Tel (020) 8318 1295 Fax (020) 8318 1446

KIRK, George. b 14. Kelham Th Coll 32. **d** 38 **p** 39. C Norbury St Oswald *Cant* 38-41; C Sheff St Cuth *Sheff* 41-43; Chapl City Gen Hosp 41-43; P-in-c Brightside St Thos 43-44; V 44-48; V Bentley 48-56; R Aston cum Aughton 56-80; P-in-c Ulley 57-65; V 65-80; RD Laughton 72-79; rtd 80; Chapl to Rtd Clergy and Clergy Widows Officer *Sheff* 80-86; Lic to Offic 86-93; Perm to Offic from 93. *3 Borrowdale Crescent, North Anston, Sheffield S25 4JW* Tel (01909) 566774

KIRK, Miss Geraldine Mercedes. b 49. Hull Univ MA89. **d** 87 **p** 94. Ind Chapl *Linc* 87-99; P-in-c Bridgwater St Jo *B & W* from 99; Chapl Taunton and Somerset NHS Trust from 99. *St John's Vicarage, Blake Place, Bridgwater TA6 5AU* Tel (01278) 422540 E-mail geraldine@kirk50.freeserve.co.uk

KIRK, Henry Logan. b 52. Adelaide Univ BA74 New Coll Edin BD77 K Coll Lon MA96. **d** 80 **p** 81. S Africa 80-85; Asst Master Haileybury Sch Herts 86; Asst Chapl Rugby Sch 86-93; Dep Hd Dulwich Coll Prep Sch 93-94; NSM S Dulwich St Steph *S'wark* 93-94; C Linslade *Ox* 94-96; Chapl Birkenhead Sch Merseyside from 96; Hd of Th and Philosophy from 96. *61 Shrewsbury Road, Prenton CH43 2JA*

KIRK, John Andrew. b 37. Lon Univ BD61 AKC61 MPhil75 Fitzw Ho Cam BA63. Ridley Hall Cam 61. **d** 63 **p** 64. C Finchley Ch Ch *Lon* 63-66; Argentina 66-79; SAMS 79-81; CMS 82-90; Dean of Miss Selly Oak Coll Birm 90-99; Dept of Th Birm Univ *Birm* 99-02; Perm to Offic *Glouc* from 99; rtd 02. *The Old Stable, Market Square, Lechlade GL7 3AB* Tel (01367) 253254

KIRK, Peter Fenwick. b 30. **d** 83 **p** 84. NSM Bathgate *Edin* 83-91; NSM Linlithgow 83-91; NSM Bathgate from 92. *18 Inch Crescent, Bathgate EH48 1EU* Tel (01506) 655369

KIRK, Steven Paul. b 59. Ex Univ LLB80 Univ of Wales (Cardiff) BD87 LLM94. St Mich Coll Llan 84. **d** 87 **p** 88. C Ebbw Vale *Mon* 87-89; PV Llan Cathl *Llan* 89-91; PV and Succ 91-94; V Port Talbot St Agnes w Oakwood 94-01; TR Aberavon from 01. *The Rectory, 29 Ynys Street, Port Talbot SA13 1YW* Tel (01639) 883630

KIRK-DUNCAN, The Ven Brian Andrew Campbell. b 15. Pemb Coll Ox BA46 MA47 TCD MA59 DPhil64. Cuddesdon Coll 39. **d** 41 **p** 42. C Summertown *Ox* 41-43; Asst Master Dragon Sch Ox 41-43; C Headington Quarry *Ox* 43-44; V Sevenhampton w Charlton Abbots *Glouc* 44-47; P-in-c Hawling w Cold Salperton 46-47; R Bredon w Bredon's Norton *Worc* 47-62; R St Mary at Hill w St Andr Hubbard etc *Lon* from 62; Prin Becket Coll Lon 63-67; Dep Min Can St Paul's Cathl *Lon* from 69; Hon Adn Guinea from 87; Perm to Offic *St E* from 91; *Chelmsf* from 92; Asst Chapl OStJ 76-79; Sub-Chapl 79-81; Offg Chapl 81-99; Sub-Prelate from 99. *The Rectory, St Mary-at-Hill, London EC3R 8EE* Tel (020) 7626 4184 Fax 7283 4421

KIRKBRIDE, Martin Lea. b 51. Oak Hill Th Coll BA94. **d** 97 **p** 98. C Lancaster St Thos *Blackb* 97-00; TV Hampreston *Sarum* from 00. *The Vicarage, 3 Dudsbury Road, West Parley, Ferndown BH22 8RA* Tel (01202) 876552

KIRKBY, John Victor Michael. b 39. Lon Univ BScEng62 DipMaths64 BD73. Ridley Hall Cam 65. **d** 67 **p** 68. C Muswell Hill St Jas *Lon* 67-70; Chapl Hatf Poly *St Alb* 71-75; V Wootton 75-86; RD Elstow 82-86; R Byfleet *Guildf* 86-92; P-in-c Potten End w Nettleden *St Alb* 92-97; V from 97; Chapl Ashridge Management Coll from 92. *The Vicarage, Church Road, Potten End, Berkhamsted HP4 2QY* Tel (01442) 865217

KIRKBY, Reginald Gresham. b 16. Leeds Univ BA40. Coll of Resurr Mirfield 40. **d** 42 **p** 43. C Gorton St Mary and St Thos *Man* 42-44; C Middlesbrough All SS *York* 44-46; C Becontree St Pet *Chelmsf* 46-48; C Notting Hill St Mich and Ch Ch *Lon* 48-51; V Bow Common 51-94; rtd 94. *7 St James's Court, Bishop Street, London N1 8PH* Tel (020) 7226 5714

KIRKE, Clive Henry. b 51. Ridley Hall Cam. **d** 83 **p** 84. C Ainsdale *Liv* 83-86; Gen Asst Bootle Deanery 86-89; P-in-c Litherland St Andr 89-98; V Ingrow cum Hainworth *Bradf* from 98. *St John's Vicarage, Oakfield Road, Keighley BD21 1BT* Tel (01535) 604069

KIRKER, Richard Ennis. b 51. Sarum & Wells Th Coll 72. **d** 77. C Hitchin *St Alb* 77-78; Gen Sec LGCM from 79. *Oxford House, Derbyshire Street, London E2 6HG* Tel and fax (020) 7739 1249 *or* tel 7791 1802 E-mail lgcm@aol.com

KIRKHAM, Alan. d 01 **p** 02. OLM Parr *Liv* from 01. *73 Haven Road, Liverpool L10 1LS* Tel 0151-521 3745

KIRKHAM, Clifford Gerald Frank. b 34. Open Univ BA91. Sarum & Wells Th Coll 72. **d** 74 **p** 75. C Worle *B & W* 74-76; C E Preston w Kingston *Chich* 76-78; C Goring-by-Sea 78-80; C-in-c Maybridge CD 80-82; V Maybridge 82-88; R N Chapel w Ebernoe 88-99; Chapl for Rural Affairs 89-99; rtd 99; Perm to Offic *Nor* from 99. *5 Meadow Way, Rollesby, Great Yarmouth NR29 5HA* Tel (01493) 749036 E-mail kirkham@fish.co.uk

✠**KIRKHAM, The Rt Revd John Dudley Galtrey.** b 35. Trin Coll Cam BA59 MA63. Westcott Ho Cam 60. **d** 62 **p** 63 **c** 76. C Ipswich St Mary le Tower *St E* 62-65; Bp's Chapl *Nor* 65-69; P-in-c Rockland St Mary w Hellington 67-69; Papua New Guinea 69-70; C St Martin-in-the-Fields *Lon* 70-72; C Westmr St Marg 70-72; Abp's Dom Chapl *Cant* 72-76; Suff Bp Sherborne *Sarum* 76-81; Area Bp Sherborne 81-01; Can and Preb Sarum Cathl from 77; Abp's Adv to the Headmasters' Conf from 90; Bp HM Forces 92-01; rtd 01; Hon Asst Bp Sarum from 01; Can and Preb Sarum Cathl from 02. *Flamstone House, Flamstone Street, Bishopstone, Salisbury SP5 4BZ* Tel (01722) 780221 E-mail jsherborne@salisbury.anglican.org

KIRKHAM, June Margaret. b 54. EMMTC 99. **d** 02 **p** 03. C Nottingham St Jude *S'well* from 02. *19 Kent Road, Nottingham NG3 6BE* Tel 0115-960 9899 E-mail june@kirkham7260.fsnet.co.uk

KIRKHAM, Stephen Gawin. b 51. MC74. Ridley Hall Cam 96. **d** 98 **p** 99. C Histon and Impington *Ely* 98-02; P-in-c N Leigh *Ox* from 02. *The Vicarage, New Yatt Road, North Leigh, Witney OX29 6TT* Tel (01993) 881136 E-mail stephen.kirkham@dial.pipex.com

KIRKLAND, Richard John. b 53. Leic Univ BA75. St Jo Coll Dur 76. **d** 79 **p** 80. C Knutsford St Jo and Toft *Ches* 79-82; C Bebington 82-89; V Poulton Lancelyn H Trin 89-95; V Hoole from 95. *All Saints' Vicarage, 2 Vicarage Road, Chester CH2 3HZ* Tel (01244) 322056 E-mail j.kirkland@clara.net

KIRKMAN, Richard Marsden. b 55. Cranmer Hall Dur. **d** 87 **p** 88. C Bridlington Priory *York* 87-90; TV Thirsk 90-96; R Escrick and Stillingfleet w Naburn from 96; RD Derwent from 01. *The Rectory, York Road, Escrick, York YO19 6EY* Tel (01904) 728406 E-mail rmkquanta@telco4u.net

KIRKMAN, Trevor Harwood. b 51. Trin Hall Cam BA73 MA77. EMMTC 94. **d** 96 **p** 97. NSM Hickling w Kinoulton and Broughton Sulney *S'well* 96-01; NSM Keyworth and Stanton-on-the-Wolds and Bunny etc from 01; Dioc Registrar and Bp's Legal Adv *Leic* from 02. *The Old Vicarage, 43 Church Lane, Long Clawson, Melton Mowbray LE14 4ND* Tel (01664) 822270 Fax (01509) 238833 E-mail trevorkirkman@lathamlawyers.co.uk

KIRKPATRICK, Errol Francis. b 28. TCD MA HDipEd. **d** 52 **p** 53. C Enniscorthy *C & O* 52-55; Dioc C (Ferns) 55-56; C Wexford St Iberius 55-56; C Bridgwater St Mary w Chilton Trinity *B & W* 56-59; R Bromley All Hallows *Lon* 59-66; R Kentchurch w Llangua *Heref* 66-77; V Rowlestone w Llancillo 66-77; V Walterstone 66-77; RD Abbeydore 72-77; R Porlock w Stoke Pero *B & W* 77-83; R Lapworth *Birm* 83-89; R Baddesley Clinton 83-89; rtd 89; Perm to Offic *B & W* from 89. *51 Runnymede, Yeovil BA21 5RY*

KIRKPATRICK, The Very Revd Jonathan Richard. b 58. CA81 Goldsmiths' Coll Lon BA85. Wilson Carlile Coll IDC81 S'wark Ord Course 83. **d** 85 **p** 85. C Lewisham St Mary *S'wark* 85-87; Chapl Lewisham Hosp 85-87; Selection Sec ACCM 88-91; Sec Aston Tr Scheme 89-91; Hon C Noel Park St Mark *Lon* 88-91; New Zealand from 91; Dean Dunedin from 96; V Gen from 97. *PO Box 5205, Dunedin, New Zealand* Tel (0064) (3) 477 0276 *or* 477 2336 E-mail jonrk@xtra.co.nz

KIRKPATRICK, Nigel David Joseph. b 68. CITC BTh96. **d** 96 **p** 97. C Portadown St Columba *Arm* 96-99; C Lecale Gp *D & D* 99-01; I Killinchy w Kilmood and Tullynakill from 01. *Killinchy Rectory, 11 Whiterock Road, Killinchy, Newtownards BT23 6PR* Tel (028) 9754 1249 Fax as telephone E-mail killinchy@down.anglican.org

KIRKPATRICK, Roger James (Brother Damian). b 41. FCA. **d** 86 **p** 87. SSF from 66; Guardian Belf Friary 80-88; Birm 89-93; Prov Min 91-02; NSM Belfast St Pet *Conn* 86-88; Chapl R Victoria Hosp Belf 86-88; Lic to Offic *Linc* 94-96; *Lon* 97-01; *Sarum* 01-03; V Holy Is *Newc* from 03. *The Vicarage, Holy Island, Berwick-upon-Tweed TD15 2RX* Tel (01289) 389216 E-mail damianssf@aol.com

KIRKPATRICK, William John Ashley. b 27. SEN SRN RMN. Sarum Th Coll 63. **d** 68 **p** 70. NSM St Mary le Bow w St Pancras Soper Lane etc *Lon* 68-70; NSM Soho St Anne w St Thos and

St Pet 70-75; SSF 76-79; NSM S Kensington St Aug *Lon* 79-80; NSM Earl's Court St Cuth w St Matthias 80-98; rtd 98; Perm to Offic *Lon* from 98. *15 Child's Street, London SW5 9RY* Tel (020) 7373 1330 Fax as telephone E-mail fr.bill@lineone.net

KIRKUP, Nigel Norman. b 54. K Coll Lon BD79 AKC79. **d** 80 **p** 80. Hon C Catford (Southend) and Downham *S'wark* 80-83; Hon C Surbiton St Andr and St Mark 83-85; Hon C Shirley St Geo 85-93; Perm to Offic *Lon* from 96. *29 Peartree Lane, London E1 9SR* Tel (020) 7488 4217

KIRKWOOD, Alexander David. b 58. Ex Coll Ox BA81 Dur Univ CertEd82. Linc Th Coll 83. **d** 85 **p** 86. C Linc St Faith and St Martin w St Pet *Linc* 85-88; C Farnborough *Roch* 88-91; V Mitcham St Barn 91-98; P-in-c S Ashford Ch Ch *Cant* from 98. *112 Beaver Road, Ashford TN23 7SR* Tel (01233) 620600

KIRKWOOD, David Christopher. b 40. Pemb Coll Ox BA63. Clifton Th Coll 63. **d** 65 **p** 66. C Wilmington *Roch* 65-68; C Green Street Green 68-72; Youth and Area Sec BCMS 72-73; Educn and Youth Sec 73-80; Hon C Sidcup Ch Ch *Roch* 74-80; V Rothley *Leic* 80-92; RD Goscote II 84-88; RD Goscote 88-90; P-in-c Toxteth St Philemon w St Gabr and St Cleopas *Liv* 92-95; TR 95-01; AD Toxteth and Wavertree 96-01; TR Harlow Town Cen w Lt Parndon *Chelmsf* from 01. *The Rectory, 43 Upper Park, Harlow CM20 1TW* Tel (01279) 444292 E-mail david.kirkwood2@tinyworld.co.uk

KIRKWOOD, Jack. b 21. Worc Ord Coll 62. **d** 63 **p** 64. C Penwerris *Truro* 63-66; V Torpoint 66-73; V Turton *Man* 73-81; P-in-c Castleton All So 81-82; Hon C Heywood St Luke 82-84; rtd 86; Perm to Offic *Blackb* from 86 and *York* 89-94. *2 Westover Grove, Warton, Carnforth LA5 9QR* Tel (01524) 732552

KIRTLEY, Georgina. b 44. St Jo Coll Dur BA94. Cranmer Hall Dur. **d** 95 **p** 96. NSM Barnard Castle w Whorlton *Dur* 95-00; Chapl HM YOI Deerbolt from 00; Asst Adv to Self Supporting Ministers from 00. *Ryelands, Stainton, Barnard Castle DL12 8RB* Tel (01833) 630871

KIRTON, Canon Richard Arthur. b 43. Dur Univ BA67 MA73 DipTh68. Wycliffe Hall Ox 68. **d** 69 **p** 70. C Warsop *S'well* 69-72; C Newark St Mary 72-75; Malaysia 75-83; Dean of Studies Th Sem Kuala Lumpur 79-82; P-in-c Bleasby w Halloughton *S'well* 83-89; V Thurgarton w Hoveringham 83-89; V Thurgarton w Hoveringham and Bleasby etc 89-91; Bp's Adv on Overseas Relns 85-91; Hon Can Kuala Lumpur from 88; Tutor Wilson Carlile Coll of Evang 91-98; P-in-c Ollerton w Boughton *S'well* from 98. *St Paulinus Vicarage, 65 Larch Road, New Ollerton, Newark NG22 9SX* Tel (01623) 860323

KISH, Paul Alexander. b 68. K Coll Lon BD92 AKC92 Leeds Univ MA96. St Steph Ho Ox 96. **d** 98 **p** 99. C Prestbury *Glouc* 98-01; Chapl Sutton Valence Sch Kent from 01. *1 Holdgate House, South Lane, Sutton Valence, Maidstone ME17 3BG* Tel (01622) 842281 E-mail paulkishtwocups@teatime22.freeserve.co.uk

KISSELL, Barrington John. b 38. Lon Coll of Div 64. **d** 67 **p** 68. C Camborne *Truro* 67-71; C Chorleywood St Andr *St Alb* 71-00; Dir Faith Sharing Min from 74; C Bryanston Square St Mary w St Marylebone St Mark *Lon* from 00. *36 Lena Gardens, London W6 7PZ*

KISSELL, Jonathan Mark Barrington. b 66. Trin Coll Bris 99. **d** 01 **p** 02. C Stevenage St Pet Broadwater *St Alb* from 01. *3 Wychdell, Stevenage SG2 8JD* Tel (01438) 217842 E-mail jonathankissell@hotmail.com

KITA KANTO, Bishop of. *See* UNO, The Most Revd James Toru

KITCHEN, Ian Brian. b 60. Worc Coll Ox BA81 Southn Univ PGCE82. Wycliffe Hall Ox 98. **d** 00 **p** 01. C Brandesburton and Leven w Catwick *York* from 00. *The Rectory, 105 Main Street, Brandesburton, Driffield YO25 8RG* Tel (01964) 544453 E-mail luddite@fish.co.uk

KITCHEN, Canon Martin. b 47. N Lon Poly BA71 K Coll Lon BD76 AKC77 Man Univ PhD88. S'wark Ord Course 77. **d** 79 **p** 80. Lect C Tr Coll Blackheath Th 83; Hon C Kidbrooke St Jas *S'wark* 79-83; Chapl Man Poly *Man* 83-88; TV Man Whitworth 83-86; TR 86-88; Adv In-Service Tr *S'wark* 88-95; Dioc Co-ord of Tr 95-97; Can Res S'wark Cathl 88-97; Can Res Dur Cathl *Dur* from 97; Sub-Dean from 99. *3 The College, Durham DH1 3EQ* Tel 0191-384 2415 Fax 386 4267 E-mail martin.kitchen@durham.anglican.org

KITCHENER, Christopher William. b 46. Open Univ BA. Sarum & Wells Th Coll 82. **d** 84 **p** 85. C Bexleyheath Ch Ch *Roch* 84-88; V Gravesend St Mary 88-97; V Biggin Hill from 97. *St Mark's Vicarage, 10 Church Road, Biggin Hill, Westerham TN16 3LB* Tel (01959) 540482 E-mail chris@chriskitchener.freeserve.co.uk

KITCHENER, Mrs Evarina Carol. b 51. Stockwell Coll of Educn CertEd70 Heythrop Coll Lon MA00. Cant Sch of Min 89. **d** 92 **p** 94. NSM Gravesend St Mary *Roch* 92-97; NSM Biggin Hill from 97; Asst Chapl Bromley Hosps NHS Trust 98-99; Distr Evang Miss Enabler S Prov URC 99-01; Par Development Officer *Roch* from 01. *St Mark's Vicarage, 10 Church Road, Biggin Hill, Westerham TN16 3LB* Tel (01959) 540482 *or* tel and fax 571607 Mobile 07947-674775 E-mail carol@eckitchener.freeserve.co.uk

KITCHENER, Canon Michael Anthony. b 45. Trin Coll Cam BA67 MA70 PhD71. Cuddesdon Coll 70. **d** 71 **p** 72. C Aldwick *Chich* 71-74; C Caversham *Ox* 74-77; Tutor Coll of Resurr Mirfield 77-83; Prin NEOC *Dur* 83-90; Hon Can Newc Cathl *Newc* 84-90; Can Res and Chan Blackb Cathl *Blackb* 90-95; P-in-c Rydal *Carl* 95-99; Warden Rydal Hall 95-99; Ldr Rydal Hall Community 95-99; Can Res Nor Cathl *Nor* from 99; Dioc Dir of Ords from 99. *55 The Close, Norwich NR1 4EG* Tel (01603) 630934 E-mail michaelkitchener@norwich.anglican.org

KITCHIN, Kenneth. b 46. Trin Coll Bris. **d** 89 **p** 90. C Barrow St Mark *Carl* 89-93; C Dalton-in-Furness 93-95; P-in-c Dearham 95-01; P-in-c Clifton, Dean and Mosser from 01. *The Vicarage, 1 Clifton Gardens, Great Clifton, Workington CA14 1TT* Tel (01900) 603886

KITCHING, David Monro. b 26. New Coll Ox BA49. Ridley Hall Cam 80. **d** 82 **p** 83. C Hornchurch St Andr *Chelmsf* 82-86; P-in-c Graveley w Papworth St Agnes w Yelling etc *Ely* 86-90; rtd 91; Perm to Offic *Ely* from 91. *20 Victoria Park, Cambridge CB4 3EL* Tel (01223) 365687

KITCHING, Miss Elizabeth. b 49. Trent Park Coll of Educn CertEd74. St Jo Coll Nottm. **d** 01 **p** 02. C Northallerton w Kirby Sigston *York* from 01. *26 Helmsley Way, Romanby, Northallerton DL7 8SX* Tel (01609) 780975 Mobile 07889-425025

KITCHING, Paul. b 53. GTCL LTCL. Coll of Resurr Mirfield 80. **d** 83 **p** 84. C Hessle *York* 83-86; Youth Officer 86-98; P-in-c Crathorne 86-98; rtd 98; P-in-c Crathorne *York* from 98. *The Rectory, Crathorne, Yarm TS15 0BB* Tel (01642) 701158 Fax 700806

KITELEY, Robert John. b 51. Hull Univ BSc73 Univ of Wales (Abth) MSc75 Lon Univ PhD82. Trin Coll Bris DipTh83. **d** 83 **p** 84. C Bebington *Ches* 83-88; C Hoole 88-91; V Plas Newton 91-99; R Ashtead *Guildf* from 99. *The Rectory, Ashdene, Dene Road, Ashtead KT21 1EE* Tel (01372) 805182 Fax as telephone E-mail bobkiteley@ntlworld.com

KITLEY, David Buchan. b 53. St Jo Coll Dur BA. Trin Coll Bris 78. **d** 81 **p** 82. C Tonbridge St Steph *Roch* 81-84; C-in-c Southall Em CD *Lon* 84-91; V Dartford Ch Ch *Roch* from 91; RD Dartford from 98. *The Vicarage, 67 Shepherds Lane, Dartford DA1 2NS* Tel (01322) 220036

KITNEY, Miss Joan Olive Lily. b 22. Gilmore Ho 50. **dss** 60 **d** 87. Horsell *Guildf* 59-63; Chapl Asst Reading Hosps 63-79; Hermitage and Hampstead Norreys, Cold Ash etc *Ox* 80-84; NSM Staines St Mary and St Pet *Lon* 87-89; rtd 89; Perm to Offic *Ox* from 90. *54 Newtown Road, Newbury RG14 7BT* Tel (01635) 36416

KITTERINGHAM, Canon Ian. b 35. CCC Cam BA59 MA63. Westcott Ho Cam 59. **d** 61 **p** 62. C Rotherham *Sheff* 61-64; C Eltham H Trin *S'wark* 64-66; V Battersea St Mary-le-Park 66-73; V Reigate St Mark 73-80; V Caterham Valley 80-85; RD Caterham 84-85; V Wandsworth Common St Mary 85-00; RD Tooting 88-93; Hon Can S'wark Cathl 95-00; rtd 00; Perm to Offic *Cov* from 02. *17 Sandfield Road, Stratford-upon-Avon CV37 9AG* Tel (01789) 266384

KITTS, Joseph. b 27. Tyndale Hall Bris 59. **d** 60 **p** 61. C Parr *Liv* 60-63; C Bootle St Leon 63-66; V Southport SS Simon and Jude 66-74; USA 74-94; rtd 92. *Windyridge, Cottage Lane, St Martin's, Oswestry SY11 3BL* Tel (01691) 777090

KIVETT, Michael Stephen. b 50. Bethany Coll W Virginia BA72. Chr Th Sem Indiana MDiv76 Sarum & Wells Th Coll 76. **d** 77 **p** 78. C Harnham *Sarum* 77-80; C E Dereham *Nor* 80-83; R S Walsham 83-88; V Upton 83-88; Chapl Lt Plumstead Hosp 84-88; V Chard St Mary *B & W* 88-99; TR Chard and Distr from 99; RD Crewkerne and Ilminster 93-98. *The Vicarage, 2 Forton Road, Chard TA20 2HJ* Tel (01460) 62320 E-mail msk@fish.co.uk.

KLIMAS, Miss Lynda. b 58. Jes Coll Cam BA89 MA93. Cranmer Hall Dur 89. **d** 90 **p** 94. Par Dn Sandy *St Alb* 90-93; Par Dn Bishop's Stortford St Mich 93-94; C 94-98; P-in-c Weston from 98; C Baldock w Bygrave from 98. *The Vicarage, 14 Munts Meadow, Weston, Hitchin SG4 7AE* Tel (01462) 790330

KNAPMAN, Preb Hugh William Hartly. b 07. St D Coll Lamp BA33. **d** 32 **p** 33. C Henleaze *Bris* 32-36; C Woolcott Park 36-38; CF (TA) 33-37; V Long Ashton *B & W* 38-55; V Glastonbury St Jo 55-69; RD Glastonbury 56-69; P-in-c Greinton 60-68; Preb Wells Cathl 67-87; R Charlton Adam w Charlton Mackrell 69-75; rtd 75; Perm to Offic *B & W* 75-94. *24 Kings Gardens, Honiton EX14 1FL* Tel (01404) 44743

KNAPP, Antony Blair. b 48. Imp Coll Lon BSc68. N Ord Course 86. **d** 89 **p** 90. C Bolton St Jas w St Chrys *Bradf* 89-92; V Kettlewell w Conistone, Hubberholme etc 92-00; TR Swindon Dorcan *Bris* from 00. *23 Sedgebrook, Swindon SN3 6EY* Tel (01793) 525130 E-mail tonybknapp@aol.com

KNAPP, Bryan Thomas. b 61. Trin Coll Bris DipHE90 BA91. **d** 91 **p** 92. C S Gillingham *Roch* 91-95; V Chatham St Paul w All SS from 95. *The Vicarage, 2A Waghorn Street, Chatham ME4 5LT* Tel (01634) 845419

KNAPP, Jeremy Michael. b 67. Westhill Coll Birm BEd91. Ripon Coll Cuddesdon BTh99. **d** 99 **p** 00. C Hill *Birm* 99-02; TV Salter Street and Shirley from 02. *68 Tythe Barn Lane, Solihull B90 1RW* Tel 0121-733 6658 E-mail jeremy@toposcope.freeserve.co.uk

KNAPP (née STOCKER), Mrs Rachael Ann. b 64. Bris Univ BA86. Trin Coll Bris DipHE90 BA91. **d** 91 **p** 94. C Ditton *Roch* 91-95; C Chatham St Paul w All SS from 95. *The Vicarage, 2A Waghorn Street, Chatham ME4 5LT* Tel (01634) 845419

KNAPPER, Peter Charles. b 39. Lon Univ BA61. St Steph Ho Ox 61. **d** 63 **p** 64. C Carl H Trin *Carl* 63-68; V Westfield St Mary 68-76; V Bridekirk 76-83; P-in-c Blackheath Ascension *S'wark* 83-96; P-in-c Holmwood *Guildf* 96-03; TV Surrey Weald from 03. *The Vicarage, Horsham Road, Holmwood, Dorking RH5 4JX* Tel (01306) 889118 E-mail peter/pat@pknapper.fsnet.co.uk

KNARESBOROUGH, Suffragan Bishop of. *Vacant*

KNEE, Geoffrey. b 31. Whitelands Coll Lon CertEd71. CA Tr Coll 56 Glouc Sch of Min 91. **d** 92 **p** 93. NSM Hampton *Worc* 92-97; Chapl St Richard's Hospice Worc 95-97; NSM Badsey w Aldington and Offenham and Bretforton *Worc* 97; rtd 97; Perm to Offic *Worc* from 98. *8 Mayfair, Fairfield, Evesham WR11 1JJ* Tel (01386) 443574

KNEE, Jacob Samuel. b 66. LSE BSc(Econ)87 MSc(Econ)88 Ox Univ BA92. Ripon Coll Cuddesdon 90. **d** 93 **p** 94. C Ashby-de-la-Zouch St Helen w Coleorton *Leic* 93-96; C Boston *Linc* 96-00; Chapl Boston Coll of FE 96-00; V Cam w Stinchcombe *Glouc* from 00. *The Vicarage, Church Road, Cam, Dursley GL11 5PQ* Tel (01453) 542084 E-mail jknee@globalnet.co.uk

KNEE-ROBINSON, Keith Frederick. b 40. Thames Poly BSc75 MICE76. St Alb and Ox Min Course 99. **d** 01 **p** 02. OLM Caversham and Mapledurham *Ox* from 01. *Mill Cottage, Church Road, Bradfield, Reading RG7 6BX* Tel 0118-974 4526 E-mail kkrmill@globalnet.co.uk

KNEEN, Michael John. b 55. Univ Coll Lon BSc76 MSc77 St Jo Coll Dur BA85. Cranmer Hall Dur 83. **d** 86 **p** 87. C Bishop's Castle w Mainstone *Heref* 86-90; TV Bridgnorth, Tasley, Astley Abbotts, etc from 90. *41 Innage Lane, Bridgnorth WV16 4HS* Tel (01746) 766418 *or* 767174 E-mail mkneen@surfaid.org

KNELL, John George. b 35. Cant Sch of Min 79. **d** 82 **p** 83. Hd Master St Geo C of E Middle Sch Sheerness 80-87; NSM Sheerness H Trin w St Paul *Cant* 82-87; NSM Minster-in-Sheppey from 87. *11 Uplands Way, Queenborough Road, Sheerness ME12 3EF* Tel (01795) 665945

KNELL, Canon Raymond John. b 27. Qu Coll Cam BA48 MA52. Ridley Hall Coll 50. **d** 52 **p** 53. C Bishopwearmouth St Gabr *Dur* 52-57; C S Shields St Hilda 57-58; P-in-c Hebburn St Oswald 58-67; V Castleside 67-76; V Heworth St Mary 76-93; RD Gateshead 83-87; Hon Can Dur Cathl 87-93; rtd 93. *40 St Andrew's Drive, Low Fell, Gateshead NE9 6JU* Tel 0191-442 1069

KNICKERBOCKER, Driss Richard. b 39. Univ of Michigan BA63 MDiv68 Ox Univ DPhil81. **d** 68 **p** 69. USA 68-76 and from 85; C St Marylebone w H Trin *Lon* 78-81; C Chelsea St Luke 81-83; P-in-c Isleworth St Fran 83-85. *20 Olive Avenue, Rehoboth Beach, DE 19971, USA*

KNIFTON, Gladys Elizabeth. b 52. SRN73 SCM75 FE TCert84 Kingston Univ DipHE94 BSc95. NTMTC 95. **d** 98 **p** 99. NSM Churt *Guildf* 98-01; Chapl Surrey Hants Borders NHS Trust from 01. *Bryanston, Boundary Road, Grayshott, Hindhead GU26 6TX* Tel (01428) 604977 Fax as telephone E-mail elizabeth@knifton.com

KNIGHT, The Very Revd Alexander Francis (Alec). b 39. St Cath Coll Cam BA61 MA65. Wells Th Coll. **d** 63 **p** 64. C Hemel Hempstead *St Alb* 63-68; Chapl Taunton Sch 68-75; Dir Bloxham Project 75-81; Dir of Studies Aston Tr Scheme 81-83; P-in-c Easton and Martyr Worthy *Win* 83-91; Adn Basingstoke 90-98; Can Res Win Cathl 91-98; Dean Linc from 98. *The Deanery, Atherstone Place, 12 Eastgate, Lincoln LN2 1QG* Tel (01522) 523608 E-mail dean@lincolncathedral.com

KNIGHT, Canon Andrew James. b 50. Grey Coll Dur BA72 Ox Univ BA74 MA81. Wycliffe Hall Ox 72. **d** 75 **p** 76. Min Can Brecon Cathl *S & B* 75-78; C Brecon w Battle 75-78; C Morriston 78-82; V 89-00; V Llanwrtyd w Llanddulas in Tir Abad etc 82-89; RD Cwmtawe 94-00; Can Res Brecon Cathl from 98; V Sketty from 00. *The Vicarage, De La Beche Road, Sketty, Swansea SA2 9AR* Tel (01792) 202767

KNIGHT, Mrs Ann. b 54. Lanc Univ CertEd75. Trin Coll Bris DipHE83 DPS84. dss 84 **d** 87 **p** 94. Wigan St Jas w St Thos *Liv* 84-87; Par Dn 87-90; C Costessey *Nor* 90-96; R Gt and Lt Ellingham, Rockland and Shropham etc 96-03; Chapl Norwich Primary Care Trust 96-02; P-in-c Worthen *Heref* from 03; P-in-c Hope w Shelve from 03. *The Rectory, Worthen, Shrewsbury SY5 9HN* Tel (01743) 891930

KNIGHT, Arthur Clifford Edwin. b 42. Univ of Wales BSc64. Wells Th Coll 64. **d** 66 **p** 67. C Llangyfelach and Morriston *S & B* 66-68; C Oystermouth 68-73; Chapl RAF 73-95; Perm to Offic *Heref* 95-97; P-in-c Brant Broughton and Beckingham *Linc* 97-99; P-in-c Credenhill w Brinsop and Wormsley etc *Heref* from 99. *26 Meadow Drive, Credenhill, Hereford HR4 7EE* Tel (01432) 760530

KNIGHT, Mrs Barbara. b 46. St Alb Minl Tr Scheme 86. **d** 90 **p** 94. NSM Weston *St Alb* 90-95; NSM Ardeley 90-95; C Norton 95-97; R Barkway, Reed and Buckland w Barley from 97. *The Rectory, 135 High Street, Barkway, Royston SG8 8ED* Tel (01763) 848077 Fax as telephone

KNIGHT, Mrs Barbara Mary. b 43. SRN64 SCM70. EMMTC 94. **d** 97 **p** 98. NSM Market Harborough and The Transfiguration etc *Leic* 97-99; C Church Langton cum Tur Langton 99-02; P-in-c Billesdon and Skeffington 02; R Church Langton cum Tur Langton etc from 02. *The Vicarage, Gaulby Road, Billesdon, Leicester LE7 9AG* Tel 0116-259 6321 E-mail revbarbarak@btopenworld.com

KNIGHT, Brenda Evelyn. b 27. St Alb and Ox Min Course 96. **d** 98 **p** 99. OLM Wheatley *Ox* from 98. *22 Middle Road, Stanton St John, Oxford OX33 1HD* Tel (01865) 351227

KNIGHT, Christopher. b 61. Wycliffe Hall Ox 94. **d** 96 **p** 97. C Banbury *Ox* 96-98; C Banbury St Paul 98-01; Chapl HM Pris Lowdham Grange from 01. *HM Prison Lowdham Grange, Nottingham NG14 7DQ* Tel 0115-966 9308 E-mail 2cv@clara.net

KNIGHT, Christopher Colson. b 52. Ex Univ BSc73 Man Univ PhD77 SS Coll Cam MA90. Sarum & Wells Th Coll BTh83. **d** 81 **p** 82. Chapl St Mary's Cathl *Edin* 81-84; V Chesterton *Cov* 84-87; R Lighthorne 84-87; V Newbold Pacey w Moreton Morrell 84-87; Chapl and Fell SS Coll Cam 87-92; Sen Research Assoc St Edm Coll Cam from 92. *Hope Cottage, Hindringham Road, Walsingham NR22 6DR* Tel (01328) 820108

KNIGHT, David Alan. b 59. Lanc Univ BA81. Ripon Coll Cuddesdon 82. **d** 85 **p** 86. C Stretford All SS *Man* 85-88; C Charlestown 88-89; TV Pendleton St Thos w Charlestown 89-94; V Tysoe w Oxhill and Whatcote *Cov* from 94. *The Vicarage, Peacock Lane, Tysoe, Warwick CV35 0SG* Tel (01295) 680201 Fax as telephone E-mail david.knight20@virgin.net

KNIGHT, David Charles. b 32. Clare Coll Cam BA55 MA59. Tyndale Hall Bris 55. **d** 57 **p** 58. C Cambridge St Paul *Ely* 57-58; C St Alb Ch Ch *St Alb* 58-61; C-in-c Wimbledon Em Ridgway Prop Chpl *S'wark* 61-67; Publications Sec BCMS 67-68; Ed Asst *The Christian* 68-69; V Lannarth *Truro* 69-75; RD Carnmarth N 72-75; V Fremington *Ex* 75-83; C Edmonton All SS w St Mich *Lon* 83; Chapl N Middx Hosp 83; rtd 94; Perm to Offic *Chelmsf* from 94. *Magnolia Cottage, Cage End, Hatfield Broad Oak, Bishop's Stortford CM22 7HT* Tel (01279) 718650

KNIGHT, Canon David Charles. b 45. ATCL63 Lon Univ BA66 St Edm Hall Ox BA68 MA73. St Steph Ho Ox 68. **d** 70 **p** 71. C Northwood H Trin *Lon* 70-73; C Stevenage All SS Pin Green *St Alb* 73-77; C Cippenham CD *Ox* 77-78; TV W Slough 78-83; Dep Min Can Windsor from 81; Ecum Officer to Bp Willesden 83-91; R Lt Stanmore St Lawr *Lon* 83-91; Prec and Can Res Chelmsf Cathl *Chelmsf* 91-01; V Ranmoor *Sheff* from 01. *The Vicarage, 389A Fulwood Road, Sheffield S10 3GA* Tel 0114-230 1671 *or* 230 1199 Fax 0114-263 0158 E-mail dknight@fish.co.uk

KNIGHT, Canon David Lansley. b 33. Em Coll Cam BA58 MA61 PGCE76. Ridley Hall Cam 57. **d** 59 **p** 60. C Chatham St Steph *Roch* 59-63; C Plymouth St Andr *Ex* 63-65; V Gravesend St Aid *Roch* 65-71; V Bexley St Mary 71-98; RD Sidcup 93-97; Hon Can Roch Cathl 97; rtd 98; Perm to Offic *Chich* from 98. *1 Newlands Avenue, Bexhill-on-Sea TN39 4HA* Tel (01424) 212120

KNIGHT, Donald. b 31. Bris Univ BA55 Man Univ DASE73. Tyndale Hall Bris 51 Qu Coll Birm 82. **d** 83 **p** 84. C Chell *Lich* 83-87; R St Ruan w St Grade and Landewednack *Truro* 87-91; R High Offley and Norbury *Lich* 91-99; Perm to Offic *Lich* from 00. *4 Newman Close, Stone ST15 8FR* Tel (01785) 812427

KNIGHT, Eric Frank Walter. b 19. St Paul's Coll Grahamstown. **d** 51 **p** 52. S Africa 51-59; C Knysna 51-55; R Victoria W w Carnarvon 55-57; R Beaconsfield 57-59; R Wick *Mor* 61-63; R Girvan *Glas* 63-68; V Charlton All Saints *Sarum* 68-89; rtd 89. *clo Ms Gail Grainger, Receivership Office, Greenlane Hospital, Devizes SN10 5DS* Tel (01380) 731317

KNIGHT, Frances Mary. b 48. EMMTC. **d** 03. NSM Braunstone *Leic* from 03. *32 Aster Way, Burbage, Hinckley LE10 2UG* Tel (01455) 618218

KNIGHT, Gavin Rees. b 65. St Andr Univ MTheol94. Ripon Coll Cuddesdon MTh96. **d** 98 **p** 99. C Solihull *Birm* 98-02; P-in-c Fulham St Andr Fulham Fields *Lon* from 02. *St Andrew's Vicarage, 10 St Andrew's Road, London W14 9SX* Tel (020) 7385 5023 Fax as telephone E-mail vicar@fulhamfields.org *or* grk@fish.co.uk

KNIGHT, Henry Christian. b 34. Fitzw Ho Cam BA62 MA66. Ridley Hall Cam 62. **d** 63 **p** 64. Succ Bradf Cathl *Bradf* 63-64; Chapl 64-66; Israel 67-79; CMJ 79-86; V Allithwaite *Carl* 86-93; rtd 93; Perm to Offic *Leic* from 93. *20 Saxon Way, Ashby-de-la-Zouch LE65 2JR* Tel (01530) 460709

KNIGHT, Canon John Bernard. b 34. Fuller Th Sem California DMin91 ACIS60. Oak Hill Th Coll. **d** 65 **p** 66. C Morden *S'wark* 65-69; USA 69-71; V Summerfield *Birm* from 71; Hon Can Birm Cathl from 01. *Christ Church Vicarage, 64 Selwyn Road, Birmingham B16 0SW* Tel 0121-454 2689 E-mail lollard@online.net

KNIGHT, John Francis Alan MacDonald. b 36. Coll of Resurr Mirfield 59. **d** 61 **p** 62. S Rhodesia 61-65; Rhodesia 65-80; Zimbabwe 80-87; Dean Mutare 81-87; TR Northampton Em *Pet* 87-97; RD Northn 88-92; P-in-c Greens Norton w Bradden and Lichborough from 97; Bp's Adv for Min of Healing from 99.

The Rectory, Greens Norton, Towcester NN12 8BL Tel (01327) 359508 E-mail jfam@jfam40.freeserve.co.uk

KNIGHT, Jonathan Morshead. b 59. Fitzw Coll Cam BA81 MA85 W Lon Inst of HE PGCE82 Jes Coll Cam DipTh83 PhD91 Jes Coll Ox MA87 Worc Coll Ox DPhil02 Sheff Univ PGCE00 SNTS99. Wycliffe Hall Ox 86. **d** 88 **p** 89. C Hillingdon St Jo *Lon* 88-91; NSM Baslow *Derby* 91-92; NSM Curbar and Stoney Middleton 91-92; Lect Bibl Studies Sheff Univ *Sheff* 91-92; Research Fell 92-94; NSM Sheff St Paul 92-94; Bp's Research Asst *Ely* 94-98; Min Whittlesford LEP 95-96; Bp's Dom Chapl 96; Sec Doctrine Commn 96-98; P-in-c Holywell w Needingworth *Ely* 98-01; Tutor Westcott Ho Cam 98-99; Dir Studies Focus Chr Inst Cambridge 99-02; OCF from 99; CF (TAVR) from 00; Hon Lect Th Kent Univ from 00; Chapl Worc Coll Ox 02-03. *Address temp unknown* E-mail jonathanknight5@hotmail.com

KNIGHT, Mrs June. b 28. Glouc Sch of Min 85. **d** 87 **p** 94. NSM Leckhampton SS Phil and Jas w Cheltenham St Jas *Glouc* 87-96; rtd 96; Perm to Offic *Glouc* from 96. *31 St Michael's Road, Woodlands, Cheltenham GL51 5RP* Tel (01242) 517911

KNIGHT, Mrs June Elizabeth. b 42. St Alb Minl Tr Scheme 90. **d** 93 **p** 94. NSM Stanstead Abbots *St Alb* 93-96; NSM Gt Amwell w St Margaret's and Stanstead Abbots 96-97; NSM Lt Hadham w Albury 97-98; NSM Bishop's Stortford St Mich from 98. *The White Cottage, Albury Hall Park, Albury, Ware SG11 2HX* Tel (01279) 771756 E-mail june.knight@whitecott.f9.co.uk

KNIGHT, Keith Kenneth. b 36. Southn Univ BSc58. Wycliffe Hall Ox 59. **d** 62 **p** 63. C Lower Darwen St Jas *Blackb* 62-64; C Leyland St Andr 64-68; P-in-c Blackb All SS 68-71; Dioc Youth Chapl 71-88; Hon C Burnley St Pet 71-74; Warden Scargill Ho 88-01; rtd 01; Perm to Offic *Bradf* from 01. *4 The Hawthorns, Sutton-in-Craven, Keighley BD20 8BP* Tel (01535) 632920

KNIGHT, Kenneth William. b 15. TD50. Wycliffe Hall Ox. **d** 61 **p** 62. C Paignton Ch Ch *Ex* 61-63; V Holbeton 63-91; rtd 91; Perm to Offic *Ex* from 91. *West Heanton, Buckland Filleigh, Beaworthy EX21 5PJ* Tel (01409) 281754

KNIGHT, Mrs Margaret Owen. b 34. Oak Hill Th Coll 78. **dss** 80 **d** 87 **p** 94. Chorleywood St Andr *St Alb* 80-87; Par Dn 87-94; C from 94; rtd 94. *15A Blacketts Wood Drive, Chorleywood, Rickmansworth WD3 5PY* Tel (01923) 283832 E-mail margaret.standrews@btinternet.com

KNIGHT, Michael Richard. b 47. St Jo Coll Dur BA69 MA79 Fitzw Coll Cam BA73 MA78 St Cross Coll Ox MA92. Westcott Ho Cam 71. **d** 74 **p** 75. C Bishop's Stortford St Mich *St Alb* 74-75; C Bedford St Andr 75-79; Chapl Angl Students Glas 79-86; V Riddings and Ironville *Derby* 86-91; Lib Pusey Ho 91-94; Fell St Cross Coll Ox 92-94; V Chesterfield St Mary and All SS *Derby* from 94. *28 Cromwell Road, Chesterfield S40 4TH* Tel (01246) 232937 *or* 206506 E-mail vicar.chesterfield@virgin.net

KNIGHT, Paul James Joseph. b 50. Oak Hill Th Coll. **d** 84 **p** 85. C Broadwater St Mary *Chich* 84-87; R Itchingfield w Slinfold 87-92; Chapl Highgate Sch Lon from 92. *15A Bishopswood Road, London N6 4PB* Tel (020) 8348 9211 *or* 8340 1524

KNIGHT, Capt Paul Jeremy. b 53. **d** 94 **p** 95. CA from 77; C Moreton Say *Lich* 94-97; V Birstall *Wakef* from 97. *St Peter's Vicarage, King's Drive, Birstall, Batley WF17 9JJ* Tel (01924) 473715 Fax as telephone E-mail rev.paul@ntlworld.com

KNIGHT, Peter John. b 51. Lon Univ AKC73 CertEd77. Sarum & Wells Th Coll 79. **d** 80 **p** 81. C Greenford H Cross *Lon* 80-83; C Langley Marish *Ox* 83; NSM W Acton St Martin *Lon* 89-90; C E Acton St Dunstan w St Thos 90-92; V Malden St Jo *S'wark* 92-02; Chapl HM Pris Long Lartin from 02. *HM Prison Long Lartin, South Littleton, Evesham WR11 5TZ* Tel (01386) 835100

KNIGHT, Peter Malcolm. b 55. DA81 DRCOG83 MRCGP85 DTM&H86 Cam Univ BA76 Lon Hosp MB, BS76. Trin Coll Bris BA94. **d** 94 **p** 95. C Quidenham *Nor* 94-97; C Quidenham Gp 97; R Thurton from 97; RD Loddon from 99. *The Rectory, 29 Ashby Road, Thurton, Norwich NR14 6AX* Tel (01508) 480738

KNIGHT, Peter Michael. b 47. St Luke's Coll Ex BEd71. Trin Coll Bris DipHE92. **d** 92 **p** 93. C Bris Ch the Servant Stockwood *Bris* 92-95; Chapl St Brendan's Sixth Form Coll 92-94; C W Swindon and the Lydiards *Bris* 95-96; TV from 96. *The Vicarage, The Butts, Lydiard Millicent, Swindon SN5 3LR* Tel (01793) 772417 E-mail peter@knight15.freeserve.co.uk

KNIGHT, Philip Stephen. b 50. Ian Ramsey Coll 74. **d** 77 **p** 78. C Pennycross *Ex* 77-80; C Epsom St Martin *Guildf* 80-83; V Clay Hill St Jo *Lon* 83-86; TV Washfield, Stoodleigh, Withleigh etc *Ex* 86-90; Chapl ATC from 86; Chapl S Warks Hosps 90-94; Chapl S Warks Health Care NHS Trust from 94. *37 Lodge Crescent, Warwick CV34 5BW* and *Warwick Hospital, Lakin Road, Warwick CV34 5BW* Tel (01926) 403053 *or* 495321 ext 4121 Fax 482603 E-mail stephen.knight@swh.nhs.uk

KNIGHT, Canon Roger George. b 41. Culham Coll Ox CertEd63. Linc Th Coll 65. **d** 67 **p** 68. C Bris St Andr Hartcliffe *Bris* 67-69; Hd Master Twywell Sch Kettering 69-74; Lic to Offic *Pet* 69-74; V Naseby 74-79; P-in-c Haselbeech 74-79; R Clipston w Naseby and Haselbech 79-82; P-in-c Kelmarsh 79-82; TR Corby SS Pet and Andr w Gt and Lt Oakley 82-88; R Irthlingborough 88-99;

RD Higham 89-94; R Burton Latimer 99-03; Can Pet Cathl 92-03; rtd 03; Perm to Offic *Pet* from 03. *37 School Lane, Higham Ferrers, Rushden NN10 8HQ*

KNIGHT, Roger Ivan. b 54. K Coll Lon BD79 AKC79. Ripon Coll Cuddesdon 79. **d** 80 **p** 81. C Orpington All SS *Roch* 80-84; C St Laur in Thanet *Cant* 84-87; R Cuxton and Halling *Roch* from 87. *The Rectory, 6 Rochester Road, Cuxton, Rochester ME2 1AF* Tel (01634) 717134 E-mail rogerknight@aol.com

KNIGHT, Ms Sue Elizabeth. b 47. Southlands Coll Lon CertEd68. SEITE 01. **d** 03. *101 Lyme Farm Road, London SE12 8JH* Tel (020) 8852 1781

KNIGHT, Mrs Susan Margaret. **d** 02 **p** 03. C Clydach *S & B* from 02. *21 Faraday Road, Clydach, Swansea SA6 5JSA* Tel (01792) 846264

KNIGHT, Suzanne. **d** 00 **p** 01. NSM Reading St Jo *Ox* from 00. *9 Victoria Way, Reading RG1 3HD* Tel 0118-967 5645 E-mail suz-knight@yahoo.co.uk

KNIGHT, William Lawrence. b 39. Univ Coll Lon BSc61 PhD65. Coll of Resurr Mirfield 75. **d** 77 **p** 78. C Bp's Hatfield *St Alb* 77-81; Asst Chapl Brussels Cathl *Eur* 81-84; V Pet H Spirit Bretton *Pet* 84-89; P-in-c Marholm 84-89; TR Riverside *Ox* from 89. *St Mary's Vicarage, London Road, Datchet, Slough SL3 9JW* Tel (01753) 580467 E-mail knightsmvd@dial.pipex.com

KNIGHTS, Christopher Hammond. b 61. St Jo Coll Dur BA83 PhD88 Liv Univ PGCTH00. Linc Th Coll 87. **d** 89 **p** 90. C Stockton St Pet *Dur* 89-92; C Chich St Paul and St Pet *Chich* 92-94; Tutor Chich Th Coll 92-94; V Ashington *Newc* 94-00; V Monkseaton St Mary from 00; Dioc Moderator Reader Tr from 03. *St Mary's Vicarage, 77 Holywell Avenue, Whitley Bay NE26 3AG* Tel 0191-252 2484 *or* 251 4216 E-mail the.knights@tiscali.co.uk

KNIGHTS, James William. b 34. AKC66. **d** 67 **p** 68. C Kettering St Andr *Pet* 67-71; V Braunston w Brooke 71-81; V Dudley St Jo *Worc* 81-97; rtd 97; Perm to Offic *Worc* from 98. *192 Brook Farm Road, Malvern WR14 3SL* Tel (01684) 561358

KNIGHTS JOHNSON, Nigel Anthony. b 52. Ealing Tech Coll BA74 Westmr Coll Ox MTh99. Wycliffe Hall Ox 78. **d** 80 **p** 81. C Beckenham Ch Ch *Roch* 80-84; CF from 84; Dep Asst Chapl Gen from 00. *clo MOD Chaplains (Army)* Tel (01980) 615508 Fax 615800

KNILL-JONES, Jonathan Waring (Jack). b 58. Univ Coll Lon BSc79. St Jo Coll Nottm Dip Th Studies 90. **d** 90 **p** 91. C Northolt W End St Jos *Lon* 90-94; C Hayes St Nic CD 94-99; V Airedale w Fryston *Wakef* from 99. *The Vicarage, The Mount, Castleford WF10 3JL* Tel (01977) 553157 E-mail jackknill@aol.com

KNOPP, Alexander Edward Robert. b 09. St Jo Coll Cam BA33 MA37. Ridley Hall Cam 32. **d** 34 **p** 35. C Loughton St Mary *Chelmsf* 34-38; C Prittlewell St Mary 38-40; R Nevendon 40; R N Benfleet w Nevendon 41-48; V Walthamstow St Jo 48-50; V Pampisford *Ely* 50-59; V Babraham 50-59; R Quendon w Rickling *Chelmsf* 59-68; R Gt Yeldham 68-73; R Gt w Lt Snoring *Nor* 73-76; rtd 76; Perm to Offic *Ely* 77-00. *6 Rose Lane, Melbourn, Royston SG8 6AD* Tel (01763) 262143

KNOTT, Christopher Rodney. b 42. Open Univ BA77. Kelham Th Coll 64. **d** 68 **p** 69. C Withycombe Raleigh *Ex* 68-72; TV Aylesbeare and Farringdon 72-75; TV Woodbury Salterton 72-75; TV Clyst St George, Aylesbeare, Clyst Honiton etc 75-76; TR Lynton, Brendon, Countisbury, Lynmouth etc 76-81; R Highweek and Teigngrace from 81. *The Rectory, 15 Stoneleigh Close, Newton Abbot TQ12 1PX* Tel (01626) 354949

KNOTT, Graham Keith. b 53. Oak Hill Th Coll BA80. **d** 80 **p** 81. C Normanton *Derby* 80-83; C Ripley 83-87; TV Newark w Hawton, Cotham and Shelton *S'well* 87-89; TV Newark 89-97; P-in-c Mansfield St Jo from 97; AD Mansfield from 03. *The Vicarage, St John Street, Mansfield NG18 1QH* Tel (01623) 625999 E-mail st.johns.church@ukgateway.net

KNOTT, Janet Patricia. b 50. Avery Hill Coll CertEd71. S Dios Minl Tr Scheme MTS91. **d** 92 **p** 94. NSM Clutton w Cameley *B & W* 92-99; Chapl R Sch Bath 94-98; Chapl R High Sch Bath 98-99; R Farmborough, Marksbury and Stanton Prior *B & W* from 99; Chapl Bath Spa Univ Coll from 99. *The Rectory, Church Lane, Farmborough, Bath BA3 1AN* Tel (01761) 479311 E-mail jan@knott111.fsnet.co.uk

KNOTT, John Wensley. b 51. FIA84 Fitzw Coll Cam MA75. S Dios Minl Tr Scheme 87. **d** 90 **p** 91. NSM Canford Magna *Sarum* 90-94; Perm to Offic *St Alb* from 94. *11 Shrublands Road, Berkhamsted HP4 3JH* Tel (01442) 875005

KNOTT, Montague Hardwick. b 05. Oak Hill Th Coll 54. **d** 55 **p** 56. C Walthamstow St Mary *Chelmsf* 55-57; V Blackmore 57-80; P-in-c Stondon Massey 80; V Blackmore and Stondon Massey 80-85; rtd 85; Perm to Offic *Chelmsf* from 85. *1 Wadham Close, Ingatestone CM4 0DL* Tel (01277) 352024

KNOTT, Pamela Frances. *See* IVE, Mrs Pamela Frances

KNOWD, George Alexander. b 31. St Deiniol's Hawarden. **d** 88 **p** 89. NSM Aghalurcher w Tattykeeran, Cooneen etc *Clogh* 88-91; Dioc Communications Officer 89-90 and 92-97; NSM Ballybay w Mucknoe and Clontibret 91-92; C 92-94; I 94-97; I Clonmel w Innislounagh, Tullaghmelan etc *C & O* from 97. *The Rectory, 7 Linden Lea, Silversprings, Clonmel, Co Tipperary, Irish*

KNOWERS, Stephen John. b 49. K Coll Lon BD72 AKC72. **d** 73 **p** 74. C Bp's Hatfield *St Alb* 73-77; C Cheshunt 77-81; P-in-c Barnet Vale St Mark 81-83; V 83-85; Chapl S Bank Poly *S'wark* 85-92; Chapl S Bank Univ 92-94; V Croydon St Pet from 94. *20 Haling Park Road, South Croydon CR2 6NE* Tel (020) 8688 4715 E-mail ulbo@appleonline.net

KNOWLES, Canon Andrew William Allen. b 46. St Cath Coll Cam BA68 MA72. St Jo Coll Nottm 69. **d** 71 **p** 72. C Leic H Trin *Leic* 71-74; C Cambridge H Trin *Ely* 74-77; C Woking St Jo *Guildf* 77-81; V Goldsworth Park 81-93; V Wyke 93-98; Dioc Officer Educn and Development of Lay People 93-98; Can Res Chelmsf Cathl *Chelmsf* from 98. *2 Harlings Grove, Chelmsford CM1 1YQ* Tel (01245) 355041 E-mail andrew.knowles@btinternet.com

KNOWLES, Charles Howard. b 43. Sheff Univ BSc65 Fitzw Coll Cam BA69 MA73. Westcott Ho Cam 67. **d** 69 **p** 70. C Bilborough St Jo *S'well* 69-72; V Choral S'well Minster 72-82; V Cinderhill 82-94; AD Nottingham W 91-94; V Cov St Mary *Cov* from 94; AD Cov S from 96. *St Mary Magdalen's Vicarage, Craven Street, Coventry CV5 8DT* Tel (024) 7667 5838 E-mail charles.knowles@dial.pipex.com

KNOWLES, Clay. *See* KNOWLES, Melvin Clay

KNOWLES, Clifford. b 35. Open Univ BA82. NW Ord Course 74. **d** 77 **p** 78. C Urmston *Man* 77-80; V Chadderton St Luke 80-87; V Heywood St Luke w All So 87-95; AD Heywood and Middleton 92-95; Perm to Offic *Linc* 95-98; rtd 00. *12B Far Lane, Coleby, Lincoln LN5 0AH* Tel (01522) 810720

KNOWLES, Dorothy Joy. b 20. Gilmore Ho 64. **dss** 69 **d** 89. Finham *Cov* 69-72; Canley 72-76; Styvechale 76-84; rtd 84; Asst Chapl Harnhill Cen for Chr Healing 88-93; Perm to Offic *Ex* from 95. *8 Station Road, Topsham, Exeter EX3 0DT* Tel (01392) 874708

KNOWLES, Eric Gordon. b 44. WMMTC 79. **d** 82 **p** 83. NSM Gt Malvern St Mary *Worc* 82-83; NSM Malvern H Trin and St Jas 83-90; NSM Lt Malvern, Malvern Wells and Wyche 90-99; NSM Lt Malvern 99-00; P-in-c from 00. *45 Wykewane, Malvern WR14 2XD* Tel (01684) 567439

KNOWLES, George. b 37. **d** 95 **p** 96. NSM Hucknall Torkard *S'well* 95-02; rtd 02; Perm to Offic *S'well* from 02. *8 North Hill Avenue, Hucknall, Nottingham NG15 7FE* Tel 0115-955 9822

KNOWLES, The Ven George Woods Atkin. b 21. TCD BA44 MA47. **d** 44 **p** 45. C Ardoyne *C & O* 44-46; C Knockbreda *D & D* 46-49; I Ballyscullion *D & R* 49-63; I Drumachose 63-89; Can Derry Cathl 75-86; Adn Derry 86-89; rtd 89. *22 Shanreagh Park, Limavady BT49 0SF* Tel (028) 7172 2298

✠**KNOWLES, The Rt Revd Graeme Paul.** b 51. AKC73. St Aug Coll Cant 73. **d** 74 **p** 75 **c** 03. C St Peter-in-Thanet *Cant* 74-79; C Leeds St Pet *Ripon* 79-81; Chapl and Prec Portsm Cathl *Portsm* 81-87; Chapter Clerk 85-87; V Leigh Park 87-93; RD Havant 90-93; Adn Portsm 93-99; Dean Carl 99-03; Bp S & M from 03. *The Bishop's House, Quarterbridge Road, Douglas IM2 3RF* Tel (01624) 622108 Fax 672890

KNOWLES, Mrs Jane Frances. b 44. GGSM66 Lon Inst of Educn TCert67. Ox Min Course CBTS93. **d** 93 **p** 94. NSM Sandhurst *Ox* 93-97; C Wargrave 97-99; P-in-c Ramsden, Finstock and Fawler, Leafield etc 99-01; V from 01. *The Vicarage, Mount Skippett, Ramsden, Chipping Norton OX7 3AP* Tel (01993) 868687 Fax 868534 E-mail jane.knowles@telinco.co.uk

KNOWLES, John Geoffrey. b 48. Man Univ BSc69 Lon Univ MSc75 FRSA. WMMTC 95. **d** 98 **p** 99. NSM The Lickey *Birm* 98-99. *61 Newlands Road, Glasgow G43 2JP* Tel 0141-632 9703

KNOWLES, Margaret Irene. b 48. EAMTC 96. **d** 99 **p** 00. C Gt Yarmouth *Nor* 99-03; TV from 03; Chapl Norfolk Mental Health Care NHS Trust from 00. *21 Hamilton Road, Great Yarmouth NR30 4ND* Tel and fax (01493) 857292 Mobile 07855-165008 E-mail irene.knowles@ntlworld.com

KNOWLES, Melvin Clay. b 43. Stetson Univ (USA) BA66 Ex Univ MA73 Ox Univ DipTh76. Ripon Coll Cuddesdon 75. **d** 77 **p** 78. C Minchinhampton *Glouc* 77-80; St Helena 80-82; TV Haywards Heath St Wilfrid *Chich* 82-88; Adult Educn Adv 88-94; TR Burgess Hill St Jo w St Edw 94-00; V Burgess Hill St Jo from 00. *St John's Vicarage, Park Road, Burgess Hill RH15 8HG* Tel (01444) 232582

KNOWLES, The Very Revd Philip John. b 48. MA PhD BTh LTCL ALCM LLAM. CITC 76. **d** 76 **p** 77. C Lisburn St Paul *Conn* 76-79; I Cloonclare w Killasnett and Lurganboy *K, E & A* 79-87; I Gorey w Kilnahue *C & O* 87-89; I Gorey w Kilnahue, Leskinfere and Ballycanew 89-95; Preb Ferns Cathl 91-95; Dean Cashel from 95; I Cashel w Magorban, Tipperary, Clonbeg etc from 95; Chan Waterford Cathl from 95; Chan Lismore Cathl from 95; Can Ossory and Leighlin Cathls from 96. *The Deanery, Cashel, Co Tipperary, Irish Republic* Tel (00353) (62) 61232

KNOWLES, Richard John. b 47. EAMTC 00. **d** 01 **p** 02. C Burlingham St Edmund w Lingwood, Strumpshaw etc *Nor* from 01. *21 Hamilton Road, Great Yarmouth NR30 4ND* Tel (01493) 857292 Mobile 07855-165008

KNOWLES-BROWN, Canon John Henry. b 30. AKC53. **d** 54 **p** 55. C Hertford St Andr *St Alb* 54-58; C Bushey 58-61; Chapl RAF 61-65; C-in-c Farley Hill St Jo CD *St Alb* 65-69; V Farley Hill St Jo 69-72; V Totteridge 72-95; RD Barnet 79-89; Hon Can St Alb 85-95; rtd 95; Perm to Offic *Ex* from 97. *1 Ascerton Close, Sidmouth EX10 9BS* Tel (01395) 579286

KNOWLING, Richard Charles. b 46. K Coll Lon BSc67 St Edm Hall Ox BA70 MA89. St Steph Ho Ox 69. **d** 71 **p** 72. C Hobs Moat *Birm* 71-75; C Shrewsbury St Mary w All SS and St Mich *Lich* 75-77; V Rough Hills 77-83; Dir Past Th Coll of Resurr Mirfield 83-90; V Palmers Green St Jo *Lon* from 90; AD Enfield 96-01. *St John's Vicarage, 1 Bourne Hill, London N13 4DA* Tel (020) 8886 1348 Fax 8351 9916 E-mail richard.knowling@london.anglican.org

KNOX, Geoffrey Martin. b 44. Dur Univ BA66 DipTh67 Sheff City Coll of Educn DipEd73. St Chad's Coll Dur 63. **d** 67 **p** 68. C Newark St Mary *S'well* 67-72; Perm to Offic *Derby* 72-74; V Woodville 74-81; RD Repton 79-81; V Long Eaton St Laur 81-00; V Somercotes from 00. *The Vicarage, 114 Nottingham Road, Somercotes, Alfreton DE55 4LY* Tel (01773) 602840

KNOX, Iain John Edward. b 46. TCD BA70 MA74 Hull Univ BPhil76. Irish Sch of Ecum 74 CITC 71. **d** 71 **p** 72. C Belfast Malone St Jo *Conn* 71-74; Bp's Dom Chapl 72-74; Perm to Offic *D & R* 74-76; I Gweedore Union 76-80; I Clonmel w Innislounagh, Tullaghmelan etc *C & O* 80-96; Bp's Dom Chapl 82-97; Press & Radio Officer (Cashel) 90-95; Dioc Info Officer (Cashel and Waterford) 92-95; Lic to Offic from 96. *Rossnowlagh, Heywood Road, Clonmel, Co Tipperary, Irish Republic* Tel (00353) (52) 27107 Mobile 87-236 8186

KNOX, Thomas Anthony. b 31. BA. Ely Th Coll. **d** 56 **p** 57. C Poplar All SS w St Frideswide *Lon* 56-59; C Eastbourne St Andr *Chich* 59-61; C Welwyn *St Alb* 61-66; V Boreham Wood St Mich 66-71; R Puttenham w Long Marston 71-79; R Toddington 79-96; rtd 96. *Croft Cottage, Little Blenheim, Yarnton, Oxford OX5 1LX* Tel (01865) 378672

KOBE, Bishop of. *See* FURUMOTO, The Rt Revd John Junichiro

KOFORIDUA, Bishop of. *See* OKINE, The Most Revd Robert Garshong Allotey

KOHNER, Canon Jeno George. b 31. K Coll Lon BD56 AKC56 Concordia Univ Montreal MA82. Westcott Ho Cam 56. **d** 57 **p** 58. C Eccleston St Thos *Liv* 57-60; Canada from 60; Hon Can Montreal from 75. *850 Lakeshore Drive, Apt H3, Dorval PQ, Canada, H9S 5T9* Tel (001) (514) 631 0066

✠**KOLINI, The Most Revd Emmanuel Musaba.** b 44. Balya Bible Coll Uganda 67 Can Werner Coll Burundi 68 Bp Tucker Coll Mukono 75. **d** 69 **c** 80. Uganda 69-79; Kyangwali 69-74; Bulinda 77-79; Zaïre 80-97; Adn Bukavu 80; Asst Bp Bukavu 81-85; Bp Shaba 86-97; Bp Kigali from 97; Abp Rwanda from 98. *PO Box 61, Kigali, Rwanda* Tel (00250) 576340 Fax 573213 *or* 576504 E-mail ek@rwanda1.com

KOLOGARAS, Mrs Linda Audrey. b 48. Humberside Univ BA97. EMMTC 89. **d** 95 **p** 96. NSM Gt and Lt Coates w Bradley *Linc* 95-98; C Immingham 98-02; R Rosewood Australia from 03. *The Rectory, 28 Delvene Crescent, Rosewood, Qld, Australia 4300* Tel (0061) (7) 5464 1430

KOMOR, Michael. b 60. Univ of Wales BSc83. Chich Th Coll 83. **d** 86 **p** 87. C Mountain Ash *Llan* 86-89; C Llantwit Major 89-91; TV 91-00; V Ewenny w St Brides Major from 00. *The Vicarage, Southerndown Road, St Brides Major, Bridgend CF32 0SD* Tel (01656) 880108 E-mail mkomor@talk21.com

KONIG, Peter Montgomery. b 44. Westcott Ho Cam 80. **d** 82 **p** 83. C Oundle *Pet* 82-86; Chapl Westwood Ho Sch Pet 86-92; Chapl Pet High Sch 92-95; Chapl Worksop Coll Notts 95-99; Chapl Glenalmond Coll *St And* from 99. *Glenalmond College, Glenalmond, Perth PH1 3RY*

KONING, Hendrik Bernadus. b 20. **d** 55 **p** 61. USA 55-98; C Bala-Cynwyd St Asaph Penn 55-58; C Bala-Cynwyd St Jo Penn 58-62; V Belmont Hills St Andr Penn 62-65; Metrop Assoc Philadelphia Penn 65-71; Exec Dir Evang Inst Ch Soc 73-88; Ind Min 73-88; C St Mary-Hamilton Village Penn 73-88; rtd 98; Perm to Offic *Eur* from 99. *Hertogenlaan 50, 5663 EL Geldrop, The Netherlands*

KOPSCH, Hartmut. b 41. Sheff Univ BA63 Univ of BC MA66 Lon Univ PhD70 DipHE. Trin Coll Bris 78. **d** 80 **p** 81. C Cranham Park *Chelmsf* 80-85; V Springfield *Birm* 85-92; V Dover St Martin *Cant* 92-96; R Bath Walcot *B & W* from 96. *The Rectory, 6 River Street, Bath BA1 2PZ* Tel (01225) 425570 E-mail kopsch@lineone.net

KOREA, Presiding Bishop of. *See* CHUNG, The Most Revd Matthew Chul Bum

KORNAHRENS, Wallace Douglas. b 43. The Citadel Charleston BA66 Gen Th Sem (NY) STB69. **d** 69 **p** 70. USA 69-72; C Potters Green *Cov* 72-75; Chapl Community of Celebration Wargrave Oxon 75-76; P-in-c Cumbrae (or Millport) *Arg* 76-78; R Grantown-on-Spey *Mor* 78-83; R Rothiemurchus 78-83; R Edin H Cross *Edin* from 83. *Holy Cross Rectory, 18 Barnton Gardens, Edinburgh EH4 6AF* Tel 0131-336 2311

KOSLA, Charles Antoni. b 58. Ridley Hall Cam CTM99. **d** 99 **p** 00. C Widford *Chelmsf* from 99. *16 Wood Street, Chelmsford CM2 9AS* Tel (01245) 344929 E-mail charlie@kosla.freeserve.co.uk

KOSONEN, Ulla. p 99. Finland 99-02; Chapl Finnish Ch in Lon from 02; NSM Bermondsey Deanery *S'wark* from 02. *The Finnish Church in London, 33 Albion Street, London SE16 7JG* Tel (020) 7237 1261

KOTHARE, Jayant Sunderrao. b 41. Bombay Univ BA Heidelberg Univ MDiv. **d** 86 **p** 87. C Handsworth St Mich *Birm* 86-89; C Southall St Geo *Lon* 89-92; TV Thamesmead *S'wark* 92-97; Dioc Community Relns Officer *Man* 97-00; P-in-c Moston St Chad 97-02; rtd 02. *c/o Mrs Cavanagh, 3 Evesham Road, Manchester M9 7DS*

KOVOOR, Canon George Iype. b 57. Delhi Univ BA77 Serampore Univ BD80 Chr Medical Assn of India DCHC85. Union Bibl Sem Yavatmal 78. **d** 80 **p** 80. India 80-90; Dean St Paul's Cathl Ambala 84-88; C Derby St Aug *Derby* 90-94; Min Derby Asian Chr Min Project 90-94; Tutor Crowther Hall CMS Tr Coll Selly Oak 94-97; Prin from 97; Hon Can More Cathl *Worc* from 01; Chapl to The Queen from 03. *Crowther Hall, Weoley Park Road, Birmingham B29 6QT* Tel 0121-472 4228 *or* 415 5738

KRAFT (née STEVENS), Mrs Jane. b 45. SRN66 SCM68. NTMTC 01. **d** 03. NSM Finchley St Mary *Lon* from 03. *9 The Fairway, New Barnet, Barnet EN5 1HH* Tel (020) 8216 3633 Mobile 07803-868482 Fax (020) 8440 3434
E-mail jane@kraft09.fsnet.co.uk

KRAMER, Beaman Kristopher (Kris). b 67. Mars Hill Coll (USA) BS88 Duke Univ (USA) MTS95. Wycliffe Hall Ox MTh98. **d** 98 **p** 99. C Hersham *Guildf* 98-99; C Paddington St Jo w St Mich *Lon* 99-00; R Radford Grace USA from 00. *Grace Rectory, 212 Fourth Street, Radford, VA 24141, USA*
E-mail frkris@i-plus.net

KRAMER, Mrs Caroline Anne. b 70. Wycliffe Hall Ox BTh98. **d** 98. C Oatlands *Guildf* 98-99; USA from 00. *Grace Rectory, 212 Fourth Street, Radford, VA 24141, USA*
E-mail revkramer@cwcom.net

KROLL, Una Margaret Patricia. b 25. Girton Coll Cam MB51 BChir51. S'wark Ord Course 68. **d** 88 **p** 97. NSM Monmouth *Mon* 88-97; Lic to Offic from 97. *St Mary's Lodge, Priory Street, Monmouth NP25 3BR* Tel (01600) 713465

KRONENBERG, John Simon. b 59. Greenwich Univ BSc85 Open Univ BA00 MRICS87 MBEng94. Ripon Coll Cuddesdon 02. **d** 02 **p** 03. C Chandler's Ford *Win* from 02. *St Martin's House, 50 Randall Road, Chandler's Ford, Eastleigh SO53 5AL* Tel and fax (023) 8025 4469 Mobile 07956-517065
E-mail j.kronenberg@bctalk.net

KRONENBERG, Selwyn Thomas Denzil. b 32. Univ of Wales (Swansea) BA54 St Cath Soc Ox BA57 MA60 Leic Univ MA72 California Univ MA82. Wycliffe Hall Ox 54. **d** 57 **p** 58. C Surbiton St Matt *S'wark* 57-59; C Luton St Mary *St Alb* 59-61; P-in-c Loscoe *Derby* 61-65; Lect RE Bulmershe Coll 65-67; Whitelands Coll from 67; Perm to Offic *Guildf* from 77; rtd 97. *58 Woodfield Lane, Ashtead KT21 2BS* Tel (01372) 272505

KRZEMINSKI, Stefan. b 51. Nottm Univ BTh77. Linc Th Coll 74. **d** 77 **p** 78. C Sawley *Derby* 77-79; Asst Chapl Bluecoat Sch Nottm from 79; Hon C W Hallam and Mapperley *Derby* 84-96; Hd of RE Nottm High Sch from 88; Perm to Offic from 96. *12 Newbridge Close, West Hallam, Ilkeston DE7 6LY* Tel 0115-930 5052

KUHRT, The Ven Gordon Wilfred. b 41. Lon Univ BD63 Middx Univ DProf01. Oak Hill Th Coll 65. **d** 67 **p** 68. C Illogan *Truro* 67-70; C Wallington H Trin *S'wark* 70-73; V Shenstone *Lich* 73-79; P-in-c S Croydon Em *Cant* 79-81; V S Croydon Em *S'wark* 81-89; RD Croydon Cen *Cant* 81-86; Hon Can S'wark Cathl *S'wark* 87-89; Adn Lewisham 89-96; Chief Sec ABM 96-98; Dir Min Division from 99. *6 Layzell Walk, London SE9 4QD* Tel (020) 8857 3476

KUHRT, Martin Gordon. b 66. Nottm Univ LLB88. Trin Coll Bris 93. **d** 96 **p** 97. C Morden *S'wark* 96-00; Chapl Lee Abbey 00-02; TV Melksham *Sarum* from 02. *St Andrew's Vicarage, 33 Church Street, Melksham SN12 7EF* Tel (01225) 704056
E-mail martinannakuhrt@classicfm.net

KUHRT, Stephen John. b 69. Man Univ BA91 Lon Inst of Educn PGCE93. Wycliffe Hall Ox BA03. **d** 03. C New Malden and Coombe *S'wark* from 03. *12 Rosebery Avenue, New Malden KT3 4JS* Tel (020) 8942 2523

KURRLE, Canon Stanley Wynton. b 22. OBE82. Melbourne Univ BA47 St Cath Soc Ox BA50 MA54. Wycliffe Hall Ox 49. **d** 52 **p** 53. C Sutton *Liv* 52-54; Australia from 54; Fell St Paul's Coll Univ of Sydney from 69; Can Sydney 81-95; Can Emer 95. *25 Marieba Road, PO Box 53, Kenthurst, NSW, Australia 2156* Tel (0061) (2) 9654 1334 Mobile 427-277919 Fax 9654 1368
E-mail mathourastation@bigpond.com

KURTI, Peter Walter. b 60. Qu Mary Coll Lon LLB82 K Coll Lon MTh89. Ch Div Sch of Pacific 82 Ripon Coll Cuddesdon 83. **d** 86 **p** 87. C Prittlewell *Chelmsf* 86-90; Chapl Derby Coll of HE *Derby* 90-92; Chapl Derby Univ 92-94; Dep Hd Relig Resource and Research Cen 90-94; Australia from 94; Prec St Geo Cathl Perth 94-97; R Scarborough 97-01; R Sydney St Jas from 01. *Level 1, 169-171 Phillip Street, Sydney, NSW, Australia 2000* Tel

(0061) (2) 9363 3335 *or* 9232 3022 Mobile 412-049271 Fax 9232 4182 E-mail peter.kurti@bigpond.com

✠**KWONG KONG KIT, The Most Revd Peter. b** 36. Kenyon Coll Ohio BD65 DD86 Hong Kong Univ DD00. Bexley Hall Div Sch Ohio MTh71 DD98. **d** 65 **p** 66 **c** 81. P-in-c Hong Kong Crown of Thorns 65-66; C Hong Kong St Paul 71-72; Bp Hong Kong and Macao 81-98; Bp Hong Kong Is from 98; Abp Hong Kong Sheng Kung Hui from 98. *Bishop's House, 1 Lower Albert Road, Hong Kong, China* Tel (00852) 2526 5355 Fax 2525 2537
E-mail office1@hkskh.org

KYLE, Miss Sharon Patricia Culvinor. b 55. Open Univ BA90 Edin Univ BD94 MTh96. Coates Hall Edin 91. **d** 94 **p** 95. C Edin SS Phil and Jas *Edin* 94-96; C Neston *Ches* 96-99; TV Kirkby *Liv* 99-01. *c/o The Revd J Morrell, 1 Sandycroft Road, Liverpool L12 0LX* E-mail mother.shaz@btinternet.com

KYRIACOU, Brian George. b 42. Lon Univ LLB64. Oak Hill Th Coll 79. **d** 81 **p** 82. C Becontree St Mary *Chelmsf* 81-83; C Becontree St Cedd 83-85; C Becontree W 85; TV 85-87; V Shiregreen St Jas and St Chris *Sheff* 87-92; TV Schorne *Ox* 92-98; V Edmonton All SS w St Mich *Lon* from 98. *All Saints' Vicarage, 43 All Saints' Close, London N9 9AT* Tel (020) 8803 9199 Mobile 07970-719094 Fax (020) 8884 4348
E-mail bgk@alls.freeserve.co.uk

KYRIAKIDES-YELDHAM, Anthony Paul Richard. b 48. CPsychol91 Birkbeck Coll Lon BSc82 Goldsmiths' Coll Lon DASS83 CQSW83 Warwick Univ MSc90. K Coll Lon BD73 AKC73. **d** 74 **p** 75. C Dalston H Trin w St Phil *Lon* 74-78; NSM Lon Docks St Pet w Wapping St Jo 79-81; NSM Hackney Wick St Mary of Eton w St Aug 81-85; NSM Wandsworth Common St Mary *S'wark* 85-87; Chapl Wandsworth HA Mental Health Unit 87-93; Chapl Springfield Univ Hosp Lon 87-93; Perm to Offic *Ex* 94-98; Lic to Offic from 98; Sen Chapl Plymouth Hosps NHS Trust from 98. *The Chaplaincy, Derriford Hospital, Derriford Road, Plymouth PL6 8DH* Tel (01752) 777111 *or* 792313 Fax 768976 E-mail tony.yeldham@phnt.swest.nhs.uk

KYTE, Eric Anthony. b 62. Leeds Univ BSc84 PGCE85. Trin Coll Bris BA98. **d** 98 **p** 99. C Pudsey St Lawr and St Paul *Bradf* 98-01; P-in-c Gisburn from 01; P-in-c Hellifield from 01. *St Mary's Vicarage, Gisburn, Clitheroe BB7 4HR* Tel (01200) 415935

L

LA TOUCHE, Francis William Reginald. b 51. Linc Th Coll 73. **d** 76 **p** 77. C Yate *Bris* 76-77; C Yate New Town 77-79; Chapl Vlissingen (Flushing) Miss to Seamen *Eur* 79-83; Port Chapl Hull Miss to Seamen 83-91; V Burstwick w Thorngumbald *York* 91-02. *Address temp unknown*
E-mail frank@latouche.fsnet.co.uk

LABDON, John. b 32. Oak Hill Th Coll. **d** 84 **p** 85. C Formby H Trin *Liv* 84-87; P-in-c St Helens St Mark 87-97; rtd 97; Perm to Offic *Ches* from 97. *28 Burton Road, Little Neston, Neston CH64 9RA* Tel 0151 336 7039

LACEY, Allan John. b 48. Wycliffe Hall Ox. **d** 82 **p** 83. C Greasbrough *Sheff* 82-85; R Treeton 85-92; V Thorpe Hesley 92-00; R Rossington from 00. *The Rectory, Sheep Bridge Lane, Rossington, Doncaster DN11 0EZ* Tel (01302) 867597
E-mail laceys@easynet.co.uk

LACEY, Eric. b 33. Cranmer Hall Dur 69. **d** 71 **p** 72. C Blackpool St Jo *Blackb* 71-75; V Whittle-le-Woods 75-88; R Heysham 88-98; rtd 98; Perm to Offic *Blackb* from 98. *143 Bredon Avenue, Chorley PR7 6NS* Tel (01257) 273040

LACEY, Canon Frank Gordon. b 26. Magd Coll Cam BA47 MA51. Ely Th Coll 48. **d** 50 **p** 51. C Nottingham St Cath *S'well* 50-53; C Mansfield Woodhouse 53-56; V Rubery *Birm* 56-64; PC Dethick, Lea and Holloway *Derby* 64-69; V Ockbrook 69-73; Dir Past Studies N Ord Course 73-81; V Birtles *Ches* 73-82; Can Res Sheff Cathl *Sheff* 82-91; rtd 91; Perm to Offic *Sheff* from 91; Perm to Offic *Derby* from 91. *6 Barnes Avenue, Dronfield Woodhouse, Dronfield S18 8YG* Tel (01246) 416589

LACEY, Nigel Jeremy. b 59. St Jo Coll Nottm BTh94. **d** 94 **p** 95. C Mildenhall *St E* 94-97; C Selly Park St Steph and St Wulstan *Birm* 97-01; P-in-c W Wycombe w Bledlow Ridge, Bradenham and Radnage *Ox* from 01. *The Rectory, Church Lane, West Wycombe, High Wycombe HP14 3AH* Tel (01494) 529988
E-mail nigel.lacey@whsmithnet.co.uk

LACK, Catherine Mary. b 59. Clare Coll Cam BA81 Ox Univ MTh00 ARCM. Qu Coll Birm 00. **d** 92 **p** 94. Par Dn Leiston *St E* 92-94; C 94-95; TV Ipswich St Mary at Stoke w St Pet 95-97; TV Ipswich St Mary at Stoke w St Pet and St Fran 97-98; Chapl

Keele Univ *Lich* from 98. *Berachah House, 51 Quarry Bank Road, Keele, Newcastle ST5 5AG* Tel (01782) 627385 *or* 583393 Fax 627385 E-mail cpa02@keele.ac.uk

LACK, Martin Paul. b 57. St Jo Coll Ox MA79 MSc80. Linc Th Coll 83. **d** 86 **p** 87. C E Bowbrook and W Bowbrook *Worc* 86-89; C Bowbrook S and Bowbrook N 89-90; R Teme Valley S 90-01; rtd 01. *Colbridge Cottage, Bottom Lane, Whitbourne, Worcester WR6 5RT* Tel (01886) 821978

LACKEY, Michael Geoffrey Herbert. b 42. Oak Hill Th Coll 73. **d** 75 **p** 76. C Hatcham St Jas *S'wark* 75-81; V New Barnet St Jas *St Alb* 81-91; V Hollington St Jo *Chich* 91-02; Dir Crowhurst Chr Healing Cen from 02. *The Old Rectory, Forewood Lane, Crowhurst, Battle TN33 9AD* Tel (01424) 8302204 Fax 830053 E-mail divine@theway.co.uk

LACKEY, William Terence Charles. b 32. St Mich Coll Llan 80. **d** 82 **p** 83. C Wrexham *St As* 82-85; V Gwersyllt 85-93; R Trefnant 93-98; rtd 98. *24 Old Farm Road, Rhostyllen, Wrexham LL14 4DX* Tel (01978) 311969

LACY, Melanie June. b 75. TCD BA98 All Hallows Coll Dublin MA00. CITC 98. **d** 00. C Bangor *D & D* 00-02; N Ireland Regional Co-ord Crosslinks from 02. *Crosslinks, 60A Castlereagh Street, Belfast BT5 4NH* Tel and fax (028) 9046 6489 E-mail crosslinks@belfast.region.crosslinks.org

LACY, Sarah Frances. b 49. Sarum Th Coll 93. **d** 96 **p** 97. C Weston Zoyland w Chedzoy *B & W* 96-00; C Middlezoy and Othery and Moorlinch 00-01; R Berrow and Breane from 01. *The Rectory, 1 Manor Way, Berrow, Burnham-on-Sea TA8 2RG* Tel (01278) 751057 E-mail sally@lacys.freeserve.co.uk

LADD, Mrs Anne de Chair. b 56. Nottm Univ BA78 Birm Univ CQSW80. St Jo Coll Nottm LTh DPS86. **dss** 86 **d** 87 **p** 94. Bucknall and Bagnall *Lich* 86-91; Par Dn 87-91; NSM Bricket Wood *St Alb* 91-01; Chapl Garden Ho Hospice Letchworth from 98; Perm to Offic *Ely* from 01. *57 St Barnabas Road, Cambridge CB1 2BX* Tel (01223) 316228

LADD, John George Morgan. b 36. Univ of Wales (Ban) BA58 MA65. Trin Coll Carmarthen St Mich Coll Llan. **d** 90 **p** 91. NSM Nevern and Y Beifil w Eglwyswrw and Meline etc *St D* 90-92; NSM Llandysilio w Egremont and Llanglydwen etc 92-93; V Gwaun-cae-Gurwen from 93. *The Vicarage, 118 Heol Cae Gurwen, Gwaun-cae-Gurwen, Ammanford SA18 1PD* Tel (01269) 822430

LADD, Nicholas Mark. b 57. Ex Univ BA78 Selw Coll Cam BA81. Ridley Hall Cam 79. **d** 82 **p** 83. C Aston SS Pet and Paul *Birm* 82-86; TV Bucknall and Bagnall *Lich* 86-91; V Bricket Wood *St Alb* 91-01; V Cambridge St Barn *Ely* from 01. *The Vicarage, 57 St Barnabas Road, Cambridge CB1 2BX* Tel (01223) 316228 *or* 519526 E-mail vicar@stbs.org.uk

✠**LADDS, The Rt Revd Robert Sidney.** b 41. LRSC72 Lon Univ BEd71. Cant Sch of Min 79. **d** 80 **p** 81 **c** 99. C Hythe *Cant* 80-83; R Bretherton *Blackb* 83-91; Chapl Bp Rawstorne Sch Preston 83-87; Bp's Chapl for Min and Adv Coun for Min *Blackb* 86-91; P-in-c Preston St Jo 91-96; R Preston St Jo and St Geo 96-97; Hon Can Blackb Cathl 93-97; Adn Lancaster 97-99; Suff Bp Whitby *York* from 99. *60 West Green, Stokesley, Middlesbrough TS9 5BD* Tel (01642) 714475 E-mail bishopofwhitby@episcopus.co.uk

LADIPO, Canon Adeyemi Olalekan. b 37. Trin Coll Bris 63. **d** 66 **p** 76. C Bilston St Leon *Lich* 66-68; Nigeria 68-84; V Canonbury St Steph *Lon* 85-87; Sec for Internat Miss BCMS 87-90; Hon C Bromley SS Pet and Paul *Roch* 89-90; V Herne Hill *S'wark* 90-99; Hon Can Jos from 95; V S Malling *Chich* 99-02; rtd 02. *2A Camden Road, Eastbourne BN21 4SU* Tel (01323) 731400

LAIDLAW, Juliet. *See* MONTAGUE, Mrs Juliet

LAIN-PRIESTLEY, Ms Rosemary Jane. b 67. Kent Univ BA89 K Coll Lon MA02. Carl Dioc Tr Course 92. **d** 96 **p** 97. C Scotforth *Blackb* 96-98; C St Martin-in-the-Fields *Lon* from 98. *5 St Martin's Place, London WC2N 4JH* Tel (020) 7766 1103

LAING, Canon Alexander Burns. b 34. RD90. Edin Th Coll 57. **d** 60 **p** 61. C Falkirk *Edin* 60-62; C Edin Ch Ch 62-70; Chapl RNR 64-91; P-in-c Edin St Fillan *Edin* 70-74; Chapl Edin R Infirmary 74-77; Dioc Supernumerary *Edin* from 77; R Helensburgh *Glas* from 77; Can St Mary's Cathl from 87. *The Rectory, 16 William Street, Helensburgh G84 8BD* Tel (01436) 672500

LAING, William Sydney. b 32. TCD BA54 MA62. **d** 55 **p** 56. C Dublin Crumlin *D & G* 55-59; C Dublin St Ann 59-65; I Carbury *M & K* 65-68; I Dublin Finglas *D & G* 68-80; I Tallaght 80-91; Can Ch Ch Cathl Dublin 90-94; Preb 94-97; I Dublin Crumlin w Chapelizod 91-97; rtd 97. *42 Hazelwood Crescent, Clondalkin, Dublin 22, Irish Republic* Tel (00353) (1) 459 3893

LAIRD, Alisdair Mark. b 60. Auckland Univ BA84. Trin Coll Bris BA92. **d** 92 **p** 93. C Linthorpe *York* 92-98; V Hull St Cuth from 98. *The Vicarage, 112 Marlborough Avenue, Hull HU5 3JX* Tel (01482) 342848 E-mail laird@onetel.net.uk

LAIRD, Canon John Charles. b 32. Sheff Univ BA53 MA54 St Cath Coll Ox BA58 MA62 Lon Univ DipEd70. Ripon Hall Ox 56. **d** 58 **p** 59. C Cheshunt *St Alb* 58-62; Chapl Bps' Coll Cheshunt 62-64; Vice-Prin 64-67; Prin 67-69; V Keysoe w Bolnhurst and Lt Staughton *St Alb* 69-01; Hon Can St Alb

87-02; Lic to Offic from 01. *The Chaplaincy, Fore Street Lodge, Hatfield Park, Hatfield AL9 5NQ* Tel (01707) 274941

LAIRD, Robert George (Robin). b 40. TCD Div Sch 58 Edin Th Coll 63. **d** 65 **p** 66. C Drumragh *D & R* 65-68; CF 68-93; QHC 91-93; Sen Chapl Sedbergh Sch 93-98; Lic to Offic *Bradf* 93-98; rtd 98; Perm to Offic *Ex* and *Sarum* from 98. *Barrule, Hillside Road, Sidmouth EX10 8JD* Tel (01395) 513948

LAIRD, Stephen Charles Edward. b 66. Oriel Coll Ox BA88 MA92 MSt93 K Coll Lon MTh91 Wycliffe Hall Ox DipMin94 MPhil96 FRSA00. **d** 94 **p** 95. C Ilfracombe, Lee, Woolacombe, Bittadon etc *Ex* 94-98; Chapl Kent Univ *Cant* 98-03; Dean of Chapl from 03; Hon Lect from 98; Chapl Kent Inst of Art and Design 98-02. *Landon, Giles Lane, Canterbury CT2 7LR* Tel (01227) 827491 *or* 787476 Mobile 07970-438840 E-mail s.c.e.laird@kent.ac.uk

LAKE, Canon David Eurwyn. b 17. TD60. St D Coll Lamp BA39. **d** 40 **p** 41. C Miskin *Llan* 40-43; C Cardiff St Jo 43-50; CF (TA) 48-67; P-in-c Llansawel *Llan* 50-56; V 56-62; V Skewen 62-84; RD Neath 76-84; rtd 84; Perm to Offic *Llan* from 84. *Fairwil, 42 Brecon Road, Ystradgynlais, Swansea SA9 1HF* Tel (01639) 849541

LAKE, David Michael. b 57. St Mary's Sem Oscott 76 Nottm Univ BA01. St Jo Coll Nottm 99. **d** 01. C Lilleshall, Muxton and Sheriffhales *Lich* from 01. *16 Thornton Park Avenue, Muxton, Telford TF2 8RF* Tel (01952) 603447 *or* 670033 E-mail davidlake@mailserver97.freeserve.co.uk

LAKE, Eileen Veronica. *See* CREMIN, Mrs Eileen Veronica

LAKE, Kevin William. b 57. St Mich Coll Llan DMS99. **d** 99 **p** 00. C Penarth w Lavernock *Llan* 99-02. *7 Nurston Close, Rhoose, Barry CF62 3EF* Tel (01446) 719060

LAKE, Canon Stephen David. b 63. Southn Univ BTh. Chich Th Coll 85. **d** 88 **p** 89. C Sherborne w Castleton and Lillington *Sarum* 88-92; P-in-c Branksome St Aldhelm 92-96; V 96-01; RD Poole 00-01; Can Res and Sub-Dean St Alb from 01. *The Old Rectory, Sumpter Yard, St Albans AL1 1BY* Tel (01727) 890201 Fax 850944 E-mail subdean@stalbanscathedral.org.uk

LAKE, Vivienne Elizabeth. b 38. Lon Univ DHistA78. Westcott Ho Cam 84. **dss** 86 **d** 87 **p** 94. Chesterton Gd Shep *Ely* 86-90; C 87-90; Ecum Min K Hedges Ch Cen 87-90; NSM Bourn Deanery 90-01; NSM Papworth Everard 94-96; Perm to Offic from 01. *15 Storey's House, Mount Pleasant, Cambridge CB3 0BZ* Tel (01223) 369523

LAKE, Wynne Vaughan. b 34. St D Coll Lamp BA55. St Mich Coll Llan 55. **d** 57 **p** 58. C Cadoxton-juxta-Barry *Llan* 57-61; C Roath St Sav 61-64; V Oakwood 64-67; V Oakwood w Bryn 67-72; R Shirenewton and Newchurch *Mon* 72-77; rtd 99. *44 Cefn Celyn, Dunvant, Swansea SA2 7TU* Tel (01792) 427299

LAKER, Clive Sheridan. b 59. RGN82 DipNursing87 Greenwich Univ BSc92. Aston Tr Scheme 93 SEITE 95. **d** 98 **p** 99. C Bridlington Quay Ch Ch *York* 98-00; C Bridlington Em 00-01; TV Bucknall and Bagnall *Lich* from 01. *St John's Parsonage, 28 Greasley Road, Stoke-on-Trent ST2 8JE* Tel (01782) 542861

LAKER, Grace. *See* SWIFT, Mrs Grace

LAKEY, Elizabeth Flora. b 46. DipOT69 Open Univ BA81. St Alb and Ox Min Course 98. **d** 01 **p** 02. OLM Nettlebed w Bix, Highmoor, Pishill etc *Ox* from 01. *Bank Farm, Pishill, Henley-on-Thames RG9 6HJ* Tel and fax (01491) 638601 Mobile 07799-752933 E-mail bankfarm@btinternet.com

LAMB, Bruce. b 47. Keble Coll Ox BA69 MA73 Leeds Univ DipTh72. Coll of Resurr Mirfield 70. **d** 73 **p** 74. C Romford St Edw *Chelmsf* 73-76; C Canning Town St Cedd 76-79; V New Brompton St Luke *Roch* 79-83; Chapl R N 83-87; C Rugeley *Lich* 87-88; V Trent Vale 88-92; Bereavement Cllr Cruse 94-99; Hon C Chorlton-cum-Hardy St Clem *Man* 98-99; Asst Chapl N Man Health Care NHS Trust 99-02; P-in-c Barton w Peel Green *Man* from 02. *St Michael's Vicarage, 468 Liverpool Road, Eccles, Manchester M30 7LP* Tel 0161-789 3751

LAMB, Bryan John Harry. b 35. Leeds Univ BA60 Aston Univ Dip Counselling 72. Coll of Resurr Mirfield 60. **d** 62 **p** 63. C Solihull *Birm* 62-65 and 88-89; Asst Master Malvern Hall Sch Solihull 65-74; Alderbrook Sch and Hd of Light Hall Adult Educn Cen 74-88; V Wragby *Linc* 89; Dioc Dir of Readers 89; Perm to Offic *Birm* from 89; rtd 95. *22 Ladbrook Road, Solihull B91 3RN* Tel 0121-705 2489

LAMB, Canon Christopher Avon. b 39. Qu Coll Ox BA61 MA65 Birm Univ MA78 PhD87. Wycliffe Hall Ox BA63. **d** 63 **p** 64. C Enfield St Andr *Lon* 63-69; Pakistan 69-75; Tutor Crowther Hall CMS Tr Coll Selly Oak 75-78; Co-ord BCMS/CMS Other Faiths Th Project 78-87; Dioc Community Relns Officer *Cov* 87-92; Can Th Cov Cathl from 92; Sec Inter-Faith Relns Bd of Miss 92-99; R Warmington w Shotteswell and Radway w Ratley *Cov* from 99. *The Rectory, Warmington, Banbury OX17 1BT* Tel (01295) 690213 E-mail lamb@easynet.co.uk

LAMB, David Andrew. b 60. Liv Inst of HE BA94 Man Univ MA01. Nor Ord Course 90. **d** 94 **p** 95. C Formby H Trin *Liv* 94-97; C St Helens St Matt Thatto Heath 97-98; C Halewood 98-01; Lect Liv Hope 99-00; V Birkenhead St Jas w St Bede *Ches* from 01. *St James's Vicarage, 56 Tollemache Road, Prenton CH43 8SZ* Tel 0151-652 1016

LAMB, Graeme William. b 68. Trin Coll Bris 99. **d** 01 **p** 02. C Heald Green St Cath *Ches* from 01. *103 Baslow Drive, Heald Green, Cheadle SK8 3HW* Tel 0161-437 2395 *or* 437 0228
E-mail graeme@graemelamb.com

LAMB, Jean Evelyn. b 57. Reading Univ BA79 Nottm Univ MA88. St Steph Ho Ox 81. **dss** 84 **d** 88 **p** 01. Leic H Spirit *Leic* 84-87; Par Dn Beeston *S'well* 88-91; Hon C and Artist in Res Nottingham St Mary and St Cath 92-95; Hon Par Dn Sneinton St Steph w St Alb 97-01; NSM Rolleston w Fiskerton, Morton and Upton from 01. *St Alban's House, 4 Dale Street, Sneinton, Nottingham NG2 4JX* Tel 0115-958 5892

LAMB, John Romney. b 21. Ch Ch Ox BA48 MA53. Wells Th Coll 49. **d** 50 **p** 51. C Tenterden St Mildred w Smallhythe *Cant* 50-53; C Hythe 53-55; CF 55-70; V Horsell *Guildf* 70-76; V Dorking w Ranmore 76-82; P-in-c Charing Heath w Egerton *Cant* 82-83; P-in-c Pluckley w Pevington 82-83; R Egerton w Pluckley 84-87; rtd 87; Perm to Offic *Chich* from 87. *Wayside, Budds Hill, Singleton, Chichester PO18 0HD* Tel (01243) 811516

LAMB, Nicholas Henry. b 52. St Jo Coll Dur BA74. St Jo Coll Nottm DPS79. **d** 79 **p** 80. C Luton Lewsey St Hugh *St Alb* 79-84; Bethany Fellowship 84-86; In Bapt Min 86-94; Perm to Offic *Chich* 97-99; C E Grinstead St Swithun from 99. *11 Garden House Lane, East Grinstead RH19 4JT* Tel (01342) 328306
E-mail revnicklamb@hotmail.com

LAMB, Peter Francis Charles. b 15. St Cath Coll Cam BA37 MA41. Wells Th Coll 37. **d** 38 **p** 39. C Wellingborough All Hallows *Pet* 38-42; C Somersham w Pidley and Colne *Ely* 42-48; Chapl RNVR 46-48; C Sherborne w Castleton and Lillington *Sarum* 48-51; The Gambia 51-57; V Winkleigh *Ex* 57-70; RD Chulmleigh 62-63; R Mells w Vobster, Whatley and Chantry *B & W* 70-77; rtd 77; Perm to Offic *B & W* from 77. *6 Parsons Close, Long Sutton, Langport TA10 9LN* Tel (01458) 241481

LAMB, Philip Richard James. b 42. Sarum & Wells Th Coll. **d** 83 **p** 84. C Wotton-under-Edge w Ozleworth and N Nibley *Glouc* 83-86; TV Worc SE *Worc* 86-91; R Billingsley w Sidbury, Middleton Scriven etc *Heref* 91-96; R St Dominic, Landulph and St Mellion w Pillaton *Truro* from 96. *The Rectory, St Mellion, Saltash PL12 6RN* Tel (01579) 350061
E-mail frlamb@stmellion141.freeserve.co.uk

LAMB, Phillip. b 68. NEOC 00. **d** 03. C Bridlington Priory *York* from 03. *20 The Lawns, Bridlington YO16 6FL* Tel (01262) 401353 Mobile 07803-239611
E-mail phil_lamb2002@yahoo.co.uk

LAMB, Scott Innes. b 64. Edin Univ BSc86. Aston Tr Scheme 88 Ridley Hall Cam BA92. **d** 93 **p** 94. C E Ham w Upton Park St Alb *Chelmsf* 93-97; V W Holloway St Luke *Lon* 97-00; P-in-c Hammersmith H Innocents 00-03; Chapl RN from 03. *Royal Naval Chaplaincy Service, Room 203, Victory Building, HM Naval Base, Portsmouth PO1 3LS* Tel (01705) 727903 Fax 727112 E-mail scott@hamleylamb.fsnet.co.uk

LAMB, William Robert Stuart. b 70. Ball Coll Ox BA91 MA95 Peterho Cam MPhil94. Westcott Ho Cam CTM95. **d** 95 **p** 96. C Halifax *Wakef* 95-98; TV Penistone and Thurlstone 98-01; Chapl Sheff Univ *Sheff* from 01. *119 Ashdell Road, Sheffield S10 3DB* Tel 0114-266 9243 E-mail w.lamb@shef.ac.uk

LAMBERT, David Francis. b 40. Oak Hill Th Coll 72. **d** 74 **p** 75. C Paignton St Paul Preston *Ex* 74-77; C Woking Ch Ch *Guildf* 77-84; P-in-c Willesden Green St Gabr *Lon* 84-91; P-in-c Cricklewood St Mich 85-91; V Cricklewood St Gabr and St Mich 92-93; R Chenies and Lt Chalfont, Latimer and Flaunden *Ox* 93-01; Chapl Izmir (Smyrna) w Bornova *Eur* 01-03; TV Brixham w Churston Ferrers and Kingswear *Ex* from 03. *54 Brunel Road, Broadsands, Paignton TQ4 6HW* Tel (01803) 842476

LAMBERT, David Hardy. b 44. AKC66. **d** 67 **p** 68. C Marske in Cleveland *York* 67-72; V from 85; V N Ormesby 73-85; RD Guisborough 86-91. *The Vicarage, 6 Windy Hill Lane, Marske-by-the-Sea, Redcar TS11 7BN* Tel (01642) 482896

LAMBERT, David Joseph. b 66. Coll of Resurr Mirfield 99. **d** 01 **p** 02. C Camberwell St Geo *S'wark* from 01. *131 Coleman Road, London SE5 7TF* Tel (020) 7703 2704 Fax as telephone

LAMBERT, David Nathaniel. b 34. Headingley Meth Coll 58 Linc Th Coll 66. **d** 66 **p** 67. In Methodist Ch 58-66; C Canwick *Linc* 66-68; C-in-c Bracebridge Heath CD 68-69; R Saltfleetby All SS w St Pet 69-73; R Saltfleetby St Clem 70-73; V Skidbrooke 70-73; V Saltfleetby 73-80; R Theddlethorpe 74-80; RD Louthesk 76-82; R N Ormsby w Wyham 80-94; R Fotherby 81-94; rtd 94; Perm to Offic *Linc* 94-97. *32 Brookside Avenue, Bedale DL8 2DP* Tel (01677) 423542

LAMBERT, Gordon. b 32. Univ of Wales (Lamp) BA56. Wycliffe Hall Ox 56. **d** 58 **p** 59. C Newbarns w Hawcoat *Carl* 58-63; C-in-c Barrow St Aid CD 63-67; V Barrow St Aid 67-68; R Ousby w Melmerby 68-71; V Farlam 71-76; TV Thirsk w S Kilvington and Carlton Miniott etc *York* 76-77; TV Thirsk 77-89; RD Thirsk 81-89; V Belvedere All SS *Roch* 89-96; rtd 96; Perm to Offic *Chich* from 98. *19 The Barnhams, Bexhill-on-Sea TN39 3RE* Tel (01424) 844443

LAMBERT, Ian Anderson. b 43. Lon Univ BA72 Nottm Univ MTh87. Ridley Hall Cam 66. **d** 67 **p** 68. C Bermondsey St Mary w St Olave, St Jo etc *S'wark* 67-70; Jamaica 71-75; Chapl RAF 75-98; rtd 98; P-in-c N and S Muskham *S'well* from 01; P-in-c Averham w Kelham from 01. *St Wilfrid's Vicarage, Marsh Lane, North Muskham, Newark NG23 6HG* Tel (01636) 702655

LAMBERT, John Clement Antony. b 28. St Cath Coll Cam BA48 MA52. Cuddesdon Coll 50. **d** 52 **p** 53. C Hornsea and Goxhill *York* 52-55; C Leeds St Pet *Ripon* 55-59; R Carlton in Lindrick *S'well* 59-93; rtd 93; Perm to Offic *Derby* from 93; *S'well* 93-00. *139 Longedge Lane, Wingerworth, Chesterfield S42 6PR* Tel (01246) 551774

LAMBERT, Malcolm Eric. b 58. RMN84 Leic Univ BSc80 Fitzw Coll Cam BA89 Nottm Univ MPhil02. Ridley Hall Cam 87. **d** 90 **p** 91. C Humberstone *Leic* 90-94; R S Croxton Gp 94-99; Warden of Readers from 97; V Birstall and Wanlip from 99. *The Rectory, 251 Birstall Road, Birstall, Leicester LE4 4DJ* Tel 0116-267 4517
E-mail me.lambert@ntlworld.com

LAMBERT, Michael Roy. b 25. Univ Coll Dur BSc49. Cuddesdon Coll 52. **d** 52 **p** 53. C Middlesbrough St Oswald *York* 52-56; C Romsey *Win* 56-59; C Cottingham *York* 59-64; Chapl Hull Univ 59-64; V Saltburn-by-the-Sea 64-72; P-in-c Shaftesbury H Trin *Sarum* 72-73; R Shaston 72-78; R Corfe Mullen 78-91; rtd 91; Perm to Offic *Glouc* from 91. *16 Pheasant Way, Cirencester GL7 1BL* Tel (01285) 654657

LAMBERT, Miss Olivia Jane. b 48. Matlock Coll of Educn BEd70. Trin Coll Bris DipHE86. **dss** 86 **d** 87 **p** 94. York St Luke *York* 86-90; Par Dn 87-90; Chapl York Distr Hosp 86-90; Par Dn Huntington *York* 90-94; C 94-95; TV 95-00; TV Marfleet from 00. *St Philip's House, 107 Amethyst Road, Hull HU9 4JG* Tel (01482) 376208 E-mail oliviajlambert@aol.com

LAMBERT, Peter George. b 29. Coll of Resurr Mirfield 86. **d** 88. NSM Rothwell w Orton, Rushton w Glendon and Pipewell *Pet* 87-93; P-in-c Corby Epiphany w St Jo 93-96; rtd 96; Perm to Offic *Pet* from 96. *4 Cogan Crescent, Rothwell, Kettering NN14 6AS* Tel (01536) 710692

LAMBERT, Philip Charles. b 54. St Jo Coll Dur BA75 Fitzw Coll Cam BA77 MA81. Ridley Hall Cam 75. **d** 78 **p** 79. C Upper Tooting H Trin *S'wark* 78-81; C Whorlton *Newc* 81-84; P-in-c Alston cum Garrigill w Nenthead and Kirkhaugh 84-87; TV Alston Team 87-89; R Curry Rivel w Fivehead and Swell *B & W* 89-01; RD Crewkerne and Ilminster 98-01; TR Dorchester *Sarum* from 01; RD Dorchester from 02. *The Rectory, 17A Edward Road, Dorchester DT1 2HL* Tel (01305) 268434

LAMBERT (née JOHNSON), Mrs Ruth Alice. b 59. Leic Univ BA80 PGCE93 Nottm Univ MA01 RGN85. **d** 01 **p** 02. C Mountsorrel Ch Ch and St Pet *Leic* from 01. *The Rectory, 251 Birstall Road, Birstall, Leicester LE4 4DJ* Tel 0116-220 2625 Mobile 07808-321695 E-mail ruth.lambert@ntlworld.com

LAMBERT, Sydney Thomas. b 17. Keble Coll Ox BA39 MA44 CertEd71. Wells Th Coll 40. **d** 41 **p** 42. C Poplar *Lon* 41-44; C Ox St Barn *Ox* 44-45; India 45-49; Asst Master Bp Cotton Sch Bangalore 45-49; USA 49-50; Asst R Cincinnati the Advent 49-50; CF 50-67; R Rendcomb *Glouc* 67-74; V Colesborne 67-74; P-in-c Cheltenham St Pet 74-78; P-in-c Todenham w Lower Lemington 78-83; P-in-c Bourton on the Hill 78-83; rtd 83; Perm to Offic *Worc* from 83. *97 Elm Road, Evesham WR11 3DR* Tel (01386) 446725 Fax as telephone

LAMBETH, Archdeacon of. *Vacant*

LAMBOURN, David Malcolm. b 37. Lanc Univ BEd76 Man Univ MEd78 Warwick Univ PhD01. Linc Th Coll 63. **d** 65 **p** 66. C Camberwell St Geo *S'wark* 65-67; C Mottingham St Andr 67-70; rtd 03. *28 Frederick Road, Birmingham B15 1JN* Tel 0121-242 3953 E-mail david.lambourn@blueyonder.co.uk

LAMBOURNE, John Brian. b 36. Chich Th Coll 62. **d** 65 **p** 66. C Cant St Greg *Cant* 65-67; C St Mary in the Marsh 67-68; C E Grinstead St Swithun *Chich* 68-70; C Storrington and Sullington 70-76; CF (TA) 87-96; V Salehurst *Chich* from 76; Bp's Adv on Rural Affairs from 89; Agric Chapl from 89. *St Mary's Vicarage, Fair Lane, Robertsbridge TN32 5AR* Tel (01580) 880408

LAMDIN, Canon Keith Hamilton. b 47. Bris Univ BA69. Ripon Coll Cuddesdon 80. **d** 86 **p** 87. Adult Educn Officer *Ox* 86-98; Team Ldr Par Resources Dept from 88; Dioc Dir Tr from 94; Hon Can Ch Ch from 97; NSM Cowley St Jo from 98. *41 Stapleton Road, Headington, Oxford OX3 7LX* Tel (01865) 767160 E-mail training@oxford.anglican.org

LAMEY, Richard John. b 77. Keble Coll Ox BA98 Em Coll Cam BA01 Keble Coll Ox MA02. Westcott Ho Cam 99. **d** 02 **p** 03. C Stockport SW *Ches* from 02. *40 Beechfield Road, Stockport SK3 8SF* Tel 0161-483 3350 E-mail rjlamey@yahoo.co.uk

LAMMAS, Miss Diane Beverley. b 47. Trin Coll Bris 76. **dss** 79 **d** 87 **p** 94. Lenton Abbey *S'well* 79-84; Wollaton Park 79-84; E Regional Co-ord and Sec for Voc and Min CPAS 84-89; Hon C Cambridge St Paul *Ely* 87-90; Voc and Min Adv CPAS 89-92; Sen Voc and Min Adv CPAS 92-95; R Hethersett w Canteloff w Lt and Gt Melton *Nor* from 95; RD Humbleyard 98-03. *The Rectory, 27 Norwich Road, Hethersett, Norwich NR9 3AR* Tel (01603) 810273 E-mail di.lammas@freeuk.com

LAMMENS, Erwin Bernard Eddy. b 62. Catholic Univ Leuven. LTh. **d** 87 **p** 88. Asst Chapl Antwerp St Boniface *Eur* from 98. *Leegbracht 2, 9860 Oosterzele, Belgium* Tel (0032) (9) 362 1575 E-mail erwin.lammens@fracarita.org

LAMOND, Stephen Paul. b 64. Trin Coll Bris BA99. **d** 99 **p** 00. C Weston-super-Mare Ch Ch *B & W* 99-02; C Congresbury w Puxton and Hewish St Ann 02-03; Chapl RAF from 03. *Chaplaincy Services (RAF), HQ, Personnel and Training Command, RAF Innsworth, Gloucester GL3 1EZ* Tel (01452) 712612 ext 5164 Fax 510828

LAMONT, Euphemia Margaret (Fay). b 53. N Coll of Educn BA98. TISEC 00. **d** 00 **p** 00. C Monifieth *Bre* from 00; C Carnoustie from 00. *1 South Street, Monifieth DD5 4PJ* Tel (01382) 532576 *or* 530351 Mobile 07931-222092 E-mail faylamont@hotmail.com

LAMONT, Roger. b 37. Jes Coll Ox BA60 MA62 Dip Counselling 92. St Steph Ho Ox 59. **d** 61 **p** 62. C Northampton St Alb *Pet* 61-66; V Mitcham St Olave *S'wark* 66-73; V N Sheen St Phil and All SS 73-85; P-in-c Richmond St Luke 82-85; Chapl Lifecare NHS Trust (Caterham) 85-94; Chapl Surrey Oaklands NHS Trust 92-99 and 99-01; rtd 01; Perm to Offic *S'wark* from 01. *8 Montague Drive, Caterham CR3 5BY* Tel (01883) 340803

LAMONT, Ms Veronica Jane (Ronni). b 56. Bp Grosseteste Coll CertEd77. St Jo Coll Nottm 90. **d** 92 **p** 94. Par Dn St Alb St Pet *St Alb* 92-94; C 94-96; TV Hemel Hempstead 96-01; V Bexley St Jo *Roch* from 01. *St John's Vicarage, 29 Park Hill Road, Bexley DA5 1HX* Tel (01322) 521786 Mobile 07802-793910 E-mail ronni@fish.co.uk

LAMPARD, Ms Ruth Margaret. b 65. St Jo Coll Dur BA87 Jes Coll Cam BA99. Westcott Ho Cam 97 Berkeley Div Sch 99. **d** 00 **p** 01. C Ealing St Pet Mt Park *Lon* 00-01; C Hackney St Jas w St John w Christ Ch from 01. *1 Farthings Close, Pinner HA5 2QR* Tel (020) 8429 8034 E-mail ruth.lampard@london.anglican.org

LANCASHIRE, Douglas. b 26. SOAS Lon BA50 MA58 K Coll Lon BD55. **d** 61 **p** 79. USA 61-62; Australia 62-65; New Zealand 65-81; R Boxted w Langham *Chelmsf* 81-91; rtd 91. *15 Cecil Avenue, Enfield EN1 1PT* Tel (020) 8363 0718

LANCASTER, Mrs Jennifer. b 48. NEOC 00. **d** 03. C Walker *Newc* from 03. *2 Heathdale Gardens, Newcastle upon Tyne NE7 7QR* Tel 0191-240 1612

LANCASTER, John Rawson. b 47. BSc. N Ord Course. **d** 82 **p** 83. C Bolton St Jas w St Chrys *Bradf* 82-86; V Barnoldswick w Bracewell from 86. *The Vicarage, 131 Gisburn Road, Barnoldswick BB18 5JU* Tel (01282) 812028 Fax 850346

LANCASTER, Norman. b 13. Leeds Univ BA36. Coll of Resurr Mirfield 36. **d** 38 **p** 39. C Skegness *Linc* 38-41; C New Cleethorpes 41-42; C Gt Grimsby St Jas 42-47; V Caistor w Holton le Moor and Clixby 47-52; PC Louth H Trin 52-57; V Keddington 52-57; V Hogsthorpe 52-62; Chapl Butlin's Holiday Camps 59-62; R Panton w Wragby 62-71; V Langton by Wragby 62-71; R Gt Coates 71-77; PC Aylesby 71-77; rtd 77; Perm to Offic *Linc* 77-95. *6 Dulverton Hall, Esplanade, Scarborough YO11 2AR* Tel (01723) 340106

LANCASTER, Ronald. b 31. MBE93. FRSC83 CChem83 St Jo Coll Dur BA53 MA56. Cuddesdon Coll 55. **d** 57 **p** 58. C Morley St Pet w Churwell *Wakef* 57-60; C High Harrogate St Pet *Ripon* 60-63; Lic to Offic *Ely* 63-88; Chapl Kimbolton Sch Cambs 63-88; Asst Chapl 88-91; Perm to Offic *Ely* from 88; rtd 96. *7 High Street, Kimbolton, Huntingdon PE28 0HB* Tel (01480) 860498 Fax 861277

LANCASTER, Mrs Susan Louise. b 47. Leic Univ BA79 CPES81. EMMTC 88. **d** 93 **p** 94. NSM Clarendon Park St Jo w Knighton St Mich *Leic* 93-97; Perm to Offic from 97. *5 Hartopp Road, Leicester LE2 1WE* Tel 0116-212 8959

LANCASTER, Archdeacon of. See WILLIAMS, The Ven Colin Henry

LANCASTER, Suffragan Bishop of. See PEDLEY, The Rt Revd Geoffrey Stephen

LAND, Michael Robert John. b 43. Ripon Hall Ox 70. **d** 72 **p** 73. C Newbury St Nic *Ox* 72-75; TV Chigwell *Chelmsf* 75-80; V Walthamstow St Andr from 80. *St Andrew's Vicarage, 37 Sutton Road, London E17 5QA* Tel (020) 8527 3969

LANDALL, Capt Allan Roy. b 55. Qu Coll Birm BA98. **d** 98 **p** 99. C Thurnby w Stoughton *Leic* 98-02; R Walsoken *Ely* from 02. *The Vicarage, Church Road, Wisbech PE13 3RA* Tel (01945) 583740 E-mail arlandall@btinternet.com

LANDALL, Richard. b 57. St Jo Coll Dur 85. **d** 88 **p** 89. C Nailsea H Trin *B & W* 88-92; CF 92-99; TV Westborough *Guildf* 99-01; R Armthorpe *Sheff* from 01. *The Rectory, Church Street, Armthorpe, Doncaster DN3 3AD* Tel (01302) 831231 Fax as telephone E-mail rlandall@lineone.net

LANDEN, Edgar Sydney. b 23. ARCM46 FRCO46 St Jo Coll Dur BA54 BMus55 DipTh55. **d** 55 **p** 56. Succ Leeds 55-58; Prec Chelmsf Cathl *Chelmsf* 58-60; V Bathampton *B & W* 60-65; Perm to Offic *Glouc* 65-69; C Cirencester 69-76; Min Can Ch Ch *Ox* 76-88; R Wytham 76-88; rtd 88; Perm to Offic *B & W* 88-98. *The Old Vicarage, Bakers Hill, Tiverton EX16 5NE* Tel (01884) 256815

LANDER, Mrs Elizabeth Anne. b 69. St Andr Univ BSc93 Ox Univ PGCE94. Wycliffe Hall Ox 00. **d** 02. C Glascote and Stonydelph *Lich* from 02. *87 Belgrave Road, Wilnecote, Tamworth B77 2LS* Tel 07790-212302 (mobile) E-mail landerliz@yahoo.co.uk

LANDMAN, Denis Cooper. b 21. MBE60 OM(Ger)80. Lon Univ BA41 DipEd52. St Deiniol's Hawarden 79. **d** 82 **p** 83. Hon C Tranmere St Paul w St Luke *Ches* 82-86; Australia from 86; C Southport St Pet 86-88; P-in-c Biggera Waters 88-92; rtd 92. *1/24 Stretton Drive, Helensvale, Qld, Australia 4212* Tel (0061) (7) 5573 4660 Mobile 407-758376

LANDRETH, Mrs Mavis Isabella (Isabel). b 32. SEN81. Gilmore Ho 67. **dss** 74 **d** 87. Walthamstow St Sav *Chelmsf* 70-75; Sanderstead All SS *S'wark* 76-79; Sheff St Cuth *Sheff* 84-85; N Gen Hosp Sheff 84-85; Icklesham *Chich* 86-87; Hon Par Dn 87-89; Perm to Offic from 89. *Gossamer Cottage, Slindon, Arundel BN18 0QT* Tel (01243) 814224

LANE, Alexander John. b 71. Leeds Univ BA02. Coll of Resurr Mirfield 99. **d** 02 **p** 03. C Eastbourne St Andr *Chich* from 02. *75 Churchdale Road, Eastbourne BN22 8RX* Tel (01323) 732741 E-mail thecurate@hotmail.com

LANE, Andrew Harry John. b 49. MBE92. Lanc Univ BA71. Cuddesdon Coll 71. **d** 73 **p** 74. C Abingdon w Shippon *Ox* 73-78; Chapl Abingdon Sch 75-78; Chapl RAF 78-94; rtd 94; Perm to Offic *Nor* 94-01; Public Preacher from 01; RD Repps from 02. *Society of St Luke, 32B Beeston Common, Sheringham NR26 8ES* Tel (01263) 825623 Fax 820334

LANE, Anthony James. b 29. Leeds Univ BA53. Coll of Resurr Mirfield 53. **d** 55 **p** 56. C Tilehurst St Mich *Ox* 55-60; Min Can Win Cathl *Win* 60-63; R Handley w Pentridge *Sarum* 64-80; V Thurmaston *Leic* 80-85; TV Bournemouth St Pet w St Swithun, H Trin etc *Win* 85-93; rtd 93. *5 Richards Way, Salisbury SP2 8NT* Tel (01722) 332163

LANE, Antony Kenneth. b 58. Ripon Coll Cuddesdon 84. **d** 87 **p** 88. C Crediton and Shobrooke *Ex* 87-90; C Amblecote *Worc* 90-94; C Sedgley All SS 94-95; TV 95-00; R Crayford *Roch* from 00. *The Rectory, 1 Claremont Crescent, Crayford, Dartford DA1 4RJ* Tel (01322) 522078 Mobile 07931-603470

LANE, Bernard Charles. b 59. Cam Coll of Art & Tech BA81 Bris Univ BA91 Anglia Poly Univ MA01. Trin Coll Bris 88 Ridley Hall Cam 99. **d** 01 **p** 02. C Sittingbourne St Mary and St Mich *Cant* from 01. *88 Albany Road, Sittingbourne ME10 1EL* Tel (01795) 426947 E-mail lane@inglaterra69.freeserve.co.uk

LANE, Christopher George. b 48. NDH. Sarum & Wells Th Coll 84. **d** 86 **p** 87. C Petersfield *Portsm* 86-90; P-in-c Barton 90-95; Perm to Offic from 95. *Carisbrooke Priory, 39 Whitcombe Road, Carisbrooke, Newport PO30 1YS* Tel (01983) 523354

LANE, David John. b 35. Magd Coll Ox BA58 MA62 BD89. Coll of Resurr Mirfield 60. **d** 62 **p** 62. Barbados 61-65; C Wolvercote *Ox* 65-66; Asst Chapl Pemb Coll Ox 66-68; Lect 68-71; Tutor St Steph Ho Ox 68-71; Canada 71-83; Assoc Prof Univ of Toronto 71-83; Tutor Coll of Resurr Mirfield 83-97; Dir of Studies 84-97; Vice-Prin 87-90; Prin 90-97; rtd 97. *Overton Cottage, New Galloway, Castle Douglas DG7 3SD*

LANE, Denis John Victor. b 29. Lon Univ LLB49 BD55. Oak Hill Th Coll 50. **d** 53 **p** 54. C Deptford St Jo *S'wark* 53-56; C Cam St Steph CD *Ely* 56-59; OMF 60-94; Malaysia 60-66; Singapore 66-94; Lic to Offic *Chich* 91-94; rtd 94; Perm to Offic *Chich* from 94. *2 Parry Drive, Rustington, Littlehampton BN16 2QY* Tel (01903) 785430 Fax as telephone

LANE, Ms Elizabeth Jane Holden. b 66. St Pet Coll Ox BA89 MA93. Cranmer Hall Dur DMS93. **d** 93 **p** 94. C Blackb St Jas *Blackb* 93-96; Perm to Offic *York* 96-99; Family Life Educn Officer *Ches* 00-02; TV Stockport SW from 02. *The Vicarage, 217 Outwood Road, Heald Green, Cheadle SK8 3JS* Tel 0161-437 4614

LANE, George David Christopher. b 68. St Pet Coll Ox BA89 MA93. Cranmer Hall Dur DMS93. **d** 93 **p** 94. C Blackb St Jas *Blackb* 93-96; C Beverley Minster *York* 96-99; V Heald Green St Cath *Ches* from 99. *The Vicarage, 217 Outwood Road, Heald Green, Cheadle SK8 3JS* Tel 0161-437 4614 *or* 3685 E-mail george.lane@exalt.co.uk

LANE, Canon Gerald. b 29. Bede Coll Dur BA52 MA96. Sarum Th Coll 52. **d** 54 **p** 55. C Camberwell St Giles *S'wark* 54-58; C Gillingham St Aug *Roch* 58-59; V Camberwell St Phil and St Mark *S'wark* 59-67; V Plumstead St Nic 67-73; V Gillingham St Aug *Roch* 73-78; V Hadlow 78-94; Hon Can Roch Cathl 87-94; rtd 94; Perm to Offic *Roch* 94-97; Perm to Offic *St Alb* 97-03. *2 Popley Butts, Meltham, Holmfirth HD9 5JN* Tel (01484) 854116

LANE, Canon Iain Robert. b 61. CCC Ox BA83. Ripon Coll Cuddesdon BA86 MA88. **d** 87 **p** 88. C Rotherhithe St Mary w All SS *S'wark* 87-91; V Bierley *Bradf* 91-00; Can Res St Alb from 00. *2 Sumpter Yard, St Albans AL1 1BY* Tel (01727) 890205 E-mail edcanon@stalbanscathedral.org.uk

LANE, John Ernest. b 39. OBE94. MBIM76 Cranfield Info Tech Inst MSc80. Handsworth Coll Birm 58. **d** 80 **p** 80. In Meth Ch 62-80; Hon C Peckham St Jo w St Andr *S'wark* 80-95; Hon C Greenwich St Alfege 98-99; Dir St Mungo Housing Assn 80-94; Dir Corporate Affairs from 94; Perm to Offic 95-98. *2 Tregony Rise, Lichfield WS14 9SN* Tel (01543) 415078

LANE, Mrs Linda Mary. b 41. ACIB66 Lon Univ BD87. Gilmore Ho DipRK67. **dss** 82 **d** 87 **p** 94. Hadlow *Roch* 82-94; Hon Par Dn 87-94; Perm to Offic 94-96; C Dartford H Trin 96-97; V

Kensworth, Studham and Whipsnade *St Alb* 97-03; rtd 03. *2 Popley Butts, Meltham, Holmfirth HD9 5JN* Tel (01484) 854116

LANE, Malcolm Clifford George. b 48. JP. St D Coll Lamp. **d** 02. Par Dn Abergavenny St Mary w Llanwenarth Citra *Mon* from 02; Asst Chapl Gwent Healthcare NHS Trust from 02. *10 Cwrdy Close, Griffithstown, Pontypool NP4 5AY* Tel (01495) 755487 E-mail st8711@aol.com

LANE, Martin John. b 69. Coll of Resurr Mirfield 92. **d** 95 **p** 96. C Liss *Portsm* 95-98; C Warren Park 98-00; C Leigh Park 98-00; TV Littlehampton and Wick *Chich* from 00. *St James's Vicarage, 12 Cornwall Road, Littlehampton BN17 6EE* Tel (01903) 724311

LANE, Michael. *See* LANE, William Michael

LANE, Mrs Pamela. b 44. **d** 00 **p** 01. OLM Betley and Keele *Lich* from 00. *Brandon, Main Road, Betley, Crewe CW3 9BH* Tel (01270) 820258

LANE, Richard Peter. b 60. Linc Th Coll 85. **d** 88 **p** 89. C Towcester w Easton Neston *Pet* 88-91; Asst Chapl Oslo w Bergen, Trondheim, Stavanger etc *Eur* 91-93; V Writtle w Highwood *Chelmsf* 93-99; Chapl Whitelands Coll Roehampton Inst *S'wark* from 99. *Whitelands College, West Hill, London SW15 3SN* Tel (020) 8392 3516

LANE, Ms Rosalind Anne. b 69. Trevelyan Coll Dur BA91 Heythrop Coll Lon MTh93 Man Univ MA01. Westcott Ho Cam Cert Th & Min 95. **d** 95 **p** 96. C Huddersfield St Pet and All SS *Wakef* 95-99; Sub Chapl HM Pris and YOI New Hall 97-99; Asst Chapl HM Pris and YOI Doncaster 99-01; Chapl 01; Chapl HM Pris Wymott from 01. *HM Prison Wymott, Ulnes Walton Lane, Leyland PR26 8LW* Tel (01772) 421461 Fax 455960

LANE, Roy Albert. b 42. Bris Sch of Min 82. **d** 85 **p** 86. NSM Bedminster *Bris* 85-97; Perm to Offic 97-02; NSM Bishopsworth and Bedminster Down from 02. *20 Ashton Drive, Bristol BS3 2PW* Tel 0117-983 0747 Mobile 07747-808972 E-mail roypeg@blueyonder.co.uk

LANE, Simon. *See* DOUGLAS LANE, Charles Simon Pellew

LANE, Stuart Alexander Rhys. *See* LANE, Alexander John

LANE, Terry. b 50. STETS 94. **d** 97 **p** 98. NSM Freemantle *Win* 97-99; Chapl HM Pris Kingston (Portsm) 99-01; Chapl HM Pris Parkhurst from 01. *HM Prison Parkhurst, Newport PO30 5NX* Tel (01983) 523855 ext 416 Fax 524861

LANE, William Henry Howard. b 63. Bris Poly BA85. Trin Coll Bris 00. **d** 02 **p** 03. C Frome H Trin *B & W* from 02. *54 Oakfield Road, Frome BA11 4JE* Tel (01373) 474334 E-mail lane@fish.co.uk

LANE, William Michael. b 19. BNC Ox MA47. **d** 79 **p** 80. Asst Chapl Clifton Coll Bris 79-82; P-in-c Batts St Mich *Bris* 82-88; C 88-89; rtd 89; Perm to Offic *Bris* 89-95. *8 Fremantle Square, Bristol BS6 5TL* Tel 0117-924 7925

LANG, Geoffrey Wilfrid Francis. b 33. St Jo Coll Ox BA56 MA61. Cuddesdon Coll 56. **d** 58 **p** 59. C Spalding *Linc* 58-61; Asst Chapl Leeds Univ *Ripon* 61-62; C Chesterton St Luke *Ely* 62-63; C-in-c Chesterton Gd Shep CD 63-69; V Chesterton Gd Shep 69-72; V Willian *St Alb* 72-76; Dioc Dir of Educn 72-76; R N Lynn w St Marg and St Nic *Nor* 77-86; V Hammersmith St Pet *Lon* 86-00; rtd 00. *54 Old Oak Road, London W3 7HQ* Tel (020) 8746 1371

LANG, The Very Revd John Harley. b 27. LRAM Em Coll Cam MA60 K Coll Lon AKC49 BD60 Keele Univ Hon DLitt88. St Boniface Warminster 49. **d** 52 **p** 53. C Portsea St Mary *Portsm* 52-57; PV and Sacr S'wark Cathl *S'wark* 57-60; Chapl Em Coll Cam 60-64; Asst Hd Relig Broadcasting BBC 64-67; Hd of Relig Progr BBC Radio 67-71; Hd of Relig Broadcasting BBC 71-80; C Sacombe *St Alb* 73-80; Chapl to The Queen 77-80; Dean Lich 80-93; rtd 93; Perm to Offic *Glouc* 93-96. *1 Abbotsdene, 6 Cudnall Street, Charlton Kings, Cheltenham GL53 8HT* Tel (01242) 577742 Fax as telephone E-mail jhlang@email.com

LANG, Nicholas. b 45. DipTh97. SEITE 94. **d** 97 **p** 98. NSM Beckenham St Jo *Roch* 97-98; NSM Penge Lane H Trin 98-01; Chapl St Chris Hospice Lon 00; V Beckenham St Jo *Roch* from 01. *St John's Vicarage, 249 Eden Park Avenue, Beckenham BR3 3JN* Tel and fax (020) 8650 6110 Mobile 07968-985051 E-mail niklang@aol.com

LANG, William David. b 51. K Coll Lon BD74 AKC74. St Aug Coll Cant 74. **d** 75 **p** 76. C Fleet *Guildf* 75-79; C Ewell St Fran 79-82; C W Ewell 79-82; V Holmwood 82-92; R Elstead from 92; V Thursley from 92. *The Rectory, Thursley Road, Elstead, Godalming GU8 6DG* Tel (01252) 703251 E-mail william@lang.net

LANGAN, Mrs Eleanor Susan. b 56. Homerton Coll Cam BEd78. Ripon Coll Cuddesdon 84. **d** 87 **p** 94. Hon Par Dn Grays Thurrock *Chelmsf* 87-89; Lic to Offic 89-94; NSM Creeksea w Althorne, Latchingdon and N Fambridge 94-95; NSM S Woodham Ferrers 95-99; NSM Overstrand, Northrepps, Sidestrand etc *Nor* 99-03; Chapl Norfolk and Nor Univ Hosp NHS Trust from 00. *The Rectory, 22A Harbord Road, Overstrand, Cromer NR27 0PN* Tel (01263) 579350

LANGAN, Michael Leslie. b 54. Cam Univ BA PGCE. Cranmer Hall Dur. **d** 84 **p** 85. C Grays Thurrock *Chelmsf* 84-89; V Creeksea w Althorne, Latchingdon and N Fambridge 89-95; RD Maldon and Dengie 92-95; P-in-c S Woodham Ferrers 95-99; R

Overstrand, Northrepps, Sidestrand etc *Nor* from 99. *The Rectory, 22A Harbord Road, Overstrand, Cromer NR27 0PN* Tel (01263) 579350 E-mail mlangan@tiscali.co.uk

LANGDON, John Bonsall. b 21. Linc Coll Ox BA51 MA55. Ripon Hall Ox 52. **d** 54 **p** 55. C Erith St Jo *Roch* 54-57; C Christchurch *Win* 57-60; Min Can Ripon Cathl *Ripon* 60-63; R Swillington 63-75; P-in-c Wrangthorn 75-76; V Leeds All Hallows w St Simon 75-76; V Leeds All Hallows w Wrangthorn 76-87; P-in-c Woodhouse St Mark 85-87; V Woodhouse and Wrangthorn 87-92; rtd 92; Perm to Offic *Ripon* from 92; Hon Min Can Ripon Cathl from 02. *32 Magdalen's Road, Ripon HG4 1HT* Tel (01765) 606814

LANGDON, Ms Susan Mary. b 48. RN69. Ripon Coll Cuddesdon 01. **d** 03. C Amesbury *Sarum* from 03. *1 Devereux Road, Amesbury, Salisbury SP4 7NR* Tel (01980) 625733 E-mail slangdon@ripon-cuddeson.ac.uk

LANGDON-DAVIES, Mrs Stella Mary. b 44. Bris Univ BSc85 Nottm Univ MBA97. St Jo Coll Nottm MTh01. **d** 01 **p** 02. C Stamford All SS w St Jo *Linc* from 01. *Church House, 26 Hazel Grove, Stanford PE9 2HJ* Tel (01780) 767759 Mobile 07976-380659 E-mail stellald@onetel.net.uk

LANGDOWN, Jennifer May. b 48. STETS DipHE95. **d** 98 **p** 99. C S Petherton w the Seavingtons *B & W* 98-02; R Curry Rivel w Fivehead and Swell from 02. *Warwick House, Wiltown, Curry Rivel, Langport TA10 0JF* Tel (01458) 251375 E-mail mrsvic@care4free.net

LANGE-SMITH, Michael Leslie. b 56. Bris Univ BSc83 Lon Bible Coll MA90. Trin Coll Bris 87. **d** 90 **p** 91. Zimbabwe 90-02; C Greendale 91-92; R Melfort 93-98; Dir Th Educn by Ext Coll of Zimbabwe 99-02; R Chinnor w Emmington and Sydenham etc *Ox* from 03. *The Rectory, High Street, Chinnor OX39 4DH* Tel (01844) 351309

LANGFORD, David Laurence. b 51. LNSM course 86. **d** 88 **p** 89. OLM Scotton w Northorpe *Linc* from 88. *1 Westgate, Scotton, Gainsborough DN21 3QX* Tel (01724) 763139

LANGFORD, Prof Michael John. b 31. New Coll Ox BA54 MA58 Cam Univ MA59 Lon Univ PhD66. Westcott Ho Cam 55. **d** 56 **p** 57. C Bris St Nath w St Kath *Bris* 56-59; Chapl Qu Coll Cam 59-63; C Hampstead St Jo *Lon* 63-67; Canada 67-96; Prof Philosophy Newfoundland Univ 82-96; Prof Medical Ethics 87-96; rtd 96; Perm to Offic *Ely* from 96. *90 Field View, Bar Hill, Cambridge CB3 8SY* Tel (01954) 789593

LANGFORD, Peter Francis. b 54. Sarum & Wells Th Coll 76. **d** 79 **p** 80. C N Ormesby *York* 79-82; Ind Chapl 83-91; V Middlesbrough St Chad 91-96; R Easington w Liverton from 96. *The Rectory, Grinkle Lane, Easington, Saltburn-by-the-Sea TS13 4NT* Tel (01287) 641348 E-mail peterlan2@aol.net

LANGFORD, Peter Julian. b 33. Selw Coll Cam BA58. Westcott Ho Cam 59. **d** 60 **p** 61. C E Ham St Mary *Chelmsf* 60-67; Hon C 67-71; Hon C Beccles St Mich *St E* 71-76; Warden Ringsfield Hall Suffolk 71-87; P-in-c Ringsfield w Redisham *St E* 76-80; TV Seacroft *Ripon* 87-89; rtd 98. *36 Ringsfield Road, Beccles NR34 9PF* Tel (01502) 710034

LANGHAM, Paul Jonathan. b 60. Ex Univ BA81 DipTh83 Fitzw Coll Cam BA86 MA91. Ridley Hall Cam 84. **d** 87 **p** 88. C Bath Weston All SS w N Stoke *B & W* 87-91; Chapl and Fell St Cath Coll Cam 91-96; V Combe Down w Monkton Combe and S Stoke *B & W* from 96. *81 Church Road, Combe Down, Bath BA2 5JJ* Tel (01225) 833152 or 835835 E-mail vicar@htcd.co.uk

LANGLEY, Emma Louise. *See* BAUGHAN, Mrs Emma Louise Langley

LANGLEY, Canon Myrtle Sarah. b 39. FRAI TCD BA61 HDipEd62 MA67 Bris Univ PhD76 Lon Univ BD66. Dalton Ho Bris 64. **d** 88 **p** 94. Dir Chr Development for Miss *Liv* 87-89; Dir Dioc Tr Inst *Carl* 90-98; Dioc Dir of Tr 90-98; Hon Can Carl Cathl 91-98; P-in-c Long Marton w Dufton and w Milburn from 98. *The Rectory, Long Marton, Appleby-in-Westmorland CA16 6BN* Tel (01768) 361269 Fax 361196 E-mail canonmlangley@hotmail.com

LANGLEY, The Ven Robert. b 37. St Cath Soc Ox BA61. St Steph Ho Ox. **d** 63 **p** 64. C Aston cum Aughton *Sheff* 63-68; Midl Area Sec Chr Educn Movement 68-71; HQ Sec Chr Educn Movement 71-74; Prin Ian Ramsey Coll Brasted 74-77; Dir St Alb Minl Tr Scheme 77-85; Can Res St Alb 77-85; Dioc Dir of Min and Tr 98-01; Adn Lindisfarne from 01; Local Min Development Officer from 01. *4 Acomb Close, Stobhill, Morpeth NE61 2YH* Tel (01670) 503810 Fax 503469 E-mail b.langley@newcastle.anglican.org or kca85@dial.pipex.com

LANGMAN, Barry Edward. b 46. Master Mariner 73. Cant Sch of Min 87. **d** 90 **p** 91. NSM St Margarets-at-Cliffe w Westcliffe etc *Cant* 90-92; C Sandgate St Paul *Cant* 92-95; P-in-c Headcorn 95-01; V from 01. *The Vicarage, 64 Oak Lane, Headcorn, Ashford TN27 9TB* Tel (01622) 890342

LANGRELL, Gordon John. b 35. Cant Univ (NZ) BA58. Ridley Hall Cam 65. **d** 67 **p** 68. C Tonbridge SS Pet and Paul *Roch* 67-71; New Zealand from 71. *46A Greenhurst Street, Upper*

Riccarton, Christchurch 8004, New Zealand Tel (0064) (3) 348 9554 Fax 348 9805 E-mail gorlang@xtra.co.nz

LANGRIDGE, Molly Deirdre. b 48. Bris Poly CQSW88. LNSM course 96. **d** 98 **p** 99. OLM King's Lynn St Marg w St Nic *Nor* 98-03. *Address temp unknown* E-mail langa@tesco.net

✠**LANGRISH, The Rt Revd Michael Laurence.** b 46. Birm Univ BSocSc67 Fitzw Coll Cam BA73 MA77. Ridley Hall Cam 71. **d** 73 **p** 74 **c** 93. C Stratford-on-Avon w Bishopton *Cov* 73-76; Chapl Rugby Sch 76-81; P-in-c Offchurch *Cov* 81-87; Dioc Dir of Ords 81-87; P-in-c Rugby St Andr 87-91; Hon Can Cov Cathl 90-93; TR Rugby St Andr 91-93; Suff Bp Birkenhead *Ches* 93-00; Bp Ex from 00. *The Palace, Exeter EX1 1HY* Tel (01392) 272362 Fax 430923 E-mail bishop.of.exeter@exeter.anglican.org

LANGSTAFF, James Henry. b 56. St Cath Coll Ox BA77 MA81 Nottm Univ BA80. St Jo Coll Nottm 78. **d** 81 **p** 82. C Farnborough *Guildf* 81-84 and 85-86; P-in-c 84-85; P-in-c Duddeston w Nechells *Birm* 86; V 87-96; RD Birm City 95-96; Bp's Dom Chapl 96-00; P-in-c Short Heath 98-00; R Sutton Coldfield H Trin from 00; AD Sutton Coldfield from 02. *Holy Trinity Rectory, 5 Broome Gardens, Sutton Coldfield B75 7JE* Tel 0121-311 0474 *or* 321 1144 E-mail langstaff@btinternet.com

LANGSTON, Clinton Matthew. b 62. Derby Coll of Educn BCombStuds86. Qu Coll Birm 87. **d** 90 **p** 91. C Shirley *Birm* 90-94; CF from 94. *c/o MOD Chaplains (Army)* Tel (01980) 615804 Fax 615800

LANGTON, Canon Kenneth. b 26. Open Univ BA76. St Aid Birkenhead 52. **d** 55 **p** 56. C Oldham St Paul *Man* 55-57; C Ashton Ch Ch 57-58; P-in-c 58; V Stalybridge New St Geo 58-69; P-in-c Stalybridge Old St Geo 67-69; V Stalybridge 69-71; R Radcliffe St Mary 71-83; Hon Can Man Cathl 80-91; V Tyldesley w Shakerley 83-91; rtd 91; Perm to Offic *Man* from 91. *889 Walmersley Road, Bury BL9 5LE* Tel 0161-764 1552

LANGTON, Canon Maurice Charles. b 09. Trin Coll Cam BA30 MA34. Sarum Th Coll 33. **d** 34 **p** 35. C Horsham *Chich* 34-37; India 37-52; V Billingshurst *Chich* 52-56; Dir RE and Tr of Ord Cand 56-77; Can and Preb Chich Cathl 63-77; rtd 77; Perm to Offic *Linc* 77-86. *3 Caithness Road, Stamford PE9 2TE* Tel (01780) 51004

LANGTON, Robert. b 45. St Alb and Ox Min Course 97. **d** 00 **p** 01. C Boyne Hill *Ox* from 00. *St Paul's House, 3 Church Close, Maidenhead SL6 4HE* Tel (01628) 781617

LANHAM, Geoffrey Peter. b 62. Cam Univ MA84 Ox Univ MPhil86. Wycliffe Hall Ox 86. **d** 89 **p** 90. C Southborough St Pet w Ch Ch and St Matt *Roch* 89-92; C Harborne Heath *Birm* 92-00; C Birm St Paul from 00; Deanery Missr from 00. *117 Metchley Lane, Harborne, Birmingham B17 0JH* Tel 0121-427 6907 *or* 427 4601 E-mail online@btclick.com

LANHAM, Richard Paul White. b 42. Dur Univ BA64. Wycliffe Hall Ox 65. **d** 67 **p** 68. C Gerrards Cross *Ox* 67-69; C Horwich H Trin *Man* 69-72; C Worsley 72-74; V Accrington St Andr *Blackb* 74-80; V Shillington *St Alb* 80-85; V Upper w Lower Gravenhurst 80-85; rtd 85; Perm to Offic *St Alb* from 85. *10 Alexander Close, Clifton, Shefford SG17 5RB* Tel (01462) 813520

LANKEY, David. b 41. MBCS68 CEng88 Southn Univ BSc62. S'wark Ord Course 79. **d** 82 **p** 83. NSM W Wimbledon Ch Ch *S'wark* 82-92; C Tooting All SS 92-95; R Long Ditton *S'wark* 95-00; R Long Ditton *Guildf* 00-02; rtd 02. *15B Heathfield Road, Seaford BN25 1TH* Tel (01323) 894452

LANKSHEAR, Jane Frances. b 70. Leeds Univ BA92 Trin Coll Carmarthen MPhil97 PhD99. EAMTC 98. **d** 00 **p** 01. C Sudbury and Chilton *St E* 00-03; TV Hitchin *St Alb* from 03. *St Mark's Vicarage, St Mark's Close, Hitchin SG5 1UR* Tel (01462) 422862 *or* 434686 E-mail jane@jlankshear.freeserve.co.uk

LANSDALE, Canon Charles Roderick. b 38. Leeds Univ BA59. Coll of Resurr Mirfield 59. **d** 61 **p** 62. C Nunhead St Antony *S'wark* 61-65; Swaziland 65-71; V Benhilton *S'wark* 72-78; TR Catford (Southend) and Downham 78-87; TR Moulsecoomb *Chich* 87-97; V Eastbourne St Mary from 97; Can and Preb Chich Cathl from 98. *The Vicarage, 2 Glebe Close, Eastbourne BN20 8AW* Tel (01323) 720420

LANSLEY, Paul Sanford. b 33. Trin Coll Cam BA56 MA61. St Steph Ho Ox 56. **d** 58 **p** 59. C N Acton St Gabr *Lon* 58-60; Perm to Offic *Chelmsf* 62-69; Hon C Colchester St Jas, All SS, St Nic and St Runwald 69-91; Asst Chapl Colchester Hosps 86-00; rtd 00; Perm to Offic *Chelmsf* from 00. *31A King Coel Road, Colchester CO3 5AQ* Tel (01206) 562813 Fax 769423

LANYON JONES, Keith. b 49. Southn Univ BTh79. Sarum & Wells Th Coll 74. **d** 77 **p** 78. C Charlton Kings St Mary *Glouc* 77-81; Sen Chapl Rugby Sch 81-99; Lic to Offic *Truro* 83-00; P-in-c St Cleer from 00. *The Vicarage, St Cleer, Liskeard PL14 5DN* Tel (01579) 343240 E-mail lanyon67@hotmail.com

LAPAGE, Michael Clement. b 23. Selw Coll Cam BA47 MA73. Clifton Th Coll 60. **d** 61 **p** 62. Kenya 61-73; Chapl Bedford Sch 73-75; Chapl Lyon w Grenoble *Eur* 76-79; V Walford w Bishopswood *Heref* 79-88; P-in-c Goodrich w Welsh Bicknor and Marstow 83-88; rtd 88; Perm to Offic *Ex* from 88.

Moorlands, 20 Watts Road, Tavistock PL19 8LG Tel (01822) 615901

LAPHAM, Canon Fred. b 31. Univ of Wales (Lamp) BA53 PhD00. Vancouver Sch of Th LTh55 BD58. **d** 55 **p** 55. Canada 55-59; C Wallasey St Hilary *Ches* 59-62; V Over St Jo 62-70; V Upton Ascension 70-82; R Grappenhall 82-91; RD Gt Budworth 85-91; Hon Can Ches Cathl 88-91; rtd 91; Perm to Offic *Ches* and *Heref* from 91. *1 Coppice Gate, Lyth Hill, Shrewsbury SY3 0BT* Tel (01743) 872284

LAPWOOD, Robin Rowland John. b 57. Selw Coll Cam MA. Ridley Hall Cam 80. **d** 82 **p** 83. C Bury St Edmunds St Mary *St E* 82-86; P-in-c Bentley w Tattingstone 86-93; P-in-c Copdock w Washbrook and Belstead 86-93; TV High Wycombe *Ox* 93-96; P-in-c Marcham w Garford 96-02; Asst Master Summer Fields Sch Ox from 02. *Summer Fields School, Mayfield Road, Oxford OX2 7EN* Tel (01865) 454433 E-mail robin.lapwood@bigfoot.com

LARCOMBE, Paul Richard. b 57. Portsm Poly BSc79 CEng MIEE. Trin Coll Bris 94. **d** 96 **p** 97. C Werrington *Pet* 96-98; C Longthorpe 98-00; V Pet St Paul from 00. *St Paul's Vicarage, Lincoln Road, Peterborough PE1 2PA* Tel (01733) 343746 E-mail paul@peterborough-stpauls.org.uk

LARGE, William Roy. b 40. Dur Univ BA DipEd. Edin Th Coll 82. **d** 84 **p** 85. C Leamington Priors All SS *Cov* 84-88; V Bishop's Tachbrook 88-99; Warden of Readers and Sen Tutor 88-99; TV N Tyne and Redesdale Team *Newc* 99-01; TR from 01. *The Rectory, Bellingham, Hexham NE48 2JS* Tel (01434) 220019

LARK, William Donald Starling. b 35. Keble Coll Ox BA59 MA63. Wells Th Coll 59. **d** 61 **p** 62. C Wyken *Cov* 61-64; C Christchurch *Win* 64-66; V Yeovil St Mich *B & W* 66-75; V Earley St Pet *Ox* 75-85; V Prittlewell *Chelmsf* 85-88; V Dawlish *Ex* 88-00; rtd 00; P-in-c Lanzarote *Eur* from 00. *Calle Los Sabandenos 37, 35510 Puerto del Carmen, Lanzarote, Canary Islands, Spain* Tel (0034) (928) 514241

LARKEY, Mrs Deborah Frances. b 63. Univ of Wales (Abth) BA85 Liv Inst of Educn PGCE90. LNSM course 95. **d** 98 **p** 99. OLM Toxteth St Cypr w Ch Ch *Liv* 98-01; OLM Edge Hill St Cypr w St Mary from 01. *36 Cotswold Street, Liverpool L7 2PZ* Tel 0151-264 0097

LARKIN, Canon Peter John. b 39. ALCD62. **d** 62 **p** 63. C Liskeard w St Keyne *Truro* 62-65; C Rugby St Andr *Cov* 65-67; Sec Bp Cov Call to Miss 67-68; V Kea *Truro* 68-78; P-in-c Bromsgrove St Jo *Worc* 78-81; R Torquay St Matthias, St Mark and H Trin *Ex* 81-97; Can Sokoto Nigeria 91-98; Can Kaduna from 98; TR Plymouth Em, St Paul Efford and St Aug *Ex* 97-00; rtd 00; Perm to Offic *Ex* from 00. *Picklecombe, 57 Babbacombe Downs Road, Torquay TQ1 3LP* Tel (01803) 326888 E-mail larkin@petermolly.freeserve.co.uk

LARNER, Gordon Edward Stanley. b 30. Brasted Th Coll 54 Oak Hill Th Coll 55. **d** 59 **p** 60. C Peckham St Mary Magd *S'wark* 59-62; C Luton w E Hyde *St Alb* 62-68; V Lower Sydenham St Mich *S'wark* 68-73; Ind Chapl 73-84; Chapl HM Pris Ranby 84-92; rtd 92. *Glen Rosa, Meshaw, South Molton EX36 4NE*

LARSEN, Clive Erik. b 55. St Jo Coll Nottm LTh90. **d** 90 **p** 91. C Weaverham *Ches* 90-92; C Helsby and Dunham-on-the-Hill 92-95; P-in-c Cheadle Heath 95-02. *Address temp unknown*

LASHBROOKE, David. b 60. Ex Univ BA87. Ripon Coll Cuddesdon 90. **d** 92 **p** 93. C Sherborne w Castleton and Lillington *Sarum* 92-95; P-in-c Weymouth St Paul 95-99; V 99-02; V St Marychurch *Ex* from 02. *The Vicarage, Hampton Avenue, Torquay TQ1 3LA* Tel (01803) 329054 E-mail frdavid@wdi.co.uk

LASHBROOKE, John. b 28. Kelham Th Coll 49. **d** 53 **p** 54. C Kennington St Jo *S'wark* 53-57; Br Guiana 57-59; V Sydenham St Phil *S'wark* 59-69; R Corby Epiphany w St Jo *Pet* 69-80; V Rubery *Birm* 80-88; V Horam *Chich* 88-93; rtd 93; Perm to Offic *Ex* from 94. *11 Gracey Court, Woodland Road, Broadclyst, Exeter EX5 3GA* Tel (01392) 464934

LASKEY, Cyril Edward. b 44. RMN71 RGN74. Llan Dioc Tr Scheme 85. **d** 88 **p** 89. NSM Troedrhiwgarth *Llan* 88-93; NSM Caerau w St Cynfelin 94-01; P-in-c Glyncorrwg and Upper Afan Valley from 01. *207 Bridgend Road, Maesteg CF34 0NL* Tel (01656) 734639

LASKEY, Stephen Allan. b 56. Manitoba Univ BA85. St Jo Coll Winnipeg MDiv88. **d** 89 **p** 89. Canada 89-01; C Labrador W 89; C Battle Harbour 89-91; R 91-96; R Goulds St Paul 96-99; Assoc P Foxtrap All SS 00-01; C Paddington St Jo w St Mich *Lon* 01-02; P-in-c Sydenham H Trin *S'wark* from 02; P-in-c Forest Hill St Aug from 03. *Holy Trinity Vicarage, 1 Sydenham Park Road, London SE26 4DY* Tel (020) 8699 5303 E-mail stephenlaskey@onetel.net.uk

LAST, Eric Cyril. b 30. Oak Hill Th Coll 77. **d** 79 **p** 80. C Wandsworth St Mich *S'wark* 79-83; V England St Andr 83-88; V S Merstham 88-96; Asst RD Reigate 92-96; rtd 96; Hon C Upper Tean *Lich* from 96. *29 Vicarage Road, Tean, Stoke-on-Trent ST10 4LE* Tel (01538) 722551 Fax as telephone E-mail eric.last1@btopenworld.com

LAST, Harold Wilfred. b 17. ARCM52 ARCO53 CCC Cam BA38 MA42. Linc Th Coll 39. **d** 40 **p** 41. C Bolton St Jas *Bradf* 40-44; C

Woodbridge St Mary *St E* 44-45; Lect K Coll Lon 45-53; Dir of Music St Bees, St Olave's & Felstead Schs 53-73; rtd 73. *Flat 1, Knapton House, North Walsham Road, Knapton, North Walsham NR28 0RT* Tel (01263) 720084

LAST, Michael Leonard Eric. b 60. St Jo Coll Nottm Dip Th & Min 94. **d** 94 **p** 95. C Tettenhall Wood *Lich* 94-98; V Pelsall 98-02; V Alton w Bradley-le-Moors and Oakamoor w Cotton from 02. *The New Vicarage, Limekiln Lane, Alton, Stoke-on-Trent ST10 4AR* Tel (01538) 702469
E-mail michael.l.e.last@btinternet.com

LAST, Norman Percy George. b 31. BA CertEd ATPL. Sarum & Wells Th Coll 77 Wycliffe Hall Ox 80. **d** 81 **p** 82. C Walton-on-Thames *Guildf* 81-83; C Farnham 83-87; R Monks Eleigh w Chelsworth and Brent Eleigh etc *St E* 87-90; P-in-c Bradworthy *Ex* 91-97; rtd 97; Perm to Offic *Ex* from 98; C Stansted *Chich* 00-02. *9 Wensley Gardens, Emsworth PO10 7RA* Tel (01243) 374174

LATHAM, Christine Elizabeth. b 46. S'wark Ord Course 87. **d** 90 **p** 94. Par Dn Battersea St Pet and St Paul *S'wark* 90-94; Par Dn S'wark Ch 94; C 94-97; C Merstham and Gatton from 97; Chapl E Surrey Learning Disability NHS Trust from 97. *Epiphany House, Mansfield Drive, Merstham, Redhill RH1 3JH* Tel (01737) 642628

LATHAM, Henry Nicholas Lomax. b 64. Reading Univ BA86. Wycliffe Hall Ox BTh93. **d** 93 **p** 94. C Aberystwyth *St D* 93-99; P-in-c Stoke Poges *Ox* from 99. *The Vicarage, Park Road, Stoke Poges, Slough SL2 4PE* Tel (01753) 642521
E-mail harryandtracy@isaiah41.freeserve.co.uk

LATHAM, John Montgomery. b 37. Univ of NZ BA Cam Univ MA Cant Univ (NZ) MEd. Westcott Ho Cam 60. **d** 62 **p** 63. C Camberwell St Geo *S'wark* 62-65; Chapl Trin Coll Cam 65-70; New Zealand from 71; Chapl Wanganui Colleg Sch 71-79; Min Enabler N New Brighton 96-01; V Christchurch St Luke 98-02; rtd 02. *43 Rugby Street, Christchurch, New Zealand 8001* Tel (0064) (3) 355 6654 Fax 355 6658 E-mail latham@xtra.co.nz

LATHAM, John Westwood. b 31. Ely Th Coll 57. **d** 60 **p** 61. C Cleckheaton St Jo *Wakef* 60-63; C Hemel Hempstead *St Alb* 63-65; C Wakef Cathl *Wakef* 65-67; V Outwood 67-72; TV Daventry w Norton *Pet* 72-79; V Flore w Dodford and Brockhall 79-96; rtd 96; Perm to Offic *Leic* from 97. *53 Lubenham Hill, Market Harborough LE16 9DG* Tel (01858) 469023

LATHAM, Robert Norman. b 53. Qu Coll Birm 82. **d** 85 **p** 86. C Tamworth *Lich* 85-89; TV Wordsley 89-93; TV Wordsley *Worc* 93-96; P-in-c Hallow 96-97; R Hallow and Grimley w Holt from 97. *Hallow Vicarage, 26 Baveney Road, Worcester WR2 6PF* Tel (01905) 748711

LATHAM, Roger Allonby. b 69. Leic Univ BA90 Warwick Univ MA92 Leeds Univ PGCE93. St Jo Coll Nottm BTh98. **d** 99 **p** 00. C Paston *Pet* 99-02; TV Cartmel Peninsula *Carl* from 02. *The Vicarage, Boarbank Lane, Allithwaite, Grange-over-Sands LA11 7QR* Tel (01539) 532437
E-mail lathams@home71.swinternet.co.uk

LATHAM, Trevor Martin. b 56. BD84. Ripon Coll Cuddesdon 84. **d** 86 **p** 87. C Cantril Farm *Liv* 86-89; TV Croxteth Park 89-98; V 98-99; TR Walton-on-the-Hill from 99. *The Rectory, Walton Village, Liverpool L4 6TJ* Tel 0151-525 3130 Fax as telephone E-mail rev.trev@virgin.net

LATHE, Canon Anthony Charles Hudson. b 36. Jes Coll Ox BA59 MA64 UEA Dip Sociology 68. Lich Th Coll 59. **d** 61 **p** 62. C Selby Abbey *York* 61-63; V Hempnall *Nor* 63-72; R Woodton w Bedingham 63-72; R Fritton w Morningthorpe w Shelton and Hardwick 63-72; R Topcroft 63-72; R Banham 72-76; TR Quidenham 76-83; P-in-c New Buckenham 78-79; V Heigham St Thos 83-94; Hon Can Nor Cathl 87-99; RD Nor S 90-94; P-in-c Sheringham 94-99; rtd 99; Perm to Offic *Nor* from 99. *38 Chestnut Hill, Norwich NR4 6NL* Tel (01603) 455846

LATIFA, Andrew Murdoch. b 73. Univ of Wales (Abth) BTh96 Univ of Wales (Cardiff) MTh00. St Mich Coll Llan 99. **d** 01 **p** 02. C Betws w Ammanford *St D* 01-03; C Llangynwyd w Maesteg *Llan* from 03. *10 Upper Street, Maesteg CF34 9DU* Tel (01656) 736858

LATIMER, Clifford James. b 45. City Univ BSc68. OLM course 97. **d** 99 **p** 00. OLM Burntwood *Lich* from 99. *24 Dove Close, Burntwood WS7 9JL* Tel (01543) 671471
E-mail cliff.latimer@virgin.net

LATTIMORE, Anthony Leigh. b 35. Dur Univ BA57. Lich Th Coll 60. **d** 62 **p** 63. C Aylestone *Leic* 62-66; C-in-c Eyres Monsell CD 66-69; V Eyres Monsell 69-73; V Somerby, Burrough on the Hill and Pickwell 73-86; RD Goscote I 80-86; R Glenfield 86-95; rtd 95; Perm to Offic *Leic* and *Pet* from 95. *28 Elizabeth Way, Uppingham, Oakham LE15 9PQ* Tel (01572) 823193

LATTY, Howard James. b 54. SRCh71. WEMTC 98. **d** 01. NSM Bath St Mich w St Paul *B & W* from 01. *68 Cedric Road, Bath BA1 3PB* Tel (01225) 319403

LAU, Paul Chow Sing. b 49. Nat Chengchi Univ BA74 Chinese Univ of Hong Kong MDiv80. **d** 80 **p** 81. Hong Kong 80-82 and 83-94; C Hong Kong H Trin 80-82; Macao 82-83; V Macao St Mark 82-83; P-in-c Hong Kong Ch of Our Sav 83-94; New Zealand 94-01; V Ang Chinese Miss Ch *Wellington* 94-01; Chapl Chinese Congregation *Lon* from 01. *3 Strutton Court, 54 Great Peter Street, London SW1P 2HH* Tel (020) 7233 0723 *or* 7233 4027

LAUGHTON, Derek Basil. b 24. Worc Coll Ox BA49 MA52. Westcott Ho Cam 49. **d** 51 **p** 52. C Wareham w Arne *Sarum* 51-53; CF 53-56; C Hemel Hempstead St Mary *St Alb* 56-59; V Stretton cum Wetmoor *Lich* 59-64; Chapl Wellington Sch Somerset 64-73; Chapl Ardingly Coll 73-77; R Plumpton w E Chiltington *Chich* 77-88; Perm to Offic *B & W* from 88; rtd 88. *13 Pyles Thorne Road, Wellington TA21 8DX* Tel (01823) 667386

LAURENCE, Brother. *See* EYERS, Frederick Thomas Laurence

LAURENCE, The Ven John Harvard Christopher. b 29. Trin Hall Cam BA53 MA57. Westcott Ho Cam 53. **d** 55 **p** 56. C Linc St Nic w St Jo Newport *Linc* 55-59; V Crosby 59-74; Can and Preb Linc Cathl 74-79 and 85-94; Dioc Missr 74-79; Bp's Dir of Clergy Tr Lon 80-85; Adn Lindsey *Linc* 85-94; rtd 94; Perm to Offic *Linc* 94-97. *5 Haffenden Road, Lincoln LN2 1RP* Tel (01522) 531444

LAURENCE, Julian Bernard Vere. b 60. Kent Univ BA82. St Steph Ho Ox 86. **d** 88 **p** 89. C Yeovil St Mich *B & W* 88-91; Chapl Yeovil Coll 90-91; Chapl Yeovil Distr Gen Hosp 91; P-in-c Barwick *B & W* 91-94; V Taunton H Trin from 94. *Holy Trinity Vicarage, 18 Holway Avenue, Taunton TA1 3AR* Tel (01823) 337890 E-mail jlaurence@htvicarage.fsnet.co.uk

LAURENCE, Vere Deacon. b 11. Ex Coll Ox BA33 BSc34 MA37. Sarum Th Coll 34. **d** 36 **p** 37. C Horfield St Greg *Bris* 36-42; Sec Dioc Reorganization Cttee 42-43; C Fishponds St Jo 42-43; C Knowle St Barn 43-47; Chapl HM Pris Stafford 47-52; V Upper Sunbury St Sav *Lon* 53-74; R Jacobstow w Warbstow and Treneglos *Truro* 74-83; RD Stratton 77-83; rtd 83; Perm to Offic *B & W* 85-97. *The Manor Nursing Home, Haydon Close, Bishops Hull, Taunton TA1 5HF* Tel (01823) 336633

LAURIE, Canon Donovan Hugh. b 40. Man Univ MSc. Oak Hill NSM Course. **d** 82 **p** 83. NSM Cudham and Downe *Roch* 82-84; C Tunbridge Wells St Jas 84-88; P-in-c Ventnor St Cath *Portsm* 88-99; V from 99; P-in-c Ventnor H Trin 88-99; V from 99; Hon Chapl St Cath Sch Ventnor from 88; P-in-c Bonchurch *Portsm* from 00; Hon Can Portsm Cathl from 01. *The Vicarage, Park Avenue, Ventnor PO38 1LD* Tel (01983) 854367
E-mail don@dlaurie.fsbusiness.co.uk

LAURIE, James Andrew Stewart. b 26. Selw Coll Cam BA51 MA55. Ridley Hall Cam 51. **d** 53 **p** 54. C Neasden cum Kingsbury St Cath *Lon* 53-56; C Cricklewood St Pet 56-59; C Lancing St Jas *Chich* 59-61; V Freehay *Lich* 61-65; P-in-c Ilam w Blore Ray and Okeover 65-71; V Wetton 65-71; V Alstonfield 65-71; P-in-c Calton 66-71; V Charsfield w Debach and Monewden w Hoo *St E* 83-86; V Charsfield w Debach, Monewden, Hoo etc 86-90; rtd 90; Perm to Offic *St E* from 91. *6 Meadow Lane, Thurston, Bury St Edmunds IP31 3QG* Tel (01359) 235181

LAUT, Graham Peter. b 37. Chich Th Coll 63. **d** 67 **p** 68. C Corringham *Chelmsf* 67-68; C Leytonstone St Marg w St Columba 68-71; P-in-c Leytonstone St Andr 71-75; V 75-80; V Romford Ascension Collier Row from 80. *The Ascension Vicarage, 68 Collier Row Road, Romford RM5 2BA* Tel (01708) 741658 E-mail glaut10497@aol.com

LAUTENBACH, Edward Wayne. b 59. St Paul's Coll Grahamstown DipTh87. **d** 88 **p** 88. S Africa 88-99; C Weltevredenpark St Mich 88-89; Asst P Florida St Gabr 89-91; Sen Asst P Bryanston St Mich 91-94; R Brakpan St Pet 94-99; P-in-c Grange St Andr *Ches* from 99; P-in-c Runcorn H Trin from 99. *The Vicarage, 37 Lime Grove, Runcorn WA7 5JZ* Tel (01928) 574411 Fax as telephone
E-mail wayne.lautenbach@btopenworld.com

LAVERACK, John Justin. b 51. Keele Univ BA CertEd Bris Univ BA. Bris Bapt Coll 76 Ex & Truro NSM Scheme 81. **d** 82 **p** 83. In Bapt Ch 79-81; C Braunton *Ex* 82-84; V Ex St Mark 84-92; Perm to Offic 92-98. *Tynewydd, Cwm Rhyd, Blaenwaun, Whitland SA34 0DB* Tel (01994) 419731
E-mail laverack@connect-wales.co.uk

LAVERTY, Canon Walter Joseph Robert. b 49. CITC 70 Glouc Th Course 73. **d** 73 **p** 74. C Belfast St Donard *D & D* 73-77; C Ballymacarrett St Patr 77-82; I Kilwarlin Upper w Kilwarlin Lower 82-86; I Orangefield w Moneyreagh from 86; Warden of Readers from 96; Can Down Cathl from 97; Preb 97-00; Treas from 01. *397 Castlereagh Road, Belfast BT5 6AB* Tel (028) 9070 4493 Fax as telephone

LAVERY, Canon Edward Robinson. Lon Univ BA DipTh. St Aid Birkenhead 65. **d** 67 **p** 68. C Belfast Trin Coll Miss *Conn* 67-69; C Belfast St Mary Magd 69-71; CF (TA) 70-95; OCF from 75; I Belfast St Phil *Conn* 71-74; I Craigs w Dunaghy and Killagan 74-83; I Ballymoney w Finvoy and Rasharkin from 83; Dioc Info Officer from 83; Can Conn Cathl 96-98; Treas 98-01; Chan from 01. *The Rectory, Queen Street, Ballymoney BT53 6JA* Tel (028) 7066 2149

LAVILLE, Jocelyn Roger (Jo). b 30. Ball Coll Ox BA52 MA63. ALCD64. **d** 64 **p** 65. C Gillingham St Mark *Roch* 64-69; C Thorpe Edge *Bradf* 69-72; Philippines 72-01; India from 01; rtd 95. *Iamanda Villa, Jowai Road, Nongthymmai, Shillong 793 014, NE India* Tel (0091) (364) 223 1499 E-mail jolaville@neline.com

LAW, Andrew Philip. b 61. BNC Ox BA83 MA93 G&C Coll Cam PGCE86 Westmr Coll Ox DipTh98. WMMTC 90. **d** 93 **p** 94. C

Tupsley w Hampton Bishop *Heref* 93-95; Chapl Heref Sixth Form Coll 94-95; Chapl City of Lon Freemen's Sch Ashtead Park 95-97; Lic to Offic *Guildf* 95-97; Chapl and Hd RS Heref Cathl Sch 97-02; Chapl Malvern Coll from 02. *Malvern College, College Road, Malvern WR14 3DF* Tel (01684) 892333 Fax 572398 E-mail andrew@lawhcs.freeserve.co.uk

LAW, Bryan. b 36. Leeds Univ BA59 Lon Univ BD76. Coll of Resurr Mirfield 59. **d** 61 **p** 62. C Winshill *Derby* 61-64; R Gorton St Phil *Man* 64-70; Lic to Offic 70-71; Perm to Offic *Ox* from 71; Hd Master Page Hill Co Middle Sch Buckingham 81-95; rtd 95. *35 Little Meadow, Loughton, Milton Keynes MK5 8EH* Tel (01908) 661333

LAW, David Richard. b 60. **d** 01 **p** 02. NSM Ashton-upon-Mersey St Martin *Ches* from 01. *2 Winston Close, Sale M33 6UG* Tel 0161-962 0297

LAW, Canon Donald Edward Boughton. b 22. Lon Coll of Div 67. **d** 69 **p** 70. C Leic H Apostles *Leic* 69-73; V Cosby 73-81; RD Guthlaxton I 75-81; V Melton Mowbray w Thorpe Arnold 81-86; Hon Can Leic Cathl 81-88; RD Framland II 84-88; TR Melton Gt Framland 86-88; rtd 88; Perm to Offic *Leic* and *Pet* from 88. *36 Mill Grove, Whissendine, Oakham LE15 7EY* Tel (01664) 474411

LAW, Elizabeth Ann. b 49. Doncaster Coll of Educn CertEd70 Loughb Univ MA01. EAMTC 99. **d** 01 **p** 02. NSM Wickham Bishops w Lt Braxted *Chelmsf* from 01. *27 Dengie Close, Witham CM8 1DJ* Tel (01376) 513596 E-mail lizz@messages.co.uk

LAW, Gordon James. b 19. Worc Ord Coll 67. **d** 69 **p** 70. C Hillingdon St Jo *Lon* 69-72; C Brixham *Ex* 72-76; R Drewsteignton 76-79; V Hittisleigh 76-79; V Spreyton 76-79; C Aldershot St Mich *Guildf* 79-82; rtd 82; Perm to Offic *Ex* 83-89; *Ab* from 83; *Bris* 93-99. *69 Maunsell Way, Wroughton, Swindon SN4 9JF* Tel (01793) 812948

LAW, Gordon Peter. b 35. Bernard Gilpin Soc Dur 59 Chich Th Coll 60. **d** 64 **p** 65. C Walthamstow St Barn and St Jas Gt *Chelmsf* 64-67; C Southchurch H Trin 67-68; C Plaistow St Andr 68-69; Chapl Aldersbrook Medical Unit 69-83; P-in-c Forest Gate All SS 69-74; V 74-83; V Romford St Jo 83-97; rtd 97; Perm to Offic *Chelmsf* from 97. *40 Molram's Lane, Great Baddow, Chelmsford CM2 7AH* Tel (01245) 477272

LAW, Herbert James Wentworth. b 12. Dur Univ BA39 DipTh39 MA42. **d** 40 **p** 41. C Monkwearmouth All SS *Dur* 40-43; P-in-c Felling 43-46; C-in-c Lobley Hill CD 46-49; V Lobley Hill 49-52; V Stoke Ferry w Wretton *Ely* 52-58; V Whittington 52-58; R Welney 58-69; V Barton 69-78; RD Barton 72-76; rtd 78; Perm to Offic *Ely* 78-00. *37 Westlands, Comberton, Cambridge CB3 7EH* Tel (01223) 263406

LAW, Jeremy Stuart Alan. b 67. RMN93 Man Metrop Univ BSc96. Westcott Ho Cam. **d** 00 **p** 01. C Newton Heath *Man* 00-01; C Wythenshawe from 01. *2 Cornishway, Manchester M22 0LD* Tel 0161-436 1769

LAW, Jeremy Thomson. b 61. Univ of Wales (Abth) BSc82 South Univ BTh89 Ox Univ DPhil00. Sarum & Wells Th Coll 84. **d** 87 **p** 88. C Wimborne Minster and Holt *Sarum* 87-90; C Highfield *Ox* 90-94; Chapl Ex Univ *Ex* from 94; Lic to Offic from 94. *Theology Department, Queens Building, University of Exeter, Queens Drive, Exeter EX4 4QE* Tel (01392) 264240 *or* 435384 Fax 264377

LAW, John Francis. b 35. Bps' Coll Cheshunt 65. **d** 67 **p** 68. C Styvechale *Cov* 67-71; P-in-c Cov St Anne and All SS 71-73; TV Cov E 73-77; P-in-c Fillongley 77-82; P-in-c Corley 77-82; V Fillongley and Corley 82-00; RD Nuneaton 90-95; rtd 00; Perm to Offic *Cov* from 00. *10 Brodick Way, Nuneaton CV10 7LH* Tel (024) 7632 5582

LAW, John Michael. b 43. Open Univ BA79. Westcott Ho Cam 65. **d** 68 **p** 69. C Chapel Allerton *Ripon* 68-72; C Ryhope *Dur* 72-73; Chapl Fulbourn Hosp Cam 74-94; Chapl Ida Darwin Hosp Cam 74-98; Mental Health Chapl Addenbrooke's NHS Trust from 94; Mental Health Fell Bethlem R and Maudsley Hosps 82. *Fulbourn Hospital, Fulbourn, Cambridge CB1 5EF* Tel (01223) 218598 Fax 218973 E-mail mike.law@addenbrookes.nhs.uk

LAW, Nicholas Charles. b 58. BA89. Trin Coll Bris 86. **d** 89 **p** 90. C Goldington *St Alb* 89-92; C Teignmouth, Ideford w Luton, Ashcombe etc *Ex* 92-97; R Bere Ferrers from 97. *The Rectory, Bere Alston, Yelverton PL20 7HH* Tel (01822) 840229

LAW, Peter James. b 46. Ridley Hall Cam 85. **d** 87 **p** 88. C Bournemouth St Jo w St Mich *Win* 87-91; V Chineham 91-96; V Luton Lewsey St Hugh *St Alb* from 96. *St Hugh's Vicarage, 367 Leagrave High Street, Luton LU4 0ND* Tel (01582) 605297 *or* 664433 Fax 696332 E-mail peterlaw@sthugheslewsey.fsnet.co.uk

LAW, Peter Leslie. b 25. Bede Coll Dur BA48 DipEd49. Qu Coll Birm 53. **d** 55 **p** 56. C Tooting All SS *S'wark* 55-57; C Frome St Jo *B & W* 57-59; V Battersea St Mary-le-Park *S'wark* 59-65; R Brampton Ash w Dingley *Pet* 65-69; Chapl St Luke's Sch Southsea 69-79; Chapl Portsm Cathl *Portsm* 69-79; V Eastney 79-90; rtd 90; Perm to Offic Portsm from 90. *123 Hayling Avenue, Portsmouth PO3 6DY* Tel (023) 9261 9913

LAW, Richard Anthony Kelway. b 57. UWIST BEng79 Nottm Univ MA(TS)01. St Jo Coll Nottm 99. **d** 01 **p** 02. C Brundall w

Braydeston and Postwick *Nor* from 01. *8 Greenacre Close, Brundall, Norwich NR13 5QF* Tel (01603) 714570 E-mail richard-law@lineone.net

LAW, Canon Robert Frederick. b 43. St Aid Birkenhead 67. **d** 69 **p** 70. C Bengeo *St Alb* 69-72; C Sandy 72-76; P-in-c St Ippolyts 76-81; Chapl Jersey Gp of Hosps 81-84; V Crowan w Godolphin *Truro* 84-92; RD Kerrier 90-91; R St Columb Major w St Wenn 92-02; RD Pydar 95-02; P-in-c St Minver from 02; Hon Can Truro Cathl from 98. *The Vicarage, Churchtown, St Minver, Wadebridge PL27 6QH* Tel and fax (01208) 862398 Mobile 078819-33024 E-mail rfl@stcolumb.junglelink.co.uk

LAW, Robert James. b 31. Lon Univ MB, BS55. Ridley Hall Cam 62. **d** 64 **p** 65. C Barnehurst *Roch* 64-66; C Edgware *Lon* 66-72; V Halwell w Moreleigh *Ex* 72-94; P-in-c Woodleigh and Loddiswell 76-79; R 79-94; rtd 94. *38 Wheatlands Road, Paignton TQ4 5HU* Tel (01803) 559450

LAW, Simon Anthony. b 55. Middx Univ BA93 DipHE79. NTMTC 94. **d** 96 **p** 97. NSM Forest Gate St Mark *Chelmsf* 96-98; C Becontree W 98-99; TV 99-02; TR from 02. *St Cedd's Vicarage, 185 Lodge Avenue, Dagenham RM8 2HQ* Tel (020) 8592 5900 E-mail law@fish.co.uk

LAW-JONES, Peter Deniston. b 55. Newc Univ BA77 Man Univ PGCE81 Nottm Univ BTh87. Linc Th Coll 84. **d** 87 **p** 88. C Chorley St Laur *Blackb* 87-91; V Feniscliffe 91-96; V St Annes from 96; Chapl Blackpool, Wyre and Fylde Community NHS Trust from 97. *The Vicarage, St Thomas Road, Lytham St Annes FY8 1JL* Tel (01253) 723750 E-mail peter@law-jones.fsnet.co.uk

LAWES, David Alan. b 33. Lon Bible Coll BD57 PGCE58 AcDipEd66 Lon Inst of Educn MA70. Cranmer Hall Dur 90. **d** 91 **p** 92. NSM Shaston *Sarum* 91-94; Hon C Diptford, N Huish, Harberton and Harbertonford *Ex* 94-98; rtd 98; Perm to Offic *Sarum* from 98. *47 Grosvenor Road, Shaftesbury SP7 8DP* Tel (01747) 855621

LAWES, Geoffrey Hyland. b 37. St Jo Coll Dur BA58 DipTh62 Hertf Coll Ox BA60 MA64 Newc Univ PGCE76 MEd79. Cranmer Hall Dur 61. **d** 63 **p** 64. C Millfield St Mark *Dur* 63-66; C Jarrow Grange 66-69; Hon C 69-86; Lic to Offic 86-90; V Collierley w Annfield Plain from 90. *Collierley Vicarage, Annfield Plain, Stanley DH9 8QS* Tel (01207) 236254

LAWES, Stephen George. b 40. Nottm Univ PGCE75. St Jo Coll Nottm BTh74. **d** 82 **p** 83. NSM Hillmorton *Cov* 82-86; NSM Daventry Deanery from 87. *Oak Tree Cottage, 34 Stowe Nine Churches, Northampton NN7 4SG* Tel (01327) 349167

LAWES, Timothy Stanley. b 57. Nottm Univ BTh88. Linc Th Coll 85. **d** 88 **p** 89. C Wymondham *Nor* 88-92; R Felmingham, Skeyton, Colby, Banningham etc 92-96; Sweden from 96; Asst V Byske from 98. *Bangatan 5, 93047 Byske, Sweden* Tel (0046) (912) 10137

LAWLESS, Mrs Patricia Elizabeth. b 36. Bris Univ BA58 PGCE59 Lon Univ DipSocSc77. S Dios Minl Tr Scheme 91. **d** 93 **p** 94. NSM Frome Ch B & W 93-95; NSM Mells w Buckland Dinham, Elm, Whatley etc 96; NSM Frome St Jo and St Mary 96-00; Chapl Victoria Hosp Frome 96-98; rtd 00; Perm to Offic *B & W* from 00. *9 Sunnyside, Frome BA11 1LD* Tel (01373) 463204

LAWLEY, Peter Gerald Fitch. b 52. Chich Th Coll 77. **d** 80 **p** 81. C Pet St Jo *Pet* 80-83; C Daventry 83-87; P-in-c Syresham w Whitfield 87-90; TV Cen Telford *Lich* 90-98; V Priors Lee and St Georges from 98. *The Vicarage, Ashley Road, Telford TF2 9LF* Tel (01952) 612923 Fax as telephone

LAWLEY, Rosemary Ann. b 47. WMMTC 00. **d** 03. NSM Kinver and Enville *Lich* from 03. *White Hill Farm Cottage, White Hill, Kinver, Stourbridge DY7 6AS* Tel (01384) 873389 Mobile 07940-426399 E-mail rosemarylawley@tiscali.co.uk

LAWLOR, Colin Robert. b 63. Lanc Univ BA89 MPhil92 St Martin's Coll Lanc PGCE90. Chich Th Coll Dip Minl Th93. **d** 93 **p** 94. C Moulsecoomb *Chich* 93-97; TV 97-99; Chapl Brighton Univ from 99. *204 Bevendean Crescent, Brighton BN2 4RD* Tel 07802-580946 (mobile) E-mail cla4251245@aol.com

LAWRANCE, Hugh Norcliffe. b 49. N Riding Coll of Educn BEd79. Linc Th Coll 83. **d** 85 **p** 86. C Lindley *Wakef* 85-87; C Barkisland w W Scammonden 87-92; C Ripponden 87-92; V Knottingley 92-98; C Thorp Arch w Walton *York* 98-00; C Boston Spa 98-00; C Clifford 98-00; P-in-c Bramham from 00; P-in-c Clifford from 00. *The Vicarage, 19 Chapel Lane, Clifford, Wetherby LS23 6HU* Tel (01937) 849792 E-mail stmary's@bostonspa2.freeserve.co.uk

LAWRANCE, Robert William. b 63. Jes Coll Ox BA85 MA89. Ripon Coll Cuddesdon BA87. **d** 88 **p** 89. C Astley *Man* 88-91; Lect Bolton St Pet 91-94; V Bury St Jo w St Mark 94-00; Chapl Bury Healthcare NHS Trust 95-00; Dir of Ords *Dur* from 00; Chapl Hatf Coll Dur from 00. *20 Dickens Wynd, Durham DH1 3QR* Tel 0191-383 2035

LAWRENCE, Charles Anthony Edwin. b 53. AKC75. St Aug Coll Cant 75. **d** 76 **p** 77. C Mitcham St Mark *S'wark* 76-80; C Haslemere *Guildf* 80-82; P-in-c Ashton H Trin *Man* 82-84; V 84-93; AD Ashton-under-Lyne 91-97; V Saddleworth 93-97; V

Effingham w Lt Bookham *Guildf* from 97; Chapl Manor Ho Sch from 97. *High Limes, 4 Fiona Close, Bookham, Leatherhead KT23 3JU* Tel (01372) 458314 Fax as telephone
E-mail sally@apostle.fsnet.co.uk

LAWRENCE, Christopher David. b 55. Wycliffe Hall Ox 01. **d** 03. C Wadhurst *Chich* from 03; C Tidebrook from 03; C Stonegate from 03. *The Vicarage, Bardown Road, Stonegate, Wadhurst TN5 7EJ* Tel (01580) 201855 Mobile 07941-557537
E-mail chris d_lawrence@hotmail.com

LAWRENCE, David Ian. b 48. AIMLS71 MIBiol76 Univ Coll Lon BSc74. Glouc Sch of Min 84 Sarum & Wells Th Coll 87. **d** 88 **p** 89. C Wotton St Mary *Glouc* 88-91; P-in-c Cheltenham St Mich 91-93; V from 93. *St Michael's Vicarage, 1 Severn Road, Cheltenham GL52 5QA* Tel (01242) 222644
E-mail dlawr15948@aol.com

LAWRENCE, David John. b 53. Leeds Poly BEd77. Linc Th Coll. **d** 86 **p** 87. C Gt and Lt Coates w Bradley *Linc* 86-89; P-in-c Hemingby 89-91; R 91-98; R Belchford 98; V Fulletby 98; P-in-c St Briavels w Hewelsfield *Glouc* from 98. *The Vicarage, St Anne's Way, St Briavels, Lydney GL15 6UE* Tel (01594) 530345 Fax as telephone

LAWRENCE, George Leslie. b 11. Bp Wilson Coll 38. **d** 41 **p** 42. C Hartlepool St Hilda *Dur* 41-46; C Darlington St Cuth 46-48; R Jarrow Grange 48-53; CF (TA) 49-64; V Bradley *Wakef* 53-60; V Newsome 60-69; R Crofton 69-78; rtd 79; Perm to Offic *Wakef* 79-98. *702 Doncaster Road, Crofton, Wakefield WF4 1PX* Tel (01924) 862174

LAWRENCE, Miss Helen. b 30. St Mich Ho Ox 62. **dss** 74 **d** 87 **p** 94. Braintree *Chelmsf* 74-87; Par Dn 87-90; rtd 90; Perm to Offic *Chelmsf* from 90. *6 Reynards Close, Kirby Cross, Frinton-on-Sea CO13 0RA* Tel (01255) 673837

LAWRENCE, Miss Ida Eugenia Laura. b 14. Open Univ BA81. Gilmore Ho 45. **dss** 78 **d** 87 **p** 94. Rayleigh *Chelmsf* 78-87; NSM 87-90; Perm to Offic from 90. *Dilkusha, Hardwick Close, Rayleigh SS6 7QP* Tel (01268) 773059

LAWRENCE, James Conrad. b 62. St Jo Coll Dur BA85. Ridley Hall Cam 85. **d** 87 **p** 88. Min Bar Hill LEP *Ely* 87-93; Deanery Adv in Evang 90-93; CPAS Evang 93-98; Perm to Offic *Cov* from 93; Springboard Missr from 97; CPAS Dir Evang Projects from 99. *236 Cubbington Road, Leamington Spa CV32 7AY* Tel (01926) 316368 *or* 334242 Fax 333613

LAWRENCE, Mrs Janet Maureen. b 43. Hockerill Teacher Tr Coll TCert64. Ox Min Course CBTS92. **d** 92 **p** 94. Hon Par Dn Bletchley *Ox* 92-94; NSM N Bletchley CD from 94. *20 The Elms, Bletchley, Milton Keynes MK3 6DB* Tel (01908) 377660

LAWRENCE, John Graham Clive. b 47. ACIB. Trin Coll Bris DipTh78. **d** 78 **p** 79. C Chatham St Phil and St Jas *Roch* 78-83; V Roch St Justus 83-97; Asst Chapl HM Pris Roch 83-97; UK Dir CMJ 97-00; Internat Co-ord Light to the Nations UK from 00; Perm to Offic *St Alb* from 00. *2. 15 Rochester Road, Tonbridge TN10 4NU* Tel 07984-951534 (mobile)
E-mail john@lttn.fsnet.co.uk

LAWRENCE, John Shaw. b 27. WMMTC. **d** 81. NSM Birm St Martin *Birm* 81-85; Chapl Coun for Soc Aid 84-89; NSM Birm St Martin w Bordesley St Andr 85-89; rtd 89. *309 Grosvenor Court, 58 The Green, Kings Norton, Birmingham B38 8RU* Tel 0121-458 3853

LAWRENCE, Canon Leonard Roy. b 31. Keble Coll Ox BA56 MA59. Westcott Ho Cam 56. **d** 58 **p** 59. C Stockport St Geo *Ches* 58-62; V Thelwall 62-68; V Hyde St Geo 68-75; V Prenton 75-96; Hon Can Ches Cathl 86-96; rtd 96; Perm to Offic *Ches* from 96; Acorn Chr Healing Trust from 97. *39 Mockbeggar Drive, Wallasey CH45 3NN* Tel 0151-346 9438

LAWRENCE, Leslie. b 44. Lon Univ DipRS84. S'wark Ord Course 86. **d** 88 **p** 89. NSM Stanwell *Lon* 88-92; C Hounslow H Trin w St Paul 92-97; P-in-c Norwood St Mary from 97. *The Rectory, 26 Tentelow Lane, Norwood Green, Southall UB2 4LE* Tel (020) 8574 1362 Fax 8606 9647
E-mail leslie.lawrence@tesco.net

LAWRENCE, Martin Kenneth. b 59. Univ Coll Dur BA82. St Steph Ho Ox 94. **d** 96 **p** 97. C Wanstead St Mary w Ch Ch *Chelmsf* 96-00; PV Westmr Abbey 99-00; Chapl Malta and Gozo *Eur* 00-01; C Romford St Edw *Chelmsf* from 02. *54 Parkside Avenue, Romford RM1 4ND* Tel (01708) 727960
E-mail martin@lawrence.net

LAWRENCE, Norman. b 45. Lon Univ BEd75. S'wark Ord Course 77. **d** 80 **p** 81. NSM Hounslow H Trin *Lon* 80-88; NSM Hounslow H Trin w St Paul from 88. *89 Bulstrode Avenue, Hounslow TW3 3AE* Tel (020) 8572 6292

LAWRENCE, The Ven Patrick Henry Andrew. b 51. TCD Div Test 79 BA81. **d** 81 **p** 82. C Templemore *D & R* 81-84; C Kilkenny St Canice Cathl *C & O* 84-85; I Templebreedy w Tracton and Nohoval *C, C & R* 85-92; I Geashill w Killeigh and Ballycommon *M & K* 92-98; Can Kildare Cathl from 92; Adn Kildare from 93; Adn Meath from 97; Warden of Readers from 97; I Julianstown and Colpe w Drogheda and Duleek from 98; Preb Monmohenock St Patr Cathl Dublin from 00. *The Rectory, Eastham Road, Bettystown, Co Meath, Irish Republic* Tel (00353) (41) 982 7345 Fax 988 8555
E-mail archdeacon@meath.anglican.org

LAWRENCE, Canon Peter Anthony. b 36. Lich Th Coll 67. **d** 69 **p** 70. C Oadby *Leic* 69-74; P-in-c Northmarston and Granborough *Ox* 74-81; P-in-c Hardwick St Mary 74-81; P-in-c Quainton 76-81; P-in-c Oving w Pitchcott 76-81; TR Schorne 81-91; RD Claydon 84-88; V Ivinghoe w Pitstone and Slapton 91-97; Hon Can Ch Ch 97; rtd 97; Perm to Offic *Ox* from 99. *Hill House, Back Lane, Malvern WR14 2HJ* Tel (01684) 564075

LAWRENCE, Peter Halliday. b 47. ALCM K Alfred's Coll Win CertEd69 Nottm Univ BTh76. St Jo Coll Nottm 72. **d** 76 **p** 77. C Birm St Luke *Birm* 76-79; V Burney Lane 79-93; TV Canford Magna *Sarum* 93-95; TR from 95; RD Wimborne from 00. *The Vicarage, 359 Sopwith Crescent, Wimborne BH21 1XQ* Tel (01202) 883630

LAWRENCE, Ralph Guy. b 55. Trin Coll Bris DipHE89. **d** 89 **p** 90. C Cotmanhay *Derby* 89-93; P-in-c Tansley, Dethick, Lea and Holloway from 93. *Lea Vicarage, Common End, Lea Bridge, Matlock DE4 5JP* Tel (01629) 534275
E-mail ralph.lawrence@lineone.net

LAWRENCE, Timothy Hervey. b 25. Ripon Hall Ox 58. **d** 60 **p** 61. C Newmarket All SS *St E* 60-62; V Kentford w Higham Green 62-84; P-in-c Herringswell 78-84; rtd 84. *13 South Street, Risby, Bury St Edmunds IP28 6QU* Tel (01284) 810083

LAWRENCE (née FOREMAN), Mrs Vanessa Jane. b 73. Ch Ch Coll Cant BA95. Westcott Ho Cam. **d** 00 **p** 01. C N Stoneham Win from 00. *All Saints' Lodge, Pointout Road, Southampton SO16 7DL* Tel (023) 8079 1090
E-mail vanessa.foreman@tesco.net

LAWRENCE, Victor John. b 43. ACII. Oak Hill Th Coll. **d** 83 **p** 84. C Paddock Wood *Roch* 83-87; R Milton next Gravesend w Denton from 87. *The Rectory, Church Walk, Milton, Gravesend DA12 2QU* Tel (01474) 533434

LAWRENCE-MARCH, David Lawrence. b 61. Univ of Wales (Lamp) BA83. Coll of Resurr Mirfield 83. **d** 85 **p** 86. C Pet St Jude *Pet* 85-89; Chapl St Aug Sch Kilburn 89-92; C Kilburn St Aug w St Jo *Lon* 89-90; C Paddington St Mary 90-92; Chapl Bearwood Coll Wokingham 92-96; R Holt w High Kelling *Nor* 96-98; Sen Chapl Bedford Sch from 98; Perm to Offic *Pet* from 98. *Bedford School, De Parys Avenue, Bedford MK40 2TU* Tel (01234) 326488
E-mail dl-march@bedfordschool.beds.sch.uk

LAWRENSON, James Percival. b 12. Kelham Th Coll 30. **d** 36 **p** 37. C Atherton *Man* 36-39; Chapl Toc H (E Yorks) 39-40; C Portland All SS w St Pet *Sarum* 40-42; Acting Chapl HM Borstal Inst Portland 40-42; Chapl 42-45; Chapl HM Borstal Inst Roch 45-50; Asst Sec Lon Police Court Miss 50-56; Hon C Wandsworth St Anne *S'wark* 50-52; Public Preacher 52-56; Chapl Berkhamsted Colleg Sch Herts 56-78; rtd 78; Perm to Offic *St Alb* from 78; *Ox* 87-90. *Downside, 7 Torrington Road, Berkhamsted HP4 3DD* Tel (01442) 865999

LAWRENSON, Michael. b 43. Leeds Univ BA60 Liv Univ CertRSS65 Newc Univ DASS69. Coll of Resurr Mirfield 60. **d** 74 **p** 74. NSM Glenrothes *St And* 74-90; Dioc Supernumerary 90-95; Chapl HM Pris Perth from 91; NSM Glenrothes *St And* from 95; NSM Leven from 95; NSM Lochgelly from 95; NSM St Andrews St Andr from 95. *Hollyburn, West Port, Falkland, Cupar KY15 7BW* Tel (01337) 857311
E-mail mlawrenson@compuserve.com

LAWRENSON, Ronald David. b 41. CITC 68. **d** 71 **p** 72. C Seapatrick *D & D* 71-78; Min Can Down Cathl 78-79; V Choral Belf Cathl 79-86; Bp's C Tynan w Middletown *Arm* 86-93; Hon V Choral Arm Cathl 87-02; Bp's C Tynan w Middletown 92-93; I Donaghmore w Upper Donaghmore 93-98. *Riverbrook Apartments, 9A Brooklands Drive, Whitehead, Carrickfergus BT38 9SL* Tel (028) 9337 3625

LAWRIE, Paul Edward. b 12. Freiburg Univ LLD35 St Cath Soc Ox BA48 MA53. Wycliffe Hall Ox 46. **d** 48 **p** 49. C Walkley *Sheff* 48-51; C Thrybergh 51-54; V Drax 54-64; R Todwick 64-78; rtd 78; Chapl Rotherham Distr Gen Hosp 78-85; Hon C Handsworth Woodhouse *Sheff* 85-88; Hon C Aston cum Aughton w Swallownest, Todwick etc 88-92; Perm to Offic from 92. *15 Haddon Way, Aston, Sheffield S26 2EH* Tel 0114-287 4864

LAWRIE, Peter Sinclair. b 39. Clifton Th Coll 62. **d** 65 **p** 66. C Derby St Chad *Derby* 65-68; C Toxteth Park St Philemon w St Silas *Liv* 68-71; V Ramsey St Mary's w Ponds Bridge *Ely* 71-81; V Whitwick St Jo the Bapt *Leic* 81-96; P-in-c Felixstowe SS Pet and Paul *St E* 96-03; rtd 03. *71 Lincroft, Oakley, Bedford MK43 7SS* E-mail p.lawrie@talk21.com

LAWRINSON, Leslie Norman. b 35. IEng MIPD90 MCMI84. **d** 99 **p** 00. OLM Onchan *S & M* from 99. *Boavl Dooin, 16 Seagull Crescent, Onchan, Isle of Man IM3 3BY* Tel (01624) 627664 Mobile 07624-491980 E-mail leslaw@mcb.net

LAWRY, Mrs Fianach Alice Moir. b 35. St And Dioc Tr Course 85. **d** 88 **p** 94. NSM Dollar *St And* from 88; Chapl HM Pris Glenochil from 91. *Sunnybank, Muckhart, Dollar FK14 7JN* Tel (01259) 781426

LAWRY, Richard Henry. b 57. Bris Univ BA79 Wolfs Coll Cam PGCE81. St Jo Coll Nottm 96. **d** 99 **p** 00. C Macclesfield Team Par *Ches* 99-02; P-in-c Stalybridge St Paul from 02. *St Paul's*

LAWS, Clive Loudon. b 54. UEA BEd76 Leeds Univ CertEd75. Wycliffe Hall Ox 79. **d** 82 **p** 83. C Newcastle w Butterton *Lich* 82-85; C Gabalfa *Llan* 85-88; R Pendine w Llanmiloe and Eglwys Gymyn w Marros *St D* 89-94; CF 89-94; Perm to Offic *B & W* 95-96; C Portishead 96-02; TV from 02. *24 St Mary's Park Road, Portishead, Bristol BS20 6SL* Tel (01275) 848934

LAWS, Edwin Kingsley. b 06. LVO53 KPM39. Bps' Coll Cheshunt 56. **d** 57 **p** 58. C Shaftesbury H Trin w St Pet *Sarum* 57-60; R Winterborne Whitechurch w Clenston 60-72; R Milton Abbas w Winterborne Whitechurch etc 72-74; RD Milton 66-73; Custos St Jo Hosp Heytesbury 74-79; rtd 79; Perm to Offic *B & W* 79-97. *Abbeyfield, 58 Bath Road, Wells BA5 3LQ* Tel (01749) 679949

LAWSON, Canon Alma Felicity. b 51. St Hugh's Coll Ox BA73 MA78. St Jo Coll Nottm DPS74. **d** 98 **p** 99. Dean of Min and Dir of Ords *Wakef* 93-00; Hon C Wakef Cathl 98-00; V Gildersome from 00; Hon Can Wakef Cathl from 01. *St Peter's House, 2A Church Street, Gildersome, Morley, Leeds LS27 7AF* Tel 0113-253 3339 Fax as telephone
E-mail felicity@lawson99.fsnet.co.uk

LAWSON, David McKenzie. b 47. Glas Univ MA69 Edin Univ BD76. Edin Th Coll 73. **d** 76 **p** 77. C Glas St Mary *Glas* 76-82; V Keighley All SS *Bradf* 82-85; Chapl Asst Univ Coll Hosp Lon 85-91; Hon C St Pancras w St Jas and Ch Ch *Lon* 86-91; R Smithfield St Bart Gt 91-93; Hon C Paddington St Jas 94-00; TV Chambersbury *St Alb* from 00. *The Vicarage, 7 Belswains Lane, Hemel Hempstead HP3 9PN* Tel (01442) 261610 Mobile 07939-473717 E-mail davidmlawson@lineone.net

LAWSON, David William. b 50. ACA DipHE. Linc Th Coll. **d** 82 **p** 83. C Stafford *Lich* 82-85; TV Redruth w Lanner *Truro* 85-87; Chapl Whitley Hosp Cov 87-94; Chapl Gulson Road Hosp Cov 87-94; Chapl Cov and Warks Hosp 87-94; P-in-c Whitley Cov 87-93; V S Leamington St Jo from 93. *St John's Vicarage, Tachbrook Street, Leamington Spa CV31 3BN* Tel (01926) 422208

LAWSON, The Very Revd Frederick Quinney (Rick). b 45. Leic Univ BA. St Steph Ho Ox. **d** 83 **p** 84. Hon C Loughborough Em *Leic* 83-86; NSM Somerby, Burrough on the Hill and Pickwell 86-87; NSM Burrough Hill Pars 87; USA from 87; Hon Can Salt Lake City 87-02; Dean from 02. *4294 Adonis Drive, Salt Lake City, UT 84124, USA* Tel (001) (801) 595 5380 *or* 277 9623 Fax 278 5903 E-mail rql@xmission.com

LAWSON, Gary Austin. b 53. Man Univ BA80. Ripon Coll Cuddesdon 80. **d** 82 **p** 83. C Nunhead St Antony *S'wark* 82-86; Hon C Reddish *Man* 86-87; Hon C Longsight St Jo w St Cypr 87-88; V Wythenshawe St Rich 88-98; C Bolton St Pet 98-03; Chapl Bolton Inst of F&HE 98-03; TR Westhoughton and Wingates from 03. *1 Bramcote Avenue, Bolton BL1 1LF* Tel (01204) 535279

LAWSON, James Barry. b 68. Edin Univ MA91 New Coll Ox DPhil96. Coll of Resurr Mirfield 98. **d** 99 **p** 00. C Poplar *Lon* 99-02; Chapl CCC Cam from 02. *Corpus Christi College, Trumpington Street, Cambridge CB2 1RH* Tel (01223) 338002 Fax as telephone E-mail jbl24@cam.ac.uk

LAWSON, John Alexander. b 62. Sheff Univ BA84 Nottm Univ MA97. St Jo Coll Nottm DPS87. **d** 87 **p** 88. C Wellington, All SS w Eyton *Lich* 87-92; TV Dewsbury *Wakef* 92-98; P-in-c Birchencliffe from 98. *St Philip's Vicarage, 38 Holly Grove, Lindley, Huddersfield HD3 3NS* Tel (01484) 531667 Fax 518482 E-mail jal@bh-cc.co.uk

LAWSON, Jonathan Halford. b 68. St Chad's Coll Dur BA90. Westcott Ho Cam CTM93. **d** 93 **p** 94. C Sedgefield *Dur* 93-96; C Usworth 96-97; TV 97-00; TV Epping Distr *Chelmsf* from 00. *Theydon Garnon Vicarage, Fiddler's Hamlet, Epping CM16 7PQ* Tel (01992) 572608

LAWSON, June Margaret. b 62. Birm Univ BA83 Didsbury Coll of Educn PGCE84 St Jo Coll York MA02. N Ord Course 00. **d** 02 **p** 03. C Huddersfield H Trin w Wakef from 02. *St Philip's Vicarage, 38 Holly Grove, Lindley, Huddersfield HD3 3NS* Tel (01484) 531667 Fax 518482 E-mail jml@bh-cc.co.uk

LAWSON, Matthew James. b 67. St Andr Univ MTheol91 FRSA02. Ripon Coll Cuddesdon MTh94. **d** 94 **p** 95. C Bedford St Andr *St Alb* 94-97; Chapl and Hd RS St Jo Sch Leatherhead from 97; Tutor Dioc Min Course *Guildf* from 98. *The Chaplain's House, 4 Linden Pit Path, Leatherhead KT22 7JD* Tel (01372) 361665 Mobile 07768-515950 Fax (01372) 386606 E-mail frlawson@aol.com

LAWSON, The Ven Michael Charles. b 52. Sussex Univ BA75. Trin Coll Bris 75. **d** 78 **p** 79. C Horsham *Chich* 78-81; C St Marylebone All So w SS Pet and Jo *Lon* 81-87; V Bromley Ch Ch *Roch* 87-99; Adn Hampstead *Lon* from 99. *The Basement Office, 44 King Henry's Road, London NW3 3RP* Tel (020) 7586 3224 Fax 7586 9976
E-mail archdeacon.hampstead@london.anglican.org

LAWSON, Russell Thomas. b 70. Leeds Univ BA92 Ox Univ BTh98. St Steph Ho Ox 98. **d** 98 **p** 99. C Cheshunt *St Alb* 98-02; C Cheam *S'wark* from 02. *4 Tudor Close, Cheam, Sutton SM3 8QS* Tel (020) 8641 7911

LAWSON, Miss Sarah Anne. b 66. Chester Coll of HE BA87. Ridley Hall Cam. **d** 00 **p** 01. C Hollingworth w Tintwistle *Ches* from 00. *22 Highfield Gardens, Hollingworth, Hyde SK14 8BF* Tel (01457) 765833 E-mail revanne@lawson66.fsnet.co.uk

LAWSON-JONES, Christopher Mark. b 68. Open Univ BA98. St Mich Coll Llan 98. **d** 00 **p** 01. C Risca *Mon* 00-03; Chapl Cross Keys Campus Coleg Gwent 00-03; TV Cyncoed from 03. *40 Felbrigg Crescent, Pontprennau, Cardiff CF23 8SE* Tel (029) 2054 9795 E-mail mark@lawson-jones.freeserve.co.uk

LAWTON, David Andrew. b 62. Man Univ BA83. Cranmer Hall Dur. **d** 00 **p** 01. C Deptford St Jo w H Trin *S'wark* from 00. *3 Orchard Hill, London SE13 7QZ* Tel (020) 8694 8400 Mobile 07887-717772

LAXON, Colin John. b 44. Cant Sch of Min 86. **d** 89 **p** 90. C Folkestone St Mary and St Eanswythe *Cant* 89-94; P-in-c Barrow St Jas *Carl* 94-01; Soc Resp Officer from 01; C Brampton and Farlam and Castle Carrock w Cumrew 01-02; TV Eden, Gelt and Irthing from 02. *The Rectory, Castle Carrock, Brampton CA8 9LZ* Tel (01228) 670745 E-mail info@carlislediocese.org.uk

LAY, Brian Robert. b 37. Bernard Gilpin Soc Dur 59 Chich Th Coll 60. **d** 63 **p** 64. C Battyeford *Wakef* 63-66; C Belhus Park *Chelmsf* 66-73; P-in-c Sutton on Plym *Ex* 73-80; V from 80. *St John's Vicarage, 3 Alma Street, Cattedown, Plymouth PL4 0NL* Tel (01752) 664191

LAY, Geoffrey Arthur. b 54. Leic Poly BA77 Man Univ MA83 Lon Univ BD88. Ridley Hall Cam CTM92. **d** 92 **p** 93. C St Neots *Ely* 92-95; P-in-c Long Stanton w St Mich 95-01; P-in-c Dry Drayton 95-97; R Chailey *Chich* from 01; Chapl Chailey Heritage Hosp Lewes from 01. *Chailey Rectory, Chailey Green, Lewes BN8 4DA* Tel (01825) 722286
E-mail geofflay@ntlworld.com

LAYBOURNE, Michael Frederick. b 37. Qu Coll Birm 81. **d** 83 **p** 84. C High Elswick St Phil *Newc* 83-85; C High Elswick St Phil and Newc St Aug 86; C Cramlington 86-87; TV 87-95; C Killingworth 95-02; rtd 02; Perm to Offic *Newc* from 02. *16 Rockcliffe Gardens, Whitley Bay NE26 2NL* Tel 0191-251 0115 E-mail mikelaybourne@waitrose.com

LAYCOCK, Charles. b 37. Open Univ BA88. N Ord Course 80. **d** 83 **p** 84. C Astley Bridge *Man* 83-86; R Crumpsall 86-94; V Ashton Ch Ch 94-00; rtd 00. *23 The Mere, Ashton-under-Lyne OL6 9NH* Tel 0161-330 2824

LAYCOCK, Lawrence. b 42. HNC. St Deiniol's Hawarden 86. **d** 89 **p** 90. C Blackpool St Mich *Blackb* 89-94; P-in-c Worsthorne 94-99; P-in-c Holme 96-99; V Holme-in-Cliviger w Worsthorne from 99. *The Vicarage, Gorple Road, Worsthorne, Burnley BB10 3NN* Tel (01282) 428478

LAYNESMITH, Mark David. b 74. York Univ BA97 MA99. Ripon Coll Cuddesdon BA01. **d** 02 **p** 03. C Tadcaster w Newton Kyme *York* from 02. *3 Heatherdene, Tadcaster LS24 8EZ* Tel (01937) 830041 E-mail marklaynesmith@fish.co.uk

LAYTON, Miss Norene. b 39. Trin Coll Bris DipHE86. dss 86 **d** 87 **p** 94. Lindfield *Chich* 86-87; Par Dn 87-92; Par Dn Loughborough Em *Leic* 92-94; C Loughborough Em and St Mary in Charnwood 94-96; V Hengrove *Bris* from 96. *Christ Church Vicarage, 7 Petherton Road, Bristol BS14 9BP* Tel (01275) 832346 E-mail vicar@cchengrove.freeserve.co.uk

LAZONBY, Canon Alan Frederick. b 19. TD64. St Jo Coll Dur BA40 DipTh41 MA43. **d** 42 **p** 43. C Auckland St Helen *Dur* 42-46; C Horden 46-50; CF (TA) 49-67; CF (TAVR) 67-77; V Witton Park *Dur* 50-57; Bp's Dom Chapl 53-57; R Haughton le Skerne 57-84; RD Darlington 74-78; Hon Can Dur Cathl 75-98; rtd 84. *16 Loraine Crescent, Darlington DL1 5TF* Tel (01325) 485876

LE BILLON, Mrs Janet. b 42. STETS 99. **d** 02 **p** 03. NSM Guernsey St Jo *Win* from 02; Chapl States of Guernsey Bd of Health from 02. *Tranquillité, Clos des Quatre Vents, St Martin, Guernsey GY4 6SU* Tel (01481) 234283

LE CRAS, Allan. b 20. Linc Th Coll LTh84. **d** 84 **p** 85. Hon C Toynton All Saints w Toynton St Peter *Linc* 84-88; Hon C Marden Hill Gp 88-90; Perm to Offic 90-01. *Snipe Dales Cottage, Lusby, Spilsby PE23 4JB* Tel (01507) 588636

LE DIEU, Miss Heather Muriel. b 41. Birm Univ BA62 MA67 DipTh. St Jo Coll Dur 77. dss 79 **d** 87. Birchfield *Birm* 79-82; Kings Heath 82-84; Walsall Pleck and Bescot *Lich* 84-88; Par Dn 87-88; rtd 88. *159 Swarthmore Road, Selly Oak, Birmingham B29 4NW* Tel 0121-475 1236

LE FEUVRE, Henry Mauger. b 21. Lich Th Coll. **d** 62 **p** 63. C Cheam *S'wark* 62-65; C Dulwich St Barn 65-69; P-in-c Dorrington *Heref* 69-72; P-in-c Stapleton 69-72; P-in-c Cardington 69-72; R Smethcott w Woolstaston 69-72; R Risby w Gt and Lt Saxham and Westley *St E* 80-85; rtd 85; Perm to Offic *St E* from 85. *18 Southgate Street, Bury St Edmunds IP33 2AF* Tel (01284) 703524

LE GRICE, Elizabeth Margaret. b 53. Man Univ BA75 MA(Theol)78. Nor Bapt Coll 75 Westcott Ho Cam 87. **d** 88 **p** 97. In Bapt Ch 78-82; C Whitchurch *Llan* 88-95; Chapl among the Deaf SE Wales *Mon* from 95; Lic to Offic from 95. *9 Hawarden Road, Newport NP19 8JP*

LE GRYS, Alan Arthur. b 51. K Coll Lon BD73 AKC73 MTh90. St Aug Coll Cant 73. **d** 74 **p** 75. C Harpenden St Jo *St Alb* 74-77; C Hampstead St Jo *Lon* 77-81; Chapl Westf Coll and Bedf Coll

81-84; V Stoneleigh *Guildf* 84-91; Lect Ripon Coll Cuddesdon 91-96; Prin SEITE from 96; Hon PV Roch Cathl *Roch* from 96; Lic to Offic *S'wark* from 96. *21 Grizedale Close, Rochester ME1 2UX* Tel(01634)402678 Mobile 07958-547053 Fax 819347 E-mail principal@seite.fsnet.co.uk

LE PREVOST, Carl Andrew. b 63. Sarum & Wells Th Coll 85. **d** 88 **p** 89. C Chandler's Ford *Win* 88-91; C Southampton Maybush St Pet 91; Asst Chapl Bryanston Sch 91-93; R Burghclere w Newtown and Ecchinswell w Sydmonton *Win* 93-98; Chapl Milton Abbey Sch Dorset 98-01; P-in-c S Trin Broads *Nor* from 03. *Hollydene, Main Road, Filby, Great Yarmouth NR29 3AA* Tel (01493) 368210

LE ROSSIGNOL, Richard Lewis. b 52. Aston Univ BSc75. Oak Hill Th Coll BA79. **d** 79 **p** 80. C E Ham St Paul *Chelmsf* 79-81; C Willesborough w Hinxhill *Cant* 81-85; Perm to Offic 85-94; NSM Brabourne w Smeeth 94-03; NSM Smeeth w Monks Horton and Stowting and Brabourne from 03. *64 Osborne Road, Willesborough, Ashford TN24 0EF* Tel (01233) 625193

LE SUEUR, Paul John. b 38. Lon Univ BSc59. Wycliffe Hall Ox 60. **d** 62 **p** 63. C Mortlake w E Sheen *S'wark* 62-65; C Witney Ox 65-69; R Sarsden w Churchill 69-74; P-in-c Clifton Hampden 74-77; P-in-c Rotherfield Greys H Trin 77-82; V 82-90; V Blacklands Hastings Ch Ch and St Andr *Chich* 90-97; V Ticehurst and Flimwell 97-00; rtd 00; Perm to Offic *Chich* from 01. *80 Barnhorn Road, Bexhill-on-Sea TN39 4QA* Tel (01424) 844747 E-mail halomanpaul@talk21.com

LE VASSEUR, Mrs Linda Susan. b 48. Shenstone Coll of Educn CertEd70. S Dios Minl Tr Scheme 92. **d** 95 **p** 96. NSM Guernsey Ste Marie du Castel *Win* 95-01; NSM Guernsey St Matt 95-01; NSM Guernsey St Sav from 01; NSM Guernsey St Marguerite de la Foret from 01. *Coin des Arquets, Les Arquets, St Pierre du Bois, Guernsey GY7 9HE* Tel (01481) 64047

LE VAY, Clare Forbes Agard Bramhall Joanna. b 41. St Anne's Coll Ox BA64 MA66 Univ of Wales (Abth) MSc72 PhD86. Westcott Ho Cam 86. **d** 88 **p** 94. C Stamford Hill St Thos *Lon* 88-89; C Hackney 89-92; Asst Chapl Brook Gen Hosp *Lon* 92-95; Asst Chapl Greenwich Distr Hosp Lon 92-95; Chapl Greenwich Healthcare NHS Trust 95-01; Perm to Offic *S'wark* from 02. *91 Mildenhall Road, London E5 0RY* Tel (020) 8985 3150 E-mail clarelevay@yahoo.com

LE-WORTHY, Michael Raymond. b 50. LNSM course 97. **d** 98 **p** 99. OLM Glascote and Stonydelph *Lich* from 98. *15 Abbey Road, Glascote, Tamworth B77 2QE* Tel (01827) 55762

LEA, Carolyn Jane. *See* COOKE, Mrs Carolyn Jane

LEA, His Honour Christopher Gerald. b 17. MC. RMC Called to the Bar (Inner Temple) 48. Ox Min Course 91. **d** 92 **p** 93. NSM Stratfield Mortimer *Ox* 92-99; NSM Stratfield Mortimer and Mortimer W End etc from 99. *Simms Farm House, Simms Lane, Mortimer, Reading RG7 2JP* Tel 0118-933 2360

LEA, Canon Montague Brian. b 34. OBE00. St Jo Coll Cam BA55 Lon Univ BD71. St Jo Coll Nottm 68. **d** 71 **p** 72. C Abington Em *Lon* 71-74; Chapl Barcelona *Eur* 74-79; V Hove Bp Hannington Memorial Ch *Chich* 79-86; Adn N France *Eur* 86-94; Chapl Paris St Mich 86-94; Hon Can Gib Cathl from 95; R Chiddingly w E Hoathly *Chich* 94-96; Chapl The Hague *Eur* 96-00; rtd 01; Perm to Offic *Chich* from 01. *35 Summerdown Lane, East Dean, Eastbourne BN20 0LE* Tel (01323) 423226 E-mail brian.lea@freedom255.co.uk

LEA, Norman. b 42. JP89. Univ of Wales (Lamp) BA67. Coll of Resurr Mirfield 66. **d** 68 **p** 69. C Newton St Pet *S & B* 68-71; C Oystermouth 71-73; C Brecon w Battle 73-74; TV Cwmbran *Mon* 74-77; V Talgarth and Llanelieu *S & B* 77-84; V Port Talbot St Theodore *Llan* 84-95; Hon Chapl Miss to Seafarers from 84; V Cadoxton-juxta-Neath *Llan* from 95. *The Vicarage, Cadoxton, Neath SA10 8AS* Tel (01639) 644625

LEA, Canon Richard John Rutland. b 40. Trin Hall Cam BA63 MA67. Westcott Ho Cam 63. **d** 65 **p** 66. C Edenbridge *Roch* 65-68; C Hayes 68-71; V Larkfield 71-86; P-in-c Leybourne 76-86; RD Malling 79-84; V Chatham St Steph 86-88; Can Res and Prec Roch Cathl 88-98; V Iffley *Ox* from 98. *The Rectory, Mill Lane, Iffley, Oxford OX4 4EJ* Tel (01865) 773516 E-mail richard.lea@lineone.net

LEACH, Alan William Brickett. b 28. MSc CEng FIStructE FASI FICE. S'wark Ord Course. **d** 89 **p** 90. NSM Forest Row *Chich* 89-98; Perm to Offic from 98. *Hathaway, Ashdown Road, Forest Row RH18 5BN* Tel (01342) 823778

LEACH, Miss Bethia Morag. b 62. Sheff Univ BA84 Liv Inst of Educn PGCE85. Ripon Coll Cuddesdon 95. **d** 97 **p** 98. C Stafford *Lich* 97-00; TV Bilston from 00. *St Mary's Vicarage, 43 Willenhall Road, Bilston, Wolverhampton WV14 6NW* Tel (01902) 490255

LEACH, Gerald. b 27. Sarum & Wells Th Coll 85. **d** 73 **p** 74. NSM Cyncoed *Mon* 73-86; C 86-87; V Dingestow and Llangovan w Penyclawdd etc 87-94; rtd 94; Perm to Offic *Heref* from 95; Lic to Offic *Mon* from 98. *19 Grange Park, Whitchurch, Ross-on-Wye HR9 6EA* Tel (01600) 890397

LEACH, James Roger. b 66. Ball Coll Ox BA89 MA99. Wycliffe Hall Ox BA98. **d** 99 **p** 00. C Knowle *Birm* from 99. *49 Newton Road, Knowle, Solihull B93 9HN* Tel (01564) 779783 E-mail james@jrleach.freeserve.co.uk

LEACH, John. b 52. K Coll Lon BD79 AKC79 St Jo Coll Dur MA. **d** 81 **p** 82. C N Walsham w Antingham *Nor* 81-85; C Crookes St Thos *Sheff* 85-89; V Styvechale *Cov* 89-97; Dir Angl Renewal Min from 97. *Anglican Renewal Ministries, 4 Bramble Street, Derby DE1 1HU* Tel (01332) 200175 Fax 200185 E-mail armderby@aol.com

LEACH, Robert Neville. b 54. Trin Coll Bris DipHE93. **d** 93 **p** 94. C Towcester w Easton Neston *Pet* 93-96; P-in-c Cowley *Lon* 96-01; P-in-c Brandon and Santon Downham w Elveden *St E* from 01; P-in-c Lakenheath from 02. *The Rectory, 40 London Road, Brandon IP27 0EL* Tel (01842) 811907

LEACH, Stephen Lance. b 42. St Steph Ho Ox 66. **d** 69 **p** 70. C Higham Ferrers w Chelveston *Pet* 69-72; TV Ilfracombe H Trin *Ex* 72-74; V Barnstaple St Mary 74-77; R Goodleigh 74-77; P-in-c Barnstaple St Pet w H Trin 76-77; P-in-c Landkey 77-79; TR Barnstaple and Goodleigh 77-79; TR Barnstaple, Goodleigh and Landkey 79-82; V Paignton St Jo 82-95; Gen Sec ACS from 95; Public Preacher *Birm* from 95. *Gordon Browning House, 8 Spitfire Road, Birmingham B24 9PB* Tel 0121-382 5533 *or* 354 9885 Fax 382 6999

LEACH, Stephen Windsor. b 47. St Chad's Coll Dur BSc70 Linacre Coll Ox BA72 MA76. Ripon Hall Ox 70. **d** 73 **p** 74. C Swinton St Pet *Man* 73-77; C Oldham St Chad Limeside 77-79; V Shaw 79-87; V St Just in Penwith *Truro* from 87; V Sancreed from 87. *The Vicarage, St Just, Penzance TR19 7UB* Tel (01736) 788672

LEACH, Timothy Edmund. b 41. Dur Univ BA63. Ridley Hall Cam 63. **d** 65 **p** 66. C Ecclesfield *Sheff* 65-68; C Stocksbridge 68-71; C-in-c W Ecclesacarr CD 71-80; V Goole 80-95; Hon Chapl Miss to Seamen 80-95; V Wath-upon-Dearne *Sheff* from 95. *The Vicarage, Church Street, Wath-upon-Dearne, Rotherham S63 7RD* Tel (01709) 872299 E-mail comedy@tinyonline.co.uk

LEADBEATER, Canon Nicolas James. b 20. Univ of Wales BA43 LLM95. St Steph Ho Ox 43. **d** 45 **p** 46. C Abergavenny H Trin *Mon* 45-47; C Coleford w Staunton *Glouc* 47-55; PC Moreton Valence and V Whitminster 55-67; V Westcote 67-72; P-in-c Icomb 67-72; V Westcote w Icomb 72-79; V Westcote w Icomb and Bledington 79-88; Hon Can Glouc Cathl 83-88; rtd 88; Perm to Offic *Glouc* from 88. *39 Park Farm, Bourton-on-the-Water, Cheltenham GL54 2HF* Tel (01451) 810192

LEADER, Miss Janette Patricia. b 46. Cam Coll of Art and Tech DipHCM66. EAMTC 94. **d** 97 **p** 98. C Desborough, Brampton Ash, Dingley and Braybrooke *Pet* 97-01; V Wellingborough St Barn from 01. *St Barnabas' Vicarage, St Barnabas Street, Wellingborough NN8 3HB* Tel (01933) 226337 Fax as telephone E-mail revdjan@aol.com

LEADER, Stephen. b 64. City Univ DipN97. Ripon Coll Cuddesdon 99. **d** 01 **p** 02. C Battersea St Luke *S'wark* from 01. *30 Canford Road, London SW11 6NZ* Tel (020) 7640 9932 E-mail therevstelea@waitrose.com

LEAF, Edward David Hugh. b 65. Oak Hill Th Coll BA97. **d** 98 **p** 99. C Bath St Bart *B & W* 98-01; C Minehead from 01. *75 Summerland Avenue, Minehead TA24 5BW* Tel (01643) 706882 E-mail dave@dleaf.fslife.co.uk

LEAH, William Albert. b 34. K Coll Lon BA56 AKC57 K Coll Cam MA63. Ripon Hall Ox 60. **d** 62 **p** 63. C Falmouth K Chas *Truro* 62-63; Chapl K Coll Cam 63-67; Min Can Westmr Abbey 67-74; V Hawkhurst *Cant* 74-83; Hon Min Can Cant Cathl 78-83; V St Ives *Truro* 83-94; rtd 98. *Trerice Cottage, Sancreed Newbridge, Penzance TR20 8QR* Tel (01736) 810987

LEAHY, David Adrian. b 56. Open Univ BA90. Qu Coll Birm. **d** 85 **p** 86. C Tile Cross *Birm* 85-88; C Warley Woods 88-91; V Hobs Moat from 91; AD Solihull from 97. *St Mary's House, 30 Hobs Meadow, Solihull B92 8PN* Tel 0121-743 4955

LEAK, Adrian Scudamore. b 38. Ch Ox BA60 MA65 BD89. Cuddesdon Coll 64. **d** 66 **p** 67. C Cov St Mark *Cov* 66-69; C Dorchester *Ox* 69-73; V Badsey *Worc* 73-80; V Wickhamford 73-80; P-in-c Monkwearmouth St Pet *Dur* 80-81; V Choral and Archivist York Minster *York* 81-86; Can Res and Prec Guildf Cathl *Guildf* 86-90; Hon Cur Guildf H Trin w St Mary 96-00; Hon C Worplesdon from 00. *St Alban's House, 96 Oak Hill, Wood Street Village, Guildford GU3 3ES* Tel (01483) 235136 E-mail adrianleak@8kingsroad.fsnet.co.uk

LEAK, Harry Duncan. b 30. St Cath Coll Cam BA53 MA57. Ely Th Coll 53. **d** 54 **p** 55. S Africa 54-57; Portuguese E Africa 57-61; C Eccleshall *Lich* 62-64; V Normacot 64-66; C Stoke upon Trent 66-68; V Hanley All SS 68-71; R Swynnerton 71-80; Perm to Offic from 80; rtd 92. *15 Sutherland Road, Tittensor, Stoke-on-Trent ST12 9JQ* Tel (01782) 351024 *or* 351036

LEAK, John Michael. b 42. St Jo Coll Nottm. **d** 84 **p** 85. NSM Beeston *Ripon* 84-87; C Far Headingley St Chad 87-88; Hon C 88-90; C Headingley 90-95; TV Bramley 95-98; rtd 98. *23 Arthington Close, Tingley, Wakefield WF3 1BT* Tel 0113-253 3763

✠**LEAKE, The Rt Revd David.** b 35. CBE03. ALCD59 LTh74. **d** 59 **p** 60 **c** 69. C Watford *St Alb* 59-61; Lect 61-63; SAMS Argentina 63-69; Asst Bp Paraguay 69-73; Asst Bp N Argentina

69-80; Bp 80-90; Bp Argentina 90-02; rtd 02; Hon Asst Bp Nor from 03. *The Anchorage, Lower Common, East Runton, Cromer NR27 9PG* Tel (01263) 513536 E-mail dleake@0800dial.com

LEAKE, Duncan Burton. b 49. Leeds Univ BA71 Leeds and Carnegie Coll PGCE72 Birm Univ Ad Dip RE78 Keele Univ MA85. Oak Hill Th Coll 90. **d** 92 **p** 93. C Stanwix *Carl* 92-97; C Chasetown *Lich* 97-00; V Chase Terrace from 00. *The Vicarage, 3 Chapel Street, Burntwood WS7 1NL* Tel (01543) 306649 *or* 304611 Fax (01543) 304642
E-mail duncan.leake@ntlworld.com

LEAKEY, Ian Raymond Arundell. b 24. K Coll Cam BA47 MA49. Ridley Hall Cam 48. **d** 50 **p** 51. C Litherland St Jo and St Jas *Liv* 50-53; Rwanda Miss 53-73; Can Burundi 66; V Cudham *Roch* 73-76; P-in-c Downe 76; V Cudham and Downe 76-89; rtd 89; Perm to Offic *Sarum* from 89. *5 Shelley Drive, Salisbury SP1 3JZ* Tel (01722) 329243

LEAKEY, Canon Peter Wippell. b 39. Lon Univ BSc60. Trin Coll Bris 73. **d** 75 **p** 76. C Colne St Bart *Blackb* 75-79; V Copp 79-85; V Pennington *Man* from 85; AD Leigh 93-00; Hon Can Man Cathl from 02. *The Vicarage, Schofield Street, Leigh WN7 4HT* Tel (01942) 673619

LEAL, Malcolm Colin. b 33. Chich Th Coll 72. **d** 75 **p** 76. Hon C Shoreham St Giles CD *Chich* 75-87; Chapl NE Surrey Coll Ewell 87-95; Hon C Arundel w Tortington and S Stoke *Chich* 88-95; Perm to Offic from 95. *8 West Park Lane, Goring-by-Sea, Worthing BN12 4EK* Tel (01903) 244160

LEAMING, Ralph Desmond. b 21. Ripon Coll Cuddesdon 79. **d** 81 **p** 82. C Darlington H Trin *Dur* 81-84; V Hamsterley 84-92; rtd 92. *The Gables, 5 Tower Mews, Wolsingham, Bishop Auckland DL13 3DA* Tel (01388) 526610

LEAMY, Stuart Nigel. b 46. Pemb Coll Ox BA68 MA73 ACA76 FCA81. Sarum Th Coll 68. **d** 70 **p** 71. C Upholland *Liv* 70-78; Lic to Offic *Lon* 78-83 and 94-97; NSM Pimlico St Mary Bourne Street from 97. *92 Gloucester Road, Hampton TW12 2UJ* Tel (020) 8979 9068 Fax 8255 1112 E-mail leamy@globalnet.co.uk

LEAN, Canon David Jonathan Rees. b 52. Univ of Wales (Lamp) DipTh74. Coll of Resurr Mirfield 74. **d** 75 **p** 76. C Tenby *St D* 75-81; V Llanrhian w Llanhywel and Carnhedryn etc 81-88; V Haverfordwest St Martin w Lambston 88-00; RD Roose 99-00; Can St D Cathl from 00; TV Dewisland from 01. *The Archdeaconry, The Close, St Davids, Haverfordwest SA62 6PE* Tel (01437) 720456

LEANING, The Very Revd David. b 36. Lambeth MA01. Lich Th Coll 58. **d** 60 **p** 61. C Gainsborough All SS *Linc* 60-65; R Warsop *S'well* 65-76; RD Kington and Weobley *Heref* 76-80; R Kington w Huntington 76-80; Adn Newark *S'well* 80-91; Provost S'well 91-00; Dean S'well from 00; P-in-c Rolleston w Fiskerton, Morton and Upton 91-93; P-in-c Edingley w Halam from 02. *The Residence, Southwell NG25 0HP* Tel (01636) 812593 *or* 812649 Fax 812782 E-mail david@leaning.prestel.co.uk

LEAR, Peter Malcolm. b 45. FCMA Kent Univ DipTh98. SEITE 95. **d** 98 **p** 99. NSM Ham St Andr *S'wark* 98-03; NSM Wandsworth St Anne from 03. *68 Crescent Road, Kingston upon Thames KT2 7RF* Tel (020) 8541 1207 *or* 7233 1894 Fax 8547 3596 E-mail peter@learpm.demon.co.uk

LEARMOUTH, Michael Walter. b 50. FCA. Oak Hill Th Coll 84. **d** 84 **p** 85. C Harlow St Mary and St Hugh w St Jo the Bapt *Chelmsf* 84-89; V Hainault 89-97; TR Harlow Town Cen w Lt Parndon 97-00; TR Barnsbury *Lon* from 00. *10 Thornhill Square, London N1 1BQ* Tel (020) 7607 4552

LEARY, Thomas Glasbrook. b 42. AKC66. **d** 67 **p** 68. C W Bromwich All SS *Lich* 67-70; TV Croydon *Cant* 70-75; C Limpsfield and Titsey *S'wark* 75-83; V Sutton New Town St Barn 83-92; V Merton St Mary from 92; RD Merton from 98. *The Vicarage, 3 Church Path, London SW19 3HJ* Tel (020) 8543 6192

LEATHARD, Brian. b 56. Sussex Univ BA Cam Univ MA Loughb Univ PhD91. Westcott Ho Cam 79. **d** 82 **p** 83. C Seaford w Sutton *Chich* 82-85; Chapl Loughb Univ *Leic* 85-89; V Hampton Hill *Lon* from 89; Dir of Ords from 99. *The Vicarage, 46 St James's Road, Hampton TW12 1DQ* Tel (020) 8979 2069 Fax 8255 8095 E-mail brian@leathard.fsnet.co.uk

LEATHERBARROW, Ronald. b 35. Chester Coll TCert59. NW Ord Course 71. **d** 75 **p** 76. C Eccleston Ch Ch *Liv* 75-80; C Eccleston St Thos 80-83; R Kirklinton w Hethersgill and Scaleby *Carl* 83-86; R Blackley White Moss St Mark *Man* 86-99; rtd 99. *1 Chapel Street, St Helens WA10 2BG* Tel (01744) 614426

LEATHERS, Brian Stanley Peter. b 61. Nottm Univ BSc83. Oak Hill Th Coll BA89. **d** 89 **p** 90. C Watford *St Alb* 89-92; C Welwyn w Ayot St Peter 92-96; V Heacham *Nor* 96-99; P-in-c Stapenhill Immanuel *Derby* 99-00; V from 00. *Immanuel Vicarage, 150 Hawthorn Crescent, Burton-on-Trent DE15 9QW* Tel (01283) 563959 E-mail brian@topsey.worldonline.co.uk

LEATHES, David Burlton de Mussenden. b 49. R Agric Coll Cirencester Dip Estate Mgt 70. St Jo Coll Nottm DCM92. **d** 92 **p** 93. C Kirkby Stephen w Mallerstang etc *Carl* 92-00; C Brough w Stainmore, Musgrave and Warcop 94-00. *Low Beck House, Rookby, Kirkby Stephen CA17 4HX* Tel (01768) 371713

LEATHLEY, Susan Mary. b 57. Bath Univ BPharm78 MRPharmS. Oak Hill Th Coll DTPS94 Trin Coll Bris MA98.

d 94 **p** 98. C Weston-super-Mare Ch Ch *B & W* 94-95; C Toxteth St Philemon w St Gabr and St Cleopas *Liv* 97-01; TV Maghull from 01. *23 Green Link, Maghull, Liverpool L31 8DW* Tel 0151-526 6626

LEATHLEY, Terence Michael. b 63. Coll of Resurr Mirfield 99. **d** 01 **p** 02. C Whitby w Aislaby and Ruswarp *York* from 01. *19 Eskdale Road, Whitby YO22 4JH* Tel (01947) 603099 Mobile 07678-986916

LEATON, Martin John. b 46. Clifton Th Coll 68. **d** 71 **p** 72. C Kenilworth St Jo *Cov* 71-74; C Stratford-on-Avon w Bishopton 74-77; P-in-c Meriden 77-81; R Meriden and Packington 82-84; R Heanton Punchardon w Marwood *Ex* 84-87; Perm to Offic 95-97; P-in-c Rampton w Laneham, Treswell, Cottam and Stokeham *S'well* from 97; P-in-c N and S Leverton from 03. *The Rectory, Main Street, Rampton, Retford DN22 0HR* Tel (01777) 248143 E-mail martinleaton@yahoo.co.uk

LEAVER, David Noel. b 63. Hatf Coll Dur BA85. Wycliffe Hall Ox 89. **d** 91 **p** 92. C Blackheath Park St Mich *S'wark* 91-95; C Upton (Overchurch) *Ches* 95-98; C Wilmslow 98-99; Perm to Offic from 99. *34 Lorna Road, Cheadle Hulme, Cheadle SK8 5BJ* E-mail davidleaver@btconnect.com

LEAVER (née SMYTH), Mrs Lucinda Elizabeth Jane (Liz). b 67. New Hall Cam BA88 MA92. Wycliffe Hall Ox BTh93. **d** 93 **p** 94. C Cambridge St Barn *Ely* 93-97; Chapl St Kath Hall Liv Inst of HE 97-98; TV Stockport SW *Ches* 99-01; Chapl Stockport Gr Sch from 99. *34 Lorna Road, Cheadle Hulme, Cheadle SK8 5BJ* Tel 0161-485 4302 E-mail liz.leaver@boltblue.net

LEAVER, Prof Robin Alan. b 39. Groningen Univ DTh87. Clifton Th Coll 62. **d** 64 **p** 65. C Gipsy Hill Ch Ch *S'wark* 64-67; C Gt Baddow *Chelmsf* 67-71; P-in-c Reading St Mary Castle Street Prop Chpl *Ox* 71-77; Chapl Luckley-Oakfield Sch Wokingham 73-75; P-in-c Cogges *Ox* 77-84; Lect Wycliffe Hall Ox 84-85; USA from 84; Prof Ch Music Westmr Choir Coll from 84; Visiting Liturgy Lect Drew Univ from 88. *Westminster Choir College, 101 Walnut Lane, Princeton, NJ 08540, USA* Tel (001) (609) 921 7100 E-mail leaver@rider.edu

LEAVES (née CRAIG), Julie Elizabeth. b 63. Southn Univ BTh87. Sarum & Wells Th Coll 82. **dss** 86 **d** 87 **p** 92. Thatcham *Ox* 86-87; Par Dn 87-88; Hong Kong 88-92; Australia from 92; Assoc P Fremantle 92-95; Chapl St Mary's Angl Girls' Sch Karrinyup from 96. *Wollaston College, Wollaston Road, Mount Claremont, W Australia 6010* Tel (0061) (8) 9341 9111 *or* tel and fax 9402 0998 Fax 9341 9222 E-mail leaves@iinet.net.au

LEAVES, Nigel. b 58. Keble Coll Ox BA80 MA83 K Coll Lon PGCE81 MA86. Sarum & Wells Th Coll 84. **d** 86 **p** 87. C Boyne Hill *Ox* 86-88; Chapl Hong Kong Cathl 88-92; Australia from 92; Abp's Chapl and R W Perth *Perth* 92-98; Tutor and Research Fell Murdoch Univ 98-00; Warden Wollaston Coll & Dir Cen for Belief, Spirituality and Aus Culture from 00. *Wollaston College, Wollaston Road, Mount Claremont, W Australia 6010* Tel (0061) (8) 9384 5511 *or* tel and fax 9383 2774 Fax 9385 3364
E-mail leaves@iinet.net.au

LEAWORTHY, John Owen. b 40. Univ of Wales (Swansea) BSc62. Oak Hill Th Coll DipHE82. **d** 82 **p** 83. C Compton Gifford *Ex* 82-85; C Plymouth Em w Efford 85-86; P-in-c Marks Tey w Aldham and Lt Tey *Chelmsf* 86-88; R 88-89; Chapl HM Pris Full Sutton 89-91; Perm to Offic *Ely* 96; NSM Portree *Arg* from 96. *Mo Dhachaidh, Fiscavaig Road, Portnalong, Carbost IV47 8SL* Tel (01478) 640492
E-mail john.leaworthy@mail.which.net

LECKEY, The Very Revd Hamilton. b 29. TCD BA51 MA58. **d** 51 **p** 52. C Ballymacarrett St Martin *D & D* 51-55; C Bangor St Comgall 55-60; I Drumgooland w Kilcoo 60-62; I Comber 62-79; Private Chapl Bp Down 62-73; Dir of Ords 62-87; I Bangor Abbey 79-96; Can Down Cathl 74-87; Dean Down 87-96; rtd 96. *34 Beechfield Drive, Bangor BT19 7ZW* Tel (028) 9146 9370

LECKEY, Paul Robert. b 61. QUB Ripon Coll Cuddesdon Adn Tr Scheme. **d** 96 **p** 97. C Eastleigh *Win* 96-01; P-in-c Upton St Leonards *Glouc* from 01. *The Rectory, Bond End Road, Upton St Leonards, Gloucester GL4 8AG* Tel (01452) 617443
E-mail paul@pleckey.abel.co.uk

LEDBETTER, Shannon Carroll. b 64. Louisville Univ (USA) BA85 Liv Univ PhD00. Virginia Th Sem MTS96. **d** 03. NSM Knowsley *Liv* from 03. *Liverpool Hope, Hope Park, Liverpool L16 9JD* Tel 0151-291 3761 Fax 291 3669
E-mail ledbets@hope.ac.uk

LEDGARD, Canon Frank William Armitage. b 24. Wells Th Coll 49. **d** 52 **p** 53. C Ipswich St Mary le Tower *St E* 52-55; V Tottington *Man* 55-62; V Kirkby Malzeard w Dallow Gill *Ripon* 62-66; R Bedale 66-87; RD Wensley 79-85; Hon Can Ripon Cathl 80-89; Bp's Adv on Chr Healing 87-89; rtd 89; Perm to Offic *Ripon* from 89. *c/o Wrigleys Solicitors, 19 Cookridge Street, Leeds LS2 3AG* Tel 0113-244 6100 Fax 244 6101

LEDGER, James Henry. b 23. Oak Hill Th Coll 68. **d** 70 **p** 71. C Spitalfields Ch Ch w All SS *Lon* 70-75; V Chitts Hill St Cuth 75-91; rtd 91; Perm to Offic *Lon* 93-96; *St Alb* from 93. *6 Acorn Street, Hunsdon, Ware SG12 8PB* Tel (01279) 842878

LEDWARD, John Archibald. b 30. FRSA85 Lon Univ BD58 Man Univ DSPT78 MA81 ThD. ALCD57. **d** 58 **p** 59. C

St Helens St Helen *Liv* 58-62; V Dearham *Carl* 62-66; V Mirehouse 66-71; V Daubhill *Man* 71-77; R Newcastle w Butterton *Lich* 77-88; R Rockland St Mary w Hellington, Bramerton etc *Nor* 88-94; P-in-c Kirby Bedon w Bixley and Whitlingham 92-94; R Rockland St Mary w Hellington, Bramerton etc 94-95; RD Loddon 92-95; rtd 95; Perm to Offic *Nor* from 95. *41 Lackford Close, Brundall, Norwich NR13 5NL* Tel (01603) 714745

LEE, Agnes Elizabeth. b 31. Whitelands Coll Lon TCert51 Coll of Preceptors ACP76 Open Univ BA87. Bp Otter Coll CertRE52 Nor Ord Course 97. **d** 98 **p** 99. NSM Dewsbury *Wakef* from 98. *1 Moor Park Court, Dewsbury WF12 7AU* Tel (01924) 467319 Fax as telephone

LEE, Alan Charles. b 32. S'wark Ord Course 77. **d** 79 **p** 80. NSM Acton Green St Pet *Lon* 79-82; Chapl RADD 82-83; P-in-c St Magnus the Martyr w St Marg New Fish Street *Lon* 83-84; NSM Barnes St Mich *S'wark* 84-90; Perm to Offic *Lon* 89-91; C Brighton St Pet and St Nic w Chpl Royal *Chich* 90-92; C Brighton St Bart 92-94; rtd 92; Hon C Holborn St Alb w Saffron Hill St Pet *Lon* from 02. *27 Leigh Court, Avonmore Road, London W14 8RJ*

LEE, Mrs Anne Louise. b 65. St Jo Coll Nottm BTh90 Wycliffe Hall Ox 94. **d** 95 **p** 96. C Wembley St Jo *Lon* 95-98; NSM S Gillingham *Roch* from 98. *26 Pear Tree Lane, Hempstead, Gillingham ME7 3PT* Tel (01634) 387892
E-mail annerichard@blueyonder.co.uk

LEE, Anthony Maurice. b 35. Bps' Coll Cheshunt 62. **d** 65 **p** 66. C Pinner *Lon* 65-71; Asst Youth Chapl *Glouc* 71-72; V Childswyckham 72-73; R Aston Somerville 72-73; V Childswyckham w Aston Somerville 73-91; P-in-c Buckland 88-91; P-in-c Stanton w Snowshill 88-91; R Childswyckham w Aston Somerville, Buckland etc 91-94; RD Winchcombe 86-94; rtd 94. *11 Holly Close, Broadclyst, Exeter EX5 3JB*

LEE, Canon Arthur Gordon. b 32. Univ of Wales (Swansea) BA52 DipSocSc53. St Mich Coll Llan 53. **d** 55 **p** 56. C Brynmawr *S & B* 55-57; C Llangyfelach and Morriston 57-60; V Llanddewi Ystradenni and Abbey Cwmhir 60-69; V Swansea St Pet 69-98; RD Penderi 90-98; Hon Can Brecon Cathl 91-95; Can Res Brecon Cathl 95-98; rtd 98. *51 Dunvant Road, Killay, Swansea SA2 7NL* Tel (01792) 207715

LEE, Canon Brian. b 37. Linc Th Coll 78. **d** 80 **p** 81. C Duston *Pet* 80-84; P-in-c Spratton 84-89; V from 89; Jt P-in-c Maidwell w Draughton, Lamport w Faxton 89-01; Jt P-in-c Cottesbrooke w Gt Creaton and Thornby from 89; RD Brixworth 94-01; Can Pet Cathl from 98. *The Vicarage, 2 Church Road, Spratton, Northampton NN6 8HR* Tel (01604) 847212

LEE, Canon Brian Ernest. b 32. ACA59 FCA70. Linc Th Coll 60. **d** 62 **p** 63. C Birch St Jas *Man* 62-65; V Withington St Paul 65-66; R Abbey Hey 66-70; Hon C Gatley *Ches* 86-88; V Egremont St Jo 88-97; RD Wallasey 91-96; OGS from 92; Hon Can Ches Cathl *Ches* 96-97; rtd 97; Perm to Offic *Nor* from 97. *St Fursey's House, Convent of All Hallows, Ditchingham, Bungay NR35 2DZ* Tel (01986) 892308 Fax as telephone

LEE, Brian John. b 51. K Coll Lon BD78 AKC78. Coll of Resurr Mirfield 78. **d** 79 **p** 80. C Ham St Rich *S'wark* 79-82; C Surbiton St Andr and St Mark 82-85; V Shirley St Geo 85-93; V St Botolph Aldgate w H Trin Minories *Lon* from 93. *St Botolph's Vestry, Aldgate, London EC3N 1AB* Tel (020) 7283 1670 *or* 7283 1990 Fax 7283 9302
E-mail brian.stbotolphsaldgate@eggconnect.net

LEE, Christopher Garfield. b 41. St Deiniol's Hawarden 80. **d** 80 **p** 81. C Swansea St Pet *S & B* 80-81; C Oystermouth 81-83; R Cromhall w Tortworth and Tytherington *Glouc* 83-93; R Bishopston *S & B* from 93; UK Field Dir Educn for Min Progr from 93. *The Rectory, 4 Portway, Bishopston, Swansea SA3 3JR* Tel (01792) 232140 Fax 233123

LEE, Clifford Samuel (Sam). b 53. **d** 95 **p** 96. NSM S Elmham and Ilketshall *St E* from 95. *Packway Lodge, Flixton, Bungay NR35 1NR* Tel (01986) 782300

LEE, Clive Warwick. b 34. St Pet Coll Ox BA58 MA62 Ox Univ PGCE73. Coll of Resurr Mirfield 58. **d** 60 **p** 61. C W End *Win* 60-64; C Upper Norwood St Jo *Cant* 65-69; Chapl Vinehall Sch E Sussex 69-94; rtd 94. *28 St Radigund's Street, Canterbury CT1 2AA* Tel (01227) 780624

LEE, Colin John Willmot. b 21. Wycliffe Hall Ox 57. **d** 59 **p** 59. C Gravesend St Jas *Roch* 59-62; V Dartford St Edm 62-67; Bp's Ind Adv *Derby* 67-91; C-in-c Ilkeston St Bart CD 67-69; P-in-c Stanton by Dale 69-75; V Ilkeston St Jo 76-91; rtd 91; Perm to Offic *Derby* and *S'well* from 91. *3 Buttermead Close, Trowell, Nottingham NG9 3QT* Tel 0115-949 0100

LEE, Canon David John. b 46. Bris Univ BSc67 Lon Univ DipTh73 Fitzw Coll Cam BA76 Cam Univ MA79 Birm Univ PhD96. Ridley Hall Cam 74. **d** 77 **p** 78. C Putney St Marg *S'wark* 77-80; Uganda 80-86; Tutor Crowther Hall CMS Tr Coll Selly Oak 86-91; Lic to Offic *Birm* 87-91; P-in-c Wishaw 91-96; P-in-c Middleton 91-96; Can Res Birm Cathl from 96; Dir Dioc Bd for Miss from 96. *134 Oakfield Road, Selly Oak, Birmingham B29 7ED* Tel 0121-472 0715 *or* 426 0422 Fax 428 1114
E-mail davidjlee@birmingham.anglican.org

LEE, The Ven David Stanley. b 30. Univ of Wales (Cardiff) BSc51. St Mich Coll Llan 56. **d** 57 **p** 58. C Caerau w Ely *Llan* 57-60; C Port Talbot St Agnes 60-70; Ind Chapl 60-70; R Merthyr Tydfil 70-72; Chapl Merthyr Tydfil Hosp 70-91; R Merthyr Tydfil and Cyfarthfa *Llan* 72-91; RD Merthyr Tydfil 82-91; Can Llan Cathl 84-97; Adn Llan 91-97; R Llanfabon 91-97; rtd 97; Perm to Offic *Llan* from 97; *Mon* from 98. *2 Old Vicarage, Llanishen, Cardiff CF14 5UZ* Tel (029) 2075 2431

LEE, David Wight Dunsmore. b 39. Wells Th Coll 61. **d** 63 **p** 64. C Middlesbrough St Oswald *York* 63-67; C Northallerton w Kirby Sigston 67-69; Malawi 69-75; V Newington Transfiguration *York* 76-81; P-in-c Sheriff Hutton 81-85; P-in-c Sheriff Hutton and Farlington 85-97; V Sheriff Hutton, Farlington, Stillington etc from 97. *The Vicarage, New Lane, Sheriff Hutton, York YO60 1QU* Tel (01347) 878336
E-mail dwdlee@talk21.com

LEE, Derek Alfred. **d** 00. OLM Llantilio Pertholey w Bettws Chpl etc *Mon* from 00. *4 Croesonen Parc, Abergavenny NP7 6PF*

LEE, Edmund Hugh. b 53. Trin Coll Ox BA75 MA79 Goldsmiths' Coll Lon BMus83 K Coll Lon MA98. Ripon Coll Cuddesdon 93. **d** 95 **p** 96. C Malden St Jas *S'wark* 95-99; TV Mortlake w E Sheen from 99. *17 Sheen Gate Gardens, London SW14 7PD* Tel (020) 8876 5002 Fax as telephone
E-mail edknife@aol.com

LEE, Frederick Roydon. b 13. OBE69. S'wark Ord Course 76. **d** 77 **p** 78. NSM Sundridge w Ide Hill *Roch* 77-81; rtd 81; Perm to Offic *Roch* 81-99. *40 Tudor Court, 210 Main Road, Biggin Hill, Westerham TN16 3BB* Tel (01959) 540785

LEE, Gilbert (Sai Kuen). b 51. Hong Kong Univ BD80 Kent Univ MA98. Chung Chi Coll Hong Kong 77. **d** 80 **p** 81. Hong Kong 80-88; C Angl Ch Hong Kong 80-81; V 81-88; NSM St Martin-in-the-Fields *Lon* 88-00; Chapl to Chinese in London 88-00; Canada from 00; I St Jo Chinese Ch Toronto from 00. *135 First Avenue, Toronto ON, Canada, M4M 1W9* Tel (001) (416) 461 0692

LEE, Gordon. *See* LEE, Canon Arthur Gordon

LEE, Henry. b 31. St Chad's Coll Dur BA53 DipTh55 Bede Coll Dur PGCE71. **d** 55 **p** 56. C Hendon St Ignatius *Dur* 55-60; C Dur St Marg 60-65; V Medomsley 65-75; Chapl Darlington Memorial Hosp 75-79; V Darlington H Trin *Dur* 75-82; V Brompton w Deighton *York* 82-90; rtd 90; Perm to Offic *York* from 90. *103 Benfieldside Road, Consett DH8 0RS* Tel (01207) 592170

LEE, Hugh Gordon Cassels. b 41. St Andr Univ BSc64. Edin Th Coll 64. **d** 67 **p** 68. C Dumfries *Glas* 67-70; C Totteridge *St Alb* 70-73; R Glas St Jas *Glas* 73-80; R Bishopbriggs 80-86; R St Fillans *St And* 86-89; R Crieff and Comrie 86-01; P-in-c Muthill 86-01; P-in-c Lochearnhead 89-01; R Dunoon *Arg* from 01. *Holy Trinity Rectory, Kilbright Road, Dunoon PA23 7LN* Tel (01369) 702444

LEE, Miss Iris Audrey Olive. b 26. St Andr Coll Southsea 54 Gilmore Ho 76. **dss** 76 **d** 87. N Weald Bassett *Chelmsf* 76-87; rtd 87; NSM Clacton St Jas *Chelmsf* 87-00; Chapl Clacton Hosp 90-95; Perm to Offic from 00. *30 Marine Court, Marine Parade West, Clacton-on-Sea CO15 1ND* Tel (01255) 423719

LEE, Mrs Jennifer. b 42. Westf Coll Lon BA64 CQSW78. N Ord Course 01. **d** 03. NSM Millhouses H Trin *Sheff* from 03. *Whirlow Croft, Whirlow Lane, Sheffield S11 9QF* Tel 0114-236 7938
E-mail leejandm@aol.com

LEE, John. b 47. Univ of Wales (Swansea) BSc70 MSc73 MInstGA87. Ripon Hall Ox 73. **d** 75 **p** 76. C Swansea St Pet *S & B* 75-78; C St Botolph Aldgate w H Trin Minories *Lon* 79-84; P-in-c Chiddingstone w Chiddingstone Causeway *Roch* 84-89; R 89-98; Clergy Appts Adv from 98. *Cowley House, 9 Little College Street, London SW1P 3SH* Tel (020) 7898 1898 Fax 7898 1899
E-mail sue.manners@caa.c-of-e.org.uk

LEE, John Charles Hugh Mellanby. b 44. Trin Hall Cam BA66 MA69 Brunel Univ MTech71. Ox NSM Course 78. **d** 81 **p** 82. NSM Amersham on the Hill *Ox* 81-88; NSM Ox St Aldate w St Matt 88-91; NSM Wheatley 93-95; Dioc Development Officer for Miss in Work and Economic Life 95-02; P-in-c Ox St Mich w St Martin and All SS from 02. *12 Walton Street, Oxford OX1 2HG* Tel (01865) 316245 Fax as telephone
E-mail hugh.lee@btinternet.com

LEE, John Foden. b 34. AKC61. **d** 61 **p** 62. C Pet All SS *Pet* 61-63; C Sudbury St Andr *Lon* 63-65; C Sherborne w Castleton and Lillington *Sarum* 65-67; V Erlestoke 67-68; R Gt Cheverell 67; V Erlestoke and Gt Cheverell 68-79; V Seend and Bulkington 79-86; Ind Chapl *Derby* 86-99; V Derby St Paul 86-99; rtd 99; Perm to Offic *Guildf* from 01. *3 Eddystone Court, Churt, Farnham GU10 2NU* Tel (01428) 717837

LEE, John Michael Andrew. b 62. Leeds Univ BA84. Trin Coll Bris 88. **d** 90 **p** 91. C Norbiton *S'wark* 90-94; C Leic H Trin w St Jo *Leic* 94-02; R York St Paul *York* from 02. *St Paul's Rectory, 100 Acomb Road, York YO2 4ER* Tel (01904) 792304
E-mail john_lee@lineone.net

LEE, John Samuel. b 47. Chich Th Coll 74. **d** 77 **p** 78. C Bramley *Ripon* 77-80; C Bideford *Ex* 81-84; TV Littleham w Exmouth

84-90; P-in-c Sidbury 90-91; TV Sidmouth, Woolbrook, Salcombe Regis, Sidbury etc from 91. *The Vicarage, Harcombe Lane, Sidford, Sidmouth EX10 9QN* Tel (01395) 579520 E-mail johnslee@glensidf.freeserve.co.uk

LEE, Joseph Patrick. b 53. St Jos Coll Upholland 72 Ushaw Coll Dur 75. **d** 78 **p** 79. In RC Ch 78-99; Hon C Charlton *S'wark* from 99. *45 Chestnut Rise, London SE18 1RJ* Tel (020) 8316 4674 Mobile07956-294429 Fax83177304 E-mail joe_lee@lineone.net

LEE, Kenneth Peter. b 45. Em Coll Cam BA67 MA71. Cuddesdon Coll 67. **d** 69 **p** 70. C Stoke Poges *Ox* 69-72; C Witton *Ches* 72-74; V Frankby w Greasby 74-92; R Christleton from 92. *The Rectory, Birch Heath Lane, Christleton, Chester CH3 7AP* Tel (01244) 335663 E-mail kpeter.lee@btinternet.com

LEE, Luke Gun-Hong. b 37. Univ of Yon Sei BTh62. St Jo Coll Morpeth 64. **d** 67 **p** 68. Korea 67-79; C Bloxwich *Lich* 79-83; TV Dunstable *St Alb* 83-90; V Croxley Green All SS from 90. *All Saints' Vicarage, Croxley Green, Rickmansworth WD3 3HJ* Tel (01923) 772109 E-mail luke.lee@talk21.com

LEE, Miss Lynley Hoe. b 52. Trin Coll Bris DipHE81. St Jo Coll Nottm BTh89 K Coll Lon MA93. **d** 90 **p** 94. Par Dn Pitsea *Chelmsf* 90-95; Singapore 95-98; C Gt Ilford St Andr *Chelmsf* 99-02; TV Grays Thurrock from 02. *Wendover, College Avenue, Grays RM17 5UW* Tel (01375) 373468 *or* 371566 E-mail lynley@lee49ie.freeserve.co.uk

LEE, Martin Paul. b 66. Aston Tr Scheme 91 Linc Th Coll 93 St Steph Ho Ox 94. **d** 96 **p** 97. C Wells St Thos w Horrington *B & W*96-00; P-in-c Brent Knoll, E Brent and Lympsham 00-01; R from 01; RD Axbridge from 03. *The Rectory, 3 Ash Trees, East Brent, Highbridge TA9 4DQ* Tel (01278) 760874 E-mail frmlee@aol.com

LEE, Nicholas Knyvett. b 54. MA. Cranmer Hall Dur. **d** 85 **p** 86. C Brompton H Trin w Onslow Square St Paul *Lon* from 85. *St Paul's Church House, Onslow Square, London SW7 3NX* Tel (020) 7589 3933

LEE, Peter Alexander. b 44. Hull Univ BSc(Econ)65. Ex & Truro NSM Scheme 80. **d** 83 **p** 84. NSM Ex St Sidwell and St Matt *Ex* 83-89; NSM Ex St Dav 90-98; C Paignton St Jo 98-01; Perm to Offic 01-03; Hon C Ex St Dav from 03. *Windyridge, Beech Avenue, Exeter EX4 6HF* Tel (01392) 254118

✠LEE, The Rt Revd Peter John. b 47. St Jo Coll Cam BA69 CertEd70 MA73. Ridley Hall Cam 70 St Jo Coll Nottm 72. **d** 73 **p** 74. C 90. C Onslow Square St Paul *Lon* 73-76; S Africa from 76; V-Gen and Bp C'the K from 90. *PO Box 1653, Rosettenville, 2130 South Africa* Tel (0027) (11) 435 0097 *or* 942 1179 Fax 435 2868 E-mail dckpeter@netactive.co.za

LEE, Peter Kenneth. b 44. Selw Coll Cam BA66 MA69. Cuddesdon Coll 67. **d** 69 **p** 70. C Manston *Ripon* 69-72; C Bingley All SS *Bradf* 72-77; Chapl Bingley Coll of Educn 72-77; V Cross Roads cum Lees *Bradf* 77-90; V Auckland St Pet *Dur* from 90; Tutor NEOC from 91. *St Peter's Vicarage, 39 Etherley Lane, Bishop Auckland DL14 7QZ* Tel (01388) 661856

LEE, Canon Raymond John. b 30. St Edm Hall Ox BA53 MA57. Tyndale Hall Bris 54. **d** 56 **p** 57. C Tooting Graveney St Nic *S'wark* 56-59; C Muswell Hill St Jas *Lon* 59-62; V Woking St Mary *Guildf* 62-70; V Gt Crosby St Luke *Liv* 70-82; Dioc Adv NSM 79-95; V Allerton 82-94; Hon Can Liv Cathl 89-95; rtd 95; P-in-c Altcar *Liv* 94-98; Perm to Offic from 98. *15 Barkfield Lane, Formby, Liverpool L37 1LY* Tel (01704) 872670

LEE, Richard Alexander. b 63. St Jo Coll Nottm BTh91. **d** 91 **p** 92. C Gt Stanmore *Lon* 91-95; C Edgware 95-98; TV S Gillingham *Roch* from 98. *26 Pear Tree Lane, Hempstead, Gillingham ME7 3PT* Tel (01634) 387892 E-mail annerichard@blueyonder.co.uk

LEE, Robert David. b 53. QUB BD75. CITC 77. **d** 77 **p** 78. C Comber *D & D* 77-83; I Mt Merrion 83-87; CMS 89-92; Egypt 89-97; R Peebles *Edin* from 97; P-in-c Innerleithen from 97. *St Peter's Rectory, 36 Wemyss Place, Peebles EH45 8JT* Tel (01721) 720571 Fax as telephone E-mail robert.l@virgin.net

LEE, Robert William. b 31. Keele Univ BA54 St Cath Soc Ox BA58 MA63. Ripon Hall Ox 56. **d** 59 **p** 60. C Dawley St Jerome *Lon* 59-62; C Bromley H Trin *Roch* 62-65; R Clayton *Man* 65-70; P-in-c Man St Paul 65-70; TV Hemel Hempstead *St Alb* 70-72; TV Corby SS Pet and Andr w Gt and Lt Oakley *Pet* 72-80; V Weedon Lois w Plumpton and Moreton Pinkney etc 80-88; R Thornhams Magna and Parva, Gislingham and Mellis *St E* 88-96; rtd 96; Perm to Offic *Bradf* and Carl from 96. *2 Guldrey Fold, Sedbergh LA10 5DY* Tel (01539) 621907

LEE, Sai Kuen. See LEE, Gilbert

LEE, Sam. See LEE, Clifford Samuel

LEE, Simon Margeison. b 43. Brighton Coll of Educn TCert66. Cant Sch of Min 90. **d** 93 **p** 94. NSM Walmer *Cant* from 93. *26 Greenacre Drive, Deal CT14 7UQ* Tel (01304) 362585

LEE, Steven Michael. b 56. Dur Univ BA. Trin Coll Bris 80. **d** 83 **p** 84. C Beckenham St Jo *Roch* 83-86; C Leic Martyrs *Leic* 86-90; V Coalville and Bardon Hill 90-95; P-in-c Kibworth and Smeeton Westerby and Saddington 95-00; P-in-c Foxton w Gumley and Laughton and Lubenham 96-97; P-in-c Foxton w Gumley and Laughton 97-00; R Kibworth and Smeeton Westerby and Saddington from 00. *The Rectory, 25 Church Road, Kibworth, Leicester LE8 0NB* Tel 0116-279 2294 E-mail lee.fam@btinternet.com

LEE, Stuart Graham. b 73. Roehampton Inst BA94. St Steph Ho Ox BTh00. **d** 00 **p** 01. C Eltham H Trin *S'wark* from 00. *59A Southend Crescent, London SE9 2SD* Tel (020) 8850 2796 Fax as telephone

LEE, Thomas Richard. b 52. AKC73. St Aug Coll Cant 74. **d** 75 **p** 76. C Leam Lane CD *Dur* 75-80; Chapl RAF from 80. *Chaplaincy Services (RAF), HQ, Personnel and Training Command, RAF Innsworth, Gloucester GL3 1EZ* Tel (01452) 712612 ext 5164 Fax 510828

LEE, William George. b 11. TCD BA33 MA48. **d** 34 **p** 35. C Southport St Andr *Liv* 34-37; C Cambridge St Paul *Ely* 37-44; V Matlock Bath *Derby* 44-49; V Deptford St Jo *S'wark* 49-61; RD Greenwich and Deptford 60; V Chislehurst Ch Ch *Roch* 61-76; rtd 76. *Dale Garth, Harmby, Leyburn DL8 5PD* Tel (01969) 622649

LEE WARNER, Canon Theodore John. b 22. Univ Coll Ox BA49 MA54. Wells Th Coll 50. **d** 51 **p** 52. C S Westoe *Dur* 51-55; P-in-c Cassop cum Quarrington 55-59; V Peterlee 59-63; V Darlington H Trin 63-74; Chapl Darlington Memorial Hosp 63-74; V Norton St Mary *Dur* 74-80; RD Barnard Castle 80-87; V Gainford 80-87; R Winston 80-87; Hon Can Dur Cathl 83-87; rtd 87. *112 Cleveland Terrace, Darlington DL3 8JA* Tel (01325) 467585

LEECE, Roderick Neil Stephen. b 59. ARCM85 Wadh Coll Ox BA81 MA85 Leeds Univ BA84. Coll of Resurr Mirfield 82. **d** 85 **p** 86. C Portsea St Mary *Portsm* 85-91; V Stamford Hill St Bart *Lon* from 91. *St Bartholomew's Vicarage, Craven Park Road, London N15 6AA* Tel (020) 8800 1554 E-mail rleece@lineone.net

LEECH, Christopher. b 16. Linc Th Coll 37. **d** 39 **p** 40. C Cudworth *Wakef* 39-41; C Twerton *B & W* 41-43; R Walcot 43-47; S Rhodesia 47-52 and 54-57; V Easton *B & W* 53-54; V Wigan St Geo *Liv* 57-60; R Combe Pyne w Rousdon *Ex* 60-76; P-in-c 76-82; C Axminster 77-79; rtd 82; Perm to Offic *Ex* from 82. *Nestor, Hillhead, Colyton EX24 6HH* Tel (01297) 552034

LEECH, Kenneth. b 39. Lon Univ BA61 AKC61 Trin Coll Ox BA63 MA71 Lambeth DD98. St Steph Ho Ox 62. **d** 64 **p** 65. C Hoxton H Trin w St Mary *Lon* 64-67; C Soho St Anne w St Thos and St Pet 67-71; Tutor St Aug Coll Cant 71-74; R Bethnal Green St Matt *Lon* 74-79; Field Officer Community & Race Relns Unit BCC 80; Race Relns Officer Gen Syn Bd for Soc Resp 81-87; Hon C Notting Hill St Clem and St Mark *Lon* 82-85; Hon C Notting Dale St Clem w St Mark and St Jas 85-88; Dir Runnymede Trust 87-90; Hon C St Botolph Aldgate w H Trin Minories *Lon* from 91. *St Botolph's Vestry, Aldgate, London EC3N 1AB* Tel (020) 7377 0721 Fax 7375 3692 E-mail kenleech@aol.com

LEECH, Miss Peggy Irene. b 29. Lon Univ CertRK58 DipSocSc77 DipRS80 DipPsychP&C82. CA Tr Coll 56. **dss** 85 **d** 87 **p** 94. Dss Oxhey All SS *St Alb* 86-87; Par Dn 87-91; NSM 91-99; Perm to Offic from 99. *2 Bucklands, Gibbs Couch, Watford WD19 5DL* Tel (020) 8428 9446

LEEDS, Archdeacon of. See OLIVER, The Ven John Michael

LEEFIELD, Michael John. b 37. Liv Univ BA60 K Coll Lon BD65 AKC65. St Boniface Warminster 62. **d** 66 **p** 67. C Gt Yarmouth *Nor* 66-70; V Trowse 70-75; V Arminghall 70-75; R Caistor w Markshall 70-75; Chapl Norfolk and Nor Hosp 70-75; V Aylesbury w Aylburton *Glouc* 75-84; RD Forest S 82-84; Lic to Offic from 85; rtd 01. *Brays Court, Awre, Newnham GL14 1EP* Tel (01594) 510483

LEEKE, Charles Browne. b 39. TCD DipTh83 Stranmillis Coll CertEd62. CITC 80. **d** 83 **p** 84. C Ballymoney w Finvoy and Rasharkin *Conn* 83-86; I Faughanvale *D & R* 86-97; Chapl Port Londonderry Miss to Seamen 92-97; Bp's Dom Chapl *D & R* 92-96; Can Derry Cathl 96-00; I Drumragh w Mountfield 97-00; Reconciliation Development Officer *D & D* from 00. *41 Beechfield Lodge, Aghalee, Craigavon BT67 0GA* Tel (028) 9265 2838 *or* 9032 3188 Fax 9265 0178 *or* 9032 1635 E-mail charlie@reconcile-thinkagain.fsnet.co.uk

LEEKE, Stephen Owen. b 50. EAMTC 82 Ridley Hall Cam 83. **d** 84 **p** 85. C Cherry Hinton St Andr *Ely* 84-87; P-in-c Warboys 87-91; P-in-c Wistow 87-91; P-in-c Bury 87-91; R Warboys w Broughton and Bury w Wistow 91-01; RD St Ives 92-01; V Cambridge St Martin from 01. *St Martin's Vicarage, 127 Suez Road, Cambridge CB1 3QD* Tel (01223) 214203 E-mail stephen@leekes.freeserve.co.uk

LEEMAN, John Graham. b 41. N Ord Course 78. **d** 80 **p** 81. NSM Hull St Mary Sculcoates *York* 80-96; Perm to Offic 96-99;

Hon C Hull St Steph Sculcoates from 99; Hon C Hull St Mary Sculcoates from 99; Hon C Hull St Mary Sculcoates from 99; Hon C Hull St Mary Sculcoates from 99; Hon C Sculcoates St Paul w Ch Ch and St Silas from 99. *1 Snuff Mill Lane, Cottingham HU16 4RY* Tel (01482) 840355

LEEMING, Jack. b 34. Kelham Th Coll 56. **d** 61 **p** 62. C Sydenham St Phil *S'wark* 61-64; Chapl RAF 64-84; Chapl Salisbury Gen Infirmary 84-89; R Barford St Martin, Dinton, Baverstock etc *Sarum* 89-99; rtd 99; Perm to Offic *Sarum* from 01. *8 Bower Gardens, Salisbury SP1 2RL* Tel (01722) 416800

LEEMING, Mrs Janice Doreen. b 45. EMMTC 97. **d** 00 **p** 01. NSM Lenton *S'well* from 00. *5 Hollinwell Avenue, Wollaton, Nottingham NG8 1JY* Tel 0115-928 2145

LEEMING, John Maurice. b 24. CEng MIMechE MIProdE FIED. NW Ord Course 72. **d** 75 **p** 76. NSM Endcliffe *Sheff* 75-78; C Norton 78-80; V Bolsterstone 80-89; Jt Min Stocksbridge Chr Cen LEP 80-89; Ind Chapl 81-89; rtd 89; Perm to Offic *S'well* from 89; *Sheff* from 93; *Derby* from 98. *Beck House, Toftdyke Lane, Clayworth, Retford DN22 9AH* Tel (01777) 817795 E-mail maurice@leeming02.freeserve.co.uk

LEES, Allan Garside. b 39. OLM course 96. **d** 99 **p** 00. OLM Hurst *Man* from 99. *1 Exeter Drive, Ashton-under-Lyne OL6 8BZ* Tel 0161-339 3105

LEES, Charles Alan. b 38. RGN OND FE TCert. WMMTC 78. **d** 81 **p** 82. NSM Yardley St Cypr Hay Mill *Birm* 81-84 and 86-87; Hon C Dorridge 84-86; Chapl E Birm Hosp 85-87; Hon C Leamington Spa H Trin and Old Milverton *Cov* 89-90; Perm to Offic *Birm* 95-96 and from 98. *49 Gordon Street, Leamington Spa CV31 1HR* Tel (01926) 772711

LEES, John Raymond. b 57. Selw Coll Cam BA78 MA82. St Steph Ho Ox 89. **d** 91 **p** 92. C Eastbourne St Mary *Chich* 91-93; Min Can and Succ St Paul's Cathl *Lon* 93-98; TR Swindon New Town *Bris* 98-01; C Highworth w Sevenhampton and Inglesham etc 01-02; Asst to AD Swindon 01-02; Perm to Offic *Lon* 02-03. *27 St Margaret's Road, Peterborough PE2 9EA* Tel (01733) 312404 Mobile 07769-606947 E-mail johnlees@onetel.net.uk

LEES, Mrs Kathleen Marion. b 30. Birkbeck Coll Lon BA60 DipRS80. S'wark Ord Course 77. **dss** 80 **d** 87 **p** 94. Epping St Jo *Chelmsf* 80-86; Hon C Hunstanton St Mary w Ringstead Parva, Holme etc *Nor* 87-88; Perm to Offic 88-94; Chapl King's Lynn and Wisbech Hosps NHS Trust 94-00; NSM Gaywood *Nor* 94-00; rtd 00; Perm to Offic *Nor* from 00. *20 North Hirne Court, St Anns Street, King's Lynn PE31 1LT* Tel (01553) 661294

LEES, Peter John. b 35 **p** 95 **p** 96. NSM Buckie *Ab* 95-00; NSM Turriff 95-00; P-in-c Fraserburgh from 00. *7 Whitefield Court, Buckpool, Buckie AB56 1EY* Tel (01542) 835011 or 835261

LEES, Stephen. b 55. St Jo Coll York CertEd77 BEd78 Nottm Univ MA96. St Jo Coll Nottm 88. **d** 90 **p** 91. C Mansfield St Jo *S'well* 90-93; TV Bestwood 93-98; V Baxenden *Blackb* from 98. *The Vicarage, Langford Street, Baxenden, Accrington BB5 2RF* Tel (01254) 232471

E-mail steve.lees@stjohnsbaxenden.org.uk

LEES, Stuart Charles Roderick. b 62. Trin Coll Bris BA. **d** 89 **p** 90. C Woodford Wells *Chelmsf* 89-93; C Brompton H Trin w Onslow Square St Paul *Lon* 93-97; Chapl Stewards Trust 93-97; P-in-c Fulham Ch Ch 97-03; V from 03. *Christ Church Vicarage, 40 Clancarty Road, London SW6 3AA* Tel (020) 7736 4261 Fax as telephone

LEES-SMITH, Christopher John (Brother Edward). b 21. CCC Ox BA49 MA65. Cuddesdon Coll 48. **d** 50 **p** 51. C Pallion *Dur* 50-54; SSF from 54; Lic to Offic *Sarum* 57-62; Perm to Offic *Newc* 62-74; Guardian Almouth Friary 65-74; Chapl Third Order SSF 74-91; rtd 91. *The Friary, Alnmouth, Alnwick NE66 6NJ* Tel (01665) 830213

LEESE, Arthur Selwyn Mountford. b 09. K Coll Lon BD31 AKC31 St Cath Soc Ox BA33 MA44. Ripon Hall Ox 31. **d** 33 **p** 34. C Bexleyheath Ch Ch *Roch* 33-37; C Cockington *Ex* 37-39; C Langley Mill *Derby* 39-51; V Hawkhurst *Cant* 51-74; rtd 74; Perm to Offic *Cant* from 74; *Chich* from 75. *84 Wickham Avenue, Bexhill-on-Sea TN39 3ER* Tel (01424) 213137

LEESE, Frederick Henry Brooke. b 24. AKC47. **d** 47 **p** 48. C Mitcham St Mark *S'wark* 47-50; C Bourne *Guildf* 50-54; V Croydon St Martin *Cant* 54-60; V Pagham *Chich* 60-70; V Chorley *Ches* 70-82; R Rogate w Terwick and Trotton w Chithurst *Chich* 82-90; RD Midhurst 85-90; rtd 90; Perm to Offic *B & W* from 90. *Treetops, Furnham Crescent, Chard TA20 1AZ* Tel (01460) 65524

LEESE, Mrs Jane Elizabeth. b 50. Man Univ BA(Econ)72 Avery Hill Coll PGCE73. Sarum Th Coll 93. **d** 96 **p** 97. NSM Kempshott *Win* 96-01; NSM Herriard w Winslade and Long Sutton etc from 01. *The Parsonage, Gaston Lane, South Warnborough, Hook RG29 1RH* Tel (01256) 862843
E-mail jane.leese@ukgateway.net

LEESON, Bernard Alan. b 47. FCollP92 FRSA92 Bris Univ CertEd68 Open Univ BA75 Southn Univ MA78 Sheff Univ PhD97. EMMTC 84. **d** 92 **p** 93. Dep Hd Master Ripley Mill Hill Sch 80-91; NSM Breadsall *Derby* 87-91; Hd St Aid CE High Sch Lancs from 91; Perm to Offic *Blackb* 91-92; Lic to Offic from 92; NSM Officer 92-96. *The Lodge, Daggers Lane, Preesall, Poulton-le-Fylde FY6 0QN* Tel (01253) 811020 *or* 810504 Fax 810244 E-mail alan-leeson@st-aidans.lancs.sch.uk

LEESON, David Harry Stanley. b 45. Glouc Th Course 82. **d** 85 **p** 86. NSM Stratton w Baunton *Glouc* 85-94; NSM N Cerney w Bagendon 91-94; NSM Stratton, N Cerney, Baunton and Bagendon from 95. *83 Cheltenham Road, Stratton, Cirencester GL7 2JB* Tel (01285) 651186

LEESON, Mrs Sally Elizabeth. b 57. Sussex Univ BA79. Westcott Ho Cam 83. **dss** 85 **d** 87 **p** 94. Battersea St Pet and St Paul *S'wark* 85-87; Par Dn 87-90; Par Dn Limpsfield and Titsey 90-94; C 94; Perm to Offic from 94. *The Parsonage, Upp Hill Lane, Priest Hutton, Carnforth LA6 1JL* Tel (01524) 781264

LEFEVER, Henry Charles. b 06. Lon Univ BA30 BD32 Tübingen Univ PhD34. **d** 65 **p** 66. Hon C S'wark St Sav w All Hallows *S'wark* 65-69; Hon C Blackheath Ascension 69-75; rtd 75; Perm to Offic *Cant* 76-98. *Address temp unknown*

LEFFLER, Christopher. b 33. Em Coll Cam BA57 MA61. Linc Th Coll. **d** 59 **p** 60. C Bermondsey St Mary w St Olave and St Jo *S'wark* 59-60; C Herne Hill St Paul 60-63; Ch-in-c Canley CD *Cov* 63-67; R Gt and Lt Glemham *St E* 67-72; R Badwell Ash w Gt Ashfield, Stowlangtoft etc 72-82; R Trimley 82-99; rtd 99. *308 High Street, Felixstowe IP11 9QJ* Tel (01394) 672279
E-mail chrisleffler@quista.net

LEFFLER, Jeremy Paul (Jem). b 62. Westmr Coll Ox BEd88. Wycliffe Hall Ox BTh94. **d** 94 **p** 95. C Ormskirk *Liv* 94-97; C Much Woolton 97-00; P-in-c Widnes St Ambrose from 00. *St Ambrose Vicarage, 45 Hargreaves Court, Widnes WA8 0QA* Tel 0151-420 8044 Fax as telephone
E-mail info@stambrose.fsnet.co.uk

LEFROY, John Perceval. b 40. Trin Coll Cam BA62. Cuddesdon Coll 64. **d** 66 **p** 67. C Maidstone St Martin *Cant* 66-69; C St Peter-in-Thanet 69-74; V Barming Heath 74-82; V Upchurch w Lower Halstow from 82; P-in-c Iwade from 95. *The Vicarage, 15 Oak Lane, Upchurch, Sittingbourne ME9 7AT* Tel (01634) 387227

LEFROY (née CLARK), Mrs Kathleen Christine. b 33. Newton Park Coll Bris TCert53 Lon Univ DipTh58. St Mich Ho Ox 56 Trin Coll Bris 90. **d** 90 **p** 02. Personnel Sec SAMS 83-91; Asst Gen Sec 87-92; rtd 92; NSM Eastbourne H Trin *Chich* 90-02; NSM Eastbourne St Jo from 02; Chmn SEAN (Internat) and SOMA (UK) from 91; Dioc Voc Adv from 92. *12 Rodmill Drive, Eastbourne BN21 2SG* Tel (01323) 640294
E-mail kathleenclefroy@macunlimited.net

LEFROY, Matthew William. b 62. Trin Coll Cam BA84 Keele Univ PGCE91. St Jo Coll Nottm MTh02. **d** 02 **p** 03. C Portswood Ch Ch *Win* from 02. *6 Royston Close, Southampton SO17 1TB* Tel (023) 8055 5883 *or* (023) 8059 5015
E-mail matthew@mjlefroy.freeserve.co.uk

LEFROY-OWEN, Neal. b 62. Bradf Univ BA99. N Ord Course 00. **d** 03. C Sandal St Cath *Wakef* from 03. *The Vicarage, Johnston Street, Wakefield WF1 4DZ* Tel (01924) 200449
E-mail revneal@amserve.com

LEGG, Adrian James. b 52. St Jo Coll Nottm LTh82 BTh82. **d** 82 **p** 83. C Haughton le Skerne *Dur* 82-85; C Llanishen and Lisvane *Llan* 85-89; V Llanwddyn and Llanfihangel-yng-Nghwynfa etc *St As* 89-93; V Llansadwrn w Llanwrda and Manordeilo *St D* from 93. *The Vicarage, Llanwrda SA19 8HD* Tel (01550) 777343
E-mail alegg94523@aol.com

LEGG, Joanna Susan Penberthy. *See* PENBERTHY, Ms Joanna Susan

LEGG, John Andrew Douglas. b 32. Selw Coll Cam BA55 MA57. Wells Th Coll 57. **d** 59 **p** 59. Australia 59-63; Chapl Rugby Sch 63-64; P-in-c Ashford w Sheldon *Derby* 64-67; Kuwait 67-69; Solomon Is 70-71; Asst Master Lt Ilford Comp Sch 72-83; P-in-c Stapleford Tawney w Theydon Mt *Chelmsf* 78-83; R Hemingby *Linc* 83-88; Greece from 88; rtd 92. *Prastos, Kynorias, Arkadia, Greece 22006* Tel (0030) (755) 51693

LEGG, Richard. b 37. Selw Coll Cam BA62 MA66 Brunel Univ MPhil77 NY Th Sem DMin85. Coll of Resurr Mirfield 63. **d** 65 **p** 66. C Ealing St Pet Mt Park *Lon* 65-68; Chapl Brunel Univ 68-78; Wychcroft Ho (Dioc Retreat Cen) *S'wark* 78-81; C Chipping Barnet w Arkley *St Alb* 81-83; TV 83-85; R St Buryan, St Levan and Sennen *Truro* 85-93; Subwarden St Deiniol's Lib Hawarden 93; Perm to Offic *Ches* 93; TV Beaminster Area *Sarum* 93-97; P-in-c Veryan w Ruan Lanihorne *Truro* 97-00; rtd 01. *Sans Bruit, Plain-an-Gwarry, Marazion TR17 0DR* Tel (01736) 710712 E-mail richard.legg@tesco.net

LEGG, Robert Richard. b 16. MBE45. Open Univ BA74 Wells Cam Coll Cant 36. **d** 59 **p** 60. C Andover w Foxcott *Win* 59-62; V W w E Tytherley 62-71; V Kingsclere 71-83; rtd 83; Perm to Offic *Win* from 83. *The Furrow, Evingar Road, Whitchurch RG28 7EU* Tel (01256) 892126

LEGG, Roger Keith. b 35. Lich Th Coll 61. **d** 63 **p** 64. C Petersfield w Sheet *Portsm* 63-66; C Portsea St Mary 66-70; Rhodesia 70-75; V Clayton *Lich* 75-00; rtd 01; Perm to Offic *Lich* from 01. *High Crest, Chapel Lane, Hookgate, Market Drayton TF9 4QP* Tel (01630) 672766 E-mail rogjud@aol.com

LEGG, Miss Ruth Helen Margaret. b 52. Hull Univ BA74 Homerton Coll Cam CertEd75. Trin Coll Bris DipHE88. **d** 88 **p** 94. C Clevedon St Andr and Ch Ch *B & W* 88-92; C Nailsea Ch

Ch 92-96; C Nailsea Ch Ch w Tickenham 96-97; V Pill w Easton in Gordano and Portbury from 97. *The Rectory, 17 Church Road, Easton in Gordano, Bristol BS20 0PQ* Tel (01275) 372804

LEGGATE, Colin Archibald Gunson. b 44. Bris Sch of Min 86. **d** 88 **p** 89. NSM Brislington St Luke *Bris* 88-97; Asst Chapl Frenchay Healthcare NHS Trust Bris 97-99; Asst Chapl N Bris NHS Trust from 99. *Frenchay Hospital, Frenchay Park Road, Bristol BS16 1LE* Tel 0117-970 1212

LEGGETT, James Henry Aufrere. b 61. Oak Hill Th Coll DipHE93. **d** 93 **p** 94. C Hensingham *Carl* 93-97; C-in-c Ryde St Jas Prop Chpl *Portsm* from 97. *84 Pellhurst Road, Ryde PO33 3BS* Tel (01983) 565621 *or* 566381
E-mail jleggett@onetel.net.uk

LEGGETT, Nicholas William Michael. b 62. St Steph Ho Ox 00. **d** 02. C Clevedon St Jo *B & W* from 02. *103 Cannons Gate, Clevedon BS21 5HZ* Tel (01275) 342043 Mobile 07762-156380 E-mail leggett1uwe@yahoo.co.uk

LEGGETT, Vanessa Gisela. See CATO, Ms Vanessa Gisela

LEGOOD, Giles Leslie. b 67. K Coll Lon BD88 AKC88 Heythrop Coll Lon MTh98. Ripon Coll Cuddesdon 90. **d** 92 **p** 93. C N Mymms *St Alb* 92-95; Chapl R Veterinary Coll *Lon* from 95; Chapl R Free Medical Sch from 95; Chapl Univ Coll Medical Sch from 95. *15 Ormonde Mansions, 106 Southampton Row, London WC1B 4BP* Tel (020) 7242 2574
E-mail glegood@rvc.ac.uk

LEGRAND, Nigel Stuart. b 51. STETS 96. **d** 99 **p** 00. NSM Boscombe St Jo *Win* from 99. *50 Meon Road, Bournemouth BH7 6PP* Tel (01202) 428603 Fax 300400
E-mail legrandfamily@netscapeonline.co.uk

LEHANEY, Frank George. b 44. City of Lon Poly 64 MCIT75 MILT99 MIAM78. Dioc OLM tr scheme 96. **d** 99 **p** 00. OLM Brockham Green *S'wark* from 99; OLM Leigh from 99. *Twelve Trees, Small's Hill Road, Leigh, Reigate RH2 8PE* Tel (01306) 611201

LEICESTER, Archdeacon of. See ATKINSON, The Ven Richard William Bryant

LEICESTER, Bishop of. See STEVENS, The Rt Revd Timothy John

LEICESTER, Dean of. See FAULL, The Very Revd Vivienne Frances

LEIGH, Mrs Alison Margaret. b 40. CertEd63 Goldsmiths' Coll Lon BEd75. Sarum & Wells Th Coll 85. **d** 87 **p** 94. C Chessington *Guildf* 87-90; C Green Street Green *Roch* 90-92; Dn-in-c E Peckham and Nettlestead 92-94; P-in-c 94-95; R 95-01; rtd 01; Perm to Offic *Heref* from 02. *17 Orchard Green, Marden, Hereford HR1 3ED* Tel (01432) 882032
E-mail alison.leigh@which.net

LEIGH, Arnold Robert. b 36. AKC60. **d** 61 **p** 62. C Lewisham St Mary *S'wark* 61-66; C Stockwell Green St Andr 66-69; V 69-72; TV Withycombe Raleigh *Ex* 72-74; TR 74-80; V Devonport St Bart 80-93; P-in-c Moretonhampstead, N Bovey and Manaton 93-96; R Moretonhampstead, Manaton, N Bovey and Lustleigh 96-00; rtd 00. *1 Southwick Road, Bournemouth BH6 5PR* Tel (01202) 420135

LEIGH, Dennis Herbert. b 34. Lon Univ BSc56 DipTh68. Chich Th Coll 58. **d** 60 **p** 61. C Roehampton H Trin *S'wark* 60-62; C E Wickham 62-67; C Plumstead St Mark and St Marg 67-73; C Corby Epiphany w St Jo *Pet* 73-74; C Paston 84-86; C Aylestone St Andr w St Jas *Leic* 86-95; rtd 95; Perm to Offic *Pet* from 95; *Leic* from 00. *14 Willowbrook Road, Corby NN17 2EB* Tel (01536) 263405

LEIGH, Canon James Ronald. b 32. S'wark Ord Course 63. **d** 67 **p** 68. C Purley St Barn *S'wark* 67-71; Prec St Ninian's Cathl Perth *St And* 71-73; R Leven 73-79; R Kirkcaldy 79-98; R Kinghorn 81-98; Can St Ninian's Cathl Perth from 90; rtd 98. *8 Pan Ha', Dysart, Kirkcaldy KY1 2TL* Tel (01592) 653113

LEIGH, Martin Francis. b 40. Sheff Univ BSc63. Cuddesdon Coll 65. **d** 67 **p** 68. C St Mary-at-Lambeth *S'wark* 67-70; C Bakewell *Derby* 70-74; V Ockbrook 74-82; RD Ilkeston 78-82; V Baslow 82-92; Bp's Ecum Officer 82-92; TR Kings Norton *Birm* 92-99; V Cheddleton *Lich* from 99; RD Leek from 01. *The Vicarage, Hollow Lane, Cheddleton, Leek ST13 7HP* Tel (01538) 360226 Mobile 07751-984122 Fax (07092) 330994
E-mail revmleigh@btopenworld.com *or* martin.f.leigh@stud.man.ac.uk

LEIGH, Mary Elizabeth. b 42. K Coll Lon BA64. Westcott Ho Cam 89. **d** 91 **p** 94. NSM Chesterfield St Mary and All SS *Derby* 91-92; C Hall Green Ascension *Birm* 92-94; Asst P Yardley St Edburgha 94-97; Chapl and Tutor N Ord Course from 97; Lic Preacher *Man* from 97; Perm to Offic *Lich* from 99. *The Vicarage, Hollow Lane, Cheddleton, Leek ST13 7HP* Tel (01538) 360226 E-mail mary@thenoc.co.uk

LEIGH, Michael John. b 69. Leeds Univ BA02 LWCMD93. Coll of Resurr Mirfield 00. **d** 02. C N Hull St Mich *York* from 02. *1 Clergy Houses, Orchard Park Road, Hull HU6 9BX* Tel (01482) 802206 E-mail mach@fish.co.uk

LEIGH, Raymond. b 37. Lon Univ BEd81. Clifton Th Coll 65. **d** 68 **p** 69. C Chadwell *Chelmsf* 68-71; Chapl RAF 71-77; Asst Master Swakeleys Sch Hillingdon 81-88; NSM Hillingdon St Jo

Lon 87-88; C Rowley Regis *Birm* 88-90; V Londonderry 90-95; R Westbury w Turweston, Shalstone and Biddlesden *Ox* 95-99; CF (ACF) 95-02; rtd 99; Perm to Offic *Chich* from 99. *39 Pryors Lane, Bognor Regis PO21 4LH* Tel and fax (01243) 263076 Mobile 07745-493014 E-mail rayleigh306@aol.com

LEIGH, Richenda Mary Celia. b 71. St Mary's Coll Strawberry Hill BA93. Ripon Coll Cuddesdon BTh98. **d** 99 **p** 00. C Dalston H Trin w St Phil and Haggerston All SS *Lon* 99-02; Chapl R Free Hampstead NHS Trust from 02. *29 New End, London NW3 1JD* Tel (020) 7435 6919 E-mail richenda.leigh@rfh.nthames.nhs.uk

LEIGH, Roy Stephen. b 28. Imp Coll Lon BSc49. S'wark Ord Course 87. **d** 90 **p** 92. NSM Green Street Green *Roch* 90-92; NSM E Peckham and Nettlestead 92-00; Perm to Offic *Roch* 01 and *Heref* from 02. *17 Orchard Green, Marden, Hereford HR1 3ED* Tel (01432) 882032 E-mail r.s.leigh@reading.ac.uk

LEIGH-HUNT, Edward Christopher. b 22. Univ Coll Dur BA47. Ely Th Coll 48. **d** 50 **p** 51. C Wandsworth St Anne *S'wark* 50-54; C Bethnal Green St Matt *Lon* 54-56; C Lewisham St Jo Southend *S'wark* 56-57; C Ealing St Barn *Lon* 57-66; Chapl Asst St Bart Hosp Lon 66-73; C St Bart Less *Lon* 66-73; Chapl Middx Hosp 73-86; rtd 87; Perm to Offic *Lon* from 95. *14 Cain Court, Castlebar Mews, London W5 1RY* Tel (020) 8991 1171

LEIGH-HUNT, Nicolas Adrian. b 46. MIEx70. Qu Coll Birm 85. **d** 87 **p** 88. C Tilehurst St Geo *Ox* 87-91; TV Wexcombe *Sarum* 91-99; TR 99-02; TR Savernake from 02; RD Pewsey from 97. *The Vicarage, 5 Eastcourt, Burbage, Marlborough SN8 3AG* Tel (01672) 810258 Fax 810696 E-mail leighhunt@aol.com

LEIGH-WILLIAMS, Owen Charles. b 32. BNC Ox BA56 MA60. Wycliffe Hall Ox 56. **d** 58 **p** 59. C Southgate *Chich* 64-62; C Gt Warley Ch Ch *Chelmsf* 64-68; Asst Chapl Warley Hosp Brentwood 64-68; C Dagenham *Chelmsf* 68-72; R Basildon St Andr 72-86; rtd 96. *309A Church Road, Basildon SS14 2NE* Tel (01268) 521628

LEIGHLIN, Dean of. See FAULL, The Very Revd Cecil Albert

LEIGHTON, Adrian Barry. b 44. LTh. Lon Coll of Div 65. **d** 69 **p** 70. C Erith St Paul *Roch* 69-72; C Ipswich St Marg *St E* 72-75; P-in-c Ipswich St Helen 75-82; R 82-88; P-in-c Holbrook w Freston and Woolverstone 88-97; P-in-c Wherstead 94-97; R Holbrook, Freston, Woolverstone and Wherstead 97-98; RD Samford 90-93; P-in-c Woore and Norton in Hales *Lich* from 98; Local Min Adv (Shrewsbury) from 99. *The Vicarage, Nantwich Road, Woore, Crewe CW3 9SA* Tel (01630) 647316
E-mail adrian.leighton@lichfield.anglican.org

LEIGHTON, Alan Granville Clyde. b 37. MInstM AMIDHE Lon Univ DipRS. S'wark Ord Course 73. **d** 76 **p** 77. C Silverhill St Matt *Chich* 76-79; C Eston *York* 79-82; V 82-84; TR Eston w Normanby 84-02; rtd 02; Perm to Offic *York* from 02. *Priory Lodge, Bush Church Lane, Eston, Middlesbrough TS6 9QR* Tel (01642) 504798 Fax 283016 E-mail aleighton@argonet.co.uk

LEIGHTON, Anthony Robert. b 56. Trin Coll Bris BA88. **d** 88 **p** 89. C Harrow Trin St Mich *Lon* 88-92; TV Ratby cum Groby *Leic* 92-94; TR Bradgate Team 94-00; P-in-c Newtown Linford 95-98; V Thorpe Acre w Dishley from 00. *The Vicarage, Thorpe Acre Road, Loughborough LE11 4LF* Tel (01509) 214553 *or* 236789 E-mail tonyleighton@compuserve.com

LEIGHTON, Mrs Susan. Bretton Hall Coll BEd80. Trin Coll Bris BA89. **d** 89 **p** 94. Par Dn Harrow Weald All SS *Lon* 89-92; NSM Ratby cum Groby *Leic* 92-96; C Bradgate Team 96-00; NSM from 00. *The Vicarage, Thorpe Acre Road, Loughborough LE11 4LF* Tel 0116-231 3090 *or* (01509) 214553
E-mail tonyleighton@compuserve.com

LEIPER, Nicholas Keith. b 34. SS Coll Cam BA55 MB58 BChir58 MA65. St Jo Coll Nottm LTh82. **d** 84 **p** 85. C Bidston *Ches* 84-87; TV Gateacre *Liv* 87-92; P-in-c Bickerstaffe 92-94; P-in-c Melling 92-94; V Bickerstaffe and Melling 94-00; rtd 00; Perm to Offic *Liv* from 00. *31 Weldale House, Chase Close, Southport PR8 2DX* Tel (01704) 566393

LEITCH, Peter William. b 36. FCA58 ATII59. Coll of Resurr Mirfield 83. **d** 85 **p** 86. C Newsome *Wakef* 85; C Newsome and Armitage Bridge 85-88; P-in-c Upper Hopton 88-91; P-in-c Mirfield Eastthorpe St Paul 88-91; Chapl Rouen Miss to Seamen *Eur* 92-94; Sen Chapl Rotterdam Miss to Seamen 94-97; Chapl Felixstowe Miss to Seafarers *St E* 97-01; rtd 01; Perm to Offic *St E* from 01. *104 St Andrew's Road, Felixstowe IP11 7ED* Tel (01394) 285320

LEMMON, Canon Rowland. b 09. Keble Coll Ox BA31 MA40. Wells Th Coll 31. **d** 32 **p** 33. C Barrow St Jas *Carl* 32-36; C Carl St Aid and Ch Ch 36-40; V Beckermet St Bridget 40-49; V Ponsonby 41-49; V Millom H Trin 49-62; RD Gosforth 51-62; Hon Can Carl Cathl 60-62; R Hexham *Newc* 62-75; Hon Can Newc Cathl 70-75; rtd 75; Perm to Offic *Ex* from 82. *4 Arundel Close, Alphington, Exeter EX2 8UQ* Tel (01392) 270365

LEMPRIERE, Norman Everard. b 28. Liv Univ BEng54. Ridley Hall Cam 55. **d** 57 **p** 58. C Ware Ch Ch *St Alb* 57-61; R Lt Munden 61-64; R Sacombe 61-64; Lee Abbey 64-66; Perm to Offic *Ex* 64-66; C Witheridge 66-69; R Nymet Rowland w Coldridge 69-75; R Denton w S Heighton and Tarring Neville *Chich* 75-81; R Sullington and Thakeham w Warminghurst

81-92; rtd 92; Perm to Offic *B & W* from 92. *38 Woodbury Avenue, Wells BA5 2XP* Tel (01749) 673368

LENDRUM, Canon William Henry. b 24. TCD BA50 MA62. CITC 50. **d** 50 **p** 51. C Belfast St Mich *Conn* 50-53; C Lisburn Ch Ch Cathl 53-61; P-in-c Belfast Whiterock 61-69; I Belfast St Mary Magd 69-91; Can Conn Cathl from 87; rtd 91. *38 Lancefield Road, Belfast BT9 6LL* Tel (028) 9028 0635

LENG, Bruce Edgar. b 38. St Aid Birkenhead 68. **d** 69 **p** 70. C Sheff St Swithun *Sheff* 69-74; TV Speke St Aid *Liv* 74-78; TV Yate New Town *Bris* 78-82; R Handsworth *Sheff* 82-95; P-in-c Thrybergh w Hooton Roberts 95; R Thrybergh from 95; Warden for Past Workers from 96. *The Rectory, 14 Manor Farm Court, Thrybergh, Rotherham S65 4NZ* Tel (01709) 850336

LENNARD, Mrs Elizabeth Jemima Mary Patricia (Mary Pat). b 21. Edin Dioc NSM Course 78. **dss** 82 **d** 86 **p** 94. Falkirk *Edin* 82-86; Hon C 86-91; Asst Dioc Supernumerary 91-96; Hon C Grangemouth from 96; Hon C Bo'ness from 96. *36 Heugh Street, Falkirk FK1 5QR* Tel (01324) 623240

LENNARD, Thomas Jay. b 21. MBE54. Edin Dioc NSM Course 74. **d** 76 **p** 77. Hon C Kelso *Edin* 74-82; Hon C Falkirk 82-91; Asst Dioc Supernumerary 91-96; Hon C Grangemouth from 96; Hon C Bo'ness from 96. *36 Heugh Street, Falkirk FK1 5QR* Tel (01324) 623240

LENNON, Alfred Dennis. b 32. Oak Hill Th Coll 72. **d** 74 **p** 74. C Cambridge H Sepulchre w All SS *Ely* 74-77; P-in-c Cambridge St Barn 77-83; R Edin St Thos *Edin* 83-90; P-in-c Burghwallis *Sheff* 90-97; Dioc Adv for Evang 90-97; rtd 97; Perm to Offic *Pet* from 98. *5 Stockerston Crescent, Uppingham, Oakham LE15 9UA* Tel (01572) 822452

LENNOX, James. b 12. TCD BA36 MA40. Div Test 37. **d** 38 **p** 39. C Houghton le Spring *Dur* 38-43; C Darlington St Cuth 43-47; V Woodhouse *Wakef* 47-63; V Bingley All SS *Bradf* 63-77; rtd 77; Perm to Offic *Bradf* from 77. *30 Hazel Beck, Cottingley Bridge, Bingley BD16 1LZ* Tel (01274) 560189

LENNOX, Joan Baxter. b 50. Strathclyde Univ BA70 Dip Counselling 94. St Jo Coll Nottm 90. **d** 96. C Baillieston *Glas* 96-97. *Address temp unknown*

LENNOX, William Ernest Michael. b 28. Selw Coll Cam BA52 MA63 Leeds Univ CertEd55. K Coll Lon 62. **d** 63 **p** 64. C Bramley *Ripon* 63-66; C Margate St Jo *Cant* 66-71; R Kingsnorth 71-73; R Shadoxhurst 71-73; R Kingsnorth w Shadoxhurst 73-93; rtd 93. *6 rue Aux Savons, Le Boisle, 80150 Crecy en Ponthieu, France*

LENON, Philip John FitzMaurice. b 24. ARIBA52 Lon Univ BD60. Wycliffe Hall Ox 55. **d** 57 **p** 58. C Hornsey Ch Ch *Lon* 57-60; C-in-c Sidcup St Andr CD *Roch* 60-67; V Crowborough *Chich* 67-89; rtd 89; Perm to Offic *Sarum* from 89. *Snowhill Cottage, Dinton, Salisbury SP3 5HN* Tel (01722) 716754

LENOX-CONYNGHAM, Andrew George. b 44. Magd Coll Ox BA65 MA73 CCC Cam PhD73. Westcott Ho Cam 72. **d** 74 **p** 75. C Poplar *Lon* 74-77; TV Crowborough *Eur* 80-82 and 91-96; Chapl Ch Coll Cam 82-86; Chapl and Fell St Cath Coll Cam 86-91; V Birm St Luke *Birm* from 96. *St Luke's Vicarage, 10 St Luke's Road, Birmingham B5 7DA* Tel 0121-666 6089 or 622 2435 Fax 622 4532 E-mail andrew@stlukesbirm.freeserve.co.uk

LENS VAN RIJN, Robert Adriaan. b 47. St Jo Coll Nottm 78. **d** 80 **p** 81. C Gt Baddow *Chelmsf* 80-83; C Edgware *Lon* 83-86; C Derby St Pet and Ch Ch w H Trin *Derby* 86-90; Chapl Eindhoven *Eur* 91-00. *Pinkelbergen 21, 5683 LN Best, The Netherlands* Tel (0031) (499) 330222 Fax 330224 E-mail rlvr@iae.nl

LENTHALL, Mrs Nicola Yvonne. b 73. Southn Univ BA95. Westcott Ho Cam CTM99. **d** 99 **p** 00. C Leighton Buzzard w Eggington, Hockliffe etc *St Alb* from 99. *138 Brooklands Drive, Leighton Buzzard LU7 8PG* Tel (01525) 850204

LENTON, Colin William. b 23. CertEd. Cuddesdon Coll 80. **d** 81 **p** 81. Hon C Cowley St Jo *Ox* 81-82; Hon C Oakley 82-85; V Langtoft w Foxholes, Butterwick, Cottam etc *York* 85-89; rtd 89; Perm to Offic *Liv* 83-95; *S'wark* from 98; *Chich* from 99. *Flat 3, 24 South Drive, Harrogate HG2 8AU* Tel (01423) 564751

LENTON, John Robert. b 46. Ex Coll Ox BA69 Harvard Univ MBA74. Oak Hill Th Coll. **d** 00. NSM Muswell Hill St Jas w St Matt *Lon* from 00. *Garden Flat, 31A King's Avenue, London N10 1PA* Tel (020) 8444 3374 Mobile 07714-237235 Fax (020) 8444 4760 E-mail johnlenton@iname.com

LENTON, Robert Vincent. b 15. Clifton Th Coll 62. **d** 63 **p** 63. Kenya 63-71; V Lacock w Bowden Hill *Bris* 71-83; rtd 83; Perm to Offic *Liv* 83-95; *S'wark* from 98; *Chich* from 99. *College of St Barnabas, Blackberry Lane, Lingfield RH7 6NJ* Tel (01342) 870260

LEONARD, Ms Ann Cressey. b 50. Open Univ BA90. S Dios Minl Tr Scheme 90. **d** 94 **p** 95. C Portsea St Cuth *Portsm* 94-96; C Farlington 96-00; Asst to RD Petersfield from 00; Deanery Co-ord for Educn and Tr from 00; Dioc Ecum Officer from 02. *13 Kelsey Close, Liss GU33 7HR* Tel (01730) 893173 E-mail ann.leonard@uk.gateway.net

LEONARD, John Francis. b 48. Lich Th Coll 69. **d** 72 **p** 73. C Chorley St Geo *Blackb* 72-75; C S Shore H Trin 75-80; V Marton Moss 81-89; V Kingskerswell w Coffinswell *Ex* from 89. *The*

Vicarage, Pound Lane, Kingskerswell, Newton Abbot TQ12 5DW
Tel (01803) 407217 *or* 873006
E-mail kingskerswell.parish.church@tinyworld.co.uk

LEONARD, Canon John James. b 41. Southn Univ BSc62. Sarum Th Coll 63. **d** 65 **p** 66. C Loughborough Em *Leic* 65-70; V New Humberstone 70-78; C-in-c Rushey Mead CD 78-85; V Leic St Theodore from 85; Hon Can Leic Cathl from 97; RD Christianity N from 97. *St Theodore's House, 4 Sandfield Close, Leicester LE4 7RE* Tel 0116-266 9956
E-mail jleonard@leicester.anglican.org

LEONARD, Peter Michael. b 47. MRTPI Portsm Poly BSc Trent Poly Dip Town Planning. Sarum & Wells Th Coll 82. **d** 84 **p** 85. C Llantwit Major *Llan* 84-88; V Cymmer and Porth 88-96; R Colwinston w Llandow and Llysworney from 96; AD Llantwit Major and Cowbridge from 02. *The Rectory, Llandow, Cowbridge CF71 7NT* Tel (01656) 890205 Fax as telephone E-mail leonards@fdn.co.uk

LEONARD, Peter Philip. b 70. Trin Coll Bris BA94. **d** 97 **p** 98. C Haslemere *Guildf* 97-00; C Haslemere and Grayswood 00-01; C Woodham from 01. *St Michael's House, 288 Albert Drive, Sheerwater, Woking GU21 5TX* Tel (01932) 341694 *or* 340166 Mobile 07730-311830 E-mail pleonard@fish.co.uk

LEONARD, Vaughan Thomas. b 51. Coll of Resurr Mirfield 94. **d** 96 **p** 97. C Broadstone *Sarum* 96-99; C Worth *Chich* 99-00; TV from 00. *St Barnabas' Vicarage, 2 Crawley Lane, Crawley RH10 7EB* Tel (01293) 513398

LEONARD-JOHNSON, Canon Philip Anthony. b 35. Selw Coll Cam BA58 MA60. Linc Th Coll 63. **d** 65 **p** 66. C Wymondham *Nor* 65-68; Zimbabwe 69-82; V Drayton in Hales *Lich* 82-92; R Adderley 82-92; P-in-c Moreton Say 88-92; S Africa 92-98; rtd 97; Hon Can Grahamstown from 97; Perm to Offic *Lich* from 99. *Hillside, Mount Lane, Market Drayton TF9 1AG* Tel (01630) 655480

LEONARDI, Jeffrey. b 49. Warwick Univ BA71 Aston Univ Dip Counselling 79. Carl Dioc Tr Course 85. **d** 88 **p** 89. C Netherton *Carl* 88-91; V Cross Canonby 91-97; V Allonby 91-97; Bp's Adv for Past Care and Counselling *Lich* from 97; Asst Min Colton, Colwich and Gt Haywood from 97. *The New Rectory, Bellamour Way, Colton, Rugeley WS15 3JW* Tel (01889) 570897 Fax as telephone E-mail jeff.leonardi@btinternet.com

LEPINE, Jeremy John. b 56. BA. St Jo Coll Nottm 82. **d** 84 **p** 85. C Harrow Trin St Mich *Lon* 84-88; TV Horley *S'wark* 88-95; Evang Adv Croydon Area Miss Team 95-02; Dioc Evang Adv and Hon Chapl *S'wark* Cathl 97-02; R Wollaton *S'well* from 02. *St Leonard's Rectory, 143 Russell Drive, Nottingham NG8 2BD* Tel 0115-928 1798 E-mail jerry.lepine@btopenworld.com

LEPPINGTON, Canon Dian Marjorie. b 46. Leeds Univ BA85. Cranmer Hall Dur 81. **dss** 83 **d** 87 **p** 94. Potternewton *Ripon* 83-85; Ind Chapl 85-97; Chapl Teesside Univ *York* from 97; Can and Preb York Minster from 03. *The Rectory, Old Byland, York YO62 5LG* Tel (01439) 798355 *or* (01642) 342264 Fax (01439) 798482

LERRY, Keith Doyle. b 49. Univ of Wales (Cardiff) DipTh72. St Mich Coll Llan 69. **d** 72 **p** 73. C Caerau w Ely *Llan* 72-75; C Roath St Martin 75-84; V Glyntaff from 84. *The Vicarage, Glyntaff Road, Pontypridd CF37 4AS* Tel (01443) 402535

LERVY, Hugh Martin. b 68. Univ of Wales (Lamp) BA89. Qu Coll Birm 89. **d** 91 **p** 92. C Brecon St Mary and Battle w Llanddew *S & B* 91-93; C Oystermouth 93-95; V Glantawe 95-00; V Morriston from 00. *The Vicarage, Vicarage Road, Morriston, Swansea SA6 6DR* Tel (01792) 771329 Mobile 07976-725644 E-mail hugh@lervy.freeserve.co.uk

LESITER, The Ven Malcolm Leslie. b 37. Selw Coll Cam BA61 MA65. Cuddesdon Coll 61. **d** 63 **p** 64. C Eastney *Portsm* 63-66; C Hemel Hempstead *St Alb* from 71. TV 71-73; V Leavesden All SS 73-88; RD Watford 81-88; V Radlett 88-93; Hon Can St Alb Abbey 90-93; Adn Bedford 93-03; rtd 03. *349 Ipswich Road, Colchester CO4 0HN*

LESLIE, David Rodney. b 43. AKC67 Liv Univ MEd94 Birm Univ PhD01. **d** 68 **p** 69. C Belmont *Lon* 68-71; C St Giles Cripplegate w St Bart Moor Lane etc 71-75; TV Kirkby *Liv* 76-84; TR Ditton St Mich 84-98; V Ditton St Mich w St Thos 98-03; V Croxteth Park from 03. *The Vicarage, 1 Sandicroft Road, Liverpool L12 0LX* Tel 0151-549 2202 Fax as telephone E-mail david_leslie@lineone.net

LESLIE, Richard Charles Alan. b 46. ACIB71. St Alb Minl Tr Scheme 76. **d** 79 **p** 91. NSM Redbourn *St Alb* 79-88; Hon C Newport Pagnell w Lathbury and Moulsoe *Ox* 88-94; Stewardship Adv to RD St Alb Adnry *St Alb* 94-97; TV Borehamwood from 97. *St Michael's Vicarage, 142 Brook Road, Borehamwood WD6 5EQ* Tel (020) 8953 2362

LESTER, David Charles. b 46. BSc. **d** 99 **p** 00. NSM Trowell *S'well* 99-02; NSM Trowell, Awsworth and Cossall from 02. *The Vicarage, The Lane, Awsworth, Nottingham NG16 2QP* Tel 0115-944 0473 E-mail david-lester@msn.com

LESTER, The Very Revd Trevor Rashleigh. b 50. CITC 83 St Deiniol's Hawarden 92. **d** 89 **p** 90. NSM Douglas Union w Frankfield *C, C & R* 89-93; C Kilkenny w Aghour and Kilmanagh *C & O* 93-95; Bp's V Ossory Cathl 93-95; Dioc Registrar (Ossory, Ferns and Leighlin) 93-95; Dioc Lib

St Canice's Lib 93-95; I Abbeystrewry Union *C, C & R* 95-03; Dean Waterford *C & O* from 03; I Waterford w Killea, Drumcannon and Dunhill from 03. *The Deanery, 41 Grange Park Road, Waterford, Irish Republic* Tel (00353) (51) 874119
E-mail dean@waterford.anglican.org

L'ESTRANGE, Timothy John Nicholas. b 67. Surrey Univ BA90 St Steph Ho Ox BA92 MA96. **d** 93 **p** 94. C Halesworth w Linstead, Chediston, Holton etc *St E* 93-96; Dom Chapl to Bp Horsham *Chich* 96-98; R Beeding and Bramber w Botolphs from 98. *The Rectory, Church Lane, Upper Beeding, Steyning BN44 3HP* Tel (01903) 815474 *or* 815850 Fax 816698
E-mail rector@upper-beeding.fsnet.co.uk

LETALL, Ronald Richard. b 29. ACIl76 SSC. Linc Th Coll 82. **d** 84 **p** 85. C Scarborough St Martin *York* 84-86; C Middlesbrough St Thos 86-88; R Kirby Misperton w Normanby, Edston and Salton 88-90; TV Louth *Linc* 90-94; rtd 94; Perm to Offic *Sheff* from 95; *Wakef* 95-97; *Chich* 97-99; and from 01. *20 Greenwood Drive, Angmering, Littlehampton BN16 4ND* Tel (01903) 859469 E-mail ronald@letall.fsnet.co.uk

LETCHER, Canon David John. b 34. K Coll Lon 54. Chich Th Coll 56. **d** 58 **p** 59. C St Austell *Truro* 58-62; C Southbroom *Sarum* 62-64; R Odstock w Nunton and Bodenham 64-72; RD Alderbury 68-73 and 77-82; V Downton 72-85; Can and Preb Sarum Cathl 79-99; TV Dorchester 85-97; RD Dorchester 89-95; rtd 97; Perm to Offic *Sarum* from 97; CF (ACF) 97-00. *6 Longmoor Street, Poundbury, Dorchester DT1 3GN* Tel (01305) 257764

LETHBRIDGE, Christopher David. b 43. N Ord Course 90. **d** 93 **p** 94. NSM S Elmsall *Wakef* 93-95; C Knottingley 95-97; R Badsworth 97-01; P-in-c Bilham *Sheff* from 01; Chapl HM YOI Hatfield from 01. *Bilham Vicarage, Churchfield Road, Clayton, Doncaster DN5 7DH* Tel (01977) 643756

LETHEREN, William Neils. b 37. Lon Univ DipTh63. St Aid Birkenhead 61. **d** 64 **p** 65. C Liv St Mich *Liv* 64-67; V 71-75; C Kirkdale St Athanasius 67-69; C Walsall Wood *Lich* 69-71; V W Derby St Jas *Liv* 75-84; R Newton in Makerfield Em 84-88; V Garston from 88. *The Vicarage, Horrocks Avenue, Garston, Liverpool L19 5NY* Tel 0151-427 4204

LETSON, Barry. b 55. Univ of Wales (Lamp) BA77. St Deiniol's Hawarden 82. **d** 83 **p** 84. C Flint *St As* 83-86; V Llansantffraid Glyn Ceirog and Llanarmon etc 86-89; R Montgomery and Forden and Llandyssil 89-96; RD Pool 92-96; V Mountain Ash *Llan* 96-97; V Mountain Ash and Miskin 97-02; V Crickhowell w Cwmdu and Tretower *S & B* from 02. *The Rectory, Rectory Road, Crickhowell NP8 1DW* Tel (01873) 810017

LETTS, Gerald Vincent. b 33. Univ of Wales BA63. Qu Coll Birm DipTh65 NY Th Sem DMin. **d** 65 **p** 66. C Birstall *Leic* 65-68; V Belgrave St Mich 68-75; P-in-c Brightside All SS *Sheff* 75-78; V Sheff St Cuth 75-91; R Bradfield 91-00; rtd 00; Perm to Offic *Ely* from 01. *12 Norico Bay, March PE15 9MJ* Tel (01354) 650820

LETTS, Kenneth John. b 42. Melbourne Univ BA65 DipEd67. Coll of Resurr Mirfield 68. **d** 71 **p** 72. Australia 71-94; C Mt Waverley St Steph 71-74; Chapl Melbourne C of E Gr Sch 74-81; P-in-c Albert Park 81-94; Sen Chapl St Mich Sch 82-94; Chapl Nice w Vence *Eur* from 94. *11 rue de la Buffa, 06000 Nice, France* Tel (0033) (4) 93 87 19 83 E-mail anglican@worldnet.fr

LEUNG, Peter. b 36. Trin Coll Singapore BTh60 St Andr Univ PhD73. SE Asia Sch of Th MTh69. **d** 60 **p** 61. Singapore 60-62 and 65-76; Br N Borneo 62-63; Malaysia 63-65; Lect Congr Coll Man 76-77; USPG 77-83; Perm to Offic *Roch* 83-89; BCC 83-90; CTBI from 90; Perm to Offic *S'wark* 89-90; Regional Sec (S and E Asia) CMS 91-99; rtd 99. *35 Tufton Gardens, West Molesey KT8 1TD* Tel (020) 8650 4157

LEVELL, Peter John. b 40. Bris Univ BA62 CertEd63. STETS 99. **d** 02 **p** 03. NSM Guildf St Sav *Guildf* from 02. *23 Mountside, Guildford GU2 4JD* Tel (01483) 871656
E-mail plevell@ntlworld.com

LEVER, Julian Lawrence Gerrard. b 36. Fitzw Coll Cam BA60 MA64. Sarum Th Coll 60. **d** 62 **p** 63. C Amesbury *Sarum* 62-66; R Corfe Mullen 66-78; RD Wimborne 73-75; P-in-c Wilton w Netherhampton and Fugglestone 78-82; R 82-86; R Salisbury St Martin 86-94; Perm to Offic *Win* from 96; rtd 98. *6 St John's Close, Wimborne BH21 1LY* Tel (01202) 848249

LEVERTON, Michael John. b 52. K Coll Lon BD76 AKC76 MTh77. Cant Sch of Min 84. **d** 87 **p** 88. NSM Elham w Denton and Wootton *Cant* 87-92; C Yelverton, Meavy, Sheepstor and Walkhampton *Ex* 92-93; TV 93-98; C Tavistock and Gulworthy 98-00; P-in-c Stevenage All SS Pin Green *St Alb* from 00. *All Saints' Vicarage, 100 Derby Way, Stevenage SG1 5TJ* Tel (01438) 318706 E-mail revmleve@aol.com

LEVERTON, Peter James Austin. b 33. Nottm Univ BA55. Ripon Coll Cuddesdon 79. **d** 81 **p** 82. C St Jo in Bedwardine *Worc* 81-84; V Worc St Mich 84-88; TR Worc St Barn w Ch Ch 88-92; V Riddings and Ironville *Derby* 92-00; rtd 00; Perm to Offic *Derby* from 00. *2 George Street, Langley Mill, Nottingham NG16 4DJ* Tel (01773) 710243 E-mail jim@rev-levs.freeserve.co.uk

LEVERTON, Peter Robert. b 25. Lich Th Coll 59. **d** 60 **p** 61. C Shepshed *Leic* 60-64; Australia 64-69; V Marshchapel *Linc* 70-73; V Grainthorpe w Conisholme 70-73; R N Coates 70-73;

Miss to Seamen 73-77; P-in-c Brislington St Luke *Bris* 77-84; V Avonmouth St Andr 84-87; Ind Chapl 84-87; P-in-c Ugborough *Ex* 87-91; P-in-c Ermington 88-91; rtd 91; Perm to Offic *Ex* from 91. *4 Drakes Avenue, Sidford, Sidmouth EX10 9QY* Tel (01395) 579835

LEVETT, The Ven Howard. b 44. K Coll Lon AKC67. **d** 68 **p** 69. C Rotherhithe St Mary w All SS *S'wark* 68-72; P-in-c Walworth St Jo 72-77; V Walworth St Jo 77-80; P-in-c Walworth Lady Marg w St Mary 78; RD S'wark and Newington 78-80; Adn Egypt 80-94; Miss to Seafarers from 80; JMECA from 80; V Holborn St Alb w Saffron Hill St Pet *Lon* from 94. *St Alban's Clergy House, 18 Brooke Street, London EC1N 7RD* Tel (020) 7405 1831 Mobile 07815-111429 Fax (020) 7430 2551
E-mail secretary@saintalbanthemartyr.org.uk

LEVICK, Brian William. b 30. Solicitor 51. Westcott Ho Cam 63. **d** 64 **p** 65. C Bourne *Linc* 64-69; C Deeping St James 69-70; C Hemel Hempstead *St Alb* 70-71; TV 71-77; Hon C Sedbergh, Cautley and Garsdale *Bradf* 77-83; V Firbank, Howgill and Killington 77-83; V Cononley w Bradley 83-90; Methodist Min 83-90; rtd 90; C Kettlewell w Conistone, Hubberholme etc *Bradf* 90-93; Hon C New Sleaford *Linc* 93-97; Dioc Ecum Officer 93-97; Ecum Officer Chs Together Lincs and S Humberside 93-97; Perm to Offic *Bradf* from 99. *42 Robin Lane, Bentham, Lancaster LA2 7AG* Tel (01524) 261473

LEVICK, Canon Frank Hemsley. b 29. Kelham Th Coll 49. **d** 54 **p** 55. C Anfield St Marg *Liv* 54-58; V 58-67; V Ribbleton *Blackb* 67-80; TR 80-85; Hon Can Blackb Cathl 75-90; R Ribchester w Stidd 85-90; rtd 90; Perm to Offic *S'well* from 90; *Linc* 96-99. *The Old Nurseries, Low Street, Beckingham, Doncaster DN10 4PS* Tel (01427) 848668 E-mail frank.canon@virgin.net

LEVISEUR, Nicholas Templer. b 56. Magd Coll Ox MA82 Barrister 79. STETS 97 Ven English Coll Rome 00. **d** 00 **p** 01. NSM Hartfield w Coleman's Hatch *Chich* from 00. *Tye House East, Edenbridge Road, Hartfield TN7 4JR* Tel (01892) 770451

LEVY, Christopher Charles. b 51. Southn Univ BTh82. Sarum & Wells Th Coll 79. **d** 82 **p** 83. C Rubery *Birm* 82-85; C Stratford-on-Avon w Bishopton *Cov* 85-87; TV Clifton *S'well* 87-95; V Egmanton from 95; R Kirton from 95; V Walesby from 95; Chapl Center Parcs Holiday Village from 01. *St Edmund's Vicarage, Walesby, Newark NG22 9PA* Tel (01623) 860522
E-mail chris@walesbyvic.fsnet.co.uk

LEW, Henry E A. b 39. **d** 96 **p** 97. NSM Dublin Whitechurch *D & G* 96-99; Manager Brabazon Trust Sheltered Housing 96-00; Lic to Offic 99-00; I Bray from 00. *51 Butterfield Park, Rathfarnham, Dublin 14, Irish Republic* Tel (00353) (1) 493 1483 *or* 269 1677 Mobile 87-628 8049 Fax (1) 283 9508
E-mail healew@iol.ie

LEWER ALLEN, Mrs Patricia (Paddy). b 47. SRN70 UNISA BA79 HDipEd85 Cape Town Univ BA86. Th Ext Educn Coll DipTh94. **d** 97 **p** 98. Dn-in-c Dunbar *Edin* 98; P-in-c from 98. *St Anne's House, 1 Westgate, Dunbar EH42 1JL* Tel (01368) 865711 Fax as telephone E-mail paddyallen@aol.com

LEWERS, The Very Revd Benjamin Hugh. b 32. Selw Coll Cam BA60 MA64. Linc Th Coll. **d** 62 **p** 63. C Northampton St Mary *Pet* 62-65; C Hounslow Heath St Paul *Lon* 65-68; C-in-c Hounslow Gd Shep Beavers Lane CD 65-68; Chapl Heathrow Airport 68-75; V Newark St Mary *S'well* 75-80; TR Newark w Hawton, Cotham and Shelton 80-81; P-in-c Averham w Kelham 79-81; Provost Derby 81-97; rtd 98; Perm to Offic *Sarum* from 98; *B & W* from 00. *Thimble Cottage, Marshwood, Bridport DT6 5QF* Tel (01297) 678515

LEWES AND HASTINGS, Archdeacon of. See READE, The Ven Nicholas Stewart

LEWES, Area Bishop of. See BENN, The Rt Revd Wallace Parke

LEWIS, The Ven Albert John Francis. b 21. Univ Coll of S Wales BA(Econ)45. St Mich Coll Llan 46. **d** 48 **p** 49. C Cardiff St Jo *Llan* 48-61; Dioc Dir RE 60-91; V Pendoylan 61-73; P-in-c Welsh St Donats 70-73; V Pendoylan w Welsh St Donats 73-81; RD Llan 69-81; Can Llan Cathl 76-81; Treas 81-88; Adn Margam 81-88; Adn Llan 88-91; rtd 91; Chapl to Rtd Clerics and Widows of Clergy *Llan* from 91; Perm to Offic from 91. *11 Downs View Close, Aberthin, Cowbridge CF71 7HG* Tel (01446) 773320

LEWIS, Ann Theodora Rachel. b 33. Univ of Wales (Ban) BA55. Qu Coll Birm 78. **d** 80 **p** 97. C Swansea St Mary w H Trin *S & B* 80-96; Chapl St Mary's Coll 90-96; rtd 96; Public Preacher *St D* from 96. *Fisherywish, Maes yr Eglwys, Llansaint, Kidwelly SA17 5JE* Tel (01267) 267386

LEWIS, Canon Arthur Griffith. b 15. Univ of Wales (Lamp) BA40. **d** 47 **p** 48. C Clydach *S & B* 47-55; R Aberyscir and Llanfihangel Nantbran 55-63; V Ystalyfera 63-87; RD Cwmtawe 79-85; Hon Can Brecon Cathl 80-89; Can 81-85; P-in-c Capel Coelbren 85-89; rtd 89. *14 Pontwillim, Brecon LD3 9BT* Tel (01874) 622869

LEWIS, Arthur Jenkin Llewellyn. b 42. Univ of Wales (Cardiff) MPS67 BPharm. Coll of Resurr Mirfield 73. **d** 73 **p** 74. C Cardiff St Jo *Llan* 73-78; C Christchurch *Win* 78-82; R Lightbowne *Man* from 82. *St Luke's Rectory, Kenyon Lane, Manchester M40 5HS* Tel 0161-681 1308

LEWIS, Arthur Roland. b 20. St Edm Hall Ox BA41 MA45. St Steph Ho Ox 41. d 43 p 44. C Sutton in Ashfield St Mich *S'well* 43-45; C Stirchley *Birm* 45-47; Zanzibar and Tanganyika 47-58; S Rhodesia 58-65; Rhodesia 65-80; Adn Inyanga 66-69; S Africa 80-87; rtd 87; Perm to Offic *Birm* 88-99. *The College of St Barnabas, Blackberry Lane, Lingfield RH7 6NJ* Tel (01342) 870028 Fax 870731 E-mail arthur_r_lewis@compuserve.com

LEWIS, The Very Revd Bertie. b 31. Univ of Wales (Lamp) BA54 St Cath Soc Ox BA57 MA60. Wycliffe Hall Ox 54. d 57 p 58. C Cwmaman *St D* 57-60; C Aberystwyth St Mich 60-62; V Llanddewi Brefi w Llanbadarn Odwyn 62-65; V Henfynyw w Aberaeron and Llanddewi Aberarth 65-75; V Lampeter 75-80; Can St D Cathl 78-86; Chapl Abth Hosps 80-88; R Aberystwyth *St D* 80-88; Adn Cardigan 86-90; V Nevern and Y Beifil w Eglwyswrw and Meline etc 88-90 and 94-96; Dean St D 90-94; V St D Cathl 90-94; Hon Can St D Cathl 94-97; rtd 96. *Bryn Golau, Llanfarian, Aberystwyth SY23 4BT* Tel (01970) 612492

LEWIS, Brian James. b 52. Cant Univ (NZ) BA75. St Jo Coll Auckland 76. d 78 p 79. New Zealand 78-80; C Shrub End *Chelmsf* 80-82; P-in-c Colchester St Barn 82-84; V 84-88; P-in-c Romford St Andr 88-90; R 90-99; RD Havering 93-97; R Lt Ilford St Mich from 99. *The Rectory, Church Road, London E12 6HA* Tel (020) 8478 2182 E-mail brian@littleilford.fsnet.co.uk

LEWIS, The Very Revd Christopher Andrew. b 44. Bris Univ BA69 CCC Cam PhD74. Westcott Ho Cam 71. d 73 p 74. C Barnard Castle *Dur* 73-76; Dir Ox Inst for Ch and Soc 76-79; Tutor Ripon Coll Cuddesdon 76-79; P-in-c Aston Rowant w Crowell *Ox* 78-81; Sen Tutor Ripon Coll Cuddesdon 79-81; Vice-Prin 81-82; V Spalding *Linc* 82-87; Can Res Cant Cathl *Cant* 87-94; Dir of Minl Tr 89-94; Dean St Alb from 94. *The Deanery, Sumpter Yard, St Albans AL1 1BY* Tel (01727) 890236 or 890202 Fax 890227 E-mail dean@stalbanscathedral.org.uk

LEWIS, Christopher Gouldson. b 42. K Coll Cam BA64 MA68. Cuddesdon Coll 65. d 67 p 68. C Gosforth All SS *Newc* 67-71; Sarawak 71-74; V Luton St Chris Round Green *St Alb* 74-80; RD Reculver *Cant* 80-86 and 92-93; V Whitstable All SS w St Pet 80-84; TR Whitstable 84-93; Dir Post-Ord Tr 88-93; Hon Can Cant Cathl 91-93; Can Res Bradf Cathl *Bradf* 93-01; Bp's Officer for Min and Tr 93-01; P-in-c Riding Mill *Newc* from 01; Chapl Shepherd's Dene Retreat Ho from 01. *The Vicarage, Riding Mill NE44 6AT* Tel (01434) 682811

LEWIS, David Antony. b 48. Dur Univ BA69 Nottm Univ MTh84. St Jo Coll Nottm 81. d 83 p 84. C Gateacre *Liv* 83-86; V Toxteth St Cypr w Ch Ch 86-01; V Edge Hill St Cypr w St Mary from 01; AD Liv N 94-03. *The Vicarage, 48 John Lennon Drive, Liverpool L6 9HT* Tel 0151-260 3262

LEWIS, David Hugh. b 45. Oak Hill Th Coll 88. d 90 p 91. C Oakham, Hambleton, Egleton, Braunston and Brooke *Pet* 90-94; R Ewhurst *Guildf* 94-99; V Southway *Ex* 99-03; RD Plymouth Moorside 01-03; P-in-c Anglesey Gp *Ely* from 03; P-in-c Swaffham Bulbeck and Swaffham Prior w Reach from 03. *The Vicarage, 86 High Street, Bottisham, Cambridge CB5 9BA* Tel (01223) 812367 E-mail david.hlewis@tinyworld.co.uk

LEWIS, David Roy. b 18. St D Coll Lamp BA39. St Mich Coll Llan 40. d 40 p 42. C Cardiff St Jo *Llan* 40-46; Br Guiana 46-54; Trinidad and Tobago 54-66; V Seven Sisters *Llan* 66-77; R Colwinston w Llandow and Llysworney 77-86; rtd 86. *Rockleigh, Colwinstone, Cowbridge CF7 7ND* Tel (01656) 654797

LEWIS, David Tudor. b 61. Jes Coll Cam BA83. Trin Coll Bris BA88. d 88 p 89. C Tile Cross *Birm* 88-91; C Woking St Jo *Guildf* 91-95; TV Carl H Trin and St Barn *Carl* 95-97; Asst Chapl Oslo w Bergen, Trondheim and Stavanger *Eur* from 97. *Vallhallveien 9, 4043 Håfrsfjord, Norway* Tel (0047) (51) 556712

LEWIS, David Tudor Bowes. b 63. Keele Univ BA85 Univ of Wales (Cardiff) BTh90. St Mich Coll Llan 87. d 90 p 91. C Llangollen w Trevor and Llantysilio *St As* 90-93; C Bistre 93-97; V Berse and Southsea 97-02; V Bwlchgwyn w Berse w Southsea from 02. *The Vicarage, 8 Whiteoaks, Bwlchgwyn, Wrexham LL11 5UB* Tel (01978) 752627

LEWIS, Canon David Vaughan. b 36. Trin Coll Cam BA60 MA64. Ridley Hall Cam 60. d 62 p 63. C Rugby St Matt *Cov* 62-65; Asst Chapl K Edw Sch Witley 65-71; Hon C Rainham *Chelmsf* 71-76; V Stoke Hill *Guildf* 76-87; V Wallington H Trin *S'wark* 87-03; Hon Can S'wark Cathl 95-03; RD Sutton 97-00; rtd 03. *11 The Meadows, Haslingfield, Cambridge CB3 7JD* Tel (01223) 874029

LEWIS, Canon David Watkin. b 40. Univ of Wales (Lamp) BA61 Univ of Wales (Swansea) DipYL65. Wycliffe Hall Ox 61. d 63 p 64. C Skewen *Llan* 63-66; Field Tr Officer Prov Youth Coun Ch in Wales 66-68; C Gabalfa 68-71; P-in-c Marcross w Monknash and Wick 71-73; R 73-83; RD Llantwit Major and Cowbridge 81-83; V Baglan from 83; Can Llan Cathl from 00. *The Vicarage, 29 Church Road, Port Talbot SA12 8ST* Tel (01639) 812199

LEWIS, Edward John. b 15. Qu Coll Cam BA36 MA40. Ridley Hall Cam 36. d 38 p 39. C Litherland St Phil *Liv* 38-41; C Prescot 41-43; Chapl RNVR 43-46; R Brechin *Bre* 47-53; V Copt Oak *Leic* 53-56; V Swanwick and Pentrich *Derby* 56-74; P-in-c Longstone 74-80; rtd 80; Perm to Offic *Derby* 80-95; Perm to

LEWIS, Edward John. b 58. JP93. Univ of Wales BEd80 BA82 FRSA97. Chich Th Coll 82. d 83 p 84. C Llangiwg *S & B* 83-85; C Morriston 85-87; Asst Chapl Morriston Hosp 85-87; V Tregaron w Ystrad Meurig and Strata Florida *St D* 87-89; Chapl Tregaron Hosp 87-89; Chapl Manor Hosp Walsall 89-92; Distr Co-ord Chapl Walsall Hosps 90-92; Sen Chapl Walsall Hosps NHS Trust 92-00; Chapl Walsall Community Health Trust 92-00; Chief Exec and Dir Tr Gen Syn Hosp Chapl Coun from 00; Perm to Offic *Lich* from 00. *Hospital Chaplaincies Council, Church House, Great Smith Street, London SW1P 3NZ* Tel (020) 7898 1894 Fax 7898 1891 E-mail edward.lewis@c-of-e.org.uk

LEWIS, Elinor Glenys. b 11. CBE93. SRN34 SCM35. St Chris Coll Blackheath 44. dss 49 d 78 p 78. Hd Dss *Cov* 49-60; New Zealand from 60; rtd 71. *Bishop Selwyn Life Care Centre, 350 Selwyn Street, Christchurch 8002, New Zealand* Tel (0064) (3) 377 9636

LEWIS, Ella Pauline. b 41. SW Minl Tr Course 94. d 98. NSM Paignton St Paul Preston *Ex* 98-02; NSM Paignton Ch Ch and Preston St Paul from 03. *Roselands, 5 Great Headland Road, Paignton TQ3 2DY* Tel (01803) 555171 E-mail paulinelewis@eclipse.co.uk

LEWIS, Elsie Leonora. b 26. Cranmer Hall Dur 72. dss 78 d 87 p 94. S Westoe *Dur* 78-80; Ryton 80-86; rtd 86. *53 Cushy Cow Lane, Ryton NE40 3NL* Tel 0191-413 5845

LEWIS, Eric. b 36. Sarum & Wells Th Coll 74. d 77 p 78. NSM Oldbury *Sarum* 77-92; C Weymouth St Paul 92-94; P-in-c Portland St Jo 94-99; Chapl Weymouth Coll 94-97; Asst Chapl Dorset Community NHS Trust 95-99; rtd 99; Chapl Costa Blanca *Eur* from 01. *Buzon T765, Tabaira 03724, Moraira, Alicante, Spain* Tel (0034) (965) 744493 Mobile 696-754439 E-mail fatherlewis@wanadoo.es

LEWIS, Frederick Norman. b 23. Leeds Univ BA47. Coll of Resurr Mirfield 47. d 49 p 50. C Haydock St Jas *Liv* 49-51; C Dresden *Lich* 51-55; C Stafford St Mary 55-56; V Wednesfield St Thos 56-65; V Shrewsbury St Chad 65-69; V Kingswinford St Mary 69-88; rtd 88; Perm to Offic *Lich* from 88. *27 Bramblewood Drive, Finchfield, Wolverhampton WV3 9DB* Tel (01902) 334934

LEWIS, Gary. b 61. Lanc Univ BA85. Ripon Coll Cuddesdon 86. d 89 p 90. C Blackb St Mich w St Jo and H Trin *Blackb* 89-92; C Altham w Clayton le Moors 92-95; V Lea 95-01; V Skerton St Luke from 01. *St Luke's Vicarage, Slyne Road, Lancaster LA1 2HU* Tel (01524) 63249

LEWIS, Graham Rhys. b 54. Loughb Univ BTech76 Cranfield Inst of Tech MBA89. SEITE 95. d 98 p 99. NSM S Gillingham *Roch* from 98. *53 Oastview, Gillingham ME8 8JG* Tel (01634) 373036 E-mail graham@53oastview.fsnet.co.uk

LEWIS, Ms Hannah Margaret. b 71. CCC Cam BA93 MA96. Qu Coll Birm 95. d 97 p 98. C Cannock *Lich* 97-00; Perm to Offic from 00. *53 Derwent Drive, Priorslee, Telford TF2 9QN*

LEWIS, Hubert Godfrey. b 33. Univ of Wales (Lamp) BA59 DipTh60. d 60 p 61. C Merthyr Tydfil *Llan* 60-64; C Caerphilly 64-66; Perm to Offic *S'wark* 66-76; Perm to Offic *Cant* 76-82; Hon C Shirley St Jo *S'wark* 82-93; Hon C Whitchurch *Llan* from 94. *2 Heol Wernlas, Cardiff CF14 1RY* Tel (029) 2061 3079

LEWIS, Hywel Gwynne. b 37. FCA75. St D Dioc Tr Course 94. d 97 p 98. NSM Henfynyw w Aberaeron and Llanddewi Aberarth *St D* from 97. *Danycoed, Lampeter Road, Aberaeron SA46 0ED* Tel (01545) 570577

LEWIS, Ian. b 33. Lon Univ MB, BS57. Oak Hill Th Coll 61. d 63 p 64. C Heatherlands St Jo *Sarum* 63-66; Ethiopia 66-73; Hon C Bath Walcot *B & W* 75-77; Lic to Offic 78-98; rtd 98. *22C Ashley Road, Bathford, Bath BA1 7TT* Tel (01225) 859818 E-mail i.lewis@btinvemev.com

LEWIS, Ian Richard. b 54. Sheff Univ BA76 Ox Univ BA83 MA87. Wycliffe Hall Ox 81. d 84 p 85. C Rusholme H Trin *Man* 84-88; C Sandal St Helen *Wakef* 88-91; V Bath St Bart *B & W* from 91. *St Bartholomew's Vicarage, 5 Oldfield Road, Bath BA2 3ND* Tel (01225) 422070 Fax as telephone E-mail ianlewis@stbartsbath.com

LEWIS, James Edward. b 22. St D Coll Lamp BA50. d 51 p 52. C Gorseinon *S & B* 52-57; C Defynnog 52-56; R Llangynllo w Troed-yr-aur *St D* 56-61; V Brynamman 61-72; R Llangathen w Llanfihangel Cilfargen 72-82; V Llangathen w Llanfihangel Cilfargen etc 82-90; RD Llangadog and Llandeilo 85-89; rtd 90. *The Flat, 3 St Mary Street, Carmarthen SA31 1TN* Tel (01267) 221660

LEWIS, James Michael. b 51. Trin Coll Carmarthen CertEd73 Open Univ BA86 MA91. St Mich Coll Llan 98. d 02 p 03. NSM Laleston w Tythegston and Merthyr Mawr *Llan* from 02. *19 Austin Avenue, Laleston, Bridgend CF32 0LG* Tel (01656) 660648 Mobile 07951-300206 E-mail mike.lewis11@virgin.net

LEWIS, Jocelyn Vivien. b 49. Trevelyan Coll Dur BSc70 Sheff Univ PhD75. EMMTC DTPS94. d 94 p 95. NSM Brimington *Derby* 94-99; P-in-c Whittington from 99; Dioc Dir Reader Tr from 99. *Whittington Rectory, Church Street North, Old*

Whittington, Chesterfield S41 9QP Tel (01246) 450651
E-mail bart@jocelyn.fsbusiness.co.uk

LEWIS, The Ven John Arthur. b 34. Jes Coll Ox BA56 MA60. Cuddesdon Coll 58. **d** 60 **p** 61. C Prestbury *Glouc* 60-63; C Wimborne Minster *Sarum* 63-66; R Eastington and Frocester *Glouc* 66-70; V Nailsworth 70-78; Chapl Memorial and Querns Hosp Cirencester 78-88; V Cirencester *Glouc* 78-88; RD Cirencester 84-88; Hon Can Glouc Cathl 85-98; Adn Cheltenham 88-98; rtd 98; Perm to Offic *Glouc* from 98. *5 Vilverie Mead, Bishop's Cleeve, Cheltenham GL52 7YY* Tel (01242) 678425

LEWIS, John Edward. b 31. SS Mark & Jo Coll Chelsea CertEd53. Qu Coll Birm 83. **d** 85 **p** 86. C Leominster *Heref* 85-87; TV 87-95; rtd 95; Perm to Offic *Heref* from 97. *The Holms, 253 Godiva Road, Leominster HR6 8TB* Tel (01568) 612280

LEWIS, John Goddard. b 52. Houston Bapt Univ (USA) BA74 JD77 Ox Univ 98. Virginia Th Sem MDiv97. **d** 97. USA 97-98 and from 01; Hon C Bladon w Woodstock *Ox* 98-01; Min Cen for Faith in the Work Place San Antonio from 01. *c/o The Lord Bishop of West Texas DD, PO Box 6885, San Antonio, TX 78209, USA* E-mail lewbrid@aol.com

LEWIS, John Herbert. b 42. Selw Coll Cam BA64 MA68. Westcott Ho Cam 64. **d** 66 **p** 67. C Wyken *Cov* 66-70; C Bedford St Andr *St Alb* 70-73; Lib Pusey Ho 73-77; Bp's Chapl for Graduates *Ox* 73-77; TV Woughton 78-82; TV Gt Chesham 82-88; P-in-c Newport Pagnell w Lathbury and Moulsoe 88-91; R from 91. *New Rectory, 81 High Street, Newport Pagnell MK16 8AB* Tel (01908) 611145

LEWIS, John Horatio George. b 47. Southn Univ BEd72 MA85. Ox NSM Course 86. **d** 89 **p** 90. NSM Newbury *Ox* from 89. *36 Glendale Avenue, Newbury RG14 6RU* Tel (01635) 821127 E-mail frjohn1@saintjohn.co.uk

✠**LEWIS, The Rt Revd John Hubert Richard.** b 43. AKC66. **d** 67 **p** 68 **c** 92. C Hexham *Newc* 67-70; Ind Chapl 70-77; Communications Officer *Dur* 77-82; Chapl for Agric *Heref* 82-87; Adn Ludlow 87-92; Suff Bp Taunton *B & W* 92-97; Bp St E from 97. *The Bishop's House, 4 Park Road, Ipswich IP1 3ST* Tel (01473) 252829 Fax 232552
E-mail bishop.richard@stedmundsbury.anglican.org

LEWIS, John Malcolm. b 41. Reading Univ BEd. Trin Coll Bris. **d** 82 **p** 83. C Kingswood *Bris* 82-85; TV Weston-super-Mare Cen Par *B & W* 85-91; Dioc Children's Adv *Nor* 91-97; TV Bishopsworth and Bedminster Down *Bris* from 97. *St Oswald's Vicarage, Cheddar Grove, Bedminster Down, Bristol BS13 7EN* Tel 0117-964 2649 Fax as telephone
E-mail john@stoswalds.freeserve.co.uk

LEWIS, The Very Revd John Percival. b 19. TCD BA44. CITC 47. **d** 47 **p** 48. C Galway *T, K & A* 47-51; I Knappagh 51-74; Can Tuam Cathl from 70; I Omey w Ballynakill, Errislannan and Roundstone 73-91; Provost Tuam 73-91; rtd 91. *Albany, Pheasant Hill, Castlebar, Co Mayo, Irish Republic* Tel (00353) (94) 22747

LEWIS, John Pryce. b 65. Trin Coll Carmarthen BA87. Wycliffe Hall Ox 92. **d** 94 **p** 95. C Carmarthen St Pet *St D* 94-97; V Nevern and Y Beifil w Eglwyswrw and Meline etc from 97. *The Vicarage, Nevern, Newport SA42 0NF* Tel (01239) 820427

LEWIS, The Very Revd John Thomas. b 47. Jes Coll Ox BA69 MA73 St Jo Coll Cam BA72 MA92. Westcott Ho Cam 71. **d** 73 **p** 74. C Whitchurch *Llan* 73-77; C Llanishen and Lisvane 77-80; Asst Chapl Univ of Wales (Cardiff) 80-85; Warden of Ords 81-85; V Brecon St David w Llanspyddid and Llanilltyd *S & B* 85-91; Sec Prov Selection Panel and Bd Ch in Wales 87-94; V Bassaleg *Mon* 91-96; TR 96-00; Bp's Chapl for CME 98-00; Dean Llan from 00; V Llandaff from 00. *The Deanery, The Cathedral Green, Llandaff, Cardiff CF5 2YF* Tel (029) 2056 1545

LEWIS, Kenneth Lionel. b 22. Univ of Wales (Swansea) 42 Keble Coll Ox BA50 MA54 Ch Coll Cam CertEd52. Wycliffe Hall Ox 52. **d** 52 **p** 53. C Bromley St Jo *Roch* 52-55; C Streatham Hill St Marg *S'wark* 55-57; R Tatsfield 57-72; Lic to Offic 72-78 and from 89; Perm to Offic *Roch* 75-78 and 83-93; Perm to Offic *Cant* 75-78. *3 Towerfields, Westerham Road, Keston BR2 6HF* Tel (01689) 851125

LEWIS, Leslie. b 25. Qu Coll Birm 82. **d** 83 **p** 84. NSM Garretts Green *Birm* 83-88; NSM Coleshill 88-92; NSM Maxstoke 88-92; rtd 92; Perm to Offic *Birm* from 92. *54 Bellevue Road, Birmingham B26 2QA* Tel 0121-742 3662

LEWIS, Leslie. b 28. LRAM56. St Aid Birkenhead 61. **d** 63 **p** 64. C Eastham *Ches* 63-66; C W Kirby St Bridget 66-72; V Rainow w Saltersford 72-73; V Rainow w Saltersford and Forest 73-02; Dioc Clergy Widows and Retirement Officer 88-93; rtd 02. *25 Appleby Close, Macclesfield SK11 8XB* Tel (01625) 616395

LEWIS, Mrs Mary Carola Melton. b 51. LRAM72 S Glam Inst HE CertEd76 Lon Univ BD93. St Mich Coll Llan 77. **d** 98 **p** 99. NSM Aberedw w Llandeilo Graban and Llanbadarn etc *S & B* from 98. *The Skreen, Erwood, Builth Wells LD2 3SJ* Tel (01982) 560210 Fax 560470 E-mail marylewis@btinternet.com

LEWIS, Maureen. b 50. Chester Coll BA92. St Jo Coll Nottm DipMM94. **d** 94 **p** 95. C Ellesmere Port *Ches* 94-98; C Prenton

98-00; C New Brighton St Jas w Em from 00. *32 Magazine Brow, Wallasey CH45 1HP* Tel 0151-630 7203

LEWIS, Melville. *See* LEWIS, William George Melville

LEWIS, Michael. *See* LEWIS, James Michael

✠**LEWIS, The Rt Revd Michael Augustine Owen.** b 53. Mert Coll Ox BA75 MA79. Cuddesdon Coll 75. **d** 78 **p** 79 **c** 99. C Salfords *S'wark* 78-80; Chapl Thames Poly 80-84; V Welling 84-91; TR Worc SE *Worc* 91-99; RD Worc E 93-99; Hon Can Worc Cathl 98-99; Suff Bp Middleton *Man* from 99. *The Hollies, Manchester Road, Rochdale OL11 3QY* Tel (01706) 358550 Fax 354851 E-mail maolewis_2000@yahoo.com

LEWIS, Michael David Bennett. b 41. Univ of Wales DipTh68 Portsm Univ MA01. St Mich Coll Llan 65. **d** 68 **p** 69. C Penarth w Lavernock *Llan* 68-72; Chapl RAF 72-74; C Llanishen and Lisvane *Llan* 74-77; V Penyfai w Tondu 77-82; Chapl Ardingly Coll 82-90; R Merrow *Guildf* 90-95; RD Guildf 94-95; V Southsea H Spirit *Portsm* from 95. *The Vicarage, 26 Victoria Grove, Southsea PO5 1NY* Tel (023) 9287 3535 Mobile 07808-609912

LEWIS, Michael John. b 37. LLAM86. St Aid Birkenhead 64. **d** 66 **p** 67. C Whitnash *Cov* 66-69; C Nuneaton St Nic 69-73; TV Basildon St Martin w H Cross and Laindon *Chelmsf* 73-79; V W Bromwich St Jas *Lich* 79-85; TV Buxton w Burbage and King Sterndale *Derby* 85-95; P-in-c Brampton St Mark 95-02; rtd 02. *15 Langley Street, Basford, Stoke-on-Trent ST4 6DX* Tel (01782) 622762

LEWIS, Norman Eric. b 34. SRN55 Open Univ BA77. Roch Th Coll 59 Lich Th Coll 60. **d** 63 **p** 64. C Hope St Jas *Man* 63-67; V Hindsford 67-77; V Bolton SS Simon and Jude 77-90; rtd 90; Perm to Offic *York* from 90. *Millbank Cottage, Kirby Misperton, Malton YO17 6XZ* Tel (01653) 668526 E-mail normanl@btinternet.com

LEWIS, Paul Wilfred. b 37. Ch Ch Ox BA60 DipEd61 MA64 DipTh72. Chich Th Coll 62. **d** 64 **p** 65. C St Pancras H Cross w St Jude and St Pet *Lon* 64-66; C Tottenham St Jo 66-68; Barbados 68-71; Lect Sarum & Wells Th Coll 72-74; Chapl 73-74; Chapl LSE *Lon* 74-80; Chapl St Chris Hospice Lon 80-86; C St Giles Cripplegate w St Bart Moor Lane etc *Lon* 86-89; Chapl Nat Hosp for Neurology and Neurosurgery Lon 89-99; Chapl Univ Coll Lon Hosps NHS Trust 96-99; P-in-c St Pancras H Cross w St Jude and St Pet *Lon* from 99. *Holy Cross Vicarage, 47 Argyle Square, London WC1H 8AL* Tel (020) 7278 3706

LEWIS, Peter. *See* LEWIS, Thomas Peter

LEWIS, Peter Andrew. b 67. Pemb Coll Ox MA PhD Univ of Wales (Abth) Bris Univ BA. Trin Coll Bris. **d** 96 **p** 97. C Cardigan w Mwnt and Y Ferwig *St D* 96-98; C Gabalfa *Llan* 98-01; V Aberpergwm and Blaengwrach from 01. *The Vicarage, 11 Roberts Close, Glynneath, Neath SA11 5HR* Tel (01639) 721964 E-mail peterlewis@net.ntl.com

LEWIS, Canon Peter Goulstone. b 25. St D Coll Lamp BA48. **d** 50 **p** 51. C Aberystwyth H Trin *St D* 50-54; C Caerphilly *Llan* 54-60; V Cwmbach 60-66; V Tongwynlais 66-79; V Llantrisant 79-90; Can Llan Cathl 80-91; RD Pontypridd 88-90; rtd 91; Perm to Offic *Llan* from 91. *73 Pinecroft Avenue, Cwmbach, Aberdare CF44 0NB* Tel (01685) 882257

LEWIS, Peter Richard. b 40. Dur Univ BA62 Birm Univ DipTh64. Qu Coll Birm 62. **d** 64 **p** 65. C Moseley St Mary *Birm* 64-67; C Sherborne w Castleton and Lillington *Sarum* 67-71; P-in-c Bishopstone w Stratford Tony 72-80; V Amesbury 80-02; Offg Chapl RAF from 80; rtd 02. *Rose Cottage, Silton Road, Bourton, Gillingham SP8 5DE*

LEWIS, Miss Rachel Veronica Clare. b 59. St Jo Coll Dur BA80 Man Univ PGCE81 Univ of Wales (Cardiff) MSc. Sarum & Wells Th Coll 86. **d** 86 **p** 94. C Caereithin *S & B* 86-88; Par Dn Bolton St Pet *Man* 88-91; Chapl Bolton Colls of H&FE 88-91; Chapl Trin Coll Carmarthen 91-94; C Yatton Keynell *Bris* 94-97; P-in-c 97-99; C Biddestone w Slaughterford 94-97; P-in-c 97-99; C Castle Combe 94-97; P-in-c 97-99; C W Kington 94-97; P-in-c 97-99; C Nettleton w Littleton Drew 94-97; P-in-c 97-99; P-in-c Grittleton and Leigh Delamere 94-99; TR By Brook 99-02; I Adare and Kilmallock w Kilpeacon, Croom etc *L & K* from 02. *The Rectory, Adare, Co Limerick, Irish Republic* Tel (00353) (61) 396227 Fax as telephone

LEWIS, Ray Arthur. b 63. Oak Hill Th Coll 87. **d** 90 **p** 91. C Holloway St Mary Magd *Lon* 90-93; TV Forest Gate St Sav w W Ham St Matt *Chelmsf* 93-97; St Vincent 97-98; Grenada 98-99. *45 Avenue Road, London E7 0LA*

LEWIS, Raymond James. b 34. Univ of Wales (Cardiff) BA Open Univ BSc. St Mich Coll Llan. **d** 91 **p** 92. C Llanelli *St D* 91-94; rtd 99. *36 Yorath Road, Whitchurch, Cardiff CF14 1QD*

LEWIS, Richard. *See* LEWIS, The Rt Revd John Hubert Richard

LEWIS, The Very Revd Richard. b 35. Fitzw Ho Cam BA78 MA63. Ripon Hall Ox 58. **d** 60 **p** 61. C Hinckley St Mary *Leic* 60-63; C Sanderstead All SS *S'wark* 63-66; V Merstham 67-72; V Wimbledon H Trin 72-74; P-in-c S Wimbledon St Pet 72-74; V S Wimbledon H Trin and St Pet 74-79; V Dulwich St Barn 79-90; Chapl Alleyn's Foundn Dulwich 79-90; RD Dulwich *S'wark* 83-90; Hon Can *S'wark* Cathl 87-90; Dean Wells *B & W* 90-03; Warden of Readers 91-03; rtd 03. *Wells House, 152 Lower*

Howsell Road, Malvern WR14 1DL Tel (01886) 833820
E-mail dean.richard@btopenworld.com

LEWIS, Canon Richard Charles. b 44. Lon Univ DipTh68 DipSocSc78 Univ of Wales (Lamp) MA94 Sheff Univ MEd96. ALCD69. **d** 69 **p** 70. C Kendal H Trin *Carl* 69-72; C Chipping Barnet *St Alb* 72-76; V Watford Ch Ch from 76; Chapl Abbots Hill Sch Hemel Hempstead 81-96; Hon Can St Alb Abbey from 90. *Christ Church Vicarage, Leggatts Way, Watford WD2 6BQ* Tel (01923) 672240 Fax as telephone
E-mail vicar@ccwatford.u-net.com *or* rts@ccwatford.u-net.com

LEWIS, Robert. b 38. St Pet Coll Ox BA62 MA66. Cuddesdon Coll 62. **d** 64 **p** 65. C Kirkby *Liv* 64-67 and 70-71; TV 71-75; Chapl St Boniface Coll Warminster 68-69; Tutor St Aug Coll Cant 69-70; Abp's Dom Chapl *York* 76-79; Dir of Ords 76-79; TR Thirsk 79-92; Chapl Oslo w Bergen, Trondheim, Stavanger etc *Eur* 93-96; P-in-c Danby *York* 96-98; V from 98; RD Whitby from 98. *The Vicarage, Danby, Whitby YO21 2NQ* Tel (01287) 660388

LEWIS, Canon Robert George. b 53. Lanc Univ BEd76. Ripon Coll Cuddesdon. **d** 78 **p** 79. C Liv Our Lady and St Nic w St Anne *Liv* 78-81; Asst Dir of Educn 81-88; P-in-c Newchurch 88-89; R Newchurch 94; P-in-c Glazebury 88-89; R Newchurch and Glazebury 89-94; R Winwick from 94; AD Winwick from 01; Hon Can Liv Cathl from 01. *The Rectory, Golborne Road, Winwick, Warrington WA2 8SZ* Tel (01925) 632760

LEWIS, Canon Robert Hugh Cecil. b 25. New Coll Ox BA50 MA50. Westcott Ho Cam 50. **d** 52 **p** 53. C Crumpsall St Matt *Man* 52-54; C New Bury 54-56; V Bury St Pet 56-63; V Poynton *Ches* 63-91; RD Stockport 72-85; Hon Can Ches Cathl 75-91; RD Cheadle 85-87; Dioc Ecum Officer 87-91; Chapl to The Queen 85-95; rtd 91; Perm to Offic *Ches* from 91. *78 Dean Drive, Wilmslow SK9 2EY* Tel (01625) 524761

LEWIS, Roger Edward. b 24. Qu Coll Cam BA45 MA49. Ridley Hall Cam 47. **d** 49 **p** 50. C Handsworth St Mary *Birm* 49-52; R Hadleigh St Jas *Chelmsf* 52-58; V Clacton St Paul 58-71; V Surbiton St Matt *S'wark* 71-89; rtd 89; Perm to Offic *S'wark* from 89. *Rose Cottage, 40 Grove Road, Horley RH6 8EL* Tel (01293) 771197

LEWIS, Roger Gilbert. b 49. St Jo Coll Dur BA70. Ripon Hall Ox 70. **d** 72 **p** 73. C Boldmere *Birm* 72-76; C Birm St Pet 76-77; TV Tettenhall Regis *Lich* 77-81; V Ward End *Birm* 81-91; rtd 91; Perm to Offic *Birm* from 91. *8 Tudor Terrace, Ravenhurst Road, Birmingham B17 8SB* Tel 0121-427 4915

LEWIS, Stuart William. b 54. Newc Univ BA79 Newc Poly PGCE80. Edin Th Coll 86. **d** 86 **p** 87. C Ledbury w Eastnor *Heref* 86-89; Chapl Malvern Coll 89-96; Chapl and Prec Portsm Cathl *Portsm* 96-97; TV Ross *Heref* 97-01; P-in-c Lower Wharfedale *Ripon* 01-03; R from 03; Chapl St Aid Sch Harrogate from 01. *The Rectory, Main Street, Kirkby Overblow, Harrogate HG3 1HD* Tel (01423) 872314

LEWIS, Thomas Peter. b 45. Selw Coll Cam BA67 MA. Ripon Hall Ox 68. **d** 70 **p** 71. C Bp's Hatfield *St Alb* 70-74; C Boreham Wood All SS 74-78; Chapl Haileybury Coll 78-85; Chapl Abingdon Sch 86-03; R Narberth w Mounton w Robeston Wathen and Crinow *St D* from 03. *The Rectory, Adams Drive, Narberth SA67 7AE* Tel (01834) 860370

LEWIS, Timothy John. b 56. Univ of Wales (Swansea) BA76. Sarum & Wells Th Coll 83. **d** 86 **p** 87. C Taunton St Mary *B & W* 86-89; Chapl RN 89-02. *Address temp unknown*

LEWIS, Trevor Charlton Haselden. b 22. Qu Coll Birm 49. **d** 51 **p** 52. C Glouc St Aldate *Glouc* 51-54; C Cirencester 54-55; C-in-c Churchdown St Jo CD 55-64; V Churchdown St Jo 64-65; R Dursley 65-70; Chapl RN 70-71; USA from 71; rtd 94. *115 Alpine, Carbondale, CO 81623, USA*

LEWIS, Vera Elizabeth. b 45. Lon Univ BA66 Univ of Wales (Abth) DipEd67 Dip Librarianship 73. St As Minl Tr Course 82. **d** 85 **p** 97. NSM Garthbeibio and Llanerfyl and Llangadfan *St As* 85-86; C 87-88; NSM Llanfair Caereinion w Llanllugan 85-86; C 87-88; Dn-in-c Llanrhaeadr-ym-Mochnant etc 88-96; Dn-in-c Llanddulas and Llysfaen 96-97; R 97-03; rtd 03. *Heulwen, Bronwylfa Square, St Asaph LL17 0BU*

LEWIS, Canon Walter Arnold. b 45. NUI BA68 TCD MPhil91. TCD Div Sch 71. **d** 71 **p** 72. C Belfast Whiterock *Conn* 71-73; C Belfast St Mark 73-80; Bp's C Belfast St Andr 80-84; I Belfast St Thos from 84; Can Belf Cathl from 97. *St Thomas Rectory, 1A Eglantine Avenue, Belfast BT9 6DW* Tel (028) 9080 8343 Fax as telephone E-mail walter.lewis@ntlworld.com

LEWIS, William George Melville. b 31. Open Univ BA. S'wark Ord Course. **d** 69 **p** 70. C Coulsdon St Jo *S'wark* 69-71; C Perry Hill St Geo 71-74; V Eltham St Barn 74-80; V Reigate St Mark 80-89; V Ham St Rich 89-97; rtd 97; Hon C Kew *S'wark* 97-00. *20 Avenue Court, The Avenue, Tadworth KT20 5BG* Tel (01737) 819748

LEWIS, William George Rees. b 35. Hertf Coll Ox BA59 MA63. Tyndale Hall Bris 61. **d** 63 **p** 64. C Tenby w Gumfreston *St D* 63-66; C Llanelli St Paul 66-69; R Letterston 69-84; R Jordanston w Llanstinan 73-78; R Punctestown and Lt Newc 78-84; R Hubberston w Herbrandston and Hasguard etc 84-90; Prov Officer for Evang and Adult Educn 90-94; V Gabalfa *Llan* 94-00;

rtd 00. *5 Westaway Drive, Hakin, Milford Haven SA73 3EG* Tel (01646) 692280

LEWIS, William Rhys. b 20. St Mich Coll Llan 53. **d** 55 **p** 56. C Ystrad Mynach *Llan* 55-58; C Bassaleg *Mon* 58-59; V Cwmtillery 59-62; V Newport St Andr 62-64; TR Ebbw Vale 64-73; R Llangattock and Llangynidr *S & B* 73-78; V Swansea St Luke 78-85; rtd 85; Perm to Offic *Llan* from 85. *6 Beech Avenue, Llantwit Major CF61 1RT* Tel (01446) 796741

LEWIS-ANTHONY, Justin Griffith. b 64. LSE BA86. Ripon Coll Cuddesdon BA91 MA97. **d** 92 **p** 93. C Cirencester *Glouc* 92-98; Prec Ch Ch *Ox* 98-03; R Hackington *Cant* from 03. *The Rectory, St Stephen's Green, Canterbury CT2 7JU* Tel (01227) 765391 E-mail rector@ststephenscanterbury.net

LEWIS-JENKINS, Christopher Robin. b 50. St Mich Coll Llan Dip Past Th 96. **d** 96 **p** 97. C Barry All SS *Llan* 96-01; V Dinas and Penygraig w Williamstown from 01. *The Vicarage, 1 Llanfair Road, Penygraig, Tonypandy CF40 1TA* Tel (01443) 422677

LEWIS LLOYD, Canon Timothy David. b 37. Clare Coll Cam BA58 MA62. Cuddesdon Coll 58. **d** 60 **p** 61. C Stepney St Dunstan and All SS *Lon* 60-64; C St Alb Abbey *St Alb* 64-67; Prec St Alb Abbey 67-69; V St Paul's Walden 69-78; V Braughing w Furneux Pelham and Stocking Pelham 78-79; P-in-c Lt Hadham 78-79; V Braughing, Lt Hadham, Albury, Furneux Pelham etc 79-82; V Cheshunt 82-95; RD Cheshunt 89-94; Hon Can St Alb 94-01; V Sawbridgeworth 95-01; rtd 01. *c/o M Lewis Lloyd Esq, 42F Forest Lane, London E15 1HA* Tel (020) 8534 1693

LEWIS-NICHOLSON, Russell John. b 45. Caulfield Inst of Tech Dip Civil Engineering 68. Oak Hill Th Coll DipTh81. **d** 81 **p** 82. C Clayton *Bradf* 81-84; Australia from 84. *14 Cedar Grove, Highton, Vic, Australia 3216* Tel (0061) (3) 5241 2408 Mobile 429-358490

LEWISHAM, Archdeacon of. See HARDMAN, The Ven Christine Elizabeth

LEWORTHY, Graham Llewelyn. b 47. Reading Univ BA69. S Dios Minl Tr Scheme 91. **d** 94 **p** 95. NSM Sark *Win* 94-96; C from 96. *Baleine Studio, La Collenette, Sark, Guernsey GY9 0SB* Tel (01481) 832140

LEY, John Andrew. b 16. St Deiniol's Hawarden 70. **d** 72 **p** 73. Hon C Leintwardine *Heref* 72-76; Hon C Wigmore Abbey 76-77; Asst P Pulloxhill w Flitton *St Alb* 77-79; Lic to Offic *Blackb* 80-81; C Stoke Lacy, Moreton Jeffries w Much Cowarne etc *Heref* 81-87; rtd 87; Perm to Offic *Lich* 87-98; Perm to Offic *Heref* from 98. *5 Glendale Close, Hereford HR4 9QF* Tel (01432) 344148

LEYLAND, Derek James. b 34. Lon Univ BSc55 Birm Univ DipTh60. Qu Coll Birm 58. **d** 60 **p** 61. C Ashton-on-Ribble *St Andr Blackb* 60-63; V 80-87; C Salesbury 63-65; V Preston St Oswald 65-67; V Pendleton 67-74; Dioc Youth Chapl 67-69; Ind Youth Chapl 70-74; R Brindle 74-80; V Garstang St Helen Churchtown 87-94; Sec SOSc 90-94; rtd 94; Perm to Offic *Blackb* from 94. *Greystocks, Goosnargh Lane, Goosnargh, Preston PR3 2BP* Tel (01772) 865682

LEYLAND, Tyrone John. b 49. Aston Univ BSc68. St Jo Coll Nottm 89. **d** 91 **p** 92. C Lich St Mary w St Mich *Lich* 91-94; TV Willenhall H Trin 94-99; P-in-c The Ridwares and Kings Bromley from 99. *The Rectory, Alrewas Road, Kings Bromley, Burton-on-Trent DE13 7HP* Tel (01543) 472932 Fax as telephone

LEYSHON, Philip Alan. b 76. Glam Univ BA. Ripon Coll Cuddesdon BTh03. **d** 03. C Newton Nottage *Llan* from 03. *79 Meadow Lane, Porthcawl CF36 5EY* Tel (01656) 788176

LEYSHON, Simon. b 63. Trin Coll Carmarthen BA86 Southn Univ BTh89 Glam Univ CertMS96. Sarum & Wells Th Coll. **d** 89 **p** 90. C Tenby *St D* 89-92; TV 92-96; Chapl and Hd RS Llandovery Coll 96-02; Chapl Ld Wandsworth Coll Basingstoke from 02. *Kimbers, Lord Wandsworth College, Long Sutton, Hook, Basingstoke RG29 1TB* Tel (01256) 862206
E-mail simonleyshon@hotmail.com

LIBBY, John Ralph. b 55. Trin Coll Cam BA(Econ)83. Ridley Hall Cam 83. **d** 91 **p** 92. C Enfield St Andr *Lon* 91-93; C Northwood Em 93-96; V Denton Holme *Carl* from 96. *St James's Vicarage, Goschen Road, Carlisle CA2 5PF* Tel (01228) 515639 *or* 810616 Fax 524569
E-mail saintjames.carlisle@talk21.com

LICHFIELD, Archdeacon of. See LILEY, The Ven Christopher Frank

LICHFIELD, Bishop of. See GLEDHILL, The Rt Revd Jonathan Michael

LICHFIELD, Dean of. See YORKE, The Very Revd Michael Leslie

LICHTENBERGER, Miss Ruth Eileen. b 34. NY Th Sem 64 Nor Ord Course 95. **d** 96 **p** 97. NSM Warrington H Trin *Liv* from 96. *8 Towers Court, Warrington WA5 1AA* Tel (01925) 656763 Fax as telephone E-mail ruthel@compuserve.com

LICKESS, Canon David Frederick. b 37. St Chad's Coll Dur BA63 DipTh65. **d** 65 **p** 66. C Howden *York* 65-70; V Rudby in Cleveland w Middleton from 70; Can and Preb York Minster from 90; RD Stokesley 93-00. *The Vicarage, Hutton Rudby, Yarm*

TS15 0HY Tel (01642) 700223 Fax as telephone
E-mail david.lickess@btinternet.com

LIDDELL, Mark. b 55. Birm Univ BA00. Coll of Resurr Mirfield 96. **d** 98 **p** 99. C Wednesbury St Jas and St Jo *Lich* 98-00; C Walsall St Andr 00-01; P-in-c from 01. *St Andrew's Vicarage, 119 Hollyhedge Lane, Birchills, Walsall WS2 8PZ* Tel (01922) 721658

LIDDELL, Canon Peter Gregory. b 40. St Andr Univ MA63 Linacre Ho Ox BA65 MA70. Andover Newton Th Sem DMin75 Ripon Hall Ox 63. **d** 65 **p** 66. C Bp's Hatfield *St Alb* 65-71; USA 71-76; P-in-c Kimpton w Ayot St Lawrence *St Alb* 77-83; Dir of Past Counselling from 80; Hon Can St Alb from 99. *The Coach House, Hitchin Road, Kimpton, Hitchin SG4 8EF* Tel (01438) 832266 *or* (01727) 868585

LIDDELOW, Peter William. b 33. Oak Hill NSM Course. **d** 82 **p** 83. NSM Finchley Ch Ch *Lon* 82-84; NSM S Mimms Ch Ch from 84; Perm to Offic *St Alb* from 95. *23 King's Road, Barnet EN5 4EF* Tel (020) 8441 2968

LIDDLE, George. b 48. NEOC 88. **d** 90 **p** 91. C Auckland St Andr and St Anne *Dur* 90-92; C Crook 92-94; C Stanley 92-94; P-in-c Evenwood 94-96; V from 96. *St Paul's Vicarage, Evenwood, Bishop Auckland DL14 9RA* Tel (01388) 834594
E-mail george@st-pauls.freeserve.co.uk

LIDDLE, Harry. b 36. Wadh Coll Ox BA57 MA61. Wycliffe Hall Ox 62. **d** 64 **p** 65. C Withington St Paul *Man* 64-68; R Broughton St Jo 68-73; V Balby *Sheff* 73-82; R Firbeck w Letwell 82-94; V Woodsetts 82-94; TV Aston cum Aughton w Swallownest, Todwick etc 94-01; rtd 01; Perm to Offic *Sheff* from 01. *30 Meadow Grove Road, Totley, Sheffield S17 4FF* Tel 0114-236 4941

LIDDLE, Stephen John. b 60. St Jo Coll Ox BA81 PGCE82. Linc Th Coll 88. **d** 91 **p** 92. C Morpeth *Newc* 91-95; P-in-c Byker St Mich w St Lawr 95-98; R Bothal and Pegswood w Longhirst from 98. *Bothal Rectory, Longhirst Road, Pegswood, Morpeth NE61 6XF* Tel (01670) 510793

LIDSTONE, Vernon Henry. b 43. SW Minl Tr Course 89. **d** 92 **p** 93. NSM Bovey Tracey SS Pet, Paul and Thos w Hennock *Ex* 92-94; Sub-Chapl HM Pris Channings Wood 92-96; Asst Dioc Chr Stewardship Adv 92-93; Dioc Chr Stewardship Adv 93-96; Dioc Officer for Par Development *Glouc* 96-97; Chapl HM Pris Leyhill 97-03; rtd 03. *The Pike House, Saul, Gloucester GL2 7JD* Tel (01452) 741410 E-mail vernon@lidstone.net

LIDWILL, Canon Mark Robert. b 57. TCD DipTh87. **d** 87 **p** 88. C Annagh w Drumgoon, Ashfield etc *K, E & A* 87-90; I Urney w Denn and Derryheen from 90; Dioc Youth Adv from 97; Preb Kilmore Cathl from 98. *The Rectory, Keadue Lane, Cavan, Co Cavan, Irish Republic* Tel (00353) (49) 61016

LIEVESLEY, Mrs Joy Margaret. b 48. Lady Mabel Coll CertEd69. Guildf Dioc Min Course 98. **d** 00 **p** 01. NSM Farnham *Guildf* from 00. *3 Kingfisher Close, Church Crookham, Fleet GU13 0JP* Tel (01252) 690223
E-mail lievesley@ntlworld.com

LIGHT, Mrs Madeline Margaret. b 54. Girton Coll Cam BA77 MA80 Lon Inst of Educn PGCE78. EAMTC DipHE99. **d** 99 **p** 00. C Eaton *Nor* 99-02; P-in-c Nor St Helen from 02; Chapl Gt Hosp Nor from 02. *The Vicarage, St Martins Palace Plain, Norwich NR3 1RW* Tel (01603) 219927

LIGHTFOOT, The Very Revd Vernon Keith. b 34. St Jo Coll Dur BA58. Ripon Hall Ox 58. **d** 60 **p** 61. C Rainhill *Liv* 60-62; C Liv Our Lady and St Nic 62-65; V Stanley 65-75; Chapl St Edm Coll Liv 66-68; Chapl Rathbone Hosp Liv 70-75; New Zealand from 75; V Mt Albert St Luke 75-85; Dean Waikato 85-97; rtd 98. *16C Acacia Crescent, Hamilton, New Zealand* Tel (0064) (7) 843 5538 Fax as telephone E-mail keith.jennie@xtra.co.nz

LIGHTOWLER, Joseph Trevor. b 33. **d** 79 **p** 80. Hon C Leverstock Green *St Alb* 79-80; Hon C Chambersbury 80-84; C Woodmansterne *S'wark* 84-88; R Odell and Pavenham *St Alb* 88-97; rtd 97; Perm to Offic *St Alb* from 97. *41 Oakwood Drive, St Albans AL4 0UL* Tel (01727) 833422

LIKEMAN, Canon Martin Kaye. b 34. St Mich Coll Llan 55. **d** 57 **p** 58. C Llanwnog w Penstrowed *Ban* 57-60; C Llandudno 60-64; V Llanrhian w Llanhywel and Carnhedryn *St D* 64-73; RD Dewisland and Fishguard 71-73; V Llanstadwel 73-99; Can St D Cathl 88-99; rtd 99. *10 Lawrenny Street, Neyland, Milford Haven SA73 1TB* Tel (01646) 600983

LILES, Malcolm David. b 48. Nottm Univ BA69. St Steph Ho Ox 69. **d** 71 **p** 72. C Corby Epiphany w St Jo *Pet* 71-74; C New Cleethorpes *Linc* 74-76; TV Lt Coates 76-77; TV Gt and Lt Coates w Bradley 78-82; Soc Resp Sec 82-93; Hon C Gt Grimsby St Mary and St Jas 82-93; P-in-c Grimsby All SS 88-93; TV Dronfield w Holmesfield *Derby* 93-98; TR Crawley *Chich* from 98. *The Rectory, 1 Southgate Road, Crawley RH10 6BL* Tel (01293) 535856 *or* 520421
E-mail rectorcrawley@btinternet.com

LILEY, The Ven Christopher Frank. b 47. Nottm Univ BEd70. Linc Th Coll 72. **d** 74 **p** 75. C Kingswinford H Trin *Lich* 74-79; TV Stafford 79-84; V Norton *St Alb* 84-96; RD Hitchin 89-94; TV Shrewsbury St Chad w St Mary *Lich* 96-01; P-in-c Shrewsbury St Alkmund 96-01; Adn Lich from 01; Can Res and Treas Lich

Cathl from 01. *24 The Close, Lichfield WS13 7LD* Tel (01543) 306145 Fax 306147
E-mail archdeacon.lichfield@lichfield.anglican.org

LILEY, Peter James. b 60. Liv Univ BA82 Westmr Coll Ox PGCE83. Oak Hill Th Coll DipHE93. **d** 93 **p** 94. C Exning St Martin w Landwade *St E* 93-96; V Acton w St Waldingfield 96-00; TV Bottesford w Ashby *Linc* from 00. *The Vicarage, 10 Old School Lane, Bottesford, Scunthorpe DN16 3RD* Tel and fax (01724) 867256 *or* 842732 E-mail peter.liley@ntlworld.com

LILEY, Stephen John. b 65. Liv Univ BA87 MMus88 ARCM93. Wycliffe Hall Ox 97. **d** 99 **p** 00. C Throop *Win* 99-03; V Clapham *St Alb* from 03. *The Vicarage, Green Lane, Clapham, Bedford MK41 6ER* Tel (01234) 352814

LILLEY, Christopher Howard. b 51. FCA75 FTII83. St Jo Coll Nottm DCM93 LNSM course 83. **d** 85 **p** 86. OLM Skegness and Winthorpe *Linc* 85-93; C Limber Magna w Brocklesby 93-96; Perm to Offic *S'well* 93-96; P-in-c Middle Rasen Gp *Linc* 96-97; R 97-02; V Scawby, Redbourne and Hibaldstow from 02; RD Yarborough from 02. *St Hybald's Vicarage, Vicarage Lane, Scawby, Brigg DN20 9LX* Tel (01652) 652725
E-mail lilley@btinternet.com

LILLEY, Ivan Ray. b 32. Bps' Coll Cheshunt 58. **d** 61 **p** 62. C Kettering SS Pet and Paul *Pet* 61-64; C Gt Yarmouth *Nor* 64-75; P-in-c Watlington w Wormegay *Ely* 75-83; P-in-c Watlington 76-83; P-in-c Holme Runcton w S Runcton and Wallington 76-83; V Tysoe w Oxhill and Whatcote *Cov* 83-86; C Langold *S'well* 87-93; P-in-c 91-98; rtd 98; Perm to Offic *Nor* from 99. *Linden Lea, 41 Cedar Drive, Attleborough NR17 2EY* Tel (01953) 452710 Fax as telephone

LILLIAN, Sister. See MORRIS, Lillian Rosina

LILLICRAP, Peter Andrew. b 65. Hatf Poly BEng87 CEng93 MIMechE93. Trin Coll Bris 00. **d** 02 **p** 03. C Kineton *Cov* from 02. *7 Green Farm End, Kineton, Warwick CV35 0LD* Tel (01926) 640451 Mobile 07762-230189
E-mail peterlillicrap@tiscali.co.uk

LILLICRAP, Stephen Hunter. b 58. Newc Univ MB, BS81 DRCOG84 MRCGP85. SEITE 00. **d** 03. C Wye w Brook *Cant* from 03. *The Vicarage, Pilgrims Way, Hastingleigh, Ashford TN25 5HP* Tel (01233) 750140 Mobile 07971-224094
E-mail steve.lillicrap@btopenworld.com

LILLIE, Judith Virginia. See THOMPSON, Mrs Judith Virginia

LILLIE, Mrs Shona Lorimer. b 49. St Jo Coll Nottm BA03. **d** 03. C Bishopbriggs *Glas* from 03. *7 Meadowburn, Bishopbriggs, Glasgow G64 3HA* Tel 0141-772 Mobile 07773-501706 E-mail shonalillie@hotmail.com

LILLINGTON, Brian Ray. b 36. RMN60 FRSH84. S Dios Minl Tr Scheme 87. **d** 90 **p** 91. NSM Yateley *Win* 90-98; NSM Eversley 98-02; rtd 03. *Kaos, Little Vigo, Yateley GU46 6ES* Tel (01252) 872760 Fax as telephone E-mail andragrask@aol.com

LILLINGTON (née POLLIT), Mrs Ruth Mary. b 65. SS Paul & Mary Coll Cheltenham BA88. St Jo Coll Nottm DPS90. **d** 90 **p** 94. Par Dn Caverswall *Lich* 90-92; Par Dn Caverswall and Weston Coyney w Dilhorne 92-93; Par Dn Luton St Mary *St Alb* 93-94; C 94-97; Chapl Luton Univ 93-97. *20 Harcourt Road, Bracknell RG12 7JD* Tel (01344) 423025

LILLISTONE, Canon Brian David. b 38. SS Coll Cam BA61 MA65. St Steph Ho Ox 61. **d** 63 **p** 64. C Ipswich All Hallows *St E* 63-66; C Stokesay *Heref* 66-71; P-in-c Lyonshall w Titley 71-76; R Martlesham w Brightwell *St E* 76-03; Hon Can St E Cathl 98-03; rtd 03; Perm to Offic *St E* from 03. *23 Woodland Close, Risby, Bury St Edmunds IP28 6QN* Tel (01284) 811330 E-mail brian@lillistone.freeserve.co.uk

LIMBERT, Kenneth Edward. b 25. CEng69 MIMechE. S'wark Ord Course 72. **d** 75 **p** 76. NSM Northwood Hills St Edm *Lon* 75-90; Perm to Offic from 90. *55 York Road, Northwood HA6 1JJ* Tel (01923) 825791

LIMBRICK, Gordon. b 36. Open Univ BA88. St Jo Coll Nottm CertCS90. **d** 87 **p** 91. Hon C Troon *Glas* 87-90; Hon C Yaxley *Ely* 90-97; Hon C Yaxley and Holme w Conington from 97; Perm to Offic *Pet* from 98. *271 Broadway, Yaxley, Peterborough PE7 3NR* Tel (01733) 243170 E-mail moandgol@tesco.com

LIMERICK AND ARDFERT, Dean of. See SIRR, The Very Revd John Maurice Glover

LIMERICK, Archdeacon of. *Vacant*

LIMERICK, ARDFERT, AGHADOE, KILLALOE, KILFENORA, CLONFERT, KILMACDUAGH AND EMLY, Bishop of. See MAYES, The Rt Revd Michael

LINAKER, David Julian John Ramage. b 65. Ripon Coll Cuddesdon BTh95. **d** 95 **p** 96. C Colehill *Sarum* 95-99; V Mere w W Knoyle and Maiden Bradley from 99. *The Vicarage, Angel Lane, Mere, Warminster BA12 6DH* Tel (01747) 860292

LINCOLN, Archdeacon of. See HAWES, The Ven Arthur John

LINCOLN, Bishop of. See SAXBEE, The Rt Revd John Charles

LINCOLN, Dean of. See KNIGHT, The Very Revd Alexander Francis

LIND-JACKSON, Peter Wilfrid. b 35. Leeds Univ BA67. Linc Th Coll 67. **d** 68 **p** 69. C Heref St Martin *Heref* 68-71; P-in-c Burghill 71-78; V 78-82; V Barnard Castle *Dur* 82-83; P-in-c Whorlton 82-83; V Barnard Castle w Whorlton 83-00; rtd 00. *15 Greenbank, Eggleston, Barnard Castle DL12 0BQ* Tel (01833) 650014

LINDARS, Frank. b 23. Wycliffe Hall Ox 54. **d** 56 **p** 57. C Beeston Hill St Luke *Ripon* 56-59; C Harrogate St Wilfrid 59-61; V Shadwell 61-80; RD Allerton 73-78; V Masham and Healey 80-88; rtd 88. *Hope Cottage, Reeth, Richmond DL11 6SF* Tel (01748) 884685

LINDECK, Peter Stephen. b 31. Oak Hill Th Coll 57. **d** 59 **p** 60. C Homerton St Luke *Lon* 59-62; C Salterhebble All SS *Wakef* 62-63; C Islington St Andr w St Thos and St Matthias *Lon* 64-67; V Toxteth Park St Bede *Liv* 68-74; Nigeria 74-76; C Netherton *Liv* 76-77; C Ollerton *S'well* 77-80; C Boughton 77-80; V Whitgift w Adlingfleet and Eastoft *Sheff* 80-86; P-in-c Swinefleet 81-86; V Kilnhurst 86-94; Chapl Montagu Hosp Mexborough 86-94; rtd 94; Perm to Offic *Sheff* from 94. *41 Church Lane, Doncaster DN4 0XB* Tel (01302) 855957

LINDEN, Gregory. b 25. Roch Th Coll. **d** 65 **p** 66. C Roundhay St Edm *Ripon* 65-68; C Highweek *Ex* 68-72; V Brampford Speke 72-82; R Upton Pyne 72-82; R Middleton-in-Teesdale *Dur* 82-85; V Eggleston 85-95; R Middleton-in-Teesdale w Forest and Frith 85-95; rtd 95. *15 Ashdown Court, Little Crakehall, Bedale DL8 1LQ* Tel (01677) 426380

LINDISFARNE, Archdeacon of. *See* LANGLEY, The Ven Robert

LINDLAR, Christopher Max Dierichs. b 55. Leeds Univ BA00. Coll of Resurr Mirfield 98. **d** 00 **p** 01. C Lancing w Coombes *Chich* from 00. *30 Greenoaks, Lancing BN15 0HE* Tel (01903) 767077 Mobile 07710-090195

LINDLEY, Geoffrey. b 22. St Jo Coll Ox BA45 MA47. Westcott Ho Cam 47. **d** 47 **p** 48. C E Wickham *S'wark* 47-51; C Welling 51-52; V Lambeth St Phil 52-56; V Ox St Marg *Ox* 56-72; P-in-c Pyrton w Shirburn 72-79; P-in-c Lewknor 72-79; P-in-c Milton-under-Wychwood 79-80; P-in-c Shipton-under-Wychwood 79-80; V Shipton-under-Wychwood w Milton, Fifield etc 80-85; Perm to Offic from 86; rtd 87. *St John's Home, St Mary's Road, Oxford OX4 1QE* Tel (01865) 247725

LINDLEY, Graham William. b 47. Man Poly CIPFA77. LNSM course 94. **d** 97 **p** 98. OLM E Crompton *Man* 97-02; NSM Newhey from 02. *37 Jordan Avenue, Shaw, Oldham OL2 8DQ* Tel (01706) 845677

LINDLEY, Harold Thomas. b 28. St Jo Coll Ox BA51 MA73. Wells Th Coll 51. **d** 53 **p** 54. C Normanton *Wakef* 53-57; C-in-c Rawthorpe CD 57-63; P-in-c Longstone *Derby* 63-68; V 68-74; P-in-c Barrow w Twyford 74-84; V Barrow-on-Trent w Twyford and Swarkestone 84-93; rtd 93. *Gorwel, 35 Nant Bychan, Moelfre LL72 8HE* Tel (01248) 410484

LINDLEY, The Ven Ralph Adrian. b 20. CBE75. St Jo Coll Dur BA51 DipTh53. **d** 53 **p** 54. C Burnley St Steph *Blackb* 53-55; Chapl RAF 55-70; UAE 70-78; Adn Gulf 70-78; Gen Sec JMECA 78-85; rtd 86; Perm to Offic *Glouc* from 86. *Taffrail, Lower Road, St Briavels, Lydney GL15 6SA* Tel (01594) 530230

LINDLEY, Canon Richard Adrian. b 44. Hull Univ BA65 Man Univ MA79 Birm Univ DPS68 Birm Poly DMS91. Cuddesdon Coll 66. **d** 68 **p** 69. C Ingrow cum Hainworth *Bradf* 68-70; Perm to Offic *Birm* 70-74; TV Ellesmere Port *Ches* 74-79; R Westborough *Guildf* 79-80; TR 80-84; Dir of Educn *Birm* 84-96; Dir of Educn *Win* from 96; Hon Can Win Cathl from 03. *Church House, 9 The Close, Winchester SO23 9LS* Tel (01962) 844644 Fax 841815

LINDO, Leithland Oscar. b 29. St Aug Coll Cant 57 St Pet Coll Jamaica 53. **d** 56 **p** 57. Jamaica 56-58; C Edmonton St Mary w St Jo *Lon* 58-62; C Heston 62-66; V Staines Ch Ch from 66. *Christ Church Vicarage, Kenilworth Gardens, Staines TW18 1DR* Tel (01784) 455457

LINDOP, Andrew John. b 57. Cam Univ MA. Cranmer Hall Dur 80. **d** 82 **p** 83. C Brinsworth w Catcliffe *Sheff* 82-85; C S Shoebury *Chelmsf* 85-89; V Mosley Common *Man* 89-99; V Astley Bridge from 99; AD Walmsley from 02. *St Paul's Vicarage, Sweetloves Lane, Bolton BL1 7ET* Tel (01204) 304119 Fax as telephone E-mail andy.lindop@tesco.net

LINDOP, Kenneth. b 45. Linc Th Coll 71. **d** 74 **p** 75. C Leic St Phil *Leic* 74-77; C Cov H Trin *Cov* 77-80; P-in-c Cubbington 80-82; V from 82; RD Warwick and Leamington 91-96; Jt P-in-c Leamington Spa H Trin and Old Milverton from 03. *St Mary's Vicarage, 15 Pinehurst, Cubbington, Leamington Spa CV32 7XA* Tel (01926) 423056

LINDSAY, Alexandra Jane (Sandra). b 43. CITC 90. **d** 93 **p** 94. Lic to Offic *K, E & A* 93-94; NSM Bailieborough w Knockbride, Shercock and Mullagh 94-97; NSM Kilmore w Ballintemple, Kildallon etc from 97. *Clementstown House, Cootehill, Co Cavan, Irish Republic* Tel (00353) (49) 555 2207 Fax as telephone

LINDSAY, Anthony. b 38. Trin Coll Bris DipHE93 St Jo Coll Nottm CertCS88. **d** 89 **p** 90. CMS 76-92; Sierra Leone 88-92; C Rainham w Wennington *Chelmsf* 92-96; R Quendon w Rickling and Wicken Bonhunt etc from 96. *The Rectory, Cambridge Road, Quendon, Saffron Walden CB11 3XJ* Tel (01799) 543238 E-mail tony@quendonrectory.freeserve.co.uk

LINDSAY, Ashley. *See* LINDSAY, Robert Ashley Charles

LINDSAY, Cecil. b 43. Iona Coll (NY) BBA68. CITC 85. **d** 88 **p** 88. NSM Kilmore w Ballintemple, Kildallon etc *K, E & A* 88-90; Lic to Offic 90-91; NSM Roscommon w Donamon, Rathcline, Kilkeevin etc 91-96; NSM Killeshandra w Killegar

and Derrylane 96-02; NSM Mohill w Farnaught, Aughavas, Oughteragh etc from 02; Dioc Registrar from 97. *Clementstown House, Cootehill, Co Cavan, Irish Republic* Tel (00353) (49) 555 2207 Fax as telephone

LINDSAY, David Macintyre. b 46. Trin Hall Cam BA68 MA72 Ox Univ DipTh70. Cuddesdon Coll 68. **d** 71 **p** 72. C Gosforth All SS *Newc* 71-74; C Keele *Lich* 74-78; Perm to Offic *St E* 79-80; Chapl Haberdashers' Aske's Sch Elstree from 80; Lic to Offic *St Alb* from 80. *36 Cranbourne Drive, Harpenden AL5 1RU* Tel (01582) 765660

LINDSAY, Eric Graham. b 30. Witwatersrand Univ BA51 Lon Univ DipAdEd78 MA80 Heythrop Coll Lon DipTh82. Coll of Resurr Mirfield 55. **d** 57 **p** 59. C Stella *Dur* 57-58; C W Hartlepool St Aid 58-60; Grenada 60-61; Perm to Offic *Win* 61-65; Perm to Offic *Roch* 65-72; Perm to Offic *Chelmsf* 72-84; C Stepney St Dunstan and All SS *Lon* 84-85; P-in-c Stepney St Dunstan LEP 84-85; R Bridge of Weir *Glas* 85-98; R Kilmacolm 85-98. *Endure Fort, 1 Rannoch Road, Kilmacolm PA13 4LT* Tel (01505) 874668

LINDSAY, John Carruthers. b 50. Edin Univ MA72 BD82. Edin Th Coll 79. **d** 82 **p** 83. C Broughty Ferry *Bre* 82-84; C Edin St Hilda *Edin* 84-85; TP 85-88; C Edin St Fillan 84-85; TP 85-88; R N Berwick from 88; R Gullane from 88. *The Rectory, 2 May Terrace, North Berwick EH39 4BA* Tel (01620) 892154 Fax as telephone E-mail jclscot@aol.com

LINDSAY, Keith Malcolm. b 18. Adelaide Univ BA39. ACT ThL41. **d** 41 **p** 42. Australia 41-49 and from 53; C N Adelaide Ch Ch 41-42; Chapl Kensington Miss 42-44; Brotherhood of St Jo 44-47; P-in-c Tailem Bend 47-49; C W Derby St Jo *Liv* 50-53; R Yorketown 53-57; RD Yorke Peninsula 54-57; R Adelaide St Mary Magd 57-67; Chapl R Adelaide Hosp 58-65; Chapl Magill Reform Inst 66-67; R Ararat 67-71; R Port Fairy 71-74; P-in-c Maylands w Firle 74-79; R Toorak Gardens 79-83; rtd 83; Lic to Offic *Adelaide* from 83; Chapl Glenside Hosp 87-90. *2 Canterbury Avenue, Trinity Gardens, S Australia 5068* Tel (0061) (8) 8332 9228 E-mail kml@bns.com.au

LINDSAY (née CLEALL), Mrs Mary Jane Anne. b 54. Keele Univ BA77 Herts Univ PGCE92. St Alb and Ox Min Course 00. **d** 03. NSM Chipping Barnet w Arkley *St Alb* from 03. *36 Cranbourne Drive, Harpenden AL5 1RU*

LINDSAY, Richard John. b 46. Sarum & Wells Th Coll 74. **d** 78 **p** 79. C Aldwick *Chich* 78-81; C Almondbury *Wakef* 81-82; C Almondbury w Farnley Tyas 82-84; V Mossley *Man* from 84. *The Vicarage, Stamford Street, Mossley, Ashton-under-Lyne OL5 0LP* Tel (01457) 832219

LINDSAY, Canon Richard John Alan. b 24. TCD BA46 BD52. **d** 49 **p** 50. C Denton Holme *Carl* 49-52; CMS Burundi 52-64; Chapl and Tutor CMS Tr Coll Chislehurst 65-68; R Chich St Pancras and St Jo *Chich* 68-74; Chapl Maisons-Laffitte *Eur* 74-82; Can Brussels Cathl 81-88; Chapl The Hague w Leiden and Voorschoten 82-89; rtd 89; Perm to Offic *Heref* 88-01; *Portsm* from 01. *The Bothy, Hewshott Lane, Liphook GU30 7SU* Tel (01428) 723645

LINDSAY, Canon Robert. b 16. St Jo Coll Dur BA37 DipTh38 MA40. **d** 39 **p** 40. C Gateshead St Mary *Dur* 39-43; P-in-c Sacriston 43-45; P-in-c Benfieldside 45-46; V Lanercost w Kirkcambeck *Carl* 46-55; V Hawkshead and Low Wray 55-70; R Dean 70-74; RD Derwent 70-81; Hon Can Carl Cathl 72-81; V Loweswater w Buttermere 74-81; rtd 81; Perm to Offic *Ex* from 81. *58 Primley Road, Sidmouth EX10 9LF* Tel (01395) 577882

LINDSAY, Robert Ashley Charles. b 43. Leeds Univ BA66 Ex Univ BPhil81. Coll of Resurr Mirfield 66. **d** 68 **p** 69. C Mill Hill Jo Keble Ch *Lon* 68-72; C Sherborne w Castleton and Lillington *Sarum* 73-78; Chapl Coldharbour Hosp Dorset 73-78; Perm to Offic *Leic* 87-92. *79 Castledine Street, Loughborough LE11 2DX* Tel (01509) 264360

LINDSAY, Sandra. *See* LINDSAY, Alexandra Jane

LINDSAY-PARKINSON, Michael. b 28. Edin Th Coll 66. **d** 67 **p** 68. C Edin Ch Ch *Edin* 67-70; C Helensburgh *Glas* 70-72; R Lockerbie 72-83; R Annan 72-83; S Africa 83-88; V Alsager St Mary *Ches* 88-93; rtd 93; Perm to Offic *Ches* 93-98. *10 Cherry Tree Avenue, Church Lawton, Stoke-on-Trent ST7 3EL* Tel (01270) 875574

LINDSEY, Archdeacon of. *Vacant*

LINES, Canon Andrew John. b 60. Univ Coll Dur BA82. All Nations Chr Coll DipMM90. **d** 97 **p** 98. Paraguay 91-99; Dir Caleb Bible Cen 91-99; SAMS 97-00; Hon Can Paraguay from 00; Gen Sec Crosslinks from 00. *59 Woodside Road, New Malden KT3 3AW* Tel (020) 8942 2179 E-mail gensec@crosslinks.org

LINES, Graham Martin. b 55. **d** 99 **p** 00. C Crosby *Linc* 99-02; C Bottesford w Ashby 02-03; TV from 03. *Holy Spirit Vicarage, 180 Enderby Road, Scunthorpe DN17 2JX* Tel (01724) 842083

LINES, Nicholas David John. b 64. St Jo Coll Nottm 94. **d** 96 **p** 97. C Burton All SS w Ch Ch *Lich* 96-01; P-in-c Rodbourne Cheney *Bris* 01-02; V from 02. *St Mary's Rectory, 298 Cheney Manor Road, Swindon SN2 2PF* Tel (01793) 522379 E-mail nick.lines@lineone.net

LINFORD, Preb John Kenneth. b 31. Liv Univ BA52. Chich Th Coll 54. **d** 56 **p** 57. C Stoke upon Trent *Lich* 56-61; V Tunstall Ch Ch 61-70; V Sedgley All SS 70-78; Chapl Chase Hosp Cannock

78-91; TR Cannock *Lich* 78-91; V Hatherton 80-91; Preb Lich Cathl 88-98; rtd 91; Perm to Offic *Lich* 91-00. *16 School Lane, Hill Ridware, Rugeley WS15 3QN* Tel (01543) 492831

LING, Adrian Roger. b 66. Goldsmiths' Coll Lon BA89 Leeds Univ BA02. Coll of Resurr Mirfield 00. **d** 02 **p** 03. C Mill End and Heronsgate w W Hyde *St Alb* from 02. *St Thomas's House, 46 Chalfont Road, Rickmansworth WD3 9TB* Tel (01923) 771022 E-mail aling@myrealbox.com

LING, Andrew Joyner. b 35. ACP69 St Luke's Coll Ex TCert63 Open Univ BA80. SW Minl Tr Course 83. **d** 86 **p** 87. NSM St Dominic, Landulph and St Mellion w Pillaton *Truro* 86-90; C Saltash 90-94; TV 94-97; Chapl Montreux w Gstaad *Eur* 98-03; rtd 03. *Martinets, Chemin des Martinets 7, 1872 Troistorrents, Switzerland* Tel (0041) (24) 477 2408

LING, Timothy Charles. b 61. Ex Univ BA85 Selw Coll Cam BA91. Ridley Hall Cam CTM92. **d** 92 **p** 93. C Gerrards Cross and Fulmer *Ox* 92-96; C Woking St Pet *Guildf* 96-00; V Bathford *B & W* from 00. *The Vicarage, 27 Church Street, Bathford, Bath BA1 7RS* Tel (01225) 858325 E-mail lingtim@hotmail.com

LINGARD, Colin. b 36. Kelham Th Coll 58. **d** 63 **p** 64. C Middlesbrough St Martin *York* 63-66; C Stainton-in-Cleveland 66-71; V Eskdaleside w Ugglebarnby 71-77; P-in-c Redcar w Kirkleatham 77; V Kirkleatham 78-86; RD Guisborough 83-86; V Linc St Botolph *Linc* 86-89; Dioc Dir of Readers 86-89; R Washington *Dur* 89-93; P-in-c Middleton St Geo 93-97; R 97-01; Chapl Teesside Airport from 97; rtd 01. *29 Belgrave Terrace, Hurworth Place, Darlington DL2 2DW* Tel 07752-179418 (mobile)

LINGARD, Keith Patrick. b 30. AKC53. **d** 54 **p** 55. C Bedford Park *Lon* 54-56; C Ruislip St Martin 56-58; C Kempston *St Alb* 58-63; Metrop Area Sec UMCA 63-65; V S Farnborough *Guildf* 65-75; R Glaston w Bisbrooke *Pet* 75-76; R Morcott w Glaston and Bisbrooke 77-95; rtd 95; Perm to Offic *Linc* from 95. *13 Woodside East, Thurlby, Bourne PE10 0HT* Tel (01778) 425572

LINGS, George William. b 49. Nottm Univ BTh74 Ox Univ PGCE75. Lambeth Hon MLitt93 St Jo Coll Nottm 70. **d** 75 **p** 76. C Harold Wood *Chelmsf* 75-78; C Reigate St Mary *S'wark* 78-85; V Deal St Geo *Cant* 85-97; First Dir CA Sheff Cen for Ch Planting and Evang from 97; NSM Norfolk Park St Leonard CD *Sheff* from 97. *The Sheffield Centre, 50 Cavendish Street, Sheffield S3 7RZ* Tel 0114-272 7451
E-mail g.lings@sheffieldcentre.org.uk

LINGWOOD, Preb David Peter. b 51. Lon Univ BEd73 Southn Univ BTh80. Sarum & Wells Th Coll 75. **d** 78 **p** 79. C Ashford St Hilda *Lon* 78-81; C Astwood Bank w Crabbs Cross *Worc* 81; TV Redditch, The Ridge 81-86; TR Blakenall Heath *Lich* 86-96; V Rushall from 96; RD Walsall from 98; Preb Lich Cathl from 02. *Rushall Vicarage, 10 Tetley Avenue, Walsall WS4 2HE* Tel (01922) 624677 E-mail david@dplingwood.freeserve.co.uk

LINKENS, Timothy Martin. b 67. Strathclyde Univ MEng90. Wycliffe Hall Ox BTh99. **d** 99 **p** 00. C Blackheath St Jo *S'wark* 99-03; V Kidbrooke St Nic from 03. *66A Whetstone Road, London SE3 8PZ* Tel (020) 8856 6317

LINN, Frederick Hugh. b 37. Em Coll Cam BA61 MA65. Ripon Hall Ox 61. **d** 63 **p** 64. C Bramhall *Ches* 63-68; V Liscard St Mary 68-71; V Liscard St Mary w St Columba 71-74; V Wybunbury 74-82; R Eccleston and Pulford 82-98; rtd 98; Perm to Offic *Ches* from 98. *4 Stonewalls, Rossett, Wrexham LL12 0LG* Tel (01244) 571942 *or* (01407) 810372

LINNEGAR, George Leonard. b 33. CGA. Kelham Th Coll 63. **d** 62 **p** 63. C Wellingborough St Mary *Pet* 62-65; Lic to Offic *Lich* 65-69; Lic to Offic *B & W* 69-80; Hon C Lewes All SS, St Anne, St Mich and St Thos *Chich* 80-86; C 87-99; rtd 99; Perm to Offic *Chich* from 99. *20 Morris Road, Lewes BN7 2AT* Tel (01273) 478145

LINNEY, Barry James. b 64. Spurgeon's Coll BD97 Anglia Poly Univ MA02. Westcott Ho Cam 99. **d** 01 **p** 02. C Chingford SS Pet and Paul *Chelmsf* from 01. *2 Sunnyside Drive, London E4 7DZ* Tel (020) 8529 3929
E-mail barry-linney@arising.freeserve.co.uk

LINNEY, the Ven Gordon Charles Scott. b 39. CITC 66. **d** 69 **p** 70. C Agherton *Conn* 69-72; Min Can Down Cathl *D & D* 72-75; V Dublin St Cath w St Jas *D & G* 75-80; Preb Tipperkevin St Patr Cathl Dublin 77-80; I Glenageary *D & G* from 80; Adn Dublin from 88; Lect CITC 89-93. *St Paul's Vicarage, Silchester Road, Glenageary, Co Dublin, Irish Republic* Tel (00353) (1) 280 1616 Fax 280 9459 E-mail glinney@eircom.net

LINNING, Alexander. b 19. Birm Univ BA40 Lon Univ BD42. **d** 61 **p** 62. Hon C W Bridgford *S'well* 61-80; Lic to Offic 80-95. *7 Kingston Road, Nottingham NG2 7AQ* Tel 0115-981 2959

LINTERN, John. b 61. Linc Th Coll BTh93. **d** 93 **p** 94. C Preston on Tees *Dur* 93-96; P-in-c W Pelton from 96; P-in-c Pelton from 99; Asst Dioc Youth Adv 96-99. *The Vicarage, West Pelton, Stanley DH9 6RT* Tel 0191-370 2146 Fax 0797-111 4359
E-mail john.lintern@durham.anglican.org

LINTHICUM, James Douglas. b 58. Towson State Univ (USA) BSc81 Leeds Univ MA00. Wesley Th Sem Washington MDiv86. **d** 01 **p** 02. Chapl Barnet and Chase Farm Hosps NHS Trust from

01; NSM Monken Hadley *Lon* from 01. *102 Bells Hill, Barnet EN5 2SQ* Tel (020) 8441 5319 Mobile 07931-562189
E-mail jlinth5481@aol.com

LINTON, Alan Ross. b 28. Lon Univ DipTh60. St Aid Birkenhead 57. **d** 60 **p** 61. C Blundellsands St Nic *Liv* 60-62; C Southport St Phil 62-63; C Aigburth 63-66; V Glazebury 66-67; C Formby St Pet 67-69; C Douglas *Blackb* 69-71; P-in-c Appley Bridge All SS CD 71-76; P-in-c Scorton 76-85; P-in-c Calder Vale w Admarsh 76-85; R Hoole 85-93; rtd 93; Perm to Offic *Blackb* from 93. *12 Clive Road, Penwortham, Preston PR1 0AT* Tel (01772) 747813

LINTON, Mrs Angela Margaret. b 45. St Alb and Ox Min Course 97. **d** 00 **p** 01. NSM Langtree *Ox* from 00. *10 Yew Tree Court, Goring, Reading RG8 9HF* Tel and fax (01491) 874236 Mobile 07884-346552

LINTON, Joseph Edmund. b 19. St Andr Univ MA46. Sarum Th Coll 46. **d** 48 **p** 49. C Monkseaton St Mary *Newc* 48-53; CF (TA) 50-54; C-in-c Lynemouth St Aid CD *Newc* 53-59; V Beltingham w Henshaw 59-93; rtd 93; Perm to Offic *Newc* from 93. *4 Dipton Close, Eastwood Grange, Hexham NE46 1UG* Tel (01434) 601457

LINTON, Sydney. b 07. Pemb Coll Ox BA30 MA34. Westcott Ho Cam 31. **d** 32 **p** 33. C Morley St Pet w Churwell *Wakef* 32-39; Hon Chapl Helsinki w Moscow 48-51; C Limpsfield and Titsey *S'wark* 51-57; V Barnes H Trin 57-71; R Codford *Sarum* 71-73; R Upton Lovell 71-73; R Codford, Upton Lovell and Stockton 73-77; rtd 77. *Lord Harris Court, Wokingham RG41 5EA* Tel 0118-978 7496

LINTOTT, William Ince. b 36. St Cath Coll Cam BA58. Ely Th Coll 58. **d** 60 **p** 61. C Brighton St Wilfrid *Chich* 60-62; C Chingford SS Pet and Paul *Chelmsf* 62-66; Chapl Fulbourn Hosp Cam 66-73; Lic to Offic *Ely* 66-97; rtd 01. *7 Haverhill Road, Stapleford, Cambridge CB2 5BX* Tel (01223) 842008

LINZEY, Prof Andrew. b 52. K Coll Lon BD73 PhD86 AKC73 Lambeth DD01 Univ of Wales (Cardiff) DPS74. St Aug Coll Cant 75. **d** 75 **p** 76. C Charlton-by-Dover SS Pet and Paul *Cant* 75-77; Chapl and Lect Th NE Surrey Coll of Tech 77-81; Chapl Essex Univ *Chelmsf* 81-92; Dir of Studies Cen for Study of Th 87-92; Sen Research Fell Mansf Coll Ox 92-00; Tutor Chr Ethics 93-00; Special Prof Th Nottm Univ 92-96; Special Prof St Xavier Univ Chicago from 96; Hon Prof Birm Univ from 97; Sen Research Fell Blackfriars Hall Ox from 00. *91 Iffley Road, Oxford OX4 1EG* Tel (01865) 201565 E-mail andrewlinzey@aol.com

LIONEL, Brother. *See* PEIRIS, Lionel James Harold

LIPP-NATHANIEL, Julie Christiane. b 41. Melbourne Univ BA63 MA72 DipSocSc63 Lon Univ 93. **d** 95 **p** 95. Tutor United Coll of Ascension Selly Oak 96-99; Lic to Offic *Birm* 96-99; Regional Desk Officer S Asia & Middle East USPG from 99; Perm to Offic *S'wark* from 00. *USPG, Partnership House, 157 Waterloo Road, London SE1 8XA* Tel (020) 7928 8681 Fax 7928 2371 E-mail julieln@uspg.org.uk

LIPPIATT, Michael Charles. b 39. Oak Hill Th Coll BD71. **d** 71 **p** 72. C Ardsley *Sheff* 71-74; C Lenton *S'well* 74-78; V Jesmond H Trin *Newc* 78-96; rtd 96. *69 Lansdowne Crescent, Stanwix, Carlisle CA3 9ES* Tel (01228) 537080

LIPPIETT, Peter Vernon. b 47. Lon Univ MB, BS73 DRCOG79 MRCGP80. Ripon Coll Cuddesdon 86. **d** 88 **p** 89. C Pinner *Lon* 88-91; V Twyford and Owslebury and Morestead *Win* 91-99; Warden Rydal Hall *Carl* 99-03; P-in-c Rydal 99-03; Dioc Spirituality Adv *Portsm* from 03. *50 Penny Street, Portsmouth PO1 2NL* Tel (023) 9282 6120

LIPSCOMB, Ian Craig. b 30. ACT ThL67 Wells Th Coll 61. **d** 63 **p** 64. C Feltham *Lon* 63-65; Australia from 65; rtd 94. *South Hill, Garroorigang Road, PO Box 118, Goulburn, NSW, Australia 2580* Tel (0061) (2) 4821 9591 Fax as telephone

LIPSCOMB, Timothy William. b 52. Chich Th Coll 82. **d** 85 **p** 86. C Sevenoaks St Jo *Roch* 85-89; C Stanningley St Thos *Ripon* 89-92; V Armley w New Wortley from 92; AD Armley from 98. *Armley Vicarage, Wesley Road, Leeds LS12 1SR* Tel 0113-263 8620

LIPSCOMBE, Brian. b 37. Bris Univ BA62. Tyndale Hall Bris 62. **d** 64 **p** 65. C Eccleston Ch Ch *Liv* 64-66; C Halliwell St Pet *Man* 66-67; C Frogmore *St Alb* 69-72; V Richmond Ch Ch *S'wark* 72-75; TV Mortlake w E Sheen 76-80; P-in-c Streatham Vale H Redeemer 80-85; V 85-91; R Norris Bank *Man* 91-96; V Droylsden St Martin 96-02; rtd 02. *15 St Anne's Drive, Leeds LS4 2SA* Tel 0113-275 1893

LISK, Stewart. b 62. Regent's Park Coll Ox BA84 MA88 Univ of Wales (Cardiff) DPS87. St Mich Coll Llan 86. **d** 88 **p** 89. C Glan Ely *Llan* 88-92; Chapl Cardiff Inst of HE 92-96; Chapl Welsh Coll of Music and Drama 92-96; Asst Chapl Univ of Wales (Cardiff) 92-96; V Glan Ely from 96. *Church House, Grand Avenue, Ely, Cardiff CF5 4HX* Tel (029) 2059 1633

LISMORE, Dean of. *See* BEARE, The Very Revd William

LISTER, Anthony Galen. b 27. Hull Univ DipArch53 RIBA54. NEOC 80. **d** 83 **p** 84. Hon C Anlaby St Pet *York* 83-87. *Hunter's Colt, Glenborrodale, Ardnamurchan PH36 4JP* Tel (01972) 500219

LISTER, David Ian. b 26. Roch Th Coll 61. **d** 62 **p** 64. C Scarborough St Mary w Ch Ch, St Paul and St Thos *York* 62-66;

C Buttershaw St Aid *Bradf* 66-68; V Tufnell Park St Geo *Lon* 68-83; V Tufnell Park St Geo and All SS 83-92; rtd 92; Perm to Offic *York* from 92. *8 Stonethwaite, Woodthorpe, York YO24 2SY* Tel (01904) 704586

LISTER, Mrs Jennifer Grace. b 44. Totley Hall Coll CertEd65. Nor Ord Course 87. **d** 92 **p** 94. C Cowgate *Newc* 92-95; C Lich St Mary w St Mich *Lich* 95-96; C Wall 95-96; P-in-c Yoxall from 96; Asst P The Ridwares and Kings Bromley from 96. *The Rectory, Savey Lane, Yoxall, Burton-on-Trent DE13 8PD* Tel (01543) 472528 E-mail jenny.lister@talk21.com

LISTER (née AISBITT), Mrs Joanne. b 69. St Jo Coll Dur BA91. St Steph Ho Ox 91. **d** 93. NSM Mill End and Heronsgate w W Hyde *St Alb* 93-96. *Address temp unknown* E-mail listerwilliam@hotmail.com

LISTER, The Very Revd John Field. b 16. Keble Coll Ox BA38 MA42. Cuddesdon Coll 38. **d** 39 **p** 41. C Radford *Cov* 39-44; C Cov St Jo 44-45; V Huddersfield St Jo *Wakef* 45-54; V Brighouse 54-71; Adn Halifax 61-72; Chapl to The Queen 66-72; RD Wakef 72-80; Provost Wakef 72-82; rtd 82; Perm to Offic *Cant* from 82. *5 Larkscliff Court, The Parade, Birchington CT7 9NB* Tel (01843) 42543

LISTER, Joseph Hugh. b 38. Tyndale Hall Bris 61. **d** 64 **p** 65. C Pemberton St Mark Newtown *Liv* 64-68; Hon C Braintree *Chelmsf* 68-71; C Darfield *Sheff* 71-73; P-in-c Sheff St Swithun 73-76; TV Sheff Manor 76-80; P-in-c Burston *Nor* 80-81; P-in-c Tivetshall 80-81; P-in-c Gissing 80-81; TR Winfarthing w Shelfanger 80-81; R Winfarthing w Shelfanger w Burston w Gissing etc 81-88; P-in-c Sandon, Wallington and Rushden w Clothall *St Alb* 88-89; R 89-93; R Nether and Over Seale *Derby* 93-96; V Lullington 93-96; R Seale and Lullington 96-98; RD Repton 96-98; Dean Ndola Zambia 99-02; rtd 02; Hon C Hartington, Biggin and Earl Sterndale *Derby* from 02. *The New Vicarage, Hide Lane, Hartington, Buxton SK17 0AP* Tel (01298) 84280 E-mail jandglister@tesco.net

LISTER, Miss Mary Phyllis. b 28. St Andr Ho Portsm 52. **dss** 80 **d** 87. Inkberrow w Cookhill and Kington w Dormston *Worc* 80-82; Ancaster *Linc* 82-87; C 87-88; rtd 88; Perm to Offic *Worc* 88-00. *6 Stuart Court, High Street, Kibworth, Leicester LE8 0LR* Tel 0116-279 3763

LISTER, Peter. b 42. Leeds Univ BA64 Newc Univ PGCE75. Coll of Resurr Mirfield 63. **d** 65 **p** 66. C Monkseaton St Pet *Newc* 65-68; C Cramlington 68-70; Hon C 71-78; C Morpeth 79-83; V Shilbottle 83-88; Asst Dioc Dir of Educn 83-88; Dir of Educn 88-95; Hon Can Newc Cathl 88-95; Dioc Dir of Educn *Lich* from 95. *The Rectory, Savey Lane, Yoxall, Burton-on-Trent DE13 8PD* Tel (01543) 472528 *or* 306030 Fax 306039 E-mail peter.lister@lichfield.anglican.org

LISTER, William Bernard. b 67. Keble Coll Ox BA88 MA92. St Steph Ho Ox BA91. **d** 92 **p** 93. C Mill End and Heronsgate w W Hyde *St Alb* 92-96; CF from 96. *c/o MOD Chaplains (Army)* Tel (01980) 615804 Fax 615800 E-mail listerwilliam@hotmail.com

LISTON, Scott Carnie. b 62. Edin Univ BD87. Edin Th Coll. **d** 88 **p** 88. C Edin St Martin *Edin* 88-91; C Edin St Luke 88-91; C Edin St Dav 91-92; Chapl HM YOI Guys Marsh 92-97; Perm to Offic *B & W* 92-97; Chapl HM YOI Onley 97-03; Chapl HM Pris Woodhill from 03. *The Chaplain's Office, HM Prison Woodhill, Wisewood Road, Milton Keynes MK4 4DA* Tel (01908) 722000

LITHERLAND, Norman Richard. b 30. Lon Univ BA51 BA52 Man Univ MEd72. N Ord Course 78. **d** 81 **p** 82. NSM Flixton St Mich *Man* 81-94; rtd 94; Perm to Offic *Man* from 94. *1 Overdale Crescent, Urmston, Manchester M41 5GR* Tel 0161-748 4243

LITHERLAND, Terence. b 46. LNSM course 90. **d** 93 **p** 94. OLM Horwich and Rivington *Man* from 93. *61 Tomlinson Street, Horwich, Bolton BL6 5QR* Tel (01204) 692201

LITJENS, Shan Elizabeth. b 55. **d** 95. C Fareham SS Pet and Paul *Portsm* 95-96; C Fareham H Trin 96-99; NSM Hedge End St Jo *Win* from 00. *11 Abraham Close, Botley, Southampton SO30 2RQ* Tel (01489) 796321 E-mail shanlitjens@aol.com

LITTLE, Andrew. b 27. Open Univ BA83 UEA BA03. AKC51. **d** 52 **p** 53. C Fulham All SS *Lon* 52-54; C Epsom St Barn *Guildf* 54-61; V Northwood *Lich* 61-72; P-in-c Hixon 72-86; V Stowe 72-86; V Hixon w Stowe-by-Chartley 86-89; rtd 89; Perm to Offic *Nor* from 89; Hon PV Nor Cathl from 93. *5 Damocles Court, Norwich NR2 1HN* Tel (01603) 662241

LITTLE, Ms Christine. b 60. Lanc Univ BA83. St Jo Coll Nottm Dip Th Studies 90 DPS91. **d** 91 **p** 94. Par Dn Meltham *Wakef* 91-94; C Hatcham St Jas *S'wark* 94-99; P-in-c from 99. *St James's Vicarage, St James's, London SE14 6AD* Tel (020) 8691 2167

LITTLE, David John. b 65. Oak Hill Th Coll BA94. **d** 94 **p** 95. C Chislehurst Ch Ch *Roch* 94-98; TV Bath Twerton-on-Avon *B & W* 98; Dep Chapl HM Pris Bris 98-99; Chapl HM Pris Reading from 99. *The Chaplain's Office, HM Prison, Forbury Road, Reading RG1 3HY* Tel (01734) 587031 Fax 591058

LITTLE, Derek Peter. b 50. St Jo Coll Dur BA72 DipTh75. Trin Coll Bris. **d** 75 **p** 76. C Bradley *Wakef* 75-78; C Kidderminster St Geo *Worc* 78-82; V Lepton *Wakef* 82-85; E Regional Sec CPAS 85-88; Lic to Offic *Ely* 86-88; V Canonbury St Steph *Lon*

88-96; R Bedhampton *Portsm* 96-99. *61 Hart Plain Lane, Waterlooville PO8 8RG*

LITTLE, Canon George Nelson. b 39. CITC 70. **d** 72 **p** 73. C Portadown St Mark *Arm* 72-76; I Newtownhamilton w Ballymoyer and Belleek 76-80; I Aghaderg w Donaghmore *D & D* 80-82; I Aghaderg w Donaghmore and Scarva from 82; Can Dromore Cathl from 93; Treas from 93; Chan from 03. *Aghaderg Rectory, 32 Banbridge Road, Loughbrickland, Banbridge BT32 3YB* Tel (028) 4062 4073

LITTLE, Herbert Edwin Samuel. b 21. Lon Univ BA54 BD68. NEOC 79. **d** 80 **p** 81. NSM Dur St Cuth *Dur* 80-88; rtd 88. *3 Whitesmocks Avenue, Durham DH1 4HP* Tel 0191-384 2897

LITTLE, Ian Dawtry Torrance. b 49. Keele Univ BEd72. SW Minl Tr Course 81. **d** 85 **p** 86. NSM St Stythians w Perranarworthal and Gwennap *Truro* 85-97; NSM Chacewater w St Day and Carharrack from 97. *Kernyk, Crellow Fields, Stithians, Truro TR3 7RE*

LITTLE, James Harry. b 57. York Univ BA79 Birm Univ DipTh86. Qu Coll Birm 84. **d** 87 **p** 88. C Wollaton *S'well* 87-90; C N Wheatley, W Burton, Bole, Saundby, Sturton etc 90-93; R E Markham w Askham, Headon w Upton and Grove from 93. *The Rectory, Lincoln Road, East Markham, Newark NG22 0SH* Tel (01777) 871731 E-mail revjlittle@aol.com

LITTLE, Nigel James. b 73. Middx Univ BA93. Oak Hill Th Coll 98. **d** 01 **p** 02. C Highgate St Mich *Lon* from 01. *17 Bisham Gardens, London N6 6DJ* Tel (020) 8340 7676 E-mail nigel_little@yahoo.com

LITTLE, Rebekah Mary. b 70. Oak Hill Th Coll. **d** 97. NSM Chislehurst Ch Ch *Roch* 97-98; NSM Bath Twerton-on-Avon *B & W* 98; Perm to Offic *Ox* from 00. *Address withheld by request*

LITTLE, Stephen. b 59. LNSM course 95. **d** 98 **p** 99. OLM Everton St Geo *Liv* from 98. *110 Granton Road, Anfield, Liverpool L5 6QW* Tel 0151-260 5031

LITTLE, Canon Stephen Clifford. b 47. Man Univ MEd81. AKC72. **d** 72 **p** 73. C Grange St Andr *Ches* 72-73; C E Runcorn w Halton 73-75; P-in-c Newbold *Man* 75-77; P-in-c Broughton and Milton Keynes *Ox* 77-82; Sector Min Milton Keynes Chr Coun 77-84; TR Warwick *Cov* 84-93; R Harvington and Norton and Lenchwick *Worc* 93-96; R Harvington 96-98; Exec Officer Dioc Bd for Ch and Soc *Man* from 98; Exec Officer Dioc Bd for Min and Soc from 01; Hon Can Man Cathl from 00. *St James's Vicarage, Lower Leigh Road, Westhoughton, Bolton BL5 2EH* Tel (01942) 859251 *or* 0161-832 5253 Fax 0161-832 2869 E-mail stephenlittle@manchester.anglican.org

LITTLEFAIR, David. b 38. ACCA71 FCCA85 Lon Univ BD79. Trin Coll Bris 76. **d** 79 **p** 80. C Bursledon *Win* 79-82; V Charles w Plymouth St Matthias *Ex* 82-89; Warden Lee Abbey Internat Students' Club Kensington 89-94; V Malmesbury w Westport and Brokenborough *Bris* 94-03; rtd 03. *6 Matford Mews, Matford, Exeter EX2 8XP* Tel (01392) 218784

LITTLEFORD, Peter John. b 40. St Mark & St Jo Coll Lon CertEd63 ACP65 Birkbeck Coll Lon BSc70 Lon Inst of Educn DipEd73 MA76. St Alb and Ox Min Course 96. **d** 99 **p** 00. NSM Bedf St Mark *St Alb* from 99; Chapl De Montfort Univ *Leic* from 99. *15 Harrington Drive, Putnoe, Bedford MK41 8DB* Tel (01234) 356645 E-mail plittlef@dmu.ac.uk

LITTLEJOHN, Keith Douglas. b 59. Ripon Coll Cuddesdon BTh03. **d** 03. C Horsham *Chich* from 03. *187 Comptons Lane, Horsham RH13 6BW* Tel (01403) 250329 Mobile 07905-595041 E-mail keithdlj@aol.com

LITTLER, Eric Raymond. b 36. Lon Univ DipTh67 AMIC93. Roch Th Coll 65. **d** 68 **p** 69. C Hatfield Hyde *St Alb* 68-73; Chapl Welwyn Garden City Hosp 70-73; TV Pemberton St Jo *Liv* 73-78; Chapl Billinge Hosp Wigan 76-81; V Pemberton St Fran Kitt Green *Liv* 78-81; V White Notley, Faulkbourne and Cressing *Chelmsf* 81-88; V Westcliff St Andr 88-96; Chapl Westcliff Hosp 88-96; Chapl Southend HA 89-96; R E and W Tilbury and Linford *Chelmsf* 96-98; Chapl Orsett Hosp 96-98; RD Thurrock *Chelmsf* 96-98; R Gt Oakley w Wix and Wrabness 98-02; Chapl Essex Rivers Healthcare NHS Trust 98-02; rtd 02; Perm to Offic *Sarum* from 98; *Chelmsf* and *B & W* from 02. *Minster Hall, 1 Pound Row, Warminster BA12 8NQ* Tel (01985) 218818

LITTLER, Keith Trevor. b 35. Lon Univ BSc(Soc)63 TCert64 York Univ MA82 Hull Univ PhD89 Westmr Coll Ox MTh98. St D Dioc Tr Course 89 St Mich Coll Llan 94. **d** 92 **p** 93. NSM Betws w Ammanford *St D* 92-94; C 94; R Pendine w Llanmiloe and Eglwys Gymyn w Marros from 94; RD St Clears from 98. *The Rectory, Pendine, Carmarthen SA33 4PD* Tel (01994) 453405

LITTLER, Malcolm Kenneth. b 34. Univ of Wales (Lamp) BA55. **d** 57 **p** 58. C Llanelli *St D* 57-60; C Llandeilo Fawr 60-61; R Puncheston, Lt Newcastle and Castle Bythe 61-64; R Lamp Velfrey 64-68; V Llanwnda w Goodwick and Manorowen 68-74; V Llanfynydd 74-78; V The Suttons w Tydd *Linc* 87-90; V Graffoe 90-94; rtd 94; Perm to Offic *Linc* from 94. *Ivy Cottage, 11 Chapel Lane, Lincoln LN1 3BA*

LITTLEWOOD, Alan James. b 51. Man Poly BEd77. LNSM course 91. **d** 95 **p** 96. OLM Gosberton *Linc* 95-97; OLM Gosberton, Gosberton Clough and Quadring 97-01; C Bourne 01-03; P-in-c Leasingham from 03; P-in-c Cranwell from 03. *The*

Rectory, 3 Moor Lane, Leasingham, Sleaford NG34 8JN Tel (01529) 309239 E-mail alan@littlewood35.freeserve.co.uk

LITTLEWOOD, Alistair David. b 68. St Cath Coll Ox BA89. Qu Coll Birm 93. **d** 96 **p** 97. C Keyworth *S'well* 96-00; Chapl Birm Univ *Birm* from 00. *258 Mary Vale Road, Bournville, Birmingham B30 1PJ* Tel 0121-458 7432 Fax 414 7002 E-mail a.littlewood@bham.ac.uk

LITTLEWOOD, Miss Jacqueline Patricia. b 52. Linc Th Coll 77. dss 80 **d** 87 **p** 94. Crayford *Roch* 80-84; Gravesend H Family w Ifield 84-87; Par Dn 87-93; rtd 93; NSM Gravesend St Aid *Roch* from 93. *25 Beltana Drive, Gravesend DA12 4BT* Tel (01474) 560106

LITTLEWOOD, John Richard. b 37. Ridley Hall Cam 69. **d** 72 **p** 73. C Rushden w Newton Bromswold *Pet* 72-75; Chapl Scargill Ho 75-77; V Werrington *Pet* 77-91; V Highbury Ch Ch w St Jo and St Sav Lon 91-02; rtd 02; Perm to Offic *York* from 03. *8 Aldersyde Court, York YO24 1QN* Tel (01904) 778879

LITTLEWOOD, Philip Nigel. b 59. Sarum & Wells Th Coll 87. **d** 90 **p** 91. C Frome St Jo and St Mary *B & W* 90-95; P-in-c Keinton Mandeville w Lydford-on-Fosse etc 95-00; R Wheathill Priory Gp of Par from 00. *Wheathill Priory Rectory, Church Street, Keinton Mandeville, Somerton TA11 6ER* Tel (01458) 223216 E-mail philiplittlewood@keinton.fsbusiness.co.uk

LITTON, Alan. b 42. Ridley Hall Cam 66. **d** 69 **p** 70. C Bolton St Bede *Man* 69-71; C Ashton St Mich 71-73; V Haslingden St Jo Stonefold *Blackb* 73-77; Ind Chapl *York* 77-81; V Crewe All SS and St Paul *Ches* 81-84; Ind Chapl 84-89; V Spotland *Man* 89-94; R Newchurch *Liv* 94-02; P-in-c Croft w Southworth 99-02; R Newchurch w Croft 02; rtd 02. *3 Rosemary Close, Great Sankey, Warrington WA5 1TL* Tel (01925) 453264

LIVERPOOL, Archdeacon of. *See* PANTER, The Ven Richard James Graham

LIVERPOOL, Bishop of. *See* JONES, The Rt Revd James Stuart

LIVERPOOL, Dean of. *See* HOARE, The Rt Revd Rupert William Noel

LIVERSIDGE, Mrs Linda Sheila. b 48. Oak Hill Th Coll BA98. **d** 98 **p** 99. C Kensal Rise St Mark and St Martin *Lon* 98-01; TV N Wingfield, Clay Cross and Pilsley *Derby* from 01. *The Vicarage, Morton Road, Pilsley, Chesterfield S45 8EF* Tel and fax (01773) 590529 Mobile 07941-667616 E-mail linda@lindalan.free-online.co.uk

LIVERSUCH, Ian Martin. b 56. St Jo Coll Dur BA79 Univ of Wales (Cardiff) DPS84. Wycliffe Hall Ox 79. **d** 83 **p** 84. C Newport St Mark *Mon* 83-85; C Risca 85-88; P-in-c Newport All SS 88-91; Canada from 91; R Hemmingford w Clarenceville 92-98; R La Salle St Lawr from 98. *350 12th Avenue, La Salle QC, Canada, L18P 3P7* Tel (001) (514) 364 5718 E-mail islwyn@total.net

LIVESEY, Kenneth. b 29. Codrington Coll Barbados 57. **d** 59 **p** 60. Br Guiana 59-66; Guyana 66-72 and 84-89; P-in-c Royton St Paul *Man* 72-73; V 73-81; P-in-c Bury H Trin 81-82; TR Bury Ch King w H Trin 82-84; V Oldham St Steph and All Martyrs 89-91; rtd 91; Perm to Offic *Man* 91-97. *2 Malvern Close, Royton, Oldham OL2 5HH* Tel 0161-628 8617

LIVINGSTON, Bertram. TCD BA56. **d** 57 **p** 58. C Enniscorthy *C & O* 57-59; I Carrickmacross *Clogh* 59-61; I Carrickmacross w Magheracloone 61-63; C-in-c Derryvolgie *Conn* 63-78; I 78-79; I Monaghan *Clogh* 79-86; I Desertlyn w Ballyeglish *Arm* 86-94; rtd 94. *6 The Green, Portadown, Craigavon BT63 5LH* Tel (028) 3835 1859

LIVINGSTON, Richard. b 46. Qu Coll Birm. **d** 83 **p** 84. C Hobs Moat *Birm* 83-87; V Droylsden St Martin *Man* 87-95; P-in-c Wolverton w Norton Lindsey and Langley *Cov* from 95; Chapl to the Deaf from 95. *The Rectory, Wolverton, Stratford-upon-Avon CV37 0HF* Tel (01789) 731278 E-mail richard@livingstonr.freeserve.co.uk

LIVINGSTONE, Canon Francis Kenneth. b 26. TCD BA48 MA64. TCD Div Sch Div Test49. **d** 49 **p** 50. C Dublin Santry Union w Coolock *D & G* 49-52; C Dublin St Geo 52-57; I Castledermot Union 57-62; C Arm St Mark *Arm* 62-66; Hon V Choral Arm Cathl 63-92; I Portadown St Sav 66-78; I Kilmore St Aid w St Sav 78-83; I Donaghmore w Upper Donaghmore 83-92; Preb Yagoe St Patr Cathl Dublin 85-92; rtd 92. *9 Castle Parade, Richhill, Armagh BT61 9QQ* Tel (028) 3887 1574

LIVINGSTONE, Canon John Morris. b 28. Peterho Cam BA53 MA56. Cuddesdon Coll 53. **d** 55 **p** 56. C Hunslet St Mary and Stourton *Ripon* 55-60; Chapl Liddon Ho Lon 60-63; V Notting Hill St Jo Lon 63-74; P-in-c Notting Hill St Mark 66-73; P-in-c Notting Hill All SS w St Columb 67-74; P-in-c Notting Hill St Clem 68-74; TR Notting Hill 74-75; Chapl Paris St Geo *Eur* 75-84; Adn N France 79-84; Adn Riviera 84-93; Chapl Nice w Vence 84-93; Biarritz from 93; rtd 93. *47 Côte des Basques, 64200 Biarritz, France* Tel (0033) (5) 59 24 71 18 Fax as telephone E-mail biarritz.cofe@infonie.fr

LIVINGSTONE, John Philip. b 51. Univ of Wales (Abth) BA PGCE. St D Dioc Tr Course. **d** 96 **p** 97. NSM Maenclochog and New Moat etc St D 96-02; V Elerch w Penrhyncoch w Capel Bangor and Goginan from 02. *The Vicarage, 78 Ger y Llan, Penrhyncoch, Aberystwyth SY23 3HQ* Tel (01970) 820988

LLANDAFF, Archdeacon of. *See* THOMAS, The Ven William Phillip

LLANDAFF, Bishop of. *See* MORGAN, The Most Revd Barry Cennydd

LLANDAFF, Dean of. *See* LEWIS, The Very Revd John Thomas

✠**LLEWELLIN, The Rt Revd John Richard Allan.** b 38. Fitzw Ho Cam BA64 MA78. Westcott Ho Cam 61. **d** 64 **p** 65 **c** 85. C Radlett *St Alb* 64-68; C Johannesburg Cathl S Africa 68-71; V Waltham Cross *St Alb* 71-79; R Harpenden St Nic 79-85; Hon Can Truro Cathl *Truro* 85-92; Suff Bp St Germans 85-92; Suff Bp Dover *Cant* 92-99; Bp at Lambeth (Hd of Staff) from 99. *Lambeth Palace, Lambeth Palace Road, London SE1 7JU* Tel (020) 7898 1200 Fax 7898 1210 E-mail richard.llewellin@lampal.c-of-e.org.uk

LLEWELLYN, Christine Ann. b 46. Univ of Wales (Ban) BA69 DipEd70. **d** 89 **p** 97. NSM Arthog w Fairbourne w Llangelynnin w Rhoslefain *Ban* 90-93; NSM Holyhead w Rhoscolyn w Llanfair-yn-Neubwll 93-94; C 94-95; C Holyhead 95-97; TV from 97. *The Old School, Rhoscolyn, Holyhead LL65 2RQ* Tel (01407) 741593

LLEWELLYN, David John Patrick. b 16. AKC40. Wells Th Coll. **d** 46 **p** 47. C Dorking *Guildf* 46-49; C Dudley St Fran *Worc* 49-50; C Redditch St Steph 50-52; V Bretforton 52-59; V Wolverley 59-60; S Africa 60-65; Rhodesia 65-69; I Kinneigh Union *C, C & R* 76-83; rtd 83. *Anne's Cottage, Hamilton Row, Courtmacsherry, Bandon, Co Cork, Irish Republic* Tel (00353) (23) 46381

LLEWELLYN, Neil Alexander. b 55. LWCMD78. Westcott Ho Cam 79 Sarum & Wells Th Coll 83. **d** 84 **p** 85. C Heref St Martin *Heref* 84-86; Chapl Rotterdam Miss to Seamen *Eur* 86-89; R Docking w The Birchams and Stanhoe w Barwick *Nor* 89-92; Chapl Ypres *Eur* 92-95; Toc H 92-95; CF from 95; Perm to Offic *Newc* from 01. *c/o MOD Chaplains (Army)* Tel (01980) 615804 Fax 615800

LLEWELLYN, Richard Morgan. b 37. CB91 OBE79 MBE76. FCMI81. Sarum & Wells Th Coll 91. **d** 93 **p** 94. C Brecon St Mary and Battle w Llanddew *S & B* 93-95; Min Can Brecon Cathl 93-95; Chapl Ch Coll Brecon from 95. *Llangattock Court, Llangattock, Crickhowell NP8 1PH* Tel (01873) 810116

LLEWELLYN, William David. b 22. Univ of Wales (Lamp) BA43. **d** 48 **p** 49. C Llanishen and Lisvane *Llan* 48-51; C Whitchurch 51-63; V Treharris 63-70; V Penmaen *Mon* 70-77; V St Mellons 77-87; rtd 87. *262 Cardiff Road, Newport NP20 3AH* Tel (01633) 817278

LLEWELLYN-MACDUFF, Ms Lindsay. b 75. Kent Univ BA97. St Mich Coll Llan 97. **d** 99 **p** 00. C Milton next Sittingbourne *Cant* 99-01; C Barham w Bishopsbourne and Kingston from 01. *20 Pilgrims Way, Canterbury CT1 1XU* Tel (01227) 454704 E-mail lindsay@hercomputer.fsworld.co.uk

LLEWELYN, John Dilwyn. b 18. St D Coll Lamp BA40 AKC42. **d** 42 **p** 43. C Battersea Rise St Mark *S'wark* 42-45; C Thame *Ox* 45-47; C Towersey w Aston Sandford 45-47; C Maidenhead St Andr and St Mary 47-51; P-in-c Devonport St Aubyn *Ex* 51-56; C Merton St Mary *S'wark* 56-61; V Plymouth St Simon *Ex* 61-82; rtd 82; Perm to Offic *Ex* 84-97. *25 Oakley Close, Pinhoe, Exeter EX1 3SB* Tel (01392) 467169

LLEWELYN, Robert Charles. b 09. Pemb Coll Cam BA32 MA36. **d** 36 **p** 37. Asst Master Westmr Sch 32-47; Chapl 46-47; C Westmr St Steph w St Mary Lon 36-40; India 41-45; Bahamas 47-51; India 51-71; Adn Poona 69-71; Warden Bede Ho Staplehurst 72-75; rtd 74; Chapl Shrine of St Julian 76-90. *80A King Street, Norwich NR1 1PG* Tel (01603) 662600

LLEWELYN, Canon Robert John. b 32. Keble Coll Ox BA54 MA58 Cheltenham & Glouc Coll of HE PhD01. Cuddesdon Coll 65. **d** 66 **p** 67. C Bedford St Andr *St Alb* 66-69; C Cheltenham St Luke and St Jo *Glouc* 69-75; V S Cerney w Cerney Wick 75-86; V Glouc St Cath 86-89; P-in-c Glouc St Mark 87-89; Hon Can Glouc Cathl 94-99; rtd 99; Perm to Offic *Glouc* from 99. *11 Sandhurst Road, Gloucester GL1 2SE* Tel (01452) 537313 E-mail robert4.freeserve.co.uk

LLEWELYN-EVANS, Catherine Ruth. b 55. St Mary's Coll Dur BA76 Southlands Coll Lon PGCE78. STETS 99. **d** 02 **p** 03. NSM Yatton Moor *B & W* from 02. *The Court House, The Triangle, Wrington, Bristol BS40 5LB* Tel (01934) 863269 E-mail cllewelynevans@globalnet.co.uk

LLOYD, Canon Bernard James. b 29. AKC56. **d** 57 **p** 58. C Laindon w Basildon *Chelmsf* 57-65; V E Ham St Geo 65-82; RD Newham 76-82; Hon Can Chelmsf Cathl 82-94; R Danbury 82-94; P-in-c Woodham Ferrers 87-90; rtd 94; Perm to Offic *Chelmsf* from 94. *Chanterelle, 47 Seaview Avenue, West Mersea, Colchester CO5 8HE* Tel (01206) 383892

LLOYD, Bertram John. b 26. St Mich Coll Llan 81. **d** 83 **p** 84. C Malpas *Mon* 83-85; V Blaenavon w Capel Newydd 85-93; rtd 93; Lic to Offic *Mon* 93-96; St Vincent 96-02. *91 Hillside Avenue, Blaenavon, Pontypool NP4 9JL* Tel (01495) 792616
E-mail llwydunion@caribsurf.com

LLOYD, The Ven Bertram Trevor. b 38. Hertf Coll Ox BA60 MA64. Clifton Th Coll 62. **d** 64 **p** 65. C S Mimms Ch Ch *Lon* 64-70; V Wealdstone H Trin 70-84; RD Harrow 77-82; P-in-c Harrow Weald St Mich 80-84; V Harrow Trin St Mich 84-89; Adn Barnstaple *Ex* 89-02; Preb Ex Cathl 91-02; rtd 02. *8 Pebbleridge Road, Westward Ho!, Bideford EX39 1HN* Tel (01237) 424701

LLOYD, Mrs Carole Barbara. b 53. Sheff Univ BA74 Leeds Metrop Univ PGCE93. N Ord Course 00. **d** 03. C Bolton St Jas w St Chrys *Bradf* from 03. *37 Cricketers Green, Yeadon, Leeds LS19 7YS* Tel 0113-250 6485
E-mail carolelloyd@cricketers.fsnet.co.uk

LLOYD, Canon Charles Henry. b 13. TCD BA34. CITC 36. **d** 36 **p** 37. C Dublin St Geo *D & G* 36-39; C Dublin Rathfarnham 39-43; I Moynalty w Moybologue *M & K* 43-54; Gen Sec Hibernian CMS 54-70; I New Ross *C & O* 70-82; Dioc Sec (Ferns) 72-80; Preb Tassagard St Patr Cathl Dublin 73-82; rtd 82. *74 The Rise, Woodpark, Ballinteer, Dublin 16, Irish Republic* Tel (00353) (1) 295 1181

LLOYD, David Edgar Charles. b 59. Univ of Wales (Cardiff) Dip Past Th 99. St Mich Coll Llan DMS98. **d** 99 **p** 00. C Newton Nottage *Llan* 99-03; V Newcastle from 03. *The Vicarage, 1 Walters Road, Bridgend CF31 4HE* Tel (01656) 655999
E-mail revd.lloyd@virgin.net

LLOYD, David Hanbury. b 28. Univ of Wales (Abth) BSc49 Reading Univ PhD70. LNSM course 97. **d** 97 **p** 98. NSM Swanage and Studland *Sarum* 97-98; Perm to Offic from 98. *Scar Bank House, Russell Avenue, Swanage BH19 2ED* Tel (01929) 426015

LLOYD, David John. b 52. Lon Univ BD82. St D Coll Lamp DipTh76. **d** 76 **p** 77. C Pembroke St Mary w St Mich *St D* 76-77; C Llanelli 77-80; V Cil-y-Cwm and Ystrad-ffin w Rhandir-mwyn etc 80-82; Oman 82-84; R Llanllwchaearn and Llanina *St D* 84-88; V Llangennech and Hendy 88-90; Perm to Offic *St Alb* 91-95; P-in-c Bampton w Clanfield Ox 96-97; V from 97; AD Witney 02-03. *5 Deanery Court, Broad Street, Bampton OX18 2LY* Tel (01993) 851222 E-mail revdjlloyd@aol.com

LLOYD, David John Silk. b 33. Univ of Wales (Lamp) BA62. St Steph Ho Ox 71. **d** 73 **p** 74. C Brentwood St Thos *Chelmsf* 73-77; C Hockley 77-80; C Wickford 80-81; C Wickford and Runwell 81-83; TV 83-88; Chapl Runwell Hosp Wickford 81-88; S Africa from 88; Perm to Offic *Chelmsf* from 88; rtd 97. *D4 Argyll House, Seaforth Road, Westcliff-on-Sea SS0 7SJ*

LLOYD, David Peter. b 58. Kingston Poly BA81 DipArch84. Sarum & Wells Th Coll 88. **d** 90 **p** 91. C N Dulwich St Faith *S'wark* 90-94; TV Bedminster *Bris* 94-00; V Henbury from 00. *St Mary's Vicarage, Station Road, Bristol BS10 7QQ* Tel and fax 0117-950 0536 Mobile 07939-264261
E-mail rev.david@talk21.com

LLOYD, Dennis John. b 46. BSc70 MSc74 PhD81. S Dios Minl Tr Scheme. **d** 90 **p** 91. C Hamworthy *Sarum* 90-92; Chapl UEA *Nor* 92-97; P-in-c Malvern St Andr *Worc* 97-99; V 99-01; Chapl Defence Evaluation Research Agency 97-01; RD Malvern 98-01; P-in-c Rowlands Castle *Portsm* from 01; Warden of Readers from 01. *The Rectory, 9 College Close, Rowland's Castle PO9 6AJ* Tel (023) 9241 2605 E-mail djlloyd@btinternet.com

LLOYD, Edward Gareth. b 60. K Coll Cam BA81 MA85 Dur Univ PhD98. Ridley Hall Cam 85. **d** 88 **p** 89. C Jarrow *Dur* 88-91; C Monkwearmouth St Pet 91-92; P-in-c 92-96; TV Monkwearmouth 97-99; V Birtley from 99. *6 Ruskin Road, Birtley, Chester le Street DH3 1AD* Tel 0191-410 2115 or 374 3500 E-mail gareth@dunelm.org.uk

LLOYD, Eileen. See TAVERNER, Mrs Eileen

LLOYD, Canon Elizabeth Jane. b 52. HND73 GRIC74 CChem MRIC77 Nottm Univ DipTh79. Linc Th Coll 77. **dss** 80 **d** 87 **p** 94. Linc St Nic w St Jo Newport *Linc* 80-81; Lic to Offic *Sarum* 81-87; Hon Par Dn Lytchett Matravers 87-92; Chapl Poole Gen Hosp 85-94; Chapl Poole Hosp NHS Trust from 94; Can and Preb Sarum Cathl *Sarum* from 03; Pres Coll of Health Care Chapl 02-04. *The Rectory, 19 Springfield Road, Poole BH14 0LG* Tel (01202) 748860 or 442167 E-mail jane.lloyd@poole.nhs.uk

LLOYD, Geoffrey. See LLOYD, William Geoffrey

LLOYD, Graham. b 36. Brasted Th Coll 62 St Aid Birkenhead 64 Glouc Sch of Min 86. **d** 89 **p** 90. NSM Churchstoke w Hyssington and Sarn *Heref* 89-97; NSM Lydbury N w Hopesay and Edgton 97-01; rtd 01; Perm to Offic *Heref* from 01. *The Pullets Cottage, Church Stoke, Montgomery SY15 6TL* Tel (01588) 620285

LLOYD, Gwilym Wyn. b 50. Leic Univ BA72 Birm Univ MSc73 Lon Univ LLB78. Trin Coll Bris DipHE85. **d** 87 **p** 88. C Bexleyheath Ch Ch *Roch* 87-91; R Darlaston St Lawr *Lich* 91-98. *24 Grosvenor Avenue, Streetly, Sutton Coldfield B74 3PB*

LLOYD, Hamilton William John Marteine. b 19. Jes Coll Ox BA41 MA45. Ripon Hall Ox. **d** 43 **p** 44. C Falmouth K Chas *Truro* 43-47; R Gerrans w St Anthony in Roseland 47-51; Min

Bournemouth H Epiphany CD 51-53; V Bournemouth H Epiphany *Win* 53-60; V Whitchurch w Tufton 60-68; V Whitchurch w Tufton and Litchfield 68-71; V Lyndhurst 71-73; V Lyndhurst and Emery Down 73-84; rtd 84; Perm to Offic *Win* from 86. *Post Office House, North Litchfield, Whitchurch RG28 7PT* Tel (01256) 893507

LLOYD, Harry James. b 22. Univ of Wales (Lamp) BA50. **d** 51 **p** 52. C Hay *S & B* 51-55; C Llanigon 51-55; C Hillingdon St Jo *Lon* 55-56; C Marlborough *Sarum* 56-60; V Kingston and Worth Matravers 60-83; C Milton Abbas, Hilton w Cheselbourne etc 83-87; rtd 87; Perm to Offic *Sarum* 87-00. *Riverside Cottage, 35 Rockbridge Park, Presteigne LD8 2NF* Tel (01547) 560115

LLOYD, Canon Herbert James. b 31. TD. St D Coll Lamp BA57. **d** 58 **p** 59. C Wrexham *St As* 58-65; TV 71-74; R Llanferres 65-67; R Llanferres, Nercwys and Eryrys 67-71; V Rhyl w St Ann 74-96; CF (TA) from 74; Can St As Cathl *St As* from 81; Prec St As Cathl from 89. *The Orchard, 8 Stoneby Drive, Prestatyn LL19 9PE* Tel (01745) 851185

LLOYD, Jane. See LLOYD, Canon Elizabeth Jane

LLOYD, John. **d** 01. OLM Tettenhall Regis *Lich* from 01. *The Barn, West Trescott Farm, Bridgnorth Road, Trescott, Wolverhampton WV6 7EU* Tel (01902) 765612

LLOYD, John Everard. b 27. LSE BSc50 FCMA60. St Alb Minl Tr Scheme 84. **d** 87 **p** 88. NSM Harpenden St Nic *St Alb* 87-90; Hon C Addingham *Bradf* 90-92; rtd 92; Perm to Offic *Bradf* 92-99. *2 High Springs, Owler Park Road, Ilkley LS29 0BG* Tel (01943) 609267

LLOYD, John James. b 14. St D Coll Lamp BA36. **d** 37 **p** 38. C Ferndale *Llan* 37-38; C Grangetown 38-41; C Aberavon 41-50; V Porth 50-63; V Cadoxton-juxta-Neath 63-79; rtd 79; Perm to Offic *Llan* from 79. *16 Spoonbill Close, Rest Bay, Porthcawl CF36 3UR* Tel (01656) 715470

LLOYD, Jonathan Wilford. b 56. Surrey Univ & City of Lon Poly BSc80 Goldsmiths' Coll Lon CQSW82 DASS82 N Lon Poly MA86. S'wark Ord Course 87. **d** 90 **p** 91. Hon C Sydenham St Bart *S'wark* 90-93; P-in-c 93-94; Dir of Soc Resp 91-95; Bp's Officer for Ch in Soc 95-97; Hon PV S'wark Cathl 91-97; Chapl Team Ldr Bath Univ *B & W* from 97; Perm to Offic *Bris* from 00. *Ecumenical Chaplaincy Centre, University of Bath, Bath BA2 7AY* Tel (01225) 386458 or 386193 Fax 384662
E-mail j.w.lloyd@bath.ac.uk

LLOYD, Michael Francis. b 57. Down Coll Cam BA79 MA82 St Jo Coll Dur BA83 Worc Coll Ox DPhil97. Cranmer Hall Dur 81. **d** 84 **p** 85. C Locks Heath *Portsm* 84-87; Asst Chapl Worc Coll Ox 89-90; Chapl Ch Coll Cam 90-94; Chapl Fitzw Coll Cam 95-96; Hon C Westminster St Jas the Less *Lon* 96-03; Tutor St Steph Ho Ox from 03. *St Stephen's House, 16 Marston Street, Oxford OX4 1JX* Tel (01865) 247874

LLOYD, Canon Nigel James Clifford. b 51. Nottm Univ BTh81 Lambeth STh90. Linc Th Coll 77. **d** 81 **p** 82. C Sherborne w Castleton and Lillington *Sarum* 81-84; R Lytchett Matravers 84-92; TR Parkstone St Pet w Branksea and St Osmund 92-02; R Parkstone St Pet and St Osmund w Branksea from 02; Ecum Officer (Sherborne Episc Area) from 92; Dioc Ecum Officer 00-01; RD Poole from 01; Can and Preb Sarum Cathl from 02. *The Rectory, 19 Springfield Road, Poole BH14 0LG* Tel (01202) 748860 or 749085 Fax 0870-558534
E-mail nigel@branksea.co.uk

LLOYD, Mrs Pamela Valpy. b 25. Gilmore Ho 48 St Aug Coll Cant 76. **dss** 76 **d** 87 **p** 94. Chartham *Cant* 76-78; Cant All SS 78-85; rtd 85; Chapl Asst Kent and Cant Hosp 87; Chapl Chaucer Hosp Cant 87-90; NSM Elham w Denton and Wootton *Cant* 87-93; Sub-Chapl HM Pris Cant 88-96; Perm to Offic *Cant* from 96; Hon C Cant St Martin and St Paul 93-95. *Cavendish House, 9 North Holmes Road, Canterbury CT1 1QJ* Tel (01227) 457782

LLOYD, Canon Peter John. b 32. TD78. Leic Univ DipSocSc53. Wells Th Coll 59. **d** 61 **p** 62. C Walmer *Cant* 61-63; CF (TA) 62-73 and 77-87; C Maidstone All SS w St Phil *Cant* 63-66; V Milton next Sittingbourne 66-69; R Brinkley, Burrough Green and Carlton *Ely* 69-73; CF 73-77; V Chessington *Guildf* 77-85; RD Epsom 82-87; V Epsom St Martin 85-92; rtd 92; Perm to Offic *B & W* from 92. *74 Southover, Wells BA5 1UH* Tel (01749) 672213

LLOYD, Peter Vernon James. b 36. St Jo Coll Cam BA61 MA. Ridley Hall Cam 60. **d** 62 **p** 63. C Keynsham w Queen Charlton *B & W* 62-65; Perm to Offic *Sarum* from 65; NSM Bournemouth St Jo w St Mich *Win* 87-90; NSM Bournemouth St Pet w St Swithun, H Trin etc 90-93; Perm to Offic *Win* 93-95; rtd 01. *18 Cornelia Crescent, Branksome, Poole BH12 1LU* Tel (01202) 741422 Fax as telephone

LLOYD, Richard Gary. b 75. Ex Coll Ox BA98 St Jo Coll Dur MA00. Cranmer Hall Dur. **d** 00 **p** 01. C Dibden *Win* from 00. *Church House, 2 Corsair Drive, Dibden, Southampton SO45 5UF* Tel (023) 8084 4376

LLOYD, Robert Graham. b 42. St Jo Coll Nottm 82. **d** 84 **p** 85. C Tonyrefail *Llan* 84-87; V Martletwy w Lawrenny and Minwear and Yerbeston *St D* 87-91; V Monkton 91-96; V Cymmer and Porth *Llan* from 96. *The Vicarage, Maesgwyn, Cymmer, Porth CF39 9HW* Tel (01443) 682219

LLOYD, Robert James Clifford. b 18. Selw Coll Cam BA41 MA49. Linc Th Coll 46. **d** 47 **p** 48. C Clapham H Trin *S'wark* 47-50; C High Wycombe All SS *Ox* 50-53; CF (TA) 50-53; C Hampstead St Jo *Lon* 53-55; V Wellington w W Buckland *B & W* 55-66; P-in-c Nynehead 56-57; V 57-66; RD Wellington 59-66; R Chartham *Cant* 66-81; RD W Bridge 75-81; Hon C Elham w Denton and Wootton 81-92; rtd 92; Perm to Offic *Cant* from 83. *Cavendish House, 9 North Holmes Road, Canterbury CT1 1QJ* Tel (01227) 457782

LLOYD, Roger Bernard. b 58. K Coll Lon BA. Cranmer Hall Dur. **d** 84 **p** 85. C Hornchurch St Andr *Chelmsf* 84-87; C Gt Parndon 87-94; V Elm Park St Nic Hornchurch 94-99. *494 Heathway, Dagenham RM10 7SH* Tel (020) 8984 9887 Mobile 07703-383176

LLOYD, Ronald. b 37. St Mich Coll Llan. **d** 83 **p** 84. C Penarth All SS *Llan* 83-85; V Cwmbach 85-91; Perm to Offic from 91. *23 Teilo Street, Cardiff CF11 9JN*

LLOYD, Canon Ronald Henry. b 32. Univ of Wales (Lamp) BA52 LTh54. **d** 54 **p** 56. C Manselton *S & B* 54-56; C Sketty 56-59; C Swansea St Mary 59-63; CF (TA) 59-65; V Elmley Castle w Netherton and Bricklehampton *Worc* 63-69; Chapl Dragon Sch Ox 69-82; Chapl St Hugh's Coll Ox 75-80; P-in-c Ox St Marg *Ox* 75-76; Chapl Magd Coll Ox 75-82; Prec and Chapl Ch Ch *Ox* 82-87; R Alvescot w Black Bourton, Shilton, Holwell etc 87-95; P-in-c Broughton Poggs w Filkins, Broadwell etc 94-95; R Shill Valley and Broadshire 95-01; rtd 01; Perm to Offic *Glouc* and *Ox* from 02. *2 The Farriers, Southrop, Lechlade GL7 3RL* Tel (01367) 850071

LLOYD, Mrs Sandra Edith. b 48. Sarum & Wells Th Coll 83. **dss** 86 **d** 87 **p** 94. Freshwater *Portsm* 86-87; C 87-89; C Whitwell 89-95; V from 95; C Niton 89-95; P-in-c 95-96; R from 96; R St Lawrence from 96. *The Rectory, Pan Lane, Niton, Ventnor PO38 2BT* Tel (01983) 730595 Fax as telephone E-mail rhadegunde@aol.com

LLOYD, Simon David. b 58. Portsm Poly BA79 RGN91 RSCN95. Wycliffe Hall Ox 80. **d** 83 **p** 84. C Cotmanhay *Derby* 83-85; Chapl Asst Nottm City Hosp 85-87; Chapl Basford Hosp Nottm 85-87; Perm to Offic *Birm* 91-97; TV Solihull from 97. *St Michael's Church Centre, Oak Cottage, Bryanston Road, Solihull B91 1BS* Tel 0121-704 4730

LLOYD, Stephen Russell. b 47. Worc Coll Ox BA69 MA77 CertEd DipTh. Oak Hill Th Coll 76. **d** 77 **p** 78. C Canonbury St Steph *Lon* 77-80; C Braintree *Chelmsf* 80-92; V Braintree St Paul 92-01; V Ipswich St Andr *St E* from 01. *The Vicarage, 286 Britannia Road, Ipswich IP4 5HF* Tel (01473) 714341 E-mail rev.lloyd@tiscali.co.uk

LLOYD, Canon Stuart George Errington. b 49. TCD BA72. **d** 75 **p** 76. C Cloughfern *Conn* 75-79; C Cregagh *D & D* 79-82; I Eglantine *Conn* 82-89; I Ballinaclay *Ballyclug* from 89; Can Conn Cathl from 97; Preb 97-01; Prec from 01. *St Patrick's Rectory, 102 Galgorm Road, Ballymena BT42 1AE* Tel and fax (028) 2565 2253 *or* tel 2563 0741 E-mail ballymena@connor.anglican.org

LLOYD, Timothy David Lewis. *See* LEWIS LLOYD, Canon Timothy David

LLOYD, William Geoffrey. b 48. Man Univ BA70. Oak Hill Th Coll 92. **d** 94 **p** 96. C Plaistow St Mary *Roch* 95-99; TV Ottery St Mary, Alfington, W Hill, Tipton etc *Ex* from 99. *The Vicarage, Newton Poppleford, Sidmouth EX10 0HB* Tel (01395) 568390 Fax as telephone E-mail geofflloyd@ukgateway.net

LLOYD-DAVIES, Arthur (Lloyd). b 31. Univ of Wales BA55. Cuddesdon Coll 55. **d** 57 **p** 58. C Tonypandy w Clydach Vale *Llan* 57-59; C Merthyr Dyfan 59-62; C Amersham *Ox* 62-65; V Tilehurst St Geo 65-73; R Wokingham St Paul 73-84; R Nuthurst *Chich* 84-90; I Fiddown w Clonegam, Guilcagh and Kilmeaden *C & O* 90-96; rtd 96; Hon C Bratton, Edington and Imber, Erlestoke etc *Sarum* 96-99. *The Gatehouse Lodge, Terrys Cross House, Brighton Road, Woodmancote, Henfield BN5 9SX* Tel (01273) 491210

LLOYD HUGHES, Gwilym. *See* HUGHES, Gwilym Lloyd

LLOYD-JAMES, Duncan Geraint. b 66. St Steph Ho Ox BTh94. **d** 94 **p** 96. C St Leonards Ch Ch and St Mary *Chich* 94-96; C Rottingdean 96-99; R Brede w Udimore from 99. *The Rectory, Brede, Rye TN31 6DX* Tel (01424) 882457 E-mail djlj@btinternet.com

LLOYD-JAMES, Canon John Eifion. b 39. Brasted Th Coll 60 Clifton Th Coll 63. **d** 65 **p** 66. C Burgess Hill St Andr *Chich* 65-68; C-in-c Portslade Gd Shep CD 68-74; V Lancing St Mich 74-88; V Billingshurst 88-93; Chapl St Mary's Hall Brighton 93-96; V Kemp Town St Mary *Chich* 93-99; P-in-c Bishopstone 99-01; V from 01; Can and Preb Chich Cathl from 00. *The Vicarage, Bishopstone Road, Bishopstone, Seaford BN25 2UD* Tel (01323) 892972

LLOYD JONES, Ieuan. b 31. FBIM St Cath Coll Cam BA51 MA54. Sarum & Wells Th Coll 80. **d** 83 **p** 84. Hon C Claygate *Guildf* 83-89; Perm to Offic *Ox* from 89. *11 Southcroft, Old Marston, Oxford OX3 0PF* Tel (01865) 793098

LLOYD MORGAN, Richard Edward. b 48. Trin Coll Cam MA70 Ox Univ DipEd71. SEITE 95. **d** 98 **p** 99. NSM Clapham St Paul

S'wark from 98. *111 Narbonne Avenue, London SW4 9LQ* Tel (020) 8673 4149 Fax as telephone

LLOYD-RICHARDS, David Robert. b 48. Open Univ BA84 Hull Univ MA87. St D Coll Lamp DipTh70. **d** 71 **p** 72. C Skewen *Llan* 71-73; C Neath w Llantwit 73-76; Miss to Seamen 76-77; V Pontlottyn w Fochriw *Llan* 77-84; R Merthyr Dyfan 84-90; Chapl Barry Neale-Kent Hosp 84-90; Tutor Open Univ from 85; Sen Chapl Univ Hosp of Wales Cardiff 90-95; Sen Chapl Univ Hosp of Wales and Llandough NHS Trust from 95. *University Hospital of Wales, Heath Park, Cardiff CF14 4XW* Tel (029) 2074 7747 ext 4854 or 2074 7747 E-mail lloyd-richards@cf.co.uk

LLOYD WILLIAMS, Martin Clifford. b 65. Westmr Coll Lon BEd87. Trin Coll Bris BA93. **d** 93 **p** 94. C Bath Walcot *B & W* 93-97; R Bath St Mich w St Paul from 97. *71 Priory Close, Combe Down, Bath BA2 5AP* Tel (01225) 835490

LO, Peter Kwan Ho. b 54. **d** 85. Hong Kong 85-01; Perm to Offic *Chich* 02-03; C Uckfield from 03. *7 Park View Road, Uckfield TN22 1JP* Tel (01825) 763775

lo POLITO, Nicola. b 59. Catholic Th Union Chicago MDiv85 MA(Theol)87. Comboni Miss. **d** 85 **p** 86. In RC Ch 85-94; Egypt 86-88; Sudan 88-91; Italy 91-94; Asst Chapl Malta and Gozo *Eur* 94-98; C Castle Bromwich SS Mary and Marg *Birm* 98-01; TV Salter Street and Shirley from 01. *18 Widney Lane, Solihull, Birmingham B91 3LS* Tel 0121-705 6586 E-mail nlopolito@hotmail.com

LOAT, Canon Andrew Graham. b 61. Aber Univ BD83 Univ of Wales (Ban) MTh00. St Jo Coll Nottm DPS87. **d** 87 **p** 88. C Llangynwyd w Maesteg *Llan* 87-90; C Llansamlet *S & B* 90-91; R Whitton and Pilleth and Cascob etc 91-98; R Llandrindod w Cefnllys and Disserth from 98; Warden of Readers from 02; Can Res Brecon Cathl from 03. *The Rectory, Broadway, Llandrindod Wells LD1 5HT* Tel (01597) 822043 E-mail aloat@cactus90.freeserve.co.uk

LOBB, Edward Eric. b 51. Magd Coll Ox BA74 MA76. Wycliffe Hall Ox 73. **d** 76 **p** 77. C Haughton St Mary *Man* 76-80; C Rusholme H Trin 80-84; P-in-c Whitfield *Derby* 84-90; V 90-92; V Stapenhill w Cauldwell 92-03; rtd 03. *6 Clay Street, Stapenhill, Burton-on-Trent DE15 9BB* Tel (01283) 561437

LOBB, Miss Josephine Mary. b 57. SRN83 Plymouth Univ Dip Nursing89. LNSM course 94. **d** 96 **p** 97. OLM St Germans *Truro* from 96. *19 Lowertown Close, Landrake, Saltash PL12 5DG* Tel (01752) 851488

LOBLEY, Mrs Shirley Bruce Fenwick. b 44. Moray Ho Coll of Educn TCert64. TISEC 98. **d** 01. C Alloa *St And* from 01. *20 Parkdyke, Stirling FK7 9LR* Tel (01786) 462799 E-mail shirley.lobley@fslife.co.uk

LOCK, David Stephen. b 28. **d** 63 **p** 64. C Streatham Vale H Redeemer *S'wark* 63-66; C Hatcham St Jas 66-75; V Leyton All SS *Chelmsf* 75-95; rtd 95; Perm to Offic *Roch* from 95. *26 Eldred Drive, Orpington BR5 4PF* Tel (01689) 601726

LOCK, Graham Robert. b 39. Hertf Coll Ox BA63 MA67. Ridley Hall Cam 62. **d** 64 **p** 65. C Bexleyheath St Pet *Roch* 64-66; C Roch St Justus 66-71; C St Mary Cray and St Paul's Cray 71-75; V Chatham St Paul w All SS 75-83; R Lambourne w Abridge and Stapleford Abbotts *Chelmsf* 83-92; V Barkingside St Laur from 92. *St Laurence's Vicarage, Donington Avenue, Ilford IG6 1AJ* Tel (020) 8518 3113

LOCK, Paul Alan. b 65. St Chad's Coll Dur BA86. Coll of Resurr Mirfield 87. **d** 89 **p** 90. C Upholland *Liv* 89-92; C Teddington SS Pet and Paul and Fulwell *Lon* 92-95; V 95-99; V Wigan St Anne *Liv* from 99. *St Anne's Vicarage, 154 Beech Hill Avenue, Wigan WN6 7TA* Tel (01942) 241930 Fax as telephone E-mail revpaul.lock@btopenworld.com

LOCK, The Ven Peter Harcourt D'Arcy. b 44. AKC67. **d** 68 **p** 69. C Meopham *Roch* 68-72; C Wigmore w Hempstead 72; C S Gillingham 72-77; R Hartley 77-83; R Fawkham and Hartley 83-84; V Dartford H Trin 84-93; Hon Can Roch Cathl 90-01; V Bromley SS Pet and Paul 93-01; RD Bromley 96-01; Adn Roch from 01; Can Res Roch Cathl from 01. *The Archdeaconry, King's Orchard, Rochester ME1 1TG* Tel (01634) 843366 ext 111 E-mail phdlock@ukonline.co.uk

LOCKE, Nigel Richard. *See* HESFORD-LOCKE, Richard Nigel

LOCKE, Robert Andrew. b 62. St Steph Ho Ox 89. **d** 92 **p** 93. C Colchester St Jas, All SS, St Nic and St Runwald *Chelmsf* 92-95; CF 95-00; V Burnham *Chelmsf* from 00. *The Vicarage, 2A Church Road, Burnham-on-Crouch CM0 8DA* Tel (01621) 782071 E-mail boblocke@lineone.net

LOCKE, Stephen John. b 60. St Chad's Coll Dur BA82. Sarum & Wells Th Coll 84. **d** 86 **p** 87. C Blackb St Mich w St Jo and H Trin *Blackb* 86-89; C Oswaldtwistle Immanuel and All SS 89-92; V Blackb St Mich w St Jo and H Trin 92-98; Chapl to the Deaf from 98. *30 Swallowfields, Pleckgate, Blackburn BB1 8NR* Tel (01254) 583790

LOCKER, Dorothea Isobel Leslie. b 19. MRPharmS41 Heriot-Watt Coll PhC41. LNSM course 79. **dss** 85 **d** 87. NSM Edin St Pet *Edin* 85-91; rtd 91. *27/220 West Saville Terrace, Edinburgh EH9 3DR* Tel 0131-667 3509

LOCKETT, Paul. b 48. Sarum & Wells Th Coll 73. **d** 76 **p** 77. C Horninglow *Lich* 76-78; C Tewkesbury w Walton Cardiff *Glouc*

78-81; P-in-c W Bromwich St Pet *Lich* 81-90; R Norton Canes 90-95; Dean's V Lich Cathl from 91; V Longton St Mary and St Chad from 95. *St Mary and St Chad's Presbytery, 269 Anchor Road, Stoke-on-Trent ST3 5DH* Tel (01782) 313142

LOCKETT, Simon David. b 66. Stirling Univ BA96. Wycliffe Hall Ox 00. **d** 02 **p** 03. C Ray Valley *Ox* from 02. *3 The Rise, Islip, Kidlington OX5 2TG* Tel (01865) 849497
E-mail simonlizlockett@hotmail.com

LOCKEY, Malcolm. b 45. Sunderland Poly BA67 Newc Univ DipEd68 FRSA75 SSC. NEOC 87. **d** 90 **p** 91. NSM Yarm *York* 90-97; C 97-98; TV Whitby w Aislaby and Ruswarp from 98; Hon Chapl Miss to Seafarers from 98; Chapl R Nat Lifeboat Inst from 00. *The Vicarage, 26 Egton Road, Aislaby, Whitby YO21 1SU* Tel (01947) 811527 Fax as telephone
E-mail macbrac@hotmail.com

LOCKHART, Antony William Castleton. b 25. GIMechE. Wells Th Coll 63. **d** 65 **p** 66. C Hale *Guildf* 65-69; C Worplesdon 69-73; V Weston 73-79; TV Westborough 79-84; V Shamley Green 84-87; RD Cranleigh 85-87; Perm to Offic *Cant* 88-03; Dioc Widows Officer 89-90; rtd 90. *22 Manormead, Tilford Road, Hindhead GU26 6RA* Tel (01428) 602573

LOCKHART, Clare Patricia Anne (Sister Clare). b 44. Bris Univ BA74. St Jo Coll Dur 84. **d** 87 **p** 94. Sisters of Charity from 63; Chapl Asst Sunderland Distr Gen Hosp 84-89; Chapl 89-95; NSM N Hylton St Marg Castletown *Dur* 87-95; P-in-c 95-99; NSM Eorropaidh *Arg* from 99; Perm to Offic *Dur* from 02. *The Sisters of Charity, Carmel, 7A Anson, Isle of Lewis HS2 0NB* Tel (01851) 820734 E-mail sistersofcharity@netscapeonline.co.uk

LOCKHART, David. b 68. QUB BSc90 TCD BTh93. CITC 90. **d** 93 **p** 94. C Belfast St Mary w H Redeemer *Conn* 93-96; I Belfast St Steph w St Luke 96-03; I Cloughfern from 03. *Cloughfern Rectory, 126 Doagh Road, Newtownabbey BT37 9QR* Tel (028) 9086 2437

LOCKHART, Eileen Ann. b 52. ACII74 Open Univ BA93. EAMTC 95. **d** 98 **p** 99. NSM Shenfield *Chelmsf* from 98. *6 Granary Meadow, Wyatts Green, Brentwood CM15 0QD* Tel (01277) 822537 Fax as telephone

LOCKHART, Ms Michelle. b 68. Man Univ BA89. Ripon Coll Cuddesdon 90. **d** 92 **p** 94. Par Dn Leigh St Mary *Man* 92-94; Asst Chapl HM Pris Full Sutton 95-97; V York St Hilda *York* 97-00; Dir Reader Tr and Local Min Development *Man* from 00. *15 Fairy Street, Elton, Bury BL8 2QQ* Tel 0161-761 2373

LOCKHART, Raymond William. b 37. Qu Coll Cam BA58 MA61 LLB60. St Jo Coll Nottm 72. **d** 74 **p** 75. C Aspley *S'well* 74-76; V 81-88; R Knebworth *St Alb* 76-81; Warden Stella Carmel Haifa (CMJ) 88-91; R Jerusalem Ch Ch 91-99; Dir CMJ Israel 99-02; rtd 02. *2 Paddock Woods, Combe Down, Bath BA2 7AD* Tel (01225) 840432 Mobile 07817-330831
E-mail lockhart@xalt.co.uk

LOCKHART, The Very Revd Robert Joseph Norman. b 24. TCD BA46 MA53. **d** 46 **p** 48. C Belfast St Mary Magd *Conn* 46-49; C Knockbreda *D & D* 49-54; P-in-c Killaney w Carryduff 54-60; I Comber 60-62; I Belfast St Donard 62-70; I Lurgan Ch the Redeemer 70-89; Prec Dromore Cathl 71-75; Dean Dromore 75-89; rtd 89; Lic to Offic *D & D* from 90. *30 Church Road, Belfast BT8 7AQ* Tel (028) 9049 1588

LOCKLEY, The Ven Harold. b 16. Lon Univ BA37 BD43 MTh49 Nottm Univ PhD55 Em Coll Cam MLitt91. Westcott Ho Cam 46. **d** 46 **p** 47. Chapl Loughb Coll 46-51; C Loughborough All SS *Leic* 46-48; V Glen Parva and S Wigston 51-58; Dir of Ords 51-79; Can Res and Chan Leic Cathl 53-63; V Leic All SS 63-78; Adn Loughborough 63-86; rtd 86; Perm to Offic *Leic* from 86. *21 Saxon Close, Market Harborough LE16 7PR* Tel (01858) 465605

LOCKWOOD, David Nicholas. b 23. Birm Univ MA81. St D Coll Lamp BA51 Qu Coll Birm 51. **d** 53 **p** 54. C Halesowen *Worc* 53-57; C Ribbesford w Bewdley and Dowles 57-60; R Gt w Lt Witley 60-64; V Hanley Castle w Hanley Swan 64-79; V Hanley Castle, Hanley Swan and Welland 79-81; Perm to Offic *S & B* from 81; rtd 88. *Church Row, Llowes, Hereford HR3 5JB* Tel (01497) 847664

LOCKWOOD, Richard. d 01. OLM Glascote and Stonydelph *Lich* from 01. *26 Mossdale, Wilnecote, Tamworth B77 4PJ* Tel (01827) 738105 *or* 330306

LOCKWOOD, Thelma. b 42. WEMTC. **d** 03. NSM Bourton-on-the-Water w Clapton *Glouc* from 03. *Keilder, Letch Hill Drive, Bourton-on-the-Water, Cheltenham GL54 2DQ* Tel (01451) 810974

LOCKWOOD, Wilfred Eric. b 18. Leeds Univ BA49. Coll of Resurr Mirfield 49. **d** 51 **p** 52. C Tettenhall Regis *Lich* 51-53; C Bournemouth St Fran *Win* 53-57; V Wardleworth St Mary *Man* 57-62; V Leeds Ch Ch and St Jo and St Barn Holbeck *Ripon* 62-71; R Ducklington *Ox* 71-83; CF (ACF) 62-83; rtd 83; Perm to Offic *Nor* from 83. *15A Wells Road, Walsingham NR22 6DL* Tel (01328) 820723

LOCKYER, David Ralph George. b 41. Wells Th Coll 65. **d** 67 **p** 68. C Bottesford *Linc* 67-69; C Eling *Win* 69-73; TV Eling, Testwood and Marchwood 73-77; TR Speke St Aid *Liv* 77-84; V Halifax St Jude *Wakef* 84-96; Chapl Halifax R Infirmary 84-96; V

Banwell *B & W* from 96. *The Vicarage, 3 East Street, Banwell, Weston-super-Mare BS29 6BN* Tel (01934) 822320

LOCKYER, Desmond Edward Weston. b 18. AKC49. **d** 50 **p** 51. C Norwood St Luke *S'wark* 50-52; C Surbiton St Matt 52-54; Chapl Asst United Sheff Hosps 54-56; C Sheff St Anne and St Phil *Sheff* 54-56; C Eastbourne St Mary *Chich* 56-59; V Hellingly 59-68; V Upper Dicker 62-68; V Eastbourne St Mich 68-75; V Preston 75-87; rtd 87; Perm to Offic *Chich* from 87. *Pilgrims, Nep Town Road, Henfield BN5 9DY* Tel (01273) 493681

LOCKYER, Maurice David. b 19. AKC43. **d** 43 **p** 44. C Talbot Village *Sarum* 43-46; C Laindon w Basildon *Chelmsf* 46-50; C Horfield H Trin *Bris* 50-64; V Huncote *Leic* 64-77; rtd 77. *c/o M Terrell Esq, Rix and Kay Solicitors, 84 High Street, Heathfield TN21 8JG*

LOCKYER, Peter Weston. b 60. Linc Coll Ox BA80 MA83 PGCE98. St Jo Coll Nottm 84. **d** 87 **p** 88. C Rowner *Portsm* 87-90; C Beaconsfield *Ox* 90-91; TV 91-95; Dep Chapl HM YOI Glen Parva 95; Chapl Wellingborough Sch 96-00; R Ewhurst *Guildf* 00-03; Hd Schs & Youth Chr Aid from 03. *38 Rushes Road, Petersfield GU32 3BW*

LOCOCK (née MILES), Mrs Jillian Maud. b 33. Lon Univ BSc53 Man Univ Cert Counselling 89. N Ord Course 81. **dss** 84 **d** 87 **p** 95. Didsbury Ch Ch *Man* 84-86; Chapl Asst Man R Infirmary 85-87; Chapl Asst Withington Hosp 86-88; Chapl Asst RN 88-93; NSM Dumbarton *Glas* 93-96. *Address temp unknown* E-mail rjbirtles@aol.com

LODER, Sister Helen. b 43. Goldsmiths' Coll Lon 65. S'wark Ord Course 91. **d** 94 **p** 95. Soc of St Marg from 70; NSM S Hackney St Mich w Haggerston St Paul *Lon* 94-01. *St Saviour's Priory, 18 Queensbridge Road, London E2 8NS* Tel (020) 7739 9976

LODGE, Anthony William Rayner. b 26. Wadh Coll Ox BA51 MA55. Cuddesdon Coll 65. **d** 66 **p** 67. Asst Chapl Forest Sch Snaresbrook 66-68; C Walthamstow St Pet *Chelmsf* 66-68; Chapl Ripon Gr Sch 68-91; rtd 91; Perm to Offic *Heref* from 92. *Church Cottage, Diddlebury, Craven Arms SY7 9DH* Tel (01584) 841340

LODGE, Canon John Alfred Ainley. b 29. Wells Th Coll 54. **d** 57 **p** 58. C Huddersfield St Jo *Wakef* 57-60; V Shepley 60-64; V Salterhebble St Jude 64-69; C-in-c Mixenden CD 69-75; V Mixenden 75-76; V Almondbury 76-79; RD Almondbury 76-79; V Warmfield 79-88; Bp's Dom Chapl 79-87; Hon Can Wakef Cathl 85-92; RD Kirkburton 88-92; P-in-c Emley 88-92; R 92; rtd 92; Perm to Offic *Ripon* from 92; Perm to Offic *Wakef* from 92. *Bygate, 2 Station Court, Morton on Swale, Northallerton DL7 9TQ* Tel (01609) 778551

LODGE, Michael John. b 53. Wycliffe Hall Ox 87. **d** 89 **p** 90. C Highworth w Sevenhampton and Inglesham etc *Bris* 89-93; P-in-c Cheltenham St Luke and St Jo *Glouc* from 93. *St Luke's Vicarage, 38 College Road, Cheltenham GL53 7HX* Tel (01242) 513940 E-mail mike.lodge@stlukes-church.org.uk

LODGE, Robin Paul. b 60. Bris Univ BA82 Ch Ch Coll Cant PGCE83. Chich Th Coll 88. **d** 90 **p** 91. C Calne and Blackland *Sarum* 90-94; Asst Chapl St Mary's Sch Calne 90-94; TV Wellington and Distr *B & W* 94-03; V Highbridge from 03. *The Vicarage, 81A Church Street, Highbridge TA9 3HS* Tel (01278) 783671 E-mail rp.lodge@btinternet.com

LODGE, Roy Frederick. b 38. MBE97. BTh Dip Sociology 62 DPhil93. Tyndale Hall Bris 63. **d** 66 **p** 67. C Tardebigge *Worc* 66-67; Chapl and Warden Probation Hostel Redditch 67-69; Chapl RAF 69-75; C Kinson *Sarum* 76; Lic to Offic *Pet* 76-77; Asst Chapl HM Pris Stafford 77-78; Chapl HM Pris Ranby 78-84; Chapl HM Pris Long Lartin 84-93; Chapl HM Pris Service Coll 87-93; Chapl HM Pris Hewell Grange 93-98; Chapl HM Pris Brockhill 93-98; rtd 98; Perm to Offic *Cov* from 98; Perm to Offic *Glouc* from 99. *44 Eton Road, Stratford-upon-Avon CV37 7ER*

LODWICK, Chan Brian Martin. b 40. Leeds Univ BA61 MPhil76 Linacre Coll Ox BA63 MA67 Univ of Wales PhD87. St Steph Ho Ox 63. **d** 64 **p** 65. C Aberaman *Llan* 64-66; C Newton Nottage 66-73; R Llansannor and Llanfrynach w Penllyn etc 73-94; R Llandough w Leckwith from 94; RD Llantwit Major and Cowbridge 83-94; Warden of Readers from 92; Chan Llan Cathl 92-02; Treas from 02; Chapl Llandough Hosp 94-99; Chapl Univ Hosp of Wales and Llandough NHS Trust from 99. *The Rectory, Llandough Hill, Llandough, Penarth CF64 2NA* Tel (029) 2070 3349

LODWICK, Stephen Huw. b 64. Plymouth Poly BSc85. St Mich Coll Llan DipTh94. **d** 94 **p** 95. C Clydach *S & B* 94-95; Chapl St Woolos Cathl *Mon* 95-98; R Grosmont and Skenfrith and Llangattock etc 98-01; CF from 01. *c/o MOD Chaplains (Army)* Tel (01980) 615804 Fax 615800

LOEWE, Jost Andreas. b 73. St Pet Coll Ox BA95 MA99 MPhil97 Selw Coll Cam PhD01. Westcott Ho Cam 97. **d** 01 **p** 02. C Upton cum Chalvey *Ox* from 01. *134 Albert Street, Slough SL1 2AU* Tel (01753) 694803

LOEWENDAHL, David Jacob (Jake). b 50. SS Coll Cam BA74 MA77. Ripon Coll Cuddesdon 75. **d** 77 **p** 78. C Walworth *S'wark* 77-80; Chapl St Alb Abbey *St Alb* 80-83; Chapl St Alb Sch 80-83; Team Ldr Community Service Volunteers 84-90; Perm to Offic *Lon* 83-90; R E and W Tilbury and Linford *Chelmsf* 90-95; V Menheniot *Truro* 95-98; RD W Wivelshire

97-98; rtd 98; Perm to Offic *Truro* from 98. *Ashpark House, Ash Park Terrace, Liskeard PL14 4DN* Tel (01579) 348205

LOFGREN, Ms Claire. b 54. Univ of California BA76. Cranmer Hall Dur 88 MDiv89. **d** 90 **p** 94. Par Dn Usworth *Dur* 90-91; C Heworth St Mary 91-93; USA from 93. *17 Highland Park Street, Boston, MA 02119, USA*

LOFT, Edmund Martin Boswell. b 25. St Jo Coll Cam BA49 MA55. Ely Th Coll 49. **d** 51 **p** 52. C Carl H Trin *Carl* 51-54; C Barrow St Geo 54-56; V Allonby w W Newton 56-62; V Fillongley *Cov* 62-77; V Earlsdon 77-90; rtd 90; Perm to Offic *Sheff* from 90. *10 Quarry Road, Sheffield S17 4DA* Tel 0114-236 0759

LOFTHOUSE, Canon Alexander Francis Joseph. b 30. Keble Coll Ox BA54 MA58. St Steph Ho Ox 54. **d** 56 **p** 57. C Barrow St Jas *Carl* 56-59; C Castleford All SS *Wakef* 59-60; V Airedale w Fryston 60-70; V Maryport *Carl* 70-78; V Helsington 78-95; V Underbarrow 78-95; V Levens 78-95; Hon Can Carl Cathl 85-95; rtd 95; Perm to Offic *Blackb* and *Carl* from 95. *Hazel Grove House, Yealand Redmayne, Carnforth LA5 9RW* Tel (01524) 782405

LOFTHOUSE, Canon Brenda. b 33. RGN60 RM62 RNT69. N Ord Course 84. **d** 87 **p** 94. Hon Par Dn Greengates *Bradf* 87-89; Par Dn Farsley 89-94; V Bolton St Jas w St Chrys 94-00; Hon Can Bradf Cathl 98-00; rtd 00; Perm to Offic *Bradf* from 00. *22 Heaton Drive, Baildon, Shipley BD17 5PH* Tel (01274) 584030

LOFTUS, Francis. b 52. Newc Univ BA73 St Andr Univ BPhil76 Coll of Ripon & York St Jo PGCE76 FRSA94. NEOC 93. **d** 96 **p** 97. Hd Master Barlby High Sch from 90; NSM Barlby w Riccall *York* from 96. *19 Green Lane, North Duffield, Selby YO8 5RR* Tel (01757) 288030 Fax 213699 E-mail francis-loftus2@supanet.com

LOFTUS, John Michael. b 52. Sheff Univ BSc74 Solicitor 77. Dioc OLM tr scheme 97. **d** 00 **p** 01. OLM Hundred River *St E* from 00. *Keld House, Hulver Street, Henstead, Beccles NR34 7UE* Tel (01502) 476257 Fax 533001 E-mail jjloftus@nortonpeskett.co.uk

LOGAN, Ms Alexandra Jane. b 73. Trin Coll Carmarthen BA94 St Martin's Coll Lanc CYCW97. Ridley Hall Cam 99. **d** 02 **p** 03. C Penwortham St Mary *Blackb* from 02. *4 Hill Road, Penwortham, Preston PR1 9XH* Tel (01772) 750060 E-mail alexandra.logan@btopenworld.com

LOGAN, Kevin. b 43. Oak Hill Th Coll 73. **d** 75 **p** 76. C Blackb Sav *Blackb* 75-78; C Leyland St Andr 78-82; V Gt Harwood St Jo 82-91; V Accrington Ch Ch from 91. *Christ Church Vicarage, 3 Bentcliff Gardens, Accrington BB5 2NX* Tel (01254) 235089 E-mail kevin@logan10.freeserve.co.uk

LOGAN, Samuel Desmond. b 39. TEng. CITC. **d** 78 **p** 79. NSM Belvoir *D & D* 78-85; NSM Knock 85-87; NSM Belfast St Brendan 87-91; Lic to Offic 91-95; C Bangor Abbey 95-97; I Belfast St Clem from 97. *8 Casaeldona Crescent, Belfast BT6 9RE* Tel (028) 9079 5473

LOGUE, Mrs Rosemary Christine. TCD BTh93. CITC 90. **d** 93 **p** 94. C Clooney w Strathfoyle *D & R* 93-96; I Londonderry St Aug 96-03; I Tullyaughnish w Kilmacrennan and Killygarvan from 03. *The Rectory, Ramelton, Letterkenny, Co Donegal* Tel (00353) (74) 915 1013 E-mail r.logue@btinternet.com

LOMAS, David Xavier. b 39. St Jo Coll Dur 75. Cranmer Hall Dur 75. **d** 78 **p** 79. C Chester le Street *Dur* 78-81; C-in-c Newton Hall LEP 81-85; Gen Preacher *Linc* from 85; Chapl Scunthorpe Distr HA 85-93; Sen Chapl Linc and Louth NHS Trust 93-01; Sen Chapl Chapl Manager United Lincs Hosps NHS Trust from 01. *Lincoln County Hospital, Greetwell Road, Lincoln LN2 5QY* Tel (01522) 573403 E-mail david.lomas@ulh.nhs.uk or xavlomas@aol.com

LOMAS, John Derrick Percy. b 58. St Mich Coll Llan 94. **d** 94 **p** 95. C Rhyl w St Ann *St As* 94-00; Chapl RN 00-01; V Holywell *St As* from 01. *The Vicarage, Fron Park Road, Holywell CH8 7UT* Tel (01352) 710010

LOMAX, Canon Barry Walter John. b 39. Lambeth STh Lon Coll of Div 63. **d** 66 **p** 67. C Sevenoaks St Nic *Roch* 66-71; C Southport Ch Ch *Liv* 71-73; V Bootle St Matt 73-78; P-in-c Litherland St Andr 76-78; V New Borough and Leigh *Sarum* 78-94; Can and Preb Sarum Cathl 91-02; R Blandford Forum and Langton Long 94-02; rtd 02. *Shiloh, 2 Colborne Avenue, Wimborne BH21 2PZ* Tel (01202) 856104 E-mail barry.lomax@virgin.net

LOMAX, Eric John. b 64. St Jo Coll Dur BA93. Wilson Carlile Coll Dip Evang88 Cranmer Hall Dur 90. **d** 96 **p** 97. C Goodshaw and Crawshawbooth *Man* 96-00; V Copmanthorpe *York* 00-01. *Address withheld by request*

LOMAX, Canon Frank. b 20. Leeds Univ BA42. Coll of Resurr Mirfield 42. **d** 44 **p** 45. C Byker St Ant *Newc* 44-50; Borneo 50-63; P-in-c Sandakan 50-63; Can Borneo 60-62; Can Jesselton 62-63; V Pudhoe *Newc* 64-74; Singapore from 75; Hon Can and V St Andr Cathl from 75; rtd 87. *100 Clemenceau Avenue North, #03-103 Cavenagh House, Singapore 229491*

LOMAX, Mrs Katie Jane. b 73. RGN96. St Jo Coll Nottm BA02. **d** 02 **p** 03. C Luton St Mary *St Alb* from 02. *72 Crawley Green Road, Luton LU2 0QU* Tel (01582) 735548

LONDON (St Paul's), Dean of. *See* MOSES, The Very Revd John Henry

LONDON, Archdeacon of. *See* DELANEY, The Ven Peter Anthony

LONDON, Bishop of. *See* CHARTRES, The Rt Revd and Rt Hon Richard John Carew

LONEY, Mark. **d** 03. C Larne and Inver *Conn* from 03. *23 Glenburn Avenue, Glynn, Larne BT40 3DJ* Tel (028) 2827 6129

LONG, Canon Anne Christine. b 33. Leic Univ BA56 Ox Univ DipEd57 Lon Univ BD65. **dss** 80 **d** 87 **p** 94. Lect St Jo Coll Nottm 73-84; Acorn Chr Healing Trust 85-98; Stanstead Abbots *St Alb* 85-92; Hon Par Dn 87-92; Hon Par Dn Camberley St Paul *Guildf* 92-94; Hon C from 94; Hon Can Guildf Cathl from 96. *8 Loweswater Walk, Heatherside, Camberley GU15 1BH* Tel (01276) 677591

LONG, Anthony Auguste. b 45. Linc Th Coll 79. **d** 81 **p** 82. C Kingswinford St Mary *Lich* 81-84; TV Ellesmere Port *Ches* 84-87; V Witton 87-97; P-in-c Wybunbury w Doddington 97-02; V from 02. *The Vicarage, Main Road, Wybunbury, Nantwich CW5 7LS* Tel (01270) 841178

LONG, Anthony Robert. b 48. SS Mark & Jo Coll Chelsea CertEd70 Southn Univ BTh93 UEA MA96. Chich Th Coll 74. **d** 77 **p** 78. C Chiswick St Nic w St Mary *Lon* 77-80; C Earley St Pet *Ox* 80-85; P-in-c Worstead w Westwick and Sloley *Nor* 85-92; P-in-c Swanton w Sco' Ruston from 85; R Worstead, Westwick, Sloley, Swanton Abbot etc from 92; Chapl Nor Cathl from 85. *The Vicarage, Withergate, Worstead, North Walsham NR28 9SE* Tel (01692) 536800

LONG, Christopher William. b 47. OBE94. Nottm Univ BTh78 Open Univ BA80. Linc Th Coll 75. **d** 78 **p** 79. C Shiregreen St Jas and St Chris *Sheff* 78-81; V 81-82; Chapl RAF from 82; Perm to Offic *St E* from 91; Perm to Offic *Nor* from 00. *Chaplaincy Services (RAF), HQ, Personnel and Training Command, RAF Innsworth, Gloucester GL3 1EZ* Tel (01452) 712612 ext 5164 Fax 510828

LONG, Canon David William. b 47. K Coll Lon 67. St Aug Coll Cant 70. **d** 72 **p** 73. C Stanley *Liv* 72-73; C W Derby St Luke 73-76; C Cantril Farm 76-79; V Warrington St Barn 79-81; V Westbrook St Jas 82-96; V Ince St Mary from 96; AD Wigan E from 03; Hon Can Liv Cathl from 03. *St Mary's Vicarage, 240A Warrington Road, Ince, Wigan WN3 4NH* Tel (01942) 864383 E-mail david@scars.demon.co.uk

LONG, Edward Percy Eades (Bill). b 14. Liv Univ BA36 MA38. Linc Th Coll 73. **d** 73 **p** 74. C Sedbergh, Cautley and Garsdale *Bradf* 73-84; rtd 85; Perm to Offic *Bradf* from 85. *4 Derry Cottages, Sedbergh LA10 5SN* Tel (01539) 620577

LONG, Mrs Frances Mary. b 58. SEITE 98. **d** 01 **p** 02. NSM Caterham *S'wark* from 01; Chapl Surrey and Sussex Healthcare NHS Trust from 01. *56 Roffes Lane, Caterham CR3 5PT* Tel (01883) 342273 E-mail franyb8@hotmail.com

LONG, Frederick Hugh. b 43. EMMTC 90. **d** 90 **p** 91. NSM Grantham *Linc* 90-00; C 00-01; TV 01-02; V Grantham St Anne New Somerby and Spitalgate from 02. *St Anne's Vicarage, Harrowby Road, Grantham NG31 9ED* Tel (01476) 562822

LONG, Geoffrey Lawrence. b 47. La Sainte Union Coll BTh93 PGCE94. Portsm Dioc Tr Course 88. **d** 89 **p** 98. NSM Whippingham w E Cowes *Portsm* 89-01; Chapl HM Pris Maidstone from 01. *HM Prison, County Road, Maidstone ME14 1UZ* Tel (01622) 755611

LONG, The Ven John Sanderson. b 13. Qu Coll Cam BA35 MA39. Cuddesdon Coll 35. **d** 36 **p** 37. C Folkestone St Mary and St Eanswythe *Cant* 36-41; Chapl RNVR 41-46; C St Peter-in-Thanet *Cant* 46; Abp's Dom Chapl 46-53; V Bearsted 53-59; V Petersfield w Sheet *Portsm* 59-70; RD Petersfield 62-70; Hon Can Portsm Cathl 67-70; Adn Ely 70-81; R Cambridge St Botolph 70-81; Hon Can Ely Cathl 70-81; rtd 81; Perm to Offic *Ely* from 81. *23 Thornton Road, Girton, Cambridge CB3 0NP* Tel (01223) 276421

LONG, Canon John Sydney. b 25. Lon Univ BSc49. Wycliffe Hall Ox 50. **d** 51 **p** 52. C Plaistow St Andr *Chelmsf* 51-54; C Keighley *Bradf* 54-57; C-in-c Horton Bank Top CD 57-59; V Buttershaw St Aid 59-64; V Barnoldswick w Bracewell 64-85; Hon Can Bradf Cathl 77-91; RD Skipton 83-90; R Broughton, Marton and Thornton 85-91; rtd 91; Perm to Offic *Bradf* from 91. *1 Church Villa, Carleton, Skipton BD23 3DQ* Tel (01756) 799095

LONG, Kingsley Edward. b 41. CITC 90. **d** 93 **p** 94. NSM Howth *D & G* 93-96; NSM Swords w Donabate and Kilsallaghan 96-01; NSM Holmpatrick w Balbriggan and Kenure from 01. *Crimond, 125 Seapark, Malahide, Co Dublin, Irish Republic* Tel (00353) (1) 845 3179

LONG, Canon Michael David Barnby. b 32. AKC55. **d** 56 **p** 57. C Whitby *York* 56-59; C Cottingham 59-61; V Elloughton 61-66; P-in-c Brantingham 61-66; V Sheff Parson Cross St Cecilia *Sheff* 66-68; V Flamborough 68-73; R Litcham w Kempston w E and W Lexham *Nor* 73-75; P-in-c York St Luke *York* 75-77; V 77-80; V Hatton w Haseley and Rowington w Lowsonford *Cov* 80-82; V Derringham Bank *York* 82-85; V Castle Acre w Newton *Nor* 85; R Southacre 85; R Castleacre w Newton, Rougham and Southacre 85-86; TV Grantham *Linc* 86-89; V Cayton w

Eastfield *York* 89-98; RD Scarborough 94-98; Can and Preb York Minster 97-03; rtd 98; P-in-c York St Clem w St Mary Bishophill Senior *York* 98-03; P-in-c Trowse *Nor* from 03. *St Clement's Rectory, 13 Nunthorpe Avenue, York YO23 1PF* Tel (01904) 624425 E-mail michael-long@amserve.com

LONG, Peter Ronald. b 48. Nottm Univ BA69 Man Univ CertEd70 Dip Past Th 71 MA83 PhD84. Cuddesdon Coll 71. **d** 73 **p** 74. Chapl RAFVR 74-99; C Bodmin *Truro* 73-75; C Newquay 75-76; Asst Youth Chapl 75-76; Dioc Youth Chapl 76-79; Perm to Offic *Eur* 76, 78-85 and 87-98; Public Preacher *Truro* 77; P-in-c Mawgan w St Martin-in-Meneage 79-82; Chapl Helston-Meneage Community and Geriatric Hosp 80-95; Miss to Seamen 80-98; P-in-c Cury w Gunwalloe *Truro* 80-82; R Cury and Gunwalloe w Mawgan 83-98; Perm to Offic *Ex* 82-93; Ecum Th Rail Ind from 97. *26 Jubilee Street, Newquay TR7 1LA* Tel 07780-976113 (mobile) Fax 0117-930 9982 E-mail forum@railpassengers.org.uk

LONG, Roger Eric. b 36. Univ Coll Dur BSc59 PhD62. NEOC 90. **d** 93 **p** 94. C Street *York* 93-97; P-in-c Coxwold and Husthwaite 97-02; rtd 02. *Ivy House, Coxwold, York YO61 4AD* Tel (01347) 868301

LONG, Canon Samuel Ernest. b 18. JP68. ALCD50. **d** 49 **p** 50. C Belfast St Clem *D & D* 49-52; C Willowfield 52-56; I Dromara w Garvaghy 56-85; Can Dromore Cathl 81-85; Treas 82-85; rtd 85. *9 Cairnshill Court, Saintfield Road, Belfast BT8 4TX* Tel (028) 9079 3401

LONG, Simon Richard. b 40. Birm Univ DPS69. Bernard Gilpin Soc Dur 61 Ely Th Coll 62 Coll of Resurr Mirfield 64. **d** 65 **p** 66. C Bournemouth St Fran *Win* 65-68; Belgium 68; USA 69-88; P-in-c Medbourne cum Holt w Stockerston and Blaston *Leic* 88-89; P-in-c Bringhurst w Gt Easton 88-89; R Six Saints circa Holt 90-99; RD Gartree I 93-97; rtd 99. *17C Craft Village, Balnakeil, Durness, Lairg IV27 4PT* Tel (01971) 511777

LONG, William Thomas. b 53. Dur Univ MA88 QUB PhD99. **d** 81 **p** 82. C Orangefield *D & D* 81-84; C Portadown St Mark *Arm* 84-86; I Dromara w Garvaghy *D & D* 86-91; I Aghalurcher w Tattykeeran, Cooneen etc *Clogh* 91-96; I Annalong *D & D* 96-03; I Belfast St Simon w St Phil *Conn* from 03. *106 Upper Lisburn Road, Belfast BT10 0BB* Tel (028) 9061 7562 Mobile 07715-773979 E-mail wlhudhud@bushinternet.com

LONGBOTHAM, Richard Ashley. b 14. AKC36. Sarum Th Coll 37. **d** 37 **p** 38. C Eastbourne Ch Ch *Chich* 37-40; S Africa 41-46 and 62-00; S Rhodesia 46-54 and 59-60; C Durban St Paul 41-44; C Pietermaritzburg St Pet 44-46; R Gatooma 47-52; R Salisbury S 53-54; CF 54-57; V Aldingbourne *Chich* 57-59; R Gwanda 59-60; V Aston w Benington *St Alb* 60-62; R Irene 62-72; R Richmond 72-74; R Eersterust Gd Shep w Silverton All SS 75-80; rtd 80. *c/o Messrs Ford Simey, 8 Cathedral Close, Exeter EX1 1EW*

LONGBOTTOM, Canon Frank. b 41. Lon Univ DipTh68 Birm Univ DPS74. Ripon Hall Ox 65. **d** 68 **p** 69. C Epsom St Martin *Guildf* 68-72; Asst Chapl St Ebbas Hosp Epsom 68-72; Asst Chapl Qu Mary's Hosp Carshalton 68-72; Asst Chapl Henderson Hosp Sutton 68-72; Chapl Highcroft Hosp Birm 72-94; Chapl Northcroft Hosp Birm 74-94; Dioc Adv for Past Care of Clergy & Families from 89; Bp's Adv from 94; Hon Can Birm Cathl *Birm* from 91; P-in-c Middleton 99-00; Bp's Adv on Health and Soc Care from 01. *46 Sunnybank Road, Sutton Coldfield B73 5RE* Tel and fax 0121-350 5823 *or* tel 378 2211

LONGBOTTOM, Canon Paul Edward. b 44. AKC67. **d** 68 **p** 69. C Rainham *Roch* 68-71; C Riverhead 71-75; C Dunton Green 71-75; V Penge Lane H Trin 75-84; V Chatham St Wm 84-94; V Shorne from 94; Dioc Dir of Ords from 94; Hon Can Roch Cathl from 96. *The Vicarage, Butcher's Hill, Shorne, Gravesend DA12 3EB* Tel (01474) 822239 Fax 824502 E-mail paul.longbottom@rochester.anglican.org

LONGFOOT, Richard. b 46. Oak Hill Th Coll 76. **d** 78 **p** 79. C Chaddesden St Mary *Derby* 78-81; C Cambridge St Martin *Ely* 81-83; R Folksworth w Morborne 83-89; R Stilton w Denton and Caldecote 83-89; R Stilton w Denton and Caldecote etc from 90; RD Yaxley from 02. *The Rectory, Stilton, Peterborough PE7 3RF* Tel (01733) 240282 E-mail richard.lfoot@lineone.net

LONGFORD, Canon Edward de Toesny Wingfield. b 25. Ch Ch Ox BA48 MA53. Wells Th Coll 49. **d** 51 **p** 52. C Stevenage *St Alb* 51-54; C Chettisham 55-68; Min Can, Prec and Sacr Ely Cathl *Ely* 55-68; P-in-c Everton w Tetworth 68-71; V 71-73; R Gamlingay 68-80; P-in-c Hatley 78-80; Hon Can Ely Cathl 79-90; R Gamlingay w Hatley St Geo and E Hatley 80-90; RD St Neots 82-90; rtd 90; Perm to Offic *Ely* from 90. *9 Philippa Close, Ely CB6 1BT* Tel (01353) 667495

LONGMAN, Edward. b 37. Hatf Coll Dur BSc62 Fitzw Coll Cam BA66 MA70. Clifton Th Coll 62. **d** 66 **p** 67. C Lower Homerton St Paul *Lon* 66-72; C Parr *Liv* 72-73; TV 74-85; Perm to Offic *Liv* 87-02; *Ches* from 96. *21 Canadian Avenue, Hoole, Chester CH2 3HG* Tel (01244) 317544 Mobile 07779-650791 Fax (01244) 400450 E-mail elongman@onetel.net.uk

LONGMAN, Edward George. b 35. St Pet Hall Ox BA58 MA62. Westcott Ho Cam 59. **d** 61 **p** 62. C Sheff St Mark Broomhall *Sheff* 61-65; V Brightside St Thos 65-74; V Yardley St Edburgha

Birm 74-84; RD Yardley 77-84; Hon Can Birm Cathl 81-96; R Sutton Coldfield H Trin 84-96; RD Sutton Coldfield 94-96; Chapl Gd Hope Distr Gen Hosp Sutton Coldfield 84-90; P-in-c Cerne Abbas w Godmanstone and Minterne Magna *Sarum* 96-02; RD Dorchester 00-02; rtd 02. *Bagbury Close, Bagborough Lane, Pylle, Shepton Mallet BA4 6SX* Tel (01749) 831319 E-mail geoffh@dircon.co.uk

LONGRIDGE, Richard Nevile. b 15. Sarum Th Coll 46. **d** 48 **p** 49. C Portsea N End St Mark *Portsm* 48-51; R Bourton w Silton *Sarum* 51-63; R Okeford Fitzpaine 63-67; R Spetisbury w Charlton Marshall 67-77; rtd 77; Perm to Offic *Ex* from 78. *The Lodge, 22 Spicer Road, Exeter EX1 1SY* Tel (01392) 494660

LONGUET-HIGGINS, John. b 62. Leeds Univ BA85. St Jo Coll Nottm Dip Th Studies 90 DPS91. **d** 91 **p** 92. C Kidlington w Hampton Poyle *Ox* 91-95; TV N Huddersfield *Wakef* 95-01; V Painswick, Sheepscombe, Cranham, The Edge etc *Glouc* from 02. *The Vicarage, Orchard Mead, Painswick, Stroud GL6 6YD* Tel (01452) 812334

LONSDALE, Mrs Gillian. b 36. Qu Mary Coll Lon BA57 MA59 Ex Univ MPhil81 Bedf Coll Lon DipSocSc60 AIMSW61. SW Minl Tr Course 96. **d** 99 **p** 00. NSM Duloe, Herodsfoot, Morval and St Pinnock *Truro* from 99; NSM Lansallos from 01; NSM Talland from 01. *Trehere Cottage, Trewidland, Liskeard PL14 4SR* Tel (01503) 240536 Mobile 07801-301031 E-mail gill@glonsdale.freeserve.co.uk

LOOKER, Miss Clare Margaret. b 55. Liv Univ CertEd DipRE. Westcott Ho Cam 85. **d** 87 **p** 02. Par Dn Prestwood and Gt Hampden *Ox* 87-90; Hon C Olney w Emberton 90-92; Hon C Blunham, Gt Barford, Roxton and Tempsford etc *St Alb* 01-03; P-in-c Welford w Sibbertoft and Marston Trussell *Pet* from 03. *The Vicarage, 35 The Leys, Welford, Northampton NN6 6HS* Tel (01858) 575252

LOOMES, Gaenor Mary. See HOCKEY, Gaenor Mary

LOONE, Sean Joseph Patrick. b 60. Cov Poly BA83 Wolv Poly CertEd84 Leeds Univ BA88 Birm Univ MEd94. Coll of Resurr Mirfield 86. **d** 89 **p** 90. C Solihull *Birm* 89-92; Hd RE Bromsgrove Jun Sch from 93. *9 Broomfield Road, Solihull B91 2ND* Tel 0121-705 5117

LOPDELL-BRADSHAW, Canon Humphrey Maitland. b 32. Edin Th Coll 58. **d** 61 **p** 62. C Edin H Cross *Edin* 61-65; C Edin St Barn 65-67; P-in-c Oldbury *Birm* 67-68; V 68-72; R Edin St Hilda *Edin* 72-77; R Hawick 77-88; R Huntly *Mor* 88-97; R Aberchirder 88-97; R Keith 88-97; Can St Andr Cathl Inverness from 91; rtd 97. *58 Cortachy Crescent, Northmuir, Kirriemuir DD8 4TP* Tel (01575) 573729

✠**LÓPEZ LOZANO, The Rt Revd Carlos.** b 62. Madrid Univ BA89 Pontifical Univ Salamanca PhD93. United Th Sem Madrid MTh91. **d** 90 **p** 90 **c** 95. Spain from 90; Bp's Chapl 90-91; R Espiritu Santo 92-95; Adn Cen and N Spain 94-95; Bp in Madrid from 95; Hon Asst Bp Eur from 95. *Calle Beneficencia 18, 28004 Madrid, Spain* Tel (0034) (91) 445 2560 Fax 594 4572 E-mail eclesiae@arrakis.es

LORAINE, Kenneth. b 34. Cranmer Hall Dur 63. **d** 66 **p** 67. C Hartlepool All SS Stranton *Dur* 66-69; C Darlington St Cuth 69-72; V Preston on Tees 72-79; V Staindrop 79-87; P-in-c Haynes *St Alb* 87-96; Dioc Stewardship Adv 87-96; rtd 96; Perm to Offic *York* from 96. *116 Turker Lane, Northallerton DL6 1QD* Tel (01609) 771277

LORD, Alexander. b 13. ALCD43. **d** 43 **p** 44. C Wakef St Mary *Wakef* 43-45; P-in-c Thornham St Jas *Man* 45-47; R Clitheroe St Jas *Blackb* 47-55; V Madeley *Heref* 55-69; R Illogan *Truro* 70-81; rtd 81; C Letton w Staunton, Byford, Mansel Gamage etc *Heref* 81-84. *43 Narrow Lane, Llandudno Junction LL31 9SZ* Tel (01492) 584647

LORD, Andrew Michael. b 66. Warwick Univ BSc87 Birm Univ MA99 Fitzw Coll Cam BA02. Ridley Hall Cam 00. **d** 03. C Long Buckby w Watford *Pet* from 03; C W Haddon w Winwick and Ravensthorpe from 03. *The Vicarage, 4 West Road, West Haddon, Northampton NN6 7AY* Tel (01788) 510535 E-mail andylord@freenet.co.uk

LORD, Clive Gavin. b 69. St Martin's Coll Lanc BA. St Steph Ho Ox BTh. **d** 96 **p** 97. C Penwortham St Leon *Blackb* 96-98; C Blackpool St Mary 98-01; P-in-c from 01. *St Mary's Vicarage, 59 Stony Hill Avenue, Blackpool FY4 1PR* Tel (01253) 342713 E-mail livecg@aol.com

LORD, Canon John Fairbourne. b 19. Kelham Th Coll 38. **d** 43 **p** 44. C Dallington *Pet* 43-45; C Langley Marish *Ox* 47-51; RD Holt *Nor* 64-79; R Thornage w Brinton w Hunworth and Stody 64-84; Hon Can Nor Cathl 77-84; rtd 84; Perm to Offic *Nor* from 84. *25 Melton Road, Hindolveston, Dereham NR20 5DB* Tel (01263) 860819

LORD, Stuart James. b 59. K Coll Lon BD81 AKC81. Sarum & Wells Th Coll 83. **d** 85 **p** 86. C Darwen St Pet w Hoddlesden *Blackb* 85-88; C Otley *Bradf* 88-93; P-in-c Low Moor St Mark 93-02; TV Brighouse and Clifton *Wakef* from 02. *31 Robin Hood Way, Clifton, Brighouse HD6 4LA* Tel (01484) 713290 E-mail kuriosmba@hotmail.com

LORDING, Miss Claire Ann. b 75. Roehampton Inst BA96. Ripon Coll Cuddesdon BTh96. **d** 99 **p** 00. C Ledbury *Heref*

99-02; TV Tenbury from 02. *The Vicarage, Church Street, Tenbury Wells WR15 8BP* Tel (01584) 810811 E-mail claire.lording@virgin.net

LORIMER, Eileen Jean. b 35. CertEd56. Dalton Ho Bris 62. **dss** 84 **d** 89 **p** 94. Chiddingstone w Chiddingstone Causeway *Roch* 84-89; NSM from 89. *3 Causeway Cottages, Chiddingstone Causeway, Tonbridge TN11 8JR* Tel (01892) 871393

LOSACK, Marcus Charles. b 53. Ch Coll Cam BA76 MA78 MPhil. Sarum & Wells Th Coll 78. **d** 80 **p** 81. C Hattersley *Ches* 80-82; C Dublin Zion Ch *D & G* 83-86; Libya 86-89; CMS 89-92; Jerusalem 89-92; I Newcastle w Newtownmountkennedy and Calary *D & G* 93-95; Exec Dir Ceile De from 95. *Céile Dé, Castlekevin, Annamoe, Bray, Co Wicklow, Irish Republic* Tel (00353) (404) 45595 Fax as telephone

LOSEBY, Everitt James Carnall. b 22. Launde Abbey. **d** 66 **p** 67. C Thurmaston *Leic* 66-70; R Seagrave w Walton le Wolds 70-75; V Thurnby Lodge 75-84; V Swinford w Catthorpe, Shawell and Stanford 84-87; rtd 87; Perm to Offic *Leic* from 87. *63 Willow Road, Blaby, Leicester LE8 4BG* Tel 0116-277 1983

LOTT, Eric John. b 34. Lon Univ BA65 Lanc Univ MLitt70 PhD77. Richmond Th Coll BD59. **d** 60 **p** 61. India 60-88; Prof United Th Coll Bangalore 77-88; Wesley Hall Ch and Community Project Leics 88-94; rtd 94; Perm to Offic *Leic* from 94. *16 Main Road, Old Dalby, Melton Mowbray LE14 3LR* Tel (01664) 822405 E-mail eric.lott@breathemail.net

LOUDEN, Canon Terence Edmund. b 48. Ch Coll Cam BA70 MA74. Sarum & Wells Th Coll 72. **d** 75 **p** 76. C Portsea N End St Mark *Portsm* 75-78; C-in-c Leigh Park St Clare CD 78-81; R Chale 81-88; R Niton 81-88; P-in-c Whitwell 82-84; V Cosham 88-96; Hon Can Portsm Cathl from 92; V E Meon from 96; V Langrish from 96; Dir CME 96-03. *The Vicarage, Church Street, East Meon, Petersfield GU32 1NH* Tel (01730) 823221 Mobile 07711-319752 E-mail telouden@cwcom.net

LOUGHBOROUGH, Archdeacon of. *See* STANES, The Ven Ian Thomas

LOUGHEED, Canon Brian Frederick Britain. b 38. TCD BA60. CITC 61. **d** 61 **p** 62. C Dublin St Pet w St Audoen *D & G* 61-63; C Glenageary 63-66; I Rathmolyon Union *M & K* 66-79; I Killarney w Aghadoe and Muckross *L & K* from 79; Can Limerick and Killaloe Cathls 87-95; Preb Taney St Patr Cathl Dublin from 89; Dioc Info Officer (Limerick) *L & K* 90-91; Radio Officer from 91. *St Mary's Rectory, Rookery Close, Killarney, Co Kerry, Irish Republic* Tel (00353) (64) 31832 Fax as telephone E-mail brianfbl@iolfree.ie

LOUGHLIN, Canon Alfred. b 10. Clifton Th Coll 37. **d** 39 **p** 40. C Preston St Mark *Blackb* 39-44; Chapl RAFVR 41-43; Org Sec (SE Area) CPAS 44-48; V Sneinton St Chris *S'well* 48-54; R Kinson *Sarum* 54-81; Can and Preb Sarum Cathl 75-81; rtd 81. *18 Donnelly Road, Bournemouth BH6 5NW* Tel (01202) 422306

LOUGHLIN, George Alfred Graham. b 43. Lon Univ DipTh68. Clifton Th Coll 65. **d** 69 **p** 70. C Plumstead All SS *S'wark* 69-73; C Bromley Ch Ch *Roch* 73-76; P-in-c Bothenhampton w Walditch *Sarum* 76-79; TV Bridport 79-83; V Heatherlands St Jo from 83. *St John's Vicarage, 72 Alexandra Road, Poole BH14 9EW* Tel (01202) 741276

LOUGHTON, Michael. b 34. K Coll Lon BD58 AKC58. **d** 59 **p** 60. C Chingford SS Pet and Paul *Chelmsf* 59-62; C Eastbourne St Eliz *Chich* 62-65; R Lewes St Jo sub Castro 65-74; Perm to Offic from 87; rtd 94. *Follers Manor, Seaford Road, Alfriston, Polegate BN26 5TT* Tel (01323) 870252

LOUIS, Ms Emma Christine. b 69. Coll of Ripon & York St Jo 89 Leeds Univ BA92 St Jo Coll Dur BA96. Cranmer Hall Dur 94. **d** 97 **p** 98. C Birm St Martin w Bordesley St Andr *Birm* 97-00; Arts Development Officer 97-00; Asst Chapl Harrogate Health Care NHS Trust 00-02; C Bilton *Ripon* 01; Chapl Co-ord St Mich Hospice Harrogate 01-02; Chapl Birm Heartlands and Solihull NHS Trust from 02. *2 Castleford Grove, Blackford Road, Birmingham B11 3SJ* Tel 0121-773 7158 Mobile 07946-451954 E-mail musicalpriest@hotmail.com

LOUIS, Peter Anthony. b 41. St Cath Coll Cam BA63 MA77 Jes Coll Cam CertEd64 Man Univ MPhil85. Wells Th Coll 66. **d** 68 **p** 70. C E Grinstead St Mary *Chich* 68-75; C Radcliffe-on-Trent *S'well* 75-80; Hd Master Blue Coat Comp Sch Cov 80-85; V Welwyn Garden City *St Alb* from 85; Chapl Oaklands Coll from 93. *The Vicarage, 48 Parkway, Welwyn Garden City AL8 6HH* Tel (01707) 323316 E-mail plouis@ntlworld.com

LOVATT, Bernard James. b 31. Lich Th Coll 64. **d** 65 **p** 66. C Burford III w Lt Heref 65-67; C Cleobury Mortimer w Hopton Wafers 67-68; C Bradford-on-Avon *Sarum* 68-69; C Wootton Bassett 69-72; C Broad Town 69-72; R Bishopstrow and Boreham 72-79; P-in-c Brighton St Geo *Chich* 79-83; V Brighton St Anne 79-83; V Brighton St Geo and St Anne 83-86; P-in-c Kemp Town St Mark and St Matt 85-86; V Brighton St Geo w St Anne and St Mark 86-95; rtd 95; Perm to Offic *Ex* from 95. *7 Cambridge Terrace, Salcombe Road, Sidmouth EX10 8PL* Tel (01395) 514154

LOVATT, Mrs Pamela. b 50. LNSM course 95. **d** 98 **p** 99. OLM Warrington St Ann *Liv* from 98; Chapl Warrington Community

Health Care NHS Trust from 99. *59 Amelia Street, Warrington WA2 7QD* Tel (01925) 650849 *or* 655221

LOVATT, William Robert. b 54. SS Coll Cam MA75 K Coll Lon PGCE77 MA78. Oak Hill Th Coll 85. **d** 87 **p** 88. C Devonport St Budeaux *Ex* 87-90; Asst Chapl Paris St Mich *Eur* 90-94; P-in-c Lenton *S'well* 94-00; V from 00. *The Vicarage, 35A Church Street, Nottingham NG7 2FF* Tel 0115-970 1059 E-mail wrlovatt@msn.com

LOVE, Ms Anette. b 53. Matlock Coll of Educn CertEd74 Nottm Univ BEd75. St Jo Coll Dur 88. **d** 90 **p** 94. Par Dn Gresley *Derby* 90-92; C Heanor 92-94; C Loscoe 94-02; V Heath from 02. *The Vicarage, Main Road, Heath, Chesterfield S44 5RX* Tel (01246) 850339

LOVE, Richard Angus. b 45. AKC67. **d** 68 **p** 69. C Balham Hill Ascension *S'wark* 68-71; C Amersham *Ox* 71-73; R Scotter w E Ferry *Linc* 73-79; P-in-c Petham w Waltham and Lower Hardres w Nackington *Cant* 79-85; R Petham and Waltham w Lower Hardres etc 85-90; V Sittingbourne H Trin w Bobbing 90-02; P-in-c Aldington w Bonnington and Bilsington etc from 02. *The Rectory, Roman Road, Aldington, Ashford TN25 7EF* Tel (01233) 720898 E-mail revralove@msn.com

LOVE, Robert. b 45. Bradf Univ BSc68 PhD74 NE Lon Poly PGCE89. Trin Coll Bris DipTh75. **d** 75 **p** 76. C Bowling St Jo *Bradf* 75-79; TV Forest Gate St Sav w W Ham St Matt *Chelmsf* 79-85; P-in-c Becontree St Elisabeth 85-96; V S Hornchurch St Jo and St Matt from 96. *St John's Vicarage, South End Road, Rainham RM13 7XT* Tel (01708) 555260

LOVEDAY, Joseph Michael. b 54. AKC75. St Aug Coll Cant 75. **d** 78 **p** 79. C Kettering SS Pet and Paul *Pet* 78-81; C Upper Teddington SS Pet and Paul *Lon* 81-84; CF from 84. *clo MOD Chaplains (Army)* Tel (01980) 615804 Fax 615800

LOVEDAY, Susan Mary. b 49. Sussex Univ BA70 Surrey Univ MSc81. STETS 94. **d** 97 **p** 98. NSM New Haw *Guildf* 97-03; NSM Egham Hythe from 03; Ecum Co-ord Churches Together in Surrey from 00. *10 Abbey Gardens, Chertsey KT16 8RQ* Tel (01932) 566920 E-mail sue.loveday.ctsurrey@lineone.net

LOVEGROVE, Mrs Anne Maureen. b 44. DipHE90. Oak Hill Th Coll 88. **d** 90 **p** 94. Par Dn Thorley *St Alb* 90-94; C 94-95; V Croxley Green St Oswald 95-02; V Letchworth St Paul w Willian from 02. *St Paul's Vicarage, 177 Pixmore Way, Letchworth Garden City SG6 1QT* Tel (01462) 637373

LOVEGROVE, Michael John Bennett. b 42. FCII FCIPD ACIArb. SEITE. **d** 00 **p** 01. NSM Saffron Walden w Wendens Ambo, Littlebury etc *Chelmsf* from 00. *8 Beck Road, Saffron Walden CB11 4EH* Tel (01799) 528232 Mobile 07980-103541 E-mail lovegrove8_@hotmail.com

LOVEJOY, Geoffrey William. b 08. St Chad's Coll Dur BA31 LTh31 MA47. Dorchester Miss Coll 28. **d** 32 **p** 33. C Hendford *B & W* 32-34; Australia 34-40; India 40-44; C Tottenham All Hallows *Lon* 45-46; S Rhodesia 46-52; C St Marychurch *Ex* 52-54; P-in-c Shiphay Collaton 54-57; V 57-59; R Cumberworth *Wakef* 59-65; R Stoke Goldington w Gayhurst *Ox* 65-72; P-in-c Ravenstone w Weston Underwood 67-72; rtd 73; Chapl Sevenoaks Hosp 73-78; Hon C Sevenoaks St Jo *Roch* 73-88; Perm to Offic 88-93. *61 Old Mill Close, Eynsford, Dartford DA4 0BN* Tel (01322) 866186

LOVELAND, John Michael. b 30. Roch Th Coll 65. **d** 67 **p** 68. C Ashford St Hilda CD *Lon* 67-71; P-in-c Earley St Nic *Ox* 71-76; V 76-79; V Kennington 79-84; V Reading St Mark 84-89; P-in-c Drayton St Pet (Berks) 89-92; rtd 92; Perm to Offic *Ox* 95-99. *Chantry House, Radley Road, Abingdon OX14 3SN*

LOVELESS, Christopher Hugh. b 61. Trin Coll Bris BA84 MA91. Linc Th Coll 89. **d** 91 **p** 92. C Willingdon *Chich* 91-95; C Goring-by-Sea 95-99; V Warnham from 99. *The Vicarage, Church Street, Warnham, Horsham RH12 3QW* Tel (01403) 265041

LOVELESS, Martin Frank. b 46. Wycliffe Hall Ox 72. **d** 75 **p** 76. C Caversham *Ox* 75-81; V Carterton 81-86; Chapl RAF 86-02; Chapl K Coll Taunton from 02. *40 South Road, Taunton TA1 3DY*

LOVELESS, Robert Alfred. b 43. Birm Univ BA66. Westcott Ho Cam 66. **d** 68 **p** 69. C Kenilworth St Nic *Cov* 68-72; C Costessey *Nor* 73-75; R Colney 75-80; R Lt w Gt Melton, Marlingford and Bawburgh 75-80; V Lt and Gt Melton w Bawburgh 80-82; P-in-c Westwood *Sarum* 82-83; Chapl Stonar Sch Melksham 82-87; P-in-c Wingfield w Rowley *Sarum* 82-83; R Westwood and Wingfield 83-87; R Paston *Pet* 87-93; V Nassington w Yarwell and Woodnewton from 93. *The Vicarage, 34 Station Road, Nassington, Peterborough PE8 6QB* Tel (01780) 782271

LOVELESS, Canon William Harry. b 21. Lon Univ BSc60. Ridley Hall Cam 61. **d** 63 **p** 64. C Danbury *Chelmsf* 63-65; C Cambridge Gt St Mary w St Mich *Ely* 65-67; V Cambridge St Mark 67-87; RD Cambridge 81-84; Hon Can Ely Cathl 81-87; rtd 87; Perm to Offic *Ely* from 87. *103 High Street, Swaffham Bulbeck, Cambridge CB5 0LX*

LOVELL, Charles Nelson. b 34. Oriel Coll Ox BA57 MA61. Wycliffe Hall Ox. **d** 59 **p** 60. C Walsall St Matt *Lich* 59-63; C St Giles-in-the-Fields *Lon* 63; Argentina 64-67; C Cambridge H Trin *Ely* 64; V Esh *Dur* 67-75; V Hamsteels 67-75; Chapl Winterton Hosp Sedgefield 75-83; R Stanhope *Dur* 83-86; Chapl

Horn Hall Hosp Weardale 83-97; R Stanhope w Frosterley *Dur* 86-97; V Eastgate w Rookhope 86-97; RD Stanhope 87-97; rtd 97. *10 Riverside, Wolsingham, Bishop Auckland DL13 3BP* Tel (01388) 527038 E-mail charles@thefreeinternet.co.uk

LOVELL, David John. b 38. JP89. Univ of Tasmania BEcon86. Qu Coll Birm 60. **d** 60 **p** 62. C Glouc St Steph *Glouc* 60-64; C Lower Tuffley St Geo CD 64-67; V Lydbrook 67-73; Australia from 73; rtd 98. *26 Lynden Road, Bonnet Hill, Tas, Australia 7053*

LOVELL, Helen Sarah. *See* HOUSTON, Helen Sarah

LOVELL, Keith Michael Beard. b 43. K Coll Lon 67. **d** 68 **p** 69. C Romford St Edw *Chelmsf* 68-73; P-in-c Elmstead 73-79; V Tollesbury w Salcot Virley from 79. *The Vicarage, 12 King's Walk, Tollesbury, Maldon CM9 8XH* Tel (01621) 869393 *or* 868441 E-mail keith@mary.freewire.co.uk

LOVELL, Laurence John. b 31. St D Coll Lamp BA54 Tyndale Hall Bris 54. **d** 56 **p** 57. C Penge Ch Ch w H Trin *Roch* 56-61; C Illogan *Truro* 61-63; V St Keverne 63-68; Australia from 68; rtd 95. *1/64 Cambridge Street, Penshurst, NSW, Australia 2222* Tel (0061) (2) 9580 7554 Fax as telephone E-mail laurence@can.net.au

LOVELUCK, Canon Allan (Illtyd). b 30. Queensland Univ MSocWork79 BSW74. St D Coll Lamp BA52 St Mich Coll Llan 54. **d** 55 **p** 56. C Dowlais *Llan* 55-58; SSF 58-79; Lic to Offic *Chelmsf* 62-64; Australia from 64; Hon Can Brisbane 92-00; rtd 95. *5/48 Dunmore Terrace, Auchenflower, Qld, Australia 4066* Tel (0061) (7) 3719 5342 *or* 3870 2566 Mobile 414-500837

LOVELUCK, Canon Graham David. b 34. Univ of Wales (Abth) BSc55 PhD58 CChem FRSC. St Deiniol's Hawarden 77. **d** 78 **p** 79. Hon C Llanfair Mathafarn Eithaf w Llanbedrgoch *Ban* 78-87; NSM Llaneugrad w Llanallgo and Penrhoslligwy etc 87-96; P-in-c 96-03; R from 03; Dioc Dir of Educn from 92; Can Cursal Ban Cathl from 00. *Gwenallt, Marianglas LL73 8PE* Tel (01248) 853741

LOVELY, Canon Leslie Walter. b 09. Dur Univ LTh32. **d** 32 **p** 33. C Southampton St Alb *Win* 32-35; Egypt 35-43; S Africa from 43; Hon Can Johannesburg from 95. *168 Darrenwood Village, Private Bag X5, Linden, 2104 South Africa* Tel (0027) (11) 678 7303

LOVERIDGE, Douglas Henry. b 52. Sarum & Wells Th Coll. **d** 84 **p** 85. C Earley St Pet *Ox* 84-88; V Hurst 88-03; Asst Chapl R Berks and Battle Hosps NHS Trust from 03. *The Rectory, Hollybush Lane, Burghfield Common, Reading RG7 3JL* Tel 0118-983 4433 E-mail dhloveridge@hotmail.com

LOVERIDGE, Emma Warren. b 65. St Jo Coll Cam BA87 MA90 PhD01. **d** 99 **p** 00. NSM Highbury Ch Ch w St Jo and St Sav Lon 99-02; NSM Islington St Mary from 03. *Rafan House, 6 Tyndale Terrace, London N1 2AT* Tel 07000-777977 (mobile) E-mail eloveridge@windsandstars.org

LOVERIDGE (née RODEN), Ms Joan Margaretha Holland (Jo). b 57. K Coll Lon BD78 AKC78 Regent's Park Coll Ox MTh98. St Alb and Ox Min Course 95. **d** 97 **p** 98. NSM Caversham St Jo *Ox* 97-98; C Earley St Pet 98-03; P-in-c Burghfield from 03. *The Rectory, Hollybush Lane, Burghfield Common, Reading RG7 3JL* Tel 0118-983 4433 E-mail jonloveridge@hotmail.com

LOVERING, Mrs Jennifer Mary. b 39. Eastbourne Tr Coll CertEd59. Wycliffe Hall Ox 81. **dss** 84 **d** 87 **p** 94. Abingdon w Shippon *Ox* 84-87; Par Dn Abingdon 87-94; C 94-97; rtd 98. *5 Monksmead, Brightwell-cum-Sotwell, Wallingford OX10 0RL* Tel (01491) 825329

LOVERING, Martin. b 35. Imp Coll Lon BScEng57 DMS66. Wycliffe Hall Ox 82. **d** 84 **p** 85. NSM Abingdon w Shippon *Ox* 84-88; C Abingdon 88-89; TV 89-00; rtd 01. *5 Monks Mead, Brightwell-cum-Sotwell, Wallingford OX10 0RL* Tel (01491) 825329

LOVESEY, Katharine Patience Beresford. b 62. **d** 03. C Nor Lakenham St Jo and All SS and Tuckswood *Nor* from 03. *23 Lindford Drive, Eaton, Norwich NR4 0LL* Tel (01603) 501619

LOVETT, Mrs Frances Mary Anderson. b 46. Plymouth Univ BA92. N Ord Course 00. **d** 03. NSM Newton in Makerfield St Pet *Liv* from 03. *8 The Parchments, Newton-le-Willows WA12 0DY* Tel (01925) 220586 Fax as telephone E-mail franian.lovett@virgin.net

LOVETT, Francis Roland. b 25. Glouc Th Course. **d** 85 **p** 86. NSM Ludlow *Heref* 85-91; rtd 92; Perm to Offic *Heref* from 96. *7 Poyner Road, Ludlow SY8 1QT* Tel (01584) 872470

LOVETT, Ian Arthur. b 43. NE Lon Poly BSc74 Ox Poly Dip Town Planning 78. Linc Th Coll 85. **d** 87 **p** 88. C Uppingham w Ayston and Wardley w Belton *Pet* 87-91; R Polebrook w Lutton w Hemington and Luddington from 91. *The Rectory, Polebrook, Peterborough PE8 5LN* Tel (01832) 274041

LOVETT, Ian James. b 49. JP99. CertEd72 BTh89 MA92. S'wark Ord Course 73. **d** 76 **p** 77. NSM Gravesend St Geo *Roch* 76-77; NSM Willesborough w Hinxhill *Cant* 77-83; NSM Landness, Littleham, Monkleigh etc *Ex* 83-85; C Compton Gifford 85-86; TV Plymouth Em w Efford 86-92; TV Plymouth Em, St Paul Efford and St Aug 93-97; Chapl Aintree Hosps NHS Trust Liv from 97. *University Hospital Aintree, Lower Lane, Fazakerley, Liverpool L9 7AL* Tel 0151-525 5980 *or* 529 2203

LOVEWELL, Robert Antony. b 34. Lich Th Coll. **d** 62 **p** 63. C Endcliffe *Sheff* 62-65; Miss to Seamen 65-79; Portuguese E Africa 65-73; V Wilton *York* 73-79; TV Thornaby on Tees 79-81; Ind Chapl *Ex* 81-97; rtd 98; Perm to Offic *Truro* from 99. *20 Whitley Grange, Liskeard PL14 6DQ* Tel (01579) 342722 E-mail tonylovewell@aol.com

LOVITT, Gerald Elliott. b 25. St Mich Coll Llan 59. **d** 61 **p** 62. C Aberdare *Llan* 61-66; C Whitchurch 66-71; V Grangetown 71-76; V Rockfield and Llangattock w St Maughan's *Mon* 76-83; V Rockfield and St Maughen's w Llangattock etc 83-93; rtd 93; Perm to Offic *Llan* from 93; Lic to Offic *Mon* from 93. *78 Ninian Road, Penylan, Cardiff CF23 5EN*

LOW, Alastair Graham. b 43. Brunel Univ BSc68 Reading Univ PhD74. Ripon Coll Cuddesdon 90. **d** 92 **p** 93. C Brighton Gd Shep Preston *Chich* 92-96; TV Ifield 96-99; TV Horsham from 99; Chapl Surrey and Sussex Healthcare NHS Trust from 02. *Trinity House, Blunts Way, Horsham RH12 2BL* Tel (01403) 265401 *or* 227000 ext 7338 E-mail graham@glowpigs.freeserve.co.uk

LOW, Christine Mabel. b 48. SS Mark & Jo Coll Plymouth BEd87. SW Minl Tr Course DTPS99. **d** 99 **p** 00. NSM Bideford, Northam, Westward Ho, Appledore etc *Ex* from 99. *11 Harvest Lane, Bideford EX39 3RU* Tel (01237) 424249 E-mail jandclow@low.freeserve.co.uk

LOW, Canon David Anthony. b 42. AKC66. **d** 67 **p** 68. C Gillingham St Barn *Roch* 67-70; V 82-88; C Wallingford *Ox* 70-73; V Spencer's Wood 73-82; P-in-c Grazeley and Beech Hill 77-82; Chapl Medway Hosp Gillingham 86-88; V Hoo St Werburgh *Roch* 88-02; RD Strood 97-02; Hon Can Roch Cathl 01-02; rtd 02. *12 Stonecrop Close, St Mary's Island, Chatham ME4 3HA*

LOW, Canon David Michael. b 39. Cape Town Univ BA60. Cuddesdon Coll 61. **d** 63 **p** 64. C Portsea St Cuth *Portsm* 63-65; S Africa 65-69; C Havant *Portsm* 69-72; V St Helens 72-88; V Sea View 81-88; V Sandown Ch Ch 88-95; V Lower Sandown St Jo 88-95; R Brading w Yaverland 95-01; Hon Can Portsm Cathl 00-01; rtd 01. *Copeland, Lane End Close, Bembridge PO35 5UF* Tel (01983) 874306

LOW, Mrs Jennifer Anne. b 49. St Anne's Coll Ox MA70 Nottm Univ PGCE71. Trin Coll Bris 01. **d** 03. C Bris St Andr Hartcliffe *Bris* from 03. *404 Bishport Avenue, Bristol BS13 0HX* Tel 0117-978 4052

LOW, Peter James. b 52. Nottm Univ BTh89. Linc Th Coll 86. **d** 89 **p** 90. C Dartford H Trin *Roch* 89-92; C Plympton St Mary *Ex* 92-94; TR Devonport St Boniface and St Phil from 94. *St Boniface Vicarage, 1 Normandy Way, Plymouth PL5 1SW* Tel (01752) 361137

LOW, Stafford. b 42. N Lon Poly BSc65. Trin Coll Bris 82. **d** 85 **p** 86. C Yeovil *B & W* 85-88; C Glastonbury w Meare, W Pennard and Godney 88-92; R Berrow and Breane 92-00; R Wincanton from 00; R Pen Selwood from 00; Chapl Voc and Min from 97; RD Bruton from 03; RD Cary from 03. *The Rectory, Bayford Hill, Wincanton BA9 9LQ* Tel (01963) 33367 E-mail lowandco@aol.com

LOW, Terence John Gordon. b 37. Oak Hill Th Coll 75. **d** 77 **p** 78. C Kensal Rise St Martin *Lon* 77-79; C Longfleet *Sarum* 79-83; P-in-c Maiden Newton and Valleys 83-84; TV Melbury 84-88; TV Buckhurst Hill *Chelmsf* 88-92; R Gt Hallingbury and Lt Hallingbury 92-01; rtd 01. *37 Vicarage Lane, Charminster, Dorchester DT2 9QF* Tel (01305) 260180

LOW, William Roberson (Robbie). b 50. Pemb Coll Cam BA73 MA77. Westcott Ho Cam 76. **d** 79 **p** 80. C Poplar Lon 79-83; Chapl St Alb Abbey *St Alb* 83-88; V Bushey Heath 88-03. *3 Trewince Lane, Bodmin Hill, Lostwithiel PL22 0AJ* Tel (01208) 871517

LOWATER, Canon Jennifer Blanche. b 34. Eastbourne Tr Coll TCert54. Sarum & Wells Th Coll 82. **dss** 85 **d** 87 **p** 94. Locks Heath *Portsm* 85-88; Hon C 87-88; NSM Southsea St Pet 88-94; Asst Dir of Ords 91-99; NSM Hook w Warsash 94-01; Hon Can Portsm Cathl 95-97. *Lower Gubbles, Hook Lane, Warsash, Southampton SO31 9HH* Tel (01489) 572156 Fax 572252 E-mail jenny.lowater@care4free.net

LOWE, Anthony Richard. b 45. York Univ BA66 Birm Univ DipTh68. Qu Coll Birm 69. **d** 69 **p** 70. C Greasbrough *Sheff* 69-71; C Thrybergh 71-75; P-in-c Sheff St Mary w St Simon w St Matthias 75-78; V Shiregreen St Hilda 78-85; V Hoxne w Denham St Jo and Syleham *St E* 85-89; P-in-c Wingfield 86-89; R Hoxne w Denham, Syleham and Wingfield from 90. *The Vicarage, Church Hill, Hoxne, Eye IP21 5AT* Tel (01379) 75246

LOWE, Mrs Brenda June. b 53. Cranmer Hall Dur 75. **d** 88 **p** 94. Chapl to Families Trin Coll and Mortimer Ho Bris 86-91; NSM Clifton Ch Ch w Em *Bris* 88-91; Asst Chapl Southmead Health Services NHS Trust 86-91; NSM Marple All SS *Ches* from 91; Perm to Offic *Man* 91-97; Asst Chapl Wythenshawe Hosp Man 94-96; Chapl Stockport Acute Services NHS Trust 96-98; Sen Chapl Stockport NHS Trust from 98. *4 Greenway Road, Heald Green, Cheadle SK8 3NR* Tel 0161-282 3850 *or* 419 5889 E-mail malowe@mail.com

LOWE, Canon David Charles. b 43. Kelham Th Coll 62. **d** 67 **p** 68. C Wingerworth *Derby* 67-70; C Greenhill St Pet 70-73; TV

Eckington 73-74; TV Eckington w Handley and Ridgeway 74-78; V Bury St Edmunds St Geo *St E* 78-86; V Leiston 86-98; RD Saxmundham 88-96; Hon Can St E Cathl from 98; P-in-c Felixstowe St Jo from 98. *5 Barton Road, Felixstowe IP11 7JH* Tel (01394) 284226

LOWE, David Reginald. b 42. K Coll Lon BD65 AKC65. St Boniface Warminster 65. **d** 66 **p** 67. C Tupsley *Heref* 66-69; C Lewes St Anne *Chich* 69-73; C Heref H Trin *Heref* 73-77; P-in-c Lyonshall w Titley 77-88; V Lyonshall w Titley, Almeley and Kinnersley 88-96; Perm to Offic 97-00; rtd 00. *26 Chapel Street, Penzance TR18 4AP* Tel (01736) 331068

LOWE, Donald. b 33. Lich Th Coll 57. **d** 60 **p** 61. C Horwich H Trin *Man* 60; C Wythenshawe St Martin CD 60-62; C Bury St Paul 62-65; S Africa 65-73; V Gannow *Blackb* 70-73; V Colne H Trin 81-89; TV Melbury *Sarum* 89-94; RD Beaminster 93-94; rtd 94; Perm to Offic *Bradf* from 94. *28 High Bank, Threshfield, Skipton BD23 5BU* Tel (01756) 752344

LOWE, Mrs Elaine Mary. b 55. LNSM course 95. **d** 98 **p** 99. OLM Bardsley *Man* from 98. *5 Danisher Lane, Bardsley, Oldham OL8 3HU* Tel 0161-633 4535

LOWE, Canon Eric. b 29. Trin Coll Ox BA50 MA54. St Steph Ho Ox 50. **d** 52 **p** 53. C Ellesmere Port *Ches* 52-55; C Hucknall Torkard *S'well* 55-56; C Solihull *Birm* 56-58; Area Sec (NW England) UMCA 58-65; Area Sec USPG *Ches, Ban* and *St As* 65-88; *Liv* 73-85; V Frodsham *Ches* 88-95; Can Ndola (Zambia) from 88; rtd 95; Perm to Offic *Liv* from 95. Ches 95-01. *55 Wetherby Way, Little Sutton, Ellesmere Port CH66 4TB* Tel 0151-339 1468 E-mail frelowe@candola.freeserve.co.uk

LOWE, The Ven Frank McLean Rhodes. b 26. ACT 59. **d** 61 **p** 63. Australia 61-86 and from 87; Hon Can Gippsland 73-81; Adn Latrobe Valley 81-86; Adn Gippsland 81-86; P-in-c Kirkby in Ashfield St Thos *S'well* 86-87; C Mansfield Woodhouse 87; rtd 91. *12A Lysbeth Street, McKinnon, Vic, Australia 3204* Tel (0061) (3) 9576 9818

LOWE, Mrs Janet Eleanor. b 56. Univ Coll Lon BSc77. NTMTC 98. **d** 01 **p** 02. C Hendon St Paul Mill Hill *Lon* from 01. *12 Frobisher Road, London N8 0QS* Tel (020) 8340 8764 E-mail janlowe@btinternet.com

LOWE, Canon John Bethel. b 30. TCD BA52 BD65. Ridley Hall Cam 55. **d** 55 **p** 56. C Belfast St Mary Magd *Conn* 55-57; Sudan 59-64; Uganda 64-74; Warden CMS Fellowship Ho Foxbury 74-76; V Kippington *Roch* 76-96; Dioc Dir of Ords 82-96; Hon Can Roch Cathl 85-96; rtd 96; Perm to Offic *Ely* from 96. *228 Cambridge Road, Great Shelford, Cambridge CB2 5JU* Tel (01223) 840019

LOWE, John Forrester. b 39. Nottm Univ BA61. Lich Th Coll 61. **d** 64 **p** 65. C N Woolwich *Chelmsf* 64-70; V Marks Gate 70-74; V Moulsham St Jo 74-79; V N Woolwich w Silvertown 79-82; V Birm St Pet *Birm* 82-86; Gen Sec SOMA UK 86-91; V Heckmondwike *Wakef* 92-98; rtd 98. *37 Jubilee Close, Ledbury HR8 2XA* Tel (01531) 631890

LOWE, Keith Gregory. b 50. Sarum & Wells Th Coll DCM93. **d** 93 **p** 94. C Wallasey St Hilary *Ches* 93-94; C W Kirby St Bridget 94-98; V Sandbach Heath w Wheelock 98-01; V High Lane from 01; Chapl Stockport NHS Trust from 01. *The Vicarage, 85 Buxton Road, High Lane, Stockport SK6 8DX* Tel (01663) 762627 E-mail keithglowe@mail.com

LOWE, Canon Michael Arthur. b 46. Lon Univ BD67 Hull Univ MA85. Cranmer Hall Dur DipTh75. **d** 76 **p** 77. C Thorpe Edge *Bradf* 76-79; C N Ferriby *York* 79-84; TV 84-86; Dir Past Studies Trin Coll Bris 86-91; V Marple All SS *Ches* 91-00; RD Chadkirk 95-00; Hon Can Ches Cathl from 00; Dir of Miss and Unity from 00; C Delamere 00-02. *4 Greenway Road, Heald Green, Cheadle SK8 3NR* Tel 0161-282 3850 E-mail malowe@mail.com

LOWE, Samuel. b 35. St D Coll Lamp. **d** 65 **p** 66. C Tenby w Gumfreston *St D* 65-67; C Lower Mitton *Worc* 67-69; C Halesowen 69-72; R Droitwich St Nic w St Pet 72-73; TV Droitwich 73-77; P-in-c Claines St Geo 77-78; P-in-c Worc St Mary the Tything 77-78; V 84-00; rtd 00. *57 Camp Hill Road, Worcester WR5 2HG* Tel (01905) 357807

LOWE, Stephen Arthur. b 49. Nottm Univ BSc71 DipTh. Cuddesdon Coll 71. **d** 74 **p** 75. C Mansfield St Mark *S'well* 74-77; Papua New Guinea 77-79; V Kirkby Woodhouse *S'well* 80-86; V Beeston 86-99; TR Wenlock *Heref* from 99. *The Rectory, New Road, Much Wenlock TF13 6EQ* Tel (01952) 727396

✠**LOWE, The Rt Revd Stephen Richard.** b 44. Lon Univ BSc66. Ripon Hall Ox 68. **d** 68 **p** 69 **c** 99. C Gospel Lane St Mich *Birm* 68-72; C-in-c Woodgate Valley CD 72-75; V E Ham w Upton Park *Chelmsf* 75-76; TR E Ham w Upton Park St Alb 76-88; Hon Can Chelmsf Cathl 85-88; Adn Sheff 88-99; Can Res Sheff Cathl 88-99; Suff Bp Hulme *Man* from 99. *14 Moorgate Avenue, Withington, Manchester M20 1HE* Tel 0161-445 5922 Mobile 07801-505277 Fax 0161-448 9687 E-mail lowehulme@btinternet.com

LOWELL, Ian Russell. b 53. AKC75. St Aug Coll Cant 75. **d** 76 **p** 77. C Llwynderw *S & B* 76-79; C Swansea St Mary w H Trin and St Mark 79-81; Chapl Ox Hosps 81-83; TV Gt and Lt Coates

w Bradley *Linc* 83-88; V Wellingborough St Mark *Pet* 88-02; V Northampton St Alb from 02; Chapl Northants Ambulance Service from 92. *St Alban's Vicarage, Broadmead Avenue, Northampton NN3 2RA* Tel (01604) 407074 E-mail irlowell@aol.com

LOWEN, David John. b 42. Sussex Univ BSc74 Univ of Wales (Lamp) MA84. Llan Dioc Tr Scheme 86. **d** 88 **p** 89. C Carmarthen St Pet *St D* 88-90; P-in-c Walwyn's Castle w Robeston W 90-92; R from 92. *The Rectory, Walwyn's Castle, Haverfordwest SA62 3ED* Tel (01437) 781257

LOWEN, John Michael. b 47. Nottm Univ BTh77. Linc Th Coll 73. **d** 77 **p** 78. C Beeston *S'well* 77-80; C Stratford-on-Avon w Bishopton *Cov* 80-82; V Monkseaton St Mary *Newc* 82-90; V Ponteland 90-95; Chapl HM Pris Leeds 95; P-in-c Sutton St Mary *Linc* 95-00; R Dunvegan Canada from 00. *10900, Box 787, 103 Avenue, Fairview AB, Canada, T0H 1L0* Tel (001) (780) 835 2580

LOWERSON, John Ridley. b 41. FRHistS83 Leeds Univ BA62 MA65. S Dios Minl Tr Scheme 85. **d** 88 **p** 89. NSM Ringmer *Chich* 88-00; NSM Lewes St Anne from 00. *9 Bradford Road, Lewes BN7 9RB* Tel (01273) 473413

LOWLES, Martin John. b 48. Thames Poly BSc72. St Jo Coll Dur DipTh78. **d** 78 **p** 79. C Leyton St Mary w St Edw *Chelmsf* 78-81; C Waltham Abbey 81-85; V E Ham St Paul 85-95; Asst AD Newham 91-95; TR N Huddersfield *Wakef* from 95. *The Rectory, 10 The Dell, Fixby, Huddersfield HD2 2FD* Tel (01484) 534564

LOWMAN, The Ven David Walter. b 48. K Coll Lon BD73 AKC73. St Aug Coll Cant 73. **d** 75 **p** 76. C Notting Hill *Lon* 75-78; C Kilburn St Aug w St Jo 78-81; Selection Sec Adv Adv ACCM 81-86; TR Wickford and Runwell *Chelmsf* 86-93; Dioc Dir of Ords 93-01; C Chelmsf All SS 93-01; C Chelmsf Ascension 93-01; Hon Can Chelmsf Cathl from 93; Adn Southend from 01. *The Archdeacon's Lodge, 136 Broomfield Road, Chelmsford CM1 1RN* Tel (01245) 258257 Fax 250845 E-mail a.southend@chelmsford.anglican.org

LOWNDES, Charles. b 22. MISW57 CQSW72 Rotherham Poly Dip Deaf Welfare 57. **d** 87 **p** 88. NSM Hanley H Ev *Lich* from 87. *7 Beacon Rise, Stone ST15 0AL* Tel (01785) 812698

LOWNDES, Harold John (Nobby). b 31. St Alb and Ox Min Course 96. **d** 99 **p** 00. OLM Lamp *Ox* from 99. *98 Wolverton Road, Haversham, Milton Keynes MK19 7AB* Tel (01908) 319939 E-mail hlowndes@vivao.net

LOWNDES, Richard Owen Lewis. b 63. Univ of Wales (Ban) BD86. Coll of Resurr Mirfield 87. **d** 89 **p** 90. C Milford Haven *St D* 89-91; C Roath St German *Llan* 91-94; Chapl Cardiff Royal Infirmary 91-94; V Tylorstown w Ynyshir *Llan* 94-96; Asst Chapl St Helier NHS Trust 96-98; Chapl Team Ldr W Middx Univ Hosp NHS Trust 98-03; Chapl Team Ldr Ealing Hosp NHS Trust 01-03; Chapl Team Ldr Southn Univ Hosps NHS Trust from 03. *Trust Management Offices, Southampton General Hospital, Tremona Road, Southampton SO16 6TD* Tel (023) 8077 7222 Fax 8079 4153

LOWRIE, Ronald Malcolm. b 48. Ripon Hall Ox 70. **d** 72 **p** 73. C Knowle *Birm* 72-75; C Bourton-on-the-Water w Clapton *Glouc* 75-79; R Broadwell, Evenlode, Oddington and Adlestrop 79-81; TV Trowbridge H Trin *Sarum* 81-88; P-in-c Westwood and Wingfield 88-90; R from 90; P-in-c Bradford-on-Avon Ch Ch from 03; Chapl Wilts and Swindon Healthcare NHS Trust from 88. *The Rectory, Westwood, Bradford-on-Avon BA15 2AF* Tel and fax (01225) 863109 *or* tel and fax 867040 E-mail parishoffice@christchurchboa.fsnet.co.uk

LOWRY, Canon Robert Harold. b 19. TCD BA44 MA49. CITC 44. **d** 44 **p** 45. C Belfast St Mary Magd *Conn* 44-48; C Belfast St Donard *D & D* 48-52; I Drumgooland w Kilcoo 52-59; I Willowfield 62-75; I Lambeg *Conn* 75-89; Can Conn Cathl from 82; rtd 90; Lic to Offic *D & D* from 90. *9 Innisfayle Park, Bangor BT19 1DP* Tel (028) 9147 2423

LOWRY, The Very Revd Stephen Harold. b 58. QUB BSc79 CertEd80. CITC DipTh85. **d** 85 **p** 86. C Coleraine *Conn* 85-88; I Greenisland 88-98; I Dromore Cathl *D & D* from 98; Dean Dromore from 02. *Dromore Cathedral Rectory, 28 Church Street, Dromore BT25 1AA* Tel (028) 9269 2275 E-mail cathedral@dromore.anglican.org

LOWSON, The Ven Christopher. b 53. AKC75 Heythrop Coll Lon MTh96. Pacific Sch of Religion Berkeley STM78 St Aug Coll Cant 76. **d** 77 **p** 78. C Richmond St Mary *S'wark* 77-79; C Richmond St Mary w St Matthias and St Jo 79-82; P-in-c Eltham H Trin 82-83; V 83-91; R Buriton *Portsm* 91-99; V Petersfield 91-99; RD Petersfield 95-99; Adn Portsdown from 99; Bp's Liaison Officer for Pris from 00. *5 Brading Avenue, Southsea PO4 9QJ* Tel (023) 9243 2693 Mobile 07957-657312 Fax 9229 8788 E-mail lowson@surfaid.org

LOWSON, Geoffrey Addison. b 47. Bede Coll Dur BEd70 DipHE98. NEOC 95. **d** 98 **p** 99. NSM Sherburn in Elmet w Saxton *York* from 98; Fieldworker (NE England) USPG from 98; Perm to Offic *Dur* from 98. *25 Mill Lane, Acaster Malbis, York YO23 2UJ* Tel (01904) 702304 Fax as telephone E-mail geofflowson@compuserve.com

LOWTHER, Ms Kareen Anne. b 59. Loughb Univ BSc81. WMMTC 98. **d** 01. C Lich St Mich w St Mary and Wall *Lich* from 01. *28 The Spires, Lichfield WS14 9RP* Tel (01543) 417274 Mobile 07940-936033

LOWTON, Nicholas Gerard. b 53. St Jo Coll Ox BA76 FRSA94. Glouc Sch of Min 86. **d** 89 **p** 90. NSM Prestbury *Glouc* 89-94. *Hazelwell, College Road, Cheltenham GL53 7JD* Tel (01242) 265609 *or* 513540 ext 209 Fax 265688 E-mail ngl@cheltcoll.gloucs.sch.uk

LOXHAM, Geoffrey Richard. b 40. Hull Univ BA62. Cranmer Hall Dur. **d** 65 **p** 66. C Darwen St Barn *Blackb* 65-68; C Leyland St Andr 68-72; V Preston St Mark 72-79; V Edgeside *Man* 79-91; P-in-c Heapey St Barnabas and Withnell St Paul *Blackb* 91-92; V 92-99; V Grimsargh from 99. *St Michael's Vicarage, 46 Preston Road, Preston PR2 5SD* Tel (01772) 653283

LOXLEY, Deirdre. b 41. DipEd72. LNSM course 94. **d** 96 **p** 97. OLM Heacham *Nor* from 96. *3 Marea Meadows, Heacham, King's Lynn PE31 7SR* Tel (01485) 570994

LOXLEY, Harold. b 43. N Ord Course 79. **d** 82 **p** 83. NSM Sheff Parson Cross St Cecilia *Sheff* 82-87; C Gleadless 87-90; V Sheff St Cath Richmond Road from 90. *St Catherine's Vicarage, 300 Hastilar Road South, Sheffield S13 8EJ* Tel 0114-239 9598 Fax as telephone

LOXLEY, Ronald Alan Keith. b 26. St Jo Coll Ox BA51 MA55. Wm Temple Coll Rugby 66 Cuddesdon Coll 67. **d** 68 **p** 69. C Swindon Ch Ch *Bris* 68-71; Ind Chapl *Lon* 71-83; Ind Chapl *Chelmsf* 83-92; P-in-c Theydon Garnon 83-92; rtd 92; Perm to Offic *Linc* 92-01. *15 Wainwell Mews, Winnowsty Lane, Lincoln LN2 4BF* Tel (01522) 511738

LOXTON, John Sherwood. b 29. Bris Univ BSc50 Birm Univ BA53. Handsworth Coll Birm 50 Chich Th Coll 80. **d** 80 **p** 81. In Meth Ch 50-80; C Haywards Heath St Wilfrid *Chich* 80-82; TV 82-89; V Turners Hill 89-96; rtd 96; Perm to Offic *Chich* from 96. *3 Ashurst Drive, Worth, Crawley RH10 7FS* Tel (01293) 887762

LOZADA-UZURIAGA, Ernesto. b 61. Wycliffe Hall Ox. **d** 02 **p** 03. C Henley w Remenham Ox from 02. *3 Walton Avenue, Henley-on-Thames RG9 1LA* Tel (01491) 575608 E-mail leon-juda@hotmail.com

LUBBOCK, David John. b 34. S'wark Ord Course. **d** 87 **p** 88. NSM Tulse Hill H Trin and St Matthias *S'wark* from 87. *The Old Vicarage, 107 Upper Tulse Hill, London SW2 2RD* Tel (020) 8674 6146

LUBKOWSKI, Richard Jan. b 51. Westmr Coll Ox BEd75 Warw Univ MA79. St Jo Coll Dur 86. **d** 88 **p** 89. C Duston *Pet* 88-90; C Hellesdon *Nor* 90-91; Perm to Offic *Sheff* 91-94; In RC Ch 94-00; Chapl HM Pris Ashwell from 00. *HM Prison Ashwell, Oakham LE15 7LS* Tel (01572) 774100 Mobile 07449-122406

LUCAS, Anthony Stanley. b 41. Man Univ BA62 K Coll Lon MA99. Qu Coll Birm 63. **d** 65 **p** 66. C N Hammersmith St Kath *Lon* 65-69; C W Wimbledon Ch Ch *S'wark* 69-74; C Caterham 74-78; P-in-c Stockwell St Mich 78-86; V 86-91; P-in-c S'wark St Geo 91; R S'wark St Geo the Martyr w St Jude 91-94; P-in-c S'wark St Alphege 92-94; R S'wark St Geo the Martyr w St Alphege & St Jude from 95. *St George's Rectory, Manciple Street, London SE1 4LW* Tel (020) 7407 2796 Fax as telephone E-mail tonyslucas@btinternet.com

LUCAS, Arthur Edgar. b 24. Clifton Th Coll 60. **d** 62 **p** 63. C Hyson Green *S'well* 62-66; V Willoughby-on-the-Wolds w Wysall 66-74; P-in-c Widmerpool 71-74; R Collyhurst *Man* 75-80; V Heapey *Blackb* 80-91; rtd 91; Perm to Offic *Blackb* and *Liv* 91-00. *18 Parkway, Standish, Wigan WN6 0SJ*

LUCAS, The Ven Brian Humphrey. b 40. CB93. FRSA93 Univ of Wales (Lamp) BA62. St Steph Ho Ox 62. **d** 64 **p** 65. C Llandaff w Capel Llanilltern *Llan* 64-67; C Neath w Llantwit 67-70; Chapl RAF 70-87; Asst Chapl-in-Chief RAF 87-91; Chapl-in-Chief RAF 91-95; QHC from 88; Perm to Offic *Llan* from 88; Can and Preb Linc Cathl *Linc* 91-95; P-in-c Caythorpe *Linc* 96-00; R from 00. *Pen-y-Coed, 6 Arnhem Drive, Caythorpe, Grantham NG32 3DQ* Tel (01400) 272085 E-mail brian.lucas@savageclub.com

LUCAS, Mrs Jane Eleanor. b 49. SW Minl Tr Course 99. **d** 03. NSM N Creedy *Ex* from 03. *Lakehead Farm, Chulmleigh EX18 7AG* Tel (01769) 580339 Fax as telephone E-mail j.e.lucas@btinternet.com

LUCAS, John Arthur. b 27. Keble Coll Ox BA29 MA45. Cuddesdon Coll 29. **d** 33 **p** 34. C Ox St Thos *Ox* 33-35; C Brighton St Wilfrid *Chich* 35-37; C London Docks St Pet *Lon* 37-39; V Swanley St Mary *Roch* 39-47; V St Thos *Ox* 47-74; P-in-c 74-79; Hon Can Ch Ch 70-85; rtd 74; Hon C Ox St Mary V w St Cross and St Pet *Ox* 78-85; Perm to Offic 85-96. *12 Lucas Place, Iffley, Oxford OX4 4HA* Tel (01865) 774508

LUCAS, John Kenneth. b 32. LNSM course 92. **d** 95 **p** 96. NSM Deptford St Nic and St Luke *S'wark* 95-97; Perm to Offic 97-00. *4 The Colonnade, Grove Street, London SE8 3AY* Tel (020) 8691 3161

LUCAS, John Maxwell. b 34. TD85. Cranmer Hall Dur 59. **d** 62 **p** 63. C Lancaster St Mary *Blackb* 62-65; C Lytham St Cuth 65-68; V Blackb St Aid 68-72; V Sparkhill St Jo *Birm* 72-78; CF (TAVR) from 73; V Edgbaston St Aug *Birm* 78-85; V Slyne w

Hest *Blackb* 85-89; Chapl HM YOI Stoke Heath 89-93; rtd 93. *2 Glendon Close, Market Drayton TF9 1NX* Tel (01630) 652977

LUCAS, Kenneth Ashley. b 18. Wells Th Coll 68. **d** 69 **p** 70. C Rye w Rye Harbour and Playden *Chich* 69-73; R W Chiltington 74-83; rtd 83; Perm to Offic *Chich* from 83. *c/o Mrs C J Huke, Meadow Lodge, The Tye, East Hanningfield, Chelmsford CM3 8BU* Tel (01273) 813150

LUCAS, Lorna Yvonne. b 48. Bp Lonsdale Coll TCert69. EMMTC DipTh98. **d** 98 **p** 99. NSM Haxey *Linc* 98-00; NSM Owston 98-00; NSM Scawby, Redbourne and Hibaldstow from 00. *4 Willingham Road, Lea, Gainsborough DN21 5EH*

LUCAS, Mark Wesley. b 62. Man Univ BSc83. Oak Hill Th Coll BA94. **d** 94 **p** 95. C Harold Wood *Chelmsf* 94-98; Dir Oast Ho Retreat Cen *Chich* 98-00; Co-ord for Adult Educn (E Sussex Area) 98-00; V Polegate from 00. *St John's Vicarage, 1 Church Road, Polegate BN26 5BX* Tel (01323) 483259 Mobile 07788-100757 Fax (01323) 483305 E-mail vicar@polegate.org.uk

LUCAS, Ms Pamela Turnbull. b 68. Westmr Coll Ox BA91 Warwick Univ PGD94 Glas Univ MSW98 New Coll Edin MTh99 Liv Univ PGCE03. TISEC 98. **d** 00 **p** 01. C Easington, Easington Colliery and S Hetton *Dur* from 00. *St Mary's House, 4 Brampton Court, Easington, Peterlee SR8 3XG* Tel 0191-527 2795 E-mail pamela@ptlucas.demon.co.uk

LUCAS, Canon Paul de Neufville. b 33. Ch Ch Ox BA59 MA59 Cam Univ MA63. Cuddesdon Coll 57. **d** 59 **p** 60. C Westmr St Steph w St Jo *Lon* 59-63; Chapl Trin Hall Cam 63-69; V Greenside *Dur* 69-73; Chapl Shrewsbury Sch 73-78; V Batheaston w St Cath *B & W* 78-88; Preb Wells Cathl 87-88; Can Res and Prec 88-99; rtd 99. *11 Fisherton Island, Salisbury SP2 7TG* Tel (01722) 325266 Fax as telephone

LUCAS, Peter Stanley. b 21. Sarum Th Coll 48. **d** 50 **p** 51. C Gillingham *Sarum* 50-53; Min Heald Green St Cath CD *Ches* 53-58; V Heald Green St Cath 58-62; V Egremont St Jo 62-65; Canada from 66. *Apt 404, 1241 Fairfield Road, Victoria BC, Canada, V8V 3B3* E-mail pmlucas@smartt.com

LUCAS, Raymond Charles Henry. b 15. ALCD41. **d** 41 **p** 42. C Southborough St Pet *Roch* 41-43; C Bris H Trin *Bris* 43-47; C Worthing H Trin *Chich* 47-50; V Island St Jude Mildmay Park *Lon* 50-54; V Southborough St Matt *Roch* 54-61; R Branston *Linc* 61-76; R Parkham, Alwington and Buckland Brewer *Ex* 76-79; rtd 80. *3 Walnut Court, Walnut Road, Chelston, Torquay TQ2 6HS* Tel (01803) 606703

LUCAS, Preb Richard Charles. b 25. Trin Coll Cam BA49 MA57. Ridley Hall Cam. **d** 51 **p** 52. C Sevenoaks St Nic *Roch* 51-55; Cand Sec CPAS 55-61; Asst Sec 61-67; R St Helen Bishopsgate w St Martin Outwich *Lon* 61-80; P-in-c St Andr Undershaft w St Mary Axe 77-80; R St Helen Bishopsgate w St Andr Undershaft etc 80-98; Preb St Paul's Cathl 85-98; rtd 98. *16 Merrick Square, London SE1 4JB* Tel (020) 7407 4164

LUCAS, Ronald James. b 38. St Aid Birkenhead 64. **d** 67 **p** 68. C Swindon Ch Ch *Bris* 67-71; C Knowle St Martin 71-74; V Swindon St Jo 74-77; TR Swindon St Jo and St Andr 77-81; V Wroughton 81-83; TV Liskeard w St Keyne, St Pinnock and Morval *Truro* 83-87; R St Ive w Quethiock 87-91; R St Ive and Pensilva w Quethiock 91-01; rtd 01; Perm to Offic *Truro* from 01. *Ough's Folly, Castle Lane, Liskeard PL14 3AH* Tel (01579) 345611 E-mail m009kj00@mcmail.com

LUCAS, Ms Susan Catherine. b 59. City of Lon Poly BSc90. STETS 97. **d** 00 **p** 01. C Streetly *Lich* 00-02; C Pheasey from 02. *The Vicarage, 88 Hillingford Avenue, Birmingham B43 7HN*

LUCAS, Mrs Vivienne Kathleen. b 44. Sarum & Wells Th Coll 84. **d** 87 **p** 94. Chapl Asst W Middx Univ Hosp Isleworth 87-92; Par Dn Whitton St Aug *Lon* 87-94; C Isleworth St Jo 94-97; P-in-c Isleworth St Mary 97-01; P-in-c Pirbright *Guildf* from 01. *The Vicarage, The Green, Pirbright, Woking GU24 0JE* Tel (01483) 473332 E-mail viviennelucas@beeb.net

LUCAS, William Wallace. b 29. Sarum Th Coll 56. **d** 59 **p** 60. C Stockton St Jo *Dur* 59-63; V Norton St Mich 63-81; R Broseley w Benthall *Heref* 81-93; P-in-c Jackfield 81-93; P-in-c Linley w Willey and Barrow 81-93; rtd 93; Perm to Offic *Dur* from 93. *105 Side Cliff Road, Sunderland SR6 9JR* Tel 0191-549 1573

LUCK, Benjamin Paul. b 53. BD. St Mich Coll Llan 80. **d** 83 **p** 84. C Blakenall Heath *Lich* 83-87; C Torpoint *Truro* 87-89; V Tuckingmill 89-96; C Knowle St Barn and H Cross Inns Court *Bris* 96-02; V Inns Court H Cross from 02. *7A Novers Park Drive, Bristol BS4 1RF* Tel 0117-966 4123

LUCKCUCK, Anthony Michael. b 47. Lon Univ BA70. Wycliffe Hall Ox 70. **d** 77 **p** 78. C Mansfield Woodhouse *S'well* 77-79; C Beeston 79-82; V Harworth 82-85; V Carlton from 85. *St John's Vicarage, 261 Oakdale Road, Nottingham NG4 1BP* Tel 0115-987 4882 E-mail amelclerc@btinternet.com

LUCKETT, Nicholas Frank. b 43. Ch Ch Ox BA65 DipEd66 MA69. OLM course 95. **d** 98 **p** 99. Hd Master St Edw C of E Middle Sch Leek 94-00; OLM Ipstones w Berkhamsytch and Onecote w Bradnop *Lich* 98-02; NSM Siddington w Preston *Glouc* from 02. *The Rectory, Preston, Cirencester GL7 5PR* Tel (01285) 654187

LUCKMAN, David Thomas William. b 71. Oak Hill Th Coll BA95 K Coll Lon PGCE. CITC 98. **d** 00 **p** 01. C Portadown

St Mark *Arm* 00-02; C Enniskillen *Clogh* from 02. *2 Halls Lane, Enniskillen BT74 7DR* Tel (028) 6632 5882
E-mail daveluckman@hotmail.com *or* curate@enniskillencathedral.org

LUCKRAFT, Christopher John. b 50. K Coll Lon BD80 AKC80. Ripon Coll Cuddesdon 80. **d** 81 **p** 82. C Sherborne w Castleton and Lillington *Sarum* 81-84; Bermuda 84-87; Chapl RN from 87. *The Chaplain's Office, Royal Hospital Haslar, Gosport PO12 2AA* Tel (023) 9258 4255 ext 2266

LUCY CLARE, Sister. *See* WALKER, Margaret

LUDLOW, Lady Margaret Maude. b 56. WEMTC 98. **d** 01 **p** 02. C Winchcombe, Gretton, Sudeley Manor etc *Glouc* from 01. *38 Riverside, Winchcombe, Cheltenham GL54 5JP* Tel (01242) 602585

LUDLOW, Archdeacon of. *See* HOOPER, The Rt Revd Michael Wrenford

LUDLOW, Suffragan Bishop of. *See* HOOPER, The Rt Revd Michael Wrenford

LUFF, Canon Alan Harold Frank. b 28. ARCM77 Univ Coll Ox DipTh52 MA54 Hon FGMS93. Westcott Ho Cam 54. **d** 56 **p** 57. C Stretford St Matt *Man* 56-59; C Swinton St Pet 59-61; Prec Man Cathl 61-68; V Dwygyfylchi *Ban* 68-79; Prec and Sacr Westmr Abbey 79-86; Prec 86-92; Can Res Birm Cathl *Birm* 92-96; rtd 96; Perm to Offic from 96. *12 Heol Ty'n-y-Cae, Cardiff CF14 6DJ* Tel (029) 2061 6023 Fax as telephone
E-mail luff@fish.co.uk

LUFF, Mrs Caroline Margaret Synia. b 44. St Hild Coll Dur BA65 Bris Univ CertEd66. SW Minl Tr Course 87. **d** 90 **p** 94. Par Dn Teignmouth, Ideford w Luton, Ashcombe etc *Ex* 90-94; C from 94; Chapl Trin Sch Teignmouth from 97. *The Rectory, 30 Dawlish Road, Teignmouth TQ14 8TG* Tel (01626) 774495

LUFF, Preb Philip Garth. b 42. St Chad's Coll Dur BA63 DipTh64. **d** 65 **p** 66. C Sidmouth St Nic *Ex* 65-69; C Plymstock 69-71; Asst Chapl Worksop Coll Notts 71-74; V Gainsborough St Jo *Linc* 74-80; V E Teignmouth *Ex* 80-89; P-in-c W Teignmouth 85-89; Chapl S Devon Healthcare NHS Trust from 85; Chapl Trin Sch Teignmouth 88-97; TR Teignmouth, Ideford w Luton, Ashcombe etc *Ex* from 89; RD Kenn from 01; Preb Ex Cathl from 02. *The Rectory, 30 Dawlish Road, Teignmouth TQ14 8TG* Tel (01626) 774495

LUGG, Donald Arthur. b 31. St Aid Birkenhead 56. **d** 59 **p** 60. C Folkestone H Trin w Ch Ch *Cant* 59-62; V Seasalter 62-66; Iran 67-73; V Cliftonville *Cant* 74-94; rtd 94; Perm to Offic *Cant* from 94; Reculver from 94. *Redcroft, Vulcan Close, Whitstable CT9 1DF* Tel (01227) 770434

LUGG, Stuart John. b 26. Glouc Th Course 74. **d** 76 **p** 77. NSM Fairford *Glouc* 76-79; P-in-c Kempsford w Welford 80-88; Perm to Offic from 88. *Content, Station Road, South Cerney, Cirencester GL7 5UB* Tel (01285) 860498

LUKE, Anthony. b 58. Down Coll Cam BA81 MA85 Geneva Univ Cert Ecum Studies 84. Ridley Hall Cam 82. **d** 84 **p** 85. C Allestree *Derby* 84-87; C Oakham, Hambleton, Egleton, Braunston and Brooke *Pet* 87-88; V Allenton and Shelton Lock *Derby* 88-02; Dir Reader Tr 95-97; Warden of Readers 97-00; R Aston on Trent, Elvaston, Weston on Trent etc from 02. *The Rectory, Rectory Gardens, Aston-on-Trent, Derby DE72 2AZ* Tel (01332) 792658 E-mail tonyluke@lineone.net

LUMB, David Leslie. b 28. Jes Coll Cam BA52 MA56. Oak Hill Th Coll 52. **d** 54 **p** 55. C Walcot *B & W* 54-58; C Lenton *S'well* 58-60; V Handforth *Ches* 60-71; V Plymouth St Jude *Ex* 71-87; V Southminster *Chelmsf* 87-93; rtd 93; Perm to Offic *Worc* from 93. *13 Glebe Road, Redditch B98 0AW* Tel (01527) 528623

LUMB, Dennis. b 36. Oak Hill Th Coll 77. **d** 79 **p** 80. C Penn Fields *Lich* 79-84; P-in-c Tibberton, Kinnersley and Preston Wealdmoors 84-88; P-in-c Bolas Magna and Waters Upton 89-91; P-in-c Saltfleetby *Linc* 91-96; P-in-c Theddlethorpe 91-96; rtd 96; NSM Wombourne w Trysull and Bobbington *Lich* 96-01; Perm to Offic from 01. *60 Woodhall Drive, Wombourne, Wolverhampton WV5 0DY* Tel (01902) 898403

LUMBY, Jonathan Bertram. b 39. Em Coll Cam BA62 MA66 Lon Univ PGCE66. Ripon Hall Ox 62. **d** 64 **p** 65. C Moseley St Mary *Birm* 64-65; Asst Master Enfield Gr Sch 66-67; C Hall Green Ascension 67-70; V Melling *Liv* 71-81; P-in-c Milverton w Halse and Fitzhead *B & W* 81-82; R 82-86; P-in-c Gisburn *Bradf* 90-93; Dioc Rural Adv 90-93; P-in-c Easton w Colton and Marlingford *Nor* 95-98; Dioc Missr 95-98; R Eccleston and Pulford *Ches* from 98. *The Rectory, Eccleston, Chester CH4 9HT* Tel (01244) 674703

LUMBY, Simon. b 70. Coll of Resurr Mirfield 99. **d** 02 **p** 03. C Worksop Priory *S'well* from 02. *18 Cheapside, Worksop S80 2HU* Tel (01909) 473427 Mobile 07929-388181
E-mail simon_lumby@hotmail.com

LUMBY, Simon John. b 56. Hull Univ BSc80 Open Univ MTh01. St Jo Coll Nottm 99. **d** 01 **p** 02. C Wirksworth *Derby* from 01. *57 Yokecliffe Drive, Wirksworth, Matlock DE4 4PF* Tel (01629) 820049 Fax 820235 E-mail revd.s.j.lumby@ntlworld.com

LUMGAIR, Michael Hugh Crawford. b 43. Lon Univ BD71. Oak Hill Th Coll 66. **d** 71 **p** 72. C Chorleywood Ch Ch *St Alb* 71-74; C Prestonville St Luke *Chich* 74-75; C Attenborough *S'well* 75-80; R Tollerton 80-91; V Bexleyheath St Pet *Roch* from 91.

St Peter's Vicarage, 50 Bristow Road, Bexleyheath DA7 4QA Tel (020) 8303 8713 E-mail michael@mlumgair.co.uk

LUMLEY, William. b 22. TCD BA44 MA49 BD49 QUB PhD77. Edgehill Th Coll Belf 49. **d** 50 **p** 51. C Dublin Drumcondra w N Strand *D & G* 50-52; Clerical V Ch Ch Cathl Dublin 52-53; C Clooney *D & R* 55-59; I Aghabog *Clogh* 59-63; V Newhey *Man* 63-66; I Ballybay *Clogh* 66-73; I Derryvullen S w Garvary 73-82; I Killucan w Clonard and Castlelost *M & K* 82-88; rtd 88. *15 Roe Fold, Main Street, Limavady BT49 0EL* Tel (028) 7776 6174

LUMMIS, Elizabeth Howieson. *See* McNAB, Mrs Elizabeth Howieson

LUMSDEN, Frank. b 20. Edin Th Coll 51. **d** 53 **p** 54. C Usworth *Dur* 53-56; V Lynesack 56-76; R Castle Eden w Monkhesleden 76-86; rtd 86; Perm to Offic *Dur* from 86; Perm to Offic *Ripon* from 90. *Cloud High, Eggleston, Barnard Castle DL12 0AU* Tel (01833) 650644

LUMSDON, Keith. b 45. Linc Th Coll 68. **d** 71 **p** 72. C S Westoe *Dur* 71-74; C Jarrow St Paul 74-77; TV Jarrow 77-88; V Ferryhill from 88; P-in-c Cornforth from 03. *St Luke's Vicarage, Church Lane, Ferryhill DL17 8LT* Tel (01740) 651438

LUND, Clare Marion. b 51. Bris Univ BA73. SW Minl Tr Course DTPS99. **d** 99. NSM Christow, Ashton, Trusham and Bridford *Ex* 99. *Amerys, Bridford, Exeter EX6 7JA* Tel (01647) 252485 Fax as telephone

LUND, David Peter. b 46. N Ord Course 88. **d** 91 **p** 92. C Maghull *Liv* 91-94; V Hindley All SS 94-01; V Teddington St Mark and Hampton Wick St Jo *Lon* from 01. *The Vicarage, 23 St Mark's Road, Teddington TW11 9DE* Tel and fax (020) 8977 4067 Mobile 07813-493761 E-mail saintseddington@aol.com

LUND, John Edward. b 48. St Jo Coll Dur 78. **d** 80 **p** 81. C Peterlee *Dur* 80-83; C Bishopton w Gt Stainton 83-85; C Redmarshall 83-85; C Grindon and Stillington 83-85; V Hart w Elwick Hall from 85; Hon Chapl Miss to Seamen 85-99; Chapl Hartlepool and E Durham NHS Trust 94-99; Chapl N Tees and Hartlepool NHS Trust from 99. *The Vicarage, Hart, Hartlepool TS27 3AP* Tel (01429) 262340 E-mail lund@telco4u.net

LUNGLEY, Canon John Sydney. b 41. St Pet Coll Ox BA64 MA70. St Steph Ho Ox 64. **d** 66 **p** 67. C Burslem St Werburgh *Lich* 66-70; C Codsall 70-73; V Ocker Hill 73-88; RD Wednesbury 84-88; V Kingswinford St Mary 88-93; V Kingswinford St Mary *Worc* 93-96; TR from 96; Hon Can Worc Cathl from 94. *The Vicarage, 17 Penzer Street, Kingswinford DY6 7AA* Tel (01384) 273716

LUNN, Preb Brooke Kingsmill. b 32. TCD BA62 MA66. Chich Th Coll 62. **d** 64 **p** 65. C Northolt Park St Barn *Lon* 64-66; C N St Pancras All Hallows 66-68; P-in-c Hornsey St Luke 68-79; V Stroud Green H Trin 79-02; AD W Haringey 90-95; Preb St Paul's Cathl 96-02; rtd 02. *The Charterhouse, Charterhouse Square, London EC1M 6AN* Tel (020) 7251 5143

LUNN, Christopher James Edward. b 34. AKC58. **d** 59 **p** 60. C Clapham H Trin *S'wark* 59-62; C Cranleigh *Guildf* 63-64; C Ham St Andr *S'wark* 64-66; V Ham St Rich 66-75; V Coulsdon St Andr 75-96; rtd 96. *24 Penally Heights, Penally, Tenby SA70 7QP* Tel (01834) 845277

LUNN, David. b 47. Bris Univ BSc69 Dur Univ BA73 DipTh74. St Jo Coll Dur 71. **d** 74 **p** 75. C Aigburth *Liv* 74-77; C Slough *Ox* 77-81; P-in-c Haversham w Lt Linford 81-84; R Haversham w Lt Linford, Tyringham w Filgrave 84-93; RD Newport 86-92; TR Walton Milton Keynes from 93; Dioc Ecum Officer from 00. *The Rectory, Walton Road, Wavendon, Milton Keynes MK17 8LW* Tel (01908) 582839

✠**LUNN, The Rt Revd David Ramsay.** b 30. K Coll Cam BA53 MA57. Cuddesdon Coll 53. **d** 55 **p** 56 **c** 80. C Sugley *Newc* 55-59; C N Gosforth 59-63; Chapl Linc Th Coll 63-66; Sub-Warden 66-70; V Cullercoats St Geo *Newc* 71-72; TR 72-80; RD Tynemouth 75-80; Bp Sheff 80-97; rtd 97; Perm to Offic *York* 97-99; Hon Asst Bp York from 99. *Rivendell, 28 Southfield Road, Wetwang, Driffield YO25 9XX* Tel (01377) 236657

LUNN, Leonard Arthur. b 42. Trin Coll Bris 69. **d** 72 **p** 73. C Walthamstow St Mary w St Steph *Chelmsf* 72-75; V Collier Row St Jas 75-85; V Collier Row St Jas and Havering-atte-Bower 86-87; Sen Chapl St Chris Hospice Sydenham *S'wark* from 87; Hon Chapl S'wark Cathl from 97. *St Christopher's Hospice, 51-59 Lawrie Park Road, London SE26 6DZ* Tel (020) 8778 9252 *or* 8699 3305 Fax 8659 8680

LUNN, Mrs Rosemary Christine. b 51. Bris Univ BA72. Trin Coll Bris 98. **d** 00 **p** 01. NSM Stoke Bishop *Bris* 00-01; C Chippenham St Pet from 01; Hon Min Can Bris Cathl from 02. *11 Aintree Drive, Chippenham SN14 0FA* Tel (01249) 464116 Mobile 07799-497533

LUNN, Sarah Anne. b 63. Lanc Univ BMus84 Man Metrop Univ MA93. Cranmer Hall Dur 00. **d** 02 **p** 03. C Kirkby Lonsdale *Carl* from 02. *6 Mill Brow, Kirkby Lonsdale, Carnforth LA6 2AT* Tel (015242) 71928 E-mail sarahlunn@care4free.net

LUNNEY, Canon Henry. b 31. ACIB57. Wycliffe Hall Ox 73. **d** 74 **p** 75. C Ipswich St Aug *St E* 74-77; P-in-c Westerfield w Tuddenham St Martin 77-83; R Westerfield and Tuddenham w Witnesham 83-97; Asst Dioc Chr Stewardship Adv 78-83; Hon

Can St E Cathl 92-97; rtd 97. *6 Karen Close, Ipswich IP1 4LP* Tel (01473) 252876

LUNNON, Canon Robert Reginald. b 31. K Coll Lon BD55 AKC55 Kent Univ MA99. St Boniface Warminster 55. **d** 56 **p** 57. C Maidstone St Mich *Cant* 56-58; C Deal St Leon 58-62; V Sturry 63-68; V Norbury St Steph 68-77; V Orpington All SS *Roch* 77-96; RD Orpington 79-95; Hon Can Roch Cathl 96; rtd 96; Perm to Offic *Cant* from 96. *10 King Edward Road, Deal CT14 6QL* Tel (01304) 364898

LUNT, Colin Peter. b 54. York Univ BA75 Leeds Poly Dip Librarianship 77. Trin Coll Bris 95. **d** 97 **p** 98. C Westbury-on-Trym H Trin *Bris* 97-00; V Coalpit Heath from 00. *The Vicarage, Beesmoor Road, Coalpit Heath, Bristol BS36 2RP* Tel (01454) 775129 Fax as telephone E-mail colin@lunt.co.uk

LUNT, Derek. b 32. St Jo Coll Dur 51. St Aid Birkenhead 55. **d** 57 **p** 58. C Toxteth Park Ch Ch *Liv* 57-59; C Prescot 59-61; V Much Dewchurch w Llanwarne and Llandinabo *Heref* 61-67; R Pembridge 67-74; Chapl Lucton Sch 71-74; rtd 91; Perm to Offic *Worc* from 93. *Olcote, 5 Mansfield Road, Malvern WR14 2WE* Tel (01684) 573932

LUNT, Margaret Joan. b 44. Leeds Univ MB, ChB68. Cranmer Hall Dur 91. **d** 94 **p** 95. C Stanford-le-Hope w Mucking *Chelmsf* 94-97; C Rayleigh 97-00; TV 00-03; TV Attercliffe, Darnall and Tinsley *Sheff* from 03. *24 Highgate, Tinsley, Sheffield S9 1WL* Tel 0114-244 1740 E-mail robertlunt@luntrfreeserve.co.uk

LURIE, Miss Gillian Ruth. b 42. LRAM62 GNSM63 ACertCM80. Gilmore Ho 68. **dss** 74 **d** 87 **p** 94. Camberwell St Phil and St Mark *S'wark* 74-76; Haddenham *Ely* 76-79; Dioc Lay Min Adv 79-86; Longthorpe *Pet* 79-81; Pet H Spirit Bretton 81-86; Bramley *Ripon* 86-93; C 87-88; TD 88-93; P-in-c Methley w Mickletown 93-98; R 98-01; rtd 02; Perm to Offic *Cant* from 02. *42A Cuthbert Road, Westgate-on-Sea CT8 8NR* Tel (01843) 831698 Fax as telephone E-mail gillandjean@hotmail.com

LURKINGS, Edward Henry. b 28. AKC53 Lon Univ BSc68 MSc70 PhD81. **d** 54 **p** 55. C Brookfield St Mary *Lon* 54-59; C Cricklewood St Pet 59-62; Ind Chapl 62-71; Lect Middx Poly 71-73; Sen Lect 73-84; Hon C Luton St Mary *St Alb* 72-84; V Potterspury, Furtho, Yardley Gobion and Cosgrove *Pet* 84-92; rtd 92. *Glasfryn, Abercych, Boncath SA37 0HA* Tel (01239) 687576

LURY, Anthony Patrick. b 49. K Coll Lon BD71 AKC71. St Aug Coll Cant 71. **d** 72 **p** 73. C Richmond St Mary *S'wark* 72-76; P-in-c Streatham Hill St Marg 76-81; V Salfords 81-90; V Emscote *Cov* 90-01; P-in-c Ascot Heath *Ox* from 01. *All Saints' Rectory, London Road, Ascot SL5 8DQ* Tel (01344) 621200 E-mail anthony@all-saints-ascot.org

LUSBY, Dennis John. b 27. Brentwood Coll of Educn CertEd70. **d** 93 **p** 94. NSM Grayshott *Guildf* 93-99; Perm to Offic from 99. *Squirrels Drey, Waggoners Way, Grayshott, Hindhead GU26 6DX* Tel (01428) 604419

LUSCOMBE, John Nickels. b 45. St Jo Coll Nottm Dip Past Counselling 97 Birm Univ BA99. AKC68. **d** 69 **p** 70. C Stoke Newington St Faith, St Matthias and All SS *Lon* 69-74; V Tottenham St Phil 74-81; Zimbabwe 82-86; V Queensbury All SS *Lon* 86-99; V Estover *Ex* 99-01; Dioc Ecum Officer 99-01; V Norton *St Alb* from 01; RD Hitchin from 02. *Norton Vicarage, 17 Norton Way North, Letchworth Garden City SG6 1BY* Tel (01462) 685059 *or* 678133 E-mail jluscombe@callnetuk.com

✠**LUSCOMBE, The Rt Revd Lawrence Edward (Ted).** b 24. Dundee Univ LLD87 MPhil91 PhD93 ACA52 FSA80 FRSA87. K Coll Lon 63. **d** 63 **p** 64 **c** 75. C Glas St Marg *Glas* 63-66; R Paisley St Barn 66-71; Provost St Paul's Cathl Dundee *Bre* 71-75; R Dundee St Paul 71-75; Bp Bre 75-90; Primus 85-90; OStJ from 85; Chapl from 96; rtd 90; Perm to Offic *Bre* from 90. *Woodville, Kirkton of Tealing, Dundee DD4 0RD* Tel (01382) 380331

LUSITANIAN CHURCH, Bishop of the. See SOARES, The Rt Revd Fernando da Luz

LUSTED, Jack Andrew. b 58. Sussex Univ BSc79 PGCE81. St Steph Ho Ox 88. **d** 90 **p** 91. C Moulsecoomb *Chich* 90-93; C Southwick St Mich 93-97; R Lurgashall, Lodsworth and Selham from 97. *The Rectory, Lodsworth, Petworth GU28 9DE* Tel (01798) 861274 E-mail jack.lusted@btinternet.com

LUSTY, Tom Peter. b 71. Glas Univ BD94 Leeds Univ MA99. Coll of Resurr Mirfield 97. **d** 99 **p** 00. C Billingshurst *Chich* 99-02; Asst Chapl Leeds Teaching Hosps NHS Trust from 02. *Leeds Teaching Hospitals NHS Trust, St James University Hospital, Beckett Street, Leeds LS9 7TF* Tel 0113-243 3144 Mobile 07710-323716

LUTHER, Canon Richard Grenville Litton. b 42. Lon Univ BD64. Tyndale Hall Bris 66. **d** 68 **p** 69. C Preston St Mary *Blackb* 68-70; C Bishopsworth *Bris* 70-71; C Radipole *Sarum* 72-76; TV Radipole and Melcombe Regis 77-90; TR Hampreston from 90; Can and Preb Sarum Cathl from 00. *The Rectory, 9 Pinewood Road, Ferndown, Wimborne BH22 9RW* Tel (01202) 872084

LUTHER THOMAS, The Ven Ilar Roy. b 30. St D Coll Lamp BA51. St Mich Coll Llan 51. **d** 53 **p** 54. C Oystermouth *S & B* 53-56; C Gorseinon 56-59; R Llanbadarn Fawr and Llandegley

59-60; R Llanbadarn Fawr, Llandegley and Llanfihangel etc 60-65; CF (ACF) 62-90; Children's Adv *S & B* 63-77; V Knighton and Norton 65-79; RD Knighton 66-79; V Sketty 79-89; Can Brecon Cathl from 75; Treas 87-88; Chan 88-90; Adn Gower 90-95; rtd 95. *2 Druids Close, Mumbles, Swansea SA3 5TY* Tel (01792) 419455

LUTTON, Percy Theodore Bell Boyce. b 24. TCD BA45 MA48. **d** 46 **p** 48. C Whitehouse *Conn* 47-49; C Dudley St Jo *Worc* 49-52; V Stambermill 52-61; V Wribbenhall 61-80; R Castlemorton, Hollybush and Birtsmorton 80-89; rtd 89; Perm to Offic *Lich* from 90. *23 Bridgeman Road, Oswestry SY11 2JP* Tel (01691) 656425

✠**LUXMOORE, The Rt Revd Christopher Charles.** b 26. Trin Coll Cam BA50 MA54. Chich Th Coll 50. **d** 52 **p** 53 **c** 84. C Newc St Jo *Newc* 52-55; C-in-c Newsham St Bede CD 55-57; V Newsham 57-58; Trinidad and Tobago 58-66; V Headingley *Ripon* 67-81; Hon Can Ripon Cathl 80-81; Can Res and Prec Chich Cathl *Chich* 81-84; Bp Bermuda 84-89; Adn Lewes and Hastings *Chich* 89-91; rtd 91; Provost Woodard Corp (S Division) 89-96; Asst Bp Chich from 91. *42 Willowbed Drive, Chichester PO19 8JB* Tel (01243) 784680

LYALL, Canon Graham. b 37. Univ of Wales (Lamp) BA61 Birm Univ DipTh63. Qu Coll Birm 61. **d** 63 **p** 64. C Middlesbrough Ascension *York* 63-67; C Kidderminster St Mary *Worc* 67-72; V Dudley St Aug Holly Hall 72-79; P-in-c Barbourne 79-81; V 81-93; RD Worc E 83-89; Hon Can Worc Cathl from 85; TR Malvern Link w Cowleigh from 93. *St Matthias' Rectory, 12 Lambourne Avenue, Malvern WR14 1NL* Tel (01684) 573834

LYALL, Richard Keith. b 70. Glas Univ BSc92 MSc95 Strathclyde Univ MSc97. Trin Coll Bris BA02. **d** 02. C Gateacre *Liv* from 02. *24 Lee Vale Road, Gateacre, Liverpool L25 3RW* Tel 0151-487 9391 E-mail rklyall@yahoo.com

LYDDON, David Andrew. b 47. LDSRCSEng70 Lon Univ BDS70. SW Minl Tr Course 90. **d** 93 **p** 94. NSM Tiverton St Pet *Ex* 93-95; NSM Tiverton St Pet w Chevithorne 95-96; NSM W Exe 96-01; NSM Tiverton St Geo and St Paul from 01. *Hightrees, 19 Patches Road, Tiverton EX16 5AH* Tel (01884) 257250 E-mail dlyddon597@aol.uk

LYDON, Mrs Barbara. b 34. Gilmore Ho 64. **dss** 72 **d** 87 **p** 94. Rastrick St Matt *Wakef* 72-85; Upper Hopton 85-87; Par Dn 87; Dn-in-c Kellington w Whitley 87-94; P-in-c 94-95; rtd 95; Perm to Offic *Wakef* from 95. *17 Garlick Street, Brighouse HD6 3PW* Tel (01484) 722704

LYES-WILSDON, Canon Patricia Mary. b 45. Open Univ BA87 ALA65. Glouc Sch of Min 84 Qu Coll Birm 86. **d** 87 **p** 94. C Thornbury *Glouc* 87-94; P-in-c Cromhall w Tortworth and Tytherington from 94; Asst Dioc Dir of Ords 90-98; Dioc Voc Officer 94-01; RD Hawkesbury from 98; Dioc Adv for Women's Min from 01; Hon Can Glouc Cathl from 02; P-in-c Falfield w Rockhampton from 02. *The New Rectory, Rectory Lane, Cromhall, Wotton-under-Edge GL12 8AN* Tel (01454) 294767 E-mail revd.pat@virgin.net

LYMBERY, Peter. b 32. JP73. St Alb and Ox Min Course 95. **d** 98 **p** 99. SBStJ from 77; OStJ from 89; OLM Stewkley w Soulbury and Drayton Parslow *Ox* from 98; P Assoc Shrine of Our Lady of Walsingham from 00. *17 Hartwell Crescent, Leighton Buzzard LU7 1NP* Tel (01525) 371235

LYNAS, Mrs Judith. b 53. S Dios Minl Tr Scheme 89. **d** 92 **p** 94. Par Dn Lytchett Minster *Sarum* 92-94; C 94-96; Hon C Longfleet 97-99. *Address temp unknown*

LYNAS, The Very Revd Norman Noel. b 55. St Andr Univ MTheol78. CITC 78. **d** 79 **p** 80. C Knockbreda *D & D* 79-81; C Holywood 81-85; I Portadown St Columba *Arm* 85-91; Dioc Communications Officer 86-89; Tutor for Aux Min (Arm) 88-91; Radio Officer (Arm) 90-91; I Kilkenny w Aghour and Kilmanagh *C & O* from 91; Dean Ossory from 91; Can Leighlin Cathl from 91. *The Deanery, Kilkenny, Irish Republic* Tel (00353) (56) 772 1516 Fax 775 1817 E-mail lynas@gofree.indigo.ie

LYNAS, Stephen Brian. b 52. MBE00. St Jo Coll Nottm BTh77. **d** 78 **p** 79. C Penn *Lich* 78-81; Relig Progr Org BBC Radio Stoke-on-Trent 81-84; C Hanley H Ev 81-82; C Edensor 82-84; Relig Progr Producer BBC Bris 85-88; Relig Progr Sen Producer BBC S & W England 88-91; Hd Relig Progr TV South 91-92; Community (and Relig) Affairs Ed Westcountry TV from 92; Abps' Officer for Millennium 96-01; Dioc Resources Adv *B & W* from 01. *Old Honeygar Cottage, Honeygar Lane, Westhay, Glastonbury BA6 9TS* Tel (01458) 860763 *or* (01749) 670777 E-mail stephen.lynas@bathwells.anglican.org

LYNCH, Eithne Elizabeth Mary. b 45. CITC BTh94. **d** 97 **p** 98. C Douglas Union w Frankfield *C, C & R* 97-01; Min Can Cork Cathl from 99; Bp's Dom Chapl from 99; I Kilmoe Union from 01. *Altar Rectory, Toormore, Skibbereen, Co Cork, Irish Republic* Tel (00353) (28) 28259 Mobile 86-253 5002 E-mail kilmoe@cork.anglican.org

LYNCH, James. EAMTC 93. **d** 96 **p** 97. NSM High Oak *Nor* 96-97; NSM High Oak, Hingham and Scoulton w Wood Rising 97-99; Asst Chapl Norfolk Mental Health Care NHS Trust 99-03; P-in-c Nor St Steph 99-03; NSM Blanchland w

Hunstanworth and Edmundbyers etc *Newc* from 03; NSM Slaley from 03; NSM Healey from 03; NSM Whittonstall from 03. *The Vicarage, Blanchland, Consett DH8 9ST* Tel (01434) 675141 E-mail jcrescent@fish.co.uk

LYNCH-WATSON, Graham Leslie. b 30. AKC55. **d** 56 **p** 57. C New Eltham All SS *S'wark* 56-60; C W Brompton St Mary *Lon* 60-62; V Camberwell St Bart *S'wark* 62-66; V Purley St Barn 67-77; C Caversham *Ox* 77-81; C Caversham St Pet and Mapledurham etc 81-85; P-in-c Warwick St Paul *Cov* 85-86; V 86-92; rtd 92; Perm to Offic *Ox* 96-00. *11 Crouch Street, Banbury OX16 9PP* Tel (01295) 263172

LYNE, Peter. b 27. Sheff Univ BA51. Qu Coll Birm 51. **d** 53 **p** 54. C Newland St Aug *York* 53-55; C Harworth *S'well* 55-56; C Burbage *Derby* 56-58; V Horsley Woodhouse 58-62; V Rawcliffe *Sheff* 62-69; V Elvaston and Shardlow *Derby* 69-74; P-in-c Ashbourne St Jo 74-80; P-in-c Kniveton w Hognaston 75-80; P-in-c Fenny Bentley, Thorpe and Tissington 77-78; P-in-c Osmaston w Edlaston 78-80; P-in-c Lt Eaton 80-84; P-in-c Holbrook 80-84; V Holbrook and Lt Eaton 84-91; rtd 91; Perm to Offic *Derby* from 91. *3 Vicarage Close, High Street, Belper DE56 1TB* Tel (01773) 829188

LYNE, Roger Howard. b 28. Mert Coll Ox BA52 MA56. Oak Hill Th Coll 52. **d** 54 **p** 55. C Rugby St Matt *Cov* 54-58; C Weymouth St Jo *Sarum* 58-61; V Newchapel *Lich* 61-65; C Bucknall and Bagnall 76-81; Perm to Offic *Win* from 82; rtd 88. *21 Copse Road, Burley, Ringwood BH24 4EG* Tel (01425) 402232

LYNESS, Nicholas Jonathan. b 55. Oak Hill Th Coll BA97. **d** 97. C Reading Greyfriars *Ox* 97-98. *3 Roe Green Cottages, Roe Green, Sandon, Buntingford SG9 0QE* Tel (01763) 288172 Mobile 07802-730485

LYNETT, Anthony Martin. b 54. K Coll Lon BD75 AKC75 Darw Coll Cam PGCE76. Sarum & Wells Th Coll 77. **d** 78 **p** 79. C Swindon Ch Ch *Bris* 78-81; C Leckhampton SS Phil and Jas w Cheltenham St Jas *Glouc* 81-83; Asst Chapl HM Pris Glouc 83-88; Chapl 91-98; V Coney Hill *Glouc* 83-88; Chapl HM YOI Deerbolt 88-91; P-in-c Glouc St Mark *Glouc* 91-99; P-in-c Glouc St Mary de Crypt w St Jo, Ch Ch etc 98-99; Chapl HM Pris Wellingborough 99-01; V Wellingborough All SS *Pet* from 01. *The Vicarage, 154 Midland Road, Wellingborough NN8 1NF* Tel (01933) 227101
E-mail tony.lynett@cableinet.co.uk

LYNN, Anthony Hilton. b 44. Golds Coll Lon TCert66 Open Univ BA80. St Alb and Ox Min Course 95. **d** 98 **p** 99. NSM Stanford in the Vale w Goosey and Hatford *Ox* 98-00; NSM Cherbury w Gainfield 00-03; TV Hermitage from 03. *The Rectory, Yattendon, Thatcham RG18 0UR* Tel (01635) 201203
E-mail tony@hlynn.fsnet.co.uk

LYNN, Mrs Antonia Jane. b 59. Girton Coll Cam BA80 MA84. St Steph Ho Ox 82. dss 84 **d** 87. Portsm Cathl *Portsm* 84-87; Dn-in-c Camberwell St Mich w All So w Em *S'wark* 87-91; Par Dn Newington St Mary 87-91; Perm to Offic 91-94; Chapl Horton Hosp Epsom 91-94; Gen Sec Guild of Health from 94; Hon Par Dn Ewell *Guildf* 94-99; Perm to Offic *Lon* from 94. *7 Kingsmead Close, West Ewell, Epsom KT19 9RD* Tel (020) 8786 8983

LYNN, Frank Trevor. b 36. Keble Coll Ox BA61 MA63. St Steph Ho Ox 61. **d** 63 **p** 64. C W Derby St Mary *Liv* 63-65; C Chorley *Ches* 65-68; V Altrincham St Jo 68-72; Chapl RN 72-88; Hon C Walworth St Jo *S'wark* 88-90; C Cheam 90-96; rtd 99. *7 Kingsmead Close, West Ewell, Epsom KT19 9RD* Tel (020) 8786 8983

LYNN, Jeffrey. b 39. Moore Th Coll Sydney 67 EMMTC 76. **d** 79 **p** 80. C Littleover *Derby* 79-80; Hon C Allestree 80-85; Chapl HM Pris Man 85-86; Chapl HM Pris Kirkham 86-93; Chapl HM Pris Wakef 93-95; Chapl HM Pris Sudbury 95-96; Chapl HM Pris Foston Hall 95-96; rtd 96; Perm to Offic *Blackb* from 98. *48 South Park, Lytham St Annes FY8 4QQ* Tel (01253) 730490

LYNN, Peter Anthony. b 38. Keele Univ BA62 St Jo Coll Cam BA64 MA68 PhD72. Westcott Ho Cam 67. **d** 68 **p** 69. C Soham *Ely* 68-72; Min Can St Paul's Cathl *Lon* 72-78; Perm to Offic *St Alb* 78-86; Min Can and Sacr St Paul's Cathl *Lon* 86-88; C Westmr St Matt 89-91; V Glynde, W Firle and Beddingham *Chich* 91-03; rtd 03. *119 Stanford Avenue, Brighton BN1 6FA* Tel (01273) 553361

LYNN, Archdeacon of. *See* GRAY, The Ven Martin Clifford

LYNN, Suffragan Bishop of. *See* FOOTTIT, The Rt Revd Anthony Charles

LYON, Adrian David. b 55. Coll of Resurr Mirfield 84. **d** 87 **p** 88. C Crewe St Andr *Ches* 87-90; C Altrincham St Geo 90-91; TV Accrington *Blackb* 91-00; TR Accrington Ch the King from 00. *St Peter's Vicarage, 151 Willows Lane, Accrington BB5 0LR* Tel (01254) 382173 Fax as telephone
E-mail lyons@ddens.freeserve.co.uk

LYON, Christopher David. b 55. Strathclyde Univ LLB75 Edin Univ BD81. Edin Th Coll 78. **d** 81 **p** 82. C Dumfries *Glas* 81-84; P-in-c Alexandria 84-88; R Greenock 88-00; R Ayr, Girvan and Maybole 00-02; Chapl Luxembourg *Eur* from 02. *98 rue de Mühlenbach, L-2168 Luxembourg* Tel (00352) 439593 Fax as telephone

LYON, Dennis. b 36. Lon Univ DipTh66. Wycliffe Hall Ox 64. **d** 67 **p** 68. C Woodthorpe *S'well* 67-70; Warden Walton Cen 70-72; V W Derby Gd Shep *Liv* 72-81; V Billinge 81-00; AD Wigan W 89-00; rtd 00. *10 Arniam Road, Rainford, St Helens WA11 8BU* Tel (01744) 885623

LYON, Canon Donald Robert. b 20. Trin Coll Cam BA41 PhD44 MA45. Linc Th Coll 46. **d** 47 **p** 48. C Dursley *Glouc* 47-51; C Brislington St Luke *Bris* 51-52; V Glouc St Mark *Glouc* 52-85; Hon Can Glouc Cathl 74-90; RD Glouc City 77-83; rtd 85; Perm to Offic *Glouc* 86-97. *12 Doverdale Drive, Longlevens, Gloucester GL2 0NN* Tel (01452) 524070

LYON, Joan Baxter. b 50. Strathclyde Univ BA70. TISEC 94. **d** 96 **p** 00. NSM Glas E End *Glas* 96-00. *98 rue de Mühlenbach, L-2168 Luxembourg* Tel (00352) 439593 Fax as telephone
E-mail joanblyon@hotmail.com

LYON, John Forrester. b 39. Edin Th Coll CertEd95. **d** 95 **p** 96. C Greenock *Glas* 95-98; C Gourock 95-98; Chapl Ardgowan Hospice 95-98; P-in-c Glas Gd Shep and Ascension *Glas* from 98. *31 Westfield Drive, Glasgow G52 2SG* Tel 0141-882 4996

LYON, John Harry. b 51. S Dios Minl Tr Scheme 86. **d** 89 **p** 90. NSM S Patcham *Chich* 89-91; C Chich St Paul and St Pet 91-94; R Earnley and E Wittering from 94. *The Rectory, East Wittering, Chichester PO20 8PS* Tel (01243) 672260

LYON, Canon Stephen Paul. b 49. Univ of Wales (Swansea) BSc71. Trin Coll Bris 74. **d** 77 **p** 78. C Hull Newland St Jo *York* 77-81; Chapl Lee Abbey 81-84; V Norbiton *S'wark* 84-92; RD Kingston 88-92; Prin *S'wark* OLM Scheme 92-00; Partnership Sec Gen Syn Bd for Miss from 00; Perm to Offic *S'wark* from 01; Hon Can S'wark Cathl from 01; Perm to Offic *Cant* from 02. *Partnership House, 157 Waterloo Road, London SE1 8XA* Tel (020) 7928 8681 *or* 8480 5145 Fax 7633 0185 *or* 8480 6088
E-mail stephen.lyon@c-of-e.org.uk

LYONS, Bruce Twyford. b 37. K Alfred's Coll Win CertEd61. Tyndale Hall Bris DipTh69. **d** 70 **p** 71. C Virginia Water *Guildf* 70-73; Chapl Ostend w Knokke and Bruges *Eur* 73-78; V E Ham St Paul *Chelmsf* 78-85; V St Alb Ch Ch *St Alb* 85-91; Chapl Wellingborough Sch 92-95; P-in-c Stogumber w Nettlecombe and Monksilver *B & W* 96-98; P-in-c Ostend w Knokke and Bruges *Eur* 98-00; NSM Newbury Deanery *Ox* 01; Chapl Milton Abbey Sch Dorset 01-02; Perm to Offic *Sarum* from 01; rtd 02. *Tudor Barn, Spring Street, Wool, Wareham BH20 6DB* Tel (01929) 462901
E-mail blyons@fish.co.uk

LYONS, Edward Charles. b 44. Nottm Univ BTh75 LTh. St Jo Coll Nottm 71. **d** 75 **p** 76. C Cambridge St Martin *Ely* 75-78; P-in-c Bestwood Park *S'well* 78-85; R W Hallam and Mapperley *Derby* 85-98; P-in-c Brownsover CD *Cov* 98-02; V Brownsover from 02; AD Rugby from 99; Dioc Ecum Officer from 03. *43 Bowfell, Brownsover, Rugby CV21 1JF* Tel (01788) 573696
E-mail ted.lyons@btinternet.com

LYONS, Graham Selby. b 29. MBE84. Open Univ BA79. LNSM course 94. **d** 97 **p** 98. OLM New Eltham All SS *S'wark* from 97. *56 Cadwallon Road, London SE9 3PY* Tel (020) 8850 6576
E-mail holyons2@aol.com

LYONS, Margaret Rose Marie. b 47. LNSM course 89. **d** 89. OLM Gainsborough All SS *Linc* 89-91. *1C Common Road, Low Moor, Bradford BD12 0NT*

LYONS, Paul. b 67. Ulster Univ BA91 DipM92. TCD Div Sch BTh98. **d** 98 **p** 99. C Seapatrick *D & D* 98-03; I Greenisland *Conn* from 03. *4 Tinamara, Greenisland, Carrickfergus BT38 8FE* Tel (028) 9086 3421
E-mail paul@plyons.fsnet.co.uk

LYONS, Paul Benson. b 44. Qu Coll Birm 68. **d** 69 **p** 70. C Rugby St Andr *Cov* 69-70; C Moston St Jo *Man* 70-72; PV Llan Cathl *Llan* 73-74; C Brookfield St Anne, Highgate Rise *Lon* 74-75; Perm to Offic 76-82; C Westmr St Sav and St Jas Less 82-86; V Gt Cambridge Road St Jo and St Jas from 86. *St John's Vicarage, 113 Creighton Road, London N17 8JS* Tel (020) 8808 4077

LYONS, William. b 22. LNSM course 78. **d** 80 **p** 81. NSM Glenrothes *St And* 80-81; NSM Kirkcaldy 81-91; NSM Kinghorn 81-91; rtd 91. *44 Annandale Gardens, Glenrothes KY6 1JD* Tel (01592) 751905

✠**LYTH, The Rt Revd Richard Edward.** b 16. St Edm Hall Ox BA38 MA55. Oak Hill Th Coll. **d** 56 **p** 57 **c** 67. C Arthuret *Carl* 56-59; Uganda 59-72; Bp Kigezi 67-72; C Chorleywood St Andr *St Alb* 74-81; rtd 81. *31 Backwoods Lane, Lindfield, Haywards Heath RH16 2EQ* Tel (01444) 482500

LYTLE, Canon John Deaville. b 23. Wadh Coll Ox BA50 MA52. Wycliffe Hall Ox 50. **d** 51 **p** 52. C Ilkeston St Mary *Derby* 51-56; P-in-c Brassington 56-59; P-in-c Bradbourne and Brassington 59-89; RD Wirksworth 78-88; Hon Can Derby Cathl 82-89; rtd 89; Perm to Offic *Derby* from 89. *14 Manor Road, Ashbourne DE6 1EH* Tel (01335) 346588

LYTTLE, Norma Irene. b 47. CITC. **d** 01 **p** 02. NSM Drumachose *D & R* from 01. *18 Windyhill Road, Limavady BT49 0RA* Tel and fax (028) 7776 3166 Mobile 07714-350317

M

M'CAW, Stephen Aragorn. b 61. Magd Coll Cam BA83 Lon Univ MB, BS86 FRCS90 MRCGP92. Cranmer Hall Dur 97. **d** 99 **p** 00. C Thetford *Nor* 99-02; R Steeple Aston w N Aston and Tackley *Ox* from 02. *The Rectory, Fir Lane, Steeple Aston, Bicester OX25 4SF* Tel (01869) 347793 E-mail samcaw@talk21.com

MABBS, Miss Margaret Joyce. b 24. St Hilda's Coll Ox BA45 MA47 DipEd46 DipRS82. S'wark Ord Course 79. **dss** 82 **d** 87 **p** 94. Eltham Park St Luke *S'wark* 82-87; NSM from 87. *70 Westmount Road, London SE9 1JE* Tel (020) 8850 4621

McADAM, Gordon Paul. b 66. QUB BSc88 TCD BTh93. CITC 90. **d** 93 **p** 94. C Drumglass w Moygashel *Arm* 93-96; I Dungiven w Bovevagh *D & R* 96-02; I Loughgall w Grange *Arm* from 02. *The Rectory, 2 Main Street, Loughgall, Armagh BT61 8HZ* Tel (028) 3889 1587 E-mail dungiven@derry.anglican.org *or* gp@pmcadam.freeserve.co.uk

McADAM, Canon Michael Anthony. b 30. K Coll Cam BA52 MA56. Westcott Ho Cam 54. **d** 56 **p** 57. C Towcester w Easton Neston *Pet* 56-59; Chapl Hurstpierpoint Coll 60-68; Bp's Chapl *Lon* 69-73; R Much Hadham *St Alb* 73-95; Hon Can St Alb 89-95; rtd 95; RD Oundle *Pet* 96-97; Perm to Offic *Pet* from 98 and *St Alb* from 03. *Parkers Patch, 55 Barnwell, Peterborough PE8 5PG* Tel (01832) 273451

McALISTER, David. b 39. St Jo Coll Nottm 83. **d** 87 **p** 88. NSM Arpafeelie *Mor* 87-93; NSM Cromarty 87-93; NSM Fortrose 87-93; C Broughty Ferry *Bre* 93-95; P-in-c Nairn *Mor* from 95. *1 Clova Crescent, Nairn IV12 4TE* Tel (01667) 452458

McALISTER, Kenneth Bloomer. b 25. TCD BA51. **d** 51 **p** 53. C Cregagh *D & D* 51-54; C Monaghan *Clogh* 54-57; C Portadown St Mark *Arm* 57-62; R Ripley *Ripon* 62-91; rtd 91; Perm to Offic *Ripon* from 91. *31 Wetherby Road, Knaresborough HG5 8LH* Tel (01423) 860705

McALISTER, Margaret Elizabeth Anne (Sister Margaret Anne). b 55. St Mary's Coll Dur BA78 Ex Univ PGCE79. Wycliffe Hall Ox 83 St Alb and Ox Min Course 99. **d** 01 **p** 02. ASSP from 91; NSM Cowley St Jas *Ox* from 01. *All Saints Convent, St Mary's Road, Oxford OX4 1RU* Tel (01865) 249127 Fax 726547

MacALLISTER, The Very Revd Randal George Leslie. b 41. TCD BA63 Div Test 64 MA66. **d** 64 **p** 66. C Portadown St Mark *Arm* 64-67; I Keady w Armaghbreague and Derrynoose 67-74; R Kirriemuir *St And* 74-81; R Greenock *Glas* 81-87; R Forfar *St And* 87-95; R Lunan Head 87-95; Chapl Sophia Antipolis *Eur* 95-98; R Auchterarder *St And* from 98; R Muthill from 98; Dean St Andr from 98. *St Kessog's Rectory, High Street, Auchterarder PH3 1AD* Tel (01764) 662525

McALISTER, Thomas George. b 20. TCD BA42 MA47. **d** 43 **p** 44. C Aghalee *D & D* 43-45; C Belfast St Pet *Conn* 45-53; V Southport St Andr *Liv* 53-59; V Spring Grove St Mary *Lon* 59-69; Chapl Wispers Sch Surrey 69-79; R Haslemere *Guildf* 69-79; V Slyne w Hest *Blackb* 79-85; rtd 85; Perm to Offic *Guildf* 86-96; Portsm 86-98; P-in-c Linchmere *Chich* 92-93. *4 Rosemary Court, Church Road, Haslemere GU27 1BH* Tel (01428) 643516

McALLEN, James. b 38. Lon Univ BD71. Oak Hill Th Coll 63. **d** 66 **p** 67. C Blackheath St Jo *S'wark* 66-69; C Edin St Thos *Edin* 69-73; V Selby St Jas *York* 73-80; V Wistow 75-80; V Houghton *Carl* 80-91; Gen Sec Lon City Miss from 92; Hon C Blackheath St Jo *S'wark* from 94. *192 Charlton Road, London SE7 7DW* Tel (020) 8856 7306

McALLEN, Robert Roy. b 41. Bps' Coll Cheshunt 62. **d** 65 **p** 66. C Seagoe *D & D* 65-67; C Knockbreda 67-70; CF 70-96; Chapl R Memorial Chpl Sandhurst 87-92; Perm to Offic *Guildf* 96-98; R Ockley, Okewood and Forest Green from 98. *The Rectory, Stane Street, Ockley, Dorking RH5 5SY* Tel (01306) 711550

MACAN, Peter John Erdley. b 36. Bp Gray Coll Cape Town 58 LTh60. **d** 60 **p** 61. S Africa 60-67; C S Lambeth St Ann *S'wark* 68-71; V Nunhead St Silas 72-81; P-in-c Clapham H Spirit 81-87; TV Clapham TM 87-90; V Dulwich St Clem w St Pet 90-02; rtd 02. *The Windings, South Croydon CR2 0HW* Tel (020) 8657 1398 E-mail peter.macan@virgin.net

McARTHUR, Duncan Walker. b 50. Strathclyde Univ BSc73 Moore Th Coll Sydney ThL80 Melbourne Univ BD82 Newc Univ MA94. **d** 82 **p** 82. Australia 82-90 and from 93; C Hornsby 82-85; Asst Min 88-89; Asst Chapl Barker Coll Hornsby 86-88; P-in-c Harraby *Carl* 90-93; R Hurstville 93-95; Hon Asst P Wauchope St Matt from 99. *43 Narran River Road, Wauchope, NSW, Australia 2446* Tel (0061) (2) 6585 1147 *or* 6583 6999 Mobile 412-828341 Fax (2) 6583 6982 E-mail duncanmcarthur@tsn.cc

McARTHUR-EDWARDS, Mrs Judith Sarah. b 71. Westmr Coll Ox BTh94. Cranmer Hall Dur Dip Minl Studies 99. **d** 99 **p** 00. C Cradley *Worc* 99-02; C Quarry Bank from 02. *9 Carpenter Glade, Halesowen B63 2BG* Tel (01384) 567601

MACARTNEY, Prof Fergus James. b 40. MRCP68 FACC76 FRCP77 Qu Coll Cam BA62 MA84 St Thos Hosp Cam BCh66

MB67. EAMTC 86 SW Minl Tr Course 88. d 90 **p** 91. Chapl Lee Abbey 90-91; NSM Shirwell, Loxhore, Kentisbury, Arlington, etc *Ex* 90-91; Asst Chapl Amsterdam w Den Helder and Heiloo *Eur* 91-98; Perm to Offic *Ely* from 99. *2 Tenison Court, Tenison Road, Cambridge CB1 2EF*

MACARTNEY, Gerald Willam. b 52. TCD BTh03. CITC. **d** 03. C Drumglass w Moygashel *Arm* from 03. *Kinore, 84 Killyman Road, Dungannon BT71 6DQ* Tel (028) 8772 7131 Mobile 07850-040027 E-mail gwmac@btinternet.com

McATEER, John Alexander. b 18. TCD BA44 MA50. CITC 44. **d** 44 **p** 45. C Limerick Cathl *L & K* 44-47; C Dublin St Bart *D & G* 47-51; C S Kensington St Steph *Lon* 51-52; C Notting Hill All SS w St Columb 52-59; V Hammersmith H Innocents 59-83; rtd 83; Perm to Offic *Lon* 83-93. *162 Sutton Court Road, London W4 3HR* Tel (020) 8995 5317

MACAULAY (née BRAYBROOKS), Mrs Bridget Ann. b 63. DipCOT84 Trin Coll Bris BA92. TISEC 96. **d** 98 **p** 99. C Edin Old St Paul *Edin* 98-01; C Edin St Pet from 01. *10 Hope Park Crescent, Edinburgh EH8 9NA* Tel 0131-667 4537

MACAULAY, John Roland. b 39. Man Univ BSc61 Liv Inst of Educn PGCE80. Wells Th Coll 61. **d** 63 **p** 64. C Padgate Ch Ch *Liv* 63-66; C Upholland 66-73; TV 73-75; V Hindley St Pet 75-81; Chapl Liv Coll 81-96; Sub-Chapl HM Pris Risley from 85; R Lowton St Luke *Liv* from 96. *The Rectory, 246 Slag Lane, Lowton, Warrington WA3 2ED* Tel (01942) 728434

MACAULAY, Kenneth Lionel. b 55. Edin Univ BD78. Edin Th Coll 74. **d** 78 **p** 79. C Glas St Ninian *Glas* 78-80; Dioc Youth Chapl 80-87; P-in-c Glas St Matt 80-87; R Glenrothes *St And* 87-89; Chapl St Mary's Cathl *Glas* 89-92; Min Glas St Mary 89-92; Min Glas St Serf 92-94; Perm to Offic *Glas* 94-96; NSM Glas St Oswald 96-98; P-in-c 98-01; Chapl HM Pris Glas (Barlinnie) 99-00; P-in-c Dumbarton *Glas* from 01. *The Rectory, 45 St Andrews Crescent, Dumbarton G82 3ES* Tel (01389) 765425 *or* 734514 E-mail kennethmacaulay@aol.com

MACAULAY, Kenneth Russell. b 63. Strathclyde Univ BSc85. TISEC 95. **d** 98 **p** 99. C Edin Old St Paul *Edin* 98-01; C Edin St Pet from 01. *10 Hope Park Crescent, Edinburgh EH8 9NA* Tel 0131-667 4537

McAUSLAND, Canon William James. b 36. Edin Th Coll 56. **d** 59 **p** 60. C Dundee St Mary Magd *Bre* 59-64; R 71-79; R Glas H Cross *Glas* 64-71; Chapl St Marg Old People's Home 79-85; R Dundee St Marg *Bre* 79-01; Chapl St Mary's Sisterhood 82-87; Chapl Ninewells Hosp 85-01; Can St Paul's Cathl Dundee 93-01; Hon Can St Paul's Cathl Dundee from 01; rtd 01. *18 Broadford Terrace, Broughty Ferry DD5 3EF* Tel (01382) 737721 E-mail williammcausland@care4free.net *or* womca@fish.co.uk

McAVOY, George Brian. b 41. MBE78. TCD BA61 MA72. Div Test 63. **d** 63 **p** 65. C Cork St Luke w St Ann *C, C & R* 63-66; I Timoleague w Abbeymahon 66-68; Chapl RAF 68-88; Asst Chapl-in-Chief RAF 88-95; QHC 91-95; Chapl Fosse Health NHS Trust 95-98; Chapl Oakham Sch from 98. *1 The Leas, Cottesmore, Oakham LE15 7DG* Tel (01572) 812404 *or* 758500 Fax 755786 E-mail gbm@oakham.rutland.sch.uk

McAVOY, Philip George. b 63. Imp Coll Lon BSc85 SS Coll Cam BA90. Westcott Ho Cam 88. **d** 91 **p** 92. C W End *Win* 91-95; TV Swanage and Studland *Sarum* 95-00; P-in-c Littleton *Lon* from 00. *Littleton Rectory, Squires Bridge Road, Shepperton TW17 0QE* Tel (01932) 562249 E-mail philmac@littletonrectory.fsnet.co.uk

McBRIDE, Murray. b 61. Wilson Carlile Coll Trin Coll Bris BA00. **d** 00 **p** 01. C S Lawres Gp *Linc* from 00. *The Rectory, Reepham Road, Fiskerton, Lincoln LN3 4EZ* Tel (01522) 752359 E-mail k.e.mcbride@bgc.ac.uk

McBRIDE, The Ven Stephen Richard. b 61. QUB BSc84 TCD DipTh87 BTh89 MA92 QUB PhD96. CITC 84. **d** 87 **p** 88. C Antrim All SS *Conn* 87-90; I Belfast St Pet 90-95; Bp's Dom Chapl 94-02; I Antrim All SS from 95; Adn Conn from 02. *The Vicarage, 10 Vicarage Gardens, Antrim BT41 4JP* Tel and fax (028) 9446 2186 Mobile 07718-588191 E-mail archdeacon@connor.anglican.org

McCABE, Alan. b 37. Lon Univ BScEng61. Ridley Hall Cam 61. **d** 63 **p** 64. C Bromley SS Pet and Paul *Roch* 63-67; PV Roch Cathl 67-70; V Bromley H Trin 70-77; V Westerham 77-88; V Eastbourne St Jo *Chich* 88-99; rtd 00; Perm to Offic *Chich* from 00. *94 Baldwin Avenue, Eastbourne BN21 1UP* Tel (01323) 643731 Fax as telephone E-mail alanmcc37@hotmail.com

McCABE, Carol. b 49. Man OLM Scheme 00. **d** 03. OLM Blackrod *Man* from 03. *27 Lymbridge Drive, Blackrod, Bolton BL6 5TH* Tel (01204) 669775

McCABE, John Hamilton. b 59. St Edm Hall Ox MA82 PGCE84 Bris Univ MA01. Trin Coll Bris 99. **d** 01 **p** 02. C Burpham *Guildf* from 01. *8 Selbourne Road, Burpham, Guildford GU4 7PJ* Tel and fax (01483) 456602 Mobile 07710-094357 E-mail jh.mccabe@ntlworld.com

McCABE, The Ven John Trevor. b 33. RD78. Nottm Univ BA55 St Cath Soc Ox DipTh59. Wycliffe Hall Ox 57. **d** 59 **p** 60. C Compton Gifford *Ex* 59-63; P-in-c Ex St Martin, St Steph, St Laur etc 63-66; Chapl RNR from 63; Chapl Ex Sch 64-66; V Capel *Guildf* 66-71; V Scilly Is *Truro* 71-74; TR Is of Scilly 74-81; Can Res Bris Cathl *Bris* 81-83; V Manaccan w St Anthony-in-

Meneage and St Martin *Truro* 83-96; RD Kerrier 87-90 and 94-96; Chmn Cornwall NHS Trust for Mental Handicap 91-00; Hon Can Truro Cathl from 93; Adn Cornwall 96-99; rtd 00; Non Exec Dir Cornwall Healthcare Trust from 99; Perm to Offic *Truro* from 99. *Sunhill, Budock Water, Falmouth TR11 5DG* Tel (01326) 378095

McCABE, Terence John. b 46. Sarum Th Coll 71. **d** 74 **p** 75. C Radford *Cov* 74-77; P-in-c Bris St Paul w St Barn *Bris* 77-80; TV E Bris 80-84; USA 84-90; R Eynesbury *Ely* from 90. *The Rectory, 7 Howitt's Lane, Eynesbury, St Neots PE19 2AJ* Tel (01480) 403884 *or* 385364 E-mail mccabe@nildram.co.uk

McCABE, William Alexander Beck. b 27. QUB BA50 PhD65. **d** 74 **p** 74. Sec Sheff Coun of Chs 74-80; Hon C Millhouses H Trin *Sheff* 74-80; TV Sheff Manor 80-83; C Mosbrough 83; C Portsea St Cuth *Portsm* 83-86; C S w N Hayling 86-87; V Mickleover St Jo *Derby* 87-91; rtd 91; Perm to Offic *Derby* from 91. *Tawelfan, Ruthin Road, Cadole, Mold CH7 5LL* Tel (01352) 810435

McCAFFERTY, Canon Christine Ann. b 43. FCA76. Gilmore Course 76. **dss** 79 **d** 87 **p** 94. Writtle *Chelmsf* 79-81; Writtle w Highwood 81-94; C 87-94; NSM Officer 88-94; Dom Chapl to Bp Bradwell 88-93; Hon Can Chelmsf Cathl from 91; TR Wickford and Runwell 94-00; rtd 00; Hon C Lt Baddow *Chelmsf* from 00. *3 Hanlee Brook, Great Baddow, Chelmsford CM2 8GB* Tel (01245) 476371 E-mail mccafferty@jcmcc.freeserve.co.uk

McCAFFERTY (née BACK), Mrs Esther Elaine. b 52. Saffron Walden Coll CertEd74. Trin Coll Bris 79 Oak Hill Th Coll BA81. **dss** 81 **d** 87 **p** 94. Collyhurst *Man* 81-84; Upton (Overchurch) *Ches* 84-88; Par Dn 87-88; Par Dn Upper Holloway St Pet w St Jo *Lon* 88-90; Min in charge 90-97; P-in-c Pitsea w Nevendon *Chelmsf* 97-02; R Basildon St Martin from 02; RD Basildon from 99. *The Rectory, St Martin's Square, Basildon SS14 1DX* Tel (01268) 522455 Fax as telephone E-mail emccafferty@talk21.com

McCAFFERTY, Keith Alexander. *See* DUCKETT, Keith Alexander

McCAFFERTY, William Andrew (Andy). b 49. Open Univ BA93. SW Minl Tr Course 94. **d** 97 **p** 98. NSM Lapford, Nymet Rowland and Coldridge *Ex* 97-03; CF from 00; NSM N Creedy *Ex* from 03. *c/o MOD Chaplains (Army)* Tel (01980) 615804 Fax 615800 E-mail andrew.mccafferty@care4free.net

McCAGHREY, Mark Allan. b 66. Warwick Univ BSc87. St Jo Coll Nottm BTh93. **d** 94 **p** 95. C Byfleet *Guildf* 94-97; V Lowestoft St Andr *Nor* from 97. *The Vicarage, 51 Beresford Road, Lowestoft NR32 2NQ* Tel (01502) 511521 Fax 08701-377567 E-mail mark@romanhill.org.uk

McCALLA, Robert Ian. b 31. AKC55. St Boniface Warminster 56. **d** 56 **p** 57. C Barrow St Jo *Carl* 56-58; C Penrith St Andr 58-61; R Greenheys St Clem *Man* 61-64; V Glodwick 64-71; R Distington *Carl* 71-73; V Howe Bridge *Man* 73-87; Chapl Atherleigh Hosp 75-98; R Heaton Mersey *Man* 73-87; V Tyldesley w Shakerley 92-98; rtd 98; Perm to Offic *Carl* from 98. *17 Brunswick Square, Penrith CA11 7LW* Tel (01768) 895212

MacCALLUM, Canon Norman Donald. b 47. Edin Univ LTh70. Edin Th Coll 67. **d** 71 **p** 72. TV Livingston LEP *Edin* 71-82; P-in-c Bo'ness from 82; R Grangemouth from 82; Miss to Seafarers from 82; Syn Clerk *Edin* from 96; Can St Mary's Cathl from 96. *33 Carronflats Road, Grangemouth FK3 9DG* Tel (01324) 482438 Fax as telephone

McCAMLEY, The Ven Gregor Alexander. b 42. TCD BA64 MA67. CITC 65. **d** 65 **p** 66. C Holywood *D & D* 65-68; C Bangor St Comgall 68-72; I Carnalea 72-80; I Knock from 80; Stewardship Adv from 89; Can Down Cathl from 90; Dioc Registrar 90-95; Adn Down from 95; Chan Belf Cathl from 95. *The Rectory, 29 King's Road, Belfast BT5 6JG* Tel (028) 9047 1514 E-mail stcolumbaknock@talk21.com

McCAMMON, John Taylor. b 42. QUB BSc65 Lon Univ BD70. Clifton Th Coll 67. **d** 71 **p** 72. C Lurgan Ch the Redeemer *D & D* 71-75; I Kilkeel 75-82; I Lisburn Ch Ch Cathl *Conn* 82-98; Treas 94-96; Prec 96; Chan 96-98; Can Conn Cathl 85-98; CMS Kenya from 98. *CMS, Partnership House, 157 Waterloo Road, London SE1 8UU* Tel (020) 7928 8681

McCANDLESS, John Hamilton Moore. b 24. QUB BA Ulster Poly BEd. **d** 63 **p** 64. C Belfast St Matt *Conn* 63-66; I Termonmaguirke *Arm* 66-69; C Jordanstown *Conn* 69-70; I Ballinderry, Tamlaght and Arboe *Arm* 70-74; I Kilbarron w Rossnowlagh and Drumholm *D & R* 84-87; rtd 87. *4 Greenhill Drive, Ballymoney BT53 6DE* Tel (028) 7066 2078 E-mail jack@theloughan.fsnet.co.uk

McCANN, Hilda. b 03. OLM Parr *Liv* from 03. *Address temp unknown*

McCANN, Michael Joseph. b 61. Man Univ BSc82 TCD BTh91 FCA. **d** 91 **p** 92. C Derryloran *Arm* 91-94; I Dunmurry *Conn* 94-99; I Kilroot and Templecorran from 99. *Kilroot Rectory, 29 Downshire Gardens, Carrickfergus BT38 7LW* Tel (028) 9336 2387

McCANN, Roland Neil. b 39. Serampore Coll BD73. Bp's Coll Calcutta DipTh70. **d** 70 **p** 73. India 70-74; C Earley St Bart *Ox*

74-77; C-in-c Harlington Ch Ch CD *Lon* 77-99; rtd 99. *195 Park Road, Uxbridge UB8 1NP* Tel (01895) 259265

McCANN, Thomas Alan George. b 66. Ulster Univ BA90 TCD BTh93 QUB MPhil99. CITC 90. **d** 93 **p** 94. C Carrickfergus *Conn* 93-00; I Woodburn H Trin from 00. *20 Meadow Hill Close, Carrickfergus BT38 9RQ* Tel (028) 9336 2126 E-mail alan@thehobbit.fsnet.co.uk

McCARRAHER, Seymour. b 26. Magd Coll Cam BA48 MA55. St Steph Ho Ox. **d** 55 **p** 56. C Southwick St Columba *Dur* 55-59; Chapl RN 59-75; C Christchurch *Win* 75-81; V Darton *Wakef* 81-92; rtd 92; Perm to Offic *York* from 93. *34 Moorside, Boston Spa, Wetherby LS23 6PN* Tel (01937) 843948

McCARTHY, David William. b 63. Edin Th Coll BD88. **d** 88 **p** 89. C Edin St Paul and St Geo *Edin* 88-91; P-in-c S Queensferry 91-95; R Glas St Silas *Glas* from 95. *77 Southbrae Drive, Glasgow G13 1PU* Tel 0141-954 9368 E-mail dwmccarthy@pastors.com

McCARTHY, The Very Revd John Francis. b 38. TCD BA61 MA72. **d** 62 **p** 63. C Seapatrick *D & D* 62-66; C Seagoe 66-71; I Moira 71-75; I Dundalk *Arm* 75-86; I Enniskillen *Clogh* 86-94; Dean Clogh 89-94; USA from 94. *St John's Anglican Church, 7th and Hampshire Street, Quincy, IL 62301, USA*

McCARTHY, Peter James. b 25. OBE. Cranmer Hall Dur. **d** 85 **p** 86. Hon C Farnham w Scotton, Staveley, Copgrove etc *Ripon* 85-87; V Startforth w Bowes 87-92; rtd 92; C Dufftown *Ab* 92-95; Perm to Offic *Ripon* from 95; Perm to Offic *Newc* from 99. *Manderley, Farnham Lane, Ferrensby, Knaresborough HG5 9JG* Tel (01423) 340503

MacCARTHY, The Very Revd Robert Brian. b 40. TCD BA63 MA66 PhD83 NUI MA65 Ox Univ MA82. Cuddesdon Coll 77. **d** 79 **p** 80. C Carlow w Urglin and Staplestown *C & O* 79-81; Lic to Offic (Cashel, Waterford and Lismore) 81-86; Lib Pusey Ho 81-82; Fell St Cross Coll Ox 81-82; C Bracknell *Ox* 82-83; TV 83-86; C Kilkenny w Aghour and Kilmanagh *C & O* 86-88; Bp's V and Lib Kilkenny Cathl 86-88; Chapl Kilkenny Coll 86-88; Bp's Dom Chapl 86-89; I Castlecomer w Colliery Ch, Mothel and Bilbo 88-95; Dioc Info Officer (Ossory and Leighlin) 88-90; Glebes Sec (Ossory and Leighlin) 92-94; Preb Monmohenock St Patr Cathl Dublin 94-99; Provost Tuam *T, K & A* 95-99; I Galway w Kilcummin 95-99; Chapl Univ Coll Galway 95-99; Dean St Patr Cathl Dublin from 99. *The Deanery, Upper Kevin Street, Dublin 8, Irish Republic* Tel (00353) (1) 475 5449 *or* 453 9472 Fax 464 6374

McCARTHY, Miss Sandra Ellen. b 56. Man Univ MusB77 Goldsmiths' Coll Lon PGCE79 ARCM75 FRCO77 GRNCM78. S'wark Ord Course 92. **d** 95 **p** 96. C Beckenham St Geo *Roch* 95-99; V Heybridge w Langford *Chelmsf* from 99. *The Vicarage, 1A Crescent Road, Heybridge, Maldon CM9 4SJ* Tel and fax (01621) 841274 Mobile 07904-292036 E-mail sandra@revdsmcc.fsnet.co.uk

McCARTHY, Stephen Samuel. b 49. ACII81 Sussex Univ 92. **d** 01. NSM Burgess Hill St Edw *Chich* from 01. *St Edward's House, 9 Coopers Close, Burgess Hill RH15 8AN* Tel (01444) 248520 Mobile 07802-734903 E-mail ssmaccarthy@aol.com

McCARTHY, Terence Arthur. b 46. Open Univ BA90. Kelham Th Coll 66. **d** 70 **p** 71. C Gt Burstead *Chelmsf* 70-74; C Wickford 74-76; TV E Runcorn w Halton *Ches* 76-80; V Runcorn H Trin 80-84; Chapl HM Pris Liv 84; Chapl HM Pris Acklington 84-92; Chapl HM Pris Holme Ho from 92. *The Chaplaincy, HM Prison Holme House, Stockton-on-Tees TS18 2QU* Tel (01642) 744115

McCARTNEY, Adrian Alexander. b 57. Stranmillis Coll BEd79 TCD BTh88. St Jo Coll Nottm LTh86. **d** 88 **p** 89. C Jordanstown w Monkstown *Conn* 88-91; Bp's C Monkstown 91-94; I 94-96; C Belvoir *D & D* from 02. *73 Dunlady Manor, Dundonald, Belfast BT16 1YP* Tel (028) 9048 1197 *or* 9067 3379 E-mail adrian@summermadness.co.uk

McCARTNEY, Ellis. b 47. Univ Coll Lon BSc73 Goldsmiths' Coll Lon DipRE80 Lon Inst of Educn MA82 Cert Counselling 94. NTMTC 94. **d** 97 **p** 98. NSM Tollington *Lon* from 97. *6 Elfort Road, London N5 1AZ* Tel (020) 7226 1533

McCARTNEY, Robert Charles. TCD DipTh85. **d** 85 **p** 85. C Portadown St Mark *Arm* 85-88; I Errigle Keerogue w Ballygawley and Killeshil 88-89; CF from 89. *c/o MOD Chaplains (Army)* Tel (01980) 615804 Fax 615800

McCARTY, Colin Terence. b 46. Loughb Univ BTech68 PhD71 Lon Univ PGCE73 FRSA89. EAMTC 91. **d** 94 **p** 95. NSM Exning St Martin w Landwade *St E* from 94; Perm to Offic *Ely* 96-01. *1 Seymour Close, Newmarket CB8 8EL* Tel (01638) 669400 *or* (01223) 552716 Mobile 07711-825157 Fax (01223) 553537 E-mail mccarty.c@ucles.org.uk *or* gly02@dial.pipex.com

MacCARTY, Paul Andrew. b 34. Sarum & Wells Th Coll 73. **d** 75 **p** 76. Ind Chapl *Win* 75-80; C Bournemouth St Andr 75-84; Hon C Christchurch 80-91; C 91-99; rtd 99; Perm to Offic *Win* from 01. *3 Douglas Avenue, Christchurch BH23 1JT* Tel (01202) 483807

McCAUGHEY, Canon Robert Morley. b 07. MA35. **d** 35 **p** 36. C Walker *Newc* 35-38; C Ponteland 38-41; C Benwell St Jas 41-43; V Wallsend St Luke 43-52; V Berwick H Trin 52-61; V Wisbech SS Pet and Paul *Ely* 61-74; RD Wisbech 62-72; Hon Can Ely

Cathl 72-74; rtd 74; Perm to Offic *D & R* from 76. *51 Ballinahone House, Knockcloughrim, Magherafelt BT45 8PT* Tel (028) 7964 2110

McCAULAY, Stephen Thomas John. b 61. Coll of Resurr Mirfield BA98. **d** 98 **p** 99. C Chaddesden St Phil *Derby* 98-02; V Mackworth St Fran from 02. *St Francis's Vicarage, 78 Collingham Gardens, Derby DE22 4FQ* Tel (01332) 347690

McCAULEY, Craig William Leslie. b 72. Glam Univ BA95 Dip Humanities 96 TCD BTh99. CITC 96. **d** 99 **p** 00. C Seapatrick *D & D* 99-02; C Kill *D & G* from 02. *22 Stradbrook Hall, Stradbrook Road, Blackrock, Co Dublin, Irish Republic* Tel (00353) (1) 284 5692 E-mail curate@eircom.net

McCAUSLAND, Norman. b 58. TCD BTh89. CITC 89. **d** 89 **p** 90. C Portadown St Columba *Arm* 89-91; P-in-c Clonmel Union *C, C & R* 91-94; Miss to Seamen 91-94; CMS 94-95; Bp's V and Lib Ossory Cathl *C & O* 96; Chapl and Tutor CITC 96-00; PV Ch Ch Cathl Dublin *D & G* 96-00; CMS 00-01; Lic to Offic *D & G* from 01. *17 Congress Gardens, Glasthule, Dun Laoghaire, Co Dublin, Irish Republic* E-mail mccausln@tcd.ie

McCLAUGHRY, Victor Thomas. b 13. TCD BA34 MA46. **d** 36 **p** 37. C Cork St Fin Barre's Cathl *C, C & R* 36-41; C Taney *D & G* 41-45; C S'wark Cathl *S'wark* 45-48; Chapl Guy's Hosp Lon 45-48; Chapl Holloway Sanatorium Virginia Water 48-54; V Gaydon w Chadshunt *Cov* 54-56; Chapl Mickleover Hosp Derby 56-60; PC Derby St Jo *Derby* 60-63; Chapl The Dorothy Kerin Trust Burrswood 63-66; V Peasmarsh *Chich* 66-70; V E Preston w Kingston 70-79; rtd 79; Perm to Offic *Chich* from 79. *16 Woodland Avenue, High Salvington, Worthing BN13 3AF* Tel (01903) 692971

McCLAY, David Alexander. b 59. TCD MA87. **d** 87 **p** 88. C Magheralin w Dollingstown *D & D* 87-90; I Kilkeel 90-01; I Willowfield from 01. *Willowfield Rectory, 149 My Lady's Road, Belfast BT6 8FE* Tel (028) 9045 7654 *or* tel and fax 9046 0105 E-mail admin@willowfieldcoi.freeserve.co.uk

McCLEAN, Lydia Margaret Sheelagh. See COOK, Mrs Lydia Margaret Sheelagh

McCLEAN, Robert Mervyn. b 38. Greenwich Univ BTh91. Edgehill Th Coll Belf 57. **d** 85 **p** 88. NSM Seapatrick *D & D* from 85. *2 Kiloanin Crescent, Banbridge BT32 4NU* Tel (028) 4062 7419 E-mail r.m.mcclean@btinternet.com

MACCLESFIELD, Archdeacon of. See GILLINGS, The Ven Richard John

McCLINTOCK, Darren John. b 77. Hull Univ BA98 Open Univ MA(TS)00. St Jo Coll Nottm 98. **d** 01 **p** 02. C Drypool *York* from 01. *St Andrew's House, 2 Harcourt Drive, Hull HU9 2AR* E-mail darrenjmcc@hotmail.com

McCLOSKEY, Robert Johnson. b 42. Stetson Univ (USA) AB63. Gen Th Sem NY STB67. **d** 67 **p** 68. USA from 67; C Gt Medford 67-69; R Somerville W St Jas and Chapl Tufts Univ 69-72; Dioc Adv for Liturgy and Music Massachusetts 71-76; R Westford St Mark 72-76; R Blowing Rock St Mary 76-82; Liturg and Musical Adv and Ecum Officer Dio W N Carolina 76-81; Dio SE Florida 90-93; Ecum Officer Dio Long Is 81-89; R Bay Shore St Pet and St Pet Sch 82-89; R Miami St Steph and St Steph Sch 89-01; Staff Officer Lambeth Conf 98; rtd 01; Perm to Offic *Glouc* from 00. *7 West End, Kingham, Chipping Norton OX7 6YH* Tel (01608) 658896

McCLOUGHLIN, Joshua. b 27. CITC 69. **d** 70 **p** 71. C Magheraculmoney *Clogh* 70-72; C Cloughfern *Conn* 73-77; I Dunfanaghy *D & R* 77-79; I Drumkeeran w Templecarne and Muckross *Clogh* 79-83; I Aghavea 83-96; rtd 96. *31A Fintona Road, Clogher BT76 0TG* Tel (028) 8554 8318

McCLURE, Mrs Catherine Abigail. b 63. Birm Univ BA84 SS Hild & Bede Coll Dur PGCE85. Ripon Coll Cuddesdon 01. **d** 03. C Cirencester *Glouc* from 03. *15 Partridge Way, Cirencester GL7 1BH* Tel (01285) 654775 Mobile 07711-476749 E-mail mcclure.staverton@virgin.net

McCLURE, Robert (Roy). b 30. Open Univ BA92. TCD Div Sch 68. **d** 70 **p** 71. C Monaghan *Clogh* 70-72; C Belfast St Matt *Conn* 72-76; Chapl HM Pris Liv 76-77; Chapl HM Pris Preston 77-82; V Foulridge *Blackb* 82-88; rtd 88; Perm to Offic *Liv* from 89. *4 Mill Lane Crescent, Southport PR9 7PF* Tel (01704) 27476

McCLURE, The Ven Timothy Elston. b 46. St Jo Coll Dur BA68. Ridley Hall Cam 68. **d** 70 **p** 71. C Kirkheaton *Wakef* 70-73; C Chorlton upon Medlock *Man* 74-79; Chapl Man Poly 74-82; TR Man Whitworth 79-82; Gen Sec SCM 82-92; Bp's Soc and Ind Adv and Dir Chs' Coun for Ind and Soc Resp LEP *Bris* 92-99; Hon Can Bris Cathl from 92; Hon C Cotham St Sav w St Mary 96; Chapl Lord Mayor's Chpl 96-99; Adn Bris from 99. *Church House, 23 Great George Street, Bristol BS1 5QZ* Tel 0117-906 0102 Fax 925 0460 E-mail tim.mcclure@bristoldiocese.org

McCLUSKEY, Coralie Christine. b 52. Univ of Wales (Cardiff) BEd74. St Alb and Ox Min Course 98. **d** 01 **p** 02. C Welwyn w Ayot St Peter *St Alb* from 01. *St Michael's House, 3 London Road, Woolmer Green, Knebworth SG3 6JU* Tel (01438) 813043 Fax as telephone E-mail curate@welwyn.org.uk

McCLUSKEY, James Terence. b 65. Coll of Resurr Mirfield 01. **d** 03. *77 Pinks Hill, Swanley BR8 8NN* Tel (01322) 480860 Mobile 07761-632734 E-mail mccluskey@katy-james.freeserve.co.uk

McCLUSKEY, Miss Lesley. b 45. Hull Univ LLB72 Bolton Coll of Educn PGCE77. N Ord Course 89. **d** 92 **p** 94. C Bootle St Mary w St Paul *Liv* 92-94; C Wigan St Anne 94-98; P-in-c Newton in Makerfield Em from 98; Chapl St Helen's and Knowsley Hosps Trust from 98. *The Rectory, Wargrave Road, Newton-le-Willows WA12 8RR* Tel (01925) 224920 E-mail lesley-mccluskey@yahoo.com

McCOACH, Jennifer Sara. b 69. Leeds Univ BSc94. Ripon Coll Cuddesdon 99. **d** 01 **p** 02. C Lillington *Cov* from 01. *34 Lime Avenue, Lillington, Leamington Spa CV32 7DF* Tel (01926) 339030 E-mail jmccoach@fish.co.uk

McCOLLUM, Alastair Colston. b 69. Whitelands Coll Lon BA91. Westcott Ho Cam 95. **d** 96 **p** 97. C Hampton All SS *Lon* 96-98; C S Kensington St Aug 98-00; Chapl Imp Coll 98-00; TV Papworth *Ely* from 00. *The Rectory, The Green, Eltisley, St Neots PE19 6TG* Tel (01480) 880152 E-mail alastair.mccollum@ely.anglican.org

McCOLLUM, Charles James. b 41. TCD BTh89. CITC 85. **d** 89 **p** 90. C Larne and Inver *Conn* 89-91; Bp's C Belfast Whiterock 91-96; I Belfast St Pet and St Jas from 96. *The Rectory, 17 Waterloo Park South, Belfast BT15 5HX* Tel and fax (028) 9077 7053 Fax 9078 1132 *or* 9077 4764

McCOMB, Canon Samuel. b 33. CITC 70. **d** 71 **p** 72. C Belfast St Mich *Conn* 71-74; C Lisburn Ch Ch 74-79; I Ballinderry *Arm* 79-83; I Lisburn Ch Ch *Conn* from 83; Can Conn Cathl from 98; Treas from 01. *Christ Church Rectory, 27 Hillsborough Road, Lisburn BT28 1JL* Tel (028) 9266 2163 *or* 9267 3271

McCONACHIE, Robert Noel. b 40. Goldsmiths' Coll Lon BA86. Oak Hill Th Coll 86. **d** 88 **p** 89. C Larkfield *Roch* 88-93; R Mereworth w W Peckham from 93. *The Rectory, The Street, Mereworth, Maidstone ME18 5NA* Tel (01622) 812214

McCONKEY, Brian Robert. b 62. Carl Dioc Tr Inst 92. **d** 95 **p** 96. C Blackb St Gabr *Blackb* 95-98; Dioc Youth Officer from 99. *7 Billinge Close, Blackburn BB2 6SB* Tel (01254) 53442 *or* 54421 Fax 699963 E-mail brian.mcconkey@blackburn.anglican.org

McCONKEY, David Benton. b 53. Kansas Wesleyan Univ (USA) BA75 Yale Univ MusM77 SSC. Yale Div Sch MDiv79. **d** 83 **p** 84. Dn Ch Cathl Salina USA 83-84; C S Lake Anchorage 84-85; P-in-c Louisville St Luke 85-86; R Warrensburgh H Cross 86-94; Can Capitular All SS Cath Albany 88-93; R Belvedere St Eliz Zimbabwe 94-03; P-in-c Norton St Fran and St Jas 94-99; Lect Bp Gaul Coll 94-01; TR Swindon New Town *Bris* from 03. *St Mark's Rectory, 5 Gold View, Swindon SN5 8ZG* Tel (01793) 873140 *or* 533280 Fax 491065 E-mail frdbmcconkey@yahoo.co.uk

McCONNEL, Canon Brian Roy. b 46. St Paul's Coll Grahamstown DipTh71. **d** 71 **p** 72. S Africa 71-77 and 79-85; C Plumstead 71-74; C St Geo Cathl Cape Town 74-77; C Prestwich St Marg *Man* 77-79; V Liscard St Mary w St Columba *Ches* 85-90; V Altrincham St Geo from 90; RD Bowdon 95-03; Hon Can Ches Cathl from 97. *St George's Vicarage, Townfield Road, Altrincham WA14 4DS* Tel 0161-928 1279 Fax 929 8826

McCONNELL, Peter Stuart. b 54. Linc Th Coll 89. **d** 91 **p** 92. C N Shields *Newc* 91-95; V Balkwell from 95; Sen Chapl Northumbria Police from 98. *St Peter's Vicarage, The Quadrant, North Shields NE29 7JA* Tel 0191-257 0952 *or* 258 3380 E-mail mcconnell@balkwell.freeserve.co.uk

McCONNELL, Robert Mark. b 60. Oak Hill Th Coll BA88. **d** 89 **p** 90. C Knock *D & D* 96-98; C Bangor St Comgall *D & D* 92-94; I Killyleagh 94-99; I Ballynure and Ballyeaston *Conn* from 99. *The Rectory, 11 Church Road, Ballyclare BT39 9UF* Tel (028) 9332 2350 E-mail coiballynure@excite.co.uk

McCORMACK, Alan William. b 68. Jes Coll Ox BA90 MA94 DPhil94. CITC 93. **d** 96 **p** 97. C Knock *D & D* 96-98; Dean of Res and Chapl TCD from 98; Succ St Patr Cathl Dublin *D & G* from 98; Abp's Dom Chapl from 03. *House 27, Trinity College, Dublin 2, Irish Republic* Tel (00353) (1) 608 1402 Fax 679 0335 E-mail mccorma@tcd.ie

McCORMACK, Colin. b 47. QUB BSc70 DipEd71 Nottm Univ BA77. St Jo Coll Nottm 75. **d** 78 **p** 79. C Carl St Jo *Carl* 78-81; C Ballynafeigh St Jude *D & D* 81-84; V Harraby *Carl* 84-89; NSM Carl H Trin and St Barn 95-99; Asst Chapl Costa Blanca *Eur* from 00. *Portal 3 1 G, Carrer Octobre 9, 03520 Polod de Marine, Alicante, Spain* E-mail cormack@euroseek.com

McCORMACK, Canon David Eugene. b 34. Wells Th Coll 66. **d** 68 **p** 69. C Lillington *Cov* 68-71; C The Lickey *Birm* 71-75; V Highters Heath 75-82; V Four Oaks 82-00; Hon Can Birm Cathl 95-00; rtd 00; Perm to Offic *Linc* and *Pet* from 00. *27 Rockingham Close, Market Deeping, Peterborough PE6 8BY* Tel (01778) 347569

McCORMACK, George Brash. b 32. ACIS65 FCIS75 Lon Univ DipRS85. S'wark Ord Course 82. **d** 85 **p** 86. Hon C Crofton St Paul *Roch* 85-89; C Crayford 89-91; R Fawkham and Hartley 91-97; rtd 97; Perm to Offic *Roch* from 98. *11 Turnpike Drive, Pratts Bottom, Orpington BR6 7SJ*

McCORMACK, John Heddon. b 58. Chich Th Coll 85. **d** 88 **p** 89. C Cleobury Mortimer w Hopton Wafers *Heref* 88-90; C

Lymington *Win* 90-92; C Portsea N End St Mark *Portsm* 92-95; Chapl St Barn Hospice Worthing from 95. *St Barnabas Hospice, Columbia Drive, Worthing BN13 2QF* Tel (01903) 264222 ext 205 *or* 534035 E-mail john.mccormack@stbarnabas-hospice.org.uk

McCORMACK, Kevan Sean. b 50. Chich Th Coll 77. **d** 80 **p** 81. C Ross *Heref* 80-81; C Ross w Brampton Abbotts, Bridstow and Peterstow 81-83; C Leominster 83; TV 84-87; Chapl R Hosp Sch Holbrook 87-00; P-in-c Woodbridge St Mary *St E* 00; R from 00. *St Mary's Rectory, Church Street, Woodbridge IP12 1DS* Tel (01394) 610424 Fax as telephone

McCORMACK, Canon Lesley Sharman. b 50. EAMTC. **d** 88 **p** 94. Hon Par Dn Chevington w Hargrave and Whepstead w Brockley *St E* 88-95; Asst Chapl W Suffolk Hosp Bury St Edm 88-95; Chapl Kettering Gen Hosp NHS Trust from 95; Bp's Hosp Chapl Adv *Pet* from 00; Can Pet Cathl from 03. *Kettering General Hospital, Rothwell Road, Kettering NN16 8UZ* Tel (01536) 492170 Fax 493767
E-mail lesley.mccormack@kgh.nhs.uk

McCORMACK, Mrs Susan. b 60. NEOC 00. **d** 03. C Newburn *Newc* from 03. *St Mary's Parsonage, Newburn Road, Newcastle upon Tyne NE15 9AB* Tel 0191-267 4553

McCORMICK, Mrs Anne Irene. b 67. Sheff Univ BA89 Hull Univ PGCE90. Ripon Coll Cuddesdon 90. **d** 92 **p** 94. C Spalding *Linc* 92-96; C Gt Grimsby St Mary and St Jas 96-01; C Gt and Lt Coates w Bradley from 98. *The Glebe House, 11 Church Lane, Limber, Grimsby DN37 8JN* Tel (01469) 561068
E-mail mccormickdavid@talk21.com

McCORMICK, David Mark. b 68. Univ of Wales (Ban) BD89. Ripon Coll Cuddesdon 90. **d** 92 **p** 93. C Holbeach *Linc* 92-96; TV Gt Grimsby St Mary and St Jas 96-01; Min Development Adv (N) from 01. *The Glebe House, 11 Church Lane, Limber, Grimsby DN37 8JN* Tel (01469) 561068
E-mail mccormickdavid@talk21.com

McCOSH, Duncan Ian. b 50. Edin Dioc NSM Course 82. **d** 91 **p** 92. C Dalkeith *Edin* 91-96; C Lasswade 91-96; P-in-c Falkirk 96-97; R 97-03; R Galashiels from 03. *The Rectory, Parsonage Road, Parsonage Road, Galashiels TD1 3HS* Tel (01896) 753118

McCOUBREY, William Arthur. b 36. CEng MIMechE. Sarum & Wells Th Coll 86. **d** 89 **p** 90. C Bedhampton *Portsm* 89-92; V Stokenham w Sherford *Ex* 92-96; R Stokenham w Sherford and Beesands, and Slapton 96-02; rtd 02; Perm to Offic *Chich* and *Portsm* from 02. *19 Warblington Road, Emsworth PO10 7HE* Tel (01243) 374011

McCOULOUGH, David. b 61. Man Univ BA84 St Jo Coll Dur BA88. Cranmer Hall Dur 86. **d** 89 **p** 90. C Man Apostles w Miles Platting *Man* 89-92; C Elton All SS 92-94; V Halliwell St Marg 94-98; Min Can Ripon Cathl *Ripon* 98-01; Chapl Univ Coll of Ripon and York St Jo 98-01; Ind Chapl *S'well* from 01; Chapl Boots PLC from 01; C Nottingham St Pet and St Jas 01-02; C Nottingham St Pet and All SS from 02. *13 Rolleston Drive, Lenton, Nottingham NG7 1JS* Tel 0115-958 7883
E-mail office@stpetersnottingham.org

McCOULOUGH, Thomas Alexander. b 32. AKC59. **d** 60 **p** 61. C Norton St Mich *Dur* 60-63; India 63-67; P-in-c Derby St Jas *Derby* 67-72; Ind Chapl *York* 72-82; P-in-c Sutton on the Forest 82-96; Dioc Sec for Local Min 82-89; Lay Tr Officer 89-96; rtd 96; Perm to Offic *Newc* from 96. *1 Horsley Gardens, Holywell, Whitley Bay NE25 0TU* Tel 0191-298 0332

McCREA, Basil Wolfe. b 21. QUB BA49. Wycliffe Hall Ox 51. **d** 53 **p** 54. C Kingston upon Hull H Trin *York* 53-56; C Dundela St Mark *D & D* 56-59; C Cork H Trin w St Paul, St Pet and St Mary *C, C & R* 59-61; I Tullyaughnish *D & R* 61-65; I Rathkeale *L & K* 65-68; I Cork H Trin *C, C & R* 68-72; I Carrigaline Union 72-90; rtd 90. *30 Somerville, Carrigaline, Co Cork, Irish Republic* Tel (00353) (21) 437 1538

McCREA, Francis. b 53. BTh. **d** 91 **p** 92. C Dundonald *D & D* 91-94; I Belfast St Brendan from 94. *St Brendan's Rectory, 36 Circular Road, Belfast BT4 2GA* Tel (028) 9076 3458

McCREADY, Kennedy Lemar. b 26. Woolwich Poly CEng56 FIEE56 Garnett Coll Lon TCert54 Birkbeck Coll Lon BSc59 Sussex Univ Dip Bibl Studies 92 MA94. Chich Th Coll 91. **d** 92 **p** 99. NSM Mayfield *Chich* 92-97; Perm to Offic 97-00; NSM New Groombridge 99-01; Perm to Offic from 01. *Quarry House, Groombridge, Tunbridge Wells TN3 9PS* Tel (01892) 864297

McCREADY, Marcus Diarmaid Julian. b 63. NUU BA85 TCD BTh88 MA MPhil93. CITC 82. **d** 88 **p** 89. C Seagoe *D & D* 88-91; I Clonallon w Warrenpoint 91-96; Chapl Liv Coll 96-97; Chapl HM Pris Lindholme from 97. *HMP Lindholme, Bawtry Road, Hatfield, Doncaster DN7 6EE* Tel (01302) 848829 *or* 848700 Fax 843352 E-mail julian@mccready.u-net.com

McCREADY, Maurice Shaun. b 55. Fitzw Coll Cam BA77 MA81 PGCE95. Ripon Coll Cuddesdon 80. **d** 83 **p** 84. C Bridgwater St Fran *B & W* 83-86; C Walton-on-Thames *Guildf* 86-88; C Elm Park St Nic Hornchurch *Chelmsf* 88-97; NSM 93-01; P-in-c Bridgwater H Trin *B & W* from 02. *Holy Trinity Vicarage, Hamp Street, Bridgwater TA6 6AR* Tel (01278) 422610 Fax as telephone

McCREERY, Canon William Robert Desmond. b 35. QUB BD. Oak Hill Th Coll 59. **d** 62 **p** 63. C Dundonald *D & D* 62-66; C

Belfast St Donard 66-69; I Annalong 69-78; I Knockbreda 78-89; I Bangor St Comgall from 89; Can Belf Cathl from 88. *2 Raglan Road, Bangor BT20 3TL* Tel (028) 9146 5230

McCRORY, Canon Peter. b 34. Chich Th Coll 63. **d** 67 **p** 68. C St Marychurch *Ex* 67-72; R Kenn w Mamhead 72-76; R Kenn 76-78; Bp's Dom Chapl *S'wark* 78-81; V Kew 81-00; RD Richmond and Barnes 84-89; Hon Can S'wark Cathl 90-00; rtd 00; Perm to Offic *Nor* from 00. *Dane House, The Street, Kettlestone, Fakenham NR21 0AU* Tel (01328) 878455

McCROSKERY, Andrew. b 74. Glas Univ BD96. Irish Sch of Ecum 97. **d** 99 **p** 00. C Newtownards *D & D* 99-02; Dean's V Cork Cathl *C, C & R* from 02; Bp's Dom Chapl from 03. *23 Firgrove Gardens, Bishopstown, Cork, Irish Republic* Tel (00353) (21) 434 5889

McCRUM, Michael Scott. b 35. Glas Univ BSc57 UNISA BTh85. **d** 85 **p** 85. S Africa 85-89; Asst P Lynnwood 86-87; P-in-c Mamelodi 87; P-in-c Villieria 87-88; Kerygma Internat Chr Min 89-92; Perm to Offic *Nor* 93-94; NSM Chesham Bois *Ox* 94-95; Perm to Offic *St Alb* 95-98; Hon C Chorleywood St Andr from 98. *Cranbrook, 31 South Road, Chorleywood, Rickmansworth WD3 5AS* Tel and fax (01923) 336897 Mobile 07971-393721
E-mail misamccrum@aol.com

McCULLAGH, Elspeth Jane Alexandra. *See* SAVILLE, Mrs Elspeth Jane Alexandra

McCULLAGH, Canon John Eric. b 46. TCD BA68 BTh88 QUB DipEd70. **d** 88 **p** 89. C Stillorgan w Blackrock *D & G* 88-91; Chapl and Hd of RE Newpark Sch Dub 90-99; I Clondalkin w Rathcoole 91-99; Sec Gen Syn Bd of Educn 99-02; Can Ch Ch Cathl Dublin *D & G* from 99. *Harcourt Villa, Kimberley Road, Greystones, Co Wicklow, Irish Republic* Tel (00353) (1) 497 8422

McCULLAGH, Canon Mervyn Alexander. b 44. TCD BA BAI68. CITC 79. **d** 79 **p** 80. C Larne and Inver *Conn* 79-83; C Ballymacash 83-85; C Dublin St Ann w St Mark and St Steph *D & G* 85-88; I Baltinglass w Ballynure etc *C & O* from 88; Warden of Readers from 90; Can Ossory and Leighlin Cathls 92-96; Treas Ossory and Leighlin Cathls from 96; P-in-c Kiltegan w Hacketstown, Clonmore and Moyne from 00. *The Rectory, Baltinglass, Co Wicklow, Irish Republic* Tel (00353) (59) 648 1321

McCULLAGH, Alistair John. b 59. Univ of Wales (Lamp) BA81 Leeds Univ BA86. Coll of Resurr Mirfield 84. **d** 87 **p** 88. C Portsm Cathl *Portsm* 87-90; C Portsea St Mary 90-94; V Reading St Matt *Ox* 94-95; Perm to Offic *S'wark* 99; Chapl King's Healthcare NHS Trust from 00. *The Chaplaincy, King's College Hospital, Denmark Hill, London SE5 9RS* Tel (020) 7346 3522
E-mail alistair.mcculloch@kingshc.nhs.uk

MacCULLOCH, Prof Diarmaid Ninian John. b 51. Chu Coll Cam BA72 MA76 PhD77 Liv Univ DAA73 FSA78 FRHistS81. Ripon Coll Cuddesdon DipTh87. **d** 87. NSM Clifton All SS w St Jo *Bris* 87-88. *St Cross College, St Giles, Oxford OX1 3LZ* Tel (01865) 270794 Fax 270795
E-mail diarmaid.macculloch@theology.ox.ac.uk

McCULLOCH, Geoffrey Kenneth. b 10. OBE57. Lon Coll of Div 62. **d** 64 **p** 65. C Kingston upon Hull H Trin *York* 64-67; P-in-c Kingston upon Hull St Matt 68-71; P-in-c Kingston upon Hull St Barn 70-71; V Kingston upon Hull St Matt w St Barn 71-79; rtd 79; Perm to Offic *Lon* 79-96. *5 Roy Road, Northwood HA6 1EQ* Tel (01923) 827438

✠**McCULLOCH, The Rt Revd Nigel Simeon.** b 42. Selw Coll Cam BA64 MA69. Cuddesdon Coll 64. **d** 66 **p** 67 **c** 86. C Ellesmere Port *Ches* 66-70; Dir Th Studies Ch Coll Cam 70-75; Chapl 70-73; Dioc Missr *Nor* 73-78; P-in-c Salisbury St Thos and St Edm *Sarum* 78-81; R 81-86; Adn Sarum 79-86; Can and Preb Sarum Cathl 79-86; Suff Bp Taunton *B & W* 86-92; Preb Wells Cathl 86-92; Bp Wakef 92-03; Bp Man from 03; High Almoner from 97. *Bishopscourt, Bury New Road, Salford, Manchester M7 4LE* Tel 0161-792 2096 Fax 792 6826
E-mail bishop@bishopscourt.manchester.anglican.org

McCULLOCH, Mrs Patricia Ann. b 46. CertEd72. EMMTC 87. **d** 90 **p** 94. C Bottesford w Ashby *Linc* 90-95; P-in-c Wragby 95-98; Chapl N Lincs Coll of FE 95-98; Ind Chapl 98-01; rtd 01; Perm to Offic *Linc* from 01. *36 Deepdale Lane, Nettleham, Lincoln LN2 2LT* Tel (01522) 595470
E-mail patricia.mcculloch@virgin.net

McCULLOUGH, Mrs Aphrodite Maria. b 47. Derby Univ MSc96. EMMTC. **d** 00 **p** 01. NSM Kirby Muxloe *Leic* from 00. *33 Alton Road, Leicester LE2 8QB* Tel 0116-288 8733 Mobile 07944-425241

McCULLOUGH, Canon Roy. b 46. Linc Th Coll 70. **d** 73 **p** 74. Chapl Highfield Priory Sch Lancs 73-77; C Ashton-on-Ribble St Andr *Blackb* 73-77; V Rishton 77-86; V Burnley St Matt w H Trin 86-97; RD Burnley 91-97; Chapl Victoria Hosp Blackpool 91-97; V Walton-le-Dale St Leon w Samlesbury St Leon *Blackb* from 97; Hon Can Blackb Cathl from 97. *The Vicarage, Church Brow, Preston PR5 4BH* Tel (01772) 880233 Fax 880289

McCURDY, Hugh Kyle. b 58. Portsm Poly BA Univ of Wales (Cardiff) PGCE. Trin Coll Bris. **d** 85 **p** 86. C Egham *Guildf* 85-88; C Woking St Jo 88-91; V Histon *Ely* from 91; RD N Stowe

from 94; P-in-c Impington from 98. *The Vicarage, 9A Church Street, Histon, Cambridge CB4 9EP* Tel (01223) 232255
E-mail st.andrews.histon@dial.pipex.com

McDERMID, The Ven Norman George Lloyd Roberts. b 27. St Edm Hall Ox BA49 MA52. Wells Th Coll 49. d 51 p 52. C Leeds St Pet *Ripon* 51-56; V Bramley 56-64; Dioc Stewardship Adv 64-76; R Kirkby Overblow 64-80; Hon Can Ripon Cathl 72-93; Dioc Stewardship Adv *Wakef* 73-76; Dioc Stewardship Adv *Bradf* 73-76; RD Harrogate *Ripon* 77-83; V Knaresborough 80-83; Adn Richmond 83-93; rtd 93; Perm to Offic *Ripon* from 93. *Greystones, 10 North End, Bedale DL8 1AB* Tel (01677) 422210

McDERMOTT, Christopher Francis Patrick. b 54. Southeastern Coll USA BA84 Wheaton Coll Illinois MA87. EAMTC. d 95 p 96. C Gt Ilford St Clem and St Marg *Chelmsf* 95-99. *17 Benton Road, Ilford IG1 4AT*

McDERMOTT, Fraser Graeme. b 65. NTMTC 97. d 98 p 00. NSM Oak Tree Angl Fellowship *Lon* 98-02; V N Wembley St Cuth from 02. *St Cuthbert's Vicarage, 214 Carlton Avenue West, Wembley HA0 3QY* Tel (020) 8904 7657

MACDONALD, Alan Hendry. b 49. St Steph Ho Ox 86. d 88 p 89. C Heavitree w Ex St Paul *Ex* 88-91; C Withycombe Raleigh 91-92; TV 92-95; R Silverton, Butterleigh, Bickleigh and Cadeleigh from 95; RD Tiverton 00-02. *The Rectory, 21A King Street, Silverton, Exeter EX5 4JG* Tel (01392) 860350
E-mail almac01@tinyonline.co.uk

MACDONALD, Alastair Douglas. b 48. St Jo Coll Dur 71. d 74 p 75. C Mottingham St Andr *S'wark* 74-78; C Woolwich St Mary w St Mich 78-81; V S Wimbledon St Andr 81-89; V Brighton St Matthias *Chich* 89-94; Chapl Southampton Community Services NHS Trust from 94; Mental Health Chapl W Hants NHS Trust from 02. *Royal South Hants Hospital, Brintons Terrace, Southampton SO14 0YG* Tel (023) 8082 2666

MacDONALD, Alastair Robert. b 72. Edin Univ MA94. TISEC. d 02. C Edin St Thos *Edin* from 02. *15/5 Grierson Gardens, Edinburgh EH5 2AS* Tel 0131-551 3448
E-mail asmacdonald@hotmail.com

MACDONALD, Cameron. b 51. Open Univ BA89. Wilson Carlile Coll 76 NEOC 89. d 90 p 91. CA from 76; C Nairn *Mor* 90-92; P-in-c 92-95; CF from 95; Perm to Offic *Ely* from 00. *c/o MOD Chaplains (Army)* Tel (01980) 615804 Fax 615800

MACDONALD, Christopher Kenneth. b 57. Ex Univ BA79 PGCE80. Trin Coll Bris DipHE93. d 93 p 94. C Eastbourne All SS *Chich* 93-96; C Polegate 96-99; Chapl Eastbourne Coll from 99. *14A Grange Road, Eastbourne BN21 4HJ* Tel (01323) 452317

MACDONALD, Colin. b 47. St Jo Coll Nottm 87. d 89 p 90. C Limber Magna w Brocklesby *Linc* 89-92; P-in-c Barrow and Goxhill 92-97; V 97-99; R Hemingby 99-02; V Fulletby 99-02; R Belchford 99-02; TV Wilford Peninsula *St E* from 02. *33 Fountains Road, Watersfield Park, Rendlesham, Woodbridge IP12 2UF* Tel (01394) 460547
E-mail cmacdonald4@compuserve.com

MACDONALD, Canon Donald Courtenay. b 45. Nottm Univ BTh74 St Martin's Coll Lanc CertEd75. Kelham Th Coll 70. d 75 p 76. C Clifton All SS w Tyndalls Park *Bris* 75-78; C Clifton All SS w St Jo 78-79; Chapl Derby Lonsdale Coll *Derby* 79-84; V Derby St Andr w St Osmund from 84; RD Derby S 89-99; Dioc Communications Officer 89-93; Hon Can Derby Cathl from 95. *St Osmund's Vicarage, London Road, Derby DE24 8UW* Tel (01332) 571329 E-mail donald.c.macdonald@btinternet.com

McDONALD, Douglas Mark. b 28. Linc Coll Ox BA54 MA59. Wells Th Coll 68. d 69 p 70. C Horsham *Chich* 69-76; TV Kirkby Lonsdale *Carl* 76-79; P-in-c Tidmarsh w Sulham *Ox* 79-83; Chapl St Audries Sch W Quantoxhead 83-91; rtd 91; Perm to Offic *B & W* 91-97. *18 Lower Park, Minehead TA24 8AX* Tel (01643) 703104

McDONALD, Gordon James Joseph. b 17. Wycliffe Hall Ox 50. d 52 p 53. C Southall H Trin *Lon* 52-55; CMS 55-59; Uganda 56-59; P-in-c Dallam CD *Liv* 59-63; V Pemberton St Mark Newtown 63-80; R Easton w Letheringham *St E* 80-83; rtd 83. *21 Capel Court, The Burgage, Cheltenham GL52 3EL* Tel (01242) 579463

MACDONALD, Helen Maria. b 56. Lon Bible Coll BA83 St Mary's Univ Coll Belf PGCE98. Cranmer Hall Dur 01 St Jo Coll Dur MA03. d 03. C Wisley w Pyrford *Guildf* from 03. *Church House, Coldharbour Road, Woking GU22 8SP* Tel (01932) 336278 E-mail curate@wisleywithpyrford.org

McDONALD, Canon Ian Henry. b 40. TD. St Aid Birkenhead 65. d 68 p 69. C Kingston upon Hull H Trin *York* 68-70; C Drumglass *Arm* 70-73; I Eglish w Killylea 73-80; I Maghera w Killelagh *D & R* 80-91; I Killowen 91-98; CF (TAVR) from 91; Can Derry Cathl *D & R* from 94; Preb from 00; I Errigal w Garvagh from 98. *St Paul's Rectory, 58 Station Road, Garvagh, Coleraine BT51 5LA* Tel (028) 2555 8226

McDONALD, James Damian (Jack). b 66. Pemb Coll Cam BA87 MA91 SS Hild & Bede Coll Dur PGCE88 K Coll Lon MA96. Qu Coll Birm 90. d 92 p 93. C Camberwell St Geo *S'wark* 92-95; Chapl G&C Coll Cam 95-99; Fell and Dean from 99; Lic to Offic

Ely from 95. *Gonville and Caius College, Cambridge CB2 1TA* Tel (01223) 332408 *or* 332482 Fax 332336
E-mail jdm39@cam.ac.uk

MacDONALD, John. b 16. St Cath Soc Ox BA38 MA42 BLitt58. St Steph Ho Ox 39. d 41 p 42. C Birkdale St Jo *Liv* 41-44; C Walton St Mary 44-49; Chapl St Steph Ho Ox 49-54; Chapl Ch Ch Ox 51-60; Chapl New Coll Ox 52-60; Lib Pusey Ho 54-60; Chapl Burgess Hall Lamp 60-76; Sub-Warden 62-76; V Edstaston *Lich* 76-82; V Whixall 76-82; Chapl Choral Ches Cathl *Ches* 82-85; rtd 85; Perm to Offic *Ches* from 85. *47 The Links, Gwernaffield, Mold CH7 5DZ* Tel (01352) 740015

McDONALD, John Richard Burleigh. b 17. TCD BA40 BD41 UKRC Reg Ind Cllr BAC Acc. d 41 p 42. C Belfast St Pet *Conn* 41-45; Uganda 46-61; Educn Officer Ch of Ireland 61-64; Hd RE Stranmills Coll of Educn Belf 66-86; Dir Post-Ord Tr *Conn* 86-94; rtd 94. *76 Osborne Drive, Belfast BT9 6LJ* Tel (028) 9066 6737

McDONALD, Lawrence Ronald. b 32. St Alb Minl Tr Scheme 84. d 87 p 88. NSM Sharnbrook and Knotting w Souldrop *St Alb* 87-90; C Bromham w Oakley and Stagsden 90-93; P-in-c Renhold 93-98; rtd 99; Perm to Offic *St Alb* from 99. *16 Townsend Road, Sharnbrook, Bedford MK44 1HY* Tel (01234) 782849 E-mail fathermac@ukgateway.net

MACDONALD, Malcolm James. b 42. Sarum Th Coll 70. d 71 p 73. C Hounslow St Steph *Lon* 71-72; C Hammersmith St Sav 72-76; P-in-c Hammersmith St Luke 76-79; V 79-87; V Kirkby Woodhouse *S'well* from 87. *The Vicarage, 57 Skegby Road, Kirkby-in-Ashfield, Nottingham NG17 9JE* Tel (01623) 759094

MACDONALD, Martin Stanley Harrison. b 51. Dur Univ BSc72 ACA75 FCA82. St Alb and Ox Min Course. d 01 p 02. NSM Tring *St Alb* from 01. *9 Hall Park, Berkhamsted HP4 2NU* Tel (01442) 384953 Mobile 07710-390115
E-mail mshmacdonald@ntlworld.com

MACDONALD, Canon Murray Somerled. b 23. Pemb Coll Cam BA46 MA49. Ely Th Coll 47. d 48 p 49. C Hendon St Mary *Lon* 48-51; C Hanover Square St Geo 51-53; P-in-c Upton and Copmanford *Ely* 53-54; R Sawtry 53-54; R Sawtry, Upton and Copmanford 54-57; V Upwood w Gt and Lt Raveley 57-62; R Wood Walton 57-62; V Fenstanton 62-70; V Hilton 62-70; RD Huntingdon 69-76; R Huntingdon All SS w St Jo 70-82; R Huntingdon St Mary w St Benedict 71-82; Hon Can Ely Cathl 72-82; Can Res 82-88; rtd 89; Perm to Offic *Linc* 89-01; *Ely* 89-97. *4 Hacconby Lane, Morton, Bourne PE10 0NT* Tel (01778) 570711

MACDONALD, Stephen Calliss. b 35. Selw Coll Cam BA58. Westcott Ho Cam 58. d 60 p 61. C Norwood All SS *Cant* 60-64; Chapl Cov Cathl *Cov* 64-68; Chr Aid 68-70; rtd 96. *c/o Mrs G M Macdonald, Linden House, Meadow Lane, Huntingdon PE28 2BP* Tel (01480) 492807

MacDONALD, Trevor John. b 33. Hertf Coll Ox BA55 MA59. Chich Th Coll 92. d 93 p 94. NSM Hove St Barn and St Agnes *Chich* from 93. *31 Orchard Gardens, Hove BN3 7BH* Tel (01273) 771228

MACDONALD, Warren. Monash Univ Aus BEng Leeds Univ MPhil Gothenburg Univ PhD00 CEng CPEng MIEAust. Trin Coll Bris DipHE95. d 95 p 96. NSM Iford *Win* 95-98; Perm to Offic from 98. *5 St James Square, Pokesdown, Bournemouth BH5 2BX* Tel (01202) 422131 Fax 422101
E-mail warren.macdonald@dial.pipex.com

MACDONALD-MILNE, Brian James. b 35. CCC Cam BA58 MA62 St Pet Coll Ox MA81. Cuddesdon Coll 58. d 60 p 61. C Fleetwood *Blackb* 60-63; Solomon Is 64-78; New Hebrides 78-80; Acting Chapl Trin Coll Ox 81; Acting Chapl St Pet Coll Ox 81-82; Relief Chapl HM Pris Grendon and Spring Hill 82; Research Fell Qu Coll Birm 82-83; Hon Asst P Bordesley SS Alb and Patr *Birm* 82-83; R Landbeach *Ely* 83-88; V Waterbeach 83-88; OCF 83-88; R Radwinter w Hempstead *Chelmsf* 88-97; RD Saffron Walden 91-97; P-in-c The Sampfords 95-97; rtd 97; Perm to Offic *Ely* from 97; Dioc Rep Melanesian Miss and Papua New Guinea Ch Partnership from 99; Chapl Ely Chapter Guild of Servants of the Sanctuary from 00; Perm to Offic *Chelmsf* from 02. *39 Way Lane, Waterbeach, Cambridge CB5 9NQ* Tel (01223) 861631
E-mail macdonaldmilne@talk21.com

McDONNELL, Mrs Mavis Marian. b 42. LNSM course 95. d 98 p 99. OLM Warrington St Ann *Liv* from 98. *32 Shaws Avenue, Warrington WA2 8AX* Tel (01925) 634408

McDONOUGH, David Sean. b 55. d 89 p 90. C Moseley St Mary *Birm* 89-92; TV Glascote and Stonydelph *Lich* from 92. *90 Briar, Tamworth B77 4DZ* Tel (01827) 52754 *or* 330306
E-mail david@dmcdonough.freeserve.co.uk

McDONOUGH, Terence. b 57. St Jo Coll Nottm LTh86. d 89 p 90. C Linthorpe *York* 89-94; TV Heworth H Trin 94-98; V Heworth Ch Ch from 98. *95 Stockton Lane, York YO31 1JA* Tel (01904) 425678

McDOUGAL, John Anthony Phelps Standen. *See* STANDEN-McDOUGAL, Canon John Anthony Phelps

McDOUGALL, David Robin. b 61. Avery Hill Coll CertEd BEd84. Ridley Hall Cam 85. d 87 p 88. C Bletchley *Ox* 87-91; C High Wycombe 91-93; C E Twickenham St Steph *Lon* 93-02; P-in-c Upper Sunbury St Sav from 02. *St Saviour's Vicarage,*

205 Vicarage Road, Sunbury-on-Thames TW16 7TP Tel (01932) 782800

McDOUGALL, Mrs Denise Alma. b 48. Ban Coll TCert69. N Ord Course 00. **d** 03. NSM Waterloo Ch Ch and St Jo *Liv* from 03. *27 Mayfair Avenue, Crosby, Liverpool L23 2TL* Tel 0151-924 8870 E-mail denisemcdougall@yahoo.co.uk

MacDOUGALL, Canon Iain William. b 20. TCD BA43 MA59. CITC 43. **d** 43 **p** 44. C Belfast St Steph *Conn* 43-45; C Enniskillen and Trory *Clogh* 45-48; I Drumlane *K, E & A* 48-50; I Ballinaclash *D & G* 51-54; I Moate *M & K* 54-58; I Ballyloughloe 54-58; I Ferbane 54-58; I Mullingar, Portnashangan, Moyliscar, Kilbixy etc 58-85; Can Meath 81-85; rtd 85. *18 Denville Court, Killiney, Co Dublin, Irish Republic* Tel (00353) (1) 285 4751

McDOUGALL, Stuart Ronald. b 28. Leeds Univ DipAdEd MEd84. Roch Th Coll 64. **d** 66 **p** 67. C Gravesend St Aid *Roch* 66-69; C Wells St Thos w Horrington *B & W* 69-70; TV Tong *Bradf* 70-73; V Cononley w Bradley 73-82; C Thornthwaite w Thruscross and Darley *Ripon* 82-83; P-in-c Dacre w Hartwith 83-86; rtd 86; Perm to Offic *Sarum* from 90. *Portman Chase Lodge, Chalbury, Wimborne BH21 7EU* Tel (01258) 840558

MACDOUGALL, William Duncan. b 47. Nottm Univ BTh74 LTh74. St Jo Coll Nottm 69. **d** 74 **p** 75. C Highbury New Park St Aug *Lon* 74-77; SAMS 77 and 78-82; Argentina 78-82; V Rashcliffe and Lockwood *Wakef* 83-87; V Tonbridge St Steph *Roch* from 87; RD Tonbridge 01-03; Dir Past and Evang Studies Trin Coll Bris from 03. *15 Cranleigh Gardens, Bristol BS9 1HD* Tel 0117-968 2028 E-mail billmacdougall@clara.net

McDOWALL, Julian Thomas. b 39. CCC Cam BA62 MA67. Linc Th Coll 62. **d** 64 **p** 65. C Rugby St Andr *Cov* 64-70; C-in-c Stoke Hill CD *Guildf* 70-72; V Stoke Hill 72-76; R Elstead 76-91; V Thursley 82-91; TV Wellington and Distr *B & W* 91-93; C Lymington *Win* from 93. *20 Solent Avenue, Lymington SO41 3SD* Tel (01590) 676750

McDOWALL, Robert Angus (Robin). b 39. AKC66. **d** 67 **p** 68. C Bishopwearmouth St Mich w St Hilda *Dur* 67-69; CF from 69; Sen CF 80-91; Asst Chapl Gen 91-94; QHC from 93. *c/o MOD Chaplains (Army)* Tel (01980) 615804 Fax 615800

McDOWALL, Roger Ian. b 40. AKC64. **d** 65 **p** 66. C Peterlee *Dur* 65-68; C Weaste *Man* 68-70; C Tonge Moor 70-73; V Whitworth St Bart 73-80; TV Torre *Ex* 80-88; V Torre All SS 88-00; Chapl S Devon Tech Coll Torbay 80-00. *1 Dunanellerich, Dunvegan, Isle of Skye IV55 8ZH* Tel (01470) 521271

McDOWELL, Francis John. b 56. QUB BA78 LSE DipBS84. CITC BTh93. **d** 96 **p** 97. C Antrim *Conn* 96-99; I Ballyrashane w Kildollagh 99-02; I Dundela St Mark *D & D* from 02. *St Mark's Rectory, 4 Sydenham Avenue, Belfast BT4 2DR* Tel (028) 9065 9047

McDOWELL, Ian. b 67. Ch Coll Cam MA88 BA92. Westcott Ho Cam CTM93. **d** 93 **p** 94. C Hackney *Lon* 93-96; Asst Chapl Homerton Hosp NHS Trust *Lon* 96-98; Chapl Newham Healthcare NHS Trust Lon from 98. *Newham General Hospital, Glen Road, London E13 8SL* Tel (020) 7363 8053 *or* 7476 4000 ext 4369 E-mail mcdow@dircon.co.uk

McDOWELL, Ian James. b 37. St Jo Coll Morpeth ACT ThL60 St Aug Coll Cant. **d** 61 **p** 62. Australia 61-66; C Naracoorte 61-63; P-in-c Elliston Miss 63-66; C S Harrow St Paul *Lon* 66; C Southgate Ch Ch 67; V Ganton *York* 67-71; P-in-c Foxholes and Butterwick 67-68; R 68-71; Australia from 71; R Angaston 71-76; R Colonel Light Gardens 76-94; R Gawler 94-98; R Merriwa from 98. *20 Gooch Street, PO Box 58, Merriwa, NSW, Australia 2329* Tel (0061) (2) 6548 2218 *or* 4930 9051

McDOWELL, Peter Kerr. b 69. QUB BA91. CITC BTh94. **d** 94 **p** 95. C Lisburn St Paul *Conn* 94-98; C Arm St Mark *Arm* 98-99; I Belfast Upper Malone (Epiphany) *Conn* from 99. *The Rectory, 74 Locksley Park, Upper Lisburn Road, Belfast BT10 0AS* Tel (028) 9060 1588 E-mail mcdowell1@ntlworld.com

MACE, Alan Herbert. b 28. Lon Univ BA49 Ex Inst of Educn TCert50. Wycliffe Hall Ox 59. **d** 60 **p** 61. C Disley *Ches* 60-63; C Folkestone H Trin w Ch Ch *Cant* 63-67; Lic to Offic *Win* 67-93; rtd 93; Perm to Offic *Win* 93-97. *15 Bassett Heath Avenue, Southampton SO16 7GP* Tel (023) 8076 8161

MACE, David Sinclair. b 37. **d** 95 **p** 96. OLM Godalming *Guildf* from 95. *Torridon, Grosevenor Road, Godalming GU7 1NZ* Tel (01483) 414646

MACE, Mrs Helen Elizabeth. b 31. Ox Univ MA52 Solicitor 56. Coll of Ascension 92. **dss** 74 **d** 87 **p** 94. Tadcaster *York* 77-84; Asst Chapl Leeds Gen Infirmary 84-94; C Woodhouse and Wrangthorn *Ripon* 94-96; Perm to Offic from 96. *Hobthrush, Wath, Harrogate HG3 5PL* E-mail hppriest@cstone.net

MACE, Robert Alfred Beasley. b 16. Leeds Univ BA49. Coll of Resurr Mirfield 48. **d** 50 **p** 51. C Callander *St And* 50-53; C Newc St Mary *Newc* 53-54; C Penton Street St Silas w All SS *Lon* 54-56; C Aylesbury *Ox* 56-59; P-in-c Glas St Gabr *Glas* 59-61; R Campbeltown *Arg* 61-65; V Barnsley St Pet *Wakef* 65-72; V Barnsley St Pet and St Jo 72-84; rtd 85; Perm to Offic *Wakef* from 85. *18 Chestnut Court, Cope Street, Barnsley S70 4HW* Tel (01226) 280729

McELHINNEY, Mrs Mary Elizabeth Ellen (Liz). b 45. TCD BSSc67 BA67. CITC BTh94. **d** 97 **p** 98. C Magheralin w

Dollingstown *D & D* 97-01; I Calry *K, E & A* from 01. *Calry Rectory, The Mall, Co Sligo, Irish Republic* Tel (00353) (71) 914 6513 E-mail lizmcelhinney@hotmail.com

McENDOO, Canon Neil Gilbert. b 50. TCD BA72. CITC 75. **d** 75 **p** 76. C Cregagh *D & D* 75-79; C Dublin St Ann *D & G* 79-82; I Dublin Rathmines w Harold's Cross from 82; Can Ch Ch Cathl Dublin from 92. *The Rectory, Purser Gardens, Church Avenue, Rathmines, Dublin 6, Irish Republic* Tel (00353) (1) 497 1797

McEVITT, Peter Benedict. b 58. Coll of Resurr Mirfield 91. **d** 93 **p** 94. C Swinton and Pendlebury *Man* 93-96; TV 96-97; V Darwen St Cuth w Tockholes St Steph *Blackb* 97-02; P-in-c Failsworth H Family *Man* from 02; AD Oldham from 02. *The Rectory, 190 Lord Lane, Failsworth, Manchester M35 0PG* Tel 0161-681 3644

MACEY, Anthony Keith Frank. b 46. Univ of Wales (Cardiff) DipTh69. St Steph Ho Ox 69. **d** 71 **p** 72. C Ex St Thos *Ex* 71-76; V Wembury 76-88; RD Ivybridge 83-91; V Cockington from 88; RD Torbay 98-03. *The Vicarage, 22 Monterey Close, Torquay TQ2 6QW* Tel (01803) 607957 Fax 690338 E-mail smacey@lineone.net *or* cockington@lineone.net

McFADDEN, Canon Ronald Bayle. b 30. TCD BA53 MA55. **d** 54 **p** 55. C Drumglass *Arm* 54-58; S Africa 58-62; Bp's Dom Chapl *D & D* 62-64; C Dundela St Mark 62-64; V Pateley Bridge and Greenhow Hill *Ripon* 64-73; V Knaresborough St Jo 73-79; P-in-c Knaresborough H Trin 78-79; Can Res Ripon Cathl 79-90; rtd 90; Chapl Qu Mary's Sch Baldersby Park 90-00; Perm to Offic *Ripon* from 90; *York* from 97. *12 Ure Bank Terrace, Ripon HG4 1JG* Tel (01765) 604043

McFADYEN, Donald Colin Ross. b 63. Wolfs Coll Cam BTh00 Peterho Cam MPhil02. Ridley Hall Cam 97. **d** 01 **p** 02. NSM Haslingfield w Harlton and Gt and Lt Eversden *Ely* from 01. *6 The Meadows, Haslingfield, Cambridge CB3 7JD* Tel (01223) 873159 Mobile 07763-401567 E-mail dm240@cam.ac.uk

McFADYEN, Canon Phillip. b 44. K Coll Lon BD69 AKC69 MTh70 ATD. St Aug Coll Cant 69. **d** 71 **p** 72. C Sheff St Mark Broomhall *Sheff* 71-74; Chapl Keswick Hall Coll of Educn 74-79; V Swardeston *Nor* 79-81; P-in-c E Carleton 79-81; P-in-c Intwood w Keswick 79-81; R Swardeston w E Carleton, Intwood, Keswick etc 81-90; R Ranworth w Panxworth, Woodbastwick etc from 90; Dioc Clergy Tr Officer 90-98; Hon Can Nor Cathl from 97; Bp's Officer for Visual Arts from 01; Relig Adv Anglia TV from 01. *The Vicarage, Woodbastwick Road, Ranworth, Norwich NR13 6HT* Tel (01603) 270263 Fax 270597 E-mail phillipmcfadyen@aol.com

McFARLAND, Alan Malcolm. b 24. Lon Univ BA53. Bris Sch of Min 82. **d** 85 **p** 86. NSM Westbury-on-Trym H Trin *Bris* 85-88; Asst Lect Bris Sch of Min 85-88; Perm to Offic *Glouc* 88-89; NSM Lechlade 89-93; Perm to Offic *Lon* from 92; Perm to Offic *Sarum* from 93. *11 The Sea Horse, Higher Sea Lane, Charmouth, Bridport DT6 6BB* Tel (01297) 560414

McFARLAND, Darren William. b 71. QUB BA93. CITC BTh96. **d** 96 **p** 97. C Greystones *D & G* 96-98; PV Ch Ch Cathl Dublin 97-99; P-in-c Clydebank *Glas* 99-02; Asst Dioc Miss 21 Co-ord 99-02; R Paisley St Barn from 02; R Paisley H Trin from 02. *11 Tantallon Drive, Paisley PA2 9JT* Tel (01505) 812359 Mobile 07773-772610 E-mail rector@paisley.freeserve.co.uk

MACFARLANE, Miss Elizabeth Clare. b 71. St Hugh's Coll Ox BA92. Ripon Coll Cuddesdon BA02. **d** 03. C Watford St Mich *St Alb* from 03. *57 Whippendell Road, Watford WD1 7LY* Tel (01923) 248739

MACFARLANE, Iain Philip. b 64. Essex Univ BSc85 W Sussex Inst of HE PGCE88. Trin Coll Bris BA99. **d** 99 **p** 00. C Fishponds St Jo *Bris* 99-03; TV Yate New Town from 03. *The Vicarage, 57 Brockworth, Bristol BS37 8SJ* Tel (01454) 322921 E-mail imacfarlane@ukonline.co.uk

MACFARLANE, Janet Elizabeth. b 64. Sheff Univ BMedSci87 St Jo Coll Dur BA92 DipMin93. Cranmer Hall Dur 93. **d** 93 **p** 94. Par Dn Stafford *Lich* 93-94; C 94-96; Chapl and Min Can Ely Cathl *Ely* 96-99; Dioc Communications Officer *Nor* from 99; Hon PV Nor Cathl from 00; Bp's Chapl from 01. *Bishop's House, Norwich NR3 1SB* Tel (01603) 614172 *or* 880853 E-mail communications@norwich.anglican.org

MACFARLANE, William Angus. b 17. Worc Coll Ox BA39 MA43. Wycliffe Hall Ox 39. **d** 40 **p** 41. C Charles w Plymouth St Luke *Ex* 40-45; C Reading St Jo *Ox* 45-47; CMS Tr Coll Blackheath 47-48; C Brompton H Trin *Lon* 48-49; R Bighton *Win* 49-52; V Bishop's Sutton 49-52; V Southwold *St E* 52-59; V Plaistow St Mary *Roch* 59-71; V Bexleyheath Ch Ch 71-79; Perm to Offic *B & W* 79-95; Chapl Sandhill Park Hosp Taunton 80-87; rtd 82. *Moorlands, Blue Anchor, Minehead TA24 6JZ* Tel (01643) 821564

McFIE, Canon James Ian. b 28. Open Univ BA99. Lich Th Coll 59. **d** 61 **p** 62. C Salford St Phil w St Steph *Man* 61-65; V Hey 65-75; V Elton All SS 75-85; V Walmsley 85-95; AD Walmsley 85-95; Hon Can Man Cathl 90-95; rtd 95; Perm to Offic *Carl* from 95. *4 Devonshire Road, Millom LA18 4JF* Tel (01229) 775192

McGANITY, Steven. b 61. Nottm Univ BTh93. St Jo Coll Nottm 90. **d** 93 **p** 94. C Gateacre *Liv* 93-97; V Clubmoor from 97. *St Andrew's Vicarage, 176 Queen's Drive, Liverpool L13 0AL* Tel 0151-226 1977

McGARAHAN, Kevin Francis. b 51. Man Poly NEBSS84. Cliff Th Coll DipTh73 Oak Hill Th Coll BA84 MA90. **d** 84 **p** 85. C Balderstone *Man* 84-87; Olympic Sports Chapl from 84; C Stoughton *Guildf* 87-89; Par Lec Ashton St Mich *Man* 89-92; TV Madeley *Heref* 92-96; CF 96-99; TV Woughton *Ox* from 99. *The Vicarage, 5 Newport Road, Woolstones, Milton Keynes MK15 0AR* Tel (01908) 667611

McGEARY, Peter. b 59. K Coll Lon BD AKC. Chich Th Coll 84. **d** 86 **p** 87. C Brighton St Pet and St Nic w Chpl Royal *Chich* 86-90; C St Marylebone All SS *Lon* 90-95; P-in-c Hayes St Anselm 95-97; V 97-98; V St Geo-in-the-East St Mary from 98; PV Westmr Abbey from 00. *The Clergy House, All Saints Court, 68 Johnson Street, London E1 0BQ* Tel (020) 7790 0973 Fax as telephone E-mail mcgeary@pmcg.demon.co.uk

McGEE, Preb Peter John. b 36. Trin Coll Cam BA60 MA. Chich Th Coll 60. **d** 62 **p** 63. C N Keyham *Ex* 62-63; C St Marychurch 63-65; C Townstall w Dartmouth 65-68; C Cockington 68-71; V Exminster 71-78; V Alfington 78-82; V Ottery St Mary 78-82; RD Ottery 82-90; Preb Ex Cathl 82-97; TR Ottery St Mary, Alfington and W Hill 82-87; TR Ottery St Mary, Alfington, W Hill, Tipton etc 87-96; P-in-c Woodbury 96-97; rtd 97; Perm to Offic *Ex* from 97. *177 Exeter Road, Exmouth EX8 3DX* Tel (01395) 272279

McGEE, The Very Revd Stuart Irwin. b 30. TCD BA53 MA68. **d** 53 **p** 54. C Belfast St Simon *Conn* 53-55; Singapore 55-58; I Drumholm and Rossnowlagh *D & R* 58-65; CF 65-77; Dep Asst Chapl Gen 77-88; Can Achonry Cathl *T, K & A* 89-92; I Achonry w Tubbercurry and Killoran 89-92; Dean Elphin and Ardagh *K, E & A* 92-99; I Sligo w Knocknarea and Rosses Pt 92-99; rtd 99. *Teach na Mara, Strandhill, Sligo, Irish Republic* Tel (00353) (71) 916 8910

MacGEOCH, David John Lamont. b 64. Bath Univ BSc90 CQSW90. Westcott Ho Cam CTM99. **d** 99 **p** 00. C Midsomer Norton w Clandown *B & W* 99-03; V Puriton and Pawlett from 03. *The Vicarage, 1 The Rye, Puriton, Bridgwater TA7 8BZ* Tel (01278) 683500 E-mail all@macgeoch.fsnet.co.uk

McGHIE, Clinton Adolphus. b 44. Univ of W Indies. CA Tr Coll. **d** 78 **p** 79. Jamaica 78-96; Perm to Offic *Chelmsf* 96-97; P-in-c Highams Park All SS 97-02; V from 02. *All Saints' Vicarage, 12A Castle Avenue, London E4 9QD* Tel (020) 8527 3269

McGILL, Francis Leonard. b 31. **d** 93 **p** 94. NSM Howell Hill *Guildf* 93-01; Perm to Offic from 02. *27 Hampton Grove, Ewell, Epsom KT17 1LA* Tel (020) 8393 2226

MacGILLIVRAY, Canon Alexander Buchan. b 33. Edin Univ MA55 Aber Univ DipEd67. Edin Th Coll 55. **d** 57 **p** 58. Chapl St Ninian's Cathl Perth *St And* 57-59; Chapl Aberlour Orphanage 59-62; C Aberlour *Mor* 59-62; R Oldmeldrum *Ab* from 62; R Whiterashes from 62; R Fyvie from 74; R Insch from 74; Can St Andr Cathl from 78. *The Rectory, Oldmeldrum, Inverurie AB51 0AD* Tel (01651) 872208

MacGILLIVRAY, Jonathan Martin. b 53. Aber Univ MA75. Coll of Resurr Mirfield. **d** 80 **p** 81. C Hulme Ascension *Man* 80-84; P-in-c Birch St Agnes 84-85; R 85-91; V Hurst 91-96; Chapl Tameside Gen Hosp 92-96; Dir of Ords and OLM Officer *Man* 96-02; V Carrington *S'well* from 02. *Carrington Vicarage, 6 Watcombe Circus, Nottingham NG5 2DT* Tel 0115-962 1291

McGINLEY, Canon Jack Francis. b 36. ALCD65. **d** 65 **p** 66. C Erith St Paul *Roch* 65-70; C Morden *S'wark* 70-74; V New Catton Ch Ch *Nor* 74-94; RD Nor N 84-89; Hon Can Nor Cathl 90-94; R Carlton-in-the-Willows *S'well* 94-02; R Colwick 96-02; rtd 02; Perm to Offic *Nor* from 03. *14 Clovelly Drive, Norwich NR6 5EY* Tel (01603) 788848
E-mail jack.mcginley@talk21.com

McGINLEY, John Charles. b 69. Birm Univ BSocSc90. Trin Coll Bris BA96. **d** 96 **p** 97. C Hounslow H Trin w St Paul *Lon* 96-00; TV Hinckley H Trin *Leic* from 00. *7 Rosemary Way, Hinckley LE10 0LN* Tel (01455) 446088
E-mail john.mcginley@virgin.net

McGIRR, Canon William Eric. b 43. CITC 68. **d** 71 **p** 72. C Carrickfergus *Conn* 71-74; C Mt Merrion *D & D* 74-77; I Donacavey w Barr *Clogh* 77-88; I Ballybeen *D & D* 88-94; I Magheraculmoney *Clogh* from 94; Can Clogh Cathl from 95. *The Rectory, Kesh, Enniskillen BT93 1TF* Tel (028) 6863 221

McGLASHAN, Alastair Robin. b 33. SAP90 Ch Ch Ox BA57 MA58 St Jo Coll Cam BA59 MA63. Ridley Hall Cam 58. **d** 60 **p** 61. C St Helens St Helen *Liv* 60; C Ormskirk 60-62; India 63-74; USA 74-75; C Lamorbey H Redeemer *Roch* 75-77; Chapl W Park Hosp Epsom 77-85; Chapl Maudsley Hosp Lon 85-87; Perm to Offic *S'wark* from 86; rtd 98. *102 Westway, London SW20 9LS* Tel (020) 8542 2125

McGLINCHEY, Patrick Gerard. b 59. NUU BA82 Nottm Univ BTh95. St Jo Coll Nottm 93. **d** 95 **p** 96. C Kettering Ch the King *Pet* 95-97; C Gorleston St Andr *Nor* 97-02; Assoc Min Cliff Park Community Ch 99-02; Chapl and Dean of Res QUB from 03. *20 Elmwood Avenue, Belfast BT9 6AY* Tel (028) 9066 7754

McGONIGLE, Martin Leo Thomas. b 64. Univ of Greenwich BA94 Anglia Poly Univ MA99. EAMTC 96. **d** 98 **p** 99. C Forest Gate All SS and St Edm *Chelmsf* 98-01. *Address temp unknown*

McGONIGLE, Canon Thomas. b 22. TCD BA45 MA65. TCD Div Sch 43. **d** 46 **p** 47. C Drumglass *Arm* 46-50; I Clogherny 50-53; I Magherafelt 53-61; I Portadown St Mark 61-74; Can Arm Cathl 72-88; Treas 79-83; Chan 83-88; Prec 88; rtd 88; Lic to Offic *Arm* from 88. *91 Kernan Gardens, Portadown, Craigavon BT63 5RA* Tel (028) 3833 0892

McGOWAN, Anthony Charles. b 57. Jes Coll Cam BA79 MA83. Coll of Resurr Mirfield. **d** 82 **p** 83. C Milford Haven *St D* 82-85; C Penistone *Wakef* 85-86; C Thurlstone 85-86; C Penistone and Thurlstone 86-88; CR from 88; Asst Chapl Radcliffe Infirmary Ox 91-94; Chapl Radcliffe Infirmary NHS Trust 94-99; Chapl Ox Radcliffe Hosps NHS Trust from 99. *Radcliffe Infirmary, Woodstock Road, Oxford OX2 6HE* Tel (01865) 224664 *or* 311188

McGOWAN, Daniel Richard Hugh. b 71. Oak Hill Th Coll. **d** 03. C Peterlee *Dur* from 03. *The Rectory, 5 Tudor Grange, Easington, Peterlee SR8 3DF* Tel 0191-527 0287

McGOWN, Robert Jackson. b 20. Keble Coll Ox BA42 MA46. Linc Th Coll 42. **d** 45 **p** 46. C Ipswich St Mary le Tower *St E* 45-47; Chapl Brockhurst Sch 47-49; Perm to Offic *Ox* 49-50; C Astbury *Ches* 50-51; C Glouc St Mary de Lode and St Nic *Glouc* 51-54; Min Can Glouc Cathl 51-54; C W Kirby St Bridget *Ches* 64-71; Perm to Offic from 76; rtd 85. *16 Church Road, West Kirby, Wirral CH48 0RW* Tel 0151-625 9481

McGRANAGHAN, Patrick Joseph Colum. b 46. Glas Univ BSc68 Lanc Univ MA72. St Alb Minl Tr Scheme 82. **d** 85 **p** 86. NSM Markyate Street *St Alb* 85-91; NSM Johnstone *Glas* 91-99; NSM Renfrew 97-99; P-in-c Kilmacolm from 99; P-in-c Bridge of Weir from 99. *The Rectory, 4 Balmore Court, Kilmacolm PA13 4LX* Tel (01505) 872733 *or* tel and fax 872961 E-mail cmcgranagh@aol.com

McGRATH, Prof Alister Edgar. b 53. Wadh Coll Ox BA75 Mert Coll Ox MA78 DPhil78 BD83 DD01. Westcott Ho Cam 78. **d** 80 **p** 81. C Wollaton *S'well* 80-83; Chapl St Hilda's Coll Ox 83-87; Tutor Wycliffe Hall Ox from 83; Prin from 95; Prof Systematic Th Regent Coll Vancouver 93-97; Research Lect in Th Ox Univ 93-99; Prof Hist Th from 99. *Wycliffe Hall, 54 Banbury Road, Oxford OX2 6PW* Tel (01865) 274200 Fax 274215

McGRATH, Gavin John. b 53. Marietta Coll (USA) BA76 Trin Episc Sch for Min MDiv81 Dur Univ PhD90. **d** 81 **p** 82. USA 81-87 and from 99; Assoc Th Prof Trin Episc Sch for Min Ambridge from 99; C Fulwood *Sheff* 87-95. *412 Little Street, Sewickley, PA 15143, USA* Tel (001) (412) 259 6446 *or* (724) 266 3838 ext 203 E-mail gavinmcgrath@tesm.edu

McGRATH, Ian Denver. b 42. Leeds Univ CertEd72. LNSM course 85. **d** 87 **p** 88. OLM Ancaster *Linc* 87-89; OLM Ancaster Wilsford Gp 89-92; C Spilsby w Hundleby 92-95; P-in-c Asterby Gp 95-99; R from 99. *The Rectory, 6 Simons Close, Donington-on-Bain, Louth LN11 9TX* Tel (01507) 343345 Fax as telephone E-mail ian@idmcgrath.fsnet.co.uk

McGRATH, John. b 49. Salford Univ BSc78 Man Poly CertEd79. N Ord Course 82. **d** 85 **p** 86. C Horwich *Man* 85-88; P-in-c Hillock 88-89; V 89-94; V York St Luke *York* 94-97; V Hollinwood *Man* 97-02; P-in-c Oldham St Chad Limeside 97-02; V Hollinwood and Limeside 02-03; TV Turton Moorland Min from 03. *Walmsley Vicarage, Blackburn Road, Bolton BL7 9RZ* Tel (01204) 304283

McGRATH, Kenneth. **d** 03. C Lisburn Ch Ch Cathl *Conn* from 03. *Address temp unknown*

McGRATH, Patrick Desmond. b 64. Liv Univ LLB86. Wycliffe Hall Ox 92. **d** 96 **p** 97. C Netherton *Liv* 96-98; C Ravenhead 98-02; P-in-c Ightham *Roch* from 02. *The Rectory, Bates Hill, Ightham, Sevenoaks TN15 9BG* Tel (01732) 884176

McGREGOR, Alan John. b 31. Jes Coll Ox MA57 Lon Univ DBRS61 Lon Inst of Educn DipRE71. S Tr Scheme 94. **d** 97 **p** 98. NSM Worting *Win* 97-00; Perm to Offic *Lon* 01 and *Sarum* from 03. *7 Sterte Avenue, Poole BH15 2AJ* Tel (01202) 667267

McGREGOR, Alistair Darrant. b 45. ALCD69. **d** 69 **p** 70. C Streatham Immanuel w St Anselm *S'wark* 69-73; Bermuda 73-76; Warden St Mich Cen New Cross 76-80; C Hatcham St Jas *S'wark* 76-80; V Nor Heartsease St Fran *Nor* 80-87; TR Thetford 87-96; P-in-c Kilverstone 87-90; P-in-c Croxton 87-90; RD Thetford and Rockland 90-95; TR St Baddow *Chelmsf* from 96. *The Rectory, 12 Church Street, Great Baddow, Chelmsford CM2 7HZ* Tel (01245) 471740 E-mail amcgregor@care4free.net

MacGREGOR, Colin Highmoor. b 19. Lon Univ BSc45 Magd Coll Cam BA47 MA50. Wells Th Coll 54. **d** 56 **p** 57. C Camberwell St Giles *S'wark* 56-60; V Clapham St Pet 60-73; V Riddlesdown 73-87; rtd 87. *Flat 3, Longacre Court, 21 Mayfield Road, South Croydon CR2 0BG* Tel (020) 8651 2615

MacGREGOR, Donald Alexander Thomson. b 52. Loughb Univ BSc75 Leic Univ CertEd78 Nottm Univ MA97. St Jo Coll Nottm 93. **d** 93 **p** 94. C Walmley *Birm* 93-96; C Braunstone *Leic* 96-97; TV 97-99; Chapl Loughb Univ from 99. *1 Holywell Drive, Loughborough LE11 3JU* Tel (01509) 268203 *or* 223741 Fax 223740 E-mail d.macgregor@lboro.ac.uk

McGREGOR, Mrs Lynn. b 61. Chester Coll of HE BTh00. N Ord Course 97. **d** 00 **p** 01. C Colne and Villages *Blackb* 00-03; C Gt Harwood St Bart from 03; C Gt Harwood St Jo from 03. *3 Bostons, Great Harwood, Blackburn BB6 7HJ* Tel 07944-801952 (mobile) E-mail revmac@dirtbiker.co.uk

MacGREGOR, Preb Neil. b 35. Keble Coll Ox BA60 MA80. Wells Th Coll. **d** 65 **p** 66. C Bath Bathwick St Mary w Woolley *B & W* 65-70; R Oare w Culbone 70-74; C Lynton, Brendon, Countisbury and Lynmouth *Ex* 70-74; P-in-c Kenn w Kingston Seymour *B & W* 74-76; R 76-80; R Wem *Lich* 80-01; V Lee Brockhurst 80-01; P-in-c Loppington w Newtown 95-01; RD Wem and Whitchurch 95-01; Preb Lich Cathl 97-01; rtd 01. *19 Castle View Terrace, Ludlow SY8 2NG* Tel (01584) 872671 E-mail neil@nandmmacgregor.fsnet.co

McGREGOR, Nigel Selwyn. b 47. FCA69. Sarum & Wells Th Coll 87. **d** 89 **p** 90. C Charlton Kings St Mary *Glouc* 89-92; P-in-c Seale *Guildf* 92-95; P-in-c Puttenham and Wanborough 92-95; R Seale, Puttenham and Wanborough from 95. *The Rectory, Seale, Farnham GU10 1JA* Tel (01252) 783057 E-mail mcgregorn@aol.com

McGREGOR, Stephen Paul. b 55. Man OLM Scheme. **d** 03. OLM Tonge Fold *Man* from 03. *32 Rawcliffe Avenue, Bolton BL2 6JX* Tel (01204) 391205 E-mail steve.mcgregor2@ntlworld.com

McGUFFIE, Duncan Stuart. b 45. Man Univ MA70 Regent's Park Coll Ox DPhil80. S Dios Minl Tr Scheme 84. **d** 85 **p** 85. C Sholing *Win* 85-89; V Clavering w Langley and Arkesden *Chelmsf* from 89. *The Vicarage, 54 Pelham Road, Clavering, Saffron Walden CB11 4PQ* Tel (01799) 550703

McGUINNESS, Gordon Baxter. b 57. St Andr Univ BSc79 BNC Ox MSc80. Oak Hill NSM Course 86. **d** 89 **p** 90. NSM Loudwater *Ox* 89-92; C Chilwell S*'well* 92-01; TR Ellesmere Port *Ches* from 01. *The Rectory, Vale Road, Whitby, Ellesmere Port CH65 9AY* Tel 0151-355 2516 *or* 356 8351 E-mail rev@gordon239.freeserve.co.uk

McGUIRE, Alec John. b 51. K Coll Cam BA73 MA76 Societas Liturgica 85 MRSH86 BAC Acc 90 FRSH90. Westcott Ho Cam 74. **d** 78 **p** 79. C Hungerford and Denford *Ox* 78-81; Prec Leeds St Pet *Ripon* 81-86; Perm to Offic from 86; rtd 01. *34 Gledhow Wood Road, Leeds LS8 4BZ* Tel 0113-240 0336

McGUIRE, John. b 31. Oak Hill Th Coll. **d** 62 **p** 65. C Tooting Graveney St Nic S*'wark* 62-64; C Normanton *Derby* 64-67; N Area Sec ICM 67-71; Chapl RNR 67-81; R Biddulph Moor *Lich* 71-00; rtd 00; Perm to Offic *Blackb* from 00. *25 Victoria Road, Fulwood, Preston PR2 8NE* Tel (01772) 719549 E-mail jmcguire@argonet.co.uk

MACHA, David. b 65. Keele Univ BA88 CertEd88 St Jo Coll Dur BA97. **d** 97 **p** 98. C Loughborough Em and St Mary in Charnwood *Leic* 97-01; CMS from 01; Tanzania from 02. *St Margaret's Church, PO Box 306, Moshi, Tanzania* E-mail david@dmacha.idps.co.uk

McHAFFIE, Alistair. b 57. Oak Hill Th Coll DipHE94. **d** 94 **p** 95. C Braintree *Chelmsf* 94-98; R Falkland Is 98-03; V Leyland St Jo *Blackb* from 03. *St John's Vicarage, Leyland Lane, Leyland PR25 1XB* Tel (01772) 621646 E-mail alistair@mchaffie.com

McHARDY, David William. b 61. Aber Coll of Educn DCE82 Edin Univ BD88 BD90 Strathclyde Univ Additional Teaching Qualification94 Edin Univ PhD97. Ab Dioc Tr Course 82 Edin Th Coll 85. **d** 88. C Dumfries *Glas* 88-89; Lect in World Religions Open Univ from 97; Hon C Oldmeldrum *Ab* from 99. *17 Kirkhill View, Blackburn, Aberdeen AB21 0XX* Tel (01224) 791758 Mobile 07788-712090 E-mail david.mchardy@talk21.com

MACHELL, Leigh Douglas. b 64. Leic Poly BSc85. St Jo Coll Nottm MTh03. **d** 03. C Beoley *Worc* from 03. *4 Marshfield Close, Redditch B98 8RW* Tel (01527) 60457 Mobile 07939-203787 E-mail rev.leigh@ntlworld.com

MACHIN, Roy Anthony. b 38. BA79. Oak Hill Th Coll 76. **d** 79 **p** 80. C Halliwell St Pet *Man* 79-83; V Eccleston St Luke *Liv* 83-91; V Kendal St Thos and Crook *Carl* 91-99; V Wigan St Barn Marsh Green *Liv* 99-03; rtd 03. *56 Ferndown Road, Harwood, Bolton BL2 3NN* Tel (01204) 362220 Fax as telephone E-mail roy.machin@btinternet.com

McHUGH, Brian Robert. b 50. York Univ BA72 Keele Univ CertEd73 Southn Univ Cert Eur Studies 78 Portsm Poly Cert Computing 84 DPSE90 IEng92 MIMA98 CMath98. S Dios Minl Tr Scheme 79. **d** 82 **p** 83. NSM Sarisbury *Portsm* 82-86; NSM Shedfield from 86. *28 Siskin Close, Bishops Waltham, Southampton SO32 1RQ* Tel (01489) 896658 E-mail brian.mchugh@bcs.org.uk *or* mchughb@tauntons.ac.uk

McILROY, Sister Honor Margaret. b 24. LRAM44 GRSM45. **d** 98 **p** 99. CSMV from 98. *St Mary's Convent, Challow Road, Wantage OX12 9DJ* Tel (01235) 763141 E-mail sistercsmv@btinternet.com

MACINNES, Canon David Rennie. b 32. Jes Coll Cam BA55 MA59. Ridley Hall Cam 55. **d** 57 **p** 58. C Gillingham St Mark *Roch* 57-61; C St Helen Bishopsgate w St Martin Outwich *Lon* 61-67; Prec Birm Cathl *Birm* 67-78; Angl Adv ATV 67-82; Angl Adv Cen TV 82-93; Dioc Missr *Birm* 79-87; Hon Can Birm Cathl 81-87; R Ox St Aldate w St Matt *Ox* 87-94; R Ox St Aldate 95-02;

Hon Can Ch Ch 98-02; rtd 02. *Pear Tree Cottage, Milcombe, Banbury OX15 4RS* Tel (01295) 721119

MACINNES, Harry Campbell. b 67. Nottm Poly BA89. Wycliffe Hall Ox BTh94. **d** 97 **p** 98. C E Twickenham St Steph *Lon* 97-00; P-in-c St Margaret's-on-Thames from 00. *295 St Margaret's Road, Twickenham TW1 1PN* Tel (020) 8891 3504 Fax 8744 3044

MACINTOSH, Andrew Alexander. b 36. St Jo Coll Cam BA59 MA63 BD80 DD97. Ridley Hall Cam 60. **d** 62 **p** 63. C S Ormsby Gp *Linc* 62-64; Lect St D Coll Lamp 64-67; Lic to Offic *Ely* from 67; Chapl St Jo Coll Cam 67-69; Asst Dean 69-79; Dean 79-02; Lect Th from 70; Pres 95-99. *St John's College, Cambridge CB2 1TP* Tel (01223) 338709 E-mail aam1003@cus.cam.ac.uk

McINTOSH, Andrew Malcolm Ashwell. b 43. Chich Th Coll 67. **d** 70 **p** 71. C Brentwood St Thos *Chelmsf* 70-74; C Chingford SS Pet and Paul 74-79; P-in-c Maldon St Mary w Mundon 79-83; R from 83. *St Mary's Rectory, Park Drive, Maldon CM9 7JG* Tel (01621) 857191

MacINTOSH, Canon George Grant. b 41. St Jo Coll Dur BA75 DipTh76. **d** 76 **p** 77. C Ecclesall *Sheff* 76-79; Hon C Sheff St Oswald 79-81; Research Fell Sheff Univ 79-81; Dioc Adult Educn Officer 81-88; V Crookes St Tim 81-88; V Abbeydale St Jo 88-97; RD Ecclesall 89-94; P-in-c Turriff *Ab* from 97; P-in-c Cuminestown from 97; Can St Andr Cathl from 01. *The Rectory, 9 Deveron Road, Turriff AB53 4BB* Tel and telephone (01888) 563238 Mobile 07974-748080 E-mail ggrant@macintosh99.freeserve.co.uk

McINTOSH, Ian MacDonald. b 64. Jes Coll Cam BA86. Trin Coll Bris BA90. **d** 90 **p** 91. C Belmont *Lon* 90-92; C Pinner 92-95; Chapl Leic Univ *Leic* 96-02; TV Leic H Spirit 96-02; Co-ord Reader Tr 00-02; C Milton Ernest, Pavenham and Thurleigh *St Alb* from 02. *The Vicarage, Thurleigh Road, Milton Ernest, Bedford MK44 1RF* Tel (01234) 822885 E-mail imm4@le.ac.uk

McINTOSH, Mrs Nicola Ann. b 60. Trin Coll Bris DipHE89 ADPS90. **d** 90 **p** 94. Par Dn Queensbury All SS *Lon* 90-93; Par Dn Ruislip Manor St Paul 93-94; C 94-95; NSM Clarendon Park St Jo w Knighton St Mich *Leic* 96-02; Asst Dioc Dir of Ords 00-02; V Milton Ernest, Pavenham and Thurleigh *St Alb* from 02. *The Vicarage, Thurleigh Road, Milton Ernest, Bedford MK44 1RF* Tel (01234) 822885 E-mail vicarage@fish.co.uk

McINTYRE, Robert Mark. b 69. Nottm Univ BA91. Coll of Resurr Mirfield 92. **d** 94 **p** 95. C Wednesbury St Jas and St Jo *Lich* 94-97; TV Wolstanton from 97. *14 Dorrington Grove, Porthill, Newcastle ST5 0HY* Tel (01782) 715001 E-mail m-mcintyre@netlineuk.net

McINTYRE DE ROMERO, Ms Iris Evelyn. b 60. Worc Coll Ox MA82 MA90. St Steph Ho Ox 82. **dss** 84 **d** 87 **p** 97. Southbroom *Sarum* 84-86; Oakdale 86-88; Par Dn 87-88; Par Dn Ireland Wood *Ripon* 88-89; Area Co-ord (NW) Chr Aid 92-94; Hon C W Derby St Mary *Liv* 94-98; R Bangor Monachorum and Worthenbury *St As* 98-03; Chapl HM Pris Brockhill from 03. *HM Prison and YOI, Brockhill, Redditch B97 6RD* Tel (01527) 552650 E-mail iris.marco@virgin.net

MACK, Mrs Gillian Frances. b 50. SCM72. Cant Sch of Min 84. **d** 87 **p** 94. NSM Deal St Geo *Cant* 87-88; NSM Deal St Leon and St Rich and Sholden 88-92; Par Dn 93-94; C 94-97; rtd 97; Perm to Offic *Cant* from 97; Hon Chapl Cautley Trust from 98. *4 Palm Beach Avenue, Hythe CT21 6NH* Tel (01303) 268523

McKAE, William John. b 42. Liv Univ BSc63 St Mark & St Jo Coll Lon PGCE64 Bris Univ DipTh70. Wells Th Coll 68. **d** 71 **p** 72. C Tranmere St Paul w St Luke *Ches* 71-74; C Midsomer Norton *B & W* 74-75; TV Birkenhead Priory *Ches* 75-80; R Oughtrington 80-91; Chapl Asst Hope, Salford R and Ladywell Hosps *Man* 91-92; Lic Preacher *Man* 91-92; R Heaton Reddish from 92. *The Rectory, St Mary's Drive, Stockport SK5 7AX* Tel 0161-477 6702

McKAVANAGH, Dermot James. b 51. TCD BA75 MA78 K Coll Lon BD78 AKC78. **d** 78 **p** 79. C Croydon H Sav *Cant* 78-82; Asst Chapl Wellington Coll Berks 82-87; Chapl RAF 87-00; rtd 02. *42 Freshfields, Lea, Preston PR2 1TJ*

McKAY, Brian Andrew. b 39. Sarum Th Coll 69. **d** 71 **p** 72. C Walker *Newc* 71-74; C Wooler Gp 74-77; TV 77-81; V Long Benton St Mary 81-89; TV Bellingham/Otterburn Gp 89-91; TV N Tyne and Redesdale Team 91-02; rtd 02. *26 Punchards Down, Totnes TQ9 5FB* Tel (01803) 840675

MACKAY, Canon Douglas Brysson. b 27. Edin Th Coll 56. **d** 58 **p** 59. Prec St Andr Cathl Inverness *Mor* 58-61; P-in-c Fochabers 61-70; R 70-72; Chapl Aberlour Orphanage 64-67; P-in-c Aberlour 64-72; Syn Clerk 65-72; Can St Andr Cathl Inverness 65-72; Hon Can 72; R Carnoustie *Bre* 72-98; Can St Paul's Cathl Dundee 81-97; Hon Can from 98; Syn Clerk 81-97; rtd 97; Tutor Dundee Univ *Bre* from 97. *24 Philip Street, Carnoustie DD7 6ED*

MACKAY, Hedley Neill. b 27. St Aid Birkenhead 53. **d** 56 **p** 57. C Beverley St Mary *York* 56-59; C Scarborough St Mary 59-60; Nigeria 61-70; C Wawne *York* 70-71; TV Sutton St Jas and Wawne 72-76; V Huntington *Yo* 76-82; TR 82-93; Perm to Offic from 93; rtd 93; Rtd Clergy and Widows Officer (York Adnry) *York* 94-98. *2 Elmfield Terrace, Heworth, York YO31 1EH* Tel (01904) 412971

MACKAY, Ian Stuart Reay. b 31. St Aid Birkenhead 56. **d** 58 **p** 59. C Selly Oak St Mary *Birm* 58-60; Ind Chapl *Sheff* 60-66; C Pitsmoor 61-63; C Rotherham 63-66; V Bolton Sav *Man* 66-71; Lect Liv Educn Authority 71-74; Regional Officer Nat Assn for Teachers in F&HE 75-91; rtd 92. *5 East Meade, Chorltonville, Manchester M21 2DX* Tel 0161-881 1228

McKAY, John Andrew. b 38. HDipEd. Chich Th Coll. **d** 74 **p** 75. C Primrose Hill St Mary w Avenue Road St Paul *Lon* 74-77; V Battersea Ch Ch and St Steph *S'wark* 77-82; I Rathkeale w Askeaton and Kilcornan *L & K* 82-85; I Dublin St Bart w Leeson Park *D & G* 85-00; Chapl Venice w Trieste *Eur* 00-03; rtd 03. *5 St Peter's Place, Drogheda, Co Louth, Irish Republic* Tel (00353) (41) 987 3277

McKAY, Margaret McLeish. *See* HALE, Mrs Margaret McLeish

MACKAY, Paul Douglas. b 60. Trin Coll Bris. **d** 00 **p** 01. C Becontree St Mary *Chelmsf* from 00; V Mile Cross *Nor* from 03. *St Catherine's Vicarage, Aylsham Road, Norwich NR3 2RJ* Tel (01603) 426767 E-mail mackay@fish.co.uk

MACKAY, Rupert. b 61. Oak Hill Th Coll BA00. **d** 00 **p** 01. C Knutsford St Jo and Toft *Ches* from 00. *Mallard House, 24 Goughs Lane, Knutsford WA16 8QL* Tel (01565) 632894 E-mail rupertmackay@rmackay.fsnet.co.uk

McKEACHIE, The Very Revd William Noble. b 43. Univ of the South (USA) BA66. Trin Coll Toronto STB70. **d** 70 **p** 70. Asst Chapl St Jo Coll Ox 70-72; Dioc Th Toronto Canada 73-78; USA from 78; Dir Ch Relns and Tutor Univ of the South 78-80; R Baltimore St Paul 81-95; Dean S Carolina and R Charleston Cathl from 95. *126 Coming Street, Charleston, SC 29403, USA* Tel (001) (843) 722 7345 Fax 722 2105 E-mail cathchlp@dycon.com

McKEARNEY, Andrew Richard. b 57. Selw Coll Cam MA. Edin Th Coll 81. **d** 82 **p** 83. Prec St Ninian's Cathl Perth *St And* 82-84; Chapl St Mary's Cathl *Edin* 84-88; R Hardwick *Ely* 88-94; R Toft w Caldecote and Childerley 88-94; V Chesterton Gd Shep from 94. *The Good Shepherd Vicarage, 51 Highworth Avenue, Cambridge CB4 2BQ* Tel (01223) 312933 *or* 351844 E-mail theophan@surfaid.org

McKECHNIE, John Gregg. b 30. Em Coll Cam BA54 MA57. Ridley Hall Cam 54. **d** 55 **p** 56. C Morden *S'wark* 55-57; Tutor Clifton Th Coll 57-62; R Chich St Pancras and St Jo *Chich* 62-68; V Reading St Jo *Ox* 68-85; RD Reading 83-85; V Lindfield *Chich* 85-95; rtd 95; Perm to Offic *Chich* from 95. *3 The Courtyard, Stockbridge Road, Chichester PO19 8GP* Tel (01243) 531703

McKEE, Douglas John Dunstan. b 34. Univ of W Aus BA65. St Mich Th Coll Crafers 54. **d** 57 **p** 58. Australia 57-72 and from 85; SSM from 58; Lic to Offic *S'well* 73-85. *St John's Priory, 14 St John Street, Adelaide, South Australia 5000* Tel (0061) (8) 8223 1014 *or* 8416 8445 Fax (0061) (8) 8223 2764 *or* 8416 8450 E-mail dunstan.mckee@flinders.edu.au

McKEE, Patrick Joseph. b 49. Ripon Coll Cuddesdon DipMin94. **d** 94 **p** 95. C Oakham, Hambleton, Egleton, Braunston and Brooke *Pet* 94-97; V Ryhall w Essendine and Carlby from 97. *The Vicarage, Church Street, Ryhall, Stamford PE9 4HR* Tel (01780) 762398 E-mail pmkee@ryhall.clara.co.uk

McKEEMAN, David Christopher. b 36. AKC58 DipEd76. **d** 60 **p** 61. C Catford St Andr *S'wark* 60-64; P-in-c W Dulwich Em 64-69; Lic to Offic *Win* 70-82; R Silchester 82-01; rtd 01. *The Maltings, Woodend Lane, Stoke Lacy, Bromyard HR7 4HQ* Tel (01885) 490705 E-mail david.mckeeman@ntlworld.com

McKEGNEY, Canon John Wade. b 47. TCD BA70 MA81. CITC 70. **d** 72 **p** 73. C Ballynafeigh St Jude *D & D* 72-75; C Bangor St Comgall 75-80; I Drumgath w Drumgooland and Clonduff 80-83; I Gilnahirk 83-90; I Arm St Mark *Arm* from 90; Can Arm Cathl from 01. *St Mark's Rectory, 14 Portadown Road, Armagh BT61 9EE* Tel (028) 3752 2970 Fax as telephone E-mail john.mckegney@virgin.net *or* armagh@armagh.anglican.org

MacKEITH (née GODFREY), Mrs Ann Veronica. b 35. Bris Univ BSc57 CertEd. Gilmore Course 78. **dss** 79 **d** 87 **p** 94. Bishopwearmouth Ch Ch *Dur* 79-83; Bishopwearmouth St Gabr 83-86; Ryhope 86-88; Par Dn 87-88; Par Dn Darlington H Trin 88-94; C 94-95; Family Life Officer 95-97; rtd 98. *135 Hummersknott Avenue, Darlington DL3 8RR* Tel (01325) 463481 E-mail annmackeith@webportal.co.uk

McKELLAR, John Lorne. b 19. Sarum Th Coll 70. **d** 72 **p** 73. C Warminster St Denys *Sarum* 72-75; USA 75-79 and 81-84; P-in-c Colchester St Barn *Chelmsf* 79-81; rtd 84; Perm to Offic *Sarum* from 84. *Corrie, 105A Clay Street, Crockerton, Warminster BA12 8AG* Tel (01985) 213161

McKELLEN, Pamela Joyce. b 47. Homerton Coll Cam TCert69 BEd70. Cranmer Hall Dur 01. **d** 02. C Ox St Matt *Ox* from 02. *91 Marlborough Road, Oxford OX1 4LX* Tel (01865) 251670 E-mail pjmck@compuserve.com

McKELVEY, Mrs Jane Lilian. b 48. Liv Inst of Educn BA94. Nor Bapt Coll 94. **d** 97 **p** 98. C Aughton St Mich *Liv* 97-01; TV Gateacre from 01. *St Mark's Vicarage, Cranwell Road, Liverpool L25 1NZ* Tel 0151-487 9634

McKELVEY, The Very Revd Robert Samuel James Houston. b 42. QVRM00 TD. QUB BA65 MA(Ed)88 Garrett-Evang Th

Sem DMin93. CITC 67. **d** 67 **p** 68. C Dunmurry *Conn* 67-70; CF (TAVR) 70-99; P-in-c Kilmakee *Conn* 70-77; I 77-81; Sec Gen Syn Bd of Educn (N Ireland) 81-01; Preb Newcastle St Patr Cathl Dublin 89-01; Dean Belf from 01. *Belfast Cathedral, Donegal Street, Belfast BT1 2HB* Tel (028) 9032 8332 Fax 9023 8855 E-mail mckelvey@unite.co.uk

McKELVIE, Canon Alfred. b 10. TCD BA34 MA43. CITC 35. **d** 35 **p** 36. C Lisburn Ch Ch *Conn* 35-38; C Ballynafeigh St Jude *D & D* 38-42; I Templecorran w Islandmagee *Conn* 42-46; I Belfast St Donard *D & D* 46-56; I Ballynafeigh St Jude 56-70; Adn Down 70-75; Chan Down Cathl 75-80; rtd 80. *50 Blenheim Park, Carryduff, Belfast BT8 8NN* Tel (028) 9081 2682

McKEMEY, Canon Robert. b 15. St Aid Birkenhead 50. **d** 52 **p** 53. C Blackb Ch Ch *Blackb* 52-53; PC Blackb St Barn 53-57; Kenya 57-69; Schs Supervisor 57-64; Adn Nakuru 64-69; I Kilrea *D & R* 69-73; R Meysey Hampton w Marston Meysey *Glouc* 73-81; RD Fairford 77-81; I Clondevaddock *D & R* 81-85; rtd 85. *3 Sevenoaks Road, Reading RG6 7NT* Tel 0118-966 0501

McKENDRY, Susan. b 02. NSM Allonby *Carl* 02-03; NSM Cross Canonby 02-03; NSM Dearham 02-03; NSM Allonby, Cross Canonby and Dearham from 03. *14 Ghyll Bank, Little Broughton, Cockermouth CA13 0LJ*

McKENNA, Dermot William. b 41. TCD BA63 MA66. CITC 64. **d** 64 **p** 65. C Enniscorthy *C & O* 64-66; I Killeshin 66-84; rtd 84. *20 Sherwood, Pollerton, Carlow, Irish Republic* Tel (00353) (59) 913 0915 E-mail mckenna@itcarlow.ie

McKENNA, Lindsay Taylor. b 62. Glas Univ MA83 Aber Univ BD86. Edin Th Coll 87. **d** 87 **p** 88. C Broughty Ferry *Bre* 87-90; C Wantage *Ox* 90-93; V Illingworth *Wakef* 93-99; Dir CARA 99-02; V Hanworth All SS *Lon* from 02. *All Saints' Vicarage, Uxbridge Road, Feltham TW13 5EE* Tel (020) 8894 9330 E-mail macdolly@clara.co.uk

MACKENNA, Richard William. b 49. Pemb Coll Cam BA71 MA75. Ripon Coll Cuddesdon BA77 MA81. **d** 78 **p** 79. C Fulham St Dionis Parson's Green *Lon* 78-81; C Paddington St Jas 81-85; Tutor Westcott Ho Cam 85-89; V Kingston All SS w St Jo *S'wark* 90-91; Perm to Offic from 94; Perm to Offic *Nor* from 99. *Didworthy House, Holman Road, Aylsham NR11 6BY* Tel (01263) 732228

MACKENNA, Robert Christopher Douglass. b 44. Oriel Coll Ox BA72 MA75 MBAP85. Cuddesdon Coll 71. **d** 73 **p** 74. C Farncombe *Guildf* 73-77; C Tattenham Corner and Burgh Heath 77-80; P-in-c Hascombe 80-90; R 90-00; RD Godalming 91-96; Hon Can Guildf Cathl 99-00; Dir St Marylebone Healing and Counselling Cen from 00; NSM St Marylebone w H Trin *Lon* from 00. *Flat 5, 38 Nottingham Place, London W1M 3FD* Tel (020) 7486 9363 *or* 7935 5066 Fax 7486 5493 E-mail cmack96891@aol.com

MACKENZIE, Alfred Arthur. b 25. Bps' Coll Cheshunt 61. **d** 61 **p** 62. C Waltham Abbey *Chelmsf* 61-64; V Barking St Erkenwald 64-72; V Broomfield 72-83; P-in-c Willerby w Ganton and Folkton *York* 83-91; R 91-95; rtd 95; Perm to Offic *Linc* 96-99. *7 Lovett Street, Cleethorpes DN35 7BJ* Tel 07791-864393 (mobile)

MACKENZIE, Andrew John Kett. b 46. Southn Univ BA68. LNSM course 88 Guildf Dioc Min Course 98. **d** 91 **p** 92. Fullbrook Sch New Haw 76-99; OLM Woodham *Guildf* 91-99; C Aldershot St Mich from 99. *Ascension House, Ayling Hill, Aldershot GU11 3LL* Tel and fax (01252) 330224 Mobile 07703-983312 E-mail andrew.mackenzie1@ntlworld.com

MACKENZIE, Miss Ann. b 54. CertEd76 DipHE82 DPS86. Trin Coll Bris 82. **dss** 85 **d** 87 **p** 94. Normanton *Wakef* 85-90; Par Dn 87-90; Par Dn Bletchley *Ox* 90-94; C 94-98; TV W Swindon and the Lydiards *Bris* from 98. *1 Brandon Close, Grange Park, Swindon SN5 6AA* Tel (01793) 870244

McKENZIE, Mrs Ann Elizabeth. b 45. Leic Univ BA67 PGCE68. STETS 95. **d** 98 **p** 99. NSM Appleshaw, Kimpton, Thruxton, Fyfield etc *Win* from 98. *The Post House, Thruxton, Andover SP11 8LZ* Tel (01264) 772788 E-mail ann.mckenzie@tinyonline.co.uk

McKENZIE, Cilla. *See* McKENZIE, Mrs Priscilla Ann

MACKENZIE, David Stuart. b 45. Open Univ BA95 FRSA00. Linc Th Coll 66. **d** 69 **p** 70. C Bishopwearmouth St Mary V w St Pet CD *Dur* 69-72; C Pontefract St Giles *Wakef* 72-74; Chapl RAF 74-02; QHC from 00; Chapl OHP from 02. *St Hilda's Priory, Sneaton Castle, Whitby YO21 3QN* Tel (01947) 602079 Fax 820854 E-mail ohppriorywhitby@btinternet.com

MACKENZIE, George. b 09. MBE46 TD50. Worc Coll Ox BA31 MA35. Wells Th Coll 32. **d** 33 **p** 34. C Whalley *Blackb* 33-36; C Ashton-on-Ribble St Andr 36-44; CF (TA) 35-59; CF (TA - R of O) 59-64; V Whaddon w Tattenhoe *Ox* 45-47; R W Grinstead *Chich* 47-52; R Sullington 52-74; R Storrington 53-74; RD Storrington 63-70; rtd 74; Perm to Offic *Chich* from 74. *c/o G H G Mackenzie Esq, 65 Geers Wood, Heathfield TN21 0AR*

McKENZIE, Ian Colin. b 31. CA56. EMMTC 89. **d** 93. NSM Edin St Mark and Edin St Andr and St Aid *Edin* 93-94; Perm to Offic *S'well* from 01. *21 Crafts Way, Southwell NG25 0BL* Tel (01636) 815755

MACKENZIE, Ian William (Bill). b 46. Trin Coll Bris DipHE95. **d** 95 **p** 96. C Bideford *Ex* 95-96; C Bideford, Northam, Westward

Ho!, Appledore etc 96-99; TV Littleham w Exmouth from 99. *Littleham Vicarage, 96 Littleham Road, Littleham, Exmouth EX8 2RD* Tel (01395) 275085

McKENZIE, Jack Llewellyn. b 29. FRSH AMIEHO MAMIT. S'wark Ord Course. **d** 79 **p** 80. Hon C Stonebridge St Mich *Lon* 79-88; Hon C Willesden St Mary 88-91; Perm to Offic *St Alb* from 00. *2 Beckett Square, Berkhamsted HP4 1BZ* Tel (01442) 874265

McKENZIE, Preb Lawrence Duncan. b 30. St Aid Birkenhead 52. **d** 55 **p** 56. C Blackb St Gabr *Blackb* 55-58; C Burnley St Pet 58-60; C St Giles-in-the-Fields *Lon* 60-63; V Queensbury All SS 63-85; V Hillingdon St Jo 85-96; Preb St Paul's Cathl 89-96; rtd 96; NSM Gt Stanmore *Lon* 96-99; Perm to Offic *Lon* and *Ely* from 99. *1 Walnut Tree Close, Little Downham, Ely CB6 2SQ* Tel (01353) 698793 E-mail kathmac@fish.co.uk

McKENZIE, Peter Sterling. b 65. Univ Coll Lon BSc88. Oak Hill Th Coll BA95. **d** 95 **p** 96. C Roxeth *Lon* 95-99; Assoc V 99-00; TV from 00. *65 Butler Road, Harrow HA1 4DS* Tel (020) 8723 5584 E-mail peter@mackenziep.fsnet.co.uk

McKENZIE, Canon Peter Thomas. b 44. Lon Univ LLB67 Nottm Univ DipTh68 Westmr Coll Ox MTh97 Univ of E Lon MA01. Cuddesdon Coll 68. **d** 70 **p** 71. C Leigh Park *Portsm* 70-75; P-in-c Sittingbourne St Mary *Cant* 75-82; V Folkestone St Sav 82-90; RD Elham 89-90; R Cant St Martin and St Paul 90-99; RD Cant 95-99; Hon Can Cant Cathl from 97; V Goudhurst w Kilndown from 99; AD Cranbrook from 01. *The Vicarage, Back Lane, Goudhurst, Cranbrook TN17 1AN* Tel (01580) 211332 E-mail canonmack@talk21.com

McKENZIE, Mrs Priscilla Ann. b 47. St Jo Coll Nottm 87. **d** 93 **p** 94. NSM Ellon *Ab* 93-96; NSM Cruden Bay 93-96; Perm to Offic *Roch* 96-99; Chapl Medway NHS Trust from 99. *Iona, Linton Hill, Linton, Maidstone ME17 4AW* Tel (01622) 741318

McKENZIE, Richard Graham. b 49. St Aug Coll Cant 72. **d** 73 **p** 74. C Deal St Leon *Cant* 73-75; C Deal St Leon w Sholden 75-78; C Herne 78-81; Canada from 81; I Pakenham 81-88; I Richmond 88-90; I Petawawa from 90. *46 Victoria Street, Petawawa ON, Canada, K8H 2E6* Tel (001) (613) 687 2218

McKENZIE, Robin Peter. b 61. Sheff Univ BEng82 Birm Univ MSc(Eng)87 Dur Univ BA02 Warwick Univ EngD02 MIEE. Cranmer Hall Dur 00. **d** 03. C Shrewsbury St Chad w St Mary *Lich* from 03. *1 St Chad's Terrace, Shrewsbury SY1 1JL* Tel (01743) 235834 E-mail mckenzie_robin@hotmail.com

MACKENZIE, Simon Peter Munro. b 52. Univ Coll Ox BA74. Coll of Resurr Mirfield 82. **d** 85 **p** 86. C Tipton St Jo *Lich* 85-91; V Perry Beeches *Birm* from 91. *St Matthew's Vicarage, 313 Beeches Road, Birmingham B42 2QR* Tel 0121-360 2100

MACKENZIE, William. *See* MACKENZIE, Ian William

McKEON, Canon James Ernest. b 22. TCD BA45 HDipEd49 Div Test. TCD Div Sch. **d** 46 **p** 47. C Dundalk *Arm* 46-48; C Dublin St Geo *D & G* 48-52; I Kilsaran w Drumcar, Dunleer and Dunany *Arm* 52-59; I Drogheda 59-64; P-in-c Termonfeckin and Beaulieu 62-64; Warden Wilson's Hosp Sch Multyfarnham 64-83; Can Kildare Cathl *M & K* 83-88; Prec 87-88; P-in-c Geashill w Killeigh and Ballycommon 83-88; rtd 88; Dioc Info Officer (Meath) *M & K* 90-91; Radio Officer 91-96. *Araucaria, 200 Bassaleg Road, Newport NP9 3PX* Tel (01633) 661974

McKEON, Canon Victor Edward Samuel. b 39. FCA65 Lon Univ BD. CITC. **d** 68 **p** 69. C Enniskillen *Clogh* 68-72; Accountant to Conn & D & D 72-79; P-in-c Magherahamlet *D & D* 77-79; I Derryvullen N w Castlearchdale *Clogh* 79-91; Dioc Treas from 83; Can Clogh Cathl 86-89; Preb 89-95; Chan from 95; I Monaghan w Tydavnet and Kilmore 91-95; I Trory w Killadeas from 95. *Trory Rectory, Rossfad, Ballinamallard BT94 2LS* Tel (028) 6638 8477 Fax as telephone

MACKERACHER, Alasdair John. b 22. Linc Th Coll 69. **d** 71 **p** 72. C Oakdale St Geo *Sarum* 71-73; C Swanage 73-78; V W Alvington w S Milton *Ex* 78-81; R Ashreigney 81-85; R Broadwoodkelly 81-85; V Brushford 81-85; V Winkleigh 81-85; V Swimbridge and W Buckland 85-88; rtd 88; Perm to Offic *Ex* from 98. *3 Gracey Court, Woodland Road, Exeter EX5 3LP* Tel (01392) 468163

McKERRELL, Euan Harvey. b 45. Aber Univ BSc69 CChem78 MRSC78. St Jo Coll Nottm MTh01. **d** 01 **p** 02. C Ness Gp *Linc* 01-03. *Address temp unkown* Tel 07718-140239 (mobile)

MACKEY, John. b 34. Lich Th Coll. **d** 64 **p** 65. C Kells *Carl* 64-67; C Barrow St Matt 67-70; R Clayton *Man* 70-75; V Low Marple *Ches* 75-83; R Coppenhall 83-00; rtd 00; Perm to Offic *Ches* from 00. *361 Hungerford Road, Crewe CW1 5EZ* Tel (01270) 254951

McKIBBIN, Gordon. b 29. Lon Univ DipTh57. St Aid Birkenhead 55. **d** 58 **p** 59. C Dundela St Mark *D & D* 58-60; C Knotty Ash St Jo *Liv* 61-64; V Gt Sankey 64-97; rtd 97; Perm to Offic *Liv* from 97. *6 Penmark Close, Warrington WA5 5TG* Tel (01925) 445125

MacKICHAN, Gillian Margaret. b 34. Bedf Teacher Tr Coll DipPE56 Cam Univ CertEd56 Lon Univ DSS76 CQSW80. S Dios Minl Tr Scheme 90. **d** 93 **p** 94. NSM Upper Kennet *Sarum* 93; TV from 95; RD Marlborough from 02. *West Bailey, Lockeridge, Marlborough SN8 4ED* Tel (01672) 861629

MACKIE, Andrew. b 53. Glas Univ BSc74 CEng MIEE. St Alb and Ox Min Course 98. **d** 00 **p** 01. OLM Purley *Ox* from 00.

12 Church Mews, Purley-on-Thames, Pangbourne, Reading RG8 8AG Tel 0118-941 7170 E-mail mackie.family@btinternet.com

MACKIE, Ian William. b 31. Lon Univ BSc53 Ex Univ PGCE54. Linc Th Coll 81. **d** 83 **p** 84. C Market Rasen *Linc* 83-87; V Bracebridge Heath 87-96; RD Christianity 92-96; rtd 96; Perm to Offic *Sheff* 96-02. *57 Bridle Crescent, Chapeltown, Sheffield S35 2QX* Tel 0114-284 4073

MACKIE, Kenneth Johnston. b 20. Univ of NZ BA45 MA46 La Trobe Univ Vic BEd77. St Jo Coll Auckland 46. **d** 47 **p** 48. New Zealand 46-66; C Whangarei 47-51; P-in-c S Hokianga 51-53; V Opotiki 53-56; V Napier St Aug 56-61; Gen Sec NZ Coun for Chr Educn 62-66; Australia 66-72 and 74-94; Chapl Traralgon and Macleod High Schs 66-70; Chapl Univ of Papua New Guinea 72-75; Perm to Offic Melbourne and Gippsland 75-89; Hon P-in-c Nerang 91-94; Perm to Offic *Roch* from 97. *Flat 1, 21 Lime Hill Road, Tunbridge Wells TN1 1LJ* Tel (01892) 540624

McKIE, The Very Revd Kenyon Vincent. b 60. Aus Nat Univ BA83 ACT BTh88 K Coll Lon MTh92 Canberra Coll DipEd84 ACT DipMin89. **d** 86 **p** 87. Australia 86-89 and from 91; Dn Queanbeyan 86; C 87; Lucas-Tooth Scholar K Coll Lon 89-91; Hon C Coulsdon St Andr *S'wark* 89-91; R Monaro S 91-94; R Bega 94-99; Adn S Coast and Monaro 96-99; Dean Goulburn from 99. *PO Box 205, Goulburn, NSW, Australia 2580* Tel (0061) (2) 4821 9192 *or* 4821 2206 Fax 4822 2639 E-mail mesacgbn@tpgi.com.au *or* deanery@tpgi.com.au

McKILLOP, Mrs Caroline Annis. b 47. Glas Univ MB, ChB72 PhD77. Edin Th Coll 95. **d** 98 **p** 99. NSM Glas St Matt *Glas* from 98. *18 Beaumont Gate, Glasgow G12 9ED* Tel 0141-339 7000

McKINLEY, Canon Arthur Horace Nelson. b 46. TCD BA69 MA79. CITC 70. **d** 70 **p** 71. C Taney Ch Ch *D & G* 71-76; I Dublin Whitechurch from 76; Preb Dunlavin St Patr Cathl Dublin from 91. *Whitechurch Vicarage, Whitechurch Road, Rathfarnham, Dublin 16, Irish Republic* Tel (00353) (1) 493 3953 E-mail whitechurchparish@ireland.com

McKINLEY, George Henry. b 23. TCD BA44 MA51. **d** 46 **p** 47. C Waterford Ch Ch *C & O* 46-49; I Fiddown 49-51; I Fiddown w Kilmacow 51-54; C S Harrow St Paul *Lon* 54-58; V Stonebridge St Mich 58-65; R Hackney St Jo 65-72; TR Hackney 72-77; V Painswick w Sheepscombe *Glouc* 77-83; Bp's Chapl 83-87; C Sandhurst 83-85; C Twigworth, Down Hatherley, Norton, The Leigh etc 85-87; rtd 88; Perm to Offic *Heref* from 96; Perm to Offic *Worc* from 96. *Middlemarch, 2 Old Barn Court, Bircher, Leominster HR6 0AU* Tel (01568) 780795

McKINNEL, Preb Nicholas Howard Paul. b 54. Qu Coll Cam BA75 MA79. Wycliffe Hall Ox BA79 MA86. **d** 80 **p** 81. C Fulham St Mary N End *Lon* 80-83; Chapl Liv Univ *Liv* 83-87; P-in-c Hatherleigh *Ex* 87-88; R Hatherleigh, Meeth, Exbourne and Jacobstowe 88-94; P-in-c Plymouth St Andr w St Paul and St Geo 94-95; TR Plymouth St Andr and St Paul Stonehouse from 95; RD Plymouth Sutton from 01; Preb Ex Cathl from 02. *St Andrew's Vicarage, 13 Bainbridge Avenue, Plymouth PL3 5QZ* Tel (01752) 772139 *or* 661414 E-mail nick@standrewschurch.org.uk

McKINNEY, James Alexander. b 52. Ex Univ BA74 Hull Univ MA87. Ripon Coll Cuddesdon 75. **d** 78 **p** 79. C Wath-upon-Dearne w Adwick-upon-Dearne *Sheff* 78-82; V Doncaster Intake 82-87; Ind Chapl 84-87; Chapl Bramshill Police Coll *Win* 87-92; V Cleator Moor w Cleator *Carl* 92-96; Chapl Cumbria Constabulary 93-96; P-in-c Frizington and Arlecdon 94-96; V Roehampton H Trin *S'wark* from 96. *The Vicarage, 7 Ponsonby Road, London SW15 4LA* Tel (020) 8788 9460 E-mail jim.mckinney@dswark.org

McKINNEY, Mervyn Roy. b 48. St Jo Coll Nottm. **d** 81 **p** 82. C Tile Cross *Birm* 81-84; C Bickenhill w Elmdon 84-89; V Addiscombe St Mary *S'wark* 89-93; V Addiscombe St Mary Magd w St Martin 93-99; P-in-c W Wickham St Fran 99-02; V W Wickham St Fran and St Mary from 02. *7 Woodland Way, West Wickham BR4 9LL* Tel (020) 8777 5034

MacKINNON, Mrs Karen Audrey. b 64. Ex Univ BA85. Linc Th Coll 92. **d** 92 **p** 94. Par Dn Filton *Bris* 92-93; Par Dn Bris Lockleaze St Mary Magd w St Fran 93-94; C 94-96; P-in-c 96-98; V 98-00; Asst Chapl Southn Univ Hosps NHS Trust 00-03; Chapl from 03. *6 Rimington Gardens, Romsey SO51 7TT* Tel (01794) 830412

McKINNON, Neil Alexander. b 46. Wycliffe Hall Ox 71. **d** 74 **p** 75. C Deptford St Nic w Ch Ch *S'wark* 74-76; C St Helier 76-79; Min W Dulwich All SS and Em 79-81; TV Thameshead 87-95; R S'wark H Trin w St Matt from 95. *The Rectory, Meadow Row, London SE1 6RG* Tel and fax (020) 7407 1707 *or* tel 7357 8532

MACKINTOSH, Robin Geoffrey James. b 46. Rhodes Univ BCom71 Cranfield Inst of Tech MBA78 Ox Univ BA85 MA91. Ripon Coll Cuddesdon 83. **d** 86 **p** 87. C Cuddesdon Ox 86; C Cannock *Lich* 86-89; R Girton *Ely* 89-01; Exec Dir The Leadership Inst from 01; Perm to Offic *Cant* from 03. *42 Queens Avenue, Canterbury CT2 8BA* Tel (01227) 479706 E-mail rob.mackintosh@ntlworld.com

McKINTY, Norman Alexander Fionn. b 63. St D Coll Lamp BA86 Birm Univ DipHE97. Westcott Ho Cam 97. **d** 99 **p** 00. C

Yeovil St Mich *B & W* from 99. *220 Goldcroft, Yeovil BA21 4DA* Tel (01935) 425621

McKITTRICK, The Ven Douglas Henry. b 53. St Steph Ho Ox 74. **d** 77 **p** 78. C Deptford St Paul *S'wark* 77-80; C W Derby St Jo *Liv* 80-81; TV St Luke in the City 81-89; V Toxteth Park St Agnes and St Pancras 89-97; V Brighton St Pet w Chpl Royal *Chich* 97-02; RD Brighton 98-02; Can and Preb Chich Cathl 98-02; Adn Chich from 02. *2 Yorklands, Dyke Road Avenue, Hove BN3 6RW* Tel (01273) 505330 *or* 421021
E-mail archchichester@diochi.org.uk
or fr.douglas@btinternet.com

McKITTRICK, Noel Thomas Llewellyn. b 28. TCD BA50 MA57 BD71. **d** 51 **p** 53. C Londonderry Ch Ch *D & R* 51-52; C Belfast St Aid *Conn* 52-54; C Knockbreda *D & D* 54-58; C Keynsham w Queen Charlton *B & W* 58-59; V Glastonbury St Benedict 59-82; V Weston-super-Mare St Paul 82-92; rtd 93; Perm to Offic *Ex* from 94. *Priory Lodge, Latimer Road, Exeter EX4 7JP* Tel (01392) 496744

MACKLEY, Robert Michael. b 78. Ch Coll Cam BA99 MA03. Westcott Ho Cam 00. **d** 03. C Clerkenwell H Redeemer *Lon* from 03; C Clerkenwell St Mark from 03. *The Clergy House, 24 Exmouth Market, London EC1R 4QE* Tel (020) 7837 1861 E-mail father_mackley@oratorium.zzn.com

MACKLIN, Reginald John. b 29. Bris Univ BA52. Ely Th Coll 54. **d** 55 **p** 56. C W Hackney St Barn *Lon* 55-58; C E Ham St Mary *Chelmsf* 58-61; C Northolt St Mary *Lon* 61-64; Jordan 64-68; Palma de Mallorca and Balearic Is *Eur* 68-69; P-in-c Hammersmith St Matt *Lon* 69-70; V Stanwell 70-82; V Kimbolton *Ely* 82-88; V Stow Longa 82-88; RD Leightonstone 82-88; P-in-c Keyston and Bythorn 85-88; P-in-c Catworth Magna 85-88; P-in-c Tilbrook 85-88; P-in-c Covington 85-88; R Coveney 88-96; R Downham 88-96; RD Ely 89-96; rtd 96; Perm to Offic *Ely* from 96. *11 Castelhythe, Ely CB7 4BU* Tel (01353) 662205 Fax as telephone E-mail macklinrj@aol.com

MACKNESS, Paul Robert. b 73. Univ of Wales (Lamp) BA96 Univ of Wales (Cardiff) BA01. St Mich Coll Llan 98. **d** 01 **p** 02. C Llanelli *St D* from 01. *The Clergy House, 44 Coldstream Street, Llanelli SA15 3BH* Tel (01554) 752056
E-mail paulr@pmackness.fsnet.co.uk

MACKNEY, John Pearson. b 17. Univ of Wales BA39 Lon Univ MA81 PGCE73. St D Coll Lamp 39. **d** 41 **p** 42. C Gelligaer *Llan* 41-44; CF 44-47; C Llangeinor *Llan* 47-49; P-in-c Cardiff All SS 49-58; Chapl HM Pris Cardiff 49-58; V Mountain Ash *Llan* 58-69; Hon C Streatley w Moulsford *Ox* from 81. *Merlebank, Reading Road, Moulsford, Wallingford OX10 9JG* Tel (01491) 651347

McKNIGHT, Thomas Raymond. b 48. QUB BEd71. CITC 74. **d** 77 **p** 78. C Lisburn Ch Ch Cathl *Conn* 77-80; C Carrickfergus 80-82; I Kilcronaghan w Draperstown and Sixtowns *D & R* 82-86; I Magheragall *Conn* 86-91; CF from 91; Perm to Offic *Bris* from 99. *c/o MOD Chaplains (Army)* Tel (01980) 615804 Fax 615800

MACKRIELL, Peter John. b 64. Mansf Coll Ox BA85 MA93 Man Univ PGCE87. St Jo Coll Nottm BTh93 MA94. **d** 94 **p** 95. C Hale and Ashley *Ches* 94-96; C Marple All SS 96-98; V Brandwood *Birm* 98-01; V Pontblyddyn *St As* from 01; Chapl to Deaf People from 01. *The Vicarage, Wrexham Road, Pontblyddyn, Mold CH7 4HG* Tel (01352) 771489 Fax 779093 E-mail peter@jmackriell.freeserve.co.uk

MACKRILL, Robert John. b 51. RIBA79 Univ Coll Lon BSc73 DipArch76. EMMTC 92. **d** 93 **p** 94. NSM Stamford All SS w St Jo *Linc* 93-97; P-in-c Stamford Ch Ch from 97. *110 Lonsdale Road, Stamford PE9 2SF* Tel (01780) 754490 Fax 756212 E-mail bob@mackrill.freeserve.co.uk

MacLACHLAN (née GRIFFITHS), Mrs Margaret. b 44. SRN67 Birm Poly CertEd81 Open Univ BA82. WMMTC 92. **d** 95 **p** 96. NSM Tile Cross *Birm* from 95. *Wayside, 17 Chester Road, Birmingham B36 9DA* Tel 0121-747 2340

MACLACHLAN, Michael Ronald Frederic. b 39. Wycliffe Hall Ox 75. **d** 75 **p** 76. C Mansfield St Pet *S'well* 75-78; P-in-c Newark Ch Ch 78; TV Newark w Hawton, Cotham and Shelton 78-86; P-in-c Sparkhill St Jo *Birm* 86-90; P-in-c Sparkbrook Em 86-90; V Sparkhill w Greet and Sparkbrook 90-92; RD Bordesley 90-92; Canada 92-97; R Stoke-next-Guildf from 97. *St John's Rectory, 2 Joseph's Road, Guildford GU1 1DW* Tel (01483) 828692 E-mail mkanddmaclachan@btinternet.com

McLACHLAN, Ms Sheila Elizabeth. b 52. SRN73 Kent Univ MA89. Wycliffe Hall Ox 80. **dss** 83 **d** 87 **p** 94. Chapl Kent Univ *Cant* 83-94; Dep Master Rutherford Coll 87-94; Dn-in-c Kingsnorth w Shadoxhurst 94; P-in-c Kingsnorth and Shadoxhurst from 94. *The Rectory, Church Hill, Kingsnorth, Ashford TN23 3EG* Tel (01233) 620433 E-mail sem@tesco.net

MacLAREN, Mrs Clare. b 67. Edin Univ LLB88. Linc Th Coll BTh95. **d** 95 **p** 96. C Benchill *Man* 95-98; C Bilton *Ripon* 98-03; TV Seacroft from 03. *St Paul's Vicarage, 58 Whinmoor Crescent, Leeds LS14 1EW* Tel 0113-265 5649
E-mail claremac@bigfoot.com

MacLAREN, Duncan Arthur Spencer. b 69. Oriel Coll Ox BA90 MA96. Oak Hill Th Coll 92. **d** 94 **p** 95. C Ox St Clem *Ox* 94-97;

Chapl St Edm Hall Ox from 97. *1 Lawrence Road, Oxford OX4 3ER* Tel (01865) 430195
E-mail duncan.maclaren@seh.ox.ac.uk

MACLAREN, Grant. b 12. St Cath Coll Cam BA37 MA41. Wycliffe Hall Ox 37. **d** 39 **p** 40. C Greenwich H Trin and St Paul *S'wark* 39-42; C Gipsy Hill Ch Ch 42-45; C Beccles St Mich *St E* 45-48; V Oulton Broad *Nor* 48-56; PC Derby Ch Ch *Derby* 56-57; P-in-c Derby H Trin 56-57; PC Derby Ch Ch and H Trin 57-73; V Stanley 73-80; rtd 80; Perm to Offic *Derby* 80-00. *21 Tennessee Road, Chaddesden, Derby DE21 6LE* Tel (01332) 661226

MacLAREN (née ALEXANDER), Mrs Jane Louise. b 69. LMH Ox BA90 MA94. Oak Hill Th Coll BA95. **d** 95 **p** 96. C Ox St Clem *Ox* 95-98; Chapl St Aug Sch 98-02; Chapl Ox Brookes Univ from 02. *1 Lawrence Road, Oxford OX4 3ER* Tel (01865) 430195 E-mail jmaclaren@brookes.ac.uk

McLAREN, Mrs Jeanette Moira. b 59. **d** 95 **p** 96. C Dulwich St Clem w St Pet *S'wark* 95-99; P-in-c Brixton St Paul from 99. *73 Baytree Road, London SW2 5RR* Tel (020) 7274 6907

McLAREN, Richard Francis. b 46. Mansf Coll Ox DSS69. S'wark Ord Course 72. **d** 75 **p** 76. C Charlton St Luke w H Trin *S'wark* 75-78; C Kensington St Mary Abbots w St Geo *Lon* 78-81; Hon C St Marylebone w H Trin 82-96; P-in-c 96-97; Development Officer CUF 97; Chairman Art and Christianity Enquiry Trust from 97; Hon C Regent's Park St Mark 97-98. *8 Gray's Court, 51-53 Gray's Inn Road, London WC1X 8PP* Tel (020) 7404 5642 E-mail richard@mclaren7.fsnet.co.uk

McLAREN, Robert Ian (Rob). b 62. Bris Univ BSc84 St Jo Coll Dur BA87. Cranmer Hall Dur 85. **d** 88 **p** 89. C Birkenhead Ch Ch *Ches* 88-90; C Bebington 90-95; V Cheadle All Hallows from 95. *All Hallows' Vicarage, 222 Councillor Lane, Cheadle SK8 2JG* Tel 0161-428 9071 *or* 2804 E-mail vicar@orange.net

McLAREN, Ronald. b 31. Kelham Th Coll. **d** 59 **p** 60. C Redcar *York* 59-62; C Hornsea and Goxhill 62-65; V Middlesbrough St Thos 65-70; Chapl RN 70-73; Australia from 73; rtd 96. *16 Moselle Drive, Thornlands, Qld, Australia 4164* Tel (0061) (7) 3821 2069 Mobile 409-039768
E-mail ronanne@ozemail.com.au

McLAREN, William Henry. b 27. OBE94. Edin Th Coll 55. **d** 56 **p** 57. C Skipton H Trin *Bradf* 56-60; V Bingley H Trin 60-65; V Allerton 65-68; R Aberdeen St Mary *Ab* 68-73; P-in-c Newland St Aug *York* 73-74; V 74-75; V Hull St Cuth 75-81; V Hedon w Paull 81-94; RD S Holderness 84-94; rtd 94; Perm to Offic *York* from 94. *Kirklea, Ottringham Road, Keyingham, Hull HU12 9RX* Tel (01964) 624159

McLAREN-COOK, Paul Raymond. b 43. LTh66. **d** 66 **p** 67. Australia 46-76 and 76-00; C Mt Lawley 66-67; C Perth Cathl 67-69; R Carnarvon 69-72; Malaysia 72-76; V Seremban 72-75; Warden Coll of Th 75-76; R Kensington 76-79; R Narrogin 79-84; P-in-c Wellington 84-85; R Gosnells 85-86; P-in-c Berrigan 86-87; P-in-c Hay 87-88; P-in-c Yass 88; R Moruya 88-90; R Heywood 90-92; R Warracknabeal 92-95; Chapl Ballarat Base and St Jo of God Hosps 95-00; R Kansas City St Mary USA 00-03; R Stanway *Chelmsf* from 03. *The Rectory, Church Lane, Stanway, Colchester CO3 5LR* Tel (01206) 210407 E-mail mclarencook@uksprite.com

McLARNON, Mrs Sylvia Caroline Millicent. b 45. S Dios Minl Tr Scheme 92. **d** 95 **p** 96. NSM Burgess Hill St Andr *Chich* 95-99; C from 99. *75 Cants Lane, Burgess Hill RH15 0LX* Tel (01444) 233902

McLAUGHLIN, Hubert James Kenneth. b 45. Belf Coll of Tech HNC70. CITC 85 97. **d** 88 **p** 89. NSM Donagheady *D & R* 88-89; NSM Glendermott 89-98; P-in-c Inver, Mountcharles and Killaghtee from 98. *The Rectory, Inver, Co Donegal, Irish Republic* Tel (00353) (73) 36013 Mobile 0802-549380

McLAUGHLIN, Capt Michael Anthony. b 48. **d** 97 **p** 98. C Gt Chart *Cant* 97-01; C-in-c Parkwood CD from 01. *The Vicarage, Wallis Avenue, Maidstone ME15 9JJ* Tel (01622) 764170 E-mail mmcl@btinternet.com

MACLAURIN, Ms Anne Fiona. b 62. St Andr Univ MA84. Ridley Hall Cam CTM99. **d** 99 **p** 00. C Crookes St Thos *Sheff* from 99. *29 Fitzgerald Road, Sheffield S10 1GX* Tel 0114-267 1090 Fax 266 2691
E-mail anne.maclaurin@stthomaschurch.org.uk

MACLAY, Christopher Willis. b 64. Stirling Univ BA88 Reading Univ MA92 Bris Univ BA01. Trin Coll Bris 99. **d** 01 **p** 02. C Bedhampton *Portsm* from 01. *2 Lester Avenue, Havant PO9 3HE* Tel (023) 9247 0200

McLAY, Canon Robert James. b 49. Cant Univ (NZ) BA71. St Jo Coll Auckland. **d** 73 **p** 74. New Zealand 73-75 and from 77; C Fendalton 73-75; Hon C Yardley St Edburgha *Birm* 75-77; V Banks Peninsular 77-80; V Marchwiel 80-83; V Huntly 83-89; Lect St Jo Coll 86-88; V Stokes Valley 89-93; V Pauatahanui from 93; Can Wellington Cathl from 96. *4 Livet Place, Papakowhai, Porirua, New Zealand* Tel (0064) (4) 233 1211 *or* 233 9781 E-mail rmclay@xtra.co.nz

MACLEAN, The Very Revd Allan Murray. b 50. Edin Univ MA72. Cuddesdon Coll 72. **d** 76 **p** 77. Chapl St Mary's Cathl *Edin* 76-81; Tutor Edin Univ 77-80; R Dunoon *Arg* 81-86; R

Tighnabruaich 84-86; Provost St Jo Cathl Oban from 86; Can from 86; Can Cumbrae from 86; R Oban St Jo from 86; R Ardbrecknish from 86; R Ardchattan from 89. *The Rectory, Ardconnel Terrace, Oban PA34 5DJ* Tel (01631) 562323

McLEAN, Bradley Halstead. b 57. McMaster Univ Ontario BSc Toronto Univ MDiv MTh PhD. **d** 83 **p** 84. C Dur St Giles *Dur* 83-84; Canada from 84. *38 Tweedsmuir Road, Winnipeg MB, Canada, R3P 1Z2*

McLEAN, The Ven Donald Stewart. b 48. TCD BA70. CITC 70. **d** 72 **p** 73. C Glendermott *D & R* 72-75; I Castledawson 75-87; Dioc Dir of Ords 79-96; I Londonderry Ch Ch from 87; Can Derry Cathl from 91; Adn Derry from 96. *Christ Church Rectory, 80 Northland Road, Londonderry BT48 0AL* Tel (028) 7126 3279 *or* 7126 8504 Fax 7127 1621
E-mail archdeacon@derry.anglican.org

MACLEAN, Mrs Dorothy. b 31. Dundee Coll DipEd70. St And Dioc Tr Course 79. **d** 86. NSM Kirriemuir *St And* 82-93. *84 Slade Gardens, Kirriemuir DD8 5AG* Tel (01575) 572396

McLEAN, Mrs Eileen Mary. b 44. City Univ BSc67. N Ord Course 85. **d** 88 **p** 94. Par Dn Burley in Wharfedale *Bradf* 88-92; Par Dn Nottingham St Pet and St Jas *S'well* 92-94; C 94-02; AD Nottingham Cen 98-02; V Bamburgh *Newc* from 02; V Ellingham from 02. *The Vicarage, 7 The Wynding, Bamburgh NE69 7DB* Tel (01668) 214295

McLEAN, Miss Frances Ellen. b 21. RGN44 SCM45. Edin Dioc NSM Course 85. **d** 88 **p** 94. NSM Penicuik *Edin* from 88; NSM W Linton from 88. *56 Cuikenburn, Penicuik EH26 0JQ* Tel (01968) 675029

MACLEAN, John Raglan. b 19. MBE88 MM42. Univ of NZ BA47. Cuddesdon Coll 47. **d** 50 **p** 51. C Moorfields *Bris* 50-53; New Zealand from 53; P-in-c Mahora 53-58; V Whakatane 58-64; V Gisborne 64-70; Can Waiapu 66-70; P-in-c Sunnynook 70; P Asst Mt Albert 71-73; V Grey Lynn 73-85; P-in-c Mangonui 85-88; rtd 88. *PO Box 87 193, Auckland 1130, New Zealand* Tel (0064) (9) 528 9768

MACLEAN, Kenneth John Forbes. b 31. St Deiniol's Hawarden 80. **d** 81 **p** 82. C Sedgley All SS *Lich* 81-85; V Shareshill 85-90; R Bicton, Montford w Shrawardine and Fitz 90-96; rtd 96; Perm to Offic *Lich* from 99. *7 The Armoury, Wenlock Road, Shrewsbury SY2 6PA* Tel (01743) 243308

MacLEAN, Lawrence Alexander Charles. b 61. K Coll Lon BD84 AKC84. Chich Th Coll 86. **d** 88 **p** 89. C Cirencester *Glouc* 88-91; C Prestbury 91-96; Perm to Offic 01-02; Chapl Florence w Siena *Eur* from 02. *The English Church of St Mark, Via Maggio 16/18, 50125 Firenze, Italy* Tel (0039) (055) 294764

McLEAN, Ms Margaret Anne. b 62. Birm Univ BA91 Heythrop Coll Lon MA99. Qu Coll Birm 88. **d** 91 **p** 94. Par Dn Bedford All SS *St Alb* 91-94; C 94; Chapl St Alb High Sch for Girls 94-98; Asst Soc Resp Officer *Derby* 98-99; Chapl Huddersfield Univ *Wakef* 99-02; P-in-c Scholes from 02; P-in-c Cleckheaton St Luke and Whitechapel from 02. *The Vicarage, Scholes Lane, Scholes, Cleckheaton BD19 6PA* Tel (01274) 873024 Mobile 07974-125494 Fax 303374 E-mail maggie@fish.co.uk

McLEAN, Canon Michael Stuart. b 32. Dur Univ BA57. Cuddesdon Coll 57. **d** 59 **p** 60. C Camberwell St Giles *S'wark* 59-61; Lic to Offic *Nor* 61-68; R Marsham 68-74; R Burgh 68-74; RD Ingworth 70-74; P-in-c Nor St Pet Parmentergate w St Jo 74-75; TV 75-78; TR 78-86; Hon Can Nor Cathl 82-86; Can Res Nor Cathl 86-94; P-in-c Nor St Mary in the Marsh 87-94; Perm to Offic from 94; rtd 97. *30 Friars Quay, Norwich NR3 1ES* Tel (01603) 630398

McLEAN, Peter. b 50. **d** 94 **p** 95. NSM Mold *St As* 94-02; Perm to Offic 02-03; P-in-c Bodedern w Llanfaethlu *Ban* from 03. *The Rectory, 4 Tynlon Estate, Llanrhyddlad, Holyhead LL65 4HT* Tel (01407) 730142

McLEAN, Robert Hedley. b 47. St Jo Coll Dur BA69. Ripon Hall Ox 69. **d** 71 **p** 72. C Redhill St Jo *S'wark* 71-74; C S Beddington St Mich 74-77; C-in-c Raynes Park H Cross CD 77; P-in-c Motspur Park 77-80; V 80-84; V Tadworth 84-00; Asst RD Reigate 92-93; RD Reigate 93-00; R Morpeth *Newc* from 00; Chapl Northd Mental Health NHS Trust from 00; Chapl Northumbria Healthcare NHS Trust from 00. *The Rectory, Cottingwood Lane, Morpeth NE61 1ED* Tel (01670) 513517 E-mail robert@morpeth-rectory.fsnet.co.uk

McLEAN-REID, Robert. b 44. Oak Hill Th Coll DipHE83. **d** 83 **p** 84. C Rainham *Chelmsf* 83-86; R Challoch w Newton Stewart *Glas* 86-87; R Aberdeen St Pet *Ab* 87-90; P-in-c Aberdeen St Clem 89-90; V Easington Colliery *Dur* 90-95; rtd 95. *37 Middleton Close, Seaton, Seaham SR7 0PQ* Tel 0191-581 1729

MacLEAY, Angus Murdo. b 59. Univ Coll Ox BA81 MA86 Man Univ MPhil92 Solicitor 83. Wycliffe Hall Ox 83. **d** 88 **p** 89. C Rusholme H Trin *Man* 88-92; V Houghton *Carl* 92-01; R Sevenoaks St Nic *Roch* from 01. *The Rectory, Rectory Lane, Sevenoaks TN13 1JA* Tel (01732) 740340 Fax 742810 E-mail macleay@ukonline.co.uk

McLELLAN, Eric Macpherson Thompson. b 16. St Jo Coll Dur BA38 DipTh39 MA41. **d** 39 **p** 40. C Byker St Mark *Newc* 39-44; C Fazakerley Em *Liv* 44-45; V Everton Em 45-54; R Sevenoaks St Nic *Roch* 54-70; Hon Can Roch Cathl 68-70; Chapl Br

Embassy Ch Paris *Eur* 70-80; RD France 75-79; Adn N France 79-80; Perm to Offic *Chich* 80-99; Perm to Offic *Roch* from 80; rtd 81. *7 Stainer Road, Tonbridge TN10 4DS* Tel (01732) 356491

MacLEOD, Alan Roderick Hugh (Roddie). b 33. St Edm Hall Ox BA56 MA61 Ox Univ DipEd62 Lon Univ Dip Ch Development 69. Wycliffe Hall Ox 56. **d** 58 **p** 59. C Bognor St Jo *Chich* 58-61; Chapl Wadh Coll Ox 62; Hd of RE Picardy Boys' Sch Erith 62-68; C Erith St Jo *Roch* 63-69; Dean Lonsdale Coll Lanc Univ 70-72; Hd of RE K Edw VI Sch Totnes 72-73; Dir of Resources St Helier Boys' Sch Jersey 73-84; V Shipton Bellinger *Win* 84-02; rtd 02; Perm to Offic *Win* from 02. *Pippins Toft, Lashmar's Corner, East Preston, Littlehampton BN16 1EZ* Tel (01903) 783523

McLEOD, Everton William. b 57. DCR78. Oak Hill Th Coll DipHE91. **d** 91 **p** 92. C New Ferry *Ches* 91-93; C Moreton 93-98; Chapl R Liv Univ Hosp NHS Trust 98-01; TR Uphill *B & W* from 01. *Uphill Rectory, 3 Old Church Road, Uphill, Weston-super-Mare BS23 4UH* Tel (01934) 620156
E-mail mcleod@xalt.co.uk

MacLEOD, John Malcolm (Jay). b 61. Harvard Univ AB84 Pemb Coll Ox BA87 MA91. Linc Th Coll MDiv93. **d** 93 **p** 94. C Chesterfield St Aug *Derby* 93-96; C Stalybridge St Paul *Ches* 96-98; P-in-c Micklehurst 98-03; P-in-c Bedford All SS *St Alb* from 03; Dioc Interfaith Adv from 03. *All Saints' Vicarage, 1 Cutcliffe Place, Bedford MK40 4DF* Tel (01234) 266945 E-mail macasher@dial.pipex.com

MacLEOD, Paul Douglas. b 66. Cuddesdon Coll BTh95. **d** 98 **p** 99. C Morpeth *Newc* 98-02; V Newbiggin Hall from 02. *St Wilfrid's House, Trevelyan Drive, Newcastle upon Tyne NE5 4DA* Tel 0191-271 4005 E-mail revpaulmcleod@aol.com

McLEOD, Canon Ronald. b 22. Lon Univ BA39 BA50 BD71 Ex Univ BA56 Man Univ MA59 Ex Univ MPhil01. Bps' Coll Cheshunt 39. **d** 41 **p** 42. C Plymouth St Pet *Ex* 41-44; Chapl RAF 44-69; Prin RAF Chapl Sch and Asst Chapl-in-Chief 69-73; QHC 72-73; R Itchen Abbas cum Avington *Win* 73-91; Hon Can Win Cathl 84-91; rtd 91; Perm to Offic *Ex* from 92. *Melfort, High Wall, Barnstaple EX31 2DP* Tel (01271) 343636

McLEOD, Ms Susan Margaret. b 48. SEN69 Sheff Poly CQSW89 Liv Univ DATh97. N Ord Course 92. **d** 95 **p** 96. NSM Charlesworth and Dinting Vale *Derby* from 95; Chapl Asst S Man Univ Hosps NHS Trust from 97. *Withington Hospital, Nell Lane, Manchester M20 8LR* Tel 0161-291 4800 *or* 445 8111

MacLEOD-MILLER, Peter Norman. b 66. **d** 91 **p** 91. Australia 91-01; C Cardiff 91-92; C Hillston 92-94; C Fitzroy 95-97; Perm to Offic Melbourne 97-01; P-in-c Risby w Gt and Lt Saxham *St E* from 02. *The Rectory, Barrow, Bury St Edmunds IP29 5BA* Tel (01284) 810929

McLOUGHLIN, Ian Livingstone. b 38. CEng MICE64. Carl Dioc Tr Course 78. **d** 83 **p** 84. NSM Stanwix *Carl* 83-88; C Barrow St Geo w St Luke 88-90; R Kirkby Thore w Temple Sowerby and Newbiggin 90-01; rtd 01; Perm to Offic *Bradf* and *Carl* from 01. *23 Bainbridge Road, Sedbergh LA10 5AU* Tel (01539) 620496

McLUCKIE, John Mark. b 67. St Andr Univ BD89. Edin Th Coll MTh91. **d** 91 **p** 92. C Perth St Ninian *St And* 91-94; Chapl K Coll Cam 94-96; TV Glas E End *Glas* 96-00; Assoc R Edin St Jo *Edin* from 00. *21 Swinton Road, Baillieston, Glasgow G69 6DS* Tel 0141-771 3000 E-mail johnmcluckie@highlander.tfnet.com

MACLUSKIE, Mrs Linda. b 55. Lanc Univ MA99. Carl and Blackb Dioc Tr Inst 95. **d** 98 **p** 99. NSM Halton w Aughton *Blackb* 98-02; NSM Bolton-le-Sands from 02. *15 Whitendale Drive, Bolton le Sands, Carnforth LA5 8LY* Tel (01524) 822769 E-mail ian@macluskie.freeserve.co.uk

McMAHON, Brian Richard. b 39. ACII. Oak Hill NSM Course 84. **d** 87 **p** 88. NSM Colney Heath St Mark *St Alb* from 87. *23 Bluebridge Avenue, Brookmans Park, Hatfield AL9 7RY* Tel (01707) 655351

McMAHON, George Ian Robertson. b 23. Monmouth Coll Illinois BA44 Univ of N Carolina BA44 MA49 Ox Univ MLitt61 Birm Univ PhD73. Gen Th Sem NY STB52. **d** 52 **p** 53. P-in-c Roxboro, Yanceyville and Milton USA 52-57; Perm to Offic 57-64; Prin Lect Homerton Coll Cam 65-88; P-in-c Cambridge St Clem *Ely* from 89. *44 Grantchester Road, Cambridge CB3 9ED* Tel (01223) 350988

McMAHON, Stephen. b 66. Coll of Resurr Mirfield. **d** 03. C Lancaster St Mary w St John and St Anne *Blackb* from 03. *Chauntry Cottage, 1 Priory Close, Lancaster LA1 1YZ*

McMANN, Duncan. b 34. Jes Coll Ox BA55 MA60. Clifton Th Coll 55. **d** 58 **p** 59. C Southwm *Newc* 58-60; C Bishopwearmouth St Gabr *Dur* 60-62; N Area Sec BCMS 62-66; Midl and E Anglia Area Sec 66-92; Support Co-ord 84-92; Lic to Offic *Man* 62-66; Lic to Offic *Cov* 66-92; P-in-c Awsworth w Cossall *S'well* 92-99; Chapl Notts Constabulary 93-99; rtd 99; Perm to Offic *Nor* from 00. *7 Evans Drive, Lowestoft NR32 2RX*

McMANN, Mrs Judith. b 46. Hull Univ BTh96. EMMTC MA98. **d** 98 **p** 99. NSM Gt Grimsby St Mary and St Jas *Linc* from 98. *23 Grasby Crescent, Grimsby DN37 9HE* Tel (01472) 887523 E-mail mcmann@btinternet.com

McMANNERS, Prof John. b 16. CBE00. St Edm Hall Ox BA39 MA45 DLitt77 St Chad's Coll Dur DipTh47 Hon DLitt84 FBA78 FRHistS73 FAHA70. **d** 47 **p** 48. C Leeds St Pet *Ripon* 47-48; Chapl St Edm Hall Ox 48-56; Fell 49-56; Dean 51-56; Australia 56-67; Prof Th Tas Univ 56-59; Prof Th Sydney Univ 59-66; Prof Fell All So Coll Ox 65-66; Fell and Chapl 85-01; Prof Hist Leic Univ *Leic* 67-72; Regius Prof Ecclesiastical Hist Ox Univ 72-84; Can Res Ch Ch *Ox* 72-84; rtd 84. *71 Cunliffe Close, Oxford OX2 7BJ,* or *All Souls College, Oxford OX1 4AL* Tel (01865) 279368
McMANNERS, John Roland. b 46. Liv Univ LLB68. Cranmer Hall Dur 99. **d** 01 **p** 02. C Monkwearmouth *Dur* from 01. *6 Lonsdale Road, Sunderland SR6 9TB* Tel 0191-384 1353
McMANUS, James Robert. b 33. Man Univ Dip Soc & Past Th 82. Wycliffe Hall Ox 56. **d** 58 **p** 59. C Leic H Trin *Leic* 58-60; C Aylestone 60-63; India 66-79; V Oldham St Barn *Man* 79-83; Asst Regional Sec CMS 83-85; V Wolverhampton St Matt *Lich* 85-93; V Lapley w Wheaton Aston 93-99; P-in-c Blymhill w Weston-under-Lizard 93-99; rtd 99; Perm to Offic *Lich* from 99. *Delamere, McBean Road, Wolverhampton WV6 0JQ* Tel (01902) 833436 Fax 834170 E-mail jimvicar@aol.com
McMASTER, James Alexander. b 43. **d** 69 **p** 70. C Dundonald *D & D* and V All SS *Conn* 73-78; I Tempo and Clabby *Clogh* 78-83; I Knocknamuckley *D & D* 83-95; I Carrickfergus *Conn* from 95. *The Rectory, 12 Harwood Gardens, Carrickfergus BT38 7US* Tel (028) 9336 3244 *or* 9336 0061
McMASTER, Richard Ian. b 32. Edin Th Coll 57. **d** 60 **p** 61. C Carl H Trin *Carl* 60-63; Tanganyika 63-64; Tanzania 64-66; V Broughton Moor *Carl* 66-69; V Burnley St Steph *Blackb* 69-77; V New Longton 77-89; P-in-c Woodhall Spa and Kirkstead *Linc* 89-91; P-in-c Langton w Woodhall 89-91; P-in-c Bucknall w Tupholme 89-91; P-in-c Horsington w Stixwould 89-91; R Woodhall Spa Gp 92-97; rtd 97; Perm to Offic *Birm* from 97. *18 Marsden Close, Solihull B92 7JR* Tel 0121-707 6208
McMASTER, William Keith. b 45. TCD. **d** 82 **p** 84. C Portadown St Columba *Arm* 82-84; C Erdington St Barn *Birm* 84-87; TV Shirley 87-00; TV Salter Street and Shirley 00-02; rtd 02. *38 Lambscote Close, Shirley, Solihull B90 1NS*
MACMATH, Terence Handley. *See* HANDLEY MACMATH, Terence
McMICHAEL, Andrew Hamilton. b 48. Univ of Wales (Ban) BA77 Mansf Coll Ox DSS74. Chich Th Coll 87. **d** 89 **p** 90. C Chorley St Geo *Blackb* 89-92; C Burnley St Andr w St Marg 92-94; Chapl Burnley Health Care NHS Trust 92-94; R Eccleston *Blackb* 94-99; V Lt Marsden w Nelson St Mary from 99. *The Vicarage, Bentley Street, Nelson BB9 0BS* Tel (01282) 615888 Fax as telephone
MacMILLAN, Douglas Middleton. b 41. St Thos Hosp Lon MB, BS66 FRCS70 FTCL82 AMusLCM80 FLCM83. Guildf Dioc Min Course 96. **d** 00. NSM Guildf Cathl *Guildf* from 00. *Rivendell, 50 Speedwell Close, Guildford GU4 7HE* Tel (01483) 533019
McMONAGLE, William Archibald. b 36. CITC 65. **d** 68 **p** 69. C Magheralin *D & D* 68-71; C Bangor Abbey 71-81; I Grey Abbey w Kircubbin 81-00; rtd 00. *50 Ashfield Court, Donaghadee BT21 0BF* Tel (028) 9188 4306
✠**McMULLAN, The Rt Revd Gordon.** b 34. ACIS57 QUB BSc61 PhD71 Cam Univ DipRS78 Irish Sch of Ecum TCD MPhil90 Univ of the South (USA) DMin95. Ridley Hall Cam 61. **d** 62 **p** 63 **c** 80. C Ballymacarrett St Patr *D & D* 62-67; Cen Adv on Chr Stewardship to Ch of Ireland 67-70; C Knock 70-71; I 76-80; I Belfast St Brendan 71-76; Offg Chapl RAF 71-78; Bp's Dom Chapl *D & D* 73-78; Adn Down 79-80; Bp Clogh 80-86; Bp D & D 86-97; rtd 97. *26 Wellington Park, Bangor BT20 4PJ* Tel (028) 9146 0821
McMULLEN, Philip Kenneth. b 55. RMN80 Glam Univ DMS92. St Mich Coll Llan DipTh95. **d** 95 **p** 96. C Coity w Nolton *Llan* 95-98; V Fleur-de-Lis *Mon* from 98. *The Vicarage, Commercial Street, Pengam, Blackwood NP12 3TX* Tel (01443) 832904
McMULLEN, Ronald Norman. b 36. TCD BA61 MA66 Liv Univ DSS73 York Univ Dip Community Work 74 BAC Acc 89 California Inst of Integral Studies MA92. Ridley Hall Cam 61. **d** 63 **p** 64. C Fulham St Mary N End *Lon* 63-67; C Cambridge St Sepulchre *Ely* 67-70; C Everton St Ambrose w St Tim *Liv* 70-73; Community Work Course & Research Asst York Univ 73-75; P-in-c Heanor *Derby* 75-79; V 79-88; RD Heanor 76-83; USA 88-93; rtd 98. *Apple Tree Cottage, 38A Main Street, Lowick, Berwick-upon-Tweed TD15 2UA* Tel (01289) 388301
McMULLON, Andrew Brian. b 56. Sheff Univ BSc DipTh. St Jo Coll Nottm. **d** 83 **p** 84. C Stainforth *Sheff* 83-86; V Blackb Redeemer *Blackb* 86-90; Chapl RAF from 90. *Chaplaincy Services (RAF), HQ, Personnel and Training Command, RAF Innsworth, Gloucester GL3 1EZ* Tel (01452) 712612 ext 5164 Fax 510828
McNAB (née LUMMIS), Mrs Elizabeth Howieson. b 44. Lon Univ LDSRCSEng68 BDS68. St Jo Coll Nottm CertCS88. **d** 88 **p** 95. NSM Lerwick *Ab* from 88; NSM Burravoe from 88.

9 Blydoit, Scalloway, Shetland ZE1 0UG Tel (01595) 880327 Fax as telephone
MACNAB, Kenneth Edward. b 65. LMH Ox BA87 MA91. Coll of Resurr Mirfield 89. **d** 91 **p** 92. C Northampton All SS w St Kath *Pet* 91-93; Lib Pusey Ho 93-98; P-in-c Tunbridge Wells St Barn *Roch* 98-01; V from 01. *St Barnabas' Parochial House, 114 Upper Grosvenor Road, Tunbridge Wells TN1 2EX* Tel and fax (01892) 533826 E-mail father.macnab@btopenworld.com
McNAMARA, Barbara. *See* SMITH, Mrs Barbara Mary
McNAMARA, Michael Ian. b 59. Van Mildert Coll Dur BA81. Ridley Hall Cam 83. **d** 85 **p** 86. C Bedford Ch Ch *St Alb* 85-89; BCMS Tanzania 89-92; TV Bolton St Paul w Em *Man* 93-97; C Galleywood Common *Chelmsf* 97-03; R Elmswell *St E* from 03. *The Rectory, Church Road, Elmswell, Bury St Edmunds IP30 9DY* Tel (01359) 240512 E-mail mwanza@lineone.net
McNAMEE, William Graham. b 38. Birm Univ BSocSc59. Cranmer Hall Dur BA74 DipTh. **d** 75 **p** 76. C Tonbridge St Steph *Roch* 75-78; C Fazeley *Lich* 78-87; Chapl Staffs Poly 87-92; Chapl Staffs Univ 92-97; P-in-c Lt Malvern, Malvern Wells and Wyche *Worc* 97-00; P-in-c Malvern Wells and Wyche 00-01; rtd 01. *22 Leadon Road, Malvern WR14 2XF* Tel (01684) 562771
MACNAUGHTON, Mrs Diana. b 54. St Hugh's Coll Ox BA76 MA90 Dur Univ PGCE78. NEOC 98. **d** 98 **p** 99. NSM Gosforth All SS *Newc* 98-01; C Willington Team from 01. *33 Twyford Close, Cramlington NE23 1PH* Tel (01670) 712259 Mobile 0795-0627799 E-mail dmacnaughton@btinternet.com
MACNAUGHTON, Canon Donald Allan. b 17. Oriel Coll Ox BA40 MA43. Westcott Ho Cam 40. **d** 41 **p** 42. C Tynemouth Ch Ch *Newc* 41-45; C Leeds St Pet *Ripon* 45-49; V Pendleton St Barn *Man* 49-53; V Wallsend St Luke *Newc* 53-58; V Wooler 58-71; RD Glendale 58-71; P-in-c Branxton 60-71; P-in-c Ingram 61-71; P-in-c Ilderton 61-71; P-in-c Kirknewton 68-71; P-in-c Doddington 69-71; V Berwick H Trin 71-82; P-in-c Berwick St Mary 71-82; RD Norham 71-82; Hon Can Newc Cathl 71-82; rtd 82; Chapl Marseille w St Raphaël, Aix-en-Provence etc *Eur* 82-87. *Flat 2, 18 Fidra Road, North Berwick EH39 4NG* Tel (01620) 892841
MACNAUGHTON, James Alastair. b 54. St Jo Coll Ox BA78 Fitzw Coll Cam BA80. Ridley Hall Cam 78. **d** 81 **p** 82. C Rounds Green *Birm* 81-85; TV Bestwood Park *S'well* 85-86; TV Bestwood 86-90; V Amble *Newc* 90-97; TR Cramlington from 97. *33 Twyford Close, Cramlington NE23 1PH* Tel (01670) 736064 E-mail macnaughton@btinternet.com
McNAUGHTON, John. b 29. St Chad's Coll Dur DipTh54. **d** 54 **p** 55. C Thorney Close CD *Dur* 54-58; C-in-c E Herrington St Chad CD 58-62; PC E Herrington 62-66; CF 66-94; V Hutton Cranswick w Skerne, Watton and Beswick *York* 94-99; rtd 99; Perm to Offic from 99. *47 Southgate, Cranswick, Driffield YO25 9QX* Tel (01377) 270869
MACNAUGHTON, William Malcolm. b 57. Qu Coll Cam BA80. Ridley Hall Cam 79. **d** 81 **p** 82. C Haughton le Skerne *Dur* 81-85; P-in-c Newton Hall 85-90; TV Shoreditch St Leon and Hoxton St Jo *Lon* 90-00; AD Hackney 94-99; V Hoxton St Jo w Ch Ch 00-02; R Hambleden Valley *Ox* from 02. *The Rectory, Hambledon, Henley-on-Thames RG9 6RP* Tel (01491) 571231 Fax as telephone
McNEE, Canon William Creighton. FCIPD TCD DipTh Univ of Wales (Cardiff) Dip Personnel Mgt Ulster Univ MA NUU MA. **d** 82 **p** 83. C Larne and Inver *Conn* 82-84; I Donagheady *D & R* 84-91; I Kilwaughter w Cairncastle and Craigy Hill *Conn* 91-93; I Ardstraw w Baronscourt, Badoney Lower etc *D & R* from 93; Bp's Dom Chapl from 96; Can Derry Cathl from 00. *2 Bunderg Road, Newtownstewart, Omagh BT78 4NQ* Tel (028) 8266 1342 Fax as telephone
MACNEICE, Alan Donor. b 34. TCD Div Sch 62. **d** 64 **p** 65. C Ballymoney w Finvoy and Rasharkin *Conn* 64-67; Jamaica 67-70; C Winchmore Hill H Trin *Lon* 71-76; C Harringay St Paul 76-77; C Kensington St Barn 77-78; P-in-c 78-79; USA from 83; rtd 99. *PO Box 293, Kilauea, Kauai, HI 96754, USA* Tel (001) (808) 826 4510 Fax 826 4444 E-mail donor@aloha.net
McNEIL, Mrs Ann. b 41. **d** 89 **p** 94. NSM Henfield w Shermanbury and Woodmancote *Chich* 89-99; Perm to Offic from 00. *Lancasters, West End Lane, Henfield BN5 9RB* Tel (01273) 492606
McNEILE, Donald Hugh. b 30. Trin Coll Cam BA53. Coll of Resurr Mirfield 53. **d** 55 **p** 56. C Wigan All SS *Liv* 55-57; C W Derby Gd Shep 57-61; rtd 95. *Manor Farm Household, North Hinksey, Oxford OX2 0NA* Tel (01865) 245473
MACNEILL, Nicholas Terence. b 62. St Steph Ho Ox BTh93. **d** 93 **p** 94. C Ex St Thos and Em *Ex* 93-97; TV 97-98; V Cople, Moggerhanger and Willington *St Alb* from 98. *The Vicarage, 3 Grange Lane, Cople, Bedford MK44 3TT* Tel (01234) 838431 E-mail nicm@tesco.net
McNEISH, Canon John. b 34. Edin Th Coll 58. **d** 61 **p** 62. C Kirkcaldy *St And* 61-64; Prec St Andr Cathl *Ab* 64-66; Chapl RAF 66-72; C Wootton Bassett *Sarum* 72-75; P-in-c Stour Provost w Todbere 75-79; TR Gillingham 79-99; RD Blackmore Vale 81-86; Can and Preb Sarum Cathl 92-99; rtd 99; Perm to

510

Offic *Sarum* from 01. *2B Holbrook Lane, Trowbridge BA14 0PR* Tel (01225) 719029 E-mail mcneishjd@yahoo.co.uk

McNICOL, Andrew Keith. b 45. Westmr Coll of Educn CertEd69 Westmr Coll Ox DipApTh89 MA90 Open Univ BA79. Westmr Coll Cam 70 Westcott Ho Cam 92. **d** 92 **p** 93. C Whitstable *Cant* 92-95; V Ferring *Chich* 95-00; P-in-c Willesborough *Cant* from 00. *The Rectory, 66 Church Road, Willesborough, Ashford TN24 0JG* Tel (01233) 624064 E-mail keith.mcnicol@tesco.net

McNIVEN, Mrs Betty. b 47. Lanc Univ BA68. N Ord Course 83. **dss** 86 **d** 87 **p** 94. Baguley *Man* 86-87; Hon Par Dn 87-88; Par Dn Newton Heath All SS 88-91; Par Dn E Farnworth and Kearsley 91-94; TV 94-95; P-in-c Spotland 95-02; Hon Can Man Cathl 00-02; TV Cwm Gwendraeth *St D* from 02. *The Vicarage, 1 Heol Mansant, Pontyates, Llanelli SA15 5SB* Tel (01269) 860451 E-mail betty.mcniven@talk21.com

MACONACHIE, Canon Alwyn. b 21. TCD BA43 MA47 BD47. CITC 44. **d** 44 **p** 45. C Londonderry Ch Ch *D & R* 44-47; I Killowen 47-64; N Sec (Ireland) CMS 64-70; Gen Sec 70-74; I Glencraig *D & D* 74-91; Can Down Cathl 82-91; Prec 87-90; Chan 90-91; rtd 91. *16 Springhill Road, Bangor BT20 3NR* Tel (028) 9146 6999

MACONACHIE, Canon Charles Leslie. b 27. TCD BA71 MA74 MDiv85 PhD90. Em Coll Saskatoon 47. **d** 50 **p** 51. C Clooney *D & R* 50-54; P-in-c Lower Tamlaght O'Crilly 54-61; Chapl Newsham Gen Hosp Liv 61-63; Chapl RAF 63-67; C Londonderry Ch Ch *D & R* 69-75; I Belmont 75-96; Warden for Min of Healing 75-96; I Culmore w Muff and Belmont 78-96; Warden Irish Internat Order of St Luke Physician from 82; Can Derry Cathl from 85; Chmn Ch's Min of Healing from 96. *3 Broomhill Court, Waterside, Londonderry BT47 6WP* Tel (028) 7148 942

MACOURT, William Albany. b 19. TCD BA54 MA46. CITC 41. **d** 42 **p** 43. C Ballymena *Conn* 42-46; C Belf Cathl 46-48; I Duneane w Ballysculion *Conn* 48-51; I Belfast St Mark 51-64; I Ballymacarrett St Patr *D & D* 64-89; Preb Swords St Patr Cathl Dublin 75-89; Adn Down *D & D* 80-89; Chan Belf Cathl 85-89; rtd 89; Dioc Info Officer *D & D* 89-97. *19 Abbey Court, Abbey Gardens, Belfast BT5 7JE* Tel (028) 9048 2041

McPHATE, The Very Revd Gordon Ferguson. b 50. Aber Univ MB, ChB74 Fitzw Coll Cam BA77 MA81 MD88 Surrey Univ MSc86 Edin Univ MTh94 FRCPEd98. Westcott Ho Cam 75. **d** 78 **p** 79. NSM Sanderstead All SS *S'wark* 78-81; Hon PV S'wark Cathl 81-86; Lect Lon Univ 81-86; Chapl St Andr Univ *St And* 86-02; Lect 86-93; Sen Lect 93-02; Dean Ches from 02. *The Deanery, 7 Abbey Street, Chester CH1 2JF* Tel (01244) 500956 *or* 500971 Fax 341110 E-mail dean@chestercathedral.org.uk

MacPHEE, Roger Hunter. b 43. Leeds Univ BSc65. EAMTC. **d** 86 **p** 87. NSM Trunch *Nor* from 86; Dioc NSM Officer from 97. *8 Lawn Close, Knapton, North Walsham NR28 0SD* Tel (01263) 720045

McPHERSON, Andrew Lindsay. b 58. MCIPD84 St Jo Coll Dur BA79. St Jo Coll Nottm DPS88. **d** 88 **p** 89. C Bitterne *Win* 88-92; V Weston 92-99; V Holdenhurst and Iford from 99. *The Vicarage, 53A Holdenhurst Avenue, Bournemouth BH7 6RB* Tel (01202) 425978 E-mail andy.mcpherson@ukgateway.net

MacPHERSON, Anthony Stuart. b 56. Qu Coll Birm 77. **d** 80 **p** 81. C Morley St Pet w Churwell *Wakef* 80-84; C Penistone 84-85; P-in-c Thurlstone 85-86; TV Penistone and Thurlstone 86-88; V Grimethorpe 88-95; P-in-c Westgate Common 95-96; V from 96; P-in-c Horbury Junction from 02; RD Wakef from 99. *St Mary's Vicarage, Millfield Road, Horbury, Wakefield WF4 5DU* Tel (01924) 275274 Mobile 07780-990354 E-mail frtony.mac@ntlworld.com

MACPHERSON, Archibald McQuarrie. b 27. Edin Th Coll 50. **d** 52 **p** 53. Asst Chapl St Andr Cathl *Ab* 52-55; Prec 55-56; P-in-c Airdrie *Glas* 56-63; R Dumbarton 63-92; rtd 92. *29 Bramblehedge Path, Alexandria G83 8PH* Tel (01389) 753981

MacPHERSON, David Alan John. b 42. Lon Univ DipTh71 BD75 Open Univ BA83 Hatf Poly MSc89. Clifton Th Coll 69 Trin Coll Bris 72. **d** 72 **p** 73. C Drypool St Columba w St Andr and St Pet *York* 72-76; Asst Chapl HM Pris Hull 72-76; P-in-c Bessingby *York* 76-78; P-in-c Carnaby 76-78; Chapl RAF 78-83; P-in-c Chedgrave w Hardley and Langley *Nor* 83-87; R 87-97; Chapl Langley Sch Nor 83-97; P-in-c Brington w Whilton and Norton *Pet* 97-98; R Brington w Whilton and Norton etc 98-02; rtd 02. *The New Rectory, Great Brington, Northampton NN7 4JB* Tel (01604) 770402 E-mail dmacp@compuserve.com

MACPHERSON, Ewan Alexander. b 43. Toronto Univ BA74. Wycliffe Coll Toronto MDiv78. **d** 78 **p** 79. Canada 78-86; V Westbury sub Mendip w Easton *B & W* from 86; V Priddy from 86. *The Vicarage, Crow Lane, Westbury sub Mendip, Wells BA5 1HL* Tel (01749) 870293

MACPHERSON, John. b 28. Lon Univ BSc50 Ex Univ DipEd51 Univ of W Indies HDipEd65. St Alb Minl Tr Scheme 82. **d** 89 **p** 90. NSM Gt Berkhamsted *St Alb* 89-95; Perm to Offic from 00. *Little Tanglewood, Luton Road, Markyate, St Albans AL3 8PZ* Tel (01582) 841219

MACPHERSON, Peter Sinclair. b 44. Lich Th Coll 68. **d** 71 **p** 72. C Honiton, Gittisham and Combe Raleigh *Ex* 71-72; C Bideford 72-74; C Devonport St Mark Ford 74-75; V Thorncombe *Sarum* 75-79; TV Dorchester 79-85; Chapl Jersey Gp of Hosps 85-90; Chapl Derriford Hosp Plymouth 90-98; rtd 98. *North Cray, 3 Windsor Terrace, Lyme Regis DT7 3AN* Tel (01297) 444867

MACQUARRIE, Canon John. b 19. TD62. Glas Univ MA40 BD43 PhD54 DLitt64 Hon DD69 Univ of the South (USA) Hon STD67 Gen Th Sem NY Hon STD68 Ox Univ MA70 DD81 Episc Sem Austin Texas Hon DD81 Nashotah Ho Wisconsin Hon DCnL86 Duncan Univ Hon DD94 FBA84. **d** 65 **p** 65. USA 62-70; Prof Systematic Th Union Th Sem NY 62-70; Lady Marg Prof Div Ox Univ 70-86; Can Res Ch Ch *Ox* 70-86; rtd 86. *206 Headley Way, Oxford OX3 7TA* Tel (01865) 761889

MACQUIBAN, Gordon Alexander. b 24. Univ of Wales (Lamp) BA49 Crewe Coll of Educn CertEd72. Ely Th Coll 49. **d** 51 **p** 52. C Christleton *Ches* 51-53; C Disley 53-55; C Heswall 55-58; Chapl R Liv Children's Hosp 55-58; V Norley *Ches* 58-64; V Ches Ch Ch 64-71; Hon C Ches H Trin 71-85; Hon C Runcorn All SS 85-87; Hon C Frodsham 87-88; rtd 88; Perm to Offic *B & W* from 88. *12 Langham Gardens, Taunton TA1 4PE* Tel (01823) 282602

McQUILLAN, Miss Martha. b 33. St Mich Ho Ox 66. **dss** 70 **d** 87 **p** 94. Barnsbury St Andr *Lon* 70-72; Nottingham St Ann w Em *S'well* 72-79; Chapl Asst Univ Hosp Nottm 79-90; Chapl Asst Nottm Gen Hosp 79-90; rtd 90; Perm to Offic *S'well* from 90. *27 Penarth Rise, Nottingham NG5 4EE* Tel 0115-969 2249 E-mail matty.mcquillan@linby.ndo.co.uk

McQUILLEN, Brian Anthony. b 45. Ripon Hall Ox 73. **d** 75 **p** 76. C Northfield *Birm* 75-78; C Sutton Coldfield H Trin 78-80; V Bearwood 80-89; V Glouc St Geo w Whaddon *Glouc* 89-96; R St Martin w Looe *Truro* from 96; RD W Wivelshire from 98. *St Martin's Rectory, Barbican Road, Looe PL13 1NX* Tel (01503) 263070 Fax 265550 E-mail revmcq.looe@btopenworld.com

McQUILLEN-WRIGHT, Christopher Charles. b 71. Kent Univ BA92. Westcott Ho Cam CTM95. **d** 95 **p** 96. C Hayle, St Erth and Phillack w Gwithian and Gwinear *Truro* 95-96; C Godrevy 96-99; TV Bodmin w Lanhydrock and Lanivet 99-02; P-in-c St Columb Minor and St Colan from 02. *The Vicarage, Parkenbutts, Newquay TR7 3HE* Tel (01637) 873496 *or* 877165

MACRAE, Charles. b 27. RD71. Edin Univ BDS62 OGS96. S Dios Minl Tr Scheme 88. **d** 91 **p** 92. NSM Heene *Chich* 91-94; NSM Portsea St Alb *Portsm* 94-96; Perm to Offic *Chich* from 96. *64 Stone Lane, Worthing BN13 2BQ* Tel (01903) 691660

McRAE, Keith Alban. b 44. S'wark Ord Course 68. **d** 73 **p** 74. NSM Crawley *Chich* 73-78; NSM Ifield 78-90. *52 Downsview, Small Dole, Henfield BN5 9YB*

MacRAE, Mrs Rosalind Phyllis. b 41. Sarum & Wells Th Coll 81. **dss** 84 **d** 87 **p** 94. Feltham *Lon* 84-87; Par Dn 87; Asst Chapl R Cornwall Hosps Trust 87-88; Chapl Mt Edgcumbe Hospice 88-92; Chapl St Austell Hosp 88-92; Chapl Penrice Hosp St Austell 88-92; NSM St Austell *Truro* 88-92; Chapl R Cornwall Hosps Trust 92-95; rtd 95. *Nairnside Cottage, Nairnside, Inverness IV1 2BU* Tel (01463) 793804

McREYNOLDS, Kenneth Anthony. b 48. TCD DipTh83. **d** 83 **p** 84. C Ballymena w Ballyclug *Conn* 83-86; I Rathcoole 86-90; I Lambeg from 90. *Lambeg Rectory, 58 Belfast Road, Lisburn BT27 4AT* Tel (028) 9266 3872 Fax as telephone E-mail kenmcreynolds@btinternet.com

MacROBERT, Iain. b 49. Wolv Univ BA80 PGCE81 Aston Univ CertPSC83 Birm Univ MA85 PhD89. **d** 00 **p** 00. NSM S Queensferry *Edin* from 00. *21 Long Crook, South Queensferry EH30 9XR* Tel and fax 0131-319 1558 *or* tel 244 0651 E-mail iain.macrobert@talk21.com

McROSTIE, Ms Lyn. b 50. Canberra Univ BA77 CDipAF87 MIInfSc81 Portsm Univ MA03. STETS DipTh98. **d** 98 **p** 99. C Portsea St Cuth *Portsm* 98-02; C Shadwell St Paul w Ratcliffe St Jas *Lon* from 02. *The Parish Office, 302 The Highway, London E1W 3DH* Tel (020) 7488 4633 Mobile 07718-300732 E-mail lyn.mcrostie@mcrostie.info

MACROW-WOOD, Antony Charles. b 60. ACA86 York Univ BA82 Jes Coll Cam BA91. Westcott Ho Cam CTM92. **d** 92 **p** 93. C Swindon St Jo and St Andr *Bris* 92-96; TV Preston w Sutton Poyntz and Osmington w Poxwell *Sarum* from 96. *The Vicarage, 58 Littlemoor Road, Weymouth DT3 6AA* Tel (01305) 815366 Mobile 07775-574971 E-mail amacrowwood@mac.com

McSPARRON, Cecil. b 35. Regent Coll Vancouver MCS87 Bible Tr Inst Glas DipMin63 Trin Th Coll Singapore DipMin68 MMin77 MDiv86. **d** 68 **p** 69. C Glendermott *D & R* 68-70; Singapore 70-77 and 83-89; C Portadown St Mark *Arm* 78-80; UK Regional Dir OMF 80-82; Tutor Miss Studies Lon Bible Coll 90-93. *1 Tutors House, Green Lane, Northwood HA6 2UZ*

McTEER, Robert Ian. b 56. Chich Th Coll 90. **d** 92 **p** 93. C S Shields All SS *Dur* 92-95; P-in-c Auckland St Helen 95-97; V from 97; Chapl Bishop Auckland Hospitals NHS Trust 95-98; Chapl S Durham Healthcare NHS Trust from 98. *The Vicarage, 8 Manor Road, St Helen Auckland, Bishop Auckland DL14 9EN* Tel (01388) 604152 E-mail fr.r.mcteer@btinternet.com

McVEAGH, Paul Stuart. b 56. Southn Univ BA78. Oak Hill Th Coll BA88. **d** 88 **p** 89. C Bebington *Ches* 88-92; Crosslinks Portugal 92-95; R High Halstow w All Hallows and Hoo St Mary *Roch* 95-02; V Westerham from 02. *The Vicarage, Borde Hill, Vicarage Hill, Westerham TN16 1TL* Tel (01959) 563127 E-mail pmcveagh@aol.com

McVEETY, Ian. b 46. N Ord Course 82. **d** 85 **p** 86. NSM Langley and Parkfield *Man* 85-86; C 87-89; V Castleton Moor 89-99; AD Heywood and Middleton 95-99; V Baguley from 99. *St John's Vicarage, 186 Brooklands Road, Sale M33 3PB* Tel 0161-973 5947

McVEIGH, Miss Dorothy Sarah. b 67. QUB BA89 TCD BTh93. CITC 90. **d** 93 **p** 94. C Belfast St Matt *Conn* 93-96; C Carrickfergus 96-99; C Lurgan Ch the Redeemer *D & D* from 99. *136 Lough Road, Lurgan, Craigavon BT66 6JL* Tel (028) 3832 5962

McVEIGH, Canon Samuel. b 49. CITC 77. **d** 79 **p** 80. C Drumragh w Mountfield *D & R* 79-82; I Dromore *Clogh* 82-90; I Drumachose *D & R* from 90; Can Derry Cathl from 01. *49 Killane Road, Limavady BT49 0DJ* Tel (028) 7176 2680

McVEIGH, Sandra. *See* BUTLER, Mrs Sandra

MACVICAR, Miss Mary. b 23. Edin Univ MA44 Ox Univ DipEd45. Ripon Coll Cuddesdon 85. **dss** 86 **d** 87 **p** 94. Bishop's Waltham *Portsm* 86-89; Hon C 87-89; Perm to Offic 89-94; Hon C Portsm Cathl 94-95; Hon Chapl from 94; rtd 95; Perm to Offic *Portsm* from 95. *15 Roman Row, Bank Street, Bishops Waltham, Southampton SO32 1RW* Tel (01489) 895955

McWATT, Glenn Ellsworth. b 48. Birkbeck Coll Lon DipRS92. Lon Bible Coll 70 S'wark Ord Course 89. **d** 92 **p** 93. NSM Tulse Hill H Trin and St Matthias *S'wark* 92-99; C New Malden and Coombe 99-03; C Reigate St Mary from 03. *63 Chart Lane, Reigate RH2 7EA* Tel (01737) 243085 E-mail mcwatt@ic24.net

McWHIRTER, James Angus. b 58. Portsm Poly BA91 Trin Coll Carmarthen PGCE93. St Steph Ho Ox 00. **d** 02. C Shifnal *Lich* from 02. *Noost, 38 Maple Close, Shifnal TF11 8HA* Tel (01952) 461548

MacWILLIAM, The Very Revd Alexander Gordon. b 23. Univ of Wales BA43 Lon Univ BD47 PhD52. St Mich Coll Llan 43. **d** 45 **p** 46. C Llanllyfni *Ban* 46-49; Min Can Ban Cathl 49-55; C Ban St Mary 50-53; C Ban St Jas 53-55; R Llanfaethlu w Llanfwrog 55-56; R Llanfaethlu w Llanfwrog and Llanrhuddlad etc 56-58; Hd of RE Dept Lic to Offic *St D* 60-78; Trin Coll Carmarthen 60-70; Hd Sch of Soc Studies 70-84; Visiting Prof Th Cen Univ Iowa USA 83-84; Can St D Cathl *St D* 78-84; Prec, V, and Dean 84-90; rtd 90. *Pen Parc, Smyrna Road, Llangain, Carmarthen SA33 5AD* Tel (01267) 241333

McWILLIAMS, Mrs Laura Jane. b 67. Cranmer Hall Dur 01. **d** 03. C Kingston upon Hull St Aid Southcoates *York* from 03. *9 Lorenzo Way, Hull HU9 3HS* Tel (01482) 704517 Mobile 07984-003660 E-mail mcwilliams@lmcwilliams.freeserve.co.uk

MADDERN, James Thomas. b 76. Wycliffe Hall Ox 00. **d** 02. C Stratford St Jo w Ch Ch and St Jas *Chelmsf* from 02. *29 Maryland Park, London E15 1HB* Tel (020) 8534 7503 E-mail james_maddern@hotmail.com

MADDEX, Patrick John. b 31. Edin Univ BSc54. Bps' Coll Cheshunt 55. **d** 57 **p** 58. C Baldock w Bygrave and Clothall *St Alb* 57-61; C Oxhey All SS 61-64; V Codicote 64-82; R Gt and Lt Wymondley w Graveley and Chivesfield 82-96; rtd 96. *19 Bramber Road, Seaford BN25 1AG*

MADDOCK, Mrs Audrey. b 27. Lon Univ CertEd79 Open Univ BA80 MBPsS80. Bris Sch of Min 81. **dss** 84 **d** 87 **p** 94. Stanton St Quintin, Hullavington, Grittleton etc *Bris* 84-94; Par Dn 87-94; C 94; P-in-c Littleton Drew 95-97; rtd 97; Perm to Offic *Bris* from 97. *1 Brookside, Hullavington, Chippenham SN14 6HD* Tel (01666) 837275

MADDOCK, David John Newcomb. b 36. Qu Coll Cam BA60 MA64. Oak Hill Th Coll 60. **d** 62 **p** 63. C Bispham *Blackb* 62-65; R 82-93; RD Blackpool 90-93; Canada 65-70; R Walsoken *Ely* 70-77; V Ore Ch Ch *Chich* 77-82; V Fowey *Truro* 93-02; Chapl Cornwall Healthcare Trust 94-02; rtd 02; Perm to Offic *Truro* from 02. *Orchards, Biscovey Road, Par PL24 2HW* Tel (01726) 813288

MADDOCK, Francis James Wilson. b 14. Bris Univ BA36 Wadh Coll Ox BA38 MA42. Cuddesdon Coll 39. **d** 40 **p** 41. C Southfields St Barn *S'wark* 40-44; C Horfield H Trin *Bris* 44-49; PC Brislington St Anne 49-56; V Newlyn St Pet *Truro* 56-60; Perm to Offic 60-64; R Forrabury w Minster and Trevalga 64-74; P-in-c Davidstow w Otterham 64-74; RD Trigg Minor 66-69; TR Boscastle w Davidstow 74-78; P-in-c Port Isaac 78-79; rtd 79; Perm to Offic *Ex* from 87. *8 Sylvan Close, Exmouth EX8 3BQ* Tel (01395) 274381

MADDOCK, Nicholas Rokeby. b 47. ABSM72 Birm Coll of Educn CertEd73. Linc Th Coll 82. **d** 82 **p** 83. C Romford St Edw *Chelmsf* 82-87; V Sway *Win* 87-94; V Taunton St Mary *B & W* from 94. *St Mary's Vicarage, Church Square, Taunton TA1 1SA* Tel (01823) 272441 E-mail marymag-taunton@beeb.net

MADDOCK, Philip Arthur Louis. b 47. Open Univ BA82 Lanc Univ MPhil02. Oak Hill Th Coll 75. **d** 78 **p** 79. C New Ferry *Ches* 78-81; C Barnston 81-82; V Over St Jo 82-85; V Norley and

Chapl to the Deaf 85-88; P-in-c Treales and Chapl to the Deaf *Blackb* 88-96; Chapl to the Deaf *Lich* 96-02; C Yoxall and The Ridwares and Kings Bromley 98-02; Adv for Deaf and Disabled People Min Div from 03; NSM Alrewas *Lich* from 03; NSM Wychnor from 03. *Ministry Division, Church House, Great Smith Street, London SW1P 3NZ* Tel (020) 7898 1439 E-mail philip.maddock@c-of-e.org.uk *or* palm@clara.net

MADDOCK, Canon Philip Lawrence. b 20. Bris Univ BA42. Cuddesdon Coll 42. **d** 43 **p** 44. C Kilburn St Aug *Lon* 43-48; C Weston-super-Mare All SS *B & W* 48-57; Chapl Community of the Epiphany Truro 57-60; Sub-Warden 60-63; Chapl HM Pris Wandsworth 63-64; HM Pris Birm 64-67; Ex 67-69; Chapl St Lawr Hosp Bodmin 69-76; Can Res and Treas Truro Cathl *Truro* 76-88; rtd 88; Perm to Offic *Truro* from 88. *31 Trenethick Avenue, Helston TR13 8LU* Tel (01326) 564909

MADDOCKS, Alison Julie. b 63. Birm Univ BSc84 Loughb Univ MBA92. St Jo Coll Nottm MTh03. **d** 03. C Wollaton *S'well* from 03. *73 Torvill Drive, Wollaton, Nottingham NG8 2BR* Tel 0115-928 3009 E-mail alison.maddocks@handbag.com

✠**MADDOCKS, The Rt Revd Morris Henry St John.** b 28. Trin Coll Cam BA52 MA56. Chich Th Coll 52. **d** 54 **p** 55 **c** 72. C Ealing St Pet Mt Park *Lon* 54-55; C Uxbridge St Andr w St Jo 55-58; V Weaverthorpe w Helperthorpe and Luttons *York* 58-61; V Scarborough St Martin 61-71; Suff Bp Selby 72-83; Adv Min Health and Healing to Abps Cant and York 83-95; Asst Bp *B & W* 83-87; Asst Bp Chich from 87; Jt Founding Dir Acorn Chr Healing Trust from 91; Can and Preb Chich Cathl from 92; rtd 95; Perm to Offic *Guildf* 95-96. *3 The Chantry, Canon Lane, Chichester PO19 1PZ* Tel (01243) 788888

MADDOX, David John. b 34. AIMLS58. Sarum & Wells Th Coll 92. **d** 81 **p** 93. In RC Ch 81-91; NSM Wimborne Minster and Holt *Sarum* 93-95; NSM Broadstone 95-01; Perm to Offic from 00. *298 Wimborne Road, Poole BH15 3EG* Tel (01202) 672597

MADDOX, Goronwy Owen. b 23. Univ of Wales (Swansea) BA52 DipEd53. Sarum Th Coll 67. **d** 70 **p** 71. Hd Master H Trin Sch Calne 57-82; Hon C Calne and Blackland *Sarum* 70-82; C 82-83; V Llywel and Traean-glas w Llanulid *S & B* 83-92; rtd 92; Perm to Offic *Sarum* from 92. *4 St Matthews Close, Rowde, Devizes SN10 2PG* Tel (01380) 728965

MADDOX, Hugh Inglis Monteath. b 37. CCC Cam BA60. Westcott Ho Cam 61. **d** 63 **p** 64. C Attercliffe *Sheff* 63-66; C Maidstone All SS w St Phil *Cant* 66-67; C Folkestone St Mary and St Eanswythe 67-69; C St Martin-in-the-Fields *Lon* 69-73; R Sandwich *Cant* 73-81; V St Peter-in-Thanet 81-84; V Red Post *Sarum* from 84. *The Vicarage, East Morden, Wareham BH20 7DW* Tel (01929) 459244

MADDY, Kevin. b 58. GRNCM79 Selw Coll Cam BA83 FRSA96. Westcott Ho Cam 81. **d** 85 **p** 86. C St Peter-in-Thanet *Cant* 85-88; Perm to Offic *Nor* 88-91; Chapl RAF 88-02; CF from 02. *c/o MOD Chaplains (Army)* Tel (01980) 615804 Fax 615800

MADELEY, Mark Keith. b 68. DipHE92 AVCM96. Oak Hill Th Coll BA93. **d** 93 **p** 94. C Mickleover All SS *Derby* 93-96; C Charlesworth and Dinting Vale 96-99; Chapl Chr Tours (UK) Ltd 99-00; NSM Moldgreen and Rawthorpe *Wakef* 99-00; V Coley from 00. *The Vicarage, 41 Ing Head Terrace, Shelf, Halifax HX3 7LB* Tel and fax (01422) 202292 Mobile 07050-021860 E-mail mark@revmadeley.freeserve.co.uk

MADGE, Francis Sidney. b 35. AKC58. **d** 59 **p** 60. C York St Mary Bishophill Senior *York* 59-62; C Sutton St Mich 62-64; C Ex St Jas *Ex* 64-69; R Sutton by Dover w Waldershare *Cant* 69-78; P-in-c W Wickham St Mary 78-81; V 81-02; rtd 02. *1 Callums Walk, Bexhill-on-Sea TN40 2JF* Tel (01424) 222756

MADRID, Bishop in. *See* LOPEZ LOZANO, The Rt Revd Carlos

MADZIMURE, Dominic Makusha. b 52. Middx Univ MA03. **d** 77 **p** 78. Zimbabwe 77-99; Perm to Offic *Cant* 01-03; P-in-c Woodchurch from 03. *The Rectory, 6 Rectory Close, Woodchurch, Ashford TN26 3QJ* Tel (01233) 860257 E-mail dominic@madzimure.fsnet.co.uk

MAGAHY, Canon Gerald Samuel. b 23. TCD BA45 MA61 LLD80 Univ Coll Galway HDipEd55. **d** 53 **p** 54. Dioc Chapl and Hd Master Villiers Sch Limerick 53-61; Chapl and Hd Master K Hosp Sch Dub 61-83; Treas St Patr Cathl Dublin 80-89; Chan 89-91; Prec 91-95; rtd 95. *2 Maryland, Beechfield Manor, Shankill, Co Dublin, Irish Republic*

MAGEE, Frederick Hugh. b 33. Yale Univ BA57. Westcott Ho Cam 58. **d** 59 **p** 60. C Bury St Mark *Man* 59-62; USA 63-64 and from 87; Chapl St Paul's Cathl Dundee *Bre* 74-79; P-in-c Invergowrie 76-79; R St Andrews St Andr 79-83; R Forfar 83-87. *220 Cottage Avenue, Cashmere, WA 98815-1004, USA* Tel (001) (509) 782 2786 E-mail magees@nwi.net

MAGEE, Keith Robert. b 60. Bris Univ BA95 PGCE96 Anglia Poly Univ PGDPT02. Trin Coll Bris 92 Westcott Ho Cam 99. **d** 01 **p** 02. C S Woodham Ferrers *Chelmsf* from 01. *25 Benbow Drive, South Woodham Ferrers, Chelmsford CM3 5FP* Tel (01245) 327096 E-mail keith.magee@ukgateway.net

MAGEE, Canon Patrick Connor. b 15. K Coll Cam BA37 MA41. Westcott Ho Cam 38. **d** 39 **p** 40. C King Cross *Wakef* 39-42; Chapl RNVR 43-46; Chapl K Coll Cam 46-52; V Kingston All

SS *S'wark* 52-60; Chapl Bryanston Sch 60-70; V Ryde All SS *Portsm* 70-72; Chapl Tiffin Sch Kingston 72-73; V Salisbury St Mich *Sarum* 73-75; TR Bemerton 75-84; rtd 84; Perm to Offic *Sarum* from 84. *16A Donaldson Road, Salisbury SP1 3AD* Tel (01722) 324278

MAGILL, Robert James Henderson. b 59. Paisley Coll of Tech BSc81. Sarum & Wells Th Coll Dip Th & Min 94. **d** 94 **p** 95. C W Moors *Sarum* 94-98; P-in-c Hilperton w Whaddon and Staverton etc from 98; Community Affairs Chapl from 02. *The Rectory, Hilperton, Trowbridge BA14 7RL* Tel (01225) 752804

MAGILL, Waller Brian Brendan. b 20. TCD BA42 BD45. **d** 44 **p** 45. C Knock *D & D* 44-47; C Holywood 47-50; Vice-Prin Qu Coll Birm 50-55; Chapl Rugby Sch 55-62; Lect Div Nottm Coll of Educn 62-75; Hd of Dept Trent Poly 75-85; Lic to Offic *S'well* from 66; rtd 85. *16 Parkcroft Road, Nottingham NG2 6FN* Tel 0115-923 3293

MAGNESS, Anthony William John. b 37. New Coll Ox BA62 MA65. Coll of Resurr Mirfield 78. **d** 80 **p** 81. C Gt Crosby St Faith *Liv* 80-83; C Newc St Jo *Newc* 83-85; P-in-c Newc St Luke 85-88; P-in-c Newc St Andr 88; V Newc St Andr and Newc St Luke 89-99; Chapl Hunter's Moor Hosp 89-95; P-in-c Cambois *Newc* 99-00; P-in-c Sleekburn 99-00; V Cambois and Sleekburn 00-03; rtd 03. *59 Firtree Crescent, Newcastle upon Tyne NE12 7JU* Tel 0191-268 4596 Fax as telephone

MAGNUSSON, Lisbet Maria. b 50. Sundsvall Harnosand Univ BSc85 Uppsala Univ MDiv93. Past Inst Uppsala 93. **p** 94. In Ch of Sweden 94-98; C Crosby *Linc* 98-99; TV Gainsborough and Morton from 99. *St Paul's Vicarage, Morton Front, Gainsborough DN21 3AD* Tel (01427) 615126 E-mail lisbet@mariamagnusson.freeserve.co.uk

MAGOR, Robert Jolyon. b 47. Wilson Carlile Coll IDC82 Sarum & Wells Th Coll 93. **d** 93 **p** 94. C Plaistow *Chelmsf* 93-96; TV Plaistow and N Canning Town 96-99; V Leigh-on-Sea St Aid 99-01; C Thorpe Bay from 01. *254 Woodgrange Drive, Southend-on-Sea SS1 2SH* Tel (01702) 616192

MAGORRIAN, David Geoffrey. b 64. St Aid Coll Dur BSc85 York Univ DPhil89. St Jo Coll Nottm. **d** 01 **p** 02. C Bishopwearmouth St Gabr *Dur* from 01. *Upper Flat, Stier House, St Gabriel's Avenue, Sunderland SR4 7TF* Tel 0191-564 1197 E-mail fam.magorrian@btinternet.com

MAGOWAN, The Ven Alistair James. b 55. Leeds Univ BSc77 DipHE. Trin Coll Bris 78. **d** 81 **p** 82. C Owlerton *Sheff* 81-84; C Dur St Nic *Dur* 84-89; Chapl St Aid Coll 85-89; V Egham *Guildf* 89-00; RD Runnymede 93-98; Adn Dorset *Sarum* from 00; Can and Preb Sarum Cathl from 00. *Little Bailie, Dullar Lane, Sturminster Marshall, Wimborne BH21 4AD* Tel (01258) 857659 Fax 857961 E-mail addorset@salisbury.anglican.org

MAGOWAN, Harold Victor. b 34. ACII69 FCII73 Chartered Insurance Practitioner 89 QUB BA55 BSc(Econ)66 DipEd69. TCD Div Sch Div Test57. **d** 57 **p** 58. C Antrim All SS w Muckamore *Conn* 57-59. *95A Groomsport Road, Bangor BT20 5NG* Tel (028) 9146 5091

MAGUIRE, Canon Brian William. b 33. Hull Univ BTh84 MA88. Coll of Resurr Mirfield 70. **d** 72 **p** 73. C Guisborough *York* 72-76; TV Haxby w Wigginton 76-77; TR 78-89; V Huddersfield St Pet and All SS *Wakef* 89-00; Hon Can Wakef Cathl 94-00; rtd 00; Perm to Offic *Wakef* from 00. *The Vicarage, St James Court, Wakefield WF2 8DW* Tel (01924) 299889

MAGUIRE, Michael Timothy Gale (Tim). b 34. Ox Univ Inst of Educn DipEd61. Wycliffe Hall Ox 58. **d** 61 **p** 62. C Southampton St Mary Extra *Win* 61-63; Bp's Youth Chapl 63-66; Perm to Offic *Win* from 97 and *Truro* from 02; rtd 99. *Mordros, Mullion, Helston TR12 7EP* Tel (01326) 241063

MAGUIRE (formerly GRATTON), Mrs Patricia Margaret. b 46. Leeds Univ BTh94 MA96 SRN67 TCert84 CertEd88. EMMTC 89 N Ord Course 96. **d** 97 **p** 98. NSM Shipley St Pet *Bradf* 97-99; C Brighouse and Clifton *Wakef* 99-00; P-in-c Thornes St Jas w Ch Ch from 00; Chapl Wakef Cathl Sch from 00. *The Vicarage, St James Court, Wakefield WF2 8DW* Tel (01924) 299889 E-mail pat@revmaguire.freeserve.co.uk

MAHER, David James. b 70. St Jo Coll Dur BA01. Cranmer Hall Dur 98. **d** 01 **p** 02. C Hounslow H Trin w St Paul *Lon* from 01. *183 Bath Road, Hounslow TW3 3BU* Tel (020) 8577 0443 E-mail dave.maher@ntlworld.com

MAHONEY, William Denis. b 35. Sem of the Immaculate Conception (NY) 77. **d** 79 **p** 95. In RC Ch USA 79-87; NSM Egremont and Haile *Carl* 92-93; NSM Kells 93-96; USA 96-98; P-in-c Beckermet St Jo and St Bridget w Ponsonby *Carl* from 98. *St John's Vicarage, 11 Lowrey Close, Beckermet CA21 2YX* Tel (01946) 841327 E-mail vlwd17@aol.com

MAHONY, Conal Martin. b 38. Pontificio Ateneo Antoniano Rome Lic in Sacred Th 64 Lateran Univ Rome ThD66. Franciscan Ho of Studies 57. **d** 62 **p** 63. In RC Ch 62-89; Dir Folkestone Family Care Cen 86-92; Lic to Offic *Cant* 89-92; C Hempnall *Nor* 92-94; TV 94-97; TR from 97. *The Rectory, The Street, Hempnall, Norwich NR15 2AD* Tel (01508) 498157

MAIDEN, Charles Alistair Kingsley. b 60. Trent Poly BSc84. St Jo Coll Nottm LTh88. **d** 89 **p** 90. C Porchester *S'well* 89-93; C Selston 93-96; P-in-c Huthwaite from 96. *The Vicarage,*

Blackwell Road, Huthwaite, Sutton-in-Ashfield NG17 2QT Tel (01623) 555053 E-mail camaiden@supanet.com

MAIDMENT, Thomas John Louis. b 43. Lon Univ BSc65. St Steph Ho Ox. **d** 67 **p** 68. C Westmr St Steph w St Jo *Lon* 67-73; P-in-c Twickenham Common H Trin 73-77; V 77-80; V Heston 80-98; V Bolton-le-Sands *Blackb* from 98; P-in-c Tunstall w Melling and Leck 02-03; AD Tunstall from 99. *The Vicarage, Ancliffe Lane, Bolton-le-Sands, Carnforth LA5 8DS* Tel (01524) 822335 E-mail t.j.l.m@btinternet.com

MAIDSTONE, Archdeacon of. See DOWN, The Ven Philip Roy

MAIDSTONE, Suffragan Bishop. See CRAY, The Rt Revd Graham Alan

MAIN, Mrs Brigid Mary Harvey. b 49. EAMTC 96. **d** 99 **p** 00. NSM Tillingham *Chelmsf* from 99. *White Lyons Cottage, High Street, Bradwell-on-Sea CM0 7QL* Tel (01621) 776438 Fax as telephone E-mail lmm@globalnet.co.uk

MAIN, Clive Timothy. b 53. St Andr Univ MA75 Cam Univ PGCE76. Oak Hill Th Coll BA94. **d** 96 **p** 97. C Alperton *Lon* 96-00; V Highbury New Park St Aug from 00. *St Augustine's Vicarage, 108 Highbury New Park, London N5 2DR* Tel (020) 7226 6870 E-mail clivemain@blueyonder.co.uk

MAIN, Canon David Murray. b 28. Univ Coll Ox BA52 MA56. St Deiniol's Hawarden 73. **d** 73 **p** 74. C Glas St Marg *Glas* 73-75; R Challoch w Newton Stewart 75-79; R Kilmarnock 79-93; Can St Mary's Cathl 83-93; rtd 93; Hon Can St Mary's Cathl *Glas* from 93. *Sunnybrae, 50 Abercromby Road, Castle Douglas DG7 1BA* Tel (01556) 504669

MAINA, Simon Mwangi. b 52. Nairobi Univ 85. **d** 80 **p** 81. Kenya 80-95; C Acton St Mary *Lon* 95-97; Worthing Churches Homeless Project from 98. *18 Cambourne Court, Shelley Road, Worthing BN11 4BQ* Tel (01903) 600507

MAINES, Trevor. b 40. Leeds Univ BSc63. Ripon Hall Ox 63. **d** 65 **p** 66. C Speke All SS *Liv* 65-70; C Stevenage St Geo *St Alb* 70-73; V Dorridge *Birm* 73-78; Org Sec CECS *Ex* 79-80; Hon C Tiverton St Pet *Ex* 79-80; Org Sec (Wales) CECS 80-87; Hon C Newton Nottage *Llan* 81-83; Perm to Offic *Mon* 83-87; V Arlesey w Astwick *St Alb* 87-95; RD Shefford 91-95; V Goldington from 95; RD Bedford from 98. *St Mary's Vicarage, Church Lane, Goldington, Bedford MK41 0EX* Tel (01234) 355024 Fax as telephone E-mail trevor.maines@tesco.net

MAINEY, Ian George. b 51. CertEd73. Oak Hill Th Coll DipHE86 BA87. **d** 87 **p** 88. C Denton Holme *Carl* 87-91; V Hensingham 91-02; RD Calder 01-02; TR Deane *Man* from 02. *Deane Rectory, 234 Wigan Road, Bolton BL3 5QE* Tel (01204) 61819 E-mail ian.mainey@lineone.net

MAINWARING, Islwyn Paul. b 52. Univ of Wales (Swansea) BD75 DPS79. St Mich Coll Llan 77. **d** 79 **p** 80. C Llanilid w Pencoed *Llan* 79-82; C Llanishen and Lisvane 82-85; TV Cwmbran *Mon* 85-88; V Troedyrhiw w Merthyr Vale *Llan* 88-91. *Pennant, 109 Penygroes Road, Blaenau, Ammanford SA18 3BZ* Tel (01269) 850350

MAINWARING, Simon James. b 74. St Anne's Coll Ox BA96 MA03 Em Coll Cam BA02. Westcott Ho Cam 00. **d** 03. C Pensnett *Worc* from 03. *St Mark's Vicarage, Vicarage Lane, Brierley Hill DY5 4JH* Tel 07789-657174 (mobile)

MAIRS, Canon Adrian Samuel. b 43. DipHE. Oak Hill Th Coll 76. **d** 78 **p** 79. C Rugby St Matt *Cov* 78-82; P-in-c Mancetter 82-84; V from 84; P-in-c Hartshill 97-01; Hon Can Cov Cathl from 03. *The Vicarage, Quarry Lane, Mancetter, Atherstone CV9 1NL* Tel (01827) 713266

MAIS, Jeremy Hugh. b 52. **d** 00 **p** 01. NSM Bibury w Winson and Barnsley *Glouc* 00-02; NSM Stratton, N Cerney, Baunton and Bagendon from 02. *Beechwood, Perrotts Brook, Cirencester GL7 7BS* Tel (01285) 831572

MAITIN, Ito. b 36. Lon Univ DipH67 BA. Kelham Th Coll 63. **d** 68 **p** 69. C Longton St Jo *Lich* 68-69; C Leek St Edw 69-71; C Lich St Chad 71-74; C Tamworth 74-81; V Penkhull from 81. *The Vicarage, 214 Queen's Road, Stoke-on-Trent ST4 7LG* Tel (01782) 414092

MAITLAND, The Hon Sydney Milivoge Patrick. b 51. Edin Univ BSc Strathclyde Univ Dip Town Planning MRTPI. St Jo Coll Nottm. **d** 86 **p** 87. Hon C Glas St Geo *Glas* from 86. *14 Kersland Street, Glasgow G12 8BL* Tel 0141-339 4573

MAJOR, Richard James Edward. b 54. DipTh. Trin Coll Bris 78. **d** 81 **p** 82. C Parr *Liv* 81-84; V Burton Fleming w Fordon *York* 84-85; V Grindale and Ergham 84-85; P-in-c Wold Newton 84-85; V Burton Fleming w Fordon, Grindale etc 85-91; V Bilton St Pet from 91. *The Vicarage, 14 Cherrytree Close, Bilton, Hull HU11 4EZ* Tel (01482) 811441

MAJOR, Richard John Charles. b 63. Massey Univ (NZ) BA85 Ex Coll Ox BA91 MA93 Magd Coll Ox DPhil91. St Steph Ho Ox 92. **d** 94 **p** 95. C Truro Cathl *Truro* 94-97; C Putney St Mary *S'wark* 97-98; Chapl Florence w Siena *Eur* 98-01; USA from 01. *1217 Massachusetts Avenue NW, Washington, DC 20005, USA* E-mail fanthorpe@compuserve.com

MAKAMBWE, Canon Francis James. b 40. St Jo Sem Lusaka. **d** 65 **p** 67. Zambia 65-91; Miss Partner CMS from 91; C Waterloo St Jo w St Andr *S'wark* 91-96; V Hatcham St Cath from 96; Hon Can S'wark Cathl from 03. *St Catherine's Vicarage,*

102 Pepys Road, London SE14 5SG Tel (020) 7639 1050 Fax 7401 3215 E-mail fmakam@aol.com

MAKEL, Arthur. b 39. Sheff Poly DMS75. AKC63. **d** 64 **p** 65. C Beamish *Dur* 64-68; Ind Chapl *York* 68-72; P-in-c Scotton w Northorpe *Linc* 72-81; Ind Chapl 72-81; R Epworth 81-89; P-in-c Wroot 81-89; R Epworth and Wroot 89-92; R Sigglesthorne and Rise w Nunkeeling and Bewholme *York* from 92; P-in-c Aldbrough, Mappleton w Goxhill and Withernwick from 98. *The Rectory, Sigglesthorne, Hull HU11 5QA* Tel (01964) 533033

MAKEPEACE, David Norman Harry. b 51. Magd Coll Ox BA74. Trin Coll Bris 83. **d** 85 **p** 86. C Romford Gd Shep Collier Row *Chelmsf* 85-88; Tanzania 88-89; C York St Paul *York* 89-91; TV Radipole and Melcombe Regis *Sarum* 91-98; V Sandgate St Paul w Folkestone St Geo *Cant* 98-00; rtd 00; Perm to Offic *Cant* from 01. *10 Limes Road, Folkestone CT19 4AU* Tel (01303) 274011

MAKEPEACE, Preb James Dugard. b 40. Keble Coll Ox BA63 MA67. Cuddesdon Coll 63. **d** 65 **p** 66. C Cullercoats St Geo *Newc* 65-68; Chapl Wadh Coll Ox 68-72; Lib Pusey Ho 68-72; V Romford St Edw *Chelmsf* 72-79; V Tettenhall Regis *Lich* 79-80; TR 80-99; RD Trysull 87-97; Preb Lich Cathl 96-99; rtd 00; Perm to Offic *Lich* from 00. *The Retreat, 9 Clive Road, Pattingham, Wolverhampton WV6 7BU* Tel (01902) 710713

✠**MAKHULU, The Most Revd Walter Paul Khotso.** b 35. CMG00. Kent Univ Hon DD88 Gen Th Sem NY Hon DD99. St Pet Rosettenville Selly Oak Coll. **d** 57 **p** 58 **c** 79. S Africa 57-61; Bechuanaland 61-63; C Poplar All SS w St Frideswide *Lon* 64-66; C Pentonville St Silas w Barnsbury St Clem 66-68; V Battersea St Phil *S'wark* 68-73; V Battersea St Phil w St Bart 73-75; Bp Botswana 79-00; Abp Cen Africa 80-00; rtd 00. *Cheyne House, 10 Crondace Road, London SW6 4BB* Tel (020) 7371 9419

MAKIN, Hubert. b 18. ACP66 Open Univ BA74. NW Ord Course 75. **d** 78 **p** 79. Hon C Mount Pellon *Wakef* 78-91; Hon C King Cross 91-94; Perm to Offic from 94. *46 Upper Highfield, Gibb Lane, Mount Tabor, Halifax HX2 0UG* Tel (01422) 244642

MAKIN, Miss Pauline. b 45. Cranmer Hall Dur 75. **dss** 78 **d** 87 **p** 94. Ashton-in-Makerfield St Thos *Liv* 78-87; Par Dn 87-89; Par Dn Rainford 89-94; C 94-95; Asst Dioc Chapl to the Deaf 89-95; C Farnworth from 95. *43 Hampton Drive, Widnes WA8 5DA* Tel and fax and tel 0151-423 3900

MAKIN, Valerie Diana. Lon Univ DipRS83. S'wark Ord Course 86. **d** 88 **p** 94. Hon Par Dn Bryanston Square St Mary w St Marylebone St Mark *Lon* 88-95; Chapl St Marylebone Healing and Counselling Cen 88-94; NSM Godalming *Guildf* 94-95; Perm to Offic *Lon* 95-97; Perm to Offic *Guildf* from 95. *Crowts, Tuesley, Godalming GU7 1UD* Tel (01483) 416613

MAKOWER, Canon Malory. b 38. TCD BA61 MA68 St Jo Coll Ox MA64 DPhil64. Ridley Hall Cam 64. **d** 66 **p** 67. C Onslow Square St Paul *Lon* 66-69; Tutor Ridley Hall Cam 69-71; Sen Tutor 71-76; P-in-c Lode and Longmeadow *Ely* 76-84; Warden EAMTC 77-79; Prin 79-84; Dir of Post-Ord Tr for NSM *Nor* 84-90; C Gt Yarmouth 84-89; TV 89-95; Dioc NSM Officer 88-95; Hon Can Nor Cathl 94-97; Prin LNSM Tr Scheme 94-97; rtd 97; Perm to Offic *Nor* from 98. *114 Yarmouth Road, Lowestoft NR32 4AQ* Tel (01502) 574769

MALAN, Victor Christian de Roubaix. b 39. Cape Town Univ BA60 Linacre Coll Ox BA63 MA68. Wycliffe Hall Ox 61. **d** 63 **p** 64. C Springfield *Birm* 63-65; P-in-c 66-67; C New Windsor *Ox* 67-69; Chapl St Jo Coll Cam 69-74; V Northampton All SS w St Kath *Pet* 74-86; V Stockport St Geo *Ches* 86-89; R N Mundham w Hunston and Merston *Chich* from 89. *The Rectory, Church Lane, Hunston, Chichester PO20 1AJ* Tel (01243) 782003

✠**MALANGO, The Most Revd Bernard Amos.** b 43. TCD MPhil84. St Jo Sem Lusaka DipTh71. **d** 71 **p** 72 **c** 88. Malawi 71-88 and from 02; Bp N Zambia 88-02; Bp Upper Shire from 02; Abp Cen Africa from 00. *Private Bag 1, Chilema, Zomba, Malawi* Tel (00265) (1) 539203 Fax as telephone
E-mail angus@malawinet *or* bernardmalango@hotmail.com

MALBON, Canon John Allin. b 36. Oak Hill Th Coll 62. **d** 65 **p** 66. C Wolverhampton St Jude *Lich* 65-68; C Hoole *Ches* 68-71; P-in-c Crewe Ch Ch 71-75; V 75-79; V Plemstall w Guilden Sutton 79-01; Hon Can Ches Cathl 96-01; rtd 01; Perm to Offic *Ches* from 02. *22 Hawksey Drive, Nantwich CW5 7GF* Tel (01270) 611584

MALCOLM, Brother. *See* FOUNTAIN, David Roy

MALCOLM, Miss Mercia Alana. b 54. St Andr Univ MA77 Lon Univ DipRS87. S'wark Ord Course 84. **d** 87 **p** 94. C Dartford Ch *Roch* 87-91; Par Dn Stockport St Geo *Ches* 91-94; C Jordanstown *Conn* 95-99; Chapl Ulster Univ 95-03; I Carnmoney *Conn* from 03. *Coole Glebe, 20 Glebe Road, Newtownabbey BT36 6UW* Tel (028) 9084 4981
E-mail carnmoney@connor.anglican.org

MALDOOM, Ms Julie Marilyn. b 65. Jes Coll Ox BA88 PGCE88. Cuddesdon Coll BTh93. **d** 96 **p** 97. C Chinnor w Emmington and Sydenham etc *Ox* 96-99. *Address temp unknown*

MALE, David Edward. b 62. Southn Univ BA83. St Jo Coll Dur BA90 Cranmer Hall Dur 88. **d** 91 **p** 92. C Leic St Chris *Leic* 91-94; C Kirkheaton *Wakef* 94-98; P Missr Huddersfield from

99. *50 Longcroft, Almondbury, Huddersfield HD5 8XW* Tel (01484) 315511 E-mail david.male@tesco.net

MALEK, Mark Mayool. b 44. Khartoum Univ BSc69 Salford Univ BSc76 Bradf Coll of Educn PGCE93. **d** 03. NSM Horton *Bradf* from 03; NSM Bradf St Oswald Chapel Green from 03. *26 Martlett Drive, Bradford BD5 8QG* Tel (01274) 732712

MALES, Jeanne Margaret. b 49. Reading Univ BA71 Lon Univ MPhil73 Surrey Univ PhD86 AFBPsS75 CPsychol88. S'wark Ord Course 93. **d** 96 **p** 97. NSM Caterham *S'wark* 96-00; C Addington from 00. *56 Viney Bank, Court Wood Lane, Croydon CR0 9JT* Tel (020) 8657 2478 E-mail jeanne@u.genie.co.uk

MALINS, Mrs Judith. b 42. **d** 00 **p** 01. NSM Wilton w Netherhampton and Fugglestone *Sarum* from 00. *65 Shaftesbury Road, Wilton, Salisbury SP2 0DU*

MALINS, Peter. b 18. Down Coll Cam BA40 MA47. Ridley Hall Cam 40. **d** 42 **p** 43. C Earlsdon *Cov* 42-44; CF (EC) 44-47; CF 47-73; QHC 72-73; V Greenwich St Alfege w St Pet and St Paul *S'wark* 73-87; P-in-c Greenwich H Trin and St Paul 76-84; Sub-Dean Greenwich 79-81; rtd 87; Perm to Offic *Guildf* from 87. *12 Ridgeway Drive, Dorking RH4 3AN* Tel (01306) 882035

MALKIN, Thomas Ross. b 64. Hertf Coll Ox BA86. Trin Coll Bris BA98. **d** 99 **p** 00. C Stretford St Bride *Man* 99-03; P-in-c Firswood and Gorse Hill from 03. *24 Canute Road, Stretford, Manchester M32 0RJ* Tel 0161-865 1802 Mobile 07973-240023 E-mail trm@fish.co.uk

MALKINSON, Christopher Mark. b 47. Chich Th Coll 84. **d** 86 **p** 87. C Stroud and Uplands w Slad *Glouc* 86-89; V Cam w Stinchcombe 89-00; P-in-c Tywardreath w Tregaminion *Truro* 00-02; P-in-c St Sampson 00-02; V Padstow from 02; Chapl Miss to Seafarers from 00. *The Vicarage, 46 Treverbyn Road, Padstow PL28 8DN* Tel (01841) 533776 E-mail chrismalk@hotmail.com

MALKINSON, Michael Stephen. b 43. St Steph Ho Ox 65. **d** 68 **p** 69. C New Addington *Cant* 68-71; C Blackpool St Steph *Blackb* 71-74; V Wainfleet St Mary *Linc* 74-81; R Wainfleet All SS w St Thos 74-81; P-in-c Croft 80-81; V Lund *Blackb* 81-93; V Heyhouses on Sea 93-00; R Balcombe *Chich* from 00; P-in-c Staplefield Common from 00. *The Rectory, Balcombe, Haywards Heath RH17 6PA* Tel (01444) 811249 Fax 811346 E-mail stephen@malkinson.co.uk

MALLAS, Mrs Wendy Norris. b 42. Cov Coll of Educn CertEd63 Reading Univ MA91 Dip Counselling 99. STETS 00. **d** 03. NSM Liss *Portsm* from 03. *Mayfield, 45 Hogmoor Road, Whitehill, Bordon GU35 9ET* Tel (01420) 478883

MALLESON, Michael Lawson. b 42. Univ of Wales (Swansea) BA64 Nottm Univ DipTh68. Linc Th Coll 67. **d** 70 **p** 71. C Wakef St Jo *Wakef* 70-73; C-in-c Holmfield St Andr CD 73-75; V Holmfield 75-80; V Heworth St Alb *Dur* 80-93; V Killingworth *Newc* from 93. *The Vicarage, West Lane, Killingworth Village, Newcastle upon Tyne NE12 6BL* Tel 0191-268 3242

MALLETT, John Christopher. b 44. EAMTC. **d** 82 **p** 83. NSM Hethersett w Canteloff *Nor* 82-85; NSM Hethersett w Canteloff w Lt and Gt Melton 85-90; Chapl Wayland Hosp Norfolk 88-94; Chapl Norwich Community Health Partnership NHS Trust 94-00; Perm to Offic *Nor* 00-03; NSM Hethersett w Canteloff w Lt and Gt Melton from 03. *2 Bailey Close, Hethersett, Norwich NR9 3EU* Tel (01603) 811010

MALLETT, Mrs Pamela Joan. b 26. LNSM course 93. **d** 96 **p** 97. OLM Long Ditton *S'wark* 96-98; Perm to Offic *S'wark* from 98; *Guildf* from 01. *109 Ditton Hill, Long Ditton, Surbiton KT6 5EJ* Tel (020) 8398 5189

MALLINSON, Canon Ralph Edward. b 40. Oriel Coll Ox BA63 MA66. St Steph Ho Ox 63. **d** 66 **p** 67. C Bolton St Pet *Man* 66-68; C Elton All SS 68-72; V Bury St Thos 72-76; V Bury Ch King 76-81; P-in-c Goodshaw 81-82; V 82-84; V Goodshaw and Crawshawbooth 84-93; AD Rossendale 83-93; Hon Can Man Cathl from 92; V Unsworth 93; Vice Prin Dioc OLM Scheme from 98. *St George's Vicarage, Hollins Lane, Bury BL9 8JJ* Tel 0161-766 2429
E-mail ralphandhelen@rmallinson.fsnet.co.uk

MALLON, Allister. b 61. Sheff Univ BA83 TCD DipTh87 BTh89 MA. CITC. **d** 87 **p** 88. C Ballymoney w Finvoy and Rasharkin *Conn* 87-90; C Belfast St Mary w H Redeemer 90-92; Bp's C Belfast St Mary Magd 92-00; Bp's C Stoneyford from 00; Chapl R Group of Hosps Health and Soc Services Trust from 00. *St John's Rectory, 62 Stoneyford Road, Lisburn BT28 3SP* Tel (028) 9264 8300 E-mail bigal@talk21.com

MALLORY, George Henry. b 14. JP. Lon Univ BSc63. St Deiniol's Hawarden. **d** 80 **p** 81. NSM Oaks in Charnwood and Copt Oak *Leic* 80-88; rtd 88; Perm to Offic *Leic* 88-91; Perm to Offic *Worc* from 91. *Claudina, Bewdley Road North, Stourport-on-Severn DY13 8PX* Tel (01299) 827964

MALMESBURY, Archdeacon of. *See* HAWKER, The Ven Alan Fort

MALONE, Richard Patrick. b 66. Wycliffe Hall Ox BTh03. **d** 03. C Fulham Ch Ch *Lon* from 03. *76 Rylston Road, London SW6 7HR* Tel 07973-104941 (mobile)
E-mail rpmalone@yahoo.com

MALONEY, Ms Fiona Elizabeth. b 60. Bradf Univ BSc82. Cranmer Hall Dur BA91 N Ord Course 91. **d** 92 **p** 94. Par Dn

Castleton Moor *Man* 92-94; C 94-96; C Pendlebury St Jo 96-99; C Fatfield *Dur* from 99. *The Vicarage, 17 Whittonstall, Fatfield, Washington NE38 8PH* Tel 0191-416 3134
E-mail fiona@jesuschrist.freeserve.co.uk

MALONEY, Terence Mark. b 63. York Univ BSc84. Cranmer Hall Dur 88. **d** 91 **p** 92. C Blackley St Andr *Man* 91-96; P-in-c Pendlebury St Jo 96-99; P-in-c Fatfield *Dur* from 99. *The Vicarage, 17 Whittonstall, Fatfield, Washington NE38 8PH* Tel 0191-416 3134 E-mail mark@cofe.org.uk

MALPASS, Clive William. b 36. AKC60. **d** 61 **p** 62. C Malden St Jo *S'wark* 61-64; C Horley 64-69; Youth Chapl *Dur* 69-72; Adv in Lay Tr 72-76; V Wyther Ven Bede *Ripon* 76-82; V Askrigg w Stallingbusk 82-01; RD Wensley 94-98; rtd 01. *2 Hargill Drive, Redmire, Leyburn DL8 4DZ* Tel (01969) 625680

MALTBY, Canon Geoffrey. b 38. Leeds Univ BA62 Nottm Univ DipRE72 Glas Coll of Ed Cert Special Past Catechesis 92. Wells Th Coll 68. **d** 70 **p** 71. C Mansfield St Mark *S'well* 70-73; V Skegby 73-78; V Carrington 78-87; C Rainworth 87-90; Chapl for People w Learning Disability (Mental Handicap) 90-03; Hon Can S'well Minster 99-03; rtd 03. *18 Beverley Close, Rainworth, Mansfield NG21 0LW* Tel (01623) 474452

MALTBY, Canon Judith Diane. b 57. Illinois Univ BA79 Newnham Coll Cam PhD92 FRHistS99. S Dios Minl Tr Scheme 89. **d** 92 **p** 94. Tutor Sarum & Wells Th Coll 87-93; Hon Par Dn Wilton w Netherhampton and Fugglestone Sarum 92-93; Chapl and Fell CCC Ox from 93; Lic to Offic *Ox* from 93; Can Th Leic Cathl *Leic* from 04. *Corpus Christi College, Oxford OX1 4JF* Tel (01865) 276722
E-mail judith.maltby@ccc.ox.ac.uk

MALTIN, Basil St Clair Aston. b 24. Qu Coll Cam BA49 MA54. Westcott Ho Cam 50. **d** 51 **p** 52. C Dursley *Glouc* 51-53; C Bathwick w Woolley *B & W* 53-57; V Frome Ch Ch 57-63; P-in-c Marston Bigot 57-59; V Bishops Lydeard 63-71; R Pulborough *Chich* 71-90; RD Storrington 84-89; rtd 90; Perm to Offic *Chich* from 90. *13 Somerstown, Chichester PO19 6AG* Tel (01243) 786740

MALTON, William Peter Antony. b 33. K Coll Lon AKC56. **d** 57 **p** 58. C N Hammersmith St Kath *Lon* 57-60; C-in-c Blackbird Leys CD *Ox* 60-65; R Pitsford *Pet* 65-66; Canada from 66; rtd 93. *106 Hughes Road, Port Sydney ON, Canada, P0B 1L0*

MAN, Archdeacon of. See PARTINGTON, The Ven Brian Harold

MANCE, Herbert William. b 19. St Jo Coll Cam BA40 MA44. Oak Hill Th Coll 47. **d** 49 **p** 50. C Leeds St Geo *Ripon* 49-53; CF 53-57; Nigeria 58-71; Can Ibadan 70-71; C Buckhurst Hill *Chelmsf* 71-75; P-in-c Roydon 75-79; V 79-85; rtd 85; Perm to Offic *Lon* from 85. *52 Redwood Avenue, Stone ST15 0DB* Tel (01785) 816128

MANCHESTER, John Charles. b 45. Lon Univ BD69. ALCD68. **d** 69 **p** 70. C Scarborough St Martin *York* 69-73; C Selby Abbey 73-76; P-in-c Old Malton 76-79; V from 79; RD Bulmer and Malton 85-91. *The Gannock House, Old Malton, Malton YO17 7HB* Tel (01653) 692121

MANCHESTER, Simon Lorimer. b 53. Univ of NSW BA. Moore Th Coll Sydney ThL79 Melbourne Coll of Div BD80. **d** 80 **p** 80. Australia 80-82 and from 84; C Wollongong Pro-Cathl 80-82; C St Helen Bishopsgate w St Andr Undershaft etc *Lon* 82-84; R Lalor Park 84-85; R N Sydney St Thos from 99. *17 Kitchener Street, PO Box 132, Artarmon, NSW, Australia 2059* Tel (0061) (2) 9420 3661 *or* 9929 4807 Fax 9955 5180 E-mail st-thomas@st-thomas.org.au

MANCHESTER, Archdeacon of. See WOLSTENCROFT, The Ven Alan

MANCHESTER, Bishop of. See McCULLOCH, The Rt Revd Nigel Simeon

MANCHESTER, Dean of. See RILEY, The Very Revd Kenneth Joseph

MANCO, Gwenda Diane. b 54. N Ord Course 97. **d** 99 **p** 00. NSM Rochdale *Man* 99-02; NSM Dearnley 02-03; Perm to Offic from 03; Asst Chapl HM Pris Buckley Hall 99-03; Chapl HM Pris Styal from 03. *HM Prison, Styal Road, Styal, Wilmslow SK9 4HR* Tel 07966-217252 (Mobile)
E-mail gwenda.manco@tesco.net

MANCOR, Neil McKay. Univ of BC MA Reading Univ PhD. Wycliffe Hall Ox. **d** 99 **p** 00. C Llandeilo Fawr and Taliaris *St D* 99-02; Canada from 02. *1575 West 59th Avenue, Vancouver BC, Canada, V6P 1Z1* E-mail neilmancor@hotmail.com

MANDER, Peter John. b 52. Liv Univ BA85. Sarum & Wells Th Coll 85. **d** 87 **p** 88. C Hale and Ashley *Ches* 87-90; TV Grantham *Linc* 90-00; P-in-c Quarrington w Old Sleaford from 00; P-in-c Silk Willoughby from 00. *The Rectory, 5 Spire View, Northfield Road, Quarrington, Sleaford NG34 7RN* Tel (01529) 306776 E-mail peter@mander52.freeserve.co.uk

MANDER, Canon Thomas Leonard Frederick. b 33. Ely Th Coll 60. **d** 62 **p** 63. C Cov St Mary *Cov* 62-66; V Bishop's Tachbrook 66-70; V Earlsdon 70-76; V Chesterton 76-83; R Lighthorne 76-83; V Newbold Pacey w Moreton Morrell 76-83; Hon Can

Cov Cathl 80-92; P-in-c S Leamington St Jo 83-84; V 84-92; rtd 92; Perm to Offic *Cov* from 92. *59 Murcott Road East, Whitnash, Leamington Spa CV31 2JJ* Tel (01926) 339950

MANDERSON, Robert Dunlop (Leslie). b 35. RCSE FDS65 Dur Univ LDS59. Ox Min Course 92. **d** 94 **p** 95. NSM Maidenhead St Andr and St Mary *Ox* 94-00; Perm to Offic 00-02; NSM Chipping Norton from 02. *11 Langston Close, Churchill, Chipping Norton OX7 6QT* Tel (01608) 658303
E-mail lpmanderson@aol.com

MANHIRE, Ashley Lewin. b 31. AKC55. **d** 56 **p** 57. C Plymouth St Gabr *Ex* 56-59; C Cockington 59-66; V Torquay St Martin Barton 66-83; RD Ipplepen 82-87; V Shaldon 83-01; rtd 01; Perm to Offic *Ex* from 01. *15 Friars Gate, Exeter EX2 4AZ*

MANHOOD, Canon Phyllis. b 32. Aston Tr Scheme 78 Qu Coll Birm 79. dss 82 **d** 87 **p** 94. Harwich *Chelmsf* 82-83; Dovercourt and Parkeston 83-85; Fawley *Win* 85-87; Par Dn 87-92; P-in-c Bournemouth St Aug 92-99; Hon Can Win Cathl 96-99; rtd 99. *11 Rhyme Hall Mews, Fawley, Southampton SO45 1FX* Tel (023) 8089 4450

✠**MANKTELOW, The Rt Revd Michael Richard John.** b 27. Ch Coll Cam BA48 MA52. Chich Th Coll 51. **d** 53 **p** 54 **c** 77. C Boston *Linc* 53-56; Chapl Ch Coll Cam 57-61; Chapl Linc Th Coll 61-63; Sub-Warden 64-66; V Knaresborough St Jo *Ripon* 66-73; RD Harrogate 72-77; V Harrogate St Wilfrid 73-77; P-in-c Harrogate St Luke 75-77; Hon Can Ripon Cathl 75-77; Suff Bp Basingstoke *Win* 77-93; Can Res Win Cathl 77-91; Hon Can 91-93; Vice Dean 87-93; rtd 93; Hon Asst Bp Chich from 94; Hon Asst Bp Eur from 94; Wiccamical Preb Chich Cathl *Chich* 97-02. *14 Little London, Chichester PO19 1NZ* Tel (01243) 531096

MANLEY, Mrs Gillian. b 59. St Martin's Coll Lanc BEd80. St Jo Coll Nottm MA00. **d** 00 **p** 01. C Eckington and Ridgeway *Derby* from 00. *The Vicarage, 1 Aintree Avenue, Eckington, Sheffield S21 4JA* Tel (01246) 434441 *or* 431721 Mobile 07836-463416 E-mail geneva@supanet.com

MANLEY, Canon Gordon Russell Delpratt. b 33. Ch Coll Cam BA56 MA60. Linc Th Coll 57. **d** 59 **p** 60. C Westbury-on-Trym St Alb *Bris* 59-61; Chapl Ch Coll Cam 61-66; V Radlett *St Alb* 66-75; V Faversham *Cant* 75-99; RD Ospringe 84-90; Hon Can Cant Cathl 90-99; rtd 99; Perm to Offic *Cant* from 99; Retirement Officer (Cant Adnry) from 01. *170 Old Dover Road, Canterbury CT1 3EX* Tel (01227) 784016

MANLEY, Michael Alan. b 60. SS Hild & Bede Coll Dur BA82. Trin Coll Bris DipTh86. **d** 86 **p** 87. C Accrington St Jo *Blackb* 86-89; C Huncoat 88-89; C Accrington St Jo w Huncoat 89-90; V Preston St Luke and St Oswald 90-96; V Blackpool St Jo from 96. *St John's Vicarage, 19 Leamington Road, Blackpool FY1 4HD* Tel (01253) 620626 *or* 294451
E-mail manleyrev@hotmail.com

MANLEY-COOPER, Simon James. b 46. S Dios Minl Tr Scheme 91. **d** 94 **p** 95. NSM Soho St Anne w St Thos and St Pet *Lon* 94-96; Ind Chapl 94-96; P-in-c Bedford St Mich *St Alb* 96-01; Ind Chapl 96-01; R Bramfield, Stapleford, Waterford etc 01-02; Chapl E and N Herts NHS Trust from 03. *Queen Elizabeth II Hospital, Howlands, Welwyn Garden City AL7 4HQ* Tel (01707) 328111 E-mail manley-c@fish.co.uk

MANN, Alexandrina Elizabeth. b 67. Westmr Coll Ox BA92 PGCE93 Birm Univ MA95. Trin Coll Bris 01. **d** 03. C Austrey and Warton *Birm* from 03. *20 Austrey Road, Warton, Tamworth B79 0HW* Tel (01827) 897392 Mobile 07761-263849 E-mail alexandrina.shalom@virgin.net

MANN, Ms Angela. b 58. Bath Univ BA80 Bris Univ PGCE83. Trin Coll Bris DipHE94. **d** 94 **p** 95. C Marlborough *Sarum* 94-97; Perm to Offic 97-99. *11 Lansdowne Close, Calne SN11 9DR*

MANN, Lt Comdr Anthony James. b 34. Open Univ BA76. St Jo Coll Nottm 85. **d** 88 **p** 89. NSM Helensburgh *Glas* from 88. *3 Rosedale Gardens, Helensburgh G84 7RW* Tel (01436) 678375 E-mail didnpud@aol.com

MANN, Canon Charmion Anne Montgomery. b 36. Liv Univ BA57 CertEd62 AdDipEd79. Trin Coll Bris 80. dss 82 **d** 87 **p** 94. Bris St Nath w St Kath *Bris* 82-84; Bris St Matt and St Nath 84-85; Asst Chapl City Cen Hosps Bris 85-88; Chapl Bris Maternity Hosp 88-94; Chapl Bris R Hosp for Sick Children 88-94; Chapl Bris R Infirmary 88-94; Hon Can Bris Cathl *Bris* from D Lacock w Bowden Hill 94-00; C Gtr Corsham 97-00; rtd 00; Perm to Offic *Bris* from 00. *1 Kingsbury Street, Calne SN11 8DF* Tel (01249) 811228 Fax as telephone
E-mail charmion@mann7747.fsnet.co.uk

MANN, Christopher John. b 57. Glas Univ BSc79. Westcott Ho Cam 83. **d** 86 **p** 87. C Worc SE *Worc* 86-89; Min Can and Sacr St Paul's Cathl *Lon* 89-96; R Upminster *Chelmsf* from 96. *The Rectory, Gridiron Place, Upminster RM14 2BE* Tel (01708) 220174 E-mail rector@saintlaurence.com

MANN, David. b 57. BA. Ridley Hall Cam. **d** 82 **p** 83. C Monkwearmouth St Andr *Dur* 82-86; Chapl Sheff Cathl *Sheff* 86-87; C Leeds St Geo *Ripon* 87-94; V Ripon H Trin from 94.

Holy Trinity Vicarage, 3 College Road, Ripon HG4 2AE Tel (01765) 605865 *or* tel and fax 690930
E-mail dave@htripon.freeserve.co.uk

MANN, Donald Leonard. b 22. Westcott Ho Cam. **d** 47 **p** 48. C S'well Minster *S'well* 47-49; C Edwinstowe 49-51; C St Alb St Paul *St Alb* 51-54; C Baldock w Bygrave and Clothall 54-56; V Guilden Morden *Ely* 56-59; V Rocester *Lich* 59-63; V Gnosall w Knightley 63-69; V Sheen 69-76; P-in-c Calton 72-76; P-in-c Ellastone 76; rtd 76; Perm to Offic *Ches* from 93. *Bungalow 24, Lyme Green Settlement, Macclesfield SK11 0LD* Tel (01260) 252209

MANN, Gary. b 63. Nottm Univ BTh90. Linc Th Coll 87. **d** 90 **p** 91. C Knottingley *Wakef* 90-93; TV Brighouse and Clifton 93-98; V Lindley from 98. *The Vicarage, 2 The Clock Tower, Lindley, Huddersfield HD3 3JB* Tel (01484) 650996

MANN (née WELLS), Ms Gillian Mary. b 46. Bedf Coll Lon BA67 Goldsmiths' Coll Lon TCert68 Derbys Coll of HE DMS87 MCIPD89. EMMTC 99. **d** 01 **p** 02. NSM Wirksworth *Derby* from 01. *2A Warmbrook, Wirksworth, Matlock DE4 4EA* Tel (01629) 826349 Mobile 07719-470363
E-mail gillianmann@eidosnet.co.uk

MANN, Ivan John. b 52. Brunel Univ BTech74 Southn Univ BTh80. Sarum & Wells Th Coll 75. **d** 78 **p** 79. C Hadleigh w Layham and Shelley *St E* 78-81; C Whitton and Thurleston w Akenham 81-83; V Leiston 83-86; Perm to Offic 86-89; R Aldringham w Thorpe, Knodishall w Buxlow etc 89-93; V Ipswich St Jo 93-96; Chapl St Mary's Convent Wantage 96-00; Asst Chapl R Berks and Battle Hosps NHS Trust 00; TV Gt Yarmouth *Nor* 00-03; Team Member Loyola Hall Jesuit Spirituality Cen Prescot from 03. *Loyola Hall, Warrington Road, Rainhill, Prescot L35 6NZ* Tel 0151-426 4137
E-mail ivanmann@f2s.com

MANN, Joan. d 98. NSM Eastbourne St Mary *Chich* 98-02; NSM The Hydneye from 02. *39 Cherry Garden Road, Eastbourne BN20 8HF* Tel (01323) 728259

MANN, John. b 35. ISO91. Lon Univ Dip Economics 66. Oak Hill NSM Course 89. **d** 92 **p** 93. NSM Springfield All SS *Chelmsf* from 92; RD Chelmsf N from 99. *18 Humber Road, Chelmsford CM1 7PE* Tel (01245) 259596

MANN, Canon John Owen. b 55. QUB BD77 MTh86 MPhil98. CITC 79. **d** 79 **p** 81. C Cloughfern *Conn* 79-82; C Knock *D & D* 82-85; I Ballyrashane w Kildollagh *Conn* 85-89; R Bentworth and Shalden and Lasham *Win* 89-93; RD Alton 92-93; I Cloughfern *Conn* 93-02; I Belfast Malone St Jo from 02; Preb Clonmethan St Patr Cathl Dublin from 99. *St John's Rectory, 86 Maryville Park, Belfast BT9 6LQ* Tel (028) 9066 6644 *or* 9066 7861 E-mail johnmann@tinyworld.co.uk

MANN, Julian Farrer Edgar. b 64. Peterho Cam MA90. Oak Hill Th Coll BA93. **d** 96 **p** 97. C Hoole *Ches* 96-00; V Oughtibridge *Sheff* from 00. *The Vicarage, Church Street, Oughtibridge, Sheffield S35 0FU* Tel 0114-286 2317
E-mail julianlisa@oughtimann.freeserve.co.uk

✠**MANN, The Rt Revd Michael Ashley.** b 24. KCVO89. CBIM RMA 42 Harvard Univ Ad Mgt Progr 73. Wells Th Coll 55. **d** 57 **p** 58 **c** 74. C Wolborough w Newton Abbot *Ex* 57-59; V Sparkwell 59-62; Nigeria 62-67; Home Sec Miss to Seamen 67-69; Can Res Nor Cathl *Nor* 69-74; Vice-Dean 73-74; Dioc Ind Adv 69-74; Suff Bp Dudley *Worc* 74-76; Dean Windsor and Dom Chapl to The Queen 76-89; rtd 89; Hon Asst Bp Glouc from 89. *Lower End Farm Cottage, Eastington, Northleach, Cheltenham GL54 3PN* Tel (01451) 860767

MANN, Canon Peter Eric. b 51. St Jo Coll Dur BA73. Westcott Ho Cam 73. **d** 75 **p** 76. C Barrow St Jo *Carl* 75-78; C Egremont 78-80; V Carl St Luke Morton 80-86; TR Egremont and Haile 86-93; P-in-c Barrow St Geo w St Luke 93-99; TR from 99; P-in-c Barrow St Jo 95-96; RD Furness 94-01; RD Barrow from 01; Hon Can Carl Cathl from 95; P-in-c Barrow St Aid from 03. *The Rectory, 98 Roose Road, Barrow-in-Furness LA13 9RL* Tel (01229) 821641 Fax as telephone
E-mail cookbird@u.genie.co.uk

MANN, Ralph Norman. b 27. BNC Ox BA51 MA55 DipEd52. Ox NSM Course 79. **d** 82 **p** 83. NSM Kingham w Churchill, Daylesford and Sarsden *Ox* 82-85; S Area Sec BCMS 82-89; P-in-c Broadwell, Evenlode, Oddington and Adlestrop *Glouc* 89-97; rtd 97; P-in-c Upton St Leonards *Glouc* 97-00. *2 Whittons Close, Hook Norton, Banbury OX15 5QG* Tel (01608) 730327

MANN, Robin. b 45. MRTPI73 Dip Town Planning 72 Fitzw Coll Cam BA76 MA80. Ridley Hall Cam 73. **d** 77 **p** 78. C Wetherby *Ripon* 77-80; V Hipswell 80-86; V Mamble w Bayton, Rock w Heightington etc *Worc* 86-96; V Avon Valley *Sarum* 96-02; R Selworthy, Timberscombe, Wootton Courtenay etc *B & W* from 02. *The Rectory, Great House Street, Timberscombe, Minehead TA24 7TQ* Tel (01643) 841544
E-mail robin@robinandrosemarymann.freeserve.co.uk

MANN, Stephen Paul. b 52. Staffs Univ BA76 Keele Univ PGCE78. Cranmer Hall Dur 96. **d** 98 **p** 99. C Spennymoor, Whitworth and Merrington *Dur* 98-03; Chapl Dur Constabulary 99-03; TV Madeley *Heref* from 03. *Woodside Vicarage, Park Lane, Madeley, Telford TF7 5HN* Tel (01952) 273008
E-mail steveandco@blueyonder.co.uk

MANN, Terence John. b 47. GGSM68 LRSM79 FTCL79 Miami Univ MA80 Lon Univ PGCE69. Ox Min Course CBTS94. **d** 94 **p** 95. NSM Kingham w Churchill, Daylesford and Sarsden *Ox* 94-00; Chapl HM Pris Camp Hill from 00. *HM Prison, Camp Hill, Newport PO30 5PB* Tel (01983) 527661 Fax 520505

MANNALL, Michael John Frederick. b 37. St Mich Coll Llan 61. **d** 63 **p** 64. C Clapham H Spirit *S'wark* 63-66; C Brighton St Bart *Chich* 66-68; C Willesden St Matt *Lon* 68-69; C-in-c Cricklewood St Pet CD 69-73; R Broughton *Pet* 73-75; Hon C Kingston St Luke *S'wark* 76-94; rtd 84; Perm to Offic *Nor* from 95. *The Blessings, 55 Sculthorpe Road, Fakenham NR21 9ET* Tel (01328) 863496

MANNERS, Kenneth. b 29. N Ord Course. **d** 84 **p** 85. NSM Brayton *York* 84-00; rtd 00; Perm to Offic *York* from 00. *16 Wistow Road, Selby YO8 3LY* Tel (01757) 702129

MANNING, Adrian Peter. b 63. St Cath Coll Cam MA88 K Coll Lon PGCE88 St Cath Coll Cam BA84. Ridley Hall Cam CTM95. **d** 95 **p** 96. C Oxhey All SS *St Alb* 95-97; Asst Chapl Bedford Sch 97-02; Perm to Offic *St Alb* from 97; Chapl St Geo Sch Harpenden from 02. *2 Bramley Cottages, Sun Lane, Harpenden AL5 4SZ* Tel (01582) 765477

MANNING, Mrs Ann. b 42. Liv Univ CertEd75. St Jo Coll Nottm CTM94 N Ord Course 94. **d** 95 **p** 96. NSM Grasmere *Carl* 95-96; NSM Delamere *Ches* 96-99; C Middlewich w Byley 99-02; Chapl Mid Cheshire Hosps Trust 99-02; P-in-c Dunton w Wrestlingworth and Eyeworth *St Alb* from 02. *The Rectory, 7 Braggs Lane, Wrestlingworth, Sandy SG19 2ER* Tel (01767) 631596

MANNING, David Godfrey. b 47. Trin Coll Bris 73. **d** 76 **p** 77. C Richmond H Trin and Ch Ch *S'wark* 76-79; C Anston *Sheff* 79-83; V Blackpool St Mark *Blackb* 83-91; V Creech St Michael *B & W* from 91. *The Vicarage, Creech St Michael, Taunton TA3 5PP* Tel (01823) 442237

MANNING, Neville Alexander. b 41. Lon Univ BD68. ALCD68. **d** 68 **p** 69. C Belvedere All SS *Roch* 68-71; C Hollington St Leon *Chich* 71-73; C Hersham *Guildf* 73-77; V Dawley St Jerome *Lon* 77-94; R Denton w S Heighton and Tarring Neville *Chich* from 94. *The Rectory, 6 Heighton Road, Newhaven BN9 0RB* Tel (01273) 514319 E-mail nmanning@dentonrectory.fsnet.co.uk

MANNINGS, Andrew James. b 52. Trent Park Coll of Educn CertEd73. St Jo Coll Nottm DCM92. **d** 92 **p** 94. C Over St Chad *Ches* 92-93; C Sale St Anne 93-96; C Timperley 96-98; P-in-c Egremont St Jo from 98; P-in-c Liscard St Mary w St Columba from 03; RD Wallasey from 02. *St John's Vicarage, 45 Marlowe Road, Wallasey CH44 3DB* Tel 0151-638 4360
E-mail andrew.mannings4@ntlworld.com

MANNS, Edwin Ernest. b 30. Portsm Dioc Tr Course 84. **d** 85. C Paulsgrove *Portsm* 85-95; Chapl St Mary's Hosp Portsm 90-91; Team Chapl Portsm Hosp 91-95; rtd 95. *17 Kelvin Grove, Portchester, Fareham PO16 8LQ* Tel (023) 9232 4818

MANSBRIDGE, The Ven Michael Winstanley. b 32. Southn Univ BA54. Ridley Hall Cam 56. **d** 58 **p** 59. C Ware St Mary *St Alb* 58-60; C Claverdon w Preston Bagot *Cov* 60-62; Kenya 62-65; Asst P Nairobi Cathl and Chapl Nairobi Univ 62-65; V Chilvers Coton w Astley *Cov* 65-75; RD Nuneaton 66-73; V Leamington Priors H Trin 75-83; Chapl Abu Dhabi St Andr UAE 83-97; Adn the Gulf 83-91; Adn Cyprus and the Gulf 91-99; Can Nicosia 86-99; Provost 97-99; Can Bahrain 87-99; rtd 97; Hon Can Nicosia and Bahrain from 99. *Blue Skies, 7 Norman Way, Wootton Bridge, Ryde PO33 4NJ* Tel (01983) 882394
E-mail fiona_mansbridge@compuserve.com

MANSELL, Cary Stuart. b 61. St Jo Coll Morpeth LTh DipMin80 DipTh83. **d** 83 **p** 84. Australia 83-97 and from 99; C Warrnambool Australia 83-86; V Edenhope 86-91; R Camperdown 91-97; C Addlestone *Guildf* 97-99; Lic to Offic *Cant* from 97; Asst Chapl St Mich Gr Sch and Assoc P E St Kilda from 99. *St Michael's Grammar School, 20 Redan Street, St Kilda, Vic, Australia 3182* Tel (0061) (3) 8530 3200 Fax 9510 9392
E-mail cmansell@stmichaels.vic.edu.au

MANSELL, The Ven Clive Neville Ross. b 53. Leic Univ LLB74 Solicitor 77. Trin Coll Bris DipHE81. **d** 82 **p** 83. C Gt Malvern St Mary *Worc* 82-85; Min Can Ripon Cathl *Ripon* 85-89; R Kirklington w Burneston and Wath and Pickhill 89-02; Adn Wensley 98-02; Adn Tonbridge *Roch* from 02. *3 The Ridings, Blackhurst Lane, Tunbridge Wells TN2 4RU* Tel (01892) 520660
E-mail archdeacon.tonbridge@rochester.anglican.org

MANSFIELD, Alastair John Fraser. b 60. Ex Univ BA82 Ch Coll Cam PGCE84 City Univ MSc92. SEITE. **d** 99 **p** 00. C Palmers Green St Jo *Lon* 99-02; P-in-c Enfield St Mich from 02. *The Vicarage, Gordon Hill, Enfield EN2 0QP* Tel (020) 8363 1063
E-mail ajstrawber@aol.com

MANSFIELD, Gordon Reginald. b 35. Lon Univ DipTh61 CertEd BA. Clifton Th Coll 58. **d** 63 **p** 64. C Carl St Jo *Carl* 63-65; C Westcombe Park St Geo *S'wark* 65-68; C Rashcliffe *Wakef* 68-70; V Woodlands *Sheff* 70-80; V Steeple Bumpstead and Helions Bumpstead *Chelmsf* 80-02. *11 Mander Way, Mowbray Road, Cambridge CB1 7SF*

MANSFIELD, Julian Nicolas (Nick). b 59. K Coll Lon BD AKC. Edin Th Coll 83. **d** 85 **p** 86. C Kirkby *Liv* 85-89; TV Ditton

St Mich 89-96; P-in-c Preston St Oswald *Blackb* 96-01; V Penwortham St Leon from 01. *St Leonard's Vicarage, Marshall's Brow, Penwortham, Preston PR1 9HY* Tel (01772) 742367 E-mail nick-vic@fish.co.uk

MANSFIELD, Robert William. b 45. Nottm Trent Univ DipHE95. LNSM course 89. **d** 88 **p** 89. OLM Louth *Linc* from 88. *The Old Railway House, Stewton, Louth LN11 8SD* Tel (01507) 327533 E-mail mansfieldstewton@hotmail.com

MANSFIELD, Simon David. b 55. Brunel Univ BSc81 Lon Univ MA94. Ripon Coll Cuddesdon 88. **d** 90 **p** 91. C N Harrow St Alb *Lon* 90-93; C Birchington w Acol and Minnis Bay *Cant* 93-97; TV Accrington *Blackb* 97-00; TV Accrington Ch the King from 00. *The Vicarage, Barnfield Street, Accrington BB5 2AQ* Tel (01254) 399322 E-mail simon@simonmansfield.freeserve.co.uk

MANSFIELD, Stephen McLaren. b 59. FGA Dip Retail Jewellery Gemmology Dip. Cranmer Hall Dur 86. **d** 89 **p** 90. C Poynton *Ches* 89-92; C Bromborough 92-94; V Bidston 94-02; C Heswall from 02. *15 Castle Drive, Heswall, Wirral CH60 4RJ* Tel 0151-342 4841 E-mail smfield@fish.co.uk

MANSHIP, Charmain Margaret. b 45. RCM ARCM65 GRSM67 FRCO68 BMus68. St Alb and Ox Min Course 95. **d** 98 **p** 99. NSM Abingdon *Ox* from 98. *Woodlyn, Faringdon Road, Southmoor, Abingdon OX13 5AF* Tel (01865) 820885

MANSHIP, Canon David. b 27. ARCO Keble Coll Ox BA52 MA58. Qu Coll Birm 52. **d** 54 **p** 55. C Hackney St Jo *Lon* 54-58; C Preston Ascension 58-61; C St Andr Holborn 61-65; Members' Tr Officer C of E Youth Coun 65-68; Clergy Tr Officer 68-70; Dir of Educn *Win* 70-79; Hon Can Win Cathl 74-79; R Old Alresford 76-79; V Abingdon w Shippon *Ox* 79-89; TR Abingdon 89-93; V Shippon 89; RD Abingdon 87-90; rtd 93; Perm to Offic *Ox* from 93. *Woodlyn, Faringdon Road, Southmoor, Abingdon OX13 5AF* Tel (01865) 820885

MANSLEY, Colin Edward. b 56. Edin Univ MA80 BA85. Ripon Coll Cuddesdon 83. **d** 86 **p** 87. C Worle *B & W* 86-89; C Baguley *Man* 89-91; C Radcliffe St Mary 91; TV Radcliffe 91-96; V Bartley Green *Birm* from 96. *The Vicarage, 96 Romsley Road, Birmingham B32 3PS* Tel 0121-475 1508 E-mail colin@archangel.clara.co.uk

MANSON-BRAILSFORD, Andrew Henry. b 64. NUU BA86 Liv Univ MPhil98. Ripon Coll Cuddesdon 87. **d** 90 **p** 91. C Warrington St Elphin *Liv* 90-93; C Torrisholme *Blackb* 93-96; V Brighton St Geo w St Anne and St Mark *Chich* from 96; Chapl St Mary's Hall Brighton from 97. *22 Seymour Square, Kemp Town, Brighton BN2 1DW* Tel (01273) 699779 *or* 279448 E-mail stgeochuch@aol.com

MANTLE, John Ambrose Cyril. b 46. St Andr Univ MTheol74 Kent Univ MA90 Leeds Univ PhD98 FRHistS01. Edin Th Coll 66. **d** 69 **p** 70. C Broughty Ferry *Bre* 69-71; C St Andrews All SS *St And* 71-75; C Edin SS Phil and Jas *Edin* 75-77; Teacher Royal High Sch Edin 75-77; Chapl and Tutor in Th St Andr Univ *St And* 77-80; P-in-c Pittenweem 78-80; P-in-c Elie and Earlsferry 78-80; Chapl and Fell Fitzw Coll Cam 80-86; Tutor Wesley Ho Cam 80-86; Hon C Cambridge Ascension 80-86; Tutor and Vice-Prin Cant Sch of Min 86-91; Visiting Lect Th Kent Univ Cant 91-93; C Boxley w Detling 86-93; Dioc Adv for Educn and Tr of Adults *Chich* 94-99; Visiting Lect Th Sussex Univ 95-98; Abps' Adv for Bps' Min *Cant* from 99; Lic to Offic *Chich* 99-02. 28 *Gulleymoor, Peterborough PE3 8LG* Tel (01733) 765920 E-mail jacmantle@yahoo.com

MANUEL, Paul. b 55. Univ of Wales (Ban) BA76 ACIS79 FCIS88. St Alb and Ox Min Course 97. **d** 00 **p** 01. NSM Luton St Paul *St Alb* from 00. *3 St James Road, Harpenden AL5 4NX* Tel (01582) 620584 E-mail pmfrompetham@aol.com

MAPLE, David Charles. b 34. Sarum Th Coll 64. **d** 66 **p** 66. C Buckland in Dover *Cant* 66-67; C St Laur in Thanet 67-71; Chapl RAF 71-75; P-in-c Ivychurch 75-76; P-in-c Newchurch *Cant* 75-78; P-in-c Burmarsh 75-78; P-in-c St Mary in the Marsh 75-76; R Dymchurch 76-78; R Dymchurch w Burmarsh and Newchurch 78-81; Hon Min Can Cant Cathl from 79; Abp's Dioc Chapl 81-91; Chapl St Jo Hosp Cant 91-95; rtd 95; Perm to Offic *Cant* from 98. *1 Mount Pleasant, Blean, Canterbury CT2 9EU* Tel (01227) 459044

MAPLE, John Philip. b 50. Chich Th Coll 71. **d** 74 **p** 79. C Notting Hill St Mich and Ch Ch *Lon* 74-75; Lic to Offic 78-79; C Barnsbury St Dav w St Clem 79-80; C Cotham St Sav w St Mary *Bris* 80-83; TV St Marylebone Ch Ch *Lon* 83-91; R St Marylebone St Paul 91-99; P-in-c Fulham St Alb w St Aug from 99; P-in-c Fulham St Pet 99-02. *St Alban's Vicarage, 4 Margravine Road, London W6 8HJ* Tel (020) 7381 1500 *or* 7385 0724

MAPLEY, Mrs Barbara Jean. b 46. Guy's Hosp Medical Sch MCSP69. Oak Hill NSM Course 88. **d** 89 **p** 94. NSM Kelvedon *Chelmsf* 89-93; C Witham 93-94; TV 94-01; R Belbroughton w Fairfield and Clent *Worc* from 01. *The Rectory, Bradford Lane, Belbroughton, Stourbridge DY9 9TF* Tel (01562) 730531

MAPPLEBECKPALMER, Richard Warwick. b 32. CCC Cam BA56 MA60. Cuddesdon Coll 56. **d** 58 **p** 59. C Redcar *York* 58-60; C Drypool St Jo 61-63; V Pendleton St Ambrose *Man* 63-77; P-in-c Piddington *Ox* 77; P-in-c Ambrosden w Arncot and Blackthorn 77; P-in-c Merton 77; V Ambrosden w Merton

and Piddington 77-88; USA from 88; rtd 97. *472 Dale Road, Martinez, CA 94553-4829, USA* Tel (001) (510) 228 5252

MAPSON, Preb John Victor. b 31. Lon Univ BA60. Oak Hill Th Coll 55. **d** 60 **p** 61. C Littleover *Derby* 60-62; C Wandsworth St Mich *S'wark* 62-65; R Willand *Ex* 65-71; P-in-c Axmouth 71-72; V 72-75; V Axmouth w Musbury 75-77; RD Honiton 76-77; V Cullompton 77-89; R Kentisbeare w Blackborough 77-89; RD Cullompton 81-89; P-in-c Sidmouth All SS 89-96; Preb Ex Cathl from 91; RD Ottery 94-96; rtd 96; Ed *Exeter Diocesan Directory Ex* from 00. *47 Headweir Road, Cullompton EX15 1NN* Tel (01884) 38037 E-mail jmapson@care4free.net *or* diocesan.news@exeter.anglican.org

MAPSTONE, Trevor Anthony. b 63. Lanc Univ BSc84 MA96. St Jo Coll Nottm LTh88 DPS89. **d** 89 **p** 90. C Hoole *Ches* 89-92; C Lancaster St Thos *Blackb* 92-96; V Harrow Trin St Mich *Lon* 96-03; Dir of Ords Willesden Area 98-03; V S Croydon Em *S'wark* from 03. *Emmanuel Vicarage, 38 Croham Manor Road, South Croydon CR2 7BE* Tel (020) 8688 2478 *or* 8688 6676 E-mail tmapstone@blueyonder.co.uk

MARAIS, Rudolph James. b 41. St Bede's Coll Umtata BTh. **d** 81 **p** 82. S Africa 81-85 and from 87; C Belmont *S'wark* 85-87. *PO Box 119, Queenstown, 5320 South Africa* Tel (0027) (451) 3965

MARAJH, Brian Melvin. BA. d 86 **p** 87. S Africa 86-94 and from 99; Perm to Offic *Glas* 94-99; Lect Coll of Transfiguration from 99. *PO Box 77, Grahamstown, 6140 South Africa* Tel (0027) (46) 622 3112 *or* 622 3332

MARCER, Graham John. b 52. Ripon Coll Cuddesdon 75. **d** 78 **p** 79. C Sherborne w Castleton and Lillington *Sarum* 78-81; C Christchurch *Win* 81-84; V Southampton St Jude 84-90; P-in-c Moordown 90-91; C Sheff Parson Cross St Cecilia *Sheff* 91-93; V Balby 93-00; RD W Doncaster 97-00; V Radford *Cov* from 00; AD Cov N from 01. *The Vicarage, 21 Tulliver Street, Coventry CV6 3BY* Tel (024) 7659 8449 E-mail graham.marcer@btinternet.com

MARCETTI, Alvin Julian. b 41. San Jose State Univ BA66 Santa Clara Univ MA76. Cranmer Hall Dur 85. **d** 87 **p** 88. C Stepney St Dunstan and All SS *Lon* 87-91; Chapl City of Lon Poly 91-92; Chapl Lon Guildhall Univ 92-96; Chapl Homerton Univ Hosp NHS Trust Lon from 96; Chapl City and Hackney Community Services NHS Trust from 96. *Homerton Hospital, Homerton Row, London E9 6SR* Tel (020) 8510 7738 E-mail ajmr@compuserve.com

MARCH, Alan Mervyn. b 48. CPFA73 Open Univ BA91. EAMTC 00. **d** 03. NSM Northampton St Alb *Pet* from 03. *236 Beech Avenue, Northampton NN3 2LE* Tel (01604) 405722

MARCH, Charles Anthony Maclea (Tony). b 32. CCC Cam BA55 MA70. Oak Hill Th Coll 55. **d** 57 **p** 58. C S Croydon Em *Cant* 57-60; C Eastbourne H Trin *Chich* 60-63; V Whitehall Park St Andr Hornsey Lane *Lon* 63-67; V Tunbridge Wells H Trin w Ch Ch *Roch* 67-82; V Prestonville St Luke *Chich* 82-87; rtd 97; Perm to Offic *Roch* from 99. *The Barn, 2 Town Farm Dairy, Brenchley Road, Brenchley, Tonbridge TN12 7PA* Tel (01892) 722802

MARCH, Gerald. b 44. Nottm Univ BA75. Oak Hill Th Coll 92. **d** 95 **p** 96. C Sandgate St Paul w Folkestone St Geo *Cant* 95-99; P-in-c Southampton St Mark *Win* from 99. *St Mark's Vicarage, 54 Archers Road, Southampton SO15 2LU* Tel (023) 8063 6425

MARCHAND, Canon Rex Anthony Victor (Toby). b 47. K Coll Lon BD69 AKC69. St Aug Coll Cant 69. **d** 70 **p** 71. C Leigh Park *Portsm* 70-73; C Bp's Hatfield *St Alb* 73-80; R Deal St Leon and St Rich and Sholden *Cant* 80-95; RD Sandwich 91-94; Hon Can Cant Cathl 94-95; V Bishop's Stortford St Mich *St Alb* from 95. *St Michael's Vicarage, 8 Larkspur Road, Bishop's Stortford CM23 4LL* Tel (01279) 651415 E-mail tandmmarchand@ntlworld.com

MARCHANT, The Ven George John Charles. b 16. St Jo Coll Dur LTh38 BA39 MA42 BD64. Tyndale Hall Bris 35. **d** 39 **p** 40. C Whitehall Park St Andr Hornsey Lane *Lon* 39-41; Lic to Offic 41-44; C Cambridge St Andr Less *Ely* 44-48; V Skirbeck H Trin *Linc* 48-54; V Dur St Nic *Dur* 54-74; RD Dur 64-74; Hon Can Dur Cathl 72-74; Adn Auckland 74-83; Can Res Dur Cathl 74-83; rtd 83; Perm to Offic *Nor* 83-01. *28 Greenways, Eaton, Norwich NR4 6PE* Tel (01603) 58295

MARCHANT, Canon Iain William. b 26. Wells Th Coll 59. **d** 60 **p** 61. C Dalston *Carl* 60-63; V Hawkesbury *Glouc* 63-76; R Newent 76-85; Hon Can Glouc Cathl 84-92; R Newent and Gorsley w Cliffords Mesne 85-92; rtd 92; Perm to Offic *Glouc* from 92. *Daisy Green, Daisy Lane, Howley, Wotton-under-Edge GL12 7PF* Tel (01453) 844779

MARCHANT, Canon Ronald Albert. b 26. Em Coll Cam BA50 MA52 PhD57 BD64. Ridley Hall Cam 50. **d** 54 **p** 55. C Acomb St Steph *York* 54-57; C Willian *St Alb* 57-59; V Laxfield *St E* 59-92; RD Hoxne 73-78; Hon Can St E Cathl 75-92; P-in-c Wilby w Brundish 86-92; rtd 92; Perm to Offic *York* from 98. *34 The Paddock, Boroughbridge Road, York YO26 6AW* Tel (01904) 798446

✠**MARCUS, The Rt Revd Justus Mauritius.** b 55. Cape Town Univ BA78. St Pet Coll Natal 77. **d** 78 **p** 79 **c** 99. S Africa 78-86 and from 89; C Wimbledon *S'wark* 87-89; Dean Kimberley

91-99; Suff Bp Cape Town (Saldanah Bay) from 99. *PO Box 420, Malmesbury, 7299 South Africa* Tel (0027) (22) 486 6770 E-mail justusmm@xsinet.co.za

MARCUSSEN, Mrs Yolande Roberta. b 47. SEITE 98. d 01 p 02. NSM Bromley Common St Aug *Roch* 01-03; NSM Orpington All SS from 03; Asst Chapl HM Pris *Roch* from 01. *Charis, 24 Lucerne Road, Orpington BR6 0EP* Tel (01689) 833599 Mobile 07790-915697 E-mail yolande.marcussen@ntlworld.com

MARGAM, Archdeacon of. *See* MORRIS, The Ven Philip Gregory

MARGARET ANNE, Sister. *See* McALISTER, Margaret Elizabeth Anne

MARGARET JOY, Sister. *See* HARRIS, Margaret Claire

MARINER, Aris. b 43. Alexandria Univ BSc65. St Alb Minl Tr Scheme 84. d 87. NSM Stevenage H Trin *St Alb* from 87. *13 Church Lane, Stevenage SG1 3QS* Tel (01438) 365596

MARION EVA, Sister. *See* RECORD, Sister Marion Eva

MARK, Brother. *See* SHARPE, John Brebber

MARK, Timothy John. b 34. Bris Univ BA57 MLitt68 MEd71 Leeds Univ PhD79. Didsbury Methodist Coll 54. d 59 p 61. India 59-64 and 65-69; Perm to Offic *Sheff* from 73. *15 Fieldhouse Road, Sprotborough, Doncaster DN5 7RN* Tel (01302) 853022

MARKBY, Archibald Campbell. b 15. Em Coll Cam BA37 MA41. Ridley Hall Cam 37. d 39 p 39. C Bradf St Clem *Bradf* 39-42; C Ox St Aldate *Ox* 42-46; V Kilburn St Mary *Lon* 46-53; V Hornsey Ch 53-64; R Ickenham 64-68; V Crowfield w Stonham Aspal *St E* 68-71; V Damerham *Sarum* 71-80; V Martin 71-80; rtd 80; Perm to Offic *Sarum* 80-00. *8 Timbermill Court, Church Sreet, Fordingbridge SP6 1RG* Tel (01425) 656141

MARKBY, Ms Jane Elizabeth. b 67. Em Coll Cam BA88 Homerton Coll Cam PGCE89. Ridley Hall Cam 00. d 02. NSM Edmonton All SS w St Mich *Lon* from 02. *1A Uvedale Road, Enfield EN2 6HA* Tel (020) 8482 0452 E-mail janemarkby@blueyonder.co.uk

MARKBY, Peter John Jenner. b 38. Em Coll Cam BA60. Clifton Th Coll 62. d 64 p 65. C Tufnell Park St Geo *Lon* 64-68; C Crowborough *Chich* 68-73; C Polegate 73-77; R Southover 77-02; rtd 02. *66 Leylands Road, Burgess Hill RH15 8AJ* Tel (01444) 870831 E-mail petermarkby@onetel.net.uk

MARKEY, Andrew John. b 73. Univ of Wales (Swansea) BSc96. Westcott Ho Cam BTh02. d 02 p 03. C Wotton-under-Edge w Ozleworth, N Nibley etc *Glouc* from 02. *39 Parklands, Wotton-under-Edge GL12 7LT* Tel (07814) 654495

MARKHAM, Deryck O'Leary. b 28. Oak Hill Th Coll 66. d 68 p 69. C Purley Ch Ch *S'wark* 68-72; V E Budleigh and Bicton *Ex* 72-93; RD Aylesbeare 89-93; rtd 93; Perm to Offic *Ex* 93-03. *8 Milford House, Milford on Sea, Lymington SO41 0QJ* Tel (01590) 643515 E-mail dolm@onetel.net.uk

MARKHAM, Canon Gervase William. b 10. MBE00. Trin Coll Cam BA32 MA36. Westcott Ho Cam 34. d 36 p 37. C Bishopwearmouth St Mich *Dur* 36-39; Bp's Dom Chapl 39-40; CF (EC) 40-46; V Burnley St Steph *Blackb* 46-52; CF (TA) 50-52; CF (TA - R of O) from 52; V Gt Grimsby St Jas *Linc* 52-65; Can and Preb Linc Cathl 56-65; RD Grimsby and Cleethorpes 62-64; V Morland w Thrimby and Gt Strickland *Carl* 65-84; RD Lowther 65-69; Hon Can Carl Cathl 72-84; rtd 84; Perm to Offic *Carl* from 84. *The Garden Flat, Morland House, Penrith CA10 3AZ* Tel (01931) 714654

MARKLAND, Vincent Hilton. b 33. Univ of Wales (Lamp) BA55 Leic Univ PGCE58. Ripon Hall Ox 67. d 68 p 69. C Worsley *Man* 68-83; V Monton 83-95; AD Eccles 91-95; rtd 95; Perm to Offic *Man* from 95; Chapl Manchester Children's Hospitals NHS Trust 96-98. *50 Knowsley Drive, Swinton, Manchester M27 0FA* Tel 0161-794 8088

MARKS, Allan Willi. b 56. Cranmer Hall Dur CTM94. d 94 p 95. C Barnoldswick w Bracewell *Bradf* 94-96; C Willington Team *Newc* 96-98; TV 98-02; V Newc H Cross from 02. *Holy Cross Vicarage, 16 Whittington Grove, Newcastle upon Tyne NE5 2QP* Tel 0191-274 4476 E-mail fatherallan@cableinet.co.uk

MARKS, Anthony Alfred. b 28. AKC53. d 54 p 55. C Fleetwood *Blackb* 54-58; V Burnley St Cuth 58-63; Chapl RN 63-83; QHC from 81; P-in-c Bradninch *Ex* 83-88; R Bradninch and Clyst Hydon 88-90; rtd 90; Perm to Offic *B & W* from 90. *Bryony Cottage, The Combe, Compton Martin, Bristol BS40 6JD*

MARKS, Anthony Wendt. b 43. G&C Coll Cam BA63 MA67 PhD70 BNC Ox DPhil72. St Steph Ho Ox 70. d 72 p 73. C Withington St Crispin *Man* 72-75; Chapl Lon Univ Medical Students *Lon* 75-80; Warden Liddon Ho Lon 80-92; C-in-c Grosvenor Chpl *Lon* 80-92; V Shrewsbury All SS w St Mich *Lich* 92-99; V Fareham SS Pet and Paul *Portsm* from 99. *St Peter and St Paul's Vicarage, 22 Harrison Road, Fareham PO16 7EJ* Tel (01329) 280256 *or* 236003

MARKS, Timothy John. b 45. Man Univ BA76 Cert Counselling 94 Anglia Poly Univ MA97. d 88 p 89. NSM Burton and Sopley *Win* 88-91; R Croxton and Eltisley *Ely* 91-96; R Graveley w Papworth St Agnes w Yelling etc 91-96; Dir Network Counselling and Tr 96-97; Perm to Offic *B & W* 97-00. *8 Arundell Road, Weston-super-Mare BS23 2QQ* Tel (01934) 415807

MARKWELL, Donald Stanley. b 30. Victoria Univ Wellington MA53. d 79 p 80. Hon C Kingston Hill St Paul *S'wark* 79-82; Hon C Ham St Andr from 82. *12 Albany Mews, Albany Park Road, Kingston upon Thames KT2 5SL* Tel (020) 8546 0740

MARL, David John. b 42. ARCA67. d 01 p 02. OLM Child Okeford *Sarum* from 01. *Gothic Cottage, Upper Street, Child Okeford, Blandford Forum DT11 8EF* Tel (01258) 860249

MARLEY, The Very Revd Alan Gordon. b 59. Birm Univ BA89. Qu Coll Birm 87. d 89 p 90. C Blandford Forum and Langton Long *Sarum* 89-93; Chapl HM YOI Aylesbury 93-97; I Fermoy Union *C, C & R* 97-03; Bp's Dom Chapl 99-03; Dean Cloyne from 03; I Cloyne Union from 03. *The Deanery, Deanery Road, Midleton, Co Cork, Irish Republic* Tel (00353) (21) 463 1449 E-mail parsifal@esatclear.ie

MARLOW (née SIBBALD), Mrs Olwyn Eileen. b 57. Aston Tr Scheme 85 Linc Th Coll 87. d 89 p 94. Par Dn Wythenshawe St Martin *Man* 89-93; Par Dn Baguley 93-94; C 94-95; Asst Chapl Cen Man Healthcare NHS Trust 95-00; NSM Newall Green St Fran *Man* 97-98; rtd 01; NSM Wythenshawe *Man* from 01. *28 Arcadia Avenue, Sale M33 3SA* Tel 0161-962 9292

MARLOW, Walter Geoffrey. b 29. AKC57. d 57 p 58. C Long Eaton St Laur *Derby* 57-61; C Mackworth St Fran 61-63; R Stoke Albany w Wilbarston *Pet* 63-68; PC Calow *Derby* 68-73; R Wingerworth 73-82; P-in-c Islington St Jas w St Phil *Lon* 82-87; P-in-c Islington St Pet 82-87; V Islington St Jas w St Pet 87-92; AD Islington 84-90; Preb St Paul's Cathl 87-92; Bp's Dom Chapl *B & W* 92-96; Preb Wells Cathl 92-96; rtd 96; Perm to Offic *Nor* from 96. *Taverners Cottage, Park Road, Wells-next-the-Sea NR23 1DQ* Tel (01328) 710432

MARNHAM, Charles Christopher. b 51. Jes Coll Cam BA73 MA77. Cranmer Hall Dur DipTh76. d 77 p 78. C Brompton H Trin *Lon* 77-78; C Brompton H Trin w Onslow Square St Paul 78-80; C Linthorpe *York* 80-84; R Haughton le Skerne *Dur* 84-95; V Ches Square St Mich w St Phil *Lon* from 95. *St Michael's Vicarage, 4 Chester Square, London SW1W 9HH* Tel (020) 7730 8889 Fax 7730 0043 E-mail office@stmichaelschurch.org.uk

MARNS, Nigel Geoffrey. b 63. Univ of Wales (Abth) BSc(Econ)85 Birm Univ BD92. Qu Coll Birm 90. d 93 p 94. C Addington *S'wark* 93-96; P-in-c W Bromwich Gd Shep w St Jo *Lich* 96-01; V Bromsgrove St Jo *Worc* from 01. *The Vicarage, 12 Kidderminster Road, Bromsgrove B61 7JW* Tel (01527) 876517

✠MARONA, The Most Revd Joseph Biringi Hassan. b 41. Bp Gwynne Th Coll 78. d 81 p 82 c 84. Chapl Rumbek State Secondary Sch 81-82; Chapl Maridi Teachers' Tr Coll 82-83; Area Bp Maridi 85-89; Bp Maridi 89-00; Dean of Prov from 98; Abp Sudan and Bp Juba from 00. *ECS Liaison Office, PO Box 604, Khartoum, Sudan* Tel (00249) (811) 20040 *or* (11) 485720 Fax (811) 20065 *or* (11) 485717 E-mail ecsprovince@hotmail.com

MARQUEZ, Edilberto. b 57. Bible Sem Alliance Peru BA80 Westmr Coll Ox PGDTheol92 MTh93 St Steph Ho Ox PGCTh94. d 94 p 95. C Reading St Jo *Ox* 94-98; C New Malden and Coombe *S'wark* 98-01; P-in-c Bucklebury w Marlston *Ox* from 01. *Bucklebury Vicarage, Burdens Heath, Upper Bucklebury, Reading RG7 6SX* Tel (01635) 866731 E-mail emarquez@tiscali.co.uk

MARQUIS-FAULKES, Edmund. b 62. Hatf Coll Dur BA85. Ridley Hall Cam 87 Coates Hall Edin 90. d 91 p 92. C Broughty Ferry *Bre* 91-93; P-in-c Dundee St Ninian 93-02; R Bieldside *Ab* from 02. *St Devenick's Rectory, Baillieswell Road, Bieldside, Aberdeen AB15 9AP* Tel (01224) 861552 E-mail marquisfaulkes@yahoo.com

MARR (née PARKER), Mrs Anne Elizabeth. b 46. Hull Univ BSc67 CertEd68. NEOC 91. d 96. Chapl Newc City Health NHS Trust from 96; NSM Whorlton *Newc* 96-97; NSM Chapel House from 97. *26 The Chesters, Newcastle upon Tyne NE5 1AF* Tel 0191-267 4808

MARR, Derek Paul. b 33. Dur Univ TCert69. Dioc OLM tr scheme 97. d 00 p 01. OLM Chapel House *Newc* from 00. *26 The Chesters, West Denton, Newcastle upon Tyne NE5 1AF* Tel 0191-267 4808

MARR, Canon Donald Radley. b 37. K Coll Lon 57. St Aid Birkenhead 61. d 64 p 65. C Macclesfield St Mich *Ches* 64-66; C Sale St Anne 66-67; V Marthall 67-72; C W Kirby St Bridget 72-76; R Waverton 76-83; R Nantwich 83-87; RD Nantwich 86-87; RD Malpas 87-91; V Bunbury 87-91; rtd 91; Dioc Rural Officer *Ches* from 91; Hon Can Ches Cathl 91-92; Perm to Offic *Truro* from 94. *St Boniface, 5 Hockenhull Crescent, Tarvin, Chester CH3 8LJ, or The Parsonage, Tresco TR24 0QQ* Tel (01829) 741302 *or* (01720) 423176

MARR, Mrs Joan Mary. b 36. SRN58 SCM75 HVCert78 NDN79. St Jo Coll Nottm CertCS91. d 91. Hon Par Dn Moffat *Glas* 91-97; Hon Par Dn Dumfries 98-03; rtd 03; Perm to Offic *Glas* from 03. *Auburn Cottage, Templand, Lockerbie DG11 1TG* Tel (01387) 810734 Mobile 07802-823658 Fax (01387) 810994

MARR, Mrs Margaret Rose. b 36. JP81. St Mary's Coll Ban TCert56 Open Univ BA00. Ripon Coll Cuddesdon 02. d 02 p 03. NSM Tarvin *Ches* from 02; Perm to Offic *Truro* from 02. *St Boniface, 5 Hockenhull Crescent, Tarvin, Chester CH3 8LJ, or*

The Parsonage, Tresco TR24 0QQ Tel (01829) 741302 *or* (01720) 423176 E-mail therevs@marr4321.fsnet.co.uk

MARR, Peter. b 36. Reading Univ PhD78. Ox NSM Course 84. **d** 87 **p** 88. NSM Reading St Giles *Ox* 87-89; C Beverley Minster *York* 90-92; P-in-c Beckenham St Barn *Roch* 92-96; V from 96. *St Barnabas' Vicarage, Oakhill Road, Beckenham BR3 6NG* Tel (020) 8650 3332 E-mail pbmarr@dircon.co.uk

MARRIOTT (née REID), Mrs Amanda Joy. b 63. DipRSAMDA83 Nottm Univ BTh92. Linc Th Coll 89. **d** 92 **p** 96. Par Dn Rothwell *Ripon* 92-94; C 94-95; C Manston 95-97; C Wetherby 97-01; P-in-c Water Eaton *Ox* from 01. *The Vicarage, 38 Mill Road, Bletchley, Milton Keynes MK2 2LD* Tel (01908) 374585 E-mail mandy@marriott-wetherby.freeserve.co.uk

MARRIOTT, Frank Lewis. b 29. Lich Th Coll 57. **d** 60 **p** 61. C Earlsdon *Cov* 60-64; R Tysoe w Compton Winyates and Oxhill 64-70; P-in-c Cov St Marg 70-77; R Ufton 77-83; V Long Itchington 77-83; RD Southam 82-89; V Long Itchington and Marton 83-95; rtd 95; Perm to Offic *Heref* from 95. *12 Traherne Close, Ledbury HR8 2JF* Tel (01531) 634576

MARRIOTT, Stanley Richard. b 36. AKC60 Warwick Univ MA92. **d** 61 **p** 62. C Coleshill *Birm* 61-64; C Maxstoke 61-64; V Ansley *Cov* 64-78; Org Sec (E Midl) CECS 79-83; P-in-c Baxterley w Hurley and Wood End and Merevale etc *Birm* 83-84; R 84-87; R Newton Regis w Seckington and Shuttington 87-97; rtd 97; Perm to Offic *B & W* from 97. *Dunkery Pleck, Wootton Courtenay, Minehead TA24 8RH* Tel (01643) 841058

MARRISON, Geoffrey Edward. b 23. Lon Univ BA48 PhD67. Bps' Coll Cheshunt 49 Kirchliche Hochschule Berlin 50. **d** 51 **p** 52. C Wormley *St Alb* 51-52; Malaya 52-55; Singapore 55-56; C Radlett *St Alb* 56-57; C St Botolph Aldgate w H Trin Minories *Lon* 57-58; V Crookes St Tim *Sheff* 58-61; India 62-64; Perm to Offic *Cant* 64-69; Lic to Offic 69-82; Perm to Offic *Carl* from 83; Tutor Carl Dioc Tr Course from 83. *1 Ainsworth Street, Ulverston LA12 7EU* Tel (01229) 586874

MARROW, David Edward Armfield. b 42. Nottm Univ BA65 MA. Tyndale Hall Bris 65. **d** 67 **p** 68. C Clifton Ch Ch w Em *Bris* 67-70; Ethiopia 70-75; N Area Sec BCMS 75-77; C-in-c Ryde St Jas Prop Chpl *Portsm* 77-84; V Worthing St Geo *Chich* from 84. *The Vicarage, 20 Seldon Road, Worthing BN11 2LN* Tel (01903) 203309

MARSBURG, John Edward. b 53. Oak Hill Th Coll DipHE94 BA96. Coll of Resurr Mirfield 98. **d** 99 **p** 00. NSM Selby Abbey *York* 99-02; R Lenzie *Glas* from 02. *The Rectory, 1A Beech Road, Lenzie, Kirkintilloch, Glasgow G66 4HN* Tel 0141-776 4149 E-mail rev.jem@marsburg.org

MARSDEN, Andrew Philip. b 63. Keble Coll Ox BA85 MA90 Birm Univ MA86. Wycliffe Hall Ox BA90. **d** 91 **p** 92. C Newport St Jo *Portsm* 91-94; C Cowplain 94-97; V Wokingham St Sebastian *Ox* from 97. *St Sebastian's Vicarage, Nine Mile Ride, Wokingham RG40 3AT* Tel (01344) 761050

MARSDEN, Andrew Robert. b 49. AKC71. St Aug Coll Cant 68. **d** 72 **p** 73. C New Addington *Cant* 72-75; C Prudhoe *Newc* 75-77; Asst Chapl HM Pris Wakef 77; Chapl HM Borstal Portland 77-82; Chapl HM YOI Onley 82-89; V Ulceby Gp *Linc* 89-98; Chapl Calderdale Healthcare NHS Trust 98-01; Chapl Calderdale and Huddersfield NHS Trust 01; Chapl St Andr Hospice Grimsby from 01; Community Chapl *Linc* from 01; Gen Preacher from 01. *28 Chestnut Rise, Barrow-upon-Humber DN19 7SG* Tel (01469) 532155

MARSDEN, Mrs Carole. b 44. Avery Hill Coll TCert65 Sheff Poly DipEd87. N Ord Course 88. **d** 91 **p** 94. NSM Saddleworth *Man* 91-92; Par Dn 92-94; C 94-95; P-in-c Oldham St Paul 95-02; C Werneth 98-02; P-in-c Shap w Swindale and Bampton w Mardale *Carl* from 02. *The Vicarage, Shap, Penrith CA10 3LB* Tel (01931) 716232

MARSDEN, Diana Marion. Deakin Univ Australia BEd. **d** 03. NSM Hurstbourne Priors, Longparish etc *Win* from 03. *Spring Hill, St Mary Bourne, Andover SP11 6BG* Tel (01264) 738211

MARSDEN, John Joseph. b 53. York Univ BA74 Nottm Univ DipTh78 MTh81 Kent Univ PhD88. St Jo Coll Nottm 77. **d** 80 **p** 81. C Leigh St Mary *Man* 80-83; Hon C Chatham St Steph *Roch* 83-91; Ind Chapl 83-91; Lect Systematic Th CITC and TCD from 91; I Newbridge w Carnalway and Kilcullen *M & K* from 97. *The Rectory, Morristown, Newbridge, Co Kildare, Irish Republic* Tel (00353) (45) 438185

MARSDEN, John Robert. b 22. Linc Coll Ox BA48 MA49. Ripon Hall Ox 57. **d** 58 **p** 59. C Dur St Cuth *Dur* 58-61; Chapl Dur Sch 61-85; rtd 85. *Prebends, High Kilburn, York YO61 4AJ* Tel (01347) 868597

MARSDEN, Canon Joyce. b 47. Trin Coll Bris DipHE80. **dss** 83 **d** 87 **p** 94. Wavertree H Trin *Liv* 83-85; Much Woolton 85-97; Par Dn 87-94; C 94-97; TV Parr from 97; Hon Can Liv Cathl from 03. *459 Fleet Lane, St Helens WA9 2NQ* Tel (01744) 21213

MARSDEN, Michael John. b 59. St Mich Coll Llan 78. **d** 82 **p** 83. C Neath w Llantwit *Llan* 82-85; Asst Chapl Univ Hosp of Wales Cardiff 85-89; V Graig *Llan* 89-93; P-in-c Cilfynydd 89-93; R Merthyr Tydfil St Dav 93-01; Chapl Gwent Healthcare NHS

Trust from 01. *Nevill Hall Hospital, Brecon Road, Abergavenny NP7 7EG* Tel (01873) 852091

MARSDEN, Robert. b 59. Ch Ch Ox BA81 PGCE82. Oak Hill Th Coll BA92. **d** 92 **p** 93. C Sevenoaks St Nic *Roch* 92-95; Chapl Fettes Coll Edin 95-99; C-in-c Buxton Trin Prop Chpl *Derby* from 99. *37 Temple Road, Buxton SK17 9BA* Tel (01298) 73656

MARSDEN, Robert James. b 56. Ch Ch Coll Cant BEd79. Oak Hill Th Coll DipHE92. **d** 94 **p** 95. C Margate H Trin *Cant* 94-98; P-in-c Brinton, Briningham, Hunworth, Stody etc *Nor* from 98. *The Rectory, Brinton, Melton Constable NR24 2QF* Tel (01263) 860295 E-mail rbmarsden@skynow.net

MARSDEN, Canon Robert William. b 24. TCD BA49 MA52. CITC 50. **d** 50 **p** 51. C Dublin St Jas *D & G* 50-54; Asst Chapl Miss to Seamen 54-58; I Currin w Drum *Clogh* 58-66; I Clones w Killeevan 66-94; Prec Clogh Cathl 86-94; rtd 94. *30 Claremont Park, Sandymount, Dublin 4, Irish Republic* Tel (00353) (1) 668 0210

MARSDEN, Samuel Edward. b 44. Keble Coll Ox BA66 MA85. Linc Th Coll 66. **d** 68 **p** 69. C Liskeard w St Keyne *Truro* 68-72; R Gerrans w St Anthony in Roseland 72-77; Hong Kong 77-81; P-in-c Ingrave *Chelmsf* 81-82; P-in-c Gt Warley w Childerditch 81-82; R Gt Warley w Childerditch and Ingrave 82-89; Australia from 89. *12 Hill Street, PO Box 86, Parkes, NSW, Australia 2870* Tel (0061) (2) 6862 2083 *or* 6862 1868 Fax 6862 1547 E-mail samuelmarsden@hotmail.com

MARSDEN-JONES, Watkin David. b 22. St D Coll Lamp BA48. **d** 49 **p** 50. C Flint *St As* 49-54; C Forest Row *Chich* 54-56; V Copthorne 56-70; RD E Grinstead 66-70; V Bosham 70-86; rtd 86; Perm to Offic *Chich* from 86. *10 Fairfield Road, Bosham, Chichester PO18 8JH* Tel (01243) 575053 E-mail dmarjon@bctalk.net

MARSH, Anthony David. b 29. Roch Th Coll 64. **d** 66 **p** 67. C Liskeard w St Keyne *Truro* 66-69; R Wrentham w Benacre and Covehithe *St E* 69-75; R Wrentham w Benacre, Covehithe, Frostenden etc 75-80; P-in-c Beyton and Hessett 80-86; C Felixstowe St Jo 86-88; rtd 88; Perm to Offic *St E* from 88 and *B & W* from 01. *Calle Jose Cuvero Yiyo 5, Edif Diana 2, Escalera 2 7d, Fuengirola 29640, Spain* Tel (0034) (617) 223143

MARSH, Carol Ann. See HATHORNE, Mrs Carol Ann

MARSH, Colin Arthur. b 54. St Jo Coll Nottm. **d** 82 **p** 83. C Kirkby *Liv* 82-86; TV St Luke in the City 86-91; USPG Zambia 91-95; Edin Univ *Edin* from 95. *27 Ferryfield, Edinburgh EH5 2PR* Tel 0131-551 1708

MARSH, David. b 32. St Jo Coll Dur BA54 DipTh57. **d** 57 **p** 58. C Bilston St Leon *Lich* 57-62; Kenya 63-66 and 70-72; Chapl Scargill Ho 67-69; Adn S Maseno 70-72; V Meole Brace *Lich* 72-77; V Westlands St Andr 77-86; V Trentham 86-96; P-in-c Alstonfield, Butterton, Warslow w Elkstone etc 96-99; rtd 99; Perm to Offic *Ches* from 99. *31 Spring Gardens, Nantwich CW5 5SH* Tel (01270) 610079

MARSH, Donald. b 35. WMMTC. **d** 90 **p** 91. NSM Wednesbury St Bart *Lich* from 90. *Holly Rise, 19 Trouse Lane, Wednesbury WS10 7HR* Tel and fax 0121-556 0095 *or* tel (01902) 723104

MARSH, Francis John. b 47. York Univ BA69 DPhil76 ATCL65 ARCM66 ARCO71. Oak Hill Th Coll 72 Selw Coll Cam 73. **d** 75 **p** 76. C Cambridge St Matt *Ely* 75-78; C Pitsmoor w Wicker *Sheff* 79; C Pitsmoor w Ellesmere 79-81; C Crookes St Thos 81-85; V S Ossett *Wakef* 85-96; RD Dewsbury 93-96; Adn Blackb 96-01; Bp's Adv on Hosp Chapls 96-01. *137 Edge Lane, Dewsbury WF12 0HB* Tel (01924) 451233 E-mail vendocjon@aol.com

MARSH, Gordon Bloxham. b 25. Cant Sch of Min 82. **d** 85 **p** 86. NSM Loose *Cant* 85-86; NSM New Romney w Old Romney and Midley 86-90; NSM Asst to RD S Lympne 90-94; rtd 94; Perm to Offic *Cant* from 94. *Westleton, St John's Road, New Romney TN28 8EN* Tel (01797) 366506

MARSH, Lawrence Allan. b 36. Sarum Th Coll 66. **d** 67 **p** 68. C Waterlooville *Portsm* 67-70; V Shedfield 70-76; R Fen Ditton *Ely* 76-01; P-in-c Horningsea 83-01; rtd 01; Perm to Offic *Ely* from 01. *The Old Bakery, 22 High Street, Bottisham, Cambridge CB5 9DA* Tel (01223) 811314 E-mail landjmarsh@aol.com

MARSH, Leonard Stuart Alexander. b 55. Hull Univ BA77 SOAS Lon MA00. Linc Th Coll 77. **d** 79 **p** 80. C Eltham St Barn *S'wark* 79-81; C Camberwell St Giles 81-83; Hon C Clifton St Paul *Bris* 83-86; Asst Chapl Bris Univ 83-86; Area Sec (Dio S'wark) USPG 86-91; Chapl Guildhall Sch of Music and Drama *Lon* 91-97; Chapl City Univ 91-98; NSM Clerkenwell H Redeemer and St Mark 94-95; P-in-c Finsbury St Clem w St Barn and St Matt 95-01; P-in-c Upper Norwood All SS *S'wark* from 01. *All Saints' Vicarage, 12 Beulah Hill, London SE19 3LS* Tel (020) 8653 2820

MARSH, Mrs Margaret Ann. b 37. Nottm Univ BSc59 Ox Univ DipEd60 Lambeth STh87 Newc Univ MA93 Man Univ MPhil95. Carl Dioc Tr Course 86. **d** 87. Asst Chapl Garlands Hosp 87-92; Dn Carl Cathl *Carl* 87-93; NSM Carl St Luke Morton 93-94; Hon Chapl Carl Hosps NHS Trust 94-00; rtd 00; Perm to Offic *Carl* 00-02 and *St Alb* from 02. *1 The Maltings, Leighton Buzzard LU7 4BS* Tel (01525) 384655

MARSH, Mrs Margaret Evaline. b 47. STETS 96. **d** 99 **p** 00. NSM Tattenham Corner and Burgh Heath *Guildf* 99-03; NSM Epsom St Martin from 03. *9 Westways, Stoneleigh, Epsom KT19 0PH* Tel (020) 8393 2317 Mobile 07801-477635

MARSH, Miss Maxine Dorothy. b 49. Bretton Hall Coll TCert72. Westcott Ho Cam 90. **d** 92 **p** 94. C Kings Norton *Birm* 92-95; P-in-c Kingsbury 95-96; V 96-02; P-in-c Middleton 99; AD Polesworth 99-02; P-in-c Glastonbury w Meare *B & W* from 02. *The Vicarage, 24 Wells Road, Glastonbury BA6 9DJ* Tel (01458) 834281 E-mail maxinemarsh@glastonbury666.ffnet.uk

MARSH, Philip Edward. b 73. Univ of Wales (Abth) BSc94. Wycliffe Hall Ox BTh02. **d** 02 **p** 03. C Hubberston *St D* from 02. *Suncrest, St Annes Road, Milford Haven SA73 3LQ* Tel (01646) 697649 Mobile 07766-314957 E-mail snuzzgrot@hotmail.com

MARSH, Ralph. b 42. ACP65 Chester Coll CertEd63 Birm Univ BPhil77 Liv Univ MA00. St Deiniol's Hawarden 86. **d** 88 **p** 89. NSM Tranmere St Paul w St Luke *Ches* 88-90; C Guiseley w Esholt *Bradf* 90-92; V Broughton *St As* 92-94; Hon C W Derby St Jo *Liv* 94; C Ribbleton *Blackb* 94-97; NSM Man Victoria Park *Man* 98-99; NSM Croxteth *Liv* from 99. *47 Rolleston Drive, Wallasey CH45 6XE*

MARSH, Canon Richard St John Jeremy. b 60. Keble Coll Ox BA82 MA86 Dur Univ PhD91. Coll of Resurr Mirfield 83. **d** 85 **p** 86. C Grange St Andr *Ches* 85-87; Solway Fell and Chapl Univ Coll Dur 87-92; Abp's Asst Sec for Ecum Affairs *Cant* 92-95; Abp's Sec for Ecum Affairs 95-01; Hon C Westmr St Steph w St Jo *Lon* 94-96; Assoc P Westmr St Matt 96-01; Can Gib Cathl *Eur* 95-01; Hon Prov Can Cant Cathl *Cant* 98-01; Can Res Cant Cathl from 01; Dir of Educn from 01. *22 The Precincts, Canterbury CT1 2EP* Tel (01227) 865226 Fax 865222 E-mail richard.marsh@canterbury-cathedral.org

MARSH, Robert Christopher. b 53. Ex Univ BEd76. St Steph Ho Ox 86. **d** 88 **p** 89. C St Leonards Ch Ch and St Mary *Chich* 88-91; TV Crawley 91-00; V Maybridge 00-02. *67 Hythe Crescent, Seaford BN25 3TZ* Tel (01323) 492552 E-mail rmarsh6204@aol.com

MARSH, Roger Philip. b 44. K Coll Lon BD72 AKC72 Sussex Univ MA95. St Aug Coll Cant 73. **d** 73 **p** 74. C Leagrave *St Alb* 73-76; Asst Youth Officer 76-77; Resources Officer 77-80; Chapl Marlborough Coll 80-86; Master Ardingly Coll Jun Sch Haywards Heath 86-95; Hd Master St Geo Sch Windsor 95-99; Chapl Lancing Coll from 99. *Lancing College, Lancing BN15 0RW* Tel (01273) 452213

MARSH, Mrs Shelley Ann. b 54. SRN75 SCM76. St Jo Coll Nottm CertCS87 TISEC 96. **d** 89 **p** 94. Hon C Glas Gd Shep and Ascension *Glas* 89-96; P-in-c Johnstone from 96; P-in-c Renfrew from 96. *44 Atholl Crescent, Ralston, Paisley PA1 3AW* Tel 0141-883 8668 E-mail revshelleymarsh@net.ntl.com

MARSH, Simon Robert. b 59. Sarum & Wells Th Coll 79. **d** 82 **p** 83. C Mottram in Longdendale w Woodhead *Ches* 82-85; Bp's Dom Chapl *Bradf* 85-87; V Ashton Hayes *Ches* 87-90; V Macclesfield St Paul 90-96; V Ringway 96-01; V Bollington St Jo from 01. *The Vicarage, Shrigley Road, Bollington, Macclesfield SK10 5RD* Tel (01625) 573162 Fax 571146 E-mail frsimon@btinternet.com

MARSH, Susan Edith. b 42. Southn Univ BA63 CertEd64. St Alb and Ox Min Course 01. **d** 01 **p** 02. NSM Bp's Hatfield *St Alb* from 01. *141 Handside Lane, Welwyn Garden City AL8 6TA* Tel (01707) 890846

MARSHALL, Alan John. *See* WACKWITZ-MARSHALL, Alan John

MARSHALL, Alexander John. Leeds Univ BSc. **d** 95 **p** 96. OLM Holbrook, Stutton, Freston, Woolverstone etc *St E* from 95. *1 The Street, Freston, Ipswich IP9 1AF* Tel (01473) 780738

MARSHALL, Alexander Robert. b 43. Glouc Sch of Min 84. **d** 87 **p** 88. NSM Newtown w Llanllwchaiarn w Aberhafesp *St As* 87-00; P-in-c Mochdre from 00. *The Vicarage, Bettws Cedewen, Newtown SY16 3DS* Tel (01686) 650345 E-mail marshall@rhayapow.kc3ltd.co.uk

MARSHALL, Mrs Alison Mary. b 54. Middx Hosp MB, BS79 MRCGP84. St Alb and Ox Min Course 98. **d** 01 **p** 02. NSM Reading St Jo *Ox* from 01. *36 Bulmershe Road, Reading RG1 5RJ* Tel 0118-966 8794 Mobile 07740-944102 E-mail ali.marshall@ntlworld.com

MARSHALL, Ms Alison Rose Marie. b 60. Leic Univ BA83 Birkbeck Coll Lon MA86 UEA PGCE87. Ridley Hall Cam. **d** 95 **p** 96. C Whittlesey, Pondersbridge and Coates *Ely* 95-98; Dep Chapl HM Pris Nor 98-99; Chapl HM Pris Northallerton 99-03; TV Sunderland *Dur* from 03; Chapl Sunderland Univ from 03. *St Columba's Vicarage, Cornhill, Southwick, Sunderland SR5 1RU* Tel 07905-173171 (mobile) E-mail amarshal@fish.co.uk

MARSHALL, Mrs Angela. b 48. Trin Coll Bris 74. **d** 88 **p** 96. Hon Par Dn Newcastle St Geo *Lich* 88-92; Lic to Offic *Eur* 92-94; Dn Versailles 94-96; Asst Chapl from 96. *31 rue du Pont Colbert, 78000 Versailles, France* Tel (0033)(1) 39 51 47 07 or 39 02 79 45 Fax 39 50 97 29 E-mail stmarks@wanadoo.fr

MARSHALL, Basil Eustace Edwin. b 21. OBE69. Westcott Ho Cam 71. **d** 73 **p** 74. C Edenbridge *Roch* 73-78; P-in-c Matfield 78-85; P-in-c Lamberhurst 78-85; C Farnborough 85-86; rtd 86; Perm to Offic *Roch* from 86; *Chich* from 01. *7 Boyne Park, Tunbridge Wells TN4 8EL* Tel (01892) 521664

MARSHALL, Canon Bryan John. b 40. Chich Th Coll 63. **d** 65 **p** 66. C Poulton-le-Fylde *Blackb* 65-68; C S Shore H Trin 68-70; V Wesham 70-74; PV Chich Cathl *Chich* 74-82; V Boxgrove 82-91; P-in-c Tangmere 82-84; R 84-91; R Westbourne 91-95; V E Preston w Kingston 95-03; Can and Preb Chich Cathl 94-03; rtd 03. *11 Priory Close, Boxgrove, Chichester PO18 0EA* (01243) 536337

MARSHALL, Christine. *See* MARSHALL, Melinda Christine

MARSHALL, Mrs Christine Anne. b 40. Leeds Univ BSc64. **d** 95 **p** 96. OLM Holbrook, Stutton, Freston, Woolverstone etc *St E* from 95. *1 The Street, Freston, Ipswich IP9 1AF* Tel (01473) 780738

MARSHALL, Christopher John. b 56. Edge Hill Coll of HE BEd79. St Alb Minl Tr Scheme 83. **d** 86 **p** 87. C Biggleswade *St Alb* 86-89; Chapl Asst S Beds Area HA 89-91; Chapl St Helier Hosp Carshalton 91-93; Sen Chapl St Helier NHS Trust 93-98; Gen Office and Bereavement Manager Newham Healthcare NHS Trust from 98; Gen Services Manager from 99. *Newham General Hospital, Glen Road, London E13 8SL* Tel (020) 7363 8462

MARSHALL, Preb Christopher John Bickford. b 32. TD78. AKC56. **d** 57 **p** 58. C Leatherhead *Guildf* 57-60; C Crewkerne *B & W* 60-63; V Long Sutton 63-72; V Long Sutton w Long Load 72-76; V Wiveliscombe 76-93; RD Tone 78-87; Preb Wells Cathl 88-96; P-in-c Chipstable w Huish Champflower and Clatworthy 93; R Wiveliscombe w Chipstable, Huish Champflower etc 93-96; rtd 96; Perm to Offic *B & W* from 96. *Tap Cottage, High Street, Milverton, Taunton TA4 1LL* Tel (01823) 400419

MARSHALL, Christopher Robert. b 49. St Chad's Coll Dur BA71. Sarum & Wells Th Coll 72. **d** 74 **p** 75. C Sheff Parson Cross St Cecilia *Sheff* 74-77; C Walsall St Gabr Fulbrook *Lich* 77-78; C Upper Gornal 78-80; V Walsall St Andr 80-86; V Willenhall St Giles 86-00; V Tividale from 00. *St Michael's Vicarage, Tividale, Warley B69 2LQ* Tel 0121-532 7911

MARSHALL, Craig Laurence. b 64. Southn Univ BEd87 Open Univ MA93 Nottm Univ MTh01. St Jo Coll Nottm 99. **d** 01. C Staplegrove w Norton Fitzwarren *B & W* from 01. *23 Nash Green, Staplegrove, Taunton TA2 6BZ* Tel (01823) 259799

MARSHALL, David. b 66. St Kath Coll Liv CertRS88 Liv Univ BA88. Ripon Coll Cuddesdon 89. **d** 92 **p** 93. C Dovecot *Liv* 92-96; P-in-c Westbrook St Jas 96-98; Dioc Communications Officer 95-98; Dioc Communications Officer *Ches* from 98. *Church House, Lower Lane, Aldford, Chester CH3 6HP* Tel and fax (01925) 419201 or (01244) 620444 Fax (01244) 620456 E-mail dco@chester.anglican.org

MARSHALL, David Charles. b 52. St Chad's Coll Dur BA73. Trin Coll Bris 74. **d** 76 **p** 77. C Meole Brace *Lich* 76-78; C W Teignmouth *Ex* 78-80; C Broadwater St Mary *Chich* 80-84; V Newcastle St Geo *Lich* 84-92; Chapl Versailles w Chevry *Eur* from 92. *31 rue du Pont Colbert, 78000 Versailles, France* Tel (0033) (1) 39 514 707 or 39 02 79 45 Fax 39 50 97 29 E-mail stmarks@wanadoo.fr

MARSHALL, David Evelyn. b 63. New Coll Ox BA85 Birm Univ MA88 PhD96. Ridley Hall Cam 88. **d** 90 **p** 91. C Roundhay St Edm *Ripon* 90-92; Chapl Ex Coll Ox 95-98; Lect St Paul's United Th Coll Limuru Kenya 98-99; P-in-c Buckden *Ely* 99-00; P-in-c Hail Weston 99-00; Abp's Dom Chapl *Cant* from 00. *7 The Cottages, Lambeth Palace, Lambeth Palace Road, London SE1 7JU* Tel (020) 7898 1200 Fax 7898 1210 E-mail david.marshall@lampal.c-of-e.org.uk

MARSHALL, Eric. b 20. EMMTC. **d** 82 **p** 83. Chapl Grimsby Distr Hosps 82-98; Hon C Gt Grimsby St Mary and St Jas *Linc* 85-98; rtd 98; Perm to Offic *Linc* from 99. *Morn Tide, Waithe Lane, Grimsby DN37 0RJ* Tel (01472) 823681

MARSHALL, Geoffrey Osborne. b 48. St Jo Coll Dur BA71. Coll of Resurr Mirfield 71. **d** 73 **p** 74. C Waltham Cross *St Alb* 73-76; C Digswell 76-78; P-in-c Belper Ch Ch and Milford *Derby* 78-86; V Spondon 86-93; Chapl Derby High Sch 87-01; RD Derby N *Derby* 90-95; Can Res Derby Cathl 93-02; Dioc Dir of Ords 95-00; R Wrexham *St As* from 02; RD Wrexham from 02. *The Rectory, 7 Westminster Drive, Wrexham LL12 7AT* Tel (01978) 263905 E-mail geoffrey@canonry.demon.co.uk

MARSHALL, Mrs Gillian Kathryn. b 54. Glouc Sch of Min 84. **d** 87 **p** 97. NSM Newtown w Llanllwchaiarn w Aberhafesp *St As* 87-98; P-in-c Betws Cedewain and Tregynon and Llanwyddelan 98-02; V from 02. *The Vicarage, Bettws Cedewen, Newtown SY16 3DS* Tel (01686) 650345

MARSHALL, Graham George. b 38. Dur Univ BA60 St Chad's Coll Dur DipHd65. **d** 65 **p** 66. C Ashton-on-Ribble St Mich *Blackb* 65-67; C Lancaster St Mary 67-71; R Church Eaton *Lich* 71-75; Prec Man Cathl *Man* 75-78; R Reddish 78-85; V Chadderton St Luke 87-02; rtd 02; Perm to Offic *Man* from 02. *7 The Woods, Rochdale OL11 3NT* Tel (01706) 642139 E-mail ggm@manutd.com

MARSHALL (née CHADWICK), Mrs Helen Jane. b 63. UEA BA84 St Jo Coll Nottm LTh88 MTh91 DPS91. **d** 91 **p** 94. Par Dn Easton H Trin w St Gabr and St Lawr and St Jude *Bris* 91-94; C 94-95; Perm to Offic *Ox* 95-98; Lect St Paul's Th Coll Limuru Kenya 98-99; Perm to Offic *Ely* 99-00; Chapl K Coll Lon *S'wark* from 01; Perm to Offic *Lon* from 01. *7 The Cottages, Lambeth Palace, Lambeth Palace Road, London SE1 7JU* Tel (020) 7848 4343 *or* 7848 2373 E-mail helen.marshall@kcl.ac.uk

MARSHALL, Canon Hugh Phillips. b 34. SS Coll Cam BA57 MA61. Linc Th Coll 57. **d** 59 **p** 60. C Westmr St Steph w St Jo *Lon* 59-65; V Tupsley *Heref* 65-74; V Wimbledon *S'wark* 74-78; TR 78-87; RD Merton 79-86; V Mitcham SS Pet and Paul 87-90; Hon Can S'wark Cathl 89-90; Perm to Offic 90-96; Chief Sec ABM 90-96; V Wendover *Ox* 96-01; P-in-c Halton 96-01; Hon Can Bulawayo from 96; rtd 01. *7 The Daedings, Deddington, Banbury OX15 0RT* Tel (01869) 337761 E-mail hughm@fish.co.uk

MARSHALL, Mrs Jean. b 36. SW Minl Tr Course 84. **d** 87 **p** 94. NSM Stratton *Truro* 87-89; NSM Bodmin w Lanhydrock and Lanivet 89-94; P-in-c Lawhitton and S Petherwin w Trewen 94-98; rtd 98; Hon C Bodmin w Lanhydrock and Lanivet *Truro* from 00. *10 Springwell View, Love Lane, Bodmin PL31 2QP* Tel (01208) 79891

MARSHALL, John. b 37. Kelham Th Coll 53. **d** 62 **p** 63. C Winshill *Derby* 62-64; C Chaddesden St Phil 64-65; Chapl HM Borstal Morton Hall 65-75; V Swinderby *Linc* 66-77; R Church Aston *Lich* 77-84; V Auckland St Andr and St Anne *Dur* 84-02; P-in-c Hunwick 88-90; Chapl Bishop Auckland Gen Hosp 84-94; Chapl Bishop Auckland Hospitals NHS Trust 94-98; Chapl S Durham Healthcare NHS Trust 98-00; rtd 02. *Croft House, West Bank, Winster, Matlock DE4 2DQ* Tel (01629) 650310

MARSHALL, John. b 50. St Luke's Coll Ex CertEd74 W Lon Inst of HE DEHC79. S'wark Ord Course 88. **d** 91 **p** 92. Hon C Brixton Hill St Sav *S'wark* 91-95; Hon C Clapham St Jas from 95. *57A Kingscourt Road, London SW16 1JA* Tel (020) 8769 3665

MARSHALL, John Douglas. b 23. Univ of Wales (Cardiff) BA43. St Alb Minl Tr Scheme 76. **d** 79 **p** 80. Hon C Radlett *St Alb* 79-86; Lic to Offic *Llan* from 86. *Meiros, 3 River Walk, Cowbridge CF71 7DW* Tel (01446) 773930

MARSHALL, John Linton. b 42. Worc Coll Ox BA64 MA68 Bris Univ MLitt75. Wells Th Coll 66. **d** 68 **p** 69. C Bris St Mary Redcliffe w Temple etc *Bris* 68-71; Tutor Sarum & Wells Th Coll 71-73; Perm to Offic *Pet* 74-77; Lic to Offic *S'well* 77-81; V Choral S'well Minster 79-81; R Ordsall 81-88; P-in-c Grove 84-88; RD Retford 84-88; V Northowram *Wakef* 88-99; P-in-c Glouc St Mark and St Mary de Crypt w St Jo etc *Glouc* 99-00; R from 00. *The Rectory, 38 St Mary's Square, Gloucester GL1 2QT* Tel (01452) 412679 E-mail cyprian@tesco.net

MARSHALL, Kirstin Heather. b 64. St Jo Coll Nottm 90. **d** 93 **p** 95. NSM Glas St Marg *Glas* 93-96; Hon Asst P Glas St Mary 96-99; P-in-c E Kilbride from 99. *St Mark's Rectory, Telford Road, East Kilbride, Glasgow G75 0HN* Tel (01355) 244042 E-mail khm@hotmail.com

MARSHALL, Canon Lionel Alan. b 41. TEng. St Deiniol's Hawarden 84 Qu Coll Birm 86. **d** 87 **p** 88. C Llandudno *Ban* 87-90; V Rhayader and Nantmel *S & B* 90-01; RD Maelienydd from 98; Hon Can Brecon Cathl from 00; P-in-c Llanbister w Llanbadarn Fynydd w Llananno etc from 01. *The Vicarage, Llanbister, Llandrindod Wells LD1 6TN* Tel (01597) 840333

MARSHALL, Canon Maurice Peter. b 23. Oak Hill Th Coll 59. **d** 61 **p** 62. C Haydock St Mark *Liv* 61-64; V New Ferry *Ches* 64-79; V Hartford 79-89; Hon Can Ches Cathl 87-89; rtd 89; Perm to Offic *Ches* from 89. *27 East Lane, Sandiway, Northwich CW8 2QQ* Tel (01606) 888591

MARSHALL, Melinda Christine. b 54. Cov Coll of Educn CertEd76. Ridley Hall Cam. **d** 01 **p** 02. C Exning St Martin w Landwade *St E* from 01. *3 Norfolk Avenue, Newmarket CB8 0DE*

MARSHALL, Michael David. b 51. BSc. Trin Coll Bris. **d** 84 **p** 85. C Kennington St Mark *S'wark* 84-88; V Streatham Park St Alb 88-96; RD Tooting 93-96; V Blackheath St Jo from 96; RD Charlton from 01. *146 Langton Way, London SE3 7JS* Tel (020) 8293 1248

✠**MARSHALL, The Rt Revd Michael Eric.** b 36. Ch Coll Cam BA58 MA60. Cuddesdon Coll 58. **d** 60 **p** 61 **c** 75. C Birm St Pet *Birm* 60-62; Tutor Ely Th Coll 62-64; Min Can Ely Cathl *Ely* 62-64; Chapl Lon Univ Lon Inst *S'wark* 64-69; V St Marylebone All SS 69-75; Suff Bp Woolwich *S'wark* 75-84; Episc Dir Angl Inst Missouri 84-92; Abps' Adv Springboard for Decade of Evang 92-97; Hon Asst Bp Lon from 84; Hon Asst Bp Chich from 92; Can and Preb Chich Cathl 90-99; P-in-c Upper Chelsea H Trin w St Jude *Lon* 97-02; R from 02. *Upper Chelsea Rectory, 97A Cadogan Lane, London SW1X 9DU* Tel (020) 7730 7270 Mobile 07710-215131

MARSHALL (formerly WEBB), Pauline Nikola. b 49. WMMTC 84. **d** 87 **p** 94. C Walsgrave on Sowe *Cov* 87-91; TD Grantham *Linc* 91-96; Ind Chapl 91-96; TV Grantham 94-96; Perm to Offic 01-02; C Boston from 02. *42 Langrick Road, Boston PE21 8HT* Tel (01205) 352110 *or* tel and fax 366892 Mobile 07815-438831 E-mail nikola.marshall@btopenworld.com

MARSHALL, Canon Peter Arthur. b 31. AKC58. **d** 59 **p** 60. C Hutton *Chelmsf* 59-61; C Rickmansworth *St Alb* 61-66; Chapl Orchard View and Kingsmead Court Hosps 66-94; R Lexden *Chelmsf* 66-94; RD Colchester 88-93; Hon Can Chelmsf Cathl 90-94; rtd 94; Perm to Offic *Win* from 94. *21 Manor Close, Wickham, Fareham PO17 5BZ* Tel (01329) 832988

MARSHALL, Peter James. b 48. Qu Coll Birm 78. **d** 80 **p** 81. C Ormskirk *Liv* 80-83; V Dallam from 83. *St Mark's Vicarage, Longshaw Street, Warrington WA5 5DY* Tel (01925) 631193

MARSHALL, The Very Revd Peter Jerome. b 40. McGill Univ Montreal. Westcott Ho Cam 61. **d** 63 **p** 64. C E Ham St Mary *Chelmsf* 63-66; C Woodford St Mary 66-71; C-in-c S Woodford 66-71; V Walthamstow St Pet 71-81; Dep Dir of Tr 81-84; Can Res Chelmsf Cathl 81-85; Dioc Dir of Tr *Ripon* 85-97; Can Res Ripon Cathl 85-97; Dean Worc from 97. *The Deanery, 10 College Green, Worcester WR1 2LH* Tel (01905) 27821 E-mail petermarshall@worcestercathedral.org.uk

MARSHALL, Peter John Charles. b 35. Bris Univ BA60. Ridley Hall Cam 60. **d** 62 **p** 63. C Lindfield *Chich* 62-65; Travelling Sec Scripture Union 65-83; Hon C Nottingham St Nic *S'well* 65-67; Hon C Cheadle Hulme St Andr *Ches* 67-83; V Ilkley All SS *Bradf* 83-98; RD Otley 92-97; rtd 98; Perm to Offic *Ches* from 00. *Creuddyn Barn, Glanwydden, Llandudno Junction LL31 9JL* Tel (01492) 547352 E-mail peter-janet_marshall@wycliffe.org

MARSHALL, Richard Arthur Howard. b 66. Regent's Park Coll Ox BA88 MA92 SS Coll Cam PGCE89. Wycliffe Hall Ox BTh99. **d** 98 **p** 99. C Broughton *Man* 98-02; Asst Chapl Sedbergh Sch 02-03; Sub Chapl HM Pris Man from 02. *The Old Rectory, 10 Rectory Road, Manchester M8 5EA* Tel 0161-795 8589 Mobile 07803-455475

MARSHALL, Robert. b 52. TCD BA75 MA00 Solicitor 77. CITC 99. **d** 02. NSM Stillorgan w Blackrock *D & G* from 02. *The Tontine, 84 The Rise, Mount Merrion, Co Dublin, Irish Republic* Tel (00353) (1) 288 6170 E-mail curate@stillorgan.dublin.anglican.org

MARSHALL, Robert Paul. b 60. Sheff Univ BA81 Dur Univ MA85. Cranmer Hall Dur 81. **d** 83 **p** 84. C Kirkstall *Ripon* 83-85; C Otley *Bradf* 85-87; Dioc Communications Officer 87-91; P-in-c Embsay w Eastby 87-91; Dioc Communications Officer *Lon* 91-95; P-in-c S Kensington St Aug 95-00; Media Adv to Abp *York* from 95; Perm to Offic *Bradf* from 02. *37 Nab Wood, Shipley BD18 4HQ* Tel (01274) 599622

MARSHALL, Rodney Henry. b 46. Bernard Gilpin Soc Dur 71 St Steph Ho Ox 72. **d** 75 **p** 76. C Gorton St Mary and St Thos *Man* 75-78; C Bedford Leigh 78-82; V Goldthorpe w Hickleton *Sheff* 82-90; Dioc Dir of In-Service Tr 89-90; NSM Hemsworth *Wakef* 96-97; P-in-c Athersley from 97. *St Helen's Vicarage, 27 Laithes Lane, Barnsley S71 3AF* Tel (01226) 245361

MARSHALL, Simon. b 54. Kingston Poly BSc77 Leeds Univ PGCE78 MA(Ed)79. Qu Coll Birm DipTh93. **d** 93 **p** 94. C Gt Clacton *Chelmsf* 93-97; TV Chigwell and Chigwell Row 97-02; C Woodford Wells from 02. *107 Monkhams Avenue, Woodford Green IG8 0ER* Tel (020) 8220 5143 E-mail simon.marshall17@ntlworld.com

MARSHALL, Simon Hardy. b 69. Bp Grosseteste Coll BA92. St Jo Coll Nottm 00. **d** 02 **p** 03. C Bartley Green *Birm* from 02. *19 Elmcroft Avenue, Birmingham B32 4LZ* Tel 0121-422 1436 E-mail themarshalls@fish.co.uk

MARSHALL, Mrs Sonia Margaret Cecilia. b 49. Westf Coll Lon BA71. EMMTC 01. **d** 03. NSM Deeping St James *Linc* from 03. *135C Eastgate, Deeping St James, Peterborough PE6 8RB* Tel (01778) 346420 E-mail curate@dsj.org.uk

MARSHALL, Susan. See PANTER MARSHALL, Mrs Susan Lesley

MARSHALL, Canon Timothy James. b 26. Barrister-at-Law (Middle Temple) 50 BNC Ox BA48 BCL49 MA53. St Steph Ho Ox DipTh51. **d** 52 **p** 53. C Staveley *Derby* 52-60; V Shirebrook 60-92; Hon Can Derby Cathl 86-92; rtd 92. *43 Charleston Road, Penrhyn Bay, Llandudno LL30 3HB* Tel (01492) 543541

MARSHALL, Timothy John. b 53. GRSM74. Oak Hill Th Coll BA79. **d** 79 **p** 80. C Muswell Hill St Jas w St Matt *Lon* 79-85; V Hammersmith St Simon 85-92; V Bovingdon *St Alb* from 92; RD Rickmansworth from 01. *The Vicarage, Vicarage Lane, Bovingdon, Hemel Hempstead HP3 0LP* Tel (01442) 833298

MARSHALL, William John. b 35. TCD BA57 BD61 PhD75. TCD Div Sch 59. **d** 59 **p** 60. C Ballyholme *D & G* 59-61; India 62-72; Asst Dean of Residence TCD 73-76; I Rathmichael *D & G* 76-92; Can Ch Cathl Dublin 90-02; Chan 91-02; Vice-Prin CITC 92-02; rtd 02. *115 The Elms, Abberley, Killiney, Co Dublin, Irish Republic* Tel (00353) (1) 239 0832

MARSHALL, William Michael. b 30. Pemb Coll Ox BA53 MA57 DipEd65 Lon Univ DipH67 Bris Univ MLitt72 PhD79. Wells Th Coll 63 Sarum & Wells Th Coll 79. **d** 80 **p** 81. Asst Chapl Millfield Sch Somerset 80-96; Hon C Glastonbury St Jo w Godney *B & W* 80-84; Hon C Glastonbury w Meare, W Pennard and Godney 84-96; rtd 96; Perm to Offic *Portsm* and *Win* from 96; *Ely* from 01; Hon Chapl ATC 97-00. *7 The Paddock, Ely CB6 1TP* Tel (01353) 612287 Fax as telephone E-mail william.m@ukonline.co.uk

MARSTON, David Howarth. b 48. St Jo Coll Dur BA69. Edin Th Coll 69. **d** 71 **p** 72. C Kendal H Trin *Carl* 71-75; Perm to Offic *Glas* 75-78; NSM Barrow St Matt *Carl* 79-86; Perm to Offic *York* 86-91; *Liv* 91-93 and 99-00; NSM Southport All SS and All So *Liv* 93-99; NSM Southport St Luke from 00. *33 Sandringham Road, Ainsdale, Southport PR8 2NY* Tel (01704) 578303

MARSTON, Neville Charles. b 37. Univ of Wales (Cardiff) DipSocSc62 BA65 Waterloo Univ (Canada) MA67. Ox Cen for Miss Studies 95. **d** 97 **p** 99. Dioc Dir Tr Seychelles 92-00; C Coven *Lich* 00-02; rtd 02. *88 Mill Rise, Swanland, North Ferriby HU14 3PW* Tel 07866-935844 (mobile)
E-mail nevillemarston@aol.com

MARSTON, William Thornton. b 59. Worc Coll Ox BA81 MA85 Cam Univ CertEd83. St Steph Ho Ox BA87. **d** 88 **p** 89. C Beckenham St Geo *Roch* 88-92; TV Ifield *Chich* 92-97; C-in-c Middleton-on-Sea CD 97-99; V Middleton from 99. *The Vicarage, 106 Elmer Road, Middleton-on-Sea, Bognor Regis PO22 6LJ* Tel (01243) 586348
E-mail w.marston@btopenworld.com

MART, Terence Eugene. b 47. CertEd76 BA82. St Jo Coll Nottm LTh87. **d** 87 **p** 88. C Prestatyn *St As* 87-91; Chapl Theatr Clwyd Mold 87-91; R Llangystennin 91-01; RD Llanrwst 96-00; V Llanfair DC, Derwen, Llanelidan and Efenechtyd from 01. *The Vicarage, Llanfair Dyffryn Clwyd, Ruthin LL15 2SA* Tel (01824) 704551

MARTIN, Alexander Lewendon. b 26. Em Coll Cam BA47 MA51. Ridley Hall Cam 56. **d** 57 **p** 58. C Ashtead *Guildf* 57-59; Asst Chapl Tonbridge Sch 59-64; Chapl Felsted Sch 64-74; Chapl Sedbergh Sch 74-84; R Askerswell, Loders and Powerstock *Sarum* 84-89; RD Lyme Bay 86-89; rtd 89; Perm to Offic *Ex* from 89. *Thirtover, 7 Alexandra Way, Crediton EX17 2EA* Tel (01363) 776206

MARTIN, Angela Lee. EMMTC 00. **d** 03. NSM Derby St Barn *Derby* from 03. *The Joiners' Arms, 60 Church Road, Quarndon, Derby DE22 5JA* Tel (01332) 552876 Mobile 07967-180531
E-mail trevor@joinersarms.com

MARTIN, Canon Anthony Bluett. b 29. St Jo Coll Cam BA52 MA56. Ridley Hall Cam 52. **d** 54 **p** 55. C Rushden *Pet* 54-57; C Worthing St Geo *Chich* 57-59; CSSM 59-63; Lic to Offic *Man* 59-63; V Hoole *Ches* 63-84; Hon Can Ches Cathl 83-94; V Bowdon 84-94; rtd 94; Perm to Offic *Ches* from 94. *8 Eaton Mews, Chester CH4 7EJ* Tel (01244) 680307

MARTIN, Blyth. *See* MARTIN, William Henry Blyth

MARTIN, Ms Briony June. b 71. St Cath Coll Cam BA92 MA96. Trin Coll Bris BA96 MA97. **d** 02 **p** 03. C Leatherhead and Mickleham *Guildf* from 02. *58 Kingscroft Road, Leatherhead KT22 7BU* Tel (01372) 379954 E-mail pmbm@fish.co.uk

MARTIN, Brother. *See* COOMBE, John Morrell

MARTIN, Bryan Robert. b 71. TCD BTh01. CITC 98. **d** 01 **p** 02. C Magheralin w Dollingstown *D & D* from 01. *22 Cottage Hill, Lurgan, Craigavon BT67 9NJ* E-mail brymrtn@aol.com

MARTIN, Christopher John. b 45. Ball Coll Ox BA67 MA87. Wycliffe Hall Ox 86. **d** 88 **p** 89. C Edin St Thos *Edin* 88-90; R Duns 90-00; Chapl Lyon *Eur* from 00. *38 Chemin de Taffignon, 69110 Ste-Foy-lès-Lyon, France* Tel (0033) (4) 78 59 67 06
E-mail lyonchurch@aol.com

MARTIN, Prof David Alfred. b 29. LSE BSc PhD. Westcott Ho Cam. **d** 83 **p** 84. Hon C Guildf Cathl *Guildf* 83-99; Perm to Offic from 99. *174 St John's Road, Woking GU21 7PQ* Tel (01483) 762134

MARTIN, David Geoffrey. b 34. K Coll Lon BD60 AKC61. **d** 61 **p** 62. C Liv Our Lady and St Nic *Liv* 61-63; Australia 63-66; Chapl and Lect K Coll Lon 66-70; V Kennington St Jo *S'wark* 70-77; P-in-c Camberwell St Jas 76-77; Hon C Clapham Ch Ch and St Jo 77-81; Lic to Offic 81-85; V S Wimbledon All SS 85-90; V Upper Norwood St Jo from 90. *St John's Vicarage, 2 Sylvan Road, London SE19 2RX* Tel (020) 8653 0378 Fax 8653 1970
E-mail dmartin169@aol.com

MARTIN, David Howard. b 47. Worc Coll Ox BEd79. AKC70 St Aug Coll Cant 70. **d** 71 **p** 72. C Sedgley All SS *Lich* 71-75; Dioc Youth Chapl *Worc* 75-81; P-in-c Worc St Andr and All SS w St Helen 75-81; R Newland, Guarlford and Madresfield 81-91; R Alvechurch from 91. *The Rectory, Alvechurch, Birmingham B48 7SB* Tel 0121-445 1087
E-mail david@martinalve.freeserve.co.uk

MARTIN, Donald Philip (Ralph). b 30. Trin Coll Toronto MA55 STB55. **d** 54 **p** 55. Canada 54-57; Tutor Kelham Th Coll 57-73; SSM from 60; P-in-c Willen *Ox* 73-81; Japan 81-82; Ghana 83-89; Dir Cleveland Lay Tr Course 89-91; C Middlesbrough All SS *York* 89-91; Kuwait 92-93; Italy 93-94; Canada 94-95; Tutor St Alb and Ox Min Course *Ox* 95-96; Chapl OHP 96; Lesotho from 97; rtd 98. *PO Box 1579, Maseru, Lesotho*

MARTIN, Edward Eldred William. b 37. Cranfield Inst of Tech MSc84 Herts Univ MA88. S'wark Ord Course 65. **d** 68 **p** 69. C Greenwich St Alfege w St Pet *S'wark* 68-71; C Kidbrooke St Jas 71-75; V Peckham St Jo 75-78; P-in-c Peckham St Andr w All SS 76-78; V Peckham St Jo w St Andr 78-81; Hon Chapl S'wark Cathl 81-02; Chapl Guy's Hosp Lon 81-88; rtd 02; Perm to Offic *S'wark* from 02; Hon C Lee St Marg from 03. *17 Honor Oak Rise,*

London SE23 3QY Tel (020) 8699 2303 Mobile 07956-204869 Fax (020) 8291 9237 E-mail emartin@horise.fsnet.co.uk

MARTIN, Edward James Russell. b 76. Hull Univ BA98 Leeds Univ BA02. Coll of Resurr Mirfield 00. **d** 03. C Carrington *S'well* from 03. *St John's House, 65 Osborne Grove, Nottingham NG5 2HE* Tel 0115-844 9805 Mobile 07736-711360

MARTIN, Miss Eileen Susan Kirkland. b 45. LCST66. Lon Bible Coll DipTh71 Cranmer Hall Dur 77. **dss** 83 **d** 86. Kilmarnock *Glas* 84-86; Par Dn Heanor *Derby* 87-92; Perm to Offic 92-95. *303 Cressex Road, High Wycombe HP12 4QF*

MARTIN, George Cobain. b 34. TCD BA57 MA65. **d** 57 **p** 58. C Bangor St Comgall *D & D* 57-64; I Kircubbin 64-74; R Ashby by Partney *Linc* 75-78; R Partney w Dalby 75-78; V Skendleby 75-78; P-in-c Candlesby w Scremby 77-78; R Partney 78-95; rtd 95; Perm to Offic *Linc* 95-98. *Southwold, Main Road, East Keal, Spilsby PE23 4BA* Tel (01790) 752988

MARTIN, Glenn. b 52. Qu Coll Birm 84. **d** 86 **p** 87. C Chatham St Wm *Roch* 86-89; Chapl Pastures Hosp Derby 89-94; Chapl Kingsway Hosp Derby 89-94; Sen Chapl S Derbys Mental Health NHS Trust 94-97; Sen Chapl Community Health Sheff NHS Trust 97-01; Professional Development Officer for Chapl and Spiritual Healthcare from 01. *North Trent Workforce Confederation, 2nd Floor, Saville Street East, Sheffield S4 7UQ* Tel 0114-226 4463 Fax 226 4442
E-mail glenn.martin@wdconfed.nhs.uk

MARTIN, Canon Gordon Albion John. b 30. AKC54. **d** 55 **p** 56. C Enfield Chase St Mary *Lon* 55-59; C Palmers Green St Jo 59-61; V Edmonton St Martin 61-64; V Culham *Ox* 64-67; Bp's Youth Chapl *St Alb* 67-73; P-in-c Wareside 69-73; V Harpenden St Jo 73-96; RD Wheathampstead 76-87; Hon Can St Alb 85-96; rtd 96; Perm to Offic *Ex* from 96. *2 Pottery Court, Church Road, Dartmouth TQ6 9SN* Tel (01803) 835628

MARTIN, Graham Rowland. b 39. LCP FRSA Liv Univ CertEd58 Nottm Univ DipRE65 Lon Univ DipTh BD70 Bris Univ BEd73 Bris Poly Dip Educn Mgt 80. Wells Th Coll 71. **d** 71 **p** 72. Hon C Glouc St Cath *Glouc* 71-76; P-in-c Brookthorpe w Whaddon 76-78; Perm to Offic 78-80; Hon C Hucclecote 80-82; Hon C Tuffley 82-88; NSM Hardwicke, Quedgeley and Elmore w Longney 88-89; V Kemble, Poole Keynes, Somerford Keynes etc 89-96; P-in-c Bibury w Winson and Barnsley from 96; Dioc Ecum Officer from 96. *The Vicarage, Bibury, Cirencester GL7 5NT* Tel (01285) 740387

MARTIN, Henry Rowland Felix. b 67. Leeds Univ BA89 SS Coll Cam BA95. Ridley Hall Cam CTM96. **d** 96 **p** 97. C Becontree St Mary *Chelmsf* 96-00; C Broughton *Man* 00-02; TR from 02. *St James' Vicarage, 396 Great Cheetham Street East, Salford M7 4UH* Tel 0161-792 1208
E-mail felixmartin@ukonline.co.uk

MARTIN, James Davidson. b 35. Glas Univ MA57 BD60 PhD70. **d** 89 **p** 89. NSM St Andrews St Andr *St And* 89-94; Chapl St Andr Univ 89-94; TV Glenrothes from 94; TV Leven from 94; TV Lochgelly from 94. *32 Craigievar Drive, Glenrothes KY7 4PH* Tel (01592) 772956 E-mail jdm32@compuserve.com

MARTIN, James Smiley. b 32. MBE98. TCD 65. **d** 67 **p** 68. C Glenavy *Conn* 67-70; C Belfast St Mary 70-73; I Carnmoney 73-74; I Mallusk 74-94; rtd 94. *21 Dundesert Road, Nutts Corner, Crumlin BT29 4SL* Tel (028) 9082 5636

MARTIN, Jessica Heloise. b 63. Trin Hall Cam BA86 PhD93. EAMTC 00. **d** 03. NSM Trin Coll Cam from 03. *82 Ditton Walk, Cambridge CB5 8QE* Tel (01223) 411196 Mobile 07870-704006
E-mail jhm28@cam.ac.uk

MARTIN, Canon John Albert. TCD DipTh85. **d** 85 **p** 86. C Drumachose *D & R* 85-88; I Cumber Upper w Learmount from 88; I Cumber Lower w Banagher from 88; Bp's Dom Chapl from 91; Dioc Warden of Readers from 92; Can Derry Cathl from 00. *Alla Rectory, 87 Cumber Road, Claudy, Londonderry BT47 4JA* Tel (028) 7133 8214

MARTIN, John Henry. b 42. St Jo Coll Cam BA63 MA67. St Jo Coll Nottm BA73. **d** 73 **p** 74. C Ecclesall *Sheff* 73-77; C Hednesford *Lich* 77-82; V Walsall Pleck and Bescot 82-92; V Whittington w Weeford from 92. *The Vicarage, Whittington, Lichfield WS14 9LH* Tel (01543) 432233

MARTIN, John Hunter. b 42. AKC64. **d** 65 **p** 66. C Mortlake w E Sheen *S'wark* 65-69; C-in-c Bermondsey St Hugh CD 69-72; V Bermondsey St Anne 72-78; P-in-c Lt Ouse *Ely* 78; V Littleport 78-89; V Attercliffe *Sheff* 89-90; P-in-c Darnall 90; TR Darnall-cum-Attercliffe 90-96; TR Attercliffe, Darnall and Tinsley 96; R Kirk Sandall and Edenthorpe from 96. *The Rectory, 31 Doncaster Road, Kirk Sandall, Doncaster DN3 1HP* Tel (01302) 882861

MARTIN, John Keith. b 32. Sarum & Wells Th Coll 76. **d** 79 **p** 80. C Bath Bathwick *B & W* 79-82; V Weston-super-Mare St Andr Bournville 82-85; V Cinderford St Jo *Glouc* 85-94; rtd 97. *Glen Cairn, 39 Laflouder Fields, Mullion, Helston TR12 7EJ* Tel (01326) 240613

MARTIN, Canon John Pringle. b 24. Bris Univ BA50. Clifton Th Coll 50. **d** 52 **p** 53. C Braintree *Chelmsf* 52-56; C St Paul *St Alb* 56-59; V Congleton St Pet *Ches* 59-81; RD Congleton 74-85; Hon Can Ches Cathl 80-90; R Brereton w Swettenham

81-90; rtd 90; Perm to Offic *B & W* from 90. *49 Parkhouse Road, Minehead TA24 8AD* Tel (01643) 706769

MARTIN, John Stuart. b 11. St Jo Coll Dur BA34. Wycliffe Hall Ox. **d** 35 **p** 36. C Mansfield St Pet *S'well* 35-37; C Newhaven *Chich* 37-39; C Barcombe 39-43; V Ox H Trin *Ox* 43-46; V Leafield w Wychwood 46-51; R Rotherfield Greys 51-63; V Highmore 55-63; R Bow w Broad Nymet *Ex* 63-65; V Upottery 65-72; TV Farway w Northleigh and Southleigh 72-73; rtd 73. *Church Villa, 8 Church Road, Bawdrip, Bridgwater TA7 8PU* Tel (01278) 684092

MARTIN, Canon John Tidswell. b 24. Em Coll Cam BA48 MA52. Kelham Th Coll 48. **d** 53 **p** 54. C Yardley Wood *Birm* 53-55; Asst Gen Sec and Sec Th Colls Dept SCM 55-58; Gen Sec 58-62; R Withington St Chris *Man* 62-68; V Kingston All SS *S'wark* 68-76; V Kingston All SS w St Jo 76-89; Hon Can S'wark Cathl 87-89; rtd 89; NSM Twickenham St Mary *Lon* from 89; Perm to Offic *S'wark* from 89; Perm to Offic *Lon* from 93. *175 Lincoln Avenue, Twickenham TW2 6NL*

MARTIN, Jonathan Patrick McLeod. b 55. Leic Univ BA81. Sarum & Wells Th Coll 84. **d** 86 **p** 87. C Southampton Thornhill St Chris *Win* 86-89; Perm to Offic 89-92; C Heatherlands St Jo *Sarum* 92-97; Dioc Link Officer for ACUPA 95-97; Chief Exec Dame Agnes Weston's R Sailors' Rests from 97; Lic to Offic *Portsm* from 97; Perm to Offic *Sarum* 98-01; NSM Parkstone St Pet and St Osmund w Branksea from 01. *3 Jennings Road, Poole BH14 8RY* Tel (01202) 748566 E-mail aggies@globalnet.co.uk

MARTIN, Joseph Edward. b 35. NDD55. Bps' Coll Cheshunt 58. **d** 60 **p** 61. C Short Heath *Birm* 60-62; C Caterham Valley *S'wark* 63-66; R W Hallam and Mapperley *Derby* 66-70; P-in-c Mapperley 66-67; V Wykeham and Hutton Buscel *York* 71-78; Chapl HM Pris Askham Grange 78-82; V Askham Bryan w Askham Richard *York* 78-82; R Amotherby w Appleton and Barton-le-Street 82-84; C Banbury *Ox* 85-88; C Warsop *S'well* 88-90; V Tuxford w Weston and Markham Clinton 90-00; rtd 00. *Windsmead, Allithwaite Road, Cartmel, Grange-over-Sands LA11 7SB* Tel (01777) 870497

MARTIN, Kenneth. b 20. Univ of Wales (Lamp) BA47. Bp Burgess Hall Lamp. **d** 48 **p** 49. C Rumney *Mon* 48-49; C Griffithstown 49-51; CF (TA) from 52; Perm to Offic *Llan* from 51. *21 Earls Court Road, Penylan, Cardiff CF23 9DE* Tel (029) 2049 3796

MARTIN, Kenneth Cyril. b 31. AIGCM53. S'wark Ord Course 71. **d** 73 **p** 74. C Hollington St Leon *Chich* 73-76; C Horsham 76-79; P-in-c Broadwaters *Worc* 79-81; V 81; P-in-c Worc H Trin 81-86; R Stoulton w Drake's Broughton and Pirton etc 86-91; rtd 91; Perm to Offic *Chich* from 95. *190 Gossops Drive, Crawley RH11 8LD* Tel (01293) 529172

MARTIN, Lee. See MARTIN, Angela Lee

MARTIN, Miss Marion. b 47. Oak Hill Th Coll DipHE85. **dss** 86 **d** 87. Ditton Roch 86-88; C 87-88; rtd 88; Perm to Offic *Glouc* 89-02. *33 Campden Road, Cheltenham GL51 6AA* Tel (01242) 239477

MARTIN, Nicholas Roger. b 53. St Jo Coll Dur BA74. Ripon Coll Cuddesdon 75. **d** 77 **p** 78. C Wolvercote w Summertown *Ox* 77-80; C Kidlington 80-82; TV 82-84; V Happisburgh w Walcot *Nor* 84-85; P-in-c Hempstead w Lessingham and Eccles 84-85; R Happisburgh w Walcot, Hempstead, Lessingham etc 85-89; R Blakeney w Cley, Wiveton, Glandford etc 89-97; TR Totnes w Bridgetown, Berry Pomeroy etc *Ex* from 97; RD Totnes 99-03. *The Rectory, Northgate, Totnes TQ9 5NX* Tel (01803) 862104 Fax 865615 E-mail nmartin497@aol.com

MARTIN, Nicholas Worsley. b 52. Sarum & Wells Th Coll 71. **d** 75 **p** 76. C Llandaff w Capel Llanilltern *Llan* 75-79; C Cardiff St Jo 79-83; C Caerphilly 79-83; TV Hemel Hempstead *St Alb* 83-93; Chapl Hemel Hempstead Gen Hosp 83-93; Perm to Offic *Chich* 94-98; *Truro* 99-00; NSM Penzance St Mary w St Paul *Truro* 99-02; NSM Penzance St Mary w St Paul and St Jo from 02. *Flat 4, 14 Regent Terrace, Penzance TR18 4DW* Tel (01736) 350506

MARTIN, Norman George. b 22. Sarum & Wells Th Coll 74. **d** 77 **p** 78. NSM Long Ashton *B & W* 77-81; NSM Walton in Gordano 81-82; NSM E Clevedon and Walton w Weston w Clapton 82-87; Chapl Barrow Hosp Bris 87-91; Chapl United Bris Healthcare NHS Trust 91-00; Chapl Farleigh Hosp 87-00; Perm to Offic *B & W* 87-00; Perm to Offic *Mon* from 00. *27 Fairview, High Beech, Chepstow NP16 5BX*

MARTIN, Paul Dexter. b 50. Wabash Coll (USA) BA72 Univ of the South (USA) MDiv75. **d** 75 **p** 76. Educn Tutor Cov Cathl 75-76; C Norbury St Phil *Cant* 76-80; USA from 80. *275 Southfield Road, Shreveport, LA 71105, USA* E-mail pdmartin@iamerica.net

MARTIN, Canon Penelope Elizabeth. b 44. Cranmer Hall Dur 83. **dss** 86 **d** 87 **p** 94. Seaham w Seaham Harbour *Dur* 86-89; Par Dn 87-89; Par Dn Cassop cum Quarrington 89-93; Par Dn Sherburn w Pittington 93-94; C 94-95; V 95-02; R Shadforth 95-02; R Pittington, Shadforth and Sherburn 02-03; Hon Can Dur Cathl 01-03; rtd 03. *3AA Rosemount, Durham DH1 5GA* Tel 0191-386 1742 E-mail penny.martin@charis.co.uk

MARTIN, Peter. b 50. MCIH75. Linc Th Coll 82. **d** 84 **p** 85. C Taunton H Trin *B & W* 84-86; C Bath Bathwick 86-88; R

Cannington, Otterhampton, Combwich and Stockland from 88; RD Sedgemoor from 00; Chapl Cannington Coll from 89. *The Rectory, 27 Brook Street, Cannington, Bridgwater TA5 2HP* Tel (01278) 652953 E-mail petermartin@petermmartin.fsnet.co.uk

MARTIN, Peter. b 66. Univ of Wales (Ban) BD89. Qu Coll Birm 90. **d** 92 **p** 93. C Kingswinford St Mary *Lich* 92-93; C Kingswinford St Mary *Worc* 93-95; Chapl Redbridge Health Care NHS Trust from 95. *The Chaplain's Office, King George Hospital, Barley Lane, Goodmayes, Ilford IG3 8YB* Tel (020) 8983 8000 ext 8841

MARTIN, Philip James. b 58. Cam Univ BA. Coll of Resurr Mirfield. **d** 84 **p** 85. C Pontefract St Giles *Wakef* 84-88; C Wantage *Ox* 88-90; C Didcot All SS 90; V Alderholt *Sarum* from 90; Dioc USPG Rep from 90. *The Vicarage, Daggons Road, Alderholt, Fordingbridge SP6 3DN* Tel (01425) 653179

MARTIN, Ralph. See MARTIN, Donald Philip

MARTIN, Raymond William. b 32. MBIM Lon Univ BSc66 DMA. Glouc Th Course 73. **d** 76 **p** 76. Hon C Glouc St Mary de Lode and St Nic *Glouc* 76-77; Hon C Redmarley D'Abitot, Bromesberrow w Pauntley etc 77-84; R 84-91; P-in-c Falfield w Rockhampton 91-98; P-in-c Oldbury-on-Severn 91-98; Chapl HM YOI Eastwood Park 91-92; rtd 98; Perm to Offic *Glouc* 98-00 and from 02; Clergy Widows' Officer (Glouc Adnry) from 99; P-in-c Shipton Moyne w Westonbirt and Lasborough 00-02; Perm to Offic *Heref* and *Worc* from 03. *Tree Tops, 35 Thirlstane Road, Malvern WR14 3PL* Tel (01684) 562714

MARTIN, Rhys Jonathan. b 68. Heythrop Coll Lon BD98. EAMTC 98. **d** 00 **p** 01. C Stansted Mountfitchet w Birchanger and Farnham *Chelmsf* 00-02; C Dovercourt and Parkeston w Harwich from 02. *19 Beacon Hill Avenue, Harwich CO12 3NR* Tel (01225) 504322 E-mail rhys.martin@zetnet.co.uk

MARTIN, Richard. b 34. Rhodes Univ BA54 Em Coll Cam BA57 MA58. Wells Th Coll 57. **d** 59 **p** 60. C Portsea St Mary *Portsm* 59-60; S Africa 60-87; C Bloemfontein Cathl 60-62; R Wepener 62-64; R Odendaalsrus 64-67; R Newton Park St Hugh 67-76; Chapl St Bede's Coll Umtata 77-79; R Hillcrest 79-87; C Aldershot St Mich *Guildf* 87-94; R Wick *Mor* 94-99; P-in-c Thurso 94-99; rtd 99; Hon C Diptford, N Huish, Harberton, Harbertonford etc *Ex* 99-01; Perm to Offic from 01. *16 Palace Meadow, Chudleigh, Newton Abbot TQ13 0PJ* Tel (01626) 853716 E-mail dosrich@gillscross.fsnet.co.uk

MARTIN, Richard Charles de Villeral. b 41. St Jo Coll Ox BA63 MA67. Ox Ord Course. **d** 84 **p** 85. NSM Ox St Thos w St Frideswide and Binsey *Ox* from 84; Asst Chapl Highgate Sch Lon 86-92; Magd Coll Sch Ox from 92; Chapl from 94. *11 Benson Place, Oxford OX2 6QH* Tel (01865) 510694

MARTIN, Richard Hugh. b 55. Van Mildert Coll Dur BA78 St Jo Coll Nottm BA81 Leeds Univ MA01. Cranmer Hall Dur 79. **d** 82 **p** 83. C Gateshead *Dur* 82-85; C Redmarshall 85-88; V Scarborough St Jas w H Trin *York* 88-96; Chapl R Wolv Hosps NHS Trust 96-02; V Bris St Andr Hartcliffe *Bris* from 02. *St Andrew's Vicarage, Peterson Square, Bristol BS13 0EE* Tel 0117-964 3554 Mobile 07870-147355 E-mail richardtherev@blueyonder.co.uk

MARTIN, Robert David Markland. b 51. FCA80 Trin Coll Cam BA71 MA74. Trin Coll Bris BA91. **d** 91 **p** 92. C Kingswood *Bris* 91-95; V Frome H Trin *B & W* from 95. *Holy Trinity Vicarage, Orchard Street, Frome BA11 3BX* Tel (01373) 462586 E-mail rob@holytrinityfrome.info

MARTIN, Robert Paul Peter. b 58. Chich Th Coll. **d** 83 **p** 84. C Anfield St Columba *Liv* 83-86; C Orford St Marg 86-87; R Blackley H Trin *Man* 87-90; C Oseney Crescent St Luke *Lon* 90-93; C Kentish Town 93-96; V Harringay St Paul from 96. *St Paul's Vicarage, Wightman Road, London N4 1RW* Tel (020) 8340 5299 Fax as telephone

MARTIN, Robin. See MARTIN, Thomas Robin

MARTIN, Robin Hugh. b 35. Rhodes Univ BA56 Birm Univ DipTh57. **d** 58 **p** 59. C Darnall *Sheff* 58-62; C-in-c Kimberworth Park 62-65; Lic to Offic 65-66; Lic to Offic *Newc* 67-71; Perm to Offic *Man* 79-93; Perm to Offic *Heref* from 97; Perm to Offic *Lich* 97-99; P-in-c Maesbury from 99. *Offa House, Treflach, Oswestry SY10 9HQ* Tel (01691) 657090

MARTIN, Roger Allen. b 38. Westmr Coll Lon CertEd59 Birkbeck Coll Lon BA64 FRMetS79. St Alb and Ox Min Course 97. **d** 99 **p** 00. NSM Bramfield, Stapleford, Waterford etc *St Alb* from 99. *41 The Avenue, Bengeo, Hertford SG14 3DS* Tel (01992) 422441 E-mail roger.martin@net.ntl.com

MARTIN, Roger Ivor. b 42. DMS76 MCMI. Cant Sch of Min. **d** 85 **p** 86. NSM Saltwood *Cant* 85-90; P-in-c Crundale w Godmersham 90-01; Dioc Exec Officer for Adult Educn and Lay Tr 90-96; CME Officer 94-96; Chapl to Bp Maidstone 96-01; R Saltwood from 01. *The Rectory, Rectory Lane, Saltwood, Hythe CT21 4QA* Tel (01303) 266932 Fax 261667 E-mail rogmartin@clara.co.uk

MARTIN, Mrs Rosanna Stuart. b 60. Bris Univ BA81. Wycliffe Hall Ox 89. **d** 92 **p** 94. Par Dn Stanford in the Vale w Goosey and Hatford *Ox* 92-94; C 94-96; C Abingdon 96-00; Perm to Offic from 00. *7 Limetrees, Chilton, Didcot OX11 1AH* Tel (01235) 821861

MARTIN, Rupert Gresley. b 57. Worc Coll Ox BA78 Ox Univ MA95. Trin Coll Bris DipHE91. **d** 91 **p** 92. C Yateley *Win* 91-95; V Sandal St Helen *Wakef* from 95. *The Vicarage, 333 Barnsley Road, Wakefield WF2 6EJ* Tel (01924) 255441 E-mail srsth@netscapeonline.co.uk

MARTIN, Russell Derek. b 47. St Jo Coll Dur 71. **d** 74 **p** 75. C Hartlepool H Trin *Dur* 74-78; C Swindon St Jo and St Andr *Bris* 78-79; V Penhill 79-91; V Haselbury Plucknett, Misterton and N Perrott *B & W* 91-99. *59 North Street, Martock TA12 6EH* Tel (01935) 829266 Mobile 07770-783893

MARTIN, Mrs Sara Galloway. b 19. MCSP40. N Ord Course 71. **dss** 79 **d** 87 **p** 94. Ainsworth *Man* 79-82; Tottington 82-87; Par Dn 87-88; Hon C from 94; rtd 89; Perm to Offic *Man* 89-94. *36 Victoria Street, Tottington, Bury BL8 4AG* Tel (01204) 882868

MARTIN, Miss Susan. b 56. Nottm Univ BA77. Edin Th Coll 86. **d** 88 **p** 94. C Leigh Park *Portsm* 88-91; C Sandown Ch Ch 91-94; C Portsea St Cuth 94-95; rtd 95; Perm to Offic *Portsm* from 95; NSM Portsea St Geo from 01. *7 Farthingdale Terrace, Peacock Lane, Portsmouth PO1 2TL* Tel (023) 9229 7994

MARTIN, Sylvia. b 24. **dss** 75 **d** 87 **p** 94. NSM Selsdon St Jo w St Fran *S'wark* 87-99; Perm to Offic from 99. *42 Upper Selsdon Road, Selsdon, Croydon CR2 8DE* Tel (020) 8657 3422

MARTIN, Sylvia. b 43. Dip Counselling 93 Dip Chr Th and Min 97. Sarum Th Coll 94. **d** 97 **p** 98. NSM Locks Heath *Portsm* 97-02; Perm to Offic from 02. *9 Harvester Drive, Catisfield, Fareham PO15 5NR* Tel (01329) 841737

MARTIN, Thomas Robin. b 40. Bps' Coll Cheshunt 64. **d** 67 **p** 68. C Ripley *Derby* 67-70; C Ilkeston St Mary 70-74; V Chinley w Buxworth 74-83; V Knighton St Mich *Leic* 83-85; V Thurmaston from 85. *The Vicarage, 828 Melton Road, Thurmaston, Leicester LE4 8BE* Tel 0116-269 2555

MARTIN, William Harrison. b 38. Sarum & Wells Th Coll 91. **d** 87 **p** 88. NSM Rushen *S & M* 87-92; C German 92-97; V Lonan from 97; V Laxey from 97. *The Vicarage, 56 Ard Reayrt, Ramsey Road, Laxey, Isle of Man IM4 7QQ* Tel (01624) 862050

MARTIN, William Henry Blyth. b 10. Keble Coll Ox BA33 MA36. Cuddesdon Coll 35. **d** 36 **p** 37. C S Shields St Mary *Dur* 36-39; Chapl Bps' Coll Cheshunt 39-45; Vice-Prin Bp's Coll Cheshunt 45-48; CF (EC) 41-45; V Chesterfield St Aug *Derby* 49-62; V Long Eaton St Laur 62-80; rtd 81; Perm to Offic *Cov* 81-01; *Pet* 85-94. *22 Clifton Court Nursing Home, Lilbourne Road, Clifton on Dunsmore, Rugby CV23 0BB* Tel (01788) 572669

MARTIN, William Matthew. b 28. C&G81 FE TCert81 Ch Coll Cam BA52 MA56. Ridley Hall Cam 52. **d** 54 **p** 55. C Weaste *Man* 54-56; V 56-61; CF (TA) 58-61; CF 61-82; Dep Asst Chapl Gen 73-82; Asst Master St Jo Southworth RC High Sch Preston 82-88; Lic to Offic *Blackb* 82-93; rtd 93; Perm to Offic *Blackb* from 93. *2B The Farthings, Chorley PR7 1TP* Tel (01257) 262772

MARTIN-DOYLE, Mrs Audrey Brenda. b 35. Cranmer Hall Dur 80. **dss** 82 **d** 87 **p** 95. The Lye and Stambermill *Worc* 82-86; Chapl Lee Abbey 86-88; Ldr Aston Cottage Community 88-93; C Cheltenham St Mary, St Matt, St Paul and H Trin *Glouc* 94-97; rtd 97; Perm to Offic *Glouc* from 97. *39 Moorend Street, Cheltenham GL53 0EH* Tel (01242) 510352 E-mail audrey@martin-doyle.freeserve.co.uk

MARTIN PHILIP, Brother. See **FREEMAN, Philip Martin**

MARTIN-SMITH, Paul. b 38. TCD BA64 Lon Univ MSc67 FIPEM88. WMMTC 94. **d** 97 **p** 98. NSM Tile Hill *Cov* 97-99; Perm to Offic *Ex* from 00. *12 Emmasfield, Exmouth EX8 2LS* Tel (01395) 269505

MARTINDALE, Mrs Patricia Ann. b 24. Qu Coll Birm. **dss** 84 **d** 87 **p** 94. Rugby St Andr *Cov* 84-94; NSM 87-94; Perm to Offic from 95. *54 Hillmorton Road, Rugby CV22 5AD* Tel (01788) 543038

MARTINEAU, Canon Christopher Lee. b 16. Trin Hall Cam BA38 MA70. Linc Th Coll 39. **d** 41 **p** 42. C Hinckley St Mary *Leic* 41-43; Chapl RNVR 43-46; C St Alb Abbey *St Alb* 46-48; V Balsall Heath St Paul *Birm* 48-54; P-in-c Shard End 54-58; V 58-65; R Skipton H Trin *Bradf* 65-83; Hon Can Bradf Cathl 72-83; rtd 83; Perm to Offic *Bradf* 83-02. *70 New Street, Ledbury HR8 2EE* Tel (01531) 635479

MARTINEAU, Canon David Richards Durani. b 36. AKC59. **d** 60 **p** 61. C Ches St Jo *Ches* 60-64; S Africa 64-69; C St Mark's Cathl George 64; C Riversdale 64-66; R Beaufort W and Victoria W 66-69; C Jarrow St Paul *Dur* 69-72; TV 72-75; TR Jarrow 76-85; V Gildersome *Wakef* 85-00; Hon Can Wakef Cathl 94-00; rtd 00; Perm to Offic *Linc* from 00; Hon Asst Chapl Voorschoten *Eur* 02-03. *Harlough, St Chad, Barrow-upon-Humber DN19 7AU* Tel (01469) 531475 E-mail david-martineau@harlough.freeserve.co.uk

MARTINEAU, Canon Jeremy Fletcher. b 40. K Coll Lon BD65 AKC65. **d** 66 **p** 67. C Jarrow St Paul *Dur* 66-73; Bp's Ind Adv 69-73; P-in-c Raughton Head w Gatesgill *Carl* 73-80; Chapl to Agric 73-80; Ind Chapl *Bris* 80-90; Abps' Rural Officer *Cant* 90-93; Nat Rural Officer Gen Syn Bd of Miss from 94; Hon Can Cov Cathl *Cov* from 01. *The Arthur Rank Centre, National Agricultural Centre, Stoneleigh Park, Kenilworth CV8 2LZ* Tel (024) 7669 6969 *or* (01926) 812130 Fax 7669 6460 E-mail j.martineau@ruralnet.org.uk

MARTLEW, Andrew Charles. b 50. Nottm Univ BTh76 Lanc Univ MA80. Linc Th Coll 72. **d** 76 **p** 77. C Poulton-le-Fylde *Blackb* 76-79; Hon C Lancaster Ch Ch 79-80; Malaysia 81-83; V Golcar *Wakef* 83-89; Dioc Schs Officer 89-95; V Warmfield 89-95; Dioc Dir of Educn *York* 95-02; CF from 02. *clo MOD Chaplains (Army),* Tel (01980) 615804 Fax 615800 E-mail andrew@elk.demon.co.uk

MARVELL, John. b 32. Lon Univ BD63 Leic Univ MEd73 PhD85. Oak Hill Th Coll 79. **d** 80 **p** 81. NSM Colchester Ch Ch w St Mary V *Chelmsf* 80-85; Perm to Offic 85-87; P-in-c Stisted w Bradwell and Pattiswick 87-98; rtd 98. *3 Impasse de Genets, Vicomte, 35800 Dinard, France* Tel (0033) (2) 9916 5674 E-mail jmarvell@ctacom.fr

MARVIN, David Arthur. b 51. HND73. St Jo Coll Nottm 96. **d** 97 **p** 98. C Mansfield St Jo *S'well* 97-01; P-in-c Greasley from 01. *The Vicarage, 36 Moorgreen, Newthorpe, Nottingham NG16 2FB* Tel (01773) 712509 E-mail dmarvin@fish.co.uk

MARWOOD, Timothy John Edmonds. b 51. Whitelands Coll Lon CertEd72 Open Univ BA89 Lon Inst of Educn MA91. S'wark Ord Course 92. **d** 95 **p** 96. NSM Putney St Mary *S'wark* from 95; Perm to Offic *Ex* from 00. *54 Eversleigh Road, London SW11 5XA* Tel (020) 7223 0510 *or* 8788 9591

MASCALL, Mrs Margaret Ann. b 43. LRAM64 Bris Univ CertEd65 St Jo Coll Dur BA71 MA79. Cranmer Hall Dur 69. **dss** 76 **d** 87 **p** 94. Hertford St Andr *St Alb* 75-79; Herne Bay Ch Ch *Cant* 79-82; Seasalter 82-84; Whitstable 84-90; Par Dn 87-90; Perm to Offic 91-94; Hon C Hackington 94-95; V Newington w Hartlip and Stockbury from 95; rtd 03. *Address temp unknown*

MASCARENHAS, Felix Pedro Antonio. b 55. Bombay Univ BA80 Pontifical Univ Rome JCD88. Pilar Major Th Sem Goa BTh81. **d** 82 **p** 82. In RC Ch 82-02; C Chich St Paul and Westhampnett *Chich* from 02. *The Vicarage, 11 Old Arundel Road, Westhampnett, Chichester PO18 0TH* Tel (01243) 783010 Mobile 07814-739312 E-mail felixmas@hotmail.com

MASDING, John William. b 39. Magd Coll Ox BA61 DipEd63 MA65 Univ of Wales (Cardiff) LLM94 FRSA96. Ridley Hall Cam 63. **d** 65 **p** 66. C Boldmere *Birm* 65-71; V Hamstead St Paul 71-97; rtd 97; Perm to Offic *B & W* from 97 and *Bris* from 00. *The Old School House, Norton Hawkfield, Pensford, Bristol BS39 4HB* Tel (01275) 830017 Fax as telephone E-mail masding@breathe.co.uk

MASH, William Edward John. b 54. ARCS Imp Coll Lon BSc75 Open Univ MA00. St Jo Coll Nottm 87. **d** 89 **p** 90. C Beverley Minster *York* 89-93; V Elloughton and Brough w Brantingham 93-01; P-in-c Newcastle St Geo *Lich* from 01; Chapl Town Cen and Newcastle Coll of H&FE from 01. *St George's Vicarage, 28 Hempstalls Lane, Newcastle ST5 0SS* Tel (01782) 710056 E-mail william@mashecbwb.freeserve.co.uk

MASHEDER, Peter Timothy Charles. b 49. AKC71. St Aug Coll Cant 71. **d** 72 **p** 73. C Barkingside St Fran *Chelmsf* 72-75; C Chingford SS Pet and Paul 75-91; P-in-c High Laver w Magdalen Laver and Lt Laver etc 91-98; R from 98; RD Ongar from 98. *The Lavers Rectory, Magdalen Laver, Ongar CM5 0ES* Tel (01279) 426774 E-mail chasmash@ic24.net

MASHEDER, Richard. b 36. AKC59. **d** 60 **p** 61. C Preston St Matt *Blackb* 60-62; C Padiham 62-65; P-in-c Worsthorne 65; 65-74; CF (TA) 65-67; P-in-c Blackb St Jude *Blackb* 74-78; V Blackb St Thos 76-78; V Blackb St Thos w St Jude 78-82; V Silverdale 82-01; rtd 01; Perm to Offic *Blackb* from 01. *59 Twemlow Parade, Heysham, Morecambe LA3 2AL* Tel (01524) 851151 Fax as telephone E-mail revakela@talk21.com

MASKELL, John Michael. b 45. Sarum & Wells Th Coll 86. **d** 88 **p** 89. C Swanborough *Sarum* 88-91; Chapl RAF 91-95; P-in-c Ollerton w Boughton *S'well* 95-97; P-in-c Guild *Guildf* 97-02; TV Walton H Trin *Ox* 02-03; Healing Co-ord Acorn Chr Healing Trust from 03. *1 Milland House Cottages, Milland Lane, Liphook GU30 7JN* Tel (01428) 741615 *or* (01420) 478121 Mobile 07929-134962 E-mail jmaskell@acornchristian.org

MASKELL, Miss Rosemary Helen. b 58. Ripon Coll Cuddesdon. **d** 00 **p** 01. C Goodrington *Ex* from 00. *40 Steed Close, Paignton TQ4 7SN* Tel (01803) 842877 Mobile 07803-499755 E-mail revrose@goodevon.fsnet.co.uk

MASKREY, Mrs Susan Elizabeth. b 43. Cranmer Hall Dur IDC70 St Jo Coll Dur CertRK70. **dss** 76 **d** 92 **p** 94. Littleover *Derby* 76-77; Sec to Publicity Manager CMS Lon 77-78; Stantonbury and Willen *Ox* 78-88; Billingham St Aid *Dur* 88-95; C 92-95; Asst Chapl HM Pris Holme Ho 94-95; Asst Chapl HM Pris Preston 95-01; Chapl HM Pris Kirkham from 01. *HM Prison, Freckleton Road, Kirkham, Preston PR4 2RA* Tel (01772) 684343

MASLEN, Darren Robert Dunstan. b 71. St Martin's Coll Lanc BA93 Open Univ MA97 Leeds Univ BA99. Coll of Resurr Mirfield 97. **d** 00 **p** 01. C Shaston *Sarum* from 00. *1 Gower Road, Shaftesbury SP7 8RU* Tel (01747) 855969

MASLEN (formerly CHILD), Mrs Margaret Mary. b 44. ALA76 Open Univ BA79. S Dios Min Tr Scheme 89. **d** 92 **p** 94. C Portishead *B & W* 92-93; C Ilminster w Whitelackington 93-94; C Ilminster and Distr 94-96; C Tatworth 96-00; Chapl Taunton and Somerset NHS Trust from 97; TV Chard and Distr

B & W from 00. *The Vicarage, 3 Home Farm, Tatworth, Chard TA20 2SH* Tel (01460) 220404

MASLEN, Richard Ernest. b 34. S Dios Minl Tr Scheme 89. **d** 92 **p** 93. NSM Sherston Magna, Easton Grey, Luckington etc *Bris* 92-93; NSM Ilminster w Whitelackington *B & W* 93-94; NSM Ilminster and Distr 94-96; P-in-c Tatworth 96-99; TV Chard and Distr 99-00; rtd 00; Perm to Offic *B & W* from 00. *The Vicarage, 3 Home Farm, Tatworth, Chard TA20 2SH* Tel (01460) 220404

MASLEN, Canon Stephen Henry. b 37. CCC Ox BA62 MA65. Ridley Hall Cam 62. **d** 64 **p** 65. C Keynsham w Queen Charlton *B & W* 64-67; C Cheltenham St Mary *Glouc* 67-71; P-in-c St Mary-at-Lambeth *S'wark* 72-74; TV N Lambeth 74-79; V Horley 79-84; TR 84-94; RD Reigate 86-91; R Coulsdon St Jo 94-02; Hon Can S'wark Cathl 95-02; rtd 02. *The Red House, Back Lane, Bredon, Tewkesbury GL20 7LH* Tel (01684) 772575

MASLEN, Trevor. b 51. Chich Th Coll 77. **d** 80 **p** 81. C Harlow St Mary Magd *Chelmsf* 80-83; C Huntingdon St Barn *Ely* 83-86; P-in-c Huntingdon 86-87; TV 87-92; V Southampton St Jude *Win* 92-97. *116 Fotheringham Road, Enfield EN1 1QE*

MASON, Adrian Stanley. b 54. Hatf Poly BSc77. Ripon Coll Cuddesdon 77. **d** 80 **p** 81. C Mill End and Heronsgate w W Hyde *St Alb* 80-83; TV Axminster, Chardstock, Combe Pyne and Rousdon *Ex* 83-87; TV Halesworth w Linstead, Chediston, Holton etc *St E* 87-88; R Brandon and Santon Downham 88-91; R Glem Valley United Benefice 91-95; Min Can St E Cathl 95-97. *42 Duddery Road, Haverhill CB9 8EA* Tel (01440) 703581

MASON, Alan Hambleton. b 27. Lon Univ BD59. Wycliffe Hall Ox 56. **d** 59 **p** 60. C Norbiton *S'wark* 59-63; V Thornton St Jas *Bradf* 63-73; V Norbiton *S'wark* 73-84; V Wavertree St Thos *Liv* 84-92; rtd 92; Perm to Offic *Liv* from 92. *17 Lovelace Road, Liverpool L19 1QE* Tel 0151-427 5678

MASON, Ambrose. *See* MASON, Canon Thomas Henry Ambrose

MASON, Miss Beverley Anne. Trin Coll Bris BA00. **d** 01 **p** 03. C Rusthall *Roch* 01-02; C Rainham from 02. *123 Station Road, Rainham, Gillingham ME8 7SP* Tel 07786-541730 (mobile) E-mail revd@bamason.fsnet.co.uk

MASON, Charles Oliver. b 51. Jes Coll Cam BA73 MA99 St Jo Coll Dur BA79. **d** 80 **p** 81. C Cheltenham St Mary, St Matt, St Paul and H Trin *Glouc* 80-84; C Enfield Ch Ch Trent Park *Lon* 84-88; P-in-c W Hampstead St Cuth 88-93; V 93-01; AD N Camden 98-01; V Braintree *Chelmsf* from 01. *St Michael's Vicarage, 10A Marshalls Road, Braintree CM7 2LL* Tel (01376) 322840 E-mail comason@beeb.net

MASON, Mrs Christine Mary. b 43. Sarum & Wells Th Coll 91. **d** 93 **p** 94. Par Dn Blakenall Heath *Lich* 93-94; C 94-97; TV Rugeley from 97. *The Vicarage, 14 Peakes Road, Rugeley WS15 2LY* Tel (01889) 582809

MASON, Christopher David. b 51. Lanc Univ BA72 Leic Univ MEd82 Pet Regional Coll ACertC98. EAMTC 91. **d** 94 **p** 95. NSM Pet St Mary Boongate *Pet* 94-00; P-in-c Newborough 00-02; NSM Pet St Mary Boongate from 03. *74 Derby Drive, Peterborough PE1 4NQ* Tel (01733) 700000 E-mail mason.cd@virgin.net

MASON, Clive Ray. b 34. St Chad's Coll Dur BA57. Qu Coll Birm 57. **d** 59 **p** 60. C Gateshead St Mary *Dur* 59-62; C Bishopwearmouth Ch Ch 62-64; V Darlington St Jo 64-74; P-in-c Southwick H Trin 75-84; R 84-89; V Bearpark 89-95; rtd 95; Perm to Offic *Dur* from 95. *41 Harbour View, Littlehaven, South Shields NE33 1LS* Tel 0191-454 0234

MASON, David Gray. b 37. MPhil LDS RCS. St Alb Minl Tr Scheme 83. **d** 95 **p** 95. NSM Biddenham *St Alb* 95-98; P-in-c Felmersham from 98. *2A Devon Road, Bedford MK40 3DF* Tel (01234) 309737 E-mail david@devon.powernet.co.uk

MASON, Dawn Lavinia. b 53. Ripon Coll Cuddesdon 95. **d** 97 **p** 98. C Wisbech St Aug *Ely* 97-00; V Emneth and Marshland St James from 00. *The Vicarage, 72 Church Road, Emneth, Wisbech PE14 8AF* Tel (01945) 583089 E-mail dawnmason@augustine12.freeserve.co.uk

MASON, Dennis Wardell. b 28. Ox NSM Course 83. **d** 86 **p** 87. NSM Ox St Barn and St Paul *Ox* from 86. *26 John Lopes Road, Eynsham, Witney OX29 4JR* Tel (01865) 880440

MASON, Edward. *See* MASON, Thomas Edward

MASON, Mrs Elizabeth Ann. b 42. Homerton Coll Cam TCert64 Open Univ BA90. Ox Min Course CBTS94. **d** 94 **p** 95. NSM Worminghall w Ickford, Oakley and Shabbington *Ox* 94-95; NSM Swan 95-98; TV from 98. *The Rectory, Grendon Underwood, Aylesbury HP18 0SY* Tel (01296) 770240 E-mail elizabeth@swanuk.freeserve.co.uk

MASON, Francis Robert Anthony. b 56. Trin Coll Bris BA90. **d** 90 **p** 91. C Denham *Ox* 90-94; P-in-c Jersey Grouville *Win* 94-98; R from 98. *The Rectory, Rue a Don, Grouville, Jersey JE3 9DA* Tel (01534) 853073 Fax 853529 E-mail francismason@jerseymail.co.uk

MASON, Geoffrey Charles. b 48. K Coll Lon BD74 AKC74. St Aug Coll Cant 74. **d** 75 **p** 76. C Hatcham Park All SS *S'wark* 75-78; V Bellingham St Dunstan 78-87; RD E Lewisham 82-87; C Catford (Southend) and Downham 87-88; Bp's Adv for Min

Development from 88. *32 King's Orchard, London SE9 5TJ* Tel (020) 8859 7614 *or* 7378 7506 Fax 7403 6497

MASON, John Evans. b 32. RD. Linc Th Coll 57. **d** 59 **p** 60. C Putney St Mary *S'wark* 59-62; C Berry Pomeroy *Ex* 62-64; Chapl RN 64-68; V Hopton *Nor* 68-72; Chapl RNR 69-82; P-in-c Roydon St Remigius *Nor* 72-76; R Diss 72-80; Dir YMCA Cam 80-85; Prin YMCA Dunford Coll 85-88; Perm to Offic *Glouc* 88-97; Perm to Offic *Ox* 89-99; rtd 96; Perm to Offic *Nor* 98-02. *41 Church Street, Westbury BA13 3NZ* Tel (01373) 822445

MASON, John Graham. b 44. Sydney Univ BA67 Lon Univ BD69 Dur Univ MA76. Moore Th Coll Sydney ThL68. **d** 69 **p** 70. Australia 69-74 and 76-00; C Chester le Street *Dur* 74-76; USA from 01. *Suite 1600, 271 Madison Avenue, New York City, NY 10016, USA* Tel (001) (212) 808 4460 Fax 808 4465 E-mail rpcnyc@aol.com

MASON, John Martin. b 41. UMIST BSc63. Glouc Sch of Min 80 Qu Coll Birm 82. **d** 84 **p** 85. C Tuffley *Glouc* 84-87; P-in-c Willersey, Saintbury, Weston-sub-Edge etc 87-92; R 92-96; P-in-c Selling w Throwley, Sheldwich w Badlesmere etc *Cant* from 96; Dioc Rural Officer from 96. *The Rectory, Vicarage Lane, Selling, Faversham ME13 9RD* Tel (01227) 752221 Fax 752658 E-mail ruraljoe@aol.com

MASON, Jonathan Patrick. b 55. Edin Th Coll 90. **d** 92 **p** 93. C Edin Ch Ch *Edin* 92-94; C Edin Old St Paul 94-96; R St Andrews All SS *St And* from 96; Chapl St Andr Univ from 97. *All Saints' Rectory, North Street, St Andrews KY16 9AQ* Tel (01334) 473193 Fax as telephone E-mail jpm2@st-and.ac.uk

MASON, Ms Josephine Margaret. b 41. Edin Univ BMus64. WMMTC 88. **d** 93 **p** 94. Chapl Asst S Birm Mental Health NHS Trust from 91; C Birm St Jo Ladywood *Birm* 93-01; C Ladywood St Jo and St Pet from 01. *340 Selly Oak Road, Birmingham B30 1HP* Tel 0121-451 1412

MASON, Julia Ann. b 43. St Jo Coll Nottm 89. **d** 91 **p** 95. NSM Troon *Glas* 91-93; NSM Ayr from 93; NSM Maybole from 93; NSM Girvan from 93. *27A Bellevue Crescent, Ayr KA7 2DP* Tel (01292) 263673

MASON, Canon Kenneth Staveley. b 31. ARCS53 Lon Univ BSc53 BD64. Wells Th Coll 56. **d** 58 **p** 59. C Kingston upon Hull St Martin *York* 58-61; C Pocklington w Yapham-cum-Meltonby, Owsthorpe etc 61-63; C Millington w Gt Givendale 61-63; V Thornton w Allerthorpe 63-69; Sub-Warden St Aug Coll Cant 69-76; Abp's Adv in Past Min 76-77; Dir Cant Sch of Min 77-81; Prin 81-89; Sec to Dioc Bd of Min *Cant* 77-87; Six Preacher Cant Cathl 79-84; Hon Can Cant Cathl 84-89; Prin Edin Th Coll 89-95; Can St Mary's Cathl *Edin* 89-96; rtd 95; Perm to Offic *Ripon* from 96. *2 Williamson Close, Ripon HG4 1AZ* Tel (01765) 607041

MASON, Nigel Frederick. b 60. Wycliffe Hall Ox DipMin95. **d** 95 **p** 96. C Highbury Ch Ch w St Jo and St Sav *Lon* 95-98; C Seaford w Sutton *Chich* 98-01; R Rotherfield w Mark Cross from 01. *The Rectory, Mayfield Road, Rotherfield, Crowborough TN6 3LU* Tel (01892) 852536

MASON, Nigel James. b 56. Culham Coll of Educn BEd78 Dip Law84. St Steph Ho Ox 95. **d** 97 **p** 98. C Hove *Chich* 97-00; V Kemp Town St Mary from 00. *St Mary's Vicarage, 11 West Drive, Brighton BN2 0GD* Tel (01273) 698601

MASON, Paul. b 51. Cranmer Hall Dur 93. **d** 93 **p** 94. C Handforth *Ches* 93-97; V Partington and Carrington from 97. *St Mary's Vicarage, Manchester Road, Partington, Manchester M31 4FB* Tel 0161-775 3542 Fax as telephone

MASON, Peter Charles. b 45. K Coll Lon BD72 AKC72 Birm Univ PGCE89. St Aug Coll Cant 72. **d** 73 **p** 74. C Ilkeston St Mary *Derby* 73-76; C Bridgnorth St Mary *Heref* 76-78; TV Bridgnorth, Tasley, Astley Abbotts, etc 78-88; RE Teacher from 89; Perm to Offic from 89. *4 Woodberry Close, Bridgnorth WV16 4PT* Tel (01746) 762235

MASON, Canon Peter Joseph. b 34. Lon Univ BA58. Coll of Resurr Mirfield 58. **d** 60 **p** 61. C Belhus Park CD *Chelmsf* 60-63; Lic to Offic *Eur* 63-64; Asst Chapl Lon Univ *Lon* 64-70; Chapl City Univ 66-70; R Stoke Newington St Mary 70-78; V Writtle *Chelmsf* 78-81; P-in-c Highwood 78-81; V Writtle w Highwood 81-86; R Shenfield 86-93; Hon Can Chelmsf Cathl 89-00; P-in-c Maldon All SS w St Pet 93-95; V 95-00; RD Maldon and Dengie 95-00; rtd 00; Perm to Offic from 00. *32 Providence, Burnham-on-Crouch CM0 8JU* Tel (01621) 785921 E-mail peter@franknox.demon.co.uk

MASON, Robert Herbert George. b 48. ACII. Oak Hill Th Coll 82. **d** 84 **p** 85. C Ware Ch Ch *St Alb* 84-87; V Eastbourne All So *Chich* 88-98; P-in-c Poole *Sarum* 98-01; R from 01; Chapl Miss to Seafarers from 98. *The Rectory, 10 Poplar Close, Poole BH15 1LP* Tel (01202) 672694 Fax 677117 E-mail revbobmelmason@hotmail.com

MASON, Canon Roger Arthur. b 41. Lon Univ BSc65 K Coll Lon BD68 AKC68. **d** 69 **p** 70. C Enfield St Andr *Lon* 69-72; P-in-c Westbury *Heref* 72-78; P-in-c Yockleton 72-78; P-in-c Gt Wollaston 77-78; V Willesden St Mary *Lon* 78-88; V Prittlewell *Chelmsf* from 88; P-in-c Prittlewell St Steph from 92; Hon Can Chelmsf Cathl from 01. *Prittlewell Vicarage, 489 Victoria Avenue, Southend-on-Sea SS2 6NL* Tel (01702) 343470 E-mail rogeramason@lineone.net

MASON, Simon Duncan. b 61. Strathclyde Univ BA83 St Jo Coll Dur PhD89 Nottm Univ BTh92. Linc Th Coll 89. **d** 92 **p** 93. C Grays Thurrock *Chelmsf* 92-96; TV Plaistow and N Canning Town 96-02; TR from 02. *45 Mafeking Road, London E16 4NS* Tel (020) 7511 7848 E-mail simond.mason@virgin.net

MASON, Simon Ion Vincent. b 60. Birm Univ BA82. Trin Coll Bris BA00. **d** 00 **p** 01. C Nottingham St Nic *S'well* from 00. *99 Seymour Road, West Bridgford, Nottingham NG2 5EE* Tel 0115-914 8946 *or* 952 4600 E-mail simon@stnics.org

MASON, Stephen David. b 65. Univ of Wales (Lamp) BA87. Ripon Coll Cuddesdon 89. **d** 92 **p** 93. C Gt Grimsby St Mary and St Jas *Linc* 92-97; V Southborough St Thos *Roch* 97-02; V Paddington St Jo w St Mich *Lon* from 02. *18 Somers Crescent, London W2 2PN* Tel (020) 7706 8101 *or* 7262 1732 Fax 7706 4475 E-mail stjohnhp@netcomuk.co.uk

MASON, Terry Mathew. b 56. Trin Coll Bris 94. **d** 96 **p** 97. C Bexleyheath Ch Ch *Roch* 96-99; P-in-c Stone from 99. *The Rectory, Church Road, Greenhithe DA9 9BE* Tel (01322) 382076

MASON, Thomas Edward. b 52. Bris Univ MEd80. Trin Coll Bris BA91. **d** 91 **p** 92. C Glouc St Jas and All SS *Glouc* 91-94; V Churchdown from 94; RD Glouc N from 99. *The Vicarage, 5 Vicarage Close, Churchdown, Gloucester GL3 2NE* Tel (01452) 713203 E-mail temason@cableinet.co.uk

MASON, Canon Thomas Henry Ambrose. b 51. BA86. **d** 86 **p** 87. C W Drayton *Lon* 86-89; Field Officer Oak Hill Ext Coll 89-94; Eur Sec ICS 94-95; Dir of Tr *Eur* from 95; Can Brussels Cathl from 00; Dir Min and Dir of Ords from 01. *72 Byne Road, London SE26 5JD, or 14 Tufton Street, Gloucester SW1P 3QZ* Tel (020) 8659 3249 *or* 7898 1162 Fax 7898 1166 E-mail ambrose.mason@europe.c-of-e.org.uk

MASON, William Frederick. b 48. Linc Th Coll 75. **d** 78 **p** 79. C Ipswich St Aug *St E* 78-81; TV Dronfield *Derby* 81-88; V Ellesmere St Pet *Sheff* 88-91; V Bedgrove *Ox* 91-00; C Hazlemere from 00. *17 Southcote Way, Penn, High Wycombe HP10 8JG* Tel (01494) 812648

MASSEY, George Douglas. b 44. St Jo Coll Nottm DCM93. **d** 93 **p** 94. C Higher Bebington *Ches* 93-98; V Messingham *Linc* from 98. *The Vicarage, 12 Holme Lane, Messingham, Scunthorpe DN17 3SG* Tel (01724) 762823 E-mail george.massey@ntlworld.com

MASSEY, Keith John. b 46. Oak Hill Th Coll 69. **d** 72 **p** 73. C Bermondsey St Jas w Ch Ch *S'wark* 72-76; C Benchill *Man* 76-82; V Clifton Green 82-97; V Flixton St Jo from 97. *St John's Vicarage, Irlam Road, Urmston, Manchester M41 6AP* Tel 0161-748 6754

MASSEY, Nigel John. b 60. Birm Univ BA81 MA82. Wycliffe Hall Ox. **d** 87 **p** 88. C Bearwood *Birm* 87-90; C Warley Woods 90; C Tottenham St Paul *Lon* 91-94; USA from 94. *French Church du St Spirit, 111 East 60th Street #4, NY 10022, USA* Tel (001) (212) 838 5680

MASSEY, Paul Daniel Shaw. b 70. Nottm Univ BA93. Westcott Ho Cam 94. **d** 96 **p** 97. C Ashby-de-la-Zouch St Helen w Coleorton *Leic* 96-01; R Cotgrave *S'well* from 01; P-in-c Owthorpe from 01. *The Rectory, 2 Thurman Drive, Cotgrave, Nottingham NG12 3LG* Tel 0115-989 2223 Fax as telephone

MASSEY, Peter William. b 45. St Mark & St Jo Coll Lon TCert66 Open Univ BA75. WMMTC 96. **d** 99 **p** 00. NSM Holmer w Huntington *Heref* 99-03; NSM Heref St Pet w St Owen and St Jas from 03. *5 Nursery Drive, Moreton-on-Lugg, Hereford HR4 8DJ* Tel and fax (01432) 761794 Mobile 07803-826728 E-mail petermassey@lineone.net

MASSEY, Preb William Cyril. b 32. Lich Th Coll 58. **d** 61 **p** 62. C Heref St Martin *Heref* 61-66; V Kimbolton w Middleton-on-the-Hill 66-75; V Alveley 75-83; P-in-c Quatt 81-83; R Alveley and Quatt 84-85; R Llangarron w Llangrove, Whitchurch and Ganarew 85-97; Preb Heref Cathl 92-97; rtd 97; Perm to Offic *Heref* from 97. *7 Hollybush Cottage, Pencombe, Bromyard HR7 4RW* Tel (01885) 400713

MASSEY, William Peter. b 50. NDH72. CITC 96. **d** 99 **p** 00. C Fermoy Union *C, C & R* 99-00; C Carrigrohane Union from 00; C Kinsale Union from 00. *Shanballyreagh, Knockraha, Co Cork, Irish Republic* Tel (00353) (21) 488 9222 Mobile 86-821 9545 E-mail revpetemass@esatclear.ie

MASSHEDAR, John Frederick. b 50. Dur Univ BEd74. Linc Th Coll 76. **d** 78 **p** 79. C Pocklington w Yapham-cum-Meltonby, Owsthorpe etc *York* 78-81; C Middlesbrough Ascension 81-82; V 82-85; V Eskdaleside w Ugglebarnby and Sneaton 85-87; V Shotton *Dur* 87-99; V Haswell, Shotton and Thornley from 99. *The Vicarage, Shotton Colliery, Durham DH6 2JW* Tel 0191-526 1156

MASSHEDAR, Richard Eric. b 57. Nottm Univ BTh86. Linc Th Coll 83. **d** 86 **p** 87. C Cassop cum Quarrington *Dur* 86-89; C Ferryhill 89-91; V Leam Lane 91-94; P-in-c Hartlepool St Paul 94-96; V from 96. *St Paul's Vicarage, 6 Hutton Avenue, Hartlepool TS26 9PN* Tel (01429) 272934 E-mail r.masshedar@ntlworld.com

MASSINGBERD-MUNDY, John. b 07. Pemb Coll Cam BA30 MA46. Cuddesdon Coll 31. **d** 32 **p** 33. C Dagenham St Martin *Chelmsf* 32-34; C Sheff St Cuth *Sheff* 34-37; C Linthorpe *York* 37-40; V Sewerby cum Marton and Grindale 40-43; V Market Weighton 43-50; R Goodmanham 46-50; P-in-c Bedale *Ripon* 50-59; R 59-65; V Limber Magna w Brocklesby *Linc* 65-72; V Kirmington 65-72; rtd 72. *Norwood, 14 Park Road, Ipswich IP1 3ST* Tel (01473) 225622

MASSINGBERD-MUNDY, Roger William Burrell. b 36. TD. Univ of Wales (Lamp) BA59. Ridley Hall Cam 59. **d** 61 **p** 62. C Benwell St Jas *Newc* 61-64; CF (TA) 63-68; CF (TAVR) 71-83; C Wholrton *Newc* 64-72; TV 73; P-in-c Healey 73-85; Dioc Stewardship Adv 73-85; Hon Can Newc Cathl 82-85; R S Ormsby w Ketsby, Calceby and Driby *Linc* 85-86; P-in-c Harrington w Brinkhill 85-86; P-in-c Haugh 85-86; P-in-c Oxcombe 85-86; P-in-c Ruckland w Farforth and Maidenwell 85-86; P-in-c Somersby w Bag Enderby 85-86; P-in-c Tetford and Salmonby 85-86; R S Ormsby Gp 86-96; RD Bolingbroke 88-96; rtd 96. *Bates Hill, Ninebanks, Hexham NE47 8DB*

MASSON, Canon Philip Roy. b 52. Hertf Coll Ox BA75 Leeds Univ BA77. Coll of Resurr Mirfield 75. **d** 78 **p** 79. C Port Talbot St Theodore *Llan* 78-82; V Penyfai w Tondu 82-92; Dioc Dir Post-Ord Tr 85-88; Warden of Ords 88-01; R Newton Nottage from 92; RD Margam from 01; Can Llan Cathl from 02. *The Rectory, 64 Victoria Avenue, Porthcawl CF36 3HE* Tel (01656) 782042 *or* 786899 Fax as telephone E-mail philipmasson@hotmail.com

MASTERMAN, Malcolm. b 49. K Coll Lon 73 City Univ MSc00. Chich Th Coll 76. **d** 77 **p** 78. C Peterlee *Dur* 77-80; Chapl Basingstoke Distr Hosp 80-85; Chapl Freeman Hosp Newc 85-95; Tr and Development Officer Hosp Chapl Coun 96-00; Sen Chapl N Dur Healthcare NHS Trust from 00. *Chaplain's Office, University Hospital of North Durham, Durham DH1 5TW* Tel 0191-333 2183

MASTERMAN, Miss Patricia Hope. b 28. St Mich Ho Ox 59. **dss** 79 **d** 87. Asst CF 77-90; rtd 90; Perm to Offic *Chich* from 90. *33 Sea Lane Gardens, Ferring, Worthing BN12 5EQ* Tel (01903) 245231

MASTERS, John Francis. b 62. St Jo Sem Wonersh 82. **d** 87 **p** 88. In RC Ch 87-89; NSM Newbury *Ox* 00-02; C Hermitage 02-03. *Address temp unknown* E-mail john.masters@btinternet.com

MASTERS, Kenneth Leslie. b 44. Leeds Univ BA68. Cuddesdon Coll 68. **d** 70 **p** 71. C Wednesbury St Paul Wood Green *Lich* 70-71; C Tettenhall Regis 71-75; TV Chelmsley Wood *Birm* 75-79; R Harting *Chich* 79-87; V Rustington 87-00; TR Beaminster Area *Sarum* from 00. *The Rectory, 3 Clay Lane, Beaminster DT8 3BU* Tel (01308) 862150 E-mail kmasters@ukonline.co.uk

MASTERS, Leslie. b 31. Ripon Hall Ox 73. **d** 75 **p** 76. C Hanham *Bris* 75-78; TV Bris St Agnes and St Simon w St Werburgh 78-84; Asst Chapl HM Pris Man 84; Chapl HM Pris Northeye 84-88; Chapl HM Pris Littlehey 88-94; rtd 94; P-in-c St Goran w Caerhays *Truro* 94-00; Perm to Offic *Chich* from 01. *46 Manor Road, Bexhill-on-Sea TN40 1SN* Tel (01424) 218294

MASTERS, Canon Raymond Austin. b 26. Kelham Th Coll 45. **d** 52 **p** 53. SSM from 51; S Africa 52-65; Can Bloemfontein Cathl 58-65; Perm to Offic *Blackb* 66-68; Chapl St Martin's Coll of Educn Lanc 68-70; Asst Sec Gen Syn Bd for Miss and Unity 71-77; Hon C Harrow St Pet *Lon* 72-77; TV Cen Ex 78-82; Dioc Miss and Ecum Officer 78-82; Warden Windsor Convent 79-95; Can Res Heref Cathl *Heref* 82-93; Treas 85-93; Bp's Co-ord for Min 82-93; rtd 95. *2 Whitehall, South Petherton TA13 5AQ* Tel (01460) 242272

MASTERS, Stephen Michael. b 52. **d** 87 **p** 88. C Primrose Hill St Mary w Avenue Road St Paul *Lon* 87-90; C Hornsey St Mary w St Geo 90-91; Bp's Dom Chapl *Chich* 91-96; V Brighton St Mich 96-99; C Eastbourne St Andr 00-01; Chapl to Bp Lewes 00-01; Asst to Adn Lewes and Hastings 00-01; P-in-c Alderney *Win* from 01; V from 03. *The New Vicarage, La Vallee, Alderney, Guernsey GY9 3XA* Tel (01481) 824866

MASTIN, Brian Arthur. b 38. Peterho Cam BA60 MA63 BD80 Mert Coll Ox MA63. Ripon Hall Ox 62. **d** 63 **p** 64. Asst Lect Hebrew Univ Coll of N Wales (Ban) 63-65; Lect Hebrew 65-82; Sen Lect 82-98; Chapl Ban Cathl *Ban* 63-65; Lic to Offic 65-98; rtd 98; Perm to Offic *Ely* from 98. *2A Gurney Way, Cambridge CB4 2ED* Tel (01223) 355078

MATABELELAND, Bishop of. See SITSHEBO, The Rt Revd Wilson Timothy

MATCHETT, Alan William. b 70. TCD BTh01. CITC 98. **d** 01 **p** 02. C Limerick City *L & K* 01-03; C Stillorgan w Blackrock *D & G* from 03. *Address temp unknown*

MATCHETT, Christopher Jonathan. b 65. BSSc TCD BTh98. **d** 98 **p** 99. C Ballynafeigh St Jude *D & D* 98-01; C Holywood from 01. *51 Princess Gardens, Holywood BT18 0PN* Tel (028) 9042 4554 *or* 9042 3622 E-mail curate.holywood@down.anglican.org

MATCHETT, Edward James Boyd. b 19. TCD BA43 MA60. **d** 43 **p** 44. C Belfast St Mary *Conn* 43-45; Miss to Seamen 45-86; Chapl Basrah Iraq 47-50; Chapl Sunderland 50-52; Chapl Belfast 52-64; Chapl RNR 60-65; Chapl Wellington New Zealand 64-69; Area Sec Miss to Seamen E England 69-74; Chapl Hong Kong 74-83; Chapl Cornish Ports 83-86; Perm to

Offic *Nor* 86-00. *10 Southern Reach, Mulbarton, Norwich NR14 8BU* Tel (01508) 570337

MATHER, Bernard Herbert. b 26. Univ Coll Dur BA51. Sarum Th Coll 53. **d** 55 **p** 56. C Wallsend St Luke *Newc* 55-60; USPG 60-94; India 60-94; rtd 94. *9 Lindisfarne Road, Shipley BD18 4RD* Tel (01274) 583693

MATHER, Cuthbert. b 15. Tyndale Hall Bris 36. **d** 40 **p** 41. C Bebington *Ches* 40-42; C Stapenhill w Cauldwell *Derby* 43-51; C Cambridge St Andr Less *Ely* 51-52; C Dagenham *Chelmsf* 53-57; V Needham w Rushall *Nor* 57-80; rtd 80; Perm to Offic *Nor* from 80. *2 Church Close, Hunstanton PE36 6BE* Tel (01485) 533084

MATHER, David Jonathan. b 65. New Coll Ox BA88 MA95. St Steph Ho Ox BTh95. **d** 95 **p** 96. C Pickering w Lockton and Levisham *York* 95-98; P-in-c Bridlington H Trin and Sewerby w Marton 98-99; V from 99. *Sewerby Vicarage, Cloverley Road, Bridlington YO16 5TX* Tel (01262) 675725

MATHER, Mrs Elizabeth Ann. b 45. CertEd66. Dalton Ho Bris IDC70 St Jo Coll Nottm 92. **d** 94 **p** 95. NSM Littleover *Derby* 94-02; Lic to Offic *St Alb* from 02. *13 Heath Park Drive, Leighton Buzzard LU7 3BF* Tel (01525) 377128
E-mail revlib@libbymather.freeserve.co.uk

MATHER, James William. b 63. Sheff Univ BA86. St Steph Ho Ox 88. **d** 91 **p** 92. C Doncaster St Leon and St Jude *Sheff* 91-94; C Cantley 94-95; V Lakenheath *St E* 95-01; P-in-c Downham Market w Bexwell *Ely* 01-02; P-in-c Crimplesham w Stradsett 01-02; R Downham Market and Crimplesham w Stradsett from 02. *The Rectory, King's Walk, Downham Market PE38 9LF* Tel (01366) 382187 E-mail j.w.mather@virgin.net

MATHER, Stephen Albert. b 54. Qu Coll Birm 85. **d** 87 **p** 88. C Sutton *Liv* 87-90; TV 90-96; V Abram 96-99; V Bickershaw 96-99; V Hindley St Pet from 99. *St Peter's Vicarage, 122 Wigan Road, Hindley, Wigan WN2 3DF* Tel (01942) 55505

MATHER, William Bernard George. b 45. St Jo Coll Nottm 77. **d** 79 **p** 80. C St Leonards St Leon *Chich* 79-82; TR Netherthorpe *Sheff* 82-90; V Littleover *Derby* 90-02; Assoc Dir SOMA UK from 02. *13 Heath Park Drive, Leighton Buzzard LU7 3BF* Tel (01525) 377128 *or* 237953 E-mail william.mather@somauk.org

MATHERS, Alan Edward. b 36. FPhS Lon Univ BA BTh. Oak Hill Th Coll 61. **d** 64 **p** 65. C Ox St Matt *Ox* 64-66; C Bootle St Leon *Liv* 66-68; C Hampreston *Sarum* 68-70; P-in-c Damerham 70-71; V Queniborough *Leic* 71-76; USA 76-77; P-in-c Tipton St Paul *Lich* 77-84; V Tipton St Matt 77-86; V Sutton Ch Ch *S'wark* 86-95; Chapl Cannes *Eur* 95-98; rtd 98; Perm to Offic *S'wark* and *Chich* from 98. *52 The Meadow, Copthorne, Crawley RH10 3AQ* Tel (01342) 713325

MATHERS, David Michael Brownlow. b 43. Em Coll Cam BA65 MA69. Clifton Th Coll 65. **d** 67 **p** 68. C Branksome St Clem *Sarum* 67-70; C Bromley Ch Ch *Roch* 70-73; V Bures *St E* 73-80; Brazil 80-82; P-in-c Old Newton w Stowupland *St E* 82-86; V 87-90; V Thurston from 90; RD Ixworth 94-03. *The Vicarage, Church Road, Thurston, Bury St Edmunds IP31 3RU* Tel (01359) 230301

MATHERS, Derek. b 32. N Ord Course 82. **d** 85 **p** 86. C Huddersfield St Jo *Wakef* 85-86; C N Huddersfield 86-88; TV Almondbury w Farnley Tyas 88-92; V Marsden 92-02; R Badsworth from 02. *The Rectory, Main Street, Badsworth, Pontefract WF9 1AF* Tel (01977) 643642

MATHERS, Kenneth Ernest William. b 56. Portsm Coll of Tech TDip82 HND84. Trin Coll Bris DipHE95. **d** 95 **p** 96. C Bournemouth St Jo w St Mich *Win* 95-99; NSM Darenth *Roch* from 99; Chapl Dartford and Gravesham NHS Trust from 01. *Darenth Vicarage, Lane End, Dartford DA2 7JR* Tel (01322) 227153 Fax as telephone E-mail revkmathers@yahoo.com

MATHERS, Mrs Kim Deborah. b 61. Southn Univ LLB82. All So Coll of Applied Th DipApTh86 Trin Coll Bris DipHE88 ADPS89. **d** 89 **p** 94. Par Dn Bitterne *Win* 89-93; Hon C Stoke Bishop *Bris* 93-95; Hon C Bournemouth St Jo w St Mich *Win* 95-99; P-in-c Darenth *Roch* from 99. *Darenth Vicarage, Lane End, Dartford DA2 7JR* Tel (01322) 227153 Fax as telephone E-mail revkmathers@yahoo.com

MATHESON, Alexander John. b 59. Lon Bible Coll BA84 S Tr Scheme 94. **d** 97 **p** 98. NSM Cowplain *Portsm* 97-01; C Portchester from 01. *190 Dore Avenue, Fareham PO16 8EP* Tel (01329) 319042 E-mail sandy@mathesonuk.com

MATHEWS, Richard Twitchell. b 27. Bps' Coll Cheshunt 57. **d** 59 **p** 60. C Leic St Phil *Leic* 59-62; Chapl Beirut 62-63; Qatar 63-67; V Riddlesden *Bradf* 67-74; Australia 74-78; P-in-c Medbourne cum Holt w Stockerston and Blaston *Leic* 78-82; Chapl Alassio *Eur* 82-83; Chapl San Remo 82-83; Chapl Palma and Balearic Is w Ibiza etc 83-87; P-in-c Witchford w Wentworth *Ely* 87-91; Perm to Offic *Cant* from 96. *Rosecroft, Church Lane, Ringwould, Deal CT14 8HR* Tel (01304) 365244

MATHEWS, Ronald Peel Beresford. b 24. TCD Dip Bibl Studies DipYL. **d** 64 **p** 65. C Waterford w Killea, Drumcannon and Dunhill *C & O* 64-66; I Clonbroney w Killoe *K, E & A* 66-71; I Drumgoon and Ashfield 71-74; Dep Sec Leprosy Miss 74-84; I Kinneigh Union *C, C & R* 84-93; rtd 93. *19 Kingston College, Mitchelstown, Co Cork, Irish Republic* Tel (00353) (25) 84779

MATHEWS, Trevor John. b 50. HonLMStJ83. Anglia Poly Univ CertPSC94 Goldsmiths' Coll Lon DipCACP95 MSc98 DipREBT95. St Steph Ho Ox 87. **d** 89 **p** 90. C Cheltenham St Steph *Glouc* 89-91; C Up Hatherley 89-91. *11 Arundel Mews, Billericay CM12 0FW* Tel (01277) 634817
E-mail mathews@conflict.co.uk

MATHIAS, John Maelgwyn. b 15. St D Coll Lamp BA38 St Mich Coll Llan 40. **d** 40 **p** 41. C Ban St Mary *Ban* 40-44; C Swansea St Pet *S & B* 44-49; V Mydroilyn w Dihewyd *St D* 49-54; R Cellan w Llanfair Clydogau 54-83; Lect St Jo Ch Coll Ystrad Meurig 67-77; rtd 83. *Bronallt, Capel Seion Road, Drefach, Llanelli SA14 7BN* Tel (01269) 844350

MATHIAS, Ms Lesley. b 49. Portsm Poly BA72 Nottm Univ MTh90. EMMTC 93. **d** 96 **p** 97. C Oadby *Leic* 96-98; Asst Chapl United Bris Healthcare NHS Trust 98-99; C Pet St Mary Boongate *Pet* 99-01; V Kings Heath from 01; TV Bp's Interfaith Adv from 01; Perm to Offic *B & W* 99-01. *1 Nene Drive, Northampton NN5 7NQ* Tel (01604) 756809
E-mail lesley@l.mathias.freeserve.co.uk

MATHIAS-JONES, Edward Lloyd. b 71. SSC98 Univ of Wales (Lamp) BA93. St Mich Coll Llan BD96 Dip Past Counselling 97. **d** 97 **p** 98. C Llanelli *St D* 97-00; C Milford Haven from 00. *5 Priory Lodge Close, Milford Haven SA73 2BZ* Tel (01646) 698368 E-mail frmathias-jones@aol.com

MATHIE, Patricia Jean (Sister Donella). b 22. Worc Coll of Educn CertEd49. CertRK74. dss 79 **d** 87. CSA from 74; Asst Superior 82-94; Mother Superior 94-00; Notting Hill St Jo *Lon* 79-80; Abbey Ho Malmesbury 81-82; Notting Hill St Clem and St Mark 82-84; Kensal Town St Thos w St Andr and St Phil 85-87; Hon C 87-96; Perm to Offic from 00. *8/9 Verona Court, London W4 2JD* Tel (020) 8987 2799

MATLOOB, Nazir Ahmad Barnabas. b 48. Punjab Univ BA79. Gujranwala Th Sem 74 BD81 MDiv85 NTMTC 95. **d** 78 **p** 78. Pakistan 78-93; Perm to Offic *Chelmsf* 94-97; C Forest Gate All SS and St Edm from 98. *64 Henderson Road, London E7 8EF* Tel (020) 8552 4280

MATON, Oswald. b 24. St Aug Coll Cant 75. **d** 77 **p** 78. NSM Chatham St Steph *Roch* 77-94; Perm to Offic from 94. *304 Maidstone Road, Chatham ME4 6JJ* Tel (01634) 843568

MATSON de LAURIER, Mrs Sarah Kennerley. b 46. EMMTC 00. **d** 02 **p** 03. NSM Hilton w Marston-on-Dove *Derby* from 02. *1 Park Way, Etwall, Derby DE65 6HU* Tel (01283) 732859
E-mail pskmd@aol.com

MATTEN, Derek Norman William. b 30. Man Univ BA51. Wycliffe Hall Ox 54. **d** 56 **p** 57. C Farnworth *Liv* 56-59; C Walton H Trin *Ox* 59-62; Uganda 62-69; Lic to Offic *Eur* 69-93; W Germany 69-90; Germany 90-93; Perm to Offic *Ex* 90-93; rtd 93; Hon C Modbury, Bigbury, Ringmore w Kingston etc *Ex* 95-00. *9 Celandine Lawns, Willand, Cullompton EX15 2TN* Tel (01884) 821083 E-mail dnwm@supanet.com

MATTHEWS, Adrian James. b 51. Edge Hill Coll of HE CertEd73. N Ord Course. **d** 87 **p** 88. C Blackley St Andr *Man* 87-90; NSM Tonge w Alkrington 96-01; R Failsworth St Jo from 01. *St John's Rectory, Pole Lane, Manchester M35 9PB* Tel 0161-681 2734 Fax as telephone

MATTHEWS, The Rt Revd Alan Montague (Dom Basil). b 37. Ex Univ BA86. **d** 02 **p** 02. OSB from 65; Abbot Elmore Abbey from 88. *Elmore Abbey, Church Lane, Speen, Newbury RG14 1SA* Tel (01635) 33080 Fax 580729

MATTHEWS, Anita Kathryn. b 70. Dur Univ BTh91. Ripon Coll Cuddesdon DipMin93. **d** 97 **p** 98. C E Barnet *St Alb* 97-01; Chapl Derby High Sch from 01. *Derby High School, Hillsway, Littleover, Derby DE23 7DT* Tel (01332) 514267 Fax 516085

MATTHEWS, Mrs Anna Ruth. b 78. Rob Coll Cam BA99 MPhil03. Westcott Ho Cam 01. **d** 03. C Abbots Langley *St Alb* from 03. *40 Kindersley Way, Abbots Langley WD5 0DQ* Tel (01923) 265729 Mobile 07974-647226

MATTHEWS, Barry Alan. b 46. AKC68. St Boniface Warminster 68 St Paul's Coll Grahamstown 69. **d** 69 **p** 70. S Africa 69-74, 77-83 and from 01; C De Aar 69-72; C Kimberley St Aug 72-74; P-in-c Kimberley St Matt 74-75; C Leeds St Aid *Ripon* 75-77; R Vryburg St Steph 77-81; Dioc Missr 81-82; R Kimberley St Aug 82-83; C Shotton *St As* 83-84; Zimbabwe 84-01; R Hwange St Jas 84-89; R Bulawayo N St Marg 89-95; R Nkulumane H Family 95-97; Adn N Matabeleland 89-97; Sen P St Mary's Cathl Harare 97-00. *The Presbytery, 9 Cybelle Street, PO Box 3043, Reygersdal, 7352 South Africa* Tel (0027) (21) 572 4783 Fax as telephone E-mail revbarry@intekom.co.za

MATTHEWS, Basil. See MATTHEWS, The Rt Revd Alan Montague

MATTHEWS, Brian. b 32. ARIC55. Cranmer Hall Dur 59. **d** 62 **p** 63. C Belgrave St Pet *Leic* 62-65; C Whitwick St Jo the Bapt 65-69; C Kirby Muxloe 69-71; P-in-c Bardon Hill 71-78; V Thringstone St Andr 78-97; rtd 97; Perm to Offic *Leic* from 97. *44 Pennine Way, Ashby-de-la-Zouch LE65 1EW* Tel (01530) 417917

MATTHEWS, Canon Campbell Thurlow. b 33. Lon Univ BA56 Dur Univ DipEd57. St Jo Coll Nottm 70. **d** 71 **p** 72. C Ryton *Dur* 71-74; Chapl R Victoria Infirmary Newc 74-82; V Greenside *Dur*

74-82; R Wetheral w Warwick *Carl* 82-93; RD Brampton 83-91; P-in-c Farlam and Nether Denton 87-93; P-in-c Gilsland 87-93; Hon Can Carl Cathl 87-00; P-in-c Thornthwaite cum Braithwaite and Newlands 93-00; P-in-c Borrowdale 97-00; rtd 00; Perm to Offic *Carl* from 00; *Newc* from 01. *The Hayes, Newcastle Road, Corbridge NE45 5LP* Tel (01434) 632010

MATTHEWS, Celia Inger. b 30. St Chris Coll Blackheath 50. **d** 86 **p** 94. Dioc Missr *St And* from 86; rtd 95. *24 Barossa Place, Perth PH1 5HH* Tel (01738) 623578

MATTHEWS, Cilla. *See* MATTHEWS, Mrs Francilla Lacey

MATTHEWS, Canon Colin John. b 44. Jes Coll Ox BA67 MA71 Fitzw Coll Cam BA70 MA74. Ridley Hall Cam 68. **d** 71 **p** 72. C Onslow Square St Paul *Lon* 71-74; C Leic H Apostles *Leic* 74-78; Bible Use Sec Scripture Union 78-89; Dir Ch Cen Guildf St Sav *Guildf* 89-95; V Burpham from 95; RD Guildf from 01; Hon Can Guildf Cathl from 02. *The Vicarage, 5 Orchard Road, Burpham, Guildford GU4 7JH* Tel (01483) 853023 Mobile 07787-575923 Fax (01483) 855645 E-mail vicarage@dial.pipex.com

MATTHEWS, David Charles. b 61. TCD BA84 HDipEd86 MA87 BTh95 Lille Univ LèsL85 QUB Cert Counselling 97. CITC 95. **d** 95 **p** 96. C Arm St Mark *Arm* 95-97; Hon V Choral Arm Cathl 96-97; Min Can and Chapl St Woolos Cathl *Mon* 97-01; V Marshfield and Peterstone Wentloog etc from 01. *The Vicarage, Church Lane, Marshfield, Cardiff CF3 2UF* Tel (01633) 680257 E-mail david@hebron97.freeserve.co.uk

MATTHEWS, David William. St Paul's Coll Grahamstown. **d** 90 **p** 91. S Africa 90-03; R Zwartkops River Par 95-00; Chapl Miss to Seafarers 00-03; R Boxford, Edwardstone, Groton etc *St E* from 03. *The Rectory, Boxford, Sudbury CO10 5JT*

MATTHEWS, David William Grover. b 73. Acadia Univ (NS) BA93 Toronto Univ MDiv98. Trin Coll Toronto 95. **d** 98 **p** 99. C Newport St Teilo *Mon* 98-00; NSM Cobbold Road St Sav w St Mary *Lon* 00-03; P-in-c Hammersmith H Innocents from 03. *35 Paddenswick Road, London W6 0UA* Tel (020) 8741 6480 E-mail fr_grover@yahoo.com

MATTHEWS, Mrs Deborah Lynne. b 57. Southn Univ BTh98 MIPD92 Ox Univ MTh01. Ripon Coll Cuddesdon 98. **d** 00 **p** 01. C Southampton (City Cen) *Win* from 00. *9 Amey Gardens, Calmore, Southampton SO40 2BB* Tel (023) 8042 8332 E-mail deborahmatthews@yahoo.com

MATTHEWS, Mrs Diana Elizabeth Charlotte. b 43. MCSP65. LNSM course 92. **d** 93 **p** 96. OLM Merrow *Guildf* from 93. *Avila, 13 Wells Road, Guildford GU4 7XQ* Tel (01483) 839738 E-mail diana.matthews@ntlworld.com

MATTHEWS, Mrs Francilla Lacey. b 37. S'wark Ord Course 83. **dss** 86 **d** 87 **p** 94. Bromley St Mark *Roch* 86-90; Hon Par Dn 87-90; Par Dn Hayes 90-94; C 94-02; rtd 02. *71 Hayes Road, Bromley BR2 9AE* Tel (020) 8464 6840

MATTHEWS, Frederick Peter. b 45. Grey Coll Dur BA66 MA68 K Coll Lon PGCE68 Lon Univ BSc(Econ)75. Sarum & Wells Th Coll 70. **d** 72 **p** 73. C W Wickham St Jo *Cant* 72-74; C Sholing *Win* 74-77; Lic to Offic 78-79; V Woolston 79-03; P-in-c Over Wallop w Nether Wallop from 03; Dioc Ecum Officer from 03. *The Rectory, Over Wallop, Stockbridge SO20 8HT* Tel (01264) 781345 E-mail peter.matthews1@telinco.co.uk

MATTHEWS, George Charles Wallace. b 27. Sarum Th Coll 58. **d** 60 **p** 61. C Coppenhall St Paul *Ches* 60-63; C Lewes St Anne *Chich* 63-67; V Wheelock *Ches* 67-76; V Mossley 76-93; rtd 93; Perm to Offic *Ches* from 93. *145 Primrose Avenue, Haslington, Crewe CW1 5QB* Tel (01270) 587463

MATTHEWS, Gerald Lancelot. b 31. Bris Univ LLB50. Ripon Hall Ox 54. **d** 57 **p** 58. C The Quinton *Birm* 57-60; C Olton 60-63; V Brent Tor *Ex* 63-72; P-in-c Lydford w Bridestowe and Sourton 70-72; TR Lydford, Brent Tor, Bridestowe and Sourton 72-78; P-in-c Black Torrington, Bradf w Cookbury etc 78-90; Perm to Offic from 90; rtd 94. *The Larches, Black Torrington, Beaworthy EX21 5PU* Tel (01409) 231228

MATTHEWS, Gilbert Brian Reeves. b 19. Keble Coll Ox BA42 MA48. St Steph Ho Ox 42. **d** 44 **p** 45. C Brighton St Wilfrid *Chich* 45-49; C St Leonards Ch Ch 49-55; C Finedon *Pet* 55-58; Youth Chapl 58-64; R Rushton and Glendon 58-79; P-in-c Thorpe Malsor 76-79; R Rushton and Glendon w Thorpe Malsor 79-81; Chapl Bp Stopford Sch Kettering 77-81; C Spondon *Derby* 81-87; rtd 87; Hon C Walsall St Gabr Fulbrook *Lich* 88-90; Hon C Glen Parva and S Wigston *Leic* 90-93; Asst Chapl HM YOI Glen Parva 90-93; Hon C Wrington w Butcombe *B & W* 93-97; Perm to Offic *Chelmsf* 97-98; Hon C Thorpe Bay 98-01. *2 Faversham Lodge, 203 Eastern Esplanade, Southend-on-Sea SS1 3AD* Tel (01702) 588251

MATTHEWS, Harold James. b 46. Leeds Univ BSc68 Fitzw Coll Cam BA70 MA74. Westcott Ho Cam 68. **d** 71 **p** 72. C Mossley Hill St Matt and St Jas *Liv* 71-74; C Stanley 74-76; TV Hackney *Lon* 76-78; Chapl Forest Sch Snaresbrook 78-83; Hd Master Vernon Holme Sch Cant 83-88; Perm to Offic *Cant* 83-88; Hd Master Heath Mt Sch Hertf from 88; Lic to Offic *St Alb* from 88. *Heath Mount School, Woodhall Park, Watton at Stone, Hertford SG14 3NG* Tel (01920) 830230 *or* 830541 E-mail hmatth1568@aol.com

MATTHEWS, Mrs Heather Ann. b 49. Bris Univ BA71 Lon Univ CertEd72. Trin Coll Bris 87. **d** 89 **p** 94. C Blagdon w Compton Martin and Ubley *B & W* 89-93; Dn-in-c 93-94; P-in-c 94; R 94-01; R Hodnet w Weston under Redcastle *Lich* from 01. *The Rectory, Abbots Way, Hodnet, Market Drayton TF9 3NQ* Tel (01630) 685491

MATTHEWS, Mrs Joan Muriel. b 53. N Ord Course 89. **d** 92 **p** 94. C Aughton St Mich *Liv* 92-97; R Wavertree St Mary from 97. *St Mary's Rectory, 1 South Drive, Wavertree, Liverpool L15 8JJ* Tel 0151-734 3103

MATTHEWS, Canon John. b 22. TD66. Trin Coll Cam BA48 MA51. Bps' Coll Cheshunt 49. **d** 51 **p** 52. C Woodlands *Sheff* 51-54; CF (TA) from 53; C Sharrow St Andr *Sheff* 54-57; V Sheff St Barn 57-62; P-in-c Lt Canfield *Chelmsf* 62-70; V Gt Dunmow 62-88; P-in-c Gt Easton 70-83; RD Dunmow 75-88; Hon Can Chelmsf Cathl 85-88; rtd 88; Perm to Offic *St E* from 88; Perm to Offic *Ely* from 99. *Moorside Cottage, The Common, Walberswick, Southwold IP18 6TE* Tel (01502) 722783

MATTHEWS, John Goodman. b 77. Univ of Wales BTh99. St Mich Coll Llan 99. **d** 02 **p** 03. C Lampeter and Llanddewibrefi Gp *St D* from 02. *Dwyfor, Maes-y-Llan, Lampeter SA48 7EN* Tel (01570) 422706

MATTHEWS, Lewis William (Bill). b 29. St Jo Coll Dur BA53 DipTh55 MSc76. **d** 55 **p** 56. C Eston *York* 55-57; C Wicker w Neepsend *Sheff* 57; Ind Chapl 57-61; V Copt Oak *Leic* 61-64; R Braunstone 64-70; V Thornaby on Tees St Paul *York* 70-72; TR Thornaby on Tees 72-78; Dir Dioc Bd for Soc Resp *Lon* 79-84; Perm to Offic 84-94; Warden Durning Hall Chr Community Cen Forest Gate 84-94; rtd 94; Hon C Jersey Gouray St Martin *Win* from 94. *Gouray Vicarage, La grande route de Faldouet, St Martin, Jersey JE3 6UA* Tel (01534) 853255

MATTHEWS, Liam. *See* MATTHEWS, William Temple Atkinson

MATTHEWS, Canon Melvyn William. b 40. St Edm Hall Ox BA63 MA68. K Coll Lon BD66 AKC67. **d** 67 **p** 68. C Enfield St Andr *Lon* 67-70; Asst Chapl Southn Univ *Win* 70-73; Lect Univ of Nairobi Kenya 73-76; V Highgate All SS *Lon* 76-79; P-in-c Clifton St Paul *Bris* 79-87; Sen Chapl Bris Univ 79-87; Dir Ammerdown Cen for Study and Renewal 87-93; V Chew Magna w Dundry *B & W* 93-97; Can and Chan Wells Cathl from 97. *8 The Liberty, Wells BA5 2SU* Tel (01749) 678763 Fax 679587 E-mail mwmatthews@firenet.ws

MATTHEWS, Oswald John. b 13. St Edm Hall Ox BA37 MA40. Ripon Hall Ox 35. **d** 37 **p** 38. C Beverley Minster *York* 37-41; V Drypool St Andr and St Pet 41-48; Chapl RAF 41-45; V Fridaythorpe w Fimber and Thixendale *York* 48-52; Miss to Seamen 52-64; Argentina 52-54; New Zealand from 54. *12 Kenneth Small Crescent, Point Chevalier, Auckland 2, New Zealand* Tel (0064) (9) 815 3846

MATTHEWS, Paul. b 47. Brunel Univ BTech70 S Bank Poly DipEED72. S Dios Minl Tr Scheme 89. **d** 92 **p** 93. NSM Goring-by-Sea *Chich* from 92. *Rose Cottage, The Court House, Sea Lane, Goring-by-Sea, Worthing BN12 4NY* Tel (01903) 502011

MATTHEWS, Peter. *See* MATTHEWS, Frederick Peter

MATTHEWS, Peter Henry. b 22. Sarum Th Coll 62. **d** 64 **p** 65. C Wareham w Arne *Sarum* 64-67; P-in-c Houghton 67; C Sholing *Win* 67-69; R Hilperton w Whaddon *Sarum* 70-78; P-in-c Staverton 71-73; V 72-78; P-in-c Milborne St Andrew w Dewlish 78-87; rtd 87; Perm to Offic *B & W* from 87. *Holmlands, Lambrook Road, Shepton Beauchamp, Ilminster TA19 0LZ* Tel (01460) 40938

MATTHEWS, Canon Rodney Charles. b 36. Sarum Th Coll 62. **d** 64 **p** 65. C Gt Clacton *Chelmsf* 64-68; C Loughton St Mary 68-74; TV 74-76; V Goodmayes All SS 76-87; V Woodford Bridge 87-02; Hon Chapl Sail Tr Assn from 89; P-in-c Barkingside St Cedd 90-92; Hon Can Chelmsf Cathl 99-02; rtd 02. *93 Kings Head Hill, London E4 7JG* Tel (020) 8529 4372

MATTHEWS, Canon Roger Charles. b 54. MBCS82 CEng90 Man Univ BSc75 CDipAF78 Nottm Univ MA02. Trin Coll Bris 87. **d** 89 **p** 90. C Gt Baddow *Chelmsf* 89-93; P-in-c Chigwell Row 93-94; TV Chigwell and Chigwell Row 94-96; Dioc Miss Officer 96-00; Millennium Ecum Officer 98-00; Bp's Adv for Miss and Min from 01; Hon C Gt Baddow from 01; Hon Can Chelmsf Cathl from 00. *62 Longmead Avenue, Great Baddow, Chelmsford CM2 7EY* Tel (01245) 478959 *or* 294445 Fax 294477 E-mail rmatthews@chelmsford.anglican.org

MATTHEWS, Canon Roy Ian John. b 27. TD71. St Cath Soc Ox BA52 MA56. St Steph Ho Ox 52. **d** 54 **p** 55. C Barnsley St Mary *Wakef* 54-58; V Staincliffe 58-65; CF (TA) 58-92; V Penistone w Midhope *Wakef* 65-72; V Brighouse 72-84; Hon Can Wakef Cathl 76-92; V Darrington 84-92; Dioc Schs Officer 84-89; Dep Dir of Educn 85-89; rtd 92; Perm to Offic *Wakef* and *York* from 92; P-in-c Selby Abbey from 96. *14 Spring Walk, Brayton, Selby YO8 9DS* Tel (01757) 707259

MATTHEWS, Royston Peter. b 39. Univ of Wales (Lamp) BA61 DipTh64. St Mich Coll Llan 61. **d** 64 **p** 65. C Fairwater CD *Llan* 64-67; C Cadoxton-juxta-Barry 67-71; V Bettws *Mon* 71-84; V Abergavenny H Trin from 84. *Holy Trinity Vicarage, Baker Street, Abergavenny NP7 5BH* Tel (01873) 853203

MATTHEWS, Canon Stuart James. b 37. St Jo Coll Dur BA60. Bps' Coll Cheshunt 60. d 62 p 63. C Horsham *Chich* 62-65; C Rednal *Birm* 65-67; Min Brandwood St Bede CD 67-68; C Northfield 68-73; V Thurcroft *Sheff* 73-82; RD Laughton 79-82; R Sprotbrough 82-00; RD Adwick 84-89; Hon Can Sheff Cathl 92-00; rtd 00; Perm to Offic *Sheff* from 00. *43 Dinnington Road, Woodsetts, Worksop S81 8RL* Tel (01909) 560160

MATTHEWS, Terence Leslie. b 35. Handsworth Coll Birm 55. d 61 p 62. C W Acklam *York* 61-64; V Horden *Dur* 64-72; R Witton Gilbert 72-77; P-in-c Grangetown 77-85; V Cleadon 85-86; V Hebburn St Cuth 86-88; rtd 88. *7 Holmlands Park South, Sunderland SR2 7SG* Tel 0191-522 6466

MATTHEWS, William. *See* MATTHEWS, Lewis William

MATTHEWS, Canon William Andrew. b 44. Reading Univ BA65 MA94. St Steph Ho Ox 65. d 67 p 68. C Westbury-on-Trym St Alb *Bris* 67-70; C Marlborough *Sarum* 70-73; P-in-c Winsley 73-75; V 75-81; V Bradford-on-Avon from 81; RD Bradford 84-94; Can and Preb Sarum Cathl from 88; Chapl to The Queen from 01. *Holy Trinity Vicarage, 18A Woolley Street, Bradford-on-Avon BA15 1AF* Tel (01225) 864444 Fax 863623
E-mail w.a.matthews@btinternet.com

MATTHEWS, William Temple Atkinson (Liam). b 47. DipApTh98. EMMTC 86. d 83 p 83. SSF 83-86; C Brinsley w Underwood *S'well* 86-89; TV Hitchin *St Alb* 89-97; R Toddington and V Chalgrave 97-03; R N Albury Australia from 03. *St Mark's Rectory, 328 Gulpha Street, North Albury, NSW, Australia 2640* Tel (0061) (2) 5794 2443

MATTHEWS-LOYDALL, Mrs Elaine. b 63. Bp Otter Coll BA85 St Jo Coll Nottm LTh89 DPS90. d 90 p 94. Par Dn Nottingham All SS *S'well* 90-94; C 94-95; Asst Chapl to the Deaf 91-93; Chapl to the Deaf 93-99; TV Leic H Spirit *Leic* from 99; Chapl for Deaf People from 99. *Pumpkin Cottage, 54 Wilne Road, Long Eaton, Nottingham NG10 3AN* Tel 0115-972 8943

MATTHEWS-PAYNE, James. b 19. St D Coll Lamp BA41. Lich Th Coll 41 St Mich Coll Llan 46. d 46 p 47. C Barry All SS *Llan* 46-51; C Canton St Cath 51-53; P-in-c Aberavon 53-55; Bermuda 55-60; V Woolston *Win* 60-65; Australia from 65; R Bridgetown 65-68; R Narrogin 68-70; R Morley 70-79; rtd 80. *12/11 Freedman Road, Mount Lawley, W Australia 6050* Tel (0061) (8) 9272 5253

MATTHIAE, Canon David. b 40. Fitzw Ho Cam BA63 MA69. Linc Th Coll 63. d 65 p 66. C New Addington *Cant* 65-70; C Charlton-by-Dover SS Pet and Paul 70-75; V Cant All SS 75-84; P-in-c Tunstall 84-87; R Tunstall w Rodmersham from 87; RD Sittingbourne 88-94; Hon Can Cant Cathl from 99. *The Rectory, Tunstall, Sittingbourne ME9 8DU* Tel (01795) 423907
E-mail david@matthiae.demon.co.uk

MATTHIAS, Edwin. b 23. AKC50. d 51 p 52. C Hinckley St Mary *Leic* 51-54; C Putney St Mary *S'wark* 54-58; V Bolney *Chich* 58-65; R Chailey 65-82; rtd 92; Perm to Offic *Chich* from 92. *Oak Cottage, South Chailey, Lewes BN8 4AT* Tel (01273) 400894

MATTHIAS, George Ronald. b 30. CertEd51. St Deiniol's Hawarden 76. d 78 p 79. NSM Broughton *St As* 78-83; NSM Wrexham 83-85; C 85-87; V Brymbo 87-95; rtd 95. *Bryn Adref, Pisgah Hill, Pentre Hill, Wrexham LL11 5DB* Tel (01978) 750757

MATTHIAS, John Rex. b 61. St Mich Coll Llan DMS94. d 94 p 95. C Llandrillo-yn-Rhos *St As* 94-98; R Llanfair Talhaearn and Llansannan etc 98-03; R Betws-yn-Rhos w Petryal from 03. *The Rectory, Llanfairtalhaiarn, Abergele LL22 8ST* Tel (01745) 720273 E-mail r.matthias@tesco.net

MATTHIAS, Paul. b 47. Philippa Fawcett Coll CertEd75 Kent Univ DipEd84. Cant Sch of Min 92. d 94 p 95. Head RE Hever Sch Maidstone 80-94; Chapl Ch Ch High Sch Ashford from 94; NSM Gillingham St Aug *Roch* from 94. *33 Malvern Road, Gillingham ME7 4BA* Tel (01634) 576197
E-mail matthias@surfaid.org

MATTOCK, Colin Graham. b 38. Chich Th Coll. d 84 p 85. C Hove All SS *Chich* 84-87; C Bexhill St Pet 87-90; V Henlow *St Alb* 90-96; V Linslade *Ox* 96-00; P-in-c Pebworth w Dorsington and Honeybourne *Glouc* 00-02; R Pebworth, Dorsington, Honeybourne etc from 02. *The Vicarage, Stratford Road, Honeybourne, Evesham WR11 7PP* Tel (01386) 830302

MATTY, Horace Anthony (Tony). b 36. Ely Th Coll 61. d 63 p 64. C Minchinhampton *Glouc* 63-66; C Hunslet St Mary and Stourton *Ripon* 66-69; TV Wendy w Shingay *Ely* 69-71; V Parson Drove 71-74; V Southea cum Murrow 71-74; V Coven *Lich* 74-82; TV Hednesford 82-85; TV Basildon St Martin w Nevendon *Chelmsf* 85-92; P-in-c Basildon St Andr w H Cross 85-92; P-in-c Sandon 92-98; P-in-c E Hanningfield 92-98; rtd 98. *Ladymead, 15 Marshallen Road, Mount Hawke, Truro TR4 8EF* Tel (01209) 891553

MAUCHAN, Andrew. b 44. Hertf Coll Ox BA65 MA69 Man Univ CertEd66. Oak Hill Th Coll DipHE90. d 90 p 91. C Bridlington Priory *York* 90-94; V Alverthorpe *Wakef* 94-01; R Wombwell *Sheff* from 01. *The Rectory, 1 Rectory Close, Wombwell, Barnsley S73 8EY* Tel (01226) 211100

MAUDE, Canon Alan. b 41. Lon Univ DipTh67 BD69 Newc Univ MSc90. Lambeth STh74 Oak Hill Th Coll 66. d 69 p 70. C Balderstone *Man* 69-73; Asst Chapl Crumpsall and Springfield

Hosps 73-75; C Crumpsall St Matt 73-75; Chapl R Victoria Infirmary Newc 75-94; Chapl R Victoria Infirmary and Assoc Hosps NHS Trust 94-98; Chapl Newcastle upon Tyne Hosps NHS Trust from 98; Hon Can Newc Cathl *Newc* from 88. *Royal Victoria Infirmary, Queen Victoria Road, Newcastle upon Tyne NE1 4LP* Tel 0191-284 4966 *or* 232 5131

MAUDE, Alexander. b 53. Bingley Coll of Educn TCert74. N Ord Course. d 02 p 03. NSM Erringden *Wakef* from 02; Chapl Ravenscliffe High Sch from 02. *47 Vicar Park Drive, Norton Tower, Halifax HX2 0NN* Tel (01422) 355856 Mobile 07816-597074 E-mail sandie@maude47.fsnet.co.uk

MAUDE, Gillian Hamer. b 53. St Anne's Coll Ox BA75 MA79 Edin Univ MSc77. St Steph Ho Ox 99. d 01 p 02. C Hackney Wick St Mary of Eton w St Aug *Lon* from 01. *159 Cassland Road, London E9 5BS* Tel and fax (020) 8985 9696 Mobile 07932-056071 E-mail gillian.maude@london.anglican.org

MAUDLIN, David. b 39. EAMTC 92. d 95 p 96. NSM Bury St Edmunds St Jo *St E* 95-97; NSM Haverhill w Withersfield 97-98; P-in-c The Sampfords and Radwinter w Hempstead *Chelmsf* from 98; RD Saffron Walden from 00. *The Rectory, Walden Road, Radwinter, Saffron Walden CB10 2SW* Tel (01799) 599332 Fax as telephone

MAUDSLEY, Canon George Lambert. b 27. St Jo Coll Nottm 74. d 75 p 76. C Binley *Cov* 75-77; Chapl Barn Fellowship Winterborne Whitechurch 77-83; V Salford Priors *Cov* 83-94; RD Alcester 82-92; Hon Can Cov Cathl 91-94; rtd 94; Perm to Offic *Cov* and *Worc* from 94. *7 Flax Piece, Upton Snodsbury, Worcester WR7 4PA* Tel (01905) 381034

MAUDSLEY, Keith. b 51. York Univ BA72. Ripon Hall Ox 72. d 75 p 76. C Rugby St Andr *Cov* 75-79; C Cambridge Gt St Mary w St Mich *Ely* 79-82; Chapl Girton Coll 79-82; P-in-c Binley *Cov* 82-89; RD Cov E 87-89; P-in-c Leek Wootton 89-91; Dioc Policy Development Adv 89-91; Dioc Adv on UPA *Liv* 91-97; Soc Resp Officer 91-97; R Lymm *Ches* from 97. *The Rectory, 46 Rectory Lane, Lymm WA13 0AL* Tel (01925) 752164
E-mail keith@maudsleykms.freeserve.co.uk

MAUDSLEY, Michael Peter. b 38. St Andr Univ BSc61. Oak Hill Th Coll 65. d 67 p 68. C Blackpool St Mark *Blackb* 67-70; C Hartford *Ches* 70-72; R Balerno *Edin* 72-82; V Stapenhill w Cauldwell *Derby* 82-91; TV Edin St Paul and St Geo *Edin* 91-95; Assoc R from 95. *21 Barony Street, Edinburgh EH3 6PD* Tel 0131-558 1157 E-mail office@pandgchurch.org.uk

MAUGHAN, Angela. b 54. Newc Univ 93. NEOC 94. d 97 p 98. C Willington Team *Newc* 97-01; V Weetslade from 01. *Weetslade Vicarage, 59 Kirklands, Burradon, Cramlington NE23 7LE* Tel 0191-268 9366

MAUGHAN, Geoffrey Nigel. b 48. CCC Cam BA69 MA73. Oak Hill Th Coll 75. d 77 p 78. C New Malden and Coombe *S'wark* 77-81; C Abingdon w Shippon *Ox* 81-89; TV Abingdon 89-98; Dir of Min and Chapl Wycliffe Hall Ox from 98. *Wycliffe Hall, 54 Banbury Road, Oxford OX2 6PW* Tel (01865) 274207
E-mail geoffrey.maughan@wycliffe.ox.ac.uk

MAUGHAN, John. b 28. Keble Coll Ox BA51 MA55. Linc Th Coll 51. d 53 p 54. C Heworth St Mary *Dur* 53-56; C Winlaton 56-59; R Penshaw 59-72; V Cleadon Park 72-93; rtd 93. *2 Struddar's Farm Court, Bates Lane, Blaydon-on-Tyne NE21 5TF* Tel 0191-414 8350

MAUND, Mrs Margaret Jennifer. b 42. RGN64 RM65 DTM66 Midwife Teacher's Dip 72. Llan Dioc Tr Scheme 89. d 94 p 97. NSM Cymmer and Porth *Llan* 94-97; NSM Pwllgwaun w Llanddewi Rhondda from 97. *27 Mill Street, Tonyrefail, Porth CF39 8AB* Tel (01443) 670085

MAUNDER, Alan John. b 52. UWIST BSc74. Oak Hill Th Coll 88. d 90 p 91. C Birkenhead Ch Ch *Ches* 90-95; P-in-c Poulton from 95. *St Luke's Vicarage, Mill Lane, Wallasey CH44 3BP* Tel 0151-638 4663 E-mail ajmaunder@lineone.net

MAUNDER, Miss Vicky Alexandra. b 73. Leeds Univ BA95. Ripon Coll Cuddesdon BA. d 02 p 03. C Swaythling *Win* from 02. *12 Willis Road, Southampton SO16 2NT* Tel (023) 8058 6002 E-mail vickymaunder2000@yahoo.co.uk

MAUNDRELL, Canon Wolseley David. b 20. New Coll Ox BA41 DipTh42 MA45. d 43 p 44. C Haslemere *Guildf* 43-49; Bp's Dom Chapl *Chich* 49-50; V Sparsholt w Lainston *Win* 50-56; R Weeke 56-61; Can Res and Treas Win Cathl 61-70; Vice-Dean Win 66-70; Asst Chapl Brussels *Eur* 70-71; V Icklesham *Chich* 72-82; RD Rye 78-84; Can and Preb Chich Cathl 81-89; TR Rye 82-89; rtd 89; P-in-c Stonegate *Chich* 89-95; Perm to Offic from 95. *13 North Walls, Chichester PO19 1DA* Tel (01243) 537359

MAUNSELL, Colin Wray Dymock. b 35. Clare Coll Cam BA56 MA59 Lon Univ DipTh58. Tyndale Hall Bris 56. d 58 p 59. C Virginia Water *Guildf* 58-60; BCMS 60-93; Ethiopia 61-79 and from 91; Portugal 81-91; Crosslinks 93-94; rtd 94. *PO Box 18984, Addis Ababa, Ethiopia*

MAURICE, David Pierce. b 50. Pemb Coll Cam BA72 MA76 BChir76. Dioc OLM tr scheme. d 01 p 02. OLM Marlborough *Sarum* from 01. *Isbury House, Kingsbury Street, Marlborough SN8 1JA* Tel (01672) 514119
E-mail david.maurice2000@yahoo.com

MAURICE, Peter David. b 51. St Chad's Coll Dur BA72. Coll of Resurr Mirfield. **d** 75 **p** 76. C Wandsworth St Paul *S'wark* 75-79; TV Mortlake w E Sheen 79-85; V Rotherhithe H Trin 85-96; RD Bermondsey 91-96; V Tooting All SS from 96. *All Saints' Vicarage, 84 Franciscan Road, London SW17 8DQ* Tel (020) 8672 3706

MAWBEY, Miss Diane. b 55. Birm Univ MMedSc97. Cranmer Hall Dur. **d** 89 **p** 94. Par Dn Menston w Woodhead *Bradf* 89-92; C Barnoldswick w Bracewell 92-93; Chapl Asst Birm Children's Hosp 93-96; Chapl Asst Birm Maternity Hosp 93-96; Chapl Birm Women's Healthcare NHS Trust 96-98; R The Whitacres and Shustoke *Birm* from 98. *The Rectory, Dog Lane, Coleshill, Birmingham B46 2DU* Tel (01675) 481252 Mobile 0410-281648

MAWDITT, Stephen Donald Harvey. b 56. LNSM course 94. **d** 96 **p** 97. OLM Ashill w Saham Toney *Nor* from 96; OLM Watton w Carbrooke and Ovington from 00. *Cutbush House, Whitehall Lane, Saham Toney, Thetford IP25 7HB* Tel (01953) 883390

MAWER, Canon David Ronald. b 32. Keble Coll Ox BA55 MA58 Dur Univ BA57 McGill Univ Montreal PhD77. Wells Th Coll 58. **d** 59 **p** 60. C Cullercoats St Geo *Newc* 59-61; Canada 61-92; Co-ord Angl Studies St Paul Univ Ottawa 81-92; Can Ottawa from 85; rtd 92; Perm to Offic *Newc* from 93. *Moorside, Church Lane, Thropton, Morpeth NE65 7JA* Tel (01669) 620597

MAWSON, Canon Arthur Cyril. b 35. St Pet Coll Ox BA56 MA61. Wycliffe Hall Ox 61. **d** 62 **p** 63. C Walsall *Lich* 62-66; V Millhouses H Trin *Sheff* 66-73; Selection Sec ACCM 73-79; Can Res and Treas Ex Cathl *Ex* 79-98; Dioc Dir of Ords 81-87; rtd 99. *4 Woodlands Close, Headington, Oxford OX3 7RY* Tel (01865) 764099

MAWSON, David Frank. b 44. Selw Coll Cam BA65 MA69. Linc Th Coll 79 SSC. **d** 80 **p** 81. C Tunstall *Lich* 80-83; C Blakenall Heath 83-84; TV 84-90; Chapl Goscote Hosp Walsall 87-90; V Pelsall *Lich* 90-94; V Tividale 94-99; V Shrewsbury All SS w St Mich from 99. *All Saints' Vicarage, 5 Lingen Close, Shrewsbury SY1 2UN* Tel (01743) 358820 Fax 243409
E-mail david.mawson@virgin.net

MAWSON, Frank. b 18. ACIS70 FHSM53. NW Ord Course 74. **d** 77 **p** 78. NSM Stockport St Mary *Ches* 77-79; P-in-c Harthill and Burwardsley 79-82; rtd 82; Perm to Offic *Ches* and *St A* from 82; *Lich* from 88; *Heref* from 95. *16 College Court, Ludlow SY8 1BZ* Tel (01584) 873869 Fax as telephone

MAXTED, Neil Andrew. b 58. GradIMI80. Sarum & Wells Th Coll 92 Aston Tr Scheme 88. **d** 92 **p** 93. C Folkestone St Sav *Cant* 92-96; CF from 96. *clo MOD Chaplains (Army)* Tel (01980) 615802 Fax 615800

MAXWELL, Christopher John Moore (Bill). b 31. MRCS59 LRCP59 Qu Coll Cam MA75. Trin Coll Bris 74. **d** 75 **p** 76. Chile 75-81; C Clevedon Ch Ch *B & W* 75; Hon C Homerton St Luke *Lon* 81-94; Chapl Ibiza *Eur* 94-99; rtd 99; Perm to Offic *Chich* from 99. *Boscobel, Brightling Road, Robertsbridge TN32 5EJ* Tel (01580) 880475

MAXWELL, Marcus Howard. b 54. Liv Univ BSc76 Man Univ MPhil89. St Jo Coll Nottm BA79. **d** 80 **p** 81. C Chadderton St Matt *Man* 80-84; V Bircle 84-93; P-in-c Heaton Mersey 93-02; TR Heatons from 02; AD Heaton from 98. *St John's Rectory, 15 Priestnall Road, Stockport SK4 3HR* Tel 0161-432 2165

MAXWELL, Ralph. b 25. Lic to Offic. **d** 86 **p** 87. NSM Belfast St Mich *Conn* 86-87; Lic to Offic 87-89; NSM Belfast St Jas w St Silas 89-97; NSM Belfast St Pet 97-02; rtd 02. *69 Woodvale Road, Belfast BT13 3BN* Tel (028) 9074 2421

MAXWELL, Richard Renwick. b 23. Mert Coll Ox BA49 MA49. Westcott Ho Cam 49. **d** 51 **p** 52. C Moordown *Win* 51-55; N Rhodesia 55-64; Zambia 64-65; C N Holmwood *Guildf* 65-67; R Harrietsham *Cant* 67-73; V Blean 73-84; Hon C Hindhead *Guildf* 84-88; Perm to Offic *Cant* from 85; rtd 88; Perm to Offic *Guildf* 88-99, *Sarum* and *Win* from 88. *4 St Birinus Road, Woodfalls, Salisbury SP5 2LE* Tel (01725) 512037

MAY, Charles Henry. b 29. Lon Coll of Div ALCD58 LTh74. **d** 58 **p** 59. C Bethnal Green St Jas Less *Lon* 58-61; C Woking St Pet *Guildf* 61-64; Area Sec (W Midl) CPAS 64-67; V Homerton St Luke *Lon* 67-80; Home Sec SAMS 80-84; V Fulham Ch Ch *Lon* 84-94; rtd 94; Perm to Offic *Ely* and *Pet* from 94; *Linc* from 95. *16 Kilverstone, Werrington, Peterborough PE4 5DX* Tel (01733) 328108 E-mail cclergyman@aol.com

MAY, Mrs Deborah Kim. b 60. Trin Coll Bris DipTh01. **d** 01 **p** 02. C Haughley w Wetherden and Stowupland *St E* from 01. *11 Walton Close, Stowmarket IP14 1TL* Tel (01449) 672865 Fax as telephone E-mail debbie.may@btinternet.com

MAY, Donald Charles Leonard. b 25. Chich Th Coll 72. **d** 73 **p** 74. C Barkingside St Francis *Chelmsf* 73-77; V Aldersbrook 77-91; rtd 92; Perm to Offic *Chelmsf* from 92. *236 Prospect Road, Woodford Green IG8 7NQ* Tel (020) 8504 6119

MAY, George Louis. b 27. Selw Coll Cam BA52 MA55 Cam Univ PGCE67 AdDipEd78. Ridley Hall Cam 52. **d** 54 **p** 55. C St Mary Cray and St Paul's Cray *Roch* 54-56; C St Paul's Cray St Barn CD 56-57; C-in-c Elburton CD *Ex* 57-66; Asst Master Guthlaxton Sch Wigston 67-70; Ixworth Sch 70-72; Thurston Upper Sch 73-74; Perias Sch New Alresford 75-85; Hon C Ropley w W

Tisted *Win* 78-79; Perm to Offic 79-96; rtd 92. *Oven House, Water Lane, Eyam, Hope Valley S32 5RG* Tel (01433) 630599

MAY, Janet Isabel. b 51. Lon Univ CertEd72. Dioc OLM tr scheme 99. **d** 00 **p** 01. OLM Attleborough w Besthorpe *Nor* from 00. *The Mill House, Church Street, Great Ellingham, Attleborough NR17 1LE* Tel (01953) 452198

MAY, John Alexander Cyril. b 52. K Coll Lon BD77 PhD98 Ch Ch Ox PGCE78. Linc Th Coll 79. **d** 80 **p** 81. C Tynemouth Ch Ch *Newc* 80-82; C Tynemouth Ch Ch w H Trin 82-85; C Tynemouth St Aug 82-85; TV Glendale Gp 85-90; V Wotton-under-Edge w Ozleworth, N Nibley etc *Glouc* from 90. *The Vicarage, Culverhay, Wotton-under-Edge GL12 7LS* Tel (01453) 842175 E-mail john@wotvic.freeserve.co.uk

MAY, Peter Richard. b 43. St Jo Coll Cam BA64 MA68 MICE70. Trin Coll Bris 77. **d** 79 **p** 80. C Lancaster St Thos *Blackb* 79-85; V Darwen St Barn 85-91; Chapl Lyon w Grenoble *Eur* 91-92; Chapl Lyon 92-94; Perm to Offic *S'wark* 94-95; TR Horley 95-02; rtd 03. *83 Military Road, Rye TN31 7NY* Tel (01797) 222847 E-mail rev@petermay.fsnet.co.uk

MAY, Simon George. b 47. FCA77 Ex Univ BA69 Univ of Wales (Ban) CertEd72. Sarum & Wells Th Coll 86. **d** 88 **p** 89. C Tamworth *Lich* 88-92; V Whitchurch *Ex* from 92; Warden of Readers (Plymouth Adnry) from 00; RD Tavistock from 02. *The Vicarage, 204 Whitchurch Road, Tavistock PL19 9DQ* Tel (01822) 610364

MAY, Stephen Charles Arthur. b 52. Mert Coll Ox BA73 Edin Univ BD78 Aber Univ PhD86. Ridley Hall Cam 84. **d** 86 **p** 87. C Sawley *Derby* 86-88; Lect St Jo Coll Auckland New Zealand 88-01; V Norden w Ashworth *Man* from 01. *St Paul's Vicarage, Heap Road, Rochdale OL12 7SN* Tel (01706) 641001 E-mail smaysfiction@hotmail.com

MAY, Toby Sebstian. b 67. Bris Univ BEng89. St Jo Coll Nottm MTh02. **d** 02 **p** 03. C Kendal St Thos *Carl* from 02. *79 High Garth, Kendal LA9 5NR* Tel (01539) 732602 E-mail toby@mays-in-grace.co.uk

MAYBURY, David Kaines. b 32. G&C Coll Cam BA55 MA59. Ridley Hall Cam 55. **d** 57 **p** 58. C Sydenham H Trin *S'wark* 57-60; C Rainham *Chelmsf* 60-63; R Edin St Jas *Edin* 63-75; R Jedburgh 75-84; NSM Duns 84-91; Warden Whitchester Conf Cen 84-91; NSM Hawick *Edin* 91-97; Warden Whitchester Chr Guest Ho and Retreat Cen 91-97; rtd 97. *DaDo Heights, Borthaugh, Hawick TD9 7LN* Tel (01450) 370809 Fax as telephone E-mail 100734.503@compuserve.com

MAYBURY, Doreen Lorna. b 33. RGN54 SCM56. Edin Th Coll 76. **dss** 81 **d** 95 **p** 95. Jedburgh *Edin* 81-84; Warden Whitchester Conf Cen 84-91; Duns 84-91; Hawick 91-97; NSM 95-97; rtd 97; Chapl Borders Gen Hosp NHS Trust from 98. *DaDo Heights, Borthaugh, Hawick TD9 7LN* Tel and fax (01450) 370809 Mobile 0780-1354134 E-mail 100734.503@compuserve.com

MAYBURY, Canon John Montague. b 30. G&C Coll Cam BA53 MA57. Ridley Hall Cam 53. **d** 55 **p** 56. C Allerton *Liv* 55-59; C Rowner *Portsm* 59-62; V Wroxall 62-67; V Southsea St Simon 67-78; V Crofton 78-91; Hon Can Portsm Cathl 81-95; C Locks Heath 91-95; rtd 95; Perm to Offic *Portsm* from 95. *19 Netley Road, Titchfield Common, Fareham PO14 4PE* Tel (01489) 584168

MAYBURY, Paul. b 31. St Deiniol's Hawarden 87. **d** 88 **p** 90. NSM Sutton St Geo *Ches* 88-94; Perm to Offic 94-98 and from 01; P-in-c Towednack *Truro* 98-00. *43 Flowerscroft, Nantwich CW5 7GN* Tel (01270) 620639

MAYBURY, Paul Dorian. b 58. Trin Coll Bris DipHE95. **d** 95 **p** 96. C Spondon *Derby* 95-99; V Gawthorpe and Chickenley Heath *Wakef* 99-02; P-in-c Ossett cum Gawthorpe 01-02; V Ossett and Gawthorpe from 02. *The Vicarage, 12 Fearnley Avenue, Ossett WF5 9ET* Tel (01924) 217379 or 263497 Fax 08701-375994 E-mail maybury@xncommunity.org.uk

MAYCOCK, Ms Jane Ellen. b 66. Somerville Coll Ox BA90 MA95 Glas Univ MPhil98. Cranmer Hall Dur 90. **d** 92 **p** 94. Par Dn Harrow Trin St Mich *Lon* 92-94; C 94-95; C Kendal H Trin *Carl* 95-99; Dir of Ords from 98. *The Rectory, Longlands Road, Bowness-on-Windermere, Windermere LA23 3AS* Tel (01539) 443063 E-mail jemaycock@lineone.net

MAYELL, Howard John. b 50. Bris Sch of Min 81. **d** 84 **p** 88. NSM Patchway *Bris* 84-86; NSM Weston-super-Mare Cen Par *B & W* 87-88; C N Stoneham *Win* 89-91; P-in-c Black Torrington, Bradf w Cookbury etc *Ex* 91-97; C Ledbury w Eastnor *Heref* 97-98; TV Ledbury from 98. *27 Hazle Close, Ledbury HR8 2XX* Tel (01531) 631530

MAYER, Alan John. b 46. AKC70. St Aug Coll Cant 70. **d** 71 **p** 72. C Stanningley St Thos *Ripon* 71-74; C St Helier *S'wark* 74-79; TV Wimbledon 79-85; V Reigate St Luke S Park 85-00; R Oxted and Tandridge from 00. *The Rectory, 29 Chichele Road, Oxted RH8 0AE* Tel (01883) 712955 or 0771-4661911 E-mail alanmayer1@compuserve.com

MAYER, Graham Keith. b 46. St Cath Coll Ox BA68 Nottm Univ PGCE69 Ex Univ MA93 Plymouth Univ Dip Counselling 95. Linc Th Coll 78. **d** 80 **p** 81. C Paignton St Jo *Ex* 80-93; Perm to Offic 93-96; P-in-c Christow, Ashton and Bridford from 96; P-in-c Dunchideock and Shillingford St George w Ide from 97.

The Rectory, Dry Lane, Christow, Exeter EX6 7PE Tel (01647) 252845

MAYER, Mrs Paula Denise. b 45. St Hilda's Coll Ox BA68 Nottm Univ CertEd69. SW Minl Tr Course 84. **d** 88. Hon Par Dn Paignton St Jo *Ex* 88-90; Par Dn 90-93; Perm to Offic from 93. *367A Torquay Road, Paignton TQ3 2BJ* Tel (01803) 558727

MAYERSON, Paul Strom. b 28. PhD MEd MusBac. Ridley Hall Cam 80. **d** 82 **p** 83. C New Romney w Old Romney and Midley *Cant* 82-85; P-in-c Ospringe 85; P-in-c Eastling 85; R Eastling w Ospringe and Stalisfield w Otterden 85-90; rtd 90; Perm to Offic *Cant* 90-95. *360 Piper Hill Road, Center Harbour, NH 03226, USA*

MAYES, Canon Andrew Dennis. b 56. Dartmouth Coll (USA) 78 K Coll Lon BD79 AKC79 Armenian Orthodox Sem Jerusalem 79 Man Univ MA97. St Steph Ho Ox 80. **d** 81 **p** 82. C Hendon St Alphage *Lon* 81-84; C Hockley *Chelmsf* 84-87; V Kingstanding St Mark *Birm* 87-92; V Saltdean *Chich* 92-01; CME Officer from 01; P-in-c Ovingdean from 01; Hon Can Niger Delta from 96. *St Wulfran's Rectory, 43 Ainsworth Avenue, Brighton BN2 7BG* Tel (01273) 303633

MAYES, Anthony Bernard Duncan. b 29. Down Coll Cam BA53 MA57. Coll of Resurr Mirfield 56. **d** 58 **p** 59. C Leeds Halton St Wilfrid *Ripon* 58-60; USA from 61; V Fairfax St Aug California 61-63; Dir The Parsonage Center San Francisco 72-82; Asst Dean Charlottesville Univ of Virginia from 86; Fell Brown Coll Univ of Virginia from 86. *1624 Corcoram Street North West, Washington, DC 20009, USA* Tel (001) (202) 319 8191 E-mail b.dm3g@virginia.edu

MAYES, The Very Revd Gilbert. b 15. TCD BA43 MA61. CITC 44. **d** 44 **p** 45. C Arm St Mark *Arm* 44-47; Hd Master Cathl Sch Arm 47-48; Dioc C 47-48; I Upper Donaghmore w Pomeroy 48-52; I Dundalk 52-61; Dean Lismore *C & O* 61-87; I Lismore w Cappoquin, Kilwatermoy, Dungarvan etc 61-87; Prec Waterford Cathl 84-87; Preb Stagonil St Patr Cathl Dublin 85-87; rtd 87. *Woodford, Ballybride Road, Rathmichael, Shankill, Co Dublin, Irish Republic* Tel (00353) (1) 282 4089

MAYES, Canon John Charles Dougan. b 44. Bps' Coll Cheshunt 63. **d** 67 **p** 68. C Portadown St Mark *Arm* 67-74; I Aghadowey w Kilrea *D & R* 74-86; USPG Area Sec 77-94; I Clooney w Strathfoyle from 86; Can Derry Cathl from 92. *All Saints' Rectory, 20 Limavady Road, Londonderry BT47 6JD* Tel (028) 7134 4306

MAYES, Leonard Harry. b 25. Ely Th Coll 59. **d** 61 **p** 62. C Norton *St Alb* 61-65; C Biscot 65-69; V Watford St Mich 69-78; V Liscard St Mary w St Columba *Ches* 78-82; R Moreton and Church Eaton *Lich* 82-90; rtd 90; Perm to Offic *Lich* 90-99. *11 Covert Close, Great Haywood, Stafford ST18 0RN* Tel (01889) 882994

✠**MAYES, The Rt Revd Michael Hugh Gunton.** b 41. TCD BA62 Lon Univ BD85. TCD Div Sch Div Test64. **d** 64 **p** 65 **c** 93. C Portadown St Columba *Arm* 64-68; Japan 68-74; Area Sec (Dios Cashel, Cork, Lim and Tuam) USPG 75-93; I Cork St Mich Union *C, C & R* 75-86; Adn Cork, Cloyne and Ross 86-93; I Moviddy Union 86-88; I Rathcooney Union 88-93; Bp K, E & A 93-00; Can Elphin Cathl 93-00; Bp L & K from 00. *Bishop's House, North Circular Road, Limerick, Irish Republic* Tel (00353) (61) 451532 Fax 451100 E-mail bishop@limerick.anglican.org

MAYES, Stephen Thomas. b 47. St Jo Coll Nottm 67. **d** 71 **p** 72. C Cullompton *Ex* 71-75; C Cheltenham St Mark *Glouc* 76-84; P-in-c Water Orton *Birm* 84-91; V from 91; AD Coleshill from 99. *The Vicarage, Water Orton, Birmingham B46 1RX* Tel 0121-747 2751 Fax 749 7294 E-mail stephentmayes@classicfm.net

MAYES, Suzanne Janette. b 55. NTMTC 95. **d** 98 **p** 99. NSM E Ham w Upton Park St Alb *Chelmsf* 98-02; Chapl HM Pris Wellingborough from 02. *Chaplaincy, HM Prison, Millers Park, Wellingborough NN8 2NH* Tel (01933) 224151 Fax 273903

✠**MAYFIELD, The Rt Revd Christopher John.** b 35. G&C Coll Cam BA57 MA61 Linacre Ho Ox DipTh63 Cranfield Inst of Tech MSc83. Wycliffe Hall Ox 61. **d** 63 **p** 64 **c** 85. C Birm St Martin *Birm* 63-67; Lect 67-71; V Luton St Mary *St Alb* 71-80; RD Luton 74-80; Adn Bedford 80-85; Suff Bp Wolverhampton *Lich* 85-92; Area Bp Wolverhampton 92-93; Bp Man 93-02; rtd 02. *Harewood House, 54 Primrose Crescent, Worcester WR5 3HT* Tel (01905) 764822

MAYFIELD, Timothy James Edward. b 60. LMH Ox BA82. Trin Coll Bris BA88. **d** 88 **p** 89. C Ovenden *Wakef* 88-92; V Mount Pellon from 92. *The Vicarage, Church Lane, Halifax HX2 0EF* Tel (01422) 365027

MAYFIELD, Timothy John Joseph. b 59. BA MA. **d** 99 **p** 00. C Battersea Rise St Mark *S'wark* from 99. *93A Bolingbroke Grove, London SW11 6HA* Tel (020) 7924 6833 or 7223 6188

MAYHEW, Canon Charles. b 40. K Coll Lon BD64 AKC64. **d** 65 **p** 66. C Nottingham St Mary *S'well* 65-69; R Cawston *Nor* 69-74; P-in-c Felthorpe w Haveringland 69-74; R Barnack w Ufford and Bainton *Pet* 74-86; RD Barnack 77-86; Can Pet Cathl 83-94; V Oakham, Hambleton, Egleton, Braunston and Brooke 86-94; Chapl Catmose Vale & Rutland Memorial Hosps 86-94; rtd 94; Perm to Offic *Pet* from 94. *Thorndon Green, Church Road, Lyndon, Oakham LE15 8TU* Tel (01572) 737594

MAYHEW, David Francis. b 51. Ch Ch Ox BA72 MA76 Newc Poly DCG76. Wycliffe Hall Ox BA75 NEOC 89. **d** 91 **p** 92. NSM High Elswick St Paul *Newc* 91-94; Toc H 91-94; V Mitford *Newc* from 94; Chapl Northgate and Prudhoe NHS Trust from 94. *The Vicarage, Stable Green, Mitford, Morpeth NE61 3PZ* Tel (01670) 511468 E-mail dfmayhew@aol.com

MAYLAND, Mrs Jean Mary. b 36. JP77. LMH Ox BA58 DipTh59 MA61 TCert60. St Deiniol's Hawarden 91. **d** 91 **p** 94. NSM York Minster *York* 91-93; Lect and Tutor N Ord Course 91-93; Lect NEOC 93-96; Dioc Ecum Officer *Dur* 93-96; Local Unity Officer Dur Ecum Relns Gp 93-96; Assoc Sec CCBI 96-99; Sec for Ch Life CTBI from 99; Perm to Offic *S'wark* 97-00; *Lon* from 97; *Chelmsf* from 00. *Inter-Church House, 35-41 Lower Marsh, London SE1 7RL* Tel (020) 7620 4444 Fax 7928 0010 E-mail jean.mayland@ctbi.org.uk

MAYLAND, Canon Ralph. b 27. VRD63. Ripon Hall Ox 57. **d** 59 **p** 60. C Lambeth St Andr w St Thos *S'wark* 59-62; Chapl RNR 61-94; C-in-c Worksop St Paul CD *S'well* 62-68; V Brightside St Marg *Sheff* 68-72; Ind Chapl 68-81; V Ecclesfield 72-81; Can Res and Treas York Minster *York* 82-94; rtd 94; Hon C Brancepeth *Dur* 94-96; Perm to Offic *York* from 96. *Minster Cottage, 51 Sands Lane, Barmston, Driffield YO25 8PQ* Tel (01262) 468709

MAYLOR, David Charles. b 59. Lanc Univ BSc80 Edge Hill Coll of HE PGCE81. St Jo Coll Nottm 89. **d** 91 **p** 92. C Hindley All SS *Liv* 91-94; P-in-c Spalding St Paul *Linc* from 94. *St Paul's Vicarage, 60 Holbeach Road, Spalding PE11 2HY* Tel (01775) 722532 E-mail dave@stpauls-spalding.co.uk

MAYNARD, John William. b 37. Lon Univ BSc58. Ripon Hall Ox 60. **d** 62 **p** 63. C St Laur in Thanet *Cant* 62-67; C S Ashford Ch Ch 67-70; V Pagham *Chich* 70-00; rtd 00. *Two Hedges, Lower Budleigh, East Budleigh, Budleigh Salterton EX9 7DL* Tel (01395) 443869

MAYNARD, Raymond. b 30. S'wark Ord Course 75 Ox Ord Course 76. **d** 77 **p** 78. NSM Hedsor and Bourne End *Ox* 77-80; C Newport Pagnell w Lathbury 80-83; P-in-c Lacey Green 83-89; V 89; Perm to Offic *Guildf* 90-01. *Hardore, Ven Ottery, Ottery St Mary EX11 1RY* Tel (01404) 814307

MAYNARD, Canon Richard Edward Buller. b 42. AKC66. **d** 67 **p** 68. C St Ives *Truro* 67-71; C Falmouth K Chas 71-74; V St Germans 74-84; V Tideford 74-84; RD E Wivelshire 81-85; Hon Can Truro Cathl from 82; V St Germans 84-85; TR Saltash from 85; Chapl St Barn Hosp Saltash 90-93; Chapl Cornwall Healthcare Trust from 93. *The Vicarage, 11 Higher Port View, Saltash PL12 4BU* Tel (01752) 843142

MAYNE, Brian John. b 52. Univ of Wales (Cardiff) BA73 LTCL75 ARICS81 MRICS01. NEOC 82 Coll of Resurr Mirfield 84. **d** 85 **p** 86. C Stainton-in-Cleveland *York* 85-89; P-in-c Rounton w Welbury 89-96; Chapl HM YOI Northallerton 89-96; Chapl HM YOI Lanc Farms from 96. *HM Young Offender Institution, Lancaster Farms, Stone Row Head, Lancaster LA1 3QZ* Tel (01524) 848745 E-mail brianmayne@excite.co.uk *or* brianmayne@lycos.co.uk

MAYNE, Canon John Andrew Brian. b 34. QUB BA55 Lon Univ BD62. TCD Div Sch Div Test 57. **d** 57 **p** 58. C Ballymoney *Conn* 57-60; C Knock *D & D* 60-62; P-in-c Knocknagoney 62-68; P-in-c Belvoir 68-71; I 71-80; Dean Waterford *C & O* 80-84; I Lecale Gp *D & D* 84-01; Can Down Cathl 87-01; Prec 91-00; Chan 00-01; Sec Gen Syn Liturg Cttee 89-99; rtd 01. *114 Ballydugan Road, Downpatrick BT30 8HF* Tel (028) 4461 2521 Mobile 07092-207229 E-mail jab@brianmayne.co.uk *or* editor.bcp@ireland.anglican.org

MAYNE, The Very Revd Michael Clement Otway. b 29. KCVO96. CCC Cam BA55 MA56. Cuddesdon Coll 55. **d** 57 **p** 58. C Harpenden St Jo *St Alb* 57-59; Bp's Dom Chapl *S'wark* 59-65; V Norton *St Alb* 65-72; Hd of Relig Progr BBC Radio 72-79; Hon Can *S'wark* Cathl *S'wark* 75-79; V Cambridge Gt St Mary w St Mich *Ely* 79-86; Dean Westmr 86-96; rtd 96; Perm to Offic *Sarum* from 97. *37 St Mark's Road, Salisbury SP1 3AY* Tel (01722) 331069

MAYO, Christopher Paul. b 68. Heythrop Coll Lon BD91 Birm Univ PGCE96. Qu Coll Birm 91. **d** 93 **p** 94. C Wednesfield *Lich* 93-94; C Bilston 94-95. *73 Gorse Road, Wednesfield, Wolverhampton WV11 2PY* Tel (01902) 733163

MAYO, Deborah Ann. *See* MURPHY, Deborah Ann

MAYO, Canon Gordon Edwin. b 18. St Jo Coll Dur LTh42 BA45 MA61. Oak Hill Th Coll. **d** 42 **p** 43. C Cheadle *Ches* 42-44; C Dur St Nic *Dur* 44-45; Chapl RAFVR 45-48; C St Marylebone All So w SS Pet and Jo 48-50; Kenya 50-59; Can Mombasa 57-59; Asst Warden Lee Abbey 60-64; Warden Lee Abbey Internat Students' Club Kensington 64-71; R Coulsdon St Jo *S'wark* 71-78; Dir of Chr Stewardship 78-85; Hon Can *S'wark* Cathl 83-85; rtd 85; P-in-c Limpsfield and Titsey *S'wark* 85-89; Perm to Offic *Chich* from 90. *1 Kings Mews, Horsham RH12 1QL* Tel (01403) 273508

MAYO, Inglis John. b 46. FCA. Ripon Coll Cuddesdon 74. **d** 77 **p** 78. C Bitterne Park *Win* 77-81; C Christchurch 81-86; P-in-c Sturminster Marshall *Sarum* 86-89; P-in-c Kingston Lacy and Shapwick 86-89; V Sturminster Marshall, Kingston Lacy and

Shapwick 89-00; P-in-c Lilliput from 00. *The Vicarage, 55 Lilliput Road, Parkstone, Poole BH14 8JX* Tel (01202) 708567 E-mail holyangelschurchlilliput@fish.co.uk

MAYO, Robert William. b 61. Keble Coll Ox BA83. Cranmer Hall Dur 85. **d** 87 **p** 88. C Luton Lewsey St Hugh *St Alb* 87-90; Hd Cam Univ Miss 90-95; Hon C Bermondsey St Jas w Ch Ch *S'wark* 90-95; Chapl S Bank Univ 95-98; Dir of Youth Work Tr Ridley Hall Cam from 98. *Ridley Hall, Cambridge CB3 9HG* Tel (01223) 741067 E-mail bm231@cam.ac.uk

MAYOH, Margaret Evelyn. b 38. Open Univ BA87 Matlock Coll of Educn TCert87. Trin Coll Bris DipHE82. **dss** 82 **d** 87 **p** 94. Halliwell St Paul *Man* 82-87; Hon Par Dn 87-91; Hon Par Dn Walmersley 91-94; Hon C 94-97; NSM Heaton Ch Ch from 97. *40 Hillside Avenue, Bromley Cross, Bolton BL7 9NJ* Tel (01204) 305423

MAYOR, Henry William. b 39. Oriel Coll Ox BA62 Birm Univ DPS67. Westcott Ho Cam 62. **d** 64 **p** 65. C The Quinton *Birm* 64-66; C Dudley St Thos *Worc* 67-71; R Birch St Agnes *Man* 71-83; Community Chapl Aylesbury *Ox* 83-89; Community Chapl Aylesbury w Bierton and Hulcott 89; R Cheetham St Luke and Lower Crumpsall St Thos *Man* 89-96; R Cheetham and Lower Crumpsall 97-01; rtd 01. *57 Hill Street, Manchester M20 3FY* Tel (07960) 767155 E-mail henrywmayor@hotmail.com

MAYOSS, Anthony (Aidan). b 31. Leeds Univ BA55. Coll of Resurr Mirfield 55. **d** 57 **p** 58. C Meir *Lich* 57-62; Lic to Offic *Wakef* 62-72 and from 78; CR from 64; S Africa 73-75; Asst Chapl Lon Univ *Lon* 76-78; Bursar CR 84-90; rtd 98; Perm to Offic *Lon* from 98. *St Michael's Priory, 14 Burleigh Street, London WC2E 7PX* Tel (020) 7379 6669 E-mail amayoss@mirfield.org.uk

MAYOSS-HURD, Mrs Susan Patricia. b 59. Lanc Univ BA81. Cranmer Hall Dur 82. **dss** 84 **d** 87 **p** 94. Ribbesford w Bewdley and Dowles *Worc* 84-88; Par Dn 87-88; Chapl W Heath Hosp 88-96; C W Heath *Birm* 88-96; V from 96. *St Anne's Vicarage, Lilley Lane, Birmingham B31 3JT* Tel (0121-475 5587

MBALI, Escourt Zolile. b 40. Fort Hare Univ BA68 Ox Univ BA71. St Bede's Coll Umtata 62. **d** 71 **p** 72. S Africa 71-74 and from 93; Botswana 74-81; V Preston on Tees *Dur* 81-83; C Knighton St Mary Magd *Leic* 84-88; P-in-c Church Langton w Tur Langton, Thorpe Langton etc 88-92; Community Relns Officer 88-93; Hon Can Leic Cathl 92-93; rtd 02. *1 Halford Road, Berea, Durban, 4001 South Africa* Tel (0027) (31) 201 6195

MDUMULLA, Jonas Habel. b 50. Nairobi Univ Hull Univ BTh87 MA89. St Phil Coll Kongwa DipTh74. **d** 74 **p** 75. Tanzania 74-82; C Sutton St Jas and Wawne *York* 82-96; P-in-c Carlton and Drax from 96; Ind Chapl from 96. *The Vicarage, 2 Church Dike Lane, Drax, Selby YO8 8NZ* Tel (01757) 618313

MEACHAM, John David. b 24. AKC51 Open Univ MPhil90. Lambeth STh77. **d** 52 **p** 53. C Maidenhead St Luke *Ox* 52-55; Asst Master Linton Ho Maidenhead 52-55; C Croydon *Cant* 55-58; V Sittingbourne St Mich 58-74; V Brenchley *Roch* 74-83; Bp's Chapl and Research Asst 83-86; P-in-c Gt Wishford *Sarum* 83-88; P-in-c S Newton 83-88; Sec C of E Doctrine Commn 84-89; rtd 88; Perm to Offic *Sarum* 88-98. *Trewinnard, Grams Road, Walmer, Deal CT14 7NT* Tel (01304) 239613

MEAD, Arthur Hugh. b 39. K Coll Cam BA60 MA64 New Coll Ox BLitt66. St Steph Ho Ox 61. **d** 80 **p** 80. NSM Hammersmith St Jo *Lon* from 80; Chapl St Paul's Sch Barnes 82-97; Dep P in O 85-90 and from 95; P in O 90-95; Reader of The Temple from 95; rtd 97. *11 Dungarvan Avenue, London SW15 5QU* Tel (020) 8876 5833

MEAD, Colin Harvey. b 26. FCA. S Dios Minl Tr Scheme 81. **d** 84 **p** 85. NSM Talbot Village *Sarum* 84-96; rtd 96; Perm to Offic *Sarum* from 96. *59 Alyth Road, Bournemouth BH3 7HB* Tel (01202) 763647

MEAD, Canon John Harold. b 37. Wells Th Coll 69. **d** 71 **p** 72. C Charlton Kings St Mary *Glouc* 71-75; R Stratton w Baunton 75-82; R Bishop's Cleeve 82-00; RD Tewkesbury 88-97; Hon Can Glouc Cathl 90-00; rtd 00; Perm to Offic *Glouc* from 00. *13 Cleevemount Close, Cheltenham GL52 3HW* Tel (01242) 241050

MEAD, Mrs Lynda Roberta. b 44. Open Univ BA91. STETS DipTh99. **d** 99 **p** 00. NSM Hythe *Win* from 99. *22 Furzedale Park, Hythe, Southampton SO45 3HW* Tel (023) 8084 8901

MEAD, Nicholas Charles. b 50. Newc Univ BEd73 Reading Univ MA76. Ridley Hall Cam 83. **d** 85 **p** 86. C Bilton *Cov* 85-88; C Whittlesea *Ely* 88-89; Hd of Relig Studies Neale-Wade Community Coll March 89-97; Fell Farmington Inst for Chr Studies Ox from 96; Sen Lect RE Westmr Coll Ox from 97. *Westminster College, Harcourt Hill, Oxford OX2 9AT* Tel (01865) 253380 E-mail n.mead@ox-west.ac.uk

MEADEN, Philip George William. b 40. Open Univ BA75. Lich Th Coll 63. **d** 66 **p** 67. C Aston SS Pet and Paul *Birm* 66-70; V Lozells St Paul 70-76; Asst Chapl HM Pris Brixton 76-77; Chapl HM Pris Lewes 77-84; Chapl HM Pris Aylesbury 84-88; Chapl HM Pris Wandsworth 88-01; rtd 01; Perm to Offic *St E* from 01. *Rose Cottage, The Street, Horham, Eye IP21 5DX* Tel (01379) 384680

MEADER, Jennifer Lindsay. b 68. UEA BA89. Westcott Ho Cam. **d** 01 **p** 02. C Cherry Hinton St Andr *Ely* from 01; C Teversham from 01. *39 Eland Way, Cherry Hinton, Cambridge CB1 9XQ* Tel (01223) 474542 E-mail revlindsay@ntlworld.com

MEADER, Philip John. b 44. Oak Hill Th Coll 73. **d** 75 **p** 76. C E Ham St Paul *Chelmsf* 75-77; CMJ 77-90; TV Lowestoft and Kirkley *Nor* 90-94; V Lowestoft St Andr 94-96; R Panfield and Rayne *Chelmsf* from 96. *The Rectory, Shalford Lane, Rayne, Braintree CM77 6BT* Tel (01376) 320517

MEADOWS, Mrs Freda Angela. b 46. CertEd68. Oak Hill Th Coll 93. **d** 96 **p** 97. NSM N Wembley St Cuth *Lon* 96-01; NSM Roxeth from 01. *48 Torrington Drive, Harrow HA2 8NF* Tel (020) 8248 3523

MEADOWS, John Michael. b 27. St Jo Coll Cam BA50. Ridley Hall Cam 51. **d** 53 **p** 54. C Daubhill *Man* 53-55; Overseas Miss Fellowship 56-87; Malaya 57-61; Vietnam 62-75; Refugee Reception Cen Sopley *Win* 79-82; NSM Canford Magna *Sarum* 86-88; C Radipole and Melcombe Regis 89-94; rtd 94; Perm to Offic *Win* from 94. *18 Wellington Avenue, Southampton SO18 5DD* Tel (023) 8046 5167

MEADOWS, Philip Michael. b 71. Univ of Wales (Lamp) BA95. St Steph Ho Ox BTh01. **d** 01 **p** 03. C W Bromwich St Fran *Lich* 01; C Leeds Belle Is St Jo and St Barn *Ripon* from 02. *St Barnabas' House, 28 Low Grange View, Leeds LS10 3DT* Tel 0113-271 8346 E-mail fatherphilip@ssjohnandbarnabas.fsnet.co.uk

MEADOWS, Canon Stanley Percival. b 14. TD61. St D Coll Lamp BA46. **d** 47 **p** 48. C Worsley *Man* 47-49; C Littleborough 49-51; V Charlestown 51-61; R Man St Geo w St Barn 61-72; R Man Miles Platting 72-82; RD Ardwick 77-82; rtd 82; Perm to Offic *Man* from 82. *20 Dantall Avenue, Manchester M9 7BH* Tel 0161-795 9478

MEADS, William Ivan. b 35. ACIS67 ACMA75 Qu Mary Coll Lon BA56. Linc Th Coll 75. **d** 77 **p** 78. C Cheltenham St Luke and St Jo *Glouc* 77-81; Chapl HM Pris Pentonville 81-82; Preston 82-85; Wakef 85-88; Chapl HM Pris Wakef 85-88; P-in-c Wroxton w Balscote and Shenington w Alkerton *Ox* 88-90; R Broughton w N Newington and Shutford etc 90-95; P-in-c Week St Mary w Poundstock and Whitstone *Truro* 95-97; rtd 97; Perm to Offic *B & W* 97-00. *15 Southlands, St Daniels Hill, Pembroke SA71 5QY* E-mail nanmeads@whsmithnet.co.uk

MEADWAY, Jeanette Valerie. b 47. FRCP87 FRCPEd87 Edin Univ MB, ChB69. Oak Hill NSM Course 89. **d** 93 **p** 94. NSM Stratford St Jo w Ch Ch and St Jas *Chelmsf* from 93. *4 Glebe Avenue, Woodford Green IG8 9HB* Tel (020) 8491 6040 Fax as telephone E-mail meadway@dial.pipex.com

MEAKIN, Canon Anthony John. b 28. TD76. Down Coll Cam BA52 MA56. Westcott Ho Cam 52. **d** 54 **p** 55. C Gosforth All SS *Newc* 54-60; V Alnwick St Paul 60-71; V Edlingham 62-71; CF (TA) 63-83; R Whickham *Dur* 71-88; RD Gateshead W 78-88; Hon Can Dur Cathl 83-93; Bp's Sen Chapl and Exec Officer for Dioc Affairs 88-93; rtd 93. *73 Oakfields, Burnopfield, Newcastle upon Tyne NE16 6PQ* Tel (01207) 270429

MEAKIN, David John. b 61. Hull Univ BA82 Hughes Hall Cam PGCE83 Lambeth STh88. Westcott Ho Cam 86. **d** 88 **p** 89. C Upminster *Chelmsf* 88-92; Prec and Sacr Dur Cathl *Dur* 92-97; V Ryhope from 97. *St Paul's Vicarage, Ryhope, Sunderland SR2 0HH* Tel 0191-523 7884 E-mail d.meakin@btinternet.com

MEAKIN, The Ven John Ernest. b 13. Kelham Th Coll 30. **d** 36 **p** 37. C Stepney St Matt *Lon* 36-39; C Cheltenham St Steph *Glouc* 39-41; C Knottingley *Wakef* 41-43; P-in-c Stepney St Phil *Lon* 43-46; Argentina 46-51; Singapore 51-55; Australia from 55; Adn Eyre Peninsula 68-70; Adn Willoch 70-80; Adn Willoch (Outer) 80-87; rtd 80. *Staddlestones, Elder Street, Moonta Mines, S Australia 5558* Tel (0061) (8) 8825 2816 E-mail meakin@yp-connect.net

MEARA, Canon David Gwynne. b 47. Oriel Coll Ox BA70 MA74. Lambeth STh76 Cuddesdon Coll 71. **d** 73 **p** 74. C Whitley Ch Ch *Ox* 73-77; Chapl Reading Univ 77-82; V Basildon 82-87; P-in-c Aldworth and Ashampstead 85-87; V Basildon w Aldworth and Ashampstead 87-94; RD Bradfield 90-94; V Buckingham w Radclive cum Chackmore 94-97; P-in-c Nash w Thornton, Beachampton and Thornborough 96-97; R Buckingham 97-00; RD Buckingham 95-00; Hon Can Ch Ch 98-00; R St Bride Fleet Street w Bridewell etc *Lon* from 00. *St Bride's Rectory, Fleet Street, London EC4Y 8AU* Tel (020) 7353 7999 or 7427 0133 Fax 7583 4867 E-mail info@stbrides.com

MEARDON, Canon Brian Henry. b 44. Reading Univ BSc66 PhD71. Oak Hill Th Coll DipHE79 MPhil84. **d** 79 **p** 80. C Reading St Jo *Ox* 79-82; V Warfield from 82; Hon Can Ch Ch from 03. *The Vicarage, Church Lane, Warfield, Bracknell RG42 6EE* Tel (01344) 882228 E-mail brian.h.meardon@btinternet.com

MEARNS, Christopher Lee. b 40. Worc Coll Ox BA54 MA58. Ripon Hall Ox BTh56. **d** 57 **p** 58. C Greenhill St Jo *Lon* 57-60; Canada 60-62; Lect Ripon Coll of Educn 63-75; Sen Lect Coll of Ripon and York St Jo 75-85; USA 87 and 89; Tutor Ridley Hall Cam 88; Seychelles 88 and 89-90; Perm to Offic *Ripon* from 90. *14 Primrose Drive, Ripon HG4 1EY* Tel (01765) 602695

✠MEARS, The Rt Revd John Cledan. b 22. Univ of Wales (Abth) BA43 Univ of Wales MA48. Wycliffe Hall Ox 43. d 47 p 48 c 82. C Mostyn *St As* 47-49; C Rhosllannerchrugog 49-56; V Cwm 56-59; Lic to Offic *Llan* 59-73; Chapl St Mich Coll Llan 59-67; Lect Th Univ of Wales (Cardiff) 59-73; Sub-Warden St Mich Coll Llan 67-73; V Gabalfa *Llan* 73-82; Hon Can Llan Cathl 81-82; Bp Ban 82-92; rtd 92; Perm to Offic *Llan* from 92. *Isfryn, 23 Avonridge, Cardiff CF14 9AU* Tel (029) 2061 5505

MEARS, Phillip David. b 40. Dur Univ BA62 DipTh63. d 65 p 66. C Sandylands *Blackb* 65-68; C Chorley St Geo 68-71; V Leyland St Ambrose 71-81; Perm to Offic *Ches* from 81; Chapl Warrington Distr Gen Hosp 81-00. *20 Kingsley Drive, Appleton, Warrington WA4 5AE* Tel (01925) 264082 *or* 662146

MEASEY, George. b 08. Roch Th Coll 67. d 68 p 69. C Rowner *Portsm* 68-72; C Worthing St Geo *Chich* 72-78; rtd 78; Perm to Offic *Chich* from 78. *clo J Measey Esq, Pinehurst, Stoke Poges Lane, Slough SL2 4NP*

MEATH AND KILDARE, Bishop of. *See* CLARKE, The Most Revd Richard Lionel

MEATH, Archdeacon of. *See* LAWRENCE, The Ven Patrick Henry Andrew

MEATS, Canon Alan John. b 41. Univ of Wales (Cardiff) BA62 DipEd63 Lon Univ BD70. St Mich Coll Llan 68. d 70 p 71. C Pontypridd St Cath *Llan* 70-73; TV Ystradyfodwg 73-75; Dioc Insp of Schs 73-75 and 83-89; V Llandeilo Tal-y-bont *S & B* 75-83; RD Llwchwr 81-83; V Aberdare St Fagan *Llan* 83-89; V Felin-foel *St D* 89-01; Asst Dioc Dir of Educn 89-92; Dioc Dir of Educn 92-97; Can St D Cathl from 94; V Pen-bre from 01. *The Vicarage, Ar y Bryn, Pembrey, Burry Port SA16 0AJ* Tel (01554) 832403

MEATYARD, Mrs Christina. b 51. SRN74. STETS 96. d 99 p 01. NSM S Hayling *Portsm* from 99. *28 Staunton Avenue, Hayling Island PO11 0EW* Tel (023) 9234 8886 *or* 9263 7649 Mobile 0797-9096779
E-mail parishoffice@haylinganglicans.freeserve.com.uk

MECHANIC, Rodney Ian (Roni). b 48. Man Univ MA(Theol)00. d 78 p 78. S Africa 78-98; P-in-c Shebbear, Buckland Filleigh, Sheepwash etc *Ex* 98-01; Australia 01-02; TV Heatons *Man* from 02. *The Rectory, 110 Crescent Park, Stockport SK4 2JE* Tel 0161-432 3537 E-mail ronimechanic@ntlworld.com *or* roni@mechanic777.fsnet.co.uk

MEDCALF, James Gordon. b 31. CB. Solicitor 63. S'wark Ord Course 87. d 90 p 91. NSM Shortlands *Roch* 90-00. *15 Losecoat Close, Stamford PE9 1DU* Tel (01780) 482583

MEDCALF, John Edward. b 19. Oak Hill Th Coll 47. d 50 p 51. C Rugby St Matt *Cov* 50-53; TR Chell *Lich* 53-61; V Wednesfield Heath 61-85; rtd 85; Perm to Offic *Heref* from 86. *Clee View, Kilforge, Bolstone, Hereford HR2 6NE* Tel (01432) 840339

MEDCALF, William Henry. b 15. TCD BA45 MA49. CITC 46. d 46 p 47. C Belfast St Mich *Conn* 46-48; C Bedford St Pet *St Alb* 48-50; SE Sec CMJ 50-63; Dir Exhibitions CMJ 63-80; rtd 80; Perm to Offic *Lon* from 80. *185 Dibdin House, Maida Vale, London W9 1QQ* Tel (020) 7328 3133

MEDFORTH, Allan Hargreaves. b 27. Qu Coll Cam BA48 MA52. Westcott Ho Cam 50. d 51 p 52. C Hexham *Newc* 51-55; PV S'well Minster *S'well* 55-59; V Farnsfield 59-72; RD S'well 66-72; V St Alb St Pet *St Alb* 72-95; RD St Alb 74-84; rtd 95; Perm to Offic *St Alb* from 95. *62 Cuckman's Drive, St Albans AL2 3AF* Tel (01727) 836437

MEDHURST, Mrs June. b 44. St Hild Coll Dur TCert66. N Ord Course 99. d 02 p 03. C Silsden *Bradf* from 02. *12 Westerley Crescent, Silsden, Keighley BD20 0BW* Tel (01535) 658465
E-mail kenm@btinternet.com

MEDHURST, Prof Kenneth Noel. b 38. Edin Univ MA61 Man Univ PhD69. d 91 p 93. NSM Baildon *Bradf* from 91; Can Th Bradf Cathl from 00. *12 Westerley Crescent, Silsden, Keighley BD20 0BW* Tel (01535) 658465

MEDHURST, Leslie John. b 56. TCD DipTh85 BTh90 MA93 Open Univ BA91. d 85 p 86. C Seapatrick *D & D* 85-90; I Belfast St Mark *Conn* 90-97; I Helen's Bay *D & D* from 97. *2 Woodland Avenue, Helens Bay, Bangor BT19 1TX* Tel (028) 9185 3601

MEDLEY, Canon Philip Roger. b 46. FTC69 Birm Univ CertEd73 Sheff Univ MA00. SW Minl Tr Course. d 85 p 86. NSM Ottery St Mary, Alfington and W Hill *Ex* 85-86; C S Hill w Callington *Truro* 86-89; C Linkinhorne *V* 89-03; Dioc Officer for Evang 93-00; Warden Cornwall Preachers' Coll from 93; Hon Can Truro Cathl 01-02; Dioc Missr *B & W* from 03. *The Vicarage, Linkinhorne, Callington PL17 7LY* Tel and fax (01579) 362560 *or* tel (01749) 670777 E-mail roger.medley@lineone.net

MEDWAY, Mrs Christine Jean. b 57. Qu Coll Birm 93. d 95 p 98. C Milton *Win* 95-97; C Southampton St Mary Extra 97-01; P-in-c Haselbury Plucknett, Misterton and N Perrott *B & W* 01-03; rtd 03. *18 Wellington Avenue, Southampton SO18 5DD* Tel (023) 8046 2286 E-mail cjmx2@fish.co.uk

MEE, Colin Henry. b 36. Reading Univ BSc58. Bris Sch of Min 83. d 85 p 86. NSM Stanton St Quintin, Hullavington, Grittleton etc *Bris* 85-87; C Swindon Ch Ch 88-90; TV Washfield, Stoodleigh, Withleigh etc *Ex* 90-95; TR 95-99; Chapl Marie Curie Foundn (Tidcombe Hall) 95-99; rtd 99. *Rickstones, Burgundy Road, Minehead TA24 5QJ* Tel (01643) 706048

MEE, James Alexander. b 08. TCD BA30 MA39. Div Test. d 31 p 32. C Drumragh *D & R* 31-35; India 35-47; Hon CF 47; New Zealand from 48; P-in-c St Mary's Cathl 48-49; V Papatoetoe 49-51; V St Heliers Bay 51-70; rtd 70. *Selwyn Oaks, 21 Youngs Road, Papakura, Auckland, New Zealand* Tel (0064) (9) 296 3808

MEEHAN, Cyril Frederick. b 52. St Jo Coll Nottm BTh80. d 80 p 81. C Keresley and Coundon *Cov* 80-83; P-in-c Linton and Castle Gresley *Derby* 83-90; P-in-c Alvaston 90-00; V 00; Chapl Asst Freeman Gp of Hosps NHS Trust 00-03; Chapl Northumbria Healthcare NHS Trust from 03. *North Tyneside General Hospital, Rake Lane, North Shields NE29 8NH* Tel 0191-259 6660

MEEK, Anthony William. b 45. ACIB. Ox NSM Course 80. d 83 p 84. NSM Gt Chesham *Ox* 83-01; Perm to Offic *S & B* from 01. *The Willows, Orley Road, Ipplepen, Newton Abbot TQ12 5SA* Tel (01803) 814370 Fax 814369 E-mail tony.meek@cwcom.net

MEERE, Mrs Alison Elizabeth. b 44. SRN65 HVCert67. Ripon Coll Cuddesdon 85. d 87 p 94. Par Dn Hengrove *Bris* 87-88; Par Dn Winterbourne 88-91; Par Dn Southmead 91-93; Par Dn Hackney *Lon* 93-94; TV 94-95; Asst Chapl R Berks Hosp Reading 95-96; Asst Chapl Battle Hosp Reading 95-96; Indonesia 02-03; rtd 03. *19 St Elmos Road, London SE16 1SA* Tel 07754-808579 (mobile)

MEERING, Laurence Piers Ralph. b 48. Man Univ BSc70. Trin Coll Bris 79. d 81 p 82. C Downend *Bris* 81-84; C Crofton *Portsm* 84-87; V Witheridge, Thelbridge, Creacombe, Meshaw etc *Ex* 87-94; TV Southgate *Chich* 94-02; TV Walton H Trin *Ox* from 02. *Walton Rectory, 42 Redwood Drive, Aylesbury HP21 7TN* Tel (01296) 394906 E-mail lawrence.meering@btinternet.com

MEESE, Dudley Noel. b 63. Leic Univ BA86 Nottm Univ PGCE87. Ridley Hall Cam 99. d 01 p 02. C Sheff St Jo *Sheff* from 01. *4 Manor Oaks Drive, Sheffield S2 5LZ* Tel 0114-296 6107

MEGAHEY, Alan John. b 44. Selw Coll Cam BA65 MA69 QUB PhD69. Westcott Ho Cam 69. d 70 p 71. Asst Chapl Wrekin Coll Telford 70-73; Ho Master Cranleigh Sch Surrey 73-83; Zimbabwe 84-93; Chapl Uppingham Sch Leics 93-01; R Brant Broughton and Beckingham *Linc* from 01; R Leadenham from 01; R Welbourn from 01. *The Rectory, Church End, Leadenham, Lincoln LN5 0PX* Tel (01400) 273987 E-mail rector.leadenham@btopenworld.com

MEGARRELL, Joanne Myrtle. d 03. C Moira *D & D* from 03. *27 Danesfoot, Moira, Craigavon BT67 0SG* Tel (028) 9261 7346

✠MEHAFFEY, The Rt Revd James. b 31. TCD BA52 MA56 BD56 QUB PhD75 Ulster Univ Hon DLitt99. d 54 p 55 c 80. C Ballymacarrett St Patr *D & D* 54-56; C Deptford St Jo *S'wark* 56-58; C Down Cathl *D & D* 58-60; C-in-c Ballymacarrett St Chris 60-62; I Kilkeel 62-66; I Cregagh 66-80; Bp's Private Chapl 72-76; Preb Down Cathl 76-80; Dioc Missr 76-80; Bp D & R 80-02; rtd 02. *10 Clearwater, Londonderry BT47 6BE* Tel (028) 7134 2624 Fax as telephone E-mail mehaffey@iol.ie

MEHEN, Donald Wilfred. b 44. Birkbeck Coll Lon BSc72 CertEd66. Dioc OLM tr scheme 97. d 00 p 01. OLM Sproughton w Burstall, Copdock w Washbrook etc *St E* from 00. *19 The Link, Bentley, Ipswich IP9 2DJ* Tel (01473) 310383 E-mail donmehen@hotmail.com

MEIER, Paul. b 64. St Jo Coll Nottm BA98. d 98 p 99. C Highley w Billingsley, Glazeley etc *Heref* 98-01; C Hildenborough *Roch* from 01. *12 Fellows Way, Hildenborough, Tonbridge TN11 9DG* Tel (01732) 838674 E-mail paul-meier@virgin.net

MEIKLE, Canon David Skene. b 39. St Cath Coll Cam BA60 MA89. Westcott Ho Cam. d 63 p 64. C Hawick *Edin* 63-67; C Edin SS Phil and Jas 67-72; C Banbury *Ox* 72-73; TV 74-78; R Ipswich St Matt *St E* 78-91; Hon Can St E Cathl 90-01; TR Mildenhall 91-01; rtd 01; Perm to Offic *St E* from 01. *172 Nacton Road, Ipswich IP3 9JN* Tel (01473) 439113 E-mail david.meikle@talk21.com

MEIN, The Very Revd James Adlington. b 38. Nottm Univ BA60. Westcott Ho Cam 61. d 63 p 64. C Edin St Columba *Edin* 63-67; Bp's Dom Chapl 65-67; Malawi 67-72; R Grangemouth *Edin* 72-82; P-in-c Bo'ness 76-82; TV Livingston LEP 82-90; R Edin Ch Ch from 90; Can St Mary's Cathl 90-01; Dean Edin from 01. *4 Morningside Road, Edinburgh EH10 4DD* Tel 0131-229 6556 Fax 228 5949 E-mail chchmorned@aol.com

MEIN, Canon Peter Simon. b 27. Nottm Univ BA55 MA59. Kelham Th Coll 48. d 55 p 56. SSM 54-70; Chapl Kelham Th Coll 55-61; Warden 62-70; Prior 64-70; USA from 71; Chapl St Andr Sch Delaware 71-92; Hon Can Delaware 89; rtd 92; Assoc Member S Delaware TM 92. *St Andrew's School, 350 Noxontown Road, Middletown, DE 19709, USA* Tel (001) (302) 645 7235 Fax 378 7120 E-mail nsmein@earthlink.net

MEIRION-JONES, Dafydd Padrig ap Geraint. b 70. Magd Coll Cam BA91 PGCE92 Oak Hill Th Coll BA01. d 01 p 02. C Ex St Leon w H Trin *Ex* from 01. *27 Barnardo Road, Exeter EX2 4ND* Tel (01392) 277540 Mobile 07989-390028 E-mail dafandboo@hotmail.com

MEIRION-JONES, Canon Huw Geraint (Gary). b 39. R Agric Coll Cirencester NDA61 MRAC61 K Coll Lon AKC69 BD71 MA84. St Aug Coll Cant 69. **d** 70 **p** 71. C Harlescott *Lich* 70-73; C Worplesdon *Guildf* 73-77; V Ash Vale 77-85; TR Westborough 85-96; Dioc Press Officer 85-94; P-in-c Shere 96-98; P-in-c Albury 97-98; R Shere, Albury and Chilworth from 98; Hon Can Guildf Cathl from 99; Dioc Rural Adv 99-03; RD Cranleigh from 00. *The Rectory, Spinning Walk, Shere, Guildford GU5 9HN* Tel (01483) 202394

MEIRIONNYDD, Archdeacon of. See WILLIAMS, The Ven Arfon

MELANESIA, Archbishop of. See POGO, The Most Revd Sir Ellison Leslie

MELANIPHY, Miss Angela Ellen. b 55. SRN79. Cranmer Hall Dur 87. **d** 90 **p** 94. Par Dn Leytonstone St Jo *Chelmsf* 90-94; C 94-95; TV Harlow Town Cen w Lt Parndon from 95. *4A The Drive, Harlow CM20 3QD* Tel (01279) 439721
E-mail angie@melaniphy.freeserve.co.uk

MELBOURNE, Brian Kenneth. b 45. York Univ Toronto 77. Trin Coll Toronto LTh82. **d** 82 **p** 82. Canada 82-87; Bermuda 88-94; P-in-c Biddenden and Smarden *Cant* 94-97; Hon C Isfield *Chich* from 01. *The Parsonage, Station Road, Isfield, Uckfield TN22 5EY* Tel (01825) 750247

MELDRUM, Andrew John Bruce. b 66. Univ of Wales (Abth) LLB89 Lon Univ MA98. Westcott Ho Cam CTM94. **d** 94 **p** 95. C Paddington St Jas *Lon* 94-99; P-in-c Brookfield St Anne, Highgate Rise 99-02; V from 02; Communications Adv to Bp Edmonton from 00. *St Anne's Vicarage, 106 Highgate West Hill, London N6 6AP* Tel (020) 8340 5190

MELDRUM, David Peter John. b 73. St Andr Univ MA95. Oak Hill Th Coll BA01. **d** 01 **p** 02. C Leyton St Mary w St Edw and St Luke *Chelmsf* from 01. *27 Crawley Road, London E10 6RJ* Tel (020) 8556 5325 E-mail davidpjmeldrum@yahoo.com

MELINSKY, Canon Michael Arthur Hugh. b 24. Ch Coll Cam BA47 MA49. Ripon Hall Ox 57. **d** 57 **p** 59. C Wimborne Minster *Sarum* 57-59; C Wareham w Arne 59-61; V Nor St Steph *Nor* 61-68; Chapl Norfolk and Nor Hosp 61-68; Hon Can Nor Cathl and Can Missr *Nor* 68-73; Chief Sec ACCM 73-78; Prin N Ord Course 78-88; rtd 88; Perm to Offic *Nor* from 88. *15 Parson's Mead, Norwich NR4 6PG* Tel (01603) 455042

MELLERUP, Miss Eiler Mary. b 52. Saffron Walden Coll CertEd58. LNSM course 94. **d** 96 **p** 97. OLM Happisburgh, Walcott, Hempstead w Eccles etc *Nor* from 96. *Channings, The Crescent, Walcott, Norwich NR12 0NH* Tel (01692) 651393

MELLING, Canon Leonard Richard. b 13. St Aid Birkenhead 38. **d** 41 **p** 42. C W Acklam *York* 41-45; C Scarborough St Mary 45-48; V Newby 48-54; Borneo 54-59; Area Sec USPG *Ox* and *Cov* 59-64; *York* 64-67; V Osbaldwick w Murton *York* 67-78; RD Bulmer 72-78; Malaysia 78-81; Dean Kuching 78-81; rtd 81; Perm to Offic *York* from 81. *82 Tranby Avenue, Osbaldwick, York YO10 3NN* Tel (01904) 413796

MELLISH, John. b 26. Cranmer Hall Dur 67. **d** 69 **p** 70. C Ulverston St Mary w H Trin *Carl* 69-72; V Bromfield 72-73; V Bromfield w Waverton 73-79; P-in-c Allonby w W Newton 77-79; V Shap w Swindale 79-86; RD Appleby 82-86; V Bassenthwaite, Isel and Setmurthy 86-90; rtd 90; Perm to Offic *Carl* from 90. *Wyndham, 3 Old Road, Longtown, Carlisle CA6 5TH* Tel (01228) 791441

MELLISS, Laurence John Albert. b 21. DSM45 RD69. AKC52. **d** 53 **p** 54. C Norbury St Steph *Cant* 53-56; C Folkestone St Mary and St Eanswythe 56-60; Chapl RNVR 56-59; Chapl RNR 59-76; R Upper St Leonards St Jo *Chich* 60-64; V Littlehampton St Mary 64-76; RD Arundel 75-76; V Findon 76-81; R Catsfield and Crowhurst 81-86; rtd 86; Perm to Offic *Sarum* from 95. *4 St Osmond Close, Yetminster, Sherborne DT9 6LU* Tel (01935) 872536

MELLOR, Frederick Charles Walter (Tony). b 24. Oak Hill NSM Course 80. **d** 83 **p** 84. NSM Loughton St Jo *Chelmsf* 83-93; Chapl Asst Whipps Cross Hosp Lon from 87; Perm to Offic from 93. *4 Scotland Road, Buckhurst Hill IG9 5NR* Tel (020) 8504 6203

MELLOR, Canon Kenneth Paul. b 49. Southn Univ BA71 Leeds Univ MA72. Cuddesdon Coll 72. **d** 73 **p** 74. C Cottingham *York* 73-76; C Ascot Heath *Ox* 76-80; V Tilehurst St Mary 80-85; V Menheniot *Truro* 85-94; RD W Wivelshire 88-96; Hon Can Truro Cathl 90-94; Can Treas from 94; Can Res and Treas Truro Cathl from 94. *Lemon Lodge, Lemon Street, Truro TR1 2PE* Tel (01872) 272094 E-mail paul@trurocathedral.org.uk

MELLOR, Roy. b 52. Lanc Univ BA92. Cuddesdon Coll 94. **d** 96 **p** 97. C Oakdale *Sarum* 96-00; TV Kingsthorpe w Northampton St Dav *Pet* from 00; R Blisworth and Stoke Bruerne w Grafton Regis etc from 03. *The Rectory, High Street, Blisworth, Northampton NN7 3BJ* Tel (01604) 879112
E-mail roy_mellor2002@yahoo.co.uk

MELLORS, Derek George. b 38. Bris Univ CertEd60 Lon Univ BSc71 Nottm Univ DipEd74 Liv Univ MEd83. N Ord Course 81. **d** 84 **p** 85. NSM Eccleston Ch Ch *Liv* 84-92; C Lowton St Mary 92-93; V Ashton-in-Makerfield St Thos 93-99; rtd 99. *20 Millbrook Lane, Eccleston, St Helens WA10 4QU* Tel (01744) 28424

MELLORS, James. b 32. Kelham Th Coll 52. **d** 56 **p** 57. C Horbury *Wakef* 56-61; V Scholes 61-72; V Mirfield 72-88; Hon Can Wakef Cathl 83-88; V Leyburn w Bellerby *Ripon* 88-93; rtd 93; Perm to Offic *Ripon* from 93. *Langthwaite Cottage, Main Street, West Witton, Leyburn DL8 4LR* Tel (01969) 622452

MELLOWS, Canon Alan Frank. b 23. Qu Coll Cam BA45 MA49. Tyndale Hall Bris 47. **d** 49 **p** 50. C Morden *S'wark* 49-54; V Brimscombe *Glouc* 54-62; R Mileham *Nor* 62-74; P-in-c Beeston next Mileham 62-66; R 66-74; P-in-c Stanfield 62-74; P-in-c Gt w Lt Dunham 70-73; R Ashill 74-79; P-in-c Saham Toney 78-79; R Ashill w Saham Toney 79-88; Hon Can Nor Cathl 82-88; rtd 88; Perm to Offic *Nor* from 88. *8 Smugglers Close, Hunstanton PE36 6JU* Tel (01485) 534271

MELLOWSHIP, Robert John. b 52. St Mich Coll Llan BD92. **d** 92 **p** 93. C Brecon St Mary and Battle w Llanddew *S & B* 92-94; Min Can Brecon Cathl 92-94; C Pontypool *Mon* 94-95; TV 95-97; P-in-c Bressingham w N and S Lopham and Fersfield *Nor* from 97. *The Rectory, High Street, Bressingham, Diss IP22 2AT* Tel (01379) 688267 Fax as telephone
E-mail rob.mellowship1@btinternet.com

MELLUISH, Mark Peter. b 59. Oak Hill Th Coll. **d** 89 **p** 90. C Ashtead *Guildf* 89-93; V Ealing St Paul *Lon* from 93. *St Paul's Vicarage, 102 Elers Road, London W13 9QE* Tel and fax (020) 8567 4628 *or* tel 8579 5953
E-mail mark.melluish@new-wine.org

MELLUISH, Stephen. b 60. Trin Coll Bris DipHE93. **d** 93 **p** 94. C Gipsy Hill Ch Ch *S'wark* 93-96; V Wandsworth St Steph from 96; P-in-c Wandsworth St Mich from 01. *St Stephen's Vicarage, 2A Oakhill Road, London SW15 2QU* Tel (020) 8874 5610
E-mail smelluish@aol.com

MELLY, Aleck Emerson. b 24. Oak Hill Th Coll 50. **d** 53 **p** 54. C Chadderton Ch Ch *Man* 53-56; C Cheltenham St Mark *Glouc* 56-59; V Tipton St Paul *Lich* 59-68; R Kemberton w Sutton Maddock 68-80; P-in-c Stockton 74-80; R Kemberton, Sutton Maddock and Stockton 81-89; rtd 89; Perm to Offic *Lich* from 89; Perm to Offic *Heref* from 90. *Bethany, 47 Greenfields Road, Bridgnorth WV16 4JG* Tel (01746) 762711

MELROSE, Kenneth Mark Cecil. b 15. Ex Coll Ox BA37 DipTh38 MA41. Ripon Hall Ox 37. **d** 39 **p** 40. C Clifton St Jo *Bris* 39-41; Lic to Offic *Glouc* 41-42; Chapl RNVR 42-46; Lic to Offic *St Alb* 47-49; V Bedminster St Aldhelm *Bris* 49-55; V Hurstbourne Tarrant *Win* 55-63; V Portswood St Denys 63-71; V Bovey Tracey SS Pet and Paul *Ex* 71-85; rtd 85; Perm to Offic *Cant* 87-03. *23 Ramsay Hall, 11-13 Byron Road, Worthing BN11 3HN* Tel (01903) 235422

MELROSE, Michael James Gervase. b 47. St Chad's Coll Dur BA69 DipTh70. **d** 71 **p** 72. C Chelmsf All SS *Chelmsf* 71-74; C Pimlico St Pet w Westmr Ch Ch *Lon* 74-80; R Man Victoria Park *Man* 80-94; P-in-c Cheetwood St Alb 85-91; R Reading St Giles *Ox* from 94. *St Giles's Rectory, Church Street, Reading RG1 2SB* Tel 0118-957 2831

MELTON, Mrs Anne. b 44. N Riding Coll of Educn CertEd65. St Jo Coll Dur 80. **dss** 83 **d** 87 **p** 94. Newton Aycliffe *Dur* 83-87; Par Dn 87-88; Par Dn Shildon w Eldon 88-94; Asst Dir of Ords 88-94; C Shildon w Eldon 94-96; P-in-c Usworth from 96. *4 Highbury Close, Springwell, Gateshead NE9 7PU* Tel 0191-416 3533

MELVILLE, Dominic. b 63. Sussex Univ BA84 Southn Univ BTh90. Sarum & Wells Th Coll 87. **d** 90 **p** 91. C Willenhall H Trin *Lich* 90-94; V Wednesfield St Greg 94-99; V Worc St Wulstan *Worc* from 99. *The Vicarage, Cranham Drive, Worcester WR4 9PA* Tel (01905) 456944 Fax as telephone

MELVIN, Gordon Thomas. b 55. BA86. Sarum & Wells Th Coll 86. **d** 88 **p** 89. C Linc St Faith and St Martin w St Pet *Linc* 88-91; TV Horsham *Chich* 91-94; Chapl Horsham Gen Hosp 91-94; Chapl Ipswich Hosp NHS Trust from 94. *50 Constable Road, Ipswich IP4 2UZ, or Ipswich Hospital, Heath Road, Ipswich IP4 5PD* Tel (01473) 704100 *or* 712233

MEMBERY, Donald Percy. b 20. K Coll Lon BSc50 DipEd51 AKC51. Ox NSM Course. **d** 79 **p** 80. NSM Aston Rowant w Crowell *Ox* 79-81; P-in-c Swyncombe 81-85; R Swyncombe w Britwell Salome 85-88; rtd 88; Perm to Offic *Ripon* from 88. *11 Carr Manor Gardens, Leeds LS17 5DQ* Tel 0113-269 1578 E-mail donald@heretics.demon.co.uk

MENDEL, Thomas Oliver. b 52. Down Coll Cam BA79 MA82. Cranmer Hall Dur 79. **d** 81 **p** 82. Lic to Offic *Ely* 81-86; Chapl Down Coll Cam 81-86; Hon C Cambridge St Mary Less *Ely* 81-86; V Minsterley *Heref* 86-92; R Habberley 86-92; Chapl Shrewsbury Sch 93-95; Chapl Milan w Genoa and Varese *Eur* 95-96; Chapl Copenhagen w Aarhus from 96. *St Alban's House, Tuborgvej 82, 2900 Hellerup, Denmark* Tel (0045) 3962 7736 Fax 39627735 E-mail chaplain@paradis.dk

✠**MENIN, The Rt Revd Malcolm James.** b 32. Univ Coll Ox BA55 MA59. Cuddesdon Coll 55. **d** 57 **p** 58 **c** 86. C Southsea H Spirit *Portsm* 57-59; C Fareham SS Pet and Paul 59-62; V Nor St Jas w Pockthorpe *Nor* 62-72; P-in-c Nor St Martin 62-74; P-in-c Nor St Mary Magd 68-72; V Nor St Mary Magd w St Jas 72-86; RD Nor E 81-86; Hon Can Nor Cathl 82-86; Suff Bp Knaresborough *Ripon* 86-97; rtd 97; Perm to Offic *Nor* from 97;

Hon Asst Bp Nor from 00. *32C Bracondale, Norwich NR1 2AN* Tel (01603) 627987

MENNISS, Andrew Philip. b 49. Univ of Wales (Swansea) BSc73. Sarum & Wells Th Coll 83. **d** 85 **p** 86. C Horsell *Guildf* 85-89; V Bembridge *Portsm* from 89; RD E Wight 95-00. *The Vicarage, Church Road, Bembridge PO35 5NA* Tel (01983) 872175 Fax 875255 E-mail apmenniss@aol.com

MENON, Nicholas Anthony Thotekat. b 39. Mert Coll Ox BA61 MA65 DipTh62. St Steph Ho Ox 61. **d** 63 **p** 64. C Paddington Ch Ch *Lon* 63-66; Hon C 66-70; V Thorpe *Guildf* 70-76; V Ox SS Phil and Jas w St Marg *Ox* 76-79; Chapl Surrey Univ *Guildf* 79-81; Chapl Cranleigh Sch Surrey 82-90 and 98-00; Ho Master 90-98; Asst Chapl Malvern Coll from 00; Perm to Offic *Worc* from 00. *Pilgrim Cottage, 187 West Malvern Road, Malvern WR14 4BB* Tel (01648) 577189

MENON, Suresh. b 64. Man Poly BA88. Oak Hill Th Coll 96. **d** 98 **p** 99. C Braintree *Chelmsf* 98-02; C Leic H Trin w St Jo *Leic* from 02. *St Philip's House, 2A Stoughton Drive North, Leicester LE5 5UB* Tel 0116-273 8979 E-mail suresh@menon64.freeserve.co.uk

MENSAH, Isaac Kingsley. b 48. **d** 01 **p** 02. Asst Chapl Brussels *Eur* from 01. *Rue de l'Intendant 152, B-1080 Brussels, Belgium* Tel (0032) (2) 420 0604 or 512 4796 Fax 511 1028 E-mail mkingsle@be.packardbell.com

MENSINGH, Gregg Richard. b 69. Portsm Univ BSc94. Westcott Ho Cam 95. **d** 97 **p** 98. C Birchfield *Birm* 97-01; V Gravelly Hill from 01. *All Saints' Vicarage, Broomfield Road, Birmingham B23 7QA* Tel 0121-373 0730 E-mail greggie@onetel.net.uk

MENTZEL, Kevin David. b 60. Reading Univ BSc82 Down Coll Cam BA87 MA91. Ridley Hall Cam 85. **d** 88 **p** 89. C Ditton *Roch* 88-91; Asst Chapl Eton Coll 91-93; Asst Chapl R Hosp Sch Holbrook 93-94; Sen C Fulham St Dionis Parson's Green *Lon* 94-97; CF from 97. *c/o MOD Chaplains (Army)* Tel (01980) 615804 Fax 615800

MENZIES, Stanley Hay. b 33. Edin Univ MA55 BD58. New Coll Edin 55. **d** 02. NSM Boston Spa *York* from 02. *Cairn Croft, 2 Crag Gardens, Bramham, Wetherby LS23 6RP* Tel (01937) 541047 Fax as telephone

MEON, Archdeacon of the. *See* HANCOCK, The Ven Peter

MEPHAM, Kevin Aubrey. b 55. Sarum & Wells Th Coll 85. **d** 88 **p** 89. NSM Sidley *Chich* 88-90; C Hollington St Leon 90-94; V Horam 94-99; P-in-c Hastings All So 99-03; V Alkham w Capel le Ferne and Hougham *Cant* from 03. *The Vicarage, 20 Alexandra Road, Capel-le-Ferne, Folkestone CT18 7LD* Tel (01303) 244119 E-mail krevkevman@aol.com

MEPHAM, Stephen Richard. b 64. K Coll Lon BD85 AKC85. Linc Th Coll 87. **d** 89 **p** 90. C Newark *S'well* 89-92; C Cheshunt *St Alb* 92-95; C-in-c Turnford St Clem CD 95-98; V Rickmansworth from 98. *The Vicarage, Bury Lane, Rickmansworth WD3 1ED* Tel (01923) 772627 E-mail srmepham@aol.com

✠**MERCER, The Rt Revd Eric Arthur John.** b 17. Kelham Th Coll. **d** 47 **p** 48 **c** 65. C Coppenhall *Ches* 47-51; C-in-c Heald Green St Cath CD 51-53; R Stockport St Thos 53-59; R Ches St Bridget w St Martin 59-65; Dioc Missr 59-65; Hon Can Ches Cathl 64-65; Suff Bp Birkenhead 65-73; Bp Ex 73-85; rtd 85; P-in-c E Knoyle, Hindon w Chicklade and Pertwood *Sarum* 85-86; P-in-c Hindon w Chicklade and Pertwood 86-88. *Frickers House, Cow Drove, Chilmark, Salisbury SP3 5AJ* Tel (01722) 716400

MERCER, James John. b 56. Bp Otter Coll Chich BEd79 Lon Inst of Educn MA85. Ridley Hall Cam 00. **d** 02. C Heref St Pet w St Owen and St Jas *Heref* from 02. *15 Belgravia Gardens, Hereford HR1 1RB* Tel (01432) 267287 Mobile 07940-506188 E-mail jjmercer@fish.co.uk

MERCER, Canon John James Glendinning. b 20. TCD BA49 MA55. **d** 50 **p** 51. C Newtownards *D & D* 50-53; C Bangor St Comgall 53-55; I Ballyholme 55-90; Can Belf Cathl 76-88; Preb Wicklow St Patr Cathl Dublin 88-90; rtd 90. *6 Hillfoot, Groomsport, Bangor BT19 6JJ* Tel (028) 9147 2979

MERCER, Nicholas Stanley. b 49. Selw Coll Cam BA72 PGCE73 MA76. Spurgeon's Coll BA78 Lon Bible Coll MPhil86 Cranmer Hall Dur 93. **d** 95 **p** 95. C Northwood Hills St Edm *Lon* 95-98; C Pimlico St Mary Bourne Street from 98. *St Mary's Presbytery, 30 Bourne Street, London SW1W 8JJ* Tel (020) 7730 6607 Mobile 07973-226153 Fax (020) 7730 7455 E-mail fr.nick@stmarythevirgin.org.uk

✠**MERCER, The Rt Revd Robert William Stanley.** b 35. St Paul's Coll Grahamstown LTh59. **d** 59 **p** 60 **c** 77. S Rhodesia 59-63; Lic to Offic *Wakef* 64-66; CR from 65; Perm to Offic *Llan* 66-68; S Africa 68-70; Rhodesia 70-80; Zimbabwe 80-87; Sub-Prelate OStJ from 80; Bp Matabeleland 77-87; Canada from 87. *225 First Avenue, Ottawa ON, Canada, K1S 2G5* Tel (001) (613) 594 8637 Fax 233 4399

MERCER, Timothy James. b 54. Fitzw Coll Cam BA76 MA80. Westcott Ho Cam 80. **d** 81 **p** 82. C Bromley SS Pet and Paul *Roch* 81-85; R Swanscombe 85-96; Chapl Bromley Hosps NHS Trust from 96. *Farnborough Hospital, Farnborough Common, Orpington BR6 8ND* Tel (01689) 814000 or 821171

MERCERON, Daniel John. b 58. Lon Univ BA81. Westcott Ho Cam 88. **d** 90 **p** 91. C Clevedon St B & W 90-94; CF from 94. *c/o MOD Chaplains (Army)* Tel (01980) 615804 Fax 615800

MERCHANT, Robert Ian. b 73. Keele Univ BA98. Wycliffe Hall Ox BA00. **d** 01 **p** 02. C Harborne Heath *Birm* from 01. *55 Albert Road, Harborne, Birmingham B17 0AP* Tel 0121-426 2548 Mobile 07957-519699 E-mail rob@uk.com

MERCHANT, Mrs Tamsin Laetitia Rachel. b 70. Wycliffe Hall Ox BTh01. **d** 01 **p** 02. C Harborne Heath *Birm* from 01. *55 Albert Road, Harborne, Birmingham B17 0AP* Tel 0121-426 2548 Mobile 07957-519699 E-mail tamsin@uk.com

MERCIER, David Cuthbert. b 10. St Pet Hall Ox BA32 MA36. Wycliffe Hall Ox 35. **d** 37 **p** 38. C Edge Hill St Mary *Liv* 37-41; C Gt Sankey 41-44; C Parr 44-49; V Langford Budville w Runnington *B & W* 49-54; R Phillack w Gwithian *Truro* 55-59; New Zealand from 59. *44 Haumoana Road, Haumoana, Hawkes Bay, New Zealand* Tel (0064) (6) 875 0147

MERCURIO, Frank James Charles. b 46. Webster Univ (USA) BA73 MA75. St Alb Minl Tr Scheme 87. **d** 89 **p** 90. C Cheshunt *St Alb* 89-93; TV Hitchin 93-00; RD Hitchin 94-00; TR Tring from 00. *The Rectory, Church Yard, Tring HP23 5AE* Tel (01442) 822170 Fax 07092-177459 E-mail frankmercurio@dialstart.net

MEREDITH, Andrew James MacPherson. b 59. St Jo Coll Nottm DCM93. **d** 93 **p** 94. C Killay *S & B* 93-97; V Waunarllwydd 97-00; V Swansea St Thos and Kilvey from 00. *The Vicarage, Lewis Street, St Thomas, Swansea SA1 8BP* Tel (01792) 652891

MEREDITH, Ian. b 53. Univ of Wales BA85 Lon Univ MTh89 Edin Univ MTh96. K Coll Lon 86. **d** 02. NSM Dumfries *Glas* from 02. *Skedholm, Greenhill, Lockerbie DG11 1JB* Tel (01387) 810843 E-mail imeredith2001@aol.com

MEREDITH, James Noel Michael Creed. b 17. Keble Coll Ox BA40 MA43. Westcott Ho Cam 39. **d** 40 **p** 42. C Woolwich St Mary w H Trin *S'wark* 40-44; CF 44-47; Chapl St Jo Sch Leatherhead 47-48; R Moss Side Ch Ch *Man* 48-56; Jamaica 56-61; R Stoke *Cov* 61-71; RD Cov E 69-71; V Hessle *York* 71-78; R Milton Abbas, Hilton w Cheselbourne etc *Sarum* 78-80; TV Llandudno *Ban* 80-84; rtd 82; Perm to Offic *Sarum* from 84. *11 Pascoe Close, Poole BH14 0NT* Tel (01202) 737108

MEREDITH, Robert. b 21. Bps' Coll Cheshunt 56. **d** 58 **p** 59. C Bedford St Andr *St Alb* 58-61; V Luton All SS 61-67; V Kimpton 67-75; RD Wheathampstead 72-76; R Kimpton w Ayot St Lawrence 75-76; R Hunsdon 76-80; R Widford 76-80; R Hunsdon w Widford and Wareside 80-84; P-in-c Braughing, Lt Hadham, Albury, Furneux Pelham etc 84-88; R Braughing w Furneux Pelham and Stocking Pelham 88-90; rtd 90; Perm to Offic *St Alb* 90-97; *Worc* from 98. *57 Ledwych Road, Droitwich WR9 9LA* Tel (01905) 797568

MEREDITH, Canon Roland Evan. b 32. Trin Coll Cam BA55 MA59. Cuddesdon Coll 55. **d** 57 **p** 58. C Bishopwearmouth St Mich *Dur* 57-59; Dioc Chapl *Birm* 59-60; C Kirkby Liv 60-63; V Hitchin St Mary *St Alb* 63-72; V Preston St Jo *Blackb* 72-76; TR 76-79; RD Preston 72-79; Hon Can Blackb Cathl 77-79; TR Witney *Ox* 79-94; P-in-c Hailey w Crawley 79-82; RD Witney 89-97; Hon Can Ch Ch 92-97; rtd 94; Perm to Offic *Ox* from 97; Perm to Offic *Eur* from 98. *1 Deanery Court, Broad Street, Bampton, Oxford OX18 2LY* Tel (01993) 851142

MEREDITH, Ronald Duncan d'Esterre. b 09. K Coll Lon BD32 AKC32. **d** 32 **p** 33. C Milton Regis St Mary *Cant* 32-35; C Croydon St Sav 35-39; C St Peter-in-Thanet 32-42; C-in-c 42-44; Chapl RNVR 44-45; V Chislet *Cant* 45-50; V Sittingbourne H Trin 50-62; R Dymchurch w Eastbridge, Orgarswick etc 62-63; R Dymchurch 63-68; V Seasalter 68-76; Six Preacher Cant Cathl 73-76; rtd 76; Perm to Offic *Cant* 76-99. *Erwgoch Farmhouse, Waunfawr, Aberystwyth SY23 3AY* Tel (01970) 623773

MEREDITH-JONES, Richard. b 26. JP79. K Coll Lon 50. **d** 54 **p** 55. C Perry Hill St Geo *S'wark* 54-56; P-in-c New Charlton H Trin 56-58; V Cinderford St Jo *Glouc* 58-62; Chapl Dilke Hosp Cinderford 58-62; V Richmond St Jo *S'wark* 62-66; Chapl Royal Hosp Richmond 62-66; Ind Chapl *Wakef* 66-70; Chapl Glenside Hosp Bris from 70; Perm to Offic *Glouc* 70-88; CF (TAVR) 78-91; Perm to Offic *Ban* 88-93; rtd 91; Perm to Offic *St D* and *B & W* from 91. *18 Wetlands Lane, Portishead, Bristol BS20 6RA* Tel (01275) 817217

MERIVALE, Charles Christian Robert. b 44. Cranmer Hall Dur 76. **d** 78 **p** 79. C Highbury Ch Ch w St Jo *Lon* 78-81; P-in-c Hawes *Ripon* 81-82; P-in-c Hardrow and Jo w Lunds 81-82; V Hawes and Hardraw 82-84; Chapl R Cornwall Hosps Trust 85-92; Perm to Offic *B & W* 92-00; *Ex* 00-02; TV Shebbear, Buckland Filleigh, Sheepwash etc *Ex* from 02. *The Rectory, Petrockstowe, Okehampton EX20 3HQ* Tel (01837) 810499 or 08454-589942 E-mail christian@phonebox50.co.uk

MERRETT, Jonathan Charles. b 55. Univ of Wales (Ban) BMus77 MMus78 Warwick Univ PGCE87 Birm Univ MPhil95. Ripon Coll Cuddesdon 78. **d** 81 **p** 82. C Kenilworth St Nic *Cov* 81-84; C Grandborough w Willoughby and Flecknoe 84-87; Asst Dioc Educn Officer 87-94. *Address temp unknown*

MERRICK, Canon John. b 51. New Univ of Ulster BA72 DipAdEd75 TCD HDipEd73 DipAdEd. CITC 89. **d** 92 **p** 93. Hd Master Sligo Gr Sch from 86; Lic to Offic *K, E & A* from 92;

Preb Elphin Cathl from 01. *The Headmaster's Residence, Sligo Grammar School, The Mall, Sligo, Irish Republic* Tel (00353) (71) 914 2775

MERRIMAN, Stephen Richard. b 74. Leeds Univ BA02. Coll of Resurr Mirfield 99. **d** 02 **p** 03. C Littlehampton and Wick *Chich* from 02. *95 The Winter Knoll, Littlehampton BN17 6NQ* Tel (01903) 733618

MERRINGTON, Canon Bill. b 55. Sheff Hallam Univ BSc78 Birm Univ MPhil95 Warwick Univ PhD03. Cranmer Hall Dur 80. **d** 83 **p** 84. C Harborne Heath *Birm* 83-88; V Leamington Priors St Paul *Cov* 88-99; RD Warwick and Leamington 97-99; R Ilmington w Stretton-on-Fosse etc from 99; RD Shipston from 99; Hon Can Cov Cathl from 01. *The Rectory, Valenders Lane, Ilmington, Shipston-on-Stour CV36 4LB* Tel (01608) 682210 Fax as telephone E-mail billmerri@aol.com

MERRY, David Thomas (Tom). b 48. St Chad's Coll Dur BA70. AKC73. **d** 74 **p** 75. C Cirencester *Glouc* 74-78; TV Bridgnorth, Tasley, Astley Abbotts and Oldbury *Heref* 78-83; P-in-c Quatford 81-83; P-in-c Stroud H Trin *Glouc* 83-87; V 87-01; Chapl Stroud Gen Hosp 83-93; Chapl Severn NHS Trust 93-01; Chapl Cheltenham Ladies' Coll from 01. *The Cheltenham Ladies' College, Bayshill Road, Cheltenham GL50 3EP* Tel (01242) 520691

MERRY, Ivor John. b 28. WMMTC 84. **d** 87 **p** 88. NSM Redditch, The Ridge *Worc* 87-94; NSM Astwood Bank 94-98; Perm to Offic from 98. *5 Church Road, Astwood Bank, Redditch B96 6EH* Tel (01527) 892887

MERRY, Rex Edwin. b 38. AKC67. **d** 68 **p** 69. C Spalding St Jo *Linc* 68-73; C Boxmoor St Jo *St Alb* 73-83; TV Hemel Hempstead 83-95; V Farley Hill St Jo from 95. *The Vicarage, 47 Rotherham Avenue, Luton LU1 5PP* Tel (01582) 729466

MERRYWEATHER, Mrs Rosalynd. b 50. Hull Coll of Educn CertEd72. NEOC. **d** 00 **p** 01. NSM Beverley St Nic *York* from 00. *10 West Close, Beverley HU17 7JZ* Tel (01482) 867958

MERWOOD, Raymond George. b 27. K Coll Lon. **d** 54 **p** 56. C Wareham w Arne *Sarum* 54-55; C Rawmarsh *Sheff* 55-58; C Thrybergh 58-62; C Brixham *Ex* 62-67; V Newton Poppleford w Harpford 67-91; rtd 91; Perm to Offic *Ex* from 92. *1 Elsdon House, Elsdon, West Hill, Ottery St Mary EX11 1UA* Tel (01404) 811035

MESLEY, Mark Terence. b 59. Plymouth Poly BSc88. St Steph Ho Ox 98. **d** 00 **p** 01. C Bickleigh and Shaugh Prior *Ex* from 00; P-in-c Llanhilleth *Mon* from 03. *The Rectory, Pendarren Road, Aberbeeg, Abertillery NP13 2DA* Tel (01495) 214236 E-mail mesleyrev@eurobell.co.uk

MESSAM, Paul James. b 65. Lon Coll of Printing BA87. Cranmer Hall Dur 01. **d** 03. C Market Harborough and The Transfiguration *Leic* from 03. *109 Tymecrosse Gardens, Market Harborough LE16 7US* Tel (01858) 463062 Mobile 07711-098209 E-mail paul.messam@virgin.net

MESSENGER, Paul. b 38. Univ of Wales (Lamp) BA63. Coll of Resurr Mirfield 63. **d** 65 **p** 66. C Battersea St Luke *S'wark* 65-69; C Ainsdale *Liv* 69-71; V Wigan St Steph 71-74; Asst Chapl St Marg Convent E Grinstead 74-76; Chapl Kingsley St Mich Sch W Sussex 74-76; P-in-c Southwater *Chich* 76-81; V 81-97; R Sullington and Thakeham w Warminghurst from 97. *The Rectory, Thakeham, Pulborough RH20 3EP* Tel (01798) 813121

MESSENGER, Canon Reginald James. b 13. Univ Coll Dur LTh38 BA39 MA57. St Aug Coll Cant 35. **d** 39 **p** 40. C E Dulwich St Jo *S'wark* 39-42; Miss India 43-64; V Sturminster Newton and Hinton St Mary *Sarum* 65-68; Miss India 68-80; rtd 80; Perm to Offic *Chich* from 80. *Flat 3, 46 Norfolk Road, Littlehampton BN17 5HE* Tel (01903) 714113

MESSHAM, Mrs Barbara Lynn. b 52. Bretton Hall Coll CertEd75. STETS DipTh99. **d** 99 **p** 00. C The Bourne and Tilford *Guildf* 99-03; V Guildf All SS from 03. *All Saints' Vicarage, 18 Vicarage Gate, Guildford GU2 7QJ* Tel (01483) 572006 Mobile 07932-615132 E-mail barbara@messhams.co.uk

MESSOM, Alan George. b 42. St Chad's Coll Dur BA63 DipTh65. **d** 65 **p** 66. C Newc St Gabr *Newc* 65-68; Korea 69-77; V Derby St Bart *Derby* from 78. *St Bartholomew's Vicarage, Addison Road, Derby DE24 8FH* Tel (01332) 347709

METCALF, Preb Michael Ralph. b 37. Clare Coll Cam BA61 MA65 Birm Univ MA80. Ridley Hall Cam 63. **d** 64 **p** 65. C Downend *Bris* 64-67; Perm to Offic *Birm* 68-78; Perm to Offic *Lich* 72-81; Dioc Dir of Educn 83-94; Perm to Offic *Heref* from 87; Preb Lich Cathl *Lich* from 91; V Stafford St Paul Forebridge from 94; RD Stafford from 00. *St Paul's Vicarage, 31 The Oval, Stafford ST17 4LQ* Tel (01785) 251683 Fax 660234 E-mail prebmetcalf@hotmail.com or berylm@ntlworld.com

METCALF, The Ven Robert Laurence. b 35. Dur Univ BA60. Cranmer Hall Dur DipTh62. **d** 62 **p** 63. C Bootle Ch Ch *Liv* 62-65; C Farnworth 65-67; V Wigan St Cath 67-75; R Wavertree H Trin 75-94; Chapl Blue Coat Sch Liv 75-94; Dir of Ords *Liv* 82-94; Hon Can Liv Cathl 87-02; Adn Liv 94-02; rtd 02. *32 Storrsdale Road, Liverpool L18 7JZ* Tel 0151-724 3956 Fax 729 0587 E-mail bobmetcalf@ukgateway.net

METCALFE, Alan. b 22. St Aid Birkenhead 49. **d** 52 **p** 53. C Cleckheaton St Jo *Wakef* 52-55; C Todmorden 55-56; C Thornhill Lees 56-58; V Middlestown 58-60; V S Crosland 60-64; V Upwood w Gt and Lt Raveley *Ely* 64-69; Chapl RAF 64-68; V Dewsbury St Matt and St Jo *Wakef* 69-71; Warden Bridgehead Hostel Cardiff 71-73; Field View Hostel Stoke Prior 73-75; McIntyre Ho Nuneaton 75-79; C Southam w Stockton *Cov* 79-84; P-in-c Kinwarton w Gt Alne and Haselor 84-87; rtd 87; Hon C Yarcombe w Membury and Upottery *Ex* 89-92; Perm to Offic *St E* from 92. *3 Mays Court, Garrison Road, Felixstowe IP11 7ST* Tel (01394) 271585

METCALFE, James. b 17. St Pet Hall Ox BA39 MA44. Wycliffe Hall Ox 39. **d** 41 **p** 42. C Dartford Ch Ch *Roch* 41-43; CF (EC) 43-47; C Goole *Sheff* 47-49; V Batley St Thos *Wakef* 49-55; V Mexborough *Sheff* 55-71; R Wickersley 71-82; rtd 82; Perm to Offic *Bradf* 83-99. *Scar Fields, The Mains, Giggleswick, Settle BD24 0AX* Tel (01729) 823983

METCALFE, Reginald Herbert. b 38. **d** 79. Hon C Aspley Guise *St Alb* 79; Hon C Aspley Guise w Husborne Crawley and Ridgmont 80-84; Hon C Bovingdon from 84. *30 Manorville Road, Hemel Hempstead HP3 0AP* Tel (01442) 242952 Fax 213137

METCALFE, Canon Ronald. b 41. BA. Edin Th Coll 67. **d** 69 **p** 70. C Saltburn-by-the-Sea *York* 69-72; P-in-c Crathorne 73-77; Youth Officer 73-77; Dioc Adult Tr Officer 78-88; Can Res York Minster 88-00; Sec for Miss and Min 88-00; V Kendal H Trin *Carl* from 00. *Holy Trinity Vicarage, 2 Lynngarth Drive, Kendal LA9 4JA* Tel (01539) 721541 or 721248 E-mail ronald.metcalfe@ukonline.co.uk

METCALFE, William Bernard. b 47. St Jo Coll Cam BA69 MA73 Ball Coll Ox BA71. Ripon Hall Ox 70. **d** 72 **p** 73. C Caversham *Ox* 72-75; C Aylesbury 75-79; Ind Chapl 75-79; TV Thamesmead *S'wark* 79-84; TR Totton *Win* 84-94; R Gt Bentley and Frating w Thorrington *Chelmsf* from 94; RD St Osyth from 00. *The Rectory, Moors Close, Great Bentley, Colchester CO7 8QL* Tel (01206) 250476 E-mail wellmet@netcomuk.co.uk

METHUEN, Charlotte Mary. b 64. Girton Coll Cam BA85 MA89 New Coll Edin BD91 PhD95. Edin Th Coll 87. **d** 98 **p** 99. C E Netherlands *Eur* 98-01; C Bonn w Cologne 01-03; Hon Asst Chapl from 03. *Lotharstrasse 8, 45131 Essen, Germany* Tel (0049) (201) 425660 Fax 423834 E-mail charlotte.methuen@ruhr-uni-bochum.de

METHUEN, The Very Revd John Alan Robert. b 47. BNC Ox BA69 MA74. Cuddesdon Coll 69. **d** 71 **p** 72. C Fenny Stratford *Ox* 71-73; C Fenny Stratford and Water Eaton 74; Asst Chapl Eton Coll 74-77; P-in-c Dorney *Ox* 74-77; Warden Dorney/Eton Coll Conf Cen 74-77; V Reading St Mark 77-83; R Hulme Ascension *Man* 83-95; Dean Ripon from 95. *The Minster House, Ripon HG4 1PE* Tel (01765) 603615 *or* 603462 Fax 690530 E-mail postmaster@riponcathedral.org.uk

METHVEN, Alexander George. b 26. Lon Univ BD52 Em Coll Cam BA54 MA58. ACT ThL47 Lon Coll of Div 50. **d** 52 **p** 53. C Cambridge St Andr Less *Ely* 52-54; Chapl RAF 55-60; V Lower Sydenham St Mich *S'wark* 60-67; Australia from 68; rtd 91. *PO Box 494, Belgrave, Vic, Australia 3160* Tel (0061) (3) 9754 8056 E-mail agmethven@hotmail.com

METIVIER, Canon Robert John. b 31. Lon Univ BA68. Lambeth STh61 Ch Div Sch of the Pacific (USA) BD66 MDiv69 Codrington Coll Barbados 56. **d** 60 **p** 61. Trinidad and Tobago 61-64 and 68-78; USPG 66-67; C Gt Berkhamsted *St Alb* 78-82; V Goff's Oak St Jas 82-90; V Tokyngton St Mich *Lon* 90-01; Hon Can Trinidad from 98; rtd 01. *17 Willowcourt Avenue, Kenton, Harrow HA3 8ET* Tel (020) 8909 1371

METTERS, Anthony John Francis. b 43. AKC65. **d** 68 **p** 69. C Heavitree *Ex* 68-74; V Plymouth Crownhill Ascension 74-79; RD Plymouth 77-79; Chapl RN 79-99; rtd 99. *Knightshayes, 1 De Port Heights, Corhampton, Southampton SO32 3DA*

METTHAM, Maurice Desmond. b 20. Sarum & Wells Th Coll 73. **d** 74 **p** 75. C Guernsey St Sav *Win* 74-81; Perm to Offic 81-96. *La Masse Residential Home, Grande Capelles Road, St Sampsons, Guernsey GY2 4UT* Tel (01481) 49334

METZNER (née JEFFREY), Mrs Katrina. b 73. St Jo Coll Ox BA96 MA01. St Steph Ho Ox 97. **d** 99 **p** 00. C Glouc St Geo w Whaddon *Glouc* 99-00; C Parkstone St Pet and St Osmund w Branksea *Sarum* from 00. *St Francis House, 105A Winston Avenue, Branksome, Poole BH12 1PB* Tel (01202) 566496

METZNER, Simon David. b 64. Magd Coll Ox BA85 K Coll Lon MA95 St Luke's Coll Ex PGCE93. St Steph Ho Ox. **d** 00 **p** 01. C Branksome St Aldhelm *Sarum* from 00. *St Francis House, 105A Winston Avenue, Branksome, Poole BH12 1PB* Tel (01202) 247523

MEWIS, Canon David William. b 47. Leeds Inst of Educn CertEd68 Leeds Poly BEd83. N Ord Course 87. **d** 90 **p** 91. C Skipton Ch Ch *Bradf* 90-92; R Bolton by Bowland w Grindleton from 92; RD Bowland from 99; Hon Can Bradf Cathl from 00. *The Rectory, Sawley Road, Grindleton, Clitheroe BB7 4QS* Tel (01200) 441154 E-mail dwm@dmewis.freeserve.co.uk

MEWS, Stuart Paul. b 44. Leeds Univ BA64 MA67 Trin Hall Cam PhD74 FRHistS75. Westcott Ho Cam 86. **d** 87 **p** 88. Lect

Lanc Univ 68-92; NSM Caton w Littledale *Blackb* 87-90; Hon C Lancaster St Mary 88-92; Reader RS Cheltenham and Glouc Coll of HE 92-00; Acting P-in-c Croxton and Eltisley *Ely* 97-98; P-in-c Tilbrook from 00; P-in-c Covington from 00; P-in-c Catworth Magna from 00; P-in-c Keyston and Bythorn from 00. *The Rectory, Church Lane, Tilbrook, Huntingdon PE18 0JS* Tel (01480) 860147

MEYER, Donovan Candido. b 60. d 91 p 91. S Africa 91-03; TV Oldham *Man* from 03. *Holy Trinity Vicarage, 46 Godson Street, Oldham OL1 2DB* Tel 0161-627 1640 E-mail donnymeyer15@hotmail.com

MEYER, Stuart Thomas. b 45. GLCM69 Open Univ BA85. Trin Coll Bris 76. d 78 p 79. C Heref St Pet w St Owen *Heref* 78-79; C Heref St Pet w St Owen and St Jas 79-80; Chapl K Coll Cam 80-84; Chapl Lon Univ Medical Schs *S'wark* 84-87; Hon C Streatham St Pet from 87; Chapl Dulwich Hosp 87-93; Chapl Camberwell Distr HA 90-93; Chapl K Coll Hosp Lon 90-93; Sen Chapl King's Healthcare NHS Trust from 93. *King's College Hospital, London SE5 9RS* Tel (020) 7346 3522 E-mail stuart.meyer@kingsch.nhs.uk

MEYER, William John. b 46. ACIB. Cranmer Hall Dur 83. d 85 p 86. C Merrow *Guildf* 85-89; V Grayshott 89-98; R Binfield *Ox* from 98. *The Rectory, Terrace Road North, Bracknell RG12 5JG* Tel (01344) 454406 Fax as telephone E-mail bill@meyer.freeserve.co.uk

MEYNELL, Canon Andrew Francis. b 43. Westcott Ho Cam 70. d 73 p 74. C Cowley St Jas *Ox* 73-79; TV 79-81; P-in-c Halton 81-95; V Wendover 81-95; P-in-c Monks Risborough 95-98; TV Risborough from 98; Dir Ords Bucks Adnry from 95; Hon Can Ch Ch from 01. *The Rectory, Mill Lane, Monks Risborough, Princes Risborough HP27 9JE* Tel (01844) 342556 Fax as telephone E-mail andrew.meynell@oxford.anglican.org

MEYNELL, Mrs Honor Mary. b 37. EMMTC 84. d 87 p 94. NSM Kirk Langley *Derby* from 87; NSM Mackworth All SS from 87; NSM Mugginton and Kedleston from 87. *Meynell Langley, Kirk Langley, Ashbourne DE6 4NT* Tel (01332) 824207

MEYNELL, Canon Mark. b 14. Ch Ch Ox BA37 MA44. Cuddesdon Coll. d 40 p 41. C St Alb Abbey *St Alb* 40-46; R Folkington *Chich* 46-49; R Marlesford *St E* 49-56; R Campsey Ashe 51-56; R Cogenhoe *Pet* 56-63; V Leamington Hastings *Cov* 65-79; R Birdingbury 74-79; Can Th Cov Cathl 73-78; rtd 79; Perm to Offic *St E* from 80. *2 Double Street, Framlingham, Woodbridge IP13 9BN* Tel (01728) 723898

MEYNELL, Mark John Henrik. b 70. New Coll Ox MA93. Ridley Hall Cam MA95. d 97 p 98. C Fulwood *Sheff* 97-01; Kampala Evang Sch of Th Uganda from 01. *KEST, PO Box 16704, Kampala, Uganda* Tel (00256) (41) 267104 Mobile (71) 611611 E-mail markmeynell@hotmail.com

MEYRICK, Canon Cyril Jonathan. b 52. St Jo Coll Ox BA73 MA77. Sarum & Wells Th Coll 74. d 76 p 77. C Bicester *Ox* 76-78; Bp's Dom Chapl 78-81; Barbados 81-84; TV Burnham w Dropmore, Hitcham and Taplow *Ox* 84-90; TR Tisbury *Sarum* 90-98; Link Officer Black Anglican Concerns 90-98; RD Chalke 97-98; Can Res Roch Cathl *Roch* from 98. *East Canonry, Kings Orchard, The Precinct, Rochester ME1 1TG* Tel (01634) 841491

MEYRICK, Thomas Henry Corfe. b 67. Magd Coll Ox BA88 MA92. St Steph Ho Ox BA94. d 95 p 96. C Bierley *Bradf* 95-99; Chapl Oriel Coll Ox from 99. *Oriel College, Oxford OX1 4EW* Tel (01865) 276580 *or* 276555 E-mail t.meyrick@bigfoot.com

MIALL, Peter Brian. b 30. Scawsby Coll of Educn TCert69. d 89 p 89. Hon C Bolsterstone *Sheff* 89-98; Perm to Offic from 98. *Waldershaigh Cottage, Heads Lane, Bolsterstone, Sheffield S36 3ZH* Tel 0114-288 5558

MICHAEL, Brother. *See* FISHER, The Rt Revd Reginald Lindsay

MICHAEL, Canon Ian MacRae. b 40. Aber Univ MA62 Hertf Coll Ox DPhil66. Westcott Ho Cam 77. d 79 p 80. C Kings Heath *Birm* 79-82; Vice-Provost St Paul's Cathl Dundee *Bre* 82-88; V Harborne St Faith and St Laur *Birm* from 88; RD Edgbaston 91-98; Hon Can Birm Cathl 00-03; rtd 03. *46 Argyle Court, St Andrews KY16 9BW* Tel (01334) 473901

MICHAEL, Stephen David. b 71. Ripon Coll Cuddesdon 01. d 03. C St Blazey *Truro* from 03. *4 Churchfield Place, Fore Street, St Blazey PL24 2NT* Tel (01726) 815669 E-mail sd.michael@virgin.net

MICHAELS, David Albert Emmanuel. b 49. Barrister-at-Law (Inner Temple) 73 Bede Coll Dur BA72. Westcott Ho Cam 86. d 88 p 89. C Hampstead St Jo *Lon* 88-91; TV Wolvercote w Summertown *Ox* from 91. *The Vicarage, 1 Mere Road, Wolvercote, Oxford OX2 8AN* Tel (01865) 515640 Fax 516440 E-mail david.michaels@dunelm.org.uk

MICHELL, Canon Douglas Reginald. b 19. St Jo Coll Dur BA41 MA44. Westcott Ho Cam 41. d 43 p 44. C Wanstead H Trin Hermon Hill *Chelmsf* 43-45; Chapl St Jo Coll Dur 45-48; Lic to Offic *Dur* 45-48; R Moss Side St Jas *Man* 48-53; V Horwich H Trin 53-61; V Evington *Leic* 61-80; Hon Can Leic Cathl 67-84; RD Christianity N 74-79; V Billesdon w Goadby and Rolleston 80-82; RD Gartree I 81-84; V Billesdon and Skeffington 82-84;

rtd 85; Perm to Offic *St Alb* 85-97; *Chich* from 97. *9 Ramsay Hall, 11-13 Byron Road, Worthing BN11 3HN* Tel (01903) 207294

MICHELL, Francis Richard Noel. b 42. St Cath Coll Cam BA64 MA68. Tyndale Hall Bris 64. d 66 p 67. C Northampton St Giles *Pet* 66-69; C Gateacre *Liv* 69-72; V Litherland St Paul Hatton Hill 72-79; V Rainhill 79-88; V Rainford from 88. *The Vicarage, Church Road, Rainford, St Helens WA11 8HD* Tel (01744) 882200

MICKLETHWAITE, Andrew Quentin. b 67. Univ Coll Dur BA89. Trin Coll Bris BA94. d 94 p 95. C Abington *Pet* 94-97; TV Duston Team from 97. *7 Pine Copse Close, New Duston, Northampton NN5 6NF* Tel (01604) 590256 E-mail andrew@duston.org.uk

MICKLETHWAITE, Mrs Dorothy Eileen. b 41. St Alb and Ox Min Course 98. d 01 p 02. NSM Helmdon w Stuchbury and Radstone etc *Pet* from 01; Asst Chapl Ox Radcliffe Hosps NHS Trust from 02; Perm to Offic *Ox* from 02. *54 Stuart Road, Brackley NN13 6HZ* Tel (01280) 703697 E-mail dorothymick@aol.com

MICKLETHWAITE, Jane Catherine. b 56. Lanc Univ BSc78. Trin Coll Bris DipHE94. d 95 p 96. C Kings Heath *Pet* 95-98; Chapl Nene Coll of HE Northn 97-98; Perm to Offic *Pet* 98-01; NSM Kings Heath from 01. *7 Pine Copse Close, New Duston, Northampton NN5 6NF* Tel (01604) 590256 E-mail j.micklethwaite@talk21.com

MICKLETHWAITE, Peter William. b 62. Peterho Cam BA84 MA88. St Jo Coll Nottm DipTh89 DPS90. d 90 p 91. C Leatherhead *Guildf* 90-93; C Wisley w Pyrford 93-97; R Windlesham from 97. *The Rectory, Kennel Lane, Windlesham GU20 6AA* Tel (01276) 472363 E-mail rector@windleshamchurch.org.uk

MIDDLEBROOK, Bryan. b 33. Dur Univ BA55 DipEd58 Newc Univ MEd74. NEOC 85. d 88 p 88. NSM Dur St Cuth *Dur* 88-99; NSM Witton Gilbert 97-99. *5 Fieldhouse Terrace, Durham DH1 4NA* Tel 0191-386 6665

MIDDLEBROOK, David John. b 61. Newc Univ BSc83 Cranfield Inst of Tech MSc85. Trin Coll Bris BA98. d 98 p 99. C Chorleywood Ch Ch *St Alb* 98-02; TV Hemel Hempstead from 02. *St Barnabas Vicarage, Everest Way, Hemel Hempstead HP2 4HY* Tel (01442) 253681 E-mail dave.middlebrook@btinternet.com

MIDDLEDITCH, Terry Gordon. b 30. Univ of Wales (Lamp) BA62 St Martin's Coll Lanc PGCE68. St D Coll Lamp 59. d 63 p 64. C Poulton-le-Fylde *Blackb* 63-65; C-in-c Heysham 65-67; Sch Master 68-88; Hon C Cheltenham St Pet *Glouc* 75-87; Hon C Badgeworth w Shurdington 75-87; Hon C Up Hatherley 75-87; C Poulton-le-Sands w Morecambe St Laur *Blackb* 88-91; V Stalmine 91-00; rtd 00; Perm to Offic *Blackb* from 00. *93 Thornton Road, Morecambe LA4 5PG* Tel (01524) 413378 Mobile 07879-426173

MIDDLEMISS, Fritha Leonora. b 47. Man Univ BA68 CertEd69. Glouc Sch of Min 86. d 89 p 94. NSM Bengeworth *Worc* 89-94; NSM Stoulton w Drake's Broughton and Pirton etc 94-96; Chapl Malvern Girls' Coll from 96; Asst Chapl HM Pris Long Lartin from 03. *HM Prison Long Lartin, South Littleton, Evesham WR11 8TZ* Tel (01386) 835100

MIDDLEMISS, Jeffrey Thomas. b 50. Padgate Coll of Educn BEd79 Edge Hill Coll of HE DASE85. N Ord Course 87. d 90 p 91. C Gateacre *Liv* 90-93; V W Derby Gd Shep 93-94; V Wigan St Cath 94-00; TV Leominster *Heref* from 01. *The New Vicarage, Kimbolton, Leominster HR6 0EJ* Tel (01568) 615295 E-mail jeff_middlemiss@lineone.net

MIDDLEMISS, Mrs Justine. b 68. Aston Univ BSc90. Ripon Coll Cuddesdon 00. d 02 p 03. C Sat St Marg *S'wark* from 02. *55 Longhurst Road, London SE13 5NA* Tel (020) 8318 6875 E-mail gandj@fish.co.uk

MIDDLESEX, Archdeacon of. *See* COLMER, The Ven Malcolm John

MIDDLETON, Alan Derek. b 46. St Jo Coll Dur BA68 MA85 Bris Univ PGCE70 Sheff Univ MMin00. Qu Coll Birm DipTh71 DPS72. d 72 p 73. C Cannock *Lich* 72-76; Warden St Helen's Youth & Community Cen Bp Auckd 76-79; V Darlington St Jo *Dur* 79-89; TR E Darlington 89-90; V Upper Norwood All SS *S'wark* 90-99; Bp's Ecum Adv from 96; TR Warlingham w Chelsham and Farleigh from 99. *The Rectory, 35 Dane Road, Warlingham CR6 9NP* Tel (01883) 624125 Fax 624490 E-mail alan.middleton@dswark.org.uk

MIDDLETON, Arthur. *See* MIDDLETON, Canon Thomas Arthur

MIDDLETON, Barry Glen. b 41. Lich Th Coll 68. d 70 p 71. C Westhoughton *Man* 70-73; C Prestwich St Marg 73-74; TV Buxton w Burbage and King Sterndale *Derby* 74-77; Chapl Worc R Infirmary 77-83; Chapl Fairfield Hosp Hitchin 83-85; P-in-c Erpingham w Calthorpe *Nor* 85-86; R Erpingham w Calthorpe, Ingworth, Aldborough etc 86-92; R Badingham w Bruisyard, Cransford and Dennington *St E* 92-96; V Sidcup St Jo *Roch* 96-98; V Gt and Lt Bardfield w Gt and Lt Saling *Chelmsf* 98-00; rtd 00; Perm to Offic *St E* from 00. *49 Constable Road, Felixstowe IP11 7HP* Tel (01394) 286506 Mobile 07798-782264

MIDDLETON, David Jeremy. b 68. Ex Univ BSc90. Wycliffe Hall Ox 01. **d** 03. C Ipswich St Jo *St E* from 03. *2A Norbury Road, Ipswich IP4 4RQ* Tel (01473) 710025

MIDDLETON, Hugh Charles. b 50. Nottm Univ BTh77. Linc Th Coll 73. **d** 77 **p** 78. C New Sleaford *Linc* 77-81; C Grantham 81; TV 81-83; R Caythorpe 83-95; P-in-c Bracebridge Heath 97-00; V from 00. *The Vicarage, 11 Salisbury Drive, Bracebridge Heath, Lincoln LN4 2SW* Tel (01522) 540460

MIDDLETON, Canon Kenneth Frank. b 28. Keble Coll Ox BA52 MA64. St Steph Ho Ox 52. **d** 55 **p** 56. C Leic St Matt *Leic* 55-58; C W Hackney St Barn *Lon* 58-60; V Leic St Matt and St Geo *Leic* 60-82; RD Christianity N 79-82; P-in-c Leic St Alb 80-82; Hon Can Leic Cathl 80-82; P-in-c Belgrave St Mich 81-82; TR Bridgnorth, Tasley, Astley Abbotts, etc *Heref* 82-87; P-in-c Quatford 83; RD Bridgnorth 83-87; TR Littleham w Exmouth *Ex* 87-99; Chapl Ex and Distr Community Health Service NHS Trust 87-99; rtd 99; Perm to Offic *Ex* from 99. *15 Strawberry Hill, Lympstone, Exmouth EX8 5JZ* Tel (01395) 272227

MIDDLETON, Canon Michael John. b 40. Dur Univ BSc62 Fitzw Ho Cam BA66 MA70. Westcott Ho Cam 63. **d** 66 **p** 67. C Newc St Geo *Newc* 66-69; V 77-85; Chapl St Geo Gr Sch Cape Town 69-72; Chapl K Sch Tynemouth 72-77; R Hexham *Newc* 85-92; Hon Can Newc Cathl 90-92; Can and Treas Adn Swindon *Bris* 92-97; Can Westmr Abbey from 97. *1 Little Cloister, London SW1P 3PL* Tel (020) 7654 4804 Fax 7654 4811 E-mail michael.middleton@westminster-abbey.org

MIDDLETON, Rodney. b 54. St Andr Univ BD80. St Steph Ho Ox 80. **d** 82 **p** 83. C Walton St Mary *Liv* 82-87; C-in-c Kew St Fran CD 87-94; V Kew 94-95; Chapl Southport and Formby Distr Gen Hosp 87-95; V Haydock St Jas from 95. *The Vicarage, 169 Church Road, Haydock, St Helens WA11 0NJ* Tel (01942) 727956 E-mail rodmid@aol.com

MIDDLETON, Canon Thomas Arthur. b 36. Dur Univ MLitt95. K Coll Lon AKC61 St Boniface Warminster 61. **d** 62 **p** 63. C Sunderland *Dur* 62-63; C Auckland St Helen 63-67; C Winlaton 67-70; C-in-c Pennywell St Thos and Grindon St Oswald CD 70-79; Chapl Grindon Hall Hosp 73-79; R Boldon 79-03; Adv in Stewardship Dur Adnry 87-92; Acting Prin St Chad's Coll Dur 97; Hon Can Dur Cathl *Dur* 98-03; rtd 03. *1 St Mary's Drive, Sherburn, Durham DH6 1RL* Tel 0191-372 3436 E-mail thomas.arthur.middleton@virgin.net

MIDDLETON-DANSKY, Brother Serge Wladimir. b 45. Cuddesdon Coll 74. **d** 77 **p** 78. C Wisbech SS Pet and Paul *Ely* 77-79; Lic to Offic Adnry Riviera *Eur* from 80; C Ox St Giles and SS Phil and Jas w St Marg *Ox* 83-86; Perm to Offic 86-88; Perm to Offic *Truro* 88-90; P-in-c Zennor 90-96; P-in-c Towednack 90-96; Perm to Offic 97-99; Lic to Offic from 99. *The Old Vicarage, Zennor, St Ives TR26 3BY* Tel (01736) 796955

MIDDLETON, Suffragan Bishop of. *See* LEWIS, The Rt Revd Michael Augustine Owen

MIDDLEWICK, Robert James. b 44. K Alfred's Coll Win CertEd67 Lon Univ BD76. Ripon Coll Cuddesdon 75. **d** 77 **p** 78. C Bromley SS Pet and Paul *Roch* 77-81; C Belvedere All SS 81-84; P-in-c Lamberhurst 85-88; P-in-c Matfield 85-88; V Lamberhurst and Matfield 88-99. *12 Mill Stream Place, Tonbridge TN9 1QJ* Tel (01580) 212054

MIDGLEY, George William. b 38. N Ord Course. **d** 83 **p** 84. C Penistone and Thurlstone *Wakef* 88-89; TV 89-94; TR from 94. *The Vicarage, Shrewsbury Road, Penistone, Sheffield S36 6DY* Tel (01226) 763241 pager 01523-470596

MIDGLEY, Stephen Nicholas. b 60. Jes Coll Cam BA83 MA86 Lon Hosp MB, BS86. Wycliffe Hall Ox DipMin97. **d** 97 **p** 98. C Hove Bp Hannington Memorial *Chich* 97-01; C Cambridge H Sepulchre *Ely* from 01. *1 Pretoria Road, Cambridge CB4 1HD* Tel (01223) 518299 E-mail steve.midgley@stag.org

MIDLANE, Colin John. b 50. Qu Mary Coll Lon BA72. Westcott Ho Cam 73 Sarum & Wells Th Coll 77. **d** 78 **p** 79. C Bethnal Green St Pet w St Thos *Lon* 78-82; P-in-c Haggerston All SS 82-88; Chapl Hengrave Hall Ecum Cen 88-89; P Cllr St Botolph Aldgate *Lon* 89-94; C St Botolph Aldgate w H Trin Minories 93-94; TV Haywards Heath St Wilfrid *Chich* 94-97; C Brighton St Geo w St Anne and St Mark 97-01; Chapl Brighton Health Care NHS Trust from 01. *Royal Sussex County Hospital, Eastern Road, Brighton BN2 5BE* Tel (01273) 696955

MIDWINTER, Sister Josie Isabel. b 46. Open Univ BA84 Univ of Wales (Lamp) MA98. CA Tr Coll IDC71 ACT DipTh77. **d** 87 **p** 99. CA from 71; CMS 84-93; Uganda 85-91; Kenya 92-96; C Didcot All SS *Ox* from 98. *12 Trent Road, Didcot, Oxford OX11 7RB* Tel (01235) 819036

MIDWOOD, Peter Stanley. b 47. CertEd69. Linc Th Coll 80. **d** 82 **p** 83. C Garforth *Ripon* 82-85; C-in-c Grinton w Arkengarthdale, Downholme and Marske 85-86; C-in-c Melbecks and Muker 85-86; V Swaledale 86-97; AD Richmond from 97; R Romaldkirk w Laithkirk from 97. *The Rectory, Romaldkirk, Barnard Castle DL12 9EE* Tel (01833) 650202

MIELL, David Keith. b 57. BSc PhD BA. Westcott Ho Cam 83. **d** 86 **p** 87. C Blackbird Leys CD *Ox* 86-89; C Walton 89-90; TV Walton Milton Keynes 90-96; RD Milton Keynes 93-95; TR Upton cum Chalvey from 96; AD Burnham and Slough from 02.

The Rectory, 18 Albert Street, Slough SL1 2BU Tel (01753) 529988 E-mail drdmiell@surfaid.org

MIER, Ms Catherine Elizabeth. b 60. Bris Univ BSc81 Chelsea Coll Lon MSc84 Dur Univ BA95. Cranmer Hall Dur 93. **d** 96 **p** 97. C Royston *St Alb* 96-00; C Bilton *Cov* from 00. *51 Falstaff Drive, Bilton, Rugby CV22 6LJ* Tel (01788) 810761 E-mail kate.mier@virgin.net

MIGHALL, Robert. b 33. St Pet Coll Ox BA57 MA61. Wycliffe Hall Ox 57. **d** 58 **p** 59. C Stoke *Cov* 58-62; C Rugby St Andr 62-64; V Newbold on Avon 64-76; V Combroke w Compton Verney 76-96; V Kineton 76-96; rtd 96; Perm to Offic *Glouc* from 97. *The Dairy House, Quarleston Farm, Clenston Road, Winterborne Stickland, Blandford Forum DT11 0NP* Tel (01258) 881467 E-mail robert@rmighall.fsnet.co.uk

MIHILL, Dennis George. b 31. St Alb Minl Tr Scheme 78. **d** 81 **p** 82. NSM Harpenden St Nic *St Alb* 81-86; C Sawbridgeworth 86-89; V Motspur Park *S'wark* 89-96; rtd 96; Perm to Offic *St Alb* 96-98; Hon C Biddenham 98-01; Perm to Offic from 01. *5 Regents Mews, Biddenham, Bedford MK40 4DL* Tel (01234) 269903

MIKHAIL, Stella Frances. BTh. **d** 02. C Bandon Union *C, C & R* from 02. *3 The Pines, Kilbrittain Road, Bandon, Co Cork, Irish Republic* Tel (00353) (23) 41053

MILBURN, John Frederick. b 56. Westmr Coll Ox BA84. Sarum & Wells Th Coll 84. **d** 86 **p** 87. C Leavesden All SS *St Alb* 86-89; C Broxbourne w Wormley 89-93; CF (TA) 90-93; Australia from 93; R Inglewood St Jo w Texas Qld 93-98; P-in-c Holland Park St Matt from 98. *PO Box 248, Holland Park, Qld, Australia 4121* Tel and fax (0061) (7) 3397 0390 *or* Tel 3397 2300 E-mail john.milburn@optushome.com.au

MILES, Damian Stewart. b 76. Fitzw Coll Cam BTh02. Westcott Ho Cam 99. **d** 02 **p** 03. C Willingdon *Chich* from 02. *11 Winchester Way, Eastbourne BN22 0JP* Tel (01323) 520928 Mobile 07815-848735 E-mail damomiles@hotmail.com

MILES, Gerald Christopher Morgan. b 36. Peterho Cam BA57 MA72 Cranfield Inst of Tech MSc72 CEng MIEE. Wycliffe Hall Ox 74. **d** 76 **p** 77. C Tunbridge Wells St Jas *Roch* 76-80; V Leigh 80-90; R Addington w Trottiscliffe 90-91; P-in-c Ryarsh w Birling 90-91; R Birling, Addington, Ryarsh and Trottiscliffe 91-00; Hon Chapl London and SE Region ATC from 96; rtd 00; Perm to Offic *Roch* from 00. *2 Spa Close, Maidstone Road, Hadlow, Tonbridge TN11 0JX* Tel (01732) 852323 Fax as telephone E-mail cmiles@supanet.com

MILES (née HOARE), Ms Janet Francis Mary. b 48. St Aid Coll Dur BA70 Bris Univ MEd84. Sarum & Wells Th Coll DipMin93. **d** 93 **p** 94. C Bruton and Distr *B & W* 93-98; P-in-c Llangarron w Llangrove, Whitchurch and Ganarew *Heref* 98-02; P-in-c Dixton from 02. *The Vicarage, 38 Hillcrest Road, Wyesham, Monmouth NP25 3LJ* Tel (01600) 712565

MILES, Malcolm Robert. b 36. AKC60. **d** 61 **p** 62. C Northampton St Mary *Pet* 61-63; C E Haddon 63-67; R Broughton 67-73; Asst Chapl Nottm Univ *S'well* 73-74; V Northampton H Trin *Pet* 75-84; V Painswick w Sheepscombe *Glouc* 84-97; V Painswick w Sheepscombe and Cranham 97-01; RD Bisley 90-94; rtd 01; P-in-c Wensley *Ripon* from 01; P-in-c W Witton from 01. *The Rectory, Wensley, Leyburn DL8 4HS* Tel (01969) 623736 E-mail rachel@milesr.freeserve.co.uk

MILES, Mrs Marion Claire. b 41. S Dios Minl Tr Scheme 86. **d** 88 **p** 94. Hon Par Dn Blandford Forum and Langton Long *Sarum* 88-94; Hon C 94-01; Chapl Blandford Community Hosp from 88; NSM The Winterbournes and Compton Valence from 01. *153 Salisbury Road, Blandford Forum DT11 7SW* Tel (01258) 452010

MILES, Patricia. STETS. **d** 03. NSM Verwood *Sarum* from 03. *4 Firs Glen Road, Verwood BH31 6JB* Tel (01202) 824211

MILES, Canon Robert William. b 27. Magd Coll Cam BA50 MA55. Westcott Ho Cam 50. **d** 52 **p** 53. C Bury St Mary *Man* 52-55; Bp's Dom Chapl *Chich* 55-58; Kenya 58-63; Provost Mombasa 58-63; R Dalmahoy *Edin* 65-70; R Batsford w Moreton-in-Marsh *Glouc* 70-77; rtd 77; Perm to Offic *Glouc* from 79. *Boilingwell, Winchcombe, Cheltenham GL54 5JB* Tel (01242) 603337

MILES, Mrs Ruth Cecilia. b 11. St Cath Ho Lon 37 St Mich Ho Ox 38. **dss** 40 **d** 87. Byker St Ant *Newc* 40-44; Stocksbridge *Sheff* 44-47; Attercliffe w Carbrook 47-52; Dioc Adv in Children's Voluntary RE 52-60; Adv in Children's RE *Linc* 60-71; Sec Bd of Women's Work 60-71; rtd 71; Perm to Offic *Glouc* 83-94. *18 Capel Court, The Burgage, Prestbury, Cheltenham GL52 3EL* Tel (01242) 526800

MILES, Miss Sharon Elizabeth Ann. b 66. Westcott Ho Cam 00. **d** 02 **p** 03. C Shrub End *Chelmsf* from 02. *St Cedd's House, 47 Eldred Avenue, Colchester CO2 9AR* Tel (01206) 572017 E-mail revdsmiles@hotmail.com

MILES, Stephen John. b 44. Monash Univ Aus BA66 Worc Coll Ox DipEd68 Univ Coll Lon MA75 California Univ PhD83. Melbourne Coll of Div BTheol86. **d** 87 **p** 88. Australia 87-97 and from 03; C E Malvern St Jo 87; C Clifton Hill St Andr 87-89; Chapl Co-ord and Angl Chapl Monash Medical Cen 89-97; Asst Chapl Bonn w Cologne *Eur* 97-00; Chapl 00-03; rtd 03.

67 Caroline Street, South Yarra, Vic, Australia 3141 Tel (0061) (3) 9866 1463

MILFORD, Canon Catherine Helena. b 39. LMH Ox BA61 DipTh62 MA65 FRSA92. Gilmore Course 81. **dss** 82 **d** 87 **p** 94. Heaton St Barn *Bradf* 82-88; Par Dn 87-88; Adult Educn Adv *Win* 88-96; TR Barnham Broom *Nor* 96-00; P-in-c Reymerston w Cranworth, Letton, Southburgh etc 96-00; TR Barnham Broom and Upper Yare from 00; Hon Can Nor Cathl from 00. *The Vicarage, Honingham Road, Barnham Broom, Norwich NR9 4DB* Tel (01603) 759204

MILFORD, Graham Alan. b 57. Trin Coll Bris 00. **d** 02 **p** 03. C Wolborough and Ogwell *Ex* from 02. *5 Gothic Road, Newton Abbot TQ12 1LD* Tel (01626) 368412

MILLAM, Peter John. b 36. Univ of Wales (Lamp) BA58. Ridley Hall Cam 58. **d** 63 **p** 64. C Cheltenham Ch Ch *Glouc* 63-66; Falkland Is 66-70; V Pulloxhill w Flitton *St Alb* 70-79; V Luton St Paul 79-89; V Chipping Campden w Ebrington *Glouc* 89-94; rtd 94; Perm to Offic *Chich* from 94. *22 Willowhale Avenue, Aldwick, Bognor Regis PO21 4AY* Tel (01243) 268316

MILLAR, Alan Askwith. b 26. Qu Coll Birm 59. **d** 60 **p** 61. C Redcar *York* 60-64; C Kirkleatham 60-64; V Middlesbrough St Aid 64-72; V Cayton w Eastfield 72-88; Chapl to RD of Scarborough 88-89; rtd 89; Perm to Offic *Bradf* from 89. *20 Guardian Court, Wells Promenade, Ilkley LS29 9JT* Tel (01943) 602081

MILLAR, Alan William. b 46. Toronto Univ MDiv. **d** 00 **p** 01. C Drumglass w Moygashel *Arm* from 00. *Kinore, 84 Killyman Road, Dungannon BT71 6DQ* Tel (028) 8772 7131

MILLAR, Andrew Charles. b 48. Hull Univ BSc69. Cuddesdon Coll 71. **d** 73 **p** 74. C Rushmere *St E* 73-76; C Ipswich All Hallows 76-79; Dioc Youth Chapl *Sheff* 79-83; Youth Chapl *Win* 83-92; V Colden from 92. *The Vicarage, Colden Common, Winchester SO21 1TL* Tel (01962) 712505

MILLAR, Christine. See WHEELER, Mrs Christine

MILLAR, Gary. b 67. Poly of Wales Univ of Wales (Cardiff). St Mich Coll Llan 88. **d** 91 **p** 92. C Tonyrefail w Gilfach Goch *Llan* 91-93; C Barry All SS 93-95; TV Cowbridge 95-97; I Dromara w Garvaghy *D & D* 97-01; I Kilkeel from 01. *44 Manse Road, Kilkeel, Newry BT34 4BN* Tel (028) 4176 2300 E-mail garymillar@tesco.net

MILLAR, Preb John Alexander Kirkpatrick (Sandy). b 39. Trin Coll Cam BA62 MA66. St Jo Coll Dur 74. **d** 76 **p** 77. C Brompton H Trin *Lon* 76-78; C Brompton H Trin w Onslow Square St Paul 78-85; V from 85; AD Chelsea 89-94; Preb St Paul's Cathl from 97. *Holy Trinity Vicarage, 73 Prince's Gate Mews, London SW7 2PP* Tel (020) 7584 8957 *or* 7581 8255

MILLAR, Sandra Doreen. b 57. Univ of Wales (Cardiff) BA79 Warwick Univ MA94 PhD99. Ripon Coll Cuddesdon. **d** 00 **p** 01. C Chipping Barnet w Arkley *St Alb* from 00. *13 Cedar Lawn Avenue, Barnet EN5 2LW* Tel (020) 8449 4797 E-mail sandra@mailcity.com

MILLARD, Albert George. b 17. Chich Th Coll. **d** 64 **p** 65. C Wokingham All SS Ox 64-71; V Kintbury w Avington 71-82; rtd 82; Perm to Offic *Portsm* 91-03. *2 New Home Farm Cottages, St Michael's Lane, Sulhamstead, Reading RG7 4DL* Tel 0118-930 2661

MILLARD, Canon Jane Mary. b 43. Open Univ BA80. Edin Dioc NSM Course 81. **d** 90 **p** 94. NSM Edin St Mary *Edin* from 90; Chapl HIV/AIDS from 90; Can St Mary's Cathl from 95; Vice Provost from 98. *Honeybrae, Ninemileburn, Penicuik EH26 9NB* Tel

MILLARD, Jonathan Neil. b 62. Aston Univ BSc83 Barrister-at-Law (Gray's Inn) 84. Wycliffe Hall Ox 89. **d** 92 **p** 93. C Haddenham w Cuddington, Kingsey etc Ox 92-94; USA 94-00; R Church Stretton *Heref* from 00. *The Rectory, Ashbrook Meadow, Carding Mill Valley, Church Stretton SY6 6JF* Tel (01694) 722585 Fax 720054 E-mail j.millard@ntl.world

MILLARD, Malcolm Edoric. b 38. Lon Univ BA60 AKC60 Lon Inst of Educn PGCE61. St Jo Coll Nottm 80. **d** 77 **p** 81. The Gambia 77-79; Deacon Banjul Cathl 77-79; Deacon Lamin St Andr 79-81; P-in-c 81-82; P-in-c Fajara St Paul 82-88; V Gen 86-88; P-in-c Farafenni Ch of African Martyrs 89-95; C S Shoebury *Chelmsf* 95-97; C Rainham w Wennington 97-02; P-in-c N Ockendon from 02. *52 Birch Crescent, South Ockendon RM15 6TZ* Tel (01708) 857859

MILLARD, Canon Murray Clinton. b 29. Ex Coll Ox BA50 DipTh52 MA58. St Steph Ho Ox 51. **d** 53 **p** 54. C Horfield St Greg *Bris* 53-55; C Guernsey St Steph *Win* 55-61; R Jersey St Mary 61-71; R Guernsey St Sampson 71-82; V Guernsey St Steph from 82; Hon Can Win Cathl from 83. *St Stephen's Vicarage, De Beauvoir, St Peter Port, Guernsey GY1 1RN* Tel (01481) 720268 Fax 723330

MILLARD, Richard Stuart Marsh. b 33. St Pet Coll Ox BA57 MA. Oak Hill NSM Course 90. **d** 93 **p** 94. NSM Laleham *Lon* 93-94; NSM Neatishead, Barton Turf and Irstead *Nor* 94-95; NSM Ashmanhaugh, Barton Turf etc 95-99; rtd 99; Perm to Offic *Nor* from 99. *Semaphore Lodge, 30 Weybourne Road, Sheringham NR25 8HF*

MILLER, Andrew. See MILLER, Ronald Andrew John

MILLER, Anthony Talbot. b 37. Univ of Wales (Lamp) BA59. Coll of Resurr Mirfield. **d** 61 **p** 62. C Panteg w Llanddewi Fach and Llandegfeth *Mon* 61-63; C Monmouth 63-65; V Holme Cultram St Mary *Carl* 65-76; Lic to Offic *Lich* 76-78; P-in-c Wrockwardine Wood 78-80; R 80-94; OCF 92-94; rtd 94. *Smallthwe, 26 Rosemary Lane, Whitchurch SY13 1EG* Tel (01948) 662120

MILLER, Barry. b 42. Bede Coll Dur TCert63 Open Univ BA79 Leic Univ MEd86. Linc Th Coll 63. **d** 65 **p** 66. C Greenside *Dur* 65-68; C Auckland St Andr and St Anne 68-71; Adv in Educn *Leic* 71-77; C Leic St Nic 77-80; Asst Chapl Leic Univ 77-80; Lect RS Leic Poly 77-80; Children's Officer Gen Syn Bd of Educn 80-84; Hd RS W Midl Coll of HE 84-89; Hd Initial Teacher Educn Wolv Poly 89-92; Wolv Univ 92-93; Hd Teacher Educn Bradf Coll from 94. *Bradford College, Great Horton Road, Bradford BD7 1AY* Tel (01274) 433472 E-mail b.miller@bilk.ac.uk

MILLER, Charles. See MILLER, Ernest Charles

MILLER, Charles Irvine. b 35. Nottm Univ BEd76. Bps' Coll Cheshunt 61. **d** 63 **p** 64. C Anlaby Common St Mark *York* 63-66; C Whitby 66-68; R Ingoldmells w Addlethorpe *Linc* 68-72; P-in-c Bishop Norton 72-76; V Scunthorpe St Jo 76-83; Chapl Manor Hosp Walsall 83-89; rtd 89; Perm to Offic *Ely* 98-99 and from 99; P-in-c Isleham 98-99. *The Old Studio, 6 Chapel Street, Duxford, Cambridge CB2 4RJ*

MILLER, Darren Noel. b 67. Birm Univ BSocSc89. Chich Th Coll BTh95 Coll of Resurr Mirfield 94. **d** 95 **p** 96. C Weoley Castle *Birm* 95-98; C Shard End 98-00; V Castle Vale St Cuth from 00. *The Vicarage, Reed Square, Castle Vale, Birmingham B35 7PS* Tel 0121-747 4041

MILLER, David George. b 54. Oriel Coll Ox BA76 MA80. Ripon Coll Cuddesdon 78. **d** 81 **p** 82. C Henfield w Shermanbury and Woodmancote *Chich* 81-84; C Monk Bretton *Wakef* 84-87; V Rastrick St Jo 87-93; TR Helston and Wendron *Truro* from 93; Chapl R Cornwall Hosps Trust from 95. *St Michael's Rectory, Church Lane, Helston TR13 8PF* Tel (01326) 572516

MILLER, David James Tringham. b 45. AKC70. Sarum & Wells Th Coll 76. **d** 77 **p** 78. C Abington *Pet* 77-80; TV Corby SS Pet and Andr w Gt and Lt Oakley 80-83; V Kettering All SS 83-94; RD Kettering 87-94; V Pet All SS from 94. *All Saints' Vicarage, 208 Park Road, Peterborough PE1 2UJ* Tel (01733) 554130 E-mail 208prp@totalise.co.uk

MILLER, David John. b 37. Louvain Univ Belgium Lic en Sciences Catéchétiques 68. Chich Th Coll 60. **d** 62 **p** 63. C Southsea H Spirit *Portsm* 62-65; C Roehampton H Trin *S'wark* 67-68; Chapl Luxembourg *Eur* 68-72; Chapl Lausanne 72-91; Asst Chapl 91-93; Chapl Le Rosey Sch Switzerland 72-02; Perm to Offic from 94; rtd 02. *1 bis avenue de l'Eglise Anglaise, 1006 Lausanne, Switzerland* Tel (0041) (21) 616 2636

MILLER, David Samuel. b 31. Lich Th Coll 62. **d** 63 **p** 64. C Leek St Edw *Lich* 63-66; C Blurton 66; C Southbourne St Kath *Win* 66-71; V E and W Worldham, Hartley Mauditt w Kingsley etc 71-76; TV Buckhurst Hill *Chelmsf* 76-80; V Elm Park St Nic Hornchurch 80-93; rtd 93; Chapl Torrevieja *Eur* 95-97. *8 Church Road, Lowestoft NR32 1TQ*

MILLER, Ernest Charles. b 56. Franklin & Marshall Coll (USA) BA78 Univ of Michigan MA79 Keble Coll Ox DPhil90. Nashotah Ho MDiv82. **d** 82 **p** 83. USA 82-84 and from 96; Asst Chapl Keble Coll Ox 84-88; Warden Ho of SS Greg and Macrina 84-90; Lic to Offic *Ox* 87-91; P-in-c New Marston 91-96; Prof Hist and Ascetical Th Nashotah Ho Wisconsin from 96. *Bishopstead, W153 Oakwood Drive, Delafield, WI 53018, USA*

MILLER, Francis Rogers. b 54. Ex Univ BA86. St Steph Ho Ox 86. **d** 88 **p** 89. C Wednesfield *Lich* 88-93; P-in-c Caldmore 93-99; V 99-02; C Walsall St Mary and All SS Palfrey 93-97; P-in-c 97-02; V Caldmore w Palfrey from 02. *St Michael's Vicarage, 12 St Michael's Street, Walsall WS1 3RQ* Tel (01922) 623445

MILLER, Gareth. See MILLER, John Gareth

MILLER, Geoffrey Edward. b 28. Leeds Univ BA56. Coll of Resurr Mirfield 53. **d** 57 **p** 58. C Birm St Aid Small Heath *Birm* 57-59; C Chiswick St Paul Grove Park *Lon* 59-61; C Barnsley St Pet *Wakef* 61-63; R Claypole *Linc* 63-76; P-in-c Westborough w Dry Doddington and Stubton 63-65; R 65-76; P-in-c Bierley *Bradf* 76-78; V 78-91; rtd 91; Chantry Priest Chpl St Mich & H So Walsingham from 91; Perm to Offic *Nor* from 91. *20 Cleaves Drive, Walsingham NR22 6EQ* Tel (01328) 820591

MILLER, Canon Geoffrey Vincent. b 56. Dur Univ BEd Newc Univ MA94. St Jo Coll Nottm. **d** 83 **p** 84. C Jarrow *Dur* 83-86; TV Billingham St Aid 86-92; Dioc Urban Development Officer 91-97; Community Chapl Stockton-on-Tees 92-94; P-in-c Darlington St Cuth 94-96; V 96-99; Soc Resp Officer 97-99; Can Res Newc Cathl *Newc* from 99; Dioc Urban Officer from 99. *58 Baronswood, Gosforth, Newcastle upon Tyne NE3 3NB* Tel 0191-285 3667 *or* 232 1939 Fax 230 0735 E-mail stnicholas@aol.com

MILLER, The Ven George Charles Alexander. b 20. TCD BA45. CITC Div Test 46. **d** 46 **p** 47. C Wexford w Rathaspeck *C & O* 46-49; Asst Chapl Miss to Seamen Belf 49; Chapl Miss to

Seamen Immingham 49-51; Chapl Pernis Miss to Seamen *Eur* 51-55; I Billis w Ballyjamesduff *K, E & A* 55-57; I Knockbride w Shercock 57-65; I Urney w Denn and Derryheen 65-89; Preb Kilmore Cathl 77-87; Adn Kilmore 87-89; rtd 89. *Wavecrest, Blenacup, Cavan, Irish Republic* Tel (00353) (49) 436 1270

MILLER, Graham William. b 71. St Andr Univ BD94 Dur Univ MA98. Westcott Ho Cam 99. **d** 01 **p** 02. C Ex St Dav *Ex* 01-03; C Sunderland St Mary and St Pet *Dur* from 03; C Sunderland Pennywell St Thos from 03. *72 Sevenoaks Drive, Sunderland SR4 9NU* Tel 0191-534 3009 E-mail grahamwmiller@aol.com

✠**MILLER, The Rt Revd Harold Creeth.** b 50. TCD BA73 MA78 Nottm Univ BA75. St Jo Coll Nottm 73. **d** 76 **p** 77 **c** 97. C Carrickfergus *Conn* 76-79; Dir Ext Studies St Jo Coll Nottm 79-84; Chapl QUB 84-89; I Carrigrohane Union *C, C & R* 89-97; Bp's Dom Chapl 91-97; Can Cork and Cloyne Cathls 94-96; Treas Cork Cathl 96-97; Can Cork Cathl 96-97; Preb Tymothan St Patr Cathl Dublin from 96; Bp D & D from 97. *The See House, 32 Knockdene Park South, Belfast BT5 7AB* Tel (028) 9047 1973 Fax 9065 0584 E-mail bishop@down.anglican.org

MILLER (née BLUNDEN), Mrs Jacqueline Ann. b 63. Leic Univ BA86 SS Coll Cam BA90. Ridley Hall Cam 88. **d** 91. Par Dn Bedford St Paul *St Alb* 91-94; C *Hmds.* 94-. *St Mary's Vicarage, Lansdowne Road, London N17 9XE* Tel (020) 8808 6644

MILLER, James Ivimey. b 33. Trin Hall Cam BA55 MA59. Ridley Hall Cam 56. **d** 61 **p** 62. C Beccles St Mich *St E* 61-63; C Blackpool St Jo *Blackb* 63-67; C Kirk Ella *York* 67-73; R Cockfield *St E* 73-78; rtd 78; Perm to Offic *St E* from 78. *3 Grosvenor Gardens, Bury St Edmunds IP33 2JS* Tel (01284) 762839

MILLER, John David. b 50. Nottm Univ BTh73 Lanc Univ GradCertEd74 Newc Univ MA93. Kelham Th Coll 68. **d** 74 **p** 75. C Horden *Dur* 74-79; C Billingham St Aid 79-80; TV 80-84; TR S Shields All SS from 84. *The Rectory, Tyne Terrace, South Shields NE34 0NF* Tel 0191-456 1851

MILLER, John Douglas. b 24. FCA60. N Ord Course 74. **d** 77 **p** 78. C Prestbury *Ches* 77-80; V Ashton Hayes 80-87; rtd 87; Perm to Offic *Ex* from 87. *35 Branscombe Close, Colyford, Colyton EX24 6RF* Tel (01297) 553581

MILLER, John Forster. b 32. Ss NSM Course. **d** 83 **p** 84. NSM Patcham *Chich* 83-86; NSM Radlett *St Alb* 86-93; Perm to Offic 93-00; Perm to Offic *Sarum* from 00. *Wedgwood, 29 Lansdowne Crescent, Derry Hill, Calne SN11 9NT* Tel (01249) 819252

MILLER, John Gareth. b 57. St Jo Coll Dur BA78. Ridley Hall Cam 79 Ven English Coll Rome 80. **d** 81 **p** 82. C Addiscombe St Mary *Cant* 81-84; TV Melbury *Sarum* 84-88; TR 88-91; V Leamington Priors All SS *Cov* 91-94. *Chelwood, Market Street, Charlbury, Chipping Norton OX7 3PL* Tel (01608) 811410

MILLER, John Selborne. b 32. RMN70 Lon Univ Dip Bibl Studies 68. S'wark Ord Course 64. **d** 71 **p** 72. C Kenton *Lon* 71-74; C Fulham St Etheldreda w St Clem 74-78; Asst at Convent of the Epiphany Truro 79-80; Hon C Pimlico St Sav 80-84; C Shirley *Birm* 84-86; rtd 86; Perm to Offic *Nor* 86-01. *28 Knight Street, Walsingham NR22 6DA* Tel (01328) 820824

MILLER, Kenneth Leslie. b 50. Lanc Univ BEd74 Liv Univ BPhil94 FRSA. N Ord Course 78. **d** 80 **p** 81. NSM Formby St Pet *Liv* 80-87; Chapl St Marg High Sch from 86; NSM Anfield St Columba from 87. *9 Hampton Road, Formby, Liverpool L37 6EJ* Tel (01704) 831256

MILLER, Kim Hurst. b 49. Ex Univ PhD89. Canberra Coll of Min BTh82 DipMin82. **d** 82 **p** 83. Australia 82-85 and from 89; C Goulburn Cathl 83-84; P-in-c Koorawatha 84-85; Perm to Offic *Ex* 85-89; R Wagga Wagga St Alb 89-98; Chapl Bathurst Gaol from 98. *3 Oates Place, Eglinton, NSW, Australia 2795* Tel (0061) (2) 6337 1841 or 6338 3282 E-mail kkmiller@globalfreeway.com.au

MILLER, Luke Jonathan. b 66. SS Coll Cam BA87 MA91. St Steph Ho Ox BA90. **d** 91 **p** 92. C Oxhey St Matt *St Alb* 91-94; C Tottenham St Mary *Lon* 94-95; V from 95. *St Mary's Vicarage, Lansdowne Road, London N17 9XE* Tel (020) 8808 6644

MILLER, Martin Michael. b 55. St Jo Coll Dur BSc78. Trin Coll Bris 94. **d** 96 **p** 97. C Leamington Priors St Paul *Cov* 96-99; C Bermondsey St Anne and St Aug *S'wark* from 99. *2 Thurland Road, London SE16 4AA* Tel (020) 7237 8741 E-mail martinmrev@aol.com

MILLER, Michael Daukes. b 46. MRCGP74 DRCOG Qu Coll Cam MA71 Lon Univ BCh70 MB71 DCH. Glouc Th Course 82. **d** 85 **p** 94. NSM Lydney w Aylburton *Glouc* 85-95; NSM Lydney from 95. *Highmead House, Blakeney GL15 4DY* Tel (01594) 516668

MILLER, Patrick Figgis. b 33. Ch Coll Cam BA56 MA60 Surrey Univ PhD95. Cuddesdon Coll 56. **d** 58 **p** 59. C Portsea St Cuth *Portsm* 58-61; C Cambridge Gt St Mary w St Mich *Ely* 61-63; Chapl SCM 61-63; Hd RS Man Gr Sch 63-69; Can Res and Lib S'wark Cathl *S'wark* 69-72; Dir of Soc Studies Qu Mary's Coll Basingstoke 72-79; Prin Sunbury Coll 79-80; Prin Esher Coll 81-98; Project Dir Learning for Living from 00; Perm to Offic *Guildf* from 01. *9 Fairfax Avenue, Epsom KT17 2QN* Tel (020) 8394 0593 Mobile 07740-503259 E-mail patrickmiller@ewell3.freeserve.co.uk

MILLER, Canon Paul. b 49. Oak Hill Th Coll 71. **d** 74 **p** 75. C Upton *Ex* 74-77; C Farnborough *Guildf* 77-78; P-in-c Torquay St Luke *Ex* 78-81; V 81-86; V Green Street Green *Roch* 86-94; V Green Street Green and Pratts Bottom 94-01; RD Orpington 96-01; Hon Can Roch Cathl from 00; V Shortlands from 01. *The Vicarage, 37 Kingswood Road, Bromley BR2 0HG* Tel (020) 8460 4989 Mobile 07940-582040 Fax (020) 8289 7577 E-mail pmiller@amserve.net

MILLER, Paul Richard. b 37. K Coll Lon BSc60 AKC60. Linc Th Coll 60. **d** 62 **p** 63. C Sheff St Geo *Sheff* 62-65; C Bottesford *Linc* 65-67; Bp's Youth Chapl 67-69; C Corringham 67-69; Dioc Youth Officer *Ripon* 69-74; Sec Nat Coun for Voluntary Youth Services 74-79; Hd Youth Nat Coun of Soc Services 74-79; P-in-c Battlesden and Pottesgrove *St Alb* 79-80; P-in-c Eversholt w Milton Bryan 79-80; P-in-c Woburn 79-80; V Woburn w Eversholt, Milton Bryan, Battlesden etc 80-98; rtd 98; Perm to Offic *Heref* from 98 and *Lich* from 03. *6 Elms Paddock, Little Stretton, Church Stretton SY6 6RD* Tel (01694) 724596 E-mail paulmiller@macunlimited.net

MILLER, Peter Tennant. b 21. Keble Coll Ox BA47 MA63. Ripon Hall Ox 62. **d** 63 **p** 64. C Wigmore w Hempstead *Roch* 63-68; V Worksop St Paul *S'well* 68-73; P-in-c Nottingham St Cath 74-75; C Nottingham St Mary 75-77; R Edith Weston w N Luffenham and Lyndon w Manton *Pet* 77-86; rtd 86; Perm to Offic *Cov* from 86. *Regency Cottage, 9 Cross Road, Leamington Spa CV32 5PD* Tel (01926) 314236

MILLER, Philip Harry. b 58. Leeds Univ BA79. Chich Th Coll 80. **d** 82 **p** 83. C Reddish *Man* 82-86; R Lower Broughton Ascension 86-94; P-in-c Cheetwood *St Alb* 91-94; P-in-c Langley and Parkfield 95-00; TR from 00. *The Rectory, Wood Street, Middleton, Manchester M24 5GL* Tel 0161-643 5013

MILLER, Philip Howard. b 40. Tyndale Hall Bris 67. **d** 72 **p** 73. Argentina 72-73; C Rusholme H Trin *Man* 73-74; Paraguay 74-77; C Toxteth St Cypr w Ch Ch *Liv* 78-80; V Burscough Bridge 80-85; V Woodbridge St Jo *St E* 85-91; P-in-c Combs 91-92 and 93-96; Chapl Burrswood Cen for Divine Healing 92-93; V Yoxford and Peasenhall w Sibton *St E* 96-01; rtd 01. *Salta, 54 Orchard Close, Melton, Woodbridge IP12 1LD* Tel (01394) 388615 E-mail phm914@lineone.net

MILLER, Richard Bracebridge. b 45. Wycliffe Hall Ox 68. **d** 70 **p** 71. C Lee Gd Shep w St Pet *S'wark* 70-74; C Roehampton H Trin 74-77; C Earley St Pet *Ox* 77-80; V Aldermaston w Wasing and Brimpton 80-96; C Newbury 96-01; Perm to Offic from 03. *14 Burcot Park, Burcot, Abingdon OX14 3DH* Tel (01865) 407521 E-mail rbmoxford@breathe.com

MILLER, Robert Stephen. b 71. QUB BSc92. CITC BTh95. **d** 95 **p** 96. C Lurgan Ch the Redeemer *D & D* 95-99; I Tullylish from 99. *Tullyish Rectory, 100 Banbridge Road, Gilford, Craigavon BT63 6DL* Tel (028) 3883 1298 Fax as telephone E-mail tullylish@dromore.anglican.org *or* robsmiller@aol.com

MILLER, Ronald Andrew John. b 46. LNSM course 96. **d** 96 **p** 97. OLM Heywood *Man* from 96. *153 Rochdale Road East, Heywood OL10 1QU* Tel (01706) 624326 Fax as telephone E-mail andrew.miller1@virgin.net

MILLER, Ronald Anthony Tony. b 41. CEng CPA MRAeS City Univ BSc63. S'wark Ord Course 69. **d** 72 **p** 80. NSM Crookham *Guildf* 72-73 and 80-85; NSM New Haw 85-95; NSM Effingham w Lt Bookham from 95. *Glen Anton, Horsley Road, Downside, Cobham KT11 3JZ* Tel (01932) 863394 Fax (01980) 613529 E-mail glenantont@cs.com

MILLER, Rosamund Joy. See SEAL, Mrs Rosamund Joy

MILLER, Mrs Rosslyn Leslie. b 43. St Andr Univ MA65 Ox Univ DipEd66 Cam Univ DipRK69. **dss** 72 **d** 87. Dir of Studies Inst of Chr Studies 72; St Marylebone All SS *Lon* 72; Adult Educn Officer 73-78; Alford w Rigsby *Linc* 86-87; C 87-90; Dioc Dir of Readers 90-03; rtd 03. *120A Station Road, Waddington, Lincoln LN5 9QS* Tel (01522) 720819 Fax 721620 E-mail rosslyn.miller@aol.com

MILLER, Roy. b 29. **d** 88 **p** 93. NSM Leic Cathl *Leic* 88-91; NSM Leic H Apostles 91-97; Perm to Offic 97-99. *5 Bratmyr, Fleckney, Leicester LE8 8BJ* Tel 0116-240 2004

MILLER, Miss Sarah Lydia. b 65. St Andr Univ BD90 Hughes Hall Cam PGCE91. EAMTC 98. **d** 01. Miss Adv USPG *Ely, Chelmsf, Nor* and *St E* 00-03; NSM Nor St Pet Mancroft w St Jo Maddermarket *Nor* 01-03; C Wythenshawe *Man* from 03. *St Luke's House, Brownley Road, Manchester M22 4PT* Tel 0161-945 7399

MILLER, Stephen Michael. b 63. NE Lon Poly BSc86 Nottm Univ BTh91. Linc Th Coll 88. **d** 91 **p** 92. C Dudley St Fran *Worc* 91-94; V Sedgley St Mary 94-99; Miss to Seafarers from 99; Chapl Rotterdam w Schiedam Miss to Seafarers *Eur* 99-03. *Ghijseland 146, 3161 VI Rhoon, The Netherlands* E-mail vichill@aol.com

MILLER, Stuart William. b 71. Univ of Wales (Cardiff) BA92. Trin Coll Bris BA97. **d** 97 **p** 98. C Fordingbridge *Win* 97-98; C Bursledon 98-02; V W Moors *Sarum* from 02; Asst Educn Officer (Sherborne Episc Area) from 03. *The Vicarage, 57 Glenwood Road, West Moors, Wimborne BH22 0EN* Tel (01202) 893197 E-mail stu@fish.co.uk

MILLER, William David. b 45. Man Univ BA66. Linc Th Coll 69. **d** 71 **p** 72. C Newc St Geo *Newc* 71-74; C Corbridge w Halton 74-77; C N Gosforth 77-81; TV Whorlton 81-90; Chapl K Sch Tynemouth from 90. *7 Strawberry Terrace, Hazelrigg, Newcastle upon Tyne NE13 7AR* Tel 0191-236 5024 *or* 258 5995

MILLETT, Maxwell Roy (Max). b 45. Clare Coll Cam BA67. S Dios Minl Tr Scheme 92. **d** 95 **p** 96. NSM Southsea St Pet *Portsm* from 95. *32 Belmont Street, Southsea PO5 1ND* Tel (023) 9281 7216

MILLETT, William Hugh. b 21. AKC49. **d** 50 **p** 51. C Barbourne *Worc* 50-53; V Catshill 53-58; R Richard's Castle *Heref* 58-78; P-in-c Stoke Lacy, Moreton Jeffries w Much Cowarne etc 78-82; Perm to Offic *Worc* from 83; rtd 86; Perm to Offic *Heref* from 93. *18 Shirley Close, Malvern WR14 2NH* Tel (01684) 567056

MILLGATE, Victor Frederick. b 44. St Mich Coll Llan 81. **d** 83 **p** 84. C Pembroke St Mary w St Mich *St D* 83-85; V Manorbier and St Florence w Redberth from 85; AD Castlemartin from 03. *The Vicarage, Manorbier, Tenby SA70 7TN* Tel (01834) 871617 E-mail ed@edmill.force9.co.uk

MILLICHAMP, Mrs Penelope Mary. b 39. CertEd60. WMMTC 82. **dss** 85 **d** 87 **p** 94. Wednesfield *Lich* 85-94; Par Dn 87-90; TD 90-94; Perm to Offic 94-95; NSM Wrockwardine Deanery 95-99; rtd 99; Perm to Offic *Lich* 99-00. *3 Mathon Lodge, 16 Stockwell Road, Wolverhampton WV6 9PQ* Tel (01902) 741996 Mobile 07971-421562 E-mail penny@millichamp.com

MILLIER, Gordon. b 28. St Aid Birkenhead 63. **d** 65 **p** 66. C Congresbury *B & W* 65-69; P-in-c Badgworth w Biddisham 69-76; R Weare w Badgworth and Biddisham 76-84; R Pilton w Croscombe, N Wootton and Dinder 84-93; rtd 93; Perm to Offic *Ex* from 93. *28 Withy Close, Canal Hill, Tiverton EX16 4HZ* Tel (01884) 253128

MILLIGAN, Peter John. **d** 01 **p** 02. NSM Putney St Marg *S'wark* from 01. *39 Stapleton Road, London SW17 8BA* Tel (020) 8767 3497

MILLIGAN, Canon William John (Barney). b 28. OBE95. Em Coll Cam BA49. Cuddesdon Coll 53. **d** 55 **p** 56. C Portsea N End St Mark *Portsm* 55-62; V New Eltham All SS *S'wark* 62-71; V Roehampton H Trin 71-79; Can Res St Alb 79-86; Chapl Strasbourg *Eur* 86-95; Angl Rep Eur Insts 90-95; rtd 95; Perm to Offic *S'wark* from 98. *3 East Street, Beaminster DT8 3DS* Tel (01308) 862806

MILLINER, Llewelyn Douglas. b 14. Univ of Wales BSc35. **d** 38 **p** 39. C Aberdare St Fagan *Llan* 38-41; C Wellingborough St Mary *Pet* 41-43; CF 43-63; Asst Master K Sch Worc 63-66; C-in-c Chelmsf St Luke CD *Chelmsf* 66-69; Dep Hd Master Widford Lodge Sch Chelmsf 69-80; Perm to Offic *Chelmsf* 69-80; rtd 80; Perm to Offic *Ex* from 80. *Fordings, Weare Giffard, Bideford EX39 4QS* Tel (01237) 473729

MILLING, David Horace. b 29. Oriel Coll Ox BA51 MA54 Cam Univ PhD73. Cuddesdon Coll 54. **d** 56 **p** 57. C Bris St Mary Redcliffe w Temple *Bris* 56-59; C Fishponds St Jo 59-62; India 62-69; Lect St D Coll Lamp 73-75; C Caversham *Ox* 77-81; C Mapledurham 77-81; C Caversham St Andr 81-86; TV Upper Kennet *Sarum* 86-88; rtd 88; Perm to Offic *Glouc* 90-99; Perm to Offic *Ex* from 00. *14 Matford Mews, Matford, Alphington, Exeter EX2 8XP* Tel (01392) 219718

MILLINGTON, Robert William Ernest. b 51. Sheff Univ BA73 St Jo Coll Dur DipTh75. **d** 76 **p** 77. C Ormskirk *Liv* 76-79; C Litherland St Paul Hatton Hill 79-81; V Bootle Ch Ch 81-88; Chapl K Edw Sch Witley from 88. *Queen's House, 3 Gurdon's Lane, Wormley, Godalming GU8 5TF* Tel (01428) 684298

MILLINGTON, Stuart. b 45. Lich Th Coll 67. **d** 70 **p** 71. C Boulton *Derby* 70-73; C Moseley St Mary *Birm* 73-76; TV Staveley and Barrow Hill *Derby* 76-82; R Wingerworth 82-99; RD Chesterfield 91-97; P-in-c Elton All SS *Man* from 99. *All Saints' Vicarage, 10 Kirkburn View, Bury BL8 1DL* Tel 0161-797 1595

MILLS, Alan Francis. b 29. Ch Coll Cam BA52 MA91. Linc Th Coll 52. **d** 54 **p** 55. C Hucknall Torkard *S'well* 54-58; C Bath Bathwick St Jo *B & W* 58-70; V Drayton 70-76; V Muchelney 70-76; V Alcombe 76-99; rtd 99; Perm to Offic *B & W* from 00. *194 Locking Road, Weston-super-Mare BS23 3LU* Tel (01934) 622679

MILLS, Alexandra. b 56. Univ of Wales (Abth) BMus78 CertEd79. Ripon Coll Cuddesdon 88. **d** 90 **p** 94. Par Dn Earlsfield St Andr *S'wark* 90-94; C Kingston All SS w St Jo 94-99; C Brixton Road Ch Ch 99-00. *Address temp unknown*

MILLS, Anthony James. b 55. Nottm Univ BA. Linc Th Coll. **d** 84 **p** 85. C Mexborough *Sheff* 84-86; C Howden *York* 86-89; V Fylingdales and Hawsker cum Stainsacre 89-95; V Scarborough St Sav w All SS from 95; P-in-c Scarborough St Martin from 02. *St Martin's Vicarage, Craven Street, Scarborough YO11 2BY* Tel (01723) 360437

MILLS, David Bryn. b 49. Ox NSM Course. **d** 83 **p** 84. NSM Stantonbury *Ox* 83-87; NSM Deanery of Milton Keynes 87-00; NSM Brampton and Farlam and Castle Carrock w Cumrew *Carl* 00-02; NSM Eden, Gelt and Irthing from 02. *The Barn, Far Long Park, Scaleby, Carlisle CA6 4JP*

MILLS, David Francis. b 51. DipHE78. Oak Hill Th Coll 76. **d** 79 **p** 80. C Rodbourne Cheney *Bris* 79-82; C Wolverhampton

St Matt *Lich* 82-85; CF 85-88; TV Braunstone *Leic* 88-95; Past Asst to Adn Leic 95-97; C Barkestone w Plungar, Redmile and Stathern 97-99; C Bottesford and Muston 97-99; C Harby, Long Clawson and Hose 97-99; C Vale of Belvoir Par 00-02; R Winfarthing w Shelfanger w Burston w Gissing etc *Nor* from 02. *The Rectory, Church Lane, Winfarthing, Diss IP22 2EA* Tel (01379) 642543 E-mail dmills@leicester.anglican.org

MILLS, Canon Geoffrey Charles Malcolm. b 33. Wycliffe Hall Ox 59. **d** 61 **p** 62. C Buckhurst Hill *Chelmsf* 61-65; C Ecclesall *Sheff* 65-69; V Endcliffe 69-78; R Whiston 78-99; Hon Can Sheff Cathl 96-99; rtd 99; Perm to Offic *Sheff* from 99. *8 Hall Road, Rotherham S60 2BP* Tel (01709) 373863

MILLS, Miss Glenys Christine. b 38. Open Univ BA81. Dalton Ho Bris DipTh64. **d** 87 **p** 94. Par Dn Clifton Ch Ch w Em *Bris* 87-94; C 94-95; P-in-c Gt w Lt Abington *Ely* 95-00; Chapl Arthur Rank Hospice Cam 95-00; Perm to Offic *Bris* from 00. *14 St Bartholemew's Close, Ashley Down, Bristol BS7 9BJ* Tel 0117-909 8859

MILLS, Gordon Derek. b 35. Lich Th Coll 60. **d** 63 **p** 64. C W Derby St Mary *Liv* 63-65; C Clifton w Glapton *S'well* 65-67; V N Wilford St Faith 67-72; V Farnsfield 72-82; P-in-c Kirklington w Hockerton 77-82; Asst Dir of Educn *Blackb* 82-86; P-in-c Brindle 82-86; V Gt Budworth *Ches* 86-88; P-in-c Antrobus 87-88; V Gt Budworth and Antrobus 88-92; V Budworth 92-00; rtd 00; Perm to Offic *Blackb* from 01. *The Reader's House, Slaidburn Road, Waddington, Clitheroe BB7 3JQ* Tel (01200) 422348

MILLS, Canon Hubert Cecil. b 44. TCD BA66 MA71 HDipEd73. CITC 67. **d** 67 **p** 68. C Dublin Rathfarnham *D & G* 67-72; Min Can St Patr Cathl Dublin 69-92; Succ 77-92; Preb Rathmichael St Patr Cathl Dublin 92-02; Treas from 02; C Dublin St Steph and St Ann *D & G* 72-77; I Holmpatrick w Balbriggan and Kenure 77-86; I Killiney H Trin from 86. *Holy Trinity Rectory, Killiney Road, Killiney, Co Dublin, Irish Republic* Tel (00353) (1) 285 2695 Fax 235 4811 E-mail revcecilmills@club.ie

MILLS, Ian Anderson. b 35. Coll of Resurr Mirfield 60 K Coll Lon AKC65. **d** 65 **p** 70. C S'wark St Alphege *S'wark* 65-67; C Hartlepool St Paul *Dur* 69-72; NSM Hartlepool St Hilda 90-95; Perm to Offic from 95. *7 Claypool Farm Close, Hutton Henry, Hartlepool TS27 4QZ* Tel (01429) 836204

MILLS, Jack Herbert. b 14. Selw Coll Cam BA38 MA42. Cuddesdon Coll 39. **d** 40 **p** 41. C Camberwell St Geo *S'wark* 40-42; C Southfields St Barn 42-46; USPG 46-47; Chapl Hurstpierpoint Coll 47-52; New Zealand 52-56, 59-61 and from 87; Australia 57-59 and 62-73; Hd Master St Wilfrid's Sch Ex 74-79; Chapl Community of St Wilfrid 74-79; Hon C Ewhurst *Chich* 79-81; Hon C Bodiam 79-81; Perm to Offic *Ex* 81-85; Perm to Offic *Chich* 85-87; rtd 87. *3 St Chad's Square, Selwyn Village, Point Chevalier, Auckland 2, New Zealand* Tel (0064) (9) 849 2243

MILLS, Jennifer Clare. See TOMLINSON, Mrs Jennifer Clare

MILLS, John Kettlewell. b 53. BA. Cranmer Hall Dur. **d** 84 **p** 85. C Ashton-upon-Mersey St Mary *Ches* 84-87; TV Didsbury St Jas and Em *Man* 87-98; V Styvechale *Cov* from 98. *Styvechale Vicarage, 16 Armorial Road, Coventry CV3 6GJ* Tel (024) 7641 6074 *or* 7669 2299 E-mail jkm@stivichall.freeserve.co.uk

MILLS, Leslie. b 17. Open Univ BSc94 Reading Univ MA95. Wycliffe Hall Ox 68. **d** 68 **p** 69. C Basingstoke *Win* 68-77; C Basing 78-80; C York Town St Mich *Guildf* 80-84; rtd 84; Perm to Offic *Win* from 84; Perm to Offic *Guildf* from 85; Perm to Offic *Ox* from 86. *21 Mill Lane, Yateley GU46 7TE* Tel (01252) 870689

MILLS, Mrs Leslie Anne. b 44. K Alfred's Coll Win CertEd65. SW Minl Tr Course 99. **d** 02 **p** 03. NSM Kilmington, Stockland, Dalwood, Yarcombe etc *Ex* from 02. *Gorse Bungalow, Cotleigh, Honiton EX14 9JB* Tel (01404) 861430 E-mail anne@stockland.cx

MILLS, Michael Henry. b 51. AKC73. St Aug Coll Cant. **d** 74 **p** 75. C Newton Aycliffe *Dur* 74-78; C Padgate *Liv* 78-79; TV 79-95; V Frodsham *Ches* from 95. *The Vicarage, Vicarage Lane, Frodsham, Warrington WA6 7DU* Tel (01928) 733378 E-mail michael.mills3@virgin.net

MILLS, Michael John. b 52. St Andr Univ BSc75 Cam Univ PGCE76. Cranmer Hall Dur 97. **d** 99 **p** 00. C Brockmoor *Worc* 99-03. *Address temp unknown* E-mail michael.mills1@ntlworld.com

MILLS, Michael Shane. b 68. Nashotah Ho Wisconsin MDiv. **d** 95 **p** 96. C Dallas Incarnation USA 95-98 and from 00; NSM Pelton *Dur* 98-99. *6006 Penrose Avenue, Dallas, TX 75206, USA* E-mail father.michael.mills@worldnet.att.net

MILLS, Mrs Anne. See MILLS, Mrs Leslie Anne

MILLS, Pamela Ann. b 44. Southn Univ DAES82. S Tr Scheme 94. **d** 97 **p** 98. NSM Hurstbourne Tarrant, Faccombe, Vernham Dean etc *Win* from 97. *Sunnyside, The Dene, Hurstbourne Tarrant, Andover SP11 0AS* Tel (01264) 736286

MILLS, Peter James. b 32. Univ Coll Lon LLB58. **d** 99 **p** 00. NSM Woodchurch *Ches* from 99. *6 West Heath Court, Gerard Road, West Kirby, Wirral CH48 4ES* Tel and fax 0151-625 3314 Mobile 07989-374499

MILLS, Peter John. b 52. Sarum & Wells Th Coll 87. **d** 89 **p** 90. C Chatham St Wm *Roch* 89-92; V Perry Street 92-95; V E Malling

95-00; CF from 00. *c/o MOD Chaplains (Army)* Tel (01980) 615804 Fax 615800

MILLS, Roger Conrad. b 58. Selw Coll Cam BA79 MA83. St Jo Coll Nottm DPS85. **d** 85 **p** 86. C Jesmond H Trin *Newc* 85-88; C Alnwick 88-91; Chapl Newc Univ 91-00; P-in-c Newc St Barn and St Jude 95-97; V Kingston Park from 00. *12 Shannon Court, Newcastle upon Tyne NE3 2XF* Tel 0191-286 4050 Fax as telephone E-mail rogermills123@yahoo.co.uk

MILLS, Timothy John. b 57. Wye Coll Lon BSc79. Trin Coll Bris 01. **d** 03. C Chislehurst Ch Ch *Roch* from 03. *56 Walden Road, Chislehurst BR7 5JX* Tel (020) 8467 6669 Mobile 07786-540819 E-mail hoppy@tmills33.fsnet.co.uk

MILLS-POWELL, Mark Oliver McLay. b 55. Edin Th Sem Virginia. **d** 83 **p** 84. C Huyton St Mich *Liv* 83-86; USA 86-95; P-in-c Basildon w Aldworth and Ashampstead *Ox* 95-02; TR Linton *Ely* from 02. *The Vicarage, Church Lane, Linton, Cambridge CB1 6JX* Tel (01223) 891251

MILLSON, Brian Douglas. b 53. Univ of W Ontario BA76 Huron Coll MDiv84. Westcott Ho Cam 82. **d** 83 **p** 84. C Walton-on-Thames *Guildf* 83-86; Canada 86-98; R Par of the Six Nations 86-89; Canadian Forces Chapl 89-98; CF from 98. *c/o MOD Chaplains (Army)* Tel (01980) 615804 Fax 615800 E-mail brian.millson@btinternet.com

MILLSON, Mrs Margaret Lily. b 41. CertEd61. EMMTC 83. **dss** 86 **d** 87 **p** 94. NSM Bottesford w Ashby *Linc* 86-01; P-in-c St Tudy w St Mabyn and Michaelstow *Truro* from 01. *The Rectory, Glebe Parc, St Tudy, Bodmin PL30 3AS* Tel (01208) 851691 Fax as telephone E-mail mlmillson@aol.com

MILLWARD, Mark Anthony. b 61. Leeds Poly BSc RGN83 Newc Univ MA93 New Coll Dur PGCE99. St Steph Ho Ox 83. **d** 86 **p** 87. C Sunderland Red Ho *Dur* 86-89; C Leic Ch Sav *Leic* 89-90; V Sunderland Pennywell St Thos *Dur* 90-96; Chapl City Hosps Sunderland NHS Trust from 96. *The Chaplain's Office, Sunderland Royal Hospital, Kayll Road, Sunderland SR4 7TP* Tel 0191-569 9180 or 565 6256 ext 42538

MILLWARD, Miss Pauline Freda. b 50. AMA74. N Ord Course 89. **d** 92 **p** 94. NSM Warley *Wakef* 92-95; P-in-c Halifax St Hilda from 95; Missr for Halifax Town Cen from 95. *8 Hill Park Mount, Sowerby Bridge HX6 3JB* Tel (01422) 823576 Pager 07666-750242 Fax 354448

MILLWOOD, Stephen Grant. b 44. Sheff Tech Coll HNC66 Sheff City Coll of Educn CertEd77 Open Univ BA92. St Jo Coll Nottm Dip Th & Min 92. **d** 94 **p** 95. C Anston *Sheff* 94-98; V Kimberworth Park from 98. *The Vicarage, 21 Birks Road, Rotherham S61 3JX* Tel (01709) 552268 E-mail restegram@lineone.net

MILLYARD, Alexander John. b 29. St Jo Coll Dur BA53. Qu Coll Birm 53. **d** 54 **p** 55. C Middlesbrough St Aid *York* 54-56; C Pocklington w Yapham-cum-Meltonby, Owsthorpe etc 56-58; C Millington w Gt Givendale 56-58; C Rickmansworth *St Alb* 58-61; R Wormley 61-65; Asst Chapl HM Pris Pentonville 65-67; Chapl HM Pris Leeds 67-69; Chapl HM Pris Ex 69-71; Chapl HM Pris Wandsworth 72-73; V Snibston *Leic* 73-75; V Leic All So 75-79; V Blakesley and Adstone *Pet* 79-89; R Blakesley w Adstone and Maidford etc 89-91; rtd 91; Perm to Offic *Chich* from 91. *6 Gainsborough House, Eaton Gardens, Hove BN3 3UA* Tel (01273) 728722

✠**MILMINE, The Rt Revd Douglas.** b 21. CBE83. St Pet Hall Ox BA46 MA46. Clifton Th Coll 47. **d** 47 **p** 48 **c** 73. C Ilfracombe SS Phil and Jas *Ex* 47-50; C Slough *Ox* 50-53; Chile 54-69; Adn N Chile, Bolivia and Peru 63-69; Hon Can Chile from 69; Area Sec SAMS 69-72; Bp Paraguay 73-85; rtd 86. *1C Clive Court, 24 Grand Parade, Eastbourne BN21 3DD* Tel (01323) 734159

MILMINE, Canon Neil Edward Douglas. b 46. Kent Univ BSc70. Wycliffe Hall Ox 80. **d** 82 **p** 83. C Hailsham *Chich* 82-86; C Horsham 86; TV 86-93; V Patcham from 93; Can and Preb Chich Cathl from 00; RD Brighton from 03. *The Vicarage, 12 Church Hill, Brighton BN1 8YE* Tel (01273) 552157 E-mail neil@milmine.freeserve.co.uk

MILNE, Alan. b 54. RMN SRN FE TCert. Cranmer Hall Dur 89. **d** 91 **p** 92. C Hartlepool St Luke *Dur* 91-94; P-in-c Dalton le Dale 94-00; V from 00; P-in-c Hawthorn 94-00; R from 00; AD Easington from 03. *The Vicarage, Church Lane, Murton, Seaham SR7 9RD* Tel 0191-526 2410

MILNE, Miss Christine Helen. b 48. LTCL71 Lon Univ DipRS86. S'wark Ord Course 83. **dss** 86 **d** 87 **p** 90. S Lambeth St Steph *S'wark* 86-89; Par Dn 87-89; New Zealand from 89. *NGA Tawa School, Private Bag 1101, Marton, New Zealand* Tel (0064) (6) 327 7955 *or* 327 6429 Fax 327 7954

MILNE, Glenn Alexander Roscoe. b 62. Oriel Coll Ox BA85 MA89. Westcott Ho Cam 87. **d** 89 **p** 90. C Hexham *Newc* 89-92; CF 92-95; I Castlepollard and Oldcastle w Loughcrew etc *M & K* from 95; OGS from 01. *St Michael's Rectory, Castlepollard, Mullingar, Co Westmeath, Irish Republic* Tel (00353) (44) 61123 Fax as telephone

MILNE, James Harley. b 73. Univ of Wales (Lamp) BD94 New Coll Edin MTh96. TISEC 95. **d** 98 **p** 99. C Dundee St Mary Magd *Bre* 98-01; Chapl St Marg Res Home Dundee 98-01; R

Dundee St Marg from 01. *St Margaret's Rectory, 19 Ancrum Road, Dundee DD2 2JL* Tel (01382) 667227

MILNER, Ms Catherine Mary (Kitty). b 56. OLM course 96. **d** 99 **p** 00. OLM Uttoxeter Area *Lich* from 99. *Glebe Cottage, Church Lane, Checkley, Stoke-on-Trent ST10 4NJ* Tel (01538) 723681 Fax 723380 E-mail revkit@kitty21.fsnet.co.uk

MILNER, Darryl Vickers. b 43. Natal Univ BA63 DipTh66. St Chad's Coll Dur 64. **d** 66 **p** 67. C Oswestry H Trin *Lich* 66-69; S Africa 69-76; New Zealand from 76. *The Vicarage, 47 Church Street, Northcote, North Shore 1309, New Zealand* Tel (0064) (9) 480 7568 Fax 419 7459 E-mail dvmilner@clear.net.nz

MILNER, David. b 38. St Aid Birkenhead 63. **d** 66 **p** 67. C Ulverston H Trin *Carl* 66-68; C Mickleover All SS *Derby* 68-71; C Mickleover St Jo 68-71; V 71-82; P-in-c Sandiacre 82-86; P-in-c Doveridge 86-97; RD Longford 86-96 and from 01; P-in-c Sudbury and Somersal Herbert 92-97; R Doveridge, Scropton, Sudbury etc from 98. *The Vicarage, Church Lane, Doveridge, Ashbourne DE6 5NN* Tel (01889) 563420

MILNER, Leslie. b 35. MBE93. Birm Univ BSc57 St Jo Coll Cam BA59. Wells Th Coll 61. **d** 63 **p** 64. C Yardley St Edburgha *Birm* 63-66; C Seacroft *Ripon* 66-71; Dir St Basil's Cen Deritend 71-00; Lic to Offic *Birm* 71-86; Perm to Offic 86-00; rtd 00. *Torride House, 29 St John's Road, Turnchapel, Plymouth PL9 9ST* Tel (01752) 492553 E-mail milner29@tinyworld.co.uk

✠**MILNER, The Rt Revd Ronald James.** b 27. Pemb Coll Cam BA49 MA52. Wycliffe Hall Ox 51. **d** 53 **p** 54 **c** 88. Succ Sheff Cathl *Sheff* 53-58; V Westwood *Cov* 58-64; V Fletchamstead 64-70; R Southampton St Mary w H Trin *Win* 70-72; P-in-c Southampton St Matt 70-72; Lic to Offic 72-73; TR Southampton (City Cen) 73-83; Hon Can Win Cathl 75-83; Adn Linc 83-88; Can and Preb Linc Cathl 83-88; Suff Bp Burnley *Blackb* 88-93; rtd 93; Asst Bp S'well from 94. *7 Crafts Way, Southwell NG25 0BL* Tel (01636) 816256

MILNER, William David. b 52. St Jo Coll Nottm DCM93. **d** 93 **p** 94. C Wollaton *S'well* 93-97; P-in-c Daybrook 97; C W Bridgford 98-99; TV Clifton from 99. *St Mary's House, 58 Village Road, Clifton, Nottingham NG11 8NE* Tel 0115-921 1856

MILNES, David Ian. b 45. Chich Th Coll 74. **d** 76 **p** 77. C Walthamstow St Sav *Chelmsf* 76-80; C Chingford SS Pet and Paul 80-83; P-in-c Gt Ilford St Alb 83-87; V from 87. *The Vicarage, 99 Albert Road, Ilford IG1 1HS* Tel (020) 8478 2428 E-mail frmilnes@aol.com

MILROY, Mrs Ethel Doreen. b 33. Bedf Coll Lon BSc54 Bris Univ PGCE92 Nottm Univ MEd79. N Ord Course 88. **d** 91 **p** 94. NSM Tideswell *Derby* 91-95; P-in-c Rowsley 95-02; rtd 02; Perm to Offic *Derby* from 02. *40 Eccles Close, Hope Valley S33 6RG* Tel (01433) 623582

MILTON, Andrew John. b 54. BD. St Steph Ho Ox. **d** 83 **p** 84. C Highfield *Ox* 83-87; TV Banbury 87-95; P-in-c Thorney Abbey *Ely* 95-02; TR Huntingdon from 02. *The Rectory, 1 The Walks East, Huntingdon PE29 3AP* Tel (01480) 412674 E-mail miltons@walkseast.fsnet.co.uk

MILTON, Miss Angela Daphne. b 50. FILEx79. Oak Hill Th Coll 84. **d** 92 **p** 94. NSM Watford *St Alb* 87-95; NSM St Alb St Mary Marshalswick 95-97; C Stevenage St Mary Sheppall w Aston 97-02; P-in-c E Molesey St Paul *Guildf* from 02. *St Paul's Vicarage, 101 Palace Road, East Molesey KT8 9DU* Tel (020) 8979 1580 E-mail angelamilton@msn.com

MILTON, Claudius James Barton. b 29. K Coll Lon BD52 AKC53. **d** 53 **p** 54. C Sudbury St Andr *Lon* 53-56; Asst Chapl Bedford Sch 57-65; Asst Master 57-65; Chapl Cranbrook Sch Kent 65-74; Asst Master and Housemaster 65-74; Chapl & Asst Master Clayesmore Sch Blandford 74-89; Clayesmore Prep Sch 74-89; rtd 89. *28 Oakwood Drive, Iwerne Minster, Blandford Forum DT11 8QT* Tel (01747) 811751

MILTON, Derek Rees. b 45. Open Univ BA76 Lon Univ BD80 Ex Univ MA95 Bris Univ CertEd81. St Jo Sem Wonersh 63. **d** 69 **p** 69. In RC Ch 68-84; Hon C Luton Lewsey St Hugh *St Alb* 84-85; Hon C Houghton Regis 85-86; C 86-89; TV Brixham w Churston Ferrers and Kingswear *Ex* 89-99; V Newport St Teilo *Mon* 99-02; C Chepstow from 02. *St Christopher's House, Bulwark Road, Bulwark, Chepstow NP16 5JW* Tel (01291) 622848

MILTON-THOMPSON, David Gerald. b 17. OBE76. Em Coll Cam BA39 MA MB BChir49 MRCS LRCP42. Lon Coll of Div 62. **d** 63 **p** 64. CMS 49-81 and 85-88; Kenya 52-81; C Chadwell *Chelmsf* 81-82; Hon C 82-85; Uganda 85-88; rtd 88; Hon C Sevenoaks St Nic *Roch* from 88. *Room 26, Rockdale House, Rockdale Road, Sevenoaks TN13 1JT* Tel (01732) 462977

MILTON-THOMPSON, Jonathan Patrick. b 51. Nottm Univ BA76. Oak Hill Th Coll 86. **d** 88 **p** 89. C Bispham *Blackb* 88-92; C Darfield *Sheff* 92; C-in-c Gt Houghton CD from 92. *16 High Street, Great Houghton, Barnsley S72 0AB* Tel (01226) 752320

MILVERTON, The Revd and Rt Hon Lord (Fraser Arthur Richard Richards). b 30. Bps' Coll Cheshunt. **d** 57 **p** 58. C Beckenham St Geo *Roch* 57-59; C Sevenoaks St Jo 59-60; C Gt Bookham *Guildf* 60-63; V Okewood 63-67; R Christian Malford w Sutton Benger etc *Bris* 73-93; Public Preacher 93-95; rtd 95;

Perm to Offic *Sarum* from 96. *7 Betjeman Road, Marlborough SN8 1TL* Tel (01672) 86568

MILVERTON, Frederic Jack. b 15. Lon Univ BSc37 Leeds Univ MEd40. Ripon Hall Ox 56. **d** 57 **p** 58. C Ecclesall *Sheff* 57-60; V Thurcroft 60-61; Lect Nottm Coll of Educn 61-67; Lect Weymouth Coll of Educn 67-76; Hd of Educn 70-76; Dean Educn Dorset Inst of HE 76-79; TV Oakdale St Geo *Sarum* 79-82; rtd 82; Perm to Offic *Sarum* from 82. *Flat 4, Compass South, Rodwell Road, Weymouth DT4 8QT* Tel (01305) 788930 E-mail rev.milv.compass@care4free.net

MILVERTON, Mrs Ruth Erica. b 32. Open Univ BA78 Southn Univ MA82. Sarum Th Coll 83. **dss** 86 **d** 87 **p** 95. Weymouth H Trin *Sarum* 86-87; Hon Par Dn 87-95; NSM 95-02; Dioc NSM Officer 89-97; rtd 02; Perm to Offic *Sarum* from 02. *Flat 4, Compass South, Rodwell Road, Weymouth DT4 8QT* Tel (01305) 788930 E-mail rev.milv.compass@care4free.net

MILWARD, Terence George. b 23. Ripon Hall Ox 66. **d** 68 **p** 69. C Selly Oak St Mary *Birm* 68-70; C Edgbaston St Bart 70-75; TV Bournemouth St Pet w St Swithun, H Trin etc *Win* 75-81; R Smannell w Enham Alamein 81-88; rtd 88; Perm to Offic *Guildf* from 88. *Church House Flat, Church Lane, Witley, Godalming GU8 5PN* Tel (01428) 685308

MILWAUKEE, Bishop of. *See* WHITE, The Rt Revd Roger John

MINALL, Peter. b 26. Lon Univ BSc47. Bps' Coll Cheshunt 51. **d** 53 **p** 54. C Bishop's Stortford St Mich *St Alb* 53-57; C Luton w E Hyde 57-63; C Tuffley *Glouc* 63-65; Asst Youth Chapl 65-69; V Stroud 69-84; RD Bisley 78-84; P-in-c Barnwood 84-91; rtd 91; Lic to Offic *Glouc* from 91; Chapl Coney Hill Hosp Glouc 86-95. *Amberwood, Knapp Lane, Painswick, Stroud GL6 6YE* Tel (01452) 813730 E-mail therev@pminall.freeserve.co.uk

MINAY, Francis Arthur Rodney. b 44. Edin Coll of Art BA65. Westcott Ho Cam 66. **d** 68 **p** 69. C Edenbridge *Roch* 68-73; C Bromley St Mark 73-75; V Tudeley w Capel 75-79; TV Littleham w Exmouth *Ex* 79-82; P-in-c Bolton Percy *York* from 82; Asst Chapl to Arts and Recreation in the NE from 82. *The Rectory, Bolton Percy, York YO23 7AL* Tel (01904) 744213

MINCHER, John Derek Bernard. b 31. **d** 60 **p** 61. OSB 54-80; Lic to Offic *Ox* 60-80; Perm to Offic *St E* 81-87; C Halesworth w Linstead, Chediston, Holton etc 87-90; P-in-c Worlingworth, Southolt, Tannington, Bedfield etc 90-91; R 91-96; rtd 96; Perm to Offic *St E* from 96. *3 Bracken Row, Thurston, Bury St Edmunds IP31 3AT* Tel (01359) 231976

MINCHEW, Donald Patrick. b 48. Univ of Wales (Cardiff) BD76. St Mich Coll Llan 74. **d** 76 **p** 77. C Glouc St Aldate *Glouc* 76-80; P-in-c Sharpness CD 80-81; V Sharpness w Purton and Brookend 81-95; Miss to Seafarers from 81; V Croydon St Mich w St Jas *S'wark* from 95. *St Michael's Vicarage, 39 Oakfield Road, Croydon CR0 2UX* Tel (020) 8680 8413

MINCHIN, Anthony John. b 35. St Cath Coll Cam BA59 MA. Wells Th Coll 59. **d** 61 **p** 62. C Cheltenham St Pet *Glouc* 61-64; C Bushey *St Alb* 64-67; V Cheltenham St Mich *Glouc* 67-74; V Lower Cam 74-82; V Tuffley 82-92; R Huntley and Longhope 92-00; rtd 00; Perm to Offic *Glouc* from 00. *2 Melbourne Drive, Stonehouse GL10 2PJ* Tel (01453) 828899

MINCHIN, Charles Scott. b 51. Trin Coll Cam BA72 MA75. Linc Th Coll 73. **d** 75 **p** 76. C Gt Wyrley *Lich* 75-78; TV Wilnecote 78-82; C Tamworth 82-84; C-in-c Glascote CD 84-88; R Brierley Hill 88-93; R Brierley Hill *Worc* from 93. *The Rectory, 2 Church Hill, Brierley Hill DY5 3PX* Tel (01384) 78146 E-mail cminchin@lineone.net

MINGINS, Canon Marion Elizabeth. b 52. Birm Univ BSocSc73 CQSW75. Cam DipRS78. **d** 87 **p** 94. CA 79-89; NSM Battersea Park All SS *S'wark* 87-88; Sen Selection Sec ACCM 87-88; OHP 89-91; Asst Dioc Dir of Ords *St E* 91-92; Dioc Dir of Ords 92-99; Min Can St E Cathl 91-92; Hon Can 92-93; Can Res 93-02; Can Pastor 99-02; Chapl to The Queen from 96; rtd 02; Perm to Offic *St E* from 02. *54 College Street, Bury St Edmunds IP33 1NH* Tel (01284) 753396 E-mail marionmingins@freezone.co.uk

MINHINNICK, Leslie. b 18. Jes Coll Ox BA39 MA43. Wycliffe Hall Ox 40. **d** 41 **p** 42. C Briton Ferry *Llan* 41-43; C Canton St Jo 43-45; Tutor St Aid Birkenhead 45-50; Vice-Prin 50-51; V Over St Jo *Ches* 51-54; V Birkenhead St Mark 54-60; V Preston St Jo *Blackb* 60-61; V Chipping 61-66; V Lytham St Jo 66-81; rtd 81; Perm to Offic *Ban* from 81. *The Old School House, Cemaes Bay LL67 0NG* Tel (01407) 710601

MINICH, Mason Faulconer. b 38. **d** 66 **p** 67. USA 66-71 and from 81; C Alverstoke *Portsm* 80; C Romford Ascension Collier Row *Chelmsf* 80-81. *5055 Seminary Road, Apartment 1319, Alexandria, VA 22311, USA*

MINION, Arthur. b 65. TCD BTh92. CITC 89. **d** 92 **p** 93. C Bandon Union *C, C & R* 92-95; I Taunagh w Kilmactranny, Ballysumaghan etc *K, E & A* 95-99; I Shinrone w Aghancon etc *L & K* from 99. *St Mary's Rectory, Shinrone, Birr, Co Offaly, Irish Republic* Tel (00353) (505) 47164 Fax as telephone

MINION, Hazel. **d** 03. NSM Templebreedy w Tracton and Nohoval *C, C & R* from 03. *22 Inchvale Drive, Shamrock Lawn, Douglas, Cork, Irish Republic* Tel (00353) (21) 436 1924

MINNS, David Andrew. b 59. St Jo Coll Nottm 95. **d** 97 **p** 98. C Burpham *Guildf* 97-00; C Knaphill w Brookwood from 00. *13 Heath Drive, Brookwood, Woking GU24 0HG* Tel (01483) 857890 Mobile 07779-519807 E-mail dlkminns@tinyworld.co.uk

MINNS, John Alfred. b 38. Oak Hill Th Coll 63. **d** 68 **p** 69. C Cheadle Hulme St Andr *Ches* 68-72; C Hartford 72-74; V Wharton 74-85; V Halliwell St Paul *Man* 85-87; C Halliwell St Pet 87-91; rtd 91; Perm to Offic *Glouc* 91-97. *39 Hambidge Lane, Lechlade GL7 3BJ* Tel (01367) 253549

MINNS, John Charles. b 42. EAMTC. **d** 85 **p** 86. NSM Heigham St Barn w St Bart *Nor* 85-91; NSM Nor St Geo Tombland from 91; Asst Chapl Norfolk and Nor Hosp 92-95; Chapl Nor Sch of Art and Design from 99. *18 Thunder Lane, Thorpe St Andrew, Norwich NR7 0PX* Tel (01603) 437000 E-mail stgeorge.tombland@virgin.net

MINORS, Graham Glyndwr Cavil. b 44. Glouc Sch of Min. **d** 79 **p** 79. Hon C Lower Cam *Glouc* 79-83; C Leckhampton SS Phil and Jas w Cheltenham St Jas 83-89; V Cainscross w Selsley 89-99; RD Stonehouse 97-99; TR Bodmin w Lanhydrock and Lanivet *Truro* from 99; Chapl Cornwall Healthcare Trust from 02. *The Rectory, Priory Road, Bodmin PL31 2AB* Tel (01208) 73867 E-mail revgminors@hotmail.com

MINSON, Roger Graham. b 41. Leeds Univ BA64. Coll of Resurr Mirfield 64. **d** 66 **p** 67. C Horfield St Greg *Bris* 66-70; C Southmead 70-73; V Lawrence Weston 74-81; TV Knowle 81-93; V Knowle St Martin 93-95; V Fishponds St Mary from 95. *St Mary's Vicarage, Vicar's Close, Bristol BS16 3TH* Tel 0117-965 4462 *or* 958 6412 E-mail stmary's.fishponds@virgin.net

MINTY, Kenneth Desmond. b 25. Ch Ch Ox BA48 MA51. Lich Th Coll 71 Qu Coll Birm 72. **d** 73 **p** 74. Asst Chapl Wrekin Coll Telford 73-84; Chapl 84-86; Hon C Lawley *Lich* 74-75; Hon C Cen Telford 75-81; Hon C Longdon-upon-Tern, Rodington, Uppington etc 81-89; V Ercall Magna 89-95; V Rowton 89-95; rtd 95; Perm to Offic *Lich* from 95. *9 Shawbirch Road, Telford TF5 0AD* Tel (01952) 244218

MINTY, Selwyn Francis. b 34. St D Coll Lamp 58. **d** 61 **p** 62. C Tonyrefail *Llan* 61-66; C Pontypridd St Cath 66-69; V Cilfynydd 69-84; V Crynant 84-00; rtd 00. *24 Derwen Fawr, Crynant, Neath SA10 8NX*

MIR, Amene Rahman. b 58. Man Univ BA81 PhD93. Coll of Resurr Mirfield 81. **d** 83 **p** 84. C Walton St Mary *Liv* 83-87; Chapl Walton Hosp Liv 83-87; Perm to Offic *Man* 87-90; Asst Chapl Salford Mental Health Unit 90-94; Chapl Salford Mental Health Services NHS Trust 94-96; Chapl R Marsden NHS Trust Lon and Surrey from 96; Lic to Offic *Lon* from 96; Perm to Offic *S'wark* 96-00. *The Chaplain's Office, Royal Marsden Hospital, Fulham Road, London SW3 6JJ* Tel (020) 7808 2818 *or* 7352 8171 E-mail mir.amene@rmh.nthames.nhs.uk

MITCHAM, Andrew Mark. b 66. Kent Univ BA87 Leeds Univ BA90. Coll of Resurr Mirfield 88. **d** 91 **p** 92. C Downham Market w Bexwell *Ely* 91-94; P Shrine of Our Lady of Walsingham 94-96; V W Worthing St Jo *Chich* from 96. *St John's Vicarage, 15 Reigate Road, Worthing BN11 5NF* Tel (01903) 247340 E-mail andrew@redmail.co.uk

MITCHELL, Alastair. b 60. Wellington Univ (NZ) BA81. St Jo Coll Auckland 86. **d** 88 **p** 89. New Zealand 88-97; Perm to Offic *Roch* 97-00; Hon C Beckenham St Mich from 00. *3 Reddons Road, Beckenham BR3 9LY* Tel (020) 7898 1610 Fax 7898 1769 E-mail amitchel@fish.co.uk

MITCHELL, Canon Albert George. b 25. TCD MA. **d** 88 **p** 89. Bp's C Skreen w Kilmacshalgan and Dromard *T, K & A* 88-00; Can Killala Cathl 96-00; rtd 00. *The Glebe, Kilglass, Enniscrone, Co Sligo, Irish Republic* Tel (00353) (96) 36258

MITCHELL, Alec Silas. b 52. Man Univ BA75 MPhil95. Nor Bapt Coll 77 Coll of Resurr Mirfield 98. **d** 99 **p** 99. C Ashton *Man* from 99; Dioc Officer for Racial Justice from 02. *St John's Vicarage, Carrhill Road, Mossley, Ashton-under-Lyne OL5 0BL* Tel (01457) 836139

MITCHELL, Allan. b 52. Kelham Th Coll 74 Linc Th Coll 78. **d** 78 **p** 79. C Kells *Carl* 78-81; C Upperby St Jo 81-83; V Pennington w Lindal and Marton 83-88; V Westfield St Mary 88-98; P-in-c Dalton-in-Furness 98-02; V Dalton-in-Furness and Ireleth-with-Askam from 02. *The Vicarage, Market Place, Dalton-in-Furness LA15 8AZ* Tel (01229) 462526 *or* 464402

MITCHELL, Andrew Patrick (Paddy). b 37. Ripon Coll Cuddesdon 84 English Coll Valladolid 59. **d** 64 **p** 65. In RC Ch 64-85; C Woolwich St Mary w St Mich *S'wark* 85-87; V E Wickham 87-94; P-in-c Walsall St Andr *Lich* 94-00; TV Sedgley All SS *Worc* 00-03. *48 Fordhouse Lane, Stirchley, Birmingham B30 3BS* Tel 0121-459 7357

MITCHELL, Cecil Robert. b 32. QUB BScEng54. CITC 65. **d** 65 **p** 66. C Belfast St Mary Magd *Conn* 65-68; C Belfast St Mark 68-69; Dioc Sec 70-74; Dioc Sec *D & D* 70-74; I Ballywalter 74-82; V Malew *S & M* 82-84; I Bright w Ballee and Killough *D & D* 84-89; I Killyleagh 89-94; rtd 94. *20 Innisfayle Crescent, Bangor BT19 1DT* Tel (028) 9146 6167

MITCHELL, Christopher Allan. b 51. Newc Univ BA72. Oak Hill Th Coll 82. **d** 84 **p** 85. C Guisborough *York* 84-87; C

Thornaby on Tees 87-88; TV 88-92; V Dent w Cowgill *Bradf* 92-98; R Barney, Fulmodeston w Croxton, Hindringham etc *Nor* from 98; R Hulland, Atlow, Kniveton, Bradley and Hognaston *Derby* from 03. *The Rectory, 16 Eaton Close, Hulland Ward, Ashbourne DE6 3EX* E-mail revchris8@aol.com

MITCHELL, Christopher Ashley. b 69. Leeds Univ BA(Econ)91. Ridley Hall Cam CTM92. d 95 p 96. Min Can St As Cathl *St As* 95-98; CF 98-02; Chapl RAF from 02; Perm to Offic *Ely* from 01. *Chaplaincy Services (RAF), HQ, Personnel and Training Command, RAF Innsworth, Gloucester GL3 1EZ* Tel (01452) 712612 ext 5164 Fax 615800

MITCHELL, Christopher Derek. b 61. Univ of Wales (Lamp) BA85 Leic Univ MA86 Qu Coll Cam BA88 MA92. Westcott Ho Cam 87. d 89 p 90. C Streetly *Lich* 89-92; C Brookfield St Mary *Lon* 92-96. *Address temp unknown*

MITCHELL, Clare. *See* GRIFFITHS, Mrs Clare

MITCHELL, David. *See* MITCHELL, Leonard David

MITCHELL, Canon David George. b 35. QUB BA56. Sarum Th Coll 59. d 61 p 62. C Westbury-on-Trym H Trin *Bris* 61-64; C Cricklade w Latton 64-68; V Fishponds St Jo 68-77; RD Stapleton 76-77; TR E Bris 77-87; Hon Can Bris Cathl from 87; R Syston 87-94; V Warmley 87-94; P-in-c Bitton 87-94; R Warmley, Syston and Bitton 94-01; RD Bitton 87-93; rtd 01; Lic to Offic *Glouc* from 01; P-in-c Chedworth, Yanworth and Stowell, Coln Rogers etc from 01. *The Vicarage, Cheap Street, Chedworth, Cheltenham GL54 4AA* Tel (01285) 720392 E-mail canongeorgemitchell@btinternet.com

MITCHELL, Preb David Norman. b 35. Tyndale Hall Bris 64. d 67 p 68. C Marple All SS *Ches* 67-70; C St Helens St Helen *Liv* 70-72; V S Lambeth St Steph *S'wark* 72-78; P-in-c Brixton Road Ch 73-75; SE Area Sec CPAS 78-81; R Uphill *B & W* 81-92; TR 92-01; Chapl Weston Area Health Trust 86-01; Preb Wells Cathl *B & W* from 90; rtd 01. *3 Pizey Close, Clevedon BS21 7TP* Tel (01275) 349176

MITCHELL, Edwin. b 44. St Jo Coll Nottm BTh74. d 74 p 75. C Worksop St Jo *S'well* 74-77; C Waltham Abbey *Chelmsf* 77-80; V Whiston *Liv* 80-91; R Wombwell *Sheff* 91-99; V Mortomley St Sav High Green from 99; AD Ecclesfield from 01. *The Vicarage, Mortomley Lane, High Green, Sheffield S35 3HS* Tel 0114-284 8231 E-mail edmitchell@rectory.force9.net

MITCHELL, Eric Sidney. b 24. S Dios Minl Tr Scheme 77. d 80 p 81. NSM Portland All SS w St Pet *Sarum* 80-83; C 88-92; Bermuda 83-88; Chapl HM Pris The Verne 91-92; rtd 92; Perm to Offic *Sarum* from 92. *10 Underheage Gardens, Portland DT5 2DX* Tel (01305) 821059

MITCHELL, Frank. b 21. Ely Th Coll 49. d 51 p 52. C Leeds St Aid *Ripon* 51-54; V Bramham *York* 54-62; V Scarborough St Sav 62-73; V Scarborough St Sav w All SS 73-83; rtd 83; Perm to Offic *York* from 83. *6 Sitwell Street, Scarborough YO11 5EX* Tel (01723) 367948

MITCHELL, Geoffrey. b 36. SS Coll Cam BA60 MA64 Nottm Univ BA97 CEng66 FIMechE76 FCIT92. EMMTC 88. d 91 p 92. NSM Oaks in Charnwood and Copt Oak *Leic* 91-94; NSM Loughborough All SS w N Trin 94-00; P-in-c Oaks in Charnwood and Copt Oak 00-03; NSM Shepshed and Oaks in Charnwood from 03; Dioc NSM Officer 98-02. *36 Brick Kiln Lane, Shepshed, Loughborough LE12 9EL* Tel (01509) 502280 E-mail mitchell.household@talk21.com

MITCHELL, Geoffrey Peter. b 30. Liv Univ BEng57 Man Univ MSc68. Wells Th Coll 57. d 59 p 60. C Bradford cum Beswick *Man* 59-61; R Man St Pet Oldham Road w St Jas 61-64; Lic to Offic 64-68; Hon C Unsworth 68-86; V Woolfold 86-95; rtd 95; Perm to Offic *Man* from 95. *14 Redfearn Wood, Rochdale OL12 7GA* Tel (01706) 638180

MITCHELL, George. *See* MITCHELL, Canon David George

MITCHELL, Canon George Alfred. b 23. TCD BA45 MA56. d 46 p 47. C Belfast St Matt *Conn* 46-48; C Ballymoney 48-51; C Belf Cathl Miss 51-52; I Broomhedge 52-58; I Carrickfergus 59-70; I Bangor St Comgall *D & D* 70-88; Can Belf Cathl 78-88; rtd 88. *2 Glendun Park, Bangor BT20 4UX* Tel (028) 9146 0882

MITCHELL, Geraint Owain. b 71. Lincs & Humberside Univ BA96 Leeds Univ BA99. Coll of Resurr Mirfield 99. d 02. C Bridlington Em *York* from 02. *40 Georgian Way, Bridlington YO15 3TB* Tel (01262) 678560

MITCHELL, Gordon Frank Henry. b 26. QFSM. FIFireE. Sarum & Wells Th Coll 74. d 77 p 78. NSM Alderbury and W Grimstead *Sarum* 77-91; NSM Alderbury Team 91-96; Perm to Offic from 96. *Seefeld, Southampton Road, Whaddon, Salisbury SP5 3EB* Tel (01722) 710516

MITCHELL, Graham Bell. b 40. Otago Univ BA64 MA65 Worc Coll Ox BA73 MA76. St Chad's Coll Dur 66. d 68 p 69. C Bris St Agnes w St Simon *Bris* 68-71; C Bedminster St Mich 73-76; V Auckland St Pet *Dur* 76-78; Vice-Prin Chich Th Coll 78-83; C Brighton St Pet w Chpl Royal and St Jo *Chich* 83-86; P-in-c Scaynes Hill 86-96; V from 96. *The Vicarage, Scaynes Hill, Haywards Heath RH17 7PB* Tel (01444) 831265 E-mail gbm@nzlon.freeserve.co.uk

MITCHELL, Ian. *See* MITCHELL, Stuart Ian

MITCHELL, Jolyon Peter. b 64. Selw Coll Cam BA88 MA90 Edin Univ PhD97. St Jo Coll Dur MA93. d 93 p 94. NSM St Mary's Cathl *Edin* 93-97; NSM Edin Ch Ch from 97; Lect Edin Univ from 93. *4 Bruntsfield Terrace, Edinburgh EH10 4EX* Tel 0131-229 8154 *or* 650 8921 E-mail jolyon.mitchell@ed.ac.uk

MITCHELL, Miss Josephine Dorothy. b 36. Dalton Ho Bris 65. dss 76 d 87 p 94. Hailsham *Chich* 75-85; Enfield St Jas *Lon* 85-96; Par Dn 87-94; C 94-96; rtd 96; Perm to Offic *St Alb* from 96. *24 Benedictine Gate, Waltham Cross EN8 0XB* Tel (01992) 470115

MITCHELL, Kevin. b 49. Newc Univ BSc71 Ox Univ BA83. Ripon Coll Cuddesdon 81. d 83 p 84. C Cantril Farm *Liv* 83-86; Chapl N Middx Hosp 86-90; C Gt Cambridge Road St Jo and St Jas *Lon* 86-90; P-in-c Cricklewood St Pet 90-96; V Whetstone St Jo from 96. *St John's Vicarage, 1163 High Road, London N20 0PG* Tel (020) 8445 4569

MITCHELL, Leonard David. b 30. ACA56 FCA66. Wells Th Coll 60 Canadian Th Sem DMin94. d 61 p 62. C Hilborough w Bodney *Nor* 61-64; C Oxborough w Foulden and Caldecote 61-64; C Cockley Cley w Gooderstone 61-64; C Gt and Lt Cressingham w Threxton 61-64; V Ernesettle *Ex* 64-67; Canada from 67; rtd 95; Assoc P Picton St Mary Magd from 98. *8 Jane Street, PO Box 4101, Picton ON, Canada, K0K 2T0* Tel (001) (613) 476 5203 Fax 476 1395 E-mail davidmitchell@sympatico.ca

MITCHELL, Owain. *See* MITCHELL, Geraint Owain

MITCHELL, Paddy. *See* MITCHELL, Andrew Patrick

MITCHELL, The Very Revd Patrick Reynolds. b 30. FSA81 Mert Coll Ox BA52 MA56. Wells Th Coll 52. d 54 p 55. C Mansfield St Mark *S'well* 54-57; Chapl Wells Th Coll and PV Wells Cathl *B & W* 57-61; V Milton *Portsm* 61-67; V Frome St Jo and P-in-c Woodlands *B & W* 67-73; Dir of Ords 70-74; Dean Wells 73-89; Dean Windsor and Dom Chapl to The Queen 89-98; rtd 98; Perm to Offic *Ex* from 98; Perm to Offic *Sarum* from 00. *Wolford Lodge, Dunkeswell, Honiton EX14 4SQ* Tel (01404) 841244

MITCHELL, Peter Derek. b 30. Nuch Th Coll. d 69 p 70. C Wargrave *Ox* 69-72; V Lund *Blackb* 72-80; V Badsey w Aldington and Wickhamford *Worc* 80-96; rtd 96. *Althaea, 29 Lavender Walk, Evesham WR11 2LN*

MITCHELL, Richard John Anthony. b 64. St Martin's Coll Lanc BA85 PGCE86. Sarum & Wells Th Coll 88. d 91 p 92. C Kendal H Trin *Carl* 91-95; TV Kirkby Lonsdale from 95. *The Vicarage, Vicarage Lane, Kirkby Lonsdale, Carnforth LA6 2BA* Tel (015242) 72078 E-mail richard.mitchell@talk21.com

MITCHELL, Robert Hugh. b 53. Ripon Coll Cuddesdon. d 82 p 83. C E Dulwich St Jo *S'wark* 82-86; C Cambridge Gt St Mary w St Mich *Ely* 86-90; Chapl Girton Coll Cam 86-90; Asst Chapl Win Coll 90-91; Assoc Chapl Addenbrooke's Hosp Cam 91-93; Chapl Portsm Hosps NHS Trust 93-95; Chapl St Mary's Hosp Portsm 93-95; Chapl R Free Hampstead NHS Trust from 95. *The Chaplains' Office, The Royal Free Hospital, Pond Street, London NW3 2QG* Tel (020) 7830 2742 *or* 7794 0500

MITCHELL, Robert McFarlane. b 50. Man Univ BA72. Wycliffe Hall Ox 73. d 75 p 76. C Tonbridge SS Pet and Paul *Roch* 75-80; CF from 80. *c/o MOD Chaplains (Army)* Tel (01980) 615804 Fax 615800

MITCHELL, Roger Sulway. b 36. Chich Th Coll 70. d 71 p 71. C Sidcup St Jo *Roch* 71-74; C Pembury 74-76; Chapl St Lawr Hosp Bodmin 76-96; Chapl Cornwall and St Scilly Mental Health Unit 88-96; Chapl Cornwall Healthcare Trust 96-00; TV Bodmin w Lanhydrock and Lanivet *Truro* 97-00; rtd 00. *12 Beacon Road, Bodmin PL31 1AS* Tel (01208) 76357 Mobile 07771-881258

MITCHELL, Sheila Rosemary. b 53. Univ Coll Ches CertEd74 AdDipEd80 PGDPT98. Nor Ord Course 93. d 96 p 97. NSM Plemstall w Guilden Sutton *Ches* 96-98; C New Brighton St Jas w Em 98-00; C New Brighton All SS 98-00; P-in-c Weston 00-02; V from 02. *All Saints' Vicarage, 13 Cemetery Road, Weston, Crewe CW2 5LQ* Tel (01270) 582585 E-mail remitch@compuserve.com

MITCHELL, Stephen Andrew John. b 56. Ch Ch Coll Cant CertEd78 K Coll Lon AKC77 BD80 Lambeth STh90. Coll of Resurr Mirfield 80. d 82 p 83. C Chatham St Steph *Roch* 82-87; C Edenbridge 87-91; V from 91; P-in-c Crockham Hill H Trin from 91; Chapl Invicta Community Care NHS Trust from 91. *The Vicarage, Mill Hill, Edenbridge TN8 5DA* Tel (01732) 862258 Fax 864335

MITCHELL, Stephen John. b 51. Ex Univ BA73 Fitzw Coll Cam BA78 MA. Ridley Hall Cam 76. d 79 p 80. C Gt Malvern St Mary *Worc* 79-81; Prec Leic Cathl *Leic* 82-85; R Barrow upon Soar w Walton le Wolds 85-02; P-in-c Gazeley w Dalham, Moulton and Kentford *St E* from 02. *All Saints' Vicarage, The Street, Gazeley, Newmarket CB8 8RB* Tel (01638) 552379 E-mail smitch4517@aol.com

MITCHELL, Steven. b 58. BTh. St Jo Coll Nottm. d 83 p 84. C Ovenden *Wakef* 83-87; V Gawthorpe and Chickenley Heath 87-98; V Birkenshaw w Hunsworth from 98. *St Paul's Vicarage, 6 Vicarage Gardens, Birkenshaw, Bradford BD11 2EF* Tel (01274) 683776

MITCHELL, Stuart. b 53. Cranmer Hall Dur 01. **d** 03. C Pocklington and Owsthorpe and Kilnwick Percy etc *York* from 03. *110 Wold Road, Pocklington, York YO42 2QG* Tel (01759) 306966

MITCHELL, Stuart Ian. b 50. Wadh Coll Ox BA71 DPhil74. S'wark Ord Course DipRS84. **d** 85 **p** 87. NSM Charlton St Luke w H Trin *S'wark* 85-86; NSM Kidbrooke St Jas 86-88; NSM Newbold w Dunston *Derby* 88-94; C 94-96; C Newbold and Gt Barlow 96-97; P-in-c Matlock Bank from 97; RD Wirksworth from 98. *All Saints' Vicarage, Smedley Street, Matlock DE4 3JG* Tel (01629) 582235
E-mail ianandmary@allsaintsmatlock.fsnet.co.uk

MITCHELL, Tim. b 63. Trin Coll Bris DipHE95. **d** 97 **p** 98. C Cromer *Nor* 97-01; P-in-c Selston *S'well* from 01. *The Vicarage, 58 Church Lane, Selston, Nottingham NG16 6EW* Tel (01773) 810247

MITCHELL, Tom Good. b 21. K Coll (NS) STh62. **d** 63 **p** 64. Canada 63-81 and from 98; V Misterton and W Stockwith *S'well* 81-87; rtd 87; Perm to Offic *Glouc* 87-98. *3136 Plummer Avenue, New Waterford NS, Canada, B1H 4W4* Tel (001) (902) 862 7155

MITCHELL, Wendy Mary. b 47. Glas Univ MA70 Callendar Park Coll of Educn Falkirk PGCE71. Trin Coll Bris DipTh01. **d** 01. C Yatton Moor *B & W* from 01. *129 High Street, Yatton, Bristol BS49 4DH* Tel (01934) 832734

MITCHELL, William Blanchard. b 26. Lon Univ DipTh54. St Aid Birkenhead 53. **d** 55 **p** 56. C Kendal H Trin *Carl* 55-59; C Dalton-in-Furness 59-60; V Nichol Forest 60-61; CF 61-77; V Nicholforest and Kirkandrews on Esk *Carl* 77-84; R Kirkby Thore w Temple Sowerby and Newbiggin 84-89; rtd 89; Perm to Offic *Carl* from 89. *Koi Hai, 23 Longlands Road, Carlisle CA3 9AD* Tel (01228) 546230

MITCHELL-INNES, Charles William. b 47. Pemb Coll Cam BA69 MA73. Sarum Th Coll 83. **d** 86 **p** 87. Asst Chapl Sherborne Sch 86-89; Chapl Milton Abbey Sch Dorset 90-96; Conduct Eton Coll from 96. *3 Savile House, Eton College, Windsor SL4 6DT* Tel (01753) 671004

MITCHELL-INNES, James Alexander. b 39. Ch Ch Ox BA64 MA66. Lon Coll of Div 65. **d** 67 **p** 68. C Cullompton *Ex* 67-71; Nigeria 71-75; P-in-c Puddletown w Athelhampton and Burleston *Sarum* 75-78; R Puddletown and Tolpuddle 78-82; V Win Ch Ch *Win* 82-92; V Titchfield *Portsm* 92-98; rtd 98. *The Cherries, 14 Test Rise, Chilbolton, Stockbridge SO20 6AF* Tel (01264) 860815 E-mail jamesmi@tiscali.co.uk

MITCHINSON, Frank. b 37. AKC60. **d** 61 **p** 62. C Cross Heath *Lich* 61-64; C Forrabury w Minster and Trevalga *Truro* 64-68; C Harpenden St Nic *St Alb* 68-70; R Southwick St Mich *Chich* 70-83; V Billingshurst 83-88; V Preston 88-02; rtd 02; P-in-c Bolney *Chich* from 02. *The Vicarage, Cowfold Road, Bolney, Haywards Heath RH17 5QR* Tel (01444) 881301

MITCHINSON, Canon Ronald. b 35. Westmr Coll Ox MA91. Linc Th Coll 66. **d** 68 **p** 69. C Heworth St Mary *Dur* 68-72; C Banbury *Ox* 72-73; TV 73-76; New Zealand 76-82; TR Banbury *Ox* 82-86; RD Deddington 84-86; Ind Chapl 86-92; Hon Can Ch Ch 90-92; TV Brayton *York* 92-96; Sen Chapl Selby Coalfield Ind Chapl 92-96; rtd 96. *6 St John's Crescent, York YO31 7QP* Tel (01904) 642382

MITFORD, Bertram William Jeremy (Bill). b 27. Wells Th Coll 62. **d** 64 **p** 65. C Hollinwood *Man* 64-67; C Atherton 67-68; C Frome St Jo *B & W* 68-71; V Cleeve 72-74; V Cleeve w Chelvey and Brockley 74-79; Chapl HM Pris Shepton Mallet 79-92; C Shepton Mallet *B & W* 79-84; C Shepton Mallet w Doulting 84-92; rtd 92. *2 Charlton Road, Shepton Mallet BA4 5NY* Tel (01749) 342825

MITRA, Avijit. b 53. Keble Coll Ox BA76. Ox NSM Course 84. **d** 88 **p** 89. NSM Abingdon *Ox* 88-96; Asst Chapl Abingdon Sch 88-96; Sen Chapl Ch Hosp Horsham from 96. *Cornerways, Christ's Hospital, Horsham RH13 0LD* Tel (01403) 258348

MITRA, Mrs Nicola Jane. b 54. St Hugh's Coll Ox BA76 PGCE77 MA81. Ox Min Course DipMin94. **d** 94 **p** 95. NSM Abingdon *Ox* 94-96; Asst Chapl Ch Hosp Horsham from 96. *Cornerways, Christ's Hospital, Horsham RH13 0LD* Tel (01403) 258348

MITSON, Mrs Carol Mae. b 46. SRN SCM HVCert. Oak Hill NSM Course 89. **d** 93 **p** 94. NSM Lawford *Chelmsf* 93-96; NSM Elmstead 96-98; NSM Harwich 96-98; NSM Dedham 98-00; Perm to Offic from 01. *Drift Cottage, The Drift, Dedham, Colchester CO7 6AH* Tel (01206) 323116 Fax as telephone

MITSON, John Dane. b 29. Solicitor 56 SS Coll Cam MA53 LLM54. Oak Hill Th Coll 91 EAMTC 93. **d** 94 **p** 95. Dioc Registrar and Legal Sec to Bp St E 75-97; NSM Greenstead *Chelmsf* 94-96; NSM Elmstead 96-98; NSM Dedham 98-00; Perm to Offic from 00. *Drift Cottage, The Drift, Dedham, Colchester CO7 6AH* Tel (01206) 323116 Fax as telephone

MITSON, Miss Joyce. b 37. Man Univ CertEd64. Trin Coll Bris DipHE79. **dss** 79 **d** 87 **p** 94. Wellington w Eyton *Lich* 79-85; Farnworth *Liv* 85-91; Par Dn 87-91; TD Bilston *Lich* 91-94; TV 94; Lich Local Min Adv 91-94; C W Bromwich St Jas 94-97; C W Bromwich St Jas w St Paul 97-98; rtd 98. *13 Birkenhills Drive, Bolton BL3 4TX* Tel (01204) 655081

MITTON, Michael Simon. b 53. Ex Univ BA75. St Jo Coll Nottm 76. **d** 78 **p** 79. C High Wycombe *Ox* 78-82; C Kidderminster St Geo *Worc* 82; TV 82-89; Dir Angl Renewal Min 89-97; Deputy Dir Acorn Chr Healing Trust from 97. *50 Kedleston Road, Derby DE22 1GW* Tel (01332) 370955 E-mail mmitton@aol.com

MLEMETA, Kedmon Hezron. b 60. CertEd78. CA Tr Coll Nairobi 86. **d** 89 **p** 90. Tanzania 89-96 and from 99; P-in-c Loughb Gd Shep *Leic* 96-99. *The Diocese of Mount Kilimanjaro, PO Box 1057, Arusha, Tanzania*

MNGOMEZULU, Sipho Percy. **d** 78 **p** 78. Swaziland 78-96 and from 03; NSM Cricklewood St Gabr and St Mich *Lon* 96-03. *Address temp unknown*

MOATE, Gerard Grigglestone. b 54. BA FRSA01. Oak Hill Th Coll 79. **d** 82 **p** 83. C Mildmay Grove St Jude and St Paul *Lon* 82-85; C Hampstead St Jo 85-88; P-in-c Pinxton *Derby* 88; V Charlesworth and Dinting Vale 88-95; V Dedham *Chelmsf* from 95; RD Dedham and Tey 98-03. *The Vicarage, High Street, Dedham, Colchester CO7 6DE* Tel (01206) 322136
E-mail gerard@moate.org

MOATE, Phillip. b 47. RGN70 Lon Univ DN73 RNT75 Leeds Univ Cert Counselling 94. N Ord Course 87. **d** 90 **p** 91. NSM Upper Holme Valley *Wakef* 90-92; NSM Almondbury Deanery 92-94; NSM Honley 94-95; P-in-c Roos and Garton in Holderness w Tunstall etc *York* 95-02; R Lockington and Lund and Scorborough w Leconfield from 02. *Rectory House, Church Lane, Lockington, Driffield YO25 9SU* Tel (01430) 810604
E-mail pmoate@tiscali.co.uk

MOATT, Richard Albert. b 54. K Coll Lon BD76 AKC76. Linc Th Coll 80. **d** 81 **p** 82. C Egremont and Haile *Carl* 81-85; V Addingham, Edenhall, Langwathby and Culgaith from 85; P-in-c Skirwith, Ousby and Melmerby w Kirkland from 98. *The Vicarage, Langwathby, Penrith CA10 1LW* Tel (01768) 881212
E-mail moatt@btinternet.com

MOBBERLEY, Keith John. b 56. BA. Westcott Ho Cam. **d** 84 **p** 85. C Coventry Caludon *Cov* 84-87; C Kenilworth St Nic 87-92; V Keresley and Coundon 92-98; P-in-c Hatton w Haseley, Rowington w Lowsonford etc 98-00; R from 00. *North Ferncumbe Rectory, Hatton Green, Hatton, Warwick CV35 7LA* Tel (01926) 484332

MOBBERLEY, Mrs Susan. b 57. Kent Univ BA79. Westcott Ho Cam 81. **dss** 84 **d** 90 **p** 94. Coventry Caludon *Cov* 84-87; Lic to Offic 87-92; NSM Keresley and Coundon 92-98; NSM Hatton w Haseley, Rowington w Lowsonford etc from 98. *North Ferncumbe Rectory, Hatton Green, Hatton, Warwick CV35 7LA* Tel (01926) 484332

MOBBS, Bernard Frederick. b 26. S'wark Ord Course 71. **d** 72 **p** 73. C Purley St Barn *S'wark* 72-74; S'wark Ord Course 74-80; P-in-c Sydenham St Bart *S'wark* 80-87; V Dormansland 87-92; rtd 92; Perm to Offic *Chich* from 92. *Fair Havens, Fletching Street, Mayfield TN20 6TH* Tel (01435) 872910

MOBERLY (née McCLURE), Mrs Jennifer Lynne. b 62. Ball State Univ (USA) BSc84. Cranmer Hall Dur 98. **d** 01 **p** 02. C Belmont *Dur* from 01. *8 Princes Street, Durham DH1 4RP* Tel 0191-386 4255

MOBERLY, Richard Hamilton. b 30. Trin Hall Cam BA53 MA57. Cuddesdon Coll 53. **d** 55 **p** 56. C Walton St Mary *Liv* 55-59; C Kensington St Mary Abbots w St Geo *Lon* 59-63; R Chingola 63-66; N Rhodesia 63-64; Zambia 64-66; V Kennington Cross St Anselm *S'wark* 67-73; TV N Lambeth 74-80; Ind Chapl 80-95; rtd 95; Perm to Offic *S'wark* from 95. *24 Wincott Street, London SE11 4NT* Tel (020) 7735 2233 Fax 7793 9021 E-mail richard@richardmoberly.org.uk

MOBERLY, Robert Walter Lambert. b 52. New Coll Ox MA77 Selw Coll Cam MA80 Trin Coll Cam PhD81. Ridley Hall Cam 74. **d** 81 **p** 82. C Knowle *Birm* 81-85; Lect Dur Univ from 85; Perm to Offic *Dur* from 85. *8 Princes Street, Durham DH1 4RP* Tel 0191-386 4255 *or* 374 2067
E-mail r.w.l.moberly@durham.ac.uk

MOCK, David Lawrence. b 64. Whitman Coll Washington BA86 Heythrop Coll Lon MTh01. Trin Coll Bris BA98. **d** 98 **p** 99. C Tadworth *S'wark* 98-01; P-in-c Sutton St Geo *Ches* 01-02; C Macclesfield Team Par 01-02; TV from 02. *St George's Vicarage, 88 Byrons Lane, Macclesfield SK11 7JS* Tel (01625) 432919 E-mail dave@mockcrew.freeserve.co.uk

MOCKFORD (née WATKINS), Mrs Betty Anne. b 45. Leeds Univ BA66 Nottm Univ CertEd67 UEA DipHE98. EAMTC 94. **d** 97 **p** 98. C Ipswich St Aug *St E* 97-00; P-in-c Charsfield w Debach, Monewden, Hoo etc from 01. *Mirembe, 10 Castle Brooks, Framlingham, Woodbridge IP13 9SF* Tel (01728) 724193 Mobile 07890-110741

MOCKFORD, Canon John Frederick. b 28. Em Coll Cam BA52 MA56 DipRS00. Ridley Hall Cam 52. **d** 54 **p** 55. C Walsall St Silas *Man* 54; C Harpurhey Ch Ch 54-57; V Bootle St Leon *Liv* 57-64; CMS 65-73; Uganda 66-73; Can Missr Kampala 72-73; V Bushbury *Lich* 73-77; TR 77-84; Preb Lich Cathl 81-84; Dir Miss and Past Studies Ridley Hall Cam 84-88; V Ipswich St Marg *St E* 88-93; rtd 93; Perm to Offic *St E* from 93. *Mirembe, 10 Castle Brooks, Framlingham, Woodbridge IP13 9SF* Tel (01728) 724193

MOCKFORD, Peter John. b 57. Nottm Univ BSc79 St Jo Coll Dur BA88. Cranmer Hall Dur 86. **d** 89 **p** 90. C Tamworth *Lich* 89-94; V Blurton from 94. *The Vicarage, School Lane, Stoke-on-Trent ST3 3DU* Tel (01782) 312163
E-mail p.mockford@ukgateway.net

MODY, Rohintan Keki. b 63. New Coll Ox BA85 MA88. Oak Hill Th Coll BA00. **d** 00 **p** 01. C Wolverhampton St Luke *Lich* from 00. *36 Pencombe Drive, Wolverhampton WV4 5EW* Tel (01902) 620211 E-mail romody@hotmail.com

MOESEL, Joseph Sams. b 65. Villanova Univ USA BA90 Harris Man Coll Ox BTh93. Ripon Coll Cuddesdon DipMin95. **d** 95 **p** 96. C Twigworth, Down Hatherley, Norton, The Leigh etc *Glouc* 95-98; CF from 98; Perm to Offic *Cant* 98-01. *c/o MOD Chaplains (Army)* Tel (01980) 615804 Fax 615800

MOFFAT, Canon George. b 46. Edin Univ BD77 Open Univ BA87. Edin Th Coll 67. **d** 72 **p** 73. C Falkirk *Edin* 73-76; C Edin St Pet 76-81; Chapl Edin Univ 77-81; C Heston *Lon* 81-84; V S Elmsall *Wakef* 84-93; TR Manningham *Bradf* from 93; Chapl to The Queen from 00; Hon Can Bradf Cathl *Bradf* from 02. *1 Selborne Grove, Bradford BD9 4NL* Tel (01274) 498566

MOFFATT, Joseph Barnaby. b 72. Fitzw Coll Cam BA96 MA99. Ripon Coll Cuddesdon 97. **d** 99 **p** 00. C Cen Wolverhampton *Lich* 99-03; C Chelsea St Luke and Ch Ch *Lon* from 03. *29 Burnsall Street, London SW3 3SR* Tel (020) 7352 5608
E-mail joemoffatt@supanet.com

MOFFATT, Neil Thomas. b 46. Fitzw Coll Cam BA68 MA72. Qu Coll Birm 69. **d** 71 **p** 72. C Charlton St Luke w St Paul *S'wark* 71-74; C Walworth St Pet 74-75; C Walworth 75-77; V Dormansland 77-86; TR Padgate *Liv* 86-96; V Padgate 96-98; TR Thatcham *Ox* from 98; AD Newbury from 02. *The Rectory, 17 Church Gate, Thatcham RG19 3PN* Tel (01635) 862616
E-mail tom@moffatt20.freeserve.co.uk

MOFFETT, Mrs Marie-Louise. b 25. St Andr Univ MA46 Cam Univ DipRS76. **d** 87 **p** 94. St Andr Univ Angl Chapl Team 87-91; C St Andrews All SS *St And* from 91. *10 Queen's Gardens, St Andrews KY16 9TA* Tel (01334) 473678

MOFFITT, Mrs Vivien Louisa. b 37. LSE BSc59 Dip Personnel Mgt 60. Sarum & Wells Th Coll 90. **d** 91 **p** 94. NSM Chandler's Ford *Win* 91-99; NSM Twyford and Owslebury and Morestead 99-01; rtd 01. *13 Velmore Road, Eastleigh SO53 3HD* Tel (023) 8026 5327

MOGER, Peter John. b 64. Mert Coll Ox BA85 BMus86 MA89 St Jo Coll Dur BA93. Cranmer Hall Dur 89. **d** 93 **p** 94. C Whitby *York* 93-95; Prec, Sacr and Min Can Ely Cathl *Ely* 95-01; V Godmanchester from 01. *The Vicarage, 59 Post Street, Godmanchester, Huntingdon PE29 2AQ* Tel (01480) 436400 Mobile 07970-694021 Fax (01480) 453354
E-mail peter.moger@ntlworld.com

MOGFORD, Canon Stanley Howard. b 13. St Pet Hall Ox BA35 DipTh36 MA39. Westcott Ho Cam 36. **d** 37 **p** 38. C Aberdare *Llan* 37-41; C Llan Cathl 41-48; V Cyfarthfa 48-54; V Pontypridd St Cath 54-63; V Llanblethian w Cowbridge 63-66; V Llanblethian w Cowbridge and Llandough etc 66-80; RD Llantwit Major and Cowbridge 69-80; Can Llan Cathl 71-80; rtd 80; Perm to Offic *Llan* from 80. *Fortis Green, 19 Plas Treoda, Cardiff CF14 1PT* Tel (029) 2061 8839

MOGRIDGE, Christopher James. b 31. Culham Coll of Educn CertEd62 LCP70 FCollP85. St Steph Ho Ox 93. **d** 94 **p** 95. NSM Wellingborough St Andr 94-98; NSM Ecton 98-02; rtd 02; Perm to Offic *Pet* from 02. *April Cottage, Little Harrowden, Wellingborough NN9 5BB* Tel (01933) 678412

MOIR, Canon David William. b 38. St Aid Birkenhead 64. **d** 67 **p** 68. C Danbury *Chelmsf* 67-70; C Bollington St Jo *Ches* 70-72; V Sutton St Jas 72-81; V Prestbury 81-95; RD Macclesfield 88-98; P-in-c Bosley and N Rode w Wincle and Wildboarclough 95-98; V from 98; Hon Can Ches Cathl from 96; Chapl E Cheshire NHS Trust from 96. *The Vicarage, Wincle, Macclesfield SK11 0QH* Tel (01260) 227234
E-mail moirdl@compuserve.com

MOIR, Nicholas Ian. b 61. G&C Coll Cam BA82 MA86 Ox Univ BA86 MA91 Lon Univ MTh92. Wycliffe Hall Ox 84. **d** 87 **p** 88. C Enfield St Andr *Lon* 87-91; Bp's Dom Chapl *St Alb* 91-94; Chapl St Jo Coll Cam 94-98; V Waterbeach *Ely* from 98; R Landbeach from 98. *The Vicarage, 8 Chapel Street, Waterbeach, Cambridge CB5 9HR* Tel (01223) 860353
E-mail nicholas.moir@ntlworld.com

MOLD, Peter John. b 33. **d** 63 **p** 64. C Boston *Linc* 63-66; C Scarborough St Mary w Ch Ch, St Paul and St Thos *York* 67-68; Australia from 68; rtd 94. *Stone Grange, 29 Newcastle Street, York, PO Box 355, W Australia 6302* Tel (0061) (8) 9641 1965

MOLE, Arthur Penton. b 10. Whitewatersrand Univ BA30. Bps' Coll Cheshunt 35. **d** 35 **p** 36. C Pokesdown All SS *Win* 35-37; C Wolborough w Newton Abbot *Ex* 37-44; R Goldsborough *Ripon* 44-49; Dioc Dir of Educn *Lit Alb* 49-51; V Barnet Vale St Mark 51-59; RD Barnet 55-59; V Southbourne St Kath *Win* 59-71; R Old Alresford 71-76; P-in-c Brown and Chilton Candover w Northington etc 72-74; R 74-76; rtd 76; Perm to Offic *Worc* from 76. *15 Garden Styles, Pershore WR10 1JW* Tel (01386) 554167

MOLE, David Eric Harton. b 33. Em Coll Cam BA54 MA58 PhD62. Ridley Hall Cam 55. **d** 59 **p** 59. C Selly Hill St Steph *Birm* 59-62; Tutor St Aid Birkenhead 62-63; Chapl Peterho Cam 63-69; Ghana 69-72; Lect Qu Coll Birm 72-76; Tutor USPG Coll of the Ascension Selly Oak 76-87; C Burton *Lich* 87-93; Chapl Burton Gen Hosp 90-93; Chapl Ostend w Knokke and Bruges *Eur* 93-98; rtd 98; Perm to Offic *Birm* from 99. *48 Green Meadow Road, Selly Oak, Birmingham B29 4DE* Tel 0121-475 1589
E-mail susananddavidmole@yahoo.co.uk

MOLE, Jennifer Vera. b 49. CertEd70. Qu Coll Birm 82. **d** 84 **p** 97. C Pontypool *Mon* 84-87; C Cyncoed 87-88; TV 88-96; C Caerleon 96-99; V Maesglas and Duffryn from 99. *The Vicarage, Old Cardiff Road, Newport NP20 3AT* Tel (01633) 815738

MOLESWORTH, Canon Anthony Edward Nassau. b 23. Pemb Coll Cam BA45 MA48. Coll of Resurr Mirfield 45. **d** 46 **p** 47. C Blyth St Mary *Newc* 46-51; C High Elswick St Phil 51-52; C Swaziland 52-68; Can 68-71; Can Zululand 63-68; R Huish Episcopi w Pitney *B & W* 71-78; P-in-c High Ham 76-78; TR Langport Area Chs 78-84; R Charlton Musgrove, Cucklington and Stoke Trister 84-90; RD Bruton 86-90; rtd 90; Perm to Offic *B & W* from 90; Perm to Offic *Sarum* from 90. *3 Barrow Hill, Stourton Caundle, Sturminster Newton DT10 2LD* Tel (01963) 362337

MOLL, Christopher David Edward. b 67. St Cath Coll Cam BA89 MA93. Ridley Hall Cam CTM97. **d** 98 **p** 99. C Byker St Mark and Walkergate St Oswald *Newc* 98-02; C Eastrop *Win* from 02. *15 Camwood Close, Basingstoke RG21 3BL* Tel (01256) 332454
E-mail ed.moll@ukgateway.net

MOLL, David Henry. b 27. St Chad's Coll Dur 50. **d** 54 **p** 55. C Wallsend St Pet *Newc* 54-58; C Wymondham *Nor* 59-62; R Yaxham 62-68; R Welborne 62-68; R Gt w Lt Poringland and Howe 69-75; R Framingham Earl 79-92; rtd 92. *6 Overlands, North Curry, Taunton TA3 6JL* Tel (01823) 491303

MOLL, Randell Tabrum. b 41. Lon Univ BD65. Wycliffe Hall Ox 62. **d** 66 **p** 67. C Drypool St Columba w St Andr and St Pet *York* 66-70; Asst Chapl HM Pris Hull 66-70; Asst Master Hull Gr Sch 66-70; C Netherton *Liv* 70-74; C Sefton 70-72; Ind Chapl 70-74 and 92-99; Belgium 75-76; P-in-c Brockmoor *Lich* 76-81; Team Ldr Black Country Urban Ind Miss 76-81; Dir Chilworth Home Services 81-84; Asst Master Bp Reindorp Sch Guildf 84-90; France and Iraq 91; Chapl Sedbergh Sch 92; Sen Chapl Miss in the Economy (Merseyside) 92-99; Hon Can Liv Cathl *Liv* 97-99; Chapl Campsfield Ho Immigration and Detention Cen 00-02; Sen Chapl Immigration Detention Servies 01-02; Team Ldr Workplace Min *St Alb* from 03. *Penn Cottage, Green End, Granborough, Buckingham MK18 3NT* Tel (01296) 670970 Fax as telephone E-mail rmoll@stalbans.anglican.org

MOLLAN, Patricia Ann Fairbank. b 44. QUB BSc67 PhD70 BD97. **d** 97 **p** 98. Aux Min *D & D* from 97; Aux Min Lecale Gp from 02. *Echo Sound, 69 Killyleagh Road, Downpatrick BT30 9BN* Tel (028) 4482 1620 E-mail pat@mollan.net

MOLLAN, Prof Raymond Alexander Boyce. b 43. QUB MB, BCh69 BAO69 MD84 FRCS. CITC 97. **d** 97 **p** 98. Aux Min *D & D* from 97; Aux Min Comber from 02. *Echo Sound, 69 Killyleagh Road, Downpatrick BT30 9BN* Tel (028) 4482 1620 E-mail rab@mollan.net

MOLLER, The Very Revd George Brian. b 35. TCD BA60 MA64 Div Test 61 Lon Univ BD84. **d** 61 **p** 62. C Belfast St Pet *Conn* 61-64; C Larne and Inver 64-68; P-in-c Rathcoole 68-69; I 69-86; Dioc Dir Ords 82-92; I Belfast St Bart 86-01; Chapl Stranmillis Univ Coll Belf 88-01; Preb Conn Cathl *Conn* 90-96; Treas 96; Prec 96-98; Dean 98-01; rtd 01. *7 Sunningdale Park, Bangor BT20 4UU* Tel (028) 9145 5903
E-mail bg@moller2.freeserve.co.uk

MOLLOY, Mrs Heather. b 54. Bradf Univ BTech76. LNSM course 92. **d** 95 **p** 96. OLM Harwood *Man* from 95. *7 Fellside, Bolton BL2 4HB* Tel (01204) 520395

MOLLOY, Terence Harold. b 36. St Jo Coll Dur BA67 Birm Univ DipTh70 MA78. Qu Coll Birm 67. **d** 70 **p** 71. C Beaconsfield *Ox* 70-75; P-in-c Chesham Ch Ch 75-80; TV Gt Chesham 80-81; P-in-c Weston Turville 81-90; P-in-c Stoke Mandeville 87-89; P-in-c Gt Marlow 90-93; P-in-c Bisham 90-93; TR Gt Marlow w Marlow Bottom, Lt Marlow and Bisham from 93. *The Rectory, The Causeway, Marlow SL7 2AA* Tel (01628) 482660 or 481806 E-mail nick.molony@btinternet.com

MONBERG, Ms Ulla Stefan. b 52. Copenhagen Univ BA79. Westcott Ho Cam 88. **d** 90 **p** 94. C Westmr St Jas *Lon* 90-94; Dean Women's Min and Area Dir of Ords Cen Lon 94-99; Dean Women's Min Kensington 94-99; Sec Dioc Bd of Women Candidates for Ord 94-99; C Paddington St Jo w St Mich 96-98; P-in-c S Kensington H Trin w All SS 98-02; Dir of Ords Two Cities Area 99-02; Denmark from 02. *Address temp unknown*

✠**MONDAL, The Rt Revd Barnabas Dwijen.** b 37. Dhaka Univ BA61 Serampore Univ BD64. Bp's Coll Calcutta 61. **d** 64 **p** 65 **c** 75. Barisal 64-67; Khulna 67-69; Rhode Is USA 69-70; Bollorepur 70-71; Thakurpukur 71-72; Prin Coll of Chr Th 72-74; Dhaka St Thos 74-75; Asst Bp Dhaka 75; Bp Dhaka and Moderator Ch of Bangladesh 75-03; rtd 03. *Address temp unknown*

MONDON, Simon Charles. b 57. WEMTC. **d** 02. OLM Worfield *Heref* from 02. *Duken Lane Cottage, Duken Lane, Wootton, Bridgnorth WV15 6EA* Tel (01746) 780265

MONDS, Anthony John Beatty. b 53. Solicitor 77. LNSM course 96. **d** 97 **p** 00. OLM Queen Thorne *Sarum* from 97. *East Field Cottage, Sandford Orcas, Sherborne DT9 4RP* Tel (01963) 220676 E-mail tonymonds@tmonds.freeserve.co.uk

MONEY, John. b 69. Wycliffe Hall Ox. **d** 03. C Porchester *S'well* from 03. *127A Digby Avenue, Nottingham NG3 6DT* Tel 0115-952 4610

MONGER, John Dennis. b 26. Univ of Wales (Cardiff) DipTh51. **d** 99 **p** 99. NSM Ewyas Harold w Dulas, Kenderchurch etc *Heref* from 99; RD Abbeydore 00-02. *Chapel Cottage, Longtown, Hereford HR2 0LE* Tel (01873) 860306

MONK, Mrs Mary. b 38. CertEd58. **d** 88 **p** 94. NSM Lee Gd Shep w St Pet *S'wark* 88-99; NSM Harpenden St Jo *St Alb* from 99. *3 Hawthorn Close, Harpenden AL5 1HN* Tel (01582) 462057

MONK, Nicholas John. b 32. Westcott Ho Cam 61. **d** 63 **p** 64. C Bris H Cross Inns Court *Bris* 63-67; C Stoke Bishop 67-69; V Swindon All SS 69-75; V Ashton Keynes w Leigh 75-87; P-in-c Minety w Oaksey 82-87; RD Malmesbury 85-88; V Ashton Keynes, Leigh and Minety 87-91; TR Swindon St Jo and St Andr 91-97; rtd 97; Perm to Offic *Heref* from 97. *The Riddings Cottage, Newcastle on Clun, Craven Arms SY7 8QT* Tel (01686) 670929

MONKHOUSE, Henry Alistair. b 34. **d** 99 **p** 00. OLM Quidenham Gp *Nor* from 99. *Wildwood Mill Road, Old Buckenham, Attleborough NR17 1SG* Tel (01953) 860845

MONKS, Ian Kay. b 36. K Coll Lon BA60 Lon Inst of Educn PGCE61. Oak Hill NSM Course 90. **d** 93 **p** 94. NSM Woodford Bridge *Chelmsf* from 93. *46 Summit Drive, Woodford Green IG8 8QP* Tel (020) 8550 2390

MONMOUTH, Archdeacon of. See HACKETT, The Ven Ronald Glyndwr

MONMOUTH, Bishop of. See WALKER, The Rt Revd Edward William Murray

MONMOUTH, Dean of. See FENWICK, The Very Revd Richard David

MONTAGUE (née LAIDLAW), Mrs Juliet. b 52. Nottm Univ BTh82. Linc Th Coll 78. **dss** 82 **d** 87 **p** 94. Gainsborough All SS *Linc* 82-86; Chapl Linc Cathl 86-92; Chapl Linc Colls of FE 86-92; Dn-in-c Whaplode Drove 92-94; P-in-c 94-99; Dn-in-c Gedney Hill 92-94; P-in-c 94-99; P-in-c Crawley and Littleton and Sparsholt w Lainston *Win* from 99; R from 03. *The Rectory, Church Lane, Littleton, Winchester SO22 6QY* Tel (01962) 881898 Fax as telephone E-mail jandf.montague@virgin.net

MONTAGUE-YOUENS, Canon Hubert Edward. b 30. Ripon Hall Ox 55. **d** 58 **p** 59. C Redditch St Steph *Worc* 58-59; C Halesowen 59-62; V Kempsey 62-69; V Kidderminster St Geo 69-72; R Ribbesford w Bewdley and Dowles 72-81; RD Kidderminster 74-81; Hon Can Worc Cathl 78-81; TR Bridport *Sarum* 81-86; RD Lyme Bay 82-86; V Easebourne *Chich* 86-89; Chapl K Edw VII Hosp Midhurst 86-89; rtd 89; Perm to Offic *Worc* from 89; Perm to Offic *Glouc* 89-95 and from 98; P-in-c Twyning 96-98. *6 Harbour View, Bredon Road, Tewkesbury GL20 5AZ* Tel (01684) 292363

✠**MONTEFIORE, The Rt Revd Hugh William.** b 20. St Jo Coll Ox BA46 MA47 SS Coll Cam BD63 Aber Univ Hon DD77 Birm Univ Hon DD85. Westcott Ho Cam 48. **d** 49 **p** 50 **c** 70. C Newc St Geo *Newc* 49-51; Chapl and Tutor Westcott Ho Cam 51-53; Vice-Prin 53-54; Dean G&C Coll Cam 54-63; Asst Lect Th Cam Univ 56-59; Lect 59-63; Can Th Cov Cathl *Cov* 59-69; V Cambridge Gt St Mary w St Mich *Ely* 63-70; Hon Can Ely Cathl 69-70; Suff Bp Kingston *S'wark* 70-78; Bp Birm 78-87; rtd 87; Asst Bp *S'wark* from 87. *White Lodge, 23 Bellevue Road, London SW17 7EB* Tel (020) 8672 6697

MONTEITH, David Robert Malvern. b 68. St Jo Coll Dur BSc89 Nottm Univ BTh92 MA93. St Jo Coll Nottm 90. **d** 93 **p** 94. C Kings Heath *Birm* 93-97; C St Martin-in-the-Fields *Lon* 97-02; P-in-c S Wimbledon H Trin and St Pet *S'wark* from 02. *The Vicarage, 10 De Burgh Road, London SW19 1DX* Tel (020) 8543 2838 E-mail david.monteith1@btinternet.com

MONTGOMERIE, Alexander (Sandy). b 47. St Jo Coll Nottm CertCS94. **d** 94 **p** 96. NSM Irvine St Andr LEP *Glas* from 94; NSM Ardrossan from 94. *105 Sharphill Road, Saltcoats KA21 5QU* Tel (01294) 465193 Fax as telephone E-mail sandy.montgomerie@btinternet.com

MONTGOMERIE, Andrew Simon. b 60. Keble Coll Ox BA82. Ridley Hall Cam 83. **d** 85 **p** 86. C Childwall All SS *Liv* 85-87; C Yardley St Edburgha *Birm* 87-90; TV Solihull 90-96; P-in-c Balsall Common 96; V from 96. *St Peter's House, Holly Lane, Balsall Common, Coventry CV7 7EA* Tel (01676) 532721

MONTGOMERY, Canon Anthony Alan. b 33. Trin Hall Cam BA56. Edin Th Coll 56. **d** 58 **p** 59. C Dumfries *Glas* 58-63; P-in-c Airdrie 63-66; R 66-68; Asst Chapl Gordonstoun Sch 68-93; Can St Andr Cathl Inverness *Mor* from 81; rtd 93. *Easter Hillside, Mosstowie, Elgin IV30 8XE* Tel and fax (01343) 850282 Mobile 0411-565780 E-mail anthony_montgomery@compuserve.com

MONTGOMERY, Charles George Greathead. b 08. AKC33. **d** 33 **p** 34. C Perry Street *Roch* 33-40; C-in-c St Gennys 42-44; V Poundstock *Truro* 44-45; rtd 45. *Jasmine Cottage, Ash Cross, Bradworthy, Holsworthy EX22 7SP*

MONTGOMERY, Ian David. b 44. St Andr Univ LLB66 FCA69. Wycliffe Hall Ox 74. **d** 75 **p** 76. C Fulham St Dionis Parson's Green *Lon* 75-78; USA from 78. *511 Harbor Light Court, Neenham, WI 54956, USA* E-mail frianm@aol.com

MONTGOMERY (née YOUATT), Mrs Jennifer Alison. b 49. St Aid Coll Dur BSc70 Homerton Coll Cam PGCE71. N Ord Course 89. **d** 92 **p** 94. NSM Ripon H Trin *Ripon* from 92; Warden of Readers from 99. *Washington House, Littlethorpe, Ripon HG4 3LJ* Tel (01765) 605276 *or* tel and fax 690930 E-mail montgomery@littlethorpe97.freeserve.co.uk

MONTGOMERY, Canon John Alexander. b 11. TCD BA34 MA42. CITC 35. **d** 35 **p** 36. C Clogh 35-37; C Belfast St Simon *Conn* 37-40; Lic to Offic *K, E & A* 40-45; C Drumshambo 45-50; I Taunagh w Kilmactranny, Ballysumaghan etc 50-54; I Garvary *Clogh* 54-59; I Kilkeevin *K, E & A* 59-67; I Ardagh 67-71; I Ardagh w Kilcommick 71-80; Preb Elphin Cathl 78-80; rtd 80; Hon C Bathgate *Edin* 83-90. *c/o Mrs Helga Dodds, 14 King Street, Armadale, Bathgate EH48 2NW*

MONTGOMERY, Pembroke John Charles. b 24. Codrington Coll Barbados. **d** 53 **p** 55. St Vincent 55-73; Can Kingstown Cathl 63-73; P-in-c Derby St Jas *Derby* 73-74; V 74-90; rtd 90. *37 Church Street, Tetbury GL8 8JG* Tel (01666) 504817

MONTGOMERY, Miss Rachel. b 63. Reading Univ BA85. Wycliffe Hall Ox BTh94. **d** 94 **p** 95. C Tufnell Park St Geo and All SS *Lon* 94-99; V Bethnal Green St Jas Less from 99; CME Officer from 99. *St James the Less Vicarage, St James's Avenue, London E2 9JD* Tel (020) 8980 1612 E-mail rachel.montgomery@london.anglican.org

MONTGOMERY, Stanley. b 18. Lich Th Coll. **d** 52 **p** 53. P-in-c Hitcham w Lt Finborough, Kettlebaston etc 93-95; Perm to Offic *St E* from 95. *34 Drovers Rise, Stanton, Bury St Edmunds IP31 2BW* Tel (01359) 250359

MONTGOMERY, Canon Thomas Charles Osborne. b 59. Edin Univ BD81. Edin Th Coll 77. **d** 82 **p** 83. C Glas St Mary *Glas* 82-85; C Dumfries 85-88; R Hamilton 88-96; Can St Mary's Cathl from 94; R Glas St Marg from 96. *St Margaret's Rectory, 22 Monreith Road, Glasgow G43 2NY* Tel 0141-632 3292 *or* 636 1131 Fax 632 3292

MONTGOMERY, Timothy Robert. b 59. Hull Univ BA82 Cam Univ PGCE83. EAMTC 90. **d** 93 **p** 94. Dir Romsey Mill Community Cen *Ely* 93-94; NSM Cambridge St Phil 93-96; Warden Kepplewray Cen Broughton-in-Furness 96-00; NSM Kendal St Thos *Carl* 96-00; V from 00. *St Thomas's Vicarage, South View Lane, Kendal LA9 4QN* Tel (01539) 729617 *or* 730683 Fax 729010 E-mail rev.tim@virginnet.co.uk *or* vicar@saint-thomas.co.uk

MONTGOMERY, Archdeacon of. See THELWELL, The Ven John Berry

MOODY, Aubrey Rowland. b 11. Coll of Resurr Mirfield 53. **d** 55 **p** 56. C Wanstead St Mary *Chelmsf* 55-57; V Feering 57-01; rtd 01. *The Vicarage, 11 Feering Hill, Feering, Colchester CO5 9NL* Tel (01376) 570226

MOODY, Christopher John Everard. b 51. New Coll Ox BA72 Lon Univ MSc90. Cuddesdon Coll BA74. **d** 75 **p** 76. C Fulham All SS *Lon* 75-79; C Surbiton St Andr and St Mark *S'wark* 79-82; Chapl K Coll Lon 82-87; V S Lambeth St Anne and All SS *S'wark* 87-95; RD Lambeth 90-95; P-in-c Market Harborough *Leic* 95-97; P-in-c Market Harborough Transfiguration 95-97; V Market Harborough and The Transfiguration etc from 97. *The Rectory, Rectory Lane, Market Harborough LE16 8AS* Tel (01858) 462926 E-mail chris.moody@harborough-anglican.org.uk

MOODY, Colin John. b 36. Bris Univ CASS71. Chich Th Coll 61. **d** 63 **p** 64. C Hove All SS *Chich* 63-69; C Dulwich St Barn *S'wark* 69-70; Perm to Offic *Bris* 70-71; Perm to Offic *Chich* 72-78 and from 90; Lic to Offic *Ely* 78-89; rtd 01. *11 Hewitts, Henfield BN5 9DT* Tel (01273) 495062 Fax as telephone

MOODY, Derek Frank. b 41. Univ of Wales BA62. Chich Th Coll 63. **d** 65 **p** 66. C Ellesmere Port *Ches* 65-69; C Lewisham St Jo Southend *S'wark* 69-73; TV Catford (Southend) and Downham 73-75; V Ham St Rich 75-83; V Catford St Laur 83-88; TV Brighton St Pet and St Nic w Chpl Royal *Chich* 88-97; V Brighton St Nic from 97. *5 Clifton Road, Brighton BN1 3HP* Tel (01273) 321399 E-mail derek@moodyd.fsnet.co.uk

MOODY, Ms Elizabeth Jane. b 61. Hull Univ BA82 Westmr Coll Ox PGCE84. Ridley Hall Cam 00. **d** 02 **p** 03. C Uxbridge *Lon* from 02. *15 Lawn Road, Uxbridge UB8 2TJ* Tel (01895) 462883 Mobile 07796-988302 E-mail lizmoody@tiscali.co.uk

MOODY, Preb George Henry. b 27. ACIS56 ARCA68 Dip of Chapl to the Deaf 77. Cranmer Hall Dur 69. **d** 71 **p** 72. C Marske in Cleveland *York* 71-74; Chapl to the Deaf *Lich* 74-89; Preb Lich Cathl 83-89; rtd 89; Perm to Offic *York* from 90. *21 Priestcrofts, Marske-by-the-Sea, Redcar TS11 7HW* Tel (01642) 489660

MOODY, Ivor Robert. b 57. K Coll Lon BD AKC. Coll of Resurr Mirfield. **d** 82 **p** 83. C Leytonstone St Marg w St Columba *Chelmsf* 82-85; C Leigh-on-Sea St Marg 85-88; V Tilbury Docks 88-96; Chapl Anglia Poly Univ from 96. *4 Bishops Court Gardens, Chelmsford CM2 6AZ* Tel (01245) 261700 *or* 493131 E-mail i.r.moody@apu.ac.uk

MOODY, Canon John Kelvin. b 30. St Fran Coll Brisbane ThL55. **d** 56 **p** 57. Australia 56-61; C Earl's Court St Cuth w St Matthias *Lon* 61-64; Chapl Ankara *Eur* 64-69; Chapl Istanbul 64-66; Chapl Palma 69-75; Chapl Tangier 75-79; Can Gib Cathl 74-79; Hon Can from 79; Australia from 79; rtd 95. *1 Short Street, Watson's Bay, NSW, Australia 2030* Tel (0061) (2) 9337 2871

MOOKERJI, Michael Manoje. b 45. Baring Union Coll Punjab BSc69. Ridley Hall Cam 83. **d** 85 **p** 86. C Heanor *Derby* 85-92; V Codnor and Loscoe 92-93; V Codnor 93-02; V Winshill from 02. *The Vicarage, 54 Mill Hill Lane, Burton-on-Trent DE15 0BB* Tel (01283) 545043

MOON, Arthur Thomas. b 22. ACP53 LCP56 Lon Univ DipTh66. Sarum Th Coll 65. **d** 66 **p** 67. C Fulwood Ch Ch *Blackb* 66-71; Hon C Bispham 71-80; C 80-87; rtd 87; Perm to Offic *Blackb* from 87. *15 Kirkstone Drive, Thornton-Cleveleys FY5 1QQ* Tel (01253) 853521

MOON, John Charles. b 23. Sarum Th Coll 49. **d** 51 **p** 52. C Bottesford *Linc* 51-54; C Habrough 54-55; V Immingham 55-61; V Weaste *Man* 61-67; V Spalding St Jo *Linc* 67-82; V Spalding St Jo w Deeping St Nicholas 82-86; rtd 86; Perm to Offic *Linc* 87-02. *14 Harrox Road, Moulton, Spalding PE12 6PR* Tel (01406) 370111

MOON, Philip. b 59. CCC Ox BA80 Warwick Univ PhD92. Wycliffe Hall Ox BTh01. **d** 01 **p** 02. C Otley *Bradf* from 01. *30 Newall Hall Park, Otley LS21 2RD* Tel (01943) 468029 E-mail philandpam@moon27.freeserve.co.uk

MOON, Philip Russell. b 56. Em Coll Cam BA78 MA81 Reading Univ PGCE79. Wycliffe Hall Ox BA82. **d** 85 **p** 86. C Crowborough *Chich* 85-87; Hd of CYFA (CPAS) 87-94; V Lowestoft Ch Ch *Nor* from 94. *The Vicarage, 16 Corton Road, Lowestoft NR32 4PL* Tel (01502) 572444

MOON, Thomas Arnold. b 24. Lon Univ BA51. Oak Hill Th Coll 49. **d** 52 **p** 53. C Fazakerley Em *Liv* 52-56; V Everton St Benedict 56-70; V Formby St Luke 70-95; rtd 95; Perm to Offic *Liv* from 95. *8 Harington Road, Formby, Liverpool L37 1NU* Tel (01704) 872229

MOONEY, The Ven Paul Gerard. b 58. **d** 84 **p** 85. In RC Ch 84-90; Korea 90-94; Chapl Miss to Seamen 90-94; Hon Can Pusan Korea from 94; Chapl Antwerp Miss to Seamen 94-97; Asst Chapl Antwerp St Boniface *Eur* 94-97; C Galway w Kilcummin *T, K & A* 97-98; I New w Old Ross, Whitechurch, Fethard etc *C & O* from 98; Hon Chapl New Ross and Waterford Miss to Seamen from 98; Prec Ferns Cathl from 01; Adn Ferns from 02. *The Rectory, College Road, New Ross, Co Wexford, Irish Republic* Tel (00353) (51) 425004 E-mail archdeacon@ferns.anglican.org

MOOR, David Drury. b 18. St Edm Hall Ox BA39 MA44. Wells Th Coll 46. **d** 48 **p** 49. C Tuffley *Glouc* 48-52; P-in-c Symondsbury *Sarum* 52-53; R 53-61; V Bournemouth St Andr *Win* 61-69; V Bournemouth St Mich 69-83; rtd 83; Perm to Offic *Sarum* from 83; Perm to Offic *Win* from 83. *93 Western Avenue, Bournemouth BH10 6HG* Tel (01202) 512455

MOOR, Simon Alan. b 65. Nottm Univ BTh93. Linc Th Coll 90. **d** 93 **p** 94. C Skegness and Winthorpe *Linc* 93-96; C Airedale w Fryston *Wakef* 96-98; V Hoylandswaine and Silkstone w Stainborough from 98. *The Vicarage, 12 High Street, Silkstone, Barnsley S75 4JN* Tel (01226) 790232 Fax as telephone

MOORE, Albert William (Bill). b 47. Birm Poly FTC72. WMMTC 91. **d** 94 **p** 95. C Hobs Moat *Birm* 94-98; V Dosthill from 98. *The Vicarage, Dosthill, Tamworth B77 1LU* Tel (01827) 281349

MOORE, Andrew Jonathan. b 59. York Univ BA82 Wycliffe Hall Ox BA84 MA89 Worc Coll Ox DPhil99. **d** 86 **p** 86. Australia 86-90; C Camberwell St Jo Melbourne 86-87; Assoc P S Yarra Ch Ch Melbourne 87-90; Acting Chapl Worc Coll Ox 91-94; Chapl Jes Coll Ox 94-99; Voc Adv *Ox* from 98; Hon Chapl Cen for Mediaeval and Renaissance Studies Ox from 99; Research Fell Regent's Park Coll Ox from 01. *Regent's Park College, Oxford OX1 2LB* Tel (01865) 288120 Fax 288121 E-mail andrew.moore@regents-park.ox.ac.uk

MOORE, Anthony Harry. b 34. Westcott Ho Cam 88. **d** 90 **p** 91. C Eyke w Bromeswell, Rendlesham, Tunstall etc *St E* 90-93; V Aldeburgh w Hazlewood 93-02; rtd 02; Perm to Offic *St E* from

---

02. *5 Kings Meadow, Great Cornard, Sudbury CO10 0HP* Tel (01787) 377967

MOORE, Anthony Michael. b 71. Ex Univ BA94 Leeds Univ BA98 MA99. Coll of Resurr Mirfield 96. **d** 99 **p** 00. C Carnforth *Blackb* 99-03; Research Fell Coll of Resurr Mirfield from 03. *The College of the Resurrection, Stocks Bank Road, Mirfield WF14 0BW* Tel (01924) 481909 Fax 492738 E-mail amoore@mirfield.org.uk

MOORE, Anthony Richmond. b 36. Clare Coll Cam BA59 MA63. Linc Th Coll 59. **d** 61 **p** 62. C Roehampton H Trin *S'wark* 61-66; C New Eltham All SS 66-70; P Missr Blackbird Leys CD *Ox* 70-81; Dioc Ecum Officer 80-00; TV Dorchester 81-93; V Enstone and Heythrop 93-01; rtd 01. *13 Cobden Crescent, Oxford OX1 4LJ* Tel (01865) 244673 E-mail moore.t@which.net

MOORE, Arlene. b 64. Dundee Univ BSc87 N Coll of Educn PGCE90 TCD BTh95. CITC 92. **d** 95 **p** 96. C Portadown St Mark *Arm* 95-99; Perm to Offic *Sheff* 99-02; C Crookes St Thos 02-03. *Address temp unknown*

MOORE, Arthur Lewis. b 33. Dur Univ BA58 PhD64. Cranmer Hall Dur DipTh59. **d** 62 **p** 63. C Stone *Roch* 62-66; C Clevedon St Andr *B & W* 66-68; Chapl Wycliffe Hall Ox 68-70; Vice-Prin 70-83; P-in-c Ampfield *Win* 83-84; V Hursley and Ampfield 84-92; TV Ewyas Harold w Dulas, Kenderchurch etc *Heref* 92-94; P-in-c 94-98; rtd 98. *2 Tollstone Way, Grosmont, Abergavenny NP7 8ER*

MOORE, Arthur Robert (Bob). b 15. MBE98. Sarum Th Coll 62. **d** 63 **p** 64. C Calne and Blackland *Sarum* 63-67; V Steeple Ashton w Semington 67-79; V Keevil 72-79; Chapl Southwick w Boarhunt *Portsm* 79-91; rtd 84; Perm to Offic *Portsm* from 91. *1 High Street, Southwick, Fareham PO17 6EB* Tel (023) 9238 2113 Fax 9237 0991

MOORE, Canon Bernard Geoffrey. b 27. New Coll Ox BA47 MA52. Ely Th Coll 49. **d** 51 **p** 52. C Chorley St Pet *Blackb* 51-54; Bp's Dom Chapl 54-55; C-in-c Blackpool St Mich CD 55-67; Chapl Victoria Hosp Blackpool 58-67; V Morecambe St Barn *Blackb* 67-81; R Standish 81-88; Hon Can Blackb Cathl 86-92; RD Chorley 86-92; V Charnock Richard 88-92; rtd 92; Perm to Offic *Ex* from 92; *Carl* from 01. *29 Wiltshire Close, Exeter EX4 1LU* Tel (01392) 58686

MOORE, Bernard George. b 32. Imp Coll Lon DIC54. Qu Coll Birm 57. **d** 60 **p** 62. C Middlesbrough St Columba *York* 60-62; S Africa 62-70; Chapl RN 70-74; C Milton *Portsm* 74-76; New Zealand from 76; rtd 97. *45 Feasegate Street, Manurewa, South Auckland 1702, New Zealand* Tel (0064) (9) 267 6924

MOORE, Brian Philip. b 51. AKC72. St Aug Coll Cant 72. **d** 74 **p** 75. C Bp's Hatfield *St Alb* 74-78; C Radlett 78-81; V Eaton Bray w Edlesborough 81-92; RD Dunstable 85-90; V St Alb St Sav 92-03; V St Peter-in-Thanet *Cant* from 03. *The Vicarage, 14 Vicarage Street, St Peters, Broadstairs CT10 2SG* Tel (01843) 869169 *or* 866061 E-mail brian.moore90@ntlworld.com

✠**MOORE, The Rt Revd Bruce Macgregor.** b 31. Univ of NZ BA55. Coll of Resurr Mirfield. **d** 57 **p** 58 **c** 92. C Blackpool St Steph *Blackb* 57-61; New Zealand from 61; Hon Can Auckland 78-96; Adn Manukau 81-90; Asst Bp Auckland 92-97. *5 Pokaka Crescent, Wharewaka, Taupo, New Zealand* Tel (0064) (7) 378 4849 E-mail brucemoore@xtra.co.nz

MOORE, Charles David. b 59. Dundee Univ BSc82 BArch85 Open Univ MA96 RIBA86. St Jo Coll Nottm Dip Th Studies 93. **d** 93 **p** 94. C Deane *Man* 93-97; Crosslinks 98-02; R and Sub Dean Mutare Zimbabwe 98-02; R Bermondsey St Mary w St Olave, St Jo etc *S'wark* from 02. *The Rectory, 193 Bermondsey Street, London SE1 3UW* Tel (020) 7357 0984

MOORE, Canon Colin Frederick. b 49. CITC 69. **d** 72 **p** 73. C Drumglass w Moygashel *Arm* 72-80; I Newtownhamilton w Ballymoyer and Belleek from 80; Hon V Choral Arm Cathl 85-96; Can and Preb from 97. *71 Ballymoyer Road, Whitecross, Armagh BT60 2LA* Tel (028) 3750 7256

MOORE, Darren Lee. b 73. Kingston Univ BEng95 Oak Hill Th Coll BA01. **d** 01 **p** 02. C Camberwell All SS *S'wark* from 01. *The Old Vicarage, Blenheim Grove, London SE15 4QS* Tel (020) 7635 6889

MOORE, David. b 36. Univ of Wales (Lamp) BA61 Magd Coll Cam BA63 MA68. Linc Th Coll 63. **d** 65 **p** 66. C Saltburn-by-the-Sea *York* 65-69; C Northallerton w Kirby Sigston 69-72; V Kirklevington 72-02; V High and Low Worsall 73-02; Chapl HM Det Cen Kirklevington 72-89; Chapl HM YOI Kirklevington Grange 89-02; rtd 02. *15 King's Drive, Eastbourne BN21 2NX* Tel (01325) 726947

MOORE, David James Paton. b 60. Sheff Univ BEng82. Cranmer Hall Dur 88. **d** 91 **p** 92. C Pemberton St Mark Newtown *Liv* 91-94; C St Helens St Helen 94-97; V Canonbury St Steph *Lon* from 97. *St Stephen's Vicarage, 9 River Place, London N1 2DE* Tel (020) 7354 9118 *or* 7226 7526 Fax 7226 7526

MOORE, David Leonard. b 51. **d** 80 **p** 82. Hon C Brixton St Matt *S'wark* 80-82; C 82-84; TV Bris St Agnes and St Simon w St Werburgh *Bris* 84-86; Perm to Offic 86-88; Perm to Offic *Blackb* from 88. *154 Victoria Road, Fulwood, Preston PR2 8NQ*

MOORE, David Metcalfe. b 41. Hull Univ BA64 PhD69. Trin Coll Bris 76. **d** 78 **p** 79. C Marple All SS *Ches* 78-82; V Loudwater *Ox* 82-90; V Chilwell *S'well* 90-93; rtd 93. *10 Cromwell Avenue, Thame OX9 3TD* Tel (01844) 217556

MOORE, David Roy. b 39. Clare Coll Cam BA61. Ripon Hall Ox 61. **d** 63 **p** 64. C Melton Mowbray w Thorpe Arnold *Leic* 63-66; Dep Dir The Samaritans 66-73; C St Steph Walbrook and St Swithun etc *Lon* 66-73; C Daybrook *S'well* 77-80; V 80-87; V Ham St Andr *S'wark* 87-99; P-in-c Rothbury *Newc* from 99. *The Rectory, Rothbury, Morpeth NE65 7TL* Tel (01669) 620482

MOORE, Canon Dennis Charles. b 19. Lon Univ BD46. Tyndale Hall Bris 39. **d** 43 **p** 44. C Broadwater St Mary *Chich* 43-47; Org Sec (E England) CPAS 47-51; V Eccleston St Luke *Liv* 51-55; V New Catton St Luke *Nor* 55-62; V Wellington w Eyton *Lich* 62-70; RD Wrockwardine 66-70; V Watford St Mary *St Alb* 70-73; P-in-c Watford St Jas 73-74; V Watford 73-84; RD Watford 75-81; Hon Can St Alb 80-84; rtd 84; Perm to Offic *Nor* from 84. *82 Greenways, Eaton, Norwich NR4 6HF* Tel (01603) 502492

MOORE, Donald John. b 31. Chich Th Coll 86. **d** 87 **p** 88. C Uckfield *Chich* 87-88; C Southwick St Mich 88-90; Bermuda from 90; Asst P St Geo 90-97; P-in-c St Dav 90-97; Chapl St Brendan's Psychiatric Hosp 92-97; rtd 97. *West Cedars, 5A Cedars Lane, Sandys MA 03, Bermuda* Tel (001) (441) 234 1804

MOORE, Douglas Gregory. b 49. Bris Univ BA71 CertEd72. Coll of Resurr Mirfield 87. **d** 89 **p** 90. C Hessle *York* 89-93; P-in-c Micklefield w Aberford 93-95; V Aberford w Micklefield from 95. *The Vicarage, Great North Road, Micklefield, Leeds LS25 4AG* Tel 0113-286 2154

MOORE, Canon Edward James. b 32. TD85. TCD BA56 MA59. **d** 56 **p** 57. C Belfast St Luke *Conn* 56-59; CF 59-62; C Dunmurry *Conn* 62-64; P-in-c Kilmakee 64-70; I Belfast H Trin 70-80; I Jordanstown w Monkstown 80-91; I Jordanstown 91-97; Chapl Ulster Poly 80-84; Chapl Ulster Univ 84-88; CF (ACF) 66-70 and 88-97; CF (TAVR) 70-88; Can Belf Cathl 89-97; rtd 97. *16 Langford Close, Carrickfergus BT38 8HG* Tel (028) 9336 7209 E-mail ejmh@onetel.net.uk

MOORE, Canon Henry James William. b 33. TCD BA55 MA70. **d** 56 **p** 57. C Mullabrack *Arm* 56-61; C Drumglass 61-63; I Clogherny 63-81; I Ballinderry, Tamlaght and Arboe from 81; Can Arm Cathl from 90; Chan 98-01; Prec from 01. *Ballinderry Rectory, 10 Brookmount Road, Coagh, Cookstown BT80 0BB* Tel (028) 7941 8255

✠**MOORE, The Rt Revd Henry Wylie.** b 23. Liv Univ BCom50 Leeds Univ MA72. Wycliffe Hall Ox 50. **d** 52 **p** 53 **c** 83. C Farnworth *Liv* 52-54; C Middleton *Man* 54-56; CMS 56-60; Iran 57-60; R Burnage St Marg *Man* 60-63; R Middleton 60-74; Home Sec CMS 74-80; Exec Sec CMS 80-83; Bp Cyprus and the Gulf 83-86; Gen Sec CMS 86-90; rtd 90; Asst Bp Dur 90-94; Perm to Offic *Heref* from 94. *Fern Hill Cottage, Hopesay, Craven Arms SY7 8HD* Tel (01588) 660248

MOORE, Preb Hugh Desmond. b 37. St Cath Soc Ox BA58 MA64. St Steph Ho Ox 58. **d** 61 **p** 62. C Kingston St Luke *S'wark* 61-68; Asst Chapl Lon Univ *Lon* 68-70; Chapl Edgware Community Hosp 70-92; Chapl Wellhouse NHS Trust 92-99; Chapl Barnet and Chase Farm Hosps NHS Trust from 99; V Hendon St Alphage *Lon* from 70; AD W Barnet 85-90; Preb St Paul's Cathl from 95. *The Vicarage, Montrose Avenue, Edgware HA8 0DN* Tel (020) 8952 4611

MOORE, Ivan. MA BTh. **d** 90 **p** 91. C Knock *D & D* 90-93; I Taney *D & G* 97-99; Chapl Bancroft's Sch Woodford Green from 99. *Bancroft's School, 611-627 High Road, Woodford Green IG8 0RF* Tel (020) 8505 4826

✠**MOORE, The Rt Revd James Edward.** b 33. TCD BA54 MA64. **d** 56 **p** 57 **c** 95. C Knock *D & D* 56-60; C Bangor St Comgall 60-62; P-in-c Belvoir 62-68; I Groomsport 68-75; I Dundela St Mark 75-95; Can Down Cathl 85-89; Treas 87-89; Adn Down 89-95; Chan Belf Cathl 89-95; Bp Conn 95-01; rtd 01. *1 Plantation Road, Bangor BT19 6AF* Tel (028) 9147 7295

MOORE, Canon James Kenneth. b 37. AKC62. St Boniface Warminster 62. **d** 63 **p** 64. C W Hartlepool St Oswald *Dur* 63-66; C-in-c Manor Park CD *Sheff* 66-76; TV Sheff Manor 76-78; R Frecheville and Hackenthorpe 78-87; V Bilham 87-91; V Sheff St Oswald 91-02; Hon Can Sheff Cathl 93-02; rtd 02. *115 Greenhill Main Road, Sheffield S8 7RG* Tel 0114-283 9634

MOORE, John. b 22. St Aid Birkenhead 54. **d** 57 **p** 58. C Glenavy w Tunny and Crumlin *Conn* 57-59; I Kingscourt w Drumconrath, Syddan and Moybologue *M & K* 60-63; C Carnmoney *Conn* 63-65; P-in-c Templepatrick w Donegore 65-68; I Templepatrick 68-85; rtd 85. *Cuthona, 67 Prospect Road, Portstewart BT55 7NQ* Tel (028) 7083 3905 E-mail jack@cuthona.fsnet.co.uk

MOORE, John. b 26. Univ of Wales (Lamp) BA51. Oak Hill Th Coll 51. **d** 53 **p** 54. C Illogan *Truro* 53-57; C Margate H Trin *Cant* 57-58; C Abingdon w Shippon *Ox* 58-67; V Retford St Sav *S'well* 67-73; R Aspenden and Layston w Buntingford *St Alb* 73-86; V Stanstead Abbots 86-91; rtd 91; Perm to Offic *Ox* from 95. *20 Radley Road, Abingdon OX14 3PQ* Tel (01235) 532518

MOORE, John Arthur. b 33. Cuddesdon Coll 70. **d** 71 **p** 72. Hon C Gt Burstead *Chelmsf* 71-74; Chapl Barnard Castle Sch 74-97; rtd

97; Perm to Offic *Dur* from 97. *39 Woodside, Barnard Castle DL12 8DY* Tel (01833) 690947

MOORE, John Cecil. b 37. TCD BA61 MA67 BD69. CITC 62. **d** 62 **p** 63. C Belfast St Matt *Conn* 62-65; C Holywood *D & D* 65-70; I Ballyphilip w Ardquin 70-77; I Mt Merrion 77-79; I Donaghcloney w Waringstown 79-02; Treas Dromore Cathl 90-93; Chan 93-02; rtd 02. *22 Kensington Court, Dollingstown, Craigavon BT66 7HU*

MOORE, John David. b 30. St Chad's Coll Dur BA54 DipTh55 DipEd56. **d** 56 **p** 57. C Wallsend St Pet *Newc* 56-60; C Leamington Priors All SS *Cov* 60-62; V Longford 62-75; P-in-c Nuneaton St Mary 75-77; V 77-83; V St Ives *Ely* 83-00; rtd 00; Perm to Offic *Chelmsf* from 01. *25 Felmongers, Harlow CM20 3DH* Tel (01279) 436496

MOORE, John Ernest. b 24. Oak Hill NSM Course. **d** 84 **p** 85. NSM Hornchurch H Cross *Chelmsf* 84-86; NSM S Woodham Ferrers 86-91; NSM Canvey Is 91-95; Perm to Offic from 95. *St Margaret's Rectory, Maldon Road, Woodham Mortimer, Maldon CM9 6SN* Tel (01621) 843373

MOORE, John Henry. b 35. Nottm Univ BMus56 CertEd57 MA61. EMMTC 87. **d** 90 **p** 91. NSM Gotham *S'well* 90-95; NSM Kingston and Ratcliffe-on-Soar 90-95; NSM Bunny w Bradmore 95-00; P-in-c 97-00; rtd 00. *19 Hall Drive, Gotham, Nottingham NG11 0JT* Tel 0115-983 0670 E-mail john@mooreev.freeserve.co.uk

MOORE, John Keith. b 26. Sarum & Wells Th Coll 78. **d** 81 **p** 82. NSM Guildf All SS *Guildf* 81-86; NSM Guildf H Trin w St Mary 86-94; Dean of Chapter 90-94; Perm to Offic *Chich* and *Guildf* from 94. *6 Oakhurst, Crossways Road, Grayshott, Hindhead GU26 6JW* Tel (01428) 607174

MOORE, John Michael. b 48. Em Coll Cam BA70 MA73. Cuddesdon Coll 72. **d** 74 **p** 75. C Almondbury *Wakef* 74-78; TV Basingstoke *Win* 78-88; P-in-c Southampton St Alb 88-91; V Swaythling 91-99; rtd 99; Chapl St Jo Win Charity from 99. *13 Priors Way, Winchester SO22 4HQ* Tel (01962) 862341

MOORE, Canon John Richard. b 35. Nottm Univ LTh59 Lambeth MA01. St Jo Coll Nottm 56. **d** 59 **p** 60. C Northwood Em *Lon* 59-63; V Burton Dassett *Cov* 63-66; Dioc Youth Chapl 63-71; Dir Lindley Lodge Educn Trust Nuneaton 71-82; TR Kinson *Sarum* 82-88; Gen Dir CPAS 88-96; Hon Can Cov Cathl *Cov* 95-01; Internat Dir ICS 96-01; rtd 01; Perm to Offic *Cov* from 01. *26 Jourdain Park, Heathcote, Warwick CV34 6FJ* Tel (01926) 429299

MOORE, John Richard. b 45. Linc Th Coll 80. **d** 82 **p** 83. C Gt Grimsby St Mary and St Jas *Linc* 82-86; V Skirbeck Quarter 86-95; Miss to Seafarers from 86; P-in-c Coningsby w Tattershall *Linc* 95-99; R from 99. *The Rectory, 22 High Street, Coningsby, Lincoln LN4 4RA* Tel (01526) 342223

MOORE, Mrs Joyce. b 48. TCD BA70 HDipEd71 ARIAM68. CITC 98. **d** 01 **p** 02. NSM Camlough w Mullaglass *Arm* from 01. *Dundalk Road, Dunleer, Co Louth, Irish Republic* Tel (00353) (41) 51327 E-mail am.camlough@armagh.anglican.org

MOORE, Leonard Richard. b 22. Leeds Univ BA47. Coll of Resurr Mirfield 47. **d** 49 **p** 50. C Hendon St Mary *Lon* 49-54; C Stevenage *St Alb* 54-60; V Bedford All SS 60-68; Lic to Offic 68-70; P-in-c Bedford H Trin 70-74; rtd 87; Hon C Cardington *St Alb* 87-91; Perm to Offic from 92. *22 Dart Road, Bedford MK41 7BT* Tel (01234) 357536

MOORE, Mrs Margaret Doreen. b 37. Westf Coll Lon BA58 CertEd59 BD63 Lambeth STh91. Dalton Ho Bris 61. **dss** 85 **d** 87 **p** 94. Harold Hill St Paul *Chelmsf* 85-87; Hon Par Dn S Woodham Ferrers 87-91; C Canvey Is 91-95; TV Gt Baddow 95-99; P-in-c Woodham Mortimer w Hazeleigh from 99; P-in-c Woodham Walter from 99. *St Margaret's Rectory, Maldon Road, Woodham Mortimer, Maldon CM9 6SN* Tel (01621) 843373

MOORE, Matthew Edward George. b 38. Oak Hill Th Coll 77. **d** 77 **p** 78. C Larne and Inver *Conn* 77-80; I Desertmartin w Termoneeny *D & R* 80-84; I Milltown *Arm* 84-96; I Culmore w Muff and Belmont *D & R* from 96; Dioc Warden for Min of Healing from 97. *The Rectory, Heathfield, Culmore Road, Londonderry BT48 8JD* Tel (028) 7135 2396 Fax as telephone E-mail matthew.moore3@btopenworld.com

MOORE, Canon Michael Mervlyn Hamond. b 35. LVO99. Pemb Coll Ox BA60 MA63. Wells Th Coll 60. **d** 62 **p** 63. C Bethnal Green St Matt *Lon* 62-66; Chapl Bucharest w Sofia and Belgrade *Eur* 66-67; Asst Gen Sec C of E Coun on Foreign Relns 67-70; Gen Sec 70-72; Abp's Chapl on Foreign Relns *Cant* 72-82; Hon C Walworth St Pet *S'wark* 67-80; Hon Can Cant Cathl *Cant* 74-90; Chapl Chpl Royal Hampton Court Palace 82-99; Dep P in O 92-99; rtd 99. *College of St Barnabas, Blackberry Lane, Lingfield RH7 6NJ* Tel (01342) 870717

MOORE, Norman Butler. b 25. St Jo Coll Dur BA50 DipTh52. **d** 52 **p** 53. C Aston St Jas *Birm* 52-55; V 57-59; C Gravesend St Jas *Roch* 55-57; PC Warley Woods *Birm* 59-64; Bp's Youth Chapl and Asst Dir of Educn *Worc* 65-66; V Lucton w Eyton *Heref* 66-69; V Hazelwell *Birm* 69-75; V Watford St Andr *St Alb* 75-94; rtd 94; Perm to Offic *St Alb* from 94. *5 Vicarage Close, St Albans AL1 2PU* Tel (01727) 863219

MOORE, Paul Henry. b 59. Ball Coll Ox BA82 DPhil86. Wycliffe Hall Ox DipTh87. **d** 89 **p** 90. C Ox St Andr *Ox* 89-93; V Kildwick *Bradf* 93-01; V Cowplain *Portsm* from 01. *The Vicarage, Padnell Road, Cowplain, Waterlooville PO8 8DZ* Tel (023) 9226 2295 E-mail p.h.moore@btinternet.com

MOORE, Peter. b 21. Leeds Univ BA47. Coll of Resurr Mirfield 46. **d** 48 **p** 49. C N Stoneham *Win* 48-51; C Portsea St Alb *Portsm* 51-53; V Tynemouth H Trin W Town *Newc* 53-58; V Thetford St Mary *Nor* 58-65; R Mundford w Lynford 65-76; P-in-c Ickburgh w Langford 65-76; P-in-c Cranwich 65-76; RD Thetford 69; V Whitley *Newc* 76-86; Chapl Hexham Gen Hosp 76-86; Chapl War Memorial Hosp 76-86; rtd 86; Perm to Offic *Newc* from 86. *31 Glebelands, Corbridge NE45 5DS* Tel (01434) 633207

MOORE, Raymond. b 47. QUB BSc70. **d** 87 **p** 88. NSM Belfast All SS *Conn* 87-95; NSM 95-96; NSM Kilmakee from 96. *17 Royal Lodge Avenue, Knockbracken, Belfast BT8 4YR* Tel (028) 9070 5481 *or* 9026 3960 Fax 9031 4055 *or* 9026 3744 E-mail r.moore@qub.ac.uk *or* raymond@rmoore.uklinux.net

MOORE, Richard William. b 39. UCD BA70 TCD HDipEd71. CITC 98. **d** 01 **p** 02. NSM Drogheda w Ardee, Collon and Termonfeckin *Arm* from 01. *Dundalk Road, Dunleer, Co Louth, Irish Republic* Tel (00353) (41) 51327 E-mail richardmoore@eircom.ie

MOORE, Canon Richard Noel. b 34. TCD BA56 MA60. **d** 57 **p** 58. C Derry Cathl *D & R* 57-60; I Clondehorkey 60-66; I Stranorlar w Meenglas and Kilteevogue 66-76; I Glendermott 76-00; Can Derry Cathl 89-00; rtd 00. *Evergreen House, 37 Mullanahoe Road, Dungannon BT71 5AT* Tel (028) 8673 7112

MOORE, Richard Norman Theobald. b 39. St Andr Univ BSc62 Lon Univ BD66. Clifton Th Coll. **d** 66 **p** 67. C Stowmarket *St E* 66-69; C New Humberstone *Leic* 69-72; P-in-c Leic Martyrs 73; V 73-84; Chapl Manor Hosp Epsom 84-94; Chapl Surrey Oaklands NHS Trust 94-00; rtd 00; Perm to Offic *Guildf* from 02. *72 Newton Wood Road, Ashtead KT19 8NL* Tel (01372) 813999

MOORE, Robert. *See* MOORE, Arthur Robert

MOORE, Robert Allen. b 32. Univ of the Pacific BA54 Boston Univ STB58 STM59. **d** 63 **p** 63. USA 63-80; V Farington *Blackb* 80-83; TV Preston St Jo 83-85; P-in-c Fleetwood 85-87; V Leyland St Jas 87-97; rtd 97; Perm to Offic *Blackb* from 97. *19 Lea Road, Whittle-le-Woods, Chorley PR6 7PF* Tel (01257) 265701 E-mail rmoore1980@aol.com

MOORE, Canon Robert George Chaffey. b 11. Kelham Th Coll 28. **d** 39 **p** 40. C Linc St Giles *Linc* 39-42; Chapl RAF 42-47; R Compton Abbas *Sarum* 49-73; Can and Preb Sarum Cathl 72-00; TV Shaston 73-77; rtd 77; Can Emer Sarum Cathl *Sarum* from 00. *Fairfax House, 85 Castle Road, Salisbury SP1 3RW* Tel (01722) 332846

MOORE, Robin Alan. b 42. Portsm Coll of Tech DipBS65 Lon Univ BA71 Garnett Coll Lon CertEd75 Open Univ Ad Dip Educn Mgt 87 Brighton Univ Dip Counselling 95. S Dios Minl Tr Scheme 91. **d** 94 **p** 95. NSM Barcombe *Chich* from 94; Chapl St Pet and St Jas Hospice N Chailey from 99. *Yew Tree House, School Path, Barcombe, Lewes BN8 5DN* Tel (01273) 400747

MOORE, Robin Hugh. b 52. CertEd BEd QUB BD TCD DipTh. **d** 84 **p** 85. C Derryloran *Arm* 84-86; C Knock *D & D* 86-89; Bp's C Belfast St Steph w St Luke *Conn* 89-94; I 94-96; I Whitehouse 96-03; Bp's C Belfast St Mary Magd from 03. *9 Sycamore Park, Newtownabbey BT37 0NR* Tel (028) 9085 1622

MOORE, Simon Quentin. b 65. Birm Univ BA83 PGCE84. St Jo Coll Nottm MA99. **d** 00 **p** 01. C St Alb St Paul *St Alb* from 00; TV Panshanger CD from 03. *69 Hardings, Welwyn Garden City AL7 2HA* Tel (01707) 375333 E-mail simon@qmoore.freeserve.co.uk

MOORE, The Very Revd Thomas Robert. b 38. TCD 65. Lambeth DipTh79 MA84. **d** 68 **p** 69. C Dublin Drumcondra w N Strand *D & G* 68-70; C Portadown St Columba *Arm* 70-72; I Kilskeery w Trillick *Clogh* 72-85; Dioc Sec from 83; I Trory w Killadeas 85-95; Can Clogh Cathl 86-89; Preb 89-91; Preb Donaghmore St Patr Cathl Dublin 91-95; Dean Clogh from 95; I Clogh w Errigal Portclare from 95. *The Deanery, 10 Augher Road, Clogher BT76 0AD* Tel (028) 8554 8235 Fax as telephone E-mail dean.t.moore@btinternet.com *or* dean@clogher.anglican.org

MOORE, Thomas Sydney. b 50. St Paul's Coll Grahamstown DipTh77. **d** 79 **p** 80. S Africa 79-96; C Bushey *St Alb* from 97. *Trinity House, 466 Bushey Mill Lane, Bushey, Watford WD23 2AS* Tel (01923) 220565 E-mail ts.moore@virgin.net

MOORE, Mrs Wendy. b 44. Westcott Ho Cam CTM94. **d** 94 **p** 95. C Rotherham *Sheff* 94-97; V Lydham w Throapham 97-01; V Bromsgrove All SS *Worc* from 01. *All Saints' Vicarage, 20 Burcot Lane, Bromsgrove B60 1AE* Tel (01527) 576515

MOORE, William. *See* MOORE, Albert William

MOORE, William Henry. b 14. K Coll Lon 34. **d** 38 **p** 39. C Mill End *St Alb* 38-41; C Tring 41-44; C Gt Yarmouth *Nor* 44-46; New Zealand 46-52; R Houghton Conquest *St Alb* 52-56; Canada 56-59; R Filby w Thrigby *Nor* 60-62; P-in-c Mautby 60-62; Perm to Offic 62-71; Asst Master Mildenhall Sec Sch 68-73; Heartsease Sch Nor 73-75; C Mildenhall *St E* 71-73; rtd 79; Perm to Offic *Nor* from 88. *21 Green Court, Avenue Green, Norwich NR7 0DN* Tel (01603) 432758

MOORE, William Morris. b 33. QUB BSc55 TCD. **d** 61 **p** 62. C Belfast St Mich *Conn* 61-64; I 70-80; C Belfast All SS 64-70; I Ballynafeigh St Jude *D & D* 80-03; Can Belf Cathl 95-03; rtd 03. *Address temp unknown*

MOORE BROOKS, Dorothy Anne. b 66. York Univ BA87 Hughes Hall Cam PGCE88. Ridley Hall Cam 96. **d** 98 **p** 99. C S Kensington St Jude *Lon* 98-01; NSM Hoddesdon *St Alb* from 01; Chapl St Ormond Street Hosp for Children NHS Trust from 02. *11 Oxenden Drive, Hoddesdon EN11 8QF* Tel (01992) 464335 E-mail dorothy.moorebrooks@btinternet.com

MOORGAS, Geoffrey Gordon. b 30. Sarum & Wells Th Coll 80. **d** 81 **p** 82. C Brixton St Matt *S'wark* 81-84; C Clapham Old Town 84-87; C Clapham TM 87; Namibia 87-94; rtd 95; NSM Limpsfield and Titsey *S'wark* from 95. *St Silvan's House, Red Lane, Oxted RH8 0RS* Tel (01883) 723452

MOORHEAD, Michael David. b 52. BSc BA. St Steph Ho Ox. **d** 83 **p** 84. C Kilburn St Aug w St Jo *Lon* 83-87; C Kenton 87-89; Chapl Cen Middx Hosp NHS Trust from 89; V Harlesden All So *Lon* from 89; P-in-c Willesden St Matt 92-02. *All Souls' Vicarage, 3 Station Road, London NW10 4UJ* Tel (020) 8965 4988 Fax as telephone E-mail michael@allsoulschurch.fsnet.co.uk

MOORHOUSE, Christine Susan. b 49. K Coll Lon BD71 AKC71. WMMTC. **dss** 86 **d** 87 **p** 94. NSM Stourbridge St Thos *Worc* 86-99; Perm to Offic from 02. *20 High Street, Wollaston, Stourbridge DY8 4NJ* Tel (01384) 395381

MOORHOUSE, Humphrey John. b 18. Oak Hill Th Coll 37. **d** 41 **p** 42. C Dalston St Mark w St Bart *Lon* 41-42; C Chadwell Heath *Chelmsf* 42-45; R Vange 45-83; rtd 83; Perm to Offic *Chelmsf* from 83. *12 Waverley Road, Benfleet SS7 4AZ* Tel (01268) 754952

MOORHOUSE, Peter. b 42. Liv Univ BSc64 Hull Univ CertEd. Linc Th Coll 79. **d** 81 **p** 82. C Horsforth *Ripon* 81-85; R Ackworth *Wakef* 85-96; Dep Chapl HM Pris Leeds 96-97; Chapl HM Pris Stocken 97-98; Chapl HM Pris Everthorpe from 98. *HM Prison Everthorpe, Everthorpe, Brough HU15 1RB* Tel (01430) 422471 Fax 421351

MOORSE, Michael William. b 36. Culham Coll of Educn TCert63. Guildf Dioc Min Course 96. **d** 98 **p** 99. OLM Woking St Pet *Guildf* from 98. *4 Bonners Close, Woking GU22 9RA* Tel (01483) 767460

MOORSOM, Christopher Arthur Robert. b 55. Ox Univ BA. Sarum & Wells Th Coll 79. **d** 82 **p** 83. C Bradford-on-Avon *Sarum* 82-85; R Broad Town, Clyffe Pypard and Tockenham 85-89; V Banwell *B & W* 89-96; R Upper Stour *Sarum* from 96. *The Rectory, Portnells Lane, Zeals, Warminster BA12 6PG* Tel (01747) 840221

MORALEE, Thomas Edward (Tony). b 33. S'wark Ord Course. **d** 82 **p** 83. NSM Wandsworth All SS *S'wark* 82-90; NSM Gt Bookham *Guildf* 91-92; Perm to Offic from 92. *71 Eastwick Park Avenue, Bookham, Leatherhead KT23 3NH* Tel (01372) 454433

MORAY, ROSS AND CAITHNESS, Bishop of. *See* CROOK, The Rt Revd John Michael

MORAY, ROSS AND CAITHNESS, Dean of. *Vacant*

MORBY, Mrs Helen Mary. b 62. Wolv Univ BA99. Ripon Coll Cuddesdon 99. **d** 01. C Lich St Chad *Lich* from 01. *45 Giles Road, Lichfield WS13 7JY* Tel (01543) 416623 *or* 416595 E-mail helen@morby.freeserve.co.uk

MORDECAI, Mrs Betty. b 27. Birm Univ BA48 Cam Univ CertEd49. Wycliffe Hall Ox 85. **dss** 86 **d** 87 **p** 94. Leamington Priors All SS *Cov* 86-87; Hon Par Dn 87-89; C Worc City St Paul and Old St Martin etc *Worc* 89-94; rtd 94. *8 Swains Crofts, Leamington Spa CV31 1YW* Tel (01926) 882001 E-mail bettyhoward@darwen23.freeserve.co.uk

MORDECAI, Thomas Huw. b 59. Bris Univ BA81 St Jo Coll Dur BA85 MA92. Cranmer Hall Dur 83. **d** 87 **p** 88. C Gillingham St Mary *Roch* 87-90; Chapl Warw Sch 90-96; Chapl Giggleswick Sch 96-98; Chapl Westmr Sch 98-01; PV Westmr Abbey from 98. *14 Barton Street, London SW1P 3NE* Tel (020) 7963 1128

MORE, Canon Richard David Antrobus. b 43. St Jo Coll Dur BA70 DipTh71. Cranmer Hall Dur 70. **d** 72 **p** 73. C Macclesfield St Mich *Ches* 72-77; Chapl Lee Abbey 77-82; V Porchester *S'well* 82-96; RD Gedling 90-96; Bp's Dom Chapl *Chelmsf* 96-01; Dioc Dir of Ords from 01; Dioc NSM Officer from 01; Hon Can Chelmsf Cathl from 96. *25 Roxwell Road, Chelmsford CM1 2LY* Tel (01245) 264187 Fax 348759 E-mail ddo@chelmsford.anglican.org

MORECROFT, Michael William. b 40. MIBiol Man Univ MEd. WMMTC. **d** 86 **p** 87. Hd Master Polesworth Sch Warks 86-91; Educn Inspector/Consultant 92-02; Hon C Wylde Green *Birm* 86-89; Hon C Castle Bromwich St Clem 89-98; Perm to Offic

from 98. *St Clement's Croft, 11 Wood Green Road, Wednesbury WS10 9AX* Tel 0121-505 5954
E-mail mwm@fort34.freeserve.co.uk

MORETON, Ann Louise. b 32. **d** 02 **p** 03. OLM Whitstable *Cant* from 02. *Church House, 24 Freeman's Close, Seasalter, Whitstable CT5 4BB* Tel (01227) 277140
E-mail annmoreton@hotmail.com

MORETON, Preb Mark. b 39. Jes Coll Cam BA64 MA68. Westcott Ho Cam. **d** 65 **p** 66. C Portsea All SS *Portsm* 65-70; C St Martin-in-the-Fields *Lon* 70-72; Chapl Jes Coll Cam 72-77; R Stafford St Mary and St Chad *Lich* 77-79; P-in-c Stafford Ch St 77-79; P-in-c Marston w Whitgreave 77-79; TR Stafford 79-91; V W Bromwich All SS from 91; Preb Lich Cathl from 99. *All Saints' Vicarage, 90 Hall Green Road, West Bromwich B71 3LB* Tel 0121-588 3698 *or* 2647

MORETON, Michael Bernard. b 44. St Jo Coll Cam BA66 MA70 Ch Ch Ox BA66 MA69 DPhil69. St Steph Ho Ox 66. **d** 68 **p** 69. C Banstead *Guildf* 68-74; R Alburgh *Nor* 74-75; R Denton 74-75; R Middleton Cheney w Chacombe *Pet* 75-87; Perm to Offic *Cant* from 00. *Waterloo House, 56-58 High Street, Rolvenden, Cranbrook TN17 4LN* Tel (01580) 241287

MORETON, Preb Michael Joseph. b 17. Univ Coll Lon BA40 Ch Ch Ox BA47 MA53. Wells Th Coll 47. **d** 48 **p** 49. C Rowbarton *B & W* 48-52; C Ilfracombe H Trin *Ex* 52-59; Lect Th Ex Univ 57-86; R Ex St Mary Steps *Ex* 59-86; P-in-c 86-92; RD Christianity 83-89; Preb Ex Cathl 85-86; rtd 86; Perm to Offic *Ex* from 86. *3 Glenthorne Road, Duryard, Exeter EX4 4QU* Tel (01392) 438083

MORETON, Philip Norman Harley. b 28. Linc Th Coll. **d** 57 **p** 58. C Howden *York* 57-60; C Bottesford *Linc* 60-65; V Linc St Giles 65-70; V Bracebridge Heath 71-77; V Seasalter *Cant* 77-84; TV Whitstable 84-88; rtd 88; Perm to Offic *York* from 96. *The Cottage, 2 Broad Lane, Howden, Goole DN14 7DN* Tel (01430) 430552

MORETON, Rupert Robert James. b 66. TCD BA89. CITC BTh92. **d** 92 **p** 93. C Dublin Ch Ch Cathl Gp *D & G* 92-96; Asst Chapl Costa Blanca *Eur* 96-98; Chapl Helsinki from 98. *Mannerheimintie 19 A7, 00250 Helsinki, Finland* Tel (00358) (9) 490424 *or* 680 1515 Fax 698 6302
E-mail rupert.moreton@icon.fi

✠**MORGAN, The Rt Revd Alan Wyndham.** b 40. Univ of Wales (Lamp) BA62. St Mich Coll Llan 62. **d** 64 **p** 65 **c** 89. C Llangyfelach and Morriston *S & B* 64-69; C Swansea St Pet 69-72; C Cov E *Cov* 72-73; TV 73-83; Bp's Officer for Soc Resp 78-83; Adn Cov 83-89; Suff Bp Sherwood *S'well* from 89. *Dunham House, Westgate, Southwell NG25 0JL* Tel (01636) 819133 Fax 819085
E-mail bishopsherwood@southwell.anglican.org

MORGAN, Alison Jean. b 59. Girton Coll Cam BA82 MA85 Darw Coll Cam PhD86. EMMTC 93. **d** 96 **p** 97. NSM Oadby *Leic* 96; NSM Leic H Trin w St Jo from 98. *29 Holmfield Road, Leicester LE2 1SE* Tel 0116-270 4986

MORGAN, Anthony Hogarth. b 42. St Josef Missiehuis Holland 60 St Jos RC Coll Lon 62. **d** 65 **p** 66. In RC Ch 66-93; NSM Handsworth Woodhouse *Sheff* 93-94; C Sheff Norwood St Leon 94-97; P-in-c Shiregreen St Hilda from 97. *St Hilda's House, 2 Firth Park Crescent, Sheffield S5 6HE* Tel 0114-243 6308

MORGAN, Anthony Paul George. b 57. Sarum & Wells Th Coll 89. **d** 91 **p** 92. C Plymstock *Ex* 91-95; P-in-c Wolborough w Newton Abbot 95-00; V York St Hilda *York* from 01. *St Hilda's Vicarage, 155 Tang Hall Road, York YO10 3SD* Tel (01904) 413150 E-mail york@thefms.fsnet.co.uk

✠**MORGAN, The Most Revd Barry Cennydd.** b 47. Lon Univ BA69 Selw Coll Cam BA72 MA74 Univ of Wales PhD86. Westcott Ho Cam 70. **d** 72 **p** 73 **c** 93. Chapl Bryn-y-Don Community Sch 72-75; C St Andrews Major w Michaelston-le-Pit *Llan* 72-75; Ed *Welsh Churchman* 75-82; Lect Th Univ of Wales (Cardiff) 75-77; Chapl and Lect St Mich Coll Llan 75-77; Warden Ch Hostel Ban 77-84; Chapl and Lect Th Univ of Wales (Ban) 77-84; In-Service Tr Adv *Ban* 78-84; Dir of Ords 82-84; Can Ban Cathl 83-84; R Wrexham *St As* 84-86; Adn Meirionnydd *Ban* 86-93; R Criccieth w Treflys 86-93; Bp Ban 93-99; Bp Llan from 99; Abp Wales from 03. *Llys Esgob, The Cathedral Green, Llandaff, Cardiff CF5 2YE* Tel (029) 2056 2400 Fax 2057 7129 E-mail archbishop@churchinwales.org.uk

MORGAN, Miss Beryl. b 30. **dss** 62 **d** 87 **p** 94. Rickerscote *Lich* 63-69; Hd Dss 70-87; Dioc Lay Min Adv 70-93; Willenhall H Trin 80-87; Par Dn 87-93; rtd 93; Hon C Penn *Lich* 94-01; Perm to Offic from 01. *11A Church Hill, Penn, Wolverhampton WV4 5NP* Tel (01902) 337173

MORGAN, Brian. b 35. Univ Coll Lon BA58. Wells Th Coll 59. **d** 61 **p** 62. C Withington St Chris *Man* 61-63; C Rochdale 63-65; Trinidad and Tobago 65-69; R Rio Claro St Faith and St Bart 65-66; R La Brea St Aug 66-69; V Heywood St Jas *Man* 69-74; Chapl Miss to Seamen 74-80; Kenya 74-77; Pernis 77-78; Antwerp 78-80; V Skerton St Chad *Blackb* 80-84; P-in-c Oswaldtwistle Immanuel 84-87; V Oswaldtwistle All SS 84-87; V Barrowford 87-00; rtd 00. *29 St Margaret's Road, Poole BH15 2DL* Tel (01202) 683863
E-mail brian@morgoon.freeserve.co.uk

✠**MORGAN, The Rt Revd Christopher Heudebourck.** b 47. Lon Univ DipTh70 Lanc Univ BA73 Heythrop Coll Lon MTh91. Kelham Th Coll 66. **d** 73 **p** 74 **c** 01. C Birstall *Leic* 73-76; Asst Chapl Brussels *Eur* 76-80; P-in-c Redditch St Geo *Worc* 80-81; TV Redditch, The Ridge 81-85; V Sonning *Ox* 85-96; Prin Berks Chr Tr Scheme 85-89; Dir Past Studies Ox Min Course 92-96; Area Bp Colchester *Chelmsf* from 01. *1 Fitzwalter Road, Colchester CO3 3SS* Tel (01206) 576648 Fax 763868
E-mail b.colchester@chelmsford.anglican.org

MORGAN, Christopher John. b 46. Brasted Th Coll 68 Linc Th Coll 70. **d** 72 **p** 73. C Earley St Pet *Ox* 72-76; C Epsom St Martin *Guildf* 76-79; V Stoneleigh 79-83; Ind Chapl *York* 83-92; NACRO 87-91; V York St Hilda *York* 92-96; TV E Greenwich *S'wark* from 96. *Christ Church Vicarage, 52 Earlswood Street, London SE10 9ES* Tel (020) 8853 5950

MORGAN, Clive. b 41. **d** 02. Par Dn Blaina and Nantyglo *Mon* from 02. *26 Victoria Street, Blaina, Abertillery NP13 3BG* Tel (01495) 291637

MORGAN, David Farnon Charles. b 43. Leeds Univ BA68. Coll of Resurr Mirfield 68. **d** 70 **p** 71. C Swinton St Pet *Man* 70-73; C Langley All SS and Martyrs 73-75; R Salford St Clem w St Cypr Ordsall 75-76; R Salford Ordsall St Clem 76-86; V Adlington *Blackb* from 86; AD Chorley from 98. *St Paul's Vicarage, Railway Road, Adlington, Chorley PR6 9QZ* Tel (01257) 480253
E-mail morgyvic@tinyworld.co.uk

MORGAN, David Joseph (Joe). b 47. Bp Burgess Hall Lamp 66 St Deiniol's Hawarden 74. **d** 74 **p** 75. C Pembroke Dock *St D* 74-77; C Burry Port and Pwll 77-80; Miss to Seafarers from 80; Sen Chapl and Sec Welsh Coun from 85. *25 Glanmor Park Road, Sketty, Swansea SA2 0QG* Tel (01792) 206637

MORGAN, Deiniol. **d** 02 **p** 03. Min Can Ban Cathl *Ban* from 02. *1 Alotan Crescent, Penrhosgarnedd, Bangor LL57 2NG* Tel (01248) 362986 E-mail deiniol@fish.co.uk

MORGAN, Denis. b 36. Cuddesdon Coll 67. **d** 69 **p** 70. C Bush Hill Park St Steph *Lon* 69-72; C Stevenage St Nic *St Alb* 72-75; V Croxley Green St Oswald 75-85; V Shillington 85-95; rtd 95; Perm to Offic *Roch* from 95. *7 Fromandez Drive, Horsmonden, Tonbridge TN12 8LN* Tel (01892) 722388

MORGAN, Canon Enid Morris Roberts. b 40. St Anne's Coll Ox BA61 Univ of Wales (Ban) MA73. United Th Coll Abth BD81. **d** 84 **p** 97. C Llanfihangel w Llanafan and Llanwnnws etc *St D* 84-86; Dn-in-c 86-93; Dir Bd of Miss Ch in Wales 93-00; V Llangynwyd w Maesteg *Llan* from 00; Hon Can Llan Cathl from 02. *Yr Hen Ficerdy, Llangynwyd, Maesteg CF34 9SB* Tel (01656) 733194

MORGAN, Gareth Morison Kilby. b 33. Bris Univ BA56. Cuddesdon Coll 57 Bangalore Th Coll. **d** 61 **p** 62. C St Helier *S'wark* 61-65; Chapl Scargill Ho 65-70; Dir RE *Linc* 71-74; Dir of Educn *St E* 74-81; TR Hanley H Ev *Lich* 81-87; R Cen Telford 89-92; Warden Glenfall Ho *Glouc* 92-98; rtd 98; Perm to Offic *Win* from 00. *St Neots, Kanes Hill, Southampton SO19 6AH* Tel (023) 8046 6509

MORGAN, Geoffrey. See MORGAN, James Geoffrey Selwyn

MORGAN, Gerwyn. See MORGAN, Chan William Charles Gerwyn

MORGAN, Glyn. b 21. Oak Hill Th Coll 73. **d** 76 **p** 77. Hon C Barton Seagrave w Warkton *Pet* 76-00; Perm to Offic from 00. *St Edmund's House, Warkton, Kettering NN15 5AB* Tel (01536) 520610

MORGAN, Glyn. b 33. Univ of Wales (Ban) BA55 MA69. Coll of Resurr Mirfield 55. **d** 57 **p** 58. C Dolgellau *Ban* 57-60; C Conway 60-63; V Corris 63-68; Hd of RE Friars' Sch Ban 69-70; Lic to Offic 70-71; Hd of RE Oswestry Boys' Modern Sch 70-74; Hd of RE Oswestry High Sch for Girls 74-79; Hon C Oswestry H Trin *Lich* 71-79; Hd of RE Fitzalan Sch Oswestry 79-88; Perm to Offic 79-84; Perm to Offic *St As* 84-88; V Meifod and Llangynyw 88-01; RD Caereinion 89-01; rtd 01. *Crib y Gwynt Annexe, Trefnanney, Meifod SY22 6XX* Tel (01938) 500066

MORGAN, Graham. b 47. KBE00. S'wark Ord Course. **d** 83 **p** 84. NSM S Kensington St Steph *Lon* 83-90; NSM Hammersmith H Innocents 90-02; NSM Bedford Park from 02. *24 Charleville Court, Charleville Road, London W14 9JG* Tel (020) 7381 3211

MORGAN, Harold Evan. b 17. St D Coll Lamp BA38. **d** 40 **p** 41. C Oldbury *Birm* 40-42; C Northleach and Hampnett w Stowell and Yanworth *Glouc* 42-43; CF 43-47; PC Milford *Derby* 47-50; R Yerbeston w Loveston *St D* 50-52; V Uzmaston and Boulston 52-53; R Llanilid w Pencoed *Llan* 53-68; V Newcastle 68-83; rtd 83; Perm to Offic *Llan* from 83. *Greystones, 28 Seaview Drive, Ogmore-by-Sea, Bridgend CF32 0PB* Tel (01656) 880467

MORGAN, Henry. b 45. Hertf Coll Ox BA68. Westcott Ho Cam 68. **d** 70 **p** 71. C Lee St Marg *S'wark* 70-73; C Newington St Paul 73-76; V Camberwell St Mich w All So w Em 76-84; V Kingswood 84-93; Perm to Offic from 93. *4 Glebe Gardens, New Malden KT3 5RY* Tel (020) 8942 4362
E-mail henry.morgan1@virgin.net

MORGAN, Hogarth. See MORGAN, Anthony Hogarth

MORGAN, Ian David John. b 57. LTCL75 Hull Univ BA78. Ripon Coll Cuddesdon 80. **d** 83 **p** 84. C Heref H Trin *Heref*

83-86; C New Shoreham *Chich* 86-88; Researcher, Producer & Presenter BBC Local Radio 88-92; V Ipswich All Hallows *St E* 92-95; TR Ipswich St Mary at Stoke w St Pet 95-97; TR Ipswich St Mary at Stoke w St Pet and St Fran from 97. *The Rectory, 74 Ancaster Road, Ipswich IP2 9AJ* Tel (01473) 601895 Fax 683303 E-mail ianmorgan@aol.com

MORGAN, Ian Stephen. b 50. Open Univ BA88. Sarum & Wells Th Coll 86. **d** 88 **p** 89. C Baldock w Bygrave *St Alb* 88-91; C Rumburgh w S Elmham w the Ilketshalls *St E* 91-92; C S Elmham and Ilketshall 92-95; V Bungay H Trin w St Mary from 95. *The Vicarage, 3 Trinity Gardens, Bungay NR35 1HH* Tel (01986) 892553 Mobile 07808-451350 Fax 895369 E-mail sm01020158@aol.com

MORGAN, James Geoffrey Selwyn. b 59. Ex Univ BA81 PGCE82 Dur Univ CCSk91 Open Univ MPhil97. Cranmer Hall Dur 88. **d** 91 **p** 92. C Reading St Agnes w St Paul *Ox* 91-93; C Bromham w Oakley and Stagsden *St Alb* 94-95; Perm to Offic *Pet* 96-98; C Epsom St Martin *Guildf* 98-01; Ox Cen for Miss Studies from 01. *Oxford Centre for Mission Studies, PO Box 70, Oxford OX2 6HB* Tel (01865) 556071 Fax 510823 E-mail gmorgan@ocms.ac.uk

MORGAN, Joe. *See* MORGAN, David Joseph

MORGAN, John. *See* MORGAN, William John

MORGAN, John Geoffrey Basil. b 21. Wells Th Coll 59. **d** 60 **p** 61. C Oakdale St Geo *Sarum* 60-64; C Talbot Village 64-67; C-in-c Ensbury St Thos CD 67-69; V Ensbury 69-82; C W Parley 82-86; rtd 86; Perm to Offic *Sarum* from 01. *57 Selwood Caravan Park, Weymans Avenue, Bournemouth BH10 7JX* Tel (01202) 582327

MORGAN, John Laurence. b 41. Melbourne Univ BA62 Oriel Coll Ox BA69 MA73 DPhil76. **d** 68 **p** 69. Acting Chapl Oriel Coll Ox 69 and 70-76; USA 77-78; Australia from 78. *St John's College, College Road, St Lucia, Qld, Australia 4067* Tel (0062) (7) 3371 3741 *or* 3842 6600 Fax 3870 5124 E-mail john.morgan@mailbox.uq.edu.au

MORGAN, John Roland. b 31. Birm Univ BA54. Bps' Coll Cheshunt 54. **d** 55 **p** 56. C Selly Oak St Mary *Birm* 55-57; C Yardley Wood 57-58; C Hamstead St Paul 58-61; V Smethwick St Chad 61-68; V Balsall Common 68-82; V N Leigh *Ox* 82-95; RD Woodstock 87-92; rtd 95; Perm to Offic *Ely* from 95. *Dyn Caryn, 2 Hayling Close, Godmanchester, Huntingdon PE29 2XB* Tel (01480) 459522

MORGAN, John William Miller. b 34. Lon Univ BSc56. Wycliffe Hall Ox 61. **d** 63 **p** 64. C St Alb Ch Ch *St Alb* 63-68; V Luton St Matt High Town 68-79; V Mangotsfield *Bris* 79-90; P-in-c Stanton St Quintin, Hullavington, Grittleton etc 90-95; R Hullavington, Norton and Stanton St Quintin 95-99; rtd 99; Perm to Offic *Bris* from 00. *3 Bouverie Park, Stanton St Quintin, Chippenham SN14 6EE* Tel (01666) 837670 E-mail johnwmmorgan@compuserve.com

MORGAN, Mrs Judith. b 62. Carl and Blackb Dioc Tr Inst 96. **d** 99 **p** 00. C Gt Broughton and Broughton Moor *Carl* from 99; C Brigham from 99. *The Vicarage, 1 High Brigham, Cockermouth CA14 0TE* Tel (01900) 825383

MORGAN, Katharine. b 41. **d** 91 **p** 97. NSM Loughor *S & B* from 91. *68 Borough Road, Lougher, Swansea SA4 6RT*

MORGAN, Kathleen Irene. b 52. St Martin's Coll Lanc CertEd74. WEMTC 93. **d** 96 **p** 97. NSM Barnwood *Glouc* 96-99; C Coney Hill 99-02; V Churchdown St Jo from 02. *The Vicarage, St John's Avenue, Churchdown, Gloucester GL3 2DA* Tel (01452) 713421 E-mail revkaty@aol.com

MORGAN, Kenneth James. b 14. Selw Coll Cam BA36 MA43. Wells Th Coll 36. **d** 38 **p** 39. C Moulsecoomb *Chich* 38-40; C Preston 40-41; Chapl RAFVR 41-47; Chapl Miss to Seamen 47; Lic to Offic *Dur* 47; Chapl Oslo Norway 47-51; V Blacklands Ch Ch *Chich* 51-58; V Weston St Jo *B & W* 58-66; V Shalford *Guildf* 66-84; rtd 84; Perm to Offic *Guildf* from 85. *Greenwood, The Close, Wonersh, Guildford GU5 0PA* Tel (01483) 898791

MORGAN, Linda Marianne. b 44. Bris Univ BSc69 Surrey Univ MSc72 Lon Univ PhD77 FRCPath01. STETS 99. **d** 02 **p** 03. NSM Claygate *Guildf* from 02. *8 Melbury Close, Claygate KT10 0EX* Tel (01372) 462911 E-mail l.morgan@surrey.ac.uk

MORGAN, Mrs Marian Kathleen Eleanor. b 38. Birm Univ MA94 FCMI82. WEMTC. **d** 00 **p** 01. NSM Cusop w Blakemere, Bredwardine w Brobury etc *Heref* from 00. *Castle View, Clifford, Hereford HR3 5EX* Tel and fax (01497) 831329 Mobile 07977-477212

MORGAN, Mark Anthony. b 58. LLB. Chich Th Coll. **d** 84 **p** 85. C Thorpe *Nor* 84-87; C Eaton 87-90; V Southtown 90-92; Perm to Offic from 92. *Nethergate End, The Street, Saxlingham, Nethergate, Norwich NR15 1AJ* Tel (01603) 762850

MORGAN, Mark Steven Glyn. b 60. Essex Univ BSc83 RGN86. Ridley Hall Cam 95. **d** 97 **p** 99. C Herne Bay Ch Ch *Cant* 97-02; TV Ipswich St Mary at Stoke w St Pet and St Fran *St E* from 02. *St Peter's Church House, Stoke Park Drive, Ipswich IP2 9TH* Tel (01473) 601438 E-mail hama.morgan-@tinyworld.co.uk

MORGAN, Martin Paul. b 46. St Steph Ho Ox 71. **d** 73 **p** 74. C Kettering St Mary *Pet* 73-76; C Fareham SS Pet and Paul *Portsm* 76-80; V Portsea Ascension 80-94; V Rottingdean *Chich* from 94.

The Vicarage, Steyning Road, Rottingdean, Brighton BN2 7GA Tel (01273) 309216

MORGAN, Mrs Melanie Jane. b 54. RMN. Qu Coll Birm 98. **d** 02 **p** 03. NSM Derby St Andr w St Osmund *Derby* from 02. *16 Brading Close, Alvaston, Derby DE24 0UW* Tel (01332) 754419 E-mail clifden@btinternet.com

MORGAN, Michael. b 32. Lon Univ BSc57 MSc67 PhD63. **d** 74 **p** 75. NSM Portsdown *Portsm* 74-98; Perm to Offic from 98. *12 East Cosham Road, Cosham, Portsmouth PO6 2JS* Tel (023) 9237 7442

MORGAN, Michael John. b 45. Nottm Univ BA66 MEd71. Linc Th Coll 80. **d** 82 **p** 83. C Bulkington *Cov* 82-83; C Bulkington w Shilton and Ansty 83-85; V Longford 85-89; R Norton *Sheff* 89-99; R Lapworth *Birm* from 99; R Baddesley Clinton from 99. *The Rectory, Church Lane, Lapworth, Solihull B94 5NX* Tel (01564) 782098

MORGAN, Morley Roland. b 47. Univ of Wales (Lamp) BA76. St Steph Ho Ox 76. **d** 77 **p** 78. C Merthyr Dyfan *Llan* 77-78; C Llantrisant 78-80; TV Coventry Caludon *Cov* 80-86; Chapl N Man Gen Hosp 86-93; Chapl N Man Health Care NHS Trust from 93. *North Manchester General Hospital, Delaunays Road, Crumpsall, Manchester M8 6RL* Tel 0161-720 2990 *or* 795 4567 ext 2990 Fax 720 2748

MORGAN, Canon Nicholas John. b 50. K Coll Lon BD71 AKC71 CertEd. St Aug Coll Cant 72. **d** 73 **p** 74. C Wythenshawe Wm Temple *Ch Man* 73-76; C Southam w Stockton *Cov* 76-79; V Braíles from 79; R Sutton under Braíles from 79; RD Shipston 90-98; Hon Can Cov Cathl from 03. *The Vicarage, Braíles, Banbury OX15 5HT* Tel (01608) 685230

MORGAN, Nicola. b 64. Nottm Univ BA86. Linc Th Coll BTh95. **d** 95 **p** 96. C Lillington *Cov* 95-98; C Gospel Lane St Mich *Birm* 98-01; P-in-c Lt Paxton *Ely* from 01; P-in-c Gt Paxton from 01; P-in-c Diddington from 01. *The Vicarage, 24 St James's Road, Little Paxton, St Neots, Huntingdon PE19 4QW* Tel (01480) 214280 *or* 475085 E-mail revnickmorg@stmicks.freeserve.co.uk

MORGAN, Peter Neville. b 36. Univ of Wales (Cardiff) BSc60 BD63 PGCE80. **d** 98 **p** 99. NSM Ardingly *Chich* from 98. *12 Victoria Close, Burgess Hill RH15 9QS* Tel (01444) 247647 E-mail revpnm98@aol.com

MORGAN, Philip. b 51. Lon Univ BSc75 Univ of Wales (Cardiff) BD78. St Mich Coll Llan 75. **d** 78 **p** 79. C Swansea St Nic *S & B* 78-81; C Morriston 81-83; C Swansea St Mary w H Trin 83-84; USA from 84. *17476 Hawthorne Avenue, Culpeper, VA 22701, USA* E-mail padre4u@hotmail.com

MORGAN, Canon Philip Brendan. b 35. G&C Coll Cam BA59 MA63. Wells Th Coll 59. **d** 61 **p** 62. C Paddington Ch Ch *Lon* 61-66; C Trunch w Swafield *Nor* 66-68; P-in-c Nor St Steph 68-72; Sacr Nor Cathl 72-74; Can Res and Sub-Dean St Alb 74-81; Hon Can St Alb 81-94; R Bushey 81-94; RD Aldenham 91-94; Can Res and Treas Win Cathl *Win* 94-01; rtd 01; Perm to Offic *Win* from 01. *9 Clifton Hill, Winchester SO22 5BL* Tel (01962) 867549

MORGAN, Canon Philip Reginald Strange. b 27. St D Coll Lamp BA51 Keble Coll Ox BA53 MA57. Wells Th Coll 57. **d** 57 **p** 58. C Fleur-de-Lis *Mon* 57-59; C Bassaleg 59-62; CF (TA) 62-74; V Dingestow and Wanastow *Mon* 62-65; V Dingestow and Penrhos 65-66; R Machen and Rudry 66-75; R Machen 75-76; V Caerleon 76-95; Can St Woolos Cathl 84-95; rtd 95; Lic to Offic *Mon* from 95. *4 Anthony Drive, Caerleon, Newport NP18 3DS* Tel (01633) 422238

MORGAN, Philip Richard Llewelyn. b 27. Wadh Coll Ox BA50 MA52. St Steph Ho Ox 53. **d** 55 **p** 56. C Warlingham w Chelsham and Farleigh *S'wark* 55-58; Chapl Haileybury Coll 58-73; Hd Master Haileybury Jun Sch Berks 73-87; R The Deverills *Sarum* 87-94; rtd 94; Perm to Offic *Guildf* and *Win* from 95. *6 Phillips Close, Headley, Bordon GU35 8LY* Tel (01428) 712194 Fax as telephone E-mail philipmorgan@msn.com

MORGAN, Canon Reginald Graham. b 25. St D Coll Lamp BA46 LTh48. **d** 48 **p** 49. C Chirk *St As* 48-50; C Llangollen and Trevor 50-55; R Llanwyddelan w Manafon 55-66; V Rhuddlan 66-94; RD St As 78-94; Hon Can St As Cathl 83-89; Can from 89; rtd 94. *Manafon, 49 Ffordd Ffynnon, Rhuddlan, Rhyl LL18 2SP* Tel (01745) 591036

MORGAN, The Ven Reginald Graham Tharle. b 46. St Jo Coll Nottm LTh75. **d** 75 **p** 76. C Oadby *Leic* 75-78; S Africa from 79; R Greytown St Jas from 88; Adn Estcourt from 95. *PO Box 112, Greytown, Natal, 3250 South Africa* Tel and fax (0027) (334) 71240 *or* tel 71241 E-mail beehive@cybertrade.co.za

MORGAN, Rhys Bryn. b 65. E Lon Univ BA94. St Mich Coll Llan 00. **d** 02 **p** 03. C Carmarthen St Pet *St D* from 02. *St Peter's Clergy House, 10A The Parade, Carmarthen SA31 1LY* Tel (01267) 237303 Mobile 07973-254062 E-mail rhys.morgan@btinternet.com

MORGAN, Richard Mervyn. b 50. Wadh Coll Ox BA73 MA75 K Alfred's Coll Win PGCE74. **d** 92 **p** 93. CMS 85-94; Kenya 88-94; Perm to Offic *S'wark* 95-96; R Therfield w Kelshall *St Alb* from 96; Tutor EAMTC *Ely* from 99. *The Rectory, Church Lane, Therfield, Royston SG8 9QD* Tel (01763) 287364

MORGAN, Richard Thomas. b 70. Peterho Cam BA91 MA95. Wycliffe Hall Ox 94. **d** 96 **p** 97. C Bath Twerton-on-Avon *B & W* 96-99; Chapl Lee Abbey 99-01; R Marks Tey and Aldham *Chelmsf* from 01. *The Rectory, Church Lane, Marks Tey, Colchester CO6 1LW* Tel (01206) 210396 *or* 213231 E-mail richardtmorgan@ic24.net *or* rector@marksteychurch.org

MORGAN, Robert Chowen. b 40. St Cath Coll Cam BA63 MA67. St Chad's Coll Dur 64. **d** 66 **p** 67. C Lancaster St Mary *Blackb* 66-76; Lect Th Lanc Univ 67-76; Fell Linacre Coll Ox from 76; Lect Th Ox Univ 76-97; Reader from 97; P-in-c Sandford-on-Thames *Ox* from 87. *Lower Farm, Sandford-on-Thames, Oxford OX4 4YR* Tel (01865) 748848 E-mail robert.morgan@theology.oxford.ac.uk

MORGAN, Canon Robert Harman. b 28. OBE94. Univ of Wales (Cardiff) BA55. Coll of Resurr Mirfield 55. **d** 57 **p** 58. C Penarth w Lavernock *Llan* 57-61; C Caerau w Ely 61-67; V Glan Ely 67-95; Hon Can Llan Cathl 94-95; rtd 95; Perm to Offic *St D* and *Llan* from 95. *Y Felin Wynt, St Davids, Haverfordwest SA62 6QS* Tel (01437) 720130

MORGAN, Robert Hugh. b 49. Univ of Wales (Cardiff) BD. St Mich Coll Llan 88. **d** 91 **p** 92. C Swansea St Pet *S & B* 91-94; V Oxwich w Penmaen and Nicholaston from 94. *The Rectory, Penmaen, Swansea SA3 2HH* Tel (01792) 371241

MORGAN, Roger William. b 40. Mert Coll Ox BA62 Cam Univ MA67. Ridley Hall Cam 80. **d** 81 **p** 82. NSM Cambridge St Paul *Ely* 81-84; V Corby St Columba *Pet* 84-90; V Leic H Trin w St Jo *Leic* from 90; C-in-c Leic St Leon CD from 01. *29 Holmfield Road, Leicester LE2 1SE* Tel 0116-270 4986

MORGAN, Canon Samuel. b 07. St D Coll Lamp BA32. **d** 32 **p** 33. C Llandysul *St D* 32-35; Argentina 35-42; V Llanwenog w Llanwnen *St D* 42-64; RD Lampeter 54-64; V Felin-foel 64-77; RD Kidwelly 72-77; Can St D Cathl 72-79; rtd 77. *10 Ty'r Fran Avenue, Llanelli SA15 3LP* Tel (01554) 772977

MORGAN, Simon John. b 58. Univ of Wales (Swansea) BA81 Univ of Wales (Cardiff) BD86 MA94. St Mich Coll Llan 83. **d** 86 **p** 87. C Penarth All SS *Llan* 86-87; C Port Talbot St Theodore 87-89; C Gelligaer 89-91; R Dowlais 91-96; Asst P Peacehaven *Chich* 96; Asst P Telscombe w Piddinghoe and Southease 96; P-in-c E Dean w Friston and Jevington 96-99; NSM Hellingly and Upper Dicker from 99; Chapl St Bede's Sch Upper Dicker from 99. *Providence House, Upper Dicker, Hailsham BN27 3QE* Tel (01323) 843887

MORGAN, Stephen. See MORGAN, Ian Stephen

MORGAN, Canon Steve Shelley. b 48. Univ of Wales DipTh70. St Mich Coll Llan 67. **d** 71 **p** 72. C Llanharan w Peterston-super-Montem *Llan* 71; C Llandaff w Capel Llanilltern 71-74; C Neath w Llantwit 74-77; TV Merthyr Tydfil and Cyfarthfa 77-91; V Merthyr Tydfil Ch Ch from 91; RD Merthyr Tydfil from 93; Can Llan Cathl from 98. *24 Pen y Bryn View, Incline Top, Merthyr Tydfil CF47 0GB* Tel (01685) 723272

MORGAN, Teresa Jean. b 68. Clare Coll Cam BA90 MA94 PhD95 Oriel Coll Ox MA98 BA01 LRAM91. St Alb and Ox Min Course 00. **d** 02 **p** 03. NSM Littlemore *Ox* from 02. *Oriel College, Oxford OX1 4EW* Tel (01865) 276579 E-mail teresa.morgan@classics.ox.ac.uk

MORGAN, Thomas John Walford. b 16. Univ of Wales BA37. St D Coll Lamp 37. **d** 39 **p** 40. C Roath *Llan* 39-42; C Heavitree *Ex* 42-45; C Merton St Mary *S'wark* 45-50; CF 50-71; V Swallowfield *Ox* 71-81; rtd 81. *57 Felinfoel Road, Llanelli SA15 3JQ* Tel (01554) 752223

MORGAN, Trevor. d 01. OLM Fleur-de-Lis *Mon* from 01. *The Tidings, Woodfieldside, Blackwood NP12 0PJ* Tel (01495) 222198

MORGAN, Verna Ireta. b 42. NEOC. **d** 89 **p** 94. NSM Potternewton *Ripon* 89-92; Par Dn Longsight St Luke *Man* 92-94; C 94-95; P-in-c Gorton St Phil 95-02; rtd 02. *Butler's Village, St James's Parish, Nevis, West Indies*

MORGAN, Chan William Charles Gerwyn. b 30. Univ of Wales (Lamp) BA52. St Mich Coll Llan 52. **d** 56 **p** 57. C Hubberston *St D* 56-62; V Ambleston w St Dogwells 62-68; Miss to Seamen 68-93; V Fishguard w Llanychar *St D* 68-85; V Fishguard w Llanychar and Pontfaen w Morfil etc 85-93; Can St D Cathl 85-93; Chan 91-93; rtd 93. *Wrth y Llan, Pontyceifion, Cardigan SA43 1DW* Tel (01239) 613943

MORGAN, William John. b 38. Selw Coll Cam BA62 MA66. Cuddesdon Coll 62. **d** 65 **p** 66. C Cardiff St Jo *Llan* 65-68; Asst Chapl Univ of Wales (Cardiff) 68-70; Perm to Offic *Lon* 70-73; C Albany Street Ch Ch 73-78; P-in-c E Acton St Dunstan 78-80; V E Acton St Dunstan w St Thos 80-95; V Isleworth All SS from 95; P-in-c St Margaret's-on-Thames 95-00. *All Saints' Vicarage, 63 Church Street, Isleworth TW7 6BE* Tel (020) 8560 6379 Fax 8758 2611

MORGAN, William Stanley Timothy. b 41. Univ of Wales (Lamp) BA63. Wycliffe Hall Ox 63. **d** 66 **p** 67. C Aberystwyth St Mich *St D* 66-69; V Ambleston w St Dogwells 69-70; V Ambleston, St Dogwells, Walton E and Llysyfran 70-74; V Llan-non 74-80; V Lampeter 80-87; V Lampeter Pont Steffan w Silian 87-01; V Llanbadarn Fawr from 01. *The Vicarage, Llanbadarn Fawr, Aberystwyth SY23 3TT* Tel (01970) 623368

MORGAN-GUY, John Richard. b 44. FRHistS80 FRSM81. St D Coll Lamp BA65 PhD85 St Steph Ho Ox 65. **d** 67 **p** 68. C Canton St Cath *Llan* 67-68; C Roath St Sav 68-70; C Machen and Rudry *Mon* 71-74; R Wolvesnewton w Kilgwrrwg and Devauden 74-80; Perm to Offic *B & W* 80-93; V Betws Cedewain and Tregynon and Llanwyddelan *St As* 93-97; RD Cedewain 97; Lect Univ of Wales (Lamp) from 98; Research Fell Cen for Adv Welsh & Celtic Studies from 99. *Tyngors, Silian, Lampeter SA48 8AS* Tel (01570) 422710

MORGAN-JONES, Canon Christopher John. b 43. Bris Univ BA66 Chicago Univ MBA68 McMaster Univ Ontario MA69. Cuddesdon Coll 70. **d** 73 **p** 74. C Folkestone St Sav *Cant* 73-76; P-in-c Swalecliffe 76-82; V Addington 82-84; V Addington S'wark 85-92; RD Croydon Addington 85-90; V Maidstone All SS and St Phil w Tovil *Cant* from 92; Hon Can Cant Cathl from 99. *The Vicarage, Priory Road, Maidstone ME15 6NL* Tel (01622) 756002 Fax 692320 E-mail ramj@allsaints.u-net.com

MORGAN-JONES, Richard James. b 46. Em Coll Cam BA68. Ripon Hall Ox 73. **d** 75 **p** 76. C Bromley St Mark *Roch* 75-77; Perm to Offic 77-84. *25 Lewes Road, Eastbourne BN21 2BY*

MORGANNWG, Archdeacon of. See WILLIAMS, The Ven Martin Infield

MORGANS, Paul Hywel. b 61. LWCMD83. Chich Th Coll 86. **d** 90 **p** 91. C Johnston w Steynton *St D* 90-92; C Caerau w Ely *Llan* 92-95; V Pentre 95-99; Hon C Roath St German 99-00. *129 Bishopston Road, Caerau, Cardiff CF5 5DX*

MORIARTY, Mrs Susan Margaret. b 43. Cartrefle Coll of Educn TCert65. St As Minl Tr Course. **d** 02. Par Dn Gorsedd w Brynford, Ysgeifiog and Whitford *St As* from 02. *7 St Michael's Drive, Caerwys, Mold CH7 5BS* Tel (01352) 720874

MORISON, John Donald. b 34. ALCD60. **d** 61 **p** 62. C Rayleigh *Chelmsf* 61-64; C St Austell *Truro* 64-67; V Meltham Mills *Wakef* 67-71; Youth Chapl *Cov* 71-76; S Africa 76-82; Can Port Elizabeth 80-82; Bardsley Missr 82-86; Lic to Offic *S'wark* 82-86; Dioc Missr *Derby* 86-99; V Quarndon 86-99; rtd 99; Perm to Offic *Sarum* from 01. *Flat 1, Canford Place, 59 Cliff Drive, Canford Cliffs, Poole BH13 7JX* Tel (01202) 709377

MORLEY, Athelstan John. b 29. Linc Coll Ox BA52 MA56. Ridley Hall Cam. **d** 54 **p** 55. C Surbiton St Matt *S'wark* 54-57; Succ Chelmsf Cathl *Chelmsf* 57-60; R Mistley w Manningtree 60-69; R Hadleigh St Jas 69-94; rtd 94; Hon C Prittlewell *Chelmsf* 94-97; Perm to Offic from 94; P-in-c St Martin Ludgate *Lon* from 01. *38 Bridgwater Drive, Westcliff-on-Sea SS0 0DH* Tel (01702) 339335

MORLEY, Georgina Laura (George). b 63. Dur Univ BA84 Nottm Univ MTh95 DPhil99. Cranmer Hall Dur. **d** 03. Dir Studies NEOC from 99; NSM Osmotherley w Harlsey and Ingleby Arncliffe *York* from 03. *18 Station Road, Brompton, Northallerton DL6 2RE* Tel (01609) 780760 E-mail gmorley@fish.co.uk

MORLEY, Miss Gillian Dorothy. b 21. Greyladies Coll 49. dss 70 **d** 87. Lewisham St Swithun *S'wark* 70-82; Sturry w Fordwich and Westbere w Hersden *Cant* 82-87; Perm to Offic from 87. *28 Glen Iris Avenue, Canterbury CT2 8HP* Tel (01227) 459992

MORLEY, John. b 43. K Coll Lon AKC67 St Deiniol's Hawarden 67. **d** 68 **p** 69. C Newbold on Avon *Cov* 69-73; C Solihull *Birm* 73-77; C-in-c Elmdon Heath CD 76-77; Chapl RAF 77-93; TR Wallingford w Crowmarsh Gifford etc *Ox* 93-98; TR Wallingford 98-99; RD Wallingford 95-99; Provost Nicosia 99-02; V Henlow and Langford *St Alb* from 02. *The Vicarage, 65 Church Street, Langford, Biggleswade SG18 9QT* Tel (01462) 700248 Mobile 07900-892566 E-mail revjohnmorley@aol.com

MORLEY, Keith. b 44. St Chad's Coll Dur BA66 DipTh67 Open Univ BSc93. **d** 67 **p** 68. C S Yardley St Mich *Birm* 67-70; C Solihull 70-73; V Shaw Hill 73-77; P-in-c Burton Coggles *Linc* 77-79; P-in-c Boothby Pagnell 77-79; V Lenton w Ingoldsby 77-79; P-in-c Bassingthorpe w Bitchfield 77-79; R Ingoldsby 79-87; RD Beltisloe 84-87; P-in-c Old Dalby and Nether Broughton *Leic* 87-94; RD Framland 88-90. *11 Swallow Close, Quarrington, Sleaford NG34 7UU*

MORLEY, Canon Leslie James. b 45. K Coll Lon BD67 AKC67 MTh68. St Boniface Warminster 68. **d** 69 **p** 70. C Birm St Pet *Birm* 69-72; C W Brompton St Mary *Lon* 72; C W Brompton St Mary w St Pet 73-74; Chapl Nottm Univ *S'well* 74-80; Dir Post-Ord Tr 80-85; Can Res and Vice-Provost S'well Minster 80-85; Hon Can 85-99; Chapl Bluecoat Sch Nottm 85-90; R Nottingham St Pet and St Jas *S'well* 85-99; AD Nottingham Cen 90-93; Rural Officer *Ripon* from 99; Perm to Offic *York* from 00. *18 Station Road, Brompton, Northallerton DL6 2RE* Tel (01609) 780734 Fax 780760 E-mail leslie.morley@virgin.net

MORLEY, Peter. b 36. St Jo Coll Nottm 81. **d** 83 **p** 84. C Sheff St Jo *Sheff* 83-87; Chapl The Shrewsbury Hosp Sheff 85-87; V Worsbrough Common *Sheff* 87-93; Chapl Mt Vernon Hosp Barnsley 87-93; R Harthill and Thorpe Salvin *Sheff* 93-99; rtd 99. *39 Hallcroft Road, Retford DN22 7LE* Tel (01777) 719081

MORLEY, Terence Martin Simon. b 49. SS Hild & Bede Coll Dur CertEd78. St Steph Ho Ox 71. **d** 74 **p** 75. C Kingston upon Hull St Alb *York* 74-76; C Middlesbrough All SS 76-77; Perm to Offic *Dur* 77-78; Hon C Worthing St Andr *Chich* 78-80; C Brighton Ch

Ch 80-82; C Hove St Patr 80-82; C Ayr *Glas* 83-86; C Mayboie 83-84; P-in-c Coatbridge 86-88; R 88-92; P-in-c 92; V Plymouth St Jas Ham *Ex* from 93; Chapl Plymouth Community Services NHS Trust 96-98. *St James's Presbytery, Ham Drive, Plymouth PL2 2NJ* Tel (01752) 362485

MORLEY, Trevor. b 39. Man Univ BSc62 MPS62 MRSH84. Ripon Hall Ox 65. d 67 p 68. C Compton Gifford *Ex* 67-70; Chapl Hammersmith Hosp Lon 70-83; Hon C N Hammersmith St Kath *Lon* 70-83; Chapl Univ Coll Hosp Lon 83-94; Chapl Univ Coll Lon Hosps NHS Trust 94-99; Hon Chapl St Luke's Hosp for the Clergy 89-99; V Linthwaite *Wakef* from 99. *The Vicarage, Church Lane, Linthwaite, Huddersfield HD7 5TA* Tel (01484) 842591

MORLEY-BUNKER, John Arthur. b 27. Wells Th Coll 67. d 68 p 69. C Horfield H Trin *Bris* 68-71; P-in-c Easton All Hallows 71-75; V 75-82; RD Bris City 74-79; V Horfield St Greg 82-93; rtd 93; Perm to Offic *Bris* from 93. *1 Knoll Court, Knoll Hill, Bristol BS9 1QX* Tel 0117-968 5837

MORLING, David Arthur. b 48. Saltley Tr Coll Birm CertEd66 Open Univ BA78. S Dios Minl Tr Scheme 83 Linc Th Coll. d 85 p 86. NSM Chich 85-97; P-in-c Doncaster Intake *Sheff* 97-02; P-in-c Doncaster H Trin 97-02; rtd 02. *Lorindell, 61 Layton Lane, Rawdon, Leeds LS19 6RA* Tel 0113-250 3488

MORONEY, Kevin John. b 61. Valley Forge Chr Coll Pennsylvania BS86. Gen Th Sem NY MDiv92. d 92 p 93. USA 92-00; Asst Pastor Metuchen St Luke New Jersey 92-94; R Metuchen All SS 94-98; Chapl St James Sch St James Maryland 98-00; Chapl and Tutor CITC from 00; P-in-c Dublin Sandymount *D & G* from 01. *CITC, Braemor Park, Dublin 14, Irish Republic* Tel (00353) (1) 492 3506 Fax 492 3082

MORPHY, George David. b 49. Birm Univ BEd71 Lon Univ BA75 Warwick Univ MA90. WMMTC. d 89 p 90. Hon C Ribbesford w Bewdley and Dowles *Worc* from 89; Dioc Dir of Educn from 99. *41 Hallow Road, Worcester WR2 6BX* Tel (01905) 422007

MORPHY, Michael John. b 43. Newc Univ BSc65 Dur Univ MSc66 QUB PhD73. Ripon Coll Cuddesdon 82. d 84 p 85. C Halifax *Wakef* 84-86; V Luddenden w Luddenden Foot 86-97; V Corbridge w Halton and Newton Hall *Newc* from 97. *The Vicarage, Greencroft Avenue, Corbridge NE45 5DW* Tel (01434) 632128 E-mail mj.morphy@btinternet.com

MORRELL, Geoffrey Bernard. b 45. AKC68. d 69 p 71. C W Leigh CD *Portsm* 69-76; V Shedfield 76-02; RD Bishop's Waltham 82-88; rtd 02. *28 Chase Farm Close, Waltham Chase, Southampton SO32 2UD* Tel (01489) 896880 E-mail geoff@dogcollar.freeserve.co.uk

MORRELL, Mrs Jennifer Mary. b 49. N Ord Course 84. d 87 p 94. Par Dn Crewe All SS and St Paul *Ches* 87-90; Par Dn Padgate *Liv* 90-94; C 94-95; TV Kirkby 95-00; V Croxteth Park 00-02. *24 Oak Tree Close, Kingsbury, Tamworth B78 2JF* Tel (01827) 874445

MORRELL, Canon Nigel Paul. b 38. S'wark Ord Course 73. d 76 p 77. C Letchworth St Paul w Willian *St Alb* 76-85; V Farley Hill St Jo 85-95; RD Luton 90-94; V Cardington from 95; Hon Can St Alb from 01; RD Elstow from 02. *22 Sunderland Place, Shortstown, Bedford MK42 0FD* Tel (01234) 743202 Fax as telephone

MORRELL, Paul Rodney. b 49. SRN70. SW Minl Tr Course 91. d 93 p 95. NSM Heavitree w Ex St Paul *Ex* 93-00; C 00-02; C Heavitree and St Mary Steps from 02. *65 Quarry Park Road, Exeter EX2 5PD* Tel (01392) 431367

MORRELL, Robin Mark George. b 29. Cuddesdon Coll 58. d 60 p 61. C Petersfield w Sheet *Portsm* 60-63; C-in-c Stockwood CD *Bris* 63-71; Lic to Offic 71-72; R Honiton, Gittisham and Combe Raleigh *Ex* 72-78; Lay Tr Officer *S'wark* 78-81; Asst Chapl HM Pris Brixton 81-85; Past Cllr from 85; Hon C Hatcham St Cath *S'wark* 91-97; rtd 94; Perm to Offic *S'wark* from 97. *46 Erlanger Road, London SE14 5TG* Tel (020) 7252 9346

MORRELL, Mrs Susan Marjorie. b 46. Open Univ BA94. SEITE 93. d 96 p 97. NSM E Peckham and Nettlestead *Roch* from 96; Chapl Kent Coll Pembury from 99. *7 Pippin Road, East Peckham, Tonbridge TN12 5BT* Tel (01622) 871150

MORRIS, Alan Ralph Oakden. b 29. Roch Th Coll 59. d 61 p 62. C Riverhead *Roch* 61-62; C Roch St Pet w St Marg 62-66; C Wrotham 66-74; V Biggin Hill 74-82; R Kingsdown 82-88; V Seal St Pet 88-92; rtd 92; P-in-c Renhold *St Alb* 92-93; Perm to Offic *Roch* 93-02. *268 Woolwich Road, London SE2 0DW* Tel (020) 8310 7860

MORRIS, Canon Alexander Dorner. b 23. Jes Coll Cam BA48 MA53. Linc Th Coll 49. d 51 p 52. C Wincobank *Sheff* 51-53; C Rotherham 53-54; C-in-c Manor Park CD 54-59; India 59-63; V Bexley St Mary *Roch* 63-71; V Leatherhead *Guildf* 71-89; RD Leatherhead 72-77; Hon Can Guildf Cathl 86-89; rtd 89; Perm to Offic *Guildf* from 89. *9 Roses Cottages, West Street, Dorking RH4 1QL* Tel (01306) 882485

MORRIS, Andy. See MORRIS, Edward Andrew

MORRIS, Mrs Ann. b 52. N Co Coll Newc CertEd73. WEMTC 00. d 03. C Churchdown St Jo *Glouc* from 03. *24 Sandycroft Road, Churchdown, Gloucester GL3 1JH* Tel (01452) 712608

MORRIS, Mrs Ann Veronica Marsham. b 46. Open Univ BA83. WEMTC 99. d 01 p 02. NSM Amberley *Glouc* from 01. *Cotswold, Amberley, Stroud GL5 5AB* Tel (01453) 872587 E-mail annmorris@hcliffe.powernet.co.uk

MORRIS, Anne. See MORRIS, Ms Margaret Anne

MORRIS, Bernard Lyn. b 28. St Aid Birkenhead 55. d 58 p 59. C-in-c Hartcliffe St Andr CD *Bris* 58-61; C Bishopston 61-63; R Ardwick St Thos *Man* 63-69; R Aylton w Pixley, Munsley and Putley *Heref* 69-79; P-in-c Tarrington w Stoke Edith 72-77; R 77-79; P-in-c Queen Camel, Marston Magna, W Camel, Rimpton etc *B & W* 79-80; R 80-87; R Queen Camel w W Camel, Corton Denham etc 87-95; rtd 95; Perm to Offic *B & W* 95-97; *Ex* from 01. *Canterbury Bells, Ansford Hill, Castle Cary BA7 7JL* Tel (01963) 351154 E-mail revblmorris@supanet.com

MORRIS, Beti Elin. b 36. CertEd57. Sarum & Wells Th Coll 87. d 89 p 97. C Llangeitho and Blaenpennal w Betws Leucu etc *St D* 89-92; C-in-c Pencarreg and Llanycrwys 92-97; V from 97. *The Vicarage, Cwmann, Lampeter SA48 8DU* Tel (01570) 422385

MORRIS, Brian Michael Charles. b 32. S Dios Minl Tr Scheme 82. d 85 p 86. NSM Denmead *Portsm* 85-89; C S w N Hayling 89-96; P-in-c Shalfleet 96-97; rtd 97; Perm to Offic *Portsm* from 97. *Ashleigh, 5 Ashwood Close, Hayling Island PO11 9AX* Tel (023) 9246 7292 E-mail rev_b_morris@talk21.com

MORRIS, Ms Catharine Mary. b 75. Regent's Park Coll Ox BA96 MA00. Ridley Hall Cam 99. d 01. C Malpas *Mon* from 01. *4 Aspen Way, Malpas, Newport NP20 6LB* Tel (01633) 821362 E-mail catharine@stmarysmalpas.freeserve.co.uk

MORRIS, Catherine. d 01 p 02. C Malpas *Mon* from 01. *4 Aspen Way, Malpas, Newport NP20 6LB* Tel (01633) 821362

MORRIS, Canon Christopher John. b 45. K Coll Lon AKC67 BD68. d 68 p 69. C W Bromwich All SS *Lich* 68-72; C Porthill 72-74; Min Can Carl Cathl *Carl* 74-77; Ecum Liaison Officer BBC Radio Carl 74-77; Dioc Communications Officer *Carl* 77-83; V Thursby 77-83; Angl Adv Border TV from 82; V Upperby St Jo *Carl* 83-91; P-in-c Lanercost w Kirkcambeck and Walton 91-99; P-in-c Gilsland w Nether Denton 96-99; R Lanercost, Walton, Gilsland and Nether Denton from 99; RD Brampton from 98; Hon Can Carl Cathl from 98. *The Vicarage, Lanercost, Brampton CA8 2HQ* Tel (01697) 72478 E-mail chris@ca8morris.fsnet.co.uk

MORRIS, Christopher Mangan. b 47. Chich Th Coll 71. d 73 p 74. C Ashersley *Wakef* 73-76; C Kippax *Ripon* 76-78; TV Seacroft 78-81; V Oulton w Woodlesford 81-86; V Hawksworth Wood 86-93; V Rawdon *Bradf* from 93. *The Vicarage, Layton Avenue, Rawdon, Leeds LS19 6QQ* Tel 0113-250 3263

MORRIS, Prof Colin. b 28. Qu Coll Ox BA48 BA51 MA53 FRHistS71. Linc Th Coll 51. d 53 p 54. Fell and Chapl Pemb Coll Ox 53-69; Lic to Offic *Ox* 53-69; Prof Medieval Hist Southn Univ 69-92; Lic to Offic *Win* from 69; rtd 92. *12 Bassett Crescent East, Southampton SO16 7PB* Tel (023) 8076 8176

MORRIS, Canon David Edmond. b 27. Univ of Wales (Cardiff) BA55. St D Coll Lamp 55. d 57 p 58. C Llanfihangel-ar-arth *St D* 57-59; C Ysbyty Ystwyth w Ystradmeurig 59-61; Asst Master St Jo Coll 59-61; CF 61-81; QHC 78-93; V Penllergaer *S & B* 81-93; RD Llwchwr 86-93; Warden of Readers 87-92; Can Brecon Cathl 90-93; Hon Can from 93; rtd 93; Perm to Offic *St D* from 93. *21 Brynglas Crescent, Llangunnor, Carmarthen SA31 2HT* Tel (01267) 223536

MORRIS, Preb David Meeson. b 35. Trin Coll Ox BA56 MA60. Chich Th Coll 57. d 60 p 61. C Westmr St Steph w St Jo *Lon* 60-65; Lib Pusey Ho 65-68; Chapl Wadh Coll Ox 67-68; C Sheff Norwood St Leon *Sheff* 68-69; Ind Chapl 68-72; C Brightside St Marg 69-72; R Adderley *Lich* 72-82; V Drayton in Hales 72-82; RD Tutbury 82-95; Chapl Burton Gen Hosp 82-90; P-in-c Burton St Modwen *Lich* 82; V Burton 82-99; Preb Lich Cathl 93-99; P-in-c Shobnall 94-99; rtd 99; Perm to Offic *Lich* from 99. *Watling House, All Stretton, Church Stretton SY6 6HH* Tel (01694) 722243

MORRIS, David Michael. b 59. Ox Univ MA84 Cam Univ PGCE91. Sarum & Wells Th Coll 82. d 84 p 85. C Angell Town St Jo *S'wark* 84-87; C Mitcham SS Pet and Paul 87-90; V Llandygwydd and Cenarth w Cilrhedyn etc *St D* 90-98; Lect Th St D Coll Lamp from 90; Hd RE Lampeter Comp Sch from 98. *Bronant, Rhydargaeau, Carmarthen SA32 7DR*

MORRIS, Canon David Pryce. b 39. Univ of Wales (Ban) DipTh62. Kelham Th Coll 55 St Mich Coll Llan 62. d 63 p 64. C Colwyn Bay *St As* 63-70; R St George 70-76; Dioc Children's Adv 75-87; V Bodelwyddan St George 76-79; V Connah's Quay 79-95; St As Dioc Adult Lay Tr Team from 88; Ed St As Dioc News from 89; Dioc Communications Officer from 90; V Shotton from 95; Hon Can St As Cathl 96-00; Can Cursal St As Cathl from 00. *The Vicarage, Chester Road East, Shotton, Deeside CH5 1QD* Tel and fax (01244) 812183 Mobile 07711-519752 E-mail dprycemorris@care4free.net

MORRIS, Dennis Gordon. b 41. ALCM58. St D Coll Lamp DipTh67. d 67 p 68. C Neath w Llantwit *Llan* 67-92; V Troedrhiwgarth from 92. *Garth Vicarage, 72 Bridgend Road, Maesteg CF34 0NL* Tel (01656) 732441

MORRIS, Edward. b 42. **d** 72 **p** 73. C Darlington H Trin *Dur* 72-75; Tutor St Steph Ho Ox 75-82; Sen Tutor 79-82; R Shadforth *Dur* 82-86; Chapl Hammersmith Hosp Lon 86-94; Chapl Qu Charlotte's Hosp Lon 86-94; Chapl Hammersmith Hosps NHS Trust from 94. *The Chaplain's Office, Hammersmith Hospital, Du Cane Road, London W12 0HS* Tel (020) 8383 1701 *or* 8743 2030 ext 4574

MORRIS, Edward Andrew (Andy). b 57. St Jo Coll Nottm 90. **d** 96 **p** 97. C Conisbrough *Sheff* 96-01; Perm to Offic *S'well* from 01. *42 Henrietta Street, Bulwell, Nottingham NG6 9JO* Tel 0115-8772 2469

MORRIS, Canon Edwin Alfred. b 32. Wells Th Coll 62. **d** 64 **p** 65. C Wood End *Cov* 64-66; Lic to Offic 66-68; Ind Chapl 68-85; P-in-c Churchover w Willey 74-85; RD Rugby 78-85; R City of Bris 85-97; Hon Can Bris Cathl 89-97; RD Bris City 91-94; rtd 97; Perm to Offic *Cov* 97-00. *117 Lower Hillmorton Road, Rugby CV21 3TN* Tel (01788) 546980

MORRIS, Mrs Elizabeth Anne. b 59. Dioc OLM tr scheme 97. **d** 00 **p** 01. OLM Westleton w Dunwich *St E* from 00; OLM Darsham from 00. *Central House, The Street, Westleton, Saxmundham IP17 3AA* Tel (01728) 648297
E-mail elizabethannes@talk21.com

MORRIS, Mrs Elizabeth Mary. b 22. Univ Coll Lon BSc50 DipRS82. S'wark Ord Course 82. **dss** 83 **d** 87 **p** 94. Purley St Mark *S'wark* 83-87; Hon C Littleham w Exmouth *Ex* 87-96; Perm to Offic 96-99. *7 Strawberry Hill, Lympstone, Exmouth EX8 5JZ* Tel (01395) 265727

MORRIS, Canon Frank Leo. b 20. St Steph Ho Ox 50. **d** 53 **p** 54. C Bickley *Roch* 53-55; C Letchworth *St Alb* 55-61; V Wareside 61-65; R Wyddial 65-79; P-in-c 79-82; V Gt w Lt Hormead 65-79; RD Buntingford 68-75; V Gt w Lt Hormead, Anstey, Brent Pelham etc 79-82; V Hormead, Wyddial, Anstey, Brent Pelham etc 82-89; Hon Can St Alb 85-89; rtd 89; Perm to Offic *St Alb* from 00. *9 Manland Avenue, Harpenden AL5 4RG* Tel (01582) 462348

MORRIS, Geoffrey. *See* MORRIS, Canon Martin Geoffrey Roger

MORRIS, Geoffrey David. b 43. Fitzw Coll Cam BA65 MA69 Westmr Coll Ox DipEd67. N Ord Course. **d** 82 **p** 83. C Man Clayton St Cross w St Paul *Man* 82-85; V Lower Kersal from 85; P-in-c Priors Hardwick, Priors Marston and Wormleighton *Cov* from 03; Asst Chapl HM Pris Rye Hill from 03. *The Vicarage, Vicarage Lane, Priors Marston, Southam CV47 7RT* Tel (01327) 260053

MORRIS, Canon George Erskine. b 34. Dalhousie Univ Canada MSW77. Codrington Coll Barbados 53 Qu Coll Birm 60. **d** 62 **p** 63. C Kidderminster St Jo *Worc* 62-66; Canada from 66; R Edmonton St Mary from 87. *3802-109 Avenue NW, Edmonton AB, Canada, T5W 0G8* Tel (001) (780) 477 1896

MORRIS, Graham Edwin. b 60. Sarum & Wells Th Coll 83. **d** 86 **p** 87. C Coalbrookdale, Iron-Bridge and Lt Wenlock *Heref* 86-90; TV Bilston *Lich* 90-99; R Northwood *Portsm* from 99; V Gurnard from 99. *The Rectory, Chawton Lane, Cowes PO31 8PR* Tel (01983) 292050
E-mail graham.morris@btinternet.com

MORRIS, Henry James. b 47. Lon Univ BSc69. Wycliffe Hall Ox MA. **d** 79 **p** 80. C Woodford Wells *Chelmsf* 79-82; C Gt Baddow 82-87; R Siddington w Preston *Glouc* 87-01; RD Cirencester 97-01; TR Madeley *Heref* from 01. *St Michael's Vicarage, Church Street, Madeley, Telford TF7 5BN* Tel and fax (01952) 586645 *or* tel 585718 E-mail henrym@dircon.co.uk

MORRIS, Ian Henry. b 42. Sarum & Wells Th Coll 73. **d** 75 **p** 76. C Lawrence Weston *Bris* 75-78; C St Buryan, St Levan and Sennen *Truro* 78-81; P-in-c Lanteglos by Fowey 81-84; V 84-85; R Lanteglos by Camelford w Advent 85-95; RD Trigg Minor and Bodmin 93-95; TR Probus, Ladock and Grampound w Creed and St Erme from 95; RD Powder from 01. *The Sanctuary, Wagg Lane, Probus, Truro TR2 4JX* Tel (01726) 882746

MORRIS, Ian James Patrick. b 43. Dur Univ BA65. Westcott Ho Cam 67. **d** 69 **p** 70. C Wisbech SS Pet and Paul *Ely* 69-72; C Gaywood, Bawsey and Mintlyn *Nor* 72-76; Asst Chapl Basingstoke Distr Hosp 76-78; Chapl Meanwood Park Hosp Gp Leeds 78-88; Chapl Addenbrooke's Hosp Cam 88-94; Chapl Addenbrooke's NHS Trust from 94. *Addenbrooke's Hospital, Box 105, Hills Road, Cambridge CB2 2QQ* Tel (01223) 217769 *or* 245151

MORRIS, Ivor Leslie. b 50. Chich Th Coll 82. **d** 84 **p** 85. C Southend *Chelmsf* 84-87; C Somers Town Lon 87-90; P-in-c Chelmsf Ascension *Chelmsf* 90-96; V from 96; P-in-c Chelmsf All SS 92-96. *The Vicarage, 57 Maltese Road, Chelmsford CM1 2PB* Tel (01245) 353914 E-mail il.morris@virgin.net

MORRIS, Miss Jane Elizabeth. b 50. York Univ BA71 CertEd72 MSc80. NEOC 92. **d** 92 **p** 94. NSM York St Mich-le-Belfrey *York* 92-95; C Leeds St Geo *Ripon* from 95. *46 Vesper Lane, Leeds LS5 3NR* Tel 0113-274 2300
E-mail jane.morris@stgeorgesleeds.org.uk

MORRIS, Jeremy Nigel. b 60. Ball Coll Ox MA81 DPhil86 Clare Coll Cam BA92. Westcott Ho Cam CTM93. **d** 93 **p** 94. C Battersea St Mary *S'wark* 93-96; Dir Studies Westcott Ho Cam

96-01; Vice-Prin 97-01; Dean and Chapl Trin Hall Cam from 01. *Trinity Hall, Cambridge CB2 1TJ* Tel (01223) 332500
E-mail jnm20@cam.ac.uk

MORRIS, Canon John. b 25. Westcott Ho Cam. **d** 65 **p** 66. C St Alb St Mich *St Alb* 65-68; V Leverstock Green 68-80; TR Chambersbury 80-82; V N Mymms 82-90; RD Hatfield 83-88; Hon Can St Alb 89-90; rtd 90; Perm to Offic *St Alb* from 90; *Nor* 92-94 and from 95; P-in-c Barney, Fulmodeston w Croxton, Hindringham etc *Nor* 94-95. *Elba, Croxton Road, Fulmodeston, Fakenham NR21 0NJ* Tel (01328) 878685

MORRIS, John Derrick. b 18. MRCS43 LRCP43. Lon Coll of Div 62. **d** 64 **p** 65. C Cromer *Nor* 64-67; V Broadway *Worc* 67-71; Hon C St Leonards St Leon *Chich* 71-83; rtd 83; Perm to Offic *Chich* from 84. *17 Bourne Way, Midhurst GU29 9HZ* Tel (01730) 814084

MORRIS, John Douglas. b 37. Cam Univ BA58 Lon Inst of Educn PGCE60 Univ of E Africa MEd67 Ex Univ PhD87. S Dios Minl Tr Scheme 94. **d** 95 **p** 96. NSM Twyford and Owslebury and Morestead *Win* 95-98; Perm to Offic from 01. *Gifford House, St Giles Hill, Winchester SO23 0JH* Tel (01962) 869720

MORRIS, John Dudley. b 33. Ball Coll Ox BA57 DipTh59 MA61. Wycliffe Hall Ox 58. **d** 60 **p** 61. C Tonbridge SS Pet and Paul *Roch* 60-65; C Enfield Ch Ch Trent Park *Lon* 65-69; Chapl Elstree Sch Woulnphram 70-74; Hd Master Handcross Park Sch W Sussex 74-89; V Rudgwick *Chich* 89-98; RD Horsham 93-98; rtd 98; Perm to Offic *Chich* from 98. *13 Hoadlands, Handcross, Haywards Heath RH17 6HB* Tel (01444) 400184

MORRIS, John Edgar. b 20. Keble Coll Ox BA42 MA50. Wycliffe Hall Ox 42. **d** 44 **p** 45. C Eccleston St Thos *Liv* 44-48; C Warrington H Trin 48-50; V Newton-le-Willows 50-57; R Wavertree H Trin 57-66; V Ainsdale 66-82; R Broadwell, Evenlode, Oddington and Adlestrop *Glouc* 82-88; rtd 89; Perm to Offic *Glouc* 89-97 and from 01. *29 Letch Hill Drive, Bourton-on-the-Water, Cheltenham GL54 2DQ* Tel (01451) 820571

MORRIS, John Owen. b 56. Nottm Univ BCom82. Linc Th Coll 79. **d** 82 **p** 83. C Morriston *S & B* 82-84; C Kingstone w Clehonger and Eaton Bishop *Heref* 84-87; P-in-c Lugwardine w Bartestree and Weston Beggard 87-92; Chapl RN from 92. *Royal Naval Chaplaincy Service, Room 203, Victory Building, HM Naval Base, Portsmouth PO1 3LS* Tel (023) 9272 7903 Fax 9272 7112

MORRIS, Jonathan Richard. b 57. Lanc Univ BA78 Trin Coll Ox MSc84. WEMTC 99. **d** 02 **p** 03. C Taunton St Andr *B & W* from 02. *1 Peter Street, Taunton TA2 7BZ* Tel (01823) 337668
E-mail jonbea@supanet.com

MORRIS, Kevin John. b 63. Univ of Wales (Ban) BMus84. Westcott Ho Cam 85. **d** 88 **p** 89. C Roath *Llan* 88-91; C Holborn St Alb w Saffron Hill St Pet *Lon* 91-96; V Bedford Park from 96; Dir Post-Ord Tr from 99. *St Michael's Vicarage, Priory Gardens, London W4 1TT* Tel (020) 8994 1380
E-mail kevin.morris@london.anglican.org

MORRIS, Kirsteen Helen Grace. b 44. STETS 99. **d** 02 **p** 03. NSM Cowes H Trin and St Mary *Portsm* from 02. *35 Granville Road, Cowes PO51 7JF* Tel (01983) 289585 Fax 292919
E-mail morris.scawfell@virgin.net

MORRIS, Leo. *See* MORRIS, Canon Frank Leo

MORRIS, Leslie Heber. b 26. Ox Univ MA47. Qu Coll Birm 83. **d** 84 **p** 93. NSM W Leigh *Portsm* 84-85; NSM Warblington w Emsworth 86-96. *Mermaid Cottage, 7 Slipper Road, Emsworth PO10 8BS* Tel (01243) 373389

MORRIS, Lillian Rosina (Mother Lillian). b 29. **dss** 70 **d** 87. CSA 68-97; Mother Superior 82-94 and from 00; Sherston Magna w Easton Grey *Bris* 71-73; Notting Hill All SS w St Columb *Lon* 74-82; Perm to Offic from 00. *8/9 Verona Court, London W4 2JD* Tel (020) 8987 2799

MORRIS, Lyn. *See* MORRIS, Bernard Lyn

MORRIS, Mrs Lynne Margaret. b 53. SEN. WMMTC 95. **d** 98 **p** 99. NSM Wrockwardine Wood *Lich* 98-01; Chapl Birm Specialist Community Health NHS Trust from 01; Perm to Offic *Lich* from 01. *5 Kingston Road, Trench, Telford TF2 7HT* Tel (01952) 618158

MORRIS, Ms Margaret Anne. b 61. Man Univ BA82 MA91. Nor Ord Course 94. **d** 96 **p** 97. C Bury St Pet *Man* 96-98; C Accrington St Jo w Huncoat *Blackb* 98-01; V Knuzden from 01. *St Oswald's Vicarage, 68 Bank Lane, Blackburn BB1 2AP* Tel (01254) 698321 E-mail anne_morris@ntlworld.com

MORRIS, Canon Margaret Jane. Ox Univ MTh96 Leic Univ Hon LLM96. EMMTC 86. **d** 89 **p** 94. NSM Quorndon *Leic* 89-96; Chapl for People affected by HIV from 94; NSM Loughborough All SS w H Trin 96-98; Hon Can Leic Cathl from 97; Chapl Asst Leic R Infirmary NHS Trust 98-00; Chapl Asst Univ Hosps Leic NHS Trust from 00. *10 Toller Road, Quorn, Loughborough LE12 8AH* Tel (01509) 412092 Fax as telephone

MORRIS, Canon Martin Geoffrey Roger. b 41. Trin Coll Cam BA63 MA67. St D Coll Lamp 63. **d** 66 **p** 67. C Newport St Paul *Mon* 66-72; R Lamp Velfrey *St D* 72-74; R Lamp Velfrey and Llanddewi Velfrey from 74; RD St Clears 83-98; Can St D Cathl from 92; Chan from 03. *The Rectory, Lampeter Velfrey, Narberth SA67 8UH* Tel (01834) 831241

MORRIS, Ms Mary. b 27. Birm Univ BA49 CertEd50 MA56. dss 68 **d** 87 **p** 94. Kinver *Lich* 83-87; Hon Par Dn Kinver and Enville 87-94; Hon C from 94. *12 Pavilion End, Prestwood, Stourbridge DY7 5PF* Tel (01384) 877245

MORRIS, Michael Alan. b 46. Jes Coll Cam BA70 MA74. Coll of Resurr Mirfield 79. **d** 81 **p** 82. C Leamington Priors All SS *Cov* 81-83; C Milton *Portsm* 83-88; R Petworth *Chich* 88-90; R Egdean 88-90; Chapl St Pet Hosp Chertsey 90-95; Hon C Thorpe *Guildf* 90-95; P-in-c Harbledown *Cant* 95-97; R from 97; Chapl St Nic Hosp Cant from 95. *The Rectory, Summer Hill, Harbledown, Canterbury CT2 8NW* Tel (01227) 464117 Fax 760530 E-mail michael@summer-hill.freeserve.co.uk

MORRIS, Michael James. b 70. Univ of Wales (Abth) BScEcon92. Qu Coll Birm BA. **d** 00 **p** 01. C Tupsley w Hampton Bishop *Heref* from 00. *2 Litley Close, Hereford HR1 1TN* Tel (01432) 350805 E-mail revmike.morris@virgin.net

MORRIS, Norman Foster Maxwell. b 46. Ex Univ BA68 MA71 Leic Univ PGCE69 Lon Univ DipRS77 K Coll Lon MTh85 Univ of Wales (Cardiff) MA91 Cheltenham & Glouc Coll of HE MA98. S'wark Ord Course 75. **d** 78 **p** 79. C Hackbridge and N Beddington *S'wark* 78-81; Chapl Tonbridge Sch 81-85; Chapl Mon Sch 85-00; Asst Warden Jones Almshouses Mon 89-00; R Wentnor w Ratlinghope, Myndtown, Norbury etc *Heref* from 00; CF (ACF) from 02. *The Rectory, Wentnor, Bishops Castle SY9 5EE* Tel (01588) 650244 Mobile 07974-771069 E-mail revnorm@adcomputers.co.uk

MORRIS, Paul David. b 56. St Jo Coll Nottm BTh79. **d** 80 **p** 81. C Billericay and Lt Burstead *Chelmsf* 80-84; C Luton Lewsey St Hugh *St Alb* 84-89; Dioc Adv on Evang *S'well* 89-00; Dioc Millennium Officer 97-01; Min Tommy's (ch for the unchurched) 96-01; C Barton in Fabis 01-02; C Gotham 01-02; C Thrumpton 01-02; C Kingston and Ratcliffe-on-Soar 01-02; C Sutton Bonington w Normanton-on-Soar 01-02; Dir Evang Chr Associates Internat from 02. *39 Davies Road, Nottingham NG2 5JE* Tel 0115-981 1311 E-mail pmorris@christianassociates.org

MORRIS, Peter. b 45. Leeds Univ CertEd66. Tyndale Hall Bris 68. **d** 71 **p** 72. C Southport SS Simon and Jude *Liv* 71-74; Min-in-c Ch Ch Netherley LEP 74-76; V Bryn 76-91; R Redenhall, Harleston, Wortwell and Needham *Nor* from 91. *The Rectory, 10 Swan Lane, Harleston IP20 9AN* Tel (01379) 852068

MORRIS, Canon Peter Arthur William. b 23. Bps' Coll Cheshunt 57. **d** 58 **p** 59. C Croxley Green All SS *St Alb* 58-62; V Sawbridgeworth 62-74; V S Gillingham *Roch* 74-79; Warden Pleshey Retreat Ho 79-85; P-in-c Pleshey *Chelmsf* 79-85; Hon Can Chelmsf Cathl 81-85; P-in-c Rumburgh w S Elmham w the Ilketshalls *St E* 85-89; rtd 89; Perm to Offic *St E* from 90. *The Cottage on the Common, Westleton, Saxmundham IP17 3AZ* Tel (01728) 73788

MORRIS, Canon Peter Michael Keighley. b 27. St Jo Coll Ox BA49 MA56. Westcott Ho Cam 51. **d** 54 **p** 55. C Bedwellty *Mon* 54-55; Lic to Offic *St D* 55-85; Lect Univ of Wales (Lamp) 55-69; Sen Lect 69-90; Dean Faculty of Th 77-81; Can St D Cathl 85-90; rtd 90; Can and Treas St D Cathl *St D* 92-97. *The Vicarage, Cwmann, Lampeter SA48 8DU* Tel (01570) 422385

MORRIS, The Ven Philip Gregory. b 50. Leeds Univ BA71 MPhil74. Coll of Resurr Mirfield 71. **d** 73 **p** 74. C Aberdare *Llan* 74-77; C Neath w Llantwit 77-80; V Cymmer and Porth 80-88; TV Llantwit Major 88-01; Dioc Missr 88-99; Can Res Llan Cathl 00-01; Adn Margam from 02; TV Aberavon 02; P-in-c Kenfig Hill from 02. *60 Ham Lane South, Llantwit Major CF61 1RN* Tel (01446) 793770 Fax as telephone E-mail pmorri@globalnet.co.uk

MORRIS, Philip John. b 50. FCIPD96. St Mich Coll Llan 97. **d** 99 **p** 00. NSM Builth and Llanddewi'r Cwm w Llangynog etc *S & B* from 99. *Lochaber, 22 North Road, Builth Wells LD2 3BU* Tel (01982) 552390

MORRIS, Raymond. b 48. Open Univ HND70 BA88. N Ord Course 80. **d** 83 **p** 84. C Tonge w Alkrington *Man* 83-86; R Blackley St Paul 86-91; V Heyside from 91; AD Tandle from 02. *St Mark's Vicarage, Perth Street, Royton, Oldham OL2 6LY* Tel (01706) 847177

MORRIS, Raymond Arthur. b 42. Trin Coll Ox BA64 MA66 Lon Univ LLB71 CQSW72. Clifton Th Coll 66. **d** 67 **p** 91. C Greenstead *Chelmsf* 67-68; Perm to Offic *York* 69-91; NSM Linthorpe from 91. *3 Medina Gardens, Middlesbrough TS5 8BN* Tel (01642) 593726

MORRIS, Raymond John Walton. b 08. OBE69. Em Coll Cam BA33 MA37. Lon Coll of Div 33. **d** 34 **p** 35. C E Twickenham St Steph *Lon* 34-37; C Bradf Cathl *Bradf* 37-40; V Plymouth Em *Ex* 40-45; V E Twickenham St Steph *Lon* 45-56; Chapl Br Embassy Ch Paris *Eur* 56-69; RD France 56-69; V Brompton H Trin *Lon* 69-75; rtd 75; Perm to Offic *Sarum* 75-99. *12 St Edward's Court, Shaftesbury SP7 8LZ* Tel (01747) 851950

MORRIS, Reginald Brian. b 31. St Mich Coll Llan 56. **d** 59 **p** 60. C St Jo in Bedwardine *Worc* 59-61; P-in-c Tolladine 61-62; CF 62-78; V Cheswardine *Lich* 78-84; V Hales 78-84; Perm to Offic

84-86; C Cen Telford 86-89; rtd 89; Perm to Offic *Heref* from 90. *Woodside Cottage, School Lane, Prees, Whitchurch SY13 2BU* Tel (01948) 840090

MORRIS, Canon Robert John. b 45. Leeds Univ BA67. Coll of Resurr Mirfield 74. **d** 76 **p** 77. C Beeston Hill St Luke *Ripon* 76; C Holbeck 76-78; C Moseley St Mary *Birm* 78-83; P-in-c Handsworth St Jas 83-88; V 88-99; P-in-c Handsworth St Mich 86-87; AD Handsworth 92-99; TR Kings Norton from 99; Hon Can Birm Cathl from 97. *The Rectory, 273 Pershore Road South, Kings Norton, Birmingham B30 3EX* Tel 0121-459 0560 *or* 458 3289 Fax 486 2825

MORRIS, Robert Lee. b 47. W Virginia Univ BA69. Gen Th Sem (NY) MDiv73. **d** 73 **p** 74. USA 73-74 and from 84; Community of Celebration 74-94; P-in-c Cumbrae (or Millport) *Arg* 75-76 and 79-84. *All Saints Church, 3577 McClure Avenue, Pittsburgh, PA 15212, USA*

MORRIS, Canon Robin Edward. b 32. St Jo Coll Ox BA55 MA60. Westcott Ho Cam 55. **d** 57 **p** 58. C Halliwell St Thos *Man* 57-61; V Castleton Moor 61-71; V Stalybridge 71-80; R Heswall *Ches* 80-97; Hon Can Ches Cathl 91-97; RD Wirral N 93-97; rtd 97; Perm to Offic *Man* from 97. *122 Kiln Lane, Milnrow, Rochdale OL16 3HA* Tel (01706) 642846

MORRIS, Roger Anthony Brett. b 68. ARCS89 Imp Coll Lon BSc89 Trin Coll Cam BA92. Ridley Hall Cam CTM93. **d** 93 **p** 94. C Northleach w Hampnett and Farmington *Glouc* 93-96; C Cold Aston w Notgrove and Turkdean 93-96; P-in-c Sevenhampton w Charlton Abbotts and Hawling etc 96-00; P-in-c Dowdeswell and Andoversford w the Shiptons etc 96-00; R Sevenhampton w Charlton Abbots, Hawling etc from 00; Dioc Dir Par Development and Evang *Cov* from 03. *The Rectory, Station Road, Andoversford, Cheltenham GL54 4LA* Tel (01242) 820230 E-mail roger.morris@virgin.net

MORRIS, Stanley James. b 35. Keble Coll Ox BA58 MA63. Chich Th Coll 59. **d** 61 **p** 62. C Tunstall Ch Ch *Lich* 61-64; C W Bromwich All SS 64-67; V Wilnecote 67-88; V Alrewas and Wychnor 88-00; rtd 01; Perm to Offic *Derby* from 01. *44 Pinfold Close, Repton, Derby DE65 6FR* Tel (01283) 703453

MORRIS, Stephen Bryan. b 54. Linc Th Coll 88. **d** 90 **p** 91. C Glouc St Geo w Whaddon *Glouc* 90-94; Chapl to the Deaf from 94; C Glouc St Mary de Crypt w St Jo, Ch Ch etc 94-99; C Glouc St Mark and St Mary de Crypt w St Jo etc 00-02; C Barnwood from 02. *24 Sandycroft Road, Churchdown, Gloucester GL3 1JH* Tel (01452) 712608

MORRIS, Stephen Francis. b 52. St Jo Coll Nottm BTh79. **d** 79 **p** 80. C N Hinksey *Ox* 79-82; C Leic H Apostles *Leic* 82-85; TV Shenley and Loughton *Ox* 85-88; TV Watling Valley 88-95; V Chatham St Wm *Roch* 95-98; TR S Chatham H Trin 98-00; Lect Nottingham St Mary and St Cath *S'well* from 00; AD Nottingham Cen 02-03. *6 Boyce Gardens, Mapperley, Nottingham NG3 3FB* Tel 0115-958 2996

MORRIS, Canon Stuart Collard. b 43. AKC66. St Boniface Warminster 66. **d** 67 **p** 68. C Hanham *Bris* 67-71; C Whitchurch 71-74; P-in-c Wapley w Codrington and Doddington 74-77; P-in-c Westerleigh 74-77; P-in-c Holdgate w Tugford *Heref* 77-82; P-in-c Abdon w Clee St Margaret 77-82; R Diddlebury w Bouldon and Munslow 77-82; P-in-c Sotterley, Willingham, Shadingfield, Ellough etc *St E* 82-87; RD Beccles and S Elmham 83-94; P-in-c Westhall w Brampton and Stoven 86-88; P-in-c Flixton w Homersfield and S Elmham 86-92; Hon Can St E Cathl 87-99; V Bungay H Trin w St Mary 87-94; P-in-c Hadleigh w Layham and Shelley 94-96; R Hadleigh 96-99; Dean Bocking 94-99; RD Hadleigh 94-98; rtd 99. *Ty'r Gelliffynonau, Cwm Cadlan, Penderyn, Aberdare CF44 0YJ* Tel (01685) 813196

MORRIS, Canon Timothy David. b 48. Lon Univ BSc69. Trin Coll Bris DipTh75. **d** 75 **p** 76. C Edin St Thos *Edin* 75-77; R Edin St Jas 77-83; R Troon *Glas* 83-85; R Galashiels *Edin* 85-02; Dean Edin 92-01; Hon Can St Mary's Cathl from 01; R Edin Gd Shep from 02. *9 Upper Coltbridge Terrace, Edinburgh EH12 6AD* Tel 0131-337 2698 E-mail tim@parsonage.scotborders.co.uk

MORRIS, Mrs Valerie Ruth. b 46. St Hugh's Coll Ox BA68 MA72. Qu Coll Birm 76. dss 78 **d** 87. Drayton in Hales *Lich* 78-82; Burton 82-90; Par Dn 87-90; Hon Par Dn 90-91. *Watling House, All Stretton, Church Stretton SY6 6HH* Tel (01694) 722243

MORRIS, William Humphrey Francis. b 29. Univ of Wales BA54 MA72 Birm Univ DipTh58 Trin Coll Cam BA62 MA66 PhD75 Man Univ MEd76 PhD80 Ox Univ DPhil85 DD88 FRAS84 FInstP92. Qu Coll Birm 56. **d** 58 **p** 59. C Prestbury *Ches* 58-60; C Neston 60-65; V Sandbach Heath 65-68; Lic to Offic 69-93; rtd 84; Lic to Offic *Lich* from 93; Perm to Offic *Ches* from 93. *Stonyflats Farm, Smallwood, Sandbach CW11 2XH* Tel (01477) 500354

MORRIS, William James. b 23. St Deiniol's Hawarden 72. **d** 73 **p** 74. NSM Brecon Adnry 73-78; NSM Crickhowell w Cwmdu and Tretower *S & B* 78-98; rtd 98. *The School House, Cwmdu, Crickhowell NP8 1RU* Tel (01874) 730353

MORRIS, William Richard Price. b 23. FCollP82. Glouc Sch of Min 86. **d** 88 **p** 89. Hon C Bussage *Glouc* 88-90; Perm to Offic 90-91; Hon C France Lynch 91; Hon C Chalford and France

Lynch 91-93; rtd 93; Perm to Offic *Glouc* from 93. *Langendun House, Manor Close, Michinhampton, Stroud GL6 9DG* Tel (01453) 886382

MORRISH, James William. b 65. Plymouth Univ BSc92. St Steph Ho Ox 99. **d** 01. C Porlock w Stoke Pero *B & W* from 01. *5 Lowerbourne, Porlock, Minehead TA24 8PZ* Tel (01643) 862989

MORRISON, Alexander Grant. b 37. St Fran Coll Brisbane ThL ACT St Columb's Hall Wangaratta. **d** 66 **p** 67. Australia 66-82; C Hayes St Mary *Lon* 83-84; R Black Notley *Chelmsf* from 84. *The Rectory, 71 Witham Road, Black Notley, Braintree CM77 7LJ* Tel (01376) 349619

MORRISON, Andrew Leslie. b 11. TD53. Pemb Coll Ox BA33 MA37. Westcott Ho Cam 33. **d** 35 **p** 36. C S Westoe *Dur* 35-38; V Castleside 38-42; CF (TA) 39-56; R Branston *Linc* 46-49; V Gateshead Ch Ch *Dur* 49-55; Chapl Bensham Hosp Gateshead 50-55; R Fenny Compton and Wormleighton *Cov* 55-59; RD Dassett Magna 59-64; V Bury and Houghton *Chich* 64-76; rtd 76; Perm to Offic *Chich* from 76. *14 Guildford Place, Chichester PO19 5DU* Tel (01243) 784310

MORRISON, Barbara Anne. b 29. St Andr Univ BSc50. **d** 95 **p** 96. NSM Eorropaidh *Arg* from 95. *46 Upper Coll, Back, Isle of Lewis HS2 0LT* Tel (01851) 820559 Fax as telephone
E-mail barbara@stmoluag.in2home.co.uk

MORRISON, Barry John. b 44. Pemb Coll Cam BA66 MA70. ALCD69. **d** 69 **p** 70. C Stoke Bishop *Bris* 69-72; C Edgware *Lon* 72-76; Chapl Poly Cen Lon 76-83; Hon C Langham Place All So 76-83; P-in-c W Hampstead St Luke 83-88; V 88-98; Chapl Westf Coll 84-92; R Rushden St Mary w Newton Bromswold *Pet* from 98. *The Rectory, Rectory Road, Rushden NN10 0HA* Tel (01933) 312554
E-mail morrison@barryandgill.freeserve.co.uk

MORRISON, Bryony Clare. b 47. Lon Univ CertEd77 Brentwood Coll of Educn BEd86. NTMTC 96. **d** 99 **p** 00. NSM Epping Distr *Chelmsf* 99-02; C from 02; Chapl Epping Forest Primary Care Trust from 02. *Vicarage Cottage, Hartland Road, Epping CM16 4PD* Tel (01992) 573672 Mobile 07850-876304
E-mail revbry@waitrose.com

MORRISON, Iain Edward. b 36. St Steph Ho Ox 76. **d** 78 **p** 79. C Brighton St Aug and St Sav *Chich* 78-81; C Felpham w Middleton 81-83; P-in-c Barnham and Eastergate 83-85; R Aldingbourne, Barnham and Eastergate 85-91; V Jarvis Brook 91-98; R Hastings St Clem and All SS from 98. *The Rectory, 7 High Street, Hastings TN34 3EY* Tel (01424) 422023
E-mail iain@hafodty.demon.uk

MORRISON, James Wilson Rennie. b 42. Aber Univ MA65. Linc Th Coll 76. **d** 78 **p** 79. C Whitley Ch Ch *Ox* 78-81; R Burghfield 81-87; CF 87-97; P-in-c Burghill *Heref* 97-03; V from 03; P-in-c Stretton Sugwas 97-03; R from 03; P-in-c Pipe-cum-Lyde 97-03; P-in-c Wellington w Pipe-cum-Lyde and Moreton-on-Lugg from 03. *The Vicarage, Burghill, Hereford HR4 7SG* Tel (01432) 760246

MORRISON, The Ven John Anthony. b 38. Jes Coll Cam BA60 MA64 Linc Coll Ox MA68. Chich Th Coll 61. **d** 64 **p** 65. C Birm St Pet *Birm* 64-68; C Ox St Mich *Ox* 68-71; Chapl Linc Coll Ox 68-74; C Ox St Mich w St Martin and All SS *Ox* 71-74; V Basildon 74-82; RD Bradfield 78-82; V Aylesbury 82-89; RD Aylesbury 85-89; TR Aylesbury w Bierton and Hulcott 89-90; Adn Buckingham 90-98; P-in-c Princes Risborough w Ilmer 96-97; Adn Ox and Can Res Ch Ch from 98. *Archdeacon's Lodging, Christ Church, Oxford OX1 1DP* Tel (01865) 204440 Fax 204465
E-mail archdoxf@oxford.anglican.org

MORRISON, Keith Charles. b 63. Wycliffe Hall Ox. **d** 01 **p** 02. C Ipswich St Aug *St E* from 01. *18 Fitzmaurice Road, Ipswich IP3 9AX* Tel (01473) 719562 Mobile 07798-965651
E-mail keithmorrisonk@hotmail.com

MORRISON, Richard James. b 55. Sarum & Wells Th Coll 87. **d** 89 **p** 90. C Boston *Linc* 89-93; P-in-c Digby 93-99; V Whaplode Drove from 99; V Gedney Hill from 99. *The Vicarage, 1 Broadgate, Whaplode Drove, Spalding PE12 0TN* Tel (01406) 330392

MORRISON, Robin Victor Adair. b 45. Nottm Univ BA67. Bucharest Th Inst 67 Ripon Hall Ox 68. **d** 70 **p** 71. C Hackney St Jo *Lon* 70-73; Chapl Newc Univ *Newc* 73-76; P-in-c Teversal *S'well* 76-78; Chapl Sutton Cen 76-78; Asst Hd Deans Community Sch Livingston *Edin* 78-80; R Edin St Columba 80-81; Chapl Birm Univ *Birm* 81-88; Prin Soc Resp Officer *Derby* 88-96; TV Southampton (City Cen) *Win* 96-01; Ind Chapl 96-01; Non Exec Dir Southampton and SW Hants HA 00-01; Officer for Ch and Soc Ch in Wales Prov Coun from 01. *97 South Road, Sully, Penarth CF64 5SN* Tel (029) 2053 1772
E-mail robin@sparticus.net

MORRISON, Walter John Raymond (Ray). b 30. Jes Coll Cam BA55 MA58. Westcott Ho Cam 55. **d** 57 **p** 58. C Dalston St Mark w St Bart *Lon* 57-60; C Totteridge *St Alb* 60-63; V Letchworth St Paul 63-71; RD Hitchin 70-71; R Ludlow *Heref* 72-83; RD Ludlow 78-83; Preb Heref Cathl 78-83; P-in-c Ludlow, Ludford, Ashford Carbonell etc 80-83; Chapl St Thos Hosp Lon 83-86; Chapl Eastbourne Distr Gen Hosp 86-95; rtd

95; Perm to Offic *Worc* from 95. *190 Farleigh Road, Pershore WR10 1LY* Tel (01386) 556542

MORROW, David. b 63. NUU BSc86 TCD BTh89. CITC 86. **d** 89 **p** 90. C Portadown St Mark *Arm* 89-91; C Ballymena w Ballyclug *Conn* 91-94; I Tempo and Clabby *Clogh* 94-01; I Kilcronaghan w Draperstown and Sixtowns *D & R* from 01. *Kilcronaghan Rectory, 12 Rectory Road, Tobermore, Magherafelt BT45 5QP* Tel (028) 7962 8823
E-mail morrowdavid@hotmail.com

MORROW, Canon Henry Hugh. b 26. TCD BA49 MA67 Flinders Univ Aus BSocAdmin76. TCD Div Sch Div Test49. **d** 49 **p** 50. C Dublin St Thos *D & G* 49-53; I Rathmolyon *M & K* 53-58; I Killoughter *K, E & A* 58-63; C Portadown St Columba *Arm* 63-65; I Ballinderry w Tamlaght 65-70; Australia from 70; Hon Can Adelaide from 84. *5 Allendale Grove, Stonyfell, S Australia 5066* Tel (0061) (8) 8332 5890

MORROW, Canon Joseph John. b 54. JP87. Edin Univ BD79 Dundee Univ LLB92 OStJ99 Dundee Univ DLLP93. Edin Th Coll 76 NY Th Sem DMin87. **d** 79 **p** 80. Chapl St Paul's Cathl Dundee *Bre* 79-82; P-in-c Dundee St Martin 82-85; R 85-90; P-in-c Dundee St Jo from 85; P-in-c Dundee St Ninian from 02; Can St Paul's Cathl Dundee from 00. *St Ninian's Rectory, Kingsway East, Dundee DD4 7RW* Tel (01382) 453818
E-mail jjmidt@glamis.sol.co.uk

MORSE, Mrs Elisabeth Ann. b 51. New Hall Cam MA73 Qu Eliz Coll Lon MSc74 Heythrop Coll Lon MA97. S'wark Ord Course 91. **d** 94 **p** 95. C Wimbledon *S'wark* 94-99; C Fulham All SS *Lon* from 99. *70A Fulham High Street, London SW6 3LG* Tel (020) 7371 7540

MORSHEAD, Ivo Francis Trelawny. b 27. ACA52 FCA63. Cuddesdon Coll 61. **d** 63 **p** 64. C Bris St Mary Redcliffe w Temple etc *Bris* 63-68; C Wimbledon *S'wark* 68-73; V Elham *Cant* 73-78; V Whitchurch *Ex* 78-91; rtd 91; Perm to Offic *Lon* from 91. *28 Edge Street, London W8 7PN* Tel (020) 7727 5975

MORSON, Mrs Dorothy Mary. b 29. Linc Th Coll 71. **d** 87. Par Dn Cen Telford *Lich* 87-89; rtd 89; Perm to Offic *Lich* 89-00. *Ashleigh, Hunter Street, Shrewsbury SY3 8QN* Tel (01743) 369225

MORSON, Mrs Eleanor. b 42. CA Tr Coll 63 TISEC 95. **d** 96 **p** 96. CA from 65; NSM Kirkwall *Ab* 96-01; R Edin St Mark *Edin* from 01. *32 Durham Avenue, Edinburgh EH15 1PA* Tel 0131-669 3452

MORSON, John. b 41. CA Tr Coll 62. **d** 88 **p** 92. NSM Duns *Edin* 88-89; CF 89-92; R Kirkwall *Ab* 92-01; R Stromness 92-01. *32 Durham Avenue, Edinburgh EH15 1PA* Tel 0131-669 3452

MORT, Alister. b 52. BSc BA. Oak Hill Th Coll. **d** 82 **p** 83. C Cheadle Hulme St Andr *Ches* 82-85; C Rodbourne Cheney *Bris* 86-87; TV 87-90; V New Milverton *Cov* from 90. *2 St Mark's Road, Leamington Spa CV32 6DL* Tel (01926) 421004
E-mail office@stmarkslspa.freeserve.co.uk

MORT, Ivan Laurence (Laurie). b 61. Nottm Univ BTh87. Linc Th Coll 84. **d** 87 **p** 88. C Aston cum Aughton and Ulley *Sheff* 87-90; C Greenstead *Chelmsf* 90-94; Chapl Toulouse *Eur* from 94. *19 rue Bel Soulhel, Cornebarrieu 31700, Toulouse, France* Tel (0033) (5) 61 85 17 67

MORT, Canon Margaret Marion. b 38. Edin Univ MA. S Tr Scheme 94. **d** 97 **p** 98. NSM Swanmore St Barn *Portsm* from 97; Hon Can Portsm Cathl from 01. *Rivendell, High Street, Shirrell Heath, Southampton SO3 2JN* Tel and fax (01329) 832178 Mobile 07761-225222 E-mail marion@holyharp.co.uk

MORTER, Ian Charles. b 54. AKC77. Coll of Resurr Mirfield 77. **d** 78 **p** 79. C Colchester St Jas, All SS, St Nic and St Runwald *Chelmsf* 78-82; C Brixham w Churston Ferrers *Ex* 82-83; TV 84-86; TV Sidmouth, Woolbrook and Salcombe Regis 86-91; TV Sidmouth, Woolbrook, Salcombe Regis, Sidbury etc 91-95; P-in-c Exminster and Kenn 95-00; TR Littleham w Exmouth from 00. *The Rectory, 1 Maer Road, Exmouth EX8 2DA* Tel (01395) 272227

MORTIBOYS, John William. b 45. K Coll Lon BD69 AKC69. Sarum Th Coll 71. **d** 71 **p** 72. C Reading All SS *Ox* 71-95; Perm to Offic *Portsm* from 97. *13 Oyster Street, Portsmouth PO1 2HZ* Tel (023) 9275 6676 Fax 9266 2626

MORTIMER, Anthony John. b 42. Sarum & Wells Th Coll 68. **d** 71 **p** 72. C Heref St Martin *Heref* 71-79; V Kingstone 79-85; P-in-c Clehonger 80-85; P-in-c Eaton Bishop 80-85; TR Pinhoe and Broadclyst *Ex* from 85. *The Rectory, 9 Church Hill, Pinhoe, Exeter EX4 9ER* Tel (01392) 467541

MORTIMER, Charles Philip. b 38. Linc Th Coll 68. **d** 70 **p** 71. C Penistone w Midhope *Wakef* 70-74; V Luddenden 74-77; P-in-c Luddenden Foot 74-77; Chapl RAF 77-91; Asst Chapl-in-Chief RAF 91-93; V Staincliffe *Wakef* 93-99; rtd 99. *15 Park Avenue, Liversedge Hall Lane, Liversedge WF15 7EQ* Tel (01924) 510051

MORTIMER, The Very Revd Hugh Sterling. b 23. TCD BA44 MA53. **d** 46 **p** 47. C Finaghy *Conn* 46-49; Dean's V Belf Cathl 49-53; V Choral Belf Cathl 53-55; I Tartaraghan *Arm* 55-61; Hon VC 57-85; I Magherafelt 61-66; I Arm St Mark 66-83; Can Arm Cathl 67-72; Treas 72-73; Chan 73-75; Prec 75-83; Dean

...nd Ardagh *K, E & A* 83-91; I Sligo w Knocknarea and
...t 83-91; rtd 91; Perm to Offic *Conn* from 91. *95 Sharman
..., Belfast BT9 5HE* Tel (028) 9066 9184

...RTIMER, Jonathan Michael. b 60. Bris Univ BA83. Oak Hill
Th Coll BA92. **d** 92 **p** 93. C Rugby St Matt *Cov* 92-96; C
Southgate *Chich* 96-98; TR from 98. *The Rectory, Forester Road,
Crawley RH10 6EH* Tel (01293) 523463

MORTIMER, Canon Lawrence George. b 45. St Edm Hall Ox
BA67 MA71 St Chad's Coll Dur DipTh68. **d** 70 **p** 71. C Rugby
St Andr *Cov* 70-75; V Styvechale 75-89; Dioc Broadcasting
Officer 80-89; Dioc Communications Officer from 89; P-in-c
Wootton Wawen from 95; P-in-c Claverdon w Preston Bagot
from 03; Hon Can Cov Cathl from 98. *The Vicarage, Stratford
Road, Wootton Wawen, Henley-in-Arden B95 6BD* Tel and fax
(01564) 792659 *or* tel 795545
E-mail l.mortimer@btinternet.com

MORTIMER, Peter Jackson. b 41. MBE95 TD73. St Jo Coll
York CertEd63 RTC63 Essex Univ MA71 FRSA97. EAMTC
97. **d** 98 **p** 99. OStJ from 77; NSM Needham Market w Badley
St E 98-02; NSM Ringshall w Battisford, Barking w Darmsden
etc 98-02; Bp's Ecum Adv from 02; Chapl to Suffolk Fire Service
from 03. *20 Leggatt Drive, Bramford, Ipswich IP8 4ET* Tel
(01473) 747419

MORTIMER, Richard James. b 63. Ex Univ BSc85 Lon Bible
Coll BA97. Oak Hill Th Coll. **d** 01. C Ore *Chich* from 01.
34 Fellows Road, Hastings TN34 3TY Tel (01424) 440093
E-mail richard@rmortimer.freeserve.co.uk

MORTIMER, William Raymond. b 31. GradIEE58 AMIEE66.
St Deiniol's Hawarden 68. **d** 69 **p** 70. C Flint *St As* 69-71; Lic to
Offic 72-73; V Llanwddyn and Llanfihangel-yng-Nghwynfa etc
73-85; RD Llanfyllin 83-84; R Llanrwst and Llanddoget and
Capel Garmon 85-96; rtd 96. *1 Coed Masarn, Woodlands Estate,
Abergele LL22 7EE* Tel (01745) 822306

MORTIMORE, David Jack. b 42. Master Mariner 69. St Mich
Coll Llan 90. **d** 91 **p** 92. C Pembroke St Mary w St Mich *St D*
91-92; C Bargoed and Deri w Brithdir *Llan* 92-97; Perm to
Offic 98-02; P-in-c Llangeinor from 02. *Cleddau, 6 Heol-y-Gaer,
Barry CF62 6UH* Tel (01446) 421560
E-mail cleddau@tesco.net

MORTIMORE, Robert Edward. b 39. Kelham Th Coll 61 Wells
Th Coll 66. **d** 69 **p** 70. C Byfleet *Guildf* 69-72; New Zealand from
72. *10 Otakau Road, Milford, Auckland 1309, New Zealand* Tel
(0064) (9) 486 1010 Fax as telephone

MORTIS, Lorna Anne. b 54. Moray Ho Coll of Educn DipEd76
Open Univ BA88 Heriot-Watt Univ 92. TISEC CMM95. **d** 98
p 99. C N Berwick *Edin* from 98; C Gullane from 98. *Rosebank,
2 Main Street, Athelstaneford, North Berwick EH39 5BE* Tel
(01620) 880505 E-mail anrola@aol.com

MORTON, Adrian Ian. b 65. Brighton Poly BSc87 Brunel Univ
MSc93. Ridley Hall Cam 98. **d** 00 **p** 01. C Kettering Ch the King
Pet from 00. *9 Churchill Way, Kettering NN15 5DP* Tel (01536)
485772 E-mail adrian-morton@supanet.com

MORTON, Albert George. b 34. Saskatchewan Univ BA61
McGill Univ Montreal MA73. Em Coll Saskatoon 56. **d** 61 **p** 61.
Canada 61-65; C Stanford-le-Hope *Chelmsf* 66-69; V Linc
St Geo Swallowbeck *Linc* 69-82; R Lt Munden w Sacombe
St Alb 82-89; R The Mundens w Sacombe 89-96; rtd 96; Perm to
Offic *Sarum* from 00. *10 Church Green, Bishop's Caundle,
Sherborne DT9 5NN* Tel (01963) 23383

MORTON, Andrew Edward. b 51. Lon Univ BA72 BD74
AKC74 Univ of Wales (Cardiff) MPhil93 Dip Counselling 98.
St Aug Coll Cant 75. **d** 76 **p** 77. C Feltham *Lon* 76-79; C
Pontlottyn w Fochriw *Llan* 79-81; V Ferndale w Maerdy 81-88;
V Tylorstown w Ynyshir 88-93; Dir of Studies Llan Ord
Course 91-93; R Llangybi and Coedypaen w Llanbadoc *Mon*
from 93; Chapl Coleg Gwent from 93; Dioc FE Officer from
93; Prov HE Officer from 01; Dioc Dir NSM Studies from 00.
The Rectory, Parc Road, Llangybi, Usk NP15 1NL Tel (01633)
450214

MORTON, Mrs Christine Mary. b 39. Linc Th Coll 78. **dss** 80
d 87 **p** 94. Ore *Chich* 80-84; Southwick St Mich 84-85;
Winchmore Hill St Paul *Lon* 85-87; Par Dn 87-94; C 94-99; NSM
from 00; rtd 00. *122 Bourne Hill, London N13 4BD* Tel (020) 8886
3157

MORTON, Clive Frederick. b 47. Lon Univ BA70 Birm Univ
MA98. Cranmer Hall Dur 78. **d** 80 **p** 81. C Countesthorpe w
Foston *Leic* 80-83; C Glen Parva and S Wigston 83-86; Asst
Chapl HM Youth Cust Cen Glen Parva 83-86; V Birm St Pet
Birm 86-98; Miss Partner CMS 99-02; Chapl St Petersburg *Eur*
99-02; Lect St Petersburg Th Academy and Sem 99-02; V
Kingsbury H Innocents *Lon* from 02. *Kingsbury Vicarage, 54 Roe
Green, London NW9 0PJ* Tel (020) 8204 7531 Mobile 07947-
883559 E-mail cp.morton@virgin.net

MORTON, Derek. *See* MORTON, Canon William Derek

MORTON, Howard Knyvett. b 30. St Jo Coll Cam BA51 MA67.
Linc Th Coll 55. **d** 57 **p** 58. C Hatfield Hyde *St Alb* 57-60; Head
RE Heaton Gr Sch Newc 60-66 and 72-75; CMS 66-72; Heworth
Grange Sch Dur 75-83; Regional Org Oxfam 88-91; Grainger Gr
Sch Newc 91-94; Lic to Offic *Newc* 73-93; Dioc World

Development Officer 94-95; rtd 95; Perm to Offic *Dur* 95-98;
Perm to Offic *Newc* from 96. *Daisy Cottage, Hawthorn Lane,
Rothbury, Morpeth NE65 7TL*

MORTON, Mrs Jacqueline Mavis. b 46. UEA BSc67 York Univ
BSc82. EMMTC 97. **d** 00 **p** 01. NSM Sibsey w Frithville *Linc*
from 00. *8 Lucan Close, Sibsey, Boston PE22 0SH* Tel (01205)
751378 E-mail jacqui.morton@jmorton.fsnet.co.uk

MORTON, Jennifer. b 50. Bedf Coll Lon BA72 Leic Univ
PGCE73. EMMTC 87. **d** 90 **p** 94. C New Mills *Derby* 90-94;
Chapl Asst Nottm City Hosp NHS Trust 94-98; Chapl
Basford Hosp Nottm 94-98; Chapl S Derbyshire Acute Hosps
NHS Trust 98-02; Vice Prin EMMTC *S'well* from 02.
56 Marshall Drive, Beeston, Nottingham NG9 3LD Tel 0115-939
5784 *or* 951 4852 Fax 951 4817
E-mail jenny.morton@nottingham.ac.uk

MORTON, Mark Paul. b 58. Univ of Wales (Swansea) BA79
Univ of Wales (Lamp) MA99. Ridley Hall Cam CTM92. **d** 92
p 93. C Daventry, Ashby St Ledgers, Braunston etc *Pet* 92-95; CF
(TA) 93-95; CF from 95. *clo MOD Chaplains (Army)* Tel
(01980) 615804 Fax 615800

MORTON, Michelle. b 67. Ripon Coll Cuddesdon 00. **d** 02 **p** 03.
C Buckingham *Ox* from 02. *17 Otters Brook, Buckingham
MK18 7EB* Tel (01280) 824269
E-mail squarenalo@hotmail.com

MORTON, Rex Gerald. b 61. St Jo Coll Nottm DipTh98. **d** 98
p 99. C Bury St Edmunds All SS *St E* 98-01; C Woodside Park
St Barn *Lon* from 01. *12 Courthouse Road, London N12 7PJ* Tel
(020) 8446 7506 Mobile 07968-088714
E-mail sj@morton4.swinternet.co.uk

MORTON, Sister Rita. b 34. Wilson Carlile Coll. **dss** 85 **d** 87 **p** 94.
CA from 76; Par Dn Harlow New Town w Lt Parndon *Chelmsf*
87-89; C Harold Hill St Geo 89-94; rtd 94; NSM Elm Park St Nic
Hornchurch *Chelmsf* from 94. *16 Cheviot Road, Hornchurch
RH11 1LP* Tel (01708) 709842

MORTON, Robert Hart. b 28. Moray Ord Course 91. **d** 94. Hon C
St Andr Cathl Inverness *Mor* from 94. *75 Fairfield Road, Inverness
IV3 5LJ* Tel (01463) 223525

MORTON, Rupert Neville. b 25. St Steph Ho Ox 51. **d** 54 **p** 55. C
Aldershot St Mich *Guildf* 54-57; Prec Guildf Cathl 57-58; V
Middlesbrough St Chad *York* 58-62; Chapl Carter Bequest Hosp
58-62; V Bramley *Guildf* 62-79; V Grafham 62-79; RD Cranleigh
71-76; R Haslemere 79-91; rtd 91; Perm to Offic *Guildf* and *Chich*
from 91. *Rock House, Wormley, Godalming GU8 5SN* Tel
(01428) 682614

MORTON, Mrs Sheila. b 44. Leeds Univ DipTh92. Sarum &
Wells Th Coll 79. **dss** 84 **d** 87 **p** 94. HM Forces Dusseldorf 84-86;
Cov St Mary *Cov* 86-89; Par Dn 87-89; Par Dn Boston Spa *York*
89-92; C Flitwick *St Alb* 93-00; R Wilden w Colmworth and
Ravensden from 00. *The New Rectory, High Street, Wilden,
Bedford MK44 2PB* Tel (01234) 772895
E-mail revsheila@vicarage727freeserve.co.uk

MORTON, Canon William Derek. b 28. Wells Th Coll 67. **d** 69
p 70. C Kibworth Beauchamp *Leic* 69-72; Ind Chapl *Nor* 72-93;
Hon Can Nor Cathl 90-93; RD Nor E 90-93; rtd 93; Perm to
Offic *Nor* from 93. *55 Cameron Green, Taverham, Norwich
NR8 6UA* Tel (01603) 861240

MORTON, The Very Revd William Wright. b 56. ALAM TCD
BTh88 MA95 QUB PhD96. CITC. **d** 88 **p** 89. C Drumachose
D & R 88-91; I Conwal Union w Gartan 91-97; Bp's Dom Chapl
92-97; Can Raphoe Cathl 94-97; Dean Derry from 97; I
Templemore from 97. *The Deanery, 30 Bishop Street,
Londonderry BT48 6PP* Tel (028) 7126 2746
E-mail dean@derry.anglican.org

MOSDOL, Halvard. b 00. C Norwegian Ch and Seamen's Miss
Lon from 02; NSM Bermondsey Deanery *S'wark* from 02.
*St Olav's Church, 1 St Olav's Square, Albion Street, London
SE16 1JB* Tel (020) 8852 3264

MOSEDALE, Hugh Alfred. b 14. AKC48. **d** 49 **p** 50. C W Derby
St Mary *Liv* 49-52; C Lewisham St Mary *S'wark* 52-55; C Walton
St Mary *Liv* 55-57; V Middleton Junction *Man* 57-61; R
Boxworth *Ely* 61-96; R Elsworth w Knapwell 61-96; RD Bourn
72-81; rtd 96; Perm to Offic *St Alb* from 96. *23 Bridgefoot, St Ives
PE27 5EP*

MOSELEY, Arthur William. b 27. Lich Th Coll. **d** 60 **p** 61. C
Castle Church *Lich* 60-64; C Bloxwich 64-66; V Bradley
St Martin 66-72; C Stoke upon Trent 73-74; V Brown Edge 74-85;
V Criftins 85-93; V Dudleston 85-93; rtd 93. *Pentre Collen, 2 Cil-
y-Coed, Ruabon, Wrexham LL14 6TA* Tel (01978) 810063

MOSELEY, David John Reading. b 30. Univ Coll Ox BA54
MA58. Wells Th Coll 54. **d** 56 **p** 57. C Farnworth and Kearsley
Man 56-59; Trinidad and Tobago 59-63; V Bedminster St Paul
Bris 63-75; TV Bedminster 75-78; V Kilmington w Shute *Ex*
78-95; P-in-c Stockland w Dalwood 90; rtd 95; Perm to Offic *Ex*
from 95. *1B Seaton Down Road, Seaton EX12 2RZ* Tel (01297)
24174

MOSELEY, Hugh Martin. b 47. St Jo Coll Dur BA70. Westcott
Ho Cam 71. **d** 73 **p** 74. C Hythe *Cant* 73-77; P-in-c Eythorne w
Waldershare 77-83; V Ringmer *Chich* 83-99; RD Lewes and
Seaford 93-97; P-in-c E Dean w Friston and Jevington 99-00; R

00-03; TR Rye from 03. *St Mary's Rectory, Gungarden, Rye TN31 7HH* Tel (01797) 222430

MOSELEY, Roger Henry. b 38. Edin Th Coll 60. **d** 63 **p** 64. C Friern Barnet All SS *Lon* 63-66; C Grantham St Wulfram *Linc* 66-69; P-in-c Swaton w Spanby 69-73; P-in-c Horbling 69-73; V Soberton w Newtown *Portsm* 73-80; V Sarisbury 80-03; rtd 03; Perm to Offic *Portsm* from 03. *53B St Michael's Road, St Helens, Ryde PO33 1YJ* Tel (01983) 875203 E-mail rhmoseley@talk21.com

MOSELING, Peter. b 48. WMMTC 92. **d** 95 **p** 96. C Daventry, Ashby St Ledgers, Braunston etc *Pet* 95-97; P-in-c Northampton H Trin 97-99; P-in-c Northampton St Paul 98-99; V Northampton H Trin and St Paul from 99; Chapl Northampton Univ Coll from 99. *The Vicarage, 24 Edinburgh Road, Northampton NN2 6PH* Tel (01604) 711468 E-mail p.moseling@amserve.net

MOSES, The Very Revd John Henry. b 38. Nottm Univ BA59 PhD65. Linc Th Coll 62. **d** 64 **p** 65. C Bedford St Andr *St Alb* 64-70; P-in-c Cov St Pet *Cov* 70-73; P-in-c Cov St Mark 71-73; TR Cov E 73-77; RD Cov E 73-77; Adn Southend *Chelmsf* 77-82; Provost Chelmsf 82-96; Chmn Coun of Cen for Th Study Essex Univ 87-96; Dean St Paul's *Lon* from 96. *The Deanery, 9 Amen Court, London EC4M 7BU* Tel (020) 7236 2827 Fax 7332 0298 E-mail dean.stpauls@dial.pipex.com

MOSES, Leslie Alan. b 49. Hull Univ BA71 Edin Univ BD76. Edin Th Coll 73. **d** 76 **p** 77. C Edin Old St Paul *Edin* 76-79; R Leven *St And* 79-85; R Edin Old St Paul *Edin* 85-95; P-in-c Edin St Marg 86-92; V St Marylebone All SS *Lon* from 95; AD Westmr St Marylebone from 01. *All Saints' Vicarage, 7 Margaret Street, London W1W 8JG* Tel (020) 7636 1788 *or* 7636 9961 Fax 7436 4470 E-mail alan@moses.org

MOSFORD, Denzil Huw Erasmus. b 56. St D Coll Lamp DipTh77 AKC78 Sarum & Wells Th Coll 77. **d** 79 **p** 80. C Clydach *S & B* 79-82; V 87-97; Jamaica 82-85; V Ystalyfera *S & B* 85-87; Dioc World Miss Officer from 91; RD Cwmtawe 93-97; V Gorseinon from 97; RD Llwchwr from 00. *The Vicarage, 42 Princess Street, Gorseinon, Swansea SA4 4US* Tel (01792) 892849 E-mail huw@mosford.freeserve.co.uk

MOSFORD, Denzil Joseph. b 28. St Deiniol's Hawarden 84. **d** 86 **p** 87. C Manselton *S & B* 86-89; R Port Eynon w Rhosili and Llanddewi and Knelston 89-99; rtd 99. *10 Pontardulais Road, Penllergaer, Swansea SA4 9AY* Tel (01792) 229660

MOSLEY, Edward Peter. b 38. Clifton Th Coll 62. **d** 67 **p** 68. C Mirehouse *Carl* 67-69; C Newbarns w Hawcoat 69-72; R Aikton 72-77; R Orton St Giles 72-77; V Silloth 77-78; CF 78-94; Hon C Grantown-on-Spey *Mor* 94-95; Hon C Rothiemurchus 94-95; rtd 98; P-in-c Strathnairn St Paul *Mor* from 03. *St Paul's Parsonage, Croachy, Inverness IV2 6UB* Tel (01808) 521397 E-mail epmos@onetel.net.uk

MOSS, Barbara Penelope. b 46. St Anne's Coll Ox BA66 MA70 Lon Univ BD97 Middx Univ MA00. EAMTC 95. **d** 97 **p** 98. NSM Leytonstone H Trin Harrow Green *Chelmsf* 97-00; C Cambridge Gt St Mary w St Mich *Ely* from 00. *38 Eachard Road, Cambridge CB3 0HY* Tel (01223) 353838 *or* 741719 E-mail bar@barmoss.demon.co.uk *or* bpm23@cam.ac.uk

MOSS, The Very Revd Basil Stanley. b 18. Qu Coll Ox BA41 MA45. Linc Th Coll 42. **d** 43 **p** 44. C Leigh St Mary *Man* 43-45; Tutor Linc Th Coll 45-46; Sub-Warden 46-51; Tutor St Cath Cumberland Lodge 51-53; V Bris St Nath w St Kath *Bris* 53-60; Dioc Dir of Ords 56-66; Hon Can Bris Cathl 59-60 and 66-73; Can Res Bris Cathl 60-66; Chief Sec ACCM 66-73; Provost Birm 73-85; rtd 85; Perm to Offic *Worc* from 85; Perm to Offic *Birm* from 86. *c/o Mrs Margaret Manson, 92 Sefton Park Road, St Andrews, Bristol BS7 9AL*

MOSS (née BELL), Mrs Catherine Ann. b 63. Trin Coll Bris BA88. **d** 89 **p** 94. Par Dn Southsea St Jude *Portsm* 89-94; C 94-97; C Luton St Mary *St Alb* 97-02; NSM from 02; Chapl Luton Univ 97-02. *2 Saxtead Close, Luton LU2 9SQ* Tel (01582) 391125

MOSS, Christopher Ashley. b 52. Ex Univ BA73 Southn Univ DASS78 CQSW78. Wycliffe Hall Ox 89. **d** 91 **p** 92. C Malvern H Trin and St Jas *Worc* 91-96; V Longdon, Castlemorton, Bushley, Queenhill etc from 96. *The Vicarage, Longdon, Tewkesbury GL20 6AT* Tel (01684) 833256

MOSS, David Glyn. b 62. St Anne's Coll Ox BA83 Em Coll Cam BA89. Westcott Ho Cam 87. **d** 90 **p** 91. C Halesowen *Worc* 90-93; Tutor St Steph Ho Ox 93-03; Vice-Prin 00-03; Dioc Tr Officer *Ex* from 03. *Address temp unknown*

MOSS, David Sefton. b 59. MRPharmS81 Sunderland Poly BSc80. Ridley Hall Cam CTM93. **d** 93 **p** 94. C Highworth w Sevenhampton and Inglesham etc *Bris* 93-97; V Bedminster St Mich from 97. *St Michael's Vicarage, 153 St John's Lane, Bedminster, Bristol BS3 5AE* Tel 0117-977 6132 Fax as telephone E-mail david.moss@iname.com

MOSS, Canon Denis. b 32. St Jo Coll Auckland LTh83. **d** 74 **p** 75. New Zealand 74-92; Chapl Budapest *Eur* from 92; Hon Can Malta Cathl from 01. *The Rectory, 2092 Budakeszi, Pf 25, Hungary* Tel (0036) (23) 452023 Fax as telephone

MOSS, James Wilfred. b 15. Oak Hill Th Coll 75. **d** 76 **p** 77. Hon C Frogmore *St Alb* 76-78 and 81-93; Hon C Watford St Luke

78-81; Perm to Offic from 93. *8A The Rise, Park Street, St Albans AL2 2NT* Tel (01727) 872467

MOSS, Preb Kenneth Charles. b 37. Imp Coll Lon BSc59 PhD62 DIC62 ARCS59. **d** 66 **p** 67. Canada 66-73; Chapl Ex Univ *Ex* 73-83; V St Marychurch 83-02; RD Ipplepen 87-93; Preb Ex Cathl from 92; rtd 02. *3 Mondeville Way, Northam, Bideford EX39 1DQ* Tel (01237) 422251

MOSS, The Ven Leonard Godfrey. b 32. K Coll Lon BD59 AKC59. **d** 60 **p** 61. C Putney St Marg *S'wark* 60-63; C Cheam 63-67; V Much Dewchurch w Llanwarne and Llandinabo *Heref* 67-72; Dioc Ecum Officer 69-83; V Marden w Amberley 72-80; V Marden w Amberley and Wisteston 80-84; P-in-c 92-94; Preb Heref Cathl 79-97; Can Heref Cathl 84-91; Dioc Soc Resp Officer 84-91; Adn Heref 91-97; rtd 97; Perm to Offic *Heref* from 97. *10 Saxon Way, Ledbury HR8 2QY* Tel (01531) 631195

MOSS, Leslie. b 02. OLM Ditton St Mich w St Thos *Liv* from 02. *105 Heath Road, Widnes WA8 7NU* Tel 0151-423 1100

MOSS, Mrs Nelva Elizabeth. b 44. Bp Grosseteste Coll TCert66 Sussex Univ BEd73. S Dios Minl Tr Scheme 90. **d** 93 **p** 94. NSM Bincombe w Broadwey, Upwey and Buckland Ripers *Sarum* 93-96; NSM Langtree *Ox* 96-98; TV from 98. *The Vicarage, Reading Road, Woodcote, Reading RG8 0QX* Tel (01491) 680979

MOSS, Peter Hextall. b 34. Clare Coll Cam BA59 MA62. Linc Th Coll 59. **d** 61 **p** 62. C Easington Colliery *Dur* 61-63; C Whickham 63-65; C-in-c Town End Farm CD 65-72; TV Mattishall *Nor* 72-75; P-in-c Welborne 75-84; P-in-c Mattishall w Mattishall Burgh 75-84; P-in-c Yaxham 80-84; TR Hempnall 84-89. *High House Cottage, Gunn Street, Foulsham, Dereham NR20 5RN* Tel (01362) 683823

MOSS, Peter John. b 41. K Coll Cam BA64 MA67. Westcott Ho Cam 63. **d** 84 **p** 85. Hon C Leighton Buzzard w Eggington, Hockliffe etc *St Alb* 84-93; NSM Luton St Sav 93-98. *84 Regent Street, Leighton Buzzard LU7 8JZ* Tel (01525) 853128

MOSS, Stephen. b 51. Lon Univ BSc69. S'wark Ord Course. **d** 85 **p** 86. NSM Clapham Ch and St Jo *S'wark* 85-87 and from 02; NSM Clapham TM 87-01. *59A Bromfelde Road, London SW4 6PP* Tel (020) 7720 3152

MOSS, Victor Charles. b 25. Oak Hill Th Coll BD65. **d** 66 **p** 67. C Macclesfield St Mich *Ches* 66-68; C Belper *Derby* 69-71; V Chesterfield St Aug 71-93; rtd 93; Perm to Offic *Derby* from 93. *16 Nether Croft Road, Brimington, Chesterfield S43 1QD* Tel (01246) 206260

MOSS, Wilfrid Maurice. b 10. St Jo Coll Dur LTh34 BA35 MA41. Tyndale Hall Bris 31. **d** 35 **p** 36. C Preston All SS *Blackb* 35-38; Min Buxton Trin Prop Chpl *Derby* 38-42; R Man Albert Memorial Ch *Man* 42-50; V Sidcup Ch Ch *Roch* 50-75; RD Sidcup 70-75; rtd 75; Perm to Offic *Ex* 75-85; Perm to Offic *B & W* from 85. *Stonehaven, 4 West View Close, Middlezoy, Bridgwater TA7 0NP* Tel (01823) 698851

MOSSE, Mrs Barbara Ann. b 51. CertEd73 Open Univ BA77 Univ of Wales (Lamp) MA99. CA Tr Coll IDC81 Lambeth STh83. **d** 90 **p** 95. CA 81-91; NSM Southbourne w W Thorney *Chich* 90-93; Perm to Offic 93-95; Community Mental Health Chapl Fareham/Gosport 94-97; NSM Purbrook *Portsm* from 95; Team Chapl Portsm Hosps NHS Trust from 01. *Drogo, 1 Grenfield Court, Birch Tree Drive, Emsworth PO10 7SA* Tel (01243) 376155 E-mail bamosse@aol.com

MOSSLEY, Iain Stephen. b 72. Univ of Wales (Ban) DipTh93 BTh94. Chich Th Coll 94. **d** 98 **p** 99. C Ribbleton *Blackb* 98-01; C Marton Moss 01-03; V Burnley St Matt w H Trin from 03. *St Matthew's Vicarage, Harriet Street, Burnley BB11 4JH* Tel (01282) 424839 E-mail father.iain@btinternet.com

MOSSMAN, Mrs Margaret. b 46. N Ord Course 97. **d** 00 **p** 01. NSM Beighton *Sheff* 00-02; C from 02. *56 Longstone Crescent, Sheffield S12 4WP* Tel 0114-265 6610

MOSSOP, Patrick John. b 48. Solicitor St Jo Coll Cam MA LLB. Linc Th Coll BTh93. **d** 93 **p** 94. C Halstead St Andr w H Trin and Greenstead Green *Chelmsf* 93-97; Assoc Chapl Essex Univ 97-99; Chapl from 99. *The Chaplaincy Office, University of Essex, Wivenhoe Park, Colchester CO4 3SQ* Tel (01206) 873108 *or* 791227 E-mail patm@essex.ac.uk

MOTE, Gregory Justin. b 60. Oak Hill Th Coll BA83. **d** 86 **p** 87. C W Ealing St Jo w St Jas *Lon* 86-90; C St Helen Bishopsgate w St Andr Undershaft etc 90-95; V Poulton Lancelyn H Trin *Ches* from 96. *6 Chorley Way, Wirral CH63 9LS* Tel 0151-334 6780 *or* 334 2683 E-mail motes@compuserve.com

MOTH, Miss Susan. b 44. Leic Univ BA65 K Coll Lon CertEd66. Linc Th Coll 83. **dss** 85 **d** 87 **p** 94. Churchdown St Jo *Glouc* 85-87; C 87-93; Dn-in-c The Rissingtons 93-94; P-in-c from 94. *The Rectory, Great Rissington, Cheltenham GL54 2LL* Tel (01451) 810611

MOTHERSDALE, Paul John. b 52. N Ord Course 94. **d** 97 **p** 98. C Kirkleatham *York* 97-00; V Middlesbrough St Agnes from 00. *St Agnes' Vicarage, 1 Broughton Avenue, Middlesbrough TS4 3PX* Tel (01642) 323804 E-mail paulmothersdale@bigfoot.com

MOTHERSOLE, John Robert. b 25. Lon Univ MA99. Chich Th Coll. **d** 84 **p** 85. NSM Hayes St Anselm *Lon* 84-93; NSM Hayes St Edm 93-98; P-in-c St Mary Aldermary from 98. *116 Nestles Avenue, Hayes UB3 4QD* Tel (020) 8848 0626

MOTT, Julian Ward. b 52. Loughb Univ BSc77. Ripon Coll Cuddesdon 78. **d** 81 **p** 82. C Aylestone *Leic* 81-84; C Gt Ilford St Mary *Chelmsf* 84-88; R Chevington w Hargrave and Whepstead w Brockley *St E* 88-99; V Lower Gornal *Worc* from 99. *The Vicarage, Church Street, Lower Gornal, Dudley DY3 2PF* Tel (01902) 882023

MOTT, Peter John. b 49. Ch Coll Cam BA70 MA75 Dundee Univ PhD73 Nottm Univ BA79. St Jo Coll Nottm 77. **d** 80 **p** 81. C Hull Newland St Jo *York* 80-83; C Selly Park St Steph and St Wulstan *Birm* 83-87; C Mosbrough *Sheff* 87-92; R Colne St Bart *Blackb* 92-98; TV Colne and Villages 98-01; P-in-c Keighley St Andr *Bradf* from 01. *The Rectory, 13 Westview Grove, Keighley BD20 6JJ* Tel (01535) 601499
E-mail peter@mottp.freeserve.co.uk

✠**MOTTAHEDEH, The Most Revd Iraj.** United Th Coll Bangalore. **d** 59 **p** 60. Bp Iran; Pres Bp Episc Ch Jerusalem and Middle E 00-02. *PO Box 135, 81465 Isfahan, Iran* Tel (0098) (21) 880 1383 *or* (31) 1233 4675 Fax (21) 890 6908
E-mail ian@glasspage.demon.co.uk *or* bishraj@chavoosh.com

MOTTERSHEAD, Derek. b 39. Open Univ BA74 BEd. Chich Th Coll 65. **d** 69 **p** 70. C Walthamstow St Barn and St Jas Gt *Chelmsf* 69-72; C Chelmsf All SS 72-77; P-in-c Cold Norton w Stow Maries 77-80; V Leytonstone St Andr 80-92; V Eastbourne St Sav and St Pet *Chich* from 92; Miss to Seafarers from 92. *St Saviour's Vicarage, Spencer Road, Eastbourne BN21 4PA* Tel (01323) 722317

MOTTRAM, Andrew Peter. b 53. AKC77. Ripon Coll Cuddesdon 77. **d** 78 **p** 79. C E Bedfont *Lon* 78-81; C Bp's Hatfield *St Alb* 81-84; V Milton Ernest 84-91; V Thurleigh 84-91; P-in-c Heref All SS *Heref* from 91; RD Heref City from 02. *10 St Barnabas Close, Hereford HR1 1EY* Tel (01432) 266588 Fax 344428 E-mail itsall@allsaintshfd.demon.co.uk

MOTYER, John Alexander. b 24. TCD BA46 MA51 BD51 Lambeth DD97. Wycliffe Hall Ox 47. **d** 47 **p** 48. C Penn Fields *Lich* 47-50; C Bris H Trin *Bris* 51-54; Tutor Clifton Th Coll 51-54; Tutor Tyndale Hall Bris 52-54; Vice-Prin Clifton Th Coll 54-65; V W Hampstead St Luke *Lon* 65-70; Dep Prin Tyndale Hall Bris 70-71; Prin and Dean Trin Coll Bris 71-81; Min Westbourne Ch Ch Prop Chpl *Win* 81-89; rtd 89; Perm to Offic *Ex* from 90. *10 Littlefield, Bishopsteignton, Teignmouth TQ14 9SG* Tel (01626) 770986

MOTYER, Stephen. b 50. Pemb Coll Cam BA73 MA77 Bris Univ MLitt79 K Coll Lon PhD93. Trin Coll Bris 73. **d** 76 **p** 77. Lect Oak Hill Th Coll 76-83; C Braughing, Lt Hadham, Albury, Furneux Pelham etc *St Alb* 83-87; Lect Lon Bible Coll from 87; Perm to Offic *Lon* and *St Alb* from 87. *7 Hangar Ruding, Watford WD1 5BH* Tel (020) 8386 6829
E-mail s.motyer@londonbiblecollege.ac.uk

MOUGHTIN, Ross. b 48. St Cath Coll Cam BA70 St Jo Coll Dur BA75. **d** 76 **p** 77. C Litherland St Paul Hatton Hill *Liv* 76-79; C Heswall *Ches* 79-84; Chapl Edw Unit Rochdale Infirmary 83-92; V Thornham w Gravel Hole *Man* 84-92; V Aughton Ch Ch *Liv* from 92; Chapl W Lancashire NHS Trust from 94. *Christ Church Vicarage, 22 Long Lane, Aughton, Ormskirk L39 5AT* Tel (01695) 422175

MOUL, Russell Derek. b 56. Reading Univ BA83. Oak Hill Th Coll DipTh99. **d** 99 **p** 00. C Harold Wood *Chelmsf* 99-02; C Harold Hill St Paul 02-03; V from 03. *St Paul's Vicarage, Redcar Road, Romford RM3 9PT* Tel (01708) 341225
E-mail russell@themouls.fslife.co.uk

MOULAND, Norman Francis. b 38. OLM course 98. **d** 99 **p** 00. OLM Verwood *Sarum* from 99. *13 Park Drive, Verwood BH31 7PE* Tel (01202) 825320

MOULD, Mrs Jacqueline. b 66. QUB BD88. CITC BTh91. **d** 91 **p** 92. C Belfast St Aid *Conn* 91-94; C Drumragh w Mountfield *D & R* 94-96; NSM Kinson *Sarum* 97-00. *10 Lower Parklands, Dungannon BT71 7JN* Tel (028) 8775 3468

MOULD, James Michael. b 46. SEITE 95. **d** 98 **p** 99. NSM Wallington H Trin *S'wark* 98-03. *Address temp unknown*

MOULD, Jeremy James. b 63. Nottm Univ BA85. CITC BTh88. **d** 91 **p** 92. C Mossley *Conn* 91-94; C Drumragh w Mountfield *D & R* 94-96; C Kinson *Sarum* 97-00. *10 Lower Parklands, Dungannon BT71 7JN* Tel (028) 8775 3468

MOULDER, John William Michael Cornock. b 39. City of Lon Poly ACIB67. Glouc Sch of Min 82. **d** 86 **p** 86. Australia 86-98; C Tividale *Lich* 98-01; P-in-c W Bromwich St Pet from 01. *St Peter's Vicarage, 194 Oldbury Road, West Bromwich B70 9DP* Tel 0121-525 5147 Fax as telephone
E-mail fatherm@enterprise.net

MOULDER, Kenneth. b 53. Lon Univ BEd75. Ridley Hall Cam 78. **d** 81 **p** 82. C Harold Wood *Chelmsf* 81-84; C Darfield *Sheff* 84-88; V Walkergate *Newc* 88-92; P-in-c Byker St Mark 90-92; V Byker St Mark and Walkergate St Oswald from 92. *St Oswald's Parsonage, Woodhead Road, Newcastle upon Tyne NE6 4RX* Tel 0191-263 6249

MOULE, Prof Charles Francis Digby. b 08. CBE85. FBA66 Em Coll Cam BA31 MA34 St Andr Univ Hon DD58 Cam Univ Hon DD88. Ridley Hall Cam 31. **d** 33 **p** 34. C Cambridge St Mark *Ely* 33-34; Tutor Ridley Hall Cam 33-34; C Rugby

St Andr *Cov* 34-36; C Cambridge Gt St Mary w St Mich *Ely* 36-40; Vice-Prin Ridley Hall Cam 36-44; Dean Clare Coll Cam 44-51; Fell from 44; Select Preacher Cam Univ 42, 48 and 53; Select Preacher Ox Univ 54 and 73; Lect Div Cam Univ 47-51; Lady Marg Prof Div Cam Univ 51-76; Can Th Leic Cathl *Leic* 55-76; rtd 76; Perm to Offic *Chich* from 81. *1 King's Houses, Pevensey BN24 5JR* Tel (01323) 762436

MOULE, Kevin David. b 54. Coll of Resurr Mirfield 77. **d** 80 **p** 81. C E Finchley All SS *Lon* 80-84; C Notting Hill St Mich and Ch Ch 84-91; P-in-c Isleworth St Fran 91-94; P-in-c Walham Green St Jo w St Jas 94-00. *124 Midhurst Road, London W13 9TP*

MOULT, Jane Elizabeth Kate. b 61. Trin Coll Bris DipHE93. **d** 94 **p** 95. C St Jo in Bedwardine *Worc* 94-97; NSM Bilton *Cov* 97-99; Chapl Staunton Harold Hosp 00; Chapl Leics and Rutland Healthcare NHS Trust from 01. *The Vicarage, 44 Talbot Lane, Whitwick, Coalville LE67 5NQ* Tel (01530) 838993

MOULT, Simon Paul. b 66. Nene Coll Northampton Dip Chiropody 88. Trin Coll Bris BA94. **d** 94 **p** 95. C St Jo in Bedwardine *Worc* 94-97; C Bilton *Cov* 97-99; P-in-c Thringstone St Andr *Leic* from 99; RD Akeley S from 03. *44 Talbot Lane, Whitwick, Coalville LE67 5NQ* Tel (01530) 833823 *or* 838993

MOULTON, Paul Oliver. b 43. BSc. N Ord Course 77. **d** 80 **p** 81. C Wilmslow *Ches* 80-85; V Knutsford St Cross 85-92; Chapl Mary Dendy Hosp Knutsford 86-92; V Gatley *Ches* 92-01; Chapl Cen Man Healthcare NHS Trust 92-01; P-in-c Capesthorne w Siddington and Marton *Ches* from 01. *The Vicarage, School Lane, Marton, Macclesfield SK11 9HD* Tel (01260) 224447

MOUNCER, David Peter. b 65. Univ of Wales (Abth) BA86. Oak Hill Th Coll BA94. **d** 94 **p** 95. C Foord St Jo *Cant* 94-98; Min Grove Green LEP from 98; P-in-c Brampton St Thos *Derby* from 03. *674 Chatsworth Road, Chesterfield S40 3NU* Tel (01246) 567634

MOUNSEY, William Lawrence Fraser. b 51. St Andr Univ BD75. Edin Th Coll 76. **d** 78 **p** 79. C Edin St Mark *Edin* 78-81; Chapl RAF from 81; R Dalmahoy *Edin* 90-96; Chapl Heriot-Watt Univ 90-96; Perm to Offic *Edin* and *St And* from 02. *Chaplaincy Services (RAF), HQ, Personnel and Training Command, RAF Innsworth, Gloucester GL3 1EZ* Tel (01452) 712612 ext 5164 Fax 510828

MOUNSTEPHEN, Philip Ian. b 59. Southn Univ BA80 Magd Coll Ox MA87 PGCE. Wycliffe Hall Ox 85. **d** 88 **p** 89. C Gerrards Cross and Fulmer *Ox* 88-92; V W Streatham St Jas *S'wark* 92-98; Hd Pathfinders CPAS 98-02; Dir CY Network 01-02; Hd Min from 02; Perm to Offic *Cov* and *Glouc* from 99. *CPAS, Athena Drive, Tachbrook Park, Warwick CV34 6NG* Tel (01926) 458446 E-mail philip@cpas.org.uk

MOUNT, Canon Judith Mary. b 35. Bedf Coll Lon BA56 Lon Univ CertEd57. Ripon Coll Cuddesdon 81. **dss** 83 **d** 87 **p** 94. Carterton *Ox* 83-85; Charlton on Otmoor and Oddington 85-87; Dioc Lay Min Adv and Asst Dir of Ords 86-89; Par Dn Islip w Charlton on Otmoor, Oddington, Noke etc 87-94; C 94-95; Assoc Dioc Dir Ords and Adv for Women in Ord Min 89-95; Hon Can Ch Ch 92-95; rtd 95; Hon C Shill Valley and Broadshire *Ox* from 95; Perm to Offic *Glouc* from 99. *The Owl House, Bell Lane, Poulton, Cirencester GL7 5JF* Tel (01285) 850242

MOUNTFORD, Canon Brian Wakling. b 45. Newc Univ BA66 Cam Univ MA73 Ox Univ MA90. Westcott Ho Cam 66. **d** 68 **p** 69. C Westmr St Steph w St Jo *Lon* 68-69; C Paddington Ch Ch 69-73; Chapl SS Coll Cam 73-78; V Southgate Ch Ch *Lon* 78-86; V Ox St Mary V w St Cross and St Pet *Ox* from 86; Chapl St Hilda's Coll Ox from 89; Hon Can Ch Ch *Ox* from 98. *9A Norham Gardens, Oxford OX2 6PS* Tel (01865) 515778 *or* 279111 E-mail brian.mountford@oriel.ox.ac.uk

MOUNTFORD, Ian David. b 65. St Jo Coll Nottm BTh93. **d** 96 **p** 97. C Chilwell *S'well* 96-00; TV Thame *Ox* from 00. *22 Stuart Way, Thame OX9 3WP* Tel (01844) 216508
E-mail mounty@fish.co.uk

MOUNTFORD, John. b 55. Nottm Univ BEd77 Birm Univ MA80 Ex Univ MPhil86. Linc Th Coll 73. **d** 78 **p** 79. C Wombourne *Lich* 78-80; C Upper Gornal 80-82; C Paignton St Jo *Ex* 82-86; Papua New Guinea 86-87; Chapl Blue Coat Sch Birm 87-90; Perm to Offic *Birm* 88-90; Australia 91-94; Thailand from 94. *8 Spitfire Road, Birmingham B24 9PB* Tel 0121-382 5533

MOUNTNEY, Frederick Hugh. b 14. St Chad's Coll Dur BA36 MA39. Lich Th Coll 36. **d** 37 **p** 38. C Beighton *Derby* 37-39; C Spondon 39-40; C Byker St Laur *Newc* 40-44; Backworth St Jo 44-48; V N Gosforth 48-51; R Lillingstone Dayrell w Lillingstone Lovell *Ox* 51-56; V Heref All SS *Heref* 56-75; Chapl Victoria Eye Hosp Heref 56-75; Dioc Ecum Officer 63-69; Chapl Bonn w Cologne *Eur* 75-79; rtd 79; Perm to Offic *Heref* 79-90 and *Nor* 82-00; St *E* 82-02 and *Eur* 90-02. *St Martin's, 44 London Road, Harleston IP20 9BW* Tel (01379) 853744

MOUNTNEY, John Michael. b 47. St Chad's Coll Dur BA69 MA84. Cuddesdon Coll 69. **d** 71 **p** 72. C Morpeth *Newc* 71-75; C Longbenton St Bart 75-77; Sub-Warden Community of All Hallows Ditchingham 77-83; R Blundeston w Flixton and Lound *Nor* 83-87; TR Nor St Pet Parmentergate w St Jo 87-93;

Warden Julian Shrine 87-93; V Embleton w Rennington and Rock *Newc* from 93. *The Vicarage, Embleton, Alnwick NE66 3UW* Tel (01665) 576660

MOURANT, Julia Caroline. b 58. Sheff Univ BA79. St Jo Coll Nottm DPS84. **dss** 84 **d** 92 **p** 94. Cropwell Bishop w Colston Bassett, Granby etc *S'well* 84-86; Marple All SS *Ches* 86-89; Harlow St Mary and St Hugh w St Jo the Bapt *Chelmsf* 89-92; NSM from 92; Asst Dir of Min from 98; CME Officer 00-02. *St Mary's Vicarage, 5 Staffords, Harlow CM17 0JR* Tel and fax (01279) 450633 *or tel* 635806
E-mail jmourant@chelmsford.anglican.org

MOURANT, Sidney Eric. b 39. Lon Univ DipTh70 BD73. Oak Hill Th Coll. **d** 89 **p** 90. C Oxton *Ches* 89-92; V Douglas All SS and St Thos *S & M* 92-96; I Rathkeale w Askeaton, Kilcornan and Kilnaughtin *L & K* 96-00; I Nenagh from 00. *St Mary's Rectory, Nenagh, Co Tipperary, Irish Republic* Tel (00353) (67) 32598 E-mail mourant@gofree.indigo.ie

MOURANT, Stephen Philip Edward. b 54. Nottm Univ BTh83. St Jo Coll Nottm. **d** 83 **p** 84. C Cropwell Bishop w Colston Bassett, Granby etc *S'well* 83-86; C Marple All SS *Ches* 86-89; P-in-c Harlow St Mary and St Hugh w St Jo the Bapt *Chelmsf* 89-90; V from 90. *St Mary's Vicarage, 5 Staffords, Harlow CM17 0JR* Tel and fax (01279) 450633 *or tel* 432135
E-mail stmarys.chgate@virgin.net

MOUSIR-HARRISON, Stuart Nicholas. b 68. SW Poly Plymouth BSc89 Nottm Univ MSc92 St Martin's Coll Lanc PhD99 St Jo Coll Dur BA99. Cranmer Hall Dur. **d** 00 **p** 01. C Oadby *Leic* from 00. *62 Fairstone Hill, Oadby, Leicester LE2 5RJ* Tel 0116-271 6474 E-mail rev.moose@btinternet.com

MOVERLEY, Ruth Elaine. b 55. K Alfred's Coll Win CertEd76. St Mich Coll Llan DPS92. **d** 90 **p** 97. C Llangynwyd w Maesteg *Llan* 90-95; C Glan Ely 95-97; V Llanharan w Peterston-super-Montem from 97. *The Vicarage, Brynna Road, Llanharan, Pontyclun CF72 9QE* Tel (01443) 226307

MOWAT, Geoffrey Scott. b 17. CCC Ox BA39 MA49. Ripon Hall Ox 58. **d** 59 **p** 60. C Clifton Ch Ch *Bris* 59-61; Lect and Chapl St Mary's Coll Cheltenham 61-64; V Coln St Aldwyn w Hatherop and Quenington *Glouc* 64-77; RD Fairford 74-77; Malaysia 77-83; rtd 83; Perm to Offic *B & W* 86-87; 92-97; Min Bath St Mary Magd Holloway 87-92; Perm to Offic *Glouc* 98-00. *33 Bettertons Close, Fairford GL7 4HY* Tel (01285) 711082

MOWAT, Robert Alexander Laird (Sandy). b 50. CD80 and Bar 90. Univ Coll of Em and St Chad Saskatoon BTh96. **d** 96 **p** 96. C Saskatchewan Gateway Canada 96-01; P-in-c Kinnerley w Melverley and Knockin w Maesbrook *Lich* from 01. *The Rectory, Vicarage Lane, Kinnerley, Oswestry SY10 8DE* Tel (01691) 682233 E-mail smowat@sk.sympatico.ca

MOWBRAY, David. b 38. Fitzw Ho Cam BA60 MA64 Lon Univ BD62. Clifton Th Coll. **d** 63 **p** 64. C Northampton St Giles *Pet* 63-66; Lect Watford St Mary *St Alb* 66-70; V Broxbourne 70-77; R Broxbourne w Wormley 77-84; V Hertford All SS 84-91; V Darley Abbey *Derby* from 91; Asst Chapl Derby R Infirmary 91-94; Chapl S Derbyshire Community and Mental Health Trust 99-03; rtd 03. *Blackbird Cottage, 169 Newport, Lincoln LN1 3DZ* Tel (01522) 546753

MOWBRAY, Derek David Whitfield. b 19. Lon Univ BD42 Dur Univ MLitt52 Sheff Univ PhD58 Leeds Univ PhD59. ALCD42. **d** 42 **p** 43. C Morden *S'wark* 42-45; Asst Master Parmiter's Foundn Sch Lon 48-50; Tutor All Nations Bible Coll Ox 50-52; C Doncaster St Geo *Sheff* 54-55; V Kettlewell w Conistone *Bradf* 55-60; V Wrangthorn *Ripon* 60-70; R Bris St Jo w St Mary-le-Port *Bris* 71-74; Perm to Offic 75-84; rtd 84. *32 May Lane, Dursley GL11 4HU*

MOWBRAY, James Edward. b 78. Univ of Wales (Abth) BTh00 Leeds Univ BA03. Coll of Resurr Mirfield 01. **d** 03. C Perry Street *Roch* from 03. *6 Dene Holm Road, Northfleet, Gravesend DA11 8LE* Tel (01474) 332657

MOWBRAY, Ms Jill Valerie. b 54. Sussex Univ BEd76 Lon Inst of Educn MA86 Anglia Poly Univ MA01. Ridley Hall Cam 99. **d** 01 **p** 02. C Tufnell Park St Geo and All SS *Lon* from 01. *34 Fortnam Road, London N19 3NR* Tel (020) 7281 3133 Mobile 07761-236910

MOWER, Miss Marguerite Mary. b 36. Bris Univ BA57. Cant Sch of Min 90. **d** 93 **p** 94. NSM Eythorne and Elvington w Waldershare etc *Cant* from 93. *Meadow Bank, Eythorne Road, Shepherdswell, Dover CT15 7PN* Tel (01304) 832026

MOWFORTH, Mark. b 64. Reading Univ BSc86. Trin Coll Bris 93. **d** 96 **p** 97. C Buckingham *Ox* 96-98; C High Wycombe 98-03; P-in-c Prestwood and Gt Hampden from 03. *The Rectory, 140 Wycombe Road, Prestwood, Great Missenden HP16 0HJ* Tel (01494) 862130

MOWLL, John William Rutley. b 42. Sarum Th Coll 63. **d** 66 **p** 67. C Oughtibridge *Sheff* 66-69; C Hill *Birm* 69-73; Ind Chapl *Worc* 73-78; V Upper Arley 73-78; P-in-c Upton Snodsbury and Broughton Hackett etc 78-81; R 81-83; V Boughton under Blean w Dunkirk *Cant* 83-89; V Boughton under Blean w Dunkirk and Hernhill from 89; RD Ospringe 95-01; Hon Min Can Cant Cathl from 96; Chapl to The Queen from 00. *The Vicarage, 101 The*

Street, Boughton-under-Blean, Faversham ME13 9BG Tel (01227) 751410

MOXLEY, Cyril Edward. b 09. Ch Coll Cam BA32 MA37. Ely Th Coll 33. **d** 35 **p** 37. India 35-37; C Clerkenwell H Redeemer w St Phil *Lon* 37-41; Perm to Offic *Cant* 41-42; C Upper Norwood St Jo 42-44; Chapl RAFVR 44-50; R Charlton Adam w Charlton Mackrell *B & W* 50-52; Chapl RAF 52-65; Prin RAF Chapl Sch 60-64; Asst Chapl-in-Chief RAF Germany 64-65; V S Stoneham *Win* 65-74; rtd 74; Hon Chapl Win Cathl *Win* 79-94. *The Old Parsonage (Brendoncare), Main Road, Otterbourne, Winchester SO21 2EE* Tel (01962) 711194

MOXON, John. **d** 02 **p** 03. NSM Birm St Luke *Birm* from 02. *41 Mariner Avenue, Birmingham B16 9DF* Tel 0121-456 1628 *or* 472 0726
E-mail john.moxon@birminghamchristiancollege.ac.uk

MOXON, The Very Revd Michael Anthony. b 42. LVO98. Lon Univ BD78 MA96. Sarum Th Coll 67. **d** 70 **p** 71. C Kirkley *Nor* 70-74; Min Can St Paul's Cathl *Lon* 74-81; Sacr 77-81; Warden Coll of Min Canons 79-81; V Tewkesbury w Walton Cardiff *Glouc* 81-90; Chapl to The Queen 86-98; Can Windsor 90-98; Chapl in Windsor Gt Park 90-98; Dean Truro from 98; R Truro St Mary from 98; Chapl Cornwall Fire Brigade HQ from 98. *The Deanery, The Avenue, Truro TR1 1HR* Tel (01872) 272661 *or* 276782 Fax 277788

MOY, Mrs Joy Patricia. b 35. Cant Sch of Min 87. **d** 90 **p** 94. NSM Cranbrook *Cant* 90-96; Perm to Offic *Win* 96-02. *Address temp unknown*

MOYNAGH, David Kenneth. b 46. LRCP70 MRCS70 MRCGP76 Lon Univ MB, BS70. S Dios Minl Tr Scheme 88. **d** 91 **p** 92. NSM Ore *Chich* 91-99. *White Cottage, Jordan's Lane, Sway, Lymington SO41 6AR* Tel (01590) 682475

MOYNAGH, Michael Digby. b 50. Southn Univ BA73 Lon Univ MA74 Aus Nat Univ PhD78 Bris Univ MA85. Trin Coll Bris DipHE84. **d** 85 **p** 86. C Northwood Em *Lon* 85-89; P-in-c Wilton *B & W* 89-90; TR 90-96; Dir Cen for Third Millennium Studies St Jo Coll Nottm from 96. *St John's College, Bramcote, Nottingham NG9 3DS* Tel 0115-922 0991 Fax as telephone

MOYNAN, Canon David George. b 53. DipTh. **d** 86 **p** 87. C Seagoe *D & D* 86-88; C Taney *D & G* 88-89; I Arklow w Inch and Kilbride 89-94; Dioc Stewardship Adv from 92; Dioc Ch of Ireland Bps' Appeal Rep from 92; I Kilternan from 94; Dioc Dir for Decade of Evang from 96; Can Ch Ch Cathl Dublin from 97. *The Rectory, Kilternan, Co Dublin, Irish Republic* Tel and fax (00353) (1) 295 5603 *or tel* 295 2643 E-mail moynandg@iol.ie

MOYNAN, Canon William John. b 20. TCD BA44. **d** 44 **p** 45. C Chapelizod *D & G* 44-49; C Dublin Drumcondra w N Strand 49-56; Clerical V Ch Ch Cathl Dublin 52-56; I Portarlington w Cloneyhurke, Ballykeane and Lea *M & K* 56-63; I Donabate w Lusk *D & G* 63-68; I Swords w Donabate and Kilsallaghan 68-90; Can Ch Ch Cathl Dublin 83-90; rtd 90. *Briarwood, Ballycarnane, Tramore, Waterford, Irish Republic* Tel (00353) (51) 390199

MOYSE, Mrs Pauline Patricia. b 42. Ex Univ CertEd62. S Dios Minl Tr Scheme 88. **d** 91 **p** 94. Hon C Fleet *Guildf* 91-92; C 93-97; Chapl Farnborough Coll of Tech 96-97; P-in-c Stoneleigh *Guildf* 97-02; Warden of Readers from 97; Dioc Adv Lay Min from 01. *Beechend, 2 Hillcrest, Fleet GU51 4PZ* Tel (01252) 671382
E-mail moyseadpp@aol.com

✠**MPALANYI-NKOYOYO, The Most Revd Livingstone.** b 37. **d** 69 **p** 70 **c** 80. Kasubi 69-75; Nsangi 75-77; Adn Namirembe 77-79; Suff Bp 80-81; Suff Bp Mukono 81-94; Abp Uganda and Bp Kampala from 94. *PO Box 14123, Kampala, Uganda* Tel (00256) (41) 270218, 270219 *or* 271138 Fax 251925 *or* 245597
E-mail couab@uol.co.ug

MPUNZI, Nduna Ananias. b 46. Birm Univ DPS79 Glas Univ LTh84. Edinburgh Th Coll S Africa 69. **d** 71 **p** 72. S Africa 72-78; Lic to Offic *Glas* 82-84; C Bilston *Lich* 84-86; TV 86-90; P-in-c Walsall St Mary and All SS Palfrey 90-97; P-in-c Caldmore 90-93; P-in-c Shobnall from 02. *St Aidan's Vicarage, 114 Shobnall Road, Burton-on-Trent DE14 2BB* Tel (01283) 845130

✠**MTETEMELA, The Most Revd Donald Leo.** b 47. St Phil Th Coll Kongwa LTh71 Wycliffe Hall Ox DipTh76. **p** 71 **c** 82. Asst Bp Cen Tanganyika 82-90; Bp Ruaha from 90; Abp Tanzania from 98. *Box 1028, Iringa, Tanzania* Tel (00255) (262) 270 1211 Fax 702479 E-mail ruaha@maf.or.tz

MUDD, Mrs Linda. b 59. WMMTC 00. **d** 03. NSM Exhall w Wixford *Cov* from 03. *19 Falmouth Close, Nuneaton CV11 6GB* Tel (024) 7638 6146 Mobile 07811-929457
E-mail muddie@mudda.freeserve.co.uk

MUDDIMAN, John Bernard. b 47. Keble Coll Ox BA67 MA72 DPhil76 Selw Coll Cam BA71 MA75. Westcott Ho Cam 69. **d** 72 **p** 73. Hon C Ox St Giles *Ox* 72-83; Chapl New Coll Ox 72-76; Tutor St Steph Ho Ox 76-83; Vice-Prin 80-83; Lect Th Nottm Univ 83-90; Fell Mansf Coll Ox from 90; Chapl from 97; Lic to Offic *Ox* 90-02; NSM Littlemore from 97. *Mansfield College, Oxford OX1 3TF* Tel (01865) 270999
E-mail john.muddiman@mansfield.ox.ac.uk

MUDGE, Frederick Alfred George. b 31. Leeds Univ BSc58 Univ of Wales BD67. St Mich Coll Llan 58. **d** 61 **p** 62. C Cwmavon

Llan 61-64; PV Llan Cathl 64-70; R Llandough w Leckwith 70-88; V Penarth All SS 88-96; rtd 96. *Pathways, 6 Fairwater Road, Llandaff, Cardiff CF5 2LD*

MUDIE, Martin Bruce. b 54. Goldsmiths' Coll Lon BA76. Sarum & Wells Th Coll 92. **d** 92 **p** 93. C Bromley St Mark *Roch* 92-95; rtd 95; Perm to Offic *B & W* 02-03; Hon C Glastonbury w Meare from 03. *20 Oriel Road, Street BA16 0JL* Tel (01458) 448034

MUELLER-SCHNURR, Mrs Jutta. b 71. Bayreuth Th Sem 97. **d** 97 **p** 02. In Lutheran Ch Germany 97-02; Chapl (Asst) Bris Univ *Bris* from 02. *12 St Paul's Road, Clifton, Bristol BS8 1LR* Tel 0117-973 3963 Fax 954 6602
E-mail jutta.mueller-schnurr@bris.ac.uk

MUGAN, Miriam Ruth. b 56. RNMH77. Oak Hill Th Coll 93. **d** 96 **p** 97. NSM St Alb St Sav *St Alb* from 96. *137 Kings Road, London Colney, St Albans AL2 1ER* Tel (01727) 825971
E-mail miriam@aromacare.supanet.com

MUGGLETON, James. b 55. Bris Univ BA80. Chich Th Coll 81 EAMTC 99. **d** 01 **p** 02. NSM E Leightonstone *Ely* 01-03; C from 03. *16 Burton Way, Spaldwick, Huntingdon PE28 0YY* Tel (01480) 896592

MUGGLETON, Major George. b 25. Chich Th Coll 55. **d** 57 **p** 58. C Oldham St Mary *Man* 57-59; C Ashton St Mich 59-61; V Croydon H Trin *Cant* 61-68; R Stisted *Chelmsf* 68-69; P-in-c Pattiswick 68-69; P-in-c Bradwell 68-69; R Stisted w Bradwell and Pattiswick 69-87; rtd 87. *Curvalion House, Creech St Michael, Taunton TA3 5QF* Tel (01823) 443842

MUGRIDGE, Mrs Gloria Janet. b 45. R Holloway Coll Lon BA66 Bedf Coll Lon DipSS67. S Dios Minl Tr Scheme 92. **d** 95 **p** 96. NSM Dorchester *Sarum* 95-97; Asst Chapl Weymouth Coll 95-97; Chapl from 97; NSM Melbury *Sarum* 97-02. *63 Syward Close, Dorchester DT1 2AN* Tel (01305) 269203

MUIR, David Murray. b 49. Glas Univ MA70 Nottm Univ BA72. St Jo Coll Nottm 70. **d** 76 **p** 77. C Fulham St Mary N End *Lon* 76-80; C Aspley *S'well* 80; India 81-85; Dir Ext Studies St Jo Coll Nottm 85-02; C Upton (Overchurch) *Ches* from 02. *10 Manor Drive, Wirral CH49 6JF* Tel 0151-604 0356

MUIR, David Trevor. b 49. TCD MA MLitt93. CITC 75. **d** 78 **p** 79. C Dublin Clontarf *D & G* 78-80; C Monkstown St Mary 80-83; I Kilternan 83-94; I Delgany 94-97; Can Ch Ch Cathl Dublin 95-97; Chapl to Ch of Ireland Assn of Deaf People from 97. *Luogh North, Doolin, Co Clare, Irish Republic* Tel (00353) (65) 707 4778 Fax 707 4871

MUIR, John William. b 38. Dur Univ BA59 Mansf Coll Ox MA65. Chich Th Coll 78. **d** 78 **p** 79. In Congr Ch 62-70; United Ch of Zambia 70-78; C Brighouse *Wakef* 78-80; V Northowram 80-87; V Sowerby 87-01; rtd 01. *8 Whitley Drive, Holmfield, Halifax HX2 9SJ* Tel 07733-152089 (mobile)
E-mail jmuir@msn.com

MUKHERJEE (or MUKHOPADHYAY), Supriyo. b 42. Calcutta Univ BA70 Serampore Th Coll BD76 Derby Univ MA97. Bp's Coll Calcutta 70. **d** 75 **p** 76. India 75-91; C Crook *Dur* 91-92; V Nelson in Lt Marsden *Blackb* 92-95; Dioc Community Relns Officer *Cov* 95-02; TV Cov E 95-02; rtd 02; Perm to Offic *Cov* from 02. *16 Nunts Lane, Coventry CV6 4HB* Tel (024) 7636 3064 E-mail samukh@lineone.net

MULCOCK, Edward John. b 16. Leeds Univ BA37. Coll of Resurr Mirfield 37. **d** 39 **p** 40. C Long Eaton St Laur *Derby* 39-48; V Leeds St Hilda *Ripon* 48-55; V Roath St German *Llan* 55-60; Min S Kenton Annunciation CD *Lon* 61-66; V Fulham St Jo Walham Green 66-76; V Fulham St Jas Moore Park 69-76; V Walham Green St Jo w St Jas 76-83; rtd 84; Perm to Offic *Sarum* from 83; *Win* from 01. *Flat 2, Gardens Court, 57 Parkstone Road, Poole BH15 2NX* Tel (01202) 673162

MULHOLLAND, Nicholas Christopher John. b 44. Chich Th Coll 77. **d** 79 **p** 80. C Thornbury *Glouc* 79-83; R Boxwell, Leighterton, Didmarton, Oldbury etc from 83; RD Tetbury from 00. *The Rectory, The Meads, Leighterton, Tetbury GL8 8UW* Tel (01666) 890283 Fax 890599

MULKERN, Richard Neville. b 39. S'wark Ord Course 88. **d** 91 **p** 92. NSM Leytonstone St Andr *Chelmsf* 91-93; Min Sec and Welfare Officer Miss to Seamen 91-93; Welfare Sec 93-94; Dir N Region 94-00; Perm to Offic *Wakef* from 93; NSM Oulton w Woodlesford *Ripon* 96-99; rtd 00. *120 Norwood Road, Birkby, Huddersfield HD2 2XX* Tel (01484) 480864

MULLALLY, Sarah Elisabeth. b 62. S Bank Univ BSc84 MSc92 Bournemouth Univ Hon DSc01 RGN84. SEITE 98. **d** 01 **p** 02. NSM Battersea Fields *S'wark* from 01. *30 Wilkinson Street, London SW8 1DB* Tel (020) 7582 5440

MULLARD, George Edward. b 14. St D Coll Lamp BA38 Sarum Th Coll 38. **d** 39 **p** 40. C Hartland and Welcombe *Ex* 39-42; C Plymouth St Gabr 42-45; C Northam 45-48; V E Coker *B & W* 48-69; V E Coker w Sutton Bingham 69-79; rtd 79; Perm to Offic *B & W* from 79. *Alvington Cottage, Brympton, Yeovil BA22 8TH* Tel (01935) 471752

MULLEN, Charles William. b 64. CITC BTh92. **d** 92 **p** 93. C Lecale Gp *D & D* 92-95; I Gorey w Kilnahue, Leskinfere and Ballycanew *C & O* 95-00; Dean's V St Patr Cathl Dublin from

00. *St Kevin's Rectory, 258 South Circular Road, Dublin 8, Irish Republic* Tel (00353) (1) 454 2726 Mobile 87-261 8878
E-mail deansvicar@stpatrickscathedral.ie

MULLEN, Peter John. b 42. Liv Univ BA70 Middx Univ PhD00. St Aid Birkenhead 66. **d** 70 **p** 71. C Manston *Ripon* 70-72; C Stretford All SS *Man* 72-73; C Oldham St Mary w St Pet 73-74; Lic to Offic 74-77; V Tockwith and Bilton w Bickerton *York* 77-89; Perm to Offic 97-98; P-in-c St Mich Cornhill w St Pet le Poer etc *Lon* from 98; P-in-c St Sepulchre w Ch Ch Greyfriars etc from 98. *The Watch House, Giltspur Street, London EC1A 9DE* Tel (020) 7248 3826 Fax as telephone
E-mail citychurches@pmullen.freeserve.co.uk

MULLENGER, Canon Alan Edward Clement. b 15. Lon Univ BD64. Kelham Th Coll 35. **d** 40 **p** 41. SSM from 40; C Sheff Parson Cross St Cecilia *Sheff* 40-48; S Africa 48-56; Basutoland 56-61; Wycliffe Hall Ox 63-64; Perm to Offic *Ox* 63-64; St Aug Coll Walsingham 64-65; Perm to Offic *Nor* 64-65; Miss P Mampong Ghana 65-74; Can Kumasi 73; R Maseru St Jo Lesotho 74-98; Prov SSM 82-87; Can Lesotho 83; Warden Lelapa la Jesu Angl Sem Roma 88; Perm to Offic *Dur* 98-01. *St Antony's Priory, Claypath, Durham DH1 1QT* Tel 0191-384 3747 Fax 384 4939 E-mail ssm.durham@which.net

MULLENGER, William. b 44. Linc Th Coll 68. **d** 69 **p** 70. C Clapham St Jo *S'wark* 69-73; C Hook 73-81; P-in-c Camberwell St Phil and St Mark 81-85; V Hackbridge and N Beddington 85-93; rtd 93; Perm to Offic *Roch* from 93. *30 Constance Crescent, Bromley BR2 7QJ*

MULLER, Anton Michael. b 61. **d** 99 **p** 00. C Sandgate St Paul w Folkestone St Geo *Cant* 99-03; TV Penrith w Newton Reigny and Plumpton Wall *Carl* from 03; P-in-c Dacre from 03; Chapl N Cumbria Mental Health NHS Trust from 03. *Dacre Vicarage, 12 Keld Close, Stainton, Penrith CA11 0ES* Tel (01768) 891378
E-mail amulleruk@aol.com

MULLER, Vernon. b 40. Natal Univ BA61 St Chad's Coll Dur DipTh64 Birm Univ MPhil93. **d** 64 **p** 65. S Africa 64-76; Chapl Friern Hosp Lon 77-91; Chapl R Berks Hosp Reading 91-95; Chapl Battle Hosp Reading 91-95; Perm to Offic *Chelmsf* from 95. *8 Ruskin Road, Chelmsford CM2 6HN* Tel (01245) 345865

MULLER, Wolfgang Wilhelm Bernard Heinrich Paul. b 28. ALCD54. **d** 55 **p** 56. C Tonbridge SS Pet and Paul *Roch* 55-56; C Chatham St Steph 56-59; C-in-c Wigmore w Hempstead CD 59-65; V Wigmore w Hempstead 65-72; V S Gillingham 72-73; W Germany 73-90; Germany from 90; rtd 93. *Auf der Mauer 7, 34431 Marsberg, Germany*

MULLETT, John St Hilary. b 25. St Cath Coll Cam BA47 MA49. Linc Th Coll. **d** 50 **p** 51. C Tottenham All Hallows *Lon* 50-52; S Rhodesia 52-61; V Bollington St Jo *Ches* 61-69; V Oxton 69-77; R Ashwell *St Alb* 77-90; RD Buntingford 82-88; rtd 90; Fell St Cath Coll Cam from 90; Perm to Offic *Ely* from 90. *13 Church Lane, Madingley, Cambridge CB3 8AF* Tel (01954) 211670

MULLIGAN, Colin Arthur. b 42. Llan Ord Course 96. **d** 96 **p** 97. NSM Neath w Llantwit *Llan* 96-01; NSM Neath from 01. *12 Chestnut Road, Cimla, Neath SA11 3PB* Tel (01639) 630409

MULLIN, Horace Boies (Dan). b 44. Dioc OLM tr scheme. **d** 00 **p** 01. OLM Mildenhall *St E* from 00. *47 Oak Drive, Beck Row, Bury St Edmunds IP28 8UA* Tel (01638) 718200
E-mail dan-martha@mullin47.freeserve.co.uk

MULLINER, Denis Ratliffe. b 40. BNC Ox BA62 MA66. Linc Th Coll 70. **d** 72 **p** 73. C Sandhurst *Ox* 72-76; Chapl Bradfield Coll Berks 76-99; Chapl Chpl Royal Hampton Court Palace from 00; Dep P in O from 00. *Chapel Royal, Hampton Court Palace, East Molesey KT8 9AU* Tel (020) 8781 9598

MULLINS, Joe. b 20. MC45. Trin Coll Ox BA49 MA59. Ridley Hall Cam 48. **d** 50 **p** 51. C Portman Square St Paul *Lon* 50-52; India 52-74; Australia from 74; rtd 86. *33/31 Cockcroft Avenue, Monash, ACT, Australia 2904* Tel (0061) (2) 6291 0345
E-mail emullins@autarmetro.com.au

MULLINS, Malcolm David. b 42. St Edm Hall Ox BA63. St Steph Ho Ox 63. **d** 65 **p** 66. C Kirkby *Liv* 65-69; C Lamorbey H Redeemer *Roch* 69-75; C Solihull *Birm* 75-77. *83 Bolton Road, Harrow HA1 4SB*

MULLINS, Mrs Margaret. b 49. Southn Univ CertEd76 K Alfred's Coll Win Dip Special Educn 87. Sarum & Wells Th Coll 94. **d** 94 **p** 95. C Bishopstoke *Win* 94-98; TV Bicester w Bucknell, Caversfield and Launton *Ox* from 98. *The Vicarage, The Spinney, Launton, Bicester OX6 0EP* Tel (01869) 252377 Fax as telephone

MULLINS, Canon Peter Matthew. b 60. Ch Ch Ox BA82 MA86 Birm Univ DPS84 Irish Sch of Ecum MPhil90. Qu Coll Birm 82. **d** 84 **p** 85. C Caversham St Pet and Mapledurham etc *Ox* 84-88; Perm to Offic *D & G* 88-89; TV Old Brumby *Linc* 89-94; Clergy Tr Adv 94-99; TR Gt and Lt Coates w Bradley from 99; Can and Preb Linc Cathl from 02. *The Rectory, 26 Meadowbank, Great Coates, Grimsby DN37 9PG* Tel (01472) 329548
E-mail peter.mullins2@ntlworld.com

MULLINS, Timothy Dougal. b 59. Dur Univ. Wycliffe Hall Ox 83. **d** 85 **p** 86. C Reading Greyfriars *Ox* 85-89; C Haughton le Skerne *Dur* 89-95; Chapl Eton Coll from 95. *2 Church Close, High Street, Eton, Windsor SL4 6AP* Tel (01753) 671373

MULLIS, Robert Owen. b 49. Bris Univ BA71 CertEd71 Birm Univ AdCertEd91. St Mich Coll Llan 93. **d** 93 **p** 94. NSM Llangenni and Llanbedr Ystrad Yw w Patricio *S & B* from 93. *16 Chestnut Drive, Abergavenny NP7 5JZ* Tel (01873) 851613

MULRAINE, Miss Margaret Haskell. b 24. Birm Univ BA45 DipEd46. Sarum Th Coll 83. **dss** 86 **d** 87 **p** 94. Wareham *Sarum* 86-87; Hon Par Dn 87-93; Perm to Offic from 93. *5 Trinity Close, Trinity Lane, Wareham BH20 4LL* Tel (01929) 552523

MULRYNE, Thomas Mark. b 70. St Cath Coll Cam BA91 MA95 Lon Inst of Educn PGCE93. Oak Hill Th Coll BA02. **d** 02 **p** 03. C W Streatham St Jas *S'wark* from 02. *171 Mitcham Lane, London SW16 6NA* Tel (020) 8769 0695 *or* 8677 3947 E-mail mark_and_caroline_mulryne@hotmail.com

MUMFORD, David Bardwell. b 49. MRCPsych86 St Cath Coll Cam BA71 MA75 Bris Univ MB, ChB81 MD92 Edin Univ MPhil89. Bp's Coll Calcutta 71 Cuddesdon Coll 73. **d** 75. C Bris St Mary Redcliffe w Temple etc *Bris* 75-76; NSM Edin St Columba *Edin* 82-86; NSM Calverley *Bradf* 86-92; Perm to Offic *B & W* from 92. *14 Clifton Vale, Clifton, Bristol BS8 4PT* Tel 0117-927 2221 E-mail david.mumford@bristol.ac.uk

MUMFORD, David Christopher. b 47. Mert Coll Ox BA68 MA74 York Univ MSW CQSW81. Linc Th Coll 84. **d** 86 **p** 87. C Shiremoor *Newc* 86-89; C N Shields St Ant 91-97; RD Newc E 96-97; V Cowgate 97-02; Internat Co-ord Internat Fellowship of Reconciliation from 02. *Spoorstraat 40, 1815 BK Alkmaar, The Netherlands* Tel (0031) (72) 512 3014

MUMFORD, Geoffrey Robert. b 70. York Univ BSc92 St Jo Coll Nottm MA00. **d** 00 **p** 01. C Rowley Regis *Birm* 00-03; TV Darwen St Pet w Hoddlesden *Blackb* from 03. *St Paul's Vicarage, Johnson New Road, Hoddlesden, Darwen BB3 3NN* Tel (01254) 702598 E-mail gmumford@fish.co.uk

MUMFORD, Grenville Alan. b 34. Richmond Th Coll DipTh. **d** 78 **p** 78. C Witham *Chelmsf* 78-81; C-in-c Gt Ilford St Marg CD 81-85; V Gt Ilford St Marg 85-87; P-in-c Everton and Mattersey w Clayworth *S'well* 87-89; R 89-96; RD Bawtry 93-96; rtd 96; Perm to Offic *Ches* from 96. *146 Audlem Road, Nantwich CW5 7EB* Tel (01777) 817364

MUMFORD, Canon Hugh Raymond. b 24. Oak Hill Th Coll 50. **d** 53 **p** 54. C Bethnal Green St Jas Less *Lon* 53-57; C Watford St Mary *St Alb* 57-59; R Thetford St Pet w St Nic *Nor* 59-69; RD Thetford 68-69; V Nether Cerne *Sarum* 69-71; R Godmanstone 69-71; C Cerne Abbas w Upcerne 69-71; R Minterne Magna 71-89; RD Dorchester 75-79; Can and Preb Sarum Cathl 77-89; rtd 89; Perm to Offic *Sarum* from 89. *10 South Walks Road, Dorchester DT1 1ED* Tel (01305) 264971

MUMFORD, Michael David. b 29. **d** 79 **p** 80. Chapl Lister Hosp Stevenage 79-83; C Royston *St Alb* 83-87; P-in-c Kelshall 83-88; P-in-c Therfield 83-88; C Barkway, Reed and Buckland w Barley 87-88; R Ewhurst *Chich* 88-94; R Bodiam 88-94; RD Rye 90-91; rtd 94; Perm to Offic *Chich* from 94. *6 Whydown Place, Bexhill-on-Sea TN39 4HA* Tel (01424) 845278

MUNBY, David Philip James. b 52. Pemb Coll Ox BA75 MA80. St Jo Coll Nottm 76. **d** 78 **p** 79. C Gipsy Hill Ch Ch *S'wark* 78-82; C-in-c W Dulwich Em CD 82-88; V Barnsley St Geo *Wakef* from 88; Asst Dioc Ecum Officer from 99. *St George's Vicarage, 100 Dodworth Road, Barnsley S70 6HL* Tel (01226) 203870 E-mail david.munby@bigfoot.com

MUNCEY, William. b 49. BA80. Oak Hill Th Coll. **d** 80 **p** 81. C Wandsworth St Mich *S'wark* 80-84; C Morden 84-88; TV 88-01; RD Merton 00-01; P-in-c Croydon Ch Ch from 01. *Christ Church Vicarage, 34 Longley Road, Croydon CR0 3LH* Tel (020) 8665 9664

MUNCH, Philip Douglas. b 55. Witwatersrand Univ BMus. Cranmer Hall Dur. **d** 88 **p** 89. Namibia 88-99; C Walvis Bay 88-89; P-in-c 89-92; Warden Ho of Prayer Luderitz 92-99; Prec Port Elizabeth S Africa 99-02; Warden Emmaus Ho of Prayer Northampton from 02. *Emmaus House of Prayer, St Michael's Church, Perry Street, Northampton NN1 4HL* Tel (01604) 627669 Fax 230316

MUNCHIN, David Leighfield. b 67. Imp Coll Lon BSc88 K Coll Lon MA00. Ripon Coll Cuddesdon 89. **d** 92 **p** 93. C Golders Green *Lon* 92-96; Prec and Min Can St Alb Abbey *St Alb* 96-02; P-in-c Hatfield Hyde from 02. *St Mary Magdalene Vicarage, Hollybush Lane, Welwyn Garden City AL7 4JS* Tel and fax (01707) 322313 Mobile 07787-567747 E-mail munchin@waitrose.com

MUNCHIN, Ysmena Rachael. See PENTELOW, Mrs Ysmena Rachael

MUNDAY, Mrs Sandra Anne. b 61. St Jo Sem Wonersh BTh89 Ripon Coll Cuddesdon 97. **d** 99 **p** 00. C Esher *Guildf* 99-02; Team Chapl R United Hosp Bath NHS Trust from 02. *Royal United Hospital, Combe Park, Bath BA1 3NG* Tel (01225) 821211 E-mail sandy.munday@ruh-bath.swest.nhs.uk

MUNDEN, Alan Frederick. b 43. Nottm Univ BTh74 Birm Univ MLitt80 Dur Univ PhD87. St Jo Coll Nottm LTh74. **d** 74 **p** 75. C Cheltenham St Mary *Glouc* 74-76; C Cheltenham St Mary, St Matt, St Paul and H Trin 76; Hon C Jesmond Clayton Memorial *Newc* 76-80; C 80-83; V Cheylesmore *Cov* 83-01; R

Weddington and Caldecote 01-03; NSM Jesmond H Trin *Newc* from 03. *Address temp unknown*

MUNGAVIN, David Stewart. b 60. Stirling Univ BA80. Edin Th Coll 87. **d** 90 **p** 91. C Glas St Marg *Glas* 90-92; P-in-c Airdrie 92-96; R 96-99; P-in-c Coatbridge 92-96; R 96-99; P-in-c Gartcosh 92-96; R 96-99; R Troon from 99. *70 Bentinck Drive, Troon KA10 6HZ* Tel (01292) 313731 Fax as telephone

MUNGAVIN, Canon Gerald Clarence. b 27. Edin Th Coll 51. **d** 54 **p** 55. C Dunfermline *St And* 54-55; C Glas Gd Shep *Glas* 55-57; CF 57-60; C Stanwix *Carl* 60-62; Chapl RAF 62-75; R Turriff *Ab* 75-81; R Cuminestown 75-81; R Banff 75-81; R Banchory 81-92; R Kincardine O'Neil 81-92; Can St Andr Cathl 89-92; Hon Can from 92; rtd 92. *5 Lade Court, Lochwinnoch PA12 4BT* Tel (01505) 843972

MUNN, Carole Christine. b 45. EMMTC 83. **d** 90 **p** 94. NSM Long Bennington w Foston *Linc* 90-95; NSM Saxonwell 95-98; Asst Chapl HM Pris Linc 94-01; Chapl HM Pris Morton Hall from 01; NSM Claypole *Linc* from 98; Gen Preacher from 01. *HM Prison, Morton Hall, Swinderby, Lincoln LN6 9PT* Tel (01522) 866700

MUNN, George. b 44. Master Mariner 72. Linc Th Coll 85. **d** 87 **p** 88. C Boston *Linc* 87-90; R Claypole from 90. *The Rectory, 6 Rectory Lane, Claypole, Newark NG23 5BH* Tel (01636) 626224 E-mail george.munn@tinyworld.co.uk

MUNN, Richard Probyn. b 45. Selw Coll Cam BA67 MA69. Cuddesdon Coll 67. **d** 69 **p** 70. C Cirencester *Glouc* 69-71; USPG 71-79; Zambia 71-79; Adn S Zambia 79; P-in-c Kings Stanley *Glouc* 80-83; R Lezant w Lawhitton and S Petherwin w Trewen *Truro* 84-92; Lesotho from 93; rtd 01. *PO Box 249, Leribe, Lesotho* Tel (00266) 877 8553

MUNNS, John Millington. b 76. Univ Coll Dur BA99 MA00. Westcott Ho Cam 01. **d** 03. C Bridgwater St Mary, Chilton Trinity and Durleigh *B & W* from 03. *11 Alexandra Road, Bridgwater TA6 3HE* Tel (01278) 429565 E-mail j.m.munns@dunelm.org.uk

MUNNS, Stuart Millington. b 36. OBE77. St Cath Coll Cam BA58 MA62 MCIPD91. Cuddesdon Coll 58. **d** 60 **p** 61. C Allenton and Shelton Lock *Derby* 60-63; C Brampton St Thos 63-65; C-in-c Loundsley Green Ascension CD 65-66; Bp's Youth Chapl 66-72; Nat Dir of Community Industry 72-77; Hon C Hornsey Ch Ch *Lon* 72-77; Dioc Missr *Liv* 77-82; V Knowsley 77-82; P-in-c Stramshall *Lich* 82-88; V Uttoxeter w Bramshall 82-88; RD Uttoxeter 82-87; P-in-c Kingstone w Gratwich 84-88; P-in-c Marchington w Marchington Woodlands 84-88; P-in-c Checkley 86-88; Perm to Offic *B & W* 88-90; NSM Wells St Thos w Horrington 90-94; P-in-c Fosse Trinity 94-02; rtd 02; Dioc Pre-Th Educn Co-ord *B & W* from 02. *Applewood House, Ham Street, Baltonsborough, Glastonbury BA6 8PX* Tel (01458) 851443 E-mail munns@ukonline.co.uk

MUNOZ-TRIVINO, Daniel. b 75. Hatf Coll Dur BA99 Wycliffe Hall Ox MTh01. **d** 01 **p** 02. C Hazlemere *Ox* from 01. *Church House, 70 George's Hill, Widmer End, High Wycombe HP15 6BH* Tel (01494) 713848 Mobile 07974-724452 E-mail dani@europemail.com

MUNRO, Basil Henry. b 40. Ripon Hall Ox 73. **d** 75 **p** 76. C N Mymms *St Alb* 75-78; C St Alb St Steph 78-80; V 80-87; R Aston-on-Trent and Weston-on-Trent *Derby* 87-99; P-in-c Elvaston and Shardlow 98-99; R Aston on Trent, Elvaston, Weston on Trent etc 99-01; Chapl Aston Hall Hosp Derby 87-93; Chapl S Derbyshire Community Health Services NHS Trust 93-01; rtd 01; Perm to Offic *Derby* from 01. *40 Brisbane Road, Mickleover, Derby DE3 9JZ*

MUNRO, Duncan John Studd. b 50. Magd Coll Ox BA72 MA76 Warwick Univ MBA96. Wycliffe Hall Ox 73. **d** 76 **p** 77. C Ecclesall *Sheff* 76-77; C Sheff St Barn and St Mary 78-80; Lic to Offic 80-86 and from 97. *23 Canterbury Crescent, Sheffield S10 3RW* Tel 0114-230 4930 *or* 261 4338

MUNRO, Ingrid Phyllis. b 51. Herts Univ BEd80. St Jo Coll Nottm MA96 St Alb Minl Tr Scheme 83. **d** 98 **p** 99. NSM Walbrook Epiphany *Derby* 98-01. *40 Brisbane Road, Mickleover, Derby DE3 9JZ*

MUNRO, Robert. b 40. Leeds Univ BA62 Bris Univ PGCE63. SW Minl Tr Course 95. **d** 98 **p** 99. NSM Saltash *Truro* 98-03; NSM Calstock from 03. *15 Valley Road, Saltash PL12 4BT* Tel (01752) 844731 E-mail bobmu@valley151.fsnet.co.uk

MUNRO, Robert Speight. b 63. Bris Univ BSc84 Man Univ PGCE87. All So Coll of Applied Th DipApTh86 Oak Hill Th Coll BA93. **d** 93 **p** 94. C Hartford *Ches* 93-97; R Davenham from 97. *The Rectory, Church Street, Davenham, Northwich CW9 8NF* Tel (01606) 42450

MUNRO, Canon Terence George. b 34. Jes Coll Cam BA56 MA60. Linc Th Coll 59. **d** 61 **p** 62. C Far Headingley St Chad *Ripon* 61-64; Jamaica 64-70; R Methley w Mickletown *Ripon* 70-79; V Hunslet Moor St Pet and St Cuth 79-85; R Barwick in Elmet 85-93; V Woodhouse and Wrangthorn 93-99; Dioc Ecum Officer 93-99; Hon Can Ripon Cathl 94-99; rtd 99; Perm to Offic *York* from 00. *45 Laburnum Drive, Beverley HU17 9UQ* Tel (01482) 861237

MUNT, Cyril. b 27. AKC52. **d** 53 **p** 54. C Ashford *Cant* 53-56; C Dorking w Ranmore *Guildf* 56-60; R Cheriton w Newington *Cant* 60-68; R Harbledown 68-83; R Porlock w Stoke Pero *B & W* 83-92; rtd 92; Perm to Offic *B & W* from 92. *Applegarth, 26 Hood Close, Glastonbury BA6 8ES* Tel (01458) 831842

MUNT, Canon Donald James. b 20. ALCD53 St Jo Coll Nottm LTh74. **d** 53 **p** 54. C Purley Ch Ch *S'wark* 53-56; C Hatcham St Jas 56-61; V Oulton Broad *Nor* 61-69; V Deptford St Pet *S'wark* 69-76; R Litcham w Kempston w E and W Lexham *Nor* 76-83; P-in-c Mileham 81-83; P-in-c Beeston next Mileham 81-83; P-in-c Stanfield 81-83; R Litcham, Kempston, Lexham, Mileham, Beeston etc 84-87; RD Brisley and Elmham 85-87; Hon Can Nor Cathl 87-88; rtd 88; Perm to Offic *Nor* from 88. *7 Irwin Close, Reepham, Norwich NR10 4EQ* Tel (01603) 870618

MUNT, Mrs Linda Christine. b 55. Sunderland Univ DipHE96. NEOC 92. **d** 95 **p** 96. C Beverley St Nic *York* 95-98; Chapl E Yorkshire Hosps NHS Trust 98-99; V Bridlington Em *York* from 99; P-in-c Skipsea w Ulrome and Barmston w Fraisthorpe from 02. *Emmanuel Vicarage, 72 Cardigan Road, Bridlington YO15 3JT* Tel (01262) 604948

MUNYANGAJU, Canon Jerome Cassian. b 53. Serampore Univ BD85 Open Univ MA97. St Phil Coll Kongwa 73. **d** 75 **p** 76. Tanzania 75-80 and 85-95; India 80-85; Hon Can Kagera from 91; Overseas Resource Person *D & D* 95-97; C Bangor Abbey *D & D* 98-00; I Killyleagh from 00. *The Rectory, 34 Inishbeg, Killyleagh, Downpatrick BT80 9TR* Tel (028) 4482 8231 Fax as telephone E-mail jerome@munyangaju.freeserve.co.uk

MURCH, Canon Robin Norman. b 37. Wells Th Coll. **d** 67 **p** 68. C Wisbech St Aug *Ely* 67-70; C Basingstoke *Win* 70-73; C Whitstable All SS *Cant* 73-76; V Queenborough 76-99; Hon Can Cant Cathl 96-99; rtd 99; Perm to Offic *Ex* from 00. *Flat 3, Narenta, 2 Barton Crescent, Dawlish EX7 9QL* Tel (01626) 863532 Mobile 07836-514528

MURDIN, Frank Laurence. b 11. Leeds Univ BA34. Coll of Resurr Mirfield 34. **d** 36 **p** 37. C Pet St Paul *Pet* 36-41; R Culworth 41-58; RD Culworth 50-58; V Moreton Pinkney 55-58; R Brampton Ash w Dingley 58-65; RD Weldon 64-65; V Greetham w Stretton and Clipsham 65-76; rtd 76. *48 Pinewood Close, Bourne PE10 9RL* Tel (01778) 423696

MURDOCH, Alexander Edward Duncan. b 37. Oak Hill Th Coll 68. **d** 71 **p** 72. C Kensington St Helen w H Trin *Lon* 71-72; C Kensington St Barn 73-74; CF 74-78; C W Kirby St Bridget *Ches* 78-84; V N Shoebury *Chelmsf* 84-87; V W Poldens *B & W* 87-96; R Gayhurst w Ravenstone, Stoke Goldington etc *Ox* from 96. *The Rectory, Mount Pleasant, Stoke Goldington, Newport Pagnell MK16 8LL* Tel (01908) 551221

MURDOCH, David John. b 58. Birm Univ BSocSc81. Ripon Coll Cuddesdon 81. **d** 84 **p** 85. C Penwortham St Leon *Blackb* 84-87; C Wirksworth w Alderwasley, Carsington etc *Derby* 87-89; R Shirland 89-97; Dioc World Development Officer 96-00; P-in-c New Mills 97-01; V from 01. *St George's Vicarage, Church Lane, New Mills, Stockport SK22 4NP* Tel (01663) 743225 Fax as telephone E-mail murdochs@btopenworld.com

MURDOCH, Mrs Lucy Eleanor. b 41. STETS BTh99. **d** 99 **p** 00. NSM Warbleton and Bodle Street Green *Chich* 99-02; NSM Rye from 02; TV from 03. *The Vicarage, 39 Lydd Road, Camber, Rye TN31 7RN* Tel (01797) 225386 E-mail lucy@murdoch26.fsnet.co.uk

MURENZI, François Xavier. b 63. Man Univ BA95 TCD MPhil01. CITC and Irish Sch of Ecum 99. **d** 01 **p** 02. C Bray *D & G* 01-03; I Athy w Kilberry, Fontstown and Kilkea from 03. *The Rectory, Church Road, Athy, Co Kildare, Irish Republic* Tel (00353) (59) 863 1446 Fax as telephone E-mail murenzi@eircom.net

MURFET, Edward David. b 36. Qu Coll Cam BA59 MA63. Chich Th Coll 59. **d** 61 **p** 62. C Croydon St Mich *Cant* 61-64; C Hunslet St Mary and Stourton *Ripon* 64-65; C Hackney Wick St Mary of Eton w St Aug *Lon* 65-69; Chapl Berne *Eur* 69-71; Chapl Naples 71-74; Chapl Rome 74-77; Lic to Offic *Bris* 78-81; Gen Sec CEMS 81-86; C Leeds St Pet *Ripon* 87-89; P-in-c 89-90; C Leeds City 91-93; Min Can Ripon Cathl from 93. *17 High St Agnesgate, Ripon HG4 1QR* Tel (01765) 602609 E-mail edmurfet@bronco.co.uk

MURFET, Gwyn. b 44. Linc Th Coll 71. **d** 74 **p** 75. C Scalby w Ravenscar and Staintondale *York* 74-77; P-in-c S Milford 77-83; R 83-84; V Kirkby Ireleth *Carl* from 84. *The Vicarage, School Road, Kirkby-in-Furness LA17 7UQ* Tel (01229) 889256 Fax as telephone

MURIEL, Sister. *See* ARTHINGTON, Sister Muriel

MURPHIE, Andrew Graham. b 65. Reading Univ BA86. St Jo Coll Nottm BTh91 MA92. **d** 92 **p** 93. C Boulton *Derby* 92-96; C Marston on Dove w Scropton 96-97; V Hilton w Marston-on-Dove from 96. *The Vicarage, 28 Back Lane, Hilton, Derby DE65 5GJ* Tel (01283) 733433 E-mail andymurphie@fish.co.uk

MURPHY, Alexander Charles. b 28. St Edm Coll Ware 50. **d** 55 **p** 56. NSM Edin St Jas *Edin* 88-90; TV Edin St Mark 90-93; TV Edin St Andr and St Aid 90-93; TV Edin St Marg 93-96; rtd 96. *29 Shadepark Drive, Dalkeith EH22 1DA* Tel 0131-660 1574

MURPHY, Andrew John. b 46. Edin Univ LLB67 MA68. **d** 95. NSM Aberdeen St Marg *Ab* 95-98; NSM Fraserburgh from 98. *Old Schoolhouse, Logie, Crimond AB43 8QN* Tel (01346) 532711

MURPHY, Deborah Ann. b 67. Newc Univ BA89 Birm Univ BD92. Qu Coll Birm 90. **d** 93 **p** 94. Par Dn Bloxwich *Lich* 93-94; C 94-97; TV Gt Grimsby St Mary and St Jas *Linc* 97-00; Perm to Offic *St Alb* from 01. *77 School Lane, Bushey WD23 1BY* Tel (020) 8386 0926 E-mail john@murphy14.freeserve.co.uk

MURPHY, Jack. b 27. N Ord Course 83. **d** 86 **p** 87. C Armley w New Wortley *Ripon* 86-90; C Hawksworth Wood 90-94; rtd 94; Perm to Offic *York* from 96. *70 Avocet Way, Bridlington YO15 3NT* Tel (01262) 609477

MURPHY, James Royse. b 54. DRCOG80 MRCGP81 Bris Univ MB, ChB77. Glouc Sch of Min 89. **d** 92 **p** 94. NSM Glouc St Cath *Glouc* 92-98; NSM Glouc St Paul from 98. *52 Lansdown Road, Gloucester GL1 3JD* Tel (01452) 505080

MURPHY, Canon John Gervase Maurice Walker (Gerry). b 26. LVO87. TCD BA52 MA55. **d** 52 **p** 53. C Lurgan Ch the Redeemer *D & D* 52-55; CF 55-73; Asst Chapl Gen 73-77; V Ranworth w Panxworth *Nor* 77-79; RD Blofield 79; Dom Chapl to The Queen 79-87; Chapl to The Queen 87-96; R Sandringham w W Newton *Nor* 79-87; RD Heacham and Rising 85-87; Hon Can Nor Cathl 86-87; Chapl ICS 87-91; Falkland Is 87-91; Miss to seamen 87-91; rtd 91; Chapl St Pet-ad-Vincula at HM Tower of Lon 91-96; Dep P in O 92-96; Extra Chapl to The Queen from 96; Perm to Offic *Nor* from 98. *Saffron Close, 17 Ringstead Road, Heacham, King's Lynn PE31 7JA* Tel (01485) 572351

MURPHY, Owen. b 52. Open Univ BA85. Chich Th Coll 92. **d** 94 **p** 95. C Oxhey St Matt *St Alb* 94-96; C Watford St Mich 96-98; P-in-c Shinfield *Ox* from 98. *The Vicarage, 12 The Manor, Shinfield, Reading RG2 9DP* Tel 0118-988 3363 E-mail omurphy@globalnet.co.uk

MURPHY, Peter Frederick. b 40. AKC65. **d** 67 **p** 68. C Paddington St Jo w St Mich *Lon* 67-72; P-in-c Basingstoke *Win* 72-76; TV 76-81; V Hythe 81-92; V Lyndhurst and Emery Down 92-99; P-in-c Minstead 95-99; V Lyndhurst and Emery Down and Minstead from 99. *The Vicarage, 5 Forest Gardens, Lyndhurst SO43 7AF* Tel (023) 8028 2154 Fax 8028 2890 E-mail pmurphy@newforestparishes.com

MURPHY, Philip John Warwick. b 65. Kent Univ BA87 Southn Univ BTh93 SSC. Chich Th Coll 88. **d** 91 **p** 92. C Broadstone *Sarum* 91-94; C Teddington SS Pet and Paul and Fulwell *Lon* 94-96; V Leytonstone St Marg w St Columba *Chelmsf* 96-01; P-in-c Leytonstone St Andr 96-97; R Benalla Australia from 01. *77 Arundel Street, PO Box 250, Benalla, Vic, Australia 3672* Tel (0061) (3) 5762 2061 Mobile 409-137025 Fax 5726 7009 E-mail pjwm@bigpond.com

MURPHY, Ronald Frederick. b 38. **d** 84 **p** 85. NSM Swindon Dorcan *Bris* 84-87; P-in-c N Cerney w Bagendon *Glouc* 87-90. *Flat 1, Byron Court, 19 The Beacon, Exmouth EX8 2AF* Tel (01395) 224375

MURPHY, Royse. *See* MURPHY, James Royse

MURPHY, William Albert. b 43. MBE98. Lon Univ BD73 QUB MTh78. **d** 73 **p** 74. C Lisburn Ch Ch *Conn* 73-79; Supt & Chapl Ulster Inst for the Deaf 79-98; Chapl HM Pris Maze from 82; Dioc Dir Ords *Conn* from 92; Chapl Ch of Ireland Min to Deaf people from 98. *2 Maghaberry Manor, Moira, Craigavon BT67 0JZ* Tel (028) 9261 9140 E-mail ddo@connor.anglican.org

MURPHY, Mrs Yvonne Letita. b 52. Brunel Univ BA90 PGCE91. SEITE 95. **d** 98 **p** 99. NSM Hampton St Mary *Lon* from 98; Chapl Bp Wand Sch from 98. *41 Jersey Close, Chertsey KT16 9PA* Tel (01932) 567796 E-mail ylm.blm@virgin.net

MURRAY, Alan. b 37. St Jo Coll Nottm BTh92. **d** 92 **p** 93. C Wombwell *Sheff* 92-95; C Mortomley St Sav High Green 95-99; P-in-c Doncaster St Jas 99-01; V from 01. *The Vicarage, 54 Littlemoor Lane, Doncaster DN4 0LB* Tel (01302) 365544

MURRAY, Christine Jean. *See* MEDWAY, Mrs Christine Jean

MURRAY, Christopher James. b 49. Open Univ BA78. St Jo Coll Nottm 79. **d** 81 **p** 82. C Heatherlands St Jo *Sarum* 81-84; C Hamworthy 84-90; R Passenham *Pet* from 90. *The Rectory, Wicken Road, Deanshanger, Milton Keynes MK19 6JP* Tel (01908) 262371

MURRAY, David McIlveen. b 36. ALCD61. **d** 61 **p** 62. C Mortlake w E Sheen *S'wark* 61-64; C Lyncombe *B & W* 64-67; C Horsham *Chich* 67-73; V Devonport St Bart *Ex* 73-79; R Chalfont St Peter *Ox* 79-95; RD Amersham 86-89; R Lower Windrush 95-03; rtd 03. *Collum End Farm, 88 Church Road, Leckhampton, Cheltenham GL53 0PD* Tel (01242) 528008

MURRAY, Elizabeth Ruth. **d** 03. C Antrim All SS *Conn* from 03. *Address temp unknown*

MURRAY, Gordon John. b 33. St Cath Coll Cam BA57 MA61. Clifton Th Coll 57. **d** 59 **p** 60. C Heref St Jas *Heref* 59-61; C Uphill *B & W* 62-65; C-in-c Reading St Mary Castle Street Prop Chpl *Ox* 65-68; Ed *English Churchman* 65-71; Prin Kensit Coll Finchley 68-75; Hd of RE Saunton Wood 75-78; rtd 98. *18 Longcroft, Felixstowe IP11 9QH* Tel (01394) 273372

MURRAY, Gordon Stewart. b 33. Birkbeck Coll Lon BSc72. Ripon Coll Cuddesdon 76. **d** 78 **p** 79. C Kenilworth St Nic *Cov*

78-81; V Potterspury w Furtho and Yardley Gobion *Pet* 81-83; V Potterspury, Furtho, Yardley Gobion and Cosgrove 84; TV Wolvercote w Summertown *Ox* 84-90; P-in-c Walworth *S'wark* 90-95; TR Walworth St Pet 95-98; P-in-c Tillington *Chich* 98; P-in-c Duncton 98; P-in-c Up Waltham 98; rtd 98; P-in-c Tillington *Chich* 98-01; P-in-c Duncton 98-01; P-in-c Up Waltham 98-01. *26 Burton Stone Lane, York YO30 6BU* Tel (01904) 330401 E-mail gordon.murray11@ntlworld.com

MURRAY, Ian Hargraves. b 48. Man Univ BSc71. St Jo Coll Nottm 79. d 81 p 82. C Erith St Paul *Roch* 81-84; C Willenhall H Trin *Lich* 84-87; TV 87-92; P-in-c Moxley 92-00; C Darlaston St Lawr 99-00; TR Glascote and Stonydelph from 00. *20 Melmerby, Wilnecote, Tamworth B77 4LP* Tel (01827) 737326 *or* 330306 E-mail rockin.rev@ntlworld.com

MURRAY, Ian William. b 32. Lon Univ BA53 PGCE54. Oak Hill NSM Course 80. d 83 p 84. NSM Pinner *Lon* from 83. *4 Mansard Close, Pinner HA5 3FQ* Tel (020) 8866 2984 E-mail bimurray@talk21.com

MURRAY, James Beattie. b 67. Goldsmiths' Coll Lon BMus87 Southlands Coll Lon PGCE89. Oak Hill Th Coll 01. d 03. C Upper Holloway *Lon* from 03. *6 Zoffany Street, London N19 3ER* Tel (020) 7263 4217 E-mail jamiemurray@hotmail.com

MURRAY, Canon John Desmond. b 16. TCD BA38 MA46. CITC 39. d 39 p 40. C Dublin St Werburgh *D & G* 39-41; C Dublin Ch Ch Leeson Park 41-43; C Dublin Rathmines 43-49; Min Can St Patr Cathl Dublin 43-53; I Powerscourt *D & G* 49-53; Chapl RN 53-55; I Dalkey St Patr *D & G* 55-70; I Milltown 70-82; Hon Chapl to Abp Dublin 73-82; Can Ch Ch Cathl Dublin 79-82; rtd 82. *3 Adare Close, Killincarrig, Greystones, Co Wicklow, Irish Republic* Tel (00353) (1) 287 6359

MURRAY, The Ven John Grainger. b 45. CITC 67. d 70 p 71. C Carlow *C & O* 70-72; C Limerick St Mary *L & K* 72-77; I Rathdowney w Castlefleming, Donaghmore etc *C & O* from 77; Can Leighlin Cathl 83-88; Treas 88-89; Chan 89-90; Prec 90-92; Preb Ossory Cathl 83-88; Treas 88-89; Chan 89-90; Prec 90-92; Adn Ossory and Leighlin from 92; Adn Cashel, Waterford and Lismore from 94. *The Rectory, Rathdowney, Portlaoise, Co Laois, Irish Republic* Tel (00353) (505) 46311 Fax 46540 E-mail venjgm@iol.ie *or* archdeacon@cashel.anglican.org

MURRAY, John Louis. b 47. Keble Coll Ox BA67 MA69. d 82 p 83. Asst Chapl Strasbourg *Eur* from 82. *11 rue des Juifs, 67000 Strasbourg, France* Tel (0033) (3) 88 36 1225 Fax 88 41 27 31

MURRAY, Mrs Margaret Janice. b 46. Carl Dioc Tr Course. dss 86 d 87 p 94. Walney Is *Carl* 86-87; Hon Par Dn 87-89; Par Dn Carl H Trin and St Barn 89-94; Chapl Cumberland Infirmary 90-94; C Harraby *Carl* 94-97; P-in-c 97-00; V 00-02; Chapl to the Deaf and Hard of Hearing 94-02; rtd 02; Perm to Offic *Carl* from 02. *6 Follyskye Cottages, Tindale Fell, Brampton CA8 2QB* Tel (01697) 746400

MURRAY, Paul Ridsdale. b 55. BEd. St Steph Ho Ox. d 83 p 84. C Hartlepool St Oswald *Dur* 83-86; C S Shields All SS 86-88; V Sacriston and Kimblesworth 88-94; P-in-c Waterhouses 94-98; P-in-c Chopwell from 98; Perm to Offic *Newc* from 99. *St John's Vicarage, Derwent View, Chopwell, Newcastle upon Tyne NE17 7AN* Tel (01207) 561248 Mobile 07803-906727 Fax 563850 E-mail p.r.murray@durham.anglican.org

MURRAY, Robert Blake. b 49. EMMTC. d 00 p 01. NSM Annesley w Newstead *S'well* 00-03; P-in-c Brinsley w Underwood from 03. *The Vicarage, 102A Church Lane, Brinsley, Nottingham NG16 5AB* Tel (01773) 713978 Fax as telephone E-mail rb.murray@ntlworld.com

MURRAY, Mrs Ruth Elizabeth. b 55. Dur Univ BA77 Man Coll of Educn CertEd78. BA. d 94 p 95. NSM Alloa *St And* 94-98; Chapl Stirling Univ 94-99. *2 Wallace Street, Alloa FK10 3RZ* Tel (01259) 217432 E-mail ruthemurray@lineone.net

MURRAY (née GOULD), Mrs Susan Judith. b 61. Poly of Wales BSc83 Open Univ MA95. St Jo Coll Nottm 90. d 91 p 94. Par Dn Stokesley *York* 91-94; CMS 94-95; Argentina 95-03; P-in-c Haddlesey w Hambleton and Birkin *York* from 03. *The Rectory, Chapel Haddlesey, Selby YO8 8QF* Tel (01757) 270245

MURRAY, Canon William Robert Craufurd. b 44. St Chad's Coll Dur BA66 DipTh68. d 68 p 69. C Workington St Mich *Carl* 68-71; C Harrogate St Wilfrid *Ripon* 71-74; P-in-c Sawley 74; V Winksley cum Grantley and Aldfield w Studley 74; R Fountains 75-81; New Zealand from 81; V Hutt 81-87; V Fendalton from 87; Can Christchurch Cathl from 91. *St Barnabas's Vicarage, 7 Makora Street, Christchurch 8004, New Zealand* Tel (0064) (3) 351 7064 *or* 351 7392 Fax 351 6374 E-mail craufurd@clear.net.nz

MURRAY-LESLIE, Adrian John Gervase. b 46. Lich Th Coll 67. d 69 p 70. C Sheff St Cuth *Sheff* 69-73; C Mosbrough 73-75; C-in-c Mosborough CD 75-80; Warden Champion Ho Youth Cen Edale from 80; P-in-c Edale *Derby* from 80. *The Vicarage, Edale, Hope Valley S33 7ZA* Tel (01433) 670254

MURRAY, THE, Bishop of. *See* DAVIES, The Rt Revd Ross Owen

MURRELL, Canon John Edmund. b 28. Westcott Ho Cam. d 66 p 67. C Ivychurch w Old Romney and Midley *Cant* 66-70; R

Bardwell *St E* 70-75; Perm to Offic *Ely* 75-77; V Wenhaston w Thorington and Bramfield w Walpole *St E* 77-86; V Thorington w Wenhaston and Bramfield 86-92; P-in-c Walberswick w Blythburgh 86-92; V Thorington w Wenhaston, Bramfield etc 92-93; RD Halesworth 85-90; Hon Can St E Cathl 89-93; rtd 93; Perm to Offic *St E* from 93. *Strickland Cottage, 12 Lorne Road, Southwold IP18 6EP* Tel (01502) 722074

MURRIE, Clive Robert. b 44. BA. Ripon Coll Cuddesdon 77. d 79 p 80. C Kenton Ascension *Newc* 79-80; C Prudhoe 80-83; V Burnopfield *Dur* 83-87; R Stella 87-91; V Coalpit Heath *Bris* 91-95; P-in-c Sittingbourne St Mich *Cant* 95-98; Chapl HM Pris Stocken 98-03; Chapl HM YOI Castington from 03. *HM YOI, Castington, Morpeth NE65 9XF* Tel (01670) 762100

MURRIN, Robert Staddon. b 42. RMA 62 Reading Univ BA68 Birm Univ DPS93 Open Univ MA96. WMMTC 90 Birm Bible Inst DipRS92. d 93 p 95. NSM Peterchurch w Vowchurch, Turnastone and Dorstone *Heref* 93-95; NSM Tupsley w Hampton Bishop 95-97; Chapl Kemp Hospice Kidderminster from 97. *Albion Cottage, Peterchurch, Hereford HR2 0RP* Tel (01981) 550656 *or* 550467 Fax 550432 E-mail murrin@cuphony.net

MURSELL, The Very Revd Alfred Gordon. b 49. BNC Ox BA70 MA73 BD87 ARCM74. Cuddesdon Coll 71. d 73 p 74. C Walton St Mary *Liv* 73-77; V E Dulwich St Jo *S'wark* 77-86; Tutor Sarum Th Coll 87-91; TR Stafford *Lich* 91-99; Provost Birm 99-02; Dean Birm from 02. *103A Selly Park Road, Selly Oak, Birmingham B29 7LH* Tel and fax 0121-472 1248 *or* tel 262 1840 Fax 262 1860 E-mail dean@birminghamcathedral.com

MUSGRAVE, Canon James Robert Lord. b 20. MBE97. TCD BA43 MA51. d 44 p 45. C Belfast St Andr *Conn* 44-46; C Derriaghy 46-51; R Duneane w Ballyscullion 51-54; I Belfast St Steph 54-64; I Magheragall 64-85; Can Conn Cathl 82-85; Bp's C Killead w Gartree 87-95; rtd 95. *14 Earlsfort, Moira, Craigavon BT67 0LY* Tel (028) 9261 2047

MUSHEN, Canon Francis John. b 34. Birm Univ BA60. Ripon Hall Ox 60. d 62 p 63. C Foleshill St Laur *Cov* 62-65; C Halesowen *Worc* 65-69; V Stourbridge St Mich Norton 69-81; Hon Can Worc Cathl 81-99; P-in-c Bromsgrove St Jo 81-87; V 87-92; R Kempsey and Severn Stoke w Croome d'Abitot 92-99; rtd 99. *16 Longheadland, Ombersley, Droitwich WR9 0JB* Tel (01905) 621461

MUSINDI, Philip. b 63. Bp Tucker Coll Mukono BD91 Univ of Wales (Cardiff) MTh94. Bp Tucker Coll Mukono DipTh87 St Mich Coll Llan 91. d 87 p 90. Uganda 87-92; C Builth and Llanddewi'r Cwm w Llangynog etc *S & B* 92-94; C Newport St Teilo *Mon* 94-97; P-in-c Newport St Matt from 97. *St Matthew's Vicarage, 124 Caerleon Road, Newport NP19 7GS* Tel (01633) 769453

MUSK, Bill Andrew. b 49. Ox Univ BA70 MA75 Univ of S Africa D Litt et Phil84 Lon Univ DipTh73. Fuller Th Sem California ThM80 Trin Coll Bris DipTh81. d 81 p 82. Egypt 81-86; CMS 88-89; TV Maghull *Liv* 89-97; V Tulse Hill H Trin and St Matthias *S'wark* from 97. *The Vicarage, 49 Trinity Rise, London SW2 2QP* Tel (020) 8674 6721 E-mail billamusk@aol.com

MUSKETT, David John. b 63. Southn Univ BA85. Ripon Coll Cuddesdon 87. d 90 p 91. C Kempston Transfiguration *St Alb* 90-93; C Ampthill w Millbrook and Steppingley 93-96; V Milford *Guildf* from 96. *The Vicarage, Milford Heath Road, Godalming GU8 5BX* Tel (01483) 414710 E-mail stjohn_milford@hotmail.com

MUSSER, Ms Christine. b 55. Ex Univ 96. d 00 p 01. C Torpoint *Truro* 00-03; P-in-c Boscastle w Davidstow from 03. *The Rectory, Forrabury, Boscastle PL35 0DJ* Tel (01840) 250359 E-mail revdchrismusser@aol.com

MUSSON, David John. b 46. Open Univ BA86 Univ of Wales (Lamp) MPhil96 Univ of Wales (Ban) PhD00. Linc Th Coll 70. d 73 p 74. C New Sleaford *Linc* 73-76; C Morton 76-80; P-in-c Thurlby 80-86; R Quarrington w Old Sleaford 86-99; P-in-c Silk Willoughby 86-87; R 87-99; Perm to Offic *Chich* from 01. *Flat A, 6 Chatsworth Gardens, Eastbourne BN20 7JP* Tel (01323) 738776 E-mail david@davidmusson.fsnet.co.uk

MUSSON, John Keith. b 39. Nottm Univ BSc61 PhD66 CEng MIMechE. St As Minl Tr Course 85. d 88 p 89. Assoc Prin NE Wales Inst of HE 80-93; NSM Holywell *St As* 88-93; C 93-95; R Caerwys and Bodfari 95-02; rtd 02. *4 Hayes View, Oswestry SY11 1TP* Tel (01691) 656212

MUSSON, William John. b 58. UMIST BSc80. St Jo Coll Nottm 88. d 91 p 92. C Nantwich *Ches* 91-94; C Finchley Ch Ch *Lon* 94-97; V Lynchmere and Camelsdale *Chich* from 97. *The Vicarage, School Road, Camelsdale, Haslemere GU27 3RN* Tel (01428) 642983 E-mail the-vicar@stpandp.freeserve.co.uk

MUST, Albert Henry. b 27. Clifton Th Coll. d 63 p 64. C Becontree St Mary *Chelmsf* 63-68; V Highbury Vale St Jo *Lon* 68-78; V Highbury New Park St Aug 78-84; V Walthamstow St Jo *Chelmsf* 84-93; rtd 93; Perm to Offic *Cant* from 93. *24 Nightingale Avenue, Whitstable CT5 4TR* Tel (01227) 772160

MUST, Mrs Shirley Ann. b 35. St Mich Ho Ox 61. dss 82 d 87 p 94. Highbury New Park St Aug *Lon* 82-84; Walthamstow St Jo

Chelmsf 84-87; Hon Par Dn 87-93; Perm to Offic *Cant* 93-94; Hon C Herne Bay Ch Ch from 94. *24 Nightingale Avenue, Whitstable CT5 4TR* Tel (01227) 772160

MUSTOE, Alan Andrew. b 52. Man Univ BA74. Qu Coll Birm DipTh77. **d** 78 **p** 79. C Chatham St Wm *Roch* 78-82; R Burham and Wouldham 82-88; Dioc Info Officer 83-88; V Strood St Nic w St Mary 88-99; V Orpington All SS from 99. *The Vicarage, 1A Keswick Road, Orpington BR6 0EU* Tel (01689) 824624 Fax as telephone E-mail akmustoe@btopenworld.com

MUSTON, David Alan. b 33. Nottm Univ BA60. Ridley Hall Cam 62. **d** 64 **p** 65. C Tankersley *Sheff* 64-67; C Goole 67-70; Asst Sec Ind Cttee of Gen Syn Bd for Soc Resp 70-76; Ind Chapl *Win* 77-79; V Leigh St Mary *Man* 79-83; R Otham w Langley *Cant* 83-97; rtd 97. *7 The Homestead, Bladon, Woodstock OX20 1XA* Tel (01993) 812650

MUSTON, James Arthur. b 48. Leic Univ CertRS91 Open Univ BA92 Derby Univ MA. EMMTC 89. **d** 91 **p** 92. NSM Chaddesden St Mary *Derby* 91-95; Community Min East Marsh Grimsby *Linc* 95-99; V Gresley from 99. *The Vicarage, 120 Church Street, Church Gresley, Swadlincote DE11 9NR* Tel (01283) 223983

MUTCH, Canon Sylvia Edna. b 36. St Mich Ho Ox 57. **dss** 79 **d** 87 **p** 94. Clifton *York* 79-95; Par Dn 87-94; C 94-95; Chapl Clifton Hosp York 81-94; R Elvington w Sutton on Derwent and E Cottingwith *York* 95-01; Can and Preb York Minster 98-01; rtd 01; Perm to Offic *York* from 01. *18 Waite Close, Pocklington, York YO42 2YU* Tel (01759) 307894

MUXLOW, Judy Ann. b 47. Univ of Wales (Cardiff) BSc69 St Luke's Coll Ex CertEd73. SEITE. **d** 00 **p** 01. NSM Biddenden and Smarden *Cant* from 00; Chapl Ch Ch High Sch Ashford from 00; Perm to Offic *Roch* from 00. *29 The Meadows, Biddenden, Ashford TN27 8AW* Tel (01580) 291016

MWANGI, Capt Joel Waweru. b 59. Nairobi Univ CertRS84. CA Tr Coll Nairobi 81. **d** 93 **p** 94. Kenya 93-96 and from 00; C Sheff St Mary Bramall Lane *Sheff* 96-99. *PO Box 57227, Nairobi, Kenya*

MWAURA, Nicholas Chege. b 65. DipTh90. **d** 90 **p** 91. Nairobi 91-95; NSM Limehouse *Lon* 99-00. *Flat C, 53 Hanbury Street, London E1 5JP*

MYANMAR, Archbishop of. *See* SAN SI HTAY, The Most Revd Samuel

MYATT, Edwin Henry. b 54. MA. Ripon Coll Cuddesdon. **d** 84 **p** 85. C W Bromwich St Fran *Lich* 84-88; C Sedgley All SS 88-93; V Trent Vale 93-94. *The Conifers, 5 Prestwick Road, Kingswinford ST4 6JY*

MYATT, Francis Eric. b 60. St Jo Coll Nottm LTh92. **d** 92 **p** 93. C W Derby St Luke *Liv* 92-95; TV Sutton 95-98; V Liv St Chris Norris Green 98-01; CF from 01. *clo MOD Chaplains (Army)* Tel (01980) 615804 Fax 615800

MYATT, Philip Bryan. b 29. Wycliffe Hall Ox 54. **d** 57 **p** 58. C Fareham St Jo *Portsm* 57-61; C Westgate St Jas *Cant* 61-64; R Woodchester *Glouc* 64-70; R Bath Walcot *B & W* 70-91; R The Edge, Pitchcombe, Harescombe and Brookthorpe *Glouc* 91-94; rtd 94; Perm to Offic *Glouc* from 94. *West Cottage, Littleworth, Amberley, Stroud GL5 5AL*

MYCOCK, Geoffrey John Arthur. b 22. Open Univ BA76. St Deiniol's Hawarden 76. **d** 77 **p** 78. Hon C Ches H Trin *Ches* 77-79; Bp's Dom Chapl 79-80; P-in-c Hargrave 79-80; V Sandbach Heath 80-82; Chapl and Lect St Deiniol's Lib Hawarden 82-85; V Holt *St As* 85-90; rtd 90; Perm to Offic *St A* from 90 and *Ches* from 91. *20 Eaton Close, Broughton, Chester CH4 0RF* Tel (01244) 531214

MYERS, Canon Arnold George. b 23. Keble Coll Ox BA44 DipTh46 MA48 TCD BA51. St Steph Ho Ox. **d** 47 **p** 48. C Harrington *Carl* 47-50; C Liv Our Lady and St Nic *Liv* 50-53; V Edgehill St Dunstan 53-62; R W Derby St Mary 62-79; TR 79-84; RD W Derby 71-78; Hon Can Liv Cathl 74-84; rtd 84; Perm to Offic *Liv* from 84. *10 Surrey Drive, West Kirby, Wirral CH48 2HP* Tel 0151-625 2250

MYERS, Duncan Frank. b 57. Warwick Univ BSc. St Jo Coll Nottm 81. **d** 84 **p** 85. C Upton cum Chalvey *Ox* 84-86; C Farnborough *Guildf* 86-90; Chapl Nottm Poly *S'well* 90-92; Chapl Nottm Trent Univ 92-95; Sen Past Advr 95-02. *6A The College, Durham DH1 3EQ* Tel 0191-384 2481 E-mail duncan@myers.uk.net

MYERS, Ms Gillian Mary. b 57. Warwick Univ BSc78 Nottm Univ MA96. St Jo Coll Nottm 83. **d** 95 **p** 97. NSM Nottingham St Jude *S'well* 95-97; NSM Gedling 97-00; P-in-c Nottingham All SS 00-02; Succ, Sacr and Min Can Dur Cathl *Dur* from 02. *6A The College, Durham DH1 3EQ* Tel 0191-384 2481 E-mail gilly@myers.uk.net

MYERS, John Bulmer. b 19. Worc Ord Coll 64. **d** 66 **p** 67. C Linthorpe *York* 66-68; NSM Huddersfield St Jo *Wakef* 74-76; C 76-79; V Cornholme 79-88; rtd 88; Perm to Offic *Wakef* from 88. *284 Burnley Road, Todmorden OL14 8EW* Tel (01706) 812224

MYERS, Paul Henry. b 49. Liv Poly ALA72. Qu Coll Birm 74. **d** 77 **p** 78. C Baildon *Bradf* 77-80; C W Bromwich All SS *Lich* 80-83; Chapl RAF 83-86; V Milton *Lich* 87-92; C Baswich 96-99;

C Hixon w Stowe-by-Chartley 99-02; TV Mid Trent from 02. *2 Vicarage Way, Hixon, Stafford ST18 0FT* Tel (01889) 270418

MYERS, Peter John. b 60. St Jo Coll Dur BA81. Linc Th Coll 84. **d** 84 **p** 85. C Bulwell St Mary *S'well* 84-88; C Shrewsbury H Cross *Lich* 88-92; rtd 92. *15 Winchelsea Street, Dover CT17 9ST* Tel (01304) 204354

MYERS, Robert William John. b 57. Aus Nat Univ BSc80 Newc Univ Aus DipEd82. Trin Coll Bris DipHE95. **d** 95 **p** 96. C Addiscombe St Mary Magd w St Martin *S'wark* 95-98; C Surbiton St Matt from 98. *127 Hamilton Avenue, Surbiton KT6 7QA* Tel (020) 8397 4294 E-mail rwjmyers@netscape.net

MYERSCOUGH, Robin Nigel. b 44. K Coll Lon BD69 Nottm Univ PGCE70. Coll of Resurr Mirfield 66. **d** 81 **p** 82. Hon C Diss *Nor* 81-84; Chapl Nor Sch 81-84; Hd RS Sedbergh Sch 84-85; Chapl and Hd RS Dur Sch 85-92; Chapl Gresham's Sch Holt 92-01; Asst Chapl from 01. *Gresham's School, Cromer Road, Holt NR25 6EA* Tel (01263) 713194

MYLES, Peter Rodney. b 42. K Coll Lon 61 St Aug Coll Cant 70. **d** 71 **p** 72. C Tideswell *Derby* 71-74; C W Brompton St Mary w St Pet *Lon* 74-79; P-in-c Notting Hill St Pet 79-82; Chapl to Bp Kensington 82-87; C Kensington St Mary Abbots w St Geo 82-92; P-in-c Isleworth St Jo from 92. *The Vicarage, St John's Road, Isleworth TW7 6NY* Tel (020) 8560 4916

MYLNE, Denis Colin. b 31. Jordan Hill Coll Glas CYCW75. Kelham Th Coll 69. **d** 71. Perm to Offic *Glas* 74-84; Perm to Offic *Ab* 84-88; C Bedford All SS *St Alb* 88-91; C Harpenden St Jo 91-96; rtd 96; Perm to Offic *Newc* from 96; Hon C Kelso *Edin* from 99. *Gracegarth, Ubbanford, Norham, Berwick-upon-Tweed TD15 2JZ* Tel (01289) 382187

MYNETT, Colin. b 25. Roch Th Coll 61. **d** 63 **p** 64. C Liskeard w St Keyne *Truro* 63-66; R Lifton *Ex* 66-71; R Kelly w Bradstone 66-71; TV Devonport St Aubyn 71-75; V Cinderford St Jo *Glouc* 75-84; P-in-c Pittville All SS 84-89; rtd 89. *5 Heron Close, Cheltenham GL51 6HA* Tel (01242) 523341

MYNETT, John Alan. b 37. CEng MIMechE67 Bris Univ BSc59 MSc61. N Ord Course 82. **d** 85 **p** 86. NSM Poynton *Ches* 85-90; NSM Macclesfield Team Par 90-01; P-in-c Sutton St Geo 98-01; Perm to Offic from 01. *1 Landseer Drive, Marple Bridge, Stockport SK6 5BL* Tel 0161-285 8558 E-mail johanne@mynett46.freeserve.co.uk

MYNORS, James Baskerville. b 49. Peterho Cam BA70 MA74. Ridley Hall Cam 70 St Jo Coll Nottm 77. **d** 78 **p** 80. Hon C Leic H Apostles *Leic* 78-79; C Virginia Water *Guildf* 79-83; C Patcham *Chich* 83-88; P-in-c Fowlmere and Thriplow *Ely* 88-01; Sen Tutor EAMTC 88-90; Vice-Prin 90-97; P-in-c Gt w Lt Abington from 01; P-in-c Hildersham from 01. *The Vicarage, 35 Church Lane, Little Abington, Cambridge CB1 6BQ* Tel (01223) 891350 *or* 890971 E-mail jimmynors@aol.com

N

NADEN, Anthony Joshua. b 38. Jes Coll Ox BA62 MA64 SOAS Lon PhD73. Wycliffe Hall Ox 60. **d** 62 **p** 63. C Rowner *Portsm* 62-66; C Fisherton Anger *Sarum* 70-72; Ghana from 72. *PO Box 3, Walewale, NR, Ghana*

NADIN, Dennis Lloyd. b 37. St D Coll Lamp BA60 Man Univ MEd81. Ridley Hall Cam 60. **d** 64 **p** 65. C Childwall All SS *Liv* 64-67; P-in-c Seacroft *Ripon* 67-69; Project Officer Grubb Inst 69-70; Lect CA Tr Coll Blackheath 70-72; Community Educn Essex Co Coun 73-80; Public Preacher *Chelmsf* from 73; Perm to Offic *St Alb* from 01; rtd 02. *The Hermitage, 201 Willowfield, Harlow CM18 6RZ* Tel (01279) 325904

NADKARNI, Edward Wasant. b 41. Trin Coll Cam BA64 MA67. Cuddesdon Coll 68. **d** 69 **p** 70. C E Ham St Mary *Chelmsf* 69-71; C Hertford St Andr *St Alb* 71-74; Chapl for Educn Bedf Deanery 74-78; Chapl Lanc Univ *Blackb* 78-83; rtd 99. *Holzschumacherweg 2A, 48161 Munster-Roxel, Germany*

NAGEL, Lawson Chase Joseph. b 49. ARHistS75 Univ of Michigan BA71 K Coll Lon PhD82. Sarum & Wells Th Coll. **d** 83 **p** 84. C Chiswick St Nic w St Mary *Lon* 83-86; Sec Gen Confraternity of the Blessed Sacrament from 85; C Horsham *Chich* 86; TV 86-91; OStJ from 88; V Aldwick *Chich* from 91. *The Vicarage, 25 Gossamer Lane, Aldwick, Bognor Regis PO21 3AT* Tel (01243) 262049 E-mail lnagel@netcomuk.co.uk

NAIDU, Michael Sriram. b 28. Univ of the South (USA) 81. Ridley Hall Cam 86. **d** 80 **p** 85. Acting Chapl Stuttgart *Eur* 85-91; Chapl 91-00; rtd 00. *Kloster Kinchberg, 72172 Sulz am Neckar, Stuttgart, Germany* Tel (0049) (7454) 883136 *or* 87418 Fax 883250

NAIRN, Frederick William. b 43. TCD 64. Luther NW Th Sem DMin88. **d** 67 **p** 68. C Larne and Inver *Conn* 67-70; Chapl RAF 70-74; P-in-c Harmston *Linc* 75-77; V 77-84; V Coleby 78-84; USA from 84. *4900 Nathan Lane, Plymouth, MN 55442, USA*

NAIRN, Stuart Robert. b 51. K Coll Lon BD75 AKC75. St Aug Coll Cant 75. **d** 76 **p** 77. C E Dereham *Nor* 76-80; TV Hempnall 80-88; V Narborough w Narford 88-99; R Pentney St Mary Magd w W Bilney 88-99; R Narborough w Narford and Pentney from 99; P-in-c Castleacre, Newton, Westacre and Southacre from 97; RD Lynn 91-99. *The Rectory, Main Road, Narborough, King's Lynn PE32 1TE* Tel (01760) 338552 *or* 338562 Fax 338562 E-mail nairn@narvalleygroup.freeserve.co.uk

NAIRN-BRIGGS, The Very Revd George Peter. b 45. AKC69. St Aug Coll Cant 69. **d** 70 **p** 71. C Catford St Laur *S'wark* 70-73; C Raynes Park St Sav 73-75; V Salfords 75-81; V St Helier 81-87; Dioc Soc Resp Adv *Wakef* 87-97; Can Res Wakef Cathl 92-97; Provost Wakef 97-00; Dean Wakef from 00. *The Deanery, 1 Cathedral Close, Margaret Street, Wakefield WF1 2DP* Tel (01924) 210005 Mobile 07770-636840 Fax 210009 E-mail thedeanofwakefield@hotmail.com

NAISH, Timothy James Neville. b 57. St Jo Coll Ox BA80 MA88. WMMTC 86. **d** 87 **p** 88. CMS from 81; C Cov H Trin *Cov* 87; Dir Th Formation (Shaba) Zaïre 88-91; Research Fell, Tutor, and Lect Qu Coll Birm 92-93; Perm to Offic *Birm* 92-93; Tutor and Lect Bp Tucker Th Coll Uganda 93-00; R Hanborough and Freeland *Ox* from 00. *The Rectory, Swan Lane, Long Hanborough, Witney OX29 8BT* Tel (01993) 881270 E-mail naish@beeb.net

NAISMITH, Mrs Carol. b 37. St Andr Univ MA59 Edin Univ MTh98. Edin Dioc NSM Course 85. **d** 90 **p** 94. NSM Edin St Marg *Edin* 90-94; NSM Edin Old St Paul 90-00; C Edin St Salvador from 00. *38 Castle Avenue, Edinburgh EH12 7LB* Tel 0131-334 4486

✠**NALEDI, The Rt Revd Theophilus Tswere.** b 36. UNISA BTh82 K Coll Lon MTh84. St Bede's Coll Umtata LTh59. **d** 59 **p** 60 **c** 87. S Africa 59-70; R Kimberley St Jas 67-70; Botswana 71-83 and 85-87; R Gaborone 71-73; Adn and R Lobatse 74-83; C Wimbledon *S'wark* 83-85; Prov Sec Ch of the Prov of Cen Africa 86-87; Bp Matabeleland Zimbabwe 87-01; Bp Botswana from 01. *PO Box 769, Gaborone, Botswana* Tel (00267) 395 3779 Fax 391 3015 E-mail angli_diocese@info.bw

NALL, Sheila. b 48. **d** 03. NSM Worc St Wulstan *Worc* from 03. *108 Ombersley Road, Worcester WR3 7EZ* Tel (01905) 26284

NANCARROW, Mrs Rachel Mary. b 38. Cam Inst of Educn TCert59. EAMTC 87. **d** 90 **p** 94. NSM Girton *Ely* 90-95; P-in-c Foxton 95-01; P-in-c Shepreth 98-01; C Fulbourn from 01; C Gt Wilbraham from 01; C Lt Wilbraham from 01. *The Vicarage, 5 Benstead's End, Great Wilbraham, Cambridge CB1 5JS* Tel (01223) 880332 E-mail r.m.nancarrow@skogen.co.uk

NANKIVELL, Christopher Robert Trevelyan. b 33. Jes Coll Ox BA55 MA63 Birm Univ MSocSc79. Linc Th Coll 56. **d** 58 **p** 59. C Bloxwich *Lich* 58-60; C Stafford St Mary 60-64; P-in-c Malins Lee 64-72; Soc Welfare Sector Min to Milton Keynes Chr Coun 73-76; Tutor Qu Coll Birm 76-81; rtd 96. *77 Pereira Road, Birmingham B17 9JA* Tel 0121-427 1197

NAPIER, Graeme Stewart Patrick Columbanus. b 66. Magd Coll Ox BA MA MPhil LRSM. St Steph Ho Ox. **d** 95 **p** 96. C Inverness St Andr *Mor* 95-98; Asst P St Laurence Ch Ch Australia 98-02; Min Can and Succ Westmr Abbey from 02. *The Chapter Office, 20 Dean's Yard, London SW1P 3PA* Tel (020) 7654 4850 Fax 7233 2072 E-mail graeme.napier@westminster-abbey.org

NAPIER, Lady Jennifer Beryl. See BLACK, Lady Jennifer Beryl

NARUSAWA, Masaki Alec. b 53. K Coll Lon BD77 AKC77. Linc Th Coll 77. **d** 78 **p** 79. C Hendon St Alphage *Lon* 78-81; C Eastcote St Lawr 81-84; V Glodwick *Man* 84-99; P-in-c Withington St Crispin from 99; Perm to Offic *Blackb* from 03. *7 Clevedon Road, Blackpool FY1 2NX* Tel (01253) 625404 E-mail masaki.narusawa@lineone.net

NASCIMENTO COOK, Mrs Anesia. b 62. Mogidas Cruces Univ BA86. Porto Allegre Th Sem DipTh91. **d** 91 **p** 93. Brazil 91-94; Lic to Offic *St Alb* 96-97; C Dinnington *Sheff* 97-99; P-in-c Shiregreen St Jas and St Chris from 99. *The Vicarage, 510 Bellhouse Road, Sheffield S5 0RG* Tel 0114-245 6526

NASH, Alan Frederick. b 46. Sarum & Wells Th Coll 72. **d** 75 **p** 76. C Foley Park *Worc* 75-79; P-in-c Mildenhall *Sarum* 79-82; Wilts Adnry Youth Officer 79-82; TV N Wingfield, Pilsley and Tupton *Derby* 82-85. *33 Manvers Road, Sheffield S6 2PJ*

NASH, David. b 25. K Coll Lon BD51 AKC51. **d** 52 **p** 53. C Buckhurst Hill *Chelmsf* 52-58; Min St Cedd CD Westcliff 58-66; R Rivenhall 66-83; P-in-c Boscastle w Davidstow *Truro* 83-85; TR 85-90; rtd 90; Perm to Offic *Truro* from 90. *9 Boscundle Avenue, Falmouth TR11 5BU*

NASH, Preb David John. b 41. Pemb Coll Ox BA64 MA70. Wells Th Coll 65. **d** 67 **p** 68. C Preston Ascension *Lon* 67-70; TV Hackney 70-75; TV Clifton *S'well* 76-82; V Winchmore Hill St Paul *Lon* 82-98; AD Enfield 87-91; Preb St Paul's Cathl from 96; R Monken Hadley from 98; AD Cen Barnet from 00. *The Rectory, Hadley Common, Barnet EN5 5QD* Tel (020) 8449 2414

NASH, Mrs Ingrid. b 36. SRN57 RNT80 BEd78 Cert Counselling 89. S'wark Ord Course 91. **d** 94 **p** 95. NSM Eltham Park St Luke *S'wark* from 94; Perm to Offic *Roch* from 97. *13 Crookston Road, London SE9 1YH* Tel (020) 8850 0750

NASH, James Alexander. b 56. Seale-Hayne Agric Coll HND79. St Jo Coll Nottm BA94. **d** 97 **p** 98. C Trunch *Nor* 97-01; R Stratton St Mary w Stratton St Michael etc from 01. *The Rectory, Flowerpot Lane, Long Stratton, Norwich NR15 2TS* Tel (01508) 530238 E-mail james.nash8@btopenworld.com

NASH, James David Gifford. b 76. New Coll Ox MEng98. Wycliffe Hall Ox BTh03. **d** 03. C Plymouth St Andr and St Paul Stonehouse *Ex* from 03. *117 Lipson Road, Plymouth PL4 7NQ* Tel (01752) 661334 E-mail james.nash@wycliffe.ox.ac.uk

NASH, Paul. See NASH, William Paul

NASH, Paul. b 59. WMMTC 94. **d** 97 **p** 98. C Aston SS Pet and Paul *Birm* 97-02; Asst Chapl Birm Children's Hosp NHS Trust from 02; Tutor St Jo Coll Nottm from 02. *13 Jaffray Road, Birmingham B24 8AZ* Tel 0121-384 6034 E-mail paulandsal@msn.com

NASH, Paul Alexander. b 20. Glouc Th Course 73. **d** 76 **p** 76. NSM Coleford w Staunton *Glouc* 76-88; Perm to Offic from 98. *16 Orchard Road, Coleford GL16 8AU* Tel (01594) 832758

NASH, Reginald Frank. b 15. **d** 66 **p** 67. C Glouc St Jas *Glouc* 66-69; P-in-c Sharpness 69-75; V Dymock w Donnington 75-77; R Dymock w Donnington and Kempley 77-80; rtd 80; Perm to Offic *Glouc* 80-94. *Holcombe Glen Cottage, Minchinhampton, Stroud GL6 9AJ* Tel (01453) 835635

NASH, Richard Edward. b 10. Westcott Ho Cam 54. **d** 56 **p** 57. C Weymouth H Trin *Sarum* 56-59; R Graffham w Woolavington *Chich* 59-65; P-in-c Lewes St Thos and All SS 65-68; V Eridge Green 68-72; R Winterborne Came *Sarum* 73-75; P-in-c Stinsford 73-75; rtd 75. *Manormead, Tilford Road, Hindhead GU26 6RA* Tel (01428) 602577

NASH, Robin Louis. b 51. Open Univ BA87 SBStJ. Aston Tr Scheme 80 Chich Th Coll 82. **d** 84 **p** 85. C Lymington *Win* 84-86; C Andover w Foxcott 86-90; R Kegworth *Leic* 90-01; P-in-c Bournemouth St Alb *Win* from 01. *St Alban's Vicarage, 17 Linwood Road, Bournemouth BH9 1DW* Tel (01202) 534193

NASH, The Ven Trevor Gifford. b 30. Clare Coll Cam BA53 MA57. Cuddesdon Coll 53. **d** 55 **p** 56. C Cheshunt *St Alb* 55-57; CF (TA) 56-61; C Kingston All SS *S'wark* 57-61; C Stevenage *St Alb* 61-63; V Leagrave 63-67; Dir Luton Samaritans 66-67; Chapl St Geo Hosp Lon 67-73; R Win St Lawr and St Maurice w St Swithun *Win* 73-82; Bp's Adv Min of Healing 73-98; P-in-c Win H Trin 77-82; RD Win 75-82; Hon Can Win Cathl from 80; Adn Basingstoke 82-90; Acorn Trust Exec Co-ord 90-97; Pres Guild of Health 92-97; Warden Guild of St Raphael 95-98; Perm to Offic *Win* from 95; rtd 97; Hon Chapl Win Cathl *Win* from 98. *The Corner Stone, 50B Hyde Street, Winchester SO23 7DY* Tel (01962) 861759

NASH, William Henry. b 31. Oak Hill Th Coll 58. **d** 61 **p** 62. C New Milverton *Cov* 61-64; C Toxteth Park St Philemon w St Silas *Liv* 64-67; V Bryn 67-76; NW Area Sec CPAS 76-82; V Penn Fields *Lich* 82-99; rtd 99; Perm to Offic *Lich* from 01. *29 Peterdale Drive, Penn, Wolverhampton WV4 5NY* Tel (01902) 344745

NASH, William Paul. b 48. St Mich Coll Llan 86. **d** 87 **p** 88. C Pembroke Dock *St D* 87-89; P-in-c Llawhaden w Bletherston and Llanycefn 89-90; V 90-92; P-in-c E Brixton St Jude *S'wark* 92-96; V 96-99; V Cwmaman *St D* from 99. *The Vicarage, Vicarage Road, Twyn, Ammanford SA18 1JQ* Tel (01269) 822426

NASH-WILLIAMS, Barbara Ruth. b 66. Lanc Univ BA88. EAMTC 96. **d** 99 **p** 00. C Tettenhall Wood and Perton *Lich* 99-02. *The Rectory, Tibberton, Newport TF10 8NL* Tel (01952) 551063 E-mail barnw@fish.co.uk

NASH-WILLIAMS, Mark Christian Victor. b 64. Trin Hall Cam BA86 MA90 PGCE87. Qu Coll Birm BD01. **d** 02. C Edgmond w Kynnersley and Preston Wealdmoors *Lich* from 02. *The Rectory, Tibberton, Newport TF10 8NN* Tel (01952) 551063 E-mail mnw@fish.co.uk

NASH-WILLIAMS, Canon Piers le Sor Victor. b 35. Trin Hall Cam BA57 MA61. Cuddesdon Coll 59. **d** 61 **p** 62. C Milton *Win* 61-64; Asst Chapl Eton Coll 64-66; Perm to Offic *Chich* 66-68; C Furze Platt *Ox* 69-72; V Newbury St Geo Wash Common 72-73; TV Newbury 73-91; R Ascot Heath 91-01; Hon Can Ch Ch 01; rtd 01; Perm to Offic from 02. *18 Chiltern Close, Newbury RG14 6SZ* Tel (01635) 31762 E-mail pnashwilliams@tesco.net

NASON, David. b 44. Open Univ BA92 ACA68 FCA78. Ripon Coll Cuddesdon 84. **d** 86 **p** 87. C Banstead *Guildf* 86-89; PV Chich Cathl *Chich* from 89; Chapl Prebendal Sch Chich from 89. *1 St Richard's Walk, Canon Lane, Chichester PO19 1QA* Tel (01243) 775615

NASORO, Howard Chimvano. b 64. Zomba Th Coll 85 Qu Coll Birm BA01. **d** 88 **p** 89. Malawi 88-92; S Balaka 88-89; C St Paul's Cathl 90-92; Acting Dean 92-94; R S Highlands 94-98; R Zomba St Geo and Teacher Zomba Th Coll from 98. *Address temp unknown* E-mail howardnasoro@hotmail.com

NATERS, Charles James Reginald. b 20. Selw Coll Cam BA45 MA47. Coll of Resurr Mirfield 46. **d** 47 **p** 48. C Ardwick St Benedict *Man* 47-52; SSJE from 54; S Africa 59-68; Lic to

Offic *Ox* 69-76; *Lon* 76-85 and from 88; *Leic* 85-88; Superior Gen SSJE from 91. *St Edward's House, 22 Great College Street, London SW1P 3QA* Tel (020) 7222 9234

NATHANAEL, Brother. *See* THOMPSON, Kenneth

NATHANAEL, Martin Moses. b 43. Lon Univ BEd73 K Coll Lon MTh77. Ripon Coll Cuddesdon 77. **d** 79 **p** 80. C Hampton All SS *Lon* 79-82; P-in-c Kensal Town St Thos w St Andr and St Phil 82-83; Hd Div Bp Stopford Sch Lon 83-91; TV Tring *St Alb* 91-00; rtd 00. *23D High Street, Puckeridge, Ware SG11 1RN* Tel (01920) 822957 E-mail martinascend@aol.com

NATHANIEL, Garth Edwin Peter. b 61. Brunel Univ BTh99. Lon Bible Coll 96. **d** 98 **p** 99. NSM Hanwell St Mary w St Chris *Lon* 98-99; C Lt Stanmore St Lawr 99-01; P-in-c Brockmoor *Worc* from 02. *5 Leys Road, Brockmoor, Brierley Hill DY5 3UR* Tel (01384) 263327 Mobile 07710-125101 E-mail garthnathaniel@freeuk.co.uk

NATHANIEL, Ivan Wasim. Punjab Univ MA65. Bp's Coll Calcutta 59. **d** 62 **p** 64. India 62-68; C Newland St Aug *York* 68-70; Hon C Crawley *Chich* 70-98; Chapl H Trin Sch Crawley 76-97; Hd of Relig Studies 76-97; Perm to Offic *Chich* from 97. *13 Haywards, Crawley RH10 3TR* Tel (01293) 882932

NATTRASS, Elizabeth Jane. b 59. Carl and Blackb Dioc Tr Inst 97. **d** 00 **p** 01. C Dalston w Cumdivock, Raughton Head and Wreay *Carl* 00-03; C Barrow St Aid from 03. *St Aidan's Vicarage, 31 Middle Hill, Barrow-in-Furness LA13 9HD* Tel (01229) 830445

NATTRASS, Michael Stuart. b 41. CBE98. Man Univ BA62. Cuddesdon Coll 62. **d** 64 **p** 65. C Easington Colliery *Dur* 64-65; C Silksworth 65-68; Perm to Offic *S'well* 68-72; Lic to Offic *Dur* 72-76; Perm to Offic *Lon* 76-78; Hon C Pinner from 78. *81 Cecil Park, Pinner HA5 5HL* Tel (020) 8866 0217 Fax 8930 0622 E-mail msn@81cecilpark.freeserve.co.uk

NAUDÉ, John Donald. b 62. Ridley Hall Cam 95. **d** 97 **p** 98. C Kettering Ch the King *Pet* 97-00; C Wellingborough All Hallows from 00. *20 Ribble Close, Wellingborough NN8 5XJ* Tel 01933 679688 E-mail johnnaude@tinyworld.co.uk

NAUMANN, Canon David Sydney. b 26. Ripon Hall Ox 54. **d** 55 **p** 56. C Herne Bay Ch Ch *Cant* 55-58; Asst Chapl United Sheff Hosps 58-60; V Reculver *Cant* 60-64; Dioc Youth Chapl 63-70; R Eastwell w Boughton Aluph 65-67; V Westwell 65-67; Warden St Gabr Retreat Ho Westgate 68-70; V Littlebourne 70-82; RD E Bridge 78-82; Hon Can Cant Cathl 81-00; R Sandwich 82-91; RD Sandwich 85-90; rtd 91; Perm to Offic *Cant* from 91. *2 The Forrens, The Precincts, Canterbury CT1 2ER* Tel (01227) 458939

NAUNTON, Hugh Raymond. b 38. Whitelands Coll Lon CertEd69 Open Univ BA75. Bernard Gilpin Soc Dur 59 Chich Th Coll 60. **d** 63 **p** 64. C Stanground *Ely* 63-66; NSM Woolwich St Mary w H Trin *S'wark* 66-67; NSM Wandsworth St Anne 67-69 and 71-73; NSM Paddington St Sav *Lon* 69-71; NSM Cuddington *Guildf* 73-78; Hd RE Raynes Park High Sch 69-76; Hd RE Paddingotn Sch 76-78; Sen Teacher and Hd RE Christ's Sch Richmond 79-93; Hon C Cheam Common St Phil *S'wark* 79-95; C Cheam 95-02; Perm to Offic *Guildf* 97-02; TV Selsdon St Jo w St Fran *S'wark* 02-03; rtd 03. *35 Farm Way, Worcester Park KT4 8RZ* E-mail hugh.naunton@ukgateway.net

NAYLOR, Miss Alison Louise. b 68. St Andr Univ MTheol97 Edin Univ MTh99. TISEC 98. **d** 00. C Ayr *Glas* from 00; C Girvan from 00; C Maybole from 00. *16L Fort Street, Ayr KA7 1HU* Tel (01292) 261755 E-mail ali.naylor@clara.co.uk

NAYLOR, Canon Frank. b 36. Lon Univ BA58 Liv Univ MA63. NW Ord Course 75. **d** 75 **p** 76. NSM Eccleston Ch Ch *Liv* 75-92; Asst Dioc Chapl to the Deaf 92-94; Sen Chapl from 94; Hon Can Liv Cathl from 01. *27 Daresbury Road, Eccleston, St Helens WA10 5DR* Tel (01744) 757034

NAYLOR, Ian Frederick. b 47. AKC70 Open Univ BA92 Heythrop Coll Lon MA00 Dip Counselling 03. St Aug Coll Cant 70. **d** 71 **p** 72. C Camberwell St Giles *S'wark* 71-74; OSB 74-86; Chapl RN from 86. *Royal Naval Chaplaincy Service, Room 203, Victory Building, HM Naval Base, Portsmouth PO1 3LS* Tel (023) 9272 7903 Fax 9272 7111

NAYLOR, Ian Stuart. b 63. Wycliffe Hall Ox. **d** 01. C Ipswich St Marg *St E* from 01. *44 Corder Road, Ipswich IP4 2XD* Tel (01473) 231137 Mobile 07712-309848 E-mail ijmjf.naylor@virgin.net

NAYLOR, Canon James Barry. b 50. Lon Univ BSc71 St Benet's Hall Ox BA75. Wycliffe Hall Ox 72. **d** 76 **p** 76. C Catford (Southend) and Downham *S'wark* 76-79; TV 79-82; P-in-c Lewisham St Swithun 82-87; V E Dulwich St Jo 87-97; RD Dulwich 90-97; P-in-c Blythburgh w Reydon *St E* 97-99; P-in-c Frostenden, Henastead, Covehithe etc 97-99; P-in-c Southwold 97-99; P-in-c Uggeshall w Sotherton, Wangford and Henham 97-99; TR Sole Bay 99-02; Chapl Supervisor St Felix Sch Southwold 99-02; Can Res Leic Cathl *Leic* from 02; C The Abbey Leic from 02; C Leic H Spirit from 02. *1 Kirby Road, Leicester LE3 6BD* Tel 0116-262 0788 E-mail barry.cathedral@leicester.anglican.org

NAYLOR, Miss Jean. b 29. Linc Th Coll 77. **dss** 79 **d** 87. Charlton St Luke w H Trin *S'wark* 79-84; Crofton Park St Hilda w St Cypr 84-89; Par Dn 87-89; rtd 89; Perm to Offic *Wakef* from 89. *12 Winter Terrace, Barnsley S75 2ES* Tel (01226) 204767

NAYLOR, John Watson. b 26. Trin Hall Cam BA52 MA56. Ripon Hall Ox 64. **d** 66 **p** 67. C Newc St Andr *Newc* 66-69; C Otterburn w Elsdon and Horsley w Byrness 69-72; R Husborne Crawley w Ridgmont *St Alb* 72-76; Chapl Caldicott Sch Farnham Royal 76-80; P-in-c Chollerton w Thockrington *Newc* 80-82; R Chollerton w Birtley and Thockrington 82-91; rtd 91; Perm to Offic *Newc* from 91. *Abbeyfield House, Bellingham, Hexham NE48 2BS* Tel (01434) 220106

NAYLOR, Canon Peter Aubrey. b 33. Kelham Th Coll 54 Ely Th Coll 57. **d** 58 **p** 59. C Shepherd's Bush St Steph *Lon* 58-62; C Portsea N End St Mark *Portsm* 62-66; Chapl HM Borstal Portsm 64-66; V Foley Park *Worc* 66-74; V Maidstone All SS w St Phil and H Trin *Cant* 74-81; P-in-c Tovil 79-81; V Maidstone All SS and St Phil w Tovil 81-91; Hon Can Cant Cathl 79-93; RD Sutton 80-86; R Biddenden and Smarden 91-93; P-in-c Leic St Marg and All SS *Leic* 93-96; P-in-c Leic St Aug 93-96; TR The Abbey Leic 96; rtd 98; Perm to Offic *Chich* 98-02; P-in-c Crowborough St Jo from 02. *St John's Vicarage, St John's Road, Crowborough TN6 1RZ* Tel (01892) 654600

NAYLOR, Peter Edward. b 30. Linc Th Coll 58. **d** 61 **p** 62. C S Beddington St Mich *S'wark* 61-64; V S Lambeth St Ann 64-77; V Nork *Guildf* 77-90; R Ecton *Pet* 90-97; Warden Ecton Ho 90-97; rtd 97; Perm to Offic *Ely* 97-01. *51 avenue Du Bezet, 64000, Pau, France*

NAYLOR, Peter Henry. b 41. MIMechE HND64. Chich Th Coll 64. **d** 67 **p** 68. C Filton *Bris* 67-70; C Brixham *Ex* 70-72; C Leckhampton St Pet *Glouc* 72-76; V Brockworth 76-94; P-in-c Gt Witcombe 91-94; RD Glouc N 91-94; P-in-c The Ampneys w Driffield and Poulton 94-95; R 95-99; P-in-c Cheltenham Em w St Steph from 99. *The Vicarage, 25 Hatherley Court Road, Cheltenham GL51 5AG* Tel (01242) 523240

NAYLOR, Robert James. b 42. Liv Univ CQSW66. N Ord Course 74. **d** 77 **p** 78. C Aigburth *Liv* 77-80; Soc Resp Officer *Glouc* 80-85; Leonard Cheshire Foundn (Lon) 85-91; Dir The Stable Family Home Trust (Hants) from 91; NSM The Lulworths, Winfrith Newburgh and Chaldon *Sarum* 98-00; P-in-c from 00; RD Purbeck from 02. *The Rectory, West Road, West Lulworth, Wareham BH20 5RY* Tel (01929) 400550

NAYLOR, Russell Stephen. b 45. Leeds Univ BA70 St Chad's Coll Dur DipTh72. Ho of Resurr Mirfield 64. **d** 72 **p** 73. C Chapel Allerton *Ripon* 72-75; Ind Chapl *Liv* 75-81; P-in-c Burtonwood 81-83; V from 83. *The Vicarage, Chapel Lane, Burtonwood, Warrington WA5 4PT* Tel (01925) 225371 E-mail russ-naylor@btinternet.com

NAYLOR, Ms Vivien Frances Damaris. b 55. RGN86 DTM89 New Hall Cam BA78 MA82. Ripon Coll Cuddesdon DipMin93. **d** 93 **p** 94. C Northampton St Jas *Pet* 93-95; Chapl Asst Southn Univ Hosps NHS Trust 95-98; Chapl 98-00; Chapl Addenbrooke's NHS Trust from 00. *Addenbrooke's Hospital, Hills Road, Cambridge CB2 2QQ* Tel (01223) 245151

✠**NAZIR-ALI, The Rt Revd Michael James.** b 49. Karachi Univ BA70 St Edm Hall Ox BLitt74 MLitt81 Fitzw Coll Cam PGCTh72 MLitt77 ACT ThD85 Bath Univ Hon DLitt03 Greenwich Univ Hon DLitt03. Ridley Hall Cam 70. **d** 74 **p** 76 **c** 84. C Cambridge H Sepulchre w St SS *Ely* 74-76; Tutorial Supervisor Th Cam Univ 74-76; Pakistan 76-86; Sen Tutor Karachi Th Coll 76-81; Provost Lahore 81-84; Bp Raiwind 84-86; Asst to Abp Cant 86-89; Co-ord of Studies and Ed Lambeth Conf 86-89; Hon C Ox St Giles and SS Phil and Jas w St Marg *Ox* 86-89; Gen Sec CMS 89-94; Asst Bp S'wark 89-94; Hon C Limpsfield and Titsey 89-94; Can Th Leic Cathl *Leic* 92-94; Bp Roch from 94; Visiting Prof Th and RS Univ of Greenwich from 96; Hon Fell St Edm Hall Ox from 99. *Bishopscourt, Rochester ME1 1TS* Tel (01634) 842721 Fax 831136 E-mail bishops.secretary@rochester.anglican.org

NDAHANI, Ernest Godwin. b 69. St Phil Th Coll Kongwa 93. **d** 96 **p** 98. Teacher St Jo Jun Sem Tanzania 95-02; TV Monkwearmouth *Dur* from 03. *12 Ormesby Road, Sunderland SR6 9HS* Tel 0191-548 5379

✠**NDAYISENGA, The Most Revd Samuel.** Bp Buye; Abp Burundi. *Eglise Episcopale du Burundi, BP 94, Ngozi, Burundi* Tel (Burundi) (30) 2210 Fax 2317 E-mail diocbuye@cbinf.com

✠**NDUNGANE, The Most Revd Winston Hugh Njongonkulu.** b 41. K Coll Lon BD78 AKC78 MTh. St Pet Coll Alice 71. **d** 73 **p** 74 **c** 91. S Africa 73-75 and from 80; C Mitcham St Mark *S'wark* 75-76; C Hammersmith St Pet *Lon* 76-77; C Primrose Hill St Mary w Avenue Road St Paul 77-79; Prin St Bede's Th Coll Umtata 85-87; Prov Exec Officer 87-91; Bp Kimberley and Kuruman 91-96; Abp Cape Town from 96. *Bishopscourt, 16-20 Bishopscourt Drive, Claremont, 7708 South Africa* Tel (0027) (21) 761 2531 Fax 797 1298 or 761 4193 E-mail archbish@bishopscourt-cpsa.org.za

NEAL, Alan. b 27. Trin Coll Bris DipTh84. **d** 84 **p** 85. Hon C Broughty Ferry *Bre* 84-85; P-in-c Dundee St Ninian 85-86; R Annan *Glas* 86-94; R Lockerbie 86-94; rtd 94. *c/o Mr and Mrs Graham Rew, 3 Vallance Drive, Lockerbie DG11 2DU*

NEAL, Canon Anthony Terrence. b 42. BA CertEd. Chich Th Coll 65. **d** 68 **p** 69. C Cross Green St Sav and St Hilda *Ripon* 68-73; NSM Hawksworth Wood 73-78; Asst Chapl & Hd RE Abbey

Grange High Sch Leeds 73-81; NSM Farnley 78-81; Dioc Adv in RE *Truro* 81-85; Children's Officer 85-87; Stewardship Adv 87-88; P-in-c St Erth 81-84; V 84-96; P-in-c Phillack w Gwithian and Gwinear 94-96; P-in-c Hayle 94-96; Hon Can Truro Cathl from 94; TR Godrevy from 96. *The Rectory, Forth an Tewennow, Phillack, Hayle TR27 4QE* Tel (01736) 753541 *or* 754866 Fax 755235 E-mail a.neal1@btinternet.com

NEAL, Canon Christopher Charles. b 47. St Pet Coll Ox BA69. Ridley Hall Cam 69. **d** 72 **p** 73. C Addiscombe St Mary *Cant* 72-76; C Camberley St Paul *Guildf* 76-83; TV 83-86; V Thame w Towersey *Ox* 86-98; TR Thame 98-03; Hon Can Ch Ch from 98; Dir Miss Movement CMS from 03. *CMS, Partnership House, 157 Waterloo Road, London SE1 8XA* Tel (020) 7928 8681 E-mail katrina@stmarys.psa-online.com

NEAL, Miss Frances Mary. b 37. BEd76. S'wark Ord Course 94. **d** 96 **p** 97. NSM Catford (Southend) and Downham *S'wark* from 96. *29 Ballamore Road, Downham, Bromley BR1 5LN* Tel (020) 8698 6616

NEAL, Canon Geoffrey Martin. b 40. AKC63. **d** 64 **p** 65. C Wandsworth St Paul *S'wark* 64-66; USA 66-68; C Reigate St Mark *S'wark* 68-70; P-in-c Wandsworth St Faith 70-72; V 72-75; V Houghton Regis *St Alb* 75-95; Hon Can St Alb 93-95; rtd 00; Perm to Offic *St Alb* from 00. *63 The Moor, Carlton, Bedford MK43 7JS* Tel (01234) 720938

NEAL, James Christian. b 62. Trin Coll Cam BA84 MA88. Coll of Resurr Mirfield 93. **d** 95 **p** 96. C Lt Stanmore St Lawr *Lon* 95-98; C Wood Green St Mich w Bounds Green St Gabr etc from 98. *20 Cornwall Avenue, London N22 7DA* Tel (020) 8881 0484

NEAL, John Edward. b 44. Nottm Univ BTh74. Linc Th Coll 70. **d** 74 **p** 75. C Lee St Marg *S'wark* 74-77; C Clapham St Jo 77; C Clapham Ch Ch and St Jo 77-81; P-in-c Eltham St Barn 81-83; V 83-98; Sub-Dean Eltham 89-91; Sub-Dean Greenwich S 91-97; RD Greenwich S from 97; V Eltham St Jo from 98. *The Vicarage, Sowerby Close, London SE9 6HB* Tel (020) 8850 2731 *or* 8859 1242

NEAL, Mrs Stephanie Kae. b 34. Girton Coll Cam BA56 MA60. Dioc OLM tr scheme 97. **d** 00 **p** 01. OLM Hundred River *St E* from 00. *12 Chartres Piece, Willingham, Beccles NR34 8DA* Tel (01502) 575208

NEAL, Stephen Charles. b 44. K Coll Lon BSc66 MCMI76. N Ord Course 90. **d** 93 **p** 94. C Walmsley *Man* 93-96; P-in-c Bolton St Matt w St Barn 96-98; TV Halliwell 98-02; Chapl Bolton Hospice from 02. *47 The Woodlands, Lostock, Bolton BL6 4JD* Tel (01204) 496070 *or* 364375 E-mail steveneal@themutual.net

NEALE, Alan James Robert. b 52. LSE BSc(Econ)73. Wycliffe Hall Ox BA76 MA81. **d** 77 **p** 78. C Plymouth St Andr w St Paul and St Geo *Ex* 77-80; C Portswood Ch Ch *Win* 80-82; V Stanstead Abbots *St Alb* 82-85; Asst Master Chelmsf Hall Sch Eastbourne 85-88; USA from 88. *390 Indian Avenue, Middletown, RI 02842, USA*

NEALE, Andrew Jackson. b 58. Oak Hill Th Coll 97. **d** 99 **p** 00. C Harold Hill St Geo *Chelmsf* 99-02; C Bentley Common, Kelvedon Hatch and Navestock 02-03; TV Chigwell and Chigwell Row from 03. *The Vicarage, Romford Road, Chigwell IG7 4QD* Tel (020) 8501 5150 E-mail andy@neale2pray.freeserve.co.uk

NEALE, David. b 50. Lanchester Poly BSc72. St Mich Coll Llan BD83. **d** 83 **p** 84. Min Can St Woolos Cathl *Mon* 83-87; Chapl St Woolos Hosp Newport 85-87; R Blaina and Nantyglo *Mon* 87-91; Video and Tech Officer Bd of Miss 91-01; TV Cyncoed 99-01; Creative Resources Officer 01-03; V Maindee from 03. *St John's Vicarage, 25 St John's Road, Newport NP19 8GR* Tel (01633) 674155 E-mail dneale@ntlworld.com

NEALE, Geoffrey Arthur. b 41. Brasted Th Coll 61 St Aid Birkenhead 63. **d** 65 **p** 66. C Stoke *Cov* 65-68; C Fareham H Trin *Portsm* 68-71; TV 71-72; R Binstead 72-77; TR Bottesford w Ashby *Linc* 77-80; V Horncastle w Low Toynton 80-90; V Brigg 90-95; V Blockley w Aston Magna and Bourton on the Hill *Glouc* 95-01; Local Min Officer 95-01; V Heath and Reach *St Alb* from 01. *The Vicarage, 2 Reach Lane, Heath and Reach, Leighton Buzzard LU7 0AL* Tel (01525) 237633 Mobile 07703-174761 E-mail geoffneale@msn.com

NEALE, Hannah. b 40. SEITE. **d** 99 **p** 00. NSM Mitcham St Mark *S'wark* from 99. *3D Grenfell Road, Mitcham CR4 2BZ* Tel (020) 8646 4752

NEALE, Canon James Edward McKenzie (Eddie). b 38. Selw Coll Cam BA61. Clifton Th Coll 61. **d** 63 **p** 64. C Everton St Ambrose w St Tim *Liv* 63-72; Relig Adv BBC Radio Merseyside 72-76; V Bestwood St Matt *S'well* 76-86; Dioc Urban Officer 86-91; V Nottingham St Mary and St Cath 91-03; Hon Can S'well Minster 91-03; rtd 03. *Church Cottage, Church Lane, Maplebeck, Nottingham NG22 0BS* Tel (01636) 636449 E-mail jemneale@hotmail.com

NEALE, Mrs Jan Celia. b 42. EMMTC 92. **d** 92 **p** 94. C Gt and Lt Coates w Bradley *Linc* 92-96; TV 96-01; TV Chambersbury *St Alb* from 01. *St Benedict's Vicarage, Peascroft Road, Hemel Hempstead HP3 8EP* Tel (01442) 243934

✠**NEALE, The Rt Revd John Robert Geoffrey.** b 26. AKC54 St Boniface Warminster 54. **d** 55 **p** 56 **c** 74. C St Helier *S'wark*

55-58; Chapl Ardingly Coll 58-62; Recruitment Sec CACTM 63-66; ACCM 66-68; R Hascombe *Guildf* 68-74; Can Missr and Dir Post-Ord Tr 68-74; Hon Can Guildf Cathl 68-74; Adn Wilts *Sarum* 74-80; Suff Bp Ramsbury 74-81; Area Bp Ramsbury 81-88; Can and Preb Sarum Cathl 74-88; Sec Partnership for World Miss 89-91; Asst Bp S'wark 89-91; Asst Bp Lon 89-91; rtd 91; Asst Bp B & W from 91; Hon Asst Bp Bris from 92; Hon Asst Bp Glouc from 94. *26 Prospect, Corsham SN13 9AF* Tel (01249) 712557

NEALE, Martyn William. b 57. G&C Coll Cam BA78 MA82. Ripon Coll Cuddesdon 78. **d** 81 **p** 82. C Perry Hill St Geo *S'wark* 81-83; C Purley St Mark 83-85; V Abbey Wood 85-97; V Hawley H Trin *Guildf* from 97; V Minley from 97. *The Vicarage, Hawley, Blackwater, Camberley GU17 9BN* Tel (01276) 35287 E-mail martynneale@freenetname.co.uk

NEAUM, Canon David. b 12. Lich Th Coll 34. **d** 37 **p** 38. C Burton All SS *Lich* 37-39; C Cannock 39-43; R Kingstone w Gratwich 43-46; R Leigh 46-52; Tristan da Cunha 52-56; S Rhodesia 56-65; Rhodesia 65-80; Zimbabwe 80-81; St Helena 81-84; rtd 84; Australia from 84. *St John's Rectory, 225 Beechworth, Wodonga, Vic, Australia 3690* Tel (0061) (2) 6024 2053

NEAVE, Garry Reginald. b 51. Leic Univ BA72 MA73 PGCE74 DipMgt MCMI. S'wark Ord Course DipRS DipPSE. **d** 82 **p** 83. Hon C Harlow St Mary Magd *Chelmsf* 82-87 and from 92; Chapl Harlow Tertiary Coll 84-99; Hon C St Mary-at-Latton *Chelmsf* 87-92; Dir Student Services and Admin W Herts Coll from 99; Perm to Offic *St Alb* from 00. *35 Perry Springs, Harlow CM17 9DQ, or West Hertfordshire College, Hempstead Road, Watford WD1 3EZ* Tel (01279) 411775 *or* (01923) 812000

NEECH, Canon Alan Summons. b 15. Dur Univ LTh37. Tyndale Hall Bris 34. **d** 39 **p** 40. BCMS 39-81; India 39-66; Can Lucknow 64-66; Overseas Sec BCMS 64-66; Gen Sec 66-81; Hon Can Cen Tanganyika from 72; Hon C Slough *Ox* 75-81; rtd 80; RD Loddon *Nor* 85-90; Perm to Offic from 90. *The Gardens Cottage, Rockland St Mary, Norwich NR14 7HQ* Tel (01508) 538519

NEED, The Very Revd Philip Alan. b 54. AKC75. Chich Th Coll 76. **d** 77 **p** 78. C Clapham Ch Ch and St Jo *S'wark* 77-79; C Luton All SS w St Pet *St Alb* 80-83; V Harlow St Mary Magd *Chelmsf* 83-89; P-in-c Chaddesden St Phil *Derby* 89-91; Bp's Dom Chapl *Chelmsf* 91-96; R Bocking St Mary from 96; Dean Bocking from 96; RD Braintree from 00. *The Deanery, Deanery Hill, Braintree CM7 5SR* Tel (01376) 324887 E-mail philipneed@bocking81.freeserve.co.uk

NEEDHAM, Miss Patricia. b 32. **d** 87 **p** 94. Par Dn Warmsworth *Sheff* 87-89; Par Dn Norton Woodseats St Chad 89-92; Chapl Beauchief Abbey from 89; rtd 92; Perm to Offic *Sheff* from 01. *14 Dalewood Drive, Sheffield S8 0EA* Tel 0114-262 0250

NEEDHAM, Brother Peter Douglas. b 56. Chich Th Coll 86. **d** 88 **p** 88. SSF from 80; C S Moor *Dur* 88-90; Chapl RN 91-93; Lic to Offic *Newc* 91-96; Lic to Offic *Lon* 97-99; P-in-c Grimethorpe *Wakef* from 02. *St Luke's Vicarage, High Street, Grimethorpe, Barnsley S72 7JA* Tel (01226) 717561 E-mail neddyneedham@mcmail.com

NEEDLE, Paul Robert. b 45. Lon Univ DipTh70. Oak Hill Th Coll 67. **d** 70 **p** 71. C Gt Horton *Bradf* 70-74; C Pudsey St Lawr 74-77; Chapl St Luke's Hosp Bradf 78-80; Hon C Horton *Bradf* 78-80; NSM Irthlingborough *Pet* 87-90; NSM Gt w Lt Addington 90-94; NSM Gt w Lt Addington and Woodford 94-98; Bp's Media Adv from 97; NSM Higham Ferrers w Chelveston from 02. *106 Wharf Road, Higham Ferrers, Rushden NN10 8BH* Tel and fax (01933) 312800 Mobile 07802-731751 E-mail paulneedle@aol.com

NEEDS, Michael John. b 42. Open Univ BA82 Univ of Wales (Swansea) MSc84 PhD87. Wycliffe Hall Ox 91. **d** 93 **p** 94. C Aberystwyth *St D* 93-96; R Llanllwchaearn and Llanina from 96. *The Rectory, Llandysul Road, New Quay SA45 9RE* Tel (01545) 560059 Fax as telephone E-mail michael@mneeds.freeserve.co.uk

NEELY, Canon William George. b 32. Lon Univ BD62 QUB PhD. **d** 56 **p** 57. C Cregagh *D & D* 56-62; C-in-c Mt Merrion 62-68; I 68-76; Dioc Missr (Down) 70-76; Can Down Cathl 74-76; I Kilcooley w Littleton, Crohane and Killenaule *C & O* 76-84; P-in-c Fertagh 79-84; I Keady w Armaghbreague and Derrynoose *Arm* from 84; Tutor for Aux Min (Arm) from 86; Dir Post-Ord Tr from 86; Preb Swords St Patr Cathl Dublin from 97. *31 Crossmore Road, Keady, Armagh BT60 3JY* Tel (028) 3753 1230

NEILAND, Paul. b 62. Dip Counselling & Psychotherapy 96 Wm Glasser Inst Dub RTCert96. St Pet Coll Wexford 80 CITC 00. **d** 01 **p** 02. NSM Enniscorthy w Clone, Clonmore, Monart etc *C & O* from 01. *Butlerstown, Killinick, Co Wexford, Irish Republic* Tel (00353) (53) 35701 Mobile (87) 242 2842 Fax (53) 41784

NEILL, Barbara June. b 39. St Jo Coll Nottm. **d** 00 **p** 01. NSM Bestwood Park w Rise Park *S'well* from 00. *42 Haydn Road, Sherwood, Nottingham NG5 2JU* Tel 0115-962 1406

NEILL, James Purdon. b 41. Lon Univ DipTh63. Oak Hill Th Coll 60. **d** 64 **p** 65. C Kendal St Thos *Carl* 64-68; Chapl Park Hill Flats Sheff 68-71; P-in-c Mansfield St Jo *S'well* 71-77; V

Nottingham St Ann w Em from 77. *St Ann's Vicarage, 17 Robin Hood Chase, Nottingham NG3 4EY* Tel 0115-950 5471

✠NEILL, The Most Revd John Robert Winder. b 45. TCD BA66 MA69 Jes Coll Cam BA68 MA72. Ridley Hall Cam 67. **d** 69 **p** 70 **c** 86. C Glenageary *D & G* 69-71; Lect CITC 70-71 and 82-84; Dioc Registrar (Ossory, Ferns and Leighlin) *C & O* 71-74; Bp's V, Lib and Chapter Registrar Kilkenny Cathl 71-74; I Abbeystrewry *C, C & R* 74-78; I Dublin St Bart w Leeson Park *D & G* 78-84; Chapl Community of St Jo the Ev 78-84; Dean Waterford *C & O* 84-86; Prec Lismore Cathl 84-86; Adn Waterford 84-86; I Waterford w Killea, Drumcannon and Dunhill 84-86; Bp T, K & A 86-97; Bp C & O 97-02; Abp Dublin *D & G* from 02. *The See House, 17 Temple Road, Milltown, Dublin 6, Irish Republic* Tel (00353) (1) 497 7849 Fax 497 6355 E-mail archbishop@dublin.anglican.org

NEILL, Richard Walter. b 67. Wadh Coll Ox BA89 Em Coll Cam BA92. Westcott Ho Cam CTM93. **d** 93 **p** 94. C Abbots Langley *St Alb* 93-97; C Wisley w Pyrford *Guildf* 97-00; V Winkfield and Cranbourne *Ox* from 00. *The Vicarage, Winkfield Street, Winkfield, Windsor SL4 4SW* Tel (01344) 882322 E-mail neill.hall@care4free.net

NEILL, Robert Chapman. b 51. Lon Univ BD82. CITC 77. **d** 77 **p** 78. C Lurgan Ch the Redeemer *D & D* 77-82; I Tullylish 82-88; I Mt Merrion 88-98; I Drumbo from 98. *Drumbo Rectory, 5 Pinehill Road, Ballylesson, Belfast BT8 8LA* Tel (028) 9082 6225

NEILL, Stephen Mahon. b 69. TCD BA91. CITC 91. **d** 93 **p** 94. C Monkstown *D & G* 93-95; Dom Chapl to Bp of Killaloe and Clonfert *L & K* from 95; C Limerick City 95-98; I Cloughjordan w Borrisokane etc from 98. *Modreeny Rectory, Cloughjordan, Co Tipperary, Irish Republic* Tel and fax (00353) (505) 42183 Mobile 87-2355912 E-mail smneill@eircom.net

NEILL, The Ven William Barnet. b 30. TCD BA61. **d** 63 **p** 64. C Belfast St Clem *D & D* 63-66; C Dundonald 66-72; I Drumgath 72-80; I Drumgooland 76-80; I Mt Merrion 80-83; I Dromore Cathl 83-97; Adn Dromore 85-97; rtd 97. *10 Cairnshill Court, Saintfield Road, Belfast BT8 4TX* Tel (028) 9079 2969

NEILL, William Benjamin Alan. b 46. Open Univ BA76. CITC 68. **d** 71 **p** 72. C Dunmurry *Conn* 71-74; C Coleraine 75-77; C Dublin St Ann w St Steph *D & G* 77-78; I Convoy w Monellan and Donaghmore *D & R* 78-81; I Faughanvale 81-86; I Waterford w Killea, Drumcannon and Dunhill *C & O* 86-97; Dean Waterford 86-97; Prec Lismore Cathl 86-97; Prec Cashel Cathl 87-97; Can Ossory and Leighlin Cathls 96-97; I Dalkey St Patr *D & G* from 97. *The Rectory, Dalkey, Dun Laoghaire, Co Dublin, Irish Republic* Tel (00353) (1) 280 3369

NELLIST, Canon Valerie Ann. b 48. SRN69 SCM71. St And Dioc Tr Course 87. **d** 90 **p** 94. NSM W Fife Team Min *St And* from 90; Hon Can St Ninian's Cathl Perth from 97. *28 Glamis Gardens, Dalgety Bay, Dunfermline KY11 9TD* Tel (01383) 824066 Fax 824668 E-mail rnellist44@aol.com

NELMES, Mrs Christine. b 41. St Mary's Coll Cheltenham Dip Teaching63 UWE BA97. S Dios Minl Tr Scheme 92. **d** 95 **p** 96. NSM Winscombe *B & W* 95-99; Perm to Offic 00-03; P-in-c Mark w Allerton from 03. *Yarrow Farm, Yarrow Road, Mark, Highbridge TA9 4LW* Tel (01278) 641650

NELSON, Canon Allen James. b 29. CITC 53. **d** 55 **p** 56. C Glenageary *D & G* 55-57; C Dublin Clontarf 57-60; I Bailieborough w Mullagh *K, E & A* 60-75; P-in-c Knockbride 66-72; P-in-c Knockbride w Shercock 72-75; I Julianstown w Colpe *M & K* 75-81; I Julianstown and Colpe w Drogheda and Duleek 81-98; Dioc Glebes Sec from 81; Can Meath from 84; rtd 98. *21 Seaview Park, Mornington, Co Meath, Irish Republic* Tel (00353) (41) 982 7044 E-mail jimnelson@eircom.net

NELSON, Bishop of. See EATON, The Rt Revd Derek Lionel

NELSON, Christopher James. b 57. Preston Poly HNC80 Nottm Univ BTh88. Aston Tr Scheme 83 St Jo Coll Nottm 85. **d** 88 **p** 89. C Blackpool St Thos *Blackb* 88-90; C Altham w Clayton le Moors 90-92; V Knuzden 92-01; V Penwortham St Mary from 01. *St Mary's Vicarage, Cop Lane, Penwortham, Preston PR1 0SR* Tel (01772) 743143 E-mail kitnel@breathemail.net or kitnel@btinternet.com

NELSON, Gibson. See NELSON, Robert Gibson

NELSON, Graham William. b 61. Birm Univ CYCW85. St Jo Coll Nottm BA91. **d** 91 **p** 92. C Pype Hayes *Birm* 91-93; C Lancaster St Mary *Blackb* 94-97; Chapl HM Pris Lanc Castle 94-97; P-in-c Preston St Jude w St Paul *Blackb* from 97; P-in-c Preston St Oswald from 01. *St Jude's Vicarage, 97 Garstang Road, Preston PR1 1LD* Tel (01772) 252987

NELSON, Jane. b 42. **d** 94 **p** 99. Par Dn Muchalls *Bre* 94-99; C from 99; Asst Chapl Grampian Healthcare NHS Trust 93-97. *4 St Michael's Road, Newtonhill, Stonehaven AB39 3RW* Tel (01569) 730967

NELSON, Julie. b 52. St Aid Coll Dur BA73 Ex Univ MA95. SW Minl Tr Course 92. **d** 95 **p** 96. NSM Tavistock and Gulworthy *Ex* 95-01; Germany from 01. *21 Deer Park Road, Tavistock PL19 9HG* Tel (01822) 612736

NELSON, Kenneth Edmund. b 10. St Jo Coll Cam BA33 MA36. Qu Coll Birm 46. **d** 47 **p** 48. C Huddersfield St Pet *Wakef* 47-50;

C Pocklington *York* 50-52; R Brotton Parva 52-58; V Sheriff Hutton 58-65; Aden 65-67; P-in-c Crayke w Brandsby and Yearsley 67-68; R 68-78; rtd 78; P-in-c Wold Newton *York* 78-81; Perm to Offic from 81. *65 West Hall Garth, South Cave, Brough HU15 2HA* Tel (01430) 423123

NELSON, Michael. b 44. Newc Univ Aus BSc68 BA72 St Jo Coll Cam BA74 Cam Univ MA78. Westcott Ho Cam 74. **d** 75 **p** 76. Perm to Offic *Newc* 75; Australia from 77. *185 Bourbong Street, Chapel Hill, Qld, Australia 4069* Tel (0061) (7) 3720 1283 Fax 3720 1620 E-mail mnelson@hradvantage.com.au

NELSON, Canon Michael. b 44. Lon Univ BD66. Coll of Resurr Mirfield 66. **d** 68 **p** 69. C Newbold w Dunston *Derby* 68-72; C N Gosforth *Newc* 72-77; V Seaton Hirst 77-83; V Blyth St Mary 83-93; P-in-c Horton 86-87; RD Bedlington 88-93; R Hexham 93-03; Hon Can Newc Cathl from 94; P-in-c Ovingham from 03; RD Corbridge from 03. *St Mary's Vicarage, 2 Burnside Close, Ovingham, Prudhoe NE42 6BS* Tel (01661) 832273 E-mail canon.michael.nelson@care4free.net

NELSON, Sister Norma Margaret. b 34. Liv Univ DASS77 CQSW77. CA Tr Coll IDC60. **d** 93 **p** 94. TD Kirkby *Liv* 93-94; TV 94-95; rtd 95; Perm to Offic *Liv* from 95. *15 Pateley Close, Kirkby, Liverpool L32 4UT* Tel 0151-545 0037

NELSON, Paul John. b 52. Nottm Univ BCombStuds84. Linc Th Coll 81. **d** 84 **p** 85. C Waltham Cross *St Alb* 84-87; C Sandridge 87-90; V 90-98; R Hundred River *St E* from 98; RD Beccles and S Elmham from 03. *The Rectory, Moll's Lane, Brampton, Beccles NR34 8DB* Tel (01502) 575859

NELSON, Peter Joseph. b 46. Nottm Poly BSc73 Man Univ CertRS85. Nor Bapt Coll 82 NEOC 99. **d** 99 **p** 99. In Bapt Min 85-99; Chapl R Hull Hosps NHS Trust 94-99; Chapl Hull and E Yorks Hosps NHS Trust 99-02; Sen Chapl from 02; NSM Sutton St Mich *York* from 99. *19 Swallowfield Drive, Hull HU4 6UG* Tel (01482) 568364 Pager 01399-113732115

NELSON, Ralph Archbold. b 27. St Cuth Soc Dur BA50. Bps' Coll Cheshunt 50. **d** 52 **p** 53. C Penwortham St Mary *Blackb* 52-57; C Eglingham *Newc* 57-58; V Featherstone *Wakef* 58-80; V Kirkham *Blackb* 80-92; RD Kirkham 88-91; rtd 92; Perm to Offic *Blackb* from 92. *6 Blundell Lane, Penwortham, Preston PR1 0EA* Tel (01772) 742573

NELSON, Robert Gibson. b 34. ALCD61. **d** 61 **p** 62. C Isleworth St Mary *Lon* 61-64; C-in-c Reading St Barn CD *Ox* 64-69; Australia 69-72; V Guernsey St Jo *Win* 72-78; R Guernsey Ste Marie du Castel 78-86; V Guernsey St Matt 84-86; rtd 86; Perm to Offic *Win* from 86. *Le Petit Feugre, Clos des Mielles, Castel, Guernsey GY5 7XV* Tel (01481) 52726

NELSON, Robert Towers. b 43. MSOSc Liv Coll of Tech BSc65. NW Ord Course 76. **d** 79 **p** 80. NSM Liv Our Lady and St Nic w St Anne *Liv* 79-83; NSM Liscard St Thos *Ches* 83-87; P-in-c from 87; Ind Missr from 87; Asst Sec SOSc from 89; Perm to Offic *Liv* 89-98; Chapl Wirral and W Cheshire Community NHS Trust 98-03; Chapl Cheshire and Wirral Partnership NHS Trust from 03. *5 Sedbergh Road, Wallasey CH44 2BR* Tel 0151-630 2830

NELSON, Roger Charles. b 44. ATI74 Newc Univ LLB66 Solicitor 69. Cant Sch of Min 88. **d** 91 **p** 92. NSM Deal St Leon and St Rich and Sholden *Cant* 91-96; NSM Northbourne and Betteshanger w Tilmanstone w Ham and Ripple and Sutton by Dover 96-97; Perm to Offic *Cant* 97-00; *Wakef* from 01. *26 Meal Hill Road, Holme, Holmfirth HD9 2QQ* Tel (01484) 680309 E-mail nelsontrap@aol.com

NELSON, Warren David. b 38. TCD BA67. **d** 68 **p** 69. C Belfast St Mich *Conn* 68-70; I Kilcooley w Littleton, Crohane, Killenaule etc *C & O* 70-76; Chapl Coalbrook Fellowship Hosp Ho Thurles 76-94; Perm to Offic (Cashel, Waterford and Lismore) 93-94; I Lurgan w Billis, Killinkere and Munterconnaught *K, E & A* 94-98; rtd 98. *6 Mucklagh, Tullamore, Co Offaly, Irish Republic* Tel (00353) (506) 24218 E-mail wnelson@eircom.net

NELSON, William. b 38. Oak Hill Th Coll 74. **d** 76 **p** 77. C Hensingham *Carl* 76-81; V Widnes St Paul *Liv* 81-89; R Higher Openshaw *Man* from 89; AD Ardwick 96-00. *St Clement's Rectory, Ashton Old Road, Manchester M11 1HJ* Tel 0161-370 1538

NENER, Canon Thomas Paul Edgar. b 42. FRCSEd71 FRCS72 Liv Univ MB, ChB. Coll of Resurr Mirfield 78. **d** 80 **p** 81. C Warrington St Elphin *Liv* 80-83; V Haydock St Jas 83-95; V W Derby St Jo from 95; Hon Can Liv Cathl from 95. *St John's Vicarage, Tuebrook, Liverpool L13 7EA* Tel 0151-228 2023

NENO, David Edward. b 60. SS Mark & Jo Coll Plymouth BA85. Ripon Coll Cuddesdon 85. **d** 88 **p** 89. C Chapel Allerton *Ripon* 88-91; C Acton St Mary *Lon* 91-94; V Kingsbury H Innocents 94-02; R Brondesbury Ch Ch and St Laur from 02. *The Rectory, Chevening Road, London NW6 6DU* Tel (020) 8969 5961 Mobile 07976-905294 E-mail d.s.neno@dial.pipex.com

NESBITT, Charles Howard. b 09. St Jo Coll Dur LTh34 BA35. Bp Wilson Coll 31. **d** 35 **p** 36. C Liv St Chris Norris Green *Liv* 35-37; C Blackb St Matt *Blackb* 37-41; C Gt Harwood St Jo 41-46; V Wrightington 46-58; I Baxenden 58-68; V Stalmine 68-74; rtd 75. *c/o Miss M A Nesbitt, 20 Craiglockhart View, Edinburgh EH14 1BX* Tel 0131-443 1768

NESBITT, Heather Hastings. b 48. S'wark Ord Course 88. **d** 90 **p** 94. Par Dn Camberwell St Luke *S'wark* 90-94; C Addiscombe St Mary Magd w St Martin 94-01; TV Sutton St Jas and Wawne

York from 01. *Sutton Rectory, 25 Church Street, Sutton-on-Hull, Hull HU7 4TL* Tel (01482) 782154
E-mail h.nesbitt@tinyworld.co.uk

NESBITT, Patrick Joseph. b 72. St Martin's Coll Lanc BA96. St Jo Coll Nottm 00. **d** 03. C Blackpool St Thos *Blackb* from 03. *8 Collingwood Avenue, Blackpool FY3 8BZ* Tel (01253) 302679 Mobile 07879-660100 E-mail patricknesbitt72@hotmail.com

NESBITT, Ronald. b 58. Sheff Univ LLB TCD DipTh85. CITC 82. **d** 85 **p** 86. C Ballymena w Ballyclug *Conn* 85-88; C Holywood D & D 88-90; I Helen's Bay 90-96; I Bangor Abbey from 96. *The Abbey Rectory, 5 Downshire Road, Bangor BT20 3TW* Tel (028) 9146 0173 E-mail ronnienesbitt@aol.co.uk

NESBITT, Miss Wilhelmina. b 65. Qu Coll Birm 98. **d** 00 **p** 01. C Bridgnorth, Tasley, Astley Abbotts, etc *Heref* from 00. *9 Fir Trees, Bridgnorth WV15 5EA* Tel (01746) 761069

NESHAM, George Dove. b 20. ALCD50. Lon Coll of Div. **d** 50 **p** 51. C Harrington *Carl* 50-52; C Ferryhill *Dur* 52-55; V Stanley 55-62; V W Ardsley *Wakef* 62-77; V Ripponden 77-80; V Satley *Dur* 80-87; RD Stanhope 81-87; rtd 87. *29 Ettrick Road, Jarrow NE32 5SL* Tel 0191-489 8071

NETHERWAY, Diana Margaret. b 47. Bp Otter Coll 94. **d** 96. NSM Northwood *Portsm* from 96; NSM Gurnard from 96. *138 Bellevue Road, Cowes PO31 7LD* Tel (01983) 298505
E-mail revbob@netherway1.freeserve.co.uk

NETHERWAY, Robert Sydney. b 37. Bp Otter Coll 94. **d** 96. NSM Cowes St Faith *Portsm* from 96. *138 Bellevue Road, Cowes PO31 7LD* Tel (01983) 298505
E-mail revbob@netherway1.freeserve.co.uk

NETHERWOOD, Mrs Anne Christine. b 43. ARIBA68 Liv Univ BArch66 Lon Univ BD92. St Deiniol's Hawarden 88. **d** 91 **p** 94. NSM Ellesmere and Welsh Frankton *Lich* 91-94; C Dudleston 94-97; C Criftins 94-97; C Criftins w Dudleston and Welsh Frankton 97; P-in-c from 97. *The Vicarage, Criftins, Ellesmere SY12 9LN* Tel (01691) 690401 Fax 690778
E-mail anne_netherwood@talk21.com

NEUDEGG, Mrs Joan Mary. b 36. Cant Sch of Min 81. **dss** 84 **d** 87 **p** 94. Chalk *Roch* 84-86; Hon C Dean Forest H Trin *Glouc* 87-90; Hon C Woolaston w Alvington 90-95; Hon C Woolaston w Alvington and Aylburton 95-96; rtd 96; Perm to Offic *Ex* from 96. *48 Marker Way, Honiton EX14 2EN* Tel (01404) 43957

NEUPERT, Douglas Alan. b 46. Chris Newport Univ (USA) BA78. Dioc OLM tr scheme 97. **d** 99 **p** 00. OLM Blackbourne *St E* from 99. *Hall Farm, Troston, Bury St Edmunds IP31 1EZ* Tel (01359) 269614 Mobile 07944-214417
E-mail doug.neupert@eu.ododedea.edu

NEVILL, James Michael. b 50. Cranmer Hall Dur 84. **d** 86 **p** 87. C Sowerby Bridge w Norland *Wakef* 86-91; CF 91-94; TV Broadwater St Mary *Chich* 94-99; Chapl St Mich Hospice Hereford from 99. *St Michael's Hospice, Bartestree, Hereford HR1 4HA* Tel (01432) 851000

NEVILL, Mavis Hetty. b 45. Westhill Coll Birm CertYS68 Sheff Poly Dip Educn Mgt 85 Bradf and Ilkley Coll DipPSE85 Bradf Univ BEd95 Univ Coll Ches CertRE96. N Ord Course 92. **d** 95 **p** 96. NSM Mount Pellon *Wakef* 95-99; NSM Mixenden from 99. *11 Lane Ends, Wheatley, Halifax HX2 8TW* Tel (01422) 362280 E-mail mavisnev@aol.com

NEVILLE, Alfred John. b 21. K Coll Lon BA40. Sarum & Wells Th Coll 80. **d** 83 **p** 84. NSM Weston-super-Mare St Paul *B & W* 83-93; Perm to Offic from 93. *12 Woodford Court, 21 Clarence Road North, Weston-super-Mare BS23 4AW* Tel (01934) 631176

NEVILLE, David Bruce. b 61. Ravensbourne Coll of Art & Design BA83. St Jo Coll Nottm LTh89 St Jo Coll Nottm DPS91. **d** 91 **p** 92. C Broxtowe *S'well* 91-94; C Attenborough 94-95; Perm to Offic 95-97; C Carrington 97-99; C Bulwell St Mary 99-02; Perm to Offic from 02. *3 Inham Road, Beeston, Nottingham NG9 4FL* Tel 0115-854 5648 E-mail rev.dnev@virgin.net

NEVILLE, Canon Graham. b 22. CCC Cam BA47 MA49 CertEd Cam Univ BD94 PhD02. Chich Th Coll 48. **d** 50 **p** 51. C Sutton in Ashfield St Mary *S'well* 50-53; Chapl Sheff Univ *Sheff* 53-58; R Culworth *Pet* 58-63; R Eydon 58-63; RD Culworth 62-63; Chapl Ch Coll of HE Canc 63-68; Chapl Sutton Valence Sch Kent 68-73; Six Preacher Cant Cathl *Cant* 69-78; Prin Lect Relig Studies Eastbourne Coll of Educn 73-80; Dir of Educn *Linc* 80-87; Can and Preb Linc Cathl 82-88; rtd 87; Perm to Offic *Linc* 88-00; *Worc* from 95. *16 Silverdale Avenue, Worcester WR5 1PY* Tel (01905) 360319

NEVILLE, Michael Robert John. b 56. Hatf Coll Dur BA80 Hughes Hall Cam PGCE81. Wycliffe Hall Ox 82. **d** 85 **p** 86. C E Twickenham St Steph *Lon* 85-88; Asst Dir Proclamation Trust 88-93; R Fordham *Chelmsf* from 93. *The Rectory, Wood Lane, Fordham Heath, Colchester CO3 5TR* Tel (01206) 240221 Fax as telephone

NEVILLE, Paul Stewart David. b 61. Wycliffe Hall Ox 98. **d** 00 **p** 01. C Chester le Street *Dur* from 00. *16 Park Road North, Chester le Street DH3 3SD* Tel 0191-388 6801

NEVIN, Alan Joseph. b 51. MCIPD80 Univ Coll Galway BA72. Aux Course 92 St Deiniol's Hawarden CertRS94. **d** 92 **p** 93. Aux P Youghal Union *C, C & R* 92-94; NSM Waterford w Killea, Drumcannon and Dunhill *C & O* 94-95; C 95-98; I Bunclody w Kildavin, Clonegal and Kilrush from 98. *St Mary's Rectory,*

Bunclody, Enniscorthy, Co Wexford, Irish Republic Tel (00353) (54) 77652 Fax 76151

NEVIN, Ronald. b 32. DMin88. Wesley Coll Leeds Linc Th Coll 63. **d** 64 **p** 65. C Norton St Mary *Dur* 64-66; R Cockfield 66-70; USA from 70; rtd 95. *20940 Rivers Ford, Estero, FL 33928, USA* Tel (001) (941) 495 8696 E-mail ronnevin@naplesnet.com

NEW, David John. b 37. Lon Univ BScEng58. Chich Th Coll 65. **d** 67 **p** 68. C Folkestone St Mary and St Eanswythe *Cant* 67-72; C Kings Heath *Birm* 72-74; V S Yardley St Mich 74-83; V Moseley St Agnes 83-00; rtd 00; Perm to Offic *Birm* from 00. *6 Falmouth, Worcester WR4 0TE* Tel (01905) 458084 Fax as telephone
E-mail david@revnew.freeserve.co.uk

NEW, Derek. b 30. **d** 86 **p** 87. NSM Brondesbury St Anne w Kilburn H Trin *Lon* 86-98; NSM Willesden St Matt from 99. *20 Lynton Road, London NW6 6BL* Tel (020) 7328 0187

NEW, Canon Thomas Stephen. b 30. K Coll Cam BA52 MA56. Cuddesdon Coll 52. **d** 54 **p** 55. C Greenford H Cross *Lon* 54-55; C Old St Pancras w Bedford New Town St Matt 55-58; C Woodham *Guildf* 58-64; V Guildf All SS 64-72; V Banstead 72-93; RD Epsom 76-80; Hon Can Guildf Cathl 79-93; Sub-Chapl HM Pris Downview 88-93; rtd 93; Perm to Offic *Ex* from 94. *St Katharine's, North Street, Denbury, Newton Abbot TQ12 6DJ* Tel (01803) 813775

NEW ZEALAND, Presiding Bishop and Primate of. See PATERSON, The Rt Revd John Campbell

NEWALL, Arthur William. b 24. Univ of Wales (Lamp) BA49. Chich Th Coll 49. **d** 51 **p** 52. C Hulme St Phil *Man* 51-53; C Fallowfield 53-55; V Oldham St Barn 55-60; V Aspull *Liv* 60-68; R Foots Cray *Roch* 68-78; V Henlow *St Alb* 78-89; rtd 89; Perm to Offic *Liv* from 89. *38 Fairhaven Road, Southport PR9 9UH* Tel (01704) 26045

NEWALL, Richard Lucas. b 43. K Coll Lon AKC66. **d** 66 **p** 67. C Roby *Liv* 66-69; C Douglas St Geo and St Barn *S & M* 69-71; Lic to Offic *Man* 72-75; C Ban St Mary *Ban* 75-77; R Newborough w Llangeinwen w Llangaffo etc 77-97; R Newborough w Llanidan and Llangeinwen etc from 98; AD Tindaethwy from 03. *Newborough Rectory, Dwyran, Llanfairpwllgwyngyll LL61 6RP* Tel (01248) 440285

NEWARK, Archdeacon of. See PEYTON, The Ven Nigel

NEWBOLD, Stephen Mark. b 60. Trin Coll Bris 01. **d** 03. C Roxeth *Lon* from 03. *69 Southdown Crescent, Harrow HA2 0QT* E-mail thenewbolds@aol.com

NEWBON, Eric. b 23. Fitzw Ho Cam BA51 MA55. Ridley Hall Cam 51. **d** 53 **p** 54. C Garston *Liv* 53-57; V Bickershaw 57-65; V Southport All So 65-85; rtd 85; Perm to Offic *Ches* from 86. *33 Haymakers Way, Saughall, Chester CH1 6AR* Tel (01244) 880123

NEWBON, Kenneth. b 29. Wells Th Coll 67. **d** 69 **p** 70. C Church Stretton *Heref* 69-72; P-in-c Cressage w Sheinton 72-75; R Braunstone *Leic* 75-81; TR 81-84; P-in-c Eardisley w Bollingham and Willersley *Heref* 84-88; P-in-c Brilley w Michaelchurch on Arrow 84-88; P-in-c Whitney w Winforton 84-88; RD Kington and Weobley 87-95; R Eardisley w Bollingham, Willersley, Brilley etc 88-96; rtd 96; Perm to Offic *Heref* from 96. *Grace Dieu House, Staunton-on-Wye, Hereford HR4 7LT* Tel (01981) 500188

NEWBON, Michael Charles. b 59. Oak Hill Th Coll DipHE94. **d** 94 **p** 95. C Bedford St Jo and St Leon *St Alb* 94-99; V Luton St Fran from 99. *The Vicarage, 145 Hollybush Road, Luton LU2 9HQ* Tel (01582) 753919 E-mail lutonstfrancis@aol.com

NEWBURY, Canon Robert. b 22. St D Coll Lamp BA46. **d** 48 **p** 49. C Killay *S & B* 48-55; V Glascombe w Rhulen and Gregrina 55-63; V Manselton 63-84; V Manselton w Hafod 84-90; Hon Can Brecon Cathl from 85; rtd 90. *4 Cobham Close, Gorseinon, Swansea SA4 4FA* Tel (01792) 896438

NEWBY, Mrs Ailsa Ballantyne. b 56. Collingwood Coll Dur BA78. St Steph Ho Ox 98. **d** 98 **p** 99. C Streatham Ch Ch *S'wark* 98-01; V S Lambeth St Anne and All SS from 01. *The Vicarage, 179 Fentiman Road, London SW8 1JY* Tel (020) 7735 3191 E-mail anewby@fish.co.uk

NEWBY, Peter Gordon. b 23. **d** 64 **p** 65. C Leic St Phil *Leic* 64-69; R Lt Bowden St Nic 69-72; V Jersey Gouray St Martin *Win* 72-77; Chapl Jersey Gp of Hosps 78-80; R Much Birch w Lt Birch, Much Dewchurch etc *Heref* 80-88; rtd 89; Perm to Offic *Ex* from 90. *18 Woodfields, Seaton EX12 2UX* Tel (01297) 24562

NEWCASTLE, Bishop of. See WHARTON, The Rt Revd John Martin

NEWCASTLE, Dean of. See DALLISTON, The Very Revd Christopher Charles

NEWCOMBE, John Adrian. b 61. Univ of Wales (Lamp) BA83 SS Paul & Mary Coll Cheltenham PGCE85. Ripon Coll Cuddesdon 90. **d** 92 **p** 93. C Stroud and Uplands w Slad *Glouc* 92-96; C Nailsworth 96-01; P-in-c Childswyckham w Aston Somerville, Buckland etc from 01. *New Vicarage, Buckland Road, Childswickham, Broadway WR12 7HH* Tel (01386) 853824

NEWCOMBE, Kenneth Harry. b 27. Leic Univ DipTh68. Ridley Hall Cam 70. **d** 72 **p** 73. C Melton Mowbray w Thorpe Arnold *Leic* 72-78; P-in-c W Bridgford *S'well* 78-84; R Radcliffe-on-

Trent and Shelford etc 84-97; rtd 97. *11 Haven Close, West Bridgford, Nottingham NG12 7LP* Tel 0115-982 1899

NEWCOMBE, Canon Timothy James Grahame. b 47. AKC75. St Aug Coll Cant 75. **d** 76 **p** 77. C Heref St Martin *Heref* 76-79; C Hitchin *St Alb* 79-85; R Croft and Stoney Stanton *Leic* 85-91; P-in-c Launceston *Truro* 91-92; V Launceston 92-97; TR Launceston from 97; Chapl Cornwall Healthcare Trust from 96; Hon Can Truro Cathl *Truro* from 01. *St Mary's Vicarage, Dunheved Road, Launceston PL15 9JE* Tel (01566) 772974 E-mail canontim@silvermead.net

✠**NEWCOME, The Rt Revd James William Scobie.** b 53. Trin Coll Ox BA74 MA78 Selw Coll Cam BA77 MA81. Ridley Hall Cam 75. **d** 78 **p** 79 **c** 02. C Leavesden All SS *St Alb* 78-82; P-in-c Bar Hill LEP *Ely* 82-92; V Bar Hill 92-94; Tutor Ridley Hall Cam 83-88; P-in-c Dry Drayton *Ely* 89-94; RD N Stowe 93-94; Can Res Ches Cathl and Dioc Dir of Ords *Ches* 94-02; Dir of Educn and Tr 96-02; Suff Bp Penrith *Carl* from 02. *Holm Croft, 13 Castle Road, Kendal LA9 7AU* Tel (01539) 727836 Fax 734380 E-mail bishop.penrith@carlislediocese.org.uk

NEWELL, Aubrey Francis Thomas. b 20. St D Coll Lamp BA43. **d** 45 **p** 46. C Rhosddu *St As* 45-49; C Llanwnog *Ban* 49-50; C Gabalfa *Llan* 50-53; C Gt Marlow *Ox* 53-57; R Lavendon w Cold Brayfield 57-62; V Gawcott and Hillesden 62-77; P-in-c Radclive 69-72; RD Buckingham 70-76 and 82-84; P-in-c Padbury w Adstock 72-77; V Lenborough 77-87; rtd 87; Perm to Offic *Ox* 89-00. *5 Church View, Steeple Claydon, Buckingham MK18 2QR* Tel (01296) 738271

NEWELL, Christopher David. b 53. Cert Counselling 92. S'wark Ord Course DipRS87. **d** 87 **p** 88. C Stockwell St Mich *S'wark* 87-90; Asst Chapl R Lon Hosp (Whitechapel) 90-92; Asst Chapl R Lon Hosp (Mile End) 90-92; R Birch St Agnes *Man* 92-96; P-in-c Longsight St Jo w St Cypr 94-96; R Birch St Agnes w Longsight St Jo w St Cypr 97; R Lansallos *Truro* 97-98; V Talland 97-98; Asst P Liskeard and St Keyne 00-02; C Duloe, Herodsfoot, Morval and St Pinnock 02-03; P-in-c from 03; C Talland 02-03; P-in-c from 03; C Lansallos 02-03; P-in-c from 03. *The Rectory, Duloe, Liskeard PL14 4PW* Tel (01503) 262300 E-mail christophernewell@talk21.com

NEWELL, David Walter. b 37. Nottm Univ BSc. WEMTC. **d** 03. NSM Painswick, Sheepscombe, Cranham, The Edge etc *Glouc* from 03. *Woodside, Kingsmill Lane, Painswick, Stroud GL6 6SA* Tel (01452) 812083

NEWELL, Canon Edmund John. b 61. Univ Coll Lon BSc83 Nuff Coll Ox DPhil88 MA89 FRHistS98. Ox Min Course 89 Ripon Coll Cuddesdon 92. **d** 94 **p** 95. C Deddington w Barford, Clifton and Hempton *Ox* 94-98; Bp's Dom Chapl 98-01; Chapl Headington Sch 98-01; Can Res St Paul's Cathl *Lon* from 01. *6 Amen Court, London EC4M 7BU* Tel (020) 7248 8572 Fax as telephone E-mail newell@amencourt.freeserve.co.uk

NEWELL, Jack Ernest. b 26. CEng FIChemE ARCS BSc. Glouc Th Course 80. **d** 83 **p** 84. NSM Hempsted *Glouc* 83-96; Perm to Offic from 96. *Hempsted House, Rectory Lane, Hempsted, Gloucester GL2 5LW* Tel (01452) 523320

NEWELL, Kenneth Ernest. b 22. S Dios Minl Tr Scheme 77. **d** 79 **p** 80. NSM Lynton, Brendon, Countisbury, Lynmouth etc *Ex* 79-85; TR 85-89; RD Shirwell 84-89; rtd 89; Perm to Offic *Ex* from 89. *Mole End, Lydiate Lane, Lynton EX35 6HE*

NEWELL, Samuel James (Jim). b 28. TCD BA53 MA63. TCD Div Sch Div Test54. **d** 54 **p** 55. C Belfast St Mary Conn 54-57; C Derriaghy 57-60; C Reading St Mary V *Ox* 60-63; V Chesham Ch Ch 63-74; P-in-c Wraysbury 74-78; TV Riverside 78-94; rtd 94; Perm to Offic *Ox* from 97. *41 Redford Road, Windsor SL4 5ST* Tel (01753) 862300

NEWELL of Staffa, Gerald Frederick Watson. b 34. Sarum Th Coll 56. **d** 59 **p** 61. C Southampton SS Pet and Paul w All SS *Win* 59-61; C Overton w Laverstoke and Freefolk 61-63; CF (TA) 61-63; CF 63-66; R Spennithorne *Ripon* 66-68; R Finghall 66-68; R Hauxwell 66-68; P-in-c Steyning *Chich* 74-78; Perm to Offic *Ex* 93-95 and 99-00; P-in-c Breamore *Win* 95-98; rtd 99; P-in-c Palermo w Taormina *Eur* 00; R Glencarse *Bre* from 01. *The Rectory, Glencarse, Perth PH2 7LX* Tel (01738) 860386

NEWELL PRICE, John Charles. b 29. SS Coll Cam BA50 MA MB, BChir MRCGP. LNSM course 88. **d** 91 **p** 94. OLM Frensham *Guildf* 91-99; rtd 99; Perm to Offic *Guildf* from 99. *7 Collards Gate, High Street, Haslemere GU27 2HE* Tel (01428) 661336

NEWEY, Edmund James. b 71. Linc Coll Ox BA95 MA97 Em Coll Cam BA99. Westcott Ho Cam 97. **d** 00 **p** 01. C Birch w Fallowfield *Man* 00-03; R Newmarket St Mary w Exning St Agnes *St E* from 03. *The Rectory, 21 Hamilton Road, Newmarket CB8 0NY* Tel 07986-530511 (mobile) E-mail ejnewey@fish.co.uk

NEWHAM, Jill. b 37. Oak Hill NSM Course. **d** 89 **p** 95. NSM W w E Mersea *Chelmsf* 89-91 and 95-97; NSM Peldon w Gt and Lt Wigborough 93-97; P-in-c Bildeston w Wattisham *St E* 97-00; NSM Gt and Lt Ouseburn w Marton cum Grafton etc *Ripon* from 01. *The Vicarage, Church Street, Whixley, York YO26 8AR* Tel (01423) 330269

NEWHAM, Simon Frank Eric. b 65. Sheff Univ BSc87 MSc89 Bris Univ BA00. Trin Coll Bris 98. **d** 00 **p** 01. C Horsham *Chich* from 00. *18 Queensway, Horsham RH13 5AY* Tel (01403) 252986

✠**NEWING, The Rt Revd Dom Kenneth Albert.** b 24. Selw Coll Cam BA53 MA57. Coll of Resurr Mirfield 53. **d** 55 **p** 56 **c** 82. C Plymstock *Ex* 55-63; R Plympton St Maurice 63-82; RD Plympton 71-76; Preb Ex Cathl 75-82; Adn Plymouth 78-82; Suff Bp Plymouth 82-88; Lic to Offic *Ox* 88-93; OSB from 89; rtd 93. *Elmore Abbey, Church Lane, Newbury RG14 1SA* Tel (01635) 33080

NEWING, Peter. b 33. Birm Univ CertEd55 Dur Univ BA63 Bris Univ BEd76 State Univ NY BSc85 EdD88 Cam Univ DipRS91 FRSA60 FSAScot59 ACP67 MCollP86 FCollP95 APhS63. Cranmer Hall Dur 63. **d** 65 **p** 66. C Blockley w Aston Magna *Glouc* 65-69; P-in-c Taynton 69-75; P-in-c Tibberton 69-75; R Brimpsfield w Elkstone and Syde 75-83; R Brimpsfield, Cranham, Elkstone and Syde 83-97; P-in-c Daglingworth w the Duntisbournes and Winstone 95-97; R Brimpsfield w Birdlip, Syde, Daglingworth etc 97-01; C Redmarley D'Abitot, Bromesberrow, Pauntley etc 01-02; NSM Brimpsfield w Birdlip, Syde, Daglingworth etc from 02; rtd 02; Perm to Offic *Heref* from 02. *The Rectory, Albright Lane, Bromesberrow, Ledbury HR8 1RU* Tel (01531) 650898

NEWITT, Mark Julian. b 76. Bradf Univ BSc97 St Jo Coll Dur BA02. Cranmer Hall Dur 00. **d** 03. C Billing *Pet* from 03. *80 Worcester Close, Northampton NN3 9GD* Tel (01604) 787163

NEWLAND, Mrs Patricia Frances. b 35. Edin Univ MA56 Dip Sociology 57. EAMTC 96. **d** 97 **p** 98. NSM Duxford *Ely* 97-02; NSM Hinxton 97-02; NSM Ickleton 97-02; rtd 02; Perm to Offic *Ely* from 02. *Ickelton Lodge, 14 Frogge Street, Ickleton, Saffron Walden CB10 1SH* Tel (01799) 530268 Fax 531146 E-mail tricia.newland@ukgateway.net

NEWLANDS, Christopher William. b 57. Bris Univ BA79. Westcott Ho Cam 81. **d** 84 **p** 85. C Bishop's Waltham *Portsm* 84-87; Hon C Upham 85-87; Prec, Sacr and Min Can Dur Cathl *Dur* 87-92; Chapl Bucharest w Sofia *Eur* 92-95; V Shrub End *Chelmsf* from 96. *All Saints' Vicarage, 270 Shrub End Road, Colchester CO3 4RL* Tel (01206) 503131 E-mail christhevic@hotmail.com

NEWLANDS, Prof George McLeod. b 41. Edin Univ MA63 Heidelberg Univ BD66 PhD70 Ch Coll Cam MA73. **d** 82 **p** 82. Lect Cam Univ 73-86; Fell and Dean Trin Hall Cam 82-86; Prof Div Glas Univ from 86; Perm to Offic *Glas* from 86. *2/19 Succoth Court, Edinburgh EH12 6BZ*, or *The University, Glasgow G12 8QQ* Tel 0131-337 4941 or 0141-330 5297

NEWLYN, Canon Edwin. b 39. AKC64. **d** 65 **p** 66. C Belgrave St Mich *Leic* 65-68; Miss to Seamen 68-81; Chapl Santos Brazil 68-69; Asst Chapl Glas and C Glas St Gabr *Glas* 69-73; Chapl E Lon S Africa 73-76; R W Bank St Pet 75-76; V Fylingdales w Stainsacre 81-88; RD Whitby 85-92; Sec Dioc Adv Cttee for Care of Chs 87-01; P-in-c Goathland 88-99; Can and Preb York Minster from 90; rtd 01; Perm to Offic *York* from 01. *8 Metropole Towers, Argyle Road, Whitby YO21 3HU* Tel (01947) 604533 E-mail enewlyn@aol.com

NEWMAN, Canon Adrian. b 58. Bris Univ BSc80 DipHE85 MPhil89. Trin Coll Bris 82. **d** 85 **p** 86. C Forest Gate St Mark *Chelmsf* 85-89; V Hillsborough and Wadsley Bridge *Sheff* 89-96; RD Hallam 94-96; R Birm St Martin w Bordesley St Andr *Birm* from 96; Hon Can Birm Cathl from 01. *The Rectory, 37 Barlows Road, Birmingham B15 2PN* Tel 0121-454 0119 or 643 5428

NEWMAN, Alan George. b 18. Lich Th Coll 41. **d** 44 **p** 45. C Twerton *B & W* 44-52; V Clandown 52-56; V Bradford-on-Avon Ch Ch *Sarum* 56-76; R Monkton Farleigh w S Wraxall 76-84; rtd 84; Perm to Offic *Sarum* from 84; *B & W* from 00. *14 White Horse Road, Winsley, Bradford-on-Avon BA15 2JZ* Tel (01225) 854119

NEWMAN, Alfred John Gordon. b 19. Qu Coll Birm 71. **d** 74 **p** 74. Hon C Hall Green St Pet *Birm* 74-84; Perm to Offic *St E* 84-96; Perm to Offic *Chich* from 96. *Flat 5, Southdown Court, Bell Banks Road, Hailsham BN27 2AT* Tel (01323) 441378

NEWMAN, Mrs Alison Myra. b 55. K Coll Lon BD77. SEITE 99. **d** 02 **p** 03. C Bromley SS Pet and Paul *Roch* from 02. *13 Rochester Avenue, Bromley BR1 3DB* Tel (020) 8464 9532 E-mail newmans8@btopenworld.com

NEWMAN, Cecil Ernest. b 21. Bris Univ BA58 DipTh58. Roch Th Coll 61. **d** 62 **p** 63. C Tiverton St Pet *Ex* 62-64; C Wolborough w Newton Abbot 64-67; Lic to Offic *Roch* 67-86; Chapl Darenth Park Hosp Dartford 67-86; rtd 86; Perm to Offic *Roch* 86-98. *27 Nursery Road, Meopham, Gravesend DA13 0LR* Tel (01474) 812955

NEWMAN, David. *See* NEWMAN, Richard David

NEWMAN, David Malcolm. b 54. FSAScot81 Aber Univ LTh BTh. St Steph Ho Ox 89. **d** 91 **p** 92. C St Mary-at-Latton *Chelmsf* 91-94; R Weeley and Lt Clacton from 94. *The Vicarage, 2 Holland Road, Little Clacton, Clacton-on-Sea CO16 9RS* Tel (01255) 860241

NEWMAN, David Maurice Frederick. b 54. Hertf Coll Ox BA75 MA79. St Jo Coll Nottm. **d** 79 **p** 80. C Orpington Ch Ch *Roch* 79-83; C Bushbury *Lich* 83-86; V Ockbrook *Derby* 86-97; TR

Loughborough Em and St Mary in Charnwood *Leic* from 97; RD Akeley E from 99. *Emmanuel Rectory, 47 Forest Road, Loughborough LE11 3NW* Tel (01509) 263264 *or* 261773 E-mail davidnewman@emmanuel.fsnet.co.uk

NEWMAN, Mrs Diana Joan. b 43. Sarum Th Coll 81. **dss** 84 **d** 87 **p** 94. Parkstone St Pet w Branksea and St Osmund *Sarum* 84-87; NSM 87-96; TV Parkstone St Pet and St Osmund w Branksea from 96. *62 Vale Road, Poole BH14 9AU* Tel (01202) 745136 Fax as telephone E-mail teamdiana@aol.com

NEWMAN, Geoffrey Maurice. b 22. Ox NSM Course 77. **d** 80 **p** 81. NSM Binfield *Ox* 80-84; Chapl St Geo Sch Ascot 82-84; V Teynham *Cant* 84-87; rtd 87; Perm to Offic *Cant* from 87. *55 St Mildred's Road, Westgate-on-Sea CT8 8RJ* Tel (01843) 833837

NEWMAN, Graham Anthony. b 44. Ripon Coll Cuddesdon 79. **d** 81 **p** 82. C Walker *Newc* 81-84; C Whorlton 84-87; V Warkworth and Acklington 87-94; V Haltwhistle and Greenhead 94-99; Chapl Northd HA 94-99; TV N Shields *Newc* 99-00; rtd 00; Perm to Offic *Newc* from 01. *49 Burnbank Avenue, Wellfield, Whitley Bay NE25 9HG* Tel 0191-253 5914

NEWMAN, Mrs Helen Margaret (Greet). b 58. York Univ BA80 Nottm Univ MA02. EMMTC 99. **d** 02 **p** 03. NSM Thorpe Acre w Dishley *Leic* from 02. *Emmanuel Rectory, 47 Forest Road, Loughborough LE11 3NW* Tel (01509) 263264 Fax as telephone E-mail helen@emmanuel.fsnet.co.uk

NEWMAN, James Edwin Michael. b 59. Nottm Univ BA80 Ox Univ BA90. Wycliffe Hall Ox 88. **d** 91 **p** 92. C Bidston *Ches* 91-95; C Cheadle from 95. *4 Cuthbert Road, Cheadle SK8 2DT* Tel 0161-428 3983 E-mail mike@stcuthberts.org

NEWMAN, John Humphrey. b 17. ALCD49. **d** 49 **p** 50. C Hove Bp Hannington Memorial Ch *Chich* 49-52; V Welling *Roch* 52-64; V Penge St Jo 64-74; R Knockholt 74-82; rtd 82; Perm to Offic *Chich* from 82. *Stonegarth, Pett Level Road, Fairlight, Hastings TN35 4EA* Tel (01424) 812518

NEWMAN, Michael Alan. b 40. Chich Th Coll 67. **d** 70 **p** 71. C Kilburn St Aug *Lon* 70-73; C St Geo-in-the-East St Mary 75-78; rtd 78. *April Cottage, Georges Lane, Storrington, Pulborough RH20 3JH* Tel (01903) 744354

NEWMAN, Preb Michael John. b 50. Leic Univ BA72 MA75 Ex Coll Ox DipTh74. Cuddesdon Coll 73. **d** 75 **p** 76. C Tettenhall Regis *Lich* 75-79; C Uttoxeter w Bramshall 79-82; R Norton Canes 82-89; TR Rugeley from 89; Preb Lich Cathl from 02. *The Rectory, 20 Church Street, Rugeley WS15 2AB* Tel (01889) 582149

NEWMAN, Canon Michael Robert. b 30. K Coll Lon BD61 Massey Univ (NZ) DSS91. St Jo Coll Auckland LTh53. **d** 54 **p** 55. New Zealand 54-58; C Hampstead St Jo *Lon* 58-61; New Zealand from 61; Can Auckland 81-93. *2126 Alfriston Road, Manurewa 1702, New Zealand* Tel (0064) (9) 267 4357

NEWMAN, Paul. b 65. St Martin's Coll Lanc BA90. Oak Hill Th Coll. **d** 00 **p** 01. C Poynton *Ches* from 00. *18 Ivy Road, Poynton, Stockport SK12 1PE* Tel (01625) 872048 E-mail scallyvic@yahoo.com

NEWMAN, Paul Anthony. b 48. Lon Univ BSc70 Leeds Univ DipTh75. Coll of Resurr Mirfield 73. **d** 76 **p** 77. C Catford St Laur *S'wark* 76-81; TV Grays All SS *Chelmsf* 81-83; TV Lt Thurrock St Mary 81-83; W Ham Adnry Youth Chapl 83-87; P-in-c Forest Gate All SS 83-89; V 89-91; Dep Chapl HM Pris Wormwood Scrubs 91-92; Chapl HM Pris Downview 92-02; Chapl HM Pris Win from 02. *HM Prison Winchester, Romsey Road, Winchester SO22 5DF* Tel (01962) 854494 Fax 842560

NEWMAN, Richard David. b 38. BNC Ox BA60 MA63. Lich Th Coll 60. **d** 62 **p** 63. C E Grinstead St Swithun *Chich* 62-66; C Gt Grimsby St Jas *Linc* 66-69; C Gt Grimsby St Mary and St Jas 69-73; TV 73-74; V St Nicholas at Wade w Sarre *Cant* 74-75; P-in-c Chislet w Hoath 74-75; V St Nicholas at Wade w Sarre and Chislet w Hoath 75-81; V S Norwood H Innocents 81-84; V S Norwood H Innocents *S'wark* from 85. *Holy Innocents' Vicarage, 192A Selhurst Road, London SE25 6XX* Tel (020) 8653 2063

NEWMAN, William Nigel Edward. b 61. St Jo Coll Dur BA83 Bris Univ PGCE86. Westcott Ho Cam 99. **d** 01 **p** 02. C Halstead St Andr w H Trin and Greenstead Green *Chelmsf* from 01. *47 Tidings Hill, Halstead CO9 1BL* Tel (01787) 475528 E-mail willandot@yahoo.co.uk

NEWNHAM, Eric Robert. b 43. FCA. Sarum & Wells Th Coll 70. **d** 75 **p** 76. Hon C Blackheath Ascension *S'wark* from 75. *27 Morden Hill, London SE13 7NN* Tel (020) 8692 6507 *or* 8691 6559

NEWPORT, Derek James. b 39. Acadia Univ (NS) BA82 MEd84. Sarum & Wells Th Coll 74. **d** 76 **p** 77. C Tavistock and Gulworthy *Ex* 76-78; Canada 78-86; V Malborough w S Huish, W Alvington and Churchstow *Ex* 86-95; TR Widecombe-in-the-Moor, Leusdon, Princetown etc from 95. *The Rectory, Widecombe-in-the-Moor, Newton Abbot TQ13 7TB* Tel (01364) 621334 Fax as telephone E-mail dereknewport@dnewport.fsnet.co.uk

NEWPORT, Prof Kenneth George Charles. b 57. Andrews Univ (USA) BA83 Columbia Union Coll (USA) MA84 Linacre Coll Ox MSt85 St Hugh's Coll Ox DPhil88. N Ord Course 98. **d** 00

p 01. Reader Chr Thought Liv Hope 99-01; Prof Th and RS from 01; Hon Research Fell Man Univ 98; NSM Bolton St Pet from 00; Perm to Offic *Liv* from 00. *Theology and Religious Studies, Liverpool Hope, Hope Park, Taggart Avenue, Liverpool L16 9JD* Tel 0151-291 3510 Fax 291 3772 E-mail knewport@hope.ac.uk

NEWPORT, Archdeacon of. See SHARPE, The Ven Kenneth William

NEWSOME, David Ellis. b 55. St Jo Coll Dur BA77. Westcott Ho Cam 80. **d** 82 **p** 83. C Finchley St Mary *Lon* 82-85; C Fulham All SS 85-87; Bp's Dom Chapl *Birm* 87-91; V Gravelly Hill 91-00; P-in-c Stockland Green 93-96; AD Aston 95-00; TR Tettenhall Regis *Lich* from 00. *The Vicarage, 2 Lloyd Road, Tettenhall, Wolverhampton WV6 9AU* Tel (01902) 742801

NEWSOME, Canon John Keith. b 49. Mert Coll Ox BA73 MA76. Ripon Coll Cuddesdon 73. **d** 76 **p** 77. C Bywell *Newc* 76-78; C Berwick H Trin 78-82; Chapl Bonn w Cologne *Eur* 86-93; Chapl Hamburg 93-00; Chapl Zürich from 00; Can Brussels Cathl from 98. *Promenadengasse 9, 8001 Zürich, Switzerland* Tel (0041) (1) 252 6024 Fax 252 6042

NEWSOME, Monica Jane. b 55. WMMTC 96. **d** 99 **p** 00. NSM Kingshurst *Birm* 99-00; Asst Chapl HM YOI Stoke Heath from 00. *HM Young Offender Institution, Stoke Heath, Market Drayton TF9 2LJ* Tel (01630) 636000

NEWSON, Julie. b 60. Southn Univ BA97. Bp Otter Coll 00. **d** 03. NSM Brighton St Pet w Chpl Royal *Chich* from 03. *77 Winton Street, Brighton BN2 5PA* Tel (01273) 570978 Mobile 07803-750147 E-mail julie.newson@btinternet.com

NEWSTEAD, Dominic Gerald. b 65. Wycliffe Hall Ox BTh95. **d** 95 **p** 96. C Windlesham *Guildf* 95-00; Asst Chapl Fontainebleau *Eur* from 00. *5 La Fontaine au Bois, 25 rue Jean Mermoz, 77210 Avon, France* Tel (0033) (1) 60 74 00 07 Fax 64 69 08 11 E-mail newsteadinfrance@aol.com

NEWSUM, Alfred Turner Paul. b 28. Coll of Resurr Mirfield 52. **d** 53 **p** 54. C Roath St German *Llan* 53-59; C Westmr St Matt *Lon* 59-60; C Washwood Heath *Birm* 60-68; P-in-c Small Heath St Greg 68-78; V Birm St Aid Small Heath 72-80; V Stockland Green 80-93; rtd 93; Perm to Offic *Llan* from 93; Perm to Offic *Mon* from 93. *Ty'r Offeiriad, 18 Almond Drive, Cardiff CF23 8HD*

NEWTH, Barry Wilfred. b 33. Bris Univ BA56. ALCD58. **d** 58 **p** 59. C Upton (Overchurch) *Ches* 58-62; C Kimberworth *Sheff* 62-63; V Clifton *Man* 63-72; V Radcliffe St Thos 72-74; V Radcliffe St Thos and St Jo 74-81; R Heaton Mersey 81-86; V Kirkby Malham *Bradf* 86-87; P-in-c Coniston Cold 86-87; V Kirkby-in-Malhamdale w Coniston Cold 87-97; rtd 97; Perm to Offic *Man* from 00. *1 Higher Ridings, Bromley Cross, Bolton BL7 9HP* Tel (01204) 451927

NEWTON, Miss Ann. b 46. Trin Coll Bris 75. **d** 87 **p** 94. Par Dn Rothley *Leic* 87-91; Par Dn Becontree St Mary *Chelmsf* 91-94; C 94-01; V Canley *Cov* from 01. *St Stephen's Vicarage, 47 Glebe Close, Coventry CV4 8DJ* Tel (024) 7642 1721

NEWTON, Barrie Arthur. b 38. Dur Univ BA61. Wells Th Coll 61. **d** 63 **p** 64. C Walton St Mary *Liv* 63-67; C N Lynn w St Marg and St Nic *Nor* 67-69; Chapl Asst The Lon Hosp (Whitechapel) 69-71; Chapl K Coll Hosp Lon 72-77; P-in-c Bishops Sutton w Stowey *B & W* 77-81; P-in-c Compton Martin w Ubley 79-81; P-in-c Bridgwater St Jo w Chedzoy 81-83; Chapl St Mary's Hosp Praed Street Lon 83-94; Chapl St Mary's NHS Trust Paddington 94-99; rtd 00. *10 Brondesbury Park Mansions, 132 Salusbury Road, London NW6 6PD* Tel (020) 7328 0397 Fax as telephone

NEWTON, Brian Karl. b 30. Keble Coll Ox BA55 MA59. Wells Th Coll 56. **d** 58 **p** 59. C Barrow Ed Geo *Carl* 58-61; Trinidad and Tobago 61-69 and 71-77; Gen Ed USPG 69-71; P-in-c Gt Coates *Linc* 77; TV Gt and Lt Coates w Bradley 78-88; V Burgh le Marsh 88-94; R Bratoft w Irby-in-the-Marsh 88-94; V Orby 88-94; R Welton-le-Marsh w Gunby 88-94; rtd 94; Perm to Offic *Linc* 94-97. *27 Somersby Way, Boston PE21 9PQ* Tel (01205) 362433

NEWTON, Canon Christopher Wynne. b 25. Trin Hall Cam BA46. Westcott Ho Cam 48. **d** 50 **p** 51. C Gateshead Ch Ch *Dur* 50-52; Canada 52-55; C Harrow Weald All SS *Lon* 55-58; V Radlett *St Alb* 58-66; RD St Alb 63-66; TR Hemel Hempstead 66-72; RD Milton Keynes *Ox* 72-77; TV Swan 78-84; RD Claydon 78-84; Dioc Ecum Officer 79-84; Hon Can Ch Ch 80-83; P-in-c Lt Gaddesden *St Alb* 84-86; rtd 86; Perm to Offic *St Alb* from 86. *24 Slade Court, Watling Street, Radlett WD7 7BT* Tel (01923) 859131

NEWTON, David. See NEWTON, Raymond David

NEWTON, David Ernest. b 42. Sarum & Wells Th Coll 72. **d** 74 **p** 75. C Wigan All SS *Liv* 74-80; V Choral York Minster *York* 80-85; R Ampleforth w Oswaldkirk 85-86; P-in-c E Gilling 85-86; R Ampleforth and Oswaldkirk and Gilling E 86-97; V Ampleforth w Oswaldkirk, Gilling E etc 98-01; RD Helmsley 94-99; P-in-c Overton *Blackb* from 01. *St Helen's Vicarage, Chapel Lane, Overton, Morecambe LA3 3HU* Tel (01524) 858234 E-mail davidnoot@aol.com

NEWTON, Derek. b 50. Sunderland Poly HND72 Dur Univ ACertC95. NEOC 89. **d** 92 **p** 93. NSM Houghton le Spring *Dur*

92-96; NSM Deanery of Houghton from 97. *Pinelodge, Warwick Drive, Houghton le Spring DH5 8JR* Tel 0191-584 9169

NEWTON, Mrs Fiona Olive. b 46. GTCL67. WMMTC 96. **d** 99 **p** 00. C Southam *Cov* 99-03; C Ufton 99-03; P-in-c Laxfield *St E* from 03; P-in-c Wilby w Brundish from 03. *The Vicarage, 15 Noyes Avenue, Laxfield, Woodbridge IP13 8EB* Tel (01986) 798998 E-mail fionanewton@rmplc.co.uk

NEWTON, George Peter Howgill. b 62. Pemb Coll Cam BA84 MA88. Oak Hill Th Coll BA93. **d** 93 **p** 94. C Blackpool St Thos *Blackb* 93-99; P-in-c Aldershot H Trin *Guildf* 99-03; V from 03. *2 Cranmore Lane, Aldershot GU11 3AS* Tel (01252) 320618 E-mail g@gjsk.prestel.co.uk

NEWTON, Gerald Blamire. b 30. Lich Th Coll. **d** 69 **p** 70. C Leeds Halton St Wilfrid *Ripon* 69-73; C Gt Yarmouth *Nor* 73-74; P-in-c Cattistock w Chilfrome and Rampisham w Wraxall *Sarum* 74-77; V Coney Hill *Glouc* 77-79; V Bryneglwys and Llandegla *St As* 79-80; R Llandegla and Bryneglwys and Llanarmon-yn-Ial 80-86; P-in-c Burythorpe, Acklam and Leavening w Westow *York* 86-95; rtd 95; Perm to Offic *York* from 95. *9 Ropery Walk, Malton YO17 7JS* Tel (01653) 692084

NEWTON, Graham Hayden. b 47. AKC69. St Aug Coll Cant 70. **d** 70 **p** 71. C St Mary-at-Lambeth *S'wark* 70-73; TV Catford (Southend) and Downham 73-78; P-in-c Porthill *Lich* 78-79; TV Wolstanton 79-86; V Stevenage H Trin *St Alb* 86-96; TR Dunstable from 96; RD Dunstable from 96. *The Rectory, 8 Furness Avenue, Dunstable LU6 3BN* Tel (01582) 664467 *or* 477401 E-mail g.newton@ntlworld.com

NEWTON, Ian. b 66. Westmr Coll Ox BEd89 Leeds Univ BA03. Coll of Resurr Mirfield 01. **d** 03. C Horninglow *Lich* from 03. *10 Field Rise, Burton-on-Trent DE13 0NR* Tel (01283) 540933 E-mail fatheriannewton@yahoo.co.uk

NEWTON, John. b 39. AKC65. **d** 66 **p** 67. C Whipton *Ex* 66-68; C Plympton St Mary 68-74; V Broadwoodwidger 74-81; R Kelly w Bradstone 74-81; R Lifton 74-81; Chapl All Hallows Sch Rousdon 81-94; Lic to Offic *Ex* 81-94; rtd 99. Flat 2, 5 Eyewell Green, Seaton EX12 2BN Tel (01297) 625587

NEWTON, John Richard. b 25. FBIM. St Jo Coll Dur 76 Cranmer Hall Dur. **d** 78 **p** 79. C Cottingham *York* 78-80; R Beeford w Frodingham and Foston 80-86; R Todwick *Sheff* 86-92; rtd 92; Perm to Offic *Linc* from 92. *Quiet Corner, 12 Pelham Close, Sudbrooke, Lincoln LN2 2SQ* Tel (01522) 595123

✠**NEWTON, The Rt Revd Keith.** b 52. K Coll Lon BD73 AKC73 Ch Ch Coll Cant PGCE75. St Aug Coll Cant 74. **d** 75 **p** 76 **c** 02. C Gt Ilford St Mary *Chelmsf* 75-78; TV Wimbledon *S'wark* 78-85; Malawi 85-91; Dean Blantyre 86-91; Can S Malawi from 86; P-in-c Knowle *Bris* 91-93; V Knowle H Nativity 93-02; P-in-c Easton All Hallows 97-02; RD Brislington 95-99; AD Bris S 99-01; Hon Can Bris Cathl 00-02; Suff Bp Richborough (PEV) *Cant* from 02. *Richborough House, 6 Mellish Gardens, Woodford Green IG8 0BH* Tel (020) 8505 7259 E-mail keith@newtonfam.freeserve.co.uk

NEWTON, Louis Kalbfield. b 44. N Texas State Univ BA73. Westcott Ho Cam CTM93. **d** 93 **p** 94. C Walthamstow St Pet *Chelmsf* 93-97; USA from 97. *573 Dolores Street, San Francisco, CA 94110, USA* Tel (001) (415) 861 1372 E-mail louisknewton@hotmail.com

NEWTON, Miles Julius Albert. b 69. K Alfred's Coll Win BA91. Qu Coll Birm BTh96. **d** 97 **p** 98. C Sholing *Win* 97-01; C Bitterne Park from 01; V Woolston from 03. *St Mark's Vicarage, 117 Swift Road, Southampton SO19 9ER* Tel (023) 8032 6908

NEWTON, Nigel Ernest Hartley. b 38. St Jo Coll Nottm CertCS87. **d** 89 **p** 90. C Largs *Glas* 89-92; Angl Chapl Ashbourne Home Largs 89-92; P-in-c Eyemouth *Edin* 92-95; Chapl Miss to Seamen 92-95; P-in-c Challoch *Glas* from 95. *All Saints' Rectory, Challoch, Newton Stewart DG8 6RB* Tel and fax (01671) 402101 Mobile 07885-436892

NEWTON, Miss Pauline Dorothy. b 48. Southn Univ BA70 PGCE71 MPhil79. Sarum Th Coll 79. **dss** 82 **d** 87 **p** 94. Bemerton *Sarum* 82-87; NSM from 87; Dep Hd Malvern Girls' Coll from 86; Perm to Offic *Worc* from 86. *13 Highbury Avenue, Salisbury SP2 7EX* Tel (01722) 325707

NEWTON, Peter. b 39. St Jo Coll Nottm 73. **d** 75 **p** 76. C Porchester *S'well* 75-79; R Wilford 79-99; rtd 99. *Appletree Cottage, 20 Main Street, Eaton, Grantham NG32 1SE* Tel (01476) 870024

NEWTON, Raymond David. b 43. K Coll Lon BSc65. Linc Th Coll 65. **d** 67 **p** 68. C Ipswich St Matt *St E* 67-71; C E w W Barkwith *Linc* 71-74; R Chelmondiston w Harkstead *St E* 74-78; R Chelmondiston w Harkstead and Shotley w Erwarton 78-91; R Chelmondiston and Erwarton w Harkstead from 91. *The Rectory, Chelmondiston, Ipswich IP9 1HY* Tel (01473) 780214 Mobile 07718-808970 Fax as telephone E-mail david.newton@stedmundsbury.anglican.org

NEWTON, Richard. b 47. Lon Univ DipTh72. Trin Coll Bris 72. **d** 73 **p** 74. C Fareham St Jo *Portsm* 73-76; C Cheltenham St Mark *Glouc* 76-83; P-in-c Malvern St Andr *Worc* 83-95; TR Kingswood *Bris* 95-99; Master St Jo Hosp Bath from 00. *The Master's Lodge, Chapel Court, Bath BA1 1SL* Tel (01225) 486411 Fax 481291 E-mail richard.newton@stjohnsbath.org.uk

NEWTON, Richard John Christopher. b 60. Bris Univ BSc81 Birm Univ DipTh87. Qu Coll Birm 85. **d** 88 **p** 89. C Bris Ch the Servant Stockwood *Bris* 88-92; C Dorking w Ranmore *Guildf* 92-96; P-in-c Hagley *Worc* 96-00; R from 00. *The Rectory, 6 Middlefield Lane, Hagley, Stourbridge DY9 0PX* Tel (01562) 882442 *or* 886363 Fax 887833 E-mail richard.kathy@yescomputers.co.uk

NEWTON, Robert Keith. b 61. Man Univ BA83. St Steph Ho Ox 86. **d** 89 **p** 90. C Ludlow *Heref* 89-91; Egypt from 92. *Flat 17, 15 Ahmed Sabri, Zamalek, Cairo, Egypt*

NEWTON, Canon William Ronald. b 12. Birm Univ BA43. Westcott Ho Cam 41. **d** 43 **p** 44. C Truro St Paul *Truro* 43-48; PV Truro Cathl 45-46; V Treslothan 48-52; V Moulsecoomb *Chich* 52-56; V Stanmer w Falmer and Moulsecoomb 56-63; V Truro St Paul *Truro* 63-73; Hon Can Truro Cathl 71-83; V Penzance St Mary w St Paul 73-82; rtd 82; Perm to Offic *Chich* and *Truro* from 83. *52 Rutland Court, New Church Road, Hove BN3 4AF* Tel (01273) 773422

NIASSA, Bishop of. See VAN KOEVERING, The Rt Revd Mark Allan

NIBLETT, David John Morton. b 24. Wells Th Coll 51. **d** 54 **p** 55. C Stepney St Dunstan and All SS *Lon* 54-59; V Syston *Leic* 59-65; V Barnstaple St Pet w H Trin *Ex* 65-75; V S Brent 75-90; rtd 90; Perm to Offic *B & W* from 90. *2 Beretun Orchard, Glastonbury BA6 8AX* Tel (01458) 833101

NICE, Canon John Edmund. b 51. Univ of Wales (Ban) BA73. Coll of Resurr Mirfield 74. **d** 76 **p** 77. C Oxton *Ches* 76-79; C Liscard St Mary w St Columba 79-82; V Latchford St Jas 82-92; R Holyhead w Rhoscolyn w Llanfair-in-Neubwll *Ban* 92-95; R Holyhead from 95; RD Llifon and Talybolion 97-01; AD from 01; Can Cursal Ban Cathl from 02. *The Rectory, Newry Street, Holyhead LL65 1HP* Tel (01407) 763001 E-mail john.nice2@btopenworld.com

NICHOL, William David. b 58. Hull Univ BA84. Ridley Hall Cam 84. **d** 87 **p** 88. C Hull Newland St Jo *York* 87-90; C Kirk Ella 90-92; TV 92-98; P-in-c Powick *Worc* 98-99; R Powick and Guarlford and Madresfield w Newland from 99. *The Vicarage, 31 The Greenway, Powick, Worcester WR2 4RZ* Tel (01905) 830270

NICHOLAS, Canon Arnold Frederick. b 34. Jes Coll Cam BA58 MA62. Ely Th Coll 58. **d** 60 **p** 61. C Wisbech St Aug *Ely* 60-63; P-in-c Lt Massingham *Nor* 63-65; Youth Chapl 63-67; Chapl Bp Otter Coll Chich 67-70; R Westbourne *Chich* 70-76; V Stansted 70-76; Can and Preb Chich Cathl 76-82; RD Chich 76-80; P-in-c Chich St Pet 76-81; V Chich St Paul and St Bart 80-81; V Chich St Paul and St Pet 81-82; V Wisbech SS Pet and Paul *Ely* 82-90; RD Wisbech 82-90; V Fordham St Pet 90-95; P-in-c Kennett 90-95; Perm to Offic *Chich* from 97; rtd 99. *19 Roman Way, Chichester PO19 3QN* Tel (01243) 781388

NICHOLAS, Brian Arthur. b 19. St Edm Hall Ox BA47 MA53. Wycliffe Hall Ox 62. **d** 64 **p** 65. C Gerrards Cross *Ox* 64-66; C Whitley Ch Ch 66-69; V Chudleigh Knighton *Ex* 69-76; V Ex St Mark 76-84; rtd 84; Perm to Offic *Ex* from 84. *Windyridge, 4 Little John's Cross Hill, Exeter EX2 9PJ* Tel (01392) 219222

NICHOLAS, Ernest Milton. b 25. ACP50 Newc Univ DipAdEd69 Lanc Univ MA78. NEOC 85. **d** 86 **p** 87. NSM Hexham Newc 86-96; Perm to Offic from 96. *Hillside, Eilansgate, Hexham NE46 3EW* Tel (01434) 603609

NICHOLAS, Herbert Llewellyn. b 19. St D Coll Lamp 51. **d** 53 **p** 54. C Merthyr Tydfil *Llan* 53-65; V Pontypridd St Matt and Cilfynydd 65-89; rtd 89; Perm to Offic *Llan* from 89. *47 Meadow Crescent, Tonteg, Pontypridd CF38 1NL* Tel (01443) 206156

NICHOLAS, Malcolm Keith. b 46. FIBMS71 Open Univ BA79. S Dios Minl Tr Scheme 81. **d** 84 **p** 85. NSM Gatcombe *Portsm* 84-92; NSM Shorwell w Kingston 88-92; C Hartley Wintney, Elvetham, Winchfield and Dogmersfield *Win* 92-96; TV Grantham *Linc* 96-02; V Grantham, Harrowby w Londonthorpe 02-03; V Carr Dyke Gp from 03. *The Vicarage, 6 Walcott Road, Billinghay, Lincoln LN4 4EH* Tel (01526) 861746 E-mail revmalc@vicarage14.freeserve.co.uk

NICHOLAS, Maurice Lloyd. b 30. Kelham Th Coll 54. **d** 58 **p** 59. C Stepney St Dunstan and All SS *Lon* 58-60; C Sevenoaks St Jo *Roch* 60-65; Chapl RADD 65-75; C Northolt St Mary *Lon* 75-85; rtd 85; Hon C Upper Teddington St Pet and Paul *Lon* 85-90; Perm to Offic from 91. *58 Elton Close, Hampton Wick, Kingston upon Thames KT1 4EE* Tel (020) 8977 9340

NICHOLAS, Patrick. b 37. Selw Coll Cam BA60 MA65. Wells Th Coll 60. **d** 62 **p** 63. C Camberwell St Giles *S'wark* 62-63; C Warlingham w Chelsham and Farleigh 63-65; C Oxted 65-68; Hong Kong 68-74; C Portsea St Mary *Portsm* 75; Hd of Ho St Chris Fellowship Chiswick 76-79; Dept of Soc Services Glos Co Coun 79-92; Probation Officer Glouc Probation Service 92-97; rtd 97; Chapl St Jo Coll Hong Kong 97-00; Perm to Offic *Glouc* from 02. *35 Norwich Drive, Cheltenham GL51 3HD* Tel (01242) 510007 E-mail patnic@btinternet.com

NICHOLAS, Paul James. b 51. Univ of Wales (Lamp) DipTh73 BA. Coll of Resurr Mirfield 73. **d** 74 **p** 75. C Llanelli *St D* 74-78; C Roath *Llan* 78-84; P-in-c Leic St Pet *Leic* 84-87; V Shard End

Birm 87-96; rtd 96; Perm to Offic *Birm* from 96. *50 Delrene Road, Shirley, Solihull B90 2HJ* Tel 0121-745 7339
E-mail frpaul@oikos.screaming.net

NICHOLLS, Alan Fryer. b 26. Univ Coll Ex BA50. Sarum Th Coll 50. **d** 52 **p** 53. C Wootton Bassett *Sarum* 52-55; C Chesterfield St Mary and All SS *Derby* 55-56; V Ringley *Man* 56-60; Chapl Prebendal Sch Chich 60-63; PV Chich Cathl *Chich* 60-63; V Selmeston w Alciston 63-65; Chapl Woodbridge Sch 65-66; Asst Chapl and Ho Master 66-86; TV Bruton and Distr *B & W* 86-92; rtd 92; Perm to Offic *B & W* 92-99 and *St Alb* from 00. *36 Turpins Close, Hertford SG14 2EH* Tel (01992) 535749

NICHOLLS, Brian Albert. b 39. LBIPP LMPA. St Jo Coll Nottm CertCS84 WMMTC 90. **d** 93 **p** 94. NSM Oakham, Hambleton, Egleton, Braunston and Brooke *Pet* 93-96; R Edith Weston w N Luffenham and Lyndon w Manton from 96; P-in-c Empingham and Exton w Horn w Whitwell from 92; P-in-c Empingham w Whitwell from 02. *The Rectory, 8 Church Lane, Edith Weston, Oakham LE15 8EY* Tel (01780) 720931
E-mail whollynich@fwi.fsnet.co.uk

NICHOLLS (née HUMPHRIES), Mrs Catherine Elizabeth. b 53. Bris Univ BA87 Anglia Poly Univ MA95. Trin Coll Bris 84. **d** 87 **p** 94. C Bath Twerton-on-Avon *B & W* 87-90; Personnel Manager and Tr Officer TEAR Fund 90-95; Tr Manager for UK and Overseas Personnel 95; Hon C Norbiton *S'wark* 91-96; Perm to Offic *Ely* from 95; Dir Past Studies EAMTC from 97; Vice Prin 01-03; Hon Min Can Pet Cathl *Pet* 97-03. *King John's Thorn, Hethel, Norwich NR14 8HE* Tel (01508) 570557
E-mail cathynic@lobstermail.co.uk

✠**NICHOLLS, The Rt Revd John.** b 43. AKC66. **d** 67 **p** 68 **c** 90. C Salford St Clem Ordsall *Man* 67-69; C Langley All SS and Martyrs 69-72; V 72-78; Dir Past Th Coll of Resurr Mirfield 78-83; Lic to Offic *Wakef* 79-83; Can Res Man Cathl *Man* 83-90; Suff Bp Lancaster *Blackb* 90-97; Bp Sheff from 97. *Bishopscroft, Snaithing Lane, Sheffield S10 3LG* Tel 0114-230 2170 Fax 263 0110 E-mail bishop.jack@bishopscroft.idps.co.uk

NICHOLLS, Mark Richard. b 60. LSE BSc(Econ)82 Leeds Univ BA88. Coll of Resurr Mirfield 86. **d** 89 **p** 90. C Warrington St Elphin *Liv* 89-92; V Wigan St Andr 92-96; R North End St Marg Zimbabwe 96-00; Shrine P Shrine of Our Lady of Walsingham 00-02; V Mill End and Heronsgate w W Hyde *St Alb* from 02. *St Peter's Vicarage, Berry Lane, Rickmansworth WD3 7HQ* Tel (01923) 770369 or 772785 Mobile 07909-546659
E-mail mmarini2001@aol.com

NICHOLLS, Mark Simon. b 57. Down Coll Cam MA79. Ripon Coll Cuddesdon 92. **d** 94 **p** 95. C Farnham *Guildf* 94-98; P-in-c Crookham from 98. *The Vicarage, 14 Gally Hill Road, Church Crookham, Aldershot GU13 0LH* Tel (01252) 617130

NICHOLLS, Michael Stanley. b 34. AKC59. St Boniface Warminster 59. **d** 60 **p** 61. C Torquay St Martin Barton CD *Ex* 60-63; C E Grinstead St Mary *Chich* 63-66; C-in-c Salfords CD *S'wark* 66-68; V Salfords 68-75; V Tunbridge Wells St Barn *Roch* 75-97; rtd 97; Perm to Offic *Cant* 98-99; *Chich* from 99. *30 St Itha Road, Selsey, Chichester PO20 0AA* Tel (01243) 603837

NICHOLLS, Neil David Raymond. b 65. Univ Coll Lon BA86. Wycliffe Hall Ox BA90. **d** 91 **p** 92. C Westmr St Steph w St Jo *Lon* 91-94; C Islington St Mary 94-96; Chapl LSE 96-00; C St Bride Fleet Street w Bridewell etc 99-00; V Ealing St Barn from 00. *St Barnabas' Vicarage, 66 Woodfield Road, London W5 1SH* Tel (020) 8998 0826

NICHOLLS, Rachel. BA MPhil. **d** 00 **p** 01. NSM Chesterton St Geo *Ely* from 00. *5 Eachard Road, Cambridge CB3 0HZ* Tel (01223) 359167

NICHOLLS, Roger. Ox Univ MA Cam Univ DipEd. **d** 01 **p** 02. OLM Kenwyn w St Allen *Truro* from 01. *8 Truro Vean Terrace, Truro TR1 1HA* Tel (01872) 275753
E-mail rognicholls@tesco.net

NICHOLLS, Simon James. b 53. Trent Park Coll of Educn CertEd76. Ridley Hall Cam. **d** 00 **p** 01. C Nuneaton St Nic *Cov* from 00. *113 St Nicolas Park Drive, Nuneaton CV11 6EF* Tel (024) 7637 5830

NICHOLLS, Albert Percival. b 18. Tyndale Hall Bris. **d** 57 **p** 57. Canada 57-59; C Attenborough w Bramcote *S'well* 59-60; P-in-c Chiselborough w W Chinnock *B & W* 60-77; R E Chinnock 60-77; R Middle Chinnock 60-70; R Middle w W Chinnock 70-78; RD Martock 75-78; P-in-c Norton sub Hamdon w Chiselborough 77-78; R Norton sub Hamdon, W Chinnock, Chiselborough etc 78-86; rtd 86; Perm to Offic *Sarum* 86; *B & W* 86-98. *14 Manor Drive, Merriott TA16 5NT* Tel (01460) 72734

NICHOLLS, Barry Edward. b 40. ACA63 FCA73. S'wark Ord Course 66. **d** 69 **p** 70. NSM Surbiton St Andr and St Mark *S'wark* 69-92; Dean for MSE Kingston 90-92; Hon Can S'wark Cathl 90-92; Perm to Offic 99-01; NSM Upper Tooting H Trin from 01. *19 Arterberry Road, London SW20 8AF* Tel (020) 8879 0154 Fax as telephone E-mail barrynichols@btinternet.com

NICHOLLS, Dennis Harry. b 25. Kelham Th Coll 47. **d** 52 **p** 53. C Oakham *Pet* 52-55; C Kettering St Mary 55-57; P-in-c Spalding St Paul *Linc* 57-61; V Bury H Trin *Man* 61-81; V St Gluvias *Truro* 81-90; RD Carnmarth S 85-90; rtd 90; Perm to Offic *Truro* from 90. *The Rectory, 53 Clinton Road, Redruth TR15 2LP* Tel (01209) 215258

NICHOLS, Derek Edward. b 33. Lon Univ BD58 Monash Univ Aus DipEd82. Chich Th Coll 73. **d** 72 **p** 73. C S w N Hayling *Portsm* 73-75; Perm to Offic *Linc* 75-77; Australia from 80. *69 Carpenter Way, Sandstone Point, Qld, Australia 4511* Tel (0061) (7) 5429 5087

NICHOLS, Mrs Elizabeth Margaret. b 45. WEMTC 00. **d** 02. NSM Ledbury *Heref* from 02. *9 Woodfield Road, Ledbury HR8 2XJ* Tel (01531) 633601
E-mail elizabeth@nichols.fsworld.co.uk

NICHOLS, Howard Keith. b 41. CCC Ox BA64 MA68 CEng86 FIEE92 EurIng94. WEMTC 98. **d** 01 **p** 02. NSM Ledbury *Heref* from 01. *9 Woodfield Road, Ledbury HR8 2XJ* Tel (01531) 633601 E-mail hkn@extra-galactic.freeserve.co.uk

NICHOLS, Canon Raymond Maurice. b 22. ALCD53. **d** 53 **p** 54. C Childwall All SS *Liv* 53-56; Kenya 56-64; Home Sec SPCK 64-71; Overseas Sec 67-73; Publisher 73-74; P-in-c Dorchester *Ox* 74-78; P-in-c Newington 77-78; TR Dorchester 78-87; V Warborough 78-87; Hon Can Ch Ch 84-87; rtd 87; Perm to Offic *Sarum* from 91. *12 Abbey Court, Cerne Abbas, Dorchester DT2 7JH* Tel (01300) 341456

NICHOLS, Robert Warren. b 54. Biola Univ (USA) BA77. Fuller Th Sem California MA81 St Alb and Ox Min Course 93. **d** 96 **p** 97. NSM Headington Quarry *Ox* 96-97; C 97-00; Chapl Ox Radcliffe Hosps NHS Trust 00; Sen Asst P Wymondham *Nor* from 00; Lect from 01. *76A Norwich Road, Wymondham NR18 0SZ* Tel (01953) 604342
E-mail bob.nichols@bigfoot.com

NICHOLSON, Mrs Barbara Ruth. b 39. Nor City Coll TCert59. Dioc OLM tr scheme 99. **d** 02 **p** 03. OLM Reculver and Herne Bay St Bart *Cant* from 02. *34 Cliff Avenue, Herne Bay CT6 6LZ* Tel (01227) 364606

NICHOLSON, Brian Warburton. b 44. St Jo Coll Nottm 70 Lon Coll of Div ALCD73 LTh74. **d** 73 **p** 74. C Canford Magna *Sarum* 73-77; C E Twickenham St Steph *Lon* 77-80; V Colchester St Jo *Chelmsf* 80-96; R Oakley w Wootton St Lawrence *Win* from 96. *The Rectory, 9 The Drive, Oakley, Basingstoke RG23 7DA* Tel (01256) 780825 E-mail rectory@oakley.ndirect.co.uk

NICHOLSON, Miss Clare. b 46. RMN80 Keele Univ BA70 CertEd70 Lon Univ DN80. St Jo Coll Nottm DPS85. **dss** 85 **d** 87 **p** 94. Bletchley *Ox* 85-87; Par Dn 87-89; Par Dn Milton Keynes 89-90; Par Dn Prestwood and Gt Hampden 90-94; C 94-99; P-in-c E Springfield *Chelmsf* from 99. *The Vicarage, Ashton Place, Chelmer Village, Chelmsford CM2 6ST* Tel (01245) 462387 E-mail revclare46@aol.com

NICHOLSON, David. b 57. Sarum & Wells Th Coll 80. **d** 83 **p** 84. C Trevethin *Mon* 83-85; C Ebbw Vale 85-87; V Newport St Steph and H Trin 87-95; Hon Chapl Miss to Seamen 87-97; V Abertillery w Cwmtillery w Six Bells *Mon* 95-97; P-in-c Cudworth *Wakef* from 97; P-in-c Lundwood from 01. *The Vicarage, St John's Road, Cudworth, Barnsley S72 8DE* Tel (01226) 710279

NICHOLSON, Mrs Diane Maureen. b 45. Birm Coll of Educn CertEd68. LNSM course 95. **d** 97 **p** 98. OLM Ludham, Potter Heigham, Hickling and Catfield *Nor* from 97. *25 Latchmoor Park, Ludham, Great Yarmouth NR29 5RA* Tel (01692) 678683

NICHOLSON, Dorothy Ann. b 40. S'wark Ord Course 81. **dss** 84 **d** 87 **p** 94. Carshalton Beeches *S'wark* 84-88; Par Dn 87-88; Par Dn Brixton Road Ch Ch 88-89; C Malden St Jo 89-95; V Balham St Mary and St Jo from 95. *St Mary's Vicarage, 35 Elmsfield Road, London SW17 8AG* Tel (020) 8673 1188 Fax as telephone E-mail nicholsonda@arsenalfc.net

NICHOLSON, Eric. b 33. **d** 01 **p** 02. OLM W Wycombe w Bledlow Ridge, Bradenham and Radnage *Ox* from 01. *3 Cherry Tree Walk, Chesham HP5 3JN* Tel (01494) 785500

NICHOLSON, Prof Ernest Wilson. b 38. Comdr OM (Italy)90. TCD BA60 MA64 Glas Univ PhD64 Cam Univ MA67 BD71 DD78 Ox Univ DD79 FBA87. Westcott Ho Cam 69. **d** 69 **p** 70. Lect Div Cam Univ 67-79; Fell, Chapl and Dir of Th Studies Pemb Coll Cam 69-79; Dean 73-79; Prof of Interpr of H Scripture Oriel Coll Ox 79-90; Provost from 90; Pro-Vice-Chan Ox Univ from 93; Lic to Offic *Ox* from 84. *The Provost's Lodgings, Oriel College, Oxford OX1 4EW* Tel (01865) 276533

NICHOLSON, Gary. b 62. Open Univ BA89. Cranmer Hall Dur 91 NEOC DipHE93. **d** 95 **p** 96. NSM Whitworth w Spennymoor *Dur* 95-97; NSM Spennymoor, Whitworth and Merrington 97-00; C Coundon and Eldon 00-02; P-in-c from 02. *Redmire, West End Villas, Coundon, Bishop Auckland DL14 8PP* Tel (01388) 603312

NICHOLSON, Harold Sydney Leonard. b 35. Leic Univ HNC65 Garnett Coll Lon PGCE67 Open Univ BA77. S'wark Ord Course DipRS86 Oak Hill NSM Course 92. **d** 94 **p** 95. NSM Stanwell *Lon* from 94; NSM Sunbury from 98. *7 Academy Court, Fordbridge Road, Sunbury-on-Thames TW16 6AN* Tel (01932) 787690

NICHOLSON, John Paul. b 57. Sarum Th Coll. **d** 82 **p** 83. C Kirkby *Liv* 82-85; TV Speke St Aid 85-95; Ind Chapl *Ox* from 95. *1 Ivy Crescent, Slough SL1 5DA* Tel (01753) 528131 or tel and fax 770149 Mobile 07866-653965
E-mail johns@ivycres64.freeserve.co.uk

NICHOLSON, Mrs Julie Karina. b 53. UWE BA97. Trin Coll Bris. **d** 00 **p** 01. C Henbury *Bris* from 00. *42 Charlton Gardens, Bristol BS10 6LX* Tel 0117-950 9970

NICHOLSON, Kevin Smith. b 47. CQSW76. Edin Th Coll 89. **d** 91 **p** 92. C W Fife Team Min *St And* 91-94; P-in-c 94-95; R Kinross from 95. *St Paul's Rectory, 55 Muirs, Kinross KY13 8AU* Tel and fax (01577) 862271 Mobile 07803-963564 E-mail revkeith@cw.com

NICHOLSON, Canon Nigel Patrick. b 46. Sarum & Wells Th Coll 72. **d** 75 **p** 76. C Farnham *Guildf* 75-78; C Worplesdon 78-81; CF (ACF) from 80; P-in-c Compton *Guildf* 81-85; R Compton w Shackleford and Peper Harow 85-89; R Cranleigh from 89; RD Cranleigh from 95; Hon Can Guildf Cathl from 01. *The Rectory, High Street, Cranleigh GU6 8AS* Tel (01483) 273620 E-mail stnicoloff@aol.com

NICHOLSON, Miss Pamela Elizabeth. b 47. Ripon Coll Cuddesdon. **d** 92 **p** 94. C Balsall Heath St Paul *Birm* 92-95; V Smethwick St Matt w St Chad from 95. *1 St Matthew's Road, Smethwick, Warley B66 3TN* Tel 0121-558 1653

NICHOLSON, Paul Shannon. b 52. York Univ BA74 Middx Univ BA02 ARCO74 ARCM75. NTMTC 99. **d** 02 **p** 03. C Primrose Hill St Mary w Avenue Road St Paul *Lon* from 02. *30A Hadley Street, London NW1 8SS* Tel (020) 7482 1170 E-mail nicholsongarrison@hotmail.com

NICHOLSON, Canon Peter Charles. b 25. OBE92. Lambeth Hon MA89 Chich Th Coll 57. **d** 59 **p** 60. C Sawbridgeworth *St Alb* 59-62; Min Can, Prec and Sacr Pet Cathl *Pet* 62-67; V Wroxham w Hoveton *Nor* 67-74; V Lyme Regis *Sarum* 74-80; Gen Sec St Luke's Hosp for the Clergy 80-93; NSM Harlington *Lon* 80-87; Hon Chapl S'wark Cathl *S'wark* from 87; Can and Preb Chich Cathl *Chich* 89-93; rtd 93. *St Luke's Cottage, 13 Brearley Close, Uxbridge UB8 1JJ* Tel (01895) 233522

NICHOLSON, Peter Charles. b 44. Oak Hill Th Coll 74. **d** 76 **p** 77. C Croydon Ch Ch Broad Green *Cant* 76-80; C Gt Baddow *Chelmsf* 80-88; TV 88-96; V Westcliff St Mich from 96. *St Michael's Vicarage, 5 Mount Avenue, Westcliff-on-Sea SS0 8PS* Tel (01702) 478462 E-mail pedinic@talk21.com

NICHOLSON, Rodney. b 45. Mert Coll Ox BA68 MA71. Ridley Hall Cam 69. **d** 72 **p** 73. C Colne St Bart *Blackb* 72-75; C Blackpool St Jo 75-78; V Ewood 78-90; V Clitheroe St Paul Low Moor from 90; P-in-c Chatburn and Downham from 03. *The Vicarage, St Paul's Street, Clitheroe BB7 2LS* Tel (01200) 458019 Fax as telephone E-mail rodnic@btopenworld.com

NICHOLSON, Roland. b 40. Sarum & Wells Th Coll 72. **d** 74 **p** 75. C Morecambe St Barn *Blackb* 74-78; V Feniscliffe 78-90; V Sabden and Pendleton 90-02; C Poulton-le-Fylde from 02. *29 Moss Bourne Road, Poulton-le-Fylde FY6 7DU* Tel (01253) 884298

NICHOLSON, Mrs Samantha. b 69. St Jo Coll York BA92. St Jo Coll Nottm MA95 LTh93. **d** 96 **p** 97. C Toxteth St Cypr w Ch Ch *Liv* 96-01; P-in-c W Derby St Luke from 01. *St Luke's Vicarage, Princess Drive, West Derby, Liverpool L14 8XG* Tel 0151-228 6025

NICHOLSON, Stephen Lee. b 65. St Jo Coll Cam BA87 MA91 PhD94. St Steph Ho Ox 98. **d** 00 **p** 01. C Middlesbrough All SS *York* from 00; Asst Chapl HM Pris Holme Ho from 00. *14 Chipchase Road, Linthorpe, Middlesbrough TS5 6EY* Tel (01642) 827196 Mobile 07788-781560

NICHOLSON, Trevor Parry. b 35. St Edm Hall Ox BA58 MA. Wycliffe Hall Ox 58. **d** 60 **p** 61. C Eastbourne Ch Ch *Chich* 60-63; V Ifield 63-67; Asst Youth Chapl *Win* 67-73; Chapl Shoreham Gr Sch 73-78; P-in-c Capel *Guildf* 78-85; V 85-90; Chapl Qu Anne's Sch Caversham 90-00; rtd 00; P-in-c N Chapel w Ebernoe *Chich* from 00. *The Rectory, North Chapel, Petworth GU28 9HP* Tel (01428) 707373

NICHOLSON, Miss Velda Christine. b 44. CertEd65. Birm Bible Inst DipTh69 Cranmer Hall Dur 81. **dss** 82 **d** 87 **p** 94. Gt and Lt Driffield *York* 82-86; Newby 86-87; Par Dn 87-88; TD Cramlington *Newc* 88-94; TV 94-96; Perm to Offic from 96. *24 Glendale, Amble, Morpeth NE65 0RG* Tel (01665) 713796

NICHOLSON, Veronica Mary. See WILSON, Mrs Veronica Mary

NICKALLS, Frederick William. b 13. Oak Hill Th Coll 49. **d** 51 **p** 52. C Penge St Jo *Roch* 51-53; C-in-c Wollaton Park CD *S'well* 53-55; V Everton Em *Liv* 55-58; V Barnehurst *Roch* 58-67; R Nailsea H Trin *B & W* 67-78; rtd 78; Perm to Offic *St E* 94-98; Perm to Offic *Win* 98-01. *9 Worcester Court, Worcester Road, Bristol BS8 3JL* Tel 0117-974 5063

NICKLAS-CARTER, Mrs Derath May. b 52. N Staffs Poly LLB87. St Alb and Ox Min Course 01. **d** 02 **p** 03. C Harlington Ch Ch CD *Lon* from 02. *192 Waltham Avenue, Hayes UB3 1TF* Tel and fax (020) 8573 0112 Mobile 07776-154984 E-mail derath@fish.co.uk

NICKLESS, Christopher John. b 58. Univ of Wales BA79. Coll of Resurr Mirfield 79. **d** 81 **p** 82. C Bassaleg *Mon* 81-85; TV Ebbw Vale 85-93; V Newport St Teilo 93-99. *c/o Bishopstow, Stow Hill, Newport NP9 4EA* Tel (01633) 263510

NICKLIN, Ivor. b 41. FRSA68 BEd MTh73 PhD76 MA84. Wycliffe Hall Ox. **d** 84 **p** 85. NSM Weaverham *Ches* 84-89; P-in-c

Kings Walden *St Alb* 89-91; P-in-c Offley w Lilley 89-91; V King's Walden and Offley w Lilley 91-93; V Basford *Lich* 93-98; rtd 98; Perm to Offic *Ches* from 99; *Lich* from 00. *232 Manor Way, Crewe CW2 6PH* Tel (01270) 669080

NICKOLS, James Alexander. b 75. Regent's Park Coll Ox BA96. Ridley Hall Cam 98. **d** 00 **p** 01. C Plymouth St Jude *Ex* from 00. *120 Salisbury Road, St Judes, Plymouth PL4 8TB* Tel (01752) 224877 Mobile 07968-062339 E-mail jamesnkls@aol.com

NICKOLS-RAWLE, Peter John. b 44. St Luke's Coll Ex CertEd73. Sarum & Wells Th Coll 76. **d** 78 **p** 79. C Ex St Thos *Ex* 78-80; C Old Shoreham *Chich* 80-86; C New Shoreham 80-86; P-in-c Donnington 86-90; Chapl RAF 90-92; TV Ottery St Mary, Alfington, W Hill, Tipton etc *Ex* 92-97; V Breage w Germoe and Godolphin *Truro* 98-01; rtd 01; Perm to Offic *Truro* from 01. *2 Kroonstadt Villas, Godolphin Road, Helston TR13 8QR* Tel (01326) 569664

NICKSON, Ann Louise. b 58. New Hall Cam BA80 Fitzw Coll Cam BA95 Solicitor 81. Ridley Hall Cam PhD98. **d** 98 **p** 99. C Sanderstead All SS *S'wark* 98-01; P-in-c Norbury St Steph and Thornton Heath from 01. *St Stephen's Vicarage, 9 Warwick Road, Thornton Heath CR7 7NH* Tel (020) 8684 3820 E-mail annnickson@aol.com

NICOL, David Christopher. b 56. Westmr Coll Ox BEd84 Ox Univ Inst of Educn 91. St Alb and Ox Min Course 95. **d** 98 **p** 99. NSM Deddington w Barford, Clifton and Hempton *Ox* 98-01; V Longnor, Quarnford and Sheen *Lich* from 01. *The Vicarage, Gauledge Lane, Longnor, Buxton SK17 0PA* Tel (01298) 83742 Fax as telephone E-mail fr.david@tinyworld.co.uk

NICOL, Ernest. b 25. S'wark Ord Course 71. **d** 74 **p** 75. NSM Hornsey Ch Ch *Lon* 74-75; NSM Hornsey St Geo 76-84; C Hendon Ch Ch 85-90; rtd 90; C Steeton *Bradf* 90-96; Asst Chapl Airedale Hosp Bradf 90-96; Perm to Offic *Lon* from 96. *75 Nightingale Lane, London N8 7RA* Tel (020) 8341 5496

NICOL, Harvie Thomas. b 61. Aston Tr Scheme DipHE97 St Jo Coll Nottm DipTh99. **d** 99 **p** 00. C Balderstone *Man* 99; C S Rochdale 00-03; P-in-c Ashton St Pet from 03; TV Ashton from 03. *The Rectory, 2A Hutton Avenue, Ashton-under-Lyne OL6 6DY* Tel 0161-330 8251

NICOLE, Bruce. b 54. K Coll Lon MA96 ACIB. Wycliffe Hall Ox 89. **d** 91 **p** 92. C Headley All SS *Guildf* 91-95; V Camberley St Mich Yorktown from 95; RD Surrey Heath from 02. *The Vicarage, 286 London Road, Camberley GU15 3JP* Tel (01276) 23602 E-mail revbrucenicole@aol.com

NICOLL, Alexander Charles Fiennes Jack. b 34. Lon Univ DipTh66. Lon Coll of Div 66. **d** 68 **p** 69. C Trentham *Lich* 68-71; C Hednesford 72-74; P-in-c Quarnford 74-84; V Longnor 74-84; P-in-c Sheen 80-84; V Longnor, Quarnford and Sheen 85-00; RD Alstonfield 96-00; Perm to Offic from 00; rtd 00. *110 Stone Road, Uttoxeter ST14 7QW* Tel (01889) 569361

NICOLL, Miss Angela Olive. b 50. Linc Th Coll 77. **dss** 79 **d** 87 **p** 94. Catford St Laur *S'wark* 79-83; Peckham St Jo w St Andr 83-87; Par Dn 87-88; Par Dn New Addington 88-94; C South All SS Africa from 02. *St Monica's House of Prayer, 46 Green Street, Kimberley, South Africa*

NICOLSON, Paul Roderick. b 32. Cuddesdon Coll 65. **d** 67 **p** 68. C Farnham Royal *Ox* 67-70; Lic to Offic *St Alb* 70-82; C Hambleden Valley *Ox* 82-99; rtd 99. *93 Campbell Road, London N17 0AX* Tel (020) 8376 5455 Mobile 0796 1177889 Fax 8376 5319 E-mail paul@nicolson.com

NIE, Miss Muriel Rose. b 29. St Mich Ho Ox IDC57. **d** 87 **p** 94. NSM Leyton All SS *Chelmsf* 87-99; Perm to Offic from 99. *2 Queens Court, Manor Road, London E10 7HP* Tel (020) 8556 0457

NIGER, Bishop on the. See OKEKE, The Rt Revd Ken Sandy Edozie

NIGERIA, Archbishop of. See AKINOLA, The Most Revd Peter Jasper

NIGHTINGALE, Catherine. b 72. **d** 01 **p** 02. C Birchencliffe *Wakef* from 01; C to Dioc Chapl among Deaf People from 01. *85 New North Road, Huddersfield HD1 5ND*

NIGHTINGALE, Canon John Brodie. b 42. Pemb Coll Ox BA64 Bris Univ DSS65 Qu Coll Cam BA67. Westcott Ho Cam 65. **d** 67 **p** 68. C Wythenshawe St Martin *Man* 67-70; Nigeria 70-76; P-in-c Amberley w N Stoke *Chich* 76-79; Adult Educn Adv 76-79; Asst Home Sec Gen Syn Bd for Miss and Unity 80-84; Miss Sec 84-87; P-in-c Wolverton w Norton Lindsey and Langley *Cov* 87-95; Dioc Miss Adv 87-95; V Rowley Regis *Birm* from 95; Hon Can Birm Cathl from 01. *St Giles' Vicarage, 192 Hanover Road, Rowley Regis, Warley B65 9EQ* Tel 0121-559 1251 Fax 559 1553 E-mail john.nightingale@which.net

NIGHTINGALE, Susan Kay. b 44. Keele Univ BA66 DipSocSc66 Seabury-Western Th Sem DMin99 Coll of Ripon & York St Jo CertCS85. S'wark Ord Course 90. **d** 93 **p** 94. NSM St Giles Cripplegate w St Bart Moor Lane etc *Lon* 93-99; Perm to Offic *York* 93-99; Asst Chapl H Trin Geneva *Eur* 99-02; P-in-c Sutton on the Forest *York* from 03. *Westfield Farm, Sheriff Hutton, York YO60 6QQ* Tel (01347) 878423

NIMMO, Canon Alexander Emsley. b 53. Aber Univ BD76 PhD97 Edin Univ MPhil83 FSAScot93. Edin Th Coll 76. **d** 8

p 79. Prec St Andr Cathl Inverness *Mor* 78-81; P-in-c Stornoway *Arg* 81-83; R 84; R Edin St Mich and All SS *Edin* 84-90; Chapl HM Pris Saughton 87-90; R Aberdeen St Marg *Ab* from 90; Can St Andr Cathl from 96; Syn Clerk from 01. *St Margaret's Rectory, Gallowgate, Aberdeen AB25 1EA* Tel (01224) 644969 Fax 630767 E-mail emsley@aberdeengallowgate.fsnet.co.uk

NIND, Robert William Hampden. b 31. Ball Coll Ox BA54 MA60. Cuddesdon Coll 54. **d** 56 **p** 57. C Spalding *Linc* 56-60; Jamaica 60-67; P-in-c Battersea St Bart *S'wark* 67-70; V Brixton St Matt 70-82; Lic to Offic 82-84; Ind Chapl 84-89; Ind Chapl *Ox* 89-95; rtd 95. *19 Binswood Avenue, Headington, Oxford OX3 8NY* Tel (01865) 66604 E-mail bawalker@rwhnind.freeserve.co.uk

NINEHAM, Prof Dennis Eric. b 21. Qu Coll Ox BA43 MA46 Cam Univ BD64 Birm Univ Hon DD72. Linc Th Coll 44. **d** 44 **p** 45. Asst Chapl Qu Coll Ox 44-46; Chapl 46-54; Prof Bibl and Hist Th K Coll Lon 54-58; Prof Div Lon Univ 58-64; Regius Prof Div Cam Univ 64-69; Warden Keble Coll Ox 69-79; Hon Can Bris Cathl *Bris* 80-86; Prof Th Bris Univ 80-86; rtd 86; Perm to Offic *Ox* from 87. *9 Fitzherbert Close, Iffley, Oxford OX4 4EN* Tel (01865) 715941

NINIS, The Ven Richard Betts. b 31. Linc Coll Ox BA53 MA62 Derby Univ. Linc Th Coll 53. **d** 55 **p** 56. C Poplar All SS w St Frideswide *Lon* 55-62; V Heref St Martin *Heref* 62-71; V Upper and Lower Bullinghope w Grafton 68-71; R Dewsall w Callow 68-71; Dioc Missr 69-74; Preb Heref Cathl 70-74; Telford Planning Officer *Lich* 70-74; Can Res and Treas Lich Cathl 74-98; Adn Stafford 74-80; Adn Lich 80-98; rtd 98; Perm to Offic *B & W* from 00. *Hill View, 32 Robert Street, Williton, Taunton TA4 4QL* Tel (01984) 634987 Fax as telephone

NISBET, Mrs Gillian Ruth. b 65. N Ord Course. **d** 03. NSM Childwall St Dav *Liv* from 03. *20 Stuart Avenue, Liverpool L25 0NJ*

NISBETT, Canon Thomas Norman. b 25. OBE91. Codrington Coll Barbados. **d** 62 **p** 63. Barbados 62-64; Bermuda from 65; Hon Can Bermuda Cathl from 81; rtd 97. *2 Shelton Road, Pembroke HM 20, Bermuda* Tel (001441) 236 0537 Fax as telephone

NIXON, Mrs Annette Rose. b 37. K Coll Lon BD58 Newc Univ CertEd73. **d** 88 **p** 94. Dioc Youth Officer *Ox* 84-90; Par Dn Earley St Pet 88-93; Par Dn Olney w Emberton 93-94; C 94-96; P-in-c Worminghall w Ickford, Oakley and Shabbington 96-00; rtd 00. *3 Harington Close, Liverpool L37 1XP* Tel (01704) 872245

NIXON, David John. b 59. St Chad's Coll Dur BA81. St Steph Ho Ox 88. **d** 91 **p** 92. C Plymouth St Pet *Ex* 91-94; Chapl Ex Univ from 94. *29 Barnardo Road, Exeter EX2 4ND* Tel (01392) 420162 E-mail d.j.nixon@exeter.ac.uk

NIXON, Frances (Isobel). b 34. TCD BA62. **d** 94 **p** 95. NSM Rossory *Clogh* from 94. *63 Granshaugh Road, Enniskillen BT92 2BL* Tel (028) 6634 8723

NIXON, John David. b 38. Leeds Univ BSc60 CEng70 MICE. Linc Th Coll 76. **d** 78 **p** 79. C Rugby St Andr *Cov* 78-83; TV 83-86; TV Bicester w Bucknell, Caversfield and Launton *Ox* 86-98; USA from 98; rtd 00. *701 1/2 Illinois Street, Lawrence, KS 66044, USA* Tel (001) (785) 832 1387 E-mail frjdn@hotmail.com or allsaintskcrector@juno.com

NIXON, Ms Naomi Jane. b 75. Keele Univ BA97. St Jo Coll Nottm MA(TS)00. **d** 01 **p** 02. C Ludlow, Ludford, Ashford Carbonell etc *Heref* from 01. *St Giles's Vicarage, Sheet Road, Ludlow SY8 1LR* Tel (01584) 874213 E-mail nnixon@fish.co.uk

NIXON, Canon Phillip Edward. b 43. Ch Ch Ox MA73 DPhil73 Trin Coll Cam BA80 K Coll Lon MA00. Westcott Ho Cam 78. **d** 81 **p** 82. C Leeds Halton St Wilfrid *Ripon* 81-84; V Goring *Ox* 84; V Goring w Stoke from 84; RD Henley 94-02; Hon Can Ch Ch 00-03; P-in-c Northampton St Jas *Pet* from 03. *The Vicarage, Vicarage Road, Northampton NN5 7AX* Tel (01604) 751164 E-mail phillip@btopenworld.com

NIXON, Miss Rosemary Ann. b 45. Bp Grosseteste Coll CertEd66 Dur Univ MA83 Edin Univ MTh95. Dalton Ho Bris IDC72 DipTh72 BD73. **d** 87 **p** 94. Tutor St Jo Coll w Cranmer Hall Dur 75-89; Dir St Jo Coll Ext Progr 82-89; NSM Chester le Street *Dur* 87-89; TD Gateshead 89-92; Dir Cranmer Hall Urban Studies Unit 89-92; TISEC 92-99; Prin 95-99; Can St Mary's Cathl *Edin* 96-99; V Cleadon *Dur* from 99. *The Vicarage, 5 Sunderland Road, Cleadon, Sunderland SR6 7UR* Tel 0191-536 7147 Fax as telephone

NIXON, William Samuel. BSc BTh. **d** 00 **p** 01. C Lisburn St Paul *Conn* 00-02; V Hillsborough *D & D* from 02. *11 Ashvale Drive, Hillsborough BT26 6DN* Tel (028) 9268 9099

NIXSON, Peter. b 27. Ball Coll Ox BA51 MA59 Ex Univ PGCE67 DipEd72. Coll of Resurr Mirfield 51. **d** 53 **p** 54. C Babbacombe *Ex* 53-56; C Swindon New Town *Bris* 56-57; C Boyne Hill *Ox* 57-60; C-in-c Bayswater St Mary CD 60-66; Perm to Offic *Ex* 66-67 and 70-85; Perm to Offic *Lich* 67-69; Hd RE Oswestry Boys' High Sch 67-69; Hon C Oswestry H Trin 69-70; Sch Coun Tiverton 70-75; Newton Abbot 75-85; V Winkleigh *Ex* 85-92; R Ashreigney 85-92; R Broadwoodkelly 85-92; V Brushford 85-92; RD Chulmleigh 87-93; rtd 93; Perm to Offic *Ex* from 93. *40 Lidford Tor Avenue, Paignton TQ4 7ED* Tel (01803) 522698

NIXSON, Rosemary Clare. *See* WARD, Mrs Rosemary Clare
NJENGA, Kennedy Samuel. b 60. Oak Hill Th Coll Qu Coll Birm. **d** 01 **p** 02. C Old Trafford St Jo *Man* from 01. *11 Reynolds Road, Old Trafford, Manchester M16 9WX* Tel 0161-881 3775 E-mail njambinjenga@aol.com
✠**NJOJO, The Rt Revd Patrice Byankya.** b 38. BA76. Montreal Dioc Th Coll 79. **d** 70 **p** 80 **c** 80. Bp Boga from 80; Abp Congo 92-02. *PO Box 25586, Kampala, Uganda* Tel (00256) 77-647495 E-mail eac-mags@infocom.co.ug
NOAH, Michael John. b 44. WEMTC 00. **d** 02 **p** 03. NSM Hucclecote *Glouc* from 02. *10 Kingscroft Road, Hucclecote, Gloucester GL3 3RF* Tel (01452) 610174 E-mail mikenoah@supanet.com
NOAKES, Mrs Dorothy. b 35. Derby Coll of Educn CertEd55 Ex Univ BEd85 BPhil(Ed)92. LNSM course 94. **d** 96 **p** 97. OLM Helston and Wendron *Truro* from 96. *6 Tenderah Road, Helston TR13 8NT* Tel (01326) 573239 E-mail poppyno@tinyworld.co.uk
✠**NOAKES, The Rt Revd George.** b 24. Univ of Wales (Abth) BA48 Univ of Wales Hon DD90. Wycliffe Hall Ox 49. **d** 50 **p** 52 **c** 82. C Lampeter *St D* 50-56; V Eglwyswrw and Meline 56-59; V Tregaron 59-67; V Cardiff Dewi Sant *Llan* 67-76; R Aberystwyth *St D* 76-80; Can St D Cathl 77-79; Adn Cardigan 79-82; V Llanychaearn w Llanddeiniol 80-82; Bp St D 82-91; Abp Wales 87-91; rtd 91. *Hafod-Lon, Rhydargaeau, Carmarthen SA32 7DT* Tel (01267) 253302
NOBBS, Charles Henry ffrench. b 67. Hatf Coll Dur BSc89 St Jo Coll Dur BA99 CEng96. Cranmer Hall Dur 97. **d** 99 **p** 00. C Northampton St Giles *Pet* 99-02; C Collingtree w Courteenhall and Milton Malsor from 02. *10 Foxglove Close, Grange Park, Northampton NN4 5DD* Tel (01604) 875188 E-mail charlie@dunelm.org.uk
NOBBS, John Ernest. b 35. Tyndale Hall Bris 60. **d** 63 **p** 64. C Walthamstow St Mary *Chelmsf* 63-66; C Braintree 66-69; C Wakef St Andr and St Mary *Wakef* 69-71; C Tooting Graveney St Nic *S'wark* 71-74; C Woking St Pet *Guildf* 74-78; C Worthing St Geo *Chich* 78-88; C Rayleigh *Chelmsf* 88-94; rtd 94; Perm to Offic *Chelmsf* from 00. *89 Panfield Lane, Braintree CM7 5RP* Tel (01376) 322901
NOBLE, Alexander Frederick Innes (Sandy). b 30. Selw Coll Cam BA53 MA58. Lon Coll of Div ALCD55. **d** 55 **p** 56. C Stratton St Margaret *Bris* 55-57; C Brislington St Luke 57-59; Chapl Pierrepont Sch Frensham 59-61; Asst Chapl Repton Sch Derby 61-63; Chapl 63-66; Chapl Blundell's Sch Tiverton 66-72; St Jo C of E Sch Cowley 73-77; Chapl Cranbrook Sch Kent 77-81; Chapl St Geo Sch Harpenden 81-90; Hon C Herriard w Winslade and Long Sutton etc *Win* 90-94; rtd 95; P-in-c Oare w Culbone *B & W* 95-99; Perm to Offic from 00. *Upway, Church Street, Minehead TA24 5JU* Tel (01643) 708976
NOBLE, Canon Arthur. b 12. TCD BA35 MA38. TCD Div Sch Div Test. **d** 36 **p** 37. C Newtownards *D & D* 36-39; C Belfast St Mark *Conn* 39-41; C Lurgan Ch the Redeemer *D & D* 41-44; I Rasharkin w Finvoy *Conn* 44-49; I Belfast St Aid 49-61; I Lisburn Ch Ch 61-82; Preb Conn Cathl 74-79; Prec 79-82; rtd 82. *38 King's Road, Belfast BT5 6JJ* Tel (028) 9028 2217
NOBLE, Christopher John Lancelot. b 58. Aston Tr Scheme 88 Oak Hill Th Coll DipHE90. **d** 90 **p** 91. C Tonbridge SS Pet and Paul *Roch* 90-95; P-in-c Stansted w Fairseat and Vigo 95-98; R from 98. *The Rectory, 9 The Coach Drive, Meopham, Gravesend DA13 0SZ* Tel (01732) 822494
NOBLE, David. b 37. S Dios Minl Tr Scheme 84. **d** 87 **p** 88. C Alverstoke *Portsm* 87-89; Australia from 90; rtd 02. *Quill Studio, 9 Chaparral Crescent, Willetton, W Australia 6155* Tel 417-172542 (mobile) E-mail thenobles@surak.com.au
NOBLE, Mrs Eileen Joan. b 45. NEOC 90. **d** 93 **p** 94. C Gosforth All SS *Newc* 93-96; C Cramlington 96-97; TV 97-01; V Ashington from 01. *Holy Sepulchre Vicarage, Wansbeck Road, Ashington NE63 8HZ* Tel (01670) 813358 E-mail revnoble2000@yahoo.com
NOBLE, Graham Edward. b 49. SS Paul & Mary Coll Cheltenham CertEd71 Open Univ BA74. EAMTC 85. **d** 88 **p** 89. C Kesgrave *St E* 88-90; P-in-c Gt and Lt Blakenham w Baylham and Nettlestead 90-95; P-in-c Debenham w Aspall and Kenton from 95; P-in-c Helmingham w Framsden and Pettaugh w Winston from 99; RD Loes from 99. *The Vicarage, 34 Gracechurch Street, Debenham, Stowmarket IP14 6RE* Tel (01728) 860265
NOBLE, Paul Vincent. b 54. Leeds Univ BA75 PGCE76 Ox Univ BA81 MA85. St Steph Ho Ox 79. **d** 82 **p** 83. C Prestbury *Glouc* 82-85; P-in-c Avening w Cherington 85-90; V The Suttons w Tydd *Linc* 90-98; R Skirbeck St Nic from 98. *The Rectory, Fishtoft Road, Skirbeck, Boston PE21 0DJ* Tel (01205) 362734
NOBLE, Peter Hirst. b 37. Lon Univ BD68 Leeds Univ MPhil72. Cranmer Hall Dur 65. **d** 68 **p** 69. C Honley *Wakef* 68-72; P-in-c Moss *Sheff* 72-81; V Askern 72-92; rtd 92. *40 Broome Close, Huntington, York YO32 9RH* Tel (01904) 766203
NOBLE, Canon Philip David. b 46. Glas Univ BSc67 Edin Univ BD70. Edin Th Coll 67. **d** 70 **p** 71. C Edin Ch Ch *Edin* 70-72; Papua New Guinea 72-75; R Cambuslang *Glas* 76-83; R

Uddingston 76-83; Ev Prestwick 83-85; R Prestwick from 85; Can St Mary's Cathl from 99. *56 Ayr Road, Prestwick KA9 1RR* Tel (01292) 477108

NOBLE, Robert. b 43. TCD BA66 BD73. **d** 68 **p** 69. C Holywood *D & D* 68-71; Chapl RAF 71-98; Chapl Holmewood Ho Sch Tunbridge Wells from 98; Perm to Offic *Chich* from 01. *The Little House, Holmewood House Sch, Langton Green, Tunbridge Wells TN3 0EB* Tel (01892) 860030

NOBLET, David. b 62. Cen Lancs Univ HND95. Cranmer Hall Dur DTM99. **d** 99 **p** 00. C Carnforth *Blackb* 99; C Standish 00-03; P-in-c Langho Billington from 03. *The Vicarage, 11 Whalley New Road, Billington, Blackburn BB7 9NA* Tel (01254) 822246

NOBLETT, The Ven William Alexander. b 53. Southn Univ BTh78 Westmr Coll Ox MTh99. Sarum & Wells Th Coll 74. **d** 78 **p** 79. C Sholing *Win* 78-80; I Ardamine w Kiltennel, Glascarrig etc *C & O* 80-82; Chapl RAF 82-84; V Middlesbrough St Thos *York* 84-87; Asst Chapl HM Pris Wakef 87-89; Chapl 89-92; Chapl HM Pris Nor 92-97; Chapl HM Pris Full Sutton 97-01; Chapl Gen of Pris and Adn to HM Pris from 01; Can and Preb York Minster *York* from 01; Lic to Offic from 01. *HM Prison Service Chaplaincy, Room 621, Horseferry House, Dean Ryle Street, London SW1P 2AW* Tel (020) 7217 8997 Fax 7217 8980 E-mail wnoblett@fish.co.uk

NOCK, Peter Arthur. b 15. Keble Coll Ox BA36 MA42. Bps' Coll Cheshunt 37. **d** 39 **p** 40. C Gt Harwood St Bart *Blackb* 39-40; C Lancaster Priory Ch 40-45; V Over Wyresdale 45-50; V Darwen St Cuth 50-64; V Sparkhill St Jo *Birm* 64-71; RD Bordesley 67-71; V Maney 71-81; rtd 81; Perm to Offic *Carl* from 81. *Westlands, Linden Fold, Grange-over-Sands LA11 7AY* Tel (01539) 535139

NOCK, Roland George William. b 62. St Andr Univ BSc84 BD89. Edin Th Coll 91. **d** 91 **p** 92. C Dunfermline *St And* 91-93; C W Fife Team Min 91-93; R Cupar 93-96; CF 96-99. *46 Heol Y Parc, Cefneithin, Llanelli SA14 7DL* Tel (01269) 845847 E-mail roland@nock.screaming.net

NOCKELS, John Martin. b 46. Lich Th Coll Qu Coll Birm 73. **d** 73 **p** 74. C Eccleshill *Bradf* 73-76; C Fawley *Win* 76-78; V Southampton St Jude 78-84; R Tadley St Pet 84-98; P-in-c South Raynham, E w W Raynham, Helhoughton, etc *Nor* 98-99; P-in-c Gt and Lt Massingham and Harpley 98-99; R Gt w Lt Massingham, Harpley, Rougham etc from 99. *The Rectory, 68 Station Road, Great Massingham, King's Lynn PE32 2HW* Tel (01485) 520211

NODDER, Marcus Charles Colmore. b 67. Pemb Coll Cam BA89 PGCE90. Oak Hill Th Coll BA01. **d** 01 **p** 02. C Denton Holme *Carl* from 01. *118 Dalston Road, Carlisle CA2 5PJ* Tel (01228) 522938 E-mail mnodder@hotmail.com *or* marcus@nodder.fsbusiness.co.uk

NODDER, Thomas Arthur (Brother Arnold). b 20. K Coll Lon 58. **d** 60 **p** 61. Brotherhood of the H Cross from 49; C Rotherhithe St Mary w All SS *S'wark* 60-63; SSF from 63; Lic to Offic *Chelmsf* 63-66; C Plaistow St Andr 66-68; Lic to Offic *Newc* 69-70; Lic to Offic *Birm* 70-83; Perm to Offic 90-98; Lic to Offic *Sarum* 83-89; rtd 90; Perm to Offic *Chelmsf* from 98. *Society of St Francis, 42 Balaam Street, London E13 8AQ* Tel (020) 7476 5189

NODDINGS, John Henry. b 39. Chich Th Coll 80. **d** 81 **p** 82. C Southborough St Pet w Ch Ch and St Matt *Roch* 81-83; C Prittlewell *Chelmsf* 83-86; V Clay Hill St Jo *Lon* 86-88; V Clay Hill St Jo and St Luke 88-02; Chapl Chase Farm Hosp Enfield 88-94; Chapl Chase Farm Hosps NHS Trust 94-95; rtd 03; P-in-c Gt Coxwell w Buscot, Coleshill etc *Ox* from 03. *The Vicarage, Great Coxwell, Faringdon SN7 7NG* Tel (01367) 240665

NOEL, Brother. See ALLEN, Noel Stephen

NOEL, Canon Frank Arthur. b 20. TCD BA44 MA49. CITC 45. **d** 45 **p** 46. C Aghalee *D & D* 45-48; C Portadown St Mark *Arm* 48-51; I Ballinderry w Tamlaght 51-59; I Tullaniskin w Clonoe 59-63; I Mullabrack w Kilcluney 63-75; I Acton and Drumbanagher 75-88; Preb Arm Cathl 86-88; rtd 88; Lic to Offic *Arm* from 90. *31 Woodford Drive, Armagh BT60 7AY* Tel (028) 3752 7787

NOKES, Michael David Patrick. b 44. CA MCMI. **d** 02 **p** 03. NSM Heworth Ch Ch *York* from 02. *12 Westminster Road, Clifton, York YO30 6LY* Tel (01904) 330620 Mobile 07776-252440 E-mail michael@cpas.org.uk

NOKES, Peter Warwick. b 48. Leic Univ BA71. Westcott Ho Cam 79. **d** 81 **p** 82. C Northfield *Birm* 81-84; C Ludlow *Heref* 84-87; P-in-c Writtle w Highwood *Chelmsf* 87-91; V 91-92; P-in-c Epping St Jo 92-95; P-in-c Coopersale 93-95; TR Epping Distr 95-99; R Nor St Pet Mancroft w St Jo Maddermarket *Nor* from 99. *37 Unthank Road, Norwich NR2 2PB* Tel (01603) 627816 *or* 610443 Mobile 07711-384009 Fax (01603) 766652 E-mail petermancroft@aol.com

NOKES, Robert Harvey. b 39. Keble Coll Ox BA61 MA65 Birm Univ DipTh63. Qu Coll Birm 61. **d** 63 **p** 64. C Totteridge *St Alb* 63-67; C Dunstable 67-73; V Langford 73-90; R Braughing w Furneux Pelham and Stocking Pelham from 90. *The Rectory, 7A Green End, Braughing, Ware SG11 2PG* Tel (01920) 822619

NOLAN, James Charles William. b 44. Chich Th Coll 75. **d** 77 **p** 78. C Crewe St Andr *Ches* 77-79; C Sale St Anne 79-83; R

Holme Runcton w S Runcton and Wallington *Ely* from 83; V Tottenhill w Wormegay from 83; R Watlington from 83. *The Rectory, Downham Road, Watlington, King's Lynn PE33 0HS* Tel (01553) 810305

NOLAN, Marcus. b 54. Bris Univ BEd. Ridley Hall Cam. **d** 83 **p** 84. C Dagenham *Chelmsf* 83-86; C Finchley St Paul and St Luke *Lon* 86-90; V W Hampstead Trin 90-98; rtd 99; Perm to Offic *Derby* from 00. *55 Blanchcroft, Melbourne, Derby DE73 1GG*

NOLLAND, John Leslie. b 47. New England Univ (NSW) BSc67 Clare Coll Cam PhD78. Moore Th Coll Sydney ThL70 BD71. **d** 71 **p** 72. Australia 71-78; Canada 78-86; Asst Prof NT Studies Regent Coll Vancouver 78-86; Tutor Trin Coll Bris from 86; Vice Prin 91-97. *Trinity College, Stoke Hill, Bristol BS9 1JP* Tel 0117-968 2083 Fax 968 7470 E-mail john.nolland@trinity-bris.ac.uk

NOLLER, Hilda Elizabeth Mary (Sister Elizabeth Mary). b 26. MSR47 FSR53. **d** 95 **p** 96. Lic to Offic *Chelmsf* from 96; Sister Superior CSD from 00. *26 Ash Walk, Warminster BA12 8PZ* Tel (01985) 213020

NOON, Canon Edward Arthur. b 16. Selw Coll Cam BA38 MA42. Bps' Coll Cheshunt 38. **d** 40 **p** 41. C Kingston St Jo *S'wark* 40-43; C Dulwich St Barn 43-48; P-in-c S Wimbledon St Pet 48-50; V 50-55; V Mitcham St Mark 55-65; V Horley 65-77; RD Reigate 72-76; Hon Can S'wark Cathl 72-83; P-in-c Purley St Barn 77-83; rtd 83; Hon C Overbury w Teddington, Alstone etc *Worc* 83-86; Perm to Offic *Glouc* 86-95. *40 Shepherds Leaze, Wotton-under-Edge GL12 7LQ* Tel (01453) 844978

NOORDANUS, Francis Peter. b 61. Cant Univ (NZ) BA82 ACT BTh90. **d** 92 **p** 93. New Zealand 92-02; C Ashburton 92-94; V Masterton St Matt 94-02; Chapl Eindhoven *Eur* from 02. *Paradijslaan 76, 5611 KR Eindhoven, The Netherlands* Tel (0031) (40) 246 5219 E-mail f.p.noordanus@planet.nl

NORBURN, Christopher Richard. b 62. Cov Poly BSc85. Aston Tr Scheme 92 Ridley Hall Cam 94. **d** 96 **p** 97. C Exning St Martin w Landwade *St E* 96-99; P-in-c Redgrave cum Botesdale w Rickinghall 99-01; R from 01. *The Rectory, Bury Road, Rickinghall, Diss IP22 1HA* Tel (01379) 898685

NORBURN, The Very Revd Richard Evelyn Walter. b 21. Witwatersrand Univ BA44 TDip44. St Paul's Coll Grahamstown 49. **d** 51 **p** 53. S Africa 51-62; C Croydon St Sav *Cant* 63-64; V Norbury St Phil 65-75; V Addington 75-81; Hon Can Cant Cathl 79-81; RD Croydon Addington 81; Dean Botswana 81-88; rtd 89; Perm to Offic *Cant* from 98. *2 Nunnery Fields, Canterbury CT1 3JN* Tel (01227) 765865

NORBURN, Canon Richard Henry. b 32. MBE97. St Edm Hall Ox BA57 DipTh58. Wycliffe Hall Ox 57. **d** 59 **p** 59. C Sudbury St Greg and St Pet *St E* 59-65; Dioc Youth Officer 65-74; P-in-c Gt Livermere 74-81; R Ampton w Lt Livermere and Ingham 74-81; RD Thingoe 78-88; Hon Can St E Cathl 81-97; R Ingham w Ampton and Gt and Lt Livermere 81-92; TV Blackbourne 92-97; rtd 97; Perm to Offic *St E* from 97. *69 Churchgate Street, Bury St Edmunds IP33 1RL* Tel (01284) 702644

NORFIELD, David Jonathan. b 67. Humberside Univ BA89. Linc Th Coll 94 Westcott Ho Cam CTM95. **d** 97 **p** 98. C Halstead St Andr w H Trin and Greenstead Green *Chelmsf* 97-01; V Moulsham St Jo from 01. *St John's Vicarage, Vicarage Road, Chelmsford CM2 9PH* Tel (01245) 352344 E-mail davidnorfield@hotmail.com

NORFOLK, The Ven Edward Matheson. b 21. Leeds Univ BA44. Coll of Resurr Mirfield 41. **d** 46 **p** 47. C Greenford H Cross *Lon* 46-47; C S Mymms K Chas 47-50; C Bushey *St Alb* 50-53; PC Waltham Cross 53-59; V Welwyn Garden City 59-69; R Gt Berkhamsted 69-81; Hon Can St Alb 72-82; V Kings Langley 81-82; Adn St Alb 82-87; rtd 87; Perm to Offic *Ex* from 87. *5 Fairlawn Court, Sidmouth EX10 8UR* Tel (01395) 514222

NORFOLK, Archdeacon of. See HAYDEN, The Ven David Frank

✠**NORGATE, The Rt Revd Cecil Richard.** b 21. St Chad's Coll Dur BA47 DipTh49. **d** 49 **p** 50 **c** 84. C Wallsend St Pet *Newc* 49-54; Tanganyika 54-64; Tanzania from 64; UMCA 54-57; V-Gen Masasi 77-84; Bp Masasi 84-92; rtd 92. *St Cyprian's College, Rondo, PO Box 212, Lindi, Tanzania*

NORGATE, Norman George. b 32. Qu Coll Cam BA55 MA58. Ridley Hall Cam. **d** 57 **p** 58. C Erith St Paul *Roch* 57-60; C E Twickenham St Steph *Lon* 60-63; V Bexleyheath St Pet *Roch* 63-71; V Woking St Mary *Guildf* 71-83; V Tunbridge Wells St Jas *Roch* 83-92; TR Tunbridge Wells St Jas w St Phil 92-97; rtd 97; Perm to Offic *St E* from 97. *Crathie, 58 Sexton Meadows, Bury St Edmunds IP33 2SB* Tel (01284) 767363

NORKETT, Alan. b 45. Sarum & Wells Th Coll 85. **d** 87 **p** 88. C Shrewsbury St Giles w Sutton and Atcham *Lich* 87-90; V Mow Cop 90-94; NSM Astbury and Smallwood *Ches* 96-97; NSM Sandbach Heath w Wheelock 97-98; C Castleford All SS and Whitwood *Wakef* 98-01; C Glass Houghton 98-01; R Shrawley, Witley, Astley and Abberley *Worc* from 01. *The Rectory, Shrawley, Worcester WR6 6TS* Tel (01905) 620489 E-mail vicaralan@aol.com

NORMAN, Andrew Herbert. b 54. K Coll Lon BD77 AKC77 Lon Univ PhD88. St Steph Ho Ox 77. **d** 78 **p** 79. C Deal St Leon w

Sholden *Cant* 78-81; C Maidstone All SS and St Phil w Tovil 81-84; V Tenterden St Mich 84-93; Chapl Benenden Hosp 86-91; Dir Post-Ord Tr *Cant* 91-93; R Guildf St Nic *Guildf* from 93. *The Rectory, 3 Flower Walk, Guildford GU2 4EP* Tel (01483) 504895

NORMAN, Andrew Robert. b 63. Univ Coll Ox BA84 MA99 Newc Poly DMS90 AIL89 Selw Coll Cam BA94 MA99. Ridley Hall Cam CTM95 BA94. **d** 95 **p** 96. Asst Chapl Paris St Mich *Eur* 95-00; C Clifton Ch Ch w Em *Bris* 00-02; Abp's Asst Sec for Ecum and Angl Affairs *Cant* from 02. *Cottage 2, Lambeth Palace, Lambeth Palace Road, London SE1 7JU* Tel (020) 7620 0636 *or* 7898 1200

NORMAN, Catherine. b 51. Nottm Univ BSc73 N Counties Coll Newc CertEd74. Linc Th Coll 95. **d** 95 **p** 96. C Scartho *Linc* 95-99; V Ulceby Gp 99-02; TV Guiseley w Esholt *Bradf* from 02. *The Vicarage, 1 Tranfield Close, Guiseley, Leeds LS20 8LT* Tel (01943) 879787

NORMAN, Canon Edward Robert. b 38. Selw Coll Cam BA61 PhD64 MA65 BD67 DD78 FRHistS72 FRSA88. Linc Th Coll 65. **d** 65 **p** 71. Fell Jes Coll Cam 64-71; Lect Cam Univ 65-88; Dean Peterho Cam 71-88; Six Preacher Cant Cathl *Cant* 84-90; Dean of Chpl Ch Ch Coll of HE Cant 88-95; Can Res and Treas York Minster *York* 95-99; Can Res and Prec York Minster from 99. *1 Precentor's Court, York YO1 7EJ* Tel (01904) 673097

NORMAN, Mrs Elizabeth Ann. b 43. St Andr and Ox Min Course 95. **d** 98 **p** 99. OLM Amersham *Ox* from 98. *16 Mulberry Court, Holmer Green, High Wycombe HP15 6TF* Tel (01494) 714712

NORMAN, The Ven Garth. b 38. St Chad's Coll Dur BA62 MA68 DipTh63 Cam Inst of Educn PGCE68 UEA MEd84. **d** 63 **p** 64. C Wandsworth St Anne *S'wark* 63-66; C Trunch w Swafield *Nor* 66-71; R Gimingham 71-77; RD Repps 75-83; TR Trunch 77-83; Prin Chiltern Chr Tr Course *Ox* 83-87; C W Wycombe w Bledlow Ridge, Bradenham and Radnage 83-87; Dir of Tr *Roch* 88-94; Hon Can Roch Cathl from 91; Adn Bromley and Bexley from 94. *6 Horton Way, Farningham DA4 0DQ* Tel (01322) 864522 Fax as telephone

NORMAN, Jillianne Elizabeth. b 59. DCR80. Ridley Hall Cam 85. **d** 88 **p** 94. Par Dn Fishponds St Jo *Bris* 88-92; Perm to Offic 92-94; Hon C Warmley, Syston and Bitton from 94; Chapl United Bris Healthcare NHS Trust from 02. *74 Blackhorse Road, Mangotsfield, Bristol BS16 9AY* Tel 0117-956 1551 E-mail jensig@globalnet.co.uk

NORMAN, Canon John Ronald. b 15. GradInstT Lon Univ BA40. Linc Th Coll 40. **d** 42 **p** 43. C Yarm *York* 42-43; C Stokesley 43-46; R Muchalls *Bre* 46-50; V Kirkby Ireleth *Carl* 50-55; R Greystoke 55-60; P-in-c Matterdale 56-60; Warden Greystoke Coll Carl 56-60; Chapl St Hilda's Priory and Sch Whitby 60-61; R Dunnington *York* 61-72; RD Bulmer 65-72; R Bolton Percy 72-82; Dioc Worship Adv 72-82; Can and Preb York Minster 77-92; rtd 82; Perm to Offic *York* from 98. *Iona, 5 Northfield Close, Pocklington, York YO42 2EG* Tel (01759) 303170

NORMAN, Linda Mary. b 48. Man Univ BSc69 CertEd70 St Jo Coll Dur BA82. **dss** 83 **d** 87. York St Mich-le-Belfrey *York* 83-88; Par Dn 87-88; rtd 88. *23 Ainsty Avenue, Dringhouses, York YO24 1HH* Tel (01904) 706152

NORMAN, Lynette Dianne. b 52. Sussex Univ CertEd73 Univ of Wales (Ban) BEd89. Ripon Coll Cuddesdon 00. **d** 02 **p** 03. C Welshpool w Castle Caereinion *St As* from 02. *Adyar, Salop Road, Welshpool SY21 7EA* Tel (01938) 556330 Mobile 07895-184517

NORMAN, Canon Michael Heugh. b 18. Qu Coll Cam BA48 Kent Univ MA. Westcott Ho Cam 48. **d** 50 **p** 51. C St Peter-in-Thanet *Cant* 50-52; S Africa from 52; rtd 86; Hon Can Cape Town from 86. *5 Rosedale Cottage, Lower Nursery Road, Rosebank, 7700 South Africa* Tel (0027) (21) 685 3622

NORMAN, Michael John. b 59. Southn Univ LLB82. Wycliffe Hall Ox 82. **d** 85 **p** 86. C Woodley St Jo the Ev *Ox* 85-89; C Uphill *B & W* 89-92; TV 92-98; R Bath St Sav w Swainswick and Woolley from 98. *St Saviour's Rectory, Claremont Road, Bath BA1 6LX* Tel (01225) 311637 E-mail michael@stsaviours.org.uk

NORMAN, Michael John. b 61. St Jo Coll Ox BSc83 Univ Coll Lon MSc83. Aston Tr Scheme 89 St Jo Coll Nottm 91. **d** 93 **p** 94. C Haughton le Skerne *Dur* 93-97; R Sapcote and Sharnford w Wigston Parva *Leic* from 97; RD Sparkenhoe W from 02. *The Rectory, 4 Sharnford Road, Sapcote, Leicester LE9 4JN* Tel (01455) 272215 E-mail micknorman@msn.com

NORMAN, Peter John. b 42. Culham Coll of Educn TCert66 Lon Inst of Educn DipEd83 MA86. STETS DipTh98. **d** 98 **p** 99. NSM Bath Weston All SS w N Stoke and Langridge *B & W* from 98. *5 Rockliffe Avenue, Bathwick, Bath BA2 6QP* Tel (01225) 463348

NORMAN, Peter John. b 59. Chich Th Coll 84. **d** 87 **p** 88. C Farncombe *Guildf* 87-91; C Cockington *Ex* 91-94; V Winkleigh from 94; R Ashreigney from 94; R Broadwoodkelly from 94; V Brushford from 94. *The Vicarage, Torrington Road, Winkleigh EX19 8HR* Tel (01837) 83719

NORMAN, Richard Hudson. b 58. Louisiana State Univ BS84 MA88. Gen Th Sem NY MDiv93 STM93. **d** 92 **p** 93. C

Southgate St Andr *Lon* 92 and 97-98; USA 92-97 and from 02; Assoc New York City St Matt and St Tim 92-93; R Abbeville St Paul 93-95; Assoc R Chevy Chase All SS 95-97; V Mill Hill St Mich *Lon* 98-02; R Greenville Redeemer from 02. *101 Taniere Court, Simpsonville, SC 29680, USA* Tel (001) (864) 277 4562 Fax 277 6330

NORMAN, Timothy. b 68. Jes Coll Cam BA91 Univ Coll Lon PhD95. Spurgeon's Coll 95 Wycliffe Hall Ox BA00. **d** 01 **p** 02. C Chipping Norton *Ox* from 01. *137 Cornish Road, Chipping Norton OX7 5LA* Tel (01608) 645744 E-mail tim.norman@bigfoot.com

NORMAN, Canon William Beadon. b 26. Trin Coll Cam BA49 MA55. Ridley Hall Cam 52. **d** 52 **p** 53. C Beckenham St Jo *Roch* 52-54; Uganda 55-65; V Alne *York* 65-74; RD Warley *Birm* 74-79; V Blackheath 74-79; Hon Can Birm Cathl 78-91; TR Kings Norton 79-91; RD Kings Norton 82-87; Warden Dioc Readers Bd 84-91; rtd 91; Perm to Offic *S'wark* from 91; Perm to Offic *Lon* from 94; Preacher Lincoln's Inn from 94. *37 Cloudesdale Road, London SW17 8ET* Tel (020) 8673 9134 Fax 8675 6890

NORMAN-WALKER, Mrs Anna Elizabeth. b 67. RGN89. St Jo Coll Nottm BA03. **d** 03. C Cullompton, Willand, Uffculme, Kentisbeare etc *Ex* from 03. *16 Gravel Walk, Cullompton EX15 1DA* Tel (01884) 35480 Mobile 07986-450330 E-mail anna@norman-walker.fsnet.co.uk

NORMAND, Stephen Joseph William. b 48. N Texas State Univ BSEd80. Sarum & Wells Th Coll 90. **d** 92 **p** 93. C Norton *St Alb* 92-94; C St Alb St Pet 94-97; Chapl Oaklands Coll 95-97; TV Horsham *Chich* 97-01; R Wimbotsham w Stow Bardolph and Stow Bridge etc *Ely* from 01. *The Rectory, Church Road, Wimbotsham, King's Lynn PE34 3QG* Tel (01366) 385713

NORMINGTON, Eric. b 16. S'wark Ord Course. **d** 63 **p** 64. C Coulsdon St Jo *S'wark* 63-66; C Bath Abbey w St Jas *B & W* 66-71; V Bath Weston All SS 71-78; P-in-c N Stoke 76-78; R Bath Weston All SS w N Stoke 78-81; RD Keynsham 75-76; rtd 81; Perm to Offic *Ex* 81-98. *Flat 16, Manormead, Tilford Road, Hindhead GU26 6RA* Tel (01428) 604700

NORRINGTON, Paul Richard. b 57. Brighton Poly BSc80 Thurrock Coll Essex DMS90. Trin Coll Bris DipTh98. **d** 98 **p** 99. C Prittlewell w Westcliff *Chelmsf* 98-02; R Colchester Ch Ch w St Mary V from 02. *The Rectory, 21 Cambridge Road, Colchester CO3 3NS* Tel (01206) 563478 E-mail pnozzer@tesco.net

NORRIS, Mrs Alison. b 55. St Andr Univ MTheol77 Dur Univ PGCE78. Cant Sch of Min 80. **dss** 82 **d** 87 **p** 94. Warlingham w Chelsham and Farleigh *S'wark* 82-85; Willingham *Ely* 85-87; Hon Par Dn 87-90; Hon Par Dn Worle *B & W* 90-94; NSM Milverton w Halse and Fitzhead 94-02; P-in-c Bradford w Oake, Hillfarrance and Heathfield from 02. *The Vicarage, Parsonage Lane, Milverton, Taunton TA4 1LR* Tel (01823) 401407 Fax 400739

NORRIS, Allan Edward. b 43. St Jo Coll Dur BA72 DipTh73. Cranmer Hall Dur 69. **d** 73 **p** 74. C Plumstead St Jo w St Jas and St Paul *S'wark* 73-78; C Battersea Park St Sav 78-82; C Battersea St Geo w St Andr 78-82; V Grain w Stoke *Roch* 82-92; V Sissinghurst w Frittenden *Cant* from 92. *The Rectory, Oakleaves, Frittenden, Cranbrook TN17 2DD* Tel (01580) 852275

NORRIS, Andrew David. b 54. CPsychol St Andr Univ BSc78 Lon Univ MPhil80. EAMTC 87. **d** 90 **p** 91. C Worle *B & W* 90-94; R Milverton w Halse and Fitzhead from 94; RD Tone from 01. *The Vicarage, Parsonage Lane, Milverton, Taunton TA4 1LR* Tel (01823) 400305 E-mail revnog@tinyonline.co.uk

NORRIS, Andrew Peter. b 62. Aston Univ BSc83. St Jo Coll Nottm BA86 DPS87. **d** 87 **p** 88. C Mountsorrel Ch Ch and St Pet *Leic* 87-90; C Harborne Heath *Birm* 90-91; P-in-c Edgbaston St Germain 91-92; V 92-99; P-in-c Hook w Warsash *Portsm* 99-00; V from 00. *The Vicarage, 113 Church Road, Warsash, Southampton SO31 9GF* Tel (01489) 572324 Fax as telephone

NORRIS, Barry John. b 46. Nottm Univ CQSW75 MTh86 Open Univ BA80 K Coll Lon PhD95. St Jo Sem Wonersh. **d** 70 **p** 71. In RC Ch 70-72; C Wisbech SS Pet and Paul *Ely* 76-78; TV E Ham w Upton Park St Alb *Chelmsf* 78-81; Chapl RAF 81-87; V N Tadley St Mary *Win* from 87. *St Mary's Vicarage, Bishopswood Road, Tadley, Basingstoke RG26 4HQ* Tel 0118-981 4435

NORRIS, Canon Clifford Joseph. b 29. Codrington Coll Barbados. **d** 61 **p** 68. Antigua 61-62; C Penton Street St Silas w All SS *Lon* 68-70; C Stepney St Dunstan and All SS 70-73; P-in-c Bethnal Green St Jas the Gt w St Jude 73-82; V Aveley and Purfleet *Chelmsf* 82-98; Hon Can NE Caribbean from 95; rtd 98; Perm to Offic *Chelmsf* from 98. *20 Hayhouse Road, Earls Colne, Colchester CO6 2PD* Tel (01787) 222015

NORRIS, Eric Richard. b 43. MICFM86. Bernard Gilpin Soc Dur 65 Ripon Hall Ox 66. **d** 69 **p** 70. C Huyton St Mich *Liv* 69-72; C Mexborough *Sheff* 72-74; V Dalton 74-78; Org Sec CECS *Carl* 78-89; Area Appeals Manager N Co 89-93; TR Thirsk *York* 93-02; RD Mowbray 00-02; V Boosbeck w Moorsholm from 02; Abp's Adv in Tourism from 02. *The Vicarage, Church Drive, Boosbeck, Saltburn-by-the-Sea TS12 3AY* Tel (01287) 651728

NORRIS, Keith David. b 47. E Lon Univ BA89 MIAM76 MBIM80. NTMTC AdDipTh98 ADPS98. **d** 98 **p** 02. NSM Cranham Park *Chelmsf* 98-99; NSM S Hornchurch St Jo and

St Matt from 01. *Still Waters, 8 Hesselyn Drive, Rainham RM13 7EJ* Tel (01708) 780767

NORRIS, Mark. b 68. Brunel Univ BEng90. Oak Hill Th Coll DipHE92 BA93. **d** 93 **p** 94. C Roby *Liv* 93-97; C St Helens St Helen 97-00; TV Gateacre from 00. *Christchurch House, 44 Brownhill Bank, Liverpool L27 7AE* Tel 0151-487 7759

NORRIS, Michael Charles Latham. b 69. Reading Univ LLB. Wycliffe Hall Ox 99. **d** 01 **p** 02. C Bryanston Square St Mary w St Marylebone St Mark *Lon* from 01. *17 Homer Row, London W1H 4AP* Tel (020) 7402 4993 Mobile 07740-182880
E-mail mikenorris1@hotmail.com

NORTH, Barry Albert. b 46. **d** 82 **p** 83. C Brampton St Thos *Derby* 82-84; C Chesterfield St Aug 84-88; P-in-c Derby St Mark 88-91; R Coalbrookdale, Iron-Bridge and Lt Wenlock *Heref* 91-97; Ch and Community Worker (Manlake Deanery) *Linc* 97-00; Soc Resp Adv *Chich* from 00; C Brighton St Mich from 00. *2 Windlesham Road, Brighton BN1 3AG* Tel (01273) 778083

NORTH, Christopher David. b 69. Bris Univ BA01. Trin Coll Bris 98. **d** 01. C Bathampton w Claverton *B & W* from 01. *28 Hantone Hill, Bathampton, Bath BA2 6XD* Tel (01225) 462705
E-mail chris.north1@tesco.net

NORTH, David Roland. b 45. Lich Th Coll 70 Qu Coll Birm 72. **d** 73 **p** 74. C Salesbury *Blackb* 73-76; C Marton 76-79; C Penwortham St Leon 79-87; R Whittington St Jo *Lich* from 87; P-in-c W Felton from 96; RD Oswestry from 92; Chapl Robert Jones/Agnes Hunt Orthopaedic NHS Trust 00-01. *The Rectory, Castle Street, Whittington, Oswestry SY11 4DF* Tel (01691) 652222 E-mail davidnorth@micro-plus-web.net

NORTH, Lyndon Percival. b 55. Lon Bible Coll BA77. NTMTC. **d** 00 **p** 01. NSM Sudbury St Andr *Lon* from 00. *143 Abbots Drive, Wembley HA0 3SH* Tel (020) 8904 2408 Mobile 07774-685906
E-mail lyndon.north@astra.gb.astra.com

NORTH, Philip John. b 66. York Univ BA88. St Steph Ho Ox BA91 MA01. **d** 92 **p** 93. C Sunderland Springwell w Thorney Close *Dur* 92-95; C Sunderland St Mary and St Pet 95-96; V Hartlepool H Trin 96-02; AD Hartlepool 00-02; P Admin Shrine of Our Lady of Walsingham from 02. *The Shrine of Our Lady of Walsingham, The College, Knight Street, Walsingham NR22 6EF* Tel (01328) 824204 *or* 820323 Fax 824208
E-mail pr.adm@shrine-olw.org.uk

NORTH, Preb Robert. b 54. Lon Univ BSc77. Ripon Coll Cuddesdon 78. **d** 81 **p** 82. C Leominster *Heref* 81-86; TV Heref St Martin w St Fran 86-92; TV Dewsall w Callow 86-92; TV Holme Lacy w Dinedor 86-92; TV Lt Dewchurch, Aconbury w Ballingham and Bolstone 86-92; TV Upper and Lower Bullinghope w Grafton 86-92; P-in-c Heref St Nic 92-97; Dir of Ords 92-00; Preb Heref Cathl from 94; TR W Heref from 97; V Heref H Trin from 97; V Breinton from 97. *St Nicholas's Rectory, 76 Breinton Road, Hereford HR4 0JY* Tel (01432) 273810
E-mail robnorth@wbsnet.co.uk

NORTH, Canon Vernon Leslie. b 26. Bps' Coll Cheshunt 61. **d** 63 **p** 64. C N Holmwood *Guildf* 63-65; C Dunstable *St Alb* 65-68; V Stotfold 68-91; RD Shefford 79-91; Hon Can St Alb 89-92; R Stotfold and Radwell 91-92; rtd 92; Perm to Offic *St Alb* from 92 and *Ely* from 00. *Hunters Moon, 10 High Street, Little Paxton, St Neots PE19 6HA* Tel (01480) 471146

NORTH INDIA, Moderator of the Church of. See TEROM, The Rt Revd Zechariah James

NORTH SYDNEY, Bishop of. See DAVIES, The Rt Revd Glenn Naunton

NORTH WEST EUROPE, Archdeacon of. See ALLEN, The Ven Geoffrey Gordon

NORTHALL, Malcolm Walter. b 26. Cheshunt Coll Cam 59 Ely Th Coll 63. **d** 64 **p** 65. C Bromsgrove St Jo *Worc* 64-67; V Blockley w Aston Magna *Glouc* 67-82; P-in-c Churchdown St V 82-92; rtd 92; Perm to Offic *Ban* from 92. *5 Maethlon Close, Tywyn LL36 0BN* Tel (01654) 710123

NORTHAM, Cavell Herbert James Cavell. See CAVELL-NORTHAM, Canon Cavell Herbert James

NORTHAM, Mrs Susan Jillian. b 36. Oak Hill Th Coll DipHE87. **d** 89. NSM Enfield Ch Ch Trent Park *Lon* 89-91; Par Dn 91-94; C 94-97; rtd 97. *5 Beech Hill Avenue, Barnet EN4 0LW* Tel (020) 8440 2723 Fax as telephone
E-mail jillandjohn.northam@btinternet.com

NORTHAMPTON, Archdeacon of. See CHAPMAN, The Ven Michael Robin

NORTHCOTT, Michael Stafford. b 55. St Chad's Coll Dur BA76 MA77 Sunderland Univ PhD81. St Jo Coll Dur 80. **d** 81 **p** 82. C Chorlton-cum-Hardy St Clem *Man* 81-84; USPG 84-89; Malaysia 84-89; Sen Lect Chr Ethics New Coll Edin Univ 89-91; NSM Edin Old St Paul *Edin* 91; NSM Edin St Jas from 91; TV Edin St Marg 93-96. *8 Dudley Gardens, Edinburgh EH6 4PY* Tel 0131-554 1651 E-mail m.northcott@ed.ac.uk

NORTHCOTT, William Mark. b 36. Clifton Th Coll 61. **d** 64 **p** 65. C Walthamstow St Luke *Chelmsf* 64-68; C Idle H Trin *Bradf* 68-70; N Sec CMJ 70-79; V Withnell *Blackb* 79-90; P-in-c Glenrothes *St And* 90-91; Asst Dioc Supernumerary 90-91; Perm to Offic *Blackb* and *Liv* from 91. *30 The Laund, Leyland, Preston PR5 3XX* Tel (01772) 493932

NORTHERN, Mrs Elaine Joy. b 54. Leic Univ BSc75 Dip Counselling 97. SEITE 00. **d** 03. C Snodland All SS w Ch Ch *Roch* from 03. *7 Old Road West, Gravesend DA11 0LH* Tel (01474) 335032 E-mail thenorthers@btinternet.com

NORTHERN LUZON, Bishop of. See SOLIBA, The Most Revd Ignacio Capuyan

NORTHERN MALAWI, Bishop of. See BOYLE, The Rt Revd Christopher John

NORTHFIELD, Stephen Richmond. b 55. Lon Univ BSc77 Southn Univ BTh84. Sarum & Wells Th Coll 79. **d** 82 **p** 83. C Colchester St Jas, All SS, St Nic and St Runwald *Chelmsf* 82-85; C Chelmsf All SS 85-89; V Ramsey w Lt Oakley and Wrabness 89-95; V Hatfield Peverel w Ulting from 95. *The Vicarage, Church Road, Hatfield Peverel, Chelmsford CM3 2LE* Tel (01245) 380958

NORTHING, Ross. b 58. Wilson Carlile Coll Dip Evang87 St Steph Ho Ox DipMin94 SSC99. **d** 94 **p** 95. CA from 87; C Up Hatherley *Glouc* 94-98; C Cheltenham St Steph 94-95; C Cheltenham Em w St Steph 95-98; V Stony Stratford *Ox* from 98; R Calverton from 98. *St Mary and St Giles Vicarage, 14 Willow Lane, Stony Stratford, Milton Keynes MK11 1FG* Tel (01908) 562148 Fax 565132 E-mail r.northing@btinternet.com

NORTHOLT, Archdeacon of. See CHESSUN, The Ven Christopher Thomas James

NORTHOVER, Kevin Charles. b 57. Coll of Resurr Mirfield 89. **d** 91 **p** 92. C Kingston upon Hull St Alb *York* 91-94; V Moorends *Sheff* 94-00; R Guernsey St Michel du Valle *Win* from 00. *The Rectory, L'Abbaye, Vale, Guernsey GY3 5SF* Tel (01481) 244088 Fax 249985

NORTHRIDGE, Canon Herbert Aubrey Hamilton. b 16. TCD BA40 MA43. **d** 41 **p** 42. C Londonderry Ch Ch *D & R* 41-45; P-in-c Convoy 45-47; I 47-50; I Derg 50-70; I Derg w Termonamongan 70-81; Can Derry Cathl 72-81; rtd 81. *Goblusk, Ballinamallard BT94 2LW* Tel (028) 6681 676

NORTHUMBERLAND, Archdeacon of. See ELLIOTT, The Ven Peter

NORTHWOOD, Michael Alan. b 36. Lon Univ BSc60 MInstP69. Wells Th Coll 62. **d** 64 **p** 65. C Eastbourne St Mary *Chich* 64-66; C Sanderstead All SS *S'wark* 66-68; P-in-c Alton Barnes w Alton Priors etc *Sarum* 69-75; Lic to Offic 76-86; Perm to Offic *Ox* from 86; rtd 01. *The Garth, 31 Mill Road, Marlow SL7 1QB* Tel (01628) 488646 Mobile 07836-372021 Fax (01628) 488649 E-mail michael@mmsolutions.com

NORTON, Anthony Bernard. b 40. Man Univ BA62. Linc Th Coll 63. **d** 65 **p** 66. C Westbury-on-Trym H Trin *Bris* 65-68; C Bris St Agnes w St Simon 68-70; P-in-c Bris St Werburgh 70-72; TV Bris St Agnes and St Simon w St Werburgh 72-77; V Lakenham St Alb *Nor* 77-85; TV Trunch 85-93; TV Halesworth w Linstead, Chediston, Holton etc *St E* 93-99; TV Blyth Valley from 99; RD Halesworth 98-01. *The Vicarage, Church Road, Spexhall, Halesworth IP19 0RQ* Tel (01986) 875453 Fax as telephone

NORTON, James Herbert Kitchener. b 37. Qu Coll Birm 78. **d** 81 **p** 82. NSM Donnington Wood *Lich* 81-83; C Matson *Glouc* 83-86; V New Mills *Derby* 86-96; RD Glossop 93-96; TR Buxton w Burbage and King Sterndale 96-02; RD Buxton 99-02; rtd 02; Perm to Offic *Derby* from 02. *Heather Glen, 11 Ellis Peter's Drive, Telford TF3 1AW* Tel (01952) 595343 Mobile 07879-470172
E-mail jhknorton@lineone.net

NORTON, John Colin (Andrew). b 25. Magd Coll Ox BA50 MA54. Cuddesdon Coll 50. **d** 52 **p** 53. C Bris St Mary Redcliffe w Temple *Bris* 52-57; C Bitterne Park *Win* 57-61; C-in-c Bishopwearmouth St Mary V w St Pet CD *Dur* 63-68; V Clifton All SS w Tyndalls Park *Bris* 68-78; Hon Can Bris Cathl 77-80; V Clifton All SS w St Jo 78-80; V Penistone *Wakef* 80-83; CR from 85; rtd 95. *House of the Resurrection, Stocks Bank Road, Mirfield WF14 0BN* Tel (01924) 494318

NORTON, Mrs Lesley Gillian. b 47. STETS 99. **d** 02 **p** 03. NSM Kinson *Sarum* from 02. *21 The Bluff, Headswell Crescent, Bournemouth BH10 6LQ* Tel (01202) 548160
E-mail norton@fish.co.uk

NORTON (or HARCOURT-NORTON), Michael Clive Harcourt. b 34. Selw Coll Cam BA58 MA60 Union Th Sem (NY) STM69 Univ of NSW MCom81 MACE84. Wells Th Coll 56 Bossey Ecum Inst Geneva 57. **d** 58 **p** 59. C Gt Ilford St Jo *Chelmsf* 58-62; Australia 62-68 and from 69; NSW Sec Aus Coun Chs 62-65; C Manhattan St Steph USA 68-69; C-in-c Mortdale 69-77; R 77-79; Assoc Chapl and Hd RS Cranbrook Sch Sydney 79-85; R Hunter's Hill 85-00; rtd 00. *7 Dulwich Road, Chatswood, NSW, Australia 2067* Tel (0061) (2) 9411 8606 Mobile 417-041779 Fax (2) 9410 2069 E-mail chnorton@bigpond.com

NORTON, Michael James Murfin. b 42. Lich Th Coll 66. **d** 67 **p** 68. C W Bromwich St Fran *Lich* 67-70; C Wellington Ch Ch 70-72; C Norwood All SS *Cant* 72-76; V Elstow *St Alb* 76-82; Asst Chapl HM Pris Wakef 82-83; Chapl HM Pris Camp Hill 83-86; Chapl HM Pris Parkhurst 86-88; Chapl HM Pris Win 88-93; V Somborne w Ashley *Win* 93-03; rtd 03. *5 Ashton Cross, East Wellow, Romsey SO51 6AY* Tel (01794) 322810
E-mail revmnorton@aol.com

NORTON, Paul James. b 55. Oak Hill Th Coll BA86. **d** 86 **p** 87. C Luton St Fran *St Alb* 86-89; C Bedworth *Cov* 89-95; TV Hitchin *St Alb* 95-02; V Portsdown *Portsm* from 03. *1A London Road, Widley, Waterlooville PO7 5AT*

NORTON, Canon Peter Eric Pepler. b 38. TCD BA61 G&C Coll Cam PhD64. St Jo Coll Dur 78. **d** 80 **p** 81. C Ulverston St Mary w H Trin *Carl* 80-83; P-in-c Warcop, Musgrave, Soulby and Crosby Garrett 83-84; R 84-90; OCF 83-90; V Appleby *Carl* from 90; R Ormside from 90; P-in-c Kirkby Thore w Temple Sowerby and Newbiggin from 01; RD Appleby from 00; Hon Can Carl Cathl from 00. *The Vicarage, Appleby-in-Westmorland CA16 6QW* Tel (01768) 351461 E-mail peter.norton@pepnorton.demon.co.uk

NORTON, Sam Charles. b 70. Trin Coll Ox BA92 MA99. Westcott Ho Cam 97. **d** 99 **p** 00. C Stepney St Dunstan and All SS *Lon* 99-02; R W w E Mersea *Chelmsf* from 03; P-in-c Peldon w Gt and Lt Wigborough from 03. *93 Kingsland Road, West Mersea, Colchester CO5 8AG* Tel (01206) 385635

NORTON, William Fullerton. b 23. Selw Coll Cam BA46 MA52. Wycliffe Hall Ox 46. **d** 48 **p** 49. C Leic H Apostles *Leic* 48-52; Singapore 52-54; Malaya 54-63; Philippines 63-66; C Homerton St Luke *Lon* 67; C Tooting Graveney St Nic *S'wark* 68-71; V Hanley Road St Sav w St Paul *Lon* 71-89; rtd 89. *21 Peel Road, Brighton BN2 5ND* Tel (01273) 677332

NORWICH, Archdeacon of. See OFFER, The Ven Clifford Jocelyn

NORWICH, Bishop of. See JAMES, The Rt Revd Graham Richard

NORWICH, Dean of. *Vacant*

NORWOOD, Andrew David. b 65. Lon Bible Coll BA91. Cranmer Hall Dur DMS94. **d** 94 **p** 95. C Headingley *Ripon* 94-97; C Handsworth St Mary *Birm* 97-00; Chapl Chelsea Coll *Lon* from 02. *11 Ormonde Mansions, 106 Southampton Row, London WC1B 4BP* Tel 07766-501079 (mobile) E-mail andrew272@hotmail.com

NORWOOD, David John. b 40. SS Paul & Mary Coll Cheltenham BEd82. Linc Th Coll 65. **d** 68 **p** 69. C Hitchin St Mary *St Alb* 68-71; Zambia 72-76; C Littlehampton St Jas *Chich* 76-77; P-in-c Chacewater *Truro* 77-79; Chapl R Cornwall Hosp Treliske 77-79; Hd RE Red Maids Sch Bris 82-85; Appeals Organiser Children's Soc 86-94; P-in-c Clarkston *Glas* 94-97; R 97-99; R Dalbeattie from 99. *The Rectory, 1 Alpine Terrace, Dalbeattie DG5 4HJ* Tel (01556) 610671

NORWOOD, Philip Geoffrey Frank. b 39. Em Coll Cam BA62 MA66. Cuddesdon Coll 63. **d** 65 **p** 66. C New Addington *Cant* 65-69; Abp's Dom Chapl 69-72; V Hollingbourne 72-78; P-in-c Wormshill 74-78; P-in-c Huckinge 74-78; V St Laur in Thanet 78-88; RD Thanet 86-88; V Spalding *Linc* 88-98; RD Elloe W 96-98; R Blakeney w Cley, Wiveton, Glandford etc *Nor* from 98; RD Holt from 02. *The Rectory, Wiveton Road, Blakeney, Holt NR25 7NJ* Tel (01263) 740686 Fax 741187

NORWOOD, Robert William. b 38. Lon Univ TCert64 Keble Coll Ox BA71 MA71 Lambeth STh83. **d** 01 **p** 03. NSM St Pancras H Cross w St Jude and St Pet *Lon* from 01. *Carlton Court, 11A Hermon Hill, London E11 2AR* Tel (020) 8530 2493

NORWOOD, Timothy. b 70. Aber Univ BD94. Westcott Ho Cam 95. **d** 97 **p** 98. C Upton cum Chalvey *Ox* 97-00; TV Watling Valley from 00. *3 Daubeney Gate, Shenley Church End, Milton Keynes MK5 6EH* Tel (01908) 505812 E-mail tim@thenorwoods.fsnet.co.uk

NOTLEY, Michael James. b 41. St Edm Hall Ox BA63 MA68 DipEd64. EMMTC 84. **d** 87 **p** 88. Hon C Oadby *Leic* 87-96; P-in-c Holbeach Marsh *Linc* from 96; P-in-c Lutton w Gedney Drove End, Dawsmere from 96. *The Vicarage, Marsh Road, Holbeach Hurn, Holbeach, Spalding PE12 8JX* Tel (01406) 425816

NOTT, Canon George Thomas Michael. b 34. Ex Coll Ox BA58 MA62 Birm Univ MEd88 Cov Univ PhD95. Coll of Resurr Mirfield. **d** 60 **p** 61. C Solihull *Birm* 60-69; Min Can Worc Cathl *Worc* 69-77; Chapl K Sch Worc 69-77; P-in-c Worc St Nic *Worc* 77-84; P-in-c Worc St Andr and All SS w St Helen 82-84; Children's Officer 77-87; Droitwich Spa 87-89; V Broadheath, Crown East and Rushwick from 89; Chapl Worc Coll of HE 89-96; RD Martley and Worc W *Worc* from 95; Hon Can Worc Cathl from 99; P-in-c Worc St Mich 00-01. *The Vicarage, Crown East Lane, Rushwick, Worcester WR2 5TU* Tel (01905) 428801 E-mail michael.nott39@mgownersclub.com

NOTT, The Rt Revd Peter John. b 33. Fitzw Ho Cam BA61 MA65. Westcott Ho Cam 58. **d** 61 **p** 62 **c** 77. C Harpenden St Nic *St Alb* 61-64; Chapl Fitzw Coll Cam 64-69; Fell 66-69; Chapl New Hall Cam 66-69; R Beaconsfield *Ox* 69-76; TR 76-77; Preb Wells Cathl *B & W* 77-85; Suff Bp Taunton 77-85; Bp Nor 85-99; rtd 99. *16 St Joseph's Mews, Candlemas Lane, Beaconsfield HP9 1GA1* Tel (01494) 678007

NOTT, Philip James. b 69. Nottm Trent Univ BA92. Ridley Hall Cam CTM98. **d** 98 **p** 99. C Kersal Moor *Man* 98-01; C Ealing St Mary *Lon* from 01; Chapl Thames Valley Univ from 01. *38 Airdale Road, London W5 4SD* Tel (020) 8567 6926 E-mail nottfamily@cwcom.net

NOTTAGE, Preb Terence John. b 36. Oak Hill Th Coll 62. **d** 65 **p** 66. C Finchley St Paul Long Lane *Lon* 65-68; C Edgware 68-72; V Harlesden St Mark 72-86; V Kensal Rise St Mark and St Martin 86; TR Plymouth Em w Efford *Ex* 86-92; P-in-c Laira 88-92; TR Plymouth Em, St Paul Efford and St Aug 93-96; Preb Ex Cathl from 96; Adv for Voc and Dioc Dir of Ords 96-01; rtd 01. *4 Keyberry Close, Newton Abbot TQ12 1DA* Tel (01626) 332277 E-mail terry.nottage@tesco.net

NOTTINGHAM, Archdeacon of. See OGILVIE, The Ven Gordon

NOURSE, John. b 22. St Jo Coll Cam BA43 MA47 ACertCM90. Wells Th Coll 48. **d** 49 **p** 51. C Bournemouth St Aug *Win* 49-51; Asst Master Hurstpierpoint Coll 51-52; C Shere *Guildf* 52-57; C Eton w Boveney *Ox* 57-62; Min Can Windsor and Asst Master St Geo Choir Sch 57-67; Succ 61-67; V Amesbury *Sarum* 67-69; Offg Chapl RAF 67-69; Prec Cant Cathl *Cant* 69-73; V Charing w Lt Chart 73-83; V Charing w Charing Heath and Lt Chart 84-88; rtd 88; Perm to Offic *Ex* from 90. *High Meadow, Greenhill Avenue, Lympstone, Exmouth EX8 5HW* Tel (01395) 264480

NOWELL, Canon John David. b 44. AKC67. **d** 68 **p** 69. C Lindley *Wakef* 68-70; C Lightcliffe 70-72; V Wyke *Bradf* 72-80; V Silsden 80-92; V Baildon from 92; Hon Can Bradf Cathl from 00. *The Vicarage, Baildon, Shipley BD17 6BY* Tel (01274) 594941 Fax as telephone

NOY, Frederick William Vernon. b 47. Sarum Th Coll 67. **d** 71 **p** 72. C Swindon St Jo *Bris* 71-75; Chapl to the Deaf *Sarum* 75-80; P-in-c Stinsford, Winterborne Came w Whitcombe etc 76-80; Perm to Offic from 80. *54 Casterbridge Road, Dorchester DT1 2AG* Tel (01305) 264269

NOYCE, Colin Martley. b 45. Brasted Th Coll 73 Ridley Hall Cam 74. **d** 76 **p** 77. C Cambridge St Jas *Ely* 76-78; Chapl RN 78-82; R Mistley w Manningtree *Chelmsf* 82-86; Miss to Seamen 86-90; Kenya 86-89; Trinidad and Tobago 89-90; V Four Marks *Win* 90-99; Chapl Pilgrim's Hospices E Kent 99-01; Yemen from 01; Chapl and Team Ldr Ch Ch and Ras Morbat Clinic from 01. *PO Box 1319, Tawahi, Aden, Republic of Yemen* Tel (00967) (2) 201204

NOYCE, Graham Peter. b 62. Bedf Coll Lon BSc84. Trin Coll Bris BA92. **d** 92 **p** 93. C Sketty *S & B* 92-94; C Swansea St Jas 94-96; C Kensal Rise St Mark and St Martin *Lon* from 96. *26 Ashburnham Road, London NW10 5SD* Tel (020) 8960 6211 E-mail graham@noyceg.freeserve.co.uk

NOYES, Roger. b 39. Linc Th Coll 65. **d** 67 **p** 68. C Adel *Ripon* 67-70; Chapl Aldenham Sch Herts 70-74; V Aldborough w Boroughbridge and Roecliffe *Ripon* 74-89; Rural Min Adv 89-90; Perm to Offic from 91. *Rose Cottage, Moor End, Nun Monkton, York YO26 8DY* Tel (01423) 330846

NSHIMYE, Stephen Kamegeri. b 60. Bp Lutaya Th Coll Uganda 88. **d** 90 **p** 91. Uganda 90-93; Rwanda 94-99; Perm to Offic *S'wark* from 02. *58 Hickin Close, London SE7 8SH* Tel (020) 8305 0934 Mobile 07950-346477

NSUBUGA, Eridard Kironde. b 58. Birm Univ DipRE96. Bp Tucker Coll Mukono. **d** 84 **p** 85. Uganda 85-88 and 92-00; C St Andr Cathl Mityana 85-88; V 92-95; R Kadoma Zimbabwe 88-91; V St Mark's Cathl Luwero 96-00; Perm to Offic *Glouc* 02-03. *Redcliffe College, Wotton House, Horton Road, Gloucester GL1 3PT* Tel 07979-904397 (mobile) Fax (01452) 503949 E-mail nsubuga@bigfoot.com *or* jeridard@yahoo.com

NTEGE, Nathan Kasolo. b 59. **d** 87 **p** 89. St Paul's Cathl Namirembe 87-91; Bp Tucker Coll Mukono 91-94; V Luzira and Kabowa 94-96; Perm to Offic *S'wark* 97-02; P-in-c Thornton Heath St Jude w St Aid from 02. *St Jude's Vicarage, 11 Dunheved Road North, Thornton Heath CR7 6AH* Tel (01342) 832021 Mobile 07951-673589

NUDDS, Douglas John. b 24. St Aid Birkenhead 48. **d** 51 **p** 52. C E Dereham w Hoe *Nor* 51-55; C Birstall *Leic* 55-58; V Bardon Hill 58-62; V Belgrave St Mich 62-68; Chapl Leic R Infirmary 68-72; High Royds Hosp Menston 72-79; V Bradf St Wilfrid Lidget Green *Bradf* 79-84; Lic to Offic *St Alb* 84-93; Chapl Shenley Hosp Radlett Herts 84-89; rtd 89; Perm to Offic *Nor* from 89. *Longview, Southgate Close, Wells-next-the-Sea NR23 1HG* Tel (01328) 711926

NUGENT, Canon Alan Hubert. b 42. Dur Univ BA65 MA78. Wycliffe Hall Ox 65 United Th Coll Bangalore DipTh66. **d** 67 **p** 68. C Mossley Hill St Matt and St Jas *Liv* 67-71; C Bridgnorth St Mary *Heref* 71-72; Chapl Dur Univ *Dur* 72-78; P-in-c Bishopwearmouth Ch Ch 78-85; P-in-c Brancepeth 85-94; Dioc Dir of Educn 85-97; Hon Can Dur Cathl 86-97; Dir of Miss and Tr Development Forum *Linc* from 97; Can and Preb Linc Cathl 98-03; Can Res and Subdean from 03. *The Subdeanery, 18 Minster Yard, Lincoln LN2 1PX* E-mail alan.nugentl@lincoln.anglican.org

NUGENT, David Richard. b 54. MInstPS84 Liv Poly BA87. Oak Hill Th Coll BA95. **d** 95 **p** 96. C Birkenhead St Jas w St Bede *Ches* 95-99; V Blundellsands St Mich *Liv* 99-02; Asst Chapl Wirral and W Cheshire Community NHS Trust 02-03; Asst Chapl Cheshire and Wirral Partnership NHS Trust from 03. *Chaplains' Office, Clatterbridge Hospital, Clatterbridge Road, Wirral CH63 4JY* Tel 0151-334 4000 E-mail dave.nugent@whnt.nhs.uk

NUGENT, Eric William. b 26. Bps' Coll Cheshunt 56. **d** 58 **p** 59. C Rochford *Chelmsf* 58-61; C Eastwood 61-62; C-in-c Eastwood St Dav CD 62-66; V Eastwood St Dav 66-79; P-in-c Weeley 79-81; V Lt Clacton 80-81; R Weeley and Lt Clacton 81-93; rtd 93; Perm to Offic *Chelmsf* from 93. *1 King's Court, King's Road, Dovercourt, Harwich CO12 4DS* Tel (01255) 552640

NUNN, Ms Alice Candida. b 52. Ripon Coll Cuddesdon 95. **d** 97 **p** 98. C Margate St Jo *Cant* 97-01; V Winterton Gp *Linc* from 01. *The Vicarage, High Street, Winterton, Scunthorpe DN15 9PU* Tel (01724) 732262

NUNN, Canon Andrew Peter. b 57. Leic Poly BA79 Leeds Univ BA82. Coll of Resurr Mirfield 80. **d** 83 **p** 84. C Manston *Ripon* 83-87; C Leeds Richmond Hill 87-91; Chapl Agnes Stewart C of E High Sch Leeds 87-95; V Leeds Richmond Hill *Ripon* 91-95; Personal Asst to Bp S'wark 95-99; Hon PV S'wark Cathl 95-99; Sub-Dean, Prec and Can Res S'wark Cathl from 99; Warden Dioc Readers Assn from 01. *73 St George's Road, London SE1 6ER* Tel (020) 7735 8322 *or* 7367 6727 Mobile 07961-332051 Fax 7367 6725 E-mail andrew.nunn@dswark.org.uk

NUNN, Geoffrey William John. b 24. St Jo Coll Dur BA51. **d** 52 **p** 53. C Upminster *Chelmsf* 52-58; V Dagenham St Martin 58-94; C 95; C Becontree S 95-96; rtd 97. *194 Parkside Avenue, Romford RM1 1NP* Tel (01708) 726276

NUNN, Peter. b 32. Kelham Th Coll 53. **d** 57 **p** 58. C Wigan St Geo *Liv* 57-60; C Warrington St Elphin 60-62; V Warrington St Pet 62-65; Chapl Winwick Hosp Warrington 65-90; rtd 90; Perm to Offic *Liv* from 90. *9 Derby House, Scholes, Wigan WN1 3RN* Tel (01942) 235407

NUNN, Canon Peter Michael. b 38. MBE98. Sarum Th Coll 64. **d** 66 **p** 67. C Hornsey St Geo *Lon* 66-71; C Cleator Moor w Cleator *Carl* 71-72; V Carl St Luke Morton 72-79; V Wotton St Mary *Glouc* 79-02; Offg Chapl RAF 80-97; RD Glouc City *Glouc* 88-94; Hon Can Glouc Cathl 90-02; rtd 02. *87 South Street, Tarring, Worthing BN14 7ND* Tel (01903) 233748

NUNN, Peter Rawling. b 51. Ox Univ BA73 Sheff Univ MSc74 BA85. Oak Hill Th Coll 82. **d** 85 **p** 86. C Bispham *Blackb* 85-87; C-in-c Anchorsholme 87-89; V from 89. *The Vicarage, 36 Valeway Avenue, Thornton-Cleveleys FY5 3RN* Tel (01253) 823904 E-mail anchorsholme@ukonline.co.uk

NUNN, Richard Ernest. b 38. St Alb and Ox Min Course 96. **d** 99 **p** 00. NSM Maidenhead St Luke *Ox* 99-02; NSM Waltham St Lawrence from 02. *The Parsonage, School Road, Waltham St Lawrence, Reading RG10 0NU* Tel 0118-934 5082 Mobile 07887-930983 E-mail richard@rjnunn.fsnet.co.uk

NUNN, Stephen Robert. b 64. St Jo Coll Nottm BTh92. **d** 92 **p** 93. C Hailsham *Chich* 92-95; C Hollington St Leon 95-97; R Clymping and Yapton w Ford 97-01; Chapl HM Pris Kingston (Portsm) from 01. *HM Prison, Milton Road, Portsmouth PO3 6AS* Tel (023) 9289 1100 Fax 9289 1181

NUNNERLEY, William John Arthur. b 27. Univ of Wales (Lamp) BA54 St Chad's Coll Dur DipTh56. **d** 56 **p** 57. C Tredegar St Geo *Mon* 56-61; Chapl RN 60-81; QHC from 79; R Barnoldby le Beck *Linc* 81-92; R Waltham 81-92; rtd 92; Perm to Offic *B & W* from 00. *Juniper Cottage, 82B Lower Street, Merriott TA16 5NW* Tel (01460) 76049

NUNNEY, Miss Sheila Frances. b 49. NNEB69 SRN74 RSCN74 SCM75 RCN Sister-Tutor's Dip 81. Oak Hill Th Coll BA92. **d** 92 **p** 94. C Swaffham *Nor* 92-96; Chapl Asst Norfolk and Nor Health Care NHS Trust 96-00; Chapl 00-01; Chapl Norwich Primary Care Trust from 01. *Priscilla Bacon Lodge, Colman Hospital, Unthank Road, Norwich NR2 2PJ* Tel (01603) 288950

NURSER, Canon John Shelley. b 29. Peterho Cam BA50 MA54 PhD58. Wells Th Coll 58. **d** 58 **p** 59. C Tankersley *Sheff* 58-61; Dean Trin Hall Cam 61-68; Australia 68-74; R Freckenham w Worlington *St E* 74-76; Can Res and Chan Linc Cathl *Linc* 76-92; Can and Preb Linc Cathl 92-94; P-in-c Shudy Camps *Ely* 92-94; rtd 94; Perm to Offic *St E* from 94 and *Ely* from 00. *68 Friars Street, Sudbury CO10 2AG* Tel (01787) 378595

NURTON, Robert. b 44. Univ of Wales (Lamp) BA67. Ridley Hall Cam 67. **d** 69 **p** 70. C Bris St Andr Hartcliffe *Bris* 69-73; C Ipswich St Mary at Stoke w St Pet & St Mary Quay *St E* 73-77; Chapl RN 77-99; Chapl Morden Coll Blackheath from 99. *Morden College, 19 St Germans Place, London SE3 0PW* Tel (020) 8858 2265

NUTH, Stephen William. b 55. Nazarene Th Coll Man CertRS87 St Jo Coll Nottm LTh95. **d** 95 **p** 96. C Wadhurst *Chich* 95-99; C Stonegate 95-99; R Marks Tey and Aldham *Chelmsf* 99-01; Perm to Offic *St E* from 03. *1 Suffolk Place, Lime Kiln Quay Road, Woodbridge IP12 1XB* Tel (01394) 380528

NUTT, Susan Mary. b 45. **d** 99 **p** 00. OLM Blackbourne *St E* from 99. *Portelet, Blacksmith Lane, Barnham, Thetford IP24 2NE* Tel (01842) 890409

NUTTALL, George Herman. b 31. St Jo Coll Dur BA59 DipTh61. Cranmer Hall Dur 59. **d** 61 **p** 62. C Eccleshill *Bradf* 61-65; V Oldham St Barn *Man* 65-70; Area Sec CMS *Derby* and *Lich* 70-81; V Derby St Aug *Derby* 81-84; Chapl Bournemouth and Poole Coll of FE *Sarum* 85-97; Chapl Dorset Inst of HE 85-90; Chapl Bournemouth Poly *Win* 90-92; Chapl Bournemouth Univ 92-97; rtd 97; Perm to Offic *Sarum* from 97. *22 Colletts Close, Corfe Castle, Wareham BH20 5HG* Tel (01929) 480103

NUTTALL, Michael John Berkeley. b 36. K Coll Lon AKC60. St Boniface Warminster 61. **d** 61 **p** 62. C Chapel Allerton *Ripon* 61-64; C Stanningley St Thos 64-68; V Leeds Gipton Epiphany 68-76; P-in-c Stainby w Gunby *Linc* 76-83; R N Witham 76-83; R S Witham 76-83; TV Bottesford w Ashby 83-88; I Adare w Kilpeacon and Croom *L & K* 88-94; I Adare and Kilmallock w Kilpeacon, Croom etc 94-01; Chapl Limerick Univ 88-95; Adn Limerick 92-01; rtd 01. *11 Cluaindara, Anglesborough, Kilmallock, Co Limerick, Irish Republic* Tel (00353) (62) 46280 Mobile 87-904 5738 E-mail adnmichaelnuttall@yahoo.com

NUTTALL, Wilfrid (Bill). b 29. ACP59 Open Univ BA82. Chich Th Coll 82. **d** 84 **p** 85. C Accrington St Jo *Blackb* 84-86; C Darwen St Cuth w Tockholes St Steph 86-89; V Foulridge 89-92; rtd 92; Perm to Offic *Cant* from 92. *15 Hope Road, Deal CT14 7DG*

NUZUM, Daniel Robert. b 73. RGN94 TCD BTh99. **d** 99 **p** 00. C Bandon Union *C, C & R* 99-01; I Templebreedy w Tracton and Nohoval from 02. *The Rectory, Crosshaven, Co Cork, Irish Repubic* Tel (00353) (21) 483 1236 E-mail curate.bandon@cork.anglican.org

NYE, Canon David Charles. b 39. K Coll Lon BD65. **d** 63 **p** 64. C Charlton Kings St Mary *Glouc* 63-67; C Yeovil St Jo w Preston Plucknett *B & W* 67-70; V Lower Cam *Glouc* 70-74; Min Can Glouc Cathl 74-79; Dir of Ords 74-79; Prin Glouc Th Course 74-79; V Glouc St Mary de Lode and St Nic *Glouc* 74-76; V Maisemore 76-79; Chapl Grenville Coll Bideford 79-81; V Leckhampton SS Phil and Jas w Cheltenham St Jas *Glouc* 81-95; Hon Can Glouc Cathl from 88; RD Cheltenham 89-95; P-in-c Northleach w Hampnett and Farmington 95-00; P-in-c Cold Aston w Notgrove and Turkdean 95-00; R Northleach w Hampnett and Farmington etc from 00; RD Northleach from 99. *The Vicarage, Northleach, Cheltenham GL54 3HL* Tel (01451) 860293 E-mail norvic@tesco.net

✠**NZIMBI, The Most Revd Benjamin.** Bp All SS Cathl Dio from 02; Abp Kenya from 02. *PO Box 40502, Nairobi 00100, Kenya* Tel (00254) (2) 714753 Fax 718442 E-mail archoffice@swiftkenya.com

O

OADES, Michael Anthony John. b 45. Brasted Th Coll 69 Sarum & Wells Th Coll 71. **d** 73 **p** 74. C Eltham Park St Luke *S'wark* 73-78; C Coulsdon St Andr 78-81; P-in-c Merton St Jas 81-86; V 86-87; V Benhilton from 87. *All Saints' Vicarage, All Saints' Road, Sutton SM1 3DA* Tel (020) 8644 9070

OADES, Canon Peter Robert. b 24. Fitzw Ho Cam BA47 CertEd48 MA53. **d** 67 **p** 67. C Warblington w Emsworth *Portsm* 67-68; V Choral Sarum Cathl *Sarum* 68-74; Chapl Salisbury Cathl Sch 68-74; P-in-c Sturminster Newton and Hinton St Mary *Sarum* 74-75; V 75-81; R Stock and Lydlinch 75-81; RD Blackmore Vale 78-81; V Woodford Valley 81-89; Can and Preb Sarum Cathl 85-89; rtd 89; Hon Chapl to the Deaf *Sarum* 82-92; Perm to Offic *Win* from 89; Perm to Offic *Sarum* from 89. *28 Mulberry Gardens, Fordingbridge SP6 1BP* Tel (01425) 657113

OAKE, Barry Richard. b 47. ARICS71. Ripon Coll Cuddesdon 83. **d** 85 **p** 86. C Wantage *Ox* 85-88; C Warlingham w Chelsham and Farleigh *S'wark* 88-91; R N w S Wootton *Nor* from 91; Asst Chapl among Deaf and Hearing-Impaired People from 01. *The Rectory, 47 Castle Rising Road, South Wootton, King's Lynn PE30 3JA* Tel (01553) 671381

OAKES, Graham. b 42. Leeds Univ DipTh68. Chich Th Coll 68. **d** 70 **p** 71. C Hulme Ascension *Man* 70-74; C Clifton All SS w Tyndalls Park *Bris* 74-76; P-in-c Chadderton St Mark *Man* 76-78; V 78-82; V King Cross *Wakef* 82-95; R Bath H Trin *B & W* from 95; Chapl R United Hosp Bath NHS Trust from 99. *Holy Trinity Rectory, 9 Marlborough Lane, Bath BA1 2NQ* Tel (01225) 422311 E-mail revd@goakes.fsbusiness.co.uk

OAKES, Miss Jennifer May. b 43. Trin Coll Bris DipHE80. **dss** 82 **d** 87 **p** 94. Wilnecote *Lich* 82-85; Stoneydelph St Martin CD 82-85; Bentley 85-89; Par Dn 87-89; Par Dn Hixon w Stowe-by-Chartley 89-94; C 94-98; Par Dn Fradswell, Gayton, Milwich and Weston 93-94; C 94-98; P-in-c Standon and Cotes Heath 98-00; rtd 00; Hon C Alfrick, Lulsley, Suckley, Leigh and Bransford *Worc* from 03. *16 Nash Green, Leigh Sinton, Malvern WR13 5DR* Tel (01886) 832699

OAKES, Canon Jeremy Charles. b 51. ACA75 FCA81. Westcott Ho Cam 75. **d** 78 **p** 79. C Evington *Leic* 78-81; C Ringwood *Win* 81-84; P-in-c Thurnby Lodge *Leic* 84-89; TV Oakdale *Sarum*

89-95; P-in-c Canford Cliffs and Sandbanks 95-03; V from 03; Can and Preb Sarum Cathl from 03. *The Vicarage, 14 Flaghead Road, Canford Cliffs, Poole BH13 7JW* Tel (01202) 700341 Fax as telephone E-mail jeremy.oakes@virgin.net

OAKES, John Cyril. b 49. AKC71. St Aug Coll Cant 71. **d** 72 **p** 73. C Broseley w Benthall *Heref* 72-76; C Cannock *Lich* 76-79; TV 79-83; V Rough Hills from 83; P-in-c Wolverhampton St Steph from 94. *St Martin's Vicarage, Dixon Street, Wolverhampton WV2 2BG* Tel (01902) 341030

OAKES, Canon Leslie John. b 28. AKC53. **d** 54 **p** 55. C Bedford Leigh *Man* 54-58; C Walsall St Matt *Lich* 58-60; Chapl Selly Oak Hosp Birm 60-64; V Longbridge *Birm* 64-93; Hon Can Birm Cathl 84-93; rtd 93; Perm to Offic *Birm* from 93. *108 Hole Lane, Birmingham B31 2DF* Tel 0121-476 8514

OAKES, Melvin. b 36. Linc Th Coll 77. **d** 79 **p** 80. C Lt Ilford St Mich *Chelmsf* 79-82; V Highams Park All SS 82-96; rtd 96; Perm to Offic *Chelmsf* from 99. *115 Richmond Avenue, London E4 9RR* Tel (020) 8527 0457

OAKES, Canon Robert. b 47. Ex & Truro NSM Scheme. **d** 82 **p** 83. NSM Probus, Ladock and Grampound w Creed and St Erme *Truro* 82-84; TV Bodmin w Lanhydrock and Lanivet 85-88; R S Hill w Callington from 88; P-in-c Linkinhorne 88-89; RD E Wivelshire 95-00; Hon Can Truro Cathl from 01. *The Rectory, Liskeard Road, Callington PL17 7JD* Tel (01579) 383341 E-mail rector@revrobert.freeserve.co.uk

OAKHAM, Archdeacon of. *See* PAINTER, The Ven David Scott

OAKLAND, Mrs Sarah Marie. b 54. UEA BEd85. EAMTC 99. **d** 02 **p** 03. C Diss *Nor* from 02. *7 de Lucy Close, Diss IP22 4YL* Tel (01379) 644955 E-mail saraho@hotmail.com

OAKLEY, Barry Wyndham. b 32. TD72. SS Coll Cam BA53 MA57. Ridley Hall Cam 56. **d** 58 **p** 59. C Alverstoke *Portsm* 58-61; C Bermondsey St Mary w St Olave and St Jo *S'wark* 61-63; V Crofton *Portsm* 63-78; V Edmonton All SS *Lon* 78-82; P-in-c Edmonton St Mich 80-82; V Edmonton All SS w St Mich 82-97; rtd 97; Perm to Offic *Lon* from 98. *25 Queen's Road, Enfield EN1 1NF* Tel (020) 8363 3199

OAKLEY, Hilary Robert Mark. b 53. Univ of Wales (Ban) BSc75 Ox Univ BA78 MA81 MIPD91. Ripon Coll Cuddesdon 76. **d** 79 **p** 80. C Birm St Pet *Birm* 79-82; C Cambridge Gt St Mary w St Mich *Ely* 82-86; Chapl Girton Coll Cam 82-86; Chapl Zürich w St Gallen and Winterthur *Eur* 86-88; NSM Lon 88-92; Perm to Offic *St Alb* from 92. *55 Southdown Road, Harpenden AL5 1PQ* Tel (01582) 761514 E-mail hilary.oakley@talk21.com

OAKLEY, Jeremy Steven. b 52. Birm Univ BA99. Trin Coll Bris DipHE95. **d** 97 **p** 98. C Walsall *Lich* 97-02; V Penn Fields from 02. *St Philip's Vicarage, Church Road, Bradmore, Wolverhampton WV3 7EJ* Tel (01902) 332031 *or* 341943 E-mail jsoakley@talk21.com

OAKLEY, Mark David. b 68. K Coll Lon BD90 AKC90 FRSA96. St Steph Ho Ox 90. **d** 93 **p** 94. C St John's Wood *Lon* 93-96; Bp's Chapl 96-00; P-in-c Covent Garden St Paul from 00; Dep P in O from 96. *Flat 3, 35 Craven Street, London WC2N 5NF* Tel (020) 7836 5221 Mobile 07956-698276 Fax (020) 7240 0346 E-mail md.oakley1@virgin.net

OAKLEY, Richard John. b 46. AKC69 St Aug Coll Cant 69. **d** 70 **p** 71. C Wythenshawe Wm Temple Ch *Man* 70-75; V Ashton H Trin 75-80; CR 80-93; Lic to Offic *Carl* 88-93; V Cantley *Sheff* 93-99; V Carl St Aid and Ch Ch *Carl* from 99. *St Aidan's Vicarage, 6 Lismore Place, Carlisle CA1 1LX* Tel (01228) 522942 E-mail fr.oakley.staidan@virgin.net

OAKLEY, Robert Paul. b 51. Sheff Univ BScTech72 PGCE74. St Jo Coll Nottm DipTh89. **d** 89 **p** 90. C Heatherlands St Jo *Sarum* 89-92; V Burton All SS w Ch Ch *Lich* 92-99; V Gt Wyrley from 99. *St Mark's Vicarage, 1 Cleves Crescent, Cheslyn Hay, Walsall WS6 7LR* Tel (01922) 414309

OAKLEY, Robin Ian. b 37. Ripon Hall Ox 68. **d** 70 **p** 71. C Leighton Buzzard *St Alb* 70-73; C Watford St Mich 73-76; R Ickleford 76-80; R Ickleford w Holwell 80-02; rtd 02; Perm to Offic *St Alb* from 02. *13 Anders Road, South Wonston, Winchester SO21 3EL* Tel (01962) 880613

OAKLEY, Susan Mary. *See* HENWOOD, Mrs Susan Mary

OAKLEY, Timothy Crispin. b 45. Qu Coll Cam BA66 MA70 Bris Univ PGCE69. St Jo Coll Nottm DipTh74 DPS76. **d** 76 **p** 77. C Bromley Common St Aug *Roch* 76-79; C Fairfield *Liv* 79-81; CMS Kenya 82-90; P-in-c Beaford, Roborough and St Giles in the Wood *Ex* 91-96; Chapl St Andr Sch Turi Kenya 96-98; V Woodford Halse w Eydon *Pet* from 99; RD Brackley from 03. *The New Vicarage, Parsons Street, Woodford Halse, Daventry NN11 3RE* Tel (01327) 261477 E-mail tim@revoakley.freeserve.co.uk

OATES, Alan. b 32. S'wark Ord Course 79. **d** 80 **p** 81. NSM Rayleigh *Chelmsf* 80-87; TV Jarrow *Dur* 87-92; P-in-c Stella 92-95; R 95-97; rtd 97; Perm to Offic *Dur* from 98; *Newc* from 00. *1 The Haven, North Shields NE29 6YH* Tel 0191-258 6984

OATES, Alexander James. b 38. Clifton Th Coll 63. **d** 67 **p** 68. C Brixton Hill St Sav *S'wark* 67-68; C Westcombe Park St Geo 68-71; C Stechford *Birm* 71-74; R Greenhithe St Mary *Roch* 74-77; soc worker 77-02; rtd 03. *1 Fairlight Villas, North Road, Havering-atte-Bower, Romford RM4 1PP* Tel (01708) 760252

OATES, Douglas. b 39. Bolton Coll of Educn CertEd74. Nor Ord Course BTh97. **d** 97 **p** 98. NSM Balderstone *Man* 97-99; NSM S Rochdale 00-01; NSM Oldham St Barn 01-03; P-in-c from 03. *St Barnabas' Vicarage, 1 Arundel Street, Oldham OL4 1NL* Tel 0161-624 7708 E-mail dco@surfaid.org

OATES, Canon John. b 30. Kelham Th Coll 53. **d** 57 **p** 58. C Hackney Wick St Mary of Eton w St Aug *Lon* 57-60; Development Officer C of E Youth Coun 60-64; Sec C of E Coun Commonwealth Settlement 64-65; Gen Sec 65-72; Sec C of E Cttee on Migration & Internat Affairs 68-72; Hon Can Bunbury from 69; V Richmond St Mary *S'wark* 70-79; P-in-c Richmond St Jo 76-79; V Richmond St Mary w St Matthias and St Jo 79-84; RD Richmond and Barnes 79-84; R St Bride Fleet Street w Bridewell etc *Lon* 84-00; AD The City 97-00; Preb St Paul's Cathl 97-00; rtd 00. *7 Kings Court, Deer Park Close, Kingston-upon-Thames KT2 7RJ* Tel (020) 8974 8821 E-mail john@joates.co.uk

OATES, Michael Graham. b 62. Leic Poly BSc84. Aston Tr Scheme 87 Cranmer Hall Dur 89. **d** 92 **p** 93. C Enfield St Andr *Lon* 92-96; TV Oakdale *Sarum* from 96. *The Vicarage, 16 Rowbarrow Close, Canford Heath, Poole BH17 9EA* Tel (01202) 699807

OATES (née ADAMS), Mrs Ruth. b 47. Bris Univ BSc69. SEITE 97. **d** 00 **p** 01. C Rainham *Roch* from 00. *60 Childscroft Road, Gillingham ME8 7SN* Tel (01634) 363631 Fax 362023 E-mail ruth-oates@epiphany-rainham.fsnet.co.uk

OBAN, Provost of. *See* MACLEAN, The Very Revd Allan Murray

OBEE, Douglas Walter. b 18. Roch Th Coll 65. **d** 67 **p** 68. C Beckenham St Geo *Roch* 67-71; R Whitestone *Ex* 71-75; V Oldridge 72-75; P-in-c Harford 76-87; V Ivybridge 76-87; V Ivybridge w Harford 87; rtd 87; Perm to Offic *Ex* from 88. *16 Kerswill Road, Exeter EX4 1NY* Tel (01392) 439405

O'BENEY, Robin Mervyn. b 35. Ely Th Coll 61. **d** 64 **p** 65. C Liss *Portsm* 64-65; C Portsea St Cuth 65-68; Hon C Wymondham *Nor* 74-76; R Swainsthorpe w Newton Flotman 76-80; NSM Sparkenhoe Deanery *Leic* 87-90; V Billesdon and Skeffington 90-91; rtd 95. *19 Bridge Street, Kington HR5 3DL* Tel (01544) 230416

OBERST, Preb Simon Julian. b 57. Trin Coll Cam BA79 MA82 ACA83. Wycliffe Hall Ox DipTh90. **d** 91 **p** 92. C S Croydon Em *S'wark* 91-95; V Chipping Campden w Ebrington *Glouc* 95-01; R Bath Abbey w St Jas *B & W* from 01; Preb Wells Cathl from 03. *The Abbey Rectory, Redwood House, Trossachs Drive, Bath BA2 6RP* Tel (01225) 464930 *or* 422462

OBIORA, Arthur Cuenyem. b 42. JP91. DipSM68. LNSM course 92. **d** 95 **p** 95. OLM Hatcham St Cath *S'wark* from 95. *15 Besson Street, London SE14 5AE* Tel (020) 7732 1065

O'BOYLE, Liam Patrick Butler. b 66. Nottm Univ BA90 MA98. EMMTC 98. **d** 01 **p** 02. NSM Cinderhill *S'well* from 01. *24 Coventry Road, Beeston, Nottingham NG9 2EG* Tel 0115-943 1032

O'BRIEN, Andrew David. b 61. Nottm Univ BTh88. Linc Th Coll 85. **d** 88 **p** 89. C Clare w Poslingford *St E* 88-89; C Clare w Poslingford, Cavendish etc 89-91; V Belton *Linc* 91-97; P-in-c Melbourn *Ely* 97-99; V from 99; P-in-c Meldreth 97-99; V from 99. *The Vicarage, Vicarage Close, Melbourn, Royston SG8 6DY* Tel (01763) 260295 E-mail revobrien@tesco.net

O'BRIEN, Donogh Smith. b 34. St Pet Hall Ox BA56 MA60. Ripon Hall Ox 56. **d** 57 **p** 58. C Gt Sankey *Liv* 57-63; C Farnworth 63-66; Lic to Offic from 66; Asst Master Wade Deacon Gr Sch Widnes 66-99; rtd 99. *Fourways, 178 Lunts Heath Road, Farnworth, Widnes WA8 9AZ* Tel 0151-424 0147

O'BRIEN, Mrs Elaine. b 55. CITC 94. **d** 97 **p** 98. Aux Min Killyman *Arm* 97-00; Aux Min Gilnahirk *D & D* from 00. *9 Moorfield Gardens, Comber, Newtownards BT23 5WF* Tel (028) 9187 1055 E-mail curate.gilnahirk@down.anglican.org

O'BRIEN, George Edward. b 32. Clifton Th Coll 61. **d** 64 **p** 65. C Denton Holme *Carl* 64-68; V Castle Town *Lich* 68-88; Chapl St Geo Hosp Stafford 88-94; Chapl Kingsmead Hosp Stafford 88-94; Chapl Foundation NHS Trust Stafford 94-99; rtd 99; Perm to Offic from 99. *Abily, 185 Tixall Road, Stafford ST16 3XJ* Tel (01785) 244261

O'BRIEN, John. b 41. St Jo Coll Cam BA63 MA67. Ridley Hall Cam 63. **d** 65 **p** 66. C Wotton St Mary *Glouc* 65-69; Youth Chapl 67-69; Lect Coll of SS Paul and Mary Cheltenham 69-85; V Twigworth, Down Hatherley, Norton, The Leigh etc *Glouc* 85-03; RD Glouc N 94-99; rtd 03. *72 Albemarle Gate, Cheltenham GL50 4PJ* Tel (01242) 514423

O'BRIEN, Kevin Michael. b 60. Herts Univ BA82. St Steph Ho Ox 99. **d** 01 **p** 02. C Uppingham w Ayston and Wardley w Belton *Pet* from 01. *34B Ayston Road, Uppingham LE15 9RL* Tel (01572) 821631 E-mail kevin.obrien@rutnet.co.uk

O'BRIEN, Mary. *See* GUBBINS, Mrs Mary

O'BRIEN, Peter Thomas. b 35. Lon Univ BD61 Man Univ PhD71. Moore Th Coll Sydney ThL60. **d** 61 **p** 62. Australia 61-63 and from 74; India 64-68 and 71-73; C Cheadle *Ches* 68-71. *Moore Theological College, 1 King Street, Newtown, NSW, Australia 2042* Tel (0061) (2) 9577 9999 *or* 9557 3072 Fax 9577 9988

O'BRIEN, Shelagh Ann. *See* STACEY, Mrs Shelagh Ann

O'BRIEN, Timothy. b 43. WEMTC 01. **d** 02. OLM Bridgnorth, Tasley, Astley Abbotts, etc *Heref* from 02. *34 St James Drive, Bridgnorth WV15 6BN* Tel (01746) 768983
E-mail revtimobrien@aol.com

O'CALLAGHAN, Regan Robert Rehe. b 67. Brunel Univ BA97 K Coll Lon MA98 Anglia Poly Univ MA01. Westcott Ho Cam 99. **d** 01 **p** 02. C Whitton St Aug *Lon* from 01. *60 Powder Hill Lane, Whitton, Twickenham TW2 6ED* Tel (020) 8255 8299

OCKFORD, Paul Philip. b 62. C St Chad's Coll Dur BA42. St Steph Ho Ox 68. **d** 70 **p** 71. C Streatham St Pet *S'wark* 70-74; C Cheam 74-77; P-in-c Eastrington *York* 77-79; TV Howden 80-83; R Sherburn and W and E Heslerton w Yedingham 83-92; V Bampton, Morebath, Clayhanger and Petton *Ex* 92-98; V Market Weighton *York* from 98; R Goodmanham from 98; V Sancton from 98. *The Vicarage, 38 Cliffe Road, Market Weighton, York YO43 3BN* Tel (01430) 873230
E-mail allsaints@lineone.com

OCKWELL, Canon Herbert <u>Grant</u>. b 12. Kelham Th Coll 30. **d** 36 **p** 37. C Newington St Matt *S'wark* 36-40; CF (EC) 40-46; V Lambeth St Phil *S'wark* 46-52; V Surbiton St Andr 52-62; V Balham Hill Ascension 62-70; Hon Can S'wark Cathl 64-70; R Blendworth, Chalton and Idsworth *Portsm* 70-81; rtd 81; Perm to Offic *Portsm* from 81; *Chich* from 82. *Abbeyfield House, 30 Crockford Road, Westbourne, Emsworth PO10 8TN* Tel (01243) 374686

O'CONNELL, Miss Mary Joy. b 49. York Univ BA71 Leeds Univ CertEd74. Chich Th Coll 84. **dss** 86 **d** 87 **p** 94. Cinderhill *S'well* 86-87; Par Dn 87-94; C 94; P-in-c 94-98; V Linc St Giles *Linc* from 98. *The Vicarage, 25 Shelley Drive, Lincoln LN2 4BY* Tel (01522) 527655 E-mail mjoconnell@lineone.net

O'CONNOR, Alfred Stanley. b 20. TCD BA43 MA60. **d** 43 **p** 44. C Belfast St Mich *Conn* 43-45; C Urney Union *K, E & A* 45-49; I Killesher 49-54; I Roscrea *L & K* 54-62; I Camlough w Killeavy *Arm* 62-65; I Drumglass 65-85; Can Arm Cathl 83-85; rtd 85. *25 West Street, Stewartstown, Dungannon BT71 5HT* Tel (028) 8773 8784

O'CONNOR, Canon Brian <u>Michael</u> **McDougal.** b 42. St Cath Coll Cam BA67 MA69. Cuddesdon Coll 67. **d** 69 **p** 70. C Headington *Ox* 69-71; Sec Dioc Past and Redundant Chs Uses Cttees 72-79; P-in-c Merton 72-76; V Rainham *Roch* 79-97; RD Gillingham 81-88; Hon Can Roch Cathl 89-97; Dean Auckland 97-00; Hon Can from 00; Perm to Offic *Ox* 00-02; P-in-c Lt Missenden from 02. *The Vicarage, Little Missenden, Amersham HP7 0PX* Tel (01494) 862008 Mobile 07740-702161
E-mail canonmichaeloc@aol.com

O'CONNOR, Canon Daniel. b 33. Univ Coll Dur BA54 MA67 St Andr Univ PhD81. Cuddesdon Coll 56. **d** 58 **p** 59. C Stockton St Pet *Dur* 58-62; C W Hartlepool St Aid 62-63; Cam Miss to Delhi 63-70; USPG 70-72; India 63-72; Chapl St Andr Univ *St And* 72-77; R Edin Gd Shep *Edin* 77-82; Prin Coll of Ascension Selly Oak 82-90; Dir Scottish Chs Ho (Chs Together in Scotland) 90-93; Can Res Wakef Cathl *Wakef* 93-96; Bp's Adv on Inter-Faith Issues 93-96; rtd 96. *50 Main Street, Strathkinness, St Andrews KY16 9SA* Tel (01334) 850081
E-mail danoconnor@btinternet.com

O'CONNOR, Edward Howard. b 32. AIMLS59 FRSH65. Linc Th Coll 81 Immanuel Coll Ibadan 76. **d** 77 **p** 79. Nigeria 77-81; P-in-c Newchurch *Portsm* 81-83; V 83-91; P-in-c Arreton 82-83; V 83-91; Chapl HM Pris Kingston (Portsm) 91-97; rtd 92. *23 Arundel Road, Ryde PO33 1BW* Tel (01983) 617062

O'CONNOR, John Goodrich. b 34. Keble Coll Ox BA58 MA60. Lich Th Coll. **d** 61 **p** 62. C Blackpool St Steph *Blackb* 61-66; C Holbeck *Ripon* 66-68; C Hendon St Mary *Lon* 68-73; TV Thornaby on Tees *York* 73-79; TR 79-89; V Blyth St Cuth *Newc* 89-96; Chapl Wellesley Nautical Sch 89-96; V Feniscliffe *Blackb* from 96. *The Vicarage, St Francis Road, Feniscliffe, Blackburn BB2 2TZ* Tel (01254) 201757 E-mail johnoak@fish.co.uk

O'CONNOR, Nigel George. b 25. TD66. Linc Th Coll 53. **d** 55 **p** 56. C S Ormsby w Ketsby, Calceby and Driby *Linc* 55-58; R Partney w Dalby 58-65; V Skendleby 59-65; R Ashby by Partney 59-65; CF (TA) 62-71; R Ivychurch w Old Romney and Midley *Cant* 65-74; V Brenzett w Snargate and Snave 65-74; R Newchurch 65-74; R St Mary in the Marsh 65-74; R Burmarsh 65-74; V Brookland w Fairfield 65-74; CF (R of O) 71-91; V S w N Hayling *Portsm* 74-85; V Corby Glen *Linc* 85-91; rtd 91; Perm to Offic *Sarum* from 91. *Winterbourne House, Allington, Salisbury SP4 0BZ* Tel (01980) 611453

O'CONNOR, Rosemary Irene. b 43. St Gabr Coll Lon TCert65. WMMTC 96. **d** 99 **p** 00. NSM Cannock *Lich* 99-01; TV from 01. *St Aidan's Vicarage, Albert Street, Cannock WS11 5JD* Tel (01543) 500015 or 502131

ODA-BURNS, John Macdonald. b 31. AKC56. **d** 57 **p** 58. C St Marychurch *Ex* 57-59; S Africa 59-64; Bahamas 64-67; USA from 67; rtd 96. *611 La Mesa Drive, Portola Valley, CA 94028, USA* Tel (001) (650) 854 2831 Fax as telephone
E-mail bussels@batnet.com

ODDY, Canon Frederick Brian. b 29. Univ of Wales (Lamp) BA50. Linc Th Coll 50. **d** 52 **p** 53. C Preston Em *Blackb* 52-55; C St Annes 55-57; V Chorley St Jas 57-64; V Warton St Oswald 64-76; P-in-c Yealand Conyers 74-76; V Warton St Oswald w Yealand Conyers 76-98; RD Tunstall 84-90; Hon Can Blackb Cathl 89-98; rtd 98; Perm to Offic *Blackb* from 98. *9 Main Road, Nether Kellet, Carnforth LA6 1HG*

ODDY, Joan Winifred. b 34. LNSM course 95. **d** 97 **p** 98. OLM Kessingland w Gisleham *Nor* 97-99; OLM Kessingland, Gisleham and Rushmere from 99. *Rose Cottage, Wash Lane, Kessingland, Lowestoft NR33 7QY* Tel (01502) 742001

ODLING-SMEE, George <u>William</u>. b 35. K Coll Dur MB, BS59 FRCS68 FRCSI86. **d** 77 **p** 78. NSM Belfast St Thos *Conn* 77-90; NSM Belfast St Geo 90-02. *The Boathouse, 24 Rossglass Road South, Killough, Downpatrick BT30 7RA* Tel (028) 4484 1868 Fax 4484 1143 E-mail wodlingsmee@aol.com

ODLUM, Michael Julian. b 24. DFC45. St Mich Coll Llan 55. **d** 56 **p** 57. C Risca *Mon* 56-59; St Vincent 60-65; P-in-c Spaxton w Charlynch *B & W* 65-67; V Sampford Arundel 67-74; Asst Chapl HM Pris Wandsworth 74; Chapl HM Pris Standford Hill 74-81; Chapl HM Pris Leic 82-89; rtd 89; Perm to Offic *Leic* from 89. *67A Main Street, Kirby Muxloe, Leicester LE9 2AN*

O'DONNELL, Kevin George. b 57. Man Univ BA78 Disbury Coll Man PGCE79. St Steph Ho Ox 86. **d** 88 **p** 89. C Tokyngton St Mich *Lon* 88-90; C Ascot Heath *Ox* 90-92; Perm to Offic 94-96; Chapl Heathfield Sch Ascot 96-99; R W Chiltington *Chich* from 99. *The Rectory, East Street, West Chiltington, Pulborough RH20 2JY* Tel (01798) 813117 Mobile 07957-880404
E-mail kevino'donnell@lastlaugh.demon.co.uk

O'DONNELL, Mrs Mollie. b 39. Portsm Poly BA91. STETS 97. **d** 00 **p** 03. NSM Calbourne w Newtown *Portsm* from 00; NSM Shalfleet from 00. *1 Mill Green Cottages, Newbridge, Yarmouth PO41 0TZ* Tel (01983) 531320

O'DONOVAN, Canon Oliver Michael Timothy. b 45. Ball Coll Ox BA68 MA71 DPhil75. Wycliffe Hall Ox 68. **d** 72 **p** 73. Tutor Wycliffe Hall Ox 72-77; Canada 77-82; Regius Prof Moral and Past Th Ox Univ from 82; Can Res Ch Ch *Ox* from 82. *Christ Church, Oxford OX1 1DP* Tel (01865) 276219
E-mail oliver.odonovan@chch.ox.ac.uk

O'DWYER, John Francis Joseph. b 61. N Ord Course 00. **d** 03. C Bury St Jo w St Mark *Man* from 03. *14 Mather Road, Bury BL9 6QU* Tel 0161-764 3943
E-mail johntricia2000@yahoo.co.uk

OEHRING, Anthony Charles. b 56. Sheff City Poly BA77 CQSW79 Kent Univ MA02. Ridley Hall Cam 86. **d** 88 **p** 89. C Gillingham *Sarum* 88-91; TV S Gillingham *Roch* 91-00; P-in-c Faversham *Cant* from 00; AD Ospringe from 02; C Preston next Faversham, Goodnestone and Graveney from 02; P-in-c The Brents and Davington w Oare and Luddenham from 03. *The Vicarage, 16 Newton Road, Faversham ME13 8DY* Tel (01795) 532592 E-mail anthonyoehring@aol.com

OEPPEN, John Gerard David. b 44. St D Coll Lamp DipTh67. **d** 67 **p** 68. C-in-c Cwmmer w Abercregan CD *Llan* 67-70; V Glyncorrwg w Afan Vale and Cymmer Afan 70-71; C Whitchurch 71-74; V Aberavon H Trin 74-78; V Bargoed and Deri w Brithdir 78-86; R Barry All SS from 86. *The Rectory, 3 Park Road, Barry CF62 6NU* Tel (01446) 734629

OESTREICHER, Canon Paul. b 31. OM(Ger)97. Univ of NZ BA53 MA65 Cov Poly Hon DLitt91. Linc Th Coll 56. **d** 59 **p** 60. C Dalston H Trin w St Phil *Lon* 59-61; C S Mymms K Chas 61-68; Asst in Relig Broadcasting BBC 61-64; Assoc Sec Internat Affairs Dept BCC 64-69; V Blackheath Ascension *S'wark* 68-81; Dir of Tr 69-72; Hon Can S'wark Cathl 78-81; Asst Gen Sec BCC 81-86; Can Res Cov Cathl *Cov* 86-97; Dir of Internat Min 86-97; Humboldt Fell Inst of Th Free Univ of Berlin 92-93; rtd 98; Perm to Offic *Cov* from 98 and *Chich* from 03. *97 Furze Croft, Furze Hill, Hove BN3 1PE* Tel (01273) 728033
E-mail paulo@reconcile.org.uk

O'FERRALL, The Very Revd Basil Arthur. b 24. CB79. TCD BA48 MA65. TCD Div Sch Div Test48. **d** 48 **p** 49. C Coleraine *Conn* 48-51; Chapl RN 51-75; Chapl of the Fleet and Adn for the RN 75-80; QHC 75-80; Hon Can Gib Cathl *Eur* 77-80; Chapl to The Queen 80-85; V Ranworth w Panxworth and Woodbastwick *Nor* 80-85; Bp's Chapl Norfolk Broads 80-85; Hon Can Win Cathl *Win* 85-93; R Jersey St Helier 85-93; Dean Jersey 85-93; Pres Jersey Miss to Seamen 85-93; Angl Adv Channel TV 85-93; rtd 93; Perm to Offic *Chich* from 93. *The Stone House, Barrack Square, Winchelsea TN36 4EG* Tel (01797) 223458

O'FERRALL, Patrick Charles Kenneth. b 34. New Coll Ox BA58 MA60. Guildf Dioc Min Course 99. **d** 00 **p** 01. OLM Godalming *Guildf* from 00. *Catteshall Grange, Catteshall Road, Godalming GU7 1LZ* Tel (01483) 410134 Fax 414161
E-mail patrick.oferrall@godalming.org.uk

OFFER, The Ven Clifford Jocelyn. b 43. Ex Univ BA67 FRSA97. Westcott Ho Cam 67. **d** 69 **p** 70. C Bromley SS Pet and Paul *Roch* 69-74; TV Southampton (City Cen) *Win* 74-83; TR Hitchin *St Alb* 83-94; Adn Nor from 94; Can Res Nor Cathl from 94. *26 The Close, Norwich NR1 4DZ* Tel (01603) 620375 Fax 661104

OGADA, John Ochieng. b 56. Nairobi Univ LLB83 Univ of Wales (Cardiff) LLM89. **d** 01. Perm to Offic *York* 01-02; NSM

Hull St Martin w Transfiguration from 02. *87 Parkfield Drive, Hull HU3 6TF* Tel (01482) 505715

O'GARRO, Henry Roland Furlonge. b 30. Leeward Is TCert52. St Steph Ho Ox 00. **d** 00. NSM Kilburn St Aug w St Jo *Lon* from 00. *32 Cedar Road, London NW2 6SR* Tel (020) 8452 4530

OGDEN, Eric. b 34. NW Ord Course 73. **d** 76 **p** 77. NSM Lydgate St Anne *Man* 76-92; NSM Lydgate w Friezland 92-01; rtd 01; Perm to Offic *Man* from 01. *40 Burnedge Lane, Grasscroft, Oldham OL4 4EA* Tel (01457) 873661

OGDEN, Harry. b 30. AKC57. **d** 58 **p** 59. C Hollinwood *Man* 58-60; C Langley St Aid CD 60-61; R Lightbowne 61-69; V Farnworth and Kearsley 69-72; V Oldham St Steph and All Martyrs 72-79; R Moss Side Ch Ch 79-95; rtd 95; Perm to Offic *Man* 95-98. *3 Lygon Lodge, Newland, Malvern WR13 5AX* Tel (01684) 574664

OGILVIE, The Ven Gordon. b 42. Glas Univ MA64 Lon Univ BD67. ALCD66. **d** 67 **p** 68. C Ashtead *Guildf* 67-72; V New Barnet St Jas *St Alb* 72-80; Dir Past Studies Wycliffe Hall Ox 80-87; P-in-c Harlow New Town w Lt Parndon *Chelmsf* 87-89; R 89-94; TR Harlow Town Cen w Lt Parndon 94-96; Chapl Princess Alexandra Hosp Harlow 88-96; Hon Can Chelmsf Cathl *Chelmsf* 94-96; Adn Nottingham *S'well* from 96. *2B Spencer Avenue, Mapperley, Nottingham NG3 5SP* Tel 0115-967 0875 *or* (01636) 814490 Fax 0115-967 1014 *or* (01636) 815882 E-mail gogilvie@southwell.anglican.org

OGILVIE, Ian Douglas. b 37. Em Coll Cam BA59 MA63. Linc Th Coll 59. **d** 61 **p** 62. C Clapham H Trin *S'wark* 61-63; C Cambridge Gt St Mary w St Mich *Ely* 63-66; Chapl Sevenoaks Sch 66-77; Hon C Sevenoaks St Nic *Roch* 67-77; Chapl Malvern Coll 77-84; Hd Master St Geo Sch Harpenden 84-87; Lic to Offic *St Alb* 84-87; Bp's Dom Chapl 87-89; P-in-c Aldenham 87-91; Appeals Dir Mind 89-91; Fund Raising Dir Br Deaf Assn 91-94; NSM Tring *St Alb* 92-94; Perm to Offic from 94; Fund Raising Dir R Nat Miss to Deep Sea Fishermen from 94. *The White House, 19 Lower Icknield Way, Marsworth, Tring HP23 4LN* Tel (01296) 661479

OGILVIE, Pamela. b 56. N Lon Poly CQSW82 Brunel Univ MA89. Qu Coll Birm 01. **d** 03. C Hill *Birm* from 03. *3 Dower Road, Sutton Coldfield B75 6UA* Tel 0121-308 0759 Mobile 07789-911576 E-mail pogilvie@fish.co.uk

OGLE, Ms Catherine. b 61. Leeds Univ BA82 MPhil85 MA91 Fitzw Coll Cam BA87. Westcott Ho Cam 85. **d** 88 **p** 94. C Middleton St Mary *Ripon* 88-91; Relig Progr Ed BBC Radio Leeds 91-95; NSM Leeds St Marg and All Hallows 91-95; P-in-c Woolley *Wakef* 95-01; P-in-c Huddersfield St Pet and All SS 01-03; V Huddersfield St Pet from 03. *59 Lightridge Road, Fixby, Huddersfield HD2 2HF* Tel (01484) 544558 E-mail ogle@woolleyvic.freeserve.co.uk

OGLESBY, Ms Elizabeth Jane. b 73. Roehampton Inst BA95 Man Univ BPhil98. Westcott Ho Cam 00. **d** 03. C S Dulwich St Steph *S'wark* from 03. *161 Westwood Park, London SE23 3QL* Tel (020) 8766 7281 Mobile 07790-219725 E-mail curate@ststephensdulwich.org

OGLESBY, Leslie Ellis. b 46. Univ Coll Ox BA69 MA73 City Univ MPhil73 Fitzw Coll Cam BA73 MA77. Ripon Coll Cuddesdon 77. **d** 78 **p** 79. C Stevenage St Mary Shephall *St Alb* 78-80; Dir Alb Minl Tr Scheme 80-87; V Markyate Street *St Alb* 80-87; Dir CME 87-94; Hon Can St Alb 93-01; TR Hitchin 94-01; Adult Educn and Tr Officer *Ely* from 01. *8 Hertford Close, Ely CB6 3QS* Tel (01353) 666628 E-mail les.oglesby@ely.anglican.org

OGLEY, John. b 40. Oak Hill Th Coll 62. **d** 65 **p** 66. C Ardsley *Sheff* 65-68; C Carlton-in-the-Willows *S'well* 68-71; P-in-c Tollerton 71-79; V Skegby 79-93; R Carlton in Lindrick 93-01; P-in-c Langold 98-01; rtd 01; Perm to Offic *S'well* from 01. *Shalom, 39 Sparken Dale, Worksop S80 1BL* Tel (01909) 479462

O'GORMAN, Paul Anthony. b 46. Portsm Poly BSc79. Oak Hill Th Coll DipHE81. **d** 81 **p** 82. C Leyton St Mary w St Edw *Chelmsf* 81-83; C Rayleigh 83-84; CF 84-87; R Northiam *Chich* 87-93; V Hastings Em and St Mary in the Castle 93-99; rtd 99; NSM Southsea St Simon *Portsm* from 99. *281 Fawcett Road, Southsea PO4 0LB* Tel (023) 9283 9323

OGSTON, Russell James. b 71. La Sainte Union Coll BA94. Qu Coll Birm BD97. **d** 98 **p** 99. C Andover w Foxcott *Win* 98-01; C Southampton Maybush St Pet 01-03; Asst Chapl Homerton Univ Hosp NHS Trust Lon from 03. *Homerton Hospital, Homerton Row, London E9 6SR* Tel (020) 8510 7385 E-mail russell.ogston@btinternet.com

OGUGUO, Barnabas Ahuna. b 47. Rome Univ BA70 BD74 Glas Univ MTh84 PhD90 Strathclyde Univ PGCE93. **d** 73 **p** 74. Nigeria 73-93; RE Teacher Lenzie Academy *Glas* 93-96; Bearsden Academy from 96; Hon C Lenzie from 95. *4 Kennedy Path, Townhead, Glasgow G4 0PW* Tel 0141-552 2628 Fax as telephone E-mail boguguo@excitepost.co.uk

O'HANLON, Canon William Douglas. b 11. Peterho Cam BA32 MA37. Cuddesdon Th Coll 32. **d** 37 **p** 38. C Heatherlands St Jo *Sarum* 37-39; Chapl RAFVR 39-46; R Langton Matravers *Sarum* 46-51; V Calne 51-62; P-in-c Heddington 53-62; V Calne and Blackland 62-69; Can and Preb Sarum Cathl 61-82; V

Coombe Bissett w Homington 69-72; R Studland 72-82; rtd 82; Perm to Offic *Sarum* from 82. *Crown Hill, 14 Bon Accord Road, Swanage BH19 2DT* Tel (01929) 425416

OHS, Lt Comdr Douglas Fredrick. b 49. Saskatchewan Univ BA74. Em Coll Saskatoon LTh75. **d** 74 **p** 75. C Bridgwater St Mary w Chilton Trinity *B & W* 75-77; Canada from 77. *Chaplain (P), 17 Wing Winnipeg, PO Box 17000 STN Forces, Winnipeg MB, Canada, R3J 3Y5* Tel (001) (204) 833 2500 ext 5417 Fax 833 2565

OJI, Erasmus Oluchukwu. b 43. Lon Univ BSc66 LRCP70 MRCS70 FRCS76. Oak Hill Th Coll 75. **d** 78 **p** 79. C Ealing Dean St Jo *Lon* 78-80; Nigeria 80-90; Asst Chapl Rotherham Distr Gen Hosp 90-91; Perm to Offic *Sheff* from 92. *369 Fulwood Road, Sheffield S10 3BS* Tel 0114-266 1360

OKE, Mrs Elizabeth Mary. b 43. St Alb and Ox Min Course CTBS99. **d** 99 **p** 00. NSM Woolhampton w Midgham and Beenham Valance *Ox* from 99. *Gladstone Cottage, 18 Windmill Road, Mortimer, Reading RG7 3RN* Tel 0118-933 2829

OKE, Michael John. b 43. Ox Min Course 89. **d** 92 **p** 93. NSM Stratfield Mortimer *Ox* 92-99; NSM Stratfield Mortimer and Mortimer W End etc 99-03; NSM Tilehurst St Geo from 03; NSM Tilehurst St Mary from 03. *Gladstone Cottage, 18 Windmill Road, Mortimer, Reading RG7 3RN* Tel 0118-933 2829

OKECHI, Patrick Otosio. b 62. Chas Univ Prague MTh94. **d** 95 **p** 98. Perm to Offic *Eur* 95-02; Asst P Angl Episc Congregation Czech Republic 02; V W Bromwich Gd Shep w St Jo *Lich* from 02. *The Vicarage, 4 Bromford Lane, West Bromwich B70 7HP* Tel 0121-525 5530 E-mail pokechi@btopenworld.com

✠**OKEKE, The Rt Revd Ken Sandy Edozie.** b 41. Nigeria Univ BSc67 Man Univ MA94. Igbaja Sem Nigeria. **d** 76 **p** 76 **c** 00. Nigeria 76-80 and 87-89; Chapl to Nigerians in UK and Irish Republic 80-87; Hon Can Kwara from 85; Hon Adn from 98; C Man Whitworth *Man* 89-95; Chapl Inst of Higher Learning Man 89-95; CMS 95-01; Perm to Offic *S'wark* from 95; Bp on the Niger from 00. *PO Box 42, Onitsha, Nigeria* Tel (00234) (46) 411282 *or* 410337

OKELLO, Modicum. b 53. Nairobi Sch of Miss Dip Miss82 Haggaih Inst of Chr Leadership Dip Chr Leadership 86 Wycliffe Hall Ox 86 Trin Coll Bris BA90 St Paul's Coll Limuru DipTh78. **d** 78 **p** 79. Kenya 78-80; Uganda 80-86; NSM Goodmayes All SS *Chelmsf* 91-92; C Barking St Marg w St Patr 92-96; C Stratford St Jo and Ch Ch w Forest Gate St Jas 96-99; TV Forest Gate St Sav w W Ham St Matt from 99. *St Matthew's Vicarage, Dyson Road, Stratford E15 4JX* Tel (020) 8519 2524 E-mail modicum@mokello.freeserve.co.uk

✠**OKINE, The Most Revd Robert Garshong Allotey.** b 37. Huron Coll Ontario BMin73 Hon DD82 Vanderbilt Univ (USA) MA75. Kumasi Th Coll 58. **d** 64 **p** 65 **c** 81. C Sekondi St Andr 64-66; Chapl Adisadel Coll 66-68; R Agona-Swedru St Jas 68-69; R Bp Aglionby Memorial Par Tamale 69-71; Asst P Byron and London Canada 71-73; Asst P Nashville H Trin 73-75; Asst P Cape Coast Ch Ch 75-81; Hd Master Ch K Academy and Prin St Nic Th Coll 76-81; Adn Koforidua and R Koforidua St Pet 81; Hon Can Accra 79-81; Bp Koforidua from 81; Abp W Africa from 93. *PO Box 980, Koforidua, Ghana* Tel (00233) (81) 22329 *or* (21) 676040 Fax (81) 22060 *or* (21) 669125 E-mail archbishopwa@mokello.freeserve.org *or* robokine@yahoo.com

OKWUOSA, Canon Amaechi Chukwudube. b 64. Anambra State Univ LLB89 Nigerian Law Sch Lagos BL90. Faith Th Sem 94. **d** 96 **p** 97. Nigeria 96-98; Hon Can Nnewi from 01; Perm to Offic *Lon* 98-01; NSM Gt Ilford St Jo *Chelmsf* from 01. *97 Beehive Lane, Ilford IG1 3RN* Tel (020) 8554 4540 E-mail dubem@okwuosa.com

OLADUJI, Christopher Temitayo. b 57. Awosika Th Coll Nigeria 84. **d** 87 **p** 88. Nigeria 87-89; C Ilutitun Ebenezer 87; Asst P Ondo Cathl 88; NSM W Ham *Chelmsf* 89-93; NSM Peckham St Jo w St Andr *S'wark* 97-98; NSM E Ham St Geo *Chelmsf* 99-01; NSM Hackney Wick St Mary of Eton w St Aug *Lon* from 02. *53 Hollybush Street, London E13 9ED* Tel and fax (020) 8470 6591 Mobile 07985-465401 E-mail c.oladuji@talk21.com

OLANCZUK, Jonathan Paul Tadeusz. b 49. UEA CertRS95. EAMTC 94. **d** 96 **p** 97. C Haverhill w Withersfield *St E* 96-00; P-in-c Badingham w Bruisyard, Cransford and Dennington from 00; P-in-c Rendham w Sweffling from 00. *The Rectory, 5 Orchard Rise, Badingham, Woodbridge IP13 8LN* Tel and fax (01728) 638823 Mobile 07766-953558 *or* 07944-186526 E-mail olanczuk@suffolkonline.net *or* jolanczuk@aol.com

OLD, Arthur Anthony George (Tony). b 36. Clifton Th Coll 69. **d** 71 **p** 72. C Clitheroe St Jas *Blackb* 71-73; C Bispham 73-77; V Haslingden St Jo Stonefold 77-81; TV Lowestoft and Kirkley *Nor* 81-83; Chapl to the Deaf *Cant* 83-01; P-in-c Hernhill 83-85; C Preston next Faversham, Goodnestone and Graveney 85-01; rtd 01; Perm to Offic *Cant* from 01. *5 Harcourt Drive, Herne Bay CT6 8DJ* Tel (01227) 749196

OLDALE, Harry. b 17. Bps' Coll Cheshunt 51. **d** 53 **p** 54. C Warmsworth w Edlington *Sheff* 53-56; C Woodlands 56-58; V Moorends 58-60; R Edgefield *Nor* 60-71; V Weybourne w Upper Sheringham 71-76; R Kelling w Salthouse 76-83; V Weybourne w Upper Sheringham 76-83; rtd 83; Perm to Offic *Nor* 85-00. *St Stephen's, 24 Station Road, Holt NR25 6BS* Tel (01263) 713964

OLDFIELD, Canon Roger Fielden. b 45. Qu Coll Cam BA67 MA71 City of Lon Poly DMS69 Lon Univ BD75. Trin Coll Bris 75. **d** 75 **p** 76. C Halliwell St Pet *Man* 75-80; V from 80; AD Bolton 93-02; Hon Can Man Cathl from 00. *St Peter's Vicarage, 1 Sefton Road, Harpers Lane, Bolton BL1 6HT* Tel (01204) 849412 Fax 849440 E-mail rogerandruth@3strands.net

OLDHAM, Dale Raymond. b 40. NZ Coll of Pharmacy MPS63 Cant Univ (NZ) MA87. Ridley Hall Cam 64. **d** 67 **p** 68. C Woking St Mary *Guildf* 67-70; New Zealand 71-73 and from 81; CMS Tanzania 74-81. *PO Box 27016, Christchurch 8030, New Zealand* Tel (0064) (3) 385 6282 *or* 385 2027 Fax 385 6283 E-mail oldham@clear.net.nz

OLDNALL, Frederick Herbert. b 16. Ripon Hall Ox 56. **d** 57 **p** 58. C Radford *Cov* 57-59; C Stratford-on-Avon 59-62; V Rosliston w Coton in the Elms *Derby* 62-83; rtd 83; Perm to Offic *Cov* from 93. *4 Margetts Close, Kenilworth CV8 1EN* Tel (01926) 852417

OLDROYD, Preb Colin Mitchell. b 30. Down Coll Cam BA54 MA60. Wells Th Coll 60. **d** 61 **p** 62. C Elton All SS *Man* 61-63; C Ex St Dav *Ex* 63-66; P-in-c Neen Sollars w Milson *Heref* 66-78; P-in-c Coreley and Doddington 66-78; R Cleobury Mortimer w Hopton Wafers 66-78; RD Ludlow 75-78; P-in-c Eastnor 78-81; R Ledbury 78-81; RD Ledbury 78-81; Chapl Ledbury Cottage Hosp *Heref* 79-95; R Ledbury w Eastnor *Heref* 81-95; Preb Heref Cathl 84-95; P-in-c Lt Marcle 85-95; rtd 95; Perm to Offic *Heref* from 96. *2 Hampton Manor Close, Hereford HR1 1TG* Tel (01432) 340569

OLDROYD, David Christopher Leslie. b 42. FRICS. S Dios Min Tr Scheme. **d** 85 **p** 86. NSM Four Marks *Win* 85-90; rtd 90. *Hill House, Spring Lane, Farnham GU9 0JD* Tel (01252) 737586

OLDROYD, James Healey. b 08. Worc Ord Coll. **d** 55 **p** 56. C Kidderminster St Mary and All SS, Trimpley etc *Worc* 55-57; C Tardebigge 57-61; V Worc St Mark 61-75; rtd 75; Perm to Offic *Worc* from 75. *7 Magnolia Close, Worcester WR5 3SJ* Tel (01905) 355603

OLDROYD, Mrs Sheila Margaret. b 40. Liv Univ BSc63. St Steph Ho Ox 98. **d** 99 **p** 00. NSM Cotgrave *S'well* 99-03; NSM Keyworth and Stanton-on-the-Wolds and Bunny etc from 03. *8 Taunton Road, West Bridgford, Nottingham NG2 6EW* Tel 0115-923 5121 Mobile 07974-785242 E-mail margaretoldroyd@aol.com

OLDROYD, Trevor. b 33. Hatf Coll Dur BA55 Lon Univ BD60. Wycliffe Hall Ox 60. **d** 61 **p** 62. C Barnes St Mary *S'wark* 61-65; C Wimbledon 65-68; W Germany 68-73; Chapl Dudley Sch 73-80; Asst Chapl Wellington Coll Berks 80-82; P-in-c Rendcomb *Glouc* 82-86; Chapl Rendcomb Coll 82-86; Chapl Wrekin Coll Telford 86-90; V Deptford St Jo w H Trin *S'wark* 91-94; rtd 94; Perm to Offic *Sarum* 94-00; *Guildf* from 02. *4 The Larches, Woking GU21 4RE* Tel (01483) 720398

OLHAUSEN, William John. b 37. TCD BA60 MA63 Lon Univ PGCE69. Ridley Hall Cam 60. **d** 62 **p** 63. C Grassendale *Liv* 62-66; Asst Chapl Dur Univ *Dur* 66-70; Lect Dur Univ 66-70; V Hazlemere *Ox* 70-89; RD Wycombe 78-83; Perm to Offic 89-93; Lic to Offic from 96; rtd 02. *The Woodyard, Scotsgrove, Thame OX9 3RU* Tel (01844) 237234 Mobile 07887-781030 E-mail wjo@clara.net

OLHAUSEN, William Paul. b 67. Wycliffe Hall Ox BA97 DipMin98. **d** 98 **p** 99. C Reading Greyfriars *Ox* 98-01; Sub Chapl HM YOI Reading 98-01; C Cambridge H Trin *Ely* from 01. *42 Pretoria Road, Cambridge CB4 1HE* Tel (01223) 479473 E-mail wpolhausen@ntlworld.com *or* william@htcambridge.org.uk

OLIVE, Dan. b 29. ARIBA54. Sarum & Wells Th Coll 79. **d** 82 **p** 83. NSM Wells St Cuth w Wookey Hole *B & W* 82-85; C Yatton Moor 86-88; R Mells w Buckland Dinham, Elm, Whatley etc 88-97; RD Frome 93-97; rtd 97; Perm to Offic *B & W* from 97. *Roseleigh, Woodcombe, Minehead TA24 8SA* Tel (01643) 702218

OLIVER, Arthur Norman. b 16. Worc Ord Coll 63. **d** 65 **p** 66. C Willingdon *Chich* 65-69; C W Worthing St Jo 69-71; R Etchingham 71-85; V Hurst Green 72-85; rtd 85; Perm to Offic *Ely* 86-89; *Chich* 89-01. *c/o J Oliver Esq, 11 Lilac Court, Cambridge CB1 7AY* Tel (01223) 245385

OLIVER, Bernard John. b 31. CEng65 MIMechE. S'wark Ord Course 75. **d** 78 **p** 79. NSM Chipping Ongar *Chelmsf* 78-81; C Waltham Abbey 81-85; C High Ongar w Norton Mandeville 85-87; C Somerton w Compton Dundon, the Charltons etc *B & W* 87-88; rtd 96; Perm to Offic *Sarum* from 01. *1 Orchard Way, Mosterton, Beaminster DT8 3LT* Tel (01308) 868037

OLIVER, Canon Beverley Stephen. b 29. Lich Th Coll 58. **d** 60 **p** 61. S Africa 61-96; Adn of the Ordinary 80-96; Lect and Preacher Newland Almshouses from 96. *The Lecturer's House, Almshouse Road, Newland, Coleford GL16 8NL* Tel (01594) 832441

OLIVER, Canon David Ryland. b 34. Univ of Wales (Lamp) BA56 St Cath Coll Ox BA58 MA62. Wycliffe Hall Ox 56. **d** 58 **p** 59. C Carmarthen St Pet *St D* 58-61; C Llangyfelach and

Morriston *S & B* 61-63; R Aberedw w Llandeilo Graban etc 63-66; R Llanbadarn Fawr, Llandegley and Llanfihangel etc 66-67; Lic to Offic *Llan* 68-70; Lic to Offic *Ban* 70-73; V Nefyn w Pistyll w Tudweiliog w Llandudwen etc 73-74; V Abercraf and Callwen *S & B* 74-77; V Llangyfelach 77-79; R Llanllwchaearn and Llanina *St D* 79-83; V Cwmaman 83-94; Can St D Cathl from 90; RD Dyffryn Aman 93-94; V Cynwyl Gaeo w Llansawel and Talley 94-99; rtd 99. *Maes y Gelynen, 40 Heol Bryngwili, Cross Hands, Llanelli SA14 6LR*

OLIVER, Gordon. *See* OLIVER, Canon Thomas Gordon

OLIVER, Graham Frank. b 42. St Barn Coll Adelaide. **d** 68 **p** 69. Australia 68-86; C Ealing Ch the Sav *Lon* 86-93; Perm to Offic 94-97 and from 00; Asst Chapl Ypres *Eur* 97-99; P-in-c 99-00. *Flat 1, 4 High Street, London NW10 4LY* Tel (020) 8963 0477

OLIVER, John Andrew George. b 28. OBE83. St Jo Coll Dur BA53 DipTh55. **d** 55 **p** 56. C Bermondsey St Mary w St Olave and St Jo *S'wark* 55-58; C Dulwich St Barn 58-61; Chapl RN 61-83; QHC 79-83; R Guisborough *York* 83-89; Tutor and Chapl Whittington Coll Felbridge 89-93; rtd 93; Perm to Offic *Carl* from 93. *Allandale, Thacka Lane, Penrith CA11 9HX* Tel (01768) 892096

OLIVER, The Ven John Graham Wyand. b 47. Ridley Hall Cam 76. **d** 78 **p** 79. C Shortlands *Roch* 78-81; C Hammersmith St Paul *Lon* 81-85; Zambia from 85; Adn S Zambia from 89. *USPG, Partnership House, 157 Waterloo Road, London SE1 8XA* Tel (020) 7928 8681 Fax 7928 2371

✠**OLIVER, The Rt Revd John Keith.** b 35. G&C Coll Cam BA59 MA63 MLitt65. Westcott Ho Cam. **d** 64 **p** 65 **c** 90. C Hilborough w Bodney *Nor* 64-68; Chapl Eton Coll 68-72; R S Molton w Nymet St George *Ex* 73-75; P-in-c Filleigh w E Buckland 73-75; P-in-c Warkleigh w Satterleigh and Chittlehamholt 73-75; P-in-c High Bray w Charles 73-75; RD S Molton 74-80; TR S Molton, Nymet St George, High Bray etc 75-82; P-in-c N Molton w Twitchen 77-79; TR Cen Ex 82-85; Adn Sherborne *Sarum* 85-90; P-in-c W Stafford w Frome Billet 85-90; Can Res Sarum Cathl 85-90; Bp Heref from 90. *Bishop's House, The Palace, Hereford HR4 9BN* Tel (01432) 271355 Fax 343047 E-mail bishop@diooffice.freeserve.co.uk

OLIVER, John Kenneth. b 47. Brunel Univ MA92 ALBC70. EAMTC 98. **d** 00 **p** 01. C E Ham St Paul *Chelmsf* 00-03; V Stratford New Town St Paul from 03. *St Paul's Vicarage, Maryland Road, London E15 1JL* Tel (020) 8534 4243 E-mail j.k.oliver@tesco.net

OLIVER, The Ven John Michael. b 39. Univ of Wales (Lamp) BA62. Ripon Hall Ox 62. **d** 64 **p** 65. C High Harrogate St Pet *Ripon* 64-67; C Bramley 67-72; V Low Harrogate St Mary 72-78; V Beeston 78-92; RD Armley 86-92; Hon Can Ripon Cathl from 87; Adn Leeds from 92. *Archdeacon's Lodge, 3 West Park Grove, Leeds LS8 2HQ* Tel and fax 0113-269 0594 Mobile 07970 421880 E-mail archdeacon.leeds@riponleeds.anglican.org

OLIVER, The Ven John Rodney. b 31. Melbourne Univ BA53 Lon Univ MTh73. Bps' Coll Cheshunt 54 ACT ThSchol03. **d** 56 **p** 57. C Much Hadham *St Alb* 56-57; Australia 58-69; Chapl Ballarat GS 58-69; C Thorley *St Alb* 70-73; C Bishop's Stortford H Trin 70-73; Australia from 73; I Aberfeldie 74-77; Chapl Trin Coll Melbourne 77-81; I Dandenong 81-91; Adn Box Hill 87-00; I East Kew St Paul 91-00; rtd 00. *27 Asquith Street, Box Hill South, Vic, Australia 3128* Tel (0061) (3) 9888 7517 Fax 9888 7598 E-mail rodley@smartchat.net.au

OLIVER, Mrs Josephine May. b 48. Cranmer Hall Dur. **d** 01 **p** 02. C Buckrose Carrs *York* from 01. *2 High Street, Rillington, Malton YO17 8LA* Tel (01944) 758567 Mobile 07885-448331 E-mail jo@j-oliver.freeserve.co.uk

OLIVER, Mrs Judith Anne. b 54. WMMTC. **d** 96 **p** 97. C Old Swinford Stourbridge *Worc* 96-99; C Pennsett 99-01; Asst to Suff Bp Dudley 99-01; P-in-c Dudley Wood from 01. *The Vicarage, 57 Lantern Road, Dudley DY2 0DL* Tel (01384) 832164 E-mail revjao@aol.com

OLIVER, Canon Paul Robert. b 41. Lon Univ DipTh65. Tyndale Hall Bris 63. **d** 66 **p** 67. C Virginia Water *Guildf* 66-70; Scripture Union (E Region) 70-74; TV Thetford *Nor* 75-83; V Earlham St Anne 83-98; RD Nor S 94-98; Hon Can Nor Cathl 96-98; rtd 98; Perm to Offic *Nor* from 98. *Cherry Tree Cottage, 91 High Road, Needham, Harleston IP20 9LF* Tel (01379) 852892

OLIVER, Canon Philip Maule. b 38. Birm Univ LLB59. Wells Th Coll 62. **d** 64 **p** 65. C Chesterton *Lich* 64-67; C Tettenhall Wood 67-71; V Milton 71-78; V Ixworth and Bardwell *St E* 78-92; P-in-c Honington w Sapiston and Troston 81-92; TR Blackbourne from 92; RD Ixworth 85-94; Hon Can St E Cathl from 00. *The Vicarage, Ixworth, Bury St Edmunds IP31 2HE* Tel (01359) 230311

OLIVER, Mrs Philippa Mary Olive (Penny). b 30. R Holloway Coll Lon BA52. Cant Sch of Min 89. **d** 92 **p** 95. NSM Eythorne and Elvington w Waldershare etc *Cant* 92-01; Perm to Offic from 01. *34 Milner Road, Elvington, Dover CT15 4EL*

OLIVER, Ryland. *See* OLIVER, Canon David Ryland

OLIVER, Simon Andrew. b 71. Mansf Coll Ox BA93 MA98 Peterho Cam BA97 MA00 PhD03. Westcott Ho Cam 95. **d** 98 **p** 99. NSM Teversham *Ely* 98-01; NSM Cherry Hinton St Andr

98-01; Chapl Hertf Coll Ox from 01. *Hertford College, Oxford OX1 3BW* Tel (01865) 279411
E-mail simon.oliver@hertford.ox.ac.uk

✠OLIVER, The Rt Revd Stephen John. b 48. AKC69. St Aug Coll Cant 70. **d** 71 **p** 72 **c** 03. C Clifton w Glapton *S'well* 71-75; P-in-c Newark Ch Ch 75-79; R Plumtree 79-85; Sen Producer BBC Relig Broadcasting Dept Lon 85-87; Chief Producer 87-91; TR Leeds City *Ripon* 91-97; Can Res and Prec St Paul's Cathl Lon 97-03; Area Bp Stepney from 03. *63 Coborn Road, London E3 2DB* Tel (020) 8981 2323 Fax 8981 8015
E-mail bishop.stepney@london.anglican.org

OLIVER, Suzanne Marie. *See* PATTLE, Mrs Suzanne Marie

OLIVER, Canon Thomas Gordon. b 48. Nottm Univ BTh72 LTh74 DipAdEd80. St Jo Coll Nottm 68 ALCD72. **d** 72 **p** 73. C Thorpe Edge *Bradf* 72-76; C Woodthorpe *S'well* 76-80; V Huthwaite 80-85; Dir Past Studies St Jo Coll Nottm 85-94; Dir of Min and Tr *Roch* from 94; Hon Can Roch Cathl from 95. *18 King's Avenue, Rochester ME1 3DS* Tel (01634) 841232 *or* 830333 Fax 829463 E-mail gordon.oliver@rochdiooff.co.uk

OLIVER, Ms Wendy Louise. b 54. Aston Tr Scheme 93 Oak Hill Th Coll DipHE94. **d** 96 **p** 97. C Walmsley *Man* 96-99; P-in-c Goodshaw and Crawshawbooth from 99. *Goodshaw Vicarage, Goodshawfold Road, Rossendale BB4 8QN* Tel (01706) 213969
Fax as telephone E-mail wendyloliver@hotmail.com

OLIVEY, Hugh Charles Tony. b 35. St Mich Coll Llan 77. **d** 79 **p** 80. C St Winnow *Truro* 79-81; C Lanhydrock 81-82; C Lostwithiel 81-82; C Lanivet 81-82; P-in-c 82-83; TV Bodmin w Lanhydrock and Lanivet 84-89; P-in-c St Neot 89-90; P-in-c Warleggan 89-90; R St Neot and Warleggan 90-99; P-in-c Cardynham 97-99; rtd 99; Perm to Offic *Truro* from 99. *The Bungalow, 2 Lower Hugus Road, Threemilestone, Truro TR3 6BD* Tel (01872) 223103

OLIVIER, Bertrand Maurice Daniel. b 62. BA84. S'wark Ord Course 93. **d** 96 **p** 97. C Walworth St Jo *S'wark* 96-00; V Southfields St Barn from 00; RD Wandsworth from 03. *St Barnabas' Vicarage, 430 Merton Road, London SW18 5AE* Tel (020) 8874 7768 Mobile 07958-411529
E-mail vicar@stbarnabas-online.org

OLLIER, Canon Timothy John Douglas. b 44. Trin Hall Cam BA66 MA69. Cuddesdon Coll 66. **d** 68 **p** 69. C Silksworth *Dur* 68-71; C St Marylebone w H Trin *Lon* 71-74; C Winlaton *Dur* 74-77; V Bishopton w Gt Stainton 77-88; R Redmarshall 77-88; P-in-c Grindon and Stillington 83-88; V Gainford 88-00; R Winston 88-00; AD Barnard Castle 88-00; P-in-c Egglescliffe 00-03; R from 03; AD Stockton from 01; Hon Can Dur Cathl from 94. *The Rectory, 10 Butts Lane, Egglescliffe, Stockton-on-Tees TS16 9BT* Tel (01642) 780188 Fax 791886
E-mail timollier@onyxnet.co.uk

OLLIFF, Roland. b 61. Coll of Resurr Mirfield CPS95. **d** 95 **p** 96. C Bickleigh and Shaugh Prior 95-98; CF from 98. *c/o MOD Chaplains (Army)* Tel (01980) 615804 Fax 615800
E-mail olliff@btinternet.com

OLNEY, Dorian Frederick. b 50. Kingston Poly BA71 MIL88 MIPD88 Anglia Poly Univ MA03. All Nations Chr Coll 75 Ridley Hall Cam CTM98. **d** 98 **p** 99. C Glenfield *Leic* 98-02; Chapl ATC 99-01; TV Newark *S'well* from 02. *Christ Church Vicarage, Boundary Road, Newark NG24 4AJ* Tel (01636) 704969 E-mail fred.olney@webleicester.co.uk

O'LOUGHLIN, Gordon Raymond. b 32. Linc Coll Ox BA56 MA60. Wells Th Coll 56. **d** 58 **p** 59. C Bournemouth St Fran *Win* 58-62; C Tunbridge Wells St Barn *Roch* 62-65; Chapl Roch Th Coll 65-67; Sub-Warden 67-69; V Kingston upon Hull St Alb York 69-78; Dir Post-Ord Tr 77-82; Can and Preb York Minster 78-81; TV York All SS Pavement w St Crux and St Martin etc 78-82; V Bromley St Andr *Roch* 82-87; P-in-c Brighton St Paul *Chich* 87-94; V 94-02; rtd 02. *4 Bramwell Lodge, Brighton Road, Woodmancote, Henfield BN5 9SX* Tel (01273) 491143

O'LOUGHLIN, Mrs Kathryn. b 60. Man Univ BSc81. STETS 96. **d** 99 **p** 00. NSM Basing *Win* from 99. *45 Pyotts Copse, Old Basing, Basingstoke RG24 8WE* Tel (01256) 354248

OLSEN, Arthur Barry. b 37. Univ of NZ BA61 Melbourne Coll of Div BD73. ACT ThL64. **d** 64 **p** 64. New Zealand 64-81; C Nelson All SS 64-67; V Ahuara 67-69; V Motupiko 69-70; V Amuri 70-73; Maori Miss and C Dunedin St Matt 73-76; V Brooklyn 77-81; C Hersham *Guildf* 81-84; P-in-c Botleys and Lyne 84-95; V from 95; P-in-c Long Cross 84-95; V from 95; Chapl NW Surrey Mental Health NHS Trust from 85. *The Vicarage, Lyne Lane, Lyne, Chertsey KT16 0AJ* Tel (01932) 874405 E-mail abandmolsen@tinyworld.co.uk

OLUKANMI, Miss Stella Grace Oluwafunmilayo Olanrewaju. b 57. St Jo Coll Nottm BTh95 LTh92. **d** 96 **p** 97. C Gt Ilford St Jo *Chelmsf* 96-01; V Barkingside St Cedd from 01. *The Vicarage, 10 Marston Road, Ilford IG5 0LY* Tel (020) 8551 3406 E-mail olukanmi@fish.co.uk

OLUMIDE, The Ven Oluseye Abiola Abisogun Okikiade ('Seye). b 42. Westhill Coll Birm CLCE66 Bradf Univ BA89 MSc92. Clifton Th Coll 68. **d** 71 **p** 72. C Halliwell St Pet *Man* 71-72; C Salford St Phil w St Steph 72; P-in-c Wood Green St Mich *Lon* 73; C Stanmer w Falmer and Moulsecoomb *Chich* 73-76; C Hulme

Ascension *Man* 76-77; Chapl Asst N Man Gen Hosp 77-80; Chapl St Bernard's and Ealing Hosps 80-86; Chapl Bradf R Infirmary 86-91; Chapl Lynfield Mt Hosp Bradf 86-91; Chapl St Luke's Hosp Bradf 86-91; Chapl Bradf Hosps NHS Trust 91-96; Chapl Co-ord Parkside Community NHS Trust Lon 96-01; rtd 01; Can Lagos Cathl from 98; Adn in Egba from 00. *11 Walters Road, Cwmllynfell, Swansea SA9 2FH*

OLYOTT, The Ven Leonard Eric. b 26. Lon Univ BA50. Westcott Ho Cam 50. **d** 52 **p** 53. C Camberwell St Geo *S'wark* 52-55; C Bp's Hatfield *St Alb* 55-60; V Chipperfield St Paul 60-68; V Crewkerne *B & W* 68-71; R Crewkerne w Wayford 71-77; RD Crewkerne 72-77; Preb Wells Cathl 76-92; Adn Taunton 77-92; rtd 92; Perm to Offic *B & W* from 92. *5 Greendale, Ilminster TA19 0EB* Tel (01460) 55062

O'MALLEY, Canon Brian Denis Brendan. b 40. Birm Univ LicH77 Gwent Coll of HE Dip Counselling 94 Univ of Wales (Lamp) MA97 MHCIMA60. Nunraw Abbey (RC) 60 Oscott Coll (RC) 74 Coll of Resurr Mirfield 82. **d** 77 **p** 83. In RC Ch 77-81; Warden St Greg Retreat Rhandirmwyn *St D* 80-83; Lic to Offic 82-83; Chapl and Min Can St D Cathl 83-85; V Wiston w Ambleston, St Dogwells, Walton E etc 85-89; V Wiston w Clarbeston and Walton E 89; R Walton W w Talbenny and Haroldston W 89-98; Chapl Pembrokeshire Coll of FE 93-98; Chapl St D Coll Lamp from 98; Can St D Cathl *St D* from 01. *Fairfield, North Road, Lampeter SA48 7HZ* Tel (01570) 422148
E-mail b.o.malley@lamp.ac.uk

OMAN, Brian Malcolm. b 14. Qu Coll Cam BA36 MA46. Chich Th Coll 36. **d** 37 **p** 38. C Gorton St Mary and St Thos *Man* 37-40; OGS from 39; Perm to Offic *Ox* 40-42; Chapl St Mary's Abbey W Malling 42-46; C Tunbridge Wells St Barn *Roch* 46-55; V Cardiff St Mary *Llan* 55-62; R Greenford H Cross *Lon* 62-74; V Kings Sutton *Pet* 74-88; rtd 88; Perm to Offic *Pet* from 88. *The Old Post Office, Church Street, Sulgrave, Banbury OX17 2RP* Tel (01295) 768317

O'MEARA, Colette Margaret Mary. *See* THORNBOROUGH, Ms Colette Margaret Mary

OMOYAJOWO, Justus Akinwale. b 65. Obafemi Awolowo Univ BA87 Ibadan Univ Nigeria MA90 Bayreuth Univ PhD99. Vining Coll Th 90. **d** 92 **p** 93. Nigeria 92-94; C Akure St Andr 92; Chapl Ondo-State Pris 93; Chapl Ondo-State Univ 94; Asst Lect Bayreuth Univ Germany 95-97; Perm to Offic *S'wark* 98-99 and 00-01; C Hatcham St Jas 99-00; Chapl Goldsmiths' Coll Lon 99-00; P-in-c Sutton New Town St Barn 01-03; P-in-c Yardley St Edburgha *Birm* from 03. *The Vicarage, 541 Church Road, Yardley, Birmingham B33 8PG* Tel 0121-785 2848
E-mail justus@omoyajowo.freeserve.co.uk

O'NEILL, Mrs Caroline Lois. b 55. Trin Coll Bris BA00. **d** 00 **p** 01. C Bath St Sav w Swainswick and Woolley *B & W* 00-03; C Charlcombe w Bath St Steph from 03. *40 Fairfield Avenue, Bath BA1 6NH* Tel (01225) 311796

O'NEILL, Christopher John. b 53. Worc Coll Ox BA75 MA80 CertEd91 ALAM LGSM Dip Th & Min 91 Cert Counselling 91 DCH98. Ripon Coll Cuddesdon 77. **d** 78 **p** 79. Asst Chapl Rugby Sch 78-80; Chapl Charterhouse Sch Godalming 81-98; Hd of Counselling from 98. *14 Chapelfields, Charterhouse Road, Godalming GU7 2BF* Tel (01483) 414437

O'NEILL, Edward Daniel. b 42. Man Univ BA62 Bradf Univ MSc76. N Ord Course 89. **d** 92 **p** 93. NSM Prenton *Ches* 92-94; NSM Newton 94-95; Perm to Offic *Liv* 97-98; NSM W Derby Gd Shep 98-99; C 99-02; V Stockbridge Village from 02. *1 The Cross, Stanley Road, Huyton, Liverpool L36 9XL* Tel 0151-449 3800

O'NEILL, Canon Gary. b 57. K Coll Lon BD79 AKC79. Westcott Ho Cam 80. **d** 81 **p** 82. C Oldham *Man* 81-84; C Birch w Fallowfield 84-87; R Moston St Chad 87-97; Can Res Birm Cathl *Birm* from 97. *119 Selly Park Road, Birmingham B29 7HY* Tel 0121-472 0146 *or* 236 4333 Fax 212 0868

O'NEILL, Irene. *See* CARTER, Mrs Irene

ONIONS, Mrs Angela Ann. b 33. STETS 01. **d** 02. NSM Bradford-on-Avon *Sarum* from 02. *27 Berryfield Road, Bradford-on-Avon BA15 1SX* Tel (01225) 309001 Mobile 07719-726461

ONIONS, Martin Giles. b 63. TC Bp Otter Coll Chich BA99 Univ Coll Chich MA02. Chich Th Coll 85. **d** 88 **p** 89. C Eastbourne St Mary *Chich* 88-91; C-in-c The Hydneye CD 91-96; V The Hydneye 96-97; V Findon Valley 97-01; V Willingdon from 01. *The Vicarage, 35A Church Street, Willingdon, Eastbourne BN20 9HR* Tel (01323) 502079 Fax as telephone E-mail martin.onions@btinternet.com

ONSLOW, Sister Denzil Octavia. b 19. CertRK58. **dss** 61 **d** 87 **p** 94. CSA from 56; Novice Guardian 68-73 and 90-94; R Foundn of St Kath in Ratcliffe 73-79; Notting Hill St Jo and St Pet *Lon* 80-87; Hon Par Dn 87-94; Hon C 94-01; Perm to Offic from 01. *8/9 Verona Court, London W4 2JD* Tel (020) 8987 2799

ONUNWA, The Ven Udobata Rufus. b 47. Nigeria Univ BA78 MA81 PhD85. Trin Coll Nigeria DipTh74. **d** 74 **p** 75. Nigeria 74-96; Tutor Crowther Hall CMS Tr Coll Selly Oak from 96. *14 Bowood End, New Hall, Sutton Coldfield B76 1LU* Tel 0121-311 1542

ORAM, Canon Geoffrey William James. b 14. Em Coll Cam BA37 MA40. Ridley Hall Cam 36. **d** 38 **p** 39. C Tooting Graveney St Nic *S'wark* 38-40; C Rugby St Andr *Cov* 40-41; V Ipswich St Thos *St E* 41-49; R E Bergholt 49-64; Bp's Chapl 54-67; Hon Can St E Cathl 59-80; RD Samford 59-64; V Aldeburgh w Hazlewood 64-80; rtd 80; Perm to Offic *St E* 80-81 and from 86; P-in-c Ipswich St Mich 81-86. *Pantiles, Spring Meadow, Hillfarm Road, Playford, Ipswich IP6 9ED* Tel (01473) 622566

ORAM, John Ernest Donald. b 34. Open Univ BA74. Tyndale Hall Bris. **d** 61 **p** 62. C Cheetham Hill *Man* 61-64; C Gt Baddow *Chelmsf* 64-67; V Blackb St Barn *Blackb* 67-72; Bp's Chapl for Soc Resp *Sheff* 72-86; Chapl Psychotherapist 79-86; Perm to Offic from 86; rtd 99. *12 Montgomery Road, Sheffield S7 1LQ* Tel 0114-221 4982

ORAM, Roland Martin David. b 45. ARCM70 Trin Coll Cam BA68. Cranmer Hall Dur DipTh78. **d** 78 **p** 79. C Aspley *S'well* 78-81; Chapl Alleyn's Sch Dulwich 81-88; Chapl Versailles w Grandchamp and Chevry *Eur* 88-92; Chapl Denstone Coll Uttoxeter 92-01; C Hanford *Lich* from 01; C Trentham from 02. *Hanford Vicarage, 76 Church Lane, Stoke-on-Trent ST4 4QD* Tel (01782) 657848

ORAM, Stephen John. b 58. **d** 84 **p** 85. C Kidderminster St Jo *Worc* 84-88; Chapl RAF 88-92; P-in-c Brislington St Anne *Bris* 92-97; V Cricklade w Latton from 97. *3 Ockwells, Cricklade, Swindon SN6 6ED* Tel (01793) 750300
E-mail stephen.oram@ntlworld.com

ORAM, Vincent Charles. b 55. Rhodes Univ BA78 Fort Hare Univ BTh84. St Paul's Coll Grahamstown DipTh81. **d** 81 **p** 82. S Africa 81-99; C King Williams Town H Trin 81-85; R Barkly East St Steph 85-90; Can Grahamstown Cathl 96; Adn East London South 97-99; P-in-c Shenley *St Alb* from 00. *The Rectory, 63 London Road, Shenley, Radlett WD7 9BW* Tel (01923) 855383 E-mail voram@onetel.net.uk

O'RAW, Neal John. b 02. C Killala w Dunfeeny, Crossmolina, Kilmoremoy etc *T, K & A* from 02. *The Rectory, Ballina Road, Crossmolina, Co Mayo, Irish Republic* Tel (00353) (96) 31384 E-mail revdoraw@hotmail.com

ORCHARD, Canon George Richard. b 41. Ex Coll Ox BA62 BA64 MA66. Ripon Hall Ox 62. **d** 65 **p** 66. C Greenhill St Pet *Derby* 65-70; Member Ecum Team Min Sinfin Moor 70-78; V Sinfin Moor 76-78; TR Dronfield 78-86; Can Res Derby Cathl 86-92; Hon Can Derby Cathl from 92; P-in-c Baslow 92-93; P-in-c Curbar and Stoney Middleton 92-93; V Baslow w Curbar and Stoney Middleton from 93. *The Vicarage, Curbar Lane, Calver, Hope Valley S32 3YF* Tel (01433) 630387 Fax as telephone

ORCHARD, Harry Frank. b 23. Roch Th Coll. **d** 63 **p** 64. C Sturminster Newton *Sarum* 63-65; Argentina 65-67; V Preston *Sarum* 67-71; R Teffont Evias and Teffont Magna 71-73; V Dinton 71-73; C Fovant w Compton Chamberlayne etc 76-78; Lic to Offic 78-02; RD Chalke 80-82; rtd 88. *49 Highfields, Ashby Meadows, Ashby Road, Spilsby PE23 5DN* Tel (01790) 753044

ORCHARD, Helen Claire. b 65. Sheff Univ BA87 PhD96 Em Coll Cam MPhil02. Westcott Ho Cam 01. **d** 03. C Merrow *Guildf* from 03. *5 Gilliat Drive, Guildford GU4 7EN* Tel (01483) 506294 Mobile 07879-622920 E-mail hco@hcorchard.freeserve.co.uk

ORCHARD, Nigel John. b 56. CertEd78. St Steph Ho Ox 82. **d** 85 **p** 86. C Tottenham St Paul *Lon* 85-89; C Is of Dogs Ch Ch and St Jo w St Luke 89-90; TV 90-92; P-in-c Southall Ch Redeemer 92-99; V from 99. *Christ The Redeemer Vicarage, 299 Allenby Road, Southall UB1 2HE* Tel (020) 8578 2711

ORCHARD, Mrs Tryphena Jane. b 35. Westf Coll Lon BA57. S'wark Ord Course 87. **d** 92 **p** 94. NSM Shaston *Sarum* 92-01; rtd 01. *Old Cann Rectory, Salisbury Road, Shaftesbury SP7 8ER* Tel (01747) 855228 Fax as telephone

ORCHIN, Robert Andrew. b 71. K Coll Lon BD92. Ripon Coll Cuddesdon DipMin95. **d** 95 **p** 96. C Leigh Park *Portsm* 95-98; C Warren Park 96-98; Perm to Offic *Portsm* 98-99; *S'wark* 99-00; P-in-c Portsea St Geo 00-02. *Snaefell, Woodland Close, Ryde PO33 1PW* Tel (01983) 612607 E-mail rorchin@aol.com

O'REILLY, Clare Maria. *See* KING, Clare Maria

O'REILLY, Ms Eileen Catherine. b 47. TCD BTh95. **d** 96 **p** 97. C Annagh w Drumgoon, Ashfield etc *K, E & A* 96-98; Bp's C 98-00; Dioc Communications Officer 98-00; Dioc Sec (Kilmore) 98-00; USA from 00. *c/o Speer, 7926 Meida Drive, Cincinnati, OH 45069, USA*

O'REILLY, Philip Jonathon. b 66. Portsm Poly BSc87 Kent Univ MA97 ARICS MRICS01. Westcott Ho Cam 93. **d** 93 **p** 94. C Selsdon St Jo w St Fran *S'wark* 93-96; TV Staveley and Barrow Hill *Derby* 96-01; V Wistow *Leic* from 01. *The Vicarage, 12 Saddington Road, Fleckney, Leicester LE8 8AW* Tel 0116-240 2215

ORFORD, Barry Antony. b 49. Univ of Wales (Ban) BA71 MTh97 PhD01. St Steph Ho Ox 71. **d** 73 **p** 74. C Monmouth *Mon* 73-77; V Choral St As Cathl *St As* 77-81; CR 83-96; Perm to Offic *St As* from 96; Hon Asst Chapl Univ of Wales (Ban) *Ban* 99-01; P Lib Pusey Ho Ox from 01. *Pusey House, St Giles, Oxford OX1 3LZ* Tel (01865) 278415

ORFORD, Canon Keith John. b 40. FCIT. EMMTC 76. **d** 79 **p** 80. NSM Matlock Bank *Derby* 79-99; NSM Wirksworth from 99; Hon Can Derby Cathl from 00. *27 Lums Hill Rise, Matlock DE4 3FX* Tel (01629) 55349
E-mail keith.orford@btinternet.com

ORGAN, Peter. b 73. K Coll Lon BA97 Birm Univ MA01. Qu Coll Birm 99. **d** 01 **p** 02. C E Wickham *S'wark* from 01. *28 Dryden Road, Welling DA16 3ND* Tel (020) 8317 9749
E-mail organs@whsmithnet.co.uk

ORLAND, Canon Ernest George. b 28. Lich Th Coll 61. **d** 62 **p** 63. C Northampton St Mich *Pet* 62-65; R Gayton w Tiffield 65-69; R Corby SS Pet and Andr 69-72; TR Corby SS Pet and Andr w Gt and Lt Oakley 72-81; RD Corby 79-81; Can Pet Cathl 79-93; V Pet All SS 81-93; rtd 93; Perm to Offic *Pet* from 93; *Linc* 95-02. *43 Godsey Lane, Market Deeping, Peterborough PE6 8HY* Tel (01778) 380724

ORME, John. b 29. Sarum Th Coll 58. **d** 60 **p** 61. C Heald Green St Cath *Ches* 60-64; C Ellesmere Port 64-67; Chapl Harperbury Hosp Radlett 67-73; P-in-c Luton All SS w St Pet *St Alb* 73-79; V 79-87; V Oxhey St Matt 87-96; rtd 96; Perm to Offic *St Alb* from 97. *1 Alzey Gardens, Harpenden AL5 5SZ* Tel (01582) 761931 E-mail john@orme117.freeserve.co.uk

ORME, Sydney. b 27. Oak Hill Th Coll 54. **d** 58 **p** 59. C Halliwell St Pet *Man* 58-61; V Friarmere 61-73; V Knypersley *Lich* 73-92; rtd 92; Perm to Offic *Ches* from 92. *10 Elworth Road, Sandbach CW11 9HQ* Tel (01270) 759233

ORMEROD, Henry Lawrence. b 35. Pemb Coll Cam BA58 MA63. Qu Coll Birm DipTh59. **d** 60 **p** 61. C Chigwell *Chelmsf* 60-64; C Thundersley 64-68; C Canvey Is 68-72; V Stanground *Ely* 72-77; TR Stanground and Farcet 77-81; TR Swindon St Jo and St Andr *Bris* 81-90; TR N Wingfield, Clay Cross and Pilsley *Derby* 90-97; rtd 97; Hon C Ironstone *Ox* 98-03; Perm to Offic from 03. *5 Waterloo Drive, Banbury OX16 3QN* Tel (01295) 278483 E-mail henryormerod@aol.com

ORMISTON, Albert Edward. b 26. AMCT46. Oak Hill Th Coll 53. **d** 56 **p** 57. C Worksop St Jo *S'well* 56-58; P-in-c Everton St Polycarp *Liv* 58-59; V 59-63; Org Sec SAMS 63-67; R Gateacre *Liv* 67-73; V Tonbridge St Steph *Roch* 73-86; V Dent w Cowgill *Bradf* 86-91; rtd 91; Perm to Offic *Ches* 91-00; *Glouc* from 02. *30 Capel Court, The Burgage, Prestbury, Cheltenham GL52 3EL* Tel (01242) 518625

ORMROD, Paul William. b 57. Liv Univ BA80. Westcott Ho Cam 80. **d** 83 **p** 84. C Prescot *Liv* 83-86; TV Padgate 86-95; V Formby St Pet from 95. *St Peter's Vicarage, Cricket Path, Formby, Liverpool L37 7DP* Tel (01704) 873369

ORMSBY, Diana Clare. b 21. CertEd41. Sarum & Wells Th Coll 77 Gilmore Course 78. **dss** 80 **d** 87 **p** 94. Lydford, Brent Tor, Bridestowe and Sourton *Ex* 80-87; Hon C Lydford and Brent Tor 87-96; Perm to Offic from 96. *Lipscliffe, Coryton, Okehampton EX20 4AB* Tel (01822) 860344

ORMSBY, Robert Daly. b 22. CCC Ox BA42 MA48. Sarum & Wells Th Coll 77. **d** 78 **p** 79. Hon C Lydford and Brent Tor *Ex* 78-96; Hon C Peter Tavy, Mary Tavy, Lydford and Brent Tor from 96. *Lipscliffe, Coryton, Okehampton EX20 4AB* Tel (01822) 860344

ORMSTON, Derek. b 43. Univ of Wales (Lamp) DipTh67. **d** 67 **p** 68. C Ogley Hay *Lich* 67-70; C Tettenhall Regis 70-74; P-in-c Leek All SS 74-79; TV Leek and Meerbrook 79-83; Youth Chapl *Bris* 83-87; R Brinkworth w Dauntsey from 87; Chapl New Coll Swindon from 87. *The Rectory, Brinkworth, Chippenham SN15 5AF* Tel (01666) 510207

ORMSTON, Canon Richard Jeremy. b 61. Southlands Coll Lon BA83 Brunel Univ MTh98. Oak Hill Th Coll BA87. **d** 87 **p** 88. C Rodbourne Cheney *Bris* 87-91; R Collingtree w Courteenhall and Milton Malsor *Pet* 91-01; RD Wootton 96-01; R Oundle w Ashton and Benefield w Glapthorn from 01; Can Pet Cathl from 03. *The Vicarage, 12 New Street, Oundle, Peterborough PE8 4EA* Tel (01832) 273595 E-mail rjo@talk21.com

O'ROURKE, Brian Joseph Gerard. b 58. TCD BA82 HDipEd83. CITC 89. **d** 92 **p** 93. Chapl Glendalough Sch 90-96; C Newcastle w Newtownmountkennedy and Calary *D & G* 92-96; Bp's C 96-98; I 98-00; I Cork St Luke Union C, *C & R* from 00. *The Rectory, 49 Ard na Laoi, Montenotte, Co Cork, Irish Republic* Tel and fax (00353) (21) 450456 Mobile 87-686 8260 E-mail stlukescork@eircom.net

ORPIN, Mrs Gillian. b 32. SRN53. Oak Hill Th Coll 82. **d** 87 **p** 95. Par Dn Passenham *Pet* 87-92; rtd 92; NSM Oban St Jo *Arg* 92-95; Dioc Chapl 95-98; Perm to Offic *St Alb* from 98. *11 Berwick Way, Sandy SG19 1TR* Tel (01767) 680629

ORR, Andrew Dermot Harman. b 66. Sheff Univ BSc89. CITC BTh92. **d** 92 **p** 93. C Ballymacash *Conn* 92-95; I Castlecomer w Colliery Ch, Mothel and Bilbo *C & O* 95-00; Dioc Registrar 95-00; I Castleknock and Mulhuddart, w Clonsilla *D & G* from 00. *Castleknock Rectory, 12 Hawthorn Lawn, Castleknock, Dublin 15, Irish Republic* Tel (00353) (1) 821 3083 E-mail greenorr@esatclear.ie

ORR, David Cecil. b 33. TCD BA56 MA68. **d** 57 **p** 58. C Drumragh *D & R* 57-60; I Convoy 60-70; I Maghera 70-80; I Drumragh w Mountfield 80-84; Dean Derry 84-97; I

Templemore 84-97; Miss to Seamen 84-97; rtd 97. *Kilrory, 11 Broomhill Court, Londonderry BT47 6WP* Tel (028) 7134 8183 E-mail cecil.orr@talk21.com

ORR, Robert Vernon. b 50. Westmr Univ 80 MIQA89. Wycliffe Hall Ox 96. **d** 98 **p** 99. C Cowley St Jo *Ox* 98-01; P-in-c Reading St Agnes w St Paul 01-02; R Reading St Agnes w St Paul and St Barn from 02. *The Vicarage, 290 Northumberland Avenue, Reading RG2 8DD* Tel 0118-987 4448 E-mail vernon.orr@lineone.net

ORR, William James Craig. FLICH BTh01. CITC 98. **d** 01 **p** 02. C Lurgan Ch the Redeemer *D & D* from 01. *14 Sandhill Park, Lurgan, Craigavon BT66 7AX* Tel (028) 3832 6040 E-mail worrshankill@hotmail.com *or* willy.orr@btinternet.com

ORR-EWING, Francis Ian Lance (Frog). b 75. Regent's Park Coll Ox BA97. Wycliffe Hall Ox MTh00. **d** 00 **p** 01. C Ox St Aldate *Ox* 00-03; V Camberwell All SS *S'wark* from 03. *All Saints' Church, Blenheim Grove, London SE15 4QS* Tel (020) 7639 3052 E-mail vicar@allsaintspeckham.co.uk

ORTON, Peter Joseph. b 57. **d** 03. OLM Burton St Chad *Lich* from 03. *237 Wetmore Road, Burton-on-Trent DE14 1RB* Tel (01283) 537574 E-mail lightcommunity@yahoo.co.uk

ORTON, Canon Richard. b 33. Keble Coll Ox BA56 MA60 Leeds Univ. Lich Th Coll 60. **d** 61 **p** 64. C Penistone w Midhope *Wakef* 61-62; Hon C Meltham 62-69; Hon C Horsforth *Ripon* 69-72; C Far Headingley St Chad 72-75; V Hellifield *Bradf* 75-80; RD Bowland 78-80; R Hutton *Chelmsf* 80-87; R Wallasey St Hilary *Ches* 87-90; Dioc Ecum Officer 92-99; RD Wallasey 96-99; Hon Can Ches Cathl 97-00; rtd 00; C Gt Sutton *Ches* from 01. *137 Brimstage Road, Barnston, Wirral CH60 1XF* Tel 0151-348 4911

OSBORN, Miss Anne. b 40. Reading Univ BA62 MA64 Lon Univ PGCE67. Oak Hill NSM Course 87. **d** 92. Chapl Lon Univ *Lon* 92-94; Chapl Lon Guildhall Univ 94-96; Chapl Univ Westmr 94-95; Assoc Tutor NTMTC from 97. *8 Beaufort House, Talbot Road, London N15 4DR* Tel (020) 8801 0115

OSBORN, David Ronald. b 42. Bris Univ BA66 Leeds Univ CertEd77 Bath Univ MEd80. Clifton Th Coll 62. **d** 66 **p** 67. C Farndon *S'well* 66-69; P-in-c W Bridgford 69-72; Asst Dioc Dir Educn *Carl* 72-77; P-in-c Kirkandrews-on-Eden w Beaumont and Grinsdale 72-77; Hd RE and Chapl Dauntsey's Sch Devizes 77-83; USA 83; V Southbroom *Sarum* 83-86; Consultant to Lay Tr Schemes *Ox* 86; Hd RE Bexhill High Sch 86-93; TV Langtree 93-95; TR 95-97; TR Bracknell from 97. *The Rectory, 26 Park Road, Bracknell RG12 2LU* Tel and fax (01344) 445090 Mobile 07803-618464 E-mail davidosborn@ntlworld.com

OSBORN, David Thomas. b 58. PGCE80 K Coll Lon BD79 AKC79. Linc Th Coll 82. **d** 83 **p** 84. C Bearsted w Thurnham *Cant* 83-86; Chapl RAF 86-90; R Bassingham *Linc* 90-91; V Aubourn w Haddington 90-91; V Carlton-le-Moorland w Stapleford 90-91; R Thurlby w Norton Disney 90-91; Chapl RAF from 91. *Chaplaincy Services (RAF), HQ, Personnel and Training Command, Innsworth, Gloucester GL3 1EZ* Tel (01452) 712612 ext 5164 Fax 510828

OSBORN, Mrs Diana Marian. b 52. R Holloway Coll Lon BSc74 Birm Univ PGCE75. NEOC 81. **dss** 84 **d** 87 **p** 94. Malden St Jo *S'wark* 84-89; Par Dn 87-89; Par Dn Brampton *Ely* 89-92; Par Dn Richmond H Trin and Ch Ch *S'wark* 92-93; Chapl Ridley Hall Cam 94-96; Chapl Milton Children's Hospice 96-98; Chapl E Anglia's Children's Hospices from 98. *70 Thrapston Road, Brampton, Huntingdon PE28 4TD* Tel (01480) 353701 *or* (01223) 860306

OSBORN, Preb John Geoffrey Rowland. b 33. Jes Coll Cam BA55 MA59. Wells Th Coll 63. **d** 65 **p** 66. C Easthampstead *Ox* 65-68; Lic to Offic *Blackb* 68-70; Brunei 70-75; Asst Dir RE *Blackb* 75-77; V Tockholes 75-77; Dir RE *B & W* 77-83; Dir and Sec Lon Dioc Bd for Schs *Lon* 83-95; Preb St Paul's Cathl 86-95; rtd 96. *4 Musson Close, Abingdon OX14 5RE* Tel (01235) 528701

OSBORN, Maurice. b 25. Univ of Wales BA50. Wycliffe Hall Ox 55. **d** 55 **p** 56. C E Wickham *S'wark* 55-57; Chapl Dauntsey's Sch Devizes 57-72; Asst Master 58-78; P-in-c Bishop's Lavington *Sarum* 79-83; P-in-c Lt Cheverell 82-83; P-in-c W Lavington and the Cheverells 83-90; rtd 90; Perm to Offic *Sarum* from 90. *Greensand Cottage, West Lavington, Devizes SN10 4LB* Tel (01380) 813244

OSBORNE, Alexander Deas. b 34. Liv Univ BSc54 PhD57. Oak Hill NSM Course 78. **d** 81 **p** 82. NSM Redbourn *St Alb* 81-98; rtd 98; Perm to Offic *Ely* and *St Alb* from 00. *6 Cam Farm, North End, Meldreth, Royston SG8 6NT* Tel (01763) 260456

OSBORNE, Anthony Russell. b 47. Sarum & Wells Th Coll 77. **d** 79 **p** 80. C Heref St Martin *Heref* 79-81; TV 82-86; TV Hanley H Ev *Lich* 86-92; Dioc Soc Resp Officer *Heref* 92-97; Can Heref Cathl 92-97; TR Cannock *Lich* from 97; V Hatherton from 97. *The Rectory, 11 Sherbrook Road, Cannock WS11 1HJ* Tel (01543) 578381 *or* 502131 E-mail aandb.osborne@cwcom.net

OSBORNE, Canon Brian Charles. b 38. St Andr Univ MA61 Lon Univ DipTh80. Clifton Th Coll 61. **d** 63 **p** 64. C Skirbeck H Trin *Linc* 63-68; V 80-03; P-in-c New Clee 68-71; V 71-75; V Derby St Aug *Derby* 75-80; Chapl Pilgrim Hosp Boston 84-88; RD Holland E *Linc* 85-95; Can and Preb Linc Cathl 92-03; Chapl to

The Queen from 97; rtd 03. *3 Newlands Road, Haconby, Bourne PE10 0UT* Tel (01778) 570818 E-mail revbrianosborne@ukonline.co.uk

OSBORNE, Christopher Hazell. b 60. Aston Tr Scheme 89 Sarum & Wells Th Coll DCM93. **d** 93 **p** 94. C Paignton St Jo *Ex* 93-96; C Hooe 96-97; TV Plymstock and Hooe 97-01; V Ivybridge w Harford from 01. *The Vicarage, Blachford Road, Ivybridge PL21 0AD* Tel (01752) 690193

OSBORNE, David Robert. b 50. Birm Univ BSc71 MEd86 Nottm Univ DipTh72 Bris Univ PGCE73. St Jo Coll Dur 78. **d** 80 **p** 81. C Penkridge w Stretton *Lich* 80-85; R Longdon-upon-Tern, Rodington, Uppington etc 85-94; R Pilton w Croscombe, N Wootton and Dinder *B & W* from 94; RD Shepton Mallet from 01. *The Rectory, Pilton, Shepton Mallet BA4 4DX* Tel (01749) 890423

OSBORNE, David Victor. b 36. Dur Univ BA59 Univ of Wales MA99. Cranmer Hall Dur DipTh62. **d** 62 **p** 63. C Kennington Cross St Anselm *S'wark* 62-66; C Sandal St Helen *Wakef* 66-67; R Ancoats *Man* 67-73; V Claremont H Angels 73-80; R Breedon cum Isley Walton and Worthington *Leic* 80-87; V Beaumont Leys 87-92; V Billesdon and Skeffington 92-01; rtd 01; Perm to Offic *Pet* from 02. *Rose Cottage, 12 Barlows Lane, Wilbarston, Market Harborough LE16 8QB* Tel (01536) 770400

OSBORNE, Canon Derek James. b 32. Tyndale Hall Bris 53. **d** 57 **p** 58. C Heworth St Mary *Sarum* 57-60; C Southgate Chich 60-63; V Croydon Ch Ch Broad Green *Cant* 63-71; V Cromer *Nor* 71-83; P-in-c Gresham w Bessingham 71-83; Hon Can Nor Cathl 77-83; V Northwood Em *Lon* 83-94; Chapl Lee Abbey 94-97; rtd 97; Perm to Offic *Nor* from 97. *50 Clifton Park, Cromer NR27 9BG* Tel (01263) 511272

OSBORNE, Gerald Edward Richard. b 63. Ch Ch Ox MA85 Wye Coll Lon MSc86. LNSM course 98. **d** 99 **p** 00. OLM Pewsey and Swanborough *Sarum* from 99. *Lawn Farm, Milton Lilbourne, Pewsey SN9 5LQ* Tel (01672) 563459 Mobile 07798-942118 Fax 564271 E-mail gerald.osborne@farmline.com

OSBORNE, Graham Daking. b 51. City Univ ACII74 FCII77. Cuddesdon Coll 94. **d** 96 **p** 97. C Cirencester *Glouc* 96-00; V Glouc St Cath from 00; RD Glouc City from 03. *St Catharine's Vicarage, 29 Denmark Road, Gloucester GL1 3JQ* Tel (01452) 524497 Fax as telephone E-mail gdosborne@bigfoot.com

OSBORNE, The Ven Hayward John. b 48. New Coll Ox BA70 MA73. Westcott Ho Cam 71. **d** 73 **p** 74. C Bromley SS Pet and Paul *Roch* 73-77; C Halesowen *Worc* 77-80; TV 80-83; TR Worc St Barn w Ch Ch 83-88; V Moseley St Mary *Birm* 88-01; AD Moseley 94-01; Hon Can Birm Cathl 00-01; Adn Birm from 01. *15 Park Hill, Birmingham B13 8DU* Tel 0121-449 1071 *or* 426 0441 Fax 428 1114 E-mail archdeaconofbham@birmingham.anglican.org

OSBORNE, Jonathan Lloyd. b 62. Ripon Coll Cuddesdon 95. **d** 97 **p** 98. C Mill End and Heronsgate w W Hyde *St Alb* 97-00; Asst Chapl Ealing Hosp NHS Trust from 00; Asst Chapl W Middx Univ Hosp NHS Trust from 00. *3 Teignmouth Gardens, Greenford UB6 8BX* Tel (020) 8997 7371 *or* 8967 5130

OSBORNE, Canon June. b 53. Man Univ BA74. St Jo Coll Nottm. **dss** 80 **d** 87 **p** 94. Birm St Martin *Birm* 80-84; Old Ford St Paul and St Mark *Lon* 84-95; Par Dn Old Ford St Paul w St Steph and St Mark 87-94; P-in-c Old Ford St Paul and St Mark 94-95; Can Res and Treas Sarum Cathl *Sarum* from 95; Bp's Dom Chapl 95-97. *Loders, 23 The Close, Salisbury SP1 2EH* Tel (01722) 555176 Fax 555177 E-mail treasurer@salcath.co.uk

OSBORNE, Malcolm Eric (Max). b 64. EN(G)87 RMN92. St Jo Coll Nottm 94. **d** 96 **p** 97. C Walton *St E* 96-99; C Ipswich St Matt 99-02; Soc Resp Adv 99-02; V Newmarket All SS from 02. *All Saints' Vicarage, 32 Warrington Street, Newmarket CB8 8BA* Tel (01638) 662514 E-mail max.osborne@stedmundsbury.anglican.org

OSBORNE, Mark William. b 67. Univ of Wales BA89. Coll of Resurr Mirfield 92. **d** 94 **p** 95. C Goldthorpe w Hickleton *Sheff* 94-97; C-in-c Southey Green St Bernard CD 97-01; P-in-c Walham Green St Jo w St Jas *Lon* from 01. *The Vicarage, 40 Racton Road, London SW6 1LP* Tel (020) 7385 3676 Fax as telephone E-mail mark@mosborne67.freeserve.co.uk

OSBORNE, Ralph. b 38. Kent Univ DipTh80. Bernard Gilpin Soc Dur 62 Clifton Th Coll 63. **d** 66 **p** 67. C Harpurhey Ch Ch *Man* 66-68; C Chorlton on Medlock St Sav 68-71; C Wilmington *Roch* 71-74; V St Mary Cray and St Paul's Cray 74-85; P-in-c Bath St Steph *B & W* 85-88; P-in-c Charlcombe 86-88; R Charlcombe w Bath St Steph from 88. *St Stephen's Rectory, Richmond Place, Bath BA1 5PZ* Tel (01225) 317535 E-mail ralph.osborne@ic24.net

OSBORNE, Canon Robin Orbell. b 29. Leeds Univ BA54. Coll of Resurr Mirfield 52. **d** 54 **p** 55. C Wellingborough All Hallows *Pet* 54-58; C Oxhey St Matt *St Alb* 60-61; V Woburn 61-65; V Battlesden and Pottesgrove 61-65; RD Cheshunt 65-82; RD Cheshunt 70-81; Hon Can St Alb 76-82; V Cheshunt St Mary w St Paul *Truro* 82-88; Can Res and Treas Truro Cathl 88-94; Perm to Offic *B & W* from 94; rtd 94. *7 The Judge's Lodgings, 19 New Street, Wells BA5 2LD* Tel (01749) 672326

OSBOURNE, David John. b 56. Linc Th Coll 78. **d** 79 **p** 80. C Houghton le Spring *Dur* 79-82; C Spalding St Jo *Linc* 82-83; C Spalding St Jo w Deeping St Nicholas 83-84; V Swineshead 84-94; RD Holland W 86-92; P-in-c Boultham 94-01; R from 01. *The Rectory, 2A St Helen's Avenue, Lincoln LN6 7RA* Tel (01522) 682026 *or* tel and fax 686527 E-mail daosbourne@supanet.com

OSBOURNE, Steven John. b 59. St Jo Coll Nottm 92. **d** 94 **p** 95. C Bushbury *Lich* 94-98; C Tamworth from 98. *St Francis' Vicarage, Masefield Drive, Tamworth B79 8JB* Tel (01827) 701918 E-mail steveosbourne@ntlworld.com

OSEI, Robert Emmanuel. b 56. **d** 76 **p** 77. Kumasi 76-83; C Hangleton *Chich* 83-84; Perm to Offic *S'wark* from 00. *8 Plummer Court, London SE13 6RA*

OSGERBY, John Martin. b 34. Sheff Univ BSc56 PhD59. Linc Th Coll 75. **d** 77 **p** 78. C Rotherham *Sheff* 77-80; C-in-c W Bessacarr CD 80-84; V W Bessacarr 84-87; Warden of Readers 86-99; R Fishlake w Sykehouse and Kirk Bramwith etc 87-99; RD Snaith and Hatfield 93-99; rtd 99; Perm to Offic *Sheff* from 99; *Linc* 00-02. *4 Marlborough Avenue, Haxey, Doncaster DN9 2HL* Tel (01427) 754815

OSGOOD, Graham Dean. b 39. Lon Univ BSc62. ALCD71 St Jo Coll Nottm 71. **d** 71 **p** 72. C Bebington *Ches* 71-76; V Gee Cross from 76. *The Vicarage, 16 Higham Lane, Hyde SK14 5LX* Tel 0161-368 2337 E-mail graham.htgx@btinternet.com

OSGOOD, Sylvia Joy. b 47. QUB BSc68 Lon Univ BD78 Man Univ PhD92. St Jo Coll Nottm MA98. **d** 97 **p** 98. NSM Bredbury St Mark *Ches* 97-01; Chapl Spurgeon's Coll from 01. *The Vicarage, 16 Higham Lane, Hyde SK14 5LX* Tel 0161-368 2337 E-mail j.osgood@spurgeons.ac.uk

O'SHAUGHNESSY, Mrs Janice Florence. b 51. STETS 95. **d** 98 **p** 99. NSM Bembridge *Portsm* 98-02; Asst Chapl Isle of Wight Healthcare NHS Trust 99-02; C Catherington and Clanfield *Portsm* from 02. *23 Pipers Mead, Clanfield, Waterlooville PO8 0ST* Tel (023) 9259 1357

O'SHEA, Mrs Helen Mary. b 55. Univ of Wales (Abth) BA77 SRN79. Llan Ord Course 94. **d** 98 **p** 99. NSM Skewen *Llan* 98-01; C Llangynwyd w Maesteg 01-02; P-in-c Cwmavon from 02. *Y Berth, 11 Tabernacle Terrace, Cwmavon, Port Talbot SA12 9HS*

OSLER, Philip. b 55. SEITE 99. **d** 02. NSM Staplehurst *Cant* from 02. *39 Marden Road, Staplehurst, Tonbridge TN12 0NE* Tel (01580) 892626 E-mail phil.osler@ukgateway.net

OSMAN, David Thomas. b 49. Bradf Univ BTech72 Newc Univ MA93. Trin Coll Bris 75. **d** 78 **p** 79. C Stranton *Dur* 78-81; C Denton Holme *Carl* 81-84; V Preston on Tees *Dur* 84-97; P-in-c Hebburn St Jo from 97; P-in-c Jarrow Grange from 00. *St John's Vicarage, 23 St John's Avenue, Hebburn NE31 2TZ* Tel 0191-422 7505

OSMAN, Ernest. b 35. St Aid Birkenhead 61. **d** 64 **p** 65. C Heaton Ch Ch *Man* 64-68; V Farnworth St Pet 68-77; V St Martin's *Lich* 77-85; V Endon w Stanley 85-00; rtd 01; Hon C Llanyblodwel and Trefonen *Lich* from 01. *The Rectory, Rectory Close, Trefonen, Oswestry SY10 9DY* Tel (01691) 654184 E-mail ern.osman@talk21.com

OSMAN, Stephen William. b 53. Matlock Coll of Educn CertEd74 Teesside Poly CQSW80. St Jo Coll Dur 88. **d** 90 **p** 91. C Newbarns w Hawcoat *Carl* 90-93; TV Marfleet *York* 93-00; P-in-c Gotham *S'well* from 00; P-in-c Barton in Fabis from 02; P-in-c Thrumpton from 02; P-in-c Kingston and Ratcliffe-on-Soar from 02. *The New Rectory, 39 Leake Road, Gotham, Nottingham NG11 0JL* Tel 0115-983 0608

OSMASTON, Miss Amiel Mary Ellinor. b 51. Ex Univ BA73 St Jo Coll Dur BA84. St Jo Coll Nottm DPS77 Cranmer Hall Dur 82. **dss** 84 **d** 87 **p** 94. Chester le Street *Dur* 84-88; Par Dn 87-88; Dir Miss and Past Studies Ridley Hall Cam 89-96; Min Development Officer *Ches* 96-03; C Lache cum Saltney 00-03; Min Development Officer *Carl* from 03; C Penrith w Newton Reigny and Plumpton Wall from 03. *The New Vicarage, Plumpton, Penrith CA11 9PA* Tel (01768) 885756 *or* (01228) 522573 Fax (01758) 885773

✠**OSMERS, The Rt Revd John Robert.** b 35. Cant Univ (NZ) MA58. Coll of Resurr Mirfield 59. **d** 61 **p** 62 **c** 95. C Rawmarsh w Parkgate *Sheff* 61-65; Lesotho 65-81; Par P Quthing 65-73; R Masite Miss 73-81; Botswana 81-88; Asst P H Cross Cathl 82-87; R Molepolole 82-88; Zambia from 88; Chapl ANC 88-91; Dioc Tr Chapl Lusaka 90-95; Bp E Zambia from 95. *PO Box 510154, Chipata, Zambia* Tel (00260) (62) 21294 Fax as telephone E-mail josmers@zamnet.zm

OSMOND, Andrew Mark. b 62. Leeds Univ LLB85. Wycliffe Hall Ox. **d** 02. C Cheltenham St Mary, St Matt, St Paul and H Trin *Glouc* from 02. *27 Cleeve View Road, Cheltenham GL52 5NJ* Tel 07866-987943 (mobile) E-mail andyos@osmon.freeserve.co.uk

OSMOND, David Methuen. b 38. Qu Coll Birm 75. **d** 77 **p** 78. C Yardley St Edburgha *Birm* 77-80; V Withall 80-89; R W Coker w Hardington Mandeville, E Chinnock etc *B & W* 89-95; Perm to Offic 96-98; rtd 98; Hon C Castle Town *Lich* from 01. *St Thomas's Vicarage, Doxey, Stafford ST16 1EQ* Tel (01785) 258796

OSMOND, Mrs Heather Christine. b 44. ABSM64 ARCM65 Birm Poly CertEd65. Qu Coll Birm 83. **dss** 84 **d** 87 **p** 97.

Brandwood *Birm* 84-85; Withall 85-89; Par Dn 87-89; Perm to Offic *B & W* 89-01; P-in-c Castle Town from 01. *St Thomas's Vicarage, Doxey, Stafford ST16 1EQ* Tel (01785) 258796

OSMOND, Oliver Robert. b 44. Ch Coll Cam BA66 MA70. Cuddesdon Coll 66 Trin Coll Toronto STB69. **d** 69 **p** 70. Canada 69-81; V Mill Hill Jo Keble Ch *Lon* from 81. *John Keble Vicarage, 142 Deans Lane, Edgware HA8 9NT* Tel (020) 8959 1312 Fax 8931 2433 E-mail oro@johnkeble.org.uk

OSMOND, Tobias Charles. b 74. Plymouth Univ BSc96. Ripon Coll Cuddesdon BTh99. **d** 99 **p** 00. C Wilton *B & W* 99-02; C Bath Abbey w St Jas from 02. *48 Devonshire Buildings, Bath BA2 4SU* Tel (01225) 422506 Mobile 07808-695732 E-mail tobes@freenet.co.uk *or* tobie@fish.co.uk

OSSORY AND LEIGHLIN, Archdeacon of. *See* MURRAY, The Ven John Grainger

OSSORY, Dean of. *See* LYNAS, The Very Revd Norman Noel

O'SULLIVAN, Mrs Hazel. b 50. S Dios Minl Tr Scheme 91. **d** 94 **p** 95. C Cove St Jo *Guildf* 94-98; TV Headley All SS 98-02; V Bordon from 02; Perm to Offic *Portsm* from 02. *58 Forest Road, Bordon GU35 0BP* Tel (01420) 477550 E-mail hazel@revd.fsnet.co.uk

O'SULLIVAN, Richard Norton. b 59. Glas Coll of Tech BSc80. Gregorian Univ Rome PhB85 STB88 STL90. **d** 89 **p** 90. In RC Ch 89-96; NSM Clarkston *Glas* 00-02; P-in-c Glas St Oswald from 02. *36 Kingsbridge Crescent, Glasgow G44 4JU* Tel 0141-583 7207 *or* 616 6446

OSWALD, John Edward Guy. b 39. Qu Coll Cam BA63 MA67. Ridley Hall Cam. **d** 68 **p** 69. C Chippenham St Paul w Langley Burrell *Bris* 68-72; C Hengrove 72-75; P-in-c Hardenhuish 75-79; P-in-c Kington St Michael 75-79; TV Chippenham St Paul w Hardenhuish etc 79-82; P-in-c Gt w Lt Somerford and Seagry 82-86; P-in-c Corston w Rodbourne 84-86; R Gt Somerford, Lt Somerford, Seagry, Corston etc from 86. *The Rectory, Frog Lane, Great Somerford, Chippenham SN15 5JA* Tel (01249) 720220

OSWIN, Frank Anthony (Tony). b 43. Chich Th Coll 69. **d** 71 **p** 72. C Radford *Cov* 71-74; C Shrub End *Chelmsf* 74-76; V Layer de la Haye 76-80; V Eastwood St Dav 80-93; TR Withycombe Raleigh *Ex* from 93. *The Rectory, 74 Withycombe Village Road, Exmouth EX8 3AE* Tel (01395) 264182

OTTAWAY, Michael John. b 17. Mert Coll Ox BA40 MA44. Cuddesdon Coll 40. **d** 41 **p** 42. C Leytonstone St Marg *Chelmsf* 41-45; C Kettering SS Pet and Paul *Pet* 45-48; C Kibworth Beauchamp *Leic* 48-49; V Wolvercote *Ox* 49-76; TV Wolvercote w Summertown 76-83; rtd 83; Perm to Offic *Chich* from 84. *3 Lower Drive, Seaford BN25 3AR* Tel (01323) 899179

OTTER, Anthony Frank. b 32. Kelham Th Coll 54. **d** 59 **p** 60. C Bethnal Green St Jo w St Simon *Lon* 59-63; C Aylesbury *Ox* 63-68; V Hanslope w Castlethorpe 68-77; P-in-c N w S Moreton 77-79; P-in-c Aston Tirrold w Aston Upthorpe 77-79; R S w N Moreton, Aston Tirrold and Aston Upthorpe 79-97; rtd 97; Perm to Offic *Ox* from 97. *4 Emden House, Barton Lane, Headington, Oxford OX3 9JU* Tel (01865) 765447

OTTERWELL, Anthony David. b 40. **d** 89 **p** 90. NSM Brighton Resurr *Chich* 89-97; Perm to Offic from 97. *11 Welesmere Road, Rottingdean, Brighton BN2 7DN* Tel (01273) 301339

OTTEWELL, David. b 42. Sheff Univ BSc65 Leic Univ PhD69. N Ord Course 90. **d** 93 **p** 94. NSM Barnby Dun *Sheff* 93-97; Perm to Offic from 97; P-in-c Finningley w Auckley *S'well* from 97. *The Rectory, Rectory Lane, Finningley, Doncaster DN9 3DA* Tel (01302) 770240

OTTEY, Canon John Leonard. b 34. AKC60 Nottm Univ BA70. **d** 61 **p** 62. C Grantham St Wulfram *Linc* 61-64; R Keyworth *S'well* 70-85; P-in-c Stanton-on-the-Wolds 71-85; P-in-c E Retford 85-87; V 87-99; P-in-c w Retford 85-87; R 87-99; Hon Can S'well Minster 93-99; rtd 99; Perm to Offic *Linc* from 00. *1 The Orchards, Grantham NG31 9GW* Tel (01476) 578762

OTTLEY, David Ronald. b 57. Lanc Univ BA78. Sarum & Wells Th Coll 79. **d** 81 **p** 82. C Urmston *Man* 81-85; Lect Bolton St Pet 85-87; P-in-c Halliwell St Thos 87-88; V Bolton St Thos 88-98; TR Halliwell from 98. *St Thomas's Vicarage, Cloister Street, Bolton BL1 3HA* Tel (01204) 841731

OTTLEY, Ronald. b 28. St Deiniol's Hawarden 81. **d** 83 **p** 84. Hon C Prestbury *Ches* 83-95; rtd 95; Perm to Offic *Ches* from 95. *2 Brocklehurst Court, Tytherington Drive, Macclesfield SK10 2HD* Tel (01625) 432649

OTTO, Andrew James. b 63. St Pet Coll Ox BA86 MA90 Bris Univ BA01. Trin Coll Bris 99. **d** 01 **p** 02. C Trowbridge H Trin *Sarum* from 01. *22 Barnes Close, Trowbridge BA14 9ER* Tel (01225) 769480 Pager 07625-735246

OTTO, Francis James Reeve. b 42. New Coll Ox BA64 BA68 Ex Univ 82. St Steph Ho Ox 66 Wells Th Coll 68. **d** 69 **p** 70. C St Stephen by Saltash *Truro* 69-72; C Newquay 72-73; V Lanteglos by Fowey 73-79; V St Goran w Caerhays 79-82; Chapl St Mary's Hall Brighton 82-88; Chapl Reading Sch 88-90; Teacher The Abbey Sch Reading 91-93; Chapl Lic Victuallers' Sch Ascot 93-94; Lic to Offic *Ox* 89-95; C Boyne Hill 95; P-in-c Cocking, Bepton and W Lavington *Chich* 95-99; Chapl Heathfield Sch Ascot from 99. *14 Locton Chase, Ascot SL5 8TP* Tel (01344) 626713

OUGH, John Christopher. b 51. Lon Univ CertEd74 Open Univ BA82. SW Minl Tr Course 91. **d** 94 **p** 95. C Plymouth Em, St Paul Efford and St Aug *Ex* 94-97; P-in-c Diptford, N Huish, Harberton and Harbertonford 97-01; P-in-c Halwell w Moreleigh 97-01; R Diptford, N Huish, Harberton, Harbertonford etc from 01. *The Rectory, Diptford, Totnes TQ9 7NY* Tel (01548) 821148
E-mail john@diptfordough.freeserve.co.uk

OULD, Julian Charles. b 57. MHCIMA77. Coll of Resurr Mirfield 80. **d** 83 **p** 84. C Hebburn St Cuth *Dur* 83-86; C Pet H Spirit Bretton *Pet* 86-90; R Peakirk w Glinton 90-95; R Peakirk w Glinton and Northborough 95-96; TR Is of Scilly *Truro* 96-98; R from 98. *The Chaplaincy, Church Road, St Mary's TR21 0NA* Tel (01720) 423128 Fax as telephone
E-mail ypj69@dial.pipex.com

OULESS, John Michael. b 22. AKC49. Ridley Hall Cam 49. **d** 50 **p** 51. C Dallington *Pet* 50-55; C Evesham *Worc* 55-56; C Halewood *Liv* 56-62; V Southwick w Glapthorn *Pet* 62-71; Chapl Glapthorn Road Hosp Oundle 63-71; R Cogenhoe *Pet* 71-89; R Whiston 71-89; rtd 89; Perm to Offic *Win* from 92. *2 Clos du Roncherez, St Brelade, Jersey JE3 8FG* Tel (01534) 44916

OUTEN (née BAILEY), Mrs Joyce Mary Josephine. b 33. St Gabr Coll Lon CertEd69 DipRS83. S'wark Ord Course 80. **dss** 83 **d** 87 **p** 94. Par Dn Woolwich St Mary w St Mich *S'wark* 87-89; Par Dn Rusthall *Roch* 89-94; C 94-97; rtd 97; Asst Chapl Kent and Cant Hosps NHS Trust 97-99; Asst Chapl E Kent Hosps NHS Trust 99-00; Hon C Whitstable *Cant* from 00. *10 Foxgrove Road, Whitstable CT5 1PB* Tel (01227) 273643
E-mail outen@foxgrove.fsnet.co.uk

OUTHWAITE, Stephen Anthony (Tony). b 35. Wells Th Coll 62. **d** 64 **p** 65. C Bitterne Park *Win* 64-67; C-in-c N Tadley CD 67-71; R Milton 71-93; RD Christchurch 82-90; V Win St Cross w St Faith from 93; Master St Cross Hosp from 93. *The Master's Lodge, St Cross Hospital, Winchester SO23 9SD* Tel (01962) 852888

OUTRAM, David Michael. b 42. Univ of Wales (Ban) BA77 BD79. Coll of Resurr Mirfield 79. **d** 80 **p** 81. C Llandegfan and Beaumaris w Llanfaes w Penmon etc *Ban* 80-82; Chapl Prebendal Sch Chich 82-86; PV Chich Cathl *Chich* 82-86; Asst Chapl Wellington Coll Berks 86-89; Hd Div from 87; Chapl from 89. *7 Chaucer Road, Wellington Chase, Crowthorne RG45 7QN* Tel (01344) 778373 or 772262

OVENDEN, Canon John Anthony. b 45. Open Univ BA80 BA93 K Coll Lon MA96. Sarum & Wells Th Coll 71. **d** 74 **p** 75. C Handsworth *Sheff* 74-77; C Isfield *Chich* 77-80; C Uckfield 77-80; P-in-c Stuntney *Ely* 80-85; Min Can, Prec and Sacr Ely Cathl 80-85; V Primrose Hill St Mary w Avenue Road St Paul *Lon* 85-98; Dir English Hymnal Co from 93; Can Windsor and Chapl in Windsor Gt Park from 98. *Chaplain's Lodge, Windsor Great Park, Windsor SL4 2HP* Tel (01784) 432434

OVEREND, Alan. b 53. Sheff Univ BA75. Oak Hill Th Coll 84. **d** 86 **p** 87. C Aughton St Mich *Liv* 86-89; P-in-c Eccleston Park 89-92; V 92-99; V Ainsdale from 99. *St John's Vicarage, 708 Liverpool Road, Ainsdale, Southport PR8 3QE* Tel (01704) 577760

OVEREND, Barry Malcolm. b 49. K Coll Lon BD71 AKC71 DipMin88. St Aug Coll Cant 71. **d** 72 **p** 73. C Nailsworth *Glouc* 72-74; C High Harrogate Ch Ch *Ripon* 75-78; V Collingham w Harewood 78-87; V Far Headingley St Chad from 87. *St Chad's Vicarage, Otley Road, Leeds LS16 5JT* Tel 0113-275 2224 or 274 4322 E-mail st.chads@virgin.net

OVEREND, Paul. b 66. Coll of Ripon & York St Jo BA88 Hull Univ MA97. Coll of Resurr Mirfield 88. **d** 93 **p** 94. C Cayton w Eastfield *York* 93-96; Asst Chapl Univ of Wales (Cardiff) *Llan* 96; Sen Chapl from 97. *University Anglican Chaplaincy, 61 Park Place, Cardiff CF10 3AT* Tel (029) 2023 2550 or 2050 6170 Fax 0870-130 5358 E-mail overend@cardiff.ac.uk

OVERINGTON, Canon David Vernon. b 34. W Aus Advanced Ed Coll DipRE90. ALCD60. **d** 60 **p** 61. C Penge Ch Ch w H Trin *Roch* 60-62; C Lenton *S'well* 62-65; PC Brackenfield w Wessington *Derby* 65-71; P-in-c Cubley w Marston Montgomery 71-76; Australia 76-99; Can Bunbury 84-85; Hon Can Perth from 96; P-in-c Longside *Ab* from 99; P-in-c Old Deer from 99; P-in-c Strichen 99. *12 Bain Terrace, Mintlaw, Peterhead AB42 5HB* Tel (01771) 622553
E-mail davidjoyce@doverington.freeserve.co.uk

OVERTHROW, Royston John. b 45. Southn Univ BTh94. Portsm Dioc Tr Course 84. **d** 85. NSM Portsm Cathl *Portsm* 85-91; Perm to Offic 91-94; Bp's Dom Chapl *Sarum* 94-02; NSM Marlborough from 02. *10 Alexandra Terrace, Blowhorn Street, Marlborough SN8 1DA* Tel (01672) 515983
E-mail liznroyuk@supanet.com

OVERTON, Charles Henry. b 51. CCC Ox BA74 MA77 Fitzw Coll Cam PGCE78 BA79 MA85. Ridley Hall Cam 77. **d** 80 **p** 81. C Tonbridge SS Pet and Paul *Roch* 80-84; Lic to Offic *Cant* 84-87; Asst Chapl St Lawr Coll Ramsgate 84-87; P-in-c Aythorpe w High and Leaden Roding *Chelmsf* 88-95; P-in-c Hughenden *Ox* 95-01. *13 The Haystacks, High Wycombe HP13 6PY* Tel (01494) 447217 or 459130

OVERTON, David Malcolm. b 52. Surrey Univ BA97. Chich Th Coll. **d** 84 **p** 85. C Ches H Trin *Ches* 84-86; C Woodchurch 86-88; C Coppenhall 88-91; C Croydon St Jo *S'wark* 91-94; Perm to Offic *Lon* 97-00; C Selsey *Chich* 98-02; Miss P Ribbleton *Blackb* from 02. *140 Teil Green, Fulwood, Preston PR2 9PE* Tel (01772) 701383

OVERTON, Keith Charles. b 28. EAMTC 78. **d** 81 **p** 82. NSM Duxford *Ely* 81-84; NSM Whittlesford 84-88; P-in-c 88-94; P-in-c Pampisford 88-90; Perm to Offic *Bris* from 94. *86 Pittsfield, Cricklade, Swindon SN6 6AW* Tel (01793) 750321

OVERTON, Thomas Vincent Edersheim. b 34. New Coll Ox BA58 DipTh59 MA61. Wycliffe Hall Ox 58. **d** 60 **p** 61. C W Hampstead Trin *Lon* 60-63; C Leeds St Geo *Ripon* 63-67; Perm to Offic *Lon* 68-71; Thailand 71-78; R Knossington and Cold Overton *Leic* 78-81; V Owston and Withcote 78-81; R Bedford St Jo and St Leon *St Alb* 81-90; Perm to Offic *B & W* 90-91; V Leigh *Roch* 91-99; rtd 99. *14 The Broadwalk, Northwood HA6 2XD* Tel (01923) 829612

OVERTON-BENGE, Mrs Angela Margaret. b 46. UEA BA99. EAMTC 94. **d** 97 **p** 98. NSM Moulsham St Jo *Chelmsf* 97-01; C Aveley and Purfleet from 01; Ind Chapl from 01. *St Stephen's House, Church Lane, Purfleet RM19 1QD* Tel (01708) 689757

OVERY, Arthur William. b 19. JP. Nor Ord Course 73. **d** 76 **p** 77. NSM Lowestoft St Marg *Nor* 76-78; NSM Lowestoft and Kirkley 79-89; Perm to Offic from 89. *The Hollies, Warren Road, Lowestoft NR32 4QD* Tel (01502) 561289

OVEY, Michael John. b 58. Ball Coll Ox BA81 BCL82 ACT MTh00. Ridley Hall Cam 88. **d** 91 **p** 92. C Crowborough *Chich* 91-95; Australia 95-98; Kingham Hill Fell Oak Hill Th Coll from 98. *Oak Hill Theological College, Chase Side, London N14 4PS* Tel (020) 8449 0467 ext 248 E-mail mikeo@oakhill.ac.uk

OWEN, Bryan Philip. b 47. Keswick Hall Coll CertEd70 Coll of Ripon & York St Jo Cert Counselling 82. Cant Sch of Min 83. **d** 86 **p** 87. NSM Deal St Geo *Cant* 86-87; C Herne 87-89; R Clarkston *Glas* 89-93; Warden Scottish Chs Ho (Chs Together in Scotland) 93-96; V Cuddington *Guildf* 96-01; rtd 01; Perm to Offic *Glas* from 01. *10 Waverley Park, Kirkintilloch, Glasgow G66 2BP* Tel 0141-776 0407 Mobile 07796-155560
E-mail owen@clara.co.uk

OWEN, Mrs Carole Janice. b 55. **d** 01 **p** 02. NSM Cley Hill Warminster *Sarum* from 01. *11 Stuart Green, Warminster BA12 9NU* Tel (01985) 214849

OWEN, Christine Rose. b 62. Univ of Wales (Ban) BA83 PGCE84. Qu Coll Birm 86. **d** 88 **p** 94. C Ynyscynhaearn w Penmorfa and Porthmadog *Ban* 88-90; Chapl Lon Univ *Lon* 90-96; Hon C St Marylebone w H Trin 94-96; Min Can and Prec Worc Cathl *Worc* 96-00; R Llansantffraid Glan Conwy and Eglwysbach *St As* from 00. *The Rectory, 16 Y Bryn, Glan Conwy, Colwyn Bay LL28 5NJ* Tel (01492) 583099

OWEN, Clifford. *See* OWEN, Phillip Clifford

OWEN, Dafydd Gwyn. b 62. St Steph Ho Ox 95. **d** 97 **p** 98. C Whitchurch *Bris* 97-01; V Bris Ch the Servant Stockwood from 01. *The Vicarage, Goslet Road, Stockwood, Bristol BS14 8SP* Tel (01275) 831138

OWEN, Daniel James. b 71. Anglia Poly Univ BSc94 TCD BTh00. CITC 97. **d** 00 **p** 01. C Belfast St Donard *D & D* 00-03; I Rathcooney Union *C, C & R* from 03. *The Rectory, Fota View, Glounthaune, Cork, Irish Republic* Tel (00353) (21) 435 5208 E-mail danieljowen@email.com

OWEN, David Cadwaladr. b 56. Grey Coll Dur BSc77 Univ Coll Worc PGCE99. WEMTC 00. **d** 03. NSM Pershore w Pinvin, Wick and Birlingham *Worc* from 03. *Caedmon, Main Street, Pinvin, Pershore WR10 2ER* Tel (01386) 554249 Mobile 07947-624801 E-mail dc.owen@dunelm.org.uk

OWEN, Canon David William. b 31. Down Coll Cam BA55 MA58. Linc Th Coll 55. **d** 57 **p** 58. C Salford St Phil w St Steph *Man* 57-61; C Grantham St Wulfram *Linc* 61-65; V Messingham 65-70; V Spilsby w Hundleby 70-77; R Aswardby w Sausthorpe 71-77; R Langton w Sutterby 71-77; R Halton Holgate 73-77; P-in-c Firsby w Gt Steeping 75-77; P-in-c Lt Steeping 75-77; R Louth 77-92; Chapl Louth Co Hosp 77-92; RD Louthesk *Linc* 82-89; Can and Preb Linc Cathl 85-92; TR Swan *Ox* 92-97; RD Claydon 94-96; rtd 97. *19 Stephen Road, Headington, Oxford OX3 9AY* Tel (01865) 766585

OWEN, Derek Malden. b 29. Oak Hill Th Coll 74. **d** 76 **p** 77. C Eastbourne H Trin *Chich* 76-78; C Walthamstow St Mary w St Steph *Chelmsf* 78-81; R Ditcheat w E Pennard and Pylle *B & W* 81-83; Warden Shaftesbury Housing Assn 86-94; rtd 94; Hon C Fairlight, Guestling and Pett *Chich* 94-97; P-in-c Llanishen w Trellech Grange and Llanfihangel etc *Mon* from 00. *The Vicarage, Llanishen, Chepstow NP16 6QL* Tel (01600) 860845

OWEN, Edgar. b 26. WMMTC. **d** 82 **p** 83. NSM Garretts Green *Birm* 82-88; NSM Stechford 88-94; rtd 94; Perm to Offic *Birm* from 94. *36 Colbourne Court, 116 Frederick Road, Stechford, Birmingham B33 8AE* Tel 0121-783 5603

✠**OWEN, The Rt Revd Edwin.** b 10. TCD BA32 MA41. **d** 34 **p** 35 **c** 72. C Glenageary *D & G* 34-36; C Dublin Ch Ch Leeson Park 36-38; Min Can St Patr Cathl Dub 35-36; Chan V 36-38; Succ

38-42; I Birr w Eglish *L & K* 42-57; Can Killaloe Cathl 54-57; Dean Killaloe 57-72; Dioc Sec (Killaloe etc) 57-72; Bp Killaloe 72-76; Bp L & K 76-81; rtd 81. *4 Cypress, Hazeldene, Anglesea Road, Donnybrook, Dublin 4, Irish Republic* Tel (00353) (1) 660 8260

OWEN, Emyr. b 69. Lancs Poly BSc91. Westcott Ho Cam BA94 CTM95. **d** 95 **p** 96. C Llanbeblig w Caernarfon and Betws Garmon etc *Ban* 95-96; C Llanberis w Llanrug 96-98; TV Bangor 98-02; P-in-c Llandygai and Maes y Groes 98-02; V Nefyn w Tudweiliog w Llandudwen w Edern from 02. *The Vicarage, Lon Isaf, Morfa Nefyn, Pwllheli LL53 6BS* Tel (01758) 720494 E-mail emyr_owen@hotmail.com

OWEN, Eric Cyril Hammersley. b 46. Liv Univ LLB68 Barrister 69. St As Minl Tr Course 95. **d** 97 **p** 98. NSM Gresford *St As* 97-03; NSM Rhosymedre w Penycae from 03. *Thistle Patch, 28 Wynnstay Lane, Marford, Wrexham LL12 8LG* Tel (01978) 856495 E-mail eowen@lineone.net

OWEN, Ethelston John Charles. b 20. St D Coll Lamp BA42. **d** 48 **p** 49. C Gresford *St As* 48-50; C Abergele 50-55; R Llanfynydd 55-58; Chapl Mersey Miss to Seamen 58-60; V Clehonger *Heref* 60-80; R Eaton Bishop 60-80; rtd 80; Perm to Offic *Heref* 81-98. *22 Capel Court, The Burgage, Prestbury, Cheltenham GL52 3EL* Tel (01242) 576389

OWEN, Gary John. b 72. City Univ BSc93. Ridley Hall Cam BA97 CTM98. **d** 98 **p** 99. C Welshpool w Castle Caereinion *St As* 98-01; TV Wrexham from 01. *The Vicarage, 160 Borras Road, Wrexham LL13 9ER* Tel (01978) 350202

OWEN, Geoffrey Neill. b 55. Chich Th Coll. **d** 85 **p** 86. C Streatham St Pet *S'wark* 85-89; C Battersea Ch Ch and St Steph 89-91; TV Surbiton St Andr and St Mark 91-97; V Merton St Jas from 97. *St James's Vicarage, Beaford Grove, London SW20 9LB* Tel (020) 8540 3122

OWEN, Gerald. b 16. St D Coll Lamp BA49. **d** 50 **p** 51. C Minera *St As* 50-54; V Foxt w Whiston *Lich* 54-57; V Shrewsbury St Mich 57-63; V Wednesbury St Bart 64-83; rtd 83; Perm to Offic *Worc* from 83. *35 Troon Place, Wordsley, Stourbridge DY8 5EN* Tel (01384) 294952

OWEN, Glyn John. b 56. Open Univ BA91 Nottm Univ MSc93. Cranmer Hall Dur 01. **d** 03. C Whiston *Sheff* from 03. *40 Flat Lane, Whiston, Rotherham S60 4EF* Tel (01709) 837388 E-mail revglynowen@blueyonder.co.uk

OWEN, Gordon Campbell. b 41. FRMetS65 MRAeS66 Univ of Wales (Ban) BD76 PGCE77 Ox Univ DipApTh97. Ban Ord Course 79. **d** 81 **p** 82. Hd RE Eirias High Sch Colwyn Bay 77-88; Chapl RAFVR from 81; Asst P Ban Cathl *Ban* 82-88; Chapl St Kath Coll and Liv Inst of HE 88-91; Dioc Liaison Officer for RE *Liv* 88-91; V Llanfair-is-gaer and Llanddeiniolen *Ban* 91-97; Educn Officer 91-97; Lic to Offic 97-00. *The Shieling, Penrhosgarnedd, Bangor LL57 2NH* Tel (01248) 352841

OWEN, Graham Anthony. b 54. Birm Univ BA77. Trin Coll Bris DipHE94. **d** 94 **p** 95. C Wiveliscombe w Chipstable, Huish Champflower etc *B & W* 94-98; V from 98. *The Vicarage, South Street, Wiveliscombe, Taunton TA4 2LZ* Tel (01984) 623309 E-mail graham@owen31.freeserve.co.uk

OWEN, Graham Wynne. b 46. GTCL67 FTCL70 Lon Inst of Educn MA81. Cant Sch of Min 90. **d** 93 **p** 94. C Eltham H Trin *S'wark* 93-97; P-in-c Shooters Hill Ch Ch 97-00; V 00-01; TV Sole Bay *St E* from 01. *The Vicarage, Park Gate, High Street, Wangford, Beccles NR34 8RL* Tel (01502) 578468

OWEN, Gwyn. *See* OWEN, Dafydd Gwyn

OWEN, Harry Dennis. b 47. Oak Hill Th Coll 73. **d** 76 **p** 77. C Fulham Ch Ch *Lon* 76-81; V Byker St Mark *Newc* 81-89; V Plumstead All SS *S'wark* from 89; RD Plumstead from 03. *All Saints' Vicarage, 106 Herbert Road, London SE18 3PU* Tel (020) 8854 2995

OWEN, James Thomas. b 48. Liv Univ MA00. Linc Th Coll 77. **d** 80 **p** 81. C Palmers Green St Jo *Lon* 80-84; C Timperley *Ches* 84-87; C Bramhall 87-92; V Latchford St Jas from 92; RD Gt Budworth from 96. *St James's Vicarage, Manx Road, Warrington WA4 6AJ* Tel (01925) 631893

OWEN, John Edward. b 52. Middx Poly BA75. Sarum & Wells Th Coll BTh81. **d** 81 **p** 82. C S Ashford Ch Ch *Cant* 81-85; TV Bemerton *Sarum* 85-91; V St Leonards and St Ives *Win* 91-95; R N Stoneham from 95. *The Rectory, 62 Glen Eyre Road, Southampton SO16 3NL* Tel (023) 8076 8123 E-mail jeowen@fish.co.uk

OWEN, Keith Robert. b 57. Warwick Univ BA Ox Univ BA MA85 Hull Univ MA(Ed)89. St Steph Ho Ox 79. **d** 82 **p** 83. C Headingley *Ripon* 82-85; Chapl Grimsby Colls of H&FE 85-90; Chapl for Educn *Linc* 85-90; P-in-c Linc St Botolph 90-95; Chapl to Caring Agencies Linc City Cen 90-95; V Steeton *Bradf* 95-01; Chapl Airedale NHS Trust 95-01; P-in-c Penzance St Mary w St Paul *Truro* 01-02; P-in-c Penzance St Jo 01-02; TR Penzance St Mary St Paul and St Jo from 02. *St Mary's Vicarage, Chapel Street, Penzance TR18 4AP* Tel (01736) 363079

OWEN, Kenneth Phillip. b 56. Liv Univ BA77 PGCE78. N Ord Course 92. **d** 95 **p** 96. C Heswall *Ches* 95-01; V Frankby w Greasby from 01. *The Vicarage, 14 Arrowe Road, Greasby, Wirral CH49 1RA* Tel 0151-678 6155 E-mail ken.owen@heswallcofe.ukf.net

OWEN, Lionel Edward Joseph. b 19. S'wark Ord Course 66. **d** 69 **p** 70. C Hythe *Cant* 69-73; C Deal St Leon 73-75; V Teynham 75-84; RD Ospringe 80-84; rtd 84; Perm to Offic *Cant* 84-02. *5 The Dene, Hillside Street, Hythe CT21 5DH* Tel (01303) 267642

OWEN, Paul Jonathan. b 59. S Bank Poly BSc81. Ridley Hall Cam 00. **d** 02 **p** 03. C Seaford w Sutton *Chich* from 02. *2 Benenden Close, Seaford BN25 3PG* Tel (01323) 891831 E-mail paulowen@freenet.co.uk

OWEN, Peter Russell. b 35. St Mich Coll Llan DipTh63. **d** 63 **p** 64. C Wrexham *St As* 63-64; C Connah's Quay 64-65; Asst Chapl Miss to Seamen 66-69; P-in-c Upper Norwood All SS w St Marg *Cant* 69-72; C Hawarden *St As* 72-75; V Cilcain and Nannerch 75-79; R Cilcain and Nannerch and Rhyd-y-mwyn 79-83; V Brymbo and Bwlchgwyn 83-87; R Llangynhafal and Llanbedr Dyffryn Clwyd 87-99; P-in-c Llanychan 87-99; rtd 00. *Telpyn Forge, Rhewl, Ruthin LL15 1TP* Tel (01824) 704051

OWEN, Ms Petra Davine. b 65. Liv Univ BA87 Lanc Univ PGCE88. St Jo Coll Nottm MA97 and 98. **d** 98 **p** 99. C Brampton St Thos *Derby* 98-01; USA from 01. *The Church of the Good Shepherd, 345 South 312th, Federal Way, WA 95003, USA*

OWEN, Phillip Clifford. b 42. G&C Coll Cam BA65 MA69. Ridley Hall Cam 71. **d** 73 **p** 74. C Stowmarket *St E* 73-76; C Headley All SS *Guildf* 76-81; TV 81-89; P-in-c Clifton-on-Teme, Lower Sapey and the Shelsleys *Worc* 89-97; R 97-02; Dioc Ecum Officer 89-02; P-in-c Corfu *Eur* from 03. *Holy Trinity Anglican Church, 21 L Mavili St, Kerkira TK 49131, Corfu, Greece* Tel and fax (0661) 031467 E-mail clavis@hotmail.com *or* holytrin@otenet.gr

OWEN, Raymond Philip. b 37. Man Univ BScTech60 AMCST60 Teesside Poly DMS83. Chich Th Coll 65. **d** 67 **p** 68. C Elland *Wakef* 67-70; C Lindley 70-73; V Bradshaw 73-80; Ind Chapl *Dur* 80-91; TR Hanley H Ev *Lich* 91-99; Bp Lich's Past Aux from 03. *Address withheld by request* Tel 07747-601379 (mobile) Fax (01782) 201390 E-mail revrayowen@hotmail.com

OWEN, Richard Ellis. b 12. Clifton Th Coll 48. **d** 50 **p** 51. C Littleover *Derby* 50-53; C Whitchurch *Lich* 53-55; R Elkstone w Syde and Winstone *Glouc* 55-61; V Badminton w Acton Turville 61-71; V Kemble w Poole Keynes 71-73; R Pebworth w Dorsington 73-83; rtd 83; Perm to Offic *Glouc* 83-94. *40 Ballards Close, Mickleton, Chipping Camden GL55 6TN* Tel (01386) 438755

OWEN, Canon Richard Llewelyn. b 27. Univ of Wales (Lamp) BA51. St Mich Coll Llan 51. **d** 53 **p** 54. C Holyhead w Rhoscolyn w Llanfair-yn-Neubwll *Ban* 53-57; C Porthmadog 57-59; R Llanfechell w Bodewryd, Rhosbeirio etc 59-67; Youth Chapl 66-67; V Penrhyndeudraeth and Llanfrothen 67-77; R Llangefni w Tregaean and Llangristiolus etc 77-89; Can Ban Cathl 82-93; Hon Can from 93; Treas 86-93; Can Missr and V Bangor Cathl Par 89-93; RD Arfon 92-93; rtd 93; Perm to Offic *Ban* from 93. *Bodowen, Great Orme's Road, Llandudno LL30 2BF* Tel (01492) 872765

OWEN, Richard Matthew. b 49. Sheff Univ BA70 Leeds Univ CertEd73. N Ord Course 84. **d** 87 **p** 88. NSM Chorlton-cum-Hardy St Werburgh *Man* 87-89; C N Reddish 89-91; Perm to Offic *York* 91-96; NSM York St Olave w St Giles 96-97; Perm to Offic 97-03. *The Old Mill, High Street, Lamberhurst, Tunbridge Wells TN3 8EQ*

OWEN, Robert Glynne. b 33. St Mich Coll Llan 56. **d** 58 **p** 59. C Machynlleth and Llanwrin *Ban* 58-62; C Llanbeblig w Caernarfon 62-65; V Carno and Trefeglwys 65-69; Hon C Dorking w Ranmore *Guildf* 69-75; Perm to Offic *St As* 75-94; V Broughton 94-99; rtd 99. *Briarcroft, Minera Road, Cefn y Bedd, Wrexham LL12 9TR* Tel (01978) 752864

OWEN, Robert Lee. b 56. Univ of Wales (Cardiff) BD79. Qu Coll Birm 79. **d** 81 **p** 82. C Holywell *St As* 81-84; Perm to Offic *Birm* 85-87; Chapl Blue Coat Sch Birm 85-87; Chapl St Elphin's Sch Matlock 87-94; Chapl Qu Marg Sch York from 94. *Queen Margaret's School, Escrick Park, Escrick, York YO19 6EU* Tel (01904) 728261

OWEN, Ronald Alfred. b 44. Wilson Carlile Coll 73 Sarum & Wells Th Coll 80. **d** 81 **p** 82. C Wotton St Mary *Glouc* 81-83; CF 83-97; P-in-c Salcombe *Ex* 97-02; V Salcombe and Malborough w S Huish from 02; RD Woodleigh 00-03. *The Vicarage, Devon Road, Salcombe TQ8 8HJ* Tel and fax (01548) 842626 Mobile 07970-727229 E-mail revraowen@hotmail.com

OWEN, Roy Meredith. b 21. Univ of Wales BA43. St Mich Coll Llan 43. **d** 45 **p** 46. C Roath St Martin *Llan* 45-47; C Penarth w Lavernock 47-51; C Merthyr Dyfan 51-56; V Llangeinor 56-62; V Pontyclun w Talygarn 62-75; C Cadoxton-juxta-Barry 82-85; rtd 85; Perm to Offic *Llan* 86-88. *20 Mary Street, Llandaff North, Cardiff CF14 2JQ* Tel (029) 2021 4555

OWEN, Canon Stanley Alfred George. b 17. Worc Ord Coll 57. **d** 59 **p** 60. C Bickenhill w Elmdon *Birm* 59-60; V 60-86; rtd 86; Perm to Offic *Birm* from 86; Chmn and Sec Assn Csh Fellowships from 88. *Bickenhill House, 154 Lode Lane, Solihull B91 2HP* Tel 0121-704 9281

OWEN, Stuart James. b 68. Sunderland Poly BA91. Ripon Coll Cuddesdon BTh00. **d** 00 **p** 01. C Hendon St Mary *Lon* 00-01; C

Hendon St Mary and Ch Ch from 01. *St Mary's Cottage, 48 Church End, London NW4 4JT* Tel (020) 8203 4673 E-mail fr_stuart@hotmail.com

OWEN, Mrs Susan Margaret. b 38. St Andr Univ MA61 Univ of Wales (Swansea) MPhil91 Univ of Wales (Ban) BD93. Qu Coll Birm 94. **d** 95 **p** 96. NSM Shrewsbury St Geo *Lich* 95-98; P-in-c Penrhyndeudraeth w Llanfrothen w Beddgelert *Ban* 98-99; V from 99. *The Vicarage, Penrhyndeudraeth LL48 6LG* Tel (01766) 770021 E-mail sowen@vicarage.fsnet.co.uk

OWEN-JONES, Peter Charles. b 57. Ridley Hall Cam CTM94. **d** 94 **p** 95. C Leverington *Ely* 94-97; C Wisbech St Mary 94-97; R Haslingfield w Harlton and Gt and Lt Eversden from 97. *The Rectory, Broad Lane, Haslingfield, Cambridge CB3 7JF* Tel (01223) 870285 Fax as telephone E-mail poj@lineone.net

OWEN-JONES, Peter John. b 47. RMCS BScEng68 CEng84 MIMechE84 MBIM87. EMMTC 85. **d** 88 **p** 89. NSM Hulbrook and Lt Eaton *Derby* 88-00; NSM W Hallam and Mapperley w Stanley from 01. *Bridge Cottage, 63 Derby Road, Stanley, Ilkeston DE7 6EX* Tel 0115-932 0764 Fax as telephone E-mail jowenjones@aol.com

OWENS, Mrs Ann Lindsay. b 47. St Hild Coll Dur CertEd68 Man Univ BA94. N Ord Course 92. **d** 95 **p** 96. Chapl St Jas Sch Farnworth 94-97; NSM New Bury *Man* 95-97; C Heywood St Luke w All So 97-98; C Heywood 98-99; P-in-c Chadderton St Matt from 99; P-in-c Chadderton St Luke from 03. *St Matthew's Vicarage, Mill Brow, Chadderton, Oldham OL1 2RT* Tel 0161-624 8600 E-mail ann-lindsay.owens@virgin.net

OWENS, Christopher Lee. b 42. SS Mark & Jo Coll Chelsea 61 Lon Inst of Educn TCert. Linc Th Coll 66. **d** 69 **p** 70. C Dalston H Trin w St Phil *Lon* 69-72; C Portsea N End St Mark *Portsm* 72-81; TV E Ham w Upton Park St Alb *Chelmsf* 81-92; C Is of Dogs Ch Ch and St Jo w St Luke *Lon* 92-98; P-in-c Chingford St Edm *Chelmsf* 98-02; V from 02. *St Edmund's Vicarage, Larkswood Road, London E4 9DS* Tel (020) 8529 5226 E-mail christopher@owenseaster.freeserve.co.uk

OWENS, Mrs Margaret Jean. b 49. Man Univ BSc70 Birm Univ MSc72. St Jo Coll Nottm 99. **d** 01 **p** 02. NSM Hurdsfield *Ches* from 01. *44 Ryles Park Road, Macclesfield SK11 8AH* Tel (01625) 262335 Mobile 07775-801613 Fax (01625) 430284 E-mail mowens44@hotmail.com

OWENS, Philip Roger. b 47. Univ of Wales (Ban) DipTh70. Wells Th Coll 71. **d** 71 **p** 72. C Colwyn Bay *St As* 71-74; C Wrexham 74-77; TV 77-80; P-in-c Yoxford *St E* 80-85; Asst Stewardship and Resources Adv 80-85; R Bangor Monachorum and Worthenbury *St As* 85-98; Sec Dioc Stewardship Cttee 89-98; RD Bangor Isycoed 92-98; R Flint 98-03; RD Holywell 02-03. *3 Turnberry Avenue, Wrexham LL13 9GG* Tel 07808-167147 (mobile)

OWENS, Stephen Graham Frank. b 49. Ch Coll Cam BA71 MA75 CertEd72. Qu Coll Birm 73. **d** 75 **p** 76. C Stourbridge St Mich Norton *Worc* 75-80; Tanzania 80-88; V Dudley Wood *Worc* 88-99; P-in-c Mamble w Bayton, Rock w Heightington etc 99-02; V from 02. *The Vicarage, Church Lane, Rock, Kidderminster DY14 9TT* Tel (01299) 266580 E-mail stephen.owens@ffvicarage.fsnet.co.uk

OWERS, Ian Humphrey. b 46. Em Coll Cam BA68 MA72. Westcott Ho Cam 71. **d** 73 **p** 74. C Champion Hill St Sav *S'wark* 73-77; V Peckham St Sav 77-82; P-in-c E Greenwich Ch Ch w St Andr and St Mich 82-83; V 83-94; P-in-c Westcombe Park St Geo 85-94; RD Greenwich 92-94; Perm to Offic *St E* from 01. *29 Avondale Road, Shipley BD18 4QR* Tel 0113-278 3779

OXBROW, Canon Mark. b 51. Reading Univ BSc72 Fitzw Ho Cam BA75 MA79. Ridley Hall Cam 73. **d** 76 **p** 77. C Luton Ch Ch *Roch* 76-80; TV Newc Epiphany *Newc* 80-88; Chapl Newc Mental Health Unit 80-88; Regional Sec Eur CMS from 88; Communication Resources Sec from 94; Internat Miss Dir from 01; Hon Can Brussels Cathl *Eur* from 98. *10 Nettleden Avenue, Wembley HA9 6DP, or CMS, Partnership House, 157 Waterloo Road, London SE1 8UU* Tel (020) 8900 2485 *or* 7928 8681 Fax 7401 3215 E-mail markoxbrow@aol.com

OXENFORTH, Colin Bryan. b 45. St Chad's Coll Dur BA67 DipTh69. **d** 69 **p** 70. C Bromley St Andr *Roch* 69-72; C Nunhead St Antony *S'wark* 72-76; V Toxteth St Marg *Liv* 76-89; V Brixton St Matt *S'wark* 89-00; V Pemberton St Jo *Liv* from 00. *2 Shelley Drive, Orrell, Wigan WN5 8HW* Tel (01942) 222237 Fax as telephone

OXFORD (Christ Church), Dean of. *See* DRURY, The Very Revd John Henry

OXFORD, Archdeacon of. *See* MORRISON, The Ven John Anthony

OXFORD, Bishop of. *See* HARRIES, The Rt Revd Richard Douglas

OXLEY, Christopher Robert. b 51. Sheff Univ BA73 PGCE74 Ox Univ BA78 MA83. Wycliffe Hall Ox 76. **d** 79 **p** 80. C Greasbrough *Sheff* 79-82; C Doncaster St Leon and St Jude 82-84; Asst Chapl Brussels *Eur* 84-87; V Humberstone *Leic*

87-93; V Beaumont Leys from 93; RD Christianity S 98-01. *The Vicarage, 10 Parkside Close, Leicester LE4 1EP* Tel 0116-235 2667 E-mail oxley@leicester.anglican.org

OXLEY, David William. b 63. TCD BA85 BTh89. CITC 85. **d** 89 **p** 90. C Dublin Ch Ch Cathl Gp *D & G* 89-92; Clerical V Ch Ch Cathl Dublin 90-92; I Templebreedy w Tracton and Nohoval *C, C & R* 92-96; Min Can Cork Cathl 95-96; I Tullow w Shillelagh, Aghold and Mullinacuff *C & O* 96-02; I Dublin Santry w Glasnevin and Finglas *D & G* from 02. *The Rectory, Church Street, Finglass, Dublin 11, Irish Republic* Tel (00353) (1) 834 1015 Mobile 86-881 6486 E-mail revdwo@hotmail.com

OXLEY, Martin Neil. b 65. Birm Univ BA86 Edin Univ BD95. Edin Th Coll CECM95. **d** 95 **p** 96. C Glas St Mary *Glas* 95-97; C Glas St Matt 95-97; C Clydebank 95-97; P-in-c Glas St Matt 97-00; Dir Studies Edin Th Coll 97-00; P-in-c Lerwick *Ab* from 00; P-in-c Burravoe from 00; Warden Soc of Our Lady of the Is from 00. *St Magnus Rectory, Greenfield Place, Lerwick, Shetland ZE1 0AQ* Tel (01595) 693862 Mobile 07970-266578 E-mail frmartin@globalnet.co.uk

OXLEY, Mrs Paula Jane. b 51. Sheff Univ BA74 Nottm Univ MA00 PGCE75. EMMTC 93. **d** 93 **p** 94. NSM Birstall and Wanlip *Leic* 93-95; NSM Beaumont Leys 95-96; C from 96. *The Vicarage, 10 Parkside Close, Leicester LE4 1EP* Tel 0116-235 2667 E-mail oxley@leicester.anglican.org

OYET, Canon Julius Isotuk. b 34. Concordia Coll (USA) MA79. Immanuel Coll Ibadan DipTh70. **d** 70 **p** 72. Nigeria 70-90 and from 96; Hon Can Ondo from 88; Miss Partner CMS from 91; C Warblington w Emsworth *Portsm* 91-95; C Kirkby *Liv* 95-96; V Port Harcourt St Cyprian and Dioc Dir Tr 97-99; rtd 00. *c/o U J Oyet Esq, 41A Garland Road, Poole BH15 2LB* E-mail ugbanaoyet@poole.hoarelea.com

P

PACEY, Edgar Prentice. b 29. Edin Univ MA50. Edin Th Coll 52. **d** 54 **p** 55. C Motherwell *Glas* 54-56; C Glas St Mary 56-61; R Coatbridge 61-70; Perm to Offic 70-77; Hon C Glas St Martin 77-83; Hon C Glas St Ninian 83-87; R Rothesay *Arg* 86; P-in-c 89-94; P-in-c Tighnabruaich 90-94; Perm to Offic *Glas* from 91; Perm to Offic *Arg* from 93; rtd 94; NSM Dunoon *Arg* 94-98. *Dunstan, 16 Broomfield Drive, Dunoon PA23 7LJ* Tel (01369) 702972

PACEY, Graham John. b 52. Leeds Univ CertEd74 Open Univ BA81 Teesside Poly AdDipEd85. NEOC 90. **d** 93 **p** 94. C Kirkleatham *York* 93-96; V Middlesbrough St Agnes 96-00; R Skelton w Upleatham from 00. *The Rectory, North Terrace, Skelton-in-Cleveland, Saltburn-by-the-Sea TS12 2ES* Tel (01287) 650329 E-mail graham.pacey@ntlworld.com

PACEY, Michael John. b 96 **p** 97. NSM Tamworth *Lich* from 96. *1 Benson View, Tamworth B79 8TD* Tel (01827) 700410

PACKER, Catherine Ruth. *See* PICKFORD, Mrs Catherine Ruth

PACKER, Prof James Innell. b 26. CCC Ox BA48 MA52 DPhil55. Wycliffe Hall Ox 49. **d** 52 **p** 53. C Harborne Heath *Birm* 52-54; Lect Tyndale Hall Bris 55-61; Lib Latimer Ho Ox 61-62; Warden 62-69; Prin Tyndale Hall Bris 70-72; Assoc Prin Trin Coll Bris 72-79; Prof Hist Th Regent Coll Vancouver 79-89; Prof Th from 89; rtd 91. *6017 Holland Street, Vancouver BC, Canada, V6N 2B2*

✠**PACKER, The Rt Revd John Richard.** b 46. Keble Coll Ox BA67 MA. Ripon Hall Ox 67. **d** 70 **p** 71 **c** 96. C St Helier *S'wark* 70-73; Chapl Abingdon St Nic *Ox* 73-77; Tutor Ripon Hall Ox 73-75; Tutor Ripon Coll Cuddesdon 75-77; V Wath-upon-Dearne w Adwick-upon-Dearne *Sheff* 77-86; RD Wath 83-86; TR Sheff Manor 86-91; RD Attercliffe 90-91; Adn W Cumberland *Carl* 91-96; P-in-c Bridekirk 95-96; Suff Bp Warrington *Liv* 96-00; Bp Ripon and Leeds *Ripon* from 00. *Bishop Mount, Hutton Bank, Ripon HG4 5DP* Tel (01765) 604148 *or* 602045 Fax 600758 E-mail bishop.riponleeds@virgin.net

PACKER, Canon John William. b 18. K Coll Lon BA40 AKC40 BD41 MTh48. **d** 41 **p** 42. C Attenborough w Bramcote *S'well* 41-44; Asst Master Lant Gr Sch 44-49; Lect RE Leeds Univ 50-53; Hd Master Canon Slade Gr Sch Bolton 53-77; Lic to Offic *Man* 53-77; Hon Can Man Cathl 75-78; rtd 77; Perm to Offic *Cant* from 78. *Netherbury, Meadow Close, Bridge, Canterbury CT4 5AT* Tel (01227) 830364

PACKER, Canon Aelred. b 48. St Jo Coll Dur BA70 St Chad's Coll Dur PhD79 Warwick Univ PGC Gp Psychotherapy 94 Ven English Coll Rome 95. **d** 96 **p** 97. SSM 93-99; Hon C S Lambeth St Anne and All SS *S'wark* 96-98; Lic to Offic *Ox* 97-99; Bp's Adv in Miss and Resources *Glas* from 99. *34 Burdon Terrace, Jesmond,*

Newcastle upon Tyne NE2 3AE Tel 07932-648034 (mobile)
E-mail peterapacker@aol.com
PACKER, Preb Roger Ernest John. b 37. ARCO59 Pemb Coll
Cam BA60 MA64. Cuddesdon Coll 60. **d** 62 **p** 63. C
Chippenham St Andr w Tytherton Lucas *Bris* 62-65; C
Caversham *Ox* 65-70; R Sandhurst 70-91; V Bridgwater St Mary,
Chilton Trinity and Durleigh *B & W* 91-00; RD Bridgwater
94-00; Preb Wells Cathl 96-00; rtd 00; Perm to Offic *Chelmsf*
from 00. *3 Kreswell Grove, Harwich CO12 3SZ* Tel (01255)
502239
PACKHAM, Ms Elizabeth Daisy. b 33. Goldsmiths' Coll Lon
BSc54 CertEd55. N Ord Course. **dss** 83 **d** 87 **p** 94. Fairfield *Derby*
83-84; Buxton w Burbage and King Sterndale 84-95; Par Dn
87-94; C 94-95; P-in-c Chinley w Buxworth 95-98; Perm to Offic
from 98; rtd 98. *100 Manchester Road, Chapel-en-le-Frith,
Stockport SK23 9TP* Tel (01298) 812921
PADDICK, Graham. b 47. S'work Ord Course. **d** 89 **p** 90. C
St Helier S'work 89-93; P-in-c Thornton Heath St Paul 93-96; V
96-98; V Dormansland from 98. *St John's Vicarage, The Platt,
Dormansland, Lingfield RH7 6QU* Tel (01342) 832391
PADDISON, Canon Michael David William. b 41. Oak Hill Th
Coll 75. **d** 77 **p** 78. C Gt Warley Ch Ch *Chelmsf* 77-80; C
Rayleigh 80-83; R Scole, Brockdish, Billingford, Thorpe Abbots
etc *Nor* 83-95; RD Redenhall 89-95; R Reepham, Hackford w
Whitwell, Kerdiston from 95; RD Sparham from 00; Hon
Can Nor Cathl from 02. *The Rectory, Station Road, Reepham,
Norwich NR10 4LJ* Tel (01603) 870220
PADDOCK, John Allan Barnes. b 51. Liv Univ BA74 MA91 Man
Univ PGCE75 Ox Univ BA77 MA81 FRSA94 CertTESOL95.
St Steph Ho Ox 75. **d** 80 **p** 81. C Matson *Glouc* 80-82; Asst Chapl
Madrid *Eur* 82-83; Chapl R Gr Sch Lanc 83-86; Hon C Blackb
Ch Ch w St Matt *Blackb* 83-86; Chapl RAF 86-91; Offg Chapl
RAF 92-94; Chapl St Olave's Gr Sch Orpington 91-94; Perm to
Offic *Blackb* 94-97; Chapl R Russell Sch Croydon 97-00; Hon C
Bickley *Roch* 97-00; V Folkestone St Pet *Cant* from 00; Hon Min
Can Cant Cathl from 01. *St Peter's Vicarage, The Durlocks,
Folkestone CT19 6AL* Tel (01303) 254472 Fax as telephone
PADFIELD, Stephen James. b 68. Ex Univ BA90 Bris Univ BA00
MA01 Univ Coll Dur PGCE92. Trin Coll Bris 98. **d** 01 **p** 02. C
Luton Ch Ch *Roch* from 01. *11 Fallowfield, Chatham ME5 0DU*
Tel (01634) 302349 Mobile 07747-775385
E-mail stevepadfield@hotmail.com
PADGET, William Thomas. b 19. **d** 77 **p** 78. NSM Rodbourne
Cheney *Bris* 77-90; rtd 90; Perm to Offic *Bris* from 90. *39 George
Tweed Gardens, Ramleaze Drive, Swindon SN5 8WB* Tel (01793)
723789
PADLEY, Miss Karen. b 68. RGN89. St Jo Coll Nottm MA00.
d 00 **p** 01. C Broxtowe *S'well* from 00. *234 Lindfield Road,
Nottingham NG8 6HR* Tel (0115) 9163474
E-mail karen@hpadley.fsnet.co.uk
PAGAN, Canon Keith Vivian. b 37. St Jo Coll Dur BA60 MA66.
Chich Th Coll 60. **d** 62 **p** 63. C Clacton St Jas *Chelmsf* 62-64; C
Wymondham *Nor* 64-70; P-in-c Guestwick 70-80; P-in-c
Kettlestone 70-79; V Hindolveston 70-80; R Islay *Arg* 80-98; R
Campbeltown 80-98; Miss to Seamen 80-98; Can St Jo Cathl
Oban *Arg* 85-98; Can Cumbrae 85-98; rtd 98. *Mariefield,
Southend, Campbeltown PA28 6RW* Tel (01586) 830310
PAGE, Canon Alan George. b 24. Em Coll Cam BA48 MA52.
Wycliffe Hall Ox 49. **d** 51 **p** 52. C Islington St Andr w St Thos and
St Matthias *Lon* 51-53; Kenya 53-71; Hon Can Mt Kenya 71-75;
Hon Can Mt Kenya S 75-84; C S Lyncombe *B & W* 71-72; R
Freshford w Limpley Stoke 72-76; R Freshford, Limpley Stoke
and Hinton Charterhouse 76-84; Can Mt Kenya Cen from 84; C
Fulham St Mary N End *Lon* 87-89; rtd 89; Perm to Offic *B & W*
from 89. *45 Ashley Avenue, Bath BA1 3DS* Tel (01225) 310532
E-mail ag.page@ukonline.co.uk
PAGE, Alan Richard Benjamin. b 38. Univ of Wales (Lamp) BA60
BSc. St Mich Coll Llan 60. **d** 62 **p** 63. C Cardiff St Andr and
St Teilo *Llan* 62-64; C Newport St Julian *Mon* 64-67; C Hoxton H
Trin w St Mary *Lon* 67-69; C Winchmore Hill H Trin 69-71; V
Camden Town St Mich w All SS and St Thos 71-98; Public
Preacher 98-02; rtd 02. *7 Four Ash Street, Usk NP15 1BW*
PAGE, Arthur Henry. b 21. Open Univ BA79. Sarum & Wells Th
Coll. **d** 82 **p** 82. NSM Gtr Corsham *Bris* 82-87; Perm to Offic
Dur 88; NSM Shadforth 89-91; rtd 91. *9 Foxton Way, High Shincliffe, Durham DH1 2PJ* Tel 0191-
386 2141
PAGE, David. b 48. Bris Univ BA70 Leic Univ MA74 Southn
Univ PGCE74 Nottm Univ DipTh82. St Jo Coll Nottm 81. **d** 83
p 84. C Morden *S'work* 83-86; V Wimbledon St Luke 86-91;
P-in-c Clapham Common St Barn 91-92; V from 92. *St Barnabas'
Vicarage, 12 Lavender Gardens, London SW11 1DL* Tel (020)
7223 5953 E-mail dp@fish.co.uk
PAGE, David James. b 62. Liv Univ BSc83 Qu Coll Ox DPhil87.
Trin Coll Bris BA93 MA95. **d** 96 **p** 97. C Knutsford St Jo and
Toft *Ches* 96-99; R Elworth and Warmingham from 99. *The
Rectory, 38 Roman Way, Sandbach CW11 9EW* Tel (01270)
762415
✠**PAGE, The Rt Revd Dennis Fountain.** b 19. G&C Coll Cam
BA41 MA45 Open Univ BSc96. Linc Th Coll 41. **d** 43 **p** 44 **c** 75.

C Rugby St Andr *Cov* 43-49; R Weeting *Ely* 49-65; R Hockwold
w Wilton 49-65; RD Feltwell 53-65; Hon Can Ely Cathl 63-65
and 68-75; V Yaxley 65-75; Adn Huntingdon 65-75; Suff Bp
Lancaster *Blackb* 75-85; rtd 85; Perm to Offic *St E* from 85.
Larkrise, Hartest, Bury St Edmunds IP29 4ES Tel (01284) 830694
PAGE, Mrs Dorothy Jean. b 29. Portsm Poly CertEd50. Ox NSM
Course 84. **d** 87 **p** 94. NSM Wantage Downs *Ox* from 87.
11 North Street, Marcham, Abingdon OX13 6NG Tel (01865)
391462
PAGE, The Ven Gilbert Alfred Derek. b 35. **d** 93 **p** 94. Australia
from 79; Dir Miss Tas 89-94; Asst P Launceston St Jo 94-95;
P-in-c George Town 95-98; Chapl Miss to Seamen Bell Bay
95-98; Adn Burnie 97-00; R Devonport 98-01; Miss Support
Officer from 01. *17 Hoskin Street, North Nowra, NSW, Australia
2541* Tel (0061) (2) 4422 3403 Mobile 419-241950
E-mail gandrpage@shoal.net.au
PAGE, Mrs Irene May. b 38. Birm Univ BA58. NEOC 85. **d** 87
p 94. Par Dn Cockfield *Dur* 87-90; Par Dn Waterloo St Jo w
St Andr S'work 90-94; C 94-95; R Old Charlton St Thos 95-02; C
Charlton 02-03; rtd 03. *40 Wolverton Road, Rednal, Birmingham
B45 8RN* Tel 0121-460 1745
PAGE, Jacqueline Anne. b 57. St Alb and Ox Min Course 96. **d** 99
p 00. NSM Stevenage H Trin *St Alb* from 99. *5 Sinfield Close,
Stevenage SG1 1LQ* Tel (01438) 368502
PAGE, John Jeremy. b 56. Keble Coll Ox BA79 MA82 New Coll
Edin BD86. Edin Th Coll 83. **d** 86 **p** 87. C Wetherby *Ripon* 86-89;
TV Wrexham *St As* 89-92; Chapl Hymers Coll Hull 92-98; Chapl
Charterhouse Sch Godalming 98-03; TR Hale w Badshot Lea
Guildf from 03. *The Rectory, 25 Upper Hale Road, Farnham
GU9 0NX* Tel (01252) 716469 Fax 713862
E-mail john@padblack.co.uk
PAGE, John Laurance Howard. b 40. ALCD. **d** 65 **p** 66. C
Spitalfields Ch Ch w All SS *Lon* 65-69; C Win Ch Ch *Win* 69-72;
C Ringwood 72-76; V Lockerley and E Dean w E and W
Tytherley 76-89; R Romsey 85-89; V Lord's Hill 89-97; P-in-c
Darby Green 97-02; V from 02. *St Barnabas House, Green Lane,
Blackwater, Camberley GU17 0NU* Tel (01252) 877817
PAGE, Jonathan Michael. b 58. Ripon Coll Cuddesdon. **d** 99
p 00. C Littlemore *Ox* 99-02; V Chaddesden St Phil *Derby* from
02. *St Philip's Vicarage, Taddington Road, Chaddesden, Derby
DE21 4JU* Tel (01332) 660072 E-mail chadphil@fish.co.uk
PAGE, Canon Michael John. b 42. K Coll Lon BD66 AKC66. **d** 67
p 68. C Rawmarsh w Parkgate *Sheff* 67-72; C-in-c Gleadless
Valley CD 72-74; TR Gleadless Valley 74-77; V Lechlade *Glouc*
77-86; RD Fairford 81-86; V Winchcombe, Gretton, Sudeley
Manor etc 86-02; Hon Can Glouc Cathl 91-02; RD
Winchcombe 94-99; Chapl E Glos NHS Trust 94-02; rtd 02.
18 Brocco Bank, Sheffield S11 8RR Tel 0114-266 3798
E-mail michael_j_page@hotmail.com
PAGE, Owen Richard. b 53. Trent Poly HNC77 Derby Coll of
Educn DMS85 FIBMS83. Linc Th Coll 89. **d** 91 **p** 92. C Gt
Bookham *Guildf* 91-94; V Kings Heath *Pet* 94-99; TR Daventry,
Ashby St Ledgers, Braunston etc from 99; RD Daventry from 00;
ACUPA Link Officer from 00; CUF Project Officer from 00. *The
Rectory, Golding Close, Daventry NN11 5PE* Tel (01327) 702638
E-mail owen@opage.freeserve.co.uk
PAGE, Canon Richard Dennis. b 23. G&C Coll Cam BA48
MA50. Ridley Hall Cam 48. **d** 50 **p** 51. C Ecclesfield *Sheff* 50-52;
Chapl St Lawr Coll Ramsgate 52-58; Chapl Dean Close Sch
Cheltenham 58-60 and 62-64; Chapl Netherton Tr Sch Morpeth
60-62; V Ecclesfield *Sheff* 64-71; RD Ecclesfield 66-71; P-in-c
Holkham w Egmere and Waterden *Nor* 71-78; R Wells next the
Sea 71-78; RD Burnham and Walsingham 72-78; V Hemsby
78-83; P-in-c Brooke w Kirstead 83-85; P-in-c Mundham w
Seething 83-85; P-in-c Thwaite 83-85; R Brooke, Kirstead,
Mundham w Seething and Thwaite 85-89; Hon Can Nor Cathl
87-89; rtd 90; Perm to Offic *Nor* from 90. *The Greyhound, Back
Street, Reepham, Norwich NR10 4SJ* Tel (01603) 870886
PAGE, Robert William Charles. b 67. St Steph Ho Ox 90. **d** 93
p 94. C Hockerill *St Alb* 93-95; C Kilburn St Aug w St Jo *Lon*
95-02; V Leytonstone St Marg w St Columba *Chelmsf* from 02.
St Margaret's Vicarage, 15 Woodhouse Road, London E11 3NG
Tel (020) 8519 0813 E-mail rob@stmandstc.fsnet.co.uk
PAGE, Teehan Dawson. b 61. Ch Ch Ox BA83 MA87 K Coll Lon
MA96. St Steph Ho Ox 91. **d** 93 **p** 94. C Surbiton St Andr and
St Mark S'work 93-96; Chapl Reed's Sch Cobham 96-99; Asst
Chapl Tonbridge Sch 99-00; Sen Chapl from 00. *1 Dry Hill Road,
Tonbridge TN9 1LT* Tel (01732) 353468
E-mail tdp@tonbschl.demon.co.uk
PAGE, Thomas William. b 65. Sarum & Wells Th Coll 84. **d** 87
p 88. C Caterham S'work 87-91; C Cheam 91-95; P-in-c
Cranham *Chelmsf* from 95; Dioc NSM Officer from 99. *All
Saints House, 107 Courtney Gardens, Upminster RM14 1DH* Tel
(01708) 501482 E-mail frtompage@hotmail.com
PAGE, Canon Trevor Melvyn. b 41. Dur Univ BA63 Fitzw Coll
Cam BA67 MA72. Westcott Ho Cam 64. **d** 67 **p** 68. C
Millhouses H Trin *Sheff* 67-69; Chapl Sheff Univ 69-74; V
Doncaster Intake 74-82; Can Res Sheff Cathl 82-00; Dioc Dir of
In-Service Tr 82-95; Dioc Dir of Ords and Post-Ord Tr 82-00; R

Bradfield from 00; Hon Can Sheff Cathl from 01. *The Rectory, High Bradfield, Bradfield, Sheffield S6 6LG* Tel 0114-285 1225

PAGE, William George. b 42. Linc Th Coll 83. **d** 85 **p** 86. C Boston *Linc* 85-89; V Sibsey w Frithville from 89; RD Holland E 95-97. *The Vicarage, Vicarage Lane, Sibsey, Boston PE22 0RT* Tel (01205) 750305 Fax as telephone
E-mail pageatsibseyvicarage@care4free.net

PAGE-CHESTNEY, Michael William. b 47. Linc Th Coll 80. **d** 82 **p** 83. C Barton upon Humber *Linc* 82-85; TV Gt Grimsby St Mary and St Jas 85-91; V E Stockwith 91-96; V Blyton w Pilham and Laughton w Wildsworth 91-93; V Corringham and Blyton Gp 93-03; P-in-c Immingham from 03; P-in-c Habrough Gp from 03. *The Vicarage, 344 Pelham Road, Immingham DN40 1PU* Tel (01469) 572560
E-mail mike@page-chestney.co.uk

PAGE-CHESTNEY, Mrs Susan Valerie. b 49. EMMTC DipTh86. **dss** 86 **d** 87 **p** 94. NSM Gt Grimsby St Mary and St Jas *Linc* 86-91; NSM Blyton w Pilham and Laughton w Wildsworth 91-93; NSM Corringham and Blyton Gp 93-03; Chapl W Lindsey NHS Trust 94-99; Chapl Linc and Louth NHS Trust 99-01; Chapl United Lincs Hosps NHS Trust 01-03; NSM Immingham *Linc* from 03; NSM Habrough Gp from 03. *The Vicarage, 344 Pelham Road, Immingham DN40 1PU* Tel (01469) 572560 E-mail sue@heavenlyhugs.com

PAGE-CLARK, Howard David. b 53. Fitzw Coll Cam MA77. LNSM course 96. **d** 97 **p** 98. OLM Lytchett Minster *Sarum* from 97. *37 Gorse Lane, Poole BH16 5RR* Tel (01202) 620239

PAGE DAVIES, David John. b 36. St Cath Soc Ox BA58 MA62. St D Coll Lamp 58. **d** 60 **p** 61. C Rhosddu *St As* 60-68; Chr Aid Area Sec (Glos, Herefords and Worcs) 68-85; Midl Regional Co-ord 78-85; Area Co-ord (Devon and Cornwall) 86-01; Lic to Offic *Truro* 86-01; Perm to Offic from 01; rtd 01. *3 Chyenhal Cottages, Buryas Bridge, Penzance TR19 6AN* Tel (01736) 732466 E-mail jpagedavies@aol.com

PAGE-TURNER, Canon Edward Gregory Ambrose Wilford. b 31. Qu Coll Birm 57. **d** 60 **p** 61. C Helmsley *York* 60-64; C Kensington St Phil Earl's Court *Lon* 64-67; C Walton-on-Thames *Guildf* 67-70; V Seend *Sarum* 70-71; V Seend and Bulkington 71-79; R Bladon w Woodstock *Ox* 79-87; P-in-c Begbroke 80-86; P-in-c Shipton-on-Cherwell 80-86; P-in-c Hampton Gay 80-85; RD Woodstock 84-87; R Patterdale *Carl* 87-89; R Askerswell, Loders and Powerstock *Sarum* 89-01; RD Lyme Bay 92-98; RD Beaminster 94-98; Can and Preb Sarum Cathl 99-01; rtd 01. *The Old School House, 9 School House Close, Beaminster DT8 3AH* Tel (01308) 861410 Fax as telephone

PAGET, Alfred Ivor. b 24. St Aid Birkenhead 56. **d** 59 **p** 60. C Hoylake *Ches* 59-62; Hong Kong 62-63; Australia 63-64; C Hyde St Geo *Ches* 64-66; R Gt and Lt Henny w Middleton *Chelmsf* 66-74; C Gt Holland 74-79; V Holland-on-Sea 79-92; rtd 92; Perm to Offic S'wark 92-98; *Lon* from 96; *Chelmsf* from 99. *The Hyrne, Guelphs Lane, Thaxted CM6 2PT* Tel (01371) 831022

PAGET, Richard Campbell. b 54. Collingwood Coll Dur BA76 Rob Coll Cam BA87. Ridley Hall Cam 85. **d** 88 **p** 89. C Gipsy Hill Ch Ch S'wark 88-92; R Chatham St Mary w St Jo *Roch* 92-98; P-in-c Brenchley 99-00; V from 00. *The Vicarage, 8 Broadoak, Brenchley, Tonbridge TN12 7NN* Tel (01892) 722140

PAGET, Robert James Innes. b 35. AKC59. **d** 60 **p** 61. C Attenborough w Bramcote S'well 60-63; C Cheltenham St Mark *Glouc* 63-72; P-in-c Pilsley *Derby* 72-73; TV N Wingfield, Pilsley and Tupton 73-89; R Pinxton 89-97; P-in-c Ambergate and Heage from 97. *The Vicarage, 65 Derby Road, Ambergate, Belper DE56 2GD* Tel (01773) 852072

PAGET-WILKES, The Ven Michael Jocelyn James. b 41. NDA64 ALCD69. **d** 69 **p** 70. C Wandsworth All SS S'wark 69-74; V Hatcham St Jas 74-82; V Rugby St Matt *Cov* 82-90; Adn Warwick from 90. *10 Northumberland Road, Leamington Spa CV32 6HA* Tel (01926) 313337 or 674328
E-mail archdeacon.michael@covdioc.org

PAGETT, Andrew Stephen. b 45. Bris & Glouc Tr Course. **d** 82 **p** 83. NSM Swindon New Town *Bris* 82-01; C Paignton St Jo *Ex* from 01. *73 Dartmouth Road, Paignton TQ4 5AF* Tel (01803) 698412

PAICE, Alan. b 26. AKC53. **d** 55 **p** 56. C Leek St Edw *Lich* 55-59; C Haslemere *Guildf* 59-63; C Eton w Boveney *Ox* 63-74; P-in-c Hawridge w Cholesbury 74-83; P-in-c The Lee 74-83; V 83-86; P-in-c Aston Clinton St Leon 79-83; R Hawridge w Cholesbury and St Leonard 83-86; rtd 86. *2 The Poplars, Park Lane, Pinhoe, Exeter EX4 9HH* Tel (01392) 464741

PAICE, Michael Antony. b 35. Kelham Th Coll 55. **d** 60 **p** 61. C Skegby S'well 60-62; C Carlton 62-66; V Misterton and W Stockwith 66-81; P-in-c Littleton on Severn w Elberton *Bris* 81-83; V Olveston 81-83; Deputation Appeals Org CECS 83-89; R Sutton St Nicholas w Sutton St Michael *Heref* 89-96; R Withington w Westhide 89-96; rtd 96. *Frankhurst, Sutton St Nicholas, Hereford HR1 3BN* Tel (01432) 880279

PAICE, Richard James Rowland. b 72. Ch Ch Ox BA94 MA99. Oak Hill Th Coll BA00. **d** 00 **p** 01. C Eastbourne All So *Chich*

from 00; Chapl Bp Bell Sch from 00. *24 Charleston Road, Eastbourne BN21 1SF* Tel (07980) 740718
E-mail rjrpaice@yahoo.com

PAILING, Crispin Alexander. b 75. Qu Coll Ox BA98 MA01. Ripon Coll Cuddesdon BA02. **d** 03. C Four Oaks *Birm* from 03. *12 Clarence Gardens, Sutton Coldfield B74 4AP* Tel 0121-308 6279

PAILING, Rowena Fay. b 77. Qu Coll Ox BA99 MA02. Ripon Coll Cuddesdon BA02. **d** 03. C Kings Heath *Birm* 03; C Four Oaks from 03. *12 Clarence Gardens, Sutton Coldfield B74 4AP* Tel 0121-308 6279

PAIN, Canon David Clinton. b 36. K Coll Lon 56. **d** 64 **p** 64. Benin 64-67; Ghana 67-86; Hon Can Accra 80-86; V Kemp Town St Mary *Chich* 86-93; Chapl St Mary's Hall Brighton 88-93; V Billingshurst *Chich* from 93; RD Horsham 98-02. *The Vicarage, East Street, Billingshurst RH14 9PY* Tel (01403) 786540 or 782332

PAIN, Michael Broughton George. b 37. Dur Univ BA61. Wycliffe Hall Ox 61. **d** 63 **p** 64. C Downend *Bris* 63-67; C Swindon Ch Ch 67-70; V Alveston 70-78; V Guildf Ch Ch *Guildf* 78-90; TR Melksham *Sarum* 90-98; Chapl Melksham Hosp 90-98; TR Redhorn *Sarum* from 98. *The Rectory, High Street, Urchfont, Devizes SN10 4QP* Tel (01380) 840672

PAIN, Richard Edward. b 56. Bris Univ BA79 Univ of Wales (Cardiff) BD84. St Mich Coll Llan 81. **d** 84 **p** 85. C Caldicot *Mon* 84-86; P-in-c Cwmtillery 86-88; V 88-91; V Six Bells 88-91; V Risca 91-98; V Overmonnow w Wonastow and Michel Troy 98-03; V Monmouth w Overmonnow etc from 03; Dioc Warden of Ord from 01. *The Vicarage, The Parade, Monmouth NP25 3PA* Tel (01600) 714454

PAINE, Alasdair David Maconnell. b 60. Trin Coll Cam BA82 MA86 MSc84. Wycliffe Hall Ox 94. **d** 96 **p** 97. C Ex St Leon w Trin *Ex* 96-01. *134 Alumhurst Road, Bournemouth BH4 8HU* Tel (01202) 762164 E-mail alastair@claranet.co.uk

PAINE, Peter Stanley. b 46. K Coll Lon BD69 AKC69. Linc Th Coll DipMin89 Cuddesdon Coll 69. **d** 71 **p** 72. C Leeds St Aid *Ripon* 71-74; C Harrogate St Wilfrid 74-78; V Beeston Hill H Spirit 78-82; TV Seacroft 82-90; V Martham w Repps w Bastwick *Nor* 90-94; V Martham and Repps with Bastwick, Thurne etc from 94. *The Vicarage, 68 Black Street, Martham, Great Yarmouth NR29 4PR* Tel (01493) 740240
E-mail peter@ppaine.free-online.co.uk

PAINE, William Barry. b 58. TCD DipTh84. CITC. **d** 84 **p** 85. C Glendermott *D & R* 84-86; C Lurgan St Jo *D & D* 86-88; I Kilbarron w Rossnowlagh and Drumholm *D & R* 88-91; CF 91-00; I Tynan w Middletown and Aghavilly *Arm* from 00. *The Rectory, 16 Derryhaw Road, Tynan BT60 4SS* Tel (028) 3756 8619

PAINE DAVEY, Nathan Paul. b 64. Barrister-at-Law 88 Birm Poly LLB86. St Steph Ho Ox 89. **d** 92 **p** 93. C Palmers Green St Jo *Lon* 92-95; C Kentish Town St Silas 95-98; C Haverstock Hill H Trin w Kentish Town St Barn 95-98; C Kentish Town St Silas and H Trin w St Barn 98-01; Perm to Offic from 01. *30A Hadley Street, London NW1 8SS* Tel (020) 7482 1170

PAINTER, Christopher Mark. b 65. Cranmer Hall Dur. **d** 00 **p** 01. C Melksham *Sarum* from 00; Chapl Wilts and Swindon Healthcare NHS Trust 02-03. *Christchurch Vicarage, 5 Brampton Court, Bowerhill, Melksham SN12 6TH* Tel (01225) 344787 E-mail ckpainter@blueyonder.co.uk

PAINTER, The Ven David Scott. b 44. Worc Coll Ox BA68 MA72 LTCL65. Cuddesdon Coll 68. **d** 70 **p** 71. C Plymouth St Andr *Ex* 70-73; Chapl Plymouth Poly 71-73; C St Marylebone All SS *Lon* 73-76; Abp's Dom Chapl *Cant* 76-80; Dir of Ords 76-80; V Roehampton H Trin S'wark 80-91; PV Westmr Abbey 81-91; RD Wandsworth S'wark 85-90; Perm to Offic 91; Can Res and Treas S'wark Cathl 91-00; Dioc Dir of Ords 91-00; Adn Oakham *Pet* from 00. *7 Minster Precincts, Peterborough PE1 1XS* Tel (01733) 891360 Fax 554524
E-mail david.painter@peterborough-cathedral.org.uk

PAINTER, John. b 25. Selw Coll Cam BA48 MA53. Ripon Hall Ox 48. **d** 50 **p** 51. C Stoke Newington St Mary *Lon* 50-55; C Woodside Park St Barn 55-56; C Llangiwg *S & B* 56-59; C-in-c Swansea St Jo 59-60; R Chipstable w Raddington *B & W* 61-64; V Audenshaw St Steph *Man* 64-66; V Sandown Ch Ch *Portsm* 66-72; R Keinton Mandeville *B & W* 72-77; P-in-c Lydford-on-Fosse 76-77; R Keinton Mandeville w Lydford on Fosse 77-90; RD Cary 81-90; RD Bruton 82-85; rtd 90; Perm to Offic *B & W* from 90; Perm to Offic *Sarum* from 96. *2 Juniper Gardens, Gillingham SP8 4RF* Tel (01747) 823818

PAINTING, Stephen Nigel. b 60. Trin Coll Bris 01. **d** 03. C Heanton Punchardon w Marwood *Ex* from 03. *Fig Tree House, 58A Poyers, Wrafton, Braunton EX33 2DN* Tel (01271) 812112 E-mail painting@fish.co.uk

PAIRMAN, David Drummond. b 47. GGSM CertEd. Chich Th Coll 82. **d** 84 **p** 85. C Cowes St Mary *Portsm* 84-87; C Marshwood Vale *Sarum* 87-90; C Hawkchurch 87-90; C Marshwood Vale from 90; rtd 95. *Achilles, Old Pinn Lane, Exeter EX1 3RF* Tel (01392) 464488

PAISEY, Gerald Herbert John. b 31. Wm Booth Memorial Coll 51 Lon Univ CertRS60 Leic Univ CertEd62 Nottm Univ

DipRE68 DipAdEd70 MPhil77 Lanc Univ MA78 K Coll Lon PhD91. St Alb Minl Tr Scheme 80. **d** 88 **p** 90. NSM Montrose *Bre* 88-90; NSM Inverbervie 88-90; Lect Robert Gordon Univ *Ab* 89-97; P-in-c Stonehaven and Catterline *Bre* 90-01; rtd 01; Tutor Open Univ from 90; Perm to Offic *Bre* from 01. *20 St Michael's Way, Newtonhill, Stonehaven AB3 2GS* Tel (01569) 730338

PAISEY, Jeremy Mark. b 58. Aber Univ LLB81 Solicitor 83. Coates Hall Edin 92. **d** 94 **p** 95. C Turriff *Ab* 94-97; C Buckie 94-97; C Banff 94-97; C Cuminestown 94-97; C Portsoy 94-97; P-in-c Buckie from 97; P-in-c Portsoy from 97; P-in-c Banff from 98. *All Saints House, 14 Cluny Square, Buckie AB56 1HA* Tel (01542) 832312 Mobile 0788-789 3582 Fax 832299
E-mail jpaisey@compuserve.com

PAISLEY, James. b 05. Edin Th Coll 27. **d** 29 **p** 30. C Dalton-in-Furness *Carl* 29-31; Borneo 31-42; Australia 42-45; V Compton *Ox* 47-70; V Hampstead Norris 47-70; rtd 70; Perm to Offic *Ex* 70-98. *clo Mrs M Hughes, 99 Southfield Avenue, Paignton TQ3 1LQ*

PAISLEY, Samuel Robinson (Robin). b 51. Man Univ BSc72. Edin Th Coll BD91. **d** 91 **p** 92. C St Mary's Cathl *Glas* 91-95; P-in-c Bishopbriggs from 95; Chapl Stobhill NHS Trust 95-99; Teaching Consultant Glas Univ *Glas* 95-99; Bp's Adv in Min *Glas* from 99. *St James's Rectory, 9 Meadowburn, Bishopbriggs, Glasgow G64 3HA* Tel 0141-772 4514 Fax 569 7508
E-mail robin.paisley@ntlworld.com

PAJUNEN, Mika Kari Tapani. b 76. Helsinki Univ MTh00. **p** 01. C Helsinki *Eur* from 02. *Stålhbergintie 3E 41, 00570 Helsinki, Finland* Tel (00358) (9) 682 3816
E-mail mika.pajunen@helsinki.fi

PAKENHAM, Charles Wilfrid. b 18. Trin Coll Ox BA40 MA52. Wycliffe Hall Ox 40. **d** 41 **p** 42. C Sutton *Liv* 41-44; CMS 44-49; Nigeria 44-49; C Darlaston St Mary *Glouc* 49-52; V Litherland Ch Ch *Liv* 52-84; rtd 84; Perm to Offic *Sarum* from 90; P-in-c W Woodhay w Enborne, Hampstead Marshall etc *Ox* 91-92; Perm to Offic 92-00. *15 Cook Road, Marlborough SN8 2EG* Tel (01672) 40531

PAKENHAM, Stephen Walter. b 29. Qu Coll Cam BA57 MA61. Linc Th Coll 57. **d** 59 **p** 60. C Handsworth St Jas *Birm* 59-61; C Handsworth St Andr 61-64; V Donnington *Chich* 64-75; V Appledram 64-75; V Durrington 75-81; V St Mary Bourne and Woodcott *Win* 81-88; rtd 88; Perm to Offic *Ex* 88-98; Perm to Offic *Win* from 98. *9 Chattis Hill Stables, Spitfire Lane, Stockbridge SO20 6JS* Tel (01264) 810225

PAKISTAN, Moderator of the Church of. *See* AZARIAH, The Rt Revd Samuel

PALIN, John Edward. b 47. Univ of Wales (Cardiff) DipTh70 DPS71 Open Univ BA83 Leeds Univ MA89. St Mich Coll Llan 67. **d** 71 **p** 72. C Staveley *Derby* 71-74; C Nottingham St Mary *S'well* 75-77; P-in-c Thistleton 77-79; V Greetham w Stretton and Clipsham *Pet* 77-79; V Greetham and Thistleton w Stretton and Clipsham 79-83; TR Staveley and Barrow Hill *Derby* 83-87; Chapl R Hallamshire Hosp Sheff 87-88; Perm to Offic *Sheff* 88-90; C Bramley *Ripon* 90-91; TV 91-93; Chapl Doncaster and S Humber Healthcare NHS Trust from 93. *St Catherine's Hospital, Tickhill Road, Doncaster DN4 8QN* Tel (01302) 796018

PALIN, Roy. b 34. Man Univ BA56. Ripon Hall Ox 65. **d** 67 **p** 68. C Ilkeston St Mary *Derby* 67-70; V Wollaton *S'well* 70-71; V Harby w Swinethorpe 71-79; V Thorney w Wigsley and Broadholme 71-79; P-in-c N Clifton 75-79; R Harby w Thorney and N and S Clifton 79-80; V Tuxford 80-81; P-in-c Laxton 80-81; P-in-c Markham Clinton 80-81; P-in-c Weston 80-81; V Tuxford w Weston and Markham Clinton 81-90; R Nuthall 90-99; rtd 99; Perm to Offic *Nor* from 00. *31 Pine Walk, Weybourne, Holt NR25 7HJ* Tel (01263) 588146

PALK, Mrs Deirdre Elizabeth Pauline. b 41. AIL77 Reading Univ BA63 City of Lon Poly DipBS74 DipRS84 Lon Univ MA94 FIOSH96. S'wark Ord Course 81. **dss** 84 **d** 87. Wanstead H Trin Hermon Hill *Chelmsf* 84-87; Hon Par Dn 87-88; Hon Par Dn Walthamstow St Pet 88-93; Hon Chapl UPA Projects 93-97; Tutor NTMTC from 97. *3 Ashdon Close, Woodford Green IG8 0EF* Tel (020) 8505 3547 Fax as telephone

PALLANT, Canon Roger Frank. b 35. Trin Coll Cam BA57 MA61. Wells Th Coll 57. **d** 59 **p** 60. C Stafford St Mary *Lich* 59-62; C Ipswich St Mary le Tower *St E* 62-65; Dioc Youth Chapl 62-65; Development Officer for C of E Youth Coun 65-70; Hon C Putney St Mary *S'wark* 66-71; Org Sec New Syn Gp 70-71; R Hintlesham w Chattisham *St E* 71-80; V Ipswich All Hallows 80-88; Hon Can St E Cathl 85-00; P-in-c Sproughton w Burstall 88-00; Dioc Officer for OLM 88-00; RD Samford 93-99; rtd 00; Perm to Offic *St E* from 00. *163 Fircroft Road, Ipswich IP1 6PT* Tel (01473) 461148

PALLETT, Ian Nigel. b 59. Leeds Univ BA80. Linc Th Coll 81. **d** 84 **p** 85. C Halesowen *Worc* 84-88; C Mansfield Woodhouse *S'well* 88-91; R Morton and Stonebroom *Derby* 91-98; P-in-c Heanor from 98. *The Vicarage, 1A Mundy Street, Heanor DE75 7EB* Tel (01773) 719800

PALLIS, Mrs Maria. b 60. N Ord Course 96. **d** 99 **p** 00. C Chapel Allerton *Ripon* 99-03; P-in-c Collingham w Harewood from 03.

The Vicarage, Church Lane, Collingham, Wetherby LS22 5AU Tel (01937) 573975 E-mail revdmp@aol.com

PALMER, Alister Gordon. b 46. Univ of Tasmania BA73 DipEd74. Trin Coll Bris 76 Ridley Hall Cam 78. **d** 80 **p** 81. C Patchway *Bris* 80-83; C Bushbury *Lich* 83-86; V Wednesfield Heath 86-93; NSM Independent Ch Community Work 93-98; Dioc Officer for Min Tas Australia 98-02; Dir Angl Miss 99-02; C Smestow Vale *Lich* 02-03; V Knowle St Barn *Bris* from 03. *St Barnabas' Vicarage, Daventry Road, Bristol BS4 1DQ* Tel 0117-966 4139 E-mail agpal@btopenworld.com

PALMER, Angus Douglas. b 40. St Chad's Coll Dur BA62 DipTh63. **d** 63 **p** 64. C Wallsend St Pet *Newc* 63-66; C Newc H Cross 66-69; C Bottesford *Linc* 69-70; St Mary's Cathl *Edin* 70-84; R W Linton 77-84. *6 Hackworth Gardens, Wylam NE41 8EJ* Tel (01661) 853786

PALMER, Christopher. b 71. **d** 98 **p** 99. C Emscote *Cov* 98-02; TV Mortlake w E Sheen *S'wark* from 02. *86 East Sheen Avenue, London SW14 8AU* Tel (020) 8487 8208
E-mail christopherpalmer@talk21.com

PALMER, David Michael. b 53. QUB BA95 MSc. CITC 95. **d** 97 **p** 98. C Glenageary *D & G* 97-99; C Agherton *Conn* 99-00; I Ramoan w Ballycastle and Culfeightrin from 00. *Ramoan Rectory, 12 Novally Road, Ballycastle BT54 6HB* Tel (028) 2076 8854 *or* 2076 2461 E-mail ramoan@connor.anglican.org

PALMER, David Michael Robert. b 70. St Jo Coll Nottm BA99. **d** 99 **p** 00. C Gillingham St Mark *Roch* 99-03; TV Clifton *S'well* from 03. *The Rectory, 19A Park Lane, Sutton Bonington, Loughborough LE12 5NH* Tel 07734-035607 (mobile)
E-mail revdavidp@hotmail.com

PALMER, David Philip. b 50. Sarum & Wells Th Coll. **d** 84 **p** 85. C St Ives *Ely* 84-86; C Luton All SS w St Pet *St Alb* 86-88; V Stocksbridge *Sheff* 88-97; P-in-c Seaton Hirst *Newc* 97-98; TR from 98; Chapl Northd Coll from 98. *The Vicarage, Newbiggin Road, Ashington NE63 0TQ* Tel (01670) 813218

PALMER, David Roderick. b 34. St Jo Coll Dur BA56 Birm Univ DipTh58 Trin Coll Ox. Qu Coll Birm 56. **d** 60 **p** 61. C Loughton St Jo *Chelmsf* 60-63; C Pimlico St Gabr *Lon* 63-64; Miss to Seamen 64-67; CF 67-74; Chapl Luxembourg *Eur* 74-80; P-in-c Exton and Winsford and Cutcombe w Luxborough *B & W* 80-82; P-in-c Wrington w Butcombe 82-84; Dep Dir of Tr Inst Wednesbury St Jas *Lich* 84-86; C Gt Wyrley 86-89; V Wilshamstead and Houghton Conquest *St Alb* 90-00; rtd 01. *14B Place du Marche, Ceauce, 61330 Normandie, France*

PALMER, Derek James. b 54. Man Univ BA77. Qu Coll Birm 77. **d** 79 **p** 80. C Leek *Lich* 79-83; CF 83-92; USA 92-95; C S Ockendon and Belhus Park *Chelmsf* 95-98; V Walthamstow St Mich 98-00; Chapl Salford Univ *Man* from 00; AD Salford from 02; Bp's Adv on New Relig Movements from 02. *The Chaplaincy, University of Salford, The Crescent, Salford M5 4WT* Tel 0161-295 4660 Mobile 07702-384945
E-mail father.derek@ntlworld.com *or* salfordunichaps@yahoo.co.uk

PALMER, Elizabeth. *See* BLATCHLEY, Ms Elizabeth Palmer

PALMER, Miss Elizabeth Anne. b 46. Reading Univ BA68 Nottm Univ PGCE69 MEd78 MA97. St Jo Coll Nottm 91. **d** 94 **p** 94. C Scartho *Linc* 91-96; P-in-c Ilkeston St Jo *Derby* 96-01; V from 01. *St John's Vicarage, 41 St John's Road, Ilkeston DE7 5PA* Tel 0115-932 5446

PALMER, Preb Francis Harvey. b 30. Jes Coll Cam BA52 MA56. Wycliffe Hall Ox 53. **d** 55 **p** 56. C Knotty Ash St Jo *Liv* 55-57; C Southgate *Chich* 58-60; Chapl Fitzw Ho Cam 60-64; V Cambridge H Trin *Ely* 64-71; Chapl to Cam Pastorate 64-71; Prin Ridley Hall Cam 71-72; R Worplesdon *Guildf* 72-80; Bp's Ecum Officer 74-80; P-in-c Blymhill w Weston-under-Lizard *Lich* 80-82; Dioc Missr and Sec to Bd for Miss and Unity 80-90; Preb Lich Cathl 86-89; TV Walsall 87-90; rtd 90; Perm to Offic *Lich* 90-99; *Glouc* from 93. *The Old Vicarage, Claverley, Wolverhampton WV5 7DT* Tel (01746) 710746

PALMER, Graham. b 31. Em Coll Cam BA53 MA57. Qu Coll Birm 56. **d** 58 **p** 59. C Camberwell St Giles *S'wark* 58-61; C Kilburn St Aug *Lon* 61-67; P-in-c Fulham St Alb 67-73; V 73-92; V Fulham St Alb w St Aug 92-97; rtd 97; Perm to Offic from 97. *7 Wellington Court, 116 Knightsbridge, London SW1X 7PL* Tel (020) 7584 4036

PALMER, Canon Hugh. b 50. Pemb Coll Cam BA72 MA76. Ridley Hall Cam 73. **d** 76 **p** 77. C Heigham H Trin *Nor* 76-80; Bp's Chapl for Tr and Miss 80-84; C St Helen Bishopsgate w St Andr Undershaft etc *Lon* 85-95; C Fulwood *Sheff* 95-97; V from 97; Hon Can Sheff Cathl from 01. *The Vicarage, 2 Chorley Drive, Sheffield S10 3RR* Tel 0114-230 1911

PALMER, Hugh Maurice Webber. b 28. Magd Coll Cam BA51 MA55. Cuddesdon Coll 51. **d** 53 **p** 54. C Bitterne Park *Win* 53-57; N Rhodesia 57-62; V Owslebury w Morestead *Win* 62-65; Rhodesia 65-70; C Headbourne Worthy *Win* 70-71; P-in-c Stratton Strawless *Nor* 72-77; R Hainford 72-77; R Haynford w Stratton Strawless 77-80; Chapl HM Pris Stafford 80-82; Chapl HM Pris Stafford 82-89; Sub-Chapl HM Pris Nor 89-91; rtd 91. *29 Mayfield Way, North Walsham NR28 0DQ* Tel (01692) 403664

PALMER, The Ven Ian Stanley. b 50. K Coll Lon BD71. Cranmer Hall Dur 73. **d** 75 **p** 76. C Huyton St Mich *Liv* 75-78; Chapl Dur Univ *Dur* 78-83; V Collierley w Annfield Plain 83-90; Australia from 90; Adn Upper Hunter from 00; R Muswellbrook from 00. *19 Brook Street, PO Box 125, Muswellbrook, NSW, Australia 2333* Tel (0061) (2) 6541 2713 Mobile 411-242596 Fax 6541 2306 E-mail palmeris@hunterlink.net.au

PALMER, John Richard Henry. b 29. AKC52. **d** 53 **p** 54. C Englefield Green *Guildf* 53-57; P-in-c Brewarrina Australia 57-62; C Wareham w Arne *Sarum* 62-63; PC Derby St Jo *Derby* 63-66; Chapl Holloway Sanatorium Virginia Water 66-70; Chapl Brookwood Hosp Woking 70-94; rtd 94; Perm to Offic *Truro* from 94. *Lightning Ridge, Pentreath Road, The Lizard, Helston TR12 7NY* Tel (01326) 290654
E-mail vsp@oldlizardhead.freeserve.co.uk

PALMER, John Russell. b 25. Birm Univ BSc46. Cuddesdon Coll 70. **d** 71 **p** 72. C Weeke *Win* 71-76; V Four Marks 76-90; rtd 90; Perm to Offic *Win* from 90. *33 Montague Road, Bournemouth BH5 2EW* Tel (01202) 426536

PALMER, Mrs Julia Elizabeth. b 57. Hull Univ BA80. St Jo Coll Nottm MA98. **d** 99 **p** 00. C Snodland All SS w Ch Ch *Roch* 99-03; P-in-c Sutton Bonington w Normanton-on-Soar *S'well* from 03. *The Rectory, 19A Park Lane, Sutton Bonington, Loughborough LE12 5NH* E-mail revjuliap@msn.com

PALMER, Kevin Anthony. b 59. St Steph Ho Ox. **d** 01. C Tunstall *Lich* from 01. *7 Park Terrace, Tunstall, Stoke-on-Trent ST6 6BP* Tel (01782) 819175

PALMER, Malcolm Leonard. b 46. Sarum & Wells Th Coll 80. **d** 82 **p** 83. C Cannock *Lich* 82-85; Chapl RAF 85-89; Asst Chapl HM Pris *Dur* 89-90; Chapl HM YOI Hewell Grange 90-93; Chapl HM Rem Cen Brockhill 90-93; Chapl HM Pris Blakenhurst 93-01; Miss P Kugluktuk Canada from 01. *PO Box 296, NT, Canada, X0E 0E0* Tel (001) (867) 982 3073

PALMER, Marc Richard. b 72. St Jo Coll Dur BA96. Cranmer Hall Dur 93. **d** 98 **p** 99. C Chester le Street *Dur* 98-03; TV Bensham from 03. *12 Red Admiral Court, Gateshead NE11 9TW* Tel 0191-460 1932 E-mail mizpar@aol.com

PALMER, Marion Denise. b 42. SRN64 SCM66 Open Univ BA82. Linc Th Coll 84. **dss** 86 **d** 87 **p** 94. Poplar *Lon* 86-90; Par Dn 87-90; Par Dn Gillingham St Mary *Roch* 90-94; C 94-96; C Farnborough 96-02; rtd 02. *14 Prestwick Avenue, Felixstowe IP11 9LF* Tel (01394) 671588

PALMER, Canon Maureen Florence. b 38. Qu Eliz Coll Lon BSc60 PhD64 DipRS79. Ripon Coll Cuddesdon DipTh84. **dss** 85 **d** 87 **p** 94. Par Dss Tupsley *Heref* 85-87; C 87-88; Par Dn Talbot Village *Sarum* 88-91; Chapl Birm Cathl *Birm* 91-96; Can Pastor and Can Res Guildf Cathl *Guildf* from 96; Sub-Dean from 99. *2 Cathedral Close, Guildford GU2 7TL* Tel (01483) 560329 *or* 565283 E-mail maureen@guildford-cathedral.org

PALMER, Michael Christopher. b 43. MBE00. AKC67 S Bank Poly CQSW76. **d** 68 **p** 69. C Easthampstead *Ox* 68-71; Miss to Seamen 71-73; Hong Kong 73; Lic to Offic *Ox* 76-79; Lic to Offic *Truro* 79-83; Dioc Soc Resp Adv 83-98; Bp's Dom Chapl 85-87; V Devoran 87-98; rtd 98; Perm to Offic *Truro* from 98. *Vine Cottages, 13 High Steet, Cuddesdon, Oxford OX44 9HP* Tel (01865) 875284

PALMER, Norman Ernest. b 28. Lon Univ DipTh56 BD59. Roch Th Coll 66. **d** 67 **p** 67. C Chipping Norton *Ox* 67-69; V Bozeat w Easton Maudit *Pet* 69-90; rtd 90; Perm to Offic *Chich* from 90. *15 Coombe Shaw, Ninfield, Battle TN33 9LQ* Tel (01424) 892138

PALMER, Canon Peter Malcolm. b 31. Chich Th Coll 56. **d** 59 **p** 60. C Leighton Buzzard *St Alb* 59-63; C Apsley End 63-65; C Hitchin H Sav 65-69; R Ickleford 69-76; V Oxhey St Matt 76-86; V Kensworth, Studham and Whipsnade 86-96; Hon Can St Alb 94-96; rtd 97; Perm to Offic *St Alb* from 97; Bishop's Retirement Officer from 97. *4 Sefton Close, St Albans AL1 4PF* Tel (01727) 763196

PALMER, Peter Parsons. b 27. **d** 59 **p** 61. SSJE from 59; Canada 59-79; Perm to Offic *Leic* 80-86; Perm to Offic *Lon* 86-94; Lic to Offic 94-97. *St Edward's House, 22 Great College Street, London SW1 3QA* Tel (020) 7222 9234

PALMER, Philip Edward Hitchen. b 35. St Jo Coll Cam MA61 DipAdEd74. Ridley Hall Cam 61 EAMTC 87. **d** 90 **p** 91. NSM Gt Oakley w Wix *Chelmsf* 90-96; NSM Gt Oakley w Wix and Wrabness 96-00; Perm to Offic from 00. *Glebe House, Great Oakley, Harwich CO12 5BJ* Tel (01255) 880737

PALMER, Robert William. b 28. DMS. Wells Th Coll 63. **d** 65 **p** 66. C Earlsdon *Cov* 65-69; P-in-c Cov St Mark 69-71; Chapl Cov and Warks Hosp 69-71; Hon C Binley *Cov* 72-76; V Sheff St Paul *Sheff* 76-84; V Deepcar 84-93; rtd 93; Perm to Offic *Sheff* from 93. *Moorlands, 26 Coal Pit Lane, Stocksbridge, Sheffield S36 1AW*

PALMER, Canon Stephen Charles. b 47. FRGS98 FLS01. Oak Hill Th Coll 71. **d** 74 **p** 75. C Crofton *Portsm* 74-77; Bp's Dom Chapl 77-80; Chapl RNR from 78; R Brighstone and Brooke w Mottistone *Portsm* 80-91; P-in-c Shorwell w Kingston 82-86; RD W Wight 87-91; Hon Can Portsm Cathl from 91; Falkland Is 91-96; V Portsdown *Portsm* 96-02; V Newport St Jo from 02; V Newport St Thos from 02; Bp's Ecological Adv from 00. *72A*

Medina Avenue, Newport PO30 1HF Tel (01983) 539580 Fax 821961 E-mail stephen.palmer@fish.co.uk

PALMER, Steven Roy. b 51. Birm Univ BSc71. WMMTC 91. **d** 94 **p** 95. C Sheldon *Birm* 94-97; P-in-c Duddeston w Nechells 97-99; V Nechells 99-03; R Billing *Pet* from 03. *The Rectory, 25 Church Walk, Great Billing, Northampton NN3 4ED* Tel (01604) 784870 Fax 401641

PALMER, Canon Terence Henry James. b 34. Univ of Wales (Lamp) BA55 LTh57 St Edm Hall Ox BA65 MA69. **d** 57 **p** 58. C Griffithstown *Mon* 57-60; Min Can and C St D Cathl *St D* 60-63; Perm to Offic *B & W* and *Ox* 63-65; C Monmouth *Mon* 65-69; C-in-c St Hilary Greenway CD 69-72; R Roggiett w Llanfihangel Roggiett 72-80; R Portskewett and Roggiet w Llanfihangel Rogiet 80-00; RD Netherwent 89-00; Dir NSM Studies 91-99; Can St Woolos Cathl 96-00; rtd 00; Perm to Offic *Eur* from 99; Lic to Offic *Mon* from 00; P-in-c Newport St Teilo from 03. *12 Windsor Park, Magor, Caldicot NP26 3NJ* Tel (01633) 881927

PALMER-PALMER-FFYNCHE, Barry Marshall. b 23. Hertf Coll Ox BA47 MA48. Westcott Ho Cam 47. **d** 49 **p** 50. C Alrewas *Lich* 49-52; C Wychnor 49-52; C Birchington w Acol *Cant* 52-56; R Harrietsham 56-66; Chapl Westmr Hosp Lon 66-73; V Chipping Sodbury and Old Sodbury *Glouc* 73-88; rtd 88; Perm to Offic *Glouc* and *Bris* from 90; *Lon* 90-00. *Finch's Folly, 45 Hay Street, Marshfield, Chippenham SN14 8PF* Tel (01225) 891096

PAMMENT, Canon Gordon Charles. b 31. TCD BA54. Linc Th Coll 56. **d** 58 **p** 60. C Hemel Hempstead *St Alb* 58-63; C Gedney Drove End *Linc* 63-65; I Macroom Union *C, C & R* 65-72; I Rathcormac Union 72-78; I Fermoy Union 78-91; Can Ross Cathl 89-91; Can Cork Cathl 89-91; rtd 91. *5 Langford Place, Co Cork, Irish Republic*

PAMPLIN, Richard Lawrence. b 46. Lon Univ BScEng68 Dur Univ BA75. NY Th Sem DMin85 Wycliffe Hall Ox 75. **d** 77 **p** 78. C Greenside *Dur* 77-80; C Sheff St Barn and St Mary *Sheff* 80-84; R Wombwell 84-90; P-in-c Madeley *Heref* 90-91; TR 91-01; Chapl Berne w Neuchâtel *Eur* from 01. *St Ursula's, Jubiläumsplatz 2, CH 3005 Bern, Switzerland* Tel (0041) (31) 351 0343 *or* 352 8567 Fax 351 0548
E-mail chaplain@bluewin.ch

PANG, Wing-On. b 43. BA67 Lon Univ MA70. Oak Hill Th Coll DipHE87. **d** 87 **p** 88. C Pennycross *Ex* 87-91; TV Mildenhall *St E* 91-96; Hong Kong from 96. *St Andrew's Church, 138 Nathan Road, Tsim Sha Tsui, Kowloon, Hong Kong* Tel (00852) 2367 1478 Fax 2367 6562 E-mail standrew@hk.super.net

PANGBOURNE, John Godfrey. b 36. Ridley Hall Cam 82. **d** 84 **p** 85. C Ashtead *Guildf* 84-88; V Ore Ch Ch *Chich* from 88. *Christ Church Vicarage, 76 Canute Road, Hastings TN35 5HT* Tel (01424) 421439 E-mail christchurch-ore@parish.co.uk

PANKHURST, Donald Araunah. b 28. Qu Coll Birm DipTh64. **d** 64 **p** 65. C Pemberton St Jo *Liv* 64-68; V Aspull 68-76; R Newchurch 76-88; R Winwick 88-94; rtd 94; Perm to Offic *Carl* from 94. *4 St Mary's Park, Windermere LA23 1AY* Tel (01539) 446390

PANNETT, Philip Anthony. b 36. Brighton Poly MPS59 MRPharmS59. K Coll Lon AKC63 St Boniface Warminster 63. **d** 64 **p** 65. C Stanmer w Falmer and Moulsecoomb *Chich* 64-68; C Hangleton 68-72; Teacher Finchden Manor Sch Tenterden 72-74; Teacher Bodiam Manor Sch 74-76; Perm to Offic from 76; rtd 01. *1 Fitzjohns Road, Lewes BN7 1PP* Tel (01273) 472804

PANTER, The Ven Richard James Graham. b 48. Oak Hill Th Coll 73. **d** 76 **p** 77. C Rusholme H Trin *Man* 76-80; C Toxteth St Cypr w Ch Ch *Liv* 80-85; V Clubmoor 85-96; P-in-c Litherland St Jo and St Jas 96-02; AD Bootle 99-02; Adn Liv from 02; V Orrell Hey St Jo and St Jas from 02. *St John and St James Vicarage, 2A Monfa Road, Bootle L20 6BQ* Tel 0151-922 3758 Fax as telephone E-mail rickyp@cableinet.co.uk

PANTER MARSHALL, Mrs Susan Lesley. b 49. Portsm Poly BSc72 Grad LI84. S Dios Minl Tr Scheme 88. **d** 91 **p** 94. NSM Southover *Chich* 91-95; C Iford w Kingston and Rodmell 95-98; C Hollington St Jo 98-02; P-in-c Herstmonceux and Wartling from 02. *The Rectory, West End, Herstmonceux, Hailsham BN27 4NY* Tel (01323) 833124 E-mail sapan@fish.co.uk

PANTLING, Mrs Rosemary Caroline. b 60. Ex Coll Ox BA83 MA Birm Univ PGCE84. EAMTC 98. **d** 01 **p** 02. NSM Bishop's Tachbrook *Cov* from 01. *22 Touchstone Road, Heathcote, Warwick CV34 6EE* Tel (01926) 316597
E-mail krpantling@waitrose.com

PANTON, Alan Edward. b 45. K Coll Lon BD67 AKC67. **d** 68 **p** 69. C Eltham St Jo *S'wark* 68-73; C Horley 73-78; V Dallington *Pet* from 78. *The Vicarage, The Barton's Close, Dallington, Northampton NN5 7HQ* Tel (01604) 751478

PANTRY, John Richard. b 46. Oak Hill Non Course DipTh93. **d** 93 **p** 94. NSM Alresford *Chelmsf* from 93. *2 Conifers Close, Alresford, Colchester CO7 8AW* Tel (01206) 824257 Fax as telephone E-mail johnpantry@fsmail.net

PAPADOPULOS, Nicholas Charles. b 66. G&C Coll Cam BA88 MA92 Barrister-at-Law (Middle Temple) 90. Ripon Coll Cuddesdon. **d** 99 **p** 00. C Portsea N End St Mark *Portsm* 99-02;

Bp's Dom Chapl *Sarum* from 02. *11 Albany Road, Salisbury SP1 3YQ* Tel (01722) 415925
E-mail nicholas.papadopoulos@care4free.net

PAPANTONIOU, Ms Frances Caroline. b 52. S Dios Minl Tr Scheme 89. **d** 92 **p** 94. Par Dn Harrow Weald All SS *Lon* 92-94; C 94-95; C Preston Ascension 95-98; Assoc V Wembley Park 98-99; TV from 99. *St Augustine's Vicarage, 13 Forty Avenue, Wembley HA9 8JL* Tel (020) 8904 0489

PAPE, David. b 54. LNSM course 95. **d** 98 **p** 99. OLM S'wark St Geo the Martyr w St Alphege & St Jude *S'wark* from 98; OLM Waterloo St Jo w St Andr from 98. *10 Stopher House, Webber Street, London SE1 0RE* Tel (020) 7928 3503

PAPE, Timothy Vernon Francis. b 39. OBE. Lon Univ BSc63. Wells Th Coll 63. **d** 65 **p** 66. C Pershore w Wick *Worc* 65-69; Perm to Offic *Bris* 69-73; NSM Southbroom *Sarum* from 75; Hd Master Chirton Primary Sch Wilts from 81; Dir Gen Shaw Trust from 90. *Mallards, Chirton, Devizes SN10 3QX* Tel (01380) 840593

PAPUA NEW GUINEA, Archbishop of. *See* AYONG, The Most Revd James Simon

PAPWORTH, Daniel John. b 69. Plymouth Poly BSc90. Trin Coll Bris BA98 MA00. **d** 99 **p** 00. C Gabalfa *Llan* 99-02. *58 Kingsfield Avenue, Harrow HA2 6AS* Tel (020) 8248 4997
E-mail revdup@lineone.net

PAPWORTH, John. b 21. Lon Univ BSc(Econ). **d** 75 **p** 76. Zambia 76-81; Hon C Paddington St Sav *Lon* 81-83; Hon C St Marylebone St Mark Hamilton Terrace 85-97; Perm to Offic *Bris* from 01. *The Fourth World, The Close, 26 High Street, Purton, Swindon SN5 4AE* Tel (01793) 772214 Fax 772521

PAPWORTH, Miss Shirley Marjorie. b 33. CA Tr Coll. **d** 88 **p** 94. Par Dn Hornchurch H Cross *Chelmsf* 88-93; rtd 93; NSM Hornchurch St Andr *Chelmsf* from 94. *4 Gosport Drive, Hornchurch RM12 6NU* Tel (01708) 524348

PARADISE, Bryan John. b 49. Southn Univ BSc Lon Bible Coll BA. Cranmer Hall Dur. **d** 82 **p** 83. C High Harrogate Ch Ch *Ripon* 82-86; Dioc Adult Educn Officer *Guildf* from 86; P-in-c Dunsfold 86-90; R 90-93; R E Horsley 93-01; RD Leatherhead from 98; R E Horsley and Ockham w Hatchford and Downside from 02. *The Rectory, Ockham Road South, East Horsley, Leatherhead KT24 6RL* Tel (01483) 282359
E-mail revbjp@mwfree.net

PARAGUAY, Bishop of. *See* ELLISON, The Rt Revd John Alexander

PARBURY, Heather Christina Winifred. b 56. **d** 01 **p** 02. C Long Compton, Whichford and Barton-on-the-Heath *Cov* from 01; C Barcheston from 01; C Cherington w Stourton from 01; C Wolford w Burmington from 01. *The Vicarage, Great Wolford, Shipton-on-Stour CV36 5NQ* Tel (01608) 674361

PARE, Stephen Charles. b 53. Sussex Univ BEd75. St Mich Coll Llan DipTh80. **d** 80 **p** 81. C Cardiff St Jo *Llan* 80-83; P-in-c Marcross w Monknash and Wick 83; TV Llantwit Major 83-91; V Penmark w Porthkerry from 91; Chapl Cardiff Wales Airport from 91. *The Vicarage, 6 Milburn Close, Rhoose, Barry CF62 3EJ* Tel (01446) 711713 E-mail penmarkporthceri@orngenet.co.uk

PARFFETT, Allan John. b 51. Keele Univ CQSW76 Spurgeon's Coll CertRS90 Open Univ DASSc95 BA97 Birm Univ MA00. Qu Coll Birm 97. **d** 98 **p** 99. C Hall Green Ascension *Birm* 98-00; Soc Worker from 00. *20 Kiln Close, Corfe Mullen, Wimbourne BH21 3UR*

PARFITT, Anthony Colin. b 44. Ox Univ Inst of Educn CertEd66 Open Univ BA71 Plymouth Poly MPhil84. SW Minl Tr Course 93. **d** 96 **p** 97. NSM Langport Area Chs *B & W* 96-00; NSM Bruton and Distr from 01. *Tile Hill Cottage, North Brewham, Bruton BA10 0JT* Tel (01749) 850188 Fax 850189
E-mail tony.parfitt@ukonline.co.uk

PARFITT, Brian John. b 49. Ex Coll Ox BA71 MA76. Wycliffe Hall Ox 71. **d** 74 **p** 75. C Magor w St Mark *Mon* 74-78; R Blaina 78-83; R Blaina and Nantyglo 83-86; Chapl Blaina and Distr Hosp Gwent 83-86; Consultant W Midlands and Wales CPAS 86-95; V Magor w Redwick and Undy *Mon* 95-98; TR Magor from 98. *The Vicarage, Newport Road, Magor, Caldicot NP26 3BZ* Tel (01633) 880266

PARFITT, David George. b 65. De Montfort Univ Leic BA87 DipArch90. Wycliffe Hall Ox BTh92. **d** 95 **p** 96. C Malpas *Mon* 95-98; C Bassaleg 98-00; TV 00-01; V Malpas from 01. *The Vicarage, Malpas Road, Newport NP20 6GQ* Tel (01633) 852047

PARFITT, George Rudolf William. b 54. WMMTC 96. **d** 99 **p** 00. OLM Highnam, Lassington, Rudford, Tibberton etc *Glouc* from 99. *8 Hillcrest, Highnam, Gloucester GL2 8LS* Tel (01452) 301635
E-mail george.parfitt@btinternet.com

PARFITT, Graeme Stanley. b 36. Qu Coll Birm 77. **d** 79 **p** 80. C Fishponds St Jo *Bris* 79-82; V Southmead 82-91; V Stockwell St Mich *S'wark* 91-01; rtd 01; Perm to Offic *Bris* from 02. *Garden Cottage, The Old House, Rectory Gardens, Henbury, Bristol BS10 7AQ* Tel 0117-959 0293

PARFITT, John Arthur. b 49. St Jo Coll Nottm BTh81. **d** 81 **p** 82. C Radcliffe-on-Trent *S'well* 81-84; C Chilwell 84-86; V Awsworth w Cossall 86-91; Perm to Offic from 91. *133 Parkside, Nottingham NG8 2NL* Tel 0115-928 1907

PARFITT, Preb John Hubert. b 29. Birm Univ DipTh66 Southn Univ MA72 BPhil. Qu Coll Birm 78. **d** 80 **p** 81. C Fladbury, Wyre Piddle and Moor *Worc* 80-82; C Malvern Link w Cowleigh 82; V Hanley Castle, Hanley Swan and Welland 82-83; Dir RE *B & W* 84-93; Preb Wells Cathl from 85; rtd 93; Perm to Offic *B & W* from 93; Master Hugh Sexey's Hosp Bruton from 95. *The Master's House, Hugh Sexey's Hospital, Bruton BA10 0AS* Tel (01749) 813369

PARFITT, Canon Keith John. b 44. K Coll Lon BD68 AKC68. St Aug Coll Cant 69. **d** 70 **p** 71. C Kettering St Andr *Pet* 70-74; Asst Soc and Ind Adv *Portsm* 74-89; RD Alverstoke 79-86; C-in-c Bridgemary CD 81-82; V Bridgemary 82-89; Dioc UPA Officer *Blackb* 89-97; Can Res Blackb Cathl 94-97; Dir Is of Wight Rural Community Coun from 97. *Downsview, Farriers Way, Shorwell, Newport PO30 3JP* Tel (01983) 740434

PARFITT, Neil. b 49. **d** 99 **p** 00. C Caerleon *Mon* 99-01; C Ebbw Vale 01-02; P-in-c Ferndale w Maerdy *Llan* 02-03; V from 03. *The Vicarage, Woodville Place, Ferndale CF43 4LS* Tel (01443) 756322

PARFITT, Susan Mary. b 42. Bris Univ BA63 CertEd68 Univ of Wales DASS70. Bris Minl Tr Scheme 82 Ripon Coll Cuddesdon. dss 84 **d** 87 **p** 94. Assoc Dir of Ords *Bris* 84-86; CME Officer 87-91; Dir Past Care and Counselling *S'wark* 91-01; rtd 01; Perm to Offic *Bris* from 02. *Garden Cottage, The Old House, Rectory Gardens, Bristol BS10 7AQ* Tel 0117-959 0293

PARGETER, Canon Muriel Elizabeth. b 28. St Mich Ho Ox 53. dss 82 **d** 87 **p** 95. Hd Dss *Roch* 82-87; Dioc Dir of Ords 87-90; Hon Can Roch Cathl 87-90; rtd 90; NSM Worthing Ch the King *Chich* from 95. *63 Pavilion Road, Worthing BN45 7EE* Tel (01903) 214476

PARISH, George Richard. b 33. ACIB60 Qu Coll Cam BA56 MA60. S'wark Ord Course 85. **d** 88 **p** 89. NSM Sunninghill *Ox* 88-96; P-in-c Withyham St Mich *Chich* from 96. *The Rectory, Withyham, Hartfield TN7 4BA* Tel (01892) 770241

PARISH, Mrs Mary Eileen. b 48. Nottm Univ BA70 Southn Univ BTh98. All Nations Chr Coll 73 STETS 95. **d** 98 **p** 99. NSM Worthing Ch the King *Chich* from 98. *The Heritage, 10 Winchester Road, Worthing BN11 4DJ* Tel (01903) 236909
E-mail frmary@theheritage.freeserve.co.uk

PARISH, Nicholas Anthony. b 58. Oak Hill Th Coll BA84 Kingston Univ MA97. Ridley Hall Cam 84. **d** 86 **p** 87. C Eltham H Trin *S'wark* 86-89; C Barnes St Mary 89-91; V Streatham St Paul 91-96; Ind Chapl *Cov* from 96. *1 Old Lands Hill, Bracknell RG12 2QX* Tel (01344) 641498 Fax as telephone
E-mail nick.parish@ntlworld.com

PARISH, Stephen Richard. b 49. Oak Hill Th Coll DipTh77. **d** 77 **p** 78. C Chadderton Ch Ch *Man* 77-81; C Chell *Lich* 81-82; TV 82-88; V Warrington St Ann *Liv* from 88. *St Ann's Vicarage, 1A Fitzherbert Street, Warrington WA2 7QG* Tel (01925) 631781

PARK, Christopher John. b 62. Sheff Poly BA83. Cranmer Hall Dur 00. **d** 02 **p** 03. C Didsbury St Jas and Em *Man* from 02. *99 Mellington Avenue, East Didsbury, Manchester M20 5WF* Tel 0161-445 9758 E-mail pasta@cjparko.freeserve.co.uk

PARK, Ernest Winston. b 10. St Paul's Cheltenham CertEd31. Moray Ord Course 89. **d** 92. C Poolewe *Mor* 92-95; rtd 95; Perm to Offic *B & W* 95-98. *Little Park, Ampthill, Bedford MK45 2RE* Tel (01525) 840435

PARK, John Charles. b 55. St Pet Coll Ox BA77 St Mary's Coll Newc PGCE81. Cranmer Hall Dur 00. **d** 02 **p** 03. C Morpeth *Newc* from 02. *23 Green Acres, Morpeth NE61 2AD* Tel (01670) 511662

PARK, Tarjei Erling Alan. b 64. W Lon Inst of HE BA88 Lanc Univ MA89 Pemb Coll Ox DPhil96. Ripon Coll Cuddesdon DipMin94. **d** 94 **p** 95. C Lancaster St Mary *Blackb* 94-98; V Enfield St Mich *Lon* 98-01; Asst Dir Post-Ord Tr from 98; V Golders Green from 01. *The Vicarage, 3 St Alban's Close, London NW11 7RA* Tel (020) 8455 4525
E-mail tarjei.park@london.anglican.org

PARK, Trevor. b 38. Lon Univ BA64 Open Univ PhD90. Lambeth STh81 Linc Th Coll 64. **d** 66 **p** 67. C Crosthwaite Kendal *Carl* 66-68; Asst Chapl Solihull Sch 69-71; Chapl St Bees Sch Cumbria 71-77; V St Bees *Carl* 71-77; V Dalton-in-Furness 77-84; V Natland 84-97; Hon Can Carl Cathl 86-97; RD Kendal 89-94; Ch Commr 93-97; Chapl Oslo w Bergen, Trondheim and Stavanger *Eur* from 97. *Harald Hårfagresgate 2, 0363 Oslo, Norway* Tel (0047) 22692214 E-mail trepar@online.no

PARKE, W/Cdr Edmund George. b 14. JP71. TCD BA37 MA47. **d** 38 **p** 39. C Newcastle w Butterton *Lich* 38-42; Chapl RAF 42-69; Chapl Soc Work Dept Dundee Corp 69-75; Tayside Regional Coun 75-79; rtd 79; Perm to Offic *St And* from 79; Perm to Offic *Bre* from 79. *45 High Street, Newport-on-Tay DD6 8AA* Tel (01382) 542048

PARKE, Simon Frederick Fenning. b 57. MA. Wycliffe Hall Ox. **d** 84 **p** 85. C Isleworth St Jo *Lon* 84-87; C St Marylebone All So w SS Pet and Jo 87-88; C Langham Place All So 88-93; V Tufnell Park St Geo and All SS from 93; P-in-c W Holloway St Luke 96-97. *The Vicarage, 72 Crayford Road, London N7 0ND* Tel (020) 7609 1645 or 7387 1360

PARKER, Alfred. b 20. Man Univ BA47. Wycliffe Hall Ox 47. **d** 49 **p** 50. C Droylsden St Mary *Man* 49-53; C New Bury 53-54;

P-in-c Bolton St Bart 54-56; V 56-61; P-in-c Gt Lever 59-61; R 61-65; V Belmont 65-87; rtd 87. *21 Edgeley Road, Whitchurch SY13 1EU*

PARKER, Angus Michael Macdonald. b 53. Bris Univ BSc74. St Jo Coll Nottm DipTh81 DPS83. d 83 p 84. C Northampton St Giles *Pet* 83-86; C Attenborough *S'well* 86-96; V Pennycross *Ex* from 96. *St Pancras Vicarage, 66 Glentor Road, Plymouth PL3 5TR* Tel (01752) 774332

PARKER, Mrs Ann Jacqueline. b 41. Dur Inst of Educn TCert63 Sunderland Poly TCert65 Open Univ BA82. WEMTC 91. d 95 p 96. NSM Pilning w Compton Greenfield *Bris* 95-98; NSM Almondsbury and Olveston 98-03; Asst Chapl N Bris NHS Trust from 98. *Wyngarth, Easter Compton, Bristol BS35 5RA* Tel (01454) 632329 E-mail annatdibley@aol.com

PARKER, Mrs Anne Margaret. b 57. Leeds Univ BSc78. EAMTC DipHE99. d 99 p 00. NSM Greenstead w Colchester St Anne *Chelmsf* 99-02; C from 02. *24 Burrows Close, Lawford, Manningtree CO11 2HE* Tel (01206) 396127 Mobile 07703-571879 E-mail amparker20@hotmail.com

PARKER, Mrs Brenda. b 36. Dioc OLM tr scheme 97. d 00 p 01. OLM Eccleston Ch Ch *Liv* from 00. *22 Selkirk Drive, Eccleston, St Helens WA10 5PE* Tel (01744) 757495

PARKER, Brian William. b 39. Ulster Univ BA88. CITC 99. d 01 p 02. NSM Knock *D & D* 01-02; NSM Glencraig from 02. *7 Cairnsville Park, Bangor BT19 6EW* Tel (028) 9145 4549 E-mail bwparker@ukgateway.net

PARKER, Carole Maureen. *See* PROUSE, Ms Carole Maureen

PARKER, David Anthony. b 38. St Chad's Coll Dur BA62 DipTh64. d 64 p 65. C Palmers Green St Jo *Lon* 64-65; C Kenton 65-71; C W Hyde St Thos *St Alb* 71-75; P-in-c Brinksway *Ches* 76-80; V 80-83; V Weston 83-92; NSM Cheadle Hulme All SS 97-98; C Offerton 98-00; TV Crosslacon *Carl* 00-02; rtd 02; C Cheadle Hulme All SS *Ches* from 02; Perm to Offic *Man* from 02. *77 Station Road, Cheadle Hulme, Cheadle SK8 7BG* Tel 0161-485 4451

PARKER, David Arthur. b 48. Lon Univ DipTh71. Kelham Th Coll. d 71 p 72. C Newc Ch Ch *Newc* 71-74; C Hendon *Dur* 74-79; C-in-c Southwick St Cuth CD 79-84; V Sunderland Red Ho 84-88; rtd 88; Perm to Offic *Ex* 88-99; Chapl Sisters of Charity from 95. *7 Woodside Court, Plympton, Plymouth PL7 1HL* Tel (01752) 330467

PARKER, David Charles. b 53. St Andr Univ MTh75 Em Coll Cam DipTh76 Univ of Leiden DTh90. Ridley Hall Cam 75. d 77 p 78. C Hendon St Paul Mill Hill *Lon* 77-80; C Bladon w Woodstock *Ox* 80-85; C-in-c Shipton-on-Cherwell 80-85; C-in-c Begbroke 80-85; C-in-c Hampton Gay 80-85; Lect Qu Coll Birm 85-93 and 89-93; Lect Birm Univ *Birm* 93-96; Sen Lect 96-98; Reader in NT Textual Criticism and Palaeography from 98. *Dumbleton Cottage, 24 Church Street, Bromyard HR7 4DP* Tel 0121-415 2415 E-mail d.c.parker@bham.ac.uk

PARKER, Canon David John. b 33. St Chad's Coll Dur BA55 Hull Univ MA85. Linc Th Coll 57. d 59 p 60. C Tynemouth Ch Ch *Newc* 59-60; C Ponteland 60-63; C Byker St Mich 63-64; C-in-c Byker St Martin CD 64-69; V Whorlton 69-73; TR 73-80; Ind Chapl *Linc* 80-84; Master Newc St Thos Prop Chpl *Newc* 84-89; Exec Officer Dioc Bd for Ch and Soc *Man* 90-98; Lic Preacher 90-98; Hon Can Man Cathl 97-98; rtd 98; Perm to Offic *Newc* from 98. *4 The Kylins, Morpeth NE61 2DJ* Tel (01670) 516218 E-mail d.j.parker@tesco.net

PARKER, David Louis. b 47. Lon Univ LLB70 Ox Univ MA82. Wycliffe Hall Ox BA79. d 80 p 81. C Broadwater St Mary *Chich* 80-84; TR Ifield 84-97; R Lavant from 97; RD Chich from 01. *The Rectory, Pook Lane, Lavant, Chichester PO18 0AH* Tel (01243) 527313

PARKER, David William. b 21. SEN CQSW MBASW. Glouc Th Course 77 Sarum & Wells Th Coll 81. d 81 p 81. Chapl HM Pris Leyhill 81-84; NSM Cromhall w Tortworth *Glouc* 81-83; NSM Wickwar w Rangeworthy 83-87; Perm to Offic from 88. *22 Durham Road, Charfield, Wotton-under-Edge GL12 8TH* Tel (01454) 260253

PARKER, Dennis. b 22. Tyndale Hall Bris 63. d 64 p 65. C Polegate *Chich* 64-68; C-in-c Reading St Mary Castle Street Prop Chpl *Ox* 68-70; R Newdigate *Guildf* 70-87; rtd 87; Perm to Offic *Guildf* from 87. *7 Harrow Close, Dorking RH4 3BB*

PARKER, George William. b 29. BS53 BD57 Lon Univ PGCE67. K Coll (NS) 49. d 53 p 54. Canada 53-59 and 68-71 and 78-93; C W Hackney St Barn *Lon* 59-61; V Haggerston St Mary w St Chad 61-68; C Portsea N End St Mark *Portsm* 72-75; V Darlington St Jo *Dur* 75-78; rtd 91. *Spider Cottage, RR3 Newport NS, Canada, B0N 2A0*

PARKER, Hugh James. b 30. ACP55 TCD MA57 Ulster Univ DASE74. d 63 p 64. Lic to Offic *Conn* 63-70 and 96-01; Dioc C 70-96; Hd Master Larne High Sch 71-92; rtd 96. *29 Ranseypt Drive, Whitehead, Carrickfergus BT38 9NW* Tel (028) 9337 8106

PARKER, John Bristo. b 26. Edin Th Coll 61. d 64 p 65. C Barrow St Jo *Carl* 64-67; V Sledmere *York* 68-74; R Cowlam 68-74; P-in-c Wetwang 69-74; V Sledmere and Wetwang w Cowlan 74-79; V Kirkby Ireleth *Carl* 79-83; V Rillington w Scampston, Wintringham etc *York* 83-87; R Bishop Wilton w Full Sutton,

Kirby Underdale etc 87-91; rtd 91; Perm to Offic *York* from 91. *East Lodge, Sledmere, Driffield YO25 3XQ* Tel (01377) 86325

PARKER, John David. b 61. Ridley Hall Cam 00. d 02. C Aston cum Aughton w Swallownest and Ulley *Sheff* from 02. *14 Cradley Drive, Aston, Sheffield S26 2FF* Tel 0114-287 9473 E-mail jdparkeruk@aol.com

PARKER, Preb Joseph French. b 09. St Chad's Coll Dur BA37 DipTh38 MA40. d 38 p 39. C Warrington St Elphin *Liv* 38-40; C Shrewsbury St Mary *Lich* 40-42; C Wolverhampton St Pet 42-46; V Kingswinford St Mary 46-51; V Toxteth Park St Agnes *Liv* 51-60; RD W Bromwich *Lich* 61-76; V W Bromwich All SS 61-76; RD W Bromwich 61-76; Preb Lich Cathl 67-76; rtd 76; Perm to Offic *Carl* 77-93. *c/o Mrs M L Parker, 36 Glebe Farm Court, Up Hatherley, Cheltenham GL51 3EB* Tel (01242) 863273

PARKER, Julian Roderick. b 57. Essex Univ BA80. Sarum & Wells Th Coll DipMin93. d 93 p 94. C Gillingham *Sarum* 93-97; V N Bradley, Southwick and Heywood from 97. *The Vicarage, 62 Church Lane, North Bradley, Trowbridge BA14 0TA* Tel (01225) 752635

PARKER, Miss Margaret. b 27. Lightfoot Ho Dur 54. dss 60 d 87 p 94. Ryhope *Dur* 56-61; Monkwearmouth St Andr 61-79; Adv for Accredited Lay Min 74-87; Adv for Accredited Lay Min *Newc* 79-87; Newc St Geo 79-87; C 87; rtd 87; Perm to Offic *Dur* and *Newc* from 87; Tutor Cranmer Hall Dur 87-92; Hon C Dur Cathl *Dur* 87-94; Min Can Dur Cathl 94-97; Chapl St Mary's Coll Dur 95-98. *53 Devonshire Road, Durham DH1 2BJ* Tel 0191-386 3233

PARKER, Margaret Grace. *See* TORDOFF, Mrs Margaret Grace

PARKER, Matthew John. b 63. Man Univ BA85 SS Coll Cam BA88. Ridley Hall Cam 85. d 88 p 89. C Twickenham St Mary *Lon* 88-91; Chapl Stockport Gr Sch 91-94; C Stockport St Geo *Ches* 91-93; P-in-c Stockport St Mark 93-94; TV Stockport SW 94-00; TR Leek and Meerbrook *Lich* from 00. *The Vicarage, 6 Church Street, Leek ST13 6AB* Tel (01538) 382515 *or* 388134 E-mail matpark01@aol.com

PARKER, Michael Alan. b 70. St Jo Coll Dur BA91. CITC BTh93. d 96 p 97. C Dundela St Mark *D & D* 96-00; I Carnalea from 00. *St Gall's Rectory, 171 Crawfordsburn Road, Bangor BT19 1BT* Tel (028) 9185 3366 E-mail carnalea@down.anglican.org

PARKER, Canon Michael John. b 54. Cam Coll of Art and Tech BA76 Lon Univ BD85. Trin Coll Bris 82. d 85 p 86. C Leic H Trin w St Jo *Leic* 85-88; P-in-c Edin Clermiston Em *Edin* 88-90; Chapl Edin St Thos from 90; Can St Mary's Cathl from 94. *16 Belgrave Road, Edinburgh EH12 6NF* Tel and fax 0131-334 1309 *or* 316 4292 E-mail mjpstthoms@aol.com

PARKER, Michael John. b 57. BSc. Wycliffe Hall Ox 80. d 83 p 84. C Heigham H Trin *Nor* 83-86; C Muswell Hill St Jas w St Matt *Lon* 86-90; R Bedford St Jo and St Leon *St Alb* 90-98; V Knowle *Birm* from 98. *The Vicarage, 1811 Warwick Road, Knowle, Solihull B93 0DS* Tel and fax (01564) 773666 *or* tel 778802 Fax 779123

PARKER, Nigel Howard. b 69. St Jo Coll Dur BSc90 CITC BTh94. d 97 p 98. C Holywood *D & D* 97-00; Outreach Development Officer Think Again from 00. *6 Carnalea Park, Bangor BT19 1HH* Tel (028) 9146 6409 E-mail nigelparker@revparker.freeserve.co.uk

PARKER, Peter Edward. b 32. FRSA Edin Univ MA55 Lon Univ PGCE56. Sarum & Wells Th Coll 73. d 74 p 75. C Kirkby Lonsdale w Mansergh *Carl* 74-76; C Kingston All SS w St Jo *S'wark* 76-80; Chapl S Bank Poly 80-85; Ind Chapl *Chelmsf* 85-90; Chapl Chelmsf Cathl 85-90; R Mistley w Manningtree and Bradfield 90-97; rtd 97; Perm to Offic *Ely* from 97. *2 Waterside, Ely CB7 4AZ* Tel (01353) 669932

PARKER, Philip Vernon. b 60. Birm Univ BSc82 PGCE83. Wycliffe Hall Ox BA89. d 90 p 91. C Walkergate *Newc* 90-93; Chapl Shiplake Coll Henley 93-96; C Lindfield *Chich* 97-99; CF (TA) from 98; Scripture Union from 99. *40 North Street, Fritwell, Bicester OX6 9QR* Tel (01869) 346273

PARKER, Ramon Lewis (Brother Raphael). b 36. Kelham Th Coll 56. d 61 p 62. C Tonge Moor *Man* 61-64; C Clerkenwell H Redeemer w St Phil *Lon* 64-65; V Prestwich St Hilda *Man* 65-71; SSF from 71; Chapl Univ of Wales (Lamp) *St D* 81-86; Lic to Offic *Sarum* from 87; rtd 97. *c/o Brother Samuel SSF, The Friary, Hilfield, Dorchester DT2 7BE* Tel (01300) 341345 Fax 341293

PARKER, Richard Bryan. b 64. Sheff Poly BA87. Coll of Resurr Mirfield 92. d 95 p 96. C Norton *Sheff* 95-98; C Hoyland 98-00; V Moorends from 00. *The Vicarage, West Road, Moorends, Doncaster DN8 4LH* Tel (01405) 741758 Fax as telephone E-mail richardparker@ukgateway.net

PARKER, Richard Frederick. b 36. Oak Hill Th Coll 72. d 74 p 75. C Wootton *St Alb* 74-76; C Hove Bp Hannington Memorial Ch *Chich* 76-81; R Northwood *Portsm* 81-88; V W Cowes H Trin 81-88; V Aldershot H Trin *Guildf* 88-98; R Spaxton w Charlynch, Goathurst, Enmore etc *B & W* from 98. *The Rectory, Church Road, Spaxton, Bridgwater TA5 1DA* Tel (01278) 671265

PARKER, Robert. b 43. Lon Univ BSc65. Cuddesdon Coll. d 67 p 68. C Sheff St Cuth *Sheff* 67-70; Asst Chapl Cheltenham Coll

70-74; R Yate *Glouc* 74-76; R Yate *Bris* 76-77; TR Yate New Town 77-80; C of E Development Officer 80-83; P-in-c Pool Quay *St As* from 99. *Pool Grange, Pool Quay, Welshpool SY21 9JU* Tel (01938) 590496

PARKER, Robert Lawrence. b 34. ALCD59. **d** 59 **p** 60. C Chippenham St Paul *Bris* 59-61; C Swindon Ch Ch 61-63; New Zealand 63-71; P-in-c Over Stowey w Aisholt *B & W* 71-73; V Nether Stowey 71-73; V Nether Stowey w Over Stowey 73-93; RD Quantock 87-93; V Pitminster w Corfe 93-99; rtd 99; Perm to Offic *B & W* from 00. *Oratia, 9 Brookfield Way, Street BA16 0UE* Tel (01458) 442906

PARKER, Robert Nicolas. b 71. Nottm Univ BA93 PGCE95. Ridley Hall Cam 95. **d** 98 **p** 99. C Yardley St Edburgha *Birm* 98-02; Asst P Eugene St Mary USA from 02. *St Mary's Episcopal Church, PO Box 50428, Eugene, OR 97405-0980, USA*

PARKER, Robert William. b 18. Linc Th Coll 81. **d** 81 **p** 82. NSM Mablethorpe w Trusthorpe *Linc* 81-83; NSM Alford w Rigsby 83-86; NSM Alberbury w Cardeston *Heref* 87-90; NSM Ford 87-90; rtd 90; Perm to Offic *Linc* 90-00. *Address temp unknown*

PARKER, Roger Thomas Donaldson. b 55. Simon Frazer Univ BC BA80 Univ of Wales (Cardiff) LLB84 Univ Coll Lon LLM85. Coll of Resurr Mirfield 95. **d** 95 **p** 96. C Swinton and Pendlebury *Man* 95-02; V Burnley St Cath w St Alb and St Paul *Blackb* from 02. *The Vicarage, 156 Todmorden Road, Burnley BB11 3ER* Tel (01282) 424587 or 423351 Fax 458579 E-mail frrogerparker@aol.com

PARKER, Roland John Graham. b 48. AKC72 Hull Univ BA(Ed)83. St Aug Coll Cant 71. **d** 74 **p** 75. C Linc St Faith and St Martin w St Pet *Linc* 74-78; V Appleby 78-84; Ind Chapl 78-84; V N Kelsey 84-92; V Cadney 84-92; P-in-c Waddington 92-97; R from 97. *The Rectory, Rectory Lane, Waddington, Lincoln LN5 9RS* Tel (01522) 720323 E-mail rolapark@btinternet.com

PARKER, Russell Edward. b 48. Lon Univ DipTh77 Man Univ BA80 Nottm Univ MTh82. St Jo Coll Nottm 80. **d** 81 **p** 82. C Walmsley *Man* 81-85; V Coalville and Bardon Hill *Leic* 85-90; Dir Acorn Chr Healing Trust from 90. *19 Newfield Road, Liss GU33 7BW* Tel (01730) 891457 E-mail rparker976@aol.com

PARKER, Stephen George. b 65. Birm Univ BEd89 MA97. Qu Coll Birm 96. **d** 98. C Harborne St Pet *Birm* 98. *Address temp unknown* E-mail sparker@westhill.ac.uk

PARKER, Thomas Henry Louis. b 16. Em Coll Cam BA38 MA42 BD50 DD61. Lon Coll of Div 38. **d** 39 **p** 40. C Chesham St Mary *Ox* 39-42; C Cambridge St Phil *Ely* 42-43; C Cambridge St Andr Less 43-45; C Luddesdowne *Roch* 45-48; V Brothertoft *Linc* 48-55; R Lt Ponton w Stroxton 55-59; R Lt Ponton 59-61; R Gt Ponton 58-61; V Oakington *Ely* 61-71; Lect Dur Univ 71-81; rtd 81; Perm to Offic *Ely* 97-00. *Ceriogh, Flaggoners Green, Bromyard HR7 4QR*

PARKER, Thomas Richard. b 52. Imp Coll Lon BScEng73 Keele Univ MEd83. Cranmer Hall Dur CTM94. **d** 94 **p** 95. C Chadkirk *Ches* from 94. *29 Urwick Road, Romiley, Stockport SK6 3JS* Tel 0161-494 0547

PARKER, Timothy Percy. b 58. Man Univ BA. St Jo Coll Nottm DipTh. **d** 85 **p** 86. C Pitsmoor Ch Ch *Sheff* 85-87; C Kimberworth 87-89; C Brightside w Wincobank *Sheff* 89-91; C Upper Armley *Ripon* 91-95; TV Billingham St Aid *Dur* 95-97; V Billingham St Luke from 97. *17 Shadforth Drive, Billingham TS23 3PW* Tel (01642) 561870 E-mail timparker@ntlworld.com

PARKES, Kevin. b 62. Trent Poly BA84. Sarum & Wells Th Coll BTh90. **d** 88 **p** 89. C Wandsworth St Anne *S'wark* 88-92; USPG 92-95; Trinidad and Tobago 93-95; Kingston Area Miss Team *S'wark* 95-01; V Wandsworth Common St Mary from 01. *The Vicarage, 291 Burntwood Lane, London SW17 0AP* Tel (020) 8874 4804

PARKES, Robert Stephen. b 12. Selw Coll Cam BA35 MA40. Linc Th Coll 37. **d** 38 **p** 39. C Eastleigh *Win* 38-48; Bp's Youth Chapl *St Alb* 49-54; Lic Preacher 49-50; V Offley 50-54; V Tilehurst St Geo *Ox* 54-65; R Pangbourne 65-77; rtd 78; Perm to Offic *Win* from 78. *9 Bailey House, Station Road, Alresford SO24 9JG* Tel (01962) 734109

PARKHILL, Alan John. b 43. TCD BA66. CITC 68. **d** 67 **p** 68. C Knockbreda *D & D* 67-70; Asst Warden Elswick Lodge Newc 71-72; C Bangor St Comgall 73-78; Bp's C Kilmore 78-82; I Kilmore and Inch 82-86; I Clonfeacle w Derrygortreavy *Arm* from 86. *4 Clonfeacle Road, Benburb, Dungannon BT71 7LQ* Tel (028) 3754 8239 Fax as telephone

PARKIN, George David. b 37. Cranmer Hall Dur BA60 DipTh62. **d** 62 **p** 63. C Balderstone *Man* 62-65; C Tunstead 65-67; C Gateshead Fell *Dur* 69-73; Nigeria 74-76; V Walton Breck *Liv* 80-92; V Rawtenstall St Mary *Man* from 92; P-in-c Constable Lee from 02. *2 Melia Close, Rawtenstall, Rossendale BB4 6RQ* Tel (01706) 215585

PARKIN, Mrs Jennifer Anne. b 47. Nene Coll Northampton BEd85. WMMTC 95. **d** 98 **p** 99. C Northampton St Alb *Pet* 98-02; P-in-c Ecton from 02; Chapl Northants Healthcare NHS Trust from 02. *The Rectory, 32 West Street, Ecton, Northampton NN6 0QF* Tel (01604) 416326 E-mail parkinjen@aol.com

PARKIN, John Edmund. b 44. Open Univ BA73. St Jo Coll Nottm 83. **d** 85 **p** 86. C Aberavon *Llan* 85-90; R Eglwysilan 90-01; P Missr Merthyr Tydfil Ch Ch from 01. *12 Heol Scwrfa, Merthyr Tydfil CF48 1HE*

PARKIN, John Francis. b 40. Linc Th Coll 65. **d** 68 **p** 69. C Cullercoats St Geo *Newc* 68-72; C Stony Stratford *Ox* 72-73; TV Lt Coates *Linc* 73-76; Perm to Offic 88-93; NSM Horncastle w Low Toynton from 93; NSM High Toynton from 93. *The Firs, 68 Louth Road, Horncastle LN9 5LJ* Tel (01507) 523208

PARKIN, Jonathon Samuel. b 73. La Sainte Union Coll BTh95 Birm Univ MA97. Qu Coll Birm 98. **d** 98 **p** 99. C Skegness and Winthorpe *Linc* 98-01; Chapl Leic Cathl *Leic* from 01; Chapl Leic Coll of FE from 01. *11 Dixon Drive, Leicester LE2 1RA* Tel 0116-270 1335

PARKIN, Melvyn Christopher. b 57. NEOC 99. **d** 02. NSM Boston Spa *York* from 02. *42 Grove Road, Boston Spa, Wetherby LS23 6AP* Tel (01937) 845303

PARKIN, Canon Trevor Kinross. b 37. Cranmer Hall Dur 63. **d** 66 **p** 67. C Kingston upon Hull St Martin *York* 66-69; C Reading St Jo *Ox* 69-73; Ind Chapl *Lon* 73-80; Hon C Langham Place All So 73-80; Ind Chapl *Ely* 80-82; V Maidenhead St Andr and St Mary *Ox* 82-02; Hon Can Butare from 00; rtd 02. *2 High Meadow Place, Chertsey KT16 9HD* Tel (01932) 560322

PARKINSON, Andrew. b 56. Keble Coll Ox BA77 MA80. Westcott Ho Cam 78. **d** 80 **p** 81. C S Shore H Trin *Blackb* 80-85; V Lea 85-94; V Longton from 94. *Longton Vicarage, Birchwood Avenue, Hutton, Preston PR4 5EE* Tel (01772) 612179 E-mail aparkinson@longtonvicarage.freeserve.co.uk

PARKINSON, Andrew. b 74. **d** 01 **p** 02. C Lancaster Ch Ch *Blackb* from 01. *36 Ambleside Road, Lancaster LA1 3HT* Tel (01524) 849186

PARKINSON, Miss Brenda. b 40. Lancs Poly CQSW. Dalton Ho Bris 65. **dss** 74 **d** 87 **p** 94. Ribbleton *Blackb* 75-80; Ingol 82-88; Par Dn 87-88; Par Dn Ashton-on-Ribble St Mich 88-91; Par Dn Ashton-on-Ribble St Mich w Preston St Mark 91-92; Par Dn Gt Marsden 92-94; C 94-98; C Gt Marsden w Nelson St Phil 99-00; rtd 00; Perm to Offic *Blackb* from 01. *18 Thorn Hill Close, Blackburn BB1 1YE* Tel (01254) 678367

PARKINSON, David Thomas. b 42. Linc Th Coll 77. **d** 79 **p** 80. C Yate New Town *Bris* 79-82; TV Keynsham *B & W* 82-88; R Bleadon from 88. *The Rectory, 17 Coronation Road, Bleadon, Weston-super-Mare BS24 0PG* Tel (01934) 812297

PARKINSON, Derek Leslie. b 29. Ripon Hall Ox 64. **d** 66 **p** 67. C Guildf Ch Ch *Guildf* 66-69; P-in-c Preston St Sav *Blackb* 69-74; P-in-c Preston St Jas 69-74; P-in-c Fontmell Magna *Sarum* 74-81; P-in-c Ashmore 74-81; P-in-c Kingswood w Alderley and Hillesley *Glouc* 81-82; R 82-94; rtd 94. *25 Fountain Crescent, Wotton-under-Edge GL12 7LD*

PARKINSON, Francis Wilson. b 37. Lon Univ DipTh62 Open Univ BA80. St Aid Birkenhead 59. **d** 62 **p** 63. C Monkwearmouth St Andr *Dur* 62-64; C Speke All SS *Liv* 64-67; CF 67-92; Perm to Offic *Ox* from 92; rtd 02. *9 Priory Mead, Longcot, Faringdon SN7 7TJ* Tel (01793) 784406

PARKINSON, George Stanley. b 20. St Jo Coll Dur BA47 DipTh48. **d** 48 **p** 49. C Widnes St Paul *Liv* 48-51; C Bradf Cathl Par *Bradf* 51-55; V Greengates 55-58; V Pennington *Man* 58-71; V Eccles St Mary 71-80; V Churt *Guildf* 80-90; RD Farnham 82-88; rtd 90; Perm to Offic *Worc* from 90. *12 Bevere Court, Bevere, Worcester WR3 7RE* Tel (01905) 457106

PARKINSON, Ian Richard. b 58. Dur Univ BA79 Lon Univ BD84. Wycliffe Hall Ox 80. **d** 83 **p** 84. C Hull Newland St Jo *York* 83-86; C Linthorpe 86-92; V Saltburn-by-the-Sea 92-01; V Marple All SS *Ches* from 01. *The Vicarage, 155 Church Lane, Marple, Stockport SK6 7LD* Tel and fax 0161-449 0950 or tel 427 2378 E-mail ian.parkinson@ukonline.co.uk

PARKINSON, The Very Revd John Fearnley. b 30. MBE90. ALCD54. **d** 55 **p** 56. C Plymouth St Andr *Ex* 55-59; Metrop Sec USCL 59-62; Relig Adv Westward TV 62-81; V Devonport St Budeaux 62-66; CF (TA) 63-77; V Kenton *Ex* 66-75; R Kenton w Mamhead 75-79; R Kenton w Mamhead and Powderham 79-83; Preb Ex Cathl 75-83; Relig Adv SW TV 82-83; Provost St Chris Cathl Bahrain 83-89; CMS 90-95; Hon Chapl Br Embassy Israel 90-95; Dean Jerusalem 90-93; rtd 95; Perm to Offic *Ex* from 95. *6 Priory Gardens, Dawlish EX7 9JN* Tel (01626) 862415

PARKINSON, John Reginald. b 32. Qu Coll Birm 79. **d** 81 **p** 82. NSM Catshill *Worc* 81-85; C Knightwick w Doddenham, Broadwas and Cotheridge 85-88; C Martley and Wichenford 85-88; P-in-c Berrow w Pendock and Eldersfield 88-89; R Berrow w Pendock, Eldersfield, Hollybush etc 89-97; RD Upton 95-97; rtd 97; Perm to Offic *Glouc* and *Worc* from 97. *8 Glebe Close, Stow on the Wold, Cheltenham GL54 1DJ* Tel (01451) 830822

PARKINSON, Leslie. *See* PARKINSON, Derek Leslie

PARKINSON, Nicholas John. b 46. FCCA75 Cranfield Inst of Tech MBA85. St Alb Minl Tr Scheme 92. **d** 95 **p** 96. NSM Woburn Sands *St Alb* 95-98; NSM Westoning w Tingrith 98-01;

NSM Woburn Sands from 01. *Thornbank House, 7 Church Road, Woburn Sands, Milton Keynes MK17 8TE* Tel (01908) 583397

PARKINSON, Peter. b 23. Roch Th Coll 61. **d** 63 **p** 64. C Linc St Mary-le-Wigford w St Martin *Linc* 63-65; C Skegness 65-68; V Newton-on-Trent 68-73; R Kettlethorpe 68-73; V Grainthorpe w Conisholme 74-83; V Marshchapel 74-83; R N Coates 74-83; V Bicker 83-88; rtd 88. *11 Waltham Road, Doddington Park, Lincoln LN6 0SD* Tel (01522) 680604

PARKINSON, Raymond Neville. b 21. Bris Univ BA53. Tyndale Hall Bris 50. **d** 54 **p** 55. C Hove Bp Hannington Memorial Ch *Chich* 54-57; C Reading St Jo *Ox* 57-59; R Folke w Long Burton, N Wootton and Haydon *Sarum* 59-69; V Ashby-de-la-Zouch H Trin *Leic* 69-79; V Swannington St Geo and Coleorton 79-87; rtd 87; Perm to Offic *Leic* 87-88; *Linc* 88-00. *31 Chestnut Crescent, Chedburgh, Bury St Edmunds IP29 4UJ* Tel (01284) 850993

PARKINSON, Simon George Denis. b 39. Univ of Wales (Lamp) BA66. Westcott Ho Cam 65. **d** 67 **p** 68. C Rothwell *Ripon* 67-70; Chapl RAF 70-73; C Leeds St Pet *Ripon* 74-75; V Horbury Junction *Wakef* 76-83; V Hanging Heaton 83-92; P-in-c Upper Hopton 92; V Eastthorpe and Upper Hopton 92-02; rtd 02. *126 Edge Lane, Dewsbury WF12 0HB* Tel (01924) 508885

PARKINSON, Thomas Alan. b 40. St Jo Coll York CertEd61 DipTh62. NW Ord Course 75. **d** 78 **p** 79. NSM Sheff Parson Cross St Cecilia *Sheff* 78-82; NSM Goldthorpe w Hickleton 82-90; C Cantley 90-01; Dioc RE and Worship Adv from 93; V Ryecroft St Nic from 02. *St Nicolas' Presbytery, Kilnhurst Road, Rawmarsh, Rotherham S62 5NG* Tel (01709) 522596

PARKINSON, Vivian Leslie. b 54. St Luke's Coll Ex CertEd76 Brighton Poly BEd82. St Jo Coll Nottm Dip Th Studies. **d** 94 **p** 95. C Cowbridge *Llan* 94-97; V Llantrisant from 97. *The Vicarage, Coed yr Esgob, Llantrisant, Pontyclun CF72 8EL* Tel (01443) 223356 or 237983 Fax 230631

PARKS, Paul. b 59. K Coll Lon BA96. St Jo Coll Nottm MA97. **d** 98 **p** 99. C S Molton w Nymet St George, High Bray etc *Ex* from 98. *Sherbourn House, 11 Duke Street, South Molton EX36 3AL* Tel (01769) 572433 E-mail paulrevjsmc@aol.com

PARMENTER, Canon Deirdre Joy. b 45. EAMTC 91. **d** 94 **p** 95. C Ipswich St Aug *St E* 94-97; P-in-c Haughley w Wetherden 97-00; V Haughley w Wetherden and Stowupland from 00; RD Stowmarket from 99; Hon Can St E Cathl from 03. *The Vicarage, The Folly, Haughley, Stowmarket IP14 3NS* Tel and fax (01449) 771647 Mobile 07721-587634 E-mail parmenter@ed-ip.freeserve.co.uk

PARNELL, Bryan Donald. b 38. JP. DipEd88. Chich Th Coll 66. **d** 69 **p** 70. C Lewisham St Jo Southend *S'wark* 69-72; Australia from 72; Asst Chapl Colleg Sch of St Pet 72-76; R Angaston 76-78; Chapl RAN 78-88; R Edwardstown 89-02; rtd 02. *PO Box 6619, Halifax Street, Adelaide, S Australia 5000* Tel (0061) (8) 4100337 Mobile 414-692340 E-mail trinitas@senet.com.au

PARNELL-HOPKINSON, Clive. b 46. SSC93 DipM75 FRSA01. Sarum & Wells Th Coll 75. **d** 78 **p** 79. C Maldon All SS w St Pet *Chelmsf* 78-81; C Chandler's Ford *Win* 81-84; Chapl RAF 84-01; P-in-c Cliddesden and Ellisfield w Farleigh Wallop etc *Win* from 01; Dioc Adv in Tourism from 01. *The Rectory, Church Lane, Ellisfield, Basingstoke RG25 2QR* Tel (01256) 381217 E-mail halo.cph@ukonline.co.uk

PARR, Clive William. b 41. FCIS. WEMTC 02. **d** 03. NSM Evesham w Norton and Lenchwick *Worc* from 03. *Grace Cottage, Mill Lane, Elmley Castle, Pershore WR10 3HP* Tel (01386) 710700 Mobile 07801-820006 Fax (01386) 710997 E-mail cwparr@parrsy.demon.co.uk

PARR, Frank. b 35. Nottm Univ BCombStuds82 Lanc Univ MA86. Linc Th Coll 79. **d** 82 **p** 83. C Padiham *Blackb* 82-85; P-in-c Accrington St Andr 85-88; V Oswaldtwistle Immanuel and All SS 88-96; V Tunstall w Melling and Leck 96-01; rtd 01; Perm to Offic *Blackb* from 01. *1 Bank View, Burton Road, Lower Bentham, Lancaster LA2 7DZ* Tel (015242) 61159 E-mail frank_parr@lineone.net

PARR, John. b 53. St Edm Hall Ox BA74 MA87 Lon Univ BD79 Sheff Univ PhD90. Trin Coll Bris 75. **d** 79 **p** 80. C Gt Crosby St Luke *Liv* 79-82; C Walton St Mary 82-84; V Ince St Mary 84-87; Tutor and Lect Ridley Hall Cam 87-95; Chapl 87-93; Dir Studies 93-95; CME Officer *Ely* 95-99; P-in-c Harston w Hauxton 95-99; P-in-c Newton 97-99; CME Officer *St E* 99-00; Can Res St E Cathl 99-00. *7A College Lane, Bury St Edmunds IP33 1NN* Tel (01284) 754247 E-mail jp1@talk21.com

PARRATT, Dennis. b 53. St Steph Ho Ox. **d** 84 **p** 85. C Cainscross w Selsley *Glouc* 84-88; C Old Shoreham *Chich* 88-91; C New Shoreham 88-91; Perm to Offic *Glouc* from 02. *The Basement Flat, 17 Montpellier Terrace, Cheltenham GL50 1UX* Tel (01242) 255812

PARRETT, Mrs Mary Margaret. b 42. Shenstone Coll of Educn DipEd63. St Alb Minl Tr Scheme 86. **d** 98 **p** 99. NSM Barton-le-Cley w Higham Gobion and Hexton *St Alb* from 98. *49 Manor Road, Barton-le-Clay, Bedford MK45 4NP* Tel (01582) 833089

PARRETT, Mrs Rosalind Virginia. b 43. Ox Brookes Univ MTh02. Cant Sch of Min 84. **d** 87 **p** 94. NSM Selling w

Throwley, Sheldwich w Badlesmere etc *Cant* 87-91; Asst Chapl Cant Hosp 87-91; Par Dn Stantonbury and Willen *Ox* 91-94; TV 94-96; P-in-c Owlsmoor 96-98; V from 98. *The Vicarage, 107 Owlsmoor Road, Owlsmoor, Sandhurst GU47 0SS* Tel (01344) 780110 or 771286 E-mail parrett.rosalind@virgin.net

PARRETT, Simon Christopher. b 60. Sarum & Wells Th Coll. **d** 87 **p** 88. C Ifield *Chich* 87-91; Chapl to the Deaf *Sarum* 91-94; NSM Bournemouth H Epiphany *Win* 94-96; Asst Chapl Poole Hosp NHS Trust from 96. *Poole Hospital, Longfleet Road, Poole BH15 2JB* Tel (01202) 442167, 665511 or 622477

PARRETT, Stanley Frederick Donald. b 24. **d** 78 **p** 79. NSM Whitchurch w Ganarew *Heref* 78-83; C Goodrich w Welsh Bicknor and Marstow 83-86; C Walford w Bishopswood 83-86; R Pembridge w Moorcourt, Shobdon, Staunton etc 86-89; rtd 89. *4 Manley Lane, Pembridge, Leominster HR6 9EE*

PARRI, Emyr. Univ of Wales BA96 FRAS. Ban & St As Minl Tr Course 98. **d** 98 **p** 99. NSM Tregarth *Ban* from 98. *The Rectory, Llanllechid, Bangor LL57 3SD* Tel (01248) 602176

PARRISH, Robert Carey. b 57. St Steph Ho Ox 89. **d** 91 **p** 92. C Abington *Pet* 91-94; C Leckhampton SS Phil and Jas w Cheltenham St Jas *Glouc* 94-97; PV Llan Cathl *Llan* 97-02; R Merthyr Dyfan from 02. *Merthyr Dyfan Rectory, 10 Buttrills Road, Barry CF62 8EF* Tel (01446) 735943

PARROTT, David Wesley. b 58. Univ of Wales (Cardiff) LLM01. Oak Hill Th Coll BA. **d** 84 **p** 85. C Thundersley *Chelmsf* 84-87; C Rainham 87-89; P-in-c Heydon w Gt and Lt Chishill 89-90; P-in-c N and S Reston 76-80; P-in-c Swaby w Claythorpe 76-80; P-in-c N and S Reston 76-80; P-in-c Swaby w S Thoresby 76-80; R Withern 80-90; V Reston 80-90; V Messingham 90-93; P-in-c Fincham *Ely* 95-02; P-in-c Marham 95-02; P-in-c Shouldham 95-02; P-in-c Shouldham Thorpe 95-02; rtd 02. *8 Anson Close, Skellingthorpe, Lincoln LN6 5TH* Tel (01522) 694417

PARROTT, George. b 37. Leeds Univ BA61. Bps' Coll Cheshunt 61. **d** 63 **p** 64. C Lower Mitton *Worc* 63-65; C-in-c Fairfield St Rich CD 65-68; Zambia 68-70; C Cleethorpes *Linc* 70-75; R Withern 75-80; P-in-c Gayton le Marsh 76-80; P-in-c Strubby and Claythorpe 76-80; P-in-c N and S Reston 76-80; P-in-c Belleau w Aby and Claythorpe 76-80; P-in-c N and S Reston 76-80; P-in-c Swaby w S Thoresby 76-80; R Withern 80-90; V Reston 80-90; V Messingham 90-93; P-in-c Fincham *Ely* 95-02; P-in-c Marham 95-02; P-in-c Shouldham 95-02; P-in-c Shouldham Thorpe 95-02; rtd 02. *8 Anson Close, Skellingthorpe, Lincoln LN6 5TH* Tel (01522) 694417

PARROTT, Canon Gerald Arthur. b 32. St Cath Coll Cam BA56 MA60. Chich Th Coll. **d** 58 **p** 59. C Ashington *Newc* 58-61; C Brighton St Pet *Chich* 61-63; V Leeds St Wilfrid *Ripon* 63-68; R Lewisham St Jo Southend *S'wark* 69-73; TR Catford (Southend) and Downham 73-77; RD E Lewisham 75-77; Can Res and Prec S'wark Cathl 77-88; TR Wimbledon 88-95; rtd 95; Perm to Offic *Chich* from 95. *10 Palings Way, Fernhurst, Haslemere GU27 3HJ*

PARROTT, Martin William. b 57. Keele Univ BA79 Lon Univ PGCE80. Ripon Coll Cuddesdon 82. **d** 85 **p** 86. C Birchfield *Birm* 85-88; Chapl Lon Univ *Lon* 88-93; P-in-c Univ Ch Ch the K Lon 90-93; V Hebden Bridge *Wakef* 93-01; Asst Chapl Pinderfields and Pontefract Hosps NHS Trust 01-02; Chapl Calderdale and Huddersfield NHS Trust from 02. *The Royal Infirmary, Acre Street, Lindley, Huddersfield HD3 3EA* Tel (01484) 342000

PARRY, Canon Alfred Charles Ascough. b 37. Natal Univ BA58. Westcott Ho Cam 59. **d** 61 **p** 62. C E Ham w Upton Park *Chelmsf* 61-63; S Africa 63-98; Sub Dean Pietermaritzburg 76-81; Adn N Natal 81-85; Can Pietermaritzburg 86-98; Hon Can from 98; Sen Asst Min Hornchurch St Andr *Chelmsf* from 99. *49 Burnway, Hornchurch RM11 3SN* Tel (01708) 443358 or 441571 E-mail burnway49@supanet.com

PARRY, Canon Bryan Horace. b 33. St Mich Coll Llan 65. **d** 67 **p** 68. C Holyhead w Rhoscolyn w Llanfair-yn-Neubwll *Ban* 67-71; TV 71-73; P-in-c Small Heath St Greg *Birm* 73-78; V 78-80; V Perry Barr 80-94; RD Handsworth 83-91; P-in-c Kingstanding St Luke 86-92; Hon Can Birm Cathl 87-94; rtd 94; Perm to Offic *Nor* from 94. *St Seiriol, Old Crown Yard, Walsingham NR22 6BU* Tel (01328) 820019

PARRY, Brychan Vaughan. b 13. Univ of Wales DipTh37. St Andr Coll Pampisford 41. **d** 42 **p** 42. C Bedminster St Paul *Bris* 42-44; CF (EC) 44-46; V Greenbank *Bris* 46-53; CF 53-69; V Gt Barton *St E* 69-78; rtd 78. *64 Cuckmere Road, Seaford BN25 4DJ* Tel (01323) 898273

PARRY, Canon David Allan. b 62. Bris Univ BSc83 Univ of Wales (Cardiff) CQSW88 DASS88. Trin Coll Bris DipHE94. **d** 94 **p** 95. C Withywood *Bris* 94-98; P-in-c Litherland St Phil *Liv* 98-02; V from 02; AD Bootle from 02; Hon Can Liv Cathl from 03. *St Philip's Vicarage, Orrell Road, Litherland, Liverpool L21 8NG* Tel 0151-928 3902

PARRY, David Thomas Newton. b 45. Selw Coll Cam BA67 MA71. Lambeth STh76 Cuddesdon Coll 67. **d** 69 **p** 70. C Oldham St Mary w St Pet *Man* 69-73; C Baguley 73-74; Tutor Sarum & Wells Th Coll 74-78; V Westleigh St Pet *Man* 78-88; TR E Farnworth and Kearsley 88-97; TR Chambersbury *St Alb*

97-03; V Blackbird Leys *Ox* from 03. *Church House, 5 Cuddesdon Way, Oxford OX4 6JH* Tel (01865) 778728
E-mail dtnparry@parsonage.u-net.com

PARRY, Denis. b 34. Sarum & Wells Th Coll 83. **d** 85 **p** 86. C Hubberston w Herbrandston and Hasguard etc *St D* 85-89; P-in-c Herbrandston and Hasguard w St Ishmael's 89-90; R 90-99; Dioc RE Adv 89-99; rtd 99. *Mayfield, Mill Stret, Kington HR5 3AL* Tel (01544) 230550

PARRY, Canon Dennis John. b 38. Univ of Wales (Lamp) BA60. St Mich Coll Llan 60. **d** 62 **p** 63. C Caerphilly *Llan* 62-64; C Aberdare St Fagan 64-67; Miss at Povungnituk Canada 67-69; R Gelligaer *Llan* 69-75; V Llanwnnog and Caersws w Carno *Ban* 75-89; V Llanidloes w Llangurig 89-01; RD Arwystli 89-01; Hon Can Ban Cathl 90-01; Can Cursal 97-01; rtd 02; Perm to Offic *Ban* from 02. *Lock Cottage, Groesfford, Brecon LD3 7UY* Tel (01874) 665400 E-mail dennis@stidloes.freeserve.co.uk

PARRY, Derek Nugent Goulding. b 32. Ely Th Coll 60. **d** 63 **p** 64. C Fareham SS Pet and Paul *Portsm* 63-67; C Portsea N End St Mark 67-74; P-in-c Piddletrenthide w Plush, Alton Pancras etc *Sarum* 74-92; rtd 92; Perm to Offic *Sarum* from 92. *Farthing Cottage, 12 Fordington Green, Dorchester DT1 1LU* Tel (01305) 269794

PARRY, Jane. See PARRY, Mrs Patricia Jane

PARRY, John Gareth. b 61. Univ of Wales (Abth) BA83 Univ of Wales (Ban) PGCE84. Westcott Ho Cam CTM96. **d** 96 **p** 97. C Holyhead *Ban* 96-99; C-in-c Llandinorwig w Penisa'r-waen 99-00; Perm to Offic from 00; Asst Master Bodedern Secondary Sch 00-01; Hd RE Pensby High Sch for Boys Wirral 02; Chapl and Hd RE Tettenhall Coll Wolv from 03. *34 Merton Park, Penmaenmawr LL34 6DH,* or *Tettenhall College, Wood Road, Wolverhampton WV6 8QX* Tel (01492) 622671 or (01902) 793010

PARRY, Keith Melville. b 31. ARICS65 Lon Univ DipRS83 MRICS01. S'wark Ord Course 80. **d** 83 **p** 84. NSM Bexley St Jo *Roch* 83-88; C Orpington All SS 88-96; rtd 96; Perm to Offic *Roch* from 96. *5 Greenside, Bexley DA5 3PA*

PARRY, Canon Kenneth Charles. b 34. Ripon Hall Ox 56. **d** 58 **p** 59. C Stoke *Cov* 58-61; Chapl RN 61-65; V Cradley *Worc* 65-70; V Gt Malvern H Trin 70-83; RD Malvern 74-83; Hon Can Worc Cathl 80-83; V Budleigh Salterton *Ex* 83-91; Can Res Ex Cathl 91-00; rtd 00. *Brook Cottage, Pye Corner, Kennford, Exeter EX6 7TB* Tel (01392) 832767 E-mail kcparry@ic24.net

PARRY, Ms Manon Ceridwen. b 69. Poly of Wales BA90 Selw Coll Cam BA93 MA97. Ridley Hall Cam CTM94. **d** 94 **p** 97. C Llandudno *Ban* 94-98; P-in-c Glanogwen w St Ann's w Llanllechid 98-99; V from 99. *Y Ficerdy, 5 Rhos-y-Nant, Bethesda, Bangor LL57 3PP* Tel (01248) 605149
E-mail manon@ogwen.demon.co.uk

PARRY, Canon Marilyn Marie. b 46. W Coll Ohio BA68 Man Univ MA77 PhD00. Epis Th Sch Cam Mass 68 Gilmore Ho 76. **dss** 79 **d** 87 **p** 94. Westleigh St Pet *Man* 78-85; Chapl Asst N Man Gen Hosp 85-90; Tutor N Ord Course 90-97; Dir Studies 91-97; Lic Preacher *Man* 90-94; Hon C E Farnworth and Kearsley 94-97; Nat Adv for Pre-Th Educn and Selection Sec Min Division Abps' Coun 97-01; Perm to Offic *St Alb* 97; Public Preacher 98-01; Can Res Ch Ch *Ox* from 01; Dioc Dir of Ords from 01. *Diocesan Church House, North Hinksey, Oxford OX2 0NB* Tel (01865) 276215 or 208289 Mobile 07712-834973 Fax (01865) 790470 or 208246
E-mail marilyn.parry@oxford.anglican.org

PARRY, Nicholas John Sinclair. b 56. Sarum & Wells Th Coll 82. **d** 85 **p** 86. C Hendon St Mary *Lon* 85-87; C Verwood *Sarum* 87-90; TV Witney *Ox* 90-96; V Costessey *Nor* from 96. *The Vicarage, Folgate Lane, Costessey, Norwich NR8 5DP* Tel (01603) 742818 E-mail nicholas.parry@btinternet.com

PARRY, Mrs Olwen Margaret. b 45. Cardiff Coll of Educn CertEd67. Llan Dioc Tr Scheme 88. **d** 92 **p** 97. NSM Newcastle *Llan* from 92. *17 Wernlys Road, Bridgend CF31 4NS* Tel (01656) 721860

PARRY, Owen Benjamin. b 42. St As Minl Tr Course 99. **d** 01 **p** 02. NSM Llangollen w Trevor and Llantysilio *St As* 01-03; C from 03. *Fairways, Halton, Chirk, Wrexham LL14 5BD* Tel (01691) 778484

PARRY, Mrs Patricia Jane. b 54. Liv Univ BTh99. N Ord Course 97. **d** 99 **p** 00. C Wilmslow *Ches* from 99. *25 Stanneylands Road, Wilmslow SK9 4EJ* Tel (01625) 533397
E-mail curate_wilmslow@hotmail.com

PARRY, Peter John. b 42. Westmr Coll Ox BTh99. EAMTC 99. **d** 01 **p** 02. NSM Montreux w Gstaad *Eur* from 01. *Les Muscaris, Route de Brent 25, CH-1807 Blonay, Switzerland* Tel (0041) (21) 943 4991 Fax as telephone E-mail pparry@compuserve.com

PARRY, Richard Neil. b 98 **p** 99. C Glan Ely *Llan* 98-00; C Merthyr Dyfan 00-02; TV Canton Cardiff from 02. *Canton Vicarage, 3A Romilly Road, Cardiff CF5 1FH* Tel (029) 2022 9683

PARRY, Richard Nigel. b 56. Univ of Wales (Cardiff) BD86. St Mich Coll Llan 82. **d** 86 **p** 87. C Holywell *St As* 86-90; V 96-00; V Berse and Southsea 90-96. *Address temp unknown*

PARRY, Miss Violet Margaret. b 30. Selly Oak Coll 53. **dss** 82 **d** 87. W Kilburn St Luke w St Simon and St Jude *Lon* 82-83;

St Marylebone St Mary 83-86; Stamford All SS w St Jo *Linc* 86-87; C 87-90; rtd 90; Perm to Offic *Linc* 90-01. *2 Stuart Court, High Street, Kibworth, Leicester LE8 0LR* Tel 0116-279 6858

PARRY, William Daniel. b 09. St Chad's Coll Dur BA31 DipTh32 MA34. **d** 32 **p** 33. C Tywyn *Ban* 32-36; C Dwygyfylchi 36-38; C Llanaber 38-45; V Arthog 45-48; V Llandinam 48-72; V Llandinam w Trefeglwys w Penstrowed 72-78; RD Arwystli 53-73; Can Ban Cathl 60-70; Chan 70-78; rtd 78; Lic to Offic *Ban* 78-96; Perm to Offic *St D* from 78. *14 Cae Mawr, Penrhyncoch, Aberystwyth SY23 3EJ* Tel (01970) 828118

PARRY-JENNINGS, Christopher William. b 34. Lon Coll of Div 57. **d** 60 **p** 62. C Claughton cum Grange *Ches* 60-63; C Folkestone H Trin w Ch Ch *Cant* 63-67; New Zealand from 67; V Lincoln 67-72; Chapl Cant Univ 68-72; V Riccarton St Jas 72-88; V Heathcote Mt Pleasant 88-96; First Gen Sec SPCK (NZ) 89-96; P Asst Upper Riccarton St Pet from 96. *22 Ambleside Drive, Burnside, Christchurch 8005, New Zealand* Tel (0064) (3) 358 9304 Fax as telephone

PARRY JONES, Leonard. b 29. Univ of Wales (Ban) BA52. St Mich Coll Llan 52. **d** 54 **p** 55. C Newtown w Llanllwchaiarn w Aberhafesp *St As* 54-58; C Abergele 58-60; V Pennant, Hirnant and Llangynog 60-65; V Llanynys w Llanychan 65-71; V Brynymaen w Trofarth 71-94; RD Rhos 77-94; rtd 94. *The Cottage, Kerry, Newtown SY16 4NU* Tel (01686) 670822

PARSELL, Howard Vivian. b 60. Univ of Wales (Lamp) BA87 Univ of Wales (Swansea) PGCE88. St Mich Coll Llan 93. **d** 94 **p** 95. C Builth and Llanddewi'r Cwm w Llangynog etc *S & B* 94-96; C Swansea St Thos and Kilvey 96-98; P-in-c Swansea St Jude from 98; Chapl to the Deaf from 98. *St Jude's Vicarage, Hillside Crescent, Uplands, Swansea SA2 0RD* Tel (01792) 473154

PARSELLE, Stephen Paul. b 53. LTh. St Jo Coll Nottm. **d** 82 **p** 83. C Boscombe St Jo *Win* 82-86; CF from 86. *c/o MOD Chaplains (Army)* Tel (01980) 615804 Fax 615800
E-mail parselle@aol.com

PARSONAGE, Robert Hugh. b 55. Nottm Trent Univ BSc78. Trin Coll Bris BA97. **d** 97 **p** 98. C Chell *Lich* 97-01; R Poringland *Nor* from 01. *The Rectory, Rectory Lane, Poringland, Norwich NR14 7SL* Tel (01508) 492215
E-mail robert@hparsonage.freeserve.co.uk

PARSONAGE, Robert Leslie. b 20. St Aid Birkenhead 43. **d** 46 **p** 47. C Farnworth *Liv* 46-47; C Bowdon *Ches* 47-51; V Everton St Geo *Liv* 51-52; CF 52-74; V Bayswater *Lon* 74-83; Perm to Offic 83-88; Preacher Newland Almshouses Glos 88-96; rtd 83; Perm to Offic *Glouc* from 96. *36 St Mary's Square, Gloucester GL1 2QT* Tel (01452) 309459

PARSONS, Andrew David. b 53. UEA BA74 Fitzw Coll Cam BA77 MA81. Westcott Ho Cam 75. **d** 78 **p** 79. C Hellesdon *Nor* 78-82; C Eaton 82-85; P-in-c Burnham Thorpe w Burnham Overy 85-87; R Burnham Sutton w Burnham Ulph etc 85-87; R Burnham Gp of Par 87-93; P-in-c Wroxham w Hoveton and Belaugh 93; R from 93; RD St Benet from 99. *The Vicarage, 11 Church Lane, Wroxham, Norwich NR12 8SH* Tel (01603) 782678 E-mail 2andrew@andrewparsons.fsnet.co.uk

PARSONS, Andrew Philip. b 50. Aston Univ BSc76 DipArch76 RIBA80. St Jo Coll Nottm Dip Th & Min 95. **d** 95 **p** 96. C Langdon Hills *Chelmsf* 95-99; P-in-c Gt Warley and Ingrave St Nic 99-01; V Ingrave St Nic and St Steph from 01. *The Rectory, Thorndon Gate, Ingrave, Brentwood CM13 3RG* Tel (01277) 812190 E-mail therector@btopenworld.com

PARSONS, Arthur. b 45. St Jo Coll Nottm LTh. **d** 75 **p** 76. C Cuddington *Guildf* 75-78; C Liskeard w St Keyne and St Pinnock *Truro* 78-81; P-in-c Ludgvan 81-83; R 83-99; Chapl Falmouth Fire Brigade 91-99; P-in-c Perranuthnoe 93-99; RD Penwith 93-98; TR Newton Tracey, Horwood, Alverdiscott etc *Ex* 99-02; C Chudleigh w Chudleigh Knighton and Trusham 02-03; C Okehampton w Inwardleigh, Bratton Clovelly etc from 03. *St Bridget's House, Bridestowe, Okehampton EX20 4ER* Tel (01837) 861612 E-mail arthur.parsons@btinternet.com

PARSONS, Arthur Gordon Boyd (Father Bob). b 20. TD50. SSC FCIPD47. Ripon Hall Ox BA54. **d** 56 **p** 57. C Doncaster St Mary *Sheff* 56-58; V N Wilford St Faith *S'well* 58-60; R W w E Allington and Sedgebrook *Linc* 60-66; P-in-c Woolsthorpe 60-64; R 64-66; V Grantham St Anne 66-69; Offg Chapl RAF 65-74; V Friskney *Linc* 69-74; R Tansor w Cotterstock and Fotheringhay *Pet* 74-76; V Forest Town *S'well* 76-78; V Sutton cum Lound 78-85; rtd 85; P-in-c Sampford Courtenay w Honeychurch *Ex* 85-87; P-in-c Exbourne w Jacobstowe 85-87; Hon C Holsworthy w Hollacombe and Milton Damerel 87-88; Hon C Bude Haven *Truro* 88-89; Hon C Stratton and Launcells 89-95; Perm to Offic *Linc* 95-96; B & W from 00; *Derby* from 01. *30 Penn Lane, Melbourne, Derby DE73 1EQ* Tel (01332) 694375

PARSONS, Bernard. b 26. Ely Th Coll 60. **d** 62 **p** 63. C Bourne *Linc* 62-64; V Pinchbeck 64-71; V Sutton Bridge 71-83; R Coningsby w Tattershall 83-93; rtd 93; Perm to Offic *Linc* from 93. *12 St Peter's Drive, Woodhall Spa LN10 6SY* Tel (01526) 353027

PARSONS, Christopher James Hutton. b 54. Univ of Wales (Ban) BA75 Birm Univ DipTh78. Qu Coll Birm. **d** 79 **p** 80. C

Crowthorne *Ox* 79-83; V Tilehurst St Cath 83-88; P-in-c Wrentham w Benacre, Covehithe, Frostenden etc *St E* 89-91; R 91-94. *35 Tufton Gardens, West Molesey KT8 1TD*
PARSONS, David. b 37. SOAS Lon 57 Qu Coll Cam BA61 MA98 ARCO75. Ridley Hall Cam 61. **d** 62 **p** 63. C Ormskirk *Liv* 62-65; C Beccles St Mich *St E* 65-68; V Woodbridge St Jo 68-73; Chapl Edgarley Hall Sch Glastonbury 73-78; Asst Master Bruton Sch for Girls 78-98; Chapl 86-98; C Downend *Bris* 98-02; rtd 02. *13 Ivythorn Road, Street BA16 0TE* Tel (01458) 446110 Mobile 07966-367099 E-mail david.parsons@ndirect.co.uk
PARSONS, David Norman. b 39. FCIB83. Trin Coll Bris 92. **d** 94 **p** 95. NSM Swindon Dorcan *Bris* 94-03. *31 Couzens Close, Chipping Sodbury, Bristol BS37 6BT* Tel (01454) 323070 E-mail david.parsons39@virgin.net
PARSONS, Desmond John. b 25. Coll of Resurr Mirfield 65. **d** 66 **p** 67. C Purley St Mark *S'wark* 66-70; V W Dulwich All SS and Em 71-83; R Limpsfield and Titsey 83-95; rtd 95; Perm to Offic *S'wark* from 96; Perm to Offic *Guildf* from 96. *Priors House, The Court, Croft Lane, Crondall, Farnham GU10 5QF* Tel (01252) 851137
PARSONS, Geoffrey Fairbanks. b 35. Trin Coll Cam BA58 MA68. Ridley Hall Cam 59. **d** 61 **p** 62. C Over St Chad *Ches* 61-64; C Heswall 64-69; V Congleton St Steph 69-75; V Weaverham 75-94; P-in-c Backford and Capenhurst 94-00; R 00-01; rtd 01; Perm to Offic *Ches* from 02. *28 Springcroft, Parkgate, South Wirral CH64 6SE* Tel (0151) 336 3354
PARSONS, George Edward. b 35. St D Coll Lamp BA60 Ripon Hall Ox 60. **d** 62 **p** 63. C Leominster *Heref* 62-66; NSM Bromfield 67-72; NSM Culmington w Onibury 67-72; NSM Stanton Lacy 67-72; NSM Ludlow 72-77; P-in-c Caynham 77-79; NSM Bishop's Cleeve *Glouc* 79-91; Sub-Chapl HM Pris Glouc 88-91; P-in-c Hasfield w Tirley and Ashleworth 91-00; P-in-c Maisemore 91-00; rtd 00; Perm to Offic *Glouc* 00-02; *Blackb* from 02. *Ballalona, 2 The Meadows, Hollins Lane, Forton, Preston PR3 0AF* Tel (01524) 792656
PARSONS, George Horace Norman. b 19. S'wark Ord Course 65. **d** 68 **p** 69. C Hatcham St Cath *S'wark* 68-72; C Horley 72-76; P-in-c S Wimbledon All SS 76-78; P-in-c Caterham 78-81; C 82-84; Chapl St Lawr Hosp Caterham 82-84; RAChD 72-84; rtd 85; Perm to Offic *S'wark* from 85. *8 Russell Road, Mitcham CR4 3AP* Tel (020) 8646 4386
PARSONS, Gilbert Harvey. b 20. St Pet Hall Ox BA46 MA46. Cuddesdon Coll 48. **d** 50 **p** 51. C Clapham St Pet *S'wark* 50-51; C Charlton St Luke w St Paul 51-56; V Stokenchurch and PC Cadmore End 56-61; V Stokenchurch and Cadmore End *Ox* 61-72; P-in-c Radnage 65-68; P-in-c Ibstone w Fingest 65-72; RD Aston 66-72; V Burford w Fulbrook 72-74; V Burford w Fulbrook and Taynton 74-85; rtd 85; Perm to Offic *Sarum* from 85. *Windrush, 23 Highlands Way, Whiteparish, Salisbury SP5 2SZ* Tel (01794) 884832
PARSONS, Jeffrey Michael Langdon. b 41. Univ of Wales (Lamp) BA72 MACE92. St Jo Coll Morpeth ThL62 OStJ81. **d** 66 **p** 68. Australia 66-68 and from 78; C Cardigan w Mwnt and Y Ferwig *St D* 69-70; C Buckhurst Hill *Chelmsf* 70-71; Chapl Bancroft's Sch Woodford Green 72-75; R Lambourne w Abridge and Stapleford Abbotts *Chelmsf* 75-78; Foundn Chapl St Pet Colleg Girls' Sch Adelaide 78-80; Dean and R St D Cathl Hobart 80-83; Foundn Chapl St Mich Coll Girls' Sch Hobart 83-86; Chapl Cranbrook Sch Sydney 87-92; Dep Hd Master 92-96; OStJ from 81; KStJ from 95; R Lakemba 99-01; rtd 01. *10 Dixon Street, Moss Vale, NSW, Australia 2577* Tel (0061) (2) 4868 2079 Mobile 410-507610 E-mail jmlparsons@yahoo.com.au
PARSONS, Jennifer Anne (Jeni). b 53. Univ of Wales (Lamp) BA76 MA78 Jes Coll Cam PhD90. Westcott Ho Cam CTM94. **d** 94 **p** 95. C Halesowen *Worc* 94-97; TV Worc St Barn w Ch Ch from 97. *214 Tolladine Road, Worcester WR4 9AU* Tel (01905) 617972 E-mail jeni@hencity.fsnet.co.uk
PARSONS, Canon John Banham. b 43. Selw Coll Cam BA65 MA68. Ridley Hall Cam 65. **d** 67 **p** 68. C Downend *Bris* 67-71; Public Preacher Withywood LEP 71-77; P-in-c Hengrove 77-78; V 78-85; V Letchworth St Paul w Willian *St Alb* 85-94; P-in-c Barking St Marg w St Patr *Chelmsf* 94-98; TR from 98; RD Barking and Dagenham from 00; Hon Can Chelmsf Cathl from 01. *The Rectory, 166 Longbridge Road, Barking IG11 8SS* Tel (020) 8594 2932 *or* 8594 4513
PARSONS, Laurie. b 19. Keble Coll Ox BA41. Wells Th Coll 41. **d** 43 **p** 44. C Westwood *Cov* 43-49; C-in-c Galley Common Stockingford CD 49-57; V Priors Marston 57-69; V Radford Semele 70-83; V Radford Semele and Ufton 83-84; rtd 84; Perm to Offic *Cov* 84-92; Perm to Offic *Pet* from 84. *86 Bull Baulk, Middleton Cheney, Banbury OX17 2SR* Tel (01295) 711829
PARSONS, Mrs Margaret Anne. b 31. Sheff Poly CQSW77. EMMTC 73. **dss** 77 **d** 87 **p** 94. Dronfield *Derby* 77-89; Par Dn 87-89; Par Dn Tidworth, Ludgershall and Faberstown *Sarum* 89-94; C 94-95; P-in-c Wold-Marsh Gp *Linc* 95-99; P-in-c Perlethorpe *S'well* 00-03. *6 Ringwood Avenue, Mansfield, Nottingham NG18 4DA* Tel (01623) 422745
PARSONS, Canon Marlene Beatrice. b 43. Wilson Carlile Coll. **dss** 76 **d** 87 **p** 94. Coulsdon St Jo *S'wark* 76-79; Hill *Birm* 79-86;

Dioc Lay Min Adv 80-90; Vice Prin WMMTC 86-90; Dioc Dir of Ords *Birm* from 90; Dean of Women's Min from 90; Hon Can Birm Cathl from 89. *20 Copperbeech Close, Birmingham B32 2HT* Tel 0121-426 4527 Fax 428 1114 E-mail ddo@birmingham.anglican.org
PARSONS, Miss Mary Elizabeth. b 43. Wilson Carlile Coll 65. **dss** 78 **d** 87 **p** 94. Chapl Asst Chu Hosp Ox 78-89; Chapl 89-93; rtd 93; NSM Sandford-on-Thames *Ox* 94-00. *20 Copperbeech Close, Birmingham B32 2HT* Tel 0121-426 4527
PARSONS, Canon Michael William Semper. b 47. St Cath Coll Ox BA69 MA74 DPhil74 Selw Coll Cam BA77 MA81. Ridley Hall Cam 75. **d** 78 **p** 79. C Edmonton All SS *Lon* 78-81; SPCK Research Fell Dur Univ 81-84; Hon Lect Th 84-85; SPCK Fell N of England Inst for Chr Educn 84-85; P-in-c Derby St Aug *Derby* 85-95; TR Walbrook Epiphany 95-96; Dioc Voc Adv 86-96; P-in-c Hempsted *Glouc* 96-00; Dir of Ords from 96; Dir Curates' Tr from 00; Hon Can Glouc Cathl from 03. *6 Spa Villas, Montpellier, Gloucester GL1 1LB* Tel (01452) 524550 E-mail mparsons@glosdioc.org.uk *or* mike.parsons@theology.ox.ac
PARSONS, Canon Robert Martin. b 43. Qu Coll Cam BA65 MA69. ALCD68. **d** 68 **p** 69. C Chapeltown *Sheff* 68-71; C Sheff St Jo 71-75; V Swadlincote *Derby* 75-91; RD Repton 81-91; P-in-c Gresley 82-86; R Etwall w Egginton 91-93; Can Res Derby Cathl 93-98; P-in-c Belper 98-03; V from 03; Hon Can Derby Cathl from 98. *St Peter's Vicarage, Chesterfield Road, Belper DE56 1FD* Tel (01773) 822148 E-mail canonparsons@totalise.co.uk
PARSONS, Roger John. b 37. Sarum Th Coll 62. **d** 65 **p** 66. C Bitterne Park *Win* 65-69; C Clerkenwell H Redeemer w St Phil *Lon* 69-72; C Willesden St Andr 72-76; C St Laur in Thanet *Cant* 76-81; Chapl Luton and Dunstable Hosp 81-86; Chapl St Mary's Hosp Luton 81-86; C Luton All SS w St Pet *St Alb* 81-86; Trustee St Benedict's Trust from 85; TV E Dereham *Nor* 86-88; TV E Dereham and Scarning 89; Perm to Offic 89-93. *478 Station Road, Sheringham NR26 8RG*
PARSONS, Stephen Christopher. b 45. Keble Coll Ox BA67 MA72 BLitt78. Cuddesdon Coll 68. **d** 70 **p** 71. C Whitstable All SS *Cant* 70-71; C Croydon St Sav 71-74; Perm to Offic *Ox* 74-76; C St Laur in Thanet *Cant* 76-79; V Lugwardine w Bartestree and Weston Beggard *Heref* 79-87; V Lechlade *Glouc* 87-03; R Edin St Cuth *Edin* from 03. *6 Westgarth Avenue, Colinton, Edinburgh EH13 0BD* Tel 0131-441 3557 E-mail stephen@parsons252262.freeserve.co.uk
PARSONS, Stephen Drury. b 54. Qu Mary Coll Lon BSc76 CCC Cam MSc79. Westcott Ho Cam 79. **d** 82 **p** 83. C Stretford All SS *Man* 82-85; C Newton Heath All SS 85-86; V Ashton St Jas 86-90; Perm to Offic from 01. *150 Henrietta Street, Ashton-under-Lyne OL6 8PH* Tel 0161-308 2852
PARTINGTON, The Ven Brian Harold. b 36. OBE02. St Aid Birkenhead 60. **d** 63 **p** 64. C Barlow Moor *Man* 63-66; C Deane 66-68; V Patrick *S & M* 68-96; Bp's Youth Chapl 68-77; RD Peel 76-96; P-in-c German St Jo 77-78; V 78-96; P-in-c Foxdale 77-78; V 78-96; Can St German's Cathl 85-96; Adn Man from 96; V Douglas St Geo from 96. *St George's Vicarage, 16 Devonshire Road, Douglas, Isle of Man IM2 3QY* Tel (01624) 675430 Fax 616136 E-mail archd-sodor@mcb.net
PARTINGTON, Kenneth. b 41. Lanc Univ MA86. Ripon Hall Ox. **d** 70 **p** 71. C Atherton *Man* 70-72; C Kippax *Ripon* 72-75; V Cartmel Fell *Carl* 75-95; V Crosthwaite Kendal 75-95; V Witherslack 75-95; V Winster 78-95; rtd 01; Perm to Offic *Carl* from 01. *The Old Cottage, Lindeth, Windermere LA23 3NH* Tel (01539) 447174
PARTINGTON, Kevin. b 51. Huddersfield Poly BA73. St Jo Coll Nottm DCM93. **d** 93 **p** 94. C Salterhebble All SS *Wakef* 93-96; V Pontefract All SS 96-03; TR Dewsbury from 03. *The Rectory, 16A Oxford Road, Dewsbury WF13 4JT* Tel (01924) 465491 *or* 457057 E-mail kevin.partington@btopenworld.com
PARTINGTON, Peter John. b 57. Peterho Cam MA. St Jo Coll Nottm 79. **d** 81 **p** 82. C Cov H Trin *Cov* 81-85; C Woking St Jo *Guildf* 85-87; C 94-99; R Busbridge 87-94; Dir of Ords from 94. *80 York Road, Woking GU22 7XR* Tel (01483) 769759 E-mail revpjp@aol.com *or* ddoguildford@aol.com
PARTRIDGE, Alan Christopher. b 55. Thames Poly BA77 Ex Univ PGCE78. St Jo Coll Nottm MA00. **d** 00 **p** 01. C Woking St Jo *Guildf* from 00; TV Ely from 03. *20 Barton Road, Ely CB7 4DE* E-mail alanc.partridge@lineone.net
PARTRIDGE, Anthony John. b 38. Univ of Wales (Lamp) BA61 Linacre Ho Ox BA63 K Coll Lon PhD77. St Steph Ho Ox 61. **d** 64 **p** 65. C Sydenham All SS *S'wark* 64-67; Hon C 68-74; Lic to Offic from 74; Prin Lect Thames Poly 75-92; Greenwich Univ from 92; rtd 03. *40 Upwood Road, London SE12 8AN,* or *University of Greenwich, Wellington Street, London SE18 6PF* Tel (020) 8318 9901 *or* 8854 2030
PARTRIDGE, Canon David John Fabian. b 36. Ball Coll Ox BA60 MA. Westcott Ho Cam 60. **d** 62 **p** 63. C Halliwell St Thos *Man* 62-65; C St Martin-in-the-Fields *Lon* 65-69; R Warblington w Emsworth *Portsm* 69-01; Hon Can Portsm Cathl 84-01; rtd 01. *83 Hamilton Road, Oxford OX2 7DP* Tel (01865) 558630

PARTRIDGE, Ian Starr. b 36. Linc Th Coll 87. **d** 89 **p** 90. C Barton upon Humber *Linc* 89-92; P-in-c Barkwith Gp 92-97; R 97-02; rtd 02; Perm to Offic *Linc* from 02; RD Calcewaithe and Candleshoe from 03. *Altair, 4 Thames Street, Louth LN11 7AD* Tel (01507) 600398 E-mail ian@altair.org.uk

PARTRIDGE, Miss Margaret Edith. b 35. Birm Univ DipTh68. Gilmore Ho 63. **dss** 85 **d** 87 **p** 94. Amblecote *Worc* 85-89; Par Dn 87-89; C Borehamwood *St Alb* 89-94; TV 94-00; rtd 00; Perm to Offic *Birm* from 01. *4 Cornerstone Drive, Maryland Drive, Birmingham B31 2AT* Tel 0121-476 0854

PARTRIDGE, Martin David Waud. b 38. Ox NSM Course 86. **d** 89 **p** 90. NSM Wargrave *Ox* 89-97; NSM Schorne from 97. *The Rectory, Church Street, Quainton, Aylesbury HP22 4AP* Tel (01296) 655237

PARTRIDGE, Michael John. b 61. St Edm Hall Ox BA83 MA89 St Jo Coll Dur BA86. Cranmer Hall Dur 84. **d** 87 **p** 88. C Amington *Birm* 87-90; C Sutton Coldfield H Trin 90-93; P-in-c W Exe *Ex* 93-01; RD Tiverton 96-00; V Tiverton St Geo and St Paul from 01. *St Paul's Vicarage, Bakers Hill, Tiverton EX16 5NE* Tel (01884) 255705
E-mail mike@stpaulstiv.freeserve.co.uk

PARTRIDGE, Ronald Malcolm. b 49. Lon Univ DipTh73 DAC94. Bris Bapt Coll LTh74 Cuddesdon Coll 74. **d** 75 **p** 76. C Bris St Andr Hartcliffe *Bris* 75-78; C E Bris 78-82; V Easton All Hallows 82-85; TV Brighton St Pet w Chpl Royal and St Jo *Chich* 85-86; TV Brighton St Pet and St Nic w Chpl Royal 86-88; C-in-c Bermondsey St Hugh CD *S'wark* 88-90; Asst Chapl Gt Ormond Street Hosp for Sick Children Lon 91-94; Asst Chapl Gt Ormond Street Hosp for Children NHS Trust 94-97. *29 All Saints Street, Hastings BN34 3BJ* Tel (01424) 715219

PARTRIDGE, Ronald William. b 42. Shimer Coll Illinois BA64. Cant Sch of Min 93. **d** 96 **p** 97. NSM Upchurch w Lower Halstow *Cant* from 96. *4 The Green, Lower Halstow, Sittingbourne ME9 7DT* Tel (01795) 842007 Fax as telephone
E-mail revdron@aol.com

PARTRIDGE, Canon Timothy Reeve. b 39. Lon Univ BSc60 AKC60. Wells Th Coll 60. **d** 62 **p** 63. C Glouc St Cath *Glouc* 62-65; C Sutton St Nicholas *Linc* 65-74; R Bugbrooke *Pet* 74-95; P-in-c Kislingbury w Rothersthorpe 95; RD Daventry 81-88; Can Pet Cathl from 83; Warden of Par Ev from 96. *The Rectory, Church Lane, Bugbrooke, Northampton NN7 3PB* Tel (01604) 830373
E-mail canontp@aol.com

PASCHAL, Brother. See WORTON, David Reginald

PASCOE, Michael Lewis. b 43. OLM course 96. **d** 99 **p** 00. OLM Crowan and Treslothan *Truro* 99-02; C from 02; OLM Penponds 01-02; C Penponds from 02. *Genesis, Bosparva Lane, Leedstown, Hayle TR27 6DN* Tel (01736) 850425
E-mail revdmike@supanet.com

PASK, Howard. b 54. St Jo Coll Nottm DipTM99. **d** 99 **p** 00. C Todmorden *Wakef* 99-02; P-in-c Hebden Bridge 02-03; P-in-c Heptonstall 02-03; V Hebden Bridge and Heptonstall from 03. *The Vicarage, 12 Becketts Close, Heptonstall, Hebden Bridge HX7 7LJ* Tel (01422) 842138 Mobile 07779-243176
E-mail howard@thepasksare.screaming.net

PASKETT, Ms Margaret Anne. b 45. York Univ BSc81 Leeds Univ MEd83. NEOC 84. **d** 87 **p** 94. Par Dn Marske in Cleveland *York* 87-91; C 92-96; Dioc Adv for Diaconal Mins 92-96; P-in-c Hemingbrough from 96. *The Vicarage, Hemingbrough, Selby YO8 7QG* Tel (01757) 638528

PASKINS, David James. b 52. Univ of Wales (Lamp) BA73 Trin Hall Cam BA76 MA81. Westcott Ho Cam 74. **d** 77 **p** 78. C St Peter-in-Thanet *Cant* 77-80; C Swanage *Sarum* 80-82; R Waldron *Chich* 82-92; R Bere Ferrers *Ex* 92-96; V Lockerley and E Dean w E and W Tytherley *Win* 96-03; R Cranborne w Boveridge, Edmondsham etc *Sarum* from 03. *The Rectory, Grugs Lane, Cranborne, Wimborne BH21 5PX* Tel (01725) 517232

PASSANT, Keith. b 39. St Jo Coll Dur BA62 CertEd70. St Alb Minl Tr Scheme 77. **d** 87 **p** 88. C Hatfield Hyde *St Alb* 87-93; rtd 93; Perm to Offic *St Alb* from 93. *26 Monk's Rise, Welwyn Garden City AL8 7NF* Tel (01707) 332889

PASTERFIELD, Canon Dunstan Patrick. b 17. Clare Coll Cam BA49 MA53. Cuddesdon Coll 49. **d** 51 **p** 51. C Dennington *St E* 51-53; Canada from 53; Hon Can Calgary 78-82. *203-83 Michener Drive, Regina SK, Canada, S4V 0L1* Tel (001) (306) 761 9185 Fax 761 2608 E-mail dppasterfield@net1fx.com

PATCH, Simon John. b 63. Aus Nat Univ BA87. Chich Th Coll BTh95. **d** 95 **p** 96. C Ifield *Chich* 95-99; TV from 99; C Stepney St Dunstan and All SS *Lon* from 03. *St Faith's House, Shandy Street, London E1 4ST*

PATCHELL, Miss Gwendoline Rosa (Wendy). b 49. Goldsmiths' Coll Lon BA69 TCert70. Trin Coll Bris DipHE92. **d** 92 **p** 94. C Ashton-upon-Mersey St Mary *Ches* 92-98; TV Hemel Hempstead *St Alb* from 98. *St Paul's Vicarage, 23 Saturn Way, Hemel Hempstead HP2 5NY* Tel (01442) 255023
E-mail wendypatchell@surfaid.org

PATCHING, Colin John. b 47. Linc Th Coll 84. **d** 86 **p** 87. C Farnley *Ripon* 86-89; C Didcot St Pet *Ox* 89-92; P-in-c Steventon

w Milton from 92. *The Vicarage, 73 Field Gardens, Steventon, Abingdon OX11 6TF* Tel (01235) 831243

PATE, Barry Emile Charles. b 50. NE Lon Poly BA80 CQSW80. S'wark Ord Course 85. **d** 88 **p** 89. NSM E Dulwich St Jo *S'wark* 88-92; C Farnborough *Roch* 92-94; C Broxbourne w Wormley *St Alb* 94-00; V Wilbury from 00. *Church House, 103 Bedford Road, Letchworth Garden City SG6 4DU* Tel (01462) 623119

PATEL, Miss Urmila Devi. b 59. Essex Univ BSc82. Chich Th Coll 90. **d** 92 **p** 94. Par Dn Leek and Meerbrook *Lich* 92-94; C 94-97; TV Hackney Marsh *Lon* 97-01. *Address withheld by request*

PATEMAN, Edward Brian. b 29. Leeds Univ BA51. Qu Coll Birm 51. **d** 53 **p** 54. C Stockton St Pet *Dur* 53-57; Lect Bolton St Pet 57-58; V Coxhoe 58-65; V Dalton le Dale 65-93; RD Houghton 72-75; R Hawthorn 88-93; rtd 93. *27 Atherton Drive, Houghton le Spring DH4 6TA* Tel 0191-385 3168

PATEN, Richard Alfred. b 32. Ch Coll Cam BA56 MA60 CEng60 MICE60. Ripon Hall Ox 61. **d** 63 **p** 64. C Oadby *Leic* 63-67; C Pet St Mark *Pet* 67-71; Chapl Community Relns 71-95; Bp's Dioc Chapl 73-85; rtd 97; Perm to Offic *Pet* from 93. *263 Eastfield Road, Peterborough PE1 4BH* Tel (01733) 562089

PATERNOSTER, Canon Michael Cosgrove. b 35. Pemb Coll Cam BA59 MA63. Cuddesdon Coll 59. **d** 61 **p** 62. C Surbiton St Andr *S'wark* 61-63; Chapl Qu Coll Dundee 63-68; Dioc Supernumerary *Bre* 63-68; Chapl Dundee Univ 67-68; Sen Fellowship of SS Alb and Sergius 68-71; R Dollar *St And* 71-75; R Stonehaven *Bre* 75-90; Hon Can St Paul's Cathl Dundee 81-00; R Aberdeen St Jas *Ab* 90-00; rtd 00; Perm to Offic *B & W* from 00. *12 Priest Row, Wells BA5 2PY*

PATERSON (née SOAR), Mrs Angela Margaret. b 59. Aston Univ MSc81 MCIPD82. St Alb and Ox Min Course 97. **d** 00 **p** 01. NSM Icknield *Ox* from 00. *86 Hill Road, Watlington OX49 5AF* Tel (01491) 614034
E-mail angela@patersonlink.co.uk

PATERSON, David. b 33. Ch Ch Ox BA55 MA58. Linc Th Coll 56. **d** 58 **p** 59. C Kidderminster St Mary *Worc* 58-60; C Wolverhampton St Geo *Lich* 60-64; V Loughborough St Pet *Leic* from 64. *St Peter's Vicarage, 129 Ashby Road, Loughborough LE11 3AB* Tel (01509) 263047

PATERSON, Douglas Monro. b 30. Em Coll Cam BA54 MA57. Tyndale Hall Bris 55. **d** 57 **p** 58. C Walcot *B & W* 57-60; C Portman Square St Paul *Lon* 60-62; Lect Oak Hill Th Coll 60-62; Min Hampstead St Jo Downshire Hill Prop Chpl *Lon* 62-65; Lect All Nations Chr Coll Ware 62-65; Rwanda 67-73; C Edin St Thos *Edin* 73-75; Lect Northumbria Bible Coll 73-94; Perm to Offic *Edin* 75-94; Lic to Offic *Newc* 76-94; rtd 94; Perm to Offic *Ox* from 94. *3 Penn Mead, Church Road, Penn, High Wycombe HP10 8NY* Tel (01494) 812496

PATERSON, Geoffrey Gordon. b 45. Cant Univ (NZ) LTh69. **d** 69 **p** 70. New Zealand 69-74; P-in-c Astwood Bank w Crabbs Cross *Worc* 78-80; New Zealand from 80; V Halswell-Prebbleton from 80. *19 Ridder Place, Christchurch 8003, New Zealand* Tel (0064) (3) 322 7787 or 365 3211

PATERSON, Gordon Ronald (Ron). b 16. MBE57. Ripon Hall Ox 58. **d** 59 **p** 60. C Warblington w Emsworth *Portsm* 59-62; V Swanmore St Barn 62-85; RD Bishop's Waltham 79-82; rtd 85; Perm to Offic *Win* 85-95; Perm to Offic *Portsm* from 85. *28 Eastways, Bishops Waltham, Southampton SO32 1EX* Tel (01489) 895671

PATERSON, James Beresford. b 21. DSC42. St Andr Univ MPhil85 FRSA93. Westcott Ho Cam 59. **d** 61 **p** 62. C Woodbridge St Mary *St E* 61-64; R Broughty Ferry *Bre* 64-72; Dioc Supernumerary 72-75; Sec Scottish Ch Action for World Development 72-79; P-in-c Glencarse 76-84; Dioc Sec 79-84; Hon Can St Paul's Cathl Dundee 79-89; rtd 84; Perm to Offic *Bre* from 84; Perm to Offic *St E* from 84. *67 Ipswich Road, Woodbridge IP12 4BT* Tel (01394) 383512

PATERSON, Mrs Jennifer Ann. b 49. Brooklands Tech Coll 69. S Dios Minl Tr Scheme 85. **d** 88 **p** 95. C Hale *Guildf* 88-92; NSM Seale, Puttenham and Wanborough 95-01; rtd 01; Perm to Offic *Guildf* 94-95 and from 01. *4 St George's Close, Badshot Lea, Farnham GU9 9LZ* Tel (01252) 316775
E-mail buao91@exchange.uk.com

✠**PATERSON, The Rt Revd John Campbell.** b 45. Auckland Univ BA66 LTh69. **d** 69 **p** 70. C 95. C Waimangu 69-71; V Waimate N Maori Pastorate 71-76; P-in-c S Hokianga 73-74; P-in-c S Bay of Is 74-75; P Asst Maori Miss Auckland 76-82; Temp CF 76-84; Chapl Qu Victoria Sch 76-82; Sec Bishopric of Aotearoa 78-87; Prov Sec 86-92; Gen Sec Angl Ch in Aotearoa, NZ and Polynesia 92-95; Bp Auckland from 95; Presiding Bp and Primate New Zealand from 98. *PO Box 37 242, Parnell, Auckland 1033, New Zealand* Tel (0064) (9) 302 7202 Fax 302 7217 E-mail bishop.auckland@xtra.co.nz

PATERSON, The Very Revd John Thomas Farquhar. b 38. TCD BA61 MA64 BD71. CITC 63. **d** 63 **p** 64. C Drumglass *Arm* 63-65; C Dublin St Bart *D & G* 66-68; Min Can St Patr Cathl Dublin 67-83; Asst Dean of Residence TCD 68-72; C-in-c Dublin St Mark *D & G* 68-71; I Dublin St Bart w Leeson Park 72-78; Dean Kildare *M & K* 78-89; I Kildare w Kilmeague and

Curragh 78-89; Lect Past Liturgy CITC 85-91; Hon Sec Gen Syn 85-91; Dean Ch Ch Cathl Dublin *D & G* from 89; I Dublin Ch Ch Cathl Gp from 89; Dio Radio Officer 91-94. *The Deanery, St Werburgh Street, Dublin 8, Irish Republic* Tel (00353) (1) 478 1797 *or* 677 8099 Fax 475 3442 *or* 679 8991
E-mail dean@dublin.anglican.org *or* paterson@iol.ie

PATERSON, Nigel John Merrick. b 53. Lanc Univ BEd75 Open Univ MA89. Dioc OLM tr scheme 99. **d** 01. OLM N Walsham w Antingham *Nor* from 01. *Marshgate Cottage, Marshgate, North Walsham NR28 9LG* Tel (01692) 406259 Mobile 07786-381361
E-mail nigelpaterson@marshgatecottage.freeserve.co.uk

PATERSON, Rex Douglas Trevor. b 27. AKC54. **d** 55 **p** 56. C Maidenhead St Luke *Ox* 55-58; C Littlehampton St Mary *Chich* 58-62; V Woodingdean 62-73; V Ferring 73-94; rtd 94; Perm to Offic *Chich* from 94. *4 Clapham Close, Clapham, Worthing BN13 3XA* Tel (01906) 74396

PATERSON, Robert Mar Erskine. b 49. St Jo Coll Dur BA71 DipTh72 MA82. **d** 72 **p** 73. C Harpurhey St Steph and Harpurhey Ch Ch *Man* 72-73; C Sketty *S & B* 73-78; R Llangattock and Llangynidr *Llan* 78-83; V Gabalfa *Llan* 83-94; TR Cowbridge 94-00; Prin Officer Ch in Wales Coun for Miss and Min from 00. *Council for Mission and Ministry, 39 Cathedral Road, Cardiff CF11 9XF* Tel (029) 2034 8209 *or* (01446) 793150 Fax (029) 2038 7835
E-mail principal.cmm@churchinwales.org.uk

PATERSON, Robin Fergus (Robert). b 32. Moore Th Coll Sydney 83. **d** 87 **p** 89. Singapore 87-88; NSM Crieff *St And* 88-92; NSM Comrie 88-92; R Dunkeld 93-98; R Strathtay 93-98; rtd 98; Lic to Offic *St And* and *Eur* from 98. *Corsie Hill House, Corsiehill, Perth PH2 7BN* Tel (01738) 446621

PATERSON, Robin Lennox Andrew. b 43. N Ord Course 84. **d** 87 **p** 88. C Manston *Ripon* 87-91; P-in-c Leeds All So 91-95; V 95-98; V Middleton St Mary from 98. *Middleton Vicarage, 198 Town Street, Leeds LS10 3TJ* Tel 0113-270 5689 Mobile 07778-860178 E-mail rlap@ntlworld.com

PATERSON, Rodney John. b 62. Keele Univ BA84. St Jo Coll Nottm MA98. **d** 98 **p** 99. C Huddersfield H Trin *Wakef* 98-01; P-in-c Charlton Kings H Apostles *Glouc* from 01. *The Vicarage, Langton Grove Road, Charlton Kings, Cheltenham GL52 6JA* Tel (01242) 512254 E-mail rodpaterson@fish.co.uk

PATERSON, Ron. *See* PATERSON, Gordon Ronald

PATERSON, Stuart Maxwell. b 37. Kelham Th Coll 57 Lich Th Coll 58. **d** 60 **p** 61. C Ilkeston St Mary *Derby* 60-64; V Somercotes 64-70; R Wingerworth 70-73; P-in-c Hawick *Edin* 92-95; R 95-00; rtd 00. *40 North Street, Inverurie AB51 4RS* Tel (01467) 624727 E-mail mpate37706@aol.com

PATERSON, Mrs Susan Ann. b 57. St Hilda's Coll Ox MA84. EMMTC DTPS95. **d** 95 **p** 96. NSM Evington *Leic* 95-98; NSM Humberstone 98-99; C 99-03; TV Melton Mowbray from 03. *26 Firwood Road, Melton Mowbray LE13 1SA*
E-mail spaterson@leicester.anglican.org

PATEY, The Very Revd Edward Henry. b 15. Liv Univ Hon LLD80. **d** 39 **p** 40. C Colchester St Mary V *Chelmsf* 39-42; C Bishopwearmouth St Mich *Dur* 42-50; Youth Chapl 46-50; V Oldland *Bris* 50-52; Youth Sec BCC 52-56; Asst Gen Sec 56-58; Can Res Cov Cathl 62-64; Select Preacher Ox Univ 61; Dean Liv 64-82; rtd 82; Perm to Offic *Bris* 82-03. *7 Stuart Court, High Street, Kibworth, Leicester LE8 0LR* Tel 0116-279 6358

PATIENT, Peter Leslie. b 39. Chich Th Coll 63. **d** 66 **p** 67. C Headington *Ox* 66-69; C Stroud *Glouc* 69-72; C Welwyn *St Alb* 72-75. *28 Young's Rise, Welwyn Garden City AL8 6RU* Tel (01707) 328830

PATIENT, Terence Ian. b 35. Open Univ BA83. LNSM course 94. **d** 96 **p** 97. OLM Old Catton *Nor* from 96. *8 Players Way, Old Catton, Norwich NR6 7AU* Tel (01603) 427899

PATO, Luke Luscombe Lungile. b 49. Fort Hare Univ BA76 Manitoba Univ MA80. St Bede's Coll Umtata DipTh71. **d** 73 **p** 75. S Africa 73-81 and from 92; Canada 81-90; Tutor Coll of Ascension Selly Oak 90-92. *College of the Transfiguration, PO Box 77, Grahamstown, 6140 South Africa* Tel (0027) (46) 622 3332 *or* 636 2964 Fax 622 3877 E-mail pato@st_figs.ru.ac.za

PATON, George Hemsell. b 23. Wadh Coll Ox MA49. Oak Hill Th Coll 50. **d** 52 **p** 53. C Earlham St Anne *Nor* 52-54; C Darfield *Sheff* 54-56; Area Sec CMS *Ely* 56-62; Area Sec CMS *St E* and *Nor* 56-66; P-in-c Kemp Town St Mark *Chich* 66-67; V Kemp Town St Mark and St Matt 67-71; R Ripe w Chalvington 71-76; R Laughton w Ripe and Chalvington 77-78; V Iford w Kingston and Rodmell 78-90; rtd 90; Perm to Offic *Chich* from 90. *77 Springett Avenue, Ringmer, Lewes BN8 5QT* Tel (01273) 812754

PATON, Ian James. b 57. Jes Coll Cam MA78 PGCE79. Westcott Ho Cam MA81. **d** 82 **p** 83. C Whitley Ch Ch *Ox* 82-84; Bp's Dom Chapl 84-86; Chapl Wadh Coll Ox 86-90; C Ox St Mary V w St Cross and St Pet *Ox* 86-90; Can and Vice Provost St Mary's Cathl Edin 90-94; R Edin St Mary 90-94; R Haddington 94-97; R Dunbar 94-97; R Edin Old St Paul from 97. *Lauder House, 39 Jeffrey Street, Edinburgh EH1 1DH* Tel 0131-556 3332
E-mail rector@osp.org.uk

PATON, John David Marshall. b 47. Barrister 70. St Steph Ho Ox 81. **d** 83 **p** 84. C Bethnal Green St Matt *Lon* 83-84; C Bethnal Green St Matt w St Jas the Gt 84-86; P-in-c St Geo-in-the-East St Mary 86-89; V 89-92; AD Tower Hamlets 92-96; Dir Post-Ord Tr from 92; P-in-c Bethnal Green St Barn 92-96; P-in-c St Vedast w St Mich-le-Querne etc from 97; P-in-c St Botolph without Bishopgate from 97; AD The City from 00. *St Vedast's Rectory, 4 Foster Lane, London EC2V 6HH* Tel (020) 7606 3998 Fax as telephone

PATON, John William Scholar. b 52. Mert Coll Ox BA74 MA95. St Steph Ho Ox 93. **d** 95 **p** 96. C Sherborne w Castleton and Lillington *Sarum* 95-98; Succ S'wark Cathl *S'wark* 98-01; Chapl Medical and Dental Students K Coll Lon 98-01; P-in-c Purley St Mark from 01. *St Mark's Vicarage, 22 Peaks Hill, Purley CR8 3JE* Tel (020) 8660 7204
E-mail john_w_s_paton@email.msn.com

PATON, The Ven Michael John Macdonald. b 22. Magd Coll Ox BA49 MA54. Linc Th Coll 52. **d** 54 **p** 55. C Gosforth All SS *Newc* 54-57; V Norton Woodseats St Chad *Sheff* 57-67; Sen Chapl Sheff United Hosps 67-70; Chapl Weston Park Hosp Sheff 70-78; V Sheff St Mark Broomhall *Sheff* 70-78; Adn Sheff 78-87; Can Res Sheff Cathl 78-87; rtd 88; Perm to Offic *Sheff* from 88. *947 Abbeydale Road, Sheffield S7 2QD* Tel 0114-236 6148

PATON-WILLIAMS, David Graham. b 58. Warwick Univ BA81 Trin Coll Ox DipTh82 Selw Coll Cam BA86 MA90 Newc Univ MA92. Ridley Hall Cam 84. **d** 87 **p** 88. C S Westoe *Dur* 87-90; C Newton Aycliffe 90-91; TV 91-93; Chapl Univ Coll of Ripon and York St Jo 93-98; Min Can Ripon Cathl *Ripon* 93-98; R Bedale 98-02; P-in-c Leeming 98-02; R Bedale and Leeming from 03; AD Wensley from 03. *The Rectory, North End, Bedale DL8 1AF* Tel (01677) 422103
E-mail david@paton-williams.freeserve.co.uk

PATRICIA, Sister. *See* PERKINS, Sister Patricia Doris

PATRICIA ANN, Sister. *See* GORDON, Sister Patricia Ann

PATRICK, Hugh Joseph. b 37. TCD BA62 MA66. **d** 63 **p** 64. C Dromore Cathl *D & D* 63-66; C Lurgan Ch the Redeemer 66-70; C Rothwell *Ripon* 70-73; V Thurnscoe St Hilda *Sheff* 73-78; V Wales 78-02; P-in-c Thorpe Salvin 78-82; RD Laughton 93-98; rtd 02; Perm to Offic *Sheff* from 02. *5 Fairfax Avenue, Worksop S81 7RH* Tel (01909) 477622
E-mail hugh@patrick46.fsnet.co.uk

PATRICK, James Harry Johnson. b 67. Birm Poly LLB88 Barrister 89. STETS 96 St Steph Ho Ox 99. **d** 99 **p** 00. NSM Clifton All SS w St Jo *Bris* from 99. *50 Hampton Park, Bristol BS6 6LJ* Tel 0117-909 5849 Fax 922 5896
E-mail jp@guildhallchambers.com

PATRICK, John Andrew. b 62. St Jo Coll Dur BA84. Ripon Coll Cuddesdon 87. **d** 89 **p** 90. C Frankby w Greasby *Ches* 89-92; C Boston *Linc* 92-95; P-in-c Graffoe Gp 95-97; V 97-02; P-in-c New Sleaford from 02. *The Vicarage, Market Place, Sleaford NG34 7SH* Tel (01529) 302177 E-mail japatrick1@aol.com

PATRICK, John Peter. b 23. AKC. **d** 52 **p** 53. C S Westoe *Dur* 52-55; C Woodhouse *Wakef* 55-58; C Batley All SS 58-59; V Upperthong 59-75; V Slaithwaite w E Scammonden 75-80; V Donington *Linc* 80-92; rtd 92; Perm to Offic *Linc* 92-01. *Little Paddock, 140 Main Road, Hundleby, Spilsby PE23 5NQ* Tel (01790) 752304

PATRICK, Peter Charles. b 64. Leeds Univ BA86 Fitzw Coll Cam BA91 MA95. Ridley Hall Cam 89. **d** 92 **p** 93. C Barton upon Humber *Linc* 92-96; TV Gt Grimsby St Mary and St Jas 96-03; RD Grimsby and Cleethorpes 99-03; R Middle Rasen Gp from 03. *The Vicarage, North Street, Middle Rasen, Market Rasen LN8 3TS* Tel (01673) 842249
E-mail charles.patrick@talk21.com

PATSTON, Raymond Sidney Richard. b 26. Kelham Th Coll 47. **d** 51 **p** 52. C Hammersmith H Innocents *Lon* 51-53; C Acton Green St Pet 53-56; Area Sec E Counties UMCA 56-62; C Chesterton St Luke *Ely* 56-59; R Downham Market w Bexwell 61-71; V Clee *Linc* 71-97; rtd 97. *75 Littlefield Lane, Grimsby DN34 4NU* Tel (01472) 349788

PATTEN (née STARNS), Mrs Helen Edna. b 43. St Hilda's Coll Ox BA65 Lon Univ CertEd70 DipTh75. Trin Coll Bris 73 Oak Hill Th Coll 81. **dss** 82 **d** 87 **p** 94. Tunbridge Wells St Jo *Roch* 82-86; Patcham *Chich* 86-91; Par Dn 87-91; Par Dn Eckington w Handley and Ridgeway *Derby* 91-94; C 94-95; TV 95-98; Chapl St Mich Hospice from 98. *Flat 1, 8 Upper Maze Hill, St Leonards-on-Sea TN38 0LQ* Tel (01424) 435113 *or* 445177

PATTERSON, Alfred Percy. d 85 **p** 87. NSM Aghalee *D & D* 85-91; C Gilford 91-93; Bp's C 93-95; I 95-00; rtd 00. *723 Upper Newtownards Road, Belfast BT4 3NU* Tel (028) 9029 4741

PATTERSON, Andrew John. b 56. Master Mariner 85 Riversdale Coll OND76. Qu Coll Birm 85. **d** 88 **p** 89. C Newc St Phil and St Aug *Newc* 88-92; Chapl Hunter's Moor Hosp 91-92; Asst Chapl R Victoria Infirmary Newc 92-96; V Whitley *Newc* from 96; Chapl Hexham Gen Hosp from 96. *The Vicarage, Whitley, Hexham NE46 2LA* Tel (01434) 673379

PATTERSON, Anthony. b 43. Moore Th Coll Sydney BTh82. **d** 83 **p** 83. Australia 83-91; C Darfield *Sheff* 91-94; TR Marfleet

York 94-99; TV Heeley and Gleadless Valley *Sheff* from 99. *Heeley Vicarage, 151 Gleadless Road, Sheffield S2 3AE* Tel 0114-255 7718 E-mail tony@yahoo.co.uk

PATTERSON, Charles David Gilliat. b 40. Lon Univ DipTh74. Oak Hill Th Coll 71. **d** 74 **p** 75. C Brompton H Trin *Lon* 74-77; C Spring Grove St Mary 77-80; V Bures *St E* 80-92; R Bath Weston St Jo w Kelston *B & W* 92-01; rtd 01; Perm to Offic *Ox* from 02. *Grove Mill, Mill Lane, Grove, Wantage OX12 7HU* Tel (01235) 772013

PATTERSON, Colin Hugh. b 52. CertEd75 St Pet Coll Ox MA77 Univ of Wales (Cardiff) MPhil90. Trin Coll Bris DipHE86. **d** 87 **p** 88. C Blackb Sav *Blackb* 87-90; C Haughton le Skerne *Dur* 90-93; Adult Educn Adv from 93. *24 Monks Crescent, Durham DH1 1HD* Tel 0191-386 1691 *or* 374 6013 Fax 384 7529 E-mail colin.patterson@durham.anglican.org

PATTERSON, Colin Peter Matthew. b 62. Newc Poly BA84. St Steph Ho Ox 92. **d** 94 **p** 95. C Cullercoats St Geo *Newc* 94-97; Shrine P Shrine of Our Lady of Walsingham 97-99; P-in-c Harlow St Mary Magd *Chelmsf* 99-00; V from 00. *St Mary Magdalene's Vicarage, 3 Oaklands Drive, Harlow CM17 9BE* Tel (01279) 453848 E-mail frcolin@mmharlow.fsnet.co.uk

PATTERSON, Mrs Diane Rosemary. b 46. WMMTC 88. **d** 91 **p** 94. C Hill *Birm* 91-95; Perm to Offic 95-96; C Shottery St Andr *Cov* 96-01; C Hunningham from 01; C Wappenbury w Weston under Wetherley from 01; C Long Itchington and Marton from 01; C Offchurch from 01; RD Southam from 02. *The Vicarage, School Lane, Hunningham, Leamington Spa CV33 9DS* Tel (01926) 633630

PATTERSON, Hugh John. b 38. Southn Univ MPhil76. AKC63. **d** 64 **p** 65. C Epsom St Martin *Guildf* 64-65; Chapl Ewell Coll 65-68; Asst Chapl and Lect Bp Otter Coll *Chich* 68-71; Lect Dudley Coll of Educn 71-77; Lect Wolv Poly 77-92; Wolv Univ 92-00; Chapl 89-00; Hon C Morville w Aston Eyre *Heref* from 82; Hon C Upton Cressett w Monk Hopton from 82; Hon C Acton Round from 82; rtd 01. *6 Victoria Road, Bridgnorth WV16 4LA* Tel (01746) 765298

PATTERSON, Ian Francis Riddell. b 31. TCD BA55. **d** 55 **p** 56. C Belfast St Mary *Conn* 55-59; C Finaghy 59-63; I Craigs w Dunaghy and Killagan 63-66; Belfast Trin Coll Miss 66-68; I Belfast H Redeemer 68-80; I Kilroot 80-90; I Kilroot and Templecorran 90-92; I Donagh w Tyholland and Errigal Truagh *Clogh* 92-97; rtd 97. *6 Orchard Park, Aughnacloy BT69 6HT* Tel (028) 8555 7854

PATTERSON, Jennifer Mary. *See* TAYLOR, Sister Jennifer Mary

PATTERSON, John. b 27. MBIM76 Regent St Poly Lon DMS58. Bps' Coll Cheshunt 60. **d** 61 **p** 62. C Maidenhead St Luke *Ox* 61-65; Chapl RAF 65-72; V Ashton St Jas *Man* 72-78; USA 78-90; R Somercotes and Grainthorpe w Conisholme *Linc* 90-92; rtd 92; Perm to Offic *Linc* from 92. *9 Simpson Close, Barrow-upon-Humber DN19 7BL* Tel (01469) 30867

PATTERSON, The Ven John Norton. b 39. TCD BA64 MA68. **d** 65 **p** 66. C Belfast St Paul *Conn* 65-68; C Larne and Inver 68-72; I Ballintoy w Rathlin and Dunseverick from 72; Miss to Seafarers from 72; Can Belf Cathl from 97; Adn Dalriada *Conn* from 01. *The Rectory, 2 Ballinlea Road, Ballintoy, Ballycastle BT54 6NQ* Tel (028) 7076 2411

PATTERSON, Marjorie Jean. *See* BROWN, Mrs Marjorie Jean

PATTERSON, Norman John. b 47. Peterho Cam BA69. Lon Coll of Div ALCD DPS St Jo Coll Nottm 70. **d** 73 **p** 74. C Everton St Ambrose w St Tim *Liv* 73-74; C Everton St Pet 74-78; TV 79-84; C Aigburth 84-92; Dioc Adv Past Care and Counselling from 84; V Gt Crosby All SS from 92. *All Saints' Vicarage, 17 Moor Coppice, Crosby, Liverpool L23 2XJ* Tel 0151-924 6436 E-mail njohn.patterson@ukgateway.net

PATTERSON, Patric Douglas MacRae. b 51. Wycliffe Hall Ox 73. **d** 76 **p** 77. C Bebington *Ches* 76-79; Canada from 79. *The Rectory, PO Box 10, Milford ON, Canada, K0K 2P0*

PATTERSON, Canon Philip Fredrick. b 50. Ulster Univ BSc QUB BD. **d** 82 **p** 83. C Lurgan Ch the Redeemer *D & D* 82-86; I Carrowdore w Millisle 86-89; I Knockbreda from 89; Dioc Registrar from 00; Preb Down Cathl from 00. *Knockbreda Rectory, 69 Church Road, Newtownbreda, Belfast BT8 4AN* Tel (028) 9064 1493 Fax as telephone E-mail pfpatterson@hotmail.com

PATTERSON, Susan Margaret. b 48. Otago Univ BA71 BD89 PhD92. Knox Coll Dunedin 84. **d** 88 **p** 89. New Zealand 88-91 and 92-97; C Dunedin St Martin 88-91; Tutor Otago Univ and Knox Coll 89-91; USA 91-92; Assoc P Hawke's Bay 92-96; Lect Trin Coll Bris 97-00; C Kilmore w Ballintemple, Kildallon etc *K, E & A* from 00. *Kildallon Rectory, Ardlougher, Ballyconnell, Co Cavan, Irish Republic* Tel (00353) (49) 952 6938 Fax as telephone E-mail kildallan@kilmore.anglican.org

PATTERSON, Trevor Harold. b 60. QUB BA82 Stranmillis Coll PGCE83. Trin Coll Bris DipHE93. **d** 93 **p** 94. C Ashtead *Guildf* 93-98; V Richmond H Trin and Ch Ch *S'wark* from 98. *Holy Trinity Vicarage, Sheen Park, Richmond TW9 1UP* Tel (020) 8404 1114 E-mail trevor-patterson@holy-trinity-richmond.fsnet.co.uk

PATTERSON, William Alfred. b 54. Wycliffe Hall Ox 77. **d** 79 **p** 80. C Partington and Carrington *Ches* 79-81; Canada from 81. *Address temp unknown*

PATTIMORE, Daniel James. b 64. Nottm Univ MEng88 Lon Bible Coll BA94. Wycliffe Hall Ox 97. **d** 99 **p** 00. C Charlesworth and Dinting Vale *Derby* 99-03. *39 Badger Close, Palacefields, Runcorn WA7 2QW* Tel 07973-406022 (mobile) E-mail dan@pattimore.com

PATTIMORE (née GORDON), Mrs Kristy. b 72. Leeds Univ BA94 Newc Univ PGCE95. Wycliffe Hall Ox 98. **d** 01 **p** 02. C Hallwood *Ches* from 01. *39 Badger Close, Palacefields, Runcorn WA7 2QW* Tel (01928) 715688 E-mail kristygordon@hotmail.com

PATTINSON, Richard Clive. b 46. Keble Coll Ox BA68 MA84. Carl and Blackb Dioc Tr Inst 98. **d** 00 **p** 01. C Hesket-in-the-Forest and Armathwaite *Carl* from 00. *The Rectory, Skelton, Penrith CA11 9SE* Tel (017684) 84295

PATTINSON, Sir William Derek. b 30. Kt90. Qu Coll Ox BA52 MA56. St Deiniol's Hawarden 90 Coll of Resurr Mirfield 92. **d** 91 **p** 92. NSM Pimlico St Gabr *Lon* from 91. *9 Strutton Court, Great Peter Street, London SW1P 2HH* Tel (020) 7222 6307

PATTISON, Anthony. b 50. MRPharmS73 Heriot-Watt Univ BSc72. Sarum & Wells Th Coll 85. **d** 87 **p** 88. C Cullercoats St Geo *Newc* 87-89; Ind Chapl 89-99; C Cramlington 89-91; TV 91-99; TR Benwell Team from 99. *Benwell Rectory, 5 Lynnwood Avenue, Newcastle upon Tyne NE4 6XB* Tel 0191-256 7020 Fax 256 7010 E-mail pattison@lineone.net

PATTISON, George Linsley. b 50. Edin Univ MA72 BD77 Dur Univ PhD. Edin Th Coll 74. **d** 77 **p** 78. C Benwell St Jas *Newc* 77-80; P-in-c Kimblesworth *Dur* 80-83; R Badwell Ash w Gt Ashfield, Stowlangtoft etc *St E* 83-91; Dean of Chapl K Coll Cam 91-01; Lect Aarhus Univ Denmark from 01. *Aarhus Universitet, Nordre Ringgade 1, 8000 Aarhus C, Denmark*

PATTISON, Stephen Bewley. b 53. Selw Coll Cam BA76. Edin Th Coll 76. **d** 78 **p** 80. C Gosforth All SS *Newc* 78-79; NSM St Nic Hosp *Newc* 78-82; Hon C Newc St Thos Prop Chpl *Newc* 80-82; Chapl Edin Th Coll 82-83; Lect Past Studies Birm Univ 83-88; Perm to Offic *Birm* 83-86 and 87-00; Hon C Moseley St Mary 86-87. *11A Salisbury Road, Moseley, Birmingham B13 8JS* Tel 0121-449 3023

PATTLE (née OLIVER), Mrs Suzanne Marie. b 66. LMH Ox BA88 SSEES Lon MA91. Trin Coll Bris BTS03. **d** 03. C Rainham *Roch* from 03. *26 Beverley Close, Gillingham ME8 9HG* Tel 07973-853959 (mobile) E-mail suzanne@pattle.charitydays.co.uk

PATTON, Desmond Hilton. b 12. TCD BA35. **d** 36 **p** 37. C Killermogh *C & O* 36-38; C Wexford 38-40; I Mothel 40-41; I Aghade w Ardoyne 41-51; I Clonenagh w Roskelton 51-59; I Ballyfin 58-59; I Carlow w Urglin and Staplestown 59-77; Can Leighlin Cathl 60-71; Can Ossory Cathl 60-62; Adn Ossory and Leighlin 62-76; rtd 76; Chapl Mageough Home *D & G* 78-88. *Kinvara Nursing Home, The Esplanade, Bray, Co Wicklow, Irish Republic* Tel (00353) (1) 286 6153

PAUL, Brother. *See* SINGLETON, Ernest George

PAUL, Ian Benjamin. b 62. St Jo Coll Ox BA84 AM88 Southn Univ MSc85 Nottm Univ BTh91 PhD98. St Jo Coll Nottm 89. **d** 96 **p** 97. C Longfleet *Sarum* 96-00; NSM from 00; Th Adv Dioc Bd of Min from 00. *32 Penn Hill Avenue, Poole BH14 9LZ* Tel (01202) 745963 Fax 385539 E-mail ian.b.paul@btinternet.com

PAUL, Canon John Douglas. b 28. Edin Univ MA52. Ely Th Coll 52. **d** 54 **p** 55. C Portsea Ascension *Portsm* 54-56; Nyasaland 56-60; Portuguese E Africa 60-70; Adn Metangula 65-70; R Castle Douglas *Glas* 70-75; R Edin St Mark *Edin* 75-80; R Elgin w Lossiemouth *Mor* 80-92; Syn Clerk 89-91; Hon Can St Andr Cathl Inverness from 89; Dean Mor 91-92; rtd 92. *2 The Avenue, Gifford, Haddington EH41 4QX* Tel (01620) 810547

PAUL, John Matthew. b 61. K Coll Lon BA84 Fitzw Coll Cam BA88 MA92. Westcott Ho Cam 86. **d** 89 **p** 90. C Writtle w Highwood *Chelmsf* 89-94; Min Can and Chapl St Paul's Cathl *Lon* 94-96; Min Can and Sacr St Paul's Cathl 96-99; V Winchmore Hill St Paul from 99. *St Paul's Vicarage, Church Hill, London N21 1JA* Tel (020) 8886 3545

PAUL, Naunihal Chand (Nihal). b 40. Allahabad Univ MA. Bangalore Th Coll BD. **d** 69 **p** 70. India 70-74; C Urmston *Man* 75-77; P-in-c Farnworth St Pet 77-80; TV E Farnworth and Kearsley 80-83; TV Laindon St Martin and St Nic w Nevendon *Chelmsf* 83-90; R Laindon w Dunton from 90. *38 Claremont Road, Laindon, Basildon SS15 5PZ* Tel (01268) 411190 E-mail rupniwas@aol.com

PAUL, Roger Philip. b 53. Clare Coll Cam BA74 MA88 CertEd76. Westcott Ho Cam 78. **d** 81 **p** 82. C Coventry Caludon *Cov* 81-85; R Warmington w Shotteswell and Radway w Ratley 85-98; R Kirkby Stephen w Mallerstang etc *Carl* from 98. *The Vicarage, Vicarage Lane, Kirkby Stephen CA17 4QX* Tel (01768) 371204 *or* 372919

PAUL, Simon Nicholas. b 56. Hull Univ BA81 PGCE82. Trin Coll Bris BA95. **d** 95 **p** 96. C Cranleigh *Guildf* 95-99; P-in-c

Broughton and Duddon *Carl* from 99. *The Vicarage, Broughton-in-Furness LA20 6HS* Tel (01229) 716305

PAVEY, Canon Angela Mary. b 55. Hull Univ BA77 Nottm Univ BCombStuds84. Linc Th Coll 81. **dss** 84 **d** 87 **p** 94. Linc St Faith and St Martin w St Pet *Linc* 84-86; Chapl Boston Coll of FE 87-95; Asst Min Officer *Linc* 89-95; C Birchwood 95-97; Dioc Dir of Ords from 97; Can and Preb Linc Cathl from 00. *St Luke's Vicarage, Jasmine Road, Lincoln LN6 0YR* Tel (01522) 683507 Fax 804741 E-mail angela.pavey@virgin.net

PAVEY, Gordon Sidney Alfred. b 19. Lon Univ BD47 Leeds Univ MEd58. Chich Th Coll 40. **d** 42 **p** 43. C S Mymms K Chas *Lon* 42-44; C Bedford Park 44-48; C Taunton H Trin *B & W* 48-50; Area Sec (N Midl) UMCA 50-54; V Huddersfield St Thos *Wakef* 54-64; Youth Chapl 54-57; Lic to Offic *Blackb* 64-68; Lic to Offic *Bris* 68-95; Prin Lect Th Bris Poly 77-92; Prin Lect Th Univ of the W of England, Bris from 92; rtd 84. *12 Chartley, The Avenue, Sneyd Park, Bristol BS9 1PE* Tel 0117-968 4762

PAVEY, John Bertram. b 51. Keele Univ BA73 Hull Univ PGCE74 MEd95. Linc Th Coll 81. **d** 83 **p** 84. C Boultham *Linc* 83-86; R Fishtoft 86-95; P-in-c Birchwood 95-01; V from 01. *St Luke's Vicarage, Jasmin Road, Lincoln LN6 0YR* Tel (01522) 688665 E-mail j.pavey@ntlworld.com

PAVEY, Michael Trevor. b 32. Lon Univ BA80 Bris Univ MPhil92. ALCD59. **d** 59 **p** 60. C Nor St Pet Mancroft *Nor* 59-61; C N Walsham w Antingham 61-63; Chapl RAF 63-83; R Mark w Allerton *B & W* 83-02; rtd 02. *17 Millgreen Close, West Huntspill, Highbridge TA9 3QY* Tel (01278) 782814

PAVLIBEYI, Andrew Christos. b 53. Trent Poly CertEd76. Oak Hill Th Coll BA88 Wycliffe Hall Ox 84. **d** 86 **p** 87. C Finchley Ch Ch *Lon* 86-89; Chapl Lon Univ 89-92; P-in-c S Hampstead St Sav 92-98; V from 98. *St Saviour's Vicarage, 30 Eton Villas, London NW3 4SQ* Tel (020) 7722 4621

PAVYER, Miss Jennifer Elizabeth. b 75. Ex Univ BSc96 Cam Univ BTh02. Westcott Ho Cam 99. **d** 02 **p** 03. C Stevenage St Andr and St Geo *St Alb* from 02. *90 Ferrier Road, Stevenage SG2 0NZ* Tel (01438) 351833
E-mail jenny.pavyer@ukgateway.net

PAWSEY, Jack Edward. b 35. Trin Coll Ox BA59 MA65. Westcott Ho Cam 64. **d** 66 **p** 67. Sec Coun Soc Aid S'wark 66-75; Race Relns Worker 75-78; Acting Sec Coun Soc Aid 78-82; Perm to Offic 84-86; Hon C Camberwell St Geo 86-98; Staff Cllr Westmr Past Foundn 87-97; Perm to Offic *S'wark* from 98. *20 Addington Square, London SE5 7JZ* Tel (020) 7701 8920

PAWSON (née ROYLE), Mrs Gillian Mary. b 57. Kingston Univ BA79 Roehampton Inst PGCE82. SEITE 99. **d** 02. C Wimbledon *S'wark* from 02. *50 Evelyn Road, London SW19 8NT* Tel (020) 8286 1030 E-mail gillypawson@blueyonder.co.uk

PAWSON, John. b 66. Moorlands Th Coll BA00 Wycliffe Hall Ox. **d** 02 **p** 03. C Bursledon *Win* from 02. *13 Redcroft Lane, Bursledon, Southampton SO31 8GS* Tel (023) 8040 4902 Mobile 07762-246947 E-mail john.pawson@virgin.net

PAWSON, Preb John Walker. b 38. Kelham Th Coll 58. **d** 63 **p** 64. C N Hull St Mich *York* 63-67; C Lower Gornal *Lich* 67-70; V Tipton St Jo 70-78; V Meir Heath from 78; RD Stoke 88-98; Preb Lich Cathl from 93. *St Francis's Vicarage, Meir Heath, Stoke-on-Trent ST3 7LH* Tel (01782) 393189 Fax as telephone E-mail pawson.meirton@virgin.net

PAXON, Robin Michael Cuninghame. b 46. St Jo Coll Dur BA69. Westcott Ho Cam 69. **d** 71 **p** 72. C Croydon St Pet S End *Cant* 71-77; C Saffron Walden w Wendens Ambo and Littlebury *Chelmsf* 77-80; P-in-c Plaistow St Mary 80-83; TV Plaistow 83-89; TV Dovercourt and Parkeston 90-95; rtd 95. *20 Park Road, Harwich CO12 3BJ* Tel (01255) 551139

PAXTON, John Ernest. b 49. Ex Univ BA71. Westcott Ho Cam 74. **d** 74 **p** 75. C Redditch St Steph *Worc* 74-77; UAE 77-81; C Bolton St Pet *Man* 81-91; Ind Missr 81-91; TV Southampton (City Cen) *Win* 91-96; R S'wark Ch Ch *S'wark* from 96; Sen Chapl S Lon Ind Miss from 96. *Christ Church Rectory, 49 Colombo Street, London SE1 8DP* Tel (020) 7633 9979 or 7928 3970 Fax 7928 1148 E-mail slim@dswark.org.uk

PAY, Norman John. b 50. St Jo Coll Dur BA72 DipTh73. Cranmer Hall Dur. **d** 74 **p** 75. C S Moor *Dur* 74-78; C Rawmarsh w Parkgate *Sheff* 78-80; C-in-c New Cantley CD 80-82; V New Cantley 82-89; V Doncaster St Leon and St Jude from 89; Asst Clergy In-Service Tr Officer from 90. *St Leonard's Vicarage, Barnsley Road, Doncaster DN5 8QE* Tel (01302) 784858

PAYN, Peter Richard. b 33. Moore Th Coll Sydney LTh59. **d** 60 **p** 60. Australia 60-79; C Pittwater 60-61; C Kensington St Matt 61-63; C Melbourne St Jas w St Barn *Ripon* 83-88; Chapl St Hilda's Sch Whitby 88-97; R Loftus and Carlin How w Skinningrove *York* 97-99; Chapl OHP 99-01; Teacher Qu Mary's Sch Thirsk from 02. *21 Wellington Gardens, Ripon HG4 1DL* Tel (01765) 609786 E-mail johnp-virgil@connectfree.co.uk

St Peter's Vicarage, Bayhall Road, Tunbridge Wells TN2 4TP Tel (01892) 530384 E-mail richardpayn@aol.com

PAYNE, Alan. See PAYNE, Kenneth Alan

PAYNE, Alan Frank. b 19. Bps' Coll Cheshunt 63. **d** 65 **p** 66. C Horsforth *Ripon* 65-69; V Oulton w Woodlesford 69-80; V Thurgoland *Wakef* 80-82; rtd 82; Perm to Offic *Wakef* 82-96; Perm to Offic *Ripon* from 96. *602 King Lane, Alwoodley Park, Leeds LS17 7AN* Tel 0113-266 0221

PAYNE, Arthur Edwin. b 37. K Alfred's Coll Win TCert59 Ban Coll DipRE60 Univ of Wales (Swansea) AdCertEd68. St Mich Coll Llan 86. **d** 87 **p** 88. C Swansea St Gabr *S & B* 87-90; Chapl Univ of Wales (Swansea) 87-90; V Brynmawr 90-91; TV Wickford and Runwell *Chelmsf* 91-94; Chapl Runwell Hosp Wickford 91-94; P-in-c Wraxall *B & W* 94-95; Perm to Offic 95-97; V Rhymney *Mon* 97-98; rtd 98. *131 Howard Road, Upminster RM14 2UQ* Tel (01708) 640451

PAYNE, Cyril Gordon. b 26. Bris Univ BA53. Linc Th Coll 53. **d** 55 **p** 56. C Southall H Trin *Lon* 55-58; C Christchurch *Win* 58-63; V Otterbourne 63-75; V Milford 75-90; rtd 90; Perm to Offic *Win* from 90. *11 Oaklands, Lymington SO41 3TH* Tel (01590) 671274

PAYNE, David Charles. b 62. Univ of Wales (Abth) BLib84. St Jo Coll Nottm MA95. **d** 95 **p** 96. C Horncastle w Low Toynton *Linc* 95-99; V Metheringham w Blankney and Dunston from 99. *The Vicarage, 38 Drury Street, Metheringham, Lincoln LN4 3EZ* Tel (01526) 321115

PAYNE, David James. b 31. Clare Coll Cam BA54 MA61. Wycliffe Hall Ox 60. **d** 62 **p** 63. C Gt Faringdon w Lt Coxwell *Ox* 62-63; C Guildf Ch Ch *Guildf* 63-66; R Shackleford 66-73; R Peper Harow 66-73; R Odell *St Alb* 73-78; V Pavenham 73-78; Warden Home of Divine Healing Crowhurst 78-84; R Wraxall *B & W* 84-92; rtd 92; Perm to Offic *Glouc* from 92; *Bris* from 00. *Langet End, Upper Up, South Cerney, Cirencester GL7 5US* Tel (01285) 860677

PAYNE, David Ronald. b 49. DMS77 Open Univ BA87. St Mich Coll Llan 88. **d** 90 **p** 91. C Oystermouth *S & B* 90-93; V Penllergaer 93-02; TV Llanelli *St D* from 02. *The Vicarage, Swiss Valley, Felinfoel, Llanelli SA14 8BS* Tel (01554) 773159

PAYNE, Canon Denis Alfred. b 22. Oriel Coll Ox BA50 MA53. Wells Th Coll 50. **d** 51 **p** 52. C Sheff St Geo and St Steph *Sheff* 51-55; Chapl Makerere Univ Uganda 55-67; Min Sec ACCM 67-69; Sen Selection Sec 69-73; Dir Post-Ord Tr and Further Tr for Clergy *St E* 73-84; Dioc Dir of Ords 73-87; Can Res St E Cathl 73-89; rtd 89; Perm to Offic *St E* from 90. *The Crooked House, Brussels Green, Darsham, Saxmundham IP17 3RN* Tel (01728) 668705

PAYNE, Elizabeth. b 50. Univ Coll Lon BSc92 Univ of Wales (Cardiff) Dip Past Th 98. St Mich Coll Llan 96. **d** 98 **p** 99. C Cyncoed *Mon* 98-03; TV from 03. *13 Clos Alyn, Pontprennau, Cardiff CF23 8LB* Tel (029) 2054 0071

PAYNE, Frederick Gates (Eric). b 19. Jes Coll Cam BA40 MA43. Lon Coll of Div 40. **d** 42 **p** 43. C Walcot *B & W* 42-45; CF (EC) 45-48; Ethiopia 48-67; SW Org Sec CMJ 68-85; rtd 84; Perm to Offic *B & W* from 85. *83 Penn Lea Road, Bath BA1 3RQ* Tel (01225) 423092

PAYNE, James John Henry. b 26. MBE69. St Pet Hall Ox BA53 MA59. Tyndale Hall Bris 48 Linc Th Coll 53. **d** 53 **p** 54. Chapl Supt Mersey Miss to Seamen 53-55; C Stoneycroft All SS *Liv* 55-57; Nigeria 57-88; Hon Can Lagos 71-88; rtd 88; Perm to Offic *Ox* 88-93; Hon C Uffington, Shellingford, Woolstone and Baulking from 93. *1 Timberyard Cottages, Church Street, Shellingford, Faringdon SN7 7QA* Tel (01367) 710274

PAYNE, John. See PAYNE, Victor John

PAYNE, John. b 58. Glas Univ BSc80 Edin Univ BD84. Edin Th Coll 81. **d** 90 **p** 90. C Dur St Nic *Dur* 90-94; Australia from 94; Chapl Toorak Coll Melbourne from 02. *11 Feathertop Chase, Burwood East, Melbourne, Vic, Australia 3151* Tel (0061) (3) 9887 8748 E-mail johnpayne@rabbit.com.au

PAYNE, John Percival. b 49. Nottm Univ BA70. Cuddesdon Coll 70. **d** 72 **p** 73. C Tilehurst St Mich *Ox* 72-76; C Cross Green St Sav and St Hilda *Ripon* 76-79; Chapl St Hilda's Priory Whitby 79-83; V Leeds Belle Is St Jo and St Barn *Ripon* 83-88; Chapl St Hilda's Sch Whitby 88-97; R Loftus and Carlin How w Skinningrove *York* 97-99; Chapl OHP 99-01; Teacher Qu Mary's Sch Thirsk from 02. *21 Wellington Gardens, Ripon HG4 1DL* Tel (01765) 609786 E-mail johnp-virgil@connectfree.co.uk

PAYNE, John Rogan. b 44. Episc Th Coll Sao Paulo. **d** 78 **p** 79. Brazil 78-86; C Ilkley All SS *Bradf* 86-88; R Elvington w Sutton on Derwent and E Cottingwith *York* 88-94. *Manor Farm House, East Flotmanby Road, Filey YO14 0HX* Tel (01723) 513969

PAYNE, Canon Joseph Marshall. b 17. TCD BA38 MA52. **d** 40 **p** 41. C Belfast St Aid *Conn* 40-43; C Ballynafeigh St Jude *D & D* 43-44; Chapl RAF 44-65; Asst Chapl-in-Chief RAF 65-72; QHC 70-72; V Malew *S & M* 72-82; RD Castletown 77-82; Can St German's Cathl 78-84; Treas 80-84; rtd 82; Perm to Offic *S & M* from 84. *Ard-ny-Shee, 3 Viking Close, Ballakillowey, Colby, Isle of Man IM9 4BH* Tel (01624) 832039

PAYNE, Julia Kathleen. See PEATY, Julia Kathleen

PAYNE, Kenneth Alan. b 45. Pemb Coll Ox BA68 MA71. Qu Coll Birm 71. **d** 74 **p** 74. Hon C Perry Barr *Birm* 74-78; Hon C Ruislip Manor St Paul *Lon* 78-79; C Hawksworth Wood *Ripon* 79-84; R Stanningley St Thos 84-94; TR Kippax w Allerton Bywater 94-00; AD Whitkirk 95-00; P-in-c Lambley *S'well* from 00; Dioc Min Development Adv from 00; Dioc Dir of Min from 02. *The Rectory, 2 Cocker Beck, Lambley, Nottingham NG4 4QP* Tel 0115-931 3531 or (01636) 814331

PAYNE, Leonard John. b 49. St Jo Coll Nottm Dip Th & Min 95. **d** 95 **p** 96. C Trimley *St E* 95-98; TV Sole Bay from 98. *The Rectory, 59 Southwold Road, Wrentham, Beccles NR34 7JE* Tel (01502) 675208 Mobile 07879-457902
E-mail leonard.payne@stedmundsbury.anglican.org
PAYNE, Mark James Townsend. b 69. Van Mildert Coll Dur BA90. Ridley Hall Cam CTM94. **d** 94 **p** 95. C Angmering *Chich* 94-98; Dioc Ev from 98; C Prestonville St Luke from 98. *12 Walsingham Road, Hove BN3 4FF* Tel (01273) 326193
PAYNE, Matthew Charles. b 62. Ex Univ LLB85 All Nations Chr Coll BA95 Solicitor 89. Oak Hill Th Coll 99. **d** 01. C Angmering *Chich* from 01. *7 Beech View, Angmering, Littlehampton BN16 4DE* Tel (01903) 784664 Fax 784459
E-mail revmatt@talk21.com
PAYNE, Michael Frederick. b 49. NE Surrey Coll of Tech HND72. St Jo Coll Nottm 81. **d** 83 **p** 84. C Hyson Green *S'well* 83-86; P-in-c Peckham St Mary Magd *S'wark* 86-90; V from 90. *St Mary's Vicarage, 22 St Mary's Road, London SE15 2DW* Tel (020) 7639 4596 Fax as telephone
E-mail mikefpayne@hotmail.com
PAYNE, Mrs Norma. b 48. Bris Univ BA70 Homerton Coll Cam PGCE71. STETS 98. **d** 01 **p** 02. NSM Cley Hill Warminster *Sarum* from 01. *87 Boreham Road, Warminster BA12 9JX* Tel (01985) 214030 Fax as telephone
PAYNE, Mrs Penelope Kenward. b 42. LGSM64. Bp Otter Coll 94. **d** 94 **p** 98. NSM Portsea N End St Mark *Portsm* from 94. *35 Saltmarsh Lane, Hayling Island PO11 0JT* Tel and fax (023) 9246 5259 *or* tel 9266 5753 E-mail peace@ppayne.f9.co.uk
PAYNE, Ralfe Dudley. b 22. Lon Univ BA50. Qu Coll Birm 50. **d** 52 **p** 53. C Tettenhall Wood *Lich* 52-57; C Tamworth 57-60; V Gayton w Fradswell 60-63; V Brockmoor 63-75; C Kinver 76-79; R Himley 79-89; V Swindon 79-89; rtd 89; Perm to Offic *Lich* from 89; Perm to Offic *Worc* from 89. *Highfield, Dunsley, Kinver, Stourbridge DY7 6LY* Tel (01384) 873612
PAYNE, Robert Christian. b 42. St Mich Coll Llan DipTh65. **d** 65 **p** 66. C Charlton Kings St Mary *Glouc* 65-69; C Waltham Cross *St Alb* 69-71; V Falfield *Glouc* 71-72; P-in-c Rockhampton 71-72; V Falfield w Rockhampton 72-76; Chapl HM Det Cen Eastwood Park 71-76; Chapl HM Youth Cust Cen Everthorpe 76-79; Chapl HM Youth Cust Cen Glen Parva 79-85; Pris Service Chapl Tr Officer 85-88; Chapl HM Pris Swinfen Hall 85-88; Asst Chapl Gen of Pris (SW) 88-90; Asst Chapl Gen of Pris 90-02; rtd 02; Sub Chapl HM YOI Stoke Heath from 02; Sub Chapl HM Pris Stafford from 02. *The Chaplaincy Team, HM Young Offender Institution, Stoke Heath, Market Drayton TF9 2JL* Tel (01630) 636116 E-mail bob.payne@ukgateway.net *or* bob.payne@hmps.gsi.gov.uk
PAYNE, Robert Harold Vincent. b 44. St Jo Coll York CertEd69. St Jo Coll Nottm 77. **d** 79 **p** 80. C Didsbury St Jas *Man* 79-80; C Didsbury St Jas and Em 80-83; V Southchurch Ch Ch *Chelmsf* 83-90; P-in-c Charles w Plymouth St Matthias *Ex* 90-94; Warden Lee Abbey 94-02; R Thorley *St Alb* from 02. *The Rectory, Vicerons Place, Bishop's Stortford CM23 4EL* Tel (01279) 654955 Fax 755179
E-mail bobpayne@stjamesthorley.freeserve.co.uk
PAYNE, Robert Sandon. b 48. ARICS72 Reading Univ BSc69 MRICS01. Ripon Coll Cuddesdon 78. **d** 80 **p** 81. C Bridgnorth, Tasley, Astley Abbotts and Oldbury *Heref* 80-83; P-in-c Wistanstow 83-92; P-in-c Acton Scott 86-92; P-in-c Dorrington 92-94; P-in-c Leebotwood w Longnor 92-94; P-in-c Smethcott w Woolstaston 92-94; P-in-c Stapleton 92-94; R Dorrington w Leebotwood, Longnor, Stapleton etc from 94. *The Rectory, Dorrington, Shrewsbury SY5 7JL* Tel (01743) 718578
PAYNE, Rosemary Ann. b 46. SSC71 LSE LLB68. St Alb and Ox Min Course 97. **d** 00 **p** 01. NSM Wooburn *Ox* from 00. *30 Goddington Road, Bourne End SL8 5TZ* Tel (01628) 521677
PAYNE, Stephen Michael. b 55. **d** 03. C Plymouth Em, St Paul Efford and St Aug *Ex* from 03. *1 Yeo Close, Efford, Plymouth PL3 6ER* Tel (01752) 785576
PAYNE, Victor John. b 45. Open Univ BA81 Dip Psychotherapy 96. St Mich Coll Llan DipTh69 DPS70. **d** 70 **p** 71. C Ystrad Mynach *Llan* 70-72; C Whitchurch 72-75; CF (TA) 74-75; CF 75-93; V Talgarth and Llanelieu *S & B* 85-87; Chapl Mid-Wales Hosp 85-87; C Bassaleg *Mon* 93-96; TV 96-01; V Tongwynlais *Llan* from 01. *The Vicarage, 1 Merthyr Road, Tongwynlais, Cardiff CF15 7LE* Tel (029) 2081 0437
PAYNE, Warwick Martin. b 26. AKC51. **d** 52 **p** 53. C Mansfield St Pet *S'well* 52-56; The Gambia 56-58; C Winlaton *Dur* 59-62; S Africa from 63; rtd 97. *7 Harvey Road, Harfield Village, Claremont, Cape Town, 7708 South Africa* Tel and fax (0027) (21) 683 0224
PAYNE COOK, John Andrew Somerset. b 43. St Pet Coll Ox BA65 MA65. Coll of Resurr Mirfield 65. **d** 68 **p** 69. C St Mary-at-Latton *Chelmsf* 68-71; C Gt Berkhamsted *St Alb* 71-76; C-in-c N Brickhill CD *Ox* 76-85; V N Brickhill and Putnoe 83-85; TR Tring 85-99; RD Berkhamsted 92-97; Hon Can St Alb 98-99; USPG 99-03; P-in-c Sandy Pt St Anne St Kitts-Nevis 00-03; P-in-c Ickleford w Holwell *St Alb* from 03; P-in-c Pirton from 03.

The Vicarage, Crabtree Lane, Pirton, Hitchin SG5 3QE Tel (01462) 712230 Fax 713597
PAYNTER, Stephen Denis. b 59. Bath Univ BSc82 CertEd82. Trin Coll Bris BA89. **d** 89 **p** 90. C Nailsea Ch Ch *B & W* 89-92; C Farnborough *Guildf* 92-97; TV N Farnborough 97-98; V Ealing St Mary *Lon* from 98. *St Mary's Vicarage, St Mary's Road, London W5 5RH* Tel (020) 8567 0414 *or* 8579 7134
PAYNTON, Paul Alexander. b 42. Hull Univ DipMin88. Linc Th Coll 72. **d** 74 **p** 75. C Uppingham w Ayston *Pet* 74-77; P-in-c Market Overton w Thistleton 77-79; R Teigh w Whissendine 77-79; R Teigh w Whissendine and Market Overton 79-95; V Irchester 95-00. *11 Mount Street, Lincoln LN1 3JE* Tel (01522) 560428
PAYTON, Canon Arthur Edward. b 16. Lambeth MA81. **d** 39 **p** 41. Brotherhood of St Paul from 36; St Kitts-Nevis 39-42; C Bedminster Down *Bris* 42-44; OCF 43-45; Org Sec Br Empire Leprosy Relief Assoc 44-49; P-in-c Toxteth Park St Jo and St Thos *Liv* 49-50; V 50-56; R Gt and Lt Wigborough w Salcot Virley *Chelmsf* 56-64; V Highwood 64-66; Hon C Feering 66-69; Hon C Kelvedon 69-82; Managing Dir Inter Ch Travel 54-82; Hon Can Gib Cathl *Eur* 73-84; rtd 81; P-in-c Wickmere w Lt Barningham and Itteringham *Nor* 84-88; Perm to Offic 88-00. *The Grange, Sandy Lane, West Runton, Cromer NR27 9LT* Tel (01263) 837400
PEACE, Brian. b 38. St Jo Coll Nottm DCM92. **d** 92 **p** 93. C Huddersfield H Trin *Wakef* 92-95; R Cheswardine, Childs Ercall, Hales, Hinstock etc *Lich* 95-00; TR 00-03; RD Hodnet 00-03; rtd 03. *2 Mouldsworth Close, Northwich CW9 8FT* Tel (01606) 333013 E-mail brian@peace6.freeserve.co.uk
PEACE, Geoffrey. b 23. S'wark Ord Course. **d** 68 **p** 69. NSM Ashford St Hilda CD *Lon* 68-73; NSM Ashford St Hilda 73-80; C Spilsby w Hundleby *Linc* 80-83; C Sandhurst *Ox* 83-85; V Owlsmoor 85-88; rtd 88; Perm to Offic *Win* from 91. *9 Barley Mow Close, Winchfield, Basingstoke RG27 8ZZ* Tel (01252) 843337
PEACH, Malcolm Thompson. b 31. St Chad's Coll Dur BA56. Sarum Th Coll 56. **d** 58 **p** 59. C Beamish *Dur* 58-61; Chapl Dur Univ 61-65; NE England Sec SCM 61-65; C-in-c Stockton St Mark CD *Dur* 65-72; P-in-c Bishopwearmouth St Nic 72-81; V 81-85; V S Shields St Hilda w St Thos 85-95; Hon Chapl Miss to Seamen 85-95; P-in-c S Shields St Aid w St Steph *Dur* 92-95; rtd 95; Perm to Offic *Dur* from 95. *116 Mount Road, Sunderland SR4 7QD* Tel 0191-522 6216
PEACHELL, David John. b 45. Oak Hill Th Coll 85. **d** 86 **p** 87. C Prescot *Liv* 86-89; CF 89-98; P-in-c Hockering, Honingham, E and N Tuddenham *Nor* 98-02; rtd 02. *21 Brentwood, Eaton, Norwich NR4 6PN* Tel (01603) 880121
PEACOCK, Canon David. b 39. Liv Univ BA61 Lanc Univ MA71 Univ of the South (USA) Hon DD00 FRSA95. Westcott Ho Cam 84. **d** 84 **p** 85. Prin Lect St Martin's Coll Lanc 81-85; Hon C Lancaster St Mary *Blackb* 84-85; Prin Whitelands Coll 85-00; Pro Rector Surrey Univ 93-00; Hon C Roehampton H Trin *S'wark* 85-92; Hon C Putney St Mary 92-00; Hon Can S'wark Cathl 97-00; Perm to Offic *Blackb* from 00. *The Old Dairy, Keerside, Arkholme, Carnforth LA6 1AP* Tel (01524) 221706 E-mail keersidecowshed@aol.com
PEACOCK, David Christopher. b 57. York Univ BA78 DPhil83. Wycliffe Hall Ox 89. **d** 91 **p** 92. C Old Brumby *Linc* 91-95; TV Bottesford w Ashby 95-00; R Cleethorpes from 00. *The Rectory, 42 Queens Parade, Cleethorpes DN35 0DG* Tel (01472) 200659 *or* 231198 E-mail dcpeacock@ntlworld.com
PEACOCK, John. b 34. ALCD60. **d** 60 **p** 61. C Addiscombe St Mary *Cant* 60-62; C Felixstowe St Jo *St E* 62-65; Chapl RAF 65-70; Australia from 71; C Panania 71-74; R Strathfield 74-80; Chapl Gladesville Hosp Sydney 81-94; Chapl Angl Retirement Villages Sydney 94-99; rtd 99. *511/6 Tarragal Glen Avenue, Erina, NSW, Australia 2250* Tel (0061) (2) 4367 0936
PEACOCK, Mrs Kate Rebecca. b 78. Hatf Coll Dur BA00. Westcott Ho Cam 01. **d** 03. C Cambridge Ascension *Ely* from 03. *2 Stretten Avenue, Cambridge CB4 3EP* Tel (01223) 462414 E-mail kate.peacock@btopenworld.com
PEACOCKE, Canon Arthur Robert. b 24. MBE93. Ex Coll Ox BA45 BSc47 MA48 DPhil48 DSc62 DD82 Birm Univ DipTh60 BD71. **d** 71 **p** 71. Fell and Tutor St Pet Coll Ox 65-73; Dean Clare Coll Cam 73-84; Lic to Offic *Ely* 73-85; Lic to Offic *Ox* from 85; Dir Ian Ramsey Cen Ox 85-88; Warden SOSc from 87; Hon Chapl Ch Ch Ox from 88; Hon C Church Ch Ox from 94. *55 St John's Street, Oxford OX1 2LQ* Tel (01865) 512041
PEAD, Charles Henry. b 31. **d** 87 **p** 88. NSM Llanfrechfa and Llanddewi Fach w Llandegveth *Mon* 87-92; NSM Mamhilad and Llanfihangel Pontymoile 92-95; Lic to Offic from 96. *Jasmine, Caerleon Road, Llanfrechfa, Cwmbran NP44 8DQ* Tel (01633) 482685
PEAKE, Robert Ernest. b 27. Univ Coll Lon BSc51 FSS. Coll of Resurr Mirfield 83. **d** 85 **p** 86. C Linslade *Ox* 85-88; TV Gt Chesham 88-89; rtd 89; Hon C Princes Risborough w Ilmer *Ox* 93-98; Hon C Risborough from 98. *Butley Cottage, Chestnut Way, Longwick, Princes Risborough HP27 9SD* Tel (01844) 344952

PEAKE, Canon Simon Jeremy Brinsley. b 30. Worc Coll Ox BA53 MA56. St Steph Ho Ox 53. **d** 57 **p** 58. C Eastbourne St Andr *Chich* 57-60; S Africa 60-69; C Claremont Ch the K 60-61; R Roodebloem All SS 61-65; R Maitland Gd Shep 65-69; Zambia 69-77; Assoc R Kitwe St Mich 69-71; Chapl Mindolo Ecum Foundn 71-77; Chapl Athens w Kifissia *Eur* 77-87; Chapl Vienna w Budapest and Prague 87-98; Chapl Vienna w Prague 98-00; Hon Can Malta Cathl 87-00; Adn E Adnry 95-00; rtd 00; Perm to Offic *B & W* and *Eur* from 00. *Rosedale, Queen Street, Keinton Mandeville, Somerton TA11 6EG* Tel (01458) 224483

PEAKE, Ms Sue. b 42. K Coll Dur BA63. SEITE 99. **d** 02. NSM Clapham Ch Ch and St Jo *S'wark* from 02. *20 Gauden Road, London SW4 6LT* Tel (020) 7627 4060

PEAL, Jacqueline. b 46. MCSP70. Cant Sch of Min 88. **d** 91 **p** 94. NSM Bexley St Jo *Roch* 91-97; NSM Crayford 91-94; C 94-97 and 00-01; C Dartford H Trin 97-00; Asst Chapl Thames Gateway NHS Trust from 01. *The Rectory, The Street, Ash, Sevenoaks TN15 7HA* Tel (01474) 872209 Fax as telephone E-mail peal@btinternet.com

PEAL, John Arthur. b 46. K Coll Lon BD70 AKC. **d** 71 **p** 72. C Portsea All SS w St Jo Rudmore *Portsm* 71-74; C Westbury *Sarum* 71-77; V Borstal *Roch* 77-82; Chapl HM Pris Cookham Wood 78-82; Chapl Erith and Distr Hosp 82-93; Chapl Qu Mary's Sidcup NHS Trust from 93; V Erith Ch Ch *Roch* 82-91; P-in-c Erith St Jo 86-91; V Bexley St Jo 91-00; R Ash from 00; R Ridley from 00. *The Rectory, The Street, Ash, Sevenoaks TN15 7HA* Tel and fax (01474) 872209 Mobile 07798-851583 E-mail peal@btinternet.com

PEAL, William John. b 26. K Coll Lon BSc47 AKC PhD52. St Jo Coll Nottm 79. **d** 80 **p** 81. C Coalville and Bardon Hill *Leic* 80-83; TV Melton Mowbray w Thorpe Arnold 83-86; TV Melton Gt Framland 86-90; rtd 90; Perm to Offic *Lich* from 91; *Ches* 91-99. *20 Conway Road, Knypersley, Stoke-on-Trent ST8 7AL* Tel (01782) 513580

PEALL, Mrs Linda Grace. b 66. Westmr Coll Ox BEd88. EAMTC 99. **d** 02 **p** 03. NSM Blackwell All SS and Salutation *Dur* from 02. *3 Westfield Drive, Darlington DL3 9BB* Tel (01325) 362650 E-mail linda.peall@btopenworld.com

PEARCE, Adrian Francis. b 55. S Dios Minl Tr Scheme 92. **d** 95 **p** 96. NSM Jersey St Jas *Win* from 95; NSM Jersey St Luke from 95. *24 Richelieu Park, Tower Road, St Helier, Jersey JE2 3HT* Tel (01534) 873115

PEARCE, Andrew John. b 66. Ex Univ BA89 Homerton Coll Cam PGCE93. St Mich Coll Llan Dip Past Th 94. **d** 96 **p** 97. C Llansamlet *S & B* 96-99; C Clydach 99-00; P-in-c Knighton, Norton, Whitton, Pilleth and Cascob 00-02; V from 02. *The Vicarage, Church Street, Knighton LD7 1AG* Tel (01547) 528566

PEARCE, Mrs Angela Elizabeth. b 36. K Coll Lon BSc58 CertEd59 BD79 AKC79. dss 79 **d** 87. Chapl Raines Sch 79-97; Homerton St Barn w St Paul *Lon* 79-85; Upper Chelsea St Simon 85-89; Hon Par Dn 87-89; Hon Par Dn Limehouse 89-97; Perm to Offic *St E* from 97. *50 Crown Street, Bury St Edmunds IP33 1QX* Tel (01284) 760016

PEARCE, Canon Brian Edward. b 39. Kelham Th Coll 59. **d** 64 **p** 65. C Smethwick St Matt *Birm* 64-68; C Kings Norton 68-72; TV 73-80; TR Swindon Dorcan *Bris* 80-91; Min Withywood CD 91-94; RD Bedminster 92-98; V Withywood 94-98; Hon Can Bris Cathl from 97; V Fishponds All SS from 98. *All Saints' Vicarage, Grove Road, Fishponds, Bristol BS16 2BW* Tel 0117-965 4143

PEARCE, Clive. b 40. Univ of Wales (Lamp) BA63 Heythrop Coll Lon MA01. St Steph Ho Ox 63. **d** 65 **p** 66. C Acton Green St Pet *Lon* 65-67; C Eastcote St Lawr 67-73; V Hatch End St Anselm from 73. *Hatch End Vicarage, 50 Cedar Drive, Pinner HA5 4DE* Tel and fax (020) 8428 4111 Mobile 07710-900545 E-mail ecclesiaenavis@aol.com

PEARCE, Colin James. b 51. Trin Coll Bris DipTh96. **d** 96 **p** 97. C Kingswood *Bris* 96-00; TV Bedminster from 00. *St Dunstan's Vicarage, 66 Bedminster Down Road, Bristol BS13 7AA* Tel 0117-963 5977 E-mail colinpearce@blueyonder.co.uk

PEARCE, Canon Denis William Wilfrid. b 25. Bps' Coll Cheshunt 55. **d** 58 **p** 59. C Lt Ilford St Mich *Chelmsf* 58-62; C Leytonstone St Jo 62-65; C-in-c Leytonstone St Aug CD 65-74; V Leytonstone H Trin Harrow Green 65-81; P-in-c Leyton St Luke 78-81; R Capel w Lt Wenham *St E* 81-86; P-in-c Lavenham 86-89; R 89-93; RD Lavenham 87-93; Hon Can St E Cathl 90-93; rtd 93; Clergy Retirement Officer *St E* 93-01. *74 Hintlesham Drive, Felixstowe IP11 2YL*

PEARCE, Desmond. b 30. Univ of Wales (Abth) BA52. EMMTC 85. **d** 88 **p** 89. NSM Chellaston *Derby* 88-90; NSM Walsall St Gabr Fulbrook *Lich* 90; C Stoke Lacy, Moreton Jeffries w Much Cowarne etc *Heref* 91-97; Perm to Offic *Mon* 98-00; P-in-c New Tredegar 00-03. *56 Bedwellty Road, Cefn Forest, Blackwood NP12 3HB*

PEARCE, Preb Eustace Kenneth Victor. b 13. Univ Coll Lon BSc65 St Pet Coll Ox Dip Anthropology 64 FRAI64. ALCD37. **d** 37 **p** 38. C Toxteth Park St Clem *Liv* 37-40; R Sutton 40-42; C Fordington *Sarum* 42-44; V Camberwell All SS *S'wark* 44-50; R Bucknall and Bagnall *Lich* 50-71; CF (TA) 66-81; V Audley *Lich*

71-81; Preb Lich Cathl 67-81; rtd 81; Chief Exec Evidence for Truth Broadcasting Assn from 83; Perm to Offic *Ches* and *Chich* from 83; *Lich* 83-95. *15 Kinnersley Avenue, Kidsgrove, Stoke-on-Trent ST7 1AP,* or *13 Lismore Road, Eastbourne BN21 3AY* Tel (01782) 773325, (01332) 725231 or (01782) 642000 Fax (01782) 641121 E-mail ucb@ucb.co.uk

PEARCE, Canon Frank. b 31. St Aid Birkenhead. **d** 57 **p** 58. C Worksop Priory *S'well* 57-61; P-in-c W Retford 61-62; R 62-70; R Kettering SS Pet and Paul *Pet* 70-94; Chapl Kettering Gen and St Mary's Hosps 70-94; Can Pet Cathl *Pet* 78-94; rtd 94. *Sherwood Lodge, 36 Queen Eleanor Road, Geddington, Kettering NN14 1AY* Tel (01536) 742334

PEARCE, Canon Gerald Nettleton. b 25. St Jo Coll Dur BA49 DipTh51. **d** 51 **p** 52. C Bury St Edmunds St Mary *St E* 51-54; C Attenborough w Bramcote and Chilwell *S'well* 54-56; V Selston 56-61; R Wilford 61-73; RD Bingham 73-84; P-in-c Holme Pierrepont w Adbolton 73-84; V Radcliffe-on-Trent 73-84; V Shelford 73-84; Hon Can S'well Minster 77-84; R Sigglesthorne and Rise w Nunkeeling and Bewholme *York* 84-91; RD N Holderness 86-90; Perm to Offic from 91; rtd 91; Rtd Clergy and Widows Officer (E Riding) *York* from 91. *Sutherland Bridge, Cropton, Pickering YO18 8EU* Tel (01751) 417420

PEARCE, Mrs Iris Rose. b 27. **d** 00 **p** 03. OLM Parkstone St Pet and St Osmund w Branksea *Sarum* 00-03; Chapl Asst Poole Hosp NHS Trust 00-03; Perm to Offic from 03. *Flat 1 Pelham, 34 Lindsay Road, Poole BH13 6AY* Tel (01202) 769301 E-mail iris1pelham@aol.com

PEARCE, Mrs Janet Elizabeth. b 49. Somerville Coll Ox BA72 MA76 CertEd74. N Ord Course 85. **d** 88 **p** 94. Par Dn Helsby and Dunham-on-the-Hill *Ches* 88-94; C 94-96; C Norley, Crowton and Kingsley from 96; Dioc Adv in Spirituality from 02. *St John's House, Pike Lane, Kingsley, Frodsham WA6 8EH* Tel (01928) 788386

PEARCE, Preb John Frederick Dilke. b 32. Ex Coll Ox BA55 MA59. Westcott Ho Cam. **d** 57 **p** 58. C Dalston St Mark w St Bart *Lon* 57-60; C Chelsea Ch Ch 60-63; R Lower Homerton St Paul 63-81; Preb St Paul's Cathl 70-97; P-in-c Clapton Park All So 72-77; V 77-84; RD Hackney 74-79; R Homerton St Barn w St Paul 81-85; TR Hackney Marsh 85; P-in-c Upper Chelsea St Simon 85-89; AD Chelsea 88-89; R Limehouse 89-97; rtd 97; Perm to Offic *St E* from 97. *50 Crown Street, Bury St Edmunds IP33 1QX* Tel (01284) 760016 Fax 756306 E-mail john@jfdp.freeserve.co.uk

PEARCE, Jonathan. b 55. St Jo Coll Nottm BTh85. **d** 85 **p** 86. C Gt Chesham *Ox* 85-89; C Newport Pagnell w Lathbury and Moulsoe 89-93; TV Waltham H Cross *Chelmsf* from 93. *The Vicarage, Church Road, High Beach, Loughton IG10 4AJ* Tel (020) 8508 1791

PEARCE, Kenneth Jack. b 25. CIPFA. Linc Th Coll 62. **d** 63 **p** 64. C Wootton Bassett *Sarum* 63-66; C Broad Town 63-66; P-in-c Derby St Andr *Derby* 66-68; V Derby St Mark 68-87; rtd 87; Perm to Offic *St Alb* from 91. *117 Oaks Cross, Stevenage SG2 8LT* Tel (01438) 317385

PEARCE, Michael Hawkins. b 29. Sarum Th Coll 61. **d** 62 **p** 63. C Bedminster St Aldhelm *Bris* 62-65; C Bishopston 65-68; R Jacobstow w Warbstow *Truro* 68-74; V Treneglos 68-74; V St Teath 74-94; rtd 94; Perm to Offic *Truro* from 94. *32 Trenant Road, Tywardreath, Par PL24 2QJ* Tel (01726) 813658

PEARCE, Neville John Lewis. b 33. CBIM88 Leeds Univ LLB53 LLM54. Trin Coll Bris 90. **d** 91 **p** 92. NSM Bath Walcot *B & W* 91-93; P-in-c Swainswick w Langridge and Woolley 93-98; Perm to Offic from 98. *Penshurst, Weston Lane, Bath BA1 4AB* Tel (01225) 426925

PEARCE, Robert John. b 47. GLCM LLCM72 Birm Univ PGCE73. Ripon Coll Cuddesdon 79. **d** 82 **p** 83. C Broseley w Benthall *Heref* 82-83; C Kington w Huntington, Old Radnor, Kinnerton etc 83-85; R Westbury 85-94; R Yockleton 85-94; V Gt Wollaston 85-94; V Gwersyllt *St As* 94-99; V Northop from 99. *The Vicarage, Sychdyn Road, Northop, Mold CH7 6AW* Tel (01352) 840842

PEARCE, Sacha Jane. b 64. Reading Univ BA92. RGN86 Ripon Coll Cuddesdon. **d** 00 **p** 01. C Tisbury *Sarum* 00-01; C Nadder Valley from 01. *7 Church Street Close, Tisbury, Salisbury SP3 6QY* Tel (01747) 870790 E-mail sachapearce@piran.org.uk

PEARCE, Trevor John. b 27. FSR57. Roch Th Coll 65. **d** 67 **p** 68. C Cheriton Street *Cant* 67-69; C Willesborough w Hinxhill 69-73; V Devonport St Barn *Ex* 73-79; Chapl N Devon Healthcare NHS Trust 79-83; V Derby St Andr w St Osmund *Derby* 83-84; Chapl Derbyshire R Infirmary 83-92; Lic to Offic *Derby* 84-92; rtd 92; Perm to Offic *Derby* from 92. *4 Morrell Wood Drive, Belper DE56 0JD* Tel (01773) 828450

PEARCE, Sister Valerie Olive. b 46. Whitelands Coll Lon CertEd67. SEITE 96. **d** 97. Sisters of the Ch from 77; Lic to Offic *S'wark* from 97. *St Michael's Convent, 56 Ham Common, Richmond TW10 7JH* Tel (020) 8940 8711 Mobile 07932-060075 Fax (020) 8332 2927 E-mail valerie.csc@which.net

PEARCE, Victor. See PEARCE, Preb Eustace Kenneth Victor

PEARCE, William Philip Daniel. b 26. Stanford Univ BA48 Leeds Univ CertEd64 MA75. Cuddesdon Coll 54. **d** 56 **p** 57.

USA 56-60 and from 86; CR 60-84; C St Geo-in-the-East w
St Paul *Lon* 84-86; rtd 02. *1037 Olympic Lane, Seaside, CA 93955,
USA* Tel (001) (831) 393 2176 E-mail philipearce@juno.com

PEARKES, Nicholas Robin Clement. b 49. Ex Univ BA. Linc Th
Coll. **d** 82 **p** 83. C Plymstock *Ex* 82-85; P-in-c Weston Mill 85-86;
TV Devonport St Boniface and St Phil 86-99; R Broadhempston,
Woodland, Staverton etc from 99. *The Rectory, Broadhempston,
Totnes TQ9 6AU* Tel (01803) 813754
E-mail platypus@wordoflife.fsnet.co.uk

PEARMAIN, Andrew Neil. b 55. K Coll Lon BD79 AKC79.
Ridley Hall Cam 79. **d** 81 **p** 82. C Cranleigh *Guildf* 81-84; P-in-c
Frimley 85-86; C 86-87; Chapl Frimley Park Hosp 87. *Address
temp unknown*

PEARMAIN, Canon Brian Albert John. b 34. Lon Univ BD68.
Roch Th Coll 63. **d** 66 **p** 67. C Shirley St Jo *Cant* 66-69; C Selsdon
St Jo w St Fran 69-73; P-in-c Louth H Trin *Linc* 73-75; TV Louth
75-79; R Scartho 79-97; RD Grimsby and Cleethorpes 89-94;
Can and Preb Linc Cathl 94-97; rtd 97; Perm to Offic *Linc* from
00. *69 Riverside Road, Newark NG24 4RL* Tel (01636) 659266
E-mail vandb.pearmain@ntlworld.com

PEARS, Anthony John. b 58. Ripon Coll Cuddesdon 00. **d** 02
p 03. C Watton w Carbrooke and Ovington *Nor* from 02.
44 Jubilee Road, Watton, Thetford IP25 6BJ Tel (01953) 773296
E-mail tony.pears@virgin.net

PEARSE, Andrew George. b 46. Wycliffe Hall Ox 71. **d** 74 **p** 75. C
Homerton St Luke *Lon* 74-77; C Chadderton Em *Man* 77-81; R
Collyhurst 81-89; Area Sec (NE, E Midl and Scotland) SAMS
89-03; rtd 03; Chapl Co-ord St Leon Hospice York from 03.
9 Troutsdale Avenue, Rawcliffe, York YO30 5TR Tel (01904)
332373 E-mail andrew.stleonards@virgin.net

PEARSE, Ronald Thomas Hennessy. b 26. AKC52. **d** 53 **p** 54. C
Leic St Pet *Leic* 53-55; C Hanwell St Thos *Lon* 55-58; R Asfordby
Leic 58-84; P-in-c Scalford w Wycombe and Chadwell 75-76; R
Thurcaston 84-89; rtd 89; Perm to Offic *Leic* 89-90. *15 Burton
Street, Loughborough LE11 2DT* Tel (01509) 215478

PEARSON, Andrew George Campbell. b 41. Qu Coll Ox BA63
BA66. Wycliffe Hall Ox 63. **d** 71 **p** 72. C Gillingham St Mark
Roch 71-72; C Billingshurst *Chich* 72-77; C Ches Square St Mich
w St Phil *Lon* 77-82; Co-ord Busoga Trust from 82; P-in-c
St Marg Pattens *Lon* from 90; C Kensington St Mary Abbots w
St Geo from 96. *15 Chadwin Road, London E13 8ND* Tel (020)
7476 6730 *or* 7623 6630

PEARSON, Andrew John. b 59. Humberside Coll of Educn
HND83. Westcott Ho Cam 86. **d** 89 **p** 90. C Knaresborough
Ripon 89-92; C Wetherby 92-94; P-in-c Hunslet Moor St Pet and
St Cuth 94-96; V 96-01; Dioc Environment Officer from 97; V
Hawksworth Wood from 01. *St Mary's Vicarage, 50 Cragside
Walk, Leeds LS5 3QE* Tel 0113-258 2923
E-mail lindrew@pearley.fsnet.co.uk

PEARSON, Ms Brenda Elizabeth Frances (Brandy). b 51. SEITE
00. **d** 03. NSM Finsbury Park St Thos *Lon* from 03. *42 Grenoble
Gardens, London N13 6JG* Tel (020) 8365 8971
E-mail brandy@brandywine999.fsnet.co.uk

PEARSON, Brian. b 29. LTCL53 Lon Inst of Educn CertEd54.
Sarum & Wells Th Coll 71. **d** 73 **p** 74. C Rainham *Roch* 73-77;
Chapl East Pembury Hosp Tunbridge Wells 77-80; C Pembury
Roch 77-80; V Gravesend St Aid 80-97; Chapl Gravesend and
N Kent Hosp 81-83; rtd 97; Perm to Offic *Roch* from 97; Dioc
Clergy Widows and Retirement Officer from 97. *32 Swan Street,
West Malling ME19 6LP* Tel (01732) 848462

PEARSON, Canon Brian Robert. b 35. Leeds Univ BA59. Coll of
Resurr Mirfield 59. **d** 61 **p** 62. C Chesterfield St Mary and All SS
Derby 61-66; P-in-c Derby St Jo 66-72; P-in-c Derby St Anne
66-72; R Thorpe *Nor* 72-90; Hon Can Nor Cathl 85-90; RD Nor
E 86-90; V Harrogate St Wilfrid *Ripon* 90-00; rtd 00; Perm to
Offic *York* from 00. *Green Garth, 13 Cedar Glade, Dunnington,
York YO19 5QZ* Tel (01904) 481232

PEARSON, Canon Brian William. b 49. FHSM Brighton Poly
BSc71 City Univ MSc80 Westmr Coll Ox MTh94. S'wark Ord
Course & Clapham Ord Scheme 76. **d** 79 **p** 80. Hon C Plumstead
All SS *S'wark* 79-81; Perm to Offic *Chich* 81-83; Hon C
Broadwater St Mary 83-88; Bp's Research and Dioc
Communications Officer *B & W* 88-90; Dioc Missr 91; Abp's
Officer for Miss and Evang and Tait Missr *Cant* 91-97; Abp's
Dioc Chapl 91-97; Hon Can Cant Cathl 92-97; Gen Dir CPAS
97-00; P-in-c Leek Wootton *Cov* from 00; Dioc Officer for OLM
from 00. *The Vicarage, 4 Hill Wootton Road, Leek Wootton,
Warwick CV35 7QL* Tel (01926) 854832 Fax 859117
E-mail brian@bwpvic.fslife.co.uk

PEARSON, Mrs Béatrice Levasseur. b 53. Sorbonne Univ Paris
LèsL74 MèsL75 Lon Inst of Educn PGCE76. Ripon Coll
Cuddesdon 01. **d** 03. C Easthampstead *Ox* from 03. *St Michael's
House, Crowthorne Road, Bracknell RG12 7ER* Tel (01344)
460041 Mobile 07786-653184
E-mail bea.acumen@zetnet.co.uk

PEARSON, Christian David John (Brother Christian). b 42.
Open Univ BA76 CCC Cam BA79 MA83. AKC65. **d** 66 **p** 67. C
Pallion *Dur* 66-68; C Peterlee 68-71; SSF from 71; Lic to Offic
Sarum 71-73; Tanzania 74-75; Lic to Offic *Ely* 75-90; Asst Chapl

Keble Coll Ox 82-83; Chapl St Cath Coll Cam 83-86; Chapl
Down Coll Cam 86-90; Lic to Offic *Lon* from 90; Dep Warden
and Chapl Lon Ho Trust 90-93; Dep Warden and Chapl Lon
Goodenough Trust 93-95. *Holy Trinity House, Orsett Terrace,
London W2 6AH* Tel (020) 7723 9735

PEARSON, Christopher Ian. b 65. Thames Poly BA91 K Coll Lon
MA96. Coll of Resurr Mirfield CPS93. **d** 93 **p** 94. C Newington
St Mary *S'wark* 93-95; C Streatham St Pet 95-97; V Kennington
Park St Agnes from 97. *The Vicarage, 37 St Agnes Place, London
SE11 4BB* Tel (020) 7735 3860 E-mail vicar@saintagnes.org.uk

PEARSON, Christopher John. b 49. GRSM LRAM ARCM.
Oak Hill NSM Course 81. **d** 84 **p** 85. NSM Barton Seagrave w
Warkton *Pet* 84-86; C Kettering St Andr 86-88; V Nassington w
Yarwell and Woodnewton 88-91; V Pet St Mark 91-03; P-in-c Gt
Doddington and Wilby from 03. *The Vicarage, 72 High Street,
Great Doddington, Wellingborough NN9 7TH* Tel (01933)
226711 Fax as telephone

PEARSON, David. *See* PEARSON, James David

PEARSON, David. b 57. Man Poly BA78. Trin Coll Bris 85. **d** 88
p 89. C Shawbury *Lich* 88-91; C Morton 88-91; C Stanton on
Hine Heath 88-91; R Mattishall w Mattishall Burgh, Welborne
etc *Nor* 91-00; RD Dereham in Mitford 98-00; Asst P Tawa
Linden New Zealand from 00. *38 Westhaven Drive, Tawa,
Wellington, New Zealand* Tel (0064) (4) 232 1929 *or* (4) 232 8448
E-mail dpearson.tawa@xtra.co.nz

PEARSON, Edgar. b 13. Tyndale Hall Bris 37. **d** 41 **p** 42. C
Handforth *Ches* 41; Burma 42; India 42-47; Hon CF 47; Chile
50-55; Australia 55-65; R Dallinghoo and Pettistree St E 65-83;
P-in-c Bredfield w Boulge 74-86; rtd 83; P-in-c Dallinghoo and
Pettistree *St E* 83-86; Perm to Offic *Mon* from 86. *Maendy
House, Penrhos, Raglan, Usk NP15 2LQ* Tel (01600) 780398

PEARSON, Fergus Tom. b 58. Middx Poly BA81 Moore Th Coll
Sydney MA98. Oak Hill Th Coll BA95. **d** 92 **p** 93. C Mildmay
Grove St Jude and St Paul *Lon* 92-95; Australia 96-98; C
Heatherlands St Jo *Sarum* 98-03; V Hensingham *Carl* from 03.
*St John's Vicarage, Egremont Road, Hensingham, Whitehaven
CA28 8QW* Tel (01946) 692822
E-mail fpe@rson.justbrowsing.com

PEARSON, Geoffrey Charles. b 49. BSc ARCS. Oak Hill Th
Coll. **d** 82 **p** 83. C Foord St Jo *Cant* 82-86; V Ramsgate St Luke
86-93; Chapl to People at Work in Cam *Ely* 93-01; Chapl HM
Pris Chelmsf from 01. *HM Prison, 200 Springfield Road,
Chelmsford CM2 6LQ* Tel (01245) 268651
E-mail geoffcp@aol.com

PEARSON, Canon Geoffrey Seagrave. b 51. St Jo Coll Dur BA72
DipTh73. Cranmer Hall Dur 72. **d** 74 **p** 75. C Kirkheaton *Wakef*
74-77; C-in-c Blackb Redeemer *Blackb* 77-82; V 82-85; Asst
Home Sec Gen Syn Bd for Miss and Unity 85-89; Hon C Forty
Hill Jes Ch *Lon* 85-89; Exec Sec BCC Evang Cttee 86-89; V Roby
Liv from 89; AD Huyton from 02; Hon Can Liv Cathl from 03.
The Vicarage, 11 Church Road, Liverpool L36 9TL Tel 0151-489
1438 Fax as telephone E-mail geoffpeo@hotmail.com

PEARSON, George Michael. b 31. FCA FBCS MIMC. Qu Coll
Birm 86 Coll of Resurr Mirfield 89. **d** 88 **p** 90. NSM Solihull
Birm 88-95; Perm to Offic from 95. *The Parsonage, 67A Hampton
Lane, Solihull B91 2QD* Tel 0121-705 0288 Fax 704 0466
E-mail parsonpearson@pearwood.org.uk

PEARSON, Canon Harold (Brother Geoffrey). b 21. Ch Coll
Cam BA43 MA46. Chich Th Coll 43. **d** 45 **p** 46. C Weymouth H
Trin *Sarum* 45-48; SSF from 48; P-in-c Plaistow St Andr *Chelmsf*
53-57; Chapl Denstone Coll Uttoxeter 58; Papua New Guinea
59-70; Min Gen SSF 70-85; Hon Can Win Cathl *Win* from 81;
Zimbabwe 80-81; rtd 91. *The Friary, Hilfield, Dorchester
DT2 7BE* Tel (01300) 341345 Fax 341293

PEARSON, Canon Henry Gervis. b 47. Mansf Coll Ox BA72
MA76. St Jo Coll Nottm 72. **d** 74 **p** 75. C Southgate *Chich* 74-76;
TV 76-82; V Debenham w Aspall and Kenton *St E* 82-91; Chapl
to Suffolk Fire Service 88-91; RD Loes 89-91; TR Marlborough
Sarum 91-02; RD Marlborough 94-02; Can and Preb Sarum
Cathl from 99; Chapl Savernake Hosp Marlborough 91-94;
Chapl E Wilts Health Care NHS Trust from 94; R Queen
Thorne *Sarum* from 02. *The Rectory, Trent, Sherborne DT9 4SL*
Tel (01935) 851049

PEARSON, Ian. b 49. Liv Univ BA71 DAA72. S'wark Ord
Course 79. **d** 82 **p** 83. Hon C Lavender Hill Ascension *S'wark*
82-84; Archivist USPG 82-85; Archivist Nat Soc 85-91; Lic to
Offic *Lon* 84-86 and 89-90; Hon C Westmr St Matt 86-88; Perm to
Offic *S'wark* 85-90; Perm to Offic *St Alb* 90-91; C Chesterfield
St Mary and All SS *Derby* 91-95; R Bengeo *St Alb* from 95. *The
Rectory, Byde Street, Hertford SG14 3BS* Tel (01992) 504997
Fax as telephone E-mail ianandlizpearson@waitrose.com

PEARSON, James David. b 51. Cape Town Univ BSocSc74.
St Paul's Coll Grahamstown DipTh78. **d** 78 **p** 79. S Africa 78-99;
C St Geo Cathl Cape Town 78-80; R Caledon H Trin 80-84; R
Tristan da Cunha St Mary 84-86; R Camps Bay St Pet 86-89; R
Kuruman St Mary-le-Bourne w Wrenchville St Pet 89-91; R
Amalinda Ch 92-96; Asst P Cambridge St Mark 96-98; Asst
P-in-c Kidds Beach St Mary and St Andr 99; C Prittlewell

St Steph *Chelmsf* from 00. *St Stephen's Vicarage, 213 Manners Way, Southend-on-Sea SS2 6QS* Tel (01702) 345190 E-mail jdavidp@blueyonder.co.uk

PEARSON, Canon James Stuart. b 28. St Jo Coll Dur BA57. Cranmer Hall Dur 57. **d** 58 **p** 59. C Halifax St Jo Bapt *Wakef* 58-63; V Alverthorpe 63-70; V Knottingley 70-78; Dioc Soc Resp Adv 78-87; V Woolley 78-94; Chapl Bretton Hall Coll of Educn 87-94; Hon Can Wakef Cathl 89-94; RD Chevet 93-94; rtd 94; Perm to Offic *York* from 96. *21 Orrin Close, York YO24 2RA* Tel (01904) 708521

PEARSON, James William. b 20. FCA59. Qu Coll Birm 75. **d** 78 **p** 79. NSM Beoley *Worc* 78-90; Perm to Offic from 90. *Ringwood, Rowney Green, Alvechurch, Birmingham B48 7QE* Tel (01527) 66952

PEARSON, John Nigel. b 45. CA Tr Coll IDC75 EMMTC 78. **d** 81 **p** 82. C Stapenhill w Cauldwell *Derby* 81-83; V Measham *Leic* from 83; P-in-c Packington w Normanton-le-Heath from 02. *The Vicarage, High Street, Measham, Swadlincote DE12 7HZ* Tel (01530) 270354

PEARSON, Canon Kevin. b 54. Leeds Univ BA75 Edin Univ BD79. Edin Th Coll 76. **d** 79 **p** 80. C Horden *Dur* 79-81; Chapl Leeds Univ *Ripon* 81-87; R Edin St Salvador *Edin* 87-93; Chapl Napier Poly 88-92; Chapl Napier Univ 92-94; Dioc Dir of Ords 90-95; Prov Dir of Ords from 91; Assoc R Edin Old St Paul 93-94; P-in-c Linlithgow 94-95; R Edin St Mich and All SS from 95; Can St Mary's Cathl from 03. *The Rectory, 203 Gilmore Place, Edinburgh EH3 9PN* Tel 0131-229 6368

PEARSON, Mrs Lindsey Carole. b 61. Cov Poly BA85 CQSW85. Westcott Ho Cam 86. **d** 89 **p** 94. Par Dn Halton St Pet *Ripon* 89-93; Par Dn Moor Allerton 93-94; C 94-96; TV Seacroft from 96; World Development Officer from 99. *St Mary's Vicarage, 50 Cragside Walk, Leeds LS14 3QE* Tel 0113-258 2923 E-mail lindrew@pearley.fsnet.co.uk

PEARSON, Michael Carden. b 38. Guy's Hosp Medical Sch MB63 BChir63 Down Coll Cam MA64 Lon Univ MSc94 FRCR75 FRCP94. St Steph Ho Ox DipMin98. **d** 98 **p** 99. NSM Horsted Keynes *Chich* 98-99; NSM Worth 99-00; Chapl Gtr Athens *Eur* 00-01. *Bleak House, Station Road, Horsted Keynes, Haywards Heath RH17 7ED* Tel (01825) 790617

PEARSON, Michael John. b 53. Southn Univ BTh78. Sarum Th Coll 74. **d** 78 **p** 79. C Paignton St Jo *Ex* 78-82; TV Ilfracombe, Lee, W Down, Woolacombe and Bittadon 82-85; TV Ilfracombe, Lee, Woolacombe, Bittadon etc 85-86; TV Barnstaple 86-97; TV Barnstaple from 97; Chapl N Devon Healthcare NHS Trust 86-96; RD Barnstaple *Ex* 97-01. *The Rectory, Sowden Lane, Barnstaple EX32 8BU* Tel (01271) 373837

PEARSON, Mrs Priscilla Dawn. b 45. Oak Hill Th Coll BA90. **d** 90 **p** 94. Par Dn Stanford-le-Hope w Mucking *Chelmsf* 90-94; C 94; C Colchester St Jo 94-96. *Talywain Cottage, Cwmavon Road, Blaenavon, Pontypool NP4 9DZ* Tel (01495) 774132

PEARSON, Raymond Joseph. b 44. AKC71. St Aug Coll Cant 71. **d** 72 **p** 73. C Wetherby *Ripon* 72-75; C Goring-by-Sea *Chich* 75-77; C Bramley *Ripon* 77-82; V Patrick Brompton and Hunton 82-94; V Crakehall 82-94; V Hornby 82-94; World Miss Officer 88-94; RD Wensley 92-94; V Bardsey from 94. *The Vicarage, Wood Acre Lane, Bardsey, Leeds LS17 9DG* Tel (01937) 572243

PEARSON, Robert James Stephen. b 52. Cov Poly BA74. St Steph Ho Ox 85. **d** 87 **p** 88. C Stoke Newington St Mary *Lon* 87-90; C Haggerston All SS 90-97; C Dalston H Trin w St Phil and Haggerston All SS 97-98; Chapl HM Pris Wandsworth 98-02; Chapl HM Pris Pentonville from 02. *HM Prison Pentonville, Caledonian Road, London N7 8TT* Tel (020) 7607 5353

PEARSON, Robert Lyon. b 57. St Jo Coll Nottm DCM92. **d** 92 **p** 93. C Netherton *Liv* 92-96; V Woolston 96-02; V Highfield from 02. *St Matthew's Vicarage, Billinge Road, Wigan WN3 6BL* Tel (01942) 222121

PEARSON, Roderick Percy. b 21. Linc Th Coll 74. **d** 75 **p** 76. C Darlington St Cuth w St Hilda *Dur* 75-80; V Bishop Middleham 80-91; rtd 91. *The Lever Flat, Christ's Hospital in Sherburn, Sherburn House, Durham DH1 2SE* Tel 0191-372 1753

PEARSON, Preb Roy Barthram. b 35. K Coll Lon 56. **d** 60 **p** 61. C Brookfield St Mary *Lon* 60-64; C St Marylebone St Cypr 64-70; V Tottenham All Hallows from 70; AD E Haringey 95-00; Preb St Paul's Cathl from 96. *The Priory, Church Lane, London N17 7AA* Tel (020) 8808 2470

PEARSON-MILES, David. b 37. St Jo Coll Nottm 74. **d** 76 **p** 77. C Hazlemere *Ox* 76-79; R Waddesdon w Over Winchendon and Fleet Marston 79-82; CF 82-92; P-in-c Barcombe *Chich* 92-94; R 94-00; rtd 00. *The Coach House, Holme Place, Oakford, Tiverton EX16 9DH* Tel (01398) 351495

PEART, John Graham. b 36. Bps' Coll Cheshunt 65. **d** 68 **p** 69. C Cheshunt *St Alb* 68-70; C St Alb St Pet 70-73; R Hunsdon 73-76; R Widford 73-76; Ind Chapl 76-82; Chapl St Geo Hosp and Distr Gen Hosp Stafford 82-87; Qu Eliz Hosp and Benham Hosp Gateshead 87-89; Garlands Hosp 89-94; P-in-c Cotehill and Cumwhinton *Carl* 89-94; V Irthington, Crosby-on-Eden and Scaleby 94-98; rtd 98; Chapl Douglas MacMillan Hospice Stoke-on-Trent 98-01; P-in-c Salt and Sandon w Burston *Lich* 01-02; TV Mid Trent from 02. *The Vicarage, Salt, Stafford ST18 0BW* Tel (01889) 508341

PEART, Patricia Isidora. b 55. Westcott Ho Cam CTM99. **d** 99. C Holland-on-Sea *Chelmsf* 99-00; C Shrub End 00-01. *6 Whitsand Road, Manchester M22 4ZA*

PEAT, Mrs Ann Kathleen. b 40. TCert60. LNSM course 93. **d** 98 **p** 99. OLM Brumby *Linc* from 98. *36 Glover Road, Scunthorpe DN17 1AS* Tel (01724) 852609

PEAT, David James. b 62. Leeds Univ BA84. Cranmer Hall Dur 86. **d** 89 **p** 90. C Wetherby *Ripon* 89-92; C Beeston 92-95; Chapl St Lawr Coll Ramsgate from 95. *St Lawrence College, College Road, Ramsgate CT11 7AE* Tel (01843) 582084 *or* 587666

PEAT, David William. b 37. Clare Coll Cam MA59 PhD62 FRAS63. Westcott Ho Cam 72. **d** 75 **p** 76. C Chesterton St Andr *Ely* 75-77; Chapl Univ Coll of Ripon and York St Jo 77-83; V E Ardsley *Wakef* 83-87; Prin Willesden Min Tr Scheme 87-94; NSM Headingley *Ripon* from 94; Research Lect Leeds Univ from 94; rtd 97. *12 North Grange Mews, Headingley, Leeds LS6 2EW* Tel 0113-275 3179 E-mail phy6dwp@phys-irc.leeds.ac.uk

PEAT, The Ven Lawrence Joseph. b 28. Linc Th Coll 55. **d** 58 **p** 59. C Bramley *Ripon* 58-61; V 65-73; R Heaton Norris All SS *Man* 61-65; P-in-c Southend St Erkenwald *Chelmsf* 73-74; TR Southend St Jo w St Mark, All SS w St Fran etc 74-79; V Skelsmergh w Selside and Longsleddale *Carl* 79-86; RD Kendal 84-89; TV Kirkby Lonsdale 86-89; Hon Can Carl Cathl 88-95; Adn Westmorland and Furness 89-95; rtd 95; Perm to Offic *Carl* from 95. *32 White Stiles, Kendal LA9 6DJ* Tel (01539) 733829

PEAT, Matthew. b 71. Bradf and Ilkley Coll BA97. Ripon Coll Cuddesdon BTh03. **d** 03. C Walney Is *Carl* from 03. *7 Irwell Road, Walney, Barrow-in-Furness LA14 3WA* Tel (01229) 474663 E-mail mpeat@fish.co.uk

PEATFIELD, Canon Alfred Charles Henry. b 22. New Coll Ox BA48 MA48. Ripon Hall Ox 48. **d** 51 **p** 52. C Hackney St Jo *Lon* 51-54; V Battersea St Paul *S'wark* 54-56; Malaya 56-63; Malaysia 63-70; Adn N Malaya 64-70; V Hornchurch St Andr *Chelmsf* 70-92; RD Havering 76-80; Hon Can Chelmsf Cathl 80-92; rtd 92; Perm to Offic *Chelmsf* from 92. *28 Moor Lane, Upminster RM14 1EB* Tel (01708) 220598

PEATMAN (née HUGHES), Mrs Debbie Ann. b 62. SS Hild & Bede Coll Dur BA83 St Jo Coll Dur BA89. Cranmer Hall Dur 87. **d** 90 **p** 94. C Edin Old St Paul *Edin* 90-91; NSM Greasley *S'well* 92-94; NSM Whitley *Cov* 94-02; C Lancaster St Thos *Blackb* from 02. *6 Beechwood Gardens, Lancaster LA1 4PH* Tel (01524) 66295 E-mail debbie@peatman.org.uk

PEATMAN, Michael Robert. b 61. Keble Coll Ox BA85 MA89 St Jo Coll Dur BA89. Cranmer Hall Dur 87. **d** 90 **p** 91. C Greasley *S'well* 90-94; P-in-c Whitley *Cov* 94-02; Dio Stewardship Adv 94-02; Sen Chapl St Martin's Coll *Blackb* from 02. *6 Beechwood Gardens, Lancaster LA1 4PH* Tel (01524) 66295 *or* 384260 E-mail mikepeat@bigfoot.com *or* m.peatman@ucsm.ac.uk

PEATTIE, Colin Hulme Reid. b 39. Natal Univ BSc59. Ripon Hall Ox 61. **d** 63 **p** 64. C Belmont *Lon* 65-83; S Africa 65-83 and from 85; V S Ossett *Wakef* 83-85. *PO Box 98, Salt Rock, 4391 South Africa* Tel (0027) (0322) 525 4004 Fax as telephone E-mail allsouls@saol.com

PEATY, Julia Kathleen. b 53. Salford Univ BSc75. STETS 96. **d** 99 **p** 00. NSM E Grinstead St Swithun *Chich* from 99. *15 Overton Shaw, East Grinstead RH19 2HN* Tel (01342) 322386 E-mail jkpeaty@aol.com

PEBERDY (née GARNETT), Mrs Alyson Susan. b 48. Trevelyan Coll Dur BA69 Reading Univ MA75 St Ant Coll Ox Dip Soc Anthropology 77. Ox Min Course 95. **d** 96 **p** 97. C New Windsor *Ox* 96-99; V Brockley Hill St Sav *S'wark* from 99; P-in-c Forest Hill St Aug from 00. *St Saviour's Vicarage, 5 Lowther Hill, London SE23 1PZ* Tel (020) 8690 2499 E-mail alyson.peberdy@ukgateway.net

PECK, David Warner. b 66. American Univ (Washington) BA88 Selw Coll Cam BA94 Cam Univ MA99. Westcott Ho Cam CTM95. **d** 95 **p** 96. C Weybridge *Guildf* 95-99; Bp's Chapl from 99. *19 Thorn Bank, Guildford GU2 7PL* Tel (01483) 302680 *or* 590500 Fax 590501 E-mail david.peck@cofeguildford.org.uk

PECK, Robert John. b 49. Bath Univ BSc72. STETS 00. **d** 03. NSM Stoke-next-Guildf from 03. *10 Eastgate Gardens, Guildford GU1 4AZ* Tel (01483) 854224 E-mail r.peck@ntlworld.com

PECKETT, Desmonde Claude Brown. b 19. Ex & Truro NSM Scheme. **d** 77 **p** 78. NSM Charlestown *Truro* 77-89; Perm to Offic from 89. *Smugglers, Porthpean, St Austell PL26 6AY* Tel (01726) 72768

PECKHAM, Richard Graham. b 51. Sarum & Wells Th Coll 84. **d** 86 **p** 87. C Bishop's Cleeve *Glouc* 86-89; TV Ilfracombe, Lee, Woolacombe, Bittadon etc *Ex* 89-96; TV Sidmouth, Woolbrook, Salcombe Regis, Sidbury etc from 96; RD Ottery 98-02; Hon Chapl ATC from 98. *St Francis's Vicarage, Woolbrook Road, Sidmouth EX10 9XH* Tel (01395) 514522 E-mail rikpeckham@lineone.net *or* rikpeckham@hotmail.com

PEDDER, Brian. b 38. Carl Dioc Tr Inst 88. **d** 91 **p** 92. NSM Wigton *Carl* 91-93; C Cleator Moor w Cleator 93-96; P-in-c Grayrigg, Old Hutton and New Hutton from 96. *The Vicarage, Grayrigg, Kendal LA8 9BU* Tel (01539) 824272

PEDLAR, John Glanville. b 43. Ex Univ BA68. St Steph Ho Ox 68. **d** 70 **p** 71. C Tavistock and Gulworthy *Ex* 70-73; Prec Portsm Cathl *Portsm* 74-77; Prec St Alb Abbey *St Alb* 77-81; V Redbourn 81-98; PV Westmr Abbey from 87; V Bedford St Paul *St Alb* from 98. *St Paul's Vicarage, 12 The Embankment, Bedford MK40 3PD* Tel (01234) 364638

PEDLEY, Canon Betty. b 49. ALCM78 Leeds Univ BEd71 Ripon Coll of Educn CertEd70 Coll of Preceptors Dip Special Educn 81. N Ord Course 85. **d** 88. Par Dn Sowerby *Wakef* 88-92; Par Educn Adv from 92; Youth Chapl from 92; Hon Can Wakef Cathl from 00. *27 Pye Nest Grove, Halifax HX2 7JY* Tel (01422) 346007 Fax 365479

✠**PEDLEY, The Rt Revd Geoffrey Stephen.** b 40. Qu Coll Cam BA64 MA67. Cuddesdon Coll 64. **d** 66 **p** 67 **c** 98. C Liv Our Lady and St Nic *Liv* 66-69; C Cov H Trin *Cov* 69-71; Zambia 71-77; P-in-c Stockton H Trin *Dur* 77-83; V Stockton St Pet 77-88; Chapl to The Queen 84-98; R Whickham *Dur* 88-93; Can Res Dur Cathl 93-98; Suff Bp Lancaster *Blackb* from 98; Hon Can Blackb Cathl from 98. *Shireshead Vicarage, Whinney Brow, Forton, Preston PR3 0AE* Tel (01524) 799900 Fax 799901 E-mail bishop.lancaster@ukonline.co.uk

PEDLEY, Nicholas Charles. b 48. CQSW75. Qu Coll Birm 88. **d** 90 **p** 91. C Stafford St Jo and Tixall w Ingestre *Lich* 90-93; C Kingswinford St Mary *Worc* 93-96; TV 96-97; C Cheswardine, Childs Ercall, Hales, Hinstock etc *Lich* 97-99; Chapl HM YOI Stoke Heath 97-99; rtd 99; Perm to Offic *Worc* from 00. *33 Comber Grove, Kinver, Stourbridge DY7 6EN* Tel (01384) 877219 E-mail nick@npedley48.freeserve.co.uk

PEDLOW, Henry Noel. b 37. QUB BA59. **d** 61 **p** 62. C Belfast St Phil *Conn* 61-66; C Belfast St Nic 66-70; I Eglantine 70-82; I Kilkeel *D & D* 82-89; I Belfast St Donard 89-03; rtd 03. *8 Old Mill Dale, Dundonalad, Belfast BT16 1WG* Tel (028) 9048 5416

PEEBLES, David Thomas. b 64. Bris Univ BA85 St Chad's Coll Dur PGCE86 Man Univ MA94. Coll of Resurr Mirfield 90. **d** 90 **p** 91. C Crewe St Andr *Ches* 90-93; Lect and Asst Dir Studies Mirfield 93-95; Chapl Qu Mary and Westf Coll *Lon* 95-00; P-in-c Bethnal Green St Matt w St Jas the Gt 97-99; Chapl LSE from 00; Bp's Adv on New Relig Movements from 01. *3 Bristol House, 80A Southampton Row, London WC1B 4BA* Tel (020) 7242 4794 E-mail d.peebles@lse.ac.uk

PEEK, John Richard. b 51. Bris Univ BSc72 Nottm Univ BA75. St Jo Coll Nottm. **d** 76 **p** 77. C Hebburn St Jo *Dur* 76-78; C Dunston 78-81; R Armthorpe *Sheff* 81-86; RE Teacher K Edw VI Sch Southn 87-88; Chapl and Hd RE Casterton Sch Cumbria 89; Teacher Furze Platt Comp Sch Berks 89-90; Perm to Offic *Portsm* 90-96; Chapl Bearwood Coll Wokingham 96-98. *Address temp unknown*

PEEL, Mrs Christine Mary. b 44. Whitelands Coll Lon CertEd66. Portsm Dioc Tr Course. **d** 90. NSM Sheet *Portsm* 90-03. *11 Whiteoak Avenue, Easingwold, York YO61 3GB* Tel (01347) 823548

PEEL, David Charles. b 41. AKC75. St Aug Coll Cant 75. **d** 76 **p** 77. C Tynemouth Cullercoats St Paul *Newc* 76-79; C Tynemouth St Jo 79-84; Ldr Cedarwood Project 84-88 and from 91; Warden Communicare Ho 89-91; Min Killingworth 89-91. *116 Grey Street, North Shields NE30 2EG* Tel 0191-272 8743

PEEL, Derrick. b 50. Open Univ BA82. Linc Th Coll 75. **d** 78 **p** 79. C Otley *Bradf* 78-82; V Shelf 82-94; P-in-c Buttershaw St Aid 89-94; TR Shelf St Mich w Buttershaw St Aid 94-95; V E Crompton *Man* from 95. *East Crompton Vicarage, Salts Street, Shaw, Oldham OL2 7TE* Tel (01706) 847454

PEEL, John Bruce. b 30. TCD BA54 MA68. Wells Th Coll 69. **d** 70 **p** 71. C Wilmslow *Ches* 70-75; V Weston 75-83; V Henbury 83-95; Chapl Parkside Hosp Ches 83-95; rtd 95; Perm to Offic *Ches* from 95. *Winneba, 29 Hungerford Terrace, Crewe CW1 1HF* Tel (01270) 587464

PEEL, Capt Jonathan Sidney. b 37. CBE95 MC57 DL75. St Jo Coll Cam BA70 MA75. Dioc OLM tr scheme 97. **d** 00 **p** 01. NSM Ashmanhaugh, Barton Turf etc *Nor* from 00. *Barton Hall, Barton Turf, Norwich NR12 8AU* Tel (01692) 536250 Fax 536135

PEEL, Michael Jerome. b 31. Bris Univ BA55 MLitt73 St Cath Soc Ox DipTh59 Man Univ BD65 K Coll Lon PhD88. Wycliffe Hall Ox 57. **d** 59 **p** 60. C Stretford St Matt *Man* 59-61; C Chorlton upon Medlock 61-62; Chapl Man Univ 61-62; C Chorlton-cum-Hardy St Clem 62-65; V Chirbury *Heref* 65-68; P-in-c Marton 65-68; R Iver Heath *Ox* 68-87; V Linslade 87-95; rtd 95; Warden Coll of St Barn Lingfield 95-00; Lic to Offic *S'wark* 95-00; Perm to Offic *Chich* and Roch 95-00; St E from 00; Chelmsf from 01. *Poplar Meadow, Thedwastre Road, Thurston, Bury St Edmunds IP31 3QY* Tel (01359) 270296

PEELING, Mrs Pamela Mary Alberta. b 44. Oak Hill Th Coll 83. dss 86 **d** 87 **p** 94. NSM Moulsham St Luke *Chelmsf* 86-88; NSM N Springfield 88-95; C Basildon St Martin 95-97; TV Grays Thurrock from 97. *The Vicarage, Clockhouse Lane, Chafford Hundred, Grays RM16 6YW* Tel (01375) 482252 E-mail pam@ppeeling.freeserve.co.uk

PEER, Charles Scott. b 69. Bris Univ BSc91 PGCE94. Trin Coll Bris BA02. **d** 02 **p** 03. C Dawlish *Ex* from 02. *1 Kingsdown Crescent, Dawlish EX7 0HP* Tel (01626) 863848 E-mail cspeer316@aol.com

PEERS, John Edward. b 39. Bps' Coll Cheshunt 60. **d** 63 **p** 64. C Crayford *Roch* 63-67; C Beckenham St Jas 67-69; C Winlaton *Dur* 69-72; P-in-c Silksworth 72-81; R Lt Bowden St Nic *Leic* 81-86; P-in-c Lt Bowden St Hugh 83-86; RD Gartree I 84-88; R Market Harborough Transfiguration 86-88; V Skipton Ch Ch *Bradf* 88-99; V Hambleton w Out Rawcliffe *Blackb* from 99. *The Vicarage, Church Lane, Hambleton, Poulton-le-Fylde FY6 9BZ* Tel (01253) 700231 E-mail sreep@hotmail.com

✠**PEERS, The Most Revd Michael Geoffrey.** b 34. Univ of BC BA56. Trin Coll Toronto LTh59 Hon DD78. **d** 59 **p** 60 **c** 77. C Ottawa St Thos 59-61; C Ottawa Trin 61-65; Chapl Carleton Univ 61-66; R Winnipeg St Bede 66-72; R Winnipeg St Martin w Middlechurch St Paul 72-74; Adn Winnipeg 69-74; R St Paul's Cathl Regina and Dean Qu'Appelle 74-77; Bp Qu'Appelle 77-82; Abp Qu'Appelle and Metrop Rupert's Land 82-86; Primate Angl Ch of Canada from 86. *600 Jarvis Street, Toronto ON, Canada, M4Y 2J6* Tel (001) (416) 924 9199 Fax 924 0211 E-mail primate@national.anglican.ca

PEERS, Michael John. b 65. SS Paul & Mary Coll Cheltenham BA86. Ripon Coll Cuddesdon 88. **d** 91 **p** 92. C Birstall and Wanlip *Leic* 91-94; C Leic St Marg and All SS 94-96; TV The Abbey Leic 96-00; P-in-c Langley Park *Dur* 00-01; V from 01; P-in-c Esh 00-01; V from 01; P-in-c Hamsteels 00-01; V from 01; P-in-c Waterhouses 00-01; V from 01. *The Vicarage, Church Street, Langley Park, Durham DH7 9TZ* Tel 0191-373 9509 E-mail mjpeers@aol.com

PEERS, Richard Charles. b 65. K Alfred's Coll Win BEd88. Chich Th Coll BTh93. **d** 93 **p** 94. C Grangetown *York* 93-95; C Portsea St Mary *Portsm* 95-97; Perm to Offic 99-01; Chapl St Luke's Sch Southsea 01-03; Hon Chapl Portsm Cathl *Portsm* 01-03; Dep Hd Ch Sch Richmond from 03. *1 Glebe House, Waynflete Street, London SW18 3QG* Tel (020) 8879 7298 *or* 8940 6982 E-mail richard.peers1@btopenworld.com

PEET, Derek Edwin. b 26. Sheff Univ BA51 DipEd52 Lon Univ DipTh57. Qu Coll Birm 66. **d** 67 **p** 68. C Hebden Bridge *Wakef* 67-70; V Darton 70-79; TR Gleadless Valley *Sheff* 79-85; V Kirk Hallam *Derby* 85-96; rtd 96; Perm to Offic *Ripon* from 96. *44 Parkways Grove, Woodlesford, Leeds LS26 8TP* Tel 0113-282 3079

PEET, John Christopher. b 56. Oriel Coll Ox BA80 MA83 Clare Coll Cam BA82 MA87. Ridley Hall Cam 80. **d** 83 **p** 84. C Menston w Woodhead *Bradf* 83-86; C Prenton *Ches* 86-89; V Harden and Wilsden *Bradf* 89-97; V Cononley w Bradley from 97. *The Vicarage, 3 Meadow Close, Cononley, Keighley BD20 8LZ* Tel (01535) 634369

PEET, John Michael. b 44. AKC67. **d** 68 **p** 72. C Battersea St Pet *S'wark* 68-69; C Sutton St Nic 69-74; C Perry Hill St Geo 74-78; TV Stepney St Dunstan and All SS *Lon* 78-81; P-in-c Stamford Hill St Bart 81-86; V 87-89; P-in-c Mile End Old Town H Trin 89-90; P-in-c Bromley All Hallows 89-90; TR Bow H Trin and All Hallows 90-03; V Mile End H Trin from 03. *Holy Trinity Vicarage, 28 Coborn Street, London E3 2AB* Tel (020) 8980 2074 Fax 8980 2247 E-mail michael@mpeet.fsnet.co.uk

PEGG, Brian Peter Richard (Bill). b 30. Ox NSM Course 77 Sarum & Wells Th Coll 82. **d** 83 **p** 84. C Furze Platt *Ox* 83-85; V Ashbury, Compton Beauchamp and Longcot w Fernham 85-94; Chapl Malaga *Eur* 94-97; rtd 97; Hon C Shere, Albury and Chilworth *Guildf* 98-02. *31 King Street, Winterton, Scunthorpe DN15 9TP* Tel (01724) 734860

PEGG, Gerald Francis. b 37. FCII69 Birkbeck Coll Lon DipRS91. S'wark Ord Course 88. **d** 91 **p** 92. NSM Belmont *S'wark* 91-95; NSM Winchelsea and Icklesham *Chich* 95-02; rtd 02. Perm to Offic *Chich* from 02. *Lorien, 19 Manor Close, Icklesham, Winchelsea TN36 4BT* Tel (01424) 814735 Mobile 07711-582710 E-mail geraldpegg@cwcom.net

PEGLER, Frederic Arthur. b 19. Selw Coll Cam BA46 MA48. Qu Coll Birm 46. **d** 47 **p** 48. C Crawley *Chich* 47-49; C Rickmansworth *St Alb* 49-50; V Sark *Win* 50-52; PV S'well Minster *S'well* 52-55; Canada 55-84; rtd 84; Perm to Offic *St Alb* 84-85. *206 Chateauneuf, 1149 Rockland Avenue, Victoria, BC, Canada, V8V 4T5* Tel (001) (250) 386 6514

PEILOW, Lynda Elizabeth Anne. b 74. CITC BTh97. **d** 97 **p** 98. C Castleknock and Mulhuddart, w Clonsilla *D & G* 97-00; C Dublin St Ann and St Steph 00-01; Min Can St Patr Cathl Dublin 00-01; I Clonsast w Rathangan, Thomastown etc *M & K* from 01. *The Rectory, Monasteroris, Edenderry, Co Offaly, Irish Republic* Tel (00353) (46) 973 1585 E-mail lpeilow@oceanfree.net

PEIRCE, John. b 35. Worc Coll Ox BA59 MA64 Kent Univ MA96. Wycliffe Hall Ox 59. **d** 61 **p** 62. C Brompton H Trin *Lon* 61-64; C Wareham w Arne *Sarum* 64-68; V Sturminster Newton and Hinton St Mary 68-74; V Kingswood *Bris* 74-79; Dir Coun Chr Care *Ex* 79-89; Public Preacher 89-92; NSM Hackney Lon 90-94; NSM St Botolph Aldgate w H Trin Minories from 94; Co-ord Ch Action on Disability 90-98; Perm to Offic *Ex* 92-98. *3 Mile End Place, London E1 4BH* Tel (020) 7790 9418

PEIRCE, Canon John Martin. b 36. Jes Coll Cam BA59 MA65. Westcott Ho Cam 65. **d** 66 **p** 67. C Croydon *Cant* 66-70; C Fareham H Trin *Portsm* 70-71; TV 71-76; TR Langley Marish *Ox* 76-85; RD Burnham 78-82; Dir of Ords and Post-Ord Tr 85-01; Can Res Ch Ch 87-01; rtd 01. *8 Burwell Meadow, Witney, Oxford OX28 5JQ*

PEIRIS, Lionel James Harold (Brother Lionel). b 45. Serampore Coll BD71. Bp's Coll Calcutta 67. **d** 70 **p** 71. Sri Lanka 70-76 and 78-95; P Lect Colombo Coll 71-76 and 78-95; C Shirley *Birm* 76-78; P Brother SSF Auckland New Zealand 96-97; Australia from 97; Asst Chapl and Past Asst Annerley Hosp 97-98; Hon C Annerley St Phil 97-98; P-in-c from 99. *115 Cornwall Street, Annerley, Qld, Australia 4103* Tel (0061) (7) 3391 3915 Fax 3391 3916

PELHAM, John. b 36. New Coll Ox BA61 MA65. **d** 79 **p** 80. NSM Balerno *Edin* 79-91; Hon C W Linton 91-94; Hon C Penicuik 91-94; Dioc Supernumerary from 94. *2 Horsburgh Bank, Balerno EH14 7DA* Tel 0131-449 3934

PELL, Charles Andrew. b 54. Leeds Univ CertEd77. Aston Tr Scheme 87 St Jo Coll Nottm 87. **d** 89 **p** 90. C Mottram in Longdendale w Woodhead *Ches* 89-90; C Handforth 90-93; P-in-c Walton Breck *Liv* 93-94; V 94-96; P-in-c Glyndyfrdwy and Llansantffraid Glyn Dyfrdwy *St As* 96-01; CF (ACF) from 93; V Rhodes *Man* from 01. *Rhodes Vicarage, Boardman Lane, Middleton, Manchester M24 4PU* Tel 0161-643 3224 Mobile 07831-279429 E-mail padre@milnet.uk.net

PELLANT, Walter Reginald Guy. b 14. OBE79. AKC42. Cuddesdon Coll 42. **d** 43 **p** 44. C Newington St Paul *S'wark* 43-45; C Kennington St Jo 45-48; Chapl RAF 48-69; Asst Chapl-in-Chief RAF 69-71; Chapl Geneva *Eur* 71-80; QHC from 70; rtd 80. *clo Mrs F M T Bennett, 29 Little Adelphi, 10 John Adam Street, London WC2N 6HA*

PELLEY, John Lawless. b 34. Oak Hill Th Coll 67. **d** 69 **p** 70. C Fareham St Jo *Portsm* 69-72; C Frogmore *St Alb* 72-76; V Standon 76-96; RD Bishop's Stortford 91-95; rtd 96; Perm to Offic *Ely* from 96. *7 Home Close, Histon, Cambridge CB4 9JL* Tel (01223) 234636

PELLY, Raymond Blake. b 38. Worc Coll Ox BA61 MA69 Geneva Univ DTh71. Linc Th Coll. **d** 63 **p** 64. C Gosforth All SS *Newc* 63-65; C N Lynn w St Marg and St Nic *Nor* 69-70; Vice-Prin Westcott Ho Cam 71-76; Warden St Jo Coll Auckland New Zealand 77-85; Visiting Lect Univ of Mass Boston USA 86-88 and 96; Chapl Victoria Univ of Wellington New Zealand 90-94; Asst P Wellington St Pet 92-94 and from 96; rtd 03. *12 Kio Crescent, Hataitai, Wellington 2, New Zealand* Tel (0064) (4) 386 3972 Fax 386 3729 E-mail raymond.pelly@xtra.co.nz

PELTOR, Lawrence Frank. b 08. Keble Coll Ox BA33 MA37. Linc Th Coll 33. **d** 34 **p** 35. C Linc St Nic w St Jo Newport *Linc* 34-37; C Middlesbrough St Paul *York* 37-39; C Whitby 39-40; CF 40-45; V Spittlegate *Linc* 46-55; Chapl Hill View Hosp Grantham 46-55; V Thirkleby w Kilburn and Bagby *York* 55-60; Hon CF 45; R Willey w Barrow *Heref* 60-72; C Wybunbury *Ches* 72-73; rtd 73; Perm to Offic *Heref* 73-98. *5 Cliff Gardens, Cliff Road, Bridgnorth WV16 4EZ* Tel (01746) 763173

PELZ, Werner. b 21. Lon Univ BA49. Linc Th Coll 50. **d** 51 **p** 52. C Birch St Jas *Man* 51-54; C-in-c Lostock CD 54-63; rtd 86. *44 Crowley Road, Healesville, Vic, Australia 3777*

PEMBERTON, Anthony Thomas Christie (Chris). b 57. BA. Cranmer Hall Dur 82. **d** 84 **p** 85. C Maidstone St Luke *Cant* 84-88; Chapl Ox Pastorate 88-98; V Cant St Mary Bredin *Cant* from 98. *St Mary Bredin Vicarage, 57 Nunnery Fields, Canterbury CT1 3JN* Tel (01227) 453777 E-mail vicar@smb.org.uk

PEMBERTON, Carrie Mary. b 55. St Hilda's Coll Ox BA78 Cam Univ PGCE42 Leeds Univ MA92 Newnham Coll Cam PhD98. Cranmer Hall Dur 83 NEOC 84. **dss** 86 **d** 87 **p** 94. NSM Leeds St Geo *Ripon* 86-87; Miss Partner CMS 87-91; Dir Women's Studies Angl Th Inst Zaïre 87-91; Perm to Offic *Pet* 92-94; NSM Bourn and Kingston w Caxton and Longstowe *Ely* 94-99; TV Elsworth w Knapwell 99; Min Cambourne LEP 00-01; Chapl Yarlswood Immigration and Detention Cen 01-03; Perm to Offic *Ely* from 03. *Elsworth Rectory, 6 The Drift, Elsworth, Cambridge CB3 8JN* Tel (01954) 267722 E-mail carrie.pemberton@ely.anglican.org

PEMBERTON, Crispin Mark Rugman. b 59. St Andr Univ MTh83. St Steph Ho Ox 84. **d** 86 **p** 87. C Acton St Alb w All SS *Lon* 86-88; C Acton Green 88-90; C Leckhampton SS Phil and Jas w Cheltenham St Jas *Glouc* 90-93; V Tuffley 93-97; RE Teacher Cheltenham Coll Jun Sch from 97; Perm to Offic *Glouc* 97-00. *Cheltenham College (Junior School), Bath Road, Cheltenham GL53 7LD* Tel (01242) 265617

PEMBERTON, David Charles. b 35. K Coll Lon 57. **d** 61 **p** 62. C Pokesdown St Jas *Win* 61-65; C W Derby St Mary *Liv* 65-67; C-in-c Cantril Farm St Jude CD 67-71; V Cantril Farm 71-74; V Devonport St Boniface *Ex* 75-83; V Stanwell *Lon* 83-00; AD Spelthorne 92-97; rtd 00. *23C Gordon Road, Ashford TW15 3ES* Tel (01784) 253420

PEMBERTON, Jeremy Charles Baring. b 56. Mert Coll Ox MA77 Fitzw Ho Cam BA80 Leeds Univ MA92. Ridley Hall Cam 78. **d** 81 **p** 82. C Stranton *Dur* 81-84; C Leeds St Geo *Ripon*

84-87; CMS Miss Partner and Dir Angl Th Inst Zaïre 87-91; V Irchester *Pet* 92-94; P-in-c Bourn and Kingston w Caxton and Longstowe *Ely* 94; R 94-00; P-in-c Elsworth w Knapwell 99-00; P-in-c Boxworth 99-00; TR Papworth from 00; RD Bourn from 98. *Elsworth Rectory, 6 The Drift, Elsworth, Cambridge CB3 8JN* Tel (01954) 267722 E-mail jeremy.pemberton@ely.anglican.org

PEMBERY, Gerald Marcus. b 29. Glouc Sch of Min 89. **d** 90 **p** 91. NSM Bream *Glouc* 90-97; rtd 97; Perm to Offic *Glouc* from 97. *Kings Wood, The Tufts, Bream, Lydney GL15 6HW* Tel (01594) 562750

PENBERTHY (formerly LEGG), Ms Joanna Susan. b 60. Newnham Coll Cam BA81 MA85. St Jo Coll Nottm DipTh82 MTh84 St Jo Coll Dur 83. **dss** 84 **d** 87 **p** 97. Haughton le Skerne *Dur* 84-85; Llanishen and Lisvane *Llan* 85-87; NSM 87-89; NSM Llanwddyn and Llanfihangel-yng-Nghwynfa etc *St As* 89-93; NSM Llansadwrn w Llanwrda and Manordeilo *St D* 93-95; Officer Div for Par Development Ch in Wales 95-99; P-in-c Cynwyl Gaeo w Llansawel and Talley *St D* 99-01; V from 01. *The Vicarage, Llanwrda SA19 8HD* Tel (01550) 777343 E-mail penber6487@aol.com

PENDLEBURY, Stephen Thomas. b 50. ACA78 Southn Univ BSc73. Ridley Hall Cam 86. **d** 88 **p** 89. C Birkenhead St Jas w St Bede *Ches* 88-91; V 91-00; V Ches St Paul from 00. *St Paul's Vicarage, 10 Sandy Lane, Chester CH3 5UL* Tel (01244) 351377 E-mail stpendleby@aol.com

PENDORF, Canon James Gordon. b 45. Drew Univ New Jersey BA67. Episc Th Sch Cam Mass STB71. **d** 71 **p** 71. USA 71-76; V Colne H Trin *Blackb* 76-80; Sen Dioc Stewardship Adv *Chelmsf* 80-83; Dioc Sec *Birm* 83-95; Hon Can Birm Cathl from 90; P-in-c Highgate 95-97; V from 97; Dioc Stewardship Adv from 95; AD Birm City Cen 96-02. *St Alban's Vicarage, 120 Stanhope Street, Birmingham B12 0XB* Tel 0121-440 4605 Mobile 07973-265037 Fax 446 6867 E-mail pendorfs@compuserve.com

PENFOLD, Brian Robert. b 54. Lon Univ BSc75 Bris Univ PGCE77. Oak Hill Th Coll BA84. **d** 84 **p** 85. C Norwood St Luke *S'wark* 84-88; C Rayleigh *Chelmsf* 88-92; V New Barnet St Jas *St Alb* from 92. *The Vicarage, 11 Park Road, Barnet EN4 9QA* Tel and fax (020) 8449 4043 Mobile 07753-680839 E-mail brian@brpenfold.freeserve.co.uk

PENFOLD, Colin Richard. b 52. St Pet Coll Ox BA74 MA78. Ridley Hall Cam 83. **d** 84 **p** 85. C Buckhurst Hill *Chelmsf* 84-87; C Greenside *Dur* 87-90; V Cononley w Bradley *Bradf* 90-97; P-in-c Shipley St Paul and Frizinghall 97; V Shipley St Paul from 98. *The Vicarage, 47 Kirkgate, Shipley BD18 3EH* Tel (01274) 583652 Fax as telephone E-mail colin@thepenfolds.org.uk

PENFOLD, Marion Jean. b 49. NEOC 96. **d** 99 **p** 00. NSM Lesbury w Alnmouth *Newc* 99-02; C from 02; NSM Longhoughton w Howick 99-02; C from 02. *7 Bisley Road, Amble, Morpeth NE65 0NW* Tel (01665) 712698 E-mail marion.penfold@btinternet.com

PENFOLD, Susan Irene. b 52. York Univ BA73 Bris Univ PhD77 Selw Coll Cam BA83 MA87. Ridley Hall Cam 81. **dss** 84 **d** 87 **p** 94. Buckhurst Hill *Chelmsf* 84-87; Hon C Greenside *Dur* 87-90; Hon C Cononley w Bradley *Bradf* 90-97; Assoc Dioc Dir of Ords 96-01; Hon C Shipley St Paul 97-00; Dir of Ords and CME Officer *Wakef* from 01. *The Vicarage, 47 Kirkgate, Shipley BD18 3EH* Tel (01274) 583652 or (01924) 371802 Fax (01274) 583652 E-mail sue.penfold@wakefield.anglican.org

PENGELLEY, Peter John. b 22. Sarum & Wells Th Coll 72. **d** 74 **p** 75. C Midsomer Norton *B & W* 74-78; R Stogursey w Fiddington 78-88; Ind Chapl 80-88; rtd 88; Perm to Offic *B & W* from 89. *Rosslyn Cottage, Roadwater, Watchet TA23 0RB* Tel (01984) 40798

PENGELLY, Canon Geoffrey. b 50. Oak Hill Th Coll 86. **d** 88 **p** 89. C Redruth w Lanner and Treleigh *Truro* 88-91; TV Bolventor 91-92; V Gloskerry, N Petherwin, Tremaine and Tresmere from 92; Hon Can Truro Cathl from 03. *The Vicarage, Egloskerry, Launceston PL15 8RX* Tel (01566) 785365

PENISTAN, Richard Luke. b 74. Newc Univ BA97 St Jo Coll Cam BA02. Ridley Hall Cam 00. **d** 03. C E Twickenham St Steph *Lon* from 03. *Address temp unknown* E-mail penistans@xalt.co.uk

PENMAN, John Bain. b 67. Aber Univ BD89 New Coll Edin MTh93 SSC96. Edin Th Coll CECM93. **d** 93 **p** 94. C Glas St Ninian *Glas* 93-96; C Ealing Ch the Sav *Lon* 96-98; P-in-c Kirkcaldy *St And* from 98. *The Rectory, 1 Longbraes Gardens, Kirkcaldy KY2 5YJ* Tel (01592) 268101 Mobile 07801-800633 E-mail frjbp@compuserve.com

PENMAN, Miss Margaret Heather. b 50. St Martin's Coll Lanc CertEd71 Lanc Univ DipEd82 DipRE87 FRSA95. Carl Dioc Tr Inst 90. **d** 93 **p** 94. Headteacher Hesketh w Becconsall All SS C of E Sch 85-00; RE/Schools Adv *Liv* from 00; NSM Lostock Hall *Blackb* 93-95; NSM Leyland St Jas from 95. *9 Oakfield Drive, Leyland, Preston PR5 3XE* Tel (01772) 435927 or 812630 Fax 814721 E-mail heatherpenman@onetel.net.uk

PENMAN, Robert George. b 42. St Jo Coll Auckland LTh66. **d** 65 **p** 66. New Zealand 65-73; C Alverstoke *Portsm* 73-74; CF 74-77; C Bridgwater St Mary w Chilton Trinity *B & W* 77-80; P-in-c Haselbury Plucknett w N Perrott 80-81; P-in-c Misterton 80-81;

V Haselbury Plucknett, Misterton and N Perrott 81-89; P-in-c Appleton *Ox* from 89; P-in-c Besselsleigh w Dry Sandford 89-00; P-in-c Besselsleigh from 00. *The Rectory, Oaksmere, Appleton, Abingdon OX13 5JS* Tel (01865) 862458
E-mail bobpenman@aol.com

PENN, Canon Arthur William. b 22. Man Univ BA49. Wycliffe Hall Ox 49. **d** 51 **p** 52. C Bowdon *Ches* 51-53; C Alston w Garrigill *Newc* 53-56; V Kirkdale *York* 56-67; V Brampton *Carl* 67-83; RD Brampton 74-83; P-in-c Gilsland w Nether Denton 75-81; Hon Can Carl Cathl 78-88; P-in-c Gilsland 81-83; V Rockcliffe and Blackford 83-88; rtd 88; Perm to Offic *Carl* 88-99. *1 Well Lane, Warton, Carnforth LA5 9QZ* Tel (01524) 733079

PENN, Barry Edwin. b 46. Univ of Wales (Swansea) BA72. St Jo Coll Nottm 77. **d** 79 **p** 80. C New Barnet St Jas *St Alb* 79-83; TV Preston St Jo *Blackb* 83-92; V Patchway *Bris* 92-01; Perm to Offic from 01. *50 Eastfield Road, Westbury-on-Trym, Bristol BS9 4AG* Tel 0117-962 2862

PENN, Christopher Francis. b 34. ACII63. Wells Th Coll 68. **d** 70 **p** 71. C Andover w Foxcott *Win* 70-72; C Odiham w S Warnborough 72-75; C Keynsham w Queen Charlton *B & W* 75; C Keynsham 75-76; TV 76-82; R Chilcompton w Downside and Stratton on the Fosse 82-87; RD Midsomer Norton 84-86; V Bathford 87-90; V Avonmouth St Andr *Bris* 90-96; Ind Chapl 90-96; rtd 96; Perm to Offic *B & W* from 96; Perm to Offic *Bris* from 96. *53 Caernarvon Road, Keynsham, Bristol BS31 2PF* Tel 0117-986 2367

PENN, Christopher Wilson. b 60. Cranmer Hall Dur 98. **d** 00 **p** 01. C Wrockwardine Deanery *Lich* from 00. *The Parsonage, Upton Magna, Shrewsbury SY4 4TZ* Tel (01743) 709283
E-mail chrispy@fish.co.uk

PENN, Clive Llewellyn. b 12. Oak Hill Th Coll 47. **d** 48 **p** 49. C Deptford St Luke *S'wark* 48-50; C Guernsey St Sampson *Win* 50-54; Australia 55-65; V Jersey Gouray St Martin *Win* 66-71; rtd 77; Lic to Offic *Win* 71-86. *PO Box 679, Williamstown, S Australia 5061*

PENNAL, David Bernard. b 37. Ripon Hall Ox 64. **d** 67 **p** 68. C Moseley St Mary *Birm* 67-71; C Bridgwater St Mary w Chilton Trinity *B & W* 71-73; P-in-c Hilton w Cheselbourne and Melcombe Horsey *Sarum* 73-76; R Milton Abbas, Hilton w Cheselbourne etc 76-78; P-in-c Spetisbury w Charlton Marshall 78-88; R Spetisbury w Charlton Marshall etc 89-00; rtd 00. *2 St Leonard's Terrace, Blandford Forum DT11 7PF* Tel (01258) 454238

PENNANT, David Falconer. b 51. Trin Coll Cam MA73. Trin Coll Bris BD84 PhD88. **d** 86 **p** 87. C Bramcote *S'well* 86-88; C Woking St Jo *Guildf* 88-93. *30 Oriental Road, Woking GU22 7AW* Tel (01483) 768055 E-mail david.pennant@ntlworld.com

PENNELL (also COFFIN), Ms Pamela. b 45. EAMTC 94. **d** 97 **p** 98. NSM Moulsham St Luke *Chelmsf* 97-98; NSM Writtle w Highwood 98-00; Perm to Offic from 01. *33 Birch Lane, Stock, Ingatestone CM4 9NA* Tel (01277) 841270

PENNEY, David Richard John. b 39. St Jo Coll Dur BA63 DipTh65. Cranmer Hall Dur 63. **d** 67 **p** 68. C Chilvers Coton w Astley *Cov* 67-70; C Styvechale 70-72; P-in-c Shilton w Ansty 72-77; P-in-c Withybrook 72-77; R Easington w Liverton *York* 77-85; Dir Soc Resp *Sarum* 85-93; Perm to Offic *Blackb* from 93; rtd 01. *8 William Street, Colne BB8 0HH* Tel (01282) 870076 Mobile 07966-157697

PENNEY, William Affleck. b 41. MBIM75 FRSA91. K Coll Lon BD63 AKC63 St Boniface Warminster 65. **d** 66 **p** 67. C Chatham St Steph *Roch* 66-70; Ind Chapl 70-77; P-in-c Bredhurst 70-72; Hon C S Gillingham 72-74; Hon C Eynsford w Farningham and Lullingstone 74-77; Bp's Dom Chapl 74-88; Hon Ind Chapl 77-88; Hon C Balham St Mary and St Jo *S'wark* 89-91; Perm to Offic *St Alb* 91-94; Hon C Bushey from 94. *Michael Hall House, Aldenham Road, Elstree, Borehamwood WD6 3BT* Tel (020) 8207 5745 E-mail bill@ashtonpenney.com

PENNICEARD, Clifford Ashley. b 42. Monash Univ Aus BA65 DipEd71 Linacre Coll Ox BA67 Ox Univ MA70. St Steph Ho Ox 65. **d** 68 **p** 69. C S Leamington St Jo *Cov* 68-70; Australia from 70; P-in-c Wantirna 74; Assoc P N Brighton 76-80; P-in-c Euroa 84-91; P-in-c Nagumbie 93-95; R Manly St Paul from 98. *99 Ernest Street, Manly, Qld, Australia 4179* Tel (0061) (7) 3396 2746 Mobile 0416-177732 Fax (7) 3396 3796
E-mail cliffpenn@powerup.com.au

PENNIECOOKE, Dorothy Victoria. b 45. Dioc OLM tr scheme 97. **d** 00 **p** 01. NSM Balham Hill Ascension *S'wark* from 00. *56 Lysias Road, London SW12 8BP* Tel (020) 8673 0037

PENNINGTON, Mrs Catherine Prudence. b 56. Man Poly BSc82 Brighton Poly MSc87 Flinders Univ Aus BTh00. ACT. **d** 00 **p** 01. C Glenelg Australia 00-01; C Is of Dogs Ch Ch and St Jo w St Luke *Lon* from 02. *St Luke's House, 36 Strafford Street, London E14 8LT* Tel 07817-389778 (mobile)

PENNINGTON, Emma Louise. b 71. Ex Univ BA92 Kent Univ MA96. Ripon Coll Cuddesdon BA00. **d** 00 **p** 01. C Shepperton *Lon* from 00. *Flat 2, The Rectory, Church Square, Shepperton TW17 9JY* Tel (01932) 241846

PENNINGTON, Frederick William. b 11. K Coll Lon. **d** 55 **p** 56. C Tiverton St Pet *Ex* 55-58; R Bradford 58-66; R Thornbury

58-66; V N Molton w Twitchen 66-77; P-in-c Molland 68-77; rtd 77; Lic to Offic *Ex* 77-95; Perm to Offic from 95. *Sunset Cottage, 103 West Street, Hartland, Bideford EX39 6BQ* Tel (01237) 441206

PENNINGTON, John Kenneth. b 27. Man Univ LLB48. Linc Th Coll 51. **d** 52 **p** 53. C Wavertree H Trin *Liv* 52-56; C Rotherham *Sheff* 56-59; India 59-63; V Nelson St Phil *Blackb* 64-66; Area Sec USPG (Dios Derby, Leic and S'well) 66-71; (Dios Derby and Sheff) 71-75; C Nottingham St Mary *S'well* 75-78; C Nottingham St Mary and St Cath 78-92; rtd 93; Perm to Offic *S'well* from 93. *3 St Jude's Avenue, Nottingham NG3 5FG* Tel 0115-962 3420

PENNINGTON, John Michael. b 32. Em Coll Cam BA54 MA58 IEng AMIEE MIHEEM. Wells Th Coll 58. **d** 60 **p** 61. C Stockport St Geo *Ches* 60-64; V Congleton St Steph 64-68; Chapl Nor Sch 68-70; V Hattersley *Ches* 70-72; C-in-c Upton Priory CD 72-75; V Upton Priory 75-79; Perm to Offic *Newc* 83-87; V Tynemouth St Jo 87-94; P-in-c Cambois 94-97; Chapl Northd HA 94-97; Ashington and Wansbeck Hosps 94-97; rtd 97; Perm to Offic *Newc* from 97. *297 Wingrove Road North, Fenham, Newcastle upon Tyne NE4 9EE* Tel 0191-274 5281 Fax as telephone

PENNOCK, Mrs Christine. b 48. Bp Grosseteste Coll BEd71 Leeds Univ PGCE94 Teesside Univ PGDE95. NEOC 98. **d** 01 **p** 02. C Crowland *Linc* from 01. *38 Beccelm Drive, Crowland, Peterborough PE6 0AG* Tel (01733) 210763 Mobile 07813-954043 E-mail chris@cpennock.fsnet.co.uk

PENNY, Alexander Stuart Egerton. b 52. Wolv Art Coll BA75. Ridley Hall Cam MA00. **d** 00 **p** 01. C Uttoxeter Area *Lich* from 00; V Crosthwaite Keswick *Carl* from 03. *Crosthwaite Vicarage, Vicarage Hill, Keswick CA12 5QB* Tel (01768) 772509

PENNY, David Roy. b 67. Wilson Carlile Coll 89 N Ord Course 00. **d** 03. C Hey *Man* from 03. C Waterhead from 03. *91 New Street, Lees, Oldham OL4 3LP* Tel 0161-621 0104
E-mail dpennyca@aol.com

PENNY, Diana Eleanor. b 51. Open Univ BA87. Nor Ord Course 87. **d** 89 **p** 94. NSM Gillingham w Geldeston, Stockton, Ellingham etc *Nor* 89-93; NSM Upton St Leonards *Glouc* 93-97; NSM Stiffkey and Cockthorpe w Morston, Langham etc *Nor* from 97. *The Vicarage, 2 Holt Road, Langham, Holt NR25 7BX* Tel (01328) 830246

PENNY, Edwin John. b 43. Leeds Univ BA64. Coll of Resurr Mirfield 64. **d** 66 **p** 67. C Acocks Green *Birm* 66-69; C Wombourne *Lich* 69-71; C Wednesbury St Paul Wood Green 71-74; V Kingshurst *Birm* 74-79; Chapl All Hallows Convent Norfolk 79-82; Hon Chapl Overgate Hospice Yorkshire 82-84; Hon C Raveningham *Nor* 84-90; All Hallows Hosp Nor Past Team 90-93; P-in-c Upton St Leonards *Glouc* 93-97; Dioc Communications Officer 93-97; P-in-c Stiffkey and Cockthorpe w Morston, Langham etc *Nor* from 97; P-in-c Gunthorpe w Bale w Field Dalling, Saxlingham etc from 99. *The Vicarage, 2 Holt Road, Langham, Holt NR25 7BX* Tel (01328) 830246 Fax as telephone

PENNY, Michael John. b 36. Linc Th Coll 78. **d** 80 **p** 81. C Knighton St Mary Magd *Leic* 80-83; TV Leic Resurr 83-85; V Blackfordby 85-95; V Blackfordby and Woodville 95-00; RD Akeley W 88-93; rtd 00; Perm to Offic *Nor* from 00. *15 Sarah's Road, Hunstanton PE36 5PA* Tel (01485) 534957

PENRITH, Suffragan Bishop of. *See* NEWCOME, The Rt Revd James William Scobie

PENTELOW, Mrs Ysmena Rachael. b 73. St Andr Univ BD96 MLitt99. EAMTC 01. **d** 03. C Stevenage H Trin *St Alb* from 03. *413 Scarborough Avenue, Stevenage SG1 2QA* Tel (01707) 331053 Mobile 07798-654194 E-mail pentelow@waitrose.com

PENTLAND, Raymond Jackson. b 57. Open Univ BA90. St Jo Coll Nottm DPS88. **d** 88 **p** 89. C Nottingham St Jude *S'well* 88-90; Chapl RAF Coll Cranwell from 90. *Chaplaincy Services (RAF), HQ, Personnel and Training Command, RAF Innsworth, Gloucester GL3 1EZ* Tel (01452) 712612 ext 5164 Fax 510828

PENTREATH, Canon Harvey. b 29. Wells Th Coll 54. **d** 57 **p** 58. C Bris St Ambrose Whitehall *Bris* 57-60; C Leatherhead *Guildf* 60-63; C Haslemere 63-65; R Elstead 65-72; V Cuddington 73-80; Hon Can Guildf Cathl 80; V Helston *Truro* 80-85; RD Kerrier 84-86; TR Helston and Wendron 85-92; Hon Can Truro Cathl 88-92; rtd 93; Perm to Offic *Truro* from 93. *Penmar, 15 Penarwyn Crescent, Heamoor, Penzance TR18 3JU* Tel (01736) 360133

PEOPLES, James Scott. b 59. TCD BA DipTh HDipEd90. **d** 85 **p** 86. C Carlow w Urglin and Staplestown *C & O* 85-90; Chapl Kilkenny Coll 90-91; I Portarlington w Cloneyhurke and Lea *M & K* 91-99; Dioc Youth Officer (Kildare) 92-99; I Lucan w Leixlip *D & G* from 99. *5 Uppercross, Ballyowen Lane, Ballydowd, Lucan, Co Dublin, Irish Republic* Tel (00353) (1) 624 9147

PEPPER, David Reginald. b 50. Lon Bible Coll. St Alb Minl Tr Scheme 89. **d** 92 **p** 93. NSM Cheshunt *St Alb* 92-95. *36 Salisbury Road, Hoddesdon EN11 0HX* Tel (01992) 410544

PEPPER, Leonard Edwin. b 44. Ex Univ BA71. Ripon Hall Ox 71. **d** 73 **p** 74. C Kingston *Birm* 73-76; C Kingshurst *Birm* 76-79; Dir Past Studies St Steph Ho Ox 80-89; TV Aylesbury w Bierton and Hulcott *Ox* 89-91; TV High Wycombe 91-96; rtd 96. *19 Gardiner Street, Oxford OX3 7AW* Tel (01865) 66191

PEPPIATT, Martin Guy. b 33. Trin Coll Ox BA57 MA60. Wycliffe Hall Ox 57. **d** 59 **p** 60. C St Marylebone All So w SS Pet and Jo *Lon* 59-63; Kenya 65-69; V E Twickenham St Steph *Lon* 69-96; rtd 96. *Pipers Cottage, East End, North Leigh, Witney OX8 6PZ* Tel (01993) 883001

PEPPIATT, Quintin Brian Duncombe. b 63. Ex Univ BSc85 St Luke's Coll Ex PGCE86. Ripon Coll Cuddesdon 89 Ch Div Sch of the Pacific (USA) 90. **d** 92 **p** 93. C Gt Ilford St Clem and St Marg *Chelmsf* 92-95; TV E Ham w Upton Park St Alb from 95. *1 Norman Road, London E6 6HN* Tel (020) 8471 8751 E-mail quintinpeppiatt@aol.com

PERCIVAL, Brian Sydney. b 37. Univ of Wales (Ban) BA61. N Ord Course 81. **d** 84 **p** 85. NSM Norbury *Ches* 84-88; P-in-c Werneth from 88; RD Chadkirk from 00. *The Vicarage, Compstall, Stockport SK6 5HU* Tel 0161-427 1259

PERCIVAL, Geoffrey. b 46. Ridley Hall Cam 73. **d** 76 **p** 77. C Eccleshall *Bradf* 76-79; C Otley 79-82; V Windhill 82-02; P-in-c Oakenshaw cum Woodlands from 03. *St Andrew's Vicarage, 589 Bradford Road, Bradford BD12 7ES* Tel (01274) 608173

PERCIVAL, James Edward Charles. b 50. C&G69. N Ord Course 92. **d** 95 **p** 96. C Broughton *Blackb* 95-99; P-in-c Blackb St Steph from 99. *St Stephen's Vicarage, 285 Whalley Old Road, Blackburn BB1 5RS* Tel (01254) 255546

PERCIVAL, James Frederick. b 74. New Coll Ox BA96 MA01 Barrister-at-Law (Middle Temple) 99. Ripon Coll Cuddesdon MA02. **d** 03. C Redhill St Matt *S'wark* from 03. *44 Ridgeway Road, Redhill RH1 6PH* Tel (01737) 213681 E-mail james.percival@fish.co.uk

PERCIVAL, Joanna Vera. b 52. Univ of San Francisco BA87. Ch Div Sch of Pacific MDiv94. **d** 94 **p** 94. Asst to R Almaden USA 94-95; NSM Ockham w Hatchford *Guildf* 95-96; C Cobham 96-00; Dioc Spirituality Adv 00-02; V Weston from 02. *All Saints' Vicarage, 1 Chestnut Avenue, Esher KT10 8JL* Tel (020) 8398 1849 E-mail joanna.percival@tesco.net

PERCIVAL, Martin Eric. b 45. Lon Univ BSc66 Linacre Coll Ox BA70 MA74. Wycliffe Hall Ox 67. **d** 70 **p** 71. C Anfield St Marg *Liv* 70-73; C Witney *Ox* 73-74; TV Bottesford w Ashby *Linc* 74-76; TV Grantham 76-80; R Coningsby w Tattershall 80-82; P-in-c Coleford w Holcombe *B & W* 82-83; V 83-84; Chapl Rossall Sch Fleetwood 84-88; Chapl Woodbridge Sch 88-02; R Downham w S Hanningfield *Chelmsf* from 02; P-in-c Ramsden Bellhouse from 02. *The Rectory, Castledon Road, Downham, Billericay CM11 1LD* Tel (01268) 710370 E-mail revmepercival@yahoo.co.uk

PERCIVAL, Richard Thomas. b 33. Edin Coll of Art Dip Town Planning 67 ARICS59 MRTPI67 FRICS71 MRICS01. Edin Dioc NSM Course 73. **d** 91 **p** 98. S Africa 91-94; NSM Edin St Ninian *Edin* from 94. *2/1 Fettes Rise, Edinburgh EH4 1QH* Tel 0131-552 5271

PERCIVAL, Robert Standring. b 27. Sheff Univ BA55 Aston Univ Dip Counselling 83. Qu Coll Birm 57. **d** 59 **p** 60. C Lightbowne *Man* 59-62; C Prestwich St Marg 62-63; V Pendlebury St Aug 63-68; Lect Glos Coll of Arts and Tech 68-93; NSM Glouc St Mary de Crypt w St Jo and Ch *Glouc* 68-82; Perm to Offic 82-97 and from 01; rtd 92. *5 Firwood Drive, Gloucester GL4 0AB* Tel (01452) 522739

PERCY, Brian. b 34. LNSM course 91. **d** 93 **p** 94. OLM Walton *St E* 93-00; OLM Walton and Trimley from 00. *16 Lynwood Avenue, Felixstowe IP11 9HS* Tel (01394) 286782

PERCY, Donald. b 45. Kelham Th Coll 66. **d** 71 **p** 72. C Hendon St Ignatius *Dur* 71-75; C Gorton St Mary and St Thos *Man* 75-77; C Middlesbrough St Thos *York* 77-82; Guyana 82-86; P-in-c S Moor *Dur* 86-90; V 90-95. *8 Ritson Street, Stanley DH9 0NH*

PERCY, Mrs Emma Margaret. b 63. Jes Coll Cam BA85 MA89 St Jo Coll Dur BA88. Cranmer Hall Dur 87. **d** 90 **p** 94. C Bedford St Andr *St Alb* 90-94; Chapl Anglia Poly Univ *Ely* 94-97; P-in-c Millhouses H Trin *Sheff* 97-03; V from 03. *Holy Trinity Vicarage, 80 Millhouses Lane, Sheffield S7 2HB* Tel 0114-236 2838

PERCY, Gordon Reid. b 46. St Jo Coll Dur BA68 DipTh70. Cranmer Hall Dur 69. **d** 71 **p** 72. C Flixton St Jo *Man* 71-76; C Charlesworth *Derby* 76-77; P-in-c 77-87; P-in-c Dinting Vale 80-87; V Long Eaton St Jo 87-98; RD Ilkeston 92-98; R Torquay St Matthias, St Mark and H Trin *Ex* from 98. *The Rectory, Wellswood Avenue, Torquay TQ1 2QE* Tel (01803) 293280 or 214175 E-mail gordonpercy@minister.com or stmathiaschurch@minister.com

PERCY, Canon Martyn William. b 62. Bris Univ BA84 K Coll Lon PhD92 Sheff Univ MEd St Jo Coll Dur CCSk90. Cranmer Hall Dur 88. **d** 90 **p** 91. C Bedford St Andr *St Alb* 90-94; Chapl and Dir Th and RS Ch Coll Cam 94-97; Dir Th and RS SS Coll Cam 95-97; Dir Linc Th Inst from 97; Sen Lect Relig and Soc Sheff Univ *Sheff* 97-00; Reader 00-03; Hon Can Sheff Cathl from 97; Hon C Millhouses H Trin from 97. *The Lincoln Theological Institute, Dept of Religions and Theology, Oxford Road, Manchester M13 9PL* Tel 0161-275 8594 or 0114-236 2838 Mobile 07941-072542 Fax 0161-275 3264 E-mail martyn.percy@man.ac.uk

PERDUE, Ernon Cope Todd. b 30. TCD BA52 MA BD56 MEd73 UCD Dip Psychology 76 MPsychSc80. TCD Div Sch 53. **d** 54 **p** 55. C Dublin Drumcondra w N Strand *D & G* 54-58; C

Dublin Booterstown w Carysfort 58-60; Dean of Res TCD 60-68; C-in-c Dublin St Mark *D & G* 66-68; C-in-c Dublin St Steph 68-69; I Rathmichael 69-76; Careers Counsellor Wicklow Voc Sch 76-82; I Limerick *L & K* 82-87; Can Limerick Cathl 82-87; Dean Killaloe, Kilfenora and Clonfert 87-95; I Killaloe w Stradbally 87-95; rtd 95. *177 The Ash, Charleville Square Apt, Butterfield Avenue, Rathfarnham, Dublin, Irish Republic* E-mail eperduc@gofree.indigo.ie

PERERA, Chandrika Kumudhini. b 61. Qu Coll Birm. **d** 03. C Luton All SS w Pet *St Alb* from 03. *St. Peter's House, Harefield Road, Luton LU1 1TH*

PERERA, George Anthony. b 51. Edin Univ BD74. Linc Th Coll 74. **d** 76 **p** 77. C Bishopwearmouth St Gabr *Dur* 76-79; C Wavertree H Trin *Liv* 76-79; TV Maghull 79-94; Chapl Park Lane Hosp Maghull 79-89; Asst Chapl Ashworth Hosp Magull from 89; V Hunts Cross *Liv* from 94. *The Vicarage, 7 Kingsmead Drive, Liverpool L25 0NG* Tel 0151-486 1220

PERHAM, The Very Revd Michael Francis. b 47. Keble Coll Ox BA74 MA78. Cuddesdon Coll 74. **d** 76 **p** 77. C Addington *Cant* 76-81; Sec C of E Doctrine Commn 79-84; Bp's Dom Chapl *Win* 81-84; TR Oakdale *Sarum* 84-92; Prec and Can Res Nor Cathl *Nor* 92-98; Provost Derby 98-00; Dean Derby from 00. *The Deanery, 9 Highfield Road, Derby DE22 1GX* Tel and fax (01332) 342971 or tel 341201 Fax 203991 E-mail dean@derbycathedral.org

PERKES, Brian Robert Keith. b 46. St Andr Univ BSc68. Nor Ord Course 91. **d** 94 **p** 95. NSM Witton *Ches* 94-98; Bp's Chapl 98-00; P-in-c Ashton Hayes from 98; P-in-c Delamere from 00. *The Vicarage, Church Road, Ashton, Chester CH3 8AB* Tel (01829) 751265 E-mail brkperkes@tinyworld.co.uk

PERKIN, David Arthur. b 30. Pemb Coll Ox BA54 MA58. Linc Th Coll 54. **d** 56 **p** 57. C St John's Wood *Lon* 56-61; Chapl Loughb Univ *Leic* 61-84; V Paddington St Jas *Lon* 84-92; rtd 92. *14 Englewood Road, London SW12 9NZ*

PERKIN, Jonathan Guy. b 52. Westmr Coll Ox BEd76. Trin Coll Bris 89. **d** 91 **p** 92. C Cullompton *Ex* 91-96; C Ashtead *Guildf* 96-01; V Egham from 01. *Mauley Cottage, 13 Manorcrofts Road, Egham TW20 9LU* Tel (01784) 432066 E-mail jonathanperkin@barclays.net

PERKIN, Paul John Stanley. b 50. Ch Ch Ox BA71 MA75 CertEd. Wycliffe Hall Ox 78. **d** 80 **p** 81. C Gillingham St Mark *Roch* 80-84; C Brompton H Trin w Onslow Square St Paul *Lon* 84-87; P-in-c Battersea Rise St Mark *S'wark* 87-92; V from 92; P-in-c Battersea St Pet and St Paul from 00. *St Mark's Vicarage, 7 Elsynge Road, London SW18 2HW* Tel (020) 8874 6023 or 7223 6188 E-mail mark.mail@ukonline.co.uk

PERKINS, Canon Alban Leslie Tate. b 08. Kelham Th Coll 28. **d** 34 **p** 35. SSM from 33; C Nottingham St Geo w St Jo *S'well* 34-37 and 68-72; S Africa 37-67 and 76-80; Can Bloemfontein Cathl from 52; Lesotho 72-76; Perm to Offic *Man* 81-86 and *Blackb* 86-90. *Society of the Sacred Mission, Willows End, 6 Sterrymere Gardens, Kinver, Stourbridge DY7 4ET* Tel (01384) 877250

PERKINS, Colin Blackmore. b 35. FCII65. Lon Coll of Div 68. **d** 70 **p** 71. C Hyson Green *S'well* 70-73; V Clarborough w Hayton 73-79; P-in-c Cropwell Bishop 79-84; P-in-c Colston Bassett 79-84; P-in-c Granby w Elton 79-84; P-in-c Langar 79-84; V Tithby w Cropwell Butler 79-84; R Cropwell Bishop w Colston Bassett, Granby etc 84-94; P-in-c Sutton Bonington w Normanton-on-Soar 94-01; rtd 01; Perm to Offic *Newc* from 01. *6 Ravensmede, Alnwick NE66 2PX* Tel (01665) 510445 E-mail cperk68836@aol.com

PERKINS, David. b 51. Sarum & Wells Th Coll. **d** 87 **p** 88. C New Mills *Derby* 87-90; V Marlpool 90-95; P-in-c Turnditch 95-02; Min in charge Belper Ch Ch and Milford 95-02; V Belper Ch Ch w Turnditch from 02; RD Duffield from 99; Chapl S Derbyshire Community and Mental Health Trust from 95. *Christ Church Vicarage, Bridge Street, Belper DE56 1BA* Tel (01773) 824974

PERKINS, David John Elmslie. b 45. Dur Univ BA66 DipTh68 ATII75. Cranmer Hall Dur 66. **d** 69 **p** 70. C Wadsley *Sheff* 69-71; C Shortlands *Roch* 71-73; Perm to Offic *Lon* 76-78; Perm to Offic *B & W* 78-80 and from 02; Lic to Offic 80-02; rtd 02. *Rainbow's End, Montacute Road, Stoke-sub-Hamdon TA14 6UQ* Tel (01935) 823314

PERKINS, Miss Julia Margaret. b 49. Linc Th Coll 85. **d** 87 **p** 94. Par Dn Owton Manor *Dur* 87-89; Par Dn Leam Lane 89-94; C 94; P-in-c Stockton St Chad 94-96; V 96-00; C Eppleton and Hetton le Hole from 00. *Lyons Rectory, High Street, Easington Lane, Houghton le Spring DH5 0JN* Tel 0191-526 8918

PERKINS, Julian John. b 67. Southn Univ BSc90 MSc92 Bris Univ BA00. Trin Coll Bris 97. **d** 01 **p** 02. C Thornbury *Glouc* from 01. *50 Park Road, Thornbury, Bristol BS35 1HR* Tel (01454) 857212 E-mail julian-sarah@perkill.freeserve.co.uk

PERKINS, Malcolm Bryan. b 20. SS Coll Cam BA41 MA45. Wycliffe Hall Ox 41. **d** 43 **p** 44. C Rainham *Roch* 43-47; C Bexley St Jo 47-50; P-in-c Chalk 50-51; V 51-56; V Borstal 56-61; Chapl St Bart Hosp Roch 59-74; P-in-c Strood St Mary *Roch* 61-65; R Wouldham 65-73; Chapl Medway Hosp Gillingham 65-67; Toc H Staff Padre (SE Region) 73-85; Hon C Roch 74-85; rtd 85; Perm to Offic *Roch* from 85; Perm to Offic *Cant* from 85. *Roke*

Cottage, 3 Belgrave Terrace, Laddingford, Maidstone ME18 6BP Tel (01622) 871774

PERKINS, Sister Patricia Doris (Sister Patricia). b 29. Gilmore Ho 60. **dss** 73 **d** 87 **p** 01. CSA from 71; Sherston Magna w Easton Grey *Bris* 73-75; Cant St Martin and St Paul *Cant* 76-78; Kilburn St Aug w St Jo *Lon* 80-84; Abbey Ho Malmesbury 84-87; Hon Par Dn Bayswater 87-94; Chapl St Mary's Hosp Praed Street Lon 88-89; Chapl St Chas Hosp Ladbroke Grove 88-89; Dean of Women's Min *Lon* from 89; Dioc Dir of Ords 90-94; Hon Par Dn St Olave Hart Street w All Hallows Staining etc 94-01. *8/9 Verona Court, London W4 2JD* Tel (020) 8987 2799

PERKINSON, Neil Donald. b 46. Wycliffe Hall Ox 84. **d** 85 **p** 86. C Workington St Jo *Carl* 85-88; TV Cockermouth w Embleton and Wythop 88-93; TV St Laur in Thanet *Cant* 93-01; P-in-c Darlaston All SS *Lich* from 01; Ind Chapl Black Country Urban Ind Miss from 01. *All Saints' Vicarage, Walsall Road, Wednesbury WS10 9SQ* Tel 0121-526 6898 *or* (01902) 710407 E-mail n.perkinson@btinternet.com

PERKINTON, Keith Glyn. b 61. Humberside Poly BA83 Leeds Univ BA92. Coll of Resurr Mirfield 93. **d** 93 **p** 94. C Knowle H Nativity *Bris* 93-97; TV Brighton Resurr *Chich* from 97. *St Luke's Vicarage, Queen's Park Terrace, Brighton BN2 9YA* Tel (01273) 603946

PERKS, David Leonard Irving. b 38. Avery Hill Coll TCert61 Sussex Univ MA76. S Dios Minl Tr Scheme 84. **d** 87 **p** 88. NSM Lewes All SS, St Anne, St Mich and St Thos *Chich* 87-91; Chapl HM Pris Lewes 91-94; NSM Deanery of Lewes and Seaford *Chich* 94-96; C Peacehaven and Telscombe Cliffs 96-00; C Telscombe w Piddinghoe and Southease 96-00; rtd 00; Asst to RD Lewes and Seaford *Chich* from 00; Chapl S Downs Health NHS Trust from 01. *45 Fitzjohn Road, Lewes BN7 1PR* Tel (01273) 478719

PERKS, Edgar Harold Martin. b 31. Open Univ BA87. Glouc Sch of Min 85. **d** 88 **p** 89. NSM Bromfield *Heref* 88-89; NSM Culmington w Onibury 88-89; NSM Stanton Lacy 88-89; NSM Culmington w Onibury, Bromfield etc 90-98; Perm to Offic from 98. *The Oaklands, Bromfield Road, Ludlow SY8 1DW* Tel (01584) 875525

PERRENS, Everard George. b 15. St Cath Coll Cam BA37 MA42. Linc Th Coll 40. **d** 42 **p** 43. C Rugby St Andr *Cov* 42-44; CF 44-47; CMS 47-65; Uganda 47-65; Chapl St Marg Sch Bushey 65-74; Hon C Earlsdon *Cov* 75-79 and 80-83; C Allesley Park 79-80; rtd 80; Perm to Offic *Cov* from 83. *2 Beechwood Court, Rochester Road, Earlsdon, Coventry CV5 6AE* Tel (024) 7671 2821 E-mail eg@ukf.net

PERRETT, David Thomas. b 48. Cranmer Hall Dur 80. **d** 82 **p** 83. C Stapleford *S'well* 82-86; V Ollerton 86-87; P-in-c Boughton 86-87; V Ollerton w Boughton 87-93; V Winklebury *Win* from 93. *The Vicarage, Willoughby Way, Basingstoke RG23 8BD* Tel (01256) 323941 *or* 359431

PERRETT, Mrs Jill. b 59. Trent Poly BA80 Leeds Poly CQSW82. STETS 99. **d** 02 **p** 03. C Mere w W Knoyle and Maiden Bradley *Sarum* from 02. *6 Ash Grove, Mere, Warminster BA12 6BX* Tel 0117-952 0708

PERRICONE, Vincent James. b 50. Connecticut Univ BA74 Pontifical Univ Rome STB88 STL90 Glas Univ PhD98. **d** 89 **p** 90. In RC Ch 89-94; C Glas St Mary *Glas* 94-95; P-in-c Knightswood H Cross Miss from 95; P-in-c Glas All SS from 95. *2 Skaterigg Drive, Burlington Gate, Glasgow G13 1SR* Tel 0141-959 3730

PERRIN, Michael Leonard. b 47. Shenstone Coll of Educn CertEd66 Lanc Univ BEd71. Dioc OLM tr scheme 97. **d** 01 **p** 02. OLM Aspull St Eliz *Liv* from 01. *21 Firs Park Crescent, Aspull, Wigan WN2 2SJ* Tel (01942) 257418 E-mail mikeperrin99@hotmail.com

PERRINS, Christopher Neville. b 68. St Steph Ho Ox 01. **d** 03. C Warrington St Elphin *Liv* from 03. *41 Parr Street, Warrington WA1 2JN* Tel (01925) 419211 E-mail revdcnperrins@aol.com

PERRINS, Harold. b 21. Kelham Th Coll 38. **d** 44 **p** 45. C Fenton *Lich* 44-49; C Talke 49-53; R Armitage 53-61; V Lapley w Wheaton Aston 61-65; V Priorslee 65-69; V Edingale 69-77; R Harlaston 69-77; V Shobnall 77-86; rtd 86; Perm to Offic *Lich* from 86. *20 Meadow Rise, Barton under Needwood, Burton-on-Trent DE13 8DT* Tel (01283) 713515

PERRINS, Mrs Lesley. b 53. St Hugh's Coll Ox BA74 S Bank Poly DCG75. S Dios Minl Tr Scheme CECM93. **d** 93 **p** 95. NSM Stoneleigh *Guildf* 93-94; NSM Haxby w Wigginton *York* 94-00; Asst Chapl York Health Services NHS Trust 99-00. *37 St John's Rise, Woking GU21 7PN* Tel (01483) 761427

PERRIS, Anthony. b 48. Univ of Wales (Abth) BSc69 Selw Coll Cam BA76 MA79. Ridley Hall Cam 74. **d** 77 **p** 78. C Sandal St Helen *Wakef* 77-80; C Plymouth St Andr w St Paul and St Geo *Ex* 80-87; TV Yeovil *B & W* 87-88; V Preston Plucknett from 88. *St James's Vicarage, 1 Old School House, Yeovil BA21 3UB* Tel (01935) 429398

PERRIS, John Martin. b 44. Liv Univ BSc66 Bris Univ DipTh70. Trin Coll Bris 69. **d** 72 **p** 73. C Sevenoaks St Nic *Roch* 72-76; C Bebington *Ches* 76-79; V Redland *Bris* 79-97; RD Horfield 91-97; R Barton Seagrave w Warkton *Pet* from 97. *The Rectory,*

St Botolph's Road, Kettering NN15 6SR Tel (01536) 513629 *or* 414052 E-mail st.botolphs@ukgateway.net

PERROTT, John Alastair Croome. b 36. Univ of NZ LLB60. Clifton Th Coll 62. **d** 64 **p** 65. C Tunbridge Wells St Pet *Roch* 64-67; C Stanford-le-Hope *Chelmsf* 67-78; R Elmswell *St E* 78-02; rtd 02. *7 Millfield Road, Barningham, Bury St Edmunds IP31 1DX*

PERRY, Alan David. b 64. Avery Hill Coll BA86 Lon Inst of Educn PGCE87 Greenwich Univ MA99. NTMTC 01. **d** 03. NSM Romford St Edw *Chelmsf* from 03. *1A Lyndhurst Drive, Hornchurch RM11 1JL* Tel (01708) 437852 Mobile 07946-730291 E-mail alan.perry80@ntlworld.com

PERRY, Andrew John. b 65. Wilson Carlile Coll St Steph Ho Ox BTh00. **d** 00 **p** 01. C Southwick St Mich *Chich* 00-03; P-in-c Upper St Leonards St Jo from 03. *St John's Rectory, 53 Brittany Road, St Leonards-on-Sea TN38 0RD* Tel (01424) 423367 Mobile 07900-981345 E-mail perry.rickard@virgin.net

PERRY, Andrew Nicholas. b 62. Westmr Coll Ox BA86. Trin Coll Bris MA91. **d** 91 **p** 92. C Bath Weston All SS w N Stoke *B & W* 91-93; C Bath Weston All SS w N Stoke and Langridge 93-95; P-in-c Longfleet *Sarum* 95-00; V from 00. *The Vicarage, 32 Alverton Avenue, Poole BH15 2QJ* Tel (01202) 723359 *or* tel and fax 253527 E-mail andrewperry@ukgateway.net

PERRY, Andrew William. b 64. R Agric Coll Cirencester NDA65 MRAC65 ADFM66. WMMTC 91. **d** 94 **p** 95. NSM Redmarley D'Abitot, Bromesberrow, Pauntley etc *Glouc* from 94. *Rye Cottage, Broomsgreen, Dymock GL18 2DP* Tel (01531) 890489 Fax 632552 E-mail aw@perry.net

PERRY, Anthony Henry. b 54. Leic Univ BA76. Aston Tr Scheme 89 Linc Th Coll 93. **d** 93 **p** 94. C Bartley Green *Birm* 93-97; V Bearwood from 97. *St Mary's Vicarage, 27 Poplar Avenue, Birmingham B17 8EG* Tel 0121-429 2165 E-mail trinity20@btopenworld.co.uk

PERRY, Anthony Robert. b 21. Birkbeck Coll Lon 39 Natal Univ 40. Kelham Th Coll 48. **d** 52 **p** 53. SSM 52-01; C Sheff Parson Cross St Cecilia *Sheff* 52-56; S Africa 56-59 and 70-88; Min Modderpoort St Aug 56-58 and 83-88; Lesotho 59-70; Min Chooko St Jas 59; Min Teyateyaneng St Agnes 60; Min Morija 66-67 and 76; Chapl Natal Univ 70-74 and 76-77; Melbourne Australia 79; Asst P Durban St Paul 78; Chapl Addington Hosp Durban 79-82; Chapl Chich Th Coll 88-90; Willen Priory 90-92; St Ant Priory 92-97; Vassall Road Priory 98-99; Warminster Priory 99; Perm to Offic *S'wark* from 98. *2 Saxon's Acre, Warminster BA12 8HT* Tel (01985) 212510 *or* 308818 Fax 308818

PERRY, Christopher Richard. b 78. St Jo Coll Dur BA00. Coll of Resurr Mirfield 00. **d** 02 **p** 03. C Penzance St Mary w St Paul and St Jo *Truro* from 02. *11 Pendarves Road, Penzance TR18 2AJ* Tel (01736) 359041 Mobile 07803-176789

PERRY, Canon Colin Charles. b 16. K Coll Cam BA38 MA42. Westcott Ho Cam 39. **d** 40 **p** 41. C Champion Hill St Sav *S'wark* 40-42; C Redhill St Jo 42-44; Ghana 45-56; V Aldbourne *Sarum* 56-64; V Baydon 57-64; PC Salisbury St Fran 64-69; V 69-71; V Preston 71-81; RD Weymouth 75-79; Can and Preb Sarum Cathl 77-82; TR Preston w Sutton Poyntz and Osmington w Poxwell 81-82; rtd 82; Perm to Offic *Sarum* from 82. *6 The Ridgeway, Corfe Mullen, Wimborne BH21 3HS* Tel (01202) 697298

PERRY, David William. b 42. St Chad's Coll Dur BA64 DipTh66. **d** 66 **p** 67. C Middleton St Mary *Ripon* 66-69; C Bedale 69-71; C Marton-in-Cleveland *York* 71-75; V Skirlaugh w Long Riston from 75; N Humberside Ecum Officer from 75. *The Vicarage, Skirlaugh, Hull HU11 5HE* Tel (01964) 562259 E-mail david@perryskirlaugh.karoo.co.uk

PERRY, Edward John. b 35. AKC62. **d** 63 **p** 64. C Honicknowle *Ex* 63-65; C Ashburton w Buckland-in-the-Moor 65-70; V Cornwood 70-92; Asst Dir of Educn 71-92; Chapl Moorhaven Hosp 91-93; V Ermington and Ugborough *Ex* 92-00; rtd 00. *32 Finches Close, Elburton, Plymouth PL9 8DP* Tel (01752) 405364

PERRY, Mrs Joanna Teresa. b 60. K Coll Lon BD82. Trin Coll Bris ADMT96. **d** 96 **p** 00. C Thornbury *Glouc* 96-97; C Winchcombe, Gretton, Sudeley Manor etc 97-99; Sub Chapl HM Pris and YOI New Hall from 99. *HM Prison and YOI New Hall, Dial Wood, Flockton, Wakefield WF4 4AX* Tel (01924) 848307

✠PERRY, The Rt Revd John Freeman. b 35. Lon Coll of Div ALCD59 LTh74 MPhil86. **d** 59 **p** 60 **c** 89. C Woking Ch Ch *Guildf* 59-62; C Chorleywood Ch Ch *St Alb* 62; Min Chorleywood St Andr CD 63-66; V Chorleywood St Andr 66-77; RD Rickmansworth 72-77; Warden Lee Abbey 77-89; RD Shirwell *Ex* 80-84; Hon Can Win Cathl *Win* 89-96; Suff Bp Southampton 89-96; Bp Chelmsf 96-03; rtd 03. *Foxbury, Gutch Common, Shaftesbury SP7 9AZ* Tel (01747) 828416

PERRY, John Neville. b 20. Leeds Univ BA41. Coll of Resurr Mirfield 41. **d** 43 **p** 44. C Poplar All SS w St Frideswide *Lon* 43-50; V De Beauvoir Town St Pet 50-63; V Feltham 63-75; RD Hounslow 67-75; Adn Middx 75-82; R Orlestone w Snave and Ruckinge w Warehorne *Cant* 82-86; rtd 86; Perm to Offic *Chich* from 90. *73 Elizabeth Crescent, East Grinstead RH19 3JG* Tel (01342) 315446

PERRY, John Walton Beauchamp. b 43. Ex Coll Ox BA64 Sussex Univ MA67. EAMTC 82 Westcott Ho Cam 84. **d** 85 **p** 86. C Shrewsbury St Chad w St Mary *Lich* 85-89; V Batheaston w St Cath *B & W* 89-99; V Milborne Port w Goathill from 99. *The Vicarage, Bathwell Lane, Milborne Port, Sherborne DT9 5AN* Tel (01963) 250248 E-mail jwbperry@hotmail.com

PERRY, Jonathan Robert. b 55. St Jo Coll Nottm DipTh. **d** 82 **p** 83. C Filey *York* 82-84; C Rayleigh *Chelmsf* 84-88; Asst Chapl St Geo Hosp Linc 88-90; Chapl Gateshead Hosps NHS Trust 90-98; Chapl Gateshead Health NHS Trust from 98. *Queen Elizabeth Hospital, Sheriff Hill, Gateshead NE9 6SX* Tel 0191-403 2072 *or* 482 0000 ext 2072

PERRY, Lesley Anne. b 52. K Coll Lon BA73 MIPR99. SEITE DipTh99. **d** 99 **p** 00. NSM Fulham All SS *Lon* from 99. *Flat 3, 76 Philbeach Gardens, London SW5 9EY* Tel (020) 7373 3085 *or* 7419 5404

PERRY, Mrs Lynne Janice. b 48. **d** 90 **p** 97. NSM Llanfair Mathafarn Eithaf w Llanbedrgoch *Ban* 90-97; C Bangor 97-99; TV from 99; AD Ogwen from 02. *Tre-wen, 39 Tal-y-Cae, Tregarth, Bangor LL57 4AE* Tel (01248) 600997

PERRY, Martin Herbert. b 43. Cranmer Hall Dur 66. **d** 70 **p** 71. C Millfield St Mark *Dur* 70-74; C Haughton le Skerne 74-77; V Darlington St Matt 77-79; V Darlington St Matt and St Luke 79-84; TR Oldland *Bris* 84-91; V 91-01; rtd 01. *Address withheld by request*

PERRY, Martyn. b 57. S Wales Bapt Coll DipTh85 DPS86 Coll of Resurr Mirfield 89. **d** 90 **p** 91. In Bapt Ch 85-89; C Hornsey St Mary w St Geo *Lon* 90-93; V Pontlottyn w Fochriw *Llan* 93-97; R Cilybebyll from 97. *The Rectory, 7 Cwmnantllwyd Road, Gellinudd, Pontardawe, Swansea SA8 3DT* Tel (01792) 862118

PERRY, Canon Michael Charles. b 33. Trin Coll Cam BA55 MA59. Westcott Ho Cam 56. **d** 58 **p** 59. C Baswich *Lich* 58-60; Chapl Ripon Hall Ox 61-63; Chief Asst Home Publishing SPCK 63-70; Can Res Dur Cathl *Dur* 70-98; Adn Dur 70-93; Bp's Sen Chapl 93-98; rtd 98. *57 Ferens Park, Durham DH1 1NU* Tel 0191-386 1891

PERRY, Michael James Matthew. b 66. Bris Univ BSc87 MSc89 PhD93. Trin Coll Bris BA99. **d** 99 **p** 00. C Keynsham *B & W* 99-03; R Queen Camel w W Camel, Corton Denham etc from 03. *The Rectory, Englands Lane, Queen Camel, Yeovil BA22 7NN* Tel (01935) 850326 E-mail michaelperry@firenet.uk.com

PERRY, The Very Revd Robert Anthony. b 21. Leeds Univ BA47. Coll of Resurr Mirfield 47. **d** 49 **p** 50. C Middlesbrough St Jo the Ev *York* 49-54; Sarawak 54-66 and 76-79; Provost Kuching 60-66; R Hasfield w Tirley *Glouc* 66-69; Asst Chapl HM Pris Man 69; Chapl HM Pris Gartree 70-73; P-in-c Mottingham St Edw *S'wark* 73-75; P-in-c Presteigne w Discoed *Heref* 80-83; R Presteigne w Discoed, Kinsham and Lingen 83-86; rtd 86; Perm to Offic *Heref* 87-93; *Linc* from 95; Chapl Laslett's *Worc* 91-92; P-in-c Ryhall w Essendine *Pet* 94-95; P-in-c Ryhall w Essendine and Carlby 95-96. *The Brambles, 19A Station Road, Heckington, Sleaford NG34 9JH* Tel (01529) 461686 E-mail valtone@ukonline.co.uk

PERRY, Russell Lee. b 38. Worc Coll Ox BA60 MA64. Carl and Blackb Dioc Tr Inst 98. **d** 98 **p** 99. NSM Grasmere *Carl* 98-01; rtd 01; Perm to Offic *S'well* from 01. *Dumble Howe, 3 Byron Gardens, Southwell NG25 0DW* Tel (01636) 815813

PERRY, Timothy Richard. b 64. Trin Coll Bris BA93. **d** 93 **p** 95. C Abingdon *Ox* 93-97; New Life Outreach from 97. *Address temp unknown*

PERRY, Valerie Evelyn. b 39. Southn Univ CertEd59 Lon Univ DipRS85. S'wark Ord Course 82. **dss** 85 **d** 87 **p** 94. NSM Romford St Edw *Chelmsf* 85-89; Par Dn 89-91; Asst Chapl Middx Hosp Lon 92-94; Chapl S Kent Hosps NHS Trust 94-98; Hon C Aylesham w Adisham *Cant* 98-00; Hon C Nonington w Wymynswold and Goodnestone etc 98-00; rtd 99; Perm to Offic *Truro* from 01. *115 Century Close, St Austell PL25 3UZ*

PERRY, William Francis Pitfield. b 61. Keble Coll Ox BA84 MA87. Ripon Coll Cuddesdon 94. **d** 96 **p** 97. C Brockworth *Glouc* 96-01; P-in-c Millbrook *Win* from 01. *58 Shirley Avenue, Shirley, Southampton SO15 5NJ* Tel (023) 8070 1896 E-mail fr.will@icxc.org

PERRY-GORE, Canon Walter Keith. b 34. Univ of Wales (Lamp) BA59. Westcott Ho Cam 60. **d** 61 **p** 62. C St Austell *Truro* 61-64; R H Innocents Barbados 64-71; Canada from 71; R New Carlisle 71-74; R N Hatley 74-96. *1115 Rue Massawippi, North Hatley PQ, Canada, J0B 2C0* Tel (001) (819) 842 4665 Fax 842 2176

PERRYMAN, Preb David Francis. b 42. Brunel Univ BSc64. Oak Hill Th Coll 74. **d** 76 **p** 77. C Margate H Trin *Cant* 76-80; R Ardingly *Chich* 80-90; V Bath St Luke *B & W* from 90; RD Bath 96-03; Preb Wells Cathl from 01. *St Luke's Vicarage, Hatfield Road, Bath BA2 2BD* Tel (01225) 311904 Fax 400975 E-mail david@stlukebath.org.uk

PERRYMAN, Graham Frederick. b 56. Southn Univ BA78 Reading Univ PGCE80. Aston Tr Scheme 90 Trin Coll Bris DipHE94. **d** 94 **p** 95. C Hamworthy *Sarum* 94-98; P-in-c Moreton and Woodsford w Tincleton 98-02; R from 02. *The*

Rectory, 17 Warmwell Road, Crossways, Dorchester DT2 8BS Tel (01305) 854046 Fax as telephone E-mail revgfp@btopenworld.com

PERRYMAN, James Edward. b 56. Lon Bible Coll BA85 Oak Hill Th Coll 86. **d** 88 **p** 89. C Gidea Park *Chelmsf* 88-91; C Becontree St Mary 91-94; Chapl Lyon *Eur* 94-00; R Allington and Maidstone St Pet *Cant* from 00; Dioc Ecum Officer from 02. *The Rectory, 35 Poplar Grove, Allington, Maidstone ME16 0DE* Tel (01622) 758704 E-mail jim_perryman@onetel.net.uk

PERRYMAN, Canon John Frederick Charles. b 49. Mert Coll Ox BA71 MA74 MInstGA98. Ridley Hall Cam 72. **d** 74 **p** 75. C Shortlands *Roch* 74-78; Asst Chapl St Geo Hosp Lon 78-82; Chapl Withington Hosp Man 83-94; Chapl S Man Univ Hosps NHS Trust from 94; Hon Can Man Cathl *Man* from 00. *Withington Hospital, Nell Lane, Manchester M20 2LR, or 24 Alan Road, Withington, Manchester M20 4WG* Tel 0161-291 4800 *or* 445 8111

PERSSON, Matthew Stephen. b 60. Dundee Univ BSc82 Bris Univ MA98. Wycliffe Hall Ox 88. **d** 91 **p** 92. C Bath Twerton-on-Avon *B & W* 91-94; Chapl HM Pris Shepton Mallet 94-97; Perm to Offic *B & W* 97-98; C Shepton Mallet w Doulting 98-00. *Ham Manor, Bowlish, Shepton Mallet BA4 5JR*

✠**PERSSON, The Rt Revd William Michael Dermot.** b 27. Oriel Coll Ox BA51 MA55. Wycliffe Hall Ox 51. **d** 53 **p** 54 c 82. C S Croydon Em *Cant* 53-55; C Tunbridge Wells St Jo *Roch* 55-58; V S Mimms Ch Ch *Lon* 58-67; R Bebington *Ches* 67-79; V Knutsford St Jo and Toft 79-82; Suff Bp Doncaster *Sheff* 82-92; rtd 93; Asst Bp B & W from 93. *Ryalls Cottage, Burton Street, Marnhull, Sturminster Newton DT10 1PS* Tel (01258) 820452

PERTH, Archbishop of. See CARNLEY, The Most Revd Peter Frederick

PERTH, Provost of. See FARQUHARSON, The Very Revd Hunter Buchanan

PERU, Bishop of. See GODFREY, The Rt Revd Harold William

PESCOD, John Gordon. b 44. Leeds Univ BSc70. Qu Coll Birm DipTh71. **d** 72 **p** 73. C Camberwell St Geo *S'wark* 72-75; Chapl R Philanthropic Soc Sch Redhill 75-80; P-in-c Nunney w Wanstrow and Cloford *B & W* 80-84; R Nunney and Witham Friary, Marston Bigot etc 84-87; R Milverton w Halse and Fitzhead 87-93; V Frome St Jo and St Mary 93-00; V Frome St Jo 01; V Woodlands 93-01; RD Frome 97-01; V Castle Cary w Ansford from 01. *The Vicarage, Church Street, Castle Cary BA7 7EJ* Tel (01963) 351615 E-mail jjpescod@fish.co.uk

PESKETT, Canon Osmond Fletcher. b 12. Dur Univ LTh44. Tyndale Hall Bris. **d** 37 **p** 38. China 38-43 and 45-50; C Felixstowe SS Pet and Paul *St E* 45; V Chadderton Ch Ch *Man* 51-55; V Tonbridge St Steph *Roch* 55-65; Tanzania 65-68; Chan Morogoro 65-68; Hon Can Morogoro from 68; V St Keverne *Truro* 68-77; rtd 77; Perm to Offic *Ex* from 91. *Gairloch, Hensleigh Drive, St Leonards, Exeter EX2 4NZ* Tel (01392) 214387

PESKETT, Richard Howard. b 42. Selw Coll Cam BA64 MA67. Ridley Hall Cam 64. **d** 68 **p** 69. C Jesmond H Trin *Newc* 68-71; Singapore 71-91; Lect Trin Coll Bris from 91; Vice-Prin Trin Coll Bris from 98. *Trinity College, Stoke Hill, Bristol BS9 1JP* Tel 0117-968 2803 *or* 968 3996 E-mail howard.peskett@trinity-bris.ac.uk

PESKETT, Timothy Lewis. b 64. St Kath Coll Liv BA86. Chich Th Coll BTh90. **d** 90 **p** 91. C Verwood *Sarum* 90-91; C Southsea H Spirit *Portsm* 91-95; TV Burgess Hill St Jo w St Edw *Chich* 95-00; V Burgess Hill St Edw from 00. *7 Bramble Gardens, Burgess Hill RH15 8UQ* Tel (01444) 241300

PESTELL, Robert Carlyle. b 54. Aston Tr Scheme 89 Linc Th Coll 91. **d** 93 **p** 94. C Matson *Glouc* 93-97; P-in-c Charfield 97-01; R Charfield and Kingswood from 02. *The Rectory, 36 Wotton Road, Charfield, Wotton-under-Edge GL12 8TG* Tel (01454) 260489

PETCH, Douglas Roodge. b 57. Nottm Univ BSc79. All Nations Chr Coll Cam DipRS81 St Jo Coll Nottm MTS95. **d** 94 **p** 94. Nigeria 94-96; C Pendleton *Man* 96-98; P-in-c Werneth 98-03; C Oldham St Paul 98-03; CMS from 03. *CMS, 157 Waterloo Road, London SE1 8XA* Tel (020) 7928 8681 E-mail rodger@petchr.freeserve.co.uk

PETER, Christopher Javed. b 51. BA75. Qu Coll Birm 94. **d** 96 **p** 97. C Darwen St Pet w Hoddlesden *Blackb* 96-98; C Accrington 98-99; C Burnley St Andr w St Marg and St Jas from 99. *60 Chichester Close, Burnley BB10 4AL* Tel (01282) 413234

PETER DOUGLAS, Brother. See NEEDHAM, Brother Peter Douglas

PETERBOROUGH, Bishop of. See CUNDY, The Rt Revd Ian Patrick Martyn

PETERBOROUGH, Dean of. See BUNKER, The Very Revd Michael

PETERKEN, Canon Peter Donald. b 28. K Coll Lon BD51 AKC51. **d** 52 **p** 53. C Swanley St Mary *Roch* 52-55 and 62-65; Is of Dogs Ch Ch and St Jo w St Luke *Lon* 55-57; R S Perrott w Mosterton and Chedington *Sarum* 57-59; Br Guiana 59-62; R Killamarsh *Derby* 65-70; V Derby St Luke 70-90; RD Derby N 79-90; Hon Can Derby Cathl 85-95; R Matlock 90-95; rtd 95;

Perm to Offic *Derby* from 95. *64 Brayfield Road, Littleover, Derby DE23 6GT* Tel (01332) 766285

PETERS, Carl Richard. b 62. Ripon Coll Cuddesdon 95. **d** 97 **p** 98. C Coventry Caludon *Cov* 97-01; V Gt Grimsby St Andr w St Luke and All SS *Linc* 01-02; TV Leek and Meerbrook *Lich* from 02. *All Saints Vicarage, Compton, Leek ST13 5PT* Tel (01538) 382588 E-mail carljackie@petersc.freeserve.co.uk

PETERS, The Very Revd Christopher Lind. b 56. Oak Hill Th Coll. **d** 82 **p** 83. C Knockbreda *D & D* 82-84; C Lisburn Ch Ch Cathl *Conn* 84-87; I Kilmocomogue Union *C, C & R* 87-93; P-in-c Beara 92-93; I Killiney Ballybrack *D & G* 93-98; Dean Ross *C, C & R* from 98; Chan Cork Cathl from 98. *The Deanery, Rosscarbery, Co Cork, Irish Republic* Tel (00353) (23) 48166 E-mail peters@esatclear.ie

PETERS, Canon Cyril John (Bill). b 19. Fitzw Ho Cam BA42 MA45. Chich Th Coll 40. **d** 42 **p** 43. C Brighton St Mich *Chich* 42-45 and 47-50; CF (EC) 45-47; Hon CF from 47; Chapl Brighton Coll 50-69; R Uckfield *Chich* 69-96; R Isfield 69-96; R Lt Horsted 69-96; RD Uckfield 73-96; Can and Preb Chich Cathl 81-89; rtd 96; Perm to Offic *Chich* from 96. *Canon's Lodge, 9 Calvert Road, Uckfield TN22 2DB* Tel (01825) 766397

PETERS, David Alexander. b 72. K Coll Lon BA94. St Steph Ho Ox BA98 DipTh99. **d** 99 **p** 00. C Paddington St Jas *Lon* 99-03; PV Westmr Abbey from 01; V Reading H Trin *Ox* from 03; V Reading St Mark from 03. *Holy Trinity Presbytery, 32 Baker Street, Reading RG1 7XY* Tel 0118-957 2650 E-mail frpeters@aol.com

PETERS, David Lewis. b 38. Ch Ch Ox BA62 MA66. Westcott Ho Cam 63. **d** 65 **p** 66. C Oldham St Mary w St Pet *Man* 65-69; C Stand 70-74; P-in-c Hillock 70-74; V 74-82; V Haslingden w Haslingden Grane *Blackb* 82-88; rtd 88; Perm to Offic *Man* from 88; Perm to Offic *Blackb* from 88. *2 Mount Terrace, Earnshaw Road, Bacup OL13 9BP* Tel (01706) 876863

PETERS, Geoffrey John. b 51. BCom BSc MDiv MInstC(Glas). Oak Hill Th Coll 85 Gujranwala Th Sem 90. **d** 87 **p** 88. C Forest Gate St Sav w W Ham St Matt *Chelmsf* 87-90; C Wembley St Jo *Lon* 90-92; Chapl Wembley Hosp 90-92; TV Manningham *Bradf* 92-97; Res Scheme Manager Anchor Trust from 02. *20 Pembroke Court, St Leonards Road, Bradford BD8 9QS* Tel (01274) 480884 *or* 544670 E-mail peters379@hotmail.com

PETERS, John Peter Thomas. b 63. Keble Coll Ox BL85. Wycliffe Hall Ox BA91. **d** 95 **p** 96. C Brompton H Trin w Onslow Square St Paul *Lon* 95-99; P-in-c Bryanston Square St Mary w St Marylebone St Mark from 00. *73 Gloucester Place, London W1 3PF* Tel (020) 7487 3224 *or* 7723 0466

PETERS, John Thomas. b 58. Connecticut Univ BA80 LTh. St Jo Coll Nottm 84. **d** 87 **p** 88. C Virginia Water *Guildf* 87-93; R Grand Rapids Ch Ch USA from 93; Perm to Offic *Lon* 96-00. *710 NW 20th Avenue #202, Grand Rapids, MN 55744, USA* Tel (001) (218) 327 0828

PETERS, Canon Kenneth. b 54. Univ of Wales (Cardiff) DipTh77 Newport Univ Tokyo MBA88 Greenwich Univ MA02 MIW96 CNI95. St Mich Coll Llan 74. **d** 77 **p** 78. C Mountain Ash *Llan* 77-80; Asst Chapl Mersey Miss to Seamen 80-82; Chapl RNR from 80; Chapl Miss to Seamen Japan 82-89; Hon Can Kobe from 85; Chapl Supt Mersey Miss to Seamen 89-93; Justice and Welfare Sec from 94; Hon C St Mich Paternoster Royal *Lon* from 94. *The Mission to Seafarers, St Michael Paternoster Royal, College Hill, London EC4R 2RL* Tel (020) 7248 5202 Fax 7248 4761 E-mail justice@missiontoseafarers.org

PETERS, Malcolm John. b 71. Leic Univ BA92. Oak Hill Th Coll BA03. **d** 03. C Braintree *Chelmsf* from 03. *183 Notley Road, Braintree CM7 1HG* Tel (01376) 326755 E-mail malcolm.peters@ukgateway.net

PETERS, Marilyn Ann. b 49. Open Univ BA90 Bris Poly DMS92. Qu Coll Birm 96. **d** 98 **p** 99. C Blakenall Heath *Lich* 98-01; TV Cen Telford from 01. *The Vicarage, Church Road, Dawley, Telford TF4 2AS* Tel (01952) 501655 Mobile 07754-435272 E-mail marilyn.peters1@virgin.net

PETERS, Canon Michael. b 41. Chich Th Coll 75. **d** 77 **p** 78. C Redruth *Truro* 77-79; TV 79-80; TV Redruth w Lanner 80-82; R St Mawgan w St Ervan and St Eval 82-86; Chapl HM Pris Liv 86-87; Chapl HM Pris Bris 87-01; Hon Can Bris Cathl *Bris* 96-01; P-in-c Middlezoy and Othery and Moorlinch *B & W* from 01. *The Vicarage, North Lane, Othery, Bridgwater TA7 0QG* Tel (01823) 698953 E-mail mikesandra@ukgateway.net

PETERS, Robert David. b 54. Oak Hill Th Coll 78. **d** 79 **p** 80. C Hyde St Geo *Ches* 79-83; C Hartford 83-86; V Lindow 86-96; V Throop *Win* from 96; AD Bournemouth from 03. *St Paul's Vicarage, 1 Chesildene Avenue, Bournemouth BH8 0AZ* Tel (01202) 531064

PETERS, Stephen Eric. b 45. Westcott Ho Cam 74. **d** 77 **p** 78. C Wanstead St Mary *Chelmsf* 77-79; C Leigh-on-Sea St Marg 79-81; P-in-c Purleigh 81-82; P-in-c Cold Norton w Stow Maries 81-82; R Purleigh, Cold Norton and Stow Maries 83-84; V Bedford Park *Lon* 84-87; Perm to Offic *Ex* 87-88 and from 93; TR Totnes and Berry Pomeroy 88-90; Chapl Ex Sch 91-93; Chapl St Marg Sch Ex 91-93. *20 South Street, Totnes TQ9 5DZ* Tel (01803) 867199

PETERSEN, Miss Jennifer Elizabeth. b 55. Aus Nat Univ BA78. Moore Th Coll Sydney BTh82 Wycliffe Hall Ox 92. **d** 94 **p** 95. In Presbyterian Ch 85-94; C Elloughton and Brough w Brantingham *York* 94-96; C Ealing St Mary *Lon* 96-00; Chapl Thames Valley Univ 96-00; Chapl Qu Mary and Westf Coll from 00. *24 Sidney Square, London E1 2EY* Tel (020) 7791 1973 E-mail j.e.petersen@qmul.ac.uk

PETERSON, David Gilbert. Sydney Univ BA65 MA74 Lon Univ BD68 Man Univ PhD78. Moore Th Coll Sydney ThL68. **d** 68 **p** 69. Australia 68-75 and 80-96; C Manly St Matt 68-70; Lect Moore Th Coll 71-75; C Cheadle *Ches* 75-78; Sen Can and R Wollongong Cathl 80-84; Lect Moore Th Coll 84-96; Prin Oak Hill Th Coll from 96; Perm to Offic *Lon* and *St Alb* from 96. *Oak Hill Theological College, Chase Side, London N14 4PS* Tel (020) 8449 0467 Fax 8441 5996 E-mail davidp@oakhill.ac.uk

PETERSON, Dennis. b 35. Oak Hill Th Coll 51. **d** 54 **p** 55. C Leyton All SS *Chelmsf* 54-56; C Leeds St Geo *Ripon* 56-58; V E Brixton St Jude *S'wark* 58-91; rtd 91; Perm to Offic *Chelmsf* from 91. *79 Cavendish Gardens, Westcliff-on-Sea SS0 9XP* Tel (01702) 334400

PETERSON, Canon John Louis. b 42. Concordia Coll (USA) BA65. Harvard Div Sch STB68 Virginia Th Sem Hon DD93. **d** 76 **p** 77. USA 76-82; Dean St Geo Coll Jerusalem 82-94; Can Res 82-94; Hon Can from 95; Hon Can Kalamazoo from 82; Hon Prov Can Cant Cathl *Cant* from 95; Sec Gen ACC from 95; Hon Can Kaduna from 99; Hon Can St Paul's Cathl *Lon* from 00. *Anglican Consultative Council, 157 Waterloo Road, London SE1 8UT* Tel (020) 7620 1110 Fax 7620 1070 E-mail john.l.peterson@anglicancommunion.org

PETERSON, Paul John. b 67. Trin Coll Bris 94. **d** 97 **p** 98. C Burney Lane *Birm* 97-01; C-in-c Bradley Stoke N CD *Bris* from 01. *106 Cooks Close, Bradley Stoke, Bristol BS32 0BB* Tel (01454) 856947 E-mail paul@petersonp.freeserve.co.uk

PETFIELD, Bruce le Gay. b 34. FHA. NEOC 76. **d** 79 **p** 80. NSM Morpeth *Newc* 79-86; C Knaresborough *Ripon* 86-87; V Flamborough *York* 87-94; V Bempton 87-94; rtd 94; Perm to Offic *York* from 94. *36 Maple Road, Bridlington YO16 6TE*

PETIT, Andrew Michael. b 53. Solicitor Cam Univ MA. Trin Coll Bris DipHE82. **d** 83 **p** 84. C Stoughton *Guildf* 83-87; C Shirley *Win* 87-92; V Cholsey *Ox* from 92; P-in-c Moulsford from 03; Chapl W Berks Priority Care Services NHS Trust 92-03. *The Vicarage, Church Road, Cholsey, Wallingford OX10 9PP* Tel (01491) 651216 E-mail apetit@lineone.net

PETITT, Michael David. b 53. BCombStuds. Linc Th Coll 79. **d** 82 **p** 83. C Arnold *S'well* 82-86; Asst Chapl HM Youth Cust Cen Glen Parva 86-87; V Blaby *Leic* 87-94; V Leagrave *St Alb* 94-98; R Badby w Newham and Charwelton w Fawsley etc *Pet* from 98; Dioc Voc Adv from 00; Dir Tr for Past Assts 01-03. *The Vicarage, Vicarage Hill, Badby, Daventry NN11 3AP* Tel (01327) 310239

PETRIE, Alistair Philip. b 50. Lon Univ DipTh76 Fuller Th Sem California DMin99. Oak Hill Th Coll 76. **d** 76 **p** 77. C Eston *York* 76-79; P-in-c Prestwick *Glas* 79-81; R 81-82; Canada from 82. *1224 Mission Ridge Road, Kelowna BC, Canada V1W 3B2* Tel (001) (250) 764 8590 Fax 764 0663 E-mail alistair@partnershipministries.org

PETRIE, Ian Robert (Eric). b 53. Avery Hill Coll PGCE84. Oak Hill Th Coll BA83 Qu Coll Birm 93. **d** 95 **p** 96. C Sedgley All SS *Worc* 95-98; P-in-c Salwarpe and Hindlip w Martin Hussingtree from 98; Co-ord Chapl W Mercia Police from 98. *The Rectory, Salwarpe, Droitwich WR9 0AH* Tel (01905) 778757

PETT, Douglas Ellory. b 24. Lon Univ BD46 BD48 AKC48 PhD74. K Coll Lon 50. **d** 50 **p** 50. C Prittlewell St Mary *Chelmsf* 49-54; C Glouc St Mary de Lode and St Nic *Glouc* 54-58; Min Can Glouc Cathl 54-58; Lic to Offic *Nor* 54-58; C Ches Square St Mich w St Phil *Lon* 58-61; V Gulval *Truro* 61-66; Chapl St Mary's Hosp Praed Street Lon 66-83; rtd 83. *23 Polsue Way, Tresillian, Truro TR2 4BE* Tel (01872) 520573

PETTENGILL, Ernest Terence. b 43. K Coll Lon. **d** 69 **p** 70. C Chesham St Mary *Ox* 69-72; C Farnborough *Guildf* 72-75; Asst Master K Alfred Sch Burnham-on-Sea 75-78; C Bishop's Cleeve *Glouc* 78-80; Chapl Westonbirt Sch 80-85; P-in-c Shipton Moyne w Westonbirt and Lasborough *Glouc* 80-85; V Berkeley w Wick, Breadstone and Newport 85-92; TV Weston-super-Mare Cen Par *B & W* 92-95; P-in-c Weston super Mare Em 96-99; Chapl Staffs Univ *Lich* 99-03; V Douglas All SS and St Thos *S & M* from 03. *St Thomas's Vicarage, Marathon Avenue, Douglas IM2 4JA* Tel (01624) 611503 E-mail e.t.pettengill@staffs.ac.uk

PETTERSEN, Canon Alvyn Lorang. b 51. TCD BA73 Dur Univ BA75 PhD81. Sarum & Wells Th Coll 78. **d** 81 **p** 82. Chapl Clare Coll Cam 81-85; Fell and Chapl Ex Coll Ox 85-92; Research Fell Linc Coll Ox 92-93; V Frensham *Guildf* 93-02; Can Res Worc Cathl *Worc* from 02. *2 College Green, Worcester WR1 2LH* Tel (01905) 28854 E-mail alvynpettersen@worcestercathedral.org.uk

PETTERSSEN, Helge. b 44. Oslo Univ. **p** 71. Brazil 71-75; USA 75-77; Belgium 77-83; Norway 83-88; R Norwegian Ch and Seamen's Miss Lon from 88; Perm to Offic *S'wark* 96-00; Chapl S'wark Cathl from 00; NSM Bermondsey Deanery *S'wark* from

02. *St Olav's Church, 1 St Olav's Square, Albion Street, London SE16 1JB* Tel (020) 7237 5587 *or* 8852 3264 Mobile 07802-301090 Fax 7237 7280 E-mail helge.pettersson@sifh.no

PETTET, Christopher Farley. b 54. Ox Univ BEd78. St Jo Coll Nottm 87. **d** 90 **p** 91. C Luton St Mary *St Alb* 90-93; C Fawley *Win* 93-97; P-in-c Amport, Grateley, Monxton and Quarley from 97. *The Vicarage, Amport, Andover SP11 8BE* Tel (01264) 772950 E-mail chrispettet@yahoo.co.uk

PETTIFER, Bryan George Ernest. b 32. Qu Coll Cam BA55 MA59 Bris Univ MEd74. Wm Temple Coll Rugby 56 Ridley Hall Cam 57. **d** 59 **p** 60. C Attercliffe w Carbrook *Sheff* 59-61; C Ecclesall 61-65; Chapl City of Bath Tech Coll 65-74; Adult Educn Officer *Bris* 75-80; Dir Past Th Sarum & Wells Th Coll 80-85; Can Res St Alb 85-92; Prin St Alb Minl Tr Scheme 85-92; Prin Ox Area Chr Tr Scheme *Ox* 92-94; Perm to Offic 94-98; Min and Deployment Officer/Selection Sec ABM 94-97; rtd 97; Perm to Offic *Bris* and *Sarum* from 98; *Glouc* 98-00. *23 Curlew Drive, Chippenham SN14 6 YG* Tel (01249) 659823

PETTIFER, John Barrie. b 38. Linc Th Coll 63. **d** 65 **p** 66. C Stretford St Matt *Man* 65-67; C Stand 67-71; V Littleborough 71-00; rtd 00. *Littleborough Christian Centre, 43 Todmorden Road, Littleborough OL15 9EL* Tel (01706) 374074

PETTIFOR, David Thomas. b 42. Ripon Coll Cuddesdon 78. **d** 81 **p** 82. C Binley *Cov* 81-84; P-in-c Wood End 84-88; V 88-92; V Finham 92-98; TV Coventry Caludon from 98. *Holy Cross Vicarage, 14 St Austell Road, Coventry CV2 5AE* Tel (024) 7663 5734 E-mail david@dtpettifor.fsnet.co.uk

PETTIGREW, Miss Claire Gabrielle. b 23. St Mich Ho Ox 55. **dss** 77 **d** 87 **p** 95. Nor Heartsease St Fran *Nor* 77-81; Heigham H Trin 81-87; Dioc Lay Min Adv 83-87; Asst Dir of Ords 87-89; rtd 89; Lic to Offic *Nor* 89-97. *26 Capel Court, The Burgage, Prestbury, Cheltenham GL52 3EL* Tel (01242) 577541

PETTIGREW, Canon Stanley. b 27. TCD BA49 MA62. Div Test. **d** 50 **p** 51. C Newcastle *D & D* 50-53; C Dublin Clontarf *D & G* 53-57; I Derralossary 57-62; Miss to Seamen 62-92; I Wicklow w Killiskey *D & G* 62-92; Can Ch Ch Cathl Dublin 87-92; rtd 92. *Corr Riasc, Bollarney South, Wicklow, Irish Republic* Tel (00353) (404) 69755

PETTINGELL, Hubert (Hugh). b 32. ACA54 FCA65 AKC58. **d** 59 **p** 60. C Mansfield St Pet *S'well* 59-61; CMS Iran 61-66; C Wellington w W Buckland and Nynehead *B & W* 67-68; Warden Student Movement Ho Lon 68-69; R Holywell w Needingworth *Ely* 69-71; Dir Finance WCC 80-96; Perm to Offic *Eur* from 94; rtd 97. *Chemin du Pommier 22, CH-1218 Le Grand Saconnex, Geneva, Switzerland* Tel (0041) (22) 798 8586 E-mail hpettingell@hotmail.com

PETTIT, Anthony David. b 72. Univ of Cen England in Birm BA94 MA95 St Jo Coll Dur BA01. Cranmer Hall Dur 98. **d** 01 **p** 02. C Gt Malvern St Mary *Worc* from 01. *1 The Moorlands, Malvern Wells WR14 4PS* Tel (01684) 575123 E-mail revant@fish.co.uk

PETTITT, Maurice. b 13. Clare Coll Cam BA35 MA57 MusBac37. Lich Th Coll 56. **d** 57 **p** 58. Asst Chapl Wellingborough Sch 57-62; R Rounton w Welbury *York* 62-69; V Riccall 69-73; RD Escrick 73-78; rtd 78; Perm to Offic *York* from 78. *Holbeck House, Low Street, Lastingham, York YO62 6TJ* Tel (01751) 417517

PETTITT, Mervyn Francis. b 39. Qu Coll Birm DipTh66. **d** 66 **p** 67. C Colchester St Jas, All SS, St Nic and St Runwald *Chelmsf* 66-69; C Loughton St Jo 69-72; R Downham w S Hanningfield 72-82; P-in-c W w S Hanningfield 77-78; C Leigh-on-Sea St Marg 82-85; rtd 85. *60 Suffolk Avenue, Leigh-on-Sea SS9 3HF* Tel (01702) 716894

PETTITT, Robin Adrian. b 50. MRTPI79 Newc Univ BA77. St Steph Ho Ox 81. **d** 83 **p** 84. C Warrington St Elphin *Liv* 83-87; C Torrisholme *Blackb* 87-93; P-in-c Charnock Richard 93-00; Dioc Par Development Officer 93-98; Sec Dioc Adv Cttee for the Care of Chs 98-99; C Broughton 00-01; rtd 01. *The Vicarage, 169 Church Road, Haydock, St Helens WA11 0NJ* Tel (01942) 727956

PETTITT, Canon Simon. b 50. Nottm Univ BTh74 CertEd. Kelham Th Coll 70. **d** 75 **p** 76. C Penistone *Wakef* 75-78; Dioc Youth Officer 78-80; Dioc Schs Officer *St E* 80-86; P-in-c Hintlesham w Chattisham 80-86; V Bury St Edmunds St Jo 86-93; RD Thingoe 88-92; Dioc Communications Officer 93-00; Hon Can St E Cathl from 93; P-in-c Exning St Martin w Landwade 00-01; V from 01; RD Mildenhall from 01. *The Vicarage, New River Green, Exning, Newmarket CB8 7HS* Tel (01638) 577413 Mobile 07850-480533 Fax (01638) 578792 E-mail simon.pettitt@stedmundsbury.anglican.org

PETTS, Anna Carolyn. Sarum Dioc Tr Coll CertEd. STETS. **d** 03. NSM Hordle *Win* from 03. *65 Ferndale Road, New Milton BH25 5EX* Tel (01425) 620856

PETTY, Alicia Christina Margaret. b 64. Wycliffe Hall Ox 01. **d** 03. C Ockbrook *Derby* from 03. *12 Appian Close, Borrowash, Derby DE72 3LY* Tel (01332) 666205

PETTY, Brian. b 34. Man Univ BA90 Melbourne Univ DipRE. St Aid Birkenhead 59. **d** 62 **p** 63. C Meole Brace *Lich* 62-65; Chapl RAF 65-69; Australia 70-75; P-in-c Kimbolton w Middleton-on-the-Hill *Heref* 76-79; P-in-c Pudleston-cum-

Whyle w Hatfield, Docklow etc 76-79; P-in-c Haddenham *Ely* 79-80; V 80-84; V Fairfield *Derby* 84-90; Chapl St Geo Sch Ascot 90-93; TR Sampford Peverell, Uplowman, Holcombe Rogus etc *Ex* 93-99; RD Cullompton 95-99; rtd 99; Perm to Offic *Ex* 99-02; Hon C Diptford, N Huish, Harberton, Harbertonford etc from 02. *Woodrising, Fortescue Road, Sidmouth EX10 9QB* Tel (01395) 514203

PETTY, The Very Revd John Fitzmaurice. b 35. Trin Hall Cam BA59 MA65. Cuddesdon Coll 64. **d** 66 **p** 67. C Sheff St Cuth *Sheff* 66-69; C St Helier *S'wark* 69-75; V Hurst *Man* 75-88; AD Ashton-under-Lyne 83-87; Hon Can Man Cathl 86-88; Provost Cov 88-00; Dean Cov 00; rtd 00; Perm to Offic *Lich* from 01. *4 Granville Street, Copthorne, Shrewsbury SY3 8NE* Tel (01743) 231513

PETTY, Capt Stuart. b 56. Wilson Carlile Coll Dip Evang85 Chich Th Coll 91. **d** 93 **p** 94. CA from 88; C W Bromwich St Andr w Ch Ch *Lich* 93-96; Asst Chapl Walsall Hosps NHS Trust 96-00; Sen Chapl 00-03; Chapl Team Ldr R Wolv Hosps NHS Trust from 03. *The Chaplain's Office, New Cross Hospital, Wednesfield Road, Wolverhampton WV10 0QP* Tel (01902) 307999

PETTY, William Duncan. b 55. Ex Univ BSc76 Leic Univ PGCE77. Oak Hill Th Coll DipTh99. **d** 99 **p** 00. C Burscough Bridge *Liv* from 99. *29 Weaver Avenue, Burscough, Ormskirk L40 4LE* Tel (01704) 892 444 E-mail duncan@thepettys.freeserve.co.uk

PETZER, Garth Stephen. MBE99. St Paul's Coll Grahamstown. **d** 88 **p** 91. S Africa 88-95; Chapl RN 96-03; CF from 03. *c/o MOD Chaplains (Army)* Tel (01980) 615804 Fax 615844

PETZSCH, Diana Frances Louise. b 54. BA73 MA74 MLitt79 CertEd81. Edin Th Coll 93. **d** 96 **p** 97. C Perth St Jo *St And* 96-99; Asst Chapl Maidstone and Tunbridge Wells NHS Trust 99-01; Chapl from 01; Chapl HM Pris E Sutton Park 01. *1 Wheatfield Way, Cranbrook TN17 3LS* Tel (01580) 713113 E-mail dpetzsch@hotmail.com

PETZSCH, Hugo Max David. b 57. Edin Univ MA79 BD83 PhD95 FSAScot91. Edin Th Coll 80. **d** 83 **p** 84. C Dollar *St And* 83-86; New Zealand 86-90; P-in-c Alyth, Blairgowrie and Coupar Angus 90-91; Chapl Glenalmond Coll *St And* 91-98; Dep Headmaster Benenden Sch from 99; Perm to Offic *Cant* from 99. *Benenden School, Cranbrook TN17 4AA* Tel (01580) 240592

PEVERELL, Paul Harrison. b 57. Ripon Coll Cuddesdon. **d** 82 **p** 83. C Cottingham *York* 82-85; V Middlesbrough St Martin 85-93; V Gt Ayton w Easby and Newton in Cleveland from 93. *The Vicarage, Low Green, Great Ayton, Middlesbrough TS9 6NN* Tel (01642) 722333 E-mail revpev@clergy.net

PEYTON, The Ven Nigel. b 51. JP87. Edin Univ MA73 BD76. Union Th Sem (NY) STM77 Edin Th Coll 73. **d** 76 **p** 77. Chapl St Paul's Cathl Dundee *Bre* 76-82; Dioc Youth Chapl 76-85; Chapl Invergowrie 79-82; P-in-c 82-85; Chapl Univ Hosp Dundee 82-85; P-in-c Nottingham All SS *S'well* 85; V 86-91; Chapl Bluecoat Sch Nottm 90-92; P-in-c Lambley *S'well* 91-99; Dioc Min Development Adv 91-99; Adn Newark from 99. *Dunham House, Westgate, Southwell NG25 0JL,* or *4 The Woodwards, Newark NG24 3GG* Tel (01636) 814490 or 612249 Fax 815882 or 611952 E-mail archdeacon-newark@southwell.anglican.org

PEYTON JONES, Donald Lewis. b 14. DSC42. K Coll Lon 59. **d** 61 **p** 62. C Withycombe Raleigh *Ex* 61-62; V Salcombe Regis 62-72; C-in-c Lundy Is 73-78; V Appledore 73-78; rtd 79; Chapl Miss to Seafarers from 79; Lic to Offic *Ex* 79-95; Perm to Offic from 95. *Nazareth House Residential Home, Durnford Street, Plymouth PL1 3QR* Tel (01752) 660943

PEYTON JONES, Mrs Dorothy Helen. b 58. LMH Ox BA79 MPhil80. Trin Coll Bris DipTh86. **dss** 86 **d** 87 **p** 94. W Holloway St Luke *Lon* 86-87; Par Dn 87-89; C Glas St Oswald *Glas* 89-92; NSM Drumchapel 92-98; Perm to Offic *Ely* from 98. *71 Humberstone Road, Cambridge CB4 1JD* Tel (01223) 523485 E-mail dorothy@the-pjs.freeserve.co.uk

PHAIR, Neal David Stewart. b 70. Limerick Univ BA98 UCD HDipEd99 TCD MPhil02. CITC 99. **d** 02. C Ballymena w Ballyclug *Conn* from 02. *38 Ballee Road East, Ballymena BT42 3DH* Tel (028) 2564 7038 E-mail nealphair@hotmail.com

PHARAOH, Carol Helen. b 63. Preston Poly BTech84. St Jo Coll Dur 96. **d** 98 **p** 99. C Heaton Ch Ch *Man* 98-02; TV Walkden and Lt Hulton from 02. *St John's Vicarage, Algernon Road, Walkden, Manchester M28 3RD* Tel 0161-790 2338 E-mail pharaohingham@freenetname.co.uk

PHARAOH, Douglas William. b 18. MSHAA56. Worc Ord Coll 68. **d** 69 **p** 70. C Gt Malvern Ch Ch *Worc* 69-71; Area Sec Leprosy Miss 71-72; P-in-c Gateshead St Cuth *Dur* 72-73; V New Seaham 73-76; P-in-c Wymeswold *Leic* 76-78; V Wymeswold and Prestwold w Hoton 78-80; P-in-c Grandborough w Willoughby and Flecknoe *Cov* 80-81; V 81-83; rtd 83; Perm to Offic *Cov* from 83; KStJ from 85. *5 Margetts Close, Kenilworth CV8 1EN* Tel (01926) 779026

PHARAOH, Donald James. b 05. AKC27. **d** 28 **p** 29. C Sevenoaks St Jo *Roch* 28-32; C Lamorbey H Trin 32-33; C Deal St Andr *Cant* 33-39; V Cant St Greg 39-57; Chapl St Jo Hosp Cant 39-57;

RD Cant 51-57; V Headcorn 57-71; rtd 71; Perm to Offic *Roch* 71-94. *Pinehurst House, Pinehurst, Sevenoaks TN14 5AQ*

PHEELY, William Rattray. b 35. EN(M)88. Edin Th Coll 57. **d** 60 **p** 61. C Glas St Mary *Glas* 60-63; C Salisbury St Martin *Sarum* 63-66; Guyana 66-82; V Bordesley St Oswald *Birm* 82-86; Perm to Offic 86-00; rtd 00; Perm to Offic *Ex* from 00. *Flat C, The Old Vicarage, Case Gardens, Seaton EX12 2AP* Tel (01297) 20493

PHEIFFER, John Leslie. b 18. Wells Th Coll. **d** 67 **p** 68. C Northwood Hills St Edm *Lon* 67-69; Chapl Twickenham Prep Sch 69-71; C Chobham w Valley End *Guildf* 71-76; C Highcliffe w Hinton Admiral *Win* 77-79; V Portswood St Denys 79-85; rtd 86. *4 Haywards Close, Felpham, Bognor Regis PO22 8HF* Tel (01243) 828985

PHELAN, Thomas Sylvester Patrick. b 36. Leic Univ DSS62 Southn Univ DASS79 CQSW79. Chich Th Coll DipTh94. **d** 94 **p** 95. C Somers Town *Lon* 94-96; C Old St Pancras w Bedford New Town St Matt 96-97; Chapl Camden and Islington Community Health NHS Trust 96-97; OSB from 97; Lic Preacher *Ox* 97-02; Hon C Nor St Pet Parmentergate w St Jo *Nor* from 02. *14 Cyprus Street, Norwich NR1 3AX* Tel (01603) 610104

PHELPS, Canon Arthur Charles. b 26. St Cath Coll Cam BA50 MA55. Ridley Hall Cam 51. **d** 53 **p** 54. C Kirkdale St Lawr *Liv* 53-56; C Rainham *Chelmsf* 56-60; Min Collier Row St Jas CD 60-65; V Collier Row St Jas 65-75; R Thorpe Morieux w Preston and Brettenham *St E* 75-84; R Rattlesden w Thorpe Morieux and Brettenham 84-90; Hon Can St E Cathl 89-90; rtd 90; Perm to Offic *Truro* 90-00; *St E* from 01. *8 Northfield Court, Aldeburgh IP15 5LU* Tel (01728) 454772

PHELPS, Ian James. b 29. Oak Hill Th Coll 53. **d** 56 **p** 57. C Peckham St Mary *S'wark* 56-59; R Gaddesby w S Croxton *Leic* 59-67; R Beeby 59-67; Asst Dioc Youth Chapl and Rural Youth Adv 65-67; CF (TA) 60-67; CF (R of O) 67-84; Youth Chapl *Leic* 67-85; Dioc Adult Educn Officer 85-91; Past Asst to Bp and Adn Leic 91-94; rtd 94; Perm to Offic *Leic* 94-99; *S'wark* from 99. *6 Montague Grange Court, Kidbrooke Gardens, London SE3 0PD* Tel (020) 8305 2150

PHELPS, Ian Ronald. b 28. FLS58 Lon Univ BSc53 PhD57. Chich Th Coll 57. **d** 59 **p** 60. C Brighton Gd Shep Preston *Chich* 59-61; C Sullington 62-64; C Storrington 62-64; R Newtimber w Pyecombe 64-68; V Brighton St Luke 68-74; TV Brighton Resurr 74-76; V Peacehaven 76-94; rtd 94; Perm to Offic *Chich* from 94. *2 Kingston Green, Seaford BN25 4NB* Tel (01323) 899511

PHENNA, Timothy Peter. b 69. Ridley Hall Cam BTh01. **d** 01 **p** 02. C Woodseats St Chad *Sheff* from 01. *25 Greenhill Road, Sheffield S8 0BA* Tel 0114-274 9394 E-mail tpphenna@aol.com

PHILBRICK, Gary James. b 57. Southn Univ BA78 K Alfred's Coll Win CertEd79 ACertCM84 MA(Theol)00 Edin Univ BD86. Edin Th Coll 83. **d** 86 **p** 87. C Southampton Maybush St Pet *Win* 86-90; R Fawley 90-00; P-in-c Swaythling from 00. *Swaythling Vicarage, 357 Burgess Road, Southampton SO16 3BD* Tel (023) 8055 4231 Fax 8067 9787 E-mail gary.philbrick@dial.pipex.com

PHILIP, Peter Wells. b 35. Ridley Hall Cam 64. **d** 67 **p** 68. C Tollington Park St Mark w St Anne *Lon* 67-70; C Battersea St Pet *S'wark* 70-72; Hon C Kennington St Mark 72-73; New Zealand 74-92 and from 94; Hon C Auckland St Paul 74; V Titirangi 74-80; Hon C Blockhouse Bay 80-92; Past Dir Chr Advance Min 80-84; Dir Evang Fellowship of NZ 87-90; C Finchley Ch Ch *Lon* 92-93; V Frankton 94-00; rtd 00. *608 Rolleston Street, Thames 2801, New Zealand* Tel (0064) (7) 868 5028 E-mail peterphilip@paradise.net.nz

PHILIP BARTHOLOMEW, Brother. *See* KENNEDY, Brother Philip Bartholomew

PHILIPPINES, Prime Bishop of the Episcopal Church in the. *See* SOLIBA, The Most Revd Ignacio Capuyan

PHILLIP, Isaiah Ezekiel. b 59. Univ of W Indies BA88. Codrington Coll Barbados 85. **d** 88 **p** 89. C St Jo Cathl Antigua 88-91; R St Geo Dominica 91-96; R All SS Antigua 96-01; P-in-c Handsworth St Mich *Birm* from 02. *St Michael's Vicarage, 20 Soho Avenue, Birmingham B18 5LB* Tel 0121-554 3521 Mobile 07985-680705 E-mail phillipisaiah@hotmail.com

PHILLIPS, Andrew Graham. b 58. Ex Univ BSc79. Chich Th Coll 84. **d** 87 **p** 88. C Frankby w Greasby *Ches* 87-89; C Liv St Chris Norris Green *Liv* 89-92; CF 92-97; Chapl RN from 00. *Royal Naval Chaplaincy Service, Room 203, Victory Building, HM Naval Base, Portsmouth PO1 3LS* Tel (023) 9272 7903 Fax 9272 7111

PHILLIPS, Canon Anthony Charles Julian. b 36. Lon Univ BD63 AKC63 G&C Coll Cam PhD67 St Jo Coll Ox MA75 DPhil80. Coll of Resurr Mirfield 66. **d** 66 **p** 67. C-in-c Chesterton Gd Shep CD *Ely* 66-69; Dean, Chapl and Fell Trin Hall Cam 69-74; Hon Bp's Chapl *Nor* 70-71; Chapl and Fell St Jo Coll Ox 75-86; Lect Th Jes Coll Ox 75-86; Lect Th Hertf Coll Ox 84-86; Hd Master K Sch Cant 86-96; Hon Can Cant Cathl *Cant* 87-96; Can Th Truro Cathl *Truro* 86-02; Perm to Offic from 02; rtd 01. *10 St Peter's Road, Flushing, Falmouth TR11 5TP* Tel (01326) 377217

PHILLIPS, Mrs Audrey Katherine. b 32. Lorain Coll Ohio BS73. Ox Min Course 88. **d** 91 **p** 94. NSM Princes Risborough w Ilmer *Ox* 91-94; P Assoc Marco Is St Mark USA 94-98; NSM Akeman

Ox 98-00. *1 The Chestnuts, Kirtlington, Kidlington OX5 3UB* Tel (01869) 350194 E-mail 110145,601@compuserve.com

PHILLIPS, Benjamin Guy. b 75. Wycliffe Hall Ox. **d** 02 **p** 03. C Cockermouth w Embleton and Wythop *Carl* from 02. *35 Gable Avenue, Cockermouth CA13 9RJ*

PHILLIPS, Benjamin Lambert Meyrick. b 64. K Coll Cam BA86 MA90. Ridley Hall Cam 87. **d** 90 **p** 91. C Wareham *Sarum* 90-94; C Chipping Barnet w Arkley *St Alb* 94-96; V Bodicote *Ox* from 96. *The Vicarage, Wykham Lane, Bodicote, Banbury OX15 4BW* Tel (01295) 270174

PHILLIPS, Beryl. *See* PHILLIPS, Mrs Elizabeth Beryl

PHILLIPS, Brian Edward Dorian William. b 36. Bris Univ BA58. Ripon Hall Ox 58. **d** 60 **p** 61. Chapl RAF 64-68; Hon C Fringford w Hethe and Newton Purcell *Ox* 68-73; Chapl Howell's Sch Denbigh 73-76; C Cleobury Mortimer w Hopton Wafers *Heref* 76-80; V Dixton 80-02; rtd 02. *37 Duxmere Drive, Ross-on-Wye HR9 5UW* Tel (01989) 562993 Mobile 07712-071558 E-mail brianphillips@u-genie.co.uk

PHILLIPS, Canon Brian Robert. b 31. Clare Coll Cam BA53 MA57. Linc Th Coll 54. **d** 56 **p** 57. C Tuffley *Glouc* 56-59; C Southgate Ch Ch *Lon* 59-62; R Luckington w Alderton *Bris* 62-69; V Highworth w Sevenhampton and Inglesham etc 69-84; Hon Can Bris Cathl 84-90; P-in-c Long Newnton 84-87; P-in-c Crudwell w Ashley, Crudwell, Hankerton, Long Newnton etc 87-90; rtd 90; Perm to Offic *Portsm* from 90; Perm to Offic *Win* from 90. *Hannington, Hospital Road, Shirrell Heath, Southampton SO32 2JR* Tel (01329) 834547

PHILLIPS, The Very Revd Christopher John. b 46. **d** 79 **p** 80. Hong Kong from 79; Chapl Hong Kong Cathl 83-87; Dean Hong Kong from 88. *c/o St John's Cathedral, Garden Road, Hong Kong* Tel (00852) 523 4157 Fax 521 7830 E-mail cjphil@netvigator.com

PHILLIPS, David Arthur. b 36. S Dios Minl Tr Scheme 90. **d** 94 **p** 95. NSM Canford Magna *Sarum* from 94. *32 Lynwood Drive, Wimborne BH21 1UG* Tel (01202) 848725

PHILLIPS, David Elwyn. b 17. St D Coll Lamp 62. **d** 64 **p** 65. C Ferndale *Llan* 64-68; C Port Talbot St Theodore 68-70; V Abercanaid 70-87; rtd 87; Perm to Offic *Llan* from 87. *Carmel, 13 Tyleri Gardens, Victor Road, Abertillery NP13 1EZ*

PHILLIPS, David Keith. b 61. New Coll Ox MA90. St Jo Coll Dur BA90. **d** 91 **p** 92. C Denton Holme *Carl* 91-94; C Chadderton Ch Ch *Man* 94-98; Sec Ch Soc from 98; Public Preacher *St Alb* from 98. *The Flat, 16 Rosslyn Road, Watford WD18 0JY* Tel (01923) 235111 E-mail director@churchsociety.org.uk

PHILLIPS, Edward Leigh Bill. b 12. St Edm Hall Ox BA34 MA47. Wycliffe Hall Ox 33. **d** 35 **p** 36. Asst Chapl Dean Close Sch Cheltenham 35-37; C Highfield *Ox* 37-38; C-in-c Patcham Chr the K CD *Chich* 39-41; CF (EC) 41-46; R Ide Hill *Roch* 46-49; V Moulsecoomb *Chich* 49-52; V Kingston w Iford 52-75; V Iford w Kingston and Rodmell 75-78; RD Lewes 65-77; rtd 78; Perm to Offic *Glouc* from 78. *35 Woodland Green, Upton St Leonards, Gloucester GL4 8BD* Tel (01452) 619894

PHILLIPS, Edwin George. b 35. N Wales Baptist Coll 64. **d** 03 **p** 03. NSM Morriston *S & B* from 03. *146 Lingfield Avenue, Port Talbot SA12 6QA* Tel (01639) 886784 Mobile 07815-969913

PHILLIPS, Mrs Elizabeth Beryl. b 34. **d** 94 **p** 95. C N Farnborough *Guildf* 94-99; rtd 99; Perm to Offic *Sarum* from 00. *8 Byron Road, Wimborne BH21 1NX* Tel (01202) 883328

PHILLIPS, Mrs Emma Catharine. b 62. St Anne's Coll Ox BA84. Trin Coll Bris BA99. **d** 99 **p** 00. C Shawbury *Lich* 99-01; C Moreton Corbet 99-01; C Stanton on Hine Heath 99-01; C Cen Telford 01-02; TV from 03. *Church House, 15 Carwood, Stirchley, Telford TF3 1YA* Tel (01952) 595482

PHILLIPS, Canon Frederick Wallace (Ferdie). b 12. MC43. Univ of Wales BA34. St Mich Coll Llan 34. **d** 36 **p** 37. C Fochriw w Deri *Llan* 36-38; C Roath 38-40; CF 40-46; C Epsom Common Ch Ch *Guildf* 46-47; R Harrietsham *Cant* 47-56; V Faversham 56-64; V Margate St Jo 64-74; Hon Can Cant Cathl 66-84; R Smarden 74-82; R Biddenden 80-82; rtd 82; Perm to Offic *Cant* from 84; Almoner Cant Cathl 85-93; Retirement Officer (Cant Adnry) 93-01. *15A The Precincts, Canterbury CT1 2EL* Tel (01227) 450891

PHILLIPS, Canon Geoffrey John. b 23. BNC Ox BA47 MA56. Ridley Hall Cam 54. **d** 56 **p** 57. C Kettering St Andr *Pet* 56-59; C Tideswell *Derby* 59-62; Ceylon 62-65; R Gillingham w Geldeston and Stockton *Nor* 65-70; V Eaton 70-81; RD Nor S 71-81; Hon Can Nor Cathl 78-81; Chapl Vienna w Budapest and Prague *Eur* 81-87; rtd 87; Perm to Offic *Nor* from 87. *Mere Farmhouse, White Heath Road, Bergh Apton, Norwich NR15 1AY* Tel (01508) 480656

PHILLIPS, Horace George. b 38. Man Univ BA60 Birm Univ DipTh62 MEd84. Qu Coll Birm 60. **d** 62 **p** 63. C Wotton St Mary *Glouc* 62-65; V Standish w Hardwicke and Haresfield 65-68; C Cirencester 68-74; V Churchdown St Jo 74-79; P-in-c Beckford w Ashton under Hill 79-85; P-in-c Overbury w Alstone, Teddington and Lt Washbourne *Worc* 84-85; V Overbury w Teddington, Alstone etc 85-88; P-in-c Peopleton and White Ladies Aston w Churchill etc 88-94; R 94-02; Dioc Sch Officer 88-97; rtd 02. *16 Fountain Gardens, Evesham WR11 1JY* Tel (01386) 47038

PHILLIPS, Ivor Lynn. b 44. Leeds Univ BA70. Cuddesdon Coll 69. **d** 71 **p** 72. C Bedlinog *Llan* 71-73; C Roath 73-77; TV Wolverhampton All SS *Lich* 77-78; TV Wolverhampton 78-81; Chapl Charing Cross Hosp Lon 81-91; Chapl Milan w Genoa and Lugano *Eur* 91-94; C Hampstead St Jo Lon 95-00; V Whitton St Aug from 00. *St Augustine's Vicarage, Hospital Bridge Road, Whitton, Twickenham TW2 6DE* Tel (020) 8894 3764 Fax 8894 4543 E-mail staug@respite.demon.co.uk

PHILLIPS, Mrs Janet Elizabeth. b 37. Bp Grosseteste Coll CertEd57. EMMTC 81. **dss** 84 **d** 87 **p** 94. Wisbech St Aug *Ely* 84-86; Cambridge St Jas 86-87; Par Dn 87-91; Par Dn Wisbech SS Pet and Paul 91-94; C 94-02; rtd 02. *St Peter's Lodge, Love Lane, Wisbech PE13 1HP* Tel (01945) 476149

PHILLIPS, Jeffery Llewellyn. b 32. Sarum & Wells Th Coll. **d** 87 **p** 88. C Ringwood *Win* 87-90; V Somborne w Ashley 90-93; rtd 93; Perm to Offic *Win* from 93. *Queen's Acre, 3 Solent Avenue, Lymington SO41 3SD* Tel (01590) 673955

PHILLIPS, Mrs Jennifer Jean. b 36. Guildf Dioc Min Course 98. **d** 01 **p** 02. OLM New Haw *Guildf* from 01. *20 Lindsay Road, New Haw, Addlestone KT15 3BD* Tel (01932) 343853 E-mail jenny@20lindsayroad.fsnet.co.uk

PHILLIPS, John David. b 29. G&C Coll Cam BA50 MA54 CertEd69. SW Minl Tr Course 85. **d** 87 **p** 88. NSM St Martin w E and W Looe *Truro* 87-88; NSM St Merryn 88-94; rtd 94; Perm to Offic *Truro* from 94. *Restings, Plaidy, Looe PL13 1LF* Tel (01503) 262121

PHILLIPS, John Eldon. b 50. Univ of Wales (Cardiff) BEd85 MEd92. St Mich Coll Llan. **d** 90 **p** 91. NSM Merthyr Cynog and Dyffryn Honddu etc *S & B* 90-94; Lic to Offic *St D* 94-99; NSM Ystradgynlais *S & B* 95-99; Chapl Trin Coll Carmarthen 95-99; P-in-c Llanrhidian w Llanmadoc and Cheriton *S & B* from 99. *The Vicarage, Llanrhidian, Swansea SA3 1EH* Tel (01792) 390144

PHILLIPS, John Reginald. b 64. St Steph Ho Ox BTh93. **d** 96 **p** 97. C Bognor *Chich* 96-99; TV Moulsecoomb 99-00; C Hove from 00. *83 Davigdor Road, Hove BN3 1RA* Tel (01273) 733971

PHILLIPS, John William Burbridge. b 39. Dur Univ BSc60 Lon Univ BD68. Tyndale Hall Bris 65. **d** 68 **p** 69. C Barton Seagrave *Pet* 68-71; C Northampton All SS w St Kath 71-75; R Irthlingborough 75-88; V Weedon Lois w Plumpton and Moreton Pinkney etc 88-95; rtd 95; Perm to Offic *Pet* 95-96. *Finca Morito 8, 12579 Alcoceber, Castellon, Spain*

PHILLIPS, Joseph Benedict. b 11. **d** 37 **p** 38. In RC Ch 37-43; C St Mary-at-Lambeth *S'wark* 47-50; C Woking St Jo *Guildf* 50-53; V Burton in Kendal *Carl* 53-59; V Bradf St Andr *Bradf* 59-66; rtd 76. *100 Ruskin Avenue, Lincoln LN2 4BT* Tel (01522) 534411

PHILLIPS, Judith Mary. b 46. Reading Univ BA67 Cardiff Coll of Educn PGCE86. St Mich Coll Llan 93. **d** 95 **p** 97. Lect Neath Coll 84-00; NSM Clydach *S & B* 95-00; Dep Chapl HM Pris Bris 00-01; Chapl HM Pris Eastwood Park from 01. *HM Prison, Eastwood Park, Falfield, Wotton-under-Edge GL12 8DB* Tel (01454) 262100 Fax 262101

PHILLIPS, Canon Kenneth John. b 37. Coll of Resurr Mirfield 67. **d** 67 **p** 68. C Blackb St Jas *Blackb* 67-69; C-in-c Lea CD 70-80; V Lea 80-84; P-in-c Priors Hardwick, Priors Marston and Wormleighton *Cov* 85-02; Sec Dioc Adv Cttee 85-99; RD Southam 89-95; Hon Can Cov Cathl 94-02; Dioc Rural Chs Officer 00-02; rtd 02; Hon C Gisburn *Bradf* from 02; Hon C Hellifield from 02. *10 Park Avenue, Hellifield, Skipton BD23 4EZ* Tel (01729) 850340 E-mail kcanonic@aol.com

PHILLIPS, Lamont Wellington Sanderson. b 33. S'wark Ord Course 73. **d** 76 **p** 78. NSM Tottenham St Paul *Lon* 76-83; P-in-c Upper Clapton St Matt 83-88; V 88-97; rtd 98. *24 Berkshire Gardens, London N18 2LF* Tel (020) 8807 7025

PHILLIPS, Lynn. *see* PHILLIPS, Ivor Lynn

PHILLIPS, Canon Martin Nicholas. b 32. Em Coll Cam BA57 MA61. Linc Th Coll 57. **d** 59 **p** 60. C Stocking Farm CD *Leic* 59-63; V Sheff Gillcar St Silas *Sheff* 63-71; V Birstall *Leic* 72-82; R Wanlip 72-82; V Birstall and Wanlip 82-88; TR Loughborough Em and St Mary in Charnwood 88-96; Hon Can Leic Cathl 90-96; rtd 96; Perm to Offic *Leic* from 96. *Foxhollow, 40A Lodge Close, Barrow upon Soar, Loughborough LE12 8ZL* Tel (01509) 416361

PHILLIPS, Mary Alice. b 53. Ripon Coll Cuddesdon 97. **d** 99 **p** 00. C Addiscombe St Mildred *S'wark* 99-02; TV Basingstoke *Win* from 02. *219 Paddock Road, Basingstoke RG22 6QP* Tel (01256) 464393 E-mail map13@tinyworld.co.uk

PHILLIPS, Michael John. b 54. JP. Trent Poly BA77. Sarum & Wells Th Coll 78. **d** 81 **p** 82. C Killay *S & B* 81-83; C Treboeth 83-85; Hong Kong 85-88; Japan 88-91; TR Is of Scilly *Truro* 91-95; TR Cwmbran *Mon* from 95. *The Rectory, Clomendy Road, Cwmbran NP44 3LS* Tel (01633) 489718

PHILLIPS, Michael Thomas. b 46. CQSW81. Linc Th Coll 89. **d** 90 **p** 91. C Hyson Green *S'well* 90-91; C Basford w Hyson Green 91-93; Chapl HM Pris Gartree 93-99; Chapl HM Pris Nottm from 99. *The Chaplaincy Office, HM Prison Nottingham, Perry Road, Sherwood, Nottingham NG5 3AG* Tel 0115-962 5022 Fax 960 3605

PHILLIPS, Mrs Patricia. b 45. Glouc Sch of Min 83. **dss** 86 **d** 87 **p** 94. Newent and Gorsley w Cliffords Mesne *Glouc* 86-95; C 87-95; P-in-c Childswyckham w Aston Somerville, Buckland etc 95-97; R 97-00; R Redmarley D'Abitot, Bromesberrow, Pauntley etc from 00. *The Rectory, Redmarley, Gloucester GL19 3HS* Tel (01531) 620715 Fax as telephone E-mail revpp@tesco.net

PHILLIPS, Patrick Noble Stowell. b 22. Edin Univ MA50 CertEd63. ALCD52. **d** 52 **p** 53. CMS 52-55; St Mark Nibo Nisi Niger 52-55; St Paul Awka 52-55; C Mossley Hill St Matt and St Jas *Liv* 55-57; V Milverton, Milbank and Elma Canada 57-60; Hd Ang Grammar Sch Benin 60-63; R Moresby *Carl* 63-66; V Mapleton and Clandeboye Canada 66-71; R Arthuret 71-88; rtd 88. *14 Gipsy Lane, Reading RG6 7HB* Tel 0118-926 4654

PHILLIPS, Miss Pauline. b 54. LNSM course 96. **d** 96 **p** 97. OLM Mossley *Man* from 96. *38 Lorne Street, Mossley, Ashton-under-Lyne OL5 0HQ* Tel (01457) 832363

PHILLIPS, Percy Graham. b 26. St Aid Birkenhead 46. **d** 51 **p** 52. C Wallasey St Hilary *Ches* 51-54; C Thrybergh *Sheff* 54-58; C Guernsey St Michel du Valle *Win* 58-60; V Heytesbury w Tytherington and Knook *Sarum* 60-65; V Stonebridge St Mich *Lon* 65-70; R Vernham Dean w Linkenholt and Upton *Win* 70-78; C Farnham *Guildf* 78-82; TV Cove St Jo 82-89; rtd 89. *22 Charts Close, Cranleigh GU6 8BH*

PHILLIPS, Peter. b 26. Oak Hill Th Coll 63. **d** 65 **p** 66. C Eastbourne All SS *Chich* 65-69; C St Alb St Paul *St Alb* 69-73; V Riseley w Bletsoe 73-84; R Arley *Cov* 84-91; rtd 91; Perm to Offic *B & W* from 91; Clergy Retirement and Widows' Officer from 99. *Milford House, 10 Albert Road, Clevedon BS21 7RP* Tel (01275) 875801

PHILLIPS, Peter Miles Lucas. b 44. Reading Univ BA66 QUB DipEd69 Univ of Wales (Cardiff) MEd88. St Mich Coll Llan DMS93. **d** 92 **p** 93. Dep Hd Teacher Dynevor Sch 82-96; NSM Llangyfelach *S & B* 92-96; Dep Chapl HM Pris Liv 96-97; Chapl HM Pris Usk and HM Pris and YOI Prescoed 97-01; Chapl HM Pris Bris from 01. *The Chaplain's Office, HM Prison, Cambridge Road, Bristol BS7 8PS* Tel 0117-980 8100

PHILLIPS, Robin Michael. b 33. AKC58. **d** 59 **p** 60. C Hanwell St Mellitus *Lon* 59-61; C St Margaret's-on-Thames 61-64; C Hangleton *Chich* 64-68; V Mellor *Derby* 68-95; RD Glossop 89-93; rtd 95; Hon C Bredekirk *Carl* 95-96. *87 George Lane, Bredbury, Stockport SK6 1DH*

PHILLIPS, Canon Stephen. b 38. QUB BA60. Linc Th Coll 60. **d** 62 **p** 63. C Waddington *Linc* 62-65; C Gt Grimsby St Jas 65-72; V Kirmington 72-97; V Limber Magna w Brocklesby 73-97; V Brocklesby Park from 97; R Croxton from 97; RD Yarborough 92-00; Can and Preb Linc Cathl from 98. *Great Limber Vicarage, 2 Church Lane, Great Limber, Grimsby DN37 8JN* Tel (01469) 560641 Fax 569515

PHILLIPS, Thomas Wynford. b 15. Univ of Wales BA37 BD40. St Mich Coll Llan. **d** 43 **p** 44. C Shotton *St As* 43-46; C Rhyl 46-50; C Hall Green Ascension *Birm* 50-52; R Shustoke 52-55; P-in-c Maxstoke 52-55; V Clay Cross *Derby* 55-68; R Upton Magna *Lich* 68-73; V Withington 68-73; R Roche *Truro* 73-80; R Withiel 73-80; RD St Austell 76-80; rtd 80; Perm to Offic *Truro* from 80. *Brynawelon, Wheal Quoit Avenue, St Agnes TR5 0SJ* Tel (01872) 552862

PHILLIPS, Timothy Leo. b 72. Bris Univ BSc95 PhD99. Trin Coll Bris BA01 MA02. **d** 02 **p** 03. C Leic H Trin w St Jo *Leic* from 02. *46 Brading Road, Leicester LE3 9BG* Tel 0116-262 4452 E-mail tim@bradingroad.fsnet.co.uk

PHILLIPS-SMITH, Edward Charles. b 50. AKC71. **d** 73 **p** 74. C Wolverhampton *Lich* 73-76; Chapl St Pet Colleg Sch Wolv 77-87; Hon C Wolverhampton *Lich* 78-87; V Stevenage St Pet Broadwater *St Alb* 87-89; Chapl Millfield Jun Sch Somerset 89-95; Lic to Offic *Ox* from 95. *Papplewick School, Windsor Road, Ascot SL5 7LH* Tel (01344) 621488

PHILLIPSON, Christopher Quintin. b 14. Ch Coll Cam BA36 MA40. Ridley Hall Cam 36. **d** 38 **p** 39. C Turnham Green Ch Ch *Lon* 38-40; C Stamford Hill St Ann 40-44; CMS Miss India 44-54; V Southbourne *Chich* 54-62; R W Thorney 56-62; R Ardingly 62-70; V Aldingbourne 70-81; rtd 81; Perm to Offic *Chich* from 82. *15 Ramsay Hall, 11-13 Byron Road, Worthing BN11 3HN* Tel (01903) 214860

PHILLIPSON-MASTERS, Miss Susan Patricia. b 52. FIST76 ACP80 Sussex Univ CertEd73 K Alfred's Coll Win BEd81 ACertCM99. Trin Coll Bris DipHE88. **d** 89 **p** 95. C Saltford w Corston and Newton St Loe *B & W* 89-94; C Uphill 94-97; C Nailsea Ch Ch w Tickenham 97-98; P-in-c Tredington and Darlingscott w Newbold on Stour *Cov* 98-00; P-in-c The Stanleys *Glouc* from 00. *The Rectory, Church Road, Leonard Stanley, Stonehouse GL10 3NP* Tel (01453) 826698 Fax 826712 E-mail sue.pm@btinternet.com

PHILLPOT, Donald John. b 27. St Jo Coll Dur BA53 DipTh55. **d** 55 **p** 56. C Southmead *Bris* 55-60; C Brislington St Luke 60-63; R Stapleton *Heref* 63-68; V Dorrington 63-68; P-in-c Astley Abbotts 68-78; R Bridgnorth w Tasley 68-78; V Lillington *Cov* 78-92; rtd 92; Perm to Offic *Glouc* from 92. *22 Williams Orchard, Highnam, Gloucester GL2 8EL* Tel (01452) 386844

PHILP (née NOBLE), Mrs Ann Carol. b 42. Sarum Dioc Tr Coll CertEd63 Southn Univ MA(Ed)89 MCIPD. S Dios Minl Tr Scheme 93. **d** 95 **p** 96. Dir Sarum Chr Cen *Sarum* 93-98; Chapl Sarum Cathl 95-02; Dioc NSM Officer 98-02; P-in-c Woodford Valley from 02; Dioc Dir of Ords from 02. *The Vicarage, Middle Woodford, Salisbury SP4 6NR* Tel (01722) 782310 E-mail ann.philp@salisbury.anglican.org

PHILPOTT, Barbara May. *See* WILKINSON, Barbara May

PHILPOTT, Canon John David. b 43. Leic Univ BA64. Trin Coll Bris 69. **d** 72 **p** 73. C Knutsford St Jo *Ches* 72-75; C Toft 72-75; C Bickenhill w Elmdon *Birm* 75-79; V Birm St Luke 79-91; RD Birm City 83-88; Hon Can Birm Cathl 89-91; V Chilvers Coton w Astley *Cov* 91-00; RD Nuneaton 95-00; Hon Can Cov Cathl 96-00; P-in-C Prague St Clem *Eur* from 00. *Vrsni 27, Praha 8, 18200 Kobylisy, Czech Republic* Tel (00420) (2) 688 8575 E-mail philpott@volny.cz

PHILPOTT, John Wilfred. b 44. K Coll Lon BD67 AKC67. **d** 68 **p** 69. C Norbury St Steph *Cant* 68-71; C Addiscombe St Mildred 71-75; V Whitfield w Guston 75-01; rtd 02. *9 Mannering Close, River, Dover CT17 0UD* Tel (01304) 825875

PHILPOTT, Ronald. b 38. IPFA69. Cranmer Hall Dur 88. **d** 89 **p** 90. NSM S Ossett *Wakef* 89-93; R Clitheroe St Jas *Blackb* 93-03; rtd 03. Perm to Offic *York* from 00. *8 Headland Close, Haxby, York YO32 3HW* Tel (01904) 758697

PHILPOTT, Preb Samuel. b 41. Kelham Th Coll 60. **d** 65 **p** 66. C Swindon New Town *Bris* 65-70; C Torquay St Martin Barton *Ex* 70-73; TV Withycombe Raleigh 73-76; V Shaldon 76-78; P-in-c Plymouth St Pet 78-80; V from 80; RD Plymouth Devonport 86-93 and 95-01; Preb Ex Cathl from 91. *St Peter's Vicarage, 23 Wyndham Square, Plymouth PL1 5EG* Tel (01752) 222007 Fax 257973 E-mail sam@plymstpeters.demon.co.uk

PHILPOTT-HOWARD, John Nigel. b 54. Univ of Wales Coll of Medicine MB, BCh77 FRCPath83. SEITE 99. **d** 02. NSM Shooters Hill Ch Ch *S'wark* from 02. *80 Charlton Road, London SE7 7EY* Tel (020) 8858 4692 E-mail jphilpotth@cs.com

PHILPS, Mark Seymour. b 51. Worc Coll Ox BA73 MA78 Lon Univ MA75 Nottm Univ BA79. St Jo Coll Nottm 77. **d** 80 **p** 81. C Chadwell Heath *Chelmsf* 80-83; C Woodford Wells 83-87; V Tipton St Matt *Lich* 87-02; C Roxeth *Lon* 02-03; TR from 03. *Christ Church Vicarage, Roxeth Hill, Harrow HA2 0JN* Tel (020) 8423 3168 E-mail mphilps@aol.com

PHILSON, James Alexander Summers (Hamish). b 20. Edin Th Coll 48. **d** 51 **p** 52. C Falkirk *Edin* 51-53; R Dunblane *St And* 53-62; Australia from 62; R Beverley 62-64; R Victoria Park 64-75; R Cottesloe 75-85; rtd 85. *38 Allenswood Road, Greenwood, W Australia 6024* Tel (0061) (8) 9447 9523 Mobile 0416-001620 E-mail jasp@smartchat.net.au

PHIPPS, David John. b 46. Bris Univ BSc68 Ex Univ PhD94 Nottm Univ PGCE69. Trin Coll Bris 75. **d** 78 **p** 79. C Madron w Morvah *Truro* 78-80; C Kenilworth St Jo *Cov* 80-83; TV Barnstaple *Ex* 83-95; I Abercraf w Callwen w Capel Coelbren *S & B* 95-02; P-in-c Gulval and Madron *Truro* from 02. *The Rectory, Madron, Penzance TR20 8SW* Tel (01736) 360992 E-mail phippsdv@dialstart.net

PHIPPS, Canon Frederick George. b 30. Kelham Th Coll 50. **d** 54 **p** 55. C Staveley *Derby* 54-59; Korea 59-65; Australia from 65; Can Ballarat Ch Cathl 84-95; rtd 95. *240 Lava Street, PO Box 297, Warrnambool, Vic, Australia 3280* Tel (0061) (3) 5562 6738

PHIPPS, John Maclean. b 14. Em Coll Cam BA38 MA50. Cuddesdon Coll 38. **d** 39 **p** 40. C Banbury *Ox* 39-41; P-in-c Cambois *Newc* 44-46; C Newport Pagnell *Ox* 47-53; V Speenhamland 53-71; V Buckland 72-79; V Littleworth 72-79; R Pusey 72-79; rtd 79; Perm to Offic *Chich* 84-93; Perm to Offic *St Alb* from 93. *Bushmead Court, Bushmead Avenue, Bedford MK40 3QW* Tel (01234) 365137

PHIZACKERLEY, The Ven Gerald Robert. b 29. Univ Coll Ox BA52 MA56. Wells Th Coll 52. **d** 54 **p** 55. C Carl St Barn *Carl* 54-57; Chapl Abingdon Sch 57-64; R Gaywood, Bawsey and Mintlyn *Nor* 64-78; RD Lynn 68-78; Hon Can Nor Cathl 75-78; Hon Can Derby Cathl *Derby* 78-96; P-in-c Ashford w Sheldon 78-90; Adn Chesterfield 78-96; rtd 96; Perm to Offic *Derby* and *Cov* from 96. *Archway Cottage, Hall Road, Leamington Spa CV32 5RA* Tel (01926) 332740

PHYPERS, David John. b 39. Leic Univ BA60 CertEd61 Lon Univ BD65. Linc Th Coll 76. **d** 78 **p** 79. NSM Normanton *Derby* 78-80; NSM Sinfin 80-87; Lic to Offic 87-88; P-in-c Denby and Horsley Woodhouse 88-00; P-in-c Wormhill, Peak Forest w Peak Dale and Dove Holes from 00; Adv for Chr Giving from 00. *Shalom, Hallsteads, Dove Holes, Buxton SK17 8BJ* Tel (01298) 813344 E-mail davidp@dial.webs.co.uk

PIACHAUD, Preb François Allen. b 12. Lon Univ BA32 BD35 Selw Coll Cam BA37 MA41. Westcott Ho Cam 37. **d** 37 **p** 38. C Walkergate *Newc* 37-40; C Edin St Jo *Edin* 40-44; V Wrangthorn *Ripon* 44-51; V Chelsea Ch Lon 51-86; Preb St Paul's Cathl 61-86; RD Chelsea 74-77; rtd 86; Perm to Offic *Ox* 86-96. *clo Dixon Ward Solicitors, 16 The Green, Richmond TW9 1QD* Tel (020) 8940 4401

PICK, David. b 44. Linc Th Coll 85. **d** 87 **p** 88. C Howden *York* 87-90; P-in-c Sledmere and Cowlam w Fridaythorpe, Fimer etc

90-91; V 91-96; rtd 96; Perm to Offic *York* from 96. *Westwood Close, 16 North Street, Nafferton, Driffield YO25 4JW* Tel (01377) 240360

PICK, William Harry. b 23. Open Univ BA77. St Aid Birkenhead 51. **d** 54 **p** 55. C Wigan St Geo *Liv* 54-57; V Newton-le-Willows 57-67; V Stoneycroft All SS 67-79; R N Meols 79-88; rtd 88; Perm to Offic *Liv* from 88. *8 Morley Road, Southport PR9 9JS* Tel (01704) 541428

PICKARD, Canon Frank Eustace. b 31. Lon Univ BSc52 St Cath Soc Ox BA56 MA63. St Steph Ho Ox. **d** 57 **p** 58. C Haydock St Jas *Liv* 57-59; C Davenham *Ches* 59-60; Asst Master St Dunstan's Sch Lon 60-63; Min Can Pet Cathl *Pet* 63-72; P-in-c Newborough 67-68; V 68-72; R Isham w Pytchley 72-76; R Abington 76-96; Can Pet Cathl 86-02; rtd 97; P-in-c Weedon Lois w Plumpton and Moreton Pinkney etc *Pet* 97-02; Perm to Offic from 02. *19 Watersmeet, Northampton NN1 5SQ* Tel (01604) 239667

PICKARD, Stephen Kim. b 52. Newc Univ Aus BCom74 Van Mildert Coll Dur PhD90. Melbourne Coll of Div BD79 St Jo Coll Morpeth 77. **d** 80 **p** 80. Australia 80-82 and from 91; C Singleton 80-82; C Dur St Cuth *Dur* 82-84; Chapl Van Mildert Coll Dur 84-90; Chapl Trev Coll Dur 84-90; Lect United Th Coll Sydney 91-97; Dir St Mark's Nat Th Cen from 98; Assoc Prof and Hd Th Chas Sturt Univ from 99. *St Mark's National Theological Centre, 15 Blackall Street, Barton, ACT, Australia 2607* Tel (0061) (2) 6249 8647 or 6273 1572 Mobile 419-638020 Fax (2) 6273 4067 E-mail spickard@csu.edu.au

PICKARD, William Priestley. b 31. Clifton Th Coll 56. **d** 59 **p** 60. C Upper Tulse Hill St Matthias *S'wark* 59-63; Asst Warden Shaftesbury Crusade Bris from 64; rtd 96. *Circle in the Square, 45 Totterdown Road, Weston-super-Mare BS23 4LJ* Tel (01934) 628994

PICKEN, David Anthony. b 63. Lon Univ BA84 Kent Univ PGCE85 Nottm Univ MA96. Linc Th Coll 87. **d** 90 **p** 91. C Worth *Chich* 90-93; TV Wordsley *Worc* 93-97; TR from 97; RD Himley from 01. *The Rectory, 13 Dunsley Drive, Wordsley, Stourbridge DY8 5RA* Tel (01384) 277215 E-mail dap@dircon.co.uk

PICKEN, James Hugh. b 51. Victoria Univ (BC) BMus75 ARCT73 Ox Univ MA94. Ripon Coll Cuddesdon BA79. **d** 80 **p** 81. C Jarrow *Dur* 80-83; SSF 83-93; Perm to Offic *Sarum* 86-92; Guardian Alnmouth Friary 92-94; Lic to Offic *Newc* 92-94; Canada from 94. *929-4th Street NW, Calgary AB, Canada T2N 1P4* Tel (001) (403) 270 9661

PICKERING, David Colville. b 41. Kelham Th Coll 61. **d** 66 **p** 67. C Chaddesden St Phil *Derby* 66-70; C New Mills 70-72; C Buxton 72-74; V Chesterfield St Aug 74-90; R Whittington 90-99; P-in-c Hathersage 99; P-in-c Bamford 99; R Hathersage w Bamford and Derwent from 00. *The Vicarage, Church Bank, Hathersage, Hope Valley S32 1AJ* Tel (01433) 650215 E-mail crispy@kupola.com

PICKERING, The Ven Fred. b 19. St Pet Hall Ox BA41 MA45. St Aid Birkenhead 41. **d** 43 **p** 44. C Leyland St Andr *Blackb* 43-46; C Islington St Mary *Lon* 46-48; NE Area Sec CPAS 48-51; V Burton All SS *Lich* 51-56; V Carl St Jo *Carl* 56-63; V Chitts Hill St Cuth *Lon* 63-74; RD E Haringey 68-73; Adn Hampstead 74-84; rtd 84; Perm to Offic *Pet* 84-93; Perm to Offic *Linc* from 93. *16 The Close, Easton on the Hill, Stamford PE9 3NA* Tel (01780) 481318

PICKERING, Geoffrey Craig. b 40. Newc Coll of Arts NDD61 Leic Coll of Art & Design ATD62 Leic Univ CertEd62. S Dios Minl Tr Scheme 90. **d** 93 **p** 94. C Horsham *Chich* 93-97; V Heathfield from 97. *The Vicarage, Old Heathfield, Heathfield TN21 9AB* Tel (01435) 862457

PICKERING, John Alexander. b 41. TCD BA63 MA66. CITC 65. **d** 65 **p** 66. C Magheralin *D & D* 65-67; C-in-c Outeragh *K, E & A* 67-68; I 68-71; Deputation Sec Hibernian Bible Soc 71-74; C-in-c Drumgoon and Ashfield 74-80; I Keady w Armaghbreague and Derrynoose *Arm* 80-83; I Drumcree from 83. *Drumcree Rectory, 78 Drumcree Road, Portadown, Craigavon BT62 1PE* Tel (028) 3833 3711

PICKERING, John David. b 38. **d** 86 **p** 86. NSM Ellon *Ab* 86-88; NSM Cruden Bay 86-88; Ind Chapl *Dur* 88-97; TV Jarrow 91-97; P-in-c Newton Hall 97-02; TV Dur N from 02. *31 York Crescent, Durham DH1 5PT* Tel 0191-386 8049

PICKERING, John Michael Staunton. b 34. Sarum & Wells Th Coll 71. **d** 72 **p** 73. C Gaywood, Bawsey and Mintlyn *Nor* 72-77; P-in-c Foulsham 77-81; R Foulsham w Hindolveston and Guestwick 81-88; P-in-c Bacton w Edingthorpe w Witton and Ridlington 88-98; rtd 98. *East Lodge, Wardley Hill Road, Kirby Cane, Bungay NR35 2PQ*

PICKERING, John Roger. b 28. Fitzw Ho Cam BA52 MA56. Linc Th Coll 62. **d** 63 **p** 66. C Haxby w Wigginton *York* 63-64; CF 66-69; C Folkestone H Trin w Ch Ch *Cant* 71-73; P-in-c Buckland Newton *Sarum* 73-77; P-in-c Wootton Glanville and Holnest 73-77; P-in-c Osmington w Poxwell 77-80; C Eston w Normanby *York* 83-84; P-in-c Swine 84-90; rtd 90; Perm to Offic *Truro* from 90. *The Bull Pens, Treworder Farm, Ruan Minor,*

Helston TR12 7JL Tel (01326) 290908 Fax 0870-0553945
E-mail pickering@ministry.demon.co.uk
PICKERING, Malcolm. b 37. Sarum Th Coll 65. **d** 68 **p** 69. C
Milton *Portsm* 68-70; C Stanmer w Falmer and Moulsecoomb
Chich 70-75; Chapl Brighton Coll of Educn 71-75; V Hooe *Chich*
75-80; R Ninfield 75-80; V Ventnor H Trin *Portsm* 80-88; V
Ventnor St Catb 80-88; Chapl St Cath Sch Ventnor 87-88; V
Marton *Blackb* 88-97; P-in-c Badingham w Bruisyard,
Cransford and Dennington *St E* 97-99; V Leiston from 99.
St Margaret's Vicarage, 2 King Edward Road, Leiston IP16 4HQ
Tel (01728) 831059 Fax as telephone
E-mail malcolm@totland-a.freeserve.co.uk
PICKERING, Mark Penrhyn. b 36. Liv Univ BA59 St Cath Coll
Ox BA62 MA67. Wycliffe Hall Ox 60. **d** 63 **p** 64. C Claughton
cum Grange *Ches* 63-67; C Newland St Jo *York* 67-72; TV
Marfleet 72-76; V Kingston upon Hull St Nic 76-85; V
Elloughton and Brough w Brantingham 85-88; Chapl R Hull
Hosps NHS Trust 88-01; Perm to Offic *York* from 01.
*St Nicholas, Beech Hill Road, Swanland, North Ferriby
HU14 3QY* Tel (01482) 634892
PICKERING, Stephen Philip. b 52. St Jo Coll York CertEd75.
Coll of Resurr Mirfield 77. **d** 79 **p** 80. C Wallsend St Luke *Newc*
79-82; Chapl RN 82-92; C-in-c Ryecroft St Nic CD *Sheff* 92-97;
V Ryecroft St Nic 97-01; V Plymouth St Simon and St Mary *Ex*
from 01. *St Simon's Vicarage, 86 Edith Avenue, Plymouth
PL4 8TL* Tel (01752) 660654
PICKERING, William Stuart Frederick. b 22. K Coll Lon BD49
AKC49 PhD58 Manitoba Univ Hon DCL81. **d** 50 **p** 51. C
Frodingham *Linc* 50-53; Lic to Offic Guildf & Linc 55-56; Tutor
K Coll Lon 53-56; Canada 58-66; Lic to Offic *Newc* 66-87; rtd
87; Perm to Offic *Ely* 87-97. *1 Brookfield Road, Coton, Cambridge
CB3 7PT* Tel (01954) 210525
PICKETT, Brian Laurence. b 48. Reading Univ BA70. Qu Coll
Birm BA73 MA77 Ripon Coll Cuddesdon. **d** 88 **p** 88. C
Highcliffe w Hinton Admiral *Win* 88-91; P-in-c Colbury 91-01;
P-in-c W End from 01. *St James's Vicarage, Elizabeth Close,
Southampton SO30 3LT* Tel (023) 8047 2180 Fax 8047 7661
PICKETT, Ms Joanna Elizabeth. b 53. Leic Univ BA74 MA80
Lon Univ MTh95. Wycliffe Hall Ox DipTh89. **d** 89 **p** 94. Chapl
Southn Univ *Win* 89-94; C N Stoneham 94-95; NSM Colbury
97-01; NSM W End from 01. *St James's Vicarage, Elizabeth
Close, Southampton SO30 3LT* Tel (023) 8047 2180 Fax 8047
7661
PICKETT, Mark William Leslie. b 60. Westhill Coll Birm BEd84.
Trin Coll Bris DipHE95. **d** 95 **p** 96. C Hellesdon *Nor* 95-98; TV
Thetford from 98; R Clitheroe St Jas *Blackb* from 03. *The
Rectory, Woone Lane, Clitheroe BB7 1BJ* Tel (01200) 423608
E-mail cloverfieldchurch@talk21.com
PICKETT, Peter Leslie. b 28. Guy's Hosp Medical Sch LDS RCS.
S Dios Minl Tr Scheme 83. **d** 86 **p** 87. NSM Eastbourne H Trin
Chich 86-88; P-in-c Danehill 88-93; rtd 93; Perm to Offic *Chich*
from 93. *Springfield, 76 Meads Road, Eastbourne BN20 7QJ* Tel
(01323) 731709 E-mail janpickett@lineone.net
PICKFORD (née PACKER), Mrs Catherine Ruth. b 76. Nottm
Univ BA97 Anglia Poly Univ MA00. Westcott Ho Cam MA00.
d 00 **p** 01. C Gosforth All SS *Newc* from 00. *1 Northfield Road,
Gosforth, Newcastle upon Tyne NE3 3UL* Tel 0191-284 8568
E-mail catherine.p@blueyonder.co.uk
PICKLES, Mark Andrew. b 62. Edin Univ BA83. Cranmer Hall
Dur 85. **d** 88 **p** 89. C Rock Ferry *Ches* 88-91; C Hartford 91-93; V
Wharton 93-00; P-in-c Duffield *Derby* from 00. *St Alkmund's
Vicarage, Vicarage Lane, Duffield, Belper DE56 4EB* Tel (01332)
841168
PICKSTONE, Charles Faulkner. b 55. BNC Ox BA77 MA81
Leeds Univ BA80. Coll of Resurr Mirfield 78. **d** 81 **p** 82. C
Birkenhead Priory *Ches* 81-84; Chapl Paris St Geo *Eur* 84; C
Camberwell St Giles w St Matt *S'wark* 84-89; V Catford St Laur
from 89; Asst RD E Lewisham 92-99. *St Laurence's Vicarage,
31 Bromley Road, London SE6 2TS* Tel (020) 8698 2871 *or* 8698
9706 E-mail charlston@mailbox.co.uk
PICKTHORN, Canon Charles Howard. b 25. Linc Coll Ox BA48
MA52. Sarum Th Coll 48. **d** 50 **p** 51. C High Harrogate Ch Ch
Ripon 50-54; C Cheam *S'wark* 54-60; R Bourton-on-the-Water w
Clapton *Glouc* 60-91; Chapl RAF 60-76; RD Stow *Glouc* 67-90;
P-in-c Gt Rissington 68-81; Hon Can Glouc Cathl from 77; rtd
91; Perm to Offic *Glouc* from 91. *267 Prestbury Road, Prestbury,
Cheltenham GL52 2EX* Tel (01242) 521447
PICKUP, Harold. b 17. St Pet Hall Ox BA39 MA46. Ridley Hall
Cam 46 Melbourne Coll of Div DipRE67. **d** 47 **p** 48. C
Middleton *Man* 47-50; V Gravesend St Mary *Roch* 51-57;
Australia from 57; rtd 82. *7 Farview Avenue, Riverside, Tas,
Australia 7250* Tel (0061) (3) 6327 4891
PICTON, Arthur David. b 39. Ch Ch Ox BA62 MA67. Chich Th
Coll. **d** 65 **p** 66. C Hulme St Phil *Man* 65-67; C Swinton St Pet
67-71; R Stretford St Pet 71-79; P-in-c Knights Enham *Win*
79-86; R 86-89; V Basing 89-02; RD Basingstoke 93-99; Hon
Can Win Cathl 96-02; rtd 02. *11 Millers Road, Tadley RG26 4LW*
Tel 0118-981 5782

PIDGEON, Warner Mark. b 68. Trin Coll Bris 00. **d** 02 **p** 03. C
Fair Oak *Win* from 02. *Windfall, Chapel Drove, Horton Heath,
Eastleigh SO50 7DL* Tel (023) 8069 4577 Mobile 07876-085054
E-mail warnermoira@supanet.com
PIDOUX, Ian George. b 32. Univ Coll Ox BA55 MA60. Coll of
Resurr Mirfield 54. **d** 57 **p** 58. C Middlesbrough All SS *York*
57-60; C Haggerston St Aug w St Steph *Lon* 60-62; C Aylesford
Roch 80-81; TV Rye *Chich* 81-84; P-in-c Bridgwater St Jo *B & W*
84-86; V 86-98; Chapl Bridgwater Hosp 91-98; rtd 98; Perm to
Offic *B & W* from 98. *Pear Tree Cottage, 9 Greenway, North
Curry, Taunton TA3 6NQ* Tel (01823) 490647 Fax as telephone
E-mail igsepidoux@aol.com
PIDSLEY, Preb Christopher Thomas. b 36. ALCD61. **d** 61 **p** 62.
C Enfield Ch Ch Trent Park *Lon* 61-66; C Rainham *Chelmsf*
66-70; V Chudleigh *Ex* 70-98; RD Moreton 86-91; Preb Ex Cathl
92-98; rtd 98. *Bellever, Shillingford Abbot, Exeter EX2 9QF* Tel
(01392) 833588
PIERARD, Canon Beaumont Harold. b 21. MBE72 JP68. St Jo
Coll Auckland. **d** 46 **p** 51. New Zealand 46-53; Chapl
Hurstpierpoint Coll 53-54; Chapl Worksop Coll Notts 54-57;
New Zealand from 57; Hon Can St Peter's Cathl Waikato 64-82.
287 Peachgrove Road, Hamilton, New Zealand Tel (0064) (7) 855
7000
PIERCE, Alan. b 46. St Mark & St Jo Coll Lon TCert68
Southlands Coll Lon BEd75 K Coll Lon MA85. Lon Bible Coll
DipTh72 N Ord Course 89. **d** 92 **p** 93. NSM Bolton St Thos *Man*
92-98; NSM Halliwell 98-00; NSM Bolton Breightmet St Jas
from 00. *3 Astley Road, Bolton BL2 4BR* Tel (01204) 300071 Fax
401556
✠**PIERCE, The Rt Revd Anthony Edward.** b 41. Univ of Wales
(Swansea) BA63 Linacre Coll Ox BA65 MA71. Ripon Hall Ox
63. **d** 65 **p** 66 c 99. C Swansea St Pet *S & B* 65-67; C Swansea
St Mary and H Trin 67-74; Chapl Univ of Wales (Swansea)
71-74; V Llwynderw 74-92; P-in-c Swansea St Barn 92-96; Dioc
Dir of Educn 93-96; Can Brecon Cathl 93-99; Adn Gower 95-99;
V Swansea St Mary w H Trin 96-99; Bp S & B from 99. *Ely
Tower, The Avenue, Brecon LD3 9DE* Tel (01874) 622008 Fax as
telephone
PIERCE, Brian William. b 42. St Steph Ho Ox 86. **d** 88 **p** 89. C
Cudworth *Wakef* 88-93; TV Manningham *Bradf* 93-98; V Tipton
St Jo *Lich* from 98. *St John's Vicarage, Upper Church Lane, Tipton
DY4 9ND* Tel 0121-557 1793
PIERCE, Bruce Andrew. b 58. TCD BBS80 BTh89. CITC 86. **d** 89
p 90. C Raheny w Coolock *D & G* 89-92; C Taney 92-93; I Lucan
w Leixlip 93-98; Chapl Adelaide and Meath Hosp Dublin 98-01;
Canada 02-03. *Address temp unknown*
E-mail brupierce@hotmail.com
PIERCE, Canon Claude Anthony (Tony). b 19. OBE46. Magd
Coll Cam BA47 MA49 BD53. Ely Th Coll 47. **d** 48 **p** 49. C
Chesterfield St Mary and All SS *Derby* 48-51; Chapl Magd Coll
Cam 51-56; Lect Th 54-56; Select Preacher Cam Univ 54;
Australia from 56; Warden Wollaston Th Coll 56-70; Hon Can
Perth 64-66; Can 66-85; Chapl Actors Ch Union 77-90; Chapl
Univ of W Australia 81-84; Chapl and Sub-Warden St Geo Coll
Crawley 81-84; rtd 85; Perm to Offic *Perth* from 85. *4 Hawkstone
Street, Cottesloe, W Australia 6011* Tel (0061) (8) 9383 2719
PIERCE, Jeffrey Hyam. b 29. FBIM80 Chelsea Coll Lon BSc51.
Ox NSM Course 86. **d** 88 **p** 89. NSM Gt Missenden w Ballinger
and Lt Hampden *Ox* 88-93; NSM Penn 93-97; rtd 97; Perm to
Offic *Ox* from 97. *Glebe Cottage, Manor Road, Penn, High
Wycombe HP10 8HY* Tel (01494) 817179
PIERCE, Jonathan Douglas Marshall. b 70. UCD BA91. CITC
BTh96. **d** 96 **p** 97. C Knockbreda *D & D* 96-99; L'Arche
Community Dublin 99-00; C Taney from 00. *Church
Lodge, 19 Taney Road, Dun Drum, Dublin 14, Irish Republic* Tel
(00353) (1) 298 5491 E-mail jonopierce@iegateway.net
PIERCE, Stephen Barry. b 60. Birm Univ BA81 MA82. Cranmer
Hall Dur. **d** 85 **p** 86. C Huyton St Mich *Liv* 85-89; V Walton
Breck Ch Ch 89-00; P-in-c Walton Breck 98-00; Resources
Officer from 00. *24 Ince Crescent, Liverpool L37 1XR* Tel (01704)
877460
PIERCE, Thomas David Benjamin. b 67. Ulster Univ BA88. Oak
Hill Th Coll DipHE92 BA94. **d** 94 **p** 95. C Cromer *Nor* 94-97; C
Belfast St Donard *D & D* 97-99; C Holywood 99-00; I Kilwarlin
Upper w Kilwarlin Lower from 00. *Kilwarlin Rectory, 9 St John's
Road, Hillsborough BT26 6ED* Tel (028) 9268 3299
PIERCE, William Johnston. b 32. N Ord Course. **d** 89 **p** 90. NSM
Gt Crosby St Luke *Liv* 89-96; Perm to Offic from 96. *1 Forton
Lodge, Blundellsands Road East, Liverpool L23 8SA* Tel 0151-
924 2400
PIERCE JONES, Alan. b 74. Coll of Ripon & York St Jo BA98.
St Mich Coll Llan 98. **d** 00 **p** 01. C Port Talbot St Theodore *Llan*
00-02; TV Neath from 02. *35 Trevallen Avenue, Cimla, Neath
SA11 3US* Tel (01639) 644434 E-mail fr.alan@lineone.net
PIERCY, Miss Elizabeth Claire. b 66. Qu Mary Coll Lon BSc87.
Wycliffe Hall Ox DipMin99. **d** 99 **p** 00. C Dronfield w
Holmesfield *Derby* 99-03; V Allestree from 03. *St Edmund's
Vicarage, Kings Croft, Allestree, Derby DE22 2FN* Tel (01332)
557396 E-mail elizabeth_piercy@hotmail.com

PIERPOINT, Canon David Alfred. b 56. **d** 86 **p** 88. NSM Athboy w Ballivor and Killallon *M & K* 86-88; NSM Killiney Ballybrack *D & G* 88-89; NSM Narraghmore and Timolin w Castledermot etc 89-91; Chan V St Patr Cathl Dublin 90-96; C Dublin St Patr Cathl Gp *D & G* 92-95; I Dublin Ch Ch Cathl Gp from 95; Can Ch Ch Cathl Dublin from 95. *The Vicarage, 30 Phibsborough Road, Dublin 7, Irish Republic* Tel (00353) (1) 830 4601 Mobile 087-263 0402 E-mail dpier@iol.ie

PIGGOT, Alan Robert Lennox. b 62. Peterho Cam BA84 MA88. Westcott Ho Cam 00. **d** 02. C Dalston H Trin w St Phil and Haggerston All SS *Lon* from 02. *Holy Trinity Vicarage, 89 Forest Road, London E8 3BL* Tel (020) 7254 5942 E-mail anglicalan@onetel.uk.net

PIGGOTT, Andrew John. b 51. Qu Mary Coll Lon BSc(Econ)72. St Jo Coll Nottm 83. **d** 86 **p** 87. C Dorridge *Birm* 86-89; TV Kidderminster St Geo *Worc* 89-94; V Biddulph *Lich* 94-99; Min and Voc Adv CPAS from 99; Perm to Offic *Cov* from 99. *3 Riversleigh Road, Leamington Spa CV32 6BG* Tel (01926) 413203

PIGGOTT, Clive. b 47. St Luke's Coll Ex CertEd69. LNSM course 93. **d** 96 **p** 97. OLM Malden St Jas *S'wark* from 96. *84 Manor Drive North, New Malden KT3 5PA* Tel (020) 8337 0801

PIGGOTT, Raymond George. b 16. Leeds Univ BA38. Coll of Resurr Mirfield 38. **d** 40 **p** 41. C Leic St Mark *Leic* 40-42; C Munster Square St Mary Magd *Lon* 42-47; Chapl RN 47-53; C Felixstowe St Jo *St E* 53-54; V Barney w Thursford *Nor* 54-56; V Ilkley St Marg *Bradf* 56-65; V Roughey *Chich* 65-80; P-in-c Lynch w Iping Marsh 80-83; rtd 83; Perm to Offic *Chich* from 85. *Flat 3, Bramwell Lodge, Brighton Road, Terry's Cross, Woodmancote, Henfield BN5 9SX* Tel (01273) 493749

PIGOTT, Graham John. b 44. Kingston Coll of Art NDD64 Lon Univ DipTh71 BD73 Nottm Univ MPhil84 MEd94. St Jo Coll Nottm DPS81. **d** 81 **p** 82. C Beeston *S'well* 81-84; P-in-c W Bridgford 84-88; V Wilford Hill from 88; AD W Bingham from 97. *The Parsonage, Boundary Road, West Bridgford, Nottingham NG2 7DB* Tel 0115-923 3492 E-mail graham@gjpigott.fsnet.co.uk

PIGOTT, Canon John Drummond. b 26. TCD Div Test50 BA50 MA56. **d** 51 **p** 52. C Belfast St Phil *Conn* 51-54; C Jordanstown 54-56; Chapl RAF 56-59; R Upper Clatford w Goodworth Clatford *Win* 59-65; V Warley Woods *Birm* 65-74; RD Warley 72-74; V Boldmere 74-97; Hon Can Birm Cathl 81-97; RD Sutton Coldfield 88-93; rtd 97; Perm to Offic *B & W* from 97. *Clatford House, 41 Farriers Green, Monkton Heathfield, Taunton TA2 8PP* Tel (01823) 413552

PIGOTT, Nicholas John Capel. b 48. Qu Coll Birm 75. **d** 78 **p** 79. C Belmont *Dur* 78-79; C Folkestone St Sav *Cant* 79-82; C Birm St Geo *Birm* 82-85; V Stevenage St Hugh and St Jo *St Alb* 85-91; TV Totnes and Berry Pomeroy *Ex* 91; TV Totnes, Bridgetown and Berry Pomeroy etc 91-02; Asst P Totnes w Bridgetown, Berry Pomeroy etc from 02. *St John's Vicarage, Crosspark, Totnes TQ9 5BQ* Tel (01803) 867961 E-mail njsa@lineone.net

PIGREM, Terence John (Tim). b 39. Oak Hill Th Coll 66. **d** 69 **p** 70. C Islington St Andr w St Thos and St Matthias *Lon* 69-73; C Barking St Marg w St Patr *Chelmsf* 73-75; TV 75-76; C W Holloway St Luke *Lon* 76-79; V 79-95; P-in-c Abbess Roding, Beauchamp Roding and White Roding *Chelmsf* 95-96; R Leaden Roding and Abbess Roding etc from 96; RD Dunmow 97-02. *The Rectory, Stortford Road, Leaden Roding, Dunmow CM6 1GY* Tel (01279) 876387 E-mail pigrem@btinternet.com

PIKE, Mrs Amanda Shirley Gail. b 69. Cranmer Hall Dur 99. **d** 01 **p** 02. C Boston Spa *York* from 01. *The Vicarage, Church Causeway, Thorp Arch, Wetherby LS23 7AE* Tel (01937) 842430 Mobile 07811-569802 E-mail ichthos@lineone.net

PIKE, David Frank. b 35. CEng MIMechE BA Lon Univ TCert. S Dios Minl Tr Scheme 82. **d** 85 **p** 86. NSM Lancing w Coombes *Chich* 85-88; R Albourne w Sayers Common and Twineham 88-94; V Wisborough Green from 94. *The Vicarage, Wisborough Green, Billingshurst RH14 0DZ* Tel (01403) 700339

PIKE, George Richard. b 38. BSc. WMMTC 79. **d** 82 **p** 83. NSM Edgbaston St Bart *Birm* 82-89; NSM S Yardley St Mich from 89. *138 Charlbury Crescent, Birmingham B26 2LW* Tel 0121-783 2818 Fax as telephone

PIKE, Horace Douglas. b 13. AKC48. **d** 48 **p** 49. C Todmorden *Wakef* 48-52; P-in-c Lundwood 52-55; V Gawber 55-59; V Baildon *Bradf* 59-71; R Burnsall 72-78; rtd 78; P-in-c Birdsall w Langton *York* 81-86; Perm to Offic from 86. *18 Southfield Close, Rufforth, York YO23 3RE* Tel (01904) 738418

PIKE, James. b 22. TCD 66. **d** 68 **p** 69. C Clooney *D & R* 68-72; I Ardstraw 72-76; I Ardstraw w Baronscourt 76-86; I Ardstraw w Baronscourt, Badoney Lower etc 76-92; Can Derry Cathl 90-92; rtd 92. *19 Knockgreenan Avenue, Omagh BT79 0EB* Tel (028) 8224 9007 Fax 8225 1382 E-mail jamespike@utvinternet.com

PIKE, Paul Alfred. b 38. Southn Univ CertEd58 Lon Univ DipTh67 MIL88. Wycliffe Hall Ox. **d** 84 **p** 85. C Penn Fields *Lich* 84-89; OMF Internat Japan from 89. *OMF International (UK), Station Approach, Borough Green, Sevenoaks TN15 8BG* Tel (01732) 887299 Fax 887224

PIKE, Peter John. b 53. Southn Univ BTh86 Lanc Univ PhD00. Sarum & Wells Th Coll 81. **d** 84 **p** 85. C Broughton *Blackb* 84-88; V Woodplumpton 88-93; Asst Dir of Ords and Voc Adv 89-93; P-in-c Barnacre w Calder Vale 93-98; Carl Dioc Tr Course from 93; V Briercliffe *Blackb* from 00. *St James's Vicarage, Briercliffe, Burnley BB10 2HU* Tel (01282) 423700 Fax as telephone E-mail revpeterpike@hotmail.com

PIKE, Robert James. b 47. Kelham Th Coll 66. **d** 70 **p** 71. C Cov St Pet *Cov* 70-74; C Bilton 74-76; P-in-c Southall St Geo *Lon* 76-81; V S Harrow St Paul 81-86; C Hillingdon St Jo 86-88; Chapl Hillingdon Hosp & Mt Vernon Hosp Uxbridge 88-90; Perm to Offic 91-96. *6 Salt Hill Close, Uxbridge UB8 1PZ* Tel (01895) 235212

PIKE, Canon Roger Walter. b 31. Roch Th Coll 65. **d** 67 **p** 68. C Wokingham St Paul *Ox* 67-70; C Whitley Ch Ch 70-76; C-in-c California CD 76-80; V Cowes St Faith *Portsm* 80-94; Hon Can Portsm Cathl 92-94; rtd 94; Perm to Offic *Truro* from 94 and *Portsm* from 98. *45 Conway Road, Falmouth TR11 4LA* Tel (01326) 315901

PIKE, Timothy David. b 68. Collingwood Coll Dur BA90 Leeds Univ BA94. Coll of Resurr Mirfield 92. **d** 95 **p** 96. C Owton Manor *Dur* 95-98; C Old St Pancras w Bedford New Town St Matt *Lon* 98-03; CR from 03. *The Community of the Resurrection, Stocks Bank Road, Mirfield WF14 0BN* Tel (01924) 483337

PILDITCH, Miss Patricia Desiree. b 21. dss 82 **d** 87 **p** 94. Barnstaple *Ex* 83-87; NSM Barnstaple from 87; Asst Chapl N Devon Healthcare NHS Trust from 82. *4 The Mews, Bydown, Swimbridge, Barnstaple EX32 0QB* Tel (01271) 830770

PILGRIM, Colin Mark. b 56. BA77 Geneva Univ Cert Ecum Studies 84. Westcott Ho Cam 81. **d** 84 **p** 85. C Chorlton-cum-Hardy St Clem *Man* 84-87; C Whitchurch *Bris* 87-89; V Bedminster Down 89-95; Dioc Youth Officer 95-01; Hon C Stoke Bishop 96-01; V Henleaze from 01. *St Peter's Vicarage, 17 The Drive, Henleaze, Bristol BS9 4LD* Tel 0117-962 0636 or 962 3196 E-mail mark@prtbristoldiocese.fsnet.co.uk

PILGRIM, Donald Eric. b 55. Cant Univ (NZ) BA80 LTh87. St Jo Coll Auckland 81. **d** 81 **p** 82. New Zealand 81-85 and from 86; C Southampton Maybush St Pet *Win* 85-86. *212 Hoon Hay Road, Christchurch 2, New Zealand* Tel (0064) (3) 338 4277 Fax as telephone

PILGRIM, Ms Judith Mary. b 44. Westcott Ho Cam 88. **d** 90 **p** 94. C Probus, Ladock and Grampound w Creed and St Erme *Truro* 90-94; Par Dn Nottingham All SS *S'well* 94; C 94-97; Asst Chapl to the Deaf 94-97; Perm to Offic *S'well* 97-00; *Ox* 00-01; P-in-c Zennor *Truro* from 02; P-in-c Towednack from 02. *The Vicarage, Nancledra, Penzance TR20 8LQ* Tel (01736) 740548

PILGRIM, Kenneth George. b 49. **d** 01 **p** 02. OLM Alkham w Capel le Ferne and Hougham *Cant* from 01. *12 Godwyne Road, Dover CT16 1SW* Tel (01304) 202197 E-mail ken@prilgrim12.freeserve.co.uk

PILKINGTON, Miss Anne. b 57. Aston Tr Scheme 88 N Ord Course 90. **d** 93 **p** 94. C Wythenshawe Wm Temple Ch *Man* 93-96; P-in-c 96-99; TV Wythenshawe from 99. *William Temple Vicarage, Robinswood Road, Manchester M22 6BU* Tel 0161-437 3194 E-mail a.pilky@fish.co.uk

PILKINGTON, Charles George Willink. b 21. Trin Coll Cam BA42 MA64. Westcott Ho Cam. **d** 63 **p** 64. C Pendleton St Thos *Man* 63-65; C Brindle Heath 63-65; C Chorlton-cum-Hardy St Clem 65-68; R Withington St Chris 68-88; rtd 88; Perm to Offic *Man* from 88. *32 Rathen Road, Withington, Manchester M20 9GH* Tel 0161-434 5365

PILKINGTON, Canon Christopher Frost. b 23. Trin Coll Cam BA50 MA60. Ridley Hall Cam 50. **d** 52 **p** 53. C St Jo in Bedwardine *Worc* 52-55; V Worc St Mark 55-60; V Bromsgrove St Jo 60-68; R Bris St Steph w St Nic and St Leon *Bris* 68-81; P-in-c 81-82; Hon Can Bris Cathl 79-82; Hon Chapl Cancer Help Cen Bris 82-89; rtd 89; Perm to Offic *Bris* from 90. *Apple Acre, Tunbridge Road, Chew Magna, Bristol BS40 8SP* Tel (01275) 333545

PILKINGTON, Edward Russell. b 39. ALCD65. **d** 65 **p** 66. C Eccleshill *Bradf* 65-68; C Billericay St Mary *Chelmsf* 68-72; V New Thundersley 72-78; R Theydon Garnon 78-82; V Gidea Park from 82. *St Michael's Vicarage, Main Road, Romford RM2 5EL* Tel (01708) 741084

PILKINGTON, John Rowan. b 32. Magd Coll Cam BA55 MA59. Ridley Hall Cam 57. **d** 59 **p** 60. C Ashtead *Guildf* 59-61; C Wimbledon *S'wark* 62-65; R Newhaven *Chich* 65-75; R Farlington *Portsm* 75-89; V Darlington St Mark w St Paul *Dur* 89-97; rtd 97; Perm to Offic *Portsm* from 98. *38 Main Road, Emsworth PO10 8AU* Tel (01243) 375830

PILKINGTON, Miss Margaret. b 30. Univ Coll Leic BA51 PGCE52 Liv Inst of HE DipRE79. **d** 01 **p** 02. NSM Kirkby Lonsdale *Carl* from 01. *5 Fern Croft, Casterton, Carnforth LA6 2RY* Tel (015242) 71619

PILKINGTON, Timothy William. b 54. Nottm Univ BA85. Linc Th Coll 82. **d** 85 **p** 86. C Newquay *Truro* 85-88; C Cockington *Ex* 88-91; R St John w Millbrook *Truro* 91-97; V Northampton St Matt *Pet* 97-02; TR Solihull *Birm* from 02. *The Rectory,*

St Alphege Close, Church Hill Road, Solihull B91 3RQ Tel 0121-705 0069 *or* 705 5350 Fax 704 0646

PILKINGTON OF OXENFORD, The Revd Canon Lord (Peter). b 33. Jes Coll Cam BA55 MA59. Westcott Ho Cam 58. **d** 59 **p** 60. C Bakewell *Derby* 59-62; Chapl Eton Coll 62-75; Hd Master K Sch Cant 75-85; Hon Can Cant Cathl *Cant* 75-90; High Master St Paul's Sch Barnes 86-92; Chmn Broadcasting Complaints Commn 92-96; Hon C Pimlico St Mary Bourne Street *Lon* from 92. *The Presbytery, 30 Bourne Street, London SW1W 8JS,* or *Oxenford House, Dowlish Wake, Ilminster TA19 0PP* Tel (020) 7730 4883 *or* (01460) 52813 Fax (01460) 55280

✠**PILLAR, The Rt Revd Kenneth Harold.** b 24. Qu Coll Cam BA48 MA53. Ridley Hall Cam 48. **d** 50 **p** 51 **c** 82. C Childwall All SS *Liv* 50-53; Chapl Lee Abbey 53-57; V New Beckenham St Paul *Roch* 57-62; V Cant St Mary Bredin *Cant* 62-65; Warden Lee Abbey 65-70; V Waltham Abbey *Chelmsf* 70-82; RD Chigwell 76-78; RD Epping Forest 78-82; Suff Bp Hertford *St Alb* 82-89; rtd 89; Asst Bp Sheff from 89. *75 Dobcroft Road, Sheffield S7 2LS* Tel 0114-236 7902

PILLAR, Kenneth James. b 50. St Jo Coll Nottm 70. **d** 74 **p** 75. C Wilmington *Roch* 74-79; CF 79-87 and from 89; R Curry Rivel w Fivehead and Swell *B & W* 87-89. *clo MOD Chaplains (Army)* Tel (01980) 615804 Fax 615800

PILLING, Neville. b 32. ACMA60 FCCA81 CertEd71. Is of Man Tr Inst 88. **d** 92 **p** 93. NSM Douglas St Matt *S & M* from 92. *Morwenna, Athol Park, Port Erin, Isle of Man IM9 6ES* Tel (01624) 832382

PIMENTEL, Peter Eric. b 55. BA. Ridley Hall Cam. **d** 82 **p** 83. C Gt Ilford St Andr *Chelmsf* 82-85; Chapl Basingstoke Distr Hosp 85-88; TV Grays Thurrock *Chelmsf* 88-96; P-in-c Barton *Portsm* 96-99; V from 99; Dioc Ecum Officer 96-02. *St Paul's Vicarage, Staplers Road, Newport PO30 2HZ* Tel (01983) 522075 Mobile 07949-366625 Fax 08701-303386
E-mail peter@pimentel.freeserve.co.uk

PIMM, Robert John. b 57. Bris Univ BA78 ACIB82. Trin Coll Bris ADMT94. **d** 94 **p** 95. C Long Benton *Newc* 94-98; TV Bath Twerton-on-Avon *B & W* from 98. *Ascension Vicarage, 35A Claude Avenue, Bath BA2 1AF* Tel (01225) 405354
E-mail revrobert@lineone.net

PIMPERTON, Raymond Swindale. b 12. Linc Th Coll 77. **d** 77 **p** 78. Hon C Holbeach *Linc* 77-83; rtd 83; Perm to Offic *Linc* 83-92. *6 Chestnut Avenue, Holbeach, Spalding PE12 7NE*

PINCHBECK, Miss Caroline Rosamund. b 70. Hatf Coll Dur BA93. Wesley Ho Cam MA00. **d** 02 **p** 03. C Mawnan *Truro* from 02. *The Rectory, Old Church Road, Mawnan Smith, Falmouth TR11 5HY* Tel (01326) 250280
E-mail crp@wesley71.freeserve.co.uk

PINCHES, Donald Antony. b 32. Pemb Coll Cam BA55 MA60 Linacre Coll Ox BA67. Wycliffe Hall Ox 64. **d** 67 **p** 68. C Aylesbury *Ox* 67-71; C Compton Gifford *Ex* 71-74; TV Lydford, Brent Tor, Bridestowe and Sourton 74-77; V Shiphay Collaton 77-97; rtd 97; Perm to Offic *Ex* from 98. *3 Malderek Avenue, Preston, Paignton TQ3 2RP* Tel (01803) 698003

PINDER, Canon John Ridout. b 43. Peterho Cam BA65 MA69. Cuddesdon Coll 65. **d** 73 **p** 74. C Leavesden All SS *St Alb* 73-76; Gen Sec Melanesian Miss 77-89; P-in-c Harpsden *Ox* 82-89; R Farlington *Portsm* 89-02; R Liss from 02; RD Portsm 96-01; Hon Can Portsm Cathl from 01. *The Rectory, 111 Station Road, Liss GU33 7AQ* Tel (01730) 890085 Fax 892654
E-mail john@jrpinder.freeserve.co.uk

PINDER-PACKARD, John. b 47. Lon Univ BSc. N Ord Course 81. **d** 84 **p** 85. NSM Mosbrough *Sheff* 84-85; C Norton 85-88; V New Whittington *Derby* from 88; P-in-c Newbold and Gt Barlow 99-00; Chapl Whittington Hall Hosp from 88. *The Vicarage, 121 Handley Road, New Whittington, Chesterfield S43 2EF* Tel (01246) 455830

PINE, David Michael. b 41. Lich Th Coll 68. **d** 71 **p** 72. C Northam *Ex* 71-74; R Toft w Caldecote and Childerley *Ely* 74-80; R Hardwick 74-80; V Ipswich St Andr *St E* 80-84; P-in-c Hazelbury Bryan w Stoke Wake etc *Sarum* 84-91; R Hazelbury Bryan and the Hillside Par 91-93; V Steep and Froxfield w Privett *Portsm* 93-00; rtd 00. *Amberley, High Road, Nettlestone, Seaview PO34 5DZ* Tel (01983) 563734

PINES, Christopher Derek. b 65. Lon Univ MB, BS89. Oak Hill Th Coll DipHE93 BA93. **d** 93 **p** 94. C Heref St Pet w St Owen and St Jas *Heref* 93-97; Min Can and Chapl St Alb Abbey *St Alb* 97-03; Chapl St Alb Sch from 03. *1 Fishpool Street, St Albans AL3 4RS*

PINFIELD, Leslie Arthur. b 57. Birm Univ BMus79 Univ Coll Lon Dip Librarianship 90. St Steph Ho Ox DipMin94. **d** 94 **p** 95. C Bath Bathwick *B & W* 94-98; TV Swindon New Town *Bris* from 98. *St Luke's Vicarage, 3 Briar Fields, Swindon SN1 2QN* Tel (01793) 536679 Fax as telephone

PINK, Canon David. b 34. Qu Coll Cam BA58 MA62. Linc Th Coll 58. **d** 60 **p** 61. C Lt Ilford St Mich *Chelmsf* 60-63; Lect Boston 63-65; V Kirton in Holland *Linc* 65-71; V Spittlegate 71-77; Ecum Officer Lincs and S Humberside 77-85; Can and Preb Linc Cathl from 77; P-in-c Canwick 77-87; R

Washingborough w Heighington 87-88; R Washingborough w Heighington and Canwick 88-90; rtd 90; Perm to Offic *Linc* from 90. *The Old School, Swarby, Sleaford NG34 8TG*

PINKERTON, Ms Patricia Edith. b 38. California Univ BA72 MA75 BTh80. Ch Div Sch of the Pacific (USA). **d** 81 **p** 82. USA 81-88; C Coleford w Staunton *Glouc* 88-92; Dn-in-c St Briavels w Hewelsfield 92-94; P-in-c 94-97; rtd 97; Perm to Offic *Glouc* from 97. *Lammas Cottage, 7 Stephens Place, Broadwell, Coleford GL16 7BJ* Tel (01594) 810321

PINNELL, George. b 39. NTMTC 96. **d** 99 **p** 00. NSM Hillingdon St Jo *Lon* from 99. *30 Swan Road, West Drayton UB7 7JZ* Tel (01895) 446656

PINNER, John Philip. b 37. K Coll Lon BA59 AKC59 Lon Inst of Educn PGCE60. Westcott Ho Cam 69. **d** 71 **p** 72. C Dover St Mary *Cant* 71-74; Chapl Felsted Sch 74-81; Chapl Rathkeale Coll New Zealand 81-02; rtd 02. *159 West Street, Greytown, Wairarapa, New Zealand 5953* Tel (0064) (6) 304 8301 Fax 304 8309 E-mail john.cheri.pinner@xtra.co.nz

PINNER, Canon Terence Malcolm William. b 35. Southn Univ MA89. AKC59. **d** 60 **p** 61. C Eltham St Barn *S'wark* 60-64; S Africa 64-67 and 69-74; USPG 67-69; Sec for Home Affairs Conf of Br Miss Socs 74-76; P-in-c Hinstock *Lich* 76-79; Adult Educn Officer 76-79; Adult RE Officer 79-83; Chapl Southn Univ *Win* 83-88; Tutor S Dios Minl Tr Scheme 88-92; Dioc Dir of Ords *Win* 88-98; Hon Can Win Cathl 92-00; P-in-c Old Alresford and Bighton 93-00; rtd 00. *47 Buriton Road, Winchester SO22 6JF* Tel (01962) 884215 Mobile 07889-177203 E-mail terence.pinner@virgin.net

PINNINGTON, Mrs Gillian. b 59. St Kath Coll Liv BEd81 Chester Coll of HE BTh02. N Ord Course 99. **d** 02. C Roby *Liv* from 02. *42 Buttermere Road, Bowring Park, Liverpool L16 2NN* Tel 0151-489 5910 E-mail pinny@supanet.com

PINNINGTON, Ms Suzanne Jane. b 66. Trevelyan Coll Dur BA89. St Steph Ho Ox 95. **d** 97 **p** 98. C Oakham, Hambleton, Egleton, Braunston and Brooke *Pet* 97-00; V Cottingley *Bradf* from 00. *The Vicarage, Littlelands, Cottingley, Bingley BD16 1RR* Tel (01274) 562278

PINNOCK, Geoffrey Gilbert. b 16. K Coll Lon 47. **d** 50 **p** 51. C Paddington St Mich w All SS *Lon* 50-52; S Africa 52-57; Perm to Offic *Lon* 57-66; acting Chapl Nat Hosp Qu Square Lon 60; St Steph Hosp Chelsea 61-62; Asst Chapl Univ Coll Hosp Lon 62-66; USA 66-72; Perm to Offic *Lon* 72-73; Perm to Offic *S'wark* 73-74; C Battersea St Phil w St Bart 74-75; P-in-c Boconnoc w Bradoc *Truro* 75-81; rtd 81. *11 Drove Acre Road, Oxford OX4 3DF* Tel (01865) 247355

PINNOCK, Giles Antony. b 67. Leic Univ BA88 MA93. St Steph Ho Ox 00. **d** 02 **p** 03. C Stony Stratford *Ox* from 02; C Calverton from 02. *St Birinus' House, 9 Bunsty Court, Stony Stratford, Milton Keynes MK11 1NJ* Tel (01908) 561675 Mobile 07713-627175 Fax 08714-332362 E-mail gilespinnock@fish.co.uk

PINNOCK, Martyn Elliott. b 47. Dartmouth RN Coll 65. Linc Th Coll 93. **d** 93 **p** 94. C Fordingbridge *Win* 93-97; V St Minver *Truro* 97-01; P-in-c Luray Ch Ch USA 01-02; V Steeton *Bradf* from 02. *The Vicarage, 2 Halsteads Way, Steeton, Keighley BD20 6SN* Tel (01535) 652877 Mobile 07817-036655 Fax (01535) 653950 E-mail nguage@railwayrev.force9.co.uk

PINSENT, Ewen Macpherson. b 30. Edin Th Coll 67. **d** 69 **p** 70. C Holt *Nor* 69-72; R Kelso *Edin* 72-82; R Blendworth w Chalton w Idsworth etc *Portsm* 82-90; R Blendworth w Chalton w Idsworth 90-92; rtd 92; Perm to Offic *Sarum* from 94. *The Cross House, Childe Okeford, Blandford Forum DT11 8ED* Tel (01258) 860803

PIPER, Canon Andrew. b 58. Magd Coll Ox BA79 MA83. Chich Th Coll 80. **d** 83 **p** 84. C Eastbourne St Mary *Chich* 83-88; TV Lewes All SS, St Anne, St Mich and St Thos 88-93; TR Worth 93-03; Can Res and Prec Heref Cathl *Heref* from 03. *1 The Close, Hereford HR1 2NG* Tel (01432) 266193 Fax 374220
E-mail andrew@cantoris1.demon.co.uk

PIPER, Canon Clifford John. b 53. Aber Univ CSS88. Moray Ord Course 91. **d** 93 **p** 94. C Invergordon St Ninian *Mor* 93-96; NSM Tain 96-98; P-in-c from 98; Can St Andr Cathl Inverness from 00. *St Andrew's Rectory, Manse Road, Tain IV19 1HE* Tel (01862) 892193 E-mail cliffpiper@onet.co.uk

PIPER, Gary Quentin David. b 42. Nottm Coll of Educn TCert65 Maria Grey Coll Lon DipEd71. Oak Hill Th Coll 75. **d** 78 **p** 79. Hon C Fulham St Matt *Lon* 78-85; V from 85; AD Hammersmith 86-92. *St Matthew's Vicarage, 2 Clancarty Road, London SW6 3AB* Tel (020) 7731 3272

PIPER, Graham. b 58. Southn Univ BTh91. Chich Th Coll 88. **d** 91 **p** 92. C Horsham *Chich* 91-94; TV Haywards Heath St Wilfrid 94-99; Dioc Voc Adv 96-99; V Bamber Bridge St Aid *Blackb* from 99. *St Aidan's Vicarage, Longworth Street, Bamber Bridge, Preston PR5 6GN* Tel (01772) 335310
E-mail fatherpiper@longworthstreet.freeserve.co.uk

PIPER, John Howard. b 09. St Chad's Coll Dur BA31. **d** 32 **p** 34. Asst Chapl Denstone Coll Uttoxeter 32-34; C Knowle H Nativity *Bris* 34-41; C Sidmouth St Nic *Ex* 41-44; Chapl RAFVR 44-46; C Cov St Mark *Cov* 46-49; C Paignton St Jo *Ex* 49-55; C Devonport St Budeaux 55-57; V Whiteleigh 57-68; R Rearsby w Ratcliffe on the Wreake *Leic* 68-78; P-in-c Thrussington 77-78; R Rearsby w Ratcliffe-on-the-Wreake etc 78-82; rtd 82; Perm to

Offic *Leic* from 82. *52 Avenue Road, Queniborough, Leicester LE7 3FA* Tel 0116-260 6605

PIPER, Kenneth John. b 29. St Luke's Coll Ex TCert53 Leeds Univ DipEd67. S Dios Minl Tr Scheme 79. **d** 82 **p** 83. NSM Bradford w Oake, Hillfarrance and Heathfield *B & W* 82-87; Chapl to Norway and Scandinavia Lay Tr Officer *Eur* 87-89; R Durrington *Sarum* 90-94; P-in-c Antony w Sheviock *Truro* 94-00; rtd 00; Perm to Offic *Truro* from 01. *2 Welman Road, Millbrook, Torpoint PL10 1QA* Tel (01752) 822580

PIPER, Canon Leonard Arthur. b 08. MBE01. Clifton Th Coll 32. **d** 35 **p** 36. C Spitalfields Ch Ch w All SS *Lon* 35-37; C Darlington St Cuth *Dur* 37-39; R Hurworth 39-73; Offg Chapl RAF 40-87; R Dinsdale w Sockburn *Dur* 61-73; Hon Can Dur Cathl 70-73; rtd 73. *Bridge Cottage, Over Dinsdale, Darlington DL2 1PW* Tel (01325) 332864

PIPPEN, Canon Brian Roy. b 50. St D Coll Lamp DipTh73. **d** 73 **p** 74. C Maindee *Mon* 73-77; TV Cwmbran 77-84; V Newport Ch Ch 84-90; R Pontypool from 90; RD Pontypool from 98; Can St Woolos Cathl from 01. *The Vicarage, Trevethin, Pontypool NP4 8JF* Tel (01495) 762228

PIRET, Michael John. b 57. State Univ NY BA79 Univ of Michigan MA80 PhD91 Mert Coll Ox MLitt89. Edin Th Coll 90. **d** 92 **p** 93. C St Andr Cathl Inverness *Mor* 92-94; Dean of Div and Chapl Magd Coll Ox from 94. *Magdalen College, Oxford OX1 4AU* Tel (01865) 276027

PIRRIE, Stephen Robin. b 56. Kent Univ BA79 Barrister 80 Cam Univ MA83. EAMTC 94. **d** 97 **p** 98. C King's Lynn St Marg w St Nic *Nor* 97-99; C Bideford, Northam, Westward Ho, Appledore etc *Ex* 99-00; TV from 00. *The Rectory, Weare Giffard, Bideford EX39 4QP* Tel (01237) 476522

PITCHER, Canon David John. b 33. Ely Th Coll 55. **d** 58 **p** 59. C Kingswinford St Mary *Lich* 58-61; C Kirkby *Liv* 61-66; R Ingham w Sutton *Nor* 66-72; V Lakenham St Jo 72-76; R Framlingham w Saxtead *St E* 76-91; RD Loes 82-89; Hon Can St E Cathl 85-99; R Woodbridge St Mary 91-99; rtd 99. *25 Coucy Close, Framlingham, Woodbridge IP13 9AX* Tel (01728) 621580

PITCHER, Robert Philip. b 47. Westhill Coll Birm DipEd70. Trin Coll Bris DipHE92. **d** 92 **p** 93. C Llansamlet *S & B* 92-96; V Caereithin 96-02; V Llanidloes w Llangurig *Ban* from 02. *The Vicarage, Trefeglwys Road, Llanidloes SY18 6HZ* Tel (01686) 412370 E-mail bob.pitcher@openworld.com

PITCHER, Ronald Charles Frederick. b 21. AKC50. **d** 51 **p** 52. C Burnage St Marg *Man* 51-53; C Heywood St Jas 53-55; C Newall Green CD 55-61; V Newall Green St Fran 61-73; Chapl Wythenshawe Hosp *Man* 64-73; C-in-c Daneshholme CD *Pet* 73-81; V Estover *Ex* 81-91; rtd 91; Perm to Offic *Sarum* from 92. *18 East Wyld Road, Weymouth DT4 0RP* Tel (01305) 771916

PITCHER, Simon John. b 63. Reading Univ BA85. Ridley Hall Cam 00. **d** 02 **p** 03. C Lightcliffe *Wakef* from 02. *Roseneath, Leeds Road, Halifax HX3 8NU* Tel (01422) 207335 E-mail sjp@ukgateway.net

PITCHFORD, Herbert John. b 34. Dur Univ BA60. Ridley Hall Cam 60. **d** 62 **p** 63. C Heref St Martin *Heref* 62-68; R Much Birch w Lt Birch 68-78; P-in-c Much Dewchurch w Llanwarne and Llandinabo 73-78; R Much Birch w Lt Birch, Much Dewchurch etc 78-80; V Grange Park St Pet *Lon* 80-91; V Wylde Green *Birm* 91-01; rtd 01; Perm to Offic *Glouc* from 03. *Woodlands, Eaton Road, Malvern WR14 4PE* Tel (01684) 575893 Mobile 07870-841150
E-mail revjpitchford@woodlands45.freeserve.co.uk

PITE, Sheila Reinhardt. See STEVENSON, Mrs Sheila Reinhardt

PITHERS, Canon Brian Hoyle. b 34. Chich Th Coll 63. **d** 66 **p** 67. C Wisbech SS Pet and Paul *Ely* 66-70; V Fenstanton 70-75; V Hilton 70-75; V Habergham Eaves St Matt *Blackb* 75-85; P-in-c Habergham Eaves H Trin 78-85; V Burnley St Matt w H Trin 85-86; TR Ribbleton 86-92; V Torrisholme 92-00; Hon Can Blackb Cathl 97-00; rtd 01; Perm to Offic *Blackb* from 01. *37 Dallam Avenue, Morecambe LA4 5BB* Tel (01524) 424786 E-mail brianpithers@supanet.com

PITKIN, James Mark. b 62. Man Univ BSc83 MRAeS90 CEng90 Glos Univ BA(Theol)03. STETS DipTh99. **d** 99 **p** 00. C Chilworth w N Baddesley *Win* 99-03; V Lockerley and E Dean w E and W Tytherley from 03. *The Vicarage, The Street, Lockerley, Romsey SO51 0JF* Tel (01794) 340635 Mobile 07931-736166 Fax 08701-674691 E-mail jamespitkin@priest.com

PITKIN, Mrs Susan Margaret. b 60. Man Univ BA84 Surrey Univ BA03. STETS 00. **d** 03. C Southampton Maybush St Pet *Win* from 03. *St Peter's House, Lockerley Crescent, Southampton SO16 4BP* Tel (023) 8077 5014 Mobile 07752-891052 E-mail suepitkin@minister.com

PITMAN, Roger Thomas. b 64. St Mich Coll Llan BTh00. **d** 00 **p** 01. C Caerphilly *Llan* 00-02; C Coity w Nolton from 02. *Y Lletty, Heol yr Ysgol, Coity, Bridgend CF35 6BL* Tel (01656) 652540 E-mail way-follower@hotmail.com

PITT, Beatrice Anne. b 50. I M Marsh Coll of Physical Educn CertEd71 Bris Univ DipHE82 Open Univ BA01. Trin Coll Bris

80. **d** 82 **p** 97. C Rhyl w St Ann *St As* 82-86; CMS 86-92; Zaïre 88-92; Jt Co-ord of Dioc Bible Schs *Bukavu* 88-92; NSM Penycae *St As* 92-98; Hon Rep for CMS *St As* and *Ban* 93-98; NSM Killesher *K, E & A* 98-01; P-in-c Killinagh w Kiltyclogher and Innismagrath 98-01; P-in-c Firbank, Howgill and Killington *Bradf* from 01. *5 Highfield Road, Sedbergh LA10 5DH* Tel (01539) 620670
E-mail anne@pittba.fsnet.co.uk

PITT, George. b 52. QUB BD79 MTh88. CITC 81. **d** 81 **p** 82. C Belfast St Mary *Conn* 81-86; CMS 86-92; Zaïre 88-92; V Penycae *St As* 92-98; I Killesher *K, E & A* 98-01; Educn Adv Ch of Ireland Bps' Appeal 01-03. *5 Highfield Road, Sedbergh LA10 5DH* Tel (01539) 620670

PITT, Karen Lesley Finella. *See* TIMMIS, Mrs Karen Lesley Finella

PITT, Robert Edgar. b 37. Chich Th Coll 70. **d** 73 **p** 74. C Knowle *Bris* 73-77; C Wells St Cuth w Coxley and Wookey Hole *B & W* 77-81; TV Wellington and Distr 81-94; V Burnham 94-02; Chapl Taunton and Somerset NHS Trust 94-02; rtd 02. *Redmaye, 119 High Street, Burbage, Marlborough SN8 3AA* Tel (01672) 810651

PITT, Canon Trevor. b 45. Hull Univ BA66 MA69 Open Univ DipEd91. Linc Th Coll 68 Union Th Sem (NY) STM70. **d** 70 **p** 71. C Sheff St Geo *Sheff* 70-74; TV Gleadless Valley 74-78; TR 78-79; P-in-c Elham *Cant* 79-82; V Elham w Denton and Wootton 82-91; Vice Prin Cant Sch of Min 81-91; Six Preacher Cant Cathl *Cant* 85-91; Prin NEOC *Newc* from 91; Hon Can Newc Cathl from 91; Perm to Offic *Ripon* and *York* from 91. *Greenview House, Hamsterley, Bishop Auckland DL13 3QF,* or *NEOC, Ushaw College, Durham DH7 9RH* Tel and fax (01388) 488898 *or* tel 0191-373 7600 Fax 0191-373 7601
E-mail trevorpitt@aol.com

PITTIS, Stephen Charles. b 52. Sheff Univ MA01. Oak Hill Th Coll DipTh75. **d** 76 **p** 77. C Win Ch Ch *Win* 76-79; Chapl Dorset Inst of HE and Bournemouth and Poole Coll of FE *Sarum* 79-84; V Woking St Paul *Guildf* 84-97; Dir of Faith Development *Win* from 97. *60 Upper Brook Street, Winchester SO23 8DG* Tel (01962) 854133

PITTS, Miss Evadne Ione (Eve). b 50. Qu Coll Birm. **d** 89 **p** 94. C Bartley Green *Birm* 89-93; TD Kings Norton 93-94; TV 94-98; P-in-c Highters Heath 98-00; V from 00. *Immanuel Vicarage, Pickenham Road, Birmingham B14 4TG* Tel 0121-430 7578

PITTS, The Very Revd Michael James. b 44. Worc Coll Ox BA67. Qu Coll Birm 67. **d** 69 **p** 70. C-in-c Pennywell St Thos and Grindon St Oswald CD *Dur* 69-72; C Darlington H Trin 72-74; Chapl Dunkerque w Lille Arras etc Miss to Seamen *Eur* 74-79; V Tudhoe *Dur* 79-81; Chapl Helsinki w Moscow *Eur* 81-85; Chapl Stockholm 85-88; Hon Can Brussels Cathl 87-88; Canada from 88; Hon Chapl Miss to Seafarers from 88; Dean and R Ch Ch Cathl Montreal from 91. *18 Weredale Park, Westmount PQ, Canada, H3A 2B8* Tel (001) (514) 843 6577 Fax 847 1316 E-mail mjpitts@ibm.net

PITYANA, Nyameko Barney. b 45. BA BD. Ripon Coll Cuddesdon. **d** 82 **p** 83. C Woughton *Ox* 82-85; V Highters Heath *Birm* 85-88; Dir Progr to Combat Racism WCC 89-92; Perm to Offic *Ox* 92-98. *Address temp unknown*

PIX, Stephen James. b 42. Ex Coll Ox BA64 MA68 DipTh65 Univ of Wales (Cardiff) LLM97. Clifton Th Coll 66. **d** 68 **p** 69. C St Helens St Helen *Liv* 68-71; Lic to Offic *S'wark* 71-76; Hon C Wallington H Trin 76-84; V Osmotherley w E Harlsey and Ingleby Arncliffe *York* 84-89; V Ox St Mich w St Martin and All SS *Ox* 89-01; rtd 01; Perm to Offic *St E* from 01. *South Farm, Windmill Hill, Long Melford, Sudbury CO10 9AD* Tel (01787) 466198

PIZZEY, Canon Lawrence Roger. b 42. Dur Univ BA64. Westcott Ho Cam 65. **d** 67 **p** 68. C Bramford *St E* 67-71; Tutor Woodbridge Abbey 71-77; Asst Chapl Woodbridge Sch 71-77; P-in-c Flempton w Hengrave and Lackford *St E* 77-85; P-in-c Culford, W Stow and Wordwell 77-85; P-in-c Acton w Gt Waldingfield 85-89; V 89-95; P-in-c Sudbury and Chilton 95-98; R from 98; RD Sudbury from 96; Hon Can St E Cathl from 00. *The Rectory, Christopher Lane, Sudbury CO10 2AS* Tel (01787) 372611 E-mail lrp.sudbury@virgin.net

PLACE, Donald Lee Andrew. b 37. **d** 74 **p** 79. C Stainton-in-Cleveland *York* 79-81; TV Loughton St Jo *Chelmsf* 81-83; Chapl Worc R Infirmary and Hosps 83-85; rtd 95. *PO Box 40241, Pittsburgh, PA 15201, USA*

PLACE, Rodger Goodson. b 37. St Chad's Coll Dur BA60 DipTh62. **d** 62 **p** 63. C Pontesbury I and II *Heref* 62-65; C Heref St Martin 65-68; V Ditton Priors 68-75; R Neenton 68-75; P-in-c Aston Botterell w Wheathill and Loughton 69-75; P-in-c Burwarton w N Cleobury 69-75; P-in-c Dacre *Ripon* 75; P-in-c Dacre w Hartwith 75-76; V Dacre w Hartwith 75-76; V Wyther Vene Bede 82-92; P-in-c Roundhay St Jo 92-97; V 97-00; rtd 00; Perm to Offic *York* from 00. *72 Field Lane, Thorpe Willoughby, Selby YO8 9FL* Tel (01757) 703174

PLACE, Thomas Richard. b 59. Ridley Hall Cam 93. **d** 93 **p** 94. C Huyton St Geo *Liv* 93-97; CF from 97. *c/o MOD Chaplains (Army)* Tel (01980) 615804 Fax 615800

PLAISTER, Keith Robin. b 43. K Coll Lon BD65 AKC65. **d** 66 **p** 67. C Laindon w Basildon *Chelmsf* 66-71; V Gt Wakering 71-78; P-in-c Foulness 78; V Gt Wakering w Foulness 78-90; C Witham 91-94; TV 94-99; P-in-c Sandon from 99; P-in-c E Hanningfield from 99. *The Rectory, Rectory Chase, Sandon, Chelmsford CM2 7SQ* Tel (01245) 472262 E-mail keithplaister@hotmail.com

PLANT, Caroline Mary. b 56. Ripon Coll Cuddesdon 01. **d** 03. C Gnosall *Lich* from 03. *17 Fountain Fold, Gnosall, Stafford ST20 0DR* Tel (01785) 822001

PLANT, Mrs Edith Winifred Irene (Ewith). b 31. Liv Univ BEd71. Cranmer Hall Dur 81. **dss** 83 **d** 87. Countesthorpe w Foston *Leic* 83-86; Loughborough All SS and H Trin 86-90; Par Dn 87-90; Par Dn Thurnby Lodge 90-91; rtd 91; Perm to Offic *Leic* 91-96. *Craighall Cottage, 26 South Road, Ellon AB41 9NP* Tel (01358) 723628

PLANT, Mrs Glenys. b 49. ALA71. EMMTC 95. **d** 98 **p** 99. C Allestree *Derby* 98-01; rtd 01; Perm to Offic *Derby* from 01. *3 Stoodley Pike Gardens, Allestree, Derby DE22 2TN* Tel (01332) 552697

PLANT, John Frederick. b 61. Man Univ BA82 MEd95 Birm Univ DPS. Qu Coll Birm 83. **d** 85 **p** 86. C Kersal Moor *Man* 85-88; Chapl Aston Univ *Birm* 88-94; TR Market Bosworth, Cadeby w Sutton Cheney etc *Leic* 94-00; P-in-c The Sheepy Gp 98-00; TR Bosworth and Sheepy Gp from 00. *The Rectory, Park Street, Market Bosworth, Nuneaton CV13 0LL* Tel (01455) 290239 E-mail jplant@leicester.anglican.org

PLANT, Michael Ian. Man Univ MEd. St Jo Coll Nottm. **d** 99 **p** 00. NSM St D Cathl *St D* 99-01; NSM Dewisland from 01. *Lower Treginnis, St Davids, Haverfordwest SA62 6RS* Tel (01437) 720840

PLANT, Nicholas. b 58. MAAT87. St Alb and Ox Min Course 95. **d** 98 **p** 99. OLM W Slough *Ox* from 98. *The Pines, 6A Green Lane, Burnham, Slough SL1 8DR* Tel (01628) 604532 Mobile 07802-363835 Pager 07625-349908

PLANT, Richard. b 41. Open Univ BSc93. Qu Coll Birm 88. **d** 90 **p** 91. C Skelmersdale St Paul *Liv* 90-93; R Golborne 93-00; R Hesketh w Becconsall *Blackb* from 00. *All Saints' Rectory, Silverdale, Hesketh Bank, Preston PR4 6RZ* Tel (01772) 814798 E-mail richard.plant1@btinternet.com

PLANT, Richard George Nicholas. b 45. Man Univ BA67. Coll of Resurr Mirfield 68. **d** 71 **p** 72. C Cleckheaton St Jo *Wakef* 71-74; P-in-c Adel *Ripon* 74-78; V Ireland Wood 78-82; V Armley w New Wortley 82-92; R Garforth from 92. *The Rectory, Church Lane, Garforth, Leeds LS25 1NR* Tel 0113-286 3737 E-mail nick@plant.go-legend.net

PLANT, Robert David. b 28. Barn Univ BSc49 Ch Ch Coll Cant MA98. St Deiniol's Hawarden 74. **d** 76 **p** 80. NSM Llandrillo-yn-Rhos *St As* 76-79; NSM St Nicholas at Wade w Sarre and Chislet w Hoath *Cant* from 79. *4 Sandalwood Drive, St Nicholas-at-Wade, Birchington CT7 0PE* Tel (01843) 847276

PLATT, Andrew Martin Robert. b 41. Oak Hill Th Coll 74. **d** 76 **p** 77. C St Alb St Paul *St Alb* 76-79; V Gazeley w Dalham and Moulton *St E* 79-85; RD Mildenhall 84-86; V Gazeley w Dalham, Moulton and Kentford 85-86; R 86-89; R 89-97; P-in-c Sudbury w Ballingdon and Brundon 97-98; V from 98. *All Saints' Vicarage, Church Street, Sudbury CO10 2BL* Tel (01787) 372400

PLATT, Harold Geoffrey. b 27. Down Coll Cam BA50 MA52. Ridley Hall Cam 51. **d** 53 **p** 54. C Cambridge St Paul *Ely* 53-56; C-in-c Cam St Martin CD 56-57; R Lower Broughton St Clem *Man* 57-66; P-in-c Salford St Matthias w St Simon 62-66; Lic to Offic 66-76; Lic to Offic *Worc* 76-82; Hon C Belbroughton 83-86; Hon C Belbroughton w Fairfield and Clent 86-90; NSM Hagley 87-90; rtd 90; Co-ord for Decade of Evang 90-95; Perm to Offic *Nor* from 95. *Brecklands Cottage, Brecklands Green, North Pickenham, Swaffham PE37 8LG* Tel (01760) 441581

PLATT, John Dendy. b 24. Magd Coll Cam BA49 MA55. Wells Th Coll 50. **d** 52 **p** 53. C Headley All SS *Guildf* 52-56; C Haslemere 56-58; R Skelton w Hutton-in-the-Forest *Carl* 59-71; rtd 89. *17 Primula Drive, Norwich NR4 7LZ* Tel (01603) 504272

PLATT, John Emerson. b 36. Pemb Coll Ox BA59 MA65 DPhil77 Hull Univ MTh72. Cuddesdon Coll 59. **d** 61 **p** 62. C Adlington *Blackb* 61-64; C Sutton St Mich *York* 64-68; C Ox St Giles *Ox* 68-71; Asst Chapl Pemb Coll Ox 68-69; Chapl 69-02; rtd 02. *377 Woodstock Road, Oxford OX2 8AA* Tel (01865) 557684

PLATT, Mrs Katherine Mary. b 29. ARIBA51 Sheff Univ BA51. Westcott Ho Cam 76. **dss** 79 **d** 87. Chesterton Gd Shep *Ely* 78-84; Whitton St Aug *Lon* 84-86; Dean of Women's Min 86-94; Hampton St Mary 86-94; Par Dn 87-94; rtd 94; Perm to Offic *Ches* from 94. *56 Mereheath Park, Knutsford WA16 6AU* Tel (01656) 651192

PLATT, Michael Robert. b 39. SS Coll Cam BA61 MA85 Nottm Univ PGCE62. Cuddesdon Coll 62. **d** 64. C Far Headingley St Chad *Ripon* 64-65; Asst Master Belmont Coll Barnstaple 65-68; Asst Master Qu Coll Taunton 68-00; Ho Master 72-83; Hd Geography 89-00; rtd 00. *8 Court Hill, Taunton TA1 4SX* Tel (01823) 270687 Fax as telephone

PLATT, William David. b 31. St Chad's Coll Dur BA54. Coll of Resurr Mirfield 54. **d** 56 **p** 57. C Bethnal Green St Jo w St Simon *Lon* 56-60; C Pinner 60-65; V N Hammersmith St Kath 65-72; V Woodham *Guildf* 72-88; Chapl Community of St Mary V Wantage 88-96; rtd 96; NSM Blewbury, Hagbourne and Upton *Ox* 96-03. *14 Radley House, Marston Ferry Road, Oxford OX2 7EA* Tel (01865) 556019

PLATTEN, Aidan Stephen George. b 76. Ripon Coll Cuddesdon BTh03. **d** 03. C Woodbridge St Mary *St E* from 03. *40 Old Barrack Road, Woodbridge IP12 4ET* Tel (01394) 384842

PLATTEN, Gregory Austin David. b 78. Worc Coll Ox BA00. Ripon Coll Cuddesdon 01. **d** 03. C St John's Wood *Lon* from 03. *3 Cochrane Street, London NW8 7PA* Tel (020) 7722 4766 Mobile 07951-748565 E-mail gregoryplatten@ukonline.co.uk

✠PLATTEN, The Rt Revd Stephen George. b 47. Lon Univ BEd72 Trin Coll Ox DipTh74 BD03 UEA Hon DLitt03. Cuddesdon Coll 72. **d** 75 **p** 76 **c** 03. C Headington *Ox* 75-78; Chapl and Tutor Linc Th Coll 78-83; Can Res Portms Cathl and Dir of Ords *Portsm* 83-89; Abp's Sec for Ecum Affairs *Cant* 90-95; Hon Can Cant Cathl 90-95; Dean *Nor* 95-03; Bp Wakef from 03. *Bishop's Lodge, Woodthorpe Lane, Wakefield WF2 6JL* Tel (01924) 255349 E-mail bishop@wakefield.anglican.org

PLATTS, Mrs Hilary Anne Norrie. b 60. SRN81 K Coll Lon BD85 AKC85. Ripon Coll Cuddesdon 86. **d** 88 **p** 94. C Moulsham St Jo *Chelmsf* 88-90; Chapl Reading Univ *Ox* 93-95; C Calcot 90-92; NSM Reading Deanery 99-00; Perm to Offic *Birm* from 00; Chapl Birm Specialist Community Health NHS Trust from 01. *All Saints' Vicarage, 2 Walsall Road, Sutton Coldfield B74 4QJ* Tel 0121-308 5315

PLATTS, Timothy Caradoc. b 61. LMH Ox BA83 MA88 St Cross Coll Ox DPhil88. Ripon Coll Cuddesdon 87. **d** 89 **p** 90. C Whitley Ch Ch *Ox* 89-95; P-in-c Earley St Nic 95-98; V 98-00; V Four Oaks *Birm* from 00. *All Saints' Vicarage, 2 Walsall Road, Sutton Coldfield B74 4QJ* Tel 0121-308 5315

PLAXTON, Canon Edmund John Swithun. b 36. AKC60. **d** 61 **p** 62. C Crofton Park St Hilda w St Cypr *S'wark* 61-65; C Coulsdon St Jo 65-69; V Forest Hill St Paul 69-80; V Belmont 80-93; V Lingfield and Crowhurst 93-01; Hon Can S'wark Cathl 97-01; rtd 01. *Tynymaes, Y Fron, Upper Llandwrog, Caernarfon LL54 7BW* Tel (01286) 880188 E-mail edmundrachel@aol.com

PLAYER, Leslie Mark. b 65. Ridley Hall Cam CTM95. **d** 95 **p** 96. C Belper *Derby* 95-98; C Hamworthy *Sarum* 98-03; R W Downland from 03. *The Rectory, 97 Mill End, Damerham, Fordingbridge SP6 3HU* Tel (01725) 518642

PLAYLE, Ms Merrin Laura. b 58. Ridley Hall Cam. **d** 01 **p** 02. C Haslemere and Grayswood *Guildf* from 01. *16 Chatsworth Avenue, Haslemere GU27 1BA* Tel (01428) 643928

PLEDGER, Miss Alison Frances. b 56. Univ of Wales (Cardiff) BA79 K Alfred's Coll Win PGCE80. Linc Th Coll 89. **d** 91 **p** 94. Par Dn Soham *Ely* 91-94; C Ely 94-96; C Rusthall *Roch* 97-00; V Alkborough *Linc* from 00. *The Vicarage, Back Street, Alkborough, Scunthorpe DN15 9JJ* Tel (01724) 721126

PLEDGER, Mrs Nicola. b 55. Lon Bible Coll BA94. St Alb and Ox Min Course 99. **d** 01 **p** 02. C Ware Ch Ch *St Alb* from 01. *10 Cromwell Road, Ware SG12 7JZ* Tel (01920) 467918 E-mail alanic@freenetname.co.uk

PLIMLEY, Canon William. b 17. St Aid Birkenhead 50. **d** 52 **p** 53. C Norbury *Ches* 52-55; V Laisterdyke *Bradf* 55-83; RD Calverley 65-78; Hon Can Bradf Cathl 67-83; rtd 83; Perm to Offic *Bradf* from 83. *465 Bradford Road, Pudsey LS28 8ED* Tel (01274) 664862

PLIMMER, Wayne Robert. b 64. St Chad's Coll Dur BA85. St Steph Ho Ox 86. **d** 88 **p** 89. C Cockerton *Dur* 88-91; C Poulton-le-Fylde *Blackb* 91-93; V Darton *Wakef* from 93. *The Vicarage, 6 Jacob's Hall Court, Darton, Barnsley S75 5LY* Tel (01226) 384596

PLOWMAN, Richard Robert Bindon. b 38. Solicitor 61. Ridley Hall Cam 76. **d** 78 **p** 79. C Combe Down w Monkton Combe *B & W* 78-81; C Combe Down w Monkton Combe and S Stoke 81-83; V Coxley w Godney, Henton and Wookey from 83; RD Shepton Mallet 95-01. *The Vicarage, Vicarage Lane, Wookey, Wells BA5 1JT* Tel (01749) 677244 Fax as telephone

PLUCK, Richard. b 60. Southn Univ BTh90. Aston Tr Scheme 84 Sarum & Wells Th Coll 86. **d** 90 **p** 91. C Harpenden St Nic *St Alb* 90-94; CF from 94. *c/o MOD Chaplains (Army)* Tel (01980) 615804 Fax 615800

PLUMB, Gordon Alan. b 42. Leeds Univ BA. Sarum & Wells Th Coll. **d** 82 **p** 83. C Biggleswade *St Alb* 82-86; TV Grantham *Linc* 86-95; P-in-c Saxby All Saints 95-97; P-in-c Bonby 95-97; P-in-c Horkstow 95-97; P-in-c S Ferriby 95-97; P-in-c Worlaby 95-97; R S Ferriby from 97; V Bonby from 97; V Horkstow from 97; R Saxby All Saints from 97; V Worlaby from 97. *The Rectory, 1 Church Lane, Saxby-All-Saints, Brigg DN20 0QE* Tel (01652) 618747 E-mail gplumb2000@aol.com

PLUMLEY, Paul Jonathan. b 42. St Jo Coll Nottm 71. **d** 74 **p** 75. C Mile Cross *Nor* 74-77; P-in-c Wickham Skeith *St E* 77-79; P-in-c Stoke Ash, Thwaite and Wetheringsett 77-79; Assoc Min

Woodbridge St Jo 80-81; Chapl RAF 81-86; Perm to Offic *Roch* 86-95; R Hever, Four Elms and Mark Beech 95-00; Chapl Maidstone and Tunbridge Wells NHS Trust from 00. *Pembury Hospital, Tonbridge Road, Tunbridge Wells TN2 4QJ* Tel (01892) 823535 Mobile 07803-703742

PLUMMER, Mrs Deborah Ann. b 49. St Hugh's Coll Ox BA71 MA75. St Alb Minl Tr Scheme 82. **dss** 85 **d** 87 **p** 94. Ickenham *Lon* 85-88; Par Dn 87-88; C Northolt St Mary 88-92; Chapl Lee Abbey 92-95; P-in-c Kintbury w Avington *Ox* 95-01; Lect Bolton St Pet *Man* from 01. *3 Ivy Bank Road, Bolton BL1 7EQ* Tel (01204) 602697 E-mail revd.debby@virgin.net

PLUMMER, Frances. b 36. Lon Univ BA DipRS. S'wark Ord Course. **dss** 82 **d** 87 **p** 94. NSM Salfords *S'wark* from 87; Dean MSE (Croydon) from 99. *50 Park View Road, Salfords, Redhill RH1 5DN* Tel (01293) 785852

PLUMMER, Miss June Alice. b 29. Bris Univ BA50 CertEd51. Sarum & Wells Th Coll 89. **d** 89 **p** 94. NSM Hanham *Bris* 89-97; rtd 97; Perm to Offic *Bris* from 97. *11 Glenwood Drive, Oldland Common, Bristol BS30 9RZ* Tel (0117-949 8667

PLUMPTON, Paul. b 50. Keble Coll Ox BA72 MA76. St Steph Ho Ox 72. **d** 74 **p** 75. C Tonge Moor *Man* 74-76; C Atherton 76-79; V Oldham St Jas 79-99; V Oldham St Jas w St Ambrose from 99. *The Vicarage, Yates Street, Oldham OL1 4AR* Tel 0161-633 4441

PLUMPTRE, John Basil. b 25. Pemb Coll Cam BA49 MA54 CertEd52. Launde Abbey 75. **d** 75 **p** 76. C Leic St Pet *Leic* 75-80; C Stanford on Soar *S'well* 81-90; C Rempstone 81-90; C Costock 81-90; C E Leake 81-90; rtd 91; Perm to Offic *Leic* 92-03; Perm to Offic *S'well* from 98. *14 Outwoods Road, Loughborough LE11 3LY* Tel (01509) 215452

PLUNKETT, Michael Edward. b 38. Leeds Univ BSc61. Ely Th Coll 61. **d** 63 **p** 64. C Kirkby *Liv* 63-68; Lect Stockton-on-Tees 68-72; Lic to Offic *Dur* 72-73; TV Stockton 73-75; V Cantril Farm *Liv* 75-81; Soc Resp Officer 81-89; V Melling 81-91; TR Speke St Aid from 91. *The Rectory, Parade Crescent, Speke, Liverpool L24 2SH* Tel 0151-486 1521

PLUNKETT, Canon Peter William. b 30. Oak Hill Th Coll. **d** 61 **p** 62. C Fazakerley Em *Liv* 61-64; C St Helens St Mark 64-68; V Kirkdale St Paul N Shore 68-79; P-in-c Bootle St Mary w St Jo 77-79; V Bootle St Mary w St Paul 79-81; V Goose Green 81-89; V W Derby St Jas 89-98; Hon Can Liv Cathl 97-98; rtd 98. *50 Trinity Crescent, West Shore, Llandudno LL30 2PQ* Tel (01492) 872109

PLYMING, Philip James John. b 74. Rob Coll Cam BA96 St Jo Coll Dur BA00 DMS01. Cranmer Hall Dur 98. **d** 01 **p** 02. C Chineham *Win* from 01. *6 Copse View Close, Chineham, Basingstoke RG24 8EZ* Tel (01256) 357030 E-mail philip.plyming@lineone.net

PLYMOUTH, Archdeacon of. *See* WILDS, The Ven Anthony Ronald

PLYMOUTH, Suffragan Bishop of. *See* GARTON, The Rt Revd John Henry

PNEMATICATOS, Nicholas Peter Anthony. b 59. N Lon Univ BA92 Lon Univ MA93. Ripon Coll Cuddesdon DipMin95. **d** 95 **p** 96. C Yeovil St Mich *B & W* 95-98; Chapl Yeovil Coll 95-96; Chapl RN 98-02; Chapl RAF from 02. *Chaplaincy Services (RAF), HQ, Personnel and Training Command, RAF Innsworth, Gloucester GL3 1EZ* Tel (01452) 712612 ext 5164 Fax 9272 7111

POARCH, Canon John Chilton. b 30. Bris Univ BA54. Ridley Hall Cam 54. **d** 56 **p** 57. C Swindon Ch Ch *Bris* 56-59; C Corsham 59-61; Seychelles 61-63; V Brislington St Cuth *Bris* 63-69; Adn Seychelles 69-72; V Warmley *Bris* 72-86; R Syston 72-86; RD Bitton 79-85; P-in-c Bitton 80-86; Hon Can Bris Cathl 82-95; P-in-c Langley Fitzurse 86-94; Dioc Dir of Ords 86-94; Dir Ord Tr 94-95; P-in-c Draycot Cerne 87-94; rtd 95; Perm to Offic *Bris* from 95; and *B & W* 98-01; Officer for the Welfare of Rtd Mins Bris Adnry from 01; Dioc Convenor Rtd Clergy Assn from 01. *86 Stanshaws Close, Bradley Stoke, Bristol BS32 9AF* Tel (01454) 619053

POCOCK, Mrs Gillian Margaret. b 35. Nottm Univ BA57. Cranmer Hall Dur 82. **dss** 83 **d** 87 **p** 94. Bearpark *Dur* 83-88; Hon Par Dn 87-88; Par Dn S Hetton w Haswell 88; Asst RD Dur 89-90; Chapl St Aid Coll Dur 89-93; Par Dn Esh *Dur* 90-92; P-in-c 92-99; P-in-c Hamsteels 97-99; P-in-c Langley Park 98-99; rtd 99. *11 Cooke's Wood, Broom Park, Durham DH7 7RL* Tel 0191-386 1140 E-mail gillian.pocock@lineone.net

POCOCK, Lynn Elizabeth. b 48. Coll of Wooster Ohio BA69 CertEd71 Birm Univ DipTh75. Qu Coll Birm 73. **dss** 82 **d** 87 **p** 94. Gleadless *Sheff* 82-85; Thorpe Hesley 85-92; Par Dn 87-92; NSM Ribbesford w Bewdley and Dowles *Worc* from 92. *The Rectory, 57 Park Lane, Bewdley DY12 2HA* Tel (01299) 402275 E-mail revlynn@bigfoot.com

POCOCK, Canon Nigel John. b 47. Lon Univ BSc68 Birm Univ MA83. Lambeth STh78 Oak Hill Th Coll 69. **d** 72 **p** 73. C Tunbridge Wells St Jas *Roch* 72-75; C Heatherlands St Jo *Sarum* 75-78; V Leic St Chris *Leic* 78-83; R Camborne *Truro* 83-97; RD Carnmarth N 91-96; Hon Can Truro Cathl 92-97; V Old Windsor *Ox* from 97. *The Vicarage, Church Road, Old Windsor, Windsor SL4 2PQ* Tel (01753) 865778 Fax as telephone E-mail njpocock@ruan.freeserve.co.uk

PODGER, Richard Philip Champeney. b 38. K Coll Cam BA61 MA66. Cuddesdon Coll 62. **d** 64 **p** 65. C Doncaster St Geo *Sheff* 64-68; C Orpington All SS *Roch* 68-74; W Germany 76-88; Chapl Kassel *Eur* 83-88; TV Whitstable *Cant* 88-94; Perm to Offic from 95; Chapl E Kent Community NHS Trust from 02. *3 Alcroft Grange, Tyler Hill, Canterbury CT2 9NN* Tel (01227) 462038 E-mail podger@centrespace.freeserve.co.uk

POGMORE, Canon Edward Clement. b 52. Sarum & Wells Th Coll 76. **d** 79 **p** 80. C Calne and Blackland *Sarum* 79-82; TV Oakdale 82-89; Min Creekmoor LEP 82-89; Chapl Geo Eliot Hosp Nuneaton 89-94; Chapl Nuneaton Hosps 89-94; Chapl Geo Eliot Hosp NHS Trust Nuneaton from 94; Chapl Co-ord for N Warks from 94; Perm to Offic *Leic* from 91; Hon Can Cov Cathl *Cov* from 00. *The Chaplaincy, George Eliot Hospital, College Street, Nuneaton CV10 7DJ* Tel (024) 7686 5046, 7686 5281 *or* 7635 1351 ext 3528 E-mail edpog@hotmail.com *or* edward.pogmore@geh.nhs.uk

✠**POGO, The Most Revd Sir Ellison Leslie.** b 47. KBE01. St Jo Coll Auckland LTh. **d** 79 **c** 81. Asst P Anderson's Bay New Zealand 79-81; Solomon Is from 81; Bp Ysabel 81-94; Abp Melanesia and Bp Cen Melanesia from 94. *Archbishop's House, PO Box 19, Honiara, Solomon Islands* Tel (00677) 21137 *or* 26101 Fax 21098 *or* 22072 E-mail epogo@comphq.org.sb

POIL, Canon Ronald Wickens. b 30. AKC56. **d** 57 **p** 58. C Willesborough *Cant* 57-60; Chapl RAF 60-76; P-in-c Edith Weston w Normanton *Pet* 65-67; V Southbourne *Chich* 76-80; P-in-c W Thorney 76-80; RD Westbourne 78-91; V Southbourne w W Thorney 80-96; Can and Preb Chich Cathl 90-96; rtd 96; Perm to Offic *Portsm* from 97. *33 Mays Lane, Stubbington, Fareham PO14 2EW*

POINTS, John David. b 43. Qu Coll Birm 78. **d** 80 **p** 81. C Wednesbury St Paul Wood Green *Lich* 80-85; V 93-01; V Sedgley St Mary 85-93; TR Wednesfield from 01; AD Wolverhampton from 03. *The Rectory, 9 Vicarage Road, Wednesfield, Wolverhampton WV11 1SB* Tel (01902) 731462

POLASHEK, Miss Stella Christine. b 44. Leic Poly MA85. EMMTC 92. **d** 95 **p** 96. NSM Appleby Gp *Leic* from 95; Chapl Leic Gen Hosp NHS Trust 99-00; Chapl Univ Hosps Leic NHS Trust from 00. *38 Mawbys Lane, Appleby Magna, Swadlincote DE12 7AA* Tel (01530) 272707

POLE, David John. b 46. Bath Academy of Art BA72. Trin Coll Bris 84. **d** 86 **p** 87. C Bris St Mary Redcliffe w Temple etc *Bris* 86-90; V Alveston 90-98; V Alveston and Littleton-on-Severn w Elberton from 98. *The Vicarage, Gloucester Road, Alveston, Bristol BS35 3QT* Tel (01454) 414810 E-mail david.pole@dial.pipex.com

POLE, Francis John Michael. b 42. FRSA64 AMInstTA65 MInstTA00 CQSW74 MCMI99. St Jo Sem Wonersh 62. **d** 67 **p** 68. In RC Ch 67-75; NSM Walthamstow St Pet *Chelmsf* 75; NSM Penge Lane H Trin *Roch* 76-77; NSM Shirley St Jo *Cant* 77-79; Assoc Chapl The Hague *Eur* 79-83; V Norbury St Steph and Thornton Heath *Cant* 83-84; *S'wark* 85-00; Sen Dioc Police Chapl 95-00; Sen Chapl Sussex Police from 00; Nat Co-ord Police Chapl from 00; TV Crawley *Chich* from 00; Ind Missr for Crawley from 00. *35 Turnpike Place, Crawley RH11 7UA* Tel (01293) 513264 Mobile 07740-941565 E-mail francis.pole@virgin.net

POLHILL, Mrs Christine. b 46. Nottm Coll of Educn CertEd67. St Alb Minl Tr Scheme 81 Qu Coll Birm BA00. **dss** 84 **d** 87 **p** 94. St Alb St Mary Marshalswick *St Alb* 84-94; Hon Par Dn 87-94; C Cottered w Broadfield and Throcking 94-96; P-in-c 96-99; C Ardeley 94-96; P-in-c 96-99; C Weston 94-96; Perm to Offic *Lich* 99-00; C Lich St Mich w St Mary and Wall from 00. *Little Hayes, Beaudesert Park, Cannock Wood, Rugeley WS15 4JJ* Tel (01543) 674474 E-mail polhill@surfaid.org.uk

POLITT, Robert William. b 47. ARCM LGSM68. Oak Hill Th Coll 73. **d** 76 **p** 77. C Bexleyheath St Pet *Roch* 76-82; TV Southgate *Chich* 82-90; Chapl N Foreland Lodge Sch Basingstoke 90-98; R Sherfield-on-Loddon and Stratfield Saye etc *Win* from 98. *The Rectory, 33 Northfield Road, Sherfield-on-Loddon, Hook RG27 0DR* Tel (01256) 882209 E-mail 113225.103@compuserve.com

POLKINGHORNE, Canon John Charlton. b 30. KBE97. Trin Coll Cam BA52 PhD55 MA56 ScD74 FRS74. Westcott Ho Cam 79. **d** 81 **p** 82. NSM Chesterton St Andr *Ely* 81-82; C Bedminster St Mich *Bris* 82-84; V Blean *Cant* 84-86; Dean Trin Hall Cam 86-89; Pres Qu Coll Cam 89-96; Can Th Cant Cathl *Liv* from 94; rtd 95; Six Preacher Cant Cathl *Cant* from 96; Perm to Offic *Ely* from 96. *74 Hurst Park Avenue, Cambridge CB4 2AF* Tel (01223) 360743

POLL, Martin George. b 61. Kent Univ BA83. Ripon Coll Cuddesdon 84. **d** 87 **p** 88. C Mill Hill Jo Keble Ch *Lon* 87-90; Chapl RN from 90. *Royal Naval Chaplaincy Service, Room 201, Victory Building, HM Naval Base, Portsmouth PO1 3LS* Tel (023) 9272 7903 Fax 9272 7111

POLLAK, Canon Peter Henry. b 18. Worc Ord Coll 67. **d** 69 **p** 70. C Claines St Jo *Worc* 69-73; R Grimley w Holt 73-88; RD Martley and Worc W 84-88; Hon Can Worc Cathl 85-88; rtd 88;

Perm to Offic *Worc* from 88. *2 Tweenways, Main Road, Kempsey, Worcester WR5 3JY* Tel (01905) 820351

POLLARD, Ann. b 46. Dioc OLM tr scheme. **d** 03. OLM Mirfield *Wakef* from 03. *9 Manor Drive, Mirfield WF14 0ER* Tel (01924) 495322

POLLARD, Mrs Christine Beryl. b 45. DCR DNM. N Ord Course 86. **d** 89 **p** 94. Par Dn Ingrow cum Hainworth *Bradf* 89-94; C Nuneaton St Nic *Cov* 94-98; P-in-c Bourton w Frankton and Stretton on Dunsmore etc from 98. *The Rectory, Main Street, Frankton, Rugby CV23 9PB* Tel (01926) 632805

POLLARD, Canon Clifford Francis. b 20. AKC49. **d** 50 **p** 51. C Leominster *Heref* 50-53; C Luton St Mary *St Alb* 53-56; V Stopsley 56-60; Chapl Toc H (Kent and Sussex) 60-64; R Mersham *Cant* 64-68; Asst Dir of Educn 68-69; Dir of Educn 69-87; Hon Can Cant Cathl 72-91; rtd 87; Perm to Offic *Cant* from 03. *6 Lady Wootton's Green, Canterbury CT1 1NG* Tel (01227) 761674

POLLARD, David. b 55. LSE BSc77. Trin Coll Bris DipHE80. **d** 80 **p** 81. Canada 81-84; C-in-c Hillsfield and Monkspath LEP *Birm* 85-89; BCMS 89-93; Crosslinks 93-95; Spain 89-94; V Doncaster St Jas *Sheff* 95-98; rtd 98. *6 Mulberry Way, Armthorpe, Doncaster DN3 3UE* Tel (01302) 833404

POLLARD, David John Athey. b 44. ACP74 Culham Coll Ox CertEd69. St Jo Coll Nottm LTh88. **d** 88 **p** 89. C Illogan *Truro* 88-91; R Roche and Withiel 91-95; TV Maidstone St Martin *Cant* 95-97; C Parkwood CD 95-97; R Lanreath *Truro* 97-99; V Pelynt 97-99; R Lanreath, Pelynt and Bradoc from 99. *The Rectory, Lanreath, Looe PL13 2NU* Tel (01503) 220131

POLLARD, Canon David Stanley. b 49. Lon Univ BD80 AKC80 Bradf Univ MA. **d** 80 **p** 81. CGA 78-89; C Manningham St Mary and Bradf St Mich *Bradf* 80-83; P-in-c 83-84; TV Manningham 84-85; C 86-87; Lic to Offic 85-89; P-in-c Sidlesham *Chich* 89-94; Chapl Chich Coll of Tech 90-94; R Petworth *Chich* from 94; RD Petworth from 95; Can and Preb Chich Cathl from 03; Chapl Sussex Weald and Downs NHS Trust from 94. *The Rectory, Rectory Lane, Petworth GU28 0DB* Tel (01798) 342505 Fax 342375
E-mail dspollard@ntlworld.com

POLLARD, Eric John. b 43. Chich Th Coll 83. **d** 85 **p** 86. C Brighton St Matthias *Chich* 85-90; C E Grinstead St Swithun 90-96; C Hove 96-00; P-in-c Brighton St Matthias from 00. *St Matthias's Vicarage, 45 Hollingbury Park Avenue, Brighton BN1 7JQ* Tel (01273) 508178
E-mail eric.pollard@btinternet.com

POLLARD, James Adrian Hunter. b 48. St Jo Coll Nottm BTh78. **d** 78 **p** 79. C Much Woolton *Liv* 78-81; CMS 81-84; V Toxteth Park Ch Ch *Liv* 85-90; CF from 90; Perm to Offic *S'wark* 92-94. *c/o MOD Chaplains (Army)* Tel (01980) 615804 Fax 615800

POLLARD, John Edward Ralph. b 40. ALCD68. **d** 67 **p** 68. C Ollerton *S'well* 67-71; C Walton H Trin *Ox* 71-74; P-in-c Cuddington w Dinton 74-77; V Haddenham 74-77; V Kingsey 75-77; V Haddenham w Cuddington and Kingsey 77-85; R Aylesbury 80-85; V Haddenham w Cuddington, Kingsey etc 85-87; V Furze Platt 87-96; rtd 97. *113 Thame Road, Haddenham, Aylesbury HP17 8EH* Tel (01844) 290582

POLLARD, Matthew Rupert. b 66. St Jo Coll Nottm. **d** 03. C Huddersfield St Pet *Wakef* from 03; Asst Chapl Huddersfield Univ from 03. *75 St John's Road, Birkby, Huddersfield HD1 5EA* Tel (01484) 303299

POLLARD, Mrs Patricia Julie. b 46. Open Univ BA97. Cant Sch of Min 94. **d** 96 **p** 97. NSM Eastling w Ospringe and Stalisfield w Otterden *Cant* from 96. *7 Arthur Salmon Close, Faversham ME13 7PS* Tel (01795) 535407 E-mail nunc.dim@tesco.net

POLLARD, Roger Frederick. b 32. Sheff Univ BSc52 K Coll Lon PGCE55 Lanc Univ MA78. Linc Th Coll 56. **d** 58 **p** 59. C Catford St Laur *S'wark* 58-63; Ghana 63-66; C Fulford *York* 66-67; C Camberwell St Geo *S'wark* 67; Asst Master Roch Valley Sch Milnrow 68-69; S Craven Sch Cross Hills 69-91; rtd 91; Perm to Offic *Bradf* 69-93; Perm to Offic *B & W* from 93. *Little Garth, Rectory Lane, Dowlish Wake, Ilminster TA19 0NX* Tel (01460) 52594

POLLARD, Stephen. b 59. Coll of Resurr Mirfield 96. **d** 98 **p** 99. C Lt Lever *Man* 98-02; P-in-c Westleigh St Pet from 02. *St Peter's Vicarage, 6 Malham Close, Leigh WN7 4SD* Tel (01942) 673626

POLLARD, Vaughan. b 59. Aston Tr Scheme 90 Trin Coll Bris DipHE92. **d** 92 **p** 93. C Nailsea H Trin *B & W* 92-95; C Acomb St Steph *York* 95-97; P-in-c Moldgreen *Wakef* 97-99; P-in-c Rawthorpe 97-99; V Moldgreen and Rawthorpe from 99. *The Vicarage, 35 Church Street, Huddersfield HD5 9DL* Tel (01484) 424432 Fax as telephone

POLLINGER (née WHITFORD), Mrs Judith. b 41. Ex Univ TCert78 BEd79 Plymouth Univ 95. SW Minl Tr Course 92. **d** 95 **p** 96. NSM St Endellion w Port Isaac and St Kew *Truro* from 95. *4 Marshalls Way, Trelights, Port Isaac PL29 3TE* Tel (01208) 880181 E-mail rev.judith@endellion.fslife.co.uk

POLLINGTON, Miss Ann Elizabeth Jane. b 56. Univ Coll Chich BA00. Ripon Coll Cuddesdon 00. **d** 02 **p** 03. C Honiton, Gittisham, Combe Raleigh, Monkton etc *Ex* from 02. *5 Glen Farm Crescent, Honiton EX14 2GX*

POLLIT, Preb Michael. b 30. Worc Coll Ox BA54 MA58. Wells Th Coll 54. **d** 56 **p** 57. C Cannock *Lich* 56-59; C Codsall 59-62; V W Bromwich St Pet 62-67; R Norton in the Moors 67-76; RD Leek 72-76; V Shrewsbury St Chad 76-87; V Shrewsbury St Chad w St Mary 87-95; Preb Lich Cathl 81-95; P-in-c Shrewsbury St Alkmund 91-95; rtd 95; Perm to Offic *Heref* 96-99. *Pentreheyling House, Churchstoke, Montgomery SY15 6HU* Tel (01588) 620273

POLLIT, Ruth Mary. See LILLINGTON, Mrs Ruth Mary

POLLITT, Graham Anthony. b 48. BA79 DipHE. Oak Hill Th Coll 76. **d** 79 **p** 80. C Rusholme H Trin *Man* 79-82; TV Southgate *Chich* 82-83; C Burgess Hill St Andr 83-86; Chapl St Martin's Coll of Educn *Blackb* 86-90; Chapl Cheltenham and Glouc Coll of HE 90-98; Perm to Offic *Glouc* 98-99; C Bispham *Blackb* from 99. *1 Prenton Gardens, Thornton-Cleveleys FY5 3RR* Tel (01253) 828041

POLLOCK, Christopher John. b 62. TCD BTh89 QUB BD. CITC 86. **d** 89 **p** 90. C Agherton *Conn* 89-91; C Ballymoney w Finvoy and Rasharkin 91-93; I Derryvolgie from 93. *53 Kennedy Drive, Belsize Road, Lisburn BT27 4JA* Tel (028) 9266 3707 E-mail chriswenda@talk21.com

POLLOCK, Duncan James Morrison. b 54. MBE95 QGM75. Nottm Univ BCombStuds83. Linc Th Coll 80. **d** 83 **p** 84. C Folkestone St Mary and St Eanswythe *Cant* 83-85; CF 85-98; R Broughton, Bossington, Houghton and Mottisfont *Win* 98-00; I Groomsport *D & D* from 00. *32 Bangor Road, Groomsport, Bangor BT19 6JF* Tel (028) 9146 4476

POLLOCK, Hugh Gillespie. b 36. Oak Hill Th Coll 61. **d** 64 **p** 65. C Maidstone St Luke *Cant* 64-68; C Washfield *Ex* 68-71; C Washfield, Stoodleigh, Withleigh etc 71-73; Chapl Lee Abbey 73-76; V Dersingham *Nor* 76-80; P-in-c Anmer 79-80; P-in-c Shernbourne 79-80; R Dersingham w Anmer and Shernborne 80-89; RD Heacham and Rising 87-89; C Barnstaple *Ex* 89-94; P-in-c Atherington and High Bickington 94-96; P-in-c Burrington 94-96; TV Newton Tracey, Horwood, Alverdiscott etc 96-98; rtd 99; Perm to Offic *Ex* 99-01; C Diptford, N Huish, Harberton, Harbertonford etc from 01. *The Vicarage, Harberton, Totnes TQ9 7SA* Tel (01803) 868445

POLLOCK, James Colin Graeme. b 53. St Chad's Coll Dur BA76. Ripon Coll Cuddesdon 77. **d** 78 **p** 79. C Hartlepool St Oswald *Dur* 78-81; C Hartlepool St Aid 81-84; V Dawdon from 84; V Seaham Harbour from 03. *The Vicarage, Melbury Street, Seaham SR7 7NF* Tel 0191-581 2317

POLLOCK, Jennifer Susan. b 51. Liv Univ BA72 PGCE73. Glouc Sch of Min 89. **d** 92 **p** 94. NSM Leominster *Heref* 92-97; P-in-c Eardisley w Bollingham, Willersley, Brilley etc 97-00; R from 00. *Church House, Church Road, Eardisley, Hereford HR3 6NN* Tel (01544) 327440

POLLOCK, John Charles. b 23. Trin Coll Cam BA46 MA48 Samford Univ (USA) Hon DLitt02. Ridley Hall Cam 49. **d** 51 **p** 52. C Portman Square St Paul *Lon* 51-53; Ed The Churchman 53-58; R Horsington *B & W* 53-58; Perm to Offic *Ex* 61-98; rtd 88. *Rose Ash House, South Molton EX36 4RB* Tel (01769) 550403

POLOMSKI, Elias Robert Michael. b 42. **d** 85 **p** 86. In RC Ch 85-90; C Headington Quarry *Ox* 91-94; Chapl St Alb Abbey *St Alb* 94-97; Chapl St Alb Sch 94-97; P-in-c Streatley w Moulsford *Ox* from 97. *The Vicarage, Streatley, Reading RG8 9HX* Tel (01491) 872191

POMERY, David John. b 45. SS Mark & Jo Coll Chelsea CertEd67. Chich Th Coll 75. **d** 77 **p** 78. C Coseley Ch Ch *Lich* 77-79; C Stocksbridge *Sheff* 79-81; V Bentley 81-87; Radlett Prep Sch 87-03; P-in-c Barton Bendish w Beachamwell and Shingham *Ely* from 03; P-in-c Fincham from 03; P-in-c Marham from 03; P-in-c Shouldham from 03; P-in-c Shouldham Thorpe from 03. *The Rectory, Barton Bendish, King's Lynn PE33 9DP* Tel (01366) 348043

POMFRET, Albert. b 23. Univ of Wales (Cardiff) BSc57 MTh95 Lon Univ MA69 FCP83 Potchefstroom Univ PhD02. Oak Hill NSM Course 92. **d** 75 **p** 76. NSM Dartford Ch Ch *Roch* 75-80; Perm to Offic 80-92; Perm to Offic *Ex* from 92. *9 St Margaret's Court, Exe Street, Topsham, Exeter EX3 0JL* Tel (01392) 873404

POND, Geraldine Phyllis. b 53. SRN74. St Jo Coll Nottm MA97. **d** 97 **p** 98. C Ancaster Wilsford Gp *Linc* 97-01; P-in-c Harlaxton Gp from 01; Chapl Linc Distr Healthcare NHS Trust from 01. *The Rectory, 6 Rectory Lane, Harlaxton, Grantham NG32 1HD* Tel (01476) 567059 E-mail revgpond@aol.com

POND, Nigel Peter Hamilton. b 40. AKC65. **d** 66 **p** 67. C E Dereham w Hoe *Nor* 66-69; C Chapl RN 69-85; TR Woughton *Ox* 85-93; Chapl Milton Keynes Gen Hosp 85-93; RD Milton Keynes *Ox* 90-93; R Olney w Emberton 93-97; R Olney from 97. *Olney Rectory, 9 Orchard Rise, Olney MK46 5HB* Tel (01234) 713308 E-mail nigel@npond.freeserve.co.uk

PONSONBY, Simon Charles Reuben. b 66. Bris Univ MLitt96. Trin Coll Bris BA94. **d** 95. C Thorpe Edge *Bradf* 95-98; Pastorate Chapl Ox St Aldate *Ox* from 98. *14 Walton Street, Oxford OX1 2HG* Tel (01865) 552849 *or* 244713 Fax 201543 E-mail simon.ponsonby@staldates.org.uk

PONT, Gordon John Harper. b 35. Glas Univ BSc56 BD65. Edin Th Coll 56. **d** 59 **p** 60. C Dunfermline *St And* 59-62; C Motherwell *Glas* 62-65; R Largs 65-68; Dioc Supernumerary *Bre* 68-71; Chapl Dundee Univ 68-73; R Dundee St Luke 71-74; NSM Dundee St Paul 74-99; Hon Chapl St Paul's Cathl Dundee 74-99; Dioc Sec from 96. *Dalhouzie, 11 West Moulin Road, Pitlochry PH16 5EA* Tel (01796) 472745

PONTEFRACT, Archdeacon of. *Vacant*

PONTEFRACT, Suffragan Bishop of. *See* ROBINSON, The Rt Revd Anthony William

PONTER, John Arthur. b 37. Univ of Wales (Abth) BA61 Linacre Coll Ox BA63 MA68 UEA PhD81. Wycliffe Hall Ox 61. **d** 63 **p** 64. C Gidea Park *Chelmsf* 63-67; C-in-c Colchester St Anne CD 67-69; V Colchester St Anne 69-72; Chapl UEA *Nor* 72-78; Chapl Chelmsf Cathl *Chelmsf* 78-79; Chapl Chelmsf Cathl Cen 78-84; V Moulsham St Jo 79-85; Dir Man Chr Inst and Chr Leadership Course 85-92; Educn Officer N Federation for Tr in Min 85-92; TR Stantonbury and Willen *Ox* 92-02; rtd 02. *1 Highveer Croft, Tattenhoe, Milton Keynes MK4 3BN* Tel (01908) 520329 E-mail ponter@msn.com

PONTIN, Colin Henry. b 37. Trin Coll Bris. **d** 83 **p** 84. C Downend *Bris* 83-86; C Riverside *Ox* 86-88; V Eton w Eton Wick and Boveney 88-90; TV Riverside 91-95; V Churt *Guildf* 95-02; rtd 02. *22 Shearsbrook Close, Bransgore, Christchurch BH23 8HF* Tel (01425) 673918 Mobile 07989-173259 E-mail colinpontin@lineone.net

POOBALAN, Isaac Munuswamy. b 62. RGN84 Edin Univ BD94 MTh97 Aber Univ MPhil98. Edin Th Coll 91. **d** 94 **p** 95. C Edin St Pet *Edin* 94-97; P-in-c Aberdeen St Clem *Ab* 97-01; R Aberdeen St Jo from 01. *15 Ashley Road, Aberdeen AB10 6RU* Tel (01224) 591527 E-mail i.poovan@abdn.ac.uk

POODHUN, Canon Lambert David. b 30. Natal Univ BA53. Edin Th Coll 54. **d** 56 **p** 57. S Africa 56-76; Adn Durban 75-76; C Upton cum Chalvey *Ox* 77-80; Chapl Kingston Hosp Surrey 80-81; Chapl Tooting Bec Hosp Lon 81-84; Chapl Hurstwood Park Hosp Haywards Heath 84-01; Chapl St Fran Hosp Haywards Heath 84-94; Chapl Mid Sussex NHS Trust 94-01; Can and Preb Chich Cathl *Chich* from 93; Hon C Haywards Heath St Rich from 01. *8 Nursery Close, Haywards Heath RH16 1HP* Tel (01444) 440938 E-mail lambertpoodhun@aol.com

POOLE, Andrew John. b 52. EMMTC 98. **d** 01 **p** 02. NSM Scraptoft *Leic* from 01. *64 Scalborough Close, Countesthorpe, Leicester LE8 5XH* Tel 0116-277 4949

POOLE, Clifford George. b 36. Keble Coll Ox BA61 MA65 Lon Univ PGCE75. S'wark Ord Course 83. **d** 86 **p** 87. C W Dulwich All SS and Em *S'wark* 86-90; Chapl Luxembourg *Eur* 90-02; rtd 02; P-in-c Alderton, Gt Washbourne, Dumbleton etc *Glouc* from 02. *The Vicarage, Church Road, Alderton, Tewkesbury GL20 8NR* Tel (01242) 620238

POOLE, Denis Tom. b 19. St Jo Coll Dur 39. St Aid Birkenhead 41. **d** 43 **p** 44. C Toxteth Park St Silas *Liv* 43-45; C Kirkdale St Lawr 45-48; Chapl Glouc Docks Mariners' Ch *Glouc* 48-51; Chapl Glouc R Infirmary 48-51; V Lambeth St Andr w St Thos *S'wark* 51-54; V New Ferry *Ches* 54-63; V Biddulph *Lich* 64-85; Chapl Biddulph Grange Hosp Staffs 64-85; rtd 85; Perm to Offic *Win* 85-97. *12 High Carr Road, Durham DH1 5AT* Tel 0191-383 2733

POOLE, Denise June. b 49. Leic Univ BSc70 Bradf and Ilkley Coll DipAdEd85. N Ord Course 90. **d** 93 **p** 94. C Horton and Bradf St Oswald Chapl Green *Bradf* 93-97; Chapl Co-ord Bradf Hosps NHS Trust 97-00; V Bradf St Aug Undercliffe *Bradf* from 00. *St Augustine's Vicarage, Undercliffe Lane, Bradford BD3 0DW* Tel (01274) 305604 E-mail denise@undercliffe.org.uk

POOLE, Edward John. b 53. Hull Univ BA81. St Steph Ho Ox 81. **d** 83 **p** 84. C Stevenage St Andr and St Geo *St Alb* 83-86; Madagascar 86-88; V Weston *St Alb* 88-96; P-in-c Ardeley 88-96; P-in-c Cottered w Broadfield and Throcking 94-96; Chapl Bucharest w Sofia *Eur* 96-98; Chapl HM Pris Lewes from 98. *HM Prison, Brighton Road, Lewes BN7 1EA* Tel (01273) 405259 Fax 405101

POOLE, Frederick Harold. b 14. Clifton Th Coll 54. **d** 56 **p** 56. C Bucknall and Bagnall *Lich* 56-60; R Chorlton on Medlock St Steph *Man* 60-68; rtd 79. *4 Bell Road, Wallasey CH44 8DJ*

POOLE, Helen Margaret. b 39. SRN. SW Minl Tr Course. **d** 94 **p** 95. NSM Ludgvan *Truro* 94-97; NSM Paul 97-02; NSM St Buryan, St Levan and Sennen from 02. *Underhill Farmhouse, St Levan, Penzance TR19 6JS* Tel (01736) 810842 Fax 810858 E-mail helena@fish.co.uk

POOLE, Ian Richard Morley. b 62. Birm Univ MB, ChB85 MRCGP90 DRCOG90 St Jo Coll Dur BA. Cranmer Hall Dur 00. **d** 02. C Willenhall H Trin *Lich* from 02. *13 Wesley Road, Willenhall WV12 5QT* E-mail ianpoole1@compuserve.com

POOLE, James Christopher. b 73. Peterho Cam BA94 MA98. Aston Tr Scheme 96 Wycliffe Hall Ox 97. **d** 00 **p** 01. C Wimbledon Park St Luke *S'wark* from 00. *5 Farquhar Road, London SW19 8DA* Tel (020) 8947 0846 E-mail james@realfire.org

POOLE, Miss Joan Wendy. b 37. Sarum Dioc Teacher Tr Coll CertEd57 Dalton Ho Bris DipTh66 Trin Coll Bris 86. **d** 87 **p** 94. Par Dn Longfleet *Sarum* 87-89; Par Dn Hamworthy 89-94; C 94-97; rtd 97; Perm to Offic *Sarum* from 97. *35 Borley Road, Poole BH17 7DT* Tel (01202) 256377

POOLE, Martin Bryce. b 59. Reading Univ BSc80 Nottm Univ DipTh82 Dip Acting 85. St Jo Coll Nottm DPS84. **d** 87 **p** 88. NSM Tulse Hill H Trin and St Matthias *S'wark* 87-99; NSM Hove *Chich* 00-01; Perm to Offic from 01. *14 Pembroke Avenue, Hove BN3 5DA* Tel (01273) 747919 Fax as telephone E-mail m.poole@virgin.net

POOLE, Martin Ronald. b 59. Aston Univ BSc81 Leeds Univ BA86. Coll of Resurr Mirfield 83. **d** 87 **p** 88. C Sheff St Cath Richmond Road *Sheff* 87-90; C W Hampstead St Jas *Lon* 90-94; V Colindale St Matthias from 94. *St Matthias' Vicarage, Rushgrove Avenue, London NW9 6QY* Tel (020) 8205 8783

POOLE, Peter William. b 35. St Pet Hall Ox BA59 MA63. Wells Th Coll 59. **d** 61 **p** 62. C Cheriton Street *Cant* 61-64; C Birchington w Acol 64-67; V Newington 67-73; P-in-c Lower Halstow 72-73; V Bearsted 73-76; V Lane End w Cadmore End *Ox* 84-89; R Chalfont St Giles 89-99; rtd 99; Perm to Offic *Guildf* from 01. *Primrose Cottage, St Nicholas Avenue, Cranleigh GU6 7AQ* Tel (01483) 272703

POOLE, Richard Eric. b 65. Huddersfield Poly BEng87. Trin Coll Bris BA98. **d** 98 **p** 99. C Sandal St Helen *Wakef* 98-01; TV Southgate *Chich* from 01. *St Andrew's Vicarage, Weald Drive, Crawley RH10 6NU* Tel (01293) 531828

POOLE, Roy John. b 26. Lon Univ BD54. St Jo Coll Lon LTh54. **d** 54 **p** 55. C Benwell St Aid *Newc* 54-57; Australia 57-61 and from 74; R Bradford cum Beswick *Man* 61-66; Area Sec Chr Aid Dept BCC 66-68; Regional Supervisor (S and E England) Chr Aid 68-74; rtd 91. *14 Chungking Grove, Stratton, W Australia 6056* Tel (0061) (8) 9250 2652 E-mail roy@echidna.id.au

POOLE, Stuart. b 33. CEng65 FIEE85 Loughb Coll DLC55 Lon Univ BScEng55 Man Univ MSc76. **d** 91 **p** 92. NSM Cheadle *Ches* 91-03; Perm to Offic from 03. *1 Dene House, Green Pastures, Stockport SK4 3RB* Tel 0161-432 6426 Fax as telephone E-mail stuart.poole@ukgateway.net

POOLE, Wendy. *See* POOLE, Miss Joan Wendy

POOLEY, Clive Nicholas. b 51. Lon Univ BEd74. NTMTC 96. **d** 99 **p** 00. C Barking St Marg w St Patr *Chelmsf* 99-02; V Barking St Erkenwald from 02. *St Erkenwald's Vicarage, Levett Road, Barking IG11 9JZ* Tel (020) 8594 2271 Fax as telephone E-mail revdclive@macunlimited.net

POOLEY, Peter Owen. b 32. Kelham Th Coll 54. **d** 58 **p** 59. C Paddington St Mary Magd *Lon* 58-62; R Rockland St Mary w Hellington *Nor* 62-67; Asst Master Thos Lethaby Sch 67-70; St Phil Gr Sch Edgbaston 70-74; Lordswood Gr Sch 74-80; Hon C Edgbaston St Geo *Birm* 77-80; R Elton *Ely* 80-01; P-in-c Stibbington and Water Newton 80-01; R Elton w Stibbington and Water Newton 01-02; rtd 02. *1 Warrenne Keep, Stamford PE9 2NX* Tel (01780) 751646

POOLMAN, Alfred John. b 46. K Coll Lon BD69 AKC69 Sheff Univ Dip Psychotherapy 83. St Aug Coll Cant 69. **d** 70 **p** 71. C Headingley *Ripon* 70-74; C Moor Allerton 75-78; C Monk Bretton *Wakef* 78-80; C Athersley 80; V Copley 80-90; Chapl Halifax Gen Hosp 80-90; R Llanfynydd *St As* from 90. *The Rectory, Llanfynydd, Wrexham LL11 5HH* Tel (01978) 762304

POOLMAN, Mrs Carole Margaret. b 53. Chelmer Inst of HE CSS80. St As & Ban Minl Tr Course 98. **d** 01 **p** 02. NSM Pontblyddyn *St As* from 01. *The Rectory, Llanfynydd, Wrexham LL11 5HH* Tel (01978) 762304

POOLTON, Martin Ronald. b 60. Kingston Poly BSc81 Salford Univ MSc83 Bp Grosseteste Coll PGCE85 FRGS81 SSC. Cuddesdon Coll DipMin95. **d** 97 **p** 98. C Penzance St Mary w St Paul *Truro* 97-99; C Northampton St Matt *Pet* 99-01; R Jersey St Pet *Win* from 01. *The Rectory, La Rue du Presbytère, St Peter, Jersey JE3 7ZH* Tel (01534) 481805 Fax as telephone E-mail poolton@onetel.net.uk

POPE, Charles Guy. b 48. AKC70. St Aug Coll Cant 70. **d** 71 **p** 72. C Southgate Ch Ch *Lon* 71-74; C N St Pancras All Hallows 74-77; C Hampstead St Steph 74-77; V New Southgate St Paul 77-86; V Brookfield St Mary from 86; P-in-c Brookfield St Anne, Highgate Rise 88-99; AD S Camden 95-00. *St Mary's Vicarage, 85 Dartmouth Park Road, London NW5 1SL* Tel (020) 7267 5941 Mobile 07770-693435 Fax 7482 2136 E-mail epopyug@aol.com

POPE, Canon Colin. b 51. Brasted Place Coll 74. Linc Th Coll 75. **d** 78 **p** 79. C W Derby Gd Shep *Liv* 78-81; C-in-c Westbrook St Phil CD 81-82; V Westbrook St Phil 82-87; V Orrell 87-96; Chapl Billinge Hosp Wigan 87-96; V Southport Em *Liv* from 96; AD N Meols from 00; Hon Can Liv Cathl from 03. *Emmanuel Vicarage, 12 Allerton Road, Southport PR9 9NJ* Tel (01704) 532743 Fax as telephone E-mail revcp@aol.com

POPE, David Allan. b 20. Oriel Coll Ox BA45 MA72. Ely Th Coll 45. **d** 47 **p** 48. C Folkestone St Mary and St Eanswythe *Cant* 47-51; V Tovil 51-54; R E Horsley *Guildf* 54-65; R Ivychurch w Old Romney and Midley *Cant* 63-65; P-in-c Brenzett w Snargate and Snave 64-65; P-in-c Newchurch 64-65; P-in-c St Mary in the Marsh 64-65; P-in-c Burmarsh 64-65; R Broadstairs 65-73;

P-in-c Berwick *Chich* 73-76; P-in-c Arlington 73-75; P-in-c Selmeston w Alciston 74-76; R Berwick w Selmeston and Alciston 76; P-in-c Rusper 76-79; R Colsterworth *Linc* 79-81; P-in-c Ingworth 81-85; P-in-c Alby w Thwaite *Nor* 81-85; P-in-c Erpingham w Calthorpe 81-85; P-in-c Aldborough w Thurgarton 83-85; rtd 85; Perm to Offic *Nor* from 85. *Burgate Lodge, Saddle Bow, King's Lynn PE34 3AR* Tel (01553) 617599

POPE, Donald Keith. b 35. Sarum & Wells Th Coll 81. **d** 76 **p** 77. Hon C Caerleon *Mon* 76-82; C 82-83; V Pontypool 83-86; R Grosmont and Skenfrith and Llangattock etc 86-98; RD Abergavenny 93-98; rtd 98. *24 Incline Way, Ridgewood Gardens, Saundersfoot SA69 9LX* Tel (01834) 812089

POPE, Miss Elizabeth Mercy. b 51. Man Univ BSc73 Ex Univ PGCE74. Trin Coll Bris 99. **d** 01 **p** 02. C Bardsley *Man* from 01. *St Cuthbert's Vicarage, Tanners Fold, Oldham OL8 2NN* Tel 0161-633 3148 E-mail elizabeth.pope@lineone.net

POPE, Michael John. b 37. Sarum Th Coll 62. **d** 65 **p** 66. C Broseley w Benthall *Heref* 65-68; C Shrewsbury St Giles *Lich* 68-71; P-in-c Shrewsbury St Geo 71-75; V 75-79; V Gnosall 79-00; RD Eccleshall 92-00; rtd 00; Perm to Offic *Lich* from 01. *Rivendell, 2 Dark Lane, Broseley TF12 5LH* Tel (01952) 883960

POPE, Michael Ronald. b 41. Bps' Coll Cheshunt 65. **d** 68 **p** 69. C Lyonsdown H Trin *St Alb* 68-72; C Seaford w Sutton *Chich* 72-76; R Hurstpierpoint 76-80; rtd 99. *34 Wilton Road, Shanklin PO37 7BZ* Tel (01983) 863602

POPEJOY, Wilfred. b 28. St Jo Coll Nottm 88. **d** 88. Hon C Donisthorpe and Moira w Stretton-en-le-Field *Leic* 88-98; rtd 98; Perm to Offic *Leic* from 99. *79 Donisthorpe Lane, Moira, Swadlincote DE12 6BB* Tel (01283) 760476

POPELY, David Charles. K Coll Lon BA00. SEITE 00. **d** 03. *143 Killearn Road, London SE6 1BS* Tel (020) 8473 4248 Mobile 07947-309197 Fax (020) 8464 7814 E-mail dave.popely@btinternet.com

POPONDOTA, Bishop of. See JUPP, The Rt Revd Roger Alan

POPP, Miss Julie Alice Gisela. b 45. Univ of BC BA71. St Jo Coll Nottm 78. **dss** 81 **d** 87 **p** 94. Woking St Mary *Guildf* 81-83; Hornsey Rise St Mary w St Steph *Lon* 83-87; Par Dn Hornsey Rise Whitehall Park Team 87-91; Par Dn Sutton St Nic *S'wark* 91-94; C 94-98; Missr Sutton Town Cen 91-98; TV Hackney Marsh *Lon* from 98. *105 Mayola Road, London E5 0RG* Tel (020) 8533 4034 Fax as telephone E-mail hackneymar@aol.com

POPPLE, The Ven Dennis. b 31. Master Mariner 58. Vancouver Sch of Th LTh72 San Francisco Th Sem DMin89 St Aid Birkenhead 59. **d** 62 **p** 63. C Walkden Moor *Man* 62-65; Canada from 65; Admin Adn 87-96; rtd 96. *8580 General Currie Road, Suite 113, Richmond BC, Canada, V6Y 3V5*

POPPLETON, Julian George. b 63. St Chad's Coll Dur BA85 PGCE86 Cam Univ DipRS94 Surrey Univ BA02. STETS 99. **d** 02 **p** 03. NSM Harnham *Sarum* from 02; Chapl K Edw VI Sch Southn from 02. *19 Thompson Close, Salisbury SP2 8QU* Tel (01722) 334272 E-mail jgp@kes.hants.sch.uk

POPPLEWELL, Andrew Frederick. b 53. St Jo Coll Dur BA75. Wycliffe Hall Ox 76. **d** 78 **p** 79. C Clifton *York* 78-81; C Lich St Chad *Lich* 82-84; V Laisterdyke *Bradf* 84-99. *Clifton, 210A Leeds Road, Eccleshill, Bradford BD2 3JU* Tel (01274) 637651

PORT MORESBY, Bishop of. See FOX, The Rt Revd Peter John

PORTEOUS, Canon Eric John. b 34. AKC58. **d** 59 **p** 60. C Wandsworth St Paul *S'wark* 59-62; C Leeds St Pet *Ripon* 62-66; V Wortley de Leeds 66-72; RD Armley 70-72; R Woolwich St Mary w H Trin *S'wark* 72-77; Sub-Dean Woolwich 74-77; P-in-c Woolwich St Mich 75-77; R Woolwich St Mary w St Mich 77-79; Chapl Whipps Cross Hosp Lon 79-96; Lic to Offic *Chelmsf* 79-86; Hon Can Chelmsf Cathl 86-96; rtd 96; Perm to Offic *Chelmsf* from 96. *128 Grove Hill, London E18 2HZ* Tel (020) 8530 5660

PORTEOUS, Michael Stanley. b 35. S'wark Ord Course 70. **d** 73 **p** 74. C Barnes St Mich *S'wark* 73-76; Chapl Greycoat Hosp Sch 76-78; C Brighton Annunciation *Chich* 78-80; Chapl Ch Hosp Horsham 80-85; TV Moulsecoomb *Chich* 85-88; R W Blatchington 88-99; rtd 99; Perm to Offic *Chich* from 99. *15 Mariners Close, Shoreham-by-Sea BN43 5LU*

PORTER, Andrew William. b 69. Bris Univ BSc91 BA01 PGCE94. Trin Coll Bris 98. **d** 01 **p** 02. C Ipsley *Worc* from 01. *77 Edgmond Close, Redditch B98 0JQ* Tel (01527) 465451 E-mail andrew.porter@bigfoot.com

PORTER, Anthony. b 43. Hertf Coll Ox BA74 MA78 Fitzw Ho Cam BA76 MA80. Ridley Hall Cam 74. **d** 77 **p** 78. C Edgware *Lon* 77-80; C Haughton St Mary *Man* 80-83; P-in-c Bacup Ch Ch 83-87; V 87-91; R Rusholme H Trin from 91. *Holy Trinity Rectory, Platt Lane, Manchester M14 5NF* Tel 0161-224 1123 Fax 224 1144 E-mail tony@plattchurch.org

PORTER, Arthur William. b 29. St Deiniol's Hawarden 70. **d** 70 **p** 71. C Ruislip St Martin *Lon* 70-80; V Kingsbury H Innocents 80-94; rtd 94; Perm to Offic *Sarum* from 94. *24 Belle Vue Road, Salisbury SP1 3YG* Tel (01722) 331314

PORTER, Barbara Judith. See JEAPES, Mrs Barbara Judith

PORTER, Brian John Henry. b 33. SW Minl Tr Course 78. **d** 81 **p** 82. NSM Plymouth St Andr w St Paul and St Geo *Ex* 81-85; Perm to Offic 85-87; NSM Devonport St Barn 87-90; C Brampton St Thos *Derby* 90-95; Asst Chapl Amsterdam w Den

Helder and Heiloo *Eur* 95-97; rtd 97; Perm to Offic *Glouc* 99-00. *Newcombes End, Elkstone, Cheltenham GL53 9PD* Tel (01242) 870258 Fax as telephone

PORTER, Brian Meredith. b 39. Monash Univ Aus BA66 Trin Hall Cam BA75 MA79 New England Univ NSW BLitt79 MLitt85 ACT ThD01. Cuddesdon Coll 68. **d** 68 **p** 71. Australia 68-73 and from 75; C Kew 68-69; K Sch Parramatta 70-73; Perm to Offic *Ely* 73; Chapl Canberra Gr Sch 75-82; Chapl Ivanhoe Gr Sch 83-97; Sen Chapl Melbourne Gr Sch from 98. *Melbourne Grammar School, Domain Road, South Yarra, Vic, Australia 3141* Tel (0061) (3) 9882 8740 *or* 9868 7157 Mobile 407-552425 Fax (3) 9882 4137 E-mail bporter@mgs.vic.edu.au

PORTER, Damian Michael. b 66. Linc Th Coll BTh92. **d** 92 **p** 93. C Pelsall *Lich* 92-96; V Greenlands *Blackb* 96-00; V Heyhouses on Sea from 00. *St Anne's Vicarage, 4 Oxford Road, Lytham St Annes FY8 2EA* Tel (01253) 722725 E-mail dmp@oxrd.fsnet.co.uk

PORTER, Canon David Anthony (Tony). b 34. Wycliffe Hall Ox 73. **d** 75 **p** 76. C Watford St Luke *St Alb* 75-78; C Worting *Win* 78-81; V Snettisham *Nor* 81-82; P-in-c Ingoldisthorpe 81-82; C Fring 81-82; R Snettisham w Ingoldisthorpe and Fring 82-84; Chapl Asst Colchester Gen Hosp 87-88; Chapl Maidstone Hosp 88-94; Chapl Mid Kent Healthcare NHS Trust 94-98; Hon Can Cant Cathl *Cant* 97-98; rtd 98; Perm to Offic *Nor* and *Ely* from 98. *The Greys, 12 Hawthorn Close, Watlington, King's Lynn PE33 0HD* Tel (01558) 811301

PORTER, David Michael. b 37. Coll of Ripon & York St Jo BA88. Ely Th Coll 61. **d** 64 **p** 65. C Clun w Chapel Lawn *Heref* 64-67; C Scarborough St Mary w Ch Ch, St Paul and St Thos *York* 67-69; C Fulford 69-71; V Strensall 71-78; Chapl Claypenny and St Monica's Hosps 78-91; V Easingwold w Raskelfe *York* 78-91; TR York All SS Pavement w St Crux and St Martin etc 91-97; R York All SS Pavement w St Crux and St Mich 97-02; rtd 02; Perm to Offic *York* from 02. *10 Hall Rise, Haxby, York YO32 3LP* Tel (01904) 769823

PORTER, David Michael. b 46. Nottm Univ BMedSci80 BM82 BS82. EMMTC 94. **d** 97 **p** 98. NSM Edwinstowe *S'well* 97-99. *Gorsethorpe Cottage, Edwinstowe, Mansfield NG21 9HJ* Tel (01623) 844657

PORTER, David Rowland Shelley. b 46. City of Liv Coll of HE CertEd69. STETS 00. **d** 03. NSM Whitehawk *Chich* from 03. *33 Warleigh Road, Brighton BN1 4NT* Tel (01273) 703499 E-mail davejanera@aol.com

PORTER, Howard. b 56. S Glam Inst HE CertEd78. St Mich Coll Llan 99. **d** 01 **p** 02. C Maindee *Mon* from 01. *16 Kensington Place, Newport NP19 8GL* Tel (01633) 281053

PORTER, John Dudley Dowell. b 33. St Edm Hall Ox BA60 MA61. Qu Coll Birm 57. **d** 59 **p** 60. C Londonderry *Birm* 59-62; C Tettenhall Regis *Lich* 62-65; Chapl RAF 65-69; V Wombourne *Lich* 69-75; V Rickerscote 75-81; P-in-c Chapel Chorlton 81-85; P-in-c Maer 81-85; P-in-c Whitmore 81-85; R Chapel Chorlton, Maer and Whitmore 85-92; TR Wednesfield 92-00; rtd 00; P-in-c Haughton St Anne *Man* 00-03. *37 rue Principale, 62130 Framecourt, France* Tel (0033) (3) 21 04 36 35

PORTER, Canon Prof Joshua Roy. b 21. Mert Coll Ox BA42 MA47. St Steph Ho Ox 42. **d** 45 **p** 46. C Portsea St Mary *Portsm* 45-47; Bp's Dom Chapl *Chich* 47-49; Chapl and Lect Oriel Coll Ox 49-62; Tutor Oriel Coll Ox 50-62; Lect Th Ox Univ 50-62; Prof Th Ex Univ 62-86; Can and Preb Chich Cathl *Chich* 65-88; Wiccamical Preb Chich Cathl from 88; rtd 86; Lic to Offic *Lon* from 87. *36 Theberton Street, London N1 0QX* Tel (020) 7354 5861

PORTER, Miss Joy Dove. b 50. Lon Univ PGCE83 Ex Univ CPS86. Lon Bible Coll BA81 Wycliffe Hall Ox 89. **d** 91 **p** 94. Par Dn Chalgrove w Berrick Salome *Ox* 91-92; Par Dn Chipping Norton 92-94; C 94-95; Hong Kong 96-97; Chapl Rouen Miss to Seamen *Eur* 97-00; P-in-c Rouen All SS 97-00. *Stable Cottage, Binfield Park, Binfield, Bracknell RG42 5JN*

PORTER, Kenneth Wilfred. b 27. St Aid Birkenhead 58. **d** 61 **p** 62. C Queensbury *Bradf* 61-63; C Oldham St Paul *Man* 63-65; V Wardle 65-91; Chapl Birch Hill Hosp 84-91; rtd 91; Perm to Offic *Man* 91-97; Perm to Offic *Liv* from 97. *19 Knowsley Drive, Leigh WN7 3LY*

PORTER, Mrs Marie-Jeanne. b 60. EMMTC 95. **d** 98 **p** 99. NSM Warsop *S'well* from 98. *Gorsethorpe Cottage, Edwinstowe, Mansfield NG21 9HJ* Tel (01623) 844657

PORTER, Matthew James. b 69. Nottm Univ BA90. Wycliffe Hall Ox BTh93. **d** 96 **p** 97. C Dore *Sheff* 96-00; V Woodseats St Chad from 00. *St Chad's Vicarage, 9 Linden Avenue, Sheffield S8 0GA* Tel 0114-274 5086 Fax as telephone E-mail mporteruk@aol.com

PORTER, Michael Edward. b 44. Trin Coll Bris 75. **d** 77 **p** 78. C Corby St Columba *Pet* 77-81; C Rainham *Chelmsf* 81-82; TV 82-92; TV Rainham w Wennington 92-95; P-in-c S Hornchurch St Jo and St Matt 92-95; V Anerley *Roch* from 95. *The Vicarage, 234 Anerley Road, London SE20 8TJ* Tel (020) 8778 4800 E-mail mike@christchurchanerley.freeserve.co.uk

PORTER, Mrs Shiela. b 50. **d** 01 **p** 02. C Deal St Geo *Cant* from 01. *25 Peter Street, Deal CT14 6DG* Tel (01304) 364108 E-mail shielaporter@hotmail.com

PORTER, Mrs Susan. STETS. d 03. NSM Wilton w Netherhampton and Fugglestone *Sarum* from 03. *24 Belle Vue Road, Salisbury SP1 3YG* Tel (01722) 331314

PORTER, William Albert. b 28. Univ of NZ BA51 MA52. Coll of Resurr Mirfield 53. d 55 p 56. C Perry Barr *Birm* 55-58; New Zealand 59-62; Fiji 62-67; Can and Prec H Trin Cathl Suva 65-67; C Wimbledon *S'wark* 68; Asst Chapl HM Pris Liv 69-70; Chapl 79-87; Chapl HM Pris Brixton 70-74; Chapl HM Pris Long Lartin 74-79; Chapl HM Pris Nottm 87-90; P-in-c Sneinton St Matthias *S'well* 90-93; rtd 94; Perm to Offic *Glouc* from 01. *40 Duke Street, Cheltenham GL52 6BP* Tel (01242) 262198

PORTER-PRYCE, Ms Julia Frances. b 57. Man Univ BA78 Leic Univ MPhil94. NTMTC 93. d 96 p 97. C Stoke Newington Common St Mich *Lon* 96-99; C Is of Dogs Ch Ch and St Jo w St Luke 99-02; V De Beauvoir Town St Pet from 02. *St Peter's Vicarage, 86 De Beauvoir Road, London N1 5AT* Tel (020) 7254 5670 E-mail julia@freeuk.com

PORTEUS, James Michael. b 34. Worc Coll Ox BA55 MA58. Cuddesdon Coll. d 57 p 58. C Fleetwood *Blackb* 57-60; C Ox St Mary V *Ox* 60-62; Staff Sec SCM Ox 60-62; USA 62-69 and 86-91; Chapl Lon Univ *Lon* 69-74; V Hampstead Garden Suburb 74-86; Min Livingston LEP *Edin* 91-96; rtd 96; P-in-c Portree *Arg* from 96. *The Rectory, Somerled Square, Portree IV51 9EH* Tel (01478) 613135

PORTEUS, Canon Robert John Norman. b 50. TCD BA72 MA76. CITC 75. d 75 p 76. C Portadown St Mark *Arm* 75-79; I Ardtrea w Desertcreat 79-83; I Annaghmore 83-98; I Derryloran from 98; Can Arm Cathl from 98; Preb from 01. *Derryloran Rectory, 13 Loy Street, Cookstown BT80 8PZ* Tel (028) 8676 2261 Fax as telephone E-mail derryloran@armagh.anglican.org

PORTHOUSE, Canon John Clive. b 32. Lon Univ BD58. Tyndale Hall Bris 55 Oak Hill Th Coll 58. d 60 p 61. C Leyton All SS *Chelmsf* 60-62; C Kendal St Thos *Carl* 62-64; V Flimby 64-68; V Sidcup St Andr *Roch* 68-74; V Beckenham St Jo 74-86; RD Beckenham 80-86; V Southborough St Pet w Ch Ch and St Matt 86-96; TR 96-97; Hon Can Roch Cathl 96-97; rtd 97; Perm to Offic *Carl* from 98. *148 Stainbank Road, Kendal LA9 5BE* Tel (01892) 528534

PORTHOUSE, Roger Gordon Hargreaves. b 39. Tyndale Hall Bris 66. d 69 p 70. C Wellington w Eyton *Lich* 69-71; C Cheadle *Ches* 71-75; R Frettenham w Stanninghall *Nor* 75-81; R Spixworth w Crostwick 75-81; V Hailsham *Chich* from 81; RD Dallington from 96. *St Mary's Vicarage, Vicarage Road, Hailsham BN27 1BL* Tel (01323) 842381 Fax 08701-637687 E-mail rporthouse@btclick.com

PORTLOCK, John Anthony. b 37. WMMTC 96. d 99 p 00. NSM Lyddington w Stoke Dry and Seaton etc *Pet* from 99. *7 Chestnut Close, Uppingham LE15 9TQ* Tel (01572) 823225 E-mail portlocklydd@aol.com

PORTSDOWN, Archdeacon of. *See* LOWSON, The Ven Christopher

PORTSMOUTH, Bishop of. *See* STEVENSON, The Rt Revd Kenneth William

PORTSMOUTH, Dean of. *See* BRINDLEY, The Very Revd David Charles

PORTWOOD, Prof Derek. b 31. Keele Univ MA69 PhD79. Lon Coll of Div ALCD57. d 57 p 58. C Laisterdyke *Bradf* 57-60; C-in-c Westlands St Andr CD *Lich* 60-66; V Westlands St Andr 66-69; rtd 96; Perm to Offic *Ely* 96-00. *51 River Lane, Cambridge CB5 8HP* Tel (01223) 311044 Fax as telephone

POSKITT, Mark Sylvester. b 63. Loughb Univ BSc84. St Jo Coll Nottm MA95. d 97 p 98. C Brigg, Wrawby and Cadney cum Howsham *Linc* 97-00; TV Howden *York* from 00. *The Vicarage, Portington Road, Eastrington, Goole DN14 7QE* Tel (01430) 410282 E-mail msposkitt@tesco.net

POST, David Charles William. b 39. Jes Coll Cam BA61 MA65. Oak Hill Th Coll 61. d 63 p 64. C Orpington Ch Ch *Roch* 63-66; C Fulwood *Sheff* 66-68; V Lathom *Liv* 68-75; V Poughill *Truro* 75-78; V Braddan S & M 78-79; Dioc Missr 78-79; P-in-c Santan 78; V 78-79; V Sherburn in Elmet *York* 79-91; P-in-c Kirk Fenton 84-85; V Thornthwaite cum Braithwaite and Newlands *Carl* 91-93; R Wheldrake w Thorganby *York* from 93. *The Rectory, 3 Church Lane, Wheldrake, York YO19 6AW* Tel (01904) 448230

POST, Oswald Julian. b 48. Derby Lonsdale Coll BEd79. EMMTC. d 84 p 85. Travelling Sec Rwanda Miss 79-89; Hon C Hulland, Atlow, Bradley and Hognaston *Derby* 84-89; V Wormhill, Peak Forest w Peak Dale and Dove Holes 89-99; P-in-c Youlgreave, Middleton, Stanton-in-Peak etc from 99. *The Vicarage, Church Street, Youlgrave, Bakewell DE45 1WL* Tel (01629) 636285

POSTILL, John Edward. b 35. Oak Hill Th Coll 64. d 67 p 68. C Southgate *Chich* 67-70; C Bowling St Jo *Bradf* 70-74; TV Winfarthing w Shelfanger *Nor* 74-79; R Slaugham *Chich* 79-97; C Busbridge and Hambledon *Guildf* from 97. *Mervil Bottom, Malthouse Lane, Hambledon, Godalming GU8 4HG* Tel (01428) 682753

POSTILL, Canon Richard Halliday. b 37. Hull Univ BSc59. Westcott Ho Cam 66. d 68 p 69. C Wylde Green *Birm* 68-72; C Kingswinford St Mary *Lich* 72-76; V Yardley Wood *Birm* 76-86; V Acocks Green 86-02; AD Yardley 93-00; Hon Can Birm Cathl 99-02; rtd 02. *32 Longmore Road, Shirley, Solihull B90 3DY* Tel 0121-744 6217

POSTLES, Donald. b 29. MPS51 Birm Univ DipTh59 MA65. Qu Coll Birm 56. d 59 p 60. C Southport H Trin *Liv* 59-62; C Prescot 62-63; V Wigan St Steph 63-71; V Farnworth 71-84; V Mossley Hill St Barn 84-92; rtd 93. *43 The Broadway, Abergele LL22 7DD* Tel (01745) 826165

POTHEN, Simon John. b 60. Westmr Coll Ox BA86. Ripon Coll Cuddesdon 86. d 88 p 89. C Southgate Ch Ch *Lon* 88-91; C Tottenham St Mary 91-93; TV Gt Grimsby St Mary and St Jas *Linc* 93-96; R Friern Barnet St Jas *Lon* 96-02; V Pinner from 02. *The Vicarage, 2 Church Lane, Pinner HA5 3AA* Tel (020) 8866 3869 Mobile 07939-523366 E-mail emmanuel.northwood@btinternet.com

POTIPHER, John Malcolm Barry. b 42. St Alb Minl Tr Scheme 79. d 82 p 83. Chapl Herts Fire Brigade 82-91; NSM Chambersbury *St Alb* 82-84; NSM Hemel Hempstead 84-86; NSM Digswell and Panshanger 86-92; P-in-c Pirton 92-95; rtd 95; Perm to Offic *St Alb* from 95. *66 Peartree Lane, Welwyn Garden City AL7 3UH* Tel (01707) 886953 Fax as telephone E-mail john.potipher@ntlworld.com

POTTER, Charles Elmer. b 42. Georgetown Univ (USA) BS65 Valparaiso Univ JD73. Wycliffe Coll Toronto MDiv81. d 81 p 82. C Southport Ch Ch *Liv* 81-84; Chapl Lee Abbey 84-87; Australia 87-93; P-in-c Aldingham and Dendron and Rampside *Carl* 94-96; P-in-c Aldingham, Dendron, Rampside and Urswick 96-99; V Bexley St Mary *Roch* from 99. *The Vicarage, 29 Hill Crescent, Bexley DA5 2DA* Tel (01322) 523457 Fax as telephone E-mail cpotter@lineone.net

POTTER, The Very Revd Christopher Nicholas Lynden. b 49. Leeds Univ BA71. St As Minl Tr Course 90. d 93 p 94. C Flint *St As* 93-96; V Llanfair DC, Derwen, Llanelidan and Efenechtyd 96-01; Dean and Lib St As Cathl from 01; V St As 01-03; TR from 03. *The Deanery, Upper Denbigh Road, St Asaph LL17 0RL* Tel (01745) 583597 E-mail chris_potter@talk21.com

POTTER, Clement. *See* POTTER, Keith Clement

POTTER, Clive Geoffrey. b 55. Aston Tr Scheme 88 Sarum & Wells Th Coll 90. d 92 p 93. C Epsom Common Ch Ch *Guildf* 92-97; TV Westborough 97-98; TR from 98. *St Francis's Vicarage, Beckingham Road, Guildford GU2 8BU* Tel (01483) 504228

POTTER, Colin Michael. b 53. Lanc Univ BA74 Birm Univ DipTh82. Qu Coll Birm 80. d 83 p 84. C Middlewich w Byley *Ches* 83-87; TV Ches Team 87-98; V Gt Sutton from 98. *St John's Vicarage, 1 Church Lane, Great Sutton, South Wirral CH66 4AP* Tel 0151-339 9916 E-mail ficer@greatsutton.fsbusiness.co.uk

POTTER, Desmond. b 59. St Paul's Coll Grahamstown DipTh85. d 88 p 88. S Africa 88-98; V Newton *Ches* from 98. *St Michael's House, 56 Queensbury Road, Wirral CH48 6EP* Tel 0151-625 8517 Fax as telephone E-mail thepotters@tinyworld.co.uk

POTTER, Harry Drummond. b 54. Em Coll Cam BA76 MA79 MPhil81 LLB92 Barrister 93. Westcott Ho Cam 79. d 81 p 82. C Deptford St Paul *S'wark* 81-84; Chapl Selw Coll Cam 84-87; Chapl Newnham Coll Cam 84-87; Chapl HM Pris Wormwood Scrubs 87-88; Chapl HM YOI Aylesbury 88-93; NSM Camberwell St Giles w St Matt *S'wark* from 93. *64 Courtlands Avenue, London SE12 8JA*

POTTER, Canon James David. b 35. AKC66. d 67 p 68. C Longbridge *Birm* 67-70; Lic to Offic 71-73; V N Harborne 73-78; V Smethwick H Trin w St Alb 78-83; V Blurton *Lich* 83-90; V Dordon *Birm* 90-98; RD Polesworth 91-96; Hon Can Birm Cathl 96-98; rtd 98; Perm to Offic *Birm* from 98. *49 Winstanley Road, Stechford, Birmingham B33 8UH* Tel 0121-783 2734

POTTER, John Daniel. b 29. Sydney Univ BA50. St Jo Coll Morpeth ThL51. d 51 p 53. Australia 52-65 and from 71; C High Harrogate Ch Ch *Ripon* 65-66; Chapl St Mary's Sch Wantage 66-68; Chapl St Jo Sch and NSM St Andr Cathl Singapore 68-71; OCF 68-71; rtd 95; Lic to Offic *Eur* 95-97. *200 Castella Road, Toolangi, Vic, Australia 3777* Tel (0061) (3) 5962 9449

POTTER, John Dennis. b 39. Ealing Tech Coll. S Dios Minl Tr Scheme 92. d 94 p 95. NSM Box w Hazlebury and Ditteridge *Bris* 94-98. *6 Fuller Road, Bath BA1 7BB* Tel (01225) 316566

POTTER, John Ellis. b 45. SSC. Sarum & Wells Th Coll 82. d 84 p 85. C Wootton Bassett *Sarum* 84-88; TV Swindon New Town *Bris* 88-96; V Milber *Ex* from 96. *St Luke's Vicarage, 10 Laburnum Road, Newton Abbot TQ12 4LQ* Tel (01626) 365837

POTTER, Canon John Henry. b 26. Lon Univ BA50. Oak Hill Th Coll 50. d 52 p 53. C Islington St Mary *Lon* 52-55; C Kinson *Sarum* 55-58; V Upper Holloway St Jo *Lon* 58-65; R Illogan *Truro* 65-69; P-in-c Ilfracombe SS Phil and Jas *Ex* 69-72; V 72-76; R Poole *Sarum* 76-87; RD Poole 80-85; Can and Preb Sarum Cathl 83-91; P-in-c Charmouth and Catherston Leweston 87-91; rtd 91; Perm to Offic *Sarum* 91-99; Perm to Offic *Win* 91-00. *11 Park Terrace, Tenby SA70 7LY* Tel (01834) 843647

POTTER, Keith Clement. b 39. Leeds Univ CertSS78 Bradf Univ MA81. Chich Th Coll 62. **d** 64 **p** 65. C Doncaster Ch Ch *Sheff* 64-68; C Tong *Bradf* 68-70; V Bradf St Columba w St Andr 70-79; V Yeadon St Andr 79-02; rtd 02. *6 Main Street, Balintore, Tain IV20 1UE*

POTTER, Kenneth Benjamin. Open Univ BA GLCM. NEOC 84. **d** 87 **p** 88. NSM Ryton w Hedgefield *Dur* 87-95; P-in-c Harby w Thorney and N and S Clifton *S'well* from 95. *The Rectory, Front Street, South Clifton, Newark NG23 7AA* Tel (01522) 778258 E-mail kenneth.b.potter@btinternet.com

POTTER, Mrs Linda. b 47. Cranmer Hall Dur 92. **d** 94 **p** 95. C Shildon w Eldon *Dur* 94-98; P-in-c Castleside from 98. *6 Hillcrest, Castleside, Consett DH8 9EB* Tel (01207) 590086 E-mail linda.vicarage@breathemail.net

POTTER, Preb Malcolm Emmerson. b 48. Bedf Coll Lon BSc70. St Jo Coll Nottm DPS75. **d** 75 **p** 76. C Upton (Overchurch) *Ches* 76-78; CPAS Staff 78-84; Development Officer St Jo Coll Nottm 84-86; P-in-c Wellington, All SS w Eyton *Lich* 86-95; V from 95; Preb Lich Cathl from 99. *All Saints' Vicarage, 35 Crescent Road, Wellington, Telford TF1 3DW* Tel (01952) 641251 E-mail malcolmepotter@blueyonder.co.uk

POTTER, Peter Maxwell. b 46. Univ of Wales (Swansea) BA69 Univ of BC MA71. Sarum & Wells Th Coll 83. **d** 85 **p** 86. C Bradford-on-Avon *Sarum* 85-88; C Harnham 88-91; P-in-c N Bradley, Southwick and Heywood 91-96; V Sale St Anne *Ches* 96-00; R Largs *Glas* from 00. *St Columba's Rectory, Aubery Crescent, Largs KA30 8PR* Tel (01475) 673143

POTTER, Canon Phillip. b 54. Stirling Univ BA75. Trin Coll Bris 82. **d** 84 **p** 85. C Yateley *Win* 84-88; V Haydock St Mark *Liv* from 88; Hon Can Liv Cathl from 03. *St Mark's Vicarage, 2 Stanley Bank Road, Haydock, St Helens WA11 0UW* Tel (01744) 23957

POTTER, Richard Antony. b 36. K Coll Cam BA60 MA64. Ridley Hall Cam 60. **d** 62 **p** 63. C Luton w E Hyde *St Alb* 62-72; V Lyonsdown H Trin 72-85; R Broxbourne w Wormley 85-02; rtd 02; C Thorverton, Cadbury, Upton Pyne etc *Ex* from 02. *The Vicarage, Newton St Cyres, Exeter EX5 5BN* Tel (01392) 851386

POTTER, Stephen Michael. b 55. Oak Hill Th Coll 93. **d** 95 **p** 96. C Chesterfield H Trin and Ch Ch *Derby* 95-99; P-in-c S Normanton from 99. *The Rectory, Church Street, South Normanton, Alfreton DE55 2BT* Tel (01773) 811273

POTTER, Canon Timothy John. b 49. Bris Univ BSc71. Oak Hill Th Coll 73. **d** 76 **p** 77. C Wallington H Trin *S'wark* 76-79; C Hampreston *Sarum* 79-81; TV Stratton St Margaret w S Marston etc *Bris* 81-87; P-in-c Hatfield Heath *Chelmsf* 87-89; P-in-c Sheering 87-89; R Hatfield Heath and Sheering from 90; Hon Can Chelmsf Cathl from 02. *The Vicarage, Broomfields, Hatfield Heath, Bishop's Stortford CM22 7EH* Tel (01279) 730288 E-mail tim.potter1@btinternet.com

POTTIER, Ronald William. b 36. S'wark Ord Course 73. **d** 76 **p** 77. NSM Lower Sydenham St Mich *S'wark* 76-98; NSM Sydenham All SS from 98. *12 Neiderwald Road, London SE26 4AD* Tel (020) 8699 4375

POTTS, Heather Dawn. b 52. **d** 98 **p** 99. C Attleborough w Besthorpe *Nor* 98-01; R Bunwell, Carleton Rode, Tibenham, Gt Moulton etc from 01; RD Depwade from 03. *The Rectory, Chapel Road, Carleton Rode, Norwich NR16 1RN* Tel (01953) 789218

POTTS, James. b 30. K Coll Lon BD56 AKC56. **d** 57 **p** 58. C Brighouse *Wakef* 57-59; Tanganyika 59-64; Tanzania 64-71; C-in-c Athersley and New Lodge CD *Wakef* 71-73; V Athersley 73-77; V Madeley *Lich* 77-85; V Baswich 85-93; RD Stafford 88-95; rtd 93. *16A Christchurch Lane, Lichfield WS13 8BA* Tel (01543) 418808

POTTS, William Gilbert. b 17. Bps' Coll Cheshunt 46. **d** 49 **p** 50. C Fenton *Lich* 49-52; C W Bromwich St Andr 52-53; C Ashbourne w Mapleton and Clifton *Derby* 53-57; V Beighton *Sheff* 57-64; V Winshill *Derby* 64-82; rtd 82; Perm to Offic *Derby* from 82. *28 Roydon Close, Mickleover, Derby DE3 0PN* Tel (01332) 516328

POULARD, Christopher. b 39. FCA. Ridley Hall Cam 82. **d** 84 **p** 85. C N Walsham w Antingham *Nor* 84-86; C Oulton Broad 86-90; TV Raveningham 90-94; R Raveningham Gp 94-99; RD Loddon 98-99; Perm to Offic *Chelmsf* from 99. *Cuddington, Colam Lane, Little Baddow, Chelmsford CM3 4SY* Tel (01245) 224221

POULSON, Ms Anna Louise. b 73. Univ Coll Dur BA94 K Coll Lon MA97. Ridley Hall Cam 98. **d** 02 **p** 03. NSM Ealing St Mary *Lon* from 02. *St John's Vicarage, Church Avenue, Southall UB2 4DH* Tel (020) 8574 2055 Mobile 07929-348621 E-mail anna.poulson@kcl.ac.uk

POULSON, Mark Alban. b 63. Bath Coll of HE BEd86 Anglia Poly Univ MA03. Ridley Hall Cam 98. **d** 00 **p** 01. C Alperton *Lon* 00-03; P-in-c Southall Green St Jo from 03. *St John's Vicarage, Church Avenue, Southall UB2 4DH* Tel (020) 8574 2055 E-mail mpoulson@fish.co.uk

POULTER, Canon Alan John. b 39. St Aid Birkenhead 64. **d** 67 **p** 68. C Heswall *Ches* 67-72; V Bredbury St Mark 72-78; V Oxton 78-97; RD Birkenhead 93-97; TR Ches Team 97-02; Hon Can

Ches Cathl 96-02; rtd 02. *21 Bevyl Road, Parkgate, Neston CH64 6RP* Tel 0151-336 6288 E-mail ajohn1@aol.com

POULTER, Joseph William. b 40. Dur Univ BA61 BA66 DipTh67. Cranmer Hall Dur 66. **d** 67 **p** 68. C Harlow New Town w Lt Parndon *Chelmsf* 67-71; C Washington *Dur* 71-77; Producer Metro Radio from 75; C-in-c Town End Farm CD 77-83; V Sunderland Town End Farm from 83. *Town End Farm House, Bootle Street, Sunderland SR5 4EY* Tel 0191-536 3823 Fax 537 3744 E-mail joepoulter@tinyworld.co.uk

POULTNEY, Wilfred Howard. b 25. SSC87. Qu Coll Birm 71. **d** 73 **p** 74. NSM S Leamington St Jo *Cov* 73-85; NSM Holbrooks 85-95; NSM Walsall St Gabr Fulbrook *Lich* from 95. *28 Walstead Road, Walsall WS5 4LX* Tel (01922) 868067

POULTON, Arthur Leslie. b 28. K Coll Lon BA53 AKC53 BD60 Leic Univ MA85. Tyndale Hall Bris 53. **d** 55 **p** 56. C New Catton St Luke *Nor* 55-56; C Earlham St Anne 56-58; C Chorleywood Ch Ch *St Alb* 58-61; R E Barnet 61-64; Ches Coll of HE 64-87; Chapl 64-84; Sen Lect 66-87; Dir of Studies Course in Chr Studies *Chelmsf* 87-94; P-in-c Gt Canfield 87-94; rtd 94; Perm to Offic *Ches* from 96. *Chaldon, Great Mollington, Chester CH1 6LG* Tel (01244) 851338

POULTON, Ian Peter. b 60. Lon Univ BSc(Econ)83 TCD DipTh86 Open Univ BA94. **d** 86 **p** 87. C Newtownards *D & D* 86-89; I Bright w Ballee and Killough 89-96; Relig Adv Downtown Radio 91-96; I Larne and Inver *Conn* 96-99; I Killiney Ballybrack *D & G* from 99. *Killiney Rectory, 21 Killiney Avenue, Killiney, Co Dublin, Irish Republic* Tel (00353) (1) 285 6180 Fax as telephone E-mail 106522.740@compuserve.com

POULTON, Katharine Margaret. b 61. Man Univ BA83 TCD DipTh87. **d** 87 **p** 91. C Bangor St Comgall *D & D* 87-91; C Seagoe 91-96; C Kilwaughter w Cairncastle and Craigy Hill *Conn* 96-99; C Greystones *D & G* 99-00; Bp's C Dublin St Geo and St Thos from 00. *Killiney Rectory, 21 Killiney Avenue, Killiney, Co Dublin, Irish Republic* Tel (00353) (1) 285 6180 Fax as telephone E-mail 106522.740@compuserve.com

POULTON, Neville John. b 48. STETS. **d** 02. NSM Portsea St Cuth *Portsm* from 02. *18 Belgravia Road, Portsmouth PO2 0DX* Tel (023) 9236 1104 Mobile 07768-661796 E-mail momac@fish.co.uk

POUNCE, Alan Gerald. b 34. Lon Univ BSc55 Dip Counselling. Wycliffe Hall Ox 57. **d** 59 **p** 60. C Wednesfield Heath *Lich* 59-61; C Heref St Pet w St Owen *Heref* 61-63; R Gt w Lt Dunham *Nor* 63-69; Asst Master Windsor Boys' Sch 69-94; rtd 94; Perm to Offic *Ox* 69-99; Lic to Offic from 99. *38 Longdown Road, Sandhurst GU47 8QG* Tel (01344) 772870

POUNCEY, Canon Cosmo Gabriel Rivers. b 11. Qu Coll Cam BA32 MA36. Cuddesdon Coll 33. **d** 34 **p** 35. C Kennington St Jo *S'wark* 34-44; Sec Ch Educn League 43-46; V Woodham *Guildf* 46-63; Hon Can Guildf Cathl 62-63; V Tewkesbury w Walton Cardiff *Glouc* 63-81; P-in-c Tredington w Stoke Orchard and Hardwicke 63-81; RD Tewkesbury 68-81; Hon Can Glouc Cathl 72-81; P-in-c Deerhurst w Apperley 74-80; Perm to Offic 81-97; rtd 81; Perm to Offic *Worc* 81-93; Perm to Offic *Sarum* from 93. *Church Walk, Littlebredy, Dorchester DT2 9HG* Tel (01308) 482356

POUND, Canon Keith Salisbury. b 33. St Cath Coll Cam BA54 MA58. Cuddesdon Coll 55. **d** 57 **p** 58. C St Helier *S'wark* 57-61; Tr Officer Hollowford Tr & Conf Cen Sheff 61-64; Warden 64-67; R S'wark H Trin 68-74; P-in-c Newington St Matt 68-74; R S'wark H Trin w St Matt 74-78; RD S'wark and Newington 73-78; TR Thamesmead 78-86; Sub-Dean Woolwich 84-86; RD Greenwich 85-86; Hon Can S'wark Cathl 85-86; Chapl Gen of Pris 86-93; Chapl to The Queen from 88; Chapl HM Pris Grendon and Spring Hill 93-98; rtd 98; Perm to Offic *Chich* from 99. *Adeleine, Pett Road, Pett, Hastings TN35 4HE* Tel (01424) 813873

POUNDE, Nigel. b 46. Edin Univ MA69 Union Th Sem (NY) STM01. Cranmer Hall Dur DipTh71. **d** 72 **p** 73. C Southsea St Simon *Portsm* 72-75; C Clayton w Keymer *Chich* 75-79; Malaysia 80-86; TV Wolverhampton *Lich* 87-97; Dioc Inter-Faith Officer 92-97; Care Services Manager Terrence Higgins Trust 97-00; USA 00-01; R Newport-on-Tay *St And* from 01. *34 Scotscraig, Boat Road, Newport-on-Tay DD6 8EU* Tel and fax (01382) 543311 *or* tel 221245 E-mail nigel.pounde@virgin.net

POUNTAIN, Eric Gordon. b 24. Sarum Th Coll 65. **d** 66 **p** 67. C New Bury *Man* 66-76; Lic to Offic *Blackb* 76-80; Chapl Lancs (Preston) Poly 80-81; P-in-c Preston St Mark 80-81; V Salesbury 81-86; rtd 86. *116 Harewood Road, Rishton, Blackburn BB1 4DZ* Tel (01254) 888091

POVEY, John Michael. b 44. St Jo Coll Nottm BTh76. **d** 76 **p** 77. USA from 76. *67 East, Pittsfield, MA 01201, USA* E-mail jmp@berkshire.net

POVEY, Canon Kenneth Vincent. b 40. AKC62. **d** 63 **p** 64. C Crewe Ch Ch *Ches* 63-66; C Neston 66-69; C Kensington St Mary Abbots w St Geo *Lon* 69-72; R Ches H Trin *Ches* 72-81; Chapl Copenhagen w Aarhus *Eur* 81-86; R Gawsworth *Ches* 86-98; Hon Can Ches Cathl 92-98; rtd 98; Perm to Offic *Ches* from 98. *The White House, Bishopton Drive, Macclesfield SK11 8TR*

POVEY, William Peter. b 36. JP85. MRCS61 LRCP61 FFPHM79 FRIPHH DRCOG HonFChS Liv Univ DPH68 Man Univ MSc82. N Ord Course 90. **d** 93 **p** 94. Dioc Drug Liaison Officer *Ches* from 93; NSM Latchford Ch Ch 93-00; NSM Daresbury from 00. *The Gables, 153 Chester Road, Grappenhall, Warrington WA4 2SB* Tel (01925) 265530 E-mail povey@excite.co.uk

POW, Mrs Enid. b 59. Carl and Blackb Dioc Tr Inst 99. **d** 02. C Broughton and Duddon *Carl* from 02. *Fernholme, 1A Broughton Park, Broughton-in-Furness LA20 6HB* Tel (01229) 716277 E-mail chavevason@yahoo.com

POW, Miss Joyce. b 29. RGN55 SCM57 RSCN60 RNT73. St Jo Coll Nottm CertCS88. **d** 88 **p** 94. Hon Par Dn Largs *Glas* 88-94; Hon C from 94. *15 Shuma Court, Skelmorlie PA17 5EJ* Tel (01475) 520289

POWE, David James Hector. b 50. Brighton Poly CertMS86. Wycliffe Hall Ox 88. **d** 90 **p** 91. C Ventnor St Cath *Portsm* 90-92; Chapl HM Pris Belmarsh 93-94; Chapl HM Pris Lewes 94-97; Chapl HM Pris Belmarsh from 98. *HM Prison Belmarsh, Western Way, London SE28 0EB* Tel (020) 8317 2436 ext 325

POWE, Eric James. b 23. Univ of Wales (Lamp) BA50 BD61. St Steph Ho Ox 50. **d** 52 **p** 53. C Ramsgate H Trin *Cant* 52-54; C Buckland in Dover 54-57; CF 57-73; Dep Asst Chapl Gen 72-73; R Broadstairs *Cant* 73-94; rtd 94; Perm to Offic *Cant* from 94. *34 Palm Bay Avenue, Cliftonville, Margate CT9 3DF* Tel (01843) 294673

POWELL, Anthony James. b 51. Sarum & Wells Th Coll 78. **d** 79 **p** 80. C Larkfield *Roch* 79-83; C Leybourne 79-83; V Borough Green from 83. *The Vicarage, 24 Maidstone Road, Borough Green, Sevenoaks TN15 8BD* Tel (01732) 882447 Fax as telephone

POWELL, Charles David. b 38. St Pet Coll Saltley CertEd61 ACP74. St Alb and Ox Min Course CBTS99. **d** 99 **p** 00. NSM Ampthill w Millbrook and Steppingley *St Alb* from 99; RD Ampthill from 03. *65 Blenheim Crescent, Luton LU3 1HD* Tel (01582) 457553 Mobile 07976-821669 E-mail cpowell8@compuserve.com

POWELL, Christopher John. b 71. K Coll Lon BA94 AKC94. Coll of Resurr Mirfield 95. **d** 97 **p** 98. C Botley *Portsm* 97-01; C Portsea N End St Mark from 01. *St Francis House, 186 Northern Parade, Portsmouth PO2 9LU* Tel (023) 9266 2467 E-mail cjp@powellcj.freeserve.co.uk

POWELL, Colin Arthur. b 32. Hatf Coll Dur BA53. Oak Hill Th Coll 56. **d** 58 **p** 59. C Leyland St Andr *Blackb* 58-61; C Lancaster St Thos 61-64; C Tranmere St Cath *Ches* 64-65; R Cheetham Hill *Man* 65-81; TV Oldham 81-86; TV Rochdale 86-97; Chapl Rochdale Healthcare NHS Trust 94-97; rtd 97; Perm to Offic *Man* 00-03. *103 Parsonage Road, Withington, Manchester M20 4NU* Tel 0161-434 2409

POWELL, Mrs Diane. b 41. SW Minl Tr Course 85. **d** 88 **p** 94. Hon C St Merryn *Truro* 88-92; Dn-in-c Gerrans w St Anthony in Roseland 92-94; P-in-c 94-00; Asst Chapl R Cornwall Hosps Trust from 00. *Royal Cornwall Hospital, Treliske, Truro TR1 3LJ* Tel (01872) 274242 or 252833

POWELL, Dudley John. b 44. Tyndale Hall Bris 65. **d** 69 **p** 70. C Blackb Sav *Blackb* 69-71; C Rodbourne Cheney *Bris* 71-74; P-in-c Kingsdown 74-79; V 79-80; V Stoke Gifford 80-90; TR 90-91; Albania from 91; Perm to Offic *Bris* from 94. *258 Jardine Crescent, Coventry CV4 9QS*

POWELL, Eleanor Ann. b 55. Gwent Coll Newport CertEd76 Univ of Wales BA82. Qu Coll Birm 82. **d** 83 **p** 94. C Caereithin *S & B* 83-86; C Bishopston 86-88; Dioc Children's Officer *Glouc* 88-94; Hon Can Glouc Cathl 94-01; P-in-c The Edge, Pitchcombe, Harescombe and Brookthorpe 94-00; Dioc Adv for Women's Min 94-01; V Churchdown St Jo 00-01; Offg Chapl RAF from 00; Chapl United Bris Healthcare NHS Trust from 01. *The Chaplaincy Office, Bristol Royal Infirmary, Marlborough Street, Bristol BS2 8HW* Tel 0117-928 2136 E-mail eleanor.powell@virgin.net

POWELL, Preb Frank. b 29. AKC52. **d** 53 **p** 54. C Stockingford *Cov* 53-56; C Netherton St Andr *Worc* 56-60; P-in-c W Bromwich St Jo *Lich* 60-66; C W Bromwich Gd Shep w St Jo 60-66; V 66-69; V Bilston St Leon 69-76; P-in-c Hanbury 76-82; V Hanbury w Newborough 83-86; V Basford 86-92; Preb Lich Cathl 87-92; rtd 92; Perm to Offic *Ches* from 92. *Pippins, 15 Jubilee Terrace, Nantwich CW5 7BT* Tel (01270) 610688 E-mail frank@fjpowell.fsnet.co.uk

POWELL, Gary Charles. b 62. UWIST BSc84. Coll of Resurr Mirfield 92. **d** 95 **p** 96. C Roath *Llan* 95-00; V Llansawel, Briton Ferry from 00. *The Vicarage, 251 Neath Road, Briton Ferry, Neath SA11 2SL* Tel (01639) 812200

POWELL, Geoffrey Peter. b 25. Chich Th Coll 54. **d** 56 **p** 57. C Bris St Agnes w St Simon *Bris* 56-58; C Sherston Magna w Easton Grey 58-62; V Wanborough 62-75; R Lyddington w Wanborough 75-80; V St Cleer *Truro* 80-90; rtd 91; Perm to Offic *Bris*; *Truro* and *Sarum* from 91. *The Old Bakery, Oare, Marlborough SN8 4JQ* Tel (01672) 562627

POWELL, John. b 44. St Luke's Coll Ex CertEd66 Univ of Wales (Lamp) MA02. Glouc Sch of Min 81. **d** 84 **p** 85. NSM Stroud

and Uplands w Slad *Glouc* 84-89; Chapl Eliz Coll Guernsey 89-92; C Llandudno *Ban* 92-93; TV 94-96; V Dwygyfylchi 96-02; V Cardigan w Mwnt and Y Ferwig w Llangoedmor *St D* from 02. *The Vicarage, Napier Gardens, Cardigan SA43 1EG* Tel (01239) 612722 E-mail parchjohnpowell@lycos.co.uk

POWELL, John Keith Lytton. b 52. E Sussex Agric Coll OND77. S Dios Minl Tr Scheme 91. **d** 94 **p** 95. NSM Bridgwater H Trin *B & W* 94-97; P-in-c Hatch Beauchamp w Beercrocombe, Curry Mallet etc 97-02; P-in-c Staple Fitzpaine, Orchard Portman, Thurlbear etc 97-02; R Beercrocombe w Curry Mallet, Hatch Beauchamp etc from 02. *The Rectory, Hatch Beauchamp, Taunton TA3 6AB* Tel (01823) 480220 Fax as telephone

POWELL, Miss Katherine. b 56. Sydney Univ BSS79 Lon Univ DipAPTh84. Wycliffe Hall Ox 84. **dss** 86 **d** 87 **p** 94. Broadwater St Mary *Chich* 86-87; Par Dn 87-91; Asst Chapl Ch Hosp Horsham 91-96; Australia from 96; Chapl Glennie Sch from 97. *The Glennie School, Herries Street, Toowoomba, Qld, Australia 4350* Tel (0061) (7) 4637 9359 or 4688 8808 Fax 4688 8848 E-mail powellk@glennie.qld.edu.au

POWELL, Kelvin. b 49. Wycliffe Hall Ox 71. **d** 74 **p** 75. C Prescot *Liv* 74-77; C Ainsdale 77-79; V Bickershaw 79-85; R Hesketh w Becconsall *Blackb* 85-99. *Address temp unknown*

POWELL, Llewellyn. b 28. Glouc Th Course 67. **d** 70 **p** 71. C Quinton *Glouc* 70-73; P-in-c 74-76; V Church Honeybourne w Cow Honeybourne 76-83; R Pebworth w Dorsington and Honeybourne 83-87; rtd 87; Perm to Offic *St D* from 87. *Bodathro Bungalow, Llangynin, St Clears, Carmarthen SA33 4LD* Tel (01994) 448301

POWELL, Mark. b 57. Bath Univ BSc78 PhD81. Ripon Coll Cuddesdon BA84 MA88. **d** 85 **p** 86. C Evesham *Worc* 85-88; V Exhall *Cov* 88-96; V Leavesden All SS *St Alb* 96-00; V Ealing St Pet Mt Park *Lon* from 00. *St Peter's Vicarage, 56 Mount Park Road, London W5 2RU* Tel (020) 8997 1620 Fax as telephone E-mail stpeter@dircon.co.uk

POWELL, Martin. b 71. St Steph Ho Ox BTh00. **d** 00 **p** 01. C Caterham *S'wark* from 00. *70 Spencer Road, Caterham CR3 5LB* Tel (01883) 340882

POWELL, Pamela. STETS. **d** 03. C Wrexham *St As* from 03. *16 Foster Road, Wrexham LL11 2LT*

POWELL, Patricia. STETS. **d** 03. NSM Woodford Valley *Sarum* from 03. *Hawthorn Cottage, Great Durnford, Salisbury SP4 6AZ* Tel (01722) 782546

POWELL, Ralph Dover. b 49. ARMCM70. Chich Th Coll 71. **d** 74 **p** 75. C Coppenhall *Ches* 74-77; C Heref H Trin *Heref* 77-80; V Crewe St Barn *Ches* from 80. *St Barnabas' Vicarage, West Street, Crewe CW1 3AX* Tel (01270) 212418 E-mail westtstreet@netscapeonline.co.uk

POWELL, Raymond Leslie. b 35. AKC61. **d** 62 **p** 63. C Hendon St Mary *Lon* 62-67; C Huntingdon All SS w St Jo *Ely* 67-75; C Huntingdon St Barn 75-79; P-in-c Sawston 79-81; V 81-00; P-in-c Babraham 85-00; RD Shelford 89-94; rtd 00; Perm to Offic *Nor* from 01. *14 Appletree Lane, Roydon, Diss IP22 4FL* Tel (01379) 641412

POWELL, Richard Michael Wheler. b 19. St Edm Hall Ox BA45. Wells Th Coll 47. **d** 49 **p** 50. C Hale *Ches* 49-52; V Crowle *Worc* 52-56; V Kempsey 57-62; R Tarporley *Ches* 62-72; P-in-c Lt Budworth 69-70; R Overton w Laverstoke and Freefolk *Win* 73-81; P-in-c Damerham *Sarum* 81-84; P-in-c Martin 81-84; rtd 84; Perm to Offic *B & W* 85-94; Perm to Offic *Ex* from 94. *38 Pine Park Road, Honiton EX14 8HR* Tel (01404) 43429

POWELL, Richard Penry. b 15. Dur Univ LTh38. St Aid Birkenhead 34. **d** 38 **p** 39. C Brierley Hill *Lich* 38-42; C Derby St Chad *Derby* 42-45; C Uttoxeter w Bramshall *Lich* 45-47; V Alton 47-60; V Bradley-in-the-Moors 48-60; R Drayton Bassett 60-64; Min Canwell CD 60-64; V Wrockwardine 64-80; V Uppington 64-80; rtd 80; Perm to Offic *Lich* from 80. *34 Herbert Avenue, Wellington, Telford TF1 2BS* Tel (01952) 242528

POWELL, Robert John. b 65. Trin Coll Bris DipHE91 MA92. **d** 92 **p** 93. C Biggin Hill *Roch* 92-95; C Edgware *Lon* 95-01; Area Sec SAMS (NW England and N Wales) from 01; Lic Preacher *Man* from 01; Perm to Offic *Blackb* from 01; *Carl* from 01. *1 Abercorn Road, Bolton BL1 6LF* Tel (01204) 843565 Fax as telephone E-mail nwareasec@samsgb.org

POWELL, Roger Roy. b 68. Thames Poly BSc91. Ripon Coll Cuddesdon BTh94. **d** 94 **p** 95. C Leic St Jas *Leic* 94-98; C The Abbey Leic 98-00; TV from 00; Youth Chapl from 98; P-in-c Leic St Paul from 01. *St Augustine's Vicarage, 8 Pool Road, Leicester LE3 9GD* Tel 0116-251 9679

POWELL, Stuart William. b 58. K Coll Lon BD80 AKC80. Ripon Coll Cuddesdon 86. **d** 88 **p** 89. C Horden *Dur* 88-90; C Northolt Park St Barn *Lon* 90-93; V Castle Vale St Cuth *Birm* 93-00; V Stockland Green from 00. *The Vicarage, Bleak Hill Road, Birmingham B23 7EL* Tel and fax 0121-373 0130 Mobile 07889-887358 Pager 07336-734456 E-mail spowell@talk21.com

POWELL, Valerie Isabelle Dawn Frances. b 69. Ripon Coll Cuddesdon BTh02. **d** 01 **p** 02. C Newport St Andr *Mon* from 01. *15 Traston Close, Newport NP19 4TG* Tel (01633) 271118 E-mail val_powell@yahoo.co.uk

POWER, Alan Edward. b 26. Worc Coll Ox BA50 MA53. Lich Th Coll. **d** 57 **p** 58. C Summerfield *Birm* 57-60; C Oldbury 60-63; V Short Heath 63-97; rtd 97; Perm to Offic *Birm* from 97. *8 Southam Drive, Sutton Coldfield B73 5PD* Tel 0121-355 8923

POWER, David Michael. b 56. BA81 BEd. Oak Hill Th Coll. **d** 81 **p** 82. C Warblington w Emsworth *Portsm* 81-84; C-in-c Hartplain CD 84-88; V Hartplain 88-91; Adv in Evang 91-97; V Portsea St Cuth from 97. *St Cuthbert's Vicarage, 2 Lichfield Road, Portsmouth PO3 6DE* Tel (023) 9282 7071 Fax as telephone

POWER, Ivor Jonathan. b 43. Lambeth STh87 CITC 66. **d** 69 **p** 70. C Dromore Cathl *D & D* 69-71; C Enniscorthy *C & O* 71-74; I Youghal *C, C & R* 74-78; I Youghal Union 78-81; I Athlone w Benown, Kiltoom and Forgney *M & K* 81-98; Can Meath 87-98; Dir of Ords (Meath) 91-97; I Dublin Crumlin w Chapelizod *D & G* from 98. *St Mary's Rectory, 118 Kimmage Road West, Dublin 12, Irish Republic* Tel (00353) (1) 455 5639 Fax 456 0006 E-mail crumlin@dublin.anglican.org

POWER, James Edward. b 58. Nottm Univ BSc81 Leeds Univ BA85. Coll of Resurr Mirfield 83. **d** 86 **p** 87. C Cadoxton-juxta-Barry *Llan* 86-89; Chapl Harrow Sch from 89. *35 West Street, Harrow HA1 3EG* Tel (020) 8872 8234

POWER, Mrs Jeanette. b 57. Oak Hill Th Coll BA81. **dss** 82 **d** 87 **p** 94. Warblington w Emsworth *Portsm* 82-84; Hartplain CD 84-87; Hon C Hartplain 87-91; Community Mental Health Chapl Havant and Petersfield from 91; NSM Wickham 93-97; NSM Portsea St Cuth from 97; Team Chapl Portsm Hosps NHS Trust from 01. *St Cuthbert's Vicarage, 2 Lichfield Road, Portsmouth PO3 6DE* Tel (023) 9282 7071 Fax as telephone

POWIS, Michael Ralph. b 63. St Jo Coll Nottm BTh95. **d** 95 **p** 96. C Dibden *Win* 95-00; V Hedge End St Luke from 00. *16 Elliot Rise, Hedge End, Southampton SO30 2RU* Tel (01489) 786717 E-mail mike.powis@ukgateway.net

POWLES, Charles Anthony. b 39. EAMTC. **d** 88 **p** 89. NSM Hemsby *Nor* 88-93. *94 Winifred Way, Caister-on-Sea, Great Yarmouth NR30 5PE*

POWLES, Michael Charles. b 34. Reading Univ BSc56 Lon Univ PGCE83. Qu Coll Birm DipTh60. **d** 60 **p** 61. C Goodmayes All SS *Chelmsf* 60-65; C Surbiton St Matt *S'wark* 65-78; Lect Woolwich Coll from 79-99; rtd 99. *Spring Cottage, 3 Rushett Close, Thames Ditton KT7 0UR* Tel (020) 8398 9654

POWLEY, Mark Thomas. b 75. Nottm Univ BA96 Birm Univ PGCE98. Wycliffe Hall Ox 01. **d** 03. C Addiscombe St Mary Magd w St Martin *S'wark* from 03. *68 Elgin Road, Croydon CR0 6XA* Tel (020) 8654 2126 E-mail mpowley@fish.co.uk

POWLEY, Canon Robert Mallinson. b 39. Fitzw Coll Cam MA65 DPS68. Ridley Hall Cam 61. **d** 63 **p** 64. C Bermondsey St Mary w St Olave, St Jo etc *S'wark* 63-67; C Moseley St Anne *Birm* 67-69; Lic to Offic *Man* 72-77; Hon C Walshaw Ch Ch 77-88; V Prestwich St Gabr 88-94; Bp's Dom Chapl 88-94; P-in-c Hargrave *Ches* from 94; Exec Officer Bd for Soc Resp from 94; Hon Can Ches Cathl from 00. *The Vicarage, Hargrave, Chester CH3 7RN* Tel (01829) 781378

POWNALL, Lydia Margaret. *See* HURLE, Mrs Lydia Margaret

POWNALL, Stephen. b 56. St Jo Coll Nottm BA02. **d** 02 **p** 03. C Herne Hill *S'wark* from 02. *8 Ruskin Walk, London SE27 9LZ* Tel (020) 7274 3663 E-mail steve@sbpownall.fsworld.co.uk

POWNE, Peter Rebbeck Lamb. b 23. Sarum & Wells Th Coll 80. **d** 83 **p** 84. C Calne and Blackland *Sarum* 83-86; V Netheravon w Fittleton and Enford 86-93; rtd 93; Perm to Offic *Sarum* from 93. *2 Oak Lane, Figheldean, Salisbury SP4 8JS* Tel (01980) 670356

POYNTING, Charles Robert Macvicar. b 23. Hertf Coll Ox BA48 MA48. Wells Th Coll 48. **d** 50 **p** 51. C Gt Bookham *Guildf* 50-52; C Epsom Common Ch Ch 52-55; V Ashton H Trin *Man* 55-62; V Belfield 62-82; V Digby *Linc* 82-92; rtd 92; Perm to Offic *Ox* 93-00. *Digby Cottage, Noke, Oxford OX3 9TX* Tel (01865) 842794

✠**POYNTZ, The Rt Revd Samuel Greenfield.** b 26. TCD BA48 MA51 BD53 PhD60 Ulster Univ Hon DLitt95. TCD Div Sch Div Test50. **d** 50 **p** 51 **c** 78. C Dublin St Geo *D & G* 50-52; C Bray 52-55; C Dublin St Michan w St Paul 55-59; Sec and Sch Insp Ch Educn Soc for Ireland 56-75; I Dublin St Steph 59-67; I Dublin St Ann 67-70; I Dublin St Ann w St Steph 70-78; Adn Dublin 74-78; Bp C, C & R 78-87; Bp Conn 87-95; rtd 95. *10 Harmony Hill, Lisburn BT27 4EP* Tel (028) 9267 9013

PRADELLA, Henry. b 54. St Mary's Coll Twickenham BEd. NTMTC 97. **d** 00 **p** 01. NSM Hainault *Chelmsf* from 00. *121 Beattyville Gardens, Ilford IG6 1JZ* Tel (020) 8270 3922 E-mail pradfam@btinternet.com

PRAGNELL, John William. b 39. Lon Univ BD65. Lambeth STh87 LTh88. **d** 65 **p** 66. C Bitterne *Win* 65-68; C Hatfield Hyde *St Alb* 68-73; Kuwait 73-75; Chapl Leavesden Hosp and Abbots Langley Hosp 75-88; Chapl Watford Gen Hosp 86-88; V St Alb St Steph *St Alb* 89-95; RD St Alb 91-95; P-in-c Copythorne *Win* 95-02; Dioc Ecum Officer 95-02; Hosp Chapl Adv (Bournemouth Adnry) 00-02; rtd 02. *10 South Mill Close, Amesbury, Salisbury SP4 7HR* Tel (01980) 622372

PRAGNELL, Michael John. b 40. Down Cathl Cam BA62 PhD65 MA66 FIQA81 MRSC CChem MSOSc88. Ox NSM Course 81. **d** 84 **p** 85. NSM High Wycombe *Ox* 84-98; NSM Beercrocombe

w Curry Mallet, Hatch Beauchamp etc *B & W* from 98. *The Rectory, Thurlbear, Taunton TA3 5BW* Tel (01823) 443581

PRAGNELL, Ms Sandra Ann. b 53. Hull Univ BA75 TCD BTh01. CITC 98. **d** 01 **p** 02. C Castleknock and Mulhuddart, w Clonsilla *D & G* from 01. *Kilbride Main Street, Castleknock, Dublin 15, Irish Republic* Tel (00353) (1) 821 2218 Mobile 87-265 8592

PRAILL, David William. b 57. FRGS90 York Univ BA79. Cranmer Hall Dur 81. **d** 82 **p** 83. C Digswell and Panshanger *St Alb* 82-84; CMS 84-89; Course Dir St Geo Coll Jerusalem 85-89; Dir McCabe Educn Trust 90-91; Dir St Luke's Hospice Harrow and Wembley from 91; Perm to Offic *S'wark* from 91; Perm to Offic *Lon* 94-97. *1A St Ann's Crescent, London SW18 2ND* Tel (020) 8870 3694

PRANCE, Jeremy Roy. b 64. DipMin90. St Jo Coll Nottm BA99. **d** 99 **p** 00. C Bramcote *S'well* from 99. *46 Rufford Avenue, Bramcote, Nottingham NG9 3JH* Tel 0115-849 9179 E-mail jez.prance@ntlworld.com

PRANCE, Nicholas David. b 55. St Luke's Coll Ex CertEd77 RMN83. EMMTC 95. **d** 98 **p** 99. NSM Radford St Pet *S'well* 98-99. *27 Stiles Road, Arnold, Nottingham NG5 6RE* Tel 0115-953 4890 Mobile 07966-524581 E-mail nick@prance.freeserve.co.uk

PRANCE, Robert Penrose. b 47. Southn Univ DipTh. Sarum & Wells Th Coll 69. **d** 72 **p** 73. C Gillingham and Fifehead Magdalen *Sarum* 72-76; P-in-c Edmondsham 76-80; P-in-c Woodlands 76-80; P-in-c Wimborne St Giles 76-80; P-in-c Cranborne 77-80; R Cranborne w Boveridge, Edmondsham etc 80-83; Chapl Sherborne Sch 83-93; V Stoke Gabriel and Collaton *Ex* 93-99; Dep PV Ex Cathl 95-99; Chapl Shiplake Coll Henley from 99. *Shiplake College, Shiplake Court, Shiplake, Henley-on-Thames RG9 4BW* Tel 0118-940 2455

PRASAD, Andrew. b 53. Ewing Coll, Allahabad BA75. Bp's Coll Calcutta BD81 Presbyterian Th Coll Seoul ThM88. **d** 79 **p** 81. *48 Ederline Avenue, Norbury, London SW16 6SA* Tel (020) 8764 0633 E-mail a.prasad@pgen.net

PRASADAM, Goruganthula Samuel Narayanamurthy (Sam). b 34. Andhra Univ India BA57. Bangalore Th Coll BD65 Union Th Sem (NY) STM68. **d** 62 **p** 65. India 62-74; C Llanbeblig w Caernarfon and Betws Garmon etc *Ban* 75-76; C Norbury *Ches* 77-78; V Aberaman and Abercwmboi *Llan* 78-83; N Sec CMS 83-87; V Luton All SS w St Pet *St Alb* 87-96; rtd 99. *15 Rossons Road, Taverham, Norwich NR8 6RE*

PRASADAM, Ms Jemima. b 38. BD61 BA87. Cranmer Hall Dur 86. **d** 87 **p** 94. Par Dn Luton All SS w St Pet *St Alb* 87-94; C 94-96; P-in-c Lozells St Paul and St Silas *Birm* from 96. *St Silas's Vicarage, 103 Heathfield Road, Birmingham B19 1HE* Tel 0121-523 5645

PRASADAM, Madhu Smitha. b 64. Qu Coll Birm. **d** 03. C Blackheath *Birm* from 03. *25 Garland Crescent, Hurst Green, Halesowen B62 9NU* Tel 0121-421 4821 E-mail prasadam@fish.co.uk

PRATT, Basil David. b 38. Ripon Hall Ox 64. **d** 67 **p** 68. C Lewisham St Jo Southend *S'wark* 67-68; C Caterham Valley 68-70; CF 70-93. *St Michael's, Bankend Road, Dumfries DG1 4AL* Tel (01387) 267933

PRATT, Christine Fiona. *See* BLACKMAN, Christine Fiona

PRATT, Edward Andrew. b 39. Clare Coll Cam BA61 MA65. Clifton Th Coll 63. **d** 66 **p** 67. C Southall Green St Jo Lon 66-69; C Drypool St Columba w St Andr and St Pet *York* 69-71; P-in-c Radbourne *Derby* 71-74; R Kirk Langley 71-78; V Mackworth All SS 71-78; V Southsea St Simon *Portsm* 78-97; rtd 97; Perm to Offic *Sarum* from 97. *7 Bay Close, Swanage BH19 1RE*

PRATT, Mrs Janet Margaret. b 40. Herts Coll BEd78. St Alb Minl Tr Scheme 78. **dss** 81 **d** 87 **p** 94. High Wych and Gilston w Eastwick *St Alb* 81-87; Hon Par Dn 87-89; Par Dn Histon *Ely* 89-91; C 94-97; Par Dn Impington 89-94; C 94-97; R Bardney *Linc* from 97. *The Rectory, 10 Church Lane, Bardney, Lincoln LN3 5TZ* Tel (01526) 398595

PRATT, John. b 37. **d** 99 **p** 00. OLM St Enoder *Truro* from 99. *Chyteg, Newquay Road, St Columb Road, St Columb TR9 6PY* Tel (01726) 860747 Fax as telephone

PRATT, John Anthony. b 38. Selw Coll Cam BA61 MA65. Qu Coll Birm DipTh66. **d** 66 **p** 67. C Harrow Weald All SS *Lon* 66-69; C St Pancras w St Jas and Ch Ch 69-74; C Saffron Walden *Chelmsf* 74-75; TV Saffron Walden w Wendens Ambo and Littlebury 75-79; V St Mary-at-Latton 79-88; Chapl Princess Alexandra Hosp Harlow 82-88; RD Harlow *Chelmsf* 83-88; R Tolleshunt Knights w Tiptree and Gt Braxted 88-03; rtd 03. *2 Erica Drive, Whitnash, Leamington Spa CV31 2RS* Tel (01926) 428609 E-mail japratt@fish.co.uk

PRATT, Kenneth George. b 21. EAMTC 81. **d** 84 **p** 85. NSM March St Jo *Ely* 84-87; Chapl Doddington Community Hosp 86-93; Chapl NW Anglia Healthcare NHS Trust from 93; P-in-c Doddington w Benwick *Ely* 87-94; rtd 94; Perm to Offic *Ely* from 94. *2 Windsor Drive, March PE15 8DF* Tel (01354) 658814 *or* 740481

PRATT, Michael. *See* HARRIS, Michael

PRATT, Canon Richard David. b 55. Linc Coll Ox BA77 MA81 Birm Univ PhD01 Nottm Univ BCombStuds84. Linc Th Coll 81. d 84 p 85. C Wellingborough All Hallows *Pet* 84-87; TV Kingsthorpe w Northampton St Dav 87-92; V Northampton St Benedict 92-97; P-in-c Carl St Cuth w St Mary *Carl* from 97; Dioc Communications Officer from 97; Hon Can Carl Cathl from 02. *St Cuthbert's Vicarage, West Walls, Carlisle CA3 8UF* Tel (01228) 521982 E-mail pratt@fish.co.uk *or* communications@carlislediocese.org.uk

PRATT, Samuel Charles. b 40. ALAM59. Oak Hill Th Coll 69. d 71 p 72. C Upper Holloway St Jo *Lon* 71-73; C Bucknall and Bagnall *Lich* 73-76; V Liv St Mich *Liv* 76-80; Chapl R Liv Hosp 80-94; Chapl R Liv Univ Hosp NHS Trust 94-01; V Billinge *Liv* from 01. *St Aidan's Vicarage, 91 Newton Road East, Billinge, Wigan WN5 7LB* Tel (01744) 892210 Mobile 07957-367114 E-mail samuel_pratt@tinyworld.co.uk

PRATT, Stephen Samuel. b 67. Univ Coll Ches BA88 Keele Univ PGCE89. Oak Hill Th Coll BA00. d 00 p 01. C Goodmayes All SS *Chelmsf* 00-03; TV Chell *Lich* from 03. *The Vicarage, 110 Sprinkbank Road, Stoke-on-Trent ST6 6HZ* Tel (01782) 823090 E-mail rev@steppratt.worldonline.co.uk

PRATT, Canon William Ralph. b 47. Keble Coll Ox BA69 MA73. Linc Th Coll 70. d 72 p 73. C Ifield *Chich* 72-78; TV 78; C Brighton St Pet w Chpl Royal and St Jo 79-83; P-in-c Hove St Jo 83-87; Dioc Communications Officer 87-00; Can and Preb Chich Cathl from 90; V Ringmer from 00. *The Vicarage, Vicarage Way, Ringmer, Lewes BN8 5LA* Tel (01273) 812243 E-mail wrpratt@btinternet.com

PREBBLE, The Ven Albert Ernest. b 08. Univ of NZ BA31 MA32 St Jo Coll Auckland 32. d 32 p 33. New Zealand 32-63; Adn Waimate 44-49; Adn Manukau 49-56; V Gen and Adn Auckland 56-63; Perm to Offic *Pet* from 59; V Greenhill St Jo *Lon* 63-72; rtd 73. *12 Saxon Court, Wessex Way, Bicester OX26 6AX* Tel (01869) 324861

PRECIOUS, Sally Joanne. *See* WRIGHT, Sally Joanne

PREECE, Barry Leslie. b 48. Lich Th Coll 68. d 71 p 72. C Ewell *Guildf* 71-74; C York Town St Mich 75-77; P-in-c Ripley 77-81; Chapl HM Det Cen Send 77-81; V Cuddington *Guildf* 81-88; V Cobham from 88. *The Vicarage, St Andrew's Walk, Cobham KT11 3EQ* Tel (01932) 862109 E-mail revpreece@aol.com

PREECE, Colin George. b 51. Bernard Gilpin Soc Dur 71 Linc Th Coll 72. d 75 p 76. C Upper Gornal *Lich* 75-78; C Wednesbury St Paul Wood Green 78-81; V Oxley 81-89; V Kennington *Cant* from 89; RD E Charing 92-98. *The Vicarage, 212 Faversham Road, Kennington, Ashford TN24 9AF* Tel (01233) 620500 E-mail cpreece@globalnet.co.uk

PREECE, Joseph. b 23. Univ of Wales (Ban) BA50 Univ of Wales (Swansea) DipSocSc51 LSE Cert Child Care 52 Lon Univ DBRS72. NW Ord Course 73. d 73 p 74. C Claughton cum Grange *Ches* 73-74; C Barnston 74-75; R Aldford and Bruera 75-80; V Wincle and Wildboarclough 80-82; P-in-c Cleeton w Silvington *Heref* 82-86; P-in-c Farlow 82-86; V Stottesdon 82-86; R Stottesdon w Farlow, Cleeton and Silvington 86-88; rtd 88; Perm to Offic *Heref* from 91. *Lingholm, Woodhall Drive, Hanwood, Shrewsbury SY5 8JU* Tel (01743) 860946

PREECE, Mark Richard. b 61. St Paul's Cheltenham BA85. Linc Th Coll 85. d 87 p 88. C Coity w Nolton *Llan* 87-89; C Penarth w Lavernock 89-92; V Ewenny w St Brides Major 92-99; V Canton St Luke 99-02; TR Canton Cardiff from 02. *Canton Rectory, 12 Thompson Avenue, Cardiff CF5 1EY* Tel (029) 2056 2022 Fax as telephone E-mail mrpreece@globalnet.co.uk

PREECE, Ronald Alexander. b 29. Lon Univ BD56. ALCD55. d 56 p 57. C Rusholme H Trin *Man* 56-59; Teacher Kidbrooke Sch Lon 59-60; Brazil 60-63; Perm to Offic *Cant* 63-70; Teacher Abp's Sch Cant 64-70; OMF 70-94; SW Regional Dir 76-94; Perm to Offic *Bris* 76-94; rtd 94; Perm to Offic *Cant* from 98. *5 Tonford Lane, Canterbury CT1 3XU* Tel (01227) 471061

PREMRAJ, Deborah Devashanthy. b 66. Bangalore Univ BSc87 BEd92 Serampore Univ BD91. United Th Coll Bangalore 87. d 96 p 97. Deacon Vedal India 96-02; Presbyter Madurantakam 97-02; Perm to Offic *S'wark* from 02. *All Saints' Vicarage, 100 Prince of Wales Drive, London SW11 4BD* Tel (020) 7498 6306 E-mail debu_csi@yahoo.com

PRENTICE, Brian. b 40. St Jo Coll Nottm 81. d 83 p 84. C W Bromwich All SS *Lich* 83-86; C Tettenhall Wood 86-89; V Essington 90-98; TR Willenhall H Trin from 98; AD Wolverhampton from 03. *Short Heath Vicarage, 20 Church Road, Willenhall WV12 5PT* Tel (01922) 476416

PRENTICE, Mark Neil. b 73. Ex Univ BA94. Wycliffe Hall Ox MTh00. d 00 p 01. C Tulse Hill H Trin and St Matthias *S'wark* from 00. *132 Trinity Rise, London SW2 2QP* Tel (020) 8674 3551

PRENTICE, Michael Charles. b 35. Bps' Coll Cheshunt 59. d 62 p 63. C Lon Docks St Pet w Wapping St Jo *Lon* 62-66; C Cranford 66-70; C Bethnal Green St Jas the Gt w St Jude 70-71; C Walsingham and Houghton *Nor* 71-73; C Southall Ch Redeemer *Lon* 73; V Acton Vale St Thos 73-78; P-in-c Stow Bardolph w Wimbotsham and Stow Bridge *Ely* 78-80; R Woodford *Pet* 80-94; rtd 98. *Doric Cottage, 1 Low Road, Wretton, King's Lynn PE33 9QN* Tel (01366) 500210

PRENTIS, Calvert Clayton. b 62. Aston Tr Scheme 93 St Jo Coll Nottm DipTh95. d 97 p 98. C Wood End *Cov* 97-00; TV Leeds St Geo *Ripon* from 00. *22 Hanover Square, Leeds LS3 1AP* Tel 0113-244 0604 E-mail calvert@prentisc.fsnet.co.uk

PRENTIS, Richard Hugh. b 36. Ch Coll Cam BA60 MA64. Sarum Th Coll 69. d 71 p 72. C Bath Bathwick St Mary *B & W* 71-76; Bp's Dom Chapl *Lich* 76-80; PV Lich Cathl 76-80; V Longton St Mary and St Chad 80-84; V Shifnal 84-94; P-in-c Badger 84-85; P-in-c Ryton 84-85; P-in-c Beckbury 84-85; rtd 94. *23A The Close, Lichfield WS13 7LD* Tel (01543) 411234

PRESCOTT, David John. b 51. St Kath Coll Liv BEd73. N Ord Course 00. d 03. C Southport Em *Liv* from 03. *28 Elswick Green, Southport PR9 9XT* Tel (01704) 227294 Mobile 07762-943138

PRESCOTT, Thomas Robert. b 41. St Mich Coll Llan DipTh95. d 95 p 96. C Abertillery w Cwmtillery w Six Bells *Mon* 95-99; V Llanhilleth 99-03; rtd 03. *70 Glandwr Street, Abertillery NP13 1TZ* Tel (01495) 216782

PRESCOTT, William Allan. b 57. d 93 p 94. C Horsell *Guildf* 93-98; R Guernsey St Sav *Win* from 98. *St Saviour's Rectory, Neuf Chemin Road, Guernsey GY7 9FQ* Tel (01481) 263045 Fax 267145 E-mail prescott@guernsey.net

PRESS, Richard James. b 45. Southn Univ CertEd67. Sarum & Wells Th Coll 92. d 92 p 93. C Bradford-on-Avon *Sarum* 92-95; P-in-c Rowde and Poulshot 95-98; R Rowde and Bromham 98-01; Chapl Wilts and Swindon Healthcare NHS Trust 98-00; P-in-c Chickerell w Fleet *Sarum* from 01. *The Rectory, East Street, Chickerell, Weymouth DT3 4DS* Tel (01305) 784915 E-mail rjpress@yifan.net

PRESS, William John. b 72. QUB MEng94 BTh. d 99 p 00. C Knockbreda *D & D* 99-03; C Dundonald from 03. *6 Mount Regan Avenue, Dundonald, Belfast BT16 1JA* Tel (028) 9048 5557

PRESTNEY, Mrs Patricia Christine Margaret. b 49. UEA BEd94. Oak Hill Th Coll 84. d 87 p 94. NSM Lawford *Chelmsf* 87-95; Chapl Benenden Sch 95-97; Chapl St Jo Coll Ipswich 97-00; R Lawford *Chelmsf* from 00. *The Rectory, Church Hill, Lawford, Manningtree CO11 2JX* Tel (01206) 392659 Fax 396039 E-mail patprestney@yahoo.com

PRESTON, David Francis. b 50. BNC Ox BA72 MA78. St Steph Ho Ox 72. d 74 p 75. C Beckenham St Jas *Roch* 74-79; C Hockley *Chelmsf* 81-83; C Lamorbey H Redeemer *Roch* 83-89; V Gillingham St Barn 89-00; Perm to Offic from 00. *109 Sunnymead Avenue, Gillingham ME7 2EA* Tel (01634) 856492

PRESTON, Donald George. b 30. St Alb Minl Tr Scheme 77. d 80 p 81. NSM Elstow *St Alb* 80-87; NSM Goldington 87-94; Perm to Offic from 95. *106 Putnoe Street, Bedford MK41 8HJ* Tel (01234) 267313

PRESTON, Frederick John. b 32. MBE72. Oak Hill Th Coll 54 St Jo Coll Northwood LTh67. d 57 p 58. C Hove Bp Hannington Memorial *Ch Chich* 57-59; C-in-c Knaphill *Guildf* 60-62; CF 62-69; V Otterton *Ex* 69-71; CF 71-79; NSM 79-84; Chapl ICS 84-89; rtd 89; Perm to Offic *Nor* 96-98; Perm to Offic *Chich* from 98. *2 The Court, Hoo Gardens, Eastbourne BN20 9AX* Tel (01323) 509221

PRESTON, James Martin. b 31. Trin Coll Cam MA55 Ch Ch Ox MA57. Virginia Th Sem 57 S'wark Ord Course 87. d 88 p 88. NSM Blackheath Ascension *S'wark* 88-95; NSM Lewisham St Mary 95-97; NSM Catford St Laur 97-99; Perm to Offic *Chich* from 99. *4 Aymer Road, Hove BN3 4GA* Tel (01273) 884177 Fax as telephone E-mail prestonm@clara.net

PRESTON, John. b 26. St Aid Birkenhead 58. d 52 p 52. In RC Ch 50-57; C Chadderton Ch Ch *Man* 58-59; C Didsbury Ch Ch 59-63; R Cheetham St Jo 63-96; rtd 96; Perm to Offic *Man* from 96. *Edelweiss, 31 Rectory Road, Crumpsall, Manchester M8 5EA* Tel 0161-740 2533

PRESTON, John Baker. b 23. Lon Univ BA49. Oak Hill Th Coll 46. d 51 p 52. C Fazakerley Em *Liv* 51-55; C Eastbourne H Trin *Chich* 55-57; V Blackheath St Jo *S'wark* 57-65; Perm to Offic *Cant* 69-91; rtd 88. *43 Wedgwood Drive, Poole BH14 8ES*

PRESTON, John Michael. b 40. K Coll Lon BD63 AKC63 Lon Univ BA81 Southn Univ PhD91. St Boniface Warminster. d 65 p 66. C Heston *Lon* 65-67; C Northolt St Mary 67-72; Trinidad and Tobago 72-74; P-in-c Aveley *Chelmsf* 74-78; V 78-82; C Eastleigh *Win* 82-84; C-in-c Boyatt Wood CD 84-87; V W End 87-00; P-in-c Newton Valence, Selborne and E Tisted w Colemore from 00. *The Vicarage, The Plestor, Selborne, Alton GU34 3JQ* Tel (01420) 511242 E-mail john.preston@ukgateway.net

PRESTON, Mrs Junko Monica. b 38. Aoyama Gakuin Tokyo BA Lon Univ. d 92 p 93. C St Paul's Cathl Wellington from 92. *12A Hobson Street, Thorndon, Wellington, New Zealand* Tel (0064) (4) 473 1902

PRESTON, Michael Christopher. b 47. Hatf Coll Dur BA68. Ripon Coll Cuddesdon 75. d 78 p 79. C Epsom St Martin *Guildf* 78-82; C Guildf H Trin w St Mary 82-86; V Epsom St Barn from 86. *St Barnabas' Vicarage, Hook Road, Epsom KT19 8TU* Tel (01372) 722874 E-mail rev@m-c-preston.demon.co.uk

PRESTON, Canon Percival Kenneth. b 16. Th Ch Ox BA38 MA48. Cuddesdon Coll 38. d 40 p 45. C Jersey St Helier *Win* 40-46; C Ox SS Phil and Jas *Ox* 46-48; C Westbury-on-Trym H

Trin *Bris* 48-50; Min Lawrence Weston CD 50-55; V Horfield St Greg 55-81; Hon Can Bris Cathl 74-82; R D Horfield 76-81; rtd 81; Perm to Offic *Bris* from 82; *Glouc* from 83. *56 Gloucester Road, Rudgeway, Bristol BS35 3RT* Tel (01454) 612794

PRESTON, Reuben James. b 65. York Univ BSc86 MEng87 Derby Coll of Educn Cert Rural Studies89 Birm Univ PGCE97. Westcott Ho Cam 88. **d** 91 **p** 92. C Weoley Castle *Birm* 91-94; TV Malvern Link w Cowleigh *Worc* 94-96; Perm to Offic *Birm* 96-99; C Bordesley St Benedict from 99. *27 Haughton Road, Handsworth, Birmingham B20 3LE* Tel 0121-686 9304 Fax 686 9276 E-mail frreuben@england.com

PRESTON, William. b 25. St Cath Coll Cam BA46 MA50 Reading Univ MSc79. Oak Hill Th Coll 48. **d** 50 **p** 51. C Hyson Green *S'well* 50-52; C Lenton 52-55; Kenya 55-62; Bethany Sch Goudhurst 62-69; Cranbrook Sch Kent 69-90; Perm to Offic *Cant* from 64; *Roch* from 66; rtd 90. *29 Orchard Way, Horsmonden, Tonbridge TN12 8LA* Tel (01892) 722616

PRESTON-THOMAS, Canon Colin Barnabas Rashleigh. b 28. K Coll Lon 48 Edin Th Coll 51. **d** 53 **p** 54. C Edin St Dav *Edin* 53-54; Chapl St Ninian's Cathl Perth *St And* 54-55; Prec St Ninian's Cathl Perth 55-60; Chapl HM Pris Perth 55-60; P-in-c Inverkeithing *St And* 60; R 61-72; P-in-c Rosyth 60; R 61-72; Syn Clerk 68-93; Can St Ninian's Cathl Perth 68-93; R Forfar 72-82; Dioc Sec 80-90; R Kilmaveonaig 82-93; R Pitlochry 82-93; rtd 93; Hon Can St Ninian's Cathl Perth *St And* from 93. *14 Muirend Grove, Perth PH1 1JW* Tel (01738) 627807

PRESTWOOD, Ms Jayne Marie. b 64. Man Univ BA86 Nottm Univ MA93. Linc Th Coll MA94. **d** 94 **p** 95. C Reddish *Man* 94-98; Dioc Drugs Misuse Project Worker 98-00; P-in-c N Reddish from 00. *St Agnes's Rectory, 551 Gorton Road, Stockport SK5 6NX* Tel 0161-223 0692 E-mail tbjp2000@fish.co.uk

PREVETT, Mark Norman. b 59. Univ of Wales (Cardiff) BD88. St Mich Coll Llan 85. **d** 88 **p** 89. C Brynmawr *S & B* 88-90; C Bassaleg *Mon* 90-92; R Blaina and Nantyglo 92-97; TV Halas *Worc* from 97; AD Dudley from 00. *St Peter's Vicarage, 15 Cricklewood Drive, Halesowen B62 8SN* Tel 0121-550 5458 Mobile 07817-622640 Fax 0121-550 9748 E-mail prevtherev@btopenworld.com

PREVITE, The Ven Anthony Michael Allen. b 41. TCD DipTh88. CITC 85. **d** 88 **p** 89. C Galway w Kilcummin *T, K & A* 88-91; I Omey w Ballynakill, Errislannan and Roundstone 91-93; Dean Tuam 93-96; I Tuam w Cong and Aasleagh 93-96; Adn Tuam from 96; Can Tuam Cathl from 96; I Omey w Ballynakill, Errislannan and Roundstone from 96. *The Rectory, Church Hill, Clifden, Co Galway, Irish Republic* Tel (00353) (95) 21147 Fax as telephone E-mail aprevite@eircom.net

PREWER, Dennis. b 31. Kelham Th Coll 50. **d** 54 **p** 55. C Stockport St Thos *Ches* 54-58; C Gt Grimsby St Mary and St Jas *Linc* 58-62; V Gt Harwood St Jo *Blackb* 62-64; V Scarcliffe *Derby* 64-70; Org Sec CECS 70-92; Dios Liv, Ban and St As 70-78; Dio Man 78-92; Lic to Offic *Ches* 70-92; Perm to Offic *Man* 78-96; rtd 92; Perm to Offic *Ches* from 92. *19 Alan Drive, Marple, Stockport SK6 6LN* Tel 0161-427 2827

PRICE, Alec John. b 32. Solicitor 58 Univ of Wales (Abth) LLB55. St Deiniol's Hawarden 77. **d** 79 **p** 80. Hon C St As *St As* 79-80; V Choral St As Cathl 79-83; Hon C St As and Tremeirchion 80-83; R Cilcain and Nannerch and Rhyd-y-mwyn 84-88; Min Can and PV Bre Cathl *S & B* 88-90; Perm to Offic *Lich* 90-91; C Shrewsbury St Chad w St Mary 91-96; Chapl Shrewsbury Town Cen 91-96; rtd 96. *Lindenhurst, Green Acre Road, Copthorne, Shrewsbury SY3 8LR* Tel (01743) 245013

PRICE, Miss Alison Jane. b 63. NNEB84. Aston Tr Scheme 91 Westcott Ho Cam CTM95. **d** 95 **p** 96. C Upper Norwood All SS *S'wark* 95-99; V Mitcham St Barn from 99. *St Barnabas' Vicarage, Thirsk Road, Mitcham CR4 2BD* Tel (020) 8648 2571 E-mail alison.price@lineone.net

PRICE, Mrs Alison Mary. b 48. K Alfred's Coll Win CertEd69. **d** 01. Par Dn Magor *Mon* from 01. *Greenwillow, Church Road, Undy, Caldicot NP26 3EN* Tel (01633) 880557

PRICE, Alun Huw. b 47. MBE91. St D Coll Lamp DipTh70. **d** 70 **p** 71. C Carmarthen St Dav *St D* 70-73; V Betws Ifan 73-77; CF 77-03. *Address temp unknown*

PRICE, Anthony Ronald. b 49. Linc Coll Ox BA71 MA83 St Jo Coll Dur BA78. **d** 79 **p** 80. C St Alb St Paul *St Alb* 79-81; C Wootton 81-85; C Lydiard Millicent w Lydiard Tregoz *Bris* 85-86; TV The Lydiards 86-91; V Marston *Ox* 91-95; V Marston w Elsfield from 95; RD Cowley 97-02. *The Vicarage, Elsfield Road, Marston, Oxford OX3 0PR* Tel (01865) 247034 E-mail tonyprice@stnicsmarston.freeserve.co.uk

PRICE, Carol Ann. b 46. St Jo Coll Nottm 02. **d** 03. NSM Derby St Alkmund and St Werburgh *Derby* from 03. *52 Statham Street, Derby DE22 1HQ* Tel (01332) 609111 Mobile 07787-522127 E-mail carol_price@ntlworld.com

PRICE, Christine. b 66. Leic Univ BA94. EAMTC 98. **d** 01 **p** 02. C Jersey St Helier *Win* from 01. *3 Myrtle Grove, 42 St Johns Road, St Helier, Jersey JE2 3LD* Tel 07971-026711 (mobile)

PRICE, Mrs Christine Janice. b 45. Sarum & Wells Th Coll 83. **dss** 86 **d** 87 **p** 94. Roxbourne St Andr *Lon* 86-90; NSM 87-90; NSM Roxeth Ch Ch and Harrow St Pet 90-93; NSM Roxeth

93-94; C 94-96; C Costessey *Nor* 96-98; rtd 98; Perm to Offic *Nor* from 98. *Kingfishers, 212A Taverham Road, Taverham, Norwich NR8 6SU* Tel (01603) 868036 Fax as telephone E-mail chrisjpri@aol.com

PRICE, Canon Clive Stanley. b 42. ALCD69. **d** 69 **p** 70. C Chenies and Lt Chalfont *Ox* 69-75; R Upper Stour *Sarum* 75-79; C-in-c Panshanger CD *St Alb* 79-82; TV Digswell and Panshanger 82-86; P-in-c St Oswald in Lee w Bingfield *Newc* from 86; Dioc Ecum Officer from 86; Hon Can Newc Cathl from 97; AD Bellingham from 00. *St Oswald's Vicarage, Wall, Hexham NE46 4DU* Tel (01434) 681354

PRICE, Dai. See PRICE, William Haydn

PRICE, David. b 27. Wycliffe Hall Ox 61. **d** 63 **p** 64. C Bucknall and Bagnall *Lich* 63-67; C Abingdon w Shippon *Ox* 67-76; Israel 76-84; V S Kensington St Luke *Lon* 84-92; P-in-c S Kensington St Jude 88-92; rtd 92; Hon C Hordle w Tiptoe *Win* 92-97; Perm to Offic *Worc* from 98. *9 Hanley Road, Malvern WR14 4PQ* Tel (01684) 568532

PRICE, David Gareth Michael. b 64. Ex Univ BA86 Kent Univ MA87 FSS. Wycliffe Hall Ox BTh94. **d** 97 **p** 98. C Godalming *Guildf* 97-00; C-in-c Elvetham Heath LEP 00-02; Min from 02. *Church House, 30 Chineham Close, Fleet GU51 1BF* Tel (01252) 695067 E-mail pricesinfleet@aol.com

PRICE, Canon David Rea. b 39. St Aid Birkenhead 61. **d** 63 **p** 64. C Green Street Green *Roch* 63-66; C Gillingham St Mary 66-69; C New Windsor St Jo *Ox* 69-72; V Winkfield 72-80; RD Bracknell 78-86; V Sunningdale 80-86; TR Wimborne Minster and Holt *Sarum* 86-96; R Wimborne Minster 96-01; Chapl Wimborne Hosp 86-01; RD Wimborne 88-98; Can and Preb Sarum Cathl 92-01; P-in-c Witchampton, Stanbridge and Long Crichel etc 00-01; rtd 01; Perm to Offic *Ex* from 01. *14 The Broadway, Exmouth EX8 2NW* Tel (01395) 269811

PRICE, Canon David Trevor William. b 43. Keble Coll Ox BA65 MA69 MEHS79 FRHistS79 FSA95. Sarum & Wells Th Coll 72. **d** 72 **p** 73. Lect Univ of Wales (Lamp) *St D* 70-87; Sen Lect 87-97; Chapl 79-80; Dean of Chpl 90-91; Public Preacher 72-86; Dioc Archivist 82-98; P-in-c Betws Bledrws 86-97; Hon Can St D Cathl 90-92; Can 92-00; V Cydweli and Llandyfaelog 97-00; P-in-c Myddle *Lich* from 00; P-in-c Broughton from 00; Perm to Offic *St As* from 01. *The Rectory, Myddle, Shrewsbury SY4 3RX* Tel (01939) 290811 Mobile 07811-712911 E-mail dtw@price2043.freeserve.co.uk

PRICE, Dawson. b 31. OBE. Peterho Cam BA52. Oak Hill NSM Course 88. **d** 91 **p** 92. NSM Harpenden St Nic *St Alb* 91-99; rtd 99. *15 Anfield Court, Fair Oak, Eastleigh SO50 7LF* Tel (023) 8069 2273

PRICE, Derek Henry. b 51. Trin Coll Bris BA98. **d** 98 **p** 99. C Bayston Hill *Lich* 98-02; R Newbarns w Hawcoat *Carl* from 02. *St Paul's Rectory, 353 Abbey Road, Barrow-in-Furness LA13 9JY* Tel (01229) 821546 E-mail dh.price@virgin.net

PRICE, Canon Derek William. b 27. St Pet Hall Ox BA51 MA55. Qu Coll Birm 51. **d** 53 **p** 54. C St Marylebone St Mark Hamilton Terrace *Lon* 53-57; C Stevenage *St Alb* 57-63; Jamaica 63-67; R Bridgham and Roudham *Nor* 67-80; R E w W Harling 69-80; Hon Can Nor Cathl 75-92; RD Thetford and Rockland 76-86; P-in-c Kilverstone 80-87; P-in-c Croxton 80-87; TR Thetford 80-87; R Castleacre w Newton, Rougham and Southacre 87-92; Perm to Offic 92-99 and from 00; P-in-c Easton w Colton and Marlingford 99-00. *Fourways, King's Road, Dereham NR19 2AG* Tel (01362) 691660

PRICE, Chan Desmond. b 23. St D Coll Lamp BA50. **d** 51 **p** 52. C Llwynypia *Llan* 51-52; C Ystradyfodwg 52-54; C Watford Ch Ch *St Alb* 54-56; Chapl RAF 56-68; R Dinas and Llanllawer *St D* 68-72; V Llandeilo Fawr w Llandyfeisant 72-79; V Llandeilo Fawr and Taliaris 79-91; Can St D Cathl 83-91; Chan 89-91; RD Llangadog and Llandeilo 90-91; rtd 91; Hon Can St D Cathl *St D* from 91. *24 Diana Road, Llandeilo SA19 6RS* Tel (01558) 824039

PRICE, Canon Edward Glyn. b 35. Univ of Wales (Lamp) BA55. Ch Div Sch of the Pacific (USA) BD58. **d** 58 **p** 59. C Denbigh *St As* 58-65; V Llanasa 65-76; V Buckley 76-91; Dioc RE Adv 77-88; RD Mold 86-91; Can St As Cathl from 87; Preb and Sacr from 95; V Llandrillo-yn-Rhos 91-00; rtd 00. *7 Rhodfa Criccieth, Bodelwyddan, Rhyl LL18 5WL* Tel (01745) 571286

PRICE, Frank Lea. b 69. SS Coll Cam BA92 Solicitor 96. Oak Hill Th Coll BA99. **d** 99 **p** 00. C Hinckley H Trin *Leic* from 99. *27 Lochmore Drive, Hinckley LE10 0TZ* Tel (01455) 447118 E-mail fandkprice@ntlworld.com

PRICE, Frank Watkin. b 22. ALCM37 Univ of Wales (Lamp) BA45. St Mich Coll Llan 45. **d** 47 **p** 48. C Cwmaman *St D* 47-50; C Llanelli 50-52; Chapl RAF 52-68; Hd RE Amman Valley Comp Sch 68-83; Hd Master Lower Sch 75-85; R St Nicholas w Bonvilston and St George-super-Ely *Llan* 85-92; rtd 92; Perm to Offic *Llan* and *St D* from 92. *13 Pedair Erw Road, Cardiff CF14 4NU* Tel (029) 2061 8356

PRICE, Frederick Leslie. b 30. Oak Hill Th Coll 59. **d** 61 **p** 62. C Hougham in Dover Ch Ch *Cant* 61-64; R Plumbland and Gilcrux *Carl* 64-95; rtd 95; Perm to Offic *Carl* from 98. *1 Beech*

Hill, Oughterside, Aspatria, Carlisle CA7 2QA Tel (01697) 320255

PRICE, Geoffrey David Gower. b 46. NDA NCA. Oak Hill Th Coll DipHE. **d** 83 **p** 84. C Gt Baddow *Chelmsf* 83-86; C Hampreston *Sarum* 86-88; TV 88-93; P-in-c Drayton in Hales *Lich* 93-97; V 97-99; P-in-c Adderley 93-97; P-in-c Moreton Say 93-97; R Ipswich St Helen, H Trin, and St Luke *St E* from 99. *The Rectory, 42 Clapgate Lane, Ipswich IP3 0RD* Tel (01473) 723467

PRICE, Gerald Andrew. b 31. NEOC. **d** 84 **p** 85. C Monkseaton St Mary *Newc* 84-87; V Cowgate 87-94; C Beltingham w Henshaw 94-96; C Haydon Bridge 94-96; rtd 96; Perm to Offic *Newc* from 96. *24 Hallstile Bank, Hexham NE46 3PQ* Tel (01434) 603374

PRICE, Mrs Jean Amelia. b 44. St Alb and Ox Min Course 99. **d** 02. OLM N Buckingham *Ox* from 02. *15 Highlands Road, Buckingham MK18 1PN* Tel (01280) 815125
E-mail jeanprice@tinyworld.co.uk

PRICE, John Francis. b 32. Qu Coll Cam BA54 MA. Ridley Hall Cam 54. **d** 56 **p** 57. C Leic H Apostles *Leic* 56-60; V Forest Gate St Mark *Chelmsf* 60-71; V Harold Hill St Geo 72-79; R Loughton St Mary 79-83; TR Loughton St Mary and St Mich 83-88; R Kirby-le-Soken w Gt Holland 88-92; rtd 92; Perm to Offic *Chelmsf* from 00. *97 Kings Parade, Holland-on-Sea, Clacton-on-Sea CO15 5JH* Tel (01255) 813202

PRICE, John Joseph. b 44. Ridley Hall Cam 89. **d** 92 **p** 93. C Glenfield *Leic* 92-97; Relig Affairs Adv BBC Radio Leics 93-97; Midl Regional Co-ord Crosslinks from 97. *Copper Beeches, 59A Peterborough Road, Castor, Peterborough PE5 7AL* Tel (01733) 380025 E-mail john@peterborough.region.crosslinks.org

PRICE, Canon John Lowry Augustine. b 13. Mercer Ho Melbourne TDip69. AKC38. **d** 39 **p** 40. C Luton St Andr *St Alb* 39-42; C Devonport St Mark Ford *Ex* 43-46; C St Alb St Sav *St Alb* 46-48; Australia from 48; P-in-c Millicent 48-53; R Colac 53-62; Can Ballarat 62-65; R Ballarat St Pet and RD Ballarat 62-65; rtd 65; Perm to Offic *Bendigo* from 89. *88 Carrington Street, Macedon, Vic, Australia 3440* Tel (0061) (3) 5426 1941

PRICE, John Newman. b 32. St Alb Minl Tr Scheme 80. **d** 83 **p** 84. NSM Bedford St Pet w St Cuth *St Alb* 83-88; C Lt Berkhamsted and Bayford, Essendon etc 88-92; P-in-c Benington w Walkern 92-99; rtd 99; Perm to Offic *St Alb* from 00. *21 Wendover Drive, Bedford MK41 9QY* Tel (01234) 313373

PRICE, Canon John Richard. b 34. Mert Coll Ox BA58 MA62. Westcott Ho Cam 58. **d** 60 **p** 61. C Man St Aid *Man* 60-63; C Bramley *Ripon* 63-67; V Leeds All Hallows w St Simon 67-74; P-in-c Wrangthorn 73-74; V Claughton cum Grange *Ches* 74-78; V Mottram in Longdendale w Woodhead 78-88; RD Mottram 79-88; Hon Can Ches Cathl 86-99; R Nantwich 88-99; rtd 99; Perm to Offic *Bradf* 99-00; P-in-c Cowling from 00. *21 Mill Croft, Cowling, Keighley BD22 0AJ* Tel (01535) 633769

PRICE, Joseph Roderick (Rod). b 45. St Mich Coll Llan 71. **d** 75 **p** 76. C Fleur-de-Lis *Mon* 75-79; CF 79-99; rtd 99. *clo MOD Chaplains (Army)* Tel (01980) 615804 Fax 615801

PRICE, Preb Lawrence Robert. b 43. LICeram71 N Staffs Poly CertCT66 Manager's Dip in Ceramic Tech 74. St Jo Coll Dur 76. **d** 78 **p** 79. C Harlescott *Lich* 78-80; C Cheddleton 80-83; P-in-c Calton 83-84; P-in-c Cauldon 83-84; P-in-c Grindon 83-84; P-in-c Waterfall 83-84; R Calton, Cauldon, Grindon and Waterfall 85-88; P-in-c Kingsley 95-01; R Kingsley and Foxt-w-Whiston from 01; RD Cheadle from 98; Preb Lich Cathl from 00. *The Rectory, Holt Lane, Kingsley, Stoke-on-Trent ST10 2BA* Tel (01538) 754754 Fax 754431 E-mail preblrprice@aol.com

PRICE, Leslie. *See* PRICE, Frederick Leslie

PRICE, Mari Josephine. b 43. St Hugh's Coll Ox BA65 Ox Univ MA69 DipEd66. Llan Dioc Tr Scheme 93. **d** 97 **p** 98. NSM Lisvane *Llan* 97-02; NSM Roath from 02. *23 Ty Draw Road, Roath, Cardiff CF23 5HB* Tel (029) 2045 6757 Mobile 07850-019883

PRICE, Martin Randall Connop. b 45. Lon Univ BSc71 Fitzw Coll Cam BA75 MA79 Univ of Wales (Swansea) PhD02. Ridley Hall Cam 73. **d** 76 **p** 77. C Keynsham *B & W* 76-79; Ind Chapl *Sheff* 79-83; V Wortley 79-83; R Hook Norton w Gt Rollright, Swerford etc *Ox* 83-91; V Shiplake w Dunsden 91-03; P-in-c Harpsden 02-03; R Shiplake w Dunsden and Harpsden from 03. *The Rectory, Shiplake, Henley-on-Thames RG9 4BS* Tel 0118-940 1306

PRICE, Michael Graham. b 62. Ex Coll Ox BA84. Linc Th Coll 84. **d** 86 **p** 87. C Salford St Phil w St Steph *Man* 86-90; R Man Gd Shep 90-95; V Netherton St Andr *Worc* 95-99; Chapl Bloxham Sch from 00. *Bloxham School, Bloxham, Banbury OX15 4PQ* Tel (01295) 720222

PRICE, Morris John. b 39. **d** 03. OLM Gt Wyrley *Lich* from 03. *42 Huthill Lane, Great Wyrley, Walsall WS6 6PB* Tel (01922) 412846 E-mail normoss@ukonline.net

PRICE, Norman. *See* PRICE, William Norman

PRICE, Canon Norman Havelock. b 28. Univ of Wales (Lamp) BA52. St Mich Coll Llan 52. **d** 54 **p** 55. C Maindee *Mon* 54-58; V Llantilio Crossenny and Llanfihangel Ystern etc 58-64; V Mon St Thos-over-Monnow 64-65; V Mon St Thos-over-Monnow and Wonastow 65-71; V Overmonnow w Wonastow and Michel Troy

71-93; RD Monmouth 84-93; Can St Woolos Cathl 91-93; rtd 93; Hon Can St Woolos Cathl *Mon* 93-96; Lic to Offic from 93. *17 Cinderhill Street, Monmouth NP25 5EY* Tel (01600) 714587

✠**PRICE, The Rt Revd Peter Bryan.** b 44. Redland Coll of Educn CertEd66. Oak Hill Th Coll DPS74. **d** 74 **p** 75 **c** 97. C Portsdown *Portsm* 74-78; Chapl Scargill Ho 78-80; P-in-c Addiscombe St Mary *Cant* 80-81; V 81-84; V Addiscombe St Mary *S'wark* 85-88; Can Res and Chan S'wark Cathl 88-92; Gen Sec USPG 92-97; Area Bp Kingston *S'wark* 97-02; Bp B & W from 02. *The Palace, Wells BA5 2PD* Tel (01749) 672341 Fax 679355
E-mail bishop@bathwells.anglican.org

PRICE, Peter Charles. b 27. Angl Th Coll (BC) DipTh61. **d** 61 **p** 62. Canada 61-66; C St Mary-at-Latton *Chelmsf* 66-68; C Bearsted *Cant* 68-74; TV Ebbw Vale *Mon* 74-77; V Llanfihangel Crucorney w Oldcastle etc 77-87; V St Paul's Cathl St Helena 87-90; V Llanishen w Trellech Grange and Llanfihangel etc *Mon* 90-94; rtd 94; Perm to Offic *Heref* from 95. *1 Kynaston, Much Marcle, Ledbury HR8 2PD* Tel (01531) 670687

PRICE, Canon Philip. b 24. Tyndale Hall Bris 50. **d** 55 **p** 56. Kenya 55-75; R Gt Horkesley *Chelmsf* 75-89; rtd 89; Perm to Offic *Chelmsf* from 89; Hon Can Kitale from 02. *229 Meadgate Avenue, Great Baddow, Chelmsford CM2 7NJ* Tel (01245) 251499

PRICE, Raymond Francklin. b 30. Wycliffe Hall Ox 61. **d** 62 **p** 63. C Bilston St Leon *Lich* 62-67; C Keighley *Bradf* 67-70; V Mangotsfield *Bris* 70-79; Ind Chapl *Birm* 79-86; C Birm St Martin 84-85; C Birm St Martin w Bordesley St Andr 85-86; V Edgbaston St Aug 86-99; rtd 99; Perm to Offic *Birm* from 00. *35 Middle Park Road, Selly Oak, Birmingham B29 4BH* Tel 0121-475 4458

PRICE, Rod. *See* PRICE, Joseph Roderick

PRICE, Roland Kendrick. b 41. Cam Univ MA64 Essex Univ PhD69. St Alb and Ox Min Course CBTS95. **d** 95 **p** 96. NSM Cholsey *Ox* 95-97; Asst Chapl The Hague *Eur* from 99. *Bentinckstraat 129, 2582 ST Den Haag, The Netherlands* Tel (0031) (70) 358 9240 *or* 355 5359 Fax 354 1023
E-mail churchoffice@stjohnandstphilip.org

PRICE, Roy Ernest. b 13. AKC38. **d** 38 **p** 39. C Ilminster w Whitelackington *B & W* 38-40; CF (EC) 40-47; CF 47-59; V Stoke w Woodcote *Ox* 59-79; rtd 79; Perm to Offic *Win* from 82. *74A London Road, Whitchurch RG28 7LY* Tel (01256) 892581

PRICE, Stanley George. b 32. FRICS69. Trin Coll Bris 84. **d** 85 **p** 86. C Newport w Longford and Chetwynd *Lich* 85-88; V Ipstones w Berkhamsytch and Onecote w Bradnop 88-97; rtd 98; Perm to Offic *B & W* 98-03; P-in-c Rodney Stoke w Draycott from 03. *St Aidan, Rectory Way, Lympsham, Weston-super-Mare BS24 0EN* Tel (01934) 750323
E-mail stanley-price@supanet.com

PRICE, Timothy Fry. b 51. NE Lon Poly CQSW. St Jo Coll Nottm 85. **d** 87 **p** 88. C Church Stretton *Heref* 87-91; V Sinfin *Derby* 91-00; Regional Adv (SW) CMJ from 00; Perm to Offic *Glouc* from 01; *B & W* from 01. *98 Furnham Road, Chard TA20 1BE* Tel (01460) 61308 E-mail southwest@cmj.org.uk

PRICE, Victor John. b 35. Oak Hill Th Coll 62. **d** 65 **p** 66. C Rainham *Chelmsf* 65-70; V Dover St Martin *Cant* 70-78; V Madeley *Heref* 78-90; P-in-c Derby St Pet and Ch w H Trin *Derby* 90-91; V 91-96; P-in-c Morley w Morley 96-00; rtd 00. *4 Holmefield, Farndon, Newark NG24 3TZ* Tel (01636) 611788

PRICE, William. *See* PRICE, Canon David Trevor William

PRICE, William Haydn (Dai). b 20. Sarum & Wells Th Coll 77. **d** 80 **p** 81. NSM Alverstoke *Portsm* 80-85; rtd 85; Perm to Offic *Portsm* from 85. *15 Amersham Close, Alverstoke, Gosport PO12 2RU* Tel (023) 9258 0965

PRICE, William Norman. b 52. GRNCM73. N Ord Course 86. **d** 89 **p** 90. C Lower Broughton Ascension *Man* 89-91; Min Can and Succ St E Cathl *St E* 92-96; Prec 94-96; V Par *Truro* 96-00; V Musbury *Blackb* from 00. *St Thomas's Vicarage, 1 Flaxmoss Close, Haslingden, Rossendale BB4 4PX* Tel (01706) 221923 Fax as telephone E-mail golfsierra999@aol.com

PRICE-ROBERTS, Mervyn. b 29. Trin Coll Carmarthen TCert51 Univ of Wales DipRE52 BEd79. St Mich Coll Llan 89 Ban Ord Course 84. **d** 87 **p** 88. NSM Bangor *Ban* 87-89; V Llandygai w Tregarth 89-97; rtd 97; Perm to Offic *Ban* from 97. *17 Parc Hen Blas Estate, Llanfairfechan LL33 0RW* Tel (01248) 680305

PRICHARD, David Malcolm. b 66. St Steph Ho Ox BTh01. **d** 01 **p** 02. C Caerphilly *Llan* from 01. *Church House, 71 Bartlett Street, Caerphilly CF83 1JT* Tel (029) 2088 2695
E-mail dm.prichard@ntlworld.com

PRICHARD, Canon Thomas John. b 16. Univ of Wales (Ban) BA38 MA72 Keele Univ PhD81 FRHistS82. Chich Th Coll 38. **d** 39 **p** 40. C Blaenau Ffestiniog *Ban* 39-41; C Machynlleth *Ban* 41-42; C Llanfabon *Llan* 42-44; C Ystradyfodwg 44-50; V Dinas w Penygraig 50-69; Rural Dn Rhondda 64-69; Can Llan Cathl 66-84; R Neath w Llantwit 69-84; Dioc Archivist 70-84; rtd 84; Perm to Offic *Ban* from 97. *Tros-yr-Afon, Llangwnnadl, Pwllheli LL53 8NS* Tel (01758) 612832

PRIDAY, Gerald Nelson. b 35. Glouc Th Course. **d** 85 **p** 88. NSM Eardisland *Heref* 85-91; NSM Aymestrey and Leinthall Earles w Wigmore etc 85-91; NSM Kingsland 85-91; NSM Eye, Croft w

Yarpole and Lucton 91-94; NSM Heref All SS 94-96; NSM Letton w Staunton, Byford, Mansel Gamage etc 96-98; rtd 98. *4 Lime Close, Ludlow SY8 2PP* Tel (01584) 876910

PRIDDIN, Mrs Maureen Anne. b 46. Leeds Univ BA67 Nottm Univ DipEd68. EMMTC 82. **dss** 85 **d** 87 **p** 94. Mickleover St Jo *Derby* 85-87; Hon Par Dn 87-94; Assoc P from 94; Dioc World Development Officer 87-90. *7 Portland Close, Mickleover, Derby DE3 9BZ* Tel (01332) 513672 E-mail mpriddin@argonet.co.uk

✣**PRIDDIS, The Rt Revd Anthony Martin.** b 48. CCC Cam BA69 MA73 New Coll Ox DipTh71 MA75. Cuddesdon Coll 69. **d** 72 **p** 73 **c** 96. C New Addington *Cant* 72-75; Chapl Ch Ox 75-80; Lic to Offic *Ox* 76-80; TV High Wycombe 80-86; P-in-c Amersham 86-90; R 90-96; RD Amersham 92-96; Hon Can Ch Ch 95-96; Suff Bp Warw *Cov* from 96; Hon Can Cov Cathl from 96. *Warwick House, 139 Kenilworth Road, Coventry CV4 7AF* Tel (024) 7641 6200 Fax 7641 5254 E-mail bishopwarwick@clara.net

PRIDEAUX, Humphrey Grevile. b 36. CCC Ox BA59 MA63 Birm Univ CertEd66 Lon Univ DipEd73 Open Univ BA87. Linc Th Coll 59. **d** 61 **p** 62. C Northampton St Matt *Pet* 61-62; C Milton *Portsm* 62-65; Perm to Offic *Birm* 65-66; Hd of RE Qu Mary's Gr Sch Walsall 66-69; Lic to Offic *Lich* 66-69; Lect St Martin's Coll Lanc 69-80; Lic to Offic *Blackb* 69-80; Perm to Offic *Portsm* 80-86; Hon C Fareham H Trin 86-87; Hon C Bishop's Waltham 87-94; NSM P-in-c W Meon and Warnford from 94. *The Rectory, Doctors Lane, West Meon, Petersfield GU32 1LR* Tel (01730) 829226

PRIDGEON, Paul Garth Walsingham. b 45. Sussex Univ BA69 CertEd. Glouc Sch of Min 87. **d** 87 **p** 88. NSM Cirencester *Glouc* 87-97; NSM Northleach w Hampnett and Farmington etc 97-03; Perm to Offic from 03. *4 Abbey Way, Cirencester GL7 2DT* Tel (01285) 656860

PRIDIE, William Raleigh. b 49. Bris Univ BEd72 Dip Mgt82 ACP82 FCollP83. SW Minl Tr Course 90. **d** 93 **p** 94. C Kingstone w Clehonger, Eaton Bishop etc *Heref* 93-96; P-in-c Kimbolton w Hamnish and Middleton-on-the-Hill 96-97; P-in-c Bockleton w Leysters 96-97; CME Officer 96-00; TV Leominster 97-00; R Fownhope w Mordiford, Brockhampton etc from 00. *The Rectory, Fownhope, Hereford HR1 4PS* Tel (01432) 860365

PRIDMORE, John Stuart. b 36. Nottm Univ BA62 Lon Univ PhD00 Nottm Univ MA67. Ridley Hall Cam 62. **d** 65 **p** 66. C Camborne *Truro* 65-67; Tutor Ridley Hall Cam 67-68; Chapl 68-71; Asst Chapl K Edw Sch Witley 71-75; Chapl 75-86; Tanzania 86-88; Angl Chapl Hengrave Hall Cen 88-89; C St Martin-in-the-Fields *Lon* 89-95; TR Hackney 95-03; V St John-at-Hackney from 03. *The Rectory, 356 Mare Street, London E8 1HR* Tel (020) 8985 5374

PRIEST, David. b 44. Chich Th Coll 69. **d** 73 **p** 74. C S Harrow St Paul *Lon* 73-76; C S Kensington St Steph 76-83; Perm to Offic 83-90; Hon C Pimlico St Mary Graham-street 90-94; Perm to Offic 97-98; NSM Pimlico St Gabr 98-01; rtd 02. *78 Lupus Street, London SW1V 3EL* Tel (020) 7821 0978 E-mail pimlicoboy@aol.com

PRIEST, Helen Elizabeth. *See* MACE, Mrs Helen Elizabeth

PRIEST, Richard Mark. b 63. Oak Hill Th Coll BA90. **d** 90 **p** 91. C Okehampton w Inwardleigh *Ex* 90-94; C Okehampton w Inwardleigh, Bratton Clovelly etc 94; CF from 94. *c/o MOD Chaplains (Army)* Tel (01980) 615804 Fax 615800

PRIESTLEY, Canon Alan Charles. b 41. Lon Univ BD69. Kelham Th Coll 64 Wm Temple Coll Rugby 65. **d** 65 **p** 66. C Edgbaston St Aug *Birm* 65-68; C Chelmsley Wood 68-72; TV 72-76; V Hazelwell from 76; Dioc Communications Officer 83-94; Bp's Press Officer from 85; Hon Can Birm Cathl from 87. *The Vicarage, 316 Vicarage Road, Birmingham B14 7NH* Tel 0121-444 4469 Mobile 07720-936729 Fax 0121-444 8184 E-mail apriestley@waitrose.com

PRIESTLEY, Canon John Christopher. b 39. Trin Coll Ox BA60. Wells Th Coll 61. **d** 68 **p** 69. C Habergham All SS *Blackb* 68-70; C Padiham 70-75; V Colne Ch Ch 75-98; Chapl to The Queen from 90; RD Pendle *Blackb* 91-96; P-in-c Foulridge 97-98; TV Colne and Villages 98-02; Hon Can Blackb Cathl 00-02; rtd 02; Perm to Offic *Blackb* from 02. *11 Chapman Court, Barnoldswick BB18 5EE* Tel (01282) 812308

PRIESTLEY, Rosemary Jane. *See* LAIN-PRIESTLEY, Ms Rosemary Jane

PRIESTLY, Thomas Herbert. b 67. Ulster Univ BA91. CITC BTh94. **d** 94 **p** 95. C Ballymena w Ballyclug *Conn* 94-99; I Dunmurry from 99. *The Rectory, 27 Church Avenue, Dunmurry, Belfast BT17 9RS* Tel (028) 9061 0984

PRIESTNALL, Reginald Hayward. b 22. Jes Coll Cam BA44 MA47. Ridley Hall Cam 44. **d** 45 **p** 46. C Streatham Immanuel *S'wark* 45-48; C Barking St Marg *Chelmsf* 48-51; R Bonsall *Derby* 51-53; P-in-c Mackworth St Fran 53-54; V 54-67; Chapl Kingsway Hosp Derby 61-67; V Rockingham w Caldecote *Pet* 67-71; V Northampton St Mich 71-77; V Ketton 77-89; RD Barnack 86-89; rtd 89. *Lavender Cottage, 486 Earlham Road, Norwich NR4 7HP* Tel (01603) 503435

PRIESTNER, Hugh. b 45. Nottm Univ BTh75. Linc Th Coll 71. **d** 75 **p** 76. C Seaton Hirst *Newc* 75-78; C Longbenton St Bart 78-81; P-in-c Glendale Gp 81-82; TV 83-88; Chapl Stafford

Acute Hosps 88-89; Tr Co-ord W Cumberland Hosp 89-92; Chapl Fair Havens Hospice 94-98; Chapl Walsgrave Hosps NHS Trust Cov from 98. *Walsgrave Hospital, Clifford Bridge Road, Walsgrave on Sowe, Coventry CV2 2DX* Tel (024) 7653 8950 *or* 7660 2020 ext 8950 E-mail hughpriestner@netscapeonline.co.uk

PRIGG, Patrick John. b 53. K Coll Lon BD82. Sarum & Wells Th Coll 89. **d** 92 **p** 93. C Wavertree St Mary *Liv* 92-96; Chapl Sandown Coll 92-96; P-in-c Glem Valley United Benefice *St E* 96-99; R from 99. *The Rectory, 6 Lion Road, Glemsford, Sudbury CO10 7RF* Tel (01787) 282164 E-mail revpat@glemsfordirectory.freeserve.co.uk

PRIME, Geoffrey Daniel. b 12. Lich Th Coll 32. **d** 35 **p** 36. C Uttoxeter w Bramshall *Lich* 35-42; P-in-c Newborough w Ch Ch on Needwood 42-43; V Pattingham 43-55; V Longstone *Derby* 55-62; Org Sec CECS *Derby, Linc, Sheff* and *S'well* 62-65; Perm to Offic *Derby* 62-00; rtd 77. *Westside Mill Farm, Hulme End, Buxton SK17 0EY* Tel (01298) 84461

PRIMROSE, David Edward Snodgrass. b 55. St Jo Coll Cam MA80. Trin Coll Bris BA92. **d** 87 **p** 92. Pakistan 87-89; C Glouc St Paul *Glouc* 92-96; R Badgeworth, Shurdington and Witcombe w Bentham 96-03; V Thornbury from 03; V Oldbury-on-Severn w Shepperdine from 03. *The Vicarage, 27 Castle Street, Thornbury, Bristol BS35 1HQ* Tel (01454) 413209 *or* 281900 E-mail primrose@blueyonder.co.uk

PRINCE (née RUMBLE), Mrs Alison Merle. b 49. Surrey Univ BSc71. Trin Coll Bris BA89. **d** 89 **p** 94. Par Dn Willesden Green St Gabr *Lon* 89-91; Par Dn Cricklewood St Gabr and St Mich 92; Par Dn Herne Hill *S'wark* 92-94; C 94-95; Chapl Greenwich Healthcare NHS Trust 95-96; TV Sanderstead All SS *S'wark* from 97. *4 Mitchley Avenue, Purley CR8 1EA* Tel (020) 8660 8123

PRINCE (née GRIFFITHS), Caroline Heidi Ann. b 66. Ex Univ BA88. Linc Th Coll 90. **d** 90 **p** 97. Chapl St Woolos Cathl *Mon* 90-94; C Newport St Woolos 90-94; C Abergavenny Deanery 94-96; TV Cwmbran 96-97; V Llantilio Crossenny w Penrhos, Llanvetherine etc from 97. *The Vicarage, Llantilio Crossenny, Abergavenny NP7 8SU* Tel (01600) 780240

PRINCE, Helena. b 23. Lightfoot Ho Dur 59. **dss** 66 **d** 87 **p** 94. W Derby St Mary *Liv* 65-85; rtd 85; Perm to Offic *Liv* 85-87; Hon C Stanley from 87. *5 Dominic Close, Liverpool L16 1JZ* Tel 0151-722 0263

PRINCE, Mrs Melanie Amanda. b 71. St D Coll Lamp BA92 Univ of Wales (Cardiff) MPhil93. St Mich Coll Llan 96. **d** 98 **p** 99. C Aberavon *Llan* 98-01; C Gabalfa from 01. *27 Pen-y-Bryn Road, Gabalfa, Cardiff CF14 3LG* Tel (029) 2025 4089

PRING, Althon Kerrigan (Kerry). b 34. AKC58. **d** 59 **p** 60. C Limehouse St Anne *Lon* 59-61; C Lt Stanmore St Lawr 61-64; C Langley Marish *Ox* 64-68; P-in-c Radnage 68-72; P-in-c Ravenstone w Weston Underwood 72-75; P-in-c Stoke Goldington w Gayhurst 72-75; R Gayhurst w Ravenstone, Stoke Goldington etc 75-85; P-in-c 85-86; RD Newport 78-80; TV Woughton 86-90; P-in-c Nash w Thornton, Beachampton and Thornborough 90-94; R 94-96; rtd 96; Perm to Offic *Ox* from 99. *Firtree Cottage, 17 High Street, Stoke Goldington, Newport Pagnell MK16 8NP* Tel (01908) 551343

PRINGLE, The Ven Cecil Thomas. b 43. TCD BA65. CITC 66. **d** 66 **p** 67. C Belfast St Donard *D & D* 66-69; I Cleenish *Clogh* 69-80; I Mullaghdun 78-80; I Rossory from 80; Preb Clogh Cathl 86-89; Adn Clogh from 89. *Rossory Rectory, Derryhonnelly Road, Enniskillen BT74 7JE* Tel (028) 6632 2874

PRINGLE, Graeme Lindsley. b 59. St Cath Coll Cam BA81 MA85. St Jo Coll Nottm Dip Th Studies 94. **d** 94 **p** 95. C Binley *Cov* 94-99; V Allesley Park and Whoberley from 99. *St Christopher's Vicarage, 99 Buckingham Rise, Coventry CV5 9HF* Tel (024) 7667 2879 E-mail graeme@stchristopher.org.uk

PRINGLE, Miss Janyce Mary. b 32. ARCM53 LRAM54 Ex Univ DipAdEd70 MPhil85. SW Minl Tr Course 83. **dss** 86 **d** 87 **p** 94. NSM Torquay St Matthias, St Mark and H Trin *Ex* 86-98; Chapl Asst Torbay Hosp Torquay 86-89; Perm to Offic *Ex* from 98. *Pendower, Wheatridge Lane, Torquay TQ2 6RA* Tel (01803) 607136

PRINGLE, John Richard. b 55. Lon Univ AKC76 CertEd77 Open Univ BA84. Chich Th Coll 78. **d** 78 **p** 79. C Northampton St Matt *Pet* 78-81; C Delaval *Newc* 81-84; V Newsham from 84; RD Bedlington 93-98. *St Bede's Vicarage, Newcastle Road, Newsham, Blyth NE24 4AS* Tel (01670) 352391 Fax as telephone

PRINGLE, Victor. b 43. St Barn Coll Adelaide BA72 ACT ThDip72. **d** 73 **p** 75. Australia 73-80; C Murray Bridge 75; C O'Halloran Hill 76; Chapl R Adelaide Hosp and C Wakerville 77-78; R Clarence Town 78-80; C Lavender Hill Ascension *S'wark* 80-81; Australia from 81; Asst P Sydney St Laur from 82. *3/1A Avenue Road, Mosman, Sydney, NSW, Australia 2008* Tel (0061) (2) 9969 8294

PRINS, Canon Stanley Vernon. b 30. TD76. Dur Univ BSc54 MA69. Ripon Hall Ox 56. **d** 58 **p** 59. C Benwell St Jas *Newc* 58-61; Asst Chapl Newc Univ 61-65; CF (TA) from 64; C-in-c Whorlton H Nativity Chpl Ho Estate *Newc* 65-72; TV Whorlton 73-76; V Humshaugh 76-83; P-in-c Simonburn 82-83; P-in-c Wark 82-83; RD Bellingham 83-93; R Humshaugh w

Simonburn and Wark 83-96; Hon Can Newc Cathl 88-96; rtd 96; Perm to Offic *Newc* from 96. *Woodside Cottage, Scrogwood, Bardon Mill, Hexham NE47 7AA* Tel (01434) 344876

PRIOR, The Ven Christopher. b 12. CB68. Keble Coll Ox BA37 MA41. Cuddesdon Coll 37. **d** 38 **p** 39. C Hornsea and Goxhill *York* 38-41; Chapl RN 41-69; Chapl of the Fleet and Adn for the RN 66-69; QHC 66-69; Adn Portsm 69-77; rtd 77; Perm to Offic *Sarum* from 77. *Ponies End, West Melbury, Shaftesbury SP7 0LY* Tel (01747) 811239

PRIOR, David Clement Lyndon. b 40. Trin Coll Ox BA63 MA66. Ridley Hall Cam 65. **d** 67 **p** 68. C Reigate St Mary *S'wark* 67-72; S Africa 72-79; Can Cape Town 76-79; C Ox St Aldate w H Trin *Ox* 79-82; C Ox St Aldate w St Matt 82-84; USA 84-85; V Ches Square St Mich w St Phil *Lon* 85-95; P-in-c Mayfair Ch Ch 85-97; Public Preacher from 95; P-in-c St Botolph without Aldersgate 97-00. *2 North Lane, Wiston, Steyning BN44 3DQ* Tel (01903) 893566

PRIOR, Canon Ian Graham. b 44. Lon Univ BSc(Econ)71. Oak Hill Th Coll DipHE80. **d** 80 **p** 81. C Luton Ch Ch *Roch* 80-83; TV Southgate *Chich* 83-93; V Burgess Hill St Andr from 93; RD Hurst from 98; Can and Preb Chich Cathl from 03. *St Andrew's Vicarage, 2 Cants Lane, Burgess Hill RH15 0LG* Tel (01444) 232023

PRIOR, Ian Roger Lyndon. b 46. St Jo Coll Dur BA68. Lon Coll of Div 68. **d** 70 **p** 71. C S Croydon Em *Cant* 70-73; Perm to Offic *S'wark* 73-85; Dir Overseas Personnel TEAR Fund 73-79; Dep Dir 79-83; Fin and Admin Dir CARE Trust and CARE Campaigns 85-92; NSM New Malden and Coombe *S'wark* from 85; Dir Careforce from 92. *39 Cambridge Avenue, New Malden KT3 4LD* Tel (020) 8949 0912 *or* 8942 3331

PRIOR, James Murray. b 39. Edin Univ BCom64. St And Dioc Tr Course 85. **d** 90 **p** 91. NSM Kirriemuir *St And* from 90; NSM Forfar from 90. *Horniehaugh, Glenquiech, Forfar DD8 3UG* Tel (01575) 540420

PRIOR, John Gilman Leathes. b 15. Qu Coll Cam BA37 MA41. Ridley Hall Cam 37. **d** 39 **p** 40. C Springfield St Marg *St E* 39-41; CF 41-46; V Springfield H Trin *Chelmsf* 46-49; V Guildf Ch Ch *Guildf* 49-63; V Camberley St Paul 63-74; V Crondall 75-77; V Crondall and Ewshot 77-80; rtd 80; Perm to Offic *Win* from 80; Perm to Offic *Guildf* 82-96; Perm to Offic *Portsm* from 84. *River Cottage, Station Road, Bentley, Farnham GU10 5JY* Tel (01420) 23413

PRIOR, Preb John Miskin. b 27. Lon Univ BSc(Econ)48. Westcott Ho Cam 49. **d** 51 **p** 52. C Bedminster St Fran *Bris* 51-55; C Sherston Magna w Easton Grey 55-57; C Yatton Keynell 57-61; C Castle Combe 57-61; C Biddestone w Slaughterford 57-61; V Bishopstone w Hinton Parva 61-66; V Marshfield w Cold Ashton 66-82; P-in-c Tormarton w W Littleton 68-82; RD Bitton 73-79; R Trull w Angersleigh *B & W* 82-91; RD Taunton 84-90; Preb Wells Cathl 90-91; Chapl Huggens Coll Northfleet 91-97; rtd 92; Hon PV Roch Cathl *Roch* from 98; Perm to Offic from 99. *Buff Cottage, 7 St Margarets Street, Rochester ME1 1TU* Tel (01634) 846422

PRIOR, Canon Kenneth Francis William. b 26. St Jo Coll Dur BA49. Oak Hill Th Coll 46. **d** 49 **p** 50. C S Mimms Ch Ch *Lon* 49-52; C Eastbourne H Trin *Chich* 52-53; V Onslow Square St Paul *Lon* 53-65; V Hove Bp Hannington Memorial Ch *Chich* 65-70; R Sevenoaks St Nic *Roch* 70-87; Hon Can Roch Cathl 82-87; C-in-c Hampstead St Jo Downshire Hill Prop Chpl *Lon* 87-90; rtd 89; Perm to Offic *Chelmsf* from 89; Perm to Offic *Lon* from 90; Perm to Offic *St Alb* 90-99. *22 Barnfield Road, Torquay TQ2 6TN* Tel (01803) 606760

PRIOR, Canon Kenneth George William. b 17. Bris Univ BA39. Bible Churchmen's Coll Bris 35. **d** 40 **p** 41. C Toxteth Park St Clem *Liv* 40-43; C Edge Hill St Cypr 43-45; C Garston 45-48; V Plymouth St Jude *Ex* 48-55; V Longfleet *Sarum* 55-82; Chapl Poole Gen Hosp 55-76; RD Poole *Sarum* 75-80; Can and Preb Sarum Cathl 77-82; rtd 82; Perm to Offic *Sarum* 82-00. *22 Ramsay Hall, 11-13 Byron Road, Worthing BN11 3HN* Tel (01903) 214880 E-mail kgwprior@aol.com

PRIOR, Nigel John. b 56. Bris Univ BA78. Westcott Ho Cam 79. **d** 81 **p** 82. C Langley All SS and Martyrs *Man* 81-82; C Langley and Parkfield 82-84; C Bury St Jo w St Mark 84-87; R Man Clayton St Cross w St Paul 87-99; P-in-c Mark Cross *Chich* 99-00; V Mayfield from 99. *The Vicarage, High Street, Mayfield TN20 6AB* Tel (01435) 873180

PRIOR, Stephen Kenneth. b 55. Rhode Is Coll (USA) BA78. Wycliffe Hall Ox 79. **d** 82 **p** 83. C Aberavon *Llan* 82-85; P-in-c New Radnor and Llanfihangel Nantmelan etc *S & B* 85-86; R 86-90; V Llansamlet 90-94; P-in-c Chester le Street *Dur* 94-96; R 96-01; R Caldbeck, Castle Sowerby and Sebergham *Carl* from 01. *The Rectory, Caldbeck, Wigton CA7 8EW* Tel (016974) 78233

PRIORY, Barry Edwin. b 44. FCIS Open Univ BA81. Qu Coll Birm 84. **d** 86 **p** 87. C Boldmere *Birm* 86-89; C Somerton w Compton Dundon, the Charltons etc *B & W* 89-93; R Porlock w Stoke Pero from 93; RD Exmoor from 97. *The Rectory, Parsons Street, Porlock, Minehead TA24 8QL* Tel (01643) 863172 E-mail barry.priory@virgin.net

PRISTON, David Leslie. b 28. Lon Bible Coll 49 Oak Hill Th Coll 66. **d** 66 **p** 67. C Heref St Pet w St Owen *Heref* 66-71; R Beeby *Leic* 72-88; R Gaddesby w S Croxton 72-88; R S Croxton Gp 88-93; rtd 93; Perm to Offic *S'well* from 93. *20 Central Avenue, Chilwell, Nottingham NG9 4DU* Tel 0115-922 7643

PRITCHARD, Antony Robin. b 53. Van Mildert Coll Dur BSc74 SS Paul & Mary Coll Cheltenham CertEd75. St Jo Coll Nottm DipTh82 DPS84. **d** 84 **p** 85. C Desborough *Pet* 84-87; C Rushden w Newton Bromswold 87-91; R Oulton St Mich *Nor* from 91. *The Rectory, Christmas Lane, Oulton, Lowestoft NR32 3JX* Tel (01502) 565722

PRITCHARD, Brian James. ACIS85. St Alb and Ox Min Course 99. **d** 01 **p** 02. NSM Newbury *Ox* from 01. *The Chase, Garden Close Lane, Wash Common, Newbury RG14 6PP* Tel (01635) 42613 Fax 35976 E-mail brianjp@waitrose.com

PRITCHARD, Brian James Pallister. b 27. CCC Cam BA51 MA66. Westcott Ho Cam 51. **d** 53 **p** 54. C Attercliffe w Carbrook *Sheff* 53-58; V New Bentley 58-60; Chapl Park Hill Flats Sheff 60-67; P-in-c Sheff St Swithun *Sheff* 67-72; V Welton *Linc* 72-92; RD Lawres 86-92; rtd 92; Perm to Offic *Derby* from 92. *Bridgeways, Milford Lane, Bakewell DE45 1DX* Tel (01629) 813553

PRITCHARD, Mrs Carol Sandra. b 52. St Aid Coll Dur BA74 Bris Univ PGCE75 UEA 95. EAMTC DipHE99. **d** 99 **p** 00. NSM Oulton St Mich *Nor* from 99. *The Rectory, Christmas Lane, Oulton, Lowestoft NR32 3JX* Tel (01502) 565722

PRITCHARD, Colin Ivor. b 44. Lon Inst of Educn TCert65. Chich Th Coll 66. **d** 69 **p** 70. C Kettering St Mary *Pet* 69-72; Chapl Clayesmore Sch Blandford 72-74; Asst Chapl Ellesmere Coll Shropshire 74-77; C Duston *Pet* 77-80; V Wellingborough St Andr 80-89; R Sedlescombe w Whatlington *Chich* 89-01; V Bexhill St Barn from 01. *St Barnabas' Vicarage, Cantelupe Road, Bexhill-on-Sea TN40 1JG* Tel (01424) 212036

PRITCHARD, Colin Wentworth. b 38. K Coll Lon 59 St Boniface Warminster 59. **d** 63 **p** 64. C Putney St Marg *S'wark* 63-67; C Brixton St Matt 67-70; C Milton *Portsm* 70-74; V Mitcham St Mark *S'wark* 74-82; R Long Ditton 82-94; V Earlsfield St Andr from 94; RD Wandsworth 98-03; rtd 03. *38 Hartfield Road, Seaford BN25 4TW* E-mail colin@loavesandfishes.f2s.com

PRITCHARD, Mrs Coral. b 37. F L Calder Coll Liv TCert58 Lanc Univ BA97. Carl and Blackb Dioc Tr Inst 99. **d** 02 **p** 03. OLM Stalmine w Pilling *Blackb* from 02. *Heyswood House, Head Dyke Lane, Pilling, Preston PR3 6SJ* Tel (01253) 790335 E-mail pritchard@heyswood.freeserve.co.uk

PRITCHARD, David Paul. b 47. FRCO LTCL BA. Wycliffe Hall Ox 80. **d** 82 **p** 83. C Kidlington *Ox* 82-84; P-in-c Marcham w Garford 84-85; V 86-96; RD Abingdon 91-96; R Henley w Remenham from 96. *The Rectory, Hart Street, Henley-on-Thames RG9 2AU* Tel (01491) 577340 Fax as telephone E-mail rector.hwr@lineone.net

PRITCHARD, Donald Oliver. b 22. Qu Coll Birm 73. **d** 75 **p** 76. Hon C Dunchurch *Cov* 75-83; P-in-c Mells w Buckland Dinham, Elm, Whatley etc *B & W* 83-84; R 84-88; rtd 88; Perm to Offic *Truro* from 88. *Moonrakers, Pengelly, Callington PL17 7DZ* Tel (01579) 84329

✠**PRITCHARD, The Rt Revd John Lawrence.** b 48. St Pet Coll Ox BA70 MA73 DipTh70 Dur Univ MLitt93. Ridley Hall Cam 70. **d** 72 **p** 73 **c** 02. C Birm St Martin *Birm* 72-76; Asst Dir RE *B & W* 76-80; Youth Chapl 76-80; P-in-c Wilton 80-88; Dir Past Studies Cranmer Hall Dur 89-93; Warden 93-96; Adn Cant and Can Res Cant Cathl *Cant* 96-02; Suff Bp Jarrow *Dur* from 02. *Bishop's House, Ivy Lane, Gateshead NE9 6QD* Tel 0191-491 0917 Fax 491 5116 E-mail bishop.of.jarrow@durham.anglican.org

PRITCHARD, Jonathan Llewelyn. b 64. Edin Univ MA87 Leeds Univ MA89 PhD99. Ripon Coll Cuddesdon 98. **d** 00 **p** 01. C Skipton H Trin *Bradf* from 00. *7 Princes Drive, Skipton BD23 1HN* Tel (01756) 701063 E-mail jonathan@japritchard.me.uk

PRITCHARD, Miss Kathryn Anne. b 60. St Cath Coll Ox MA Bradf Univ DIT. St Jo Coll Dur. **d** 87. Par Dn Addiscombe St Mary *S'wark* 87-90; CPAS Staff 90-92; Perm to Offic *Cov* 92-95; Producer Worship Progr BBC Relig Broadcasting 94-99; Publicity Manager Hodder & Stoughton Relig Books 99-01; Commissioning and Product Development Manager Ch Ho Publishing from 01. *Church House, Great Smith Street, London SW1P 3NZ* Tel (020) 7898 1485 E-mail kathryn.pritchard@c-of-e.org.uk

PRITCHARD, Kenneth John. b 30. Liv Univ BEng51. NW Ord Course 72. **d** 74 **p** 75. C Ches Team *Ches* 74-78; Miss to Seamen 78-84; V Runcorn St Jo Weston *Ches* 78-84; V Gt Meols 84-98; rtd 98; Perm to Offic *Ches* from 99; Perm to Offic *Liv* from 99. *13 Fieldlands, Scarisbrick, Southport PR8 5HQ* Tel (01704) 514600

PRITCHARD, Malcolm John. b 55. Bradf Univ BA85 CQSW85. St Jo Coll Nottm 86. **d** 88 **p** 89. C Peckham St Mary Magd *S'wark* 88-93; V Luton St Matt High Town *St Alb* from 93. *St Matthew's Vicarage, 85 Wenlock Street, Luton LU2 0NN* Tel (01582) 732320 E-mail b4mjp2c@ntlworld.com

PRITCHARD, Michael Owen. b 49. Trin Coll Carmarthen CertEd71. St Mich Coll Llan 71. **d** 73 **p** 74. C Conwy w Gyffin *Ban* 73-76; TV Dolgellau w Llanfachreth and Brithdir etc 76-78; Dioc Children's Officer 77-86; V Betws y Coed and Capel Curig 78-83; CF (TAVR) from 79. V Betws-y-Coed and Capel Curig w Penmachno etc *Ban* 83-86; Chapl Claybury Hosp Woodford Bridge 86-96; Chapl Team Leader Forest Healthcare NHS Trust Lon from 96. *Dept of Spiritual and Religious Care, Whipps Cross Hospital, Whipps Cross Road, London E11 1NR* Tel (020) 8539 5522 *or* 8989 3813 E-mail mopritchard@aol.com
PRITCHARD, Mrs Norma Kathleen. b 32. Birm Univ BA53 CertEd54. EMMTC 81. **dss** 84 **d** 87 **p** 94. Derby St Alkmund and St Werburgh *Derby* 84-90; Par Dn 87-90; Par Dn Derby St Andr w St Osmund 90-94; C 94-96; Assoc Min Alvaston 96-02; rtd 02; Perm to Offic *S'wark* from 02. *44 Evans Avenue, Allestree, Derby DE22 2EN* Tel (01332) 557702
PRITCHARD, Peter Benson. b 30. FPhsS60 LCP68 Univ of Wales (Lamp) BA51 St Cath Coll Ox DipTh57 Lon Univ PGCE68 DipEd70 Liv Univ MEd74 PhD81. Ripon Hall Ox 55. **d** 58 **p** 59. C Wavertree H Trin *Liv* 58-60; C Sefton 60-61; C-in-c Thornton CD 61-64; Chapl Liv Coll Boys' Sch 64-70; Hon C Wavertree St Bridget 70-89; Lect CF Mott Coll of Educn 70-76; Sen Lect Liv Coll of HE 76-83; Liv Poly 83-87; Perm to Offic 90-96; *Ches* from 90; Chapl St Jo Hospice Wirral from 93; Tutor Open Univ 90-95; rtd 95. *68 Gleggside, West Kirby, Wirral CH48 6EA* Tel 0151-625 8093
PRITCHARD, Peter Humphrey. b 47. Univ of Wales (Ban) BA70 MA98 Liv Univ PGCE73 Birm Univ DipTh87. Qu Coll Birm 85. **d** 87 **p** 88. C Llanbeblig w Caernarfon and Betws Garmon etc *Ban* 87-90; R Llanberis w Llanrug 90-94; R Llanfaethlu w Llanfwrog and Llanrhuddlad etc 94-99; R Llanfair Mathafarn Eithaf w Llanbedrgoch from 99. *The Rectory, 3 Swn-y-Don, Benllech, Tyn-y-Gongl LL74 8PR* Tel (01248) 853744
PRITCHARD, Simon Geraint. b 61. Coll of Ripon & York St Jo BA85 Ex Univ PGCE88. Cranmer Hall Dur 98. **d** 00 **p** 01. C Heysham *Blackb* 00-01; C Morecambe St Barn 01-03; C Standish from 03. *St Wilfrid's House, 7 Rectory Lane, Standish, Wigan WN6 0XA* Tel (01257) 425806
PRITCHARD, Thomas. b 14. Ch Ch Ox BA37 MA40. Westcott Ho Cam 37. **d** 38 **p** 39. C Rugby St Andr *Cov* 38-45; Mauritius 45-49; V Ipswich All Hallows *St E* 49-61; Hon Can St E Cathl 58-61; V Ex St Dav *Ex* 62-81; rtd 81; Perm to Offic *Ex* from 81. *3 Mill Cottages, Exton, Exeter EX3 0PH* Tel (01392) 873018
PRITCHARD, Thomas James Benbow. b 47. St Paul's Cheltenham CertEd69 Univ of Wales (Cardiff) BEd79 MSc85. SW Minl Tr Course 96. **d** 99 **p** 00. NSM St Enoder *Truro* 99-01; P-in-c Roche and Withiel from 01. *The Vicarage, Fore Street, Roche, St Austell PL26 8EP* Tel (01726) 890301 E-mail tjb_pritchard@btopenworld.com
PRITCHARD, The Ven Thomas William. b 33. Keele Univ BA55 DipEd55 Univ of Wales (Cardiff) LLM94. St Mich Coll Llan 55. **d** 57 **p** 58. C Holywell *St As* 57-61; C Ruabon 61-63; V 77-87; R Pontfadog 63-71; R Llanferres, Nercwys and Eryrys 71-77; Dioc Archivist 76-98; Can St As Cathl 84-98; RD Llangollen 86-87; Adn Montgomery 87-98; V Berriew and Manafon 87-98; rtd 98. *4 Glynne Way, Hawarden, Deeside CH5 3NL* Tel (01244) 538381
PRITCHETT, Antony. b 63. Kent Univ BA86. Westcott Ho Cam 96. **d** 98 **p** 99. C Broughton Astley and Croft w Stoney Stanton *Leic* 98-02; V Gawber *Wakef* from 02; Chapl Barnsley Hospice from 02. *The Vicarage, Church Street, Gawber, Barnsley S75 2RL* Tel (01226) 207140 E-mail antony.pritchett@tinyworld.co.uk
PRITT, Stephen. b 06. AKC31. **d** 31 **p** 32. C Witton *Blackb* 31-34; C St Annes 34-37; PC Ennerdale *Carl* 37-40; V Amblecote *Worc* 40-45; V Wolverley 46-48; V Warrington H Trin *Liv* 48-55; V Thornham w Titchwell *Nor* 55-58; Clerical Org Sec CECS *Cant, Chich, Roch* and *Win* 58-60; R Helhoughton w Raynham *Nor* 60-80; rtd 80; Perm to Offic *Glouc* 80-93. *23 Addiscombe Road, Weston-super-Mare BS23 4LT* Tel (01934) 622795
PRIVETT, Peter John. b 48. Qu Coll Birm 75. **d** 78 **p** 79. C Moseley St Agnes *Birm* 78-81; V Kingsbury 81-87; P-in-c Dilwyn and Stretford *Heref* 87-90; Dioc Children's Adv 87-01; TV Leominster 90-98; NSM from 98; Dioc Millennium Officer 98-01. *165 Bargates, Leominster HR6 8QT* Tel (01568) 613176
PROBART, Raymond. b 21. Sarum Th Coll 49. **d** 51 **p** 52. C Padiham *Blackb* 51-54; C Burnley St Pet 54-56; V Heyhouses 56-60; V Douglas 60-88; rtd 88; Perm to Offic *B & W* 88-98; *Glouc* from 03. *6 Capel Court, The Burgage, Prestbury, Cheltenham GL52 3EL* Tel (01242) 235771
PROBERT, Beverley Stuart. b 42. Dioc OLM tr scheme. **d** 01 **p** 02. OLM Canford Magna *Sarum* from 01. *Blaenafon, 102 Knights Road, Bournemouth BH11 9SY* Tel (01202) 571731
PROBERT, Christopher John Dixon. b 54. Univ of Wales (Cardiff) DipTh77 DPS78 Univ of Wales (Ban) BPhS95 MTh97. St Mich Coll Llan 74. **d** 78 **p** 79. C Aberdare St Fagan *Llan* 78-79; C Cadoxton-juxta-Barry 79-81; R Llanfynydd *St As* 81-84; V Gosberton Clough and Quadring *Linc* 84-86; TV Coventry Caludon *Cov* 86-88; V Llanrhian w Llanhywel and Llanrheithan *St D* 88-91; V Tregaron w Ystrad Meurig and Strata Florida 91-93; Chapl Tregaron Hosp 91-93; Tutor St D NSM Course

89-93; V Betws-y-Coed and Capel Curig w Penmachno etc *Ban* 93-98; Warden of Readers 96-98; V Lt Drayton *Lich* from 98; OCF from 01. *The Vicarage, Christ Church Lane, Market Drayton TF9 1DY* Tel and fax (01630) 652801 Mobile 07718-667177 E-mail chris@probert1.co.uk
PROBERT, Edward Cleasby. b 58. St Cath Coll Cam BA80 MA84. Ripon Coll Cuddesdon BA84. **d** 85 **p** 86. C Esher *Guildf* 85-89; V Earlsfield St Andr *S'wark* 89-94; V Belmont from 94. *The Vicarage, Belmont Rise, Sutton SM2 6EA* Tel (020) 8642 2363 E-mail eprobert@ukgateway.packardbell.org
PROBETS, Canon Desmond. b 26. AKC50. **d** 51 **p** 52. C Finsbury St Clem *Lon* 51-52; C Kenton 52-62; Solomon Is 62-72; Dean Honiara 69-72; V Timperley *Ches* 72-92; RD Bowdon 77-87; Hon Can Ches Cathl 82-92; rtd 92; Perm to Offic *Wakef* from 92. *24 Shelley Close, Penistone, Sheffield S36 4GT* Tel (01226) 766402
PROCTER, Andrew David. b 52. St Jo Coll Ox BA74 MA86. Trin Coll Bris 74. **d** 77 **p** 78. C Barnoldswick w Bracewell *Bradf* 77-80; P-in-c Kelbrook 80-82; V 82-87; V Heaton St Barn 87-93; V Swanley St Paul *Roch* from 93. *The Vicarage, Rowhill Road, Swanley BR8 7RL* Tel (01322) 662320
PROCTER, Robert Hendy. b 31. Trin Hall Cam BA54 MA. Edin Dioc NSM Course 88. **d** 93 **p** 94. NSM Edin Ch Ch *Edin* from 93. *2 Braid Avenue, Edinburgh EH10 6DR* Tel 0131-447 1140
PROCTOR, Kenneth Noel. b 33. St Aid Birkenhead 61. **d** 63 **p** 64. C Oldham St Paul *Man* 63-66; C Davyhulme St Mary 66-69; V Norden w Ashworth 69-00; rtd 00. *4 Bankscroft, Hopwood, Heywood OL10 2NG* Tel (01706) 364197
PROCTOR, Michael John. b 59. Longlands Coll of FE C&G78 BTEC NC81. Cranmer Hall Dur 93. **d** 93 **p** 94. C Leatherhead *Guildf* 93-98; V Henlow and Langford *St Alb* 98-01; V Marton-in-Cleveland *York* from 01. *The Vicarage, Stokesley Road, Marton-in-Cleveland, Middlesbrough TS7 8JU* Tel (01642) 326305 E-mail mlm.proctor@virgin.net
PROCTOR, Michael Thomas. b 41. Ch Ch Ox BA65 MA67. Westcott Ho Cam 63. **d** 65 **p** 66. C Monkseaton St Mary *Newc* 65-69; Pakistan 69-72; C Willington *Newc* 72-77; TV Willington Team 77-79; Ed Sec Nat Soc 79-84; P-in-c Roxwell *Chelmsf* 79-84; Dir of Miss and Unity 85-94; Bp's Ecum Officer 85-00; Hon Can Chelmsf Cathl 85-00; P-in-c Gt Waltham w Ford End 94-00; rtd 00; Dir Chelmsf Counselling Foundn from 00. *22 Raymead, Great Waltham, Chelmsford CM3 1AR* Tel (01245) 360334 E-mail mtproctor@lineone.net
PROCTOR, Canon Noel. b 30. MBE93. St Aid Birkenhead 62. **d** 64 **p** 65. C Haughton le Skerne *Dur* 64-67; R Byers Green 67-70; Chapl HM Pris Eastchurch 70-74; Chapl HM Pris Dartmoor 74-79; Chapl HM Pris Man 79-95; Hon Can Man Cathl *Man* 91-95; rtd 95; Perm to Offic *Man* from 95. *222 Moor Lane, Salford M7 3QH* Tel 0161-792 1284
PROCTOR, Canon Susan Katherine. b 44. **d** 89 **p** 94. Par Dn Beighton *Sheff* 89-91; Par Dn Aston cum Aughton and Ulley 91-93; Par Dn Aston cum Aughton w Swallownest, Todwick etc 93-94; TV 94-96; R Dinnington 96-01; P-in-c Aston cum Aughton w Swallownest and Ulley 01-02; TR from 02; AD Laughton from 98; Hon Can Sheff Cathl from 98. *The Rectory, 91 Worksop Road, Aston, Sheffield S26 2EB* Tel 0114-287 2272 E-mail sueproctor@lineone.net
PROFIT, David Hollingworth. b 17. Man Univ BA38. Cuddesdon Coll 40. **d** 41 **p** 42. C Kings Heath *Birm* 41-43; S Africa from 43. *Braehead House, 1 Braehead Road, Kenilworth, 7708 South Africa* Tel (0027) (21) 762 6041
PROPHET, Canon John Roy Henderson. b 10. Dur Univ LTh48 BA49. ALCD34. **d** 34 **p** 35. C Low Leyton *Chelmsf* 34-37; C Canvey Is 37-38; P-in-c Walthamstow St Andr 38-39; V 39-44; V Jesmond H Trin *Newc* 44-48; V Fenham St Jas and St Basil 48-61; V Blaby *Leic* 61-73; Hon Can Leic Cathl 70-80; R Church Langton w Thorpe Langton and Tur Langton 73-80; rtd 80; Perm to Offic *Leic* and *Pet* from 80. *24 Stuart Court, High Street, Kibworth, Leicester LE8 0LR* Tel 0116-279 6880
PROSSER, Gillian Margaret. b 40. Lon Inst of Educn TCert61. **d** 99. OLM Cwmbran *Mon* from 99. *25 Forest Close, Coed Eva, Cwmbran NP44 4TE* Tel (01633) 866716
PROSSER, Jean. b 40. Open Univ BA84 Surrey Univ PhD94. **d** 02. OLM Grosmont and Skenfrith and Llangattock etc *Mon* from 01. *Yew Tree Farm, Llangattock Lingoed, Abergavenny NP7 8NS* Tel (01873) 821405 E-mail jean.prosser@talk21.com
PROSSER, Malcolm George. b 22. Univ of Wales (Lamp) BA44. St Mich Coll Llan 44. **d** 45 **p** 46. C Llantwit Fardre *Llan* 45-49; C Roath 49-58; V Trealaw 58-66; V High Littleton *B & W* 66-87; rtd 87. *141 Westway, Broadstone BH18 9LQ* Tel (01202) 694280
PROSSER, Rhys. b 51. BA74 Bris Univ CertEd75 Southn Univ BTh83 Hull Univ MA93. Sarum & Wells Th Coll 77. **d** 80 **p** 81. C Wimbledon *S'wark* 80-83; C St Helier 83-88; TV Gt and Lt Coates w Bradley *Linc* 88-95; P-in-c Saxilby Gp 95-97; R from 97; RD Corringham from 01. *The Rectory, 1 Westcroft Drive, Saxilby, Lincoln LN1 2PT* Tel (01522) 702427
PROSSER, Richard Hugh Keble. b 31. Trin Coll Cam BA53 MA57 Leeds Univ PGCE63. Cuddesdon Coll 55. **d** 57 **p** 58. C Wigan All SS *Liv* 57-60; CR 62-87; St Aug Miss Penhalonga Zimbabwe 64-90; R Pocklington and Owsthorpe and Kilnwick

Percy etc *York* 90-00; rtd 01. *26 Fleur de Lis, Middlemarsh Street, Poundbury, Dorchester DT1 3GX* Tel (01305) 260329

PROSSER, Stephanie. b 42. Linc Th Coll 94. **d** 96 **p** 99. NSM Linc St Nic w St Jo Newport *Linc* 96-99; NSM Saxilby Gp from 99. *The Rectory, 1 Westcroft Drive, Saxilby, Lincoln LN1 2PT* Tel (01522) 702427

PROTHERO, Brian Douglas. b 52. St Andr Univ MTh75 Dundee Univ CertEd77. Linc Th Coll 84. **d** 86 **p** 87. C Thornbury *Glouc* 86-89; V Goodrington *Ex* from 89. *Goodrington Vicarage, 16 Cliff Park Avenue, Paignton TQ4 6LT* Tel (01803) 556476

PROTHERO, David John. b 43. St Pet Coll Ox BA66 MA70. St Steph Ho Ox 68. **d** 70 **p** 71. C Kirkby *Liv* 70-72; C St Marychurch *Ex* 72-74; V Marldon 74-83; Chapl HM Pris Channings Wood 78-83; V Torquay St Martin Barton *Ex* 83-91; P-in-c Bath Bathwick *B & W* 91-93; R from 93. *Bathwick Rectory, Sham Castle Lane, Bath BA2 6JL* Tel (01225) 460052 E-mail david@djprothero.fsnet.co.uk

PROTHERO, John Martin. b 32. Oak Hill Th Coll 64. **d** 66 **p** 67. C Tipton St Martin *Lich* 66-69; C Wednesfield Heath 69-72; Distr Sec BFBS 72-85; Lic to Offic *S'well* 73-86; Hon C Gedling 73; V Willoughby-on-the-Wolds w Wysall and Widmerpool 86-97; rtd 98. *The Elms, Vicarage Hill, Aberaeron SA46 0DY* Tel (01545) 570568

PROTHEROE, Rhys Illtyd. b 50. St D Coll Lamp DipTh74. **d** 74 **p** 75. C Pen-bre *St D* 74-76; C Carmarthen St Dav 76-78; V Llanegwad 78-79; V Llanegwad w Llanfynydd 79-82; V Gors-las 82-95; RD Dyffryn Aman 94-95; V Llan-llwch w Llangain and Llangynog from 95. *The Vicarage, Llan-llwch, Carmarthen SA31 3RN* Tel (01267) 236805

PROTHEROE, Canon Robin Philip. b 33. St Chad's Coll Dur BA54 DipTh56 MA60 Nottm Univ MPhil75 Ox Univ DipEd62. **d** 57 **p** 58. C Roath *Llan* 57-60; Asst Chapl Culham Coll Abingdon 60-64; Sen Lect RS Trent (Nottm) Poly *S'well* 64-84; Perm to Offic 64-66; Lic to Offic 66-84; P-in-c Barton in Fabis 70-73; P-in-c Thrumpton 70-73; Dir of Educn *Bris* 84-98; Hon Can Bris Cathl 85-98; Selector for ACCM 88-91; ABM from 91; Bp's Insp of Th Colls from 88; Perm to Offic from 98. *29 Barley Croft, Bristol BS9 3TG* Tel 0117-968 3245 Fax 968 4826 E-mail robinprotheroe@aol.com

PROUD, Andrew John. b 54. K Coll Lon BD79 AKC79. Linc Th Coll 79. **d** 80 **p** 81. C Stansted Mountfitchet *Chelmsf* 80-83; TV Borehamwood *St Alb* 83-90; C Bp's Hatfield 90-92; R E Barnet 92-01; Chapl Adis Abeba St Matt Ethiopia from 02. *PO Box 109, Adis Ababa, Ethiopia* Tel (00251) (1) 112623 Fax 551907 E-mail smac@telecom.net.et

PROUD, David John. b 56. Leeds Univ BA77 Dur Univ CertEd78. Ridley Hall Cam 85. **d** 88 **p** 89. C Lindfield *Chich* 88-91; TV Horsham 91-97; V Ware Ch Ch *St Alb* from 97; Chapl E Herts NHS Trust 97-00; Chapl E and N Herts NHS Trust from 00. *The Vicarage, 15 Hanbury Close, Ware SG12 7BZ* Tel (01920) 463165 E-mail david@vicproud.demon.co.uk

PROUDLEY, Sister Anne. b 38. Edin Univ BSc60. St Alb and Ox Min Course 97. **d** 00 **p** 01. CSJB from 00; Lic to Offic *Ox* from 00. *The Priory, 2 Springhill Road, Begbroke, Kidlington OX5 1RX* Tel (01865) 855331 *or* 849531 E-mail csjbclewer@dial.pipex.com

PROUDLOVE, Lee Jason. b 70. Lon Bible Coll BA94 Bris Univ MA01. Trin Coll Bris 00. **d** 01 **p** 02. NSM Morden *S'wark* from 01. *192 Central Road, Morden SM4 5RQ* Tel (020) 8646 6278 Mobile 07941-896235 E-mail lproudlove@hotmail.com

PROUDMAN, Canon Colin Leslie John. b 34. K Coll Lon BD60 MTh63. Wells Th Coll 60. **d** 61 **p** 62. C Radlett *St Alb* 61-64; Canada from 64; Hon Can Toronto from 86; Dean Div Toronto Div Coll 90-92; rtd 97. *#1802, 77 Maitland Place, Toronto ON, Canada M4Y 2V6* Tel (001) (416) 923 4235

PROUSE, Ms Carole Maureen. b 45. N Ord Course. **dss** 86 **d** 87 **p** 95. NSM Coalville and Bardon Hill *Leic* 87-90; Perm to Offic 90-95; NSM Thorpe Acre w Dishley 95-96; P-in-c Packington w Normanton-le-Heath 96-01; Chapl HM Pris Low Newton from 01. *HM Prison Low Newton, Finchale Avenue, Brasside, Durham DH1 5YA* Tel 0191-386 1141

PROUT, Hubert Douglas. b 18. St D Coll Lamp BA38. **d** 41 **p** 42. C Low Leyton *Chelmsf* 41-44; CF 44-47; C Wanstead St Mary *Chelmsf* 47-50; Perm to Offic *Llan* 52-56; C Wirksworth w Carsington *Derby* 56-58; C Idridgehay 56-58; V Kirk Hallam 58-84; rtd 84; Perm to Offic *Llan* from 85. *9 Caldy Close, Porthcawl CF36 3QL* Tel (01656) 786479

PROUT, Mrs Joan. b 42. Gipsy Hill Coll of Educn TCert63. LNSM course 95. **d** 97 **p** 98. OLM Whitton *Sarum* from 97. *22 Ermin Close, Baydon, Marlborough SN8 2JQ* Tel (01672) 540465

PROVOST, Ian Keith. b 47. CA Tr Coll IDC73 Ridley Hall Cam CTM93. **d** 93 **p** 94. C Verwood *Sarum* 93-97; P-in-c Redlynch and Morgan's Vale 97-02; TV Plymstock and Hooe *Ex* from 02. *The Vicarage, 9 St John's Drive, Hooe, Plymouth PL9 9SD* Tel (01752) 403076 E-mail ian@provost.free-online.co.uk

PROWSE, Mrs Barbara Bridgette Christmas. b 41. R Holloway Coll Lon BA62. **d** 91 **p** 94. C Kingsthorpe w Northampton St Dav *Pet* 91-97; V Northampton St Jas 97-02; rtd 02; Perm to

Offic *Truro* from 02. *36 Carn Basavern, St Just, Penzance TR19 7QX* Tel (01736) 787994 E-mail bbc@prowseb.freeserve.co.uk

PRUDOM, William Haigh. b 26. STh79 APhS81 Hull Univ MPhil88. St D Coll Lamp 60. **d** 62 **p** 63. C Aylesford *Roch* 62-63; C Margate St Jo *Cant* 63-66; V Long Preston *Bradf* 66-73; C Darlington St Cuth *Dur* 73-75; V Ticehurst *Chich* 75-79; P-in-c Flimwell 78-79; V Ticehurst and Flimwell 79-81; R Spennithorne w Finghall and Hauxwell *Ripon* 81-91; rtd 91; Perm to Offic *Ripon* from 91. *9 Sydall's Way, Catterick Village, Richmond DL10 7ND* Tel (01748) 818604

PRUEN, Edward Binney. b 56. K Coll Lon BD77 AKC77. St Jo Coll Nottm DPS79. **d** 79 **p** 80. C Kidderminster St Mary *Worc* 79-82; C Woking St Jo *Guildf* 82-84; Chapl Asst R Marsden Hosp Lon and Surrey 84-86; C Stapleford *S'well* 86-88; Min Winklebury CD *Win* 88; V Winklebury 88-93; Chapl Ld Mayor Treloar Coll Alton from 93. *2 St Joseph's Cottage, Upper Froyle, Alton GU34 4JY* Tel (01420) 23893 *or* 526400 Fax 526426 E-mail edpruen@aol.com

PRUEN, Hugh Barrington. b 18. AKC50. **d** 50 **p** 51. C Westmr St Steph w St Jo *Lon* 50-53; R Didmarton w Oldbury-on-the-Hill and Sopworth *Glouc* 53-56; V Ches St Jo *Ches* 56-64; R Skegness *Linc* 64-71; V Heckington w Howell 71-79; R Ashley w Weston by Welland and Sutton Bassett *Pet* 79-83; rtd 83; Perm to Offic *Linc* 83-00. *Ashleigh, Church Road, Old Bolingbroke, Spilsby PE23 4HF* Tel (01790) 763504

PRYCE, Donald Keith. b 36. Man Univ BSc. Linc Th Coll 69. **d** 71 **p** 72. C Heywood St Jas *Man* 71-74; P-in-c 74-75; V 75-86; R Ladybarn from 86; Chapl S Man Coll from 87; Chapl Christie Hosp NHS Trust Man from 93. *St Chad's Rectory, Withington, Manchester M20 9WH* Tel 0161-445 1185

PRYCE, Robin Mark. b 60. Sussex Univ BA82 Cam Univ MA94. Westcroft Ho Cam 84 United Th Coll Bangalore 85. **d** 87 **p** 88. C W Bromwich All SS *Lich* 87-90; Chapl Sandwell Distr Gen Hosp 90; Fell and Chapl CCC Cam 90-02; Tutor 92-02; Dean of Chpl 96-02; V Smethwick *Birm* from 02. *Old Church Vicarage, 93A Church Road, Smethwick, Warley B67 6EE* Tel 0121-558 1763 Fax as telephone E-mail rmp31@cam.ac.uk

PRYCE, William Robert. b 28. MBE91. **d** 79 **p** 80. NSM Leverstock Green *St Alb* 79-80; Perm to Offic *Sheff* 80-84; NSM Sheff St Barn and St Mary 84-90; NSM Alveley and Quatt *Heref* 91-93; Perm to Offic from 93. *5 Wren Way, Westbury Park View, Bicester OX26 6UJ*

PRYKE, Jonathan Justin Speaight. b 59. Trin Coll Cam BA80 MA85. Trin Coll Bris BD85. **d** 85 **p** 86. C Corby St Columba *Pet* 85-88; C Jesmond Clayton Memorial *Newc* from 88. *15 Lily Avenue, Jesmond, Newcastle upon Tyne NE2 2SQ* Tel 0191-281 9854

PRYOR, Derek John. b 39. Lon Univ DipTh57 BD63 Birm Univ MEd74. Linc Th Coll 79 Chich Th Coll 79. **d** 80 **p** 81. Hon C Youlgreave *Derby* 80-82; Hon C Stanton-in-Peak 80-82; Hon C Ingham w Cammeringham w Fillingham *Linc* 82-87 and from 92; Chapl Bp Grosseteste Coll Linc 83-84; Dioc Schs Officer *Linc* 87-92; rtd 92; Perm to Offic *Linc* 99-02. *Walnut Cottage, Chapel Lane, Fillingham, Gainsborough DN21 5BP* Tel (01427) 668276 Fax 667956 E-mail john.pryor@btinternet.com

PRYOR, William Lister Archibald. b 39. Trin Coll Cam BA67 MA69 DipEd68. Ox NSM Course 72. **d** 75 **p** 90. NSM Summertown *Ox* 75-76; NSM Wolvercote w Summertown from 76; Perm to Offic *Nor* from 93. *23 Harbord Road, Oxford OX2 8LH* Tel (01865) 515102 Fax as telephone

PRYS, Deiniol. b 53. Univ of Wales (Ban) DipTh82 BTh91 Univ of Wales (Cardiff) DPS83. St Mich Coll Llan 82. **d** 83 **p** 84. C Llanbeblig w Caernarfon and Betws Garmon etc *Ban* 83-86; TV Amlwch 86-88; V Llanerch-y-medd 89-92; R Llansadwrn w Llanddona and Llaniestyn etc from 92. *The Rectory, Llansadwrn, Porthaethwy LL59 5SL* Tel (01248) 810534 Mobile 07740-541316

PRYSE, Hugh Henry David. b 58. St Chad's Coll Dur BA81 SS Coll Cam PGCE82 K Coll Lon MA96. St Steph Ho Ox 94. **d** 96 **p** 97. C Branksome St Aldhelm *Sarum* 96-00; TV Hove *Chich* from 00. *The Vicarage, 17 Vallance Gardens, Hove BN3 2DB* Tel (01273) 734859

PRYSOR-JONES, John Glynne. b 47. Heythrop Coll Lon MA94 Liv Univ CQSW73 Birm Univ DPS80. Westcott Ho Cam 88. **d** 90 **p** 91. C Mitcham St Mark *S'wark* 90-93; V Dudley St Fran *Worc* 93-99; R Woodchurch *Ches* 99-01; Hd Past Care Services Chorley and S Ribble NHS Trust 01-02; Hd Past Care Services Preston Acute Hosps NHS Trust 01-02; Hd Past Care Services Lanc Teaching Hosps NHS Trust from 02. *Royal Preston Hospital, Sharoe Green Lane, Fulwood, Preston PR2 9HT* Tel (01772) 522350 *or* 700797 Fax 522447 E-mail john.prysor-jones@lthtr.nhs.uk

PRYTHERCH, David. b 30. Down Coll Cam BA54 MA58 Lon Univ CertEd68 DipAdEd71. Coll of Resurr Mirfield 54. **d** 56 **p** 57. C Blackpool St Steph *Blackb* 56-61; R Mantson *Glouc* 61-65; Chapl St Elphin's Sch Matlock 65-85; V Thornton-le-Fylde *Blackb* 85-94; RD Poulton 91-94; rtd 94; Perm to Offic *Ches* from 96. *8A Dunraven Road, West Kirby, Wirral CH48 4DS*

PUCKRIN, Christopher. b 47. Oak Hill Th Coll. **d** 82 **p** 83. C Heworth H Trin *York* 82-84; C Sherburn in Elmet 84-85; P-in-c Kirk Fenton 85-86; P-in-c Kirkby Wharfe 85-86; V Kirk Fenton w Kirkby Wharfe and Ulleskelfe 86-87; C York St Mich-le-Belfrey 87-94; P-in-c Barnstaple *Ex* 94-97; TV 97-00; V Woodside *Ripon* from 00. *St James's Vicarage, 1 Scotland Close, Horsforth, Leeds LS18 5SG* Tel 0113-258 2433

PUDDEFOOT, John Charles. b 52. St Pet Coll Ox BA74 Edin Univ BD78. Edin Th Coll 76. **d** 78 **p** 79. C Darlington H Trin *Dur* 78-81; Ind Chapl *Chich* 81-84; Asst Master Eton Coll 84-93; Hd Mathematics from 93; Lic to Offic *Ox* from 85. *Eton College, Windsor SL4 6DB* Tel (01753) 671320
E-mail j.puddefoot@etoncollege.org.uk

PUDGE, Mark Samuel. b 67. K Coll Lon BD90 AKC90. Ripon Coll Cuddesdon DipMin93. **d** 93 **p** 94. C Thorpe Bay *Chelmsf* 93-96; TV Wickford and Runwell 97-00; Development Officer Citizens' Advice Bureau from 00. *9 Lyon House, 53 Riding House Street, London W1W 7ED* Tel 07773-396749 (mobile)
E-mail markpudge@msp1.demon.co.uk

PUDNEY, Malcolm Lloyd. b 48. SEITE 99. **d** 01 **p** 02. NSM S Nutfield w Outwood *S'wark* from 01. *The Rookery, Broadbridge Lane, Smallfield, Horley RH6 9RF* Tel (01342) 842463 Mobile 07860-464836 E-mail yendup@xalt.co.uk

PUERTO RICO, Bishop of. See ALVAREZ-VELAZQUEZ, The Rt Revd David Andres

PUGH, Brian. See PUGH, William Bryan

PUGH, Canon David. b 22. Univ of Wales (Abth) BA48. St D Coll Lamp 48. **d** 50 **p** 51. C Llanllwchaiarn *St D* 50-57; R Bangor Teifi w Henllan 57-70; R Bangor Teifi w Henllan and Llanfairorllwyn 70-81; RD Emlyn 73-91; R Bangor Teifi w Henllan and Llanfairorllwyn etc 81-91; Can St D Cathl 88-92; rtd 92; Hon Can St D Cathl *St D* from 92. *2 Bro Dewi, Henllan, Llandyssul SA44 5TL* Tel (01559) 370619

PUGH, Harry. b 48. K Coll Lon BD70 AKC71 Lanc Univ MA89. **d** 72 **p** 73. C Milnrow *Man* 72-75; P-in-c Rochdale Gd Shep 75-78; TV Rochdale 78-79; Perm to Offic *Liv* 79-82; C Darwen St Cuth *Blackb* 82-85; C Darwen St Cuth w Tockholes St Steph 85-86; V Burnley St Steph 86-93; R Hoole 93-01; P-in-c Porthleven w Sithney *Truro* from 01. *The Vicarage, Pendeen Road, Porthleven, Helston TR13 9AL* Tel (01326) 562419

PUGH, Ronald Keith. b 32. Jes Coll Ox BA54 MA57 DPhil57. Ripon Hall Ox 56. **d** 59 **p** 60. C Bournemouth St Mich *Win* 59-61; Asst Chapl Bryanston Sch 61-66; Chapl Cranleigh Sch Surrey 66-68; Lic to Offic *Win* from 68; Lect K Alfred Coll Winchester 68-97; rtd 97; Sec and Treas Win and Portsm Dioc Clerical Registry from 97. *Church House, 9 The Close, Winchester SO23 9LS* Tel (01962) 844644 *or* 857249 Fax 877316
E-mail clerical.registry@ukgateway.net

PUGH, Stephen Gregory. Southn Univ BEd77. Linc Th Coll 85. **d** 87 **p** 88. C Harpenden St Nic *St Alb* 87-90; C Stevenage All SS Pin Green 90-93; R Stotfold and Radwell 93-00; V Gt Ilford St Marg and St Clem *Chelmsf* from 00. *The Vicarage, 70 Brisbane Road, Ilford IG1 4SL* Tel (020) 8554 7542 Mobile 07905-370410 E-mail sgpugh@waitrose.com

PUGH, Miss Wendy Kathleen. b 48. Newnham Coll Cam BA69 MA75. Trin Coll Bris DipTh95. **d** 95 **p** 96. C Hailsham *Chich* 95-99; C Frimley *Guildf* from 99. *4 Warren Rise, Frimley, Camberley GU16 8SH* Tel (01276) 66740
E-mail wkpaugh@aol.com

PUGH, William Bryan (Brian). b 34. Man Univ CertBibKnowl57. Ridley Hall Cam 59. **d** 61 **p** 62. C Oseney Crescent St Luke w Camden Square St Paul *Lon* 61-64; C N Wembley St Cuth 64-67; CF 67-88; QHC 85-88; Chapl Heathfield Sch Ascot 88-95; rtd 99; Perm to Offic *Ox* and *Guildf* from 99. *3 College Close, Camberley GU15 4JU* Tel (01276) 503702 E-mail w.pugh@ntlworld.com

PUGMIRE, Canon Alan. b 37. Lon Univ DipTh63. Tyndale Hall Bris 61. **d** 64 **p** 65. C Islington St Steph w St Bart and St Matt *Lon* 64-66; C St Helens St Mark *Liv* 66-71; R Stretford St Bride *Man* 71-82; R Burnage St Marg 82-02; AD Heaton 88-98; Hon Can Man Cathl 98-02; rtd 02; Perm to Offic *Man* from 02. *20 Shortland Crescent, Manchester M19 1SZ* Tel 0161-431 3476 Fax as telephone E-mail alan@apugmire.freeserve.co.uk

PUGSLEY, Anthony John. b 39. ACIB. Oak Hill Th Coll 89. **d** 90 **p** 91. C Chadwell *Chelmsf* 90-94; P-in-c Gt Warley Ch Ch 94-01; V Warley Ch Ch and Gt Warley St Mary from 01. *Christ Church Vicarage, 79 Mount Crescent, Brentwood CM14 5DD* Tel (01277) 220428 E-mail revtony@aol.com

PULESTON, Mervyn Pedley. b 35. K Coll Lon BD60 AKC60. **d** 61 **p** 62. C Gt Marlow *Ox* 61-65; P Missr Blackbird Leys CD 65-70; V Kidlington 70-85; R Hampton Poyle 70-85; TR Kidlington w Hampton Poyle 85-86; Chapl Geneva *Eur* 86-92; TV Dorchester *Ox* 92-00; rtd 00. *36 Benmead Road, Kidlington OX5 2DB* Tel (01865) 372360 E-mail mpuleston@aol.com

PULFORD, Christopher. b 59. Pemb Coll Ox BA81 MA87. Trin Coll Bris 82. **d** 84 **p** 85. C Parr *Liv* 84-87; Chapl Berkhamsted Colleg Sch Herts 87-92; Development Dir React from 92. *c/o React, St Luke's House, 270 Sandycombe Road, Kew, Richmond TW9 3NA* Tel (020) 8940 2575 Fax 8940 2050

PULFORD, John Shirley Walter. b 31. Jes Coll Cam BA55 MA59 Lon Univ DipC&G79. Cuddesdon Coll 55. **d** 57 **p** 58. C Blackpool St Steph *Blackb* 57-60; N Rhodesia 60-63; V Newington St Paul *S'wark* 63-68; C Seacroft *Ripon* 68-70; Chapl HM Pris Liv 70-72; Chapl HM Pris Linc 72-73; Student Cllr Linc Colls of Art and Tech 73-79; Cam Univ Counselling Service 79-96; Dir 82-96; rtd 96. *59 Cromer Road, North Walsham NR28 0HB* Tel (01692) 404320

PULFORD, Canon Stephen Ian. b 25. Clifton Th Coll 53. **d** 56 **p** 57. C Heref St Jas *Heref* 56-58; R Coberley w Cowley *Glouc* 58-94; P-in-c Colesborne 75-94; Hon Can Glouc Cathl 84-94; RD Cirencester 88-89; rtd 94; Perm to Offic *Glouc* from 94. *16 Bafford Grove, Charlton Kings, Cheltenham GL53 9JE* Tel (01242) 524261

PULLAN, Ben John. b 43. MSc. **d** 77 **p** 78. NSM Westbury-on-Trym St Alb *Bris* 77-91; NSM Henleaze from 91. *52 Druid Stoke Avenue, Bristol BS9 1DQ* Tel 0117-968 2697
E-mail b.dpullan@virgin.net

PULLAN, Lionel Stephen. b 37. ARCO58 FIST77 Keble Coll Ox BA58 MA62. Cuddesdon Coll 58. **d** 60 **p** 61. C Tranmere St Paul *Ches* 60-63; C Higher Bebington 63-64; Perm to Offic 64-70; Hon C Luton St Chris Round Green *St Alb* 70-72; Hon C Hitchin H Sav 72-73; Hon C Welwyn 73-75; Hon C Welwyn w Ayot St Peter 75-78; Hon C Kimpton w Ayot St Lawrence 78-82; Hon C Stevenage St Andr and St Geo 82-85; Deputation Appeals Org CECS 85-90; V Sundon *St Alb* 90-03; rtd 03; Perm to Offic *St Alb* from 03. *139 Turnpike Drive, Luton LU3 3RB* Tel (01582) 573236 Fax as telephone

PULLAN, Mrs Pauline Margaret. b 32. N Ord Course 79. **dss** 82 **d** 87 **p** 94. Stockport St Sav *Ches* 82-83; Wilmslow 83-87; Par Dn 87-92; NSM 92-94; Sub-Chapl HM Pris Styal 89-92; rtd 92; NSM Altrincham St Jo *Ches* 94-96. *12 Acacia Avenue, Wilmslow SK9 6AX* Tel (01625) 525865

PULLEN, James Stephen. b 43. Lon Univ BSc64 PGCE65 Linacre Coll Ox BA68. St Steph Ho Ox 66. **d** 68 **p** 69. C Chorlton-cum-Hardy St Clem *Man* 68-71; C Doncaster St Leon and St Jude *Sheff* 72-73; Chapl St Olave's and St Sav Schs Orpington 73-75; Chapl Haileybury Coll 75-01; Second Master 99-01; V St Ives *Ely* from 01. *The Vicarage, Westwood Road, St Ives PE27 6DH* Tel (01480) 463254
E-mail james.pullen@ely.anglican.org

PULLEN, Paul Anthony. b 58. Trin Coll Bris 96. **d** 98 **p** 99. C Helston and Wendron *Truro* 98-01; P-in-c Carbis Bay w Lelant from 01. *The Vicarage, Porthrepta Road, Carbis Bay, St Ives TR26 2LD* Tel (01736) 796206
E-mail wendronchurch@barclays.net

PULLEN, Roger Christopher. b 43. Lon Univ BSc65 PGCE90. Wells Th Coll 65. **d** 67 **p** 68. C S w N Hayling *Portsm* 67-69; C Farlington 69-73; **d** 73 **p** 74. C Pershore w Wick *Worc* 73-75; C Pershore w Pinvin, Wick and Birlingham 75-77; TV Droitwich 77-80; V Woburn Sands *St Alb* 80-85; Perm to Offic *Ex* 85-87. *85 Weymouth Road, Frome BA11 1HJ* Tel (01373) 472170

PULLIN, Andrew Eric. b 47. Kelham Th Coll 67 Linc Th Coll 71. **d** 73 **p** 74. C Pershore w Wick *Worc* 73-75; C Pershore w Pinvin, Wick and Birlingham 75-77; TV Droitwich 77-80; V Woburn Sands *St Alb* 80-85; Perm to Offic *Ex* W 85-87. *85 Weymouth Road, Frome BA11 1HJ* Tel (01373) 472170

PULLIN, Christopher. b 56. St Chad's Coll Dur BA77. Ripon Coll Cuddesdon 79. **d** 80 **p** 81. C Tooting All SS *S'wark* 80-85; V New Eltham All SS 85-92; V St Jo in Bedwardine *Worc* from 92. *St John's Vicarage, 143 Malvern Road, Worcester WR2 4LN* Tel (01905) 422327

PULLIN, Peter Stanley. b 29. MA MSc CEng. Trin Coll Bris 87. **d** 88 **p** 89. NSM Rugby St Andr *Cov* 88-90; NSM Aylesbeare, Rockbeare, Farringdon etc *Ex* 90-98; Perm to Offic from 99. *Applegarth, 5 Minchin Orchard, Aylesbeare, Exeter EX5 2BY* Tel (01395) 232877

PULLINGER, Mrs Catherine Ann. b 54. York Univ BA76. Oak Hill Th Coll DipHE93. **d** 93 **p** 97. NSM Luton St Paul *St Alb* 93-99; NSM Luton Lewsey St Hugh from 99. *52 Wheatfield Road, Luton LU4 0TR* Tel (01582) 606996
E-mail ipullinger@compuserve.com

PULLINGER, Ian Austin. b 61. Oak Hill Th Coll. **d** 96 **p** 97. C Weston *Win* 96-00; TV The Ortons, Alwalton and Chesterton *Ely* from 00. *32 Fraserburgh Way, Orton Southgate, Peterborough PE2 6SS* Tel (01733) 394185 E-mail ianpullinger@bigfoot.com

PULLINGER, Peter Mark. b 53. Heythrop Coll Lon MA97. Ridley Hall Cam 01. **d** 03. C Clapham Park St Steph *S'wark* from 03. *6 Blenheim Gardens, London SW2 5ET*

PULMAN, Edgar James. b 17. Selw Coll Cam BA48 MA53. ALCD50. **d** 50 **p** 51. C Lee Gd Shep *S'wark* 50-52; C Stoke sub

Hamdon *B & W* 52-53; V 53-58; C Norton sub Hamdon 52-53; R 53-58; Singapore 58-62; V Finchley H Trin *Lon* 63-76; C Norton sub Hamdon, W Chinnock, Chiselborough etc *B & W* 77-78; Perm to Offic 79-01; rtd 82. *The Orangery, The Manor House, Norton-sub-Hamdon, Stoke-sub-Hamdon TA14 6SJ* Tel (01935) 881521

PULMAN, John. b 34. Nottm Univ Cert Th & Past Studies 81. EMMTC 78. **d** 81 **p** 82. NSM Mansfield St Pet *S'well* 81-83; C Mansfield Woodhouse 83-86; V Flintham 86-99; R Car Colston w Screveton 86-99; Chapl HM YOI Whatton 87-90; Chapl HM Pris Whatton 90-99; rtd 99; Perm to Offic *S'well* from 99 and *Derby* from 00. *101 Ling Forest Road, Mansfield NG18 3NQ* Tel (01623) 474707

PUMPHREY, Norman John Albert. b 21. Nor Ord Course 76. **d** 77 **p** 78. NSM Aylsham *Nor* 77-94; Chapl St Mich Hosp Aylsham 88-99; Perm to Offic *Nor* from 94. *12 Buxton Road, Aylsham, Norwich NR11 6JD* Tel (01263) 733207

PUNSHON, Carol Mary. *See* BRENNAN, Ms Carol Mary

PUNSHON, George Wilson. b 30. Bris Univ BSc Michigan State Univ MSc DipEd. Ripon Hall Ox 71 DipTh. **d** 73 **p** 74. C Knighton St Mary Magd *Leic* 73-76; V Donisthorpe and Moira w Stretton-en-le-Field 76-82; R Gt Bowden w Welham, Glooston and Cranoe 82-86; Zimbabwe 87-89 and from 00; Perm to Offic *Pet* 96-00; V Ascension Is 97-98; Chapl Peterho Sch Marondera from 00. *Peterhouse, Private Bag 3741, Marondera, Zimbabwe* Tel (00263) (79) 22200 *or* 24951 Fax 24200

PUNSHON, Canon Keith. b 48. JP. Jes Coll Cam BA69 MA73 Birm Univ DipTh73 MA77. Qu Coll Birm 71. **d** 73 **p** 74. C Yardley St Edburgha *Birm* 73-76; Chapl Eton Coll 76-79; V Hill *Birm* 79-86; CF (TA) from 79; V S Yardley St Mich *Birm* 86-96; Can Res Ripon Cathl *Ripon* from 96. *St Peter's House, Minster Close, Ripon HG4 1QP* Tel (01765) 604108 E-mail postmaster@riponcathedral.org.uk

PURCHAS, Canon Catherine Patience Ann. b 39. St Mary's Coll Dur BA61. St Alb Minl Tr Scheme 77. **dss** 80 **d** 87 **p** 94. RE Resource Cen 80-81; Relig Broadcasting Chiltern Radio 81-87; Wheathampstead *St Alb* 81-87; Hon Par Dn 87-94; Hon C 94-01; Relig Broadcasting Beds Radio from 88; Bp's Officer for Women from 93; Bp's Officer for NSMs and Asst Dir of Ords 93-00; Assoc Dioc Dir of Ords from 00; Hon Can St Alb 96-00. *14 Horn Hill, Whitwell, Hitchin SG4 8AS* Tel (01438) 871668 Fax as telephone

PURCHAS, Canon Thomas. b 35. Qu Coll Birm 59. **d** 62 **p** 63. C Bp's Hatfield *St Alb* 62-71; R Blunham 71-78; P-in-c Tempsford w Lt Barford 71-78; R Blunham w Tempsford and Lt Barford 78-80; R Wheathampstead 80-00; RD Wheathampstead 92-99; Hon Can St Alb 99-00; rtd 00; RD Hitchin 00-02; Perm to Offic *St Alb* from 00. *14 Horn Hill, Whitwell, Hitchin SG4 8AS* Tel (01438) 871668 Fax as telephone

PURDY, Canon John David. b 44. Leeds Univ BA65 DipTh74 MPhil76. Coll of Resurr Mirfield 72. **d** 75 **p** 76. C Marske in Cleveland *York* 75-78; C Marton-in-Cleveland 78-80; V Newby 80-87; V Kirkleatham 87-95; V Kirkbymoorside w Gillamoor, Farndale etc from 95; Can and Preb York Minster from 98; RD Helmsley from 99. *The Vicarage, Kirkbymoorside, York YO62 6AZ* Tel (01751) 431452

PURSER, Alan Gordon. b 51. Leic Univ BSc73. Wycliffe Hall Ox 74. **d** 77 **p** 78. C Beckenham Ch Ch *Roch* 77-81; TV Barking St Marg w St Patr *Chelmsf* 81-84; S Africa 84-88; Min Hadley Wood St Paul Prop Chpl *Lon* from 88. *34 Crescent East, Hadley Wood, Barnet EN4 0EN* Tel (020) 8449 2572 Fax 8440 2864 E-mail alan.purser@dlondon.org.uk

PURVEY-TYRER, Neil. b 66. Leeds Univ BA87 MA88. Westcott Ho Cam 88. **d** 90 **p** 91. C Denbigh and Nantglyn *St As* 90-92; Chapl Asst Basingstoke Distr Hosp 92-95; TV Cannock *Lich* 95-99; V Northampton H Sepulchre w St Andr and St Lawr *Pet* 99-02; Dioc Co-ord for Soc Resp from 99; TR Duston Team from 02. *The Vicarage, 3 Main Road, Duston, Northampton NN5 6JB* Tel (01604) 752591 E-mail ntyrer@waitrose.com

PURVIS, Canon Colin. b 19. Kelham Th Coll 37. **d** 44 **p** 45. C Hebburn St Cuth *Dur* 44-47; C Sunderland 47-50; C Darlington St Cuth 50-53; C-in-c Humbledon St Mary V CD 53-58; C-in-c Bishopwearmouth St Mary V w St Pet CD 58-62; V Heworth St Mary 62-76; RD Gateshead 69-76; R Egglescliffe 76-84; Hon Can Dur Cathl 83-92; rtd 84. *4 Duke's Drive, Newcastle upon Tyne NE3 5NT* Tel 0191-236 6394

PURVIS, Lynn. b 58. St Jo Coll Dur BA97. Cranmer Hall Dur 94. **d** 98 **p** 99. C Gt Aycliffe *Dur* 98-02; Asst Chapl N Tees and Hartlepool NHS Trust from 02. *The Rectory, 1 Clifton Avenue, Billingham TS22 5DE* Tel (01642) 551666

PURVIS, Mrs Sandra Anne. b 56. Univ Coll Ches BTh01. N Ord Course 98. **d** 01 **p** 02. C Blackpool St Jo *Blackb* from 01. *52 Leeds Road, Blackpool FY1 4HJ* Tel (01253) 624036 Mobile 07967-136992 E-mail sandraapurvis@aol.com

PURVIS, Stephen. b 48. AKC70. **d** 71 **p** 72. C Peterlee *Dur* 71-75; Dioc Recruitment Officer 75-79; V Stevenage All SS Pin Green *St Alb* 79-88; TR Borehamwood 88-00; RD Aldenham 94-98; V

Leagrave from 00. *St Luke's Vicarage, High Street, Leagrave, Luton LU4 9JY* Tel (01582) 572737 Fax as telephone E-mail stephen.purvis@excite.co.uk

PUSEY, Ian John. b 39. Sarum Th Coll 69. **d** 71 **p** 72. C Waltham Abbey *Chelmsf* 71-75; TV Stantonbury *Ox* 75-80; P-in-c Bletchley 80-84; R 84-00; RD Milton Keynes 96-00; P-in-c Lamp from 00. *The Rectory, High Street, Haversham, Milton Keynes MK19 7DT* Tel and fax (01908) 312136 E-mail ian.pusey@virginnet.co.uk

PUTNAM, Mrs Gillian. b 43. WEMTC 00. **d** 02 **p** 03. NSM Milton *B & W* from 02. *6 Miller Close, Weston-super-Mare BS23 2SQ* Tel (01934) 416917 E-mail gillianputnam@yahoo.co.uk

✠**PWAISIHO, The Rt Revd William Alaha.** b 48. Bp Patteson Th Coll (Solomon Is) 71. **d** 74 **p** 75 **c** 81. Solomon Is 74-76; New Zealand 78-79; Solomon Is 79-95; Dean Honiara 80-81; Bp Malaita 81-89; C Sale St Anne *Ches* 97-99; Asst Bp Ches from 97; R Gawsworth from 99. *The Rectory, Gawsworth, Macclesfield SK11 9RJ* Tel (01260) 223201 Mobile 07711-241625 E-mail bishop@gawsworth72.freeserve.co.uk

PYATT, Noel Watson. b 34. AKC57. **d** 58 **p** 59. C Prenton *Ches* 58-61; C Cheadle Hulme All SS 61-63; P-in-c Hattersley 63-66; V 66-70; V Ches St Paul 70-99; rtd 99; Perm to Offic *Sheff* from 99. *273 School Road, Sheffield S10 1GQ* Tel 0114-266 9944

PYBURN, Canon Alan. b 29. G&C Coll Cam BA51 MA55. Westcott Ho Cam 53. **d** 55 **p** 56. C Barnard Castle *Dur* 55-57; Chapl G&C Coll Cam 57-60; V Dallington *Pet* 60-72; V Ox St Giles *Ox* 72-79; P-in-c Remenham 79-94; R Henley 79-94; RD Henley 84-94; Hon Can Ch Ch 90-95; R Henley w Remenham 94-95; rtd 95. *Pippin Cottage, Well Hill, Finstock, Chipping Norton OX7 3BU* Tel (01993) 868651

PYBUS, Antony Frederick. b 54. Birm Univ BA77. St Jo Coll Dur 78. **d** 81 **p** 82. C Ches H Trin *Ches* 81-84; C W Hampstead St Jas *Lon* 84-89; V Alexandra Park St Andr 89-93; V Alexandra Park from 93. *The Vicarage, 34 Alexandra Park Road, London N10 2AB* Tel (020) 8444 6898 Fax 8442 1736 E-mail office@alexandrapark.org

PYE, Alexander Frederick. b 61. St Mich Coll Llan Dip Practical Th 95. **d** 95 **p** 96. C Griffithstown *Mon* 95-97; P-in-c Bistre *St As* 97-99; P-in-c Penmaen and Crumlin *Mon* 99-00; V 00-02; R Govilon w Llanfoist w Llanelen from 02. *The Rectory, Merthyr Road, Govilon, Abergavenny NP7 9PT* Tel (01873) 832703

PYE, Canon Allan Stephen. b 56. Univ of Wales (Lamp) BA78 Lanc Univ MA85 MPhil87. Westcott Ho Cam 79. **d** 81 **p** 82. C Scotforth *Blackb* 81-85; C Oswaldtwistle All SS 85-87; V Wrightington 87-91; Chapl Wrightington Hosp 87-91; P-in-c Hayton St Mary *Carl* 91-93; V Hayton w Cumwhitton 93-98; RD Brampton 96-98; Hon Can Carl Cathl from 97; P-in-c Hawkshead and Low Wray w Sawrey 98-03; V Hawkshead and Low Wray w Sawrey and Rusland etc from 03. *The Vicarage, Vicarage Lane, Hawkshead, Ambleside LA22 0PD* Tel (01539) 436301 E-mail stephen.pye@virgin.net

PYE, Gay Elizabeth. b 46. RN67 RN68. BD73. **d** 96 **p** 96. NSM Castle Church *Lich* 96-00; Chapl HM Pris Shrewsbury 97-00; Perm to Offic *Lich* from 00; *Carl, Ches* and *Derby* from 01. *Castle Church Vicarage, 18 Castle Bank, Stafford ST16 1DJ* Tel and fax (01785) 600943 *or* tel 223673 E-mail gay.pye@bfbs.org.uk

PYE, James Timothy. b 58. Oak Hill Th Coll BA90. **d** 90 **p** 91. C Normanton *Derby* 90-94; R Talke *Lich* from 94. *The Rectory, 26 Crown Bank, Talke, Stoke-on-Trent ST7 1PU* Tel (01782) 782348 E-mail jimpye@fish.co.uk

PYE, Joseph Terence Hardwidge. b 41. ARICS64 MRICS01. Trin Coll Bris 70. **d** 73 **p** 74. C Blackb Ch Ch *Blackb* 73-76; OMF 77-90; Korea 77-90; V Castle Church *Lich* from 90. *Castle Church Vicarage, 18 Castle Bank, Stafford ST16 1DJ* Tel (01785) 223673

PYE, Michael Francis. b 53. New Coll Ox BA75 MA78 DPhil78. STETS 97. **d** 00 **p** 01. C Fareham H Trin *Portsm* from 00. *12 Greenwood Close, Fareham PO16 7UF* Tel (01329) 280380 E-mail mike@pye229.freeserve.co.uk

PYE, Nicholas Richard. b 62. Univ Coll Lon BA84 Man Univ PGCE87 Anglia Poly Univ MA03. Ridley Hall Cam CTM98. **d** 98 **p** 99. C Epsom Common Ch Ch *Guildf* 98-01; C Harrow Trin St Mich *Lon* from 01; V Finchley St Paul and St Luke from 03. *St Paul's Vicarage, 50 Long Lane, London N3 2PU* Tel (020) 8346 8729 E-mail revpye@xalt.co.uk

PYE, Ms Sandra Anne. b 53. Anglia Poly Univ BA96 RMN74. EAMTC 99. **d** 02 **p** 03. C Hunstanton St Mary w Ringstead Parva etc *Nor* from 02. *The Rectory, Broad Lane, Brancaster, King's Lynn PE31 8AU* Tel (01485) 210268

PYKE, Alan. b 37. Trin Coll Bris BA87. **d** 87 **p** 88. CA 58-87; C Ipswich St Mary at Stoke w St Pet *St E* 87-90; R Creeting St Mary, Creeting St Peter etc 90-98; C S Trin Broads *Nor* 98-02; rtd 03; Perm to Offic *Nor* from 03. *20 Bell Meadow, Martham, Great Yarmouth NR29 4UA* Tel (01493) 740048 E-mail alanpyke@scs-datacom.co.uk

PYKE, Barry John. b 62. FGS84 Qu Mary Coll Lon BSc84 Southn Univ BTh94 Open Univ BA96. Sarum & Wells Th Coll BTh91. **d** 94 **p** 95. C Bengeworth *Worc* 94-96; C Worc City St Paul and Old St Martin etc 96-99; R Chipping Ongar w Shelley

Chelmsf from 99. *The Rectory, Shackletons, Ongar CM5 9AT* Tel (01277) 362173

PYKE, Richard Ernest. b 50. Sarum & Wells Th Coll. **d** 82 **p** 83. C Bushey *St Alb* 82-85; C Gt Berkhamsted 85-89; V St Alb St Mary Marshalswick 89-00; TR Bp's Hatfield from 00. *The Rectory, 1 Fore Street, Hatfield AL9 5AN* Tel (01707) 262072

PYKE, Mrs Ruth Cheryl. b 56. Bath Coll of HE BA78 W Lon Inst of HE PGCE80. St Alb and Ox Min Course 95. **d** 98 **p** 99. C Leavesden All SS *St Alb* 98-02; C St Alb St Steph from 02. *The Rectory, 1 Fore Street, Hatfield AL9 5AN* Tel (01707) 262072 E-mail ruth.pyke@tesco.net

PYKE, Thomas Fortune. b 62. St Chad's Coll Dur BA85 Fitzw Coll Cam BA88. Ridley Hall Cam 86. **d** 89 **p** 90. C Hitchin *St Alb* 89-94; Chapl Aston Univ *Birm* 94-99; V Birm St Paul from 99; Th Ecum Officer Birm Bd for Miss from 01. *71 Wellington Road, Birmingham B15 2ET* Tel 0121-440 3407 E-mail tom.pyke@virgin.net

PYLE, John Alan. b 31. Qu Coll Birm. **d** 69 **p** 70. C Fenham St Jas and St Basil *Newc* 69-72; C Monkseaton St Pet 72-74; C Morpeth 74-78; R Bothal 78-83; TV Willington Team 83-91; R Chollerton w Birtley and Thockrington 91-97; rtd 97; Perm to Offic *Newc* from 97. *37 Ullswater Drive, Killingworth, Newcastle upon Tyne NE12 6GX* Tel 0191-268 6044

PYM, David Pitfield. b 45. Nottm Univ BA65 Ex Coll Ox DPhil68. Ripon Hall Ox 66. **d** 68 **p** 69. C Nottingham St Mary *S'well* 68-72; Chapl RN 72-76 and 79-84; Chapl Worksop Coll Notts 76-79; R Avon Dassett w Farnborough and Fenny Compton *Cov* from 84. *The Rectory, Avon Dassett, Leamington Spa CV47 2AS* Tel (01295) 690305

PYM, Francis Victor. b 24. ARIBA52 DipArch52. St Jo Coll Dur 74. **d** 76 **p** 77. C Keighley *Bradf* 76-79; Chapl Bethany Fellowship 79-87; Lic to Offic *Chich* from 87; Dir Joshua Chr Trust from 88; Research Asst Ho of Lords from 89; Dir Gp Apologetics Initiative from 92. *Bolney House, Bolney, Haywards Heath RH17 5QR* Tel (01444) 881877

PYM, Gordon Sydney. b 19. Worc Ord Coll 59. **d** 61 **p** 62. C Highweek *Ex* 61-63; C Plymouth Em 63-66; V Kilnhurst *Sheff* 66-69; V Owston 69-72; V Hensall 72-75; rtd 75; Perm to Offic *Sheff* from 75. *6 Greno Road, Swinton, Mexborough S64 8RP* Tel (01709) 586884

PYNE, Robert Leslie. b 51. Lanchester Poly BA72 Solicitor 75 Leeds Univ DipTh78 Dundee Univ Dip Criminal Justice Studies 98. Coll of Resurr Mirfield 76. **d** 79 **p** 80. C Clifton All SS w St Jo *Bris* 79-81; Bp's Dom Chapl *Ox* 81-84; TV High Wycombe 84-90; Chapl RN from 90. *Royal Naval Chaplaincy Service, Room 203, Victory Building, HM Naval Base, Portsmouth PO1 3LS* Tel (023) 9272 7903 Fax 9272 7111

PYNN, Catherine. b 45. Reading Univ BSc67. St Alb and Ox Min Course 93. **d** 96 **p** 97. NSM Caversham St Pet and Mapledurham etc *Ox* from 96; Chapl Bradfield Coll Berks from 00. *21 Ridge Hall Close, Caversham, Reading RG4 7EP* Tel 0118-947 6065 Mobile 07947-437948

✠**PYTCHES, The Rt Revd George Edward David.** b 31. Bris Univ BA54 Nottm Univ MPhil84. Tyndale Hall Bris 51. **d** 55 **p** 56 **c** 70. C Ox St Ebbe *Ox* 55-58; C Wallington H Trin *S'wark* 58-59; Chile 59-77; Suff Bp Valparaiso 70-72; Bp Chile, Bolivia and Peru 72-77; V Chorleywood St Andr *St Alb* 77-96; rtd 96; Perm to Offic *St Alb* from 96. *Red Tiles, Homefield Road, Chorleywood, Rickmansworth WD3 5QJ* Tel (01923) 283763 Fax 283762

PYTCHES, Preb Peter Norman Lambert. b 32. Univ Coll Lon 52 Lon Univ BD57 Bris Univ MLitt67 Southn Univ PhD81 K Coll Lon MA00 Potchefstroom Univ MTh03 Lambeth STh74. Tyndale Hall Bris 53. **d** 57 **p** 58. C Heatherlands St Jo *Sarum* 57-61; C Cromer *Nor* 61-63; V Plymouth St Jude *Ex* 63-71; V Heatherlands St Jo *Sarum* 71-76; Dir Past Tr Oak Hill Th Coll 76-81; V Finchley Ch Ch *Lon* 81-91; dir Can Barnet 86-91; V Forty Hill Jes Ch 91-97; Preb St Paul's Cathl 92-97; rtd 97; Perm to Offic *Lon* from 98. *25 Weardale Gardens, Enfield EN2 0BA* Tel (020) 8366 5126 Fax as telephone

Q

QUANCE, John David. b 42. Kelham Th Coll 61. **d** 67 **p** 68. C Southgate Ch Ch *Lon* 67-70; C Norbury St Phil *Cant* 70-73; Asst Chapl Middx Hosp Lon 73-80; R Failsworth St Jo *Man* 80-95; Australia 84-85; P-in-c Healey *Man* from 95. *Healey Vicarage, Gandy Lane, Rochdale OL12 6EF* Tel (01706) 657386

QUARMBY, David John. b 43. St Jo Coll Dur BA64 Lon Univ CertEd70 Man Univ MEd89 Sheff Univ MA99. Ridley Hall Cam 65. **d** 67 **p** 68. C Bournville *Birm* 67-71; V Erdington St Chad 71-73; Lic to Offic *Blackb* 73-83; Perm to Offic *Man* 83-90; C Oldham St Paul 90-98; Hon C from 98; Cllr Huddersfield Poly 90-92; Huddersfield Univ 92-01; Perm to Offic *Man* from 00. *30 College Avenue, Oldham OL8 4DS* Tel 0161-626 2771 E-mail davidquarmby@dqnet.freeserve.co.uk

QUARRELL, John Beck. b 39. Hull Coll of Educn CertEd59. Chich Th Coll 67. **d** 70 **p** 71. C Horbury *Wakef* 70-71; C Sowerby 71-73; V Brotherton 74-80; Chapl Pontefract Gen Hosp 78-80; Staincliffe Hosp Wakef 82-88; V Staincliffe *Wakef* 80-88; R Farndon w Thorpe, Hawton and Cotham *S'well* from 89. *The Rectory, 3 Marsh Lane, Farndon, Newark NG24 3SS* Tel (01636) 705048

QUARTON, Robert Edward. b 43. EMMTC 84. **d** 87 **p** 88. C Gresley *Derby* 87-88; C Clay Cross 88-90; C N Wingfield, Clay Cross and Pilsley 90-91; R Darley from 91; P-in-c S Darley, Elton and Winster from 03. *The Rectory, 15 Hall Rise, Darley Dale, Matlock DE4 2FW* Tel (01629) 734257

QUASH, Jonathan Ben. b 68. Peterho Cam BA90 MA94 PhD99. Westcott Ho Cam 91. **d** 95 **p** 96. NSM Cambridge St Mary Less *Ely* 95-96; Asst Chapl Peterho Cam 95-96; Chapl Fitzw Coll Cam 96-99; Fell 98-99; Tutor Wesley Ho Cam 96-99; Fell and Dean Peterho Cam from 99. *Peterhouse, Cambridge CB2 1RD* Tel (01223) 338217 E-mail jbq1000@cam.ac.uk

✠**QUASHIE, The Rt Revd Kobina Adduah.** b 34. ACIS60 Univ of Ghana LLB71 LLM74 DipTh80. **d** 78 **p** 78 **c** 92. Ghana 78-80 and 92-02; Chapl Middx Hosp Lon 80; Funding Officer USPG 80-92; Hon Can Kumasi from 86; Hon Can Koforidua from 86; Hon Can Accra from 87; Bp Cape Coast 92-02; rtd 02. *32 Chandos Road, London NW2 4LU* Tel (020) 8452 5721

QUAYLE, Margaret Grace. b 28. Gipsy Hill Coll of Educn TCert48 Lon Univ BA53 Liv Univ MPhil78. LNSM course 95. **d** 98 **p** 99. OLM Gt Crosby St Luke *Liv* from 98. *Chwyd, 9 Myers Road West, Crosby, Liverpool L23 0RS* Tel 0151-924 1659

QUENNELL, Brian Michael. b 19. **d** 74 **p** 75. C Oakham w Hambleton and Egleton *Pet* 74-78; V Denford w Ringstead 78-87; Perm to Offic 87-99; rtd 87. *9 The Hollies, St Christopher's Home, Abington Park Crescent, Northampton NN3 3AD* Tel (01604) 232729

QUIBELL, Edward Villiers. b 71. Anglia Poly BSc93 Hughes Hall Cam PGCE94. Trin Coll Bris BA03. **d** 03. C Swindon Ch Ch *Bris* from 03. *58 Upham Road, Swindon SN3 1DN* Tel (01793) 521296 Mobile 07771-854980 E-mail ed@equibell.fsnet.co.uk

QUIBELL, Mrs Susan Elizabeth. b 50. **d** 03. OLM Aldridge *Lich* from 03. *23 Highfield Way, Aldridge, Walsall WS9 8XF* Tel (01922) 456083 E-mail sue.quibell@virgin.net

QUICK, John Michael. b 46. N Counties Coll Newc TCert68 Birkbeck Coll Lon BSc73 FRGS70. St Alb and Ox Min Course 97. **d** 00 **p** 01. OLM New Windsor *Ox* from 00. *White Roses, 45 York Road, Windsor SL4 3PA* Tel (01753) 865557 Mobile 07977-754822 E-mail littlefrquick@aol.com

QUICK, Roger Aelfred Melvin Tricquet. b 55. Leeds Univ BA79 PGCE81. Coll of Resurr Mirfield BA94. **d** 96 **p** 97. C Chapel Allerton *Ripon* 96-00; C Ireland Wood 00-03; Hon C from 03; rtd 03. *6 Holt Park Gardens, Leeds LS16 7RB* Tel 0113-281 7854

QUIGLEY, Adam. b 03. NSM Castlerock w Dunboe and Fermoyle *D & R* from 03. *41 Queens Park, Coleraine BT51 3JS* Tel (028) 7035 5191

QUIGLEY, Donna Maree. Ulster Univ BEd BTh. **d** 01 **p** 02. C Portadown St Columba *Arm* from 01. *14 Ardmore Crescent, Portadown BT62 4DU* Tel (028) 3833 1916

QUIGLEY, John Molesworth. b 21. BNC Ox BA43 MA47. Wycliffe Hall Ox 43. **d** 44 **p** 45. C Wembley St Jo *Lon* 44-46; Hon C Ellesmere Port *Ches* 75; Hon C Bromborough 75-77 and 80-82; Hon C Prenton 77-80; Hon C Wallasey St Hilary 82-84; Hon C Perm to Offic *Bradf* 85-99. *31 The Crofts, St Bees CA27 0BH* Tel (01946) 824812

QUIGLEY, William. b 46. Ulster Univ BA86. CITC BTh98. **d** 98 **p** 99. C Ballymoney w Finvoy and Rasharkin *Conn* 98-01; I Eglish w Killylea *Arm* from 01. *154 Killylea Road, Armagh BT60 4LN* Tel (028) 3756 8320

QUILL, John Stephen. b 51. Nottm Univ DipTh78. Linc Th Coll 76. **d** 79 **p** 80. C Sawbridgeworth *St Alb* 79-81; C Watford Ch Ch 81-85; Dioc Soc Services Adv *Worc* 85-90; Adv to Bd of Soc Resp 90-95. *Address temp unknown*

QUILL, Canon Walter Paterson. b 35. **d** 60 **p** 61. C Glendermott *D & R* 60-63; I Kilbarron 63-66; I Kilcronaghan w Ballynascreen 66-81; I Derg w Termonamongan from 81; Can Derry Cathl from 89; Preb Howth St Patr Cathl Dublin from 04. *13 Strabane Road, Castledreg BT81 7HZ* Tel (028) 8267 1362 E-mail derg@iol.ie

QUILLIAM, Miss Anne Eleanor Scott. b 31. Bedf Coll Lon BA54 CertEd55. Dalton Ho Bris 59. **d** 87. Par Dn Toxteth St Philemon w St Gabr and St Cleopas *Liv* 87-92; rtd 92; Perm to Offic *S & M* from 92. *13 Raad ny Gabbil, Castletown, Isle of Man IM9 1HH* Tel (01624) 822375

QUIN, David Christopher. b 42. St Alb and Ox Min Course 97. **d** 00 **p** 01. NSM Blunham, Gt Barford, Roxton and Tempsford etc *St Alb* from 00. *The Rectory, Park Lane, Blunham, Bedford MK44 3NJ* Tel and fax (01767) 640690 Mobile 07867-664924

QUIN, Eric Arthur. b 22. Magd Coll Cam BA46 MA48 Lon Univ BD56. Bps' Coll Cheshunt 46. **d** 48 **p** 49. C Luton St Andr *St Alb* 48-50; C Barnoldswick w Bracewell *Bradf* 50-52; PC Bradf St Sav 52-57; P-in-c Gt w Lt Wymondley *St Alb* 57-58; P-in-c St Ippolyts 57-58; V 58-70; RD Hitchin 68-70; V Haynes 70-87; rtd 87; Perm to Offic *Ches* from 87. *Annabel's Cottage, The Lydiate, Wirral CH60 8PR* Tel 0151-342 8650

QUIN, John James Neil. b 31. Ox Univ MA DipEd53. Qu Coll Birm 61. **d** 63 **p** 64. C Cannock *Lich* 63-68; V Sneyd Green 68-78; V Stafford St Paul Forebridge 78-90; TV Tettenhall Regis 90-98; rtd 98; Perm to Offic *Ex* from 00. *Watcombe House, 28 Barnpark Road, Teignmouth TQ14 8PN* Tel (01626) 772525

QUINE, Christopher Andrew. b 38. St Aid Birkenhead 61. **d** 64 **p** 65. C Hunts Cross *Liv* 64-67; C Farnworth 67-71; C-in-c Widnes St Jo 67-71; V Clubmoor 71-78; V Formby H Trin 78-99; V Santan *S & M* from 99; V Arbory from 99. *Arbory Vicarage, Main Road, Ballabeg, Castletown, Isle of Man IM9 4LG* Tel (01624) 823595

QUINE, David Anthony. b 28. Qu Coll Cam BA52 MA59. Ridley Hall Cam 53. **d** 55 **p** 56. C Beckenham Ch Ch *Roch* 55-59; C Normanton *Derby* 59-60; V Low Elswick *Newc* 60-66; V Houghton *Carl* 66-68; Lic to Offic *York* 68-71; Chapl Monkton Combe Sch Bath 71-85; rtd 85; Perm to Offic *Carl* from 85. *Briar Cragg, Gale Rigg, Ambleside LA22 0AZ* Tel (015394) 433563

QUINE, Canon Ernest Kendrick Leigh. b 21. St Jo Coll Dur BA50 MA55 DipTh51 Nottm Univ DPhil68. **d** 51 **p** 52. C Grassendale *Liv* 51-52; C Shrewsbury St Alkmund *Lich* 52-54; C-in-c Park Estate St Chris CD *Leic* 54-61; V Belgrave St Pet 61-93; Hon Can Leic Cathl 67-93; rtd 93; Perm to Offic *Leic* from 93. *63 Somerset Drive, Glenfield, Leicester LE3 8QW* Tel 0116-232 1994

✠**QUINLAN, The Rt Revd Alan Geoffrey.** b 33. Kelham Th Coll 54. **d** 58 **p** 59 **c** 88. C Bedford Leigh *Man* 58-61; S Africa from 61; Suff Bp Cape Town (Cen Region) 88-98; rtd 98. *132 Woodley Road, Plumstead, Cape Town, 7800 South Africa*

QUINN, Canon Arthur Hamilton Riddel. b 37. TCD BA60 MA64 BD67. **d** 61 **p** 62. C Belfast H Trin *Conn* 61-63; C Belfast St Mary Magd 63-64; Chapl Hull Univ *York* 64-69; Chapl Keele Univ *Lich* 69-74; P-in-c Keele 72-74; V Shirley St Jo *Cant* 74-84; V Shirley St Jo *S'wark* from 85; RD Croydon Addington from 95; Hon Can S'wark Cathl from 03. *The Vicarage, 49 Shirley Church Road, Croydon CR0 5EF* Tel (020) 8654 1013 Fax 8656 4568 E-mail stjohn@shirleychurchrd.freeserve.co.uk

QUINN, Cecil Hugh. b 24. Oak Hill Th Coll 74. **d** 76 **p** 77. C Bedford St Jo and St Leon *St Alb* 76-79; Deputation Sec Irish Ch Miss 79-89; I Rathmullan w Tyrella *D & D* 80-96; rtd 96. *Riverside Court, 9/1 Warriston Road, Edinburgh EH7 4HJ* Tel 0131-557 6438

QUINN, Derek John. b 55. TCD BTh88. **d** 88 **p** 89. C Mossley *Conn* 88-91; I Cappagh w Lislimnaghan *D & R* from 91. *Erganagh Rectory, 1 Erganagh Road, Omagh BT79 7SX* Tel (028) 8224 2572

QUINN, Eugene Frederick. b 35. Allegheny Coll (USA) AB57 Univ of California MA66 MA69 PhD70. Vancouver Sch of Th DipTh74. **d** 74 **p** 75. C Washington St Columba USA 74-75 and 78-81; Chapl Prague *Eur* 75-78; C Chevy Chase All SS USA 81-82 and 86-90; Chapl Nat Cathl Washington 81-82 and from 95; C Washington Epiphany 83 and 86-88; V Bowie St Jas 83-84; Chapl Warsaw 93-95. *5702 Kirkside Drive, Chevy Chase, MD 20815-7116, USA* E-mail efquinn@msn.com

QUINN, George Bruce. b 23. **d** 82 **p** 83. NSM Douglas St Ninian *S & M* from 82. *85 Port-e-Chee Avenue, Douglas IM2 5EZ* Tel (01624) 674080

QUINN, John James. b 46. TCD BA70 PhD76. St Jo Coll Nottm DipTh80. **d** 81 **p** 82. C Gorleston St Andr *Nor* 81-84; R Belton 84-90; R Burgh Castle 84-90; R Belton and Burgh Castle from 90. *The Rectory, Belton, Great Yarmouth NR31 9JQ* Tel (01493) 780210

QUINN, Kenneth Norman. b 40. QUB BSc62 CEng MICE. CITC 80. **d** 85 **p** 86. NSM Seapatrick *D & D* 85-91; Lic to Offic from 91. *4 Knollwood, Seapatrick, Banbridge BT32 4PE* Tel (028) 4062 3515 E-mail ken.quinn@btinternet.com

QUINN, Marjorie. **d** 94 **p** 97. NSM Hawarden *St As* from 94. *21 Hawarden Way, Mancot, Deeside CH5 2EL* Tel (01244) 531639

QUINNELL, Peter Francis. b 48. St Steph Ho Ox DipMin95. **d** 95 **p** 96. C Tewkesbury w Walton Cardiff *Glouc* 95-99; R Stratton, N Cerney, Baunton and Bagendon from 99. *The Rectory, 94 Gloucester Road, Cirencester GL7 2LJ* Tel (01285) 653359 E-mail quinnell.rectory@amserve.net

QUINNEY, Canon William Elliott. b 33. Linc Th Coll 62. **d** 64 **p** 65. C Coalville *Leic* 64-68; P-in-c Ibstock 68-69; R Nailstone w Carlton 69-79; R Nailstone and Carlton w Shackerstone from 79; Hon Can Leic Cathl from 97. *The Rectory, Rectory Lane, Nailstone, Nuneaton CV13 0QQ* Tel (01530) 260281

QUINT, Mrs Patricia Mary. b 51. Milton Keynes Coll of Ed CertEd76 Open Univ BA77. St Alb Minl Tr Scheme 90. **d** 93 **p** 94. C Hertford St Andr *St Alb* 93-96; C Bromham w Oakley and Stagsden 96-00; R Stotfold and Radwell from 00. *The Vicarage, 61 Church Road, Stotfold, Hitchin SG5 4NE* Tel (01462) 730218

QUIREY, Mrs Edith. b 56. CITC 98. **d** 01 **p** 02. C Belfast St Mich *Conn* from 01. *696 Crumlin Road, Belfast BT14 8AD* Tel (028) 9029 9057

R

✠**RABENIRINA, The Most Revd Remi Joseph.** b 38. Antananarivo Univ LèsL83. St Paul's Coll Ambatoharanana 61 St Chad's Coll Dur 64 Bossey Ecum Inst Geneva. **d** 67 **p** 68 **c** 84. Dn Toamasina St Jas Madagascar 67; R St Matt Pro-Cathl Antsiranana 68-73; R Ambohimangakely St Jo 73-84; Angl Chapl Antananarivo Univ 73-84; Bp Antananarivo from 84; Abp Indian Ocean from 95. *Evêché Anglican, Lot VK 57 Ter Ambohimanoro, 101 Antananarivo, Madagascar* Tel (00261) (20) 222 0827 Mobile 3311-20827 Fax (20) 226 1331 E-mail eemdanta@dts.mg

RABIN, Peter David. b 62. Southlands Coll Lon BA86. Aston Tr Scheme 88 Ripon Coll Cuddesdon BTh93. **d** 93 **p** 94. C Hornsey St Mary w St Geo *Lon* 93-97; V Cricklewood St Pet from 97. *St Peter's Vicarage, 5 Farm Avenue, London NW2 2EG* Tel (020) 8450 9043 Fax 8208 4146 E-mail frrabin@aol.com

RABJOHNS, Alan. b 40. Leeds Univ BA62. Coll of Resurr Mirfield 62. **d** 64 **p** 65. C Ashington *Newc* 64-67; C Upton cum Chalvey *Ox* 67-76; V Roath St Sav *Llan* from 76; AD Cardiff from 03. *St Saviour's Vicarage, 115 Splott Road, Cardiff CF24 2BY* Tel (029) 2046 1203

RABLEN, Antony Ford. b 52. St Jo Coll Nottm. **d** 82 **p** 83. C Clifton *York* 82-85; TV Marfleet 85-92; P-in-c Wawne w Melton 92-00; TR Sutton St Jas and Wawne from 00. *St John's Vicarage, Wawne Road, Sutton-on-Hull, Hull HU7 4YR* Tel (01482) 820979

RABLEN, Mrs Christine Mary. b 52. Trevelyan Coll Dur BA74 Hull Univ BA92 Leeds Univ MA94. N Ord Course 00. **d** 02 **p** 03. C Sutton St Mich *York* from 02. *St John's Vicarage, Wawne Road, Sutton-on-Hull, Hull HU7 4YR* Tel (01482) 820979

RABY, Malcolm Ernest. b 47. St Jo Coll York BEd73. N Ord Course 81. **d** 84 **p** 85. NSM Chadkirk *Ches* 84-88; Consultant E England CPAS 88-94; C Ely 94-96; TV Ely 96-98; P-in-c Over from 98; Dioc Adv in Miss and Evang from 98; P-in-c Long Stanton w St Mich from 02. *The Vicarage, Horseware, Over, Cambridge CB4 5NX* Tel (01954) 230329 E-mail mission@ely.anglican.org

RACE, Alan. b 51. Bradf Univ BTech73 Birm Univ MA82. Ripon Coll Cuddesdon 73. **d** 76 **p** 77. C Tupsley *Heref* 76-79; Asst Chapl Kent Univ *Cant* 79-84; Dir Studies S'wark Ord Course 84-94; R Aylestone St Andr w St Jas *Leic* from 94. *The Rectory, Old Church Street, Leicester LE2 8ND* Tel 0116-299 7624 Fax 299 7653 E-mail arace@leicester.anglican.org

RACE, Christopher Keith. b 43. St Paul's Coll Grahamstown DipTh78. **d** 78 **p** 80. S Africa 78-83; Angl Chapl Stellenbosch Univ 79-81; R Kalk Bay 81-83; Dioc Admin Botswana and Personal asst to Abp Cen Africa 83-86; P-in-c E Kalahari 83-86; V Tanworth St Patr Salter Street *Birm* 86-96; P-in-c Rothiemurchus *Mor* 96-01; Perm to Offic *Glouc* 02-03; P-in-c Kemble, Poole Keynes, Somerford Keynes etc from 03. *1 Ross Road, English Bicknor, Coleford GL16 7PA* Tel (01594) 860195 E-mail mcrace@msn.com

RACE, John Arthur. b 37. St Alb and Ox Min Course 95. **d** 98 **p** 99. OLM Haddenham w Cuddington, Kingsey etc *Ox* from 98. *8 The Closes, Haddenham, Aylesbury HP17 8JN* Tel (01844) 290180

RACE, Stephen Peter. b 69. SS Hild & Bede Coll Dur BA93. St Steph Ho Ox 00. **d** 02 **p** 03. C Wigton *Carl* from 02. *44 The Hawthorns, Syke Road, Wigton CA7 9LE* Tel (016973) 49010

RACTLIFFE, Dudley John. b 38. Man Univ BA62 Birm Univ DPS69. Ridley Hall Cam 63. **d** 66 **p** 67. C Radford *Cov* 66-68; C Haslemere *Guildf* 69-73; V Perry Beeches *Birm* 73-78; V Worle *B & W* 78-88; Dioc Ecum Officer 88-93; R Dowlishwake w Kingstone, Chillington etc 88-93; TR Swanage and Studland *Sarum* 93-01; rtd 01. *12 Sid Lane, Sidmouth EX10 9AN* Tel (01395) 579712

RADCLIFFE, Canon Albert Edward. b 34. Lon Univ BD63. St Aid Birkenhead Ch Div Sch of the Pacific (USA) 61. **d** 62 **p** 63.

C Knotty Ash St Jo *Liv* 62-64; C Blundellsands St Nic 64-66; Chapl Haifa St Luke Israel 66-69; V Tonge w Alkrington *Man* 69-77; R Ashton St Mich 77-91; AD Ashton-under-Lyne 87-91; Can Res Man Cathl 91-00; rtd 00; Perm to Offic *Man* from 01. *26 St Chad's Road, Withington, Manchester M20 4WH* Tel 0161-445 1327

RADCLIFFE, David Jeffrey. b 52. Linc Th Coll 77. **d** 79 **p** 80. C Poulton-le-Fylde *Blackb* 79-84; V Ingol 84-88; R Lowther and Askham *Carl* 88-96; R Lowther and Askham and Clifton and Brougham from 96. *The Rectory, Lilac House, Lowther, Penrith CA10 2HH* Tel (01931) 712277

RADCLIFFE, Eileen Rose (Rosie). b 54. Carl Dioc Tr Inst 92. **d** 95 **p** 96. NSM Gt Salkeld w Lazonby *Carl* 95-96; NSM Dacre 99-02; Perm to Offic from 02. *The Rectory, Lilac House, Lowther, Penrith CA10 2HH* Tel (01931) 712277

RADCLIFFE, John Frederick. b 39. Dioc OLM tr scheme 99. **d** 01 **p** 02. OLM Meltham *Wakef* from 01. *13 Orchard Close, Meltham, Huddersfield HD9 4EG* Tel (01484) 348806

RADCLIFFE, Mrs Rosemary. b 45. SW Minl Tr Course 87. **d** 90 **p** 94. NSM Devoran *Truro* 90-93; Dn-in-c N Newton w St Michaelchurch, Thurloxton etc *B & W* 93-94; P-in-c 94-00; Chapl to the Deaf 93-96; P-in-c Whipton *Ex* 00-01; rtd 01. *3 Southleigh House, Lemon Street, Truro TR1 2PE* Tel (01872) 273906

✠**RADFORD, The Rt Revd Andrew John.** b 44. Trin Coll Bris 72. **d** 74 **p** 75 **c** 98. C Shirehampton *Bris* 74-78; C Henleaze 78-80; Producer Relig Progr BBC Radio Bris 74-80; V Bath St Barn w Englishcombe *B & W* 80-85; Dioc Communications Officer *Glouc* 85-93; Producer Relig Progr Severn Sound Radio 85-93; Hon Can Glouc Cathl 91-98; Development and Tr Officer Ch Ho Westmr 93-98; Abps' Adv for Bps' Min 98; Suff Bp Taunton *B & W* from 98; Preb Wells Cathl from 98. *Bishop's Lodge, West Monkton, Taunton TA2 8LU* Tel (01823) 413526 Fax 412805 E-mail bishoptaunton@talk21.com

RADFORD, Leslie. b 24. Lon Univ DipPT75. LNSM course. **d** 85 **p** 86. OLM Scotter w E Ferry *Linc* 85-94. *Address temp unknown*

RADLEY, Mrs Jean Frances. b 40. Man Univ RGN62 Univ Coll Lon RSCN65 Preston Poly DN89 Cen Lancs Univ BSc95. Carl and Blackb Dioc Tr Inst 98. **d** 00 **p** 01. OLM Kendal St Geo *Carl* from 00. *3 Castle Street, Kendal LA9 7AD* Tel (01539) 740811 Mobile 07714-020189 E-mail jeanradley@onetel.net.uk

RADLEY, Stephen Gavin. b 62. K Coll Lon BSc83 AKC83 St Jo Coll Dur BA87. Cranmer Hall Dur 85. **d** 89 **p** 90. C Darlington St Matt and St Luke *Dur* 89-92; P-in-c Chilton 92-96; P-in-c Marley Hill 96-01. *Address temp unknown*

RADLEY, Stephen John. b 68. Lancs Coll of Agric NDA89. St Jo Coll Nottm BTh96. **d** 96 **p** 97. C Boulton *Derby* 96-00; Chapl RAF from 00. *Chaplaincy Services (RAF), HQ, Personnel and Training Command, RAF Ainsworth, Gloucester GL3 1EZ* Tel (01452) 712612 ext 5164 Fax 510828 E-mail steve.radley@cwcom.net

RAFFAY, Julian Paul. b 60. Stirling Univ BSc84. Cranmer Hall Dur BA90. **d** 90 **p** 91. C Adel *Ripon* 90-93; C Leeds Halton St Wilfrid 93-95; Asst Chapl S Derbys Mental Health NHS Trust 95-97; TV Gleadless *Sheff* 97-01; V Deepcar from 01. *St John's Vicarage, 27 Carr Road, Deepcar, Sheffield S36 2PQ* Tel 0114-288 5138 E-mail julian@saintjohns.co.uk *or* julian.raffay@saintjohns.co.uk

RAGAN, Mrs Jennifer Mary. b 39. Linc Th Coll 71. **dss** 80 **d** 87 **p** 94. Hackney *Lon* 80-84; Hornchurch St Andr *Chelmsf* 84-88; Par Dn 87-88; Par Dn Ingrave St Steph CD 88-90; Par Dn Gt Parndon 90-94; C 94-99; TV from 99. *14 Deer Park, Harlow CM19 4LD* Tel (01279) 431133

RAGBOURNE, Miss Pamela Mary. b 27. CertEd47. Dalton Ho Bris 53. **dss** 76 **d** 87 **p** 94. CPAS Staff 68-79; Tottenham St Jo *Lon* 79-81; Gt Cambridge Road St Jo and St Jas 82-84; Camberley St Paul *Guildf* 84-86; rtd 87; Perm to Offic *Glouc* 87-93; and from 97; NSM Winchcombe, Gretton, Sudeley Manor etc 93-97. *14 Crispin Close, Winchcombe, Cheltenham GL54 5JY* Tel (01242) 603469

RAHI, Hakim Banta Singh. b 36. Union Bibl Sem Yavatmal BD71. **d** 74 **p** 74. India 74-83; In URC 83-88; Perm to Offic *Birm* 88-93; Ecum Evang Asian Community 88-93. *3 Hobson Close, Norton Street, Birmingham B18 5RH* Tel 0121-554 2144

RAHILLY, Philip James. b 54. Univ of Wales (Cardiff) BD86. Wycliffe Hall Ox 86. **d** 88 **p** 89. C Knightwick w Doddenham, Broadwas and Cotheridge *Worc* 88; C Martley and Wichenford, Knightwick etc 89-91; C Worc St Barn w Ch Ch 91-92; TV Kidderminster St Mary and All SS w Trimpley etc 92-95; P-in-c Childe Okeford, Okeford Fitzpaine, Manston etc *Sarum* 95-00; P-in-c Shilling Okeford 99-00; R Okeford from 00. *The Rectory, Rectory Lane, Childe Okeford, Blandford Forum DT11 8DT* Tel (01258) 860547

RAI, Mrs Mary Anne. b 61. La Sainte Union Coll BTh83 PGCE84. Trin Coll Bris DipTh85. **dss** 86 **d** 87 **p** 99. Bury St Edmunds St Mary *St E* 86-89; Par Dn 87-89; Perm to Offic 90-93; *Cov* 94-99 and from 02; NSM Styvechale *Cov* 99-01. *331A Anstey Road, Coventry CV2 3FN* Tel (024) 7661 2534 E-mail kal.rai@virgin.net

RAIKES, Miss Gwynneth <u>Marian</u> Napier. b 51. Somerville Coll Ox MA72 Lon Univ BD81. Trin Coll Bris 79. **dss** 81 **d** 98 **p** 98. Asst Chapl Bris Poly *Bris* 81-86; Beckenham Ch Ch *Roch* 86-98; C 98-00; Dean of Women and Dir Past Tr Oak Hill Th Coll from 00. *5 Farm Lane, London N14 4PP* Tel (020) 8441 0490 Mobile 07866-651272 E-mail marianr@oakhill.ac.uk

RAIKES, Canon Myles Kenneth. b 23. New Coll Ox BA47 MA51. Wells Th Coll 47. **d** 49 **p** 50. C Chelmsf Cathl *Chelmsf* 49-51; C Stratford St Jo 51-53; P-in-c Hockerill *St Alb* 53-55; V 55-63; Chapl Herts and Essex Hosp Bp's Stortford 56-63; V Bushey Heath *St Alb* 63-70; R Digswell 70-77; Hon Can St Alb 76-77; P-in-c Meare *B & W* 77-81; P-in-c W Coker 82-83; Dioc Ecum Officer 84-88; C Ilminster w Whitelackington 84-85; C S Petherton w the Seavingtons 85-87; rtd 88; Perm to Offic *B & W* from 88. *7 West Street, South Petherton TA13 5DQ* Tel (01460) 241056

RAIKES, Canon Peter. b 37. St Mich Coll Llan 78. **d** 80 **p** 81. C Roath *Llan* 80-82; V Resolven 82-86; V Resolven w Tonna 86-92; RD Neath 89-01; V Skewen 92-02; Can Llan Cathl 97-02; rtd 02. *2 Kennedy Drive, Pencoed, Bridgend CF35 6TW* Tel (01656) 862317

RAIKES, Robert Laybourne. b 32. Wells Th Coll 59. **d** 61 **p** 62. C Poplar All SS w St Frideswide *Lon* 61-66; C Grendon Underwood w Edgcott *Ox* 66-68; C Swan 68-71; V Whitchurch Canonicorum w Wooton Fitzpaine etc *Sarum* 71-81; P-in-c Branksome St Aldhelm 81-82; V 82-91; V Pitminster w Corfe *B & W* 91-92; rtd 92; Chapl Madeira *Eur* 93-95; Perm to Offic *Glouc* 95-98; Hon C Broadwell, Evenlode, Oddington, Adlestrop etc 98-01; Lic to Offic *Eur* from 02. *28 Coopers Lane, Abingdon OX14 5GW* Tel (01235) 523426

RAILTON, John Robert Henry. b 45. FCIB79 Reading Univ BSc68 PhD82. S Dios Minl Tr Scheme 82. **d** 85 **p** 86. NSM Wickham *Portsm* 85-89; C Bridgemary 89-90; V 90-96; TR Ridgeway *Sarum* 96-02; TR Whitton from 02. *The Vicarage, Back Lane, Ramsbury, Marlborough SN8 2QH* Tel (01672) 520235 E-mail johnrailton@webleicester.co.uk

RAILTON, Sandra. b 46. S Dios Minl Tr Scheme 82. **dss** 85 **d** 87 **p** 94. Catherington and Clanfield *Portsm* 85-86; Lee-on-the-Solent 86-89; C 87-89; Par Dn Burnham w Dropmore, Hitcham and Taplow *Ox* 89-94; TV Wallingford w Crowmarsh Gifford etc 94-98; Dioc Dir Ords (OLM) Berks 96-99; TV Ridgeway *Sarum* 98-02; Dioc Voc Adv 99-02; TV Whitton from 02. *The Rectory, Back Lane, Ramsbury, Marlborough SN8 2QH* Tel (01672) 520235 E-mail vicar@whittonteam.org.uk

RAILTON-CROWDER, Mrs Mary. b 51. RN72 RM91 MIOSH93 Luton Univ BA96. St Alb and Ox Min Course 98. **d** 01 **p** 02. NSM Elstow *St Alb* from 01; Ecum Chapl De Montford Univ from 02. *21 Fulmar Road, Bedford MK41 7JX* Tel (01234) 216779 E-mail revmaryrailton-crowder@fsmail.net

RAINBIRD, Ms Ruth Patricia. b 40. SRN62. OLM course 98. **d** 01 **p** 02. OLM Limpsfield and Titsey *S'wark* from 01. *73 Stoneleigh Road, Oxted RH8 0TP* Tel (01883) 713683

RAINBOW, Preb Gerald Anton Hayward. b 15. St Edm Hall Ox BA38 MA41. Linc Th Coll 38. **d** 39 **p** 40. C Monkwearmouth St Andr *Dur* 39-43; Chapl RAFVR 43-47; V Claverley *Heref* 47-57; V Leominster 57-80; RD Leominster 60-80; Preb Heref Cathl 67-95; P-in-c Eyton 69-80; rtd 80; Perm to Offic *Heref* 89-01. *Whingate Cottage, Corby Hill, Carlisle CA4 8PN* Tel (01228) 562586

RAINE, Alan. b 49. MIPD93. NEOC DipHE95. **d** 95 **p** 96. NSM Jarrow *Dur* from 95; Chapl S Tyneside Coll from 97. *49 Brixham Crescent, Jarrow NE32 3SL* Tel 0191-489 3042 Fax as telephone

RAINE, Patrick John Wallace. b 21. DFC. Sarum & Wells Th Coll 72. **d** 74 **p** 75. C Chandler's Ford *Win* 74-76; R Highclere and Ashmansworth w Crux Easton 76-84; R Copythorne and Minstead 84-87; rtd 87; P-in-c Breamore *Win* 91-95; Perm to Offic from 95; *Sarum* from 98. *11 Wenbrook Close, Attleborough, Nuneaton CV11 4LJ* Tel (024) 7634 9871

RAINE, Stephen James. b 49. Lanchester Poly DipAD69 Sheff Poly BA80. N Ord Course 85. **d** 86 **p** 87. C Cottingham *York* 86-90; V Dunscroft Ch Ch *Sheff* 90-92; V Dunscroft St Edwin 92-96; V Kettering St Mary *Pet* from 96. *The Vicarage, 175 Avondale Road, Kettering NN16 8PN* Tel (01536) 512736 Fax as telephone E-mail evangelist24@aol.com

RAINER, John Charles. b 54. Ex Univ BA76 DipTh78 CertEd78. St Jo Coll Nottm 86. **d** 88 **p** 89. C Fletchamstead *Cov* 88-94; V Leic H Apostles *Leic* 94-03; V Shipley St Pet *Bradf* from 03. *The Vicarage, 2 Glenhurst Road, Shipley BD18 4DZ* Tel (01274) 584488 E-mail jrainer@nationwideisp.net

RAINES, Mrs Gisela Rolanda. b 58. Groningen Univ Kandidaats 84. K Coll Lon BD83. **dss** 84 **d** 87 **p** 94. Charlton St Luke w H Trin *S'wark* 84-87; Par Dn 87; Chapl Imp Coll Lon 87-91; Hon C Birch w Fallowfield *Man* 94-95; P-in-c Withington St Chris 95-03; C Man St Ann from 03. *197 Old Hall Lane, Manchester M14 6HJ* Tel 0161-224 6643 E-mail gisela@fish.co.uk

RAINES, William Guy. b 46. Lon Univ BSc69 MSc70 Ox Univ BA80. Ripon Coll Cuddesdon 78. **d** 81 **p** 82. C W Drayton *Lon* 81-84; C Charlton St Luke w H Trin *S'wark* 84-87; Chapl K Coll

Lon 87-94; Chapl Imp Coll 91-94; P-in-c Birch w Fallowfield *Man* 94-95; R from 95. *197 Old Hall Lane, Manchester M14 6HJ* Tel 0161-224 1310 E-mail wraines@emmental.demon.co.uk

RAINEY, Graeme Norman. b 66. Van Mildert Coll Dur BA88 Reading Univ MA01. Ridley Hall Cam 93. **d** 93 **p** 94. C Maltby *Sheff* 93-96; Chapl Reading Univ *Ox* from 96. *The University of Reading Chaplaincy, Park House Lodge, Whiteknights, Reading RG6 6AH2* Tel 0118-931 8797 E-mail g.n.rainey@reading.ac.uk

RAINFORD, Canon Robert Graham. b 55. Lanc Univ CertEd76 BEd77. St Steph Ho Ox 81. **d** 83 **p** 84. C Burnley St Cath w St Alb and St Paul *Blackb* 83-86; C-in-c Hawes Side St Chris CD 86-89; V Hawes Side from 89; AD Blackpool from 00; Hon Can Blackb Cathl from 01; P-in-c Marton Moss from 01. *St Christopher's Vicarage, Hawes Side Lane, Blackpool FY4 5AH* Tel (01253) 697937 Fax 839294 E-mail graham.rainford@virgin.net

RAINSBERRY, Edward John. b 24. TCD BA48 MA58. TCD Div Sch Div Test49. **d** 49 **p** 50. C Abbeystrewry Union *C, C & R* 49-52; Chapl RAF 52-58; V Long Compton *Cov* 58-84; R Whichford 58-84; V Long Compton, Whichford and Barton-on-the-Heath 84-95; rtd 95; Perm to Offic *Cov* 95-01; *Ox* and *Pet* from 95. *12 Portway Gardens, Aynho, Banbury OX17 3AR* Tel (01869) 810417

RAINSBURY, Mark James. b 56. NE Lon Poly BA79. Oak Hill Th Coll BA87. **d** 88 **p** 89. C Tonbridge St Steph *Roch* 88-95; C Hampreston *Sarum* 95-97; TV 97-99. *Address temp unknown*

RAINSFORD, Peter John. b 31. FCP72. Qu Coll Birm 75. **d** 77 **p** 78. Hon C Lich St Chad *Lich* 77-81; C 82; C Coseley Ch Ch 82-84; V Wednesbury St Bart 84-91; Chapl Sandwell Distr Gen Hosp 89-91; rtd 91; Perm to Offic *Lich* from 91. *157 Broadway, Walsall WS1 3HD* Tel (01922) 624526 E-mail p.j.rainsford@tinyonline.co.uk

RAISTRICK, Brian. b 38. St Paul's Cheltenham TCert60 Ex Univ AdDipEd68 Newc Univ MEd76 UEA PhD86. Westcott Ho Cam 92. **d** 93 **p** 94. C Haverhill w Withersfield, the Wrattings etc *St E* 93-95; P-in-c Horringer cum Ickworth 95-02; P-in-c Risby w Gt and Lt Saxham and Westley 99-02; P-in-c Chevington w Hargrave and Whepstead w Brockley 00-02; R Horringer 02; RD Thingoe 99-01; rtd 03; Perm to Offic *St E* from 03. *Greenways, Westwood, Great Barton, Bury St Edmunds IP31 2SF* Tel (01284) 787372 *or* 747372 E-mail brian@raistrick.freeserve.co.uk

RAITH, Robert. b 31. Edin Univ MA61. Coll of Resurr Mirfield 57. **d** 59 **p** 60. C Edin St Jas *Edin* 59-61; P-in-c 76-77; Asst Prov Youth Org 61-65; C Dalmahoy 61-65; C Edin St Mark 66-76; Dioc Supernumerary 77-78; P-in-c Edin St Luke 78-79; Perm to Offic from 79; Pilsdon Community 87-90. *Address withheld by request*

RAITT, Derek. b 41. K Coll Lon BD63 AKC63. **d** 64 **p** 65. C Blackb St Jas *Blackb* 64-67; C Burnley St Pet 67-69; V Foulridge 69-74; V Euxton 74-91; V Penwortham St Mary 91-00; P-in-c Halton w Aughton from 00. *The Rectory, High Road, Halton, Lancaster LA2 6PU* Tel (01524) 811370

RAIWIND, Bishop of. *See* AZARIAH, The Rt Revd Samuel

RAJA, John Joshva. b 65. Serampore Coll MTh93 Leic Univ MA96 New Coll Edin 96. **d** 93 **p** 94. India 93-95; Hon C Leic H Spirit *Leic* 95-96; Hon C Edin H Cross *Edin* 96-99. *43 Scotland Street, Edinburgh EH3 6PY* Tel 0131-557 3797 Fax as telephone E-mail j.raja@sms.ed.ac.uk

RAJKOVIC, Michael. b 52. Sheff Univ BMet74 MMet75 PhD79. St Jo Coll Nottm MA95. **d** 95 **p** 96. C Harrow Weald All SS *Lon* 95-98; C Woodford Wells *Chelmsf* 98-02; V Bricket Wood *St Alb* from 02. *20 West Riding, Bricket Wood, St Albans AL2 3QP* Tel (01923) 681107 E-mail mrajk30852@aol.com

RAKE, David John. b 47. Nottm Univ BA68 PhD73. Wycliffe Hall Ox DipTh73. **d** 74 **p** 75. C Radcliffe-on-Trent *S'well* 74-77; P-in-c Upwell St Pet *Ely* 77-79; P-in-c Outwell 77-79; Chapl Warw Univ *Cov* 79-86; V Kenilworth St Nic 86-98; P-in-c Tintagel *Truro* from 98; Bp's Adv on Spiritual Formation from 98. *The Vicarage, Vicarage Hill, Tintagel PL34 0DJ* Tel (01840) 770315

RALPH, Brian Charles. b 66. St Steph Ho Ox 89. **d** 92 **p** 93. C Yeovil St Mich *B & W* 92-95; TV St Jo on Bethnal Green *Lon* 95-01; P-in-c Bethnal Green St Barn 01-03; V from 03. *12 Chisenhale Road, London E3 5TG* Tel (020) 8983 3426 *or* 8806 4130

RALPH, Charles. b 15. TCD BA47 MA58. **d** 47 **p** 48. C Kilmegan *D & D* 47-49; C Drumcree *Arm* 49-50; I Arboe 50-51; C Arm St Mark 51-53; I Durrus *C, C & R* 53-54; I Kilcooley *C & O* 54-58; V Toxteth Park St Cleopas *Liv* 58-62; I Kilscoran *C & O* 62-64; R Fordley w Middleton *St E* 64-81; R Theberton 64-81; rtd 82; Perm to Offic *St E* from 82; TV Raveningham *Nor* 82; P-in-c Rossinver *K, E & A* 85-86. *5 Gayfer Avenue, Kesgrave, Ipswich IP5 2PZ* Tel (01473) 622154

RALPH, Nicholas Robert. b 63. Lanc Univ BSc85. Westcott Ho Cam BA91 CTM92. **d** 92 **p** 93. C Fareham H Trin *Portsm* 92-95; C Portsea St Cuth 95-96; V Hayling Is St Andr 96-03; V N Hayling St Pet 96-03; Soc Resp Adv from 03. *100 St Thomas's Street, Portsmouth PO1 2HE* E-mail nralph@bigfoot.com

RALPH, Richard Gale. b 51. Pemb Coll Ox BA73 MA78 DPhil78 FRSA90. S Dios Minl Tr Scheme 84. **d** 87 **p** 88. NSM St Leonards Ch Ch and St Mary *Chich* from 87; NSM St Pancras H Cross w St Jude and St Pet *Lon* 87-94; Prin Westmr Coll Ox from 96. *Westminster College, Harcourt Hill, Oxford OX2 9AT,* or *St Alban, 11 The Mount, St Leonards-on-Sea TN38 0HR* Tel (01865) 247644 *or* (01424) 422722

RALPHS, John Eric. b 26. MBAP66 St Cath Coll Ox BA52 MA56. Wycliffe Hall Ox 53. **d** 53 **p** 54. C Wolvercote *Ox* 53-55; Chapl Asst Radcliffe Infirmary Ox 54-62; Lic to Offic *Ox* 55-66; Chapl Dragon Sch Ox 55-68; Asst Chapl HM Pris Ox 58-61; Jun Chapl Mert Coll Ox 59-62; Chapl St Hugh's Coll Ox 62-67; Priest-Psychotherapist from 68; Lic to Offic *Ox* from 83; rtd 91. *209 Woodstock Road, Oxford OX2 7AB* Tel (01865) 515550

RALPHS, Robert Brian. b 31. Qu Coll Birm 75. **d** 78 **p** 79. Hon C Wednesbury St Jo *Lich* 78-80; Hon C Wednesbury St Paul Wood Green 80-81; Perm to Offic 81-96; Hon C W Bromwich Gd Shep w St Jo 96. *204 Bromford Lane, West Bromwich B70 7HX* Tel 0121-553 0119

RALPHS, Sharon Ann. *See* SIMPSON, Mrs Sharon Ann

RAMELL, John Edwin. b 25. Bris Univ BA55. Tyndale Hall Bris. **d** 56 **p** 57. C New Milverton *Cov* 56-60; V Wombridge *Lich* 60-70; TR Chell 70-82; V Congleton St Pet *Ches* 82-90; rtd 90; Perm to Offic from 92. *10 Newland Close, Eynsham, Witney OX29 4LE* Tel (01865) 880180

RAMPTON, Paul Michael. b 47. St Jo Coll Dur BA69 DipTh70 MA73 K Coll Lon PhD85 Westmr Coll Ox MTh99. Wycliffe Hall Ox 72. **d** 73 **p** 74. C Folkestone H Trin w Ch Ch *Cant* 73-77; P-in-c Kingsdown 77-79; P-in-c Ringwould w Oxney 77-79; R Ringwould w Kingsdown 79-83; V Maidstone St Paul 83-88; V Maidstone St Martin 88-95; V Steyning *Chich* from 95; R Ashurst from 95; RD Storrington from 99. *St Andrew's Vicarage, Station Road, Steyning BN44 3YL* Tel (01903) 813256 Fax as telephone

RAMPTON, Canon Valerie Edith. b 41. Nottm Univ BSc63 MSc66 BA79. Gilmore Course 78. **dss** 82 **d** 87 **p** 94. Sneinton St Chris w St Phil *S'well* 80-87; Par Dn 87-88; Par Dn Stapleford 88-93; Dioc Adv on Women in Min 90-01; Dn-in-c Kneesall w Laxton and Wellow 93-94; V 94-02; Hon Can S'well Minster 97-02; rtd 02. *Tansy Cottage, Hillside, Beckingham, Lincoln LN5 0RQ* Tel (01636) 626665 E-mail valerie.rampton@btinternet.com

RAMSARAN (or COOPER), Susan Mira. b 49. K Coll Lon BA70 Univ Coll Lon MA72 PhD78. Ripon Coll Cuddesdon BA92. **d** 93 **p** 94. C Selling w Throwley, Sheldwich w Badlesmere etc *Cant* 93-97; P-in-c Plaxtol *Roch* 97-99; P-in-c Shipbourne 97-99; R Shipbourne w Plaxtol from 99; RD Shoreham from 01. *The Rectory, The Street, Plaxtol, Sevenoaks TN15 0QG* Tel (01732) 810319

RAMSAY, Canon Alan Burnett. b 34. AKC62. **d** 63 **p** 64. C Clapham H Trin *S'wark* 63-67; C Warlingham w Chelsham and Farleigh 67-71; P-in-c Stockwell St Mich 71-78; V Lingfield 78-85; P-in-c Crowhurst 83-85; V Lingfield and Crowhurst 85-92; RD Godstone 88-92; V Mitcham St Mark 92-00; Hon Can S'wark Cathl 93-00; rtd 00; Perm to Offic *Cant* from 00. *Kent House, 9 Scotton Street, Wye, Ashford TN25 5BU* Tel (01233) 813730

RAMSAY, Carl Anthoney St Aubyn. b 55. WMMTC 88. **d** 90 **p** 91. C Wednesfield Heath *Lich* 90-94; V Willenhall St Anne from 94. *St Anne's Vicarage, Ann Street, Willenhall WV13 1EN* Tel (01902) 606516 E-mail spreeboy@talk21.com

RAMSAY, Christopher. b 68. St Jo Coll Dur BA90. Wycliffe Hall Ox BTh94. **d** 97 **p** 98. C Cricklewood St Gabr and St Mich *Lon* 97-01; P-in-c Southall St Geo from 01. *1 Lancaster Road, Southall UB1 1NP* Tel (020) 8574 1876

RAMSAY, Eric Nicolson. b 29. **d** 94 **p** 95. C Forfar *St And* 94-99; C Kirriemuir 94-99; Asst Chapl Gtr Athens *Eur* 99-00. *Address temp unknown*

RAMSAY, James Anthony. b 52. Wadh Coll Ox BA75 MA. **d** 86 **p** 87. C Olney w Emberton *Ox* 86-89; V Blackbird Leys 89-02; Chapl Bucharest w Sofia *Eur* from 02. *The Church of the Resurrection, Str Xenepol nr 2, Sector 1, Bucharest, Romania*

RAMSAY, Kenneth William. b 18. ALCD48. **d** 52 **p** 53. C Southall Green St Jo *Lon* 52-57; Asst Chapl Lee Abbey 57-60; Perm to Offic *Portsm* 69-80; Perm to Offic *Sarum* 77-87; rtd 87; Hon C Burstow *S'wark* 87-98; Perm to Offic from 98. *3 Park Close, Strood Green, Betchworth RH3 7JB* Tel (01737) 843470

RAMSAY, Kerry. b 59. Heythrop Coll Lon MA94. Westcott Ho Cam CTM92. **d** 94 **p** 96. S Africa 95-96; C Dulwich St Barn *S'wark* 96; C Charlton St Luke w H Trin 96-99; C Cambridge Gt St Mary w St Mich *Ely* from 99. *35 Pakenham Close, Cambridge CB4 1PW* Tel (01223) 329590 E-mail kerry@lineone.net

RAMSAY, Max Roy MacGregor. b 34. Ball Coll Ox MA58. Qu Coll Birm 82. **d** 84 **p** 85. C Hale *Ches* 84-86; C Nantwich 87-91; V Haslington w Crewe Green 87-91; P-in-c Dunham Massey St Marg 92-93; P-in-c Dunham Massey St Mark 92-93; P-in-c Dunham Massey St Marg and St Mark 93-95; rtd 95; Perm to Offic *Ches* from 95. *6 Comber Way, Knutsford WA16 9BT* Tel (01565) 632362 E-mail max@rmramsay.fsnet.co.uk

RAMSBOTTOM, Mrs Julie Frances. b 54. Trevelyan Coll Dur BA76. S'wark Ord Course 88. **d** 91 **p** 94. Par Dn Bray and Braywood *Ox* 91-94; C 94-97; R W Woodhay w Enborne, Hampstead Marshall etc from 97. *The Rectory, Enborne, Newbury RG20 0HD* Tel (01635) 34427
E-mail julie.ramsbottom@talk21.com

RAMSBURY, Area Bishop of. *See* HULLAH, The Rt Revd Peter Fearnley

RAMSDEN, Canon Arthur Stuart. b 34. Kelham Th Coll 56. **d** 61 **p** 62. C Featherstone *Wakef* 61-63; C Barnsley St Pet 63-67; V Charlestown 67-70; V Middlestown 70-77; V Purston cum S Featherstone from 77; Hon Can Wakef Cathl from 95. *The Vicarage, Victoria Street, Featherstone, Pontefract WF7 5EZ* Tel (01977) 792288

RAMSDEN, Peter Stockton. b 51. Univ Coll Lon BSc74 Leeds Univ DipTh76 MA92. Coll of Resurr Mirfield 74. **d** 77 **p** 78. C Houghton le Spring *Dur* 77-80; C S Shields All SS 80-83; Papua New Guinea 83-90 and 93-96; P-in-c Micklefield *York* 90-93; V Long Benton *Newc* from 96. *The Vicarage, 3 Station Road, Benton, Newcastle upon Tyne NE12 8AN* Tel 0191-266 2015
E-mail vicar@stbarts@talk21.com

RAMSDEN, Raymond Leslie. b 49. Open Univ BA86. **d** 78 **p** 79. C Greenhill St Jo *Lon* 78-85; C Staines St Mary and St Pet 85-90; V Hounslow St Steph from 90. *St Stephen's Vicarage, Parkside Road, Hounslow TW3 2BP* Tel (020) 8570 3056
E-mail raymondramsden@hotmail.com

RAMSEY-HARDY, Stuart John Andrew. b 46. St Jo Coll Dur BA69. Wycliffe Hall Ox 69. **d** 74 **p** 75. C Stoke Newington St Mary *Lon* 74-77; C Hersham *Guildf* 78-79; Hon C Thames Ditton 79-83. *23 New Row, London WC2N 4LA* Tel (020) 7836 2217

RAMSHAW, Marcus John. b 71. St Andr Univ MTheol93 York Univ MA94. Cranmer Hall Dur DipMin96. **d** 96 **p** 97. C Hythe *Cant* 96-00; Chapl Down Coll Cam 01-03. *Downing College, Cambridge CB2 1DQ* Tel (01223) 334800 Fax 337334
E-mail marcusramshaw@hotmail.com

RANCE, Miss Eleanor Jane. b 72. K Coll Lon BA93 AKC93 Dur Univ MA96. Cranmer Hall Dur DMS96. **d** 96 **p** 97. C Barnes St Mary *S'wark* 96-97; C Barnes 97-99; Chapl RAF from 99. *Chaplaincy Services (RAF), HQ, Personnel and Training Command, RAF Innsworth, Gloucester GL3 1EZ* Tel (01452) 712612 ext 5164 Fax 510828

RANDALL, Anthony. *See* RANDALL, James Anthony

RANDALL, Colin Antony. b 57. SS Paul & Mary Coll Cheltenham BEd78 Bris Univ DipHE82 Lon Univ BD84. Trin Coll Bris 80. **d** 84 **p** 85. C Denton Holme *Carl* 84-87; C Brampton RD 87-90; R Hanborough and Freeland *Ox* 90-99; P-in-c Holme Eden *Carl* from 99; P-in-c Croglin from 99; P-in-c Wetheral w Warwick from 99. *St Paul's Vicarage, Warwick Bridge, Carlisle CA4 8RF* Tel (01228) 560332
E-mail carandall@freeuk.com

RANDALL, Colin Michael Sebastian. b 50. Aston Univ BSc72. Qu Coll Birm 72. **d** 75 **p** 76. C Tonge w Alkrington *Man* 75-78; C Elton All SS 78-82; P-in-c Bridgwater H Trin *B & W* 82-86; V 86-90; V Bishops Hull 90-00; TR Wellington and Distr from 00. *The Rectory, 72 High Street, Wellington TA21 8RF* Tel (01823) 662248 E-mail colinms.randall@virgin.net

RANDALL, Canon Edmund Laurence. b 20. AM80. CCC Cam BA40 MA47. Wells Th Coll 47. **d** 49 **p** 50. C Bournemouth St Luke *Win* 49-52; Fell and Lect Selw Coll Cam 52-57; Chapl 53-57; Prin Ely Th Coll 57-59; Can Res Ely Cathl *Ely* 57-59; Australia from 60; Chapl St Fran Coll Brisbane 60-64; Warden St Barn Coll Adelaide 64-85; Hon Can Wangaratta from 89; rtd 85. *44 Mackay Street, Wangaratta, Vic, Australia 3677* Tel (0061) (3) 5721 9007

RANDALL, Elizabeth. *See* BILLETT, Mrs Elizabeth

RANDALL, Gareth John. b 49. Southn Univ BA72 PGCE73 ACP80. Oak Hill Th Coll 90. **d** 93 **p** 94. Dir of Studies Dame Alice Owen's Sch Potters Bar 84-95; Dir of Personnel 95-00; Asst Hd from 00; NSM S Mymms K Chas *St Alb* 93-98; NSM Potters Bar from 98. *Petersleia, 196 Barnet Road, Potters Bar EN6 2SE* Tel (01707) 651958 *or* 622847
E-mail randallg42@thegrid.org.uk

RANDALL, Ian Neville. b 39. Oriel Coll Ox BA62 MA65. St Steph Ho Ox 62. **d** 65 **p** 66. C Perivale *Lon* 65-68; C Fulham St Jo Walham Green 68-73; C Cowley St Jas *Ox* 73-79; TV 79-82; V Didcot St Pet 82-93; P-in-c Clewer St Andr from 93. *Clewer Rectory, 16 Parsonage Lane, Windsor SL4 5EN* Tel (01753) 865185

RANDALL, James Anthony. b 36. ACIB69 Kent Univ DipTh80. Ridley Hall Cam 68. **d** 70 **p** 71. C Rusthall *Roch* 70-74; V Shorne 74-79; V Bexleyheath Ch Ch 79-89; R Stone 89-98; rtd 98; Perm to Offic *Roch* from 99. *6 Sandling Way, St Mary's Island, Chatham ME4 3AZ* Tel (01634) 890603

RANDALL, Canon John Terence. b 29. St Cath Coll Cam BA52 MA59. Ely Th Coll 52. **d** 54 **p** 55. C Luton Ch Ch *St Alb* 54; C Dunstable 54-57; C Ely 57-60; C March St Jo 60-62; Area Sec (S Midl) UMCA 62-64; Area Sec USPG *Birm* and *Cov* 65-76; P-in-c Avon Dassett w Farnborough *Cov* 76-78; P-in-c Fenny Compton 76-78; R Avon Dassett w Farnborough and Fenny

Compton 78-84; V New Bilton 84-94; RD Rugby 89-94; Hon Can Cov Cathl 93-94; rtd 94; Perm to Offic *Cov* and *Pet* from 94; *Leic* from 96. *52 Cymbeline Way, Rugby CV22 6LA* Tel (01788) 816659

RANDALL, Julian Adrian. b 45. Open Univ BA78 Stirling Univ MSc94 MIPD. St Jo Sem Wonersh 68. **d** 70 **p** 71. Asst P Mortlake w E Sheen *S'wark* 71-72; Asst P Welling 72-74; Asst P Tunbridge Wells H Trin w Ch Ch *Roch* 74-79; NSM Dunfermline *St And* 96-98; P-in-c Elie and Earlsferry from 98; P-in-c Pittenweem from 98. *The Great House, Priory Court, Pittenweem, Anstruther KY10 2LJ* Tel (01333) 311532 Fax 312212
E-mail rector@randall.co.uk

RANDALL, Kelvin John. b 49. JP80. K Coll Lon BD71 AKC71 Birm Univ PGCE72 Trin Coll Carmarthen MPhil97 Univ of Wales (Ban) PhD00. St Jo Coll Nottm DPS73. **d** 74 **p** 75. C Peckham St Mary Magd *S'wark* 74-78; C Portsdown *Portsm* 78-81; C-in-c Crookhorn Ch Cen CD 81-82; R Bedhampton 82-90; Bp's Chapl for Post-Ord Tr 84-89; RD Havant 87-89; P-in-c Bournemouth St Jo w St Mich *Win* 90-94; V 94-97; Chapl Talbot Heath Sch Bournemouth 90-94; Research Fell Trin Coll Carmarthen from 97; C Portswood St Denys *Win* from 00. *The Vicarage, 54 Whitworth Crescent, Southampton SO18 1GD* Tel (023) 8067 2108 Fax 8067 1757 E-mail kjrandall@argonet.co.uk

RANDALL, Mrs Lynda Lorraine. b 44. Sarum & Wells Th Coll 89. **d** 91 **p** 94. Par Dn Chesterton St Andr *Ely* 91-94; C 94-95; C Linton 95-96; TV Linton 96-99; R Byfield w Boddington and Aston le Walls *Pet* from 99. *The Rectory, Church Lane, Byfield, Daventry NN11 6XN* Tel (01327) 260204
E-mail lynda@chrislyn.demon.co.uk

RANDALL, Miss Marian Sally. b 49. Trin Coll Bris 75. **dss** 89 **d** 87 **p** 94. Peckham St Mary Magd *S'wark* 80-83; Sutton Ch Ch 83-97; Par Dn 87-94; C 94-97; P-in-c S Merstham from 97. *The Vicarage, Battlebridge Lane, Redhill RH1 3LH* Tel (01737) 642722

RANDALL, Martin Trevor. b 51. St Jo Coll Dur BA74. Trin Coll Bris 74. **d** 77 **p** 78. C Ashton-upon-Mersey St Mary *Ches* 77-80; C Everton St Sav w St Cuth *Liv* 80-82; V W Derby Gd Shep 82-91; P-in-c Toxteth Park Ch Ch 91-94; P-in-c Toxteth Park St Bede 91-94; V Toxteth Park Ch Ch w St Bede 95-97; Chapl HM Pris Altcourse from 97. *HM Prison Altcourse, Higher Lane, Liverpool L9 7LH* Tel 0151-522 2000 ext 2395 Fax 522 2011

RANDALL, Samuel Paul. b 59. Leeds Univ MA90. Ridley Hall Cam 84. **d** 87 **p** 88. C Kingston upon Hull St Nic *York* 87-89; CF 89-93; TV Bramley *Ripon* 93-96; Dioc Ecum Officer *Dur* 97-01; P-in-c Holmside 97-01; Bp's Officer for Ch in the World *Bradf* from 02. *The Vicarage, Morton Lane, East Morton, Keighley BD20 5RS* Tel (01274) 561640

RANDELL, David Peter. b 48. Trin Coll Bris BA88. **d** 92 **p** 93. C Wells St Cuth w Wookey Hole *B & W* 92-95; TV Wellington and Distr from 95. *22 Dyers Close, West Buckland, Wellington TA21 9JU* Tel (01823) 664925 E-mail revrandell@supanet.com

RANDELL, John Harrison. b 35. Lon Univ BD62. Chich Th Coll 77. **d** 78 **p** 78. C Ribbleton *Blackb* 78-82; V Barton 82-00; rtd 00; Perm to Offic *Blackb* from 00. *6 Royds Avenue, Morecambe LA3 1PA* Tel (01524) 850269

RANDELL, Phillip John. b 45. Lon Univ DipTh68 BD73 CertEd. Linc Th Coll 67. **d** 68 **p** 69. C Henbury *Bris* 68-71; C Summertown *Ox* 71-73; C Liskeard w St Keyne *Truro* 73-75; Chapl Coll of SS Mark and Jo Plymouth *Ex* 75-79; Tanzania 80-82; R Alvescot w Black Bourton, Shilton, Holwell etc *Ox* 82-87; R St Gennys, Jacobstow w Warbstow and Treneglos *Truro* 87-97; rtd 97; Perm to Offic *Truro* from 01. *14 Merlin's Way, Tintagel PL34 0PB* Tel (01840) 770559

RANDOLPH-HORN, David Henry. b 47. Nottm Univ BA69 Keele Univ CQSW71. Qu Coll Birm 80. **d** 82 **p** 83. C Hamstead St Paul *Birm* 82-84; V Aston St Jas 84-94; Hon C Leytonstone H Trin Harrow Green *Chelmsf* 93-99; Sec Inner Cities Relig Coun 94-99; Assoc Dir Leeds Ch Inst from 99; P-in-c Heptonstall *Wakef* 99-02; P-in-c Farnley *Ripon* from 03. *20 New Market Street, Leeds LS1 6DG* Tel 0113-245 4700 Fax 391 7939
E-mail david@edrh.demon.co.uk

RANGER, Keith Brian. b 34. Down Coll Cam BA58 MA63. Glas NSM Course 58. **d** 81 **p** 82. OMF Internat 81-99; Ethnic Min Co-ord 90-99; Hong Kong 81-89; Perm to Offic *Ches* 89-93 and from 99; *Man* 93-99. *144 Newton Street, Macclesfield SK11 6RW* Tel (01625) 439184
E-mail 101613.3107@compuserve.com

RANKIN, John Cooper. b 24. Glas Univ MA44 Lon Univ BD53. Edin Th Coll 48. **d** 50 **p** 51. C Dundee St Mary Magd *Bre* 50-52; Chapl R Merchant Navy Sch Bearwood 53-60; Min Can Bris Cathl *Bris* 60-66; Lic to Offic *Lich* 66-69; Prin Lect Bp Otter Coll Chich 69-84; rtd 84. *28 Worcester Road, Chichester PO19 5DW* Tel (01243) 789467 E-mail johnrankin@cs.com

RANKIN, Joyce. **d** 03. C Dublin St Ann and St Steph *D & G* from 03. *Address temp unknown*

RANKIN, Stephen Brian. b 65. Salford Univ BSc88. Trin Coll Bris 95. **d** 97 **p** 98. C Ashton-upon-Mersey St Mary *Ches* from 97. *109 Ascot Avenue, Sale M33 4GT* Tel 0161-976 1693
E-mail srankin@breathemail.net

RANKIN, William John Alexander. b 45. Van Mildert Coll Dur BA68 Fitzw Coll Cam BA73 MA77. Westcott Ho Cam 71. **d** 74 **p** 75. C St John's Wood *Lon* 74-78; Chapl Clifton Coll Bris 78-86; P-in-c The Claydons *Ox* 86-91; R 91-93; R Clare w Poslingford, Cavendish etc *St E* from 93. *The Vicarage, 14 High Street, Clare, Sudbury CO10 8NY* Tel (01787) 278501

RANKINE, Christopher Barry. b 66. Portsm Poly BA88. Linc Th Coll BTh93. **d** 93 **p** 95. C Farlington *Portsm* 93-96; C Alverstoke 96-98; C Romsey *Win* 98-00; P-in-c W Andover from 00. *The Vicarage, 17 Millway Road, Andover SP10 3EU* Tel (01264) 392541

RANN, Preb Harry Harvey. b 18. Sarum Th Coll 47. **d** 50 **p** 51. C Victoria Docks Ascension *Chelmsf* 50-52; C Christchurch *Win* 52-56; C Mill Hill Jo Keble Ch *Lon* 56-57; V Woolfold *Man* 57-62; Dean's Chapl and PV Ex Cathl *Ex* 62-77; Sacr 65-77; Succ 73-77; V Colyton 77-84; R Colyton and Southleigh 84-86; RD Honiton 84-86; Preb Ex Cathl 84-87; TR Colyton, Southleigh, Offwell, Widworthy etc 86-87; rtd 87; Perm to Offic *Ex* from 87. *4 Scattor View, Bridford, Exeter EX6 7JF* Tel (01647) 252741

RANSOM, Nigel Lester. b 60. Leeds Univ BA81. Wycliffe Hall Ox 83 SE Asia Sch of Th MTh83. **d** 85 **p** 86. C Gidea Park *Chelmsf* 85-88; C Widford 88-91; V Eastwood from 91. *The Vicarage, Eastwoodbury Lane, Southend-on-Sea SS2 6UH* Tel (01702) 525272 E-mail nlran@btinternet.com

RANSOME, Arthur. b 21. St Jo Coll Nottm 71. **d** 72 **p** 72. Israel 72-76; C Virginia Water *Guildf* 76-79; P-in-c Peper Harow 79-82; P-in-c Shackleford 79-82; P-in-c Seale 82-89; rtd 89; Perm to Offic *Truro* 89-99. *Tudor Lodge, 60 East Church Street, Xenia, OH 45385, USA*

RANSON, Canon Arthur Frankland. b 50. St Jo Coll Dur BA73. Wycliffe Hall Ox 73. **d** 75 **p** 76. C Bare *Blackb* 75-78; C Scotforth 78-81; V Leyland St Ambrose 81-82; AD Leyland 96-02; Hon Can Blackb Cathl from 00; P-in-c Blackb St Silas from 02. *St Silas's Vicarage, Preston New Road, Blackburn BB2 6PS* Tel (01254) 671293 E-mail arthur.ranson@ntlworld.com

RANSON, George Sidney. b 28. Open Univ BA78. NEOC 85. **d** 86 **p** 87. NSM Acomb H Redeemer *York* 86-88; C Warton St Oswald w Yealand Conyers *Blackb* 88-90; V Pilling 90-95; rtd 95; Perm to Offic *Blackb* from 95. *18 Cotswold Road, Lytham St Annes FY8 4NN*

RANSON, Terence William James. b 42. AFAIM91 AKC64 MTh87 STM88. St Boniface Warminster 64. **d** 65 **p** 66. C Walton St Mary *Liv* 65-69; C Ipswich St Mary le Tower *St E* 69-71; Chapl Mersey Miss to Seamen 71-74; V N Keyham *Ex* 74-79; Australia 79-91; Sen Chapl and State Sec Fremantle Miss to Seamen 79-91; V N Mymms *St Alb* from 91. *The Vicarage, North Mymms Park, Hatfield AL9 7TN* Tel (01727) 822062 Fax as telephone

RANTALA, Tapani Pellervo. b 61. Helsinki Univ 81. **d** 91 **p**. Finland 91-02; Project Sec Par Work Cen 01-94; Asst Sec to Abp Turku and Finland 94-00; Dir and Chapl Finnish Ch in Lon from 02; NSM Bermondsey Deanery *S'wark* from 02. *The Finnish Church in London, 33 Albion Street, London SE16 7JG* Tel (020) 7237 1261 Fax 7237 1245 E-mail tapani.rantala@btclick.com

RANYARD, Michael Taylor. b 43. Nottm Univ BTh74. Linc Th Coll 71. **d** 74 **p** 75. C Sutton in Ashfield St Mary *S'well* 74-76; Hon C Lewisham St Mary *S'wark* 76-77; C Rushmere *St E* 77-79; R Hopton, Market Weston, Barningham etc 79-83; Chr Educn and Resources Adv *Dur* 83-93; Prin Adv to Dioc Bd of Educn *Blackb* 93-98; Asst P Blackb Cathl 98-99; rtd 99. *72 Wyedean Rise, Belmont, Hereford HR2 7XZ* Tel (01432) 355452 Fax as telephone E-mail smranyard@xalt.co.uk *or* michaelranyard@beeb.net

RAO, Norma Ruoman. b 63. Westmr Coll Ox BTh97. Westcott Ho Cam 99. **d** 01 **p** 02. C Endcliffe *Sheff* from 01. *22 Neill Road, Sheffield S11 8QG* Tel 0114-266 8674 E-mail norma@rrao.junglelink.co.uk

RAPHAEL, Brother. *See* PARKER, Ramon Lewis

RAPHAEL, The Ven Timothy John. b 29. Leeds Univ BA53. Coll of Resurr Mirfield. **d** 55 **p** 56. C Westmr St Steph w St Jo *Lon* 55-60; V Welling *S'wark* 60-63; New Zealand 63-72; Dean Dunedin 65-72; V St John's Wood *Lon* 72-83; AD Westmr St Marylebone 82-83; Adn Middx 83-96; rtd 96; Perm to Offic *Glouc* from 96. *121 Hales Road, Cheltenham GL52 6ST* Tel (01242) 256075

RAPHOE, Archdeacon of. *See* HARTE, The Ven Matthew Scott

RAPHOE, Dean of. *See* HAY, The Very Revd John

RAPKIN, Kevern. b 39. Univ of Wales (Lamp) BA62 BD72. Lich Th Coll 63. **d** 65 **p** 66. C Hanley w Hope *Lich* 65-68; C Woodchurch *Ches* 68-70; C Abbots Langley *St Alb* 70-73; Australia 73-00; R Mt Pleasant 73-80; R Rockingham and Safety Bay 80-90; R Lesmurdie 90-00; C Sholing *Win* from 00. *St Francis House, 75 Montague Avenue, Southampton SO19 0QB* Tel (023) 8044 3733

RAPLEY, Frederick Arthur. b 27. Roch Th Coll 67. **d** 69 **p** 70. C Tenterden St Mildred w Smallhythe *Cant* 69-75; P-in-c Sittingbourne H Trin w Bobbing 75-85; V 85-89; rtd 89; Hon C Luton St Andr *St Alb* 89-92; Perm to Offic *St Alb* 92-98; Cant 98-02; *St E* from 02. *The Rectory, Clopton, Woodbridge IP13 6SE* Tel (01473) 738943

RAPLEY, Mrs Joy Naomi. b 41. Portsm Poly CertEd63 Open Univ BA79. Sarum & Wells Th Coll 87. **d** 89 **p** 94. Par Dn Welwyn Garden City *St Alb* 89-92; Chapl S Beds Community Healthcare Trust 92-98; C Wilbury *St Alb* 94-95; NSM St Mary's Bay w St Mary-in-the-Marsh etc *Cant* 98-02; NSM New Romney w Old Romney and Midley 98-02; Asst Chapl E Kent Community NHS Trust 99-02; P-in-c Clopton w Otley, Swilland and Ashbocking *St E* from 02. *The Rectory, Clopton, Woodbridge IP13 6SE* Tel (01473) 738943 E-mail revraps@aol.com

RAPSEY, Peter Nigel. b 46. K Coll Lon BD68 AKC68. St Boniface Warminster. **d** 69 **p** 70. C Walton-on-Thames *Guildf* 69-73; C Fleet 73-77; P-in-c The Collingbournes and Everleigh *Sarum* 77-79; TV Wexcombe 79-84; R Wokingham St Paul *Ox* 84-93; Chapl Warminster Sch 93-96; V Frome Ch Ch *B & W* from 96; RD Frome from 01. *Christ Church Vicarage, 73 Weymouth Road, Frome BA11 1HJ* Tel (01373) 473249 Fax 454394 E-mail ccfrome@fish.co.uk

RASHBROOK, Alan Victor. b 42. S'wark Ord Course. **d** 75 **p** 76. Hon C Woking St Mary *Guildf* 75-83. *Hope Cottage, Robin Hood Lane, Sutton Green, Guildford GU4 7QG* Tel (01483) 762760

RASON, Frederick George. b 26. Qu Coll Birm 68. **d** 69 **p** 70. C Weymouth H Trin *Sarum* 69-72; P-in-c Yatesbury 72-73; P-in-c Cherhill 72-73; R Oldbury 73-76; R W Parley 76-91; rtd 91; Perm to Offic *Sarum* from 91 and *Win* from 92. *4 Knoll Gardens, St Ives, Ringwood BH24 2LW* Tel (01425) 475761

RASTALL, Preb Thomas Eric. b 19. St Aid Birkenhead 62. **d** 63 **p** 64. C Leek St Luke *Lich* 64-67; V Brown Edge 67-74; P-in-c Croxden 74-78; V Denstone 74-81; P-in-c Ellastone 78-81; V Denstone w Ellastone and Stanton 81-91; RD Uttoxeter 87-91; Preb Lich Cathl 89-91; rtd 91; Perm to Offic *Cov* 91-01. *21 Hammerton Way, Wellesbourne, Warwick CV35 9NS* Tel (01789) 842422

RATCLIFF, The Ven David William. b 37. K Coll Lon DipAdEd82. Edin Th Coll 59. **d** 62 **p** 63. C Croydon St Aug *Cant* 62-65; C Selsdon St Jo w St Fran 65-69; V Milton Regis St Mary 69-75; Hon Min Can Cant Cathl 75-91; Asst Dir of Educn 75-91; Dioc Adv in Adult Educn and Lay Tr 75-91; Hon Pres Protestant Assn for Adult Educn in Eur 88-91; Chapl Frankfurt-am-Main 91-98; Adn Scandinavia *Eur* from 96; Chapl Stockholm w Gävle and Västerås 98-02; rtd 02; Perm to Offic *Cant* from 02. *9 The Orchards, Elham, Canterbury CT4 6TR* Tel (01303) 840624 E-mail archdeacon.david@ratcliff1137.freeserve.co.uk

RATCLIFFE, Canon Michael David. b 43. Lon Univ BSc65 Southn Univ PGCE67 Lon Univ BA75 Dur Univ DipTh77 Lanc Univ MA84. Cranmer Hall Dur 75. **d** 77 **p** 78. C Blackpool St Thos *Blackb* 77-81; V Oswaldtwistle St Paul from 81; RD Accrington 97-03; Hon Can Blackb Cathl from 00. *29 Mayfield Avenue, Oswaldtwistle, Accrington BB5 3AA* Tel (01254) 231038 Fax 390273 E-mail mratossy@tiscali.co.uk

RATCLIFFE, Peter William Lewis. b 30. Birm Univ BSc55 Lon Univ BD58. Tyndale Hall Bris 55. **d** 58 **p** 59. C Cambridge St Andr Less *Ely* 58-61; R Wistow 61-74; R Bury 61-74; V Rainham *Chelmsf* 74-85; R Wennington 75-85; V Heacham *Nor* 85-87; P-in-c Sedgeford w Southmere 85-87; V Heacham and Sedgeford 87-95; rtd 95; Perm to Offic *Nor* from 95. *22 Birchfield Gardens, Mulbarton, Norwich NR14 8BT* Tel (01508) 570511 E-mail p&mratcliffe@mulb.fsnet.co.uk

RATCLIFFE, Mrs Roosevelta (Rosie). b 60. K Coll Lon BA97 MA99. SEITE 98. **d** 01 **p** 02. C Croydon St Matt *S'wark* from 01. *117 Shirley Avenue, Croydon CR0 8SQ* Tel (020) 8654 2529

RATHBAND, Kenneth William. b 60. Edin Univ BD86. Edin Th Coll 82. **d** 86 **p** 87. NSM Dundee St Paul *Bre* 86-88; TV Dundee St Martin 88-89; NSM Edin SS Phil and Jas *Edin* 90-91; R Alyth *St And* from 91; R Blairgowrie from 91; R Coupar Angus from 91. *Carnach, Back Road, Bridge of Cally, Blairgowrie PH10 7JL* Tel (01250) 886224 *or* 874583 E-mail krathband@zetnet.co.uk

RATHBONE, Mrs Elizabeth. b 51. Lon Univ MB, BS76 MRCGP80. WMMTC 03. **d** 03. C Tettenhall Regis *Lich* from 03. *11 Harwin Close, Wolverhampton WV6 9LF* E-mail liz.rathbone1@btinternet.com

RATHBONE, Paul. b 36. BNC Ox BA58 MA62. Wycliffe Hall Ox 58. **d** 60 **p** 61. C Carl St Jo *Carl* 60-63; C Heworth w Peasholme St Cuth *York* 63-68; V Thorganby w Skipwith and N Duffield 68-83; V Bishopthorpe and Acaster Malbis 83-01; rtd 01; Perm to Offic *York* from 01. *12 Whitelass Close, Thirsk YO7 1FG* Tel (01845) 523347 E-mail prathbon@fish.co.uk

RATHBONE, Stephen Derek. b 61. Wycliffe Hall Ox. **d** 00 **p** 01. C W Kirby St Bridget *Ches* 00-03; P-in-c Rainow w Saltersford and Forest from 03. *The Vicarage, Rainow, Macclesfield SK10 5TZ* Tel (01625) 572013 E-mail steve.rathbone@virgin.net

RATINGS, Canon John William. b 37. St Pet Coll Ox BA62 MA71. Cuddesdon Coll 62. **d** 64 **p** 65. C Langley All SS and Martyrs *Man* 64-68; C Easthampstead *Ox* 68-71; V Wargrave 71-02; RD Sonning 88-98; Hon Can Ch Ch from 97; V Wargrave w Knowl Hill from 02; Provost Woodard Corp (S Division) from 00. *The Vicarage, Wargrave, Reading RG10 8EU* Tel 0118-940 2202 Fax 940 1470 E-mail jratings@aol.com

RATTENBERRY, Christopher James. b 59. Solicitor York Univ BA80. St Jo Coll Nottm Dip Th Studies 93. **d** 93 **p** 94. C Porchester *S'well* 93-98; P-in-c Daybrook from 98; Sen Chapl Notts Constabulary from 00; AD Nottingham N from 01. *St Paul's Vicarage, 241 Oxclose Lane, Nottingham NG5 6FB* Tel 0115-926 2686 E-mail revdcjr.aol.com

✠**RATTERAY, The Rt Revd Alexander Ewen.** b 42. Codrington Coll Barbados 61. **d** 65 **p** 66 **c** 96. C S Kirkby *Wakef* 66-68; C Sowerby St Geo 68-71; V Airedale w Fryston 71-80; Bermuda from 80; Adn Bermuda 94-96; Bp Bermuda from 96. *Bishop's Lodge, PO Box HM 769, Hamilton HM CX, Bermuda* Tel (001) (441) 292 2967 *or* 292 6987 Fax 296 0592 *or* 292 5421 E-mail bishopratteray@ibl.bm

RATTIGAN, Paul Damian. b 61. Reading Univ BSc87 MA Sussex Univ PGCE88. Qu Coll Birm DipTh95. **d** 95 **p** 96. C Parr *Liv* 95-99; P-in-c St Helens St Matt Thatto Heath 99-01; V from 01. *St Matthew's Vicarage, St Matthew's Grove, St Helens WA10 3SE* Tel (01744) 24644 E-mail r@tigan.freeserve.co.uk *or* paul@st.matthewschurch.com

RAVALDE, Canon Geoffrey Paul. b 54. St Cuth Soc Dur BA76 SS Coll Cam BA86 MA90 Lon Univ MTh91 Barrister 78. Westcott Ho Cam 84. **d** 87 **p** 88. C Spalding *Linc* 87-91; P-in-c Wigton *Carl* 91-92; V from 92; RD Carl 95-00; Hon Can Carl Cathl from 96. *The Vicarage, Longthwaite Road, Wigton CA7 9JR* Tel (01697) 342337

RAVEN, Barry. b 48. Sarum & Wells Th Coll 69. **d** 72 **p** 73. C Henbury *Bris* 72-76; P-in-c S Marston w Stanton Fitzwarren 76-78; TV Stratton St Margaret w S Marston etc 78-80; P-in-c Coalpit Heath 80-84; V 84-91; R Ashley, Crudwell, Hankerton, Long Newnton etc from 91; RD N Wilts from 99. *The Rectory, 1 Days Court, Crudwell, Malmesbury SN16 9HG* Tel (01666) 577118 E-mail barry.raven@talk21.com

RAVEN, Margaret Hilary. b 45. Dur Univ BA67 Man Univ MEd73. Wesley Th Sem Washington MDiv95. **d** 96 **p** 97. USA 96-01; Asst R Martinsburg Trin Ch 96-99; Assoc R Toms River Ch 99-00; Perm to Offic *Edin* from 02. *32 Montpelier Park, Edinburgh EH10 4NJ* Tel 0131-228 4790 E-mail mthrraven@hotmail.com

RAVEN, Roger Ian Thomas-Ambrose. b 65. Girton Coll Cam BA87 MA91 PGCE92 Cranfield Univ MSc92 Leeds Univ BA01. Coll of Resurr Mirfield 99. **d** 01 **p** 02. C Cantley *Sheff* from 01. *33 Stone Font Grove, Cantley, Doncaster DN4 6UQ* Tel (01302) 538362 E-mail r.raven@btinternet.com

RAVEN, Tony. b 39. MIEE72 CEng72 Garnett Coll Lon CertEd65. St Alb and Ox Min Course 94. **d** 97 **p** 98. NSM Lt Berkhamsted and Bayford, Essendon etc *St Alb* 97-01; P-in-c Lt Hadham w Albury from 01. *The Vicarage, Parsonage Lane, Albury, Ware SG11 2HU* Tel (01279) 771361 E-mail tony.raven@ntlworld.com

RAVENS, David Arthur Stanley. b 30. Jes Coll Ox BA53 MA61 Lon Univ BD63. Wells Th Coll 61. **d** 63 **p** 64. C Seacroft *Ripon* 63-70; TV 70-73; Sir Wm Borcase's Sch Marlow 73-87; rtd 95. *44 Arthursdale Grange, Scholes, Leeds LS15 4AW* Tel 0113-273 6648

RAVENSCROFT, The Ven Raymond Lockwood. b 31. Leeds Univ BA53. Coll of Resurr Mirfield 54. **d** 55 **p** 56. S Africa 55-57; S Rhodesia 57-59; Bechuanaland 59-62; C St Ives *Truro* 62-64; V Falmouth All SS 64-68; V St Stephens by Launceston 68-73; P-in-c Launceston St Thos 68-73; V Launceston St Steph w St Thos 73-74; TR Probus, Ladock and Grampound w Creed and St Erme 74-88; RD Powder 77-81; Hon Can Truro Cathl 82-88; P-in-c St Erme 84-85; Adn Cornwall and Can Lib Truro Cathl 88-96; rtd 96; Perm to Offic *Truro* from 96 and *Ex* from 00. *19 Innismoor Court, St David's Hill, Exeter EX4 4DP* Tel (01392) 430607

RAVENSDALE, Jonathan Christopher. b 56. Aston Tr Scheme 90 Chich Th Coll DipTh94. **d** 94 **p** 95. C Leytonstone St Marg w St Columba *Chelmsf* 94-97; P-in-c Leytonstone St Andr 97-01; Voc Adv Richborough *Cant* and Barking from 97; V Walthamstow St Mich from 01. *St Michael's Vicarage, 9 Palmerston Road, London E17 6PQ* Tel (020) 8520 6328

✠**RAWCLIFFE, The Rt Revd Derek Alec.** b 21. OBE71. Leeds Univ BA42. Coll of Resurr Mirfield 42. **d** 44 **p** 45 **c** 74. C Claines St Geo *Worc* 44-47; Solomon Is 47-58; New Hebrides 58-80; Adn S Melanesia 59-74; Asst Bp Melanesia 74-75; Bp New Hebrides 75-80; Bp Glas 81-91; rtd 91; Asst Bp Ripon 91-96; Lic to Offic from 96. *7 Dorset Avenue, Leeds LS8 3RA* Tel 0113-249 2670

RAWDING, Andrew. b 70. St Jo Coll Nottm 00. **d** 02 **p** 03. C Enfield St Andr *Lon* from 02. *159 Parsonage Lane, Enfield EN1 3UJ* Tel (020) 8364 6628 E-mail therawdings@fish.co.uk

RAWDON-MOGG, Timothy David. b 45. St Jo Coll Dur BA76. Cuddesdon Coll 75. **d** 77 **p** 78. C Wotton St Mary *Glouc* 77-80; C Ascot Heath *Ox* 80-82; V Woodford Halse w Eydon *Pet* 82-88; V Shrivenham w Watchfield and Bourton *Ox* 88-00; R Horsted Keynes *Chich* from 00. *The Rectory, Station Road, Horsted Keynes, Haywards Heath RH17 7ED* Tel (01825) 790317

RAWE, Alan Charles George. b 29. ALCD56. **d** 56 **p** 57. C W Kilburn St Luke w St Simon and St Jude *Lon* 56-59; Lect Watford St Mary *St Alb* 59-61; R Ore *Chich* 61-69; R Moreton *Ches*

69-80; V Coppull *Blackb* 80-83; Miss to Seamen 83-94; Felixstowe Seafarers' Cen 88-94; rtd 94; Perm to Offic *Blackb* from 94. *15 Starfield Close, Lytham St Annes FY8 4QA* Tel (01253) 733647

RAWLING, Miss Jane Elizabeth. b 51. Birm Univ BSc73 St Jo Coll York CertEd75. St Jo Coll Nottm LTh84. **dss** 84 **d** 87 **p** 94. Southsea St Jude *Portsm* 84-87; C 87-88; C St Paul's Cray St Barn *Roch* 88-91; Hon C from 91; SE Regional Co-ord BCMS Crosslinks 91-01; Perm to Offic *S'wark* 97-01; Sec for Bps' Selection Conf and CME Sec Min Division from 01. *50 Batchwood Green, Orpington BR5 2NF* or *Church House, Great Smith Street, London SW1P 3NZ* Tel (01689) 871467 *or* (020) 7898 1424 Fax 7898 1421 E-mail jane.rawling@c-of-e.org.uk

RAWLING, Stephen Charles. b 43. Man Univ BSc64 Bris Univ MSc71 DipTh73. Sarum & Wells Th Coll 71. **d** 73 **p** 74. C Bris St Andr Hartcliffe *Bris* 73-76; C Westlands St Andr *Lich* 76-78; R Darlaston St Lawr 78-90; TR Bloxwich from 90. *All Saints' Vicarage, 3 Elmore Row, Bloxwich, Walsall WS3 2HR* Tel (01922) 476598

RAWLINGS, Miss Brenda Susan. b 48. Sussex Univ CertEd69 DipHE81. Oak Hill Th Coll 85. **d** 87 **p** 94. Par Dn Green Street Green *Roch* 87-90; Par Dn Collier Row St Jas and Havering-atte-Bower *Chelmsf* 90-94; C 94; C Greenstead 94-98; R 98-00; TR Greenstead w Colchester St Anne from 00. *The Rectory, 74 Howe Close, Colchester CO4 3XD* Tel (01206) 865762

RAWLINGS, Gayle Ann Mary. b 53. Toronto Univ MD76 BA88 K Coll Lon MA89 FRCP(C)81. Westcott Ho Cam 01. **d** 03. C Ex St Thos and Em *Ex* from 03. *13 Sydney Road, Exeter EX2 9AJ* Tel (01392) 213445 E-mail rawlings@fish.co.uk

RAWLINGS, Preb John Edmund Frank. b 47. AKC69. St Aug Coll Cant 69. **d** 70 **p** 71. C Rainham *Roch* 70-73; C Tattenham Corner and Burgh Heath *Guildf* 73-76; Chapl RN 76-92; V Tavistock and Gulworthy *Ex* from 92; Chapl Kelly Coll Tavistock 93-02; RD Tavistock *Ex* 97-02; Preb Ex Cathl from 99. *The Vicarage, 5A Plymouth Road, Tavistock PL19 8AU* Tel (01822) 612162 *or* 616673 E-mail john@tavychurch.freeserve.co.uk

RAWLINGS, Philip John. b 53. St Jo Coll Nottm BTh83. **d** 83 **p** 84. C Blackley St Andr *Man* 83-87; C Halliwell St Pet 87-93; R Stretford St Bride from 93; AD Stretford from 98. *St Bride's Rectory, 29 Shrewsbury Street, Old Trafford, Manchester M16 9BB* Tel 0161-226 6064 E-mail philjr@zetnet.co.uk

RAWLINS, Clyde Thomas. b 28. **d** 02. NSM Saints St Aid *Ripon* from 02. *26 Gledhow Wood Close, Leeds LS8 1PN* Tel 0113-266 7731

RAWLINS, Geoffrey Ernest Francis. b 30. **d** 56 **p** 57. C St Marylebone All So w SS Pet and Jo *Lon* 56-66; Hon C 66-67; USA 67-95; rtd 95. *Flat 2, 60 Elm Park Road, London SW3 6AU* Tel (020) 7352 4076

RAWLINSON, Curwen. b 32. MBE73. Leeds Univ CertEd55 Man Univ DipEd56 Open Univ BA80. Sarum Th Coll 59. **d** 61 **p** 62. C Wigan St Mich *Liv* 61-63; CF 63-78; Dep Asst Chapl Gen 78-80; Asst Chapl Gen 80-85; QHC 83-98; R Uley w Owlpen and Nympsfield *Glouc* 85-98; RD Dursley 89-96; rtd 98; Perm to Offic *Glouc* from 98. *Cark House, 6 Groves Place, Fairford GL7 4BJ* Tel (01285) 711009

RAWLINSON, James Nigel. b 56. Em Coll Cam BA77 MB, BCh80 FRCSE86 FFAEM98. WMMTC 95. **d** 98 **p** 99. NSM Bath Weston All SS w N Stoke and Langridge *B & W* from 98; Perm to Offic *Bris* from 98; Consultant Bris R Infirmary from 99. *Glen Boyd House, 38 Court View, Wick, Bristol BS30 5QP*

RAWLINSON, John. b 47. Guy's Hosp Medical Sch BSc67 MB, BS71 MRCS. EAMTC 89. **d** 92 **p** 93. NSM Tilbrook *Ely* from 92; NSM Covington from 92; NSM Catworth Magna from 92; NSM Keyston and Bythorn from 92; Chapl Chu Coll Cam from 98. *The Malt House, 42 Stonely, Huntingdon PE28 0EH* Tel (01480) 860263 Fax 861590 E-mail dingleberry@lineone.net

RAWLINSON, Rowland. b 20. Leeds Univ CertEd41 Liv Univ DipAdEd68 Open Univ BA74. St Deiniol's Hawarden 79. **d** 80 **p** 81. Hon C Barnston *Ches* 80-82; C 82-85; Hon C Higher Bebington 85-92; rtd 92; Perm to Offic *Ches* from 94. *18 Winston Grove, Moreton, Wirral CH46 0PQ* Tel 0151-677 5641

RAWSON, Christopher Derek. b 39. Ox Min Course CBTS95. **d** 95 **p** 96. NSM Shill Valley and Broadshire *Ox* from 95. *Little Hay, Broadwell, Lechlade GL7 3QS* Tel (01367) 860255

RAWSON, Michael Graeme. b 62. York Univ BA84 Ox Univ BA88. St Steph Ho Ox 86. **d** 89 **p** 90. C Brighouse St Martin *Wakef* 89-92; C Brighouse and Clifton 92-93; V Gomersal from 93. *The Vicarage, 404 Spen Lane, Gomersal, Cleckheaton BD19 4LS* Tel (01274) 872131 E-mail michael.rawson@ntlworld.com

RAY, Mrs Joanna Zorina. b 55. AIMLS78 K Coll Lon BSc77 Garnett Coll Lon PGCE80 Lon Inst of Educn MA92. S'wark Ord Course 84. **d** 87 **p** 94. NSM Carshalton *S'wark* 87-91; NSM Sutton New Town St Barn 91-93; NSM Knighton St Mary Magd *Leic* 93-94; C Leic H Spirit 94-98; Chapl for Deaf People 94-98; Chapl and Andr Hosp Northn from 99. *St Andrew's Hospital,*

Billing Road, Northampton NN1 5DG Tel (01604) 629696 *or* (01858) 463951 Mobile 07802-300799
E-mail revdjoannaray@cs.com

RAY, John Mead. b 28. OBE79. St Andr Univ MA50 DipEd51. CMS Tr Coll Chislehurst 60. **d** 70 **p** 71. Miss Partner CMS 70-95; C Sparkhill St Jo *Birm* 87-90; C Sparkbrook Em 87-90; C Sparkhill w Greet and Sparkbrook 90; Deanery Missr 90-95; rtd 95; Perm to Offic *Birm* from 95. *190 Sarehole Road, Birmingham B28 8EF* Tel 0121-777 6143

RAY, Robin John. b 44. Sarum & Wells Th Coll 72. **d** 74 **p** 75. C Bourne Valley *Sarum* 74-78; P-in-c Dilton's-Marsh 78-82; V 82-87; V Taunton Lyngford *B & W* 87-93; R Exford, Exmoor, Hawkridge and Withypool from 93; Rural Affairs Officer from 93; ACORA Link Officer from 93. *The Rectory, Exford, Minehead TA24 7LX* Tel (01643) 831586
E-mail rays@exfordrectory.freeserve.co.uk

RAYBOULD, James Clive Ransford. b 37. Wolv Univ BSc62 Anglia Poly Univ MBA94 PhD01. Cranmer Hall Dur 81. **d** 83 **p** 84. C Cannock *Lich* 83-86; P-in-c Leek Wootton *Cov* 86-89; Dioc Tr Adv 86-89; TV Cannock *Lich* 89; Assoc Lect Anglia Poly Univ *Chelmsf* from 90; rtd 00. *73 Eastwood Old Road, Leigh-on-Sea SS9 4RS* Tel (01702) 522277

RAYBOULD, Norman William. b 18. Lich Th Coll 51. **d** 54 **p** 55. C Bloxwich *Lich* 54-57; C Tettenhall Wood 57-60; C Stoke upon Trent 60-61; P-in-c Hanley H Ev 61-67; V St Martin's 67-76; V Sheriffhales w Woodcote 76-83; rtd 83; Perm to Offic *Lich* from 83. *19 Cedar Close, St Martins, Oswestry SY11 3QF* Tel (01691) 774083

RAYFIELD, Lee Stephen. b 55. Southn Univ BSc78 Lon Univ PhD81 SOSc95. Ridley Hall Cam 93. **d** 93 **p** 94. C Woodford Wells *Chelmsf* 93-97; P-in-c Furze Platt *Ox* from 97; RD Maidenhead from 00. *The Vicarage, 259 Courthouse Road, Maidenhead SL6 6HF* Tel (01628) 621961 *or* 784053
E-mail rayfield@btinternet.com

RAYMENT, Mrs Helen Elizabeth. b 46. Keswick Hall Coll CertEd67. EAMTC 92. **d** 95 **p** 96. NSM Old Catton *Nor* 95-96; Perm to Offic *Pet* 01-02; P-in-c Weedon Bec w Everdon and Dodford from 02. *The Vicarage, Church Street, Weedon, Northampton NN7 4PL* Tel (01327) 340359

RAYMENT-PICKARD, Hugh Douglas John. b 61. Kent Univ BA84 Em Coll Cam BA87 Lon Univ PhD97. Westcott Ho Cam 85. **d** 88 **p** 89. C St Jo on Bethnal Green *Lon* 88-91; C Hackney 91-92; TV 92-95; V Notting Dale St Clem w St Mark and St Jas from 95; AD Kensington from 01. *12 St Ann's Villas, London W11 4RS* Tel (020) 7221 3548 Fax 7460 6989
E-mail hugh@clementjames.co.uk

RAYMER, Victoria Elizabeth. b 46. Wellesley Coll (USA) BA68 Harvard Univ MA69 JD78 PhD81. St Steph Ho Ox MA91 Qu Coll Birm DPS89. **d** 89 **p** 94. Par Dn Bushey *St Alb* 89-94; C Eaton Socon 94-98; V Milton Ernest, Pavenham and Thurleigh 98-01; Dir Studies Westcott Ho Cam from 01. *1 Short Street, Cambridge CB1 1LB* Tel (01223) 352922 *or* tel and fax 741011
E-mail ver21@cam.ac.uk

RAYNER, David. b 49. Trin Hall Cam BA72 MA75. Westcott Ho Cam 75. **d** 78 **p** 79. C Chorlton-cum-Hardy St Clem *Man* 78-81; C Cambridge Gt St Mary w St Mich *Ely* 81-84; V Camberwell St Geo *S'wark* 84-88; Warden Trin Coll Cen Camberwell 84-88; Warden Bp Mascall Cen *Heref* 89-90; V Smethwick H Trin w St Alb *Birm* 90-92; P-in-c W Smethwick 90-92; P-in-c Smethwick SS Steph and Mich 92-95; V Smethwick Resurr 92-99; RD Warley 93-97; Sec Inner Cities Relig Coun 99-03; Perm to Offic *Lon* from 99. *Address temp unknown*

RAYNER, Canon George Charles. b 26. Bps' Coll Cheshunt 50. **d** 52 **p** 53. C Rowbarton *B & W* 52-56; V Taunton H Trin 56-63; Chapl Taunton and Somerset Hosp 60-63; V Lower Sandown St Jo *Portsm* 63-69; R Wootton 69-89; Hon Can Portsm Cathl 84-89; rtd 89; Perm to Offic *B & W* 89-92 and *Portsm* from 98; P-in-c Six Pilgrims *B & W* 93-02. *The Bungalow, 1 Alresford Road, Shanklin PO37 6HX* Tel (01983) 867304

RAYNER, Paul Anthony George. b 39. Dur Univ BA60 Lon Univ BD68 Cape Town Univ MA79. Lon Coll of Div 65. **d** 68 **p** 69. C Crookes St Thos *Sheff* 68-72; S Africa 72-79; P-in-c S Shoebury *Chelmsf* 80-84; R 84-97; V Loughton St Mich from 97. *St Michael's House, Roding Road, Loughton IG10 3EJ* Tel (020) 8508 1489 E-mail prayner@globalnet.co.uk

RAYNER, Richard Noel. b 24. Lon Univ BD51. Oak Hill Th Coll 50. **d** 52 **p** 53. C Plymouth St Jude *Ex* 52-55; V Walthamstow St Luke *Chelmsf* 55-61; V Romford Gd Shep Collier Row 61-65; V Slough *Ox* 65-72; V Heworth w Peasholme St Cuth *York* 72-75; V Heworth H Trin 75-81; V Okehampton w Inwardleigh *Ex* 81-89; RD Okehampton 87-89; rtd 89; Perm to Offic *Ex* 90-98 and *B & W* from 90. *Redlands, 5 Ladymeade, Ilminster TA19 0EA* Tel (01460) 52491

RAYNER, Stewart Leslie. b 39. St Jo Coll Dur BA61 DipTh66 MA73. Cranmer Hall Dur. **d** 67 **p** 68. C Whiston *Sheff* 67-70; C Doncaster St Geo 70-74; Chapl Doncaster R Infirmary 70-74; R Adwick-le-Street *Sheff* 74-85; V Totley 85-91; Asst Chapl Pastures Hosp Derby 91-94; Asst Chapl Kingsway Hosp Derby 91-94; Asst Chapl S Derby Mental Health Services 91-94; P-in-c

Etwall w Egginton *Derby* 94-99; R from 99; RD Longford 96-01. *St Helen's Rectory, Main Street, Etwall, Derby DE6 6LP* Tel (01283) 732349 E-mail slrayner@fish.co.uk

RAYNES, Andrew. b 60. R Holloway Coll Lon BA83. Wycliffe Hall Ox DipMin95. **d** 95 **p** 96. C Crowborough *Chich* 95-99; V Blackb Ch Ch w St Matt *Blackb* from 99; AD Blackb and Darwen from 03. *The Vicarage, Brandy House Brow, Blackburn BB2 3EY* Tel (01254) 56292 E-mail andrewraynes@xalt.co.uk

RAYNHAM, Mrs Penelope Anne. b 44. SW Minl Tr Course 97. **d** 00 **p** 01. OLM S Hill w Callington *Truro* from 00. *Bramblings, Honicombe Corner, Harrowbarrow, Callington PL17 8JN* Tel (01822) 833065 E-mail penny@bramvista.co.uk

RAYNOR, Duncan Hope. b 58. Ex Coll Ox MA80 MA82 Birm Univ PGCE88 MLitt93. Qu Coll Birm 82. **d** 84 **p** 85. C Kings Heath *Birm* 84-87; Perm to Offic from 87; Hd of RE Alderbrook Sch Solihull 88-94; Chapl K Edw Sch Birm from 94. *134 Addison Road, Birmingham B14 7EP* Tel 0121-684 3407 *or* 472 1672 E-mail dhr@kes.bham.sch.uk

RAYNOR, Canon Michael. b 53. Lanc Univ BA74 MSc75. Ripon Coll Cuddesdon BA84 MA99. **d** 85 **p** 86. C Gt Crosby St Faith *Liv* 85-88; V Warrington St Barn 88-97; V Orford St Andr from 97; AD Warrington from 99; Hon Can Liv Cathl from 03. *St Andrew's Vicarage, Poplars Avenue, Orford, Warrington WA2 9UE* Tel (01925) 631903 E-mail mjraynor@care4free.net

RAYNOR-SMITH, Charles Alfred Walter. b 12. Sarum Th Coll. **d** 55 **p** 56. C Oakdale St Geo *Sarum* 55-58; C Swanage 58-62; V Colehill 62-81; rtd 81; Perm to Offic *Sarum* from 81. *19 Tatnam Road, Poole BH15 2OW* Tel (01202) 681996

RAZZALL, Charles Humphrey. b 55. Worc Coll Ox BA76 MA81 Qu Coll Cam BA78. Westcott Ho Cam 76. **d** 79 **p** 80. C Catford (Southend) and Downham *S'wark* 79-83; V Crofton Park St Hilda w St Cypr 83-87; UPA Officer 87-92; TV Oldham *Man* 87-01; AD Oldham 92-99; Hon Can Man Cathl 98-01; R Coppenhall *Ches* from 01. *The Rectory, 198 Ford Lane, Crewe CW1 3TN* Tel (01270) 215151

READ, Andrew Gordon. b 40. Nottm Univ BA69 ARICS63 FRICS86. Cuddesdon Coll 70. **d** 70 **p** 71. C E Retford *S'well* 70-72; C Woodthorpe 72-76; P-in-c Newark St Leon 76-78; Perm to Offic *Roch* 79-91. *1 Border Road, London SE26 6HB* Tel (020) 8778 6140

READ, Charles William. b 60. Man Univ BA81 Man Poly CertEd82. St Jo Coll Nottm 86. **d** 88 **p** 89. C Oldham *Man* 88-90; C Urmston 90-94; P-in-c Broughton St Jas w St Clem and St Matthias 94-96; TV Broughton 96-99; Tutor Cranmer Hall Dur from 99. *St John's College, 3 South Bailey, Durham DH1 3RJ* Tel 0191-374 3579 Fax 374 3573
E-mail c.w.read@durham.ac.uk

READ, Christopher Holditch. b 19. Qu Coll Birm 50. **d** 53 **p** 54. C Portishead *B & W* 53-56; C Walton on Trent, Coton in the Elms and Rosliston *Derby* 56-58; R Bonsall 58-63; V Cromford 58-63; R Grangemouth *Edin* 63-72; V Parwich w Alsop-en-le-Dale *Derby* 72-87; P-in-c Fenny Bentley, Thorpe and Tissington 77; rtd 87; Perm to Offic *Mor* 88-89. *Eastdene Residential Hotel, 7 Albany Road, Bexhill-on-Sea TN40 1BY* Tel (01424) 215100

READ, Geoffrey Philip. b 61. Bris Univ LLB82. Wycliffe Hall Ox 85. **d** 88 **p** 89. C Dorking St Paul *Guildf* 88-92; TV Westborough 92-97; TR 97-98; Chapl Basle *Eur* from 98; P-in-c Freiburg-im-Breisau 98-01. *St Johanns-Ring 92, CH-4056 Basle, Switzerland* Tel (0041) (61) 321 7477 Fax 321 7476
E-mail geoff.read@datacomm.ch

READ, Jack. b 19. Qu Coll Birm 67. **d** 68 **p** 69. C Tong *Bradf* 68-70; C Baildon 70-72; V Queensbury 72-86; rtd 86; Perm to Offic *Bradf* from 86. *7 Silver Birch Grove, Wyke, Bradford BD12 9ET* Tel (01274) 670737

READ, James Arthur. b 51. Nottm Coll of Educn BEd74. EMMTC 84. **d** 87 **p** 88. C Weoley Castle *Birm* 87-91; C W Smethwick 91-92; C Smethwick Resurrection 92; TV Atherton *Man* 92-97; P-in-c Facit 97-00; V Whitworth w Facit from 00. *The Vicarage, Market Street, Whitworth, Rochdale OL12 8LU* Tel (01706) 853931 E-mail james.read@phonecoop.coop

READ, John. b 33. Worc Coll Ox BA56 MA60. Chich Th Coll 56. **d** 58 **p** 59. C Babbacombe *Ex* 58-60; C Heavitree 60-63; V Swimbridge 63-69; V Ex St Matt 69-80; P-in-c Ex St Sidwell 79-80; R Ex St Sidwell and St Matt 80-83; Chapl Warneford Hosp Leamington Spa 83-89; Chapl S Warks Hosps 83-89; Chapl Dur and Ches le Street Hosps 89-95; Chapl Dryburn Hosp 89-95; rtd 95; NSM Tamworth *Lich* 95-98; Perm to Offic *Cov* from 02. *30 Wattfield Close, Rugeley WS15 1ER* Tel (01889) 575427

READ, John du Sautoy. **d** 66 **p** 67. V Choral Derry Cathl *D & R* 66-67; Dean's V Derry Cathl 67; S Africa from 69. *33 Town Street, Potchefstroom, 2520 South Africa* Tel (0027) (148) 297 8580

READ, John Hanson. b 17. St Jo Coll Ox BA49 MA53. Qu Coll Birm 49. **d** 50 **p** 51. C Eastbourne St Mary *Chich* 50-53; C Horsham 53-57; V Brighton St Wilfrid 57-61; R Beddington *S'wark* 61-78; RD Sutton 65-70; P-in-c Guestling *Chich* 78; P-in-c Pett 78; R Guestling and Pett 78-83; rtd 83; Perm to Offic *Chich* from 84; RD Rye 89-90. *6 Oast House Road, Icklesham, Winchelsea TN36 4BN* Tel (01424) 814440

READ, John Samuel. b 33. Fitzw Ho Cam BA56. Clifton Th Coll 62. **d** 64 **p** 65. C Sneinton St Chris w St Phil *S'well* 64-67; C Huyton St Geo *Liv* 67-70; Lic to Offic *Blackb* 70-72; V Moldgreen *Wakef* 72-84; V Rawtenstall St Mary *Man* 84-91; Chapl Rossendale Gen Hosp 84-91; R Earsham w Alburgh and Denton *Nor* 91-98; P-in-c Ditchingham, Hedenham and Broome 94-98; rtd 98; Perm to Offic *Nor* from 98. *7 Pine Tree Close, Worlingham, Beccles NE34 7EE* Tel (01502) 712585

READ, Mrs Julie Margaret. b 61. Keble Coll Ox BA82 Univ of Wales (Ban) PGCE83. WEMTC 97. **d** 00 **p** 01. C Bishop's Castle w Mainstone *Heref* 00-01; C Bishop's Castle w Mainstone, Lydbury N etc from 01. *The Vicarage, Lydbury North SY7 8AU* Tel (01588) 680633

READ, Maureen Elizabeth. b 52. Man Metrop Univ BEd93 Chester Coll of HE BTh99. N Ord Course 95. **d** 98 **p** 99. NSM Leesfield *Man* 98-99; C 99-02; TV Heywood from 02. *The Vicarage, 27 Heys Lane, Heywood OL10 3RD* Tel (01706) 368053

READ, Michael Antony. b 75. Lanc Univ BA99 St Jo Coll Dur BA01. Cranmer Hall Dur 99. **d** 02. C Stanley *Liv* from 02. *25 Eaton Road, West Derby, Liverpool L12 7JJ* Tel 0151-228 5252

READ, Nicholas George. b 51. Chelsea Coll Lon BSc72 PhD81 Spurgeon's Coll Dip Counselling 97. SEITE 97. **d** 00 **p** 01. NSM Beckenham St Jo *Roch* from 00. *16 Stanhope Grove, Beckenham BR3 3BS* Tel and fax (020) 8658 5035 Mobile 07904-317488 E-mail hancompro@aol.com

READ, Nicholas John. b 59. OBE99. Keble Coll Ox BA81 MSc82 MA85. Ox Min Course 92. **d** 95 **p** 96. NSM Charlbury w Shorthampton *Ox* 95-98; Dir Rural Stress Information Network 96-00; Chapl for Agric *Heref* from 98. *The Vicarage, Lydbury North SY7 8AU* Tel (01588) 680609

READ, Canon Robert Edgar. b 47. Kelham Th Coll 66. **d** 70 **p** 71. C Harton Colliery *Dur* 70-75; C Wilmslow *Ches* 76-80; V Gatley 80-92; V Offerton from 92; RD Stockport from 00; Hon Can Ches Cathl from 03. *St Alban's Vicarage, 1A Salcombe Road, Offerton, Stockport SK2 5AG* Tel 0161-480 3773 E-mail reread@talk21.com

READ, Victor. b 29. Lon Univ BD58. ALCD57. **d** 58 **p** 59. C Wimbledon *S'wark* 58-61; C Lt Marlow *Ox* 61-64; V Wootton *Linc* 64-67; R Croxton 64-67; V Ulceby 64-67; V Linc St Pet in Eastgate w St Marg 67-73; V W Wimbledon Ch Ch *S'wark* 73-94; rtd 94; Perm to Offic *Pet* from 94. *27 Nightingale Drive, Towcester NN12 6RA* Tel (01327) 352027

READE, The Ven Nicholas Stewart. b 46. Leeds Univ BA70 DipTh72. Coll of Resurr Mirfield 70. **d** 73 **p** 74. C Coseley St Chad *Lich* 73-75; C Codsall 75-78; V Upper Gornal 78-82; V Mayfield *Chich* 82-88; RD Dallington 82-88; V Eastbourne St Mary 88-97; RD Eastbourne 88-97; Can and Preb Chich Cathl 90-97; Can from 97; Min The Hydneye CD 91-93; Adn Lewes and Hastings from 97. *27 The Avenue, Lewes BN7 1QT* Tel (01273) 479530 Fax 476529 E-mail archlewes@pavilion.co.uk

READE, Richard Barton. b 66. Wolv Poly BA88. Ripon Coll Cuddesdon BA91. **d** 92 **p** 93. C Wilnecote *Lich* 92-96; C Penkridge Team 96-98; P-in-c Basford from 98. *211 Basford Park Road, Basford, Newcastle ST5 0PG* Tel (01782) 619045 E-mail richardreade@supanet.com

READER, Christine Sarah. STETS. **d** 00 **p** 01. NSM N Waltham and Steventon etc *Win* from 00. *5 Church Farm Close, North Waltham, Basingstoke RG25 2BN* Tel (01256) 397503

READER, John. b 53. Trin Coll Ox BA75 MA79 Man Univ DSPT83 MPhil87. Ripon Coll Cuddesdon 76. **d** 78 **p** 79. C Ely 78-80; C Baguley *Man* 80-83; TV Kirkby Lonsdale *Carl* 83-86; V Lydbury N *Heref* 86-89; P-in-c Hopesay w Edgton 86-89; R Lydbury N w Hopesay and Edgton 89-90; Tutor Glouc Sch for Min 86-88; Vice-Prin 88-90; Dir Past Th Sarum & Wells Th Coll 90-92; P-in-c Elmley Lovett w Hampton Lovett and Elmbridge etc *Worc* from 92; Assoc Tr and Educn Officer 92-02; Ind Chapl from 01. *The Rectory, Elmley Lovett, Droitwich WR9 0PU* Tel (01299) 251798 E-mail john-reader@4thenet.co.uk

READER, The Ven Trevor Alan John. b 46. Lon Univ BSc68 MSc70 Portsm Poly PhD72. S Dios Minl Tr Scheme 83. **d** 86 **p** 87. C Alverstoke *Portsm* 86-89; P-in-c Hook w Warsash 89-95; V 95-98; P-in-c Blendworth w Chalton w Idsworth from 98; Dir NSM from 98; Adn Is of Wight from 03. *The Boltons, Kite Hill, Wootton Bridge, Ryde PO33 4PB* Tel (01983) 884432

READER-MOORE, Anthony. b 43. Kent Univ BA80 Hull Univ MA83. Linc Th Coll. **d** 82 **p** 83. C Addiscombe St Mildred *Cant* 82-84; C Addiscombe St Mildred *S'wark* 85-86; R N Wheatley, W Burton, Bole, Saundby, Sturton etc *S'well* 86-93; Rural Officer 89-93; P-in-c Alford w Rigsby *Linc* 93-97; V 97-00; P-in-c Bilsby w Farlesthorpe 93-97; V 97-00; P-in-c Hannah cum Hagnaby w Markby 93-97; R 97-00; P-in-c Saleby w Beesby and Maltby 93-97; R 97-00; V Wellingborough All Hallows *Pet* from 00. *12 Bush Close, Wellingborough NN8 3GL* Tel (01933) 222002

READING, Canon Laurence John. b 14. DSC44. Lon Univ BD39 AKC39. **d** 39 **p** 40. C Prittlewell *Chelmsf* 39-42; Chapl RNVR 42-46; C-in-c Prittlewell St Pet CD 46-60; V Shrub End *Chelmsf* 60-64; Tr Officer Bd of Educn Adult Cttee 64; Sec 65-72; Can Heref Cathl *Heref* 72-82; rtd 82; Perm to Offic *Chelmsf* from 82. *11 Wakelin Way, Witham CM8 2TX* Tel (01376) 513251

READING, Mrs Lesley Jean. b 49. GNSM70 Trent Park Coll of Educn CertEd71. N Ord Course 98. **d** 01 **p** 02. NSM Eccles *Man* from 01. *Ryders Farm, Manchester Road, Kearsley, Bolton BL4 8RU* Tel 0161-380 1809 Fax 794 1446 E-mail readinglesley@hotmail.com

READING, Miss Siân Jacqueline Mary. b 64. Westcott Ho Cam CTM95. **d** 95 **p** 96. C Northampton St Alb *Pet* 95-98; TV Duston Team from 98. *St Francis House, Eastfield Road, Duston, Northampton NN5 6TQ* Tel (01604) 753679 E-mail sianreading@tinyonline.co.uk

READING, Area Bishop of. Vacant

REAGON, Darrol Franklin. b 46. Univ of Wales (Cardiff) DipTh76. St Mich Coll Llan 74. **d** 76 **p** 77. C Llandrillo-yn-Rhos *St As* 76-78; C Hawarden 78-81; V Northwich St Luke and H Trin *Ches* 81-85; V Moulton *Linc* 85-91; V Scunthorpe Resurr 91-92; P-in-c Branston 92-94; TV Heywood from 02. *The Rectory, Branston, Lincoln LN4 1NN* Tel (01522) 791296

REAKES-WILLIAMS, Gordon Martin. b 63. St Cath Coll Cam BA86 MA89. St Jo Coll Dur BA90. **d** 91 **p** 92. C Harold Wood *Chelmsf* 91-94; Chapl Leipzig *Eur* from 95. *Schreberstrasse 14B, 04109 Leipzig, Germany* Tel (0049) (341) 302 7951 Mobile 177-240 4207 Fax (341) 993 8844 E-mail earwig@t-online.de

REALE, Mrs Kathleen. b 38. Carl Dioc Tr Course 83. **dss** 86 **d** 87 **p** 94. Dalston *Carl* 86-87; Par Dn 87-90; Par Dn Westward, Rosley-w-Woodside and Welton 87-90; Par Dn Thursby 89-90; Dn-in-c Gt Salkeld w Lazonby 90-94; P-in-c 94-97; rtd 97; Perm to Offic *Carl* from 98. *4 Low Moorlands, Carlisle CA5 7NX* Tel (01228) 711749

REANEY, Mrs Beverly Jane. b 58. Nottm Univ BA81. S Wales Ord Course 00. **d** 03. NSM Llanharry *Llan* from 03. *The Rectory, High Street, Nelson, Treharris CF46 6HA* Tel (01443) 450335 Fax as telephone E-mail beverly.j.reaney@rhondda-cynon-taf.gov.uk

REANEY, Christopher Thomas. b 60. Univ of Wales (Lamp) BA82. St Mich Coll Llan DipTh85. **d** 85 **p** 86. C Maindee *Mon* 85-87; C Griffithstown 88-89; V Treherbert w Treorchy *Llan* 89-99; V Treorchy and Treherbert 99-02; R Llanfabon from 02. *The Rectory, High Street, Nelson, Treharris CF46 6HA* Tel (01443) 450335 Fax as telephone

REARDON, Bernard Morris Garvin. b 13. Keble Coll Ox BA35 MA38. Ripon Hall Ox 35. **d** 37 **p** 38. C Saffron Walden *Chelmsf* 37-38; C Shenfield 38-40; P-in-c 40-41; CF (EC) 41-46; V Hornchurch H Cross *Chelmsf* 46-47; R Kelly w Bradstone *Ex* 47-59; R Parham and Wiggonholt w Greatham *Chich* 59-63; Sen Lect, Reader, and Hd Relig Studies Newc Univ 63-78; rtd 78; Perm to Offic *Newc* from 78. *2 The Grove, Benton, Newcastle upon Tyne NE12 9PE* Tel 0191-266 1574

REARDON, Canon Martin Alan. b 32. OBE97. Selw Coll Cam BA54 MA58. Cuddesdon Coll 56. **d** 58 **p** 59. C Rugby St Andr *Cov* 58-60; Lic to Offic *Sheff* 61-71; Sub-Warden Linc Th Coll 71-78; Gen Sec Gen Syn Bd for Miss and Unity 78-89; Can and Preb Linc Cathl *Linc* 79-02; R Plumpton w E Chiltington *Chich* 89-90; Gen Sec Chs Together in England 90-97; Perm to Offic *S'wark* 95-00; rtd 97; Perm to Offic *St Alb* from 00. *Little School House, High Street, Turvey, Bedford MK43 8DB* Tel (01234) 888992 E-mail aifreardon@talk21.com

REASON, Jack. b 28. St Alb Minl Tr Scheme 77. **d** 80 **p** 81. NSM Luton Lewsey St Hugh *St Alb* 80-85; C Bideford *Ex* 85-88; R Northlew w Ashbury 88-93; R Bratton Clovelly w Germansweek 88-93; rtd 93; Perm to Offic *Ex* from 94. *5 Merryfield Road, Bideford EX39 4BX* Tel (01237) 472150

REAST, Eileen Joan. *See* BANGAY, Mrs Eileen Joan

REAVIL, Michael Edward. b 51. Qu Coll Birm 89. **d** 91 **p** 92. C Cofton Hackett w Barnt Green *Birm* 91-94; C Stevenage St Mary Sheppall w Aston *St Alb* 94-97; P-in-c Lt Leigh and Lower Whitley *Ches* 97-98; P-in-c Antrobus 97-98; P-in-c Aston by Sutton 97-98; rtd 98. *13 Huntgate Court, Beccles NR34 9TR*

RECORD, Canon John. b 47. St Chad's Coll Dur BA71. Westcott Ho Cam 71. **d** 73 **p** 74. C Paddington St Jo w St Mich *Lon* 73-75; C Witney *Ox* 75-78; P-in-c Lt Compton and Chastleton 78-80; R Lt Compton w Chastleton, Cornwell etc 80-83; V Hawkhurst *Cant* 83-97; RD W Charing 89-95; Hon Can Cant Cathl 96-97; P-in-c Devizes St Jo w St Mary *Sarum* from 97; P-in-c Devizes St Pet from 00; RD Devizes from 98; Can and Preb Sarum Cathl from 02. *The Rectory, 39 Long Street, Devizes SN10 1NS* Tel (01380) 723705 E-mail rector@stjohndevizes.fsnet.co.uk

RECORD, Sister Marion Eva. b 25. MRCS50 LRCP50 Leeds Univ FFARCS57 Lon Univ BD79. **dss** 78 **d** 87 **p** 94. OHP from 72; Chapl Hull Univ *York* 72-78; Chapl York Univ 78-80; Lic to Offic 80-95; Perm to Offic from 95; rtd 96. *St Hilda's Priory, Sneaton Castle, Whitby YO21 3QN* Tel (01947) 602079

REDDING, Roger Charles. b 45. Chich Th Coll 87. **d** 89 **p** 90. C Yeovil St Mich *B & W* 89-93; P-in-c Salisbury St Mark *Sarum* 93-94; Lic to Offic 94-96; TV Chalke Valley from 96; Chapl to Travelling People from 02. *The Vicarage, May Lane, Ebbesbourne Wake, Salisbury SP5 5JL* Tel (01722) 780408

REDDINGTON, Gerald Alfred. b 34. Lon Univ DipRS79. S'wark Ord Course 76. **d** 79 **p** 79. NSM St Vedast w St Mich-le-Querne etc *Lon* 79-85; Dir Past Support Gp Scheme 83-86;

Hon C St Marylebone All SS 85-90; Perm to Offic *Portsm* from 88; V Ealing St Barn *Lon* 90-99; rtd 99. *The Orange Tree, Madeira Road, Seaview PO34 5BA* Tel (01983) 617026
E-mail rev.redd@btinternet.com

REDEYOFF, Neil Martyn. b 69. Nottm Univ BA01. St Jo Coll Nottm 98. **d** 01 **p** 02. C Grange St Andr *Ches* from 01; C Runcorn H Trin from 01. *Holy Trinity Vicarage, Grange Park Avenue, Runcorn WA7 5UT* Tel (01928) 572299
E-mail nredeyoff@ntlworld.com

REDFEARN, James Jonathan. b 62. Newc Univ BA83 PGCE89. Cranmer Hall Dur 95. **d** 95 **p** 96. C Kidsgrove *Lich* 95-97. *56 Holly Avenue, Jesmond, Newcastle upon Tyne NE2 2QA* Tel 0191-281 9046 E-mail jaredfearn@compuserve.com

REDFEARN, John William Holmes. Sheff Univ BA30 MA31 DipEd31. **d** 33 **p** 34. C Bishopwearmouth St Mich *Dur* 33-35; Asst Master Bede Coll Sch Sunderland 31-45; Chapl Berkhamsted Colleg Sch Herts 45-55; Chapl Haberdashers' Aske's Sch Elstree 56-72; Perm to Offic *Lon* 61-76; rtd 72. *184 Cardiff Road, Llandaff, Cardiff CF5 2AD* Tel (029) 2056 7692

REDFEARN, Michael. b 42. Open Univ BA78 Hull Univ MA84 BA86. Bernard Gilpin Soc Dur 63 St Aid Birkenhead 64. **d** 68 **p** 69. C Bury St Pet *Man* 68-71; C Swinton St Pet 71-74; Ind Chapl *Bris* 74-79 and 80-81; Ind Chapl Australia 79-80; Ind Chapl *York* 81-86; V Southill and Course Dir St Alb Minl Tr Scheme 86-93; Dep Chapl HM Pris Wandsworth 94; Chapl HM YOI and Rem Cen Feltham 94-97; Chapl HM YOI Aylesbury 97-02; rtd 02. *Las Frondarojas, Apartado de Correos 9, 04800 Albox, Almeria, Spain* Tel (0034) (696) 391584

REDFEARN, Ms Tracy Anne. b 66. Heythrop Coll Lon BD88. Ripon Coll Cuddesdon 91. **d** 93 **p** 94. C Haslemere *Guildf* 93-97; TV Gt Grimsby St Mary and St Jas *Linc* 97-00; P-in-c Legbourne 00-01; P-in-c Raithby 00-01; P-in-c Wold-Marsh Gp 00-01; V Legbourne and Wold Marsh from 01. *The Rectory, Church Lane, Legbourne, Louth LN11 8LN* Tel (01507) 601223
E-mail therev@supanet.com

✠**REDFERN, The Rt Revd Alastair Llewellyn John.** b 48. Ch Ch Ox BA70 MA74 Trin Coll Cam BA74 MA79 Bris Univ PhD01. Qu Coll Birm 75. **d** 76 **p** 77 **c** 97. C Tettenhall Regis *Lich* 76-79; Tutor Ripon Coll Cuddesdon 79-87; Hon C Cuddesdon *Ox* 83-87; Can Res Bris Cathl from 94; Dioc Dir Tr 91-97; Suff Bp Grantham *Linc* from 97; Dean Stamford from 98; Can and Preb Linc Cathl from 00. *243 Barrowby Road, Grantham NG31 8NP* Tel (01476) 564722 Fax 592468
E-mail bishop.grantham@btopenworld.com

REDFERN, Paul. b 48. Ulster Univ BA88. CITC BTh94. **d** 94 **p** 95. C Belfast St Aid *Conn* 94-97; I Belfast St Mark 97-03; I Kilbride from 03. *Kilbride Rectory, 1 Rectory Road, Doagh, Ballyclare BT39 0PT* Tel (028) 9334 0225

REDGERS, Brian. b 42. St Jo Coll Dur BA65 Keswick Hall Coll PGCE75. Westcott Ho Cam 65. **d** 67 **p** 68. C Rushmere *St E* 67-73; Lic to Offic from 73. *44 Belvedere Road, Ipswich IP4 4AB* Tel (01473) 273829

REDGRAVE, Cecil Goulden. b 14. Oak Hill Th Coll 37. **d** 41 **p** 42. C Higher Openshaw *Man* 41-43; C Ashton St Jas 43-44; C Chadderton Ch Ch 44-46; V Thornton *Leic* 46-49; V Fairlight *Chich* 49-60; V New Milverton *Cov* 60-76; R Tredington and Darlingscott w Newbold on Stour 76-83; rtd 83; Perm to Offic *Cov* from 83. *30 Elmdene Road, Kenilworth CV8 2BX* Tel (01926) 857118

REDGRAVE, Canon Christine Howick. b 50. AIAT73. Trin Coll Bris 75. **dss** 78 **d** 87 **p** 94. Watford *St Alb* 78-83; Maidenhead St Andr and St Mary *Ox* 83-85; Bracknell 85-96; Par Dn 87-94; TV 94-96; Asst Dir of Ords from 95; P-in-c Woolhampton w Midgham and Beenham Valance from 96; Hon Can Ch Ch from 00. *The Rectory, Birds Lane, Midgham, Reading RG7 5UL* Tel 0118-971 2186 Fax as telephone
E-mail ordberk@oxford.anglican.org

REDGRAVE, Ronald Oliver. b 18. Ox NSM Course. **d** 83 **p** 84. NSM Boyne Hill *Ox* 83-85; Perm to Offic *St E* 85-86; P-in-c Alderton w Ramsholt and Bawdsey 86-88; rtd 88; Perm to Offic *Ox* from 97. *The Rectory, Birds Lane, Midgham, Reading RG7 5UL* Tel 0118-972 3035

REDHEAD, Edward. b 30. St Deiniol's Hawarden 60. **d** 63 **p** 64. C Mottram in Longdendale w Woodhead *Ches* 63-67; V Rivington *Man* 67-72; V Bloxwich *Lich* 72-75; Hon C Lich St Chad 82-84; P-in-c Bromfield w Waverton *Carl* 84-85; V 85-90; P-in-c W Newton 84-85; V 85-90; R Harrington 90-93; rtd 93. *Tigh-na-Mara, 2-3 Caroy, Struan, Isle of Skye IV56 8FQ* Tel (01470) 572338

REDHOUSE, Mark David. b 67. BTEC NC86. Oak Hill Th Coll BA94. **d** 94 **p** 95. C Fulham St Mary N End *Lon* 94-96; C Hove Bp Hannington Memorial Ch *Chich* 96-01; V Horam from 01. *The Vicarage, Horebeech Lane, Horam, Heathfield TN21 0DT* Tel (01435) 812563

REDKNAP, Clive Douglas. b 53. Trin Coll Bris BA95. **d** 95 **p** 96. C Patcham *Chich* 95-00; C Wadhurst and Stonegate 00-03; P-in-c Hollington St Jo from 03. *The Vicarage, 94 Lower Glen Road, St Leonards-on-Sea TN37 7AR* Tel (01424) 751103

REDMAN, Anthony James. b 51. Reading Univ BSc72 FRICS95. EAMTC 01. **d** 03. NSM Bury St Edmunds All SS w St Jo and St Geo *St E* from 03. *The Cottage, Great Livermere, Bury St Edmunds IP31 1JG* Tel (01359) 269335 Fax (01284) 704734
E-mail tony@tandcredman.fsnet.co.uk

REDMAN, Canon Arthur Thomas. b 28. Dur Univ BA52 PGCE. Ridley Hall Cam 62. **d** 63 **p** 64. C Heaton St Barn *Bradf* 63-66; C Hitchin St Mary *St Alb* 66-70; P Missr 72-75; Hd RE Stopsley High Sch Luton 66-70; Hd Humanities and Modern Studies Hewett Sch Nor 70-72; Perm to Offic *Nor* 70-72; V Swanwick and Pentrich *Derby* 75-80; Warden of Readers 78-97; Dir Bp's Cert 78-88; V Allestree 80-96; P-in-c Morley 82-85; Hon Can Derby Cathl 86-96; RD Duffield 88-96; rtd 96; Hon C Bretby w Newton Solney *Derby* 96-97; Chapl and Development Officer Children in Distress 97-01; Dir St Barn Project Romania from 01. *9 Ludgate Walk, Mackworth, Derby DE22 4HQ* Tel (01332) 521733 Fax 551569

REDMAN, Canon Douglas Stuart Raymond. b 35. MCIOB64. Roch Th Coll 66. **d** 68 **p** 69. C Shortlands *Roch* 68-71; V 80-00; R Kingsdown 71-76; R Chatham St Mary w St Jo 76-80; RD Beckenham 90-00; Hon Can Roch Cathl 93-00; rtd 00; Perm to Offic *Cant* from 01. *25 Hovendens, Sissinghurst, Cranbrook TN17 2LA* Tel (01580) 714600 Fax as telephone

REDMAN, Julia Elizabeth Hithersay. *See* WHITE, Mrs Julia Elizabeth Hithersay

REDVERS HARRIS, Jonathan Francis. b 60. Solicitor 87 Southn Univ LLB81 Univ of Wales (Cardiff) LLM94. Ridley Hall Cam 87. **d** 90 **p** 91. C Enfield St Jas *Lon* 90-93; PV Llan Cathl *Llan* 93-96; Succ 94-96; V Houghton Regis *St Alb* 96-03; V Ryde All SS *Portsm* from 03. *14 Argyll Street, Ryde PO33 3BZ* Tel (01983) 565953 E-mail j.redvers_harris@virgin.net

REDWOOD, Canon David Leigh. b 32. Glas Univ DipSW78. Edin Th Coll 57. **d** 59 **p** 60. C Stirling *Edin* 59-61; C Glas Ch Ch *Glas* 61-64; P-in-c Glas Ascension 64-66; R 66-69; R Hamilton 69-74; R Callander *St And* 74-76; Hon C 76-78; R Lochearnhead 74-76; R Killin 74-76; Hon C Doune 76-78; Hon C Aberfoyle 78-85; R Dunfermline 85-97; TR W Fife Team Min 85-97; Can St Ninian's Cathl Perth 90-97; Syn Clerk 93-97; rtd 97. *8 Strathmore Avenue, Dunblane FK15 9HX* Tel (01786) 825493
E-mail dlredwood@talk21.com

REDWOOD, Marion. b 47. **d** 00. NSM Abercarn and Cwmcarn *Mon* from 00. *30 John Street, Cwmcarn, Crosskeys, Newport NP11 7EH* Tel (01495) 271910

REECE, Donald Malcolm Hayden. b 36. CCC Cam BA58 MA62. Cuddesdon Coll 58. **d** 60 **p** 61. C Latchford St Jas *Ches* 60-63; C Matlock and Tansley *Derby* 63-67; C-in-c Hackenthorpe Ch Ch CD 67-70; Rhodesia 70-73; V Leic St Pet *Leic* 74-82; V Putney St Marg *S'wark* 82-91; Home Sec Coun for Chr Unity from 92; Perm to Offic *S'wark* and *Lon* from 92; C Wandsworth St Anne 94-97; V Shepherd's Bush St Steph w St Thos *Lon* from 97. *St Stephen's Vicarage, Coverdale Road, London W12 8JJ* Tel (020) 8743 3166 Fax as telephone E-mail stephenw12@lineone.net

REECE, Paul Michael. b 60. Southn Univ BA81. Coll of Resurr Mirfield 83. **d** 85 **p** 86. C Borehamwood *St Alb* 85-89; C Potters Bar 89-92; R Lt Stanmore St Lawr *Lon* from 92; AD Harrow 97-02; Chapl R Nat Orthopaedic Hosp NHS Trust from 92. *Whitchurch Rectory, St Lawrence Close, Edgware HA8 6RB* Tel (020) 8952 0019 Mobile 07860-690503 Fax 8537 0547
E-mail paul.reece@london.anglican.org

REECE, Roger Walton Arden. b 56. Dioc OLM tr scheme 97. **d** 00 **p** 01. OLM Chadderton St Luke *Man* from 00. *186 Broadway, Chadderton, Oldham OL9 9JH* Tel 0161-284 6824 Mobile 07855-234862 E-mail rogerandhilary@aol.com

REED, Adam Michael Frederick. b 73. Humberside Univ BA95. Cranmer Hall Dur 96. **d** 99 **p** 00. C Northallerton w Kirby Sigston *York* 99-03; R Middleton, Newton and Sinnington from 03. *St Andrew's House, 15 Carr Lane, Middleton, Pickering YO18 8PU* Tel (01751) 474858

REED, Alan Ronald. b 44. Sarum Th Coll 66. **d** 68 **p** 70. C Ifield *Chich* 68-71; C Perivale *Lon* 71-72; C Ruislip St Martin 72-75; C Burgess Hill St Jo *Chich* 76-78; V Shoreham Beach 78-80; V Roughey 80-97; P-in-c Rusper 84-86; V Hove St Barn and St Agnes from 97. *St Barnabas' Vicarage, 88 Sackville Road, Hove BN3 3HE* Tel (01273) 732427

REED, Allan Norman. b 31. Keble Coll Ox BA55 MA59 Didsbury Coll Man CertEd72. Wycliffe Hall Ox 55. **d** 57 **p** 58. C Beverley Minster *York* 57-60; C Marfleet 60-64; R S Levenshulme *Man* 64-71; Lic Preacher from 71; rtd 92; Perm to Offic *Ripon* from 92. *21 Lyons Road, Richmond DL10 4UA* Tel (01748) 825767

REED, Ms Annette Susan. b 54. Birm Univ BA76 Univ of Wales (Cardiff) CQSW78. Qu Coll Birm 84. **d** 87 **p** 94. C Churchover w Willey *Cov* 89-92; C Clifton upon Dunsmore and Newton 89-92; C Walsgrave on Sowe 92-95; C Cov E 92-95; C Burbage w Aston Flamville *Leic* 95-98; C Hinckley St Mary 95-98; C The Sheepy Gp 98-00; TV Bosworth and Sheepy Gp from 00. *The Rectory, Church Lane, Sheepy Magna, Atherstone CV9 3QS* Tel (01827) 881082 E-mail annettereed@greatsheep.freeserve.co.uk

REED, Brian. b 43. Bris Univ BSc65 Nottm Univ DipTh76. Linc Th Coll 73. **d** 76 **p** 77. C S Ashford Ch Ch *Cant* 76-78; C Spring

Park 78-83; V Barming Heath from 83. *St Andrew's Vicarage, 416 Tonbridge Road, Maidstone ME16 9LW* Tel (01622) 726245

REED, Bruce Douglas. b 20. Fitzw Ho Cam BA52 MA56 Lambeth Hon MLitt90. Moore Th Coll Sydney LTh45. **d** 46 **p** 46. Australia 46-49; Chapl Fitzw Ho Cam 50-54; C Cambridge St Paul *Ely* 53-54; Chmn Grubb Inst from 69; rtd 85. *The Grubb Institute, Cloudesley Street, London N1 0HU* Tel (020) 7278 8061 Fax 7278 0728

REED, Christopher John. b 42. Selw Coll Cam BA64 MA68 Dur Univ DipTh66. Cranmer Hall Dur 64. **d** 67 **p** 68. C Gt Ilford St Andr *Chelmsf* 67-70; P-in-c Bordesley St Andr *Birm* 70-72; V 72-80; V Crofton St Paul *Roch* 80-98; V Yalding w Collier Street from 98; RD Paddock Wood from 01. *The Vicarage, Vicarage Road, Yalding, Maidstone ME18 6DR* Tel (01622) 814182 E-mail chris.lysbeth@yaldingvicarage.freeserve.co.uk

REED, Colin Bryher. b 58. York Univ BA80 RGN86. Ridley Hall Cam CTM95. **d** 95 **p** 96. C Grays North *Chelmsf* 95-99; Chapl Plymouth Hosps NHS Trust 99-02; Hd Chapl Services Norfolk and Nor Univ Hosp NHS Trust from 02. *The Chaplaincy, Norfolk and Norwich University Hosp, Colney Lane, Norwich NR4 7UZ* Tel (01603) 86286 *or* 287470

REED, Colin Charles Gilmour. b 40. LCP75 FCP86 St Luke's Coll Ex TCert63 Lon Univ DipTh69 La Trobe Univ Vic MA94. Tyndale Hall Brisbane 67. **d** 69 **p** 70. C Weston-super-Mare Ch Ch *B & W* 69-71; Kenya 71-79; Australia 80-99; CMS from 84; Tanzania from 99. *SLP 282, Iringa, Tanzania* E-mail colinreed@maf.org *or* cwreed@cms.org.au

REED, David. See REED, Richard David

REED, Canon Douglas Victor. b 19. AKC41 Middlebury Coll (USA) Hon DD51. St Steph Ho Ox 41. **d** 42 **p** 43. C Poplar St Sav w St Gabr and St Steph *Lon* 42-44; C Bedford St Paul *St Alb* 44-45; Asst Org Sec SPCK 46-47; V Belvedere St Aug *Roch* 47-52; V Chislehurst Annunciation 52-85; Hon Can Roch Cathl 81-85; rtd 85; Perm to Offic *Roch* 85-94. *6 Crown Lane, Chislehurst BR7 5PL* Tel (020) 8467 3360

REED, Duncan Esmond Bousfield. b 51. AKC74 Ch Ch Coll Cant PGCE75. St Aug Coll Cant 76. **d** 76 **p** 77. C Houghton le Spring *Dur* 76-79; C Stockton St Pet 79-83; V Darlington St Mark w St Paul 83-88; V Benfieldside 88-93; P-in-c Whickham 93-95; R 95-03. *Top House, 27 Hill End, Frosterley, Bishop Auckland DL13 2SY* Tel (01388) 529227 E-mail duncan@churchfaze.freeserve.co.uk

REED, Mrs Elizabeth Christine. b 43. Lon Bible Coll Lon Univ BD65. WMMTC 95. **d** 97 **p** 98. NSM Ledbury *Heref* from 97; Chapl Bromsgrove Sch from 99. *The Old Barn, Perrystone Hill, Ross-on-Wye HR9 7QX* Tel (01989) 780439

REED, Ethel Patricia Ivy. See WESTBROOK, Mrs Ethel Patricia Ivy

REED, Geoffrey Martin. b 51. Univ of Wales (Cardiff) BA73 Open Univ PGCE98. Oak Hill Th Coll 73. **d** 76 **p** 77. C Swansea St Nic *S & B* 76-78; C Sketty 78-84; V Glasbury and Llowes 84-86; V Glasbury and Llowes w Clyro and Betws 86-01; R Teme Valley S *Worc* from 01. *The Rectory, Broadheath, Tenbury Wells WR15 8QW* Tel (01886) 853286 Mobile 07977-229103 E-mail martin.reed@clara.co.uk

REED, Harvey. See REED, William Harvey

REED, Jack. b 23. Bris Univ BA49 Lon Univ BD51. Tyndale Hall Bris. **d** 51 **p** 52. C Crookes St Thos *Sheff* 51-54; C Cheltenham St Mark *Glouc* 54-56; R Bickenhill w Elmdon *Birm* 56-60; V Sparkbrook Ch Ch 60-66; V Drypool St Columba w St Andr and St Pet *York* 66-80; TR Drypool 80-83; P-in-c Thwing 83-85; P-in-c Rudston w Boynton and Kilham 83-85; V 85-87; Perm to Offic from 87; rtd 85. *32 Dower Rise, Swanland, North Ferriby HU14 3QT* Tel (01482) 632649

REED, The Ven John Peter Cyril. b 51. BD78 AKC78. Ripon Coll Cuddesdon 78. **d** 79 **p** 80. C Croydon *Cant* 79-82; Prec St Alb Abbey *St Alb* 82-86; R Timsbury and Priston *B & W* 86-93; Chapl Rural Affairs Bath Adnry 87-93; P-in-c Ilminster w Whitelackington 93-94; TR Ilminster and Distr 94-99; Adn Taunton from 99. *4 Westerkirk Gate, Staplegrove, Taunton TA2 6BQ* Tel (01823) 323838 Fax 325420 E-mail adtaunton@bathwells.anglican.org

REED, Capt John William. b 57. Sussex Univ BSc79 Ch Ch Coll Cant DipHE93. N Ord Course 95. **d** 97 **p** 98. C Padgate *Liv* 97-99; C Orford St Marg 99-01; V from 01. *St Margaret's Vicarage, St Margaret's Avenue, Orford, Warrington WA2 8DT* Tel (01925) 631937 Fax as telephone E-mail john@scobiem.freeserve.co.uk

REED, Matthew Colin. b 50. Edin Univ BD82. Edin Th Coll 72. **d** 84 **p** 85. C Edin St Pet *Edin* 84-87; P-in-c Linlithgow 87-94; P-in-c Bathgate 87-91; Chapl HM Pris Polmont 91-94; R Motherwell *Glas* 94-97; R Wishaw 94-97; Chapl HM Pris Edin from 02. *HM Prison Edinburgh, 33 Stenhouse Road, Edinburgh EH11 3LN* Tel 0131-444 3115

REED, Matthew Graham. b 68. Nottm Univ BEng89 Roehampton Inst MSc03. Ripon Coll Cuddesdon BA92 MA97. **d** 93 **p** 94. C Oxton *Ches* 93-97; TV Gt Marlow w Marlow Bottom, Lt Marlow and Bisham *Ox* 97-02; Hd Lon and SE Team Chr Aid from 02. *52A Oak Tree Road, Marlow SL7 3EG* Tel (01628) 483568 E-mail mreed@christian-aid.org

REED, Canon Pamela Kathleen. b 38. EMMTC. **dss** 84 **d** 87 **p** 94. Cambridge Ascension *Ely* 84-88; Par Dn 87-88; Par Dn Cherry Hinton St Andr 88-90; C 91-95; C Teversham 91-95; V Chesterton St Geo from 95; Hon Can Ely Cathl from 00. *St George's Vicarage, 8 Chesterfield Road, Cambridge CB4 1LN* Tel (01223) 423374

REED, Richard David. b 32. Trin Coll Carmarthen K Alfred's Coll Win CertEd54 Ex Univ MA02. **d** 91 **p** 92. NSM Dale and St Brides w Marloes *St D* 91-96; P-in-c Blisland w St Breward *Truro* 96-99; rtd 99; Perm to Offic *Truro* from 99; *St D* from 02. *25 Westhaven, Cosheston, Pembroke Dock SA62 4UL* Tel (01646) 685806

REED, Robert Chase. b 47. Emerson Coll Boston (USA) BSc70 TCD HDipEd72. **d** 87 **p** 88. Aux Min Taney *D & G* 87-97; Res Hd Master Wesley Coll Dub from 87; Succ St Patr Cathl Dublin 93-97; Treas St Patr Cathl Dublin from 96. *Embury House, Wesley College, Dublin 16, Irish Republic* Tel (00353) (1) 269 3150 Fax as telephone E-mail bobreed@indigo.ie

REED, Simon John. b 63. Trin Coll Ox BA86 MA90. Wycliffe Hall Ox BA90. **d** 91 **p** 92. C Walton H Trin *Ox* 91-96; P-in-c Hanger Hill Ascension and W Twyford St Mary *Lon* 96-01; V from 01. *The Ascension Vicarage, Beaufort Road, London W5 3EB* Tel (020) 8566 9920 Fax as telephone E-mail coa@surfaid.org

REED, William Harvey. b 47. K Coll Lon BD69 AKC69. St Aug Coll Cant 69. **d** 70 **p** 71. C Stockton St Mark CD *Dur* 70-72; C Billingham St Cuth 72-76; C S Westoe 76-79; V Chilton Moor 79-87; R Hutton *Chelmsf* 87-95; V Hullbridge from 95. *The Vicarage, 93 Ferry Road, Hullbridge, Hockley SS5 6EL* Tel (01702) 232017 E-mail revharveyreed@whsmithnet.co.uk

REEDE, Samuel William. b 24. TCD BA48 MA52 BD55. CITC 50. **d** 50 **p** 51. C Waterford Ch Ch *C & O* 50-54; C Cregagh *D & D* 54-55; Hd S Ch Miss Ballymacarrett 59-67; Chapl Stranmillis Coll Belf 64-68; Can Raphoe Cathl *D & R* 67-92; I Raphoe w Raymochy 67-68; I Raphoe w Raymochy and Clonleigh 68-92; Dean Raphoe 80-92; rtd 92. *Rooskey, Newtowncunningham, Co Donegal, Irish Republic* Tel (00353) (74) 915 6426

REEDER, Angela Lilian. **d** 99 **p** 00. OLM Eastington, Frocester, Haresfield etc *Glouc* from 99. *St Loy Cottage, West End, Stonehouse GL10 3SN* Tel (01453) 827446

REES, Anthony John. b 49. St Jo Coll Dur BA72 DipTh73 MA77 Man Univ MEd89. **d** 74 **p** 75. C Smethwick St Matt w St Chad *Birm* 74-77; C Bolton St Pet *Man* 77-80; R Cheetham St Mark 80-88; V Mottram in Longdendale w Woodhead *Ches* 88-93; V Mottram in Longdendale 93-02; V Chirk *St As* from 02. *The Vicarage, Trevor Road, Chirk, Wrexham LL14 5HD* Tel (01691) 778519

REES, Antony. See REES, Percival Antony Everard

REES, Brian. b 48. McGill Univ Montreal BA74 St Andr Univ BD76 PhD80. Montreal Dioc Th Coll 76. **d** 80 **p** 81. Canada 80-85; Lic to Offic *St Alb* 85-94; Chapl Bedford Sch 85-92; Hd Master Bedf Prep Sch from 92. *Pemberley House, 17 Park Avenue, Bedford MK40 2LF* Tel (01234) 355999

REES, Brynley Mervyn. b 18. Univ of Wales BA38. Lon Coll of Div 40. **d** 41 **p** 42. C Walthamstow St Luke *Chelmsf* 41-43; C Birm Bp Ryder *Birm* 43-46; V W Bromwich St Paul *Lich* 46-52; V Handforth *Ches* 52-60; V St Alb Ch Ch *St Alb* 60-84; rtd 84; C Weobley w Sarnesfield and Norton Canon *Heref* 84-91; Perm to Offic from 92. *2 Nelson Cottage, Bridge Sollars, Hereford HR4 7JN* Tel (01981) 590296

REES, Celia Pamela. b 48. St D Coll Lamp BA70. LNSM course 97. **d** 98 **p** 99. OLM Leominster *Heref* from 98. *Rivendell, 50 Oldfields Close, Leominster HR6 8TL* Tel (01568) 616581 *or* 612124

REES, Mrs Christine Deryn Irving. b 57. Nottm Univ BSc Sheff Univ MA. Qu Coll Birm. **d** 00 **p** 01. NSM Astwood Bank *Worc* 00-01; C from 01. *367 Birchfield Road, Redditch B97 4NE* Tel (01527) 544417

REES, Christopher John. b 40. Dur Univ BA62. Ridley Hall Cam 62. **d** 64 **p** 65. C Wilmslow *Ches* 64-70; C Birkenhead St Pet w St Matt 70-75; V Lostock Gralam 75-83; R Davenham 83-96; P-in-c Aldford and Bruera from 96. *The Rectory, Middle Lane, Aldford, Chester CH3 6JA* Tel (01244) 620281 E-mail cjrees@surfaid.org

REES, Canon David Frederick. b 21. SS Coll Cam BA48 MA52. Sarum Th Coll 48. **d** 50 **p** 51. C Blackb St Luke *Blackb* 50-53; C St James 53-55; V Choral York Minster *York* 55-62; V Penwortham St Mary *Blackb* 62-90; RD Leyland 70-84; Hon Can Blackb Cathl 79-90; rtd 90; Perm to Offic *Blackb* from 91. *4 Queensdale Close, Walton-le-Dale, Preston PR5 4JU* Tel (01772) 259010

REES, David Grenfell. b 18. St D Coll Lamp BA40 Qu Coll Birm 42. **d** 43 **p** 44. C Llangeinor *Llan* 43-47; C Cadoxton-juxta-Barry 47-53; C St Andrews Major 53-60; V Dyffryn 60-84; rtd 84; Perm to Offic *Llan* from 84. *10 Tyn-yr-Heol Road, Bryncoch, Neath SA10 7EA* Tel (01639) 644488

REES, Chan David Philip Dunn Hugh. b 38. Jes Coll Ox BA60 MA64 Ox Univ DipEd67. Westcott Ho Cam 62. **d** 64 **p** 65. C

Salford St Phil w St Steph *Man* 64-66; Perm to Offic *St As* 66-67; Perm to Offic *Derby* 67-74; Chapl St Marg C of E High Sch Aigburth Liv 74-83; V Meliden and Gwaenysgor *St As* from 84; Dioc Adv for Schs 85-91; Warden of Readers 89-91; Dioc Dir of Ords from 91; Hon Can St As Cathl 93-95 and from 95; Chan from 96. *The Vicarage, Meliden, Prestatyn LL19 8HN* Tel (01745) 856220

REES, David Richard. b 60. St Mich Coll Llan DipTh84. **d** 84 **p** 85. C Llanstadwel *St D* 84-86; C Carmarthen St Dav 86-91; V Llanrhian w Llanhywel and Carnhedryn etc 91-99; V Spittal w Trefgarn and Ambleston w St Dogwells from 99. *The Vicarage, Spittal, Haverfordwest SA62 5QP* Tel (01437) 741505

REES, Ms Diane Eluned. b 61. Univ of Wales (Ban) BSc82 Em Coll Cam PGCE83 Univ of Wales (Swansea) MEd87 CPsychol AFBPsS. St Jo Coll Nottm CTM93 BTh95 MA96. **d** 96 **p** 97. C Hall Green St Pet *Birm* 96-00; P-in-c Bozeat w Easton Maudit *Pet* 00-03; C Putney St Mary *S'wark* from 03. *17 Fanthorpe Street, London SW15 1DZ* Tel (020) 8887 7164
E-mail dereeswdt@aol.com

REES, Eric Vernon. b 19. St Jo Coll Dur BA41 MA44. St Andr Pampisford 43. **d** 43 **p** 44. C Tollington Park St Mark *Lon* 43-51; C Edmonton All SS 51-66; C N St Pancras All Hallows 66-68; C-in-c Enfield St Giles CD 68-80; C Edmonton All SS 80-82; C Edmonton All SS w St Mich 82-90; rtd 90; Perm to Offic *Lon* from 90. *45 Monmouth Road, London N9 0JB* Tel (020) 8807 4329

REES, Glyn. b 63. St Bede's Coll Umtata DipTh87. **d** 87 **p** 87. S Africa 87-00; C Turffontein 87-88; Chapl S African Defence Force 89-90; P-in-c Nigel 91-92; C Kempton Park and Edenvale 92-93; TR Secunda 94-98; R Brakpan 99-00; R Whitwell *Derby* from 00. *The Rectory, High Street, Whitwell, Worksop S80 4RE* Tel (01909) 720220 Fax as telephone

REES, Gruffydd Nicholas. b 23. Univ of Wales (Lamp) BA46. Wycliffe Hall Ox 46. **d** 48 **p** 49. C Fishguard *St D* 48-51; C Betws w Ammanford 51-53; C Carmarthen St Dav 53-57; C Epsom St Martin *Guildf* 57-62; V Llanbister and Llanbadarn Fynydd w Llananno *S & B* 62-75; R New Radnor and Llanfihangel Nantmelan etc 75-84; R Llangenni and Llanbedr Ystrad Yw w Patricio 84-88; rtd 88. *Trefilan, 26 Lakeside Avenue, Llandrindod Wells LD1 5NT* Tel (01597) 825451

REES, Ian Kendall. **d** 00 **p** 01. C Barry All SS *Llan* from 00. *4 Alwen Drive, Barry CF62 7LH* Tel (01446) 722548

REES, Jennifer Mary. *See* MORRELL, Mrs Jennifer Mary

REES, Joanna Mary. *See* STOKER, Mrs Joanna Mary

REES, John. *See* REES, Canon Vivian John Howard

✠**REES, The Rt Revd John Ivor.** b 26. Univ of Wales (Abth) BA50. Westcott Ho Cam 50. **d** 52 **p** 53 **c** 88. C Fishguard w Llanychar *St D* 52-55; C Llangathen w Llanfihangel Cilfargen 55-57; P-in-c Uzmaston and Boulston 57-59; V Slebech and Uzmaston w Boulston 59-65; V Llangollen and Trevor *St As* 65-74; RD Llangollen 70-74; R Wrexham 74-76; Can St As Cathl 75-76; Dean Ban 76-88; V Ban Cathl Par 79-88; Asst Bp St D 88-91; Adn St D 88-91; Bp St D 91-95; Sub-Prelate OStJ from 93; rtd 95; Hon Fell Trin Coll Carmarthen from 96. *Llys Dewi, 45 Clover Park, Haverfordwest SA61 1UE* Tel (01437) 764846

REES, Canon John Martin Rawlins Gore. b 30. St D Coll Lamp BA53. **d** 55 **p** 57. C Mold *St As* 55-56; C Broughton 56-59; C Newtown 59-61; V Penycae 61-73; V Northop 73-83; V Bickerton w Bickley *Ches* 83-91; Lic to Offic 91-95; rtd 95. *Hafod, 9 High Park, Gwernaffield, Mold CH7 5EE* Tel (01352) 740412

REES, John Philip Walford. b 41. St D Coll Lamp BA62 Linacre Coll Ox BA64 MA69 Univ of Wales (Cardiff) BD73. Wycliffe Hall Ox 62. **d** 64 **p** 65. C Reading St Jo *Ox* 64-67; V Patrick *S & M* 67-68; C Pontypool *Mon* 68-70; Area Sec CMS *Glouc, Heref* and *Worc* 70-75; V Bream *Glouc* 75-91; Team Ldr Ichthus Chr Fellowship 91-96; TV Glyncorrwg w Afan Vale and Cymmer Afan *Llan* 96-99; R Llandogo and Tintern *Mon* 99-00; R Llandogo w Whitebrook Chpl and Tintern Parva from 00; RD Monmouth from 02. *The Rectory, Llandogo, Monmouth NP25 4TW* Tel (01594) 530887

REES, The Ven John Wynford Joshua. b 24. Univ of Wales (Lamp) BA52. **d** 53 **p** 54. C Aberystwyth *St D* 53-60; V Llanyre w Llanfihangel Helygen, Llanwrthwl etc *S & B* 60-71; R Llanyre w Llanfihangel Helygen and Diserth 71-87; V Llanllyr-yn-Rhos w Llanfihangel Helygen 87-94; Hon Can Brecon Cathl 77-79; Can Res 79-94; Treas 83-87; Adn Brecon 87-94; rtd 94. *Denebrook, Ithan Road, Llandrindod Wells LD1 6AS* Tel (01597) 823573

REES, Canon Judith Margaret. b 39. Southn Univ BTh89. dss 86 **d** 87 **p** 94. Sanderstead All SS *S'wark* 86-87; Par Dn 87; Dir Cottesloe Chr Tr Progr *Ox* 89-99; Par Dn Gt Horwood 89-91; Par Dn Winslow w Gt Horwood and Addington 91-94; C 94-99; RD Claydon 96-99; Hon Can Ch Ch 97-99; rtd 99. *Sidney Cottage, 111 Lower Road, Salisbury SP2 9NH* Tel (01722) 410050

✠**REES, The Rt Revd Leslie Lloyd.** b 19. Keinton Hall Coll 36. **d** 42 **p** 43 **c** 80. C Roath St Sav *Llan* 42-45; Asst Chapl HM Pris Cardiff 42-45; Chapl HM Pris Dur 45-48; V Princetown *Ex* 48-55; Chapl HM Pris Dartmoor 48-55; Chapl HM Pris Win

55-62; Chapl Gen of Pris 62-80; Hon Can Cant Cathl *Cant* 66-80; Chapl to The Queen 71-80; Suff Bp Shrewsbury *Lich* 80-86; rtd 86; Asst Bp Win from 87. *Kingfisher Lodge, 20 Arle Gardens, Alresford SO24 9BA* Tel (01962) 734619

REES, Michael Lloyd. b 51. St D Coll Lamp DipTh74. **d** 74 **p** 75. C Cardigan w Mwnt and Y Ferwig *St D* 74-77; Min Can St D Cathl 77-81; TV Aberystwyth 81-83; Dioc Children's Adv 83-92; V Pen-boyr 83-88; V Henfynyw w Aberaeron and Llanddewi Aberarth 88-99; RD Glyn Aeron 95-99; V Gors-las from 99. *The Vicarage, 56 Black Lion Road, Cross Hands, Llanelli SA14 6RU* Tel (01269) 842561

REES (née CURRY), Mrs Pauline Carol. b 46. WMMTC 94. **d** 98 **p** 99. OLM Leominster *Heref* from 98. *Crossways Cottage, Leysters, Leominster HR6 0HR* Tel (01568) 750300 Mobile 07702-238395

REES, Percival Antony Everard. b 35. Pemb Coll Ox BA56 MA59. Clifton Th Coll 58. **d** 60 **p** 61. C Heatherlands St Jo *Sarum* 60-65 and 69-70; India 65-69; V W Hampstead St Luke *Lon* 70-82; Lect Oak Hill Th Coll 82-86; V Enfield Ch Ch Trent Park *Lon* 87-00; rtd 00; Perm to Offic *Chelmsf* from 00. *10 Winchester Road, Frinton-on-Sea CO13 9JB* Tel (01255) 679258

REES, Philip. *See* REES, John Philip Walford

REES, Canon Richard John Edward Williams. b 36. Univ of Wales (Lamp) BA58. St Mich Coll Llan 58. **d** 60 **p** 61. C St Issells *St D* 60-64; C Llanedy 64-67; V Whitchurch w Solva and St Elvis 67-77; V Whitchurch w Solva and St Elvis w Brawdy etc 77-01; RD Dewisland and Fishguard 73-01; Can St D Cathl 87-01; Treas 97-01; rtd 01. *The Smithy, Cheriton, Stackpole, Pembroke SA71 5BZ*

REES, Canon Richard Michael. b 35. St Pet Hall Ox BA57 MA61. Tyndale Hall Bris 57. **d** 59 **p** 60. C Crowborough *Chich* 59-62; C Clifton Ch Ch w Em *Bris* 62-64; V Clevedon Ch Ch *B & W* 64-72; V Cambridge H Trin *Ely* 72-84; Chief Sec CA 84-90; Can Res Ches Cathl *Ches* 90-00; Vice-Dean 93-00; Dioc Missr 90-00; Cheshire Co Ecum Officer 91-99; rtd 00; Perm to Offic *Nor* from 01. *56 Tennyson Avenue, King's Lynn PE30 2QJ* Tel (01553) 691982

REES, Ronald Benjamin Dennis. b 44. Univ of Wales (Ban) BTh00. St Mich Coll Llan 00. **d** 00 **p** 01. C Llanbedrog w Llannor and Llangian *Ban* 00-02; P-in-c Llanllyfni from 02. *Y Rheithordy, 2 Môr Awel, Pen-y-groes Estate, Caernarfon LL54 6RA* Tel (01286) 881124

REES, Stephen Philip. b 70. St Luke's Coll Ex BA. Oak Hill Th Coll BA03. **d** 03. C Moreton-in-Marsh w Batsford, Todenham etc *Glouc* from 03. *32 Croft Holm, Moreton-in-Marsh, Gloucester GL56 0JH* E-mail zipyzac@globalnet.com

REES, Miss Susan Mary. b 61. Univ of Wales (Cardiff) BSc82. Ripon Coll Cuddesdon 00. **d** 02 **p** 03. C Penarth All SS *Llan* from 02. *84 Coleridge Avenue, Penarth, Cardiff CF64 2SR* Tel (029) 2070 8044

REES, Canon Vivian John Howard. b 51. Southn Univ LLB72 Ox Univ BA79 MA84 Leeds Univ MPhil84. Wycliffe Hall Ox 76. **d** 79 **p** 80. C Moor Allerton *Ripon* 79-82; Sierra Leone 82-86; Lic to Offic *Ox* from 86; Jt Dioc Reg from 98; Dep Prov Reg 98-00; Prov Reg from 00; Legal Adv ACC from 98; Hon Prov Can Cant Cathl *Cant* from 01. *Oxford Diocesan Registry, 16 Beaumont Street, Oxford OX1 2LZ* Tel (01865) 241974 Fax 726274
E-mail oxford@winckworths.co.uk

REES, William David Cledwyn. b 25. FRGS54 Qu Coll Cam BA49 DipEd50 MA52 Univ of Wales MA75 PhD81. St Deiniol's Hawarden 63. **d** 65 **p** 66. C Rhyl w St Ann *St As* 65-72; Chapl and Lect St Mary's Coll Ban 72-77; Lic to Offic *Ban* 72-77; Lect Univ of Wales (Ban) from 77; Chapl 77-84; Sec Dioc Schs Cttee 84-86. *Anwylfa, Fron Park Avenue, Llanfairfechan LL33 0AS* Tel (01248) 680054

REESE, Preb John David. b 49. Cuddesdon Coll 73. **d** 76 **p** 77. C Kidderminster St Mary *Worc* 76-81; Malaysia 81-85; V Bishop's Castle w Mainstone *Heref* 85-91; RD Clun Forest 87-91; V Tupsley 91-93; P-in-c Hampton Bishop and Mordiford w Dormington 91-93; V Tupsley w Hampton Bishop from 93; RD Heref City 96-02; Preb Heref Cathl from 96. *The Vicarage, 107 Church Road, Hereford HR1 1RT* Tel (01432) 274490

REEVE, Canon Brian Charles. b 36. Lon Univ BSc57 BD60. Tyndale Hall Bris 58. **d** 61 **p** 62. C Eccleston St Luke *Liv* 61-63; C Upton (Overchurch) *Ches* 63-65; C Pemberton St Mark Newtown *Liv* 65-68; V Macclesfield Ch Ch *Ches* 68-74; V Stone Ch Ch *Lich* 74-84; RD Trentham 77-84; V Hoole *Ches* 84-94; Chapl Ches City Hosp 84-91; P-in-c Alderley *Ches* 94-01; Dioc Warden of Readers 84-91; Hon Can Ches Cathl 94-01; rtd 01; Perm to Offic *Ches* from 02. *73 Spring Gardens, Leek ST13 8DD* Tel (01538) 387321

REEVE, David Michael. b 44. St Cath Coll Cam BA67 MA71. Coll of Resurr Mirfield 68. **d** 70 **p** 71. C Willingdon *Chich* 70-73; C Hove All SS 73-76; C Moulsecoomb 76-80; R Singleton 80-90; V E Dean 80-90; V W Dean 80-90; R Hurstpierpoint 90-99; R Kingston Buci from 99. *The Rectory, Rectory Road, Shoreham-by-Sea BN43 6EB* Tel (01273) 592591

REEVE, John Richard. b 65. Southn Univ BA86 La Sainte Union Coll PGCE88. Ripon Coll Cuddesdon 95. **d** 97 **p** 98. C Hale w Badshot Lea *Guildf* 97-00; TV Totton *Win* from 00. *The Vicarage, Ringwood Road, Woodlands, Southampton SO40 7GX* Tel (023) 8066 3267

REEVE, Kenneth John. b 42. Sarum & Wells Th Coll DCM93. **d** 93 **p** 94. C Thorpe St Matt *Nor* 93-96; P-in-c S Lynn 96-99. *Address temp unknown*

REEVE, Kenneth Robert. b 23. St Cath Coll Ox BA49 MA53. Sarum Th Coll 64. **d** 68 **p** 69. Hon C Farleigh Hungerford w Tellisford *B & W* 68-71; Perm to Offic Virgin Is 71-72; Hon C Norton St Philip 72-74; Hon C Hinton Charterhouse 72-74; Seychelles 74-76; Perm to Offic *B & W* 77-89; *Chich* 78-82. *Sundial, Hill Close, Wincanton BA9 9NF* Tel (01963) 33369

REEVE, Richard Malcolm. b 64. Reading Univ BSc85. Trin Coll Bris BA92. **d** 92 **p** 93. C Northolt St Mary *Lon* 92-95; C Acton Green 95-98; V Hayes St Edm from 98. *St Edmund's Vicarage, 1 Edmund's Close, Hayes UB4 0HA* Tel (020) 8573 6913

REEVE, Richard Noel. b 29. MB, ChB. St Deiniol's Hawarden. **d** 84 **p** 85. Hon C Norton *Ches* 84-85; C Filey *York* 85-87; TV Brayton 87-90; rtd 90; Perm to Offic *Man* 90-93; Res Min Bicton, Montford w Shrawardine and Fitz *Lich* 97-99; Perm to Offic from 99. *26 Windsor Road, Stafford ST17 4PA* Tel (01785) 252607

REEVE, Preb Roger Patrick. b 42. Fitzw Coll Cam BA65 MA68. Coll of Resurr Mirfield. **d** 67 **p** 68. C Barnstaple St Pet w H Trin *Ex* 67-74; V Ernesettle 74-78; V Braunton from 78; RD Barnstaple 85-93 and from 01; Preb Ex Cathl from 92. *The Vicarage, Church Street, Braunton EX33 2EL* Tel (01271) 813367 Fax as telephone E-mail rogerreeve@cwcom.net

REEVES, Christopher. b 30. Nottm Univ BA53. Wells Th Coll 53. **d** 55 **p** 56. C Rowbarton *B & W* 55-59; C Cant St Greg *Cant* 59-61; Chapl Schiedam Miss to Seamen *Eur* 61-67; V Barkingside H Trin *Chelmsf* 67-97; rtd 97. *3 Albany Close, Goonown, St Agnes TR5 0XE* Tel (01872) 552976

REEVES, David Eric. b 46. Sarum Th Coll 68. **d** 71 **p** 72. C Guildf H Trin w St Mary *Guildf* 71-74; C Warmsworth *Sheff* 74-78; V Herringthorpe 78-90; V Cleveleys *Blackb* from 90; RD Poulton 94-00. *The Vicarage, Rough Lea Road, Thornton-Cleveleys FY5 1DP* Tel (01253) 852153

REEVES, Donald St John. b 34. Qu Coll Cam BA57 MA61. Cuddesdon Coll 62. **d** 63 **p** 64. C Maidstone All SS w St Phil *Cant* 63-65; Bp's Dom Chapl *S'wark* 65-68; V St Helier 69-80; R Westmr St Jas *Lon* 80-98; Dir Soul of Eur Project from 98; rtd 98; Perm to Offic *Ex* from 00. *The Coach House, Church Street, Crediton EX17 2AQ* Tel (01363) 775100 Fax 773911 E-mail donalreeves@aol.com

REEVES, Elizabeth Anne. See THOMAS, Mrs Elizabeth Anne

REEVES, Gillian Patricia. b 46. S'wark Ord Course 87. **d** 90 **p** 94. Par Dn Shirley St Geo *S'wark* 90-94; C 94-96; C Caterham 96-98; TV from 98. *St Luke's Vicarage, 8 Whyteleafe Hill, Whyteleafe CR3 0AA* Tel (020) 8660 4015

REEVES, Graham. b 65. Chich Th Coll BTh94. **d** 94 **p** 95. C Cardiff St Mary and St Steph w St Dyfrig etc *Llan* 94-95; C Roath 95-98; Chapl Sussex Weald and Downs NHS Trust from 98. *1A Havenstoke Close, Chichester PO19 4RR*

REEVES, John Graham. b 44. Kelham Th Coll 64. **d** 69 **p** 71. C Aston cum Aughton *Sheff* 69-71; C Ribbleton *Blackb* 72-74; C Cleveleys 74-75; P-in-c Huncoat 75-77; V 77-82; V Knuzden 82-92; V Sandylands from 92. *St John's Vicarage, 2 St John's Avenue, Morecambe LA3 1EU* Tel (01524) 411299

REEVES, Kenneth William. b 38. TCD 67 NUI DipSocSc76. **d** 69 **p** 70. C Killowen *D & R* 69-70; I Ardara 70-76; TV Quidenham *Nor* 76-81; V Swaffham 81-86; Chapl Nor Coll of Educn 86-91; P-in-c Lakenham St Alb *Nor* 86-91; rtd 92; Perm to Offic *Nor* 92-98; P-in-c Trowse 99-03; P-in-c Nerja and Almuñécar *Eur* from 03. *Calle Condal 21, 29780 Nerja, Malaga, Spain* Tel (0034) 95 252 5406 Fax as telephone E-mail revkenn@aol.com

REEVES, Maria Elizabeth Ann. See COULTER, Mrs Maria Elizabeth Ann

REEVES, Michael Richard Ewert. b 74. Girton Coll Cam MA00. Oak Hill Th Coll 98. **d** 02 **p** 03. NSM Langham Place All So *Lon* from 02. *83 Boundary Road, London NW8 0RG* Tel (020) 7625 5840 *or* 7580 3522 E-mail mre.reeves@virgin.net

REEVES, Nicholas John Harding. b 44. Open Th Coll BA99 Nottm Univ MA02. ALCD69. **d** 69 **p** 70. C Upton (Overchurch) *Ches* 69-72; C Woodlands *Sheff* 72-74; C-in-c Cranham Park CD *Chelmsf* 74-79; V Cranham Park 79-88; R Aldridge *Lich* 88-02. *90 Nottingham Road, Long Eaton, Nottingham NG10 2BZ* Tel 0115-973 6029 E-mail john@thereeves.freeserve.co.uk

✠**REEVES, The Rt Revd Sir Paul Alfred.** b 32. GCMG85 GCVO86 QSO90. Univ of NZ BA55 MA56 St Pet Coll Ox BA61 MA65 Hon DCL85 Wellington Univ (NZ) Hon LLD89 Gen Th Sem NY Hon DD92. St Jo Coll Auckland LTh58. **d** 58 **p** 60 **c** 71. New Zealand 58-59 and from 64; C Ox St Mary V *Ox* 59-61; C Kirkley *Nor* 61-63; C Lewisham St Mary *S'wark* 63-64; Bp Waiapu 71-79; Bp Auckland 79-85; Abp New Zealand 80-85; Gov Gen NZ 85-90; KStJ from 86; ACC Rep at United Nations 91-93; Asst Bp New York 91-94; Dean Te Rau Kahikatea Th

Coll Auckland 94-95. *16E Cathedral Place, Parnell, Auckland, New Zealand* Tel (0064) (9) 302 2913 *or* 373 7599 ext 4754 Fax 308 2312 E-mail sirpaulreeves@dra.co.nz

REGAN, Brian. b 46. MBIM80. WMMTC 88. **d** 91 **p** 92. C Cov St Jo *Cov* 91-94; FSJ from 93; V Tile Hill *Cov* from 94. *St Oswald's Vicarage, 228 Jardine Crescent, Coventry CV4 9PL* Tel (024) 7646 5072 E-mail brian@revregan.freeserve.co.uk

REGAN, Noel Henry Likely. b 49. **d** 99 **p** 00. C Taunagh w Kilmactranny, Ballysumaghan etc *K, E & A* from 99. *Gurteen Farm, Cliffoney, Co Sligo, Irish Republic* Tel (00353) (71) 916 6253

REGAN, Paul John. b 67. Southn Univ BA88 PhD96 St Jo Coll Dur BA98. Cranmer Hall Dur 96. **d** 99 **p** 00. C St Alb St Pet *St Alb* 99-03; TV Smestow Vale *Lich* from 03. *Swindon Vicarage, 12 St John's Close, Swindon, Dudley DY3 4PQ* Tel (01384) 273429 *or* (01902) 897700

REGAN, Philip. b 49. Qu Mary Coll Lon BSc MSc. Wycliffe Hall Ox 81. **d** 83 **p** 84. Hon C Scotforth *Blackb* 83-89; P-in-c Combe St Nicholas w Wambrook *B & W* 89-01; V from 01; P-in-c Whitestaunton 89-01; R from 01. *The Vicarage, Combe St Nicholas, Chard TA20 3NJ* Tel (01460) 62121

REGINALD, Brother. See BOX, Reginald Gilbert

REID, Alec. See REID, William Alexander

REID, Amanda Joy. See MARRIOTT, Mrs Amanda Joy

REID, Andrew John. b 47. Birm Univ BEd70 Man Univ MEd76 Lon Univ DipRS88. S'wark Ord Course 88. **d** 88 **p** 89. NSM Westerham *Roch* 88-90; Chapl Abp Tenison's Sch Kennington from 90. *Archbishop Tenison's School, 55 Kennington Oval, London SE11 5SR* Tel (020) 7435 3771 *or* 7435 6126

REID, Christopher Jason. b 69. Trin Coll Bris 01. **d** 03. C Woodley *Ox* from 03. *8 Caldbeck Drive, Woodley, Reading RG5 4LA* Tel 0118-944 0690 E-mail cjasonreid@hotmail.com

REID, Canon Colin Guthrie. b 30. **d** 56 **p** 57. C Kendal St Thos *Carl* 56-59; C Crosthwaite Keswick 59-60; R Caldbeck w Castle Sowerby 60-76; RD Wigton 69-70; P-in-c Sebergham 75-76; R Caldbeck, Castle Sowerby and Sebergham 76-93; Hon Can Carl Cathl 89-93; Perm to Offic *Carl* from 93. *Mellbreak, Longthwaite Road, Wigton CA7 9JR* Tel (01697) 345625

REID, Donald. b 58. Glas Univ LLB79 Pemb Coll Ox MPhil81 Edin Univ BD85. Edin Th Coll 82. **d** 85 **p** 86. C Greenock *Glas* 85-88; C Baillieston 88-91; R 91-95; C Glas St Serf 88-91; R 91-95; Chapl Glas Univ 89-00; Chapl Glas Caledonian Univ 89-00; Chapl Strathclyde Univ 89-00. *212 Wilton Street, Glasgow G20 6BL* Tel 0141-946 1145 Fax 576 5906 E-mail dreid212@aol.com

REID, Eric. See REID, Canon William Frederick

✠**REID, The Rt Revd Gavin Hunter.** b 34. OBE00. K Coll Lon BA56. Oak Hill Th Coll 56. **d** 60 **p** 61 **c** 92. C E Ham St Paul *Chelmsf* 60-63; C Rainham 63-66; Publications Sec CPAS 66-71; Hon C St Paul's Cray St Barn *Roch* 68-71; Ed Sec USCL 71-74; Hon C Woking St Jo *Guildf* 72-92; Sec for Evang CPAS 74-92; Consultant Missr CPAS and BMU Adv 90-92; Suff Bp Maidstone *Cant* 92-00; Six Preacher Cant Cathl 92-97; rtd 00; Perm to Offic *Nor* and *St E* from 00. *Furzefield, 17 Richard Crampton Road, Beccles NR34 9HN* Tel (01502) 717042 Mobile 07941-770549 Fax (01502) 710739 E-mail gavin@reids.org

REID, Geraldine Felicity (Jo). b 47. RGN69. EMMTC 95. **d** 98 **p** 99. NSM Skellingthorpe w Doddington *Linc* 98-02; NSM Hykeham from 02. *Tol Peden, Monson Park, Skellingthorpe, Lincoln LN6 5UE* Tel (01522) 828402 *or* 828403

REID, Gordon. See REID, The Ven William Gordon

REID, Herbert Alan. b 31. AKC55. **d** 56 **p** 57. C Penwortham St Mary *Blackb* 56-59; C-in-c Penwortham St Leon CD 59-63; V Brierfield 63-72; V Warton St Paul 72-79; V Read in Whalley 79-98; rtd 98; Perm to Offic *Blackb* from 98. *Paslew House, 6 The Sands, Whalley, Blackburn BB7 9TL* Tel (01254) 824620

REID, Hugh Gamble. b 33. Roch Th Coll 63. **d** 64 **p** 64. C Martin w Thornton *Linc* 64-66; Bp's Youth Chapl 66-69; C Alford w Rigsby 66-69; Chapl HM Borstal Everthorpe 69-71; Chapl HM Pris Dur 71-74; Chapl HM Pris Wakef 74-77; V Northowram *Wakef* 77-79; Chapl HM Pris Coldingley 79-81; Chapl HM Rem Cen Risley 81-85; Chapl HM Pris Holloway 85-88; C Guilden Morden *Ely* 88-89; C Shingay Gp of Par 90; R Upwell Ch Ch 90-93; R Welney 90-93; Perm to Offic *Ely* from 93. *Banff, 23 Northwold, Ely CB6 1BG* Tel (01353) 663924

REID, James. b 46. Strathclyde Univ BSc69. WMMTC 88. **d** 91 **p** 92. C Attleborough *Cov* 91-95; V Walsall Pleck and Bescot *Lich* 95-99; TR Chell from 99. *The Rectory, 203 St Michael's Road, Stoke-on-Trent ST6 6JT* Tel (01782) 838708

REID, Jason. See REID, Christopher Jason

REID, Lucinda Jane. b 57. Dur Univ BA78. Ripon Coll Cuddesdon 79. **dss** 81 **d** 85 **p** 85. Birtley *Dur* 81-84; Canada from 84. *127 Glasgow Street North, Guelph ON, Canada, N1H 4W5* Tel (001) (519) 821 7419 E-mail lreid@uoguelpha.ca

REID, Mrs Pauline Ann. b 57. EAMTC 00. **d** 03. C Silverstone and Abthorpe w Slapton etc *Pet* from 03. *The Rectory, 2 Tews End Lane, Paulerspury, Towcester NN12 7NQ* Tel (01327) 811670 Mobile 07812-831869 E-mail p.reid@tiscali.co.uk

REID, Peter Ivor. b 30. Qu Coll Cam BA53 MA72. St Mich Coll Llan 78. **d** 80 **p** 81. C Llantwit Major and St Donat's *Llan* 80-83; C Llantwit Major 83-84; V Laleston w Tythegston 84; V Laleston w Tythegston and Merthyr Mawr 84-88; V Roath 88-98; rtd 98. *18 Woolaston Avenue, Cardiff CF23 5AD* Tel (029) 2075 3306

REID, Robert. *See* McLEAN-REID, Robert

REID, Stewart Thomas. b 45. Liv Hope MA01. Oak Hill Th Coll 66. **d** 70 **p** 71. C Normanton *Derby* 70-73; C Leyland St Andr *Blackb* 73-78; V Halliwell St Luke *Man* 78-95; V Southport Ch Ch *Liv* from 95. *The Vicarage, 12 Gloucester Road, Southport PR8 2AU* Tel (01704) 565120

REID, William Alexander (Alec). b 23. Melbourne Univ BA48 ACT ThL50. Trin Coll Melbourne 46. **d** 51 **p** 52. Australia 51-52, 58-71 and from 81; C Kennington St Jo *S'wark* 53; C Westmr St Matt *Lon* 53-56; C Balkwell *Newc* 56-58; Malaysia 71-76; Papua New Guinea 76-81; and 89. *7/55A Coorigil Road, Carnegie, Vic, Australia 3163* Tel (0061) (3) 9569 9217

REID, Canon William Frederick (Eric). b 22. OBE88. TCD BA45 MA53. **d** 46 **p** 47. C Belfast Ardoyne *Conn* 46-49; C Finaghy 49-52; C Dublin Donnybrook *D & G* 52-54; I Carbury *M & K* 54-59; Dep Dir The Samaritans 59-67; C St Steph Walbrook and St Swithun etc *Lon* 59-67; Chapl Netherne Hosp Coulsdon 67-76; C-in-c Netherne St Luke CD *S'wark* 67-76; Lic to Offic 76-99; Sec and Dir Tr Gen Syn Hosp Chapl Coun 76-87; Hon Can Newc Cathl *Newc* 79-88; rtd 88; Perm to Offic *S'wark* from 99. *65 Lagham Park, South Godstone, Godstone RH9 8EP* Tel (01342) 893312

REID, The Ven William Gordon. b 43. Edin Univ MA63 Keble Coll Ox BA66 MA72. Edin Th Coll 63 Cuddesdon Coll 66. **d** 67 **p** 68. C Edin St Salvador *Edin* 67-69; Chapl and Tutor Sarum Th Coll 69-72; R Edin St Mich and All SS *Edin* 72-84; Provost St Andr Cathl Inverness *Mor* 84-87; Chapl Ankara *Eur* 87-89; Chapl Stockholm w Gävle and Västerås 89-92; V Gen to Bp Eur 92-02; Can Gib Cathl 92-98; Adn in Eur 96-98; P-in-c St Mich Cornhill w St Pet le Poer etc *Lon* 97-98; Dean Gib *Eur* 98-00; Chapl Milan w Genoa and Varese from 00; Adn Italy and Malta from 00; Chapl Liguria from 00. *All Saints' Church, Via Solferino 17, 20121 Milan, Italy* Tel (0039) (02) 655 2258 Fax as telephone E-mail allsaint@tin.it *or* gordon reid@libero.it

REIGATE, Archdeacon of. *See* KAJUMBA, The Ven Daniel Steven Kimbugwe

REILLY, Canon Frederick James. b 29. CITC 70. **d** 73 **p** 74. C Agherton *Conn* 73-75; C Ballymena 75-82; I Ballyscullion *D & R* from 82; Hon Can Derry Cathl from 03. *The Rectory, 8 Ballynease Road, Bellaghy, Magherafelt BT45 8JD* Tel (028) 7938 6214

REILLY, Thomas Gerard. b 38. **d** 64 **p** 64. In RC Ch 64-73; Hon C Clapton Park All So *Lon* 73-76; Hon C Haggerston All SS 76-78; Hon C Walthamstow St Sav *Chelmsf* 79-85; P-in-c Forest Gate Em w Upton Cross 85-89; V 89-92; V Chaddesden St Phil *Derby* 92-01; RD Derby N 95-00; rtd 01; Perm to Offic *B & W* from 01. *4 Rose Lane, Crewkerne TA18 7ER* Tel (01460) 72613 E-mail ger_mon@totalise.co.uk

REILY, Paul Alan. b 59. UEA BA81. St Jo Coll Nottm DTS91 MA92. **d** 92 **p** 93. C Westcliff St Mich *Chelmsf* 92-96; P-in-c Barkingside St Cedd 96-98; V 98-01; V Leyton St Cath and St Paul from 01. *St Catherine's Vicarage, Fairlop Road, London E11 1BL* Tel (020) 8539 6361 E-mail paulreily@pipeonline.net

REINDORP, David Peter Edington. b 52. Trin Coll Cam BA82 MA86 CQSW77 DASS77. Westcott Ho Cam 79. **d** 83 **p** 84. C Chesterton Gd Shep *Ely* 83-85; C Hitchin *St Alb* 85-88; V Waterbeach *Ely* 88-97; R Landbeach 88-97; OCF 88-97; CF(V) from 92; RD Quy *Ely* 94-97; V Cherry Hinton St Jo from 97. *St John's Vicarage, 9 Luard Road, Cambridge CB2 2PJ* Tel (01223) 247451 *or* tel and fax 241316 E-mail david.reindorp@talk21.com

REINDORP, Canon Michael Christopher Julian. b 44. Trin Coll Cam BA67 MA70 K Coll Lon MA99. Cuddesdon Coll 67 United Th Coll Bangalore 68. **d** 69 **p** 70. C Poplar *Lon* 69-74; V Chatham St Wm *Roch* 74-84; R Stantonbury *Ox* 84-87; TR Stantonbury and Willen 87-92; P-in-c Richmond St Mary w St Matthias and St John's *S'wark* 92-95; TR from 96; Hon Can S'wark Cathl from 03. *The Vicarage, Ormond Road, Richmond TW10 6TH* Tel (020) 8940 0362 Fax as telephone E-mail rector@richmondteam.freeserve.co.uk

REISS, Prof Michael Jonathan. b 58. Trin Coll Cam BA78 MA82 PhD82 PGCE83 FIBiol90. EAMTC 87. **d** 90 **p** 91. Lect Cam Univ 88-94; Reader 94-00; NSM Comberton *Ely* 90-94; NSM Deanery of Bourn 94-96 and 99-00; P-in-c Boxworth and Elsworth w Knapwell 96-99; Perm to Offic from 99; Prof Science Educn Inst of Educn Lon Univ from 01. *Institute of Education, University of London, 20 Bedford Way, London WC1H 0AL* Tel (020) 7612 6776 E-mail m.reiss@ioe.ac.uk

REISS, Peter Henry. b 62. Hertf Coll Ox BA85 MA91 Natal Univ MA95. Trin Coll Bris DipHE90 St Jo Coll Nottm 95. **d** 95 **p** 96. C Sherwood *S'well* 95-00; TV Bestwood 00-03; V Bestwood Park w Rise Park from 03. *81 Cherry Orchard Mount, Nottingham NG5 5TJ* Tel 0115-919 8820 E-mail p.reiss@ntlworld.com

REISS, The Ven Robert Paul. b 43. Trin Coll Cam BA67 MA71. Westcott Ho Cam 67. **d** 69 **p** 70. C St John's Wood *Lon* 69-73; Bangladesh 73; Chapl Trin Coll Cam 73-78; Selection Sec ACCM 78-85; Sen Selection Sec 83; TR Grantham *Linc* 86-96; RD Grantham 92-96; Adn Surrey *Guildf* from 96; Hon Can Guildf Cathl from 96. *The Archdeacon's House, New Road, Wormley, Godalming GU8 5SU* Tel (01428) 682563 Fax 682993 E-mail bob.reiss@cofeguildford.org.uk

REITH, Ivor Stuart Weston. b 16. Ridley Hall Cam 65. **d** 66 **p** 67. C Eastbourne H Trin *Chich* 66-69; R Angmering 69-81; rtd 81; Perm to Offic *Chich* from 84. *8 Windmill Close, Hove BN3 7LJ* Tel (01273) 733187

REITH, Robert Michael. b 55. Oak Hill Th Coll BA83. **d** 83 **p** 84. C Kendal St Thos *Carl* 83-87; C Leyland St Andr *Blackb* 87-92; V Leyland St Jo 92-94; TR Dagenham *Chelmsf* 94-03; V from 03. *The Vicarage, Church Lane, Dagenham RM10 9UL* Tel (020) 8592 1339 E-mail mikereith@aol.com

REMPEY, Philip Roland. b 19. Glouc Th Course 74. **d** 76 **p** 76. NSM Charlton Kings St Mary *Glouc* 76-88; Perm to Offic from 88. *87 Ravensgate Road, Charlton Kings, Cheltenham GL53 8NS* Tel (01242) 519313

RENDALL, Canon John Albert. b 43. Hull Univ BTh84 MA89. Ripon Hall Ox 65. **d** 68 **p** 69. C Southsea St Simon *Portsm* 68-71; C Wallington H Trin *S'wark* 71-77; P-in-c Rufforth w Moor Monkton and Hessay *York* 77-79; R from 79; P-in-c Long Marston 77-79; R from 79; RD New Ainsty 85-97; P-in-c Healaugh w Wighill, Bilbrough and Askham Richard from 02; P-in-c Tockwith and Bilton w Bickerton from 03; Can and Preb York Minster from 94; Chapl Purey Cust Nuffield Hosp from 82. *The Vicarage, Wetherby Road, Rufforth, York YO23 3QF* Tel (01904) 738262 E-mail nata@supanet.com

RENDALL, Richard John. b 54. Solicitor 78 Wadh Coll Ox BA76 LLB76 MA92. Wycliffe Hall Ox 90. **d** 92 **p** 93. C Heswall *Ches* 92-98; R High Ongar w Norton Mandeville *Chelmsf* from 98. *The Rectory, The Street, High Ongar, Ongar CM5 9NQ* Tel (01277) 362593 E-mail rendalls@talk21.com

RENDLE, Graham Barton. b 40. **d** 99 **p** 00. OLM Rougham, Beyton w Hessett and Rushbrooke *St E* from 99. *Appletrees, Bury Road, Beyton, Bury St Edmunds IP30 9AB* Tel (01359) 270924

RENFREY, Edward Donald John-Baptist. b 53. ACT DipTh76. **d** 76 **p** 77. Australia 76-84 and from 99; C Naracoorte 76-77; P-in-c Kingston w Robe 78-81; R 81-84; Chapl RN 84-99; Chapl R Aus Navy from 99. *4/7 Bambra Crescent, Larrakeyah, NT, Australia 0820* Tel (0061) (8) 8935 4282 Mobile 409-662823 E-mail edwardrenfrey@hotmail.com.au

RENISON, Gary James. b 62. SS Hild & Bede Coll Dur BA83. Ridley Hall Cam 84. **d** 86 **p** 87. C Stapenhill w Cauldwell *Derby* 86-89; C Cheadle Hulme St Andr *Ches* 89-92; Min Cheadle Hulme Em CD 92-95; P-in-c Bar Hill from 95. *108 Stonefield, Bar Hill, Cambridge CB3 8TE* Tel (01954) 781629 *or* tel and fax 206120 E-mail gjr@renison.ndo.co.uk

RENNARD, Edward Lionel. b 51. CertEd72 Nottm Univ BTh80. Linc Th Coll 76. **d** 80 **p** 81. C Old Brumby *Linc* 80-82; C-in-c Gt Grimsby St Matt Fairfield CD 82-86; V Fairfield St Matt 86-88; V Hykeham 88-91; TR 91-00; TR Blyth Valley *St E* from 00. *The Rectory, Highfield Road, Halesworth IP19 8SJ* Tel and fax (01986) 872331 *or* tel 872602 Mobile 07939-220416 E-mail e.l.rennard@ntlworld.com

RENNARD, Margaret Rose. b 49. CertEd75. Linc Th Coll 76. **d** 87 **p** 94. C Fairfield St Matt *Linc* 87-88; C Hykeham 88-00; Chapl HM Pris Morton Hall 91-00; Asst Chapl HM Pris Blundeston from 00; Chapl Allington NHS Trust from 00; Perm to Offic *St E* from 01. *The Rectory, Highfield Road, Halesworth IP19 8SU* Tel and fax (01986) 872331 *or* tel 872602 E-mail margaret.rennard@ntlworld.com

RENNIE, Iain Hugh. b 43. Ripon Coll Cuddesdon 88. **d** 90 **p** 91. C Poulton-le-Sands w Morecambe St Laur *Blackb* 90-94; V Hornby w Claughton 94-02; V Hornby w Claughton and Whittington etc from 02. *The Vicarage, Arkholme, Carnforth LA6 1AX* Tel (015242) 21238 Fax as telephone

RENNIE, Paul Antony. b 58. Heriot-Watt Univ BSc82 Edin Univ LTh. **d** 87 **p** 88. C Nairn *Mor* 87-90; C Forres 87-90; C Edin St Pet *Edin* 90-92; Dep Chapl HM Pris Leeds 92; Chapl HM YOI Hindley 93-95; Chapl HM Pris Liv 95-97; Chapl RAF from 97. *Chaplaincy Services (RAF), HQ, Personnel and Training Command, RAF Ainsworth, Gloucester GL3 1EZ* Tel (01452) 712612 ext 5164 Fax 510828

RENNISON, Walter Patrick. b 18. MBE52. TCD BA40 MA45. **d** 42 **p** 43. C Ballymacarrett St Martin *D & D* 42-45; CF 45-73; V Milland *Chich* 73-87; rtd 87; Perm to Offic *Guildf* from 87. *Woodlands Elderly Persons' Residence, 174-178 Reading Road South, Church Crookham, Fleet GU52 6AE* Tel (01252) 615358

RENNIX, Raymond. d 03. NSM Killaney w Carryduff *D & D* from 03. *5 Brompton Court, Dromara, Dromore BT25 2DQ* Tel (028) 9753 3167 E-mail ray.rennix@u.genie.co.uk

RENOUF, Peter Mark. b 30. Down Coll Cam BA55 MA59 Cam Univ DipEd56. Ridley Hall Cam. **d** 58 **p** 59. C Rainham *Chelmsf* 58-61; Asst Chapl Wellington Coll Berks 61-63; Chapl 63-69; V

Eastbourne All SS *Chich* 69-78; R Farnborough *Guildf* 78-84; C Welford w Wickham and Gt Shefford *Ox* 85-86; C Welford w Wickham and Gt Shefford, Boxford etc 86-89; P-in-c Beedon and Peasemore w W Ilsley and Farnborough 89-97. *1 King James Terrace, 2 Broad Street, Portsmouth PO1 2LL*

RENOUF, Canon Robert Wilson. b 28. Niagara Univ BSc51 Pacific State Univ PhD77. Claremont Sch of Th DMin81 Lambeth STh86 Selly Oak Coll Cert Min & Miss 86 Gen Th Sem (NY) MDiv54. **d** 54 **p** 55. USA 54-56 and 58-82 and from 91; Nicaragua 56-58 and 82-85; Fell and Tutor Coll of the Ascension Selly Oak 85-86; Hon PV S'wark Cathl *S'wark* 86-91; Miss Personnel Sec USPG 86-88; Adv Decade of Evang ACC 89-91; rtd 92. *4502 North Caminito de la Puerta, Tuscon, AZ 85718, USA* E-mail tacheria@aol.com

RENSHAW, Ms Anne-Marie Louise. b 71. St Hilda's Coll Ox MA96 Fitzw Coll Cam BA97. Ridley Hall Cam 95. **d** 98 **p** 99. C Norton *St Alb* 98-02; TV Borehamwood from 02. *Holy Cross Vicarage, 1 Warren Grove, Borehamwood WD6 2QU* Tel (020) 8953 2183 E-mail alr@fish.co.uk

RENSHAW, Anthony. b 40. McGill Univ Montreal LTh87 DipMin87. Montreal Dioc Th Coll 83. **d** 87 **p** 88. Canada 87-90; P-in-c Ainsdale *Liv* 90-91; V 91-98; V Singleton w Weeton *Blackb* from 98. *St Michael's Vicarage, Church Road, Weeton, Preston PR4 3WD* Tel (01253) 836249
E-mail tonyrenshaw@tiscali.co.uk

RENSHAW, David William. b 59. Oak Hill Th Coll BA85. **d** 85 **p** 86. C Shawbury *Lich* 85-88; V Childs Ercall and R Stoke upon Tern 88-92; V Stoneleigh *Guildf* 92-97; RD Epsom 95-97; Chapl Scarborough and NE Yorks Healthcare NHS Trust 97-99; Chapl St Cath Hospice Scarborough 97-99; R Meppershall w Campton and Stondon *St Alb* 99-01; C Bedford St Andr 02; rtd 02. *11 Albany Road, Bexhill-on-Sea TN40 1BY* Tel (01424) 731526 E-mail dwrenshaw@onetel.net.uk

RENSHAW, Peter Selwyn Kay. b 29. Keble Coll Ox BA52 MA64. St Steph Ho Ox 52. **d** 64 **p** 65. Lic to Offic *Ox* 64-66; Chapl RN 66-70; Chapl Br Emb and Athens St Paul *Eur* 71-74; Gothenburg 74-75; Chapl RN Sch Haslemere 75-81; Costa Blanca *Eur* 81-82; R Ewelme *Ox* 83-85; R Ewelme, Brightwell Baldwin, Cuxham w Easington 85-92; rtd 92. *Lovedays House, Painswick, Stroud GL6 6QB* Tel (01452) 812811

RENSHAW, Susan Kathryn. b 55. Shenstone Coll of Educn CertEd77. WMMTC 99. **d** 02 **p** 03. C Sedgley All SS *Worc* from 02. *23 Sunningdale Road, Sedgley, Dudley DY3 3PP* Tel (01902) 661184 Mobile 07932-750410
E-mail skrenshaw23@hotmail.com

RENSHAW, Timothy John. b 65. Trin Coll Carmarthen BA86. St Jo Coll Nottm MA97. **d** 97 **p** 98. C Calverton *S'well* 97-01; C Epperstone 97-01; C Gonalston 97-01; C Oxton 97-01; P-in-c Shireoaks from 01; Dioc Adv on Notts Coalfield from 01. *1 Potter's Nook, Shireoaks, Worksop S81 8NF* Tel (01909) 479350

RENWICK, Canon Colin. b 30. St Aid Birkenhead. **d** 59 **p** 60. C Drypool St Columba w St Andr and St Pet *York* 59-62; C Wigan St Cath *Liv* 62-64; Min Thornton CD 64-77; V Thornton 77-97; RD Bootle 83-89; Hon Can Bauchi from 93; rtd 97; Perm to Offic *Ches* from 97. *27 Briar Drive, Heswall, Wirral CH60 5RN* Tel 0151-342 3308

RENYARD, Christopher. b 52. Open Univ BA87. Coll of Resurr Mirfield 81. **d** 84 **p** 85. C Heckmondwike *Wakef* 84-88; C Harpenden St Nic *St Alb* 88-95; Asst Chapl Salisbury Health Care NHS Trust from 95. *The Chaplain's Office, Salisbury District Hospital, Salisbury SP2 8BJ* Tel (01722) 336262 ext 4271

RENYARD, Paul Holmwood. b 42. K Coll Lon BD65 AKC65. **d** 66 **p** 67. C Croydon St Aug *Cant* 66-69; C Farnham *Guildf* 69-72; V Capel 72-78; Asst Dir RE 72-78; Asst Dir RE *Roch* 78-83; Hon C Roch 78-83; V Holdenhurst *Win* 83-95; V Pennington from 95. *The Vicarage, 29 Ramley Road, Pennington, Lymington SO41 8LH* Tel (01590) 672646
E-mail paul@renyard.fsnet.co.uk

REPATH, George David. b 43. Univ of Wales (Lamp) DipTh68 Kellogg Coll Ox MSt96. **d** 68 **p** 69. C Cardiff St Jo *Llan* 68-73; C Gt Stanmore *Lon* 73-77; V Stratfield Mortimer *Ox* 77-85; RD Bradfield 82-85; P-in-c Mortimer W End w Padworth 83-85; V Bray and Braywood from 85. *The Vicarage, Bray, Maidenhead SL6 2AB* Tel (01628) 621527

REPATH, John Richard. b 48. Univ of Wales (Cardiff) DipTh75. St Mich Coll Llan 72. **d** 75 **p** 76. C Canton St Jo *Llan* 75-79; C Burghclere w Newtown and Ecchinswell w Sydmonton *Win* 80-83; R Bewcastle and Stapleton *Carl* 83-88; P-in-c Kirklinton w Hethersgill and Scaleby 86-88; R Bewcastle, Stapleton and Kirklinton etc 88-97; rtd 97; P-in-c New Galloway *Glas* from 97. *The Rectory, Kenbridge Road, New Galloway, Castle Douglas DG7 3RP* Tel (01644) 420235

REPTON, Suffragan Bishop of. *See* HAWTIN, The Rt Revd David Christopher

RESCH, Michael Johann. b 63. NTMTC DTPS99. **d** 99 **p** 00. C Cullompton *Ex* 99-01; C Cullompton, Willand, Uffculme, Kentisbeare etc 01-03; P-in-c Sittingbourne H Trin w Bobbing

Cant from 03. *Holy Trinity Vicarage, 47 London Road, Sittingbourne ME10 1NQ* Tel (01795) 472724 Mobile 07866-922918 E-mail mikeresch@aol.com

RESTALL, Gerald Dalton. b 22. K Coll Lon BD50 AKC50. **d** 51 **p** 52. C Grays Thurrock *Chelmsf* 51-55; C-in-c Rush Green St Aug CD 55-58; Youth Chapl 58-62; CF (TA) 58-69; V Becontree St Elisabeth *Chelmsf* 62-71; P-in-c Becontree St Geo 62-65; CF (R of O) 69-77; R and V Reading St Mary V *Ox* 72-77; R Reading St Mary w St Laur 77-88; rtd 88; Perm to Offic *Heref* from 91. *20 Sudbury Avenue, Hereford HR1 1YB* Tel (01432) 279194

RESTALL, Miss Susan Roberta. b 45. MSc. Sarum & Wells Th Coll 79. **dss** 82 **d** 87 **p** 94. Dorchester *Sarum* 82-84; Portland All SS w St Pet 84-87; Par Dn 87; TD Yate New Town *Bris* 87-94; TV 94-95; Chapl Birm Heartlands and Solihull NHS Trust 95-01; rtd 01. *12 Croft Road, Yardley, Birmingham B26 1SG* Tel 0121-783 3325

REVELEY, James Stewart. b 69. Goldsmiths' Coll Lon BMus92. Ch Div Sch of the Pacific (USA) 95 Ripon Coll Cuddesdon BA97. **d** 96 **p** 97. C Goldington *St Alb* 96-00; C Harpenden St Nic from 00. *86 Tuffnells Way, Harpenden AL5 3HG* Tel (01582) 762485 E-mail revjumble@aol.com

REVELEY, Mrs Valerie Mary. b 39. Lon Inst of Educn BEd77. St Alb and Ox Min Course 96. **d** 99 **p** 00. OLM Olney *Ox* from 99. *36 Oxleys, Olney MK46 5PH* Tel (01234) 713989

REVELL, Patrick Walter Millard. b 32. Wells Th Coll 65. **d** 67 **p** 68. C Leic St Jas *Leic* 67-74; V Quorndon 74-82; TR Camelot Par *B & W* 82-90; RD Cary 90-96; RD Bruton 90-96; V Castle Cary w Ansford 90-97; rtd 97; Perm to Offic *B & W* and *Sarum* from 97. *80 Sheepland Lane, Sherborne DT9 4BP* Tel (01935) 813083

REVERA, Susan Mary. *See* LEATHLEY, Susan Mary

REVETT, Canon Graham Francis. b 40. AKC63. **d** 64 **p** 65. C Pennywell St Thos and Grindon St Oswald CD *Dur* 64-68; C Hartlepool St Aid 68-71; V Shiney Row 71-80; V Herrington 73-80; RD Houghton 76-80; TR Cullercoats St Geo *Newc* 80-97; RD Tynemouth 87-92; Hon Can Newc Cathl from 94; R Bolam w Whalton and Hartburn w Meldon from 97; V Nether Witton from 97; Chapl Kirkley Hall Coll from 98. *The Rectory, Whalton, Morpeth NE61 3UX* Tel (01670) 775360 Fax as telephone E-mail gfrevett@yahoo.co.uk

REW, Eric Malcolm. b 63. UEA BSc84 PGCE89. Qu Coll Birm 98. **d** 00 **p** 01. C Shepshed *Leic* 00-03; C Shepshed and Oaks in Charnwood from 03. *28 Forest Street, Shepshed, Loughborough LE12 9DA* Tel (01509) 505882 E-mail revd.rew@virgin.net

REX, Keith Leslie Herbert. b 30. K Coll Lon 53. **d** 55 **p** 56. C Shepton Mallet *B & W* 55-58; C Cheshunt *St Alb* 58-60; V Weston-super-Mare St Andr Bournville *B & W* 60-67; R Charlton Adam w Charlton Mackrell 67-69; rtd 90. *46 Petherton Gardens, Hengrove, Bristol BS14 9BS*

REYNISH, David Stuart. b 52. Nottm Univ BEd75. Linc Th Coll 72. **d** 77 **p** 78. C Boston *Linc* 77-80; C Chalfont St Peter *Ox* 80-84; V Thursby *Carl* 84-88; R Iver Heath *Ox* 88-03; V Kelvedon and Feering *Chelmsf* from 03. *The Vicarage, Church Street, Kelvedon, Colchester CO5 9AL* Tel (01376) 571172

REYNOLDS, Alan Martin. b 53. Sarum & Wells Th Coll 73. **d** 77 **p** 78. C Glan Ely *Llan* 77-84; V Pontyclun w Talygarn 84-97; Perm to Offic from 97. *22 Osborn Square, Cardiff CF11 8BG* Tel (029) 2023 9344

REYNOLDS, Alan Thomas William. b 43. Lon Univ BSc64. Linc Th Coll 64. **d** 66 **p** 67. C Leic St Pet *Leic* 66-70; C Huntington *York* 70-72; Jamaica 72-76; V Stechford *Birm* 76-83; P-in-c Hampton in Arden 83-86; V 87-93; Chapl E Birm Hosp 86-88; Chapl Parkway Hosp Solihull 88-93; V Moseley St Anne *Birm* 93-02; V Kerry and Llanmerewig and Dolfor *St As* from 02; AD Cedewain from 03. *The Vicarage, 47 Willans Drive, Kerry, Newtown SY16 4DB* Tel (01686) 670466

REYNOLDS, Alfred Stanley. b 18. Birm Univ BSc39 Open Univ BA88. St Deiniol's Hawarden 69. **d** 70 **p** 71. NSM Illogan *Truro* 70-85; Perm to Offic *Sarum* from 86. *42 Cloford Close, Trowbridge BA14 9DH* Tel (01225) 763542

REYNOLDS, Mrs Angela Heather. b 44. Wye Coll Lon BSc66 Birm Univ CertEd67. EAMTC 94. **d** 97 **p** 98. NSM Barnham Broom *Nor* 99-00; C Easton w Colton and Marlingford 99-00; P-in-c Easton, Colton, Marlingford and Bawburgh from 00. *Easton Vicarage, Dereham Road, Easton, Norwich NR9 5ES* Tel (01603) 880197 E-mail revangel@fish.co.uk

REYNOLDS, David Hammerton. b 39. St Jo Coll Dur BA62. Qu Coll Birm DipTh63. **d** 65 **p** 66. C N Ormesby *York* 65-68; C Hessle 68-71; V Sherburn in Elmet 71-79; V Fulford 79-87; Resp for Clergy In-Service Tr York Area 82-87; C Egloskerry *Truro* 87; TV Bolventor 87-90; TR Brayton *York* from 90. *The Rectory, Doncaster Road, Brayton, Selby YO8 9HE* Tel (01757) 704707 E-mail dhr@breathemail.net

REYNOLDS, David James. b 48. St Jo Coll Dur BA72 DipTh73 Lanc Univ MA85. Cranmer Hall Dur 69. **d** 73 **p** 74. C Formby H Trin *Liv* 73-77; P-in-c Widnes St Paul 77-80; V Southport St Paul 80-87; P-in-c Mawdesley *Blackb* 87-91; R from 91; Chapl Derian

Ho Children's Hospice 93-97. *Mawdesley Rectory, Green Lane, Ormskirk L40 3TH* Tel (01704) 822203
E-mail davidreynolds@tinyworld.co.uk

REYNOLDS, Canon John Lionel. b 34. JP. Westmr Coll Ox MTh00. Chich Th Coll 58. **d** 61 **p** 62. C Whitkirk *Ripon* 61-64; C Tong *Bradf* 64-68; V Chisledon and Draycot Foliatt *Sarum* 68-74; TR Ridgeway 74-76; RD Marlborough 74-76; V Calne and Blackland 76-89; RD Calne 77-84; Can and Preb Sarum Cathl 80-02; V Woodford Valley 89-02; rtd 02. *Rose Court, Church Hill, Lover, Salisbury SP5 2PL* Tel (01725) 512311

REYNOLDS, John Stewart. b 19. FSA81 St Edm Hall Ox BA42 MA45 BLitt50. Ridley Hall Cam 42. **d** 44 **p** 45. C Ox St Clem *Ox* 44-46; C-in-c Ox All SS w St Martin 46-49; R Easton-on-the-Hill *Pet* 49-56; R Besselsleigh w Dry Sandford *Ox* 56-85; Lect Wycliffe Hall Ox 71-78; rtd 85; Perm to Offic *Ox* from 85. *Linden Lodge, 59 St Mary's Road, Oxford OX4 1PZ* Tel (01865) 727386

REYNOLDS, Mandy Elizabeth. b 59. NTMTC 99. **d** 02 **p** 03. NSM Wembley St Jo *Lon* from 02. *73 Beverley Gardens, Wembley HA9 9RB* Tel (020) 8933 0222
E-mail mandyreynoldsuk@yahoo.co.uk

REYNOLDS, Paul Andrew. b 57. BA86. Trin Coll Bris 83. **d** 86 **p** 87. C Reading St Jo *Ox* 86-90; C Dorridge *Birm* 90-95; TV Riverside *Ox* from 95. *The Vicarage, 69A Eton Wick Road, Windsor SL4 6NE* Tel (01753) 852268

REYNOLDS, Paul Frederick. b 56. Lon Bible Coll DRBS78 St Jo Coll Nottm 90. **d** 92 **p** 93. C Hyde St Geo *Ches* 92-96; P-in-c Delamere 96-00; Asst Dir Par Support and Development 96-98; Acting Dir 98-00; V Handforth from 00. *The Vicarage, 36 Sagars Road, Handforth, Wilmslow SK9 3EE* Tel (01625) 250559 *or* 532145 E-mail paul.reynolds@saintchads.fsnet.co.uk

REYNOLDS, Philip Delamere. b 53. Leeds Univ CertEd74 Nottm Univ BCombStuds82. Linc Th Coll 79. **d** 82 **p** 83. C Huddersfield St Jo *Wakef* 82-85; C Barkisland w W Scammonden 85-87; P-in-c Skelmanthorpe from 87. *St Aidan's Vicarage, Radcliffe Street, Skelmanthorpe, Huddersfield HD8 9AF* Tel (01484) 863232 E-mail northmist@thales.demon.co.uk

REYNOLDS, Raymond Ernest. b 29. Nottm Univ MPhil89. Lambeth STh84 CA Tr Coll 50 Chich Th Coll 58. **d** 60 **p** 61. C Leeds St Marg *Ripon* 60-62; C Beeston *S'well* 62-64; R Farnley *Ripon* 64-76; R Higham-on-the-Hill w Fenny Drayton *Leic* 76-81; R Higham-on-the-Hill w Fenny Drayton and Witherley 81-90; V Sutton *Ely* 90-94; R Witcham w Mepal 90-94; rtd 94; C Nantwich *Ches* 94-96; Perm to Offic from 96. *4 St Alban's Drive, Nantwich CW5 7DW* Tel (01270) 623534

REYNOLDS, Richard Michael. b 42. St Steph Ho Ox 65. **d** 67 **p** 68. C Kidderminster St Mary *Worc* 67-70; Guyana 70-73; TV N Creedy *Ex* 73-80; R Holsworthy w Hollacombe 80-86; R Holsworthy w Hollacombe and Milton Damerel from 86; Chapl N Devon Healthcare NHS Trust from 94. *The Rectory, Bodmin Street, Holsworthy EX22 6BH* Tel (01409) 253435
E-mail michael@rnlds85.freeserve.co.uk

REYNOLDS, Roderick Breedon (Rory). b 58. Man Univ BA80. Ripon Coll Cuddesdon DipMin95. **d** 95 **p** 96. C Hitchin *St Alb* 95-98; C Stevenage St Andr and St Geo 98-00; P-in-c High Wych and Gilston w Eastwick from 00. *The Rectory, High Wych, Sawbridgeworth CM21 0HX* Tel (01279) 600894 Mobile 07970-070827 E-mail roryreynolds@mac.com

REYNOLDS, Mrs Rosemary Joan. b 46. WMMTC 00. **d** 03. NSM Brandwood *Birm* from 03. *23 Chanston Avenue, Birmingham B14 5BD* Tel 0121-444 7015
E-mail hello@frankandrosemary.freeserve.co.uk

REYNOLDS, Simon Andrew. b 65. ARCM85 Univ of Wales (Cardiff) 85 MA00. Westcott Ho Cam 98. **d** 00 **p** 01. C Ex St Thos and Em *Ex* 00-03; Min Can and Succ St Paul's Cathl *Lon* from 03. *8A Amen Court, London EC4M 7BU* Tel (020) 7248 6115 *or* 7246 8338 E-mail succentor@stpaulscathedral.org.uk

REYNOLDS, Canon Stanley Kenneth. b 14. Bps' Coll Cheshunt 47. **d** 50 **p** 51. C Derby St Anne *Derby* 50-57; PC Stonebroom 57-64; V Chaddesden St Phil 64-70; V Greenhill St Pet 70-74; V Greenhill *Sheff* 74-81; P-in-c Burghwallis w Skelbrooke 81-89; Hon Can Sheff Cathl 83-89; rtd 89; Perm to Offic *Nor* from 89. *4 Burton Close, Diss IP22 3YJ* Tel (01379) 650562

RHAM, Canon John Theodore. b 27. Magd Coll Cam BA50 MA65. Sarum Th Coll 50. **d** 52 **p** 53. C Harborne St Pet *Birm* 52-54; C Coleshill 54-56; C Falmouth K Chas *Truro* 56-59; R St Ewe 59-68; RD St Austell 65-68; V Budock 68-93; RD Carnmarth S 77-84; Hon Can Truro Cathl 80-93; rtd 93; France from 94. *Villa Budoc, 36 Route de Bernis, Langlade, 30980 Gard, France*

RHODES, Adrian Michael. b 48. K Coll Lon BD71 AKC71 DPST76. Qu Coll Birm 71. **d** 72 **p** 73. C Bury St Jo *Man* 73-75; Chapl N Man Gen Hosp 75-77; C Crumpsall *Man* 75-77; Chapl Walsall Manor and Bloxwich Hosps 77-83; Chapl Walsall Gen Hosp 81-83; Chapl Man R Infirmary 83-94; Chapl St Mary's Hosp Man 83-94; Chapl Man R Eye Hosp 83-94; Chapl Cen Man Healthcare NHS Trust 94-00; Perm to Offic *Man* from 00. *58 Errwood Road, Burnage, Manchester M19 2QH* Tel 0161-224 1739 E-mail adrian@rhodes.net

RHODES, Anthony John. b 27. Mert Coll Ox BA50 MA53 DipTh53. St Steph Ho Ox 52. **d** 54 **p** 55. C Northampton St Alb

Pet 54-57; C Oakham 57-60; P-in-c S Queensferry *Edin* 60-74; V Mitcham St Olave *S'wark* 74-81; V Owston *Linc* 81-92; V W Butterwick 81-92; rtd 92. *1 Trentside, Owston Ferry, Doncaster DN9 1RS* Tel (01427) 728237

RHODES, Arthur. b 31. Dur Univ BA58. Cranmer Hall Dur 57. **d** 59 **p** 60. C Kirkdale St Lawr *Liv* 59-61; C Litherland St Phil 61-64; V St Helens St Matt Thatto Heath 64-67; V Samlesbury *Blackb* 67-79; Lic to Offic 80-01; Perm to Offic from 01. *88 Deborah Avenue, Fulwood, Preston PR2 9HU* Tel (01772) 712212

RHODES, Benjamin. b 71. Portsm Univ BSc93 Anglia Poly Univ PGDPT02. Westcott Ho Cam 94. **d** 97 **p** 98. C Upminster *Chelmsf* 97-01; Asst Chapl Lewisham Hosp NHS Trust from 01. *University Hospital, Lewisham High Street, London SE13 6LH* Tel (020) 8333 3000 *or* 8333 3299 Fax 8333 3333
E-mail ben_rhodes@beeb.net *or* ben.rhodes@uhl.nhs.uk

RHODES, Christine. See RHODES, Lois Christine

RHODES, David. b 34. St Chad's Coll Dur BA60. **d** 61 **p** 62. C Dudley St Jo *Worc* 61-64; C-in-c Stourbridge St Mich Norton CD 64-68; V Astwood Bank w Crabbs Cross 69-78; Dioc Ecum Officer 73-78; TR Hackney *Lon* 78-88; R St Giles Cripplegate w St Bart Moor Lane etc 88-00; rtd 00; Perm to Offic *Chelmsf* from 00. *4 Freshwell Gardens, Saffron Walden CB10 1BZ* Tel (01799) 522912

RHODES, David George. b 45. Univ of Wales (Abth) BA66. Trin Coll Bris 83. **d** 85 **p** 86. C Brinsworth w Catcliffe *Sheff* 85-89; V Mortomley St Sav 89-90; V Mortomley St Sav High Green 90-99; V Totley from 99. *All Saints' Vicarage, 37 Sunnyvale Road, Sheffield S17 4FA* Tel 0114-236 2322
E-mail allfiveofus@totley37.freeserve.co.uk

RHODES, David Grant. b 43. Ex Univ BA66 Leeds Univ DipAdEd75. Sarum & Wells Th Coll 69. **d** 72 **p** 73. C Mirfield *Wakef* 72-75; V Batley St Thos 75-80; Dioc Adult Educn Officer 76-80; Hon C Huddersfield St Jo 85-86; Dir BRF 86-87; V Robert Town *Wakef* 87-94; Project Worker 'Faith in Leeds' 94-99; Hon C Potternewton *Ripon* 99; Chapl Missr Children's Soc 99-03; Hon C Leeds City *Ripon* from 99; rtd 03. *111 Potternewton Lane, Leeds LS7 3LW* Tel 0113-262 7247 Fax as telephone
E-mail rhodes@freeuk.com

RHODES, Duncan. b 35. Leeds Univ BSc56. Local Minl Tr Course 90. **d** 93 **p** 94. OLM Saddleworth *Man* from 93. *Holden Cottage, 21 Spurn Lane, Diggle, Oldham OL3 5QP* Tel (01457) 872399 E-mail dunrhodes@aol.com

RHODES, Mrs Heather. b 52. **d** 88. Par Dn Purley St Mark *S'wark* 89-94; C 94-98; rtd 98; Hon C Purley St Mark *S'wark* from 00. *24 Highfield Road, Purley CR8 2JG* Tel (020) 8660 1486

RHODES, Canon John Lovell. b 33. MBE81. Lon Univ BD59. St Aid Birkenhead 55. **d** 59 **p** 60. C Bradf St Clem *Bradf* 59-61; C Heeley *Sheff* 61-66; Ind Chapl *Linc* 66-81; Sen Ind Chapl 81-98; RD Grimsby and Cleethorpes 76-83; Can and Preb Linc Cathl 77-98; Chapl Franklin Coll 92-98; rtd 98; Perm to Offic *Linc* 98-01. *19 Augusta Close, Grimsby DN34 4TQ* Tel (01472) 343167

RHODES, Lois Christine. b 34. Lon Univ BSc61. Glouc Sch of Min 84. **d** 87 **p** 94. NSM Weobley w Sarnesfield and Norton Canon *Heref* 87-92; NSM Letton w Staunton, Byford, Mansel Gamage etc 87-92; Asst Chapl Heref Hosps NHS Trust from 93. *Bellbrook, Bell Square, Weobley, Hereford HR4 8SE* Tel (01544) 318410 *or* (01432) 355444

RHODES, Matthew Ivan. b 66. Bris Univ BA89 Birm Univ MPhil95. Qu Coll Birm BD93. **d** 94 **p** 95. C Willenhall H Trin *Lich* 94-97; Chapl Maadi St Jo Egypt 97-00; P-in-c Middleton *Birm* from 00; P-in-c Wishaw from 00. *The Rectory, Coppice Lane, Middleton, Tamworth B78 2AR* Tel 0121-323 4906 Fax as telephone E-mail catmat30@hotmail.com

RHODES, Robert George. b 41. Man Univ BSc62. Ripon Hall Ox DipTh73. **d** 74 **p** 75. C Banbury *Ox* 74-77; TV Banbury 77-81; P-in-c Long Horsley *Newc* 81-86; Adult Educn Adv 81-86; TR Wolverton *Ox* 86-97; P-in-c Bledlow w Saunderton and Horsenden 97-98; TV Risborough 98-02; Warden of Readers 97-02; USPG Belize from 02. *6 Sixth Street, King's Park, Belize City, Belize* Tel (00501) (2) 237949, 233660 *or* 233664
E-mail bandjrhodes@hotmail.com

RHODES-WRIGLEY, James. b 35. AKC59. **d** 60 **p** 61. C S Harrow St Paul *Lon* 60-66; V Hendon Ch Ch 66-71; V Northolt Park St Barn 71-92; rtd 92; Hon C Whyke w Rumboldswhyke and Portfield *Chich* from 96. *4 Gordon Avenue, Donnington, Chichester PO19 8QY* Tel (01243) 781664

RHYDDERCH, David Huw. b 48. Univ of Wales (Cardiff) DipTh73. St Mich Coll Llan 70. **d** 73 **p** 74. C Gelligaer *Llan* 73-76; C Penarth All SS 76-78; V Resolven 78-81; V Ystrad Rhondda w Ynyscynon 81-93; RD Rhondda 89-93; R St Andrews Major w Michaelston-le-Pit from 93. *The Rectory, Lettons Way, Dinas Powys CF64 4BY* Tel (029) 2051 2555

RICE, Brian Keith. b 32. Peterho Cam BA55 MA59. Seabury-Western Th Sem BD57 STM67 MDiv79 Linc Th Coll. **d** 57 **p** 58. C Winchmore Hill St Paul *Lon* 57-60; C Derby St Werburgh *Derby* 60-63; C Mackworth St Frpar 63-66; Chapl Kingsway Hosp Derby 63-66; Educn Sec USPG 66-72; Dir of Educn *Birm* 72-84; Chapl St Chad's Hosp Birm 77-84; Soc Resp Officer *Dur* 84-97; rtd 97; Perm to Offic *Dur* from 97; *York* from 98. *Jasmine*

Cottage, 16 Forest Lane, Kirklevington, Yarm TS15 9LY Tel (01642) 780396

RICE, Brian Thomas. b 46. Univ of Wales (Cardiff) BD77. St Mich Coll Llan 75. **d** 77 **p** 78. C Llanelli *St D* 77-79; P-in-c Llandygwydd and Cenarth w Cilrhedyn 79-80; V 80-83; V Llandingat w Myddfai from 83; RD Llangadog and Llandeilo from 91. *The Vicarage, Towy Avenue, Llandovery SA20 0EH* Tel (01550) 720524

RICE, David. b 57. Nottm Univ BA79. Ripon Coll Cuddesdon 80. **d** 82 **p** 83. C Cirencester *Glouc* 82-86; R Theale and Englefield *Ox* 86-00; TR Wallingford from 00. *The Rectory, 22 Castle Street, Wallingford OX10 8DW* Tel (01491) 202188

RICE, Franklin Arthur. b 20. FRICS49. St Alb Minl Tr Scheme 77. **d** 80 **p** 81. NSM Hoddesdon *St Alb* 80-84; Perm to Offic *Guildf* from 85. *1 Oatlands Court, St Mary's Road, Weybridge KT13 9QE* Tel (01932) 846462

RICE, John Leslie Hale. b 38. Lon Univ BScEng60 BD68 FCMI. EMMTC 73. **d** 76 **p** 77. NSM Allestree St Nic *Derby* 76-90; Lic to Offic from 90. *14 Gisborne Crescent, Allestree, Derby DE22 2FL* Tel (01332) 557222

RICE, Lt Cdr Peter Langford. b 49. RN Coll Dartmouth 70 RN Coll Greenwich 78. STETS 97. **d** 00 **p** 01. Hon C Salisbury St Fran and Stratford sub Castle *Sarum* from 00. *Oak Lodge, Laverstock Park, Salisbury SP2 1QJ* Tel (01722) 332949 Pager 07666-732761 E-mail rowley1@btinternet.com

RICE-OXLEY, John Richard. b 44. Keble Coll Ox BA66 MA69 Dur Univ MA85. Lon Coll of Div 68. **d** 70 **p** 71. C Eastwood *S'well* 70-73; Youth Adv CMS 73-78; V Mansfield St Jo *S'well* 78-82; P-in-c Thornley *Dur* 82-85; P-in-c Darlington St Matt and St Luke 85-87; V 87-98; V Hornsea w Atwick *York* from 98. *The Vicarage, 9 Newbeggin, Hornsea HU18 1AB* Tel (01964) 532531 E-mail rowley1@btinternet.com

RICH, Brian John. b 49. Reading Univ BSc70. Guildf Dioc Min Course 94. **d** 97 **p** 98. OLM Stoke Hill *Guildf* from 97. *Roewen, 1 Trentham Crescent, Old Woking, Woking GU22 9EW* Tel (01483) 829541 E-mail st-peters@stoke-hill.freeserve.co.uk

RICH, Canon Christopher Robin. b 49. LSE MSc(Econ)95. Brasted Th Coll 70 Sarum & Wells Th Coll 72. **d** 74 **p** 75. C Sholing *Win* 74-76; C Southampton Maybush St Pet 76-79; R Fawley 79-90; Ind Chapl 83-84; Dir Soc Resp 90-99; Hon Can Win Cathl 96-99; Dir Soc Resp *Blackb* from 99. *24 Bosburn Drive, Mellor Brook, Blackburn BB2 7PA* Tel (01254) 676281 E-mail chris.rich@blackburn.anglican.org

RICH, Nicholas Philip. b 49. St Cuth Soc Dur BA74 PGCE75 Coll of Ripon & York St Jo CertEd83. Linc Th Coll 86. **d** 88 **p** 89. C W Acklam *York* 88-91; Chapl St Geo Sch Harpenden 91-95; Lic to Offic *St Alb* 91-95; rtd 95. *57 Knowlwood Road, Todmorden OL14 6PB* Tel (01706) 810551

RICH, Paul Michael. b 36. OBE87. Sarum Th Coll 62. **d** 65 **p** 66. C Woodbridge St Mary *St E* 65-68; C W Wycombe *Ox* 68-70; CF 70-88; Lic to Offic *S & B* 88-90; V Crondall and Ewshot *Guildf* from 91. *The Vicarage, Farm Lane, Crondall, Farnham GU10 5QE* Tel (01252) 850379

RICH, Peter Geoffrey. b 45. Oak Hill Th Coll 74. **d** 77 **p** 78. C Blackheath St Jo *S'wark* 77-80; C Surbiton St Matt 80-87; V St Alb St Luke *St Alb* 87-98; V Gravesend St Aid *Roch* from 98. *The Vicarage, St Gregory's Crescent, Gravesend DA12 4JL* Tel (01474) 352500 E-mail angela_richuk@yahoo.co.uk

RICH, Thomas. b 52. St Jo Coll Nottm 86. **d** 88 **p** 89. C Netherton Liv 88-91; P-in-c Bootle Ch Ch 91-93; V from 93. *Christ Church Vicarage, 1 Breeze Hill, Bootle L20 9EY* Tel 0151-525 2565

RICHARDS, Alan Grenville. b 41. Kelham Th Coll 64. **d** 69 **p** 70. C Northolt St Mary *Lon* 69-75; V Fatfield *Dur* 75-84; V Beighton *Sheff* 84-91; V Endcliffe 91-94; Deputation Appeals Org Children's Soc 94-98; V Cheriton All So w Newington *Cant* from 98. *All Souls Vicarage, 1 Ashley Avenue, Cheriton, Folkestone CT19 4PX* Tel (01303) 275483

RICHARDS, Andrew David Thomas. b 55. St Jo Coll Dur BA76 Roehampton Inst PGCE84 FRSA96. St Steph Ho Ox 76. **d** 78 **p** 79. C Shirley *Birm* 78-80; C Cowley St Jo *Ox* 80-82; Perm to Offic *Win* 84-88 and *Sarum* 88-92; NSM Hazelbury Bryan and the Hillside Par *Sarum* 92-94; Chapl Rossall Sch Fleetwood 94-99; Min Can Ely Cathl and Chapl K Sch Ely 99-03; Chapl Wellington Coll Berks from 03. *20 Goldsmith Way, Crowthorne RG45 7QP* Tel 07952-341837 (mobile)

RICHARDS, Anthony Francis. b 26. Edin Univ 45 Wadh Coll Ox BA51 MA54. Ridley Hall Cam 50. **d** 52 **p** 53. C Finchley Ch Ch *Lon* 52-55; C Maidenhead St Andr and St Mary *Ox* 55-59; Lect All Nations Chr Coll Ware Herts 59-63; V Wycombe Ch Ch *Ox* 59-63; P-in-c 63-66; V Terriers 63-73; USA 70-71; V Cinderford St Steph w Littledean *Glouc* 73-80; V Clacton St Paul *Chelmsf* 80-93; New Zealand 88-89; rtd 93. *Mont, 58230 Ouroux-en-Morvan, Montsauche, France* Tel (0033) (3) 86 78 24 44 E-mail anthony.richards@libertysurf.fr

RICHARDS, Antony. *See* RICHARDS, William Antony

RICHARDS, Mrs April Deborah. b 42. Man Univ BSc63. S dios Minl Tr Scheme 82. **dss** 85 **d** 87 **p** 94. Catherington and Clanfield *Portsm* 85-87; C 87-89; C E Meon 89-95; C Langrish 89-95; Chapl St Mary's Hosp Portsm 92-93; Chapl Portsm Hosps NHS Trust 93-95; P-in-c Blackmoor and Whitehill *Portsm* 95-98; V

from 98; RD Petersfield from 99. *The Vicarage, Blackmoor, Liss GU33 6BN* Tel (01420) 473548

RICHARDS, Basil Ernest. b 18. Lich Th Coll 51. **d** 53 **p** 54. C Kidderminster St Mary *Worc* 53-55; C Northfield *Birm* 55-56; Hon C Gt Malvern Ch Ch *Worc* 78-84; Perm to Offic from 84; Chapl Laslett's Almshouses 84-88; rtd 88. *42 Viscount Cobham Court, Pickersleigh Road, Malvern WR14 2RJ* Tel (01684) 565441

RICHARDS, Brian. b 39. Open Univ BA78. N Ord Course 65 St Deiniol's Hawarden 94. **d** 94 **p** 94. C St Mellons and Michaelston-y-Fedw *Mon* 94-96; P-in-c Michaelston-y-Fedw 96-02; P-in-c Haarlem *Eur* from 02. *Closenberg Bastion 8, 1991 SP Velserbroek, The Netherlands* Tel (0031) (23) 547 3760

RICHARDS, Brian William. b 45. **d** 03. NSM Howell Hill *Guildf* from 03. *2 Canford Court, 88A Epsom Road, Sutton SM3 9ES* Tel (020) 8330 1196 E-mail brianmeg@globalnet.co.uk

RICHARDS, Charles Dennis Vincent. b 37. AKC61. **d** 62 **p** 63. Chapl St Ninian's Cathl Perth *St And* 62-64; C Pimlico St Mary Graham-street *Lon* 64-66; C St Marylebone Ch Ch w St Barn 66-68; C Wood Green St Mich 68-69; Min S Kenton Annunciation CD 69-77; P-in-c Wembley Park St Aug 70-73; Hon C Paddington St Jo w St Mich 77-94; Perm to Offic 77-79; Lic to Offic from 79; rtd 02. *Flat B, 10 Bathurst Street, London W2 2SD* Tel (020) 7262 5633

RICHARDS, Charles Edmund Nicholas. b 42. Trin Coll Cam BA64 MA68. Westcott Ho Cam 64. **d** 66 **p** 67. C Rugby St Andr *Cov* 66-72; TV Basingstoke *Win* 72-77; R Rotherhithe St Mary w All SS *S'wark* from 77; RD Bermondsey 81-91. *The Rectory, 72 St Marychurch Street, London SE16 4JE* Tel (020) 7231 2465

RICHARDS, Christopher Mordaunt. b 40. New Coll Ox BA63 MA72 Bris Univ MB, ChB72. Cuddesdon Coll 63. **d** 65 **p** 81. C Bris St Mary Redcliffe w Temple etc *Bris* 65-66; Perm to Offic 66-72; Hon C Keynsham *B & W* 81-90; Perm to Offic 90-93. *4 St Ronans Avenue, Bristol BS6 6EP* Tel 0117-974 4062

RICHARDS, Daniel James. b 40. St D Coll Lamp DipTh66. **d** 66 **p** 67. C Kingswinford H Trin *Lich* 66-69; C Banbury *Ox* 69-71; C Aylesbury 71-73; C-in-c Stoke Poges St Jo Manor Park CD 73-78; R W Slough 78-80; R Ilchester w Northover, Limington, Yeovilton etc *B & W* 80-90; RD Ilchester 81-91; RD Martock 89-91; TR Bruton and Distr 90-97; R Axbridge w Shipham and Rowberrow from 97. *The Rectory, Cheddar Road, Axbridge BS26 2DL* Tel (01934) 732261 E-mail revdanrich@aol.com

RICHARDS, Canon David. b 30. Bris Univ BA52. St Mich Coll Llan 52. **d** 54 **p** 55. C Llangynwyd w Maesteg *Llan* 54-56; Iran 57-61 and 62-66; C Skewen *Llan* 61-62; V Cwmbach 66-76; Warden of Ords 71-77; R Coity w Nolton 76-96; Can Llan Cathl 88-96; rtd 96; Perm to Offic *Llan* and *Mon* from 96. *Inglewood, 5 Hopewell Close, Bulwark, Chepstow NP16 5ST* Tel (01291) 628912

RICHARDS, David Arnold. b 56. Wycliffe Hall Ox 76. **d** 81 **p** 82. C Skewen *Llan* 81-84; C Barking St Marg w St Patr *Chelmsf* 84-85; TV 85-90; Chapl Barking Hosp 87-88; P-in-c Stratford St Jo and Ch Ch w Forest Gate St Jas *Chelmsf* 90-97; V Stratford St Jo w Ch Ch and St Jas from 97. *Stratford Vicarage, 20 Deanery Road, London E15 4LP* Tel (020) 8534 8388 *or* 8503 1913 E-mail office@stjohnse15.freeserve.co.uk

RICHARDS, David Gareth. b 60. Hull Univ BA83 Birm Univ DipTh91. Qu Coll Birm 89. **d** 92 **p** 93. C Knowle *Birm* 92-96; Assoc R Edin St Paul and St Geo *Edin* 96-00; R from 00. *11 East Fettes Avenue, Edinburgh EH4 1DN* Tel 0131-332 3904 *or* 556 1355 Fax 556 0492 E-mail drichards4@compuserve.com

RICHARDS, Dennis. b 48. St Mich Coll Llan DipTh95. **d** 97 **p** 98. C Cwmbran *Mon* 97-00; TV from 00. *St Peter's Vicarage, 30 Longhouse Grove, Henllys, Cwmbran NP44 6HQ* Tel (01633) 867613 E-mail rockrchrds@aol.com

RICHARDS, Canon Irving St Clair. b 40. Coll of Resurr Mirfield 72. **d** 74 **p** 75. C Wigston Magna *Leic* 74-78; P-in-c N Evington from 78; Hon Can Leic Cathl from 97; Bp's Officer for Race and Community Relns from 94. *The Vicarage, 214 East Park Road, Leicester LE5 5FD* Tel 0116-273 6752

RICHARDS, James Johnston. b 59. Solicitor 84 Lon Bible Coll BA90 Dur Univ MA97. Cranmer Hall Dur 90. **d** 92 **p** 93. C Harrow Trin St Mich *Lon* 92-95; C Kendal H Trin *Carl* 95-99; R Windermere from 99. *The Rectory, Longlands Road, Bowness-on-Windermere, Windermere LA23 3AS* Tel (01539) 443563 E-mail jamesjrichards@lineone.net *or* rector@stmartin.org.uk

RICHARDS, Mrs Jane Valerie. b 43. Westf Coll Lon BA64 Birm Univ CertEd65. S Dios Minl Tr Scheme 84. **d** 87 **p** 94. NSM Locks Heath *Portsm* 87-90; Asst Chapl Qu Alexandra Hosp Portsm 90-92; Chapl Portsm Hosps NHS Trust 92-95; Asst to RD Fareham *Portsm* 96-95; C Locks Heath 95-96; Chapl Southn Univ Hosps NHS Trust 96-03; rtd 03; Perm to Offic *Portsm* from 97. *16 Lodge Road, Locks Heath, Southampton SO31 6QY* Tel (01489) 573891 E-mail dick@richards9934.freeserve.co.uk

RICHARDS, John. b 20. Univ of Wales (Lamp) BA40 Keble Coll Ox BA42 MA46 BLitt48 FSA70. Westcott Ho Cam DipTh43. **d** 43 **p** 44. C Chirk *St As* 43; CF 44-45; C Bollington St Jo *Ches* 46-50; V Macclesfield St Pet 50-56; Lect Macclesfield Coll of FE 53-56; V New Brighton All SS 56-67; Master Wellington Sch

Wirral 61-65 and 67-82; CF (TA) 62-69; Sen CF (TA) 69-86; V Hoylake *Ches* 61-86; Chapl Hoylake Cottage Hosp 67-86; rtd 86; Perm to Offic *Ches* from 86. *Ithaca, 56 Cleveley Road, Wirral CH47 8XR* Tel 0151-632 5135

✠**RICHARDS, The Rt Revd John.** b 33. SS Coll Cam BA55 MA59. Ely Th Coll 57. **d** 59 **p** 60 **c** 94. C Ex St Thos *Ex* 59-64; R Holsworthy w Cookbury 64-74; R Hollacombe 64-74; RD Holsworthy 70-74; V Heavitree 74-77; TR Heavitree w Ex St Paul 78-81; RD Christianity 78-81; Adn Ex and Can Res Ex Cathl 81-94; Suff Bp Ebbsfleet (PEV) *Cant* 94-98; Asst Bp B & W 96-98; rtd 98. *Penberth, Stoney Road, Lewdown, Okehampton EX20 4DQ* Tel (01566) 783144

RICHARDS, Preb John Francis. b 37. Dur Univ BA61. Wells Th Coll 61. **d** 63 **p** 64. C Sherwood *S'well* 63-67; C Bishopwearmouth St Mich *Dur* 67-69; C Egg Buckland *Ex* 69-75; CF (ACF) 72-02; V Plymouth St Jas Ham *Ex* 75-83; V Plympton St Mary 83-02; RD Plymouth Moorside 88-93 and 96-01; Preb Ex Cathl from 91; rtd 02. *24 Trewithy Drive, Plymouth PL6 5TY* Tel (01752) 214442
E-mail jfr-sjr@fish.co.uk

RICHARDS, John George. b 48. Qu Coll Birm 87. **d** 89 **p** 90. C Acocks Green *Birm* 89-92; TV Shirley 92-96; P-in-c Yardley Wood 96-00; V from 00. *Christ Church Vicarage, School Road, Yardley Wood, Birmingham B14 4AP* Tel 0121-436 7726

RICHARDS, John Henry. b 34. CCC Cam BA57 MA75. St Mich Coll Llan BD77. **d** 77 **p** 78. C Llangynwyd w Maesteg *Llan* 77-79; C Cardiff St Jo 79-82; Asst Chapl Univ of Wales (Cardiff) 79-82; V Penmark w Porthkerry 82-83; R Stackpole Elidor w St Petrox *St D* 83-85; R St Petrox w Stackpole Elidor and Bosherston etc 85-99; rtd 99. *20 Williamson Street, Pembroke SA71 4ER* Tel (01646) 672472

RICHARDS, John Michael. b 53. Coll of Ripon & York St Jo TCert76 Open Univ BA81. Cranmer Hall Dur 93. **d** 93 **p** 94. C Wath-upon-Dearne *Sheff* 93-95; R Warmsworth 95-01; R Sprotbrough from 01. *The Rectory, 42A Spring Lane, Sprotborough, Doncaster DN5 7QG* Tel (01302) 853203 Fax as telephone

RICHARDS, John Stanley. b 39. St Jo Coll Dur BA60. Ridley Hall Cam 61. **d** 64 **p** 65. C Fordingbridge w Ibsley *Win* 64-67; CF (TA) 64-68; C Bitterne Park *Win* 67-68; C Pokesdown All SS 68-70; Fell Qu Coll Birm 70-71; C Chesterton St Andr *Ely* 71-73; Asst Chapl Canford Sch Wimborne 73-77; Assoc Dir Fountain Trust 77-80; Dir Renewal Servicing from 81; NSM New Haw *Guildf* 81-84; rtd 02. *Amstel, River Ash Estate, Shepperton TW17 8NG* Tel (01932) 244737

RICHARDS, John William. b 29. Southn Univ BSc55. Sarum & Wells Th Coll 78. **d** 81 **p** 82. NSM Woking St Mary *Guildf* 81-85; C Addlestone 85-87; C S Gillingham *Roch* 87-89; Hon C W Byfleet *Guildf* 91-95; rtd 94; Perm to Offic *Sarum* from 95. *16 Normandy Way, Poundbury Whitfield, Dorchester DT1 2PP* Tel (01305) 251529

RICHARDS, Julian. b 25. Wycliffe Hall Ox 71. **d** 73 **p** 74. C Hessle *York* 73-76; P-in-c Rowley 76-82; Chapl HM Pris Hull 79-82; P-in-c Boldre w S Baddesley 83; P-in-c Boldre w S Baddesley 83; V 83-93; rtd 93; RD Alton *Win* 93-98; Perm to Offic *Portsm* and *Win* from 98; Clergy Widows Officer (Win Adnry) from 00. *Manor End, Worldham Hill, East Worldham, Alton GU34 3AX* Tel (01420) 86894
E-mail julian.richards@manorend.fsnet.co.uk

RICHARDS, Keith David. b 50. Didsbury Coll of Educn CertEd72. S'wark Ord Course 79. **d** 82 **p** 83. NSM Walworth *S'wark* 82-85; Chapl Derbyshire Coll of HE 85-87; V Rottingdean *Chich* 87-93; TR Crawley 93-97; V Arundel w Tortington and S Stoke from 97. *The Vicarage, 26 Maltravers Street, Arundel BN18 9BU* Tel (01903) 885209 or 882262 Fax 882201 E-mail keith@arundel2000.freeserve.co.uk

RICHARDS, Kelvin. b 58. Univ of Wales (Abth) BSc80 MA88. Ripon Coll Cuddesdon BA82. **d** 83 **p** 84. C Killay *S & B* 83-86; C Morriston 86-89; R Llangattock and Llangynidr from 89; RD Crickhowell from 02. *The Rectory, Llangattock, Crickhowell NP8 1PH* Tel (01873) 810270

RICHARDS, Kendrick Steven William. b 55. DMS81 Nottm Univ BTh87. St Jo Coll Nottm 84. **d** 87 **p** 88. C Belper *Derby* 87-91; V Ilkeston St Jo 91-95; rtd 95; Perm to Offic *Derby* from 95. *30 Newstead Road North, Shipley View, Ilkeston DE7 8UB*

RICHARDS, Llewelyn. b 15. St Deiniol's Hawarden 73. **d** 75 **p** 76. NSM Corwen and Llangar *St As* 75-85; Past Care Gwyddelwern 78-85; rtd 85. *120 Maesyfallen, Corwen LL21 9AD* Tel (01490) 412195

RICHARDS, Mrs Mary Edith. b 33. SW Minl Tr Course 85. **d** 87 **p** 94. NSM Kea *Truro* 87-88; Asst Chapl Bris Poly *Bris* 88-91; C E Clevedon and Walton w Weston w Clapton *B & W* 91-96; rtd 96; Hon C Probus, Ladock and Grampound w Creed and St Erme *Truro* from 96; Mental Health Chapl Cornwall Healthcare Trust 97-01. *62 Midway Drive, Uplands Park, Truro TR1 1NQ* Tel (01872) 277556

RICHARDS, Nicholas. See RICHARDS, Charles Edmund Nicholas

RICHARDS, Norman John. b 47. BSc. Ridley Hall Cam. **d** 83 **p** 84. C Luton St Fran *St Alb* 83-86; R Aspenden and Layston w

Buntingford 86-95; P-in-c Westmill 94-95; R Aspenden, Buntingford and Westmill from 95. *The Vicarage, Vicarage Road, Buntingford SG9 9BH* Tel (01763) 271552

RICHARDS, Peter Garth. b 30. Lon Univ BA51 Ex Univ PGCE72. St Chad's Coll Dur DipTh55. **d** 55 **p** 56. C Manston *Ripon* 55-57; C Adel 57-62; V Holbeck St Matt 62-66; C Clyst St George *Ex* 66-75; TV Clyst St George, Aylesbeare, Clyst Honiton etc 75-81; rtd 92. *61 Tattenhill Lane, Branston, Burton-on-Trent DE14 3EZ*

RICHARDS, Robert Graham. b 42. St Jo Coll Nottm LTh80. **d** 80 **p** 81. C Radipole and Melcombe Regis *Sarum* 80-83; TV Billericay and Lt Burstead *Chelmsf* 84-91; UK Dir CMJ 91-95; Chief Exec Nat Bibl Heritage Cen Ltd Trust 95-97; C Chorleywood St Andr *St Alb* 97-00. *33 Stowell Crescent, Wareham BH20 4PT* Tel (01929) 557124 Fax as telephone E-mail revrob@jireh.co.uk

RICHARDS, Ronald Jervis. b 16. St D Coll Lamp BA37 St Mich Coll Llan 38. **d** 39 **p** 40. C Minera *St As* 39-43; Chapl RAF 43-71; R Quendon w Rickling *Chelmsf* 71-75; V Dedham 75-83; rtd 83; Perm to Offic *Ex* from 00. *2 Hollies Road, St Stephens, Launceston PL15 8HB* Tel (01566) 776296

RICHARDS, Shaun. b 62. SSC. St Steph Ho Ox DipMin95. **d** 97 **p** 98. C Willesden Green St Andr and St Fran *Lon* 97-01; P-in-c Pentonville St Silas w All SS and V from 01; V from 02. *St Silas House, 45 Cloudesley Road, London N1 0EL* Tel (020) 7278 1101 E-mail fathershaun@one-richards.freeserve.co.uk

RICHARDS, Simon Granston. b 47. Nottm Univ BTh72. St Jo Coll Nottm 68 ALCD72. **d** 72 **p** 73. C Waltham Abbey *Chelmsf* 72-77; TV Basildon St Martin w H Cross and Laindon etc 77-80; V Grayshott *Guildf* 80-89; V Eccleston Ch Ch *Liv* 88-92; V Berkeley w Wick, Breadstone and Newport *Glouc* 92-02; P-in-c Stone w Woodford and Hill 99-02; V Berkeley w Wick, Breadstone, Newport, Stone etc from 02; RD Dursley 96-02; Chapl Severn NHS Trust from 94. *The Vicarage, Church Lane, Berkeley GL13 9BN* Tel (01453) 810294
E-mail simongr@tiscali.co.uk

RICHARDS, Stuart Anthony. b 70. K Coll Lon BA92 Keble Coll Ox BA97. St Steph Ho Ox 97. **d** 99 **p** 00. C Reading All SS *Ox* 99-02; C Solihull *Birm* from 02. *17 Church Hill Close, Solihull B91 3JB* Tel 0121-704 0897 Mobile 07811-467244

RICHARDS, Canon Thomas John Wynzie. b 25. St D Coll Lamp BA49. **d** 51 **p** 52. C Llandybie *St D* 51-53; V 71-87; C Llandegai *Ban* 53-56; R Llanymawddwy 56-57; Chapl Nat Nautical Sch Portishead 57-71; RD Dyffryn Aman *St D* 78-85; Can St D Cathl 83-92; Treas St D Cathl 89-92; V Pencarreg and Llanycrwys 87-92; rtd 92. *Maes Teifi, Cwmann, Lampeter SA48 8DT* Tel (01570) 423354

RICHARDS, William Antony. b 28. Ex Coll Ox BA52 MA56. St Steph Ho Ox 52. **d** 54 **p** 55. C Fenton *Lich* 54-55; C Kingswinford St Mary 55-60; V Meir 60-64; R Warmington w Shotteswell *Cov* 64-75; RD Dassett Magna 70-74; Org Sec CECS *Cov, Leic* and *Pet* 75-81; V Bidford-on-Avon *Cov* 81-92; rtd 92; Perm to Offic *Cov* and *Worc* from 92. *4 Harbour Close, Bidford-on-Avon, Alcester B50 4EW* Tel (01789) 772699

RICHARDS, Canon William Hughes. b 37. St D Coll Lamp BA58. **d** 60 **p** 61. C Llandysul *St D* 60-63; C Llanelli 63-65; V Llanddewi Brefi w Llanbadarn Odwyn 65-73; V Pen-bre 73-83; V Llangunnor w Cwmffrwd 83-88; V Cardigan w Mwnt and Y Ferwig 88-99; V Cardigan w Mwnt and Y Ferwig w Llangoedmor 99-01; Can St D Cathl 89-01; Treas 01; rtd 01. *Hafan Gobaith, 6 Cwrt y Gloch, Peniel, Carmarthen SA32 7HW* Tel (01267) 235995

RICHARDS, Canon William Neal. b 38. ALCD63. **d** 63 **p** 64. C Otley *Bradf* 63-65; C Leamington Priors St Mary *Cov* 65-67; CMS 67-69; Kenya 69-74; Asst Provost and Can Res Nairobi 70-74; V Gt Malvern St Mary *Worc* 74-86; Chapl Kidderminster Health Distr 86-91; RD Kidderminster *Worc* 89-91; R Martley and Wichenford, Knightwick etc 91-01; rtd 01. *Bay Tree Cottage, 32 Pump Street, Malvern WR14 4LU* Tel (01684) 569658

RICHARDSON, Aidan. See RICHARDSON, James Aidan

RICHARDSON, Andrew John. b 44. Ex Univ CertEd69. Trin Coll Bris 83. **d** 82 **p** 83. Kenya 82-87; Dioc Educn Sec *Maseno N* 83-89; Chapl Brentwood Sch Essex 88; Chapl Scarborough Coll 88-01; TV Parkham, Alwington, Buckland Brewer etc *Ex* from 01; RD Hartland from 03. *The Rectory, Old Market Drive, Woolsery, Bideford EX39 5QF* Tel (01237) 431571
E-mail rev.andy-ros@care4free.net

RICHARDSON, Aubrey. See RICHARDSON, John Aubrey

RICHARDSON, Canon Charles. b 13. AKC35. Linc Th Coll 35. **d** 36 **p** 37. C Eltham St Barn *S'wark* 36-40; C St Helier 40-45; Chapl RNVR 45-47; Min Mitcham Ascension CD *S'wark* 47-53; PC 53-54; R Rawmarsh *Sheff* 54-60; R Rawmarsh w Parkgate 60-76; RD Rotherham 74-76; Hon Can Sheff Cathl 76-84; R Harthill 76-80; rtd 80; Perm to Offic *Sheff* from 81. *41 Nether Green Road, Sheffield S11 7EH* Tel 0114-230 4699

RICHARDSON, Canon Charles Leslie Joseph. b 54. St Jo Coll Dur BA76. Coll of Resurr Mirfield 76. **d** 79 **p** 80. C Folkestone St Mary and St Eanswythe *Cant* 79-83; C Maidstone St Martin 83-86; Selection Sec and Voc Adv ACCM 86-91; PV Westmr

Abbey 87-91; R Hastings St Clem and All SS *Chich* 91-98; RD Hastings 92-97; V E Dulwich St Jo *S'wark* from 98; Dioc Voc Adv from 99. *St John's Vicarage, 62 East Dulwich Road, London SE22 9AU* Tel (020) 7639 3807

RICHARDSON, Clive. b 57. Trin Coll Bris DipHE82 Oak Hill Th Coll BA83 Bris Univ MA00. **d** 83 **p** 84. C Woking St Pet *Guildf* 83-86; C Worplesdon 86-90; V Rowledge 90-03; V Rowledge and Frensham from 03. *The Vicarage, Church Lane, Rowledge, Farnham GU10 4EN* Tel (01252) 792402 E-mail clive@rowvic.freeserve.co.uk

RICHARDSON, David. b 71. Edin Univ MA93 Stranmillis Coll PGCE94 PhD98. CITC BTh02. **d** 02. C Coleraine *Conn* from 02. *49 Avonbrook Gardens, Coleraine BT52 1SS* Tel (028) 7034 3671

RICHARDSON, David Anthony. b 41. Kelham Th Coll 57. **d** 66 **p** 67. C Tong *Bradf* 66-68; C Richmond St Mary *S'wark* 68-71; C Sanderstead All SS 71-74; TV 74-78; R Beddington 78-92; V Dormansland 92-98; RD Godstone 95-98; USA from 98; Assoc R Tucson St Phil in the Hills from 98. *St Philip's in the Hills, PO Box 65840, Tucson, AZ 85728-5840, USA* Tel (001) (520) 299 6421 Fax 299 0712 E-mail richardsond@juno.com

RICHARDSON, Canon David Gwynne. b 39. AMIMinE. K Coll Lon 60. **d** 64 **p** 65. C Birtley *Dur* 64-67; Bp's Soc and Ind Adv 67-77; TV Brayton *York* 78-92; Ind Chapl 78-92; Chapl IMinE from 85; R Monk Fryston and S Milford from 92; RD Selby from 93; Can and Preb York Minster from 03. *The Rectory, Main Street, Hillam, Leeds LS25 5HH* Tel (01977) 682357 Fax (01757) 703742 E-mail gwynnerichardson@aol.com

RICHARDSON, David John. b 50. MA LLB FCIArb. S'wark Ord Course. **d** 85 **p** 86. NSM S Croydon Em *S'wark* from 85. *20 Hurst View Road, South Croydon CR2 7AG* Tel (020) 8688 4947 *or* 8688 6676 E-mail dr.personal@13kbw.law.co.uk

RICHARDSON, The Very Revd David John Leyburn. b 46. Queensland Univ BA69. St Barn Coll Adelaide ACT ThL70 Melbourne Coll of Div BD75 Qu Coll Birm DPS76. **d** 70 **p** 71. Australia 70-75 and from 79; Perm to Offic *Birm* 75-76; C Cambridge Gt St Mary w St Mich *Ely* 76-79; Dean Adelaide 89-99; Dean Melbourne from 99. *St Paul's Cathedral, 209 Flinders Lane, Melbourne, Vic, Australia 3000* Tel (0061) (3) 9650 3791 *or* 9419 3364 Fax 9419 4364 E-mail drichardson@stpaulscathedral.org.au

RICHARDSON, Preb Douglas Stanley. b 23. Bps' Coll Cheshunt 55. **d** 57 **p** 58. C Hampton St Mary *Lon* 57-61; V W Twyford 61-69; V Notting Hill St Pet 69-78; V Staines St Pet 78-83; P-in-c Staines St Mary 81-83; V Staines St Mary and St Pet 83-92; AD Spelthorne 83-92; Preb St Paul's Cathl 92; rtd 92; Perm to Offic *Win* from 92. *22 Rooks Down Road, Badgers Farm, Winchester SO22 4LT* Tel (01962) 863687

RICHARDSON, Edward John. b 39. ONC60 Guildf Co Coll of Tech HNC62 Westmr Coll Ox MTh98. Lich Th Coll 62. **d** 65 **p** 66. C Chessington *Guildf* 65-70; TV Trunch *Nor* 70-75; V Stoneleigh *Guildf* 75-79; Perm to Offic *S'wark* 92-94; Hon C Kingston All SS w St Jo 94-99; C from 99. *Church House, 30 Bloomfield Road, Kingston upon Thames KT1 2SE* Tel (020) 8546 9882

RICHARDSON (née WOOD), Elaine Mary. b 51. SRN74. SEITE 00. **d** 03. C Hythe *Cant* from 03. *2 Palmarsh Avenue, Hythe CT21 6NT* Tel (01303) 261699 E-mail elaine.longview@virgin.net

RICHARDSON, Canon Eric Hatherley Humphrey. b 12. Qu Coll Ox BA35 MA46. Wescott Ho Cam 35. **d** 36 **p** 37. C Stoke Newington St Mary *Lon* 36-39; S Africa from 39. *PO Box 2289, Cramerview, 2060 South Africa* Tel (0027) (11) 787 7813 E-mail ceric@kon.co.za

RICHARDSON, Geoffrey Stewart. b 47. St Jo Coll Ox BA69 MA73. St Steph Ho Ox 70. **d** 72 **p** 73. C Roxbourne St Andr *Lon* 72-75; C Woodford St Barn *Chelmsf* 75-80; V Goodmayes St Paul 80-87; R Stow in Lindsey *Linc* 87-92; P-in-c Coates 87-92; P-in-c Willingham 87-92; R Stow Gp 92-01; RD Corringham 93-01; R Shaldon, Stokeinteignhead, Combeinteignhead etc *Ex* from 01. *The Rectory, Torquay Road, Shaldon, Teignmouth TQ14 0AX* Tel (01626) 872396

RICHARDSON, Graeme James. b 75. Oriel Coll Ox BA97. Ripon Coll Cuddesdon MPhil02. **d** 03. C Hatfield Hyde *St Alb* from 03. *Church House, Hollybush Lane, Welwyn Garden City AL7 4JS* Tel (01707) 338835 E-mail graeme.richardson@theology.ox.ac.uk

RICHARDSON, Gwynne. *See* RICHARDSON, Canon David Gwynne

RICHARDSON, Harold. b 22. Worc Ord Coll 62. **d** 64 **p** 65. C Carl St Barn *Carl* 64-66; V Rockcliffe 66-74; rtd 87. *21 St Catherine's Place, Edinburgh EH9 1NU* Tel 0131-667 8040

RICHARDSON, Canon Jack Cyril. b 11. Leeds Univ BSc36. Coll of Resurr Mirfield 35. **d** 35 **p** 36. C Mottingham St Andr *S'wark* 35-38; S Africa 38-45; CF 40-45; C Farnham Royal *Ox* 45-53; V S Stoneham *Win* 53-65; R Upper Clatford w Goodworth Clatford 65-77; RD Andover 67-75; Hon Can Win Cathl 73-77; rtd 77; Perm to Offic *St Alb* from 78. *St Audrey's, Church Street, Hatfield AL9 5AR* Tel (01707) 260042 *or* 272264

RICHARDSON, James Aidan. b 28. St Chad's Coll Dur BA51 DipTh54. **d** 54 **p** 55. C Ferryhill *Dur* 54-56; C Stirling *Edin* 56-58; P-in-c Bo'ness 58-64; P-in-c Linlithgow 58-64; V Linthwaite *Wakef* 64-79; RD Blackmoorfoot 77-79; V Clifton 79-92; P-in-c Hartshead 83-88; rtd 92; Perm to Offic *Wakef* from 92. *10B Brooke Street, Cleckheaton BD19 3RY* Tel (01274) 874587

RICHARDSON, James Arthur. b 19. MC44. ARICS53 Lon Univ BSc51 MRICS01. Ridley Hall Cam 60. **d** 62 **p** 62. C Wandsworth All SS *S'wark* 62-65; V Streatham Park St Alb 65-87; rtd 87; Perm to Offic *Chich* from 87. *18 Crunden Road, Eastbourne BN20 8LW* Tel (01323) 737711

RICHARDSON, James Horner. b 19. Ch Coll Cam BA42 MA45. Ridley Hall Cam 41. **d** 43 **p** 44. C Normanton *Derby* 43-47; C Far Headingley St Chad *Ripon* 47-48; C High Harrogate St Pet 48-50; CF 50-53; Hon CF from 53; V Chadderton Em *Man* 53-59; V Huyton St Mich *Liv* 59-70; V Ormskirk 70-80; Hon Chapl ATC 71-80; V Giggleswick *Bradf* 80-82; P-in-c Rathmell 80-82; V Giggleswick and Rathmell w Wigglesworth 82-84; rtd 84; Hon Chapl Spennithorne Hall *Ripon* from 84; Hon C Aysgarth and Bolton cum Redmire from 84; Perm to Offic *Bradf* from 97. *25 Longdale Avenue, Settle BD24 9BB* Tel (01729) 823793

RICHARDSON, Canon James John. b 41. Hull Univ BA63 Sheff Univ DipEd64 FRSA91. Cuddesdon Coll 66. **d** 69 **p** 70. C Wolverhampton St Pet *Lich* 69-72; P-in-c Hanley All SS 72-75; R Nantwich *Ches* 75-82; Hon Can Ripon Cathl *Ripon* 82-88; V Leeds St Pet 82-88; Exec Dir Coun of Chrs and Jews 88-92; P-in-c Brington w Whilton and Norton *Pet* 93-96; P-in-c Church Brampton, Chapel Brampton, Harleston etc 94-96; TR Bournemouth St Pet w St Swithun, H Trin etc *Win* from 96; P-in-c Bournemouth St Aug from 01. *St Peter's Rectory, 18 Wimborne Road, Bournemouth BH2 6NT* Tel (01202) 554058 Fax as telephone E-mail canonjim@stprectory.freeserve.co.uk

RICHARDSON, John. *See* RICHARDSON, Edward John

RICHARDSON, John. b 41. Qu Coll Birm 69. **d** 72 **p** 73. C Ormskirk *Liv* 72-74; C Doncaster St Geo *Sheff* 74-77; R Hemsworth *Wakef* 77-79; V Penallt *Mon* 79-85; R Amotherby w Appleton and Barton-le-Street *York* 85-89; P-in-c Hovingham 86-89; C 89; P-in-c Slingsby 86-89; TR Street 89-90; R Skelton w Shipton and Newton on Ouse 90-93; V Alsager St Mary *Ches* 93-96; V Grangetown *York* 96-00; V E Coatham 00-02; V Coatham and Dormanstown from 02. *Coatham Vicarage, 9 Blenheim Terrace, Redcar TS10 1QP* Tel (01642) 482870

RICHARDSON, John. b 47. Linc Th Coll 78. **d** 80 **p** 81. C Keighley St Andr *Bradf* 80-83; V Hugglescote w Donington *Leic* 83-84; V Hugglescote w Donington-le-Heath and Ellistown 84-86; TR Hugglescote w Donington, Ellistown and Snibston 86-97; RD Akeley S 87-96; R Hallaton w Horninghold, Allexton, Tugby etc 97-00; rtd 00. *13 Normanton Drive, Oakham LE15 6FG* Tel (01572) 770755

RICHARDSON, John. b 55. Lon Univ BEd BD Kent Univ MA. St Steph Ho Ox. **d** 83 **p** 84. C Thornbury *Glouc* 83-86; C Sheff Parson Cross St Cecilia *Sheff* 86-87; C Clacton St Jas *Chelmsf* 87-90; R Gt and Lt Tey w Wakes Colne and Chappel from 90. *The Rectory, Brook Road, Great Tey, Colchester CO6 1JF* Tel (01206) 211481 E-mail revjohn.richardson@virgin.net

RICHARDSON, John Aubrey. b 33. NEOC 90. **d** 93 **p** 94. NSM Warkworth and Acklington *Newc* from 93. *Harvest Lodge, 27 Acklington Village, Morpeth NE65 9BL* Tel (01670) 760761

RICHARDSON, John Hedley. b 45. Leeds Univ BA72. Qu Coll Birm 72. **d** 74 **p** 75. C Chaddesden St Phil *Derby* 74-76; Perm to Offic 76-86; TV Old Brampton and Loundsley Green 86-91; R Caston w Griston, Merton, Thompson etc *Nor* 91-95; RD Breckland 94-99; P-in-c Hockham w Shropham Gp of Par 94-95; R Caston, Griston, Merton, Thompson etc 95-02; P-in-c Clifton St Jas *Sheff* 02-03; V from 03. *Clifton Vicarage, 10 Clifton Crescent North, Rotherham S65 2AS* Tel (01709) 363082 *or* 836308 Fax as telephone

✠**RICHARDSON, The Rt Revd John Henry.** b 37. Trin Hall Cam BA61 MA65. Cuddesdon Coll 61. **d** 63 **p** 64 **c** 94. C Stevenage *St Alb* 63-66; C Eastbourne St Mary *Chich* 66-68; V Chipperfield St Paul *St Alb* 68-75; V Rickmansworth 75-86; RD Rickmansworth 77-86; V Bishop's Stortford St Mich *Bris* 86-94; Hon Can St Alb 87-94; Suff Bp Bedford 94-02; rtd 02. *The Old Rectory, Bewscastle, Carlisle CA6 6PS* Tel (01697) 748338

RICHARDSON, John Humphrey. b 33. Dur Univ BA57. Chich Th Coll 57. **d** 59 **p** 60. C Bexhill St Barn *Chich* 59-61; C Stanmer w Falmer and Moulsecoomb 61-64; C Ifield 64-70; R Earnley and E Wittering 70-79; V Stamford All SS w St Pet *Linc* 79-81; R Stamford St Jo w St Clem 79-81; RD Aveland and Ness w Stamford 80-87; V Stamford All SS w St Jo 81-92; P-in-c Metheringham w Blankney 92-94; V Metheringham w Blankney and Dunston 94-98; rtd 98; Perm to Offic *Chich* from 99. *68 Bishopsgate Walk, Chichester PO19 6FQ* Tel (01243) 536864

RICHARDSON, Canon John Malcolm. b 39. Glas Univ MA60 BD63. Andover Newton Th Coll STM65 Edin Th Coll 84. **d** 84 **p** 85. C Edin Old St Paul *Edin* 84-86; R Leven St And 86-90; R Newport-on-Tay 90-96; R Tayport 90-96; Can St Ninian's Cathl Perth from 93; R Forfar from 96. *The Rectory, 24 St James's Road, Forfar DD8 1LG* Tel (01307) 463440 Fax as telephone

RICHARDSON, John Peter. b 50. Keele Univ BA72. St Jo Coll Nottm 73. **d** 76 **p** 77. C Blackheath *Birm* 76-81; P-in-c Sparkbrook Ch Ch 81-83; Chapl NE Lon Poly *Chelmsf* 83-92; Chapl E Lon Univ 92-99; Hon C Stratford St Jo w Ch Ch and St Jas 83-99; C 99-00; C Henham and Elsenham w Ugley from 00. *39 Oziers, Elsenham, Bishop's Stortford CM22 6LS* Tel (01279) 813703 Mobile 07931-506913
E-mail j.p.richardson@btinternet.com
RICHARDSON, John Stephen. b 50. Southn Univ BA71. St Jo Coll Nottm 72. **d** 74 **p** 75. C Bramcote *S'well* 74-77; C Radipole and Melcombe Regis *Sarum* 77-80; P-in-c Stinsford, Winterborne Came w Whitcombe etc 80-83; Asst Dioc Missr 80-83; V Nailsea Ch Ch *B & W* 83-90; Adv on Evang 86-90; Provost Bradf 90-00; Dean Bradf 00-01; V Wye w Brook *Cant* from 01; AD W Bridge from 03; Chapl Wye Coll Kent *Lon* from 01. *The Vicarage, Cherry Garden Crescent, Wye, Ashford TN25 5AS* Tel (01233) 812450
RICHARDSON, Prof John Stuart. b 46. Trin Coll Ox BA68 MA71 DPhil73 FRSE96. **d** 79 **p** 80. NSM St Andrews St Andr *St And* 79-87; Chapl St Andr Univ 80-87; Prof Classics Edin Univ from 87; TV Edin St Columba *Edin* from 87. *29 Merchiston Avenue, Edinburgh EH10 4PH* Tel 0131-228 3094
E-mail j.richardson@ed.ac.uk
RICHARDSON, John Thandule. b 49. Bradf and Ilkley Coll Dip Community Educn 78 BSc80 Lanc Univ MA97. Carl and Blackb Dioc Tr Inst 94. **d** 97 **p** 98. NSM Lea *Blackb* 97-02; NSM Broughton from 02. *65 Lower Bank Road, Fulwood, Preston PR2 8NU* Tel (01772) 787689 E-mail j.richardson@ucsm.ac.uk
RICHARDSON, John William. b 56. Bp Otter Coll BA85 Chich Th Coll 85. **d** 87 **p** 88. C E Preston w Kingston *Chich* 87-89; C Goring-by-Sea 89-90; TV Aldrington 91-92; V Sompting 92-02; P-in-c Margate All SS *Cant* from 02; P-in-c Westgate St Sav from 02. *The Vicarage, Thanet Road, Westgate-on-Sea CT8 8PB* Tel (01843) 831869
RICHARDSON, Joseph Edmund. b 27. St Chad's Coll Dur BA49. Sarum Th Coll 51. **d** 52 **p** 53. C Far Headingley St Chad *Ripon* 52-56; C Hoylake Ches 56-58; R Halton *Ox* 58-65; R Davenham *Ches* 65-76; V Sale St Anne 76-84; R Delamere 84-88; rtd 88; Perm to Offic *Ex* 94-99. *10 Glenthorne Road, Exeter EX4 4QU* Tel (01392) 438539
RICHARDSON, Laurence Leigh. b 71. Trin Coll Carmarthen BA92 PGCE93 Univ of Wales (Cardiff) DipTh96 BTh97. St Mich Coll Llan 94. **d** 97 **p** 98. C Carmarthen St Pet *St D* 97-01; Chapl Carmarthenshire Coll 99-01; P-in-c Abergwili w Llanfihangel-uwch-Gwili etc *St D* 01-03; V from 03. *The Vicarage, Wellfield Road, Abergwili, Carmarthen SA31 2JQ* Tel (01267) 234189 E-mail landcat10a@aol.com
RICHARDSON, Maurice. b 12. **d** 66 **p** 67. C Hawksworth w Scarrington *S'well* 66-69; V Lowdham 69-77; rtd 77; Perm to Offic *S'well* and *Leic* from 82. *Old Orchard, Granby, Nottingham NG13 9PR* Tel (01949) 50860
RICHARDSON, Preb Neil. b 46. Southn Univ BTh83. Sarum & Wells Th Coll 71. **d** 74 **p** 75. C Oldham St Mary w St Pet *Man* 74-77; C-in-c Holts CD 77-82; R Greenford H Cross from 82; Preb St Paul's Cathl from 02. *The Rectory, Oldfield Lane, Greenford UB6 9JS* Tel (020) 8578 1543
E-mail neil@holycross.ndo.co.uk
or neilandmarion2001@hotmail.com
✠**RICHARDSON, The Rt Revd Paul.** b 47. Qu Coll Ox BA68 BA70 MA75. Harvard Div Sch 70 Cuddesdon Coll 71. **d** 72 **p** 73 **c** 87. C Earlsfield St Jo *S'wark* 72-75; Asst Chapl Oslo St Edm *Eur* 75-77; Papua New Guinea 77-95; Miss P Nambaiyufu 77-79; Lect Newton Th Coll 79-81; Prin 81-85; Dean Port Moresby 85-86; Bp Aipo Rongo 87-95; Bp Wangaratta 95-97; Asst Bp Newc from 95. *Close House, St George's Close, Jesmond, Newcastle upon Tyne NE2 2TF* Tel 0191-281 2556 *or* 285 2220 Fax 284 6933
RICHARDSON, Paul. b 58. Univ of Wales (Cardiff) BSc80. Ridley Hall Cam 81. **d** 84 **p** 85. C Stanwix *Carl* 84-87; Ind Chapl 87-89; Staff P Dalton-in-Furness 87-89; V Marton Moss *Blackb* 89-95; P-in-c Prestwich St Gabr *Man* 95-00; Bp's Dom Chapl 95-00; V Westbury *Sarum* 00-02; TR Whine Horse from 02. *The Vicarage, Bitham Lane, Westbury BA13 3BU* Tel (01373) 822209
RICHARDSON, Pauline Kate. See JENKINS, Pauline Kate
RICHARDSON, Robin John. b 71. Bris Univ BA01 Loughb Univ BEng92 PGCE93. Trin Coll Bris 98. **d** 01 **p** 02. C Sidmouth, Woolbrook, Salcombe Regis, Sidbury etc *Ex* from 01. *25 Lymebourne Park, Sidmouth EX10 9HZ* Tel (01395) 519741
E-mail strangways@xalt.co.uk
RICHARDSON, Ronald Eric. b 48. York Univ CertEd Leeds Univ BEd. N Ord Course. **d** 82 **p** 83. NSM St Andr and St Mary *Wakef* 82-83; C 83-90; NSM S Ossett 90-95; Perm to Offic from 95. *37 Stanley Road, Wakefield WF1 4NA* Tel (01924) 381047
RICHARDSON, Simon James. b 51. Loughb Univ BSc82 Nottm Univ MA99. EMMTC 96. **d** 99 **p** 00. C Market Harborough and The Transfiguration etc *Leic* 99-02; Chapl Loughb Univ from 02; C Loughborough All SS w H Trin from 02. *13 Spinney Hill Drive, Loughborough LE11 3LB* Tel (01509) 237761

RICHARDSON, Simon Kay Caoimhín. b 74. St Jo Coll Dur BA96. Wycliffe Hall Ox 01. **d** 03. C Sandgate St Paul w Folkestone St Geo *Cant* from 03. *St George's House, 133 Shorncliffe Road, Folkestone CT20 3PB* Tel (01303) 248675 Mobile 07771-800846
E-mail simonkcrichardson@hotmail.com
RICHARDSON, Miss Susan. b 58. Cranmer Hall Dur. **d** 87 **p** 94. Par Dn Stokesley *York* 87-91; Par Dn Beverley St Nic 91-94; P-in-c Cloughton 94-97; Tr Officer E Riding Adnry from 94; V Cloughton and Burniston w Ravenscar etc 97-99; V Middlesbrough St Oswald from 99. *St Oswald's Vicarage, Lambton Road, Middlesbrough TS4 2RG* Tel (01642) 816156
RICHBOROUGH, Suffragan Bishop of (Provincial Episcopal Visit or). See NEWTON, The Rt Revd Keith
RICHENS, Canon Geoffrey Roger. b 23. ALCD52. **d** 52 **p** 53. C St Helens St Helen *Liv* 52-56; V Widnes St Mary 56-80; V Skelmersdale St Paul 80-93; Hon Can Liv Cathl 89-93; rtd 93; Perm to Offic *Liv* from 93 and *Blackb* from 98. *43 West View, Parbold, Wigan WN8 7NT* Tel (01257) 463143
RICHERBY, Canon Glynn. b 51. K Coll Lon BD73 AKC73. St Aug Coll Cant 73. **d** 74 **p** 75. C Weston Favell *Pet* 74-78; Prec Leic Cathl *Leic* 78-81; V Glen Parva and S Wigston 81-93; Dir Post-Ord Tr 86-95; V Leic St Jas from 93; Dir CME from 95; Hon Can Leic Cathl from 98. *St James the Greater Vicarage, 216 London Road, Leicester LE2 1NE* Tel 0116-254 4113
E-mail glynn@leicester.anglican.org
RICHES, Prof John Kenneth. b 39. CCC Cam BA61 MA65. Kirchliche Hochschule Bethel 61 Westcott Ho Cam 62. **d** 65 **p** 66. C Costessey *Nor* 65-68; Chapl and Fell SS Coll Cam 68-72; Lect Glas Univ 72-86; Sen Lect 86-91; Prof Div and Bibl Criticism Glas Univ from 91; Chmn Balmore Trust from 80; Lic to Offic *Glas* from 85. *Viewfield, Balmore, Torrance, Glasgow G64 4AE* Tel (01360) 620254 E-mail j.riches@divinity.gla.ac.uk
RICHES, Malcolm Leslie. b 46. St Jo Coll Nottm Dip Th & Min 94. **d** 94 **p** 95. C Swaythling *Win* 94-97; P-in-c Boldre w S Baddesley 97-01; V from 01. *The Vicarage, Pilley Hill, Pilley, Lymington SO41 5QF* Tel (01590) 677538 Fax 677767
E-mail malcolm.riches@ukgateway.net
RICHEUX, Marc Stephen. b 66. Man Univ BA89. Trin Coll Bris BA00. **d** 00 **p** 01. C Plumstead St Jo w St Jas and St Paul *S'wark* from 00. *34 Earl Rise, London SE18 7NH* Tel (020) 8855 1311 *or* 8317 3271 E-mail richeux@mail.clara.net
RICHEY, Robert Samuel Payne. b 23. TCD BA46. **d** 48 **p** 49. C Moy *Arm* 48-50; I Killinagh w Kiltyclogher *K, E & A* 50-60; I Killinagh w Kiltyclogher and Innismagrath 60-72; I Killinagh w Kiltyclogher, Killargue etc 72-91; I Killinagh w Kiltyclogher and Innismagrath 91-98; Sec Dioc Bd Educn 64-98; Dioc Sec (Kilmore) 72-98; Dioc Info Officer (Kilmore) 81-98; Can Kilmore Cathl 80-98; Preb Mulhuddart St Patr Cathl Dublin 94-98; rtd 98. *Rockview, Blacklion, Co Cavan, Irish Republic* Tel (00353) (71) 985 3010
✠**RICHMOND, The Rt Revd Francis Henry Arthur.** b 36. TCD BA59 MA66 Strasbourg Univ BTh60 Linacre Coll Ox MLitt64. Wycliffe Hall Ox 60. **d** 63 **p** 64 **c** 86. C Woodlands *Sheff* 63-66; Chapl Sheff Cathl 66-69; V Sheff St Geo 69-77; Chapl Sheff Univ *Linc* 77-86; Warden Linc Th Coll 77-86; Can and Preb Linc Cathl *Linc* 77-86; Suff Bp Repton *Derby* 86-98; Hon Can Derby Cathl 86-98; rtd 98. *39 Hodges Court, Oxford OX1 4NZ* Tel (01865) 790466
RICHMOND, Gordon Hazlewood. b 33. Launde Abbey 77. **d** 79 **p** 80. C Leic St Paul *Leic* 79-81; C Shepshed 81-84; V Ryhall w Essendine *Pet* 84-91; RD Barnack 89-91; V Gretton w Rockingham 91-98; rtd 98; Perm to Offic *Pet* from 98; *Leic* from 99. *Malvern, 2 Linwal Avenue, Houghton-on-the-Hill, Leicester LE7 9HD* Tel 0116-241 7638
RICHMOND, Patrick Henry. b 69. Ball Coll Ox BA90 Green Coll Ox MA94 DPhil94. Wycliffe Hall Ox BA96. **d** 97 **p** 98. C Leic Martyrs *Leic* 97-01; Chapl St Cath Coll Cam from 01. *8 South Green Road, Cambridge CB3 9JP* Tel (01223) 324035 *or* 338300 E-mail chaplain@caths.cam.ac.uk
RICHMOND, Peter James. b 54. Writtle Agric Coll HND76 Ex Univ PGCE95. St Jo Coll Nottm LTh80. **d** 80 **p** 81. C Ogley Hay *Lich* 80-83; C Trentham 83-85; P-in-c Wolverhampton St Jo 85-89; P-in-c Loppington w Newtown 89-93; P-in-c Edstaston 89-93; Perm to Offic *Ex* 94-95; P-in-c Weston Zoyland w Chedzoy *B & W* from 95. *The Vicarage, Church Lane, Weston Zoyland, Bridgwater TA7 0EP* Tel (01278) 691743
E-mail peterzoyland@yahoo.co.uk
RICHMOND, Mrs Yvonne Lorraine. b 63. WEMTC DipApTh99. **d** 99 **p** 00. NSM Magor *Mon* 99-00; NSM Kenilworth St Jo *Cov* from 00. *Birchwood, Red Lane, Kenilworth CV8 1PB* Tel (024) 7647 1039
E-mail yvonne.richmond@care4free.net
RICHMOND, Archdeacon of. See GOOD, The Ven Kenneth Roy
RICKARDS, Bruce Walter. b 69. NTMTC 98. **d** 01 **p** 02. NSM St Marg Lothbury and St Steph Coleman Street etc *Lon* from 01. *85A Toynbee Road, London SW20 8SJ* Tel (020) 8540 4150 Mobile 07850-655102 E-mail byrickards@btinternet.com

RICKETTS, Allan Fenn. b 46. Open Univ BA76. Cranmer Hall Dur 68. **d** 71 **p** 72. C Rowley Regis *Birm* 71-72; C The Quinton 72-74; C Brierley Hill *Lich* 74-77; TV Chelmsley Wood *Birm* 77-82; TV Ross w Brampton Abbotts, Bridstow and Peterstow *Heref* 82-88; R Linton w Upton Bishop and Aston Ingham 88-96. *13 Falaise Close, Ross-on-Wye HR9 5UT* Tel (01989) 565077

RICKETTS, Mrs Diane. NTMTC. **d** 01 **p** 02. NSM Nazeing *Chelmsf* from 01; NSM Roydon from 01. *38 Paternoster Close, Waltham Abbey EN9 3JX* Tel (01992) 764415
E-mail diane_ricketts@yahoo.co.uk

RICKETTS, Canon Kathleen Mary. b 39. Southlands Coll Lon TCert59 Univ of W Aus BA79. Westcott Ho Cam 81. **dss** 83 **d** 87 **p** 94. All Hallows by the Tower etc *Lon* 83-88; C 87-88; C Hall Green Ascension *Birm* 88-91; Chapl Birm Children's Hosp 91-94; Chapl Birm Children's Hosp NHS Trust 94-99; Hon Can Birm Cathl *Birm* 96-99; rtd 99. *22 Holly Drive, Birmingham B27 7NF* Tel 0121-706 1087

RICKETTS, Mrs Linda Elizabeth. b 52. RNMH85. EAMTC 98. **d** 01 **p** 02. C Loddon, Sisland, Chedgrave, Hardley and Langley *Nor* from 01. *6 Farm Close, Chedgrave, Norwich NR14 6HQ* Tel (01508) 528310

RICKETTS, Peter William. b 28. DLC53. St Alb Minl Tr Scheme 76. **d** 79 **p** 80. NSM Hertford All SS *St Alb* 79-86; R Blunham w Tempsford and Lt Barford 86-93; rtd 93; Perm to Offic *St Alb* 93-02. *7 Rashley Road, Chickerell, Weymouth DT3 4AT* Tel (01305) 781892

RICKMAN, Peter Alan. b 68. Ripon Coll Cuddesdon BTh94. **d** 97 **p** 98. C Bitterne Park *Win* 97-01; Chapl St Paul's Colleg Sch Hamilton NZ from 01. *St Paul's Collegiate School, Private Bag 3069, Hukanui Road, Hamilton, New Zealand*

RIDDEL, Canon Robert John. b 37. CITC 65. **d** 68 **p** 69. C Derryloran *Arm* 68-74; I Keady w Armaghbreague and Derrynoose 74-80; I Mullaghdun *Clogh* 80-84; I Cleenish 80-84; I Fivemiletown from 84; Can Clogh Cathl from 91; Preb Donaghmore St Patr Cathl Dublin from 95. *The Rectory, 160 Ballagh Road, Fivemiletown BT75 0QP* Tel (028) 6652 1030
E-mail r.j.riddel@btinternet.com

RIDDELL, Morris Stroyan. b 34. Lon Univ DipTh59 BD69. Tyndale Hall Bris 57. **d** 60 **p** 60. S Africa 60-63; C Mowbray 60-62; V Addington Ch Ch 62-63; V N Grimston w Wharram Percy and Wharram-le-Street *York* 63-67; V Kirby Grindalythe 63-67; P-in-c Weaverthorpe w Helperthorpe and Luttons 65-67; P-in-c Settrington 65-67; P-in-c Wintringham 65-67; P-in-c Thorpe Bassett 65-67; R Bris St Jo w St Mary-le-Port *Bris* 67-70; Dir Bris Samaritans 67-70; Chapl HM Pris Long Lartin 71-74; Chapl HM Pris Brixton 74-78; Chapl Cane Hill Hosp Coulsdon 78-85; Chapl HM Rem Cen Latchmere Ho 85-89; rtd 95. *Flat 5, 30 Montpelier Crescent, Brighton BN1 3JJ* Tel (01273) 329229

RIDDELSDELL, Canon John Creffield. b 23. Selw Coll Cam BA47 MA52 Lon Univ BD70. Ridley Hall Cam 47. **d** 49 **p** 50. C Kilburn St Mary *Lon* 49-52; Kenya 52-77; V Gt Ilford St Andr *Chelmsf* 77-88; rtd 88; Perm to Offic *Chelmsf* from 88. *Waverley, Mill Lane, Walton on the Naze CO14 8PE* Tel (01255) 850213

RIDDING, George. b 24. Oriel Coll Ox BA50 MA57. Wells Th Coll 60. **d** 61 **p** 62. C Countess Wear *Ex* 61-62; Chapl Ex Sch 62-64; India 64-68; Hd Master W Buckland Sch Barnstaple 68-78; USPG 78-82; P-in-c Broadhembury w Payhembury *Ex* 82-83; P-in-c Plymtree 82-83; R Broadhembury, Payhembury and Plymtree 83-89; rtd 89; Perm to Offic *Sarum* from 89. *Cherwell, Higher Blandford Road, Shaftesbury SP7 8DA* Tel (01747) 851390

RIDDING, William Thomas. b 54. Southn Univ BTh. Sarum & Wells Th Coll 80. **d** 83 **p** 84. C Verwood *Sarum* 83-86; TV Gillingham 86-01; RD Blackmore Vale 95-01; P-in-c Stalbridge 01-02; R Stalbridge and Stock from 02. *The Rectory, Church Hill, Stalbridge, Sturminster Newton DT10 2LR* Tel (01963) 362859
E-mail williamridding@beeb.net

RIDDLE, Kenneth Wilkinson. b 20. St Cath Soc Ox BA42 MA46. Ripon Hall Ox 42. **d** 43 **p** 44. C Lowestoft St Marg *Nor* 43-47; C Luton St Mary *St Alb* 47-49; V Sundon w Streatley 49-52; R Pakefield *Nor* 52-59; V Nor St Pet Mancroft 59-60; R E w W Harling 60-65; P-in-c Bridgham and Roudham 60-61; R 61-65; R Lowestoft St Marg 65-68; rtd 85. *9 Clare Court, Clarence Road, Fleet GU51 3XX* Tel (01252) 617450

RIDEOUT, Canon Gordon Trevor. b 38. BA87 Westmr Coll Ox MTh96. Linc Coll of Div 58. **d** 62 **p** 63. C Southgate *Chich* 62-65; Chapl Dr Barnardo's Barkingside & Woodford Br 65-67; CF 67-73; V Nutley *Chich* 73-79; V Eastbourne All SS from 79; Chapl Moira Ho Sch E Sussex from 79; Chapl Brighton Poly *Chich* 80-92; Chapl Brighton Univ from 92; Can and Preb Chich Cathl from 90; RD Eastbourne 91-97. *All Saints' Vicarage, Grange Road, Eastbourne BN21 4HE* Tel (01323) 410033

RIDER, Andrew. b 62. RMN85 Nottm Univ BTh90 K Coll Lon MA96. Aston Tr Scheme 85 St Jo Coll Nottm 87. **d** 90 **p** 91. C Luton Ch Ch *Roch* 90-93; C w resp for Clubhouse Langham Place All So *Lon* from 93. *25 Fitzroy Street, London W1T 6DR* Tel (020) 7580 3745 *or* 7387 1360 Fax 7387 2593
E-mail arider@clara.co.uk

RIDER, Canon Dennis William Austin. b 34. Lon Univ DipTh61. St Aid Birkenhead 58. **d** 61 **p** 62. C Derby St Aug *Derby* 61-64; C Sutton *Liv* 64-67; R Stiffkey w Morston, Langham Episcopi etc *Nor* 67-71; V Buxton w Oxnead 71-79; R Lammas w Lt Hautbois 72-79; R Gaywood, Bawsey and Mintlyn 79-91; RD Lynn 89-91; Hon Can Nor Cathl 90-99; R E Dereham and Scarning 91-98; TR 98-99; RD Dereham in Mitford 95-98; rtd 99; Perm to Offic *Nor* from 01. *37A Holt Road, Fakenham NR21 8BW* Tel (01328) 856018

RIDER, Geoffrey Malcolm. b 29. Selw Coll Cam BA53 MA56 Lon Inst of Educn PGCE68. Coll of Resurr Mirfield 53. **d** 55 **p** 56. C S Elmsall *Wakef* 55-60; C Barnsley St Mary 60-63; V Cleckheaton St Jo 63-67; Public Preacher *S'wark* 67-92; rtd 92; S Africa 92-95; Perm to Offic *S'wark* from 95. *35 Kirkby Road, Ripon HG4 2EY* Tel (01765) 690517

RIDER, Neil Wilding. b 35. St Jo Coll Dur BA59 DipTh61 Univ of Wales (Lamp) MA00. Cranmer Hall Dur 59. **d** 62 **p** 63. C Blackb St Barn *Blackb* 62-64; C Chadderton Em *Man* 64-69; C Deane 69-72; V Coldhurst 72-75; Perm to Offic *Ely* 76-78; C Didsbury Ch Ch *Man* 78-80; Perm to Offic *St D* from 80; rtd 00. *Caergrawnt, Cwmann, Lampeter SA48 8EL* Tel (01570) 422921

RIDGE, Aubrey. b 25. Oak Hill Th Coll 67. **d** 68 **p** 69. C Gorleston St Andr *Nor* 68-70; C Hamworthy *Sarum* 70-75; P-in-c Pitsea *Chelmsf* 75-78; R 78-81; P-in-c Stoke Ash, Thwaite and Wetheringsett *St E* 81-85; P-in-c Bedingfield and Thorndon w Rishangles 81-85; P-in-c Thorndon w Rishangles, Stoke Ash, Thwaite etc 85-86; P-in-c Risby w Gt and Lt Saxham and Westley 86-90; rtd 90; Perm to Offic *Sarum* 90-93; Hon C Milford *Win* 93-96; Perm to Offic 96-99. *5 Oak Tree Court, Whitby Road, Milford on Sea, Lymington SO41 0UJ* Tel (01590) 643504

RIDGE, Haydn Stanley. b 24. Univ of Wales (Lamp) BA51 Bris Univ CertEd52. Qu Coll Birm 56. **d** 56 **p** 57. C Blackheath *Birm* 56-60; Div Master Guernsey Gr Sch 60-75; Perm to Offic *Win* 60-62; Hon C Guernsey St Steph 62-96; Dep Hd Master St Peter Port Sch 75-80; Hd Master St Sampson Sch 75-87; rtd 91; Perm to Offic *Win* 96-00. *St David, Les Cherfs, Castel, Guernsey GY5 7HG* Tel (01481) 56209

RIDGEWAY, David. b 59. St Chad's Coll Dur BSc80 Cam Univ CertEd81. Ripon Coll Cuddesdon 84. **d** 87 **p** 88. C Kempston Transfiguration *St Alb* 87-90; C Radlett 90-95; P-in-c Heath and Reach 95-98; V 98-01; V St Alb St Steph from 01. *St Stephen's Vicarage, 14 Watling Street, St Albans AL1 2PX* Tel (01727) 862598 E-mail davidridgeway@eggconnect.net

RIDGEWELL, Graham Edgar Charles. b 46. LGSM71 Open Univ BA82 UEA DPSE88. **d** 02 **p** 03. NSM Whitby w Aislaby and Ruswarp *York* from 02. *Fernlea, The Avenue, Sleights, Whitby YO22 5BS* Tel (01947) 810504
E-mail ridgwell@onetel.net.uk

RIDGEWELL, Miss Mary Jean. b 54. Dur Univ BA76 PGCE77. Ridley Hall Cam 88. **d** 91 **p** 94. Par Dn Trowbridge St Jas *Sarum* 91-94; C 94-95; Chapl Lee Abbey 95-96; NSM Bradford Peverell, Stratton, Frampton etc *Sarum* 96-97; Chapl HM Pris and Young Offender Inst Guys Marsh from 97. *HM Prison and YOI, Guy's Marsh, Shaftesbury SP7 0AH* Tel (01747) 853344 ext 325 Fax 851584

RIDGWAY, David. b 28. Trin Hall Cam BA54 MA58. Westcott Ho Cam 54. **d** 56 **p** 57. C Milton *Portsm* 56-59; CF 59-63; R Gosforth *Carl* 63-70; V Walney Is 70-76; P-in-c Irthington 76-78; P-in-c Crosby-on-Eden 77-78; V Irthington, Crosby-on-Eden and Scaleby 79-93; rtd 93. *11 Woodleigh, Walton, Brampton CA8 2DS* Tel (01697) 73252

RIDGWAY, Mrs Janet Elizabeth Knight. b 40. St Alb Minl Tr Scheme 83. **dss** 86 **d** 87 **p** 94. Tring *St Alb* 86-87; Hon Par Dn 87-94; Hon C from 94. *Barleycombe, Trooper Road, Aldbury, Tring HP23 5RW* Tel (01442) 851303
E-mail mrs.v.j.ridgway@breathemail.net

RIDING, Pauline Alison. *See* BICKNELL, Mrs Pauline Alison

RIDINGS, Neil Arthur. b 66. Man Poly BEd90. St Jo Coll Nottm 01. **d** 01 **p** 02. C Holyhead *Ban* from 01. *Tŷ Sant Elbod, 3 Harbour View, Holyhead LL65 2HL* Tel (01407) 760841

RIDLEY, Alfred Forbes. b 34. Bps' Coll Cheshunt 62. **d** 65 **p** 66. C Prittlewell St Mary *Chelmsf* 65-69; R Paulerspury *Pet* 69-73; P-in-c Wicken 71-73; V W Haddon w Winwick 73-83; RD Brixworth 80-83; R Guernsey St Philippe de Torteval *Win* 83-92; R Guernsey St Pierre du Bois 83-92; R Blakesley w Adstone and Maidford etc *Pet* 92-99; rtd 99; Perm to Offic *Pet* from 99. *4 Plessey Close, Towcester NN12 6HY* Tel (01327) 358664

RIDLEY, Andrew Roy. b 55. St Pet Coll Ox BA77. Ripon Coll Cuddesdon 78. **d** 79 **p** 80. C Bollington St Jo *Ches* 79-83; V Runcorn St Mich 83-94; Dioc Chapl to MU 92-98; RD Frodsham 94-98; V Helsby and Dunham-on-the-Hill 94-98; P-in-c Alvanley 94-98; R Whitchurch *Lich* from 98; RD Wem and Whitchurch from 01. *The Rectory, Church Street, Whitchurch SY13 1LB* Tel (01948) 662342 Fax as telephone

RIDLEY, David Gerhard. b 60. Southn Univ BSc82 Bath Univ PGCE83. Qu Coll Birm 91. **d** 93 **p** 94. C Faversham *Cant* 93-97; Min Folkestone St Aug CD 97-01; V Dover St Mary from 01; P-in-c Guston from 02. *The Vicarage, Taswell Street, Dover CT16 1SE* Tel (01304) 206842 E-mail davidridley@bigfoot.com

RIDLEY, Derek. b 40. Newc Univ BSc74. Cranmer Hall Dur 75. **d** 78 **p** 79. C Upperby St Jo *Carl* 78-81; C Penrith w Newton Reigny 81; C Penrith w Newton Reigny and Plumpton Wall 81-82; TV 82-86; V Cadishead *Man* 86-99; R Asfordby and P-in-c Ab Kettleby Gp *Leic* 99-02; P-in-c Old Dalby and Nether Broughton 99-01; rtd 02. *32 Carleton Place, Penrith CA11 8LW* Tel (01768) 890676

RIDLEY, Jay. b 41. Birm Univ BA63. St Steph Ho Ox 63. **d** 65 **p** 66. C Woodford St Mary *Chelmsf* 65-67; C Prittlewell St Mary 67-70; C-in-c Dunscroft CD *Sheff* 70-74; Asst Chapl HM Pris Wormwood Scrubs 75-77; Chapl HM Rem Cen Ashford 77-84; Chapl HM YOI Feltham 84-91; Chapl HM Pris Ashwell 91-00; C Oakham, Hambleton, Egleton, Braunston and Brooke *Pet* from 00. *45 Trent Road, Oakham LE15 6HE* Tel (01572) 756086 E-mail j.ridley@zetnet.co.uk

RIDLEY, Mrs Lesley. b 46. Cranmer Hall Dur 75. **dss** 78 **d** 87 **p** 94. Upperby St Jo *Carl* 78-81; Penrith w Newton Reigny and Plumpton Wall 81-86; Cadishead *Man* 86-99; Par Dn 87-94; C 94-99; C Asfordby and Ab Kettleby Gp *Leic* 99-02; rtd 02. *32 Carleton Place, Penrith CA11 8LW* Tel (01768) 890676

RIDLEY, Louise. b 59. Lanc Univ BA81 LGSM83. Cranmer Hall Dur 01. **d** 03. C Sheff St Cuth *Sheff* from 03. *112 Whiteways Road, Sheffield S4 8EU* Tel 0114-261 1605

RIDLEY, Canon Michael Edward. b 37. Ex Univ MA90. St Boniface Warminster AKC62. **d** 63 **p** 64. C Chapel Allerton *Ripon* 63-67; C Epsom St Martin *Guildf* 67-70; C Claxby w Normanby-le-Wold etc *Linc* 70-72; V Leake 72-75; R Harlaxton w Wyville and Hungerton 75-80; R Stroxton 76-80; Dioc Stewardship Adv *Portsm* 80-86; P-in-c Rowlands Castle 80-82; C Blendworth w Chalton w Idsworth etc 83-86; TV N Creedy *Ex* 86-90; R W Downland *Sarum* 90-02; RD Chalke 92-97 and 98-00; Can and Preb Sarum Cathl 00-02; rtd 02. *6 Cole Moore Meadow, Tavistock PL19 0ES* Tel (01822) 610799

RIDLEY, Michael Laurence. b 59. BA81. Ripon Coll Cuddesdon 81. **d** 83 **p** 84. C Bollington St Jo *Ches* 83-88; V Thelwall 88-95; V Weaverham from 95; RD Middlewich from 99. *The Vicarage, Weaverham, Northwich CW8 3NJ* Tel (01606) 852110 E-mail michael@stmarysvicarage.fsnet.co.uk

RIDLEY, Peter John. b 39. Keble Coll Ox BA61. Tyndale Hall Bris 61. **d** 63 **p** 64. C Clifton Ch Ch w Em *Bris* 63-67; C Lambeth St Andr w St Thos *S'wark* 67-69; V W Hampstead St Cuth *Lon* 69-77; V Eynsham *Ox* 77-85; RD Woodstock 82-84; V Nicholforest and Kirkandrews on Esk *Carl* 85-96; P-in-c E Knoyle, Semley and Sedgehill *Sarum* from 96. *The Rectory, Semley, Shaftesbury SP7 9AU* Tel (01747) 830362 Fax as telephone

RIDLEY, Simon. b 33. Magd Coll Ox BA54 MA58 BD66. Linc Th Coll 54. **d** 57 **p** 58. C St John's Wood *Lon* 57-60; Abp's Dom Chapl *Cant* 60-61; V N Wootton *B & W* 61-66; Lect Wells Th Coll 61-65; Hong Kong 66-70; TR Basingstoke *Win* 70-73; rtd 96; Perm to Offic *Cant* from 96. *Oxney House, The Street, Wittersham, Tenterden TN30 7ED* Tel (01797) 270215

RIDLEY, Stephen James. b 57. St Pet Coll Ox MA83. Ripon Coll Cuddesdon 80. **d** 82 **p** 83. C Heald Green St Cath *Ches* 82-85; Chapl Ches Coll 85-90; Dioc Press Officer 85-90; Chapl Birkenhead Sch Merseyside 90-96; Lic to Offic *Ches* 90-96; Chapl Barnard Castle Sch from 96. *3 Old Courts, Barnard Castle School, Newgate, Barnard Castle DL12 8UN* Tel (01833) 690222

RIDLEY, Stewart Gordon. b 47. K Coll Lon AKC72. St Aug Coll Cant 72. **d** 73 **p** 74. C Armley w New Wortley *Ripon* 73-77; C Hawksworth Wood 77-79; C Rothwell w Lofthouse 79-81; R Whitwood *Wakef* 81-87; R Ingoldmells w Addlethorpe *Linc* 87-92; RD Calcewaithe and Candleshoe 89-92; V Settle *Bradf* from 92; Dioc Chapl MU from 93. *The Vicarage, 2 Town Head, Settle BD24 9RG* Tel (01729) 822288

RIDLEY, Vic. *See* RIDLEY, David Gerhard

RIDOUT, Canon Christopher John. b 33. K Coll Lon BD57 AKC57 MA92. **d** 58 **p** 59. C Roxeth Ch Ch *Lon* 58-62; CMS 62-63; Kenya 63-75; C Gt Malvern St Mary *Worc* 75-79; R Bredon w Bredon's Norton 79-98; RD Pershore 91-97; Hon Can Worc Cathl 92-98; rtd 98; Perm to Offic *Glouc* from 98. *5 Belworth Drive, Hatherley, Cheltenham GL51 6EL* Tel (01242) 231765

RIDYARD, Preb John Gordon. b 33. St Aid Birkenhead 59. **d** 62 **p** 63. C Lancaster St Mary *Blackb* 62-65; C Bushbury *Lich* 65-68; V Darlaston All SS 68-76; TV Wolverhampton St Mark 76-78; TV Wolverhampton 78-82; Preb Lich Cathl from 82; V Bishopswood 82-89; V Brewood 82-89; RD Penkridge 83-89; R Newcastle w Butterton 89-98; rtd 98; V in the Close *Lich* from 98. *Upper Flat, Vicars Hall, Beacon Street, Lichfield WS13 7AD* Tel (01543) 306297

RIDYARD, Malcolm Charles. b 32. St D Coll Lamp BA54 Wycliffe Hall Ox 54. **d** 56 **p** 57. C Widnes St Paul *Liv* 56-59; C Ashton-in-Makerfield St Thos 59-61; India 62-71; Area Sec CMS *B & W*, *Bris* and *Sarum* 71-80; P-in-c Church Coniston *Carl* 80-87; P-in-c Torver 80-87; R Bootle, Corney, Whicham and Whitbeck 87-97; rtd 98; Perm to Offic *Birm* from 98. *140 Quinton Road West, Quinton, Birmingham B32 2RH* Tel 0121-422 3895

RIEM, Roland Gerardus Anthony. b 60. St Chad's Coll Dur BSc82 Kent Univ PhD86 Heythrop Coll Lon MA99. St Jo Coll Nottm

DipTh87 DPS89. **d** 89 **p** 90. C Deal St Leon and St Rich and Sholden *Cant* 89-92; Sen Chapl Nottm Univ *S'well* 92-98; Minl Development Officer STETS from 98. *Sarum College, 19 The Close, Salisbury SP1 2EE* Tel (01722) 424814 Fax 424811 E-mail rgariem@stets.ac.uk

RIESS, Trevor William. b 54. Down Coll Cam MA76 CertEd77. St Jo Coll Nottm 84. **d** 86 **p** 87. C Stainforth *Sheff* 86-88; Chapl St Jas Choir Sch Grimsby 89; C Lowestoft and Kirkley *Nor* 89-90; TV 90-94; TV Lowestoft St Marg 94-95; Lothingland Hosp 90-95; V Gorleston St Mary *Nor* from 95. *The Vicarage, 41 Nuffield Crescent, Gorleston, Great Yarmouth NR31 7LL* Tel (01493) 661741

RIGBY, Francis Michael. b 29. Glouc Sch of Min. **d** 90 **p** 91. NSM Alvescot w Black Bourton, Shilton, Holwell etc *Ox* 90-92; P-in-c Gt w Lt Tew 92-95; P-in-c Bishop's Frome w Castle Frome and Fromes Hill *Heref* 96-99; P-in-c Acton Beauchamp and Evesbatch 96-99. *Barn Acre, Bishop's Frome, Worcester WR6 5AV* Tel (01885) 490204

RIGBY, Harold. b 34. Nottm Univ BA56 St Cath Soc Ox BA58 MA62 Man Poly PGCE77. Ripon Hall Ox 56. **d** 58 **p** 59. C Didsbury St Jas and Em *Man* 58-61; C Bury St Jo 61-64; P-in-c Lostock St Thos and St Jo 64-76; Hon C Davyhulme St Mary 76-79; Lic Preacher from 79; Perm to Offic *Ches* from 79; rtd 99. *17 Atwood Road, Didsbury, Manchester M20 0TA* Tel 0161-445 7454

RIGBY, Joseph. b 37. Open Univ BA72. Ox NSM Course. **d** 78 **p** 79. NSM Earley St Pet *Ox* 78-80; C Penzance St Mary w St Paul *Truro* 80-82; V Mevagissey 82-83; P-in-c St Ewe 83; R Mevagissey and St Ewe 83-90; rtd 90; Perm to Offic *Truro* from 90. *5 The Close, Upland Crescent, Truro TR1 1LY* Tel (01872) 240440

RIGBY, Michael John. b 52. MA MSc. Ridley Hall Cam. **d** 82 **p** 83. C Reading St Jo *Ox* 82-86; C Wallington H Trin *S'wark* 86-92; Pastor Foundns Chr Fellowship Trust Ch from 92. *14 Dinorben Court, Woodcote Road, Wallington SM6 0PZ* Tel (020) 8647 8649

RIGBY, William. b 51. Leic Univ BSc(Econ)72 Newc Poly BSc82. Cranmer Hall Dur 86. **d** 88 **p** 89. C Morpeth *Newc* 88-92; R St John Lee 92-00; Chapl to the Deaf from 92; P-in-c Chapel House from 00. *The Vicarage, 44 Queensbury Drive, North Walbottle, Newcastle upon Tyne NE15 9XF* Tel 0191-267 4069 Fax 229 0232 E-mail riggers@rigby.enta.net

RIGELSFORD, Mrs Anne Catharina (Ank). b 44. EAMTC 99. **d** 02 **p** 03. NSM Cambridge H Cross *Ely* from 02. *19 Clare Street, Cambridge CB4 3BY* Tel (01223) 368150 Mobile 07932-846395 E-mail ank@rigelsford.freeserve.co.uk

RIGGS, Sidney James. b 39. Bps' Coll Cheshunt 62. **d** 63 **p** 64. C S'wark St Geo *S'wark* 63-66; C Plymouth Crownhill Ascension *Ex* 66-69; Asst Youth Chapl *Glouc* 69-71; Hon Min Can Glouc Cathl 71-74; Min Can Glouc Cathl 74-76; V Glouc St Mary de Lode and St Nic 76-92; R Rodborough from 92; RD Stonehouse 94-96. *The Rectory, Walkley Hill, Rodborough, Stroud GL5 3TX* Tel (01453) 764399

RIGNEY, James Thomas Walpole. b 59. Sydney Univ BA82 MA88 Pemb Coll Ox DPhil95 CCC Cam BA00. Westcott Ho Cam 98. **d** 01 **p** 02. C Cambridge St Jas *Ely* from 01. *130 Hulatt Road, Cambridge CB1 8TH* Tel (01223) 212516 E-mail jamesrigney@hotmail.com

RILEY, David Leo. b 51. S Bank Univ MSc95. Dioc OLM tr scheme 97. **d** 00 **p** 01. NSM Bellingham St Dunstan *S'wark* from 00. *117 Whitefoot Lane, Bromley BR1 5SB* Tel (020) 8516 4544 E-mail driley3020@aol.com

RILEY, John Graeme. b 55. St Jo Coll Dur BA78. Trin Coll Bris 79. **d** 81 **p** 82. C Hensingham *Carl* 81-84; C Preston St Cuth *Blackb* 84-87; V Blackb Ch Ch w St Matt 87-98; Chapl Qu Park Hosp Blackb 87-94; V Shevington *Blackb* from 98. *St Anne's Vicarage, 81 Gathurst Lane, Shevington, Wigan WN6 8HW* Tel (01257) 252136

RILEY, Preb John Martin. b 37. St D Coll Lamp BA62 DipTh63. **d** 63 **p** 64. C Conwy w Gyffin *Ban* 63-68; P-in-c Llanfachraeth 68-70; TV Dolgellau, Llanfachreth, Brithdir etc 70-72; V Beddgelert 72-78; Dioc Youth Chapl 72-78; V Tywyn 78-82; V Tywyn w Aberdyfi 82-95; V Llanegryn w Aberdyfi w Tywyn from 95; RD Ystumaner 87-01; AD from 01; Can Ban Cathl 90-97; Preb from 97. *The Vicarage, Tywyn LL36 9BF* Tel (01654) 710295 Fax as telephone E-mail martinriley@fish.co.uk

RILEY, The Very Revd Kenneth Joseph. b 40. OBE03. Univ of Wales BA61 Linacre Ho Ox BA64 MA68. Wycliffe Hall Ox 61. **d** 64 **p** 65. C Fazakerley Em *Liv* 64-66; Chapl Brasted Place Coll Westerham 66-69; Chapl Oundle Sch 69-74; Chapl Liv Cathl *Liv* 74-75; Chapl Liv Univ 74-93; V Mossley Hill St Matt and St Jas 75-83; RD Childwall 82-83; Can Res Liv Cathl 83-93; Treas 83-87; Prec 87-93; Dean Man from 93. *1 Booth Clibborn Court, Salford M7 9JY* Tel 0161-792 2801 or 833 2220 Fax 839 6218 E-mail dean@manchestercathedral.com

RILEY, Mrs Lesley Anne. b 54. Totley Thornbridge Coll TCert75. Trin Coll Bris DipHE81. **dss** 83 **d** 87 **p** 94. Hensingham *Carl* 81-84; Preston St Cuth *Blackb* 84-87; Hon Par Dn Blackb Ch Ch w St Matt 87-98; Asst Dir of Ords 96-00; Dir of Ords from 00; Hon C Shevington from 98. *St Anne's Vicarage, 81 Gathurst Lane,*

Shevington, Wigan WN6 8HW Tel (01257) 252136 *or* tel and fax (01772) 456180

RILEY, Ms Linda. b 67. St Jo Coll Nottm BA00. **d** 00 **p** 01. C Ince Ch Ch *Liv* from 00. *140 Ince Green Lane, Ince, Wigan WN2 2DA* Tel 07944-377732 (mobile)

RILEY, Martin Shaw. b 47. Selw Coll Cam BA71 Cam Univ CertEd72 MA75. Sarum & Wells Th Coll 85. **d** 87 **p** 88. C Tuffley *Glouc* 87-91; Hon Min Can Glouc Cathl from 88; P-in-c Barnwood 91-94; V 94-99; P-in-c Highnam, Lassington, Rudford, Tibberton etc from 99. *The Rectory, Maidenhall, Highnam, Gloucester GL2 8DL* Tel (01452) 525567
E-mail rileys25@tesco.net

RILEY, Michael Charles. b 57. Ball Coll Ox BA79 MA83 Ex Univ CertEd80. Edin Th Coll 84. **d** 86 **p** 87. C Newc St Geo *Newc* 86-89; C Chiswick St Nic w St Mary *Lon* 89-90; V Chiswick St Paul Grove Park from 90. *St Paul's Vicarage, 64 Grove Park Road, London W4 3SB* Tel (020) 8987 0312

RILEY, Preb Patrick John. b 39. Leeds Univ BA62. Coll of Resurr Mirfield 62. **d** 64 **p** 65. C Rowbarton *B & W* 64-72; P-in-c Farleigh Hungerford w Tellisford 72-73; P-in-c Rode, Rode Hill and Woolverton 72-73; R Rode Major 73-85; RD Frome 78-85; V Glastonbury w Meare and W Pennard 85-01; Preb Wells Cathl 90-01; rtd 01. *24 Tanyard Lane, Shaftesbury SP7 8HW* Tel (01747) 850361

RILEY, Peter Arthur. b 23. Kelham Th Coll 40. **d** 51 **p** 52. C Aston cum Aughton *Sheff* 51-53; C Doncaster Ch 53-55; C Trinidad and Tobago 55-59; C-in-c Leic St Chad CD *Leic* 59-62; Jamaica 62-77; V Abertillery *Mon* 77-83; R Panteg 83-88; rtd 88; Hon C Dartmouth *Ex* 88-99; Lic to Offic *Mon* from 99. *The Bungalow, Clewer Court, Newport NP20 4LQ* Tel (01633) 766870

RILEY, Canon William. b 24. St Aid Birkenhead 48. **d** 51 **p** 52. C Edgehill St Dunstan *Liv* 51-53; C Halsall 53-57; V Prestolee *Man* 57-62; P-in-c Ringley 60-62; R Tarleton *Blackb* 62-92; RD Leyland 84-89; Hon Can Blackb Cathl 90-92; rtd 92; Perm to Offic *Blackb* from 92. *114 Liverpool Road, Hutton, Preston PR4 5SL* Tel (01772) 614267

RILEY-BRALEY, Robert James. b 57. Ch Ch Ox BA82 Ch Ch Ox MA82 Down Coll Cam BA83 MA87 K Coll Lon MA98 Surrey Univ PGCE92. Ridley Hall Cam 81. **d** 84 **p** 85. C Thames Ditton *Guildf* 84-87; C Gravesend St Geo *Roch* 87-91; Perm to Offic *Lon* 91-92; *Blackb* 92-95; *S'wark* 95-02; C Stevenage St Mary Sheppall w Aston *St Alb* from 02. *31 Harefield, Stevenage SG2 9NG* Tel (01438) 749695
E-mail ril.bral@virgin.net

RIMELL, Gilbert William. b 22. Llan Dioc Tr Scheme 76. **d** 81 **p** 82. NSM Laleston w Tythegston and Merthyr Mawr *Llan* 81-94; rtd 94; Perm to Offic *Llan* from 94. *75 Bryntirion Hill, Bridgend CF31 4BY* Tel (01656) 658002

RIMMER, Andrew Malcolm. b 62. Magd Coll Cam BA84 MA88. Wycliffe Hall Ox 86. **d** 88 **p** 89. C Romford Gd Shep Collier Row *Chelmsf* 88-92; C Hazlemere *Ox* 92-97; V Crookhorn *Portsm* from 97. *The Vicarage, 87 Perseus Place, Waterlooville PO7 8AW* Tel (023) 9226 7647 *or* tel and fax 9225 5527
E-mail a.rimmer@tesco.net

RIMMER, Anthony Robert Walters. b 41. Hull Univ BA63. Coll of Resurr Mirfield 64. **d** 66 **p** 67. C Leeds All SS *Ripon* 66-69; C Kippax 69-72; C Preston St Jo *Blackb* 72-76; TV 76-83; P-in-c Glasson Ch Ch 83-86; Chapl Lanc R Infirmary 83-86; Chapl Dunkirk Miss to Seafarers *Eur* 86-01; rtd 01; Perm to Offic *Blackb* from 02. *The Haws, 1 Wartonwood View, Carnforth LA5 9DE* Tel (01524) 733974 Mobile 07967-004850

RIMMER, Canon David Henry. b 36. Ex Coll Ox BA60 MA65. Linc Th Coll 62. **d** 64 **p** 65. C Liv Our Lady and St Nic *Liv* 64-66; C Daybrook *S'well* 66-69; Chapl St Mary's Cathl *Edin* 69-71; R Kirkcaldy *St And* 71-78; R Haddington *Edin* 78-83; R Dunbar 79-83; R Edin Gd Shep 83-01; Hon Can St Mary's Cathl 98-01; rtd 01. *4/15 Orchard Brae Avenue, Edinburgh EH4 2HW* Tel 0131-539 0283

RIMMER, Janet. *See* SPICER, Dorothy Janet Rosalind

RIMMER, John Clive. b 25. Oak Hill Th Coll 63. **d** 65 **p** 66. C Earlestown *Liv* 65-69; C-in-c Dallam CD 69-74; V Southport SS Simon and Jude 74-83; V Westhead 83-90; Chapl Ormskirk Hosp Liv 84-90; rtd 90; Perm to Offic *Liv* from 90. *14 Hurlston Drive, Ormskirk L39 1LD* Tel (01695) 570838

RIMMER, Mrs Margaret. b 55. SRN77 SCM78. Cranmer Hall Dur 00. **d** 02 **p** 03. C Aysgarth and Bolton cum Redmire *Ripon* from 02. *Swan Farm Bungalow, Redmire, Leyburn DL8 4HA* Tel (01969) 625031 Mobile 07815-297758
E-mail margaret.rimmer@talk21.com

RIMMER, Paul Nathanael. b 25. Jes Coll Ox BA48 MA50. Wycliffe Hall Ox 48. **d** 50 **p** 51. C Douglas St Thos *S & M* 50-52; C Windermere St Martin *Carl* 52-55; India 55-59; V Marston *Ox* 59-90; RD Cowley 69-73; rtd 90. *32 Ulfgar Road, Wolvercote, Oxford OX2 8AZ* Tel (01865) 552567

RIMMER, Peter Anthony. b 39. St As Minl Tr Course 90. **d** 96 **p** 97. NSM Abergele *St As* 96-00; C Bodelywddan from 00. *17 Lon-y-Mes, Abergele LL22 7JG* Tel (01745) 833222

RIMMER, Roy Malcolm. b 31. Fitzw Ho Cam BA58 MA62. Tyndale Hall Bris 54. **d** 59 **p** 60. C Ox St Clem *Ox* 59-62; The

Navigators 62-70; Oslo St Edm *Eur* 62-64; Public Preacher *S'wark* 64-66; Perm to Offic *Ox* 66-70; C Portman Square St Paul *Lon* 70-75; R Rougham *St E* 75-87; P-in-c Rushbrooke 78-87; P-in-c Beyton and Hessett 86-87; V Newmarket All SS 87-93; rtd 93; Perm to Offic *Ely* from 93. *Ramsey House, 3 Oakfield Place, Old Station Road, Newmarket CB8 8GA* Tel (01638) 660852

RIMMINGTON, Gerald Thorneycroft. b 30. FCP66 Lon Univ BSc56 PhD64 Leic Univ MA59 Nottm Univ MEd72 PhD75. **d** 76 **p** 78. Canada 76-79; Lic to Offic *Leic* 79-80; R Paston *Pet* 81-86; V Cosby *Leic* 86-90; Dir CME 87-90; R Barwell w Potters Marston and Stapleton 90-95; rtd 95; Perm to Offic *Leic* 95-03; RD Guthlaxton I from 03. *7 Beechings Close, Countesthorpe, Leicester LE8 5PA* Tel 0116-277 7155

RINDL, Antony William. b 64. Doncaster Coll of Educn HND88. St Jo Coll Nottm Dip Th & Min 99. **d** 99 **p** 00. C Syston *Leic* 99-03; TV Colne and Villages *Blackb* from 03. *The Vicarage, Skipton Road, Foulridge, Colne BB8 7NP* Tel (01282) 870959

RINGER, Philip James. b 47. Ox Min Course 88. **d** 91 **p** 92. NSM Chalfont St Peter *Ox* 91-95; TV Combe Martin, Berrynarbor, Lynton, Brendon etc *Ex* 96-03; R Wriggle Valley *Sarum* from 03. *The Rectory, Church Street, Yetminster, Sherborne DT9 6LG* Tel (01935) 872237 E-mail revphil@supanet.com

RINGLAND, Tom Laurence. b 61. SS Hild & Bede Coll Dur BSc83. Trin Coll Bris BA89. **d** 89 **p** 90. C Southgate *Chich* 89-92; C Polegate 92-96; P-in-c Coalville and Bardon Hill *Leic* 96-98; V from 98. *Christ Church Vicarage, London Road, Coalville LE67 3JA* Tel (01530) 838287 E-mail tringland@aol.com

RINGROSE, Brian Sefton. b 31. Clare Coll Cam BA54 MA58. Tyndale Hall Bris 56. **d** 58 **p** 59. C Ox St Ebbe *Ox* 58-60; C Erith St Paul *Roch* 60-61; India 61-75; P-in-c Ox St Matt *Ox* 75-78; Interserve (Scotland) 78-96; Perm to Offic *Glas* 78-96; rtd 96. *1 Napier Road, Edinburgh EH10 5BE* Tel 0131-447 2012
E-mail brianringrose@aol.com

RINGROSE, The Ven Hedley Sidney. b 42. Open Univ BA79. Sarum Th Coll 65. **d** 68 **p** 69. C Bishopston *Bris* 68-71; C Easthampstead *Ox* 71-75; V Glouc St Geo w Whaddon *Glouc* 75-88; RD Glouc City 83-88; Hon Can Glouc Cathl 86-98; V Cirencester 88-98; RD Cirencester 89-97; Adn Cheltenham from 98; Hon Can Glouc Cathl from 98. *The Sanderlings, Thorncliffe Drive, Cheltenham GL51 6PY* Tel (01242) 522923 Fax 235925
E-mail archdchelt@star.co.uk

RIO GRANDE, Bishop of. *See* KELSHAW, The Rt Revd Terence

RIOCH, Mrs Wenda Jean. b 35. Sarum & Wells Th Coll 84. **d** 87 **p** 94. Par Dn Basingstoke *Win* 87-91; Par Dn Catshill and Dodford *Worc* 91-94; C 94-98; TV Ottery St Mary, Alfington, W Hill, Tipton etc *Ex* from 98. *The Vicarage, Bendarroch Road, West Hill, Ottery St Mary EX11 1UW* Tel (01404) 812094
E-mail vicarofwesthill@aol.com

RIORDAN, Sean Charles. b 67. Loughb Univ BA89. St Jo Coll Nottm MA(TS)98. **d** 99 **p** 00. C Ockbrook *Derby* 99-03; Asst Chapl Tervuren *Eur* from 03. *Zikkelstraat 13, 1970 Wezembeek-Oppem, Belgium* Tel (0032) (2) 688 0988
E-mail sean.riordan@stpaulstervuren.org

RIPLEY, Preb Geoffrey Alan. b 39. Dur Univ BA62. St Aid Birkenhead. **d** 64 **p** 65. C E Herrington *Dur* 64-67; Hon C Hodge Hill CD *Birm* 68-70; Youth Chapl *Liv* 70-75; Chapl Liv Cathl 70-78; Bp's Dom Chapl 75-78; V Wavertree St Bridget 78-87; Lay Tr Adv *B & W* 87-95; Dioc Chapl MU 92-01; R S Petherton w the Seavingtons 95-01; Chapl E Somerset NHS Trust 95-01; Preb Wells Cathl *B & W* 97-01; rtd 02. *20 Overleigh, Street BA16 0TL* Tel (01458) 446766

RIPON AND LEEDS, Bishop of. *See* PACKER, The Rt Revd John Richard

RIPON, Dean of. *See* METHUEN, The Very Revd John Alan Robert

RIPPINGALE, Denis Michael. b 29. Leeds Univ BA52. Coll of Resurr Mirfield 52. **d** 54 **p** 55. C S Kirkby *Wakef* 54-58; C King Cross 58-60; C Derby St Thos *Derby* 60-63; V Altofts *Wakef* 63-71; V S Elmsall 71-84; V Marsden 84-92; rtd 92. *61 Viking Road, Bridlington YO16 7PW* Tel (01262) 601838

RISBY, John. b 40. Lon Univ DipT66. Lambeth STh82 Oak Hill Th Coll 64. **d** 67 **p** 68. C Fulham Ch Ch *Lon* 67-68; C Ealing St Mary 68-70; C Chitts Hill St Cuth 70-73; C Hove Bp Hannington Memorial Ch *Chich* 73-76; V Islington St Jude Mildmay Park *Lon* 76-82; P-in-c Islington St Paul Ball's Pond 78-82; V Mildmay Grove St Jude and St Paul 82-84; R Hunsdon w Widford and Wareside *St Alb* from 84; RD Hertford 91-96. *The Rectory, Acorn Street, Hunsdon, Ware SG12 8PB* Tel (01920) 870171 E-mail johnrisby@compuserve.com

RISDON, John Alexander. b 42. Lon Univ DipT66. Clifton Th Coll 66. **d** 68 **p** 69. C Ealing Dean St Jo *Lon* 68-72; C Heref St Pet w St Owen *Heref* 72-74; Ord Cand Sec CPAS 74-77; Hon C Bromley Ch Ch *Roch* 74-77; TV Cheltenham St Mary, St Matt, St Paul and H Trin *Glouc* 77-86; R Stapleton *Bris* 86-00; R Bedhampton *Portsm* from 00. *The Rectory, Bidbury Lane, Bedhampton, Havant PO9 3JG* Tel (023) 9248 3013 Fax as telephone E-mail pam@bedhamptonrectory.freeserve.co.uk

RISING, Sidney Frederick. b 28. EMMTC 73. **d** 76 **p** 77. NSM W Bridgford *S'well* 76-79; C 79-82; V Whatton w Aslockton,

Hawksworth, Scarrington etc 82-87; Chapl HM Det Cen Whatton 82-87; Chapl Notts Police 87-93; Rural Officer *S'well* 87-89; P-in-c Perlethorpe 88-90; P-in-c Norton Cuckney 89-90; P-in-c Staunton w Flawborough 90-93; P-in-c Kilvington 90-93; rtd 93. *18 St Leonard's Cottages, London Road, Newark NG24 1QT* Tel (01636) 610318

RITCHIE, Angus William Mark. b 74. Magd Coll Ox BA94 BPhil96 MA98. Westcott Ho Cam 96. **d** 98 **p** 99. C Plaistow and N Canning Town *Chelmsf* 98-02; TV from 02. *The Vicarage, 34 St Martin's Avenue, London E6 3DX* Tel (020) 8552 6991
E-mail angus.ritchie@virgin.net

RITCHIE, Brian Albert. b 34. Open Univ BA80 Birm Univ MA84. Qu Coll Birm 60. **d** 63 **p** 64. C S Leamington St Jo *Cov* 63-67; C-in-c Canley CD 67-70; Perm to Offic 71-80; Hon C Cov H Trin 82-88; R Hatton w Haseley, Rowington w Lowsonford etc 88-97; rtd 97; Perm to Offic *Cov* from 98. *10 Margetts Close, Kenilworth CV8 1EN*

RITCHIE, David John Rose. b 48. St Jo Coll Dur BA72 DipTh74. **d** 74 **p** 75. C Harold Wood *Chelmsf* 74-79; TV Ipsley *Worc* 79-84; Chapl Vevey w Château d'Oex and Villars *Eur* 84-93; V Stoke Bishop *Bris* from 93. *The Vicarage, Mariner's Drive, Bristol BS9 1QJ* Tel 0117-968 1858 *or* 968 7449

RITCHIE, David Philip. b 60. Hatf Coll Dur BA85. Wycliffe Hall Ox 85. **d** 87 **p** 88. C Chadwell *Chelmsf* 87-90; C Waltham H Cross 90-94; TV Becontree W 94-98; TR 98-01; Lay Tr Officer from 01; C Lt Waltham from 02. *Glebelands, Boreham Road, Great Leighs, Chelmsford CM3 1PP* Tel (01245) 362644
E-mail pritchie@chelmsford.anglican.org

RITCHIE, Miss Jean. b 30. Lon Univ CertEd51 Dip Ch Development 71. Trin Coll Bris DipTh79. **dss** 79 **d** 87 **p** 94. Ox St Ebbe w H Trin and St Pet *Ox* 79-87; Par Dn 87-91; rtd 91; Perm to Offic *B & W* 91-94 and from 96; NSM Clevedon St Andr and Ch Ch 94-96. *63 Holland Road, Clevedon BS21 7YJ* Tel (01275) 871762

RITCHIE, John Young Wylie. b 45. Aber Univ MA69 Univ of Wales (Cardiff) BD76. St Mich Coll Llan 73. **d** 76 **p** 77. C Trevethin *Mon* 76-78; C Cwmbran 78-81; TV 81-82; C Ind Chapl *York* 82-91; P-in-c Micklefield 82-88; P-in-c Aislaby and Ruswarp 88-89; C Scalby w Ravenscar and Staintondale 89-91; C Shelf *Bradf* 91-94; C Shelf St Mich w Buttershaw St Aid 94-97; V Owston *Sheff* from 97. *The Vicarage, 11 Crabgate Lane, Skellow, Doncaster DN6 8LE* Tel (01302) 337101 Fax as telephone
E-mail jywr.tradcath@btinternet.com

RITCHIE, Philip Simon James. b 68. Man Univ BA90 Sussex Univ MA98 Leeds Univ MA01 Man Metrop Univ PGCE92. Coll of Resurr Mirfield 99. **d** 01 **p** 02. C Brighton St Nic *Chich* from 01. *30 Bigwood Avenue, Hove BN3 6FQ* Tel (01273) 725811
E-mail phil@sonrit.fsnet.co.uk

RITCHIE, Robert Peter. MA MPhil. **d** 00 **p** 01. NSM Kingston All SS w St Jo *S'wark* from 00. *143 Canbury Park Road, Kingston-upon-Thames KT2 6LH*

RITCHIE, Canon Samuel. b 31. Lon Coll of Div 65. **d** 67 **p** 68. C Westlands St Andr *Lich* 67-70; V Springfield H Trin *Chelmsf* 70-82; Chapl HM Pris Chelmsf 70-82; Chapl HM Pris Brixton 82-84; Chapl HM Pris Hull 84-86; Sen Chapl HM Prison Wymott 86-95; NW Area Chapl Co-ord 86-95; rtd 95; P-in-c Helmingham w Framsden and Pettaugh w Winston *St E* 96-97. *Hillcrest, 3 Highfield Drive, Claydon, Ipswich IP6 0EY* Tel (01473) 833798

RITCHIE, William James. b 62. TCD MA84 DipTh86. **d** 86 **p** 87. C Enniscorthy *C & O* 86-89; Asst Chapl Alexandria Egypt 89-91; Bp's C Kells Gp *C & O* 91-92; I Kells Union *M & K* 92-99; Warden of Readers 93-97; Dioc Ecum Officer 97-99; Min Can St Patr Cathl Dublin 97-99; I Clondehorkey w Cashel *D & R* 99-00; I Dublin St Bart w Leeson Park *D & G* from 00. *The Rectory, 12 Merlyn Road, Ballsbridge, Dublin 4, Irish Republic* Tel (00353) (1) 269 4813 Fax as telephone
E-mail stbartholomew@dublin.anglican.org

RITSON, Canon Gerald Richard Stanley (Bill). b 35. CCC Cam BA59 MA63. Linc Th Coll 59. **d** 61 **p** 62. C Harpenden St Jo *St Alb* 61-65; C Goldington 65-69; R Clifton 69-76; Sec to Dioc Past Cttee 76-87; P-in-c Aldenham 76-87; Hon Can St Alb 80-87; Can Res St Alb 87-00; rtd 00; Perm to Offic *S'wark* from 00. *97 Mitre Road, London SE1 8PT* Tel (020) 7633 0012

RIVERS, Arthur. b 20. Oak Hill Th Coll 52. **d** 53 **p** 54. C Wigan St Cath *Liv* 53-56; V Parr Mt 56-60; V Burscough Bridge 60-79; V Holmesfield *Derby* 79-86; rtd 86; Hon C Warton St Oswald w Yealand Conyers *Blackb* 86-88; Perm to Offic *Blackb* and *Carl* from 88. *Holmlea, Hale, Milnthorpe LA7 7BL* Tel (01539) 563588

RIVERS, David John. b 51. St Jo Coll Nottm. **d** 84 **p** 85. C Woodthorpe *S'well* 84-88; C Hyson Green St Paul w St Steph 88; Asst Chapl Colchester Gen Hosp 89-91; Chapl Leeds Teaching Hosps NHS Trust from 91. *Leeds General Infirmary, Great George Street, Leeds LS1 3EX* Tel 0113-292 3527 *or* 292 2914
E-mail davidri@ulth.northy.nhs.uk

RIVERS, John Arthur. b 21. EAMTC 79. **d** 81 **p** 82. NSM Blakeney w Cley, Wiveton, Glandford etc *Nor* 81-86; Hon C

Cromer 86-87; Perm to Offic from 87. *28 Compit Hills, Cromer NR27 9LJ* Tel (01263) 513051

RIVETT, Andrew George. b 52. Lon Univ MB, BS76 LRCP76 MRCS76. Oak Hill Th Coll 85. **d** 87 **p** 88. C Stanford-le-Hope w Mucking *Chelmsf* 87-90; C Slough *Ox* 90-93; TV Totton *Win* 93-99. *NHS Library, South Academic Block, Southampton General Hospital, Tremonar Road, Southampton SO16 6YD* Tel (023) 8077 7222

RIVETT, Leonard Stanley. b 23. MSSCLE82 St Jo Coll Dur BA47 DipTh49 York Univ Cert Local Hist 88. **d** 49 **p** 50. C Chorlton-cum-Hardy St Clem *Man* 49-53; C-in-c Wythenshawe Wm Temple Ch CD 53-57; Area Chapl Toc H (E and W Yorkshire) 57-62; V Norton juxta Malton *York* 62-74; Warden Wydale Hall 74-83; R Elvington w Sutton on Derwent and E Cottingwith 83-88; rtd 88; Perm to Offic *York* from 88; Offg Chapl RAF from 90. *47 Ryecroft Avenue, York YO24 2SD* Tel (01904) 705364

RIVETT, Peter John. b 42. St Jo Coll Dur BA71 DipTh72. Cranmer Hall Dur. **d** 72 **p** 73. C Newland St Jo *York* 72-76; TV Marfleet 76-82; V Oxhey All SS *St Alb* 82-93; TR Swanborough *Sarum* 93-98; TV Pewsey and Swanborough 98-01; USPG from 01. *United College of the Ascension, Weoley Park Road, Birmingham B29 6RD* Tel 0121-415 6810

RIVETT-CARNAC, Canon Sir Thomas Nicholas, Bt. b 27. Westcott Ho Cam. **d** 63 **p** 64. C Rotherhithe H Trin *S'wark* 63-68; C Bromham H Trin *Lon* 68-72; P-in-c Kennington St Mark *S'wark* 72-87; V 87-89; RD Lambeth 79-83; Hon Can S'wark Cathl 80-89; rtd 89; Perm to Offic *Chich* from 89. *The Haven, Sandhurst Lane, Bexhill-on-Sea TN39 4RH* Tel (01424) 846074

RIVIERE, Jonathan Byam Valentine. b 54. Cuddesdon Coll. **d** 83 **p** 84. C Wymondham *Nor* 83-88; TV Quidenham 88-94; P-in-c Somerleyton w Ashby, Fritton and Herringfleet 94; R Somerleyton, Ashby, Fritton, Herringfleet etc 95-03; R Sandringham w W Newton and Appleton etc from 03; P-in-c Castle Rising from 03; Dom Chapl to The Queen from 03. *The Rectory, Sandringham PE35 6EH* Tel (01485) 540587

RIVIERE, Mrs Tanagra June (Tana). b 41. S Dios Minl Tr Scheme 88. **d** 91. NSM Medstead cum Wield *Win* 91-94; NSM Bishop's Sutton and Ropley and W Tisted 94-96. *The Drey, Paice Lane, Medstead, Alton GU34 5PT* Tel (01420) 563330 Fax as telephone

RIX, Patrick George. b 30. Magd Coll Ox BA54 DipEd55 MA57. Ridley Hall Cam 58. **d** 60 **p** 61. C Dur St Nic *Dur* 60-62; Asst Chapl Wrekin Coll Telford 62-70; Asst Chapl Gresham's Sch Holt 70-80; Chapl Bloxham Sch 80-86; rtd 86; P-in-c Swanton Abbott w Skeyton *Nor* 89; Perm to Offic from 89. *5 Rye Close, North Walsham NR28 9EY* Tel (01692) 402649

ROACH, Kenneth Thomas. b 43. St Andr Univ BD69 Fitzw Coll Cam BA71 MA76. Westcott Ho Cam 69. **d** 71 **p** 72. C Glas St Marg *Glas* 71-73; CF 73-76; R Johnstone *Glas* 76-85; R Bearsden 85-96; TR from 96; CF (TA) from 86. *34 Roman Road, Bearsden, Glasgow G61 2SQ* Tel 0141-942 0386

ROACH, Lynne Elisabeth. *See* DAVIES, Mrs Lynne Elisabeth

ROACHE, Anthony. b 60. Nazarene Th Coll Man BA78 Qu Coll Birm PDATS99. **d** 99 **p** 00. C Bury St Mary *Man* 99-02; P-in-c Ringley w Prestolee from 02. *The Vicarage, 9 Stoneleigh Drive, Radcliffe, Manchester M26 1FZ* Tel (01204) 573742
E-mail tonyroache@yahoo.com

ROAKE, Anthony Richard. b 52. Keble Coll Ox BA75 MA80. Wycliffe Hall Ox 75. **d** 77 **p** 78. C Clifton *S'well* 77-80; V Lapley w Wheaton Aston *Lich* 80-86; V Bournemouth St Andr *Win* 86-98; V Fernhurst *Chich* from 98. *The Vicarage, Church Road, Fernhurst, Haslemere GU27 3HZ* Tel (01428) 652229
E-mail tony@fernhurst1.demon.co.uk

ROAN, Canon William Forster. b 21. St Chad's Coll Dur BA47 DipTh49. **d** 49 **p** 50. C Barrow St Jas *Carl* 49-52; C-in-c Westf St Mary CD 52-58; V Westfield St Mary 58-61; R Greystoke 61-69; V Workington St Jo 70-86; Hon Can Carl Cathl 72-86; RD Solway 77-84; rtd 86; Perm to Offic *Carl* from 86. *41 Chiswick Street, Carlisle CA1 1HJ* Tel (01228) 521756

ROBB, Ian Archibald. b 48. K Coll Lon 68. **d** 72 **p** 73. C E Ham w Upton Park *Chelmsf* 72-74; C Leckhampton SS Phil and Jas w Cheltenham St Jas *Glouc* 74-79; P-in-c Cheltenham St Mich 79-90; V Lower Cam w Coaley from 90. *St Bartholomew's Vicarage, Upper Cam, Dursley GL11 5JR* Tel (01453) 542679 E-mail ia jdr@lineone.net

ROBB, Robert Hammond Neill. b 46. Open Univ BA89 Man Univ 66. St Deiniol's Hawarden 87. **d** 87 **p** 88. C Lache cum Saltney *Ches* 87-89; V Norley and Crowton 89-97; P-in-c Kingsley 95-97; V Norley, Crowton and Kingsley 97-98; V Neston from 98. *The Vicarage, High Street, Neston CH64 9TZ* Tel 0151-353 1000

ROBB, Timothy Simon. b 72. Cant Univ (NZ) BMus94 LTCL94 Lon Bible Coll BTh98. Trin Coll Bris MA03. **d** 03. C Bedford Ch Ch *St Alb* from 03. *161 Dudley Street, Bedford MK40 3SY* Tel (01234) 301708 Mobile 07808-521382
E-mail curate@christchurchbedford.org.uk

ROBBINS, Angela Mary. *See* WEAVER, Ms Angela Mary

ROBBINS, David Leslie. b 43. Univ Coll Lon BSc65 Nottm Univ CertEd66. EMMTC 96. **d** 00 **p** 01. NSM Newark *S'well* from 00.

21 Woodland View, Southwell NG25 0AG Tel (01636) 812641 Mobile 07773-361042 E-mail dlrobbins@freenetname.uk

ROBBINS, David Ronald Walter. b 47. Sarum & Wells Th Coll 85. **d** 87 **p** 88. C Meir Heath *Lich* 87-89; C Collier Row St Jas and Havering-atte-Bower *Chelmsf* 89-93; C Tamworth *Lich* 97-98; P-in-c Hulland, Atlow, Bradley and Hognaston *Derby* 97-98; P-in-c Kniveton 97-98; R Hulland, Atlow, Kniveton, Bradley and Hognaston 98-02; R Widford *Chelmsf* from 02. *The Rectory, 3 Canuden Road, Widford, Chelmsford CM1 2SU* Tel (01245) 346329 Fax 346365 E-mail robbinsdrw@aol.com

ROBBINS, Mrs Janet Carey. b 41. Ox Univ BA63 MA95 PGCE81 Univ of Wales (Lamp) 92. St D Dioc Tr Course 96. **d** 98 **p** 99. NSM Llanfihangel Ystrad and Cilcennin w Trefilan etc *St D* 98-01; NSM Quantock Towers *B & W* from 02. *The Rectory, Vellow Road, Stogumber, Taunton TA4 3TL* Tel (01984) 656949

ROBBINS, Martin Charles. b 68. Thames Valley Univ BA91. Ripon Coll Cuddesdon BTh00. **d** 00 **p** 01. C Thatcham *Ox* from 00. *23 Crowfield Drive, Thatcham RG19 3RX* Tel (01635) 872217

ROBBINS, Peter Tyndall. b 25. Magd Coll Ox BA46 DipTh47 MA51. Westcott Ho Cam 48. **d** 50 **p** 51. C Bury St Paul *Man* 50-53; C Swinton St Pet 53-55; V Prestwich St Hilda 55-59; V Lower Halstow *Cant* 59-63; V Charing w Lt Chart 63-73; V Basing *Win* 73-83; V Kingsclere 83-90; rtd 90; Perm to Offic *Birm* 91-00; Asst RD Tamworth *Lich* 91-95; Perm to Offic from 95. *1 Smyth Flat, St John's Hospital, St John Street, Lichfield WS13 6PB* Tel (01543) 415197 E-mail robbinspb@tesco.net

ROBBINS, Richard Harry. b 14. Lon Univ BD47 Keble Coll Ox DipTh50. ALCD41. **d** 41 **p** 42. C Enfield St Geo *Lon* 41-44; Chile 63-86; rtd 86. *61 Richmond Wood Road, Bournemouth BH8 9DQ* Tel (01202) 512247

ROBBINS, Stephen. b 53. K Coll Lon BD74 AKC74. St Aug Coll Cant 75. **d** 76 **p** 77. C Tudhoe Grange *Dur* 76-80; C-in-c Harlow Green CD 80-84; V Gateshead Harlow Green 84-87; CF from 87. *c/o MOD Chaplains (Army)* Tel (01980) 615804 Fax 615800

ROBBINS, Walter. b 35. **d** 72 **p** 73. Argentina 73-82; Adn N Argentina 80-82; C Southborough St Pet w Ch Ch and St Matt *Roch* 82-86; V Sidcup St Andr 86-95; V Grain w Stoke 95-00; rtd 00; Perm to Offic *Roch* from 00; *Cant* from 01. *Mariners, Imperial Avenue, Minster on Sea, Sheerness ME12 2HG* Tel (01795) 876588

ROBBINS-COLE, Adrian Peter. b 62. LSE BSc(Econ)84 K Coll Lon MA96. Ch Div Sch of the Pacific (USA) 90 Ripon Coll Cuddesdon BA92. **d** 93 **p** 94. C S Dulwich St Steph *S'wark* 93-97; V Motspur Park from 97; RD Merton from 01. *The Vicarage, 2 Douglas Avenue, New Malden KT3 6HT* Tel (020) 8942 3117 E-mail 100561.72@compuserve.com

ROBBINS-COLE, Ms Sarah Jane. b 68. Vermont Univ BA90 K Coll Lon MA00. Ch Div Sch of the Pacific (USA) 92 Ripon Coll Cuddesdon BA95. **d** 95 **p** 96. C W Dulwich All SS *S'wark* 95-98; Chapl K Coll Sch Wimbledon from 98; Hon C Motspur Park *S'wark* from 98. *The Vicarage, 2 Douglas Avenue, New Malden KT3 6HT* Tel (020) 8942 3117 E-mail _src@kcs.org.uk

ROBERT, Brother. *See* ATWELL, Robert Ronald

ROBERT HUGH, Brother. *See* KING-SMITH, Philip Hugh

ROBERTS, Aelwyn. *See* ROBERTS, Joseph Aelwyn

ROBERTS, Alan Moss. b 39. CEng68 MIMechE68 MIMarE68. St Jo Coll Nottm 77. **d** 79 **p** 80. C Bromsgrove St Jo *Worc* 79-83; C Edgbaston St Germain *Birm* 83-89; R Broadhembury, Payhembury and Plymtree *Ex* from 89. *The Rectory, Broadhembury, Honiton EX14 3LT* Tel (01404) 841240 E-mail alanmossroberts@lineone.net

ROBERTS, Preb Andrew Alexander. b 49. Open Univ BA75. Bp Otter Coll CertEd70 Sarum & Wells Th Coll 76. **d** 80 **p** 81. NSM Dorchester *Sarum* 80-85; C Swanage and Studland 85-87; TV 87-94; TR Bridgnorth, Tasley, Astley Abbotts, etc *Heref* from 94; Preb Heref Cathl from 03. *The Rectory, 16 East Castle Street, Bridgnorth WV16 4AL* Tel (01746) 763256 or 767174 E-mail andyaroberts@talk21.com

ROBERTS, Andrew John. b 55. BA. EMMTC. **d** 03. NSM Church Langton cum Tur Langton etc *Leic* from 03. *Oaks Ridge House, 53A Oaks Road, Great Glen, Leicester LE8 9EG* Tel 0116-259 3392

ROBERTS, Anne Judith. b 44. CertEd65 DipEd78 Open Univ BA82 Dip Counselling 91. S Dios Minl Tr Scheme 86. **d** 89 **p** 94. Hon Par Dn S Kensington H Trin w All SS *Lon* 89-92; NSM Barnes *S'wark* from 92; S'wark OLM Scheme from 98. *5 Avenue Gardens, London SW14 8BP* Tel (020) 8878 5642 E-mail revjr@surfaid.org

ROBERTS, Mrs Anne Marie. b 55. York Univ BA77 Nottm Univ DipTh81. St Jo Coll Nottm 80 WMMTC 93. **d** 96 **p** 97. NSM Meole Brace *Lich* from 96; Chapl Robert Jones/Agnes Hunt Orthopaedic NHS Trust from 98; Chapl Prestfelde Sch Shrewsbury from 99. *The Vicarage, Vicarage Road, Shrewsbury SY3 9EZ* Tel (01743) 231744 or 362399 E-mail mbvicarage@aol.com

ROBERTS, Arthur. *See* ROBERTS, John Arthur

ROBERTS, Bernard John. b 21. Ox NSM Course 79. **d** 82 **p** 83. NSM Wendover *Ox* 82-01. *19 The Paddocks, Wendover, Aylesbury HP22 6HE* Tel (01296) 623445

ROBERTS, Brian David. b 44. Ball Coll Ox BA66 FRSA00. Guildf Dioc Min Course 00. **d** 03. OLM Guildf H Trin w St Mary *Guildf* from 03. *Risby, Upper Guildown Road, Guildford GU2 4EZ* Tel (01483) 570556 Mobile 07979-766471 Fax (020) 7631 6224 E-mail roberts@risby83.freeserve.co.uk

ROBERTS, Bryan Richard. b 55. Univ of Wales (Cardiff) DipTh78 BD80. St Mich Coll Llan 78. **d** 80 **p** 81. C Finham *Cov* 80-83; Asst Youth Officer *Nor* 83-86; R N and S Creake w Waterden 86-91; P-in-c E w N and W Barsham 86-91; Chapl Epsom Coll 91-01; Chapl Gresham's Sch Holt from 01. *10 Kelling Road, Holt NR25 6RT* Tel (01263) 713234

ROBERTS, Charles Richard Meyrick. b 53. Huddersfield Poly ARCM75 BA75. St Paul's Coll Grahamstown DipTH91. **d** 92 **p** 92. S Africa 92-94; C Bath Abbey w St Jas *B & W* 94-98; P-in-c Chew Magna w Dundry 98-00; R Chew Magna w Dundry and Norton Malreward from 00; P-in-c Chew Stoke w Nempnett Thrubwell from 03. *The Rectory, 24 High Street, Chew Magna, Bristol BS40 8PW* Tel (01275) 332199 E-mail chewrector@hotmail.com

ROBERTS, Christopher Michael. b 39. CCSk93 Man Univ DipAE79. Qu Coll Birm 62. **d** 64 **p** 65. C Milton next Gravesend Ch Ch *Roch* 64-68; C Thirsk w S Kilvington *York* 68-69; V Castleton *Derby* 69-75; TV Buxton w Burbage and King Sterndale 75-79; Perm to Offic 84-87; NSM Marple All SS *Ches* 87-90; Asst Chapl Rainhill Hosp Liv 90-91; Asst Chapl St Helens Hosp Liv 90-91; Chapl Asst Whiston Co Hosp Prescot 90-91; Chapl R United Hosp Bath 91-94; Chapl R United Hosp Bath NHS Trust 94-99; Sen Chapl Birm Children's Hosp NHS Trust from 99. *The Chaplain's Office, Birmingham Children's Hospital NHS Trust, Steelhouse Lane, Birmingham B4 6NH* Tel 0121-333 8527 *or* 333 9999 Fax 333 9998 E-mail dept.chaplaincy@birminghamchildrens.wmids.nhs.uk

ROBERTS, Colin Edward. b 50. Sarum & Wells Th Coll. **d** 83 **p** 84. C Harton *Dur* 83; C S Shields All SS 83-85; C Thamesmead *S'wark* 85-87; TV 87-89; C Streatham St Pet 89-90 and 92; Zimbabwe 90-92; V Earlsfield St Jo *S'wark* from 92. *St John's Vicarage, 40 Atheldene Road, London SW18 3BW* Tel (020) 8874 2837 Fax (080) 8874 2816 E-mail vicar@stjohnthedivine.freeserve.co.uk

ROBERTS, Cyril. b 41. St Deiniol's Hawarden. **d** 84 **p** 85. C Maltby *Sheff* 84-86; TR Gt Snaith from 86; AD Snaith and Hatfield from 03. *The Orchard, Pontefract Road, Snaith, Goole DN14 9JS* Tel (01405) 860866 Mobile 07702-004870 E-mail cyril.roberts@tesco.net

ROBERTS, David. b 44. Ex Univ BA65. St Steph Ho Ox 65. **d** 67 **p** 68. C Southwick St Columba *Dur* 67-72; C-in-c Southwick St Cuth CD 72-79; R Alyth *St And* 79-84; R Blairgowrie 79-84; R Coupar Angus 79-84; P-in-c Taunton St Jo *B & W* from 84; Chapl Somerset Coll of Arts and Tech from 84. *17 Henley Road, Taunton TA1 5BW* Tel (01823) 284176 E-mail scat.chap@virgin.net

ROBERTS, David Alan. b 38. Open Univ BA82. Ripon Hall Ox 71. **d** 73 **p** 74. C W Bridgford *S'well* 73-77; V Awsworth w Cossall 77-82; V Oxclose *Dur* 82-94; P-in-c New Seaham from 94. *The Vicarage, 269 Station Road, Seaham SR7 0BH* Tel 0191-581 3270

ROBERTS, David Charles. b 53. Poly of Wales CertEd76 Open Univ BA82 BA93 Univ of Wales MEd87. St Mich Coll Llan 96. **d** 98 **p** 99. C Whitchurch *Llan* 98-00; Chapl Univ of Wales (Cardiff) from 00. *27 Anthony Grove, Abercanaid, Merthyr Tydfil CF48 1YX* Tel (01685) 377224 E-mail drobberts@uwic.ac.uk

ROBERTS, Preb David Henry. b 38. St Chad's Coll Dur BA60. Qu Coll Birm DipTh62. **d** 62 **p** 63. C Stonehouse *Glouc* 62-65; C Hemsworth *Wakef* 65-69; V Newsome 69-76; R Pontesbury I and II *Heref* from 76; RD Pontesbury 83-93; Preb Heref Cathl from 85. *The Deanery, Main Road, Pontesbury, Shrewsbury SY5 0PS* Tel (01743) 790316 E-mail dhroberts@lineone.net

ROBERTS, Canon David John. b 36. Man Univ BSc58. St D Coll Lamp 65. **d** 67 **p** 68. C Rhosllannerchrugog *St As* 67-70; R Cerrigydrudion w Llanfihangel Glyn Myfyr etc 70-75; R Llanrwst and Llanddoget 75-77; R Llanrwst and Llanddoget and Capel Garmon 77-84; RD Llanrwst 77-84; V Abergele 84-01; RD Rhos 94-00; Hon Can St As Cathl 95-96; Can Cursal St As Cathl 96-01; rtd 01. *Brithdir, Abergele Road, Bodelwyddan, Rhyl LL18 5SR* Tel (01745) 585807

ROBERTS, Dewi. b 57. LWCMD77 Cyncoed Coll CertEd78. St Mich Coll Llan DipTh84. **d** 84 **p** 85. C Clydach *S & B* 84-88; V Glantawe 88-94; V Loughor from 94. *The Rectory, 109 Glebe Road, Loughor, Swansea SA4 6SR* Tel (01792) 891958

ROBERTS, Dewi James Llewelyn. b 63. United Th Coll Abth 83. **d** 96 **p** 97. C Llandudno *Ban* 96-02; C Bodedern w Llanfachraeth and Llechgynfarwy 99-02; C Llanfaethlu w Llanfwrog and Llanrhuddlad etc 99-02; V Newcastle Emlyn w Llandyfriog etc *St D* from 02. *The Vicarage, Newcastle Emlyn SA38 9LL* Tel (01239) 710385 E-mail dewi.roberts@which.net

ROBERTS, Dilwyn Carey. b 38. St Deiniol's Hawarden 74. **d** 76 **p** 77. C Glanadda *Ban* 76-77; TV Amlwch, Rhosybol, Llandyfrydog etc 77-81; V Llanllechid 81-85; V Caerhun w Llangelynin 85-87; V Caerhun w Llangelynin w Llanbedr-y-Cennin 87-92; rtd 93. *67 St Georges Drive, Conwy LL31 9PR*

ROBERTS, Donald James. b 26. Sarum & Wells Th Coll 83. **d** 86 **p** 87. NSM Corfe Castle, Church Knowle, Kimmeridge etc *Sarum* 86-88 and 91-95; C Broadstone 88-91; rtd 91; Perm to Offic *Sarum* 95-98. *42 Priory Court, Nacton, Ipswich IP10 0JU* Tel (01473) 711242

ROBERTS, Edward. *See* ROBERTS, Canon Henry Edward

ROBERTS, Edward John Walford. b 31. Trin Coll Carmarthen CertEd. St D Dioc Tr Course. **d** 79 **p** 80. NSM Burry Port and Pwll *St D* 79-98; NSM Swansea St Jas *S & B* 98-02; Lic to Offic from 02. *1A Woodlands Terrace, Uplands, Swansea SA1 6BR*

ROBERTS, Canon Edward Owen. b 38. K Coll Lon BD63 AKC63. **d** 64 **p** 65. C Auckland St Andr and St Anne *Dur* 64-67; C Cheltenham St Paul *Glouc* 67-68; Asst Master Colne Valley High Sch Linthwaite 69-71; V Meltham Mills *Wakef* 71-75; R Emley 75-88; RD Kirkburton 80-88; V Huddersfield H Trin from 88; RD Huddersfield 89-99; Hon Can Wakef Cathl from 92. *Holy Trinity Vicarage, 132 Trinity Street, Huddersfield HD1 4DT* Tel (01484) 422998

ROBERTS, Canon Elwyn. b 25. Univ of Wales (Ban) DipTh54. St Mich Coll Llan 54. **d** 55 **p** 56. C Llanfairfechan *Ban* 55-61; V Capel Curig 61-69; V Glanogwen 69-88; Hon Can Ban Cathl 84-90; R Llansadwrn w Llanddona and Llaniestyn etc 88-91; rtd 91; Perm to Offic *Ban* from 91. *Llain Delyn, 10 Cae'r Delyn, Bodffordd, Llangefni LL77 7EJ* Tel (01248) 750407

ROBERTS, The Ven Elwyn. b 31. Univ of Wales (Ban) BA52 Keble Coll Ox BA54 MA59. St Mich Coll Llan 54. **d** 55 **p** 56. C Glanadda *Ban* 55-57; V 66-71; Lib and Lect St Mich Coll Llan 57-66; Dir Post-Ord Tr *Ban* 70-90; R Llandudno 71-83; Can Ban Cathl 77-78; Chan Ban Cathl 78-83; Adn Meirionnydd 83-86; R Criccieth w Treflys 83-86; Adn Ban 86-99; rtd 99; Perm to Offic *Ban* from 99. *6 Min Menai, Eithinog, Bangor LL57 2LB* Tel (01248) 355515

ROBERTS, Eric. b 40. Ban Ord Course 90 St Mich Coll Llan 92. **d** 93 **p** 94. Min Can Ban Cathl *Ban* 93-97; R Llanllyfni 97-02; V Llandysul w Bangor Teifi w Henllan etc *St D* from 02. *The Vicarage, Tanyfron, Wells Street, Llandysul SA44 4DR* Tel (01559) 362277

ROBERTS, Graham Miles. b 59. Open Univ BA95. Trin Coll Bris DipHE92. **d** 92 **p** 93. C Charles w Plymouth St Matthias *Ex* 92-96; Chapl Plymouth Univ 92-94; TV Liskeard, St Keyne, St Pinnock, Morval etc *Truro* 96-99; P-in-c Bournemouth St Andr *Win* from 99. *St Andrew's Vicarage, 53 Bennett Road, Bournemouth BH8 8QQ* Tel (01202) 396022 E-mail graham@roberts82.freeserve.co.uk

ROBERTS, Canon Henry Edward (Ted). b 28. Oak Hill Th Coll 53. **d** 56 **p** 57. C Edgware *Lon* 56-58; C Bedworth *Cov* 58-61; V Bethnal Green St Jas Less *Lon* 61-73; V Old Ford St Mark Victoria Park 61-73; V Bethnal Green St Jas Less w Victoria Park 73-78; RD Tower Hamlets 76-78; Can Res Bradf Cathl *Bradf* 78-82; Dioc Dir Soc Resp 78-82; V Bermondsey St Jas w Ch Ch *S'wark* 82-90; P-in-c Bermondsey St Anne 82-90; Hon Can S'wark Cathl 90-93; Gen Adv for Inner City Min 90-93; rtd 93. *12 Bromeswell Road, Ipswich IP4 3AS* Tel (01473) 288956

ROBERTS, James. *See* ROBERTS, William James

ROBERTS, James Arthur. b 34. Lon Univ BSc56. Bps' Coll Cheshunt 58. **d** 60 **p** 61. C Upper Holloway St Steph *Lon* 60-62; C March St Jo *Ely* 62-65; V Coldham 65-70; V Friday Bridge 65-70; PC Ridgeway *Derby* 70-72; P-in-c Gleadless *Sheff* 72-74; TR 74-79; P-in-c Catfield *Nor* 79-82; P-in-c Ingham w Sutton 79-82; R Aldwincle w Thorpe Achurch, Pilton, Wadenhoe etc *Pet* 82-91; R Barby w Kilsby 91-96; RD Daventry 92-96; rtd 96; Perm to Offic *Ely* 96-00. *29 Whiteacres, Whittlesey, Peterborough PE7 1XR* Tel (01733) 351602

ROBERTS, Jane Elizabeth. b 53. SEITE 98. **d** 01 **p** 02. NSM Mitcham Ascension *S'wark* from 01. *39 Castleton Road, Mitcham CR4 1NZ* Tel (020) 8764 6423 Mobile 07790-703710 E-mail jaaneroberts@nasuwt.net

ROBERTS, Miss Janet Lynne. b 56. Trin Coll Bris 76. **dss** 82 **d** 87 **p** 94. Dagenham *Chelmsf* 82-86; Huyton St Mich *Liv* 86-91; Par Dn 87-91; C Aughton Ch Ch 91-98; TV Parr from 98. *St Paul's Vicarage, 75 Chain Lane, St Helens WA11 9QF* Tel (01744) 734335 Fax as telephone E-mail church@stpaulschainlane.freeserve.co.uk

ROBERTS, Mrs Jasmine Cynthia. b 46. Cant Sch of Min 88. **d** 91. NSM Sandwich *Cant* from 91; Asst Dir of Ords from 02. *The Rectory, Knightrider Street, Sandwich CT13 9ER* Tel (01304) 613138 Fax as telephone E-mail jasmineroberts@supanet.com

ROBERTS, Jeffrey David. b 25. St Cath Coll Cam BA46 MA50 Lon Univ BSc58. **d** 65 **p** 66. Hd Master Adams' Gr Sch Newport Shropshire 59-73; Hd Master St Geo Sch Gravesend 74-82. *Corner House, Keyston, Huntingdon PE28 0RD* Tel (01832) 710254

ROBERTS, John Anthony Duckworth. b 43. K Coll Lon BD65 AKC65. St Boniface Warminster 65. **d** 66 **p** 67. C Wythenshawe Wm Temple CD *Man* 66-69; C Bradford-on-Avon *Sarum* 69-72; Chapl Dauntsey's Sch Devizes 72-73; CF 73-77; P-in-c Verwood *Sarum* 77-81; V 81-86; V Clitheroe St Mary *Blackb*

86-97; R Paget St Paul Bermuda 97-03; Asst Chapl Palma de Mallorca *Eur* from 03. *Address temp unknown*

ROBERTS, John Arthur. b 37. Man Univ BScTech59 CEng68 MIEE68. Cranmer Hall Dur DipTh71. **d** 71 **p** 72. C Wellington w Eyton *Lich* 71-75; P-in-c Newton Flowery Field *Ches* 75-80; V Dunham Massey St Marg 80-91; Chapl Countess of Ches Hosp NHS Trust 91-02; Chapl W Cheshire NHS Trust 94-02; NSM Plas Newton *Ches* from 99; rtd 02. *29 Well Lane, Chester CH2 2HL* Tel (01244) 409579 Mobile 07816-752516

ROBERTS, John Charles. b 50. Nottm Univ BA71 DLLP93. Westcott Ho Cam BA73. **d** 73 **p** 74. C Newark St Mary *S'well* 73-77; Chapl RAF 77-93; Lic to Offic *Bris* 93-95. *15 Foxbrook, Wootton Bassett, Swindon SN4 8QD* Tel (01793) 851518

ROBERTS, John Charles Welch. b 39. UMIST BSc60. Oak Hill NSM Course 91 SW Minl Tr Course 92. **d** 94 **p** 95. NSM Washfield, Stoodleigh, Withleigh etc *Ex* from 94. *East Sidborough, Loxbeare, Tiverton EX16 8DA* Tel (01884) 256302 Fax as telephone E-mail john@sidborough.freeserve.co.uk

ROBERTS, Canon John Hugh. b 42. K Alfred's Coll Win CertEd72 Open Univ BA75. Wells Th Coll 65. **d** 67 **p** 68. C Wareham w Arne *Sarum* 67-70; C Twyford *Win* 70-72; Asst Teacher Rawlins Sch Leics 72-74; V Nassington w Yarwell *Pet* 74-77; Asst Teacher Sponne Sch Towcester 78-92; RD Brackley 94-03; P-in-c Helmdon w Stuchbury and Radstone etc from 93; P-in-c Weedon Lois w Plumpton and Moreton Pinkney etc from 02; Can Pet Cathl from 01. *Pimlico House, Pimlico, Brackley NN13 5TN* Tel (01280) 850378 E-mail rev.roberts@virgin.net

ROBERTS, John Mark Arnott. b 54. K Coll Lon AKC75 CertEd76. Chich Th Coll 77. **d** 77 **p** 78. C Ashford *Cant* 77-82; V St Mary's Bay w St Mary-in-the-Marsh etc 82-91; R Sandwich from 91; AD Sandwich from 00. *The Rectory, Knightrider Street, Sandwich CT13 9ER* Tel (01304) 613138 Fax as telephone E-mail revdmarkroberts@supanet.com

ROBERTS, Canon John Victor. b 34. St Edm Hall Ox BA58 MA62. Tyndale Hall Bris 58. **d** 60 **p** 61. C Southport Ch Ch *Liv* 60-62; C Pemberton St Mark Newtown 62-65; V Blackb Sav *Blackb* 65-71; Chapl Blackb and Lancs R Infirmary and Park Lee Hosp 65-71; V Parr *Liv* 71-73; TR 73-80; R Much Woolton 80-02; RD Childwall 84-89; AD Liv S 89-00; Hon Can Liv Cathl 95-02; rtd 02; Perm to Offic *Liv* from 03. *8 Cherry Vale, Liverpool L25 5PX* Tel 0151-428 8290 Fax as telephone E-mail canonjvr@hotmail.com

ROBERTS, John Victor. b 40. GIPE61. Qu Coll Birm 83. **d** 85 **p** 86. C Ludlow *Heref* 85-89 and 92-93; P-in-c Coreley and Doddington 89-92; P-in-c Knowbury 89-92; TV Ludlow, Ludford, Ashford Carbonell etc 93-02; rtd 02. *The Fold, 10 Whitemeadow Close, Craven Arms SY7 9QP* Tel (01588) 672093

ROBERTS, Jonathan George Alfred. b 60. Lon Univ BD. Qu Coll Birm. **d** 84 **p** 85. C Shepshed *Leic* 84-86; C Braunstone 86-87; Dioc Youth Adv *Dur* 88-92; Nat Youth Officer Gen Syn Bd of Educn 92-94; P-in-c Washington *Dur* 94-95; R 95-99; Regional Co-ord for Community Work Assessment Consortium for the NE from 99; Perm to Offic *Dur* from 99; *Newc* from 01. *10 Brierville, Durham DH1 4QE* Tel 0191-383 9148 E-mail cwacnee@aol.com

ROBERTS, Joseph Aelwyn. b 18. Univ of Wales (Lamp) BA40. St Mich Coll Llan 41. **d** 42 **p** 43. C Llanllyfni *Ban* 42-44; Min Can Ban Cathl 44-52; V Llandegai 52-88; Dioc Dir for Soc Work 73-88; rtd 88; Perm to Offic *Ban* from 88. *The Vicarage, Llandygai, Bangor LL57 4LA* Tel (01248) 353711

ROBERTS, Judith. *See* ROBERTS, Anne Judith

ROBERTS, Ms Judith. b 55. Collingwood Coll Dur BA76 Goldsmiths' Coll Lon PGCE77. SW Minl Tr Course 00. **d** 03. C Burrington, Chawleigh, Cheldon, Chulmleigh etc *Ex* from 03. *The Rectory, Chawleigh, Chulmleigh EX18 7HJ* Tel (01769) 580660 E-mail judith75@yahoo.com

ROBERTS, Mrs Kathleen Marie. b 50. Th Ext Educn Coll 98. **d** 00 **p** 01. S Africa 00-02; C Crediton, Shobrooke and Sandford etc *Ex* from 03. *50 Beech Park, Pounds Hill, Crediton EX17 1HW* Tel (01363) 777924

ROBERTS, Keith Mervyn. b 55. St Pet Coll Birm CertEd76 LGSM78. Qu Coll Birm 89. **d** 91 **p** 92. C Hall Green St Pet *Birm* 91-95; TV Warwick *Cov* 95-00; P-in-c Bishop's Tachbrook from 00; Dioc Broadcasting Officer from 00; Dioc Communications Officer from 03; Relig Affairs Correspondent BBC Radio Cov & Warw 95-01; Presenter/Producer from 01. *The Vicarage, 24 Mallory Road, Bishops Tachbrook, Leamington Spa CV33 9QX* Tel (01926) 426922 Fax as telephone E-mail mervynrob@aol.com

ROBERTS, Canon Kenneth William Alfred. b 26. Roch Th Coll 63. **d** 65 **p** 66. C Waterlooville *Portsm* 65-67; C Honicknowle *Ex* 67-68; C Christchurch *Win* 68-69; C Shiphay Collaton *Ex* 70-71; CF 71-74; R Bassingham *Linc* 74-75; V Carlton-le-Moorland w Stapleford 74-75; R Thurlby w Norton Disney 74-75; V Aubourn w Haddington 74-75; Chapl R Hosp Sch Holbrook 75-78; P-in-c Copdock w Washbrook and Belstead *St E* 78-79; P-in-c Brandeston w Kettleburgh 79-82; Chapl Brandeston Hall Sch 79-84; Chapl Lisbon *Eur* 84-86; Can and Chan Malta Cathl

86-89; R Wimbotsham w Stow Bardolph and Stow Bridge etc *Ely* 89-91; rtd 91; Perm to Offic *St E* from 91. *2 Valley Farm Bungalows, Combs Lane, Stowmarket IP14 2NL* Tel (01449) 674746

ROBERTS, Preb Kevin Thomas. b 55. Qu Coll Cam BA78 MA82 Nottm Univ BA82. St Jo Coll Nottm 80. **d** 83 **p** 84. C Beverley Minster *York* 83-86; C Woodley St Jo the Ev *Ox* 86-91; V Meole Brace *Lich* from 91; RD Shrewsbury from 98; Preb Lich Cathl from 02. *The Vicarage, Vicarage Road, Shrewsbury SY3 9EZ* Tel (01743) 231744 *or* tel and fax 362399
E-mail mbvicarage@aol.com

ROBERTS, Laurence James. b 51. Sussex Univ BEd73. Sarum & Wells Th Coll 75. **d** 78 **p** 79. C Rotherhithe St Mary w All SS *S'wark* 78-81; Public Preacher 81-84; Ind Chapl 81-84; Hon P Nunhead St Silas 82-84; TV Plaistow *Chelmsf* 84-89; Chapl Newham Gen Hosp and Plaistow Hosp 84-96; Tutor Community Nursing Services 89-96; Tutor Westmr Past Foundn from 90; Perm to Offic *Chelmsf* from 90; Lect E Lon Univ from 92. *Ty'n y Coed, 40 Boleyn Road, London E7 9QE* Tel (020) 8472 2430 E-mail laurence.roberts@virgin.net

ROBERTS, Ms Leanne Kelly. b 74. St Hilda's Coll Ox BA95 MA02 Em Coll Cam BA01. Westcott Ho Cam 99. **d** 02 **p** 03. C Hampton All SS *Lon* from 02. *Westwood Cottage, 44 The Avenue, Hampton TW12 3RG* Tel (020) 8255 5962
E-mail leanneroberts_uk@yahoo.co.uk

ROBERTS, Malcolm Kay. b 54. Jes Coll Ox BA76 MA82. Ripon Coll Cuddesdon 84. **d** 87 **p** 88. C Frodingham *Linc* 87-91; R Fiskerton 91-99; rtd 99. *Address withheld by request*

ROBERTS, Miss Marguerite Mary Grace. b 43. Keswick Hall Coll CertEd65 Sussex Univ BEd74 UEA MA86. EAMTC 97. **d** 00 **p** 01. Hon C Cambridge St Mark *Ely* from 00. *5 Eachard Road, Cambridge CB3 0HZ* Tel (01223) 359167

ROBERTS, Mark. *See* ROBERTS, John Mark Arnott

ROBERTS, Martin Vincent. b 53. LRAM72 Birm Univ BA76 MA77 PhD82. Ripon Coll Cuddesdon 76. **d** 78 **p** 79. C Perry Barr *Birm* 78-81; Sen Chapl and Lect W Sussex Inst of HE 81-86; Leic Poly *Leic* 86-92; Sen Chapl De Montfort Univ 92-95; TV Leic H Spirit 86-89; TR 89-95; V Baswich *Lich* 95-01; V Selly Oak St Mary *Birm* from 01. *St Mary's Vicarage, 923 Bristol Road, Selly Oak, Birmingham B29 6ND* Tel 0121-472 0250
E-mail martin@mroberts48.fsnet.co.uk

ROBERTS, Matthew Garnant. b 13. St D Coll Lamp BA37. **d** 37 **p** 38. C St Brides Minor *Llan* 37-39; C Iford *Win* 39-43; C Bournemouth St Alb 43-46; Chapl RAF 47-68; P-in-c Hinton Ampner w Bramdean *Win* 68-70; R 70-74; R Hinton Ampner w Bramdean and Kilmeston 74-78; rtd 78; Lic to Offic *B & W* 79-96. *The Granary, Quaperlake Street, Bruton BA10 0NA* Tel (01749) 812545

ROBERTS, Mervyn. *See* ROBERTS, Keith Mervyn

ROBERTS, Michael Brian. b 46. Oriel Coll Ox BA68 MA72 St Jo Coll Dur BA73 DipTh74. Cranmer Hall Dur 71. **d** 74 **p** 75. C St Helens St Helen *Liv* 74-76; C Goose Green 76-78; C Blundellsands St Nic 78-80; V Fazakerley St Nath 80-87; V Chirk *St As* 87-01; V Cockerham w Winmarleigh and Glasson *Blackb* from 01. *The Vicarage, 5 Lancaster Road, Cockerham, Lancaster LA2 0EB* Tel (01524) 791390 Fax as telephone
E-mail michael.andrea.r@ukonline.co.uk

ROBERTS, Michael Frederick. b 46. Sarum Th Coll 86. **d** 88 **p** 89. C Reading St Matt *Ox* 88-91; NSM Douglas St Geo and St Barn *S & M* 91-93; V Malew from 93. *Malew Vicarage, Crossag Road, Ballasalla, Isle of Man IM9 3EF* Tel (01624) 822469
E-mail malew@globalnet.co.uk

ROBERTS, Nia Wyn. b 64. Univ of Wales (Ban) BA86 PGCE87 CQSW90 Anglia Poly Univ MA00. Westcott Ho Cam 98. **d** 00 **p** 01. C Rhyl w St Ann *St As* from 00. *The Close, 12 Paradise Street, Rhyl LL18 3LW* Tel (01745) 350862 Mobile 07833-302312

ROBERTS, Nicholas John. b 47. Lon Univ BD70 AKC70 MTh78 Surrey Univ MSc93. St Aug Coll Cant 70. **d** 71 **p** 72. C Tividale *Lich* 71-74; C St Pancras H Cross w St Jude and St Pet *Lon* 74-76; C Camberwell St Giles *S'wark* 76-78; Chapl Ch Coll Cam 78-82; V Kingstanding St Luke *Birm* 82-85; Chapl St Chas Hosp Ladbroke Grove 85-96; Chapl Princess Louise Hosp Lon 85-96; Chapl Paddington Community Hosp 85-96; Chapl Cen Middx Hosp NHS Trust 96-99; Chapl St Mary's NHS Trust Paddington from 99. *Chaplain's Office, St Mary's Hospital, Praed Street, London W2 1NY* Tel (020) 7886 1508
E-mail nicholas@norlon.freeserve.co.uk

ROBERTS, Mrs Patricia Frances. b 62. Roehampton Inst BEd85. Trin Coll Bris 93. **d** 96 **p** 97. NSM Buckhurst Hill *Chelmsf* 96-99;

NSM Gt Baddow from 99. *124 Beehive Lane, Chelmsford CM2 9SH* Tel (01245) 269026
E-mail tudorandtricia@ezekiel124.fsnet.co.uk

ROBERTS, Paul Carlton. b 57. Worc Coll Ox BA78 MA86 CertEd. St Jo Coll Nottm 84. **d** 87 **p** 88. C Hazlemere *Ox* 87-91; C Woodley St Jo the Ev 91-92; TV Woodley from 92. *St James's Vicarage, 35 Highgate Road, Woodley, Reading RG5 3ND* Tel 0118-969 6157 Fax as telephone E-mail robertspc@fish.co.uk

ROBERTS, Paul John. b 60. Man Univ BA82 Man Poly PGCE83 Man Univ PhD91. St Jo Coll Nottm 83. **d** 85 **p** 86. C Burnage St Marg *Man* 85-88; Tutor Trin Coll Bris 88-00; R Cotham St Sav w St Mary and Clifton St Paul *Bris* from 00. *12 Belgrave Road, Bristol BS8 2AB* Tel 0117-377 1086
E-mail paul.roberts@bristol.anglican.org

ROBERTS, Peter Francis. b 59. N Illinois Univ BSc81 Leeds Univ BA87. Coll of Resurr Mirfield 85. **d** 88 **p** 89. C Leeds All So *Ripon* 88-92; Asst Dioc Youth Chapl 91-92; USPG Belize 92-94; V Collingham w Harewood *Ripon* 95-01; World Miss Officer 95-01; Chapl Dubai and Sharjah w N Emirates from 01. *Holy Trinity Church, PO Box 7415, Dubai, United Arab Emirates* Tel (00971) (4) 337 4947 *or* 337 0247 Mobile (50) 758 1479 Fax (4) 334 5788 E-mail anglican@emirates.net.ae

ROBERTS, Peter Gwilym. b 42. N Ord Course 78. **d** 81 **p** 82. NSM Seaforth *Liv* 81-83; TV Kirkby 83-88; Dioc Adv on UPA 88-91; P-in-c Southport H Trin 91-94; S Africa from 94; rtd 00. *PO Box 44108, Linden, Gauteng, 2104 South Africa* Tel (0027) (11) 475 4424 *or* 475 1314 Fax 475 8284

ROBERTS, Peter Reece. b 43. Chich Th Coll 73. **d** 75 **p** 76. C Cadoxton-juxta-Barry *Llan* 75-79; C Brixham w Churston Ferrers *Ex* 79-81; C Bexhill St Pet *Chich* 81-84; R Heene from 84; RD Worthing 89-97. *Heene Rectory, 4 Lansdowne Road, Worthing BN11 4LY* Tel (01903) 202312 Fax as telephone

ROBERTS, Philip Alan. b 59. Chich Th Coll 85. **d** 88 **p** 89. C Friern Barnet St Jas *Lon* 88-93; C Farnham Royal w Hedgerley *Ox* 93-02; TV Southend *Chelmsf* from 02. *39 St John's Road, Westcliff-on-Sea SS0 7JY* Tel (01702) 433327

ROBERTS, Philip Anthony. b 50. St Jo Coll Dur BA73. Wycliffe Hall Ox 75. **d** 77 **p** 78. C Roby *Liv* 77-79; C Ainsdale 79-80; C Pershore w Pinvin, Wick and Birlingham *Worc* 80-83; Chapl Asst Radcliffe Infirmary Ox 83-88; John Radcliffe and Littlemore Hosps Ox 83-88; Chapl R Victoria and Bournemouth Gen Hosps 88-91; Chapl Heref Co Hosp 91-94; Chapl Heref Hosps NHS Trust from 94. *The County Hospital, Union Walk, Hereford HR1 2ER* Tel (01432) 364139 *or* 355444

ROBERTS, Canon Phillip. b 21. Sarum Th Coll 55. **d** 57 **p** 58. C Salisbury St Mich *Sarum* 57-60; Australia 60-63; V Westbury *Sarum* 63-73; TR Dorchester 73-80; Can and Preb Sarum Cathl 75-87; R Upper Chelsea H Trin w St Jude *Lon* 80-87; rtd 87; Perm to Offic *Sarum* from 87; V of Close Sarum Cathl 89-95. *112 Harnham Road, Salisbury SP2 8JW* Tel (01722) 323291

ROBERTS, The Ven Raymond Harcourt. b 31. CB84. St Edm Hall Ox BA54 MA58. St Mich Coll Llan 54. **d** 56 **p** 57. C Bassaleg *Mon* 56-59; Chapl RNR 57-59; Chapl RN 59-84; Chapl of the Fleet and Adn for the RN 80-84; QHC 80-84; Hon Can Gib Cathl *Eur* 80-84; Gen Sec JMECA 85-89; C Hale *Guildf* 85-89; Hon Chapl Llan Cathl *Llan* 90-95; Lic to Offic from 95. *8 Baynton Close, Llandaff, Cardiff CF5 2NZ* Tel (029) 2057 8044

ROBERTS, Miss Rebecca Mary. b 71. Glam Univ BA92 Chelt & Glouc Coll of HE PGCE93. Qu Coll Birm BA02. **d** 03. C Greenstead w Colchester St Anne *Chelmsf* from 03. *St Anne's Vicarage, Compton Road, Colchester CO4 4BQ* Tel (01206) 522378 E-mail bricklanebek@hotmail.com

ROBERTS, Richard. b 23. Univ of Wales BA48. St Mich Coll Llan 48. **d** 50 **p** 51. C Pwllheli *Ban* 50-53; C Llangelynnin 53-57; V Llanwnog w Penstrowed 57-68; R Llanrwst and Llanddoget *St As* 68-75; RD Llanrwst 73-75; V Llandrillo-yn-Rhos 75-90; rtd 91; Perm to Offic *Ban* from 91; Perm to Offic *St As* from 97. *2 Bryn Ithel, Abergele LL22 8QB* Tel (01745) 826353

ROBERTS, Canon Richard Stephanus Jacob (Steph). b 28. TCD BA51 MA57. TCD Div Sch Div Test51. **d** 51 **p** 52. C Orangefield *D & D* 51-54; Miss to Seamen 51-94; Portuguese E Africa 51-65; Ceylon 65-68; Chapl Miss to Seamen Dublin 68-72; Chapl Miss to Seamen Southn 72-94; Sen Chapl Ch on the High Seas 72-94; Hon Can Win Cathl *Win* 82-94; rtd 94; Perm to Offic *Win* from 94. *25 Bassett Crescent West, Southampton SO16 7EB* Tel (023) 8079 0734

ROBERTS, Ronald Barry. b 40. S Dios Minl Tr Scheme 80. **d** 83 **p** 85. NSM Wedmore w Theale and Blackford *B & W* 83-85; C Odd Rode *Ches* 85-87; V Eaton and Hulme Walfield from 87. *The Vicarage, Hulme Walfield, Congleton CW12 2JG* Tel (01260) 279863 E-mail ronald@walfield.freeserve.co.uk

ROBERTS, Mrs Rosamunde Mair. b 59. RN80. STETS 98. **d** 01 **p** 02. C Farnham *Guildf* from 01. *6 High Park Road, Farnham GU9 7JL* Tel (01252) 726057 E-mail r.m.roberts@talk21.com

ROBERTS, Mrs Rosanne Elizabeth. b 51. Glouc Sch of Min 85. **d** 88 **p** 94. NSM Charlton Kings St Mary *Glouc* 88-93; C Leckhampton SS Phil and Jas w Cheltenham St Jas 93-96; R Ashchurch from 96. *The Rectory, Ashchurch, Tewkesbury GL20 8JZ* Tel (01684) 293729

ROBERTS, Miss Sandra June. b 58. Univ Coll Ches BA96. Qu Coll Birm 98. **d** 98 **p** 99. C Mold *St As* 98-01; V Llandrillo and Llandderfel from 01. *The Vicarage, Llandrillo, Corwen LL21 0SW* Tel (01490) 440224

ROBERTS, Stephen Bradley. b 66. K Coll Lon BD90 Wycliffe Hall Ox 89. **d** 91 **p** 92. C W Hampstead St Jas *Lon* 91-94; TV Uxbridge 94-98; Chapl Brunel Univ from 98. *26 Church Road, Cowley, Uxbridge UB8 3NA* Tel (01895) 238815 *or* 203308 E-mail stephen.roberts@brunel.ac.uk

ROBERTS, Canon Stephen John. b 58. BD. Westcott Ho Cam. **d** 83 **p** 84. C Riverhead w Dunton Green *Roch* 83-86; C St Martin-in-the-Fields *Lon* 86-89; Warden Trin Coll Cen Camberwell 89-99; V Camberwell St Geo *S'wark* 89-99; RD Camberwell 97-99; Treas and Can Res S'wark Cathl from 00; Sen Dioc Dir of Ords from 00. *76 Tatum Street, London SE17 1QR* Tel (020) 7277 1456 *or* 7939 9458 Fax 7939 9469 E-mail stephen.roberts@dswark.org.uk

ROBERTS, Miss Susan Emma. b 60. La Sainte Union Coll BTh93. St Steph Ho Ox DipMin94. **d** 96 **p** 97. C Petersfield *Portsm* 96-00; P-in-c Ashprington, Cornworthy and Dittisham *Ex* from 00; RD Totnes from 03. *The Rectory, Prior View, Cornworthy, Totnes TQ9 7HN* Tel (01803) 732384 E-mail sue.cornworthy@zoom.co.uk

ROBERTS, Sydney Neville Hayes. b 19. K Coll Lon 38. Cuddesdon Coll 45. **d** 47 **p** 48. C Aylesbury *Ox* 47-52; CF 52-69; R Theale w N Street *Ox* 69-76; R Theale and Englefield 76-85; rtd 85; Perm to Offic *Ox* from 89. *34 Stonebridge Road, Steventon, Abingdon OX13 6AU* Tel (01235) 834777

ROBERTS, Mrs Sylvia Ann. b 40. Stockwell Coll Lon TCert60. S Dios Minl Tr Scheme 84. **dss** 84 **d** 92. Crookhorn *Portsm* 84-88; Hon Par Dn Bedhampton 88-89; Par Dn Southampton (City Cen) *Win* 89-91; TD 91-94; TV 94-96; V Merton St Jo *S'wark* from 96; P-in-c Colliers Wood Ch Ch from 03. *St John's Vicarage, High Path, London SW19 2JY* Tel (020) 8542 3283

ROBERTS, Tegid. b 47. **d** 87 **p** 88. Lic to Offic *Ban* 87-93; NSM Llandinorwig w Penisa'r-waen 93-99; Lic to Offic 99-00; Dioc Officer for Children and Schs from 00; Min Can Ban Cathl from 00. *Arwel, Llanrug, Caernarfon LL55 3BA* Tel (01286) 870760 E-mail tr@roberts485.freeserve.co.uk

ROBERTS, Terry Harvie. b 45. Sarum & Wells Th Coll 87. **d** 89 **p** 90. C Weymouth H Trin *Sarum* 89-93; TV Basingstoke *Win* 93-98; P-in-c Win St Barn from 98. *St Barnabas' Vicarage, Trussell Crescent, Winchester SO22 6DY* Tel (01962) 882728 Fax as telephone E-mail stbarnabas.winchester@ukgateway.net

ROBERTS, Canon Thomas Ewart. b 17. VRD65. Liv Univ BA41. St Aid Birkenhead 39. **d** 41 **p** 42. C Bowdon *Ches* 41-44; V Dunham Massey St Marg 47-52; Chapl RNVR 44-47 and 53-58; Chapl RNR 58-67; Ind Chapl *S'wark* 52-55; C-in-c Woolwich H Trin CD 52-55; Chapl R Arsenal Woolwich 52-55; PC Selsdon *Cant* 55-59; V Dover St Mary 59-71; RD Dover 59-71; Hon Can Cant Cathl 67-71 and 81-84; V Chesterfield St Mary and All SS *Derby* 71-75; V Tenterden St Mildred w Smallhythe *Cant* 75-82; RD W Charing 81-82; rtd 82; Asst Chapl Kent and Cant Hosp 82-91; Perm to Offic *Cant* from 84. *2 Lesley Avenue, Canterbury CT1 3LF* Tel (01227) 451072

ROBERTS, Tudor Vaughan. b 58. Newc Univ BA81. All Nations Chr Coll 91 Trin Coll Bris BA94. **d** 96 **p** 97. C Buckhurst Hill *Chelmsf* 96-99; TV Gt Baddow from 99. *124 Beehive Lane, Chelmsford CM2 9SH* Tel (01245) 269026 E-mail tudorandtricia@ezekiel124.fsnet.co.uk

ROBERTS, Vaughan Edward. b 65. Selw Coll Cam BA88 MA91. Wycliffe Hall Ox 89. **d** 91 **p** 92. C Ox St Ebbe w H Trin and St Pet *Ox* 91-95; Student Pastor 95-98; R from 98. *St Ebbe's Rectory, 2 Roger Bacon Lane, Oxford OX1 1QE* Tel (01865) 248154 E-mail vroberts@stebbes.org.uk

ROBERTS, Vaughan Simon. b 59. Univ of Wales (Ban) BA80 Bath Univ PhD99. McCormick Th Sem Chicago MA82 Westcott Ho Cam 83. **d** 85 **p** 86. C Bourne *Guildf* 85-89; Chapl Phyllis Tuckwell Hospice Farnham 88-89; Chapl Bath Univ *B & W* 89-96; NSM Bath Ch Ch Prop Chpl 90-96; P-in-c 92-96; P-in-c Chewton Mendip w Ston Easton, Litton etc from 96; Dioc Voc Adv 96-99; Dir of Ords from 99. *The Rectory, Lower Street, Chewton Mendip, Bath BA3 4PD* Tel (01761) 241644 Fax as telephone E-mail vaughanroberts@compuserve.com

ROBERTS, Vincent Akintunde Tunde. b 55. Kingston Poly BA(Econ)81. S'wark Ord Course. **d** 91 **p** 92. Hon C Brixton Road Ch Ch *S'wark* 91-96; C Mitcham St Barn 96-99; P-in-c Stoke Newington St Olave from 99. *St Olave's Vicarage, Woodberry Down, London N4 2TW* Tel (020) 8800 1374

ROBERTS, Vivian Phillip. b 35. Univ of Wales BD78. St D Coll Lamp 57. **d** 60 **p** 61. C Cwmaman *St D* 60-64; R Puncheston, Lt Newcastle and Castle Bythe 64-72; V Brynamman 72-77; V Brynaman w Cwmllynfell 77-83; V Pen-bre 83-00; rtd 00. *40 New Road, Llanelli SA15 3DR* Tel (01554) 755506

ROBERTS, Wallace Lionel. b 31. Univ of Wales (Lamp) BA58. St D Coll Lamp 55. **d** 59 **p** 60. C Astley Bridge *Man* 59-61; Asst Master Stand Gr Sch 61-66; Hon C Stand 61-66; Hon C Aden 66-67; Lect Stockport Tech Coll 67-70; Hon C Heaton Moor *Man* 67-70; Chapl Qu Sch Rheindahlen 70-76; Hon CF 70-76;

Swaziland 76-85; Chapl Oporto *Eur* 86-89; Chapl Hordle Ho Sch Milford-on-Sea 89-90; C Portishead *B & W* 91-96; rtd 96; Perm to Offic *B & W* from 96. *44 Hallett's Way, Portishead, Bristol BS20 6BT* Tel (01275) 817484

ROBERTS, William James (Jim). b 55. Hughes Hall Cam PGCE78. Lon Bible Coll BA77 NEOC 92. **d** 94 **p** 95. NSM York St Mich-le-Belfrey *York* from 94. *12 Bishop's Way, York YO10 5JG* Tel (01904) 413479

ROBERTS, Wynne. b 61. Univ of Wales (Ban) DipTh85 BTh92. Ridley Hall Cam 85. **d** 87 **p** 88. C Ban Cathl Par *Ban* 87-90; Min Can Ban Cathl 87-90; V Ynyscynhaearn w Penmorfa and Porthmadog 90-94; TV Bangor 94-99; Chapl Ysbyty Gwynedd Hosp Ban from 99. *North West Wales NHS Trust, Ysbyty Gwynedd, Penrhosgarnedd, Bangor LL57 2PW* Tel (01248) 384384 Fax 370629 E-mail wynne.roberts@nww-tr.wales.nhs.uk

ROBERTSHAW, John Sean. b 66. Cranmer Hall Dur 90. **d** 93 **p** 94. C Morley St Pet w Churwell *Wakef* 93-96; TV Upper Holme Valley 96-01; TR from 01; CF (TA) from 98. *The Vicarage, Kirkroyds Lane, New Mill, Huddersfield HD9 1LS* Tel and fax (01484) 683375 Mobile 07980-289727 E-mail vcar@dialstart.net

ROBERTSHAW, Jonothan Kempster Pickard Sykes. b 41. AKC65. **d** 66 **p** 67. C Perranzabuloe *Truro* 66-69; Miss to Seamen 69-76; Hong Kong 69-72; Namibia 73-76; TV Probus, Ladock and Grampound w Creed and St Erme *Truro* 76-79; TV N Hill w Altarnon, Bolventor and Lewannick 79-80; P-in-c Lansallos 80-84; R 84-96; P-in-c Talland 80-84; V 84-96; V Madron 96-01; P-in-c Gulval 99-01; V Gulval and Madron 01; rtd 01. *9 Redwood Drive, Aston-on-Clun, Craven Arms SY7 8EZ* Tel (01588) 660760

ROBERTSON, Agnes Muriel Hodgson. b 20. Edin Univ MA41. St And NSM Tr Scheme. **d** 91 **p** 94. NSM Lochgelly *St And* 91-92; Par Dn Glenrothes 92-94; NSM 94-98; NSM Leven 94-98; NSM St Andrews St Andr 94-98; NSM Lochgelly 94-98; rtd 98. *96 High Street, Dunblane FK15 0ER* Tel (01786) 821679

ROBERTSON, Ms Beverley Ann. b 57. Qu Coll Birm 98. **d** 01 **p** 02. C Sutton Coldfield H Trin *Birm* from 01. *1 Trinity Hill, Sutton Coldfield B72 1TA* Tel 0121-354 4689 E-mail bev_robertson@yahoo.com

ROBERTSON, Brian Ainsley. b 50. Warwick Univ BSc72. St Jo Coll Nottm 94. **d** 94 **p** 95. C Leic Martyrs *Leic* 94-97; C Oadby 97-98; TV 98-02; P-in-c Ashby-de-la-Zouch St Helen w Coleorton from 02. *The Vicarage, Mill Street, Packington, Ashby-de-la-Zouch LE65 1WL* Tel (01530) 412215 E-mail b-robertson@sthelens-ashby.fsnet.co.uk

ROBERTSON, Charles Kevin. b 64. Virginia Poly & State Univ BA85. Virginia Th Sem MDiv93. **d** 93 **p** 94. P-in-c USA 93-96; NSM Neville's Cross St Jo CD *Dur* 96-97; NSM Esh from 97. *The Vicarage, Church Street, Langley Park, Durham DH7 9TZ* Tel 0191-373 6019 E-mail c.k.robertson@durham.ac.uk

ROBERTSON, Charles Peter. b 57. Linc Th Coll 94 Aston Tr Scheme 92. **d** 96 **p** 97. C Holbeach *Linc* 96-99; C S Lafford from 01. *The Vicarage, 1 The Drove, Osbournby, Sleaford NG34 0DH* Tel (01529) 455630

ROBERTSON, David. *See* ROBERTSON, Thomas John

ROBERTSON, David John. b 54. Sheff Univ BA76. Ridley Hall Cam 77. **d** 79 **p** 80. C Downend *Bris* 79-83; C Yate New Town 83-85; TV 85-87; TV High Wycombe *Ox* 87-97; RD Wycombe 91-97; P-in-c Haley Hill *Wakef* 97-99; V Ovenden from 97. *St George's Vicarage, 2 Bracewell Drive, Wheatley, Halifax HX3 5BT* Tel (01422) 354153

ROBERTSON, Edward Macallan. b 28. Aber Univ MA49 Qu Coll Ox BLitt51. Coll of Resurr Mirfield 53. **d** 55 **p** 56. C Swindon New Town *Bris* 55-60; R Hawick *Edin* 60-69; R Alloa *St And* 70-73; Lic to Offic *Edin* 74-78; P-in-c Bathgate 78-82; P-in-c Linlithgow 78-82; Hon C Strathtay *St And* 82-90; P-in-c Auchterarder 90-93; P-in-c Muthill 90-93; rtd 93. *Coruisk, 65 Smithfield Crescent, Blairgowrie PH10 6UE* Tel (01250) 874427

ROBERTSON, Ernest Ian. b 22. Bede Coll Dur BA49. Wycliffe Hall Ox 49. **d** 51 **p** 52. C Jarrow St Paul *Dur* 51-54; C Sedgefield 54-56; V Eighton Banks 56-60; Chapl Shotley Bridge Gen Hosp 60-81; V Benfieldside *Dur* 60-87; Chapl HM Det Cen Medomsley 61-87; rtd 87. *Flat 11, Thornley House, Sherburn House Hospital, Durham DH1 2SE* Tel 0191-372 1992

ROBERTSON, George Edward. b 14. Rhodes Univ BA35 MA35 Stellenbosch Univ MA48. Wells Th Coll 52. **d** 53 **p** 61. C Wells St Cuth *B & W* 53-54; S Africa 54-73 and 74-79; C Fort Beaufort 54-59; C Plumstead 59-64; C Pinelands 64-66; C Goodwood 66-73; Australia 73-74; Lic to Offic Dio Cape Town 74-79; rtd 79; Perm to Offic *Chich* 79-91. *clo Mr P J Kean, Methodist Annexe, PO Box 106, Simonstown, 7995 South Africa*

ROBERTSON, Ian Hugh. b 44. LGSM64 ARCM65 Makerere Univ Kampala DipTh83 Lanc Univ MA91. St Mark's Dar-es-Salaam 80. **d** 83 **p** 83. SSF 73-82; Zimbabwe 83-87; TV Barrow St Geo w St Luke *Carl* 87-90; V Reigate St Mark *S'wark* 90-98; P-in-c Accrington St Jo w Huncoat *Blackb* 98-99; V from 99.

St John's Vicarage, 11 Queen's Road, Accrington BB5 6AR Tel (01254) 234587 Fax as telephone
E-mail ian.robertson2@btinternet.com

ROBERTSON, James Alexander. b 46. Sarum & Wells Th Coll 72. **d** 75 **p** 76. C Monkseaton St Pet *Newc* 75-78; C Prudhoe 78-79; TV Brayton *York* 79-84; V Redcar 84-93; V Selby Abbey 93-96; V Monkseaton St Pet *Newc* from 96; AD Tynemouth from 98. *St Peter's Vicarage, 6 Elmwood Road, Whitley Bay NE25 8EX* Tel 0191-252 1991 Fax as telephone

ROBERTSON, James Macaulay. b 51. St Jo Coll Dur BA73. Oak Hill Th Coll. **d** 00 **p** 01. C Holdenhurst and Iford *Win* from 00. *19 Colemore Road, Boscombe, Bournemouth BH7 6RZ* Tel (01202) 431993 E-mail robo@fish.co.uk

ROBERTSON, Canon James Smith. b 17. OBE84. Glas Univ MA38. Edin Th Coll 38. **d** 40 **p** 41. C Edin St Martin *Edin* 40-41; C Edin St Salvador 41-45; Zambia 45-65; Warden St Mark's Tr Coll Mapanza 50-55; Warden Chalimbana Tr Coll 55-65; Hon Can Zambia 66-70; Hon Can Lusaka from 71; Lect St Bede Coll Dur 65-68; Sec for Ch Colls of Educn Gen Syn Bd of Educn 68-73; Sec USPG 73-83; Chapl to The Queen 80-88; rtd 83; Perm to Offic *Lon* 83-93 and from 96; Perm to Offic *S'wark* 83-95. *Flat 8, 26 Medway Street, London SW1P 2BD*

ROBERTSON, John Charles. b 61. St Pet Coll Ox BA81 Trin Coll Cam BA89. Ridley Hall Cam 87. **d** 90 **p** 91. C Kenilworth St Jo *Cov* 90-94; Chapl York Univ *York* 94-00; V Grove *Ox* from 00. *The Vicarage, Main Street, Grove, Wantage OX12 7LQ* Tel (01235) 766484 E-mail jroberts@fish.co.uk

ROBERTSON, Mrs Josephine Anne. b 51. CertEd72 Ch Ch Coll Cant BSc91. Dioc OLM tr scheme 99. **d** 02 **p** 03. OLM Folkestone H Trin w Ch Ch *Cant* from 02; Chapl Dover Coll from 02. *100 Surrenden Road, Folkestone CT19 4AQ* Tel (01303) 277330 Mobile 07905-954504
E-mail jo.robertson@ntlworld.com

ROBERTSON, Linda Margaret. Somerville Coll Ox MA Aber Univ MSc. STETS. **d** 03. NSM Hursley and Ampfield *Win* from 03. *35 Winnington, Fareham PO15 6HP* Tel (01329) 239857

ROBERTSON, Muriel. *See* ROBERTSON, Agnes Muriel Hodgson

ROBERTSON, Canon Paul Struan. b 45. St Jo Coll Dur BA73 Newc Univ Aus BEdStr79 MA95. **d** 72 **p** 73. C Chester le Street *Dur* 72-73; Australia 73-88 and from 89; C Hamilton 73-77; C Cessnock 77-79; R Scone 79-88; V Collierley w Annfield Plain *Dur* 88-89; R New Lambton from 89; AD Newc W from 96; Lect St Jo Coll Morpeth from 97; Can Newc Cathl from 01. *122 St James Road, PO Box 292, New Lambton, NSW, Australia 2305* Tel (0061) (2) 4957 1173 *or* 4952 2218 Fax 4957 1788
E-mail saints@idl.net.au

ROBERTSON, Mrs Priscilla Biddulph. b 25. St And Dioc Tr Course 87. **d** 90 **p** 94. C St Andrews St Andr *St And* from 90. *8 Balrymonth Court, St Andrews KY16 8XT* Tel (01334) 474976

ROBERTSON, Scott. b 64. Edin Univ BD90. Edin Th Coll 86. **d** 90 **p** 91. C Glas Gd Shep and Ascension *Glas* 90-92; P-in-c 92-97; P-in-c Ardrossan from 97; P-in-c Irvine St Andr LEP from 97; P-in-c Dalry from 97. *31 Milgarholm Avenue, Irvine KA12 0EL* Tel and fax (01294) 278341 Mobile 07703-709176
E-mail revscottrob@talk21.com

ROBERTSON, Stephen Andrew. b 60. Strathclyde Univ BSc82. Trin Coll Bris 92. **d** 92 **p** 93. C Vange *Chelmsf* 92-96; V Creeksea w Althorne, Latchingdon and N Fambridge from 96. *The Vicarage, Fambridge Road, Althorne, Chelmsford CM3 6BZ* Tel (01621) 740250 E-mail stephen.r@quista.net

ROBERTSON, Stuart Lang. b 40. Glas Univ MA63 Nottm Univ DipTh74 Edin Univ MTh96. St Jo Coll Nottm 72. **d** 75 **p** 76. C Litherland St Jo and St Jas *Liv* 75-78; C Edin St Thos *Edin* 78-81; Chapl Edin Univ 81-83; C Edin St Pet 81-83; R Edin St Jas 83-91; Miss to Seamen 83-91; Russia 91-98; BCMS 91-93; Crosslinks from 93; Chapl St Petersburg *Eur* 93-95; Chapl Warsaw from 98. *ul Mokotowska 12 m3, 02-679 Warszawa, Poland* Tel (0048) (22) 621 4165 Fax as telephone E-mail emmanuel@it.com.pl

ROBERTSON, Thomas John (David). b 15. Univ of Wales BA38 Lon Univ DipTh64 DipEd66. St Steph Ho Ox 38. **d** 40 **p** 41. C Welshpool *St As* 40-42; C Shotton 42-45; C Colwyn Bay 45-48; V Choral St As Cathl 48-49; R Newmarket 49-53; V Woolfold *Man* 53-57; V Bury St Thos 57-61; Hd of RE Bramhall Gr Sch 61-74; V Taddington and Chelmorton *Derby* 74-80; rtd 80; Perm to Offic *Derby* 80-87; *Ches* and *Man* 80-95; *S'wark* 95-03; *Roch* 01-03. *The Coach House, Halstead Hall, Halstead, Sevenoaks TN14 7DH*

ROBIN, John Bryan Carteret. b 22. Trin Coll Ox BA48 MA55. Cuddesdon Coll 49. **d** 77 **p** 78. Chapl Rishworth Sch Ripponden 76-81; Australia from 82; Chapl Geelong Gr Sch 82-84; P-in-c Queenscliff St Geo 86-94; rtd 94. *8 Heron Court, Point Lonsdale, Vic, Australia 3225* Tel (0061) (3) 5258 4432

ROBIN, Peter Philip King. b 23. Trin Coll Cam BA48 MA81. Cuddesdon Coll 49. **d** 51 **p** 52. C Bethnal Green St Matt *Lon* 51-54; Papua New Guinea 54-75; R Elsing w Bylaugh *Nor* 76-85; R Lyng w Sparham 76-85; P-in-c Holme Cultram St Mary *Carl* 85-88; rtd 88; Perm to Offic *Carl* 88-99 and from 02. *191 Brampton Road, Carlisle CA3 9AX* Tel (01228) 545293

ROBINS, Christopher Charles. b 41. St Mich Coll Llan 66. **d** 68 **p** 69. C Bideford *Ex* 68-71; C Dawlish 71-74; V Laira 74-81; P-in-c E Allington 81; P-in-c Dodbrooke 81-83; P-in-c Churchstow w Kingsbridge 81-83; R Kingsbridge and Dodbrooke from 83. *The Rectory, Church Street, Kingsbridge TQ7 1NW* Tel (01548) 856231

ROBINS, Douglas Geoffrey. b 45. Open Univ BA90. Ex & Truro NSM Scheme. **d** 81 **p** 83. NSM Kenwyn *Truro* 81-84; Public Preacher from 84. *4 Enys Road, Truro TR1 3TE* Tel (01872) 277469

ROBINS, Ian Donald Hall. b 28. K Coll Lon BD51 AKC51 Lanc Univ MA74. **d** 52 **p** 53. C St Annes *Blackb* 52-55; C Clitheroe St Mary 55-57; V Trawden 57-67; Hd of RE St Chris C of E Sch Accrington 67-76; P-in-c Hugill *Carl* 76-82; Asst Adv for Educn 76-82; Chapl St Martin's Coll of Educn *Blackb* 82-86; V St Annes St Marg 86-91; rtd 91; Perm to Offic *Blackb* from 91. *20 Painter Wood, Billington, Blackburn BB7 9JD* Tel (01254) 824930

ROBINS, Mrs Mary Katherine. b 34. FRGS Bris Univ BSc55 CertEd56. St Alb Minl Tr Scheme. **dss** 84 **d** 87 **p** 94. N Mymms *St Alb* 84-92; Hon Par Dn 87-92; NSM Northaw 92-95; Hon C Westmr St Jas *Lon* from 95; Perm to Offic *St Alb* from 95. *15 Bluebridge Road, Brookmans Park, Hatfield AL9 7UW* Tel (01707) 656670 E-mail maryrob@eclipse.co.uk

ROBINS, Terrence Leslie. b 38. Kingston Poly 56 CEng67 FIMechE78. Nor Ord Course 99 Coll of Resurr Mirfield 99. **d** 00 **p** 01. Bp's Adv for Elderly People in Res Care *Wakef* from 98; Hon C Cumberworth, Denby and Denby Dale 00-03; P-in-c from 03. *Cruck Cottage, Cumberworth Lane, Denby Dale, Huddersfield HD8 8RU* Tel (01484) 866000 Fax as telephone
E-mail robinslt@aol.com

ROBINS, Ms Wendy Sheridan. b 56. Lanc Univ BA77. EAMTC 93. **d** 93 **p** 94. Dir of Communications and Resources *S'wark* from 92; NSM Walthamstow St Pet *Chelmsf* from 93; Hon C S'wark Cathl *S'wark* from 02. *17 Hillcrest Road, London E17 4AP,* or *Trinity House, 4 Chapel Court, Borough High Street, London SE1 1HW* Tel (020) 8523 0016 *or* 7403 8686 Fax 7403 4770 E-mail wendy.s.robins@dswark.org.uk

ROBINSON, Alan Booker. b 27. Keble Coll Ox BA51 MA56. Sarum Th Coll 51. **d** 53 **p** 54. C Leeds All So *Ripon* 53-56; C Ilkley St Marg *Bradf* 57-59; V Carlton *Wakef* 59-66; OCF 66-92; V Hooe *Ex* 66-95; RD Plympton 81-83; RD Plymouth Sutton 86-91; rtd 95; Perm to Offic *Ripon* from 95. *1 Charlton Court, Knaresborough HG5 0BZ* Tel (01423) 860884
E-mail alrob@beeb.net

ROBINSON, Albert. b 15. Roch Th Coll 60. **d** 61 **p** 62. C Limpsfield and Titsey *S'wark* 61-64; R Grimston w Congham *Nor* 64-73; P-in-c Roydon All SS 64-73; V Gt w Lt Plumstead 73-81; rtd 81; Perm to Offic *Glouc* 81-93. *63 Marleyfield Way, Churchdown, Gloucester GL3 1JW* Tel (01452) 855178

ROBINSON, Alison Jane. b 55. WEMTC 99. **d** 02 **p** 03. C Bishop's Cleeve *Glouc* from 02. *2A Orchard Road, Bishops Cleeve, Cheltenham GL52 8LX* Tel (01242) 675471 Mobile 07773-721238 E-mail alisonjane.robinson@btinternet.com

ROBINSON, Andrew David. b 61. St Cath Coll Ox BA84 MA01 RMN89. Trin Coll Bris 97. **d** 02. C Southmead *Bris* 02-03; C Chippenham St Paul w Hardenhuish etc from 03; C Kington St Michael from 03. *3 Garth Close, Chippenham SN14 6XF* Tel (01249) 650787 E-mail room-2-live@yahoo.co.uk

ROBINSON, Canon Andrew Nesbitt. b 43. AKC67. **d** 68 **p** 69. C Balsall Heath St Paul *Birm* 68-71; C Westmr St Steph w St Jo *Lon* 71-75; Chapl Sussex Univ *Chich* from 75; Chapl Brighton Poly 75-92; Chapl Brighton Univ 92-93; P-in-c Stanmer w Falmer from 80; Can and Preb Chich Cathl from 98. *St Laurence House, Park Street, Brighton BN1 9PG* Tel (01273) 606928 *or* 606755

ROBINSON, Andrew Stephen. b 49. Lanc Univ BA71 Worc Coll of Educn PGCE72 Glam Univ Dip Educn Mgt 82. St Mich Coll Llan 90 DipTh93. **d** 95 **p** 96. NSM Llangattock and Llangynidr *S & B* from 95. *17 Pencommin, Llangynidr, Crickhowell NP8 1LT* Tel (01874) 730034

✠**ROBINSON, The Rt Revd Anthony William.** b 56. CertEd. Sarum & Wells Th Coll. **d** 82 **p** 83 **c** 02. C Tottenham St Paul *Lon* 82-85; TV Leic Resurr *Leic* 85-89; TR 89-97; RD Christianity N 92-97; P-in-c Belgrave St Pet 94-95; Hon Can Leic Cathl 94-97; Adn Pontefract *Wakef* 97-02; Suff Bp Pontefract from 02. *Pontefract House, 181A Manygates Lane, Sandal, Wakefield WF2 7DR* Tel (01924) 250781 Fax 240490
E-mail bishop.pontefract@wakefield.anglican.org

ROBINSON, Arthur Robert Basil. b 32. ACP67 St Jo Coll Dur BA56 Bradf Univ MA84. Wycliffe Hall Ox 56. **d** 58 **p** 59. C Pemberton St Mark Newtown *Liv* 58-62; CF 62-65; Asst Master Colne Valley High Sch Linthwaite 65-69; Asst Chapl HM Pris Man 69; Chapl HM Borstal Roch 69-74; Peru 74-77; V Golcar *Wakef* 77-83; Admin Sheff Fam Conciliation Service 84-91; Warden St Sampson's Cen York 91-00; rtd 00. *Morangie, 2A Brecksfield, Skelton, York YO30 1YD* Tel (01904) 470558

ROBINSON, Arthur William. b 35. Dur Univ BSc60. Clifton Th Coll 60. **d** 62 **p** 63. C Ox St Clem *Ox* 62-65; Chile 65-77; V Hoxton St Jo w Ch Ch *Lon* 78-88; TV Gateacre *Liv* 88-00; rtd 00;

Perm to Offic *Liv* from 00. *86 Kingsthorne Park, Liverpool L25 0QS* Tel 0151-486 2588 E-mail arthelrob@aol.com

ROBINSON, Brian John Watson. b 33. St Cath Coll Cam BA56 MA60. Westcott Ho Cam 57. **d** 58 **p** 59. C Whitworth w Spennymoor *Dur* 58-62; India 62-66; P-in-c Preston St Steph *Blackb* 66-72; V Ashton-on-Ribble St Andr 72-79; Lic to Offic 79-82; V Preston St Jude w St Paul 82-97; Chapl N Tyneside Health Care NHS Trust 94-97; rtd 97; Perm to Offic *Blackb* from 97. *50 Green Acres, Fulwood, Preston PR2 7DB* Tel (01772) 861516

ROBINSON, Canon Bryan. b 32. Fitzw Ho Cam BA56. Ely Th Coll 56. **d** 58 **p** 59. C Fleetwood *Blackb* 58-65; V Burnley St Andr 65-74; V Burnley St Marg 65-74; V Burnley St Andr w St Marg 74-97; RD Burnley 85-91; P-in-c Burnley St Jas 92-97; Hon Can Blackb Cathl 94-97; rtd 97; Perm to Offic *Blackb* from 97. *50 Fountains Avenue, Simonstone, Burnley BB12 7PY* Tel (01282) 776518

ROBINSON, Christopher Gordon. b 49. Ridley Hall Cam. **d** 82 **p** 83. C Stanton *St E* 82-85; C Lawshall 85-86; P-in-c Lawshall w Shimplingthorne and Alpheton 86-89; TV Oakdale *Sarum* 89-99; V Easton H Trin w St Gabr and St Lawr and St Jude *Bris* from 99. *The Vicarage, 69 Stapleton Road, Bristol BS5 0PQ* Tel 0117-955 4255 E-mail christopher.robinson@tesco.net

ROBINSON, Christopher James. b 52. St Pet Coll Birm CertEd74. OLM course 97. **d** 99 **p** 00. OLM Wilnecote *Lich* from 99. *55 Sycamore, Wilnecote, Tamworth B77 5HB* Tel (01827) 282331 E-mail chrisrobinson5@compuserve.com

ROBINSON, Daffyd Charles. b 48. Qu Coll Birm 77. **d** 80 **p** 85. C Abington *Pet* 80-82; C Immingham *Linc* 85-90; R Willoughby from 90. *The Rectory, Station Road, Willoughby, Alford LN13 9NA* Tel (01507) 462045 Fax as telephone E-mail dcr@willgp.f9.co.uk

ROBINSON, Mrs Danielle Georgette Odette. b 47. SEITE 98. **d** 01 **p** 02. NSM Reigate St Mary *S'wark* from 01; Chapl Surrey and Sussex Healthcare NHS Trust from 01; Perm to Offic *Chich* from 01. *10 Doran Gardens, Doran Drive, Redhill RH1 6AY* Tel (01737) 772380

ROBINSON, David. b 42. Sarum & Wells Th Coll. **d** 82 **p** 83. C Billingham St Cuth *Dur* 82-86; V Longwood *Wakef* 86-94; C Athersley 94-97; P-in-c Brotherton 97-02; rtd 02; Perm to Offic *York* from 03. *The Vicarage, Market Weighton Road, Holme-on-Spalding-Moor, York YO43 4AG* Tel (01430) 860379

ROBINSON, Canon David Hugh. b 47. Linc Th Coll 76. **d** 79 **p** 80. C Bulkington *Cov* 79-82; P-in-c Whitley 82-87; Chapl Walsgrave Hosp Cov 87-94; Chapl Walsgrave Hosps NHS Trust Cov 94-97; Hon Can Cov Cathl *Cov* 92-98; Perm to Offic from 98. *95 Potters Green Road, Coventry CV2 2AN* Tel (024) 7662 2683

ROBINSON, David Mark. b 55. Univ Coll Dur BSc76 Leic Univ MA80 CQSW80. Cranmer Hall Dur 86. **d** 88 **p** 89. C Shipley St Pet *Bradf* 88-92; P-in-c Ingrow cum Hainworth 92-97; V Bramhope *Ripon* from 97. *The Vicarage, 26 Leeds Road, Bramhope, Leeds LS16 9BQ* Tel 0113-284 2543

ROBINSON, David Michael Wood. b 28. Glas Univ BSc50 Lon Univ BD54. **d** 57 **p** 57. C Erith St Jo *Roch* 57-58; Japan 58-71; R Holton and Waterperry *Ox* 71-88; RD Aston and Cuddesdon 88-92; R Holton and Waterperry w Albury and Waterstock 88-94; Chapl Ox Poly 90-92; Chapl Ox Brookes Univ 92-94; rtd 94. *72 Divinity Road, Oxford OX4 1LJ* Tel (01865) 245466

ROBINSON, Capt Denis Hugh. b 53. SS Mark & Jo Coll Plymouth CertEd75. Sarum & Wells Th Coll 88. **d** 91 **p** 92. NSM Bisley and W End *Guildf* from 91; Asst Chapl Gordon's Sch Woking 91-94; Chapl from 94. *Ashleigh, Bagshot Road, West End, Woking GU24 9PX* Tel (01276) 857535 *or* 858084 Fax 855335

ROBINSON, Dennis Winston. b 42. QUB BScEng68. CITC. **d** 88 **p** 89. NSM Mullavilly *Arm* 88-92; NSM Arm St Mark 92-95; C Portadown St Mark 95-98; I Aghavea *Clogh* from 98. *The Rectory, Brookeborough, Enniskillen BT94 4EE* Tel (028) 8953 1210 E-mail dw.robinson@ukgateway.net

ROBINSON, Derek Charles. b 43. S'wark Ord Course 91. **d** 94 **p** 95. NSM Abbey Wood *S'wark* from 94. *19 Silverdale Road, Bexleyheath DA7 5AB* Tel (01322) 523870

ROBINSON, Douglas. b 48. Nottm Univ BEd70 Trin Coll Bris 71 Lon Univ BD74 Union Th Sem Virginia MA75. **d** 75 **p** 76. C Southport Ch Ch *Liv* 75-78; V Clubmoor 78-85; V Epsom Coll 85-88; Chapl Dauntsey's Sch Devizes 89-95; Perm to Offic *Eur* from 95. *Im Grünen Weg 1, Hangen Wiesheim 55234, Germany* Tel (0049) (6375) 941575 E-mail reverendrobinson@t-online.de

ROBINSON, Elizabeth Carole Lesley. b 67. CITC 99. **d** 02. NSM Clonfert Gp of Par *L & K* from 02. *Camelot, Lusmagh, Banagher, Co Offaly, Irish Republic* Tel and fax (00353) (90) 51598 Mobile 87-909 1561 E-mail kandlrobinson@eircom.net

ROBINSON, Eric Charles. b 28. Lon Univ BD71 Lanc Univ MA97. Carl and Blackb Dioc Tr Inst 94. **d** 97 **p** 98. NSM Carl St Cuth w St Mary *Carl* 97-99; C Kendal H Trin 99-01; P-in-c Arthuret from 01; P-in-c Nicholforest and Kirkandrews on Esk

from 01. *Arthuret Rectory, Arthuret Drive, Longtown, Carlisle CA6 5SG* Tel (01228) 791338

ROBINSON, Frank. *See* ROBINSON, John Francis Napier

ROBINSON, George. b 27. HNC59. Oak Hill Th Coll 59. **d** 61 **p** 62. C Branksome St Clem *Sarum* 61-64; Australia from 64; rtd 80. *24 Abingdon Road, Roseville, NSW, Australia 2069* Tel (0061) (2) 9416 4330 Fax 9416 9936 E-mail mandgrobinson@ozemail.com.au

ROBINSON, Mrs Gillian Dawn. b 69. Edin Univ BD91. Trin Coll Bris 94. **d** 96 **p** 97. C Totton *Win* 96-00; P-in-c Roughtown *Man* from 00. *The Vicarage, Woods Lane, Dobcross, Oldham OL3 5AN* Tel (01457) 877212 Fax as telephone E-mail gill@robinson.camnews.net

ROBINSON, Hugh Stanley. b 21. AKC47. **d** 47 **p** 48. C Tilehurst St Geo *Ox* 47-50; CF 50-53; C Farnham Royal *Ox* 53-59; V Wheatley 59-67; V Chiddingly *Chich* 67-83; V Laughton 67-76; Asst Chapl HM Pris Northeye 83-86; rtd 86; Perm to Offic *Lich* from 86. *2 Brook Drive, Wem, Shrewsbury SY4 5HQ* Tel (01939) 234683

ROBINSON, Ian. b 57. Nottm Univ BTh87 MA97. Linc Th Coll 84. **d** 87 **p** 88. C Bottesford w Ashby *Linc* 87-90; TV 90-95; P-in-c Caistor w Clixby 95-00; P-in-c Grasby 95-00; P-in-c Searby w Owmby 95-00; V Caistor Gp from 00; RD W Wold from 01. *The Vicarage, 1 Cromwell View, Caistor, Lincoln LN7 6UH* Tel (01472) 851339 E-mail ianrobinson5@compuserve.com

ROBINSON, Ian Cameron. b 19. OBE72. Em Coll Cam BA40 MA44. Linc Th Coll 71. **d** 72 **p** 73. C Ipswich St Aug *St E* 72-74; V Darsham 74-84; V Westleton w Dunwich 74-84; RD Saxmundham 79-83; rtd 84; Perm to Offic *St E* from 84. *Corner House, Rectory Street, Halesworth IP19 8BS* Tel (01986) 873573

ROBINSON, Mrs Jane Hippisley. b 41. Somerville Coll Ox MA66 K Coll Lon PGCE. S Dios Minl Tr Scheme 88. **d** 91. NSM Ealing St Pet Mt Park *Lon* 91-96; NSM N Acton St Gabr 96-00. *60 Madeley Road, London W5 2LU* Tel (020) 8991 0206

ROBINSON, Mrs Janet. b 34. Milton Keynes Coll of Ed CertEd77 Open Univ BA78. WMMTC 89. **d** 92 **p** 94. NSM Roade and Ashton w Hartwell *Pet* 92-94; NSM Pottersbury, Furtho, Yardley Gobion and Cosgrove 94-99; rtd 99; Perm to Offic *Pet* from 99. *73 Eastfield Crescent, Yardley Gobion, Towcester NN12 7TT* Tel (01908) 542233

ROBINSON, Mrs Jean Anne. b 50. Lon Univ BPharm72 MRPharmS73 Southn Univ BTh98. STETS 95. **d** 98 **p** 99. NSM Frimley *Guildf* 98-03; NSM Worplesdon from 03. *4 Chequer Tree Close, Knaphill, Woking GU21 2PB* Tel (01483) 481825

ROBINSON, John Francis Napier (Frank). b 42. St Edm Hall Ox BA64 MA68 Lon Univ DipTh68. Clifton Th Coll 65. **d** 68 **p** 69. C Southport Ch Ch *Liv* 68-71; C Coleraine *Conn* 71-74; Deputation Sec (Ireland) BCMS 74-76; TV Marfleet *York* 76-81; V Yeadon St Jo *Bradf* 81-95; P-in-c Rounds Green *Birm* 95-00; V 00-02; rtd 02. *61 Clumber Avenue, Beeston, Nottingham NG9 4BH* Tel 0115-922 1704

ROBINSON, John Howard. b 52. Stockport Tech Coll C&G82 Jo Dalton Coll Man HNC84. St Jo Coll Nottm DCM92. **d** 92 **p** 93. C Meole Brace *Lich* 92-96; R Baschurch and Weston Lullingfield w Hordley 96-00; V Grassendale *Liv* from 00. *St Mary's Vicarage, 22 Eaton Road, Liverpool L19 0PW* Tel 0151-427 1474

ROBINSON, The Very Revd John Kenneth. b 36. K Coll Lon BD61 AKC61. **d** 62 **p** 63. C Poulton-le-Fylde *Blackb* 62-65; C Lancaster St Mary 65-66; Chapl HM Pris Lanc 65-66; Chapl St Jo Sch Singapore 66-68; V Colne H Trin *Blackb* 68-71; Dir Educn Windward Is 71-74; V Skerton St Luke *Blackb* 74-81; Area Sec (E Anglia) USPG 81-91; Hon Min Can St E Cathl *St E* 82-91; Chapl Gtr Lisbon *Eur* 91-00; Adn Gib 94-02; Can Gib Cathl 94-00; Dean Gib 00-03; rtd 03. *9 Poplar Drive, Coppull, Chorley PR7 4LS* E-mail deangib@gibnet.gi

ROBINSON, John Leonard William. b 23. Lon Univ BA50. Bps' Coll Cheshunt 50. **d** 52 **p** 53. C Victoria Docks Ascension *Chelmsf* 52-55; C Kilburn St Aug *Lon* 55-63; C Westmr St Jas 63-81; V Compton, the Mardens, Stoughton and Racton *Chich* 81-93; V Stansted 85-93; rtd 93; Perm to Offic *St Alb* from 93 and *Lon* from 96. *19 Greenhill Park, Barnet EN5 1HQ* Tel (020) 8449 3984

ROBINSON, Jonathan William Murrell. b 42. Univ of Wales (Lamp) MA01. Sarum Th Coll 65. **d** 68 **p** 69. C Tooting All SS *S'wark* 68-71; C Bourne *Guildf* 71-76; Dir Grail Trust from 76; Dir Grail Trust Chr Community Cen Burtle *B & W* 78-82; Hon C Willesden Green St Gabr *Lon* 78-82; V Stoke St Gregory w Burrowbridge and Lyng *B & W* 82-90; Dir Grail Retreat Cen from 90; NSM Aymestrey and Leinthall Earles w Wigmore etc *Heref* 92-96; rtd 01. *The Liberty, Arthurs Gate, Montgomery SY15 6QU* Tel (01686) 668502 Fax as telephone

ROBINSON, Keith. b 48. Lon Univ BA75 BD77 AKC77. Westcott Ho Cam 77. **d** 78 **p** 79. C Bow w Bromley St Leon *Lon* 78-81; C Leighton Buzzard w Eggington, Hockliffe etc *St Alb* 81-88; PV Westmr Abbey 82-90; V Bulkington w Shilton and Ansty *Cov* 88-95; P-in-c Salisbury St Martin *Sarum* 95-00; P-in-c Laverstock 95-00; R Salisbury St Martin and Laverstock from 00; RD Salisbury from 98. *The Rectory,*

Tollgate Road, Salisbury SP1 2JJ Tel (01722) 504813 *or* tel and fax 503123 E-mail frkeithssm@yahoo.co.uk

ROBINSON, Kenneth Borwell. b 37. Lon Univ BA62. Ridley Hall Cam 68. **d** 70 **p** 71. C Walthamstow St Jo *Chelmsf* 70-74; P-in-c Becontree St Alb 74-78; P-in-c Heybridge w Langford 78-84; TV Horley *S'wark* 84-98; C Oxted and Tandridge 98-02; rtd 02; Perm to Offic *Portsm* from 03. *49 Osborne Road, East Cowes PO32 6RZ* Tel (01983) 295736

ROBINSON, Lesley. *See* ROBINSON, Elizabeth Carole Lesley

ROBINSON, Leslie. b 31. St Aid Birkenhead 56. **d** 59 **p** 60. C Hugglescote w Donington *Leic* 59-61; C Greenside *Dur* 61-63; C-in-c New Cantley CD *Sheff* 63-66; V Choral Heref Cathl *Heref* 66-67; R Easton-on-the-Hill *Pet* 67-69; Hon Min Can Pet Cathl 68-69; C Weston-super-Mare St Jo *B & W* 69-70; V Winkleigh *Ex* 70-72; V Thorpe Acre w Dishley *Leic* 72-78; V Cloughton *York* 78-79; V Hedon w Paull 79-81; V Bywell *Newc* 81-86; V Wymeswold and Prestwold w Hoton *Leic* 86-97; rtd 97; Perm to Offic *Leic* 97-98. *19 Ambleside Close, Loughborough LE11 3SH* Tel (01509) 263790

ROBINSON, Miss Margaret. b 32. S'wark Ord Course 83. **dss** 86 **d** 87 **p** 94. Finsbury St Clem w St Barn and St Matt *Lon* 86-87; Par Dn St Giles Cripplegate w St Bart Moor Lane etc 87-94; C 94-95; rtd 95; Perm to Offic *Win* 95-00; Hon Chapl Win Cathl 98-00. *10 Barnfield Road, Petersfield GU31 4DQ* Tel (01730) 268056

ROBINSON, Michael John. b 45. Nottm Univ BA66. Linc Th Coll 78. **d** 79 **p** 80. C Aston cum Aughton *Sheff* 79-80; C Rotherham 80-82; TV Howden *York* 82-86; V Heywood St Jas *Man* 86-92; V Astley 92; R Blackley St Paul 92-97; V Hale and Ashley *Ches* from 97. *St Peter's Vicarage, 1 Harrop Road, Hale, Altrincham WA15 9BU* Tel 0161-928 4182 Fax 928 9702

ROBINSON, Monica Dorothy. b 40. St Alb and Ox Min Course 99. **d** 01 **p** 02. NSM Bedford St Andr *St Alb* from 01. *Shoyswell, Radwell Road, Milton Ernest, Bedford MK44 1RY* Tel (01234) 824366

ROBINSON, The Ven Neil. b 29. St Jo Coll Dur BA52 DipTh54. **d** 54 **p** 55. C Kingston upon Hull H Trin *York* 54-58; V Glen Parva and S Wigston *Leic* 58-68; Hon Can Leic Cathl 68-83; RD Sparkenhoe I 69-83; R Market Bosworth w Shenton 69-83; Can Res Worc Cathl *Worc* 83-87; Adn Suffolk *St E* 87-94; rtd 94; Perm to Offic *Ripon* from 94. *16 Mallorie Court, Mallorie Park Drive, Ripon HG4 2QG* Tel (01765) 603075

ROBINSON, Norman Leslie. b 50. Liv Univ BSc71. Lon Bible Coll BA78 Wycliffe Hall Ox 78. **d** 80 **p** 81. C Bebington *Ches* 80-83; C St Helens St Helen *Liv* 83-90; P-in-c Westward, Rosley-w-Woodside and Welton *Carl* from 90; P-in-c Thursby from 98. *The Vicarage, Rosley, Wigton CA7 8AU* Tel (01697) 343723 E-mail normalrevs@aol.com

ROBINSON, Canon Paul Leslie. b 46. Dur Univ BA67 Nottm Univ DipTh73. Linc Th Coll 71. **d** 74 **p** 75. C Poynton *Ches* 74-76; C Prenton 76-78; V Seacombe 78-88; V Stalybridge St Paul 88-00; P-in-c Wallasey St Hilary from 00; Urban Min Officer from 96; Hon Can Ches Cathl from 98. *St Hilary's Rectory, Church Hill, Wallasey CH45 3NH* Tel 0151-638 4771 E-mail paul@revrobinson.fsnet.co.uk

ROBINSON, Paul Leslie. b 65. St Steph Ho Ox 95. **d** 97 **p** 98. C Upholland *Liv* 97-01; V Lydiate and Downholland from 01. *The Vicarage, Church Lane, Lydiate, Liverpool L31 4HL* Tel 0151-526 0512 E-mail paul@revrobinson.fsnet.co.uk

ROBINSON, Peter. b 42. Univ of Wales (Lamp) BA63 DipEd64 Univ of Wales (Cardiff) BD71. N Ord Course 78. **d** 81 **p** 82. NSM Rochdale *Man* 81-83; C Rochdale 83-86; V Shore 86-91; Chapl for Readers 90-96. *131 Starkey Street, Heywood OL10 4JH* Tel (01706) 367557

ROBINSON, Peter Charles. b 53. Open Univ BA83. Oak Hill Th Coll 85. **d** 87 **p** 88. C Nottingham St Ann w Em *S'well* 87-89; C Worksop St Anne 89-92; V S Ramsey St Paul *S & M* 92-99; Can St German's Cathl 98-99; P-in-c Goostrey *Ches* 99-03; Dioc Dir of Ords 99-03; P-in-c Aldeburgh w Hazlewood *St E* from 03. *The Vicarage, Church Walk, Aldeburgh IP15 5DU* Tel 07941-202524 (mobile) E-mail pc.robinson@virgin.net

ROBINSON, Peter Edward Barron. b 40. Open Univ BSc99. Sarum & Wells Th Coll 76. **d** 78 **p** 79. C Petersfield w Sheet *Portsm* 78-82; R Bentworth and Shalden and Lasham *Win* 82-88; R W Horsley *Guildf* 88-00; rtd 00; Perm to Offic *B & W* from 01. *Byways, Kingstone, Ilminster TA19 0NT* Tel (01460) 259016 E-mail peb.robinson@ntlworld.com

ROBINSON, Peter John Alan. b 61. St Jo Coll Cam BA83. St Jo Coll Dur BA92 PhD97. **d** 95 **p** 96. C N Shields *Newc* 95-99; P-in-c Byker St Martin from 99; P-in-c Byker St Mich w St Lawr from 01. *St Martin's Vicarage, 152 Roman Avenue, Newcastle upon Tyne NE6 2RJ* Tel 0191-265 5931 E-mail pjarobison@lineone.net

ROBINSON, Peter McCall. b 24. Worc Coll Ox BA48 MA50. Wells Th Coll 48. **d** 50 **p** 51. S Africa 50-54; C Stoke Poges *Ox* 55-57; S Africa 57-71; V Payhembury *Ex* 71-79; R Cheriton w Tichborne and Beauworth *Win* 79-81; S Africa 81-82; V Marystowe, Coryton, Stowford, Lewtrenchard etc *Ex* 82-85; V Blackawton and Stoke Fleming 85-88; rtd 88; Perm to Offic *Ex*

from 89. *4 Barton Mews, Venn Ottery, Ottery St Mary EX11 1RZ* Tel (01404) 815756

ROBINSON, Philip. b 38. JP79. S Dios Minl Tr Scheme 88. **d** 91 **p** 92. NSM Ickenham *Lon* 91-95; P-in-c from 95; P-in-c Hayes St Anselm 98-99; P-in-c Harlington 98-00; AD Hillingdon 97-03. *St Giles's Rectory, 38 Swakeleys Road, Ickenham, Uxbridge UB10 8BE* Tel and fax (01895) 622970 Mobile 07956-570176 E-mail stgilesickenham@compuserve.com

ROBINSON, Raymonde Robin. b 43. St Jo Coll Dur BA66. Chich Th Coll 67. **d** 70 **p** 71. C Ealing St Barn *Lon* 70-72; C Pinner 72-75; C Clerkenwell H Redeemer w St Phil 75-80; TV Kingsthorpe w Northampton St Dav *Pet* 80-89; R Letchworth *St Alb* 89-95; V Noel Park St Mark *Lon* from 95. *St Mark's Vicarage, Ashley Crescent, London N22 6LJ* Tel (020) 8888 3442

ROBINSON, Richard Hugh. b 35. St Jo Coll Cam BA58 MA62. Ridley Hall Cam 58. **d** 60 **p** 81. C Cheadle Hulme St Andr *Ches* 60-62; Hon C Alvanley 62-64; Perm to Offic 64-80; Hon C Elloughton and Brough w Brantingham 80-86; C 86-87; Ext Dir CMJ 87-88; NSM Appleby *Carl* 91-93; Perm to Offic *Carl* and *York* 93-98; *Ely* from 01; rtd 00. *26 Paradise Street, Cambridge CB1 1DR* Tel (01223) 328833 Fax 328838

ROBINSON, Canon Roger George. b 24. Qu Coll Cam BA46 MA50. Ridley Hall Cam 46. **d** 48 **p** 49. C Gorleston St Andr *Nor* 48-51; C Drypool St Andr and St Pet *York* 51-54; P-in-c Kingston upon Hull St Aid Southcoates 54-55; V 55-60; V Clifton 60-70; Chapl Clifton Hosp York 61-70; V Far Headingley St Chad *Ripon* 70-81; RD Headingley 72-81; Hon Can Ripon Cathl 81; Perm to Offic from 81; R Drayton w Felthorpe *Nor* 81-91; rtd 91. *24 St Matthew's Walk, Leeds LS7 3PS* Tel 0113-269 6307

ROBINSON, Ronald Frederick. b 46. Brasted Place Coll 72. Oak Hill Th Coll 74. **d** 76 **p** 77. C Pennington *Man* 76-77; C Bedhampton *Portsm* 77-79; C Portsea N End St Mark 79-82; V 90-92; R Rowner 82-90; Perm to Offic *Portsm* 93-02; P-in-c Bury and Houghton *Chich* 96-97; P-in-c Coldwaltham and Hardham 96-97; P-in-c Bury w Houghton and Coldwaltham and Hardham 97-98; V 98; Past Sec Ch Union 98-02; P-in-c Portsea Ascension *Portsm* from 02. *The Vicarage, 98 Kirby Road, Portsmouth PO2 0PW* Tel (023) 9266 0123 Fax 9266 7499 E-mail fr.robinson@talk21.com

ROBINSON, Roy David. b 35. AKC59. **d** 60 **p** 61. C Acocks Green *Birm* 60-62; C Shirley 62-65; C Haslemere *Guildf* 65-70; R Headley w Box Hill 70-85; V Hinchley Wood 85-00; rtd 00; Perm to Offic *Guildf* from 02. *1 Park Road, Slinfold, Horsham RH13 0SD* Tel (01403) 791640

ROBINSON, Simon John. b 51. Edin Univ MA72 PhD89 Ox Univ BA77. Wycliffe Hall Ox 75. **d** 78 **p** 79. C Haughton le Skerne *Dur* 78-81; Chapl Asst N Tees Hosp Stockton-on-Tees 81-83; C Norton St Mary *Dur* 81-83; Chapl Heriot-Watt Univ *Edin* 83-90; R Dalmahoy 83-90; Chapl Leeds Univ *Ripon* from 90; P-in-c Leeds Em from 90. *14 Parkside Green, Leeds LS6 4NY* Tel 0113-274 6297 *or* 233 5070 E-mail s.j.robinson@leeds.ac.uk

ROBINSON, Stuart. b 39. N Ord Course. **d** 87 **p** 88. C Hull St Martin w Transfiguration *York* 87-90; P-in-c Preston and Sproatley in Holderness 90-91; R from 91; RD S Holderness from 98. *The Rectory, Staithes Road, Preston, Hull HU12 8TB* Tel (01482) 898375

ROBINSON, Stuart Peter. b 59. Moore Th Coll Sydney BTh85 ACT DipTh86. **d** 87 **p** 87. Australia 87-98 and from 01; C Miranda St Paul 87-88; C Doonside St Jo 88-89; R Quakers Hill St Steph 89-97; Perm to Offic *Ox* from 96; Chapl Tervuren *Eur* 98-01; P-in-c Liège 98-00; Dioc Ev and Ch Growth Consultant *Sydney* from 01. *Dept of Evangelism, St Andr's House, Sydney Sq, PO Box A295, Sydney South, NSW, Australia 1235* Tel (0061) (2) 9265 1582 Fax 9267 8601 E-mail robinson.stuart@bigpond.com *or* dofe@ozemail.com

ROBINSON, Mrs Teresa Jane. b 56. St Alb and Ox Min Course 98. **d** 01 **p** 02. OLM Cookham *Ox* from 01. *7 Golden Ball Lane, Maidenhead SL6 6NW* Tel (01628) 634107 E-mail terrie@7goldenball.freeserve.co.uk

ROBINSON, Canon Thomas Fisher. b 20. St Jo Coll Dur BA49. **d** 50 **p** 51. C Pendlebury St Jo *Man* 50-54; C Davyhulme St Mary 54-56; V Litherland St Andr *Liv* 56-62; V Wigan St Cath 62-67; V Garston 67-88; Hon Can Liv Cathl 85-88; rtd 88; Perm to Offic *Liv* from 88. *208 Mather Avenue, Liverpool L18 9TG* Tel 0151-475 7870

ROBINSON, Thomas Hugh. b 34. CBE89. TCD BA55 MA71. **d** 57 **p** 58. C Belfast St Clem *D & D* 57-60; Kenya 61-64; I Youghal *C, C & R* 64-66; C 66-89; Chapl Gen 86-89; TR Cleethorpes *Linc* 90-98; R 98-99; rtd 99; Perm to Offic *Glouc* from 99. *Brailes View House, Landgate, Blockley, Moreton-in-Marsh GL56 9BY* Tel (01386) 701189

ROBINSON, Timothy James. b 59. Middx Poly BA84 Coll of Ripon & York St Jo PGCE00. St Steph Ho Ox 88. **d** 91 **p** 92. C W Acklam *York* 91-95; P-in-c N Ormesby 95-96; V 96-99; Teacher Hall Garth Sch Middlesbrough from 99; Perm to Offic *Ripon* from 99. *The Yellow House, Copt Hewick, Ripon HG4 5BY*

ROBINSON, Virgil Austin Anderson. b 38. Univ of SW Louisiana BS62 Loyola Univ Chicago MPS88. St Steph Ho Ox 77 St Geo Coll Jerusalem 81. **d** 79 **p** 80. NSM Bicester w

Bucknell, Caversfield and Launton *Ox* 79-82; USA from 82; R Northbrook St Giles 83-90; R Woodstock St Anne 91; Chapl NW Univ and R Park Ridge St Anselm 92; Dean St Paul's Cathl Fond du Lac 93-95; R Chicago St Paul and the Redeemer 96-98; R Milwaukee St Paul from 98. *1527 Chapel Court, Northbrook, IL 60062, USA*

ROBINSON, William Pitchford. b 50. Nottm Univ BTh75. Kelham Th Coll 71. **d** 75 **p** 76. C Bow w Bromley St Leon *Lon* 75-79; Hon C Barkingside St Geo *Chelmsf* 79-82; Chapl Claybury Hosp Woodford Bridge 79-85; Hon C Barkingside St Fran *Chelmsf* 82-85; Australia from 86. *5 Comet Street, Mandurah, W Australia 6210* Tel (0061) (8) 9581 1301

ROBLIN, The Ven Graham Henry. b 37. OBE83. AKC61. St Boniface Warminster 60. **d** 62 **p** 63. C St Helier *S'wark* 62-66; CF 66-81; Dep Asst Chapl Gen 81-83; Warden RAChD Cen Bagshot 83-85; Asst Chapl Gen (BOAR) 86-89; Dep Chapl Gen 89-93; Adn for the Army 90-93; QHC 87-93; R Bere Regis and Affpuddle w Turnerspuddle *Sarum* 93-01; rtd 01. *Croft Cottage, High Street, Yetminster, Sherborne DT9 6LF* Tel (01935) 873795

ROBOTTOM, David Leonard Douglas. b 40. Qu Coll Birm 80 Sarum & Wells Th Coll 81. **d** 83 **p** 84. C Uppingham w Ayston and Wardley w Belton *Pet* 83-87; TV Sidmouth, Woolbrook and Salcombe Regis *Ex* 87-91; TV Sidmouth, Woolbrook, Salcombe Regis, Sidbury etc 91-95; R Bradninch and Clyst Hydon from 95; RD Cullompton from 03. *The Rectory, 27 West End Road, Bradninch, Exeter EX5 4QS* Tel (01392) 881264 E-mail su2312@eclipse.co.uk

ROBSON, Angus William. b 13. Kelham Th Coll 32. **d** 38 **p** 39. C Regent Square St Pet *Lon* 38-40; C Mill End *St Alb* 40-45; CF 43-45; P-in-c Luton St Pet 45; Perm to Offic *St Alb* 45-46; V Sark *Win* 46-50; V Jersey St Jas 50-75; Chapl HM Pris Jersey 60-75; rtd 78; Perm to Offic *Win* 78-98. *Flat 1, La Petite Carrière, Wellington Road, St Helier, Jersey JE2 4RJ* Tel (01534) 31656

ROBSON, Claire English. b 62. Middx Poly BEd88. Westcott Ho Cam CTM99. **d** 99 **p** 00. C Dorchester *Sarum* 99-02; C Kilburn St Mary w All So and W Hampstead St Jas *Lon* from 02. *1 St James's House, Sherriff Road, London NW6 2AP* Tel (020) 7372 6441 E-mail clairerobson@clara.net

ROBSON, Featherstone. b 30. Southn Univ CertEd52 Nottm Univ DipEd74. Oak Hill Th Coll 55. **d** 58 **p** 59. C Illogan *Truro* 58-60; Chapl Bedstone Sch Shropshire 60-61; Hd RE John Hampden Gr Sch High Wycombe 61-67; Teacher Larkmead Sch Abingdon 68-71; Teacher Dorking Gr Sch 71-76; Ho Master Scarisbrick Hall Sch Ormskirk 77-78; Chapl Dean Close Jr Sch Cheltenham 78-79; Asst Chapl K Edw Sch Witley 79-81; Deputation Sec for England, Irish Ch Miss 82-86; rtd 86; Perm to Offic *Ox* 86-00. *71 Springfield Drive, Abingdon OX14 1JF* Tel (01235) 533421

ROBSON, Gilbert Alan. b 30. St Pet Hall Ox BA53 MA57. Linc Th Coll 56. **d** 57 **p** 58. C Chatham St Mary w St Jo *Roch* 57-59; Sub Warden Roch Th Coll 59-62; Min Can Roch Cathl *Roch* 59-62; Bp's Dom Chapl 61-64; Chapl Roch Th Coll 62-64; R Wouldham *Roch* 62-64; Chapl Nor Coll of Educn 65-68; Sen Lect in Div 68-72; V Shotwick *Ches* 72-74; Dioc Dir of Ords 72-74; Bp's Dom Chapl 72-74; Hd of Div Eton Coll Windsor 74-89; R Wrotham *Roch* 89-95; rtd 95; Perm to Offic *Nor* from 95. *3 Staden Park, Trimingham, Norwich NR11 8HX* Tel (01263) 834887

ROBSON, Preb Ian Leonard. b 32. K Coll Lon MA00. Bps' Coll Cheshunt 61. **d** 63 **p** 64. C Croxley Green All SS *St Alb* 63-65; C Harpenden St Nic 65-68; V Redbourn 68-72; V Ashford St Matt *Lon* 72-77; V Kensington St Mary Abbots w St Geo 77-97; AD Kensington 94-97; Preb St Paul's Cathl 96-97; rtd 97; Perm to Offic *Chich* from 97. *Wepham Lodge, Wepham, Arundel BN18 9RA* Tel (01903) 884667 E-mail robsonoblate@aol.com

ROBSON, Irwin. b 20. **d** 63 **p** 64. C Longbenton St Bart *Newc* 63-69; C-in-c Byker St Martin CD 69-74; V Willington 74-76; TR Willington Team 76-83; V Ulgham 83-87; V Widdrington 83-87; rtd 88; Perm to Offic *Newc* from 88. *8 Brinkburn Place, Amble, Morpeth NE65 0BJ* Tel (01665) 710765

ROBSON, James Edward. b 65. Pemb Coll Ox BA88. Wycliffe Hall Ox 91. **d** 94 **p** 95. C Enfield Ch Ch Trent Park *Lon* 94-98; C Oakwood St Thos 98-00; Hon C from 00; Tutor Oak Hill Th Coll from 00. *1 Ruston Gardens, London N14 4PF* Tel (020) 8440 3122 E-mail jamesr@oakhill.ac.uk

ROBSON, John Howard. b 60. Newc Univ BA81 ACIB87. Cranmer Hall Dur 98. **d** 00 **p** 01. C Hethersett w Canteloff w Lt and Gt Melton *Nor* from 00. *32 Harman Close, Hethersett, Norwich NR9 3PR* Tel (01603) 812845

ROBSON, John Phillips. b 32. LVO99. St Edm Hall Ox. AKC58. **d** 59 **p** 60. C Huddersfield St Pet and St Paul *Wakef* 59-62; Asst Chapl Ch Hosp Horsham 62-65; Chapl 65-80; Sen Chapl Wellington Coll Berks 80-89; Chapl to RVO and Qu Chpl of the Savoy 89-02; Chapl to The Queen 93-02; rtd 02; Extra Chapl to The Queen from 02. *A2 Odhams Walk, London WC2H 9SA* Tel (020) 7240 7662

ROBSON, Mrs Margery June. b 44. Darlington Tr Coll CertEd65. St Steph Ho Ox 92. **d** 94 **p** 95. C Tuffley *Glouc* 94-98; V Darlington St Mark w St Paul *Dur* 98-03; Chapl Metro Cen

Gateshead from 03. *St Mark's House, Randolph Street, Jarrow NE32 3AQ* Tel 0191-483 2092

ROBSON, Martin Douglas. b 62. St Andr Univ MTh85 Cam Univ PGCE88 Edin Univ MTh94. Edin Th Coll CECM94. **d** 94 **p** 95. C Perth St Ninian *St And* 94-97; P-in-c Lockerbie *Glas* from 97; P-in-c Moffat from 97. *The Rectory, Ashgrove Terrace, Lockerbie DG11 2BQ* Tel (01576) 202484

ROBSON, Pamela Jean. b 44. CTM97. **d** 97 **p** 98. NSM W Ewell *Guildf* 97-01; NSM Wotton and Holmbury St Mary from 02. *The Rectory, Holmbury St Mary, Dorking RH5 6NL* Tel (01306) 730285 E-mail pamandbrianrobson@hotmail.com

ROBSON, Canon Patricia Anne. b 40. MBE99. CertEd60. SW Minl Tr Course 85. **d** 87 **p** 94. Dioc Youth Officer *Truro* 87-92; Hon C Paul 87-92; Hon C Kenwyn St Geo 88-92; Dn-in-c St Enoder 92-94; P-in-c from 94; P-in-c Newlyn St Newlyn from 03; Hon Can Truro Cathl from 98; RD Pydar from 02. *St Enoder Rectory, Summercourt, Newquay TR8 5DF* Tel (01726) 860724 Fax as telephone E-mail intercelt@aol.com

ROBSON, Paul Coutt. b 37. Leeds Univ BA60. Coll of Resurr Mirfield 63. **d** 64 **p** 65. C Stokesay *Heref* 64-66; C St Geo Cathl Cape Town 66-68; R Roodebloem All SS 68-70; Chapl HM Pris Man 70-71; Chapl HM Borstal Feltham 71-74; Chapl HM Borstal Hollesley 74-78; Chapl HM Pris Grendon and Spring Hill 78-85; Chapl HM Pris Nor 85-92; Chapl HM YOI and Remand Cen Brinsford 92-99; rtd 99; Perm to Offic *Heref* 00-01; P-in-c Wistanstow from 01. *Pilgrims, Henley Common, Church Stretton SY6 6RS* Tel (01694) 781221 E-mail smrpcr@lineone.net

ROBSON, Peter Cole. b 45. Clare Coll Cam BA66 MA70 Oriel Coll Ox BLitt69 MLitt70. Coll of Resurr Mirfield 70. **d** 71 **p** 72. C Gt Grimsby St Mary and St Jas *Linc* 71-73; Chapl BNC Ox 73-76; R Timsbury *B & W* 76-79; P-in-c Blanchland w Hunstanworth *Newc* 80-83; rtd 87. *c/o J W T Robson Esq, 4 Skylark Avenue, Mountsorrel, Leicester LE12 7FY* Tel 0116-237 4369

ROBSON, Stephen Thomas. b 54. Chich Th Coll 84. **d** 86 **p** 87. C Newc St Fran *Newc* 86-89; C Gateshead St Cuth w St Paul *Dur* 89-91; TV Stanley 91-96; V Sugley *Newc* from 96. *Sugley Vicarage, Lemington, Newcastle upon Tyne NE15 8RD* Tel 0191-267 4633

ROBSON, William. b 34. FCIS66 FCCA80. Sarum & Wells Th Coll 77. **d** 79 **p** 80. C Lymington *Win* 79-81; CF 81-93; V Barton Stacey and Bullington etc *Win* 93-98; rtd 98; Hon C Knaresborough *Ripon* 98-01. *5 Townfoot Steading, Lesbury, Alnwick NE66 3AR*

ROBUS, Keith Adrian. b 59. Chich Th Coll 85. **d** 88 **p** 89. C Greenhill St Jo *Lon* 88-92; C Willesden St Matt 92-02; V N Acton St Gabr from 02. *23 St Albans Avenue, London W4 5LL* Tel (020) 8994 6017 E-mail keith@robus.demon.co.uk

ROBY, Richard James. b 33. Imp Coll Lon BSc54 Lon Inst of Educn PGCE55. St Alb Minl Tr Scheme 82. **d** 85 **p** 86. NSM Bushey *St Alb* 85-92; NSM Wootton 92-00; rtd 00; Perm to Offic *St Alb* from 00. *5 Powis Mews, Flitwick, Bedford MK45 1SU* Tel (01525) 718529

ROCHDALE, Archdeacon of. See BALLARD, The Ven Andrew Edgar

ROCHE, Miss Alison Mary. b 70. Man Univ BSc91 Nottm Univ MA(TS)00 PGCE94. St Jo Coll Nottm 98. **d** 01 **p** 02. C Leic Martyrs *Leic* from 01. *62 Ashleigh Road, Leicester LE3 0FB* Tel 0116-254 1341

ROCHE, Barry Robert Francis. b 40. Lon Univ BD66 Dur Univ DipTh67 DipApTh92 Ox Univ MTh93. Clifton Th Coll 63. **d** 68 **p** 69. C Beckenham Ch Ch *Roch* 68-72; C Chester le Street *Dur* 72-74; C-in-c N Bletchley CD *Ox* 74-78; R Luton Ch Ch *Roch* 78-92; Chapl All SS Hosp Chatham 78-92; TR Glascote and Stonydelph *Lich* 92-99; RD Tamworth 95-99; V Oulton Broad *Nor* from 99. *St Mark's Vicarage, 212 Bridge Road, Lowestoft NR33 9JX* Tel (01502) 572563 Fax as telephone

ROCHESTER, Thomas Robson. b 33. NEOC 85. **d** 90 **p** 91. NSM Glendale Gp *Newc* from 90. *Braemar, Milfield, Wooler NE71 6HT* Tel (01668) 216346

ROCHESTER, Archdeacon of. See LOCK, The Ven Peter Harcourt D'Arcy

ROCHESTER, Bishop of. See NAZIR-ALI, The Rt Revd Michael James

ROCHESTER, Dean of. *Vacant*

ROCK, Mrs Jean. b 37. Gilmore Course 76. **dss** 79 **d** 87 **p** 97. Douglas St Matt *S & M* 79-81; Marown 81-83; Chapl Asst Oswestry and Distr Hosp 83-87; Oswestry St Oswald *Lich* 83-90; Par Dn 87-90; C-in-c Pont Robert and Pont Dolanog *St As* 90-97; V 97; rtd 99; Perm to Offic *Lich* from 99. *10 Wharf Cottages, Rhoswiel, Weston Rhyn, Oswestry SY10 7TD* Tel (01691) 773766

ROCKALL, Miss Valerie Jane. b 42. City of Cov Coll CertEd63. St Alb Minl Tr Scheme 78. **dss** 81 **d** 87 **p** 94. Asst Hd Wigginton Sch Tring 73-90; Boxmoor St Jo *St Alb* 87-90; NSM Hemel Hempstead 87-90; Par Dn Ampthill w Millbrook and Steppingley 90-93; TD Southampton (City Cen) *Win* 93-94; TV 94-99; P-in-c Aveley and Purfleet *Chelmsf* from 99. *The Vicarage,*

Mill Road, Aveley, South Ockendon RM15 4SR Tel (01708) 891242

RODEN, Jo. See LOVERIDGE, Ms Joan Margaretha Holland

RODEN, John Michael. b 37. St Jo Coll York CertEd64 Open Univ BA92 York Univ DPhil96. Ripon Hall Ox 71. **d** 73 **p** 74. C Saltburn-by-the-Sea *York* 73-77; Chapl St Pet Sch York 77-82; Warden Marrick Priory *Ripon* 83; Hon C Appleton Roebuck w Acaster Selby *York* 84-85; P-in-c from 86; Youth Officer from 86; Sen Chapl Selby Coalfield Ind Chapl from 96. *All Saints' Vicarage, Appleton Roebuck, York YO23 7DG* Tel (01904) 744327 Fax as telephone E-mail rodenjohn@lineone.net

RODEN, Michael Adrian Holland. b 60. Ripon Coll Cuddesdon 82. **d** 85 **p** 86. C S Lambeth St Anne and All SS *S'wark* 85-88; C Wandsworth St Paul 88-90; C Ox St Mary V w St Cross and St Pet *Ox* 90-94; Chapl Wadh Coll Ox 90-94; R Steeple Aston w N Aston and Tackley *Ox* 94-02; TR Hitchin *St Alb* from 02. *The Rectory, 21 West Hill, Hitchin SG5 2HZ* Tel (01462) 434017

RODERICK, Philip David. b 49. Univ of Wales (Swansea) BA70 Univ of Wales (Abth) BD77 Lon Univ CertEd71.. Linc Th Coll 80. **d** 80 **p** 81. C Llanfair-is-gaer and Llanddeiniolen *Ban* 80-82; TV Holyhead w Rhoscolyn w Llanfair-yn-Neubwll 82-84; Chapl and Lect Th Univ of Wales (Ban) 84-88; Warden Angl Chapl Cen 84-88; Prin Bucks Chr Tr Scheme *Ox* 88-94; Dir Chiltern Chr Tr Progr 88-94; Dir Quiet Garden Trust from 92; V Amersham on the Hill *Ox* from 96. *The Vicarage, 70 Sycamore Road, Amersham HP6 5DR* Tel (01494) 727553 Fax as telephone E-mail philip.roderick@ukonline.co.uk

RODFORD, Canon Brian George. b 50. Hatf Poly BEd84. **d** 79 **p** 80. Hon C St Alb St Steph *St Alb* 79-85; Chapl St Mary's Sch 81-90; Sen Teacher 83-90; Hon C Hendon St Mary *Lon* 85-90; Hon C Golders Green 85-90; Hon C Winchmore Hill H Trin 90-95; V Ponders End St Matt 95-02; Dir Chain Foundn Uganda from 02; Can All SS Cathl Kampala from 02; Perm to Offic *Lon* from 02. *39 Lonfield Avenue, London NW7 2EH* Tel (020) 8203 2330

RODGER, Canon Raymond. b 39. Westmr Coll Ox DipApTh91 MTh93. Bps' Coll Cheshunt 62. **d** 63 **p** 64. C Frodingham *Linc* 63-66; Asst Chapl St Geo Hosp Lon 66-69; C Waltham *Linc* 69-73; V Nocton 73-86; P-in-c Potter Hanworth 74-86; P-in-c Dunston 77-86; RD Graffoe 81-92; Can and Preb Linc Cathl from 85; V Nocton w Dunston and Potterhanworth 86-92; Bp's Dom Chapl from 92; Sen Preacher from 92. *Bishop's House, Eastgate, Lincoln LN2 1QQ* Tel (01522) 534701 Mobile 07803-123975 Fax 511095 E-mail bishlincoln@claranet.co.uk

RODGERS, Canon Cyril George Hooper. b 20. Qu Coll Birm 50. **d** 52 **p** 53. C Bishop's Cleeve *Glouc* 52-56; V Nailsworth 56-61; Chapl Longford's Approved Sch Minchinhampton 56-57; CF (TA) 58-62; R Upwell Ch Ch *Ely* 61-66; CF (TA - R of O) 62-87; V Wiggenhall St Germans and Islington *Ely* 66-76; RD Lynn Marshland 68-76; R Woolpit *St E* 76-84; RD Lavenham 78-87; Hon Can St E Cathl 84-87; R Woolpit w Drinkstone 84-87; rtd 87; Perm to Offic *St E* from 87. *Fox Farm, Wetherden, Stowmarket IP14 3NE* Tel (01359) 40364

RODGERS, David. b 26. Sarum Th Coll 63. **d** 65 **p** 66. C Combe Down *B & W* 65-68; V Leigh Woods 68-76; R Wellow w Foxcote and Shoscombe 76-79; C Wells St Cuth w Coxley and Wookey Hole 79-82; P-in-c Wookey w Henton 79-82; V Ercall Magna *Lich* 82-89; V Rowton 82-89; RD Wrockwardine 84-88; rtd 89; Perm to Offic *B & W* from 98. *27 Wood Close, Wells BA5 2GA*

RODGERS, Preb Frank Ernest. b 46. Tyndale Hall Bris 68. **d** 71 **p** 72. C Madeley *Heref* 71-74; C Littleover *Derby* 74-77; V Clodock and Longtown w Craswell and Llanveyno *Heref* 77-79; P-in-c St Margaret's w Michaelchurch Eskley and Newton 77-79; V Clodock and Longtown w Craswall, Llanveynoe etc from 79; RD Abbeydore 90-96; Preb Heref Cathl from 96. *The Vicarage, Longtown, Hereford HR2 0LD* Tel (01873) 860289

RODGERS, John Terence Roche. b 28. TCD BA53 MA55 ACII. Bps' Coll Cheshunt. **d** 57 **p** 58. C Templecorran *Conn* 57-60; C Derriaghy 60-61; C Antrim All SS 62-64; I Belfast St Steph 64-79; I Dunmurry 79-94; Can Belf Cathl 92-94; rtd 94. *8 Aberdelghy Park, Lambeg, Lisburn BT27 4QF* Tel (028) 9266 0430

RODGERS, Richard Thomas Boycott. b 47. Lon Univ MB, BS70 FRCS81. Qu Coll Nottm DipTh77. **d** 77 **p** 78. C Littleover *Derby* 77-80; Lect Birm St Martin w Bordesley St Andr *Birm* 89-90; Perm to Offic from 90. *63 Meadow Brook Road, Birmingham B31 1ND* Tel 0121-476 0789 E-mail dick.rodgers@charis.co.uk

RODHAM, Morris. b 59. Hatf Coll Dur BA81 St Jo Coll Dur PGCE85 Bris Univ MA93. Trin Coll Bris DipHE92. **d** 93 **p** 94. C New Milverton *Cov* 93-97; V Leamington Priors St Mary from 97. *The Vicarage, 28 St Mary's Road, Leamington Spa CV31 1JP* Tel (01926) 778507 *or* tel and fax 778505 E-mail morris.rodham@stmaryschurch.swinternet.co.uk

RODLEY, Ian Tony. b 48. Qu Coll Birm 77. **d** 80 **p** 81. Dioc Children's Adv *Bradf* 80-85; C Baildon 80-85; V Bradf St Wilfrid Lidget Green 85-90; Chapl to the Deaf 88-90; V Otley 90-98; C Wolverton *Ox* 98-03; TR Bramley *Ripon* from 03. *St Peter's Vicarage, 8 Hough Lane, Bramley, Leeds LS13 3NE* Tel (01423) 561415 E-mail ianrod@clara.co.uk

RODRIGUEZ, Luis Mario. b 64. Occidental Coll (USA) BA86 S California Univ MA93. St Steph Ho Ox MTh99. **d** 98 **p** 99. C Battersea Ch Ch and St Steph *S'wark* 98-02; C Pimlico St Pet w Westmr Ch Ch *Lon* from 02. *3 St Peter's House, 119 Eaton Square, London SW1W 9AL* Tel (020) 7235 4480 E-mail lum.rod@virgin.net

RODRIGUEZ-VEGLIO, Francis Bonny. b 33. SSC. Sarum Th Coll 62. **d** 64 **p** 65. C Alnwick St Paul *Newc* 64-68; V Horton w Piddington *Pet* 68-79; P-in-c Preston Deanery 68-79; CF (ACF) 75-82; TV Is of Scilly *Truro* 79-82; Hon Chapl Miss to Seamen 79-82; Perm to Offic *Pet* 86-88; C Leic Ch Sav *Leic* 88-91; V Kirkwhelpington, Kirkharle, Kirkheaton and Cambo *Newc* 91-95; Perm to Offic *Pet* from 95; rtd 98. *Gemacq Cottage, 14 Daventry Road, Norton, Daventry NN11 5ND* Tel (01327) 872030

RODWELL, Barry John. b 39. Birm Univ CertEd59 Cam Univ DipAdEd77. Ridley Hall Cam 67. **d** 70 **p** 71. C Sudbury St Greg and St Pet *St E* 70-73; Hd RE Hedingham Sch 73-80; R Sible Hedingham *Chelmsf* 80-85; RE Adv 85-93; V St Burstead 93-00; rtd 00; Perm to Offic *Nor* from 00. *The Nutshell, 11 Filbert Road, Loddon, Norwich NR14 6LW* Tel (01508) 522949 E-mail nutshell@tesco.net

RODWELL, Prof John Stanley. b 46. Leeds Univ BSc68 Ox Univ DipTh73 Southn Univ PhD74. Cuddesdon Coll 71. **d** 74 **p** 75. Hon C Horfield H Trin *Bris* 74-75; Hon C Skerton St Luke *Blackb* 75-77; Lic to Offic from 77. *7 Derwent Road, Lancaster LA1 3ES* Tel (01524) 62726

ROE, Mrs Caroline Ruth. b 57. Birm Univ BA80 PGCE93. Wycliffe Hall Ox 81. **dss** 84 **d** 87 **p** 96. Olveston *Bris* 84-87; Par Dn 87; NSM Alveley and Quatt *Heref* 87-94; Bp's Voc Officer 90-94; Hon C Loughborough Em and St Mary in Charnwood *Leic* 97-98; C Hathern, Long Whatton and Diseworth w Belton etc 98-00. *4 John's Lee Close, Loughborough LE11 3LH* Tel (01509) 232595

ROE, Frank Ronald. b 31. Brasted Th Coll Westcott Ho Cam 55. **d** 57 **p** 58. C S w N Hayling *Portsm* 57-61; Hong Kong 61-77; Sen Chapl St Jo Cathl 61-66; Asst Chapl 77; Sen Chapl Miss to Seamen 66-69; Australia from 77; Hon Chapl Miss to Seafarers from 77; rtd 96. *166 Dempster Street, PO Box 838, Esperance, W Australia 6450* Tel (0061) (8) 9071 4207 *or* 9071 6811/22 Mobile 417-172272 Fax 9072 1073 E-mail revfrank@bigpond.com

ROE, Canon Joseph Thorley. b 22. AKC49 DipAdEd Hull Univ PhD90. K Coll Lon 46. **d** 50 **p** 51. C Methley *Ripon* 50-53; C Richmond 53-55; V Leeds Gipton Epiphany 55-60; C of E Youth Coun Tr Officer 60-64; Sec Youth Dept BCC 64-67; Prin Lect Bretton Hall Coll Wakef 67-74; Sec for Miss and Unity *Ripon* 74-78; Dioc Missr and Bp's Dom Chapl 75-78; Can Res Carl Cathl *Carl* 78-82; Dioc Dir of Tr 78-82; Dioc Adult Educn Officer *Wakef* 82-88; Hon Can Wakef Cathl 83-88; Dir of Educn 85-88; rtd 88; Perm to Offic *Wakef* from 88. *29 Milnthorpe Drive, Wakefield WF2 7HU* Tel (01924) 256938

ROE, Peter Harold. b 37. K Coll Lon BD62 AKC62. **d** 63 **p** 64. C Knowle St Barn *Bris* 63-65; C Leckhampton St Pet *Glouc* 65-68; V Shaw Hill *Birm* 68-73; V Hobs Moat 73-90; V Packwood w Hockley Heath 90-99; Perm to Offic *Blackb* from 99; rtd 99. *14 Worcester Avenue, Garstang, Preston PR3 1EY* Tel (01995) 605775

ROE, Robert Henry. b 22. LCP57. Westcott Ho Cam 72. **d** 74 **p** 75. Hd Master St Mary's Primary Sch Saffron Walden 74-83; NSM Saffron Walden w Wendens Ambo and Littlebury *Chelmsf* 75-86; Perm to Offic *Nor* from 86. *Larchmount, High Street, Cley, Holt NR25 7RG* Tel (01263) 740369

ROE, Robin. b 28. CBE MC68. TCD BA52 MA55. **d** 53 **p** 54. C Dublin Sandford *D & G* 53-55; CF 55-81; QHC 77-81; R Merrow *Guildf* 81-89; rtd 89; Perm to Offic *Guildf* from 89. *Lansdowne, 6 Mitchells Close, Shalford, Guildford GU4 8HY* Tel (01483) 563852

ROEMMELE, Michael Patrick. b 49. TCD BA72 MA76. **d** 73 **p** 74. C Portadown St Columba *Arm* 73-77; C Drumachose *D & R* 77-80; Bahrain 79-83; Cyprus 79-83; Chapl RAF 83-00; CF from 00. *c/o MOD Chaplains (Army)* Tel (01980) 615804 Fax 615800

ROESCHLAUB, Robert Friedrich. b 39. Purdue Univ BSc63. Berkeley Div Sch MDiv66. **d** 66 **p** 66. USA 66-77; Hon C Tilehurst St Cath *Ox* 78-79; Hon C Tilehurst St Mich 79-82; P-in-c Millom H Trin w Thwaites *Carl* 82-85; P-in-c Millom 85-89; R Dunstall w Rangemore and Tatenhill *Lich* 89-93; rtd 94; Perm to Offic *Carl* from 98. *20 Pannatt Hill, Millom LA18 5DB* Tel (01229) 772185

ROEST, Wilma. b 62. Utrecht Univ MA88 Roehampton Inst PGCE92. SEITE 96. **d** 99 **p** 00. C Merton St Mary *S'wark* 99-02; TV N Lambeth from 02. *De Pastorie, 10 Wincott Street, London SE11 4NT* Tel (020) 7820 9445 E-mail wilma.roest@virgin.net

ROFF, Andrew Martin. b 42. Bede Coll Dur BSc65. Westcott Ho Cam 65. **d** 70 **p** 71. C King's Norton *Birm* 70-73; Min Can Blackb Cathl *Blackb* 73-76; P-in-c Blackb St Jo 74-75; V Longton 76-81; Chapl Trin Coll Glenalmond 82-83; R Allendale w Whitfield *Newc* 83-92; V Gosforth St Nic 92-97; Dioc Supernumerary

677

Mor from 01. *Rowan Glen, Upper Braefindon, Culbokie, Dingwall IV7 8GY* Tel (01349) 877762
E-mail 106770.3175@compuserve.com

ROFF, Canon John Michael. b 47. St Chad's Coll Dur BSc69. Westcott Ho Cam 70. **d** 72 **p** 73. C Lancaster St Mary *Blackb* 72-75; C Dronfield *Derby* 75-76; TV 76-80; TR N Wingfield, Pilsley and Tupton 80-85; V Ilkeston St Mary 85-90; V Stockport St Geo *Ches* 90-94; Dioc Ecum Officer 92-99; TR Stockport SW 94-00; RD Stockport 95-00; Hon Can Ches Cathl 98-00; Can Res Ches Cathl from 00. *9 Abbey Street, Chester CH1 2JF* Tel (01244) 316144 Fax as telephone
E-mail roff@chestercathedral.com

ROGAN, Canon John. b 28. St Jo Coll Dur BA49 MA51 DipTh54 Open Univ BPhil81. **d** 54 **p** 55. C Ashton St Mich *Man* 54-57; C Sharrow St Andr *Sheff* 57-61; Ind Chapl 57-61; Sec C of E Ind Cttee 61-66; V Leigh St Mary *Man* 66-78; RD Leigh 71-78; Hon Can Man Cathl 75-78; Provost St Paul's Cathl Dundee *Bre* 78-83; R Dundee St Paul 78-83; Soc Resp Adv *Bris* 83-93; Can Res Bris Cathl 83-93; rtd 93; Perm to Offic *Bris* from 93. *84 Concorde Drive, Bristol BS10 6PX* Tel 0117-950 5803

ROGER ALEXANDER, Brother. *See* BOHUN, Brother Roger Alexander

ROGERS, Canon Alan David. b 24. K Coll Cam BA47 MA50. Cuddesdon Coll 50. **d** 52 **p** 53. C Saffron Walden *Chelmsf* 52-54; C Walthamstow St Mich 54-57; Madagascar 57-66; Qu Coll Birm 66-67; Lect Div Weymouth Coll 67-73; Lic to Offic *Sarum* from 69; Hd of Relig and Th Depts Dorset Inst of Educn 73-82; Hon Can Antananarivo from 84; rtd 89. *4 Fossett Way, Wyke Regis, Weymouth DT4 9HD* Tel (01305) 779942

✠**ROGERS, The Rt Revd Alan Francis Bright.** b 07. Lambeth MA59 Bps' Coll Cheshunt 28. **d** 30 **p** 31 **c** 59. C Shepherd's Bush St Steph *Lon* 30-32; C Twickenham Common H Trin 32-34; Mauritius 34-49; Adn 46-49; Bp 59-66; Hon Can St Jas Cathl 44-59; V Twickenham St Mary *Lon* 49-54; Hon C from 85; V Hampstead St Jo 54-59; RD Hampstead 55-59; Suff Bp Fulham 66-70; Suff Bp Edmonton 70-75; rtd 75; Asst Bp Pet 75-84; P-in-c Wappenham w Abthorpe and Slapton 77-80; C Abthorpe w Slapton 81-83; Hon Asst Bp Lon 85-91; Hon Asst Bp Eur from 96. *20 River Way, Twickenham TW2 5JP* Tel (020) 8894 2031

ROGERS, Mrs Angela. **d** 00 **p** 01. OLM Bridgnorth, Tasley, Astley Abbotts, etc *Heref* from 00. *18 St Nicholas Road, Bridgnorth WV15 5BW* Tel (01746) 762013

ROGERS, Brian Robert. b 36. Open Univ BA80. St Jo Coll Nottm 70. **d** 72 **p** 73. C Ealing St Mary *Lon* 72-74; C Greenside *Dur* 74-75; Lic to Offic 75-85; Perm to Offic *Lich* 85-95; rtd 97; Perm to Offic *Sarum* from 97. *71 Alderney Avenue, Poole BH12 4LF* Tel (01202) 772103

ROGERS, Brian Victor. b 50. Trin Coll Bris 75. **d** 78 **p** 79. C Plumstead St Jo w St Jas and St Paul *S'wark* 78-83; P-in-c Gayton *Nor* 83-85; P-in-c Gayton Thorpe w E Walton 83-85; P-in-c Westacre 83-85; P-in-c Ashwicken w Leziate 83-85; R Gayton Gp of Par 85-91; R Rackheath and Salhouse 91-96; P-in-c Warmington, Tansor, Cotterstock and Fotheringhay *Pet* 96-97; V Warmington, Tansor and Cotterstock etc from 97. *The Vicarage, Warmington, Peterborough PE8 6TE* Tel (01832) 280263 E-mail brian.rogers@cwcom.net

ROGERS, Charles Murray. b 17. Qu Coll Cam BA38 MA40 Lon Univ DipEd43. Westcott Ho Cam 38. **d** 40 **p** 41. C Plymouth St Andr *Ex* 40-42; Perm to Offic *Ely* 42; CMS 43-71; India 46-71; Jerusalem 71-80; Hong Kong 80-89; rtd 82; Canada 89-98. *St Andrew's Lodge, All Saints Convent, St Mary's Road, Oxford OX4 1RV* Tel (01865) 243659

ROGERS, Christopher Antony. b 47. N Ord Course 79. **d** 81 **p** 82. C Chesterfield St Aug *Derby* 81-84; C Chaddesden St Phil 84-86; R Whitwell 86-95; V W Burnley *Blackb* 95-01; V Ashford St Hilda *Lon* from 01. *St Hilda's Vicarage, 8 Station Crescent, Ashford TW15 3HH* Tel (01784) 254237
E-mail christopher.rogers@london.anglican.org

ROGERS, Clive William. b 62. Selw Coll Cam BA83 MA87 MEng93 Southn Univ BTh90. Chich Th Coll 87. **d** 90 **p** 91. C Leic St Aid *Leic* 90-93; P-in-c Ryhall w Essendine *Pet* 93-94; Lic to Offic *Ely* 94-03; Perm to Offic from 00. *13 St John's Street, Duxford, Cambridge CB2 4RA* Tel (01223) 513625

ROGERS, Cyril David. b 55. Birm Univ BA76 BTheol. Sarum & Wells Th Coll 80. **d** 83 **p** 84. C Leagrave *St Alb* 83-87; TV Langtree *Ox* 87-97; R Ballaugh *S & M* from 97. *The Rectory, Ballacrosha, Ballaugh, Isle of Man IM7 5AQ* Tel (01624) 897873

ROGERS, Damon. b 66. Cov Univ BEng92 Wolv Univ PGCE94 Warwick Univ BPhil(Ed)02. Cranmer Hall Dur 01. **d** 03. C Heigham St Thos *Nor* from 03. *363 Earlham Road, Norwich NR2 3RQ* Tel (01603) 506121

ROGERS, David. b 48. Univ of Wales (Ban) BA69. Westcott Ho Cam 70. **d** 72 **p** 73. C Rainbow Hill St Barn *Worc* 72-75; C Tolladine 72-75; C Astwood Bank w Crabbs Cross 75-79; V Cradley 79-90; V Beoley from 90; RD Bromsgrove from 00. *The Vicarage, Church Hill, Beoley, Redditch B98 9AR* Tel (01527) 63976

ROGERS, David Alan. b 55. City of Lon Poly BA77 MCIT82. Linc Th Coll 88. **d** 90 **p** 91. C Kingston upon Hull St Nic *York* 90-93; P-in-c Kingston upon Hull St Mary 93-96; N Humberside Ind Chapl 93-02; Dir Leeds Ch Inst *Ripon* from 02. *20 New Market Street, Leeds LS1 6DG* Tel 0113-245 4700
E-mail daverogers@leedschurchinstitute.org

ROGERS, The Ven David Arthur. b 21. Ch Coll Cam BA47 MA52. Ridley Hall Cam 47. **d** 49 **p** 50. C Stockport St Geo *Ches* 49-53; R Levenshulme St Pet *Man* 53-59; P-in-c Cautley w Dowbiggin *Bradf* 59-60; P-in-c Garsdale 59-60; V Sedbergh 59-74; RD Sedbergh 59-73; V Garsdale 60-74; V Cautley w Dowbiggin 60-74; Hon Can Bradf Cathl 67-77; P-in-c Firbank, Howgill and Killington 73-77; RD Ewecross 73-77; V Sedbergh, Cautley and Garsdale 74-79; Adn Craven 77-86; rtd 86; Lic to Offic *Bradf* from 86; Perm to Offic *Blackb* from 87 and *Carl* from 89. *Borrens Farm, Leck, Carnforth LA6 2JG* Tel (01524) 271616

ROGERS, David Barrie. b 46. S Dios Minl Tr Scheme 89. **d** 93. NSM Old Alresford and Bighton *Win* 93-96; Dep Warden Dioc Retreat Ho (Holland Ho) Cropthorne *Worc* 96-98; Warden Stacklands Retreat Ho W Kingsdown 98-03; Hon C Kingsdown *Roch* 98-03; Warden St Pet Bourne Cen from 03. *St Peter's Bourne Centre, 40 Oakleigh Park South, London N20 9JU*

ROGERS, David Martyn. b 56. Univ of Wales (Lamp) BA77 K Coll Lon BD79 AKC79 St Kath Coll Liv DipEd86 Liv Univ BPhil94. Chich Th Coll 79. **d** 80 **p** 81. C Hockerill *St Alb* 80-85; Perm to Offic *St Alb* 85-87; C Kilburn St Mary *Lon* 87-90; V New Longton *Blackb* from 90; Chapl to Lancs Constabulary from 90. *All Saints' Vicarage, Station Road, New Longton, Preston PR4 4LN* Tel (01772) 613347

ROGERS, Canon Donovan Charles Edgar. b 08. Clifton Th Coll 32. **d** 35 **p** 36. C Leyton Em *Chelmsf* 35-37; C N Woolwich 37-38; Chapl RAF 38-41; CF 41-46; S Africa from 47; Can of Prov from 65. *The Cottage, Beach Road, Noordhoek, 7985 South Africa* Tel (0027) (21) 789 1117

ROGERS, George Hutchinson. b 51. Windsor Univ Ontario BSW75. Wycliffe Coll Toronto MDiv78. **d** 78 **p** 78. Canada 78-99; C Tonbridge SS Pet and Paul *Roch* 99-03; V Werrington *Pet* from 03. *The Vicarage, 37 The Green, Werrington, Peterborough PE4 6RT* Tel (01733) 571649
E-mail ghrogers@nildram.co.uk

ROGERS, Ian Colin. b 73. Wolv Univ BA95. Coll of Resurr Mirfield BA99. **d** 00 **p** 01. C Lon Docks St Pet w Wapping St Jo *Lon* from 00. *St Peter's Mission House, Wapping Lane, London E1 2RW* Tel (020) 7702 2307

ROGERS, The Very Revd John. b 34. Univ of Wales (Lamp) BA55 Oriel Coll Ox BA58 MA61. St Steph Ho Ox 57. **d** 59 **p** 60. C Roath St Martin *Llan* 59-63; Br Guiana 63-66; Guyana 66-71; V Caldicot *Mon* 71-77; V Monmouth 77-84; RD Monmouth 81-84; TR Ebbw Vale 84-93; RD Blaenau Gwent 86-93; Can St Woolos Cathl 88-93; Dean Llan 93-99; V Llandaff w Capel Llanilltern 93-99; rtd 99. *Fron Lodge, Llandovery SA20 0LJ* Tel (01550) 720089

ROGERS, John Arthur. b 47. MBIM. Edin Dioc NSM Course 90. **d** 92. C Middlesbrough St Martin *York* 92-93; NSM The Trimdons *Dur* from 00. *9 Coronation Terrace, Trimdon Village, Trimdon Station TS29 6PQ* Tel (01429) 881119

ROGERS, John Robin. b 36. St Alb Minl Tr Scheme 78. **d** 81 **p** 82. NSM Digswell and Panshanger *St Alb* 81-84; C Welwyn w Ayot St Peter 85-92; R Wilden w Colmworth and Ravensden 92-99; rtd 99; Perm to Offic *St Alb* 99-02. *37 The Birches, Shobdon, Leominster HR6 9NG* Tel (01568) 708903

ROGERS, John William Trevor. b 28. Qu Coll Bris 85 **p** 86. NSM Dunchurch *Cov* 85-95; Perm to Offic from 95. *15 Hillyard Road, Southam, Leamington Spa CV47 0LD* Tel (01926) 813469

ROGERS, Canon Kenneth. b 33. Cuddesdon Coll 68. **d** 69 **p** 70. C Perranzabuloe *Truro* 69-71; C Truro St Paul 71-74; P-in-c Kenwyn St Geo 74-87; RD Powder 81-88; Hon Can Truro Cathl 87-98; TR Bodmin w Lanhydrock and Lanivet 87-98; RD Trigg Minor and Bodmin 89-93; rtd 98; Perm to Offic *Truro* from 98. *25 Paul Row, Truro TR1 1HH* Tel (01872) 261007

ROGERS, Canon Llewelyn. Univ of Wales (Lamp) BA59. St Mich Coll Llan. **d** 61 **p** 62. C Holywell *St As* 61-64; C Hawarden 64-70; R Bodfari 70-73; V Rhosymedre 73-78; V Llansantffraid-ym-Mechain 77-83; V Llansantffraid-ym-Mechain and Llanfechain 83-98; RD Llanfyllin 84-88; V Pont Robert, Pont Dolanog, Garthbeibio etc 98-01; Can St As Cathl 98-01; rtd 01. *17 Maes y Berllan, Llanymynech SY22 6PJ*

ROGERS, Lynne. **d** 03. NSM Ferns w Kilbride, Toombe, Kilcormack etc *C & O* from 03. *The Corner House, Clone, Ferns, Co Wexford, Irish Republic* Tel (00353) (54) 66961
E-mail lynnerogers@eircom.net

ROGERS, Malcolm Dawson. b 63. SS Hild & Bede Coll Dur BA84 Selw Coll Cam BA88. Ridley Hall Cam 86. **d** 89 **p** 90. C Ipswich St Jo *St E* 89-93; CMS 93-95; Russia 93-95; C Holloway St Mary Magd *Lon* 95-97; V from 97. *St Mary Magdalene Vicarage, 28 Witherington Road, London N5 1PP* Tel (020) 7607 3919

ROGERS, Malcolm Kenneth. b 72. Liv Inst of Educn BA93. St Jo Coll Nottm MA95 LTh96. **d** 96 **p** 97. C W Derby St Luke *Liv* 96-00; V Huyton Quarry from 00. *St Gabriel's Vicarage, 2 St Agnes Road, Huyton, Liverpool L36 5TA* Tel 0151-489 2688

ROGERS, Mark James. b 64. Univ of Wales (Lamp) BA. Qu Coll Birm. **d** 89 **p** 90. C Dudley St Aug Holly Hall *Worc* 89-93; C Worc St Barn w Ch Ch 93-94; TV 94-97; USPG Belize 97-00; Canada from 00. *St Columba's Rectory, 4020 Hingston Avenue, Montreal QC, Canada H4A 2J7*

ROGERS, Martin Brian. b 53. LNSM course 89. **d** 92 **p** 93. OLM Collyhurst *Man* from 92. *8 Greenford Road, Crumpsall, Manchester M8 0NW* Tel 0161-740 4614

ROGERS, Martin Stephen. b 28. St Edm Hall Ox BA50 MA54. Cuddesdon Coll 50. **d** 52 **p** 53. C Reading St Mary V *Ox* 52-54; C Buxton *Derby* 54-57; Australia 58-64; Lect Cuddesdon Coll 65-73; Chapl Littlemore Hosp Ox 65-74; Dept of Educn Cam Univ 73-76; Chapl Univ Coll of Ripon and York St Jo 76-93; Postgraduate Medical Educn Adv Leeds Univ 90-93; rtd 93; Perm to Offic *Ex* from 98. *Freshwater, 4 Marles Close, Awliscombe, Honiton EX14 3GA* Tel (01404) 44296

ROGERS, Maurice George Walden. b 23. AKC51. **d** 52 **p** 53. C Bedford All SS *St Alb* 52-56; C Southfields St Barn *S'wark* 56-58; C Chingford SS Pet and Paul *Chelmsf* 58-61; V Gt Ilford St Luke 61-72; V Woodford St Barn 72-89; rtd 89; Perm to Offic *Chelmsf* from 89 and *Win* from 93. *The Coach House, 13 Bodorgan Road, Bournemouth BH2 6NQ* Tel (01202) 291034

ROGERS, Michael Andrew. b 47. OBE91. FRAeS96. Ripon Coll Cuddesdon. **d** 01 **p** 02. C Bromsgrove St Jo *Worc* from 01; H Chapl ATC from 02. *74 Carol Avenue, Bromsgrove B61 8RW* Tel (01527) 874632 E-mail mrogers@holton.fsnet.co.uk

ROGERS, Michael Ernest. b 34. Sarum & Wells Th Coll 83. **d** 85 **p** 86. C Roehampton H Trin *S'wark* 85-88; V Ryhill *Wakef* 88-94; V S Elmsall 94-00; rtd 00; Perm to Offic *Derby* from 00. *The Willows, 49 Main Street, Weston-on-Trent, Derby DE72 2BL* Tel (01332) 700273

ROGERS, Canon Michael Hugh Walton. b 52. K Coll Lon BD73 AKC73. St Aug Coll Cant 74. **d** 75 **p** 76. C Eastbourne St Andr *Chich* 75-78; C Uppingham w Ayston *Pet* 78-82; V Eye 82-90; R Cottesmore and Barrow w Ashwell and Burley from 90; RD Rutland 95-00; C Greetham and Thistleton w Stretton and Clipsham from 01; Lect Peak Comm Coll from 01. *The Rectory, Cottesmore, Oakham LE15 7DJ* Tel (01572) 812202 E-mail mhwrogers@btinternet.com

ROGERS, Canon Noel Desmond. b 26. TD71. Univ of Wales (Lamp) BA51. **d** 53 **p** 54. C Rhyl w St Ann *St As* 53-58; V Everton St Geo *Liv* 58-64; CF (TA) 59-75; R Newton in Makerfield *Liv* 64-74; V Rostherne w Bollington *Ches* from 74; P-in-c Over Tabley and High Legh 93-98; CF (R of O) 75-81; RD Knutsford *Ches* 85-96; Hon Can Ches Cathl from 87. *The Vicarage, Rostherne, Knutsford WA16 6RY* Tel (01565) 830595

ROGERS, Philip John. b 52. Univ of Wales CertEd74 Nottm Univ BTh78. St Jo Coll Nottm 76. **d** 79 **p** 80. C Stretford St Bride *Man* 79-84; P-in-c Plumstead St Jo w St Jas and St Paul *S'wark* 84-85; V from 85. *St John's Vicarage, 176 Griffin Road, London SE18 7QA* Tel (020) 8855 1827 E-mail philipjrogers@ukonline.co.uk

ROGERS (née GOLDER), Mrs Rebecca Marie (Beki). b 71. Brunel Univ BA94. Trin Coll Bris BA02. **d** 02. C Short Heath *Birm* from 02. *46 Redacre Road, Sutton Coldfield B73 5EA* Tel 0121-354 8748 E-mail bekirogers@hotmail.com

ROGERS, Richard Anthony. b 46. Ex Coll Ox BA69 Birm Univ DipTh70. Qu Coll Birm 70. **d** 71 **p** 72. C Shirley *Birm* 71-74; Chapl Solihull Sch 74-78; Hon C Cotteridge *Birm* 78-84; Hon C Hill 84-93; Hd RE Kings Norton Sch from 93; Perm to Offic from 93. *48 Jordan Road, Sutton Coldfield B75 5AB* Tel 0121-308 0310

ROGERS, Richard Jonathan. b 64. Trin Coll Bris BTh96. **d** 96 **p** 97. C Carterton *Ox* 96-00; Crosslinks 00-03; Perm to Offic *B & W* from 00. *11 East End Avenue, Warminster BA12 9NF* Tel (01985) 214123

ROGERS, Canon Robert. b 42. Bernard Gilpin Soc Dur 66 St Aid Birkenhead 67 Ridley Hall Cam 69. **d** 70 **p** 71. C Childwall St Dav *Liv* 70-73; C Huntington *York* 73-76; TR Brayton 76-89; RD Selby 84-89; V New Malton 89-98; RD Bulmer and Malton 97-98; Asst Chapl York Health Services NHS Trust 98-99; Sen Chapl from 99; Can and Preb York Minster *York* from 03. *York District Hospital, Wigginton Road, York YO31 8HE* Tel (01904) 453120, 631313 or 699469

ROGERS, Robert Charles. b 55. St Pet Coll Birm CertEd77 Warwick Univ MA99 Univ Coll Worc DipEBD00. St Jo Coll Nottm 87. **d** 89 **p** 90. C Wellesbourne *Cov* 89-93; R Bourton w Frankton and Stretton on Dunsmore etc 93-97; Behaviour Support Teacher Warks LEA from 98; Lic to Offic from 98.

18 Waring Way, Dunchurch, Rugby CV22 6PH Tel (01788) 817361

ROGERS, Robin. *See* ROGERS, John Robin

ROGERS, Ronald James. b 31. Bris Univ BA56 St Cath Soc Ox BA58 MA65. Wycliffe Hall Ox 56. **d** 58 **p** 59. C Gt Yarmouth *Nor* 58-62; C Newington St Mary *S'wark* 67-69; C Liv Our Lady and St Nic w St Anne *Liv* 78-83; C Pimlico St Pet w Westmr Ch Ch *Lon* 83-85; Chapl Westmr City Sch 85-87; P-in-c Pimlico St Sav *Lon* 87-96; rtd 96; Chapl Izmir (Smyrna) w Bornova *Eur* 96-01; P-in-c Palermo w Taormina from 01. *Chaplaincy Residence, via Stabile Mariana 118B, 90139 Palermo, Sicily* Tel (0039) (09) 158 5220 Fax as telephone

ROGERS, Ms Sally Jean. b 54. Univ of Wales (Lamp) BA77 Nottm Univ BTh87. Linc Th Coll 84. **d** 87 **p** 94. Par Dn Bris St Mary Redcliffe w Temple etc *Bris* 87-90; Par Dn Greenford H Cross *Lon* 90-94; C 94-96; TV Hemel Hempstead *St Alb* 96-02; Perm to Offic from 02. *62 Clarence Road, London E17 6AQ* Tel (020) 8531 4992

ROGERS, Trevor. *See* ROGERS, John William Trevor

ROGERS, William. *See* ROGERS, Clive William

ROGERS, William Arthur. b 41. Lon Univ BA64 CertEd. Chich Th Coll 79. **d** 81 **p** 82. C Chandler's Ford *Win* 81-84; R Bentley and Binsted 84-94; P-in-c The Lulworths, Winfrith Newburgh and Chaldon *Sarum* 94-99; rtd 99. *2 Hazel Close, Teignmouth TQ14 8RN* Tel (01626) 879183

ROGERSON, Anthony Carroll. b 37. Trin Coll Ox BA59 MA63 MIPD92. St Alb and Ox Min Course 96. **d** 98 **p** 99. NSM Radley and Sunningwell *Ox* 98-02; Perm to Offic from 02. *Noggins, 35 Lower Radley, Abingdon OX14 3AY* Tel (01235) 550214 E-mail tonyrogerson@cygnet.org.uk

✠**ROGERSON, The Rt Revd Barry.** b 36. Leeds Univ BA60 Bris Univ Hon LLD93. Wells Th Coll 60. **d** 62 **p** 63 **c** 79. C S Shields St Hilda w St Thos *Dur* 62-65; C Bishopwearmouth St Nic 65-67; Lect Lich Th Coll 67-71; Vice-Prin 71-72; Lect Sarum & Wells Th Coll 72-74; V Wednesfield St Thos *Lich* 75-79; TR Wednesfield 79; Suff Bp Wolverhampton 79-85; Bp Bris 85-02; rtd 02; Hon Asst Bp B & W from 03. *Flat 2, 30 Albert Road, Clevedon BS21 7RR* Tel (01275) 541964 E-mail 106430.1040@compuserve.com

ROGERSON, Cecil Theodore. b 59. St Paul's Coll Grahamstown DipTh81. **d** 81 **p** 83. S Africa 81-97; TV Wordsley *Worc* from 97. *1 Denleigh Road, Kingswinford DY6 8QB* Tel (01384) 278692 Fax 271769 E-mail ctroger@blueyonder.co.uk

ROGERSON, Colin Scott. b 30. St Andr Univ MA55. Edin Th Coll. **d** 57 **p** 58. C Byker St Ant *Newc* 57-59; C Newc St Geo 59-63; C Wooler 63-67; V Tynemouth St Aug 67-75; C Dur St Marg *Dur* 75-88; P-in-c Hebburn St Jo 88-95; rtd 95; Perm to Offic *Dur* from 95. *6 Edlingham Road, Durham DH1 5YS* Tel 0191-386 1956

ROGERSON, Canon David George. b 38. St Chad's Coll Dur BA60 DipTh63 Newc Univ DipEd67. **d** 63 **p** 64. C Wallsend St Luke *Newc* 63-67; C Delaval 67-70; V Long Benton St Mary 70-81; V N Sunderland from 81; Warden Seahouses Dioc Hostel from 81; Miss to Seafarers from 81; Hon Can Newc Cathl *Newc* from 02. *The Vicarage, South Lane, North Sunderland, Seahouses NE68 7TU* Tel (01665) 720202

ROGERSON, Derek Russell. b 23. Lon Univ BA51. Sarum Th Coll 51. **d** 53 **p** 54. C Balham Hill Ascension *S'wark* 53-56; C Mottingham St Andr 56-60; R Sapcote *Leic* 60-64; R Harpurhey St Steph *Man* 64-70; V Rochdale Gd Shep 70-74; Asst Chapl HM Pris Man 74-76; Chapl HM Pris Kirkham 76-83; Chapl HM Pris Haverigg 84-88; rtd 88; Perm to Offic *Carl* 88-99. *26 Market Street, Millom LA18 4AH* Tel (01229) 775261

ROGERSON, Ian Matthew. b 45. Bede Coll Dur CertEd67 Open Univ BA76. Oak Hill Th Coll DipHE81. **d** 83 **p** 84. C Haughton St Mary *Man* 83-86; V Ramsbottom St Andr from 86; AD Bury from 96. *St Andrew's Vicarage, 2 Henwick Hall Avenue, Ramsbottom, Bury BL0 9YH* Tel (01706) 826482 Fax as telephone

ROGERSON, Canon Prof John William. b 35. Man Univ BD61 DD75 Linacre Ho Ox BA63 MA67 Aber Univ Hon DD98. Ripon Hall Ox 61. **d** 64 **p** 66. C Dur St Oswald *Dur* 64-67; Lect Th Dur Univ 64-75; Sen Lect 75-79; Lic to Offic *Dur* 67-79; Lic to Offic *Sheff* from 79; Prof Bibl Studies Sheff Univ 79-96; Hd of Dept 79-94; Hon Can Sheff Cathl *Sheff* 82-95. *60 Marlborough Road, Sheffield S10 1DB* Tel 0114-268 1426

ROLAND, Andrew Osborne. b 45. Mert Coll Ox BA66 DPM69. Cranmer Hall Dur BA84. **d** 84 **p** 85. C Streatham St Leon *S'wark* 84-87; C Kingston All SS w St Jo 87-94; P-in-c Hackbridge and Beddington Corner from 94. *All Saints' Vicarage, New Road, Mitcham CR4 4JL* Tel (020) 8648 3650

ROLFE, Charles Edward. b 34. Wells Th Coll 68. **d** 70 **p** 71. C Bath Twerton-on-Avon *B & W* 70-79; TV Wellington and Distr 79-85; P-in-c Frome Ch Ch 85-89; V 89-94; Chapl Victoria Hosp Frome 85-94; Chapl St Adhelm's Hosp Frome 88-94; rtd 94; NSM Fordingbridge *Win* 95-01; NSM Hale w S Charford 95-01; NSM Fordingbridge and Breamore and Hale etc from 01. *14 Ashford Close, Fordingbridge SP6 1DH* Tel (01425) 652684

ROLFE, Joseph William. b 37. Qu Coll Birm 78. **d** 81 **p** 82. NSM Tredington and Darlingscott w Newbold on Stour *Cov* 81-91;

NSM Brailes from 91; NSM Sutton under Brailes from 91; NSM Shipston Deanery from 98. *35 Manor Lane, Shipston-on-Stour CV36 4EF* Tel (01608) 661737

ROLFE, Paul Douglas. b 46. MIBC90. N Ord Course 90. **d** 93 **p** 94. C Urmston *Man* 93-96; V Lawton Moor from 96. *The Vicarage, Orton Road, Manchester M23 0LH* Tel 0161-998 2461 Fax as telephone E-mail paul@st-michael.demon.co.uk

ROLLETT, Robert Henry. b 39. Leeds Univ BA61 Leic Univ CertEd62. Linc Th Coll 77. **d** 79 **p** 80. C Littleport *Ely* 79-82; P-in-c Manea 82-83; V 83-85; P-in-c Wimblington 82-83; R 83-85; V Thorney Abbey 85-93; P-in-c The Ramseys and Upwood 93-94; TR 94-99; rtd 99; P-in-c Scalford w Goadby Marwood and Wycombe etc *Leic* 99-00. *2 Stockerston Crescent, Uppingham, Oakham LE15 9UB* Tel (01572) 823685

ROLLINS, David. b 65. Nene Coll Northampton DipSW93 De Montfort Univ BA98. St Steph Ho Ox DipMin01. **d** 01 **p** 02. C Leic St Aid *Leic* from 01. *26 Chevin Avenue, Leicester LE3 6PX* Tel 0116-287 2221

ROLLINSON, Canon John Knighton. b 14. FRCO34 Sheff Univ BMus36 AKC48. **d** 49 **p** 50. C Ilkeston St Mary *Derby* 49-53; C Wirksworth w Carsington 53-55; PC Dethick, Lea and Holloway 55-64; R Whittington 64-81; Chapl Whittington Hall Hosp 64-82; P-in-c New Whittington 78-81; rtd 81; Perm to Offic *Derby* from 81. *75 Yew Tree Drive, Somersall, Chesterfield S40 3NB* Tel (01246) 568647

ROLLS, Peter. b 40. Leeds Inst of Educn CertEd. N Ord Course 80. **d** 83 **p** 84. NSM Meltham *Wakef* from 83. *14 Heather Road, Meltham, Huddersfield HD7 3EY* Tel (01484) 850389

ROLPH, Pauline Gladys. b 30. SRN51 SCM53 HVCert65. Oak Hill Th Coll 88. **d** 90 **p** 94. Hon C Chingford St Anne *Chelmsf* 90-96; rtd 96; Perm to Offic *Sarum* from 96. *1 Black Lawn, Gillingham SP8 4SD* Tel (01747) 822502 Fax 821474

ROLPH, Reginald Lewis George. b 29. Open Univ BA74. Bps' Coll Cheshunt 55. **d** 58 **p** 59. C Perivale *Lon* 58-61; C Wokingham St Paul *Ox* 61-63; C Letchworth *St Alb* 63-78; Perm to Offic from 78; rtd 93. *22 Souberie Avenue, Letchworth Garden City SG6 3JA* Tel (01462) 684596

ROLSTON, Cyril Willis Matthias. b 29. CITC 66. **d** 68 **p** 69. C Portadown St Mark *Arm* 68-71; I Loughgilly w Clare 71-81; Dir of Ords from 72; Asst Chapl Craigavon Area Hosp Group Trust from 80; I Moy w Charlemont *Arm* 81-96; Preb Arm Cathl 92-96; rtd 96; Chapl Armagh and Dungannon Health and Soc Services from 96. *19 Lower Parklands, Dungannon BT71 7JN* Tel (028) 8772 5910

ROLSTON, John Ormsby. b 28. TCD BA51 MA59 BD63. CITC 51. **d** 51 **p** 52. C Belfast St Mary Magd *Conn* 51-55; C Knock *D & D* 55-59; P-in-c Gilnahirk 59-63; I 63-66; I Belfast St Jas *Conn* 66-79; I Belfast St Jas w St Silas 79-96; Can Belf Cathl 82-96; Prec Belf Cathl 88-96; Adn Conn 88-96; rtd 96; Dioc C *Conn* 96-98. *5 Springburn Park, Lisburn BT27 5QZ* Tel (028) 9267 8932 E-mail j.o.rolston@lineone.net

ROLTON, Patrick Hugh. b 49. Sarum & Wells Th Coll 72. **d** 74 **p** 75. C Roch 74-79; C Edenbridge 79-81; R N Cray 81-97; rtd 97. *45 Chalk Pit Avenue, Orpington BR5 3JJ* Tel (01689) 872916

ROM, Norman Charles. b 24. S'wark Ord Course 63. **d** 66 **p** 67. C Leatherhead *Guildf* 66-71; Chapl HM Pris Cant 71-74; Chapl HM Pris Pentonville 74-85; Chapl HM Pris Stocken 85-87; P-in-c Empingham *Pet* 85-87; R Empingham and Exton w Horn w Whitwell 87-94; rtd 94; Perm to Offic *Pet* from 94. *11 Dundee Drive, Stamford PE9 2TR* Tel (01780) 482051

ROMANIS, Adam John Aidan. b 57. Pemb Coll Ox BA78 MA83. Westcott Ho Cam 81. **d** 84 **p** 85. C Northfield *Birm* 84-88; TV Seaton Hirst *Newc* 88-93; V Newc Ch Ch w St Ann 93-99; V Cowley St Jo *Ox* from 99. *The Vicarage, 271 Cowley Road, Oxford OX4 2AJ* Tel (01865) 242396 E-mail adamox4@aol.com

ROMER, William Miller. b 35. Brown Univ Rhode Is BA57. MDiv60. **d** 60 **p** 60. USA 60-03; P-in-c Lake Luzerne St Mary 60-64; Asst Min Hanover St Andr 64-65; V NY St Boniface 65-70; P-in-c Troy St Luke 70-71; R Rochester Redeemer 98-03; I Rathkeale w Askeaton, Kilcornan and Kilnaughtin *L & K* from 03. *Cragmore, Askeaton, Co Limerick, Irish Republic*

RONAYNE, Peter Henry. b 34. FCA68. Oak Hill Th Coll 64. **d** 66 **p** 67. C Chesham St Mary *Ox* 66-69; C Worthing H Trin *Chich* 69-74; V Shoreditch St Leon w St Mich *Lon* 74-82; P-in-c Norwood St Luke *S'wark* 82-85; V 85-94; V W Norwood St Luke 94-99; RD Streatham 87-91; rtd 99; Perm to Offic *S'wark* from 00. *54 Maywater Close, South Croydon CR2 0LS* Tel (020) 8651 9743

RONCHETTI, Quentin Marcus. b 56. Ripon Coll Cuddesdon 79. **d** 80 **p** 81. C Eastbourne St Mary *Chich* 80-83; C Moulsecoomb 83-85; TV 85-90; V Findon Valley 90-97; V Shoreham Beach from 97. *The Vicarage, West Beach, Shoreham-by-Sea BN43 5LF* Tel (01273) 453768

RONE, The Ven James. b 35. St Steph Ho Ox 79. **d** 80 **p** 81. C Stony Stratford *Ox* 80-82; P-in-c Fordham St Pet *Ely* 82-83; V 83-89; P-in-c Kennett 82-83; R 83-89; Can Res Ely Cathl 89-95; Treas 92-95; Adn Wisbech 95-02; Hon Can Ely Cathl 95-02; Bp's Adv for Hosp Chapl 96-02; rtd 03; Perm to Offic *Ely* from 03. *Little Housing, 32 Lumley Close, Ely CB7 4FG* Tel (01353) 667088

ROOKE, Henry John Warburton. b 10. Ch Ch Ox BA32 MA35. Wycliffe Hall Ox 34. **d** 35 **p** 36. C Hayes *Roch* 35-40; CF (EC) 40-46; C Edgbaston St Geo *Birm* 48-51; V Weobley w Sarnesfield *Heref* 51-69; RD Weobley 64-67; rtd 69. *22 Manormead, Tilford Road, Hindhead GU26 6RA* Tel (01428) 605082

ROOKE, James Templeman. b 43. Saltley Tr Coll Birm CertEd65. EMMTC 82. **d** 84 **p** 85. NSM Bassingham *Linc* 84-89; NSM Hykeham 89-94; Sub Chapl HM Pris Morton Hall 94; P-in-c Borrowdale *Carl* 94-97; Chapl Keswick Sch 94-97; NSM Hykeham *Linc* 97-02; Sub Chapl HM Pris Morton Hall 97-00; NSM Swinderby *Linc* from 02; CF (ACF) from 00. *The Chestnuts, Main Street, Norton Disney, Lincoln LN6 9JU* Tel (01522) 788315

ROOKE, John George Michael. b 47. St Jo Coll Dur BA72 DipTh74. Cranmer Hall Dur 71. **d** 74 **p** 75. C Skelmersdale St Paul *Liv* 74-78; TV Speke St Aid 78-81; Ind Chapl 81-85; V Knotty Ash St Jo from 85. *St John's Vicarage, Thomas Lane, Liverpool L14 5NR* Tel 0151-228 2396

ROOKE, Canon Patrick William. b 55. Open Univ BA85. Sarum & Wells Th Coll 75. **d** 78 **p** 79. C Mossley *Conn* 78-81; C Ballywillan 81-83; I Craigs w Dunaghy and Killagan 83-88; I Ballymore *Arm* 88-94; Asst Prov and Dioc Registrar 92-94; Hon V Choral Arm Cathl 93-94; I Agherton *Conn* from 94; Preb and Can Conn Cathl from 01. *The Rectory, 59 Strand Road, Portstewart BT55 7LU* Tel (028) 7083 3277 *or* 7083 2538 E-mail rector@aghertonparish.freeserve.co.uk

ROOKWOOD, Colin John. b 40. TCD BA64 MA68 Lon Univ PGCE67 DipTh69. Clifton Th Coll 67. **d** 70 **p** 71. C Eccleston Ch Ch *Liv* 70-75; V Penge St Jo *Roch* 75-82; V Childwall All SS *Liv* 82-91; Chapl Bethany Sch Goudhurst 91-03; rtd 03; Perm to Offic *Roch* from 01. *Providence Cottage South, Curtisden Green, Goudhurst, Cranbrook TN17 1LD* Tel (01580) 211579 E-mail colin.rookwood@talk21.co.uk

ROOM, Canon Frederick John. b 24. St Jo Coll Ox BA49 MA53. Wells Th Coll 49. **d** 51 **p** 52. C Bradford cum Beswick *Man* 51-54; C Halliwell St Marg 54-56; C Farnham Royal *Ox* 56-58; Cl-in-c Farnham Royal S CD 58-70; TV Thetford *Nor* 70-89; Sen Ind Missr 75-89; Hon Can Nor Cathl 77-89; rtd 89; Perm to Offic *Nor* from 89. *61 Beechwood Drive, Thorpe St Andrew, Norwich NR7 0LN* Tel (01603) 435930

ROOME, Mrs Alison Morag Venessa. b 48. Bp Lonsdale Coll TCert71. EMMTC 98. **d** 01 **p** 02. NSM Alfreton *Derby* from 01. *55 Dovedale Crescent, Belper DE56 1HJ* Tel (01773) 825635 E-mail aliroome@lineone.net

ROOMS, Canon Nigel James. b 60. Leeds Univ BSc81 Nottm Univ MA95 CEng80 MIChemE86. St Jo Coll Nottm DipTh89. **d** 90 **p** 91. C Chell *Lich* 90-94; Min Moshi St Marg Tanzania 94-01; Dir Th Educn by Ext 94-01; Hon Can Arusha from 01; Dioc Dir of Tr *S'well* from 02. *12 Lingwood Lane, Woodborough, Nottingham NG14 6DX* Tel 0115-965 4380 *or* (01636) 817231 Fax (01636) 815084 E-mail nigel.rooms@southwell.anglican.org

ROOSE-EVANS, James Humphrey. b 27. St Benet's Hall Ox BA52 MA56. **d** 81 **p** 81. NSM Kington and Weobley *Heref* from 81; NSM Primrose Hill St Mary w Avenue Road St Paul *Lon* from 82. *71 Belsize Park Gardens, London NW3 4JP*

ROOSE FRANCIS, Leslie. See FRANCIS, Leslie

ROOT, Canon Howard Eugene. b 26. Univ of S California BA45 St Cath Soc Ox BA51 Magd Coll Cam MA53 Magd Coll Ox MA70. Ripon Hall Ox 49. **d** 53 **p** 54. C Trumpington *Ely* 53; Asst Lect Div Cam Univ 53-57; Lect 57-66; Fell and Chapl Em Coll Cam 54-56; Fell and Dean 56-66; Wilde Lect Ox Univ 57-60; Delegated Observer Second Vatican Coun 63-65; Prof Th Southn Univ 66-81; Hon Chapl Win Cathl Win 66-67; Can Th 67-80; Chmn Abp's Commn on Marriage 68-71; Consultant Lambeth Confs 68 and 88; Jt Ed *Journal of Th Studies* 69-74; Pope Adrian VI Prof Univ of Louvain 79; St Aug Can Cant Cathl *Cant* 80-91; Dir Angl Cen Rome 81-91; Abp Cant's Counsellor on Vatican Affairs 81-91; Visiting Prof Pontifical Gregorian Univ Rome 84-91; Preceptor Malling Abbey from 93. *26 St Swithun Street, Winchester SO23 9HU*

ROOT, John Brereton. b 41. Lon Univ BA64 Em Coll Cam BA66 MA. Ridley Hall Cam 64. **d** 68 **p** 69. C Harlesden St Mark *Lon* 68-73; C Lower Homerton St Paul 73-76; Chapl Ridley Hall Cam 76; Vice-Prin 76-79; V Alperton *Lon* from 79; AD Brent 95-03. *The Vicarage, 34 Stanley Avenue, Wembley HA0 4JB* Tel and fax (020) 8902 1729 Fax 8902 6231 E-mail stjames2000@breathemail.net

ROOTES, William Brian. b 44. St And NSM Tr Scheme 88. **d** 91. NSM Auchterarder *St And* 91-97; NSM Muthill 91-97; Dioc Sec from 98. *The Diocesan Office, 28A Balhousie Street, Perth PH1 5HJ* Tel (01738) 443173 *or* 880477 Fax 443174 *or* 880709 E-mail office@standrews.anglican.org

ROPER, David John. b 53. St Steph Ho Ox DipMin95. **d** 95 **p** 96. C Hunstanton St Mary w Ringstead Parva etc *Nor* 95-98; TV E Dereham and Scarning 98-00; R Barham w Bishopsbourne and Kingston *Cant* from 00; P-in-c Nonington w Wymynswold and Goodnestone etc from 00; AD E Bridge from 01. *The Rectory,*

The Street, Barham, Canterbury CT4 6PA Tel (01227) 831340 E-mail david.roper@clara.co.uk

ROPER, Douglas. b 72. Teesside Univ BA93. Oak Hill Th Coll BA00. **d** 00 **p** 01. C Rugby St Matt *Cov* 00-03; C Mancetter from 03. *The Rectory, Rectory Drive, Arley, Coventry CV7 8RD* Tel (01676) 540378 Mobile 07940-544024 E-mail doug.roper@tesco.net

ROPER, Michael Darwin Alston. b 66. Leeds Univ BA03. Coll of Resurr Mirfield 00. **d** 03. C Mortlake w E Sheen *S'wark* from 03. *5 Vernon Road, London SW14 8NH* Tel (020) 7978 1409 E-mail gore-lodge@yahoo.co.uk

ROPER, Neil Vincent James. d 98 **p** 99. C Port Talbot St Theodore *Llan* 98-00; C Newton Nottage 00-03; C Treorchy and Treherbert from 03. *The Vicarage, 58 Miskin Street, Treherbert, Treorchy CF42 5LR* Tel (01443) 772241

ROPER, Terence Chaus. b 35. K Coll Lon 56. St Boniface Warminster 59. **d** 60 **p** 61. C Forton *Portsm* 60-63; USA from 63; C Arlington St Alban 63-65; C Dallas St Thos 65-67; R Dallas Our Lady of Grace 67-73; R Irving Redeemer 73-76; R Dallas Transfiguration 76-99; R Philadelphia H Trin from 99. *1815 John F Kennedy Boulevard #2308, Philadelphia, PA 19103, USA* Tel (001) (215) 587 6873 *or* 567 1267

ROPER, Canon Timothy Hamilton. b 34. Qu Coll Cam BA57 MA61. Sarum Th Coll 57. **d** 59 **p** 60. C Kingsthorpe *Pet* 59-62; C Kirkby *Liv* 62-65; Chapl Rossall Sch Fleetwood 65-84; R Arthingworth, Harrington w Oxendon and E Farndon *Pet* 84-99; RD Brixworth 89-94; Can Pet Cathl 94-99; rtd 99. *47 Cromwell Crescent, Market Harborough LE16 8JN* Tel (01858) 468032

ROSAMOND, Derek William. b 49. Linc Th Coll 87. **d** 89 **p** 90. C Coventry Caludon *Cov* 89-93; Urban Regeneration Chapl Gateshead *Dur* from 93; TV Sunderland from 96. *21 Thornhill Terrace, Sunderland SR2 7JL* Tel 0191-567 2231 Fax 567 1002 E-mail derekrosamond@lineone.net

ROSCAMP, Alan Nicholas Harrison. b 12. Dur Univ LTh37 BA39 MA42. St Aid Birkenhead 32. **d** 36 **p** 37. C Latchford Ch Ch *Ches* 36-38; C Tarvin 39-44; P-in-c Bowdon 44-45; V Macclesfield St Paul 45-51; V Wadhurst *Chich* 51-63; V Tidebrook 52-63; Perm to Offic *Cant* from 63; rtd 78. *Horton Green, Ruckinge, Ashford TN26 2PF* Tel (01233) 732491

ROSCOE, David John. b 64. UEA BA87 Selw Coll Cam BA93. Aston Tr Scheme 89 Westcott Ho Cam CTM94. **d** 94 **p** 95. C Ditton St Mich *Liv* 94-98; TV Kirkby 98-99; V Wigan St Steph 99-03; Jt P-in-c Aspull and New Springs 02-03; V New Springs and Whelley from 03. *St Stephen's Vicarage, 141 Whelley, Wigan WN2 1BL* Tel (01942) 242579

ROSE, Andrew David. b 45. BA81. Oak Hill Th Coll 78. **d** 81 **p** 82. C Northwood Em *Lon* 81-86; V Iver *Ox* 86-95; R Frinton *Chelmsf* from 95. *The Rectory, 22 Queens Road, Frinton-on-Sea CO13 9BL* Tel (01255) 674664 E-mail rose@rectory-frinton.freeserve.co.uk

ROSE, Anthony James. b 47. Trin Coll Bris BD72. **d** 73 **p** 74. C Halliwell St Pet *Man* 73-76; CF 76-94; R Colchester Ch Ch w St Mary V *Chelmsf* 94-01; RD Colchester 98-01; P-in-c Boreham from 01. *The Vicarage, Church Road, Boreham, Chelmsford CM3 3EG* Tel (01245) 450607 E-mail 0075@dial.p17edc.com

ROSE, Anthony John. b 53. Birm Univ BA79 DipHE86. Trin Coll Bris 84. **d** 86 **p** 87. C The Quinton *Birm* 86-90; R Abbas and Templecombe w Horsington *B & W* 90-98; V New Thundersley *Chelmsf* from 98. *St George's Vicarage, 89 Rushbottom Lane, Benfleet SS7 4DN* Tel (01268) 792088 E-mail anthony.rose@ukonline.co.uk

ROSE, Canon Barry Ernest. b 35. Chich Th Coll 58. **d** 61 **p** 62. C Forest Gate St Edm *Chelmsf* 61-64; Antigua 64-66; Dominica 66-69; V St Mary-at-Latton *Chelmsf* 69-79; V Stansted Mountfitchet 79-88; V Halstead St Andr w H Trin and Greenstead Green 88-00; RD Halstead and Coggeshall 91-95; RD Hinckford 95-98; Hon Can Chelmsf Cathl 96-00; rtd 00; Perm to Offic *Chelmsf* from 00. *Farriers, St Mary's Road, Great Bentley, Colchester CO7 8NN* Tel (01206) 250295 E-mail jbrose@talk21.com

ROSE, Bernard Frederick. b 47. LNSM course. **d** 91 **p** 92. OLM Ipswich St Thos *St E* from 91. *84 Chesterfield Drive, Ipswich IP1 6DN* Tel (01473) 462390

ROSE, Charles. *See* ROSE, Westmoreland Charles Edward

ROSE, Christopher John. BSc. **d** 00 **p** 01. NSM Cambridge St Paul *Ely* from 00. *6 Montreal Road, Cambridge CB1 2NP* Tel (01223) 511241 *or* 213162

ROSE, Eve. b 63. Leeds Univ BA85. Qu Coll Birm 99. **d** 01 **p** 02. C Seacroft *Ripon* from 01. *51 St James Approach, Seacroft, Leeds LS14 6JJ* Tel 0113-273 0693 Mobile 07771-851725

ROSE, Miss Geraldine Susan. b 47. Trin Coll Bris DipTh76 BD78. **dss** 78 **d** 87 **p** 94. Tonbridge St Steph *Roch* 78-80; Littleover *Derby* 80-87; Par Dn 87-88; Par Dn Wombwell *Sheff* 88-94; C 94-96; rtd 96; Perm to Offic *Sheff* from 96. *5 Wheatcroft, Conisbrough, Doncaster DN12 2BL* Tel (01709) 867761

ROSE, Canon Gordon Henry. b 23. St Cath Soc Ox BA48 MA53. Wells Th Coll 49. **d** 50 **p** 51. C Bournemouth St Andr *Win* 50-55; R Bishopstoke 55-92; Hon Can Win Cathl 82-92; rtd 92; Perm to

Offic *Win* from 92. *44 Westbury Court, Hedge End, Southampton SO30 0HN* Tel (01489) 781309

ROSE, Ingrid Elizabeth. b 57. Univ of Wales (Abth) BA78 DipEd79. Trin Coll Carmarthen 84. **d** 87 **p** 01. NSM Ysbyty Cynfyn w Llantrisant and Eglwys Newydd *St D* 87-90 and 92-95. *Ystwyth Villa, Pontrhydygroes, Ystrad Meurig SY25 6DS* Tel (01974) 282398

ROSE, John Clement Wansey. b 46. New Coll Ox BA71 MA72. Ripon Hall Ox 70. **d** 72 **p** 73. C Harborne St Pet *Birm* 72-76; TV Kings Norton 76-81; V Maney 81-02; R Condover w Frodesley, Acton Burnell etc *Heref* from 02. *The Vicarage, Condover, Shrewsbury SY5 7AA* Tel (01743) 872251

ROSE, John David. b 40. Dioc OLM tr scheme 97. **d** 00 **p** 01. OLM Prescot *Liv* from 00. *18 Eccleston Gardens, St Helens WA10 3BL* Tel (01744) 736168 Mobile 07808-350859 Fax 0151-426 5121

ROSE, Canon Judith Anne. b 36. Newnham Coll Cam BA57 MA65 K Coll Lon PhD91. Ripon Coll Cuddesdon DipTh87. **d** 87 **p** 94. Par Dn Kettering All SS *Pet* 87-92; P-in-c Aldwincle w Thorpe Achurch, Pilton, Wadenhoe etc 92-97; R from 97; RD Oundle from 98; Adv in Women's Min from 01; Can Pet Cathl from 01. *The Rectory, Main Street, Aldwincle, Kettering NN14 3EP* Tel (01832) 720613 Mobile 07941-902628

ROSE, Judith Barbara. b 51. TCert52. St Alb and Ox Min Course 96. **d** 99 **p** 00. OLM Stantonbury and Willen *Ox* from 99. *16 Runnymede, Giffard Park, Milton Keynes MK14 5QL* Tel (01908) 618634 Fax as telephone

ROSE, The Ven Kathleen Judith. b 37. Lon Univ DipTh66. Lon Bible Coll BD73 St Mich Ho Ox 64. **dss** 76 **d** 87 **p** 94. Leeds St Geo *Ripon* 76-81; Bradf Cathl *Bradf* 81-85; S Gillingham *Roch* 85-87; Par Dn 87-90; RD Gillingham 88-90; Bp's Dom Chapl 90-95; Asst Dir of Ords 90-95; Hon Can Roch Cathl 93-02; Acting Adn Tonbridge 95-96; Adn Tonbridge 96-02; rtd 02. *4 Glebelands Close, Cheddar BS27 3XP* Tel (01934) 741708 Mobile 07736-616382

ROSE, Lionel Stafford Harry. b 38. MBE93. Wells Th Coll 69. **d** 71 **p** 72. C Minchinhampton *Glouc* 71-73; C Thornbury 73-75; R Ruardean 75-80; V Whiteshill 80-84; CF 84-93; Chapl HM Pris Kirkham 93-95; Chapl HM Pris Wymott 95-01; Chapl HM Pris Rye Hill 01; rtd 01; Perm to Offic *Ely* from 02. *39 West Avenue, Ramsey, Huntingdon PE26 1AY* Tel (01487) 813198

ROSE, Mrs Lynda Kathryn. b 51. Barrister-at-Law (Gray's Inn) 81 Ex Univ BA73 Ox Univ BA86. Wycliffe Hall Ox 87. **d** 87 **p** 94. C Highfield *Ox* 87-88; C Ox St Clem 89-93; Dir Anastasis Min 93-99; NSM Ambrosden w Merton and Piddington 94-99; Pres Assn Chr Writers from 99. *95 Staunton Road, Oxford OX3 7TR* Tel (01865) 768774

ROSE, Canon Paul Rosamond. b 32. Trin Hall Cam BA56 MA60. Westcott Ho Cam 57. **d** 59 **p** 60. C Wandsworth St Anne *S'wark* 59-61; C Tormohun *Ex* 61-64; S Rhodesia 64-65; Rhodesia 65-67; Min Can, Prec and Sacr Pet Cathl *Pet* 67-72; V Paddington St Jo w St Mich *Lon* 72-79; PV Westmr Abbey 74-79; Min Can and Prec Cant Cathl *Cant* 79-84; V Rothwell w Orton *Pet* 84-87; R Rothwell w Orton, Rushton w Glendon and Pipewell 87-97; Can Pet Cathl 94-97; rtd 97; Chapl Heidelberg *Eur* 98; Perm to Offic *Pet* from 97; *Lon* and *Eur* from 98. *15 Standish Court, Campaign Avenue, Peterborough PE2 9RR* Tel (01832) 720613

ROSE, Robert Alec Lewis. b 41. Man Univ BSc64. Wycliffe Hall Ox 85. **d** 87 **p** 88. C Vange *Chelmsf* 87-91; C Langdon Hills 91-94; P-in-c Bentley Common 94-00; P-in-c Kelvedon Hatch 94-00; R Bentley Common, Kelvedon Hatch and Navestock from 00. *The Rectory, 2 Church Road, Kelvedon Hatch, Brentwood CM14 5TJ* Tel (01277) 373486 Fax as telephone E-mail robdaphnerose@talk21.com

ROSE, Roy. b 11. Worc Ord Coll 63. **d** 64 **p** 64. C Hykeham *Linc* 64-68; V Hale 68-77; V Helpringham 68-77; P-in-c Scredington 73-77; rtd 77; Perm to Offic *Linc* from 77. *72 Lincoln Road, Ruskington, Sleaford NG34 9AP* Tel (01526) 832669

ROSE, Susan. *See* ROSE, Miss Geraldine Susan

ROSE, Mrs Susan Margaret. b 59. Westmr Coll of Educn BEd81. St Alb and Ox Min Course 95. **d** 98 **p** 99. C N Petherton w Northmoor Green *B & W* 98-01; P-in-c from 01. *The Dower House, North Petherton, Bridgwater TA6 6SE* Tel (01278) 662429

ROSE, Miss Susan Mary. b 36. Lon Univ DipTh70 TCert56. Dalton Ho Bris 68 Trin Coll Bris 74. **dss** 81 **d** 87 **p** 94. Brinsworth w Catcliffe *Sheff* 75-77; Scargill Ho 77-83; Netherthorpe *Sheff* 83-87; Tutor Trin Coll Bris 87-96; V Normanton *Wakef* 96-01; rtd 01; Perm to Offic *Sheff* from 01. *23 Kendal Vale, Worsborough Bridge, Barnsley S70 5NL*

ROSE, Timothy Edward Francis. b 72. Univ of Wales (Cardiff) BD93 MA95 K Coll Lon PhD98. Wycliffe Hall Ox 99. **d** 01 **p** 02. C Jesmond H Trin *Newc* from 01. *41 Springbank Road, Newcastle upon Tyne NE2 1PD* Tel 0191-261 7826 Mobile 07967-557897 E-mail tim.rose1@btinternet.com

ROSE, Westmoreland Charles Edward. b 32. St Jo Coll Nottm 85. **d** 87 **p** 88. C Fairfield *Derby* 87-90; V Linton and Castle Gresley 90-01; rtd 01; Perm to Offic *Derby* from 01. *17 Radcliffe Drive, Derby DE22 3LB* Tel (01332) 207271

ROSE-CASEMORE, Claire Pamela. b 63. St Paul's Cheltenham BA84 St Luke's Coll Ex PGCE85. Ridley Hall Cam 95. **d** 97 **p** 98. Par Dn Kingsthorpe w Northampton St Dav *Pet* 97-98; C 98-01; TV Daventry, Ashby St Ledgers, Braunston etc from 01. *The Rectory, 71 High Street, Braunston, Daventry NN11 7HS* Tel (01788) 890235 E-mail clairerc@btopenworld.com

ROSE-CASEMORE, John. b 27. Chich Th Coll. **d** 55 **p** 56. C Epsom Common Ch Ch *Guildf* 55-58; C Hednesford *Lich* 58-60; V Dawley 60-65; R Puttenham and Wanborough *Guildf* 65-72; R Frimley 72-83; RD Surrey Heath 76-81; R Ludgershall and Faberstown *Sarum* 83-86; R Tidworth, Ludgershall and Faberstown 86-92; rtd 92; Perm to Offic *Ex* from 93. *5 Culvery Close, Woodbury, Exeter EX5 1LZ* Tel (01395) 233426

ROSE-CASEMORE, Miss Penelope Jane. b 56. Bris Univ CertEd77 BEd78. Westcott Ho Cam DipRS82. **dss** 85 **d** 87 **p** 94. Waterloo St Jo w St Andr *S'wark* 85-87; Par Dn 87-88; Asst Chapl Gt Ormond Street Hosp for Sick Children Lon 88-90; Par Dn Balham St Mary and St Jo *S'wark* 90-94; C 94-96; Par Dn Upper Tooting H Trin 90-94; C 94-96; TV Clapham TM 96-01; V Clapham Ch Ch and St Jo from 02. *Christchurch Vicarage, 39 Union Grove, London SW8 2QT* Tel (020) 7622 3552 Fax as telephone

ROSEWEIR, Clifford John. b 43. Glas Univ MA64 Kingston Poly Dip Personnel Mgt 81 MIPD81. S'wark Ord Course 83. **d** 84 **p** 85. NSM Redhill H Trin *S'wark* 84-89; P-in-c Croydon St Martin 89-92; Perm to Offic 92-93; Hon C Wallington H Trin 93-94; V Croydon Ch Ch 94-97. *206 Bridle Road, Shirley, Croydon CR0 8HL* Tel (020) 8765 7629 *or* 8777 2820 Mobile 07850-480058

ROSHEUVEL, Canon Siegfried Winslow Patrick. b 39. Lon Univ BA86. Codrington Coll Barbados 64. **d** 68 **p** 68. Guyana 68-75; C Worksop Priory *S'well* 75-78; Area Sec USPG *Chelmsf* and *St Alb* 78-89; (Dio Lon) 78-92; Chapl HM Pris Wandsworth 92-93; Chapl HM Pris Rudgate 93-96; Chapl HM Pris Thorp Arch 93-96; Can Cape Coast from 94; Chapl HM Pris Brixton from 96; Hon Chapl S'wark Cathl *S'wark* from 97. *HM Prison Brixton, PO Box 369, Jebb Avenue, London SW2 5XF* Tel (020) 8674 9811 Fax 8674 6128 E-mail buntasq@aol.com

ROSIER, The Rt Revd Stanley Bruce. b 28. Univ of W Aus BSc48 Ox Univ BA52 MA56. Westcott Ho Cam 53 Melbourne Coll of Div DipRE63. **d** 54 **p** 55 **c** 67. C Ecclesall *Sheff* 54-57; Australia from 57; Can Perth 66-67; Adn Northam 67; Bp Willochra 70-87; Asst Bp 90-92; R Parkside 87-94; rtd 94. *5A Fowler's Road, Glenunga, S Australia 5064* Tel (0061) (8) 8379 5213 E-mail bfrosier@senet.com.au

ROSKELLY, James Hereward Emmanuel. b 57. BSc ACSM80. Cranmer Hall Dur 83. **d** 86 **p** 87. C Dunster, Carhampton and Withycombe w Rodhuish *B & W* 86-90; C Ealing St Mary *Lon* 90-93; Chapl R Marsden Hosp Lon and Surrey 93-95; CF 95-03; Perm to Offic Lon 95-98. *Address temp unknown*

ROSKILLY, John Noel. b 33. DRCOG60 MRCGP68 Man Univ MB, ChB58. St Deiniol's Hawarden 74. **d** 75 **p** 76. NSM Bramhall *Ches* 75-86; V Capesthorne w Siddington and Marton 86-91; Dioc Dir of Counselling 84-93; Bp's Officer for NSM 87-93; NSM Macclesfield St Paul 92-93; rtd 93; Perm to Offic *Ches* from 93. *North View, Hawkins Lane, Rainow, Macclesfield SK10 5TL* Tel (01625) 501014

ROSKROW, Neil. b 27. FBCO80. St Alb Minl Tr Scheme 82. **d** 85 **p** 86. NSM Digswell and Panshanger *St Alb* 85-90; P-in-c Gt Gaddesden 90-95; P-in-c Lt Gaddesden 92-95; rtd 96; Perm to Offic *St Alb* from 96. *Treunnard, 64 New Road, Welwyn AL6 0AN*

ROSKROW, Mrs Pamela Mary. b 25. St Alb Minl Tr Scheme. **dss** 85 **d** 87 **p** 94. Digswell and Panshanger *St Alb* 85-90; Hon Par Dn 87-90; Hon Par Dn Gt Gaddesden 90-94; Hon C 94-95; Hon Par Dn Lt Gaddesden 92-94; Hon C 94-95; Perm to Offic from 96. *Treunnard, 64 New Road, Welwyn AL6 0AN* Tel (01438) 714132

ROSOMAN, Richard John. b 59. Ripon Coll Cuddesdon 90. **d** 92 **p** 93. C Cradley *Worc* 92-96; Ind Chapl and C Coseley Ch Ch 96-00; V Malvern H Trin and St Jas from 00. *Holy Trinity Vicarage, 2 North Malvern Road, Malvern WR14 4LR* Tel (01684) 561126 E-mail louise@mrosoman.freeserve.co.uk

ROSS, Canon Anthony McPherson. b 38. OBE. Univ of Wales (Lamp) BA60 Lon Univ BD63. St Mich Coll Llan 60. **d** 61 **p** 62. C Gabalfa *Llan* 61-65; Chapl RN 65-93; Hon Chapl to The Queen 89-93; P-in-c Coln St Aldwyns, Hatherop, Quenington etc *Glouc* 93-95; V from 95; RD Fairford from 96; Hon Can Glouc Cathl from 02. *The Vicarage, Coln St Aldwyns, Cirencester GL7 5AG* Tel (01285) 750013 E-mail tonyross-cheqs@care4free.net

ROSS, Mrs Audrey Ruth. b 42. Herts Coll BA86. St Alb and Ox Min Course 99. **d** 02. NSM Leavesden All SS *St Alb* from 02. *33 Pine Grove, Bushey WD23 2DY* Tel (01923) 233667

ROSS, David Alexander (Alex). b 46. Lon Univ DipTh73. Oak Hill Th Coll 73. **d** 75 **p** 76. C Northwood Em *Lon* 75-80; R Eastrop *Win* 80-86; V Hove Bp Hannington Memorial Ch *Chich* 86-93; V Muswell Hill St Jas w St Matt *Lon* from 93. *St James's*

Vicarage, 2 St James's Lane, London N10 3DB Tel (020) 8444 2579 *or* 8883 6277 Fax 8883 4459 E-mail churchoffice@st-james.org.uk

ROSS, Preb Duncan Gilbert. b 48. Lon Univ BSc70. Westcott Ho Cam 75. **d** 78 **p** 79. C Stepney St Dunstan and All SS *Lon* 78-84; V Hackney Wick St Mary of Eton w St Aug 84-95; P-in-c Bow Common 95-03; V from 03; Preb St Paul's Cathl from 95. *St Paul's Vicarage, Leopold Street, London E3 4LA* Tel (020) 7987 4941 Fax as telephone E-mail duncan.ross5@btinternet.com

ROSS, Frederic Ian. b 34. Man Univ BSc56. Westcott Ho Cam 58 Episc Th Sem Mass DipTh61. **d** 62 **p** 63. C Oldham *Man* 62-65; Sec Th Colls Dept SCM 65-69; Teacher Man Gr Sch 69-84; V Shrewsbury H Cross *Lich* 84-02; rtd 02. *The Paddock, Plealey Road, Annscroft, Shrewsbury SY5 8AN* Tel (01743) 860327

ROSS, Canon Frederick. b 36. Qu Coll Birm. **d** 64 **p** 65. C Hessle *York* 64-68; V Marlpool *Derby* 68-73; P-in-c Norbury w Snelston 73-74; R 74-81; P-in-c Clifton 73-74; V 74-81; RD Ashbourne 78-81; V Melbourne 81-98; RD Melbourne 81-86 and 91-96; Hon Can Derby Cathl 92-98; rtd 98; Perm to Offic *Newc* from 98. *7 Meadow Grange, Berwick-upon-Tweed TD15 1NW* Tel (01289) 306041

ROSS, Henry Ernest. b 40. NW Ord Course 70. **d** 73 **p** 74. NSM Litherland St Phil *Liv* 73-75; C Newton-le-Willows 75-77; P-in-c Walton St Luke 77-79; V from 79; RD Walton 84-89. *46 Somerset Drive, Ainsdale, Southport PR8 3SN* Tel (01704) 571287

ROSS, John. b 41. Wells Th Coll 66. **d** 69 **p** 70. C Newc St Gabr *Newc* 69-71; C Prudhoe 71-75; Hon C Shotley 75-87; Hon C Whittonstall 75-87; P-in-c Wallsend St Pet 93-94. *11 Weston Avenue, Wideopen, Newcastle upon Tyne NE16 5TS*

ROSS, John Colin. b 50. Oak Hill Th Coll 84. **d** 86 **p** 87. C Stowmarket *St E* 86-89; C Wakef St Andr and St Mary *Wakef* 89-91; R Gt and Lt Whelnetham w Bradfield St George *St E* 91-94; V Newmarket All SS 94-02; V Erith St Paul *Roch* from 02. *The Vicarage, 44A Colyers Lane, Erith DA8 3NP* Tel (01322) 332809 Mobile 07904-124227 E-mail rev.ross@virgin.net

ROSS, Malcolm Hargrave. b 37. Dur Univ BSc58. Westcott Ho Cam 63. **d** 64 **p** 65. C Armley St Bart *Ripon* 64-67; USPG 67-71; Trinidad and Tobago 67-71; V New Rossington *Sheff* 71-75; Bp's Missr in E Lon 75-82; P-in-c Haggerston All SS 75-82; V Bedford Leigh *Man* 82-85; Area Sec USPG *Bris* and *Glouc* 85-90; Bp's Officer for Miss and Evang *Bris* 90-94; P-in-c Lacock w Bowden Hill 90-94; V Sherston Magna, Easton Grey, Luckington etc from 94. *The Vicarage, Green Lane, Sherston, Malmesbury SN16 0NP* Tel (01666) 840209 E-mail malcolmross@rossteam.freeserve.co.uk

ROSS, Oliver Charles Milligan. b 58. Lon Univ BA80 St Edm Ho Cam BA85. Ridley Hall Cam 84. **d** 87 **p** 88. C Preston St Cuth *Blackb* 87-90; C Paddington St Jo w St Mich *Lon* 90-95; V Hounslow H Trin w St Paul from 95; P-in-c Isleworth St Mary 01-02. *The Vicarage, 66 Lampton Road, Hounslow TW3 4JD* Tel (020) 8570 3892 *or* 8570 3066 Fax 8570 8886 E-mail ocmross@aol.com

ROSS, Ms Rachel Anne. b 64. York Univ BSc85 SS Coll Cam PGCE86 Sheff Univ MA97 Coll of Ripon & York St Jo MA00. N Ord Course 97. **d** 00 **p** 01. C Pendleton *Man* from 00; P-in-c Salford St Ignatius and Stowell Memorial from 03; P-in-c Salford Ordsall St Clem from 03. *The Rectory, Parsonage Close, Salford M5 3GS* Tel 0161-872 0800 Mobile 07884-371688 E-mail 106277.35@compuserve.com

ROSS, Canon Raymond John. b 28. Trin Coll Cam BA52 MA57. St Steph Ho Ox 52. **d** 54 **p** 55. C Clifton All SS *Bris* 54-58; C Solihull *Birm* 58-66; C-in-c Hobs Moat CD 66-67; V Hobs Moat 67-72; R Newbold w Dunston *Derby* 72-95; RD Chesterfield 78-91; Hon Can Derby Cathl 86-95; rtd 96; Perm to Offic *Derby* from 96. *Threeways, Bridge Hill, Belper DE56 2BY* Tel (01773) 825876

ROSS, Vernon. b 57. Portsm Poly BSc79 RGN86. Trin Coll Bris DipHE91. **d** 91 **p** 92. C Fareham St Jo *Portsm* 91-94; P-in-c Witheridge, Thelbridge, Creacombe, Meshaw etc *Ex* 94-00; TR Barnstaple from 00. *The Rectory, 4 Northfield Lane, Barnstaple EX31 1QB* Tel (01271) 345958

ROSS-McCABE, Mrs Philippa Mary Seton. b 63. Natal Univ BA83 HDipEd86 Bris Univ BA01. Trin Coll Bris 99. **d** 01 **p** 02. C Burpham *Guildf* from 01. *8 Selbourne Road, Burpham, Guildford GU4 7JP* Tel (01483) 456602 Fax as telephone E-mail p.ross-mccabe@ntlworld.com

ROSS, Dean of. *See* PETERS, The Very Revd Christopher Lind

✠**ROSSDALE, The Rt Revd David Douglas James.** b 53. Westmr Coll Ox DipApTh90 MA91 Surrey Univ MSc01. K Coll Lon 72 Chich Th Coll 80. **d** 81 **p** 82 **c** 00. C Upminster *Chelmsf* 81-86; V Moulsham St Luke 86-90; V Cookham *Ox* 90-00; RD Maidenhead 94-00; Hon Can Ch Ch *Ox* 00-00; Suff Bp Grimsby *Linc* from 00; Can and Preb Linc Cathl from 00. *Bishop's House, Church Lane, Irby, Grimsby DN37 7JR* Tel (01472) 371715 Fax 371716 E-mail rossdale@btinternet.com

ROSSETER, Miss Susan Mary. b 46. Man Univ BA67 Edin Univ DASS71. St Jo Coll Nottm LTh84. **d** 87 **p** 94. Par Dn Bromley Common St Aug *Roch* 87-88; C Pudsey St Lawr and St Paul *Bradf*

88-95; C Haughton le Skerne *Dur* 95-00; C Wilnecote *Lich* from 00. *5 Avill, Hockley, Tamworth B77 5QE* Tel (01827) 251816

ROSSITER, Donald William Frank. b 30. **d** 80 **p** 81. NSM Abergavenny St Mary w Llanwenarth Citra *Mon* 80-96; NSM Govilon w Llanfoist w Llanelen from 92. *10 Meadow Lane, Abergavenny NP7 7AY* Tel (01873) 855648

ROSSITER, Gillian Alice. b 56. SRN75 RSCN75 Chester Coll of HE Dip Counselling 96. N Ord Course 98. **d** 01 **p** 02. NSM Neston *Ches* 01-03; C from 03. *Ivy Cottage, 10 Burton Road, Little Neston, South Wirral CH64 9RE* Tel 0151-336 7369

ROSSITER, Raymond Stephen David. b 22. MBE99. St Deiniol's Hawarden 75. **d** 76 **p** 77. NSM Sale St Anne *Ches* 76-90; Perm to Offic from 90; rtd 91. *75 Temple Road, Sale M33 2FQ* Tel 0161-962 3240

ROSSLYN SMITH, Mrs Katherine Dorothy Nevill. b 40. STETS 97. **d** 00 **p** 01. NSM Tisbury *Sarum* 00-01; NSM Nadder Valley 01-03; NSM Chalke Valley from 03. *Swallowdale, The Quarry, Tisbury, Salisbury SP3 6HR* Tel (01747) 871605

ROSTILL, Brian. b 50. K Alfred's Coll Win BTh00. Cranmer Hall Dur 01. **d** 03. C Knights Enham *Win* from 03. *2 Madrid Road, Andover SO10 1JR* Tel (01264) 324269
E-mail rostill@tiscali.co.uk

ROSTRON, Derek. b 34. St Mich Coll Llan 65. **d** 67 **p** 68. C Morecambe St Barn *Blackb* 67-70; C Ribbleton 70-72; V Chorley All SS 72-79; C Woodchurch *Ches* 79-80; V Audlem from 80; RD Nantwich 87-97. *St James's Vicarage, 66 Heathfield Road, Audlem, Crewe CW3 0HG* Tel (01270) 811543 Fax as telephone

ROTHERHAM, Eric. b 36. Clifton Th Coll 63. **d** 67 **p** 68. C Gt Crosby St Luke *Liv* 67-69; C Sutton 69-71; V Warrington St Paul 72-79; Lic to Offic 79-80; Perm to Offic *Ches* and *Liv* from 80; rtd 01. *7 Paul Street, Warrington WA2 7LE* Tel (01925) 633048

ROTHERY, Cecil Ivor. b 24. St Jo Coll Winnipeg 50. **d** 53 **p** 54. Canada 53-72; C Gainsborough All SS *Linc* 72-74; R Fleet 74-79; P-in-c Wrawby 79-80; C Glanford Bridge 79-80; rtd 80; Perm to Offic *S'well* 80-83 and *Sheff* 83-93. *129 Queen Street, Retford DN22 7DA* Tel (01777) 701551

ROTHERY, Jean. b 44. **d** 98 **p** 99. NSM Purley *Ox* from 98. *Oak Lea, Tidmarsh Road, Tidmarsh, Reading RG8 8ER* Tel 0118-984 3625

ROTHERY, Robert Frederick (Fred). b 34. Lon Coll of Div 67. **d** 69 **p** 70. C Burscough Bridge *Liv* 69-72; C Chipping Campden *Glouc* 72-75; P-in-c Didmarton w Oldbury-on-the-Hill and Sopworth 75-77; R Boxwell, Leighterton, Didmarton, Oldbury etc 77-83; R Stow on the Wold 83-00; RD Stow 90-99; rtd 00. *12 Phillips Road, Marnhull, Sturminster Newton DT10 1LF* Tel (01258) 820668

ROTHWELL, Bryan. b 60. St Edm Hall Ox BA81 MA85. Trin Coll Bris. **d** 85 **p** 86. C Carl St Jo *Carl* 85-88; C Ulverston St Mary w H Trin 88-90; P-in-c Preston St Mary *Blackb* 90-96; P-in-c St John's in the Vale w Wythburn *Carl* 96-99; R St John's-in-the-Vale, Threlkeld and Wythburn from 99; Warden Dioc Youth Cen from 96. *The Rectory, Threlkeld, Keswick CA12 4RT* Tel (017687) 79714 E-mail bryan.rothwell@btinternet.com

ROTHWELL, Edwin John. b 53. Lanc Univ BA74 PhD79. Sarum & Wells Th Coll 88. **d** 90 **p** 91. C Malvern Link w Cowleigh *Worc* 90-94; R Bowbrook N 94-00; Asst Chapl Swindon and Marlborough NHS Trust 00-03; Chapl E Somerset NHS Trust from 03. *Chaplain's Office, Yeovil District Hospital, Higher Kingston, Yeovil BA21 4AT* Tel (01935) 475122

ROTHWELL, Canon Eric. b 12. Man Univ BA35. Lich Th Coll 35. **d** 37 **p** 38. C Padiham *Blackb* 37-41; P-in-c Burnley St Cath 41-42; C Blackpool St Mary 42-47; V Warton St Oswald 47-63; RD Tunstall 55-63; Hon Can Blackb Cathl 61-77; R Chorley St Laur 63-77; rtd 77; Perm to Offic *Carl* from 77 and *Blackb* from 79. *1 Town End Meadow, Cartmel, Grange-over-Sands LA11 6QG* Tel (01539) 536574

ROTHWELL, Harold. b 34. AKC58. K Coll Lon St Boniface Warminster. **d** 59 **p** 60. C Old Brumby *Linc* 59-62; P-in-c Sheff St Steph w St Phil and St Ann *Sheff* 62-64; V Caistor w Holton le Moor and Clixby *Linc* 67-77; Chapl Caistor Hosp 67-77; Org Sec CECS *Ex* and *B & W* 77-81; P-in-c Deeping Fen *Linc* 78-81; C Boston 86-88; C Spilsby w Hundleby 88-91; C Bracebridge Heath 91-94; rtd 94; Perm to Offic *Linc* from 94. *47 Ridgeway, Nettleham, Lincoln LN2 2TL* Tel (01522) 751610

ROTHWELL, Michael John Hereward. *See* HEREWARD-ROTHWELL, Canon Michael John

ROTHWELL, Steven. b 68. Roehampton Inst BA99 Cam Univ MA02. Westcott Ho Cam 00. **d** 02 **p** 03. C Chesterton Gd Shep *Ely* from 02. *19 Hurrell Road, Cambridge CB4 3RQ* Tel (01223) 464348 E-mail srothwell44@hotmail.com

ROTHWELL-JACKSON, Christopher Patrick. b 32. St Cath Soc Ox BA58 MA61 Bris Univ PGCE66. St Steph Ho Ox 55. **d** 59 **p** 60. C E Clevedon All SS *B & W* 59-62; C Midsomer Norton 62-65; Asst Teacher St Pet Primary Sch Portishead 66-68; Clevedon Junior Sch 68-72; Dep Hd Clevedon All SS Primary Sch 72-75; Lic to Offic 69-75; Hd Master Bp Pursglove Sch Tideswell 75-90; Lic to Offic *Derby* 76-95; rtd 90; Perm to Offic *Ex* from 95. *Rosedale, Hookway, Crediton EX17 3PU* Tel (01363) 772039

ROUCH, David Vaughan. b 36. Oak Hill Th Coll 67. **d** 69 **p** 70. C Denton Holme *Carl* 69-74; V Litherland St Jo and St Jas *Liv* 74-95; V Pemberton St Mark Newtown from 95; P-in-c Wigan St Barn Marsh Green from 03. *The Vicarage, Victoria Street, Wigan WN5 9BN* Tel (01942) 206954 Fax 742869
E-mail drouchatjennyr@cableinet.co.uk

ROUCH, Peter Bradford. b 66. Ox Univ MA87 ACIB89. Westcott Ho Cam BA99. **d** 99 **p** 00. C E Dulwich St Jo *S'wark* 99-02; Jun Research Fell St Steph Ho Ox from 02. *St Stephen's House, 16 Marston Street, Oxford OX4 1JX* Tel (01865) 791659 Mobile 07905-504170 E-mail peterrouch@barclays.net

ROULSTON, Joseph Ernest. b 52. MIBiol77 FRSC86 MRCPath93 FLS94 BNC Ox BA74 MA78 Lon Univ PhD81. Edin Dioc NSM Course 83. **d** 86 **p** 87. C Edin St Hilda *Edin* 86-88; C Edin St Fillan 86-88; NSM Edin St Mich and All SS 88-97; Dioc Chapl Gen from 96. *16 Summerside Street, Edinburgh EH6 4NU* Tel 0131-554 6382 *or* tel and fax 536 2703 Mobile 07703-200944 E-mail j.e.roulston@ed.ac.uk

ROUND, Keith Leonard. b 49. Sarum & Wells Th Coll 88. **d** 90 **p** 91. C Meir *Lich* 90-95; V Burslem St Werburgh from 95. *The Presbytery, Haywood Road, Stoke-on-Trent ST6 7AH* Tel (01782) 837582

ROUND, Malcolm John Harrison. b 56. Lon Univ BSc77 BA81. Oak Hill Th Coll. **d** 81 **p** 82. C Guildf St Sav w Stoke-next-Guildford *Guildf* 81-85; C Hawkwell *Chelmsf* 85-88; R Balerno *Edin* from 88. *53 Marchbank Drive, Balerno EH14 7ER* Tel 0131-449 4127

ROUNDHILL, Andrew (John). b 65. CCC Cam BA87. Ripon Coll Cuddesdon BTh93. **d** 93 **p** 94. C Lancaster Ch Ch w St Jo and St Anne *Blackb* 93-97; Chapl Loretto Sch Musselburgh 97-02; Chapl Hong Kong Cathl from 02. *D2 On Lee, 2 Mount Davis Road, Pok Fu Lam, Hong Kong* Tel (00852) 2817 8774 *or* 2523 4157 E-mail roundhill@netvigator.com

ROUNDS, Canon Philip Rigby. b 21. Wells Th Coll 49. **d** 52 **p** 53. C Weymouth H Trin *Sarum* 52-56; V Laverstock 56-67; R Wyke Regis 67-89; Can and Preb Sarum Cathl 77-89; rtd 89; Perm to Offic *Sarum* 91-00. *The College of St Barnabas, Blackberry Lane, Lingfield RH7 6NJ* Tel (01342) 871584

ROUNDTREE, James Clabern (Clay). b 75. Oklahoma Univ BFA98 York Univ MA00. St Steph Ho Ox BA02. **d** 03. C Yarm *York* from 03. *8 Merlay Close, Yarm TS15 9TE* Tel (01642) 787322 E-mail clayroundtree@hotmail.com

ROUNDTREE, Samuel William. b 19. TCD BA42 MA54. CITC 43. **d** 43 **p** 44. C Waterford Ch Ch *C & O* 44-47; I Tallow w Kilwatermoy 47-51; I Kiltegan w Stratford (and Rathvilly from 60) 51-62; Treas Leighlin Cathl 62-78; Preb Ossory Cathl 62-82; I Dunleckney 62-82; Chan Ossory and Leighlin Cathls 78-80; Prec 80-82; I New w Old Ross, Whitechurch, Fethard etc 82-88; Adn Ferns 86-88; rtd 88. *Killincarrig House, Killincarrig Road, Greystones, Co Wicklow, Irish Republic* Tel (00353) (1) 287 4428

ROUNTREE, Canon Richard Benjamin. b 52. NUI BA73. CITC 76. **d** 76 **p** 77. C Orangefield *D & D* 76-80; C Dublin Zion Ch *D & G* 80-83; I Dalkey St Patr 83-97; Dioc Dir Decade of Evang 90-96; Can Ch Ch Cathl Dublin from 92; I Powerscourt w Kilbride from 97. *Powerscourt Rectory, Enniskerry, Bray, Co Wicklow, Irish Republic* Tel (00353) (1) 286 3534 Fax as telephone E-mail rountree@indigo.ie *or* powerscourt@glendalough.anglican.org

ROUSE, Graham. b 58. Sheff City Coll of Educn CertEd79 Leic Univ DipEd84. Cranmer Hall Dur 90. **d** 92 **p** 93. C Longridge *Blackb* 92-96; P-in-c Fairhaven 96-97; V from 97. *Fairhaven Vicarage, 83 Clifton Drive, Lytham St Annes FY8 1BZ* Tel (01253) 734562 E-mail fairhavenstpaul@btopenworld.com

ROUTH, Canon Eileen Rosemary. b 41. Cant Sch of Min 82. **dss** 85 **d** 87 **p** 94. Folkestone St Sav *Cant* 85-90; Par Dn 87-90; Par Dn Woodnesborough w Worth and Staple 90-91; Dn-in-c 91-94; V 94-96; V Maidstone St Martin 96-99; Hon Can Cant Cathl 99; rtd 99; Perm to Offic *Cant* from 00. *31 Tile Kiln Hill, Blean, Canterbury CT2 9EE* Tel (01227) 464052

ROUTH, William John. b 60. Magd Coll Ox BA81 MA92. Ripon Coll Cuddesdon 93. **d** 95 **p** 96. C Longton *Blackb* 95-99; V Sutton Coldfield St Chad *Birm* from 99. *St Chad's Vicarage, 41 Hollyfield Road, Sutton Coldfield B75 7SN* Tel 0121-329 2995 E-mail john.routh@btinternet.com

ROW, Mrs Pamela Anne. b 54. Open Univ BA86 MA92 Homerton Coll Cam BEd75. N Ord Course 94. **d** 96 **p** 97. NSM Neston *Ches* 96-01; Chapl Heref Cathl Sch from 02. *4 Harley Court, Hereford HR1 2NA* Tel (01432) 363508 *or* 363509

ROWBERRY, Christopher Michael. b 58. Plymouth Univ CQSW85. Qu Coll Birm 94. **d** 96 **p** 97. C Lytchett Minster *Sarum* 96-00; TV Totton *Win* from 00. *Eling Vicarage, Eling Hill, Totton, Southampton SO40 9HF* Tel (023) 8086 6426 E-mail chrisrow@btinternet.com

ROWBERRY, Michael James. b 46. Sussex Univ BA74. Edin Th Coll 85. **d** 87 **p** 92. C Wolvercote w Summertown *Ox* 87-88; NSM Cov St Fran N Radford *Cov* 91-95; Perm to Offic 95-98; C Doncaster Intake *Sheff* 98-00; C Doncaster St Jas 98-00; C-in-c St Edm Anchorage Lane CD from 00. *St Edmund's House, Anchorage Lane, Spotbrough, Doncaster DN5 8DT* Tel (01302) 781986

ROWDON, John Michael Hooker. b 27. Witwatersrand Univ BA52. Ridley Hall Cam 52. **d** 54 **p** 55. C Broadwater St Mary *Chich* 54-56; C Streatham Immanuel w St Anselm *S'wark* 56-59; Nigeria 60-62; C All Hallows Lon Wall *Lon* 62-66; Warden Toc H Tower Hill 64-66; Australia from 66; rtd 92. *Box 116, Bridgetown, W Australia 6255*

ROWE, Andrew Gidleigh Bruce. b 37. AKC62. St Boniface Warminster. **d** 63 **p** 64. C Midsomer Norton *B & W* 63-68; Chapl RN 68-84; Chapl Heathfield Sch Ascot 84-86; Hon C Winkfield and Cranbourne *Ox* 84-86; TV Wellington and Distr *B & W* 86-95; R Chewton Mendip w Ston Easton, Litton etc 95-96; Perm to Offic *Ex* 96-99; rtd 99. *Merrymeet, Posbury, Crediton EX17 3QF* Tel (01363) 772262

ROWE, Andrew Robert. b 64. Westmr Coll Ox BA85 PGCE86. Ridley Hall Cam CTM95. **d** 95 **p** 96. C Broadheath *Ches* 95-99; V E Ardsley *Wakef* from 99. *The Vicarage, Church Lane, East Ardsley, Wakefield WF3 2LJ* Tel (01924) 822184 E-mail andyr@rowe6423.freeserve.co.uk

ROWE, Canon Antony Silvester Buckingham. b 26. St Jo Coll Dur 53. **d** 55 **p** 56. C Holbrooks *Cov* 55-59; V Cov St Mary 59-83; RD Cov S 72-82; Hon Can Cov Cathl 76-92; R Harbury and Ladbroke 83-92; rtd 92; Perm to Offic *Cov* and *Glouc* from 92. *3 Cotswold Edge, Mickleton, Chipping Campden GL55 6TR* Tel (01386) 438622

ROWE, Arthur John. b 35. TCD 73. **d** 76 **p** 77. C Bangor Abbey *D & D* 76-78; I Kilbarron *D & R* 78-79; I Kilbarron w Rossnowlagh 79-82; P-in-c Hockering *Nor* 82-85; P-in-c Honingham w E Tuddenham 82-85; P-in-c N Tuddenham 82-85; R Hockwold w Wilton *Ely* 85-95; R Weeting 85-95; rtd 95. *Orchard Villa, Back Lane, Castle Acre, King's Lynn PE32 2AR*

ROWE, Canon Bryan. b 50. Carl Dioc Tr Course 87. **d** 90 **p** 91. C Kells *Carl* 90-93; P-in-c Aspatria w Hayton 93-02; R Workington St Mich from 02; RD Solway from 99; Hon Can Carl Cathl from 99. *St Michael's Rectory, Dora Crescent, Workington CA14 2EZ* Tel (01900) 602311

ROWE, Mrs Christine Elizabeth. b 55. Southn Univ BEd77. Ripon Coll Cuddesdon 83. **dss** 86 **d** 87 **p** 94. Denham *Ox* 86-87; Par Dn 87-89; Par Dn Aylesbury 89; Par Dn Aylesbury w Bierton and Hulcott 89-93; NSM Caversham St Jo 93-99; Chapl HM Pris Reading 93-98; Chapl Mother's Union 95-00; Chapl R Berks and Battle Hosps NHS Trust 96-00; P-in-c Vancouver St Thos Canada 00-01; R from 01. *782 East King's Road, North Vancouver BC, Canada, V7K 1E3* Tel (001) (604) 987 6307 *or* 434 6111 Fax 434 9592 E-mail rowe782@aol.com

ROWE, David Brian. b 58. Trin Coll Bris DipHE82. **d** 83 **p** 84. C Radipole and Melcombe Regis *Sarum* 83-86; C Cranham Park *Chelmsf* 86-88; Assoc Min and Par Missr Eastrop *Win* 88-92; P-in-c Arborfield w Barkham *Ox* 92-97; Asst Dioc Adv in Evang *S'well* 97-02; P-in-c Wilford from 00. *The Rectory, Main Road, Nottingham NG11 7AJ* Tel 0115-981 5661 E-mail wilfordchurch@aol.com

ROWE, Geoffrey Lewis. b 44. Univ of Wales (Lamp) BA. Ripon Coll Cuddesdon 80. **d** 82 **p** 83. C Milber *Ex* 82-84; TV Withycombe Raleigh 84-90; R Clyst St Mary, Clyst St George etc from 90. *The Rectory, 40 Clyst Valley Road, Clyst St Mary, Exeter EX5 1DD* Tel (01392) 874363

ROWE, Miss Joan Patricia. b 54. Trin Coll Bris BA87. **d** 88 **p** 94. C Radstock w Writhlington *B & W* 88-92; C Nailsea H Trin 92-96; P-in-c Shapwick w Ashcott and Burtle from 96. *The Vicarage, Vicarage Lane, Shapwick, Bridgwater TA7 9LR* Tel (01458) 210260 E-mail joanrowe@ic24.net

ROWE, John Goring. b 23. McGill Univ Montreal BA48 BD51 Selw Coll Cam BA53. Montreal Dioc Th Coll LTh51. **d** 51 **p** 52. Canada 51; C Trumpington *Ely* 51-53; Hon C Bow Common *Lon* 53-84; rtd 88. *10 Cordelia Street, London E14 6DZ* Tel (020) 7515 4681

ROWE, Peter Anthony. b 46. Univ Coll Dur BA68 Birkb Coll Lon MA91 Lon Univ DipRS94 Barrister 78 Solicitor 85 Kent Univ DipTh98. SEITE 95. **d** 98 **p** 99. NSM Ashford *Cant* from 98. *1 Woodside Villas, Ashford Road, Hamstreet, Ashford TN26 2DT* Tel (01233) 732172 Fax (01227) 450498 E-mail peterrowe@girlings.com

ROWE, Peter Farquharson. b 19. Selw Coll Cam BA41. Westcott Ho Cam 41. **d** 43 **p** 44. C Putney St Mary *S'wark* 43-47; C Lewisham St Jo Southend 47-54; V Mitcham Ascension 54-65; V Eltham Park St Luke 65-77; V Ravensthorpe w E Haddon and Holdenby *Pet* 77-84; rtd 84; Perm to Offic *Ex* 84-89; *Sarum* 89-92; *Win* from 92. *28 Gordon Avenue, Winchester SO23 0QQ* Tel (01962) 869806

ROWE, Philip William. b 57. Southn Univ BSc78. Lambeth STh86 Trin Coll Bris 82. **d** 85 **p** 86. C Tooting Graveney St Nic *S'wark* 85-89; V Abbots Leigh w Leigh Woods *Bris* 89-96; V Almondsbury 96-98; P-in-c Littleton on Severn w Elberton 96-98; V Almondsbury and Olveston from 98; AD Bris W from 00. *The Vicarage, Sundays Hill, Almondsbury, Bristol BS32 4DS* Tel (01454) 613223 E-mail rowe@sundays.freeserve.co.uk

ROWE, Richard Nigel. b 41. St Pet Coll Saltley DipEd64. St Steph Ho Ox 67. **d** 70 **p** 71. C Acton Green St Pet *Lon* 70-74; C Leigh St Clem *Chelmsf* 74-80; V Leytonstone St Marg w St Columba 80-89; RD Waltham Forest 86-89; V Thaxted

ROWE, Shiela. *See* JOHNSON, Mrs Shiela

ROWE, Canon Stanley Hamilton. b 18. St Pet Hall Ox BA48 MA52. ALCD50. **d** 50 **p** 51. C Leyton St Paul *Chelmsf* 50-52; CMS Nigeria 52-65; P-in-c Becontree St Cedd *Chelmsf* 65-67; Hd of RE Jo Hampden Sch High Wycombe 67-83; Perm to Offic *Ox* 67-84 and from 86; rtd 83; Hon P-in-c Aston Rowant w Crowell *Ox* 84-86; Hon Can Oke-Osun from 94. *37 Greenwood Avenue, Chinnor OX39 4HW* Tel (01844) 351278 E-mail shrowe@fish.co.uk

ROWE, Stephen Mark Buckingham. b 59. SS Mark & Jo Coll Plymouth BA81. Ripon Coll Cuddesdon 83. **d** 86 **p** 87. C Denham *Ox* 86-89; C Aylesbury w Bierton and Hulcott 89-90; TV 90-93; V Caversham St Jo 93-00; Canada from 00; Sen Chapl Miss to Seafarers 00-01; P-in-c Surrey Epiphany 01-02; R from 02. *782 East King's Road, North Vancouver BC, Canada, V7K 1E3* Tel (001) (604) 987 6307 *or* tel and fax 588 4511 E-mail rowe782@aol.com

ROWE, Mrs Vanda Sheila. b 63. STETS 95. **d** 98 **p** 99. C Marlborough *Sarum* 98-01; TV Pewsey and Swanborough from 01. *The Vicarage, Church Road, Woodborough, Pewsey SN9 5PH* Tel (01672) 851746

ROWELL, Canon Alan. b 50. Lon Univ BSc71 AKC71. Trin Coll Bris DipTh75. **d** 75 **p** 76. C W Hampstead St Cuth *Lon* 75-78; C Camborne *Truro* 78-81; V Pendeen w Morvah from 81; Hon Can Truro Cathl from 03. *The Vicarage, Pendeen, Penzance TR19 7SE* Tel (01736) 788777

✠**ROWELL, The Rt Revd Douglas Geoffrey.** b 43. CCC Cam BA64 MA68 PhD68 Keble Coll Ox DD97. Cuddesdon Coll. **d** 68 **p** 69 **c** 94. Asst Chapl New Coll Ox 68-72; Chapl Keble Coll Ox 72-94; Wiccamical Preb Chich Cathl *Chich* from 81; Suff Bp Basingstoke *Win* 94-01; Bp Eur from 01. *Bishop's Lodge, Church Road, Worth, Crawley RH10 7RT, or, 14 Tufton Street, London SW1P 3QZ* Tel (01293) 883051 *or* (020) 7898 1155 Fax (01293) 884479 *or* (020) 7898 1166 E-mail bishop@eurobish.clara.co.uk

ROWELL, Frank. b 22. Chich Th Coll 50. **d** 52 **p** 53. C Ipswich All SS *St E* 52-58; R Earl Stonham 56-65; R Otley 65-83; R Clopton 65-83; R Clopton w Otley, Swilland and Ashbocking 83-88; rtd 88; Perm to Offic *St E* from 90. *37 Riverview, Melton, Woodbridge IP12 1QU* Tel (01394) 385449

ROWELL, Mrs Gillian Margaret. b 56. Lon Bible Coll BA96. St Alb and Ox Min Course DipMin99. **d** 99 **p** 00. NSM The Lee *Ox* from 99; NSM Hawridge w Cholesbury and St Leonard from 99. *81 Eskdale Avenue, Chesham HP5 3AY* Tel (01494) 772833

ROWELL, William Kevin. b 51. Reading Univ BSc71. Linc Th Coll 78. **d** 80 **p** 81. C Cannock *Lich* 80-83; Ind Chapl 83-86; C Ketley and Oakengates 83-86; R Norton in the Moors 86-93; RD Leek 92-93; P-in-c Minsterley and Habberley *Heref* 93-01; RD Pontesbury 99-01; Miss Adv USPG *Heref, Worc* and *Glouc* from 01; NSM Wenlock *Heref* from 02. *66 Severn Way, Cressage, Shrewsbury SY5 6DS* Tel (01952) 510195 *or* 510276 E-mail billrowell_uspg@compuserve.com *or* bilkro@btinternet.com

ROWETT, David Peter. b 55. Univ Coll Dur BA76. Ripon Coll Cuddesdon 82. **d** 84 **p** 85. C Yeovil *B & W* 84-88; C Yeovil St Mich 88-89; V Fairfield St Matt *Linc* from 89. *St Matthew's Vicarage, 8 Thirlmere Avenue, Grimsby DN33 3EA* Tel (01472) 821183 E-mail d.rowett@virgin.net

ROWETT, Mrs Margaret Pettigrew Coupar. b 33. Sarum & Wells Th Coll 84. **dss** 86 **d** 87 **p** 95. Widley w Wymering *Portsm* 86-88; C 87-88; Par Dn Plympton St Mary *Ex* 88-91; rtd 91; NSM St Mewan *Truro* from 94; Perm to Offic from 99. *Epiphany Cottage, 9 Socotra Drive, Trewoon, St Austell PL25 5SQ* Tel (01726) 71450

ROWLAND, Andrew John William. b 60. STETS 98. **d** 01 **p** 02. NSM Verwood *Sarum* 01-02; C from 02. *46 Crane Drive, Verwood BH31 6QB* Tel (01202) 825505 E-mail ar@fish.co.uk

ROWLAND, Barry William. b 59. St Jo Coll Nottm Dip Th & Min 95 BA95. **d** 95 **p** 96. C Welling *Roch* 95-98; C Green Street Green and Pratts Bottom 98-02; V New Beckenham St Paul from 02. *St Paul's Vicarage, Brackley Road, Beckenham BR3 1RB* Tel (020) 8650 3400 Mobile 07808-239668 E-mail bazzavic@hotmail.com

ROWLAND, Prof Christopher Charles. b 47. Ch Coll Cam BA69 MA73 PhD75. Ridley Hall Cam 72. **d** 75 **p** 76. Lect RS Newc Univ *Newc* 74-79; Hon C Benwell St Jas 75-78; Hon C Gosforth All SS 78-79; Dean Jes Coll Cam 79-91; Asst Lect Div Cam Univ 83-85; Lect Div 85-91; Lic to Offic *Ely* 79-91; Prof of Exegesis of H Scripture Ox Univ from 91; Fell Qu Coll Ox from 91. *Queen's College, Oxford OX1 4AW* Tel (01865) 279120

ROWLAND, Ms Dawn Jeannette. b 38. RSCN61 RGN63. S'wark Ord Course 81. **dss** 84 **d** 87 **p** 94. Par Dn Croydon H Sav S'wark 84-89; NSM Riddlesdown from 89. *9 Hartley Hill, Purley CR8 4EP* Tel (020) 8660 6270

ROWLAND, Derek John. b 47. St Jo Coll Nottm 84. **d** 86 **p** 87. C Porchester *S'well* 86-89; V Fairfield *Liv* 89-96; V Buckfastleigh w Dean Prior *Ex* from 96. *The Vicarage, Glebelands, Buckfastleigh TQ11 0BH* Tel (01364) 644228

ROWLAND, Eric Edward James. b 35. Leeds Univ BA62. Coll of Resurr Mirfield 61. **d** 63 **p** 64. C S Kirkby *Wakef* 63-65; C Headingley *Ripon* 65-70; V Osmondthorpe St Phil 70-79; R Sandy *St Alb* 79-00; RD Biggleswade 85-94; rtd 00; Perm to Offic *Ely* from 01. *3 Tower Road, Ely CB7 4HW* Tel (01353) 664359

ROWLAND, Geoffrey Watson. b 17. **d** 55 **p** 56. BCMS 55-65; Burma 55-65; C Blackheath Park St Mich *S'wark* 65-71; V W Bromwich St Paul *Lich* 71-76; Chapl Community Relns *Lon* 77-83; C Southall Green St Jo 83; rtd 83; Perm to Offic *Lon* from 83. *3 Amber Court, Longford Avenue, Southall UB1 3QR* Tel (020) 8574 3442

ROWLAND, Jennifer Norah. b 48. Worc Coll of Educn CertEd70 Open Univ BA83 AIB. WMMTC 96. **d** 99 **p** 00. C Stratford-upon-Avon, Luddington etc *Cov* from 99; P-in-c Ditton Priors w Neenton, Burwarton etc *Heref* from 03. *The Vicarage, Ditton Priors, Bridgnorth WV16 6SQ* Tel (01746) 34636
E-mail jenny@rowland4.demon.co.uk

ROWLAND, Robert William. b 51. Birm Univ BA72 Univ of Wales (Cardiff) DPS73. St Mich Coll Llan 72. **d** 74 **p** 75. C Connah's Quay *St As* 74; C Shotton 74-76; C Llanrhos 76-81; V Dyserth and Trelawnyd and Cwm from 81; RD St As from 94. *The Vicarage, Dyserth, Rhyl LL18 6DB* Tel (01745) 570750

ROWLAND, Stanley George. b 48. Middx Univ BA86. NTMTC 95. **d** 98 **p** 99. NSM Enfield St Geo *Lon* 98-02; C Grantham *Linc* 02-03; V Grantham, Earlesfield from 03. *The Vicarage, The Grove, Earlesfield, Grantham NG31 7PU* Tel (01476) 571270
E-mail sgrowland@btopenworld.com

ROWLAND JONES, Sarah Caroline. b 59. LVO93 OBE97. Newnham Coll Cam BA80 MA84 Nottm Univ BTh98. St Jo Coll Nottm 96. **d** 99 **p** 00. C Wrexham *St As* 99-02; S Africa from 02. *Bishopshaven, PO Box 420, Malmesbury, 7299 South Africa*
E-mail sarahrj@surfaid.org

ROWLANDS, The Very Revd Daniel John. b 25. Pemb Coll Cam BA49 MA54. Bps' Coll Cheshunt 49. **d** 51 **p** 52. C Woodford St Mary *Chelmsf* 51-53; Miss to Seamen 53-75; Asst Chapl Rotterdam 53-55; Port Chapl Dar-es-Salaam 55-61; Chapl The Tees 62-69; V Wilton *York* 63-69; Asst Gen Sec Miss to Seamen Paternoster R 69-75; R Woodbridge St Mary *St E* 75-82; Dean Gib *Eur* 82-86; Perm to Offic *St D* 86-88; P-in-c Llangrannog and Llandysiliogogo 88-92; RD Glyn Aeron 89-95; rtd 95. *Glyn Coed, Clos Dolwen, Aberporth, Cardigan SA43 2DE* Tel (01239) 811042 Fax as telephone

ROWLANDS, Canon Emyr Wyn. b 42. Univ of Wales (Ban) DipTh70. St Mich Coll Llan 69. **d** 70 **p** 71. C Holyhead w Rhoscolyn *Ban* 70-74; V Bodedern w Llechgynfarwy and Llechylched etc 74-88; R Machynlleth and Llanwrin 88-97; R Machynlleth w Llanwrin and Penegoes from 97; RD Cyfeiliog and Mawddwy 96-01; AD from 01; Can Ban Cathl from 97. *The Rectory, Newtown Road, Machynlleth SY20 8HE* Tel (01654) 702261

ROWLANDS, Forrest John. b 25. LSE BSc(Econ)51. Chich Th Coll 54. **d** 56 **p** 57. C Hove St Phil *Chich* 56-58; C Haywards Heath St Wilfrid 58-62; R Kingston by Sea 62-74; rtd 90. *130 Thorpe Road, Norwich NR1 1RH* Tel (01603) 473587

ROWLANDS, Gareth Richard. b 70. Univ of Wales BA93. St Steph Ho Ox BTh93. **d** 96 **p** 97. C Shotton *St As* 96-00; TV Wrexham 00-03; Chapl Co-ord Cheshire and Wirral Partnership NHS Trust from 03. *The Countess of Chester Hospital, Liverpool Road, Chester CH2 1UL* Tel (01244) 365000 ext 4543 *or* 4024
E-mail gareth.rowlands@coch.nhs.uk

ROWLANDS, Graeme Charles. b 53. K Coll Lon BD74 AKC74. St Aug Coll Cant 75. **d** 76 **p** 77. C Higham Ferrers w Chelveston *Pet* 76-79; C Gorton St Mary and St Thos *Man* 79-81; C Reading H Trin *Ox* 81-89; P-in-c Kentish Town St Silas *Lon* 89-92; V 92-98; P-in-c Haverstock Hill H Trin w Kentish Town St Barn 93-98; V Kentish Town St Silas and H Trin w St Barn from 98. *St Silas's House, 11 St Silas's Place, London NW5 3QP* Tel (020) 7485 3727

ROWLANDS, Canon John Henry Lewis. b 47. Univ of Wales (Lamp) BA68 Magd Coll Cam BA70 MA74 Dur Univ MLitt86. Westcott Ho Cam 70. **d** 72 **p** 73. C Aberystwyth *St D* 72-76; Chapl Univ of Wales (Lamp) 76-79; Youth Chapl 76-79; Dir Academic Studies St Mich Coll Llan 79-84; Sub-Warden 84-88; Warden 88-97; Lect Univ of Wales (Cardiff) *Llan* 79-97; Asst Dean 81-83; Dean 93-97; Dean of Div Univ of Wales 91-95; Dir of Ords 85-88; V Whitchurch 97-02; TR from 02; Hon Can Llan Cathl 90-97; Can from 97; Chan from 02; Chapl Cardiff Community Healthcare NHS Trust from 97. *The Vicarage, 6 Pennline Road, Cardiff CF14 2AD* Tel (029) 2062 6072 Fax as telephone E-mail office@parishofwhitchurch.freeserve.co.uk

ROWLANDS, Canon Joseph Haydn. b 36. Univ of Wales (Lamp) BA61 DipTh63. **d** 63 **p** 64. C Llanfairisgaer *Ban* 63-68; R Maentwrog w Trawsfynydd 68-75; V Henfynyw w Aberaeron and Llanddewi Aberarth *St D* 75-80; R Trefdraeth *Ban* 80-84; V Llandysul *St D* 84-98; V Llandysul w Bangor Teifi w Henllan etc 98-01; Hon Can St D Cathl 88-90; Can St D Cathl from 90; RD Emlyn 92-01; rtd 01. *1 Llys Ystrad, Johnstown, Carmarthen SA31 3PU*

ROWLANDS, Kenneth Albert. b 41. MA DipAE. NW Ord Course 70. **d** 73 **p** 74. NSM Hoylake *Ches* 73-80; NSM Oxton 80-82; Perm to Offic 82-00; C Stoneycroft All SS *Liv* 92-94; V Mossley Hill St Barn 94-03; rtd 03. *77 Queens Avenue, Meols, Wirral CH47 0LT* Tel 0151-632 3033

ROWLANDS, Marc Alun. b 62. Univ of Wales (Abth) BSc84 St D Coll Lamp MPhil89 PhD95. Wycliffe Hall Ox 97. **d** 99 **p** 00. C Betws w Ammanford *St D* 99-01; C Carmarthen St Pet 01-02; P-in-c Llanpumsaint w Llanllawddog from 02. *The Vicarage, Llanpumsaint, Carmarthen SA33 6BZ* Tel (01267) 253205
E-mail marc_rowlands@hotmail.com

ROWLANDS, Michael Huw. b 62. Birm Univ BA85 Univ of Wales (Cardiff) BD88. St Mich Coll Llan 85. **d** 88 **p** 89. C Penarth All SS *Llan* 88-91; V Martletwy w Lawrenny and Minwear etc *St D* 91-99; CF 99-02; P-in-c Nolton w Roch *St D* from 02. *Calbern, St David's Road, Haverfordwest SA61 2UR* Tel (01437) 710209

ROWLANDS, Richard. b 34. St Mich Coll Llan 59. **d** 62 **p** 63. C Tywyn *Ban* 62-65; C Dwygyfylchi 65-69; V Caerau and Trefeglwys 69-71; CF 71-83. *Rhyd Casadog, Ty'n Lon Po, Holyhead LL65 3AQ* Tel (01407) 720843

ROWLANDS, Robert. b 31. Roch Th Coll. **d** 68 **p** 69. C Hooton *Ches* 68-71; V Stretton 71-88; P-in-c Appleton Thorn and Antrobus 87-88; V Stretton and Appleton Thorn 88-00; rtd 00; Perm to Offic *Carl* from 01. *Uplands, Redhills Road, Arnside, Carnforth LA5 0AT* Tel (01524) 761612

ROWLANDS, Simon David. b 66. **d** 99 **p** 00. C St Peter-in-Thanet *Cant* from 99. *64 High Street, St Peters, Broadstairs CT10 1EB* Tel (01843) 860313

ROWLANDS, Mrs Valerie Christine. b 54. St As Minl Tr Course 99. **d** 02 **p** 03. NSM Llanbedr DC w Llangynhafal, Llanychan etc *St As* from 02. *Hafoty, 2 Tan y Bryn, Llanbedr Duffryn Clwyd, Ruthin LL15 1AQ* Tel (01824) 707407

ROWLANDSON, Gary Clyde. b 50. Lon Univ CertEd72 BA85. Oak Hill Th Coll 82. **d** 85 **p** 86. C Muswell Hill St Jas w St Matt *Lon* 85-89; C Northwood Em 89-93; R Chesham Bois *Ox* from 93. *The Rectory, Glebe Way, Chesham Bois, Amersham HP6 5ND* Tel (01494) 726139 E-mail stleoscb@aol.com

ROWLEY, Christopher Francis Elmes. b 48. St Jo Coll Dur BA70 St Luke's Coll Ex PGCE71. St Steph Ho Ox 76. **d** 78 **p** 79. C Parkstone St Pet w Branksea and St Osmund *Sarum* 78-81; TV 82-85; P-in-c Chard Gd Shep Furnham *B & W* 85-89; P-in-c Dowlishwake w Chaffcombe, Knowle St Giles etc 88-89; R Chard, Furnham w Chaffcombe, Knowle St Giles etc 89-91; V Stoke St Gregory w Burrowbridge and Lyng from 91; RD Taunton from 01. *The Vicarage, Stoke St Gregory, Taunton TA3 6EG* Tel (01823) 490247 E-mail cft-arowley@supanet.com

ROWLEY, David Michael. b 39. N Ord Course 87. **d** 90 **p** 91. C Stainland *Wakef* 90-93; V Hayfield *Derby* 93-99; RD Glossop from 96; P-in-c Chinley w Buxworth 98-99; V Glossop from 99. *The Vicarage, Church Street South, Glossop SK13 7RU* Tel (01457) 852146 Fax as telephone

ROWLEY, Jennifer Jane Elisabeth. b 61. LMH Ox BA84 MA92. EAMTC 99. **d** 02 **p** 03. C Kingsthorpe w Northampton St Dav *Pet* from 02. *22 Tollgate Close, Northampton NN2 6RP* Tel (01604) 720104 E-mail jennyrowley@tiscali.co.uk

ROWLEY, Susan. **d** 01. OLM Fazeley *Lich* from 01. *76 Reindeer Road, Fazeley, Tamworth B78 3SW* Tel (01827) 250431 *or* 289414
E-mail rowley_sue@hotmail.com

ROWLEY-BROOKE, Mrs Marie Gordon. b 46. ARIAM69. Ripon Coll Cuddesdon 00. **d** 02 **p** 03. C Leckhampton SS Phil and Jas w Cheltenham St Jas *Glouc* from 02. *32 Gratton Road, Cheltenham GL50 2BU* Tel (01242) 234156
E-mail trumpetplayer@zoom.co.uk

ROWLING, Canon Catherine. b 55. Man Poly BEd77. Westcott Ho Cam 83 NEOC 85. **dss** 86 **d** 87 **p** 94. Gt Ayton w Easby and Newton in Cleveland *York* 86-89; Par Dn 87-89; Chapl Teesside Poly 89-92; Chapl Teesside Univ 92-96; Dioc Adv for Diaconal Mins 96-98; Dean of Women's Min from 98; Co Dir of Ords from 98; Dioc Moderator Reader Tr from 99; Can and Preb York Minster from 01. *The Vicarage, Ingleby Greenhow, Great Ayton, Middlesbrough TS9 6LL* Tel (01642) 723947 *or* 724050 Fax 724773

ROWLING, Richard Francis. b 56. BA. Westcott Ho Cam. **d** 84 **p** 85. C Stokesley *York* 84-87; C Stainton-in-Cleveland 87-90; V New Marske 90-96; V Wilton 92-96; P-in-c Ingleby Greenhow w Bilsdale Priory, Kildale etc 96-98; V 98-03; TR Thirsk from 03; Abp's Adv for Rural Affairs from 98. *The Rectory, Cemetery Road, Thirsk YO7 1PR* Tel (01845) 523183
E-mail rfrowling@aol.com

ROWNTREE, Peter. b 47. St D Coll Lamp BA68 Univ of Wales (Cardiff) MA70. St Steph Ho Ox 70. **d** 72 **p** 73. C Stanwell *Lon* 72-75; C Northolt St Mary 75-79; Chapl Ealing Gen Hosp 79-83 and 87-94; Chapl Ealing Hosp NHS Trust 94-99; Chapl W Lon Healthcare NHS Trust 94-99; Chapl Cherry Knowle Hosp Sunderland 83-87; Chapl Ryhope Hosp Sunderland 83-87; Sen Co-ord Chapl Univ Coll Lon Hosps NHS Trust from 99. *The Chaplaincy, The Middlesex Hospital, Mortimer Street, London W1N 8AA* Tel (020) 7636 8333

ROWSELL, Canon John Bishop. b 25. Jes Coll Cam BA49 MA55. Ely Th Coll 49. d 51 p 52. C Hackney Wick St Mary of Eton w St Aug *Lon* 51-55; C Is of Dogs Ch Ch and St Jo w St Luke 55-56; C Reading St Mary V *Ox* 56-59; V Hightown *Wakef* 59-69; R Harlton *Ely* 69-81; V Haslingfield 69-81; V Methwold 81-95; RD Feltwell 81-95; R Northwold 82-95; Hon Can Ely Cathl 84-99; P-in-c Hockwold w Wilton 95-99; P-in-c Weeting 95-99; Perm to Offic from 00. *Reed House, High Street, Hilgay, Downham Market PE38 0LH* Tel (01366) 387662

ROWSON, Frank. b 40. CEng67 MIStructE67. Sarum & Wells Th Coll 87. d 90 p 91. NSM Ore Ch Ch *Chich* 90-98; NSM Fairlight, Guestling and Pett 98-00; rtd 00; Perm to Offic *Chich* from 01. *149 Priory Road, Hastings TN34 3JD* Tel (01424) 439802

ROWSTON, Geoffrey. b 34. Sarum Th Coll 59. d 62 p 63. C Ashburton w Buckland-in-the-Moor *Ex* 62-65; C Basingstoke *Win* 65-68; V Netley 68-78; V W End 78-87; R Alderbury and W Grimstead *Sarum* 87-91; P-in-c Whiteparish 89-91; TR Alderbury Team 91-99; rtd 99; Perm to Offic *Cov* from 99. *34 Oldbutt Road, Shipston-on-Stour CV36 4EG* Tel (01608) 663024

✠**ROWTHORN, The Rt Revd Jeffery William.** b 34. Societas Liturgica MNAAL MHSA Ch Coll Cam BA57 MA62 Oriel Coll Ox BLitt72. Berkeley Div Sch DD87 Cuddesdon Coll 61 Union Th Sem (NY) BD61. d 62 p 63 c 87. C Woolwich St Mary w H Trin *S'wark* 62-65; R Garsington *Ox* 65-68; USA from 68; Chapl and Dean Union Th Sem NY 68-73; Assoc Prof Past Th Yale and Berkeley Div Schs 73-87; Suff Bp Connecticut 87-93; Bp in Charge Convocation of American Chs in Eur 94-01; Asst Bp Eur from 95; Asst Bp Spain from 97; Asst Bp Portugal from 97; rtd 01. *17 Woodland Drive, Salem, CT 06420, USA* Tel (001) (860) 859 3377

✠**ROXBURGH, The Rt Revd James William.** b 21. St Cath Coll Cam BA42 MA46. Wycliffe Hall Ox 42. d 44 p 45 c 83. C Folkestone H Trin w Ch Ch *Cant* 44-47; C Handsworth St Mary *Birm* 47-50; V Bootle St Matt *Liv* 50-56; V Drypool St Columba w St Andr and St Pet *York* 56-65; V Barking St Marg *Chelmsf* 65-73; P-in-c Barking St Patr 65-73; Hon Can Chelmsf Cathl 72-77; V Barking St Marg w St Patr 73-75; TR 75-77; Adn Colchester 77-83; Suff Bp Barking 83-84; Area Bp Barking 84-90; rtd 90; Asst Bp Liv from 91. *53 Preston Road, Southport PR9 9EE* Tel (01704) 542927

ROXBY, Gordon George. b 39. Lon Univ BSc61. Coll of Resurr Mirfield 61. d 63 p 64. C Fleetwood *Blackb* 63-66; C Kirkham 66-68; V Runcorn St Jo Weston *Ches* 68-78; R Moston St Chad *Man* 78-86; V Bury St Pet 86-99; AD Bury 86-96; Hon Can Man Cathl 97-99; V Sandiway *Ches* from 99; Initial Minl Tr Officer from 99. *The Vicarage, Norley Road, Sandiway, Northwich CW8 2JU* Tel (01606) 883286 Fax 301505 E-mail wekan@surfaid.org

ROY, Miss Jennifer Pearl. b 53. SRN75 CSS91. Cranmer Hall Dur. d 01 p 02. C Hebburn St Jo *Dur* from 01; C Jarrow Grange from 01. *St Oswald's Vicarage, St Oswald's Road, Hebburn NE31 1HR* Tel 0191-420 8245 E-mail jennieroy@bigfoot.com

ROYALL, Preb Arthur Robert. b 19. Lambeth MA Qu Coll Birm 51. d 53 p 54. C Ashford St Matt *Lon* 53-56; V Heap Bridge *Man* 56-59; V Whitton St Aug *Lon* 59-64; P-in-c Bromley St Mich 64-71; R Poplar All SS w St Frideswide 64-71; RD Poplar 65-66; P-in-c Poplar St Sav w St Gabr and St Steph 68-71; RD Tower Hamlets 68-76; R Poplar 71-73; P-in-c Mile End Old Town H Trin 73-76; P-in-c Bethnal Green St Barn 73-75; Preb St Paul's Cathl 73-86; R Bow w Bromley St Leon 73-76; Clergy Appts Adv 76-85; Perm to Offic *Nor* 77-98; *Ely* 78-98; rtd 86; Perm to Offic *Lon* 86-91. *5 Ramsay Hall, 11-13 Byron Road, Worthing BN11 3HN* Tel (01903) 230688

ROYCROFT, James Gordon Benjamin. b 26. CITC. d 56 p 57. C Belfast St Aid *Conn* 56-58; C Crossmolina *T, K & A* 58-63; ICM Sec (N England) 63-67; I Drung w Castleterra *K, E & A* 67-83; I Larah and Lavey 67-83; I Drumkeeran w Templecarne and Muckross *Clogh* 83-91; rtd 91. *Gransha Road, Culkey, Enniskillen* Tel (028) 6632 8544

ROYDEN, Charles. b 60. Wycliffe Hall Ox BA86 MA91. d 87 p 88. C Bidston *Ches* 87-91; V N Brickhill and Putnoe *St Alb* 91-92; V Bedf St Mark from 93. *The Vicarage, Calder Rise, Bedford MK41 7UY* Tel and fax (01234) 342613 *or* tel 309175 Mobile 07973-113861 E-mail vicar@thisischurch.com

ROYDEN, Eric Ramsay. b 29. St Deiniol's Hawarden 75. d 77 p 78. Hon C Tranmere St Paul w St Luke *Ches* 77-81; C Eastham 81; V New Brighton All SS 81-95; P-in-c 95-97; rtd 95; Perm to Offic *Ches* from 97. *14 Kinglass Road, Bebington, Wirral CH63 9AJ*

ROYDEN, Ross Eric. b 55. Lon Bible Coll BA77 Nottm Univ MTh82. Wycliffe Hall Ox 79. d 81 p 82. C Moreton *Ches* 81-84; Chapl and Tutor Bedf Coll of HE *St Alb* 84-93; R Banchory *Ab* 93-00; R Kincardine O'Neil 93-00; V Kowloon Tong Ch Ch Hong Kong from 00. *Christ Church Vicarage, 2 Derby Road, Kowloon Tong, Kowloon, Hong Kong* Tel (00852) 2338 4433 Fax 2338 8422 E-mail rossroyden@aol.com

ROYDS, John Caress. b 20. Qu Coll Cam BA47 MA52. d 74 p 75. C Kettering St Andr *Pet* 74-76; P-in-c Loddington w Cransley 76;

R 76-81; Dir of Educn 76-81; V Northampton St Jas 81-85; CMS 85-86; Pakistan 85-86; rtd 87; Perm to Offic *Sarum* from 90. *16B Donaldson Road, Salisbury SP1 3AD* Tel (01722) 332293

ROYLANCE, Mrs Margaret. b 47. CertEd68. Cant Sch of Min 92. d 96 p 97. NSM Tenterden St Mildred w Smallhythe *Cant* from 96; Chapl Ashford Sch from 96. *5 Southgate Road, Tenterden TN30 7BS* Tel (01580) 762332

ROYLE, Antony Kevan. b 50. Lon Univ BSc71 FIA76. Trin Coll Bris 76. d 79 p 80. C Chell *Lich* 79-82; C Leyland St Andr *Blackb* 82-86; V Blackb Sav 86-95; Chapl Blackb R Infirmary and Park Lee Hosp 86-95; Chapl E Lancs Hospice 86-95; TR Walton H Trin *Ox* 95-01; NSM Wendover Deanery from 01. *4 Darley Close, Aylesbury HP21 7EA* Tel 07796-143905 (mobile)

ROYLE, Michael Arthur. b 38. Univ of Wales (Ban) BSc61 Lon Univ DipTh63. St Jo Coll Nottm 81. d 82 p 83. C Boulton *Derby* 82-85; C Belper 85-87; P-in-c Smalley and Morley 87-95; RD Heanor 89-94; V Charlesworth and Dinting Vale 95-02; rtd 02. *Kaiama, 55 Cross Lane, Marple, Stockport SK6 7PZ* Tel 0161-427 6453 E-mail royle@fish.co.uk

ROYLE, Canon Peter Sydney George. b 34. K Coll Lon BD57 AKC57. d 58 p 59. C St Helier *S'wark* 58-62; Australia 62-68; P-in-c Sydenham St Phil *S'wark* 69-72; V Leigh Park *Portsm* 72-85; RD Havant 77-82; V S w N Hayling 85-96; V S Hayling 96-97; Hon Can Portsm Cathl 95-97; rtd 97; Perm to Offic *Ex* from 97. *Fairbank, 74 Newton Road, Bishopsteignton TQ14 9PP* Tel (01626) 779252

ROYLE, Canon Roger Michael. b 39. AKC61 Lambeth MA90. d 62 p 63. C Portsea St Mary *Portsm* 62-65; C St Helier *S'wark* 65-68; Succ S'wark Cathl 68-71; Warden Eton Coll Dorney Par Project *Ox* 71-74; Conduct Eton Coll 74-79; Lic to Offic *S'wark* 79-90; Chapl Ld Mayor Treloar Coll Alton 90-92; Hon C Froyle and Holybourne *Win* 90-92; Hon Can and Chapl S'wark Cathl *S'wark* 93-99; Perm to Offic from 99. *Address withheld by request*

ROYLE, Canon Stanley Michael. b 43. K Coll Lon BD69 AKC69 Man Univ MA75. St Aug Coll Cant 71. d 72 p 73. C Timperley *Ches* 72-76; Perm to Offic 76-81; R Milton Abbas, Hilton w Cheselbourne etc *Sarum* 81-86; Dir of Ords 86-01; Adv on CME 86-98; Can and Preb Sarum Cathl from 89; Bp's Dom Chapl 98-01; Lic to Offic from 01. *Three Firs, Blandford Road, Sturminster Marshall, Wimborne BH21 4AF* Tel (01258) 857326

ROYSTON-BALL, Peter. b 38. St Mich Coll Llan 61. d 65 p 66. C Dartford St Alb *Roch* 65-67; C Chislehurst Annunciation 67-69; C St Marylebone Ch Ch w St Paul *Lon* 69-75; Hon C New Windsor *Ox* 75-78; Perm to Offic *S'wark* 75-88; C Leic St Eliz Nether Hall *Leic* 88-94; V Belvedere St Aug *Roch* 94-02; rtd 02. *Address withheld by request* E-mail royston38@yahoo.uk.com

RUAHA, Bishop of. *See* MTETEMELA, The Most Revd Donald Leo

RUCK, John. b 47. Bris Univ BSc68. Selly Oak Coll DipRE87 All Nations Chr Coll 77. d 80 p 83. Indonesia 80-86 and 87-91; Perm to Offic *Birm* 86-87 and 91-98. *94 Gristhorpe Road, Birmingham B29 7SL* Tel 0121-472 7460

RUDALL, Mark Edward. b 53. Regent's Park Coll Ox BA80 MA84. Ripon Coll Cuddesdon DipMin01. d 99. In Bapt Min 80-01; C Wallingford *Ox* from 01. *20 Glyn Avenue, Didcot OX11 7AH* Tel (01235) 815331 Mobile 07779-654975 E-mail mark@rudall.freeserve.co.uk

RUDD, Charles Robert Jordeson. b 34. TCD BA56 MA65 BD65. d 57 p 58. C Lurgan Redeemer *D & D* 57-61; C Lisburn Ch Ch Cathl *Conn* 61-65; C Willowfield *D & D* 62-66; I Drumgooland w Kilcoo 66-75; I Moira 75-95; I Magherally w Annaclone 95-02; Can Belf Cathl 90-02; rtd 02. *12 Thorn Heights, Banbridge BT32 4BF* Tel (028) 4062 8995

RUDD, Colin Richard. b 41. AKC64. d 65 p 66. C N Stoneham *Win* 65-70; V Rotherwick, Hook and Greywell 70-74; R Hook w Greywell 74-78; Toc H 78-89; V Buckland *Ox* 89-98; V Littleworth 89-98; R Pusey 89-98; R Gainfield 99-99; RD Vale of White Horse 96-99; rtd 99. *Alcudia, Bilbrook, Minehead TA24 6HE* Tel (01984) 640021

RUDD, Canon Julian Douglas Raymond. b 19. Leeds Univ BA40. Coll of Resurr Mirfield 40. d 42 p 43. C Bury St Edmunds St Jo *St E* 42-46; C Holborn St Alb w Saffron Hill St Pet *Lon* 46-49; V Bournemouth St Fran *Win* 49-60; R Bournemouth 56-60; R Old Alresford 60-70; RD Alresford 60-70; Hon Can Win Cathl 62-70; V Warwick St Mary *Cov* 70-76; V Warwick St Mary w St Nic 76-83; Hon Can Cov Cathl 76-84; TR Warwick 83-84; RD Warwick 77-79; rtd 84; Perm to Offic *Sarum* 84-98. *The College of St Barnabas, Blackberry Lane, Lingfield RH7 6NJ* Tel (01342) 870441

RUDD, Robert Arthur. b 33. ALCD60. d 60 p 61. C Blackb Sav *Blackb* 60-63; C Huyton St Geo *Liv* 63-65; V Bickershaw 65-72; Asst Chapl HM Pris Liv 72-73; Chapl HM Pris Birm 73-78; Chapl HM Pris Parkhurst 78-86; Chapl HM Pris Camp Hill 86-92; Chapl St Mary's Hosp Newport 92-95; rtd 95; Perm to Offic *Portsm* from 95. *The Elms, 13 Horsebridge Hill, Newport PO30 5TJ* Tel (01983) 524415

RUDDLE, Canon Donald Arthur. b 31. Linc Th Coll 64. d 66 p 67. C Kettering SS Pet and Paul *Pet* 66-70; V Earlham St Anne *Nor* 70-79; V E Malling *Roch* 79-95; RD Malling 84-93; Hon Can Roch Cathl 88-95; Chapl Nord Pas de Calais *Eur* 95-98; rtd 98.

16 rue du Calvaire, Enquine-les-Mines, 62145 Pas de Calais, France Tel (0033) 21 93 69 46 E-mail donruddle@aol.com

RUDDOCK, Brian John. b 45. Dur Univ BA66 Nottm Univ MEd91. Westcott Ho Cam 67. **d** 69 **p** 70. C Ross *Heref* 69-72; C Kettering SS Pet and Paul *Pet* 72-75; P-in-c Colchester St Steph *Chelmsf* 75-77; TR Colchester St Leon, St Mary Magd and St Steph 77-84; R March St Pet *Ely* 84-89; R March St Mary 84-89; RD March 87-89; Dioc Unemployment Officer *Sheff* 89-94; Lic to Offic from 96; Resource and Developmant Officer CCWA from 96. *36 Sandygate, Wath-upon-Dearne, Rotherham S63 7LW* Tel (01709) 873254 Fax as telephone E-mail ccwa@btinternet.com

RUDDOCK, Canon Charles Cecil. b 28. TCD Dip Bibl Studies. TCD Div Sch. **d** 57 **p** 58. C Belfast St Mary *Conn* 57-59; C Carnmoney 59-61; C Belfast St Aid 61-63; I Kiltegan w Rathvilly *C & O* 63-69; C Newtownards *D & D* 69-72; Australia 72-83; I Mallow Union *C, C & R* 83-89; I Fenagh w Myshall, Aghade and Ardoyne *C & O* 89-95; Can Ossory and Leighlin Cathls 92-95; rtd 95; Perm to Offic *Glouc* from 95. *26 Arundel Drive, Rodborough, Stroud GL5 3SH* Tel (01453) 766484

RUDDOCK, Edgar Chapman. b 48. St Jo Coll Dur BA70 MA76 DipTh73. **d** 74 **p** 75. C Birm St Geo *Birm* 74-78; R 78-83; S Africa 83-91; Dir Tr Dio St Jo 83-86; P-in-c Mandini 86-87; Prov Dir Tr 88-91; TR Stoke-upon-Trent *Lich* 91-02; Internat Relns Sec USPG from 03. *USPG, Partnership House, 157 Waterloo Road, London SE1 8XA* Tel (020) 7928 8681 E-mail edrud@cix.co.uk

RUDDOCK, Kenneth Edward. b 30. TCD BA52 QUB MTh79. CITC 53 Div Test. **d** 53 **p** 54. C Ballymena *Conn* 53-56; C Belfast St Thos 56-60; I Tomregan w Drumlane *K, E & A* 60-68; I Belfast St Luke *Conn* 68-80; Miss to Seamen 80-96; I Whitehead and Islandmagee *Conn* 80-96; Can Lisburn Cathl 90-96; Dioc Info Officer from 90; Chan Conn Cathl 96; rtd 96; Dioc C *Conn* from 98. *24 Fourtowns Manor, Ahoghill, Ballymena BT42 1RS* Tel (028) 2587 8966 Mobile 07970-639067

RUDDOCK, Leonard William. b 58. CITC 91. **d** 94 **p** 95. NSM Roscrea w Kyle, Bourney and Corbally *L & K* from 94. *Short Corville, Roscrea, Co Tipperary, Irish Republic* Tel (00353) (505) 22034

RUDDOCK, Canon Norman Trevor. b 35. TCD BA57 MA60 HDipEd62. TCD Div Sch 58. **d** 58 **p** 59. C Belfast St Steph *Conn* 58-60; C Dublin Ch Ch Leeson Park *D & G* 60-63; Perm to Offic 63-73; USA 70-72; I Kilanne *C & O* 73-81; I Castlepollard and Oldcastle w Loughcrew etc *M & K* 84-93; Can Meath 92-93; I Wexford w Ardcolm and Killurin *C & O* 93-04; I Taghmon w Horetown and Bannow 95-04; P-in-c Kilscoran w Killinick and Mulrankin 02-04; Treas Ferns Cathl 96-98; Chan 98-03; Prec 03-04; rtd 04. *5 Richmond Terrace, Spawell Road, Wexford, Irish Republic* Tel (00353) 87-791 5901 (mobile)

RUDDOCK, Canon Reginald Bruce. b 55. AGSM77. Chich Th Coll. **d** 83 **p** 84. C Felpham w Middleton *Chich* 83-86; C Portsea St Mary *Portsm* 86-88; P-in-c Barnes St Mich *S'wark* 88-95; Dir Angl Cen Rome 95-99; Hon Can American Cathl Paris from 96; Can Res Worc Cathl *Worc* from 99. *15A College Green, Worcester WR1 2LH* Tel (01905) 21961 Fax 611139 E-mail bruceruddock@worcestercathedral.org.uk

RUDDY, Canon Denys Henry. b 22. Jes Coll Ox BA48 MA53. Linc Th Coll 48. **d** 50 **p** 51. C Petersfield w Sheet *Portsm* 50-53; C Gt Grimsby St Jas *Linc* 53-58; R Longworth and Hinton Waldrist *Ox* 58-77; RD Vale of White Horse 68-75; Warden of Readers 70-87; Chapl Abingdon St Nic 77-87; Hon Can Ch Ch 79-87; RD Abingdon 79-80; rtd 87; Perm to Offic *Ox* and *Pet* 87-99; *Glouc* from 99. *23 Capel Court, The Burgage, Prestbury, Cheltenham GL52 3EL* Tel (01242) 577535

RUDEN, Lars Olav. b 43. Dioc OLM tr scheme 97. **d** 00 **p** 01. NSM Bamford *Man* from 00. *123 Harewood Way, Rochdale OL11 5TW* Tel (01706) 640609 Mobile 07713-431756

RUDIGER, David John. b 42. MCMI91. Ox Min Course CBTS94. **d** 94 **p** 95. NSM Woughton *Ox* from 94. *32 Forest Rise, Eaglestone, Milton Keynes MK6 5EU* Tel (01908) 668474 E-mail david@rudiger2.freeserve.co.uk

RUDKIN, Simon David. b 51. Bradf Univ BA74 K Coll Lon BD77 AKC77. Coll of Resurr Mirfield 77. **d** 78 **p** 79. C Flixton St Mich *Man* 78-81; C Atherton 81-84; V Lever Bridge 84-91; P-in-c Pennington w Lindal and Marton *Carl* 91-96; P-in-c Pennington and Lindal w Marton and Bardsea 96-00; V Morland, Thrimby, Gt Strickland and Cliburn from 00. *The Vicarage, Morland, Penrith CA10 3AX* Tel (01931) 714620

RUDMAN, David Walter Thomas. b 48. Lon Univ DipTh70 BD72. Oak Hill Th Coll 68. **d** 72 **p** 73. C Plymouth St Jude *Ex* 72-75; C Radipole *Sarum* 76-77; Warden St Geo Ho Braunton 77-03; R Georgeham *Ex* 88-03; Dioc Adv in Adult Tr 97-03; TV S Molton w Nymet St George, High Bray etc from 03; Dioc Adv in OLM from 03. *The Rectory, Kingsnymphton, Umberleigh EX37 9ST* Tel (01769) 580457 E-mail davidrudman@ntlworld.com

RUDMAN, Thomas Peter William. b 22. Oak Hill Th Coll 60. **d** 62 **p** 63. C St Paul's Cray St Barn CD *Roch* 62-65; C Morden *S'wark* 65-67; V Lowestoft Ch Ch *Nor* 67-73; V Stapenhill w

Cauldwell *Derby* 73-81; V Sutton le Marsh *Linc* 81-87; RD Calcewaithe and Candleshoe 85-87; rtd 87; Perm to Offic *Win* 87-96 and *Ex* from 96. *28 Gracey Court, Woodland Road, Broadclyst, Exeter EX5 3GA* Tel (01392) 466436

RUEHORN, Eric Arthur. b 33. St Aid Birkenhead 58. **d** 61 **p** 62. C Harpurhey Ch *Man* 61-65; V Roughtown 65-74; V Hawkshaw Lane 74-99; rtd 99; Perm to Offic *Man* from 00. *29 Hunstanton Drive, Bury BL8 1EG* Tel 0161-761 3983

RUFF, Brian Chisholm. b 36. Lon Univ BD66 ACA60 FCA70. Oak Hill Th Coll 63. **d** 67 **p** 68. C Cheadle *Ches* 67-72; Educn and Youth Sec CPAS 72-76; V New Milverton *Cov* 76-90; V Westbourne Ch Ch CD *Win* 90-01; rtd 02. *19 Hardy Road, West Moors, Wimborne BH22 0EX* Tel (01202) 868733 E-mail bcr@ruffys.fsnet.co.uk

RUFF, Michael Ronald. b 49. K Coll Lon BD72 AKC72. St Aug Coll Cant 72. **d** 73 **p** 74. C Old Shoreham *Chich* 73-76; Chapl Ellesmere Coll Shropshire 77-81; Chapl Grenville Coll Bideford 81-87; Chapl Stamford Sch from 87; Perm to Offic *Linc* 87-99. *9 Vence Close, Stamford PE9 2LZ1* Tel (01780) 766567

RUFFLE, Preb John Leslie. b 43. ALCD66. **d** 66 **p** 67. C Eastwood *S'well* 66-70; C Keynsham w Queen Charlton *B & W* 70-75; P-in-c Weston-super-Mare Em 75; TV Weston-super-Mare Cen Par 75-84; V Yatton Moor 84-91; TR 91-98; P-in-c Chew Stoke w Nempnett Thrubwell 98-03; Dioc Adv in Past Care and Counselling from 03; Preb Wells Cathl from 97. *16 Mendip Road, Weston-super-Mare BS23 3HA* Tel (01934) 612254 Fax 612104 E-mail john@vicpress01.freeserve.co.uk

RUFFLE, Peter Cousins. b 19. Lon Univ BD42. ALCD42. **d** 42 **p** 43. C Highbury Ch Ch *Lon* 42-46; CMS Missr Bihar India 46-52; Youth Adv CMS 52-57; Hon C Bromley St Jo *Roch* 54-57; V Walton Breck *Liv* 57-60; V Aigburth 60-66; Prin Wilson Carlile Coll of Evang 66-74; Can Res Blackb Cathl *Blackb* 74-78; V Meole Brace *Lich* 78-85; rtd 85; Perm to Offic *Win* and *Portsm* 85-03. *20 Dulverton Hall, Esplanade, Scarborough YO11 2AR* Tel (01723) 340120

RUFLI, Alan John. b 63. TCD BA89. **d** 91 **p** 92. C Donaghcloney w Waringstown *D & D* 91-94; C Knock 94-95; I Rathcoole *Conn* 95-01; I Holmpatrick w Balbriggan and Kenure *D & G* from 01. *Holmpatrick Rectory, Miller's Lane, Skerries, Co Dublin, Irish Republic* Tel (00353) (1) 849 2247 E-mail rufrev@aol.com

RUGEN, Peter. b 60. Crewe & Alsager Coll BEd86. Trin Coll Bris MA00. **d** 00 **p** 01. C Shipley St Pet *Bradf* from 00. *2B Nab Lane, Shipley BD18 4HB* Tel (01274) 583457

RUGG, Andrew Philip. b 47. Kent Univ BA82. Sarum & Wells Th Coll 83. **d** 85 **p** 86. C Harlesden All So *Lon* 85-90; TV Benwell Team *Newc* 90-97; V Weetslade 97-00; rtd 00; Perm to Offic *York* from 00. *36 Whenby Grove, York YO31 9DS* Tel and fax (01904) 652567 Mobile 07980-390051

RUGMAN, Mrs Hazel. b 47. **d** 03. NSM Sandbach *Ches* from 03. *High Trees, 157 Sandbach Road, Alsager ST7 2AX* Tel (01270) 876386

✠**RUMALSHAH, The Rt Revd Munawar Kenneth (Mano).** b 41. Punjab Univ BSc60 Serampore Coll BD65 Karachi Univ MA68 Cam Univ PGCE86. Bp's Coll Calcutta DipTh65. **d** 65 **p** 66 **c** 94. Pakistan 65-69 and 89-99; C H Trin Cathl Karachi 65-69; C Roundhay St Edm *Ripon* 70-73; Area Sec CMS *Ripon* and *York* 74-78; Asst Home Sec York Prov 73-78; Educn Sec BCC 78-81; P-in-c Southall St Geo *Lon* 81-88; USPG from 89; Gen Sec from 99; Bp Peshawar 94-99; Hon Asst Bp S'wark from 99. *USPG, Partnership House, 157 Waterloo Road, London SE1 8XA* Tel (020) 7928 8681 Fax 7928 2371 E-mail manor@uspg.org.uk

RUMBALL, Preb Frank Thomas. b 43. Sarum & Wells Th Coll 72. **d** 74 **p** 75. C Bromyard *Heref* 74-78; TV Ewyas Harold w Dulas 78-79; TV Ewyas Harold w Dulas, Kenderchurch etc 79-81; C Minsterley 81-82; P-in-c Eye, Croft w Yarpole and Lucton 82-91; R Condover w Frodesley, Acton Burnell etc 91-01; Preb Heref Cathl 97-01; rtd 01; Perm to Offic *Heref* from 01. *The Old School, Pitchford, Shrewsbury SY5 7DW* Tel (01694) 731256

RUMBALL, William Michael. b 41. Surrey Univ BSc63 Birm Univ PhD66 Open Univ BA75 MIM66 MINucE73 FIMMM03. Wycliffe Hall Ox 78. **d** 80 **p** 81. C S Molton, Nymet St George, High Bray etc *Ex* 80-83; V S Hetton w Haswell *Dur* 83-90; V S Wingfield and Wessington *Derby* 90-99; rtd 99; Hon C Brailsford w Shirley and Osmaston w Edlaston *Derby* from 01. *4 Hawthorn Close, Ashbourne DE6 1HW* Tel (01335) 343203 E-mail wm.rumball@virgin.net

RUMBLE, Alison Merle. *See* PRINCE, Mrs Alison Merle

RUMBOLD, Bernard John. b 43. **d** 73 **p** 75. Papua New Guinea 73-76; C Gt Burstead *Chelmsf* 76-77; Chapl RAF 77-93; Chapl HM Pris Featherstone 93-95; C Wordsley *Worc* 96-99; TV 96-99; Chapl Dudley Gp of Hosps NHS Trust 96-99; R Teme Valley N *Worc* 99-02; rtd 02. *41 Blackmore Road, Stalbridge, Sturminster Newton DT10 2NU* Tel (01963) 362923

RUMBOLD, Graham Charles. b 44. Open Univ BA79. S Dios Minl Tr Scheme 76. **d** 79 **p** 80. NSM Widley w Wymering *Portsm* 79-82; Chapl Cynthia Spencer Unit Manfield Hosp 82-94; Chapl Northampton Community Healthcare NHS Trust 94-01; Chapl Northants Healthcare NHS Trust from 01; NSM Weston Favell

Pet 93-95; NSM Northampton St Matt from 98. *3 Calstock Close, Northampton NN3 3BA* Tel (01604) 627389

RUMENS, Canon John Henry. b 21. AKC49. **d** 50 **p** 51. C Wareham w Arne *Sarum* 50-54; V Alderholt 54-59; R Salisbury St Edm 59-72; RD Salisbury 69-72; Can and Preb Sarum Cathl 72-85; R Trowbridge H Trin 72-79; P-in-c Sturminster Marshall 79-83; V 83-85; rtd 85; Perm to Offic *Sarum* from 85. *20 Constable Way, Salisbury SP2 8LN* Tel (01722) 334716

RUMENS, Ms Katharine Mary. b 53. UEA BEd76. Westcott Ho Cam 90. **d** 92 **p** 94. Par Dn E Ham w Upton Park St Alb *Chelmsf* 92-94; C 94-95; C Waterloo St Jo w St Andr *S'wark* 95-00; Chapl S Bank Cen and Chapl Lon Weekend TV 95-00; R St Giles Cripplegate w St Bart Moor Lane etc *Lon* from 00. *The Rectory, 4 The Postern, Wood Street, London EC2Y 8BJ* Tel and fax (020) 7588 3013 *or* tel 7638 1997 E-mail rumens@stgileschurch.com

RUMING, Canon Gordon William. b 27. Kelham Th Coll 45. **d** 52 **p** 53. C Baildon *Bradf* 52-55; C Prestbury *Glouc* 55-60; C Penzance St Mary *Truro* 60-61; R Calstock 61-92; Hon Can Truro Cathl 79-92; RD E Wivelshire 85-91; rtd 92; Perm to Offic *Truro* from 92 and *Ex* from 99. *3 Derry Avenue, Plymouth PL4 6BH* Tel (01752) 661986

RUMSEY, Andrew Paul. b 68. Reading Univ BA89. Ridley Hall Cam MA98. **d** 97 **p** 98. C Harrow Trin St Mich *Lon* 97-01; V Gipsy Hill Ch Ch *S'wark* from 01. *Christ Church Vicarage, 1 Highland Road, London SE19 1DP* Tel (020) 8670 0385 E-mail vicar@gipsyhill.org.uk

RUMSEY, Ian Mark. b 58. Van Mildert Coll Dur BSc79 St Jo Coll Dur BA89. Cranmer Hall Dur 87. **d** 90 **p** 91. C Dalston *Carl* 90-94; C Wreay 92-94; TV Cockermouth w Embleton and Wythop from 94; Adv for Post-Ord Tr 97-00. *The Vicarage, 14 Harrot Hill, Cockermouth CA13 0BL* Tel (01900) 824383

RUNCORN, David Charles. b 54. BA77 Ox Poly Dip Psychology 88. St Jo Coll Nottm 77. **d** 79 **p** 80. C Wealdstone H Trin *Lon* 79-82; Chapl Lee Abbey 82-87; C Ealing St Steph Castle Hill *Lon* 89-90; V 90-96; Dir Past and Evang Studies Trin Coll Bris 96-03; Dir Local Min Development *Lich* from 03. *The Vicarage, 35 Church Street, Littleover, Derby DE23 6GF* Tel (01332) 767802 E-mail david.runcorn@lichfield.anglican.org

RUNCORN, Canon Dennis Brookes. b 22. Ch Coll Cam BA47 MA52. Ridley Hall Cam 47. **d** 49 **p** 50. C Ashtead *Guildf* 49-53; Hong Kong 54-62; Prin CMS Tr Coll Chislehurst 62-67; V Shortlands *Roch* 67-80; RD Beckenham 73-80; Hon Can Roch Cathl 78-87; V Shorne 80-87; rtd 87; Perm to Offic *Derby* from 87. *14 Hollowood Avenue, Littleover, Derby DE23 6JD* Tel (01332) 765859

RUNCORN, Jacqueline Ann. *See* SEARLE, Ms Jacqueline Ann

RUNDELL, Simon Philip. b 67. Univ of N Lon BSc95 Leeds Univ BA01 RGN90. Coll of Resurr Mirfield 99. **d** 01 **p** 02. C Southsea H Spirit *Portsm* from 01. *Church House, 219 Fawcett Road, Southsea PO4 0DH* Tel (023) 9281 2128 E-mail simon@rundell.org.uk

RUNDLE, Mrs Beryl Rosemary. b 28. Bris Univ BA49 CertEd50. S Dios Minl Tr Scheme 83. **dss** 86 **d** 87. Tangmere *Chich* 86-87; Hon Par Dn 87-92; Boxgrove 86-87; Hon Par Dn 87-92; Hon Par Dn Eastbourne St Sav and St Pet 92-98; Perm to Offic *Portsm* and *Chich* from 98. *22 Sovereign Drive, Southsea PO4 8XX* Tel (01705) 826859

RUNDLE, Hilary. b 65. St Hugh's Coll Ox BA88 Cheltenham & Glouc Coll of HE PGCE90. Trin Coll Bris 01. **d** 03. C Chipping Sodbury and Old Sodbury *Glouc* from 03. *23 Couzens Close, Chipping Sodbury, Bristol BS37 6BT* Tel (01454) 320951 E-mail hilaryrundle@hotmail.com

RUNDLE, Nicholas John. b 59. Southn Univ BA80. St Steph Ho Ox BTh84. **d** 84 **p** 85. C E Preston w Kingston *Chich* 84-87; Chapl RAF 87-91; Australia from 91; Assoc P Magill 91-93; R Grange 93-98; R Hawthorn from 98; AD S Suburbs from 00. *3 Rosevear Street, Hawthorn, S Australia 5062* Tel (0061) (8) 8370 3583 *or* 8272 7266 Fax 8373 7144 E-mail njrundle@hotmail.com

RUNDLE, Penelope Anne. b 36. St Hugh's Coll Ox MA59 Lon Univ DAA64. S Dios Minl Tr Scheme 85. **d** 88 **p** 94. Hon Par Dn Mere w W Knoyle and Maiden Bradley *Sarum* 88-91; Hon Par Dn Upper Stour 91-94; Hon C from 94. *The Common, Kilmington, Warminster BA12 6QY* Tel (01985) 844610

RUSCHMEYER, Henry Cassell. b 44. Union Coll NY BA66 Bank St Coll of Ed NY MEd73 NY Univ MA88. Gen Th Sem (NY) MD78. **d** 78 **p** 79. USA 78-89 and from 97; NSM Wilton Place St Paul *Lon* 89-97. *2115 Brookhaven Drive, Sarasota, FL 34239, USA*

RUSCOE, Canon John Ernest. b 32. Dur Univ BA57. Qu Coll Birm 57. **d** 59 **p** 60. C Jarrow St Paul *Dur* 59-63; C Whitburn 63-65; V S Hylton from 65; Hon Can Dur Cathl from 85. *The Vicarage, South Hylton, Sunderland SR4 0QB* Tel 0191-534 2325 E-mail ruscoe@durham.anglican.org

RUSH, Paul Andrew. b 57. Lon Bible Coll BA79. Ridley Hall Cam 98. **d** 00 **p** 01. C Bar Hill *Ely* from 00. *66 Watermead, Bar Hill, Cambridge CB3 8TL* Tel (01954) 204812 E-mail rev.paul.rush@ntlworld.com

RUSHER, James Victor Francis. b 28. RMA. Ridley Hall Cam 58. **d** 60 **p** 61. C Kensington St Helen w H Trin *Lon* 60-63; C

Edgbaston St Bart *Birm* 63-66; V Summerfield 66-71; V Knowle 71-82; Perm to Offic 82-93; Chapl Parkway Hosp Solihull 85-93; rtd 93. *4 Froxmere Close, Solihull B91 3XG* Tel 0121-705 4514

RUSHFORTH, Richard Hamblin. b 40. Keble Coll Ox BA62 MA71. Chich Th Coll 62. **d** 64 **p** 65. C St Leonards Ch Ch *Chich* 64-79; Org Sec Fellowship of St Nic 79-81; V Portslade St Nic and St Andr from 81; Min Portslade Gd Shep CD 88-89. *The Vicarage, South Street, Portslade, Brighton BN41 2LE* Tel (01273) 418090

RUSHTON, David William. b 70. St Chad's Coll Dur BA96. St Steph Ho Ox DipTh98. **d** 98 **p** 99. C Hornsey St Mary w St Geo *Lon* 98-01; C Thamesmead *S'wark* 01-02; Asst Chapl King's Healthcare NHS Trust from 02. *The Chaplain's Office, King's College Hospital, Denmark Hill, London SE5 9RS* Tel (020) 7346 3522 Fax 7346 4059 E-mail rev.rushton@kingsch.nhs.uk

RUSHTON, Canon James David. b 39. Dur Univ BA61. Cranmer Hall Dur DipTh64. **d** 64 **p** 65. C Upper Armley *Ripon* 64-67; C Blackpool Ch Ch *Blackb* 67-70; V Preston St Cuth 70-79; V Denton Holme *Carl* 79-96; P-in-c Preston All SS *Blackb* 96-00; V from 00; AD Preston 98-03; Hon Can Blackb Cathl from 00. *All Saints' Vicarage, 94 Watling Street Road, Fulwood, Preston PR2 4BP* Tel (01772) 700672 E-mail jimrushton@ukonline.co.uk

RUSHTON, Ms Janet Maureen. b 46. Keele Univ BA68 Leic Univ PGCE69. Wycliffe Hall Ox BTh94. **d** 94 **p** 95. C Harrow St Mary *Lon* 94-98; C Putney St Mary *S'wark* 98-02; P-in-c Wolvercote w Summertown *Ox* from 02. *The Vicarage, 37 Lonsdale Road, Oxford OX2 7ES* Tel (01865) 556079 E-mail janrushton@lineone.net

RUSHTON, Malcolm Leslie. b 47. Bris Univ BSc69 Birm Univ PhD72 Fitzw Coll Cam BA74. Ridley Hall Cam 72. **d** 75 **p** 76. C Cullompton *Ex* 75-79; Chapl Univ Coll Lon 79-87; Chapl R Veterinary Coll Lon 87-90; Chapl R Free Medical Sch 87-90. *Flat 3, 13 Belsize Grove, London NW3 4UX* Tel (020) 7722 1989 Fax as telephone

RUSHTON, Philip William. b 38. Open Univ BA87. Clifton Th Coll 62. **d** 65 **p** 66. C Brixton St Paul *S'wark* 65-67; C Aldridge *Lich* 67-69; C Bushbury 69-71; Chapl Nat Nautical Sch Portishead 71-72; Chapl RAF 72-79; P-in-c Bolton on Swale *Ripon* 79-87; P-in-c The Cowtons 80-82; V 82-89; CF (TA) from 88; R Litcham, Kempston, Lexham, Mileham, Beeston etc *Nor* 89-95; P-in-c Tittleshall w Godwick 93-95; R Litcham w Kempston, E and W Lexham, Mileham etc 95-96; P-in-c Scole, Brockdish, Billingford, Thorpe Abbots etc 96-98; R 98-01; rtd 01; Perm to Offic *St E* and *Carl* from 01. *Helm Lea, Kirkby Thore, Penrith CA10 1UA* Tel (01768) 361597 Fax as telephone E-mail philipwrushton@hotmail.com

RUSHTON, Mrs Susan Elizabeth. b 44. Univ of Wales (Cardiff) BA65. Bris Univ BA89. **dss** 86 **d** 87 **p** 94. Westbury-on-Trym H Trin *Bris* 86-91; Hon Par Dn 87-91; C Wotton St Mary *Glouc* 91-94; Chapl United Bris Healthcare NHS Trust 94-98; P-in-c Frampton Cotterell *Bris* from 94; P-in-c Iron Acton from 98. *The Rectory, Rectory Road, Frampton Cotterell, Bristol BS36 2BP* Tel (01454) 772112 Fax as telephone E-mail s.rushton@breathemail.net

RUSHTON, Mrs Valerie Elizabeth Wendy. b 40. Birm Univ BSocSc62 DPS87. WMMTC 86. **d** 89 **p** 94. C Nuneaton St Nic *Cov* 89-93; C Stockingford 93-96; TV Watling Valley *Ox* 96-01; rtd 02; Perm to Offic *Ox* from 02. *106 Moreton Road, Buckingham MK18 1IP* Tel (01280) 824942

RUSK, The Very Revd Frederick John. b 28. QUB BA50 TCD 52. **d** 53 **p** 54. C Ballymoney *Conn* 53-56; C Belfast St Nic 56-59; I Broomhedge 59-65; RE Insp 64-66; I Belfast St Simon 65-72; I Ballymena w Ballyclug 78-88; I Belfast St Nic 88-98; Preb Conn Cathl 84-86; Treas 86-90; Prec 90; Chan Conn Cathl 90-95; Dean Conn 95-98; rtd 98. *28 Banbridge Road, Lurgan, Craigavon BT66 7EQ* Tel (028) 3832 9763

RUSK, Michael Frederick. b 58. Cam Univ BA MA Dur Univ MA98. Westcott Ho Cam 81. **d** 84 **p** 85. C Altrincham St Geo *Ches* 84-87; Chapl Collingwood and Grey Coll *Dur* 87-90; Lect Dur Univ 89-99; C-in-c Neville's Cross St Jo CD 90-99; TR Oadby *Leic* from 99; RD Gartree II from 00. *St Peter's Rectory, 1 Leicester Road, Oadby, Leicester LE2 5BD* Tel 0116-271 2135 E-mail m.f.rusk@leicester.anglican.org

RUSS, Canon Timothy John. b 41. AKC64. Sarum Th Coll 66. **d** 66 **p** 67. C Walthamstow St Pet *Chelmsf* 66-70; C Epping St Jo 70-73; C Stepney St Dunstan and All SS *Lon* 73-75; Youth Officer 75-79; Tutor YMCA Nat Coll Walthamstow 79-84; Hon C St Botolph Aldgate w H Trin Minories *Lon* 82-89; Selection Sec ACCM 84-89; Dir St Marylebone Healing and Counselling Cen 89-92; Gen Sec Inst of Relig and Medicine 89-92; Hon C Hoxton St Anne w St Columba *Lon* 90-92; P-in-c St Dennis *Truro* from 92; Par Development Adv 92-99; Dir Minl Tr from 99; Hon Can Truro Cathl from 01. *The Rectory, Carne Hill, St Dennis, St Austell PL26 8AZ* Tel (01726) 822317 Fax as telephone E-mail timrussa@tesco.net

RUSSELL, Adrian Camper. b 45. Chich Th Coll 79. **d** 81 **p** 82. C Marton *Blackb* 81-84; C Haslemere *Guildf* 84-85; V Hartlepool H Trin *Dur* 85-89; P-in-c Cornforth 89-94; R Auchterarder

St And 94-97; R Muthill 94-97; P-in-c Kenton Ascension *Newc* from 97. *Kenton Vicarage, Creighton Avenue, Newcastle upon Tyne NE3 4UN* Tel 0191-285 7803 Fax as telephone
E-mail acr0210@btinternet.com

✠**RUSSELL, The Rt Revd Anthony John.** b 43. St Chad's Coll Dur BA65 Trin Coll Ox DPhil71. Cuddesdon Coll 65. **d** 70 **p** 71 **c** 88. C Hilborough w Bodney *Nor* 70-73; P-in-c Preston-on-Stour w Whitchurch *Cov* 73-76; P-in-c Atherstone on Stour 73-76; V Preston on Stour and Whitchurch w Atherstone 77-88; Can Th Cov Cathl 77-88; Chapl Arthur Rank Cen 73-82; Dir 83-88; Chapl to The Queen 83-88; Area Bp Dorchester *Ox* 88-00; Bp Ely from 00. *The Bishop's House, Ely CB7 4DW* Tel (01353) 662749 Fax 669477 E-mail bishop@ely.anglican.org

RUSSELL, Canon Brian Kenneth. b 50. Trin Hall Cam BA73 MA76 Birm Univ MA77 PhD83. Cuddesdon Coll 74. **d** 76 **p** 77. C Redhill St Matt *S'wark* 76-79; Dir of Studies NEOC 79-83; P-in-c Merrington *Dur* 79-83; Dir of Studies and Lect Linc Th Coll 83-86; Selection Sec and Sec Cttee for Th Educn ABM 86-93; Bp's Dir for Min *Birm* from 93; Hon Can Birm Cathl from 99. *175 Harborne Park Road, Harborne, Birmingham B17 0BH* Tel 0121-426 0429 Fax 428 1114
E-mail b.russell@birmingham.anglican.org

RUSSELL, Brian Robert. b 61. QUB BA BD92 TCD DipTh85. **d** 85 **p** 86. C Dublin Drumcondra w N Strand *D & G* 85-87; C Carrickfergus *Conn* 87-90; I Kilmegan w Maghera *D & D* 90-96; I Bailieborough w Knockbride, Shercock and Mullagh *K, E & A* 96-00; I Kilbarron w Rossnowlagh and Drumholm *D & R* from 00. *The Rectory, Lisminton, Ballintra, Co Donegal, Irish Republic* Tel (00353) (74) 973 4025 E-mail bestrussell@eircom.net

RUSSELL, Bruce Harley. b 57. Ch Ch Ox BA79 Roehampton Inst PGCE80. Ripon Coll Cuddesdon DipMin99. **d** 99 **p** 00. C Bracknell *Ox* 99-03; TV Langley Marish from 03. *St Francis's Vicarage, 21 Lynward Avenue, Slough SL3 7BJ* Tel (01753) 557150 E-mail bhrussell@supanet.com

RUSSELL, Christopher Ian. b 68. St Jo Coll Dur BA91 St Edm Coll Cam MPhil96. Ridley Hall Cam 93. **d** 96 **p** 97. C Deptford St Jo w H Trin *S'wark* 96-99; Soul Survivor Watford *St Alb* 99-01; C Reading St Mary w St Laur *Ox* from 01. *Hamelsham, Downshire Square, Reading RG1 6NJ* Tel 0118-958 0960
E-mail chris@belindarussell.freeserve.co.uk

RUSSELL, David Edward. d 52 **p** 53. C St Mich Cathl Barbados 53-56; Perm to Offic *Chich* and *Roch* from 98. *31 Fair Lane, Robertsbridge TN32 5AS*

RUSSELL, David John. b 57. Sarum & Wells Th Coll BTh94. **d** 94 **p** 95. C Glouc St Geo w Whaddon *Glouc* 94-98; P-in-c Wickwar w Rangeworthy 98-01; R Wickwar, Rangeworthy and Hillesley from 02. *The Rectory, High Street, Wickwar, Wotton-under-Edge GL12 8NP* Tel (01454) 294267
E-mail davidrussell@classicfm.net

RUSSELL, David Robert. b 43. Brasted Th Coll 66 Sarum Th Coll 68. **d** 70 **p** 71. C Leintwardine *Heref* 70-73; C Bridgnorth w Tasley 73-75; Australia from 75. R Lockridge 75-80; R Bellevue and Darlington 80-87; Snr Chapl DCS 93; R Carlisle and Rivervale from 95; AD Vic Park from 98. *239 Orrong Road, Rivervale, W Australia 6103* Tel (0061) (8) 9470 5861 Fax 9470 5862 E-mail drussl@smartchat.net.au

RUSSELL, Canon Derek John. b 30. St Pet Hall Ox BA54 MA58. Qu Coll Birm 54. **d** 56 **p** 57. C Boxley *Cant* 56-59; C Whitstable All SS 59-63; Chapl HM Pris Wormwood Scrubs 63-65 and 71-89; Chapl HM Pris Stafford 65-69; Pentonville 70; SE Regional Chapl 74-81; Chapl HM Rem Cen Latchmere Ho 74-77; Asst Chapl Gen of Pris 81-83; Dep 83-90; Hon Can Cant Cathl 86-90; rtd 90; Perm to Offic *Cant* from 90. *25 Pier Avenue, Whitstable CT5 2HQ* Tel (01227) 276654

RUSSELL, Ms Elizabeth Marilyn Vivia. b 50. LRAM72 GRSM72. Westcott Ho Cam 95. **d** 97 **p** 98. C Alton St Lawr *Win* 97-01; C St Martin-in-the-Fields *Lon* from 01. *5 Aldwyn House, Davidson Gardens, London SW8 2HX* Tel (020) 7766 1108
E-mail liz.russell@smitf.org

RUSSELL, Eric. b 19. Dur Univ LTh42 BA48 MA53 Man Univ BD52 Nottm Univ MPhil87. Oak Hill Th Coll 38. **d** 42 **p** 43. C Rusholme H Trin *Man* 42-45; C Cheadle *Ches* 45-47; C Bispham *Blackb* 47-49; Org Sec NW Area CPAS 49-52; V Litherland St Jo and St Jas *Liv* 52-57; Asst Master Broadway Sch Cheadle 59-61; Div Master Wilmslow Gr Sch 61-64; Sen Lect Relig Educn W Midl Tr Coll Walsall 64-67; Hd of Relig Studies Sheff Coll of Educn 67-78; Lic to Offic *Sheff* 67-78; Lect Liv Bible Coll 78-88; rtd 88; Perm to Offic *Liv* from 88. *16A St Paul's Street, Southport PR8 1LZ* Tel (01704) 534797

RUSSELL, Eric Watson. b 39. FCA73. Clifton Th Coll 66. **d** 69 **p** 70. C Knowle *Sarum* 69-73; C Peckham St Mary Magd *S'wark* 73-77; TV Barking St Marg w St Patr *Chelmsf* 77-82; V Lozells St Paul and St Silas *Birm* 82-95; RD Aston 89-94; P-in-c Barston from 95; C Knowle from 95. *20 Slater Road, Bentley Heath, Solihull B93 8AG* Tel (01564) 776864 Fax 779123
E-mail eric-russell@supanet.com

RUSSELL, The Ven Harold Ian Lyle. b 34. Lon Coll of Div ALCD59 BD60. **d** 60 **p** 61. C Iver *Ox* 60-63; C Fulwood *Sheff* 63-67; V Chapeltown 67-75; RD Tankersley 73-75; V Nottingham St Jude *S'well* 75-89; AD Nottingham Cen 86-89;

Hon Can S'well Minster 88-89; Adn Cov 89-00; rtd 01; Chapl to The Queen from 97; Perm to Offic *S'well* from 01. *5 Old Acres, Woodborough, Nottingham NG14 6ES* Tel 0115-965 3543

RUSSELL, Isoline Lucilda. b 41. Dioc OLM tr scheme 00. **d** 03. OLM Camberwell St Giles w St Matt *S'wark* from 03. *124 Hindmans Road, London SE22 9NH* Tel (020) 8299 4431

RUSSELL, James Anthony Tomkins. b 67. Oak Hill Th Coll BA99. **d** 99 **p** 00. C Chadwell *Chelmsf* 99-03; C Patcham *Chich* from 03. *32 Fairview Rise, Brighton BN1 5GL* Tel (01273) 503926
E-mail jamesandannabel@aol.com

RUSSELL, Mrs Janet Mary. b 53. Univ of Wales BSc74 BArch76. Ox Min Course 91. **d** 94 **p** 95. C Watlington w Pyrton and Shirburn *Ox* 94-97; C Icknield 97-98; TV Wallingford from 98. *34 Thames Mead, Crowmarsh Gifford, Wallingford OX10 8EY* Tel (01491) 837626

RUSSELL, Canon John Arthur. b 29. AKC62. **d** 63 **p** 64. C Fareham H Trin *Portsm* 63-67; R Greatham w Empshott 67-79; V Ham St Andr *S'wark* 79-87; P-in-c Battersea St Luke 87-92; V 92-96; Hon Can S'wark Cathl 95-96; rtd 97; Perm to Offic *S'wark* from 97. *23 Vicarage Street, Frome BA11 1PU* Tel (01373) 472226

RUSSELL, John Bruce. b 56. Ripon Coll Cuddesdon. **d** 95 **p** 96. C Newport Pagnell w Lathbury and Moulsoe *Ox* 95-98; P-in-c Wing w Grove 98-03; AD Mursley 02-03. *21 Elm Close, Weston Turberville, Aylesbury HP22 5SS* Tel (01296) 614597
E-mail john@russvic.freeserve.co.uk

RUSSELL, John Graham. b 35. G&C Coll Cam BA58 MA62. Westcott Ho Cam 59. **d** 61 **p** 62. C Durleigh *B & W* 61-66; C Bridgwater St Mary w Chilton Trinity 61-66; C Far Headingley St Chad *Ripon* 66-72; P-in-c Leeds St Matt Lt London 72-79; V Rowley Regis *Birm* 79-84; V Hall Green Ascension 84-95; Deanery P Warley Deanery 95-00; rtd 01; Perm to Offic *Birm* from 01. *1 Stapylton Avenue, Harborne, Birmingham B17 0BA* Tel 0121-426 4529 E-mail pmr@russellp21.fsnet.co.uk

RUSSELL, John Richard. b 53. Westmr Coll Ox MTh01 FRSA02. Spurgeon's Coll 77 Ripon Coll Cuddesdon 01. **d** 01 **p** 02. Chapl RAF from 02. *Chaplaincy Services (RAF) HQ, Personnel and Training Command, RAF Innsworth, Gloucester GL3 1EZ* Tel (01452) 712612 ext 5164 Fax 510828

RUSSELL, Canon Jonathan Vincent Harman. b 43. K Coll Lon 68. **d** 69 **p** 70. C Addington *Cant* 69-73; C Buckland in Dover w Buckland Valley 73-76; P-in-c Selling 76-85; P-in-c Throwley w Stalisfield and Otterden 79-85; R Selling w Throwley, Sheldwich w Badlesmere etc 85-95; Hon Min Can Cant Cathl 83-94; Hon Can Cant Cathl from 94; RD Ospringe 90-95; P-in-c Elham w Denton and Wootton 95-01; V from 01. *The Vicarage, Vicarage Lane, Elham, Canterbury CT4 6TT* Tel (01303) 840219

RUSSELL, Jonathan Wingate. b 55. BSc BA DMS Dip Ind Mgt. St Jo Coll Nottm 81. **d** 84 **p** 85. C Southsea St Jude *Portsm* 84-87; P-in-c Shorwell w Kingston 87-92; V from 92; P-in-c Gatcombe 87-92; R from 92; P-in-c Chale 89-92; R from 92; RD W Wight 96-01. *The Vicarage, 5 Northcourt Close, Shorwell, Newport PO30 3LD* Tel (01983) 741044 Fax as telephone
E-mail russells@shorwellvicarage.freeserve.co.uk

RUSSELL, Lloyd George Winkler. b 19. Hatf Coll Dur LTh45 BA49. **d** 45 **p** 46. Jamaica 45-48, 50-52 and 82-85; Perm to Offic *Dur* 48-50; *Lon* 53-58; *S'wark* 53-59; *Roch* 58-81 and from 85; rtd 85; Perm to Offic *S'wark* from 85. *39 Pembroke Road, Bromley BR1 2RT* Tel (020) 8460 1498

RUSSELL, Martin Christopher. b 48. St Jo Coll Dur BA70. Coll of Resurr Mirfield 72. **d** 74 **p** 75. C Huddersfield St Pet *Wakef* 74-77; Trinidad and Tobago 78-85; V S Crosland *Wakef* 86-00; P-in-c Helme 86-00; P-in-c Halifax H Trin 00-02; P-in-c Halifax St Jude 00-02; V Halifax H Trin and St Jude from 02. *Holy Trinity Vicarage, 9 Love Lane, Halifax HX1 2BQ* Tel (01422) 352446

RUSSELL, Michael John. b 38. Clifton Th Coll 68. **d** 68 **p** 69. C Cranham Park CD *Chelmsf* 68-70; C Bucknall and Bagnall *Lich* 70-77; P-in-c Tintwistle *Ches* 77-79; V 79-86; New Zealand from 86; rtd 03. *144 Winchester Street, Ashurst, New Zealand* Tel (0064) (6) 326 8547

RUSSELL, Morris Charles. b 14. AKC36. **d** 37 **p** 38. C Tottenham St Phil *Lon* 37-39; C Winchmore Hill H Trin 39-41; CF (EC) 41-46; V Thornham w Titchwell *Nor* 46-51; R Newmarket St Mary *St E* 51-59; R Ipswich St Matt 59-66; V Auckland St Matt New Zealand 67-79; rtd 79. *3A Princes Street, Cambridge, New Zealand* Tel (0064) (7) 823 1128

RUSSELL, Canon Neil. b 47. Nottm Univ CPS81 Ox Univ DipApTh95. EMMTC 78. **d** 81 **p** 82. NSM Wyberton *Linc* 81-84; C 84-85; V Frampton 85-93; Agric Chapl and Countryside Officer 88-93; P-in-c Stamford All SS w St Jo 93-97; V from 97; RD Aveland and Ness w Stamford from 00; Can and Preb Linc Cathl from 02. *All Saints' Vicarage, Casterton Road, Stamford PE9 2YL* Tel (01780) 756942
E-mail nrussell@onetel.net.uk

RUSSELL, Mrs Noreen Margaret. b 39. Man Univ BA60 Lon Univ PGCE61 BD66. WMMTC 90. **d** 91 **p** 94. NSM Swynnerton and Tittensor *Lich* 91-97; C Draycott-le-Moors w Forsbrook from 97. *40 Old Road, Barlaston, Stoke-on-Trent ST12 9EQ* Tel (01785) 372992

RUSSELL, The Ven Norman Atkinson. b 43. Chu Coll Cam BA65 MA69 Lon Univ BD70. Lon Coll of Div 67. **d** 70 **p** 71. C Clifton Ch Ch w Em *Bris* 70-74; C Enfield Ch Ch Trent Park *Lon* 74-77; R Harwell w Chilton *Ox* 77-84; P-in-c Gerrards Cross 84-88; P-in-c Fulmer 85-88; R Gerrards Cross and Fulmer 88-98; Hon Can Ch 95-98; RD Amersham 96-98; Adn Berks from 98. *Foxglove House, Love Lane, Donnington, Newbury RG14 2JG* Tel (01635) 552820 Fax 522165
E-mail archdber@oxford.anglican.org
RUSSELL, Miss Pamela. b 34. SRN SCM. Coll of Resurr Mirfield 85. **dss** 86 **d** 87. Barnburgh w Melton on the Hill *Sheff* 86-93; Hon Par Dn 87-93; Chapl Asst Grimsby Distr Gen Hosp 93-94; Asst Chapl NE Lincs NHS Trust 94-99; rtd 99; Perm to Offic *Linc* 99-02. *17 Cambridge Road, Grimsby DN34 5TR* Tel (01472) 872292
RUSSELL, Paul Selwyn. b 38. ALCD61. **d** 61 **p** 62. C Gillingham St Mark *Roch* 61-64; SAMS 64-84; Chile, Peru and Bolivia 64-84; V Brinsworth w Catcliffe *Sheff* 84-91; R Brinklow *Cov* from 91; R Harborough Magna from 91; V Monks Kirby w Pailton and Stretton-under-Fosse from 91. *The Rectory, 31 Coventry Road, Brinklow, Rugby CV23 0NE* Tel (01788) 832274
E-mail psrussll@aol.com
RUSSELL, Ralph Geoffrey Major. b 19. St Aug Coll Cant 47 Sarum Th Coll 48. **d** 50 **p** 51. C Redruth *Truro* 50-55; C Hayes St Mary *Lon* 55-56; C W Wycombe *Ox* 56-62; V New Bradwell w Stantonbury 62-73; P-in-c Gt Linford w Willen and Gt and Lt Woolstone 62-64; P-in-c Linslade 74-75; V 75-87; rtd 87; Perm to Offic *Ox* from 87; *Pet* from 89. *60 Cheneys Walk, Bletchley, Milton Keynes MK3 6JY* Tel (01908) 641998
RUSSELL, Richard Alexander. b 44. Univ of Wales (Abth) BA65 McMaster Univ Ontario MA67 Bris Univ MA73 PGCE74 MEd76. Trin Coll Bris DipHE81. **d** 82 **p** 83. C Hartlepool St Paul *Dur* 82-85; P-in-c Bath Widcombe *B & W* 85-88; V 88-00; rtd 00. *76 Waterside Way, Radstock, Bath BA3 3YQ* Tel (01761) 433217
E-mail 113135.2044@compuserve.com
RUSSELL, Roger Geoffrey. b 44. Worc Coll Ox BA69 MA73. Cuddesdon Coll 70. **d** 72 **p** 73. C Anlaby Common St Mark *York* 72-75; C Wilton Place St Paul *Lon* 75-86; R Lancing w Coombes *Chich* from 86; RD Worthing from 97. *The Vicarage, 63 Manor Road, Lancing BN15 0EY* Tel (01903) 753212
RUSSELL, William Warren. b 52. QUB BSocSc74. CITC 74. **d** 77 **p** 78. C Agherton *Conn* 77-79; C Lisburn Ch Ch Cathl 79-83; I Magheradroll *D & D* from 83. *18 Church Road, Ballynahinch BT24 8LP* Tel (028) 9756 2289
E-mail vicarwarren@hotmail.com
RUSSELL-SMITH, Mark Raymond. b 46. New Coll Edin MTh91. St Jo Coll Dur BA71 Cranmer Hall Dur DipTh72. **d** 72 **p** 73. C Upton (Overchurch) *Ches* 72-75; C Deane *Man* 75-77; UCCF Travelling Sec 77-80; Lic to Offic *York* 78-81; BCMS 81-92; Kenya 81-92; P-in-c Slaidburn *Bradf* from 92; P-in-c Long Preston w Tosside from 97. *The Rectory, Slaidburn, Clitheroe BB7 3ER* Tel (01200) 446238
RUST, Jonathan Kenneth. b 62. Reading Univ BSc84. Ridley Hall Cam. **d** 00 **p** 01. C Holloway St Mary Magd *Lon* from 00. *Top Flat, St Mark's Vicarage, Sandringham Road, London E8 2LL* Tel (020) 7254 2971
RUSTED, Mrs Mary Elizabeth. b 44. **d** 00 **p** 01. OLM Mildenhall *St E* from 00. *Spring Hall Farm, Cooks Drove, West Row, Bury St Edmunds IP28 8QL* Tel (01638) 715054
RUSTELL, Anthony. b 77. Ch Ch Ox BA98 MSt01 MA02. St Steph Ho Ox 98. **d** 01 **p** 02. NSM Ox St Barn and St Paul *Ox* from 01. *Keble College, Oxford OX1 3PG*
E-mail anthony.rustell@keble.ox.ac.uk
✠**RUSTON, The Rt Revd John Harry Gerald.** b 29. SS Coll Cam BA52 MA56. Ely Th Coll 52. **d** 54 **p** 55 **c** 83. C Leic St Andr *Leic* 54-57; OGS from 55; C Cuddesdon and Tutor Cuddesdon Coll 57-61; C Sekhukhuniland S Africa 62-70; Prin St Fran Coll 67-70; Can Pretoria 68-76; Sub Dean 71-76; Adn Bloemfontein 76-83; Suff Bp Pretoria 83-91; Bp St Helena 91-99; Perm to Offic *Roch* from 99. *1 Hunsdon Drive, Sevenoaks TN13 3AX* Tel (01732) 455868
RUTHERFORD, Anthony Richard. b 37. Culham Coll Ox TCert62 Lon Univ DipAdEd68 Sussex Univ MA77. S'wark Ord Course 83. **d** 86 **p** 87. Hon C Tunbridge Wells St Luke *Roch* 86-88; C Bromley SS Pet and Paul 88-90; V Wragby *Linc* 90-94; Asst Min Officer 90-94; V Penge Lane H Trin *Roch* 94-02; rtd 02. *6 Ashley Gardens, Tunbridge Wells TN4 8TY*
E-mail tonyrutherford6ag@hotmail.com
RUTHERFORD, Arthur Ernest. b 26. Saltley Tr Coll Birm CertEd53 Loughb Coll of Educn DipEd54. Sarum & Wells Th Coll 91. **d** 92 **p** 93. NSM Lilliput *Sarum* 92-96; Perm to Offic from 96. *Kirinyaga, 8 Jennings Road, Poole BH14 8RY* Tel (01202) 748777
RUTHERFORD, Daniel Fergus Peter. b 65. Hatf Coll Dur BA86 CertEd87. Ridley Hall Cam 88. **d** 90 **p** 91. C Harold Wood *Chelmsf* 90-94; C Hove Bp Hannington Memorial Ch *Chich* 94-97; Chapl City of Lon Freemen's Sch Ashtead Park from 97. *City of London Freemen's School, Ashtead Park KT21 1ET* Tel (01372) 277933 Fax 276728

RUTHERFORD, David Lesslie Calderwood. b 29. Master Mariner 55 Open Univ BA76 Open Th Coll BA99. LNSM course 89. **d** 91 **p** 92. Dioc Moderator for Reader Tr *St E* 90-95; OLM Acton w Gt Waldingfield 91-00; rtd 00; Perm to Offic *St E* from 00. *18 Gotsfield Close, Acton, Sudbury CO10 0AS* Tel (01787) 374169 Mobile 07774-680862
E-mail david@rutherfordpriest.freeserve.co.uk
✠**RUTHERFORD, The Rt Revd Graeme Stanley.** b 43. Cranmer Hall Dur BA77 MA78 ACT 66. **d** 66 **p** 67 **c** 00. Australia 66-73 and from 77; C Holborn St Geo w H Trin and St Bart *Lon* 73-74; C Dur St Nic *Dur* 74-77; R Kyabram 77-82; I Malvern St P 82-87; I Camberwell St Jo 87-00; Can St Paul's Cath 91-00; Asst Bp Newcastle from 00. *10 Pangari Place, PO Box 9095, Wyoming, NSW, Australia 2250* Tel (0061) (2) 4329 2902 Fax 4329 5501
E-mail bishopgraeme@bigpond.com
RUTHERFORD, Ian William. b 46. Univ of Wales (Lamp) BA68. Cuddesdon Coll 68. **d** 70 **p** 71. C Gosforth All SS *Newc* 70-72; C Prestbury *Glouc* 73-76; Chapl RN 76-93; TV Redruth w Lanner and Treleigh *Truro* 93-94; V Paulsgrove *Portsm* 94-99; V Leeds Belle Is St Jo and St Barn *Ripon* from 99. *The Vicarage, 30 Low Grange View, Leeds LS10 3DT* Tel 0113-271 7821
RUTHERFORD, Janet Elizabeth. b 37. Leic Univ Dip Counselling 98. S'wark Ord Course 86. **d** 89. NSM Plaistow St Mary *Roch* 89-90; NSM Linc St Botolph *Linc* 91-93. *6 Ashley Gardens, Tunbridge Wells TN4 8TY*
RUTHERFORD, Canon John Allarton Edge. b 10. SS Coll Cam BA32 MA36. Westcott Ho Cam 32. **d** 33 **p** 34. C Portsm Cathl *Portsm* 33-40; Chapl St Jo Coll York 40-42; Chapl Abp Holgate's Gr Sch 40-42; Chapl RAFVR 42-46; Chapl Charterhouse Sch Godalming 46-70; V Walsham le Willows *St E* 70-83; P-in-c 83-85; Hon Can St E Cathl 82-85; rtd 84; Perm to Offic *St E* from 85. *Stowlangtoft Nursing Home, Stowlangtoft, Bury St Edmunds IP31 3JY*
RUTHERFORD, Canon John Bilton. b 23. Qu Coll Birm 49. **d** 52 **p** 53. C Newc H Cross *Newc* 52-57; C Longbenton St Bart 57-60; V High Elswick St Phil 60-66; V Walker 66-74; V Benwell St Jas 74-81; Hon Can Newc Cathl 80-90; V Lesbury w Alnmouth 81-90; RD Alnwick 86-89; Perm to Offic from 90; rtd 90. *68 Worcester Way, Woodlands Park, Wideopen, Newcastle upon Tyne NE4 5JE* Tel 0191-236 4785
RUTHERFORD, Peter George. b 34. Nor Ord Course 73. **d** 76 **p** 77. NSM New Catton Ch Ch *Nor* 76-79; NSM Eaton 79-80; NSM Nor St Steph 81-92; Perm to Offic 92-94; P-in-c Earlham St Mary 94-99; RD Nor S 98-99; rtd 99; Perm to Offic *Nor* from 97. *126 Colman Road, Norwich NR4 7AA* Tel (01603) 457629 Fax as telephone E-mail pgr457629@aol.com
RUTHERFORD, Peter Marshall. b 57. St Andr Univ MTheol81 Ulster Univ MA96. CITC 83. **d** 83 **p** 84. C Stormont *D & D* 83-85; CF 85-01; Asst Chapl Gen 01-02; Asst Chapl Milan w Genoa and Varese *Eur* from 03. *Via Taburi 2, 21039 Valganna, Varese, Italy* Tel (0039) (03) 3299 4607
RUTHERFORD (née ERREY), Ms Rosalind Elisabeth. b 52. St Hugh's Coll Ox BA74 Goldsmiths' Coll Lon PGCE78 Surrey Univ BA02. STETS 99. **d** 02. C Earley St Pet *Ox* from 02. *33 Clevedon Drive, Earley, Reading RG6 5XF*
E-mail rosalind@rutherfords.fsnet.co.uk
RUTLEDGE, Canon Christopher John Francis. b 44. Lon Univ BSc67 Clare Coll Cam PGCTh70 FE TCert80 Univ of Wales MPhil94 PhD99. Sarum Th Coll 67. **d** 70 **p** 71. C Birm St Pet *Birm* 70-73; C Calne and Blackland *Sarum* 73-76; P-in-c Derry Hill 76-78; V 78-81; P-in-c Talbot Village 81-82; V from 82; Can and Preb Sarum Cathl from 95. *The Vicarage, 20 Alton Road, Bournemouth BH10 4AE* Tel (01202) 513646 or 529349
E-mail christopher.rutledge@cwcom.net
RUTLEDGE, Francis George. b 62. TCD BA83 DipTh86 BTh90. **d** 86 **p** 87. C Holywood *D & D* 86-89; C Willowfield 89-91; I Kilmakee *Conn* 91-97; I Carrigrohane Union *C, C & R* from 97. *The Rectory, Church Hill, Carrigrohane, Co Cork, Irish Republic* Tel (00353) (21) 487 1106 E-mail carrigro@gofree.indigo.ie
RUTT, Mrs Celia Mary Avril. b 43. Cranmer Hall Dur. **d** 02. NSM Heworth H Trin *York* from 02. *226 Shipton Road, York YO30 5RZ* Tel (01904) 627384 E-mail crutt@fish.co.uk
RUTT, Canon Denis Frederic John. b 17. Kelham Th Coll 34. **d** 41 **p** 42. C Luton Ch Ch *St Alb* 41-46; R Yaxham *Nor* 54-61; R Welborne 54-61; R Kirkley 61-71; RD Lothingland 65-71; R N Lynn w St Marg and St Nic 71-76; Can Res and Prec Lich Cathl *Lich* 76-83; rtd 83; Perm to Offic *Bradf* 83-99. *18 Manormead, Tilford Road, Hindhead GU26 6RA*
RUTT-FIELD, Benjamin John. b 48. Chich Th Coll. **d** 90 **p** 91. C Wickford and Runwell *Chelmsf* 90-94; V Goodmayes St Paul from 94. *St Paul's Vicarage, 20 Eastwood Road, Ilford IG3 8XA* Tel (020) 8590 6596 E-mail frbenjaminruttfield@yahoo.co.uk
RUTTER, Canon Allen Edward Henry (Claude). b 28. Qu Coll Cam BA52 MA56 DipAgr53. Cranmer Hall Dur DipTh58. **d** 59 **p** 60. C Bath Abbey w St Jas *B & W* 59-60; C E Dereham w Hoe *Nor* 60-64; R Cawston 64-69; Chapl Cawston Coll 64-69; P-in-c Felthorpe w Haveringland 64-69; S Africa 69-73; P-in-c Over and Nether Compton, Trent etc *Sarum* 73-80; RD Sherborne 77-87; P-in-c Oborne w Poyntington 79-80; P-in-c Queen Thorne 80-96; Can and Preb Sarum Cathl 86-96; rtd 96; Perm to Offic

B & W 98-99; P-in-c Thorncombe w Winsham and Cricket St Thomas 99; C Chard and Distr 99-00; Perm to Offic from 00. *Home Farm, Chilson, South Chard, Chard TA20 2NX* Tel (01460) 221368

RUTTER, John Edmund Charles. b 53. Qu Coll Cam MA76. All Nations Chr Coll Dip Miss82 St Jo Coll Nottm MA93. **d** 93 **p** 94. C Penge St Jo *Roch* 93-97; Bp's C Bangor Primacy *D & D* from 97; RD Bangor from 00. *4 Glendowan Way, Bangor BT19 7SP* Tel (028) 9145 7057 Fax as telephone

RUTTER, Martin Charles. b 54. Wolv Poly BSc75 Southn Univ BTh81. Sarum & Wells Th Coll 76. **d** 79 **p** 80. C Cannock *Lich* 79-82; C Uttoxeter w Bramshall 82-86; V W Bromwich St Jas 86-97; P-in-c W Bromwich St Paul 89-97; V W Bromwich St Jas w St Paul 97-02; RD W Bromwich 94-02; V Gt Barr from 02. *22 Lodge Road, Walsall WS5 3JY* Tel 0121-357 5813

RUTTER, Ronald. b 47. SS Hild & Bede Coll Dur TCert71 Open Univ BA81 CMath MIMA. Carl and Blackb Dioc Tr Inst. **d** 00 **p** 01. NSM Heversham and Milnthorpe *Carl* from 00. *Ellerslie, Woodhouse Lane, Heversham, Milnthorpe LA7 7EW* Tel (01539) 564260 Fax as telephone E-mail ron_rutter@hotmail.com

RWANDA, Archbishop of. *See* KOLINI, The Most Revd Emmanuel Musaba

RYALL, John Francis Robert. b 30. New Coll Ox BA52 MA57. Westcott Ho Cam 52. **d** 54 **p** 55. C Petersfield w Sheet *Portsm* 54-56; C Portsea St Mary 56-62; C Warblington w Emsworth 62-65; C Freshwater 65-67; R Frating w Thorrington *Chelmsf* 67-73; R Gt Yeldham 74-76; P-in-c Lt Yeldham 75-76; R Gt w Lt Yeldham 76-80; P-in-c Thorley *Portsm* 80-82; P-in-c Shalfleet 80-82; V 82-95; V Calbourne w Newtown 82-95; rtd 95; Perm to Offic *Portsm* from 95. *Weald House, Main Road, Wellow, Yarmouth PO41 0SZ* Tel (01983) 760783

RYALL, Michael Richard. b 36. TCD BA58 MA65 HDipEd66. TCD Div Sch Div Test58. **d** 58 **p** 59. C Dublin St Geo *D & G* 58-62; CF 62-65 and 68-90; CF (TAVR) 67-68; C Dublin Rathmines *D & G* 65-66; Dungannon Sec Sch 66-68; R Yardley Hastings, Denton and Grendon etc *Pet* 90-01; rtd 01; Perm to Offic *Portsm* from 02. *Hollow House, Hill Brow Road, Liss GU33 7PX* Tel (01730) 895161 Mobile 07968-111258

RYALLS, Craig James. b 74. Bris Univ BA96 Peterho Cam BA01. Ridley Hall Cam 99. **d** 02 **p** 03. C Bearsted w Thurnham *Cant* from 02. *19 Fulbert Drive, Bearsted, Maidstone ME14 4PU* Tel (01622) 631192 E-mail craig.ryalls@btopenworld.com

RYAN, Prof Christopher John. b 43. Gregorian Univ Rome PhL65 STL69 Glas Univ MA72 St Edm Coll Cam PhD78. Scots Coll Rome 62. **d** 68 **p** 68. In RC Ch 68-86; Fell and Dean St Edm Coll Cam 75-81; Fell Th Pontifical Inst of Medieval Studies Toronto 81-87; Naden Research Student St Jo Coll Cam 87-88; Lect Italian Cam Univ 88-90; Lic to Offic *Ely* 87-90; Sen Lect Italian Sussex Univ 91-94; Prof 94-02; Perm to Offic *Ox* 91-02; Fell and Dean of Chapl K Coll Cam from 02; Lic to Offic *Ely* from 02. *King's College, Cambridge CB2 1ST* Tel (01223) 331248 E-mail dean@kings.cam.ac.uk *or* cjr48@cam.ac.uk

RYAN, David Peter. b 64. Aston Univ BSc86. Linc Th Coll BTh94. **d** 94 **p** 95. C Horsforth *Ripon* 94-97; C Bedale 97-98; P-in-c Startforth and Bowes and Rokeby w Brignall 98-00; V from 00. *The Vicarage, High Startforth, Barnard Castle DL12 9AF* Tel (01833) 637371 E-mail davidryannow@netscapeonline.co.uk

RYAN, Graham William Robert (Gregg). b 51. CITC 90 St Jo Coll Nottm CertCS93. **d** 93 **p** 94. NSM Clonsast w Rathangan, Thomastown etc *M & K* 93-97; Dioc Communications Officer 96-97; Press Officer from 97; Dioc C from 97. *Millicent Hall, Millicent South, Sallins, Naas, Co Kildare, Irish Republic* Tel (00353) (45) 879464 Fax as telephone E-mail greggwrj@iol.ie

RYAN, James Francis. b 47. Surrey Univ BSc. Trin Coll Bris DipHE St Jo Coll Nottm. **d** 83 **p** 84. C Littleover *Derby* 83-86; C Chipping Sodbury and Old Sodbury *Glouc* 86-89; V Pype Hayes *Birm* 89-99; R W Winch w Setchey, N Runcton and Middleton *Nor* from 99. *The Rectory, Rectory Lane, West Winch, King's Lynn PE33 0NR* Tel (01553) 840835

RYAN, Canon Maureen. b 98 **p** 99. C Tuam w Cong and Aasleagh *T, K & A* from 98; Preb Kilmactalway St Patr Cathl Dublin from 01. *Marshal's Park, Rinville, Oranmore, Galway, Irish Republic*

RYAN, Roger John. b 47. Surrey Univ MA00. Lon Bible Coll BA79 Oak Hill Th Coll 79. **d** 80 **p** 81. C Luton St Fran *St Alb* 80-83; R Laceby *Linc* 83-88; V Summerstown *S'wark* from 88. *St Mary's Vicarage, 46 Wimbledon Road, London SW17 0UQ* Tel (020) 8946 9853

RYAN, Canon Stephen John. b 49. Univ of Wales (Swansea) BA70 Bris Univ DipTh73. Sarum & Wells Th Coll 70. **d** 73 **p** 74. C Llantrisant *Llan* 73-77; V Treherbert w Treorchy 77-89; Youth Chapl 80-85; RD Rhondda 84-89; V Aberdare St Fagan 89-02; RD Cynon Valley 97-02; TR Neath from 02; Can Llan Cathl from 02. *The Rectory, 23 London Road, Neath SA11 1LE* Tel (01639) 644612

RYCRAFT, Mrs Rosemary Ives Stewart. b 49. Westmr Coll Ox BTh00 SRN72 SCM74. St Alb and Ox Min Course 00. **d** 03. NSM New Marston *Ox* from 03. *15 Jack Straws Lane, Headington, Oxford OX3 0DL* Tel (01865) 791075 E-mail rosemary.rycraft@btopenworld.com

RYDER, Canon Derek Michael. b 36. St Cath Coll Cam BA60 MA64. Tyndale Hall Bris 61. **d** 63 **p** 64. C Hampreston *Sarum* 63-66; Asst Chapl Brentwood Sch Essex 66-72; Chapl Ipswich Sch 72-77; Home Sec CMJ 77-87; TR Wexcombe *Sarum* 87-99; RD Pewsey 89-99; Can and Preb Sarum Cathl 97-99; rtd 99; Perm to Offic *Ox* and *Sarum* from 00. *31 The Green, Calne SN11 8DJ* Tel (01249) 821797

RYDER, John Merrick. b 55. Natal Univ BA75 BA77. St Pet Coll Natal 81. **d** 82 **p** 83. S Africa 84-88; St Helena 88-91; C Havant *Portsm* 91-95; P-in-c Godshill 95-99; V from 99; P-in-c Wroxall 99-02. *The Vicarage, Church Hill, Godshill, Ventnor PO38 3HY* Tel (01983) 840895 E-mail rfrjohn@aol.com

RYDER, Canon Lisle Robert Dudley. b 43. Selw Coll Cam BA68 MA72 Birm Univ DPS76. Sarum Th Coll 69. **d** 71 **p** 72. C Lowestoft St Marg *Nor* 71-75; Chapl Asst Oxon Area HA 76-79; C Littlehampton St Jas *Chich* 79-85; C Wick 79-85; C Littlehampton St Mary 79-85; Chapl Worc R Infirmary 85-94; Chapl Worc R Infirmary NHS Trust 94-00; Chapl Worcs Acute Hosps NHS Trust from 00; Hon Can Worc Cathl *Worc* from 89. *1 Holywell Hill, Worcester WR2 5NZ, or Worcester Royal Infirmary, Castle Street, Worcester WR1 3AS* Tel (01905) 763333 E-mail holywell@totalise.co.uk

RYDER-WEST, Keith. b 63. Sunderland Poly BSc86. Chich Th Coll 92 Coll of Resurr Mirfield BTh95. **d** 95 **p** 96. C Rawmarsh w Parkgate *Sheff* 95-96; C Armley w New Wortley *Ripon* 96-99; V Altofts *Wakef* from 99. *The Vicarage, Altofts, Normanton WF6 2QG* Tel (01924) 892299

RYDINGS, Donald. b 33. Jes Coll Ox BA57 MA61. Linc Th Coll 57. **d** 59 **p** 60. C Poulton-le-Fylde *Blackb* 59-62; C Ox St Mary V *Ox* 62-66; Staff Sec SCM 62-66; C-in-c Bourne End St Mark CD *Ox* 66-74; R Hedsor and Bourne End 74-76; P-in-c Gt Missenden w Ballinger and Lt Hampden 76-93; RD Wendover 79-89; V Gt Missenden w Ballinger and Lt Hampden 93-02; rtd 02. *16 Marroway, Weston Turville, Aylesbury HP22 5TQ* Tel (01296) 612281

RYE, David Ralph. b 33. AKC59. **d** 60 **p** 61. C Rushmere *St E* 60-64; C Barnham Broom w Kimberley, Bixton etc *Nor* 64-76; TV Barnham Broom 76-82; TR 82-95; P-in-c Reymerston w Cranworth, Letton, Southburgh etc 85-95; rtd 95; Perm to Offic *Nor* from 95. *5A Yarmouth Road, Norwich NR7 0EA*

RYELAND, John. b 58. K Coll Lon BD80 AKC80. Linc Th Coll 80. **d** 81 **p** 82. C Enfield St Jas *Lon* 81-84; C Coulsdon St Andr *S'wark* 84-87; C-in-c Ingrave St Steph CD *Chelmsf* 87-97; Dir Chr Healing Miss from 97; NSM Paddington St Steph w St Luke *Lon* 97-99. *8 Cambridge Court, 210 Shepherd's Bush Road, London W6 7NJ* Tel (020) 7603 8118 Fax 7603 5224 E-mail chm@healingmission.freeserve.co.uk

RYLAND, Colin William. b 16. TD52. MCSP. St Steph Ho Ox 61. **d** 62 **p** 63. C Plymstock *Ex* 62-66; R Church w Chapel Brampton *Pet* 66-73; V Wellingborough St Barn 73-83; Relief Chapl HM Prison Service 80-92; rtd 83; Perm to Offic *Dur* from 83; Chapl St Chad's Coll 94-96. *13 St John's Road, Durham DH1 4NU* Tel 0191-386 9638

RYLANDS, Mrs Amanda Craig. b 52. CertEd75. All Nations Chr Coll Dip Miss82 Trin Coll Bris DipHE85. **dss** 85 **d** 87 **p** 94. Chippenham St Andr w Tytherton Lucas *Bris* 85-87; Par Dn Stockport St Geo *Ches* 87-91; Par Dn Acton and Worleston, Church Minshull etc 91-94; C 94-97; Dioc Adv for Min Among Children 95-97; NSM Langport Area Chs *B & W* 97-98 and 99-02; TV 98-99; Dioc Voc Adv 00-02; Perm to Offic *Ex* from 03. *The Rectory, Church Lane, Cheriton Bishop, Exeter EX6 6HY* Tel (01647) 24702

RYLANDS, Canon Mark James. b 61. SS Hild & Bede Coll Dur BA83. Trin Coll Bris BA87. **d** 87 **p** 88. C Stockport St Geo *Ches* 87-91; V Acton and Worleston, Church Minshull etc 91-97; TR Langport Area Chs *B & W* 97-02; Dioc Missr *Ex* from 02; Can Res Ex Cathl from 02. *The Rectory, Church Lane, Cheriton Bishop, Exeter EX6 6HY* Tel (01647) 24702 *or* (01392) 459378 E-mail fishing@exeter.anglican.org

RYLANDS, Canon Thomas Michael. b 18. CCC Cam BA39 MA46. Wells Th Coll. **d** 47 **p** 48. C Nantwich *Ches* 47-51; V Wilton *B & W* 51-56; R Malpas *Ches* 56-68; R Malpas and Threapwood 68-85; RD Malpas 70-84; Hon Can Ches Cathl 72-85; rtd 85; Perm to Offic *Ches* 85-00. *Haughton Thorn, Tarporley CW6 9RN* Tel (01829) 260215

RYLE, Denis Maurice. b 16. OBE70. St Aid Birkenhead 35. **d** 39 **p** 40. C Parr *Liv* 39-42; C Widnes St Paul 42-44; C Much Woolton 44-45; CF 45-58; Sen CF 58-65; Dep Asst Chapl Gen 65-73; P-in-c Latimer w Flaunden *Ox* 73-85; rtd 85; Perm to Offic *York* from 90. *5 Church Close, Wheldrake, York YO19 6DP* Tel (01904) 898124

RYLEY, Canon Patrick Macpherson. b 30. Pemb Coll Ox BA54 Lon Univ BD56. Clifton Th Coll 54. **d** 56 **p** 57. C Ox St Clem *Ox* 56-59; Burma 60-66; Kenya 68-75; V Lynn St Jo *Nor* 76-92; V King's Lynn St Jo the Ev 92-95; RD Lynn 78-83; Hon Can Nor Cathl 90-95; rtd 95; Perm to Offic *Bradf* from 95. *106 Little Lane, Ilkley LS29 8JJ* Tel (01943) 817026

RYLEY, Timothy Patrick. b 64. Man Univ BA86. St Jo Coll Nottm Dip Th Studies 92 MA93. **d** 93 **p** 94. C Pendlebury St Jo

Man 93-97; P-in-c Norris Bank 97-01; Age Concern from 01. *213 Green Lane, Heaton Moor, Stockport SK4 2NS* Tel 0161-975 0151

RYMER, David John Talbot. b 37. Chich Th Coll 63. **d** 66 **p** 67. C Tuffley *Glouc* 66-69; Rhodesia 69-79; P-in-c S Kensington St Jude *Lon* 79-82; V 82-88; P-in-c Ambergate *Derby* 88-91; P-in-c Heage 88-91; R Ambergate and Heage 91-96; P-in-c Findern 96-01; V 01-03; P-in-c Willington 96-01; V 01-03; rtd 03. *2 Glebe Close, Long Lane, Dalbury Lees, Ashbourne DE6 5BJ* Tel (01332) 824165 E-mail david.rymer@amserve.net

RYRIE, Alexander Crawford. b 30. Edin Univ MA52 BD55 Glas Univ MLitt75. New Coll Edin 52 Union Th Sem (NY) STM56. **d** 83 **p** 83. Hon C Edin St Mary *Edin* 83-85; R Jedburgh 85-95; rtd 95. *Boisils, Bowden, Melrose TD6 0ST* Tel (01835) 823226

RYRIE, Mrs Isabel. b 31. ABPsS73 CPsychol88 Edin Univ MA51 Glas Univ MEd70. Moray Ho Edin DipRE52. **d** 89 **p** 94. Bp's Dn *Edin* 89-91; NSM Edin St Mary 91-98; rtd 98. *Boisils, Bowden, Melrose TD6 0ST* Tel (01835) 823226

S

SABAH, Bishop of. See YONG, The Most Revd Datuk Ping Chung

SABAN, Ronald Graham Street. b 28. Bps' Coll Cheshunt 60. **d** 62 **p** 63. C Maidstone St Martin *Cant* 62-66; C Croydon St Sav 66; rtd 94. *34 Kingsway, Caversham, Reading RG4 0RA* Tel 0118-947 9454

SABELL, Michael Harold. b 42. Open Univ BA78 Surrey Univ MSc. Sarum & Wells Th Coll 77. **d** 80 **p** 81. NSM Shirley *Win* 80-82; NSM Finham *Cov* 82-85; Chapl to the Deaf *Win* 81-82; *Cov* 82-85; *Sheff* 85-89; Lich 89-96; Chapl to the Deaf *St Alb* 96-01; P-in-c Gt and Lt Wymondley 96-01; R Ingoldsby *Linc* from 01; R Old Somerby from 01; R Ropsley from 01; R Sapperton w Braceby from 01. *The Rectory, Back Lane, Ingoldsby, Grantham NG33 4EW* Tel (01476) 585746

SABEY-CORKINDALE, Charmaine Clare. b 58. DipCOT87 SROT87. St Alb and Ox Min Course. **d** 02. NSM St Ippolyts *St Alb* 02-03; C Hitchin from 03. *5 Lavender Way, Hitchin SG5 2LU* Tel (01462) 435497

SADDINGTON, Peter David. b 42. Cranmer Hall Dur. **d** 84 **p** 85. C Tudhoe Grange *Dur* 84-86; C Monkwearmouth St Andr 86-88; V Burnopfield 88-94; P-in-c Greenside 94-96; V from 96. *The Vicarage, Greenside, Ryton NE40 4AA* Tel 0191-413 8281

SADGROVE, The Very Revd Michael. b 50. Ball Coll Ox BA71 MA75. Trin Coll Bris 72. **d** 75 **p** 76. Lic to Offic *Ox* 75-77; Tutor Sarum & Wells Th Coll 77-82; Vice-Prin 80-82; V Alnwick *Newc* 82-87; Vice-Provost, Can Res and Prec Cov Cathl *Cov* 87-95; Provost Sheff 95-00; Dean Sheff 00-03; Dean Dur from 03. *The Deanery, The College, Durham DH1 3EQ* Tel 0191-384 7500 Fax 386 4267 E-mail michael.sadgrove@durhamcathedral.co.uk

SADLER, Ann Penrith. b 50. STETS. **d** 01 **p** 02. C Lenham w Boughton Malherbe *Cant* 01-02; C Harrietsham w Ulcombe 01-02; C Len Valley from 02. *The Vicarage, Old Ashford Road, Lenham, Maidstone ME17 2PX* Tel (01622) 853919 E-mail sadler@ferring39.fsnet.co.uk

SADLER, The Ven Anthony Graham. b 36. Qu Coll Ox BA60 MA64. Lich Th Coll 60. **d** 62 **p** 63. C Burton St Chad *Lich* 62-65; V Rangemore 65-72; V Dunstall 65-72; V Abbots Bromley 72-79; V Pelsall 79-90; RD Walsall 82-90; Preb Lich Cathl from 87; P-in-c Uttoxeter w Bramshall 90-97; P-in-c Stramshall 90-97; P-in-c Kingstone w Gratwich 90-97; P-in-c Checkley 90-97; P-in-c Marchington w Marchington Woodlands 90-97; P-in-c Leigh 93-97; TR Uttoxeter Area 97; Adn Walsall from 97. *10 Paradise Lane, Walsall WS3 4NH* Tel (01922) 445353 Fax 445354 E-mail archdeacon.walsall@lichfield.anglican.org

SADLER, John Ernest. b 45. Nottm Univ BTh78. Linc Th Coll 74. **d** 78 **p** 79. C Brampton St Thos *Derby* 78-81; TV Coventry Caludon *Cov* 81-85; P-in-c High Elswick St Phil *Newc* 85; P-in-c Newc St Aug 85; V Newc St Phil and St Aug 86-94; P-in-c Newc Epiphany 94-99; Perm to Offic from 00; Ch Development Worker from 01. *1 Albermarle Avenue, Newcastle upon Tyne NE2 3NQ* Tel 0191-285 1724 E-mail jjsadler@btinternet.com

SADLER, Michael Stuart. b 57. Wycliffe Hall Ox 78. **d** 81 **p** 82. C Henfynyw w Aberaeron and Llanddewi Aberarth *St D* 81-88; V Llanddewi Rhydderch w Llangattock-juxta-Usk etc *Mon* from 88. *The Vicarage, Llanddewi Rhydderch, Abergavenny NP7 9TS* Tel (01873) 840373

SAGAR, Brian. b 39. Sarum & Wells Th Coll 78. **d** 80 **p** 81. C Radcliffe St Thos and St Jo *Man* 80-82; P-in-c Charlestown 82-85;

R Gt Lever 85-89; Chapl Cov Ch Housing Assn *Cov* 89-92; V Wing w Grove *Ox* 92-97; P-in-c Diddington *Ely* 97-00; P-in-c Lt Paxton 97-00; P-in-c Southoe 97-00; P-in-c Lever Bridge *Man* from 00. *St Stephen's Vicarage, Radcliffe Road, Bolton BL2 1NZ* Tel (01204) 528300

SAGE, Andrew George. b 58. Chich Th Coll 83. **d** 85 **p** 86. C Rawmarsh w Parkgate *Sheff* 85-87; C Fareham SS Pet and Paul *Portsm* 87-89; C Southsea H Spirit 89-91; P-in-c Nuthurst *Chich* 91-93; R 93-95; V Hangleton from 95; Chapl Worthing and Southlands Hosps NHS Trust from 01. *St Helen's Villa, 145 New Church Road, Hove BN3 4DB* Tel (01273) 424892 or 419409 E-mail andrewsage@aol.com

SAGE, Canon Jesse. b 35. Trin Hall Cam BA61 MA65. Chich Th Coll 61. **d** 63 **p** 64. C Feltham *Lon* 63-67; S Africa 67-72 and from 96; R Abbas and Temple Combe *B & W* 72-75; R Abbas and Templecombe w Horsington 76-77; Chapl Agric and Rural Soc in Kent *Cant* 78-95; Hon Can Cant Cathl 90-95; R Gonubie St Martin by the Sea 96-00; P-in-c Komga St Paul 98-00; Hon Can Grahamstown from 02; rtd 00. *30 Hazy Ridge, Swallow Lane, Gonubie, 5257 South Africa* Tel (0027) (43) 732 1298 Mobile 82-651 6698 Fax (43) 732 1317 E-mail jessesage@qwest.co.za

SAGE, John Arthur. b 32. MInstP Lon Univ BSc54. St Alb Minl Tr Scheme 78. **d** 81 **p** 82. NSM Stevenage St Mary Shephall *St Alb* 81-86; NSM Stevenage St Mary Sheppall w Aston 86-87; C St Peter-in-Thanet *Cant* 87-98; rtd 98. *3 West Cliff Road, Broadstairs CT10 1PU* Tel (01843) 603471

SAGOVSKY, Nicholas. b 47. CCC Ox BA69 St Edm Ho Cam PhD81. St Jo Coll Nottm BA73. **d** 74 **p** 75. C Newc St Gabr *Newc* 74-77; C Cambridge Gt St Mary w St Mich *Ely* 81; Vice-Prin Edin Th Coll 82-86; Dean of Chpl Clare Coll Cam 86-97; Wm Leech Prof Fell Newc Univ *Newc* from 97; Perm to Offic from 99. *Department of Religious Studies, Armstrong Building, Newcastle University, Newcastle upon Tyne NE1 7RU* Tel 0191-222 6000

SAINSBURY, Peter Donald. b 67. Ridley Hall Cam 98. **d** 00 **p** 01. C Longfleet *Sarum* from 00. *31 Houlton Road, Poole BH15 2LN* Tel (01202) 677829 Fax 253527 E-mail petesainsbury@yahoo.co.uk

✠**SAINSBURY, The Rt Revd Roger Frederick.** b 36. Jes Coll Cam BA58 MA62. Clifton Th Coll. **d** 60 **p** 61 **c** 91. C Spitalfields Ch Ch w All SS *Lon* 60-63; Missr Shrewsbury Ho Everton 63-74; P-in-c Everton St Ambrose w St Tim *Liv* 67-74; Warden Mayflower Family Cen Canning Town *Chelmsf* 74-81; P-in-c Victoria Docks St Luke 78-81; V Walsall *Lich* 81-87; TR 87-88; Adn W Ham *Chelmsf* 88-91; Area Bp Barking 91-02; Moderator Ch's Commn for Racial Justice 99-02; rtd 02; Hon Asst Bp B & W from 03. *Abbey Lodge, Battery Lane, Portishead, Bristol BS20 7JD* Tel (01275) 847082

SAINT, Arthur James Maxwell. b 10. St Jo Coll Ox BA31 MA35. Cuddesdon Coll 34. **d** 35 **p** 36. C Stoke upon Trent *Lich* 35-37; Hd Master St Thos Sch Kuching Sarawak 37-41; C Shrewsbury St Mary 42-43; V Shawbury 43-48; V Cheltenham St Steph *Glouc* 48-60; Chapl Guy's Hosp Lon 60-65; V Ox SS Phil and Jas *Ox* 65-76; rtd 76. *The College of St Barnabas, Blackberry Lane, Lingfield RH7 6NJ* Tel (01342) 870256

SAINT, David Gerald. b 45. Sarum & Wells Th Coll 72. **d** 75 **p** 76. C Wellingborough All Hallows *Pet* 75-79; R Kislingbury w Rothersthorpe 79-83; V Kings Heath 83-85; Relig Progr Producer BBC Radio Northn from 85; Perm to Offic *Pet* from 86. *71 Stanwell Way, Wellingborough NN8 3DD* Tel (01933) 675995

ST ALBANS, Archdeacon of. See CUNLIFFE, The Ven Helen Margaret

ST ALBANS, Bishop of. See HERBERT, The Rt Revd Christopher William

ST ALBANS, Dean of. See LEWIS, The Very Revd Christopher Andrew

ST ANDREWS, DUNKELD AND DUNBLANE, Bishop of. See HENLEY, The Rt Revd Michael Harry George

ST ANDREWS, DUNKELD AND DUNBLANE, Dean of. See MacALISTER, The Very Revd Randal George Leslie

ST ASAPH, Archdeacon of. See THOMAS, The Ven Elwyn Bernard

ST ASAPH, Bishop of. See DAVIES, The Rt Revd John Stewart

ST ASAPH, Dean of. See POTTER, The Very Revd Christopher Nicholas Lynden

ST DAVIDS, Archdeacon of. See HOLDSWORTH, The Ven John Ivor

ST DAVIDS, Bishop of. See COOPER, The Rt Revd Carl Norman

ST DAVIDS, Dean of. See EVANS, The Very Revd John Wyn

ST EDMUNDSBURY AND IPSWICH, Bishop of. See LEWIS, The Rt Revd John Hubert Richard

ST EDMUNDSBURY, Dean of. See ATWELL, The Very Revd James Edgar

ST GERMANS, Suffragan Bishop of. See SCREECH, The Rt Revd Royden

ST GILES, Miss Aysha. b 61. Nottm Univ BA84. Ripon Coll Cuddesdon 88. **d** 90 **p** 97. C Daventry *Pet* 90-91; C Corby SS Pet and Andr w Gt and Lt Oakley 91-92; C Chellaston *Derby* 97-99; R Brimington 99-03; rtd 03; Perm to Offic *Derby* from 03. *c/o Crockford, Church House, Great Smith Street, London SW1P 3NZ*

ST HELENA, Bishop of. *See* SALT, The Rt Revd John William

ST JOHN-CHANNELL, Michael Alister Morrell. b 53. Bris Univ BEd76 MA01. Ripon Coll Cuddesdon 76. **d** 78 **p** 79. C Portsea St Mary *Portsm* 78-81; PV Linc Cathl *Linc* 82-85; P-in-c Linc St Mary-le-Wigford w St Benedict etc 82-85; R Cranford *Glouc* from 99; V Staines St Mary and St Pet 92-99; V Cirencester *Glouc* from 99; RD Cirencester from 01. *Cirencester Vicarage, 1 Dollar Street, Cirencester GL7 2AJ* Tel (01285) 653142 Fax 652442 E-mail mstjc@hotmail.com

ST JOHN NICOLLE, Michael George. b 29. St Jo Coll Dur BA52 DipEd. **d** 70 **p** 71. C Lt Bowden St Nic *Leic* 70; C Knighton St Jo 71-74; R Desford 74-81; R Tarrant Valley *Sarum* 81-85; R Jersey St Jo *Win* 85-94; rtd 94; Perm to Offic *Win* from 94. *Les Noyers, Les Chenoles, St John, Jersey JE3 4FB* Tel (01534) 865276

SALENIUS, Richard Mark. b 57. K Coll Lon BD79 AKC79. Linc Th Coll 79. **d** 80 **p** 81. C St Marylebone w H Trin *Lon* 80-84; C Sale St Anne *Ches* 84-87; V Macclesfield St Jo 87-96; V Brightlingsea *Chelmsf* from 96. *The Vicarage, Richard Avenue, Brightlingsea, Colchester CO7 0LP* Tel (01206) 302407 E-mail richard.salenius@btinternet.com

SALES, Canon Patrick David. b 43. K Coll Lon AKC68 BD74 Kent Univ MA00. **d** 69 **p** 70. C Maidstone All SS w St Phil *Cant* 69-72; C Chart next Sutton Valence 72-74; C Birchington w Acol 75-77; V Boughton under Blean w Dunkirk 77-83; V Herne 83-03; P-in-c Hoath 98-03; TV Whitstable from 03; Hon Min Can Cant Cathl 83-01; Hon Can Cant from 01; RD Reculver 86-92; AD from 01; Dioc Adv in Liturgy from 00. *The Vicarage, Church Street, Whitstable CT5 1PG* Tel (01227) 272308 E-mail patrick@sales64.freeserve.co.uk

SALISBURY, Anne Ruth. b 37. Dalton Ho Bris DipTh65. **d** 87 **p** 94. C Harrow Trin St Mich *Lon* 87-98; C Paddington Em Harrow Road from 99; C W Kilburn St Luke w St Simon and St Jude from 99. *Emmanuel Vicarage, 44C Fermoy Road, London W9 3NH* Tel (020) 8969 0438

SALISBURY, Harold Gareth. b 21. St Pet Hall Ox BA42 MA46. Wycliffe Hall Ox 42. **d** 44 **p** 45. C Pet St Mark *Pet* 44-46; India 47-63; V Duddo *Newc* 63-70; V Norham 63-70; V Norham and Duddo 70-78; V Snaith *Sheff* 78-86; P-in-c Cowick 78-86; TR Gt Snaith 86; rtd 86; Perm to Offic *Pet* from 87. *33 Nightingale Drive, Towcester NN12 6RA* Tel (01327) 353674

SALISBURY, John Forbes. b 16. St Jo Coll Dur 46. **d** 50 **p** 51. C Gt Malvern Ch Ch *Worc* 50-53; C Dudley St Jo 53-57; V Manningham St Luke *Bradf* 57-62; V Riddlesden 62-67; V Tosside 67-79; Lic to Offic 80-84; rtd 81; Perm to Offic *Bradf* 84-99. *14 Victoria Mill, Belmont Wharf, Skipton BD23 1RL* Tel (01756) 701411

SALISBURY, Peter Brian Christopher. b 58. MBCS85 UMIST BSc80. Sarum & Wells Th Coll BTh92. **d** 92 **p** 93. C Stanmore *Win* 92-95; V Chilworth w N Baddesley from 95. *The Vicarage, 33 Crescent Road, North Baddesley, Southampton SO52 9HU* Tel (023) 8073 2393 E-mail peter@baddesleychurch.org

SALISBURY, Canon Roger John. b 44. Lon Univ BD67. Lon Coll of Div 66. **d** 68 **p** 69. C Harold Wood *Chelmsf* 68-73; V Dorking St Paul *Guildf* 73-82; R Rusholme H Trin *Man* 82-90; TR Gt Chesham *Ox* from 90; RD Amersham from 98; Hon Can Ch Ch from 02. *The Rectory, Church Street, Chesham HP5 1HY* Tel (01494) 783629 Fax 791745 E-mail rsalisbury@greatchesham.freeserve.co.uk

SALISBURY, Canon Tobias. b 33. Em Coll Cam BA60. Ripon Hall Ox 60. **d** 62 **p** 63. C Putney St Mary *S'wark* 62-65; C Churchdown St Jo *Glouc* 65-67; V Urchfont w Stert *Sarum* 67-73; R Burton Bradstock w Shipton Gorge and Chilcombe 73-79; P-in-c Long Bredy w Lt Bredy and Kingston Russell 75-79; TR Bride Valley 79-86; V Gt and Lt Bedwyn and Savernake Forest 86-97; Can and Preb Sarum Cathl 92-98; rtd 98; Perm to Offic *B & W* from 98. *Anfield, Hayes Lane, Compton Dundon, Somerton TA11 6PB* Tel (01458) 274459

SALISBURY, Bishop of. *See* STANCLIFFE, The Rt Revd David Staffurth

SALISBURY, Dean of. *Vacant*

SALMON, Alan Clive. b 63. SSC99 Bris Univ BA84 Univ of Wales (Cardiff) DPS85. St Mich Coll Llan 84. **d** 86 **p** 87. C Llanelli *St D* 86-88; C Roath St German *Llan* 88-90; V Nevern and Y Beifil w Eglwyswrw and Meline etc *St D* 90-92; In RC Ch 92-99; Perm to Offic *S'wark* 99-00; Hon C Lavender Hill Ascension etc from 00. *St Philip's House, St Philip's Square, London SW8 3RT* Tel (020) 7622 1929

SALMON, Andrew Ian. b 61. St Jo Coll Nottm BTh88. **d** 88 **p** 89. C Collyhurst *Man* 88-92; P-in-c Pendleton St Ambrose 92-95; TV Pendleton 95-99; TR from 99. *St Ambrose's Vicarage, 92 Fitzwarren Street, Pendleton, Salford M6 5RS* Tel 0161-745 7608 Fax 743 8211 E-mail andy@st-amb.dircon.co.uk

SALMON, Andrew Meredith Bryant. b 30. Jes Coll Cam BA54 MA58. Ridley Hall Cam 54. **d** 56 **p** 57. C Enfield Ch Ch Trent Park *Lon* 56-58; Chapl Monkton Combe Sch Bath 58-71; Chapl Milton Abbey Sch Dorset 71-89; TV Bride Valley *Sarum* 89-96; rtd 97; Perm to Offic *Sarum* from 97. *1 Barnhill Road, Wareham BH20 5BD* Tel (01929) 554039

SALMON, Anthony James Heygate. b 30. CCC Ox BA53 DipTh54 MA57. Cuddesdon Coll 54. **d** 56 **p** 57. C S Norwood St Mark *Cant* 56-59; S Africa 59-69; Chapl USPG Coll of the Ascension Selly Oak 69-74; P-in-c Frinsted 74-78; R Harrietsham 74-85; P-in-c Ulcombe 81-85; V Chobham w Valley End *Guildf* 85-95; rtd 95; Perm to Offic *St Alb* from 95. *24 Elmwood, Welwyn Garden City AL8 6LE* Tel (01707) 333694

SALMON, Bernard Bryant. b 24. Trin Hall Cam BA50 MA54. Wells Th Coll 50. **d** 52 **p** 53. C Stockton St Pet *Dur* 52-55; C Longbenton St Bart *Newc* 55-58; R Cramlington 58-71; V Winscombe *B & W* 71-91; RD Locking 78-86; rtd 91; Perm to Offic *B & W* from 91. *Scaddens House, Scaddens Lane, Rodney Stoke, Cheddar BS27 3UR* Tel (01749) 870194

SALMON, Mrs Constance Hazel. b 25. R Holloway Coll Lon BSc46. Lon Bible Coll 66 Gilmore Course 71. **dss** 80 **d** 87 **p** 96. Sidcup St Andr *Roch* 80-88; NSM 87-88; Perm to Offic 88-96; NSM Eynsford w Farningham and Lullingstone from 96. *43 Old Mill Close, Eynsford, Dartford DA4 0BN* Tel (01322) 866034

SALMON, Jonathan. b 66. Univ Coll of Swansea BSc(Econ)88 Sussex Univ MA95 MPhil95. Wycliffe Hall Ox 01. **d** 03. C Bowling St Jo *Bradf* from 03. *79 Bowling Hall Road, Bradford BD4 7LN* Tel 07814-674027 (mobile) E-mail jonathan@jsalmon1.fsnet.co.uk

SALMON, Mrs Margaret Penny. b 37. Leeds Univ BA59 CertEd60. SW Minl Tr Course 85. **d** 88 **p** 94. NSM Yelverton, Meavy, Sheepstor and Walkhampton *Ex* from 88. *Hinnies, Leg-o-Mutton Corner, Yelverton PL20 6DJ* Tel (01822) 853310 E-mail peggysalmon@compuserve.com

SALMON, Mark Harold. b 62. Trin Coll Bris. **d** 00 **p** 01. C Bath Weston All SS w N Stoke and Langridge *B & W* from 00. *23 Lucklands Road, Weston, Bath BA1 4AX* Tel (01225) 314809 E-mail mark.salmon@xalt.co.uk

SALMON, Philip John. b 63. Oak Hill Th Coll 96. **d** 98 **p** 99. C Kington w Huntington, Old Radnor, Kinnerton etc *Heref* 98-02; TV Radipole and Melcombe Regis *Sarum* from 02. *The Vicarage, 74 Field Barn Drive, Weymouth DT4 0EF* Tel (01305) 778995 Mobile 07771-688226 E-mail pip@fish.co.uk

SALMON, Richard Harold. b 35. Fitzw Ho Cam BA57. Clifton Th Coll 57. **d** 59 **p** 60. C Blackheath Park St Mich *S'wark* 59-61; C St Alb St Paul *St Alb* 61-63; Malaysia 63-75; OMF 63-65; C Telok Anson St Luke 63-65; V Kuantan Pehang Epiphany 65-75; P-in-c March St Wendreda *Ely* 75-76; R 76-85; V Congresbury w Puxton and Hewish St Ann *B & W* 85-00; rtd 00; Perm to Offic *Truro* 00-01. *2 Wisteria Avenue, Hutton, Weston-super-Mare BS24 9QF* Tel (01934) 813750 E-mail richard.salmon@talk21.com

SALMON, The Very Revd Thomas Noel Desmond Cornwall. b 13. TCD BA35 MA49 BD42. TCD Div Sch 35. **d** 37 **p** 38. C Bangor St Comgall *D & D* 37-40; C Belfast St Jas *Conn* 40-41; C Larne and Inver 42-44; Clerical V Ch Ch Cathl Dublin *D & G* 44-45; Lect TCD 45-89; I Dublin Rathfarnham *D & G* 45-50; Hon Clerical V Ch Ch Cathl Dublin 45-63; I Tullow 50-62; I Dublin St Ann 62-67; Preb Dunlavin St Patr Cathl Dublin 63-67; Dean Ch Ch Cathl Dublin *D & G* 67-89; I Dublin Ch Ch Cathl 76-89; rtd 89. *3 Glenageary Terrace, Dun Laoghaire, Co Dublin, Irish Republic* Tel (00353) (1) 280 0101

SALMON, William John. b 52. Lon Univ BSc72. St Jo Coll Dur 76. **d** 79 **p** 80. C Summerstown *S'wark* 79-81; C Hampreston *Sarum* 81-86; V Sundon *St Alb* 86-90; Dep Chapl HM Young Offender Inst Glen Parva 90-91; Chapl HM Pris Whitemoor 91-95; Chapl HM Pris Blundeston from 95. *The Chaplain's Office, HM Prison Blundeston, Lowestoft NR32 5BG* Tel (01502) 730591 ext 326 Fax 732392 E-mail bill.salmon@chalkface.net

SALMON, Yvonne. d 03. OLM Boughton Monchelsea *Cant* from 03. *Address temp unknown*

SALONIA, Ivan. b 38. Open Univ BA81 N Lon Poly MA85 CQSW78. Milan Th Coll (RC) 60. **d** 63 **p** 64. In RC Ch Hong Kong 64-73; Hon C Woolwich St Thos *S'wark* 89-91; C Greenwich St Alfege w St Pet and St Paul 91-93; C Kidbrooke St Jas 93-95; TV 95-02; rtd 02; Perm to Offic *S'wark* from 03. *247 Hook Lane, Welling DA16 2NZ* Tel (020) 8298 1309 Mobile 07946-085065 Fax (020) 8306 6859 E-mail ivanus_magnus@hotmail.com

SALOP, Archdeacon of. *See* HALL, The Ven John Barrie

SALSBURY, Harry. b 31. Lon Univ TCert62. **d** 60 **p** 61. In RC Ch 60-82; NSM Bexhill St Pet *Chich* 83-84; Chapl Brighton Coll Jun Sch 84-93; C Eastbourne St Mary *Chich* 93-94; Perm to Offic from 94. *3 Egbert Close, Eastbourne BN23 6TP* Tel (01323) 460685

SALT, Canon David Christopher. b 37. Univ of Wales (Lamp) BA59. Sarum Th Coll 59. **d** 61 **p** 62. C Bridgwater St Mary *Worc* 61-66; Ind Chapl 66-72; R Knightwick w Doddenham, Broadwas and Cotheridge 72-82; Chapl Worc Coll of HE 72-82; V Redditch St Steph *Worc* 82-02; P-in-c Tardebigge 84-88; RD

Bromsgrove 91-00; Hon Can Worc Cathl 92-02; rtd 02. *7 Longmoor Close, Redditch B97 6SX* Tel (01527) 68735

SALT, David Thomas Whitehorn. b 32. K Coll Lon AKC56 BD57. **d** 57 **p** 58. New Hebrides 57-63; Solomon Is 63-66; C Hawley H Trin *Guildf* 66-68; V Shelf *Bradf* 68-73; R Checkendon *Ox* 73-81; RD Henley 78-84; TR Langtree 81-84; Chapl Hungerford Hosp 84-89; V Hungerford and Denford *Ox* 84-89; P-in-c Harpsden 89-95; Gen Sec Melanesian Miss 89-95; rtd 95; Perm to Offic *Sarum* from 95. *7 Milton Road, Pewsey SN9 5JJ* Tel (01672) 569124

✠**SALT, The Rt Revd John William.** b 41. Kelham Th Coll 61. **d** 66 **p** 67 **c** 99. C Barrow St Matt *Carl* 66-70; Lesotho 70-77; S Africa 77-99; OGS from 81; Superior from 96; Dean Eshowe Cathl and Adn S Zululand 89-99; Bp St Helena from 99. *Bishopsholme, PO Box 62, St Helena, South Atlantic Ocean* Tel (00290) 4471 Fax 4728 E-mail bishop@helanta.sh *or* jsalt@ogs.net

SALT, Leslie. b 29. Linc Th Coll 68. **d** 69 **p** 69. C Alford w Rigsby *Linc* 69-75; V Torksey 75-94; R Kettlethorpe 77-94; V Marton 77-94; V Newton-on-Trent 77-94; rtd 94; Perm to Offic *Linc* 94-97. *2 Holdenby Close, Lincoln LN2 4TQ*

SALT, Neil. b 64. Univ of Wales (Ban) BA85 Edin Univ BD89 Man Metrop Univ BSc97. Edin Th Coll 86. **d** 89 **p** 90. C Stretford All SS *Man* 89-93; P-in-c Smallbridge 93; P-in-c Wardle 93; V Smallbridge and Wardle 93-94; Perm to Offic *Wakef* 94-01; Hon C Ripponden from 01. *Christ Church Vicarage, 6 King Meadow, Barkisland, Halifax HX4 0AR* Tel (01422) 825987

SALTER, Arthur Thomas John. b 34. TD88. AKC60. **d** 61 **p** 62. C Ealing St Pet Mt Park *Lon* 61-65; C Shepherd's Bush St Steph w St Thos 65-66; C Holborn St Alb w Saffron Hill St Pet 66-70; P-in-c Barnsbury St Clem 70-77; P-in-c Islington St Mich 70-77; V Pentonville St Silas w All SS and St Jas 70-00; CF (TAVR) from 75; Gen Sec Angl and E Chs Assn from 76; Chmn from 90; P-in-c St Dunstan in the West *Lon* 79-99; rtd 00. *1 St James's Close, Bishop Street, London N1 8PH* Tel (020) 7359 0250

SALTER, Canon George Alfred. b 25. TCD BA47 MA. CITC 49. **d** 49 **p** 50. C Rathdowney *C & O* 49-51; C Cork St Luke *C, C & R* 51-53; I Fermoy Union 53-55; I Cork St Luke w St Ann 55-73; Can Ross Cathl 69-88; Can Cork Cathl 69-88; Treas 88-94; I Cork St Luke Union 73-94; Preb Tymothan St Patr Cathl Dublin 88-94; rtd 94. *Mount Vernon House, 66 Wellington Road, Cork, Irish Republic* Tel (00353) (21) 450 6844

SALTER, Janet Elizabeth. b 48. Leeds Univ CertEd69. SW Minl Tr Course 92. **d** 95 **p** 98. C Coleshill *Birm* 95-97; Hon C St Dennis *Truro* 97-00; TV Gillingham *Sarum* from 00. *The Vicarage, Kington Magna, Gillingham SP8 5EW* Tel (01747) 838494 Fax as telephone E-mail kmvicarage@tiscali.co.uk

SALTER, Canon John Frank. b 37. Dur Univ BA62 DipTh64. Cranmer Hall Dur 62. **d** 64 **p** 65. C Bridlington Priory *York* 64-67; Travelling Sec IVF 67-70; V Stoughton *Guildf* 70-02; RD Guildf 89-94; Hon Can Guildf Cathl 99-02; rtd 03. *7 Aldershot Road, Guildford GU2 8AE* Tel (01483) 511165 E-mail j.salter@btinternet.com

SALTER, John Leslie. b 51. AKC76. Coll of Resurr Mirfield 77. **d** 78 **p** 79. C Tottenham St Paul *Lon* 78-82; P-in-c Castle Vale *Birm* 82-83; TV Curdworth w Castle Vale 83-90; V Castle Vale St Cuth 90-92; V Wantage *Ox* from 93; AD Wantage from 01. *The Vicarage, The Cloisters, Wantage OX12 8AQ* Tel (01235) 762214 E-mail thevicar@wantage.parish.clara.net

SALTER, Nigel Christopher Murray. b 46. Loughb Univ BTech. Ripon Coll Cuddesdon 79. **d** 81 **p** 82. C Glouc St Aldate *Glouc* 81-84; C Solihull *Birm* 84-88; V Highters Heath 88-97; Asst Chapl Greenwich Healthcare NHS Trust 97-01; Asst Chapl Qu Eliz Hosp NHS Trust 01-03; P-in-c Leaton and Albrighton w Battlefield *Lich* from 03. *Leaton Vicarage, Baschurch Road, Bomere Heath, Shrewsbury SY4 3PN* Tel (01939) 290259

SALTER, Richard. b 24. Edin Th Coll 46. **d** 48 **p** 49. C Dundee St Salvador *Bre* 48-51; C Watford St Andr *St Alb* 51-54; C Oxhey St Matt 54-58; V Robert Town *Wakef* 58-62; V Watford St Jo *St Alb* 62-98; rtd 98; Perm to Offic *St Alb* from 98. *1 Beechfield Court, Grandfield Avenue, Watford WD17 4UE* Tel (01923) 231659

SALTER, Roger John. b 45. Trin Coll Bris 75. **d** 79 **p** 80. C Bedminster St Mich *Bris* 79-82; C Swindon Ch Ch 82-84; V Bedminster Down 84-89; P-in-c Northwood *Portsm* 89-93; P-in-c W Cowes H Trin 89-92; V Cowes H Trin and St Mary 92-94; USA from 94. *1300 Panorama Drive, Vestavia Hills, AL 35216, USA* Tel (001) (205) 823 7747

SALTER, Samuel. b 22. St Edm Hall Ox BA49 MA53. St Steph Ho Ox 49. **d** 50 **p** 51. C Brighton St Wilfrid *Chich* 50-53; C Felpham w Middleton 53-56; V Barkston w Syston *Linc* 56-59; R Coningsby 59-65; Chapl RAF 59-65; Chapl Cheltenham Coll 65-81; TV Grantham *Linc* 81-87; rtd 87; Perm to Offic *Linc* from 87. *23 St Nicholas Close, Barkston, Grantham NG32 2ND* Tel (01400) 251864

SALTWELL, Ms Kathleen. b 48. Edin Univ BD00 Cam Univ MA02. Westcott Ho Cam 00. **d** 02 **p** 03. C Worc SE *Worc* from 02. *24 Albert Road, Worcester SR5 1EB* Tel (01905) 356656 E-mail kathsaltwell@hotmail.com

SALWAY, Canon Donald Macleay. b 31. St Pet Hall Ox BA54 MA59. Oak Hill Th Coll 54. **d** 56 **p** 57. C Holloway St Mary w St Jas *Lon* 56-67; V Cambridge St Phil *Ely* 67-81; V Mile Cross *Nor* 81-96; RD Nor N 89-95; Hon Can Nor Cathl 91-96; rtd 96; Perm to Offic *B & W* from 96; C Langport Area Chs 98-00. *Lype House, Long Load, Langport TA10 9LD* Tel (01458) 241623

SAMBELL, David John. b 31. St Aid Birkenhead 60. **d** 63 **p** 64. C Sutton St Geo *Ches* 63-67; C Alsager St Mary 67-71; V Crewe St Pet 71-81; V Upton Priory 81-99; rtd 99; Perm to Offic *Ches* from 01. *19 Woodfield Close, Connah's Quay, Deeside CH5 4RF* Tel (01244) 814462

SAMMAN, Peter Bryan. b 27. TCD BA53. Coll of Resurr Mirfield 53. **d** 55 **p** 56. C Adlington *Blackb* 55-57; C Church Kirk 57-60; V Briercliffe 60-67; V Lancaster Ch Ch 67-74; V Lostock Hall 74-85; V Morecambe St Barn 85-91; rtd 91; Perm to Offic *Blackb* from 91. *14 Wentworth Crescent, Morecambe LA3 3NX* Tel (01524) 425208

SAMMÉ, Raymond Charles. b 50. Trent Poly MIBiol80 Anglia Poly Univ MA03. Oak Hill Th Coll 85. **d** 87 **p** 88. C Holmer w Huntington *Heref* 87-90; C Derby St Alkmund and St Werburgh *Derby* 90-93; V Romford Gd Shep Collier Row *Chelmsf* from 93. *Good Shepherd Vicarage, 97 Collier Row Lane, Romford RM5 3BA* Tel (01708) 726423 E-mail ray.samme@btinternet.com

SAMMON, Helen Mary. b 57. Newnham Coll Cam MA79 Bris Univ MB, ChB82 MRCGP98. WEMTC 00. **d** 03. NSM Painswick, Sheepscombe, Cranham, The Edge etc *Glouc* from 03. *Windycot, Cranham, Gloucester GL4 8HS* Tel (01452) 813159 E-mail helen.sammon@doctors.org.uk

SAMMONS, John Trevor. b 22. Birm Univ BA48. Ripon Hall Ox. **d** 50 **p** 51. C The Quinton *Birm* 50-55; V Birm St Luke 55-70; Chapl Birm Skin Hosp 56-70; P-in-c No Man's Heath *Lich* 70-82; R Newton Regis w Seckington and Shuttington *Birm* 70-86; rtd 87; Perm to Offic *Birm* from 87. *39 Kurtus, Dosthill, Tamworth B77 1NX* Tel (01827) 283875

SAMPFORD, John Alfred. b 36. Lich Th Coll 58. **d** 61 **p** 62. C Lambeth St Phil *S'wark* 61-65; C Beddington 65-69; V Hampstead Ch Ch *Lon* 69-79; V Enfield Chase St Mary 79-02; rtd 02; Perm to Offic *Ches* from 02. *Ellisland, Bryn Gwyn Lane, Northop Hall, Mold CH7 6JT* Tel (01244) 810635

SAMPSON, Brian Andrew. b 39. **d** 94 **p** 95. C Glem Valley United Benefice *St E* 94-96; C Pentlow, Foxearth, Liston and Borley *Chelmsf* 96-97; P-in-c from 97. *The Rectory, The Street, Foxearth, Sudbury CO10 7JG* Tel (01787) 313132 E-mail captainbrianca@waitrose.co.uk

SAMPSON, Clive. b 38. St Jo Coll Cam BA61 MA64. Ridley Hall Cam 63. **d** 65 **p** 66. C Tunbridge Wells St Jo *Roch* 65-69; Travelling Sec Scripture Union 69-79; V Maidstone St Luke *Cant* 79-94; rtd 98. *64-70 rue Compans A3 274, 75019 Paris, France* Tel (0033) (1) 40 18 12 72

SAMPSON, Desmond William John. b 25. FRICS60. Roch Th Coll 63. **d** 65 **p** 66. C Hythe *Cant* 65-70; V Alkham w Capel le Ferne and Hougham 70-76; V Wingham w Elmstone and Preston w Stourmouth 76-86; RD E Bridge 81-86; C Hythe 86-91; rtd 91; Perm to Offic *Cant* from 91. *25 Albert Road, Hythe CT21 6BP* Tel (01303) 268457

SAMPSON, Jeremy John Egerton. b 23. Dur Univ BSc45. Wells Th Coll 46. **d** 48 **p** 49. C Longbenton St Bart *Newc* 48-51; Singapore 51-62; V Killingworth *Newc* 62-76; V Consett *Dur* 76-90; RD Lanchester 80-85; rtd 90; Perm to Offic *Dur* and *York* from 90. *6 Kilkenny Road, Guisborough TS14 7LE* Tel (01287) 632734

SAMPSON, Julian Robin Anthony. b 78. St D Coll Lamp BA00. St Steph Ho Ox 01. **d** 03. C Notting Hill All SS w St Columb *Lon* from 03. *12 Powis Gardens, London W11 1JG* Tel (020) 7221 2857 E-mail jrasampson@yahoo.co.uk

SAMPSON, Terence Harold Morris. b 41. ACA64 FCA75. Bps' Coll Cheshunt 64. **d** 67 **p** 68. C Penrith St Andr *Carl* 67-72; V Carl St Barn 72-80; TR Carl H Trin and St Barn 80-84; Chapl Cumberland Infirmary 83-84; R Workington St Mich *Carl* 84-01; Hon Can Carl Cathl 89-01; RD Solway 90-95. *16 Poplar Street, Keswick CA12 5BW*

SAMS, Michael Charles. b 34. FCA62. Ox NSM Course 81. **d** 84 **p** 85. NSM Abingdon *Ox* 84-92 and from 99; P-in-c Shippon 92-99. *13 Honand Close, Abingdon OX14 2LU* Tel (01235) 529084

SAMSON, Hilary Lynn. b 50. SW Minl Tr Course. **d** 03. NSM St Agnes and Mithian w Mount Hawke *Truro* from 03. *12 Newton Road, Troon, Camborne TR14 7SJ* Tel (01209) 713247 E-mail hilarysamson@lineone.net

SAMUEL, Brother. *See* DOUBLE, Richard Sydney

SAMUEL, Canon James Louis. b 30. Birm Poly CQSW72 Open Univ BA77. Sarum Th Coll 59. **d** 61 **p** 62. C Dursley *Glouc* 61-63; C Matson 63-65; C Leckhampton SS Phil and Jas 65-66; C Blakenall Heath *Lich* 67-69; P-in-c Dudley St Aug Holly Hall *Worc* 81-86; V 86-94; RD Dudley 87-93; Hon Can Worc Cathl 88-94; rtd 94; Perm to Offic *Worc* 94-96 and from 98; C Kidderminster St Mary and All SS w Trimpley etc 96-98. *44 Broadwaters Drive, Kidderminster DY10 2RY* Tel (01562) 68533

✠**SAMUEL, The Most Revd Kunnumpurathu Joseph.** b 42. Union Bibl Sem Yavatmal BRE68 Selly Oak Coll CPS85 Texas Chr Univ MDiv86. **d** 68 **c** 90. Ch of S India from 68; Bp E Kerala from 90; Moderator Ch of S India from 99. *CSI Bishop's House, Melukavumattom PO, Kottayam 686 652, Kerala State, India* Tel (0091) (482) 291026 Fax 291044

SAMUEL, Mrs Mary Rose. b 42. Newc Univ BA65 Bris Univ CQSW67. STETS 95. **d** 98 **p** 99. C Waltham on the Wolds, Stonesby, Saxby etc *Leic* 98-01; P-in-c Wymondham w Edmondthorpe, Buckminster etc from 01. *The Rectory, Sycamore Lane, Wymondham, Melton Mowbray LE14 2AZ* Tel (01572) 787238 Fax 787499

SAMUEL, Stuart. b 48. St Aug Coll Cant 70. **d** 71 **p** 72. C Golcar *Wakef* 71-77; V Brampton St Mark *Derby* 77-79; P-in-c Hathern *Leic* 79-83; R Hathern, Long Whatton and Diseworth 83-90; R Hathern, Long Whatton and Diseworth w Belton etc 90-97; RD Akeley E 92-96; P-in-c Waltham on the Wolds, Stonesby, Saxby etc 97-02; P-in-c Wymondham w Edmondthorpe, Buckminster etc 97-01; P-in-c High Framland Par 97-01; P-in-c Helpringham w Hale *Linc* from 02. *The Vicarage, 2 Vicarage Lane, Helpringham, Sleaford NG34 0RP* Tel (01529) 421435 E-mail stuart@marymag.freeserve.co.uk

SAMUEL, Preb Theophilus. b 34. BScTech59. Oak Hill Th Coll 70. **d** 72 **p** 73. C Slough *Ox* 72-73; Chapl Community Relns 73-78; Chapl Brunel Univ *Lon* 78-85; V W Drayton 85-98; Preb St Paul's Cathl 97-98; rtd 98; Perm to Offic *Leic* from 99. *The Rectory, 7 Sycamore Close, Wymondham, Melton Mowbray LE14 2AZ* Tel (01572) 787238 Fax 787499

SAMUELS, Canon Ann Elizabeth. b 51. Birm Univ BA73 CertEd74. Trin Coll Bris 85. **d** 87 **p** 94. Par Dn Runcorn *Ches* 87-91; Par Dn Halton 91-94; C 94-03; Bp's Adv for Women in Min 94-96; Asst Dir of Ords 96-03; RD Frodsham 99-03; Chapl Halton Gen Hosp NHS Trust 99-03; V Higher Bebington *Ches* from 03; Hon Can Ches Cathl from 01. *3 Beech Road, Bebington, Wirral CH63 8PE* Tel 0151-645 9074 E-mail vicar@higher.bebington.fsnet.co.uk

SAMUELS, Canon Christopher William John. b 42. AKC66. **d** 67 **p** 68. C Kirkholt *Man* 67-72; C-in-c Houghton Regis St Thos CD *St Alb* 72-76; R Tarporley *Ches* 76-83; R Ches St Mary from 83; RD Ches 95-02; Hon Can Ches Cathl from 97; Chapl to The Queen from 02. *The Rectory, Overleigh Road, St Mary-without-the-Walls, Chester CH4 7HL* Tel (01244) 671202 Fax 682034

SAMUELS, Raymond John. b 49. Qu Mary Coll Lon BSc73 Essex Univ CertEd74. Trin Coll Bris 85. **d** 87 **p** 88. C Moreton *Ches* 87-91; V Halton 91-02; Dioc Dir of Ords from 03. *3 Beech Road, Bebington, Wirral CH63 8PE* Tel 0151-645 9074 *or* 644 8480 E-mail samuels@ddo-chester.fsnet.co.uk

SAMUELS, Miss Sheila Mary. b 57. St Andr Univ MA79 Wolfs Coll Ox MLitt82 CertEd83. Trin Coll Bris BA89. **d** 89 **p** 94. C Skirbeck H Trin *Linc* 89-96; Perm to Offic from 00. *61 Oak Crescent, Boston PE21 9EZ*

SAMWAYS, Denis Robert. b 37. Leeds Univ BA62. Coll of Resurr Mirfield 62. **d** 64 **p** 65. C Clun w Chapel Lawn *Heref* 64-69; C Pocklington w Yapham-cum-Meltonby, Owsthorpe etc *York* 69-71; C Millington w Gt Givendale 69-71; R Hinderwell w Roxby 71-76; Hon C 80-91; Hon C Loftus 76-80; V Boosbeck w Moorsholm 91-95; R Kirby Misperton w Normanby, Edston and Salton 95-02; rtd 02. *7 High Street, Gatehouse of Fleet, Castle Douglas DG7 2HR* Tel (01557) 814095

SAMWAYS, John Feverel. b 44. BA DipTh. Trin Coll Bris 81. **d** 83 **p** 84. C Patcham *Chich* 83-86; C Ox St Aldate w St Matt *Ox* 86-94; R Ox St Matt 95-97; TR Keynsham *B & W* from 97. *St John's Rectory, 1 The Park, Keynsham, Bristol BS31 2BL* Tel 0117-986 3354

✠**SAN SI HTAY, The Most Revd Samuel.** BA. **d** 67 **c** 89. Burma from 67; Asst Pastor Indaw 67-69; P-in-c Mawbi 70-76; Prin H Cross Coll 76-91; Asst Bp Yangon 91-93; Gen Sec Myanmar 93-01; Abp Myanmar and Bp Yangon from 01. *Bishopscourt, 140 Pyidaungsu Yeiktha Road, Dagon, Yangon 11191, Myanmar* Tel (0095) (1) 246813 Fax 251405 E-mail cpm.140@mptmail.net.mm

✠**SANANA, The Rt Revd Rhynold Ewaruba.** b 39. Newton Th Coll 60 St Barn Coll Adelaide 71 St Aug Coll Cant 75. **d** 67 **p** 67 **c** 76. Papua New Guinea 67-72, 73-90 and from 92; Asst P Dogura Cathl 67-69; Asst P Popondetta Resurr 69-70; St Barn Coll Adelaide Australia 72-73; Dean Dogura and Adn E Region 74-76; Asst Bp New Guinea 76-77; Bp Dogura 77-89; Asst P Lakenham St Mark *Nor* 90-92; rtd 92. *Melanesian Brotherhood, Haruro, PO Box 29, Popondetta, Oro Province, Papua New Guinea*

SANDAY, Robert Ward. b 55. Sarum & Wells Th Coll 89. **d** 91 **p** 92. C Swindon Ch Ch *Bris* 91-94; V Lyddington and Wanborough and Bishopstone etc 94-00; Chapl to the Deaf *Win* from 00. *3 Wheat Close, Chandlers Ford, Eastleigh SO53 4HA* Tel (023) 8027 0551

SANDBERG, Canon Peter John. b 37. Lon Univ LLB59. Lon Coll of Div 67. **d** 69 **p** 70. C Hailsham *Chich* 69-72; C Billericay St Mary *Chelmsf* 72-77; TV Billericay and Lt Burstead 77-83; R Thundersley 83-02; RD Hadleigh 90-00; Hon Can Chelmsf

Cathl 00-02; rtd 02. *Hethersett, School Road, Pentlow, Sudbury CO10 7JR* Tel (01787) 281006 E-mail psandberg@compuserve.com

SANDELLS-REES, Kathy Louise. *See* JONES, Ms Kathy Louise

SANDERS, Colin Anthony Wakefield. b 26. Wadh Coll Ox MA55. Ox NSM Course 89. **d** 90 **p** 91. NSM Eynsham and Cassington *Ox* 90-95; NSM Bladon w Woodstock from 95. *Little Firs, 41 Bladon Road, Woodstock OX20 1QD* Tel (01993) 813357

SANDERS, Diana Louise. b 59. Southn Univ BSc80 ACA83. STETS 95. **d** 98 **p** 99. NSM Alderbury Team *Sarum* 98-01; NSM Clarendon from 01. *Park Cottage, West Dean, Salisbury SP5 1JQ* Tel (01794) 340355

SANDERS, Graham Laughton. b 32. Kelham Th Coll 52. **d** 56 **p** 57. C Glouc St Paul *Glouc* 56-60; India 61-68; V Heaton St Martin *Bradf* 68-76; V Gt Waltham *Chelmsf* 76-79; V Gt Waltham w Ford End 79-87; Sec Dioc Liturg Cttee 78-87; TR Guiseley w Esholt *Bradf* 87-94; rtd 97; Perm to Offic *Bradf* from 95 and *York* from 98. *4 Marlborough Road, Shipley BD18 3NX* Tel (01274) 587896 Fax 593529 E-mail glmcesanders@aol.com

SANDERS, Henry William. b 36. **d** 62 **p** 64. C Nottingham St Ann *S'well* 62-65; C Dagenham *Chelmsf* 65-67; C W Thurrock 67-73; C W Ham 73-78; rtd 01. *Lancaster House, Serene Place, Broadstairs CT10 1LN* Tel (01843) 862853

SANDERS, Herbert. b 21. Clifton Th Coll 51. **d** 53 **p** 54. C Laisterdyke *Bradf* 53-56; C Bingley All SS 56-59; C Oxenhope 59-66; Lic to Offic *Linc* 66-81 and from 95; rtd 81. *12 Low Toynton Road, Horncastle LN9 5LL*

SANDERS, Mrs Hilary Clare. b 57. Hull Univ BA79 UEA CertEd81. EAMTC 83. **dss** 85 **d** 87 **p** 94. Haverhill w Withersfield, the Wrattings etc *St E* 85-87; Hon Par Dn Melton 87-94; Hon C 94-99; Dioc Dir Educn (Schools) 88-99; P-in-c Earl Soham w Cretingham and Ashfield from 99. *The Rectory, Church Lane, Earl Soham, Woodbridge IP13 7SD* Tel (01728) 685778 Fax 684051 E-mail mark@stedmundsbury.anglican.org *or* msanders@fish.co.uk

SANDERS, James Alexander. b 29. **d** 65 **p** 66. Australia 65-78; C Enfield St Jas *Lon* 78-81; rtd 94. *81 Queen Street, Woollahra, NSW 2025, Australia* Tel (0061) (2) 9328 6823 Fax 9362 1692

SANDERS, Canon Mark. b 57. Hull Univ BA79 Cam Univ BA82 DipHE91. Westcott Ho Cam 80. **d** 83 **p** 84. C Haverhill w Withersfield, the Wrattings etc *St E* 83-87; P-in-c Melton 87-91; R 91-98; Dioc Dir Post-Ord Tr from 97; Asst Dioc Dir of Ords 98-99; Dioc Dir of Ords from 99; Dioc Dir of CME 99-01; Hon Can St E Cathl from 01. *The Rectory, Church Lane, Earl Soham, Woodbridge IP13 7SD* Tel (01728) 685778 Fax 684051 E-mail mark@stedmundsbury.anglican.org *or* msanders@fish.co.uk

SANDERS, Preb Michael Barry. b 45. Fitzw Coll Cam BA67 MA71 Lon Univ BD71. St Jo Coll Nottm 68 Lon Coll of Div. **d** 71 **p** 72. C Ashtead *Guildf* 71-74; Chapl St Jo Coll Cam 75-79; V Dorridge *Birm* 79-89; TR Walsall *Lich* 89-97; Preb Lich Cathl 97-01; Chapl The Hague *Eur* from 01. *Riouwstraat 2, 2585 HA The Hague, The Netherlands* Tel (0031) (70) 355 5359 Fax 306 0758 *or* 354 1023 E-mail churchoffice@stjohnandstphilip.org

SANDERS, Nigel Wilding. b 29. Mert Coll Ox MA55. Ox Min Course 91. **d** 92 **p** 93. NSM Maidenhead St Andr and St Mary *Ox* 92-97; NSM Furze Platt 97-01; Perm to Offic from 02. *Fieldway, Worster Road, Cookham, Maidenhead SL6 9JG* Tel (01628) 521516 Fax 527328 E-mail nigelsanders@worsterroad.freeserve.co.uk

SANDERS, Mrs Nora Irene. b 29. Lon Univ BA50 CertEd51. WMMTC 74. **dss** 78 **d** 87 **p** 94. Dorridge *Birm* 78-87; Par Dn 87-90; Hon C Tanworth *Birm* 94-96; Perm to Offic from 96. *8 Cransley Grove, Solihull B91 3ZA* Tel 0121-705 2391

SANDERS, Roderick David Scott. b 58. Southn Univ BA80 CertEd81. Cranmer Hall Dur 85. **d** 88 **p** 89. C Luton St Mary *St Alb* 88-93; P-in-c Clovelly *Ex* 93-94; P-in-c Woolfardisworthy and Buck Mills 93-94; TV Parkham, Alwington, Buckland Brewer etc 94-98; NSM Cove St Jo *Guildf* 98-03; NSM Guildf All SS from 03. *Christ Church Vicarage, 25 Waterden Road, Guildford GU1 2AZ* Tel (01483) 564664 Mobile 07720-856460 E-mail rod.sanders@ntlworld.com

SANDERS (née COLLINGBRIDGE), Mrs Susan Rachel. b 61. St Mary's Coll Dur BA83. Cranmer Hall Dur 85. **d** 88 **p** 94. Par Dn Luton St Mary *St Alb* 88-93; Perm to Offic *Ex* 93-94; NSM Parkham, Alwington, Buckland Brewer etc 94-98; TV Cove St Jo *Guildf* 98-03; V Guildf Ch Ch w St Martha-on-the-Hill from 03. *Christ Church Vicarage, 25 Waterden Road, Guildford GU1 2AZ* Tel (01483) 568886 Mobile 07711-549976 E-mail susie.sanders@ntlworld.com

SANDERS, Mrs Wendy Elizabeth. b 49. Carl Dioc Tr Course 87. **d** 90 **p** 94. NSM Bampton w Mardale *Carl* 90-92; C Walney Is 92-94; C Stanwix 94-98; TV Chippenham St Paul w Hardenhuish etc *Bris* 98-03; TV Kington St Michael 98-03; RD Chippenham 99-03; TR Cockermouth w Embleton and Wythop *Carl* from 03.

The Rectory, Lorton Road, Cockermouth CA13 9DU Tel (01900) 823269 Mobile 07980-598892
E-mail wendy.sanders@talk21.com *or* wes@fish.co.uk

SANDERS, William John. b 48. Liv Inst of Educn BA80. Wycliffe Hall Ox 81. **d** 83 **p** 84. C Netherton *Liv* 83-87; C Wavertree St Bridget 87-97; V Wavertree St Bridget and St Thos from 97. *The Vicarage, Ashfield, Wavertree, Liverpool L15 1EY* Tel 0151-733 1117

SANDERSON, Colin James. b 54. SEN SRN Univ of Wales MA95. St Mich Coll Llan 85. **d** 87 **p** 88. C Merthyr Dyfan *Llan* 87-90; C Cadoxton-juxta-Barry 90-91; V Llangeinor 91-99. *26 Greenhill Road, Manchester M24 2BD* Tel 0161-653 9259 Mobile 07713-742365

SANDERSON, Canon Daniel. b 40. AKC66. **d** 67 **p** 68. C Upperby St Jo *Carl* 67-72; V Addingham 72-75; V Ireleth w Askam 75-02; C Dalton-in-Furness and Ireleth-with-Askam from 02; Hon Can Carl Cathl from 95; RD Furness from 01. *St Peter's Vicarage, Duke Street, Askham-in-Furness LA16 7AD* Tel (01229) 462647 E-mail danaskireleth@btinternet.com

SANDERSON, Canon Gillian. b 47. Cranmer Hall Dur 80. **dss** 82 **d** 87 **p** 94. Allesley *Cov* 82-86; Warwick 86-87; C 87-94; TV 94-00; Hon Can Cov Cathl 94-00; Perm to Offic from 00. *5 Burbury Court, Emscote Road, Warwick CV34 5LD* Tel (01926) 492881 Mobile 07714-193776
E-mail gillian@canon-sanderson.freeserve.co.uk

SANDERSON, Harold. b 26. St Aid Birkenhead. **d** 61 **p** 62. C Pemberton St Mark Newtown *Liv* 61-64; V Warrington St Ann 64-73; P-in-c Warrington St Pet 70-73; V Orrell 73-79; V Scarisbrick 79-91; rtd 91; Perm to Offic *Liv* from 91. *29 Green Lane, Ormskirk L39 1ND* Tel (01695) 571421

SANDERSON, The Very Revd Peter Oliver. b 29. St Chad's Coll Dur BA52 DipTh54. **d** 54 **p** 55. C Houghton le Spring *Dur* 54-59; Jamaica 59-63; Chapl RAF 63-67; P-in-c Winksley cum Grantley and Aldfield w Studley *Ripon* 67-68; V 68-74; V Leeds St Aid 74-84; Can St Paul's Cathl Dundee *Bre* 84-91; Provost St Paul's Cathl Dundee 84-91; R Dundee St Paul 84-91; USA from 91; rtd 94. *201 1st Avenue North, Apt 405, Iowa City, IA 52245-3613, USA* Tel (001) (319) 466 0852

SANDERSON, Peter Richard Fallowfield. b 18. St Cath Soc Ox BA41 MA46. Chich Th Coll 41. **d** 42 **p** 44. C Bishops Hull St Jo *B & W* 42-48; C Ox St Paul *Ox* 48-49; Perm to Offic *Ex* 49-55; V Poundstock *Truro* 56-74; P-in-c Hove St Patr *Chich* 74-79; P-in-c Buxted St Mary 79-82; P-in-c Hadlow Down 79-82; P-in-c Buxted and Hadlow Down 82-83; rtd 83; Perm to Offic *Chich* 83-00. *Nova Scotia, 48 Parklands Road, Hassocks BN6 8JZ* Tel (01273) 843117

SANDERSON, Scott. b 42. Oak Hill Th Coll DipHE. **d** 82 **p** 83. C Galleywood Common *Chelmsf* 82-88; P-in-c Newport w Widdington 88-92; V Newport 92-98; V Walton le Soken from 98. *The Vicarage, Martello Road, Walton on the Naze CO14 8BP* Tel (01255) 675452 E-mail scott.sanderson@lineone.net

SANDES, Canon Denis Lindsay. b 46. CITC BTh86. **d** 89 **p** 90. C Bandon Union *C, C & R* 89-92; I Kells Gp *C & O* from 92; Can Leighlin Cathl from 03. *The Priory, Kells, Co Kilkenny, Irish Republic* Tel (00353) (56) 28367

SANDFORD, The Revd and Rt Hon Lord (John Cyril Edmondson). b 20. DSC43. Dartmouth RN Coll. Westcott Ho Cam 56. **d** 58 **p** 60. C Harpenden St Nic *St Alb* 58-63; Perm to Offic 63-66; Chapl for Miss and Ecum St Alb 63-66; Chmn Redundant Chs Cttee Ch Commrs 82-88; rtd 85. *27 Ashley Gardens, Ambrosden Avenue, London SW1P 1QD* Tel (020) 7834 5722

SANDFORD, Nicholas Robert. b 63. Kent Univ BA84 Univ of Wales (Cardiff) BD87. St Mich Coll Llan 84. **d** 87 **p** 88. C Neath w Llantwit *Llan* 87-90; C Cardiff St Jo 90-94; R Cilybebyll 94-97; Chapl HM Pris Swansea 95-97; Chapl HM Pris Parc (Bridgend) from 97. *The Chaplaincy Centre, HM Prison Parc, Heol Hopcyn John, Bridgend CF35 6AP* Tel (01656) 300200 Fax 300001

SANDFORD, Paul Richard. b 47. Em Coll Cam BA69 MA73. Wycliffe Hall Ox 72. **d** 75 **p** 76. C Upper Holloway St Pet *Lon* 75-77; C Finchley St Paul Long Lane 77-81; Ind Chapl *Newc* 81-88; TV Cramlington 81-88; TV Dronfield *Derby* 88-90; TV Dronfield w Holmesfield 90-02; P-in-c Sinfin from 02; RD Derby S from 02. *St Stephen's Vicarage, 311 Sinfin Lane, Sinfin, Derby DE24 9GP* Tel (01332) 760135
E-mail paul.sandford@dwhteamparish.free-online.co.uk

SANDHAM, Stephen McCourt. b 41. K Coll Lon BD65 AKC65. **d** 66 **p** 67. C Stockton St Pet *Dur* 66-69; C Bishopwearmouth Gd Shep 69-71; C Bishopwearmouth St Mich w St Hilda 71-75; V Darlington St Mark w St Paul 75-82; P-in-c Sunderland St Paul 82-87; R Shincliffe 87-98; P-in-c from 98; Chapl Sherburn Hosp Dur from 98. *Shincliffe House, Sherburn Hospital, Durham DH1 2SE* Tel 0191-372 2890

SANDOM, Miss Carolyn Elizabeth. b 63. Homerton Coll Cam BEd85. Wycliffe Hall Ox BTh93. **d** 94. C St Helen Bishopsgate w St Andr Undershaft etc *Lon* 94-96; C Cambridge H Sepulchre *Ely* from 96. *12 Eden Street, Cambridge CB1 1EL* Tel (01223) 578016 *or* 518218 Fax 327331 E-mail staff@shsg.org

SANDS, Colin Robert. b 38. JP84. Chester Coll CertEd64. N Ord Course 82. **d** 85 **p** 86. Hd Master St Andr Magull Primary Sch

from 80; NSM Bootle Ch Ch *Liv* 85-94; NSM Maghull from 94. *16 Strafford Drive, Bootle L20 9JW* Tel 0151-525 8709

SANDS, Frederick William. b 25. St Deiniol's Hawarden 86. **d** 87 **p** 88. Chapl Asst Leic Gen Hosp 87-89; Chapl 89-95; rtd 95; Perm to Offic *Leic* from 95. *Gwendolen Road, Leicester LE5 4PW* Tel 0116-249 0490

SANDS, Nigel Colin. b 39. Dur Univ BA64 MA68. Oak Hill Th Coll 65. **d** 67 **p** 68. C Skelmersdale St Paul *Liv* 67-71; C Childwall All SS 71-72; V Wavertree St Bridget 72-78; P-in-c Welford w Wickham and Gt Shefford *Ox* 78-86; P-in-c Boxford w Stockcross and Speen 84-86; R Welford w Wickham and Gt Shefford, Boxford etc from 86. *The Rectory, Wickham, Newbury RG20 8HD* Tel (01488) 608244

SANDS, William James. b 55. Nottm Univ LTh83 Man Univ MA99. St Jo Coll Nottm 80. **d** 83 **p** 84. C St Mary-at-Latton *Chelmsf* 83-86; R Mvurwi Zimbabwe 86-87; C-in-c Barkingside St Cedd *Chelmsf* 87-89; C Woodford St Mary w St Phil and St Jas 87-89; P-in-c Elmsett w Aldham *St E* 89-92; P-in-c Kersey w Lindsey 89-92; R Esigodini Zimbabwe 92-96; Sub Dean Harare 97; Chapl Algarve *Eur* 98-00; V Castle Bromwich St Clem *Birm* 00; V from 00. *St Clement's Vicarage, Lanchester Way, Castle Bromwich, Birmingham B36 9JG* Tel 0121-747 4460 Fax as telephone E-mail billsands@onetel.net.uk

SANGSTER, Andrew. b 45. K Coll Lon BD67 AKC67 BA71 MA84 Lon Inst of Educn MPhil93 LLB97 FCollP. St Boniface Warminster. **d** 69 **p** 70. C Aylesford *Roch* 69-72; C Shirley *Win* 73-76; V Woolston 76-79; Prov Youth Chapl Ch in Wales 79-82; Chapl Collegiate Sch New Zealand 82-89; Chapl Eton Coll 89-92; Hd Master St Edm Sch Hindhead 92-96; Perm to Offic *Guildf* 92-96; Hd Master Thos Prep Sch Lon 96-99; V Ormesby St Marg w Scratby, Ormesby St Mich etc *Nor* from 99. *The Rectory, Church View, Ormesby, Great Yarmouth NR29 3PZ* Tel (01493) 750234

SANKEY, Julian. b 52. Qu Coll Ox BA74 MA79. St Jo Coll Nottm 84. **d** 86 **p** 87. C New Barnet St Jas *St Alb* 86-89; C Mansfield St Pet *S'well* 89-94; Chapl St Luke's Hospice Sheff from 94. *St Luke's Hospice, Little Common Lane, Sheffield S11 9NE, or 2 Woodvale Road, Sheffield S10 3EX* Tel 0114-236 9911 *or* 266 5689 Fax 262 1242

SANKEY, Terence Arthur Melville. b 51. CertTS. Trin Coll Bris 87. **d** 89 **p** 90. C Chalke Valley W *Sarum* 89-93; NSM Chalke from 93; Chapl HM Pris Dorchester from 99. *HM Prison Dorchester, 7 North Square, Dorchester DT1 1JD* Tel (01305) 266021

SANSBURY, Canon Christopher John. b 34. Peterho Cam BA57 MA. Westcott Ho Cam 58. **d** 59 **p** 60. C Portsea N End St Mark *Portsm* 59-63; C Weeke *Win* 63-71; V N Eling St Mary 71-78; R Long Melford *St E* 78-00; P-in-c Shimpling and Alpheton 98-00; Hon Can St E Cathl 97-00; rtd 00; Perm to Offic *St E* from 00. *2 Deacon's Close, Lavenham, Sudbury CO10 9TT* Tel (01787) 248068

SANSOM, John Reginald. b 40. St Jo Coll Nottm 73. **d** 75 **p** 76. C Ipswich St Marg *St E* 75-79; P-in-c Emneth *Ely* 79-85; P-in-c Hartford 85-86; TV Huntingdon 86-91; R Sawtry 91-97; R Sawtry and Glatton 97-99; TV Ely from 99. *44 Bentham Way, Ely CB6 1BS* Tel (01353) 664964
E-mail jsansom@bentham44.freeserve.co.uk

SANSOM, Canon Michael Charles. b 44. Bris Univ BA66 St Jo Coll Dur PhD74. Cranmer Hall Dur 68. **d** 72 **p** 73. C Ecclesall *Sheff* 72-76; Lic to Offic *Ely* 76-88; Dir of Studies Ridley Hall Cam 76-88; Vice-Prin 79-88; Dir of Ords St Alb from 88; Can Res St Alb from 88. *4D Harpenden Road, St Albans AL3 5AB* Tel (01727) 833777

SANSOM, Robert Arthur. b 29. BA. St Aid Birkenhead 60. **d** 62 **p** 63. C Sutton in Ashfield St Mary *S'well* 62-65; V Holbrooke *Derby* 65-70; Canada from 70; R North Saanich St Andr and H Trin 70-80; R Oak Bay St Mary 80-84; R Saanichton St Mary 84-89; rtd 89. *2254 Amherst Avenue, Sidney BC, Canada, V8L 2G7* Tel (001) (250) 656 9840 E-mail swift@intertrek.com

SANSOME, Geoffrey Hubert. b 29. Man Univ BA53. Qu Coll Birm DipTh62. **d** 62 **p** 63. C Prenton *Ches* 62-68; P-in-c Liscard St Thos 68-72; V Kingsley 72-83; V Wybunbury w Doddington 83-91; V Marbury 91-99; rtd 99; Perm to Offic *Blackb* from 00; *Ches* from 01. *21 Ash Drive, Warton, Preston PR4 1DD* Tel (01772) 633799

SANSUM, Canon David Henry. b 31. Bris Univ BA52 MA63. St Aid Birkenhead 54. **d** 56 **p** 57. C Henleaze *Bris* 56-59; C Stratton St Margaret 59-60; C Stoke Bishop 60-64; V Stechford *Birm* 64-76; V Ashbourne w Mapleton *Derby* 76-98; P-in-c Thorpe 77-83; V Ashbourne St Jo 81-98; RD Ashbourne 91-98; Hon Can Derby Cathl 95-98; rtd 98; Perm to Offic *Bris* and *Glouc* from 98. *Greenleaze, Main Road, Easter Compton, Bristol BS35 5DQ* Tel (01454) 632563

✠**SANTER, The Rt Revd Mark.** b 36. Qu Coll Cam BA60 MA64 Lambeth DD99. Westcott Ho Cam. **d** 63 **p** 64 **c** 81. Tutor Cuddesdon Coll 63-67; C Cuddesdon *Ox* 63-67; Fell and Dean Clare Coll Cam 67-72; Tutor 68-72; Prin Westcott Ho Cam 73-81; Hon Can Win Cathl *Win* 78-81; Area Bp Kensington *Lon* 81-87; Bp Birm 87-02; rtd 02; Hon Asst Bp Birm from 03.

81 Clarence Road, Kings Heath, Birmingham B13 9UH Tel 0121-441 2194

✠**SANTOS DE OLIVEIRA, The Most Revd Orlando. c** 97. Bp S Brazil from 97; Primate of Brazil from 03. *Caxia Postal 11.510, Teresópolis, Porto Alegre, RS, 90870-970, Brazil* Tel (0055) (51) 3318 6200 *or* 3318 6031 Fax as telephone
E-mail osoliveira@ieab.org.br

SANTRAM, Philip James. b 27. MA Delhi Univ BSc48 Serampore Univ BD53. Bp's Coll Calcutta 49. **d** 52 **p** 54. India 52-66; Ethiopia 66-68; C Horton *Bradf* 68-71; C Whitley Ch Ch *Ox* 71-72; P Missr St Mary Magd Conv Tilehurst 72-76; V Tilehurst St Mary 76-78; Canada from 78; rtd 92. *2933 Westoak Trails Boulevard, Oakville, ON, Canada, L6M 4V2* Tel (001) (905) 465 1017

SAPSFORD, John Garnet. b 38. **d** 76 **p** 76. C Whiteshill *Glouc* 76-81; Australia from 81. *11/24A Thomas Street, Ringwood, Vic, Australia 3134* Tel (0061) (3) 9876 0609
E-mail sapsford@melbpc.org.au

SAPWELL, Mrs Lynette. b 51. Sussex Univ BEd73 Middx Univ BA03. NTMTC 00. **d** 03. NSM Rochford *Chelmsf* from 03. *23 Briar Close, Hockley SS5 4HD* Tel (01702) 207167
E-mail lyn@sapwell.fsnet.co.uk

SARALIS, Preb Christopher Herbert. b 34. Univ of Wales BA54 St Cath Coll Ox BA56 MA60. Wycliffe Hall Ox. **d** 57 **p** 58. C Abergavenny St Mary w Llanwenarth Citra *Mon* 57-61; C Bridgwater St Mary w Chilton Trinity *B & W* 61-65; V Berrow 65-72; RD Burnham 72-76; R Berrow and Breane 72-76; V Minehead 76-92; RD Exmoor 80-86; Preb Wells Cathl 84-92; V Bovey Tracey SS Pet, Paul and Thos w Hennock *Ex* 92-99; rtd 99; Perm to Offic *B & W* from 99. *1 Broadway Road, Horton, Ilminster TA19 9RX* Tel (01460) 52416 E-mail saralis@fish

SARAPUK, Susan. b 59. Lon Univ BA80 Univ of Wales PGCE81. St Mich Coll Llan DPS90. **d** 90 **p** 97. C Morriston *S & B* 90-94; C Swansea St Pet 94-97; P-in-c Llangyfelach 97-98; V 98-02; C Sketty from 02. *13 Edison Crescent, Clydach, Swansea SA6 5JF* Tel (01792) 843521

SARGANT, John Raymond. b 38. CCC Cam BA61 MA70. Westcott Ho Cam 64 Harvard Div Sch 66. **d** 67 **p** 68. C Croydon *Cant* 67-72; Sec Zambia Angl Coun 72-75; P-in-c Bradford-on-Avon Ch Ch *Sarum* 76-81; V 81-90; TV Marlborough 90-03; Dioc Inter-Faith Adv 90-00; Can and Preb Sarum Cathl 92-01; rtd 03. *48 Summerhill Road, Lyme Regis DT7 3DT* Tel (01297) 445922

SARGEANT, Anthony. d 00 **p** 01. NSM Goostrey *Ches* from 00. *Greenbank House, Astbury Village Green, Congleton CW12 4RQ* Tel (01260) 272116

✠**SARGEANT, The Rt Revd Frank Pilkington. b** 32. St Jo Coll Dur BA55 Trin Coll Bris58 Nottm Univ DipAdEd73. Cranmer Hall Dur 57. **d** 58 **p** 59 **c** 84. C Gainsborough All SS *Linc* 58-62; C Gt Grimsby St Jas 62-66; V Hykeham 66-73; Dir In-Service Tr and Adult Educn *Bradf* 73-84; Can Res Bradf Cathl 73-77; Adn Bradf 77-84; Suff Bp Stockport *Ches* 84-94; Bp at Lambeth (Hd of Staff) *Cant* 94-99; rtd 99; Hon Asst Bp Eur from 99; Perm to Offic *Ches* from 99. *23 Brotherton Drive, Trinity Gardens, Salford M3 6BH* Tel 0161-839 7045

SARGEANT, George Henry. b 19. Bps' Coll Cheshunt 60. **d** 62 **p** 63. C Woodbridge St Jo *St E* 62-64; C Ipswich St Thos 64-68; C-in-c Gt w Lt Wratting 69-70; R 70-77; C-in-c Barnardiston 69-70; R 71-77; rtd 84; Lic to Offic *Nor* 90-99; Perm to Offic *Cant* from 02. *11 Langley Gardens, Cliftonville, Margate CT9 3EB* Tel (01843) 224788

SARGEANT, Kenneth Stanley. b 19. Lon Coll of Div 68. **d** 70 **p** 71. C E Ham St Paul *Chelmsf* 70-73; C Southborough St Pet w Ch Ch and St Matt *Roch* 73-77; Chapl Joyce Green Hosp Dartford 77-88; R Greenhithe St Mary *Roch* 77-88; rtd 88; Perm to Offic *Chich* from 88. *2 Westfield Close, Polegate BN26 6EF* Tel (01323) 488151

SARGEANTSON, Kenneth William. b 30. **d** 90 **p** 91. NSM The Marshland *Sheff* 90-93; NSM Goole 93-97; Perm to Offic from 97. *19 High Street, Swinefleet, Goole DN14 8AH* Tel (01405) 704256

SARGENT, Miss Ann. b 65. **d** 98 **p** 99. C Bris St Andr Hartcliffe *Bris* 98-01; P-in-c Flax Bourton *B & W* from 01; P-in-c Barrow Gurney from 01. *The Rectory, Main Road, Flax Bourton, Bristol BS48 3QJ* Tel (01275) 462582

SARGENT, Charles Edward. b 68. K Coll Lon BD89 Leeds Univ MA96. Coll of Resurr Mirfield 94. **d** 96 **p** 97. C Notting Dale St Clem w St Mark and St Jas *Lon* 96-00; P-in-c S Kensington St Aug from 00; Chapl Imp Coll from 00. *St Augustine's Vicarage, 117 Queen's Gate, London SW7 5LW* Tel (020) 7584 6622 *or* 7581 1877 Fax 7584 4330 E-mail charles_sargent@priest.com

SARGENT, David Gareth. b 63. Sheff Univ BA85. Cranmer Hall Dur BA93. **d** 96 **p** 97. C Norbury *Ches* 96-01; V Hooton from 01. *Hooton Vicarage, Chester Road, Little Sutton, Ellesmere Port CH66 1QF* Tel 0151-339 2020
E-mail revdave.sargent@talk21.com

SARGENT, Derek Connor. b 66. TCD BTh99 St Jo Coll Nottm CertCS99 Cert Counselling 01. CITC 96. **d** 99 **p** 00. C Waterford w Killea, Drumcannon and Dunhill *C & O* 99-01; V 01-03; I Dublin Clontarf *D & G* from 03. *The Rectory, 15 Seafield Road*

West, Clontarf, Dublin, Irish Republic Tel (00353) (1) 833 1181 E-mail clontarf@dublin.anglican.org

SARGENT, Preb Richard Henry. b 24. Man Univ BA50. Ridley Hall Cam 50. **d** 52 **p** 53. C Rusholme H Trin *Man* 52-54; C Cheadle *Ches* 54-59; V Cheadle Hulme St Andr 59-67; V Bushbury *Lich* 67-73; V Castle Church 73-89; RD Stafford 81-88; Preb Lich Cathl 87-89; rtd 89. *57 Deanshill Close, Stafford ST16 1BW* Tel (01785) 605335

SARGISSON, Conrad Ralph. b 24. Keble Coll Ox BA46 MA50. Wells Th Coll 48. **d** 50 **p** 51. C Charlton Kings St Mary *Glouc* 50-53; C Prestbury 53-55; V St Briavels 55-58; V Lanteglos by Fowey *Truro* 58-62; V Penzance St Mary 62-73; RD Penwith 72-73; V Westbury-on-Trym H Trin *Bris* 73-79; P-in-c Blisland w St Breward *Truro* 79-83; V Mylor w Flushing 83-91; P-in-c St Hilary w Perranuthnoe 93-96; rtd 96; Perm to Offic *Truro* from 96. *Cassawarn Farmhouse, Blisland, Bodmin PL30 4JU* Tel (01208) 850371

SARMEZEY, George Arpad. b 61. Qu Mary Coll Lon BA83 Goldsmiths' Coll Lon PGCE86. Westcott Ho Cam CTM92. **d** 92 **p** 93. C Eastville St Anne w St Mark and St Thos *Bris* 92-94; C Stratton St Margaret w S Marston etc 94-97; Asst Chapl Northn Gen Hosp NHS Trust 97-00; Sen Chapl from 00. *Northampton General Hospital, Billing Road, Northampton NN1 5BD* Tel (01604) 545773 Fax 544608
E-mail george.sarmezey@ngh-tr.anglox.nhs.uk

SARUM, Archdeacon of. *See* JEANS, The Ven Alan Paul

SASADA, Benjamin John. b 33. MA. EAMTC. **d** 82 **p** 83. NSM Dickleburgh, Langmere, Shimpling, Thelveton etc *Nor* 82-88; Perm to Offic *St E* from 84; NSM Diss *Nor* 88-95; P-in-c Dickleburgh, Langmere, Shimpling, Thelveton etc 95-99; rtd 99; Perm to Offic *Nor* from 99. *The Grange, Walcott Green, Diss IP22 3SS* Tel (01379) 642174

SASSER, Col the Ven Howell Crawford. b 37. Maryland Univ BA72 Geo Mason Univ Virginia MA74 Westmr Coll Ox MTh97. Washington Dioc Course 75. **d** 77 **p** 78. USA 77; W Germany 77-80; Somalia 80-83; Cyprus 84-92; Chapl Montreux w Gstaad *Eur* 92-97; Chapl Oporto from 97; Adn Gib from 02. *rua do Campo Alegre 640-5DTO, 4150-171 Porto, Portugal* Tel (00351) (22) 609 1006 Fax as telephone
E-mail stjameschurch@compuserve.com

SATTERFORD, Douglas Leigh. b 18. DSC42. Ripon Hall Ox 59. **d** 60 **p** 61. C Sanderstead All SS *S'wark* 60-65; V Lyminster *Chich* 65-85; V Poling 66-85; rtd 85; Perm to Offic *Chich* 85-88; *St E* 88-00; *Cant* from 00. *5 Grovelands, Old Ashford Road, Lenham, Maidstone ME17 2QR* Tel (01622) 850675

SATTERLY, Gerald Albert. b 34. Lon Univ BA56 Ex Univ Hon BA. Wycliffe Hall Ox 58. **d** 60 **p** 61. C Southborough St Pet *Roch* 60-63; C S Lyncombe *B & W* 63-66; V Sheff St Barn *Sheff* 66-69; R Adwick-le-Street 69-73; V Awre and Blakeney *Glouc* 73-82; P-in-c Newnham 80-82; V Newnham w Awre and Blakeney 82-90; R Instow *Ex* 90-98; V Westleigh 90-98; rtd 98; Perm to Offic *Ex* and *Truro* from 99. *Tryst Lea, 2 Cameron Close, Maer Lane, Bude EX23 8SP*

✠**SATTERTHWAITE, The Rt Revd John Richard. b** 25. CMG91. Leeds Univ BA46. Coll of Resurr Mirfield 48. **d** 50 **p** 51 **c** 70. C Carl St Barn *Carl* 50-53; C Carl St Aid and Ch Ch 53-55; Asst Gen Sec C of E Coun on Foreign Relns 55-59; C St Mich Paternoster Royal *Lon* 55-59; P-in-c 59-65; Gen Sec C of E Coun on Foreign Relns 59-70; V St Dunstan in the West *Lon* 59-70; Hon Can Cant Cathl *Cant* 63-70; Gen Sec Abp's Commn on RC Relns 65-70; Suff Bp Fulham *Lon* 70-80; Bp Gib 70-80; Bp Eur 80-93; Dean Malta 70-93; rtd 93; Hon Asst Bp Carl 94-01; Perm to Offic from 01. *25 Spencer House, St Paul's Square, Carlisle CA1 1DG* Tel (01228) 594055

SAUL, Norman Stanley. b 30. St Aid Birkenhead 51. **d** 54 **p** 55. C S Shore H Trin *Blackb* 54-57; C Poulton-le-Fylde 57-59; PC Freckleton 59-66; V Blackb St Luke 66-68; V Barton 68-72; V Foxdale *S & M* 72-77; V Maughold 77-90; CF (ACF) 80-86; rtd 90; Perm to Offic *Blackb* from 90. *15 Croft Meadow, Bamber Bridge, Preston PR5 8HX* Tel (01772) 314475

SAUNDERS, Andrew Vivian. b 44. Leeds Univ BA65. Coll of Resurr Mirfield 66. **d** 68 **p** 69. C Goodmayes St Paul *Chelmsf* 68-71; C Horfield H Trin *Bris* 71-75; C Oldland 75-77; Ind Chapl *B & W* 77-80; P-in-c Buckland Dinham w Elm, Orchardleigh etc 77-78; P-in-c Buckland Dinham 78-80; V Westfield 80-90; R Clutton w Cameley 90-99; C Christchurch *Win* from 99. *All Saints' House, 22 Kestrel Drive, Christchurch BH23 4DE* Tel (01425) 276267

SAUNDERS, Barry. *See* SAUNDERS, John Barry

SAUNDERS, Brian Gerald. b 28. Pemb Coll Cam BA49 MA53. Cuddesdon Coll 63. **d** 66 **p** 67. NSM Gt Berkhamsted *St Alb* 66-87; P-in-c Lt Gaddesden 87-92; rtd 92; Perm to Offic *Ox* 92-94; *St Alb* from 92; *Pet* from 95; *Linc* from 01; Hon C Newton Longville w Stoke Hammond and Whaddon 94-01. *114 Manthorpe Road, Grantham NG31 8DL* Tel (01476) 567046

SAUNDERS, Canon Bruce Alexander. b 47. St Cath Coll Cam BA68 MA72 Ox Univ DipTh70. Cuddesdon Coll 68. **d** 71 **p** 72. C Westbury-on-Trym H Trin *Bris* 71-74; Hon C Clifton St Paul 74-78; Asst Chapl Bris Univ 74-78; TV Fareham H Trin *Portsm* 78-84; TR Mortlake w E Sheen *S'wark* 84-97; RD Richmond

and Barnes 89-94; Can Miss for Ch in Soc from 97. *7 Temple West Mews, West Square, London SE11 4TJ* Tel (020) 7735 0143 *or* 7939 9411 Fax 7939 9467
E-mail bruce.saunders@dswark.org.uk

SAUNDERS, David. b 28. Keble Coll Ox BA50 DipTh51 MA59. Cuddesdon Coll 51. **d** 53 **p** 54. C Mexborough *Sheff* 53-56; C Sheff St Cuth 56-60; V New Bentley 60-67; V Grimsby All SS *Linc* 67-78; V Caistor w Clixby 78-88; P-in-c Grasby 78-94; Chapl Caistor Hosp 78-94; P-in-c Searby w Owmby *Linc* 79-94; V Dunholme 88-92; P-in-c Welton and Dunholme w Scothern 92-94; rtd 94; Perm to Offic *Linc* from 94. *2 Oundle Close, Washingborough, Lincoln LN4 1DR* Tel (01522) 793164

SAUNDERS, David Anthony. b 48. Trin Coll Bris 76. **d** 78 **p** 79. C Bath Walcot *B & W* 78-80; Asst Dir RE 80-83; Youth Chapl 80-83; C Long Ashton 83-84; V Bath St Bart 84-90; Offg Chapl RN 84-90; V Cullompton *Ex* 90-97; R Kentisbeare w Blackborough 90-97; Dir Shiloh Min USA from 97. *11610 Grandview Road, Kansas City, MO 64137, USA*
E-mail 100717.411@compuserve.com

SAUNDERS, Edward George Humphrey. b 23. St Jo Coll Cam BA48 MA50. Ridley Hall Cam. **d** 50 **p** 51. C Ox St Ebbe *Ox* 50-52; Cand Sec CPAS 52-54; Clerical Asst Sec 54-58; V Finchley Ch Ch *Lon* 58-64; V Chipping Campden *Glouc* 64-69; P-in-c Ebrington 66-69; Lic to Offic *Leic* 69-71; V Ches Square St Mich w St Phil *Lon* 71-84; P-in-c Mayfair Ch Ch 80-84; Hon C Ox St Andr *Ox* 84-90; rtd 88. *33 Manna Grove, Belfast BT5 6AJ* Tel (028) 9079 8765

SAUNDERS, Gareth John McKeith. b 71. St Andr Univ BD93 Edin Univ MTh99. TISEC 99. **d** 99 **p** 00. C St Andr Cathl *Ab* 99-03; C Edin St Salvador *Edin* from 03; C Edin Gd Shep from 03. *St Salvador's Rectory, 54 Drum Brae Park, Edinburgh EH12 8TF* Tel 0131-467 2418 Mobile 07732-356123
E-mail gareth@garethjmsaunders.co.uk

SAUNDERS, Geoffrey David. b 51. Bris Univ BSc73. Dioc OLM tr scheme. **d** 01. OLM Rockland St Mary w Hellington, Bramerton etc *Nor* from 01. *13 The Street, Rockland St Mary, Norwich NR14 7ER* Tel (01508) 538550
E-mail geoffsaunders@waitrose.com

SAUNDERS, Graham Howard. b 53. Hatf Poly BSc77. Trin Coll Bris BA86. **d** 86 **p** 87. C Birm St Martin w Bordesley St Andr *Birm* 86-89; C Olton 89-96; TV Bedminster *Bris* 96-02; P-in-c Farnham Royal w Hedgerley *Ox* from 02. *The Rectory, Victoria Road, Farnham Common, Slough SL2 3NJ* Tel (01753) 643233 Fax 644130

SAUNDERS, James Benedict John. b 72. St Aid Coll Dur BA93 St Jo Coll Cam PhD97 St Jo Coll Dur BA00. Cranmer Hall Dur 98. **d** 01 **p** 02. C Sole Bay *St E* from 01. *31 The Firs, Jermyns Road, Reydon, Southwold IP18 6YS* Tel (01502) 725189 Mobile 07751-976137 E-mail revjames@supanet.com

SAUNDERS, Mrs Joan Mary (Jo). b 44. Univ Coll Lon BA66 PGCE67. EAMTC 00. **d** 03. NSM Gt and Lt Casterton w Pickworth and Tickencote *Pet* from 03. *Mellstock, Bourne Road, Essendine, Stamford PE9 4LH* Tel (01780) 480479
E-mail josaunders@btinternet.com

SAUNDERS, John Barry. b 40. Chich Th Coll. **d** 83 **p** 84. C St Breoke *Truro* 83-84; C St Breoke and Egloshayle 84-87; V Treverbyn 87-96; RD St Austell 91-96; V Perranzabuloe from 96. *The Vicarage, Cox Hill, Perranporth TR6 0AT* Tel (01872) 573375

SAUNDERS, Canon John Michael. b 40. Brasted Th Coll 66 Clifton Th Coll 68. **d** 70 **p** 71. C Homerton St Luke *Lon* 70-74; SAMS 74-97; Brazil 74-91; P-in-c Horsmonden *Roch* 91-97; Area Sec (SE England) SAMS 91-97; V Gillingham St Mark *Roch* from 97. *The Vicarage, Vicarage Road, Gillingham ME7 5UA* Tel (01634) 851818 Fax 570489
E-mail info@stmarkschurchgillingham.co.uk

SAUNDERS, Kenneth John. b 35. Linc Th Coll 73. **d** 75 **p** 76. C Boultham *Linc* 75-79; V Swinderby 79-87; V Cherry Willingham w Greetwell 87-95; P-in-c S Kelsey Gp 95-98; P-in-c N Kelsey 95-98; P-in-c Kelsey Gp 98-00; rtd 00; Perm to Offic *Linc* from 01. *Pew End, 17 Wentworth Drive, Dunholme, Lincoln LN2 3UH* Tel (01673) 862930

SAUNDERS, Malcolm Walter Mackenzie. b 34. Em Coll Cam BA58 MA62. Wycliffe Hall Ox 58. **d** 60 **p** 61. C Northampton St Giles *Pet* 60-63; C Northampton St Alb 63-66; V Corby St Columba 66-84; Inst Dir Evang Explosion 84-91; Lic to Offic *Pet* 84-91; V Ketton 91-92; R Ketton w Tinwell 92-01; rtd 01. *35 Main Street, Barrowden, Oakham LE15 8EQ* Tel (01572) 747036

SAUNDERS, Mrs Margaret Rose. b 49. Newnham Coll Cam BA71 St Jo Coll York PGCE72 Herts Univ Dip Counselling 96. St Alb Minl Tr Scheme 85. **d** 88 **p** 94. Hon Par Dn Gt Berkhamsted *St Alb* 88-90; Hon Chapl Asst Gt Ormond Street Hosp for Sick Children Lon 88-90; Asst Chapl Aylesbury Vale HA 90-92; Chapl Milton Keynes Gen NHS Trust 92-98; Chapl Milton Keynes Community NHS Trust 92-98; C Newport Pagnell w Lathbury and Moulsoe *Ox* 98-01; TV Grantham *Linc* 01-02; P-in-c Grantham, Manthorpe from 02; Chapl United Lincs Hosps NHS Trust from 01. *The Vicarage, 114 Manthorpe Road, Grantham NG31 8DL* Tel (01476) 567047

SAUNDERS, Mark Richard. b 74. Coll of Ripon & York St Jo BA95 St Jo Coll Dur BA00. Cranmer Hall Dur 98. **d** 01 **p** 02. C Ponteland *Newc* from 01. *2 Granger Road, Ponteland, Newcastle upon Tyne NE20 9UL* Tel (01661) 860599

SAUNDERS, Martin Paul. b 54. K Coll Lon BD76 AKC76 Univ of Northumbria at Newc DipSW96. Westcott Ho Cam 77. **d** 78 **p** 79. C Seaton Hirst *Newc* 78-81; Regional Chapl Hong Kong Miss to Seamen 81; C Egglescliffe *Dur* 81-82; Chapl to Arts and Recreation 81-84; C Jarrow 82-84; TV 84-88; V Southwick St Columba 88-94; Perm to Offic from 94. *55 The Meadows, Burnopfield, Newcastle upon Tyne NE16 6QW* Tel (01207) 271242 Mobile 07710-325197
E-mail martinsaunders@derwentheights.freeserve.co.uk

SAUNDERS, Martyn Leonard John. b 69. Magd Coll Cam MEng92. Wycliffe Hall Ox BA97. **d** 98 **p** 99. C Quinton Road W St Boniface *Birm* 98-02; TV Barnsbury *Lon* from 02. *5 Huntingdon Street, London N1 1BU* Tel (020) 7700 4097
E-mail martyn.saunders@london.anglican.org

SAUNDERS, Michael. b 38. Charing Cross Hosp Medical Sch MB, BS62 FRCPEd74 FRCP78 MSOSc84. NEOC 82. **d** 84 **p** 85. Lic to Offic *York* 84-92; Tutor NEOC 84-93; NSM Stokesley *York* 92-93; C Ripon Cathl *Ripon* 93-95; Perm to Offic *York* from 93; NSM Gt and Lt Ouseburn w Marton cum Grafton etc *Ripon* from 95. *College Grove, 2 College Lane, Masham HG4 4HE* Tel (01765) 866306 E-mail michael.saunders@btinternet.com

SAUNDERS, Michael Walter. b 58. CChem MRSC84 Grey Coll Dur BSc79. Wycliffe Hall Ox 86. **d** 89 **p** 90. C Deane *Man* 89-93; TV Eccles 93-02; Chapl Eccles Sixth Form Coll 96-02; Dioc Adv on Evang *Man* 98-02; C Yateley *Win* 02-03; C Yateley and Eversley from 03. *The Rectory, Glaston Hill Road, Eversley, Hook RG27 0LX* Tel 0118-973 6595
E-mail mikethevicar@thesaunders.plus.com

SAUNDERS, Reginald Frederick. b 15. LNSM course 76. **d** 79 **p** 80. NSM Perth St Ninian *St And* from 79; NSM Stanley from 79. *31 Muirend Road, Perth PH1 1JU* Tel (01738) 626217

SAUNDERS, Canon Richard Charles Hebblethwaite. b 17. Qu Coll Ox BA40 DipTh41 MA42. Westcott Ho Cam 41. **d** 42 **p** 43. C Darnall *Sheff* 42-45; India 46-49; V Thornton-le-Street w Thornton-le-Moor etc *York* 49-52; V Eastwood *Sheff* 52-62; V Bris St Ambrose Whitehall *Bris* 62-75; P-in-c Easton All Hallows 65-68; TR E Bris 75-77; P-in-c Colerne 77-82; P-in-c N Wraxall 77-82; RD Chippenham 80-82; Hon Can Bris Cathl 82; rtd 82; Hon C Honiton, Gittisham, Combe Raleigh, Monkton etc *Ex* from 85. *St Michael's Cottage, Gittisham, Honiton EX14 3AH* Tel (01404) 850634

SAUNDERS, Richard George. b 54. BNC Ox BA76 MA81. St Jo Coll Nottm 82. **d** 85 **p** 86. C Barrow St Mark *Carl* 85-89; C Cranham Park *Chelmsf* 89-97; TV Kinson *Sarum* 97-00; TR from 00. *St Philip's Vicarage, 41 Moore Avenue, Kinson, Bournemouth BH11 8AT* Tel (01202) 581135 Fax as telephone
E-mail dick@saundersfamily.freeserve.co.uk

SAUNDERS, Ronald. b 37. ACP67 St Pet Coll Birm CertEd62 CertRE62 Memorial Univ Newfoundland CertEd80 Columbia Univ MA82 PhD87 Cert Counselling 95. Sarum Th Coll 69. **d** 68 **p** 70. Malawi 68-72; Lic to Offic 68-70; C Blantyre 71-72; C Kensington St Mary Abbots w St Geo *Lon* 72-73; C Bournemouth St Fran *Win* 73-75; Canada 75-81; I Twillingate 76; Lic to Offic 77-81; C Gt Marlow *Ox* 81-82; Area Org Leprosy Miss 82-85; V Penycae *St As* 85-87; TV Wrexham 87-89; Lic to Offic *Ox* 90-91; Chapl Morden Coll Blackheath 91-97; Master Wyggeston's Hosp Leic 97-03. *4 Visdelou Terrace, Shotley Gate, Ipswich IP9 1RP*

SAUNDERS, Sheila Lilian. b 42. Dioc OLM tr scheme 00. **d** 03. OLM Walworth St Pet *S'wark* from 03. *9 Wooler Street, London SE17 2ED* Tel (020) 7252 5045
E-mail sheila.saunders3@btopenworld.com

SAUNDERS, Ms Wendy Jennifer. b 49. S'wark Ord Course 86. **d** 95 **p** 96. Bp's Adv for Urban Min and Leadership *S'wark* 90-91; C Thamesmead 95-98; P-in-c Eltham St Sav from 98. *St Saviour's Vicarage, 98 Middle Park Avenue, London SE9 5JH* Tel (020) 8850 6829 *or* 07802-603754
E-mail wendy.saunders@sunday.surfaid.org

SAUNT, James Peter Robert. b 36. Chich Th Coll 73. **d** 75 **p** 76. C Portland All SS w St Pet *Sarum* 75-78; P-in-c Bratton 78-81; V 81-94; Chapl HM YOI Erlestoke Ho 81-94; P-in-c Oldbury *Sarum* 94-99; R 99-01; rtd 01. *Elms, Waddon, Portesham, Weymouth DT3 4ER*

SAUSBY, John Michael. b 39. AKC. **d** 63 **p** 64. C Crosland Moor *Wakef* 63-65; C Halifax St Jo Bapt 65-67; V Birkby 67-77; V Holmfirth 77-89; TR Upper Holme Valley 89-01; rtd 01. *15 River Holme View, Brockholes, Huddersfield HD9 7BP* Tel (01484) 667228

SAVAGE, Andrew Michael. b 67. Wye Coll Lon BSc89 Cranfield Inst of Tech MSc91. Wycliffe Hall Ox 93. **d** 96 **p** 97. C Ecclesall *Sheff* 96-99; TV Kirk Ella *York* from 99. *St Luke's Vicarage, 2A Chestnut Avenue, Willerby, Hull HU10 6PA* Tel (01482) 658974
E-mail savos@btinternet.com

SAVAGE, Canon Christopher Marius. b 46. Hull Univ MA94 FRSA99. Bps' Coll Cheshunt 66 Qu Coll Birm 68. **d** 70 **p** 71. C Battersea St Luke *S'wark* 70-75; TV Newbury *Ox* 75-80; R Lich St Mary w St Mich *Lich* 80-85; V Chessington *Guildf* 85-91; Ind

Chapl *Win* 91-00; Chapl Basingstoke Coll of Tech 91-00; V Newc Ch Ch w St Ann *Newc* from 00. *The Vicarage, 11 Gibson Street, Newcastle upon Tyne NE1 6PY* Tel and fax 0191-232 0516 Mobile 07711-272567 E-mail cpsavage@btinternet.com

SAVAGE, Graham John. b 47. Univ of Wales (Ban) BSc69 PhD78. CITC 89. **d** 92 **p** 94. Lic to Offic *D & D* from 92; NSM Down Cathl 94-97; NSM Lecale Gp from 97. *7 Cedar Grove, Ardglass, Downpatrick BT30 7UE* Tel (028) 4484 1501

SAVAGE, Mrs Hilary Linda. b 48. RGN71 RM86. WMMTC 89. **d** 92 **p** 94. C Quinton Road W St Boniface *Birm* 92-96; P-in-c Edgbaston SS Mary and Ambrose 96-01; V 01-02; TV Cramlington *Newc* from 02. *1 Cateran Way, Cramlington NE23 6EX* Tel (01670) 714261

SAVAGE, Mrs Jennifer Anne. b 52. CertEd73. N Ord Course 96. **d** 99 **p** 00. C Haworth *Bradf* 99-02; R from 02. *The Rectory, 81 West Lane, Haworth, Keighley BD22 8EN* Tel (01535) 640293 *or* 642169

SAVAGE, John. b 48. Bris Univ BEd76. SW Minl Tr Course 94. **d** 97 **p** 98. C Falmouth K Chas *Truro* 97-00; P-in-c Mabe from 00; Chapl Miss to Seafarers from 00. *The Vicarage, Church Road, Mabe Burnthouse, Penryn TR10 9HN* Tel (01326) 373201

SAVAGE, Jonathan Mark. b 57. Kingston Poly BSc79 MSc89 Roehampton Inst PGCE80. Ridley Hall Cam 94. **d** 96 **p** 97. C Ely 96-99; TV Huntingdon from 99. *The Vicarage, 3A Longstaff Way, Hartford, Huntingdon PE28 7XT* Tel (01480) 434463

SAVAGE, Leslie Walter. b 15. Cranmer Hall Dur 63. **d** 65 **p** 66. C Stanwix *Carl* 65-69; V Bolton w Cliburn 69-74; V Holme *Blackb* 74-81; rtd 81; Perm to Offic *Chich* from 81. *42 Wilton Road, Bexhill-on-Sea TN40 1HX* Tel (01424) 223829

SAVAGE, Mark David John. b 55. Birm Univ BA76 Dur Univ BA82 Newc Univ MLitt83. Cranmer Hall Dur 80. **d** 83 **p** 84. C Newc St Gabr *Newc* 83-86; Adult Educn Adv 86-94; V Bedlington from 94. *The Vicarage, 21 Church Lane, Bedlington NE22 5EL* Tel (01670) 829220 Fax 823453 E-mail marksavage@beeb.net

SAVAGE, Michael Atkinson. b 33. St Pet Hall Ox BA57 MA61. Tyndale Hall Bris 57. **d** 59 **p** 60. C Rugby St Matt *Cov* 59-62; C Welling *Roch* 62-66; V Bowling St Steph *Bradf* 66-73; V Ben Rhydding 73-92; RD Otley 87-92; TR Quidenham *Nor* 92-97; R Quidenham Gp 97-99; rtd 99; Perm to Offic *Bradf* from 00. *42 Hollins Lane, Utley, Keighley BD20 6LT* Tel (01535) 606790

SAVAGE, Paul James. b 58. Liv Univ BA81. Wycliffe Hall Ox 88. **d** 91 **p** 92. C Litherland St Phil *Liv* 91-94; CMS from 94. *Church Mission Society, Partnership House, 157 Waterloo Road, London SE1 8UU* Tel (020) 7928 8681 Fax 7401 3215

SAVEGE, Timothy. b 38. **d** 00 **p** 01. OLM Blyth Valley *St E* from 00. *Grove Farm, Chediston, Halesworth IP19 0BG* Tel (01986) 785423

SAVIGEAR, Miss Elfrida Beatrice. b 49. Wye Coll Lon BSc71 Edin Univ DipAE72 Bath Univ MSc85 Lambeth STh94. Trin Coll Bris Dip Th Studies 90 Ridley Hall Cam 91. **d** 93 **p** 94. C Ross w Brampton Abbotts, Bridstow, Peterstow etc *Heref* 93-97; P-in-c Butlers Marston and the Pillertons w Ettington *Cov* 97-99; P-in-c Alderminster and Halford 97-99; P-in-c Bicknoller w Crowcombe and Sampford Brett *B & W* 99-00; P-in-c Stogumber w Nettlecombe and Monksilver 99-00; R Quantock Towers from 00. *The Rectory, 11 Trendle Lane, Bicknoller, Taunton TA4 4EG* Tel (01984) 656262 E-mail elfrida@bicknollerrectory.freeserve.co.uk

SAVILE, Canon Ian Keith Wrey. b 26. Trin Hall Cam BA50 MA54. Ridley Hall Cam 51. **d** 53 **p** 54. C Bootle St Matt *Liv* 53-56; C Birkdale St Jo 56-57; V Barrow St Mark *Carl* 57-64; V Wandsworth All SS *S'wark* 64-74; RD Wandsworth 70-74; S'well H Trin *S'well* 74-80; Bp's Adv on Evang 74-80; V Canford Magna *Sarum* 80-88; TR 88; RD Wimborne 85-88; Can and Preb Sarum Cathl 86-88; Patr Sec CPAS 88-93; rtd 93; Perm to Offic *Cov* 88-93; *Sarum* from 93. *23A Avenue Road, Wimborne BH21 1BS* Tel (01202) 880210

SAVILL, David. b 27. TD69 and Bar 75. Em Coll Cam BA49 MA52. Ridley Hall Cam 50. **d** 52 **p** 53. Chapl St E Cathl *St E* 52-54; C St Martin-in-the-Fields *Lon* 54-57; V Sunbury 57-67; V Heston 67-73; Hon C Mettingham w Ilketshall St John *St E* 73-79; Hon C Mettingham 79-80; Chapl Felixstowe Coll 80-90; rtd 90; Perm to Offic *B & W* from 90. *The Bungalow, Ashlands Meadow, Crewkerne TA18 7NN* Tel (01460) 77298 Fax 77131

SAVILLE, Andrew. b 66. Worc Coll Ox BA92 MA92 Cov Univ PhD00. Wycliffe Hall Ox DipTh. **d** 95 **p** 96. C Tonbridge SS Pet and Paul *Roch* 95-99; NSM Bromley Ch Ch from 99; Dir Bromley Chr Tr Cen from 99. *68 Warren Avenue, Bromley BR1 4BS* Tel (020) 8460 1174 E-mail asaville@ccbromley.fsnet.co.uk

SAVILLE, Preb David James. b 39. Ch Ch Ox BA60 MA64. Clifton Th Coll 61. **d** 63 **p** 64. C Darfield *Sheff* 63-66; C St Leonards St Leon *Chich* 66-68; Cand Sec CPAS 69-74; Hon C Bromley Ch Ch *Roch* 69-74; V Taunton St Jas *B & W* 74-80; RD Taunton N 78-80; V Chorleywood Ch Ch *St Alb* 80-90; RD Rickmansworth 86-90; Adv for Evang Edmonton *Lon* 91-96; Dioc Adv for Evang 96-01; TR Hackney Marsh from 01; Preb

St Paul's Cathl from 97. *St Barnabas' Rectory, 111 Homerton High Street, London E9 6DL* Tel (020) 8533 1156 E-mail david.saville@dlondon.org.uk

SAVILLE, Edward Andrew. b 47. Leeds Univ CertEd70 Open Univ BA75. Carl Dioc Tr Inst. **d** 90 **p** 91. C Accrington St Jo w Huncoat *Blackb* 90-93; C Standish 93-95; V Brierfield from 95; AD Pendle from 98. *The Vicarage, 5 Reedley Farm Close, Reedley, Burnley BB10 2RB* Tel (01282) 613235 Fax as telephone E-mail e.saville@btinternet.com

SAVILLE (née McCULLAGH), Mrs Elspeth Jane Alexandra. b 68. Man Univ BSc90. Wycliffe Hall Ox BTh95. **d** 95 **p** 96. C Huddersfield H Trin *Wakef* 95-98; NSM Tonbridge SS Pet and Paul *Roch* 98-99. NSM Bromley Ch Ch from 99. *68 Warren Avenue, Bromley BR1 4BS* Tel (020) 8460 1174

SAVILLE, Canon Jeremy David. b 35. Oriel Coll Ox BA59 MA62. Chich Th Coll 58. **d** 60 **p** 61. C Tynemouth Cullercoats St Paul *Newc* 60-63; C Hexham 63-65; Lic to Offic *Ox* 65-68; Chapl Cuddesdon Coll 65-68; R Holt *Nor* 68-73; P-in-c Kelling w Salthouse 68-71; V R Edgefield 71-73; R Hoe 73-73; R E Dereham w Hoe 73-80; V E Dereham 80-81; R Scarning w Wendling 78-81; R Beckenham St Geo *Roch* 81-89; Hon Can Roch Cathl 86-89; R Ashdon w Hadstock *Chelmsf* 89-01; RD Saffron Walden 97-01; Hon Can Chelmsf Cathl 00-01; rtd 01; Perm to Offic *Nor* from 01. *8B Hillside, Sheringham NR26 8DB* Tel (01263) 820164

SAVILLE, Mrs Margaret. b 46. SW Minl Tr Course 93. **d** 94 **p** 95. C Over St Chad *Ches* 94-98; V Crewe All SS and St Paul from 98. *All Saints' Vicarage, 79 Stewart Street, Crewe CW2 8LX* Tel (01270) 560310

SAVILLE-DEANE, Marcus. b 58. Imp Coll Lon BSc80. Wycliffe Hall Ox 83. **d** 87 **p** 88. C Spring Grove St Mary *Lon* 87-92. *Apsley Croft, 316 Woodstock Road, Oxford OX2 7NS* Tel (01865) 514265

SAWARD, Canon Michael John. b 32. Bris Univ BA55. Tyndale Hall Bris. **d** 56 **p** 57. C Croydon Ch Ch Broad Green *Cant* 56-59; C Edgware *Lon* 59-64; Sec Liv Coun of Chs 64-67; Radio and TV Officer CIO 67-72; Hon C Beckenham St Jo *Roch* 70-72; V Fulham St Matt *Lon* 72-78; V Ealing St Mary 78-91; AD Ealing E 79-84; P-in-c Ealing St Paul 86-89; Preb St Paul's Cathl 85-91; Can Res and Treas St Paul's Cathl 91-00; rtd 01. *6 Discovery Walk, London E1W 2JG* Tel (020) 7702 1130 Fax as telephone

SAWLE, Martin. b 49. Solicitor 74 Dundee Univ LLB70. N Ord Course 87. **d** 90 **p** 91. NSM Longton *Blackb* 90-92; P-in-c Hoghton from 92. *The Vicarage, Chapel Lane, Hoghton, Preston PR5 0RY* Tel (01254) 852529 E-mail martin@sawleandco.com

SAWLE, Ralph Burford. b 14. Lich Th Coll 34. **d** 37 **p** 38. C Sawley *Derby* 37-40; C Walthamstow St Barn *Chelmsf* 40-43; P-in-c Hanley All SS *Lich* 43-46; V Hanford 46-52; V Malins Lee 52-57; V Ocker Hill 57-61; V Werrington *Truro* 61-72; RD Trigg Major 66-72; V St Giles on the Heath w Virginstow 68-72; V St Neot 72-79; rtd 79; Perm to Offic *Win* from 79. *32 Cavendish Close, Romsey SO51 7HT* Tel (01794) 516132

SAWYER, Andrew William. b 49. AKC71 St Aug Coll Cant 71. **d** 72 **p** 73. C Farnham *Guildf* 72-75; C Dawlish *Ex* 75-78; R Colkirk w Oxwick, Whissonsett and Horningtoft *Nor* 78-82; R Colkirk w Oxwick w Pattesley, Whissonsett etc 82-90; V Hungerford and Denford *Ox* from 90. *The Vicarage, Parsonage Lane, Hungerford RG17 0JB* Tel (01488) 682844

SAWYER, Derek Claude. b 33. ALCD58. **d** 58 **p** 59. C Kirby Muxloe *Leic* 58-60; C Braunstone 60-65; Mauritius 65-68; V Knighton St Mich *Leic* 68-82; Chapl Kifissia *Eur* 82-85; Lic to Offic *Glouc* 85-87; V Glouc St Aldate 87-01; rtd 01; R Capisterre w Dieppe Bay Town St Kitts from 01. *St Paul's Rectory, St Paul's Village, PO Box 539, Basseterre, St Kitts* Tel (001) (869) 466 6398 Fax as telephone E-mail raitasawyer@caribsurf.com

SAWYER, Graham Anthony Christian Paul. b 61. St Chad's Coll Dur BA82. **d** 98 **p** 02. C Roseneath New Zealand 98-99; Ind Chapl Sydney Australia 99-00; C Pontypool *Mon* 01-02; TV from 02. *St James's Vicarage, Hanbury Road, Trevethin, Pontypool NP4 6JF* Tel (01495) 769006 E-mail graham.sawyer@excite.com

SAWYERS, Thomas Adam Barton. b 21. Edgehill Th Coll Belf 58. **d** 61 **p** 62. C Drumragh *D & R* 61-63; I Tamlaght O'Crilly 63-69; I Lissan *Arm* 69-82; rtd 82. *Lynwood, 82 Coleraine Road, Portrush BT56 8HN* Tel (028) 7082 3441

✠**SAXBEE, The Rt Revd John Charles.** b 46. Bris Univ BA68. Cranmer Hall Dur DipTh69 PhD74. **d** 72 **p** 74. C Compton Gifford *Ex* 72-77; P-in-c Weston Mill 77-80; V 80-81; TV Cen Ex 81-87; Jt Dir SW Minl Tr Course 81-92; Preb Ex Cathl 88-92; Adn Ludlow *Heref* 92-01; Preb Heref Cathl 92-01; P-in-c Wistanstow 92-94; P-in-c Acton Scott 92-94; Suff Bp Ludlow 94-01; Bp Linc from 01. *The Bishop's House, Eastgate, Lincoln LN2 1QQ* Tel (01522) 534701 Fax 511095 E-mail bishlincoln@claranet.co.uk

SAXBY, Martin Peter. b 52. St Jo Coll Dur BA77 DipTh78. Cranmer Hall Dur 74. **d** 78 **p** 79. C Peckham St Mary Magd *S'wark* 78-81; C Ramsey *Ely* 81-84; P-in-c Yaxham *Nor* 84-89; P-in-c Welborne 84-89; P-in-c Mattishall w Mattishall Burgh 84-89; R Mattishall w Mattishall Burgh, Welborne etc 89-90; V

Rugby St Matt *Cov* from 90. *St Matthew's Vicarage, 7 Vicarage Road, Rugby CV22 7AJ* Tel (01788) 330442 *or* 330447 Fax 08701-391160 E-mail martin@stmatthews.org.uk

SAXBY, Steven Michael Paul. b 70. Fitzw Coll Cam BA98 MA02. Aston Tr Scheme 92 Linc Th Coll 94 Westcott Ho Cam 95. **d** 98 **p** 01. C E Ham w Upton Park St Alb *Chelmsf* 98-00; C Barking St Marg w St Patr 00-02; Waltham Forest Deanery Development Worker from 02; NSM Walthamstow 02-03; V Walthamstow St Pet from 03. *St Peter's Vicarage, 121 Forest Rise, London E17 3PW* Tel (020) 8520 3854 E-mail saxby@fish.co.uk

SAXTON, James. b 54. Lanc Univ BEd77 Hull Univ MEd85. Linc Th Coll 84. **d** 86 **p** 87. C Moor Allerton *Ripon* 86-90; C Knaresborough 90-92; TV Seacroft 92-95; V Ireland Wood 95-00; TV Becontree S *Chelmsf* from 02. *114 Oval Road North, Dagenham RM10 9EP* Tel (020) 8595 1042

✠**SAY, The Rt Revd David.** b 14. KCVO88. Ch Coll Cam BA38 MA41 Lambeth DD61 Kent Univ Hon DCL87. Ridley Hall Cam 38. **d** 39 **p** 40 **c** 61. C Croydon *Cant* 39-43; C St Martin-in-the-Fields *Lon* 43-50; Asst Sec C of E Youth Coun 42-44; Gen Sec 44-47; Gen Sec BCC 47-55; R Bp's Hatfield *St Alb* 55-61; Hon Can St Alb 57-61; Bp Roch 61-88; ChStJ from 61; High Almoner 70-88; rtd 88; Hon Asst Bp Cant from 88. *23 Chequers Park, Wye, Ashford TN25 5BB* Tel (01233) 812720

SAYER, Derek John. b 32. St Steph Ho Ox 55. **d** 58 **p** 58. C Tottenham All Hallows *Lon* 58-61; C Letchworth *St Alb* 61-63; Chapl RADD 63-64 and 66-82; C Lancing St Mich *Chich* 64-66; C Dorking w Ranmore *Guildf* 89-92; V Holmwood 92-95; Perm to Offic from 95; rtd 92. *24 Chalkpit Lane, Dorking RH4 1ER* Tel (01306) 882610

SAYER, Canon William Anthony John. b 37. St Mich Coll Llan 60. **d** 64 **p** 65. C Gorleston St Andr *Nor* 64-67; P-in-c Witton w Ridlington 67-71; P-in-c Honing w Crostwight 67-71; V Bacton w Edingthorpe 67-71; CF 71-84; Miss to Seafarers from 84; R Holkham w Egmere w Warham, Wells and Wighton *Nor* 84-02; RD Burnham and Walsingham 87-92; Hon Can Nor Cathl 97-02; rtd 02; Perm to Offic *Nor* from 02. *Greenway Lodge, Mill Road, Wells-next-the-Sea NR23 1RF* Tel (01328) 711224

SAYERS, Ms Karen Jane. b 69. Sheff Univ BMus90. Ripon Coll Cuddesdon 00. **d** 02 **p** 03. C Dunstable *St Alb* from 02. *Priory Vicarage, 20 Friars Walk, Dunstable LU6 3JA* Tel (01582) 658795 E-mail karen.sayers@talk21.com

SAYERS, Simon Philip. b 59. Cam Univ MA81. Oak Hill Th Coll 83. **d** 85 **p** 86. C Alperton *Lon* 85-89; C Hornsey Rise Whitehall Park Team 89-90; TV 90-96; P-in-c Digswell and Panshanger *St Alb* 96-98; Min Panshanger CD 98-02; R Warblington w Emsworth *Portsm* from 02. *The Rectory, 20 Church Path, Emsworth PO10 7DP* Tel (01243) 372428 E-mail simonsayers@hotmail.com

SAYERS, Susan. b 46. Bp Otter Coll Chich BEd69 Middx Univ BA02. NTMTC 99. **d** 02 **p** 03. NSM Southend *Chelmsf* from 02; Asst Chapl HM Pris Bullwood Hall from 02. *3 Fairview Gardens, Leigh-on-Sea SS9 3PD* Tel (01702) 478280 E-mail susansayers@yahoo.com

SAYLE, Philip David. b 61. St Jo Coll Nottm Dip Th & Min 94. **d** 94 **p** 95. C Helston and Wendron *Truro* 94-97; R St Stephen in Brannel 97-00; R Kenwyn w St Allen from 00. *The Vicarage, Kenwyn Church Road, Kenwyn, Truro TR1 3DR* Tel (01872) 263015 Fax as telephone E-mail pdsayle@btinternet.com

SAYWELL, Philip. b 33. Linc Th Coll 57. **d** 60 **p** 61. C Stepney St Dunstan and All SS *Lon* 60-63; C Calstock *Truro* 63-66; V Lanteglos by Fowey 66-73; Iran 73-77; R Cockley Cley w Gooderstone *Nor* 78-81; V Didlington 78-81; R Gt and Lt Cressingham w Threxton 78-81; R Hilborough w Bodney 78-81; R Oxborough w Foulden and Caldecote 78-81; UAE 81-84; Perm to Offic *Chich* 84-88; Nat Co-ord (UK) SOMA UK 85-88; rtd 93. *Riverside, Exford, Minehead TA24 7PX* Tel (01643) 831619 Fax 831416 E-mail philip.saywell@virgin.net

SCAIFE, Andrew. b 50. Ex Coll Ox BA73 MA76. Wycliffe Hall Ox 74. **d** 77 **p** 78. C Everton St Geo *Liv* 77-81; P-in-c Liv St Mich 81; TV St Luke in the City 81-86; V Litherland St Phil 86-96; Snr Chapl Wirral Hosp NHS Trust from 96. *Arrowe Park Hospital, Upton, Wirral CH49 5PE* Tel 0151-678 5111 ext 2275 E-mail andrew.scaife@whnt.nhs.uk

SCALES, Barbara Marion. b 24. S'wark Ord Course. **dss** 82 **d** 87 **p** 94. St Helier *S'wark* 82-87; Hon Par Dn 87-89; Chapl Asst St Helier Hosp Carshalton 82-88; NSM Cheam Common St Phil *S'wark* 89-95; rtd 95; Perm to Offic *S'wark* from 95. *51 Tonfield Road, Sutton SM3 9JP* Tel (020) 8644 3712

SCAMMAN (née BEWES), Mrs Helen Catherine. b 71. Leeds Univ BA94 York Univ PGCE95 Cam Univ BA01. Ridley Hall Cam 99. **d** 02 **p** 03. C Win Ch Ch *Win* from 02. *8 Juniper Close, Winchester SO22 4LU* Tel (01962) 865051 E-mail scampersons@yahoo.com

SCAMMAN, Jonathan Leitch. b 73. St Andr Univ MA96 Ex Coll Ox MPhil98 Cam Univ BA01. Ridley Hall Cam 99. **d** 02 **p** 03. C Win Ch Ch *Win* from 02. *8 Juniper Close, Winchester SO22 4LU* Tel (01962) 865051 E-mail scampersons@yahoo.com

SCAMMELL, Frank. b 56. Cam Univ MA. St Jo Coll Nottm BA83. **d** 82 **p** 83. C Stapenhill w Cauldwell *Derby* 82-86; TV Swanage and Studland *Sarum* 86-92; Min Southgate LEP *St E*

92-03; V Stoughton *Guildf* from 03. *Stoughton Vicarage, 3 Shepherds Lane, Guildford GU2 9SJ* Tel (01483) 561603

SCAMMELL, John Richard Lyn. b 18. TD50. Bris Univ LLB45. Wycliffe Hall Ox 46. **d** 48 **p** 49. C Bishopston *Bris* 48-50; C Stoke Bishop 50-52; Perm to Offic Ho Cam 70. **d** 72 **p** 73. C P-in-c Bicknoller *B & W* 73-78; P-in-c Crowcombe 75-78; R Bicknoller w Crowcombe and Sampford Brett 78-81; Perm to Offic *B & W* 81-93; *Guildf* 84-00; rtd 83. *4 Pine Ridge Drive, Lower Bourne, Farnham GU10 3JW* Tel (01252) 713100

SCANDINAVIA and GERMANY, Archdeacon of. *See* RATCLIFF, The Ven David William

SCANLON, Geoffrey Edward Leyshon. b 44. Coll of Resurr Mirfield. **d** 76 **p** 77. C Beamish *Dur* 76-79; C-in-c Bishopwearmouth St Mary V w St Pet CD 79-81; USA from 81. *1226 North Vermilion, Danville, IL 61832, USA* Tel (001) (217) 442 1677

SCANTLEBURY, James Stanley. b 48. St Jo Coll Dur BA69 Heythrop Coll Lon MTh80. Westcott Ho Cam 70. **d** 72 **p** 73. C Upperby St Jo *Carl* 72-75; C Guildf H Trin w St Mary *Guildf* 75-77; Order of St Aug 77-86; Chapl Austin Friars Sch Carl 80-86; Chapl Mayfield Coll E Sussex 86-88; Chapl H Trin Sen Sch Halifax 88-90; NSM Ripponden *Wakef* 88-90; V Torpenhow *Carl* 91-94; V Allhallows 91-94; V Falmouth All SS *Truro* 94-98; V Harden and Wilsden *Bradf* 98-02; rtd 03. *5 Westhill Avenue, Cullingworth, Bradford BD13 5BB* Tel (01535) 272980

SCARBOROUGH, John Richard Derek. b 32. Lon Univ BA54. Cuddesdon Coll 68. **d** 69 **p** 70. C Fulbeck *Linc* 69-72; C Bassingham 73-74; Lic to Offic 74-76 and 78-93; R Boothby Graffoe 76-77; R Navenby 76-77; V Wellingore w Temple Bruer 76-77; V Graffoe 77-78; NSM Bassingham 93-97; NSM Auburn w Haddington 93-97; NSM Carlton-le-Moorland w Stapleford 93-97; NSM Thurlby w Norton Disney 93-97; Perm to Offic from 97. *Hales Cottage, 47 High Street, Navenby, Lincoln LN5 0DZ* Tel (01522) 811031

SCARGILL, Christopher Morris. b 57. UEA BA79 York Univ MA81 Leeds Univ CertEd81 Nottm Univ BTh89. Linc Th Coll 86. **d** 89 **p** 90. C Desborough *Pet* 89-92; C Buxton w Burbage and King Sterndale *Derby* 92-93; TV 93-98; V Ipstones w Berkhamsytch and Onecote w Bradnop *Lich* from 98. *The Vicarage, Church Lane, Ipstones, Stoke-on-Trent ST10 2LF* Tel (01538) 266313 E-mail candsscargill@aol.com

SCARISBRICK, Mrs Helen. b 60. Sheff Univ BA81 Sheff Poly PGCE82 Chester Coll of HE BTh99. N Ord Course 97. **d** 99 **p** 00. C Norbury *Ches* from 99. *45 Rowan Drive, Cheadle Hulme, Cheadle SK8 7DU* Tel 0161-486 1710 E-mail helen.scarisbrick@btopenworld.com

SCARR, Hazel Anne. b 44. Guildhall Sch of Music & Drama. St Alb and Ox Min Course. **d** 00 **p** 01. C Adderbury w Milton *Ox* from 00. *Wooden Hill Farm, Barford Road, Bloxham, Banbury OX15 4LP* Tel (01295) 720022 Fax 721050 E-mail hazel@jandhscarr.sagehost.co.uk

SCARTH, John Robert. b 34. Leeds Univ BSc55 CertEd St Jo Coll Dur DipTh65. Cranmer Hall Dur 63. **d** 65 **p** 66. C Dewsbury All SS *Wakef* 65-68; V Shepley 68-72; Asst Master Kingston-upon-Hull Gr Sch 72-78; St Mary's C of E Sch Hendon 78-81; V Ossett cum Gawthorpe 81-88; R Tarrington w Stoke Edith, Aylton, Pixley etc *Heref* 88-96; rtd 96; Perm to Offic *Wakef* 96-97 and from 98. *44 Gagewell Drive, Horbury, Wakefield WF4 6BS* Tel (01924) 272055

SCARTH, Maurice John. b 31. MInstPS AMBIM. St Deiniol's Hawarden 81. **d** 83 **p** 84. C Llandrillo-yn-Rhos *St As* 83-87; V Rhosymedre 87-91; V Kerry and Llanmerewig and Dolfor 91-93; rtd 93. *Homelands, 11A Compton Way, Abergele LL22 7BL* Tel (01745) 833783

SCATTERGOOD, William Henry. b 26. **d** 56 **p** 57. Australia 56-84; V Lonan *S & M* 84-92; V Laxey 84-92; rtd 92; Perm to Offic *Chich* from 92. *5 Sandgate Close, Seaford BN25 3LL* Tel (01323) 492203

SCEATS, Preb David Douglas. b 46. Ch Coll Cam BA68 MA72 Bris Univ MA71. Clifton Th Coll 68. **d** 71 **p** 72. C Cambridge St Paul *Ely* 71-74; Lect Trin Coll Bris 74-83; V Shenstone *Lich* 83-86; Dioc Tr Officer 86-91; P-in-c Colton 86-90; Dir Local Min Development 91-98; Warden of Readers 91-96; C Lich St Chad 94-98; Dioc Board of Min Team Ldr 96-98; Preb Lich Cathl 96-98; Prin NTMTC from 99; Preb St Paul's Cathl *Lon* from 02. *North Thames Ministerial Training Course, Oak Hill, Chase Side, London N14 4PS* Tel (020) 8364 9442 Fax 8364 8889 E-mail principal@ntmtc.org.uk *or* niblick@quista.net

SCHAEFER, Carl Richard. b 67. Coll of Resurr Mirfield CPS94. **d** 94 **p** 95. C Ribbleton *Blackb* 94-98; V Blackb St Thos w St Jude from 98; P-in-c Blackb St Mich w St Jo and H Trin from 03. *The Vicarage, Didsbury Street, Blackburn BB1 3JL* Tel (01254) 263259 E-mail carl@schaeferc.freeserve.co.uk

SCHARF, Ulrich Eduard Erich Julian. b 35. Melbourne Univ BA59 MA62 Linacre Coll Ox BA67 MA72 Lon Univ PhD81. Ripon Hall Ox 65. **d** 67 **p** 68. C Hackney St Jo *Lon* 68-71; Lic to Offic 71-75; Bp Stepney's Chapl 71-75; P-in-c Shadwell St Paul w Ratcliff St Jas 75-90; R St Geo-in-the-East w St Paul 79-86; P-in-c W Ham *Chelmsf* 90-95; V from 95. *The Vicarage, Devenay Road, London E15 4AZ* Tel (020) 8519 0955

SCHARIAH, Zechariah. b 43. Zürich Univ BD87. Baptist Th Sem Rueschlikon 83. **d** 93 **p** 93. Chapl to Miss to Minorities from 93; Perm to Offic *Eur* from 95. *Mission to Minorities, Cysatstrasse 6, 6000 Luzern 7, Switzerland*

SCHEMANOFF, Ms Natasha Anne. b 50. CertEd71 DipTh96. **d** 96 **p** 97. C Freshford, Limpley Stoke and Hinton Charterhouse *B & W* 96-99; TV Worle 99-00; V Kewstoke w Wick St Lawrence from 00; Bp's Adv for Racial Justice from 00. *The Vicarage, 35 Kewstoke Road, Kewstoke, Weston-super-Mare BS22 9YE* Tel (01934) 416162

SCHIBILD, Nigel Edmund David. b 47. Oak Hill Th Coll BA81. **d** 81 **p** 82. C Eccleston Ch Ch *Liv* 81-85; P-in-c Sydenham H Trin *S'wark* 85-87; V 87-91; Chapl Mildmay Miss Hosp 91-98; CMS Lebanon from 99. *All Saints' Church, PO Box 11-2211, Riad El Solh, Beirut 1107 2100, Lebanon* Tel (00961) (4) 530551 Mobile 3-281388 Fax (1) 739764 E-mail schibild@iname.com

SCHILD, John. b 38. ALCD64. **d** 64 **p** 65. C Cheltenham Ch Ch *Glouc* 64-67; Area Sec CMS *Sheff* and *S'well* 67-73; Area Sec CMS *Chelmsf* and *St Alb* 73-75; V Lt Heath *St Alb* 76-88; R Bedford St Pet w St Cuth 88-94; P-in-c King's Walden and Offley w Lilley 94-98; V 98-03; rtd 03. *Trenarren, St Cleer, Liskeard PL14 5DN* E-mail john@schild.demon.co.uk

SCHLEGER, Ms Maria Francesca. b 57. LSE BA78 SS Coll Cam BA84 MA89. Westcott Ho Cam 82. **dss** 85 **d** 87 **p** 94. De Beauvoir Town St Pet *Lon* 85-90; Par Dn 87-90; TD Bow H Trin and All Hallows 90-94; Dean of Women's Min (Stepney Area) 90-94; Perm to Offic *Birm* 94-98; NSM Stepney St Dunstan and All SS *Lon* from 99; Chapl Mildmay Miss Hosp from 03. *St Faith's House, Shandy Street, London E1 4ST* Tel (020) 7790 4194

SCHLUTER, Nathaniel David. b 71. Pemb Coll Ox BA93 MA97 Green Coll Ox DPhil98. Wycliffe Hall Ox BA. **d** 00 **p** 01. C Gerrards Cross and Fulmer *Ox* from 00. *Fairwood, Hay Lane, Fulmer, Slough SL3 6HJ* Tel (01753) 662468 E-mail nat@schluter.org.uk

SCHMIDT, Mrs Karen Rosemarie. b 48. Surrey Univ BSc70 Solicitor 76. STETS DipHE99. **d** 99 **p** 00. NSM Lee-on-the-Solent *Portsm* from 99. *43 Deal Close, Stubbington, Fareham PO14 2LZ* Tel (01329) 314774 *or* (023) 9285 6233 Mobile 07770-795342 E-mail mschmidt@netcomuk.co.uk

SCHNURR, Jutta. *See* MUELLER-SCHNURR, Mrs Jutta

SCHNURR, Martin. b 67. **d** 02. Chapl (Asst) Bris Univ *Bris* from 02. *12 St Paul's Road, Clifton, Bristol BS8 1LR* Tel 0117-973 3963 E-mail martin.schnurr@bris.ac.uk

SCHOFIELD, Andrew Thomas. b 47. K Coll Lon BD70 AKC71 PGCE72. St Aug Coll Cant 70. **d** 81 **p** 82. C Whittlesey *Ely* 81-84; C Ramsey 84-87; P-in-c Ellington 87-94; P-in-c Grafham 87-94; P-in-c Spaldwick w Barham and Woolley 87-94; P-in-c Easton 87-94; P-in-c March St Jo 94; R from 94. *St John's Rectory, Station Road, March PE15 8NG* Tel (01354) 653525 E-mail andrew.schofield@ely.anglican.org *or* atschofield@msn.com

SCHOFIELD, David. b 43. Linc Th Coll 74. **d** 75 **p** 76. C Gainsborough All SS *Linc* 75-78; R Bolingbroke w Hareby 78-79; P-in-c Hagnaby 78-79; P-in-c Hagworthingham w Asgarby and Lusby 78-79; P-in-c Mavis Enderby w Raithby 78-79; P-in-c E Kirkby w Miningsby 78-79; R Bolingbroke 79-81; C-in-c Stamford Ch CD 81-90; V Crowle 90-97; V Crowle Gp from 97. *The Vicarage, Church Street, Crowle, Scunthorpe DN17 4LE* Tel (01724) 710268

SCHOFIELD, David Leslie. b 40. MISM89. EMMTC 98. **d** 01 **p** 02. NSM Derby St Mark *Derby* from 01. *Windsong, 126 Longmoor Lane, Sandiacre, Nottingham NG10 5JP* Tel 0115-939 1850 E-mail david.schofield@boots-plc.com

SCHOFIELD, Edward Denis. b 20. **d** 61 **p** 62. C Addiscombe St Mildred *Cant* 61-63; P-in-c Croydon St Jas 63-64; V 64-66; V Boughton under Blean 66-75; P-in-c Dunkirk 73-75; V Boughton under Blean w Dunkirk 75-76; V Sandgate St Paul 76-85; rtd 85; Perm to Offic *Ex* from 95. *53 Haydons Park, Honiton EX14 8TA* Tel (01404) 42584

SCHOFIELD, Gary. b 64. Ripon Coll Cuddesdon 97. **d** 99 **p** 00. C Exhall *Cov* 99-02; V Wales *Sheff* from 02. *The Vicarage, Manor Road, Wales, Sheffield S26 5PD* Tel (01909) 771111

SCHOFIELD, John Martin. b 47. Selw Coll Cam BA69 MA73. St Steph Ho Ox 70. **d** 72 **p** 73. C Palmers Green St Jo *Lon* 72-75; C Friern Barnet St Jas 75-80; V Luton St Aug Limbury *St Alb* 80-89; V Biddenham 89-94; Dir CME 89-94; Dir Minl Tr *Guildf* 94-99; Can Res Guildf Cathl 95-99. *1 Addley House, 72-78 Molesey Road, Hersham, Walton-on-Thames KT12 4RG* Tel (01932) 227642

SCHOFIELD, John Verity. b 29. Jes Coll Ox BA52 DipTh53 MA56. Cuddesdon Coll 53. **d** 55 **p** 56. C Cirencester *Glouc* 55-59; R Stella *Dur* 59-67; Kenya 67-69; Asst Chapl St Paul's Sch Barnes 69-70; Chapl 71-80; Australia 81-83; Gen Sec Friends of Elderly & Gentlefolk's Help 83-94; Perm to Offic *Sarum* from 83; rtd 94. *Bishops Barn, Foots Hill, Cann, Shaftesbury SP7 0BW* Tel (01747) 853852

SCHOFIELD, Nigel Timothy. b 54. Dur Univ BA76 Nottm Univ BCombStuds83 FRCO. Linc Th Coll 80. **d** 83 **p** 84. C Cheshunt

St Alb 83-86; TV Colyton, Southleigh, Offwell, Widworthy etc *Ex* 86-94; V Seaton 94-03; P-in-c Beer and Branscombe 01-03; V Seaton and Beer from 03; RD Honiton from 99. *The Vicarage, Colyford Road, Seaton EX12 2DF* Tel (01297) 20391

SCHOFIELD, Rodney. b 44. St Jo Coll Cam BA64 MA67 St Pet Hall Ox BA70 MA73. St Steph Ho Ox 68. **d** 71 **p** 72. C Northampton St Mary *Pet* 71-76; V Irchester 76-84; Lesotho 84-86; R W Monkton *B & W* 86-00; Asst Dir of Ords 87-89; Dir of Ords 89-99; Preb Wells Cathl 90-00; Lect Zomba Th Coll Malawi from 00. *PO Box 130, Zomba, Malawi* Tel (00265) 918303

SCHOFIELD, Ms Sarah. b 70. Man Univ BA95. Qu Coll Birm 95. **d** 97 **p** 98. C Longsight St Luke *Man* 97-02; P-in-c Gorton St Phil from 02; Tutor (Man Ho) Westcott Ho Cam from 03. *St Philip's Rectory, Lavington Grove, Manchester M18 7EQ* Tel 0161-231 2201 E-mail sarahschof@aol.com

SCHOFIELD, Mrs Victoria Louise. b 56. Liv Poly BSc88 Liv Univ PGCE91. Wycliffe Hall Ox 00. **d** 02 **p** 03. C Hattersley *Ches* from 02. *58 Callington Drive, Hyde SK14 3EL* Tel 0161-366 7036

SCHOLEFIELD, John. b 27. Leeds Univ BSc50. Wells Th Coll 51. **d** 53 **p** 54. C Ossett cum Gawthorpe *Wakef* 53-56; C Hebden Bridge 56-58; V Sowerby St Geo 58-64; V Darton 64-70; V Stoke Gabriel *Ex* 70-84; P-in-c Collaton St Mary 82-84; V Stoke Gabriel and Collaton 84-92; rtd 92; Perm to Offic *Ex* from 92. *25 Droridge, Dartington, Totnes TQ9 6JQ* Tel (01803) 863192

SCHOLES, Ms Victoria Prichard. b 68. Man Univ BSc89. St Jo Coll Nottm 97. **d** 00 **p** 01. C Macclesfield St Jo *Ches* 00-02; NSM from 02. *37 Princes Way, Macclesfield SK11 8UB* Tel (01625) 425049

SCHOLEY, Donald. b 38. Leeds Univ CertEd60. Lich Th Coll 69. **d** 72 **p** 73. C Blaby *Leic* 72-75; TV Daventry w Norton *Pet* 75-78; R Wootton w Quinton and Preston Deanery from 78. *The Rectory, 67 Water Lane, Wootton, Northampton NN4 6HH* Tel (01604) 761891

SCHOLFIELD, Peter. b 35. Sarum Th Coll 64. **d** 66 **p** 67. C S Kirkby *Wakef* 66-69; P-in-c Carlton 69-90; rtd 90; Perm to Offic *Wakef* from 90. *31 Springhill Avenue, Crofton, Wakefield WF1 1HA* Tel (01924) 863430

SCHOLLAR, Canon Pamela Mary. b 39. Southn Univ DipEd80. S Dios Minl Tr Scheme 89. **d** 92 **p** 94. NSM Bournemouth St Andr *Win* 92-94; NSM Pokesdown St Jas from 94; Hon Can Win Cathl from 02. *22 Bethia Road, Bournemouth BH8 9BD* Tel (01202) 397925 E-mail schollar@ukgateway.net

SCHOLZ, Terence Brinsley. b 44. St Martin's Coll Lanc MA98. Carl and Blackb Dioc Tr Inst 94. **d** 97 **p** 98. NSM St Annes *Blackb* 97-01; NSM Broughton from 01; Perm to Offic from 02. *5 Bracken Drive, Freckleton, Preston PR4 1TH* Tel (01772) 632966 Mobile 07768-441400 Fax 635779

SCHOOLING, Bruce James. b 47. Rhodes Univ BA73. St Paul's Coll Grahamstown 76. **d** 76 **p** 77. S Africa 76-86; C Wanstead St Mary *Chelmsf* 87-90; V Leigh-on-Sea St Jas from 90. *St James's Vicarage, 103 Blenheim Chase, Leigh-on-Sea SS9 3BY* Tel (01702) 471786 Fax as telephone E-mail b.schooling@btinternet.com

SCHORAH, Michael James. b 63. Keble Coll Ox BA89 MA91. Trin Coll Bris BA95. **d** 95 **p** 96. C Cheltenham St Mary, St Matt, St Paul and H Trin *Glouc* 95-98; C Hazlemere *Ox* 98-99; P-in-c Deal, The Carpenter's Arms *Cant* from 99. *2 Toremore Mews, Rectory Road, Deal CT14 9SX* Tel (01304) 369100 Mobile 07971-834910 Fax 07970-099363 E-mail mike.schorah@cellchurch.co.uk

SCHRODER, Edward Amos. b 41. Cant Univ (NZ) BA64. Cranmer Hall Dur DipTh66. **d** 67 **p** 68. C St Marylebone All So w SS Pet and Jo *Lon* 67-71; USA from 71; Dean Gordon Coll 71-76; Asst to Bp Florida 76-79; R Orange Park 79-86; R San Antonio from 86. *510 Belknap, San Antonio, TX 78212, USA* Tel (001) (210) 736 3132 Fax 733 1432 E-mail rector@cecweb.org

SCHRYVER, Mrs Linda Jean. b 56. Ch Ch Coll Cant BSc00. SEITE 00. **d** 03. NSM Willesborough *Cant* from 03. *2 Church Cottages, Canterbury Road, Godmersham, Canterbury CT4 7DS* Tel (01227) 730750 Mobile 07768-566372 E-mail schryverl@tiscali.co.uk

SCHULD DE VERNY, Dietrich Gustave. *See* DE VERNY, David Dietrich

SCHUNEMANN, Bernhard George. b 61. LRAM83 K Coll Lon BD86 AKC86. Ripon Coll Cuddesdon 88. **d** 90 **p** 91. C Kirkby Liv 90-93; C St Martin-in-the-Fields *Lon* 93-97; Chapl Br Sch of Osteopathy 93-97; P-in-c Littlemore *Ox* from 97. *The Vicarage, St Nicholas Road, Oxford OX4 4PP* Tel (01865) 437720 Fax 437719 E-mail bschunemann@compuserve.com

✠**SCHUSTER, The Rt Revd James Leo.** b 12. Keble Coll Ox BA35 MA44. St Steph Ho Ox 36. **d** 37 **p** 38 **c** 56. Chapl St Steph Ho Ox 39-49; CF (EC) 40-46; S Africa from 49; Bp St John's 56-79; Asst Bp George from 80. *19 Aanhuizen Street, Swellendam, 6743 South Africa* Tel (0027) (291) 42115

SCHWIER, Paul David. b 55. LNSM course 94. **d** 96 **p** 97. OLM Pulham Market, Pulham St Mary and Starston *Nor* 96-99; OLM

Dickleburgh and The Pulhams from 99. *Street Farm, Pulham Market, Diss IP21 4SP* Tel (01379) 676240

SCHWIER, Peter Andrew. b 52. **d** 91 **p** 92. NSM Fressingfield, Mendham etc *St E* from 91. *Valley Farm, Metfield, Harleston IP20 0JZ* Tel (01379) 586517

SCLATER, Jennifer. d 02. Par Dn Elgin w Lossiemouth *Mor* from 02. *82 Pluscarden Road, Elgin IV30 1SU* Tel (01343) 556469

SCLATER, John Edward. b 46. Nottm Univ BA68 St Edm Hall Ox CertEd71. Cuddesdon Coll 69. **d** 71 **p** 72. C Bris St Mary Redcliffe w Temple etc *Bris* 71-75; Chapl Bede Ho Staplehurst 75-79; Chapl Warw Sch 79; P-in-c Offchurch *Cov* 79-80; Belgium 81-89; Willen Priory 89-91; C Linslade *Ox* 91-94; P-in-c Hedsor and Bourne End 94-02; rtd 02. *3 East Court, South Horrington Village, Wells BA5 3HL* Tel (01749) 671349
E-mail john@jes07.freeserve.co.uk

SCOBIE, Geoffrey Edward Winsor. b 39. Bris Univ BSc62 MSc68 Birm Univ MA70 Glas Univ PhD78 FRSA96 AFBPsS. Tyndale Hall Bris 62. **d** 65 **p** 66. C Summerfield *Birm* 65-66; C Moseley St Anne 66-67; Lect Psychology Glas Univ from 67; Hon C Glas St Silas Glas 70-83; P-in-c 83-84; Hon R 84-85; TR 85-86; Team Chapl 86-88; Hon Asst Team Chapl 88-99; Assoc P Bishopbriggs from 99. *3 Norfolk Crescent, Bishopbriggs, Glasgow G64 3BA* Tel 0141-722 2907

SCOONES, Roger Philip. b 48. DipTh. Trin Coll Bris. **d** 82 **p** 83. C Childwall All SS *Liv* 82-85; Head Cathl *Bradf* 85-90; V Congleton St Pet *Ches* 90-96; P-in-c Congleton St Steph 94-96; R Stockport St Mary from 96. *St Mary's Rectory, Gorsey Mount Street, Stockport SK1 4DU* Tel 0161-429 6564 *or* 480 1815 Fax 429 6564 E-mail roger@scoones9.freeserve.co.uk

SCORER, John Robson. b 47. Westcott Ho Cam 73. **d** 75 **p** 76. C Silksworth *Dur* 75-78; C Newton Aycliffe 78-82; V Sherburn 82-83; V Sherburn w Pittington 83-89; P-in-c Croxdale 89-93; Chapl Dur Constabulary from 89; Chapl Dur Police Tr Cen from 93. *1 Vicarage Close, Howden le Wear, Crook DL15 8RB* Tel (01388) 764938 Fax as telephone

SCOTFORD, Bethan Lynne. b 44. Univ of Wales (Cardiff) BA67 PGCE68 Man Metrop Univ Dip Educn Mgt 86. St As Minl Tr Course 95. **d** 99 **p** 00. Fieldworker (Wales) USPG from 98; C Guilsfield w Pool Quay *St As* 99-02; R Corwen and Llangar w Gwyddelwern and Llawrybetws from 02. *The Rectory, Ffordd ty Cerrig, Corwen LL21 9RP* Tel (01490) 412278 Mobile 07802-656607 E-mail 114153.2024@compuserve.com

SCOTLAND, Nigel Adrian Douglas. b 42. McGill Univ Montreal MA71 Aber Univ PhD75 CertEd75 Bris Univ MLitt85. Gordon-Conwell Th Sem MDiv70 Lon Coll of Div ALCD66 LTh74. **d** 66 **p** 67. C Harold Wood *Chelmsf* 66-69; USA 69-70; R Lakefield Canada 70-72; Lic to Offic *Ab* 72-75; Chapl and Lect St Mary's Coll Cheltenham 75-79; Sen Lect 77-79; Chapl and Sen Lect Coll of SS Paul and Mary Cheltenham 79-84; NSM Cheltenham St Mark *Glouc* 85-92; Field Chmn RS Cheltenham and Glouc Coll of HE 89-01; Glos Univ from 01; Prin Lect from 96; Perm to Offic *Glouc* from 92. *23 School Road, Charlton Kings, Cheltenham GL53 8BG* Tel (01242) 529167
E-mail nscotland@chelt.ac.uk

SCOTLAND, Primus of the Episcopal Church in. See CAMERON, The Most Revd Andrew Bruce

SCOTT, Adam. b 47. TD78. Ch Ch Ox BA68 MA72 City Univ MSc79 Barrister 72 FRSA95 CEng81 MIEE81 FIEE94. S'wark Ord Course 73. **d** 75 **p** 76. MSE Blackheath Park St Mich *S'wark* from 75; Dean for MSE, Woolwich from 90; Prof Fell St Andr Univ *St And* 96-97 and from 98; Perm to Offic from 96. *19 Blackheath Park, London SE3 9RW, or St Katharine's West, The Scores, St Andrews KY16 9AT* Tel (020) 8852 3286 *or* (01334) 462800 Fax (020) 8852 6247 *or* (01334) 426812
E-mail adam.scott@btinternet.com

SCOTT, Alfred Thomas. b 19. St Steph Ho Ox 78. **d** 81 **p** 82. NSM S Ascot *Ox* 81-85; NSM Bridport *Sarum* 85-89; Perm to Offic *Sarum* from 89-90 and *Truro* 90-02; rtd 90. *22 Castle Hill Court, Cross Lane, Bodmin PL31 2LE*

SCOTT, Preb Allan George. b 39. Man Univ BA61. Coll of Resurr Mirfield 61. **d** 63 **p** 64. C Bradford cum Beswick *Man* 63-66; P-in-c 66-72; Hon C Bramhall *Ches* 72-74; Hon C Tottenham St Jo *Lon* 74-76; Hon C Bush Hill Park St Steph 76-79; R Stoke Newington St Mary 79-02; Preb St Paul's Cathl from 91; P-in-c Brownswood Park 95-97. *St Mark's Vicarage Flat, 1A Moray Road, London N4 3LD* Tel (020) 7263 9371

SCOTT, Andrew Charles Graham. b 28. Mert Coll Ox BA57 MA. Wells Th Coll 57. **d** 59 **p** 60. C Rugby St Andr *Cov* 59-64; Chapl RN 64-68; C Prenton *Ches* 68-71; V Tow Law *Dur* 71-81; RD Stanhope 77-81; V Bampton w Clanfield *Ox* 81-95; rtd 95; Perm to Offic *Ex* from 95. *99 Speedwell Crescent, Plymouth PL6 5SZ* Tel (01752) 773570

SCOTT, Barrie. b 63. Birm Univ BA85 Goldsmiths' Coll Lon PGCE86. St Steph Ho Ox 93. **d** 95 **p** 96. C Tilehurst St Mich *Ox* 95-98; Perm to Offic *Birm* from 98. *29 Beechwood Road, Great Barr, Birmingham B43 6JN* Tel 0121-358 3877 *or* 373 4807

SCOTT, Basil John Morley. b 34. Qu Coll Cam BA59 Banaras Hindu Univ MA65. Ridley Hall Cam 58. **d** 60 **p** 61. C Woking St Pet *Guildf* 60-63; India 63-83; TR Kirby Muxloe *Leic* 83-89;

Asian Outreach Worker (Leic Martyrs) 89-95; Derby Asian Chr Min Project *Derby* 95-00; rtd 00; Perm to Offic *Ely* from 00. *14 Scotsdowne Road, Trumpington, Cambridge CB2 2HU* Tel (01223) 476565 E-mail 100600.233@compuserve.com

SCOTT, Brian. b 35. CCC Ox BA58. Coll of Resurr Mirfield 59. **d** 61 **p** 65. C Carl St Aid and Ch Ch *Carl* 61-62; Asst Master Hutton Gr Sch 63-65; Perm to Offic *Leic* 65-67; Lic to Offic 67-70; P-in-c Theddingworth 71-78; V Lubenham 71-78; Asst Chapl Oundle Sch 78-83; R Barrowden and Wakerley w S Luffenham *Pet* 83-98; rtd 98; Perm to Offic *Leic* and *Pet* from 98. *The Cedars, 3 Glaston Road, Preston, Oakham LE15 9NH* Tel (01572) 737242

SCOTT, Charles Geoffrey. b 32. St Jo Coll Cam BA54 MA58. Cuddesdon Coll 56. **d** 58 **p** 59. C Brighouse *Wakef* 58-61; C Bathwick w Woolley *B & W* 61-64; V Frome Ch Ch 64-78; R Winchelsea *Chich* 78-93; R Winchelsea and Icklesham 93-95; rtd 95; Perm to Offic *Chich* from 95. *Hickstead, Main Street, Iden, Rye TN31 7PT* Tel (01797) 280096

SCOTT, Christopher. See DAVIES, Christopher

SCOTT, Christopher John Fairfax. b 45. Magd Coll Cam BA67 MA71. Westcott Ho Cam 68. **d** 70 **p** 71. C Nor St Pet Mancroft *Nor* 70-73; Chapl Magd Coll Cam 73-79; V Hampstead Ch Ch *Lon* 79-94; rtd 00. *49 St Barnabas Road, Cambridge CB1 2BX* Tel (01223) 359421

SCOTT, Canon Christopher Michael. b 44. SS Coll Cam BA66 MA70. Cuddesdon Coll 66. **d** 68 **p** 69. C New Addington *Cant* 68-73; C Westmr St Steph w St Jo *Lon* 73-78; V Enfield St Mich 78-81; V Effingham w Lt Bookham *Guildf* 81-87; R Esher 87-98; RD Emly 91-96; R Bude Haven and Marhamchurch *Truro* from 98; Hon Can Truro Cathl from 03. *The Rectory, 8 Falcon Terrace, Bude EX23 8LJ* Tel (01288) 352318

SCOTT, Christopher Stuart. b 48. Surrey Univ BA92 MBPsS92. Sarum & Wells Th Coll 79. **d** 81 **p** 82. C Enfield Chase St Mary *Lon* 81-82; C Coalbrookdale, Iron-Bridge and Lt Wenlock *Heref* 82-86; P-in-c Breinton 86-89; Chapl Hickey's Almshouses Richmond from 89; Lic to Offic *S'wark* from 89. *164 Sheen Road, Richmond TW9 1XD* Tel (020) 8940 6560

SCOTT, Claude John. b 37. Qu Mary Coll Lon BSc60 PhD64 Lon Inst of Educn PGCE61 FRSA94. EAMTC 88. **d** 91 **p** 92. NSM Heigham H Trin *Nor* 91-98; Perm to Offic from 98. *17 Lime Tree Road, Norwich NR2 2NQ* Tel (01603) 455686
E-mail cjscott@btinternet.com

SCOTT, Colin. b 32. Dur Univ BA54. Coll of Resurr Mirfield 58. **d** 60 **p** 61. C Wallsend St Pet *Newc* 60-64; C Seaton Hirst 64-68; C Longbenton St Bart 68-70; V Benwell St Aid 70-77; V Sleekburn 77-89; P-in-c Cambois 77-88; V Longhoughton w Howick 89-96; rtd 96; Perm to Offic *Newc* from 96. *Pele Cottage, Hepple, Morpeth NE65 7LH* Tel (01669) 640258

✠**SCOTT, The Rt Revd Colin John Fraser.** b 33. Qu Coll Cam BA56 MA60. Ridley Hall Cam 56. **d** 58 **p** 59 **c** 84. C Clapham Common St Barn *S'wark* 58-61; C Hatcham St Jas 61-64; V Kennington St Mark 64-71; RD Lambeth 68-71; Vice-Chmn Dioc Past Cttee 71-77; Hon Can S'wark Cathl 73-84; TR Sanderstead All SS 77-84; Suff Bp Hulme *Man* 84-98; Chmn CCC 94-98; rtd 99; Perm to Offic *Leic* from 99; *Derby* from 00. *The Priest House, Prior Park Road, Ashby-de-la-Zouch LE65 1BH* Tel (01530) 564403

SCOTT, Cuthbert Le Messurier. b 13. Wells Th Coll 60. **d** 61 **p** 62. C Highgate St Mich *Lon* 61-64; V Paddington St Jo w St Mich 64-72; V Shamley Green *Guildf* 72-83; rtd 83; Perm to Offic *Chich* 84-88; and from 95; Chapl St Dunstan's Hosp Brighton 88-95. *30 Manormead, Tilford Road, Hindhead GU26 6RA* Tel (01428) 604768

SCOTT, David. b 40. Rhodes Univ BA63. St Paul's Coll Grahamstown LTh65. **d** 65 **p** 66. S Africa 65-91; TV Cheltenham St Mark *Glouc* 92-96; R Swanscombe *Roch* from 96. *The Rectory, Swanscombe Street, Swanscombe DA10 0JZ* Tel (01322) 843160

SCOTT, Canon David Victor. b 47. St Chad's Coll Dur BA69. Cuddesdon Coll 69. **d** 71 **p** 72. C St Mary-at-Latton *Chelmsf* 71-73; Chapl Haberdashers' Aske's Sch Elstree 73-80; V Torpenhow *Carl* 80-91; V Allhallows 80-91; R Win St Lawr and St Maurice w St Swithun *Win* from 91; Warden Sch of Spirituality *Win* from 91; Hon Can Win Cathl from 02. *The Rectory, Colebrook Street, Winchester SO23 9LH* Tel (01962) 868056

SCOTT, Edgar. b 12. Linc Th Coll 76. **d** 76 **p** 76. Hon C Wombwell *Sheff* 76-90; rtd 90; Perm to Offic *Sheff* 90-93. *17 Wood Walk, Wombwell, Barnsley S73 0LZ* Tel (01226) 753020

SCOTT, Canon Eric Walter. b 16. St Jo Coll Cam BA38 MA43. Ridley Hall Cam 38. **d** 40 **p** 41. C Reading St Jo *Ox* 40-43; C Cambridge H Trin *Ely* 43-45; C-in-c Tilehurst St Mary CD *Ox* 45-49; R Brimpton w Wasing 49-53; V Midgham 50-53; R Foothills Miss Canada 53-56; R Edmonton St Geo 56-57; V Midgham w Brimpton 57-61; Chapl Shawnigan Lake Sch Canada 61-67; I Shawnigan Lake 64-67; R Courtenay St Jo 67-81; Perm to Offic *Nor* 81-89; Perm to Offic *Ely* 90-00. *4 Allen Court, Hauxton Road, Trumpington, Cambridge CB2 2LU* Tel (01223) 841015

SCOTT, Mrs Erica Jane. b 58. Trin Coll Bris BA02. **d** 02 **p** 03. C Ilminster and Distr *B & W* from 02. *145 Blackdown View, Ilminster TA19 0BG* Tel (01460) 53427
E-mail scott@ericaj.fsnet.co.uk

SCOTT, Francis Richard. b 63. St Jo Coll Nottm. **d** 00 **p** 01. C Huntington *York* from 00; TV from 03. *49 Avon Drive, Huntington, York YO32 9YA* Tel (01904) 768423
E-mail fandfscott@aol.com

SCOTT, Gary James. b 61. Edin Univ BD87. Edin Th Coll 85. **d** 87 **p** 88. C Edin St Cuth *Edin* 87-90; R Peebles 90-92; P-in-c Innerleithen 92-96; R Penicuik 96-98; R W Linton 96-98; Lic to Offic from 98. *4 Springwood Terrace, Peebles EH45 9ET*

SCOTT, Geoffrey. *See* SCOTT, Charles Geoffrey

SCOTT, Canon Gordon. b 30. Man Univ BA51. St Jo Coll Dur 51. **d** 53 **p** 54. C Monkwearmouth St Andr *Dur* 53-55; C Stranton 55-56; C Chester le Street 56-59; V Marley Hill 59-62; Chapl Forest Sch Snaresbrook 62-66; Chapl Dunrobin Sch Sutherland 66-72; Chapl Pocklington Sch York 72-74; V Barton w Pooley Bridge *Carl* 74-80; RD Penrith 79-82; P-in-c Lazonby 80; R Gt Salkeld w Lazonby 80-90; Hon Can Carl Cathl 83-94; P-in-c Patterdale 90-94; rtd 94; Perm to Offic *Carl* 94-97. *48 Lakeland Park, Keswick CA12 4AT* Tel (01768) 775862

SCOTT, Guy Charles. b 61. Coll of Resurr Mirfield. **d** 00 **p** 01. C Abington *Pet* from 00. *21 Lime Avenue, Northampton NN3 2HA* Tel (01604) 711264

SCOTT, Mrs Helen Ruth. b 59. Surrey Univ BA97 K Coll Lon MA99 St Thos Hosp Lon SRN81 R Shrewsbury Hosp RM85. S'wark Ord Course DipRS92. **d** 92 **p** 94. NSM Richmond St Mary w St Matthias and St Jo *S'wark* from 92; Chapl Hickey's Almshouses Richmond from 01. *164 Sheen Road, Richmond TW9 1XD* Tel (020) 8940 6560

SCOTT, Ian. b 45. MBChA87 MSSCh87. Qu Coll Birm 92. **d** 94 **p** 95. C Cropthorne w Charlton *Worc* 94-97; Asst Chapl Univ Hosp Birm NHS Trust 98-99; Chapl S Warks Combined Care NHS Trust 99-02; Chapl Worcs Acute Hosps NHS Trust from 02. *Worcester Royal Infirmary, Ronkswood Branch, New Town Road, Worcester WR5 1HN* Tel (01905) 763333 Mobile 07788-416500 E-mail ian.scott@swarkpct.nhs.uk

SCOTT, Ian Michael. b 25. Bris Univ BA50 Leic Univ DipEd51 Open Univ MA99. Bps' Coll Cheshunt 52. **d** 53 **p** 54. C Rotherhithe St Mary w All SS *S'wark* 53-55; C Lavender Hill Ascension 55-59; C Camberwell St Mich w All So w Em 59-60; C Kettering St Mary *Pet* 60-63; V Haverstock Hill H Trin w Kentish Town St Barn *Lon* 63-93; rtd 93; Perm to Offic *Nor* 93-96. *Apd Correos 228, 03724 Moraira, Alicante, Spain* Tel (0034) (96) 754 5401

SCOTT, Mrs Inez Margaret Gillette. b 26. St Alb Minl Tr Scheme 76. **dss** 79 **d** 87 **p** 94. Preston w Sutton Poyntz and Osmington w Poxwell *Sarum* 83-86; Dorchester 86-96; Par Dn 87-88; NSM 88-96; rtd 88; Perm to Offic *Sarum* from 96. *14 Came View Road, Dorchester DT1 2AE* Tel (01305) 267547

SCOTT, James Alexander Gilchrist. b 32. Linc Coll Ox BA56 DipHT57 MA60. Wycliffe Hall Ox 56. **d** 58 **p** 59. C Shipley St Paul *Bradf* 58-61; Abp's Dom Chapl *York* 61-65; Brazil 65-68; V Grassendale *Liv* 68-77; V Thorp Arch *York* 77; P-in-c Walton 77; V Thorp Arch w Walton 77-89; Chapl HM Pris Rudgate 77-82; Askham Grange 82-87; RD Tadcaster 78-86; V Kirk Ella 89-92; TR 92-97; rtd 97; Perm to Offic *York* from 98. *Mount Royd, Potter Hill, Pickering YO18 8AD* Tel (01751) 476226

SCOTT, James William. b 39. S Dios Minl Tr Scheme 84. **d** 88 **p** 89. NSM Bremhill w Foxham and Hilmarton *Sarum* 88-94; NSM Derry Hill w Bremhill and Foxham from 94. *14 Bremhill, Calne SN11 9LA* Tel (01249) 813114

SCOTT, Mrs Janice Beasant. b 44. MCSP66 Middx Hosp Physiotherapy Sch Dip Town Planning 70. EAMTC 89. **d** 92 **p** 94. NSM Fakenham w Alethorpe *Nor* 92-95; C Eaton 95-99; R Dickleburgh and The Pulhams from 99; RD Redenhall from 03. *The Rectory, Station Road, Pulham Market, Diss IP21 4TE* Tel (01379) 676256 Mobile 07905-039243
E-mail revjanice@scott347.freeserve.co.uk

SCOTT, John. *See* SCOTT, Canon William John

SCOTT, John. b 54. QUB BD79. CITC 80. **d** 81 **p** 82. C Willowfield *D & D* 81-83; C Newtownards 83-85; I Kilskeery w Trillick *Clogh* 85-90; Lic to Offic *D & D* 90-96; I Bright w Ballee and Killough 96-01. *Address temp unknown*
E-mail rev.john@virgin.net

SCOTT, John. b 54. Heriot-Watt Univ BA76 Leeds Univ BA97. Coll of Resurr Mirfield 95. **d** 97 **p** 98. C Bethnal Green St Matt w St Jas the Gt *Lon* 97-00; Asst Chapl Qu Mary and Westf Coll 97-00; C Heston from 00; Inter-Faith Adviser from 00. *24 Hogarth Gardens, Hounslow TW5 0QS* Tel (020) 8577 1738 E-mail john.scott@london.anglican.org

SCOTT, John David. b 52. St Jo Coll Ox BA74 MA78 Leeds Univ BA78. Coll of Resurr Mirfield 76. **d** 78 **p** 79. C Oundle *Pet* 78-81; C Dalston H Trin w St Phil *Lon* 81-85; V Ponders End St Matt 85-91; Chapl Bede Ho Staplehurst from 91. *Bede House, Goudhurst Road, Staplehurst, Tonbridge TN12 0HQ* Tel (01580) 891995

SCOTT, John Eric. b 16. FSA St Cath Coll Ox BA38 MA42. Ripon Hall Ox 39. **d** 40 **p** 41. C Heworth St Alb *Dur* 40-43; C

SCOTT
Gateshead St Mary 43-45; Chapl and Sacr Ch Ch *Ox* 45-47; Ho Master Forest Sch Snaresbrook 55-81; P-in-c St Mich Cornhill w St Pet le Poer etc *Lon* 81-85; rtd 85. *17 Harman Avenue, Woodford Green IG8 9DS* Tel (020) 8505 7093

SCOTT, Preb John Gilbert Mortimer. b 25. St Edm Hall Ox BA49 MA52. Bps' Coll Cheshunt. **d** 51 **p** 52. C Ex St Thos *Ex* 51-54; C Wolborough w Newton Abbot 54-58; V Clawton 58-66; R Tetcott w Luffincott 58-66; RD Holsworthy 65-66; V Newton St Cyres 66-84; RD Cadbury 81-84; Preb Ex Cathl from 84; P-in-c Bampton 84; P-in-c Clayhanger 84; P-in-c Petton 84; V Bampton, Morebath, Clayhanger and Petton 84-91; rtd 91. *Trelake, Bridgetown Hill, Totnes TQ9 5BA* Tel (01803) 867754

SCOTT, John Harold. b 46. Univ of Wales (Cardiff) BSc69. St Steph Ho Ox 69. **d** 72 **p** 73. C Skewen *Llan* 72-74; C Port Talbot St Theodore 74-77; P-in-c Bedlinog 77-78; V 78-85; R Penderyn w Ystradfellte and Pontneathvaughan *S & B* from 85. *The Vicarage, Ystradfellte, Aberdare CF44 9JE* Tel (01639) 720405 Mobile 07711-961667 E-mail jhs46@hotmail.com

SCOTT, John Peter. b 47. Open Univ BA80. Lambeth STh81 K Coll Lon 69 St Aug Coll Cant 74. **d** 75 **p** 76. C Dartford St Alb *Roch* 75-78; C-in-c Goring-by-Sea *Chich* 78-81; Chapl Wells and Meare Manor Hosps 81-86; CF (TAVR) 82-90; Chapl Pangbourne Coll 86-90; Min Reigate St Phil CD *S'wark* 90-92; P-in-c Reigate St Phil from 92; Chapl St Bede's Ecum Sch Reigate from 90. *The Parsonage, 102A Nutley Lane, Reigate RH2 9HA* Tel (01737) 244542

SCOTT, Keith Brounton de Salve. b 55. QUB BD. DipTh. **d** 83 **p** 84. C Belfast St Matt *Conn* 83-87; I Ardclinis and Tickmacrevan w Layde and Cushendun 87-01. *20 Princess Gardens, Holywood, Belfast BT18 0PN* Tel (028) 9042 2266 E-mail keithbscott@msn.com

SCOTT, Kenneth James. b 46. Bris Univ BA68. Trin Coll Bris 71. **d** 73 **p** 74. C Illogan *Truro* 73-76; C Camberley St Paul *Guildf* 76-81; R Bradford Peverell, Stratton, Frampton etc *Sarum* from 81; RD Dorchester 95-99. *The Rectory, Church Lane, Frampton, Dorchester DT2 9NL* Tel (01300) 320429 Fax as telephone E-mail kenjscott@care4free.net

SCOTT, Kevin Francis. b 51. Peterho Cam MA Mert Coll Ox DPhil76 CChem MRSC. Wycliffe Hall Ox. **d** 83 **p** 84. C Ox St Ebbe w H Trin and St Pet *Ox* 83-86; P-in-c Prestonpans *Edin* 86-93; R Musselburgh 86-93; R Edin SS Phil and Jas from 93. *The Rectory, 5 Wardie Road, Edinburgh EH5 3QE* Tel 0131-552 4300 E-mail drkfs@aol.com

SCOTT, Kevin Peter. b 43. Reigate Coll of Art DipAD73. Coll of Resurr Mirfield 93. **d** 93 **p** 94. C Rushall *Lich* 93-97; P-in-c Goldenhill from 97. *St John's Vicarage, Drummond Street, Stoke-on-Trent ST6 5RF* Tel (01782) 782736

SCOTT, Kevin Willard. b 53. Westhill Coll Birm CYCW77 Open Univ BA96 Glos Univ MA03. Linc Th Coll 92. **d** 92 **p** 93. C Walton-on-Thames *Guildf* 92-97; R Matson *Glouc* 97-03; RD Glouc City 01-03; V Malden St Jo *S'wark* from 03. *5 Vicarage Close, Worcester Park KT4 7LZ* Tel (020) 8337 8830 E-mail kevinscott@fish.co.uk

SCOTT, Lester Desmond Donald. b 66. NUI BA89. CITC BTh92. **d** 92 **p** 93. C Killeshandra w Killegar and Derrylane *K, E & A* 92-95; C Kilmore w Ballintemple 92-95; I Fenagh w Myshall, Aghade and Ardoyne *C & O* from 95. *The Glebe House, Ballon, Carlow, Irish Republic* Tel and fax (00353) (59) 915 9367 Mobile 87-250 4322 E-mail lesterscott@oceanfree.net

SCOTT (née CURRELL), Mrs Linda Anne. b 62. K Alfred's Coll Win BEd84. Trin Coll Bris BA92. **d** 92 **p** 94. Par Dn Tunbridge Wells St Mark *Roch* 92-94; C 94-97; TV Walthamstow *Chelmsf* 97-02; Perm to Offic from 02. *St Margaret's Rectory, London Road, Pitsea, Basildon SS13 2DU* Tel (01268) 584760 E-mail scottlindatim@aol.com

SCOTT, Canon Malcolm Kenneth Merrett. b 30. ACA53 FCA64. Clifton Th Coll 56. **d** 58 **p** 59. C Highbury Ch Ch *Lon* 58-60; CMS 60-61; Uganda 61-74; V Sunnyside w Bourne End *St Alb* 74-90; V Clapham 90-95; rtd 95. *10 The Ring, Little Haywood, Stafford ST18 0TP* Tel (01889) 881464

SCOTT, Nicholas Charles Andrew. b 74. Univ of Wales (Ban) BD95. Westcott Ho Cam 97. **d** 99 **p** 00. C Ryde H Trin and Swanmore St Mich *Portsm* 99-01; C Burbage w Aston Flamville *Leic* from 01. *46 Salisbury Road, Burbage, Hinckley LE10 2AR* Tel (01455) 617377 E-mail ncascott@hotmail.com

SCOTT, Patrick Henry Fowlis. b 25. Jes Coll Cam BA51 MA55. Wells Th Coll 51. **d** 53 **p** 54. C Milton next Gravesend w Denton *Roch* 53-54; V New Hythe 54-57; CF 57-70; Dep Asst Chapl Gen 70-71 and 74-80; Sen CF 72-74; P-in-c Fridaythorpe w Fimber and Thixendale *York* 80-83; P-in-c Sledmere and Wetwang w Cowlan 80-83; V Sledmere and Cowlam w Fridaythorpe, Fimer etc 84-90; rtd 90; Perm to Offic *York* 90-01. *4 Hatherley Court, Hatherley Court Road, Cheltenham GL51 6EA* Tel (01242) 239179

SCOTT, Paul Malcolm. b 57. Sheff City Poly BA79 CPFA85. Ripon Coll Cuddesdon. **d** 00 **p** 01. C N Shields *Newc* from 00. *103 Billy Mill Avenue, North Shields NE29 0QW* Tel 0191-258 0554 E-mail paulmscott@scott2.freeserve.co.uk

SCOTT, Pauline Claire Michalak. b 55. St Anne's Coll Ox BA77 MA82 Dur Univ PGCE78. TISEC 98. **d** 01 **p** 02. NSM

Papworth *Ely* from 01. *16 Granary Way, Cambourne, Cambridge CB3 6BQ* Tel (01954) 200795 Mobile 07855-395840 E-mail pauline.cm.scott@ntlworld.com

SCOTT, Peter Crawford. b 35. Ch Ch Ox BA56 MA61. Cuddesdon Coll 60. **d** 62 **p** 63. C Broseley w Benthall *Heref* 62-66; P-in-c Hughenden *Ox* 66-71; C Hykeham *Linc* 71-73; P-in-c Stottesdon *Heref* 73-76; Australia from 76; rtd 97. *8 Delacombe Way, Willaura, Vic, Australia 3379* Tel (0061) (3) 5354 1557

SCOTT, Peter James Douglas Sefton. b 59. OBE03. Edin Univ BD83. Edin Th Coll 81. **d** 83 **p** 84. C Helensburgh *Glas* 83-86; C-in-c Glas St Oswald 86-89; R 89-91; Chapl RN from 91; ChJLJ from 99. *Royal Naval Chaplaincy Service, Room 203, Victory Building, HM Naval Base, Portsmouth PO1 3LS* Tel (023) 9272 7903 Fax 9272 7111

SCOTT, Peter Lindsay. b 29. Keble Coll Ox BA54 MA58. Linc Th Coll 54. **d** 56 **p** 57. C Weston-super-Mare St Sav *B & W* 56-59; C Knowle H Nativity *Bris* 59-61; P-in-c Glas St Pet *Glas* 61-63; V Heap Bridge *Man* 63-73; V Rochdale St Geo w St Alb 73-86; R Droylsden St Andr 86-94; rtd 94; Perm to Offic *Man* from 94. *2 Chancel Place, Rochdale OL16 1FB* Tel (01706) 523270

SCOTT, Ruth. *See* SCOTT, Mrs Helen Ruth

SCOTT, Sara Rosamund. b 49. Portsm Poly BSc70 Plymouth Poly MPhil74. SEITE 97. **d** 00 **p** 01. NSM Rotherhithe H Trin *S'wark* from 00. *147 Jerningham Road, London SE14 5NJ* Tel (020) 7639 6311 Fax 7639 1842 E-mail sarascott@btinternet.com

SCOTT, Simon James. b 65. Ch Ch Ox BA87 MA90. Wycliffe Hall Ox 87. **d** 91 **p** 92. C Cheadle All Hallows *Ches* 91-95; Scripture Union 95-98; C Cambridge H Sepulchre *Ely* from 98. *9 Victoria Street, Cambridge CB1 1JP* Tel (01223) 518352 *or* 327331 E-mail staff@stag.org

SCOTT, Terence. b 56. QUB BSc77. CITC 77. **d** 80 **p** 81. C Ballymena *Conn* 80-83; C Antrim All SS 83-85; P-in-c Connor w Antrim St Patr 85-88; I Magherafelt *Arm* from 88; Hon V Choral Arm Cathl from 95. *St Swithin's Rectory, 1 Churchwell Lane, Magherafelt BT45 6AL* Tel (028) 7963 2365 Fax as telephone E-mail terrscott1@aol.com

SCOTT, Mrs Theresa Anne. b 53. Bris Univ BSc75 Lon Univ PGCE76. Ox Min Course 89. **d** 92 **p** 94. NSM Wickham Bishops w Lt Braxted *Chelmsf* 92-93; NSM Drayton St Pet (Berks) *Ox* 94-01; NSM Convenor (Berks Adnry) 97-01; Bp's Officer for NSM 98-01; Bp's Adv for Women in Ordained Min from 01; P-in-c Hurley and Stubbings 01-02; V Burchetts Green from 02. *The Vicarage, Burchetts Green Road, Burchetts Green, Maidenhead SL6 6QS* Tel (01628) 824454 E-mail driftway@dial.pipex.com

SCOTT, Timothy Charles Nairne. b 61. Ex Univ BA83. Westcott Ho Cam 84. **d** 87 **p** 88. C Romford St Edw *Chelmsf* 87-89; Community Priest 89-94; P-in-c Leytonstone H Trin Harrow Green 94-97; V 97-02; Educn and Tr Adv (Bradwell Area) from 02. *St Margaret's Rectory, London Road, Pitsea, Basildon SS13 2DU* Tel (01268) 552219 E-mail scottlindatim@aol.com

SCOTT, Trevor Ian. b 57. Culham Coll Ox CertEd79. EAMTC 97. **d** 98 **p** 99. NSM Waltham H Cross *Chelmsf* from 98. *Hartland Villas, 208 High Road, Broxbourne EN10 6QF* Tel (01992) 420376 E-mail trevor.scott2@ntlworld.com

SCOTT, Vernon Malcolm. b 30. TCD BA57 MA60. TCD Div Sch Div Test56 Ridley Hall Cam 58. **d** 58 **p** 59. C Limehouse St Anne *Lon* 58-62; C N St Pancras All Hallows 62-66; V Enfield St Mich 66-77; R Tansor w Cotterstock and Fotheringhay *Pet* 77-81; R Barby w Onley 81-83; V Kilsby 81-83; R Barby w Kilsby 83-90; R Coxford Gp *Nor* 90-94; P-in-c South Raynham, E w W Raynham, Helhoughton, etc 94-96; R E and W Rudham, Houghton-next-Harpley etc 95-96; rtd 96; Perm to Offic *Nor* from 96. *5 Wells Road, Walsingham NR22 6DL* Tel (01328) 820151

SCOTT, Walter David Craig. b 22. Selw Coll Cam BA49 MA53. Sarum Th Coll 49. **d** 51 **p** 52. C Shildon *Dur* 51-55; Min Cleadon Park St Cuth CD 55-67; V Cleadon Park 67-71; V Bulkington *Cov* 72-83; RD Bedworth 76-79; V Bulkington w Shilton and Ansty 83-87; rtd 87; Perm to Offic *Cov* from 87. *8 Osprey Close, Nuneaton CV11 6TF* Tel (024) 7634 5561

SCOTT, William. b 20. MBE97. St Chad's Coll Dur BA46 Leeds Univ DipEd53 Dip Special Educn 78. **d** 60 **p** 61. CR 60-99; C Wolborough w Newton Abbot *Ex* 60-63; Chapl St Cath Sch Bramley 63-67; Chapl St Mary and St Anne's Sch Abbots Bromley 67-76; Perm to Offic *Eur* 77-90; Chapl Boulogne-sur-Mer w Calais and Lille *Eur* 87-90; Chapl Lille 90-97; rtd 97; Perm to Offic *Eur* from 97. *42 Westgate Court Avenue, Canterbury CT2 8JR* Tel (01227) 456277

SCOTT, William. b 44. **d** 03. NSM Chester le Street *Dur* from 03. *12 Pinedale Drive, South Hetton, Durham DH6 2XG* Tel 0191-526 4735

SCOTT, Canon William John. b 46. TCD BA70. CITC. **d** 71 **p** 72. C Bangor St Comgall *D & D* 71-74; C Holywood 74-80; Dioc Min of Healing Team from 75; I Carnalea 80-90; N Ireland Wing Chapl ATC from 80; I Seapatrick *D & D* from 90; Treas Dromore Cathl from 02. *The Rectory, 63 Lurgan Road, Banbridge BT32 4LY* Tel (028) 4062 2612 *or* 4062 2744 Fax 4066 9940 E-mail john@seapatrick.fsnet.co.uk

SCOTT, Preb William Sievwright. b 46. Edin Th Coll 67. **d** 70 **p** 71. C Glas St Ninian *Glas* 70-73; C Bridgwater St Fran *B & W* 73-77; R Shepton Beauchamp w Barrington, Stocklinch etc 77-81; P-in-c Cossington 82-84; P-in-c Woolavington 82-84; Chapl Community of All Hallows Ditchingham 84-91; V Pimlico St Mary Bourne Street *Lon* 91-02; P-in-c Pimlico St Barn 97-01; V 01-02; AD Westmr St Marg from 97; Preb St Paul's Cathl from 00; Chapl to RVO and Qu Chpl of the Savoy from 02; Chapl to The Queen from 03. *The Queen's Chapel of the Savoy, Savoy Hill, London WC2R 0DA* Tel (020) 7379 8088 *or* 7839 2048 E-mail bournebill@aol.com

SCOTT-BROMLEY, Mrs Deborah Joan. b 58. Surrey Univ BA01 Open Univ BA96 DipEurHum96. STETS 98. **d** 01 **p** 02. C Hale w Badshot Lea *Guildf* from 01. *195 Eton Place, Farnham GU9 0EG* Tel 07855-704849 (mobile)

SCOTT-DEMPSTER, Canon Colin Thomas. b 37. Em Coll Cam BA65 MA68. Cuddesdon Coll 64. **d** 66 **p** 67. C Caversham *Ox* 66-69; Chapl Coll of SS Mark and Jo Chelsea 69-73; V Chieveley w Winterbourne and Oare *Ox* 73-02; RD Newbury 77-98; Hon Can Ch Ch 90-02; rtd 02. *Old Faskally House, Killiecrankie, Pitlochry PH16 5LG* Tel (01796) 473575 E-mail colin@faskally25.freeserve.co.uk

SCOTT-HAMBLEN, Shane. b 66. Webster Univ (USA) BMus89 St Thos Aquinas Univ Rome STB94 MA96 STL96 St Louis Univ 90. **d** 94 **p** 95. In RC Ch 94-97; C Staines St Mary and St Pet *Lon* 97-99; USA from 99; R Highlands St Mary from 02. *The Episcopal Church of St Mary, 1 Chestnut Street, Cold Spring, NY 10516, USA* Tel (001) (845) 265 2539

✠**SCOTT-JOYNT, The Rt Revd Michael Charles.** b 43. K Coll Cam BA65 MA68. Cuddesdon Coll 65. **d** 67 **p** 68 **c** 87. C Cuddesdon *Ox* 67-70; Tutor Cuddesdon Coll 67-71; Chapl 71-72; TV Newbury St Nic *Ox* 72-75; P-in-c Bicester 75-79; P-in-c Caversfield 75-79; P-in-c Bucknell 76-79; TR Bicester w Bucknell, Caversfield and Launton 79-81; RD Bicester and Islip 76-81; Can Res St Alb 82-87; Dir of Ords and Post-Ord Tr 82-87; Suff Bp Stafford *Lich* 87-92; Area Bp Stafford 92-95; Bp Win from 95. *Wolvesey, Winchester SO23 9ND* Tel (01962) 854050 Fax 842376 E-mail joyce.cockell@dial.pipex.com

SCOTT-OLDFIELD, Ivor Erroll Lindsay. b 21. Univ Coll Dur BA49. Sarum Th Coll 49. **d** 51 **p** 52. C Trowbridge St Jas *Sarum* 51-54; C Haggerston St Paul *Lon* 54-58; V Enfield SS Pet and Paul 58-61; V Kentish Town St Benet and All SS 61-68; Dir Gen RADD 68-87; rtd 87; Perm to Offic *Lon* from 87. *11E Prior Bolton Street, London N1 2NX*

SCOTT-THOMPSON, Ian Mackenzie. b 57. Ch Ch Ox BA78. St Jo Coll Nottm BA82. **d** 83 **p** 84. C Hartley Wintney, Elvetham, Winchfield etc *Win* 83-85; C Bitterne 85-89; V Iford 89-99; P-in-c Holdenhurst 95-99; TR Cove St Jo *Guildf* from 99. *The Rectory, 55 Cove Road, Farnborough GU14 0EX* Tel (01252) 544544 E-mail ian.scott-thompson@virgin.net

SCRACE, David Peter. b 46. Sarum & Wells Th Coll 79. **d** 81 **p** 82. C Abbots Langley *St Alb* 81-85; TV Chippenham St Paul w Hardenhuish etc *Bris* 85-91; P-in-c Harnham *Sarum* 91-99; V from 99; RD Salisbury 93-98. *The Vicarage, Old Blandford Road, Salisbury SP2 8DQ* Tel (01722) 333564

SCRAGG, Michael John. b 39. BA93 Jas Cook Univ Townsville BCom97 MA01. ACT ThDip73. **d** 74 **p** 75. C Camp Hill Australia 74-77; C Chesterton Gd Shep *Ely* 77-79; Australia from 79; C Maryborough 79-80; V Biggenden 80-85; Chapl Wolston Park Hosp 85-91; P-in-c Taroom 91-96; C Noarlunga, Happy Valley and Willunga 96-97; rtd 98. *Eleebana, 1-11 Old Coach Way, PO Box 424, Yandina, Qld, Australia 4561* Tel (0061) (7) 5446 8774 Fax as telephone E-mail hapy5859@squirrel.com.au

SCREECH, Prof Michael. b 26. Ordre national du Merite 83 Chevalier Legion d'Honneur 92. Univ Coll Lon BA50 Birm Univ DLitt59 Univ Coll Lon DLitt82 All So Coll Ox MA84 DLitt90 Ex Univ Hon DLitt93 Geneva Univ Hon DD98 FBA81 FRSL87. Ox Min Course 92. **d** 93 **p** 94. NSM Ox St Giles and SS Phil and Jas w St Marg *Ox* from 93; Extraordinary Fell Wolfs Coll Ox from 93; Chapl and Fell All So Coll Ox from 01. *5 Swanston Field, Whitchurch on Thames, Reading RG8 7HP* Tel 0118-984 2513 Fax as telephone

✠**SCREECH, The Rt Revd Royden.** b 53. K Coll Lon BD74 AKC74. St Aug Coll Cant 75. **d** 76 **p** 77 **c** 00. C Hatcham St Cath *S'wark* 76-80; V Nunhead St Antony 80-87; P-in-c Nunhead St Silas 82-87; RD Camberwell 83-87; V New Addington 87-94; Selection Sec ABM 94-97; Sen Selection Sec Min Division 97-00; Suff Bp St Germans *Truro* from 00. *32 Falmouth Road, Truro TR1 2HX* Tel (01872) 273190 Fax 277883 E-mail bishop@stgermans.truro.anglican.org

SCRINE, Ralph. b 19. Bris Univ BA40 Fitzw Ho Cam BA46 MA60 Lon Univ MPhil81. Westcott Ho Cam 45. **d** 46 **p** 47. C Moorfields *Bris* 46-51; C Bishopston w Slaughterford 51-52; P-in-c Locklease CD 52-60; V St Jas Less 60-65; Chapl Eliz Coll Guernsey 60-65; Lect Div Ch Ch Coll Cant 65-68; Chapl Ch Ch Coll of HE Cant 68-75; Sen Lect Ch Ch Coll Cant 68-84; rtd 84; Perm to Offic *Cant* 84-02. *Little Henny, Stone Street, Petham, Canterbury CT4 5PP* Tel (01227) 700725

✠**SCRIVEN, The Rt Revd Henry William.** b 51. Sheff Univ BA72. St Jo Coll Nottm DPS75. **d** 75 **p** 76 **c** 95. C Wealdstone H Trin *Lon* 75-79; SAMS Argentina 79-82; USA 82-83; SAMS Spain 84-90; Chapl Madrid w Bilbao *Eur* 90-95; Suff Bp Eur 95-02; Dean Brussels 95-97; Dir of Ords 97-02; Asst Bp Pittsburgh USA from 02. *1437 Greystone Drive, Pittsburgh, PA 15206, USA* Tel (001) (412) 362 1620 *or* 281 6131 Fax 471 5591 E-mail scriven@pgh.anglican.org

SCRIVEN, Hugh Alexander. b 59. Trin Coll Cam BA80. Cranmer Hall Dur 81. **d** 84 **p** 85. C Pudsey St Lawr and St Paul *Bradf* 84-87; C Madeley *Heref* 87-91; TV 91-00; V Edgbaston St Germain *Birm* from 00. *St Germain's Vicarage, 180 Portland Road, Birmingham B16 9TD* Tel 0121-429 3431

SCRIVEN, Paul Michael. b 51. Bris Univ BSc72 Lon Univ CertEd74. S Dios Minl Tr Scheme 84. **d** 87 **p** 88. NSM Redmarley D'Abitot, Bromesberrow w Pauntley etc *Glouc* 87-90; Lic to Offic *Heref* 90-95; Lic to Offic *Mon* 94-95 and from 02; V Dingestow and Llangovan w Penyclawdd etc 95-01; Adv Rural Affairs from 98. *The Vicarage, Dingestow, Monmouth NP25 4DY* Tel (01600) 740206 E-mail scriven@btinternet.co

SCRIVENER, Robert Allan. b 54. Nottm Univ BEd78 Hull Univ BTh98 De Montfort Univ Leic MA99. Linc Th Coll 79. **d** 80 **p** 81. C Sherwood *S'well* 80-83; C Burghclere w Newtown and Ecchinswell w Sydmonton *Win* 83-86; TV Hemel Hempstead *St Alb* 86-93; V Kingston upon Hull St Nic *York* from 93. *St Nicholas' Vicarage, 898 Hessle High Road, Hull HU4 6SA* Tel (01482) 507944 E-mail allanbedbt@aol.com

SCRIVENS, Mrs Elaine. b 53. TCert74 Man Univ BEd75. NEOC. **d** 00 **p** 01. NSM E Coatham *York* 00-02; NSM Coatham and Dormanstown from 02. *14 Wheatlands Park, Redcar TS10 2PD* Tel (01642) 485144

SCRIVENS, Ernest. b 25. Lon Univ DipTh53. Wycliffe Hall Ox ThL. **d** 62 **p** 63. C Chesham St Mary *Ox* 62-64; CF (S Rhodesia) 64-67; Jamaica 67-68; R Ardington w E Lockinge *Ox* 68-69; Miss to Seamen W Australia 69-79; V Yeadon St Jo *Bradf* 79-80; Australia from 81; rtd 88. *Villa 1101, 269 Binkdale Road, Wellington Point, Qld, Australia 4160*

SCROGGIE, Mrs Felicity Marie-Louise. b 62. Pemb Coll Ox BA86 St Andr Univ MPhil87. STETS BTh99. **d** 99 **p** 00. C Brondesbury St Anne w Kilburn H Trin *Lon* 99-02; V Sudbury St Andr from 02. *St Andrew's Vicarage, 956 Harrow Road, Wembley HA0 2QA* Tel (020) 8904 4016
E-mail felicity.scroggie@london.anglican.org

SCRUBY, The Ven Ronald Victor. b 19. Trin Hall Cam BA48 MA52. Cuddesdon Coll 48. **d** 50 **p** 51. Chapl K Edw VII Hosp Midhurst 50-53; R Rogate *Chich* 50-53; Chapl Saunders-Roe E Cowes 53-58; V Eastney *Portsm* 58-65; RD Portsm 60-65; Adn Is of Wight 65-77; Adn Portsm 77-85; rtd 85; Perm to Offic *Chich* 85-94; Perm to Offic *Portsm* from 85. *Church House, Rogate, Petersfield GU31 5EA* Tel (01730) 821784

SCUFFHAM, Canon Frank Leslie. b 30. AKC56 DSRS68. **d** 57 **p** 58. C Kettering SS Pet and Paul *Pet* 57-59; Ind Chapl *Sheff* 60-61; Ind Chapl *Pet* 61-95; Can Pet Cathl 72-95; RD Corby 76-79; P-in-c Stoke Albany w Wilbarston *Pet* R 79-95; rtd 95; Perm to Offic *St E* from 95. *The Orchard, Earlsford Road, Mellis, Eye IP23 8EA* Tel (01379) 783378

SCULLY, Hazel. b 01 **p** 02. Lic to Offic *M & K* from 01. *Lowtown, Coralstown, Kinnegad, Co Westmeath, Irish Republic* Tel (00353) (44) 74352

SCULLY, Kevin John. b 55. NIDA BDA96. St Steph Ho Ox 91. **d** 93 **p** 94. C Stoke Newington St Mary *Lon* 93-97; C Stepney St Dunstan and All SS 97-00; Dir of Ords from 97; Voc Adv from 97; P-in-c Bethnal Green St Matt w St Jas the Gt 00-02; R from 02. *The Rectory, Hereford Street, London E2 6EX* Tel (020) 7739 7586 Fax as telephone

SCUTTER, Canon James Edward. b 36. OBE91. AKC59 St Boniface Warminster 59. **d** 60 **p** 61. C Tilbury Docks *Chelmsf* 60-63; Bechuanaland 63-65; Rhodesia 65-70; New Zealand 70-79; Singapore 79-81; New Zealand from 81; Prin Chapl NZ Defence Force 84-91; QHC from 84; Hon Can Wellington from 87. *4 Sunderland Avenue, Hobsonville, Auckland, New Zealand* Tel (0064) (9) 416 7206 *or* 417 7006

SEABROOK, Alan Geoffrey. b 43. ALCD65. **d** 66 **p** 67. C Bethnal Green St Jas Less *Lon* 66-70; C Madeley *Heref* 70-73; V Girlington *Bradf* 74-80; P-in-c Abdon w Clee St Margaret *Heref* 80-83; R Bitterley 80-83; P-in-c cold Weston 80-83; P-in-c Hopton Cangeford 80-83; P-in-c Stoke St Milburgh w Heath 80-83; R Bitterley w Middleton, Stoke St Milborough etc from 83; RD Ludlow from 01. *The Rectory, Bitterley, Ludlow SY8 3HJ* Tel (01584) 890239

SEABROOK, Geoffrey Barry. b 45. Open Univ BA77 DipEd Lon Univ MA(Ed)84. Chich Th Coll 66. **d** 69 **p** 70. C Tottenham All Hallows *Lon* 69-72; C Winchmore Hill H Trin 72-74; V Hornsey St Geo 74-82; P-in-c Hornsey St Mary 80-82; R Hornsey St Mary w St Geo from 82; P-in-c Hornsey H Innocents 84-92; AD W Haringey from 95. *Hornsey Rectory, 140 Cranley Gardens, London N10 3AH* Tel (020) 8883 6846 Fax 8352 0879
E-mail gb.seabrook@virgin.net

SEABROOK, Paul. b 60. Univ of Wales (Cardiff) BA81 Nottm Univ PGCE82. Ridley Hall Cam 01. **d** 03. C Wimborne Minster

Sarum from 03. *29 Venator Place, Wimborne BH21 1DQ* Tel (01202) 887557 E-mail seabrooktribe@telco4u.net

SEABROOK, Mrs Penelope Anne. b 56. Hertf Coll Ox BA77 K Coll Lon MA98. SEITE 00. **d** 03. NSM Southfields St Barn *S'wark* from 03. *121 Home Park Road, London SW19 7HT* Tel (020) 8947 3113 E-mail pennyseabrook@hotmail.com

SEABROOK, Richard Anthony. b 68. Southn Univ BTh92. Chich Th Coll 92. **d** 92 **p** 93. C Cottingham *York* 92-94; C Hawley H Trin *Guildf* 94-98; V Hockley *Chelmsf* from 98. *6A Silvertree Close, Hockley SS5 4SP* Tel (01702) 203668
E-mail sspp@incense.demon.co.uk

SEAFORD, The Very Revd John Nicholas. b 39. Dur Univ BA67 DipTh68. St Chad's Coll Dur 68. **d** 68 **p** 69. C Bush Hill Park St Mark *Lon* 68-71; C Stanmore *Win* 71-73; V N Baddesley 73-76; V Chilworth w N Baddesley 76-78; V Highcliffe w Hinton Admiral 78-93; RD Christchurch 90-93; Hon Can Win Cathl from 93; Dean Jersey from 93; R Jersey St Helier from 93; Chapl Jersey Airport from 93. *The Deanery, David Place, St Helier, Jersey JE2 4TE* Tel (01534) 720001 Fax 617488
E-mail deanofjersey@jerseymail.co.uk

SEAL, Edward Hugh. b 10. ARCM31 Lon Univ BMus36. Wells Th Coll 46. **d** 48 **p** 49. C Midsomer Norton *B & W* 48-50; V Churt *Guildf* 50-57; V Pemberton St Jo *Liv* 57-63; R Poulton-le-Sands *Blackb* 63-78; rtd 78; Perm to Offic *Blackb* from 79. *3 Fern Bank, Scotforth, Lancaster LA1 4TT* Tel (01524) 67078

SEAL, Nicholas Peter. b 57. Ex Univ BA. Linc Th Coll 81. **d** 83 **p** 84. C Wareham *Sarum* 83-87; Chapl K Alfred Coll *Win* 87-91; V Stanmore 91-01; RD Win from 99; P-in-c Win St Matt from 01; Chapl Peter Symonds Coll Win from 01. *The Rectory, 44 Cheriton Road, Winchester SO22 5AY* Tel (01962) 854849 E-mail p.seal@ukgateway.net

SEAL, Philip Trevor. b 32. AKC55. **d** 56 **p** 57. C Godalming *Guildf* 56-60; C Tamworth *Lich* 60-61; R Lich Stud 61-73; Chapl HM Youth Cust Cen Swinfen Hall 66-73; R Shere *Guildf* 74-88; RD Cranleigh 76-81; V Abbotsbury, Portesham and Langton Herring *Sarum* 88-97; rtd 97. *2 Moorlane Cottages, Poltimore, Exeter EX4 0AQ*

SEAL, Ronald Frederick. b 28. CA Tr Coll 50 Lich Th Coll 59. **d** 61 **p** 62. C Bedhampton *Portsm* 61-65; R N and S Kilworth *Leic* 65-71; R Barwell w Potters Marston and Stapleton 71-80; P-in-c Upper Stour *Sarum* 80-83; R Upper Stour 84-90; RD Heytesbury 87-89; Bermuda 90-92; Miss to Seamen 90-92; rtd 92; Perm to Offic *Sarum* from 92. *8 Briar Close, Wyke, Gillingham SP8 4SS* Tel (01747) 825462

SEAL (formerly MILLER), Mrs Rosamund Joy. b 56. Lon Univ BSc77 Whitelands Coll Lon PGCE80. EMMTC 92. **d** 94 **p** 96. NSM Grantham *Linc* 94-96; C Stamford All SS w St Jo 96-00; C Spalding from 00. *The Chantry, 7 Church Street, Spalding PE11 2PB* Tel (01775) 711355 *or* tel and fax 722631
E-mail rosamund.seal@spaldingchurches.org

SEAL, William Christopher Houston. b 50. Occidental Coll (USA) BA72. Ch Div Sch of the Pacific (USA) MDiv81. **d** 81 **p** 82. USA 81-88 and from 94; R Etton w Helpston *Pet* 88-94. *The Rectory, 171 Grove Street, Nevada City, CA 95959, USA*

SEALE, William Arthur. b 62. NUI BA84 TCD DipTh87. **d** 87 **p** 88. C Drumragh w Mountfield *D & R* 87-90; I from 01; I Drumgath w Drumgooland and Clonduff *D & D* 90-01. *Drumragh Rectory, 12 Crevenagh Way, Omagh BT79 0JE* Tel (028) 8224 2130 Fax as telephone
E-mail drumragh@derry.anglican.org

SEALY, Daniel O'Neill. b 21. Oak Hill Th Coll 62. **d** 64 **p** 65. C Walcot *B & W* 64-67; Chapl RN 67-73; Nigeria 73-79; Libya 79-82; Tunisia 82-86; rtd 86; I Kilgariffe Union *C, C & R* 87-92. *Swanhill, Culver Street, Newent GL18 1JA*

SEALY, Canon Gordon William Hugh. b 27. Leeds Univ BA53 MA64. Coll of Resurr Mirfield 55. **d** 55 **p** 56. C Greenford H Cross *Lon* 55-58; Br Honduras 58-68; R Tarrant Gunville, Tarrant Hinton etc *Sarum* 68-74; V Leic St Paul *Leic* 74-96; Hon Can Leic Cathl 86-96; rtd 96. *Church Cottage, Maker Lane, Hoar Cross, Burton-on-Trent DE13 8QR* Tel (01283) 575738

SEALY, Stephen. b 52. K Coll Lon BD86 AKC86. Linc Th Coll 86. **d** 88 **p** 89. C Botley *Portsm* 88-91; Prec Cant Cathl *Cant* 91-96; Hon Min Can Cant Cathl 91-96; V Pembury *Roch* from 96. *The Vicarage, 4 Hastings Road, Pembury, Tunbridge Wells TN2 4PD* Tel (01892) 824761

SEAMAN, Canon Arthur Roland Mostyn. b 32. TCD BA55 DipEd56 Div Test56 MA58. Westcott Ho Cam 58. **d** 58 **p** 59. C Blackley St Pet *Man* 58-61; C Sanderstead All SS *S'wark* 61-62; V Heywood St Luke *Man* 62-70; Dir of Educn 70-85; Hon Can Man Cathl 74-95; R Chorlton-cum-Hardy St Werburgh 85-95; rtd 95; Perm to Offic *Newc* from 95. *10 The Haven, Beadnell, Chathill NE67 5AW* Tel (01665) 720510

SEAMAN, Canon Brian Edward. b 35. Dur Univ BA59. Cranmer Hall Dur. **d** 61 **p** 62. C Burnage St Marg *Man* 61-65; Chapl Mayflower Family Cen Canning Town *Chelmsf* 65-75; V High Elswick St Paul *Newc* 75-96; TV Glendale Gp 96-03; Hon Can Newc Cathl 82-03; rtd 03. *13 Rosebery Street, Ringstead, Kettering NN14 4BY* Tel (01933) 622615
E-mail learners@seaman.fsworld.co.uk

SEAMAN, Christopher Robert. b 34. Solicitor 62 St Jo Coll Ox BA58 MA74. Ox Min Course 92 St Alb and Ox Min Course 94. **d** 95 **p** 96. NSM Watlington w Pyrton and Shirburn *Ox* 95-97; NSM Icknield 97-98; Perm to Offic 98-99; Hon C Shippon from 99. *5 Curtyn Close, Abingdon OX14 1SE* Tel (01235) 520380

SEAMAN, Paul Robert. b 61. Bp Grosseteste Coll BEd82. Chich Th Coll 83. **d** 86 **p** 87. C Tilehurst St Mich *Ox* 86-91; TV Moulsecoomb *Chich* 91-95; R Whyke w Rumboldswhyke and Portfield from 95. *St George's Rectory, 199 Whyke Road, Chichester PO19 7HQ* Tel (01243) 782535

SEAMAN (née HEWLINS), Mrs Pauline Elizabeth. b 47. Lon Univ BD68 AKC. Ox Min Course 93. **d** 96 **p** 97. NSM Radley and Sunningwell *Ox* 96-99; Chapl SS Helen and Kath Sch Abingdon from 96; NSM Shippon *Ox* from 99. *5 Curtyn Close, Abingdon OX14 1SE* Tel (01235) 520380

SEAMAN, Robert John. b 44. ACP DipEd. EAMTC. **d** 84 **p** 85. NSM Downham Market w Bexwell *Ely* 84-90; V Southea w Murrow and Parson Drove 90-97; V Guyhirn w Ring's End 90-97; V Newnham w Awre and Blakeney *Glouc* from 97. *The Vicarage, 1 Whetstones, Unlawater Lane, Newnham GL14 1BT* Tel (01594) 516648 Fax 510131
E-mail rj.seaman@btopenworld.com

SEAMER, Stephen James George. b 50. AKC73. Ridley Hall Cam 74. **d** 75 **p** 76. C Rustington *Chich* 75-78; C Bulwell St Jo *S'well* 78-79; P-in-c Camber and E Guldeford *Chich* 79-80; TV Rye 80-83; V Knowle *Birm* 83-87; Assoc Chapl Brussels Cathl *Eur* 87-88; P-in-c Tervuren 88-94; Chapl 94-98; P-in-c Liège 90-98; V Tonbridge SS Pet and Paul *Roch* from 98. *The Vicarage, 12 Church Street, Tonbridge TN9 1HD* Tel (01732) 770962 *or* 770961 Fax 358052
E-mail admin@tonbridgeparish.freeserve.co.uk

SEAR, Peter Lionel. b 49. Ex Univ BA72. Linc Th Coll 72. **d** 74 **p** 75. C Sheldon *Birm* 74-77; C Caversham *Ox* 77-81; C Caversham St Pet and Mapledurham etc 81-85; TR Thatcham 85-98; V Castle Cary w Ansford *B & W* 98-00; rtd 00. *Knowle Cottage, Lamyatt, Shepton Mallet BA4 6NP* Tel (01749) 813226

SEAR, Terence Frank. b 39. LDSRCSEng62 Univ Coll Lon BDS63. Portsm Dioc Tr Course 88. **d** 89. NSM Ryde H Trin *Portsm* 89-98; NSM Swanmore St Mich w Havenstreet 89-92; NSM Swanmore St Mich 92-98; NSM Wroxall 90-00; NSM Godshill 99-01; Perm to Offic from 02. *Wood Farm, Holdenhurst, Wootton Bridge, Ryde PO33 4JF* Tel (01983) 883560

SEARE, Mrs Janice Mae. b 48. SEN. STETS 99. **d** 02 **p** 03. NSM Holdenhurst and Iford *Win* from 02. *Wood Farm, Holdenhurst Village, Bournemouth BH8 0EE* Tel (01202) 302468 Fax 391281
E-mail pj.seare@zoom.co.uk

SEARL, John. b 37. Southn Univ BSc58 Edin Univ PhD69. **d** 00. NSM Edin St Cuth *Edin* from 00. *57 Bonaly Crescent, Edinburgh EH13 0EP* Tel 0131-441 5791 *or* 650 5044
E-mail searl@maths.ed.ac.uk

SEARLE, Charles Peter. b 20. Selw Coll Cam BA48 MA53. Ridley Hall Cam. **d** 50 **p** 51. C Becontree St Mary *Chelmsf* 50-53; P-in-c Bedford St Jo *St Alb* 53-56; R 56-60; V Weston-super-Mare Ch Ch *B & W* 60-70; V Woking Ch Ch *Guildf* 70-85; rtd 85; Perm to Offic *Ex* from 85. *Spinners, 15 Spindlebury, Cullompton EX15 1SY* Tel (01884) 33386
E-mail asearle@dialstart.net

SEARLE, David William. b 37. MASI89 ACIOB98. Dioc OLM tr scheme 96. **d** 99 **p** 00. OLM E Bergholt and Brantham *St E* from 99. *46 Chaplin Road, East Bergholt, Colchester CO7 6SR* Tel (01206) 298932

SEARLE, Capt Francis Robert. b 52. IDC74. CA Tr Coll 72 St Steph Ho Ox 88. **d** 90 **p** 91. CA from 72; C Lancing w Coombes *Chich* 90-93; V Hampden Park 93-00; P-in-c Eastchurch w Leysdown and Harty *Cant* from 00; V from 03. *The Rectory, Warden Road, Sheerness ME12 4EJ* Tel (01795) 880205 E-mail francis.searle@churcharmy.net

SEARLE, Canon Hugh Douglas. b 35. St Cath Coll Cam BA59 MA63 Cranfield Inst of Tech MSc85. Oak Hill Th Coll 59. **d** 61 **p** 62. C Islington H Trin Cloudesley Square *Lon* 61-64; Chapl HM Pris Lewes 64-65; Chapl HM Borstal Roch 65-69; Chapl HM Youth Cust Cen Hollesley Bay Colony 70-74; Chapl HM Pris Parkhurst 74-78; P-in-c Barton *Ely* 78-84; V 84-00; P-in-c Coton 78-84; R 84-00; RD Bourn 81-94; Hon Can Ely Cathl 97-00; rtd 00; Perm to Offic *Ely* from 00. *38 Field End, Witchford, Ely CB6 2XE* Tel (01353) 659749 E-mail cfsw@ely.anglican.org

SEARLE, Ms Jacqueline Ann. b 60. Whitelands Coll Lon BEd83 Bris Univ MA01. Trin Coll Bris DipHE92. **d** 92 **p** 94. Par Dn Roxeth Ch Ch and Harrow St Pet *Lon* 92-93; Par Dn Roxeth 93-94; C Ealing St Steph Castle Hill 94-96; Lect Trin Coll Bris 96-03; P-in-c Littleover *Derby* from 03. *The Vicarage, 35 Church Street, Littleover, Derby DE23 6GF* Tel (01332) 767802
E-mail stpeterlittloever@hotmail.com

SEARLE, John Francis. b 42. OBE98. FRCA70 FRSM84 Lon Univ MB, BS66. SW Minl Tr Course 92. **d** 95 **p** 96. NSM Ex St Leon w H Trin *Ex* 95-03; Assoc Staff Member SWMTC from 03. *Belle Isle Lodge, Belle Isle Drive, Exeter EX2 4RY* Tel (01392) 432153 E-mail johnlizex@aol.com

SEARLE, Mark Robin. b 73. Cen Sch Speech & Drama BA94. Trin Coll Bris BA03. **d** 03. C Cant St Mary Bredin *Cant* from 03.

---

38 Nunnery Road, Canterbury CT1 3LS Tel (01227) 455723
E-mail marksearle@btinternet.com

SEARLE, Michael Stanley. b 38. HNC60. AMIQ63. N Ord Course 93. **d** 95 **p** 96. NSM Hoole *Ches* 95-99; P-in-c Marbury from 99; P-in-c Tushingham and Whitewell from 02. *The Vicarage, Marbury, Whitchurch SY13 4LN* Tel (01948) 663758 Mobile 07850-720120 Fax (01948) 667479
E-mail mike.s.searle@btinternet.com

SEARLE, Michael Westran. b 47. Leeds Univ LLB68 Nottm Univ DipTh69. Cuddesdon Coll 69. **d** 71 **p** 72. C Norton St Mary *Dur* 71-74; C Westbury-on-Trym H Trin *Bris* 74-77; V Bedminster Down 77-84; V Bris Ch the Servant Stockwood 84-88; Dir of Tr *York* 88-00; R Dunnington from 00. *The Rectory, 30 Church Street, Dunnington, York YO10 5PW* Tel (01904) 489349 E-mail msearle@yorktrain.demon.co.uk

SEARLE, Philip Robert. b 67. Westcott Ho Cam. **d** 95 **p** 96. C Plymstock *Ex* 95-97; C Plymstock and Hooe 97-98; TV Stoke-upon-Trent *Lich* from 98. *All Saints' Vicarage, 540 Leek Road, Stoke-on-Trent ST1 3HH* Tel (01782) 205713
E-mail hairetic@surfaid.org

SEARLE, Ralph Alan. b 57. G&C Coll Cam BA79 MA83. Coll of Resurr Mirfield 81. **d** 83 **p** 84. C Cockerton *Dur* 83-86; C S Shields All SS 86-88; TV 88-96; Assoc P Worksop Priory *S'well* 96-97; Assoc P Paignton St Jo *Ex* 97-01; V Horfield St Greg *Bris* from 01; Hon Min Can Bris Cathl from 02. *St Gregory's Vicarage, Filton Road, Horfield, Bristol BS7 0PD* Tel 0117-969 2839
E-mail fr.ralph@tinyonline.co.uk

SEARLE-BARNES, Albert Victor. b 28. Sheff Univ BA48 Lon Univ BD53. ALCD53. **d** 53 **p** 54. C Iver *Ox* 53-55; C Attenborough w Bramcote *S'well* 55-59; C Bramcote 55-59; R Cratfield w Heveningham and Ubbeston *St E* 59-64; R Wick w Doynton *Bris* 64-70; Perm to Offic 70-72; V Downend 73-78; V Market Rasen *Linc* 78-86; R Linwood 79-86; V Legsby 79-86; R Green's Norton w Bradden *Pet* 86-88; V Hambledon *Portsm* 88-92; rtd 92; Perm to Offic *Glouc* from 92. *32 Oakland Avenue, Cheltenham GL52 3EP* Tel (01242) 227425

SEARLE-BARNES, Belinda Rosemary. b 51. ARCM72 GRSM73 Lon Univ Dip Past Th 91 MA93 Southn Univ DipMin96. Sarum Th Coll 93. **d** 96 **p** 97. NSM Pimperne, Stourpaine, Durweston and Bryanston *Sarum* 96-00; Asst Par Development Adv 98-00; Asst Chapl Bryanston Sch 98-00; TV Southampton (City Cen) *Win* from 00. *St Michael's Vicarage, 55 Bugle Street, Southampton SO14 2AG* Tel (023) 8022 4242
E-mail bsb@st-michaels.freeserve.co.uk

SEARS, Derek Lynford. b 25. St Jo Coll Cam BA49 MA53. Wycliffe Hall Ox 49. **d** 51 **p** 52. C Blackb St Steph *Blackb* 51-53; C Preston St Paul 53-56; V Burnley St Jas 56-62; Jamaica 62-66; V Freckleton *Blackb* 66-74; Jamaica 74-78; V Ashton-on-Ribble St Mich *Blackb* 78-90; P-in-c Preston St Mark 82-90; rtd 90; Perm to Offic *Blackb* from 90. *61 Greencroft, Penwortham, Preston PR1 9LB* Tel (01772) 740190

SEARS, Ms Helen. b 50. Birm Coll of Educn CertEd71. Qu Coll Birm 96. **d** 98 **p** 99. C Hadley *Lich* 98-01; C Cannock from 01. *9 Condor Grove, Heath Hayes, Cannock WS12 3YB* Tel (01543) 270107

SEARS, Jacqueline Isabella. SRN69 DN84. NTMTC 95. **d** 99 **p** 00. NSM Hanwell St Mellitus w St Mark *Lon* 99-03; Perm to Offic *St E* from 03; Asst Chapl Essex Rivers Healthcare NHS Trust from 03. *Clamp Farm, Barn One, Creeting Road, Stowmarket IP14 5BP* Tel (01449) 675863
E-mail jackie@searsfamily.fslife.co.uk

SEARS, Jeanette. b 59. Man Univ BA80 PhD84 Lon Univ PGCE85. Wycliffe Hall Ox DPS. **d** 92 **p** 94. NSM Ox St Aldate w St Matt *Ox* 92-94; NSM Ox St Aldate 95-96. *Address temp unknown*

SEARS, Michael Antony. b 50. Birm Univ BSc71 PGCE72. Linc Th Coll 78. **d** 80 **p** 81. C Willenhall H Trin *Lich* 80-83; C Caldmore 83-84; P-in-c 84-86; V 86-89; Abp Ilsley RC Sch Birm 89-97; TV Solihull *Birm* 98-02; R Castle Bromwich SS Mary and Marg from 02. *67 Chester Road, Castle Bromwich, Birmingham B36 9DP* Tel 0121-684 3031 Mobile 07740-537559
E-mail rector.castleb@fish.co.uk

SEATON, Canon James Bradbury. b 29. Ch Coll Cam BA53 MA57. Westcott Ho Cam 53. **d** 55 **p** 56. C Derby St Werburgh *Derby* 55-58; C Darlington St Cuth *Dur* 58-64; V Preston on Tees 64-72; TV Stockton H Trin 72-73; TV Cen Stockton 73-75; R Anstey *Leic* 75-89; RD Sparkenhoe III 81-89; Hon Can Leic Cathl 87-94; R Market Harborough Transfiguration 89-94; rtd 94; Perm to Offic *Glouc* from 94. *Wayside, Sheep Street, Chipping Campden GL55 6DW* Tel (01386) 841753

SEATON, Stuart Paul. b 75. Dur Univ BA96 Leeds Univ MA. Coll of Resurr Mirfield 97. **d** 99 **p** 00. C Hatfield Hyde *St Alb* 99-02; Asst Chapl Aldenham Sch Herts from 03. *1 The Orchard, Aldenham School, Aldenham Road, Elstree, Borehamwood WD6 3RL* Tel (01923) 289748
E-mail stuart@seaton.freeserve.co.uk

SEBER, Derek Morgan. b 43. Man Univ CertRS79 Man Poly Cert Trade Union Studies 83 MA87 Man Metrop Univ MPhil96. Oak Hill Th Coll 71. **d** 73 **p** 74. C Collyhurst *Man* 73-76; C

Radcliffe St Thos and St Jo 76-77; Ind Missr 77-89; P-in-c Hulme St Geo 77-83; Hon C Moss Side St Jas w St Clem 83-96; Project Officer Linking Up 89-96; Lic Preacher 90-96; P-in-c Cheetham St Jo 97; P-in-c Thornton Hough *Ches* from 97; Ind Chapl from 97. *All Saints' Vicarage, Raby Road, Thornton Hough, Wirral CH63 1JP* Tel 0151-336 3429 Fax 336 1654
E-mail derek@morganseber.freeserve.co.uk

SECCOMBE, Marcus John. b 34. Oak Hill Th Coll 60. **d** 63 **p** 64. C Woodthorpe *S'well* 63-67; C Doncaster St Mary *Sheff* 67-72; V Owston 72-90; R Rossington 90-99; rtd 99; Perm to Offic *Sheff* from 99. *39 Marlborough Road, Doncaster DN2 5DF* Tel (01302) 321505

SECOMBE, Preb Frederick Thomas. b 18. St D Coll Lamp BA40 St Mich Coll Llan 40. **d** 42 **p** 43. C Swansea St Mark *S & B* 42-44; C Knighton 44-46; C Machen *Mon* 46-49; C Newport St Woolos 49-52; Chapl St Woolos Hosp Newport 49-52; V Llanarth w Clytha, Llansantffraed and Bryngwyn *Mon* 52-54; R Machen and Rudry 54-59; V Swansea St Pet *S & B* 59-69; R Hanwell St Mary *Lon* 69-83; AD Ealing W 78-82; Preb St Paul's Cathl 81-83; rtd 83. *30 Westville Road, Penylan, Cardiff CF23 5AG* Tel (029) 2048 3978

SECRETAN, Ms Jenny Ruth. b 54. St Aid Coll Dur BA76 Ex Univ PGCE77 Nottm Univ DipTh82 Dur Univ MA97 BAC Acc98. Linc Th Coll 81 Cranmer Hall Dur 83. **dss** 84 **d** 87 **p** 94. Asst Chapl Newc Poly *Newc* 84-86; Sunderland St Chad *Dur* 84-86; Bordesley St Oswald *Birm* 86-87; Par Dn 87-91; Assoc Soc Resp Officer *Dur* 92-95; Perm to Offic *Dur* 95-99; Perm to Offic *Newc* 95-99; Perm to Offic *Dur* and *Newc* 95-99. *14 Southwood Gardens, Kenton, Newcastle upon Tyne NE3 3BU*

SEDANO, Juan Antonio. b 55. Centro de Discipulado Lima 85. **d** 88 **p** 88. Peru 88-90; Crosslinks 91-94; SAMS from 95; NSM Ingrave St Steph CD *Chelmsf* from 95. *5 The Chase, Ingrave, Brentwood CM13 3QT* Tel (01277) 810907
E-mail dan@sedano.freeserve.co.uk

SEDDON, Ernest Geoffrey. b 26. ARIBA51 Man Univ DipArch50 DipTh83 MA85. St Deiniol's Hawarden 80. **d** 80 **p** 81. C Dunham Massey St Marg *Ches* 80-83; P-in-c Warburton 82-87; P-in-c Dunham Massey St Mark 85-86; V 86-92; rtd 92; Perm to Offic *Ches* from 92. *7 Colwyn Place, Llandudno LL30 3AW* Tel (01492) 547639

SEDDON, Philip James. b 45. Jes Coll Cam BA68 MA71 Birm Univ MPhil01. Ridley Hall Cam 67. **d** 70 **p** 71. C Tonge w Alkrington *Man* 70-74; CMS Nigeria 74-78; Lect St Jo Coll Nottm 78-79; Lic to Offic *Ely* 79-85; Chapl Magd Coll Cam 79-85; Lect Bibl Studies Selly Oak Colls 86-00; Lic to Offic *Birm* from 87; Lect Th Birm Univ from 00. *Department of Theology, University of Birmingham, Edgbaston, Birmingham B15 2TT* Tel 0121-414 3613 Fax 414 6866 E-mail p.j.seddon@bham.ac.uk

SEDEN, Martin Roy. b 47. Man Univ MSc Salford Univ PhD. EMMTC 79. **d** 82 **p** 83. NSM Knighton St Mary Magd *Leic* from 82. *139 Shanklin Drive, Leicester LE2 3QG* Tel 0116-270 2128 *or* 257 7404 E-mail rseden@dmu.ac.uk

SEDGLEY, Mrs Jean. b 41. Whitelands Coll Lon CertEd63. S Dios Minl Tr Scheme 92. **d** 95 **p** 96. NSM Haywards Heath St Wilfrid *Chich* 95-01; NSM Cuckfield from 01. *25 Pasture Hill Road, Haywards Heath RH16 1LY* Tel (01444) 413974

SEDGLEY, Canon Timothy John. b 42. St Jo Coll Ox BA63 MA68 DipTh64. Westcott Ho Cam 64. **d** 66 **p** 67. C Nor St Pet Mancroft *Nor* 66-70; V Costessey 70-79; RD Nor N 75-79; V Walton-on-Thames *Guildf* from 79; RD Emly 86-91; Hon Can Guildf Cathl from 86; Dir OLMs and NSMs from 93. *The Vicarage, 53 Ashley Park Avenue, Walton-on-Thames KT12 1EV* Tel (01932) 227184

SEDGWICK, Jonathan Maurice William. b 63. BNC Ox BA85 MA89 Leeds Univ BA88. Coll of Resurr Mirfield 86. **d** 89 **p** 90. C Chich St Paul and St Pet *Chich* 89-91; Dean of Div and Chapl Magd Coll Ox 91-94; Perm to Offic *S'wark* from 00; Hon C E Dulwich St Jo from 00. *91 Landells Road, London SE22 9PH* Tel (020) 8299 2384

SEDGWICK, Peter Humphrey. b 48. Trin Hall Cam BA70 Dur Univ PhD83. Westcott Ho Cam 71. **d** 74 **p** 75. C Stepney St Dunstan and All SS *Lon* 74-77; P-in-c Ferryhill *Dur* 77-79; Lect Th Birm Univ 79-82; Hon C The Lickey *Birm* 79-82; Th Consultant for NE Ecum Gp *Dur* 82-88; Lect Th Hull Univ 88-94; Abp's Adv on Ind Issues *York* 88-94; Vice-Prin Westcott Ho Cam 94-96; Asst Sec Abps' Coun Bd for Soc Resp from 96; NSM Pet St Barn *Pet* 96-98; rtd 98; Perm to Offic *Lon* from 98; *Guildf* from 02. *38 Oasthouse Drive, Fleet GU51 2UL*, *or Church House, Great Smith Street, London SW1P 3NZ* Tel (01252) 629976 *or* (020) 7898 1531 Fax (020) 7898 1536
E-mail peter.sedgwick@c-of-e.org.uk *or* revgould@virgin.net

SEED, Richard Edward. b 55. UNISA BTh86 Westmr Coll Ox MEd. Kalk Bay Bible Inst S Africa DipTh79. **d** 80 **p** 81. S Africa 80-85 and 87-89; Zimbabwe 85-87; Asst Chapl Kingham Hill Sch 89-90; C Beckenham Ch Ch *Roch* 90-95; Chapl Düsseldorf *Eur* 96-00; CMS from 00. *CMS, Partnership House, 157 Waterloo Road, London SE1 8UU* Tel (020) 7928 8681

SEED, The Ven Richard Murray Crosland. b 49. Leeds Univ MA91. Edin Th Coll 69. **d** 72 **p** 73. C Skipton Ch Ch *Bradf*

72-75; C Baildon 75-77; Chapl HM Det Cen Kidlington 77-80; TV Kidlington *Ox* 77-80; V Boston Spa *York* 80-99; P-in-c Newton Kyme 84-85; P-in-c Clifford 89-99; P-in-c Thorp Arch w Walton 98-99; Chapl Martin House Hospice for Children Boston Spa 85-99; RD New Ainsty *York* 97-99; Adn York from 99; R Micklegate H Trin and Bishophill Junior St Mary from 00. *Holy Trinity Rectory, Micklegate, York YO1 6LE* Tel (01904) 623798 Fax 628155
E-mail richard-seed@archdeaconyork.fsnet.co.uk

SEELEY, John Frederick. b 36. AKC61. **d** 62 **p** 63. C Lower Broughton Ascension *Man* 62-64; C Chiswick St Paul Grove Park 64-66; C Ruislip St Mary 66-67; C Hampstead Garden Suburb 67-69; P-in-c St John's Wood All SS 69-71; C Stamford Hill St Bart 74-80; P-in-c Harringay St Paul 80-84; V 84-96; rtd 96. *37 Great College Street, Brighton BN2 1HJ* Tel (01273) 673670

SEELEY, Martin Alan. b 54. Jes Coll Cam BA76 MA79. Ripon Coll Cuddesdon 76 Union Th Sem (NY) STM78. **d** 78 **p** 79. C Bottesford w Ashby *Linc* 78-80; USA 80-90; Selection Sec ABM 90-96; Sec for Continuing Minl Educn 90-96; V Is of Dogs Ch Ch and St Jo w St Luke *Lon* from 96. *Christ Church Vicarage, Manchester Road, London E14 3BN* Tel (020) 7538 1766 *or* 7987 1915

SEGAL, Michael Bertram. b 20. Lon Univ BA44. Cuddesdon Coll 46. **d** 48 **p** 49. C Lewisham St Jo Southend *S'wark* 48-53; C Coulsdon St Andr 53-61; V S Wimbledon St Pet 61-71; V Crofton Park St Hilda w St Cypr 72-82; P-in-c Grendon w Castle Ashby *Pet* 82-85; V Gt Doddington 82-85; rtd 85; Perm to Offic *Cant* 85-02. *8 Manormead, Tilford Road, Hindhead GU26 6RA* Tel (01428) 602559

SEGRAVE-PRIDE, Mrs Philippa Louise. b 73. Westhill Coll Birm BTh96. Ripon Coll Cuddesdon 97. **d** 99 **p** 00. C Harborne St Pet *Birm* 99-02; TV Tring *St Alb* from 02. *The Vicarage, Watery Lane, Wilstone, Tring HP23 4PH* Tel (01442) 823008
E-mail philippa@segrave-pride.freeserve.co.uk

SELBY, Miss Carole Janis. b 50. Chelsea Coll of Physical Educn CertEd71 Sussex Univ BEd72 K Coll Lon MA03. Westcott Ho Cam CTM95. **d** 95 **p** 96. C Worc St Barn w Ch Ch *Worc* 95-99; Min Turnford St Clem CD *St Alb* from 99. *St Clements House, 44 Hillview Gardens, Cheshunt, Waltham Cross EN8 0PE* Tel (01992) 625098 Fax as telephone E-mail c_selby@talk21.com

✦**SELBY, The Rt Revd Peter Stephen Maurice.** b 41. St Jo Coll Ox BA64 MA67 Episc Th Sch Cam Mass BD66 K Coll Lon PhD75. Bps' Coll Cheshunt 66. **d** 66 **p** 67 **c** 84. C Queensbury All SS *Lon* 66-69; C Limpsfield and Titsey *S'wark* 69-77; Assoc Dir of Tr 69-73; Vice-Prin S'wark Ord Course 70-72; Asst Dioc Missr *S'wark* 73-77; Dioc Missr *Newc* 77-84; Can Res Newc Cathl 77-84; Suff Bp Kingston *S'wark* 84-91; Area Bp Kingston 91-92; Pres Modern Churchpeople's Union from 91; Wm Leech Professorial Fell Dur Univ 92-97; Asst Bp Dur 92-97; Asst Bp Newc 92-97; Bp Worc from 97; Hon Prof Univ Coll Worc from 98; Bp HM Pris from 01. *The Bishop's House, Hartlebury Castle, Kidderminster DY11 7XX* Tel (01299) 250214 Fax 250027
E-mail bishop.peter@cofe-worcester.org.uk

SELBY, Canon Sydney Arthur. b 17. K Coll Lon 41. **d** 48 **p** 49. C Menston w Woodhead *Bradf* 48-53; V Kildwick 53-74; RD S Craven 73-74; Hon Can Bradf Cathl 73-82; V Gisburn 74-82; RD Bowland 80-81; rtd 82; Perm to Offic *Bradf* 82-99. *Clough Cottage, Clough Lane, Simonstone, Burnley BB12 7HW* Tel (01282) 773108

SELBY, Suffragan Bishop of. See WALLACE, The Rt Revd Martin William

SELDON, Francis Peter. b 58. St Jo Coll Nottm 98. **d** 00 **p** 01. C Styvechale *Cov* 00-02; C Cheylesmore from 02. *11 Frankpledge Road, Coventry CV3 5GT* Tel (024) 7650 7770

SELF, Canon David Christopher. b 41. Toronto Univ BSc62 MA64 K Coll Lon BD68 AKC68. **d** 69 **p** 70. C Tupsley *Heref* 69-73; Chapl Dur Univ *Dur* 73-78; TV Southampton (City Cen) *Win* 78-84; TR Dunstable *St Alb* 84-95; RD Dunstable 90-91; TR Bris St Paul's *Bris* from 95; RD Bris City 98-99; AD City from 99; Hon Can Bris Cathl from 99. *St Paul's Rectory, 131 Ashley Road, Bristol BS6 5NU* Tel 0117-955 0150 *or* 955 1755 E-mail self@supanet.com

SELF, John Andrew. b 47. Pershore Coll of Horticulture CANP68. Trin Coll Bris 74 CMS Tr Coll Crowther Hall 76. **d** 81 **p** 83. CMS 77-91; Pakistan 77-91; Assoc V Bath Weston All SS w N Stoke *B & W* 91-92; V Sparkhill w Greet and Sparkbrook *Birm* from 92. *St John's Vicarage, 15 Phipson Road, Birmingham B11 4JE* Tel and Fax 0121-449 2760 *or* tel 753 1415
E-mail john.self@stjohnsparkhill.org.uk

SELF, Peter Allen. b 41. S Dios Minl Tr Scheme 84. **d** 87 **p** 98. NSM Wilton *B & W* 87-91; NSM Taunton Lyngford 91-96; Asst Chapl Taunton and Somerset NHS Trust from 96. *20 Dyers Close, West Buckland, Wellington TA21 9JU* Tel (01823) 663408 Fax 663448

SELFE, John Ronald. b 41. EMMTC 85. **d** 95 **p** 96. OLM Mid Marsh Gp *Linc* from 95. *Bookend, 236 Eastgate, Louth LN11 8DA* Tel (01507) 603809

SELIM, Claes Eric. b 48. Uppsala Univ MA73 BD76. **d** 77. Sweden 77-00; C Rasbo 77-80; P-in-c Hablingbo 81-85; P-in-c

Öja and Huddunge 85-89; Dep Lect Uppsala Univ 81-89; Lect 89-95; V Öja 89-92; V Vänge 95-00; C Holbeach *Linc* 00-02; R Guernsey Ste Marie du Castel *Win* from 02; V Guernsey St Matt from 02. *Castel Rectory, La Rue de la Lande, Castel, Guernsey GY5 7EJ* Tel (01481) 256793

SELLER, James Stoddart. b 16. TD64. St Jo Coll Dur LTh45. Tyndale Hall Bris 40. **d** 44 **p** 45. C Cambridge St Andr Less *Ely* 44-47; C Holborn St Geo w H Trin *Lon* 47-48; C Whitby *York* 48-50; V Ravenscar 51-53; V Sledmere 53-60; P-in-c Huttons Ambo 57-60; R Burnby 60-89; R Londesborough 60-89; R Nunburnholme 60-89; P-in-c Shiptonthorpe w Hayton 78-89; rtd 89; Perm to Offic *York* from 89. *7 Wilton Road, Hornsea HU18 1QU* Tel (01964) 533160

SELLER, Prof Mary Joan. b 40. Qu Mary Coll Lon BSc61 Lon Univ PhD64 DSc82. S'wark Ord Course 89. **d** 91 **p** 94. NSM Hurst Green *S'wark* from 91. *11 Home Park, Oxted RH8 0JS* Tel (01883) 715675

SELLERS, Anthony. b 48. Southn Univ BSc71 DipTh76. Wycliffe Hall Ox 84. **d** 86 **p** 87. C Luton St Mary *St Alb* 86-90; V Luton St Paul from 90. *37A Arthur Street, Luton LU1 3SG* Tel (01582) 481796 E-mail tsellers@route56.co.uk

SELLERS, George William. b 35. N Ord Course. **d** 89 **p** 90. NSM Rothwell *Ripon* from 89. *16 Thornegrove, Rothwell, Leeds LS26 0HP* Tel 0113-282 3522

SELLERS, Robert. b 58. Coll of Resurr Mirfield 90. **d** 92 **p** 93. C Wotton St Mary *Glouc* 92-95; TV Redruth w Lanner and Treleigh *Truro* 95-98; P-in-c Devoran from 98; Bp's Dom Chapl from 98. *The Vicarage, Devoran Lane, Devoran, Truro TR3 6PA* Tel (01872) 863116 E-mail robert.sellers@ukonline.co.uk

SELLERS, Warren John. b 43. Bp Otter Coll Chich TCert73 W Sussex Inst of HE DipAdEd88. K Coll Lon 63 Sarum Th Coll 65. **d** 68 **p** 69. C Guildf H Trin w St Mary *Guildf* 68-72; Hon C Chich St Paul and St Pet *Chich* 72-73; C Epping St Jo *Chelmsf* 73-76; Hon C Pulborough *Chich* 76-90; Hon C Fleet *Guildf* 90-92; Teacher 73-89; Waltham Abbey St Lawr and H Cross Schs Essex 73-76; Pulborough St Mary, Easebourne & Bp Tuffnell Schs 76-89; Hd Teacher St Pet Jun Sch Farnborough 90-92; TV Upper Kennet *Sarum* 92-95; TR from 95. *The Rectory, 27 High Street, Avebury, Marlborough SN8 1RF* Tel (01672) 539643 Fax as telephone E-mail warren@zeronet.org.uk

SELLEY, Paul Edward Henry. b 47. Bris Univ BEd70 ALCM67 LTCL87. Sarum Th Coll 93. **d** 96 **p** 97. C Swindon Dorcan *Bris* 96-00; V Ashton Keynes, Leigh and Minety from 00. *The Vicarage, 23 Richmond Court, Ashton Keynes, Swindon SN6 6PP* Tel (01285) 861566 Fax as telephone

SELLGREN, Eric Alfred. b 33. AKC61. **d** 62 **p** 63. C Ditton St Mich *Liv* 62-66; V Hindley Green 66-72; V Southport St Paul 72-80; Warden Barn Fellowship Winterborne Whitchurch 80-86; V The Iwernes, Sutton Waldron and Fontmell Magna *Sarum* 86-98; rtd 98; Perm to Offic *Sarum* from 98. *16 The Limes, Motcombe, Shaftesbury SP7 9QL* Tel (01747) 850747

SELLIX, Martin Gordon. b 45. Ridley Hall Cam 74. **d** 76 **p** 77. C Crofton St Paul *Roch* 76-80; Ind Chapl *Chelmsf* 80-94; R Rayne 80-86; V Blackmore and Stondon Massey 86-94; RD Ongar 89-94; TR Liskeard, St Keyne, St Pinnock, Morval etc *Truro* 94-99; V Liskeard and St Keyne from 99; Chapl Cornwall and Is of Scilly Mental Health Unit from 96. *The Rectory, Church Street, Liskeard PL14 3AQ* Tel (01579) 342178 or 347411

SELLIX, Mrs Pamela Madge. b 47. Lon Univ BA68 PGCE68. SW Minl Tr Course 00. **d** 03. *The Rectory, Church Street, Liskeard PL14 3AQ* Tel (01579) 342178

SELLORS, Michael Harry. b 36. K Coll Lon 60 St Boniface Warminster 61. **d** 61 **p** 62. C Willesden St Mary *Lon* 61-64; C Aldershot St Mich *Guildf* 64-67; V Hale 67-84; P-in-c E w W Beckham *Nor* 84-85; P-in-c Bodham 84-85; V Weybourne w Upper Sheringham 84-85; R Kelling w Salthouse 84-85; R Weybourne Gp 85-91; V Hunstanton St Edm w Ringstead 91-97; Dean Jerusalem 97-02; rtd 02. *Cranford House, 56 Cromer Road, West Runton, Cromer NR27 9AD* Tel (01263) 837293

SELMAN, Cyril Allen. b 25. Wycliffe Hall Ox 64. **d** 65 **p** 65. C Thame *Ox* 65-69; V Beedon 69-87; R Peasemore 69-87; rtd 88; Perm to Offic *Ban* from 88. *1 Market Street, North Tawton EX20 2ET* Tel (01837) 82771

SELMAN, Michael Richard. b 47. Sussex Univ BA68 Bris Univ MA70. Coll of Resurr Mirfield 71. **d** 73 **p** 74. C Hove All SS *Chich* 73-74; C Horfield H Trin *Bris* 74-78; P-in-c Landkey *Ex* 78-79; C Barnstaple and Goodleigh 78-79; TV Barnstaple, Goodleigh and Landkey 79-82; TR 82-84; P-in-c Sticklepath 83-84; TR Barnstaple 85; RD Barnstaple 83-85; TR Cen Ex 85-00; Chapl Aquitaine *Eur* from 00. *Le Presbytère, 1 Lotissement la Caussade, 33270 Floirac, France* Tel (0033) (5) 56 40 05 12 Fax as telephone E-mail mselman@fr.packardbell.org

SELMES, Brian. b 48. Nottm Univ BTh74 Dur Univ MA97. Linc Th Coll 74. **d** 74 **p** 75. C Padgate *Liv* 74-77; C Sydenham St Bart *S'wark* 77-80; Chapl Darlington Memorial Hosp from 80; Chapl Darlington Memorial Hosp NHS Trust 94-98; Chapl S Durham Healthcare NHS Trust from 98. *Darlington Memorial Hospital, Hollyhurst Road, Darlington DL3 6HX* Tel (01325) 743029 or 359688 E-mail brian.selmes@smtp.sdhc-tr.northy.nhs.uk

SELVEY, Canon John Brian. b 33. Dur Univ BA54. Cuddesdon Coll 56. **d** 58 **p** 59. C Lancaster St Mary *Blackb* 58-61; C Blackb Cathl 61-65; Cathl Chapl 64-65; V Foulridge 65-69; V Walton-le-Dale 69-82; V Cleveleys 82-89; Hon Can Bloemfontein Cathl from 88; V Slyne w Hest *Blackb* 89-97; Hon Can Blackb Cathl 93-97; rtd 97; Perm to Offic *Carl* from 98. *Low Quietways, Borrowdale Road, Keswick CA12 5UP* Tel (01768) 773538

SELWOOD, Michael. b 40. Oak Hill Th Coll DipHE90 BA91. **d** 91 **p** 92. Canada 91-95; P-in-c Sherborne, Windrush, the Barringtons etc *Glouc* from 95. *The New Vicarage, Windrush, Burford OX18 4TS* Tel (01451) 844276 E-mail 106631.11@compuserve.com

SELWOOD, Robin. b 37. ALCD61. **d** 61 **p** 62. C Lenton *S'well* 61-63; C Norbury *Ches* 63-66; V Newton Flowery Field 66-75; V Kelsall 75-89; V Sale St Paul 89-02; rtd 02; P-in-c Langtoft w Foxholes, Butterwick, Cottam etc *York* from 02. *The Rectory, Church Lane, Langtoft, Driffield YO25 3TN* Tel (01377) 267226

SELWOOD, Timothy John. b 45. Lon Univ LLB66. Sarum Th Coll. **d** 83 **p** 84. NSM Colbury *Win* 83-85; NSM Copythorne and Minstead 85-90; Perm to Offic from 98. *Long Cottage, Mews Lane, Winchester SO22 4PS* Tel (01926) 860874

SELWYN, David Gordon. b 38. MEHS Clare Coll Cam BA62 MA66 New Coll Ox MA66. Ripon Hall Ox 62. **d** 64 **p** 65. C Ecclesall *Sheff* 64-65; Asst Chapl New Coll Ox 65-68; Lect Univ of Wales (Lamp) *St D* 68-98; Reader from 98; Perm to Offic from 68. *19 Penbryn, Lampeter SA48 7EU* Tel (01570) 422748

SEMEONOFF, Canon Jean Mary Agnes. b 36. BSc56 Leic Univ CertEd57. EMMTC 84. **d** 87 **p** 94. Par Dn Leic H Spirit *Leic* 87 and 89-94; Chapl for Deaf People *Derby* 87-89; Chapl for Deaf People *Leic* 89-94; Hon Can Leic Cathl 92-99; rtd 94; Bp's Adv for Women's Min *Leic* 93-97; Min for Special Past Duties 94-99; Perm to Offic from 99. *107 Letchworth Road, Leicester LE3 6FN* Tel 0116-285 8854 E-mail semeonof@leicester.anglican.org

SEMEONOFF, Robert. b 40. Edin Univ BSc62 DipD67. EMMTC 81. **d** 84 **p** 85. NSM Leic H Spirit *Leic* 84-88 and 89-94; NSM Loughb Gd Shep 88-89; Asst Chapl Leic Univ 89-94; Min for Special Past Duties 94-98; Chapl Leic R Infirmary NHS Trust 98-01; Hon Asst Chapl Univ Hosps Leic NHS Trust from 01. *107 Letchworth Road, Leicester LE3 6FN* Tel 0116-285 8854 or 254 1414 ext 5487 E-mail semeonof@leicester.anglican.org

SEMPER, The Very Revd Colin Douglas. b 38. Keble Coll Ox BA62. Westcott Ho Cam 61. **d** 63 **p** 64. C Guildf H Trin w St Mary *Guildf* 63-67; Sec ACCM 67-69; Producer Relig Broadcasting Dept BBC 69-75; Overseas Relig Broadcasting Org BBC 75-79; Hd Relig Progr BBC Radio 79-82; Hon Can Guildf Cathl *Guildf* 80-82; Provost Cov 82-87; Can and Treas Westmr Abbey 87-97; Steward 87-90; rtd 97; Perm to Offic *Sarum* 97-03; Hon C Rowledge and Frensham *Guildf* from 03. *The Vicarage, Frensham, Farnham GU10 3DT* Tel (01252) 792137 E-mail sempers@freezone.co.uk

SEMPLE, Henry Michael. b 40. K Coll Lon BSc62 Birkbeck Coll Lon PhD67 CMath FIMA FCMI FRSA. S Dios Minl Tr Scheme. **d** 87 **p** 88. NSM Steyning *Chich* 87-91; Perm to Offic *Guildf* 87-91; Perm to Offic *Linc* 92-93; NSM Linc Cathl 93-99; TR Headley All SS *Guildf* 99-02; V from 02. *All Saints' Rectory, High Street, Headley, Bordon GU35 8PP* Tel (01428) 717321 E-mail mandpsemple@waitrose.com

SEMPLE, Patrick William. b 45. Sussex Univ BA66 Bris Univ DipTh70. Sarum & Wells Th Coll 68. **d** 72 **p** 73. C Paddington Ch Ch *Lon* 72-75; Ind Chapl Nor 75-79; P-in-c Woodbastwick 76-79; V Kensington St Barn *Lon* 79-83; V Coleford w Staunton *Glouc* from 83; P-in-c Forest of Dean Ch Ch w English Bicknor 84-89. *The Vicarage, 40 Box Bush Road, Coleford GL16 8DN* Tel (01594) 833379 E-mail patricksemple@tiscali.co.uk

SEMPLE, Studdert Patrick. b 39. TCD BA66. CITC 66. **d** 67 **p** 68. C Orangefield *D & D* 67-70; USA 70-71; I Stradbally *C & O* 71-82; Ch of Ireland Adult Educn Officer 82-88; I Donoughmore and Donard w Dunlavin *D & G* 88-96; Bp's C Dublin St Geo and St Thos 96-99; Chapl Mountjoy Pris and Mater Hosps 96-99; rtd 99. *49 Richmond Park, Monkstown, Co Dublin, Irish Republic* Tel (00353) (1) 230 1712

SEN, Arani. b 61. R Holloway Coll Lon BA84 St Martin's Coll Lanc PGCE86 Open Univ MA94 Fitzw Coll Cam BA98. Ridley Hall Cam 96. **d** 99 **p** 00. C Mildmay Grove St Jude and St Paul *Lon* 99-02; C-in-c Southall Em CD from 02. *37 Dormers Wells Lane, Southall UB1 3HX* Tel (020) 8843 9556 E-mail arani_sen@hotmail.com

SENIOR, Brian Stephen. b 55. Brighton Coll of Educn CertEd76. Oak Hill Th Coll DipHE93. **d** 93 **p** 94. C Hildenborough *Roch* 93-98; TV Tunbridge Wells St Jas w St Phil from 98. *St Philip's Vicarage, Birken Road, Tunbridge Wells TN2 3TE* Tel (01892) 512071 E-mail revbsenior@beeb.net

SENIOR, David John. b 47. Oak Hill Th Coll. **d** 82 **p** 83. C Market Harborough *Leic* 82-85; TV Marfleet *York* 85-91; R Desford and Peckleton w Tooley *Leic* 91-96; P-in-c Hall Green Ascension *Birm* 96-99; V from 99; P-in-c Gospel Lane St Mich 97-03. *The Vicarage, 592 Fox Hollies Road, Birmingham B28 9DX* Tel 0121-777 3689

SENIOR, George. b 36. Open Univ BA83. EMMTC 82. d 86 p 87. NSM Spratton *Pet* 86-90; NSM Cottesbrooke w Gt Creaton and Thornby 86-90; C Darwen St Pet w Hoddlesden *Blackb* 90-92; V Foulridge 92-97; P-in-c Swallow *Linc* 97-02; rtd 02. *21 Woodland Drive, Woodhall Spa LN10 6YF* Tel (01526) 354150

SENIOR, John Peter. b 23. Lon Univ BSc48. Edin Th Coll 63. d 65 p 66. C Marton *Blackb* 65-68; C Heysham 68-71; V Blackpool St Mich 71-79; V Heddon-on-the-Wall *Newc* 79-88; rtd 88; Perm to Offic *Wakef* from 88. *56 Thorpe Lane, Huddersfield HD5 8TA* Tel (01484) 530466

SENIOR, Patrick Nicolas Adam. b 63. Univ of Wales (Ban) BA86. Trin Coll Bris BA94. d 94 p 95. C Derringham Bank *York* 94-98; V Brownhill *Wakef* from 98. *The Vicarage, 24 Intake Lane, Brownhill, Batley WF17 0BT* Tel (01924) 471999
E-mail pals@thedogcollar.fsnet.co.uk

✠SENTAMU, The Rt Revd John Mugabi. b 47. Makerere Univ Kampala Selw Coll Cam BA76 MA. Ridley Hall Cam. d 79 p 79 c 96. Chapl HM Rem Cen Latchmere Ho 79-82; C Ham St Andr *S'wark* 79-82; C Herne Hill St Paul 82-83; P-in-c Tulse Hill H Trin 83-84; V Upper Tulse Hill St Matthias 83-84; V Tulse Hill H Trin and St Matthias 85-96; P-in-c Brixton Hill St Sav 87-89; Hon Can S'wark Cathl 93-96; Area Bp Stepney *Lon* 96-02; Bp Birm from 02. *Bishop's Croft, Old Church Road, Harborne, Birmingham B17 0BG* Tel 0121-427 1163 Fax 426 1322
E-mail bishop@birmingham.anglican.org

SEOUL, Bishop of. *See* CHUNG, The Most Revd Matthew Chul Bum

SEPHTON, John. b 43. d 01 p 02. OLM Newburgh w Westhead *Liv* from 01; Asst Chapl HM Pris Risley from 02. *2 Ruff Lane, Ormskirk L39 4QZ* Tel (01695) 576774 *or* (01925) 763871
E-mail johnsephton@postmaster.co.uk

SEPPALA, Christopher James. b 59. St Jo Coll Dur BA82 Ch Ch Coll Cant CertEd92. Chich Th Coll 83. d 85 p 86. C Whitstable *Cant* 85-88; C S Ashford Ch Ch 88-91; Perm to Offic from 01. *9 Newton Road, Whitstable CT5 2JD* Tel (01227) 266411
E-mail xpristopheros@netscapeonline.co.uk

SERBUTT, Rita Eileen. b 33. Man Univ BA54 Univ of Wales (Cardiff) DipEd56 FRSA94. Dioc OLM tr scheme 98. d 01 p 02. OLM Balham St Mary and St Jo *S'wark* from 01. *5 Veronica Road, London SW17 8QL* Tel (020) 8772 1031
E-mail eileen.serbutt@virgin.net

SERJEANT, Frederick James. b 28. Lon Inst of Educn BEd77. AKC53 St Boniface Warminster 53. d 54 p 55. C Leytonstone St Marg w St Columba *Chelmsf* 54-58; C Parkstone St Pet w Branksea Sarum 58-59; V Reigate St Luke S Park *S'wark* 59-65; V Battersea St Pet 65-71; C-in-c Battersea St Paul 67-71; V W Mersea *Chelmsf* 71-73; P-in-c E Mersea 71-73; R W w E Mersea 73-75; rtd 93. *3 Church Hill View, Sydling, Dorchester DT2 9SY* Tel (01300) 341670

SERJEANT, Mrs Heather Faith. b 60. Stirling Univ BSc80. Ripon Coll Cuddesdon 00. d 02 p 03. C Caversham and Mapledurham *Ox* from 02. *4A The Mount, Caversham, Reading RG4 7RU* Tel 0118-947 2729 E-mail heatherserjeant@aol.com

SERJEANT, John Frederick. b 33. K Coll Lon 52. d 56 p 57. C Over St Chad *Ches* 56-59; C-in-c Brinnington St Luke CD 59-63; V Brinnington 63-69; V Gatley 69-79; TV Halesworth w Linstead and Chediston *St E* 79-80; TV Halesworth w Linstead, Cheddiston, Holton etc 80-82; C Chesterfield St Mary and All SS *Derby* 82-88; Chapl Chesterfield R Hosp 82-88; Chapl Chesterfield and N Derbyshire R Hosp 88-95; rtd 95. *188 Queen Victoria Road, New Tupton, Chesterfield S42 6DW* Tel (01246) 863395

SERJEANTSON, John Cecil Mylles. b 36. Bp's Univ Lennoxville BA59 McGill Univ Montreal BD66. Montreal Dioc Th Coll LTh66. d 66 p 67. Canada 66-72 and from 79; C Westmount St Matthias 66-68; R Huntingdon w Ormstown 68-72; C Gt and Lt Driffield *York* 72-76; V Bilton St Pet 76-79; R Brome Montreal 79-01; rtd 01. *19 Mountain, South Bolton PQ, Canada, J0E 2N0* Tel (001) (450) 292 0850

SERMON, Michael John. b 61. Univ of Cen England in Birm ACIB85. Qu Coll Birm BA98 MA99. d 99 p 00. C W Heath *Birm* 99-03; V Blackheath from 03. *St Paul's Vicarage, 83 Vicarage Road, Halesowen B62 8HX* Tel 0121-559 1000
E-mail revsermon@aol.com

SERTIN, John Francis. b 22. Fitzw Ho Cam BA50 MA54. Tyndale Hall Bris. d 45 p 46. C Sidcup Ch Ch *Roch* 45-47; Chapl Fitzw Ho Cam 47-50; C-in-c St Paul's Cray St Barn CD *Roch* 50-59; V Chitts Hill St Cuth *Lon* 59-62; Sec Ch Soc 62-67; P-in-c Woburn Square Ch Ch *Lon* 67-77; R Holborn St Geo w H Trin and St Bart 67-80; R Donyatt w Horton, Broadway and Ashill *B & W* 80-92; rtd 92; Perm to Offic *B & W* 92-02. *23 Birstan Gardens, Andover SP10 4NY* Tel (01264) 334544

SERUNJOGI, David. b 59. Redcliffe Coll BA01. Bp Tucker Coll Mukono 96. d 95 p 97. Dir Miss and Evang Cen Buganda 95-00; Perm to Offic *Glouc* from 02. *Redcliffe College, Wotton House, Horton Road, Gloucester GL1 3PT* Tel 07884-060704 (mobile)
E-mail centromass@yahoo.com

SERVANT, Canon Alma Joan. b 51. Nottm Univ BA76 Dip Librarianship 79. Westcott Ho Cam 83. dss 85 d 87 p 94. Ordsall

S'well 85-88; Par Dn 87-88; Par Dn Man Whitworth *Man* 88-94; TV 94-96; Chapl Man Poly 88-92; Chapl Man Metrop Univ 92-96; P-in-c Heaton Norris St Thos 96-00; P-in-c Hulme Ascension from 00; Hon Can Man Cathl from 02. *The Rectory, Royce Road, Hulme, Manchester M15 5FQ* Tel 0161-226 5568

SERVANTE, Kenneth Edward. b 29. AKC55. d 56 p 57. C Chaddesden St Phil *Derby* 56-58; C Brampton St Thos 58-61; C Whitfield 61-63; V Derby St Paul 63-70; V Elmton 70-81; P-in-c Winster 81-82; P-in-c Elton 81-82; R S Darley, Elton and Winster 82-94; rtd 94; Perm to Offic *Derby* from 94. *13 Chestnut Avenue, Belper DE56 1LY* Tel (01773) 820513

SESSFORD, Canon Alan. b 34. Bps' Coll Cheshunt 65. d 66 p 67. C Highcliffe w Hinton Admiral *Win* 66-69; C Minehead *B & W* 70; C Chandler's Ford *Win* 70-73; V Burton and Sopley 73-00; RD Christchurch 93-98; Hon Can Win Cathl 98-00; rtd 00; Perm to Offic *Win* from 00; Chapl R Bournemouth and Christchurch Hosps NHS Trust from 01. *4 Benson Close, Bransgore, Christchurch BH23 8HX* Tel (01425) 673412

SETTERFIELD, Nicholas Manley. b 63. Colchester Inst of Educn BA89. St Steph Ho Ox 89. d 92 p 93. C Prestbury *Glouc* 92-96; R Letchworth *St Alb* from 96. *The Rectory, 39 South View, Letchworth Garden City SG6 3JJ* Tel (01462) 684822
E-mail rectory@letchworthparish.fsnet.co.uk

SETTIMBA, John Henry. b 52. Nairobi Univ BSc78 Leeds Univ MA91. Pan Africa Chr Coll BA78. d 78 p 80. Kenya 78-81; Uganda 81-85; C Allerton *Bradf* 86-87; C W Ham *Chelmsf* 87-91; C-in-c Forest Gate All SS 91-94; P-in-c 94-96; TV Hackney *Lon* 96-02. *63 Belvedere Court, Upper Richmond Road, London SW15 6HZ* Tel (020) 8789 8376

SEVILLE, Thomas Christopher John. b 57. Trin Hall Cam MA80. Coll of Resurr Mirfield 87. d 89 p 90. C Knowle *Bris* 89-93; CR from 93. *Community of the Resurrection, Stocks Bank Road, Mirfield WF14 0BN* Tel (01924) 483315
E-mail tseville@mirfield.org.uk

SEWARD, Jolyon Frantom. b 57. Univ of Wales (Cardiff) BA81. Chich Th Coll 83. d 86 p 87. C Llanblethian w Cowbridge and Llandough etc *Llan* 86-88; C Newton Nottage 88-93; Dioc Children's Officer 88-98; V Penyfai w Tondu 93-01; TV Heavitree and St Mary Steps *Ex* from 01. *St Lawrence's Vicarage, Lower Hill Barton Road, Exeter EX1 3EH* Tel (01392) 466302

SEWARD, Nicholas. b 70. Imp Coll Lon BEng91 ACGI91. Cranmer Hall Dur BA96 MA98. d 98 p 99. C Bearsted w Thurnham *Cant* 98-02; Chapl and Hd RS Magd Coll Sch *Ox* from 02. *9 Thelwall House, Herbert Close, Oxford OX4 2AY* Tel (01865) 245495 E-mail nseward@mcsoxford.org

SEWELL, Andrew William. b 61. Nottm Univ BSc83. St Jo Coll Nottm 83. d 93 p 94. C Adel *Ripon* 93-96; C Far Headingley St Chad 96-98; Asst Dioc Missr 96-98; P-in-c Otham w Langley *Cant* 98-01; R from 01. *The Rectory, Church Road, Otham, Maidstone ME15 8SB* Tel (01622) 861470
E-mail asewell@aol.com

SEWELL, Miss Elizabeth Jill. b 56. Reading Univ BSc77. Trin Coll Bris BA97. d 97 p 98. C Rothley *Leic* 97-01; TV Market Harborough and The Transfiguration etc from 01. *The Vicarage, 49 Ashley Way, Market Harborough LE16 7XD* Tel (01858) 463441 E-mail ejsewell@leicester.anglican.org

SEWELL, John Andrew Clarkson. b 58. Aston Tr Scheme 93 Ripon Coll Cuddesdon 95. d 97 p 98. C Horsham *Chich* 97-99; C Cleobury Mortimer w Hopton Wafers etc *Heref* 99-01; R 01-03; TV Ludlow, Ludford, Ashford Carbonell etc from 03. *St Mary's Vicarage, Donkey Lane, Ashford Carbonell, Ludlow SY9 4DA* Tel (01584) 831352 E-mail jacsewell@aol.com

SEWELL, John Barratt (Barry). b 39. St Bart Hosp Medical Coll MB, BS63 DRCOG66. Ridley Hall Cam CTM92. d 92 p 93. C Ulverston St Mary w H Trin *Carl* 92-94; Asst Chapl R Cornwall Hosps Trust 94-98; Chapl 98-99; P-in-c Gerrans w St Anthony-in-Roseland and Philleigh *Truro* from 00. *The Rectory, Gerrans, Portscatho, Truro TR2 5EB, or Cleswyth, Creegbrawse St Day, Redruth TR16 5QF* Tel (01872) 580277 *or* (01209) 821696
E-mail barry@cleswyth.freeserve.co.uk

SEWELL, Jonathan William. b 60. Lanc Univ BA82 BTh86. Linc Th Coll 83. d 86 p 87. C Ilkeston St Mary *Derby* 86-89; C Enfield Chase St Mary *Lon* 89-92; Dioc Youth Officer *Win* 92-97; P-in-c Headington St Mary *Ox* from 98. *St Mary's Vicarage, Bayswater Road, Oxford OX3 9EY* Tel (01865) 761886 Fax 435492
E-mail jonathan.sewell@ntlworld.com

SEWELL, Peter Alexis. b 35. Lon Univ BSc61 PhD67 FRSC86. Cyprus and the Gulf Ord Course 92. d 94 p 95. Cyprus and the Gulf 94-97; Perm to Offic *Liv* 97; NSM Ormskirk from 97. *Shakelady Hey, Sandy Lane, Lathom, Ormskirk L40 5TU* Tel (01695) 572095 Fax as telephone

SEWELL, Richard Michael. b 62. Birm Univ BA84. SEITE 99. d 02. C Putney St Mary *S'wark* from 02. *8 Deodar Road, London SW15 2NN* Tel (020) 8785 3821

SEWELL, Robin Warwick. b 42. Trin Coll Bris. d 82 p 83. C Hinckley H Trin *Leic* 82-85; C Broadwater St Mary *Chich* 85-89; Chapl Barcelona *Eur* 89-02; V Braintree St Paul *Chelmsf* from 02. *St Paul's Parsonage, Hay Lane, Braintree CM7 3DY* Tel (01376) 325095 E-mail info@stpaulsbraintree.org.uk

SEWELL, Miss Sarah Frances. b 61. Wycliffe Hall Ox 87. **d** 91 **p** 94. C Binley *Cov* 91-94; Asst Chapl Derriford Hosp Plymouth 94-96; Chapl Stoke Mandeville Hosp NHS Trust 96-00; Chapl R Marsden NHS Trust Lon and Surrey from 00. *The Chaplain's Office, Royal Marsden Hospital, Downs Road, Sutton SM2 5PT* Tel (020) 8642 3074, 8642 6011 *or* 8642 7395

SEXTON, Canon Michael Bowers. b 28. SS Coll Cam BA52 MA56. Wells Th Coll 52. **d** 54 **p** 55. C Miles Platting St Luke *Man* 54-57; C Bradford cum Beswick 57-58; C-in-c Oldham St Chad Limeside CD 58-62; R Filby w Thrigby w Mautby *Nor* 62-72; P-in-c Runham 67-72; P-in-c Stokesby w Herringby 68-72; R Hethersett w Canteloff 72-85; V Ketteringham 73-84; RD Humbleyard 81-86; Hon Can Nor Cathl 85-93; R Hethersett w Canteloff w Lt and Gt Melton 85-86; V Hunstanton St Mary w Ringstead Parva, Holme etc 86-93; rtd 94; Perm to Offic *Nor* from 94. *3 Forge Close, Poringland, Norwich NR14 7SZ* Tel (01508) 493885

SEYCHELLES, Bishop of. *See* CHANG-HIM, The Rt Revd French Kitchener

SEYMOUR, Dom Anthony Nicholas. b 39. QUB BA61. **d** 96 **p** 97. Community of Our Lady and St John from 86. *Alton Abbey, Abbey Road, Beech, Alton GU34 4AP* Tel (01420) 562145 *or* 563575 Fax 561691

SEYMOUR, David. b 43. Kelham Th Coll 60. **d** 68 **p** 69. C Cowley St Jas *Ox* 68-73; TV Lynton, Brendon, Countisbury, Lynmouth etc *Ex* 73-77; C-in-c Luton (Princes Park) CD *Roch* 78-79; V Rosherville 79-90; rtd 90. *4 Swinburne Drive, Lowry Hill, Carlisle CA3 0PY* Tel (01228) 597320
E-mail markbeech@boltblue.com

SEYMOUR, David Raymond Russell. b 56. Keble Coll Ox BA79 MA88. St Steph Ho Ox 79. **d** 81 **p** 82. C Tilehurst St Mich *Ox* 81-85; TV Parkstone St Pet w Branksea and St Osmund *Sarum* 85-91; V Bradford-on-Avon Ch Ch 91-01; P-in-c Sturminster Newton and Hinton St Mary 01-02; V Sturminster Newton, Hinton St Mary and Lydlinch from 02. *The Vicarage, Church Street, Sturminster Newton DT10 1DB* Tel (01258) 472531

SEYMOUR, Canon John Charles. b 30. Oak Hill Th Coll 51 and 55 Wycliffe Coll Toronto 54. **d** 57 **p** 58. C Islington St Andr w St Thos and St Matthias *Lon* 57-60; C Worthing St Geo *Chich* 60-63; V Thornton *Leic* 63-70; R Kirby Muxloe 70-81; TR 81-83; Hon Can Leic Cathl 82-93; RD Sparkenhoe I 83-88; R Market Bosworth w Shenton 83-87; TR Market Bosworth, Cadeby w Sutton Cheney etc 87-93; RD Sparkenhoe W 89-92; rtd 93. *7 Merton Close, Broughton Astley, Leicester LE9 6QP* Tel (01455) 282525

SEYMOUR, Paul Edward. b 62. Humberside Univ BA92. St Jo Coll Nottm 01. **d** 03. C Ingleby Barwick *York* from 03. *27 Berrington Gardens, Ingleby Barwick, Stockton-on-Tees TS17 0UH* Tel (01642) 763647 Mobile 07815-729831
E-mail paulseymour@tiscali.co.uk

SEYMOUR-WHITELEY, Richard Dudley. b 59. Leic Poly BSc80. Linc Th Coll 82. **d** 85 **p** 86. C Bushey *St Alb* 85-89; C Stevenage St Mary Sheppall w Aston 89-93; P-in-c Blunham w Tempsford and Lt Barford 93-99; P-in-c The Stodden Churches 99-01; I Grey Abbey w Kircubbin *D & D* from 01. *The Rectory, 90 Newtownards Road, Greyabbey, Newtownards BT22 2QJ* Tel (028) 4278 8216

SHACKELL, Daniel William. b 42. LNSM course 92. **d** 95 **p** 96. Dir Spires Cen from 93; OLM Streatham St Leon *S'wark* 95-99; Lic to Offic from 99; Perm to Offic *Guildf* from 01. *83 Hillside, Banstead SM7 1EZ* Tel (01737) 361345 *or* (020) 8696 0943

SHACKELL, Kenneth Norman. b 26. S'wark Ord Course 66. **d** 69 **p** 70. NSM Greenwich St Alfege w St Pet and St Paul *S'wark* 69-95; Perm to Offic *Sarum* from 95. *17 Portman Drive, Child Okeford, Blandford Forum DT11 8HU* Tel (01258) 861583 Fax as telephone

SHACKERLEY, Canon Albert Paul. b 56. Birkbeck Coll Lon DipRS86 DipTh89 Chich Tech Coll Cert Counselling 93 K Coll Lon MA97. CA Tr Coll Dip Evang83 Chich Th Coll Dip Minl Th93. **d** 93 **p** 94. C Harlesden All So *Lon* 93-96; P-in-c Chelmsf All SS *Chelmsf* 96-98; V 98-02; Can Res Sheff Cathl *Sheff* from 02. *9 Stumperlowe Hall Road, Sheffield S10 3QR* Tel 0114-230 4181 *or* 0114-263 6066 Mobile 07786-927715
E-mail paul_shackerley@btinternet.com

SHACKLADY, Mrs Thelma. b 38. Liv Univ BA60. St Alb Minl Tr Scheme 89. **d** 92 **p** 94. NSM Luton St Andr *St Alb* 92-96; NSM Luton All SS w St Pet from 96. *31 Fairford Avenue, Luton LU2 7ER* Tel (01582) 723252 E-mail bill.shacklady@virgin.net

SHACKLEFORD, Richard Neal. b 40. Univ of Denver BA64 Univ of N Colorado MA74. St Steph Ho Ox 84. **d** 86 **p** 87. C Poulton-le-Fylde *Blackb* 86-88; USA from 88; Can St Jo Cathl Colorado 88-92; C Denver St Mich 92-96; R Lindenhurst St Boniface from 96. *100 46th Street, Lindenhurst, NY 11747, USA*

SHACKLETON, Canon Alan. b 31. Sheff Univ BA53. Wells Th Coll 54. **d** 56 **p** 57. C Ladybarn *Man* 56-58; C Bolton St Pet 58-61; V Middleton Junction 61-70; V Heywood St Luke 70-84; AD Rochdale 82-92; Hon Can Man Cathl 84-97; V Heywood St Luke w All So 85-86; TV Rochdale 86-91; TR 91-97; rtd 97;

Perm to Offic *Man* from 97. *28 Taunton Avenue, Rochdale OL11 5LD* Tel (01706) 645335
E-mail alan@ashackleton.demon.co.uk

SHACKLETON, Ian Roderick. b 40. St Fran Coll Brisbane 69 ACT ThL71. **d** 72 **p** 72. Australia 72-78; C Birch St Agnes *Man* 79-80; P-in-c Newton Heath St Wilfrid and St Anne 80-87; NSM W Derby St Jo *Liv* 87-90; C 90-94; P-in-c Southport St Luke from 94; Asst Chapl HM Pris Liv from 94. *The Clergy House, 71 Hawkshead Street, Southport PR9 9BT* Tel (01704) 538703

SHACKLEY, Prof Myra Lesley. b 49. Southn Univ BA70 PhD75 Nottm Univ MA99 FRGS. EMMTC 96. **d** 99 **p** 00. NSM Ordsall *S'well* 99-02; Dioc Tourism Adv from 02; PV S'well Minster from 02. *47 Eldon Street, Tuxford, Newark NG22 0LG* Tel and fax (01777) 870838 Mobile 07889-691504
E-mail myra.shackley@ntu.ac.uk

SHAFEE, Kenneth Harold. b 30. ALA64. Ex & Truro NSM Scheme 78. **d** 81 **p** 82. NSM Littleham w Exmouth *Ex* 81-85; Custos St Jo Hosp Heytesbury 85-89; NSM Lydford, Brent Tor, Bridestowe and Sourton *Ex* 89-90; Perm to Offic *Ex* from 90. *The Firs, Exeter Road, Dawlish EX7 0LX* Tel (01626) 888326

SHAFTO, Robert James. b 38. FCA61. OLM course 96. **d** 99 **p** 00. OLM W Dulwich All SS *S'wark* from 99. *46 Cedar Close, London SE21 8HX* Tel (020) 8761 7395

SHAHZAD, Sulaiman. b 60. BA. Oak Hill Th Coll BA93. **d** 96 **p** 97. C Winchmore Hill St Paul *Lon* 96-00; TV Digswell and Panshanger *St Alb* from 00. *71 Haldens, Welwyn Garden City AL7 1DH* Tel (01707) 335537

SHAIL, Canon William Frederick. b 15. Kelham Th Coll. **d** 41 **p** 42. C Deptford St Paul *S'wark* 41-44; C Lewisham St Mary 44-47; C Christchurch *Win* 47-52; R N Stoneham 52-68; V Bournemouth St Alb 68-78; V Burley Ville 78-84; rtd 84; Perm to Offic *Win* 84-97. *19 Halton Close, Bransgore, Christchurch BH23 8HZ* Tel (01425) 673064

SHAKESPEARE, James Douglas Geoffrey. b 71. Fitzw Coll Cam BA93 MA97 Man Univ MA96. Westcott Ho Cam CTM99. **d** 99 **p** 00. C Cherry Hinton St Jo *Ely* 99-02; Bp's Chapl and Policy Adv *Leic* from 02. *32 Craighill Road, Leicester LE2 5FP* Tel 0116-270 5827
E-mail shakespeare@jdgs.freeserve.co.uk

SHAKESPEARE, Steven. b 68. CCC Cam BA89 PhD94. Westcott Ho Cam 93. **d** 96 **p** 97. C Cambridge St Jas *Ely* 96-99; V Endcliffe *Sheff* from 99. *St Augustine's Vicarage, 4 Clarke Drive, Sheffield S10 2NS* Tel 0114-266 1932
E-mail steve@bower.abel.co.uk

SHALLCROSS, Canon Martin Anthony. b 37. FRICS70. Sarum & Wells Th Coll 75. **d** 78 **p** 79. NSM Bramshaw and Landford w Plaitford *Sarum* 78-81; NSM Tisbury 81-01; NSM Nadder Valley from 01; Can and Preb Sarum Cathl from 93. *Wallmead Farm, Tisbury, Salisbury SP3 6RB* Tel (01747) 870208
E-mail shallcross.wallmead@ukgateway.net

SHAMBROOK, Roger William. b 46. Sarum & Wells Th Coll 78. **d** 83 **p** 84. OSP 76-82; C Southbourne St Kath *Win* 83-86; TV Bridport *Sarum* 86-01; Chapl Bridport Community Hosp 86-94; Chapl Dorset Community NHS Trust 94-01; P-in-c Torre All SS *Ex* from 01. *All Saints' Vicarage, 45 Barton Road, Torquay TQ1 4DT* Tel (01803) 328865

SHAND, Brian Martin. b 53. Univ Coll Lon BA76 PhD82. St Steph Ho Ox 85. **d** 87 **p** 88. C Uxbridge St Marg *Lon* 87-88; C Uxbridge 88-90; C Worplesdon *Guildf* 90-94; Relig Affairs Producer BBC Radio Surrey 90-94; V Weston 94-01; V Witley from 01. *The Vicarage, Petworth Road, Witley, Godalming GU8 5LT* Tel (01428) 682886

SHANKS, Robert Andrew Gulval. b 54. Ball Coll Ox BA75 G&C Coll Cam BA79 Leeds Univ PhD90. Westcott Ho Cam 77. **d** 80 **p** 81. C Potternewton *Ripon* 80-83; C Stanningley St Thos 84-87; Lect Leeds Univ 87-91; Teaching Fell Lanc Univ *Blackb* 91-95; Research Fell in Th Cheltenham and Glouc Coll of HE 95-96; NSM Leeds City *Ripon* 95-96; P-in-c Upper Ryedale *York* from 97; CME Officer Cleveland Adnry from 97. *The Rectory, Old Byland, York YO62 5LG* Tel (01439) 798355

SHANNON, Brian James. b 35. St Chad's Coll Dur BA59 DipTh61. **d** 61 **p** 62. C Palmers Green St Jo *Lon* 61-65; C Kenton 65-70; V Roxbourne St Andr 70-81; V Thorpe-le-Soken *Chelmsf* 81-91; V Gt Wakering w Foulness 91-99; rtd 99; Perm to Offic *Chelmsf* from 99. *154 Bournemouth Park Road, Southend-on-Sea SS2 5LT* Tel (01702) 464737

SHANNON, Canon Francis Thomas. b 16. TCD BA39 MA. CITC. **d** 39 **p** 40. C Rathdowney *C & O* 39-41; I Mothel 41-51; I Aghade w Ardoyne 51-61; I Carnew w Kilrush 61-91; Preb Ferns Cathl 71-91; Treas 80-81; Chan 81-85; Prec 85-91; rtd 91. *16 Clonattin, Gorey, Co Wexford, Irish Republic* Tel (00353) (55) 22284

SHANNON, The Ven Malcolm James Douglas. b 49. TCD BA72 MA75. CITC 75. **d** 75 **p** 76. C Clooney *D & R* 75-78; I Kilcolman w Kiltallagh, Killorglin, Knockane etc *L & K* from 78; Adn Ardfert and Aghadoe from 88; Treas Limerick Cathl from 88; Dir of Ords from 91. *Kilcolman Rectory, Miltown, Killarney, Co Kerry, Irish Republic* Tel (00353) (66) 976 7302 Mobile 086-2539906 Fax 976 7197

SHANNON, Canon Trevor Haslam. b 33. Selw Coll Cam BA57 MA61 Lon Univ BD69. Westcott Ho Cam 57. **d** 59 **p** 60. C Moss Side Ch *Man* 59-62; V Woolfold 62-66; Chapl Forest Sch Snaresbrook 66-80 and 87-88; V Gt Ilford St Marg *Chelmsf* 88-90; TR Gt Ilford St Clem and St Marg 90-96; V 96-99; RD Redbridge 90-95; Hon Can Chelmsf Cathl 93-99; rtd 99; Perm to Offic *Nor* from 00. *Honeysuckle Cottage, Clubbs Lane, Wells-next-the-Sea NR23 1DP* Tel (01328) 711409

SHAPLAND, David Edward. b 26. Cuddesdon Coll 51. **d** 53 **p** 54. C Cranbrook *Cant* 53-55; Chapl St Cath Coll Cam 55-61; R Fittleworth *Chich* 62-65; Warden Bede Ho Staplehurst 65-69; Warden Llanerchwen Trust 70-91; Lic to Offic *S & B* 70-79; Perm to Offic *Chich* 79-91; rtd 91. *21 Hayes End Manor, South Petherton TA13 5BE* Tel (01460) 242345

SHARE, David James. b 30. Sarum Th Coll 56. **d** 58 **p** 59. C Whipton *Ex* 58-63; Min Tiverton St Andr Statutory Distr 63-69; RD Tiverton 67-74; V Tiverton St Andr 69-79; P-in-c Ex St Thos 79-80; TR Ex St Thos and Em 80-83; V Woodbury 83-95; rtd 95; Corps Chapl ATC 94-02; Perm to Offic *Ex* from 95. *57 Coombeshead Road, Newton Abbot TQ12 1PZ* Tel (01626) 362516

SHARLAND, Canon Marilyn. b 40. City of Birm Coll CertEd61. Oak Hill Th Coll 84. **dss** 86 **d** 87 **p** 94. Barkingside St Laur *Chelmsf* 86-87; Hon Par Dn 87-88; Hon Par Dn Hucclecote *Glouc* 88-89; C Coney Hill 89-98; P-in-c Tuffley 98-99; V from 99; Hon Can Glouc Cathl from 02. *St Barnabas' Vicarage, 200 Reservoir Road, Tuffley, Gloucester GL4 9SB* Tel (01452) 306535 Fax 535998 E-mail reverend.marilyn@euphony.net

SHARMAN, Hilary John. b 32. Leeds Univ BA58. Coll of Resurr Mirfield 58. **d** 60 **p** 61. C Hertford St Andr *St Alb* 60-64; C Harpenden St Nic 64-72; V High Cross from 72; V Thundridge from 72. *7 Ducketts Wood, Thundridge, Ware SG12 0SR* Tel (01920) 465561

SHARP, Alfred James Frederick. b 30. Oak Hill Th Coll 62. **d** 64 **p** 65. C Hanley Road St Sav w St Paul *Lon* 64-68; P-in-c Leverton *Linc* 68-84; Chapl Pilgrim Hosp Boston 76-84; P-in-c Bennington w Leverton *Linc* 84; V Ch Broughton w Boylestone amd Sutton on the Hill *Derby* 84-89; R Ch Broughton w Barton Blount, Boylestone etc 89-94; rtd 94. *14 Edgefield, Weston, Spalding PE12 6RQ* Tel (01406) 370376

SHARP, Andrew Timothy. b 58. K Alfred's Coll Win BA79. Wycliffe Hall Ox 82. **d** 85 **p** 86. C Scarborough St Mary w Ch Ch and H Apostles *York* 85-89; C Luton St Fran *St Alb* 89-90; V 90-98; P-in-c Guernsey St Jo *Win* 98-01; V from 01; Vice-Dean Guernsey from 01. *St John's Vicarage, Les Amballes, St Peter Port, Guernsey GY1 1WY* Tel (01481) 720879 Fax as telephone

SHARP, Mrs Barbara Elaine. b 52. Open Univ BA84. Ripon Coll Cuddesdon 01. **d** 03. C Timperley *Ches* from 03. *57 Heyes Lane, Timperley, Altrincham WA15 6DZ* Tel 0161-905 1994

SHARP, Bernard Harold. b 40. Linc Th Coll 64. **d** 67 **p** 68. C Newton Aycliffe *Dur* 67-69; C Leam Lane CD 69-71; Malawi 72-75; P-in-c Blakenall Heath *Lich* 75-77; TV Gateshead *Dur* 77-79; C Warmsworth *Sheff* 84; C Caerau w Ely *Llan* 85-92; V Cwmbach from 92. *The Vicarage, Bridge Road, Cwmbach, Aberdare CF44 0LS* Tel (01685) 878674

SHARP, Brian Phillip. b 48. Cant Sch of Min 85. **d** 88 **p** 89. C S Ashford Ch Ch *Cant* 88-92; C St Laur in Thanet 92-96; V Margate St Jo from 96. *The Vicarage, 24 St Peter's Road, Margate CT9 1TH* Tel (01843) 230766 E-mail brian.stjohn@cwcom.net

SHARP, Canon David Malcolm. b 33. Hertf Coll Ox BA56 MA59. Cuddesdon Coll 56. **d** 58 **p** 59. C Bris St Mary Redcliffe w Temple *Bris* 58-65; V Henleaze 65-75; V Nor St Pet Mancroft *Nor* 75-82; R Nor St Pet Mancroft w St Jo Maddermarket 82-98; Hon Can Nor Cathl 86-98; Dioc Rural Contact from 91; rtd 98; Perm to Offic *Nor* from 98. *The Pines, Field Lane, Fakenham NR21 9QX* Tel (01328) 864121

SHARP (née BROWN), Mrs Jane Madeline. b 54. **d** 97 **p** 98. C Aylestone St Andr w St Jas *Leic* 97-00; Hon C Knighton St Mary Magd from 00. *10 St Mary's Road, Leicester LE2 1XA* Tel 0116-270 6002 E-mail jbrown@leicester.anglican.org

SHARP, Mrs Janice Anne. b 54. Aston Tr Scheme 91 N Ord Course 93. **d** 96 **p** 97. C Skipton H Trin *Bradf* 96-00; V Buttershaw St Paul 00-02; Chapl Hull and E Yorks Hosps NHS Trust from 02. *The Hull Royal Infirmary, Anlaby Road, Hull HU3 2JZ* Tel (01482) 328541

SHARP, Nicholas Leonard. b 64. Grey Coll Dur BA85. St Jo Coll Nottm Dip Th Studies 94 MA95. **d** 95 **p** 96. C Oakwood St Thos *Lon* 95-99; TV N Farnborough *Guildf* from 99; Chapl Farnborough Sixth Form Coll from 01. *The Vicarage, 45 Sand Hill, Farnborough GU14 8ER* Tel (01252) 543789 E-mail nick@sharp64.freeserve.co.uk

SHARP, Canon Reuben Thomas George (Tom). b 27. ALCD57. **d** 57 **p** 58. C Pudsey St Lawr *Bradf* 57-60; V Cononley w Bradley 60-63; Dioc Youth Chapl 60-63; Dioc Youth Officer *Wakef* 63-68; V Dewsbury All SS 68-84; RD Dewsbury 68-90; Hon Can Wakef Cathl 76-97; TR Dewsbury 84-90; V Cawthorne 90-97; rtd 97; Perm to Offic *Man* from 99. *1 St Barnabas Drive, Littleborough OL15 8EJ* Tel (01706) 379298

SHARP, Preb Robert. b 36. FLCM58. St Aid Birkenhead 64. **d** 67 **p** 68. C Shipley St Paul *Bradf* 67-70; C-in-c Thwaites Brow CD 70-74; V Thwaites Brow 74-77; P-in-c Alberbury w Cardeston *Heref* 77-78; V 78-87; V Ford 77-87; V Claverley w Tuckhill 87-97; RD Bridgnorth 89-96; Preb Heref Cathl 91-97; rtd 97; Perm to Offic *Heref* 97-99 and from 01; C Stoke Lacy, Moreton Jeffries w Much Cowarne etc 99-00. *62 Biddulph Way, Ledbury HR8 2HN* Tel (01531) 631972

SHARP, Miss Sarah Elizabeth. b 67. Bp Otter Coll Chich BA89 Anglia Poly Univ MA00 Coll of Ripon & York St Jo PGCE90. Westcott Ho Cam 98. **d** 00 **p** 01. C Ross *Heref* from 00; R Lower Windrush *Ox* from 03. *The Rectory, Main Road, Stanton Harcourt, Witney OX29 5RP* Tel (01865) 880249 E-mail sesharp@care4free.net

SHARPE, Canon Alan Brian. b 39. Lich Th Coll 64. **d** 67 **p** 68. C Croydon Woodside *Cant* 67-70; C Portsea St Mary *Portsm* 70-75; V Sheerness H Trin w St Paul *Cant* 75-83; V Hove St Patr w Ch Ch and St Andr *Chich* 83-90; V Hove St Patr from 90; Can and Preb Chich Cathl from 93. *St Patrick's Vicarage, 30 Cambridge Road, Hove BN3 1DF* Tel (01273) 327242

SHARPE, Anthony Mark. b 67. Leeds Univ BA01. Coll of Resurr Mirfield 99. **d** 01 **p** 02. C Acomb Moor *York* 01-02; C Norton juxta Malton 02-03; C W Buckrose from 03. *Inn Farmhouse, Settrington, Malton YO17 8NP* Tel (01944) 768494

SHARPE, Canon Bruce Warrington. b 41. JP88. DMS(Ed)85 MCM185. Ely Th Coll 62 St Steph Ho Ox 64. **d** 65 **p** 66. C Streatham St Pet *S'wark* 65-67; St Lucia 67-68; Hon C Leic St Matt and St Geo *Leic* 68-69; Hon C Catford St Laur *S'wark* 69-70; Hon C Deptford St Paul 70-75; Hon C Lamorbey H Redeemer *Roch* 76-83; Hon C Sidcup St Andr 88-99; Perm to Offic *Roch* 83-88 and 99-01; *Lon* from 97; *S'wark* from 98; Hon C Bickley from 01; Hon Can Windward Is from 01. *72 Faraday Avenue, Sidcup DA14 4JF* Tel (020) 8300 0695 or 8346 3522 E-mail canonbruce1@aol.com

SHARPE, Cecil Frederick. b 23. Edin Th Coll 52. **d** 54 **p** 55. C Falkirk *Edin* 54-56; C Kings Norton *Birm* 56-58; V Withall 58-80; Perm to Offic from 80; rtd 88. *35 Shirley Park Road, Shirley, Solihull B90 2BZ* Tel (0121) 744 6905

SHARPE, David Francis. b 32. Ex Coll Ox BA56 MA59. St Steph Ho Ox 57. **d** 60 **p** 61. C Hunslet St Mary and Stourton *Ripon* 60-63; C Notting Hill St Jo *Lon* 63-68; V Haggerston St Mary w St Chad 68-78; P-in-c Haggerston St Aug w St Steph 73-78; V Haggerston St Chad 78-83; V Mill Hill St Mich 83-98; rtd 98; Chapl St Raphaël *Eur* 98-02. *15 Grahame Park Way, London NW7 2LA* Tel (020) 8959 0429 E-mail davidsharpe@waitrose.com

SHARPE, Derek Martin Brereton (Pip). b 29. Birkbeck Coll Lon BA60. NEOC 90. **d** 90 **p** 91. NSM Scarborough St Luke *York* 90-92; Asst Chapl Scarborough Distr Hosp 90-92; P-in-c Sherburn and W and E Heslerton w Yedingham *York* 92-99; Hon C Buckrose Carrs 99; rtd 99; Perm to Offic *York* from 00. *Byland Lodge, 68A Low Moorgate, Rillington, Malton YO17 8JW* Tel (01944) 759063

SHARPE, Gerard John. b 23. Westcott Ho Cam. **d** 64 **p** 65. C Thetford St Cuth w H Trin *Nor* 64-70; V Holme *Ely* 70-76; R Conington 70-76; R Glatton 74-93; V Holme w Conington 76-93; RD Yaxley 82-88; rtd 93; Perm to Offic *Ely* 93-00. *24 St Margaret's Road, Girton, Cambridge CB3 0LT* Tel (01223) 574246

SHARPE, Miss Joan Valerie. b 33. EMMTC 73. **dss** 84 **d** 88 **p** 94. Hon Par Dn Warsop *S'well* 88-94; Hon C 94-98; rtd 98. *1 Forest Court, Eakring Road, Mansfield NG18 3DP* Tel (01623) 424051

SHARPE, John Brebber (Brother Mark). b 14. **d** 85. CSWG from 82; Lic to Offic *Chich* from 85. *The Monastery, 23 Cambridge Road, Hove BN3 1DE* Tel (01273) 726698

SHARPE, John Edward. b 50. Dur Univ BSc72 St Jo Coll Dur DipTh75. **d** 76 **p** 77. C Woodford Wells *Chelmsf* 76-79; C Ealing St Mary *Lon* 79-83; Min Walsall St Martin *Lich* 83-87; TV Walsall 87-96; R Glenfield *Leic* from 96. *The Rectory, Main Street, Glenfield, Leicester LE3 8DG* Tel 0116-287 1604 E-mail jesharpe@leicester.anglican.org

SHARPE, Canon John Leslie. b 33. Open Univ BA75 Birm Univ DPS72 MInstGA89. Kelham Th Coll 54. **d** 58 **p** 59. C Charlton St Luke w St Paul *S'wark* 58-61; Papua New Guinea 62-70; Adn N Distr 68-70; C-in-c Southampton SS Pet and Paul w All SS *Win* 71-73; TV Southampton (City Cen) 73-75; Chapl SW Hants Psychiatric Services 75-93; Chapl Knowle Hosp Fareham 75-93; Hon Can Portsm Cathl *Portsm* 86-93; rtd 93; Perm to Offic *Sarum* from 98. *Clare Cottage, 23 West Dean, Salisbury SP5 1JB* Tel (01794) 340028 Fax 342256 E-mail john@jlsharpe.freeserve.co.uk

SHARPE, The Ven Kenneth William. b 40. Univ of Wales (Lamp) BA61. Sarum Th Coll 61. **d** 63 **p** 64. C Hubberston *St D* 63-71; TV Cwmbran *Mon* 71-74; Dioc Children's Adv 72-82; Dioc Youth Chapl 74-82; V Dingestow and Llangovan w Penyclawdd and Tregaer 74-82; V Newport St Mark 82-97; Chapl Alltyryn Hosp Gwent 83-97; RD Newport *Mon* 93-97; Can St Woolos Cathl from 94; Adn Newport from 97. *The Archdeaconry, 93 Stow Hill, Newport NP20 4EA* Tel (01633) 215012

SHARPE, Mrs Margaret Theresa. b 48. Man Univ BEd70 Dur Univ DipTh74. Cranmer Hall Dur 72 WMMTC 90. **d** 91 **p** 94. C W Bromwich H Trin *Lich* 91-96; Asst Chapl Glenfield Hosp NHS Trust Leic 96-99; Chapl 99-00; Chapl Univ Hosps Leic NHS Trust from 00. *The Rectory, Main Street, Glenfield, Leicester LE3 8DG, or Chaplains' Department, Glenfield Hospital, Groby Road, Leicester LE3 9QP* Tel 0116-287 1604 *or* 256 3413 E-mail mtsharpe@leicester.anglican.org

SHARPE, Mark. *See* SHARPE, Anthony Mark

SHARPE, Miss Mary. b 31. CQSW71. Dalton Ho Bris 58. **dss** 78 **d** 87 **p** 94. Upton (Overchurch) *Ches* 78-83; Harlescott *Lich* 83-84; New Brighton All SS *Ches* 85-89; Par Dn 87-89; rtd 89; Perm to Offic *Ches* from 89. *13 Manor Close, Neston CH64 6TE*

SHARPE, Mrs Mary Primrose. b 22. Coll of St Matthias Bris CertEd. Gilmore Ho CertRK51 CMS Tr Coll Chislehurst. **dss** 81 **d** 87. Coley *Wakef* 81-87; Hon Par Dn 87-89; rtd 89; Perm to Offic *Bradf* 89-99. *54 Bradford Road, Menston, Ilkley LS29 6BX* Tel (01943) 877710

SHARPE, Peter Richard. b 55. Salford Univ BSc76 ACIB81. STETS 98. **d** 01 **p** 02. C Ex St Jas *Ex* from 01. *17 Culverland Close, Exeter EX4 6HR* Tel (01392) 412575 Mobile 0767-251136

SHARPE, Pip. *See* SHARPE, Derek Martin Brereton

SHARPE, Richard Gordon. b 48. Birm Univ BA69. St Jo Coll Nottm BA74. **d** 75 **p** 76. C Hinckley H Trin *Leic* 75-78; C Kingston upon Hull H Trin *York* 78-85; Chapl Marston Green Hosp Birm 85-88; Chapl Chelmsley Hosp Birm 86-88; TV Chelmsley Wood *Birm* 85-88; P-in-c Dosthill 88-93; V 93-97; R Desford and Peckleton w Tooley *Leic* from 97. *The Rectory, 27 Church Lane, Desford, Leicester LE9 9GD* Tel (01455) 822276 E-mail sharpeblackhorse@aol.com

SHARPE, Canon Roger. b 35. TCD BA60 MA63. Qu Coll Birm 60. **d** 62 **p** 63. C Stockton H Trin *Dur* 62-64; C Oakdale St Geo *Sarum* 64-68; V Redlynch and Morgan's Vale 68-86; RD Alderbury 82-86; V Warminster St Denys 86-88; R Upton Scudamore 86-88; V Horningsham 86-88; R Warminster St Denys, Upton Scudamore etc 88-95; Can and Preb Sarum Cathl 89-00; RD Heytesbury 89-95; Chmn Dioc Assn for Deaf from 91; P-in-c Corsley 92-95; TR Cley Hill Warminster 95-00; rtd 00; Perm to Offic *Sarum* from 01. *Woodside, Bugmore Lane, East Grimstead SP5 3SA* Tel (01722) 712753

SHARPE, Tony Ernest Charles. b 34. Dur Univ BA55. EAMTC 90. **d** 93 **p** 94. NSM Leigh-on-Sea St Jas *Chelmsf* 93-96; NSM Thorpe Bay 96-00; NSM Golden Cap Team *Sarum* from 00. *The Vicarage, Hawkchurch, Axminster EX13 5XB* Tel (01297) 678337

SHARPLES, Canon Alfred Cyril. b 09. Man Univ BA33. Linc Th Coll 33. **d** 35 **p** 36. C Rochdale *Man* 35-39; C Ashton St Mich 39-42; R Cheetham St Mark 42-46; V Tonge w Alkrington 46-51; V Hope St Jas 51-76; Hon Can Man Cathl 74-76; rtd 76; Perm to Offic *Ches* and *Man* from 77. *30 Greenbank Drive, Bollington, Macclesfield SK10 5LW* Tel 0161-207 5073

SHARPLES, David. b 41. Linc Th Coll 71. **d** 73 **p** 74. C Reddish *Man* 73-75; C Prestwich St Mary 76-78; V Ashton St Jas 78-86; V Hope St Jas from 86. *Hope Vicarage, Vicarage Close, Pendleton, Salford M6 8EJ* Tel 0161-789 3303

SHARPLES, David John. b 58. Lon Univ BD81 AKC81. Coll of Resurr Mirfield. **d** 82 **p** 83. C Prestwich St Mary *Man* 82-87; V Royton St Anne 87-02; AD Tandle 94-02; Dir of Ords from 02. *St Thomas's New Vicarage, Church Street, Milnrow, Rochdale OL16 3QS* Tel (01706) 291539 *or* 0161-708 9366 Fax 0161-792 6826 E-mail ddo@bishopscourt.manchester.anglican.org

SHARPLES, Derek. b 35. SS Paul & Mary Coll Cheltenham CertEd57 Liv Univ DipEd63 Man Univ MEd66 Bath Univ PhD72 Open Univ BA79 FCollP86. WMMTC 83. **d** 86 **p** 87. NSM Malvern H Trin and St Jas *Worc* 86-90; C St Jo in Bedwardine 90-92; R Belbroughton w Fairfield and Clent 92-00; rtd 00; Perm to Offic *Worc* from 00. *Witton, 16 Moorlands Road, Malvern WR14 1VA* Tel (01684) 575742 E-mail witton@clara.co.uk

SHARPLES, Canon John Charles. b 29. St Jo Coll York TCert48 Lon Univ BSc55. St Deiniol's Hawarden 87. **d** 87 **p** 88. Hon C Wigan St Mich *Liv* 87-89; P-in-c New Springs 89-96; Hon Can Liv Cathl 97; rtd 97; Perm to Offic *Liv* from 97. *New Springs Vicarage, 7 Lealholme Avenue, Wigan WN2 1EH* Tel (01942) 243071

SHARPLES, Ms Susan Margaret. b 58. SRN82 Worc Coll of Educn BA89. WMMTC 91. **d** 94 **p** 95. C Worc SE *Worc* 94-97; P-in-c Elmley Castle w Bricklehampton and Combertons 97-01; USA from 01. *Address temp unknown*

SHARPLEY, The Ven Roger Ernest Dion. b 28. Ch Ch Ox BA52 MA56. St Steph Ho Ox 52. **d** 54 **p** 55. C Southwick St Columba *Dur* 54-60; V Middlesbrough All SS *York* 60-81; P-in-c Middlesbrough St Hilda w St Pet 64-72; RD Middlesbrough 70-81; Can and Preb York Minster 74-81; P-in-c Middlesbrough St Aid 79; V 79-81; V St Andr Holborn *Lon* 81-92; Adn Hackney 81-92; rtd 92; Perm to Offic *Dur* from 92; Chapl Grey Coll Dur 96-01. *2 Hill Meadows, High Shincliffe, Durham DH1 2PE* Tel 0191-386 1908

SHAVE, Norman Rossen. b 60. G&C Coll Cam BA82 MA95 Newc Univ MB, BS85 MRCGP90. Cranmer Hall Dur 98. **d** 00

p 01. C Preston on Tees *Dur* from 00. *5 The Close, Long Newton, Stockton-on-Tees TS21 1DW* Tel (01642) 570878

SHAW, Alan. b 24. Man Univ BSc44 MSc48 PhD51. Ely Th Coll 55. **d** 57 **p** 58. C Orford St Marg *Liv* 57-59; C Bury St Mary *Man* 59-61; Perm to Offic *Liv* 61-71; V Beckermet St Jo *Carl* 71-76; V Lt Leigh and Lower Whitley *Ches* 76-80; V Latchford Ch Ch 80-91; rtd 91; Perm to Offic *Ches* and *Liv* from 91. *57 Dudlow Green Road, Appleton, Warrington WA4 5EQ* Tel (01925) 269402

SHAW, Alan Taylor. b 52. Sarum & Wells Th Coll 88. **d** 90 **p** 91. C Beeston *Ripon* 90-93; C Stanningley St Thos 93-96; TV Seacroft 96-98; V Ryhill *Wakef* 98-02; rtd 03. *65 Hollingthorpe Avenue, Hall Green, Wakefield WF4 3NP*

SHAW, Alan Walter. b 41. TCD BA63 BAI63 Chu Coll Cam MSc66. **d** 94 **p** 95. NSM Drumcliffe w Kilnasoolagh *L & K* 94-97; NSM Kenmare w Sneem, Waterville etc from 97. *St Patrick's Rectory, Kenmare, Co Kerry, Irish Republic* Tel (00353) (64) 41121 Fax as telephone E-mail shawa@eircom.net *or* kenmare@ardfert.anglican.org

SHAW, Canon Alexander Martin. b 44. AKC67. **d** 68 **p** 69. C Glas St Oswald *Glas* 68-70; C Edin Old St Paul *Edin* 70-75; Chapl K Coll Cam 75-77; C St Marylebone All SS *Lon* 77-78; R Dunoon *Arg* 78-81; Succ Ex Cathl *Ex* 81-83; Dioc Miss and Ecum Officer 83-89; TV Cen Ex 83-87; Can Res St E Cathl *St E* from 89; Prec from 96. *1 Abbey Precincts, Bury St Edmunds IP33 1RS* Tel (01284) 761982 Mobile 07801-549615 Fax (01284) 768655 E-mail alexandermartin.shaw@virgin.net

SHAW, Mrs Alison Barbara. b 55. Open Univ BA92. SW Minl Tr Course 98. **d** 01 **p** 02. NSM St Breoke and Egloshayle *Truro* 01-03; C Bodmin w Lanhydrock and Lanivet from 03. *The Vicarage, Rectory Road, Lanivet, Bodmin PL30 5HG* Tel (01208) 831743 E-mail alishaw2001@yahoo.co.uk

SHAW, Andrew Jonathan. b 50. Wycliffe Hall Ox 85. **d** 87 **p** 88. C Witton w Brundall and Braydeston *Nor* 87-89; C Brundall w Braydeston and Postwick 89-90; C Grayswood *Guildf* 90-91; P-in-c 91-99; Chapl RN Sch Haslemere 90-96; V Hendon St Paul Mill Hill *Lon* from 99. *St Paul's Vicarage, Hammers Lane, London NW7 4EA* Tel (020) 8959 1856 *or* 8906 3793

SHAW, Ms Anne Lesley. b 50. SRN SCM ONC. Linc Th Coll 77. **dss** 80 **d** 87 **p** 94. Camberwell St Luke *S'wark* 80-85; Chapl Asst Lon Hosp (Whitechapel) 85-90; Chapl Lewisham Hosp 90-94; Chapl Hither Green Hosp 90-94; Chapl Sydenham Childrens' Hosp 90-94; Chapl Lewisham Hosp NHS Trust from 94. *The Chaplain's Office, University Hospital Lewisham, High Street, London SE13 6LH* Tel (020) 8333 3299 *or* 8333 3000 E-mail annie.shaw@uhl.nhs.uk

SHAW, Anne Patricia Leslie. b 39. MB, BS63 DA68 MRCS63 LRCP63. Qu Coll Birm 79. **dss** 81 **d** 87 **p** 94. Pinner *Lon* 81-84; Rickmansworth *St Alb* 84-87; NSM from 87. *37 Sandy Lodge Road, Moor Park, Rickmansworth WD3 1LP* Tel (01923) 827663 E-mail donanne.shaw@virginnet.co.uk

SHAW, Anthony Keeble. b 36. K Alfred's Coll Win CertEd60 Birkbeck Coll Lon CPsychol98. SW Minl Tr Course 78. **d** 81 **p** 82. Hd Teacher Wolborough C of E Primary Sch 73-87; NSM E Teignmouth *Ex* 81-83; NSM Highweek and Teigngrace 83-87; Sub Chapl HM Pris Channings Wood 85-87; C Southbourne St Kath *Win* 87-89; Teaching 89-96; NSM Regent's Park St Mark *Lon* 93-96; P-in-c Winthorpe and Langford w Holme *S'well* 96-01; Dioc Chief Insp of Schs 96-01; rtd 01; Perm to Offic *Win* from 01. *Manlea Cottage, Centre Lane, Everton, Lymington SO41 0JP* Tel (01590) 645451

SHAW, Clive Ronald. b 54. UEA BA75 Hatf Coll Dur PGCE76. Carl and Blackb Dioc Tr Inst 99. **d** 02. C Westfield St Mary *Carl* from 02. *49 Sarsfield Road, Workington CA14 5DA* Tel (01900) 64976 E-mail c.shaw@rowan1.fslife.co.uk

SHAW, Colin Clement Gordon. b 39. RMN60 Thoracic Nursing Cert 62 DPS72. Linc Th Coll 65. **d** 67 **p** 68. C Tettenhall Regis *Lich* 67-70; C Tile Cross *Birm* 70-72; V Edstaston *Lich* 72-75; V Whixall 72-75; Chapl Stoke Mandeville Hosp and St Jo Hosp 75-90; Manor Ho Hosp and Tindal Gen Hosp Aylesbury 75-90; R Bledlow w Saunderton and Horsenden *Ox* 90-96; rtd 96. *5 Wyre Close, Haddenham, Aylesbury HP17 8AU* Tel (01844) 292741 E-mail ccg.shaw@btinternet.com

SHAW, Colin Martin. b 21. Oak Hill Th Coll 68. **d** 69 **p** 70. C Halliwell St Pet *Man* 69-72; V Tonge Fold 72-78; V Gresley *Derby* 78-82; V Gt Marsden *Blackb* 82-87; rtd 87; Perm to Offic *Ely* from 87. *60 Popes Lane, Warboys, Huntingdon PE17 2RN* Tel (01487) 822246

SHAW, David George. b 40. Lon Univ BD64. Tyndale Hall Bris 58. **d** 65 **p** 66. C Kirkdale St Lawr *Liv* 65-68; C Bebington *Ches* 68-70; V Swadlincote *Derby* 70-75; R Eyam from 75. *The Rectory, Eyam, Hope Valley S32 5QH* Tel (01433) 630821 Fax 630930 E-mail rector@eyamchurch.org

SHAW, David Michael. b 61. Univ Coll Dur BA83 Bris Univ BA97. Trin Coll Bris DipHE93. **d** 93 **p** 94. C Wotton-under-Edge w Ozleworth and N Nibley *Glouc* 93-97; P-in-c Jersey St Clem *Win* 97-98; R from 98. *The Rectory, La rue du Presbytere, St Clement, Jersey JE2 6RB* Tel (01534) 851992 E-mail st.clement@jerseymail.co.uk

SHAW, David Parlane. b 32. CITC. **d** 69 **p** 70. Bp's C Lower w Upper Langfield *D & R* 69-75; R Chedburgh w Depden and Rede *St E* 75-78; R Chedburgh w Depden, Rede and Hawkedon 79-82; R Desford *Leic* 82-83; R Desford and Peckleton w Tooley 84-91; P-in-c Ramsden Crays w Ramsden Bellhouse *Chelmsf* 91-95; rtd 95; Perm to Offic *Leic* from 95. *9 Hambleton Close, Leicester Forest East, Leicester LE3 3NA* Tel 0116-224 6507
SHAW, David Thomas. b 45. Open Univ BA78. WMMTC 87. **d** 90 **p** 91. C Sheldon *Birm* 90-93; R Chelmsley Wood 93-02; TR Broughton Astley and Croft w Stoney Stanton *Leic* from 02. *The Rectory, St Mary's Close, Broughton Astley, Leicester LE9 6ES* Tel (01455) 283150
SHAW, Denis Alfred Arthur. b 24. Wells Th Coll 64. **d** 65 **p** 66. C Redditch St Steph *Worc* 65-70; R Addingham *Bradf* 70-92; rtd 92; Perm to Offic *Bradf* from 92. *67 Crowther Avenue, Calverley, Pudsey LS28 5SA* Tel (0124) 611746
SHAW, Ernest Ronald. b 16. K Coll Lon BA38. Chich Th Coll 72. **d** 72 **p** 73. Chapl Cov Cathl *Cov* 72-78; Perm to Offic *Sarum* 79-80; C Semley and Sedgehill 80-85; rtd 85; Perm to Offic *Sarum* from 85. *Fairmead, Church Hill, Stour Row, Shaftesbury SP7 0QW* Tel (01747) 838350
SHAW, Mrs Felicity Mary. b 46. UEA BSc67 MSc68 Liv Inst of Educn DipRE87. N Ord Course 88. **d** 91 **p** 94. Par Dn Benchill *Man* 91-94; C 94-95; TV E Farnworth and Kearsley 95-98; TR from 98. *The Rectory, 55 Church Street, Farnworth, Bolton BL4 8AQ* Tel (01204) 572819 E-mail rev.flissshaw@tesco.net
SHAW, Frederick Hugh. b 16. CChem MRSC Dur Univ BSc49 MSc66. EMMTC 73. **d** 76 **p** 77. Hon C Wingerworth *Derby* 76-96; Perm to Offic from 96. *1 Frances Drive, Wingerworth, Chesterfield S42 6SJ* Tel (01246) 278321
SHAW, Gary Robert. b 59. **d** 85 **p** 86. C Dundonald *D & D* 85-87; I Tullaniskin w Clonoe *Arm* 87-94; Bp's C Stoneyford *Conn* 94-99; I Belfast St Nic 99-00; Chapl R Group of Hosps Health and Soc Services Trust 94-00. *64 Kilwarlin Crescent, Belfast BT8 4EN* Tel (028) 9049 3024
SHAW, Canon Geoffrey Norman. b 26. Jes Coll Ox MA50. Wycliffe Hall Ox 49. **d** 51 **p** 52. C Rushden *Pet* 51-54; C Woking Ch Ch *Guildf* 54-59; V Woking St Paul 59-62; R St Leonards St Leon *Chich* 62-68; Lic to Offic *Sheff* 68-72; Vice-Prin and Lect Oak Hill Th Coll 72-79; Prin Wycliffe Hall Ox 79-88; Hon Can Ch Ch *Ox* 86-88; rtd 88; Lic to Offic *Nor* 88-91. *15A West Street, Kingham, Chipping Norton OX7 6YF* Tel (01608) 658006
SHAW, Gerald Oliver. b 32. K Coll Lon 56. **d** 60 **p** 61. C Burnley St Cuth *Blackb* 60-62; C Heysham 62-65; C-in-c Oswaldtwistle All SS CD 65-66; V Oswaldtwistle All SS 66-69; Chapl Leavesden Hosp Abbots Langley 69-75; Chapl Broadmoor Hosp Crowthorne 75-88; C Easthampstead *Ox* 88-92; P-in-c Beech Hill, Grazeley and Spencers Wood 92-97; rtd 97; Lic to Offic *Ox* from 99. *1 Mortimer House Cottage, Mortimer Lane, Mortimer, Reading RG7 3PR* Tel 0118-933 3660
SHAW, Graham. b 44. Worc Coll Ox BA65. Cuddesdon Coll. **d** 69 **p** 70. C Esher *Guildf* 69-73; R Winford *B & W* 73-78; Chapl Ex Coll Ox 78-85; R Farnborough *Roch* 88-95. *2 Herons Place, Isleworth TW7 7BE* Tel (020) 8569 7839
SHAW, Canon Grahame David. b 44. Lich Th Coll 65. **d** 68 **p** 69. C Grange St Andr *Ches* 68-73; TV E Runcorn w Halton 73-74; TV Thamesmead *S'wark* 74-79; V Newington St Paul from 79; S'wark Adnry Ecum Officer from 90; RD S'wark and Newington 96-02; Hon Can S'wark Cathl from 99. *The Vicarage, Lorrimore Square, London SE17 3QU* Tel (020) 7735 2947 *or* 7735 8815 E-mail grahame.shaw@talk21.com
SHAW, Mrs Irene. b 45. Gilmore Course 80 NEOC 82. **dss** 83 **d** 87 **p** 94. Elloughton and Brough w Brantingham *York* 83-86; Westborough *Guildf* 86-87; C 87-88; C Shottermill 88-91; C Lamorbey H Redeemer *Roch* 91-97; V Bellavista All SS 97-02; P-in-c S Crosland *Wakef* 02-03; P-in-c Rashcliffe and Lockwood 02-03; TV Em TM from 03. *The Vicarage, 42 Beaumont Park Road, Huddersfield HD4 5JS* Tel (01484) 431163
SHAW, Jane Alison. b 63. Ox Univ BA85 MA91 Harvard Div Sch MDiv88 Univ of California Berkeley PhD94. St Alb and Ox Min Course 96. **d** 97 **p** 98. Fell Regent's Park Coll Ox 94-01; Dean 98-01; NSM Ox St Mary V w St Cross and St Pet *Ox* from 97; Hon Cathl Chapl Ch Ch Ox from 00; Fell, Chapl and Dean of Div New Coll Ox from 01. *New College, Oxford OX1 3BN* Tel (01865) 557289 E-mail jane.shaw@theology.oxford.ac.uk
SHAW, Miss Jane Elizabeth. b 47. New Hall Cam BA68 MA72 Brunel Univ MPhil79 DipHSM71. NEOC 98. **d** 01 **p** 02. NSM Moor Allerton *Ripon* from 01. *101 St Anne's Road, Leeds LS6 3NZ* Tel 0113-275 8978 Fax 233 6997 E-mail j.e.shaw@leeds.ac.uk
SHAW, Mrs Jane Louise Claridge. b 66. Birm Poly BA87. WMMTC 00. **d** 03. C Longbridge *Birm* from 03. *6 Butter Walk, Birmingham B38 8JQ* Tel 07811-886698 (mobile)
SHAW, Mrs Janet Elaine. b 53. EMMTC 94. **d** 97 **p** 98. C Cleveleys *Blackb* 97-01; P-in-c Blackpool St Paul 01-03; V from 03. *St Paul's Vicarage, 253 Warbreck Hill Road, Blackpool FY2 0SP* Tel (01253) 350007 E-mail mail@vicstp.fsnet.co.uk
SHAW, John Boyde. b 52. Nottm Univ BA00. St Jo Coll Nottm. **d** 00 **p** 01. C Gorleston St Andr *Nor* from 00. *2 Elmgrove Road, Gorleston, Great Yarmouth NR31 7PP* Tel (01493) 659410

SHAW, John Richard Astley. b 24. St Jo Coll Dur 46. ACT ThL53. **d** 51 **p** 53. Australia 51-55; C Braunstone *Leic* 55-57; R Rearsby w Ratcliffe on the Wreake 57-65; R Guernsey St Marguerite de la Foret *Win* 65-90; rtd 90; Perm to Offic *Win* from 90. *St Antony, Les Cornus, St Martin, Guernsey GY4 6PZ* Tel (01481) 237097
SHAW, Jonathan. *See* SHAW, Andrew Jonathan
SHAW, Kenneth James. b 36. St Jo Coll Nottm 85 Edin Th Coll 88. **d** 87 **p** 89. NSM Troon *Glas* 87-89; C Glas St Mary 89-90; R Lenzie 90-01; Warden of Readers 96-01; rtd 01; Hon C Glas St Mary *Glas* from 02. *19 Mailerbeg Gardens, Moodiesburn, Glasgow G69 0JP* Tel (01236) 873987 E-mail ken@kjshaw.fsnet.co.uk
SHAW, Malcolm. b 46. Trin Coll Bris. **d** 01 **p** 02. C Bolsover *Derby* from 01. *114 Horsehead Lane, Bolsover, Chesterfield S44 6XH* Tel (01246) 828296 Mobile 07713-624005 Fax (01246) 827434 E-mail malshw@aol.com
SHAW, Mrs Margaret Ann. b 58. Bp Otter Coll Chich BA80 SS Paul & Mary Coll Cheltenham PGCE81. EAMTC 00. **d** 03. C Langdon Hills *Chelmsf* from 03. *17 Oakham Close, Langdon Hills, Basildon SS16 6NX* E-mail sh.ma@btinternet.com
SHAW, Michael Howard. b 38. Leeds Univ BSc61 Kent Univ DipTh90. Linc Th Coll 64. **d** 66 **p** 67. C W Hartlepool St Paul *Dur* 66-68; Asst Master Stockbridge Co Sec Sch 68; Totton Coll 69; Gravesend Boys' Gr Sch 70-72; Maidstone Gr Sch 72-94; Perm to Offic *Cant* and *Roch* from 70; rtd 03. *2 Bredgar Close, Maidstone ME14 5NG* Tel (01622) 673415
SHAW, Neil Graham. b 61. St Jo Coll Nottm 91. **d** 94 **p** 95. C Leamington Priors St Paul *Cov* 91-95; TV Bestwood *S'well* 95-99; Chapl HM YOI Thorn Cross from 99. *HM Young Offender Institute, Arley Road, Appleton, Warrington WA4 4RL* Tel (01925) 605085 Fax 262153
SHAW, Norman. b 33. Cranmer Hall Dur. **d** 82 **p** 83. C Beamish *Dur* 82-84; P-in-c Craghead 84-89; C Cleadon 88-89; rtd 98. *3 St Mary's Drive, Sherburn, Durham DH6 1RL* Tel 0191-372 2540 E-mail normandcon@aol.com
SHAW, Peter Haslewood. b 17. Pemb Coll Cam BA39 MA65. Worc Ord Coll 65. **d** 67 **p** 68. C S Kensington St Jude *Lon* 67-69; V Alderney *Win* 69-78; V Disley *Ches* 78-82; rtd 82; Chapl Athens w Kifissia, Patras and Corfu *Eur* 82-85; Hon C Las Palmas 84-85; Hon C Breamore *Win* 85-89. *Manor Cottage, Church Road, Greatworth, Banbury OX17 2DU* Tel (01295) 712102
SHAW, Ralph. b 38. Man Univ MEd70. Sarum & Wells Th Coll 78. **d** 80 **p** 81. C Consett *Dur* 80-84; P-in-c Tanfield 84-88; V 88-97; R S Shields St Aid and St Steph from 97. *The Rectory, 45 Lawe Road, South Shields NE33 2EN* Tel 0191-456 1831
SHAW, Ralph Michael. b 45. DipAdEd. Lich Th Coll 68. **d** 70 **p** 71. C Dewsbury All SS *Wakef* 70-75; TV Redcar w Kirkleatham *York* 75-76; Dioc Youth Officer *St Alb* 76-91; Lic to Offic from 91; Chief Exec Jo Grooms from 91. *18 Wyton, Welwyn Garden City AL7 2PF* Tel (01707) 321813 *or* (020) 7452 2000 Fax (020) 7452 2101 E-mail revmshaw@aol.com *or* mshaw@johngrooms.org.uk
SHAW, Richard. *See* SHAW, John Richard Astley
SHAW, Preb Richard Tom. b 42. AKC69. St Aug Coll Cant 69. **d** 70 **p** 71. C Dunston St Nic *Dur* 70-73; C Maidstone All SS w St Phil and H Trin *Cant* 73-75; Chapl RN 75-79; V Barrow-on-Humber *Linc* 79-83; V Linc St Faith and St Martin w St Pet 83-91; V Clun w Bettws-y-Crwyn and Newcastle *Heref* from 91; RD Clun Forest from 94; P-in-c Hopesay from 98; Preb Heref Cathl from 02. *The Vicarage, Vicarage Road, Clun, Craven Arms SY7 8JG* Tel (01588) 640809
SHAW, Robert Christopher. b 34. Man Univ BA BD. Union Th Sem (NY) STM. **d** 82 **p** 83. C Sharlston *Wakef* 82-83; C Scissett St Aug 83-85; R Cumberworth w Denby Dale 85-90; P-in-c Denby 85-90; R Bolton w Ireby and Uldale *Carl* 90-95; rtd 95; Perm to Offic *York* from 95. *Stonecroft, Sproxton, York YO62 5EF* Tel (01439) 770178
SHAW, Robert William. b 46. Lon Univ BD69. St Aug Coll Cant 69. **d** 70 **p** 71. C Hunslet St Mary and Stourton *Ripon* 70-71; C Hunslet St Mary 71-74; C Hawksworth Wood 74-76; R Stanningley St Thos 76-84; V Potternewton 84-94; V Manston 94-02; P-in-c Hunslet Moor St Pet and St Cuth from 02; P-in-c Beeston Hill H Spirit from 02. *St Peter's Vicarage, 139 Dewsbury Road, Leeds LS11 5NW* Tel 0113-277 2464
SHAW, Roderick Kenneth. b 37. MBIM77. Moray Ord Course 88. **d** 92 **p** 95. Hon C Grantown-on-Spey *Mor* 92-96; Hon C Rothiemurchus from 92. *The Cottage, Balliefurth, Grantown-on-Spey PH26 3NH* Tel (01479) 821496
SHAW, Mrs Rosemary Alice. b 44. CertEd65 DipTh75 CQSW78 Heythrop Coll Lon MA96. S'wark Ord Course 87. **d** 89 **p** 94. Par Dn Walworth *S'wark* 89-92; Par Dn E Dulwich St Jo 92-95; NSM 95-96; Eileen Kerr Mental Health Fellow Maudsley Hosp 95-96; Chapl King's Healthcare NHS Trust 96-01; Hon C E Dulwich St Jo *S'wark* from 96; Chapl Guy's and St Thos' Hosps NHS Trust Lon from 02. *19 Scutari Road, London SE22 0NN* Tel (020) 8693 6325 E-mail rrosemaryshaw@aol.com
SHAYLER-WEBB, Peter. b 57. Bath Univ BSc81 BArch83. Ripon Coll Cuddesdon 93. **d** 95 **p** 96. C Bedford St Paul *St Alb*

95-99; C Dorking w Ranmore *Guildf* from 99. *79 Ashcombe Road, Dorking RH4 1LX* Tel (01306) 882065
E-mail shaylerweb@aol.com

SHEA, Guy Roland John. b 33. Trin Coll Connecticut BA55 Ch Ch Ox BA58 MA62. Coll of Resurr Mirfield 60. **d** 60 **p** 61. C Kennington St Jo *S'wark* 60-63 and 75-77; C N Audley Street St Mark *Lon* 63-67; C Hammersmith St Sav 67-70; P-in-c Gunnersbury St Jas 70-75; Perm to Offic 77-82; Hon C Fulham St Alb 82-92; Hon C Fulham St Alb w St Aug 92-97; P-in-c Fulham St Pet 95-98; rtd 98; Perm to Offic *Lon* from 98. *7 Wellington Court, 116 Knightsbridge, London SW1X 7PL* Tel (020) 7584 4036

SHEA, Martyn Paul Leathley. b 66. City Univ BSc89. Wycliffe Hall Ox. **d** 00 **p** 01. C Ches Square St Mich w St Phil *Lon* from 00. *142 Cambridge Street, London SW1V 4QF* Tel (020) 7730 8889 Mobile 07976-869467 Fax (020) 7730 0043
E-mail martyn_shea@compuserve.com *or* lizshea@hotmail.com

SHEAD, John Frederick Henry. b 38. ACP74 FCP81. Westcott Ho Cam 72. **d** 74 **p** 75. Hd Master Thaxted Co Primary Sch 70-85; Hon C Thaxted *Chelmsf* 74-85; C Saffron Walden w Wendens Ambo and Littlebury 86-88; P-in-c Wethersfield w Shalford 88-96; P-in-c Finchingfield and Cornish Hall End 94-96; RD Braintree 95-00; V Finchingfield and Cornish Hall End etc from 96. *The Vicarage, Finchingfield, Braintree CM7 4JR* Tel (01371) 810309 E-mail jshead@fish31.freeserve.co.uk

SHEARCROFT, Sister Elizabeth Marion. b 57. SRN76. **d** 94 **p** 95. CA from 84; NSM Margate H Trin *Cant* 94-98; Chapl Thanet Healthcare NHS Trust 94-98; Chapl E Kent Hosps NHS Trust 99-02; C Kendal H Trin *Carl* from 02. *7 Wattsfield Road, Kendal LA9 5JH* Tel (01539) 729572
E-mail elizabeth_shearcroft@hotmail.com

SHEARD, Andrew Frank. b 60. York Univ BA81. St Jo Coll Nottm 92. **d** 94 **p** 95. C Uxbridge *Lon* 94-96; TV 96-99; P-in-c 99-01; TR from 01. *St Margaret's Vicarage, 72 Harefield Road, Uxbridge UB8 1PL* Tel (01895) 237853 *or* 258766 Fax 812194
E-mail andrewf.sheard@btinternet.com

SHEARD, Ernest. b 29. Linc Th Coll 73. **d** 74 **p** 75. Hon C Birstall *Leic* 74-82; Hon C Birstall and Wanlip 82-84; Asst Chapl Loughb Univ and Colls 75-90; Lic to Offic *Leic* from 90. *21 Orchard Road, Birstall, Leicester LE4 4GD* Tel 0116-267 3901

SHEARD, Gillian Freda. *See* COOKE, Ms Gillian Freda

SHEARD, Preb Michael Rowland. b 42. K Coll Lon BA Man Univ PhD. **d** 95 **p** 95. World Miss Officer *Lich* from 89; Preb Lich Cathl *Lich* from 99. *68 Sneyd Lane, Essington, Wolverhampton WV11 2DX* Tel (01922) 445844 Fax 491948
E-mail michael.sheard@btinternet.com

SHEARER, John Frank. b 35. Ex Univ BSc60. Tyndale Hall Bris 62. **d** 63 **p** 64. C Blackheath St Jo *S'wark* 63-67; R Nuffield *Ox* from 67. *The Rectory, Nuffield, Henley-on-Thames RG9 5SN* Tel (01491) 641305

SHEARING, Michael James. b 39. Lanc Univ BA71. Linc Th Coll. **d** 66 **p** 67. Hon C Hartlepool St Paul *Dur* 66-76; Asst Master Dyke Ho Comp Sch Hartlepool 76-87; C Houghton le Spring 87; P-in-c Wheatley Hill 87-95; V Bishopwearmouth St Nic 95-97; R Cockfield from 97; V Lynesack from 97. *The Rectory, Cockfield, Bishop Auckland DL13 5AA* Tel (01388) 718447 E-mail michael.shearing@durham.anglican.org

SHEARLOCK, The Very Revd David John. b 32. FRSA91 Birm Univ BA55. Westcott Ho Cam 56. **d** 57 **p** 58. C Guisborough *York* 57-60; C Christchurch *Win* 60-64; V Kingsclere 64-71; V Romsey 71-82; Dioc Dir of Ords 77-82; Hon Can Win Cathl 78-82; Dean Truro 82-97; R Truro St Mary 82-97; Chapl Cornwall Fire Brigade 91-97; rtd 98; Perm to Offic *Sarum* from 98. *3 The Tanyard, Shadrack Street, Beaminster DT8 3BG* Tel (01308) 863170

SHEARMAN, Michael Alan. b 22. Down Coll Cam BA44 MA48. Coll of Resurr Mirfield 46. **d** 48 **p** 49. C Bounds Green *Lon* 48-53; C Wembley Park St Aug 53-58; V Enfield St Luke 58-87; rtd 87; Perm to Offic *Nor* from 87. *18 Thompson Avenue, Holt NR25 6EN* Tel (01263) 713072

SHEARS, Canon Michael George Frederick. b 33. Pemb Coll Cam BA57 MA68. St Steph Ho Ox 57. **d** 59 **p** 60. C Grantham St Wulfram *Linc* 59-68; R Waltham 68-80; R Barnoldby le Beck 74-80; RD Haverstoe 78-80; V Soham *Ely* 80-99; RD Fordham 83-95; Hon Can Ely Cathl 94-99; rtd 99; Perm to Offic *Nor* from 00. *Woodcutter's Cottage, 19 High Street, Wicklewood, Wymondham NR18 9QE* Tel (01953) 605535

SHEASBY, Adrian. b 29. Open Univ BA89. St Aid Birkenhead 54. **d** 57 **p** 58. C Foleshill St Paul *Cov* 57-60; C Pet St Jo *Pet* 60-65; V Maxey w Northborough 65-94; rtd 94; Perm to Offic *Pet* and *Linc* from 94. *26 Beech Close, Market Deeping, Peterborough PE6 8LL* Tel (01778) 347581

SHEATH, Allan Philip. b 48. SW Minl Tr Course 95. **d** 98 **p** 99. NSM Tiverton St Pet and Chevithorne w Cove *Ex* 98-03; C Honiton, Gittisham, Combe Raleigh, Monkton etc from 03. *The Vicarage, Awliscombe, Honiton EX14 3PJ* Tel (01404) 42983 E-mail allan.sheath@virgin.net

SHEDDEN, Mrs Valerie. b 56. Ripon Coll of Educn CertEd77. Cranmer Hall Dur 81. **dss** 84 **d** 87 **p** 94. Tudhoe Grange *Dur*

84-85; Whitworth w Spennymoor 85-91; Par Dn 87-91; Par Dn E Darlington 91-94; P-in-c Bishop Middleham 94-00; Dioc RE Adv 94-00; V Heworth St Mary from 00. *Heworth Vicarage, High Heworth Lane, Gateshead NE10 0PB* Tel 0191-469 2111
E-mail val.shedden@talk21.com

SHEEHAN, Patrick Edward Anthony. b 37. Campion Ho Middx 58 English Coll Lisbon 62. **d** 67 **p** 69. In RC Ch 67-73; C Clapham H Spirit *S'wark* 73-75; P-in-c Wimbledon 75-77; Australia from 77; R Balga Good Shep 77-80; R Melville H Cross 80-85; Chapl R Newcastle Hosp 85-91; Chapl Jo Hunter Hosp 91-97; R Terrigal 97-01; rtd 01. *22 Abby Crescent, Ashmore, Qld, Australia 4214* Tel (0061) (7) 5564 7064

SHEEHY, Jeremy Patrick. b 56. Magd Coll Ox BA78 MA81 New Coll Ox DPhil90. St Steph Ho Ox 78. **d** 81 **p** 82. C Erdington St Barn *Birm* 81-83; C Small Heath St Greg 83-84; Dean Div, Fell and Chapl New Coll Ox 84-90; V Leytonstone St Marg w St Columba *Chelmsf* 90-96; P-in-c Leytonstone St Andr 93-96; Prin St Steph Ho Ox from 96. *St Stephen's House, 16 Marston Street, Oxford OX4 1JX* Tel (01865) 247874 Fax 794338

SHEEKEY, Raymond Arthur. b 23. Chich Th Coll 51. **d** 53 **p** 54. C Ramsgate St Geo *Cant* 53-56; C Birchington w Acol 56-61; V Brabourne w Smeeth 61-79; RD N Lympne 75-78; Chapl Lenham Hosp 79-88; R Lenham w Boughton Malherbe 79-88; rtd 88; Perm to Offic *Bris* 88-97; Perm to Offic *Glouc* 98-99. *41 Barleycorn, Leybourne, West Malling ME19 5PS* Tel (01732) 847722

SHEEN, Canon John Harold. b 32. Qu Coll Cam BA54 MA58. Cuddesdon Coll 56. **d** 58 **p** 59. C Stepney St Dunstan and All SS *Lon* 58-62; V Tottenham St Jo 62-68; V Wood Green St Mich 68-78; P-in-c Southgate St Mich 77-78; R Kirkbride *S & M* 78-97; Chapl Ramsey Cottage Hosp 80-98; V Lezayre St Olave Ramsey 80-98; RD Ramsey 88-97; Can St German's Cathl 91-98; Dir of Ords 93-01; rtd 98; Perm to Offic *S & M* from 99. *Kentraugh Mill, Colby, Isle of Man IM9 4AU* Tel (01624) 832406

SHEEN, Canon Victor Alfred. b 17. Tyndale Hall Bris 47. **d** 49 **p** 50. Uganda 49-56; C Cheltenham St Mark *Glouc* 56-58; V W Streatham St Jas *S'wark* 58-65; V Clapham St Jas 65-86; RD Clapham and Brixton 75-82 and 85-86; Hon Can S'wark Cathl 80-86; rtd 86; Perm to Offic *Chich* from 86. *10 Porters Way, Polegate BN26 6AP* Tel (01323) 487487

SHEFFIELD, Michael Julian. b 53. Brentwood Coll of Educn CertEd. Sarum & Wells Th Coll 76. **d** 79 **p** 80. C Locks Heath *Portsm* 79-83; C Waterlooville 83; C Ryde All SS 83-86; P-in-c Ryde H Trin 86-92; V 92-96; P-in-c Swanmore St Mich w Havenstreet 86-92; V Swanmore St Mich 92-96; V W Leigh from 96. *St Alban's Vicarage, Martin Road, Havant PO9 5TE* Tel and fax (023) 9245 1751 Mobile 07818-031902
E-mail mikejs99@hotmail.com

SHEFFIELD, Archdeacon of. *See* BLACKBURN, The Ven Richard Finn

SHEFFIELD, Bishop of. *See* NICHOLLS, The Rt Revd John

SHEFFIELD, Dean of. *Vacant*

SHEGOG, Preb Eric Marshall. b 37. Lon Univ DipTh60 City Univ MA88 FRSA92. Lich Th Coll 64. **d** 65 **p** 66. C Benhilton *S'wark* 65-68; Asst Youth Adv 68-70; V Abbey Wood 70-76; Chapl Sunderland Town Cen 76-83; C Bishopwearmouth St Mich w St Hilda *Dur* 76-83; Hd Relig Broadcasting IBA 84-90; Perm to Offic *Lon* 85-90; Perm to Offic *St Alb* 85-89; Hon C Harpenden St Nic 89-97; Dir Communications for C of E 90-97; Dir Communications *Lon* 97-00; Preb St Paul's Cathl 97-00; Acting Dioc Gen Sec 99; rtd 00; Perm to Offic *St Alb* from 00. *9 Colbron Close, Ashwell, Baldock SG7 5TH* Tel (01462) 743251

SHEHADI, Nabil Faduzi. b 58. Wycliffe Hall Ox 00. **d** 02 **p** 03. C Cobbold Road St Sav w St Mary *Lon* from 02. *The Vicarage Cottage, Cobbold Road, London W12 9LN* Tel (020) 8749 4391
E-mail nabil.shehadi@london.anglican.org

SHEILD, Canon Edward Oscar. b 10. Univ of NZ LLB33 Qu Coll Ox BA36 MA40 BD82. **d** 36 **p** 37. C Fallowfield *Man* 36-39; New Zealand 39-46; Tutor Cuddesdon Coll 46-49; Lic to Offic *Ox* 46-58; Lic Preacher *Man* 49-58; Dioc Miss 49-58; Hon Can Man Cathl 54-58; Dean Singapore 58-64; V Chapel Allerton *Ripon* 64-75; rtd 75; Perm to Offic *Carl* 75-99; P-in-c Coldstream *Edin* 77-79. *21 Stuart Court, High Street, Kibworth, Leicester LE8 0LR* Tel 0116-279 6735

SHELDON, Jennifer Christine. b 43. K Coll Lon BA99. NTMTC 00. **d** 02. NSM Poplar *Lon* from 02. *23 Lancaster Drive, London E14 9PT* Tel (020) 7538 2375 Fax 7538 1551
E-mail jensheldon@aol.com

SHELDON, Jonathan Mark Robin. b 59. Cam Univ MA83. Ridley Hall Cam 81. **d** 83 **p** 84. C Dulwich St Barn *S'wark* 83-86; C Worle *B & W* 86-88; V Chesterton St Andr *Ely* 88-97. *21 Chancery Lane, Thrapston, Kettering NN14 4JL* Tel (01832) 731173 E-mail jsheldon@agnet.co.uk

SHELDON, Martin David. b 67. Sussex Univ BA89 Nottm Univ MTh01. St Jo Coll Nottm 99. **d** 01 **p** 02. C Milton *Win* from 01. *10 Spinacre, Barton-on-Sea, New Milton BH25 7DF* Tel (01425) 621930 E-mail martin.sheldon@lineone.net

SHELDRAKE, Varlie Ivy. b 39. **d** 03. OLM E w W Harling, Bridgham w Roudham, Larling etc *Nor* from 03. *Springfield,*

Lopham Road, East Harling, Norwich NR16 2PX Tel (01953) 717404

SHELLEY, Derrick Sydney David. b 38. Lon Univ LLB60 AKC65. Linc Th Coll. **d** 68 **p** 69. C Weybridge *Guildf* 68-72; Chapl Red Bank Schs 72-77; Lic to Offic *Blackb* 80-97; NSM Lytham St Cuth 80-97; rtd 97; Perm to Offic *Truro* from 97. *Peniel, Cox Hill, Cocks, Perranporth TR6 0AT* Tel (01872) 573886 Fax as telephone E-mail derrick@shelley.dabsol.co.uk

SHELLEY, Robin Arthur. b 34. CEng MIMechE. St Jo Coll Nottm 85. **d** 87 **p** 88. C Countesthorpe w Foston *Leic* 87-90; V Enderby w Lubbesthorpe and Thurlaston 90-00; rtd 00; Perm to Offic *Leic* 00-03; *York* from 02. *10 West Leys Park, Swanland, North Ferriby HU14 3LS* Tel (01482) 637063

SHELLOCK, Norman Stanley. b 15. ATCL53 Dur Univ LTh38. St Aug Coll Cant 34. **d** 38 **p** 39. C Biscot *St Alb* 38-41; Br Guiana 41-59; Area Sec USPG *Ely* and *St E* 59-80; rtd 80; Perm to Offic *Nor* 80-81; *St E* from 81; *Ely* 81-97. *24 Runnymede Green, Bury St Edmunds IP33 2LH* Tel (01284) 703506

SHELLS, Canon Charles Harry. b 15. Trinity Hall Cam BA38 MA43. **d** 39 **p** 40. C Almondbury *Wakef* 39-42; C Camberwell St Geo *S'wark* 42-47; V Newington St Paul 47-54; V Wandsworth St Anne 54-65; RD Wandsworth 63-65; R Trunch w Swafield *Nor* 65-71; R Bradfield 65-71; P-in-c Gimingham 65-71; P-in-c Trimingham 65-71; P-in-c Antingham w Thorpe Market 65-71; P-in-c Felmingham 65-68; P-in-c Suffield 65-68; P-in-c Gunton St Pet 65-71; RD Tunstead 65-68; Can Res Bris Cathl *Bris* 71-81; rtd 81; Lic to Offic *B & W* 81-96; and *Sarum* from 81; Perm to Offic *Bris* from 81 and *B & W* from 88. *13 Dod Lane, Glastonbury BA6 8BZ* Tel (01458) 832052

SHELTON, Ian Robert. b 52. BEd74 Lon Univ MA79. Ripon Coll Cuddesdon BA81 MA90. **d** 82 **p** 83. C Wath-upon-Dearne w Adwick-upon-Dearne *Sheff* 82-86; TV Grantham *Linc* 86-93; P-in-c Waltham 93-97; R from 97; P-in-c Barnoldby le Beck 93-97; R from 97; RD Haverstoe from 01. *The Rectory, 95 High Street, Waltham, Grimsby DN37 0PN* Tel (01472) 822172

SHELTON, Ms Pauline Mary. b 52. K Coll Lon BA73. N Ord Course 96. **d** 99 **p** 00. C Baswich *Lich* 99-02; TV Stoke-upon-Trent from 02. *The Vicarage, Upper Belgrave Road, Stoke-on-Trent ST3 4QJ* Tel (01782) 324903 E-mail rev.pauline@virgin.net

SHENTON, Canon Brian. b 43. Chich Th Coll 73. **d** 75 **p** 76. C Mill Hill Jo Keble Ch *Lon* 75-78; C New Windsor *Ox* 78-81; TV 81-82; P-in-c Cherbury 82-83; V Calcot 83-89; R Reading St Mary w St Laur from 89; RD Reading from 95; P-in-c Reading St Matt 96-00; Hon Can Ch Ch from 98. *42 Northcourt Avenue, Reading RG2 7HD* Tel 0118-931 4025 *or* 957 1057 Mobile 07710-490250 E-mail stmaryshouserdg@waitrose.com

SHENTON, David. b 57. Aston Tr Scheme 91 Ripon Coll Cuddesdon DipMin95. **d** 95 **p** 96. C Thurmaston *Leic* 95-98; C Melton Mowbray 98-99; V 99-01. *Address temp unknown*

SHEPHARD, Brian Edward. b 34. Magd Coll Cam BA56 MA60 Ox Univ DipPSA60 CertEd71 HDipRE71. Wycliffe Hall Ox 58. **d** 60 **p** 61. C Wigan St Cath *Liv* 60-62; C Kidderminster St Geo *Worc* 62-65; Lect CA Tr Coll Blackheath 65-70; Lect Hamilton Coll of Educn 70-77; Perm to Offic *Glas* 70-77; Chapl Buchan Sch Castletown 77-88; Lic to Offic *S & M* 77-88; Lic to Offic *S'wark* 88-89; Tutor Wilson Carlile Coll of Evang 88-89; C Andreas St Jude *S & M* 89-91; C Jurby 89-91; V Lezayre 91-02; rtd 02; Perm to Offic *S & M* from 02. *Keayn Ard, Queen's Road, Port St Mary, Isle of Man IM9 5EP* Tel (01624) 833315

SHEPHEARD-WALWYN, John. b 16. Oriel Coll Ox BA38 MA44. Wells Th Coll 38. **d** 40 **p** 42. C Roch St Pet w St Marg *Roch* 41-44; C Lamorbey H Redeemer 44-49; C Edenbridge 49-56; V Rosherville 56-61; R Horwood *Ex* 61-78; V Westleigh 61-78; P-in-c Harberton w Harbertonford 78-82; rtd 82; Perm to Offic *Bris* from 82. *Flat 23, Westfield House, Cote Lane, Bristol BS9 3UN* Tel 0117-949 4823

SHEPHERD, Canon Anthony Michael. b 50. Em Coll Cam BA72 MA76. Westcott Ho Cam 72. **d** 74 **p** 75. C Folkestone St Mary and St Eanswythe *Cant* 74-79; Bp's Dom Chapl *Ripon* 79-87; Dioc Communications Officer 79-87; V High Harrogate St Pet from 87; Hon Can Ripon Cathl from 99. *St Peter's Vicarage, 13 Beech Grove, Harrogate HG2 0ET* Tel (01423) 500901 E-mail asheperd@bigfoot.com

SHEPHERD, Christopher Francis Pleydell. b 44. St Steph Ho Ox 68. **d** 69 **p** 70. C Milber *Ex* 69-72; C Ex St Thos 72-74; TV Ilfracombe, Lee and W Down 74-78; TV Ilfracombe, Lee, W Down, Woolacombe and Bittadon 78-80; P-in-c Tregony w St Cuby and Cornelly *Truro* 80-83; R 83-96. *2 Cherry Meadow, Cheriton Fitzpaine, Crediton EX17 4JX* Tel (01363) 866896

SHEPHERD, David. b 42. St Jo Coll Dur BA65 MA68 MLitt76. Edin Th Coll 66. **d** 68 **p** 69. Chapl St Paul's Cathl Dundee *Bre* 68-79; Chapl Dundee Univ 73-79; R Dundee St Mary Magd from 79. *14 Albany Terrace, Dundee DD3 6HR* Tel (01382) 223510

SHEPHERD, David Mark. b 59. Reading Univ BA81 Nottm Univ BTh86. Linc Th Coll 83. **d** 86 **p** 87. C Wilmslow *Ches* 86-89; C Bromborough 89-92; V Leasowe 92-97; V Oxhey

St Matt *St Alb* from 97. *The Vicarage, St Matthew's Close, Eastbury Road, Watford WD19 4ST* Tel (01923) 241420 E-mail davidshepherd@matts52.fsnet.co.uk

SHEPHERD, Ernest John Heatley. b 27. TCD BA48 BD53. **d** 50 **p** 51. C Belfast St Mary Magd *Conn* 50-54; I Whitehouse 54-96; Can Conn Cathl 86-90; Co-ord Aux Min 87-96; Treas Conn Cathl 90; Prec Conn Cathl 90-96; rtd 96. *15 Downshire Gardens, Carrickfergus BT38 7LW* Tel (028) 9336 2243

SHEPHERD, Miss Jayne Elizabeth. b 57. Reading Univ BA78. Cranmer Hall Dur 79. **dss** 82 **d** 87 **p** 94. Wombourne *Lich* 82-85; Harlescott 85-87; Par Dn 87-90; Chapl Asst Qu Medical Cen Nottm Univ Hosp NHS Trust 90-97; Asst Chapl Cen Notts Healthcare NHS Trust 90-97; Chapl Pet Hosps NHS Trust 97-02; Chapl St Helen's and Knowsley Hosps Trust from 02. *Whiston Hospital, Warrington Road, Prescot L35 5DR* Tel 0151-426 1600 Fax 430 8478

SHEPHERD, Mrs Joan Francis Fleming. b 45. RGN66. dss 84 **d** 86 **p** 94. NSM Ellon *Ab* from 84; NSM Cruden Bay from 84; Bp's Chapl for Tr and Educn from 95. *8 Ythan Court, Ellon AB41 9BL* Tel (01358) 723241

SHEPHERD, John Donald. b 33. Cranmer Hall Dur BA59 DipTh61. **d** 61 **p** 62. C Dewsbury All SS *Wakef* 61-63; C Chapelthorpe 63-66; V Stainland 66-70; Dioc Youth Chapl *Truro* 70-74; V Newquay 74-84; RD Pydar 81-84; Chapl Borocourt Mental Handicap Hosp 84-95; TR Langtree *Ox* 84-95; rtd 98; Perm to Offic *Lich* from 99. *21 Sparkham Close, Shrewsbury SY3 6BX* Tel (01743) 244453

SHEPHERD, The Very Revd John Harley. b 42. Melbourne Univ BA64 ThL66 St Cath Coll Cam PhD80. Union Th Sem (NY) MSacMus73. **d** 67 **p** 68. Australia 67-70; from 88; C Stretford St Matt *Man* 71; Asst P Sayville Long Is USA 72-77; Jo Stewart of Rannoch Scholar St Cath Coll Cam 77-80; C Cherry Hinton St Andr *Ely* 78-80; Chapl Ch Ch Ox 80-88; Chapl Univ W Australia 88-90; Dean Perth from 90. *St George's Cathedral, 38 St George's Terrace, Perth, W Australia 6000* Tel (0061) (8) 9325 5766 *or* 9322 7265 Fax 9325 5242 E-mail thedean@perthcathedral.org

SHEPHERD, John Martin. b 68. St Jo Coll Cam BA90. Oak Hill Th Coll BA93. **d** 96 **p** 97. C Rusholme H Trin *Man* 96-00; SAMS from 00. *South American Mission Society, Allen Gardiner House, 12 Fox Hill, Birmingham B29 4AG* Tel 0121-472 2616 Fax 472 7977

SHEPHERD, Canon John Michael. b 42. BNC Ox BA63 MA72. Coll of Resurr Mirfield 64. **d** 66 **p** 67. C Clapham H Spirit *S'wark* 66-69; C Kingston All SS 69-72; V Upper Tooting H Trin 73-80; V Wandsworth St Paul 80-90; P-in-c Mitcham SS Pet and Paul 90-92; V 92-97; RD Merton 96-97; V Battersea St Luke from 97; RD Battersea from 01; Hon Can S'wark Cathl from 01. *52 Thurleigh Road, London SW12 8UD* Tel (020) 8673 6506

SHEPHERD, Mrs Julie Margaret. b 37. Man OLM Scheme 00. **d** 03. OLM Halliwell *Man* from 03. *Apple Cottage, 16 Grove Street, Bolton BL1 3PG* Tel (01204) 844508 Mobile 07742-667903 E-mail julie.shepherd@care4free.net

SHEPHERD, Keith Frederick. b 42. EMMTC 86. **d** 89 **p** 90. NSM Stocking Farm *Leic* 89-93; NSM Church Langton w Tur Langton, Thorpe Langton etc 93-99; TV Syston from 99. *The Parsonage, 20 Hoby Road, Thrussington, Leicester LE7 4TH* Tel (01664) 424962 E-mail shepherd@leicester.anglican.org

SHEPHERD, Michael John. b 54. Dur Univ BA75 St Paul Univ Ottawa LCL81 Ottawa Univ MCL81. Ushaw Coll Dur 73. **d** 77 **p** 78. In RC Ch 77-93; NSM Evesham *Worc* 95-97; NSM Evesham w Norton and Lenchwick 97-99; NSM Badsey w Aldington and Offenham and Bretforton from 99. *90 Main Street, Bretforton, Evesham WR11 7JJ* Tel (01386) 831476

SHEPHERD, Mrs Pauline. b 53. Stockwell Coll of Educn TCert73. WMMTC 00. **d** 03. C Walsall Pleck and Bescot *Lich* from 03. *134 Birmingham Road, Aldridge, Walsall WS9 0AQ* Tel (01922) 452493 Mobile 07814-680304 E-mail andrew.shepherd2@which.net

SHEPHERD, Peter James. b 38. Dur Univ BA64. Ridley Hall Cam 64. **d** 66 **p** 67. C Luton Ch Ch *Roch* 66-70; C Belvedere All SS 70-71; C Wisley w Pyrford *Guildf* 71-75; V Thorney Abbey *Ely* 75-85; V Yaxley 85-93; RD Yaxley 88-92; P-in-c Feltwell 93-95; rtd 96; Perm to Offic *Ely* from 96. *51 Middlefield Road, Sawtry, Huntingdon PE28 5SH* Tel (01487) 834084

SHEPHERD, Peter William. b 48. Reading Univ BA71 Lon Univ BD80 Brighton Poly MPhil87 Lanc Univ MA94. Chich Th Coll 77. **d** 80 **p** 81. NSM Eastbourne St Sav and St Pet *Chich* 80-82; NSM Clitheroe St Mary *Blackb* from 82; Hd Master Wm Temple Sch Preston 83-88; Hd Master Canon Slade Sch Bolton from 88; Perm to Offic *Man* from 89. *Homestead, Eastham Street, Clitheroe BB7 2HY* Tel (01200) 425053 *or* (01204) 401555 Fax (01200) 426317 *or* (01204) 401556 E-mail pws.canonslade@btconnect.com

✠**SHEPHERD, The Rt Revd Ronald Francis.** b 26. Univ of BC BA48. AKC52 St Jo Coll Winnipeg Hon DD89. **d** 52 **p** 53 **c** 85. C Westmr St Steph w St Jo *Lon* 52-57; Canada from 57; Dean Edmonton 65-70; Dean Montreal 70-82; Bp BC 85-92; rtd 92; Hon V St Barn Miss San Diego USA 95-00. *Easter Hill,*

110 Ensilwood Road, Salt Spring Island BC, Canada, V8K 1N1 Tel (001) (250) 537 1399

SHEPHERD, Thomas. b 52. SRN74 Man Univ BA79 Didsbury Coll Man PGCE83. N Ord Course 92. **d** 95 **p** 96. C Baguley *Man* 95-99; C Timperley *Ches* 99-03; V Sale St Paul from 03. *St Paul's Vicarage, 15 Springfield Road, Sale M33 7YA* Tel 0161-973 1042

SHEPHERD, Timothy Roy. b 34. Selw Coll Cam BA58. Linc Th Coll 62. **d** 64 **p** 65. C Selly Oak St Mary *Birm* 64-67; C Stockland Green 67-72; V Perry Common 72-76; V Holton-le-Clay *Linc* 76-84; V Habrough Gp 84-93; P-in-c Uffington 93-95; R Uffington Gp 95-99; rtd 99; Perm to Offic *Pet* from 99; *Linc* from 00. *Chapelside, Chapel Hill, Wootton, Woodstock OX20 1DX* Tel (01993) 813319

✠**SHEPPARD, The Rt Revd and Rt Hon Lord (David Stuart).** b 29. Trin Hall Cam BA53 MA56 Hon DD90 Liv Univ Hon LLD81 Liv Poly Hon DTech87 Ex Univ Hon DD98 Birm Univ Hon DD99 Open Univ Hon DUniv99 Univ of Wales Hon DD00. Ridley Hall Cam 53. **d** 55 **p** 56 **c** 69. C Islington St Mary *Lon* 55-58; Chapl and Warden Mayflower Family Cen Canning Town *Chelmsf* 58-69; Suff Bp Woolwich *S'wark* 69-75; Bp Liv 75-97; rtd 97; Hon Asst Bp *Ches* from 00. *11 Melloncroft Drive, West Kirby, Wirral CH48 2JA*

SHEPPARD, Ian Arthur Lough. b 33. Sarum & Wells Th Coll 71. **d** 74 **p** 75. C Bishop's Cleeve *Glouc* 74-77; Chapl RAF 77-81; V Gosberton *Linc* 81-87; V Leven Valley *Carl* 87-90; Deputation and Gen Appeals Org Children's Soc 90-98; rtd 98. *57 Seymour Grove, Eaglescliffe, Stockton-on-Tees TS16 0LE* Tel (01642) 791612 E-mail ian.sheppard@bluecarrots.com

SHEPPARD, Canon Martin. b 37. Hertf Coll Ox BA61 MA65. Chich Th Coll 63. **d** 65 **p** 66. C N Hull St Mich *York* 65-68; C Hove St Jo *Chich* 68-71; V Heathfield St Rich 71-77; V New Shoreham 77-94; V Old Shoreham 77-94; TR Rye 94-03; RD Rye 95-02; Can and Preb Chich Cathl 03; rtd 03. *62 St Pancras Road, Lewes BN7 1JG* Tel (01273) 474999

SHEPPARD, Norman George. b 32. Wolv Teacher Tr Coll CertEd73. St D Coll Lamp 57. **d** 59 **p** 60. C Burry Port and Pwll *St D* 59-64; SAMS 64-68; Chile 64-68; C Madeley *Heref* 68-69; Asst Master Madeley Court Sch 73-75; Gilbert Inglefield Sch Leighton Buzzard 75-80; USPG 80-81; Argentina from 80; rtd 95. *Santa Rosa 1650, Vincente Lopez, Province of Buenos Aires, Argentina* Tel (0054) (1) 797 9748

SHEPPARD, Roger Malcolm. WMMTC. **d** 01 **p** 02. NSM Castle Vale St Cuth *Birm* from 01. *146 Conway Road, Fordbridge, Birmingham B37 5LD* Tel 0121-788 0539

SHEPPARD, Stanley Gorton. b 18. St Jo Coll Dur 46. **d** 62 **p** 63. C Leic St Mark *Leic* 62-65; R Cole Orton 65-75; V Ashby Folville and Twyford w Thorpe Satchville 75-88; rtd 88; Perm to Offic *Ex* from 89. *1 Peak Coach House, Cotmaton Road, Sidmouth EX10 8SY* Tel (01395) 516124

SHEPPARD, Mrs Susan. b 59. Ex Univ BA80 MA99 SS Hild & Bede Coll Dur PGCE81. SW Minl Tr Course 95. **d** 98 **p** 99. NSM Stoke Canon, Poltimore w Huxham and Rewe etc *Ex* from 98; Chapl St Peter's High Sch Exeter from 99. *Autumn Haze, Rewe, Exeter EX5 4HA* Tel (01392) 841284 Fax as telephone

SHEPTON, Robert Leonard McIntyre. b 35. Jes Coll Cam BA58 MA61. Oak Hill Th Coll 59. **d** 61 **p** 62. C Weymouth St Jo *Sarum* 61-63; Boys' Ldr Cam Univ Miss Bermondsey 63-66; Warden Ox-Kilburn Club 66-69; Chapl St D Coll Llandudno 69-77; Chief Instructor Carnoch Outdoor Cen 77-80; Chapl Kingham Hill Sch Oxon 80-92; rtd 92. *Innisfree, Duror, Appin PA38 4DA* Tel (01631) 730437 Fax 730382
E-mail bob@innisfree.free-online.co.uk

SHERBORNE, Archdeacon of. *Vacant*

SHERBORNE, Area Bishop of. *See* THORNTON, The Rt Revd Timothy Martin

SHERDLEY, Mrs Margaret Ann. b 46. Chester Coll of HE BTh03. N Ord Course 00. **d** 03. NSM Fellside Team *Blackb* from 03. *23 Sandy Lane, Preesall, Poulton-le-Fylde FY6 0EJ* Tel (01253) 810894 Mobile 07931-592787
E-mail m.sherdley@btinternet.com

SHERGOLD, William Frank. b 19. St Chad's Coll Dur BA40 MA47. Coll of Resurr Mirfield 40. **d** 42 **p** 43. C Poplar All SS w St Frideswide *Lon* 42-49; V Hanworth All SS 49-58; V Hackney Wick St Mary of Eton w St Aug 59-64; V Paddington St Mary 64-69; V Charlton-by-Dover St Bart *Cant* 69-72; P-in-c Charlton-by-Dover SS Pet and Paul 70-72; R Charlton-in-Dover 72-78; R Tunstall 78-83; rtd 84; TV Poplar *Lon* 84; Hon C 84-92; Perm to Offic *Chich* 92-99 and *B & W* from 00. *78 Southover, Wells BA5 1UH* Tel (01749) 678803

SHERIDAN, Andrew Robert (Drew). b 61. Edin Univ MA83 Jordanhill Coll Glas PGCE86. TISEC 95. **d** 98 **p** 99. C Glas St Mary *Glas* from 98. *St Mary's House, 42 Hillhead Street, Glasgow G12 8PZ* Tel 0141-339 8904 *or* 339 6691 Fax 334 5669
E-mail a.sheridan@glasgow.anglican.org

SHERIDAN, Mrs Deborah Jane. b 47. ALA73 Kent Univ BA69. WMMTC 90. **d** 93 **p** 94. NSM Lich St Chad *Lich* from 93; Chapl St Giles Hospice Lich from 98. *45 High Grange, Lichfield WS13 7DU* Tel (01543) 264363 *or* 416595
E-mail d.sheridan@postman.org.uk

SHERIDAN, Peter. b 37. Saltley Tr Coll Birm CertEd59 Leic Poly BEd82. N Ord Course 89. **d** 92 **p** 93. NSM Braunstone *Leic* 92-95; NSM Ratby cum Groby 95-98; NSM Newtown Linford 95-98; TV Bradgate Team 98-00; Perm to Offic 00-01; NSM Woodhouse, Woodhouse Eaves and Swithland from 01. *16 Turnpike Way, Markfield LE67 9QT* Tel (01530) 245166

SHERIFF (née WORRALL), Canon Suzanne. b 63. Trin Coll Bris BA86. **d** 87 **p** 94. Par Dn Kingston upon Hull St Nic *York* 87-91; Par Dn Kingston upon Hull St Aid Southcoates 91-94; C 94-96; TV Marfleet 96-00; TR from 00; Can and Preb York Minster from 01. *St Hilda's Vicarage, 256 Annandale Road, Hull HU9 4JU* Tel (01482) 799100
E-mail cpsherlock@freeserve.co.uk

SHERLOCK, Charles Patrick. b 51. New Coll Ox BA73 MA76. Ripon Coll Cuddesdon 75. **d** 77 **p** 78. C Ashtead *Guildf* 77-81; Ethiopia 81-82; Chapl Belgrade w Zagreb *Eur* 82-84; USPG (Ethiopia) 84-91; R Dollar *St And* 91-97; Ethiopia 97-00; P-in-c Crieff *St And* from 01; P-in-c Comrie from 01; P-in-c Lochearnhead from 01. *Auchilhanzie, Gilmerton, Crieff PH7 3NE* Tel (01764) 652619 07740-981951
E-mail cpsherlock@msn.com

SHERLOCK, Canon Desmond. b 31. K Coll Lon BD60 AKC60. **d** 61 **p** 62. C Mitcham Ascension *S'wark* 61-64; C Reigate St Luke S Park 64-67; V Aldersbrook *Chelmsf* 67-77; RD Redbridge 74-77; TR Witham 77-97; Hon Can Chelmsf Cathl 93-97; rtd 97; Perm to Offic *Chelmsf* from 98. *20 Chalks Road, Witham CM8 2JG* Tel (01376) 513004

SHERLOCK, Thomas Alfred. b 40. Aux Course 87. **d** 90 **p** 91. NSM Kilmallock w Kilflynn, Kilfinane, Knockaney etc *L & K* 90-94; C Templemore w Thurles and Kilfithmone *C & O* 95-98; I 98-00; I Castlecomer w Colliery Ch, Mothel and Bilbo from 00. *The Rectory, Castlecomer, Co Tipperary, Irish Republic* Tel (00353) (56) 444 1677

SHERRATT, David Arthur. b 60. Univ of Wales (Lamp) BA82 Leeds Univ BA91. Coll of Resurr Mirfield 92. **d** 92 **p** 93. C St Jo on Bethnal Green *Lon* 92-95; C W Hampstead St Jas 95-98; V Abbey Wood *S'wark* from 98. *St Michael's Vicarage, 1 Conference Road, London SE2 0YH* Tel (020) 8311 0377

SHERRED, Peter William. b 47. Kent Univ BA69. SEITE 96. **d** 99 **p** 00. NSM Dover St Mary *Cant* 99-02; Perm to Offic from 02. *Copthorne, Dover Road, Guston, Dover CT15 5EN* Tel (01304) 203548 Fax 206950 E-mail copthorne@talk21.com

SHERRING, Patrick. b 55. Trent Park Coll of Educn BEd78 CertEd77 Lon Inst of Educn DipPSE88. Ridley Hall Cam CTM95. **d** 97 **p** 98. C Leyton St Mary w St Edw and St Luke *Chelmsf* 97-01; P-in-c Ingatestone w Buttsbury from 01. *The Rectory, 1 Rectory Close, Ingatestone CM4 0DB* Tel (01277) 352562
E-mail patrick.sherring@ingatestoneparishchurch.org.uk

SHERRING, Toby Bruce. b 76. Ex Univ BA97 St Luke's Coll Ex PGCE98. St Steph Ho Ox 00. **d** 02. C W Derby St Jo *Liv* from 02. *St John's Vicarage, 2 Green Lane, Stoneycroft, Liverpool L13 7EA* Tel 0151-259 8587 *or* 228 2023 E-mail father_toby@hotmail.com

SHERSBY, Brian Alfred. b 41. Clifton Th Coll 68. **d** 71 **p** 72. C Stoughton *Guildf* 71-74; C Heref St Pet w St Owen *Heref* 75-79; V Earlham St Mary *Nor* 79-91; R Murston w Bapchild and Tonge Cant from 91. *Bapchild Rectory, School Lane, Sittingbourne ME9 9NL* Tel (01795) 472929

SHERWIN, David Royston. b 56. HNC St Jo Coll Nottm 84. **d** 89 **p** 90. C Conisbrough *Sheff* 89-95; V Wheatley Park 95-01; Dioc Adv for Evang 95-01; P-in-c Martley and Wichenford, Knightwick etc *Worc* from 01. *The Rectory, Martley, Worcester WR6 6QA* Tel (01886) 888664
E-mail 101707.2036@compuserve.com

SHERWIN, Mrs Jane. b 41. Kingston Coll of Art DipAD61. Sarum Th Coll 93. **d** 96 **p** 97. NSM Brightling, Dallington, Mountfield etc *Chich* 96-02; P-in-c Waldron from 02. *The Rectory, Sheepsetting Lane, Waldron, Heathfield TN21 0UY* Tel (01435) 862816

SHERWIN, Mrs Margaret Joyce. b 65. N Ord Course BTh99. **d** 99 **p** 00. C Litherland St Phil *Liv* 99-03; V Hindley Green from 03. *The Vicarage, 848 Atherton Road, Hindley, Wigan WN2 4SA* Tel (01942) 255833

SHERWIN, Miss Margaret Miriam. b 32. dss 83 **d** 87 **p** 94. Holborn St Alb w Saffron Hill St Pet *Lon* 83-87; Par Dn 87-88; Par Dn Highgate St Mich 88-93; rtd 93; NSM Purbrook *Portsm* from 93. *16 Lombard Court, Lombard Street, Portsmouth PO1 2HU* Tel (023) 9283 8429

SHERWIN, Mrs Philippa Margaret. b 46. Lon Univ BDS70 LDSRCSEng70. LNSM course 98. **d** 99 **p** 00. OLM Queen Thorne *Sarum* from 99. *Holway Mill, Sandford Orcas, Sherborne DT9 4RZ* Tel (01963) 220380

SHERWOOD, David Charles. b 56. LRPS94. WEMTC 98. **d** 01 **p** 02. C Taunton Lyngford *B & W* from 01. *12 Eastwick Road, Taunton TA2 7HX* Tel (01823) 270708
E-mail ic_xc@yahoo.com

SHERWOOD, David James. b 45. Solicitor 69 Univ of Wales (Cardiff) LLM94. St Steph Ho Ox 81. **d** 83 **p** 84. C Westbury-on-Trym H Trin *Bris* 83-85; C Corringham *Chelmsf* 85-87; V Hullbridge 87-94; V Kenton *Lon* from 94. *St Mary's Vicarage,*

3 St Leonard's Avenue, Harrow HA3 8EJ Tel (020) 8907 2914 Fax 8933 7305

SHERWOOD, Gordon Frederick. b 29. Sarum & Wells Th Coll 77. **d** 80 **p** 81. Hon C Weeke *Win* 80-82; C Kirk Ella *York* 82-85; P-in-c Burstwick w Thorngumbald 85-87; V 87-90; R Kirby Misperton w Normanby, Edston and Salton 90-94; rtd 94; Perm to Offic *Cant* from 95. *Sandycroft, Lewson Street, Norton, Faversham ME9 9JN* Tel (01795) 522696
E-mail gsherwood@ontel.net.uk

SHERWOOD, Canon Ian Walter Lawrence. b 57. TCD BA80 DipTh82. **d** 82 **p** 84. C Dublin St Patr Cathl Gp *D & G* 82-83; Chapl Billinge Hosp Wigan 83-86; C Orrell *Liv* 83-86; Chapl Bucharest w Sofia *Eur* 86-89; Chapl Istanbul w Moda from 89; Can Malta Cathl from 97. *c/o FCO (Istanbul), King Charles Street, London SW1A 2AH* Tel (0090) (1) 244 4228

SHERWOOD, Kenneth Henry. b 37. CITC 90. **d** 93 **p** 94. NSM Malahide w Balgriffin *D & G* 93-96; NSM Castleknock and Mulhuddart, w Clonsilla 96-97; NSM Leighlin w Grange Sylvae, Shankill etc *C & O* from 97. *The Deanery, Old Leighlin, Co Carlow, Irish Republic* Tel (00353) (59) 972 1411

SHERWOOD, Nigel John Wesley. b 58. DipTh. CITC 86. **d** 86 **p** 87. C Kilmore w Ballintemple, Kildallon etc *K, E & A* 86-89; I Tullow w Shillelagh, Aghold and Mullinacuff *C & O* 89-95; I Arklow w Inch and Kilbride *D & G* from 95; Sec SPCK Glendalough from 98. *The Rectory, Emoclew Road, Arklow, Co Wicklow, Irish Republic* Tel (00353) (402) 32439

SHERWOOD, Paul Steven. b 76. Southn Univ BA(QTS)98. Ripon Coll Cuddesdon 00. **d** 03. C Chilworth w N Baddesley *Win* from 03. *18 Rownhams Lane, North Baddesley, Southampton SO52 9LQ* Tel (023) 8073 3131

SHERWOOD, Suffragan Bishop of. *See* MORGAN, The Rt Revd Alan Wyndham

SHEWAN, Alistair Boyd. b 44. Open Univ BA83 BSc95. Edin Th Coll 63. **d** 67 **p** 68. Prec St Andr Cathl Inverness *Mor* 67-69; C Shepherd's Bush St Steph w St Thos *Lon* 70-72; Hon C Edin St Mich and All SS *Edin* 73-75; Perm to Offic 75-81; Hon C Edin Old St Paul 81-86; NSM Edin St Columba 87-91; Asst Dioc Supernumerary from 91; C Edin St Ninian from 95. *3 Castle Wynd North, Edinburgh EH1 2NQ* Tel 0131-225 6537

SHEWAN, James William. b 36. Sarum Th Coll 61. **d** 63 **p** 64. C Rainbow Hill St Barn *Worc* 63-64; C Newton Aycliffe *Dur* 64-66; C Harton 66-69; V S Moor 69-72; CF 72-77; CF(V) from 81; P-in-c Benwell St Aid *Newc* 77-79; V Longhoughton w Howick 79-88; V Spittal 88-00; V Scremerston 88-00; RD Norham 96-00; rtd 00. *12 Clove Court, Tweedmouth, Berwick-upon-Tweed TD15 2FJ* Tel (01289) 306005

SHIELD, Barry Graham. b 39. Queensland Univ BA79 Univ of New England DipEd83 MLitt86 Kent Univ MA95 Washington Univ PhD00. St Fran Coll Queensland DipTh85 McAuley Coll Brisbane GradDipRE84. **d** 83 **p** 84. Australia 83-00 and from 01; P-in-c Haselbury Plucknett, Misterton and N Perrott *B & W* 00-01. *21 Miller Street, PO Box 96, Taroom, Qld, Australia 4420* Tel (0061) (7) 4627 3158 Fax as telephone
E-mail barryshield1@bigpond.com

SHIELD, Graham Friend. b 63. Ripon Coll Cuddesdon. **d** 00 **p** 01. C Camborne *Truro* from 00. *6 St Meriadoc Road, Camborne TR14 7HL* Tel (01209) 613160
E-mail graham@shieldfam.freeserve.co.uk

SHIELD, Ian Thomas. b 32. Hertf Coll Ox BA56 MA60 BLitt60. Westcott Ho Cam 59. **d** 61 **p** 62. C Shipley St Paul *Bradf* 61-64; Tutor Lich Th Coll 64-71; Chapl 67-71; V Dunston w Coppenhall *Lich* 71-79; TV Wolverhampton 79-86; rtd 87; Perm to Offic *Lich* from 87. *13 Duke Street, Penn Fields, Wolverhampton WV4 3DT* Tel (01902) 337037
E-mail ianshield@aol.com

SHIELDS, Mrs Jennifer Jill. b 39. Heref Coll of Educn CertEd74. St Alb and Ox Min Course 99. **d** 02. OLM Lenborough *Ox* from 02. *8 West Furlong, Padbury, Buckingham MK18 2BP* Tel (01280) 814474

SHIELDS, Canon Michael Penton. b 30. Bps' Coll Cheshunt. **d** 64 **p** 65. C Kingsbury St Andr *Lon* 64-67; C Friern Barnet All SS 67-69; V Colindale St Matthias 69-76; V Sevenoaks St Jo *Roch* 76-95; RD Sevenoaks 84-95; Chapl Sevenoaks Hosp 78-94; Chapl St Mich Sch Otford 90-95; Hon Can Roch Cathl *Roch* 94-95; rtd 95; Hon PV Roch Cathl *Roch* from 96; Perm to Offic from 01. *Flat 14, Bromley College, London Road, Bromley BR1 1PE* Tel (020) 8464 7906

SHILL, Kenneth Leslie. b 49. Leic Univ BA70 Lon Univ BD73 Cam Univ DipTh77. Ridley Hall Cam 75. **d** 77 **p** 78. C Harborne Heath *Birm* 77-83; V Mansfield St Jo *S'well* 83-93; Bp's Adv on Healing 89-93; Chapl Amsterdam w Heiloo *Eur* 93-95; TR Bath Twerton-on-Avon *B & W* from 95. *The Rectory, Watery Lane, Twerton-on-Avon, Bath BA2 1RL* Tel (01225) 421438
E-mail shill1@tinyworld.co.uk

SHILLAKER, Mrs Christine Frances. b 39. Lon Univ DipTh61. Gilmore Ho 74. **dss** 86 **d** 87 **p** 94. Colchester St Leon, St Mary Magd and St Steph *Chelmsf* 86-89; Par Dn 87-89; Par Dn Colchester, New Town and The Hythe 89-94; C 94-96; P-in-c Ramsey w Lt Oakley and Wrabness 96-02; rtd 02. *21 Nelson Road, Colchester CO3 9AP*

SHILLAKER, John. b 34. K Coll Lon BD60 AKC60. **d** 61 **p** 62. C Bush Hill Park St Mark *Lon* 61-65; C Milton *Win* 65-69; C-in-c Moulsham St Luke CD *Chelmsf* 69-78; V Moulsham St Luke 78-85; P-in-c Colchester St Leon, St Mary Magd and St Steph 85-86; R 86-89; R Colchester, New Town and The Hythe 89-96; rtd 96; Perm to Offic *Chelmsf* from 00. *21 Nelson Road, Colchester CO3 9AP*

SHILLING, Ms Audrey Violet. b 26. Dur Univ BA69. CA Tr Coll 51 Cranmer Hall Dur 66. **d** 87 **p** 94. CA from 53; NSM Gillingham H Trin *Roch* 87-93; NSM Rainham 94-96; Perm to Offic from 96. *13 Motney Hill Road, Gillingham ME8 7TZ* Tel (01634) 233654 Fax as telephone

SHILLINGFORD, Brian. b 39. Lich Th Coll 65. **d** 68 **p** 69. C Lewisham St Swithun *S'wark* 68-71; C Godstone 71-75; TV Croydon *Cant* 75-81; TV N Creedy *Ex* 81-93; TR from 93. *The Rectory, Morchard Bishop, Crediton EX17 6PJ* Tel (01363) 877221

SHILSON-THOMAS, Mrs Annabel Margaret. b 60. Jes Coll Ox BA82. Westcott Ho Cam 87. **d** 89 **p** 98. Par Dn Sydenham St Bart *S'wark* 89-93; Journalist CAFOD 95-03; Hon C Kingston All SS w St Jo *S'wark* 97-98; Perm to Offic *Ely* 00-03; Acting Chapl Rob Coll Cam 03; Chapl Anglia Poly Univ *Ely* from 03. *73 Oxford Road, Cambridge CB4 3PH*

SHILSON-THOMAS, Hugh David. b 64. Ex Coll Ox BA86 MA98 K Coll Lon MA99. Westcott Ho Cam 87. **d** 89 **p** 90. C Sydenham All SS *S'wark* 89-92; C Lower Sydenham St Mich 89-92; Ecum Chapl Kingston Univ 93-98; Chapl Rob Coll Cam 98-03; Nat Adv for HE/Chapl Abps' Coun from 03; Perm to Offic *Ely* from 03. *Church House, Great Smith Street, London SW1P 3NZ* Tel (020) 7898 1513
E-mail hugh.shilson-thomas@c-of-e.org.uk

SHILVOCK, Geoffrey. b 47. Univ of Wales (Lamp) BA69. Sarum Th Coll 70. **d** 72 **p** 73. C Kidderminster St Mary *Worc* 72-78; P-in-c Gt Malvern Ch Ch 78-85; V Wolverley and Cookley from 85; RD Kidderminster 95-01. *The Vicarage, Wolverley, Kidderminster DY11 5XD* Tel (01562) 851133
E-mail geoffshilvock@hotmail.com

SHIMWELL, Canon Robert John. b 46. ARCM65. Lon Bible Coll DipTh68 Trin Coll Bris 75. **d** 78 **p** 79. C Richmond H Trin *S'wark* 78-79; C Luddington *Ex* 79-81; C Kentisbeare w Blackborough 79-81; V S Cave and Ellerker w Broomfleet *York* 81-87; Chapl Lee Abbey 87-88; R Glas St Silas *Glas* 88-94; V Upton (Overchurch) *Ches* from 94; RD Wirral N 97-98; Hon Can Ches Cathl from 02. *The Vicarage, 20 Church Road, Upton, Wirral CH49 6JZ* Tel 0151-677 4810 *or* 677 1186 Fax 606 1935
E-mail rob@stm-upton.org.uk

SHINE, Aisling. **d** 03. NSM Dublin Drumcondra w N Strand *D & G* from 03. *1 Roselawn Grove, Castleknock, Dublin 15, Irish Republic* Tel (00353) (1) 820 1797 E-mail shine1@eircom.net

SHINER, Michael Joseph. b 21. Chich Th Coll 51. **d** 53 **p** 54. C Weymouth H Trin *Sarum* 53-56; V Stanbridge w Tilsworth *St Alb* 56-63; V Powerstock w W Milton, Witherstone and N Poorton *Sarum* 67-73; V Knutsford St Cross *Ches* 73-75; Area Sec Age Concern Cornwall 75-86; Perm to Offic *S'wark* 80-86; rtd 86. *55 Tennyson Drive, Malvern WR14 2UL* Tel (01684) 563269

SHINN, William Raymond. b 22. Sarum & Wells Th Coll 71. **d** 73 **p** 74. C Letchworth St Paul *St Alb* 73-75; C Dunstable 76-78; TV 78-80; V Luton St Chris Round Green 80-88; rtd 88; Perm to Offic *St Alb* from 88. *31 Coleridge Close, Hitchin SG4 0QX* Tel (01462) 641883

SHINTON, Bertram David. b 41. K Coll Lon 62 Liv Univ PGCTh97. WMMTC 95. **d** 98 **p** 99. NSM Broseley w Benthall, Jackfield, Linley etc *Heref* from 98. *Gestiana, Woodlands Road, Broseley TF12 5PU* Tel (01952) 882765 *or* 0121-311 2104

SHIPLEY, Stephen Edwin Burnham. b 52. Univ Coll Dur BA74. Westcott Ho Cam 85. **d** 87 **p** 88. C Ipswich St Marg *St E* 87-90; P-in-c Stuntney *Ely* 90-95; Min Can, Prec and Sacr Ely Cathl 90-95; Producer Worship Progr BBC Relig Broadcasting from 95; Lic to Offic *Derby* from 96. *21 Devonshire Road, Buxton SK17 6RZ* Tel (01298) 78383 *or* 0161-244 3292 Fax 0161-244 3290 E-mail stephen.shipley@bbc.co.uk

SHIPP, Linda Mary. b 49. Cranmer Hall Dur 00. **d** 02 **p** 03. C Kirkleatham *York* from 02. *44 Ayton Drive, Redcar TS10 4LR* Tel and fax (01642) 476072 Mobile 07970-908517
E-mail linda.shipp@btinternet.com

SHIPP, Susan. *See* HOLLINS, Patricia Susan

SHIPSIDES, Brian Kenneth. b 56. Reading Univ BA. Westcott Ho Cam 79. **d** 82 **p** 83. C Bramley *Ripon* 82-85; C Notting Dale St Clem w St Mark and St Jas *Lon* 85-90; Chapl N Lon Poly 90-92; Chapl Univ of N Lon 92-97; P-in-c Forest Gate All SS and St Edm *Chelmsf* from 97. *The Vicarage, 79 Claremont Road, London E7 0QA* Tel (020) 8534 2193

SHIPTON, Andrew James. b 60. Leeds Univ BA82 Univ of Northumbria at Newc MED99. Cranmer Hall Dur 83. **d** 85 **p** 86. C Fishponds St Jo *Bris* 85-88; C Gosforth All SS *Newc* 88-91; V Long Benton St Mary 91-96; Chapl Univ of Northumbria at Newc from 96. *282 Wingrove Road North, Newcastle upon Tyne NE4 9EE* Tel 0191-274 9761
E-mail andrew.shipton@unn.ac.uk

SHIPTON, Linda Anne. *See* GREEN, Mrs Linda Anne

SHIPTON (née WILSON), Mrs Marjorie Jayne. b 59. Hull Univ BA80 Leeds Univ MA01 K Alfred's Coll Win PGCE81. St Jo Coll Dur 85. **dss** 86 **d** 87 **p** 94. Ormesby *York* 86-89; Par Dn 87-89; Chapl Asst Newc Gen Hosp 89-91; Chapl 91-95; Dep Hd Chapl Newcastle upon Tyne Hosps NHS Trust from 95; NSM Whorlton *Newc* 94-97. *Royal Victoria Infirmary, Queen Victoria Road, Newcastle upon Tyne NE1 4LP* Tel 0191-232 5131

SHIRE, William Stanley. b 17. TCD BA39 MA43. **d** 40 **p** 41. C Dundalk *Arm* 40-43; C Portadown St Mark 43-45; P-in-c Mullaglass 45-51; I 51-57; C Attenborough w Bramcote and Chilwell *S'well* 57-58; V Lowdham 58-66; R Pilton w Wardenhoe and Stoke Doyle *Pet* 67-70; R Aldwincle w Thorpe Achurch, Pilton, Wadenhoe etc 70-82; rtd 82; Lic to Offic *Pet* 82-85; Perm to Offic from 85. *96 Glapthorne Road, Oundle, Peterborough PE8 4PS* Tel (01832) 272125

SHIRES, Alan William. b 36. Lon Univ BA60. Oak Hill Th Coll 57. **d** 61 **p** 62. C York St Paul *York* 61-64; C Southgate *Chich* 64-67; V Doncaster St Mary *Sheff* 67-75; Perm to Offic *Portsm* 75-96; Student Counsellor Portsm Poly 75-88; Hd Student Services Portsm Poly 88-96; rtd 96. *15 Broomfield Road, Admaston, Wellington TF5 0AR*

SHIRESS, Canon David Henry Faithfull. b 27. St Cath Coll Cam BA49 MA53. Ridley Hall Cam 51. **d** 53 **p** 54. C Southport Ch Ch *Liv* 53-55; C St Helens St Mark 55-58; V Shrewsbury St Julian *Lich* 58-67; V Blackheath Park St Mich *S'wark* 67-93; Sub-Dean Greenwich 81-90; RD Greenwich 90-91; Hon Can S'wark Cathl 89-93; rtd 93; Perm to Offic *Sarum* from 93. *35 Rempstone Road, Wimborne BH21 1SS* Tel (01202) 887845

SHIRLEY, Timothy Francis. b 25. Univ Coll Ox BA49 MA49. Qu Coll Birm 49. **d** 51 **p** 52. C Pimlico St Gabr *Lon* 51-56; C-in-c Hayes St Edm CD 56-65; V Fulham St Etheldreda 65-68; V Fulham St Etheldreda w St Clem 68-90; rtd 90; Perm to Offic *Worc* from 90. *70 St Dunstan's Crescent, Worcester WR5 2AQ* Tel (01905) 353930

SHIRLEY, Valerie Joy. b 42. LNSM course 93. **d** 96 **p** 97. OLM Sydenham H Trin *S'wark* from 96. *Flat 9, Faircroft, 5 Westwood Hill, London SE26 6BG* Tel (020) 8778 2551

SHIRRAS, The Ven Edward Scott. b 37. St Andr Univ BSc61. Clifton Th Coll 61. **d** 63 **p** 64. C Surbiton Hill Ch Ch *S'wark* 63-66; C Jesmond Clayton Memorial *Newc* 66-68; Youth Sec CPAS 68-71; Publications Sec 71-74; Asst Gen Sec 74-75; Hon C Wallington H Trin *S'wark* 69-75; V Roxeth Ch Ch *Lon* 75-82; V Roxeth Ch Ch and Harrow St Pet 82-85; AD Harrow 82-85; Adn Northolt 85-92; V Win Ch Ch *Win* 92-01; rtd 01; Perm to Offic *Ox* 01-02; P-in-c Marcham w Garford from 02. *1 All Saints Close, Marcham, Abingdon OX13 6PE* Tel (01865) 391319
E-mail shirras@ukgateway.net

SHIRRAS, Rachel Joan. *See* COLLINS, Rachel Joan

SHOCK, Rachel Alexandra. b 63. Nottm Trent Univ LLB94. EMMTC 95. **d** 98 **p** 00. NSM Radford All So w Ch Ch and St Mich *S'well* 98-99; NSM Lenton Abbey from 99. *1 May Avenue, Wollaton, Nottingham NG8 2NE* Tel 0115-928 3626
E-mail rachel@ashock.freeserve.co.uk

SHONE, The Very Revd John Terence. b 35. Selw Coll Cam BA58 MA64 Newc Univ MA92. Linc Th Coll 58. **d** 60 **p** 61. C St Pancras w St Jas and Ch Ch *Lon* 60-62; Chapl Aber Univ *Ab* 62-68; Chapl St Andr Cathl 62-65; V Gt Grimsby St Andr and St Luke *Linc* 68-69; Chapl Stirling Univ *St And* 69-80; R Bridge of Allan 69-86; P-in-c Alloa 77-85; Can St Ninian's Cathl Perth 80-89; P-in-c Dollar 81-86; Dean St Andr 82-89; Research and Development Officer 86-89; Dioc Supernumerary 86-89; TV Cullercoats St Geo *Newc* 89-00; rtd 00. *29 Redwell Place, Alloa FK10 2BT* Tel (01259) 215113 E-mail husnwif@aol.com

SHONE, Raymond. b 21. St Jo Coll Dur BA47 MA54 Brighton Poly Dip Counselling 81. Linc Th Coll 48. **d** 48 **p** 49. C Penn *Lich* 48-50; C Warblington w Emsworth *Portsm* 50-58; R Monks Risborough *Ox* 58-61; Chapl and Lect Bp Otter Coll Chich 61-66; Perm to Offic *Chich* from 66; Sen Lect Eastbourne Coll of Educn 66-76; E Sussex Coll of HE 76-79; Brighton Poly 79-80; Counsellor W Sussex Inst of HE 83-87; rtd 87. *28 Hawthorn Close, Chichester PO19 3DZ* Tel (01243) 774543

SHONE, Robert Alan. b 16. Qu Coll Cam BA38 MA42. St Steph Ho Ox 39. **d** 39 **p** 40. C W Derby Gd Shep *Liv* 39-41; C Wigan All SS 41-42; C Birch St Jas *Man* 42-45; C Wardleworth St Mary 45-47; R Withington St Chris 47-56; V Morley St Paul *Wakef* 56-63; V Wardleworth St Mary *Man* 63-73; V Wardleworth St Jas 66-73; V Wardleworth St Mary w St Jas 73-81; rtd 81; Perm to Offic *Man* from 81. *32 Tong Lane, Whitworth, Rochdale OL12 8BE* Tel (01706) 825648

SHONE, Miss Ursula Ruth. b 34. Lon Univ DBRS59 Stirling Univ BA75 Open Univ BPhil88 Chester Coll of HE DipApTh00. **dss** 81 **d** 86 **p** 94. Bridge of Allan *St And* 81-85; Lochgelly 85-87; Chapl Cov Cathl *Cov* 87-90; Ind Chapl 87-90; Par Dn Ainsdale *Liv* 90-94; Dioc Science Adv 90-99; C Ainsdale 94-96; C Childwall St Dav 99-00; rtd 00; Perm to Offic *Bre* from 00. *4 Park Road, Brechin DD9 7AF* Tel (01356) 626087

SHOOTER, Robert David. b 44. Lon Univ BSc70 Lanc Univ MA94 CQSW72 LRAM92. N Ord Course 99. **d** 02 **p** 03. NSM

Brierfield *Blackb* from 02. *234 Briercliffe Road, Burnley BB10 2NZ* Tel (01282) 412404

SHOOTER, Ms Susan. b 58. Nottm Univ BA81 PGCE82. St Jo Coll Nottm MA94. **d** 96 **p** 98. C Dartford H Trin *Roch* 96-97; C Crayford 97-00; V Bostall Heath from 00. *St Andrew's Parsonage, 276 Brampton Road, Bexleyheath DA7 5SF* Tel (020) 8303 9332
E-mail mistshoot@aol.com

SHORROCK, John Musgrave. b 29. TCD BA54 MA58. Bps' Coll Cheshunt 54. **d** 56 **p** 57. C Fleetwood *Blackb* 56-59; C Lancaster St Mary 59-61; C-in-c Blackpool St Wilfrid CD 61-65; V Blackpool St Wilfrid 65-67; Min Can and Sacr Cant Cathl *Cant* 67-70; V Chorley St Geo *Blackb* 71-78; P-in-c Bredgar w Bicknor and Huckinge *Cant* 78-82; P-in-c Frinsted w Wormshill and Milstead 78-82; R Bredgar w Bicknor and Frinsted w Wormshill etc 82-92; rtd 92; Perm to Offic *Cant* from 92; Clergy Widows Officer Cant Adnry from 97. *Bradgate, School Lane, Bekesbourne, Canterbury CT4 5ER* Tel (01227) 832133
E-mail shorrock@eurobell.co.uk

SHORT, Brian Frederick. b 29. St Jo Coll Nottm 70. **d** 72 **p** 73. C Walton St E 72-75; P-in-c Barking w Darmsden and Gt Bricett 75-78; P-in-c Ringshall w Battisford and Lt Finborough 75-78; TV Nor St Pet Parmentergate w St Jo *Nor* 78-88; R Winfarthing w Shelfanger w Burston w Gissing etc 88-90; rtd 90; Perm to Offic *Nor* from 92. *31 Nursery Gardens, Blofield, Norwich NR13 4JE* Tel (01603) 712396

SHORT, Bryan Raymond. b 37. Bris Univ BSc59 CertEd60. Dioc OLM tr scheme 00. **d** 02 **p** 03. *12 Bankfield Lane, Kirkheaton, Huddersfield HD5 0JG* Tel (01484) 425832

SHORT, Ms Clare. b 50. Leic Univ BA72 St Mary's Coll Twickenham PGCE73. All Nations Chr Coll Cert Div & RS 81 S Dios Minl Tr Scheme 89. **d** 92 **p** 94. NSM Horsham *Chich* 92-99. *19 York Close, Southwater, Horsham RH13 9XJ* Tel (01403) 730880

SHORT, Eileen. b 45. Ex Univ BA66. Nor Ord Course 93. **d** 96 **p** 97. NSM Castleton Moor *Man* 96-98; NSM Chorlton-cum-Hardy St Clem 98-00; NSM Baguley from 00. *2 Netherwood Road, Northenden, Manchester M22 4BQ*

SHORT, Mrs Heather Mary. b 50. WEMTC 98. **d** 01 **p** 02. C Heref S Wye *Heref* from 01. *26 St Clare's Court, Lower Bullingham, Hereford HR2 6PX* Tel (01432) 351687

SHORT, Canon John Sinclair. b 33. Oak Hill Th Coll 64. **d** 66 **p** 67. C Islington St Mary *Lon* 66-70; V Becontree St Mary *Chelmsf* 70-76; V New Malden and Coombe *S'wark* 76-90; RD Kingston 79-84; Hon Can S'wark Cathl 83-90; P-in-c Peldon w Gt and Lt Wigborough *Chelmsf* 90-93; rtd 93; Perm to Offic *S'wark* from 93. *22 Chart Lane, Reigate RH2 7BP* Tel (01737) 245244

SHORT, Canon John Timothy. b 43. Lon Univ DipTh67. Kelham Th Coll 63. **d** 68 **p** 69. C St Marylebone Ch Ch w St Barn *Lon* 68-70; C Southgate Ch Ch 70-72; P-in-c Mosser *Carl* 72-78; Dioc Youth Officer 72-78; R Heyford w Stowe Nine Churches *Pet* 78-87; V Northampton St Jas 87-96; RD Wootton 88-96; TR Kingsthorpe w Northampton St Dav from 96; Can Pet Cathl from 97. *The Rectory, 16 Green End, Kingsthorpe, Northampton NN2 6RD* Tel (01604) 717133 Fax as telephone
E-mail tim@kingsthorpechurches.co.uk

SHORT, Kenneth Arthur. b 33. Tyndale Hall Bris 64. **d** 67 **p** 68. C E Twickenham St Steph *Lon* 67-71; C Paddock Wood *Roch* 71-74; SE Area Sec BCMS 74-82; Hon C Sidcup Ch Ch *Roch* 74-82; V Tollington Park St Mark w St Anne *Lon* 82-86; V Holloway St Mark w Em 86-89; R Alfold and Loxwood *Guildf* 89-98; rtd 98; Perm to Offic *Roch* from 00. *228 Ralph Perring Court, Stone Park Avenue, Beckenham BR3 3LX* Tel 020-8650 4859

SHORT, Martin Peter. b 54. Peterho Cam BA77 MA81. Wycliffe Hall Ox 77. **d** 79 **p** 80. C Shipley St Pet *Bradf* 79-82; C Becontree St Mary *Chelmsf* 82-86; V Bolton St Jas w St Chrys *Bradf* 86-92; Dioc Communications Officer 92-98; C Otley 92-98; Hd Media Tr Gen Syn Communications Dept from 98; Hon C and Hon Chapl Bradf Cathl *Bradf* from 98; Lic to Offic from 98. *5 Cathedral Close, Bradford BD1 4EG* Tel (01274) 777731

SHORT, Martin Ronald. b 57. Crewe & Alsager Coll CertEd78 Leic Univ BEd85. St Jo Coll Nottm 93. **d** 93 **p** 94. C Frankby w Greasby Ches 93-97; TV Horwich and Rivington *Man* 97-02; TV Turton Moorland Min from 02. *St Anne's Vicarage, High Street, Turton, Bolton BL7 0EH* Tel (01204) 856807

SHORT, Canon Michael John. b 38. Univ of Wales (Lamp) BA59. Sarum Th Coll 59. **d** 61 **p** 62. C Swansea St Nic *S & B* 61-64; C Oystermouth 64-69; V Merthyr Vale w Aberfan *Llan* 69-82; RD Merthyr Tydfil 76-82; R Caerphilly from 82; RD Caerphilly from 83; Can Llan Cathl from 89; Prec from 02. *The Rectory, 2 St Martin's Road, Caerphilly CF83 1EJ* Tel (029) 2088 2992 Mobile 07831-742515

SHORT, Neil Robert. b 58. Loughb Univ BSc81 St Jo Coll Dur BA86. Cranmer Hall Dur 83. **d** 86 **p** 87. C Whitfield *Derby* 86-90; C Bradf St Aug Undercliffe *Bradf* 90-96; V Burscough Bridge *Liv* from 96. *St John's Vicarage, 253 Liverpool Road South, Ormskirk L40 7RE* Tel (01704) 893205

SHORT, Mrs Patricia Ann (Pip). b 41. K Coll Lon BA62 AKC62. **d** 00 **p** 01. NSM Etwall w Egginton *Derby* from 00; Chapl Asst S Derbyshire Acute Hosps NHS Trust from 00. *Ivy Cottage, 19 Monk Street, Tutbury, Burton-on-Trent DE13 9NA* Tel (01283) 813640 Mobile 07711-823082 Fax 814373 E-mail pipshort@mail.com *or* pip.short@sdah-tr.trent.nhs.uk

SHORT, Robert Leslie. b 48. Em Coll Cam BA70 MA76. Wycliffe Hall Ox 87. **d** 92 **p** 92. Mexico 92-93; Chapl Repton Sch *Derby* from 93. *Repton School, Repton, Derby DE65 6FH* Tel (01283) 559283 Fax as telephone

SHORT, Timothy. *See* SHORT, Canon John Timothy

SHORT, Vincent Charles. b 57. Oak Hill Th Coll DipHE92. **d** 97 **p** 98. C Chatham St Phil and St Jas *Roch* 97-01; V Istead Rise from 01. *The Vicarage, Upper Avenue, Gravesend DA13 9DA* Tel (01474) 832403 Fax as telephone E-mail vcshort@fish.co.uk

SHORTEN, Richard Deering. b 08. Qu Coll Cam BA30 MA48. Westcott Ho Cam 30. **d** 32 **p** 33. C Leeds St Wilfrid *Ripon* 32-35; I Hunslet St Silas 35-38; V Kirkby Wharfe *York* 38-56; Chapl RAFVR 41-48; V Preshute *Sarum* 56-75; Asst Chapl Marlborough Coll 56-75; RD Marlborough *Sarum* 64-75; rtd 75; Perm to Offic *Sarum* from 75. *c/o J H D Shorten Esq, Tanners, Hyde End Lane, Brimpton, Reading RG7 4RH* Tel 0118-971 3553 *or* 01256 844888

SHORTER, Robert Edward. b 48. Ripon Coll Cuddesdon 89. **d** 91 **p** 92. C Braunton *Ex* 91-94; C Bishopsnympton, Rose Ash, Mariansleigh etc 94-96; TV 96-98; P-in-c E w W Harptree and Hinton Blewett *B & W* 98-03; Dioc Ecum Officer 98-03. *Fleur de la Passion, 61330 Torchamp, France*

SHORTHOUSE, Raymond Trevor. b 34. DipAdEd Warwick Univ DPhil00. Ridley Hall Cam 68. **d** 70 **p** 71. C Gt Ilford St Andr *Chelmsf* 70-73; C Ludlow *Heref* 73-75; P-in-c Cressage w Sheinton 76-80; P-in-c Harley w Kenley 76-80; P-in-c Denby *Derby* 80-84; Adult Educn Officer 80-85; RD Heanor 83-84; V Chellaston 84-88; P-in-c Breadsall 88-98; Dioc Dir of Studies 88-96; rtd 98; P-in-c Symondsbury *Sarum* from 99. *The Rectory, Shutes Lane, Symondsbury, Bridport DT6 6HF* Tel (01308) 422145 E-mail justin@shorthouse.netlineuk.net

SHORTT, Canon Noel Christopher. b 36. Open Univ BA76 Ulster Univ MA Dip Continuing Educn DPhil91. Bps' Coll Cheshunt 63. **d** 63 **p** 64. C Belfast St Mary *Conn* 63-66; C Agherton 66-68; Chapl RAF 68-69; I Duneane w Ballyscullion *Conn* 69-79; I Belfast St Steph w St Luke 79-89; I Ballyrashane w Kildollagh 89-99; Can Belfast St Anne 96-99; rtd 99. *2 Woodview Park, Ballymoney BT53 6DJ*

SHOTLANDER, Lionel George. b 27. Cant Univ (NZ) BA49 MA51. **d** 51 **p** 52. New Zealand 51-58 and 60-74; C Southsea St Pet *Portsm* 58-60; V Curdridge 74-85; R Durley 79-85; V Twyford and Owslebury and Morestead *Win* 85-91; rtd 91; Perm to Offic *Win* and *Portsm* from 91. *Cambria, High Street, Shirrell Heath, Southampton SO32 2JN* Tel (01329) 832353

SHOTTER, The Very Revd Edward Frank. b 33. Univ of Wales (Lamp) BA58. St Steph Ho Ox 58. **d** 60 **p** 61. C Plymouth St Pet *Ex* 60-62; Inter-Colleg Sec SCM (Lon) 62-66; Perm to Offic *Lon* 62-69; Dir Lon Medical Gp 63-89; Chapl Lon Univ Medical Students *Lon* 69-89; Dir Inst of Medical Ethics 74-89; Preb St Paul's Cathl *Lon* 77-89; Dean Roch 89-03; rtd 03. *Hill House, Westhall, Halesworth IP19 8QZ* Tel (01502) 575364

SHOULER, Mrs Margaret Fiona. b 55. St Jo Coll Nottm. **d** 01 **p** 02. C Sherwood *S'well* from 01. *139 Appledore Avenue, Wollaton, Nottingham NG8 2RW* Tel 0115-928 3400

SHOULER, Simon Frederic. b 54. Pemb Coll Cam MA79 FRICS89. EMMTC 82. **d** 85 **p** 86. NSM Asfordby *Leic* 85-89; Lic to Offic from 89. *1 West End, Long Clawson, Melton Mowbray LE14 4PE* Tel (01664) 822549 E-mail sshouler@oldmanorhouse.u-net.com

SHOZAWA, John. **d** 64. Canada 64-78 and 95-01; USA 78-95; rtd 01; Perm to Offic *Guildf* from 00. *4 Cromwell Place, Cranleigh GU6 7LF* Tel (01483) 267295

SHREEVE, The Ven David Herbert. b 34. St Pet Hall Ox BA57 MA61. Ridley Hall Cam 57. **d** 59 **p** 60. C Plymouth St Andr *Ex* 59-64; V Bermondsey St Anne *S'wark* 64-71; V Eccleshill *Bradf* 71-84; RD Calverley 78-84; Hon Can Bradf Cathl 83-84; Adn Bradf 84-99; rtd 99; Lic to Offic *Bradf* from 99. *26 Kingsley Drive, Harrogate HG1 4TJ* Tel (01423) 886479

SHREWSBURY, Preb Michael Buller. b 30. St Jo Coll Dur BA54. Linc Th Coll 54. **d** 56 **p** 57. C Salford St Phil w St Steph *Man* 56-60; Chapl RN 60-63; Chapl HM Pris Pentonville 64-67; Bermuda 67-70; V Dalston H Trin w St Phil *Lon* 70-86; AD Hackney 79-84; Preb St Paul's Cathl 86-92; R Stepney St Dunstan and All SS 86-92; rtd 92; Perm to Offic *Lon* from 92. *Flat 1, 150 Wapping High Street, London E1W 3PH* Tel (020) 7480 5479

SHREWSBURY, Area Bishop of. *See* SMITH, The Rt Revd Alan Gregory Clayton

SHRIMPTON, Canon Aner Clive. b 14. Lon Univ BD39. ALCD39. **d** 39 **p** 40. C Ore Ch Ch *Chich* 39-41; C Battle 42-46; P-in-c S Patcham 46-52; V Ruddington *S'well* 52-84; Hon Can S'well Minster 78-84; rtd 84; Perm to Offic *S'well* from 84.

36 Brookview Drive, Keyworth, Nottingham NG12 5JN Tel 0115-937 2795

SHRIMPTON, Mrs Sheila Nan. b 32. Qu Mary Coll Lon BA54 LSE CertSS55. St Chris Coll Blackheath 57. **dss** 83 **d** 87 **p** 94. Lic to Offic *B & W* 83-90; NSM Barkston and Hough Gp *Linc* 90-97; Asst Local Min Officer 90-97; C Brant Broughton and Beckingham 97-98; P-in-c Churchstanton, Buckland St Mary and Otterford *B & W* 98-02; rtd 02. *2 King William Mews, Church Street, Curry Rivel, Langport TA10 0HD* Tel (01458) 259293

SHRINE, Robert Gerald. b 44. Birm Univ BA65 Univ of Zambia PGCE70 Lanc Univ MA74 Open Univ BA80. St Jo Coll Nottm MA97. **d** 97 **p** 98. C Blackpool St Thos *Blackb* 97-99; Dioc Chapl among Deaf People *Bradf* and *Wakef* from 99. *10 Field Close, Halifax HX3 5LS* Tel (18002) (01422) 300511 Fax (01422) 300718 E-mail bob.shrine@ukonline.co.uk

SHRINE, Mrs Susan Elaine Walmsley. b 56. N Ord Course. **d** 02 **p** 03. C Bradshaw and Holmfield *Wakef* from 02. *10 Field Close, Halifax HX3 5LS* Tel (01422) 384140 Fax 300718 E-mail sue.shrine@ukonline.co.uk

SHRISUNDER, David Shripat. b 29. Osmania Univ Hyderabad BA52 Serampore Univ BD59 Shivaji Univ Kolhapur MA69. Bp's Coll Calcutta 54. **d** 57 **p** 58. India 57-71, 72-75, 77-79 and 88-90; C Poona St Paul w Kirkee All SS 57-58; P I Bombay Em 58-61; I Solapur Epiphany 61-71, 72-75 and 88-90; Lect Dayanand Coll Solapur 69-71, 72-75 and 78-79; C Batley All SS *Wakef* 71-72; C Skegness *Linc* 75-77; C Derringham Bank *York* 80-81; TV Grays Thurrock *Chelmsf* 81-85; R Uddingston *Glas* 85-88; R Cambuslang 85-88; P-in-c Sinfin Moor *Derby* 90-94; rtd 94; Perm to Offic *Wakef* 94-96 and from 98. *8 Jessamine Street, Dewsbury WF13 3HY* Tel (01924) 517616

SHRIVES, Austen Geoffrey. b 28. Lon Univ BD68 MTh77. S'wark Ord Course. **d** 64 **p** 65. C Lower Sydenham St Mich S'wark 64-68; Miss to Seamen 68-74; V Epsom St Martin *Guildf* 74-84; V York Town St Mich 84-87; R Churchstanton, Buckland St Mary and Otterford *B & W* 87-93; rtd 93; Perm to Offic *Ex* 94-96; Perm to Offic *Heref* from 97. *16 Watling Street, Ross-on-Wye HR9 5UF*

SHUFFLEBOTHAM, Alastair Vincent. b 32. Nottm Univ CSocSc57. Lich Th Coll 63. **d** 65 **p** 66. C W Kirby St Bridget *Ches* 65-69; V Tranmere St Paul 69-71; V Tranmere St Paul w St Luke 71-78; V Neston 78-97; rtd 97. *Y-Clystyrau, 5 Tan-y-Bryn, Llanbedr Dyffryn Clwyd, Ruthin LL15 1AQ* Tel (01824) 704619

SHUKMAN, Ann Margaret. b 31. Girton Coll Cam BA53 MA58 LMH Ox DPhil74. WMMTC 80. **dss** 84 **d** 92 **p** 94. Steeple Aston w N Aston and Tackley *Ox* 84-96; NSM 92-96; rtd 96; Perm to Offic *Ox* from 96. *40 Woodstock Close, Oxford OX2 8DB* Tel (01865) 512554 Fax 310341

SHUTT, Anthony John. b 57. Brunel Univ BSc79 DipHE89. Trin Coll Bris 87. **d** 89 **p** 90. C Epsom St Martin *Guildf* 89-95; P-in-c Send from 95. *St Mary's Vicarage, Vicarage Lane, Send, Woking GU23 7JN* Tel (01483) 222193

SHUTT, Laurence John. b 42. MPS64 MRPharmS88. St Steph Ho Ox 87 Llan Dioc Tr Scheme 80. **d** 84 **p** 85. NSM Whitchurch *Llan* 84-87; C Llanishen and Lisvane 88-90; Chapl RNR from 89; V Middlestown *Wakef* 90-97; P-in-c Arnside *Carl* from 97. *The Vicarage, Church Hill, Arnside, Carnforth LA5 0DW* Tel (01524) 761319

SHUTT, Nicholas Stephen. b 58. Qu Mary Coll Lon LLB80 Solicitor 83. SW Minl Tr Course 91. **d** 94 **p** 95. NSM Yelverton, Meavy, Sheepstor and Walkhampton *Ex* from 94. *12 Blackbrook Close, Walkhampton, Yelverton PL20 6JF* Tel (01822) 854653 E-mail nickshutt@compuserve.com

SIBANDA, Melusi Francis. b 72. Univ of Zimbabwe BSc96 BA99. Bp Gaul Th Coll Harare 97. **d** 98 **p** 99. C Bulawayo Cathl Zimbabwe 98-00; R Bulawayo St Marg 01-03; C Colne and Villages *Blackb* from 03. *13 Lancaster Street, Colne BB8 9AZ* Tel (01282) 871750 E-mail mfsibanda@hotmail.com

SIBBALD, Olwyn. *See* MARLOW, Mrs Olwyn Eileen

SIBLEY, Jonathan Paul Eddolls. b 55. Newc Univ BA77. Westcott Ho Cam 78 Ripon Coll Cuddesdon 85. **d** 87 **p** 88. C Waltham Cross *St Alb* 87-90; C Chalfont St Peter *Ox* 90-96; P-in-c Sulhamstead Abbots and Bannister w Ufton Nervet 96-02; P-in-c Sutton St Mary *Linc* from 02. *The Vicarage, Market Place, Long Sutton, Spalding PE12 9JJ* Tel (01406) 362033 Fax as telephone E-mail sibley.jon_jeanne@btinternet.com

SIBLEY, Peter Linsey. b 40. Selw Coll Cam BA61 MA63 DipHE. Oak Hill Th Coll 79. **d** 81 **p** 82. C Crofton *Portsm* 81-84; TV Cheltenham St Mark *Glouc* 84-93; P-in-c Tewkesbury H Trin 93-96; V from 96; RD Tewkesbury and Winchcombe 97-02. *Holy Trinity Vicarage, 49 Barton Street, Tewkesbury GL20 5PU* Tel (01684) 293233 E-mail sibglos@aol.com

SIBSON, Canon Edward John. b 39. Brasted Th Coll 61 St Aid Birkenhead 63. **d** 65 **p** 66. C Gt Parndon *Chelmsf* 65-69; C Saffron Walden 69-72; P-in-c Colchester St Leon 72-77; Ind Chapl 72-80; TV Colchester St Leon, St Mary Magd and St Steph 77-80; V Layer de la Haye 80-90; R Chipping Ongar w Shelley 90-98; RD Ongar 94-98; P-in-c High and Gd Easter w Margaret

Roding from 98; P-in-c Gt Canfield w High Roding and Aythorpe Roding from 02; Hon Can Chelmsf Cathl from 01. *The Rectory, 3 Old Vicarage Close, High Easter, Chelmsford CM1 4RW* Tel (01245) 231429
E-mail johnsibson@easterrectory.freeserve.co.uk
SIBSON, Canon Robert Francis. b 46. Leeds Univ CertEd68. Sarum & Wells Th Coll 78. **d** 80 **p** 81. C Watford St Mich *St Alb* 80-83; TV Digswell and Panshanger 83-90; V Biggleswade 90-02; Chapl Bedford and Shires Health and Care NHS Trust 94-02; RD Biggleswade *St Alb* 96-01; Hon Can St Alb from 98; V Sawbridgeworth from 02. *The Vicarage, 144 Sheering Mill Lane, Sawbridgeworth CM21 9ND* Tel (01279) 723305
SICHEL, Stephen Mackenzie. b 59. UEA BA80 Birm Univ MA95. Ripon Coll Cuddesdon 87. **d** 90 **p** 91. C Tettenhall Regis *Lich* 90-95; C Camberwell St Giles w St Matt *S'wark* 95-01; P-in-c Brixton St Matt 01-02; V Brixton St Matt w St Jude from 02. *The Vicarage, 5 St Matthew's Road, London SW2 1ND* Tel (020) 7274 3553
SIDAWAY, The Ven Geoffrey Harold. b 42. Kelham Th Coll 61. **d** 66 **p** 67. C Beighton *Derby* 66-70; C Chesterfield St Mary and All SS 70-72; P-in-c Derby St Bart 72-74; V 74-77; V Maidstone St Martin *Cant* 77-86; V Bearsted w Thurnham 86-00; RD Sutton 92-99; Hon Can Cant Cathl 94-00; Adn Glouc from 00. *Glebe House, Church Road, Maisemore, Gloucester GL2 8EY* Tel (01452) 528500 Fax 381528 E-mail archdglos@star.co.uk
SIDDALL, Arthur. b 43. Lanc Univ MA81 DMS90 Surrey Univ PGCE94 MCMI96. Lon Coll of Div ALCD67 LTh74. **d** 67 **p** 68. C Formby H Trin *Liv* 67-70; C Childwall All SS 70-72; CMS 72-77; Bangladesh 74-77; V Clitheroe St Paul Low Moor *Blackb* 77-82; V Blackb St Gabr 82-90; Dep Gen Sec Miss to Seamen 90-93; Hon C Leatherhead *Guildf* 93-96; V Chipping and Whitewell *Blackb* from 96; Dioc Rural Chapl from 03. *The Vicarage, Garstang Road, Chipping, Preston PR3 2QH* Tel (01995) 61252 Fax as telephone
E-mail arthur.siddall@which.net
SIDDLE, Michael Edward. b 33. Dur Univ BA54. St Aid Birkenhead 55. **d** 57 **p** 58. C Fazakerley Em *Liv* 57-59; C Farnworth 59-62; V Swadlincote *Derby* 62-70; Distr Sec (Northd and Dur) BFBS 70-72; Yorkshire 72-82; V Bamber Bridge St Aid *Blackb* 82-87; V Horsforth *Ripon* 87-00; rtd 00. *28 Carr Bridge Drive, Cookridge, Leeds LS16 7JY* Tel 0113-261 0498 Mobile 07941-209069
SIDEBOTHAM, Canon Stephen Francis. b 35. Qu Coll Cam BA58 MA80. Linc Th Coll 58. **d** 60 **p** 61. C Bitterne Park *Win* 60-64; Hong Kong 64-83; Dean 76-83; Archdeacon 78-83; Chapl Gravesend and N Kent Hosp 83-94; R Gravesend St Geo *Roch* 83-94; RD Gravesend 91-94; P-in-c Rosherville 91-94; Acorn Chr Healing Trust from 94; rtd 97; Perm to Offic *Ox* 97-98. *87 Aston Abbotts Road, Weedon, Aylesbury HP22 4NH* Tel (01296) 640098
SIDEBOTTOM, Andrew John. *See* DAVIES, Andrew John
SIDEBOTTOM, George. b 16. TCD 43. **d** 49 **p** 50. C Drumholm and Rossnowlagh *D & R* 49-52; C Maghera 52-53; C Ches St Mary *Ches* 53-56; I Achill w Dugort, Castlebar and Turlough *T, K & A* 56-60; V Felmersham *St Alb* 60-81; w Bletsoe 62-79; R Bletsoe 60-62; rtd 81; Perm to Offic *St Alb* from 81. *2 Homebrook House, Cardington Road, Bedford MK42 0RL* Tel (01234) 356189
SIDES, Canon James Robert. b 37. TCD BA66. CITC 68. **d** 67 **p** 68. C Belfast St Clem *D & D* 67-70; C Antrim All SS *Conn* 70-73; I Tomregan w Drumlane *K, E & A* 73-80; I Killesher 80-97; Can Kilmore Cathl from 94; I Kildrumferton w Ballymachugh and Ballyjamesduff from 97. *Kildrumferton Rectory, Crosserlough, Co Cavan, via Kells, Irish Republic* Tel (00353) (49) 433 6211
E-mail kildrumferton@kilmore.anglican.org
SIEJKOWSKI, Piotr Jan (Peter). b 64. Warsaw Univ PhD97. Coll of Resurr Mirfield 98. **d** 91 **p** 92. Poland 92-98; C Tile Hill *Cov* 99-01; Chapl and Lect Univ Coll Chich from 01. *University College Chichester, College Lane, Chichester PO19 6PE* Tel (01243) 816041 E-mail psiejko@siejkowski.freeserve.co.uk
SIGRIST, Richard Martin. b 46. Bernard Gilpin Soc Dur 67 Sarum Th Coll 68. **d** 71 **p** 72. C Yeovil St Mich *B & W* 71-74; Chapl RN 74-84; TV Sidmouth, Woolbrook and Salcombe Regis *Ex* 84-86; TR 86-91; TR Sidmouth, Woolbrook, Salcombe Regis, Sidbury etc 91-94; RD Ottery 90-94; USA 94-99; P-in-c Devonport St Bart *Ex* 99-02; V from 02; RD Plymouth Devonport from 01. *St Bartholomew's Vicarage, 13 Outland Road, Plymouth PL2 3BZ* Tel (01752) 562623
E-mail rmsigrist@onetel.net.uk
SILCOCK, Donald John. b 30. AKC59. **d** 60 **p** 61. C Hackney St Jo *Lon* 60-63; C-in-c Plumstead Wm Temple Ch Abbey Wood CD *S'wark* 63-68; C Felpham w Middleton *Chich* 68-74; R Ightham *Roch* 74-84; R Cliffe at Hoo w Cooling 84-92; RD Strood 85-91; rtd 92; Perm to Offic *Chich* from 92. *Puck's House, 26 Ancton Way, Elmer Sands, Middleton-on-Sea, Bognor Regis PO22 6JN* Tel (01243) 582589
SILINS, Jacqueline. *See* JOHNSON, Ms Jacqueline
SILK, Ian Geoffrey. b 60. Pemb Coll Cam BA81 MA85. Trin Coll Bris BA89. **d** 89 **p** 90. C Linc St Giles *Linc* 89-93; P-in-c Linc

St Geo Swallowbeck 93-98; V from 98. *St George's Vicarage, 87 Eastbrook Road, Lincoln LN6 7EW* Tel (01522) 870881
E-mail revisilk@fish.co.uk
SILK, John Arthur. b 52. Selw Coll Cam BA73 MA77 K Coll Lon MTh80. Westcott Ho Cam 75. **d** 77 **p** 78. C Banstead *Guildf* 77-80; C Dorking w Ranmore 80-84; R Ringwould w Kingsdown Cant 84-95; V Thames Ditton *Guildf* from 95. *The Vicarage, Summer Road, Thames Ditton KT7 0QQ* Tel (020) 8398 3446
SILK, Richard Trevor. b 67. St Steph Ho Ox 01. **d** 03. C St Marychurch *Ex* from 03. *28 Barewell Road, Torquay TQ1 4PA* E-mail richardsilk@hotmail.com
✠**SILK, The Rt Revd Robert David.** b 36. Ex Univ BA58. St Steph Ho Ox 58. **d** 59 **p** 60 **c** 94. C Gillingham St Barn *Roch* 59-62; C Lamorbey H Redeemer 65-69; R Swanscombe SS Pet and Paul 69-71; P-in-c Swanscombe All SS 69-71; R Swanscombe 71-75; R Beckenham St Geo 75-80; Adn Leic 80-94; TR Leic H Spirit 82-88; Bp Ballarat 94-03; rtd 03; P-in-c Amberley w N Stoke and Parham, Wiggonholt etc *Chich* from 03. *The Vicarage, Church Street, Amberley, Arundel BN18 9ND* Tel (01798) 831500
SILK, Timothy James. b 73. Ox Brookes Univ BSc96. Oak Hill Th Coll BA99. **d** 99 **p** 00. C Stamford St Geo w St Paul *Linc* 99-02; C Arborfield w Barkham *Ox* from 02. *1 Wheatlands Manor, Meadowbarns Park Lane, Finchampstead, Wokingham RG40 4QL* Tel 0118-973 6519 Fax 976 0285
E-mail timsilk@bigfoot.com
SILKSTONE, Harry William James. b 21. St D Coll Lamp BA48. **d** 49 **p** 50. C Dowlais *Llan* 49-51; C Aberdare St Fagan 51-53; C Southall H Trin *Lon* 53-56; V Stratford New Town St Paul *Chelmsf* 56-63; R Debden 63-72; V Bocking St Pet 72-78; R Gt Hallingbury 78-86; rtd 86; Perm to Offic *B & W* 86-93. *4 Mortimer Place, Clare, Sudbury CO10 8QP* Tel (01787) 278652
SILKSTONE, Thomas William. b 27. St Edm Hall Ox BA51 MA55 BD67. Wycliffe Hall Ox 51. **d** 53 **p** 54. C Aston SS Pet and Paul *Birm* 53-56; Div Master Merchant Taylors' Sch Crosby 56-62; Lect K Alfred's Coll Win 62-65; Sen Lect 65-75; Prin Lect 75-85; Lic to Offic *Win* 62-85; Perm to Offic *Truro* from 82; rtd 92. *Trevalyon, Lansallos, Looe PL13 2PX* Tel (01503) 72110
SILLER, Canon James Robert William. b 44. Pemb Coll Ox BA65 MA70 Qu Coll Cam 69. Westcott Ho Cam 67. **d** 70 **p** 71. C Spring Grove St Mary *Lon* 70-73; C Leeds St Pet *Ripon* 73-77; P-in-c Quarry Hill 73-77; V Gilling and Kirkby Ravensworth 77-82; P-in-c Melsonby 77-82; R Farnley 82-94; V Potternewton from 94; Hon Can Ripon Cathl from 99. *St Martin's Vicarage, 2A St Martin's View, Leeds LS7 3LB* Tel 0113-262 4271
SILLETT, Angela Veronica Isabel. *See* BERNERS-WILSON, Mrs Angela Veronica Isabel
SILLEY, Michael John. b 48. Ripon Coll Cuddesdon 82. **d** 84 **p** 85. C Frodingham *Linc* 84-87; V Ingham w Cammeringham w Fillingham 87-96; R Aisthorpe w Scampton w Thorpe le Fallows etc 87-96; RD Lawres 92-96; P-in-c N w S Carlton 93-96; P-in-c Brigg 96-97; V Brigg, Wrawby and Cadney cum Howsham from 97; RD Yarborough 01-02. *The Vicarage, 10 Glanford Road, Brigg DN20 8DJ* Tel (01652) 653989
E-mail michaelsilley@aol.com
SILLIS, Andrew Keith. b 66. Wolv Poly BSc87. Aston Tr Scheme 91 Westcott Ho Cam 93. **d** 96 **p** 97. C Boyne Hill *Ox* 96-99; C Hayes St Nic CD *Lon* 99-00; C-in-c from 00. *St Nicholas' Vicarage, Raynton Drive, Hayes UB4 8BG* Tel (020) 8573 4122
E-mail asillis@aol.com
SILLIS, Eric Keith. b 41. NW Ord Course 75. **d** 78 **p** 79. C Blackpool St Steph *Blackb* 78-82; V Huncoat 82-86; V Blackpool St Wilfrid 86-95; V Fleetwood St Dav from 95; Chapl Mother's Union from 99. *St David's Vicarage, 211 Broadway, Fleetwood FY7 8AZ* Tel (01253) 779725
E-mail ksillis@stdavid.freeserve.co.uk
SILLIS, Graham William. b 46. S'wark Ord Course 73. **d** 76 **p** 77. C Palmers Green St Jo *Lon* 76-79; C Dawlish *Ex* 79-81; V Ipswich St Thos *St E* 81-87; V Babbacombe *Ex* 87-95; C Tividale *Lich* 98-00; R Winchelsea and Icklesham *Chich* from 00. *The Rectory, St Thomas Street, Winchelsea TN36 4EB* Tel (01797) 226254
SILLITOE, William John. b 37. Lich Th Coll 67. **d** 69 **p** 70. C Ettingshall *Lich* 69-71; C March St Jo *Ely* 72-74; P-in-c Kennett 74-77; V Fordham St Pet 74-77; V Castle Bromwich St Clem *Birm* 77-00; rtd 00; Perm to Offic *Birm* from 00. *St Clement's Croft, 11 Wood Green Road, Wednesbury WS10 9AX* Tel 0121-505 5954
E-mail mwm@fort34.freeserve.co.uk
SILLS, Canon Peter Michael. b 41. Barrister 76 Nottm Univ BA63 LLM68. S'wark Ord Course 78. **d** 81 **p** 82. C W Wimbledon Ch Ch *S'wark* 81-85; P-in-c Barnes H Trin 85-93; Wandsworth Adnry Ecum Officer 90-93; V Purley St Mark 93-00; Can Res Ely Cathl *Ely* from 00. *The Black Hostelry, The College, Ely CB7 4DL* Tel (01353) 645105 *or* 667735
E-mail peter.sills@cathedral.ely.anglican.org
SILVA, Peter John. b 47. Rhodes Univ BA73 HDipEd77 BEd79. St Paul's Coll Grahamstown 68. **d** 74 **p** 74. S Africa 74-98; C Bloemfontein Cathl 74-75; Chapl Dioc Sch for Girls Grahamstown 75-79 and 89-95; Lect Rhodes Univ 79-81; Dir Academic Support Services Natal Univ 81-85; Regional Manager Performance and Educn Services 86; Dir Tape Aids for

the Blind 87; R Overport Ch Ch 88-89; Dir Educn Projects Grahamstown Foundn 95-98; TV Abingdon *Ox* 99-02; Chief Exec Officer Peers Early Educn Partnership from 02. *Woodford Bridge Cottage, Drystone Hill, Enstone, Chipping Norton OX7 4AA* Tel (01608) 678627 *or* (01865) 395145 Mobile 07980-264472 E-mail peter.silva@virgin.net

SILVERMAN, Prof Bernard Walter. b 52. Jes Coll Cam BA73 MA76 PhD78 ScD89 Southn Univ BTh00 FRS97. STETS 97. **d** 99 **p** 00. Prof Statistics Bris Univ from 93; Hon C Cotham St Sav w St Mary and Clifton St Paul *Bris* from 99. *10 Canynge Square, Bristol BS8 3LA* Tel 0117-973 8202 *or* 928 9171 Fax 928 9173 E-mail b.w.silverman@bristol.ac.uk

SILVERSIDES, Mark. b 51. Lon Univ BD73. St Jo Coll Nottm 74. **d** 76 **p** 77. C Hornchurch St Andr *Chelmsf* 76-80; P-in-c Becontree St Thos 80-85; TR Becontree W 85-86; CPAS Staff 86-92; New Media Producer from 92; Perm to Offic *Dur* 93-97. *15 Glenhurst Drive, Whickham, Newcastle upon Tyne NE16 5SH* Tel 0191-488 1937 E-mail msilversides@ambitnewmedia.com

SILVERTHORN, Alan. b 37. St Mich Coll Llan 62. **d** 65 **p** 66. C Machen and Rudry *Mon* 65-71; V New Tredegar 71-83; V Llanfrechfa and Llanddewi Fach w Llandegveth from 83. *The Vicarage, Llanfrechfa, Cwmbran NP44 8DQ* Tel (01633) 482343

SILVESTER, David. b 59. Qu Mary Coll Lon BSc80 Nottm Univ BCombStuds85. Linc Th Coll 82. **d** 85 **p** 86. C Walthamstow St Mary w St Steph *Chelmsf* 85-90; TV Barking St Marg w St Patr 90-96; V Mildmay Grove St Jude and St Paul *Lon* from 96; AD Islington from 03. *The Vicarage, 71 Mildmay Road, London N1 2PT* Tel (020) 7226 5924 E-mail dsilve5737@aol.com

SILVESTER, Stephen David. b 59. Chu Coll Cam BA80 MA83 Man Univ PGCE82. St Jo Coll Nottm 88. **d** 91 **p** 92. C Nottingham St Jude *S'well* 91-96; V Gamston and Bridgford from 96. *10 Scafell Close, West Bridgford, Nottingham NG2 6RJ* Tel 0115-982 5993 E-mail steve-silvester@bigfoot.com

SIM, David Hayward. b 29. Qu Coll Birm 57. **d** 59 **p** 60. C Foleshill St Laur *Cov* 59-62; C Kenilworth St Nic 62-64; V Devonport St Aubyn *Ex* 64-69; V Frampton *Linc* 69-74; V Gainsborough St Geo 74-82; V Sturminster Newton and Hinton St Mary *Sarum* 82-89; R Stock and Lydlinch 82-89; Dorchester 89-94; Chapl HM Pris Dorchester 89-94; rtd 95; Perm to Offic *Sarum* from 95. *12 Eldridge Close, Dorchester DT1 2JS* Tel (01305) 269262

SIMCOCK, Canon Michael Pennington. b 27. Qu Coll Cam BA50 MA52. Bps' Coll Cheshunt 50. **d** 52 **p** 53. C Andover w Foxcott *Win* 52-55; C Eastleigh 55-57; Min Tadley St Mary CD 57-67; V Altarnon and Bolventor *Truro* 67-70; V Treleigh 70-87; RD Carnmarth N 75-91; Hon Can Truro Cathl 82-92; R Redruth w Lanner 87-88; TR Redruth w Lanner and Treleigh 88-92; rtd 92; Perm to Offic *Truro* from 92. *1C Stratton Place, Falmouth TR11 2ST*

SIMESTER, Paul Stephen. b 57. Oak Hill Th Coll DipHE99. **d** 99 **p** 00. C Branksome Park All SS *Sarum* 99-03; TV Wareham from 03. *St Martin's Vicarage, Keysworth Road, Sandford, Wareham BH20 7DD* Tel (01929) 552756 E-mail paul@church2.freeserve.co.uk

SIMISTER, Charles Arnold. b 19. MM44. Edin Th Coll 49. **d** 52 **p** 53. C Glas Ch Ch *Glas* 52-57; C Worsley *Man* 57-60; V Downton *Sarum* 60-63; CF 63-84; R Kirkcudbright *Glas* 63-84; R Gatehouse of Fleet 63-84; rtd 84; Perm to Offic *Glas* from 84. *98 High Street, Kirkcudbright DG6 4TX* Tel (01557) 330747

SIMISTER, Norman Harold. b 39. Bris Univ BSc60. LNSM course 91. **d** 93 **p** 94. OLM Wainford *St E* from 99. *Romaine, 1 School Road, Ringsfield, Beccles NR34 8NZ* Tel (01502) 715549

SIMM, Michael Keith. b 63. **d** 00 **p** 01. C Ipswich St Matt *St E* from 00; C-in-c Cliff Park Community Ch *Nor* from 03. *1 South Gardens, Gorleston, Great Yarmouth NR31 6TL* Tel (01493) 669401 E-mail mike_simm@talk21.com

SIMMONDS, David Brian. b 38. Selw Coll Cam BA62 MA66 Heidelberg Univ 62. Ridley Hall Cam 63. **d** 65 **p** 66. C Newcastle w Butterton *Lich* 65-69; V Branston 69-97; V Branston w Tatenhill 97; RD Tutbury 95-97; rtd 97; Perm to Offic *Pet* 97-00; P-in-c Easton on the Hill, Collyweston w Duddington etc 00-02; Hon C Ketton, Collyweston, Easton-on-the-Hill etc from 03. *The Rectory, 38 West Street, Easton on the Hill, Stamford PE9 3LS* Tel (01780) 751967 Fax as telephone E-mail davidsimmonds@btinternet.com

SIMMONDS, Edward Alan. b 32. St Edm Hall Ox MA60. Ripon Coll Cuddesdon 88. **d** 89 **p** 90. NSM Ox St Mich w St Martin and All SS *Ox* 89-92; NSM Ox St Mary V w St Cross and St Pet 92-94; Chapl Lugano *Eur* 94-98; rtd 98; Perm to Offic *Ex* from 98. *Rokesdown, Higher Duryard, Pennsylvania Road, Exeter EX4 5BQ* Tel (01392) 270311

SIMMONDS, John. b 24. Sheff Univ BA50. Ridley Hall Cam 50. **d** 52 **p** 53. C Portsdown *Portsm* 52-55; C-in-c Fareham St Jo Ev CD 55-65; V W Streatham St Jas *S'wark* 65-73; V Congresbury *B & W* 73-75; P-in-c Puxton w Hewish St Ann and Wick St Lawrence 73-75; V Congresbury w Puxton and Hewish St Ann 75-84; Warden Home of Divine Healing Crowhurst 84-89; rtd 89. *Beach Villa, 14 The Beach, Clevedon BS21 7QU* Tel (01275) 342295

SIMMONDS, Paul Andrew Howard. b 50. Nottm Univ BSc73 Lon Univ DipTh78. Trin Coll Bris 75. **d** 78 **p** 79. C Leic H Trin w St Jo *Leic* 78-82; SW Regional Co-ord CPAS 83-86; Hd Adult Tr and Resources CPAS 86-95; C Wolston and Church Lawford *Cov* 89-03; Dioc Miss Adv 95-03; Research Dir Forward Vision from 03. *31 John Simpson Close, Wolston, Coventry CV8 3HX* Tel (024) 7654 3188 Fax 7654 0042

SIMMONDS, Canon Paul Richard. b 38. AKC63. **d** 64 **p** 65. C Newington St Mary *S'wark* 64-67; C Cheam 68-73; P-in-c Stockwell Green St Andr 73-87; V from 87; Hon Can S'wark Cathl 97-03; rtd 03. *37 Ocean Drive, Ferring, Worthing BN12 5QP* Tel (01903) 242679 E-mail paulangela@hotmail.com

SIMMONDS, Robert John. b 58. Aston Tr Scheme 92 Ripon Coll Cuddesdon DipMin96. **d** 96 **p** 97. C Southampton Thornhill St Chris *Win* 96-00; TV Basingstoke from 00. *The Vicarage, 75 Cumberland Avenue, Basingstoke RG22 4BQ* Tel (01256) 465666

SIMMONDS, Robert William. b 52. Nottm Univ BTh77 Birm Poly DCG79. Linc Th Coll 72. **d** 80 **p** 81. C Roehampton H Trin *S'wark* 80-83; TV Hemel Hempstead *St Alb* 83-90; V S Woodham Ferrers *Chelmsf* 90-94; rtd 94. *30 Fitzroy Road, Whitstable CT5 2LG* Tel (01277) 275960

SIMMONDS, William Hugh Cyril. b 08. Lon Univ DipOAS47. St Jo Hall Highbury. **d** 37 **p** 38. China 30-51; P-in-c Sinfin *Derby* 52-54; V Wolverhampton St Jude *Lich* 54-67; V S Malling *Chich* 67-78; rtd 78; Perm to Offic *Roch* 96-99. *6 Cornford House, Cornford Lane, Pembury, Tunbridge Wells TN2 4QS* Tel (01892) 824196

SIMMONS, Barry Jeremy. b 32. Leeds Univ BA54 MA62. Ridley Hall Cam 61. **d** 63 **p** 64. C Buttershaw St Aid *Bradf* 63-65; Jamaica 65-68; V Earby *Bradf* 68-73; Hong Kong 73-74; Bahrain 75-79; Chapl Luxembourg *Eur* 80-91; V Shoreham *Roch* 91-00; rtd 00; Perm to Offic *Glouc* from 01. *Touchdown, 57 Griffin Close, Stow on the Wold, Cheltenham GL54 1AY* Tel (01451) 831637

SIMMONS, Bernard Peter. b 26. CA Tr Coll 48 S'wark Ord Course 86. **d** 88 **p** 88. C Chatham St Wm *Roch* 88-91; rtd 91; P-in-c Underriver *Roch* 91-95; P-in-c Seal St Lawr 91-95; Perm to Offic *Pet* from 95. *5 Sycamore Drive, Desborough, Kettering NN14 2YH* Tel (01536) 763302

SIMMONS, Canon Brian Dudley. b 35. Master Mariner. St Steph Ho Ox 62. **d** 64 **p** 65. C Bournemouth St Pet *Win* 64-67; Miss to Seamen 67-71; Hon C Milton next Gravesend w Denton *Roch* 67-70; Hon C Gravesend St Geo 70-71; V Lamorbey H Trin 71-90; R Hever w Mark Beech 90-93; P-in-c Four Elms 90-93; R Hever, Four Elms and Mark Beech 93-94; V Langton Green 94-01; Hon Can Roch Cathl 91-01; rtd 01. *17 Chancellor House, Mount Ephraim, Tunbridge Wells TN4 8BT* Tel (01892) 617262

SIMMONS, Christopher John. b 49. Mert Coll Ox MA77. NEOC 88. **d** 90 **p** 91. C Kirkleatham *York* 90-93; P-in-c Barlby 93-95; V Barlby w Riccall 95-02; RD Derwent 98-01; R Pocklington and Owsthorpe and Kilnwick Percy etc from 02. *The Rectory, 29 The Balk, Pocklington, York YO42 2QQ* Tel (01759) 302133

SIMMONS, Eric. b 30. Leeds Univ BA51. Coll of Resurr Mirfield 51. **d** 53 **p** 54. C Chesterton St Luke *Ely* 53-57; Chapl Keele Univ *Lich* 57-61; CR from 63; Warden Hostel of the Resurr Leeds 66-67; Superior CR 74-87; R Foundn of St Kath in Ratcliffe 89-92; Prior St Mich Priory 93-97; rtd 98. *House of the Resurrection, Stocks Bank Road, Mirfield WF14 0BN* Tel (01924) 494318 Fax 490489

SIMMONS, Gary David. b 59. Trin Coll Bris BA86. **d** 87 **p** 88. C Ecclesfield *Sheff* 87-90; Min Stapenhill Immanuel CD *Derby* 90-96; V Stapenhill Immanuel 97-98; R Slaugham *Chich* from 98. *The Rectory, Brighton Road, Handcross, Haywards Heath RH17 6BU* Tel (01444) 400221

SIMMONS, Godfrey John. b 39. Open Univ BA81. St And NSM Tr Scheme 71 Edin Th Coll 77. **d** 74 **p** 74. Dioc Supernumerary *St And* 74-75 and 80-81; C Strathtay and Dunkeld 75-77; C Bridge of Allan and Alloa 77-80; Asst Chapl Stirling Univ 77-80; Chapl 80; Min Crieff, Muthill and Comrie 80-81; R 81-85; Chapl HM Pris Perth 80-85; R Kirkwall and Stromness *Ab* 85-91; R Strichen 91-94; R Longside, Old Deer and Peterhead 91-92; Chapl HM Pris Peterhead 91-94; Miss to Seafarers 85-02; Hon Chapl (Scotland) 85-90; Hon Area Chapl (Scotland) 90-94; Chapl Supt Mersey Miss to Seafarers 94-02; TV Chu the K *Dur* from 02. *St George's Vicarage, South Moor, Stanley DH9 7EN* Tel and fax (01207) 230128 Mobile 07985-4458890 E-mail johnandjosimmons@onetel.net.uk

SIMMONS, Miss Joan Yvonne. b 14. Gilmore Ho 57. **dss** 61 **d** 87. Harringay St Paul *Lon* 61-63; Belsize Park 63-69; Adult Educn Officer 69-78; rtd 78; Perm to Offic *Chich* from 87. *12 Whittington College, London Road, East Grinstead RH19 2QU* Tel (01342) 312781

SIMMONS, John. b 53. Carl Dioc Tr Course 82. **d** 85 **p** 86. C Wotton St Mary *Glouc* 85-88; P-in-c Amberley 88-92; R Burton Latimer *Pet* 92-98; RD Kettering 94-98; R Paston 98-01; V Irchester from 01. *The Vicarage, 19 Station Road, Irchester, Wellingborough NN29 7EH* Tel (01933) 312674 E-mail john@simmons.freeserve.co.uk

SIMMONS, John Graham. b 54. Westf Coll Lon BSc75 Man Univ PGCE76 CertRE81. N Ord Course 89. **d** 92 **p** 93. C Thame w Towersey *Ox* 92-97; R Heydon, Gt and Lt Chishill, Chrishall etc *Chelmsf* from 97. *1 Hall Lane, Great Chishill, Royston SG8 8SG* Tel (01763) 838703 E-mail revsimm@aol.com

SIMMONS, John Harold. b 46. FCCA. Sarum & Wells Th Coll 86. **d** 89 **p** 90. NSM The Iwernes, Sutton Waldron and Fontmell Magna *Sarum* 89-01; NSM Iwerne Valley from 01. *Fourways, Shroton, Blandford Forum DT11 8QL* Tel (01258) 860515

SIMMONS, Ms Marion. b 45. N Ord Course 95. **d** 98 **p** 99. NSM Stoneycroft All SS *Liv* 98-99; C 00-01; TV Fazakerley Em from 01. *St Paul's Vicarage, Formosa Drive, Liverpool L10 7LB* Tel 0151-521 3344

SIMMONS, Canon Maurice Samuel. b 27. St Chad's Coll Dur BA50 DipTh52 Newc Univ MA99 MPhil02. **d** 52 **p** 53. C S Shields St Hilda *Dur* 52-58; Youth Chapl 56-60; R Croxdale 58-81; Soc and Ind Adv to Bp Dur 61-70; Gen Sec Soc Resp Gp 70-75; Hon Can Dur Cathl from 71; Sec Dioc Bd for Miss and Unity 75-82; V Norton St Mary 81-92; RD Stockton 85-92; rtd 92. *11 Roecliffe Grove, Stockton-on-Tees TS19 8JU* Tel (01642) 618880 E-mail m.simmons1@ntlworld.com

SIMMONS, Peter. See SIMMONS, Bernard Peter

SIMMONS, Raymond Agar. b 35. Linc Th Coll 69. **d** 71 **p** 72. C Hartlepool St Luke *Dur* 71-74; P-in-c Purleigh *Chelmsf* 74-81; Ind Chapl 74-81; P-in-c Cold Norton w Stow Maries 81; Chapl Rampton Hosp Retford 81-97; rtd 97; Perm to Offic *Linc* 98-01. *13 Caenby Road, Cleethorpes DN35 0JT*

SIMMONS, Richard Andrew Cartwright. b 46. Trin Coll Bris 73. **d** 75 **p** 76. C Worting *Win* 75-80; R Six Pilgrims *B & W* 80-92; R Bincombe w Broadwey, Upwey and Buckland Ripers *Sarum* from 92. *The Rectory, 526 Littlemoor Road, Weymouth DT3 5PA* Tel (01305) 812542

SIMMS, William Michael. b 41. DMA66 ACIS70 MCIPD75 Open Univ BA87. NEOC 84. **d** 87 **p** 88. NSM Croft *Ripon* 87; C 88; NSM Middleton Tyas and Melsonby 87; C 88; C Headingley 88-90; C Richmond w Hudswell 90-93; C-in-c Downholme and Marske 90-93; V Hawes and Hardraw from 93. *The Vicarage, Burtersett Road, Hawes DL8 3NP* Tel (01969) 667553

SIMON, Brother. See BROOK, Peter Geoffrey

SIMON, David Sidney. b 49. Univ of Wales (Abth) BSc(Econ)70 CDipAF76 Hull Univ MA83. NEOC 84. **d** 87 **p** 88. NSM Beverley St Mary *York* 87-94; NSM Beverley Deanery 94-98; Lect Humberside Coll of HE 87-90; Humberside Poly 90-92; Humberside Univ *York* 92-96; Lincs and Humberside Univ 96-98; Admin Rydal Hall *Carl* 98-01; Perm to Offic 01-02; NSM Cartmel Peninsula from 02. *3 Kents Bank House, Kentsford Road, Grange-over-Sands LA11 7BB* Tel (01539) 536762 E-mail dssimon@fish.co.uk

SIMON, Frederick Fairbanks. b 42. Ripon Coll Cuddesdon 74. **d** 77 **p** 78. C Cheddleton *Lich* 77-79; C Woodley St Jo the Ev *Ox* 79-82; V Spencer's Wood 82-85; P-in-c Steventon w Milton 85-87; Chapl Grenville Coll Bideford 87-95; rtd 96; Perm to Offic *Ex* from 96. *The Chimes, 18 Fore Street, Moretonhampstead, Newton Abbot TQ13 8LL* Tel (01647) 440979

SIMON, Haydn Henry England. See ENGLAND-SIMON, Haydn Henry

SIMON, Oliver. b 45. Dur Univ BA67 Sussex Univ MA68 Ox Univ DipTh71 Man Univ CertRS89 Sheff Univ MMinTheol94 Open Univ Dip French Studies 98. Cuddesdon Coll 69. **d** 71 **p** 72. C Kidlington *Ox* 71-74; C Bracknell 74-78; V Frodsham *Ches* 78-88; R Easthampstead *Ox* 88-00; Chapl Ripon Coll Cuddesdon from 00; Chapl Community of St Mary V Wantage from 00. *Homefield, Ham Road, Wantage OX12 9DG* Tel (01235) 224224 E-mail oliversimon@cs.com

SIMONS, Miss Christine. b 40. RGN62 RM64 RHV69. St Jo Coll Nottm 82. **dss** 84 **d** 87 **p** 94. Claygate *Guildf* 84-87; C Camberley St Paul 87-93; NSM 93-99; C Woking Ch Ch from 99. *4 Orchard Drive, Woking GU21 4BN* Tel (01483) 771551 E-mail csimons@waitrose.com

SIMONS, Preb John Trevor. b 34. Lon Univ BD67. ALCD66. **d** 67 **p** 68. C Becontree St Mary *Chelmsf* 67-71; V Cranham Park 71-78; P-in-c Nailsea H Trin *B & W* 78-83; R 83-97; Sen Asst P 97-99; Preb Wells Cathl 90-99; rtd 99; Nat Dir Crosswinds Prayer Trust from 97; Perm to Offic *B & W* from 99. *11 Spring Hill, Worle, Weston-super-Mare BS22 9AP* Tel (01934) 624302 Fax as telephone E-mail crosswinds@btinternet.com

SIMONS, Mark Anselm. b 38. ARCM62. Oak Hill Th Coll 62. **d** 65 **p** 66. C Nottingham St Ann *S'well* 65-68; C N Ferriby *York* 68-75; P-in-c Sherburn 75-78; V Gt and Lt Driffield 78-93; Perm to Offic from 93. *7 Royal Crescent, Scarborough YO11 2RN* Tel (01723) 378056

SIMONS, William Angus. b 18. Keble Coll Ox BA39 MA47. Cuddesdon Coll 40. **d** 41 **p** 42. C Poplar All SS w St Frideswide *Lon* 41-44 and 47-48; RAChD 44-47; C Is of Dogs Ch Ch and St Jo w St Luke *Lon* 48-54; V Fulham St Jas Moore Park 54-62; Ind Chapl *Worc* 62-63; Ind Missr R Foundn of St Kath in Ratcliffe 63-65; Chapl Hammersmith Hosp Lon 65-68; Chapl St Edm Hosp Northn 68-88; Chapl Northn Gen Hosp 68-72; P-in-c Northampton St Lawr *Pet* 72-76; C Northampton H

Sepulchre w St Andr and St Lawr 76-81; rtd 81; Northants Past Coun Service from 76; Founder Dir 76-84; Supervisor from 84; Perm to Offic *Pet* from 81. *54 Park Avenue North, Northampton NN3 2JE* Tel (01604) 713767

SIMONSON, Canon Juergen Werner Dietrich. b 24. Lon Univ BD52. ALCD52. **d** 52 **p** 53. C W Kilburn St Luke w St Simon and St Jude *Lon* 52-56; Nigeria 57-63; Chapl CMS Tr Coll Chislehurst 64-65; Vice-Prin 65-67; Prin CMS Tr Coll Chislehurst 67-69; V Putney St Marg *S'wark* 69-81; RD Wandsworth 74-81; Hon Can S'wark Cathl 75-90; R Barnes St Mary 81-90; rtd 90; Perm to Offic *Win* from 90. *Elm Cottage, Horseshoe Lane, Ibthorpe, Andover SP11 0BY* Tel (01264) 736381

SIMPER, Miss Rachel Dawn. b 67. K Coll Lon BD89. Westcott Ho Cam CTM92. **d** 92 **p** 94. Par Dn Clitheroe St Mary *Blackb* 92-94; C 94-95; C Nor St Pet Mancroft w St Jo Maddermarket *Nor* 95-97; V Slyne w Hest *Blackb* from 97; Women's Min Adv from 00. *The Vicarage, 2 Summerfield Drive, Slyne, Lancaster LA2 6AQ* Tel (01524) 822128

SIMPKIN, Mrs Doris Lily. b 30. EMMTC 79. **dss** 82 **d** 87 **p** 94. Mugginton and Kedleston *Derby* 82-87; NSM 87-94; Perm to Offic from 94. *71 Wheeldon Avenue, Derby DE22 1HP* Tel (01332) 343830

SIMPKIN, Paul. b 29. EMMTC. **d** 82 **p** 83. NSM Mugginton and Kedleston *Derby* 82-92; Lic to Offic from 92. *71 Wheeldon Avenue, Derby DE22 1HP* Tel (01332) 343830

SIMPKINS, Frank Charles. b 19. MCIT52 MILT99. Oak Hill Th Coll 72. **d** 75 **p** 76. C Harrow Weald St Mich *Lon* 75-78; Hon C 81-84; P-in-c Dollis Hill St Paul 78-80; Chapl Northwick Park Hosp Harrow 81-83; Hon C Harrow Trin St Mich *Lon* 84-94; Perm to Offic from 94. *7 Milne Feild, Pinner HA5 4DP* Tel (020) 8428 2477

SIMPKINS, Canon Lionel Frank. b 46. UEA BSc68. Lambeth STh77 St Jo Coll Nottm ALCD72 LTh74. **d** 73 **p** 74. C Leic H Apostles *Leic* 73-77; C Bushbury *Lich* 77-80; V Sudbury w Ballingdon and Brundon *St E* 80-96; Chapl Sudbury Hosps 80-96; RD Sudbury 88-96; Hon Can St E Cathl from 94; V Ipswich St Aug from 96; Warden of Readers from 03. *St Augustine's Vicarage, 2 Bucklesham Road, Ipswich IP3 8TJ* Tel (01473) 728654

SIMPSON, Alan Eric. b 52. Ch Ch Ox BA73 MA77 Birm Univ PhD77 CPhys77 MInstP77. Cranmer Hall Dur 96. **d** 98 **p** 99. C Long Benton *Newc* 98-02; P-in-c Cresswell and Lynemouth from 02. *The Vicarage, 33 Till Grove, Ellington, Morpeth NE61 5ER* Tel (01670) 860242 E-mail fr.alan@talk21.com

SIMPSON, Alexander. b 31. Oak Hill Th Coll 74. **d** 76 **p** 77. Hon C Lower Homerton St Paul *Lon* 76-81; Hon C Homerton St Barn w St Paul 81-85; TV Hackney Marsh 85-87; V Kensington St Helen w H Trin 87-97; rtd 97; Perm to Offic *Derby* from 01. *18 Holymoor Road, Holymoorside, Chesterfield S42 7DX* Tel (01246) 567490

SIMPSON, Alison Jane. b 60. St Andr Univ BSc83 BD86 Princeton Univ MTh87. **d** 99 **p** 99. C Ellon *Ab* 99-02; R Huntly *Mor* from 02; R Keith from 02; R Aberchirder from 02. *Holy Trinity Rectory, Seafield Avenue, Keith AB55 5BS* Tel (01542) 882782 Mobile 07811-230648

SIMPSON, Andrew. b 48. Liv Univ BEng69. Sarum Th Coll 83. **d** 86 **p** 87. NSM Canford Magna *Sarum* from 86. *17 Sopwith Crescent, Wimborne BH21 1SH* Tel (01202) 883996 E-mail andrew.simpson6@virgin.net

SIMPSON, Charles Michael. b 38. St Cath Coll Cam MA64 Campion Hall Ox MA65 Heythrop Coll Lon STL69 K Coll Lon PhD71. **d** 68 **p** 69. Lect Th Lon Univ 72-84; Chapl Prince of Peace Community Greenwich 85-87; Retreat Dir St Beuno's Clwyd 87-91; P-in-c Selkirk *Edin* 91-94; P-in-c Offchurch *Cov* 94-96; Warden Offa Retreat Ho and Dioc Spirituality Adv 94-00; P-in-c Stoke Canon, Poltimore w Huxham and Rewe etc *Ex* from 00; Dioc Adv in Adult Tr from 00. *The Vicarage, Stoke Canon, Exeter EX5 4AS* Tel (01392) 841583 Fax 330350

SIMPSON, David John. b 61. Univ Coll Dur BA85. Sarum & Wells Th Coll 89. **d** 91 **p** 92. C Selby Abbey *York* 91-94; C Romsey *Win* 94-97; Chapl Southn Univ from 97. *Chaplain's Lodge, St Mary's Church Close, South Stoneham, Southampton SO18 2ST* Tel (023) 8055 8126 E-mail chaplain@soton.ac.uk

SIMPSON, Derek. b 44. LNSM course 95. **d** 98 **p** 99. OLM Howe Bridge *Man* 98-02; OLM Atherton and Hindsford w Howe Bridge from 02. *17 Firs Road, Over Hulton, Bolton BL5 1EZ* Tel (01204) 651561

SIMPSON, Derek John. b 59. Oak Hill Th Coll BA89. **d** 89 **p** 90. C Alperton *Lon* 89-95; TR Brentford from 95; AD Hounslow from 02. *The Rectory, 3 The Butts, Brentford TW8 8BJ* Tel (020) 8568 6502 E-mail derek.simpson@btinternet.com

SIMPSON, Derrick. b 27. NW Ord Course 72. **d** 75 **p** 76. C Disley *Ches* 75-79; C Stockport St Geo 79-81; R Wistaston 81-90; Chapl Barony Hosp Nantwich 81-89; V Newton in Mottram *Ches* 90-93; rtd 93; Perm to Offic *Ches* from 93. *60 Dane Bank Avenue, Crewe CW2 8AD*

SIMPSON, Mrs Elizabeth Ann. b 59. Lon Bible Coll BA80 Trin Coll Bris 84. **dss** 86 **d** 97 **p** 98. Thornbury *Glouc* 86-87;

Beckenham Ch Ch *Roch* 87-90; Heydon, Gt and Lt Chishill, Chrishall etc *Chelmsf* 90-93; Shirwell, Loxhore, Kentisbury, Arlington, etc *Ex* 93-97; NSM S Molton w Nymet St George, High Bray etc 97-99; C 99-03; P-in-c W Buckingham *Ox* from 03. *The Vicarage, Orchard Place, Westbury, Brackley NN13 5JT* Tel (01280) 704964 E-mail ls@robandliz.freeserve.co.uk

SIMPSON, Geoffrey Sedgwick. b 32. Hamilton Coll (NY) BA54 Wisconsin Univ MA Pemb Coll Cam PhD70. Gen Th Sem (NY) STB57. **d** 57 **p** 57. USA 57-77; Chapl Birm Univ *Birm* 77-80; V Shoreham *Roch* 80-90; TR Street *York* 90-02; rtd 02. *The Laurels, Queen Street, Yetminster, Sherborne DT9 6LL* Tel (01935) 872915

SIMPSON, Mrs Georgina. b 46. Westmr Coll Ox BTh93 Birm Univ MA95 DipEd98. St Alb and Ox Min Course 95. **d** 97 **p** 98. NSM Littlemore *Ox* 97-98; C Ox St Giles and SS Phil and Jas w St Marg from 98. *85 Church Road, Sandford-on-Thames, Oxford OX4 4YA* Tel (01865) 512319 E-mail gs@stgileschurch.fsnet.co.uk

SIMPSON, Godfrey Lionel. b 42. Sarum Th Coll 63. **d** 66 **p** 67. C Leintwardine *Heref* 66-70; C Leominster 70-73; P-in-c Whitbourne 73-79; V Barlaston *Lich* 79-02; RD Trentham 85-00; P-in-c The Guitings, Cutsdean and Farmcote *Glouc* from 02; P-in-c Upper and Lower Slaughter w Eyford and Naunton from 02. *The Rectory, Copse Hill Road, Lower Slaughter, Cheltenham GL54 2HY* Tel (01451) 810812

SIMPSON, Herbert. b 20. Carl Dioc Tr Course. **d** 82 **p** 83. NSM Barrow St Aid *Carl* 82; NSM Barrow St Jo 82-90; rtd 90; Perm to Offic *Carl* from 90. *3 Glenridding Drive, Barrow-in-Furness LA14 4PE* Tel (01229) 823707

SIMPSON, Mrs Janet Mary. b 42. New Coll Edin LTh94. EAMTC 99. **d** 00 **p** 01. C Aldringham w Thorpe, Knodishall w Buxlow etc *St E* from 00. *The Rectory, Benhall Green, Benhall, Saxmundham IP17 1HT* Tel (01728) 605887 Fax as telephone E-mail simpsonjanet@lineone.net

SIMPSON, The Very Revd John Arthur. b 33. OBE01. Keble Coll Ox BA56 MA60. Clifton Th Coll 56. **d** 58 **p** 59. C Low Leyton *Chelmsf* 58-59; C Orpington Ch Ch *Roch* 59-62; Tutor Oak Hill Th Coll 62-72; V Ridge *St Alb* 72-79; P-in-c 79-81; Dir of Ords and Post-Ord Tr 75-81; Hon Can St Alb 77-79; Can Res St Alb 79-81; Adn Cant and Can Res Cant Cathl *Cant* 81-86; Dean Cant 86-00; rtd 00; Perm to Offic *Cant* from 01. *Flat D, 9 Earls Avenue, Folkestone CT20 2HW*

SIMPSON, Canon John Bernard. b 40. ACP66 St Paul's Cheltenham CertEd62 Ox Univ MTh95. **d** 93 **p** 93. In URC 63-93; Asst to RD Lothingland *Nor* 93-94; RD from 99; C Hopton w Corton 93-94; P-in-c 94-99; TR Lowestoft St Marg from 99; Hon Can Nor Cathl from 01. *St Margaret's Rectory, 147 Hollingsworth Road, Lowestoft NR32 4BW* Tel (01502) 573046 E-mail john.simpson5@tesco.net

SIMPSON, Canon John Lawrence. b 33. SS Coll Cam BA55 MA59 ARCM60 Univ of W of England Hon MMus. Wells Th Coll 63. **d** 65 **p** 66. Chapl Win Cathl *Win* 65-66; C Win St Bart 65-69; Chapl Repton Sch Derby 69-71; Hd of RE Helston Sch 71-78; P-in-c Curry Rivel *B & W* 79-80; R Curry Rivel w Fivehead and Swell 80-86; V Tunbridge Wells K Chas *Roch* 86-89; Can Res Bris Cathl *Bris* 89-99; rtd 99; Perm to Offic *B & W* from 00. *Yardes Cottage, Windmill Hill, Ilminster TA19 9NT* Tel (01823) 480593

SIMPSON, John Peter. b 39. ALCD66. **d** 66 **p** 67. C Woodside *Ripon* 66-69; C Burnage St Marg *Man* 69-72; V Rochdale Deeplish St Luke 72-80; R Lamplugh w Ennerdale *Carl* from 80. *The Rectory, Vicarage Lane, Ennerdale, Cleator CA23 3BE* Tel (01946) 861310 E-mail revpetersim@supanet.com

SIMPSON, John Raymond. b 41. NSW Sch of Hypnotic Sciences Dip Clinical Hypnotherapy 87 Univ of S Aus GradDipEd92 MASCH87. Chich Th Coll 65. **d** 67 **p** 68. C Scarborough St Martin *York* 67-71; C Grangetown 71-72; Youth Chapl Bermuda 72-75; C Lewisham St Mary *S'wark* 76; Australia 76-99 and from 00; C Albany 76-78; R Carey Park 78-84; Chapl RAN 84-90; Chapl RAAF 90-99; Grace Cathl San Francisco USA 99-00; Chapl RANSR from 00. *PO Box 1419, Albany, W Australia 6332* Tel (0061) (8) 9841 6295, 9571 7009 *or* tel and fax 9571 7007 Fax 9481 6205 E-mail johnsimpson_94108@yahoo.com

SIMPSON, John Raymond. b 55. Oak Hill Th Coll 88. **d** 90 **p** 91. C Immingham *Linc* 90-94; TV The Ramseys and Upwood *Ely* 94-99; P-in-c Brothertoft Gp *Linc* 99-02; Chapl SE Sector S Lincs Health Care NHS Trust 99-01; Chapl United Lincs Hosps NHS Trust 01-02; Asst Chapl N Lincs and Goole Hosps NHS Trust from 02. *Diana, Princess of Wales Hospital, Scartho Road, Grimsby DN33 2BA* Tel (01472) 874111 Fax 875392 E-mail john.simpson4@btinternet.com

SIMPSON, John Verrent. b 68. Univ of Wales (Cardiff) BScEcon93. Ripon Coll Cuddesdon BTh98. **d** 98 **p** 99. C Llanf St Jo *Llan* 98-00; C Cen Cardiff 00-01; C Upper Chelsea H Trin w St Jude *Lon* from 01. *12 Cambridge Mansions, Cambridge Road, London SW11 4RU* Tel (020) 7730 7270 Mobile 07779-136757 Fax (020) 7730 9287 E-mail jvs@fish.co.uk

SIMPSON, Mrs June Hall. b 31. LRAM59 Sheff Univ BEd74. EMMTC 83. **dss** 86 **d** 87 **p** 94. NSM Carlton in Lindrick *S'well*

87-01; rtd 01. *47 Thorndon Court, Eagle Way, Great Warley, Brentwood CM13 3BY* Tel (01277) 260271 E-mail revjune@91windsor.freeserve.co.uk

SIMPSON, Kevin Gordon. b 54. QPM02. Univ of Wales BEd96 MCIPD94. St Mich Coll Llan. **d** 02. NSM Llantwit Fardre *Llan* from 02. *95 St Anne's Drive, Pontypridd CF38 2PB* Tel (01443) 207033 Mobile 07870-397494 E-mail k.g.simpson@btinternet.com

SIMPSON, Miss Margery Patricia. b 36. SRN57 SCM59. Oak Hill Th Coll BA86. **dss** 86 **d** 87 **p** 94. Rodbourne Cheney *Bris* 86-87; Par Dn 87-90; Par Dn Warmley 90-94; C Warmley, Syston and Bitton 94-95; TV Yate New Town 95-96; rtd 97; Perm to Offic *Sarum* from 97. *12 Hunter Close, Colehill, Wimborne BH21 2TZ* Tel (01202) 842059

SIMPSON, Mark Lawrence. b 73. Oak Hill Th Coll BA03. **d** 03. C Leyland St Andr *Blackb* from 03. *3 Beech Avenue, Leyland PR25 3AL* Tel (01772) 622446

SIMPSON, Michael. *See* SIMPSON, William Michael

SIMPSON, Michael. *See* SIMPSON, Charles Michael

SIMPSON, Peter. *See* SIMPSON, John Peter

SIMPSON, Canon Peter Wynn. b 32. Birm Univ BA53. Ripon Hall Ox 55. **d** 57 **p** 58. C Leamington Priors H Trin *Cov* 57-60; C Croydon *Cant* 60-63; V Foleshill St Laur *Cov* 63-70; V Radford 70-79; RD Cov N 76-79; V Finham 79-91; RD Cov S 82-88; Hon Can Cov Cathl 83-91; rtd 91; Perm to Offic *Cov* from 91. *Faith Cottage, 118 Main Street, Wolston, Coventry CV8 3HP* Tel (024) 7641 8330

SIMPSON, Philip Alexander. b 54. Keele Univ BA79 CQSW79. CMS Tr Coll Selly Oak 85. **d** 89. CMS from 85; Pakistan 85-98; Regional Dir for Middle East and Pakistan from 98. *CMS, Partnership House, 157 Waterloo Road, London SE1 8UU* Tel (020) 7928 8681 Fax 7401 3215 E-mail phil.simpson@cms-uk.org

SIMPSON, Raymond James. b 40. Lon Coll of Div ALCD63 LTh74. **d** 63 **p** 64. C Longton St Jas *Lich* 63-66; C Upper Tooting H Trin *S'wark* 68-71; BFBS Distr Sec E Anglia 71-77; C-in-c Bowthorpe CD *Nor* 78-84; V Bowthorpe 84-96; Perm to Offic *Newc* from 96; Guardian Community of Aidan and Hilda from 96. *Lindisfarne Retreat, Marygate, Holy Island, Berwick-upon-Tweed TD15 2SD* Tel (01289) 389249 Fax as telephone E-mail raysimpson@ndirect.co.uk

SIMPSON, Richard Lee. b 66. Keble Coll Ox BA88 MPhil91 Westmr Coll Ox PGCE89. Wycliffe Hall Ox DipMin93. **d** 93 **p** 94. C Newc St Gabr *Newc* 93-97; P-in-c Jesmond H Trin from 97; P-in-c Newc St Barn and St Jude from 97. *Holy Trinity Vicarage, 63 Roseberry Crescent, Jesmond, Newcastle upon Tyne NE2 1EX* Tel 0191-281 1663 E-mail ricksimpson@lineone.net

SIMPSON, Robert. **d** 03. NSM Ballymoney w Finvoy and Rasharkin *Conn* from 03. *28 Willowfield Park, Coleraine BT52 2NF* Tel (028) 7035 8552 E-mail srobertheather@aol.com

SIMPSON, Robert Charles. b 46. Ridley Hall Cam. **d** 85 **p** 86. C Eastwood *S'well* 85-88; V Yardley St Cypr Hay Mill *Birm* 88-93; P-in-c Newent and Gorsley w Cliffords Mesne *Glouc* 93-95; R from 95. *The Rectory, 43 Court Road, Newent GL18 1SY* Tel (01531) 820248 E-mail stmarys.church@talk21.com

SIMPSON, Robert David. b 61. Fitzw Coll Cam BA83 MA87 Bris Univ MLitt94. Trin Coll Bris DipHE87. **d** 87 **p** 88. C Beckenham Ch Ch *Roch* 87-90; C Heydon w Gt and Lt Chishill *Chelmsf* 90; C Chrishall 90; C Elmdon w Wendon Lofts and Strethall 90; C Heydon, Gt and Lt Chishill, Chrishall etc 91-93; TV Shirwell, Loxhore, Kentisbury, Arlington, etc *Ex* 93-97; TR S Molton w Nymet St George, High Bray etc 97-03. *The Vicarage, Orchard Place, Westbury, Brackley NN13 5JT* Tel (01280) 704964 E-mail revsimpson@supanet.com

SIMPSON, Robert Theodore (Theo). b 34. Linc Coll Ox BA58 MA61 K Coll Lon PhD71 UNISA Dip Tertiary Educn 83 MEd85. Chich Th Coll 58. **d** 60 **p** 61. C Ellesmere Port *Ches* 60-63; CR 63-66; S Africa 68-88; Prin St Pet Coll 72-75; Pres Federal Th Sem 73-75; Sen Lect Th Swaziland Univ 83-87; Assoc Prof Th 87-88; Chapl and Lect Coll of SS Mark and Jo Plymouth 88-90; Tutor Simon of Cyrene Th Inst 90-92; Perm to Offic *S'wark* 91-92; P-in-c Shadwell St Paul w Ratcliffe St Jas *Lon* 92-01; rtd 01. *36 Whitton Dene, Hounslow TW3 2JT* E-mail theo@cologon.org

SIMPSON, Roger Westgarth. b 51. Lon Univ BSc72. St Jo Coll Nottm 77. **d** 79 **p** 80. C St Marylebone All So w SS Pet and Jo *Lon* 79-85; R Edin St Paul and St Geo *Edin* 85-95; R Vancouver H Trin Canada 95-99; V York St Mich-le-Belfrey *York* from 99. *St Cuthbert's Centre, Peasholme Green, York YO1 7PW* Tel (01904) 624190 *or* 412470 Fax 622290 E-mail admin@st-michael-le-belfrey.org

SIMPSON, The Ven Samuel. b 26. TCD BA55 MA69 Div Test56. TCD Div Sch. **d** 56 **p** 57. C Coleraine *Conn* 56-60; I Donagh w Cloncha and Clonmany *D & R* 60-64; I Ballyscullion 64-81; Can Derry Cathl from 78; I Errigal w Garvagh 81-96; Adn Derry 89-96; rtd 96. *53 Magheramenagh Drive, Atlantic Road, Portrush BT56 8SP* Tel (028) 7082 4292

SIMPSON (née RALPHS), Mrs Sharon Ann. b 55. St Mary's Coll Dur BA77. Cranmer Hall Dur 81. **dss** 83 **d** 87 **p** 94.

Caverswall *Lich* 83-87; Par Dn 87-89; Asst Dioc Officer for Minl Tr *St As* 90-91; NSM Selkirk *Edin* 91-94; C Offchurch *Cov* 94-96; Warden Offa Retreat Ho and Dioc Spirituality Adv 94-00; C Stoke Canon, Poltimore w Huxham and Rewe etc *Ex* from 00; Dioc Adv in Adult Tr from 00. *The Vicarage, Stoke Canon, Exeter EX5 4AS* Tel (01392) 841583 Fax 330350

SIMPSON, Mrs Susie Alexandra. b 58. Hertf Coll Ox BA81. St Steph Ho Ox BA98 DipTh99. **d** 99 **p** 00. C High Wycombe *Ox* 99-03; TV from 03. *The Vicarage, 175 Dashwood Avenue, High Wycombe HP12 3DB* Tel (01494) 449494 E-mail sas@fish.co.uk

SIMPSON, Thomas Eric. b 31. St Chad's Coll Dur BA55. Ely Th Coll 55. **d** 57 **p** 58. C Jarrow St Paul *Dur* 57-61; C Bishopwearmouth St Mary V w St Pet CD 61-63; V Chopwell 63-92; Chapl Norman Riding Hosp Tyne & Wear 79-83; Chapl Shotley Bridge Gen Hosp 83-90; rtd 92. *58 Tanmeads, Nettlesworth, Chester le Street DH2 3PY* Tel 0191-371 9814

SIMPSON, William Michael. b 45. Leeds Univ BA66 PGDipESL67. St Jo Coll Nottm 75. **d** 77 **p** 78. C Desborough *Pet* 77-80; P-in-c Arthingworth w Kelmarsh and Harrington 79-80; Hong Kong 80-85 and 92-00; P-in-c Stanley St Steph and Chapl St Steph Coll 80-85; Chapl St Jo Cathl 80-85; P-in-c Beetham and Milnthorpe *Carl* 85-92; V Kowloon Tong Ch Ch 92-00; V Ticehurst and Flimwell *Chich* from 00. *The Vicarage, Ticehurst, Wadhurst TN5 7AB* Tel (01580) 200316 E-mail mars8@tinyworld.co.uk

SIMPSON, William Thomas. b 10. St Chad's Coll Dur BA35 DipTh36 MA38. **d** 36 **p** 37. C Portsea St Cuth *Portsm* 36-46; V Kennington Park St Agnes *S'wark* 46-49; V Sheff St Matt *Sheff* 49-59; R Week St Mary *Truro* 59-81; R Whitstone 62-81; rtd 81; Perm to Offic *Truro* from 81. *c/o The Revd J A C Wilson, The Rectory, Sand Lane, Calstock PL18 9QX* Tel (01822) 832518

SIMPSON, William Vaughan. b 16. Worc Ord Coll 55. **d** 57 **p** 58. C Charlton Kings St Mary *Glouc* 57-60; R Willersey w Saintbury 60-73; RD Campden 70-73; P-in-c Cherington 74-76; V Clearwell 76-79; Perm to Offic 79-91; rtd 81; Perm to Offic *Worc* from 81. *62 Fruitlands, Malvern WR14 4XA* Tel (01684) 567009

SIMS, Bernard David. b 40. Bris Coll Dip Tech Chemistry 63 Bath Univ BSc66. Ox Min Course 91. **d** 94 **p** 95. NSM Beedon and Peasemore w W Ilsley and Farnborough *Ox* 94-98; TV Blakenall Heath *Lich* from 98. *St Chad's Vicarage, Edison Road, Walsall WS2 7HT* Tel (01922) 612081 E-mail sims@beechdale.fsnet.co.uk

SIMS, Christopher Sidney. b 49. Wycliffe Hall Ox 74. **d** 77 **p** 78. C Walmley *Birm* 77-80; V Yardley St Cypr Hay Mill 80-88; V Stanwix *Carl* 88-96; RD Carl 89-95; Hon Can Carl Cathl 91-95; P-in-c Bassenthwaite, Isel and Setmurthy 96-00; P-in-c Bolton w Ireby and Uldale 96-00; P-in-c Allhallows 96-00; P-in-c Torpenhow 96-00; TR Binsey from 00. *The Vicarage, Torpenhow, Carlisle CA5 1HT* Tel (016973) 71295 E-mail rector@binsey69.freeserve.co.uk

SIMS, Canon James Henry. b 35. St Jo Coll Nottm 87. **d** 89 **p** 91. NSM Bangor Abbey *D & D* 89-93; C Holywood 93; Bp's C Kilbroney 93-01; Min Can Belf Cathl from 99; C Clonallon w Warrenpoint *D & D* from 01; Hon Can Dromore Cathl from 03. *The Rectory, 8 Donaghaguy Road, Warrenpoint, Newry BT34 3RZ*

SIMS, Keith George. b 29. LNSM course 92. **d** 95 **p** 96. OLM Forest Hill St Aug *S'wark* from 95. *68 Forest Hill Road, London SE22 0RS* Tel (020) 8693 7225

SIMS, Michael Graeme. b 37. SW Minl Tr Course 96. **d** 98 **p** 99. NSM Parkham, Alwington, Buckland Brewer etc *Ex* 98-00; NSM Blymhill w Weston-under-Lizard *Lich* from 00. *The Rectory, Blymhill, Shifnal TF11 8LH* Tel (01952) 850273

SIMS, Peter George Russell. b 36. Univ of Wales (Swansea) BA57. St Mich Coll Llan 63. **d** 65 **p** 66. C Brecon w Battle *S & B* 65-72; Min Can Brecon Cathl 65-72; V Llanfrynach and Cantref w Llanhamlach from 72. *The Rectory, Llanfrynach, Brecon LD3 7AJ* Tel (01874) 86667

SIMS, Sidney. b 20. Wycliffe Hall Ox. **d** 64 **p** 65. C Attenborough w Bramcote *S'well* 64-67; V Ramsey St Mary's w Ponds Bridge *Ely* 67-70; V Cambridge St Matt 70-85; Algeria 85-86; rtd 86; Perm to Offic *Nor* from 86. *Cockley Cottage, 66 Morston Road, Blakeney, Holt NR25 7BE* Tel (01263) 740184

SIMS, Vickie Lela. b 56. Iowa State Univ BA79. Ripon Coll Cuddesdon 00. **d** 02 **p** 03. C Grantham *Linc* from 02. *12 Lincoln Close, Grantham NG31 8RQ* Tel (01476) 402769 E-mail simstabbat@hotmail.com

SINCLAIR, Andrew John McTaggart. b 58. Ex Univ BA80. Westcott Ho Cam 81. **d** 84 **p** 85. C Aston cum Aughton and Ulley *Sheff* 84-87; C Rotherham 87-88; TV Edin Old St Paul *Edin* 88-93; Hon Angl Chapl Edin Univ and Moray Ho Coll 89-93; TV Dunstable *St Alb* 93-00; V Verwood *Sarum* from 00. *The Vicarage, Dewlands Way, Verwood BH31 6JN* Tel (01202) 822298 E-mail a.and.j.sinclair@dial.pipex.com

SINCLAIR, Arthur Alfred. b 46. **d** 87 **p** 89. Hon C St Andr Cathl Inverness *Mor* 87-92; C 93-97; Chapl Asst Inverness Hosp 87-89; Dioc Chapl 87-89; NSM Culloden St Mary-in-the-Fields 89-92; P-in-c from 93; P-in-c Inverness St Jo from 93; Edin Th Coll 92-93; Chapl Raigmore Hosp NHS Trust Inverness from 93.

St John's Rectory, Southside Road, Inverness IV2 3BG Tel (01463) 716288

SINCLAIR, Charles Horace. b 19. Keble Coll Ox BA40 MA44. Linc Th Coll 41. **d** 42 **p** 43. C Upper Norwood St Jo *Cant* 42-45; Chapl K Coll Auckland 46-50; Asst Chapl Haileybury Coll 51; Hd Master Prebendal Sch Chich 51-53; PV Chich Cathl *Chich* 51-53; Chapl and Sen Tutor Brookland Hall Welshpool 53-57; Hd Master St Aid Sch Denby Dale 57-64; Perm to Offic *Wakef* 58-64; rtd 84; Perm to Offic *Cant* from 84. *Oakstead, 94 Harbour Way, Folkestone CT20 1NB* Tel (01303) 250882 Mobile 07974-294886

SINCLAIR, Colin. b 30. **d** 84 **p** 85. NSM Ramoan w Ballycastle and Culfeightrin *Conn* 84-92. *4 Bushfoot Cottages, Portballintrae, Bushmills BT57 8RN* Tel (028) 2073 1551

SINCLAIR, Gordon Keith. b 52. MA. Cranmer Hall Dur. **d** 84 **p** 85. C Summerfield *Birm* 84-88; V Aston SS Pet and Paul 88-01; AD Aston 00-01; Hon Can Birm Cathl 00-01; V Cov H Trin *Cov* from 01. *4 Bishop's Walk, Coventry CV5 6PY* Tel (024) 7671 2114

SINCLAIR, Canon Jane Elizabeth Margaret. b 56. St Hugh's Coll Ox BA78 MA80 Nottm Univ BA82. St Jo Coll Nottm 80. **dss** 83 **d** 87 **p** 94. Herne Hill St Paul *S'wark* 83-86; Chapl and Lect St Jo Coll Nottm 86-93; Can Res Sheff Cathl *Sheff* 93-03; V Rotherham from 03; Hon Can Sheff Cathl from 03. *The Vicarage, 2 Heather Close, Rotherham S60 2TQ* Tel (01709) 364341

SINCLAIR, John Robert. b 58. Oak Hill Th Coll DipHE92. **d** 92 **p** 93. C Ponteland *Newc* 92-96; V Long Benton St Mary 96-01; V Newburn from 01. *The Vicarage, High Street, Newburn, Newcastle upon Tyne NE15 8LQ* Tel 0191-229 0522 Fax 267 0582 E-mail john.r.sinclair@lineone.net

✠**SINCLAIR, The Rt Revd Maurice Walter.** b 37. Nottm Univ BSc59 Leic Univ PGCE60. Tyndale Hall Bris 62 Nashotah Ho Hon DD01. **d** 64 **p** 65 **c** 90. C Boscombe St Jo *Win* 64-67; SAMS 67-02; Argentina 67-78; Personnel Sec 79-83; Asst Gen Sec 83-84; Prin Crowther Hall CMS Tr Coll Selly Oak 84-90; Bp N Argentina 90-02; Primate of S Cone 95-02; rtd 02; Hon Asst Bp *Birm* from 02. *55 Selly Wick Drive, Birmingham B29 7JQ* Tel 0121-471 2617 E-mail mandg@sinclair401.fsnet.co.uk

SINCLAIR, Michael David Bradley. b 42. N Ord Course Coll of Resurr Mirfield. **d** 97 **p** 98. NSM Settrington w N Grimston, Birdsall w Langton *York* 97-99; P-in-c W Buckrose from 99. *Witham Cottage, Langton, Malton YO17 9QP* Tel (01653) 658360

SINCLAIR, Nigel Craig. b 65. Teesside Poly BA87 Coll of Ripon & York St Jo MA00. St Jo Coll Dur BA93. **d** 94 **p** 95. C Marton-in-Cleveland *York* 94-97; TV Thirsk 97-02; V Pannal w Beckwithshaw *Ripon* from 02. *St Robert's Vicarage, 21 Crimple Meadows, Pannal, Harrogate HG3 1EL* Tel (01423) 870202 E-mail nsinclair@supanet.com

SINCLAIR, Peter. b 44. Oak Hill Th Coll DipTh86. **d** 88 **p** 89. C Darlington H Trin *Dur* 88-91; C-in-c Bishop Auckland Woodhouse Close CD 91-98; P-in-c Consett from 98. *The Vicarage, 10 Aynsley Terrace, Consett DH8 5NF* Tel (01207) 502235

SINCLAIR, Peter Monteith. b 52. St Andr Univ BSc73. NEOC. **d** 01 **p** 02. NSM Darlington St Cuth *Dur* from 01. *Sundial Cottage, 7 Haughton Green, Darlington DL1 2DD* Tel (01325) 358424 Mobile 07710-017625 Fax (01325) 361572 E-mail peter@psld.co.uk

SINCLAIR, Robert Charles. b 28. Liv Univ LLB49 QUB LLM69 PhD82. Ely Th Coll 58. **d** 60 **p** 61. C Glenavy *Conn* 60-63; Chapl RN 63-67; C Cregagh *D & D* 67-68; Perm to Offic *Conn* from 69. *Juniper Cottage, 11A Glen Road, Glenavy, Crumlin BT29 4LT* Tel (028) 9445 3126

SINCLAIR, Robert Michael. b 41. CQSW81. Edin Th Coll 63. **d** 66 **p** 67. C Dunfermline *St And* 66-68; C Edin Old St Paul *Edin* 68-72; P-in-c Edin St Dav 72-77; Hon Dioc Supernumerary from 77. *121/19 Comiston Drive, Edinburgh EH10 5QU* Tel 0131-447 5068

SINDALL, Canon Christine Ann. b 42. ALA69. EAMTC 84. **d** 87 **p** 94. NSM Sutton *Ely* 87-89; C Cambridge Ascension 89-94; TV 94-96; R Cheveley from 96; R Ashley w Silverley from 96; V Kirtling from 96; V Wood Ditton w Saxon Street from 96; RD Linton from 01; Hon Can Ely Cathl from 01. *The Rectory, 130 High Street, Cheveley, Newmarket CB8 9DG* Tel (01638) 730770 *or* tel and fax 731946 E-mail csindall@surfaid.org

SINGH, Balwant. b 32. BA60. Saharanpur Th Coll 50. **d** 53 **p** 58. India 53-67 and 71-73; Hon C Handsworth St Jas *Birm* 67-71; Hon C N Hinksey *Ox* 73-80; Lic to Offic 80-81; Hon C S Hinksey from 82. *9 Jersey Road, Oxford OX4 4RT* Tel (01865) 717217

SINGH, Thomas Balwant. b 62. Westmr Coll Ox BTh98. Wycliffe Hall Ox 98. **d** 00 **p** 01. C Houghton Regis *St Alb* from 00. *The New Clergy House, Lowry Drive, Houghton Regis, Dunstable LU5 5SJ* Tel (01582) 863292 E-mail thomas.singh@ukonline.co.uk

SINGH, Vivian Soorat. b 30. Trin Coll Cam BA MA53. Westcott Ho Cam 54. **d** 55 **p** 56. C Yardley Wood *Birm* 55-57; C Birm St Paul 57-59; Asst Master Framlingham Coll 59-72; Chapl 60-72; Chapl Wymondham Coll 72-75; Dep Hd Litcham High

Sch 75-88; rtd 88; Perm to Offic *Nor* from 88. *Manor Cottage, Wendling Road, Longham, Dereham NR12 2RD* Tel (01362) 687382

SINGLETON, David Brinley (Brin). b 59. St Steph Ho Ox. **d** 00 **p** 01. C Soham *Ely* 00-01; C Soham and Wicken from 02. *5 Adelaide Close, Soham, Ely CB7 5FJ* Tel (01353) 720878
E-mail brin.singleton@ukgateway.net

SINGLETON, Mrs Editha Mary. b 27. WMMTC 85. **dss** 84 **d** 87 **p** 94. Lich St Chad *Lich* 84-90; Hon Par Dn 87-90; Hon Par Dn Beaulieu and Exbury and E Boldre *Win* 90-94; Hon C 94-97; Perm to Offic from 97. *The Peregrine, The Lane, Fawley, Southampton SO45 1EY* Tel (023) 8089 4364

SINGLETON, Ernest George (Paul). b 15. St Aug Coll Cant 38. **d** 41 **p** 42. C Portsea N End St Mark *Portsm* 41-46; C Hendon St Mary *Lon* 46-48; CR 48-68; Lic to Offic *Wakef* 49-51; Lic to Offic *Lon* 52-56; S Africa 56-60; Prior St Teilo's Priory Cardiff 61-68; Perm to Offic *Lon* 68-91 and 93-95; rtd 80; Hon C Twickenham St Mary *Lon* 91-93. *Suite 268, Postnet X31, Saxonwold, Johannesburg, 2132 South Africa* Tel (0027) (11) 880 2982 Fax 442 4732

SINGLETON, James Richard. b 56. CEng85 RN Eng Coll Plymouth BSc79 RN Coll Greenwich Dip Nuclear Tech 81. Ripon Coll Cuddesdon 90. **d** 92 **p** 93. C Bourne *Guildf* 92-96; TV Wimborne Minster and Holt *Sarum* 96; P-in-c Horton and Chalbury 96; V Horton, Chalbury, Hinton Martel and Holt St Jas 96-97; P-in-c from 97. *The Rectory, Hinton Martel, Wimborne BH21 7HD* Tel (01258) 840256

SINGLETON, Kenneth Miller. b 58. Oak Hill Th Coll DipHE91. **d** 91 **p** 92. C Grove *Ox* 91-95; P-in-c Ashbury, Compton Beauchamp and Longcot w Fernham 95-99; C Kirkheaton *Wakef* from 99. *423 Wakefield Road, Huddersfield HD5 8DB* Tel (01484) 429885 E-mail kensingleton@hotmail.com

SINNAMON, Canon William Desmond. b 43. TCD BA65 MA80 MPhil95. CITC 66. **d** 66 **p** 67. C Seapatrick *D & D* 66-70; C Arm St Mark *Arm* 70-74; V Choral Arm Cathl 73-74; I Ballinderry 75-80; I Dublin St Patr Cathl Gp *D & G* 80-83; Preb Tipperkevin St Patr Cathl Dublin 80-83; I Taney *D & G* from 83; Can St Patr Cathl Dublin from 91; Treas 91-96; Chan from 96. *Taney Rectory, 6 Stoney Road, Dundrum, Dublin 14, Irish Republic* Tel (00353) (1) 298 4497 *or* 298 5491 Fax 298 5491
E-mail taney@dublin.anglican.org
or parishoftaney@eircom.net

SINNICKSON, Charles. b 21. Princeton Univ BA44. Cuddesdon Coll 60. **d** 63 **p** 64. C Soho St Anne w St Thos and St Pet *Lon* 63-67; C Chelsea St Luke 67-72; Hon C S Kensington St Jude 72-81; NSM Upper Chelsea St Simon 81-86; NSM S Kensington St Aug 86-90; rtd 90; Perm to Offic *Lon* from 90. *4 Cranley Mansion, 160 Gloucester Road, London SW7 4QF* Tel (020) 7373 2767

SINTON, Bernard. b 43. Leic Univ BSc66. Sarum & Wells Th Coll 87. **d** 90 **p** 91. NSM Horsham *Chich* from 90. *The Vicarage, Shipley Village, Shipley, Horsham RH13 8PH* Tel (01403) 741238

SINTON, Mrs Patricia Ann. b 41. RGN62 SCM64. STETS 95. **d** 98 **p** 99. NSM Horsham *Chich* 98-01; P-in-c Shipley from 01. *The Vicarage, Shipley Village, Shipley, Horsham RH13 8PH* Tel (01403) 741238

SINTON, Vera May. b 43. Somerville Coll Ox BA65 MA69 Bris Univ CertEd66. Trin Coll Bris DipHE81. **dss** 81 **d** 87 **p** 94. Broxbourne w Wormley *St Alb* 81-87; Hon Par Dn 87; Tutor All Nations Chr Coll Ware 81-87; Chapl St Hilda's Coll Ox 87-90; Tutor Wycliffe Hall Ox 87-98; NSM Ox St Clem *Ox* from 99; Tutor Ox Cen for Youth Min from 01; rtd 03. *22 Norham Gardens, Oxford OX2 6QD* Tel (01865) 514232
E-mail vera.sinton@wycliffe.ox.ac.uk

SIRMAN, Allan George. b 34. Lon Univ BA58. Oak Hill Th Coll 55. **d** 59 **p** 60. C Uphill *B & W* 59-61; C Morden *S'wark* 61-65; R Chadwell *Chelmsf* 65-75; V Wandsworth All SS *S'wark* 75-95; rtd 95; Perm to Offic *Ripon* from 95. *Marydale, Kingsley Drive, Middleham, Leyburn DL8 4PZ* Tel (01969) 624582

SIRR, The Very Revd John Maurice Glover. b 42. TCD BA63. CITC 65. **d** 65 **p** 66. C Belfast St Mary *Conn* 65-68; C Finaghy 68-69; I Drumcliffe w Lissadell and Munninane *K, E & A* 69-87; Preb Elphin Cathl 81-87; Dean Limerick and Ardfert *L & K* from 87; I Limerick City from 87; Chapl Limerick Pris from 87. *The Deanery, 7 Kilbane, Castletroy, Limerick, Irish Republic* Tel (00353) (61) 338697 Mobile 87-254 1121 Fax (61) 332158
E-mail dean@limerick.anglican.org

SISSON, Trevor. b 54. ALCM. St Jo Coll Dur 76 St Jo Coll Nottm LTh94. **d** 79 **p** 80. C Rainworth *S'well* 79-83; C Worksop Priory 83-85; R Bilborough w Strelley 85-94; P-in-c Keyworth 94-02; P-in-c Stanton-on-the-Wolds 94-02; P-in-c Bunny w Bradmore 95-97 and 01-02; R Keyworth and Stanton-on-the-Wolds and Bunny etc from 02; AD S Bingham 95-03. *The Rectory, Nottingham Road, Keyworth, Nottingham NG12 5FD* Tel 0115-937 2017 E-mail trevmmkey@messages.co.uk

SITCH, Keith Frank. b 40. Lon Univ BA63 Lon Univ MA95. S'wark Ord Course 72. **d** 75 **p** 76. NSM Romford St Edw *Chelmsf* 75-78; NSM Kidbrooke St Jas *S'wark* from 78. *92 Kidbrooke Park Road, London SE3 0DX* Tel (020) 8856 3843

✠**SITSHEBO, The Rt Revd Wilson Timothy.** b 52. UNISA BTh82 MTh93. St Bede's Coll Umtata DipTh77. **d** 79 **p** 80 **c** 01. Zimbabwe 80-96; Tutor United Coll of Ascension Selly Oak 96-01; Bp Matabeleland from 01. *PO Box 2422, Bulawayo, Zimbabwe* Tel (00263) (9) 61370 Fax 68353

SIXSMITH, David. b 39. Lon Univ BD66 Handsworth Coll Birm DipTh62. LNSM course 96. **d** 97 **p** 98. OLM Narborough w Narford *Nor* 97-99; OLM Pentney St Mary Magd w W Bilney 97-99; OLM Westacre 97-99; OLM Castle Acre w Newton and Southacre 97-99; OLM Narborough w Narford and Pentney 99; C Hunstanton St Mary w Ringstead Parva etc 99-01; P-in-c Foulsham w Hindolveston and Guestwick from 01; P-in-c N Elmham w Billingford and Worthing from 02. *The Rectory, Guist Road, Foulsham, Dereham NR20 5RZ* Tel (01362) 683275

SIXTUS, Bernd. **d** 03. C Paris St Geo *Eur* from 03. *Address temp unknown*

SIZER, Stephen Robert. b 53. Sussex Univ BA DipHE Ox Univ MTh94. Trin Coll Bris 80. **d** 83 **p** 84. C St Leonards St Leon *Chich* 83-86; C Guildf St Sav w Stoke-next-Guildford *Guildf* 86-89; R Stoke-next-Guildf 89-97; V Virginia Water from 97. *Christ Church Vicarage, Christ Church Road, Virginia Water GU25 4LD* Tel and fax (01344) 842374 Mobile 07970-789549
E-mail stephen@sizers.org

SKELDING, Donald Brian. b 23. Trin Coll Cam BA47 MA52. Cuddesdon Coll. **d** 50 **p** 51. C Sedgley All SS *Lich* 50-54; C W Bromwich All SS 54-56; V Tong 56-61; V Walton St Jo *Liv* 61-65; V Southport St Paul 65-72; R Norton Canes *Lich* 72-81; R Hinstock and Sambrook 81-84; rtd 84; C Alderbury Team *Sarum* 91-94; Perm to Offic *Sarum* from 94 and Truro from 01. *Spindrift, 3 Quilver Close, Gorran Haven, St Austell PL26 6JT* Tel (01726) 843764

SKELDING, Mrs Hazel Betty. b 25. LGSM66 CertEd45. Gilmore Course 80. **dss** 83 **d** 87 **p** 94. Hinstock and Sambrook *Lich* 83-84; Asst Children's Adv RE 86-91; Hon Par Dn Alderbury Team *Sarum* 91-94; C 94-96; rtd 96; Perm to Offic *Sarum* from 96 and Truro from 01. *Spindrift, 3 Quilver Close, Gorran Haven, St Austell PL26 6JT* Tel (01726) 843764

SKELTON, Beresford. b 52. St Chad's Coll Dur BA74 SSC. Chich Th Coll 74. **d** 76 **p** 77. C Byker St Ant *Newc* 76-80; Chapl Asst Newc Gen Hosp 80-81; C Newc St Jo *Newc* 80-82; Chapl Asst Freeman Hosp Newc 81-82; V Cresswell and Lynemouth *Newc* 82-88; P-in-c Millfield St Mary *Dur* 88-93; V from 93. *St Mary Magdalene's Vicarage, Wilson Street, Sunderland SR4 6HJ* Tel 0191-565 6318 Fax as telephone

SKELTON, Dennis Michael. b 33. K Coll Lon BSc55. NEOC 76. **d** 79 **p** 80. NSM Pennywell St Thos and Grindon St Oswald CD *Dur* 79-84; V Heatherycleugh 84-99; V St John in Weardale 84-99; V Westgate 84-99; rtd 99; Perm to Offic *Dur* from 99. *52 Vicarage Close, New Silksworth, Sunderland SR3 1JF* Tel 0191-523 7135

SKELTON, Canon Henry John Nugent. b 13. Linc Th Coll 37. **d** 40 **p** 41. C Grantham St Wulfram *Linc* 40-43; Chapl RAFVR 43-47; V Heckington w Howell *Linc* 47-56; V Holbeach 56-73; RD Elloe E 68-73; Can and Preb Linc Cathl 70-73; rtd 78; Perm to Offic *St D* from 78. *Upton Castle, Cosheston, Pembroke Dock SA72 4SE* Tel (01646) 682435

SKELTON, Melvyn Nicholas. b 38. St Pet Coll Ox BA61 MA65 Selw Coll Cam BA63 MA68. Ridley Hall Cam 62. **d** 64 **p** 65. C St Marychurch *Ex* 64-66; C Bury St Edmunds St Mary *St E* 66-69; Hon C 69-78; Lic to Offic from 78. *22A The Street, Moulton, Newmarket CB8 8RZ* Tel (01638) 750563

SKELTON, Pamela Dora. b 38. Hull Coll of Educn DipEd58. Edin Th Coll 80. **dss** 78 **d** 86 **p** 94. Edin St Barn *Edin* 78-86; Dn-in-c 86-90; Dioc Youth Chapl 83-90; Min Edin Ch Ch 91-97; Chapl R Infirmary of Edin NHS Trust 91-99; Chapl Lothian Univ Hosps NHS Trust from 99. *112 St Alban's Road, Edinburgh EH9 2PG* Tel 0131-667 1280

SKEMP, Canon Stephen Rowland. b 12. Wadh Coll Ox BA34 MA62. Cuddesdon Coll 34. **d** 35 **p** 36. C W Hendon St Jo *Lon* 35-39; S Africa 39-46; R Publow w Pensford, Compton Dando and Chelwood *B & W* 47-50; V Hornsea and Goxhill *York* 50-62; V Atwick w Nunkeeling and Bewholme 50-62; RD N Holderness 52-62; R Gt Stanmore *Lon* 62-71; Chapl Br Embassy Ankara *Eur* 71-74; Adn Aegean 71-77; Chapl Athens St Paul 74-77; rtd 77; Can Malta Cathl *Eur* from 80; Perm to Offic *Ox* 83-96. *Orchard Bank, Goose Green, Deddington, Oxford OX15 0SZ* Tel (01869) 38487

SKEOCH, Canon David Windsor. b 37. Ch Ch Ox BA58 MA62. Westcott Ho Cam 73. **d** 74 **p** 75. NSM Pimlico St Mary Graham-street 74-79; Bp's Dom Chapl *Truro* 79-81; Bp's Chapl *Lon* 81-83; V Pimlico St Gabr from 83; Can The Murray from 92. *St Gabriel's Vicarage, 30 Warwick Square, London SW1V 2AD* Tel (020) 7834 7520 *or* 7834 2136

SKETCHLEY, Edward Sydney. b 20. Qu Coll Birm. **d** 49 **p** 50. C Bakewell *Derby* 49-53; PC Ridgeway 53-57; PC Abbey Dale 57-65; V Walsgrave on Sowe *Cov* 65-73; V Hound *Win* 73-90; rtd 90; Perm to Offic *Win* from 90; *Portsm* from 02. *Cloisters, 1 Monks Way, Fareham PO14 3LU*

SKEVINGTON, Michael James. b 56. Natal Univ BA79. St Paul's Coll Grahamstown. d 82 p 83. S Africa 82-88 and from 90; C Slough *Ox* 88-90. *PO Box 38088, Point, 4069 South Africa* Tel (0027) (31) 337 7521 *or* 337 5573

SKIDMORE, Michael Anthony. d 98 p 99. NSM Rainworth *S'well* 98-00; NSM Blidworth 98-00; P-in-c Basford St Leodegarius from 00. *The Vicarage, 152 Perry Road, Nottingham NG5 1GL* Tel 0115-960 5602 E-mail mikeskidmore@breathemail.com

SKIDMORE, Mrs Sheila Ivy. b 36. d 87 p 94. Hon Par Dn Leic Resurr *Leic* 87-91; Par Dn Clarendon Park St Jo w Knighton St Mich 91-94; TV 94-01; rtd 01. *15 School Lane, Birstall, Leicester LE4 4EA* Tel 0116-267 3318 E-mail revd.sheila@theskidmores.f9.co.uk

SKILLEN, John Clifford Tainish. b 50. NUU BA72 MA82 QUB DipEd73 TCD BTh89. CITC 86. d 89 p 90. C Bangor Abbey *D & D* 89-92; I Kilwarlin Upper w Kilwarlin Lower 92-96; I Finaghy *Conn* from 96; Dioc Rep for Bps' Appeal from 97; Asst Ed *Church of Ireland Gazette* from 99. *St Polycarp's Rectory, 104 Upper Lisburn Road, Belfast BT10 0BB* Tel (028) 9062 9764 E-mail st-polycarp@utvinternet.com

SKILLINGS, Martyn Paul. b 46. St Chad's Coll Dur BA68. Linc Th Coll 68. d 70 p 71. C Stanley *Liv* 70-72; C Warrington St Elphin 72-75; Ind Chapl 75-76; V Surfleet *Linc* 88-92; V Burton St Chad *Lich* from 92. *The Vicarage, 113 Hunter Street, Burton-on-Trent DE14 2SS* Tel and fax (01283) 564044 Mobile 07887-854525 E-mail pedaller@care4free.net

SKILTON, Christopher John. b 55. Magd Coll Cam BA76 MA80. Wycliffe Hall Ox 77. d 80 p 81. C Ealing St Mary *Lon* 80-84; C New Borough and Leigh *Sarum* 84-88; TV Gt Baddow *Chelmsf* 88-95; TR Sanderstead All SS *S'wark* from 95; P-in-c Sanderstead St Mary from 02; RD Croydon S from 00. *The Rectory, 1 Addington Road, South Croydon CR2 8RE* Tel (020) 8657 1366 *or* 8657 0665 E-mail cjs@dialpal.co.uk

SKINGLEY, Christopher George. b 49. K Coll Lon MA98. Oak Hill Th Coll BA90 Qu Coll Birm. d 00 p 01. C Enfield St Jas *Lon* from 00. *Glebe House, 146 Hertford Road, Enfield EN3 5AY* Tel (020) 8805 2974 E-mail chrisann@fish.co.uk

SKINNER, Arthur. b 38. d 97 p 98. NSM Selling w Throwley, Sheldwich w Badlesmere etc *Cant* from 97. *Bruckley Bungalow, Ashford Road, Badlesmere, Faversham ME13 0NZ* Tel (01233) 740666

✠**SKINNER, The Rt Revd Brian Antony.** b 39. Reading Univ BSc60. Tyndale Hall Bris 66. d 67 p 68 c 77. C Woking St Pet *Guildf* 67-70; Chile 70-86; Adn Valparaiso 76-77; Suff Bp Valparaiso 77-86; C Chorleywood St Andr *St Alb* 87-96; V Iver *Ox* from 96. *The Vicarage, Widecroft Road, Iver SL0 9QD* Tel (01753) 653131

SKINNER, David Malcolm. b 26. CCC Cam BA55 MA59. Wells Th Coll 55. d 57 p 58. C Bris Lockleaze St Mary Magd w St Fran *Bris* 57-60; Sec C of E Radio and TV Coun 60-64; Sec Abps' Radio and TV Coun 64-67; V Ston Easton w Farrington Gurney *B & W* 67-70; rtd 70. *Glasha, Cromane, Killorglin, Co Kerry, Irish Republic* Tel (00353) (66) 69149

SKINNER, Mrs Elaine Teresa (Terri). b 55. Bath Univ BSc78. EMMTC 99. d 02 p 03. NSM Whitwick St Jo the Bapt *Leic* from 02. *31 Stewart Drive, Loughborough LE11 5RU* Tel (01509) 843790 Mobile 07810-241381 E-mail terri.skinner@btopenworld.com

SKINNER, Graeme John. b 57. Southn Univ BSc79. Trin Coll Bris BA. d 86 p 87. C Bebington *Ches* 86-90; V Ashton-upon-Mersey St Mary from 90. *St Mary's Vicarage, 20 Beeston Road, Sale M33 5AG* Tel 0161-973 5118 Fax 973 3227 E-mail graeme@gjskinner.freeserve.co.uk

SKINNER, Mrs Jane Mary. b 59. Leeds Univ BA81. Cranmer Hall Dur 82. dss 84 d 87 p 94. Chatham St Phil and St Jas *Roch* 84-87; Hon Par Dn Church Coniston *Carl* 87-91; Hon Par Dn Torver 87-91; NSM Dalton-in-Furness 91-97; Chapl HM Pris Haverigg 92-97; Chapl Cumberland Infirmary 97-98; Chapl Carl Hosps NHS Trust 98-02; TV Carl H Trin and St Barn *Carl* 98-02; Hon C W Swindon and the Lydiards *Bris* from 02. *The Rectory, Old Shaw Lane, Shaw, Swindon SN5 5PH* Tel (01793) 770568

SKINNER, Mrs Jean. b 47. RN68 RM70. NEOC DipHE96. d 96 p 97. NSM Ch the King *Newc* 96-03; NSM City Cen Chapl from 03. *32 Easedale Avenue, Melton Park, Newcastle upon Tyne NE3 5TB* Tel 0191-236 3474 E-mail jean.skinner@tesco.net

SKINNER, Preb John Cedric. b 30. Bris Univ BA55 Lon Univ DipTh57. Tyndale Hall Bris 55. d 57 p 58. C St Leonard *Ex* 57-62; Univ Sec IVF 62-68; V Guildf St Sav *Guildf* 68-76; R Stoke next Guildf St Jo 74-76; R Guildf St Sav w Stoke-next-Guildford 76-84; R Ex St Leon w H Trin *Ex* 84-98; Chapl R W of England Sch for the Deaf 84-98; Preb Ex Cathl *Ex* 92-98; rtd 98; Perm to Offic *Ex* from 00. *386 Topsham Road, Exeter EX2 6HE* Tel (01392) 876540

SKINNER, John Richard. b 45. N Ord Course 84. d 87 p 88. C Allerton *Liv* 87-90; C Huyton St Mich 90-97; P-in-c Fairfield from 97. *St John's Vicarage, 19 Lockerby Road, Liverpool L7 0HG* Tel 0151-263 4001

SKINNER, John Timothy. b 55. Linc Th Coll 79. d 81 p 82. C Newton Aycliffe *Dur* 81-82; Perm to Offic *Newc* 95-01. *5 Peep O'Shea, Howick, Alnwick NE66 3LD* Tel (01665) 577675

SKINNER, Leonard Harold. b 36. K Coll Lon BD62 AKC62. d 63 p 64. C Hackney Wick St Mary of Eton w St Aug *Lon* 63-66; C Palmers Green St Jo 66-70; V Grange Park St Pet 70-80; TV Hanley H Ev *Lich* 80-86; Chapl Sunderland Poly *Dur* 86-92; Chapl Sunderland Univ 92-93; P-in-c Hebburn St Oswald 93-01; rtd 01; Perm to Offic *Newc* from 01. *28 Brighton Grove, Whitley Bay NE26 1QH* Tel 0191-251 4891

SKINNER, Maurice Wainwright. b 30. St Jo Coll Ox BA53 MA59 FRSC70. Ox NSM Course. d 86 p 87. NSM Furze Platt *Ox* 86-94; NSM Hurley and Stubbings 94-00; rtd 00; Perm to Offic *Ox* from 00. *5 Clarefield Close, Maidenhead SL6 5DR* Tel (01628) 624875

SKINNER, Michael Thomas. b 39. Open Univ BA88 BA90. S'wark Ord Course 73. d 78 p 79. NSM Orpington St Andr *Roch* 78-82; NSM Orpington All SS 82-99; Assoc Bp's Officer for NSMs 90-98; Bp's Officer for NSMs from 98; P-in-c Orpington St Andr from 99; Perm to Offic *S'wark* from 02. *The Vicarage, Anglesea Road, Orpington BR5 4AN* Tel (01689) 823775 E-mail michael.skinner@rochester.anglican.org

SKINNER, Mrs Nicola Jayne. b 70. Birm Univ BA92. Cuddesdon Coll MTh. d 98 p 99. C Bartley Green *Birm* 98-01; Assoc Min Aurora Trin Ch Canada from 01. *Trinity Anglican Church, 79 Victoria Street, Aurora ON, Canada, L4G 1R3*

SKINNER, Peter William. b 47. SSC. Sarum & Wells Th Coll 85. d 87 p 88. C Latchford St Jas *Ches* 87; C Weymouth St Paul *Sarum* 89; Perm to Offic *Lon* 97-99; C Leic St Aid *Leic* 99-01; TV Staveley and Barrow Hill *Derby* from 01. *The Vicarage, 30 Cedar Street, Hollingwood, Chesterfield S43 2LE* Tel (01246) 472175 Fax 471453

SKINNER, Philip Harold. b 30. d 97 p 98. OLM Tisbury *Sarum* 97-01; rtd 01. *Ladydown House, Vicarage Road, Tisbury, Salisbury SP3 6HY* Tel (01747) 870394

SKINNER, Raymond Frederick. b 45. St Jo Coll Dur BA67 Dur Univ MA93. Cranmer Hall Dur. d 70 p 71. C High Elswick St Paul *Newc* 70-76; V Newbottle *Dur* 76-87; Ind Chapl 81-87; RD Houghton 84-87; Oman 87-90; TR Morden *S'wark* from 90; Asst RD Merton from 91. *The Rectory, London Road, Morden SM4 5QT* Tel (020) 8648 3920 *or* 8658 0012 E-mail skinhicks@aol.com

SKINNER, Stephen John. b 52. AIA Bris Univ BSc St Jo Coll Dur BA Dur Univ MLitt. Cranmer Hall Dur. d 83 p 84. C Chatham St Phil and St Jas *Roch* 83-87; P-in-c Torver *Carl* 87-90; C P-in-c Church Coniston 87-90; V 90-91; V Dalton-in-Furness 91-97; TR Carl H Trin and St Barn 97-02; TR W Swindon and the Lydiards *Bris* from 02. *The Rectory, Old Shaw Lane, Shaw, Swindon SN5 5PH* Tel (01793) 770568 E-mail barne@freenetname.co.uk

SKINNER, Terri. See SKINNER, Mrs Elaine Teresa

SKIPPER, Kenneth Graham. b 34. St Aid Birkenhead 65. d 68 p 69. C Newland St Aug *York* 68-71; C Newby 71-74; V Dormanstown 74-78; C-in-c Mappleton w Goxhill 78; C-in-c Withernwick 78; V Aldbrough w Cowden Parva 78; V Aldbrough, Mappleton w Goxhill and Withernwick 79-89; R Londesborough 89-96; R Burnby 90-96; R Nunburnholme and Warter 90-96; V Shiptonthorpe w Hayton 90-96; rtd 96. *18 Elber Crescent, Bowmore PA43 7HU* Tel (01496) 810321

SKIPPER, Canon Lawrence Rainald. b 17. St Pet Hall Ox BA39 MA43. Wycliffe Hall Ox 39. d 41 p 41. C Aldershot H Trin *Guildf* 41-44; C Paignton Ch Ch *Ex* 44-48; V Paignton St Paul Preston 48-50; Chapl Trent Coll Nottm 50-56; Lic to Offic *Derby* 51-56; V Claughton cum Grange *Ches* 56-65; R Christleton 65-72; RD Ches 69-78; R Eccleston and Pulford 72-82; Hon Can Ches Cathl 74-82; rtd 82; Perm to Offic *Ches* from 82. *10 Westminster Terrace, Chester CH4 7LF* Tel (01244) 683178

SKIPPON, Kevin John. b 54. St Steph Ho Ox 78. d 81 p 82. C Gt Yarmouth *Nor* 81-84; C Kingstanding St Luke *Birm* 84-86; V Smethwick SS Steph and Mich 86-92; Chapl Derbyshire R Infirmary 92-94; Chapl Derbyshire R Infirmary NHS Trust 94-98; Chapl S Derbyshire Acute Hosps NHS Trust from 98. *Derbyshire Royal Infirmary, London Road, Derby DE1 2QY* Tel (01332) 347141 ext 2572 E-mail kevin.skippon@sdah-tr.trent.nhs.uk

SKIPWITH, Osmund Humberston. b 06. New Coll Ox BA28 MA33. Cuddesdon Coll 29. d 30 p 31. C Leic St Pet *Leic* 30-35; Zanzibar 35-41; CF (EC) 41-47; CF 47-54; R Maperton *B & W* 54-66; P-in-c 66-71; R N Cheriton 54-66; P-in-c 66-71; RD Cary 60-71; P-in-c Compton Pauncefoot w Blackford 63-71; P-in-c Yarlington 63-71; Preb Wells Cathl 64-74; R N Cadbury 66-71; C Worle 71-76; rtd 76; Perm to Offic *B & W* from 76. *24 Heathdene Manor, Langley Road, Watford WD1 3PZ* Tel (01923) 211543

SKIRROW, Paul Richard. b 52. Hull Univ BA82 Chester Coll of HE MTh00. N Ord Course 97. d 00 p 01. C St Luke in the City *Liv* from 00. *9 Hougoumont Avenue, Liverpool L22 0LL* Tel 0151-928 9053 Fax as telephone E-mail paul.skirrow@btinternet.com

SKLIROS, Michael Peter. b 33. Clare Coll Cam BA57 MA62. Ridley Hall Cam 57. d 59 p 60. C Hornchurch St Andr *Chelmsf* 59-61; Asst Chapl Denstone Coll Uttoxeter 61-65; Chapl RAF 65-77; P-in-c Stowmarket *St E* 77-78; Lic to Offic 78-85; C Gt Finborough w Onehouse and Harleston 85-91; P-in-c 91; R Gt and Lt Bealings w Playford and Culpho 91-96; rtd 96. *17 Bury Hill Close, Melton, Woodbridge IP12 1LE* Tel (01394) 388104

SKOYLES, John Alan. b 32. Breakspear Coll 50 Christleton Hall 53. d 58 p 59. In RC Ch 59-80; Soc worker 80-99; NSM The Hydneye *Chich* 99-00; C Kenton, Mamhead, Powderham, Cofton and Starcross *Ex* 00-01. *Flat 3, 31 Ceylon Place, Eastbourne BN21 3JE*

SKRINE, Charles Walkver Douglas. b 75. Qu Coll Ox BA98. Oak Hill Th Coll BA03. d 03. C St Helen Bishopsgate w St Andr Undershaft etc *Lon* from 03. *64 Arbery Road, London E3 5DD* E-mail charles@cwdskrine.freeserve.co.uk

SKUCE, David. b 56. NUU BSc79 QUB PGCE80 TCD BTh89. CITC 87. d 89 p 90. C Templemore *D & R* 89-92; I Kilbarron w Rossnowlagh and Drumholm 92-99; I Urney w Sion Mills from 99; Bp's Dom Chapl from 94. *The Rectory, 112 Melmount Road, Sion Mills, Strabane BT82 9PY* Tel (028) 8165 8020

SLACK, Canon Ellis Edward. b 23. Birm Univ BA51 MA53. Qu Coll Birm 51. d 53 p 53. C Leeds Halton St Wilfrid *Ripon* 53-56; R Stanningley St Thos 57-64; V N Dulwich St Faith *S'wark* 64-72; V Bethnal Green St Jo w St Simon *Lon* 72-78; TR Bethnal Green St Jo w St Bart 78-79; Can Res Portsm Cathl *Portsm* 79-83; Bp's Chapl for CME 79-83; V Woodplumpton *Blackb* 83-88; Dir Post-Ord Tr 83-88; rtd 88; Perm to Offic *York* from 88. *68 Ouse Lea, Shipton Road, York YO30 6SA* Tel (01904) 658263 E-mail ellis.slack@tesco.net

SLACK, Michael. b 53. RGN83 St Jo Coll Dur BA74 Lon Univ PGCE79 Newc Poly DPSN86. St Steph Ho Ox 74. d 76 p 77. C Wolverhampton St Steph *Lich* 76-77; NSM Bywell *Newc* 89-93; TV Cullercoats St Geo 93-98; TR from 98. *St George's Vicarage, Beverley Gardens, North Shields NE30 4NS* Tel 0191-252 1817 Fax as telephone

SLADDEN, Duncan Julius Edward. b 25. K Coll Cam BA50 MA51. Cuddesdon Coll 51. d 53 p 54. C Huddersfield St Pet *Wakef* 53-55; C Reading St Mary V *Ox* 55-61; R Largs *Glas* 61-65; P-in-c Stevenage *St Alb* 65-70; R Johnstone *Glas* 70-76; Prayer Gp Adv Scottish Chs Renewal 76-81; Sec Scottish Episc Renewal Fellowship 81-84; R E Kilbride 85-90; rtd 90. *17 Bruce Avenue, Dunblane FK15 9JB* Tel (01786) 825520

SLADDEN, Canon John Cyril. b 20. Mert Coll Ox BA42 MA46 BD66. Wycliffe Hall Ox 46. d 48 p 49. C Oswestry St Oswald *Lich* 48-51; Tutor St Aid Birkenhead 51-53; R Todwick *Sheff* 53-59; V Nether Peover *Ches* 59-86; RD Knutsford 80-85; Hon Can Ches Cathl 80-86; rtd 86. *Rossa, Penmon, Beaumaris LL58 8SN* Tel (01248) 490207

SLADDEN, John David. b 49. RN Eng Coll Plymouth BSc74 St Edm Coll Cam MA86. Ridley Hall Cam 80. d 83 p 84. C St Bees *Carl* 83-85; Perm to Offic *Lich* 85-87; Miss Co-ord Down to Earth Evangelistic Trust 85-87; V Doncaster St Jas *Sheff* 87-94. *9 Teal Close, Chatteris PE16 6PR* Tel (01354) 694097

SLADE, Canon Adrian Barrie. b 47. K Alfred's Coll Win DipEd68. St Jo Coll Nottm BTh73 ALCD72. d 73 p 74. C Streatham Immanuel w St Anselm *S'wark* 73-76; C Chipping Barnet *St Alb* 76-78; C Chipping Barnet w Arkley 78-80; V Sundon 80-85; Soc Resp Officer *Glouc* from 86; Hon Can Glouc Cathl from 91. *38 Sydenham Villas Road, Cheltenham GL52 6DZ* Tel (01242) 253162 Fax 242672 E-mail glossr@star.co.uk

SLADE, Alfred Laurence. b 12. ACII. Roch Th Coll 67. d 69 p 70. Hon C Cliftonville *Cant* 69-71; Hon C Westgate St Jas 71-75; Perm to Offic *Sarum* 75-81; Perm to Offic *Cant* 81-93. *21 McKinlay Court, The Parade, Minnis Bay, Birchington CT7 9QG* Tel (01843) 46882

SLADE, Michael John. b 55. Trin Coll Bris 94. d 96 p 97. C Blagdon w Compton Martin and Ubley *B & W* 96-99; V Winscombe from 99. *The Vicarage, Winscombe Hill, Winscombe BS25 1DE* Tel (01934) 843164 Fax as telephone E-mail mikeslade@compuserve.com

SLADE, Canon William Clifford. b 24. St Jo Coll Dur BA47 DipTh49 MA53. d 49 p 50. C Northallerton w Deighton and Romanby *York* 49-52; C Eston 52-54; V Anlaby Common St Mark 54-60; V Brompton w Snainton 60-67; R Stokesley 67-71; V Felixkirk w Boltby 71-82; V Kirby Knowle 71-82; Can and Preb York Minster 79-86; V Topcliffe w Dalton and Dishforth 82-86; Abp's Adv for Spiritual Direction 82-86; Perm to Offic from 86; rtd 86. *Bede House, Beck Lane, South Kilvington, Thirsk YO7 2NL* Tel (01845) 522915

SLADEN, Philip. b 50. Fitzw Coll Cam BA71 MA75 DipTh. Ripon Hall Ox 72. d 75 p 76. C Bushey Heath *St Alb* 75-78; Chapl RAF 78-99; Ind Chapl *Chelmsf* from 99. *147 Katherine Road, London E6 1ES* Tel and fax (020) 8586 6988 Mobile 07715-372935 E-mail phil575@ukonline.co.uk

SLATER, Mrs Ann. b 46. Somerville Coll Ox BA67 MA71. WMMTC 92. d 95 p 96. C Northampton St Benedict *Pet* 95-99; TV Daventry, Ashby St Ledgers, Braunston etc from 99. *The

Vicarage, 19 High Street, Welton, Daventry NN11 5JP Tel (01327) 879421 E-mail ann.slater@btinternet.com

SLATER, David. See SLATER, Canon Philip David

SLATER, James Richard David. b 61. New Univ of Ulster BA83 TCD BTh89 Univ of Ulster MA92. CITC 86. d 89 p 90. C Clooney w Strathfoyle *D & R* 89-93; I Aghadowey w Kilrea from 93. *Kilrea Rectory, 2 Moneygran Road, Kilrea, Coleraine BT51 5SJ* Tel (028) 2554 0257

SLATER, Preb John. b 45. K Coll Lon BA67 AKC67 Fitzw Coll Cam BA69 MA73. Westcott Ho Cam 67 Union Th Sem (NY) STM70. d 70 p 71. C St Marylebone All SS *Lon* 70-77; V Paddington St Sav 77-83; Dir Post-Ord Tr 82-92; V St John's Wood 83-01; AD Westmr St Marylebone 92-01; Preb St Paul's Cathl from 99; P-in-c Hanover Square St Geo w St Mark from 01. *21A Down Street, London W1J 7AW* Tel (020) 7409 3255 *or* tel and fax 7629 0874 E-mail revjslater@aol.com

SLATER, John Albert. b 25. Lon Univ BA52. Oak Hill Th Coll 47. d 52 p 53. C Everton Em *Liv* 52-55; V Kirkdale St Paul N Shore 55-61; V Bacup St Sav *Man* 61-70; V Blackpool St Thos Blackb 70-84; rtd 84; Perm to Offic *Blackb* from 84. *18 Church Road, Thornton-Cleveleys FY5 2TZ* Tel (01253) 853330

SLATER, John Ralph. b 38. Kent Univ BA90. Linc Th Coll 71. d 73 p 74. C S Hackney St Mich w Haggerston St Paul *Lon* 73-74; C Leytonstone St Marg w St Columba *Chelmsf* 74-77; C Whitstable All SS w St Pet *Cant* 77-80; V Gt Ilford St Alb *Chelmsf* 80-83; V Clipstone *S'well* 83-87; rtd 87. *117 Canterbury Road, Westgate-on-Sea CT8 8NW* Tel (01227) 831593

SLATER, Mark Andrew. b 56. ARCS79 Imp Coll Lon BSc79. Ridley Hall Cam 87. d 89 p 90. C Northampton St Giles *Pet* 89-92; C Stopsley *St Alb* 92-93; C-in-c Bushmead CD 93-99; V St Alb St Luke from 99. *St Luke's Vicarage, 46 Cell Barnes Lane, St Albans AL1 5QJ* Tel (01727) 865399 E-mail mark.slater@saint-lukes.co.uk

SLATER, Paul John. b 58. CCC Ox MA83 Dur Univ BA83. Cranmer Hall Dur 81. d 84 p 85. C Keighley St Andr *Bradf* 84-88; Dir Dioc Foundn Course 88-93; P-in-c Cullingworth 88-93; Bp's Personal Exec Asst 93-95; Warden of Readers 92-96; R Haworth 95-01; Bp's Officer for Min and Miss from 01. *6 Glenhurst Road, Shipley BD18 4DZ* Tel (01274) 586414 Fax as telephone E-mail paul.slater@dial.pipex.com

SLATER, Canon Philip David. b 27. K Coll Lon 58. d 60 p 61. C Havant *Portsm* 60-67; C Leigh Park 68-69; Hants Co RE Adv 69-74; Gosport and Fareham RE Adv 74-82; Hon C Bishop's Waltham 76-82; V Bulford, Figheldean and Milston *Sarum* 82-93; RD Avon 85-95; Can and Preb Sarum Cathl 91-95; V Avon Valley 93-95; rtd 95; V of Close Sarum Cathl *Sarum* from 95; Chapl Godolphin Sch from 95. *102 Coombe Road, Salisbury SP2 8BD* Tel (01722) 332529 E-mail voc@salcath.co.uk

SLATER, Robert Adrian. b 48. St Jo Coll Nottm 76. d 79 p 80. C Bedworth *Cov* 79-82; TV Billericay and Lt Burstead *Chelmsf* 82-88; V Rounds Green *Birm* 88-94. *11 Lewis Road, Birmingham B30 2SU* Tel 0121-689 2721 E-mail robslater@freeuk.com

SLATER, Thomas Ernest. b 37. Chelsea Coll Lon TCert60 Lon Univ BD71 NE Lon Poly DipG&C88. ALCD66. d 67 p 68. C Bootle Ch Ch *Liv* 67-72; C Stapleford *S'well* 72-75; Supt Tower Hamlets Miss 75-77; Hon C Stepney St Pet w St Benet *Lon* 78-79; Asst Chapl The Lon Hosp (Whitechapel) 79-83; Chapl 83-89; NSM Poplar *Lon* 89-92 and 94-00; Perm to Offic 92-94; rtd 02. *11 Elgin House, Cordelia Street, London E14 6EG* Tel (020) 7987 4504

SLATER, Victoria Ruth. b 59. Hertf Coll Ox BA82 MA87 Selw Coll Cam BA89 MA94. Westcott Ho Cam 86. d 89 p 94. Chapl Asst Man R Infirmary 89-90; Chapl 90-94; Chapl St Mary's Hosp Man 90-94; Chapl Ox Radcliffe Hosp NHS Trust 94-97; Chapl Sir Michael Sobell Ho Palliative Care Unit from 97. *Sir Michael Sobell House, The Churchill, Headington, Oxford OX3 7LJ* Tel (01865) 225860

SLATER, William Edward. b 51. Bolton Inst of Tech HNC77. Aston Tr Scheme 85 Oak Hill Th Coll 87. d 89 p 90. C Balderstone *Man* 89-94; V Newchapel *Lich* from 94; RD Stoke N from 99. *The Vicarage, 32 Pennyfield Road, Newchapel, Stoke-on-Trent ST7 4PN* Tel (01782) 782837 E-mail willslater@tinyworld.co.uk

SLATOR, Edward Douglas Humphreys. b 18. TCD BA41 MA47 Hull Univ BPhil75. d 43 p 44. C Taney *D & G* 43-46; Chapl St Columba's Coll Dub 46-60; I Killea *C & D* 60-73; C Taney *D & G* 74-80; P-in-c Rathmolyon w Castlerickard, Rathcore and Agher *M & K* 80-87; rtd 87; PV Ch Ch Cathl Dublin *D & G* from 93. *31 St John's, Park Avenue, Dublin 4, Irish Republic* Tel (00353) (1) 283 9395

SLATOR, Canon William Thompson Howard. b 09. TCD BA31 MA34. d 32 p 33. C Ballywillan *Conn* 33-35; P-in-c Mullaghdun *Clogh* 35-38; I Boyle w Aghanagh *K, E & A* 38-52; I Clonbroney w Killoe 52-66; I Kiltoghart 66-81; Preb Elphin Cathl 66-81; rtd 81. *c/o Naomi Maybury, 15 Wainsfort Crescent, Terenure, Dublin 6W, Irish Republic*

SLATTER, Barrie John. b 44. Nottm Univ BSc66 FRICS97. Dioc OLM tr scheme 97. d 00 p 01. OLM Hundred River *St E*

00-03; C Gt and Lt Glemham, Blaxhall etc from 03. *The Rectory, Low Road, Stratford St Andrew, Saxmundham IP17 1LJ*

SLATTERY, Maurice Michael. b 43. Southlands Coll Lon CertEd73 BEd74. S'wark Ord Course 91. **d** 94 **p** 95. NSM Malden St Jas *S'wark* 94-97; NSM Niton *Portsm* 97-99; NSM Whitwell 97-99; NSM St Lawrence 97-99; NSM Selsdon St Jo w St Fran *S'wark* 99-03. *Marlbrook, Hunts Road, St Lawrence, Ventnor PO38 1XT* Tel 07939-157892 (mobile)

SLAUGHTER, Clive Patrick. b 36. St Paul's Coll Grahamstown DipTh78. **d** 77 **p** 78. S Africa 77-87; R Thorley w Bishop's Stortford H Trin *St Alb* 87-90; R Thorley 90-01; RD Bishop's Stortford 96-01; rtd 01; Perm to Offic *St Alb* 01-03; P-in-c Much Hadham from 03. *53 High Street, Hunsdon, Ware SG12 8QB* Tel (01279) 844955 E-mail clive.slaughter@virgin.net

SLAUGHTER, Canon Maurice Basil. b 20. Leeds Univ BA42. Coll of Resurr Mirfield 42. **d** 44 **p** 45. C Kingswinford St Mary *Lich* 44-46; C Roch St Nic w St Clem *Roch* 46-47; C Luton Ch Ch *St Alb* 47-50; V Birm St Marg Ladywood *Birm* 50-52; V Newsome *Wakef* 52-60; V Queensbury *Bradf* 60-63; V Skipton Ch Ch 63-78; Hon Can Bradf Cathl 67-85; RD Skipton 73-82; P-in-c Bolton Abbey 78-85; P-in-c Rylstone 78-85; P-in-c Arncliffe w Halton Gill 79-82; rtd 85; Perm to Offic *Bradf* 85-99; Perm to Offic *Wakef* 85-96; Perm to Offic *Ely* 96-00. *107 Lisle Close, Ely CB7 4AD* Tel (01353) 664541

SLEDGE, The Ven Richard Kitson. b 30. Peterho Cam BA52 MA57. Ridley Hall Cam 52. **d** 54 **p** 55. C Compton Gifford *Ex* 54-57; C Ex St Martin, St Steph, St Laur etc 57-63; V Dronfield *Derby* 63-76; TR 76-78; RD Chesterfield 72-78; Adn Huntingdon *Ely* 78-96; R Hemingford Abbots 78-89; Hon Can Ely Cathl 78-99; rtd 96; Bp's Dom Chapl *Ely* 96-99; Dioc Retirement Officer from 98; Perm to Offic from 99. *7 Budge Close, Brampton, Huntingdon PE29 4PL* Tel (01480) 380284 *or* (01353) 662749 Fax (01480) 437789

SLEDGE, Timothy Charles Kitson. b 64. Coll of Ripon & York St Jo BA87 York Univ MA88. Trin Coll Bris DipHE95 ADUT95. **d** 95 **p** 96. C Huddersfield St Thos *Wakef* 95-98; V Luddenden w Luddenden Foot 98-03; P-in-c Sowerby 02-03; Dioc Miss Enabler *Pet* from 03. *The Vicarage, Campbell Square, Northampton NN1 3EB* Tel (01604) 230563 E-mail tim@sledgey.freeserve.co.uk

SLEE, The Very Revd Colin Bruce. b 45. OBE01. K Coll Lon BD69 AKC69 FKC01. St Aug Coll Cant 69. **d** 70 **p** 71. C Nor Heartsease St Fran *Nor* 70-73; C Cambridge Gt St Mary w St Mich *Ely* 73-76; Chapl Girton Coll Cam 73-76; Tutor and Chapl K Coll Lon 76-82; Can Res and Sub-Dean St Alb 82-94; Provost S'wark 94-00; Dean S'wark from 00; Hon Lect Harvard Div Sch from 01. *The Provost's Lodging, 51 Bankside, London SE1 9JE* Tel (020) 7928 6414 *or* 7367 6731 Fax 7367 6725 E-mail colin.slee@dswark.org.uk

SLEE, John Graham. b 51. Brunel Univ BTech73. Oak Hill Th Coll 85. **d** 87 **p** 88. C St Columb Minor and St Colan *Truro* 87-91; R St Mawgan w St Ervan and St Eval 91-02; RD Pydar 93-95; P-in-c St Just-in-Roseland and St Mawes from 02. *16 Waterloo Close, St Mawes, Truro TR2 5BD* Tel (01326) 270248 Fax as telephone E-mail jslee@priest.com

SLEEMAN, Matthew Timothy. b 68. St Cath Coll Cam BA90 MA95 PhD96. Wycliffe Hall Ox BA97. **d** 98 **p** 99. C Eynsham and Cassington *Ox* 98-02. *128 The Fairway, London N14 4NN*

SLEGG, John Edward. b 36. St Pet Coll Ox BA62 MA66. Ridley Hall Cam 62. **d** 64 **p** 65. C Perranzabuloe *Truro* 64-66; CF 66-86; V Poling *Chich* from 86; V Lyminster from 86. *The Vicarage, 3 Middle Paddock, Lyminster, Littlehampton BN17 7QH* Tel (01903) 882152 E-mail slegglymvic@aol.com

SLEIGHT, Gordon Frederick. b 47. AKC69. St Aug Coll Cant 69. **d** 70 **p** 71. C Boston *Linc* 70-74; P-in-c Louth St Mich 74-75; P-in-c Stewton 75; TV Louth 75-81; V Crosby 81-95; P-in-c Nettleham 95-97; V from 97. *The Vicarage, 2 Vicarage Lane, Nettleham, Lincoln LN2 2RH* Tel (01522) 754752 E-mail gordon@gsleight.freeserve.co.uk

SLIM, David Albert. b 49. Westhill Coll Birm CertEd72. Linc Th Coll 90. **d** 90 **p** 91. C Walmley *Birm* 90-93; R Marchwiel and Isycoed *St As* from 93. *Marchwiel Rectory, Overton Road, Marchwiel, Wrexham LL13 0TE* Tel (01978) 780640

SLIPPER, Charles Callan. b 55. Lanc Univ BA77 PhD84. S Dios Minl Tr Scheme 91. **d** 93 **p** 94. Focolare Movement from 77; NSM N Acton St Gabr *Lon* 93-96; Perm to Offic from 96. *38 Audley Road, London W5 3ET* Tel (020) 8991 2022 E-mail callan@onetel.net.uk

SLIPPER, Robert James. b 64. St Jo Coll Cam BA87 MA91. Wycliffe Hall Ox BA92. **d** 92 **p** 93. C Southgate *Chich* 92-95; C Stoughton *Guildf* 95-00; V Terrington St Clement *Ely* from 00. *The Vicarage, 27 Sutton Road, Terrington St Clement, King's Lynn PE34 4PQ* Tel (01553) 828430 E-mail robert@slipper.fsnet.co.uk

SLOANE, Isaac Reuben. b 16. TCD BA41 MA60. **d** 42 **p** 43. C Kinawley w H Trin *K, E & A* 42-44; I Gleneely w Culdaff *D & R* 44-54; I Ardstraw w Baronscourt, Badoney Lower etc 54-76; I Drumclamph w Drumquin 76-78; rtd 78. *40 Rawdon Place, Moira, Craigavon BT67 0NX* Tel (028) 9261 1547

SLOGGETT, Donald George. b 49. Trin Coll Bris 81. **d** 83 **p** 84. C Horfield H Trin *Bris* 83-86; C Highworth w Sevenhampton and Inglesham etc 86-88; P-in-c Upavon w Rushall *Sarum* 88-90; R Upavon w Rushall and Charlton 90-01; R Stoulton w Drake's Broughton and Pirton etc *Worc* from 01. *The Rectory, Manor Farm, Stoulton, Worcester WR7 4RS* Tel (01905) 840528

SLOW, Leslie John. b 47. Liv Univ BSc68 MSc69. N Ord Course 77. **d** 80 **p** 81. NSM Horton *Bradf* from 80. *25 Grasleigh Way, Bradford BD15 9BE* Tel (01274) 491808

SLUMAN, Richard Geoffrey Davies. b 34. St Jo Coll Ox BA68 MA68. Sarum Th Coll 68. **d** 70 **p** 71. C Gt Yarmouth *Nor* 70-73; V Churchdown *Glouc* 73-82; P-in-c Blockley w Aston Magna 82-83; V Blockley w Aston Magna and Bourton on the Hill 83-94; rtd 94; Perm to Offic *Cov* from 94. *21 Manor Farm Road, Tredington, Shipston-on-Stour CV36 4NZ* Tel (01608) 662317

SLY, Canon Christopher John. b 34. Selw Coll Cam BA58 MA62. Wycliffe Hall Ox. **d** 60 **p** 61. C Buckhurst Hill *Chelmsf* 60-64; V Berechurch 64-75; V Southend St Sav Westcliff 75-87; R Wickham Bishops w Lt Braxted 87-99; RD Witham 87-96; Hon Can Chelmsf Cathl 93-99; rtd 99. *Ludlow Cottage, Church Lane, Little Leighs, Chelmsford CM3 1PQ* Tel (01245) 361489

SLY, Canon Harold Kenneth. b 15. Kelham Th Coll 34. **d** 38 **p** 39. C Wigston Magna *Leic* 38-41; C Dudley St Edm *Worc* 41-43; C Redditch St Steph 43-49; V Worc St Swithun 49-57; V Hampton in Arden *Birm* 57-83; Hon Can Birm Cathl 78-83; rtd 83; Perm to Offic *Worc* 83-91; *Lich* 91-95; *Birm* 95-98; *Glouc* from 02; Hon C Wylde Green *Birm* 98-01; Chapl Convent of the H Name Malvern 83-90. *24 Capel Court, The Burgage, Prestbury, Cheltenham GL52 3EL* Tel (01242) 579632

SLYFIELD, John David. b 32. TD67. Roch Th Coll 66. **d** 68 **p** 69. C St Mary in the Marsh *Cant* 68-71; P-in-c Steeple Claydon *Ox* 71-76; P-in-c Middle w E Claydon 71-76; RD Claydon 73-78; R The Claydons 76-78; V S Westoe *Dur* 78-82; V Tideswell *Derby* 82-92; RD Buxton 84-91; rtd 92; Perm to Offic *Derby* 92-02; P-in-c Beeley and Edensor from 02. *The Vicarage, Edensor, Bakewell DE45 1PH* Tel (01246) 582180

SMAIL, Richard Charles. b 57. CCC Ox BA80 MA83. Ox Min Course 90. **d** 93 **p** 95. NSM Keble Coll Ox 93-96; Chapl, Fell and Lect BNC Ox 97-02; Perm to Offic *Ox* from 02. *Brasenose College, Oxford OX1 4AJ* E-mail richardsmail@supanet.com

SMAIL, Canon Thomas Allan. b 28. Glas Univ MA49 Edin Univ BD52. **d** 79 **p** 79. Vice-Prin St Jo Coll Nottm 80-85; TR Sanderstead All SS *S'wark* 85-94; Hon Can S'wark Cathl 91-94; rtd 94; Perm to Offic *S'wark* from 94. *36B Alexandra Road, Croydon CR0 6EU* Tel (020) 8656 9683

SMALE, Frederick Ronald. b 37. K Coll Lon BD60 AKC60. **d** 61 **p** 62. C Bearsted *Cant* 61-64; C Fishponds St Mary *Bris* 64-69; V Hartlip *Cant* 69-71; P-in-c Stockbury w Bicknor and Huckinge 69-71; V Hartlip w Stockbury 71-75; R River 75-85; V Birchington w Acol and Minnis Bay 85-00; rtd 00; Perm to Offic *Cant* from 01. *28 Margate Road, Broomfield, Herne Bay CT6 7BL* Tel (01227) 283880

SMALE, Ian Keith. b 53. Wycliffe Hall Ox. **d** 00 **p** 01. C Overton w Laverstoke and Freefolk *Win* from 00. *21 Lordsfield Gardens, Overton, Basingstoke RG25 3EW* Tel (01256) 771305 E-mail ian@smale.freewire.co.uk

SMALL, David Binney. b 39. Brasted Th Coll 61 Westcott Ho Cam 63. **d** 65 **p** 66. C Milton *Portsm* 65-69; CF 69-92; R Wickwar w Rangeworthy *Glouc* 92-97; RD Hawkesbury 94-97; rtd 97; Perm to Offic *Glouc* from 97; Sub Chapl HM Pris Glouc from 98. *16 Wotton Road, Charfield, Wotton-under-Edge GL12 8TP* Tel (01454) 261746 Fax as telephone

SMALL, Gordon Frederick. b 41. St Jo Coll Nottm 77. **d** 79 **p** 80. C Belper *Derby* 79-84; NSM Matlock Bath 90-91; C Ripley 91-93; TV Bucknall and Bagnall *Lich* 93-98; Assoc P Deal St Leon and St Rich and Sholden *Cant* from 98. *St Richard's Lodge, 7 St Richard's Road, Deal CT14 9JR* Tel (01304) 374674 E-mail gordon.small1@btopenworld.com

SMALL, Marcus Jonathan. b 67. Univ of Wales (Ban) BD94. Ripon Coll Cuddesdon 94. **d** 96 **p** 97. C Moseley St Mary *Birm* 96-99; TV Wenlock *Heref* from 99. *14 Stretton Road, Much Wenlock TF13 6AS* Tel (01952) 728211

SMALL, Simon William. b 57. Worc Coll of Tech HNC77 DMA81. Cuddesdon Coll. **d** 98 **p** 99. C Kidderminster St Mary and All SS w Trimpley etc *Worc* 98-01; Chapl to Bp Dudley from 01. *4 Hemplands Road, Stourbridge DY8 1TX* Tel (01384) 826939 Mobile 07702-693414 E-mail simon.small@virgin.net

SMALLDON, Canon Keith. b 48. Open Univ BA76 Newc Univ MA94. St Mich Coll Llan DipTh71. **d** 71 **p** 72. C Cwmbran *Mon* 71-73; C Chepstow 73-75; Dioc Youth Adv *Bradf* 75-79; P-in-c Woolfold *Man* 82-85; Dioc Youth and Community Officer 82-90; P-in-c Thursby *Carl* 90-94; Dir of Clergy Tr 90-94; TR Daventry, Ashby St Ledgers, Braunston etc *Pet* 94-98; R Llantwit Major *Llan* 98-03; Can Res Brecon Cathl *S & B* from 03. *The Clergy House, Cathedral Close, Brecon LD3 9DP* Tel (01874) 623776 E-mail ksmalldon@compuserve.com

SMALLEY, Mrs Kathleen. b 23. Linc Th Coll 81. **dss** 84 **d** 87 **p** 94. Leominster *Heref* 84-85; Bridgnorth, Tasley, Astley

Abbotts, etc 85-96; Hon C 87-96; Perm to Offic from 96. *8A Cliff Road, Bridgnorth WV16 4EY* Tel (01746) 766202

SMALLEY, The Very Revd Stephen Stewart. b 31. Jes Coll Cam BA55 MA58 PhD79. Eden Th Sem (USA) BD57 Ridley Hall Cam. **d** 58 **p** 59. C Portman Square St Paul *Lon* 58-60; Chapl Peterho Cam 60-63; Dean 62-63; Nigeria 63-69; Lect Th Man Univ 70-77; Can Res and Prec Cov Cathl *Cov* 77-87; Vice-Provost 86-87; Dean Ches 87-01; rtd 01; Perm to Offic *Glouc* from 02. *The Old Hall, The Folly, Longborough, Moreton-in-Marsh GL56 0QS* Tel (01451) 830238
E-mail stephen@ssssss.fsworld.co.uk

SMALLMAN, Miss Margaret Anne. b 43. Hull Univ BSc64 Bris Univ CertEd65. St Jo Coll Nottm DipTh82. **dss** 83 **d** 87 **p** 94. Bromsgrove St Jo *Worc* 83-87; Par Dn 87-88; Par Dn Stoke Prior, Wychbold and Upton Warren 88-90; TD Tettenhall Wood *Lich* 91-94; TV 94-99; P-in-c W Bromwich H Trin from 99; C W Bromwich Gd Shep w St Jo from 99. *Holy Trinity Vicarage, 1 Burlington Road, West Bromwich B70 6LF* Tel 0121-525 3595
E-mail mas@msmallman.fsnet.co.uk

SMALLMAN, Mrs Sheila Maxine. b 30. Lon Univ BSc51. St Jo Coll Nottm 91 Cant Sch of Min 92. **d** 97 **p** 98. NSM Benenden *Cant* 97-01; Asst Chapl Benenden Hosp 97-01; NSM Sandhurst w Newenden *Cant* from 01. *Beacon Shaw, Rolvenden Road, Benenden, Cranbrook TN17 4BU* Tel (01580) 240625 Fax as telephone

SMALLS, Peter Harry. b 34. FCCA. LNSM course 96. **d** 97 **p** 98. OLM Narborough w Narford *Nor* 97-99; OLM Pentney St Mary Magd w W Bilney 97-99; OLM Castle Acre w Newton and Southacre 97-99; OLM Westacre 97-99; OLM Narborough w Narford and Pentney 99-02; Perm to Offic from 03. *Windward, Drapers Lane, Ditchingham, Bungay NR35 2JW* Tel (01986) 894667

SMALLWOOD, Simon Laurence. b 58. St Jo Coll Dur BSc80. Cranmer Hall Dur 89. **d** 92 **p** 93. C Stapenhill w Cauldwell *Derby* 92-96; TV Dagenham *Chelmsf* 96-03; V Becontree St Geo from 03. *The Vicarage, 86 Rogers Road, Dagenham RM10 8JX* Tel (020) 8593 2760

SMART, Barry Anthony Ignatius. b 57. Lanc Univ BEd79. St Steph Ho Ox 85. **d** 88 **p** 89. C Wantage *Ox* 88-91; C Abingdon 91-93; TV 93-95; C Princes Risborough w Ilmer 95-97; C Kingstanding St Luke *Birm* 97-00; V Small Heath from 00. *All Saints' Clergy House, 85 Jenkins Street, Small Heath, Birmingham B10 0PQ* Tel 0121-772 0621 Fax as telephone

SMART, Beryl. b 33. Sheff Univ BSc55 FIMgt83. Dioc OLM tr scheme 98. **d** 01 **p** 02. OLM Newchurch w Croft *Liv* from 01. *41 Culcheth Hall Drive, Culcheth, Warrington WA3 4PT* Tel (01925) 762655

SMART, Mrs Carol. b 45. SSF SRN67. S Dios Minl Tr Scheme 89. **d** 92 **p** 94. Chapl St Mary's Hosp NHS Trust 92-99; NSM Shorwell w Kingston *Portsm* 99-02; NSM Gatcombe 92-02; NSM Chale 92-02; Perm to Offic from 02. *20 Sydney Close, Shide, Newport PO30 1YG* Tel (01983) 526242
E-mail carol_smart@tssf.freeserve.co.uk

SMART, Clifford Edward James. b 28. Kelham Th Coll 48. **d** 53 **p** 54. C Blackb St Pet *Blackb* 53-56; Korea 56-65 and 66-93; C Birm St Aid Small Heath *Birm* 65-66; rtd 93. *6430 Telegraph Road, St Louis, MO 63129-4934, USA* Tel (001) (314) 846 5927

SMART, Harry Gavin. b 67. St D Coll Lamp BA90 Selw Coll Cam DipTh92. Westcott Ho Cam CTM94. **d** 94 **p** 95. C Thirsk *York* 94-97; C Sheff Norwood St Leon *Sheff* 97-99; Mental Health Chapl Community Health Sheff NHS Trust from 99. *Longley Centre, Northern General Hospital, Herries Road, Sheffield S5 7AU* Tel 0114-271 6518 *or* 271 6310

SMART, Canon Haydn Christopher. b 38. Wells Th Coll 66. **d** 69 **p** 70. C Hillmorton *Cov* 69-72; C Duston *Pet* 72-75; V Woodford Halse 75-79; V Woodford Halse w Eydon 79-82; V Wellingborough All SS 82-92; RD Wellingborough 87-92; V Longthorpe 92-03; Can Pet Cathl 92-03; RD Pet 96-01; rtd 03; P-in-c Madeira *Eur* from 03. *The Parsonage, 20 rua do Quebra Costas, 9000 Funchal, Madeira* Tel (00351) (291) 220674 Fax (291) 220161 E-mail holytrinity@netmadeira.com

SMART, Mrs Hilary Jean. b 42. SOAS Lon BA63 CSocSc64 DASS67. EMMTC 85. **d** 88 **p** 94. Par Dn Walsall Pleck and Bescot *Lich* 88-94; C 94; TV Sheff Manor *Sheff* 94-02; Bp's Ecum Officer 94-02; rtd 02; Chapl Compton Hospice from 02. *Abbey Cottage, 42 High Street, Much Wenlock TF13 6AD* Tel (01952) 727062

SMART, John Francis. b 36. Keble Coll Ox BA59 MA69. Cuddesdon Coll 59. **d** 61 **p** 66. C Cannock *Lich* 61-63; Hon C Gt Wyrley 63-66; C Wednesfield St Thos 66-70; V Brewood 70-85; R E Clevedon and Walton w Weston w Clapton *B & W* 85-02; Chapl Southmead Health Services NHS Trust 85-99; Chapl N Bris NHS Trust 99-02; rtd 02. *Sunnymead, Ford Cross, South Zeal, Okehampton EX20 2JL* Tel (01837) 840233
E-mail andrsmart@tiscali.co.uk

SMART, Neil Robert. b 61. Bris Univ BVSc84. Ridley Hall Cam 01. **d** 03. C Shirley *Win* from 03. *16 Radway Road, Southampton SO15 7PW* Tel (023) 8077 9605
E-mail somesmarts@talk21.com

SMART, Richard Henry. b 22. St Jo Coll Dur 46 Clifton Th Coll 48. **d** 52 **p** 53. C Leeds St Geo *Ripon* 52-54; Kenya 54-56; C New Addington *Cant* 56-59; V Awsworth w Cossall *S'well* 59-63; BFBS Distr Sec E Anglia 63-70; Bp's Ecum Adv *Ely* 70-81; Dioc Missr 70-74; P-in-c Dry Drayton 74-81; Min Bar Hill LEP 74-81; P-in-c Madingley 80-81; V Sandylands *Blackb* 81-92; rtd 92; Perm to Offic *Pet* from 97; *Ely* 97-00; *Nor* from 98. *156 Ryeland Road, Duston, Northampton NN5 6XJ* Tel (01604) 758502

SMART, Richard Henry. b 23. Lon Univ BA51. Oak Hill Th Coll. **d** 53 **p** 54. C Bedworth *Cov* 53-56; C New Malden and Coombe *S'wark* 56-59; V Hanley Road St Sav w St Paul *Lon* 59-71; V Plumstead All SS *S'wark* 71-88; rtd 88; Perm to Offic *Chich* from 88. *2 Annington Road, Eastbourne BN22 8NG* Tel (01323) 726850

SMART, Canon Sydney. b 15. TCD BA37 MA43. **d** 39 **p** 40. C Belfast St Mich *Conn* 39-42; P-in-c Belfast St Barn 42-46; I 46-60; I Belfast All SS 60-83; Can Belf Cathl 76-83; rtd 83. *49 Ballylenaghan Park, Belfast BT8 6WP* Tel (028) 9079 9028

SMEATON, William Brian Alexander. b 37. CITC 69. **d** 71 **p** 72. C Belfast St Luke *Conn* 71-81; I Tullyaughnish w Kilmacrennan and Killygarvan *D & R* 81-02; Bp's Dom Chapl 87-02; Can Raphoe Cathl 88-02; Dioc Radio Officer 90-02; rtd 02. *Bearna Ghaoithe, Drumcavney, Trentagh, Letterkenny, Co Donegal, Irish Republic* Tel (0353) (91) 37917 E-mail smeaton@indigo.ie

SMEDLEY, Christopher John. b 62. Trent Poly BSc90. St Jo Coll Nottm MA98. **d** 98 **p** 99. C Cotmanhay *Derby* 98-02; R Wilne and Draycott w Breaston from 02. *The Rectory, 68 Risley Lane, Breaston, Derby DE72 3AU* Tel (01332) 872242

SMEDLEY, Paul Mark. b 59. Bris Univ BA80 Lanc Univ MA81. S Dios Minl Tr Scheme 89. **d** 92 **p** 93. NSM Acton St Mary *Lon* from 92. *12 Baldwyn Gardens, London W3 6HH* Tel (020) 8993 5527 *or* 8932 8497 E-mail paul@planningforum.co.uk

SMEJKAL, Yenda Marcel. b 68. Van Mildert Coll Dur BA97. Coll of Resurr Mirfield 97. **d** 99 **p** 00. C S Shields All SS *Dur* from 99. *4 Mitford Road, South Shields NE34 0EQ* Tel 0191-456 1300 E-mail yenda.smejkal@virgin.net

SMETHURST, David Alan. b 36. Lon Univ BD60 Man Univ MPhil84. Tyndale Hall Bris 57. **d** 61 **p** 62. C Burnage St Marg *Man* 61-63; P-in-c Whalley Range St Marg 63-65; R Haughton St Mary 65-74; R Stratford St Mary w H Trin *Carl* 74-87; Dean Hong Kong 87; Dir Acorn Chr Healing Trust Resource Cen 88-93; V Epsom St Martin *Guildf* 93-00; RD Epsom 97-00; rtd 01; Perm to Offic *Carl* from 01. *3 Friars Ground, Kirkby-in-Furness LA17 7YB* Tel (01229) 889725 Fax as telephone
E-mail friarsground@yahoo.com

SMETHURST, Gordon James. b 33. CEng FIStructE. N Ord Course 79. **d** 82 **p** 83. NSM Halliwell St Marg *Man* 82-87; NSM Bradshaw 87-88; Asst Chapl Bolton R Infirmary 88-95; Asst Chapl Bolton Gen Hosp 88-95; NSM Westhoughton and Wingates *Man* from 95. *91 Albert Road West, Bolton BL1 5ED* Tel (01204) 842561

SMETHURST, Gordon McIntyre. b 40. Man Univ BA62 BD69. Wells Th Coll 70. **d** 70 **p** 71. C Sandal St Helen *Wakef* 70-73; P-in-c Smawthorpe St Mich 73-75; Chapl HM Youth Cust 73-75; Hd RE Goole Gr Sch 75-79; S Hunsley Sch Melton 80-00; V Anlaby Common St Mark *York* 00-03; P-in-c Roos and Garton in Holderness w Tunstall etc from 03. *The Rectory, Rectory Road, Roos, Hull HU12 0LD* Tel (01964) 670384

SMETHURST, Leslie Beckett. b 22. CEng. NW Ord Course 72. **d** 75 **p** 76. C Baguley *Man* 75-78; TV Droylsden St Mary 78-81; V Droylsden St Martin 81-86; rtd 87; Perm to Offic *Blackb* from 87. *27 Calf Croft Place, Lytham St Annes FY8 4PU* Tel (01253) 733159

SMILLIE, Linda Barbara. b 46. Oak Hill Th Coll DipHE87. **d** 87 **p** 94. Par Dn Holloway St Mary w St Jas *Lon* 87-88; Par Dn Holloway St Mary Magd 88-90; Chapl W End Stores 90-91; C Holloway St Mark w Em 90-91; Hon C Islington St Mary 92-94; C-in-c Southall Em CD 95-01; rtd 01; Perm to Offic *Ox* from 01. *Lower Green Cottage, Lower Green, Towersey, Thame OX9 3QW* Tel (01844) 214757

SMITH, Adam. See SMITH, Anthony Adam Dalziel

SMITH, Alan. b 38. Tyndale Hall Bris 63. **d** 65 **p** 66. C New Milverton *Cov* 65-68; C Cheadle *Ches* 68-71; V Handforth 71-78; Asst Chapl HM Prisons Styal 75-78; Chapl HM Pris Wormwood Scrubs 78-79; Chapl HM Borstal Wellingborough 79-83; R Rushden w Newton Bromswold *Pet* 83-96; Chapl Rushden Sanatorium from 83; V Wollaston and Strixton *Pet* from 96. *The Vicarage, 81 Irchester Road, Wollaston, Wellingborough NN9 7RW* Tel (01933) 664256 Fax as telephone
E-mail revalan@fish.co.uk

✠**SMITH, The Rt Revd Alan Gregory Clayton.** b 57. Birm Univ BA78 MA79. Wycliffe Hall Ox 79. **d** 81 **p** 82 **c** 01. C Pudsey St Lawr *Bradf* 81-82; C Pudsey St Lawr and St Paul 82-84; Chapl Lee Abbey 84-90; TV Walsall *Lich* 90-97; Dioc Missr 90-97; Adn Stoke 97-01; Area Bp Shrewsbury from 01. *Athlone House, 68 London Road, Shrewsbury SY2 6PG* Tel (01743) 235867 Fax 243296 E-mail bishop.shrewsbury@lichfield.anglican.org

SMITH, Alan Leonard. b 51. Madeley Coll of Educn CertEd72. Trin Coll Bris DipTh95. **d** 95 **p** 96. C Taunton St Mary *B & W*

95-98; V Taunton Lyngford from 98. *St Peter's Vicarage, Eastwick Road, Taunton TA2 7HD* Tel (01823) 275085 E-mail alan@rasmith.fsnet.co.uk

SMITH, Alan Pearce Carlton. b 20. Trin Hall Cam BA40 MA45 LLB46. Westcott Ho Cam 76. **d** 78 **p** 79. Hon C Cherry Hinton St Jo *Ely* 78-82; P-in-c Madingley 82-83; P-in-c Dry Drayton 82-83; P-in-c Swaffham Bulbeck 84-88; Perm to Offic from 88. *38 Alpha Road, Cambridge CB4 3DG* Tel (01223) 358124

SMITH, Alan Thomas. b 35. BA DipEd. Ridley Hall Cam 82. **d** 84 **p** 85. C Bedworth *Cov* 84-89; R Carlton Colville w Mutford and Rushmere *Nor* 89-97; rtd 97; Perm to Offic *Nor* from 01. *Elderberry Cottage, The Street, Dennington, Woodbridge IP13 8JF* Tel (01728) 638006

SMITH, Alec John. b 29. AKC53. **d** 54 **p** 55. C Charlton Kings St Mary *Glouc* 54-56; C-in-c Findon Valley CD *Chich* 56-57; V Viney Hill *Glouc* 57-65; V Churchdown St Jo 65-66; V Bishop's Cannings *Sarum* 66-69; CF 69-88; V Douglas St Thos *S & M* 88-92; rtd 92; Perm to Offic *S & M* from 92. *Church Barn, Lonan Church Road, Laxey, Isle of Man IM4 7JX* Tel (01624) 861325 Fax 08701-322204 E-mail revdajsmith@talk21.com

SMITH, Alexander Montgomery. b 36. TCD BA59 MA64 BD65. TCD Div Sch Div Test60. **d** 61 **p** 62. C Knock *D & D* 61-64; C Belfast St Thos *Conn* 64-66; Lect St Kath Coll Liv 66-69; Sen Lect 69-98; Asst Chapl St Kath Coll *Liv* 66-69; Chapl 69-80; NSM Allerton 80-98; C Christchurch *Win* from 98. *11 Magdalen Lane, Christchurch BH23 1PH* Tel (01202) 476103

SMITH, Alfred Lawrence. b 23. FCP84 Open Univ BA72 Birm Univ DipEd73. EMMTC 82. **d** 85 **p** 86. NSM Ashover *Derby* 85-86; NSM Ashover and Brackenfield 86-95; Perm to Offic from 95. *Cotton House Farm, Amber Lane, Ashover, Chesterfield S45 0DZ* Tel (01246) 590265

SMITH, Andrew John. b 37. Leeds Univ BA61. Coll of Resurr Mirfield 61. **d** 63 **p** 64. C W Hackney St Barn *Lon* 63-65; Dir and Chapl Northorpe Hall Trust Yorkshire 65-72; Warden Ox Ho Bethnal Green 72-78; Dir and Chapl The Target Trust 78-86; P-in-c Gt Staughton *Ely* 86-88; Norfolk DTI Educn Adv 88-91; Perm to Offic *Ex* 92-96 and from 98; C Widecombe-in-the-Moor, Leusdon, Princetown etc 96-97; rtd 97. *6 Beacon Cottages, Buckland-in-the-Moor, Ashburton, Newton Abbot TQ13 7HL* Tel (01364) 652654

SMITH, Andrew John. b 46. ACGI Lon Univ BScEng67 DIC PhD71 Trin Coll Ox DipTh74 Bath Univ MEd88 CEng96 MIEE96. Coll of Resurr Mirfield 74. **d** 76 **p** 77. C Swindon New Town *Bris* 76-78; C Southmead 78-79; Perm to Offic 79-91. *15 Dyrham Close, Bristol BS9 4TF* Tel 0117-942 8594

SMITH, Andrew John. b 53. Loughb Univ BTech74. St Jo Coll Nottm MA98 Lon Bible Coll DipHE98. **d** 99 **p** 00. C Hailsham *Chich* 99-02; P-in-c Worc St Mich *Worc* 02-03; TV Almondbury w Farnley Tyas *Wakef* from 03. *150 Flemminghouse Lane, Huddersfield HD5 8UD* Tel (01484) 545085 Fax 08701-322204 E-mail revdajsmith@talk21.com

SMITH, Andrew John. b 59. Birm Univ BScSo80 PhD81. WMMTC 89. **d** 91 **p** 92. C Lower Mitton *Worc* 91-92; C Stourport and Wilden 92-95; TV Redditch, The Ridge from 95; P-in-c Redditch St Steph from 02. *The Vicarage, St George's Road, Redditch B98 8EE* Tel (01527) 63017

SMITH, Andrew Perry Langton. b 56. Sheff City Poly BSc79 Imp Coll Lon MSc80. Trin Coll Bris 89. **d** 91 **p** 92. C Littleover *Derby* 91-95; TV Walsall *Lich* from 95; Ind Chapl Black Country Urban Ind Miss from 95. *21 Buchanan Road, Walsall WS4 2EW* Tel (01922) 634859 *or* 710407 E-mail apl.smith@care4free.net

SMITH, Mrs Anita Elisabeth. b 57. Westhill Coll Birm BEd79. Trin Coll Bris DipHE88 ADPS88. **d** 88 **p** 94. Par Dn Bermondsey St Anne *S'wark* 88-92; Par Dn Brockley Hill St Sav 92-94; C 94-99; Miss Partner CMS Kenya from 99. *CMS, PO Box 40360, Nairobi, Kenya*

SMITH, Ann Veronica. b 38. Doncaster Coll of Educn DipEd. Edin Dioc NSM Course 88. **d** 95 **p** 96. NSM S Queensferry *Edin* 95-99; NSM Falkirk from 99. *16 Mannerston, Linlithgow EH49 7ND* Tel (01506) 834361

SMITH (née JENNINGS), Mrs Anne. b 41. CertEd63 STh Cam Univ CertRK67. Gilmore Ho 65. dss 71 **d** 87 **p** 94. Barton w Peel Green *Man* 71-76; Wythenshawe Wm Temple Ch 76-79; Rochdale 79-83; Chapl Rochdale Colls of FE 79-83; Hillock *Man* 83-87; Dn-in-c 87-88; Chapl Wakef Cathl *Wakef* 88-96; P-in-c Whitwell *Derby* 96-00; V Mansfield Woodhouse *S'well* 00-01; rtd 01; Perm to Offic *Carl* from 02. *Hazel Cottage, The Courtyard, Staffield, Penrith CA10 1EU* Tel (01768) 870153

SMITH, Anthony Adam Dalziel. b 42. Qu Coll Birm 65. **d** 68 **p** 69. C Peterlee *Dur* 68-71; C Tilehurst St Mich *Ox* 71-76; V Wootton (Boars Hill) 76-88; R Brightwalton w Catmore, Leckhampstead etc 88-01; rtd 01; Perm to Offic *Ox* from 01. *North Cottage, West Ilsey, Newbury RG20 7AL* Tel (01635) 281704

SMITH, Anthony Charles. b 43. Sarum & Wells Th Coll 90. **d** 92 **p** 93. C Dartford H Trin *Roch* 92-95; V Northfleet from 95. *The Vicarage, The Hill, Northfleet, Gravesend DA11 9EU* Tel (01474) 566400 E-mail smithab@clara.net

SMITH, Anthony Cyril. b 40. K Coll Lon 65. **d** 69 **p** 70. C Crewkerne *B & W* 69-74; TV Hemel Hempstead *St Alb* 74-76;

Asst Chapl K Coll Taunton 76-80; Chapl 80-02; rtd 02. *1 Castle Street, Stogursey, Bridgwater TA5 1TG* Tel (01278) 733577

SMITH, Anthony James. b 57. ACA Sheff Univ BA. Ridley Hall Cam 83. **d** 86 **p** 87. C Woking St Pet *Guildf* 86-90; C Reigate St Mary *S'wark* 90-94; CMS Kenya 94-00; Finance Team Leader World Vision UK from 00. *World Vision UK, 599 Avebury Boulevard, Milton Keynes MK9 3PG* Tel (01908) 841000

SMITH, The Ven Anthony Michael Percival. b 24. G&C Coll Cam BA48 MA53. Westcott Ho Cam 48. **d** 50 **p** 51. C Leamington Priors H Trin *Cov* 50-53; Abp's Dom Chapl *Cant* 53-57; Chapl Norwood and Distr Hosp 57-66; V Norwood All SS 57-66; V Yeovil St Jo w Preston Plucknett *B & W* 66-72; RD Merston 68-72; Preb Wells Cathl 70-72; V Addiscombe St Mildred *Cant* 72-79; Adn Maidstone 79-89; Dir of Ords 80-89; Hon Can Cant Cathl 80-89; rtd 89; Perm to Offic *Cant* from 90; Perm to Offic *Chich* 89-91 and from 93; RD Rye 91-93. *The Garden House, Horseshoe Lane, Beckley, Rye TN31 6RZ* Tel (01797) 260514

SMITH, Antoinette. b 47. NTMTC AdDipTh98 ADPS98. **d** 98 **p** 99. NSM Chigwell and Chigwell Row *Chelmsf* 98-02; TV from 02. *St Winifred's Church House, 115 Manor Road, Chigwell IG7 5PS* Tel (020) 8500 4608 E-mail reverend@tonismith.freeserve.co.uk

SMITH, Miss Audrey. b 47. S'wark Ord Course 89. **d** 92 **p** 94. NSM Croydon St Aug *S'wark* 92-98; P-in-c Redmarley D'Abitot, Bromesberrow w Pauntley etc *Glouc* 98-00. *Address temp unknown*

SMITH, Mrs Audrey Isabel. b 20. Lon Univ. Qu Coll Birm IDC79. dss 84 **d** 87 **p** 94. NSM Kingston All SS w St Jo *S'wark* 87-95; Perm to Offic *Truro* from 95. *31 Copes Gardens, Truro TR1 3SN* Tel (01872) 261813

SMITH, Austin John Denyer. b 40. Worc Coll Ox BA62. Cuddesdon Coll 64. **d** 66 **p** 67. C Shepherd's Bush St Steph w St Thos *Lon* 66-69; C W Drayton 69-72; Chapl Sussex Univ *Chich* 72-79; V Caddington *St Alb* from 79. *The Vicarage, Collings Wells Close, Caddington, Luton LU1 4BG* Tel (01582) 731692 E-mail ajdsmith@lineone.net

SMITH, Mrs Barbara Jean. b 39. Bris Univ BA62 Surrey Univ PGCE93. S'wark Ord Course 83. dss 86 **d** 87 **p** 94. Hon Dss Chislehurst St Nic *Roch* 86; Hon Par Dn 87-90; Hon C Wrecclesham *Guildf* 90-94; Hon C Herriard w Winslade and Long Sutton etc *Win* 94-99; P-in-c 99-03; P-in-c Newnham w Nately Scures w Mapledurwell etc 99-03; rtd 03. *Hill Cottage, 282 Lovedean Lane, Waterlooville PO8 9RY* Tel (023) 9259 4426 E-mail barbarajsmith@btopenworld.com

SMITH, Mrs Barbara Mary. b 47. Doncaster Coll of Educn CertEd68. St Jo Coll Dur 82. dss 85 **d** 87 **p** 94. Beverley St Nic *York* 85-87; Par Dn 87; NSM S'wark H Trin w St Matt *S'wark* 89-90; Ind Chapl Teesside *York* 91-95; Hon C Middlesbrough St Chad 94-95; Perm to Offic *St Alb* from 96; Locum Chapl Anglia Poly Univ *Ely* 96-98; TV Linton from 00. *The Vicarage, Park Lane, Castle Camps, Cambridge CB1 6SR* Tel (01799) 584803

SMITH, Canon Barry. b 41. Univ of Wales (Lamp) BA62 Fitzw Ho Cam BA64 MA68 Man Univ MPhil91. Ridley Hall Cam. **d** 65 **p** 66. C Rhyl w St Ann *St As* 65-70; Chapl Scargill Ho 70-72; C Flint *St As* 72-74; V Broughton 74-86; Dioc Ecum Officer 82-86; RD Wrexham 82-86; R Wrexham 86-95; Can Cursal St As Cathl 86-95; Chan 95; Perm to Offic *S'wark* from 97. *1 Acorn Keep, Rowhills, Farnham GU9 9BL* Tel (01252) 322111

SMITH, Barry Roy. b 46. STETS. **d** 00. NSM Blendworth w Chalton w Idsworth *Portsm* from 00; Asst Chapl Portsm Hosps NHS Trust from 03. *7A Durley Avenue, Waterlooville PO8 8XA* Tel (023) 9226 5620

SMITH, Canon Brian. b 44. Westmr Coll Ox MTh95. Sarum & Wells Th Coll 71. **d** 74 **p** 75. C Pennywell St Thos and Grindon St Oswald CD *Dur* 74-77; Chapl RAF 77-95; P-in-c Keswick St Jo *Carl* 95-96; V from 96; RD Derwent from 98; Hon Can Carl Cathl from 99. *St John's Vicarage, Ambleside Road, Keswick CA12 4DD* Tel (01768) 772130 E-mail keswick@fish.co.uk

✠**SMITH, The Rt Revd Brian Arthur.** b 43. Edin Univ MA66 Fitzw Coll Cam BA68 MA72 Jes Coll Cam MLitt73. Westcott Ho Cam 66. **d** 72 **p** 73 **c** 93. Tutor and Lib Cuddesdon Coll 72-75; Dir of Studies 75-78; Sen Tutor Ripon Coll Cuddesdon 78-79; C Cuddesdon *Ox* 76-79; Dir Tr *Wakef* 79-87; P-in-c Halifax St Jo 79-85; Hon Can Wakef Cathl 81-87; Adn Craven *Bradf* 87-93; Suff Bp Tonbridge *Roch* 93-01; Hon Can Roch Cathl 93-01; Bp Edin from 01. *3 Eglinton Crescent, Edinburgh, EH12 5DH, or Bishop's Office, 21A Grosvenor Crescent, Edinburgh EH2 5EL* Tel 0131-226 5099 Fax 226 7088 E-mail bishop@edinburgh.anglican.org

SMITH, Brian Godfrey. b 24. Chich Th Coll 63. **d** 65 **p** 66. C Newc H Cross *Newc* 65-68; C Redcar *York* 68-72; C Kirkleatham 68-72; V Wortley de Leeds *Ripon* 72-76; Chapl Costa del Sol E *Eur* 76-82; Chapl Estoril 82-84; V Worfield *Heref* 84-89; rtd 89; Perm to Offic *Heref* from 92. *2 Pineway, Lodge Farm, Bridgnorth WV15 5DT* Tel (01746) 764088

SMITH, Brian Michael. b 42. Kelham Th Coll 69. **d** 69 **p** 70. C Somers Town *Lon* 70-74; C Stamford Hill St Jo 74-75; C Stamford Hill St Bart 75-84; P-in-c Edmonton St Pet w St Martin

84-92; V from 92. *The Vicarage, St Peter's Road, London N9 8JP* Tel (020) 8807 2974 Fax 8887 0153 E-mail vicar@stpeteredmonton.freeserve.co.uk

SMITH, Canon Bridget Mary. b 46. Bp Otter Coll CertEd67 S Dios Minl Tr Scheme 88. **d** 91 **p** 94. C Pet H Spirit Bretton *Pet* 91-95; P-in-c Silverstone and Abthorpe w Slapton 95-03; R Silverstone and Abthorpe w Slapton etc from 03; Warden of Past Assts from 00; Can Pet Cathl from 01. *The Vicarage, High Street, Silverstone, Towcester NN12 8US* Tel (01327) 857996 E-mail quickvic@lineone.net

SMITH, Mrs Catherine Eleanor Louise. b 52. St Alb and Ox Min Course 99. **d** 02. NSM Denham *Ox* from 02. *55 Penn Road, Beaconsfield HP9 2LW* Tel (01494) 670389 Fax as telephone

SMITH, Charles Henry <u>Neville</u>. b 31. Nottm Univ BA52 MA65. Sarum Th Coll 55. **d** 57 **p** 58. C Thirsk w S Kilvington *York* 57-60; C Linthorpe 60-61; V Danby 61-66; Chapl United Cam Hosps 66-76; Chapl Lanc Moor Hosp 76-84; Hon Can Blackb Cathl *Blackb* 81-84; Asst Sec Gen Syn Hosp Chapl Coun 84-88; Hon C Lee St Marg *S'wark* 84-88; Chapl Guy's Hosp Lon 88-96; rtd 96; Hon Chapl S'wark Cathl *S'wark* from 96; Perm to Offic from 96. *57 Belmont Park, London SE13 5BW* Tel (020) 8318 9993

SMITH, Charles Rycroft (Ryc). b 46. Sarum & Wells Th Coll 76. **d** 78 **p** 79. C Heref St Martin *Heref* 78-81; C Southampton Maybush St Pet *Win* 81-83; R The Candover Valley 83-99; RD Alresford 90-99; P-in-c Guernsey St Andr 99-01; R from 01; Vice-Dean Guernsey from 02. *The Rectory, rue des Morts, St Andrews, Guernsey GY6 8XN* Tel (01481) 238568 E-mail ryc@starectory.fsnet.co.uk

SMITH, Charles Septimus. b 23. Bris & Glouc Tr Course. **d** 79 **p** 80. NSM Bris St Agnes and St Simon w St Werburgh *Bris* 79-86; C 86-87; C Bris St Paul's 87-89; rtd 89. *6521 Glenerin Drive, APT 807, Mississauga ON, Canada, L5N 2X2*

SMITH, Christine. b 46. **d** 97 **p** 98. C Salterhebble All SS *Wakef* 97-01; P-in-c Siddal from 01. *St Mark's Vicarage, 15 Whitegate Road, Siddal, Halifax HX3 9AD* Tel (01422) 369558

SMITH, Christine Lydia. See CARTER, Mrs Christine Lydia

SMITH, Christopher Blake Walters. b 63. Univ of Wales (Cardiff) BMus84 BD88 LLM95. St Mich Coll Llan 85. **d** 88 **p** 89. C Aberdare *Llan* 88-93; V Tongwynlais 93-00; Dioc Dir Post-Ord Tr from 95; Dom Chapl Bp Llan and Warden of Ords from 01. *Pendinas, The Cathedral Green, Llandaff, Cardiff CF5 2EB* Tel (029) 2056 4249 Fax as telephone E-mail cbw@csmith20.freeserve.co.uk

SMITH, Christopher Francis. b 46. K Coll Lon BD68 AKC68. St Aug Coll Cant 69. **d** 70 **p** 71. C Norwood All SS *Cant* 70-72; Asst Chapl Marlborough Coll 72-76; C Deal St Leon w Sholden *Cant* 77-81; P-in-c Benenden 81-83; V from 83; Chapl Benenden Sch 81-92; Chapl Benenden Hosp from 91. *The Vicarage, The Green, Benenden, Cranbrook TN17 4DL* Tel (01580) 240658 E-mail christopherfrancissmith@tinyworld.co.uk

SMITH, Christopher James. b 72. Newc Univ BSc94. Wycliffe Hall Ox BTh01. **d** 02 **p** 03. C Cambridge H Trin *Ely* from 02. *4 Parsonage Street, Cambridge CB5 8DN* Tel (01223) 479678 E-mail revsmith@ntlworld.com

SMITH, Christopher Matthew. b 67. New Coll Ox BA89 MA93 Homerton Coll Cam PGCE90. St Steph Ho Ox BA94. **d** 95 **p** 96. C Wantage *Ox* 95-99; Dom Chapl to Bp Horsham *Chich* 99-01; V Beckenham St Mich w St Aug *Roch* from 01. *St Michael's Vicarage, 120 Birkbeck Road, Beckenham BR3 4SS* Tel (020) 8778 6569

SMITH, Canon Christopher Milne. b 44. Selw Coll Cam BA66. Cuddesdon Coll 67. **d** 69 **p** 70. C Liv Our Lady and St Nic *Liv* 69-74; TV Kirkby 74-81; R Walton St Mary 81-91; Can Res Sheff Cathl *Sheff* 91-02; V Doncaster St Geo from 02; Bp's Adv on the Paranormal from 97; Hon Can Sheff Cathl from 03. *The Vicarage, 98 Thorne Road, Doncaster DN2 5BJ* Tel (01302) 368796 *or* 323748

SMITH, Clarice Mary. b 25. St Mich Coll Llan 76. **dss** 77 **d** 80. Llangiwg *S & B* 77-80; C Llwynderw 80-84; C Newton St Pet 84-88; rtd 88. *33 Sherringham Drive, Newton, Swansea SA3 4UG* Tel (01792) 367984

SMITH, Clifford. b 31. Lon Univ DipTh60. St Aid Birkenhead 59. **d** 61 **p** 62. C Limehouse St Anne *Lon* 61-63; C Ashtead *Guildf* 63-66; R Bromley All Hallows *Lon* 66-76; V Hillsborough and Wadsley Bridge *Sheff* 76-89; V Stainforth 89-96; rtd 96; Hon C Hurst *Ox* from 97. *33 King Street Lane, Winnersh, Wokingham RG41 5AX* Tel 0118-978 9453

SMITH, Clive Leslie. b 50. Leeds Univ BA72 MA03 Ch Coll Liv PGCE73 K Coll Lon PGDHE96. Coll of Resurr Mirfield 75. **d** 77 **p** 78. C Golddington *St Alb* 77-81; C Cheshunt 81-84; V Watford St Pet 84-89; Chapl Leavesden Hosp Abbots Langley 89-94; Chapl St Alb and Hemel Hempstead NHS Trust 94-00; Chapl W Herts Hosps NHS Trust from 01; Sen Chapl Doncaster and Bassetlaw Hosps NHS Trust from 01; Perm to Offic *S'well* from 02. *Chaplaincy Department, Doncaster Royal Infirmary, Armthorpe Road, Doncaster DN2 5LT, or 34 Tanners Hill, Abbots Langley WD5 0LT* Tel (01302) 366666 ext 3616 *or* (01923) 677977 E-mail chaplaincy.department@dbh.nhs.uk *or* clivelsmith@yahoo.co.uk

SMITH, Colin. b 39. MBE. Open Univ BA80 CChem88 FRSC88. NEOC DipHE94. **d** 97 **p** 98. NSM Jesmond H Trin *Newc* from 97; NSM Newc St Barn and St Jude from 97. *1 Cayton Grove, Newcastle-upon-Tyne NE5 1HL* Tel 0191-267 9519 E-mail colinsmith3@compuserve.com

SMITH, Colin Graham. b 59. Hatf Poly BA82 CQSW82. Trin Coll Bris BA88. **d** 88 **p** 89. C Bermondsey St Jas w Ch Ch *S'wark* 88-92; V Brockley Hill St Sav 92-99; Miss Partner CMS Kenya from 99. *CMS, PO Box 40360, Nairobi, Kenya*

SMITH, Colin Richard. b 53. Liv Poly BA80 Liv Univ MTD83. Oak Hill Th Coll 84. **d** 86 **p** 87. C Ormskirk *Liv* 86-89; V Wigan St Cath 89-94; C St Helens St Helen from 94. *211A Dentons Green Lane, St Helens WA10 6RU* Tel (01744) 453681

SMITH, Mrs Corinne Anne. b 52. St Andr Univ MTh91. St Alb and Ox Min Course 95. **d** 97. C Abingdon *Ox* 97-02; Chapl Pemb Coll Ox 02-03; Chapl Ox Radcliffe Hosps NHS Trust from 03. *The John Radcliffe Hospital, Headley Way, Headington, Oxford OX3 9DU* Tel (01865) 741166 E-mail corinne.smith@vizzavi.net

SMITH, Craig Philip. b 61. Huddersfield Poly HND82 Sheff City Poly BA86. St Jo Coll Nottm Dip Th Studies 92 DipMM93. **d** 93 **p** 94. C Bramley and Ravenfield *Sheff* 93-95; C Bramley and Ravenfield w Hooton Roberts etc 95-97; C Rainham w Wennington *Chelmsf* 97-00; TV Gainsborough and Morton *Linc* from 00. *St George's Vicarage, Heapham Road, Gainsborough DN21 1SH* Tel (01427) 612717 Fax as telephone E-mail cs3jays@nildram.co.uk

SMITH, Darren John Anthony. b 62. Nottm Univ BCombStuds84. Linc Th Coll 84. **d** 86 **p** 87. C Leic Ascension *Leic* 86-90; C Curdworth w Castle Vale *Birm* 90; C Castle Vale St Cuth 90-91; C Kingstanding St Luke 91-92; P-in-c 92-93; V from 93; P-in-c Kingstanding St Mark 01-02. *St Luke's Clergy House, 49 Caversham Road, Kingstanding, Birmingham B44 0LW* Tel 0121-354 3281

SMITH, David. See SMITH, John David Elliott

SMITH, David Charles Stuart. CertEd53 Wheaton Coll Illinois MA74. Oak Hill Th Coll 61. **d** 61 **p** 62. Australia 61-72, 75-89 and from 90; Wellington Coll Berks 72-75; C Luton Lewsey St Hugh *St Alb* 90. *45 Fairbairn Road, Toorak, Vic, Australia 3142* Tel (0061) (3) 9842 2652 E-mail sgejmsmith@bigpond.com.au

SMITH, David Earling. b 35. AKC60. **d** 61 **p** 62. C Knebworth *St Alb* 61-63; C Chipping Barnet 64-66; C S Ormsby w Ketsby, Calceby and Driby *Linc* 66-69; R Claxby w Normanby-le-Wold 69-74; R Nettleton 69-74; R Kelsey 69-74; R N Owersby w Thornton le Moor 69-74; R Stainton-le-Vale w Kirmond le Mire 69-74; V Ancaster 74-79; Warden and Chapl St Anne Bedehouses Linc 79-89; C Linc Minster Gp 79-89; rtd 89; Perm to Offic *Linc* 90-02. *17 Egerton Road, Lincoln LN2 4PJ* Tel (01522) 510336 E-mail david@limani17.fsnet.co.uk

✠**SMITH, The Rt Revd David James.** b 35. AKC58 FKC99. **d** 59 **p** 60 **c** 87. C Gosforth All SS *Newc* 59-62; C Newc St Fran 62-64; C Longbenton St Bart 64-68; V Longhirst 68-75; V Monkseaton St Mary 75-82; RD Tynemouth 80-82; Hon Can Newc Cathl 81-87; Adn Lindisfarne 81-87; V Felton 82-83; Suff Bp Maidstone *Cant* 87-92; Bp HM Forces 90-92; Bp Bradf 92-02; rtd 02; Hon Asst Bp York from 02; Hon Asst Bp Eur from 02. *34 Cedar Glade, Dunnington, York YO19 5QZ* Tel (01904) 481225

SMITH, Canon David John. b 32. Goldsmiths' Coll Lon BA76 LSE MSc79. Lon Coll of Div 68. **d** 70 **p** 71. C Clerkenwell St Jas and St Jo w St Pet *Lon* 70-73; P-in-c Penge St Paul *Roch* 74-78; V 78-89; RD Beckenham 86-89; Chapl Bromley and Sheppard's Colls 90-97; Perm to Offic *S'wark* 90-97; Dioc Clergy Widows and Retirement Officer *Roch* 90-97; Hon Can Roch Cathl 95-97; rtd 98; Perm to Offic *St Alb* from 98. *13 Park Way, Rickmansworth WD3 7AU* Tel (01923) 775963

SMITH, David John. b 42. Oak Hill Th Coll 75. **d** 77 **p** 78. C New Milverton *Cov* 77-81; V Hartshill 81-86; V Attleborough 86-95; AD Nuneaton 93-95; N Regional Co-ord Crosslinks 95-03; rtd 03; Perm to Offic *Ches* from 00. *14 Peregrine Close, Winsford CW7 1SH* Tel (01606) 860211

SMITH, David John Parker. See EVANS, David Victor

SMITH, David Leonard. b 37. St Alb Minl Tr Scheme 84. **d** 91 **p** 92. NSM Potton w Sutton and Cockayne Hatley *St Alb* from 91. *11 Judith Gardens, Potton, Sandy SG19 2RJ* Tel (01767) 260583 E-mail david.smith@lawdata.co.uk

SMITH, David Roland Mark. b 46. Dur Univ BA68 ACP78 FRSA87 SSC88. Edin Th Coll 68. **d** 70 **p** 71. C Southwick St Columba *Dur* 70-74 and 81-82; Asst Chapl Univ of Wales (Cardiff) *Llan* 74-76; Hon C E Bris 76-78; Hon C Filton 78-79; Min Leam Lane Cd *Dur* 80-81; Co-ord Chapl Service Sunderland Poly 81-86; Chapl Birm Univ *Birm* 86-95; Chapl Heathrow Airport *Lon* 95-00; rtd 00; Chapl Wolv Airport *Lich* from 00; Perm to Offic *Heref*, *Worc* from 00 and *Birm* from 02. *20 Carder Drive, Brierley Hill DY5 3SR* Tel (01384) 352045 Mobile 07778-876695 E-mail revdrmsmith@aol.com

SMITH, David Sidney Mark. b 54. Bris Univ BEd76. Ripon Coll Cuddesdon 77. **d** 79 **p** 80. C Wotton-under-Edge w Ozleworth and N Nibley *Glouc* 79-83; TV Malvern Link w Cowleigh *Worc* 83-93; Relig Affairs Producer BBC Heref and Worc 90-93; V

Clevedon St Jo *B & W* from 93. *St John's Vicarage, 1 St John's Road, Clevedon BS21 7TG* Tel (01275) 872410 Fax 544005 E-mail dsms@blueyonder.co.uk

SMITH, David Stanley. b 41. Ox NSM Course. **d** 84 **p** 85. NSM Burghfield *Ox* 84-86; NSM Stratfield Mortimer 86-88; NSM Mortimer W End w Padworth 86-88; C St Breoke and Egloshayle *Truro* 88-93; V Penwerris from 93. *Penwerris Vicarage, 12 Stratton Terrace, Falmouth TR11 2SY* Tel (01326) 314263

SMITH, David Watson. b 31. Sarum Th Coll 63. **d** 65 **p** 66. C W Wimbledon Ch Ch *S'wark* 65-69; C Cheam 69-74; V Haslington *Ches* 74-83; V Haslington w Crewe Green 83-87; V Daresbury 87-98; rtd 98; Perm to Offic *Pet* from 98. *4 Wakefield Way, Nether Heyford, Northampton NN7 3LU* Tel (01327) 341561 E-mail rev.dw.smith@freeuk.com

SMITH, David William. b 46. Sarum Th Coll 70. **d** 72 **p** 73. C Stokesley *York* 72-75; C Edin St Mich and All SS *Edin* 75-77; R Galashiels 77-85; R Yarm *York* 85-00; TR Whitby w Aislaby and Ruswarp from 00; P-in-c Fylingdales and Hawsker cum Stainsacre from 02. *The Rectory, Chubb Hill Road, Whitby YO21 1JP* Tel (01947) 602590

SMITH, Deborah Jane. b 62. Newc Poly BA83. STETS 00. **d** 03. C Dorchester *Sarum* from 03. *10 Treves Road, Dorchester DT1 2HD* Tel (01305) 260552 Mobile 07870-560354 E-mail smithsmania@btopenworld.com

SMITH, Mrs Decia Jane. b 47. ALAM66. WMMTC 92. **d** 95 **p** 96. C Edgbaston St Germain *Birm* 95-99; P-in-c Abbots Leigh w Leigh Woods *Bris* from 00. *The Vicarage, 51 Church Road, Abbots Leigh, Bristol BS8 3QU* Tel (01275) 373996 E-mail revdecia@fish.co.uk

SMITH, Denis Richard. b 53. St Jo Coll Nottm 83. **d** 85 **p** 86. C Hersham *Guildf* 85-88; C Thatcham *Ox* 88-91; V Shefford *St Alb* 91-02; P-in-c Tilehurst St Cath *Ox* from 02. *The Vicarage, Wittenham Avenue, Tilehurst, Reading RG31 5LN* Tel 0118-942 7786 E-mail revdenissmith@hotmail.com

SMITH, Dennis Austin. b 50. Lanc Univ BA71 Liv Univ PGCE72. NW Ord Course 74. **d** 77 **p** 78. NSM Seaforth *Liv* 77-83; NSM Gt Crosby St Faith 77-83; Hon C 83-98; Hon C Gt Crosby St Faith and Waterloo Park St Mary from 98; Asst Chapl Merchant Taylors' Sch Crosby 79-83; Chapl from 83. *16 Fir Road, Liverpool L22 4QL* Tel 0151-928 5065

SMITH, Dennis Peter. b 35. Qu Coll Birm 83. **d** 85 **p** 86. C Sedgley All SS *Lich* 85-89; C Penkridge w Stretton 89-90; TV Penkridge Team 90-93; V Ketley and Oakengates 93-00; RD Telford 96-00; RD Telford Severn Gorge *Heref* 96-00; rtd 00. *57 Fordbrook Lane, Pelsall, Walsall WS3 4BW* Tel (01922) 693077

SMITH, Derek Arthur. b 38. Chich Th Coll 63. **d** 66 **p** 67. C Cheadle *Lich* 66-70; C Blakenall Heath 70-72; P-in-c Pet 72-77; TR 77-86; V Knutton 72-76; R Lich St Mary w St Mich 86-96; P-in-c Wall 90-96; R Lich St Mich w St Mary and Wall 96-98; V W Bromwich St Andr w Ch Ch 98-02; rtd 02. *20 Tiverton Drive, West Bromwich B71 1DA* Tel 0121-525 0260

SMITH, Derek Arthur Byott. b 26. Hull Univ MA89. S Dios Minl Tr Scheme 78. **d** 81 **p** 82. NSM Wimborne Minster and Holt *Sarum* 81-83; C Northampton St Alb *Pet* 83-85; Ind Chapl *York* 85-89; P-in-c Kingston upon Hull St Mary 88-89; P-in-c Newington w Dairycoates 89-93; rtd 93; Perm to Offic *York* from 93. *107 Cardigan Road, Bridlington YO15 3LP* Tel (01262) 678852

SMITH, Derek Arthur Douglas. b 26. Dur Univ BA51. Qu Coll Birm 58. **d** 60 **p** 61. C Evesham *Worc* 60-63; C Bollington St Jo *Ches* 63-68; V Thelwall 68-78; V Whitegate w Lt Budworth 78-92; rtd 92; Perm to Offic *Ches* from 92. *10 Newtons Crescent, Winterley, Sandbach CW11 9NS* Tel (01270) 589130

SMITH, Derek Graham. b 53. St Cath Coll Cam BA74 MA77. Westcott Ho Cam 74. **d** 76 **p** 77. C Weymouth H Trin *Sarum* 76-79; P-in-c Bradpole 79; TV Bridport 79-84; R Monkton Farleigh, S Wraxall and Winsley 84-98; TR Melksham from 98; RD Bradford from 01; Chapl Wilts and Swindon Healthcare NHS Trust 00-02. *The Rectory, Canon Square, Melksham SN12 6LX* Tel (01225) 703262

SMITH, Diana Linnet. b 47. Sheff Univ BSc69 Goldsmiths' Coll Lon MA83 Trin Coll Carmarthen PhD99. EAMTC 02. **d** 03. C Oundle w Ashton and Benefield w Glapthorn *Pet* from 03. *The Rectory, Main Street, Aldwincle, Kettering NN14 3EP* Tel (01832) 720613 E-mail sdiana@fish.co.uk

SMITH, Donald Edgar. b 56. Oak Hill Th Coll 89. **d** 91 **p** 92. C Holloway St Mark w Em *Lon* 91-92; C Tollington 92-95; TV W Ealing St Jo w St Jas from 95. *23A Culmington Road, London W13 9NJ* Tel (020) 8566 3459 Fax 8566 3507

SMITH, The Ven Donald John. b 26. Univ of Wales LLM. Clifton Th Coll 50. **d** 53 **p** 54. C Edgware *Lon* 53-56; C Ipswich St Marg *St E* 56-58; V Hornsey Rise St Mary *Lon* 58-62; R Whitton and Thurleston w Akenham *St E* 62-75; Hon Can St E Cathl 73-91; Adn Suffolk 75-84; R The Rickinghalls 75-76; P-in-c Redgrave w Botesdale 75-76; R Redgrave cum Botesdale w Rickinghall 76-78; Adn Sudbury 84-91; rtd 91; Perm to Offic *Cov, Ox, St E* and *Worc* from 91; *Glouc* 91-96 and from 03. *St Peter's Cottage, Stretton-on-Fosse, Moreton-in-Marsh GL56 9SE* Tel (01608) 662790

✠**SMITH, The Rt Revd Donald Westwood.** b 28. Edin Th Coll 54 St D Coll Lamp 50. **d** 54 **p** 55 c 90. Asst Dioc Supernumerary *Ab* 54-55; Chapl St Andr Cathl 55-56; Canada 56-57; R Longside *Ab* 57-65; Mauritius 65-85; P-in-c St Geo-in-the-East St Mary *Lon* 85-86; Seychelles 86-87; Madagascar 87-99; Bp Toamasina 90-99. *Avenue Cote d'Emeraude, Morcellement Raffray, Albion, Mauritius* Tel (00230) 238 5966 E-mail tighdhonuil@hotmail.com

SMITH, Douglas David Frederick. b 28. Lon Univ BD53. ALCD53. **d** 53 **p** 54. C Fulham Ch Ch *Lon* 53-57; C Heatherlands St Jo *Sarum* 57-61; V Hyson Green *S'well* 61-66; Lic to Offic *York* 66-69; NE Area Sec CPAS 66-69; R Higher Openshaw *Man* 69-80; R Church w Chapel Brampton *Pet* 80-81; R Church and Chapel Brampton w Harlestone 81-86; Perm to Offic *Ox* from 86; rtd 89. *1 Maybush Walk, Olney MK46 5NA* Tel (01234) 712256

SMITH, Ms Elizabeth. b 46. Liv Inst of Educn CertEd67 Heythrop Coll Lon BD76 Lon Univ MPhil84. Westcott Ho Cam CTM92. **d** 92 **p** 94. Par Dn Moulsham St Jo *Chelmsf* 92-94; C 94-96; V Westcliff St Andr 96-00; V Sedgley St Mary *Worc* from 00. *St Mary's Vicarage, St Mary's Close, Dudley DY3 1LD* Tel (01902) 883310

SMITH (née HOWSE), Mrs Elizabeth Ann. b 39. Bath Academy of Art CertEd60 Warwick Univ BEd85 Westhill Coll Birm DipRE88. WMMTC 91. **d** 94 **p** 95. C Fletchamstead *Cov* 94-97; P-in-c Leamington Hastings and Birdingbury 97-03; P-in-c Grandborough w Willoughby and Flecknoe 97-03; V Leam Valley from 03. *The Vicarage, Leamington Hastings, Rugby CV23 8DY* Tel (01926) 632455 Fax as telephone E-mail beth.smith@iname.com

SMITH, Miss Elizabeth Jane. b 50. Birm Univ BA72 DCG73. Trin Coll Bris 88. **d** 90 **p** 95. C Lowestoft and Kirkley *Nor* 90-94; TV Rugby St Andr *Cov* 94-01; C Shepton Mallet w Doulting *B & W* 01-03; R from 03; Chapl Mendip Primary Care Trust from 01. *23 Compton Road, Shepton Mallet BA4 5QR* Tel (01749) 346184 E-mail liz@revmh.fsnet.co.uk

SMITH, Elizabeth Marion. b 52. ACA74 FCA82. Carl Dioc Tr Inst 91. **d** 94 **p** 95. C Appleby *Carl* 94-98; P-in-c Hesket-in-the-Forest and Armathwaite from 98; P-in-c Skelton and Hutton-in-the-Forest w Ivegill from 98. *St Mary's Vicarage, High Hesket, Carlisle CA4 0HU* Tel (01697) 473320 Fax 473167 E-mail revdesmith@hotmail.com

SMITH, Eric Frederick. b 19. Lon Univ BA40 BD42. ALCD42. **d** 42 **p** 43. C Talbot Village *Sarum* 42-44; C S'wark St Jude *S'wark* 44-48; P-in-c Mottingham St Edward LD 48-56; V Lee Gd Shep w St Pet 56-67; Sub-Dean Lewisham 61-67; R Long Ditton 67-81; V Deal St Geo *Cant* 81-85; RD Sandwich 82-85; rtd 85; Perm to Offic *Cant* from 85; Chapl Cant Sch of Min 88-94; Chapl SEITE from 94. *Beach Cottage, 179 Beach Street, Deal CT14 6LE* Tel (01304) 367648

SMITH, Esmond Ernest Carrington. b 22. Mert Coll Ox BA43 MA47. Westcott Ho Cam 46. **d** 46 **p** 47. V E Crompton *Man* 51-57; V Ripley *Derby* 57-65; V Aston SS Pet and Paul *Birm* 65-75; RD Aston 71-75; Asst Master Stainiforth Sch Thetford 75-78; Perm to Offic *St E* from 78; rtd 87. *The Saltings, Broad Street, Orford, Woodbridge IP12 2NQ* Tel (01394) 405234 E-mail ez@saltings.f9.co.uk

SMITH, Eustace. b 20. St Pet Hall Ox BA43 MA46. Wycliffe Hall Ox 43. **d** 46 **p** 46. C Tiverton St Pet *Ex* 46-47; C Lenton *S'well* 47-49; C Aston SS Pet and Paul *Birm* 49-53; V Bermondsey St Anne *S'wark* 53-59; V Buckminster w Sewstern *Leic* 59-74; V Buckminster w Sewstern, Sproxton and Coston 74-82; R Algarkirk *Linc* 82-88; V Fosdyke 82-88; rtd 89; Perm to Offic *Leic* from 89. *32 Wordsworth Way, Measham, Swadlincote DE12 7ER* Tel (01530) 273765

SMITH (née DAVIS), Felicity Ann. b 40. Bris Univ MB, ChB63. Qu Coll Birm 83. dss 86 **d** 87 **p** 94. NSM Dioc Bd for Soc Resp *Cov* 86-96; NSM Leamington Spa H Trin and Old Milverton from 96. *14 Oakwood Grove, Warwick CV34 5TD* Tel (01926) 492452

SMITH, Francis Armand. b 10. Sarum Th Coll 59. **d** 61 **p** 62. C Marlborough *Sarum* 61-63; V Upavon w Rushall 63-76; rtd 76; Perm to Offic *S'wark* 76-93; *St Alb* 77-93; *Chich* 78-93. *15 High Street, Cowden, Edenbridge TN8 7JQ* Tel (01342) 850484

SMITH, Francis Christian Lynford. b 36. Padgate Coll of Educn TCert59 Lon Univ DipRE66. Cuddesdon Coll 72. **d** 74 **p** 75. C Catford St Laur *S'wark* 74-79; Mauritius 79-80; Chapl Dulwich Coll 81-91; Chapl St Mich Univ Sch Victoria Canada from 91; rtd 01. *Apartment 403, 2626 Blackwood Street, Victoria BC, Canada, V8T 3W3* Tel (001) (250) 598 3459 E-mail smudge4147@hotmail.com

SMITH, Francis James Prall. b 22. Nor Ord Course 73. **d** 76 **p** 77. NSM Gunthorpe w Bale *Nor* 76-82; NSM Friston *St E* 82-86; NSM Knodishall w Buxlow 82-86; NSM Aldringham w Thorpe, Knodishall w Buxlow etc 86-89; rtd 89; Perm to Offic *St E* from 90. *6 Bluebell Way, Worlingham, Beccles NR34 7BT* Tel (01502) 711528

SMITH, Francis Malcolm. b 44. Open Univ BA82 FCMI AIB69. EAMTC 90. **d** 93 **p** 94. NSM Prittlewell *Chelmsf* from 93. *14 St*

James Avenue, Southend-on-Sea SS1 3LH Tel (01702) 586680 Fax 291166

SMITH, Canon Frank. b 39. Nottm Univ CertEd65 Open Univ BA76. Paton Congr Coll Nottm 61 Cuddesdon Coll 69. **d** 69 **p** 70. C Davyhulme St Mary *Man* 69-72; PC Peak Forest and Wormhill *Derby* 72-78; R W Hallam and Mapperley 78-85; V Henleaze *Bris* 85-01; RD Clifton 93-99; Hon Can Bris Cathl 99-01; rtd 01; Perm to Offic *Derby* from 01. *4 Hall Court, The Village, West Hallam, Ilkeston DE7 6GS* Tel 0115-944 3474

SMITH, Mrs Gabrielle Lynette Claire. b 49. St Aid Coll Dur BA70 ARCM73. St Alb and Ox Min Course 95. **d** 98 **p** 99. NSM Gt Marlow w Marlow Bottom, Lt Marlow and Bisham *Ox* from 98. *29 Bovingdon Heights, Marlow SL7 2JR* Tel (01628) 482923

SMITH (née SAMPSON), Ms Gail Sampson. b 49. Towson State Univ (USA) BA85. Virginia Th Sem MDiv93. **d** 93 **p** 94. Assoc R Ellicott City St Jo USA 93-99; Perm to Offic *S'wark* 00-01; Hon C Kew St Phil and All SS w St Luke from 01. *67 Cambridge Road, Twickenham TW1 2JT* Tel (020) 8892 4077
E-mail ukrevgss@aol.com

SMITH, Gary Russell. b 56. Southn Univ BTh94. Cuddesdon Coll 94. **d** 96 **p** 97. C Southampton Maybush St Pet *Win* 96-00. *Address temp unknown*

SMITH, Geoffrey. *See* SMITH, Richard Geoffrey

SMITH, Geoffrey. b 45. Bernard Gilpin Soc Dur 65 Sarum Th Coll 66. **d** 69 **p** 70. C Hatfield *Sheff* 69-71; C Bolton St Pet *Man* 71-74; V Lt Hulton 74-78; P-in-c Newc St Andr *Newc* 78-87; Soc Resp Adv 78-87; Hon Can Newc Cathl 84-87; Dir Cen for Applied Chr Studies 87-91; Team Ldr Home Office Birm Drug Prevention Unit 91-93; Public Preacher *Birm* 87-93; C Brampton and Farlam and Castle Carrock w Cumrew *Carl* 93-96; ACUPA Link Officer 94-96; Can Res Bradf Cathl *Bradf* 96-00; Nat Dir Toc H from 00; Perm to Offic *Ox* 00-02; Hon C Biddenham *St Alb* from 02. *7 Church End, Biddenham, Bedford MK40 4AS* Tel (01234) 218914

SMITH, Canon Geoffrey Cobley. b 30. Bps' Coll Cheshunt 63. **d** 65 **p** 66. C Hockerill *St Alb* 65-68; C Evesham *Worc* 68-72; V Walberswick w Blythburgh *St E* 72-85; RD Halesworth 81-85; R Newmarket St Mary w Exning St Agnes 85-00; RD Mildenhall 86-00; Hon Can St E Cathl 87-00; rtd 00; Perm to Offic *St E* from 00. *78 Eastgate Street, Bury St Edmunds IP33 1YR* Tel (01284) 731061

SMITH, Geoffrey Keith. b 37. Lon Coll of Div 57. **d** 60 **p** 61. C Leek St Luke *Lich* 60-63; C Trentham 63-66; V Lilleshall 66-84; P-in-c Sheriffhales w Woodcote 83-84; V Lilleshall and Sheriffhales 84-87; P-in-c Haughton 87-91; R Derrington, Haughton and Ranton 91-03; RD Stafford 95-03; rtd 03. *19 Meadow Drive, Haughton, Stafford ST18 9HU* Tel (01785) 259076

SMITH, Geoffrey Raymond. b 49. AKC71. St Aug Coll Cant 71. **d** 72 **p** 73. C Hendon St Alphage *Lon* 72-75; C Notting Hill St Mich and Ch Ch 75-78; P-in-c Isleworth St Fran 78-83; P-in-c Chipping Ongar *Chelmsf* 83-84; R 84-86; R Shelley 84-86; R Chipping Ongar w Shelley 86-89; RD Ongar 88-89; P-in-c Harlow St Mary Magd 89-90; V 90-98; R Woodford St Mary w St Phil and St Jas from 98. *The Rectory, 8 Chelmsford Road, London E18 2PL* Tel (020) 8504 3472
E-mail geoffreysmith49@aol.com

SMITH, George Frederic. b 35. AKC59. **d** 60 **p** 61. C Radford *Cov* 60-64; C Kenilworth St Nic 64-67; V Burton Dassett 67-71; CF 71-74; V Lapley w Wheaton Aston *Lich* 74-80; V Gt Wyrley 80-90; V Shareshill 90-95; rtd 95. *Beili Tew Lodge, Llansawel, Llandeilo SA19 7LJ*

SMITH, Canon George Robert Henry. b 24. Chich Th Coll 49. **d** 52 **p** 53. C Glouc St Steph *Glouc* 52-56; V Parkend 56-65; P-in-c Clearwell 60-62; V Tuffley 65-82; Hon Can Glouc Cathl 81-95; R Leckhampton St Pet 82-94; rtd 94; NSM Westcote w Icomb and Bledington *Glouc* 95-98; Perm to Offic from 98. *1 The Paddocks, Church Lane, Bledington, Chipping Norton OX7 6XB* Tel (01608) 659194

SMITH, Gerald. b 36. Sarum Th Coll 61. **d** 63 **p** 64. C Menston w Woodhead *Bradf* 63-66; Chapl RAF 66-70; C Hoylake *Ches* 70-72; R Inverurie *Ab* 72-74; R Kemnay 72-74; TV Hucknall Torkard *S'well* 74-75; Falkland Is 75-78; V Luddenden w Luddenden Foot *Wakef* 79-86; V Scopwick Gp *Linc* 86-94; P-in-c Leasingham 94-96; rtd 96; Perm to Offic *Ex* from 96 and Truro from 00. *Ivy Cottage, Woolsery, Bideford EX39 5QS* Tel (01237) 431298 Fax as telephone

SMITH, Preb Gilbert. b 14. Lon Univ BD64. Lambeth STh57 K Coll Lon 39. **d** 40 **p** 41. C Brierley Hill *Lich* 40-42; CF 42-50; R Wrockwardine Wood *Lich* 51-58; V Codsall 58-83; RD Penkridge 72-82; Preb Lich Cathl 82-88; rtd 83; P-in-c Blymhill w Weston-under-Lizard *Lich* 83-88; Perm to Offic 89-01. *4 Moatbrook Avenue, Codsall, Wolverhampton WV8 1DH*

SMITH, Mrs Gillian Angela. b 39. RGN60 RM62. All Nations Chr Coll IDC65. **d** 94 **p** 95. NSM Haydock St Mark *Liv* 94-96; Perm to Offic *Ely* 96-02; rtd 99; Hon C Milton *Win* from 02. *St Peter's House, 25 Ashley Common Road, New Milton BH25 5AJ* Tel (01425) 612644

SMITH, Godfrey Declan Burfield. b 42. TCD BA64 MA67 PGCE65. Irish Sch of Ecum Dip Ecum82 Sarum Th Coll. **d** 69 **p** 70. Zambia 70-75; Perm to Offic *D & G* 81-02; S Regional Sec (Ireland) CMS 81-99; Overseas Sec 87-93; Miss Personnel Sec 93-99; I Donoughmore and Donard w Dunlavin *D & G* from 02. *The Rectory, Donard, Co Wicklow, Irish Republic* Tel (00353) (45) 404631 E-mail smithdeclan@esatclear.ie

SMITH, Graeme Richard. b 65. Leeds Univ BA87 Birm Univ MA91 PhD97. Qu Coll Birm 87. **d** 89 **p** 90. C Daventry *Pet* 90-92; Perm to Offic *Birm* 92-97; Lect Th Westmr Coll Ox 97-02; Sen Lect Soc and Cultural Th 00-02; Co Ecum Officer *Ox* 97-02. *Address temp unknown*

SMITH, Graham. *See* SMITH, John Graham

SMITH, Graham. b 39. Univ of Wales (Ban) CertEd60 Nottm Univ DipRE68 Lon Univ DipEd75. Dioc OLM tr scheme 98. **d** 01 **p** 02. OLM Upper Holme Valley *Wakef* from 01. *Rose Cottage, 45 South Lane, Holmfirth, Huddersfield HD9 1HJ* Tel (01484) 689661 Mobile 07887-952397
E-mail graham.smith50@btopenworld.com

SMITH, Graham Arthur James. b 43. MRICS68. STETS 98 Coll of Resurr Mirfield 01. **d** 01 **p** 02. NSM Broadstone *Sarum* from 01. *5 Durlston Road, Parkstone, Poole BH14 8PQ* Tel 07710-328685 (mobile) E-mail fr.graham.smith@talk21.com

SMITH, Canon Graham Charles Morell. b 47. St Chad's Coll Dur BA74. Westcott Ho Cam 74. **d** 76 **p** 77. C Tooting All SS *S'wark* 76-80; TV Thamesmead 80-87; TR Kidlington w Hampton Poyle *Ox* 87-97; RD Ox 89-95; TR Leeds City *Ripon* from 97; Can Ripon Cathl from 97. *Leeds Rectory, 1 Vicarage View, Leeds LS5 3HF* Tel 0113-278 6237 or 245 2036
E-mail rector.deledes@virgin.net

SMITH, Graham David Noel. b 37. Oak Hill Th Coll 72. **d** 73 **p** 74. C Southborough St Pet w Ch Ch and St Matt *Roch* 73-76; C Bedworth *Cov* 76-79; R Treeton *Sheff* 79-84; V Riddlesden *Bradf* 84-96; RD S Craven 91-96; rtd 96; Hon C Ilkley All SS *Bradf* from 97. *26 Hawthorne Grove, Burley in Wharfdale, Ilkley LS29 7RF* Tel (01943) 864754
E-mail grahams@26hawthorne.freeserve.co.uk

SMITH, Canon Graham Francis. b 27. Leic Univ DSS51 Lon Univ BD57. Wells Th Coll 51. **d** 54 **p** 55. C Howe Bridge *Man* 54-57; C Hatfield Hyde *St Alb* 57-63; V Angell Town St Jo *S'wark* 63-73; V Wandsworth St Anne 73-85; P-in-c Wandsworth St Faith 75-78; RD Wandsworth 81-85; Hon Can S'wark Cathl 82-92; Mert Deanery Missr 85-92; rtd 92; Perm to Offic *Pet* from 97. *The Haven, 9 High Street, Syresham, Brackley NN13 5HL* Tel (01280) 850421

SMITH, Graham John. b 31. SSC. **d** 75 **p** 76. NSM Devonport St Mark Ford *Ex* 75-81; NSM Plympton St Maurice 81-90; V Ernesettle 90-03; P-in-c from 03; rtd 03. *St Aidan's Vicarage, 122 Rochford Crescent, Plymouth PL5 2QD* Tel (01752) 210241
E-mail graham.smith6@talk21.com

SMITH, Graham John. b 60. RN Coll Dartmouth 79 RN Eng Coll Plymouth BScEng84. Trin Coll Bris DipHE89 BA90 St Jo Coll Nottm MA00. **d** 90 **p** 91. C Herne *Cant* 90-93; Chapl RN 93-96; C Henfield w Shermanbury and Woodmancote *Chich* 96-98; Chapl Sussex Police 96-98; Chapl Portsm Hosps NHS Trust 98-00; P-in-c Cosham *Portsm* from 00; CME Officer from 03; Chapl Highbury Coll of FE Portsm from 00. *The Vicarage, 269 Hawthorn Crescent, Cosham, Portsmouth PO6 2TL* Tel (023) 9238 7162 or 9232 6179 Mobile 07970-826160 Fax 07967-446376 E-mail gjsmith@first-web.co.uk

SMITH, Grahame Clarence. b 32. Lich Th Coll 58. **d** 60 **p** 61. C New Sleaford *Linc* 60-63; R Tydd 63-76; V Barholm w Stowe 76-81; V Tallington 76-81; V Uffington 76-81; P-in-c W Deeping 76-77; R 77-81; R Uffington 81-92; rtd 92; Perm to Offic *Linc* 92-95. *Keeper's Cottage, Careby Road, Aunby, Stamford PE9 4EG* Tel (01780) 636386

SMITH, Greg Peter. b 60. Warwick Univ BA86. Qu Coll Birm 96 WMMTC. **d** 99 **p** 00. C Binley *Cov* from 99. *57 Princethorpe Way, Binley, Coventry CV3 2HG* Tel (024) 7663 6335 E-mail gregsmith31760@aol.com

SMITH, Gregory James. *See* CLIFTON-SMITH, Gregory James

SMITH, Canon Guy Howard. b 33. Man Univ BA54. Coll of Resurr Mirfield 60. **d** 62 **p** 63. C Oswestry H Trin *Lich* 62-66; Malaysia 66-69; V Willenhall St Anne *Lich* 69-79; P-in-c Willenhall St Steph 75-79; Malawi 79-82; Adn Lilongwe Lake Malawi 80-82; V Tettenhall Wood *Lich* 82-89; TR 89-91; TR Kidderminster St Jo and H Innocents *Worc* 91-99; rtd 99; Perm to Offic *Worc* from 99. *11 Church Walk, Stourport-on-Severn DY13 0AL* Tel (01299) 822281 Fax as telephone

SMITH, Mrs Gwendoline Anne. b 52. K Coll Lon BA97. SEITE DipTM97. **d** 99 **p** 00. C Erith St Paul *Roch* 99-02; V Hadlow from 02. *The Vicarage, Maidstone Road, Hadlow, Tonbridge TN11 0DJ* Tel (01732) 850238
E-mail gwensmith@kent33.freeserve.co.uk

SMITH, Harold. *See* SMITH, Robert Harold

SMITH, Harold. b 20. Qu Coll Birm 77. **d** 80 **p** 81. NSM Gravelly Hill *Birm* 80-85; NSM Duddeston w Nechells 85-93; Perm to

Offic from 93. *37 Dovey Tower, Duddeston Manor Road, Birmingham B7 4LE* Tel 0121-682 9417

SMITH, Harvey Jackson. b 44. St Jo Coll Auckland LTh68. **d** 68 **p** 69. New Zealand 68-70 and from 74; C St John's Cathl Napier 68-70; C Laindon w Basildon *Chelmsf* 71-72; C Shepherd's Bush St Steph w St Thos *Lon* 72-74; V Waikohu 74-77; V Edgecumbe 77-81; V Pukekohe 81-89; V Remuera 89-98; Adn Auckland 96-98; Bp Auckland's Chapl for Development from 98. *80A Onewa Road, Northcote, Auckland, New Zealand* Tel (0064) (9) 419 7062 Fax 419 7067 E-mail hj.smith@xtra.co.nz

SMITH, Harvey Jefferson. b 19. AMCT39 FIEE38 FIMechE52 FIPlantE67 ACIArb78. St Alb Minl Tr Scheme 81. **d** 88 **p** 97. Hon C Hemel Hempstead *St Alb* 88-92; NSM from 95; Perm to Offic 92-95 and from 00. *43 Garland Close, Hemel Hempstead HP2 5HU* Tel (01442) 266377

SMITH, Sister Hazel Ferguson Waide. b 33. Univ Coll Lon BA55. **dss** 64 **d** 87. CSA 58-77; St Etheldreda's Children's Home Bedf 64-85; Bedford St Paul *St Alb* 85-92; Par Dn 87-92; rtd 92; Perm to Offic *St Alb* from 92; Ox 93-00. *Paddock House, 6 Linford Lane, Willen, Milton Keynes MK15 9DL* Tel (01908) 661554 Mobile 07789-654881

SMITH, Henry Neville. b 25. Chich Th Coll 53. **d** 54 **p** 55. C Oldham St Mary *Man* 54-56; C Mitcham St Olave *S'wark* 57-59; Succ Leic Cathl *Leic* 59-60; Chapl St Jas Hosp Balham 60-63; V Ivinghoe w Pitstone *Ox* 63-73; Chapl St Andr's Sch Caversham 73-90; rtd 90; Perm to Offic *Chich* from 90. *4 St Mary's Mews, Felpham, Bognor Regis PO22 7PE* Tel (01243) 822716

SMITH, Henry Robert. b 41. Lanchester Poly BSc66. Qu Coll Birm 75. **d** 78 **p** 79. Hon C Hillmorton *Cov* 78-81; Lic to Offic *S'well* 81-85; Hon C Radcliffe-on-Trent and Shelford etc 85-89; C Sutton in Ashfield St Mary 89-92; P-in-c Forest Town 92-98; P-in-c Babworth w Sutton-cum-Lound 98-02; P-in-c Scofton w Osberton 98-02; R Babworth w Sutton-cum-Lound and Scofton etc from 02. *St Bartholomew's Vicarage, Mattersey Road, Retford DN22 8PW* Tel (01777) 710007 *or* 703253 E-mail babworth@dircon.co.uk

SMITH, Howard Alan. b 46. Dip Counselling 81 St Jo Coll Dur BA73 DipnTh74. **d** 74 **p** 75. C Brighton St Matthias *Chich* 74-77; C Henfield 77-78; C Henfield w Shermanbury and Woodmancote 78-80; R Northiam 80-87; Chapl St Ebba's Hosp Epsom 87-94; Chapl Qu Mary's Hosp Carshalton 87-94; Chapl Merton and Sutton Community NHS Trust 94-99; Chapl Epsom and St Helier NHS Trust 99-00; Perm to Offic *Guildf* from 01. *72 Park Lane, Wallington SM6 0TL* Tel (020) 8296 2000 E-mail hosmith@globalnet.co.uk

SMITH, Howard Gilbert. b 48. Leeds Univ BA69. St Steph Ho Ox BA71 MA75 Ridley Hall Cam 72. **d** 73 **p** 74. C Wallsend St Luke *Newc* 73-76; C Farnworth and Kearsley *Man* 76-77; P-in-c Farnworth All SS 77-78; TV E Farnworth and Kearsley 78-82; V Belfield 82-93; V Leesfield from 93. *St Thomas's Vicarage, Wild Street, Lees, Oldham OL4 5AD* Tel 0161-624 3731

SMITH, Ian. b 62. Hull Univ BA83. Oak Hill Th Coll DipHE87 BA88. **d** 88 **p** 89. C W Hampstead St Luke *Lon* 88-90; C Woking St Pet *Guildf* 90-95; V Leyland St Jo *Blackb* 95-02; C Goole *Sheff* from 02. *St Mary's Church House, Swinefleet Road, Goole DN14 5TN* Tel (01405) 761131

SMITH, Canon Ian Walker. b 29. Leeds Univ BA52. Coll of Resurr Mirfield 52. **d** 54 **p** 55. C Moulsecoomb *Chich* 54-61; Chapl K Sch Cant 61-62; C Crawley *Chich* 62-79; TV 79-81; R Clenchwarton *Ely* 81-94; RD Lynn Marshland 84-94; Hon Can Ely Cathl 88-94; Perm to Offic *Nor* 88-94; rtd 94; Perm to Offic *Ely* from 94. *27 Jubilee Drive, Dersingham, King's Lynn PE31 6YA* Tel (01485) 540203

SMITH, Irene Lillian. b 42. OLM course 96. **d** 99 **p** 00. OLM Moston St Chad *Man* 99-00; OLM Uttoxeter Area *Lich* from 00. *16 Teanhurst Close, Tean, Stoke-on-Trent ST10 4NN* Tel (01538) 722975 E-mail irenel.smith@genie.co.uk

SMITH, Mrs Irene Mary. b 43. Shenstone Coll of Educn CertEd64 Lon Univ BD77. OLM course 96. **d** 99 **p** 00. OLM Uttoxeter Area *Lich* from 99. *16 Teanhurst Close, Lower Tean, Stoke-on-Trent ST10 4NN* Tel (01538) 722975

SMITH, Miss Irene Victoria. b 45. SRN66 SCM69. Man OLM Scheme 00. **d** 03. OLM Lawton Moor *Man* from 03. *288 Wythenshawe Road, Manchester M23 9DA* Tel 0161-998 4100 Mobile 07889-116856

SMITH, James. *See* SMITH, Philip James

SMITH, James. b 26. NEOC 76. **d** 79 **p** 80. NSM Seaton Hirst *Newc* 79-82; NSM Cresswell and Lynemouth 82-88; NSM Cambois 88-93; rtd 93; Perm to Offic *Newc* from 93. *140 Pont Street, Ashington NE63 0PX* Tel (01670) 816557

SMITH, James Edward. b 30. Chich Th Coll 57. **d** 58 **p** 59. C Ellesmere Port *Ches* 58-61; C W Bromwich All SS *Lich* 61-63; Chapl RN 63-65; V Walton St Jo *Liv* 65-71; V Anfield St Columba 71-79; V Altcar 79-92; rtd 92; Perm to Offic *Linc* 93-02. *272 Skellingthorpe Road, Lincoln LN6 0EU* Tel (01522) 696865

SMITH, James Harold. b 31. Ch Coll Tasmania ThL61. **d** 61 **p** 61. Australia 61-63 and 66-85 and 92-94; Canada 64-65; Chapl St Chris Hospice *Lon* 86-87; Asst Chapl Brook Gen Hosp *Lon* 87-92; Asst Chapl Greenwich Distr Hosp *Lon* 87-92; Perm to Offic *S'wark* from 94. *Poplar Cottage, 80 Charlton Road, London SE7 7EY* Tel (020) 8858 4692

SMITH, James Henry. b 32. St Aid Birkenhead. **d** 65 **p** 66. C Wigan St Cath *Liv* 65-68; V Parkfield in Middleton *Man* 68-77; V Bolton Breightmet St Jas 77-97; rtd 97; Perm to Offic *Liv* from 97. *Flat 4, 14A Cropton Road, Formby, Liverpool L37 4AD* Tel (01704) 833682

SMITH, James William. b 47. SRN69 RMN70 MRIPHH69 MRSH92 Lambeth STh90 Sussex Coll of Tech MA95. Chich Th Coll 78. **d** 80 **p** 80. C Kenwyn *Truro* 80-82; C Haslemere *Guildf* 82-84; TV Honiton, Gittisham, Combe Raleigh, Monkton etc *Ex* 84-91; Chapl R Marsden Hosp Lon and Surrey 91-95; Perm to Offic *S'wark* 91-95; rtd 95; Perm to Offic *Sarum* from 96. *22 Thrift Close, Stalbridge, Sturminster Newton DT10 2LE* Tel (01963) 362445

SMITH, Mrs Janice Lilian. b 51. Open Univ BSc99. N Ord Course 98. **d** 01 **p** 02. NSM Yeadon St Jo *Bradf* from 01. *17 Silverdale Close, Guiseley, Leeds LS20 8BQ* Tel (01943) 877023 E-mail janice@mizzie.fsnet.co.uk

SMITH, Jeffery Donald Morris. b 23. **d** 53 **p** 54. S Rhodesia 53-61; R Old Deer *Ab* 61-63; R Fraserburgh 63-68; S Africa 68-73; P-in-c Bintree w Themelthorpe *Nor* 73-76; V Twyford w Guist 73-76; R Twyford w Guist and Bintry w Themelthorpe 76-80; RD Sparham 79-81; R Twyford w Guist w Bintry w Themelthorpe etc 81; TR Hempnall 81-84; R Catfield 84-89; R Ingham w Sutton 84-89; rtd 89; Perm to Offic *Nor* from 89. *27 Dale Road, Dereham NR19 2DD* Tel (01362) 697022

SMITH, Jeffry Bradford. b 56. BA82. Ch Div Sch of the Pacific (USA) MDiv85 Ripon Coll Cuddesdon. **d** 86 **p** 87. C Frimley *Guildf* 87-91; R E and W Clandon 91-03; Chapl HM Pris Send 94-96; Chapl HM Pris Channings Wood from 03. *HM Prison Channings Wood, Denbury, Newton Abbott TQ12 6DW* Tel (01803) 812361 ext 325 Fax 813175

SMITH, Mrs Jennifer Pamela. b 63. Girton Coll Cam BA85 MA88. Oak Hill Th Coll BA91. **d** 91 **p** 94. C Rawdon *Bradf* 91-93; Chapl Bradf Cathl 93-96; P-in-c Kelbrook 96-00; Asst Chapl Airedale NHS Trust from 01. *24 Greenacres, Skipton BD23 1BX* Tel (01756) 790852

SMITH, Jeremy John Hawthorn. b 52. Birm Univ BSc73 Lanc Univ MA97. Carl and Blackb Dioc Tr Inst 94. **d** 97 **p** 98. NSM Long Marton w Dufton and w Milburn *Carl* 97-00; NSM Hesket-in-the-Forest and Armathwaite from 00; NSM Skelton and Hutton-in-the-Forest w Ivegill from 00; NSM Ainstable from 00. *St Mary's Vicarage, High Hesket, Carlisle CA4 0HU* Tel (01697) 473320

SMITH, Jeremy Victor. b 60. Keble Coll Ox BA82. Chich Th Coll 83. **d** 85 **p** 86. C Alton St Lawr *Win* 85-88; C W Hampstead St Jas *Lon* 88-93; V St Geo-in-the-East St Mary 93-97. *18 The Grange, Grange Road, London W4 4DE* Tel (020) 8742 7104

SMITH, Jesse Lee. b 70. Man Univ BA93. Linc Th Coll DipMM94 Westcott Ho Cam MA95. **d** 96 **p** 97. C Gomersal *Wakef* 96-00; C Penarth All SS *Llan* 00-02; TV Cen Cardiff 02-03; V Hartlepool H Trin *Dur* from 03. *Holy Trinity Vicarage, Davison Drive, Hartlepool TS24 9BX* Tel (01429) 267618 E-mail jesse@frjesse.freeserve.co.uk

SMITH, John. *See* SMITH, Stephen John

SMITH, John Alec. b 37. Lon Coll of Div ALCD62 BD63. **d** 63 **p** 64. C Cromer *Nor* 63-66; C Barking St Marg *Chelmsf* 66-69; V Attercliffe *Sheff* 69-75; P-in-c Sheff St Barn 76-78; V Sheff St Barn and St Mary 78-89; Ind Chapl 78-89; RD Ecclesall 80-85; TR Chippenham St Paul w Hardenhuish etc *Bris* 89-00; V Kington St Michael 89-00; rtd 00. *82 Victoria Road, Bidford-on-Avon, Alcester B50 4AR* Tel (01793) 872932

SMITH, John Bartlett. b 50. ACIPD54 St Chad's Coll Dur BA73 Lanchester Poly Dip Ind Relns 80. Cuddesdon Coll 73. **d** 76 **p** 77. C Heref St Martin *Heref* 76-86; NSM Isleworth St Mary *Lon* 86-89; NSM Millom *Carl* 89-92; NSM Balham St Mary and St Jo *S'wark* from 92. *101 Gosberton Road, London SW12 8LG* Tel (020) 8675 1743

SMITH, John David Elliott. b 39. Dur Univ BA61. Cranmer Hall Dur 61. **d** 64 **p** 65. C Stratford-on-Avon w Bishopton *Cov* 64-70; P-in-c Tredington 70-76; P-in-c Newbold on Avon 76-81; V 81-89; P-in-c Arlington, Folkington and Wilmington *Chich* 89-99; rtd 99. *Meadsway Cottage, 22 Granville Road, Eastbourne BN20 7HA* Tel (01323) 720192

SMITH, John Denmead. b 44. Ox Univ BA65 MA69 DPhil71. Coll of Resurr Mirfield 72. **d** 75 **p** 76. Asst Chapl Win Coll from 75. *11 Kingsgate Street, Winchester SO23 9PD* Tel (01962) 861820

SMITH, John Eckersley. b 26. Univ of Wales (Lamp). St Aug Coll Cant Wycliffe Hall Ox 53. **d** 55 **p** 56. C Heywood St Jas *Man* 55-57; C Atherton 57-59; R Gorton All SS 59-65; C Northenden 73-75; V Charlestown 75-82; Perm to Offic from 85; rtd 91. *19 Arthur Street, Swinton, Manchester M27 3HP* Tel 0161-793 7707

SMITH, John Ernest. b 52. St Andr Univ MTh77. Wycliffe Hall Ox 78. **d** 79 **p** 80. C Bermondsey St Mary w St Olave, St Jo etc *S'wark* 79-87; P-in-c Whyteleafe 87-97; RD Caterham 96-98; TV Caterham 98; R Merstham and Gatton from 98. *The Rectory,*

Gatton Bottom, Merstham, Redhill RH1 3BH Tel (01737) 643755 Fax 642954 E-mail john_e_smith@talk21.com

SMITH, John Graham. b 32. **d** 78 **p** 79. NSM Hordle *Win* 78-00; rtd 00. *3 Marryat Road, New Milton BH25 5LW* Tel (01425) 615701

SMITH, John Lawrence. b 43. Birm Univ BSc65. Linc Th Coll 67. **d** 70 **p** 71. C Frodingham *Linc* 70-75; TV Gt Grimsby St Mary and St Jas 75-83; V Wolverhampton St Andr *Lich* from 83. *St Andrew's Vicarage, 66 Albert Road, Wolverhampton WV6 0AF* Tel (01902) 712935

SMITH, John Leslie. b 44. Trin Coll Cam BA65 MA71. Ripon Coll Cuddesdon 79. **d** 81 **p** 82. C Ollerton *S'well* 81-84; P-in-c Farndon 84-88; P-in-c Thorpe 84-88; P-in-c Langford w Holme 88-95; P-in-c Winthorpe 88-95; Dioc Chief Insp Ch Schs 88-95; Dir of Educn *Pet* 95-99; P-in-c Cottingham w E Carlton 97-99; Dir of Educn *Roch* from 99. *Diocesan Board of Education, Deanery Gate, The Precinct, Rochester ME1 1SJ* Tel (01634) 843667 Fax 843674 E-mail john.smith@rochester.anglican.org

SMITH, John Macdonald. b 29. Ch Coll Cam BA52 MA56. Wells Th Coll 56. **d** 58 **p** 59. C Westbury-on-Trym H Trin *Bris* 58-60; C Reading St Giles *Ox* 60-63; V Kidmore End 63-82; rtd 82. *38 Main Road, Norton, Evesham WR11 4TL* Tel (01386) 870918

SMITH, John Malcolm. b 36. ACIB60. N Ord Course 81. **d** 84 **p** 85. NSM Bury St Pet *Man* from 84. *46 Ajax Drive, Bury BL9 8EF* Tel 0161-766 8378

SMITH, John Oswald Salkeld. b 32. Oak Hill Th Coll 57. **d** 60 **p** 61. C Peckham St Mary Magd *S'wark* 60-63; C Rodbourne Cheney *Bris* 63-67; V Bradf St Aug Undercliffe *Bradf* 67-74; P-in-c Hammersmith St Simon *Lon* 74-76; V Chelsea St Jo w St Andr 76-97; rtd 98. *2 Lawn Road, Guildford GU2 4DE*

SMITH, John Roger. b 36. Dur Univ BA59. Tyndale Hall Bris 59. **d** 61 **p** 62. C Chaddesden St Mary *Derby* 61-63; C Gresley 63-66; V Burton Ch Ch *Lich* 66-76; V Doncaster St Mary *Sheff* 76-92; R Barnburgh w Melton on the Hill etc 92-01; rtd 01. *2 Fieldhead Drive, Cross Hills, Keighley BD20 7RJ* Tel (01535) 634062

SMITH, Canon John Stewart. b 18. St Cath Soc Ox BA42 MA46. Ripon Hall Ox 42. **d** 43 **p** 44. C Oldbury *Birm* 43-46; C Hengrove *Bris* 46-49; C-in-c Patchway CD 49-58; V Shirehampton 58-72; V Westbury-on-Trym St Alb 72-83; RD Clifton 73-79; Hon Can Bris Cathl 77-84; rtd 83; Chapl Hortham Hosp 83-93; Chapl Phoenix NHS Trust 93-94; Perm to Offic *Bris* from 84. *48A Downs Park West, Bristol BS6 7QL* Tel 0117-962 9208

SMITH, John Sydney. b 36. Loughb Coll ALA59 FLA68 FISM82 Lanc Univ MA97. Carl and Blackb Dioc Tr Inst 94. **d** 97 **p** 98. NSM Arthuret, Nicholforest and Kirkandrews on Esk *Carl* 97-02; rtd 02. *The Jays, 3 White House, Walton, Brampton CA8 2DJ* Tel (01697) 741114

SMITH, John Thomas. b 29. Shuttleworth Agric Coll NDA55 Keele Univ DASE72 Wolv Poly MPhil81 PhD87. WMMTC 87. **d** 91 **p** 92. NSM Drayton in Hales *Lich* 91-96; NSM Cheswardine, Childs Ercall, Hales, Hinstock etc 96-98; rtd 98; Perm to Offic *Lich* 98-00. *Red Bank House, Market Drayton TF9 1AY* Tel (01630) 652302

SMITH, John Thompson. b 30. Wycliffe Hall Ox 64. **d** 66 **p** 67. C Walsall *Lich* 66-69; V Stoke Prior *Worc* 69-75; Asst Gen Sec Red Triangle Club 75-85; R Tendring and Lt Bentley w Beaumont cum Moze *Chelmsf* 85-89; R Fairstead w Terling and White Notley etc 89-92; Chapl Heath Hosp Tendring 85-92; rtd 92; Perm to Offic *B & W* from 92. *1 Harvey Close, Weston-super-Mare BS22 7DW* Tel (01934) 514256

SMITH, John Trevor. b 47. GGSM. Coll of Resurr Mirfield 74. **d** 77 **p** 78. C Loughton St Jo *Chelmsf* 77-80; C Ruislip St Martin *Lon* 80-84; P-in-c Southall Ch Redeemer 84-91; V Kingsbury St Andr from 91. *St Andrew's Vicarage, 28 Old Church Lane, London NW9 8RZ* Tel (020) 8205 7447 Fax 8205 7652 E-mail jts@dircon.co.uk

SMITH, John William. b 51. EAMTC 00. **d** 03. NSM Erpingham w Calthorpe, Ingworth, Aldborough etc *Nor* from 03. *18 Pound Lane, Aylsham, Norwich NR11 6DR* Tel (01263) 734761

SMITH, Jonathan Paul. b 60. Univ of Wales (Lamp) BA81. Wycliffe Hall Ox 82. **d** 84 **p** 85. C Baglan *Llan* 84-88; C Gabalfa 88-90; R Llangammarch w Llanganten and Llanlleonfel etc *S & B* 90-01; Dioc Missr 95-01; R Denbigh *St As* from 01. *The Rectory, St David's Lane, Denbigh LL16 3EP* Tel (01745) 812970 E-mail mission@cadmarch.freeserve.co.uk

SMITH, Jonathan Peter. b 55. K Coll Lon BD77 AKC77 Cam Univ PGCE78. Westcott Ho Cam 79. **d** 80 **p** 81. C Gosforth All SS *Newc* 80-82; C Waltham Abbey *Chelmsf* 82-85; Chapl City Univ *Lon* 85-88; R Harrold and Carlton w Chellington *St Alb* 88-97; Chapl Beds Police 90-97; V Harpenden St Jo from 97; RD Wheathampstead from 99. *St John's Vicarage, 5 St John's Road, Harpenden AL5 1DJ* Tel (01582) 467168 *or* 712776 E-mail oldtractorboy@tiscali.co.uk

SMITH, Joyce Mary. b 52. Lon Hosp BDS74 Nottm Univ MMedSc77 Lon Univ PhD84 MCCDRCS89. EAMTC. **d** 00 **p** 01. C Harlow St Mary and St Hugh w St Jo the Bapt *Chelmsf* 00-02; C Waltham H Cross from 02. *St Lawrence House, 46 Mallion Court, Waltham Abbey EN9 3EQ* Tel (01992) 767916 E-mail joyce@smith2767fsnet.co.uk

SMITH, Julian. b 48. K Coll Lon 70. Linc Th Coll 71. **d** 73 **p** 74. C Taunton Lyngford *B & W* 73-76; TV Wellington and Distr 76-81; R Axbridge w Shipham and Rowberrow 81-96; Chapl St Jo Hosp Axbridge from 84; V Taunton St Andr *B & W* from 96. *St Andrew's Vicarage, 118 Kingston Road, Taunton TA2 7SR* Tel (01823) 332544 E-mail jandms@eurobell.co.uk

SMITH, Julian William. b 64. Liv Univ BSc85. Trin Coll Bris BA93. **d** 93 **p** 94. C Henfynyw w Aberaeron and Llanddewi Aberarth *St D* 93-97; V Llansantffraed and Llanbadarn Trefeglwys etc from 97. *The Vicarage, 11 Maes Wyre, Llanrhystud SY23 5AH* Tel (01974) 202336

SMITH, Keith. b 46. ACIB. S Dios Minl Tr Scheme 85. **d** 87 **p** 88. NSM W Worthing St Jo *Chich* 87-94; NSM Maybridge 94-96; C Durrington 96-01; V Pagham from 01. *The Vicarage, Church Lane, Pagham, Bognor Regis PO21 4NX* Tel (01243) 262713

SMITH, Kenneth Robert. b 48. K Coll Lon BD75 AKC75. St Aug Coll Cant 75. **d** 76 **p** 77. C Birtley *Dur* 76-80; V Lamesley 80-90; R Whitburn from 90. *The Rectory, 51 Front Street, Whitburn, Sunderland SR6 7JD* Tel 0191-529 2232

SMITH, Kenneth Victor George. b 37. ALCD61 Lon Univ BD62. **d** 62 **p** 63. Hon C Bromley Common St Aug *Roch* 62-66; Hon C Streatham Immanuel w St Anselm *S'wark* 66-68; Perm to Offic 68-78; Chapl Whitgift Sch and Ho Croydon 78-97; Hon C Sanderstead All SS 78-91; Hon C Croydon St Jo 91-97; rtd 02. *Bridle Ways, Haling Grove, South Croydon CR2 6DQ* Tel (020) 8680 4460

SMITH, Kevin. b 66. Westmr Coll Ox BA89. Chich Th Coll 90. **d** 92 **p** 93. C Worksop Priory *S'well* 92-96; V New Cantley *Sheff* from 96. *St Hugh's House, Levet Road, Cantley, Doncaster DN4 6JQ* Tel (01302) 535739

SMITH, Canon Laurence Kenneth Powell. b 17. Lon Coll of Div ALCD41 LTh74. **d** 41 **p** 42. C Streatham Vale H Redeemer *S'wark* 41-44; C Surbiton St Matt 44-51; V Southampton St Matt *Win* 51-57; V Iford 57-72; R Stockbridge and Houghton 72-85; RD Romsey 79-85; Hon Can Win Cathl 82-85; rtd 85; Perm to Offic *Win* from 85. *8 Riverside Gardens, Romsey SO51 8HN* Tel (01794) 518262

SMITH, Laurence Sidney. b 37. Sarum & Wells Th Coll 70. **d** 73 **p** 74. C Surbiton St Matt *S'wark* 73-76; C Horley 76-81; V W Ewell *Guildf* 81-90; V W Byfleet 90-02; rtd 02. *Candlemill Cottage, Millbank, George Street, Nailsworth, Stroud GL6 0AG* Tel (01453) 836432

SMITH, Lawrence Paul. b 51. Ch Ch Coll Cant CertEd72 Southn Univ BTh81. Chich Th Coll 76. **d** 79 **p** 80. C Margate St Jo *Cant* 79-84; R Eythorne w Waldershare 84-87; P-in-c Sibertswold w Coldred 85-87; P-in-c Barfreystone 85-87; R Eythorne and Elvington w Waldershare etc 87-97; Par Min Development Adv (Kensington Area) *Lon* from 97; NSM Isleworth St Fran from 00. *St Francis Vicarage, 865 Great West Road, Isleworth TW7 5PD* Tel (020) 8568 9098 *or* 8580 2142 Fax 8560 8113 E-mail lawrence.smith@london.anglican.org

SMITH, Canon Lewis Shand. b 52. Aber Univ MA74 Edin Univ BD78. Edin Th Coll 74. **d** 77 **p** 78. C Wishaw *Glas* 77-79; P-in-c 79-80; C Motherwell 77-79; P-in-c 79-80; R Lerwick *Ab* 80-00; R Burravoe 80-00; Miss to Seafarers from 80; Can St Andr Cathl *Ab* 93-00; R Dumfries *Glas* from 00. *8 Newall Terrace, Dumfries DG1 1LW* Tel (01387) 254126 E-mail shand.smith@talk21.com

SMITH, Mrs Linda Jean. b 61. Ripon Coll Cuddesdon DipMin99. **d** 99 **p** 00. C St Martin w Looe *Truro* from 99. *Eastfield, 57 Barbican Road, Looe PL13 7NN* Tel (01503) 262221 E-mail smith.looe@virgin.net

SMITH, Linnet. *See* SMITH, Diana Linnet

SMITH, Miss Lorna Cassandra. b 43. Open Univ BA76. Cant Sch of Min 82. **dss** 86 **d** 87 **p** 94. Birchington w Acol and Minnis Bay *Cant* 86-87; Par Dn 87-92; C Addlestone *Guildf* 92-97; V Englefield Green from 97. *The Vicarage, 21 Willow Walk, Englefield Green, Egham TW20 0DQ* Tel (01784) 432553 Fax as telephone E-mail revlcs@aol.com

SMITH, Mrs Lorna Rosalind. b 53. Oak Hill NSM Course 89. **d** 92 **p** 94. NSM Squirrels Heath *Chelmsf* 92-94; NSM Stanford-le-Hope w Mucking 94-97; P-in-c Fobbing from 97. *24 Martin's Close, Stanford-le-Hope SS17 8AB* Tel (01375) 642439 Fax 643883 E-mail lornads24@aol.com

SMITH, Lynford. *See* SMITH, Francis Christian Lynford

SMITH (née THORNTON), Mrs Magdalen Mary. b 69. Warwick Univ BA90. Qu Coll Birm BD95. **d** 96 **p** 97. C Kirkby *Liv* 96-98; C Birm St Martin w Bordesley St Andr *Birm* 00-03. *4 Woodrough Drive, Moseley, Birmingham B13 9EP* Tel 0121-449 1336 E-mail mags@smith.freeserve.co.uk

SMITH, Mrs Margaret Elizabeth. b 46. Bretton Hall Coll CertEd67. N Ord Course 85. **d** 88 **p** 94. Hon Par Dn Battyeford *Wakef* 88-91; Hon C Mirfield 89-91; Chapl HM Pris and YOI New Hall 90-95; Dn-in-c Flockton cum Denby Grange *Wakef* 91-94; P-in-c 94-96; V Scholes 96-01; P-in-c Buckden *Ely* from 01; P-in-c Offord D'Arcy w Offord Cluny from 01. *The Vicarage, Church Street, Buckden, St Neots PE19 5TL* Tel (01480) 810371 E-mail memagsmith@waitrose.com

SMITH, Mrs Marion Elizabeth. b 51. Bris Univ CertEd73 Middx Univ BA99. NTMTC AdDipTh98. **d** 98 **p** 99. NSM Cowley *Lon*

98-00; P-in-c Harlington from 00. *The Rectory, St Peter's Way, Hayes UB3 5AB* Tel (020) 8759 9569 Mobile 07803-617509 E-mail marion.smith@tiscali.co.uk

SMITH, Mark Andrew. b 59. **d** 85 **p** 86. S Africa 85-01; P St Mary Magdalene Port Elizabeth 88-89; R St Pet Cradock 89-92; R Alexandra Plurality 93; Chapl St Andr Coll Grahamstown 94-01; Chapl Denstone Coll Uttoxeter from 02. *Denstone College, Denstone, Uttoxeter ST14 5HN* Tel (01889) 590372 Mobile 07776-185474 Fax (01889) 590744

SMITH, Mark David. *See* LAYNESMITH, Mark David

SMITH, Mark Gordon Robert Davenport. b 56. St Jo Coll Dur BA77. Ridley Hall Cam 78. **d** 80 **p** 81. C Sheff St Jo *Sheff* 80-83; C Brightside w Wincobank 83-86; V Kimberworth Park 86-91; Consultant NE England CPAS 91-98; Perm to Offic 91-98; *Dur* from 95; Nat Co-ord Cert in Evang Studies (CA) from 98. *Wilson Carlile College, 50 Cavendish Street, Sheffield S3 7RZ* Tel 0114-225 7447 Mobile 07702-269608 Fax 279 5863 E-mail m.smith@sheffieldcentre.org.uk

SMITH, Mark Graham. b 63. Ex Univ BA86 Qu Coll Cam DipTh89. Westcott Ho Cam 87. **d** 90 **p** 91. C Cottingham *York* 90-92; C Guisborough 92-94; Chapl St Martin's Coll *Blackb* 94-98; V Ashton-on-Ribble St Mich w Preston St Mark 98-03; V Scotforth from 03. *St Paul's Vicarage, 24 Scotforth Road, Lancaster LA1 4ST* Tel (01524) 32106 E-mail marklisasmith@aol.com

SMITH, Mark Peter. b 61. Reading Univ BA82 Open Univ BA93 MA97 Keele Univ PGCE84 Liv Univ MTh02. N Ord Course 99. **d** 02 **p** 03. C Wingerworth *Derby* from 02. *20 Longedge Rise, Wingerworth, Chesterfield S42 6NX* Tel (01246) 229532 E-mail mark@mpsosb1.demon.co.uk

SMITH, Mark Richard Samuel. b 63. UMIST BSc84. Cranmer Hall Dur 86. **d** 89 **p** 90. C Kersal Moor *Man* 89-93; C Halliwell St Pet 93-01; TV Stockport Web *Ches* 01-02. *327 Tottington Road, Bury BL8 1SZ* Tel 07762-152755 (mobile)

SMITH, Martin David. b 52. LTCL Hull Univ BA75. Cuddesdon Coll 75. **d** 78 **p** 79. C Brentwood St Thos *Chelmsf* 78-80; C Reading St Giles *Ox* 80-91; R Colkirk w Oxwick w Pattesley, Whissonsett etc *Nor* 91-95; P-in-c Gt and Lt Ryburgh w Gateley and Testerton 94-95; P-in-c Hempton and Pudding Norton 94-95; P-in-c Nor St Pet Parmentergate w St Jo 95-03; TR Trunch 03. *The Rectory, 10 Stepping Lane, Norwich NR1 1PE* Tel (01603) 622509 Fax 628417 E-mail frmartinsmith@clara.net

SMITH, Martin Lee. b 47. Worc Coll Ox BA68 MA72. Cuddesdon Coll 68. **d** 70 **p** 71. C Digswell *St Alb* 70-71; C Cheshunt 71-73; Perm to Offic *Ox* 74-80; SSJE 76-02; USA from 81. *1245 4th Street SW E208, Washington, DC 20024, USA* E-mail martin.l.smith@worldnet.att.net

SMITH, Martin Stanley. b 53. Univ of Wales (Abth) BScEcon75. STETS DipTh99. **d** 99 **p** 00. NSM Woking Ch Ch *Guildf* from 99. *Brackenlea, Heather Close, Horsell, Woking GU21 4JR* Tel (01483) 714307

SMITH, Canon Martin William. b 40. K Coll Lon BD63 AKC63. **d** 64 **p** 65. C Ashford St Hilda *Cant* 64-67; Malaysia 67-71; V Lakenham St Mark *Nor* 72-85; V N Walsham w Antingham 85-01; P-in-c Neatishead, Barton Turf and Irstead 94-95; RD Tunstead 91-96; RD St Benet 96-99; Hon Can Nor Cathl from 93; V Wymondham from 01. *The Vicarage, 5 Vicar Street, Wymondham NR18 0PL* Tel (01953) 602269

SMITH, Martyn. b 52. CertEd73. Oak Hill Th Coll BA81. **d** 81 **p** 82. C Halliwell St Pet *Man* 81-86; V Cambridge St Martin *Ely* 86-89; Vineyard Chr Fellowship from 89. *Vineyard Centre, Unit 7, Greenheys Business Centre, 10 Pencroft Way, Manchester M15 6JJ* Tel 0161-232 0222 Fax 232 7699

SMITH, Melvyn. *See* SMITH, Canon William Melvyn

SMITH, Merrick Thomas Jack. b 37. Glos Coll of Arts & Tech ONC57 CEng65 MCIBSE65. Oak Hill NSM Course 90. **d** 92 **p** 93. NSM Isleworth St Mary *Lon* 92-94; Perm to Offic *Birm* 94-96; NSM Warfield *Ox* 96-98; TV Wallingford 98-01; P-in-c Tredington and Darlingscott w Newbold on Stour *Cov* 01-03; rtd 03. *4 Brunel Drive, Preston, Weymouth DT3 6NU* Tel (01305) 832308 E-mail smithmerrick@talk21.com

SMITH, Michael. *See* SMITH, The Ven Anthony Michael Percival

SMITH, Michael. b 54. Matlock Coll of Educn CertEd76 Nottm Univ BEd77. Ridley Hall Cam 87. **d** 89 **p** 90. C Ilkeston St Mary *Derby* 89-92; TV Wirksworth 92-98; RD Wirksworth 97-98; V Ashbourne w Mapleton from 98. *The Vicarage, Belle Vue Road, Ashbourne DE6 1AT* Tel (01335) 343129 E-mail revmikesmith@btinternet.com

SMITH, Michael Anthony. b 47. Univ of Wales (Abth) MA73. **d** 78 **p** 79. NSM Llandingat w Llanfair and Myddfai 78-82; Chapl Llandovery Coll 81-82; Chapl Pocklington Sch York from 82. *Hosmer Lodge, 35 Percy Road, Pocklington, York YO42 2LZ* Tel (01759) 304543 or 303125

SMITH, Michael David. b 57. BA80. St Steph Ho Ox 81. **d** 83 **p** 84. C Beaconsfield *Ox* 83-87; V Wing w Grove 87-92; R Farnham Royal w Hedgerley 92-01; P-in-c Cookham from 01. *The Vicarage, Church Gate, Cookham, Maidenhead SL6 9SP* Tel (01628) 523969 or 529661

SMITH, Michael Ian Antony. b 69. Warwick Univ BSc91. Oak Hill Th Coll BA95. **d** 95 **p** 96. C Cheadle *Ches* 95-98; C Hollington St Leon *Chich* 98-01; C Hartford *Ches* from 01. *52 Stones Manor Lane, Hartford, Northwich CW8 1NU* Tel (01606) 77740 or 783063 Fax 786758 E-mail miasmith@btopenworld.com

SMITH, Michael James. b 47. AKC69. St Aug Coll Cant 70. **d** 71 **p** 72. C Corby St Columba *Pet* 71-78; V Collierley *Dur* 78-80; CPAS Evang from 83. *6 Blind Lane, Chester le Street DH3 4AG* Tel 0191-388 1977

SMITH, Michael John. b 47. Lon Univ DipTh71. Kelham Th Coll 65. **d** 71 **p** 72. C Cov St Mary *Cov* 71-75; Chapl RN 75-90; CF 90-95; R Lynch w Iping Marsh and Milland *Chich* from 95; RD Midhurst 98-03. *The Rectory, Fernhurst Road, Milland, Liphook GU30 7LU* Tel (01428) 741285 E-mail revmjsmith@hotmail.com

SMITH, Michael Keith John. b 66. Thames Poly BSc88. Linc Th Coll BTh95. **d** 95 **p** 96. C Birch St Agnes w Longsight St Jo w St Cypr *Man* 95-99; TV Pendleton from 99. *The Vicarage, Moorfield Road, Salford M6 7EY* Tel 0161-736 3064 E-mail mkjsmith@supanet.com

SMITH, Michael Raymond. b 36. ARCM56 ARCO56 Qu Coll Cam BA59 MA63. Cuddesdon Coll 64. **d** 65 **p** 66. C Redcar *York* 65-70; V Dormanstown 70-73; Prec Worc Cathl *Worc* 73-77; TR Worc St Barn w Ch Ch 77-83; RD Worc E 79-83; V Eskdale, Irton, Muncaster and Waberthwaite *Carl* 83-87; Chapl Uppingham Sch Leics 87-93; P-in-c Stoke Lacy, Moreton Jeffries w Much Cowarne etc *Heref* 93-01; Dioc Schs Officer from 97 to 01. *Plough House, Wellington, Hereford HR4 8AT* Tel (01432) 839087 E-mail stolacy@aol.com

SMITH, Michael Robin. b 34. ACIB58. Sarum Th Coll 59. **d** 62 **p** 63. C Perry Hill St Geo *S'wark* 62-65; C Streatham St Leon 65-68; NSM E Brixton St Jude 68-70; Brixton Chr Counselling Min 70-79; Wandsworth Chr Inst 80-91; rtd 99. *8 Turret House, Limmer Lane, Felpham, Bognor Regis PO22 7EN* Tel (01243) 864339

SMITH, Neville. *See* SMITH, Charles Henry Neville

SMITH, Norman George. b 27. K Coll Lon BD52 AKC52. **d** 53 **p** 54. C Pennington *Man* 53-56; C Chorlton-cum-Hardy St Clem 56-57; V Heywood St Jas 57-63; R Bedhampton *Portsm* 63-81; V Win St Bart *Win* 81-92; RD Win 84-89; rtd 92; Perm to Offic *Win* from 92. *40 Goring Field, Winchester SO22 5NH* Tel (01962) 852882

SMITH, Norman Jordan. b 30. Sarum Th Coll 57. **d** 60 **p** 61. C Parkend *Glouc* 60-61; C Clearwell 60-61; C W Tarring *Chich* 61-65; Australia 65-68; V Chidham *Chich* 68-94; rtd 95. *Potters Paradise, 82 Church Road, Hayling Island PO11 0NX*

SMITH, Preb Olwen. b 44. Birm Univ BA66 DPS68. Selly Oak Coll 67. **d** 89 **p** 94. Ind Chapl Black Country Urban Ind Miss *Lich* 84-98; TV Cen Wolverhampton from 94; Preb Lich Cathl from 99. *66 Albert Road, Wolverhampton WV6 0AF* Tel (01902) 712935 or 710407 Fax 685222 E-mail bcuim3@nascr.net

SMITH, Mrs Pamela Christina. b 46. St Alb and Ox Min Course 97. **d** 00 **p** 01. NSM Ironstone *Ox* from 00; Chapl Kath Ho Hospice from 00. *The Vicarage, Horley, Banbury OX15 6BJ* Tel (01295) 730951 E-mail pamela@banx.fsnet.co.uk

SMITH, Miss Pamela Frances. b 44. St Mary's Coll Cheltenham TCert65. WEMTC 91. **d** 94 **p** 95. NSM Badgeworth, Shurdington and Witcombe w Bentham *Glouc* 94-02; NSM The Lavingtons, Cheverells, and Easterton *Sarum* 02-03; Hon C from 03. *The Vicarage, White Street, West Lavington, Devizes SN10 4LW* Tel (01380) 818388 E-mail revdpsmith@breathemail.net

SMITH, Paul. b 48. STETS 99. **d** 02 **p** 03. NSM Copthorne *Chich* from 02. *7 Heather Close, Copthorne, Crawley RH10 3PZ* Tel (01342) 714308 E-mail heatherclose@freenet.co.uk

SMITH, Paul. b 52. LNSM course 97. **d** 98 **p** 99. OLM Leominster *Heref* from 98. *32 The Meadows, Leominster HR6 8RF* Tel (01568) 615862 or 612124

SMITH, Paul Aidan. b 59. Birm Univ BA82. Wycliffe Hall Ox 82. **d** 85 **p** 86. C Selly Park St Steph and St Wulstan *Birm* 85-88; C Kensal Rise St Mark and St Martin *Lon* 88-91; V Water Eaton *Ox* 91-00; TR Hale w Badshot Lea *Guildf* 00-02; TV Stantonbury and Willen *Ox* from 02. *2 Hooper Gate, Willen, Milton Keynes MK15 9JR* Tel (01908) 606689 Mobile 07930-308644 E-mail paul_a smith@bigfoot.com

SMITH, Paul Allan. b 66. C Coll Cam BA88 MA00 PhD94. WMMTC 98 Ripon Coll Cuddesdon 99. **d** 00 **p** 01. C Moseley St Mary *Birm* from 00. *4 Woodward Drive, Birmingham B13 9EP* Tel 0121-449 1336 E-mail paul@smith291066.freeserve.co.uk

SMITH, Paul Andrew. b 55. St Chad's Coll Dur BA76. Chich Th Coll 78. **d** 80 **p** 81. C Haberghana Eaves St Matt *Blackb* 80-83; C Ribbleton 83-86; V Rishton from 86; RD Whalley 95-01. *The Vicarage, Somerset Road, Rishton, Blackburn BB1 4BP* Tel (01254) 886191 E-mail dreadnoughtfam@aol.com

SMITH, Paul Anthony. b 66. Ripon Coll Cuddesdon. **d** 00 **p** 01. C Prestwood and Gt Hampden *Ox* from 00. *28 Peter's Close, Prestwood, Great Missenden HP16 9ET* Tel (01494) 866351

SMITH, Preb Paul Gregory. b 39. Ex Univ BA61. St Steph Ho Ox 61. **d** 63 **p** 64. C Walthamstow St Mich *Chelmsf* 63-66; C Devonport St Mark Ford *Ex* 66-69; C Hemel Hempstead *St Alb* 69-71; TV 71-83; R Bideford *Ex* 83-96; TR Bideford, Northam, Westward Ho!, Appledore etc 96; Chapl Bideford and Torridge Hosps 83-96; P-in-c Ex St Jas *Ex* 96-98; R 98-03; Preb Ex Cathl from 95; rtd 03. *Valrose, Broad Lane, Appledore, Bideford EX39 1ND* Tel (01237) 423513
E-mail fatherpaulsmith@aol.com

SMITH, Mrs Pauline Frances. b 37. Bris Univ BA58 Lon Univ CertEd59. Sarum & Wells Th Coll 87. **d** 90 **p** 94. C Cobham *Guildf* 90-96; P-in-c Lower Wylye and Till Valley *Sarum* 96-97; TV Wylye and Till Valley from 97; RD Stonehenge from 01. *The Rectory, West Street, Great Wishford, Salisbury SP2 0PQ* Tel (01722) 790363

SMITH, Peter. b 36. Keele Univ BA60. Cuddesdon Coll 73. **d** 75 **p** 76. C Shrewsbury St Chad *Lich* 75-80; V Burton St Chad 80-90; P-in-c Berwick w Selmeston and Alciston *Chich* 90-91; R 91-02; rtd 02; Perm to Offic *Sarum* from 03. *40 Homefield, Child Okeford, Blandford Forum DT11 8EN* Tel (01258) 861833

SMITH, Peter. b 49. Ex Univ BSc69 PGCE73. Carl Dioc Tr Course. **d** 82 **p** 83. NSM Kendal H Trin *Carl* from 82. *55 Empson Road, Kendal LA9 5PR* Tel (01539) 721467
E-mail rev.p.smith@btinternet.com

SMITH, Peter Alexander. *See* GRAYSMITH, Peter Alexander

SMITH, Peter Denis Frank. b 52. Local Minl Tr Course. **d** 81 **p** 83. OLM Camberwell St Mich w All Sv w Em *S'wark* 81-95; OLM Croydon St Jo from 95. *57 Alton Road, Croydon CR0 4LZ* Tel (020) 8760 9656

SMITH, Peter Francis Chasen. b 28. Leeds Univ BA54. Coll of Resurr Mirfield 54. **d** 56 **p** 57. C E Dulwich St Clem *S'wark* 56-59; C Sutton St Nic 59-62; C-in-c Wrangbrook w N Elmsall CD *Wakef* 62-68; Chapl St Aid Sch Harrogate 68-85; P-in-c Lower Nidderdale *Ripon* 85-93; rtd 93; Perm to Offic *Ripon* from 93; Perm to Offic *York* from 95. *Clematis Cottage, Main Street, Kilburn, York YO61 4AH* Tel (01347) 868394
E-mail peter.f.c.smith@btinternet.com

SMITH, Peter Henry. b 62. Bris Univ BA83. SEITE 96. **d** 99 **p** 00. C Romford St Edw *Chelmsf* 99-02; V Aldersbrook from 02. *St Gabriel's Vicarage, 12 Aldersbrook Road, London E12 5HH* Tel (020) 8989 0315 E-mail phxsmith@aol.com

SMITH, Peter Howard. b 55. St Andr Univ MTh78. Trin Coll Bris 78. **d** 79 **p** 80. C Handforth *Ches* 79-82; C Eccleston St Luke *Liv* 82-85; V Leyton St Paul *Chelmsf* 85-91; V Darwen St Barn *Blackb* 91-99; TR Bushbury *Lich* from 99. *The Rectory, 382 Bushbury Lane, Wolverhampton WV10 8JP* Tel (01902) 787688 *or* 782226
E-mail phsmith@dial.pipex.com

SMITH, Peter Howard. b 57. St Jo Coll Dur BSc78 Selw Coll Cam BA82 MA85. Ridley Hall Cam 80. **d** 83 **p** 84. C Welling *Roch* 83-87; C Hubberston w Herbrandston and Hasguard etc *St D* 87-89; C Hubberston 89-91; V Canley *Cov* 91-00; V Burney Lane *Birm* from 00. *Christ Church Vicarage, Burney Lane, Birmingham B8 2AS* Tel 0121-783 7455 E-mail peter@ccbl.org.uk

SMITH, Peter James. b 23. K Coll Lon 49. **d** 53 **p** 54. C Atherton *Man* 53-55; C Wokingham All SS *Ox* 55-56; C Doncaster St Geo *Sheff* 56-59; V Whitgift w Adlingfleet 59-62; Chapl Highcroft Hosp Birm 62-71; C Wolborough w Newton Abbot *Ex* 71-74; C Furze Platt *Ox* 74-78; Travelling Sec Ch Coun for Health and Healing 78-81; P-in-c Bisham *Ox* 82-90; rtd 90; NSM Hindhead *Guildf* 90-96; Perm to Offic *Guildf* 96-97; *Portsm* from 97. *4 Copse Close, Liss GU33 7EW* Tel (01730) 894499

SMITH, Peter Michael. b 28. Open Univ BA75. K Coll Lon 52. **d** 56 **p** 57. C Pokesdown St Jas *Win* 56-59; C Weeke 59-63; V Hutton Roof *Carl* 63-69; V Barrow St Aid 69-72; V Preston Patrick 72-93; rtd 93; Chapl to the Deaf and Hard of Hearing *Carl* from 93; Perm to Offic from 93. *2 Green Road, Kendal LA9 4QR* Tel (01539) 726741 Mobile 07973-224289
E-mail peter@smith687.freeserve.co.uk

SMITH, Peter William. b 31. Glouc Th Course 74. **d** 77 **p** 77. C Coleford w Staunton *Glouc* 77; Hon C 77-87; P-in-c Alderton w Gt Washbourne 87-94; R Alderton, Gt Washbourne, Dumbleton etc 94-97; rtd 97; Perm to Offic *Ex* from 97. *5 Western Drive, Starcross, Exeter EX6 8EH* Tel (01626) 890115

SMITH, Philip. b 55. Shoreditch Coll Lon BEd78. Oak Hill Th Coll DipHE97 BA98. **d** 98 **p** 99. C Cheltenham St Mary, St Matt, St Paul and H Trin *Glouc* from 98. *60 All Saints Road, Cheltenham GL52 2HA* Tel (01242) 528567

SMITH, Philip Hathway. b 66. St Andr Univ MTh88. Coll of Resurr Mirfield 90. **d** 92 **p** 93. C Shrewsbury St Giles w Sutton and Atcham *Lich* 92-94; C Clayton 94-97; TV Hanley H Ev 97-02; C Croydon St Mich w St Jas *S'wark* from 02. *3 St Stephens Crescent, Thornton Heath CR7 7NP* Tel (020) 8683 4593

SMITH, Philip James. b 32. St Alb Minl Tr Scheme. **d** 82 **p** 83. NSM Radlett *St Alb* 82-85; C 85-89; V Codicote 89-99; RD Hatfield 95-01; rtd 99; Perm to Offic *St Alb* from 00. *34 Cherry Tree Rise, Walkern, Stevenage SG2 7JL* Tel (01438) 861958

SMITH, Philip James. b 60. ACGI82 Imp Coll Lon BScEng82 Fitzw Coll Cam BA94. Ridley Hall Cam CTM95. **d** 95 **p** 96. C Aldborough w Boroughbridge and Roecliffe *Ripon* 95-99; V

from 99. *The Vicarage, Church Lane, Boroughbridge, York YO51 9BA* Tel (01423) 322433
E-mail philip@aldwithbb.freeserve.co.uk

SMITH, Philip Lloyd Cyril. b 22. Ch Coll Cam BA47 MA49. Wycliffe Hall Ox 47. **d** 49 **p** 50. C St Helens St Helen *Liv* 49-52; C Woking St Jo *Guildf* 52-56; R Burslem St Jo *Lich* 56-83; P-in-c Burslem St Paul 82-83; R Burslem 83-86; rtd 86; Perm to Offic *Sheff* from 86. *Upper Treasurer's House, 42 Bromley College, London Road, Bromley BR1 1PE* Tel 020-8290 1566

SMITH, Ralston Antonio. b 28. St Pet Coll Jamaica 53. **d** 56 **p** 57. Jamaica 56-60 and from 72; C Ex St Thos *Ex* 60-62; C Withycombe Raleigh 62-68; V Exwick 68-72; rtd 93. *PO Box 136, Anglican House, United Theological College, Kingston 7, Jamaica*

SMITH, Raymond Charles William. b 56. K Coll Lon BD78 AKC78. Coll of Resurr Mirfield 79. **d** 80 **p** 81. C Iffley *Ox* 80-83; C Wallingford w Crowmarsh Gifford etc 83-86; V Tilehurst St Mary 86-96; TR Haywards Heath St Wilfrid *Chich* from 96. *The Rectory, St Wilfrid's Way, Haywards Heath RH16 3QH* Tel (01444) 413300

SMITH, Canon Raymond Douglas. b 31. TCD BA53 MA56 BD56. **d** 54 **p** 55. C Belfast St Mich *Conn* 54-56; C Ballymacarrett St Patr *D & D* 56-58; CMS Tr Coll Chislehurst 58-60; Kenya (CMS) 60-71; Asst Gen Sec (Hibernian) CMS 71-74; Gen Sec CMS 74-86; CMS Ireland 76-86; Hon Can N Maseno from 78; I Powerscourt w Kilbride and Annacrevy *D & G* 86-96; Can Ch Ch Cathl Dublin from 94. *Glencarrig Lodge, Kindlestown Upper, Delgany, Co Wicklow, Irish Republic* Tel (00353) (1) 287 3229

SMITH, Raymond Frederick. b 28. Lon Univ BSc51 Leeds Univ MA65. Oak Hill Th Coll 51. **d** 53 **p** 54. C Toxteth Park St Philemon *Liv* 53-56; C Halliwell St Pet *Man* 56-58; V Denton and Weston *Bradf* 58-66; V Normanton *Wakef* 66-81; RD Chevet 73-81; R Moreton *Ches* 81-90; rtd 90. *Cornerways, Station Road, Llanymynech SY22 6EG* Tel (01691) 839254

SMITH, Raymond George Richard. b 38. Univ of Wales (Ban) BSc61 MSc65. WMMTC 91. **d** 94 **p** 95. NSM Edgmond w Kynnersley and Preston Wealdmoors *Lich* 94-97; Chapl Princess R Hosp NHS Trust Telford 95-03; V Llandegfan w Llandysilio *Ban* from 03. *The Vicarage, Mona Road, Menai Bridge LL59 5EA* Tel (01248) 717265

SMITH, Raymond Horace David. b 30. Sir John Cass Coll Lon FIBMS61. Lon Coll of Div 64. **d** 67 **p** 68. C Shoreditch St Leon *Lon* 67-70; SAMS 71-73; Chile 71-80; P-in-c Castle Hedingham *Chelmsf* 80-83; P-in-c Cambridge St Phil *Ely* 83-86; V 86-91; Chapl Ibiza *Eur* 91-94; C Lowton St Mary *Liv* 94-96; rtd 96; Perm to Offic *Ely* 96-02; Perm to Offic *Win* from 02. *St Peter's House, 25 Ashley Common Road, New Milton BH25 5AJ* Tel (01425) 612644 E-mail camsmith@freeuk.com

SMITH, Canon Richard. b 47. Westmr Coll Ox MTh99. St D Coll Lamp DipTh75. **d** 75 **p** 76. C Aberavon *Llan* 75-78; Ind Chapl 78-81; TV Bournemouth St Pet w St Swithun, H Trin etc *Win* 81-85; Chapl Colchester Gen Hosp 85-94; Chapl Severalls Hosp Colchester 85-94; Sen Chapl Essex Rivers Healthcare NHS Trust from 94; Sen Chapl NE Essex Mental Health NHS Trust 94-01; Sen Chapl N Essex Mental Health Partnership NHS Trust from 01; Bp's Adv for Hosp Chapl *Chelmsf* from 99; Hon Can Chelmsf Cathl from 01. *The Chaplain's Office, Colchester General Hospital, Turner Road, Colchester CO4 5JL* Tel (01206) 742513

SMITH, Richard Geoffrey. b 46. St Jo Coll Dur BA68 MA69. St Steph Ho Ox BA74 MA78. **d** 75 **p** 76. C Brentwood St Thos *Chelmsf* 75-78; C Corringham 78-81; R Shepton Beauchamp w Barrington, Stocklinch etc *B & W* 81-83; TV Redditch, The Ridge *Worc* 85-89; R Teme Valley N 89-98; Perm to Offic *Heref* from 02. *Churchbridge, Nash, Ludlow SY8 3AX* Tel (01584) 891329

SMITH, Richard Harwood. b 34. Sarum Th Coll 57. **d** 59 **p** 60. C Kington w Huntington *Heref* 59-62; Br Guiana 62-66; Guyana 66-69; C Broseley w Benthall *Heref* 69-70; Lic to Offic 70-76; USPG Area Sec (Dios Heref and Worc) 70-76; R Wigmore Abbey 76-84; V Eye w Braiseworth and Yaxley *St E* 84-96; P-in-c Bedingfield 84-96; P-in-c Occold 84-96; rtd 96. *33 Broad Street, Leominster HR6 8DD* Tel (01568) 610676

SMITH, Canon Richard Ian. b 46. Jes Coll Ox BA69 MA80. Ripon Hall Ox 69. **d** 70 **p** 71. C Eston *York* 70-76; TV E Ham w Upton Park St Alb *Chelmsf* 76-80; R Crook *Dur* 80-86; V Stanley 80-86; V Billingham St Cuth from 86; AD Stockton 92-01; Hon Can Dur Cathl from 98. *St Cuthbert's Vicarage, Church Road, Billingham TS23 1BW* Tel (01642) 659538 Fax 553236

SMITH, Richard Keith. b 44. Harper Adams Agric Coll NDA69. St Jo Coll Nottm. **d** 84 **p** 85. C Wirksworth w Alderwasley, Carsington etc *Derby* 84-87; R Hulland, Atlow, Bradley and Hognaston 87-96; P-in-c Long Compton, Whichford and Barton-on-the-Heath *Cov* from 96; P-in-c Wolford w Burmington from 97; P-in-c Cherington w Stourton from 97; P-in-c Barcheston from 97. *The Vicarage, Broad Street, Long Compton, Shipston-on-Stour CV36 5JH* Tel (01608) 684207

SMITH, Richard Michael. b 52. Lon Univ BA74. EAMTC 79. **d** 82 **p** 83. NSM Cambridge Ascension *Ely* 82-84; C Rainham

Roch 84-88; V Southborough St Thos 88-96; P-in-c Shanklin St Sav *Portsm* 96-99; V from 99; P-in-c Lake 96-99; V from 99. *The Vicarage, Lake, Sandown PO36 9JT* Tel (01983) 405666

SMITH, Robert Harold. b 23. Lon Univ BA49. Oak Hill Th Coll 46. **d** 50 **p** 51. C Nottingham St Ann *S'well* 50-52; Chapl in Elburton CD *Ex* 52-57; V Lowestoft Ch Ch *Nor* 57-67; R Upton *Ex* 67-80; P-in-c Fersfield *Nor* 80-81; P-in-c N w S Lopham 80-81; R Bressingham w N and S Lopham and Fersfield 81-87; rtd 87; Perm to Offic *Nor* from 87. *22 St Walstan's Road, Taverham, Norwich NR8 6NG* Tel (01603) 861285

SMITH, Robert Harrison. b 62. Lon Bible Coll BA90 Nottm Univ MA(TS)00 MA(MM)01 Cam Univ PGCE93. St Jo Coll Nottm 99. **d** 01 **p** 02. C Chatham St Phil and St Jas *Roch* from 01. *3A Kit Hill Avenue, Walderslade, Chatham ME5 9ET* Tel (01634) 864348 E-mail robandesther@rhsmith.freeserve.co.uk

✠**SMITH, The Rt Revd Robin Jonathan Norman.** b 36. Worc Coll Ox BA60 MA64. Ridley Hall Cam 60. **d** 62 **p** 63 **c** 90. C Barking St Marg *Chelmsf* 62-67; Chapl Lee Abbey 67-72; V Chesham St Mary *Ox* 72-80; RD Amersham 79-82; TR Gt Chesham 80-90; Hon Can Ch Ch 88-90; Suff Bp Hertford *St Alb* 90-01; rtd 01; Hon Asst Bp St Alb from 02. *7 Aysgarth Road, Redbourn, St Albans AL3 7PJ* Tel (01582) 791962

SMITH, Rodney Frederic Brittain. b 37. Jes Coll Cam BA61 MA64. St Steph Ho Ox 87. **d** 88 **p** 89. NSM Rainworth *S'well* 88-89; C Basford St Aid 89-91; C Sneinton St Cypr 91-94; P-in-c Sneinton St Matthias 94-96; V 96-02; P-in-c Sneinton St Steph w St Alb 01-02; rtd 02. *41A Cyprus Road, Nottingham NG3 5EB* Tel 0115-962 0378

SMITH, Rodney John Boughton. b 19. AKC41. Sarum Th Coll 41. **d** 42 **p** 43. C Frome St Jo *B & W* 42-44; C Eastbourne St Andr *Chich* 45-48; C Belvedere St Aug *Roch* 48-49; C Horsham *Chich* 49-55; V Kings Bromley *Lich* 55-60; V Porthill 60-68; V E Meon *Portsm* 68-84; V Langrish 76-84; rtd 84; Perm to Offic *Ex* 84-99. *3 Barton Orchard, Tipton St John, Sidmouth EX10 0AN* Tel (01404) 814673

SMITH, Roger. *See* SMITH, Thomas Roger.

SMITH, Roger. *See* SMITH, John Roger

SMITH, Roger Owen. b 50. Univ of Wales (Abth) BA72 St Chad's Coll Dur CertEd73 FRGS. S'wark Ord Course 84. **d** 87 **p** 88. NSM Nunhead St Antony w St Silas *S'wark* 87-91; NSM Forest Hill St Aug 91-98; NSM Crofton Park St Hilda w St Cypr 91-98; NSM Brockley Hill St Sav 91-98; NSM Camberwell St Giles w St Matt 98-00; Perm to Offic *Cant* from 01. *22 Wear Bay Road, Folkestone CT19 6BN* Tel (01303) 259896

SMITH, Canon Roger Stuart. b 41. Chich Th Coll 65. **d** 66 **p** 67. C Garforth *Ripon* 66-70; C Hilborough Gp *Nor* 70-73; TV 73-78; V Mendham w Metfield and Withersdale *St E* 78-89; P-in-c Fressingfield w Weybread 86-89; R Fressingfield, Mendham etc 90-91; RD Hoxne 86-91; R Kelsale-cum-Carlton, Middleton, Theberton etc 91-01; C Yoxmere Conf from 01. RD Saxmundham from 96; Hon Can St E Cathl from 97. *The Rectory, Middleton, Saxmundham IP17 3NR* Tel (01728) 648421 E-mail canonroger@middleton3112.freeserve.co.uk

SMITH, Roger William. b 48. Imp Coll Lon BSc70. EAMTC. **d** 00 **p** 01. NSM Rothwell w Orton, Rushton w Glendon and Pipewell *Pet* from 00. *6A Kipton Close, Rothwell, Kettering NN14 6DR* Tel (01536) 710981 E-mail roger.smith@corusgroup.com

SMITH, Ronald. b 26. ALCD56. **d** 56 **p** 57. C Gravesend St Jas *Roch* 56-59; C-in-c Istead Rise CD 59-79; V Istead Rise 79-93; rtd 93; Perm to Offic *Roch* from 93. *114 Maidstone Road, Rochester ME1 3DT* Tel (01834) 829183

SMITH, Ronald Deric. b 21. Lon Univ BA46. Bps' Coll Cheshunt 59. **d** 61 **p** 62. C Crayford *Roch* 61-67; USA 67-68; C W Malling w Offham *Roch* 68-71; V Slade Green 71-78; V Bromley Common St Luke 78-91; rtd 91; Perm to Offic *S'wark* and *Roch* from 91. *5 Bromley College, London Road, Bromley BR1 1PE* Tel (020) 8464 0212

SMITH, Ronald Eric. b 43. EMMTC 93. **d** 93 **p** 94. NSM Wingerworth *Derby* 93-99; NSM Newbold w Dunston 99-01; NSM Loundsley Green from 01. *21 Windsor Drive, Wingerworth, Chesterfield S42 6TG* Tel (01246) 279004

SMITH, Canon Ronald James. b 36. Linc Th Coll 73. **d** 75 **p** 76. C Bilborough St Jo *S'well* 75-78; P-in-c Colwick 78-81; R 81-85; P-in-c Netherfield 78-81; V 81-85; C Worksop Priory 85-90; TV Langley and Parkfield *Man* 90-95; P-in-c Barton w Peel Green 95-01; Hon Can Tamale from 01; rtd 01; Perm to Offic *Man* from 01. *12 Bramhall Drive, Holmes Chapel, Crewe CW4 7EJ* Tel (01477) 544072

SMITH, Ronald William. b 45. St Jo Coll York CertEd67. Chich Th Coll 70. **d** 73 **p** 74. C Scarborough St Martin *York* 73-76; C Stainton-in-Cleveland 76-80; V E Coatham 80-89; V Brookfield from 89. *Brookfield Vicarage, 89 Low Lane, Brookfield, Middlesbrough TS5 8EF* Tel (01642) 282241 E-mail revronsmith@ntlworld.com

SMITH, The Very Revd Rowan Quentin. b 43. AKC66. St Boniface Warminster 66. **d** 67 **p** 68. C Matroosfontein 67-69; C

Bonteheuwel 70; C Plumstead All SS 71-72; P-in-c Grassy Park 72-77; CR from 80; Chapl St Martin's Sch Rosettenville 80-88; Chapl Cape Town Univ 88-90; Prov Exec Officer 90-96; Can of Prov 93-96; Can Pastor St Geo Cathl 96; Dean Cape Town from 96. *The Deanery, 29 Upper Orange Street, Oranjezicht, 8001 South Africa* Tel (0027) (21) 465 2609 *or* 423 3371 Fax 423 8466 E-mail sgcdean@icon.co.za

SMITH, Preb Roy Leonard. b 36. Clifton Th Coll 63. **d** 66 **p** 67. C Clapham St Jas *S'wark* 66-70; C Kennington St Mark 70-74; C-in-c Southall Em CD *Lon* 74-83; V Stonebridge St Mich from 83; Preb St Paul's Cathl from 96. *St Michael's Vicarage, Hillside, London NW10 8LB* Tel (020) 8965 7443

SMITH, Royston. b 55. EMMTC 87. **d** 90 **p** 91. NSM Shirland *Derby* 90-94; NSM Ashover and Brackenfield 95-01; NSM Ashover and Brackenfield w Wessington from 01. *Kirkdale Cottage, Oakstedge Lane, Milltown, Ashover, Chesterfield S45 0HA* Tel (01246) 590975 E-mail royston@kirkdalecottage.freeserve.co.uk

SMITH, Royston Burleigh. b 26. St Deiniol's Hawarden 76. **d** 79 **p** 80. C Prestatyn *St As* 79-83; V Kerry and Llanmerewig 83-90; C Rhyl w St Ann 90-91; rtd 91. *45 Clwyd Park, Kinmel Bay, Rhyl LL18 5EJ* Tel (01745) 337684

SMITH, Ruth. *See* SMITH, Ms Vivienne Ruth

SMITH, Mrs Shirley Ann. b 46. RSCN68 RM82 RGN84 RHV86 Univ of Wales PGDPT94. Sarum & Wells Th Coll 89. **d** 93 **p** 94. Par Dn Totton *Win* 93-94; C 94-96; Chapl Portsm Hosps NHS Trust 96-98; V Lord's Hill *Win* 98-01; TV Beaminster Area *Sarum* from 01. *The Vicarage, Orchard Mead, Broadwindsor, Beaminster DT8 3RA* Tel (01308) 868805 E-mail shirleysmith@winch58.freeserve.co.uk

SMITH, Stephen. b 53. Leeds Poly CQSW78. Sarum & Wells Th Coll 87. **d** 89 **p** 90. C Redcar *York* 89-92; C Leeds St Aid *Ripon* 92-96; R Lanteglos by Camelford w Advent *Truro* 96-99; Chapl Hull and E Yorks Hosps NHS Trust from 99. *The Chaplaincy, Castle Hill Hospital, Castle Road, Cottingham HU16 5JQ* Tel (01482) 875875

SMITH, Stephen John. b 46. Kelham Th Coll 65. **d** 69 **p** 70. C Warsop *S'well* 69-73; C Heaton Ch Ch *Man* 73-75; V Bolton St Bede 75-78; R Bilborough w Strelley *S'well* 78-84; R E Leake 84-92; P-in-c Costock 84-92; P-in-c Rempstone 84-92; P-in-c Stanford on Soar 84-92; R E and W Leake, Stanford-on-Soar, Rempstone etc 92-97; RD W Bingham 92-97; V Swaffham *Nor* from 97; C Gt and Lt Dunham w Gt and Lt Fransham and Sporle from 03; RD Breckland from 02; Chapl NW Anglia Healthcare NHS Trust from 99. *The Vicarage, White Cross Road, Swaffham PE37 7QY* Tel (01760) 721373 Fax as telephone E-mail frjohnsmith@aol.com

SMITH, Stephen John. b 55. Lon Univ BD80. Trin Coll Bris 77. **d** 81 **p** 82. C Fulham St Matt *Lon* 81-86; C Stoke Gifford *Bris* 86-90; TV 90-01; rtd 01; Perm to Offic *Bris* from 01. *47 Saxon Way, Bradley Stoke, Bristol BS32 9AR* Tel (01454) 616429 E-mail steve@revsmith.freeserve.co.uk

SMITH, Canon Stephen John Stanyon. b 49. Sussex Univ BA81 Birm Univ MSocSc83. Westcott Ho Cam 83. **d** 85 **p** 86. C Four Oaks *Birm* 85-89; USA from 89; Asst P Cheyenne River Reservation 89-91; Miss P Rosebud Reservation 91-94; Assoc R Ivoryton and Essex 94-98; Can St Paul's Cathl Buffalo from 98. *100 Beard Avenue, Buffalo, NY 14214, USA* Tel and fax (001) (716) 838 0240 *or* tel 855 0900 Fax 855 0910 E-mail stanyon@aol.com

SMITH, Stephen Thomas. b 55. Westcott Ho Cam 95. **d** 97 **p** 98. C Kempston Transfiguration *St Alb* 97-01; C Bromham w Oakley and Stagsden from 01. *65 Lincroft, Oakley, Bedford MK43 7SS* Tel (01234) 826153

SMITH, Steven Barnes. b 60. Cov Poly BA83 Leeds Univ BA86. Coll of Resurr Mirfield 83. **d** 87 **p** 88. C Darlington St Mark w St Paul *Dur* 87-89; C Prescot *Liv* 89-91; V Hindley Green 91-96; Asst Chapl Havering Hosps NHS Trust 96-98; Chapl Chelsea and Westmr Healthcare NHS Trust from 98. *Chelsea and Westminster Hospital, 369 Fulham Road, London SW10 9NH* Tel (020) 8746 8083 *or* 8746 8000

SMITH, Steven Gerald Crosland. b 48. Linc Th Coll 82. **d** 84 **p** 85. Chapl St Jo Sch Tiffield 84-87; C Towcester w Easton Neston *Pet* 84-87; P-in-c Kings Heath 87-89; V 89-93; TV N Creedy *Ex* from 93; RD Cadbury from 02. *The Vicarage, Cheriton Fitzpaine, Crediton EX17 4JB* Tel (01363) 866352 E-mail sgcsmith@compuserve.com

SMITH, Susan. b 48. Swansea Coll of Educn 69 Open Univ Cert Business Studies89 FInstD87. Ox Min Course 93. **d** 96 **p** 97. C Burnham w Dropmore, Hitcham and Taplow *Ox* 96-00; TV Whitton *Sarum* 00-02; TV W Slough *Ox* from 02. *St Andrew's House, Washington Drive, Slough SL1 5RE* Tel (01628) 661994

SMITH, Miss Susan Ann. b 50. Bris Univ BA72 St Jo Coll York PGCE73. Ripon Coll Cuddesdon 97. **d** 99 **p** 00. C Swaffham *Nor* 99-02; R King's Beck from 02. *The Rectory, Aylsham Road, Felmingham, North Walsham NR28 0LD* Tel (01692) 402382

SMITH, Mrs Susan Jennifer. b 52. MCIPD90 DipTM90. St Alb and Ox Min Course 94. **d** 97 **p** 98. C Ascot Heath *Ox* 97-01; P-in-c Flixton St Mich *Man* from 01. *The Rectory, 348 Church Road, Urmston, Manchester M41 6HR* Tel 0161-748 2884 Fax as telephone E-mail saxoncross@talk21.com

SMITH, Terence. b 38. Lon Univ DipTh69 Brunel Univ BSc79 Cranfield Inst of Tech MSc80. Tyndale Hall Bris 67. **d** 69 **p** 70. C Cheylesmore *Cov* 69-71; C Leamington Priors St Paul 71-74; V Halliwell St Paul *Man* 74-75; Lect Uxbridge Coll 80-86; R Medstead cum Wield *Win* 86-99; P-in-c Kennington *Ox* 99-03; V from 03. *The New Vicarage, The Avenue, Kennington, Oxford OX1 5AD* Tel (01865) 321504 E-mail ter.s@btinternet.com

SMITH, Terrence Gordon. b 34. TD83. MCSP58 SRN60. St Mich Coll Llan 68. **d** 70 **p** 71. C Gelligaer *Llan* 70-73; CF (TA) 72-99; C Aberavon *Llan* 73-75; V Pontlottyn w Fochriw 75-77; V Kenfig Hill 77-84; V Dyffryn 84-99; rtd 99. *1 Gnoll Crescent, Neath SA11 3TF*

SMITH, Thomas Robert Selwyn. b 12. Bps' Coll Cheshunt 35. **d** 37 **p** 38. C Workington St Mich *Carl* 37-40; C Wilton Place St Paul *Lon* 40-41; C Cheshunt St Alb 41-44; V Dalston *Carl* 44-55; V Box *Bris* 55-92; rtd 93; Perm to Offic *Bris* 93-01. *Woodland View, Devizes Road, Box, Corsham SN14 9EB* Tel (01225) 742405

SMITH, Thomas Roger. b 48. Cant Sch of Min 77. **d** 80 **p** 81. NSM Folkestone St Sav *Cant* 80-82; NSM Lyminge w Paddlesworth, Stanford w Postling etc 82-85; Chapl Cant Sch of Min 82-91; R Biddenden and Smarden *Cant* 86-91; TR Totnes, Bridgetown and Berry Pomeroy etc *Ex* 91-96; P-in-c Haslingden w Grane and Stonefold *Blackb* 96-98; V from 98; RD Accrington from 03. *St James's Vicarage, Church Lane, Haslingden, Rossendale BB4 5QZ* Tel (01706) 215533 E-mail rsmith9456@aol.com

SMITH, Timothy. b 58. Trin Coll Bris 00. **d** 02. C Warminster Ch Ch *Sarum* from 02. *1 Brook Close, Warminster BA12 8SG* Tel (01985) 214569

SMITH, Timothy Brian. b 62. Brisbane Coll BA(Theol)92. **d** 92 **p** 92. Australia 92-94 and from 96; C Grafton St Jo Ev 92-94; C Heald Green St Cath *Ches* 94-96; R Mid Richmond 96-01; I Belmont St Steph from 01. *42 Regent Street, Belmont, Vic, Australia 3216* Tel (0061) (3) 5243 2557 Mobile 412-673152 E-mail timsandy@turboweb.net.au

SMITH, Toni. *See* SMITH, Antoinette

SMITH, Tony. b 23. Roch Th Coll 62. **d** 64 **p** 65. Chapl TS Arethusa 64-67; C Frindsbury *Roch* 64-67; V Hadlow 67-78; R Wrotham 78-89; RD Shoreham 80-89; rtd 89; Perm to Offic *Roch* from 89. *25 Wye Road, Borough Green, Sevenoaks TN15 8DX* Tel (01732) 885884

SMITH, Trevor Andrew. b 60. St Jo Coll Dur BA86. Cranmer Hall Dur 83. **d** 87 **p** 88. C Guisborough *York* 87-90; C Northallerton w Kirby Sigston 90-95; R Middleton, Newton and Sinnington 95-01; Chapl St Luke's Hospice Plymouth from 01. *St Luke's Hospice, Stamford Road, Plymouth PL9 9XA* Tel (01752) 401172 Fax 481878

SMITH, Trevor Bernard. b 33. Culham Coll of Educn CertEd70 Ox Poly BEd82. Oak Hill Th Coll 61. **d** 64 **p** 65. C Bispham *Blackb* 64-66; C Chesham St Mary *Ox* 66-68; Perm to Offic 90-94; rtd 96. *126 The Broadway, Herne Bay CT6 8HA* Tel (01227) 362665

SMITH, Vernon Hemingway. b 33. St Alb Minl Tr Scheme 83. **d** 86 **p** 87. NSM Leighton Buzzard w Eggington, Hockliffe etc *St Alb* 86-98; NSM Newbury *Ox* from 98. *18 Old Bath Road, Newbury RG14 1QL* Tel (01635) 40889

SMITH, Ms Vivienne Ruth. b 57. St Jo Coll Dur BA79. N Ord Course 99. **d** 00 **p** 01. C Heckmondwike *Wakef* 00-03; TV Dewsbury from 03. *St John's Vicarage, 68 Staincliffe Road, Dewsbury WF13 4ED* E-mail r2cstsmith@btinternet.com

SMITH, Walter. b 37. Westcott Ho Cam 67. **d** 69 **p** 70. C N Hull St Mich *York* 69-72; C Whitby 72-74; V Newington w Dairycoates 74-77; P-in-c Skipton Bridge 77-78; P-in-c Baldersby 77-78; TV Thirsk 77-88; P-in-c Topcliffe w Dalton and Dishforth 82-87; V Lythe w Ugthorpe 88-97; rtd 97; Perm to Offic *York* from 98. *102 Upgang Lane, Whitby YO21 3JW* Tel (01947) 605456

SMITH, Miss Wendy Hamlyn. b 41. ALA70 Open Univ BA85. Ridley Hall Cam 85. **d** 87 **p** 94. C Stroud H Trin *Glouc* 87-90 and 91-92; Australia 90-91; TD Stoke-upon-Trent *Lich* 92-94; TV 94-97; V Pheasey 97-02; P-in-c Barlaston from 02. *The Vicarage, 2 Longton Road, Barlaston, Stoke-on-Trent ST12 9AA* Tel (01782) 372452 E-mail wendy@whsphea.fsnet.co.uk

SMITH, William Joseph Thomas. b 20. Chich Th Coll 54. **d** 55 **p** 56. C Laindon w Basildon *Chelmsf* 56-61; R Stifford 61-65; V Boreham 65-90; rtd 90; Perm to Offic *Chelmsf* from 90. *7 Trenam, Church Road, Boreham, Chelmsford CM3 3EF* Tel (01245) 466930

SMITH, William Manton. b 64. Univ of Wales (Abth) LLB85 St Jo Coll Dur PGCE90. United Th Coll Abth BD89 St Jo Coll Nottm 91. **d** 93 **p** 94. C Coventry Caludon *Cov* 93-97; V Exhall from 97. *Exhall Vicarage, Ash Green, Coventry CV7 9AA* Tel (024) 7636 2997 E-mail william.smith@fish.co.uk

SMITH, Canon William Melvyn. b 47. K Coll Lon BD69 AKC69 PGCE70. St Aug Coll Cant 71. **d** 71 **p** 72. C Kingswinford H Trin *Lich* 71-73; Hon C Coseley Ch Ch 73-74; C Wednesbury St Paul Wood Green 75-78; V Coseley St Chad 78-91; RD Himley 83-93; RD Himley *Worc* 93-96; TR Wordsley *Lich* 91-93; TR Wordsley *Worc* 93-96; Stewardship and Resources Officer from 97; Hon Can Worc Cathl from 03. *330 Hagley Road, Pedmore, Stourbridge DY9 0RD* Tel (01562) 720414 *or* (01905) 20537 E-mail melvynsm@aol.com

SMITH-CAMERON, Canon Ivor Gill. b 29. Madras Univ BA50 MA52. Coll of Resurr Mirfield. **d** 54 **p** 55. C Rumboldswyke *Chich* 54-58; Chapl Imp Coll *Lon* 58-72; Dioc Missr *S'wark* 72-92; Can Res S'wark Cathl 72-94; C Battersea Park All SS 92-94; Hon C 94-96; Hon C Battersea Fields from 96; Co-ord All Asian Chr Consultation 92-93; rtd 94; Chapl to The Queen 95-99. *100 Prince of Wales Drive, London SW11 4BD* Tel (020) 7622 3809 E-mail isbat@publiconline.co.uk

SMITHAM (née HARVEY-COOK), Mrs Elizabeth Ann. b 62. St D Coll Lamp BA90 St Mich Coll Llan DPS91. **d** 92 **p** 97. C Llangiwg *S & B* 92-94; C Morriston 94-98; P-in-c Llanfair-is-gaer and Llanddeiniolen *Ban* 98-00; V 00-03; V Llanddeiniolen w Llanfair-is-gaer etc from 03. *The Vicarage, Y Felinheli LL56 4SQ* Tel (01248) 671967 E-mail ann@smitham.freeserve.co.uk

✠**SMITHSON, The Rt Revd Alan.** b 36. Qu Coll Ox BA62 MA68. Qu Coll Birm DipTh64. **d** 64 **p** 65 **c** 90. C Skipton Ch Ch *Bradf* 64-68; C Ox St Mary V w St Cross and St Pet *Ox* 68-72; Chapl Qu Coll Ox 69-72; Chapl Reading Univ *Ox* 72-77; V Bracknell 77-83; TR 83-84; Can Res Carl Cathl *Carl* 84-90; Dir Dioc Tr Inst 84-90; Dioc Dir of Tr 85-90; Suff Bp Jarrow *Dur* 90-01; rtd 02. *St Crispin's, Crispin Street, Creetown, Newton Stewart DG8 7JT* Tel (01671) 820310

SMITHSON, Michael John. b 47. FRGS Newc Univ BA68 Lon Univ BD79 Dur Univ PGCE. Trin Coll Bris 76. **d** 79 **p** 80. C S Mimms Ch *Lon* 79-81; Support and Public Relations Sec UCCF 82-84; R Frating w Thorrington *Chelmsf* 84-88; V Portsea St Luke *Portsm* from 88. *St Luke's Vicarage, 19 Greetham Street, Southsea PO5 4LH* Tel (023) 9282 6073 Mobile 07802-482584 Fax 08701-629366

SMITHURST, Jonathan Peter. b 54. EMMTC DTPS94. **d** 94 **p** 95. NSM Bramcote *S'well* 94-03; NSM Attenborough from 03; Acting AD Beeston 98-99; AD from 99. *46 Sandy Lane, Beeston, Nottingham NG9 3GS* Tel 0115-922 6588

SMITS, Eric. b 29. **d** 61 **p** 62. C Thornaby on Tees St Paul *York* 61-66; R Brotton Parva 66-98; rtd 98. *7 Pikes Nurseries, Ludham, Great Yarmouth NR29 5NW* Tel (01692) 678156

SMOUT, Canon Michael John. b 37. St Pet Coll Ox BA61 MA75 DipTh62 Lon Univ BD64. Lon Coll of Div 62. **d** 64 **p** 65. C Toxteth Park St Philemon w St Silas *Liv* 64-69; C Everton St Sav 69-70; Missr E Everton Gp of Chs 70-74; V Everton St Sav w St Cuth 74-79; R Aughton St Mich 79-02; RD Ormskirk 82-89; AD 89-02; Hon Can Liv Cathl 92-02; rtd 02. *4 Victoria Road, Aughton, Ormskirk L39 5AU* Tel (01695) 423054

SMURTHWAITE, William. b 25. Brasted Th Coll 53 Edin Th Coll 54. **d** 57 **p** 58. C S Shields St Simon *Dur* 57-59; Miss to Seamen 59-72; Lagos Nigeria 59-63; Port of Spain Trinidad and Tobago 63-65; Port Chapl Immingham 65-72; Lic to Offic *Linc* 65-72; R Ladybank *St And* 73-90; R Cupar 73-90; rtd 90. *10 Park View, Balmullo, St Andrews KY16 0DN* Tel (01334) 870639

SMYTH, Anthony Irwin. b 40. TCD BA63 MA66. Clifton Th Coll 64. **d** 66 **p** 67. C Worthing St Geo *Chich* 66-69; Chile 70-75; C Woodley St Jo the Ev *Ox* 76-80; V St Leonards St Ethelburga *Chich* 80-93; R Stopham and Fittleworth from 93. *The Rectory, Church Lane, Fittleworth, Pulborough RH20 1HL* Tel (01798) 865455 E-mail anthony.smyth@btinternet.com

SMYTH, Francis George. b 20. Ridley Hall Cam 64. **d** 65 **p** 66. C Ormskirk *Liv* 65-70; V Bicton *Lich* 70-90; Chapl HM Pris Shrewsbury 71-90; rtd 90; Perm to Offic *Lich* from 90. *41 Sutton Road, Shrewsbury SY8 6DL* Tel (01743) 360030

SMYTH, Gordon William. b 47. Open Univ BA. St Jo Coll Nottm 81. **d** 83 **p** 84. C St Keverne *Truro* 83-86; V Landrake w St Erney and Botus Fleming 86-95; RD E Wivelshire 94-95; V Highertown and Baldhu from 95. *All Saints' Vicarage, Highertown, Truro TR1 3LD* Tel (01872) 261944 E-mail smyth@btinternet.com

SMYTH, Canon Kenneth James. b 44. TCD BA67 MA72. **d** 68 **p** 69. C Bangor Abbey *D & D* 68-71; C Holywood 71-74; I Gilnahirk 74-82; I Newtownards w Movilla Abbey 82-89; I Newtownards from 89; Preb Wicklow St Patr Cathl Dublin from 93. *36 Belfast Road, Newtownards BT23 4TT* Tel and fax (028) 9181 2527 *or* 9181 3193 E-mail kennethjsmyth@aol.com

SMYTH, Peter Charles Gordon. b 72. Univ of Wales (Ban) BA94 TCD BTh98. CITC. **d** 98 **p** 99. C Stillorgan w Blackrock *D & G* 98-02; Canada from 02. *Address temp unknown*

SMYTH, Robert Andrew Laine (Brother Anselm). b 30. Trin Coll Cam BA53 MA59 Lon Univ PGCE60 DipEd65. **d** 79 **p** 80. SSF from 53; Min Prov Eur Prov SSF 79-91; Lic to Offic *Linc* 84-92; P-in-c Cambridge St Benedict *Ely* 92-93; V 93-00; rtd 00.

St Clare's House, 3 Pool Field Avenue, Birmingham B31 1ER Tel 0121-476 1912

SMYTH, Trevor Cecil. b 45. Chich Th Coll 66. **d** 69 **p** 70. C Cookridge H Trin *Ripon* 69-73; C Middleton St Mary 73-75; C Felpham w Middleton *Chich* 75-78; P-in-c Wellington Ch Ch *Lich* 78-80; V 80-86; P-in-c W Wittering *Chich* 86; R W Wittering and Birdham w Itchenor 86-94; Perm to Offic 00; TV Withycombe Raleigh *Ex* from 01. *All Saints' Vicarage, Church Road, Exmouth EX8 1RZ* Tel (01395) 278534

SMYTHE, Mrs Angela Mary. b 53. St Jo Coll Nottm 85. **d** 87 **p** 94. Par Dn Forest Town *S'well* 87-90; Dn-in-c Pleasley Hill 90-94; V 94-03; AD Mansfield 98-03; P-in-c Sneinton St Chris w St Phil from 03. *St Christopher's Vicarage, 180 Sneinton Boulevard, Nottingham NG2 4GL* Tel 0115-950 5303

SMYTHE, Harry Reynolds. b 23. Sydney Univ BA45 St Pet Hall Ox BA48 MA51 Ch Ch Ox DPhil51. Moore Th Coll Sydney 43 ACT ThL45. **d** 51 **p** 53. C Tavistock and Gulworthy *Ex* 51-52; C Ex St Mary Arches 53; Australia 54-70 and 81-83; Dir Angl Cen Rome 70-81; Lib Pusey Ho 83-91; Dir of Studies 91-94; Lic to Offic *Ox* 83-94; rtd 91; Perm to Offic *Cant* from 91. *10 Eastbridge Hospital, High Street, Canterbury CT1 2BD* Tel (01227) 453436

SMYTHE, Peter John Francis. b 32. Lon Univ LLB56 Barrister-at-Law (Middle Temple) 76. Wells Th Coll 56. **d** 58 **p** 59. C Maidstone All SS *Cant* 58-62; V Barrow St Jo *Carl* 62-65; V Billesdon w Goadby and Rolleston *Leic* 65-71; rtd 97. *Sherington House, 44 Priory Road, Malvern WR14 3DN* Tel (01684) 573266

SMYTHE, Canon Ronald Ingoldsby Meade. b 25. Qu Coll Ox BA46 MA48. Ely Th Coll 51. **d** 54 **p** 55. C Wanstead St Mary *Chelmsf* 54-56; C-in-c Belhus Park CD 56-59; Min Belhus Park ED 59-62; V Hatfield Heath 62-78; Hon C Writtle 78-81; Hon C Writtle w Highwood 81-85; P-in-c Whatfield w Semer, Nedging and Naughton *St E* 85-89; Dir Ipswich Concern Counselling Cen from 85; Dioc Adv for Counselling 85-89; Dioc Adv for Counselling and Past Care 89-96; rtd 90; Hon Can St E Cathl *St E* 93-96; Perm to Offic from 96. *94 Wangford Road, Reydon, Southwold IP18 6NY* Tel (01502) 723413

SNAITH, Bryan Charles. b 33. Univ of Wales BSc55. St Mich Coll Llan 61. **d** 61 **p** 62. C Bargoed w Brithdir *Llan* 61-62; C Llanishen and Lisvane 62-71; Ind Chapl *Dur* 71-76; Ind Chapl *Worc* 76-81; P-in-c Stone 76-81; C Chaddesley Corbett 77-81; Ind Chapl *Chelmsf* from 81; TV Colchester St Leon, St Mary Magd and St Steph 81-86. *2 Colvin Close, Colchester CO3 4BS* Tel (01206) 767793 E-mail bryansnaith-colchester@msn.com

SNAPE, Sqn Ldr Bernard Reginald Roy. b 08. OBE56. Sarum Th Coll 69. **d** 69 **p** 70. C W Leigh *Portsm* 69-71; V Arreton 71-75; rtd 75; Perm to Offic *Sarum* from 75. *23 Shady Bower Close, Salisbury SP1 2RQ* Tel (01722) 328645

SNAPE, Harry. b 21. Qu Coll Birm 76. **d** 78 **p** 79. NSM Highters Heath *Birm* 78-82; NSM Stirchley 82-84; TV Corby SS Pet and Andr w Gt and Lt Oakley *Pet* 84-89; rtd 89; Perm to Offic *Chich* from 89. *Flat 19, Ramsey Hall, Byron Road, Worthing BN11 3HN* Tel (01903) 237663

SNAPE, Mrs Lorraine Elizabeth. b 52. STETS. **d** 02. NSM Titchfield *Portsm* from 02. *51 Crescent Road, Locks Heath, Southampton SO31 6PE* Tel (01489) 589205 E-mail lorrainesnape@tinyworld.co.uk

SNAPE, Paul Anthony Piper. b 44. OLM course 97. **d** 98 **p** 99. OLM Tettenhall Wood and Perton *Lich* from 98. *24 Windsor Gardens, Castlecroft, Wolverhampton WV3 8LY* Tel (01902) 763577 Pager 07625-589790 E-mail paul.snape@amserve.net

SNARE, Peter Brian. b 39. Cape Town Univ BSc63. SEITE 99. **d** 02. NSM Dymchurch w Burmarsh and Newchurch *Cant* from 02. *35 Shepherds Walk, Hythe CT21 6PW* Tel (01303) 269242 E-mail peter.snare@btinternet.com

SNASDELL, Antony John. b 39. St Chad's Coll Dur BA63 DipTh65. **d** 65 **p** 66. C Boston *Linc* 65-70; Hon C Worksop Priory *S'well* 71-82; P-in-c Gt Massingham *Nor* 82-84; P-in-c Harpley 82-84; P-in-c Lt Massingham 82-84; R Gt and Lt Massingham and Harpley 84-91; R Thorpe from 91. *The Rectory, 56A Thunder Lane, Norwich NR7 0JW* Tel (01603) 33578

SNEARY, Michael William. b 38. Brentwood Coll of Educn CertEd71 Open Univ BA79. Ely Th Coll 61. **d** 64 **p** 65. C Loughton St Jo *Chelmsf* 64-67; Youth Chapl 67-70; Hon C Ingrave 70-71; Teacher Harold Hill Gr Sch Essex 71-74; Ivybridge Sch 74-76; Coombe Dean Sch Plymouth 76-03; rtd 03. *The Lodge, 1 Lower Port View, Saltash PL12 4BY*

SNEATH, Canon Sidney Dennis. b 23. Leeds Univ BA50. Bps' Coll Cheshunt 50. **d** 52 **p** 53. C Nuneaton St Mary *Cov* 52-59; C-in-c Galley Common Stockingford CD 59-68; V Camp Hill w Galley Common from 68; Hon Can Cov Cathl from 80. *The Vicarage, Cedar Road, Nuneaton CV10 9DL* Tel (024) 7639 2523

SNELGAR, Canon Douglas John. b 17. DSC45. Trin Hall Cam BA48 MA53. Westcott Ho Cam 48. **d** 50 **p** 51. C Fareham SS Pet and Paul *Portsm* 50-53; C Ventnor St Cath 53-57; C Ventnor H Trin 53-57; V Steep 57-92; P-in-c Froxfield w Privett 88-92; Hon Can Portsm Cathl 85-92; rtd 92; Perm to Offic *Chich* from 92; Perm to Offic *Portsm* from 92. *37 South Acre, South Harting, Petersfield GU31 5LL* Tel (01730) 825142

✠**SNELGROVE, The Rt Revd Donald George.** b 25. TD72. Qu Coll Cam BA48 MA53 Hull Univ Hon DD97. Ridley Hall Cam. **d** 50 **p** 51 **c** 81. C Oakwood St Thos *Lon* 50-53; C Hatch End St Anselm 53-56; V Dronfield *Derby* 56-62; CF (TA) 60-73; V Hessle *York* 63-70; RD Hull 67-70 and 81-90; Can and Preb York Minster 69-81; Adn E Riding 70-81; R Cherry Burton 70-78; Suff Bp Hull 81-94; rtd 94; Hon Asst Bp Linc from 95. *Kingston House, 8 Park View, Barton-upon-Humber DN18 6AX* Tel (01652) 634484

SNELL, Mrs Brigitte. b 43. BA85. EAMTC 86. **d** 89 **p** 94. NSM Cambridge Gt St Mary w St Mich *Ely* 89-91; Par Dn Cambridge St Jas 91-94; C 94-95; V Sutton 95-03; R Witcham w Mepal 95-03; rtd 03. *45 London Road, Harston, Cambridge CB2 5QQ* Tel (01223) 872839 E-mail brigittesnell@aol.com

SNELL, Colin. b 53. Trin Coll Bris 94. **d** 96 **p** 97. C Martock w Ash *B & W* 96-00; TV Wilton from 00. *St Michael's House, 1 Comeytrowe Lane, Taunton TA1 5PA* Tel (01823) 326525 E-mail stmikes@fish.co.uk

SNELL, James Osborne. b 13. Selw Coll Cam BA35 MA39. Ely Th Coll 35. **d** 36 **p** 37. C Summertown *Ox* 36-38; C Fenny Stratford 38-43; C Rugeley *Lich* 43-47; V Dawley Parva 47-52; V New Bradwell w Stantonbury *Ox* 52-61; P-in-c Gt Linford 55-61; R Charlton-in-Dover *Cant* 61-69; R Ramsgate H Trin 69-78; rtd 79; Perm to Offic *Cant* from 79. *3 Glebe Close, St Margarets-at-Cliffe, Dover CT15 6AF* Tel (01304) 852210

SNELL, William Graham Brooking. b 14. Lon Coll of Div 36. **d** 39 **p** 40. C Burton Ch Ch *Lich* 39-41; C Rushden St Pet 41-46; C Ealing St Paul *Lon* 46-48; C Cheltenham St Mark *Glouc* 48-51; V Beckford w Ashton under Hill 51-54; V Everton St Polycarp *Liv* 54-57; R Ashby w Oby, Thurne and Clippesby *Nor* 57-79; rtd 79; Perm to Offic *Nor* 79-96. *5 Chestnut House, East Street, Blandford Forum DT11 7DU* Tel (01258) 456931

SNELLGROVE, Martin Kenneth. b 54. City Univ BSc77 CEng80 MICE84. Aston Tr Scheme 85 Ridley Hall Cam 87. **d** 89 **p** 90. C Four Oaks *Birm* 89-92; TV Wrexham *St As* 92-01; R Hope from 01. *The Rectory, Kiln Lane, Hope, Wrexham LL12 9PH* Tel (01978) 762127

SNELLING, Brian. b 40. Oak Hill Th Coll DipTh68. **d** 69 **p** 70. C Slough *Ox* 69-72; C Hoole *Ches* 72-76; V Millbrook 76-80; V Homerton St Luke *Lon* 80-90; R Marks Tey w Aldham and Lt Tey *Chelmsf* 90-98; V Stebbing w Lindsell from 98. *The Vicarage, 7 Ruffels Place, Stebbing, Dunmow CM6 3TJ* Tel (01371) 856080 E-mail revbrians@aol.com

SNELSON, William Thomas. b 45. Ex Coll Ox BA67 Fitzw Coll Cam BA69 MA75. Westcott Ho Cam 67. **d** 69 **p** 70. C Godalming *Guildf* 69-72; C Leeds St Pet *Ripon* 72-75; V Chapel Allerton 75-81; V Bardsey 81-93; Dioc Ecum Officer 86-93; W Yorkshire Ecum Officer *Bradf* 93-97; Gen Sec Chs Together in England from 97; Perm to Offic *St Alb* from 97. *Churches Together in England, 27 Tavistock Square, London WC1H 9HH* Tel (020) 7529 8133 Fax 7529 8134 E-mail bill.snelson@cte.org.uk

SNOOK, Mrs Margaret Ann. b 41. S Dios Minl Tr Scheme. **d** 91 **p** 94. NSM Keynsham *B & W* from 91. *32 Hurn Lane, Keynsham, Bristol BS31 1RS* Tel 0117-986 3439

SNOOK, Walter Currie. *See* CURRIE, Walter

SNOW, Campbell Martin Spencer. b 35. JP. Roch Th Coll 65. **d** 67 **p** 68. C Dover St Mary *Cant* 67-72; C Birchington w Acol 72-74; V Reculver 74-80; P-in-c New Addington 80-81; V 81-84; V New Addington *S'wark* 85-87; CF (ACF) 84-87; CF (TA) 87-92; P-in-c Caterham Valley *S'wark* 87-99; rtd 99; Perm to Offic *S'wark* from 99. *28 The Crossways, Merstham, Redhill RH1 3NA* Tel (01737) 643388

SNOW, The Ven Edward Brian. b 22. CITC 62. **d** 65 **p** 66. C Cork H Trin w St Paul, St Pet and St Mary *C, C & R* 65-67; C Dun Laoghaire *D & G* 67-72; Hon Clerical V Ch Ch Cathl Dublin 69-72; I Rathkeale *L & K* 72-77; I Kilmallock w Kilflynn, Kilfinane, Knockaney etc 77-94; Adn Limerick 81-92; Chapter Clerk Limerick, Killaloe and Clonfert 92-94; rtd 94. *Balladik, 9 St Catherine's Road, Glenageary, Co Dublin, Irish Republic* Tel (00353) (1) 284 6004 E-mail psnow@indigo.ie

SNOW, Frank. b 31. Lon Univ BD57. **d** 83 **p** 84. Hon C Tweedmouth *Newc* 83-86; Hon C Berwick H Trin 86-89; Hon C Berwick St Mary 86-89; Hon C Berwick H Trin and St Mary 89-90; R Gt Smeaton w Appleton Wiske and Birkby etc *Ripon* 90-97; rtd 97; Perm to Offic *Ripon* from 97; Perm to Offic *Sheff* from 02. *The Green, Totley, Sheffield S17 4AT* Tel 0114-235 0024 E-mail frank@fcrsnow.freeserve.co.uk

SNOW, Martyn James. b 68. Sheff Univ BSc89. Wycliffe Hall Ox BTh95. **d** 95 **p** 96. C Brinsworth w Catcliffe and Treeton *Sheff* 95-97; CMS Guinea 98-01; V Pitsmoor Ch Ch *Sheff* from 01. *The Vicarage, 257 Pitsmoor Road, Sheffield S3 9AQ* Tel 0114-272 7756

SNOW, Miss Patricia Margaret. b 21. Dub Bible Coll 45 St Mich Ho Ox 51. **dss** 72 **d** 87 **p** 96. W Ham *Chelmsf* 72-78; Acomb St Steph *York* 78-83; rtd 83; NSM Northfleet *Roch* 96-01; Perm to Offic from 01. *29 Huggens' College, College Road, Northfleet, Gravesend DA11 9DL* Tel (01474) 352963

SNOW, Peter David. b 37. St Jo Coll Cam BA61 MA67. Ridley Hall Cam 62. **d** 64 **p** 65. C Kingshurst *Birm* 64-66; USA from 67; C Santa Barbara All SS 67-71; Can Missr for Youth Los Angeles 71-75; R Jackson St Jo 75-81; Asst R Bellevue Resurr 81-85; R Redmond H Cross 89-01; rtd 01; P-in-c Edmonds SS Hilda and Patr from 02. *927 36th Avenue, Seattle, WA 98122, USA* Tel (001) (206) 329 3784 E-mail peterorlisa@cs.com

SNOW, Peter Normington. b 23. St Jo Coll Ox BA48 MA52. Ely Th Coll 48. **d** 50 **p** 51. C Lower Gornal *Lich* 50-52; C Solihull *Birm* 52-56; V Emscote *Cov* 56-89; RD Warwick 67-77; rtd 89; Perm to Offic *Cov* from 89. *3 Park Lane, Harbury, Leamington Spa CV33 9HX* Tel (01926) 612410

SNOW, Richard John. b 57. Bris Univ BSc80. **d** 90 **p** 91. C Preston Plucknett *B & W* 90-95; TV Stratton St Margaret w S Marston etc *Bris* 95-02; R Box w Hazlebury and Ditteridge from 02. *The Vicarage, Church Lane, Box, Corsham SN13 8NR* Tel (01225) 744458 E-mail snows@fish.co.uk

SNOWBALL, Dorothy Margaret. b 52. Sunderland Univ BA98. NEOC98. **d** 01 **p** 02. NSM Heworth St Mary *Dur* from 01. *2 Oval Park View, Felling, Gateshead NE10 9DS* Tel 0191-469 5059 E-mail dsnowball@talk21.com

SNOWBALL, Michael Sydney. b 44. Dur Univ BA70 MA72 St Jo Coll Dur DipTh72. **d** 72 **p** 73. C Stockton St Pet *Dur* 72-75; C Dunston St Nic 75-77; C Dunston 77-78; C Darlington St Jo 78-81; V Chilton 81-91; V Brompton w Deighton *York* from 91. *The Vicarage, Brompton, Northallerton DL6 2QA* Tel (01609) 772436 E-mail mickthevic@aol.com

SNOWDEN, Miss Alice Isabel Glass. b 55. Lanc Univ BA77 Humberside Coll of Educn PGCE84. Ripon Coll Cuddesdon 91. **d** 94 **p** 95. C Mirfield *Wakef* 94-97; TV Guiseley w Esholt *Bradf* 97-02; V Bankfoot from 02. *St Matthew's Vicarage, Carbottom Road, Bradford BD5 9AA* Tel (01274) 726529 E-mail sobak@800mdial.com

SNOWDEN (née HALL), Mrs Elizabeth. b 58. Plymouth Poly BSc79 Birm Univ BA01 Lon Inst of Educn PGCE80. Qu Coll Birm 98. **d** 01. C Burntwood *Lich* from 01. *9 Derwent Grove, Burntwood WS7 9JN* Tel (01543) 674324

SNUGGS, David Sidney. b 49. Keble Coll Ox BA71 PGCE72 MA75. S Dios Minl Tr Scheme 89. **d** 92 **p** 93. C Bitterne Win 92-96; V Fair Oak from 96. *The Vicarage, Fair Oak Court, Fair Oak, Eastleigh SO50 7BG* Tel (023) 8069 2238

SOADY, Mark. b 60. RMN84 Univ of Wales BTh. St Mich Coll Llan 96. **d** 96 **p** 97. C Tenby *St D* 96-99; TV from 99. *9 Lamack Vale, Tenby SA70 8DN* Tel (01834) 844330 Mobile 07041-520150 Fax 843766 E-mail mark_soady@freenet.co.uk

SOAR, Arthur Leslie. b 20. ACII. Linc Th Coll 82. **d** 83 **p** 84. NSM Chilham *Cant* 83-86; NSM Crundale w Godmersham 86-90; NSM Elmsted w Hastingleigh 86-90; rtd 90; Perm to Offic *Cant* from 90. *9 Redington, Lower Queens Road, Ashford TN24 8HW* Tel (01233) 625559

SOAR, Martin William. b 54. Wye Coll Lon BSc78. Wycliffe Hall Ox 86. **d** 88 **p** 89. C Henfynyw w Aberaeron and Llanddewi Aberarth *St D* 88-91; C Hubberston 91-93; P-in-c Low Harrogate St Mary *Ripon* 93-95; V from 95. *St Mary's Vicarage, 22 Harlow Oval, Harrogate HG2 0DS* Tel (01423) 502614

✠**SOARES, The Rt Revd Fernando da Luz.** b 43. Univ of Porto. **d** 71 **p** 72 **c** 80. Bp Lusitanian Ch from 80; Hon Asst Bp Eur from 95. *Rua Elias Garcia 107-1 Dto, 4430-091 Vila Nova de Gaia, Portugal* Tel (00351) (22) 375 4646 Fax 375 2016 E-mail fernandols@netc.pt *or* ilcae@mail.telepac.pt

SODOR AND MAN, Bishop of. See KNOWLES, The Rt Revd Graeme Paul

SOER, Patricia Kathleen Mary. b 40. CertEd61. OLM course 96. **d** 99 **p** 00. OLM Deptford St Jo w H Trin *S'wark* from 99. *350 Wood Vale, London SE23 3DY* Tel (020) 8699 4616

SOFIELD, Martin. b 60. Man OLM Scheme 99. **d** 02 **p** 03. OLM Clifton *Man* from 02. *16 Ross Drive, Clifton, Swinton, Manchester M27 6PS* Tel 0161-793 1677 E-mail martin.sofield@ntlworld.com

SOGA, Hector Ian. b 47. Glas Univ MA70 BMus78 PhD90 Selw Coll Cam BA72 MA76. St And NSM Tr Scheme 87. **d** 88 **p** 89. NSM Dollar *St And* from 88. *2 Harviestoun Road, Dollar FK14 7HF* Tel (01259) 743169

SOKOLOWSKI (née MAHON), Mrs Stephanie Mary. b 56. Liv Univ BSc80 SRN80. S'wark Ord Course 91. **d** 94 **p** 95. C Warlingham w Chelsham and Farleigh *S'wark* 94-97; C Godstone and Blindley Heath from 97. *The Vicarage, Blindley Heath, Lingfield RH7 6JR* Tel (01342) 832337

✠**SOLIBA, The Most Revd Ignacio Capuyan.** b 44. Univ of Philippines AB72. St Andr Th Sem Manila BTh73 MDiv88. **d** 73 **p** 74 **c** 91. Chapl St Paul's Memorial Sch 73-75; Officer-in-charge 75-76; P-in-c Balbalasang 74-76; V Balantoy 77-78 and 82-91; V Mt Data 79-81; Bp N Luzon 91-97; Prime Bp Philippines from 97. *PO Box 10321, Broadway Centrum, 1112 Quezon City, Philippines* Tel (0063) (2) 722 8478 *or* 721 5061 Fax 721 1923 E-mail soliba@edsamail.com.ph *or* soliba@hotmail.com

SOLOMON, Arthur Creagh. b 33. ACT LTh C h Coll Hobart. **d** 62 **p** 63. Australia 62-67; C Addiscombe St Mildred *Cant* 67-68; Chapl Pierrepont Sch Frensham 69-72; R Clifton Campville w

Chilcote *Lich* 72-95; P-in-c Thorpe Constantine 83-95; R Clifton Campville w Edingale 95; Perm to Offic *Derby* 96-98; rtd 98; Perm to Offic *S & M* from 98. *Poppy Cottage, Ballacannell, Laxey, Isle of Man IM4 7HD* Tel (01624) 861235

SOMERS-EDGAR, Carl John. b 46. Otago Univ BA69. St Steph Ho Ox 72. **d** 75 **p** 76. C Northwood H Trin *Lon* 75-79; C St Marylebone All SS 79-82; V Liscard St Mary w St Columba *Ches* 82-85; New Zealand from 85. *St Peter's Vicarage, 57 Baker Street, Caversham, Dunedin, New Zealand* Tel (0064) (3) 455 3961

SOMERS HESLAM, Peter. *See* HESLAM, Peter Somers

SOMERVELL, Mrs Katherine Mary. b 30. Edin Univ CQSW51. WMMTC 86. **d** 88 **p** 94. Par Dn Caldmore *Lich* 88-92; Par Dn Wilnecote 92-94; C 94-95; rtd 95; NSM Loppington w Newtown *Lich* 95-99. *3 Orchard Close, Cressage, Shrewsbury SY5 6BZ* Tel (01952) 510755

SOMERVILLE, David. b 58. QUB BEd. **d** 00 **p** 01. C Lisburn Ch Ch *Conn* 00-03; I Drumgath w Drumgooland and Clonduff *D & D* from 03. *The Rectory, 29 Cross Road, Hilltown, Newry BT34 5TF* Tel 07811-916825 (mobile) E-mail revds@btinternet.com

SOMERVILLE, John William Kenneth. b 38. St D Coll Lamp 60. **d** 63 **p** 64. C Rhosllannerchrugog *St As* 63-67; C Llangystennin 67-70; V Gorsedd 70-77; V Gorsedd w Brynford and Ysgeifiog 77-02; RD Holywell 96-02; rtd 02. *15 Bryn Marl Road, Mochdre, Colwyn Bay LL28 5DT*

SOMMERVILLE, Prof Robert Gardner. b 27. Glas Univ MB50 ChB50 MD60 FRCPGlas67 Lon Univ FRCPath68. **d** 96 **p** 96. NSM Blairgowrie *St And* 96-97; NSM Coupar Angus 96-97; NSM Alyth 96-97; P-in-c Killin 97-99; Perm to Offic 99-01; P-in-c Tayport from 01. *Monkmyre, Myreriggs Road, Coupar Angus, Blairgowrie PH13 9HS* Tel (01828) 627131 Fax as telephone E-mail rgsommer@lineone.net

SONG, James. b 32. Lon Coll of Div 57. **d** 60 **p** 61. C Virginia Water *Guildf* 60-63; C Portman Square St Paul *Lon* 63-66; V Matlock Bath *Derby* 66-76; V Woking St Jo *Guildf* 76-94; RD Woking 87-92; rtd 94; Perm to Offic *Guildf* from 94. *Ash House, Churt, Farnham GU10 2NU* Tel (01428) 714493 Fax as telephone

SOOSAINAYAGAM, Xavier. b 50. S'wark Ord Course 89 St Paul's Sem Trichy BTh77 Sri Lanka Nat Sem BPh73. **d** 76 **p** 77. In RC Ch 76-89; C Streatham St Leon *S'wark* 89-94; C Merton St Jas 94-97; V Croydon H Sav from 97. *The Vicarage, 115 St Saviour's Road, Croydon CR0 2XF* Tel (020) 8664 8975

SOPER, Brian Malcolm. b 31. Lon Univ BSc53 Mansf Coll Ox DipTh56. Ripon Hall Ox 63. **d** 63 **p** 64. C Platt Roch 63-64; Chapl K Sch Roch 64-72; Chapl Repton Sch Derby 72-75; Chapl Bennett Memorial Dioc Sch Tunbridge Wells 75-84; Perm to Offic *Cant* 70-87; Perm to Offic *Chich* from 87. *The Croft, Point Hill, Rye TN31 7NP* Tel (01797) 222897

SOPER, Jonathan Alexander James. b 64. Univ Coll Dur BA85. Wycliffe Hall Ox 94. **d** 96 **p** 97. C Bath Weston All SS w N Stoke and Langridge *B & W* 96-00; C Bryanston Square St Mary w St Marylebone St Mark *Lon* from 00. *Garden Flat, 44 St Stephens Avenue, London W12 8JH* Tel (020) 8740 4452 E-mail jon@spaf.org.uk

SOPHIANOU, Neofitos Anthony (Tony). b 47. Sarum & Wells Th Coll 86. **d** 88 **p** 89. C St Peter-in-Thanet *Cant* 88-91; Perm to Offic *St All* 97-99; C Stevenage St Nic and Graveley from 99. *69 York Road, Stevenage SG1 4ET* Tel (01438) 238231 Fax 0870-136 9325 E-mail tony.sophianou@ntlworld.com

SORENSEN, Ms Anna Katrine Elizabeth. b 58. Man Univ BA82 MPhil94 Open Univ PGCE95. Ripon Coll Cuddesdon 83. **d** 87 **p** 94. Par Dn Ashton H Trin *Man* 87-88; Asst Chapl St Felix Sch Southwold 89-90; Chapl 90-99; Hon Par Dn Reydon *St E* 89-92; Hon Par Dn Blythburgh w Reydon 92-94; Hon C 94-99; C Gislingham and Thorndon from 99. *The Vicarage, 41 Castle Street, Eye IP23 7AW* Tel and fax (01379) 870277 Mobile 07932-031479 E-mail anna_sor@yahoo.com

SOULSBY, Canon Michael. b 36. Dur Univ BSc57. Westcott Ho Cam 61. **d** 62 **p** 63. C Selly Oak St Mary *Birm* 62-66; C Kings Norton 66-72; TV 73-76; TR Sutton *Liv* 76-88; RD Prescot 84-88; P-in-c Orton Longueville *Ely* 88-96; RD Yaxley 92-02; TR The Ortons, Alwalton and Chesterton from 96; Hon Can Ely Cathl from 94. *The Rectory, Orton Longueville, Peterborough PE2 7DN* Tel (01733) 371071 *or* tel and fax 230620 E-mail m.soulsby@talk21.com

SOUPER, Patrick Charles. b 28. K Coll Lon BD55 AKC55. **d** 57 **p** 58. Chapl Derby City Hosp 57-62; Chapl Derby Cathl *Derby* 57-62; Asst Chapl Lon Univ 62-64; C St Marylebone w H Trin 64-65; Chapl St Paul's Sch Barnes 65-70; Lect in Educn Southn Univ 70-93; Lic to Offic *Win* 70-93; rtd 93. *PO Box 11, 74100 Rethymnon, Crete, Greece* Tel (0030) (831) 31521 Fax 31903 E-mail pigiaki@phl.uoc.gr

SOURBUT, Philip John. b 57. Cam Univ BA MA. Cranmer Hall Dur BA. **d** 85 **p** 86. C Springfield All SS *Chelmsf* 85-88; C Roxeth Ch Ch and Harrow St Pet *Lon* 88-91; P-in-c Bath St Sav *B & W* 91-93; R Bath St Sav w Swainswick and Woolley 93-98; V Cullompton and R Kentisbeare w Blackborough *Ex* 98-01; TR Cullompton, Willand, Uffculme, Kentisbeare etc from 01.

Windyridge, 10 Willow Road, Cullompton EX15 1AP Tel (01884) 34048 Fax 34747 E-mail psourbut@lineone.net

SOUTER, Ruth Rosemary. b 55. Dur Univ BEd77. EMMTC 00. **d** 03. C Braunstone Park CD *Leic* from 03. *16 Turville Road, Leicester LE3 1NY* Tel 0116-291 3040
E-mail ruthsouter@yahoo.com

SOUTER, William Ewen Logan. b 66. Em Coll Cam BA88 Univ Coll Lon PhD93. Trin Coll Bris BA94 MA97. **d** 97 **p** 98. C Harborne Heath *Birm* 97-01; TV Horsham *Chich* from 01. *St John's House, Church Road, Broadbridge Heath, Horsham RH12 3ND* Tel (01403) 265238 Mobile 07889-612861
E-mail ewen@souter-family.freeserve.co.uk

SOUTH, Gillian. *See* HARWOOD, Mrs Gillian

SOUTH EAST ASIA, Archbishop of. *See* YONG, The Most Revd Datuk Ping Chung

SOUTH INDIA, Moderator of the Church of. *See* SAMUEL, The Most Revd Kunnumpurathu Joseph

SOUTH WEST TANGANYIKA, Bishop of. *See* WESTALL, The Rt Revd Michael Robert

SOUTHALL, Colin Edward. b 36. Lich Th Coll 63. **d** 65 **p** 82. C Wylde Green *Birm* 65-67; Perm to Offic 68-73; Perm to Offic *Pet* 73-81; Hon C Linc St Faith and St Martin w St Pet *Linc* 82-85; Hon C Gt Glen, Stretton Magna and Wistow etc *Leic* 85-93; Chapl Asst Leic R Infirmary 93-96; Hon C Fleckney and Kilby *Leic* 96-98; Perm to Offic from 99. *1 Spinney View, Great Glen, Leicester LE8 9EP* Tel 0116-259 2959

SOUTHAMPTON, Suffragan Bishop of. *Vacant*

SOUTHEE, Mrs Sandra Margaret. b 43. EAMTC 97. **d** 00 **p** 01. NSM Galleywood Common *Chelmsf* 00-02; NSM Moulsham St Jo from 02. *6 Hampton Road, Chelmsford CM2 8ES* Tel (01245) 475456

SOUTHEND, Archdeacon of. *See* LOWMAN, The Ven David Walter

SOUTHERN, Humphrey Ivo John. b 60. Ch Ch Ox BA82 MA86. Ripon Coll Cuddesdon 83. **d** 86 **p** 87. C Rainham *Roch* 86-90; C Walton St Mary *Liv* 90-92; C Walton-on-the-Hill 92; V Hale *Guildf* 92-96; TR 96-97; TR Hale w Badshot Lea 97-99; Dioc Ecum Officer 92-99; TR Tisbury *Sarum* 99-01; TR Nadder Valley from 01; RD Chalke from 00. *The Rectory, Park Road, Tisbury, Salisbury SP3 6LF* Tel (01747) 870312

SOUTHERN, John Abbott. b 27. Leeds Univ BA47. Coll of Resurr Mirfield. **d** 51 **p** 52. C Leigh St Mary *Man* 51-55; C Gt Grimsby St Jas *Linc* 55-58; V Oldham St Jas *Man* 58-60; V Haigh *Liv* 60-75; V Pemberton St Jo 75-98; rtd 98; Perm to Offic *Liv* from 00. *145 Moor Road, Orrell, Wigan WN5 8SJ* Tel (01942) 732132

SOUTHERN, Paul Ralph. b 48. Oak Hill Th Coll DipHE. **d** 87 **p** 88. C Chadwell Heath *Chelmsf* 87-91; P-in-c Tolleshunt D'Arcy w Tolleshunt Major 91-01; V Tolleshunt D'Arcy and Tolleshunt Major from 01. *8 Vicarage Close, Tolleshunt D'Arcy, Maldon CM9 8UG* Tel (01621) 860521

SOUTHERN CONE OF AMERICA, Primate of. *See* VENABLES, The Most Revd Gregory James

SOUTHERTON, Miss Kathryn Ruth. b 66. Univ of Wales (Lamp) BA88. Sarum & Wells Th Coll 90. **d** 92 **p** 97. C Connah's Quay *St As* 92-97; R Halkyn w Caerfallwch w Rhesycae from 97. *The New Rectory, Halkyn, Holywell CH8 8BU* Tel (01352) 781297

SOUTHERTON, Canon Peter Clive. b 38. MBE01. Univ of Wales (Lamp) BA59. Qu Coll Birm DipTh60. **d** 61 **p** 62. C Llandrillo-yn-Rhos *St As* 61-68; Bermuda 68-71; V Esclusham *St As* 72-82; V Prestatyn from 82; Hon Can St As Cathl from 96. *The Vicarage, 109 High Street, Prestatyn LL19 9AR* Tel (01745) 853780

SOUTHEY, George Rubidge. b 34. St Mich Coll Llan 84. **d** 86 **p** 87. C Hessle *York* 86-89; P-in-c Scarborough St Columba 89-92; V 92-99; rtd 99; Perm to Offic *Glouc* from 00. *19 Pochard Close, Quedgeley, Gloucester GL2 4LL* Tel (01452) 724004

SOUTHGATE, Graham. b 63. GIBiol85 Bris Poly Higher Dip Applied Biology 83 NE Surrey Coll of Tech PhD89. Ripon Coll Cuddesdon BTh93. **d** 93 **p** 94. C Tisbury *Sarum* 93-97; TV Chalke Valley from 97. *The Vicarage, Nunton, Salisbury SP5 4HP* Tel (01722) 330628

SOUTHGATE, Stephen Martin. b 61. Lanc Univ BA83 St Martin's Coll Lanc PGCE84. Cranmer Hall Dur DMS98. **d** 98 **p** 99. C Witton *Ches* 98-01; R Backford and Capenhurst from 01. *The Vicarage, Grove Road, Mollington, Chester CH1 6LG* Tel (01244) 851071 E-mail thesouthgates@beeb.net

SOUTHWARD, Douglas Ambrose. b 32. St Jo Coll Nottm LTh74 FBS02. ALCD57. **d** 57 **p** 58. C Otley *Bradf* 57-61; C Sedbergh 61-63; C Cautley w Dowbiggin 61-63; C Garsdale 61-63; PV Lich Cathl *Lich* 63-65; V Hope *Derby* 65-72; V Crosby Ravensworth *Carl* 72-82; V Bolton 74-82; Sec Dioc Past and Redundant Chs Uses Cttees 78-82; RD Appleby 78-82; Hon Can Carl Cathl 81-95; R Asby 81-82; V Hawkshead and Low Wray w Sawrey 82-98; P-in-c Windermere St Jo 84-89; RD Windermere 84-89; P-in-c Satterthwaite 94-95; rtd 98; Perm to Offic *Carl* from 98. *Hawthorn House, Town End, Witherslack, Grange-over-Sands LA11 6RL* Tel (01539) 552078

SOUTHWARD, James Fisher. b 57. St Martin's Coll Lanc BEd80. Chich Th Coll 83. **d** 86 **p** 87. C Woodford St Barn *Chelmsf* 86-89; TV Crawley *Chich* 89-95; V Higham and Merston *Roch* from 95; RD Strood from 02. *The Vicarage, Hermitage Road, Higham, Rochester ME3 7NE* Tel (01634) 717360

SOUTHWARK, Archdeacon of. *See* BARTLES-SMITH, The Ven Douglas Leslie

SOUTHWARK, Bishop of. *See* BUTLER, The Rt Revd Thomas Frederick

SOUTHWARK, Dean of. *See* SLEE, The Very Revd Colin Bruce

SOUTHWELL, Peter John Mackenzie. b 43. New Coll Ox BA64 MA68. Wycliffe Hall Ox 66. **d** 67 **p** 68. C Crookes St Thos *Sheff* 67-70; Lect Sheff Univ 67-70; Sen Tutor Wycliffe Hall Ox from 70; Chapl Qu Coll Ox from 82. *The Queen's College, Oxford OX1 4AW* Tel (01865) 279143 *or* 553829 Fax 274215

SOUTHWELL, The Ven Roy. b 14. AKC42. **d** 42 **p** 43. C Wigan St Mich *Liv* 42-44; C Kennington St Jo *S'wark* 44-48; V Ixworth *St E* 48-51; P-in-c Ixworth Thorpe 48-51; V Bury St Edmunds St Jo 51-56; R Bucklesham w Brightwell and Foxhall 56-59; Dir RE 59-68; Hon Can St E Cathl 59-68; V Norton St Mary *Lon* 68-71; Adn Northolt 70-80; rtd 80; Warden Community of All Hallows Ditchingham 83-89; Lic to Offic *Nor* 83-89; Perm to Offic from 89. *397 Sprowton Road, Norwich NR3 4HY* Tel (01603) 405977

SOUTHWELL, Bishop of. *See* CASSIDY, The Rt Revd George Henry

SOUTHWELL, Dean of. *See* LEANING, The Very Revd David

SOUTHWELL-SANDER, Canon Peter George. b 41. G&C Coll Cam BA64 MA67. Westcott Ho Cam 63. **d** 65 **p** 66. C Maidstone All SS w St Phil *Cant* 65-68; C Cambridge Gt St Mary w St Mich *Ely* 68-71; Chapl Girton Coll Cam 69-73; V Clapham St Paul *S'wark* 73-77; V Merton St Mary 77-84; P-in-c Merton St Jo 77-79; Dir of Min *Chelmsf* 85-94; Can Res Chelmsf Cathl 85-94; Public Preacher 94-96; Perm to Offic 96-97; UK Adv Chicago Th Seminaries' DMin in Preaching from 95; USA from 96. *600 Salem End Road, Framingham, MA 01702, USA* Tel (001) (508) 875 5540

SOUTHWOOD, Robert Alfred. b 31. Sarum & Wells Th Coll 72. **d** 74 **p** 75. C Christchurch *Win* 74-76; C Fordingbridge w Ibsley 76-79; P-in-c Ernesettle *Ex* 79-80; V 80-83; R Stoke-in-Teignhead w Combe-in-Teignhead etc 83-01; rtd 01; Perm to Offic *Ex* from 01. *42 Reynell Road, Ogwell, Newton Abbot TQ12 6YA* Tel (01626) 200752 E-mail rsouth4001@aol.com

SOWDEN, Charles William Bartholomew. b 47. DipADO68. Local Minl Tr Course 90 LNSM course 96. **d** 97 **p** 98. OLM Saxonwell *Linc* from 97. *River View, 7 The Meadows, Long Bennington, Newark NG23 5EL* Tel and fax (01400) 281596 Mobile 07710-715409 E-mail charles.sowden@btinternet.com

SOWDEN, Geoffrey David. b 57. Kingston Poly BA79. Wycliffe Hall Ox DipMin95. **d** 97 **p** 98. C Ware Ch Ch *St Alb* 97-02; V Highworth w Sevenhampton and Inglesham etc *Bris* from 02. *The Vicarage, 10 Stonefield Drive, Highworth, Swindon SN6 7DA* Tel (01793) 765554
E-mail the.sowdens@btinternet.com

SOWDON, Henry Lewis Malcolm. b 37. TCD BA. Bps' Coll Cheshunt. **d** 64 **p** 65. C Newport w Longford *Lich* 64-66; C Caverswall 66-69; Chapl Claysmore Sch Blandford 69-72; Hon C Hornsey Ch Ch *Lon* 72-80; Chapl Gordon's Sch Woking 80-86; TV Hodge Hill *Birm* 86-91; Perm to Offic from 91; rtd 02. *157 Heathfield Road, Birmingham B19 1JD* Tel 0121-240 3557

SOWERBUTTS, Alan. b 49. Sheff Univ BSc70 PhD73 Qu Coll Cam BA75 MA79. Westcott Ho Cam 74. **d** 76 **p** 77. C Salesbury *Blackb* 76-80; V Lower Darwen St Jas 80-84; V Musbury 84-93; P-in-c Brindle 93-98; Sec Dioc Adv Cttee for the Care of Chs 93-98; V Read in Whalley from 98. *The Vicarage, George Lane, Read, Burnley BB12 7RQ* Tel (01282) 771361
E-mail anseres@ukonline.co.uk

SOWERBUTTS, Philip John. b 67. Chester Coll of HE BEd89 Edge Hill Coll of HE PGCE99. Oak Hill Th Coll BA03. **d** 03. C Kirk Ella *York* from 03. *3 Redland Drive, Kirk Ella, Hull HU10 7UE* Tel (01482) 653251 Mobile 07957-122836
E-mail philip-claire@hotmail.com

SOWERBY, Geoffrey Nigel Rake. b 35. St Aid Birkenhead 56. **d** 60 **p** 61. C Armley St Bart *Ripon* 60-63; Min Can Ripon Cathl 63-65; V Thornthwaite w Thruscross and Darley 65-69; V Leeds All SS 69-73; V Leyburn w Bellerby 73-81; R Edin Old St Paul *Edin* 81-86; V Hawes and Hardraw *Ripon* 86-92; Dioc Adv in Deliverance Min 91-92; rtd 92; Perm to Offic *Dur* and *Ripon* from 92. *6 Wycar Terrace, Bedale DL8 2AG* Tel (01677) 425860
E-mail geoffreysowerby@onetel.com

SOWERBY, Mark Crispin Rake. b 63. K Coll Lon BD85 AKC85 Lanc Univ MA94. Coll of Resurr Mirfield 85. **d** 87 **p** 88. C Knaresborough *Ripon* 87-90; C Darwen St Cuth w Tockholes St Steph *Blackb* 90-92; V Accrington St Mary 92-97; Chapl St Chris High Sch Accrington 92-97; Chapl Victoria Hosp Accrington 92-97; Asst Dir of Ords *Blackb* 93-96; Voc Officer and Selection Sec Min Division 97-01; V Harrogate St Wilfrid

Ripon from 01. *St Wilfrid's Vicarage, 51B Kent Road, Harrogate HG1 2EU* Tel (01423) 503259 Mobile 07778-451145 E-mail mcrsowerby@aol.com

SOWTER, Colin Victor. b 35. Ball Coll Ox BA56 MA59 DPhil60. Oak Hill NSM Course 88. **d** 91 **p** 92. NSM Cranleigh *Guildf* 91-93; NSM Wonersh 93-98; NSM Wonersh w Blackheath from 98. *Hollycroft, Grantley Avenue, Wonersh Park, Guildford GU5 0QN* Tel (01483) 892094

SOX, Harold David. b 36. N Carolina Univ BA58. Union Th Sem (NY) MDiv61. **d** 61 **p** 61. USA 61-74; Hon C Richmond St Mary *S'wark* 74-79; Hon C Richmond St Mary w St Matthias and St Jo 79-82; Hon C Kensington St Mary Abbots w St Geo *Lon* 82-84 and 89-93; Perm to Offic 84-89; Hon C Beedon and Peasemore w W Ilsley and Farnborough *Ox* 93-94; Perm to Offic *Ox* 93-97 and *S'wark* 97-04. *20 The Vineyard, Richmond TW10 6AN* Tel (020) 8940 0094

SPACKMAN (née MORRISON), Mrs Ailsa. b 40. Qu Univ Kingston Ontario BA82. Montreal Dioc Th Coll. **d** 83 **p** 85. Canada 83-95; Dn Caspe 83-85; I Malbay Miss Par 85-92; Chapl Drummondville Penitentiary 92-93; rtd 93; Perm to Offic *Ex* from 99. *Cofton Lodge, Cofton Hill, Cockwood, Starcross, Exeter EX6 8RB* Tel (01626) 891584

SPACKMAN, Canon Peter John. b 37. Southn Univ BSc60. Westcott Ho Cam 65. **d** 66 **p** 67. C Boxmoor St Jo *St Alb* 66-69; C Alnwick St Paul *Newc* 69-72; C-in-c Stewart Town Jamaica 72-74; Canada 74-95; I Sept-Iles 74-77; R Baie Comeau 77-80; R Gaspe 80-92; Adn Gaspe 88-92; R Richmond 92-94; Hon Can Quebec 92-94; Perm to Offic *Ex* 95-97; Hon C Kenton, Mamhead, Powderham, Cofton and Starcross from 97. *Cofton Lodge, Cofton Hill, Cockwood, Starcross, Exeter EX6 8RB* Tel (01626) 891584

SPAFFORD, The Very Revd Christopher Garnett Howsin. b 24. St Jo Coll Ox BA48 MA54. Wells Th Coll 48. **d** 50 **p** 51. C Brighouse *Wakef* 50-53; C Huddersfield St Pet 53-55; V Hebden Bridge 55-61; R Thornhill 61-69; V Shrewsbury St Chad *Lich* 69-76; V Newc St Nic *Newc* 76-89; Provost Newc 76-89; rtd 89; Perm to Offic *Heref* from 93. *Low Moor, Elm Close, Leominster HR6 8JX* Tel (01568) 614395

SPAIGHT, Robert George. b 45. Ridley Hall Cam. **d** 84 **p** 85. C St Columb Minor and St Colan *Truro* 84-87; C Worksop St Jo *S'well* 87-89; V Barlings *Linc* from 89. *The Vicarage, Station Road, Langworth, Lincoln LN3 5BB* Tel (01522) 754233

SPANISH REFORMED CHURCH, Bishop of. *See* LÓPEZ LOZANO, The Rt Revd Carlos

SPANNER, Prof Douglas Clement. b 16. Lon Univ BSc46 PhD51 DSc72. LNSM course. **d** 73 **p** 75. Hon C Ealing St Mary *Lon* 73-78; Hon C Eynsham *Ox* 79-83; Hon C Grove 83-86; Lic to Offic from 86. *Shalom, Main Street, Grove, Wantage OX12 7JY* Tel (01235) 766845

SPANNER, Handley James. b 51. Lanchester Poly BSc73 BA. Oak Hill Th Coll 82. **d** 85 **p** 86. C Cov H Trin *Cov* 85-89; V Rye Park St Cuth *St Alb* 89-01; V Colney Heath St Mark from 01. *St Mark's Vicarage, St Mark's Close, Colney Heath, St Albans AL4 0NQ* Tel (01727) 822040 E-mail james@ryepark.netscapeonline.co.uk

SPARHAM, Canon Anthony George. b 41. St Jo Coll Dur BA69 DipTh. Cranmer Hall Dur 66. **d** 71 **p** 72. C Bourne *Linc* 71-74; TV Tong *Bradf* 74-76; V Windhill 76-81; Dir of Educn *St E* 82-85; V Goostrey *Ches* 85-99; Dir Lay Tr 85-90; Jt Dir Lay Tr 90-97; Hon Can Ches Cathl from 94; R Wilmslow from 99. *The Rectory, 12 Broadway, Wilmslow SK9 1NB* Tel (01625) 523127 *or* 520309 E-mail tony.sparham@talk21.com

SPARKES, Colin Anthony. b 37. Surrey Univ MSc68 Bath Univ MEd83 MIEE. Ox NSM Course 78. **d** 81 **p** 82. NSM Shrivenham w Watchfield and Bourton *Ox* 81-84; NSM Shellingford 84-91; R Hawkinge w Acrise and Swingfield *Cant* 91-01; rtd 02. *Winkfield, Victoria Road, Kingsdown, Deal CT14 8DX* Tel (01304) 365662

SPARKES, Donald James Henry. b 33. Oak Hill Th Coll DipTh59. **d** 59 **p** 60. C Southall Green St Jo *Lon* 59-63; P-in-c Pitsmoor *Sheff* 63-70; V 70-73; P-in-c Wicker w Neepsend 70-73; V Pitsmoor w Wicker 73-79; V Pitsmoor w Ellesmere 79-86; V Pitsmoor Ch Ch 86-96; rtd 96; Perm to Offic *Derby* and *Sheff* from 96. *8 Grosvenor Mansions, Broad Walk, Buxton SK17 6JH* Tel (01298) 25134

SPARKS, Christopher Thomas. b 29. Lanc Univ PGCE69 Birm Univ 81. St D Coll Lamp BA53 Lich Th Coll 53. **d** 55 **p** 56. C Macclesfield St Mich *Ches* 55-59; C W Kirby St Bridget 59-61; V Altrincham St Jo 61-68; Lic to Offic *Blackb* 68-79; C Lancaster St Mary 79-83; Chapl HM Pris Lanc 83-84; Perm to Offic *Blackb* from 84; rtd 94. *1 Yealand Drive, Scotforth, Lancaster LA1 4AN* Tel (01524) 67507

SPARKS, Ian. b 59. Lanc Univ BSc(Econ)81. Cranmer Hall Dur 94. **d** 96 **p** 97. C Bowdon *Ches* 96-00; V Chelford w Lower Withington from 00. *The New Vicarage, Chelford, Macclesfield SK11 9AH* Tel (01625) 861231 E-mail ian@sparks5.freeserve.co.uk

SPARLING, Harold William. b 19. ARCM53 Lon Univ BD40 AKC40. Bps' Coll Cheshunt 40. **d** 41 **p** 43. C S Norwood

St Mark *Cant* 41-43; C-in-c Bradfield *Chelmsf* 43-46; R Langham 46-54; Min Can and Succ St Paul's Cathl *Lon* 54-56; R Cranham *Chelmsf* 56-60; R Upper Hardres w Stelling *Cant* 60-78; Teacher Ashford Sch Kent 75-80; Perm to Offic *St E* from 81; rtd 84. *9 Mayfield Road, Lyminge, Folkestone CT18 8HL* Tel (01303) 862319

SPARROW, Michael Kenneth. St Jo Coll Dur BA74. Coll of Resurr Mirfield 74. **d** 75 **p** 76. C N Hinksey *Ox* 75-78; C Portsea St Mary *Portsm* 78-85; V Midsomer Norton w Clandown *B & W* 85-93; Chapl Schiedam Miss to Seafarers *Eur* from 93. *Jan Steenstraat 69, 3117 TC Schiedam, The Netherlands* Tel (0031) (10) 427 0063

SPEAKMAN, Anthony Ernest. b 43. **d** 71 **p** 72. C Newtown *St As* 71-72; C Holywell 72-75; C St Marylebone w H Trin *Lon* 75-77; V Camberwell St Phil and St Mark *S'wark* 77-80; Lic to Offic *Lon* 94-96; NSM Kennington St Jo from 96; rtd 99. *24 McAuley Close, Kennington Road, London SE1 7BX* Tel (020) 7928 8721

SPEAKMAN, Joseph Frederick. b 26. NW Ord Course 75. **d** 78 **p** 79. NSM Wallasey St Hilary *Ches* 78; C 79-82; V Marthall w Over Peover 82-91; rtd 91; Perm to Offic *Ches* from 91. *1 Kinnaird Court, Cliff Road, Wallasey CH44 3AX* Tel 0151-637 0109

SPEAR, Andrew James Michael. b 60. Dur Univ BA81. Ridley Hall Cam 83. **d** 86 **p** 87. C Haughton le Skerne *Dur* 86-90; C Eastbourne H Trin *Chich* 90-95; C Patcham 95-02; V Oldland *Bris* from 02. *Oldland Vicarage, Grangeville Close, Longwell Green, Bristol BS30 9YJ* Tel 0117-932 7178 *or* 932 3291

SPEAR, Miss Jennifer Jane. b 53. Westhill Coll Birm BEd76. Trin Coll Bris DipHE84. **dss** 84 **d** 87 **p** 95. Reading St Jo *Ox* 84-90; Par Dn 87-90; Hon Par Dn Devonport St Barn *Ex* 90-91; Hon Par Dn Devonport St Mich 90-91; Par Dn Plymstock 91-94; C 94-97; TV Plymstock and Hooe from 97. *63 Plymstock Road, Plymstock, Plymouth PL9 7NX* Tel (01752) 405202

SPEAR, John Cory. b 33. Open Univ BA87. Ridley Hall Cam 68. **d** 70 **p** 71. C Gerrards Cross *Ox* 70-73; TV Washfield, Stoodleigh, Withleigh etc *Ex* 73-79; R Instow 79-90; V Westleigh 79-90; RD Hartland 82-89; V Pilton w Ashford 90-97; TR Barnstaple 97-99; rtd 99; Perm to Offic *Ex* from 00. *Abbots Lodge, Abbotsham Court, Abbotsham, Bideford EX39 5BH* Tel (01237) 476607

SPEAR, Sylvia Grace. b 36. St Chris Coll Blackheath 60. **dss** 76 **d** 87 **p** 94. S Wimbledon H Trin and St Pet *S'wark* 76-80; Lee Gd Shep w St Pet 80-95; Par Dn 87-94; C 94-95; rtd 95; Perm to Offic *Nor* from 95. *19 Grovelands, Ingoldisthorpe, King's Lynn PE31 6PG* Tel (01485) 543469

SPEARS, Reginald Robert Derek. b 48. Trin Coll Ox BA72 MA75. Cuddesdon Coll 72. **d** 75 **p** 76. C Hampton All SS *Lon* 75-79; C Caversham *Ox* 79-81; C Caversham St Pet and Mapledurham etc 81-84; V Reading St Matt 84-94; V Earley St Pet from 94. *St Peter's Vicarage, 129 Whiteknights Road, Reading RG6 7BB* Tel 0118-926 2009 Fax as telephone E-mail derekspears@compuserve.com

SPECK, Ms Jane Elisabeth. b 72. Univ of Cen England in Birm BA94 St Jo Coll Dur BA01. Cranmer Hall Dur 98. **d** 02 **p** 03. C Stourport and Wilden *Worc* from 02. *143 Sutton Park Road, Kidderminster DY11 6JQ* Tel (01562) 820678

SPECK, Preb Peter William. b 42. Univ of Wales BSc64 Birm Univ BA66 DPS67 MA71. Qu Coll Birm 64. **d** 67 **p** 68. C Rhosddu *St As* 67-71; C Wrexham 71-72; Asst Chapl United Sheff Hosps 72-73; Chapl N Gen Hosp Sheff 73-79; Chapl R Free Hosp Lon 79-95; Hon Sen Lect Sch of Med 87-95; Preb St Paul's Cathl *Lon* 92-95; Chapl Southn Univ Hosps NHS Trust 95-02; rtd 02; Public Preacher *Win* from 02; Visiting Fell Southn Univ from 02; Hon Sen Research Fell K Coll Lon from 02. *22 The Harrage, Romsey SO51 8AE* E-mail peter.speck@which.net

SPECK, Raymond George. b 39. Oak Hill Th Coll 64. **d** 67 **p** 68. C Stretford St Bride *Man* 67-70; C Roxeth Ch Ch *Lon* 70-74; V Woodbridge St Jo *St E* 74-85; R Jersey St Ouen w St Geo *Win* 85-98; rtd 98; Perm to Offic *Win* from 98. *Rosevale Lodge, rue du Craslin, St Peter, Jersey JE3 7BU* Tel (01534) 634987

SPEDDING, Geoffrey Osmond. b 46. Hull Univ BA67 Fitzw Coll Cam BA69 MA BD. **d** 70 **p** 71. C Bradf Cathl *Bradf* 70-73; C Sutton St Jas and Wawne *York* 73-76; TV Preston St Jo *Blackb* 76-82; TV Yate New Town *Bris* 82-87; TR Bestwood *S'well* 87-94; V Ravenshead from 94. *St Peter's Vicarage, 55 Sheepwalk Lane, Ravenshead, Nottingham NG15 9FD* Tel (01623) 405203 E-mail stpeters@ravensheadchurch.freeserve.co.uk

SPEDDING, William Granville. b 39. Lon Univ BD60. Tyndale Hall Bris 57. **d** 62 **p** 63. C Man Albert Memorial Ch *Man* 62-65; Co-ord Humanities Hayward Sch Bolton 65-93; Perm to Offic 65-67; Hon C New Bury 67-79; Hon C Bolton St Paul w Em 79-86; NSM Pennington 86-02. *26 Milverton Close, Lostock, Bolton BL6 4RR* Tel (01204) 841248 E-mail info@hovercraft.org.uk

SPEEDY, Canon Darrel Craven. b 35. St Chad's Coll Dur BA57. Wells Th Coll 57. **d** 59 **p** 60. C Frodingham *Linc* 59-63; V Heckington w Howell 63-71; V Barton upon Humber 71-79; R Tain *Mor* 79-85; Dioc Sec 82-85; Can St Andr Cathl Inverness 83-85; Syn Clerk 83-85; R Whaley Bridge *Ches* 85-01; RD Chadkirk 88-95; Hon Can Ches Cathl from 96; rtd 01; P-in-c

Barthomley *Ches* from 01. *The Rectory, Rushy Lane, Barthomley, Crewe CW2 5PE* Tel (01270) 877112
E-mail darrel.speedy@btopenworld.com

SPEERS, Canon Samuel Hall. b 46. TCD BA70 MA75. Cuddesdon Coll 70. d 73 p 74. C Boreham Wood All SS *St Alb* 73-76; Madagascar 76-88; Hon Can Antananarivo from 85; R S Lafford *Linc* 88-02; RD Lafford 96-02; TR Chipping Barnet w Arkley *St Alb* from 02. *The Rectory, 38 Manor Road, Barnet EN5 2JJ* Tel (020) 8449 3894 E-mail hall.speers@talk21.com

SPENCE, Brian Robin. b 39. St Chad's Coll Dur BA61 DipTh63. d 63 p 64. C Weston *Guildf* 63-67; Lesotho 67-68; C Chobham w Valley End *Guildf* 68-71; C Gt Yarmouth *Nor* 71-74; V Warnham *Chich* 74-81; V E Grinstead St Mary 81-86; V Crowthorne *Ox* from 86. *The Vicarage, 56 Duke's Ride, Crowthorne RG45 6NY* Tel (01344) 772413

SPENCE, James Knox. b 30. Worc Coll Ox BA55 MA58. Ridley Hall Cam. d 57 p 58. C W Hampstead Trin *Lon* 57-60; C Ox St Ebbe w St Pet *Ox* 61-64; Cand Sec CPAS 64-68; V Reading Greyfriars *Ox* 68-78; C St Helen Bishopsgate w St Martin Outwich *Lon* 78-80; C St Helen Bishopsgate w St Andr Undershaft etc 80-82; P-in-c Gt Baddow *Chelmsf* 82-86; V 86-88; TR 88-95; rtd 95; Hon C Wallingford *Ox* from 96. *15 High Street, Wallingford OX10 0BP* Tel (01491) 826814
E-mail jim@spence341.fsnet.co.uk

SPENCE, James Timothy. b 35. St Jo Coll Cam BA59 MA63. Wycliffe Hall Ox 59. d 61 p 62. C Stoke *Cov* 61-64; C Cambridge H Trin *Ely* 64-67; R Tarrington w Stoke Edith *Heref* 67-72; Dioc Youth Officer 67-72; Lic to Offic *Win* 72-75; R Falstone *Newc* 75-80; TV Bellingham/Otterburn Gp 80-82; Dioc Ecum Adv 82-87; V Dinnington 82-87; V Shap w Swindale *Carl* 87-93; P-in-c Bowness and Kirkbride w Newton Arlosh 93-00; rtd 00; Perm to Offic *Carl* from 02. *67 Clifford Road, Penrith CA11 8PT* Tel (01768) 866727

SPENCE, Canon John Edis. b 24. St Edm Hall Ox BA46 MA48. Westcott Ho Cam 47. d 48 p 49. C Newland St Jo *York* 48-50; Australia 50-54; C Uckfield *Chich* 54-55; Chapl RN 55-59 and 60-65; V Thornton-le-Street w Thornton-le-Moor etc *York* 59-60; Chapl RNR from 65; V St Germans *Truro* 65-73; V Tideford 65-73; P-in-c Sheviock 69-70; Perm to Offic 73-76; Dioc Chapl to Bp 76-78; C Newlyn St Newlyn 76-78; Chapl for Maintenance of the Min 78-87; Stewardship Adv 80-87; Hon Can Truro Cathl 84-89; Bp's Dom Chapl 87-89; P-in-c St Allen 87-89; rtd 89; Lic to Offic *Truro* 89-95; Perm to Offic *Ex* 91-98; Hon C Diptford, N Huish, Harberton, Harbertonford etc from 98. *26 Kerries Road, South Brent TQ10 9DA* Tel (01364) 72578

SPENCE, Mrs Moira Joan. b 44. St Alb and Ox Min Course 96. d 01 p 02. OLM Risborough *Ox* from 01. *37 Place Farm Way, Monks Risborough, Princes Risborough HP27 9JJ*

SPENCE, Canon Philip Arthur. b 29. Lon Univ BD71 Open Univ BA76. Hartley Victoria Coll DipTh67 Westcott Ho Cam 78. d 78 p 79. In Methodist Ch 67-78; C Walthamstow St Pet *Chelmsf* 78-80; Dioc Adv on Evang 80-87; Dep Dir Dept of Miss (Evang Division) 80-85; P-in-c Greensted 80-86; Bp's Adv on Tourism 81-87; Asst Dir of Miss and Unity 85-87; R Greensted-juxta-Ongar w Stanford Rivers 86-87; V Cambridge St Mark *Ely* 87-95; Chapl Wolfs Coll Cam 87-95; Relig Adv Anglia TV 91-95; V Pet St Jo *Pet* 95-01; Can Res and Warden Pet Cathl 97-01; Can from 01; P-in-c Preston and Ridlington w Wing and Pilton from 01; Adult Educn Officer from 01. *The Rectory, Ridlington Road, Preston, Oakham LE15 9NN* Tel (01572) 737287
E-mail philip.spence@talk21.com

SPENCE, The Very Revd Walter Cyril. b 19. TCD BA40 MA43 BD43. d 42 p 43. C Maghera *D & R* 43-48; C Roscommon *K, E & A* 48-50; I Ballysumaghan w Killery 50-55; I Tubbercurry w Kilmactigue *T, K & A* 55-60; I Achonry w Tubbercurry and Killoran 60-66; Can Achonry Cathl 62-66; Dean Tuam 66-81; I Tuam 66-81; Dioc Registrar 66-85; Preb Kilmactalway St Patr Cathl Dublin 67-85; I Kilmoremoy w Castleconnor, Easkey, Kilglass etc *T, K & A* 81-85; rtd 85. *Beth Shalom, 1 Gracefield Avenue, Dublin 5, Irish Republic*

SPENCELEY, Malcolm. b 40. St Jo Coll Dur 78. d 80 p 81. C Redcar *York* 78-82; V Middlesbrough Ascension 85-93; V Newby from 93. *The Vicarage, 77 Green Lane, Scarborough YO12 6HT* Tel (01723) 363205

SPENCER, Antony Wade. b 50. AIQS78 Birm Poly HNC74 Wolv Poly MCIOB76. Ridley Hall Cam CTM94. d 94 p 95. C Bury St Edmunds St Geo *St E* 94-96; Perm to Offic 96-97; C Rougham, Beyton w Hessett and Rushbrooke 97-99; TV Mildenhall from 99. *The Vicarage, 8 Church Lane, Mildenhall, Bury St Edmunds IP28 7ED* Tel(01638) 717331 Mobile 07710-298604 Fax 717557
E-mail antspencer@aol.com

SPENCER, Christopher Graham. b 61. Magd Coll Cam BA83 MA87 Bath Univ MSc84. St Jo Coll Nottm 93. d 93 p 94. C Ore *Chich* 93-97; V Deal St Geo *Cant* from 97. *The Vicarage, 8 St George's Road, Deal CT14 6BA* Tel (01304) 372587
E-mail vicar@stgeorgesdeal.org.uk

SPENCER, David William. b 43. EAMTC 80. d 81 p 82. NSM Wisbech St Aug *Ely* 81-84; C Whittlesey 84-86; R Upwell Ch Ch 86-90; R March St Pet 90-98; R March St Mary 90-98; TV Stanground and Farcet 98-01; V Farcet from 01. *The Vicarage,*

Main Street, Farcet, Peterborough PE7 3AN Tel (01733) 240286
E-mail davidspencer@freezone.co.uk

SPENCER, Mrs Gail. STETS. d 03. NSM Wilton w Netherhampton and Fugglestone *Sarum* from 03. *68 Bouverie Avenue, Salisbury SP2 8DX* Tel (01722) 331128

SPENCER, Geoffrey. b 50. ALCM76 Nottm Univ CertEd78 ACertCM79 Open Univ BA84. Linc Th Coll 85. d 87 p 88. C Skegness and Winthorpe *Linc* 87-90; V Heckington 90-93; P-in-c Bottesford and Muston *Leic* 93-98; P-in-c Harby, Long Clawson and Hose 94-98; P-in-c Barkestone w Plungar, Redmile and Stathern 94-98; RD Framland 97-98; rtd 98; Hon C Holbeach *Linc* from 03. *33 Spalding Road, Holbeach, Spalding PE12 7HG*

SPENCER, Canon Gilbert Hugh. b 43. Lon Univ BD67. ALCD66. d 67 p 68. C Bexleyheath Ch Ch *Roch* 67-73; C Bexley St Jo 73-76; P-in-c Bromley St Jo 76-78; V 78-81; R Chatham St Mary w St Jo 81-91; V Minster-in-Sheppey *Cant* from 91; P-in-c Queenborough from 99; AD Sittingbourne 94-00 and from 03; Hon Can Cant Cathl from 99; Chapl Sheppey Community Hosp 91-98; Chapl Thames Gateway NHS Trust from 98. *The Vicarage, Vicarage Road, Minster-on-Sea, Sheerness ME12 2HE* Tel (01795) 873185 Fax as telephone
E-mail gilbert_spencer@hotmail.com

SPENCER, Gordon Charles Craig. b 13. Oak Hill Th Coll 35. d 38 p 39. C Attenborough w Bramcote *S'well* 38-41; C Heanor *Derby* 41-45; P-in-c Eastwood *S'well* 45-46; R W Hallam *Derby* 46-66; PC Mapperley 51-66; RD Ilkeston 62-66; V Bathampton *B & W* 66-81; Chapl R Sch Bath 72-81; rtd 81; P-in-c Ditteridge *Bris* 81-86; Perm to Offic *B & W*; *Bris* from 86. *26 Elm Grove, Bath BA1 7AZ* Tel (01225) 316570

SPENCER, Graham Lewis. b 48. St Jo Coll Nottm 80. d 82 p 83. C Leic St Anne *Leic* 82-85; P-in-c Frisby-on-the-Wreake w Kirby Bellars 85-86; TV Melton Gt Framland 86-93; V Upper Wreake 93-99; V Glen Magna cum Stretton Magna etc from 99. *St Cuthbert's Vicarage, Church Road, Great Glen, Leicester LE8 9FE* Tel 0116-259 2238 E-mail grahamspencer@mail.com

SPENCER, Joan. b 50. HND. LNSM course 96. d 98 p 99. OLM Norwich St Mary Magd w St Jas *Nor* from 98. *94 Mousehold Avenue, Norwich NR3 4RS* Tel (01603) 404471

SPENCER, John Edward. b 36. Bris Univ BA60. Tyndale Hall Bris 60. d 61 p 62. C St Helens St Mark *Liv* 61-64; Japan 65-70; Area Sec CMS *Leic* and *Pet* 70-71; Warden and Chapl Rikkyo Japanese Sch Rudgwick 71-73; Hd Master and Chapl Pennthorpe Sch Rudgwick 74-96; NSM Rudgwick *Chich* 95-96; rtd 96; Perm to Offic *Chich* from 96; Guildf 96-98; Hd Master Ardingly Coll Jun Sch Haywards Heath 97-98; Chapl Rowcroft Hospice Torquay 99-01; Hon C Bovey Tracey SS Pet, Paul and Thos w Hennock *Ex* from 99. *101 Churchfields Drive, Bovey Tracey, Newton Abbot TQ13 9QZ* Tel (01626) 836773

SPENCER, Mrs Margot Patricia Winifred. b 48. Coll of St Matthias Bris CertEd69 Farnborough Tech Coll 91. STETS 98. d 01 p 02. NSM Wonersh w Blackheath *Guildf* from 01. *8 Binscombe Lane, Godalming GU7 3PN* Tel (01483) 416333
E-mail margotspencer@tinyworld.co.uk

SPENCER, Neil Richard. b 49. Leeds Univ BA70 ALA72. WEMTC 96. d 99 p 00. NSM Ludlow, Ludford, Ashford Carbonell etc *Heref* 99-02; C Weobley w Sarnesfield and Norton Canon from 02; C Letton w Staunton, Byford, Mansel Gamage etc from 02. *St Mary's House, Staunton-on-Wye, Hereford HR4 7LT* Tel (01981) 500257
E-mail nspencer@revd.freeserve.co.uk

SPENCER, Norman Ernest. b 07. d 74 p 75. NSM Olveston *Bris* 74-82; Perm to Offic from 82. *26 Park Crescent, Bristol BS16 1NZ* Tel 0117-956 8873

SPENCER, Peter Cecil. b 30. Lich Th Coll 58. d 61 p 62. C Alton St Lawr *Win* 61-63; C Bournemouth St Luke 63-66; C W End 67-70; C Reading St Mary V *Ox* 70-72; C-in-c Reading St Matt CD 72-76; V Reading St Matt 76-78; TV Sidmouth, Woolbrook and Salcombe Regis *Ex* 78-86; R Birch w Layer Breton and Layer Marney *Chelmsf* 86-96; rtd 96; Perm to Offic *Chelmsf* from 99. *11 Dray Court, Colchester Road, West Bergholt, Colchester CO6 3TD* Tel (01206) 243453

SPENCER, Peter Roy. b 40. CertEd. Sarum & Wells Th Coll 72. d 74 p 75. C Northampton St Alb *Pet* 74-77; TV Cov E *Cov* 77-90; V Erdington St Barn *Birm* 90-02; TR Erdington from 02. *The Vicarage, 26 Church Road, Birmingham B24 9AX* Tel 0121-373 0884 *or* 350 9945

SPENCER, Richard Dennis. b 50. Imp Coll Lon BSc71. NTMTC 93. d 96 p 97. C Leek and Meerbrook *Lich* 96-00; P-in-c Shrewsbury H Trin w St Julian from 00. *Holy Trinity Vicarage, Greyfriars Road, Shrewsbury SY3 7EP* Tel (01743) 244891
E-mail rds@htbv.org.uk

SPENCER, Richard Hugh. b 62. Univ of Wales (Cardiff) LLB84 BD88 Bris Univ MA92. St Mich Coll Llan 85. d 88 p 89. C Barry All SS *Llan* 88-90; Asst Chapl Univ of Wales (Cardiff) 90-92; Lect NT Studies 92-98; Tutor St Mich Coll Llan 92-98; R Llangenni and Llanbedr Ystrad Yw w Patricio *S & B* 98-00; Dir Post-Ord Tr 00; TV Cowbridge *Llan* from 02. *The Vicarage, 2 Court Close, Aberthin, Cowbridge CF71 7EH* Tel (01446) 773889 E-mail richardhspencer@hotmail.com

SPENCER, Richard William Edward. b 33. FSCA66. WMMTC 78. **d** 81 **p** 82. NSM The Lickey *Birm* 81-83; Area Sec (Warks and W Midl) Chr Aid 83-93; Perm to Offic *Worc* from 95 and *Heref* from 98. *Honey Hedge, 165 Godiva Road, Leominster HR6 8TB* Tel (01568) 620097

SPENCER, Robert. b 48. St Jo Coll Nottm CertCS93. **d** 93 **p** 94. NSM Ellon *Ab* from 93; NSM Cruden Bay from 93; NSM Fraserburgh w New Pitsligo 95-99. *12 Riverview Place, Ellon AB41 9NW* Tel (01358) 723193 Fax (01224) 248505 E-mail spencer@netmatters.co.uk

SPENCER, Roy Primett. b 26. Oak Hill Th Coll 50. **d** 53 **p** 54. C Bedford St Pet *St Alb* 53-55; C Luton Ch Ch 55-58; C Nottingham St Mary *S'well* 58-60; V Middlestown *Wakef* 60-61; Chapl Crumpsall Hosp Man 61-66; R Fleet *Linc* 66-69; V Accrington St Paul *Blackb* 69-78; V Woodplumpton 78-83; Chapl Preston Hosp N Shields 83-91; P-in-c Preston St Luke *Blackb* 83-89; P-in-c Preston St Luke and St Oswald 89-90; rtd 91; Perm to Offic *Blackb* from 91. *5 Hollywood Avenue, Penwortham, Preston PR1 9AS* Tel (01772) 743783

SPENCER, Stephen Christopher. b 60. Ball Coll Ox BA82 DPhil90. Edin Th Coll 88. **d** 90 **p** 91. C Harlesden All So *Lon* 90-93; Zimbabwe 93-99; V Caton w Littledale *Blackb* from 99; Dep Prin Carl and Blackb Dioc Tr Inst 99-03; Prin N Ord Course from 03. *The Vicarage, 153 Brookhouse Road, Brookhouse, Lancaster LA2 9NX* Tel (01524) 770300 Fax as telephone E-mail s.spencer@ukgateway.net

SPENCER, Stephen Nigel Howard. b 53. Pemb Coll Ox BA75 MA03 Jes Coll Cam PGCE76. Trin Coll Bris 80. **d** 82 **p** 83. C Partington and Carrington *Ches* 82-85; C Brunswick *Man* 85-88; Chapl UEA *Nor* 88-92; rtd 92; Perm to Offic *Nor* 92-95. *43 College Lane, Norwich NR4 6TW* Tel (01603) 506815 E-mail howard.spencer@btinternet.com

SPENCER, Steven Christopher. b 47. RGN69 Westmr Coll Lon HND78. NTMTC 98. **d** 98 **p** 99. NSM Chatham St Phil and St Jas *Roch* from 98. *278 Churchill Avenue, Chatham ME5 0LH* Tel (01634) 302581 E-mail steve@scspencer.freeserve.co.uk

SPENCER, Mrs Susan. b 47. EMMTC 87. **d** 90 **p** 94. Par Dn Cotgrave *S'well* 90-94; C 94-98; P-in-c Rolleston w Fiskerton, Morton and Upton from 98. *The Vicarage, 29 Marlock Close, Fiskerton, Southwell NG25 0UB* Tel (01636) 830331 E-mail sue@spencer.softnet.co.uk

SPENCER, Mrs Susan Lesley. b 55. Dioc OLM tr scheme 97. **d** 00 **p** 01. OLM Middleton w Thornham *Man* from 00. *1 Westbrook Close, Rochdale OL11 2XY* Tel (01706) 350668 E-mail suespencer@bigfoot.com

SPENCER, Sylvia. d 98. Chapl Grampian Univ Hosp NHS Trust from 98. *Aberdeen Royal Infirmary, Foresterhill, Aberdeen AB9 2ZB* Tel (01224) 681818

SPENCER-THOMAS, Owen Robert. b 40. Lon Univ BSc(Soc)70 LGSM96 MRTvS76. Westcott Ho Cam 70. **d** 72 **p** 73. C S Kensington St Luke *Lon* 72-76; Lect RS S Kensington Inst 74-76; Dir Lon Chs Radio Workshop & Relig Producer BBC 76-78; Relig Producer Anglia TV 78-95; NSM Cambridge Ascension *Ely* from 87; Chapl St Jo Coll Sch Cam 93-98; Chapl St Bede's Sch Cam 96-97; Acting Chapl Ch Coll Cam 97-01; Dioc Dir of Communications *Ely* from 02. *52 Windsor Road, Cambridge CB4 3JN* Tel and fax (01223) 358448 *or* tel (01353) 652701 E-mail owenst@btinternet.com

SPENDLOVE, Mrs Lindsay Kate. b 55. Man Univ LLB77 Essex Univ BA88. EAMTC 89. **d** 92 **p** 94. NSM Lexden *Chelmsf* 92-94; NSM Colchester Ch Ch w St Mary V 94-96; NSM Pleshey 97-02; Perm to Offic *St E* from 02. *Caer Colyn, Donkey Lane, Friston, Saxmundham IP17 1PL* Tel (01728) 688043

SPERRING, Clive Michael. b 43. Oak Hill Th Coll 71. **d** 75 **p** 76. C Hawkwell *Chelmsf* 75-78; C-in-c Gt Baddow 78-82; New Zealand from 82. *49 Te Arawa Street, Orakei, Auckland 5, New Zealand* Tel (0064) (9) 528 4400 *or* 521 0296 E-mail revclive@xtra.co.nz

SPEYER, Nicholas Anthony. b 48. Lon Univ BD78 Sydney Univ BE70 Sheff Univ MPhil84. Moore Th Coll Sydney ThL77. **d** 79 **p** 79. Australia 79-82 and from 84; C Millhouses H Trin *Sheff* 82-84. *325 Rocky Point Road, Sans Souci, NSW, Australia 2219* Tel (0061) (2) 9529 6141 E-mail nspeyer@primus.com.au

SPICER, David John. b 52. Sussex Univ BA76 Lon Univ MTh78 Dip Psychotherapy 97. Westcott Ho Cam 77. **d** 79 **p** 80. C E Dulwich St Jo *S'wark* 79-82; C Richmond St Mary w St Matthias and St Jo 82-87; V Lewisham St Swithun 87-91; Chapl Community of All Hallows Ditchingham from 91. *St Edmund's House, All Hallows Convent, Ditchingham, Bungay NR35 2DZ* Tel (01986) 892139

SPICER (formerly RIMMER), Dorothy Janet Rosalind. b 49. Cen Sch of Art Lon BA72 Middx Poly ATD74 E Lon Univ MA98. Westcott Ho Cam. **d** 00 **p** 01. C Notting Hill St Jo and St Pet *Lon* 00-02; V Totternhoe, Stanbridge and Tilsworth *St Alb* from 02. *The Vicarage, Mill Road, Stanbridge, Leighton Buzzard LU7 9HX* Tel (01525) 210253 E-mail djrspicer@hotmail.com

SPICER, Leigh Edwin. b 56. Sarum & Wells Th Coll 78. **d** 81 **p** 82. C Harborne St Pet *Birm* 81-83; C Bloxwich *Lich* 83-87; Chapl

RAF from 87. *Chaplaincy Services (RAF), HQ, Personnel and Training Command, RAF Innsworth, Gloucester GL3 1EZ* Tel (01452) 712612 ext 5164 Fax 510828

SPICER, Nicolas. b 61. Univ of Wales (Lamp) BA84. Coll of Resurr Mirfield 84. **d** 86 **p** 87. C Westbury-on-Trym H Trin *Bris* 86-89; C Willesden Green St Andr and St Fran *Lon* 89-93; Chapl Asst Charing Cross Hosp Lon 93-94; Asst Chapl Hammersmith Hosps NHS Trust 94-97; R Ardleigh and The Bromleys *Chelmsf* from 97. *The Rectory, Hall Road, Great Bromley, Colchester CO7 7TS* Tel (01206) 230344 E-mail nspicer@lineone.net

SPICER, Robert Patrick. b 39. FCA68. St Alb and Ox Min Course 94. **d** 97 **p** 98. NSM Riverside *Ox* 97-01; NSM Beaconsfield from 01; Perm to Offic *Lon* from 98. *The Parsonage, St Michael's Green, Beaconsfield HP9 2BN* Tel (01494) 673464 E-mail robspic@msn.com

SPIERS, The Ven Graeme Hendry Gordon. b 25. ALCD52. **d** 52 **p** 53. C Addiscombe St Mary *Cant* 52-56; Succ Bradf Cathl *Bradf* 56-58; V Speke All SS *Liv* 58-66; V Aigburth 66-80; RD Childwall 75-79; Hon Can Liv Cathl 77-91; Adn Liv 80-91; rtd 91; Perm to Offic *Liv* from 91. *19 Barkfield Lane, Formby, Liverpool L37 1LY* Tel (01704) 872902

SPIERS, Peter Hendry. b 61. St Jo Coll Dur BA82. Ridley Hall Cam 83. **d** 86 **p** 87. C W Derby St Luke *Liv* 86-90; TV Everton St Pet 90-95; V Everton St Geo from 95. *St George's Vicarage, 40 Northumberland Terrace, Liverpool L5 3QG* Tel 0151-263 1945

SPIKIN, Simon John Overington. b 48. Nottm Univ BTh74. Linc Th Coll 70. **d** 75 **p** 76. C Sawbridgeworth *St Alb* 75-79; C Odiham w S Warnborough and Long Sutton *Win* 79-81; R Dickleburgh w Thelveton w Frenze and Shimpling *Nor* 81-82; P-in-c Rushall 81-82; R Dickleburgh, Langmere, Shimpling, Thelveton etc 82-96; rtd 96; Perm to Offic *Cant* from 01. *Marley Court, Kingston, Canterbury CT4 6JH* Tel (01227) 832405

SPILLER, David Roger. b 44. St Jo Coll Dur BA70 Fitzw Coll Cam BA72 MA76 Nottm Univ DipAdEd80. Ridley Hall Cam 70. **d** 73 **p** 74. C Bradf Cathl *Bradf* 73-77; C Stratford-on-Avon w Bishopton *Cov* 77-80; Chapl Geo Eliot Hosp Nuneaton 80-90; V Chilvers Coton w Astley *Cov* 80-90; RD Nuneaton 84-90; Prin Aston Tr Scheme 90-97; C Kings Norton *Birm* 98-99; C Shirley 99-00; Dir of Min and Dioc Dir of Ords *Cov* from 00. *The Parsonage, Sambourne Lane, Sambourne, Redditch B96 6PA* Tel (01527) 892372 *or* (024) 7671 0504 Fax (024) 7671 0550 E-mail rogerspiller@btinternet.com

SPILLER, Edward William. b 32. Cranmer Hall Dur 80. **d** 82 **p** 83. C Kirkleatham *York* 82-85; R The Thorntons and The Otteringtons 85-00; rtd 01; Perm to Offic *York* from 01. *Carlton House, Topcliffe Road, Thirsk YO7 1RL* Tel (01845) 522811 E-mail rev.ted@skypilot.flyer.co.uk

SPILMAN, Derrick Geoffrey. b 27. Roch Th Coll 61. **d** 63 **p** 64. C Dover St Mary *Cant* 63-67; CF 67-71; Canada from 71; rtd 92. *5398 Hazel Place, Burnaby BC, Canada V5G 4K2* Tel (001) (604) 294 6816

SPILSBURY, Stephen Ronald Paul. b 39. Nottm Univ BSc69 MPhil72 Bris Univ PhD99. Linc Th Coll 71. **d** 64 **p** 65. In RC Ch 64-71; C Cricklade w Latton *Bris* 72-75; P-in-c Swindon All SS 76-81; V Lawrence Weston 81-95; RD Westbury and Severnside 89-91; rtd 99. *10 Woodside Grove, Bristol BS10 7RF* Tel 0117-959 1079 E-mail paul.spilsbury@btinternet.com

SPINDLER, Miss Jane Diana. b 54. Southn Univ BA75 CertEd76. Wycliffe Hall Ox 87. **d** 89 **p** 94. C Bishopsworth *Bris* 89-93; C Brislington St Luke 93-94; rtd 95; Perm to Offic *Bris* from 95. *143 Highridge Road, Bishopsworth, Bristol BS13 8HT* Tel 0117-935 8137

SPINK, Mrs Diana. b 40. Ex Univ BA63 PGCE64. St Alb and Ox Min Course 94. **d** 00 **p** 01. NSM Hemel Hempstead *St Alb* from 00. *48 Spooners Drive, Park Street, St Albans AL2 2HL* Tel (01727) 872361 Mobile 07808-184321 E-mail normanspink@hotmail.com

SPINK, Canon George Arthur Peter. b 26. Oak Hill Th Coll 54. **d** 56 **p** 57. C Thurnby w Stoughton *Leic* 56-58; C-in-c Thurnby Lodge CD 58-59; Chapl Bonn w Cologne *Eur* 59-62; Chapl Vienna w Budapest and Prague 62-68; Chapl Cov Cathl *Cov* 68-70; Can Res Cov Cathl 70-77; Warden The Dorothy Kerin Trust Burrswood 77-81; Prior Omega Order from 80; Lic to Offic *Roch* 80-86; Lic to Offic *B & W* 86-95; rtd 89. *The Priory, Winford Manor, Winford, Bristol BS40 8DW* Tel (01275) 472262 Fax 472065

SPINKS, Prof Bryan Douglas. b 48. FRHistS85 St Chad's Coll Dur BA70 DipTh71 BD79 K Coll Lon MTh72 Dur Univ DD88 Yale Univ Hon MA98. **d** 75 **p** 76. C Witham *Chelmsf* 75-78; C Clacton St Jas 78-79; Chapl Chu Coll Cam 80-97; Lic to Offic *Ely* 80-97; Affiliated Lect Div Cam Univ 82-97; Perm to Offic *St Alb* 84-99; Prof Liturg Studies Yale Univ and Fell Morse Coll from 98; Perm to Offic *Ely* from 02. *Institute of Sacred Music, 409 Prospect Street, New Haven, CT 06511, USA* E-mail bryan.spinks@yale.edu *or* bryspinkus@aol.com

SPINKS, Christopher George. b 53. Brighton Poly HND80. Oak Hill Th Coll BA88. **d** 88 **p** 89. C Hove Bp Hannington Memorial Ch *Chich* 88-92; Travelling Sec UCCF 92-95; Itinerant Min 95-98; Chapl Martlets Hospice Hove from 98; TV Hove *Chich*

from 99. *35 St Heliers Avenue, Hove BN3 5RE* Tel (01273) 730027
E-mail chrisgspinks@hotmail.com

SPINKS, John Frederick. b 40. Westmr Coll Ox MTh97. Oak Hill
Th Coll 79. **d** 82 **p** 83. NSM Roxbourne St Andr *Lon* 82-89; C
Northwood H Trin 89-93; P-in-c Greenhill St Jo 93-96; V from
96. *St John's Vicarage, 11 Flambard Road, Harrow HA1 2NB* Tel
and fax (020) 8907 7956 *or* tel 8863 3690
E-mail john@spinks77.freeserve.co.uk

SPINNEY, Giles Martin. b 16. Ch Coll Cam BA39 MA43.
Wycliffe Hall Ox 39. **d** 41 **p** 42. C Oakwood St Thos *Lon* 41-46; V
Roxeth Ch Ch 46-50; R Kersal Moor *Man* 50-54; R Brixton
Deverill *Sarum* 54-72; R Kingston Deverill w Monkton Deverill
55-72; R The Deverills 72-81; rtd 81; Perm to Offic *Sarum* from
81. *17 Chancery Lane, Warminster BA12 9JS* Tel (01985) 214813

SPITTLE, Christopher Bamford. b 74. St Jo Coll Dur BA95.
Ridley Hall Cam 97. **d** 99 **p** 00. C Netherton *Liv* 99-03; TR
Sutton from 03. *St Michael's Vicarage, Gartons Lane, Clock Face,
St Helens WA9 4RB* Tel (01744) 813738

SPITTLE, Robin. b 57. St Jo Coll Nottm 84. **d** 86 **p** 87. C Ipswich
St Fran *St E* 86-91; Min Shotley St Mary CD 91-92; R Shotley
92-99; P-in-c Copdock w Washbrook and Belstead 93-99; V
Kesgrave from 99. *The Vicarage, Kesgrave, Ipswich IP5 1JQ* Tel
(01473) 622181 E-mail robin.spittle@lineone.net

SPIVEY, Colin. b 35. ACII61. Oak Hill Th Coll 74. **d** 76 **p** 77. C
Egham *Guildf* 76-79; C Edgware *Lon* 79-83; R Haworth *Bradf*
83-95; Sub Chapl HM Pris Leeds 94-99; V Thorpe Edge *Bradf*
95-00; rtd 01. *2 Woodhill View, Wetherby LS22 6PP* Tel (01937)
581508

SPIVEY, Canon Peter. b 19. Edin Th Coll 46. **d** 48 **p** 49. C
Dewsbury Moor *Wakef* 48-50; C Mirfield 50-53; R Whitwood
Mere 53-61; V Meltham 61-85; RD Blackmoorfoot 79-85; Hon
Can Wakef Cathl 81-85; rtd 85; Perm to Offic *Wakef* from 85.
3 Follett Avenue, Huddersfield HD4 5LW Tel (01484) 654674

SPIVEY, Ronald. b 28. ACMA MInstAM. EMMTC 83. **d** 86
p 87. NSM Sutton St Mary *Linc* 86-98; Perm to Offic from 98.
5 Lancaster Drive, Long Sutton, Spalding PE12 9BD Tel (01406)
362084 E-mail ron@spiveyr.freeserve.co.uk

SPOKES, David Lawrence. b 57. Nottm Univ BCombStuds85.
Linc Th Coll 82. **d** 85 **p** 86. C Rushall *Lich* 85-89; TV Thornaby
on Tees *York* 89-93; R Yardley Hastings, Denton and Grendon
etc *Pet* from 02. *The Rectory, Castle Ashby Road, Yardley
Hastings, Northampton NN7 1EL* Tel (01604) 696080

SPOKES, Keith John. b 29. EAMTC. **d** 84 **p** 85. NSM Bury
St Edmunds St Mary *St E* 84-89; P-in-c Helmingham w
Framsden and Pettaugh w Winston 89-92; rtd 93; Perm to Offic
St E from 93. *16 Croft Rise, Bury St Edmunds IP33 2PY* Tel
(01284) 706742

SPONG, Terence John. b 32. CLJ80. Roch Th Coll 63. **d** 66 **p** 67.
C Forton *Portsm* 66-68; Rhodesia 68-80; Zimbabwe 80-84; R
Christow, Ashton, Trusham and Bridford *Ex* 84-86; Chapl
Puerto de la Cruz Tenerife *Eur* 86-93; Miss to Seamen 86-93; rtd
93; Perm to Offic *Win* from 93; Chapl R Bournemouth and
Christchurch Hosps NHS Trust 97-98. *14B Stuart Road,
Highcliffe, Christchurch BH23 5JS* Tel (01425) 277833

SPOONER, Anthony Patrick David. b 45. Univ Coll of Rhodesia
Univ Coll of Nyasaland BA68 Nottm Univ DipTh72. Linc Th
Coll 71. **d** 74 **p** 75. C Glynde, W Firle and Beddingham *Chich*
74-77; Rhodesia 77-80; Zimbabwe 80-86; P-in-c Clacton St Jas
Chelmsf 86-90; V from 90. *St James's Vicarage, 44 Wash Lane,
Clacton-on-Sea CO15 1DA* Tel (01255) 422007
E-mail revapdspooner@aol.com

SPOTTISWOODE, Anthony Derek. b 25. Solicitor 50 Pemb Coll
Cam BA47 MA86. Sarum & Wells Th Coll 85. **d** 86 **p** 87. C
Hampstead St Jo *Lon* 86-94; rtd 95; Perm to Offic *Lon* from 95.
Flat 2, 26 Belsize Lane, London NW3 5AB Tel (020) 7435 6756

SPRATLEY, Deryck Edward. b 30. BSc. Oak Hill Th Coll 62. **d** 64
p 65. C Ramsgate St Luke *Cant* 64-67; C W Holloway St Dav *Lon*
67-73; V Upper Holloway St Pet 73-79; V Upper Holloway St Pet
w St Jo 79-82; P-in-c Dagenham *Chelmsf* 82-88; P-in-c Becontree
St Geo 84-88; TR Dagenham 88-93; rtd 93; Perm to Offic
Chelmsf 93-01. *35 Upper Second Avenue, Frinton-on-Sea
CO13 9LP* Tel (01255) 851216

SPRATT, Laurence Herbert. b 28. Linc Th Coll 76. **d** 78 **p** 79. C
Mexborough *Sheff* 78-80; R Wrentham w Benacre, Covehithe,
Frostenden etc *St E* 80-88; Perm to Offic *Arg* 89-90 and 91-98;
P-in-c Inveraray 90-91; rtd 93. *19 Church Street, Ellesmere
SY12 0HD*

SPRATT, Robert Percival. b 31. FCIOB MRSH ABEng. Carl
Dioc Tr Inst 84. **d** 87 **p** 88. NSM Kendal St Thos *Carl* 87-89;
Chapl HM Pris Preston 89-96; Dir Miss to Pris from 96; Perm to
Offic *Blackb* from 96 and *Carl* from 97. *Missions to Prisons,
PO Box 37, Kendal LA9 6GF* Tel (01539) 720475 Fax as
telephone

SPRAY, Canon Charles Alan Francis Thomas. b 27. ARSM51
Lon Univ BScEng51. Ridley Hall Cam 57. **d** 59 **p** 60. C Chich
St Pancras and St Jo *Chich* 59-63; V Shipley 63-69; R Ore 70-85; V
Burgess Hill St Andr 85-93; Can and Preb Chich Cathl 88-93; rtd
93; Perm to Offic *Chich* from 93. *6 Silverdale Road, Burgess Hill
RH15 0EF* Tel (01444) 232149

SPRAY, John William. b 29. Sarum & Wells Th Coll 71. **d** 73 **p** 74.
C Clayton *Lich* 73-77; V Hartshill 77-82; P-in-c Aston 82-83;
P-in-c Stone St Mich 82-83; P-in-c Stone St Mich w Aston St Sav
83-84; R 84-90; rtd 90. *2 Belvoir Avenue, Trentham, Stoke-on-
Trent ST4 8SY* Tel (01782) 644959

SPRAY, Mrs Josephine Ann. b 44. Nottm Coll of Educn TCert65.
St Alb and Ox Min Course CBTS95. **d** 98 **p** 99. NSM Watford
St Mich *St Alb* 98-02; P-in-c Turvey from 02. *The Rectory,
Bamfords Lane, Turvey, Bedford MK43 8DS* Tel (01234) 881312
E-mail jas@watfordgb.freeserve.co.uk

SPRAY, Richard Alan. b 43. EMMTC 85. **d** 88 **p** 89. NSM
Cotgrave *S'well* 88-96; P-in-c Barton in Fabis 96-01; P-in-c
Thrumpton 96-01; P-in-c Kingston and Ratcliffe-on-Soar 96-01;
P-in-c Blyth 01-02; P-in-c Scrooby 01-02; V Blyth and Scrooby w
Ranskill from 02. *The Vicarage, St Martin's Close, Blyth,
Worksop S81 8DW* Tel (01909) 591229
E-mail richard.spray@care4free.net

SPREADBRIDGE, Paul Andrew. b 49. Greenwich Univ
CertEd02. SEITE 99. **d** 98 **p** 03. In RC Ch 98-01; NSM Chatham
St Steph *Roch* from 02. *5 Commissioners Court, New Stairs,
Chatham ME4 4HQ* Tel (01634) 892584
E-mail paul.spreadbridge@btopenworld.com

SPREADBURY, Joanna Mary Magdalen. b 65. Magd Coll Ox
BA90 MA93 K Coll Lon PhD99. Westcott Ho Cam MA99. **d** 99
p 00. C Watford St Mich *St Alb* 99-03; C Leavesden All Sts from
03. *49 Ross Crescent, Garston, Watford WD25 0DA* Tel (01923)
673129

SPREADBURY, John Graham. b 59. OLM course 96. **d** 99 **p** 00.
OLM Billingborough Gp *Linc* from 99. *Osbourne House, 3-5
Low Street, Billingborough, Sleaford NG34 0QJ* Tel (01529)
240440

SPRENT, Michael Francis (Brother Giles). b 34. Ex Coll Ox
BA58 MA62. Kelham Th Coll 58. **d** 61 **p** 62. C Plaistow St Andr
Chelmsf 61-63; SSF from 61; Papua New Guinea 65-69; Hilfield
Friary 69-74 and 77-78; Alnmouth Friary 74-76; Harbledown
Friary 78-82; Sweden 76-77; TV High Stoy *Sarum* 77-78;
Solomon Is 83-97; Perm to Offic *Sarum* from 97; rtd 99. *The
Friary, Hilfield, Dorchester DT2 7BE* Tel (01300) 341345 Fax
341293

SPRIGGS, John David Robert. b 36. BNC Ox BA58 MA63.
S'wark Ord Course 73. **d** 75 **p** 76. Lic to Offic *Ox* 75-97; Chapl
Pangbourne Coll 95-97; Perm to Offic *Linc* from 97. *Glen House,
Great Ponton Road, Boothby Pagnell, Grantham NG33 4DH* Tel
(01476) 585756

SPRINGATE, Paul Albert Edward. b 48. Oak Hill Th Coll 81.
d 83 **p** 84. C Pennycross *Ex* 83-87; P-in-c Cossington and
Seagrave *Leic* 87; TV Sileby, Cossington and Seagrave 87-96;
Chapl and Warden Harnhill Healing Cen from 96. *Harnhill
Christian Healing Centre, Cirencester GL7 5PX* Tel (01285)
850283 Fax 850519 E-mail office@harnhillcentre.org.uk

SPRINGETT, John Howard. b 47. Pemb Coll Cam BA70
MA74. Ridley Hall Cam 70. **d** 72 **p** 73. C Ulverston St Mary w H
Trin *Carl* 72-76; V Dewsbury Moor *Wakef* 76-84; V Hoddesdon
St Alb 84-00; RD Cheshunt 94-00; TR Shelf St Mich w
Buttershaw St Aid *Bradf* 00-03; V Woodford Bridge *Chelmsf*
from 03. *St Paul's Vicarage, 4 Cross Road, Woodford Green
IG8 8BS* Tel (020) 8504 3815
E-mail springbett25@hotmail.com

SPRINGETT, Robert Wilfred. b 62. Nottm Univ BTh89. Linc Th
Coll 86. **d** 89 **p** 90. C Colchester St Jas, All SS, St Nic and
St Runwald *Chelmsf* 89-92; C Basildon St Martin w Nevendon
92-94; P-in-c Belhus Park 94-01; P-in-c S Ockendon 94-01; RD
Thurrock 98-01; R Wanstead St Mary w Ch Ch from 01. *The
Rectory, 37 Wanstead Place, London E11 2SW* Tel (020) 8989
9101 E-mail robert.springett@lineone.net

SPRINGETT, Simon Paul. b 56. Warwick Univ LLB78. Wycliffe
Hall Ox 78. **d** 81 **p** 82. C Harlow St Mary and St Hugh w St Jo the
Bapt *Chelmsf* 81-84; C Gt Clacton 84-86; R Rayne 86-91; Chapl
RN from 91. *Royal Naval Chaplaincy Service, Room 203, Victory
Building, HM Naval Base, Portsmouth PO1 3LS* Tel (023) 9272
7903 Fax 9272 7111

SPRINGFORD, Patrick Francis Alexander. b 45. Wycliffe Hall
Ox 71. **d** 74 **p** 75. C Finchley Ch Ch *Lon* 74-79; CF from 79. *c/o
MOD Chaplains (Army)* Tel (01980) 615804 Fax 615800

SPRINGHAM, Desmond John. b 32. Bris Univ BA56. Oak Hill
Th Coll 56. **d** 58 **p** 59. C St Alb St Paul *St Alb* 58-61; C Reading
St Jo *Ox* 61-66; R Worting *Win* 66-80; V Jersey St Andr 80-97; rtd
97; Perm to Offic *Sarum* from 97. *19 Balmoral Crescent,
Dorchester DT2 8DN* Tel (01534) 34975

SPRINGTHORPE, Canon David Frederick. b 47. Open Univ
BA. AKC72. **d** 73 **p** 74. C Dartford St Alb *Roch* 73-77; C Biggin
Hill 77-80; R Ash 80-89; R Ridley 80-89; R Eynsford w
Farningham and Lullingstone 89-94; V Barnehurst from 94; RD
Erith from 98; Hon Can Roch Cathl from 02. *The Vicarage,
93 Pelham Road, Barnehurst, Bexleyheath DA7 4LY* Tel (01322)
523344

SPROSTON, Bernard Melvin. b 37. St Jo Coll Dur 77. **d** 79 **p** 80.
C Westlands St Andr *Lich* 79-82; P-in-c Heage *Derby* 82-87; V

Heath 87-02; rtd 02; Perm to Offic *Derby* from 02. *2 Upwood Close, Holmehall, Chesterfield S40 4UP* Tel (01246) 207401

SPROULE, Gerald Norman. b 26. TCD Dip Bibl Studies 60. **d** 60 **p** 61. C Monaghan *Clogh* 60-62; I Cleenish 62-68; I Magheracross 68-73; Admin Sec (Ireland) BCMS 73-79; I Belfast St Aid *Conn* 79-86; I Magherally w Annaclone *D & D* 86-94; rtd 94. *4 Hilden Park, Lisburn BT27 4UG* Tel (028) 9260 1528

SPURGEON, Michael Paul. b 53. MIEx. Linc Th Coll 83. **d** 85 **p** 86. C Lillington *Cov* 85-89; C Min Can Ripon Cathl *Ripon* 89-95; R Lower Nidderdale from 95. *Lower Nidderdale Rectory, Old Church Green, Kirk Hammerton, York YO26 8DL* Tel (01423) 331142

SPURIN, Canon Richard Mark. b 28. Peterho Cam BA52 MA60. Wycliffe Hall Ox 54. **d** 55 **p** 56. C Foleshill St Laur *Cov* 55-58; C Atherstone 58-60; CMS 60-61; Kenya 61-73; C-in-c Ewell St Paul Howell Hill CD *Guildf* 73-82; V Netherton *Liv* 82-86; V Brandwood *Birm* 86-91; C Padiham *Blackb* 91-93; Hon Can Nambale Cathl Kenya from 92; rtd 93; Perm to Offic *Blackb* from 93. *11 Rosemount Avenue, Burnley BB11 2JU* Tel (01282) 421402

SPURLING, David John. b 35. Cam Univ MA62 Leeds Univ MPhil77. LNSM course 96. **d** 97 **p** 98. OLM Quidenham Gp *Nor* 97-02. *1A rue St Sebastien, 68230 Walbach, France*

SPURR, Andrew. b 58. St Jo Coll Dur BA80 LRPS02. Ripon Coll Cuddesdon 80 Roch Div Sch (USA) 84 Qu Coll Birm 92. **d** 93 **p** 94. C Rainham *Roch* 93-96; C Stansted Mountfitchet *Chelmsf* 96; C Stansted Mountfitchet w Birchanger and Farnham 97; R from 97. *The Rectory, 5 St John's Road, Stansted CM24 8JP* Tel (01279) 812203 Fax as telephone E-mail rector@stansted.net

SPURR, Roger Colin. b 29. Linc Th Coll. **d** 82 **p** 83. C Street w Walton *B & W* 82-85; R Stogumber w Nettlecombe and Monksilver 85-95; rtd 95; Perm to Offic *Newc* from 95. *15 Abbey Gate, Morpeth NE61 2XL* Tel (01670) 514561

SPURRELL, John Mark. b 34. FSA87 CCC Ox BA57 DipTh58 MA61. Linc Th Coll 58. **d** 60 **p** 61. C Tilbury Docks *Chelmsf* 60-65; C Boston *Linc* 65-76; R Stow in Lindsey 76-85; P-in-c Willingham 76-85; P-in-c Coates 76-85; P-in-c Brightwell w Sotwell *Ox* 85-97; rtd 97; Perm to Offic *B & W* from 97. *10 The Liberty, Wells BA5 2SU* Tel (01749) 678966

SPURRIER, Richard Patrick Montague. b 25. Bris Univ BA59. Wycliffe Hall Ox 59. **d** 61 **p** 62. C S Lyncombe *B & W* 61-63; C Weston St Jo 63-64; rtd 90. *48 Longford Road, Melksham SN12 6AU* Tel (01225) 707419

SPURWAY, Christine Frances. b 54. Cuddesdon Coll DipMin98. **d** 98 **p** 99. C Coulsdon St Andr *S'wark* 98-02; P-in-c Riddlesdown from 02. *St James's Vicarage, 1B St James's Road, Purley CR8 2DL* Tel (020) 8660 5436

SQUAREY, Canon Gerald Stephen Miles. b 36. Lich Th Coll 59. **d** 62 **p** 63. C Poplar All SS w St Frideswide *Lon* 62-64; C Heston 64-67; V Bradford Abbas w Clifton Maybank *Sarum* 67-74; P-in-c Corfe Castle 74-79; R 79-84; R Steeple w Tyneham, Church Knowle and Kimmeridge 79-84; R Corfe Castle, Church Knowle, Kimmeridge etc 84-90; P-in-c Pimperne 90-91; P-in-c Stourpaine, Durweston and Bryanston 90-91; R Pimperne, Stourpaine, Durweston and Bryanston 91-01; RD Milton and Blandford 91-01; Can and Preb Sarum Cathl 92-01; rtd 01; Bp's Dom Chapl *Sarum* from 02. *4 Water Lane, Salisbury SP2 7TE* Tel (01722) 326396

SQUIRE, Clenyg. b 31. TCert53. Cuddesdon Coll 89. **d** 90 **p** 91. NSM Hale and Ashley *Ches* 90-93; P-in-c Kingsley 93-95; Perm to Offic *Ches* and *Man* from 95; *Newc* from 00. *10 Higher Downs, Altrincham WA14 2QL* Tel 0161-928 3346 Fax 0870-1641585 E-mail clenyg@bunsoga.demon.co.uk

SQUIRE, Geoffrey Frank. b 36. Ex & Truro NSM Scheme. **d** 83 **p** 84. NSM Barnstaple *Ex* 83-98; NSM Swimbridge w W Buckland and Landkey from 98. *Little Cross, Northleigh Hill, Goodleigh, Barnstaple EX32 7NR* Tel (01271) 344935

SQUIRE, Humphrey Edward. b 29. St Chad's Coll Dur BA55. Coll of Resurr Mirfield. **d** 57 **p** 58. C Newbold w Dunston *Derby* 57-59; C Thorpe *Nor* 59-61; Zanzibar 61-63; C Whittington *Derby* 63-64; R Drayton *Nor* 64-75; Chapl Dover Coll 75-83; TV Wareham *Sarum* 83-94; rtd 94; Perm to Offic *Sarum* from 94. *La Retraite, Burbidge Close, Lytchett Matravers, Poole BH16 6EG* Tel (01202) 622304

SQUIRE, Preb John Brinsmead. b 16. St Edm Hall Ox BA38 MA43. Linc Th Coll 38. **d** 40 **p** 40. C Knowle *Bris* 40-41; C Bath Bathwick *B & W* 41-45 and 48-51; C Walsall St Andr *Lich* 45-46; C Lower Gornal 47-48; V Bridgwater H Trin *B & W* 51-57; V Taunton St Andr 57-81; Preb Wells Cathl from 77; rtd 81. *Xanadu, 1 St Mary Street, Nether Stowey, Bridgwater TA5 1LJ* Tel (01278) 732957

SQUIRES, John Wallace Howden. b 45. Sydney Univ BA67 MTh97 Lon Univ BD75. Moore Th Coll Sydney ThL74 Melbourne Coll of Div DipRE75. **d** 76 **p** 76. Australia 76-78 and from 80; C Luton St Mary *St Alb* 78-79; Chapl Home of Divine Healing Crowhurst 79-80. *22 Moorehead Street, Redfern, NSW, Australia 2016* Tel (0061) (2) 9690 0206 *or* 9381 1730 Fax 9381 1909 E-mail j.squires@newcollege.unsw.edu.au

SQUIRES, The Ven Malcolm. b 46. St Chad's Coll Dur BA72. Cuddesdon Coll 72. **d** 74 **p** 75. C Headingley *Ripon* 74-77; C Stanningley St Thos 77-80; V Bradshaw *Wakef* 80-85; V Ripponden 85-89; V Barkisland w W Scammonden 85-89; V Mirfield 89-96; R Wrexham *St As* 96-02; Hon Can St As Cathl 00-01; Adn Wrexham from 01; R Llandegla from 02. *The Rectory, Llandegla, Wrexham LL11 3AW* Tel (01978) 790362 E-mail squiresmalcolm@aol.com

SSERUNKUMA, Michael Wilberforce. b 54. Trin Coll Bris DipHE88 BA90. Bp Tucker Coll Mukono 77. **d** 77 **p** 78. Uganda 77-87; C Gabalfa *Llan* 90-94; TV Cyncoed *Mon* 94-95; R Canton St Jo *Llan* 95-01; Asst Chapl R Berks and Battle Hosps NHS Trust 01-02; Chapl Team Ldr from 02. *The Chaplaincy, Royal Berkshire Hospital, London Road, Reading RG1 5AN* Tel 0118-987 7105

STABLES, Courtley Greenwood. b 13. Keble Coll Ox BA49 MA54. St Steph Ho Ox 48. **d** 50 **p** 51. C Watlington *Ox* 50-51; C Bracknell 51-55; Br Honduras 55-57; C Guildf H Trin w St Mary *Guildf* 57-61; Chapl Bedford Modern Sch 61-63; Sen Lect Coll of All SS Tottenham 63-72; Chmn Coun of Ch Schs Co 68-87; C St Andr Undershaft w St Mary Axe *Lon* 64-72; Hon C Uckfield *Chich* 72-94; rtd 78; Perm to Offic *Chich* from 94. *Abotslare, Pound Green, Buxted, Uckfield TN22 4JZ* Tel (01825) 732467

STABLES, Miss Katharine Ruth. b 45. DipInstHSM70 R Holloway Coll Lon BA67. WMMTC 90. **d** 93 **p** 94. NSM Knutton *Lich* from 93; NSM Silverdale and Alsagers Bank 93-96; Soc Resp Officer 96-99. *19 Kennet Close, Newcastle ST5 4ER* Tel (01782) 633430 *or* 553093

STACE, Michael John. b 44. Open Univ BA80 MBEng MCMI. SEITE 94. **d** 97 **p** 98. NSM Cant St Dunstan w H Cross *Cant* 97-01; NSM Cant All SS from 01. *124 St Stephen's Road, Canterbury CT2 7JS* Tel (01227) 451169 Mobile 07831-174900 Fax 455627 E-mail michaelstace@btconnect.com

STACEY, Helen Norman. Edin Univ MB, ChB45 PhD49. S'wark Ord Course 82. **dss** 83 **d** 87 **p** 94. Notting Hill St Jo and St Pet *Lon* 83-85; Upper Kennet *Sarum* 85-87; Hon Par Dn 87-93; Perm to Offic from 93. *Greystones House, Green Street, Avebury, Marlborough SN8 1RE* Tel (01672) 539289

STACEY, Nicolas David. b 27. St Edm Hall Ox BA51 MA55. Cuddesdon Coll 51. **d** 53 **p** 54. C Portsea N End St Mark *Portsm* 53-58; Bp's Dom Chapl *Birm* 58-59; R Woolwich St Mary w H Trin *S'wark* 59-68; Borough Dean Greenwich 65-68; Dep Dir Oxfam 68-70; Perm to Offic *Ox* 68-71; P-in-c Selling *Cant* 76-78; Perm to Offic 79-84 and from 90; Six Preacher Cant Cathl 84-89; rtd 92. *The Old Vicarage, Selling, Faversham ME13 9RD* Tel (01227) 752833

STACEY (née O'BRIEN), Mrs Shelagh Ann. b 55. RGN83 Bedf Coll Lon BSc77. N Ord Course 89. **d** 92 **p** 94. Par Dn S Elmsall *Wakef* 92-94; C 94-95; C Carleton 95-97; P-in-c 97-99; C E Hardwick 95-97; P-in-c 97-99; V Carleton and E Hardwick from 99. *The Vicarage, 10 East Close, Pontefract WF8 3NS* Tel (01977) 702478

STACEY, Timothy Andrew. b 58. Imp Coll Lon BSc79 York Univ PGCE83. St Jo Coll Nottm 94. **d** 94 **p** 95. C Chorleywood Ch Ch *St Alb* 94-99; P-in-c Chalfont St Giles *Ox* from 99; Chapl Bucks Chilterns Univ Coll from 99. *The Rectory, 2 Deanway, Chalfont St Giles HP8 4DX* Tel (01494) 872097 E-mail t.and.s.stacey@virgin.net

STACEY, Canon Victor George. b 44. NUI BA69 QUB MTh. CITC 72. **d** 72 **p** 73. C Derriaghy *Conn* 72-76; C Knock *D & D* 76-79; I Ballymacarrett St Martin 79-86; I Dublin Santry w Glasnevin *D & G* 86-95; Bp's Dom Chapl from 90; I Dun Laoghaire and Dioc Registrar from 95; Preb Maynooth St Patr Cathl Dublin from 97. *Christ Church Vicarage, 2 Park Road, Dun Laoghaire, Co Dublin, Irish Republic* Tel (00353) (1) 280 9537

STACKPOLE, Robert Aaron. b 59. Williams Coll Mass BA82 Oriel Coll Ox MLitt88. St Steph Ho Ox 88. **d** 90 **p** 91. C Kettering SS Pet and Paul *Pet* 90-93; Canada from 93. *Address temp unknown*

STAFF, Mrs Jean. b 44. CertEd64. EMMTC 81. **dss** 84 **d** 87 **p** 94. Old Brumby *Linc* 84-87; C 87-88; C Gainsborough St Geo 88-91; Dn-in-c 91-94; P-in-c 94-96; P-in-c Haxey 96-97; P-in-c Owston 96-97; V Haxey from 97; V Owston from 97. *The Vicarage, Church Street, Haxey, Doncaster DN9 2HY* Tel (01427) 752351

STAFF, Susan. See JACKSON, Mrs Susan

STAFFORD, Christopher James. b 67. Birm Univ BSc88 PhD92. St Jo Coll Nottm MA. DipMM99. **d** 99 **p** 00. C Westbrook St Phil *Liv* 99-03; R Newchurch w Croft from 03. *Newchurch Rectory, 17 Jackson Avenue, Culcheth, Warrington WA3 4ED* Tel (01925) 766300 E-mail cjstaff@surfaid.org

STAFFORD, David George. b 45. Qu Coll Birm 75. **d** 77 **p** 78. C Chesterfield St Aug *Derby* 77-80; C Ranmoor *Sheff* 80-83; V Bolton-upon-Dearne from 83. *The Vicarage, 41 Station Road, Bolton-on-Dearne, Rotherham S63 8AA* Tel (01709) 893163

STAFFORD, Canon John Ingham Henry. b 31. TCD BA52 MA58. **d** 53 **p** 55. C Clonallon *D & D* 53-56; C Belfast Malone St Jo *Conn* 56-59; Australia 59-64; Min Can Down Cathl *D & D* 64-68; Hd of S Ch Miss Ballymacarrett 68-73; I Bright w

Killough 73-83; C Bangor Primacy 83-92; Can Down Cathl 90-92; I Urney w Sion Mills *D & R* 92-98; rtd 98. *14 Cleland Park North, Bangor BT20 3EN* Tel (028) 9145 6311

STAFFORD, Mark Anthony. b 64. Huddersfield Univ BSc92. St Jo Coll Nottm MA98. **d** 98 **p** 99. C Stafford St Jo and Tixall w Ingestre *Lich* 98-01; C W Retford *S'well* 01; TV Retford from 02. *The Rectory, Rectory Road, Retford DN22 7AY* Tel (01777) 719816

STAFFORD, Matthew Charles. b 73. Wilson Carlile Coll 94 Ripon Coll Cuddesdon DMin99. **d** 99 **p** 00. C High Wycombe *Ox* 99-02; P-in-c Wrockwardine Wood *Lich* from 02. *The Rectory, Church Road, Wrockwardine Wood, Telford TF2 7AH* Tel (01952) 613865 Mobile 07986-754478
E-mail jules.matthew@talk21.com

STAFFORD, Richard William (Billy). b 46. Ringsent Tech Inst TCert69. CITC 96. **d** 99 **p** 00. NSM Urney w Denn and Derryheen *K, E & A* from 99; NSM Annagh w Drumgoon, Ashfield etc from 00. *12 Cherrymount, Keadue Lane, Cavan, Co Cavan, Irish Republic* Tel (00353) (49) 437 1173 Mobile 87-240 4630 E-mail rwstafford@yahoo.com

STAFFORD, Area Bishop of. *See* HILL, The Rt Revd Christopher John

STAFFORD-WHITTAKER, William Paul. b 69. Chich Th Coll DipTh94. **d** 94 **p** 95. C Brighton Resurr *Chich* 94-97; C Holborn St Alb w Saffron Hill St Pet *Lon* 97-02; V Stanwell from 02. *The Vicarage, 1 Lord Knyvett Close, Stanwell, Staines TW19 7PF* Tel (01784) 252044

STAGG, Charles Roy. b 18. G&C Coll Cam BA45 MA47. Ripon Hall Ox 47. **d** 48 **p** 49. Chapl Dur Sch 48-54; C The Lickey *Birm* 54-55; Chapl Kampala Tech Inst Uganda 55-58; Chapl Aldenham Sch Herts 58-64; Chapl Kenya High Sch Nairobi Kenya 64-66; Hd Master Kenton Coll Nairobi 66-80; Perm to Offic *Glouc* 81-96. *Wyck Cottage, Childswickham, Broadway WR12 7HF* Tel (01386) 853229

STAGG, Jeremy Michael. b 47. Leeds Univ BSc69 Fontainebleau MBA77. Sarum & Wells Th Coll 90. **d** 92 **p** 93. C Basing *Win* 92-96; P-in-c Barton, Pooley Bridge and Martindale *Carl* 96-99; Hon CMS Rep 96-99; C Burgh-by-Sands and Kirkbampton w Kirkandrews etc *Carl* 99-00; C Barony of Burgh 00-01; Dioc Past Sec from 00; P-in-c Distington from 01. *The Rectory, Church Road, Distington, Workington CA14 5TE* Tel (01946) 830384 *or* (01228) 522573 Fax (01228) 815400
E-mail pastoral@carlislediocese.org.uk

STAGG, Canon Michael Hubert. b 39. St Chad's Coll Dur 58. **d** 63 **p** 64. C Weston-super-Mare St Sav *B & W* 63-66; P-in-c Ashbrooke *Linc* 66-71; R Brompton Regis w Upton and Skilgate *B & W* 71-78; P-in-c Kidderminster St Jo *Worc* 78-80; P-in-c Cannington *B & W* 80-84; R Cannington, Otterhampton, Combwich and Stockland 84-87; Dioc Communications Officer *Nor* 88-93; Bp's Chapl 88-93; R Sprowston w Beeston 93-01; RD Nor N from 95; Hon Can Nor Cathl from 98; P-in-c Nor St Andr from 01; P-in-c Norwich St Geo Colegate from 01. *31 Ash Grove, Norwich NR3 4BE* Tel (01603) 479795
E-mail michaelstagg@waitrose.com

STAGG, Roy Ernest. b 48. **d** 01 **p** 02. OLM Birchington w Acol and Minnis Bay *Cant* from 01. *7 Minster Road, Acol, Birchington CT7 0JB* Tel (01843) 841551 E-mail roy@staggr.freeserve.co.uk

STAINER, Richard Bruce. b 62. Linc Th Coll 92. **d** 94 **p** 95. C N Walsham w Antingham *Nor* 94-97; R Cogenhoe and Gt and Lt Houghton w Brafield *Pet* from 97; RD Wootton from 01. *The Rectory, Church Street, Cogenhoe, Northampton NN7 1LS* Tel (01604) 891166 Fax as telephone E-mail r.stainer@tesco.net

STAINES, Edward Noel. b 26. Trin Coll Ox MA52 MSc85. Chich Th Coll 51 57. **d** 57 **p** 58. C Eastbourne St Mary *Chich* 57-61; V Amberley w N Stoke 61-70; V Forest Row 70-75; R Ashurst 70-75; V Bexhill St Aug 75-79; TR Ovingdean w Rottingdean and Woodingdean 79-85; V Rottingdean 85-86; Perm to Offic *Worc* from 86; Perm to Offic *Glouc* 86-88; Chapl Gtr Lisbon *Eur* 88-90; Chapl Marseille 90; rtd 90. *White House, Harpley Road, Defford, Worcester WR8 9BL* Tel (01386) 750817

STAINES, Michael John. b 28. Trin Coll Ox BA52 MA56. Wells Th Coll 62. **d** 64 **p** 65. C Southwick St Mich *Chich* 64-67; TV Harling Gp *Nor* 67-73; P Missr S Chilterns Gp *Ox* 74-75; R W Wycombe w Bledlow Ridge, Bradenham and Radnage 76-93; RD Wycombe 83-87; rtd 93; Perm to Offic *Heref* and *Worc* from 93. *Upper Town Cottage, Berrington, Tenbury Wells WR15 8TH* Tel (01584) 811533

STALKER, William John. b 49. N Ord Course 89. **d** 91 **p** 92. C Formby H Trin *Liv* 91-94; V Stoneycroft All SS 94-03; Chapl R Liv Univ Hosp NHS Trust 94-03; P-in-c Lowton St Mary *Liv* from 03. *The Vicarage, 1 Barford Drive, Lowton, Warrington WA3 1DD* Tel (01942) 607705

STALLARD, John Charles. b 34. Selw Coll Cam BA58 MA62. Ripon Hall Ox 62. **d** 64 **p** 65. C Hall Green Ascension *Birm* 64-66; C Sutton Coldfield H Trin 66-68; C-in-c Brandwood CD 68-71; Chapl Dame Allan's Schs Newc 71-74; V Warley Woods *Birm* 75-84; TR Droitwich *Worc* 84-87; P-in-c Dodderhill 84-87; TR Droitwich Spa 87-94; V Pensnett 94-00; rtd 00; Perm to Offic

St D from 00. *Greengates, Cae Melyn, Aberystwyth SY23 2HA* Tel (01970) 624269 E-mail greengates@breathemail.net

STALLARD, Ms Mary Kathleen Rose. b 67. Selw Coll Cam BA88 Lon Inst of Educn PGCE90. Qu Coll Birm 91. **d** 93 **p** 97. C Newport St Matt *Mon* 93-96; P-in-c Ysbyty Cynfyn w Llantrisant and Eglwys Newydd *St D* 96-97; V 97-02; Chapl St As Cathl *St As* from 02. *Woodcroft, Upper Denbigh Road, St Asaph LL17 0BG* Tel (01745) 730064

STALLEY, Brian Anthony. b 38. Oak Hill Th Coll 60. **d** 63 **p** 64. C Summerstown *S'wark* 63-70; Surrey BFBS Sec 70-73; Manager Action Cen BFBS 73-76; R Branston *Linc* 76-91; rtd 91; Perm to Offic *Linc* from 91. *6 Sunningdale Grove, Washingborough, Lincoln LN4 1SP* Tel (01522) 794164 Mobile 07941-508445 Fax (01522) 794663 E-mail brian@bstalley.freeserve.co.uk

STAMFORD, Brian. b 37. **d** 91 **p** 92. CMS Uganda 88-95; P-in-c North Hill and Lewannick *Truro* 95-03; P-in-c Altarnun w Bolventor, Laneast and St Clether from 03. *The Vicarage, Altarnun, Launceston PL15 7SJ* Tel (01566) 86108 Fax as telephone E-mail brianstamford@btopenworld.com

STAMFORD, Dean of. *See* REDFERN, The Rt Revd Alastair Llewellyn John

STAMP, Andrew Nicholas. b 44. Ex Univ BA67. Sarum Th Coll 67. **d** 69 **p** 70. C S Beddington St Mich *S'wark* 69-73; Tutor Sarum & Wells Th Coll 73-76; Chapl RN 76-81; C-in-c W Leigh CD *Portsm* 81-82; V W Leigh 82-87; R Botley 87-95; V Curdridge 94-95; R Durley 94-95; P-in-c Compton, the Mardens, Stoughton and Racton *Chich* from 95; P-in-c Stansted from 95; Tutor Bp Otter Coll Chich 95-98; Dioc Rural Officer *Chich* from 00. *The Vicarage, Compton, Chichester PO18 9HD* Tel (023) 9263 1252

STAMP, Ian Jack. b 47. Aston Tr Scheme 82 N Ord Course 83. **d** 86 **p** 87. C Tonge w Alkrington *Man* 86-89; V Heywood St Marg 89-98; P-in-c Heywood St Luke w All So 96-98; TR Heywood 98-01; V Bury St Jo w St Mark from 01. *St John's Vicarage, 270 Walmersley Road, Bury BL9 6NH* Tel 0161-764 3412 Fax as telephone E-mail revistamp@aol.com

STAMP, Philip Andrew. b 53. Linc Th Coll 86. **d** 88 **p** 89. C Barton w Peel Green *Man* 88-91; R Blackley H Trin from 91. *Holy Trinity Rectory, Goodman Street, Manchester M9 1FE* Tel 0161-205 2879

STAMP, Richard Mark. b 36. St Chad's Coll Dur BA60 DipTh62. **d** 62 **p** 63. Australia 62-69 and from 72; C Greenhill St Jo *Lon* 69-72; rtd 01. *127 Hilda Drive, RMB Ravenswood, Harcourt, Vic, Australia 3453* Tel (0061) (3) 5435 3576 Fax as telephone E-mail stamp@netcon.net.au

STAMPS, Canon Dennis Lee. b 55. Biola Univ (USA) BA78 Trin Evang Div Sch (USA) MDiv83 MA87 Dur Univ PhD95. Westcott Ho Cam 90. **d** 92 **p** 93. C Moseley St Mary *Birm* 92-96; Dir WMMTC 96-01; Dean Qu Coll Birm 01-02; Minl Development Officer *St Alb* from 02; Can Res St Alb from 02. *7 Corder Close, St Albans AL3 4NH* Tel (01727) 841116 E-mail dstampsuk@aol.com

✠**STANAGE, The Rt Revd Thomas Shaun.** b 32. Pemb Coll Ox BA56 MA60 Nashotah Ho Wisconsin Hon DD86. Cuddesdon Coll 56. **d** 58 **p** 59 **c** 78. C Gt Crosby St Faith *Liv* 58-61; Min Orford St Andr CD 61-63; V Orford St Andr 63-70; S Africa from 70; Dean Kimberley 75-78; Suff Bp Johannesburg 78-82; Bp Bloemfontein 82-97; rtd 97; Acting Lect Th Univ of the Free State from 97. *PO Box 13598, Noordstad, Bloemfontein, 9301 South Africa* Tel (0027) (51) 436 7282

STANBRIDGE, The Ven Leslie Cyril. b 20. St Jo Coll Dur BA47 DipTh49 MA54. **d** 49 **p** 50. C Erith St Jo *Roch* 49-51; Tutor St Jo Coll Dur 51-55; Chapl 52-55; V Kingston upon Hull St Martin *York* 55-64; R Cottingham 64-72; Can and Preb York Minster 68-00; Succ Canonicorum from 88; RD Hull 70-72; Adn York 72-88; rtd 88; Perm to Offic *York* from 00. *39 Lucombe Way, New Earswick, York YO32 4DS* Tel (01904) 750812

✠**STANCLIFFE, The Rt Revd David Staffurth.** b 42. Trin Coll Ox BA65 MA68. Cuddesdon Coll 65. **d** 67 **p** 68 **c** 93. C Armley St Bart *Ripon* 67-70; Chapl Clifton Coll Bris 70-77; Dir of Ords *Portsm* 77-82; Can Res Portsm Cathl 77-82; Provost Portsm 82-93; Bp Sarum from 93. *South Canonry, 71 The Close, Salisbury SP1 2ER* Tel (01722) 334031 Fax 413112
E-mail dsarum@salisbury.anglican.org

STANDEN, David Charles. b 68. K Coll Lon BA91 AKC91 PGCE92 Lon Univ PhD00. Westcott Ho Cam 01. **d** 03. C Prittlewell *Chelmsf* from 03. *Oakleigh Cottage, 28 East Street, Southend-on-Sea SS2 6LH* Tel (01702) 603773
E-mail davidstanden@onetel.net.uk

STANDEN, Mark Jonathan. b 63. LMH Ox BA85 Barrister 86. Ridley Hall Cam BA94 CTM95. **d** 95 **p** 96. C Sevenoaks St Nic *Roch* 95-99; R Angmering *Chich* from 99. *The Rectory, Rectory Lane, Angmering, Littlehampton BN16 4JU* Tel (01903) 784979

STANDEN McDOUGAL, Canon John Anthony Phelps. b 33. AKC58. **d** 59 **p** 60. C Ipswich St Marg *St E* 59-63; C Bury St Edmunds St Mary 63-65; C Wadhurst *Chich* 65-70; C Tidebrook 65-70; R Tollard Royal w Farnham *Sarum* 70-81; P-in-c Gussage St Michael and Gussage All Saints 71-76; R 76-81; RD Milton and Blandford 81-86; R Tollard Royal w

Farnham, Gussage St Michael etc 82-86; Can and Preb Sarum Cathl 86-94; TR Bride Valley 86-94; rtd 94; Perm to Offic *Sarum* from 94. *Silverdale Cottage, North Chideock, Bridport DT6 6LG* Tel (01297) 489408

STANDING, Victor. b 44. FRCO67 Lon Univ BMus66 Ox Univ DipTh77 Clare Coll Cam CertEd68. Ripon Coll Cuddesdon 75. **d** 78 **p** 79. C Wimborne Minster *Sarum* 78-80; TV Wimborne Minster and Holt 80-83; R Ex St Sidwell and St Matt *Ex* 83-94; Dep PV Ex Cathl 83-01; Chapl R Devon and Ex Hosp 83-94; Chapl W of England Eye Infirmary Ex 83-94; P-in-c Tedburn St Mary, Whitestone, Oldridge etc *Ex* 94-96; P-in-c Dunsford and Doddiscombsleigh 95-96; P-in-c Cheriton Bishop 95-96; R Tedburn St Mary, Whitestone, Oldridge etc 96-01; RD Kenn 97-01; V New Shoreham *Chich* from 01. *The Vicarage, Church Street, Shoreham-by-Sea BN43 5DQ* Tel (01273) 452109

STANDISH, Derrick Edgar. b 41. Univ of Wales (Lamp) BA67. Wycliffe Hall Ox 68. **d** 68 **p** 69. C Brynmawr *S & B* 68-69; C Morriston 69-74; V Merthyr Cynog and Dyffryn Honddu 74-76; R Llanwenarth Ultra *Mon* 76-83; V Abersychan and Garndiffaith 83-91. *7 Intermediate Road, Brynmawr, Ebbw Vale NP23 4SF*

STANDRING, Rupert Benjamin Charles. b 68. Pemb Coll Ox BA90 MA99. Ridley Hall Cam BA94 CTM95. **d** 95 **p** 96. C Bromley Ch Ch *Roch* 95-99; Tutor Cornhill Tr Course from 99; Hon C W Hampstead St Luke *Lon* from 99; Perm to Offic from 99. *140-148 Borough High Street, London SE1 1LB* Tel (020) 7407 0562

STANES, The Ven Ian Thomas. b 39. Sheff Univ BSc62 Linacre Coll Ox BA65 MA69. Wycliffe Hall Ox 63. **d** 65 **p** 66. C Leic H Apostles *Leic* 65-69; V Broom Leys 69-76; Warden Marrick Priory *Ripon* 76-82; Officer Miss, Min and Evang (Willesden Area) *Lon* 82-92; CME Officer 82-92; Preb St Paul's Cathl 89-92; Adn Loughborough *Leic* from 92. *The Archdeaconry, 21 Church Road, Glenfield, Leicester LE3 8DP* Tel 0116-231 1632 Fax 232 1593 E-mail stanes@leicester.anglican.org

STANESBY, Derek Malcolm. b 31. Leeds Univ BA56 Man Univ MEd75 PhD84 SOSc. Coll of Resurr Mirfield 56. **d** 58 **p** 59. C Lakenham St Jo *Nor* 58-61; C Welling *S'wark* 61-63; V Bury St Mark *Man* 63-67; R Ladybarn 67-85; Can and Steward Windsor 85-97; rtd 97; Perm to Office *Leic* and *Pet* from 00. *32 Elizabeth Way, Uppingham, Oakham LE15 9PQ* Tel (01572) 821298

STANFORD, Mark Roger. b 59. Cranmer Hall Dur DipTh98. **d** 98 **p** 99. C Aughton Ch Ch *Liv* 98-02; TV Toxteth St Philemon w St Gabr and St Cleopas from 02. *St Philemon's Vicarage,, 40 Devonshire Road, Princess Park, Liverpool L8 3TZ* Tel 0151-727 1248

STANGHAN, Eileen. b 40. Whitelands Coll Lon CertEd75. LNSM course 95. **d** 98 **p** 99. OLM Reigate St Phil *S'wark* from 98. *32 Saxon Way, Reigate RH2 9DH* Tel (01737) 240920 *or* (01293) 430043

STANIFORD, Mrs Doris Gwendoline. b 43. Gilmore Course IDC79. **dss** 80 **d** 87 **p** 94. Hangleton *Chich* 80-82; Durrington 82-89; Par Dn 87-89; Chich Th Coll 83-89; C Crawley 89-97; Chapl Crawley Gen Hosp 89-97; Chapl St Cath Hospice 92-97; Dioc Voc Adv *Chich* 92-97; C Southwick St Mich 97-99; Asst Dir of Ords from 97; TV Ifield from 99. *St Alban's Vicarage, Gossops Drive, Crawley RH11 8LD* Tel (01293) 529848

STANLEY, Arthur Patrick. b 32. TCD BA54 Div Test55 MA64. **d** 55 **p** 56. C Waterford H Trin *C & O* 55-57; CF 58-74; Dep Asst Chapl Gen 74-83; USA from 84; rtd 94. *2081 S Avenue, Stanton, IA 51573, USA* Tel (001) (712) 829 2457 Fax as telephone E-mail pnpstan@netins.net

STANLEY, Baden Thomas. b 68. TCD BA91. CITC BTh94. **d** 94 **p** 95. C Seapatrick *D & D* 94-98; I Bray *D & G* from 98. *The Rectory, Church Road, Bray, Co Wicklow, Irish Republic* Tel (00353) (1) 286 2968 E-mail bray@dublin.anglican.org

STANLEY, Canon John Alexander. b 31. OBE99. Tyndale Hall Bris DipTh56. **d** 56 **p** 57. C Preston All SS *Blackb* 56-60; C St Helens St Mark *Liv* 60-63; V Everton St Cuth 63-70; P-in-c Everton St Sav 69-70; V Everton St Sav w St Cuth 70-74; V Huyton St Mich from 74; Hon Can Liv Cathl from 87; AD Huyton 89-02; Chapl to The Queen 93-01. *The Vicarage, Huyton, Liverpool L36 7SA* Tel 0151-449 3900 Mobile 07740-621833 Fax 0151-480 6002

STANLEY, Mrs Nicola Vere. b 56. STETS 99. **d** 02 **p** 03. NSM Bedford Park *Lon* from 02. *8 Birch Grove, London W5 9SN* Tel (020) 8992 0620 E-mail nvs@mosaic.ndirect.co.uk

STANLEY, Simon Richard. b 44. Wells Th Coll 66. **d** 69 **p** 70. C Foleshill St Laur *Cov* 69-71; C Hessle *York* 71-75; P-in-c Flamborough 75-80; R Dunnington 80-92; P-in-c York St Barn 92-99; P-in-c York St Chad from 99; Relig Progr Producer BBC Radio York from 94. *St Chad's Vicarage, 36 Campleshon Road, York YO23 1EY* Tel (01904) 674524 Fax 466516 E-mail simonstanley@clara.net

STANLEY-SMITH, James. b 29. Hatf Coll Dur BA54 DipEd55. S Dios Minl Tr Scheme 81. **d** 84 **p** 85. C Bournemouth St Jo w

St Mich *Win* 84-87; R Hale w S Charford 87-94; rtd 94; Perm to Offic *Win* from 94. *10 Rownhams Way, Rownhams, Southampton SO16 8AE* Tel (023) 8073 2529

STANNARD, Miss Beryl Elizabeth. b 36. SRN62 SCM64. Oak Hill Th Coll BA92. **d** 92 **p** 94. Par Dn Streatham Park St Alb *S'wark* 92-94; C 94-96; C Gerrards Cross and Fulmer *Ox* 96-01; rtd 01; Perm to Offic *Ox* from 02. *20 Wey Lane, Chesham HP5 1JH* Tel (01494) 774715

STANNARD, Brian. b 46. MICE71 MIStructE71. Cranmer Hall Dur 86. **d** 88 **p** 89. C Burnage St Marg *Man* 88-91; V Walmersley 91-03; TV Westhoughton and Wingates from 03. *The Vicarage, 91 Chorley Road, Westhoughton, Bolton BL5 3PG* Tel (01942) 812119 E-mail brian@stannardrev.fsnet.co.uk

STANNARD, The Ven Colin Percy. b 24. TD66. Selw Coll Cam BA47 MA49. Linc Th Coll 47. **d** 49 **p** 50. C St E Cathl *St E* 49-52; C-in-c Nunsthorpe CD *Linc* 52-55; CF (TA) 53-67; V Barrow St Jas *Carl* 55-64; V Upperby St Jo 64-70; R Gosforth 70-75; RD Calder 70-75; P-in-c Natland 75-84; RD Kendal 75-84; Hon Can Carl Cathl 75-84; Can Res Carl Cathl 84-93; Adn Carl 84-93; rtd 93; Perm to Offic *Carl* from 93. *51 Longlands Road, Carlisle CA3 9AE* Tel (01228) 538584

STANNARD, Harold Frederick David. b 12. AKC37. **d** 37 **p** 38. C St Columb Major *Truro* 37-43; Chapl RAFVR 43-46; R Dunsby w Dowsby *Linc* 46-48; R W Quantoxhead *B & W* 48-77; rtd 77. *c/o J F Church Esq, Stephens and Scown, 3 Cross Lane, St Austell PL25 4AX* Tel (01726) 74433

STANNARD, Canon Peter Graville. b 59. Univ of Wales (Abth) BSc(Econ)81. St Steph Ho Ox BA85 MA86. **d** 86 **p** 87. C Worksop Priory *S'well* 86-89; Prin St Nic Th Coll Ghana 89-96; Hon Can Koforidua from 93; TR Shelf St Mich w Buttershaw St Aid *Bradf* 96-99; P-in-c Heaton Norris St Thos *Man* 00-02; TV Heatons from 02. *St Thomas's Rectory, 6 Heaton Moor Road, Stockport SK4 4NS* Tel 0161-432 1912

STANTON, Miss Barbara. b 51. Whitelands Coll Lon TCert72 DipNCTD77 Lon Univ BD86. WMMTC 89. **d** 92 **p** 94. NSM Hinckley St Mary *Leic* 92-97; Bp's Ecum Adv and P-in-c Husbands Bosworth w Mowsley and Knaptoft etc from 97; P-in-c Arnesby w Shearsby and Bruntingthorpe from 02. *The Rectory, Honeypot Lane, Husbands Bosworth, Lutterworth LE17 6LY* Tel (01858) 880351

STANTON, David John. b 60. St Andr Univ MTheol82 FSAScot89 Ex Univ MA00 FRSA98. Ripon Coll Cuddesdon 83. **d** 85 **p** 86. C Beckenham St Geo *Roch* 85-88; Asst Chapl Shrewsbury Sch 88-90; Hon C Shrewsbury All SS w St Mich *Lich* 88-90; P-in-c Abbotskerswell *Ex* 90-94; Chapl Plymouth Univ 92-97; P-in-c Bovey Tracey St Jo, Chudleigh Knighton etc 94-99; V Bovey Tracey St Jo w Heathfield from 99; Dioc Voc Advisor from 95; Warden of Readers from 96; RD Moreton from 98. *St John's Vicarage, Newton Road, Bovey Tracey, Newton Abbot TQ13 9BD* Tel (01626) 833451 E-mail stanton@bovey7.freeserve.co.uk

STANTON, Gregory John. b 47. Sarum & Wells Th Coll 84. **d** 86 **p** 87. C Willenhall H Trin *Lich* 86-89; C Plympton St Mary *Ex* 89-91; V Milton Abbot, Dunterton, Lamerton etc from 91. *The Vicarage, The Parade, Milton Abbot, Tavistock PL19 0NZ* Tel (01822) 612732 E-mail gjstanton31@hotmail.com

STANTON, John Maurice. b 18. Univ Coll Ox BA45 MA45. Wycliffe Hall Ox 51. **d** 52 **p** 53. C Tonbridge SS Pet and Paul *Roch* 52-54; Hd Master Blundell's Sch Tiverton 59-71; Public Preacher *Ex* 71-72; C Ex St Matt 72-73; R Chesham Bois *Ox* 73-83; rtd 83; Perm to Offic *Ox* from 83. *16 Emden House, Barton Lane, Headington OX3 9JU* Tel (01865) 765206

STANTON, Miss Julie Elizabeth. b 59. Matlock Coll of Educn CertEd80. EMMTC 00. **d** 03. NSM Matlock Bath and Cromford *Derby* from 03. *35 Intake Lane, Cromford, Matlock DE4 3RH* Tel (01629) 822653 Mobile 07769-748276 Fax (01629) 760903 E-mail juliestanton@ukonline.com

STANTON, Ms Karen Janis. b 55. N Ord Course 00. **d** 03. C Withington St Paul *Man* from 03. *5 Westbourne Grove, Withington, Manchester M20 1JA* Tel 0161-445 5498 Mobile 07814-254744 E-mail kaz@stanton.ndo.co.uk

STANTON, Thomas Hugh (Timothy). b 17. Trin Coll Cam BA38 MA45. Coll of Resurr Mirfield 46. **d** 47 **p** 48. C Camberwell St Geo *S'wark* 47-49; CR from 52; S Africa 54-87; rtd 87. *Community of the Resurrection, Stocks Bank Road, Mirfield WF14 0BN* Tel (01924) 494318

STANTON-HYDE, Mrs Marjorie Elizabeth. b 37. TCert58. Cranmer Hall Dur 86. **d** 88 **p** 94. Par Dn Elmley Lovett w Hampton Lovett and Elmbridge etc *Worc* 88-91; Par Dn Wilden 88-91; Par Dn Hartlebury 88-91; Dn-in-c 91-94; P-in-c 94-97; R 97-98; rtd 98; Hon C Gt Malvern St Mary *Worc* 99-02; Warden Jes Hosp Cant from 02. *The Warden's Lodge, Jesus Hospital, 2 Sturry Road, Canterbury CT1 1BS* Tel (01227) 463771

STANTON-SARINGER, Maurice Charles. b 49. Bris Univ BSc71 PGCE72 Fitzw Coll Cam BA77 MA81. Ridley Hall Cam 75. **d** 78 **p** 79. C Gerrards Cross *Ox* 78-80; C Bletchley 80-83; Lic to Offic 83-91; Chapl Stowe Sch 83-91; R Sherington w Chicheley, N Crawley, Astwood etc *Ox* from 91; RD Newport

from 95. *The Rectory, 21 School Lane, Sherington, Newport Pagnell MK16 9NF* Tel (01908) 610521
E-mail saringer@telinco.co.uk

STANWAY, Peter David. b 48. K Coll Lon BD71. St Aug Coll Cant 72. **d** 73 **p** 74. C Maidstone All SS w St Phil and H Trin *Cant* 73-77; Canada 77-84; C Waterlooville *Portsm* 84-87; R Laughton w Ripe and Chalvington *Chich* 87-90; Chapl Witney Community Hosp 90-91; C Wheatley w Forest Hill and Stanton St John *Ox* 91-92; C Cowley St Jas 93-02; rtd 02. *22 Colleywood, Kennington, Oxford OX1 5NF* Tel (01865) 739342

STAPLE, Miss Patricia Ann. b 54. Birm Univ BA75. St Steph Ho Ox 00. **d** 02. C Dartmouth *Ex* from 02. *22 Church Road, Dartmouth TQ6 9HQ* Tel and fax (01803) 834761 Mobile 07719-129008 E-mail tricia_staple@hotmail.com

STAPLEFORD, Robin Duncan. b 62. St Jo Coll Nottm DipMin94 Aston Tr Scheme 92. **d** 96 **p** 97. C Evington *Leic* 96-99; TV Vale of Belvoir Par from 00. *The Vicarage, 1 Boyers Orchard, Harby, Melton Mowbray LE14 4BA* Tel (01949) 860269
E-mail stapleford.robin.d@ukonline.co.uk

STAPLES, David. b 35. Jes Coll Ox BA59 MA63 BD75. Linc Th Coll 59. **d** 61 **p** 62. C Kettering St Andr *Pet* 61-64; C Doncaster St Geo *Sheff* 64-66; Dioc Youth Chapl 66-71; V Mexborough 71-83; Chapl Montagu Hosp Mexborough 71-83; RD Wath *Sheff* 77-83; Hon Can Sheff Cathl 80-83; V W Haddon w Winwick *Pet* 83-88; RD Brixworth 83-89; V W Haddon w Winwick and Ravensthorpe 88-00; ACUPA Link Officer 90-00; rtd 00; Perm to Offic *Linc* from 00. *1 Sycamore Close, Bourne PE10 9RS* Tel (01778) 423121

STAPLES, Jeffrey Joseph. b 61. St Jo Coll Nottm 97. **d** 99 **p** 00. C Prenton *Ches* from 99. *89 Prenton Hall Road, Prenton CH43 3BH* Tel 0151-608 4692

STAPLES, John Michael. b 45. STETS 94. **d** 97 **p** 98. C Tisbury *Sarum* 97-01; P-in-c Barford St Martin, Dinton, Baverstock etc 00-01; TV Nadder Valley from 01. *11A Tyndale's Meadow, Dinton, Salisbury SP3 5HU* Tel (01722) 717883

STAPLES, John Wedgwood. b 42. Hertf Coll Ox BA64 MA. Wycliffe Hall Ox 64. **d** 66 **p** 67. C Yardley St Edburgha *Birm* 66-69; C Knowle 69-74; R Barcombe *Chich* 74-81; V Old Windsor *Ox* 81-96; P-in-c Pangbourne w Tidmarsh and Sulham 96-99; R from 99. *The Rectory, St James's Close, Pangbourne, Reading RG8 7AP* Tel 0118-984 2928
E-mail revd_john@staplesj.fsnet.co.uk

STAPLES, Peter. b 35. Jes Coll Ox BA59. **d** 62 **p** 63. C Fairfield *Derby* 62-63; C Dore 63-66; C Wilne and Draycott w Breaston 66-71; The Netherlands from 72; Asst Chapl Utrecht w Amersfoort, Harderwijk and Zwolle *Eur* from 94. *Doldersweg 39C, 3712 BN Huis Ter Heide, Utrecht, The Netherlands* Tel (0031) (3404) 31928

STAPLES, Canon Peter Brian. b 38. Bps' Coll Cheshunt 66. **d** 68 **p** 69. C Birkdale St Jas *Liv* 68-71; C Sevenoaks St Jo *Roch* 71-74; V Treslothan *Truro* 74-80; V Truro St Paul and St Clem 80-02; Hon Can Truro Cathl 98-02; rtd 02; Perm to Offic *St E* from 03. *25 Osmund Walk, Bury St Edmunds IP33 3UU* Tel (01284) 760620

STAPLES, Terence Malcolm. b 43. Trin Coll Bris MA01. BA95. **d** 95 **p** 96. C Bath St Sav w Swainswick and Woolley *B & W* 95-99; R Exton and Winsford and Cutcombe w Luxborough from 99. *The Rectory, Winsford, Minehead TA24 7JE* Tel (01643) 851301 E-mail staplest@freenet.co.uk

STAPLETON, The Very Revd Peter Edward Champneys. b 32. FSA74 Pemb Coll Cam BA54 MA58. Ely Th Coll 54. **d** 56 **p** 57. C York St Olave w St Giles *York* 56-59; C Pocklington w Yapham-cum-Meltonby, Owsthorpe etc 59-61; R Seaton Ross w Everingham and Bielby and Harswell 61-67; RD Weighton 66-67; R Skelton by York 67-75; V Wroxham w Hoveton *Nor* 75-81; P-in-c Belaugh 76-81; Can Res and Prec Roch Cathl *Roch* 81-88; Dean Carl 88-98; rtd 98; Perm to Offic *Wakef* from 98. *Rockland House, 20 Marsh Gardens, Honley, Huddersfield HD7 2AF* Tel (01484) 666629

STAPLETON, Leonard Charles. b 37. Chich Th Coll 75. **d** 77 **p** 78. C Crayford *Roch* 77-81; C Lamorbey H Redeemer 81-83; V Belvedere St Aug 83-89; V Beckenham St Jas 89-02; rtd 02; Perm to Offic *Roch* from 03. *46 High Street, Chislehurst BR7 5AQ* Tel (020) 8467 3736

STAPLETON, Robert Michael Vorley. b 25. ALCD51. **d** 51 **p** 52. C Plymouth St Andr *Ex* 51-56; Chapl RN 56-60; C Surbiton St Matt *S'wark* 60-64; R Chenies and Lt Chalfont *Ox* 64-87; P-in-c Latimer w Flaunden 86-87; R Chenies and Lt Chalfont, Latimer and Flaunden 87-92; rtd 92. *Woodside, Swannaton Road, Dartmouth TQ6 9RL* Tel (01803) 832972

STAPLETON, Robert Vauvelle. b 47. Dur Univ BA70. Cranmer Hall Dur DipTh71. **d** 71 **p** 72. C Monkwearmouth All SS *Dur* 73-76; C Stranton 76-79; P-in-c Kelloe 79-86; V New Shildon 86-96; R Stoke Albany w Wilbarston and Ashley etc *Pet* from 96. *The Rectory, Stoe Albany, Market Harborough LE16 8PZ* Tel (01858) 535213 E-mail robertstapleton@hotmail.com

STARBUCK, Francis Tony. b 36. Kelham Th Coll 57. **d** 61 **p** 62. C Mansfield St Mark *S'well* 61-63; C Clifton H Trin CD 63-64; C Didcot *Ox* 67-71; P Missr California CD 71-75; R Barkham

74-75; V Hagbourne 75-82; V Maidenhead St Luke 82-87; New Zealand from 87; V Te Puke St Jo 87-96; Can Waiapu 90-94; V Clevedon All So 96-01; rtd 01. *17 Flora Place, Mahia Park, Manurewa, New Zealand* Tel (0064) (9) 266 2209

STARES, Brian Maurice William. b 44. St Deiniol's Hawarden 74. **d** 74 **p** 75. C Risca *Mon* 74-77; V Newport St Steph and H Trin 77-87; V Fleur-de-Lis 87-92; Chapl HM Pris Belmarsh 92-93; Chapl HM YOI Dover 93-98; Chapl HM YOI and Rem Cen Feltham 98-99; V Bishton *Mon* from 99. *The Vicarage, Station Road, Llanwern, Newport NP18 2DW* Tel (01633) 413457

STARES, Mrs Olive Beryl. b 33. Sarum Th Coll 83. **dss** 86 **d** 87 **p** 94. Crofton *Portsm* 86-87; Hon C 87-01; rtd 01. *62 Mancroft Avenue, Hill Head, Fareham PO14 2DD* Tel (01329) 668540

STARK, Mrs Beverley Ann. b 52. Bp Otter Coll CertEd73 EMMTC 92. **d** 92 **p** 94. Par Dn Bulwell St Jo *S'well* 92-94; C 94-97; TV Bestwood 97-03; V Bestwood Em w St Mark from 03. *Emmanuel Vicarage, 10 Church View Close, Arnold, Nottingham NG5 9QP* Tel 0115-920 8879
E-mail beverley.stark@ntlworld.com

STARK, John Jordan. b 40. Hull Univ BA62 St Chad's Coll Dur DipTh64. **d** 64 **p** 65. C Buxton *Derby* 64-67; C Wolborough w Newton Abbot *Ex* 67-74; R Belstone 74-79; P-in-c Plymouth St Gabr 79-80; V from 80. *The Vicarage, 1 Peverell Terrace, Plymouth PL3 4JJ* Tel (01752) 663938

STARK, Margaret Alison. b 46. Univ of Wales BA70 BA71. St Mich Coll Llan DPS90. **d** 90 **p** 97. C Llanishen and Lisvane *Llan* 90-93; C Llanishen 93-94; C Aberavon 94-98; R Llanfabon 98-01; rtd 01. *4 Penarth House, 28 Stanwell Road, Penarth CF64 2EY* Tel (029) 2070 1303

STARK, Michael. b 35. Dur Univ BSc56 SEN58. Chich Th Coll 58. **d** 60 **p** 61. C Middlesbrough St Paul *York* 60-64; C S Bank 64-66; Asst Chapl HM Pris Wormwood Scrubs 74-76; Asst Chapl HM Pris Liv 75-76; Chapl HM Pris Featherstone 76-83; Chapl HM Pris Ex 83-89; Chapl HM Pris Leic 89-97; rtd 97; Perm to Offic *Leic* and *S'well* from 99. *28 St Peters Road, Highfields, Leicester LE2 1DA*

STARKEY, Gerald Dennis. b 34. Qu Coll Birm 79. **d** 82 **p** 83. C Wilnecote *Lich* 82-86; Min Stoke-upon-Trent 86-90; P-in-c W Bromwich St Pet 90-00; rtd 00; Perm to Offic *Lich* from 01. *6 Heazewood Drive, Wednesfield, Wolverhampton WV11 1SH* Tel (01902) 726252

STARKEY, John Douglas. b 23. St Chad's Coll Dur BA47 DipTh48. **d** 48 **p** 49. C Horninglow *Lich* 48-52; C Lower Gornal 52-55; C-in-c W Bromwich Ascension CD 55-57; V Coseley Ch Ch 57-66; V Freehay 66-84; P-in-c Oakamoor w Cotton 78-84; R Dunstall w Rangemore and Tatenhill 84-88; rtd 88; Perm to Offic *Lich* and *Derby* from 88. *34 Park Crescent, Doveridge, Ashbourne DE6 5NE* Tel (01889) 566384

STARKEY, Michael Stuart. b 63. LMH Ox BA85 Nottm Univ BTh92 MA93. St Jo Coll Nottm 90. **d** 93 **p** 94. C Ealing St Mary *Lon* 93-95; C Brownswood Park 95-97; P-in-c 97-01; V Twickenham Common H Trin from 01. *Holy Trinity Vicarage, 1 Vicarage Road, Twickenham TW2 5TS* Tel (020) 8898 1168
E-mail revstarkey@yahoo.co.uk

STARKEY, Patrick Robin. b 37. **d** 64 **p** 65. C Tonbridge SS Pet and Paul *Roch* 64-68; Asst Chapl Sherborne Sch 68-72; Scripture Union 73-85; rtd 99. *14 Heol Twrch, Lower Cwmtwrch, Swansea SA9 2TD*

STARKEY, Simon Mark. b 36. Liv Univ BA78 MA. Clifton Th Coll. **d** 66 **p** 67. C Ox St Ebbe w St Pet *Ox* 66-72; Community Chapl CPAS Kirkdale 72-75; TV Toxteth Park St Bede *Liv* 75-78; P-in-c 78-80; V 80-90; RD Toxteth 81-89; Chapl Ches Coll *Ches* 90-96; TV St Luke in the City *Liv* from 96. *31 Mount Street, Liverpool L1 9HD* Tel 0151-709 2788

STARKEY, Susan Anne. b 52. St Jo Coll Nottm DipTh95. **d** 97 **p** 98. C Watford St Luke *St Alb* 97-02; C Oxhey All SS from 02. *14 The Hoe, Watford WD19 5AY* Tel (020) 8420 1047

STARKIE, Andrew Edward. b 70. Regent's Park Coll Ox BA91 MA95. Ridley Hall Cam 97. **d** 02. C Long Benton *Newc* from 02. *5 Balroy Court, Newcastle upon Tyne NE12 9AW* Tel 0191-270 2186 E-mail curate.stbarts@talk21.com

STARNES, Peter Henry. b 19. LTCL74 St Jo Coll Cam BA42 MA47 Ch Ch Coll Cant PGCE72. Linc Th Coll 42. **d** 44 **p** 45. C Gillingham *Sarum* 44-50; C St Peter-in-Thanet *Cant* 50-52; CF 52-55; Hon CF from 55; R Hothfield *Cant* 56-60; V Westwell 56-65; R Eastwell w Boughton Aluph 60-65; rtd 84. *Whitebeams, High Halden, Ashford TN26 3LY* Tel (01233) 850245

STARNS, Helen Edna. See PATTEN, Mrs Helen Edna

STARR, Michael Reginald. b 41. FICE71 Bris Univ BSc63 PhD66. Ox NSM Course 83. **d** 86 **p** 87. NSM Gt Faringdon w Lt Coxwell *Ox* 86-00; P-in-c Ashbury, Compton Beauchamp and Longcot w Fernham 00-03; NSM Shrivenham and Ashbury from 03. *The Vicarage, Ashbury, Swindon SN6 8LN* Tel (01793) 710231 E-mail michael_starr@compuserve.com

STARR, Michael Richard. b 43. Sarum Th Coll 65. **d** 68 **p** 69. C Plymouth St Pet *Ex* 68-72; C Blackpool St Paul *Blackb* 72-74; V Burnley St Cuth 74-79; C Eastbourne St Mary *Chich* 79-84; P-in-c Eastbourne Ch Ch 84-87; V 87-88; R Guernsey Ste Marie du

Castel *Win* 88-01; V Guernsey St Matt 94-01; Vice-Dean Guernsey 99-01; P-in-c Win St Bart from 01. *Hyde Vicarage, 1 Abbey Hill Close, Winchester SO23 7AZ* Tel (01962) 852032

STARRS, Lindsey Carolyn. b 49. Alsager Coll of Educn CertEd70 Liv Inst of HE BEd85. Ripon Coll Cuddesdon 00. **d** 02. C Penkridge Team *Lich* from 02. *31 Saxon Road, Penkridge, Stafford ST19 5EP* Tel (01785) 716540
E-mail starrs@lstarrs.fsnet.com

STARTIN, Geoffrey Neil. b 56. Essex Univ BA81 Ch Ch Ox MSc84 Westmr Coll Ox CertEd85. St Steph Ho Ox 86. **d** 88 **p** 89. C Coseley Ch *Lich* 88-90; C Wellingborough All Hallows *Pet* 90-92; Asst Chapl HM Pris Wormwood Scrubs 92-93; C Newton Nottage *Llan* 93-96; P-in-c Lydd *Cant* 96-99; C Rowner *Portsm* 00-02. *Address temp unknown* Tel 07718-735143 (mobile)

STARTIN, Nicola Gail. b 57. K Coll Lon LLB79. St Steph Ho Ox 88. **d** 90 **p** 96. C Wellingborough All SS *Pet* 90-92; NSM Pyle w Kenfig *Llan* 94-95; Asst Chapl Mid Kent Healthcare NHS Trust 95-97; Chapl HM Pris E Sutton Park 97-00; Chapl HM Pris Haslar from 00. *HM Prison Haslar, 2 Dolphin Way, Gosport PO12 2AW* Tel (023) 9258 0381 ext 325 Fax 9251 0266

STATHAM, Brian Edward. b 55. K Coll Lon MA AKC76. St Steph Ho Ox 77. **d** 78 **p** 79. C Ches H Trin *Ches* 78-81; C Birkenhead Priory 81-82; TV 82-86; V Newton 86-91; SSF 91-94; TV Horsham *Chich* 95-99; Chapl Horsham Gen Hosp 95-99; TV Ches Team *Ches* from 99. *St Thomas's Vicarage, 33 Abbot's Grange, Chester CH2 1AJ* Tel (01244) 371612 Fax 378535
E-mail brianstatham@aol.com

STATHAM, John Francis. b 31. Kelham Th Coll 51. **d** 56 **p** 57. C Ilkeston St Mary *Derby* 56-58; C New Mills 58-59; V 69-81; C Newbold w Dunston 59-62; PC Magheralin 62-69; RD Glossop 78-81; R Matlock 81-89; R Killamarsh 89-93; rtd 93; Perm to Offic *Derby* and *S'well* from 93. *33 Ackford Drive, The Meadows, Worksop S80 1YG* Tel (01909) 476031

STATON, Preb Geoffrey. b 40. Wells Th Coll 64. **d** 66 **p** 67. C Wednesfield St Thos *Lich* 66-69; C Cannock 69-72; V Cheddleton 72-82; RD Leek 77-82; V Harlescott 82-90; Preb Lich Cathl from 87; TR Penkridge Team from 90. *The Rectory, New Road, Penkridge, Stafford ST19 5DN* Tel (01785) 712378
E-mail geoffrey.staton@penkridgechurch.org.uk

STATTER, Deborah Hillary. b 55. Dioc OLM tr scheme. **d** 00 **p** 01. OLM Everton St Pet *Liv* 00-02; OLM Everton St Pet w St Chrys from 02. *76 Prince Edward Street, Liverpool L5 3LW* Tel 0151-207 1045

STAUNTON, Richard Steedman. b 25. Wadh Coll Ox BA49 MA50 BSc51. Cuddesdon Coll 63. **d** 64 **p** 65. C Wyken *Cov* 64-68; V Tile Hill 68-76; V Hillmorton 76-90; rtd 90; Perm to Offic *Ban* from 90. *2 Tan-y-fron, Corris Uchaf, Machynlleth SY20 9BN* Tel (01654) 761466

STAVELEY-WADHAM, Robert Andrew. b 43. ACII. Ridley Hall Cam 79. **d** 81 **p** 82. C Saffron Walden w Wendens Ambo and Littlebury *Chelmsf* 81-84; P-in-c Austrey and Warton *Birm* 84-87; Perm to Offic *Chich* 87-02; *Ely* 88-96; P-in-c Tillington from 02; P-in-c Duncton from 02; P-in-c Up Waltham from 02. *The Rectory, Tillington, Petworth GU28 9AH* Tel (01798) 345210

STEAD, Andrew Michael. b 63. BA. BA84. Coll of Resurr Mirfield 84. **d** 87 **p** 88. C Wellingborough All Hallows *Pet* 87-90; Chapl St Alb Abbey *St Alb* 90-94; Chapl Aldenham Sch Herts from 94. *1 The Orchard, Aldenham School, Elstree, Borehamwood WD6 3RL* Tel (01923) 851636 Fax 854410
E-mail andrew@theorchard.demon.co.uk

STEAD, Canon George Christopher. b 13. K Coll Cam BA35 MA38 LittD78 New Coll Ox BA35 Keble Coll Ox MA49 FBA80. Cuddesdon Coll 38. **d** 38 **p** 41. Perm to Offic *Newc* 38-39; C Newc St Jo 39; Lect Div K Coll Cam 38-49; Fell 38-49 and 71-85; Prof Fell 71-80; Asst Master Eton Coll 40-44; Fell and Chapl Keble Coll Ox 49-71; Select Preacher Ox Univ 58-59 and 61; Ely Prof Div Cam Univ 71-80; Can Res Ely Cathl *Ely* 71-80; rtd 80; Perm to Offic *Ely* from 81. *13 Station Road, Haddenham, Ely CB6 3XD* Tel (01353) 740575

STEAD, Philip John. b 60. Sheff Univ LLB82 City of Lon Poly ACII85. Linc Th Coll 95. **d** 95 **p** 96. C Warsop *S'well* 95-99; P-in-c Forest Town from 99. *The Vicarage, Old Mill Lane, Forest Town, Mansfield NG19 0EP* Tel (01623) 621120

STEAD, Timothy James. b 60. Ex Univ BSc82. St Steph Ho Ox DipMin95. **d** 95 **p** 97. C Broseley w Benthall, Jackfield, Linley etc *Heref* 95-99; TV Haywards Heath St Wilfrid *Chich* from 99. *Ascension Vicarage, 1 Sandy Vale, Haywards Heath RH16 4JH* Tel (01444) 450173

STEADMAN, Mark John. b 74. Southn Univ LLB95 Ch Coll Cam BA01 Barrister-at-Law (Inner Temple) 96. Westcott Ho Cam 99. **d** 02 **p** 03. C Portsea St Mary *Portsm* from 02. *1 St Mary Glebe, 32 Nutfield Place, Portsmouth PO1 4JF* Tel (023) 9283 0154 E-mail steadman@fish.co.uk

STEADMAN, Norman Neil. b 39. QUB BSc61 TCD Div Test63. **d** 63 **p** 64. C Newtownards *D & D* 63-65; C Belfast Whiterock *Conn* 65-67; Asst Dean of Res QUB 67-71; Perm to Offic *St Alb* 71-73; Dioc Youth Officer 73-76; P-in-c Hitchin H Sav 76; TV Hitchin 77-84; V Brampton *Carl* 84-93; R Brampton and Farlam and Castle Carrock w Cumrew 93-98; C Carl H Trin and St Barn

from 98; Chapl Carl Hosps NHS Trust from 98; Chapl North Lakeland Healthcare NHS Trust from 98. *Sandsfield Vicarage, 104 Housesteads Road, Carlisle CA2 7XG* Tel (01228) 536710

STEADMAN-ALLEN, Miss Barbara. b 53. ARCM83 Trent Park Coll of Educn CertEd74 Birm Univ BMus77. Cranmer Hall Dur 88. **d** 90 **p** 94. C Chessington *Guildf* 90-94; C Chertsey 94-99; Chapl Box Hill Sch from 99; P-in-c Mickleham *Guildf* 99-01; C Leatherhead and Mickleham from 01. *The Rectory, Old London Road, Mickleham, Dorking RH5 6EB* Tel (01372) 378335

STEADY, Miss Vilda May. b 51. Linc Th Coll 87. **d** 89 **p** 94. Par Dn Cannock *Lich* 89-91; Par Dn Hammerwich 91-94; C 94-95; Asst Chapl Eastbourne Hosps NHS Trust 95-97; Chapl Luton and Dunstable Hosp NHS Trust 97-01; Chapl Jas Paget Healthcare NHS Trust from 01. *17A Western Road, Gorleston, Great Yarmouth NR31 7QG* Tel (01493) 442232

STEAR, Michael Peter Hutchinson. b 47. Goldsmiths' Coll Lon TCert68. Wycliffe Hall Ox 71. **d** 74 **p** 75. C Streatham Vale H Redeemer *S'wark* 74-77; C-in-c Ramsgate St Mark *Cant* 77-82; V 82-83; Min Jersey St Paul Prop Chpl *Win* 83-94; TR Radipole and Melcombe Regis *Sarum* 94-00; Chapl Weymouth Coll 94-97; rtd 00; Perm to Offic *Sarum* from 01. *132 Preston Road, Preston, Weymouth DT3 6BH*

STEAR, Mrs Patricia Ann. b 38. Birm Univ BSc60. LNSM course 96. **d** 97 **p** 98. OLM Bradford Peverell, Stratton, Frampton etc *Sarum* from 97. *Westwood House, Bradford Peverell, Dorchester DT2 9SE* Tel (01305) 889227 Fax 889718
E-mail patstear@saqnet.co.uk

STEARE, Peter Douglas. b 27. S Dios Minl Tr Scheme 80. **d** 84 **p** 85. NSM Upton cum Chalvey *Ox* 84-86; Perm to Offic *Bris* 86-88; Hon C Kington St Michael 88-90; Hon C Tetbury w Beverston *Glouc* 94-95; rtd 95; Perm to Offic *Ox* 98-99; Hon C Risborough from 99. *41 Dunsmore Avenue, Monks Risborough, Princes Risborough HP27 9JX* Tel (01844) 273113

STEARN, Peter Reginald. b 38. ARCM. Linc Th Coll 75. **d** 77 **p** 78. C St Alb St Pet *St Alb* 77-79; C Bushey 79-82; V Kings Langley from 82. *The Vicarage, The Glebe, Kings Langley WD4 9HY* Tel (01923) 262939

STEBBING, Christopher Henry. b 64. G&C Coll Cam MEng87 MA90. Cranmer Hall Dur 98. **d** 00 **p** 01. C Malin Bridge *Sheff* from 00. *10 Avondale Road, Sheffield S6 4QP* Tel 0114-232 1051
E-mail stebbingfamily@blueyonder.co.uk

STEBBING, Michael Langdale (Nicolas). b 46. Univ of Zimbabwe BA68 Univ of S Africa MTh86. Coll of Resurr Mirfield. **d** 74 **p** 75. C Borrowdale *Carl* 74-76; Rhodesia 76-79; S Africa 79-86; CR from 80. *House of the Resurrection, Stocks Bank Road, Mirfield WF14 0BN* Tel (01924) 494318

STEDDON, Peter James Raymond. b 46. St Edm Hall Ox BA67 MA71 FCIPD. STETS 96. **d** 99 **p** 00. NSM Goring w S Stoke *Ox* 99-03; NSM Whitchurch St Mary from 03; Team Missr Langtree from 03. *Rectory Cottage, High Street, Whitchurch on Thames, Reading RG8 7DF* Tel 0118-984 1473 Mobile 07766-514874 E-mail petersteddon@hotmail.com

STEDMAN, Barrie John. b 49. Dioc OLM tr scheme 97. **d** 00 **p** 01. OLM Mildenhall *St E* from 00. *13 Bennett Road, Red Lodge, Bury St Edmunds IP28 8JT* Tel (01638) 750505 Mobile 07831-803622 Fax (01223) 455823

STEDMAN, Preb Michael Sydney. b 34. ARICS58 MRICS01. Clifton Th Coll 62. **d** 65 **p** 66. C Lindfield *Chich* 65-68; C Gt Baddow *Chelmsf* 68-73; TV Ashby w Thurton, Claxton and Carleton *Nor* 73-75; P-in-c 75-85; TV Rockland St Mary w Hellington 73-75; P-in-c 75-85; TV Framingham Pigot 73-75; P-in-c 75-85; TV Bramerton w Surlingham 73-75; P-in-c 75-85; TV Bergh Apton w Yelverton 73-75; P-in-c 75-85; RD Loddon 78-85; R Church Stretton *Heref* 85-99; RD Condover 88-96; Preb Heref Cathl 94-99; rtd 99; Perm to Offic *St E* from 00. *44 The Mowbrays, Framlingham, Woodbridge IP13 9DL* Tel (01728) 724479 E-mail michael@stedmanm.freeserve.co.uk

STEDMAN, Robert Alfred. b 24. Qu Coll Birm 50. **d** 52 **p** 53. C Portchester *Portsm* 52-55; V Brighton St Anne *Chich* 55-61; V Salehurst 61-76; R Newhaven 76-90; rtd 90; Perm to Offic *Chich* 90-99. *12 Lady Wootton's Green, Canterbury CT1 1NG*

STEED, Herbert Edward. b 23. St Jo Coll Dur BA51 DipTh52. **d** 52 **p** 53. C Stoneycroft All SS *Liv* 52-55; C Folkestone H Trin w Ch Ch *Cant* 55-57; V Croydon St Jas 57-63; V Strood St Fran *Roch* 63-64; R E Barnet *St Alb* 65-91; rtd 91; Perm to Offic *Guildf* 91-01. *1 Harrier Close, Cranleigh GU6 7BS* Tel (01483) 278150

STEEL, Carolie Mary. b 47. Bedf Coll Lon BA69 Solicitor 73. St Mich Coll Llan 98. **d** 01 **p** 02. NSM Llangunnor w Cwmffrwd *St D* from 01. *Llwyn Celyn, 24 Picton Terrace, Carmarthen SA31 3BX* Tel (01267) 236369 Fax 231117

STEEL, Graham Reginald. b 51. Cam Univ MA. Trin Coll Bris 80. **d** 83 **p** 84. C Gt Parndon *Chelmsf* 83-86; C Barking St Marg w St Patr 86-89; P-in-c Westcliff St Cedd 89-96; P-in-c Prittlewell St Pet 92-96; Chapl Southend Gen Hosp 89-92; V Prittlewell w Westcliff *Chelmsf* from 96. *The Vicarage, 122 Mendip Crescent, Westcliff-on-Sea SS0 0HN* Tel (01702) 525126 Fax 08701-643372 E-mail grahamsteel@blueyonder.co.uk

STEEL, Leslie Frederick. b 34. Webster Univ Geneva MA88. St Jo Coll Auckland 57 LTh65. **d** 59 **p** 60. New Zealand 59-71 and 74-86; Singapore 72-73; C Roslyn 59-62; V Waimea Plains 62-69; CF 70-73; V Dunstan 74-81; Adn Otago 77-82; V Anderson's Bay and Chapl Police Force 82-86; Can Dunedin Cathl 82-85; Adn Dunedin 85-86; Hon C Geneva *Eur* 87-90; Chapl Lausanne 90-97; Perm to Offic *Pet* 98-99; P-in-c Potterspury, Furtho, Yardley Gobion and Cosgrove 99-02; R Potterspury w Furtho and Yardley Gobion etc from 02. *The Vicarage, 11 Church Lane, Potterspury, Towcester NN12 7PU* Tel (01908) 542428 E-mail hestents@btinternet.com

STEEL, Norman William. b 53. Sarum & Wells Th Coll 85. **d** 87 **p** 88. C S Woodham Ferrers *Chelmsf* 87-91; V Woolavington w Cossington and Bawdrip *B & W* 91-99; P-in-c Pitminster w Corfe 99-02; Chapl Huish Coll Taunton from 99; rtd 02; Perm to Offic *B & W* from 02. *96 Burch's Close, Taunton TA1 4TS* Tel (01823) 423204 Fax 07986-370063 E-mail norman.steel@btinternet.com

STEEL, Richard John. b 57. Dur Univ BA79 Cam Univ MA86 Edin Univ MTh97. Ridley Hall Cam 81. **d** 84 **p** 85. C Hull Newland St Jo *York* 84-87; Relig Broadcasting Officer *Derby* 88-92; Dioc Communications Officer *Blackb* 92-97; Communication Dir CMS from 97; Perm to Offic *Guildf* 97-00; NSM Stoke-next-Guildf from 00. *CMS, Partnership House, 157 Waterloo Road, London SE1 8UU* Tel (020) 7928 8681 E-mail richard.steel@cms-uk.org

STEEL, Thomas Molyneux. b 39. Man Univ BA61 Ox Univ DipPSA62. Ripon Hall Ox 61. **d** 63 **p** 64. C Newc H Cross *Newc* 63-66; P-in-c Man St Aid *Man* 66-71; R Failsworth St Jo 71-79; P-in-c Farnham Royal *Ox* 79-81; P-in-c Hedgerley 80-81; R Farnham Royal w Hedgerley 81-91; V Prescot *Liv* 91-03; rtd 03. *20 Barnet Way, London NW7 3BH* Tel (020) 8906 0271

STEELE, Alan Christopher. b 63. Cape Town Univ BA85 Univ of Zimbabwe BA91. Gaul Ho Harare 89. **d** 91 **p** 93. Zimbabwe 91-99; C Harare St Mary Magd 91-93; C Harare St Luke 93-95; Chapl Ruzawi Sch 96-99; CF from 99. *c/o MOD Chaplains (Army)* Tel (01980) 615804 Fax 615800

STEELE, Charles Edward Ernest. b 24. Cuddesdon Coll 72. **d** 74 **p** 75. C Rubery *Birm* 74-77; P-in-c Shaw Hill 77-79; V 79-82; C Curdworth 82-83; C Curdworth w Castle Vale 83-85; rtd 85; Perm to Offic *Birm* from 85. *3 Dominic Drive, Middleton Hall Road, Birmingham B30 1DW* Tel 0121-451 3372

STEELE, David Robert. b 29. Peterho Cam BA53 MA57. Oak Hill Th Coll 53. **d** 56 **p** 57. C Portman Square St Paul *Lon* 56-59; C Sevenoaks St Nic *Roch* 59-62; Kenya 63-65; Lic to Offic *Lon* 65-83; Chapl Steward's Trust Lon 65-72; Jt Gen Sec ICS 72-81; Dir 2 Tim 2 Trust from 81; Perm to Offic *Lon* 83-91; Perm to Offic *Win* from 83; rtd 94. *Worthy Park Grove, Abbots Worthy, Winchester SO21 1AN* Tel (01962) 882082

STEELE, Derek James. b 53. St Jo Coll Nottm CertRE. **d** 97 **p** 98. Aux Min Ballywillan *Conn* from 97. *106 Mountsandel Road, Coleraine BT52 1TA* Tel (028) 7035 1633

STEELE, Gerald Robert. b 25. St D Coll Lamp BA49. **d** 51 **p** 52. C Glyntaff *Llan* 51-63; V Llangeinor 63-73; R Cadoxton-juxta-Barry 73-91; Chapl Barry Community Hosp 73-91; Miss to Seamen 73-91; rtd 91; Perm to Offic *Llan* from 91. *74 Redbrink Crescent, Barry CF62 5TU* Tel (01446) 737554

STEELE, Gordon John. b 55. Kent Univ BA76 Worc Coll Ox BA82 MA87. Coll of Resurr Mirfield 82. **d** 84 **p** 85. C Greenhill St Jo *Lon* 84-88; C Uxbridge St Andr w St Jo 88; TV Uxbridge 88-94; V Northampton St Alb *Pet* 94-01; V Pet St Jo from 01. *26 Minster Precincts, Peterborough PE1 1XX* Tel (01733) 566265 E-mail gordonsteele@fish.co.uk

STEELE, Keith Atkinson. b 28. CEng MIMechE FInstMC. Qu Coll Birm Oak Hill Th Coll 80. **d** 81 **p** 82. NSM Westoning w Tingrith *St Alb* 81-87; NSM Chalgrave 87-88; P-in-c 88-96; RD Dunstable 91-96; Perm to Offic from 96. *Mariner's Lodge, Church Road, Westoning, Bedford MK45 5JW* Tel (01525) 714111

STEELE, Peter Gerald. b 44. Bournemouth Tech Coll BSc67 Essex Univ MSc69. Sarum & Wells Th Coll DipTh93. **d** 93 **p** 94. C Beaminster Area *Sarum* 93-97; P-in-c Aldermaston w Wasing and Brimpton *Ox* from 97. *The Vicarage, Wasing Lane, Aldermaston, Reading RG7 4LX* Tel 0118-971 2281 E-mail petesteele@btopenworld.com

STEELE, Terence. b 54. Linc Th Coll 85. **d** 87 **p** 88. C New Sleaford *Linc* 87-90; V Cowbit 90-95; P-in-c Burgh le Marsh 95-97; P-in-c Orby 95-97; P-in-c Bratoft w Irby-in-the-Marsh 95-97; P-in-c Welton-le-Marsh w Gunby 95-97; V Burgh le Marsh from 97; R Bratoft w Irby-in-the-Marsh from 97; V Orby from 97; R Welton-le-Marsh w Gunby from 97. *The Vicarage, Glebe Rise, Burgh le Marsh, Skegness PE24 5BL* Tel (01754) 810216 E-mail father.steel@btclick.com

STEELE-PERKINS, Mrs Barbara Anita. b 46. Whitelands Coll Lon CertEd68 Spurgeon's Coll MTh98. STETS 99. **d** 01 **p** 02. Tutor Dioc Min Course *Guildf* from 95; NSM Wisley w Pyrford from 01. *The Rectory, Ockham Lane, Ockham, Woking GU23 6NP* Tel (01483) 224959 E-mail barbara@steeleperkins.fsnet.co.uk

STEELE-PERKINS, Richard De Courcy. b 36. Clifton Th Coll 61. **d** 64 **p** 65. C Stoke Damerel *Ex* 64-65; C Washfield 65-68; P-in-c Wimbledon *S'wark* 68-70; Chapl Lambeth Hosp 70-74; Asst Chapl St Thos Hosp Lon 70-74; P-in-c Tawstock *Ex* 74-75; R 75-81; P-in-c Sticklepath 74-75; R 75-81; V Buckfastleigh w Dean Prior 81-91; TR Camelot Par *B & W* 91-94; Asst Chapl R Surrey Co and St Luke's Hosps NHS Trust 94-99; Asst Chapl Heathlands Mental Health Trust Surrey 94-99; P-in-c Ockham w Hatchford *Guildf* 99-01; rtd 02; Hon C E Horsley and Ockham w Hatchford and Downside *Guildf* from 02. *The Rectory, Ockham Lane, Ockham, Woking GU23 6NP* Tel (01483) 210167 E-mail richard@steele-perkins.fsnet.co.uk

STEEN, Jane Elizabeth. b 64. Newnham Coll Cam BA88 MA90 PhD92 Trin Coll Cam 93. Westcott Ho Cam 93. **d** 96 **p** 97. C Chipping Barnet w Arkley *St Alb* 96-99; Chapl and Personal Asst to Bp S'wark from 99; Hon Chapl S'wark Cathl from 00. *70 Pollards Hill North, London SW16 4NY* Tel (020) 8679 4908 *or* 8769 3256 Fax 8769 4126 E-mail jane.steen@dswark.org.uk

STEINBERG, Eric Reed (Joseph). b 65. Trin Coll Bris BA94. **d** 94 **p** 95. C Chigwell and Chigwell Row *Chelmsf* 94-99; Perm to Offic from 99; Dir Y2000 from 99. *104 Pevensey Road, Eastbourne BN22 8AE* Tel (01323) 644404 E-mail jsteinberg@y-2000.com

STEINER, Eduard Samuel Ted. b 52. Liv Univ MB, ChB74 DCH76. EMMTC 93. **d** 96 **p** 97. NSM Ravenshead *S'well* from 96. *La Corbiere, Cauldwell Drive, Mansfield NG18 4SL* Tel (01623) 653615

STELL, Peter Donald. b 50. Leeds Univ 74 Southn Univ BA81 Man Univ 93 MInstM BAC Acc UKRC Reg Ind Cllr. Sarum & Wells Th Coll 78. **d** 81 **p** 82. C Rothwell w Lofthouse *Ripon* 81-85; TV Brayton *York* 85-87; Chapl Asst Leybourne Grange Hosp W Malling 87-88; Chapl Asst Kent, Sussex and Pembury Hosps Tunbridge Wells 87-88; C Spalding St Jo w Deeping St Nicholas *Linc* 87-93; Chapl S Lincs HA Mental Handicap Unit 88-93; Chapl HM Pris Liv 93-94; Chapl HM Pris Wayland 94-99; Chapl HM Pris Grendon and Spring Hill 99-02; Chapl HM Pris Rye Hill from 02. *HM Prison Rye Hill, Willoughby, Rugby CV23 8AN* Tel (01482) 320673

STENHOUSE, Joan Frances Fleming. b 45. RGN66. Ab Dioc Tr Course 82. **dss** 84 **d** 86 **p** 94. Ellon *Ab* 84-86; NSM 86-97; Cruden Bay 84-86; NSM 86-97; Bp's Chapl for Tr and Educn from 95; Asst P Cuminestown from 97. *Burnside of Teuchar, Cuminestown, Turriff AB53 8HS* Tel (01888) 544298 E-mail jstwo@netlineuk.net

STENTIFORD, Pauline Cecilia Elizabeth. b 48. Univ of Wales (Ban) DipHE02. EAMTC 98. **d** 00 **p** 01. NSM Gt and Lt Bealings w Playford and Culpho *St E* 00-03; P-in-c from 03. *Sheepstor, Boyton, Woodbridge IP12 3LH* Tel (01394) 411469 E-mail pauline.stentiford@btopenworld.com

STEPHEN, Canon Kenneth George. b 47. Strathclyde Univ BA69 Edin Univ BD72. Edin Th Coll 69. **d** 72 **p** 73. C Ayr *Glas* 72-75; R Renfrew 75-80; R Motherwell 80-93; R Wishaw 80-93; Can St Mary's Cathl from 87; Syn Clerk from 87; R Kilmarnock from 93. *The Parsonage, 1 Dundonald Road, Kilmarnock KA1 1EQ* Tel (01563) 523577 E-mail ken.stephen@ukgateway.net

STEPHENI, Frederick William. b 28. TD73. FSAScot81 FRSA82 Cranfield Inst of Tech MSc82. Lambeth STh83 Qu Coll Birm 54. **d** 55 **p** 56. C Arnold *S'well* 55-57; P-in-c 57-58; P-in-c Hucknall Torkard 58-59; Chapl Stoke-on-Trent City Gen Hosp 59-62; Chapl N Staffs R Infirmary Stoke-on-Trent 59-62; CF 62) 60-88; Chapl K Coll Hosp Lon 62-63; R Cotgrave *S'well* 63-76; V Owthorpe 63-76; Chapl Addenbrooke's Hosp Cam 76-88; Lic to Offic *Ely* 76-99; rtd 88; Perm to Offic *York* from 00. *64A Scarborough Road, Norton, Malton YO17 8AE* Tel (01653) 694995

STEPHENS, Canon Archibald John. b 15. Selw Coll Cam BA37 MA44. Wells Th Coll 46. **d** 47 **p** 48. C Gt Malvern St Mary *Worc* 47-50; Nigeria 50-68 and 70-71; Hon Can Ondo 57-71; Hon Can Owerri from 71; C Swindon Ch Ch *Bris* 68-70; C-in-c Ash Vale CD *Guildf* 71-72; V Ash Vale 72-77; P-in-c Thursley 77-82; rtd 82; Perm to Offic *Guildf* from 85. *Fernhill, 12 Vicarage Lane, Farnham GU9 8HN* Tel (01252) 722514

STEPHENS, Grahame Frank Henry. b 33. Dioc OLM tr scheme 99. **d** 02. OLM Woolwich St Mary w St Mich *S'wark* from 02. *121 The Drive, Bexley DA5 3BY* Tel (020) 8303 3546 Mobile 07775-796896 Fax (020) 8306 2155

STEPHENS, Harold William Barrow. b 47. Lon Univ BEd71. S Dios Minl Tr Scheme 80. **d** 82 **p** 83. NSM Heytesbury and Sutton Veny *Sarum* 82-83; NSM Bishopstrow and Boreham 83-91; Dep Hd Master Westwood St Thos Sch Salisbury 91-99; P-in-c Market Lavington and Easterton 99-03; P-in-c W Lavington and the Cheverells 02-03; R The Lavingtons, Cheverells, and Easterton from 03. *The Vicarage, 14 Church Street, Market Lavington, Devizes SN10 4DT* Tel (01380) 813914 E-mail harold.stephens@ukonline.co.uk

STEPHENS, James Charles. b 62. Dip Analytical Chemistry. **d** 91 **p** 92. C Kilcolman w Kiltallagh, Killorglin, Knockane etc *L & K* from 91. *Kilderry, Miltown, Co Kerry, Irish Republic* Tel (00353) (66) 67735 E-mail jstephens@klinge.ie

STEPHENS, Mrs Jean. b 46. St As Minl Tr Course. **d** 89 **p** 97. NSM Gwernaffield and Llanferres *St As* 89-02; NSM Hawarden from 02. *Noddfa, Pen-y-Fron Road, Pantymwyn, Mold CH7 5EF* Tel (01352) 740037

STEPHENS, Mrs Joan. b 38. Dioc OLM tr scheme 97. **d** 00 **p** 01. OLM Irlam *Man* from 00. *77 Baines Avenue, Irlam, Manchester M44 6AS* Tel 0161-775 7538

STEPHENS, John. See STEPHENS, Canon Archibald John

STEPHENS, John James Frederick. b 10. QUB BA34. Lon Coll of Div 34. **d** 37 **p** 38. C Stambermill *Worc* 37-40; CF (EC) 40-46; C Seapatrick H Trin *D & D* 46-47; C Wollaston *Worc* 47-48; R The Shelsleys 48-51; V Broadheath 51-82; rtd 82; Perm to Offic *Worc* from 82. *Jerred Cottage, Church Lane, Lower Broadheath, Worcester WR2 6QY* Tel (01905) 640224

STEPHENS, John Michael. b 29. ARICS52 MRICS01. Lich Th Coll 62. **d** 64 **p** 65. C Birchington w Acol *Cant* 64-70; V Tovil 70-79; V Brabourne w Smeeth 79-94; RD N Lympne 87-94; rtd 94; Perm to Offic *York* from 96. *Southacre, Kirby Mills, Kirkbymoorside, York YO62 6NR* Tel (01751) 432766

STEPHENS, Martin Nicholas. b 64. Brunel Univ BSc88 Nottm Univ MTh01. St Jo Coll Nottm 99. **d** 01. C Newchapel *Lich* from 01. *21 Powderham Close, Packmoor, Stoke-on-Trent ST6 6XN* Tel (01782) 790244

STEPHENS, Miss Mary. b 26. Reading Univ BA50 BEd51. Linc Th Coll. **d** 87 **p** 94. NSM Gt Grimsby St Mary and St Jas *Linc* 86-91; C 91-92; TD 92-94; TV 94-96; rtd 96; Perm to Offic *Linc* from 96. *33 Amesbury Avenue, Grimsby DN33 3HT* Tel (01472) 752340

STEPHENS, Paul. b 53. AGSM73 Newton Park Coll Bath PGCE74. Trin Coll Bris DipHE93. **d** 93 **p** 94. C S Molton w Nymet St George, High Bray etc *Ex* 93-97; R Norton Fitzwarren *B & W* 97-99; Chapl St Aug Sch Taunton 97-99; Chapl Monkton Combe Sch Bath from 99. *Monkton Combe School, Monkton Combe, Bath BA2 7HG* Tel (01225) 721116 *or* 721135

STEPHENS, Mrs Penny Clare. b 60. St Anne's Coll Ox BA83 Lon Inst of Educn PGCE85. Oak Hill Th Coll. **d** 99 **p** 00. C Turnham Green Ch Ch *Lon* 99-03. *Address temp unknown*

STEPHENS, Canon Peter John. b 42. Oriel Coll Ox BA64 MA67. Clifton Th Coll 63. **d** 68 **p** 68. C Lenton *S'well* 68-71; C Brixton Hill St Sav *S'wark* 71-73; P-in-c 73-82; TV Barnham Broom *Nor* 82-89; V Gorleston St Mary 89-94; RD Flegg (Gt Yarmouth) 92-94; P-in-c High Oak 94-97; RD Humbleyard 95-98; C Hingham w Wood Rising w Scoulton 96-97; TR High Oak, Hingham and Scoulton w Wood Rising 97; Hon Can Nor Cathl from 99. *The Rectory, Deopham Road, Morley St Botolph, Wymondham NR18 7DA* Tel and fax (01953) 606332 Mobile 07768-425349

STEPHENS, Preb Peter Stanley. b 33. ALCD59. **d** 59 **p** 60. C Paignton St Paul Preston *Ex* 59-64; V Buckland Monachorum 64-74; RD Tavistock 70-74; V Compton Gifford 74-85; RD Plymouth Sutton 83-86; Preb Ex Cathl from 84; TR Plymouth Em w Efford 85-86; R Thurlestone w S Milton 86-98; rtd 98. *Headland View, 14 Court Park, Thurlestone, Kingsbridge TQ7 3LX* Tel (01548) 560891 Fax as telephone

STEPHENS, Richard William. b 37. Dur Univ BSc62 DipTh64. Cranmer Hall Dur 62. **d** 64 **p** 65. C Hensingham *Carl* 64-67; C Norbury *Ches* 67-71; R Elworth and Warmingham 71-79; V Bootle St Matt *Liv* 79-89; P-in-c Litherland St Andr 79-83; P-in-c Failsworth H Trin *Man* 89-93; R 93-02; P-in-c Oldham St Barn 01-02; AD Oldham 99-02; rtd 02. *Cloverstone, 3 Craignair Street, Dalbeattie DG5 4AX* Tel (01556) 610627 E-mail revrstephens@btinternet.com

STEPHENS, Ronald John. b 13. Sarum Th Coll 56. **d** 57 **p** 58. C Calne *Sarum* 57-61; V Stanstead Abbots *St Alb* 61-82; rtd 82; Perm to Offic *Nor* from 82. *63 Beechlands Park, Southrepps, Norwich NR11 8NT* Tel (01263) 834893

STEPHENS, Canon Simon Edward. b 41. OBE92. Qu Coll Birm DPS68 PhD80. Bps' Coll Cheshunt 63. **d** 67 **p** 68. C Cov St Mark *Cov* 67-71; C Lillington 71-76; C-in-c Canley CD 76-79; V Canley 79-80; Chapl RN 80-97; Asst Chapl Menorca *Eur* 97-98; Chapl 98-99; Chapl Moscow from 99; Hon Can Malta Cathl from 01. *British Embassy - Moscow, FCO, King Charles Street, London SW1A 2AH* Tel (007) (095) 229 0990 Fax as telephone E-mail anglican@rol.ru

STEPHENS, Mrs Susanne Hilary. b 44. St Jo Coll Nottm. Guildf Dioc Min Course. **d** 00 **p** 01. OLM Camberley St Paul *Guildf* from 00. *Shire, Knightsbridge Road, Camberley GU15 3TS* Tel and fax (01276) 507693 Mobile 07714-217167 E-mail suestephens@onetel.net.uk

STEPHENSON, David John. b 65. Bris Univ BSc(Soc)87 Dur Univ BA91. Cranmer Hall Dur 92. **d** 92 **p** 93. C Whickham *Dur* 92-94; C Sunderland Pennywell St Thos 94-97; V Stockton St Jo from 97; V Stockton St Jas from 99. *St John the Baptist Vicarage, 168 Durham Road, Stockton-on-Tees TS19 0DZ* Tel (01642) 674119 E-mail david.stephenson2@ntlworld.com

STEPHENSON, Canon Eric George. b 41. Bede Coll Dur CertEd63. Qu Coll Birm DipTh65. **d** 66 **p** 67. C Wakef St Jo *Wakef* 66-69; C Seaham w Seaham Harbour *Dur* 69-73; C Cockerton 73-75; Lic to Offic 75-85; V E Boldon 85; AD Jarrow 92-01; Hon Can Dur Cathl 93; Hon Chapl to The

Queen from 02. *The Vicarage, 2 Ashleigh Villas, East Boldon NE36 0LA* Tel 0191-536 3699 Fax 536 6289 E-mail eric.stephenson@btinternet.com

STEPHENSON, Ian Clarke. b 24. Lon Univ DipTh69. Tyndale Hall Bris 52. **d** 56 **p** 57. C Bedworth *Cov* 56-58; C Edgware *Lon* 58-65; R Biddulph Moor *Lich* 65-70; Hon C Biddulph 70-88; Hon C Burslem 85-88; New Zealand from 87; rtd 89. *5 Arthur Terrace, Balclutha, Otago, New Zealand* Tel (0064) (3) 418 2657

STEPHENSON, John Joseph. b 35. St Jo Coll Dur BA74. Qu Coll Birm 75. **d** 76 **p** 77. C Whitworth w Spennymoor *Dur* 76-79; V Eppleton 79-96; rtd 96; Perm to Offic *Dur* from 96. *29 Launceston Drive, Sunderland SR3 3QB* Tel 0191-528 2144

STEPHENSON, Martin Woodard. b 55. St Cath Coll Cam BA77 MA82. Westcott Ho Cam 78. **d** 81 **p** 82. C Eastleigh *Win* 81-85; C Ferryhill *Dur* 85-87; Asst Dir of Ords 87-89; Chapl St Chad's Coll 87-89; TR Clarendon Park St Jo w Knighton St Mich *Leic* 89-98; P-in-c Hall Green St Pet *Birm* 98-99; V from 99. *St Peter's Vicarage, 33 Paradise Lane, Birmingham B28 0DY* Tel 0121-777 1935 E-mail martinw.stephenson@virgin.net

STEPHENSON, Nicolas William. b 22. Ely Th Coll. **d** 62 **p** 63. C S Westoe *Dur* 62-65; CR from 68; Hon C Westgate Common *Wakef* 74-75; Lic to Offic 75-87; Asst Chapl HM Pris *Wakef* 84-87; rtd 87; Perm to Offic *Ripon* from 87. *24 Nicholson Court, 25 Fitzroy Drive, Leeds LS8 4AP* Tel 0113-248 5166

STEPHENSON, Canon Robert. b 36. St Chad's Coll Dur BA58 DipTh60. **d** 60 **p** 61. C Whickham *Dur* 60-63; C Gateshead St Mary 63-65; PC Low Team 65-67; R Stella 67-74; V Comberton *Ely* from 74; RD Bourn 94-97; P-in-c Dry Drayton 97-01; Hon Can Ely Cathl from 01. *The Vicarage, Church Lane, Comberton, Cambridge CB3 7ED* Tel (01223) 262793

STEPHENSON, Simon George. b 44. St Jo Coll Dur BA67. Trin Coll Bris 74. **d** 76 **p** 77. C Hildenborough *Roch* 76-82; C Bishopsworth *Bris* 82-85; C-in-c Withywood CD 85-90; TV Wreningham *Nor* 90-97; P-in-c Tasburgh w Tharston, Forncett and Flordon 94-97; V Ashwellthorpe, Forncett, Fundenhall, Hapton etc 98; TV High Oak, Hingham and Scoulton w Wood Rising from 98; Chapl HM Pris Wayland from 98. *The Rectory, Attleborough Road, Hingham, Norwich NR9 4HP* Tel (01953) 850211

STEPNEY, Area Bishop of. See OLIVER, The Rt Revd Stephen John

STERLING, Anne. See HASELHURST, Mrs Anne

STERLING, John Haddon. b 40. Pemb Coll Cam BA62 MA66. Cuddesdon Coll 63. **d** 65 **p** 66. S Africa 65-70; Chapl Bris Cathl *Bris* 71-74; Member Dioc Soc and Ind Team 71-74; Ind Chapl *Linc* 74-87; Ind Chapl *Ripon* 87-92; TV Hanley H Ev *Lich* 92-97; Min in Ind 92-97; P-in-c Hixon w Stowe-by-Chartley 97-02; P-in-c Fradswell, Gayton, Milwich and Weston 97-02; TR Mid Trent from 02. *The Vicarage, Stafford Road, Weston, Stafford ST18 0HX* Tel (01889) 270490

STERRY, Christopher. b 54. K Coll Lon BD77 AKC77. Episc Sem Austin Texas 78 St Jo Coll Nottm DPS80. **d** 80 **p** 81. C Huddersfield St Jo *Wakef* 80-84; V Middlestown 84-89; Chapl and Tutor N Ord Course 89-94; Lect Ches Coll of HE 93-94; NSM Padgate *Liv* 92-94; Bp's Dom Chapl *Blackb* 94-97; Chapl Whalley Abbey 94-97; Warden from 97; V Whalley from 97. *The Vicarage, 40 The Sands, Clitheroe BB7 9TL* Tel (01254) 824679, 823249 *or* 828400 Mobile 07010-717992 Fax (01254) 828401 E-mail vicwhalley@aol.com

STERRY, Timothy John. b 34. Oriel Coll Ox BA58 MA62 DipTh60. Wycliffe Hall Ox 58. **d** 60 **p** 61. C Cromer *Nor* 60-64; Chapl Oundle Sch 64-72; Teacher Cheam Prep Sch 72-75; Hd Master Temple Grove Sch E Sussex 75-80; Team Ldr Scripture Union Independent Schs 81-99; rtd 00. *60 Amberwood, Ferndown BH22 9JT* Tel (01202) 873053 E-mail tim@sterry.org

STEVEN, Canon David Bowring. b 38. AKC64. **d** 64 **p** 65. C Grantham St Wulfram *Linc* 64-68; S Africa 68-75; C Bramley *Ripon* 76-77; V Sutton Valence w E Sutton and Chart Sutton *Cant* 77-82; P-in-c Littlebourne 82-86; V Mansfield Woodhouse *S'well* 86-98; P-in-c Mullion *Truro* 98-03; RD Kerrier 01-03; Hon Can Truro Cathl from 03; rtd 03. *5 Guinea Port Parc, Wadebridge PL27 7BY* Tel (01208) 815393

STEVEN, James Henry Stevenson. b 62. CCC Cam MA84 St Jo Coll Dur BA87 K Coll Lon PhD99. Cranmer Hall Dur 84. **d** 87 **p** 88. C Welling *Roch* 87-91; C Bournemouth St Jo w St Mich *Win* 91-94; TV Bournemouth St Pet w St Swithun, H Trin etc 94-00; Chapl Bournemouth and Poole Coll of FE 94-00; Tutor Trin Coll Bris from 00. *Trinity College, Stoke Hill, Bristol BS9 1JP* Tel 0117-968 2803

STEVENETTE, John Maclachlan. b 30. St Pet Coll Ox MA60. Ripon Hall Ox 60. **d** 61 **p** 62. C Newhaven *Chich* 61-66; R Lynch w Iping Marsh 66-74; R Birdham w W Itchenor 74-78; R Byfleet *Guildf* 78-86; V Whittlesey *Ely* 86-90; TR Whittlesey and Pondersbridge 91; R Itchen Valley *Win* 91-99; rtd 99; Perm to Offic *Bris* from 00. *35 Ballard Chase, Abingdon OX14 1XQ* Tel (01235) 526706

STEVENETTE, Simon Melville. b 62. Hull Univ BA83. Wycliffe Hall Ox 84. **d** 87 **p** 88. C Carterton *Ox* 87-90; C Keynsham *B & W* 90-91; TV 91-98; Chapl Keynsham Hosp Bris 92-98; V Swindon Ch Ch *Bris* from 98. *Christ Church Vicarage,*

26 Cricklade Street, Swindon SN1 3HG Tel (01793) 529166 Fax (07070) 754618

STEVENS, Alan Robert. b 55. Warwick Univ BA77. St Jo Coll Nottm 87. **d** 89 **p** 90. C Ex St Leon w H Trin *Ex* 89-92; TV Rugby St Andr *Cov* 92-97; P-in-c N w S Kilworth and Misterton *Leic* 97-00. *Address temp unknown*

STEVENS, Andrew. *See* STEVENS, John David Andrew

STEVENS, Andrew Graham. b 54. BEd MA. Coll of Resurr Mirfield. **d** 83 **p** 84. C Leigh Park *Portsm* 83-87; TV Brighton Resurr *Chich* 87-94; V Plumstead St Nic *S'wark* from 94. *St Nicholas's Vicarage, 64 Purrett Road, London SE18 1JP* Tel (020) 8854 0461 Fax 8265 5065 E-mail frandrew@dircon.co.uk

STEVENS, Anne Helen. b 61. Warwick Univ BA82 Fitzw Coll Cam BA90 MA94 Heythrop Coll Lon MTh99. Ridley Hall Cam 88. **d** 91 **p** 94. Par Dn E Greenwich Ch Ch w St Andr and St Mich *S'wark* 91-94; Chapl Trin Coll Cam 94-99; P-in-c Battersea St Mich *S'wark* from 99; Dir Readers' Tr from 99. *93 Bolingbroke Grove, London SW11 6HA* Tel (020) 7228 1990

STEVENS, Anthony Harold. b 46. CEng71 MIStructE71 FIStructE87 MICE75 FICE92 S Bank Univ ONC65 HNC67. St Mich Coll Llan Dip Practical Th 95. **d** 95 **p** 96. C Cardiff St Jo *Llan* 95-98; TV Cowbridge 98-01; R Eglwysilan from 01. *The Rectory, Brynhafod Road, Abertridwr, Caerphilly CF83 4BH* Tel (029) 2083 0220 E-mail tonstevens@aol.com

STEVENS, Brian Henry. b 28. Oak Hill Th Coll. **d** 69 **p** 70. C Chadwell *Chelmsf* 69-75; V Penge Ch Ch w H Trin *Roch* 75-85; V St Mary Cray and St Paul's Cray 85-93; rtd 93; Perm to Offic *Cant* from 93. *53 Middle Deal Road, Deal CT14 9RG*

STEVENS, Brian Henry. b 45. Open Univ BA80. S Dios Minl Tr Scheme 81. **d** 84 **p** 85. NSM S Malling *Chich* 84-86; C Langney 86-87; TV Wolverton *Ox* 87-88; V Welford w Sibbertoft and Marston Trussell *Pet* 88-91; V Hardingstone and Horton and Piddington from 91. *The Vicarage, 29 Back Lane, Hardingstone, Northampton NN4 6BY* Tel (01604) 760110 Mobile 07802-702036 Fax (01604) 702547 E-mail brian.stevens@tesco.net

STEVENS, Cyril David Richard. b 25. NZ Bd of Th Studies LTh66. **d** 59 **p** 60. New Zealand 59-65 and 67-68; V Playford w Culpho and Tuddenham St Martin *St E* 65-67; R Rendham w Sweffling and Cransford 69-73; RD Saxmundham 72-74; R Rendham w Sweffling 73-95; rtd 95; Perm to Offic *St E* from 95. *Meadow Cottage, Low Road, Marlesford, Woodbridge IP13 0AW* Tel (01728) 746013

STEVENS, David Charles. b 31. Keble Coll Ox BA55 DipTh56 MA59. Wycliffe Hall Ox 55. **d** 57 **p** 58. C Plymouth St Andr *Ex* 57-60; S Rhodesia 61-65; Rhodesia 65-66; Asst Chapl Bryanston Sch 66-70; Chapl 70-73; P-in-c Shilling Okeford *Sarum* 73-76; Lic to Offic *Chelmsf* 76-86; Chapl Chigwell Sch Essex 76-86; R Tarrant Valley *Sarum* 86-94; rtd 94; Perm to Offic *Sarum* from 94. *Bumble Cottage, 3 Yondover, Loders, Bridport DT6 4NW* Tel (01308) 421025

STEVENS, David John. b 45. Bris Univ BA67 Lon Univ DipTh69. Clifton Th Coll. **d** 70 **p** 71. C Ex St Leon w H Trin *Ex* 70-75; P-in-c Lt Burstead *Chelmsf* 75-77; TV Billericay and Lt Burstead 77-81; P-in-c Illogan *Truro* 81-83; R St Illogan 83-96; RD Carnmarth N 96; V Highworth w Sevenhampton and Inglesham etc *Bris* 96-01; P-in-c Constantine *Truro* from 01; RD Kerrier from 03. *The Vicarage, Charlbury Heights, Constantine, Falmouth TR11 5UR* Tel (01326) 340259

STEVENS, Canon David Johnson (Brother David Stephen). b 13. St Cath Soc Ox BA51 MA55. Wycliffe Hall Ox 49. **d** 52 **p** 53. C Wigan St Cath *Liv* 52-54; P-in-c Litherland St Paul Hatton Hill 54-57; Ind Chapl 57-77; V Warrington St Paul 61-70; Guardian of Franciscan Ho Liv 70-77; Lic to Offic Cant 71-78; SSF from 77; Lic to Offic *Newc* from 79; rtd 83. *clo Provincial Bursar, The Friary, Hilfield, Dorchester DT2 7BE* Tel (01300) 341345 Fax 341293

STEVENS, David Leonard. b 28. St Edm Hall Ox BA51 MA57. Cuddesdon Coll 60. **d** 62 **p** 63. C Old Brumby *Linc* 62-67; Chapl St Alb Sch Chorley 67-71; V Linc St Faith and St Martin w St Pet *Linc* 72-83; C Wolborough w Newton Abbot *Ex* 83-87; P-in-c 87-94; rtd 94. *Yew Tree Cottage, Sticklepath, Okehampton EX20 2NW* Tel (01837) 840098

STEVENS, David Lynne. b 59. Poly of Wales BA81. N Ord Course 99. **d** 02 **p** 03. C Horsforth *Ripon* from 02. *7 Featherbank Walk, Horsforth, Leeds LS18 4QN* Tel 0113-258 4653 Mobile 07748-477970 E-mail davidstev1@aol.com

STEVENS, David Norman. b 44. QPM91. OStJ89. EAMTC 01. **d** 03. NSM Necton, Holme Hale w N and S Pickenham *Nor* from 03. *clo Crockford, Church House, Great Smith Street, London SW1P 3NZ* E-mail david@stevens.go-plus.net

STEVENS, Douglas George. b 47. Lon Univ BA69. Westcott Ho Cam 69. **d** 72 **p** 73. C Portsea St Geo CD *Portsm* 72-75; C Portsea N End St Mark 75-79; Chapl NE Lon Poly *Chelmsf* 79-83; C-in-c Orton Goldhay CD *Ely* 83-87; V Elm 87-91; V Coldham 87-91; V Friday Bridge 87-91; R Woodston 91-98; P-in-c Fletton 94-98; rtd 98. *28 Francis Gardens, Peterborough PE1 3XX* Tel (01733) 755430

STEVENS, Frank Hayman. b 11. Univ Coll Ox BA32 MA38. Linc Th Coll 64. **d** 65 **p** 66. C Burnham *B & W* 65-68; V Kenn

68-69; P-in-c Kingston Seymour 68-69; R Kenn w Kingston Seymour 69-74; P-in-c Cossington 74-76; rtd 76; Perm to Offic *B & W* 76-98. *14 Eastgate Gardens, Taunton TA1 1RD* Tel (01823) 270436

STEVENS, Frederick Crichton. b 42. K Coll Lon BD78 AKC78. St Steph Ho Ox 78. **d** 79 **p** 80. C Newquay *Truro* 79-81; C St Martin-in-the-Fields *Lon* 81-85; P-in-c Soho St Anne w St Thos and St Pet 85-96; R 96-98; R Lostwithiel, St Winnow w St Nectan's Chpl etc *Truro* from 98. *The Rectory, 3 Springfield Close, Lostwithiel PL22 0ER* Tel (01208) 873448

STEVENS, Miss Gillian. b 51. K Alfred's Coll Win CertEd72. EAMTC 98. **d** 01 **p** 02. C March St Mary and March St Pet *Ely* 01-03; C Whittlesey, Pondersbridge and Coates from 03. *8 The Grove, Whittlesey, Peterborough PE7 2RF* E-mail gill@stevens.net

STEVENS, James Anthony. b 47. Worc Coll Ox MA69. Trin Coll Bris 78. **d** 80 **p** 81. C Heref St Pet w St Owen and St Jas *Heref* 80-84; C Lowestoft and Kirkley *Nor* 84-85; TV 85-89; V Dorridge *Birm* from 89; AD Shirley from 02. *The Vicarage, 6 Manor Road, Dorridge, Solihull B93 8DX* Tel (01564) 772472 *or* 775652

STEVENS, Jane. *See* KRAFT, Mrs Jane

STEVENS, Janice Hazel. **d** 00 **p** 01. Chapl S Lon and Maudsley NHS Trust from 00; NSM Warlingham w Chelsham and Farleigh *S'wark* from 00. *7 Harrow Road, Warlingham CR6 9EY*

STEVENS, John David Andrew. b 44. Wycliffe Hall Ox. **d** 68 **p** 69. C Standish *Blackb* 68-71; C Stonehouse *Glouc* 71-76; P-in-c Closworth *B & W* 76-77; P-in-c Barwick 76-77; TV Yeovil 77-80; R Chewton Mendip w Ston Easton, Litton etc 80-94; R Quantoxhead from 94; RD Quantock 95-01. *The New Rectory, Kilve, Bridgwater TA5 1DZ* Tel (01278) 741501 Fax as telephone E-mail andrewstevens@zetnet.co.uk

STEVENS, Martin Leonard. b 35. St Jo Coll Dur BA60 MA72. Oak Hill Th Coll 60. **d** 62 **p** 63. C Low Elswick *Newc* 62-65; C S Croydon Em *Cant* 65-69; Hon C 69-74; S England Dep Sec Instn Ch Miss 69-74; V Felling *Dur* 74-86; NSM Ches Square St Mich w St Phil *Lon* 92-96; rtd 95; Hon C Cullompton and Kentisbeare w Blackborough *Ex* 96-01. *11 Foxes Way, Warwick CV34 6AX* Tel (01926) 490864

STEVENS, Michael John. b 37. St Cath Coll Cam BA63. Coll of Resurr Mirfield 63. **d** 65 **p** 66. C Poplar All SS w St Frideswide *Lon* 65-71; Asst Chapl The Lon Hosp (Whitechapel) 71-74; Chapl St Thos Hosp Lon 75-96; Hospitaller St Bart Hosp Lon from 96; P-in-c St Bart Less *Lon* 96-99; V from 99. *The Hospitaller, St Bartholomew's Hospital, West Smithfield, London EC1A 7BE* Tel (020) 7601 8066 E-mail rev.stevens@bartsandthelondon.nhs.uk

STEVENS, Norman William. b 38. St Chad's Coll Dur BA61 DipTh63. **d** 63 **p** 99. C Wingate Grange *Dur* 63-64; NSM Bulkington w Shilton and Ansty *Cov* from 99. *60 Clinton Lane, Kenilworth CV8 1AT* Tel (01926) 858090 *or* (024) 7622 7597

STEVENS, Penelope Ann. b 46. SW Minl Tr Course DTPS99. **d** 99 **p** 00. NSM Halsetown *Truro* 99-02; P-in-c Breage w Germoe and Godolphin from 02. *The Vicarage, Breage, Helston TR13 9PN* Tel (01326) 573449 Mobile 07929-152234 E-mail revpen@lineone.net

STEVENS, Peter David. b 36. ARICS MRICS01. Oak Hill Th Coll DipHE81. **d** 81 **p** 82. C Branksome St Clem *Sarum* 81-87; R Moreton and Woodsford w Tincleton 87-98; rtd 98; Hon C Hordle *Win* 98-02; Perm to Offic from 02. *34 Wisbech Way, Hordle, Lymington SO41 0YQ* Tel (01425) 628922

STEVENS, Philip Terence. b 55. Man Univ BSc76 Lon Univ BD81 St Jo Coll Dur MA86 MCMI MIED. Cranmer Hall Dur 81. **d** 83 **p** 84. C Withington St Paul *Man* 83-86; C Middleton 86-88; V Saddleworth 88-92; V Sheff St Paul *Sheff* 93-96; TR Sheff Manor 96-00; Perm to Offic 00-02; Soc Inclusion Manager Sheff City Coun from 00. *238 Carter Knowle Road, Sheffield S7 2EB* Tel 0114-250 8044

STEVENS, Canon Ralph Samuel Osborn. b 13. Birm Univ BSc29 St Cath Soc Ox BA36 MA41. Ripon Hall Ox 34. **d** 36 **p** 37. C Aston SS Pet and Paul *Birm* 36-45; P-in-c Birm St Paul 45-50; V 50-83; RD Cen Birmingham 46-58; RD Birm City 58-73; Hon Chapl to Bp 48-83; Hon Can Birm Cathl 52-83; Ind Chapl 54-78; Chapl to The Queen 67-83; rtd 83; Perm to Offic *Birm* from 84. *10 Harrison's Green, Birmingham B15 3LH* Tel 0121-454 3089

STEVENS, Richard William. b 36. AKC59. St Boniface Warminster 59. **d** 60 **p** 61. C Greenhill St Jo *Lon* 60-63; Chapl RAF 63-79; CF 79-01; rtd 01; Perm to Offic *Cant* from 02. *The Old Vicarage, Stockbury, Sittingbourne ME9 7UN* Tel (01795) 844891

STEVENS, Robin George. b 43. Leic Univ BA65. Cuddesdon Coll 74. **d** 74 **p** 75. C Hemel Hempstead *St Alb* 74-77; Chapl K Coll Sch Wimbledon from 77; TV Wimbledon *S'wark* from 98. *9 Thornton Road, London SW19 4NE* Tel (020) 8946 3423 *or* 8947 9311

STEVENS, Simon Mark. b 72. Lon Univ BD Cam Univ MPhil. STETS 00. **d** 01 **p** 02. C Sholing *Win* from 01. *93 Spring Road, Southampton SO19 2QH* Tel (023) 8042 0371 E-mail simon.m.stevens@btinternet.com

STEVENS, Mrs Susan Marjorie Earlam. b 52. RGN74 Ox Poly HVCert76. WMMTC 97. **d** 00 **p** 01. NSM Harborne St Faith and St Laur *Birm* 00-02; C Publow w Pensford, Compton Dando and Chelwood *B & W* from 03. *Woollard Place, Woollard, Pensford, Bristol BS39 4HU* Tel (01761) 490898

STEVENS, Miss Sylvia Joyce. b 41. Qu Mary Coll Lon BA63 Bris Univ CertEd64 St Jo Coll Dur BA77 DipTh78. Cranmer Hall Dur 75. **dss** 78 **d** 87 **p** 94. Chapl Trent (Nottm) Poly *S'well* 78-92; Chapl Nottm Trent Univ 92-93; CME Officer *Bris* 93-95; Tutor Trin Coll Bris 93-95; Hon C Chippenham St Pet *Bris* 93-95; C 95-97; R Everton and Mattersey w Clayworth *S'well* from 97. *The Rectory, Abbey Lane, Mattersey, Doncaster DN10 5DX* Tel (01777) 817364

STEVENS, Thomas Walter. b 33. Bps' Coll Cheshunt. **d** 65 **p** 66. C Newc St Matt w St Mary *Newc* 65-69; C Wallsend St Luke 69-70; C Cranford *Lon* 70-87; C Fulwell St Mich and St Geo 87-90; C Teddington SS Pet and Paul and Fulwell 90-91; rtd 92; Perm to Offic *S'wark* from 92. *23A Samos Road, London SE20 7UQ*

STEVENS, Trevor. b 65. Grey Coll Dur BA86 PGCE87 FSAScot93 FRSA94. Edin Th Coll 93 Coll of Resurr Mirfield 97. **d** 98 **p** 99. C Alnwick *Newc* 98-01; R Dundee St Salvador *Bre* from 01. *The Rectory, 9 Minard Crescent, Dundee DD3 6LH* Tel (01382) 221785

STEVENSON, Canon Alastair Rice. b 42. Open Univ BA78. Ripon Coll Cuddesdon 78. **d** 80 **p** 81. C Bexhill St Pet *Chich* 80-82; C Brighton St Matthias 82-84; C Swindon Ch Ch *Bris* 84-87; Bp's Soc and Ind Adv 87-97; P-in-c Swindon All SS w St Barn 97-01; V from 01; Hon Can Bris Cathl from 02. *The Vicarage, Southbrook Street, Swindon SN2 1HF* Tel (01793) 612385 Fax as telephone
E-mail alastair@asteve.fsbusiness.co.uk

STEVENSON, Andrew James. b 63. IEng AMICE MIAT. SW Minl Tr Course 94. **d** 97 **p** 98. NSM Highertown and Baldhu *Truro* from 97. *19 Hillcrest Avenue, Truro TR1 3NE* Tel (01872) 241880 E-mail andy@blacktop.freeserve.co.uk

STEVENSON, Beaumont. *See* STEVENSON, Canon Frank Beaumont

STEVENSON, Bernard Norman. b 57. Kent Univ BA78 Fitzw Coll Cam BA81 MA86. Ridley Hall Cam. **d** 82 **p** 83. C Mortlake w E Sheen *S'wark* 82-84; C Kensal Rise St Martin *Lon* 84-88; C Headstone St Geo 88-90; V Worfield *Heref* 90-95; R Hutton *B & W* from 95. *The Rectory, Church Lane, Hutton, Weston-super-Mare BS24 9SL* Tel (01934) 812366
E-mail bstevenson@clara.net

STEVENSON, Brian. *See* STEVENSON, Canon Robert Brian

STEVENSON, Brian. b 34. JP66. NW Ord Course 76. **d** 79 **p** 80. C Padiham *Blackb* 79-82; V Clitheroe St Paul Low Moor 82-89; V Blackb St Silas 89-01; rtd 01; Perm to Offic *Blackb* from 01. *1 Chatburn Close, Great Harwood, Blackburn BB6 7TL* Tel (01254) 885051

STEVENSON, Christopher James. b 43. TCD BA65 MA73 Em Coll Cam BA69 MA73. Westcott Ho Cam 68. **d** 70 **p** 71. C Newc H Cross *Newc* 70-72; C Arm St Mark *Arm* 72-73; C Dublin Crumlin *D & G* 73-76; Hon Clerical V Ch Ch Cathl Dublin 75-76; C-in-c Appley Bridge All SS *Blackb* 76-82; P-in-c Appley Bridge 82-91; Bp's C Cloonclare w Killasnett, Lurganboy and Drumlease *K, E & A* from 91. *The Rectory, Manorhamilton, Co Leitrim, Irish Republic* Tel (00353) (71) 985 5041

STEVENSON, David Andrew. b 60. Trin Coll Bris BA92. **d** 92 **p** 93. C Nottingham St Sav *S'well* 92-96; P-in-c Darlaston All SS *Lich* 96-00; Ind Chapl Black Country Urban Ind Miss 96-00; C Darlaston St Lawr 99-00; TV Broadwater St Mary *Chich* from 00. *St Stephen's Vicarage, 37 Angola Road, Worthing BN14 8DU* Tel (01903) 523310

STEVENSON, Derick Neville. b 36. Open Univ BA76. Ridley Hall Cam 79. **d** 80 **p** 81. C Bonchurch *Portsm* 80-84; C-in-c Crookhorn Ch Cen CD 84-87; R Norton Fitzwarren *B & W* 87-96; P-in-c N Hartismere *St E* 96-01; rtd 01; Perm to Offic *Portsm* from 02. *Brambles, Main Road, Brighstone, Newport PO30 4AJ* Tel (01983) 740436

STEVENSON, Donald Macdonald. b 48. Lon Univ BSc(Econ)70 Leeds Univ MA72 Univ of Wales (Abth) PGCE73 Warwick Univ MEd78 UEA Dip Counselling 00. Oak Hill Th Coll BA88. **d** 88 **p** 89. C Gt Malvern St Mary *Worc* 88-92; Chapl Bedford Sch 92-98; Sen Chapl 96-98; Perm to Offic *St Alb* from 99; Perm to Offic *Ox* from 01. *94 Curlew Crescent, Bedford MK41 7HZ* Tel (01234) 217013 E-mail donstevenson100@hotmail.com

STEVENSON, Canon Frank Beaumont. b 39. Duke Univ (USA) BA61 MInstGA. Episc Th Sch Harvard MDiv64. **d** 64 **p** 64. USA 64-66; Zambia 66-68; Lect Th Ox Univ from 68; Bp's Tr

Officer *Ox* 69-70; Chapl Keble Coll Ox 71-72; Chapl Oxon Mental Healthcare NHS Trust from 75; Officer for Continuing Minl Educn from 90; Dioc Adv Past Care from 90; Hon Can Ch Ch *Ox* from 98. *Littlemore Mental Health Trust, Oxford OX4 4XN,* or *The School House, Stanton St John, Oxford OX33 1ET* Tel (01865) 778911 *or* 351635
E-mail 101531.3264@compuserve.com

STEVENSON, Gerald Ernest. b 35. S'wark Ord Course 80. **d** 83 **p** 84. NSM Eltham Park St Luke *S'wark* 83-88; Asst Chapl HM Pris Wormwood Scrubs 88-98; Perm to Offic *S'wark* 88-99; rtd 99; Hon C Eltham St Barn *S'wark* from 99. *7 Moira Road, London SE9 1SJ* Tel (020) 8850 2748

STEVENSON, John. b 39. Glas Univ MA64 Jordan Hill Coll Glas TCert65. St Jo Coll Nottm Edin Th Coll. **d** 87 **p** 88. NSM Moffat *Glas* 87-92; P-in-c Eastriggs 92-95; P-in-c Gretna 92-95; P-in-c Langholm 92-95; Israel 95-01; P-in-c Thurso *Mor* from 01; P-in-c Wick from 01. *5 Naver Place, Thurso KW14 8PZ* Tel (01847) 893393 E-mail john@kw147pz.co.uk

STEVENSON, John Charles. b 22. St Jo Coll Dur LTh48. Oak Hill Th Coll 45. **d** 49 **p** 50. C Davyhulme St Mary *Man* 49-51; C Thornham w Gravel Hole 51-54; V Steeple Claydon *Ox* 54-58; R Salford Stowell Memorial *Man* 58-64; RD Claydon *Ox* 58; V Bolton St Bede *Man* 64-75; Asst Chapl HM Pris Wandsworth 75-77; Chapl HM Pris Linc 77-80; R Fiskerton *Linc* 80-87; rtd 87; Perm to Offic *Blackb* from 87. *15 The Coppice, Redwood Park, Beaufort Road, Morecambe LA4 6TS* Tel (01524) 423653

STEVENSON, John William. b 44. Salford Univ BSc66 E Warks Coll Dip Mgt73 Univ of S Africa BTh89. St Paul's Coll Grahamstown DipTh86. **d** 87 **p** 87. S Africa 87-93; V Broom Leys *Leic* from 93. *St David's Vicarage, 7 Greenhill Road, Coalville LE67 4RL* Tel (01530) 836262
E-mail stevensons@vicarage30.freeserve.co.uk

STEVENSON, The Rt Revd Kenneth William. b 49. Edin Univ MA70 Southn Univ PhD75 Man Univ DD87 FRHistS90. Sarum & Wells Th Coll 70. **d** 73 **p** 74 **c** 95. C Grantham w Manthorpe *Linc* 73-76; C Boston 76-80; Chapl and Lect Man Univ *Man* 80-86; TV Man Whitworth 80-82; TR 82-86; R Guildf H Trin w St Mary *Guildf* 86-95; Bp Portsm from 95. *Bishopsgrove, 26 Osborn Road, Fareham PO16 7DQ* Tel (01329) 280247 Fax 231538 E-mail bishports@clara.co.uk

STEVENSON, Leslie Thomas Clayton. b 59. TCD BA DipTh MPhil. **d** 83 **p** 84. C Dundela St Mark *D & D* 83-87; I Kilmore and Inch 87-92; R Donaghadee 92-99; I Portarlington w Cloneyhurke and Lea *M & K* from 99. *The Rectory, Portarlington, Co Laois, Irish Republic* Tel (00353) (502) 40117 Fax as telephone

STEVENSON, Michael Richard Nevin. b 52. Lon Univ BSc MA77. CITC DipTh86. **d** 86 **p** 87. C Clooney w Strathfoyle *D & R* 86-89; CF from 89. *c/o MOD Chaplains (Army)* Tel (01980) 615804 Fax 615800

STEVENSON, Miss Pamela Mary. b 35. Lon Univ CQSW74. LNSM course 94. **d** 97 **p** 98. OLM Mitcham Ascension *S'wark* from 97. *7 Robin Hood Close, Mitcham CR4 1JN* Tel (020) 8764 8331 Mobile 07702-928204

STEVENSON, Peter John. b 70. Southn Univ BSc91 MSc93. Wycliffe Hall Ox 00. **d** 02 **p** 03. C Watford St Luke *St Alb* from 02. *19 Langley Road, Watford WD17 4PS*

STEVENSON, The Ven Richard Clayton. b 22. TCD BA48 MA56. CITC 48. **d** 49 **p** 49. C Belfast St Mary Magd *Conn* 48-51; C Bangor St Comgall *D & D* 51-54; I Comber 54-60; I Belfast St Barn *Conn* 60-70; I Belfast St Nic 70-88; Adn Conn 79-88; rtd 88. *42 Malone Heights, Belfast BT9 5PG* Tel (028) 9061 5006

STEVENSON, Canon Robert Brian. b 40. QUB BA61 Qu Coll Cam BA67 MA71 Pemb Coll Ox BA69 BD76 MA76 Birm Univ PhD70. Cuddesdon Coll 69. **d** 70 **p** 71. C Lewisham St Jo Southend *S'wark* 70-73; C Catford (Southend) and Downham 73-74; Lect and Dir Past Studies Chich Th Coll 74-81; Acting Vice-Prin 80-81; V W Malling w Offham *Roch* from 81; RD Malling 93-02; Hon Can Roch Cathl from 98. *The Vicarage, 138 High Street, West Malling ME19 6NE* Tel (01732) 842245

STEVENSON, Canon Ronald. b 17. Leeds Univ BA38. Coll of Resurr Mirfield 38. **d** 40 **p** 41. C Pontefract All SS *Wakef* 40-44; C-in-c Lundwood CD 44-47; Area Sec Miss to Seamen 47-49; Chapl Lanc Moor Hosp 49-65; Chapl N Lancs and S Westmorland Hosps 65-75; Hon Can Blackb Cathl *Blackb* 71-75. *28 Slyne Road, Torrisholme, Morecambe LA4 6PA* Tel (01524) 410957

STEVENSON (née PITE), Mrs Sheila Reinhardt. b 60. St Jo Coll Dur BA82 Nottm Univ MA98. Oak Hill Th Coll BA88. **d** 88 **p** 94. Par Dn Derby St Aug *Derby* 88-92; C Brampton St Thos 92-95; Perm to Offic *St Alb* 95-96; P-in-c The Stodden Churches 96-98; P-in-c Croxton and Eltisley *Ely* 98-99; P-in-c Graveley w Papworth St Agnes w Yelling etc 98-99; Chapl Papworth Hosp NHS Trust 98-99; TV Braunstone *Leic* 99-02; P-in-c from 02. *36 Woodcote Road, Leicester LE3 2WD* Tel 0116-282 5272 E-mail sheila.pite@talk21.com

STEVENSON, Trevor Donald. b 59. TCD Div Sch BTh. **d** 91 **p** 92. C Magheralin w Dollingstown *D & D* 91-95; CMS Uganda 95-98; Dir Fields of Life from 99. *Tree Tops, Brides Glen Road,*

Shankill, Co Dublin, Irish Republic Tel (00353) (1) 282 0150 Fax as telephone

STEVENTON, Mrs June Lesley. b 61. Aston Tr Scheme 86 Sarum & Wells Th Coll BTh91. **d** 91 **p** 94. Par Dn Chatham St Steph *Roch* 91-94; C 94-96; Perm to Offic *York* 96-97; Perm to Offic *Liv* 97-00; V Abram from 00; V Bickershaw from 00. *The Vicarage, 9 Lee Lane, Abram, Wigan WN2 5QU* Tel (01942) 866396 Fax as telephone

STEVENTON, Kenneth. b 59. Cuddesdon Coll 94. **d** 96 **p** 97. C Spalding *Linc* 96-99; R Sutterton, Fosdyke, Algarkirk and Wigtoft from 99. *The Vicarage, Station Road, Sutterton, Boston PE20 2JH* Tel (01205) 460285
E-mail ken.steventon@cwcom.net

STEVINSON, Harold John Hardy. b 34. Selw Coll Cam BA57 MA61. Qu Coll Birm. **d** 59 **p** 60. C Bris St Mary Redcliffe w Temple *Bris* 59-63; C Caversham *Ox* 63-73; Soc Resp Officer *Dur* 74-82; Sec Dioc Bd for Miss and Unity 82-88; P-in-c Croxdale 82-88; P-in-c Leamington Hastings and Birdingbury *Cov* 88-96; rtd 96; Perm to Offic *Cov* and *Glouc* from 96. *8 Greenways, Winchcombe, Cheltenham GL54 5LG* Tel (01242) 602195

STEVINSON, Mrs Josephine Mary. b 25. STh56. Cranmer Hall Dur 86. **dss** 86 **d** 87 **p** 94. Croxdale *Dur* 86-87; Lic to Offic 87-88; Lic to Offic *Cov* 88-96; NSM Leamington Hastings and Birdingbury 94-96; rtd 96; Perm to Offic *Glouc* from 96. *8 Greenways, Winchcombe, Cheltenham GL54 5LG* Tel (01242) 602195

STEWARD, Mrs Linda Christine. b 46. NE Lon Poly CQSW82. S'wark Ord Course 85. **d** 88 **p** 94. NSM E Ham w Upton Park St Alb *Chelmsf* 88-91; Chapl Newham Healthcare NHS Trust Lon 91-98; NSM Plaistow *Chelmsf* 91-96; NSM Plaistow and N Canning Town 96-98; P-in-c Rawreth w Rettendon from 98. *The Rectory, Church Road, Rawreth, Wickford SS11 8SH* Tel (01268) 766766 E-mail steward.linda@hotmail.com

STEWART, Alan. *See* STEWART, Hugh Alan.

STEWART, Alan Valentine. b 47. CGLI Lic94 Univ Coll Galway BA98. **d** 97 **p** 98. C Mullingar, Portnashangan, Moyliscar, Kilbixy etc *M & K* 97-00; C Clane w Donadea and Coolcarrigan from 00. *Baltrasna, Ashbourne, Co Meath, Irish Republic* Tel (00353) (1) 835 0997 E-mail alanstewart@fasfinglas.ie

STEWART, Canon Alexander Butler. b 25. TCD Dip Bibl Studies. **d** 58 **p** 59. C Holywood *D & D* 58-61; Miss to Seamen 61-64; Portuguese E Africa 61-64; I Donagh *D & R* 64-65; I Helen's Bay *D & D* 65-72; I Donegal w Killymard, Lough Eske and Laghey *D & R* 72-90; Can Raphoe Cathl 81-90; rtd 90; Lic to Offic *D & D* from 90. *21 Upper Ballygelagh Road, Ardkeen, Newtownards BT22 1JH* Tel (028) 4273 8601

STEWART, Alice Elizabeth. b 42. **d** 00 **p** 01. C Cloughfern *Conn* from 00. *3 Fergus Court, Carrickfergus BT38 8HT* Tel (028) 9336 5721

STEWART (née BARBER), Mrs Anne Louise. b 71. QUB BA93 PGCE94. CITC 97. **d** 00 **p** 01. C Belfast Malone St Jo *Conn* from 00. *St George's Rectory, 28 Myrtlefield Park, Belfast BT9 6NF* Tel (028) 9066 7134 E-mail revmother.stewart@breathe.com

STEWART, Miss Betty. b 25. S'wark Ord Course 91. **d** 93 **p** 94. NSM Wandsworth Common St Mary *S'wark* 93-95; Asst P Hampton Hill *Lon* from 95. *71 Ormond Drive, Hampton TW12 2TL* Tel (020) 8979 6047

STEWART, Brian. b 59. BTh. **d** 91 **p** 92. C Ballywillan *Conn* 91-94; I Belfast St Geo from 94; Bp's Dom Chapl from 94; OCF from 00. *St George's Rectory, 28 Myrtlefield Park, Belfast BT9 6NF* Tel (028) 9066 7134 *or* 9023 1275

STEWART, Canon Charles. b 55. St Jo Coll Cam BA77 MA81 CertEd79. Wycliffe Hall Ox 85. **d** 87 **p** 88. C Bowdon *Ches* 87-90; C Bath Abbey w St Jas *B & W* 90-94; Can Res, Prec and Sacr Win Cathl *Win* from 94. *8 The Close, Winchester SO23 9LS* Tel (01962) 856236 Fax as telephone
E-mail charles.stewart@winchester-cathedral.org.uk

STEWART, Hugh Alan. b 67. Lon Inst BA91 Middx Univ BA03. Lon Bible Coll 96 NTMTC 00. **d** 03. C Gt Stanmore *Lon* from 03. *St John's House, 16 The Chase, Stanmore HA7 3RY* Tel (020) 8420 6208

STEWART, Ian Guild. b 43. Edin Th Coll 89. **d** 84 **p** 85. NSM Dundee St Mary Magd *Bre* 84-87; NSM Dundee St Jo 87-90; C 90-92; NSM Dundee St Martin 87-90; C 90-92; R Montrose from 92; P-in-c Inverbervie from 92. *The Rectory, 17 Panmure Place, Montrose DD10 8ER* Tel (01674) 672652

STEWART, James. *See* STEWART, Malcolm James

STEWART, James. b 32. Div Hostel Dub. **d** 69 **p** 70. C Belfast St Donard *D & D* 69-72; C Dundonald 72-74; I Rathmullan w Tyrella 74-80; I Belfast St Clem 80-97; I Moy w Charlemont *Arm* from 97. *St James' Rectory, 37 The Square, Moy, Dungannon BT71 7SG* Tel (028) 8778 4312

STEWART, James Patrick. b 55. Keele Univ BA77 Birm Univ MA78. Ridley Hall Cam 86. **d** 88 **p** 89. C Boulton *Derby* 88-91; C Cove St Jo *Guildf* 91-92; TV 92-97; TR Tunbridge Wells St Jas w St Phil *Roch* from 97; RD Tunbridge Wells from 99. *The Vicarage, 12 Shandon Close, Tunbridge Wells TN2 3RE* Tel (01892) 530687 Fax as telephone
E-mail jim.stewart@charis.co.uk

STEWART, James Richard. b 71. St Jo Coll Ox BA93 MA99. Cranmer Hall Dur BA98 DMS99. **d** 99 **p** 00. C Consett *Dur* 99-02; TV Kidderminster St Jo and H Innocents *Worc* from 02. *143 Sutton Park Road, Kidderminster DY11 6JQ* Tel (01562) 820678 E-mail jimthevic@hotmail.com

STEWART, Mrs Janet Margaret. b 41. Roehampton Inst CertEd62. Cranmer Hall Dur DipRK70. **d** 87 **p** 94. Hon Par Dn Oulton Broad *Nor* 87-94; Hon C 94-97; Chapl Lowestoft Hosp 94-97; Perm to Offic *B & W* 97-98; C Quidenham Gp *Nor* 98-01; Asst Chapl Norfolk and Nor Univ Hosp NHS Trust from 00; rtd 01. *30 St Joseph's Road, Sheringham NR26 8JA* Tel (01263) 824497

STEWART, John. b 39. Oak Hill Th Coll 75. **d** 77 **p** 78. C Accrington Ch Ch *Blackb* 77-79; TV Darwen St Pet w Hoddlesden 79-86; R Coppull St Jo from 86. *St John's Vicarage, Darlington Street, Coppull, Chorley PR7 5AB* Tel (01257) 791258

✠**STEWART, The Rt Revd John Craig.** b 40. Ridley Coll Melbourne LTh64. **d** 65 **p** 66 **c** 84. Australia 65-68 and from 70; C Crawley *Chich* 68-70; Bp W Region 84-91; Bp N Region 91-94; Bp E Region 94-01; V Gen 88-01; R Woodend from 01. *Buckland Street, PO Box 69, Woodend, Vic, Australia 3442* Tel (0061) (3) 5427 2460 Fax as telephone
E-mail bishopjcstewart@bigpond.com

STEWART, Canon John Roberton. b 29. Sarum Th Coll 63. **d** 65 **p** 66. C Gillingham *Sarum* 65-70; R Langton Matravers 70-84; RD Purbeck 82-89; Can and Preb Sarum Cathl 83-90; R Kingston, Langton Matravers and Worth Matravers 84-90; Can Res Sarum Cathl 90-95; Treas 90-95; rtd 95; Perm to Offic *Sarum* from 95. *Hillrise, 26 Durlston Road, Swanage BH19 2HX* Tel (01929) 422802

STEWART, Canon John Wesley. b 52. QUB BD76 TCD 76. **d** 77 **p** 78. C Seagoe *D & D* 77-79; C Lisburn Ch Ch *Conn* 79-85; I Ballybay w Mucknoe and Clontibret *Clogh* 85-90; I Derryvullen S w Garvary from 90; Bp Dom Chapl 95-00; Glebes Sec from 95; Dioc Registrar from 98; Exam Can Clogh Cathl 98-00; Preb from 98. *The Rectory, Tullyharney, Enniskillen BT74 4PR* Tel (028) 6638 7236 Fax as telephone
E-mail jva.stewart@care4free.net

STEWART, Malcolm James. b 44. TD78. York Univ BA66 K Coll Lon MA68 Lon Inst of Educn PGCE69 Solicitor 79. NEOC 89. **d** 93 **p** 94. NSM Upper Nidderdale *Ripon* 93-95; C Fountains Gp 95-98; V Catterick 98-03; P-in-c Culmington w Onibury, Bromfield etc *Heref* from 03. *The Vicarage, Bromfield, Ludlow SY8 2JP* Tel (01584) 856625

STEWART, Marcus Patrick Michael. b 66. Ox Univ BA89 MSc93 Cam Univ BA92. Ven English Coll Rome 89 Westcott Ho Cam 96. **d** 98 **p** 99. C Headington Ox 98-00; Hon C S Hinksey from 00; CF from 01. *c/o MOD Chaplains (Army), or St Edmund Hall, Oxford OX1 4AR* Tel (01980) 615804 Fax 615800 E-mail frmarcus@thearmy.screaming.net

STEWART, The Very Revd Prof Maurice Evan. b 29. TCD BA50 MA53 BD67 QUB PhD75. TCD Div DMS99. **d** 52 **p** 53. C Belfast St Jas *Conn* 52-55; Chapl Bps' Coll Cheshunt 55-58; Hd of Trin Coll Miss Belf 58-61; I Newcastle *D & D* 61-69; Lect CITC 69-91; Vice-Prin 80-91; Lect Div TCD 72-91; Chan St Patr Cathl Dublin 80-89; Prec 89-91; Dean 91-99; I Dublin St Patr Cathl Gp *D & G* 91-99; rtd 99; Visiting Prof Nashotah Ho Wisconsin from 01. *12 Mount Haven, New Road, Grey Stones, Co Wicklow, Irish Republic* Tel (00353) (1) 287 1748

STEWART, Maxwell Neville Gabriel. b 33. Hertf Coll Ox BA58. Wycliffe Hall Ox DipTh59. **d** 60 **p** 61. C Perry Beeches *Birm* 60-62; Chapl Rosenberg Coll St Gallen 62-64; Perm to Offic *Chelmsf* 64-70; Warden Leics Poly 70-92; De Montfort Univ Leic 92-93; Hon C Leic St Mary *Leic* 74-79; Perm to Offic from 79; rtd 98. *25 Sidney Court, Norwich Road, Leicester LE4 0LR*

STEWART, Michael. b 65. St Jo Coll Nottm LTh89. **d** 89 **p** 90. C Ealing St Paul *Lon* 89-93; P-in-c N Wembley St Cuth 93-98; V 98-02; Assoc P Abbotsford Canada from 02. *St Matthew's Anglican Church, 2010 Guilford Drive, Abbotsford BC, Canada, V2S 5R2* E-mail mikes@stmatthewsanglicanchurch.com

STEWART, Canon Raymond John. b 55. TCD BA79 MA82. CITC 74 Div Test77. **d** 79 **p** 80. C Clooney *D & R* 79-82; I Dunfanaghy 82-87; I Gweedore Union 85-87; Dioc Youth Adv 83-87; I Castledawson 87-03; I Tamlaght O'Crilly Upper w Lower from 03; Ed *D & R Dioc News* 89-93; Stewardship Adv from 98; Can Derry Cathl from 99. *12 Station Road, Castledawson, Magherafelt BT45 8AZ* Tel (028) 7946 8235

STEWART, Stephen John. b 62. Oak Hill Th Coll DipHE99. **d** 99 **p** 00. C Mile Cross *Nor* from 99. *Glebe House, 140 Mile Cross, Norwich NR3 2LD* Tel (01603) 417352
E-mail stevestewartce@hotmail.com

STEWART, William. **d** 01 **p** 02. NSM Kilroot and Templecorran *Conn* from 01. *63 Victoria Road, Carrickfergus BT38 7JJ* Tel (028) 9336 2145

STEWART, William James. b 58. BA. CITC DipTh. **d** 83 **p** 84. C Glenageary *D & G* 83-86; Rostrevor Renewal Cen 86-87; I Naas w Kill and Rathmore *M & K* 87-93; Min Dublin Ch Ch Cathl Gp *D & G* from 93; CORE (St Cath Ch) from 93; Chapl Rotunda Hosp 94-99; Chapl Dub Coll of Catering from 94; Min Can St Patr Cathl Dublin from 00. *96 Lower Drumcondra Road,*

Dublin 9, Irish Republic Tel (00353) (1) 473 5100 Mobile 087-238 1976 Fax 473 5111 E-mail willi@corechurch.ie

STEWART, William Jones. b 32. Trin Hall Cam BA55 MA59 Cam Univ CertEd56. Edin Th Coll 67. **d** 69 **p** 69. Chapl St Ninian's Cathl Perth *St And* 69-71; Bp's Dom Chapl *Ox* 71-75; V Lambourn from 75; P-in-c Lambourne Woodlands 83-90; P-in-c Eastbury and E Garston from 83. *The Vicarage, Newbury Street, Lambourn, Hungerford RG17 8PD* Tel (01488) 71546 E-mail stewart.clan4@btopenworld.com

STEWART-DARLING, Fiona Lesley. b 58. Kingston Poly GRSC79 Lon Univ PhD82 K Coll Lon MA99. Trin Coll Bris BA91. **d** 91 **p** 94. C Cirencester *Glouc* 91-94; Chapl Cheltenham and Glouc Coll of HE 94-97; Chapl Portsm Univ *Portsm* from 97; Hon Chapl Portsm Cathl from 97. *15 Grays Court, Portsmouth PO1 2PN* Tel (023) 9273 3575 *or* 9284 3161 Fax 9284 3430 E-mail fiona.stewart-darling@port.ac.uk

STEWART ELLENS, Gordon Frederick. *See* ELLENS, Gordon Frederick Stewart

STEWART-SYKES, Alistair Charles. b 60. St Andr Univ MA83 Birm Univ PhD92. Qu Coll Birm 86. **d** 89 **p** 90. C Stevenage St Andr and St Geo *St Alb* 89-92; C Castle Vale St Cuth *Birm* 92-93; Barbados 93-96; Assoc Min Hanley H Ev *Lich* 97-98; USA 98-01; V Sturminster Marshall, Kingston Lacy and Shapwick *Sarum* from 01. *The Vicarage, Newton Road, Sturminster Marshall, Wimborne BH21 4BT* Tel (01258) 857255 Fax 08701-358049 E-mail alistairstewartsykes@fish.co.uk

STEWART-SYKES, Teresa Melanie. b 64. Bris Univ BA85. Qu Coll Birm 89. **d** 89. Par Dn Stevenage St Andr and St Geo *St Alb* 89-92; Perm to Offic *Birm* 92-93; Barbados 93-97; C Meir Heath *Lich* 97-98; USA 98-01. *The Vicarage, Newton Road, Sturminster Marshall, Wimborne BH21 4BT* Tel (01258) 857255

STEYNOR, Victor Albert. b 15. Southn Univ DipEd62. S'wark Ord Course 68. **d** 71 **p** 72. C Bognor *Chich* 71-75; P-in-c Kenton and Ashfield w Thorpe *St E* 75-81; P-in-c Aspall 75-81; V Debenham 75-81; V Debenham w Aspall and Kenton 81-82; rtd 82; Perm to Offic *St E* from 82. *57 Denmark Road, Beccles NR34 9DL* Tel (01502) 711433

STIBBE, Mrs Hazel Mary. **d** 99 **p** 00. NSM Wolverhampton St Andr *Lich* 99-02; Lic to Offic *St As* from 03. *Braemar, Kerry Street, Montgomery SY15 6PG* Tel (01686) 668912

STIBBE, Mark William Godfrey. b 60. Trin Coll Cam BA83 MA86 Nottm Univ PhD88. St Jo Coll Nottm 83. **d** 86 **p** 87. C Stapleford *S'well* 86-90; C Crookes St Thos *Sheff* 90-93; Lect Sheff Univ 90-97; V Grenoside 93-97; V Chorleywood St Andr *St Alb* from 97. *St Andrew's Vicarage, 37 Quickley Lane, Chorleywood, Rickmansworth WD3 5AE* Tel (01923) 447111 Fax 284406 E-mail mark.standrews@btinternet.com

STICKLAND, David Clifford. b 44. Surrey Univ BA01 CPFA68 MAAT77 FCCA80. STETS 98. **d** 01 **p** 02. NSM Greatham w Empshott and Hawkley w Prior's Dean *Portsm* from 01; Chapl Defence, Science and Tech Laboratory and QinetiQ from 02. *The Barn, Jolly Robins, Hawkley, Liss GU33 6NQ* Tel (01730) 827355 Mobile 07836-282561 Fax 827652 E-mail david_stickland@talk21.com

STICKLAND, Geoffrey John Brett. b 42. St D Coll Lamp DipTh66. **d** 66 **p** 67. C Aberavon H Trin *Llan* 66-69; C Llanrumney *Mon* 69-72; C Tetbury w Beverston *Glouc* 72-75; V Hardwicke 75-82; R Hardwicke, Quedgeley and Elmore w Longney 82-98; V Quedgeley from 98. *The Rectory, School Lane, Quedgeley, Gloucester GL2 6PN* Tel (01452) 720411 E-mail geoffstickland@hotmail.com

STICKLEY, Mrs Annette Frances. b 44. Bp Otter Coll Chich 67. **d** 00. NSM Worth *Chich* from 00. *12 Woodlands, Pound Hill, Crawley RH10 3DL* Tel (01293) 873023

STIDOLPH, Canon Robert Anthony. b 54. GBSM ARCM FRSA92. St Steph Ho Ox 77. **d** 80 **p** 80. C Hove All SS *Chich* 80-84; TV Brighton Resurr 84-87; Chapl Cheltenham Coll 87-94; Sen Chapl and Hd RS Wellington Coll Berks 94-01; Hon Can Ch Ch *Ox* from 00; Chapl and Asst Master Radley Coll from 01. *Radley College, Abingdon OX14 2HR* Tel (01235) 543000

STIEVENARD, Alphonse Etienne Arthur. b 34. Selw Coll Cam BA36 MA40. Lon Coll of Div 36. **d** 37 **p** 38. C Northwood Em *Lon* 37-40; P-in-c Southborough St Pet *Roch* 40-44; V Leyton Ch Ch *Chelmsf* 44-51; V Jersey Millbrook St Matt *Win* 51-78; rtd 78; Perm to Offic *Win* from 78. *Le Ruisselet, Mont Rossignol, St Ouen, Jersey JE3 2LN* Tel (01534) 481215

STIFF, Canon Derrick Malcolm. b 40. Lich Th Coll 69. **d** 72 **p** 73. C Cov St Geo *Cov* 72-75; R Benhall w Sternfield *St E* 75-79; P-in-c Snape w Friston 75-79; V Cartmel *Carl* 79-87; R Sudbury and Chilton *St E* 87-94; P-in-c Lavenham 94-95; P-in-c Preston 94-95; R Lavenham w Preston 95-03; Min Can *St E* Cathl 90-03; Hon Can 00-03; RD Lavenham 93-03; rtd 03; Perm to Offic *St E* from 03. *9 Fisherton Island, Salisbury SP2 7TG* Tel (01722) 320177 E-mail canonstiff@hotmail.com

STILEMAN, William Mark Charles. b 63. Selw Coll Cam BA85 MA89 PGCE86. Wycliffe Hall Ox DipTh89. **d** 91 **p** 92. C Ox St Andr *Ox* 91-95; C Gt Chesham 95; TV from 95. *14A Manor Way, Chesham HP5 3BG* Tel (01494) 784372

STILL, Colin Charles. b 35. Selw Coll Cam BA67 MA71. Cranmer Hall Dur DipTh68 United Th Sem Dayton STM69. **d** 69 **p** 70. C Drypool St Columba w St Andr and St Pet *York* 69-72; Abp's Dom Chapl 72-75; Recruitment Sec ACCM 76-80; P-in-c Ockham w Hatchford *Guildf* 76-80; R 80-90; Can Missr and Ecum Officer 80-90; Perm to Offic *Chich* from 92; rtd 96. *Flat 9, 16 Lewes Crescent, Brighton BN2 1GB* Tel (01273) 686014

STILL (née STACEY), Mrs Gillian. b 53. SW Minl Tr Course 94. **d** 97 **p** 98. NSM Peter Tavy, Mary Tavy, Lydford and Brent Tor *Ex* from 97. *The Rectory, Lydford, Okehampton EX20 4BH* Tel (01822) 820479 Mobile 07971-412511 E-mail gill_still@hotmail.com

STILL, Jonathan Trevor Lloyd. b 59. Ex Univ BA81 Qu Coll Cam BA84 MA88. Westcott Ho Cam 82. **d** 85 **p** 86. C Weymouth H Trin *Sarum* 85-88; Chapl for Agric *Heref* 88-93; V N Petherton w Northmoor Green *B & W* 93-00; V The Bourne and Tilford *Guildf* from 00. *The Vicarage, 2 Middle Avenue, Farnham GU9 8JL* Tel (01252) 715505

STILL, Kenneth Donald. b 37. St Aid Birkenhead 64. **d** 67 **p** 95. C Ainsdale *Liv* 67-68; C Kirkby 68-69; C Sutton 96-98; TV from 98. *316 Reginald Road, St Helens WA9 4HS* Tel (01744) 812380

STILLMAN, Roger John. b 47. St Steph Ho Ox 81. **d** 83 **p** 84. C St Helier *S'wark* 83-88; P-in-c Falinge *Man* 88; TV Rochdale 88-94; P-in-c Wokingham St Paul *Ox* 94-00; R from 00; Chapl W Berks Priority Care Services NHS Trust from 95. *St Paul's Rectory, Holt Lane, Wokingham RG41 1ED* Tel 0118-978 0629 Fax 979 2122 E-mail roger.stillman@btopenworld.com

STILLWELL, Wayne Anthony. b 68. Univ of Greenwich BA91. Oak Hill Th Coll 94. **d** 96 **p** 97. C Necton, Holme Hale w N and S Pickenham *Nor* 96-98; C Eastbourne H Trin *Chich* 98-03; V Chaddesden St Mary *Derby* from 03. *St Mary's Vicarage, 133 Chaddesden Lane, Chaddesden, Derby DE21 6LL* Tel (01332) 280924 E-mail w.stillwell@virgin.net

STILLWELL, Malcolm Thomas. b 54. Coll of Resurr Mirfield 83. **d** 86 **p** 87. C Workington St Mich *Carl* 86-90; P-in-c Flimby 90-93; Perm to Offic 93-95; NSM Westfield St Mary from 95. *18 Moorfield Avenue, Workington CA14 4HJ* Tel (01900) 66757

STILWELL, Timothy James. b 65. Birm Univ BA87. Wycliffe Hall Ox 96. **d** 98 **p** 99. C Clifton Ch Ch w Em *Bris* 98-02; C Hammersmith St Paul *Lon* from 02. *30 Rannoch Road, London W6 9SR* Tel (020) 7385 5820 E-mail tim.stilwell@sph.org

STIMPSON, Graham George. b 40. Lon Univ MB BS65 DPM. Cuddesdon Coll 69. **d** 70 **p** 71. NSM Bris St Mary Redcliffe w Temple etc *Bris* 70-92. *12 Challoner Court, Bristol BS1 4RG* Tel 0117-926 0802

STIMPSON, Nigel Leslie. b 60. St Martin's Coll Lanc BA92. Coll of Resurr Mirfield 94. **d** 94 **p** 95. C Heyhouses on Sea *Blackb* 94-96; C Torrisholme 96-99; V Ravensthorpe and Thornhill Lees w Savile Town *Wakef* from 99. *The Vicarage, Church Street, Ravensthorpe, Dewsbury WF13 3LA* Tel (01924) 465959 E-mail nls@dircon.co.uk

STINSON, William Gordon. b 29. Lon Univ BSc50. Ely Th Coll 51. **d** 52 **p** 53. C Kingston upon Hull St Alb *York* 52-56; Br Guiana 56-61; V E and W Ravendale w Hatcliffe *Linc* 61-67; R Beelsby 61-67; P-in-c Ashby w Fenby and Brigsley 62-66; R 66-67; V New Cleethorpes 67-76; RD Grimsby and Cleethorpes 73-76; P-in-c Dovercourt *Chelmsf* 76-83; TR Dovercourt and Parkeston 83-91; RD Harwich 87-91; V Gosfield 91-95; rtd 95; Perm to Offic *Chelmsf* and *St E* from 95. *14 The Columbines, Melford Road, Cavendish, Sudbury CO10 8AB* Tel (01787) 281381

STIRK, Peter Francis. b 24. Linc Coll Ox BA49 MA53. Qu Coll Birm 49. **d** 50 **p** 51. C Beeston *Ripon* 50-68; P-in-c Kirby-on-the-Moor 68-71; V 71-81; P-in-c Cundall 78-81; V Kirby-on-the-Moor, Cundall w Norton-le-Clay etc 81-90; rtd 90. *Devonshire Cottage, Marton le Moor, Ripon HG4 5AT* Tel (01423) 322330

STIRLING, Mrs Christina Dorita (Tina). b 48. Lon Univ BEd73. Wycliffe Hall Ox 87. **d** 89 **p** 94. Par Dn Thame w Towersey *Ox* 89-94; C 94-98; P-in-c Brill, Boarstall, Chilton and Dorton 98; R Bernwode from 98. *The Vicarage, 7 High Street, Brill, Aylesbury HP18 9ST* Tel (01844) 238325 Fax as telephone

STIRRUP, Roger. b 34. St Cath Coll Cam BA58 MA62. Linc Th Coll 58. **d** 60 **p** 61. C Selly Oak St Mary *Birm* 60-63; C Battersea St Mary *S'wark* 63-65; Chapl St Andr Univ *St And* 65-68; Chapl Nottm High Sch 68-80; Asst Chapl Rugby Sch 80-85; V Fordingbridge *Win* 85-92; TR Ross w Brampton Abbotts, Bridstow and Peterstow *Heref* 92-93; TR Ross 93-99; P-in-c Linton w Upton Bishop and Aston Ingham 97-99; rtd 99. *Prospect House, Lays Hill, Kerne Bridge, Ross-on-Wye HR9 5QU* Tel (01600) 890237 E-mail rstirrup@aol.com

STOBART, Mrs Judith Audrey. b 43. St Hugh's Coll Ox BA65 MA71 Lon Inst of Educn DipEd72 Heythrop Coll Lon MTh00. St Alb Minl Tr Scheme 82. **dss** 85 **d** 87 **p** 94. Bp's Hatfield *St Alb* 85-87; Par Dn Hatfield Hyde 87-91; NSM Welwyn Garden City 91-92; Par Dn 92-94; C 94-95; Perm to Offic 95-97; C Bp's Hatfield 97-00; TV from 00; Jt RD Welwyn Hatfield 01-03; P-in-c Gt w Lt Addington and Woodford *Pet* from 03. *The Rectory, Church Street, Woodford, Kettering NN14 4EX* Tel (01832) 732477 E-mail judith.a.stobart@ntlworld.com

STOCK, Lionel Crispian. b 58. ACMA85 ACIS94. Linc Th Coll BTh94. d 94 p 95. C Preston w Sutton Poyntz and Osmington w Poxwell *Sarum* 94-97; P-in-c Stalbridge 97-00; Hon C Hillingdon All SS *Lon* from 01. *38 Granville Road, Hillingdon, Uxbridge UB10 9AE* Tel (01895) 270232
E-mail 106101.545@compuserve.com

STOCK, Miss Ruth Vaughan. b 51. Birkbeck Coll Lon BA79 MA85. Wycliffe Hall Ox 91. d 93 p 94. Par Dn Toxteth St Philemon w St Gabr and St Cleopas *Liv* 93-94; C 94-97; TV from 97. *St Gabriel's Vicarage, 2 Steble Street, Liverpool L8 6QH* Tel 0151-708 7751

STOCK, The Very Revd Victor Andrew. b 44. AKC68 FRSA95. d 69 p 70. C Pinner *Lon* 69-73; Chapl Lon Univ 73-79; R Friern Barnet St Jas 79-86; R St Mary le Bow w St Pancras Soper Lane etc 86-02; P-in-c St Mary Aldermary 87-98; Dean Guildf from 02. *The Deanery, 1 Cathedral Close, Guildford GU2 7TL* Tel (01483) 560328 *or* 565287 Fax 303350
E-mail dean@guildford-cathedral.org

✠STOCK, The Rt Revd William Nigel. b 50. St Cuth Soc Dur BA72. Ripon Coll Cuddesdon DipTh75. d 76 p 77 c 00. C Stockton St Pet *Dur* 76-79; Papua New Guinea 79-84; V Shiremoor *Newc* 85-91; TR N Shields 91-98; RD Tynemouth 92-98; Hon Can Newc Cathl 97-98; Can Res Dur Cathl *Dur* 98-00; Chapl Grey Coll Dur 99-00; Suff Bp Stockport *Ches* from 00. *Bishop's Lodge, Back Lane, Dunham Town, Altrincham WA14 4SG* Tel 0161-928 5611 Fax 929 0692
E-mail bpstockport@chester.anglican.org

STOCK-HESKETH, Jonathan Philip. b 49. St Chad's Coll Dur BA Cam Univ CertEd Nottm Univ MTh PhD93 Dip Psychology 98. St Steph Ho Ox. d 83 p 84. C Leic St Phil *Leic* 83-86; C Loughborough Em 86-89; Lect Nottm Univ from 95; Perm to Offic *S'well* from 98. *Hugh Stewart Hall, Nottingham University, Nottingham NG7 2QX* Tel 0115-951 4663
E-mail jshesketh@aol.com

STOCKBRIDGE, Alan Carmichael. b 33. MBE89. Keble Coll Ox BA55 MA62. Wycliffe Hall Ox 66. d 68 p 69. CF 68-78 and 82-92; Chapl Reading Sch 78-82; R Harrietsham w Ulcombe *Cant* 92-98; rtd 98; Perm to Offic *Eur* from 00. *R165, Avenida 5, S'algar, Menorca, Spain* Tel (0034) (971) 359833 Fax as telephone

STOCKBRIDGE, Nelson William. b 35. Trin Th Coll Auckland 61. d 84 p 85. New Zealand 85-86; C Shildon w Eldon *Dur* 87; C Norton St Mary 87-88; C Cottingham *York* 88-91; V Aldbrough, Mappleton w Goxhill and Withernwick 91-96; C Baildon *Bradf* 96-01; rtd 01; New Zealand from 02. *3 Alison Street, Rotorua, New Zealand 3201* Tel (0064) (7) 348 7327
E-mail nelsonandruth@xtra.co.nz

STOCKER, David William George. b 37. Bris Univ BA58 CertEd. Qu Coll Birm 59. d 60 p 61. C Sparkhill St Jo *Birm* 60-64; C Keighley *Bradf* 64-65; V Grenoside *Sheff* 66-83; V Sandbach *Ches* 83-01; rtd 01; Perm to Offic *Ches* from 01. *18 Mill Bridge Close, Crewe CW1 5DZ* Tel (01270) 212865

STOCKER, Rachael Ann. See KNAPP, Mrs Rachael Ann

STOCKITT, Robin Philip. b 56. Liv Univ BA77 Crewe & Alsager Coll PGCE78 Open Univ Dip Special Needs 90. Ridley Hall Cam CTM95. d 97 p 98. C Billing *Pet* 97-01; P-in-c Freiburg-im-Breisau *Eur* from 01; Asst Chapl Basle from 01. *Am Kohlbach 16, 79199 Kirchzarten Burg-Hofen, Freiburg, Germany*

STOCKLEY, Mrs Alexandra Madeleine Reuss. b 43. Cranmer Hall Dur 80 Carl Dioc Tr Inst. dss 84 d 87 p 94. Upperby St Jo *Carl* 84-89; Par Dn 87-89; Dn-in-c Grayrigg, Old Hutton and New Hutton 90-94; P-in-c 94-95; P-in-c Levens 95-03; rtd 03. *Crawberry, Ulpha, Broughton-in-Furness LA20 6DZ* Tel (01229) 716875

STOCKLEY, Michael Ian. b 41. Lon Coll of Div 66. d 69 p 70. C St Helens St Mark *Liv* 69-74; C Fazakerley Em 74; TV 74-82; V Ince Ch Ch 82-92; V Birkdale St Pet from 92. *St Peter's Vicarage, 2 St Peter's Road, Southport PR8 4BY* Tel (01704) 568448

STOCKLEY, Roland. b 23. St Jo Coll Dur BA47 DipTh49. d 49 p 50. C Rainbow Hill St Barn *Worc* 49-52; CF 52-57; V Broadwaters *Worc* 57-66; V Himbleton w Huddington 66-68; R Pedmore 68-88; rtd 88; Perm to Offic *Lich* and *Worc* from 90. *64 Hyperion Road, Stourbridge DY7 6SB* Tel (01384) 393463

STOCKPORT, Suffragan Bishop of. See STOCK, The Rt Revd William Nigel

STOCKTON, Ian George. b 49. Selw Coll Cam BA72 MA76 Hull Univ PhD90. St Jo Coll Nottm PGCE74. d 75 p 76. C Chell *Lich* 75-78; C Trentham 78-80; R Dalbeattie *Glas* 80-84; P-in-c Scotton w Northorpe *Linc* 84-88; Asst Local Min Officer 84-88; Local Min Officer and LNSM Course Prin 88-97; TR Monkwearmouth *Dur* from 97. *The Rectory, 2A Park Avenue, Sunderland SR6 9PU* Tel 0191-548 6607 *or* 516 0135
E-mail ian.stockton@durham.anglican.org

STOCKWELL, John Nicholas. b 49. Trin Coll Bris 80. d 82 p 83. C Flixton St Jo *Man* 82-86; V Accrington Ch Ch *Blackb* 86-90; R Chulmleigh *Ex* 90-93; R Chawleigh w Cheldon 90-93; R Wembworthy w Eggesford 90-93; P-in-c Burwash Weald *Chich* 93-97; rtd 01. *23 John Street, Southampton SO14 3DR* Tel (023) 8033 3357 E-mail jnstockwell@aol.com

STODDART, David Easton. b 36. K Coll Dur BSc60 PhD66 CEng66 MIMechE66 FCMI72 FIQA76. WEMTC 92. d 95 p 96. OLM Stroud H Trin *Glouc* 95-99; OLM Woodchester and Brimscombe 99-00; NSM from 00; Jt Angl Chapl Severn NHS Trust from 99. *Dunelm, Pinfarthings, Amberley, Stroud GL5 5JJ* Tel (01453) 833028

STOKE-ON-TRENT, Archdeacon of. See STONE, The Ven Godfrey Owen

STOKER, Andrew. b 64. Coll of Ripon & York St Jo BA86. Coll of Resurr Mirfield 87. d 90 p 91. C Horton *Newc* 90-92; C Clifford *York* 92-96; P-in-c Cawood 96-98; P-in-c Ryther 96-98; P-in-c Wistow 96-98; R Cawood w Ryther and Wistow from 98. *The Vicarage, 41 Rythergate, Cawood, Selby YO8 3TP* Tel (01757) 268273

STOKER, Howard Charles. b 62. Linc Th Coll BTh93. d 93 p 94. C Hessle *York* 93-96; C Richmond w Hudswell *Ripon* 96-99; C Downholme and Marske 96-99; R Holt w High Kelling *Nor* from 99. *The Rectory, 11 Church Street, Holt NR25 6BB* Tel (01263) 712048 Fax 711397 E-mail holtrectory@dialstart.com

STOKER, Mrs Joanna Mary. b 57. Leic Univ BA79 Nottm Univ BCombStuds83. Linc Th Coll 80. dss 83 d 87 p 94. Greenford H Cross *Lon* 83-87; Par Dn 87-89; Par Dn Farnham Royal w Hedgerley *Ox* 89-92; Dn-in-c Seer Green and Jordans 92-94; P-in-c 94-97; TV Stantonbury and Willen 97-03; TR Basingstoke *Win* from 03. *The Rectory, Church Street, Basingstoke RG21 7QT* Tel (01256) 326654
E-mail jostoker@jstoker29.freeserve.co.uk

STOKES, Canon Albert Edward. b 21. TCD BA43 MA46 BD46. CITC 43. d 46 p 47. Lect Ch of Ireland Coll of Educn Dub 49-79; I Powerscourt w Kilbride and Annacrevy *D & G* 56-86; Ch Ch Cathl Dublin 70-86; rtd 86. *Cotehele, The Riverwalk, Ashford, Wicklow, Irish Republic* Tel (00353) (404) 40360

STOKES, Canon Andrew John. b 38. G&C Coll Cam BA60 MA64. Ripon Hall Ox 60. d 62 p 63. C Northampton All SS w St Kath *Pet* 62-65; C Endcliffe *Sheff* 65-68; Sen Ind Chapl 69-74; P-in-c Bridport *Sarum* 75-79; TR Bridport 79-80; V Holbeach Marsh *Linc* 82-88; Bp's Dom Chapl 88-92; Can Res and Prec Linc Cathl from 92; rtd 03. *2 Lupin Road, Lincoln LN2 4GD* E-mail a.j.stokes@talk21.com

STOKES, Colin Arthur (Ted). b 59. d 03. NSM Bromyard *Heref* from 03. *Solmor Paddocks, Linley Green Road, Whitbourne, Worcester WR6 5RE* Tel (01886) 821625

STOKES, David Francis Robert. b 53. Lon Inst of Educn PGCE76 Peterho Cam MA81. Trin Coll Bris BA87 Cranmer Hall Dur 01. d 03. NSM Salisbury St Mark *Sarum* from 03. *4 St Joseph's Close, Bishipdown, Salisbury SP1 3FX* E-mail dsjs_stokes@lineone.net

STOKES, David Lewis. b 49. Keble Coll Ox BA74. Westcott Ho Cam 73. d 75 p 76. C Romford St Edw *Chelmsf* 76-78; USA from 78. *114 George Street, Providence, RI 02906-1189, USA*

STOKES, Miss Mary Patricia. b 39. St Hilda's Coll Ox BA62 MA66 Lanc Univ MA80 Bris Univ CertEd63. EMMTC 78. d 87 p 94. Par Dn Pheasey *Lich* 87-93; C Walton-on-Thames *Guildf* from 93. *50 Misty's Field, Walton-on-Thames KT12 2BG* Tel (01932) 248945 E-mail marystokes1@excite.co.uk

STOKES, Michael John. b 34. Lich Th Coll 63. d 65 p 66. C Worplesdon *Guildf* 65-68; Chapl RAF 68-84; Asst Chapl-in-Chief RAF 84-89; QHC 87-95; V Chesterton w Middleton Stoney and Wendlebury *Ox* 89-95; RD Bicester and Islip 90-95; Chapl Kyrenia St Andr Cyprus 95-00; rtd 00; Perm to Offic *Ox* from 00. *Keeper's Cottage, Manor Farm Lane, Chesterton, Bicester OX6 8UD* Tel (01869) 248744 Fax as telephone

STOKES, Roger Sidney. b 47. Clare Coll Cam BA68 MA72. Sarum & Wells Th Coll 69. d 72 p 73. C Keighley *Bradf* 72-74; C Bolton St Jas w St Chrys 74-78; V Hightown *Wakef* 78-85; Dep Chapl HM Pris Wakef 85-87; Chapl HM Pris Full Sutton 87-89; Perm to Offic *Wakef* 92-95; P-in-c Carlinghow 95-99; P-in-c Bedford St Martin *St Alb* from 99. *St Martin's Vicarage, 76 Clapham Road, Bedford MK41 7PN* Tel (01234) 357862 E-mail r.s.stokes.65@cantab.net

STOKES, Simon Colin. b 62. Nene Coll Northampton BSc83. Ridley Hall Cam CTM92. d 92 p 93. C New Catton Ch Ch *Nor* 92-96; P-in-c King's Lynn St Jo the Ev from 96; Chapl Coll of W Anglia from 01. *St John's Vicarage, Blackfriars Road, King's Lynn PE30 1NT* Tel (01553) 773034
E-mail simon@simonstokes.co.uk

STOKES, Terence Harold. b 46. Man Univ DSPT84 Open Univ BA89. Sarum & Wells Th Coll 71. d 73 p 74. C Blakenall Heath *Lich* 73-75; C Walsall Wood 75-78; C Normanton St Alb *Pet* 78-81; TV Swinton St Pet *Man* 81-85; V Daisy Hill 85-92. *8 Westbury Close, Westhoughton, Bolton BL5 3UL* Tel (01942) 819057

STOKES, Terence Ronald. b 35. Linc Th Coll. d 69 p 70. C Bramley *Ripon* 69-72; C Osbournby w Scott Willoughby *Linc* 72-74; C Hykeham 74-77; V Birchwood 77-94; P-in-c Scopwick Gp 94-00; rtd 01; Perm to Offic *Linc* from 01. *47 Paddock Lane, Metheringham, Lincoln LN4 3YG* Tel (01526) 321753

STOKES, Preb Terence Walter. b 34. Bps' Coll Cheshunt 62. d 64 p 65. C Wanstead St Mary *Chelmsf* 64-67; C St Alb Abbey *St Alb* 67-70; Asst Dir RE *B & W* 70-75; Youth Chapl 70-75; P-in-c

Yeovil 75-77; TV 77-82; TR Wellington and Distr 82-99; RD Tone 89-96; Preb Wells Cathl 90-99; rtd 99; Perm to Offic *B & W* from 99. *57 Mountfields Avenue, Taunton TA1 3BW* Tel (01823) 351424

STOKES-HARRISON, David Neville Hurford. b 41. **d** 00 **p** 01. NSM Walsall *Lich* from 00. *6 Victoria Terrace, Walsall WS4 2DA* Tel (01922) 630657

STOKOE, Prof Rodney James Robert. b 20. Dur Univ BSc46 BA48 DipTh49. Crozer Th Sem Pennsylvania ThM67 Atlantic Sch of Th Halifax (NS) Hon DD87. **d** 49 **p** 50. C W Hartlepool St Paul *Dur* 49-53; R Edin Ch Ch *Edin* 53-57; P-in-c Bishopwearmouth St Gabr *Dur* 57-60; Canada from 60; Prof Div K Coll NS 60-71; Prof Past Th Atlantic Sch Th NS 71-85. *403 Prince Street, Ste 206, Truro NS, Canada, B2N 1E6* Tel (001) (902) 897 6129

STOKOE, Wayne Jeffrey Jeff. b 56. Coll of Resurr Mirfield 94. **d** 96 **p** 97. C Sheff St Cath Richmond Road *Sheff* 96-99; V Edlington from 99. *The Vicarage, Heaton Gardens, Edlington, Doncaster DN12 1SY* Tel (01709) 858358
E-mail wjs@stokoej.freeserve.co.uk

STONE, Adrian Gordon. b 68. Trent Poly BSc89 Nottm Univ PGCE92. St Jo Coll Nottm 01. **d** 03. C Bayston Hill *Lich* from 03. *4 Newbrook Drive, Bayston Hill, Shrewsbury SY3 0QG* Tel (01743) 872956 Mobile 07739-043709
E-mail adrian@the-stone-family.net

STONE, Albert John. b 44. Loughb Univ BTech67 BSc. Sarum & Wells Th Coll 83. **d** 85 **p** 86. C Plymstock *Ex* 85-88; P-in-c Whitestone 88-92; P-in-c Oldridge 88-92; P-in-c Holcombe Burnell 88-92; R Tedburn St Mary, Whitestone, Oldridge etc 93-94; P-in-c Yarcombe w Membury and Upottery 94; P-in-c Cotleigh 94; V Yarcombe, Membury, Upottery and Cotleigh 95-99; P-in-c Bampton, Morebath, Clayhanger and Petton from 99. *The Vicarage, Station Road, Bampton, Tiverton EX16 9NG* Tel (01398) 331466 Fax as telephone
E-mail ajstone@argonet.co.uk

STONE, Andrew Francis. b 43. AKC65. **d** 66 **p** 67. C Walthamstow St Mich *Chelmsf* 66-67; C Ealing St Barn *Lon* 67-70; C E Grinstead St Mary *Chich* 70-74; C-in-c The Hydneye CD 74-81; R Denton w S Heighton and Tarring Neville 81-93; V Eastbourne St Andr from 93. *St Andrew's Vicarage, 425 Seaside, Eastbourne BN22 7RT* Tel (01323) 723739

STONE, Miss Carol Ann. b 54. Leic Univ BA75 Qu Coll Cam BA77 MA81. Westcott Ho Cam 76. **d** 78 **p** 79. C Bradford-on-Avon *Sarum* 78-81; R Corsley 81-83; Chapl Dauntsey's Sch Devizes 83-88; V Studley *Sarum* 89-94; Chapl Cheltenham Coll 94-95; Venezuela 95-96; V Upper Stratton *Bris* from 96. *The Vicarage, 67 Beechcroft Road, Swindon SN2 7RE* Tel (01793) 723095 Mobile 07702-342848
E-mail revcarolstone@btopenworld.com

STONE, Christopher. *See* STONE, Canon John Christopher

STONE, Christopher John. b 49. Lanc Univ MA89 Keele Univ MA92. Lambeth STh84 Linc Th Coll 78. **d** 81 **p** 82. C Bromley St Mark *Roch* 81-84; R Burgh-by-Sands and Kirkbampton w Kirkandrews etc *Carl* 84-89; Chapl N Staffs R Infirmary Stoke-on-Trent 89-93; Co-ord Staff Support Services N Staffs Hosp from 93. *5 Honeywood, Newcastle ST5 9PT* Tel (01782) 625134

STONE, Christopher Martyn Luke. b 78. Glam Univ BA99. St Steph Ho Ox 99. **d** 02 **p** 03. C Merthyr Tydfil Ch Ch *Llan* from 02. *7 Brynteg Terrace, Merthyr Tydfil CF47 0DP* Tel (01685) 386072 E-mail chrisstoneuk@yahoo.co.uk

STONE, David Adrian. b 56. Oriel Coll Ox BA78 MA83 BM, BCh83. Wycliffe Hall Ox 85. **d** 88 **p** 89. C Holborn St Geo w H Trin and St Bart *Lon* 88-91; C S Kensington St Jude 91-93; V 93-02; AD Chelsea 96-02; TR Newbury *Ox* from 02. *The Rectory, 64 Northcroft Lane, Newbury RG14 1BN* Tel and fax (01635) 40326 or tel 47018 Mobile 07973-215927
E-mail david@dandb.org.uk

STONE, Dominic Charles. b 63. HND85. Ridley Hall Cam CTM99. **d** 99 **p** 00. C Ashbourne w Mapleton *Derby* 99-02; TV Uttoxeter Area *Lich* from 02. *13 Moisty Lane, Marchington, Uttoxeter ST14 8JY* Tel (01283) 820030
E-mail dominicstone@fish.co.uk

STONE, Elizabeth Karen Forbes. *See* FORBES STONE, Elizabeth Karen

STONE, Ernest Arthur. b 09. VRD60. AKC34 Open Univ BA81 MPhil91. **d** 34 **p** 35. C Saffron Walden *Chelmsf* 34-37; V Clavering w Langley 37-46; Chapl RNVR 44-64; V Clymping *Chich* 46-54; V Bexhill St Aug 54-74; Dioc RE Adv 54-80; rtd 74; Lic to Offic *Chich* 80-86; Perm to Offic from 89; RD Worthing 86-89. *56 Manor Road, Worthing BN11 4SQ* Tel (01903) 235120

STONE, The Ven Godfrey Owen. b 49. Ex Coll Ox BA71 MA75 W Midl Coll of Educn PGCE72 Sheff Univ Dip Leadership, Renewal & Miss Studies 97. Wycliffe Hall Ox BA78. **d** 81 **p** 82. C Rushden w Newton Bromswold *Pet* 81-87; Dir Past Studies Wycliffe Hall Ox 87-92; TR Bucknall and Bagnall *Lich* 92-02; RD Stoke 98-02; Adn Stoke from 02. *Archdeacon's House, 39 The Brackens, Newcastle ST5 4JL* Tel (01782) 663066 Fax 711165
E-mail archdeacon.stone@lichfield.anglican.org

STONE, Jeffrey Peter. b 34. Nottm Univ TCert72 BEd73. Lich Th Coll 58. **d** 61 **p** 62. C Newark St Mary *S'well* 61-65; C Sutton

in Ashfield St Mich 65-69; Robert Smyth Sch Market Harborough 72-89; Perm to Offic *Leic* 88-90; R Waltham on the Wolds, Stonesby, Saxby etc 90-96; rtd 96; Perm to Offic *Leic* from 99. *71 Redland Road, Oakham LE15 6PH* Tel (01572) 756842

STONE, John. *See* STONE, Albert John

STONE, John Anthony. b 46. St Chad's Coll Dur BA68 DipTh69. **d** 69 **p** 70. C New Addington *Cant* 69-72; C Tewkesbury w Walton Cardiff *Glouc* 72-76; C-in-c Dedworth CD *Ox* 76-82; V Dedworth 82-86; TV Chipping Barnet w Arkley *St Alb* 86-95; R Baldock w Bygrave 95-03; R Ches H Trin *Ches* from 03. *The Rectory, 50 Norris Road, Chester CH1 5DZ* Tel (01244) 372721
E-mail jastone@dunelm.org.uk

STONE, Canon John Christopher. b 53. Newc Univ BA74 Birkbeck Coll Lon MA77 MSTSD74 Member, English Speaking Bd 74 LGSM73 MIPR FRSA. Oak Hill NSM Course 89. **d** 92 **p** 93. NSM Southfleet *Roch* from 92; Dioc Communications Officer 96-03; Chapl Univ of Greenwich 98-99; Hon Can Roch Cathl from 02; Bp's Dom Chapl from 03; Bp's Media Adv from 03. *Bishopscourt Flat, St Margaret's Street, Rochester ME1 1TS* Tel (01634) 404343 *or* (01474) 707511 Fax (01634) 402793 E-mail chris.stone@rochester.anglican.org

STONE, John Geoffrey Elliot. b 20. Ch Coll Cam BA41 MA45. Ridley Hall Cam 47. **d** 49 **p** 50. C Wellingborough St Barn *Pet* 49-51; C Bexhill St Pet *Chich* 51-56; C Ifield 56-59; V Southwater 59-70; V Thornham w Titchwell *Nor* 70-74; R Copdock w Washbrook and Belstead *St E* 74-77; P-in-c Therfield *St Alb* 77-82; P-in-c Kelshall 77-82; C Littlehampton St Jas *Chich* 82-85; C Littlehampton St Mary 82-85; C Wick 82-85; TV Littlehampton and Wick 86; rtd 86; C Compton, the Mardens, Stoughton and Racton *Chich* 86-92; Perm to Offic *Nor* 92-96; Perm to Offic *Chich* from 96. *1A Tuscan Avenue, Middleton-on-Sea, Bognor Regis PO22 7TD* Tel (01243) 582226

STONE, Martyn. *See* STONE, Christopher Martyn Luke

STONE, Michael Graham. b 33. FBCS. S Dios Mini Tr Scheme. **d** 83 **p** 84. NSM Chich St Paul and St Pet *Chich* 83-95; NSM Chich 95-98; rtd 98; Perm to Offic *Chich* 98-00; Hon C Chich St Paul and Westhampnett from 00. *125 Cedar Drive, Chichester PO19 3EL* Tel (01243) 784484

STONE, Michael John. b 33. Trin Hall Cam MA56 LLB58. EAMTC 78. **d** 80 **p** 81. NSM Whitton and Thurleston w Akenham *St E* 80-84; NSM Westerfield and Tuddenham w Witnesham 84-95; Dioc Chr Stewardship Adv 93-95; P-in-c Coddenham w Gosbeck and Hemingstone w Henley 95-98; Asst P 98-02; Asst P Crowfield w Stonham Aspal and Mickfield 98-02; Dioc Voc Adv 95-99; rtd 02; Perm to Offic *St E* from 02. *Chanters Mead, School Road, Coddenham, Ipswich IP6 9PS* Tel (01449) 760631

STONE, Nigel John. b 57. Bedf Coll Lon BSc82 Lon Bible Coll MA95. St Jo Coll Nottm 82. **d** 85 **p** 86. C Battersea Park St Sav *S'wark* 85-87; C Battersea St Sav and St Geo w St Andr 87-89; P-in-c Brixton St Paul 89-92; V 92-97; Lay Tr Officer from 97; Hon Chapl S'wark Cathl from 97. *11 Wilkinson Street, London SW8 1DD* Tel (020) 7582 6424 *or* 8392 3742
E-mail nigel.stone@dswark.org.uk

STONE, Noel Alfred William. b 33. St Jo Coll Morpeth 58. **d** 62 **p** 63. Australia 62-74; C The Quinton *Birm* 74-75; Hong Kong 75-78; New Zealand 78-85; P-in-c Witham Gp *Linc* 85; R 85-93; RD Beltisloe 90-93; rtd 93; Perm to Offic *Arg* 93-98. *Wattletree, High Street, Brompton-by-Sawdon, Scarborough YO13 9DA* Tel (01723) 850636

STONE, Philip William. b 58. Ridley Hall Cam 85. **d** 88 **p** 89. C Hackney Marsh *Lon* 88-97; V Kensal Rise St Mark and St Martin from 97; AD Brent from 03. *Kensal Rise Vicarage, 93 College Road, London NW10 5EU* Tel (020) 8969 4598

STONE, Richard Anthony. b 46. Hatf Coll Dur BA68 Nottm Univ DipTh71. Linc Th Coll 70. **d** 73 **p** 74. C Marske in Cleveland *York* 73-78; TV Haxby w Wigginton 78-87; V Osbaldwick w Murton 87-96; TV Willington Team *Newc* from 96; Chapl N Tyneside Coll of FE from 99. *The Vicarage, Berwick Drive, Wallsend NE28 9ED* Tel 0191-262 7518

STONE, Rodney Cameron. b 32. Sarum Th Coll 67. **d** 69 **p** 70. C Milton *Portsm* 69-74; CF (TA) from 72; R Rowlands Castle *Portsm* 74-80; V Tividale *Lich* 80-81; C Weeke *Win* 81-88; V Win St Barn 89-97; rtd 97; Perm to Offic *Win* from 97; Asst Chapl Win and Eastleigh Healthcare NHS Trust from 97. *8 Lyndhurst Close, Harestock, Winchester SO22 6NA* Tel (01962) 883602

STONEBANKS, David Arthur. b 34. Louvain Univ Belgium MA70. Coll of Resurr Mirfield 64. **d** 66 **p** 67. C Burgess Hill St Jo *Chich* 66-68; Chapl City Univ *Lon* 70-73; Chapl Strasbourg w Stuttgart and Heidelberg *Eur* 73-80; Chapl Geneva 80-86; Chapl Zürich w St Gallen and Winterthur 86-89; R Horsted Keynes *Chich* 89-99; rtd 99. *42 Home Park, Oxted RH8 0JU* Tel (01883) 732339

STONEHOLD, Wilfred Leslie. b 33. St Luke's Coll Ex TCert71. OLM course 98. **d** 99 **p** 00. OLM Harlescott *Lich* from 99. *19 Wendsley Road, Harlescott Grange, Shrewsbury SY1 3PE* Tel (01743) 369237

STONES, John Graham. b 49. Southn Univ BSc72. SW Minl Tr Course 91. **d** 94 **p** 95. C Okehampton w Inwardleigh, Bratton

Clovelly etc *Ex* 94-97; TV Sidmouth, Woolbrook, Salcombe Regis, Sidbury etc from 97. *All Saints Vicarage, All Saints Road, Sidmouth EX10 8ES* Tel (01395) 515963
E-mail graham@saints6.freeserve.co.uk

STONESTREET, George Malcolm. b 38. AKC61. **d** 62 **p** 63. C Leeds St Pet *Ripon* 62-64; C Far Headingley St Chad 64-67; C Askrigg w Stallingbusk 67-82; V Bramley 82-85; TR 85-94; V Eskdale, Irton, Muncaster and Waberthwaite *Carl* 94-03; rtd 03. *Northside, Grange, Keswick CA12 5UQ* Tel (01768) 777671 Fax as telephone E-mail malcolm@dip.edi.co.uk

STONEY, The Ven Thomas Vesey. b 34. Oriel Coll Ox BA56 MA60. CITC 58. **d** 58 **p** 59. C Ballywillan *Conn* 58-61; C Carrickfergus 61-66; I Skerry w Rathcavan and Newtowncrommelin 66-92; Adn Dalriada 85-92; rtd 93. *Ardagh Lodge, Newport, Co Mayo, Irish Republic* Tel (00353) (98) 41150

STOODLEY, Peter Bindon. b 47. Linc Th Coll 89. **d** 91 **p** 92. C Holbeck *Ripon* 91-94; P-in-c Osmondthorpe St Phil 94-99; V Sowerby Bridge w Norland *Wakef* from 99. *The Vicarage, Park Road, Sowerby Bridge HX6 2PG* Tel (01422) 831251

STORDY, Richard Andrew. b 64. St Jo Coll Ox BA86 Ox Univ MA94 Barrister 86. Cranmer Hall Dur BA97. **d** 98 **p** 99. C Gt Horton *Bradf* 98-02; V Chapeltown *Sheff* from 02. *St John's Vicarage, 23 Housley Park, Chapeltown, Sheffield S35 2UE* Tel 0114-257 0966

STOREY, Mrs Elizabeth Mary. b 37. Cam Univ DipRS80 Man Univ BA84. Local Minl Tr Course 81. **dss** 84 **d** 87 **p** 94. Liv All So Springwood *Liv* 84-87; Par Dn 87-91; C St Helens St Helen 91-94; C Garston 94-97; Asst Chapl Liv Univ 94-98; C Mossley Hill St Matt and St Jas from 97; Asst Chapl Liv Coll from 98. *27 Mentmore Road, Mossley Hill, Liverpool L18 4PU* Tel 0151-724 2075

STOREY, Gerard Charles Alfred. b 57. GRSC80 Thames Poly BSc80 Lon Univ PhD84. Wycliffe Hall Ox 84. **d** 87 **p** 88. C Broadwater St Mary *Chich* 87-92; TV 92-95; Chapl Northbrook Coll of Design and Tech 90-95; Oman 95-99; P-in-c Guernsey H Trin *Win* 99-01; V from 01. *Holy Trinity Vicarage, Brock Road, St Peter Port, Guernsey GY1 1RS* Tel (01481) 724382 Fax as telephone E-mail gerard@storeyguernsey.freeserve.co.uk

STOREY, Canon Michael. b 36. Chich Th Coll 73. **d** 75 **p** 76. C Illingworth *Wakef* 75-78; V Rastrick St Jo 78-87; V Crosland Moor from 87; Hon Can Wakef Cathl from 00. *The Vicarage, Church Avenue, Crosland Moor, Huddersfield HD4 5DF* Tel (01484) 422381

STOREY, Mrs Patricia Louise. b 60. TCD MA83. CITC BTh94. **d** 97 **p** 98. C Ballymena w Ballyclug *Conn* 97-00; C Glenavy w Tunny and Crumlin from 00. *The Vicarage, 30 Crumlin Road, Glenavy, Crumlin BT29 4LG* Tel (028) 9442 2361
E-mail storeyp@rev.5.freeserve.co.uk

STOREY, Timothy. b 60. Trin Coll Bris DipHE94. **d** 94 **p** 95. C Bath Weston St Jo w Kelston *B & W* 94-98; C Shirley *Win* 98-03; R Blandford Forum and Langton Long *Sarum* from 03. *The Rectory, 2 Portman Place, Blandford Forum DT11 7DG* Tel (01258) 480092 E-mail t.storey@btopenworld.com

STOREY, William Earl Cosbey. b 58. Kent Univ BA MPhil. CITC DipTh86. **d** 82 **p** 83. C Drumglass w Moygashel *Arm* 82-86; I Crinken *D & G* 86-96; I Glenavy w Tunny and Crumlin *Conn* from 96. *The Vicarage, 30 Crumlin Road, Glenavy, Crumlin BT29 4LG* Tel (028) 9442 2361 E-mail es@cofire.freeserve.co.uk

STOREY, William Leslie Maurice. b 31. Oak Hill Th Coll 67. **d** 69 **p** 70. C Wembley St Jo *Lon* 69-71; C Ealing Dean St Jo 71-75; V W Derby St Luke 75-80; V Hunts Cross 80-83; Hon C Brixton St Paul *S'wark* 83-86; P-in-c 87-88; P-in-c Brixton Hill St Sav 83-86; rtd 88; Perm to Offic *S'wark* 88-02. *124 Surbiton Hill Park, Surbiton KT5 8EP* Tel (020) 8390 2821

STORR VENTER, Phillip. b 52. Barrister-at-Law (Gray's Inn) 74. S'wark Ord Course 90. **d** 93 **p** 94. NSM Bethnal Green St Barn *Lon* 93-97; Chapl Armenia and Georgia *Eur* 97-02; P-in-c Highgate All SS *Lon* from 02. *All Saint's Vicarage, Church Road, London N6 4QH* Tel (020) 8340 1123 Fax as telephone
E-mail london@freenet.com

STORY, Victor Leonard. b 45. St Mark & St Jo Coll Lon TCert66 Brighton Poly BSc74 LIMA74. Ripon Coll Cuddesdon 80. **d** 81 **p** 82. C Evesham *Worc* 81-85; P-in-c Ilmington w Stretton on Fosse and Ditchford *Cov* 85-90; P-in-c Ilmington w Stretton-on-Fosse etc 90-96; Chapl Vlissingen (Flushing) Miss to Seamen *Eur* 96-97; Chapl Rotterdam Miss to Seamen 97-99; R Gt w Lt Milton and Gt Haseley *Ox* from 99. *The Rectory, Great Milton, Oxford OX44 7PN* Tel (01844) 279498

STOTE, Mrs Pamela Anne. b 49. Dudley Coll of Educn TCert70 Open Univ BA83. WMMTC 97. **d** 00 **p** 01. NSM Cov St Geo *Cov* 00-03; NSM Whitley from 03. *22 Chetwode Close, Coventry CV5 9NA* Tel (024) 7671 7845 Mobile 07905-230924
E-mail pam@stote.fslife.co.uk

STOTER, David John. b 43. MBE02. K Coll Lon AKC66. **d** 67 **p** 68. C Reading St Giles *Ox* 67-71; C Luton Lewsey St Hugh *St Alb* 71-73; Chapl Westmr Hosp Lon 73-79; Convenor of Chapls Notts Distr HA 79-94; Chapl Univ Hosp Nottm 79-94; Chapl Nottm Gen Hosp 79-02; Sen Chapl Qu Medical Cen Nottm Univ Hosp NHS Trust 94-02; Sen Chapl Notts

Healthcare NHS Trust 94-02; Manager Chapl and Bereavement Services 94-02; R Gedling *S'well* from 02. *The Rectory, Rectory Drive, Gedling, Nottingham NG4 4BG* Tel 0115-961 3214

STOTT, Antony. b 21. Bps' Coll Cheshunt 53. **d** 55 **p** 56. Australia 55-62; V Longbridge Deverill w Hill Deverill *Sarum* 62-66; V Bratton 66-74; R Marnhull 74-81; P-in-c Broad Chalke and Bower Chalke 81; P-in-c Ebbesbourne Wake w Fifield Bavant and Alvediston 81; P-in-c Berwick St John 81; V Chalke Valley W 81-87; rtd 87; Perm to Offic *Ex* from 87. *11 Luscombe Close, Ivybridge PL21 9TT* Tel (01752) 896142
E-mail revtony1@aol.com

STOTT, Christopher John. b 45. Lon Univ BD68. Tyndale Hall Bris. **d** 69 **p** 70. C Croydon Ch Ch Broad Green *Cant* 69-72; Ethiopia 73-76; Area Sec (SW) BCMS 76-78; Tanzania 78-85; R Harwell w Chilton *Ox* from 85; RD Wallingford 91-95. *The Rectory, Harwell, Didcot OX11 0EW* Tel (01235) 835365

STOTT, Eric. b 36. ALCD62. **d** 62 **p** 63. C Penn Fields *Lich* 62-65; C Normanton *Derby* 65-71; R Lower Broughton St Clem w St Matthias *Man* 71-79; V Chadderton Em 79-01; rtd 01; Perm to Offic *Glouc* from 01. *21 Laynes Road, Hucclecote, Gloucester GL3 3PU* Tel (01452) 534492 E-mail seric@fish.co.uk

STOTT, Frederick. b 23. Bris Univ DipFE75 Univ of Wales (Cardiff) CQSW71 Indiana Univ BD98. Sarum & Wells Th Coll 83. **d** 85 **p** 86. Hon C Sholing *Win* 85-90; Perm to Offic *Portsm* from 89; *Winch* from 90; *Sarum* from 93. *35 Broadwater Road, Southampton SO18 2DW* Tel (023) 8055 7193

STOTT, Gary. b 69. Leeds Univ BA92 St Jo Coll Dur MA99. Cranmer Hall Dur DMS99. **d** 99 **p** 00. C Farnley *Ripon* 99-03; C Manston from 03. *Manston Vicarage, Church Lane, Leeds LS15 8JB* Tel 0113-260 0348 *or* 264 5530
E-mail hgstott@surfaid.org

STOTT, John Robert Walmsley. b 21. Trin Coll Cam BA45 MA50. Lambeth DD83 Ridley Hall Cam 44. **d** 45 **p** 46. C St Marylebone All So w SS Pet and Jo *Lon* 45-50; R 50-75; Hon C 75-88; Hon C Langham Place All So from 88; Chapl to The Queen 59-91; Extra Chapl to The Queen from 91; Dir Lon Inst of Contemporary Christianity 82-86; Pres from 86; rtd 91. *12 Weymouth Street, London W1N 3FB* Tel (020) 7580 1867

STOTT, Jonathan Robert. b 67. Ripon Coll Cuddesdon. **d** 01 **p** 02. C Anfield St Columba *Liv* from 01. *98 Ince Avenue, Anfield, Liverpool L4 7UY* Tel 0151-260 0118 Mobile 07971-876517 E-mail jonathan_r_stott@hotmail.com

STOTT, Miss Teresa. b 57. Linc Th Coll 94. **d** 94 **p** 95. C Lee-on-the-Solent *Portsm* 94-97; C Spalding St Jo w Deeping St Nicholas *Linc* 97-98; P-in-c Freiston w Butterwick 98-99; R Freiston w Butterwick and Benington from 99; P-in-c Leverton from 03. *Pinchbeck House, Girls' School Lane, Butterwick, Boston PE22 0HZ* Tel (01205) 760550

STOW, John Mark. b 51. Selw Coll Cam BA73 MA77. Linc Th Coll 76. **d** 78 **p** 79. C Harpenden St Jo *St Alb* 78-82; TV Beaminster Area *Sarum* 82-87; P-in-c Hawkchurch 87-90; P-in-c Marshwood Vale 87-88; TR Marshwood Vale 88-91; Past Co-ord Millfield Jun Sch from 93. *Chestnut House, Edgarley, Glastonbury BA6 8LL* Tel (01458) 832245

STOW, Peter John. b 50. Oak Hill Th Coll. **d** 89 **p** 90. C Forest Gate St Mark *Chelmsf* 89-94; V from 94. *St Mark's Vicarage, Tylney Road, London E7 0LS* Tel (020) 8555 2988
E-mail saintmarks@clara.net

STOW, Archdeacon of. *See* ELLIS, The Ven Timothy William

STOWE, Brian. b 32. Trin Coll Cam BA55 BA56 MA59. Ridley Hall Cam 55. **d** 57 **p** 58. C New Catton St Luke *Nor* 57-59; Chapl R Masonic Sch Bushey 59-70; Tutor Rickmansworth Sch Herts 70-71; Chapl Alleyn's Foundn Dulwich 71-75; Hon C Dulwich St Barn *S'wark* 71-75; Chapl Ellerslie Sch Malvern 75-92; Chapl Malvern Coll 92-93; TV Malvern Link w Cowleigh *Worc* 93-94; rtd 95; P-in-c Malvern St Andr *Worc* 95-96; Perm to Offic from 96. *31 Park View, Grange Road, Malvern WR14 3HG* Tel 07792-515307 (mobile) E-mail brianstowe@onetel.net.uk

STOWE, Nigel James. b 36. Bris Univ BScB57. Clifton Th Coll 59. **d** 61 **p** 62. C Ware Ch Ch *St Alb* 61-64; C Reigate St Mary *S'wark* 64-67; V Islington St Jude Mildmay Park *Lon* 67-75; V Penn Street *Ox* 75-01; rtd 01. *27 Snowdrop Way, Widmer End, High Wycombe HP15 6BL* Tel (01494) 717496

STOWE, Canon Rachel Lilian. b 33. Qu Coll Birm 79. **dss** 83 **d** 87 **p** 94. Dean w Yelden, Melchbourne and Shelton *St Alb* 82-87; Pertenhall w Swineshead 82-87; Bp's Officer for NSMs and Asst Dir of Ords 87-93; rtd 93; NSM The Stodden Churches *St Alb* 87-96; Hon Can St Alb 92-96; Perm to Offic *Ripon* from 97 and *York* from 98; Convenor Dioc Adv Gp for Chr Healing *Ripon* 98-03. *The Parsonage, East Cowton, Northallerton DL7 0BD* Tel and fax (01325) 378173

STRACHAN, Donald Philip Michael. b 37. St D Coll Lamp 60. **d** 62 **p** 63. C Aberdeen St Mary *Ab* 62-64; P-in-c Aberdeen St Paul 64-66; Chapl St Andr Cathl 65-68; Itinerant Priest *Mor* 68-73; R Coatbridge *Glas* 73-85; Chapl HM Pris Glas (Barlinnie) 84-87; Dioc Supernumerary *Glas* 85-94; rtd 94; Perm to Offic *Arg* from 87. *Reul na Mara, Claddach Kirkibost, Isle of North Uist HS6 5EP* Tel (01876) 580392

STRAFFORD, Nigel Thomas Bevan. b 53. Univ of Wales (Lamp) BA80. Sarum & Wells Th Coll 80. **d** 82 **p** 94. C Kidderminster St Mary *Worc* 82; C Kidderminster St Mary and All SS, Trimpley etc 82-83; Hon C Stockton St Mark *Dur* 84-86; NSM Longwood *Wakef* 86-94; V Athersley 94-97; P-in-c Ferrybridge 97-03; P-in-c Holme and Seaton Ross Gp *York* from 03. *The Vicarage, Market Weighton Road, Holme-on-Spalding-Moor, York YO43 4AG* Tel (01430) 860248

STRAIN, Christopher Malcolm. b 56. Solicitor Southn Univ LLB77. Wycliffe Hall Ox 83. **d** 86 **p** 87. C Werrington *Pet* 86-89; C Broadwater St Mary *Chich* 89-94; TV Hampreston *Sarum* 94-00; P-in-c Parkstone St Luke 00-03; V from 03. *The Vicarage, 2 Birchwood Road, Parkstone, Poole BH14 9NP* Tel (01202) 741030

STRAIN, John Damian. b 49. Keele Univ BA72 Birkbeck Coll Lon MSc83 PhD89 AFBPsS89. STETS BTh00. **d** 00 **p** 01. NSM Hindhead *Guildf* 00-03; NSM Churt and Hindhead from 03. *Pinewoods, Church Lane, Grayshott, Hindhead GU26 6LY* Tel (01428) 607115 E-mail j.strain@surrey.ac.uk

STRANACK, The Very Revd David Arthur Claude. b 43. Chich Th Coll 65. **d** 68 **p** 69. C Forest Gate St Edm *Chelmsf* 68-69; C Colchester St Jas, All SS, St Nic and St Runwald 69-74; V Brentwood St Geo 74-82; V Nayland w Wiston *St E* 82-99; Hon Can St E Cathl from 94; R Hadleigh 99-02; V Hadleigh, Layham and Shelley from 02; RD Hadleigh from 99; Dean Bocking from 99. *The Deanery, Church Street, Hadleigh, Ipswich IP7 5DT* Tel (01473) 822218

STRANACK, Fay Rosemary. b 30. Lon Univ BSc55 PhD60. Westcott Ho Cam 88. **d** 89 **p** 94. NSM Denmead *Portsm* 89-98; rtd 98; Perm to Offic *Portsm* from 98. *35 Yew Tree Gardens, Denmead, Waterlooville PO7 6LH* Tel (023) 9225 6785

STRANACK, Canon Richard Nevill. b 40. Leeds Univ BA63. Coll of Resurr Mirfield 63. **d** 65 **p** 66. C Bush Hill Park St Mark *Lon* 65-68; C Brighton St Martin *Chich* 68-72; P-in-c Toftrees w Shereford *Nor* 72-74; V 74-81; P-in-c Pensthorpe 72-74; R 74-81; V Hempton and Pudding Norton 72-81; RD Burnham and Walsingham 78-81; V Par *Truro* 81-94; P-in-c St Blazey 87-91; Hon Chapl Miss to Seafarers from 81; V Stratton and Launcells *Truro* from 94; Hon Can Truro Cathl from 98; RD Stratton from 02; Chapl Cornwall Healthcare Trust from 97. *The Vicarage, Diddies Road, Stratton, Bude EX23 9DW* Tel (01288) 352254 Fax 356525

STRAND, Tyler Alan. b 51. Augustana Coll (USA) AB73. St Steph Ho Ox 74 Gen Th Sem (NY) MDiv78. **d** 77 **p** 78. USA 77-85 and from 93; W Germany 85-90; Chapl Helsinki w Moscow *Eur* 91-93. *1220 Cambia Drive #4310, Schaumburg, IL 60193-4606, USA* Tel (001) (847) 534 7212

STRANGE, Adam Michael. b 57. Pemb Coll Ox BA79 MA89. Wycliffe Hall Ox BA84. **d** 84 **p** 85. C York St Paul *York* 84-87; Asst Chapl Brussels Cathl *Eur* 87-91; Assoc Chapl 91-95; P-in-c Heigham H Trin *Nor* 95-99; R from 99. *The Rectory, 17 Essex Street, Norwich NR2 2BL* Tel (01603) 622225 E-mail big1al@ntlworld.com

STRANGE, Brian. b 47. QUB BA69. SW Minl Tr Course 99. **d** 01 **p** 02. NSM Georgeham *Ex* from 01. *2 Inglenook Cottages, St Mary's Road, Croyde, Braunton EX33 1PG* Tel (01271) 890961 E-mail brian@croyde.org

STRANGE, Bryan. b 26. Sarum & Wells Th Coll 73. **d** 75 **p** 76. C King's Worthy *Win* 75-78; C Wilton *B & W* 78-80; V Kewstoke w Wick St Lawrence 80-89; rtd 89; Perm to Offic *Ex* from 90. *29 Bluebell Avenue, Tiverton EX16 6SX*

STRANGE, Malcolm. b 58. Westmr Coll Ox MTh95. Sarum & Wells Th Coll 82. **d** 85 **p** 86. C Seaton Hirst *Newc* 85-88; C Ridgeway *Sarum* 88-89; TV 89-91; TV Newbury *Ox* 91-98; TR Bideford, Northam, Westward Ho, Appledore etc *Ex* 98-01; RD Hartland 99-01. *Address withheld by request*

STRANGE, Mark Jeremy. b 61. Aber Univ LTh82. Linc Th Coll 87. **d** 89 **p** 90. C Worc St Barn w Ch Ch *Worc* 89-92; V Worc St Wulstan 92-98; R Elgin w Lossiemouth *Mor* from 98. *The Rectory, 8 Gordon Street, Elgin IV30 1JQ* Tel (01343) 547505

STRANGE, Mrs Mary McKellar. b 53. FCA75 ATII77. St Jo Coll Nottm BTh93 Westcott Ho Cam 93. **d** 94 **p** 95. C Weston Favell *Pet* 94-97; C Broughton Astley and Croft w Stoney Stanton *Leic* 97-98; TV 98-03; RD Guthlaxton I 00-03; V St Helens *Portsm* from 03; V Sea View from 03. *The Vicarage, Eddington Road, Seaview PO34 5JT* Tel (01983) 567494

STRANGE, Michael Paul. b 46. Univ of Wales (Ban) BSc67 MSc71. SEITE 94. **d** 97 **p** 98. NSM Clapham TM *S'wark* 97-01; NSM Clapham H Trin and St Pet from 02; Asst Chapl HM Pris High Down 98-01; Asst Chapl HM Pris Wormwood Scrubs from 01. *HM Prison Wormwood Scrubs, Du Cane Road, London W12 0TU* Tel (020) 8588 3200 ext 3262 *or* 7228 9868 E-mail mike.strange@alfriston48.freeserve.co.uk

STRANGE, Canon Peter Robert. b 48. Univ Coll Lon BA69 Ex Coll Ox BA71 MA76. Cuddesdon Coll. **d** 72 **p** 73. C Denton *Newc* 72-74; C Newc St Jo 74-79; Chapl for Arts and Recreation 79-90; R Wallsend St Pet 79-86; Can Res Newc Cathl from 86; Angl Adv Tyne Tees TV from 90. *55 Queen's Terrace, Jesmond,*

Newcastle upon Tyne NE2 2PL Tel 0191-281 0181 *or* 232 1939 Fax 230 0735 E-mail stnicholas@aol.com

STRANGE, Preb Robert Lewis. b 45. Sarum & Wells Th Coll 72. **d** 74 **p** 75. C Walthamstow St Barn and St Jas Gt *Chelmsf* 74-77; C Wickford 77-80; P-in-c Treverbyn *Truro* 80-83; V 83-86; Asst Stewardship Adv 82-96; V Newlyn St Pet from 86; Preb Trehaverock from 94; Hon Chapl Miss to Seafarers from 86. *St Peter's Vicarage, Newlyn, Penzance TR18 5HT* Tel (01736) 362678 Fax 351174 E-mail robert.sarov@tiscali.co.uk

STRANGE, William Antony. b 53. Qu Coll Cam BA76 MA80 K Alfred's Coll Win CertEd77 Ox Univ DPhil89. Wycliffe Hall Ox 79. **d** 82 **p** 83. Tutor Wycliffe Hall Ox 82-87; C Aberystwyth *St D* 87; TV 87-91; V Llandeilo Fawr and Taliaris 91-96; Hd of Th and RS Trin Coll Carmarthen 96-01. *Address temp unknown*

STRANRAER-MULL, The Very Revd Gerald Hugh. b 42. AKC69. St Aug Coll Cant 69. **d** 70 **p** 71. C Hexham *Newc* 70-72; C Corbridge w Halton 72; R Cruden Bay *Ab* from 72; R Ellon from 72; Can St Andr Cathl from 81; Dean Ab from 88; P-in-c Peterhead from 02. *The Rectory, Ellon AB41 9NP* Tel (01358) 720366 Fax as telephone E-mail gerald.stranraer-mull@virgin.net

STRAPPS, Canon Robert David. b 28. St Edm Hall Ox BA52 MA56. Wycliffe Hall Ox 52. **d** 54 **p** 55. C Low Leyton *Chelmsf* 54-57; C Ox St Aldate w H Trin *Ox* 57-60; V Sandal St Helen *Wakef* 60-94; RD Chevet 81-93; Hon Can Wakef Cathl 92-94; rtd 94; Perm to Offic *Wakef* 94-98; *Glouc*; *Worc* from 94. *Brookside, Hill Road, Kemerton, Tewkesbury GL20 7JN* Tel (01386) 725515

STRASZAK, Edmund Norman. b 57. Coll of Resurr Mirfield 88. **d** 90 **p** 91. C Adlington *Blackb* 90-93; C Harrogate St Wilfrid and St Luke *Ripon* 93-95; V Chorley All SS *Blackb* from 95. *All Saints' Vicarage, Moor Road, Chorley PR7 2LR* Tel (01257) 265665 E-mail edmund@straszak.freeserve.co.uk

STRATFIELD, Robert John. b 42. HND ARICS67 MRICS01. SW Minl Tr Course 96. **d** 99 **p** 00. OLM Lanteglos by Camelford w Advent *Truro* from 99. *Watergate Farm, Advent, Camelford PL32 9QL* Tel (01840) 213129 Mobile 07721-646841 Fax 212590 E-mail surveybob@breathemail.net

STRATFORD, Mrs Anne Barbara. Southn Univ CertEd58 Westmr Coll Ox DipApTh98 Ox Univ MTh99. Qu Coll Birm 88. **d** 91 **p** 94. Officer Dioc Bd of Soc Resp (Family Care) *Lich* 85-97; NSM Kinnerley w Melverley and Knockin w Macsbrook 91-95; Chapl Robert Jones and Agnes Hunt Orthopaedic Hosp 95-97; NSM Maesbury *Lich* 95-96; P-in-c 96-97; Chapl Moreton Hall Sch from 96; P-in-c Ford *Heref* 97-02; V from 02; P-in-c Alberbury w Cardeston 97-02; V from 02. *The Vicarage, Ford, Shrewsbury SY5 9LZ* Tel (01743) 850254 Fax 885131

STRATFORD, David. b 46. LNSM course 94. **d** 98 **p** 99. OLM Ditton St Mich w St Thos *Liv* from 98. *96 Clincton View, Widnes WA8 8RW* Tel 0151-423 4912

STRATFORD, The Ven Ralph Montgomery. b 30. TCD BA53 MA67. CITC 53. **d** 54 **p** 54. Dioc C *C & O* 54-55; C Waterford Ch 55-56; I Ballisodare w Collooney 56-00; Adn Killala and Achonry *T, K & A* 69-00; Can Killala Cathl from 69; Preb Kilmactalway St Patr Cathl Dublin 85-00; rtd 00. *Knoxpark House, Robinstown, Mullingar, Co Westmeath, Irish Republic* Tel (00353) (44) 35292

STRATFORD, Terence Stephen. b 45. Chich Th Coll 67. **d** 69 **p** 70. C Old Shoreham *Chich* 69-73; C New Shoreham 69-73; C Uckfield 73-75; C Lt Horsted 73-75; C Isfield 73-75; P-in-c Waldron 76-80; R 80-82; V Blacklands Hastings Ch Ch and St Andr 82-89; P-in-c Ovingdean 89-95; Dioc Ecum Officer 89-95; P-in-c Staplefield Common 95-00; Sussex Ecum Officer 95-01; V Ferring from 00. *The Vicarage, 19 Grange Park, Ferring, Worthing BN12 5LS* Tel (01903) 241645

STRATFORD, Timothy Richard. b 61. York Univ BSc82. Wycliffe Hall Ox 83. **d** 86 **p** 87. C Mossley Hill St Matt and St Jas *Liv* 86-89; C St Helens St Helen 89-91; Bp's Dom Chapl 91-94; V W Derby Gd Shep 94-03; TR Kirkby from 03. *The Rectory, Old Hall Lane, Kirkby, Liverpool L32 5TH* Tel 0151-547 2155 Fax as telephone E-mail timstratford@compuserve.com

STRATHIE, Duncan John. b 58. Heythrop Coll Lon MA02. Cranmer Hall Dur BA95. **d** 97 **p** 98. C Yateley *Win* 97-01; V Kempshott from 01; Dioc Convener of Voc Adv from 03. *The Vicarage, 171 Kempshott Lane, Kempshott, Basingstoke RG22 5LF* Tel (01256) 355460 E-mail duncan.strathie@ntlworld.com

STRATON, Christopher James. b 46. DipTh74. **d** 93 **p** 94. S Africa 93-00; Chapl Miss to Seamen 93-96; Asst P Gingindlovu All SS 97-99; R 99-00; P-in-c Tyldesley w Shakerley *Man* from 00. *11 Peel Hall Avenue, Tyldesley, Manchester M29 8TA* Tel (01942) 882914

STRATTA, Antony Charles (Tony). b 36. ACIS. S'wark Ord Course 82. **d** 85 **p** 86. C Southborough St Pet w Ch Ch and St Matt *Roch* 85-88; R Gt Mongeham w Ripple and Sutton by Dover *Cant* 88-96; rtd 96; Perm to Offic *St E* from 96. *Well House, The Great Yard, Rougham Green, Bury St Edmunds IP30 9JP*

STRATTON, Henry William. b 39. Bris Univ CertEd74 BEd75. Glouc Sch of Min 80. **d** 83 **p** 84. NSM Cainscross w Selsley *Glouc* 83-87; C Odd Rode *Ches* 87-92; V Runcorn H Trin 92-96; V Lostock Gralam from 96. *The Vicarage, Station Road, Lostock Gralam, Northwich CW9 7PS* Tel (01606) 43806
E-mail harry@hstratton.fsnet.co.uk
STRATTON, John Jefferies. b 27. Bps' Coll Cheshunt 53. **d** 55 **p** 56. C Watford St Mich *St Alb* 55-60; C Stevenage 60-65; R Cottered w Broadfield and Throcking 65-82; RD Buntingford 75-82; V S Mimms St Mary and Potters Bar *Lon* 82-84; V Potters Bar *St Alb* 85-94; P-in-c Flamstead 94-96; rtd 94; Perm to Offic *B & W* from 97; Hon C Taunton H Trin from 97. *17 The Fairways, Sherford, Taunton TA1 3PA* Tel (01823) 330564
STRAUGHAN, Keith. b 60. Imp Coll Lon BSc81 Lon Univ PhD87 Imp Coll Lon ARCS81 CPhys87 MInstP87 Trin Coll Cam BA94. Westcott Ho Cam 94. **d** 97 **p** 98. C Abbots Langley *St Alb* 97-00; Chapl and Fell SS Coll Cam 00-03; Tutor from 00; Dean from 03. *The Chaplain, Sidney Sussex College, Cambridge CB2 3HU* Tel (01223) 338800 Fax 338884
E-mail chaplain@sid.cam.ac.uk
STRAW (née CAUDWELL), Mrs Juliet Lesley. b 49. Univ of Wales (Ban) BA70 Leeds Univ PGCE71. St Alb and Ox Min Course 00. **d** 03. *Clive Cottage, 68 Windmill Road, Mortimer Common, Reading RG7 3RL* Tel 0118-933 2648
E-mail juliet.straw@btinternet.com
STREATER, David Arthur. b 33. Oak Hill Th Coll 67. **d** 68 **p** 69. C Lindfield *Chich* 68-71; S Africa 71-86; R Kingham w Churchill, Daylesford and Sarsden *Ox* 86-91; Dir Ch Soc 91-98; Sec Ch Soc Trust 91-96; rtd 98; P-in-c Odell *St Alb* from 98. *The Rectory, 3 Church Lane, Odell, Bedford MK43 7AA* Tel (01234) 720234 Fax as telephone E-mail monty@ukgateway.net
STREATFEILD, Francis Richard Champion. b 22. Qu Coll Cam BA48 MA59. Cuddesdon Coll 48. **d** 50 **p** 51. C Houghton le Spring *Dur* 50-53; India 53-70; V Sacriston *Dur* 70-79; Lic to Offic *Carl* 79-85; Area Sec USPG *Carl* 79-85; C Carl St Aid and Ch Ch *Carl* 85-88; rtd 88; Perm to Offic *Carl* 88-99. *Fenton Lane Head, How Mill, Carlisle CA4 9LD* Tel (01228) 70470
STREATFEILD, Peter Michael Fremlyn. b 53. Newc Univ BSc77 St Jo Coll Dur BA03. Cranmer Hall Dur 00. **d** 03. C Solway Plain *Carl* from 03. *Ivy Cottage, Langrigg, Wigton CA7 3LL* Tel (016973) 21310 E-mail petermfs@hotmail.com
STREET, Anthony James. b 57. Trin Coll Bris DipHE81. **d** 85 **p** 87. SAMS 85-95; Chile 85-95; P-in-c Warley *Wakef* 96-99; V from 99. *The Vicarage, 466 Burnley Road, Warley, Halifax HX2 7LW* Tel (01422) 363623
E-mail familiastreet@btinternet.co.uk
STREET, Matthew Graham. b 61. Regent's Park Coll Ox BA83. Wycliffe Hall Ox 99. **d** 01. C Combe Down w Monkton Combe and S Stoke *B & W* from 01. *13A Fox Hill, Bath BA2 5QL* Tel (01225) 836092 Mobile 07710-527070
E-mail mgstreet@hotmail.com
STREET, Peter Jarman. b 29. K Coll Lon BD59 AKC59. **d** 59 **p** 60. C Highters Heath *Birm* 59-60; C Shirley 60-62; Lect Chesh Coll of Educn 62-66; St Pet Coll of Educn Birm 66-70; RE Adv Essex Co Coun 70-92; Hon C Gt Dunmow *Chelmsf* 71-85; Sen Insp RE and Humanities 74-92; R Gt w Lt Yeldham 85-92; RD Belchamp 90-92; rtd 92; Perm to Offic *Chelmsf* from 92. *18 Jubilee Court, Great Dunmow CM6 1DY* Tel (01371) 876871
STREET, Philip. b 47. Lon Univ BPharm68. NW Ord Course 75. **d** 78 **p** 79. C Heaton St Barn *Bradf* 78-81; C Evington *Leic* 82-84; R Wymondham w Edmondthorpe, Buckminster etc 84-88; V Gosberton Clough and Quadring *Linc* 88-95; Asst Local Min Officer 88-95; V Buttershaw St Paul *Bradf* 95-99; P-in-c Gt and Lt Casterton w Pickworth and Tickencote *Pet* from 99; P-in-c Exton w Horn from 02; P-in-c Empingham and Exton w Horn w Whitwell from 02. *The Rectory, Main Street, Great Casterton, Stamford PE9 4AP* Tel (01780) 764036
E-mail philipenny@streetshome.freeserve.co.uk
STREETER, Christine Mary. See HADDON-REECE, Mrs Christine Mary
STREETER, David James. b 42. Pemb Coll Cam BA64 MA68. Qu Coll Birm 65. **d** 67 **p** 68. C Saffron Walden *Chelmsf* 67-71; C Shrub End 71-73; R Rayne 73-79; V Highams Park All SS 79-82; P-in-c Stradbroke w Horham and Athelington *St E* 82-87; R Stradbroke, Horham, Athelington and Redlingfield from 87; RD Hoxne 91-00. *The Rectory, Doctors Lane, Stradbroke, Eye IP21 5HU* Tel (01379) 384363 Mobile 07798-784179
E-mail david.streeter@stedmundsbury.anglican.org
STREETING, John William. b 52. ACertCM89 Cam Inst of Educn CertEd74 Birm Univ BEd77 FGMS98 FRSA98 Anglia Poly Univ MA99. St Steph Ho Ox 90. **d** 92 **p** 93. C Upminster *Chelmsf* 92-95; C Chingford SS Pet and Paul 95-97; Assoc V Chelsea St Luke and Ch Ch *Lon* 97-03; V Sheerness H Trin w St Paul *Cant* from 03. *The Vicarage, 241 High Street, Sheerness ME12 1UR* Tel (01795) 662589
STREETING, Laurence Storey. b 14. VRD65. St Jo Coll Dur BA39 DipTh40 MA42. **d** 40 **p** 41. C Bishopwearmouth St Gabr *Dur* 40-46; Chapl RNVR 42-46; S Africa 46-49; Chapl Garden

City Woodford Bridge 49-51; Chapl Village Home Barkingside 49-51; Chapl RAF 51-56; Chapl RNR 56-90; Asst Chapl Eliz Coll Guernsey 56-60; Chapl Eshton Hall Sch Gargrave 60-64; Perm to Offic *Cant* 64-65; R Guernsey St Sampson *Win* 65-71; St Vincent 72-76; Chapl Madeira *Eur* 76-80; rtd 80; Perm to Offic *Win* from 79. *Apartment 8, de Hubie Court, Les Cotils Christian Centre, St Peter Port, Guernsey GY1 1VV*
STRETCH, Richard Mark. b 53. LNSM course 91. **d** 93 **p** 94. OLM Stowmarket *St E* from 93. *91 Kipling Way, Stowmarket IP14 1TS* Tel (01449) 676219
STRETTON, George Peter. b 22. MBE. **d** 70 **p** 71. Malaysia 70-78; V Shireoaks *S'well* 79-85; Perm to Offic *B & W* from 86; rtd 87. *9 The Lerburne, Wedmore BS28 4ED* Tel (01934) 713244
STRETTON, Reginald John. b 37. MRPharmS63 CBiol70 MIBiol70 Man Univ BSc62 Nottm Univ PhD65. EMMTC 88. **d** 91 **p** 92. NSM Loughb Gd Shep *Leic* 91-94; P-in-c Burrough Hill Pars 94-02; rtd 02. *19 Paddock Close, Quorn, Loughborough LE12 8BJ* Tel (01509) 412935
E-mail rstretton@leicester.anglican.org
STRETTON, Robert John. b 45. Lon Univ DipTh69. Kelham Th Coll. **d** 69 **p** 70. C Hendon St Ignatius *Dur* 69-73; C Middlesbrough St Thos *York* 73-77; OSB 77-78; V Brandon *Dur* 78-85; SSM from 85; Lic to Offic *Dur* 85-91; Tr in Evang Ch in Wales 91-94; Perm to Offic *S'wark* 94-01; Lesotho from 01. *Society of the Sacred Mission Priory, PO Box 1579, Maseru, Lesotho* Tel (00266) 315979
STREVENS, Brian Lloyd. b 49. St Jo Coll Dur BA70. Ripon Hall Ox 70. **d** 73 **p** 74. C Old Trafford St Jo *Man* 73-76; C Bolton St Pet 76-78; Org Sec Southn Coun of Community Service 78-92; Perm to Offic *Win* 82-86, 92-95 and from 01; Hon C Bitterne Park *Win* 86-92; Hon C N Stoneham 95-01. *186 Hill Lane, Southampton SO15 5DB* Tel (023) 8033 3301
E-mail hq@scaccs.org.uk
STREVENS, Richard Ernest Noel. b 34. Nottm Univ BA60. Linc Th Coll 60. **d** 62 **p** 63. C St Botolph Aldgate w H Trin Minories *Lon* 62-66; C Ealing St Steph Castle Hill 66-68; Hon C St Botolph without Bishopgate 68-70; V Clent *Worc* 76-86; V Pirbright *Guildf* 86-00; Perm to Offic *Ex* 69-98 and from 00; rtd 00. *83 Head Weir Road, Cullompton EX15 1NN* Tel (01884) 35823
STRIBLEY, William Charles Harold. b 29. SW Minl Tr Course 84. **d** 87 **p** 88. NSM Kenwyn St Geo *Truro* 87-92; NSM Truro St Paul and St Clem 92-98; Perm to Offic from 99. *54 Chirgwin Road, Truro TR1 1TT* Tel (01872) 272958
STRICKLAND (née CUTTS), Mrs Elizabeth Joan Gabrielle. b 61. St Jo Coll Dur BA83. Westcott Ho Cam 87. **d** 90 **p** 94. C Cayton w Eastfield *York* 90-92; NSM Biggin Hill *Roch* 93-96; Perm to Offic *Ox* 96-00; *Ely* 00-02; P-in-c Holywell w Needingworth *Ely* from 02. *Windswept, Holywell, St Ives PE27 4TQ* Tel (01480) 495275 or 460170
E-mail epstrickland@compuserve.com
STRICKLAND, Canon Ernest Armitage. b 24. Ch Coll Cam BA49 MA54. Wycliffe Hall Ox 49. **d** 51 **p** 52. C Bolton St Paul *Man* 51-53; C Hyson Green *S'well* 53-55; C-in-c Wollaton Park CD 55-57; V Wollaton Park 57-64; V Southport St Phil *Liv* 64-76; R Broughton *Linc* 76-90; RD Yarborough 81-86; Can and Preb Linc Cathl 85-00; rtd 90; Perm to Offic *Linc* 90-00; *Ely* from 00. *143 Grimsby Road, Waltham, Grimsby DN37 0PU* Tel (01472) 821126
STRICKLAND, Jonathan Edward Tully. b 56. Westf Coll Lon BSc78. Ridley Hall Cam 00. **d** 02 **p** 03. C Margate H Trin *Cant* from 02. *10 Richmond Avenue, Cliftonville, Margate CT9 2NG* Tel (01843) 295188 E-mail strickers@tesco.net
STRICKLAND, Canon Paul Lowndes. b 21. Linc Th Coll 46. **d** 49 **p** 50. C Oatlands *Guildf* 49-52; C Huddersfield St Jo *Wakef* 52-54; V Carlton 54-58; V Offton, Nettlestead and Willisham *St E* 58-61; CF (TA) 59-67; V Debenham *St E* 61-75; V Lakenheath 75-83; Hon Can St E Cathl 81-83; rtd 83. *4 Albany Gardens East, Clacton-on-Sea CO15 6HW* Tel (01255) 426303
STRIDE, Clifford Stephen. b 21. Ex & Truro NSM Scheme. **d** 81 **p** 82. NSM Chulmleigh *Ex* 81-83; NSM Hardham *Chich* 87-93; NSM Coldwaltham and Hardham 93-97; NSM Bury w Houghton and Coldwaltham and Hardham from 97. *Ambleside, Sandy Lane, Watersfield, Pulborough RH20 1NF* Tel (01798) 831851
STRIDE, Desmond William Adair. b 15. Ch Coll Cam BA37 MA41. Ridley Hall Cam 38. **d** 39 **p** 40. C Alperton *Lon* 39-41; C St Marylebone All So w SS Pet and Jo 41-42; C Milton Regis St Mary *Cant* 42-45; Chapl Dover Coll 45-57; Warden St Mich Coll Tenbury 57-65; V Tenbury St Mich *Heref* 57-65; Asst Master Tre-Arddur Ho Sch 65-67; Chapl Heathfield Sch Ascot 67-80; rtd 80; Perm to Offic *Chich* from 90. *5 Oakmede Way, Ringmer, Lewes BN8 5JL* Tel (01273) 813561
STRIDE, Edgar George. b 23. Tyndale Hall Bris 47. **d** 51 **p** 52. C Croydon Ch Ch Broad Green *Cant* 51-55; V Thurrock *Chelmsf* 55-61; V Becontree St Mary 61-70; R Spitalfields Ch Ch w All SS *Lon* 70-89; rtd 89; Perm to Offic *Pet* from 89 and *Linc* 89-01. *23 Pembroke Road, Stamford PE9 1BS* Tel (01780) 756325

STRIDE, John David. b 46. Ex Univ BSc68. Oak Hill Th Coll DipHE88. **d** 88 **p** 89. C Ashtead *Guildf* 88-96; V Lodge Moor St Luke *Sheff* from 96. *St Luke's House, 18 Blackbrook Road, Sheffield S10 4LP* Tel 0114-230 5271 Fax 230 8109 E-mail vicar@stlukeslodgemoor.org.uk

STRIDE, John Michael. b 48. Oak Hill Th Coll BA77. **d** 80 **p** 81. C Edmonton All SS *Lon* 80-82; C Edmonton All SS w St Mich 82-83; C Wembley St Jo 83-85; P-in-c Hockering *Nor* 85-89; R Hockering, Honingham, E and N Tuddenham 89-91; V Tuckswood 91-93; Chapl HM Pris Leeds 93-94; Chapl HM Pris Littlehey 94-96; V Heeley *Sheff* 96-99; TR Heeley and Gleadless Valley from 99. *The Vicarage, 5 Blackstock Close, Sheffield S14 1AE* Tel 0114-239 3897 E-mail mojnst@aol.com

STRIKE, Maurice Arthur. b 44. FRSA66 NDD66. Sarum & Wells Th Coll 85. **d** 87 **p** 88. C Chippenham St Andr w Tytherton Lucas *Bris* 87-91; R Corfe Castle, Church Knowle, Kimmeridge etc *Sarum* from 91. *The Rectory, East Street, Corfe Castle, Wareham BH20 5EE* Tel (01929) 480257

STRINGER, Adrian Nigel. b 60. Univ of Wales (Cardiff) BD82 Lanc Univ PGCE83. Sarum & Wells Th Coll 86. **d** 88 **p** 89. C Barrow St Matt *Carl* 88-92; TV Westhoughton *Man* 92-94; I Inver w Mountcharles, Killaghtee and Killybegs *D & R* 94-96; V Tuckingmill *Truro* 96-01; Chapl R Alexandra and Albert Sch Reigate 01-03; I Desertlyn w Ballyeglish *Arm* from 03. *Address temp unknown* E-mail adrianstringer@gatton-park.org.uk

STRINGER, Harold John. b 36. Peterho Cam BA58. Ripon Hall Ox 62. **d** 64 **p** 65. C Hackney St Jo *Lon* 64-68; C Roehampton H Trin *S'wark* 68-71; P-in-c Southampton St Mich w H Rood, St Lawr etc *Win* 71-73; TV Southampton (City Cen) 73-82; Ind Chapl 77-82; V Notting Hill St Jo 82-87; V Notting Hill St Pet 82-87; V Notting Hill St Jo and St Pet 87-01; AD Kensington 98-01; rtd 02. *56 Mountfield Road, London W5 2NQ* Tel (020) 8998 8049 E-mail stringer@haroldandchristina.co.uk

STRINGER, Canon John Roden. b 33. AKC61. **d** 62 **p** 63. C Auckland St Helen *Dur* 62-63; C Hebburn St Cuth 63-67; V Cassop cum Quarrington 67-88; RD Sedgefield 84-88; V Lumley 88-98; Hon Can Dur Cathl 88-98; rtd 98; Perm to Offic *Dur* 98-03. *20 Cherry Lane, Carlisle CA1 3GJ* Tel (01228) 550467

STRINGER, Leonard Gordon. b 14. Westcott Ho Cam 64. **d** 66 **p** 67. C Bath Abbey w St Jas *B & W* 66-80; rtd 80; Perm to Offic *B & W* 80-92. *8 Hockley Court, Weston Park West, Bath BA1 4AR* Tel (01225) 318286

STROMMEN, Mary. **d** 03. NSM Oslo w Bergen, Trondheim and Stavanger *Eur* from 03. *Address temp unknown*

STRONG, Christopher Patteson. b 43. Ridley Hall Cam. **d** 83 **p** 84. C Dalton-in-Furness *Carl* 83-87; V Wootton *St Alb* 87-02; RD Elstow 94-02; R Fowlmere, Foxton, Shepreth and Thriplow *Ely* from 02. *The Rectory, High Street, Fowlmere, Royston SG8 7SU* Tel (01763) 208195 Fax as telephone E-mail christopherpstrong@hotmail.com

STRONG, Jack. b 16. St Aid Birkenhead 52. **d** 54 **p** 55. C Radcliffe St Thos *Man* 54-58; V Chadderton St Mark 58-66; V Burgh-by-Sands w Kirkbampton *Carl* 66-83; R Burgh-by-Sands and Kirkbampton w Kirkandrews etc 83; rtd 83; Perm to Offic *Glouc* 84-99. *Aballava, 18 Winel Road, Winchcombe, Cheltenham GL54 5YE* Tel (01242) 603347

STRONG, Canon John David. b 34. Cuddesdon Coll 59. **d** 61 **p** 62. C Gosforth All SS *Newc* 61-65; Chapl Malvern Coll 65-71; R Welford w Weston on Avon *Glouc* 72-79; V Nailsworth 79-01; RD Tetbury 83-00; Hon Can Glouc Cathl 91-01; rtd 01. *Glebe House, The Meads, Leighterton, Tetbury GL8 8UW* Tel (01666) 890236 E-mail canondavid@penshouse.freeserve.co.uk

STRONG, Matthew John. b 60. Lon Univ BA81 Cam Univ BA84 MA89. Ridley Hall Cam 82. **d** 85 **p** 86. C Roundhay *Ripon* 85-89; C Hirwaun *Llan* 89-91; V Troedyrhiw w Merthyr Vale 91-95; Tutor Llan Ord Course 91-95. *22 Birch Lane, Oldbury B68 0NZ* Tel 0121-421 5978

STRONG, Rowan Gordon William. b 53. Victoria Univ Wellington BA76 Edin Univ PhD92. St Jo Coll (NZ) LTh80 Melbourne Coll of Div ThM88. **d** 77 **p** 78. New Zealand 77-83; Australia 83-89 and from 92; NSM Edin Old St Paul *Edin* 89-92; Tutor Edin Univ 91-92; Lect Murdoch Univ from 92. *37 Milne Street, Bicton, W Australia 6157* Tel (0061) (8) 9319 8505 *or* 9360 6470 Fax 9360 6480 E-mail strong@socs.murdoch.edu.au

STRONG, Preb Stephen Charles. b 16. Em Coll Cam BA38 MA43. Lon Coll of Div 38. **d** 40 **p** 41. C Harborne Heath *Birm* 40-43; C Dublin St Kevin *D & G* 43-45; Hd Cam Univ Miss Bermondsey 45-52; V Upper Tulse Hill St Matthias *S'wark* 52-57; V Egham *Guildf* 57-66; V Heref St Pet w St Owen *Heref* 66-79; V Heref St Pet w St Owen and St Jas 79-82; Preb Heref Cathl 78-85; rtd 82; Perm to Offic *Heref* from 83. *162 Buckfield Road, Leominster HR6 8UF* Tel (01568) 615534

STRONG, Capt William John Leonard. b 44. CA Tr Coll 64 Chich Th Coll 87. **d** 89 **p** 90. CA from 66; C Mayfield *Chich* 89-92; C Seaford w Sutton 92-94; V Crawley Down All SS 94-97; rtd 01. *21 Carroll Close, Poole BH12 1PL* Tel (01202) 733940 Mobile 07944-670125

STROUD, The Ven Ernest Charles Frederick. b 31. St Chad's Coll Dur BA59 DipTh60. **d** 60 **p** 61. C S Kirkby *Wakef* 60-63; C Whitby *York* 63-66; C-in-c Chelmsf All SS CD *Chelmsf* 66-69; V Chelmsf All SS 69-75; V Leigh-on-Sea St Marg 75-83; Asst RD Southend 76-79; RD Hadleigh 79-83; Hon Can Chelmsf Cathl 82-83; Adn Colchester 83-97; rtd 97; Perm to Offic *Chelmsf* from 97. *St Therese, 67 London Road, Hadleigh, Benfleet SS7 2QL* Tel (01702) 554941 Fax 500789

STROUD, Canon Robert Owen. b 29. AKC56. **d** 57 **p** 58. C Aylesbury *Ox* 57-60; C Bexhill St Pet *Chich* 60-64; C Gosforth All SS *Newc* 64-66; V High Elswick St Phil 66-72; V Tynemouth Cullercoats St Paul 72-77; R Orlestone w Ruckinge w Warehorne *Cant* 77-81; RD N Lympne 79-81; V Folkestone H Trin w Ch Ch 81-83; TR Folkestone H Trin and St Geo w Ch Ch 83-90; V Folkestone H Trin w Ch Ch 90-93; RD Elham 90-93; Hon Can Cant Cathl 92-93; rtd 93; Perm to Offic *Ev* 94-02; *Cant* from 02. *27 Rochester Avenue, Canterbury CT1 3YE* Tel (01227) 767312

STROYAN, John Ronald Angus. b 55. MTh. Qu Coll Birm 81 Bossey Ecum Inst Geneva 82. **d** 83 **p** 84. C Cov E *Cov* 83-87; V Smethwick St Matt w St Chad *Birm* 87-94; V Bloxham w Milcombe and S Newington *Ox* from 94; AD Deddington from 02. *The Vicarage, Church Street, Bloxham, Banbury OX15 4ET* Tel (01295) 720252 E-mail jstroyan@fish.co.uk

STRUDWICK, Canon Donald Frank. b 12. Leeds Univ BA33. Coll of Resurr Mirfield 33. **d** 35 **p** 37. C Wandsworth St Anne *S'wark* 35-39; C Plumstead Ascension 39-44; V Camberwell St Luke 44-49; V E Dulwich St Clem 49-85; RD Dulwich 57-67; Hon Can S'wark Cathl 73-85; rtd 85; Perm to Offic *Roch* 85-00. *The Old Chapel, Pencelli, Brecon LD3 7LX* Tel (01874) 665415

STRUDWICK, Canon Vincent Noel Harold. b 32. Nottm Univ BA59 DipEd. Kelham Th Coll 52. **d** 59 **p** 60. Tutor Kelham Th Coll 59-63; Sub-Warden 63-70; C Crawley *Chich* 70-73; Adult Educn Adv 73-77; R Fittleworth 73-77; Planning Officer for Educn Milton Keynes 77-80; Dir of Educn *Ox* 80-89; Hon Can Ch Ch from 82; Continuing Minl Educn Adv 85-89; Dir Dioc Inst for Th Educn 89-97; Prin Ox Min Course 89-94; Prin St Alb and Ox Min Course 94-96; Fell and Tutor Kellogg Coll Ox 94-00; C Aylesbury w Bierton and Hulcott *Ox* 97-98. *31 The Square, Brill, Aylesbury HP18 9RP* Tel (01865) 280354 Fax 270309 E-mail vincent.strudwick@conted.ox.ac.uk

STRUGNELL, John Richard. b 30. Lon Univ BA52 Leeds Univ MA61 Queensland Univ PhD77. Wells Th Coll 54. **d** 56 **p** 57. C Leeds Halton St Wilfrid *Ripon* 56-59; C Moor Allerton 59-62; Australia from 65; rtd 95. *231 Grandview Road, Pullenvale, Qld, Australia 4069* Tel (0061) (7) 3374 1776

STRUTT, Peter Edward. b 40. St Alb and Ox Min Course 94. **d** 97 **p** 98. NSM Penn Street *Ox* 97-02; Perm to Offic from 02. *59 King's Ride, Penn, High Wycombe HP10 8BP* Tel (01494) 812418

STRUTT, Mrs Susan. b 45. Glouc Sch of Min 87. **d** 90 **p** 94. NSM Eye, Croft w Yarpole and Lucton *Heref* 90-94; C Leominster 94-96; P-in-c Bosbury w Wellington Heath etc 96-98; TV Ledbury from 98; Dioc Adv on Women in Min 99-03. *The Vicarage, Bosbury, Ledbury HR8 1QA* Tel (01531) 640225

STUART, Angus Fraser. b 61. Bedf Coll Lon BA83 K Coll Lon PhD91 St Jo Coll Dur BA92. Cranmer Hall Dur 90. **d** 93 **p** 94. C Twickenham St Mary *Lon* 93-96; Sen Chapl Bris Univ *Bris* from 96; Hon C Bris St Mich and St Paul 96-98; P-in-c 98-00; Hon C Cotham St Sav w St Mary and Clifton St Paul from 00. *67 Waverley Road, Redland, Bristol BS6 6ET* Tel 0117-924 4261 *or* 954 6600 Fax 954 6602 E-mail angus.stuart@bris.ac.uk

STUART, Sister Ann-Marie Lindsay. b 41. Westmr Coll Lon CertEd69 Kent Univ BA80 Plymouth Univ DipMin93. Franciscan Study Cen 76. **d** 99 **p** 00. NSM Sherborne w Castleton and Lillington *Sarum* 99-01; TV Golden Cap Team from 01. *The Vicarage, 5 George Close, Charmouth, Bridport DT6 6RU* Tel (01297) 560409

STUART, Brother. *See* BURNS, The Rt Revd Stuart Maitland

STUART, Francis David. b 32. Barrister-at-Law Lon Univ BA54 AKC57. Ridley Hall Cam 62. **d** 64 **p** 65. C Addiscombe St Mildred *Cant* 64-67; Chapl RN 67-71; Lic to Offic *Liv* 76-80; TV Oldham *Man* 84-89; Chapl Oldham and Distr Gen Hosp 84-89; Chapl Oldham R Infirmary 86-89; Chapl R Oldham Hosp 89-94; Chapl Oldham NHS Trust 94-98; rtd 97; Perm to Offic *Man* 00-03. *3 bis Allee des Chataigniers, 56340 Carnac, France* Tel (0033) (2) 9752 8374

STUART, Canon Herbert James. b 26. CB83. TCD BA48 MA55. **d** 49 **p** 50. C Sligo Cathl *K, E & A* 49-53; C Dublin Rathmines *D & G* 53-55; Chapl RAF 55-73; Asst Chapl-in-Chief RAF 73-80; Chapl-in-Chief and Archdeacon for the RAF 80-83; Can and Preb Linc Cathl *Linc* 81-83; R Cherbury *Ox* 83-87; Perm to Offic *Glouc* 87-96; *Ox* 87-96; rtd 91. *1 Abbot's Walk, Lechlade GL7 3DB* Tel (01367) 253299

✠**STUART, The Rt Revd Ian Campbell.** b 42. New England Univ (NSW) BA70 CertEd70 Melbourne Univ DipEd77 MA92 MACE72 FAIM91. St Barn Coll Adelaide 84. **d** 85 **p** 85 **c** 92. Australia 85-99; Asst Bp N Queensland 96-99; Chapl Liv Hope from 99; Asst Bp Liv from 99. *The Chaplaincy, Liverpool Hope,*

Hope Park, Taggart Avenue, Liverpool L16 9JD Tel 0151-291 3547 Fax 291 3873 E-mail stuarti@hope.ac.uk

STUART-LEE, Nicholas. b 54. Wycliffe Hall Ox. **d** 83 **p** 84. C Costessey *Nor* 83-85; TV Dewsbury *Wakef* 85-90; R Rowlands Castle *Portsm* 90-00; V Nottingham St Jude *S'well* from 00. *St Jude's Vicarage, Woodborough Road, Nottingham NG3 5HE* Tel 0115-960 4102

STUART-SMITH, David. b 36. St Pet Coll Ox BA61 MA65. Tyndale Hall Bris. **d** 63 **p** 64. C Tooting Graveney St Nic *S'wark* 63-67; C Richmond H Trin 67-70; Lic to Offic 70-74; NSM Canonbury St Steph *Lon* 70-74; Travelling Sec IVF 70-74; Bangladesh 74-79; V Clapham Park St Steph *S'wark* 79-95; RD Streatham 83-87; Chapl Wye Coll Kent 95-01; P-in-c Wye w Brook *Cant* 95-01; P-in-c Hastingleigh 00-01; rtd 01; Perm to Offic *Cant* from 01. *40 Lancaster Close, Hamstreet, Ashford TN26 2JG* Tel (01233) 731049 E-mail dstuartsmi@aol.com

STUART-WHITE, William Robert. b 59. Ox Univ BA. Trin Coll Bris BA. **d** 86 **p** 87. C Upper Armley *Ripon* 86-91; P-in-c Austrey *Birm* 91-92; P-in-c Warton 91-92; V Austrey and Warton 92-98; R Camborne *Truro* from 98. *The Rectory, Rectory Gardens, Camborne TR14 7DN* Tel (01209) 613020 E-mail wstuartwhi@aol.com

STUBBINGS, Frank Edward. b 20. Fitzw Coll Cam BA48 MA53. Worc Ord Coll 60. **d** 61 **p** 62. C Rowbarton *B & W* 61-64; V Catcott 64-74; V Burtle 64-74; Chapl St Cath Sch Bramley 74-83; R Barkestone w Plungar, Redmile and Stathern *Leic* 83-87; rtd 87; Perm to Offic *B & W* 88-91; Hon C Lostwithiel, St Winnow w St Nectan's Chpl etc *Truro* from 91. *Gooseydown, Park Road, Lostwithiel PL22 0BU* Tel (01208) 872762

STUBBS, Anthony Richard Peter (Ælred). b 23. Ball Coll Ox BA49. Coll of Resurr Mirfield 51. **d** 54 **p** 54. Lic to Offic *Wakef* 54-57 and 82-94; CR from 54; Lic to Offic *Llan* 57-59; S Africa 60-77; Lesotho 77-81; rtd 94; Perm to Offic *Lon* 96-97. *House of the Resurrection, Stocks Bank Road, Mirfield WF14 0BN* Tel (01924) 494318 Fax 490489

STUBBS, Ian Kirtley. b 47. Man Univ DipAE90. Kelham Th Coll 66. **d** 70 **p** 71. C Chandler's Ford *Win* 70-75; C Farnham Royal *Ox* 75-80; Ind Chapl 75-80; Ind Chapl *Man* 81-86; TV Oldham 81-86; TR Langley and Parkfield 86-88; Community Work Officer Dioc Bd of Soc Resp 88-90; Dir Laity Development 90-96; Nat Adv in Adult Learning C of E Bd of Educn 97-02; V Stalybridge *Man* from 02. *The Vicarage, 2 Tintagel Court, Astley Road, Stalybridge SK15 1RA* Tel and fax 0161-338 2368 Mobile 07712-451710 E-mail ian@denshaw.freeserve.co.uk

STUBBS, Stanley Peter Handley. b 23. Lon Univ BD52 Lille 3 Univ MèsL82. Ely Th Coll 55. **d** 55 **p** 56. C Fletton *Ely* 55-58; Hon Min Can Pet Cathl *Pet* 56-58; C Hounslow Heath St Paul *Lon* 58-63; CF (TA) 59-78; V Northampton St Alb *Pet* 63-76; R Brondesbury Ch Ch and St Laur *Lon* 76-93; rtd 93; Perm to Offic *Lon* from 93. *3 Westbury Lodge Close, Pinner HA5 3FG* Tel (020) 8868 8296

STUBBS, Trevor Noel. b 48. Hull Univ DipMin AKC70. St Aug Coll Cant 73. **d** 74 **p** 75. C Heckmondwike *Wakef* 74-77; Australia 77-80; V Middleton St Cross *Ripon* 80-89; R Wool and E Stoke *Sarum* 89-95; TR Bridport from 95. *The Rectory, 84 South Street, Bridport DT6 3NW* Tel (01308) 422138 E-mail trevor.stubbs@uk.com

STUBENBORD, Jess William. b 48. BA72. Trin Coll Bris 75. **d** 78 **p** 79. C Cromer *Nor* 78-82; C Gorleston St Mary 82-85; P-in-c Saxthorpe and Corpusty 85-89; P-in-c Blickling 86-89; R Saxthorpe w Corpusty, Blickling, Oulton etc 89-93; P-in-c Mulbarton w Kenningham 93-97; P-in-c Flordon 94-97; P-in-c Wreningham 95-97; R Mulbarton w Bracon Ash, Hethel and Flordon from 98. *The Rectory, The Common, Mulbarton, Norwich NR14 8JS* Tel (01508) 570296 E-mail j.stubenbord@xalt.co.uk

STUBLEY, Peter Derek. b 28. AKC57 Dur Univ MA79 PhD91. **d** 58 **p** 59. C Stockton St Chad *Dur* 58-61; V W Hartlepool St Oswald 61-66; Ind Chapl 66-76; Ind Chapl *York* 76-96; V Gt Totham *Chelmsf* 83; P-in-c Kingston upon Hull St Mary *York* 83-88; rtd 96; Perm to Offic *York* from 96. *8 Queens Way, Cottingham HU16 4EP* Tel (01482) 848718

STUCKES, Stephen. b 62. Trin Coll Bris. **d** 96 **p** 97. C Dunster, Carhampton and Withycombe w Rodhuish *B & W* 96-00; V Alcombe from 00. *The Vicarage, 34 Manor Road, Minehead TA24 6EJ* Tel (01643) 703285 E-mail sjstuckes@hotmail.com

STUDD, Christopher Sidney. b 25. S'wark Ord Course. **d** 68 **p** 69. C Shenfield *Chelmsf* 68-73; R Stifford 73-83; P-in-c Bowers Gifford w N Benfleet 83-86; R 83-92; rtd 92; Perm to Offic *Chelmsf* from 92. *9 Stonehill Road, Roxwell, Chelmsford CM1 4PF* Tel (01245) 248824

STUDD, John Eric. b 34. Clare Coll Cam BA58 MA62. Coll of Resurr Mirfield 58. **d** 60 **p** 61. C Westmr St Steph w St Jo *Lon* 60-65; Australia 65-69; Hon C Kensington St Mary Abbots w St Geo *Lon* 70-71; P-in-c Monks Risborough *Ox* 72-77; P-in-c Gt and Lt Kimble 72-77; C Aylesbury 78; Chapl to the Deaf 78-82; Chapl Hants, Is of Wight and Channel Is Assn for Deaf 82-91; Chapl to the Deaf *Win* 91-99; Perm to Offic *Guildf* 82-96; Perm to Offic *Portsm* from 82; rtd 99. *28 Elgin Way, Flagstaff*

Hill, S Australia 5159 Tel (0061) (8) 8370 4707 Fax 8370 6517 E-mail jonea@senet.com.au

STUDDERT, Michael John de Clare. b 39. Trin Coll Cam BA64 MA67. Cuddesdon Coll 64. **d** 66 **p** 67. C Langley All SS and Martyrs *Man* 66-69; C Fleet *Guildf* 69-73; Perm to Offic 73-77; Chapl Eagle Ho Sch Sandhurst 77-88. *Southlands, Churt Road, Hindhead GU26 6PF* Tel (01428) 604620

STUDDERT-KENNEDY, Andrew Geoffrey. b 59. Ch Ch Ox BA80 MA86. Ripon Coll Cuddesdon BA88. **d** 89 **p** 90. C Wimbledon *S'wark* 89-94; V Norbury St Oswald 94-02; RD Croydon N 99-02; TR Marlborough *Sarum* from 02. *The Rectory, 1 Rawlingswell Lane, Marlborough SN8 1AU* Tel (01672) 512357

STUDDERT-KENNEDY, Canon Christopher John. b 22. BNC Ox BA49 MA53. Wells Th Coll 49. **d** 51 **p** 52. C Bermondsey St Mary w St Olave and St Jo *S'wark* 51-54; C Clapham H Trin 54-56; V Putney St Marg 56-66; R Godstone 66-91; RD Godstone 76-88; Hon Can S'wark Cathl 80-91; rtd 91; Perm to Offic *Chich* from 91. *Orchard House, The Street, Washington, Pulborough RH20 4AS* Tel (01903) 892774

STUDHOLME, Muriel Isabel. b 25. **d** 96. NSM Bromfield w Waverton *Carl* 96-02; NSM Solway Plain from 02. *Yew Tree Cottage, Dundraw, Wigton CA7 0DP* Tel (01697) 342506

STURCH, Richard Lyman. b 36. Ch Ch Ox BA58 MA61 DPhil70. Ely Th Coll. **d** 62 **p** 63. C Hove All SS *Chich* 62-65; C Burgess Hill St Jo 65-66; C Ox St Mich w St Martin and All SS *Ox* 67-68; Tutor Ripon Hall Ox 67-71; Nigeria 71-74; Lect Lon Bible Coll 75-80; Lic to Offic *Lon* 75-80; TV Wolverton *Ox* 80-86; R Islip w Charlton on Otmoor, Oddington, Noke etc 86-01; rtd 01. *35 Broomfield, Stacey Bushes, Milton Keynes MK12 6HA* Tel (01908) 316779 E-mail rsturch@compuserve.com

STURDY, William David Mark. b 28. Ch Coll Cam BA52 MA56. Qu Coll Birm. **d** 55 **p** 56. C Lutterworth w Cotesbach *Leic* 55-59; C Loughborough Em 59-61; V Thorpe Acre w Dishley 61-72; R Kegworth 72-82; V Cringleford *Nor* 82-85; R Colney 82-85; R Cringleford w Colney and Bawburgh 85-93; RD Humbleyard 87-93; rtd 94; Perm to Offic *Nor* from 94. *20 Valley Rise, Dersingham, King's Lynn PE31 6PT* Tel (01485) 543762

STURMAN, Robert George. b 50. Nottm Univ BTh79. Linc Th Coll 75. **d** 79 **p** 80. C Cainscross w Selsley *Glouc* 79-83; TV Bottesford w Ashby *Linc* 83-88; V Prescot *Liv* 88-91; P-in-c Abenhall w Mitcheldean *Glouc* 93-97; R from 97; RD Forest N from 99. *St Michael's Rectory, Hawker Hill, Mitcheldean GL17 0BS* Tel (01594) 542434

STURROCK, Marian Elizabeth. b 46. Westmr Coll Ox BTh97 Univ of Wales (Cardiff) 97. St Mich Coll Llan 98. **d** 99 **p** 00. C Swansea St Pet *S & B* 99-03; R Thundersley *Chelmsf* from 03. *St Peter's Rectory, Church Road, Thundersley, Benfleet SS7 3HG* Tel (01268) 566206

STURT, Rock André Daniel. b 56. Liv Univ BSc79 Lon Univ CertEd80. Oak Hill Th Coll DipTh88 BA88. **d** 88 **p** 89. Chapl St Bede's Sch Cam 88-90; Par Dn Cambridge St Martin *Ely* 88-90; C 90-91; P-in-c Alwalton and Chesterton 91-96; TV The Ortons, Alwalton and Chesterton from 96. *Alwalton Rectory, Church Street, Peterborough PE7 3UU* Tel (01733) 236205 E-mail rcsturt@fish.co.uk

STUTZ, Clifford Peter. b 25. **d** 83 **p** 84. OLM Cusop w Blakemere, Bredwardine w Brobury etc *Heref* from 83. *Burnt House, Dorstone, Hereford HR3 5SX* Tel (01497) 831472

STUTZ, Ms Sally Ann. b 64. Univ of Wales BSc88 Leeds Metrop Univ MSc93 Birm Univ BD95 SRD90. Qu Coll Birm 93. **d** 96 **p** 97. C Middleton St Mary *Ripon* 96-00; C Wilmslow *Ches* from 00; Dioc Adv in Chr Worship from 00. *17 Cobetts Way, Wilmslow SK9 6HN* Tel and fax (01625) 536755 or tel 530942

STYLER, Geoffrey Marsh. b 15. CCC Ox BA37 MA40 Cam Univ MA44. Union Th Sem (NY) STM39 Cuddesdon Coll 40. **d** 41 **p** 42. C Heckmondwike *Wakef* 41-44; Vice-Prin Westcott Ho Cam 44-48; Fell CCC Cam from 48; Lect Th Cam Univ 53-82; Select Preacher Ox Univ 55-57; Select Preacher Cam Univ 58 and 63; rtd 82; Perm to Offic *Ely* from 95. *Middleton Cottage, Sidgwick Avenue, Cambridge CB3 9DA* Tel (01223) 358420

STYLER, Jamie Cuming. b 36. Sarum & Wells Th Coll 70. **d** 72 **p** 73. C Whipton *Ex* 72-75; C Paignton St Jo 76-78; V Topsham 78-88; V Plymouth St Simon 88-01; Chapl Plymouth Community Services NHS Trust 94-01; rtd 01. *Drey House, 27 Langham Way, Ivybridge PL21 9BX* Tel (01752) 691592

STYLES, Clive William John. b 48. WMMTC 87. **d** 90 **p** 91. C Burslem *Lich* 90-94; TV Wednesfield 94-99; V Ashwellthorpe, Forncett, Fundenhall, Hapton etc *Nor* from 99. *The Vicarage, 16 The Fields, Tacolneston, Norwich NR16 1DG* Tel (01953) 788227

STYLES, Canon Lawrence Edgar. b 19. AM88. Pemb Coll Cam BA48 MA52. Ridley Hall Cam. **d** 50 **p** 51. C Bishop's Stortford St Mich *St Alb* 50-53; V Tyldesley w Shakerley *Man* 53-60; Australia from 60; Can Melbourne 82-86; rtd 86. *25 Carson Street, Kew, Vic, Australia 3101* Tel (0061) (3) 9853 9749 Fax as telephone E-mail lstyles@co31.aone.net.au

STYLES, Nigel Charles. b 57. Keele Univ BA79 Rob Coll Cam BA92. Ridley Hall Cam CTM93. **d** 95 **p** 96. C Bedford Ch Ch

St Alb 95-02; V Bramcote *S'well* from 02. *Bramcote Vicarage, Moss Drive, Bramcote, Beeston NG9 3NF* Tel 0115-925 5655 E-mail nigel@stylish.freeserve.co.uk

SUART, Geoffrey Hugh. b 49. Man Univ BSc70 Nottm Univ PGCE71. Oak Hill Th Coll DipHE83. d 83 p 84. C Ogley Hay *Lich* 83-86; TV Wenlock *Heref* 86-90; TR Kirby Muxloe *Leic* from 90; RD Sparkenhoe E 99-03. *The Rectory, 6 Station Road, Kirby Muxloe, Leicester LE9 2EJ* Tel 0116-238 6822 *or* 238 6811 E-mail geoffsuart@talk21.com

SUCH, Colin Royston. b 62. UEA LLB83. Ripon Coll Cuddesdon 94. d 97 p 98. C Streetly *Lich* 97-00; P-in-c Wednesfield St Greg from 00. *St Gregory's Vicarage, 112 Long Knowle Lane, Wednesfield, Wolverhampton WV11 1JQ* Tel (01902) 731677

SUCH, Canon Howard Ingram James. b 52. Southn Univ BTh81 Lon Univ MA97. Sarum & Wells Th Coll 77. d 81 p 82. C Cheam *S'wark* 81-84; Prec Cant Cathl *Cant* 84-91; Hon Min Can Cant Cathl 84-03; V Borden 91-03; AD Sittingbourne 00-03; Can Res and Prec Sheff Cathl *Sheff* from 03. *The Cathedral, Church Street, Sheffield S1 1HA* Tel 0114-275 3434 Fax 278 0244 E-mail howard.such@sheffield-cathedral.org.uk

SUCH, Paul Nigel. b 52. FGA72 BTh84. Chich Th Coll 79. d 84 p 85. C Handsworth St Andr *Birm* 84-87; C Rugeley *Lich* 87-88; TV 88-91; R Longton 91-02; R Cov St Jo *Cov* from 02. *St John's Rectory, 9 Davenport Road, Coventry CV5 6QA* Tel (024) 7667 3203 Fax as telephone

SUCH, Royston Jeffery. b 46. Solicitor Univ Coll Lon LLB67. Sarum & Wells Th Coll 83. d 83 p 84. NSM Headbourne Worthy *Win* 83-90; R Bishop's Sutton and Ropley and W Tisted from 90. *The Vicarage, Lyeway Lane, Ropley, Alresford SO24 0DW* Tel (01962) 772205

SUCKLING, Keith Edward. b 47. CChem FRSC Darw Coll Cam PhD71 Liv Univ BSc87 DSc89. Oak Hill NSM Course 91. d 94 p 95. NSM Digswell and Panshanger *St Alb* from 94. *291 Knightsfield, Welwyn Garden City AL8 7NH* Tel (01707) 330022 E-mail keith@suckling291.freeserve.co.uk

SUDAN, Archbishop of the Episcopal Church of the. *See* MARONA, The Most Revd Joseph Biringi Hassan

SUDBURY, Archdeacon of. *See* COX, The Ven John Stuart

SUDDABY, Susan Eveline. b 43. Bedf Coll of Educn CertEd64 Bp Otter Coll Chich AdvCertEd86. S'wark Ord Course 93. d 96 p 97. NSM Rusthall *Roch* 96-00; C Northfleet 00-02. *51 Bowen Road, Tunbridge Wells TN4 8SU* Tel (01892) 534100

SUDDARDS, John Martin. b 52. Trin Hall Cam BA74 MA77 Barrister-at-Law 75. Qu Coll Birm 86. d 89 p 90. C Halstead St Andr w H Trin and Greenstead Green *Chelmsf* 89-93; P-in-c Gt w Lt Yeldham 93-97; R Upper Colne 97-01; RD Hinckford 98-01; TR Witham from 01. *The Vicarage, 7 Chipping Dell, Witham CM8 2JX* Tel (01376) 513509 E-mail john@protais.ndo.co.uk

SUDELL, Philip Henry. b 61. Thames Poly BScEng84 Lon Univ PGCE85. Wycliffe Hall Ox 89. d 92 p 93. C Worthing Ch the King *Chich* 92-96; C Muswell Hill St Jas w St Matt *Lon* from 96. *8 St James's Lane, London N10 3DB* Tel (020) 8883 7417 E-mail philip.sudell@st-james.org.uk

SUDRON, David Jeffrey. b 78. Dur Univ BA99 MA00. St Steph Ho Ox 01. d 03. C Gt Grimsby St Mary and St Jas *Linc* from 03. *3 Grosvenor Street, Grimsby DN32 0QH* Tel (01472) 356931 E-mail david.sudron@dunelm.org.uk

SUDWORTH, Frank. b 43. Open Univ BA92. Oak Hill Th Coll DipHE78. d 78 p 79. C Deane *Man* 78-81; C Worksop St Jo *S'well* 82-85; V Wollaton Park 85-90; P-in-c Lenton Abbey 85-86; V 86-90; V Upper Armley *Ripon* 90-97; RD Armley 92-95; Dep Chapl HM Pris Liv 97-98; P-in-c Low Moor H Trin *Bradf* 98-03; V Low Moor from 03. *Holy Trinity Vicarage, Park House Road, Low Moor, Bradford BD12 0HR* Tel (01274) 678859

SUFFERN, Richard William Sefton. b 57. Reading Univ BSc79. Trin Coll Bris DipHE90. d 90 p 91. C Radipole and Melcombe Regis *Sarum* 90-94; TV Cheltenham St Mark *Glouc* 94-99; R Whitnash *Cov* from 99. *St Margaret's Rectory, 2 Church Close, Whitnash, Leamington Spa CV31 2HJ* Tel (01926) 425070 E-mail r.suffern@ntlworld.com

SUFFOLK, Archdeacon of. *See* ARRAND, The Ven Geoffrey William

SUFFRIN, Canon Arthur Charles Emmanuel. b 09. Selw Coll Cam BA30 MA34. Qu Coll Birm 34. d 35 p 36. C Winchmore Hill H Trin *Lon* 35-39; C Abbots Langley *St Alb* 39-42; CF (EC) 42-44; Public Preacher *St Alb* 44-47; C-in-c Luton St Chris Round Green CD 47-53; V Croxley Green All SS 53-63; V Hexton 63-68; V Pirton 68-74; Hon Can St Alb 65-75; RD Hitchin 71-74; rtd 74; Perm to Offic *Sarum* from 74. *Sampford House Nursing Home, 27 Shurnhold, Melksham SN12 8DD* Tel (01255) 707442

SUGDEN, Charles Edward. b 59. Magd Coll Cam MA81 PGCE82. Trin Coll Bris DipHE91. d 91 p 92. C Gidea Park *Chelmsf* 91-94; TV Melksham *Sarum* 94-01; NSM Poole from 02. *Hyghfoldes, Canford Magna, Wimborne BH21 3AD* Tel (01202) 887386 E-mail parsons.paddock@btinternet.com

SUGDEN, Canon Christopher Michael Neville. b 48. St Pet Coll Ox BA70 MA74 Nottm Univ MPhil74 Westmr Coll Ox PhD88. St Jo Coll Nottm 72. d 74 p 75. C Leeds St Geo *Ripon* 74-77; Assoc P Bangalore St Jo India 77-83; Lic to Offic *Ox* from 83; Can St Luke's Cathl Jos Nigeria from 00; Exec Dir Ox Cen for Miss Studies from 01. *Oxford Centre for Mission Studies, PO Box 70, Oxford OX2 6HB* Tel (01865) 556071 Fax 510823 E-mail csugden@ocms.ac.uk

SUGDEN, Kara Kerstin. b 58. Man Univ BSc81 W Midl Coll of Educn PGCE82. Trin Coll Bris BA91. d 91 p 96. NSM Gidea Park *Chelmsf* 91-94; NSM Melksham *Sarum* 95-01; Chapl Canford Sch Wimborne from 01. *Hyghfoldes, Canford Magna, Wimborne BH21 3AD* Tel (01202) 887386 *or* 841254 E-mail kks@canford.com

SULLIVAN, Adrian Michael. b 55. Sarum & Wells Th Coll 85. d 87 p 88. C Louth *Linc* 87-90; P-in-c E and W Keal 90; P-in-c Marden Hill Gp 90-92; R from 92; RD Bolingbroke 97-00. *The Rectory, Hall Lane, West Keal, Spilsby PE23 4BJ* Tel (01790) 753534 E-mail rev.sully@ic24.net

SULLIVAN, Bernard George. b 24. St Jo Coll Dur BA50. d 51 p 52. C Dudley St Thos *Worc* 51-54; C Braunstone *Leic* 54-55; Chapl RAF 55-58; Chapl Ascham Ho Sch Gosforth 59-63; Chapl St Mary's Hosp Stannington 62-91; V Stannington *Newc* 63-91; rtd 91; Perm to Offic *Newc* from 91. *1 St Aidan's Crescent, Stobhill, Morpeth NE61 2UP*

SULLIVAN, Canon Julian Charles. b 49. Lon Univ BSc74 CertEd75. Wycliffe Hall Ox 80. d 83 p 84. C Southall Green St Jo *Lon* 83-87; C Wells St Cuth w Wookey Hole *B & W* 87-90; V Sheff St Barn and St Mary *Sheff* 90-91; V Sheff St Mary w Highfield Trin 91-95; V Sheff St Mary Bramall Lane from 95; Hon Can Sheff Cathl from 01; AD Ecclesall from 01. *St Mary's Vicarage, 42 Charlotte Road, Sheffield S1 4TL* Tel 0114-272 4987 E-mail jvsull1@aol.com

SULLIVAN, Preb Nicola Ann. b 58. SRN81 RM84. Wycliffe Hall Ox BTh95. d 95 p 96. C Earlham St Anne *Nor* 95-99; Assoc V Bath Abbey w St Jas *B & W* 99-02; Chapl R Nat Hosp for Rheumatic Diseases NHS Trust 99-02; Bp's Chapl and Past Asst *B & W* from 02; Sub-Dean Wells from 03; Preb Wells Cathl from 03. *North Wing Flat, The Palace, Wells BA5 2PD* Tel (01749) 672341 Fax 679355 E-mail nicola.sullivan@bathwells.anglican.org

SULLIVAN, Canon Trevor Arnold. b 40. CITC 69. d 70 p 71. C Lurgan Ch the Redeemer *D & D* 71-72; C Tralee *L & K* 72-75; Irish Sch of Ecum 75-77; Ind Chapl *D & G* 77-80; I Ematris *Clogh* 80-84; I Aughrim w Ballinasloe etc *L & K* from 84; Can Limerick and Killaloe Cathls from 89. *The Rectory, Aughrim, Ballinasloe, Co Galway, Irish Republic* Tel and fax (00353) (90) 967 3735 Mobile 087-412194

SULLY, Andrew Charles. b 67. Southn Univ BA88 Birm Univ DPS91 MPhil95. Qu Coll Birm 90. d 93 p 94. C Maindee *Mon* 93-96; V Llanfihangel w Llanafan and Llanwnnws etc *St D* 96-02; PV St As Cathl *St As* from 02; TV St As from 03. *Woodcroft, Upper Denbigh Road, St Asaph LL17 0BG* Tel (01745) 730064

SULLY, Martin John. b 44. AIAS. St Jo Coll Nottm 80. d 82 p 83. C Lindfield *Chich* 82-86; V Walberton w Binsted 86-01; R Lewes St Jo sub Castro from 01. *St John's Rectory, 1 The Avenue, Lewes BN7 1BA* Tel (01273) 473080

SUMMERS, John Ewart. b 35. MIMechE66 Ex Univ MA95. ALCD69. d 69 p 70. C Fulham St Matt *Lon* 69-72; Chapl RN 72-81; V Devonport St Barn *Ex* 81-98; V Devonport St Mich and St Barn 98-00; rtd 00; Perm to Offic *Ex* from 00. *Box Cottage, Aish, South Brent TQ10 9JH* Tel (01364) 72976

SUMMERS (née PASCOE), Mrs Lorraine Eve. b 51. St Alb and Ox Min Course 98. d 01 p 02. NSM Sandon, Wallington and Rushden w Clothall *St Alb* from 01. *29 Stane Street, Clothall, Baldock SG7 6TS* Tel (01462) 892472 Mobile 0779-833226

SUMMERS, Neil Thomas. b 58. Roehampton Inst BA93 K Coll Lon MA94 St Mary's Coll Strawberry Hill PGCE95. SEITE 97. d 00 p 01. NSM Richmond St Mary w St Matthias and St Jo *S'wark* from 00. *2 Ravensbourne Road, Twickenham TW1 2DH* Tel (020) 8892 8313 E-mail ntsummers@aol.com

SUMMERS, Paul Anthony. b 53. Coll of Resurr Mirfield 77. d 80 p 81. C Manston *Ripon* 80-83; Min Can and Prec Ripon Cathl 83-88; Chapl Univ Coll of Ripon and York St Jo 84-88; V Whitkirk *Ripon* 88-95; R Lower Wharfedale 95-00; AD Harrogate 98-00. *16 Beacon Street, Addingham, Ilkley LS29 0QX* Tel (01943) 839552 Mobile 07747-131731 E-mail paulsummers65@hotmail.com

SUMMERS, Canon Raymond John. b 41. Univ of Wales TCert63 DPS88 Open Univ BA75. St Mich Coll Llan 77. d 77 p 78. NSM Mynyddislwyn *Mon* 77-81; C Mynyddislwyn 81-82; P-in-c 82-89; V 89-91; V Mynyddislwyn 91-95; TR from 95; RD Bedwellty from 95; Can St Woolos Cathl from 01. *The Rectory, Vicarage Lane, Pontllanfraith, Blackwood NP12 2DP* Tel (01495) 224240

SUMMERS, Stephen Bruce. b 63. St Andr Univ MTheol95. STETS 98. d 00 p 01. C Bishop's Waltham *Portsm* 00-02; R Farlington from 02. *The Rectory, 27 Farlington Avenue, Cosham, Portsmouth PO6 1DF* Tel (023) 9237 5145 E-mail summertime@tiscali.co.uk

SUMMERS, Preb Ursula Jeanne. b 35. Birm Univ BA56 Liv Univ CertEd57. Glouc Sch of Min. **dss** 85 **d** 87 **p** 94. Fownhope *Heref* 85-87; Hon C 87; Brockhampton w Fawley 85-87; Hon C 87; C Marden w Amberley and Wisteston 88-94; P-in-c 94-02; RD Heref Rural 93-99; P-in-c Moreton-on-Lugg 96-02; Preb Heref Cathl 96-02; rtd 02; Perm to Offic *Heref* from 02. *99 Walkers Green, Marden, Hereford HR1 3EA* Tel (01432) 880497 E-mail rsatmarden@aol.com

SUMNER, Preb Gillian Mansell. b 39. St Anne's Coll Ox BA61 MA65 MLitt76. Wycliffe Hall Ox BA85. **dss** 86 **d** 87 **p** 94. Ox St Andr *Ox* 86-91; Hon C 87-91; Tutor Wycliffe Hall Ox 86-89; Prin Ox Area Chr Tr Scheme *Ox* 89-91; Vice-Prin Ox Min Course 89-91; Assoc Prin 91-94; Hon C Kirtlington w Bletchingdon, Weston etc 91-94; Hon Can Ch Ch 94; Local Min Officer *Heref* 95-02; P-in-c Wistanstow 95-98; Preb Heref Cathl from 97; Adv for NSM from 02. *Black Venn, Reeves Lane, Stanage, Knighton LD7 1NA* Tel (01547) 530281 E-mail gandmsumner@compuserve.com

SUMNER, John Gordon. b 46. CCC Cam BA68 MA72. Ridley Hall Cam 69. **d** 72 **p** 73. C Liskeard w St Keyne *Truro* 72-75; C Caversham *Ox* 75-81; V Swallowfield 81-93; Asst Chapl Reading Univ 81-93; C Glastonbury w Meare *B & W* from 93; Ldr Quest Community from 93. *The White Cottage, 15 Bere Lane, Glastonbury BA6 8BD* Tel (01458) 832377 E-mail jsumner@fish.co.uk

SUMNERS, Ms Cristina Jordan. b 47. Vassar Coll (NY) BA73 BNC Ox MPhil85. Princeton Th Sem 73 Gen Th Sem (NY) MDiv76. **d** 78 **p** 82. USA 79-91 and from 02; Asst to R San Antonio St Dav 80-90; P-in-c Rockport Trin by Sea 90-91; Asst Chapl K Edw Sch Witley 93-95; Perm to Offic *Guildf* 93-96; NSM Guildf H Trin w St Mary 97-02; Educn Officer 99-02. *NDCBU 5798, Taos, NM 87571, USA*

SUMPTER, Timothy Mark. b 62. St Jo Coll Nottm BTh95. **d** 95 **p** 96. C Ockbrook *Derby* 95-98; C Wallington H Trin *S'wark* 98-01; V Ockbrook *Derby* from 01. *74 The Riddings, Ockbrook, Derby DE72 3SF* Tel (01332) 820084

SUNDERLAND, Christopher Allen. b 52. BA75 St Pet Coll Ox MA80 DPhil80 DipTh86. Trin Coll Bris 84. **d** 86 **p** 87. C Stratton St Margaret w S Marston etc *Bris* 86-90; V Barton Hill St Luke w Ch Ch 90-98; RD Bris City 94-98; Perm to Offic from 98; Research Assoc Churches' Coun for Ind & Soc Resp from 98. *50 Guest Avenue, Emersons Green, Bristol BS16 7GA* Tel 0117-957 4652 Fax as telephone E-mail csunderland@pavilion.co.uk

SUNDERLAND, Preb Geoffrey. b 21. St Edm Hall Ox BA43 MA47 DipTh47. St Steph Ho Ox 46. **d** 48 **p** 49. C Clifton All SS *Bris* 48-51; C Elland *Wakef* 52-54; C Devonport St Mark Ford *Ex* 55-56; C-in-c Plymouth St Jas Ham CD 56-59; V Plymouth St Jas Ham 59-63; Chapl K Coll Taunton 63-65; C Clifton All SS *Bris* 65-68; V Plymstock *Ex* 68-86; RD Plympton 76-81; Preb Ex Cathl 82-89; rtd 86; Perm to Offic *B & W* and *Ex* from 86. *22 Blackdown View, Sampford Peverell, Tiverton EX16 7BE* Tel (01884) 821688 E-mail geoffrey.sunderland@talk21.com

SUNDERLAND, Wendy Jillian. b 47. **d** 99 **p** 00. OLM Bury St Edmunds St Mary *St E* from 99. *9 Crown Street, Bury St Edmunds IP33 1QU* Tel (01284) 766883

SUNDERLAND, Archdeacon of. *See* BAIN, The Ven John Stuart

SURMAN, Malcolm Colin. b 48. Birm Univ CertEd72 Southn Univ BTh88. Sarum & Wells Th Coll 76. **d** 78 **p** 79. C Basingstoke *Win* 78-81; P-in-c Alton All SS 81-85; V 85-01; Chapl N Hants Loddon Community NHS Trust 84-01; P-in-c Burton and Sopley *Win* from 01. *The Vicarage, Preston Lane, Burton, Christchurch BH23 7JU* Tel (01202) 489807 Fax 475793 E-mail malcolm.surman@fish.co.uk

SURREY, Mrs Maureen. b 53. Man OLM Scheme 98. **d** 01. OLM Davyhulme Ch Ch *Man* 01-02. *56 Abingdon Road, Urmston, Manchester M41 0GN* Tel 0161-748 3961 E-mail sidandmo@hotmail.com

SURREY, Archdeacon of. *See* REISS, The Ven Robert Paul

SURRIDGE, Mrs Faith Thomas. b 45. Open Univ BA75 DipRD83 Lon Univ PGCE76 Ex Univ Dip Maths Educn 87 BPhil(Ed)96. SW Minl Tr Course 83. **dss** 85 **d** 87 **p** 94. St Breoke and Egloshayle *Truro* 85-87; NSM St Mawgan w St Ervan and St Eval 91-95; NSM St Columb Major w St Wenn 95-03; P-in-c from 03. *Oaklands, Station Road, St Columb TR9 6BX* Tel (01637) 881567 E-mail ftsurridge@portablesl.ngfl.gov.uk

SURTEES, Brian Lawrence. NTMTC. **d** 01 **p** 02. NSM Hatfield Heath and Sheering *Chelmsf* from 01. *13 Bowes Drive, Ongar CM5 9AU* Tel (01277) 363607 E-mail bsurtees@aol.com

SURTEES, Timothy John de Leybourne. b 31. G&C Coll Cam BA54 MA58. Westcott Ho Cam 54. **d** 56 **p** 57. C Guisborough *York* 56-59; C Grantham St Wulfram *Linc* 59-61; V Cayton w Eastfield *York* 61-72; R Cheam *S'wark* 72-96; rtd 96; Perm to Offic *Heref* from 96. *Dove Cottage, Leysters, Leominster HR6 0HW* Tel (01568) 750203

SUSTINS, Nigel. b 46. Lon Univ BEd70. S'wark Ord Course 86. **d** 88 **p** 90. NSM C Mitcham St Mark *S'wark* 89-93; Perm to Offic from 96. *56 Grove Road, Mitcham CR4 1SA* Tel (020) 8640 8137

SUTCH, Christopher David. b 47. TD92. AKC69. St Aug Coll Cant 69. **d** 70 **p** 71. C Bris St Andr Hartcliffe *Bris* 70-75; C

SUMMERS

Swindon Dorcan 75-78; TV 78-79; P-in-c Alveston 79-83; V 83-89; RD Westbury and Severnside 86-89; CF (TA) 80-83; TR Yate New Town *Bris* 89-99; RD Stapleton 95-99; V Cainscross w Selsley *Glouc* from 99. *The Vicarage, 58 Cashes Green Road, Stroud GL5 4RA* Tel (01453) 755148 Fax as telephone E-mail davidandmegan@sutches25.freeserve.co.uk

SUTCH, Canon Christopher Lang. b 21. Oriel Coll Ox BA47 MA47. Cuddesdon Coll 47. **d** 49 **p** 50. C Westbury-on-Trym H Trin *Bris* 49-53; V Bedminster Down 53-58; V Hanham 58-74; R Brinkworth w Dauntsey 74-86; RD Malmesbury 79-85; Hon Can Bris Cathl 82-86; rtd 86; Hon C E Bris 86-91; Perm to Offic *Bris* from 91; *Glouc* from 01. *36 Arrowsmith Drive, Stonehouse, Gloucester GL10 2QR* Tel (01453) 791896

SUTCLIFFE, Crispin Francis. b 48. Keble Coll Ox BA69. Sarum & Wells Th Coll 73. **d** 74 **p** 75. C Truro St Paul *Truro* 74-77; S Africa 77-80; P-in-c Treslothan *Truro* 80-85; V 85-91; R Ilchester w Northover, Limington, Yeovilton etc *B & W* from 91. *The Rectory, Ilchester, Yeovil BA22 8LJ* Tel (01935) 840296

SUTCLIFFE, Canon David. b 29. Lon Univ BD57. Lon Coll of Div ALCD56. **d** 57 **p** 58. C Penn *Lich* 57-61; V Ashton St Pet *Man* 61-65; V Eccleshill *Bradf* 65-71; Lic to Offic 71-74; V Manningham St Luke 74-79; V Bolton St Jas w St Chrys 79-85; V Calverley 85-94; RD Calverley 88-93; Hon Can Bradf Cathl 89-94; rtd 94; Perm to Offic *Bradf* from 94. *49 Galloway Lane, Pudsey LS28 7UG* Tel 0113-257 4053

SUTCLIFFE, Howard Guest. b 44. Fitzw Coll Cam BA66 MA70 Birm Univ MA75 Man Univ CertRS88. Westcott Ho Cam 73. **d** 74 **p** 75. C Chorlton-cum-Hardy St Clem *Man* 74-77; Chapl Chetham's Sch of Music 77-80; V Oldham St Paul *Man* 80-94; Lic to Offic 94-97; Co-ord Werneth and Freehold Community Development Project from 94; Perm to Offic from 01. *34 Lynn Street, Oldham OL9 7DW, or 155 Windsor Road, Oldham OL8 1RG* Tel 0161-628 2235 E-mail sdickson@uk.packardbell.org

SUTCLIFFE, Ian. b 31. Surrey Univ BSc69. Qu Coll Birm 61. **d** 63 **p** 65. C W Wimbledon Ch Ch *S'wark* 63-65; C Battersea St Phil 65-66; C Kingston Hill St Paul 71-73; Lic to Offic *Carl* 75-96; rtd 96. *42 Hill Street, Arbroath DD11 1AB*

SUTCLIFFE, John Leslie. b 35. Liv Univ BA56. Sarum Th Coll 58. **d** 60 **p** 61. C Lytham St Cuth *Blackb* 60-62; C Altham w Clayton le Moors 62-65; C-in-c Penwortham St Leon CD 65-71; Ind Chapl *Liv* 71-74; V Orford St Andr 74-79; V Burnley St Cuth *Blackb* 79-88; Bp's Adv on UPA *Ripon* 88-94; Hon C Leeds Gipton Epiphany 89-94; I Carrickmacross w Magheracloone *Clogh* 94-01; rtd 01; Perm to Offic *Blackb* from 02. *1 Beckside, Barley, Burnley BB12 9JZ* Tel (01282) 449687

SUTCLIFFE, Peter John. b 58. BA. Linc Th Coll. **d** 82 **p** 83. C Skipton Ch Ch *Bradf* 82-85; C Tettenhall Regis *Lich* 85-86; TV 86-89; TV Warwick *Cov* 89-93; Relig Producer BBC Radio Cov & Warks 89-93; V Burley in Wharfedale *Bradf* 93-03; RD Otley 97-02; P-in-c Yeadon St Andr from 03. *St Andrew's Vicarage, Haw Lane, Yeadon, Leeds LS19 7XQ* Tel 0113-250 3989 E-mail peter.sutcliffe@btinternet.com

SUTER, Richard Alan. b 48. Rhodes Univ BA72 St Jo Coll Dur BA74 DipTh75. Cranmer Hall Dur 72. **d** 75 **p** 76. C Darlington H Trin *Dur* 75-77; C Wrexham *St As* 77-82; R Llansantffraid Glan Conwy and Eglwysbach 82-87; V Broughton 87-92; RD Wrexham 90-97; V Rossett from 92. *The Vicarage, Rossett, Wrexham LL12 0HE* Tel (01244) 570498 E-mail sutertribe@quista.net

SUTHERLAND, Alan. b 55. Sarum & Wells Th Coll. **d** 80 **p** 81. C Hessle *York* 80-83; USA from 83. *111 Fontaine Boulevard, Winchester, KY 40391, USA*

SUTHERLAND, Alistair Campbell. b 31. MIEE CEng Lon Univ BSc50 Ex Univ BA77. Wycliffe Hall Ox 77. **d** 78 **p** 79. C Nottingham St Jude *S'well* 78-81; R Barton in Fabis 81-96; P-in-c Thrumpton 81; V 81-96; RD W Bingham 87-92; Dioc Adv on Ind Society 92-96; NSM Gotham 93-96; NSM Kingston and Ratcliffe-on-Soar 93-96; rtd 96; Perm to Offic *Ex* from 99; Perm to Offic *S'wark* from 88. *Rosehayne, Musbury, Axminster EX13 8SR* Tel (01297) 552995

SUTHERLAND, Eric. b 54. AKC76. Sarum & Wells Th Coll 76. **d** 77 **p** 78. C Roehampton H Trin *S'wark* 77-80; C Tattenham Corner and Burgh Heath *Guildf* 80-84; V Guildf All SS 84-91; Dep Chapl HM Pris Wandsworth 91-92; Chapl HM YOI Huntercombe and Finnamore 92-97; Chapl HM Pris Liv from 97. *HM Prison, 68 Hornby Road, Liverpool L9 3DF* Tel 0151-525 9571

SUTHERLAND, Mark Robert. b 55. Univ of NZ LLB77 Lon Inst of Educn MA95 Birkbeck Coll Lon DAC89. Ripon Coll Cuddesdon 82. **d** 85 **p** 86. C Pinner *Lon* 85-88; C Sudbury St Andr 88-91; Perm to Offic *S'wark* 91-92; Chapl Maudsley Hosp Lon 91-94; Chapl Bethlem R Hosp Beckenham 91-94; Chapl Bethlem and Maudsley NHS Trust Lon 94-99; Presiding Chapl S Lon and Maudsley NHS Trust from 99. *The Maudsley Hospital, London SE5 8AZ* Tel (020) 7919 2815 Fax as telephone E-mail mark.sutherland@flam-pr.nhs.uk

SUTTLE, Neville Frank. b 38. Reading Univ BSc61 Aber Univ PhD64. **d** 76 **p** 77. NSM Penicuik *Edin* from 76. *44 St James's*

Gardens, Penicuik EH26 9DU Tel (01968) 673819 Fax as telephone

SUTTON, Brian Ralph. b 33. Trin Coll Bris DPS81 Sarum & Wells Th Coll. **d** 83 **p** 84. NSM Timsbury *B & W* 83-84; NSM Timsbury and Priston 85-88; V Thorncombe w Winsham and Cricket St Thomas 89-98; rtd 98; Perm to Offic *B & W* 98-01. *The Old Coach House, Priston, Bath BA2 9ED* Tel (01761) 471494

SUTTON, Charles Edwin. b 53. Bris Univ BEd77 Ox Univ. Ripon Coll Cuddesdon 77. **d** 80 **p** 81. C Stanwix *Carl* 80-84; Warden Marrick Priory *Ripon* 84-88. *7 Beech Close, Baldersby, Thirsk YO7 4QB* Tel (01765) 640616

SUTTON, Colin Phillip. b 51. Birm Univ BA73. Chich Th Coll 73. **d** 75 **p** 76. C Penarth All SS *Llan* 75-77; C Roath 77-80; C Caerau w Ely 80-84; V Rhydyfelin from 84. *St Luke's House, 6 Fairfield Lane, Hawthorn, Pontypridd CF37 5LN* Tel (01443) 842298

SUTTON, David John. b 49. **d** 99 **p** 00. C Maesglas and Duffryn *Mon* from 99. *6 Manor Park, Duffryn, Newport NP10 8SA* Tel (01633) 815177

SUTTON, David Robert. b 49. Birm Univ BA69 Ox Univ CertEd72. St Steph Ho Ox 70. **d** 72 **p** 73. C Clitheroe St Mary *Blackb* 72-75; C Fleetwood 75-78; V Calderbrook *Man* 78-88; V Winton from 88; Chapl Salford Mental Health Services NHS Trust from 92. *The Vicarage, Albany Road, Eccles, Manchester M30 8FE* Tel 0161-788 8991
E-mail frdavid@veronicon.freeserve.co.uk

SUTTON, Eves. *See* SUTTON, The Rt Revd Peter Eves

SUTTON, James William. b 41. Oak Hill Th Coll 81. **d** 84 **p** 85. NSM Chorleywood St Andr *St Alb* 84-00; Perm to Offic from 00. *Belmount, 7 Hillside Road, Chorleywood, Rickmansworth WD3 5AP* Tel (01923) 282806 Fax 447200
E-mail sutton@7hillside.freeserve.co.uk

SUTTON, Jeremy John Ernest. b 60. Ridley Hall Cam 83. **d** 86 **p** 87. C Seacombe *Ches* 86-88; C Northwich St Luke and H Trin 88-90; TV Birkenhead Priory 90-94; V Over St Chad 94-01; V Dunham Massey St Marg and St Mark from 01. *St Margaret's Vicarage, Dunham Road, Altrincham WA14 4AQ* Tel 0161-928 1609 E-mail jerrysutton@uk.packardbell.org

SUTTON, Canon John. b 47. St Jo Coll Dur BA70. Ridley Hall Cam 70. **d** 72 **p** 73. C Denton St Lawr *Man* 72-77; R 77-82; V High Lane *Ches* 82-88; V Sale St Anne 88-96; V Timperley from 96; Hon Can Ches Cathl from 01; RD Bowdon from 03. *The Vicarage, 12 Thorley Lane, Timperley, Altrincham WA15 7AZ* Tel 0161-980 4330

SUTTON, John Stephen. b 33. Em Coll Cam BA57 MA61. Wycliffe Hall Ox 57. **d** 59 **p** 60. C Dagenham *Chelmsf* 59-62; C Bishopwearmouth St Gabr *Dur* 62-63; V Over Kellet *Blackb* 63-67; V Darwen St Barn 67-74; V Walthamstow St Jo *Chelmsf* 74-84; V Stebbing w Lindsell 84-98; RD Dunmow 94-98; rtd 98; Perm to Offic *Chich* from 98. *20 Firwood Close, Eastbourne BN22 9QL* Tel (01323) 504654

SUTTON, Canon John Wesley. b 48. Rolle Coll CertEd71. All Nations Chr Coll Dip Miss72. **d** 76 **p** 77. Chile 76-77; Peru 79-84; Area Sec SAMS 84-88; Youth Sec SAMS 88-91; Perm to Offic *Lon* 88-97; Personnel Sec SAMS from 91; Asst Gen Sec SAMS from 91; Perm to Offic *Chelmsf* from 84; *Ox* 85-96; *St Alb* from 85; Hon Can Peru from 93. *88 Horn Lane, Woodford Green IG8 9AH* Tel (020) 8505 7888 Fax (01892) 525797

✠**SUTTON, The Rt Revd Keith Norman.** b 34. Jes Coll Cam BA58 MA62. Ridley Hall Cam. **d** 59 **p** 60 **c** 78. C Plymouth St Andr *Ex* 59-61; Chapl St Jo Coll Cam 62-67; Chapl Bp Tucker Coll Uganda 68-72; Prin Ridley Hall Cam 73-78; Suff Bp Kingston *S'wark* 78-84; Bp Lich 84-03; rtd 03. *8 Summerleaze Crescent, Bude EX23 8HH* Tel (01288) 352614

SUTTON, Kingsley Edwin. b 70. TCD BTh94 CertAgric. **d** 97 **p** 98. C Belfast St Matt *Conn* 97-99; C Willowfield *D & D* 99-02; I Newry from 02. *Glebe House, Windsor Avenue, Newry BT34 1EQ* Tel (028) 3026 2621

SUTTON, Canon Malcolm David. b 26. Selw Coll Cam BA47 MA52. Ridley Hall Cam 48. **d** 50 **p** 51. C Owlerton *Sheff* 50-52; C Kew *S'wark* 52-54; C Hornchurch St Andr *Chelmsf* 54-56; V Roxeth Ch Ch *Lon* 56-63; R Beccles St Mich *St E* 63-82; TR 82-94; RD Beccles 65-73; Hon Can St E Cathl 70-94; rtd 94; Perm to Offic *St E* from 94; Perm to Offic *Nor* from 95. *10 Merville, Carlton Colville, Lowestoft NR33 8UF*

SUTTON, Peter. b 20. Ely Th Coll 60. **d** 62 **p** 63. C Kippax *Ripon* 62-64; R Hamerton *Ely* 64-77; V Winwick 64-77; V Upton and Copmanford 70-77; V Bradworthy *Ex* 77-90; rtd 90; Perm to Offic *Truro* 90-98; Perm to Offic *Ex* from 98. *Mowhay Villa, Chilsworthy, Holsworthy EX22 7BQ* Tel (01409) 254900

SUTTON, Peter Allerton. b 59. Ex Univ BA85. Linc Th Coll 85. **d** 87 **p** 88. C Fareham H Trin *Portsm* 87-93; C Alverstoke 90-93; Chapl HM Pris Haslar 90-93; V Lee-on-the-Solent *Portsm* from 93; Warden of Readers 96-00. *St Faith's Vicarage, Victoria Square, Lee-on-the-Solent PO13 9NF* Tel (023) 9255 0269

✠**SUTTON, The Rt Revd Peter Eves.** b 23. CBE90. Wellington Univ (NZ) MA54 MA47. NZ Bd of Th Studies LTh48. **d** 47 **p** 48 **c** 65. C Wanganui New Zealand 47-50; C Bethnal Green St Jo *Lon* 50-51; C Bp's Hatfield *St Alb* 51-52; New Zealand from 52; V Berhampore 52-58; V Whangarei 58-64; Adn Waimate 62-64;

Dean St Paul's Cathl Dunedin 64-65; Bp Nelson 65-90; Acting Primate of New Zealand 85-86; ChStJ from 85; Sub-Prelate OStJ from 86; rtd 90. *3 Ngatiawa Street, Nelson 7001, New Zealand* Tel (0064) (3) 546 6591 Fax as telephone

SUTTON, Philip Frank. b 55. Lon Univ HND76. St Alb and Ox Min Course CBTS95. **d** 95 **p** 96. NSM Akeman *Ox* 95-00; Chapl Ox Radcliffe Hosps NHS Trust 96-00; Sen Chapl R United Hosp Bath NHS Trust from 00. *Royal United Hospital, Combe Park, Bath BA1 3NG* Tel (01225) 824039 Pager 07659-184873
E-mail suttonp@ruh-bath.swest.nhs.uk

SUTTON, Richard Alan. b 39. Reading Univ BSc61. Wycliffe Hall Ox 70. **d** 72 **p** 73. C Galleywood Common *Chelmsf* 72-76; Pakistan 76-79; C Walsall St Martin *Lich* 79-83; V Barton Hill St Luke w Ch Ch *Bris* 83-89; V Sidcup Ch Ch *Roch* 89-95; rtd 95; Perm to Offic *Roch* 95-98. *117 Wren Road, Sidcup DA14 4NQ* Tel (020) 8302 9233

SUTTON, Richard John. b 45. Lon Inst of Educn CertEd68. St Alb Minl Tr Scheme 77 Linc Th Coll 81. **d** 82 **p** 83. C Royston *St Alb* 82-87; C Bp's Hatfield 87-95; P-in-c Kempston from 95; P-in-c Biddenham from 95. *The Vicarage, Church End, Kempston, Bedford MK43 8RH* Tel (01234) 852241
E-mail backwater@hereabouts.net

SUTTON, Ronald. b 27. FSCA. NW Ord Course 76. **d** 79 **p** 80. C Helsby and Dunham-on-the-Hill *Ches* 79-81; R Church Lawton 81-92; RD Congleton 91-92; rtd 92; Perm to Offic *Ches* from 92. *79 Thornton Avenue, Macclesfield SK11 7XL* Tel (01625) 430212

SWABEY, Brian Frank. b 44. BA. Oak Hill Th Coll 79. **d** 82 **p** 83. C Clapham St Jas *S'wark* 82-84; C Wallington H Trin 84-88; Chapl Mt Gould Hosp Plymouth 88-89; V Plymouth St Jude *Ex* 88-92; Chapl RN 92-99; V Penn Fields *Lich* 99-01; rtd 01. *2 Drax Gardens, Crownhill, Plymouth PL6 5BJ* Tel (01752) 210643
E-mail brianswabey@eurobell.co.uk

SWABY, Canon John Edwin. b 11. St Jo Coll Dur BA32 DipTh34 MA35 Leic Univ PhD83. **d** 34 **p** 35. C Louth w Welton-le-Wold *Linc* 34-40; V Scunthorpe St Jo 40-53; R Mablethorpe w Stain 53-60; P-in-c Theddlethorpe w Mablethorpe 53-54; R 54-60; RD E Louthesk 57-60; Acting RD Yarborough 64-70; V Barton upon Humber 60-71; Can and Preb Linc Cathl 69-77; V Barholm w Stowe 71-76; R Uffington 71-76; V Tallington 71-76; rtd 76; Perm to Offic *Pet* and *Linc* from 76. *6 Willoughby Drive, Empingham, Oakham LE15 8PZ* Tel (01780) 460719

SWABY, Keith Graham. b 48. Southn Univ BA75. St Steph Ho Ox 75. **d** 77 **p** 78. C Lt Stanmore St Lawr *Lon* 77-80; C Hove All SS *Chich* 80-83; C Haywards Heath St Wilfrid 83; TV 83-95; C Clayton w Keymer 95-02; rtd 02. *The Old String of Horses, 2 and 4 Stephenson's Lane, Brampton CA8 1RU* Tel (016977) 3803

SWABY, Leward Anthony Woodrow. b 60. Trin Coll Bris 86 Ripon Coll Cuddesdon 89. **d** 92 **p** 93. C Wembley St Jo *Lon* 92-95; C Northampton St Matt *Pet* 95-97; TV Kingsthorpe w Northampton St Dav 97-01; Asst Chapl Worcs Acute Hosps NHS Trust from 01. *Worcs Acute Hospitals NHS Trust, Ronkswood Hospital, Newtown Road, Worcester WR5 1HN* Tel (01905) 763333 Fax 760555

SWABY, Desrine. SEITE 00. **d** 03. NSM S'wark St Geo the Martyr w St Alphege and St Jude *S'wark* from 03. *36 Gabriel House, 10 Odessa Street, London SE16 1HQ* Tel (020) 7231 9834

SWAIN, Allan. *See* SWAIN, William Allan

SWAIN, David Noel. b 36. Wellington Univ (NZ) BA63 MA66. Coll of Resurr Mirfield 65. **d** 67 **p** 68. C Clapham H Trin *S'wark* 67-70; New Zealand 70-75; P-in-c Hermitage *Ox* 75-76; P-in-c Hampstead Norris 75-76; V Hermitage w Hampstead Norreys 76-80; TR Hermitage and Hampstead Norreys, Cold Ash etc 80-82; R Bingham *S'well* 82-94; rtd 94; Perm to Offic *S'well* from 94. *77 Trent Boulevard, West Bridgford, Nottingham NG2 5BE* Tel 0115-982 1222

SWAIN, John Edgar. b 44. Lich Th Coll 67. **d** 69 **p** 70. C E Dereham w Hoe *Nor* 69-73; V Haugh *Linc* 73-74; R S Ormsby w Ketsby, Calceby and Driby 73-74; R Harrington w Brinkhill 73-74; R Oxcombe 73-74; R Ruckland w Farforth and Maidenwell 73-74; R Somersby w Bag Enderby 73-74; R Tetford and Salmonby 73-74; R Belchford 73-74; V W Ashby 73-74; C Attleborough *Nor* 74-78; Canada 78-90 and from 01; P-in-c Oxford Cen w Eastwood and Princeton 78-84; P-in-c Oldcastle w Colchester N 84-90; P-in-c Kirton w Falkenham *St E* 90-95; Chapl Suffolk Constabulary 90-01; P-in-c Gt and Lt Whelnetham w Bradfield St George 95-01; P-in-c Lawshall 98-01; R Wawa w White River and Hawk Junction from 01. *St Paul's Anglican Rectory, Second Avenue, Wawa ON, Canada, P0S 1K0* Tel (001) (705) 856 1336 E-mail j_eswain@hotmail.com

SWAIN, Canon John Roger. b 29. Fitzw Ho Cam BA55 MA59. Bps' Coll Cheshunt 55. **d** 57 **p** 58. C Headingley *Ripon* 57-60; C Moor Allerton 60-65; V Wyther Ven Bede 65-75; V Horsforth 75-86; P-in-c Roundhay St Edm 86-88; V 88-95; RD Allerton 89-94; Hon Can Ripon Cathl 89-95; rtd 95. *3 Harlow Court, Park Avenue, Leeds LS8 2JH* Tel 0113-218 8329

SWAIN, Preb Peter Ayres. b 44. NCA63. Sarum & Wells Th Coll 86. **d** 88 **p** 89. C Beaminster Area *Sarum* 88-92; P-in-c Bromfield w Waverton *Carl* 92-98; P-in-c W Newton 92-98; Member Rural Life and Agric Team 93-96; Ldr 96-98; RD Solway 95-98; Hon

Can Carl Cathl 96-98; TR Leominster *Heref* from 98; RD Leominster from 98; Preb Heref Cathl from 03. *The Rectory, Church Street, Leominster HR6 8NH* Tel (01568) 612124

SWAIN, Raymond Thomas. b 60. Oak Hill Th Coll BA89. **d** 89 **p** 90. C New Clee *Linc* 89-93; TV Cheltenham St Mark *Glouc* 93-03; Ecum Chapl Glos Hosps NHS Trust from 03. *Cheltenham General Hospital, Sandford Road, Cheltenham GL53 7AN* Tel (01242) 222222 ext 4286 *or* 274286
E-mail redder@blueyonder.co.uk

SWAIN, Ronald Charles Herbert. b 08. Dur Univ LTh32 BA42 MA50. St Aug Coll Cant 29. **d** 32 **p** 33. C S Wimbledon H Trin *S'wark* 32-34; China 34-40; Perm to Offic *Dur* and *Newc* 41-42; P-in-c Padgate Ch Ch *Liv* 42-46; Perm to Offic *S'wark* 46-47; Chapl RAF 47-54; CF 54-62; V Walsham le Willows *St E* 62-70; V Shipley *Chich* 70-74; rtd 74; Perm to Offic *St E* from 74. *81 Westley Road, Bury St Edmunds IP33 3RU* Tel (01284) 761655

SWAIN, Mrs Sharon Juanita. b 46. Sussex Univ BA75 CertEd76. Glouc Sch of Min 84 Qu Coll Birm. **dss** 84 **d** 87 **p** 94. Upton St Leonards *Glouc* 84-88; C 87-88; Children's Officer *Worc* 88-95; Min Can Worc Cathl 94-95; V Hanley Castle, Hanley Swan and Welland 95-01; R E Bergholt and Brantham *St E* from 01; RD Samford from 01. *The Rectory, Rectory Lane, Brantham, Manningtree CO11 1PZ* Tel (01206) 392646 Mobile 07880-705630 E-mail s.swain@freeuk.com

SWAIN, William Allan. b 38. Hulme Th Coll 63. **d** 68 **p** 69. C Welwyn Garden City *St Alb* 68-72; C Romsey *Win* 72-74; C Weeke 74-78; V Bournemouth H Epiphany 78-91; P-in-c Moordown 91-94; V from 94. *St John's Vicarage, 2 Vicarage Road, Bournemouth BH9 2SA* Tel (01202) 546400
E-mail allan.swain@themail.co.uk

SWAINSON, Norman. b 38. Salford Univ MSc75. St Jo Coll Nottm 77. **d** 79 **p** 80. C Levenshulme St Pet *Man* 79-84; R Jarrow Grange *Dur* 84-97; rtd 97; Perm to Offic *Ches* from 98. *176 George Street, Compstall, Stockport SK6 5JD* Tel 0161-449 0551

SWALES, David James. b 58. Warwick Univ BA. Cranmer Hall Dur. **d** 84 **p** 85. C Eccleshill *Bradf* 84-88; C Prenton *Ches* 88-92; V Oakworth *Bradf* 92-00; V Bolton St Jas w St Chrys from 00. *St James's Vicarage, 1056 Bolton Road, Bradford BD2 4LH* Tel (01274) 637193

SWALES, Peter. b 52. ACIB78 Open Univ BA99. Ridley Hall Cam 85. **d** 87 **p** 88. C Allestree *Derby* 87-91; P-in-c Horsley 91-99; RD Heanor 97-99; V Heckmondwike *Wakef* from 99. *The Vicarage, 25 Church Street, Heckmondwike WF16 0AX* Tel (01924) 405881 Mobile 07980-548740 Fax (01924) 406215
E-mail swales.peter@talk21.com

SWALLOW, Mrs Alice Gillian. b 51. Birm Univ BA72 CertEd73. NEOC 82. **dss** 84 **d** 87 **p** 94. Morpeth *Newc* 84-86; Uttoxeter w Bramshall *Lich* 86-88; Par Dn 87-88; Par Dn Rocester 88; Chapl to the Deaf *Man* 88-90; Par Dn Goodshaw and Crawshawbooth 88-93; C Barkisland w W Scammonden *Wakef* 93-95; V Ripponden 95-97; rtd 97. *22 Scholes Lane, Scholes, Cleckheaton BD19 6NR* Tel (01274) 875529 E-mail jill_swallow@yahoo.co.uk

SWALLOW, John Allen George. b 28. St Jo Coll Dur BA53 DipTh54. **d** 54 **p** 55. C Billericay St Mary *Chelmsf* 54-57; C Bishop's Stortford St Mich *St Alb* 57-59; V Roxwell *Chelmsf* 59-64; V S Weald 64-81; R W w E Mersea 81-93; rtd 93; Perm to Offic *Chelmsf* from 93; *St E* from 95. *72 Rembrandt Way, Bury St Edmunds IP33 2LT* Tel (01284) 725136

SWALLOW, John Brian. b 36. Trent Poly 78. **d** 84 **p** 85. C Cleveleys *Blackb* 84-87; V Blackpool St Mich 87-93; P-in-c Burnley St Steph 93-98; V 98-01; RD Burnley 97-00; rtd 01; Perm to Offic *Dur* from 02. *6 Chichester Walk, Haughton-le-Skerne, Darlington DL1 2SG*

SWAN, Duncan James. b 65. Imp Coll Lon BSc88 SS Coll Cam BA91 Cam Univ MA95. Ridley Hall Cam CTM92. **d** 92 **p** 93. C Stevenage St Andr and St Geo *St Alb* 92-95; C Harpenden St Nic 95-99; V Redbourn from 99. *The Vicarage, Church End, Redbourn, St Albans AL3 7DU* Tel (01582) 793122
E-mail duncpen@hotmail.com

SWAN, Owen. b 28. ACP71. Edin Th Coll 56. **d** 59 **p** 60. C Lewisham St Jo Southend *S'wark* 59-64; CF (TA) from 60; V Richmond St Luke *S'wark* 64-82; C-in-c Darlington St Hilda and St Columba CD *Dur* 82-84; R Feltwell *Ely* 84-87; R Holywell w Needingworth 87-97; rtd 97; P-in-c St Staughton *Ely* 97-02; P-in-c Hail Weston and Southoe 00-02; Perm to Offic *Ely* and *St E* from 02. *Primrose Cottage, Hawes Lane, Norton, Bury St Edmunds IP31 3LS* Tel (01359) 231108

SWAN, Philip Douglas. b 56. Wye Coll Lon BSc78 Qu Coll Cam MA81 CertEd81 Nottm Univ DipTh87. St Jo Coll Nottm 86. **d** 88 **p** 89. C Birm St Martin w Bordesley St Andr *Birm* 88-92; C Selly Park St Steph and St Wulstan 92-96; P-in-c The Lickey 96-98; V from 98. *The Vicarage, 30 Lickey Square, Rednal, Birmingham B45 8HB* Tel 0121-445 1425

SWAN, Preb Ronald Frederick. b 35. St Cath Coll Cam BA59 MA. Coll of Resurr Mirfield. **d** 61 **p** 62. C Staveley *Derby* 61-66; Chapl Lon Univ *Lon* 66-72; C St Martin-in-the-Fields 72-77; V Ealing St Barn 77-88; V Ealing St Steph Castle Hill 81-88; AD Ealing E 84-88; V Harrow St Mary 88-97; AD Harrow 89-94;

Preb St Paul's Cathl from 91; Master R Foundn of St Kath in Ratcliffe from 97. *The Royal Foundation of St Katharine, Ratcliffe, 2 Butcher Row, London E14 8DS* Tel (020) 7790 3540 Fax 7702 7603 E-mail ron@stkatharine.demon.co.uk

SWAN, Thomas Hugh Winfield. b 26. New Coll Ox BA50 MA62 Barrister 51. Ridley Hall Cam 63. **d** 65 **p** 66. C Yaxley *Ely* 65-68; P-in-c Sawtry 69; R 69-79; P-in-c Fordham St Mary 79-82; V 82-87; P-in-c Hilgay 79-82; R 82-87; P-in-c Southery 79-82; R 82-87; rtd 91; Perm to Offic *Ely* 91-00. *24 Chiefs Street, Ely CB6 1AT* Tel (01353) 668452

SWANBOROUGH, Alan William. b 38. Southn Univ BEd75. Sarum & Wells Th Coll 77. **d** 80 **p** 81. NSM Ventnor H Trin *Portsm* 80-85; NSM Ventnor St Cath 80-85; Chapl Upper Chine Sch Shanklin 88-95; NSM Shanklin St Blasius *Portsm* 91-93; P-in-c from 93. *The Rectory, Rectory Road, Shanklin PO37 6NS* Tel (01983) 862407

SWANBOROUGH, Robert Charles. b 28. Sarum & Wells Th Coll 75. **d** 77 **p** 78. C Woodley St Jo the Ev *Ox* 77-78; C Bray and Braywood 79-80; V Gt Coxwell w Buscot, Coleshill etc 80-96; rtd 96; Perm to Offic *Ox* from 96. *76 Foxcote, Finchampstead, Wokingham RG40 3PE* Tel (0118) 973 5465

SWANEPOEL, David John. b 41. Rhodes Univ BA62 UNISA BA64 DipHE80 BTh84. **d** 75 **p** 76. S Africa 75-94; Dean George 85-89; NSM Hellingly and Upper Dicker *Chich* 94-99. *Providence House, Coldharbour Road, Upper Dicker, Hailsham BN27 3QE* Tel (01323) 843887

SWANN, Antony Keith. b 34. Lon Univ DipTh60. St Aid Birkenhead 58. **d** 61 **p** 62. C Bilston St Leon *Lich* 61-66; Sierra Leone 66-70; V W Bromwich St Phil *Lich* 70-75; Nigeria 76-78; R Church Lench w Rous Lench and Abbots Morton *Worc* 78-88; Chapl HM Pris Coldingley 88-90; Chapl HM Pris Leyhill 91-97; rtd 97; P-in-c Kemble, Poole Keynes, Somerford Keynes etc *Glouc* 97-02. *30 Perry Orchard, Upton St Leonards, Gloucester GL4 8DQ*

SWANN, The Ven Edgar John. b 42. TCD BA66 MA70 BD77 HDipEd80. CITC 68. **d** 68 **p** 69. C Crumlin *Conn* 68-70; C Howth *D & G* 70-73; I Greystones from 73; Can Ch Ch Cathl Dublin from 90; Adn Glendalough from 93. *The Rectory, Greystones, Co Wicklow, Irish Republic* Tel (00353) (1) 287 4077 Mobile 87-255 7032 Fax (1) 287 3766
E-mail edgarjswann@eircom.net

SWANN, Canon Frederick David. b 38. **d** 69 **p** 70. C Lurgan Ch the Redeemer *D & D* 69-77; I Ardmore w Craigavon 77-79; I Comber 79-85; I Drumglass w Moygashel *Arm* from 85; Can Arm Cathl from 96; Preb 98-01; Treas from 01. *The Rectory, 26 Circular Road, Dungannon BT71 6BE* Tel (028) 8772 2614 E-mail derickswann@lineone.net

SWANN, Paul David James. b 59. Ch Ch Ox BA81 MA88. St Jo Coll Nottm Dip Th Studies 89 DPS90. **d** 90 **p** 91. C Old Hill H Trin *Worc* 90-94; V 94-02; C Worc City St Paul and Old St Martin etc from 02; Chapl Worc Tech Coll from 02. *21 Tower Road, Worcester WR3 7AF* Tel (01905) 731135
E-mail pswann@hicon.co.uk

SWANSEA AND BRECON, Bishop of. *See* PIERCE, The Rt Revd Anthony Edward

SWANTON, John Joseph. b 61. Bradf and Ilkley Coll BA84 MCIH89 MRSH95. S Dios Minl Tr Scheme 92. **d** 95 **p** 96. NSM Shalford *Guildf* 95-99; NSM Compton w Shackleford and Peper Harow from 99. *90 Busbridge Lane, Godalming GU7 1QH* Tel (01483) 427160

SWARBRIGG, David Cecil. b 42. TCD BA64 MA67. **d** 65 **p** 66. C Lisburn Ch Ch *Conn* 65-67; C Thames Ditton *Guildf* 72-76; Chapl Hampton Sch Middx 76-97; rtd 97; Perm to Offic *Lon* from 97. *39 Harefield, Hinchley Wood, Esher KT10 9TY* Tel (020) 8398 3950 Fax as telephone

SWART-RUSSELL, Phoebe. b 58. Cape Town Univ BA79 MA82 DPhil88. Ox NSM Course 89. **d** 90 **p** 94. C Riverside *Ox* 90-95; Hon C Chenies and Lt Chalfont, Latimer and Flaunden from 96. *The Rectory, Latimer, Chesham HP5 1UA* Tel (01494) 762281

SWARTZ, Clifford Robert. b 71. Trin Coll Connecticut BA92 Trin Coll Cam BA99. Ridley Hall Cam 97. **d** 00 **p** 01. C Kirk Ella *York* 00-03; Regional Dir FOCUS USA from 03; Hon C Tariffville Trin Ch from 03. *242 Steele Road, West Hartford, CT 06117, USA* E-mail clifford@swartz.karoo.co.uk

SWAYNE, Jeremy Michael Deneys. b 41. Worc Coll Ox BA63 BM, BCh67 MRCGP71 FFHom91. **d** 00 **p** 01. NSM Fosse Trinity *B & W* from 00. *Greys, Ditcheat, Shepton Mallet BA4 6RB* Tel (01749) 860371 Fax 860530
E-mail jem.swayne@btinternet.com

SWEATMAN, John. b 44. Open Univ BA89. Bernard Gilpin Soc Dur 67 Oak Hill Th Coll 68. **d** 71 **p** 72. C Rayleigh *Chelmsf* 71-73; C Seaford w Sutton *Chich* 73-77; Chapl RN 77-82; CF 82-85; V Hellingly and Upper Dicker *Chich* 85-90; Hon C Mayfield 95-96; P-in-c Malborough w S Huish, W Alvington and Churchstow *Ex* 96-02; V Ash w Westmarsh *Cant* from 02. *The Vicarage, Queen's Road, Ash, Canterbury CT3 2BG* Tel (01304) 812296 E-mail ash.church@tiscali.co.uk

SWEED, John William. b 35. Bernard Gilpin Soc Dur 58 Clifton Th Coll 59. **d** 62 **p** 63. C Shrewsbury St Julian *Lich* 62-64; C Sheff

St Jo *Sheff* 64-70; V Doncaster St Jas 70-79; V Hatfield 79-00; RD Snaith and Hatfield 84-93; Perm to Offic from 00; rtd 00. *21 The Oval, Tickhill, Doncaster DN11 9HF* Tel (01302) 743293

SWEENEY, Andrew James. b 61. Wycliffe Hall Ox 96. **d** 96 **p** 97. C Bladon w Woodstock *Ox* 96-99; C Coleraine *Conn* 99-02; V Cogges and S Leigh *Ox* from 02. *Cogges Priory, Church Lane, Witney OX8 6LA* Tel (01993) 702155 Mobile 07720-472556 E-mail sweeney@coggespriory.freeserve.co.uk

SWEENEY, Robert Maxwell. b 38. Ch Ch Ox BA63 MA66 Birm Univ MA78. Cuddesdon Coll 63. **d** 65 **p** 66. C Prestbury *Glouc* 65-68; C Handsworth St Andr *Birm* 68-70; Asst Chapl Lancing Coll 70-73; Perm to Offic *Chich* 70-73; V Wotton St Mary *Glouc* 74-79; V Ox St Thos w St Frideswide and Binsey *Ox* from 79; Chapl Magd Coll Ox 82-88. *19 Botley Road, Oxford OX2 0BL* Tel (01865) 251403

SWEET, Canon John Philip McMurdo. b 27. New Coll Ox BA49 MA52 Lambeth DD94 SNTS61. Westcott Ho Cam 54.5 Yale Div Sch 54. **d** 55 **p** 56. C Mansfield St Mark *S'well* 55-58; Chapl Selw Coll Cam 58-83; Dean of Chpl 83-94; Asst Lect Div Cam Univ 60-63; Lect 64-94; Wiccamical Preb Chich Cathl *Chich* from 62; rtd 94; Perm to Offic *Ely* from 99. *97 Barton Road, Cambridge CB3 9LL* Tel (01223) 353186

SWEET, Reginald Charles. b 36. Open Univ BA74. Ripon Hall Ox 61. **d** 62 **p** 63. C Styvechale *Cov* 62-65; Chapl RN 65-69 and 74-93; R Riddlesworth w Gasthorpe and Knettishall *Nor* 69-74; R Brettenham w Rushford 69-74; Perm to Offic 93-96; Chapl Miss to Seamen 96-99; rtd 99; Chapl Win St Cross w St Faith *Win* from 99. *The Chaplain's Lodge, The Hospital of St Cross, St Cross Road, Winchester SO23 9SD* Tel (01962) 853525 Mobile 07889-375085

SWEET, Vaughan Carroll. b 46. Aston Univ BSc69 MSc70. Linc Th Coll 89. **d** 91 **p** 92. C Uttoxeter w Bramshall *Lich* 91-95; P-in-c Hadley 95-98; V from 98; RD Telford from 00; RD Telford Severn Gorge *Heref* from 00. *The Vicarage, 19 Manor Road, Hadley, Telford TF1 5PN* Tel (01952) 254251 Fax as telephone E-mail vaughan.sweet@virgin.net

SWEET-ESCOTT, Richard Mark. b 28. Hertf Coll Ox BA51 MA53. Westcott Ho Cam 56. **d** 58 **p** 59. C Leeds St Pet *Ripon* 58-62; C Littlehampton St Mary *Chich* 62-65; C Seaford w Sutton 65-72; P-in-c Burpham 72-75; V Easebourne 75-79; V Crawley Down All SS 79-93; rtd 93; Perm to Offic *Chich* from 93. *8 Buttsfield Lane, East Hoathly, Lewes BN8 6EF* Tel (01825) 841052

SWEETING, Paul Lee. b 68. Lanc Univ BSc90 St Martin's Coll Lanc PGCE92. Cranmer Hall Dur BA99. **d** 99 **p** 00. C Blackb St Gabr *Blackb* 99-03; R Falkland Is from 03. *The Deanery, 17 Ross Road, Stanley, Falkland Islands* Tel (00500) 21100 Fax 21842 E-mail sweeting@horizon.co.fk

SWEETMAN, Denis Harold. b 22. Roch Th Coll 61. **d** 63 **p** 64. C Riverhead *Roch* 63-70; C Dunton Green 67-70; Chapl Sevenoaks Hosp 70-72; R Eynsford w Lullingstone *Roch* 71-73; R Eynsford w Farningham and Lullingstone 73-89; rtd 89; Perm to Offic *Newc* from 89. *31 Gloster Park, Amble, Morpeth NE65 0JQ* Tel (01665) 711863 E-mail picrosso@mcmail.com

SWENSSON, Sister Gerd Inger. b 51. Lon Univ MPhil85 Uppsala Univ 70. **dss** 74 **d** 87. C Sweden 74-75; Notting Hill *Lon* 75-77; CSA from 75; Abbey Ho Malmesbury 77-79; R Foundn of St Kath 79-81; Notting Hill All SS w St Columb *Lon* 81-84; Kensington St Mary Abbots w St Geo 85-89; C Bedford Park 91-95; Sweden from 95. *Christens Gård, Pl 8, St Slägarp, S-231 95 Trelleborg, Sweden* Tel and fax (0046) (40) 487059 Mobile (0046) 708-743994 E-mail tedeum@mail.bip.net

SWIFT, Ainsley Laird. b 56. Liv Univ BEd80. Ripon Coll Cuddesdon. **d** 94 **p** 95. C Prescot *Liv* 94-98; TV New Windsor *Ox* 98-01; P-in-c from 01. *The Vicarage, Hermitage Lane, Windsor SL4 4AZ* Tel (01753) 858720 *or* 855447 Fax 860839 E-mail ainsley@swift9485.fsnet.co.uk

SWIFT, Christopher James. b 65. Hull Univ BA86 Man Univ MA95. Westcott Ho Cam 89. **d** 91 **p** 92. C Longton *Blackb* 91-94; TV Chipping Barnet w Arkley *St Alb* 94-97; Chapl Wellhouse NHS Trust 97-98; Chapl Dewsbury Health Care NHS Trust 98-01; Hd Chapl Services Leeds Teaching Hosps NHS Trust from 01. *The Chaplaincy, St James's University Hospital, Beckett Street, Leeds LS9 7TF* Tel 0113-206 4658 E-mail chirs.swift@leedsth.nhs.uk

SWIFT, Christopher John. b 54. Linc Coll Ox BA76 MA Selw Coll Cam BA80. Westcott Ho Cam 79. **d** 81 **p** 82. C Portsea St End St Mark *Portsm* 81-84; C Alverstoke 84-87; V Whittin SS Phil and Jas *Lon* 87-94; R Shepperton from 94; AD Spelthorne from 98. *The Rectory, Church Square, Shepperton TW17 9JY* Tel (01932) 220511 Fax as telephone E-mail christopher.swift@london.anglican.org

SWIFT (formerly LAKER), Mrs Grace. b 39. RN63. Sarum & Wells Th Coll BTh91. **d** 91 **p** 94. C Helston and Wendron *Truro* 91-95; Chapl Havering Hosps NHS Trust 95-02; NSM Rush Green *Chelmsf* 98-02; Bp's Adv for Hosp Chapl from 99. *The*

Vicarage, 111 Church Street, Billericay CM11 2TR Tel (01277) 625947 E-mail graceswift@hotmail.com

SWIFT, Ian John Edward. b 46. NTMTC 99. **d** 02 **p** 03. NSM Basildon St Martin *Chelmsf* from 02. *79 Bull Lane, Rayleigh SS6 8LD* Tel (01268) 775593 Mobile 07799-888607 E-mail ian@swiftfamily.fsnet.co.uk

SWIFT, Jessica Suzanne. b 75. Univ of New Brunswick BSc99. Wycliffe Hall Ox 99. **d** 02. C Islington St Mary *Lon* from 02. *108 Liverpool Road, London N1 0RE* Tel (020) 7226 0854 Mobile 07812-676240 E-mail swift_jessica@hotmail.com

SWIFT, Ms Pamela Joan. b 47. Liv Univ BSc68. NEOC 85. **d** 88 **p** 94. Par Dn Bermondsey St Jas w Ch Ch *S'wark* 88-91; Par Dn Middleton St Cross *Ripon* 91-92; Dioc Stewardship Adv 92-95; TR Bramley 95-99; Miss Adv USPG *Blackb*, *Bradf*, *Carl* and *Wakef* 99-01; Hon C Kildwick *Bradf* 99-01; R and Community P Glas St Matt *Glas* from 01. *2/1 17 Crosbie Street, Maryhill Park, Glasgow G20 0BQ* Tel 0141-946514 Mobile 07833-938843 E-mail pamswift@lineone.net

SWIFT, Richard Barrie. b 33. Selw Coll Cam BA58 MA64. Ripon Hall Ox. **d** 60 **p** 61. C Stepney St Dunstan and All SS *Lon* 60-64; C Sidmouth St Nic *Ex* 64-72; P-in-c W Hyde St Thos *St Alb* 72-77; V Mill End 72-77; V Mill End and Heronsgate w W Hyde 77-82; V Axminster *Ex* 82-83; P-in-c Chardstock 82-83; P-in-c Combe Pyne w Rousdon 82-83; TR Axminster, Chardstock, Combe Pyne and Rousdon 83-94; rtd 94; Perm to Offic *Ex* from 94. *15 Paternoster Row, Ottery St Mary EX11 1DP* Tel (01404) 813102

SWIFT, Selwyn. b 41. Trin Coll Bris 73. **d** 76 **p** 77. C Melksham *Sarum* 76-79; TV 79-81; TV Whitton 81-84; V Derry Hill 84-89; R Bunwell, Carleton Rode, Tibenham, Gt Moulton etc *Nor* 89-01; RD Depwade 97-01; rtd 01. *2 Kembold Close, Bury St Edmunds IP32 7EF* Tel (01284) 701258

SWIFT, Stanley. b 47. ACIS71 Nottm Univ DipTh73 Open Univ BA86. Linc Th Coll 71. **d** 74 **p** 75. C Heaton St Barn *Bradf* 74-77; C Bexhill St Pet *Chich* 77-81; R Crowland *Linc* 81-86; RD Elloe W 82-86; R Upminster *Chelmsf* 86-95; P-in-c N Ockendon 94-95; V Rush Green 95-02; V St Burstead from 02. *The Vicarage, 111 Church Street, Billericay CM11 2TR* Tel (01277) 625947 E-mail stanswift@hotmail.com

SWINBURNE, Harold Noel. b 27. Univ Coll Lon BA49 St Chad's Coll Dur DipTh. **d** 53 **p** 54. C Cockerton *Dur* 53-57; C Wisbech St Aug *Ely* 57-59; V Chilton Moor *Dur* 59-71; Lect RS New Coll Dur 71-93; Lic to Offic *Dur* 71-85; V Bishopwearmouth St Nic 85-93; rtd 93. *39 Durham Moor Crescent, Durham DH1 5AS* Tel 0191-386 2603

SWINDELL, Anthony Charles. b 50. Selw Coll Cam BA73 MA77 Leeds Univ MPhil77. Ripon Hall Ox 73. **d** 75 **p** 76. C Hessle *York* 75-78; P-in-c Litlington w W Dean *Chich* 78-80; Adult Educn Adv E Sussex 78-80; TV Heslington *York* 80-81; Chapl York Univ 80-81; R Harlaxton *Linc* 81-91; RD Grantham 85-90; R Jersey St Saw *Win* from 91; Perm to Offic *Nor* 93-96. *The Rectory, Rectory Lane, St Saviour's Hill, St Saviour, Jersey JE2 7NP* Tel (01534) 736679

SWINDELL, Brian. b 35. St Jo Coll Nottm 86. **d** 88 **p** 89. C Wombwell *Sheff* 88-91; V Brinsworth w Catcliffe 91-93; TR Brinsworth w Catcliffe and Treeton 93-99; rtd 99. *36 Wasdale Close, West Bridgford, Nottingham NG2 6RG* Tel 0115-914 1125

SWINDELL, Richard Carl. b 45. Didsbury Coll Man CertEd67 Open Univ BA73 Leeds Univ MEd86. N Ord Course 79 Qu Coll Birm 77. **d** 82 **p** 83. Hd Teacher Moorside Jun Sch 78-96; NSM Halifax St Aug *Wakef* 82-92; NSM Huddersfield H Trin from 92; Family Life and Marriage Officer 96-02; Bp's Adv for Child Protection from 02. *13 Moor Hill Court, Laund Road, Salendine Nook, Huddersfield HD3 3GQ* Tel (01484) 640473 Mobile 07946-761364 E-mail rswin25004@aol.com

SWINDELLS, Jonathan Reid. b 66. Bp Otter Coll Chich BA90 Cam Univ PGCE93 Leeds Univ BA02. Coll of Resurr Mirfield 00. **d** 02 **p** 03. C Sherborne w Castleton and Lillington *Sarum* from 02. *69 Granville Way, Sherborne DT9 4AT* Tel 07790-430070 (mobile)

SWINDELLS, Philip John. b 34. St Edm Hall Ox BA56 MA60. Ely Th Coll 56. **d** 58 **p** 59. C Upton cum Chalvey *Ox* 58-62; C Bishops Hull St Jo *B & W* 62-66; C Stevenage St Geo *St Alb* 66-71; V Stevenage All SS Pin Green 71-78; R Clophill 78-00; P-in-c Upper w Lower Gravenhurst 83-93; P-in-c Shillington 96-99; rtd 00; Perm to Offic *Ely* from 00. *10 Birchmead, Gamlingay, Sandy SG19 3ND* Tel (01767) 654136

SWINDLEHURST, Canon Michael Robert Carol. b 29. Worc Coll Ox BA52 MA56. Cuddesdon Coll 61. **d** 63 **p** 64. C Havant *Portsm* 63-66; C Hellesdon *Nor* 66-69; V Brightlingsea *Chelmsf* 69-95; Miss to Seamen 69-95; RD St Osyth *Chelmsf* 84-94; Hon Can Chelmsf Cathl 89-95; rtd 95; Perm to Offic *Chelmsf* from 95; *St Alb* 95-98. *9 Radwinter Road, Saffron Walden CB11 3HU* Tel (01799) 513788

SWINDLEY, Canon Geoffrey. b 25. St Mich Coll Llan 59. **d** 61 **p** 62. C Flint *St As* 61-68; V Buttington and Pool Quay 68-77; R Welshpool w Castle Caereinion 77-92; RD Pool 77-92; Hon Can

St As Cathl 83-93; Can Cursal St As Cathl 86; rtd 93. *2 Cobden Street, Welshpool SY21 7EH* Tel (01938) 555942

SWINDON, Suffragan Bishop of. *See* DOE, The Rt Revd Michael David

SWINGLER, Preb Jack Howell. b 19. St Jo Coll Cam BA41 MA47. Ridley Hall Cam 46. **d** 48 **p** 49. C Yeovil St Jo w Preston Plucknett *B & W* 48-53; V Henstridge 53-79; RD Merston 74-84; P-in-c Charlton Horethorne w Stowell 78-79; Preb Wells Cathl from 79; R Henstridge and Charlton Horethorne w Stowell 79-85; rtd 85; Perm to Offic *B & W* from 85. *St Andrew's, March Lane, Galhampton, Yeovil BA22 7AN* Tel (01963) 440842

SWINHOE, Terence Leslie. b 49. Man Univ BA71 PGCE72 Lon Univ BD95. N Ord Course. **d** 84 **p** 85. C Harborne St Pet *Birm* 84-87; V Warley *Wakef* 87-96; V Rastrick St Matt from 96. *St Matthew's Vicarage, 1 Vicarage Gardens, Brighouse HD6 3HD* Tel (01484) 713386 E-mail swinfam@aol.com

SWINN, Gerald Robert. b 40. Leeds Univ BSc60 Lon Univ BD70. Oak Hill Th Coll 63. **d** 66 **p** 67. C Weston-super-Mare Ch Ch *B & W* 66-69; C Harefield *Lon* 70-72; Lic to Offic *Sarum* from 72. *7 Witchampton Road, Broadstone BH18 8HY*

SWINN, Philip Daniel. b 65. Oak Hill Th Coll BA01. **d** 01 **p** 02. C Harpenden St Nic *St Alb* from 01. *37 St James Road, Harpenden AL5 4PB* Tel (01582) 462657 E-mail pd_swinn@swinns.co.uk

SWINNERTON, Edward. b 26. St Aid Birkenhead 62. **d** 64 **p** 65. C Prescot *Liv* 64-67; C St Helens w Trin *Blackb* 67-69; V Hambleton 69-88; P-in-c Out Rawcliffe 84-88; V Hambleton w Out Rawcliffe 88-89; V Barnacre w Calder Vale 89-92; rtd 92; Perm to Offic *Ripon* and *York* from 92. *The Grange, Little Hutton, Thirsk YO7 3BQ*

SWINNERTON, Ernest George Francis. b 33. Clare Coll Cam BA54 MA57. Linc Th Coll 56. **d** 58 **p** 59. C Kirkholt *Man* 58-61; C Swindon Ch Ch *Bris* 61-67; C-in-c Walcot St Andr CD 67-75; P-in-c Chilton Foliat *Sarum* 76; TV Whitton 76-85; V Bolton St Matt w St Barn *Man* 85-95; rtd 95; Perm to Offic *Man* from 95. *9 Duddon Avenue, Breightmet, Bolton BL2 5EZ* Tel (01204) 381377

SWINNEY, Fergus William. *See* DIXON-SWINNEY, Fergus William Henry

SWINTON, Garry Dunlop. b 59. SS Mark & Jo Coll Plymouth BA81 CertEd82. Ripon Coll Cuddesdon 85. **d** 88 **p** 89. C Surbiton St Andr and St Mark *S'wark* 88-92; Succ S'wark Cathl 92-97; P-in-c Wandsworth St Faith 97-01; Chapl YMCA Wimbledon 97-01; Chapl Greycoat Hosp Sch from 01; Chapl Westmr City Sch from 01; Perm to Offic *S'wark* from 01. *4 Greenham Close, London SE1 7RP* Tel 07961-422303 (mobile) E-mail garryswinton@hotmail.com

SWITHINBANK, Kim Stafford. b 53. SS Coll Cam BA77 MA80. Cranmer Hall Dur 78. **d** 80 **p** 81. C Heigham H Trin *Nor* 80-83; Chapl Monkton Combe Sch Bath 83-85; C Langham Place All So *Lon* 85-89; R Stamford St Geo w St Paul *Linc* 90-02; Chapl NW Anglia Healthcare NHS Trust 90-02; V Falls Ch Virginia USA from 02. *2344 Brittany Parc Drive, Falls Church, VA 22043, USA* Tel (001) (703) 569 2377 E-mail kswithinbank@thefallschurch.org

SWITHINBANK, Mrs Penelope Jane. b 53. St Andr Univ MTheol74 Hughes Hall Cam PGCE75. Ridley Hall Cam 00. **d** 02. Falls Ch Virginia USA from 02. *2344 Brittany Parc Drive, Falls Church, VA 22043, USA* Tel (001) (703) 569 2377 E-mail womanbydesign@hotmail.com

SWITZERLAND, Archdeacon of. *See* HAWKER, The Ven Peter John

SWYER, David Martin. b 64. Univ of Wales (Abth) BA87 PGCE89. St Mich Coll Llan DipTh91. **d** 91 **p** 92. C Killay *S & B* 91-93; C Newton St Pet 93-95; R Albourne w Sayers Common and Twineham *Chich* from 95. *The Rectory, 5 The Twitten, Albourne, Hassocks BN6 9DF* Tel (01273) 832129

SWYER (née HARRIS), Mrs Rebecca Jane. b 67. **d** 91. C Sketty *S & B* 91-95. *The Rectory, 5 The Twitten, Albourne, Hassocks BN6 9DF* Tel (01273) 832129

SWYNNERTON, Brian Thomas. b 31. JP77. Ox Univ Inst of Educn 56 NY Univ BA74 PhD75 FRGS62 LCP62. Lich Th Coll 67. **d** 69 **p** 70. C Swynnerton *Lich* 69-71; CF (TAVR) 70-80; C Eccleshall *Lich* 71-74; C Croxton w Broughton 74-80; Chapl and Lect Stafford Coll 80-84; Chapl Naples w Sorrento, Capri and Bari *Eur* 84-85; Perm to Offic *Lich* from 85; Perm to Offic *Wakef* 85-88; Chapl Rishworth Sch Ripponden 85-88; Chapl Acton Reynald Sch Shrewsbury 88-96; Chapl Telford City Tech Coll from 96. *Hales Farm, Market Drayton TF9 2PP* Tel (01630) 657156

SYER, Angela. b 48. ARCM69 Philippa Fawcett Coll CertEd71. Qu Coll Birm. **d** 00 **p** 01. C Oakdale *Sarum* from 00. *6 Wingfield Avenue, Poole BH15 3DQ* Tel (01202) 673296 or 649782

SYKES, Mrs Clare Mary. b 61. WMMTC 93. **d** 96 **p** 97. C Tupsley w Hampton Bishop *Heref* 96-01; NSM Bromyard from 01; NSM Stanford Bishop, Stoke Lacy, Moreton Jeffries w Much Cowarne etc from 01. *The Vicarage, 28 Church Lane, Bromyard HR7 4DZ* Tel (01885) 482438 E-mail sykes@quista.net

SYKES, Gerald Alfred. b 58. Univ of Wales (Abth) BSc79 PhD84 Univ of Wales (Cardiff) BD98. St Mich Coll Llan 95. **d** 98 **p** 99. C

Cardigan w Mwnt and Y Ferwig w Llangoedmor *St D* 98-01; P-in-c Brechfa w Abergorlech etc from 01. *The Rectory, Brechfa, Carmarthen SA32 7RA* Tel (01267) 202389 Fax as telephone E-mail sykesga@bigfoot.com *or* sykesga@freenet.co.uk

SYKES, Graham Timothy Gordon. b 59. ACIB89. St Jo Coll Nottm BTh92. **d** 92 **p** 93. C Kington w Huntington, Old Radnor, Kinnerton etc *Heref* 92-95; C Breinton 95-97; TV W Heref 97-98; Dioc Co-ord for Evang 95-01; V Bromyard from 01. *The Vicarage, 28 Church Lane, Bromyard HR7 4DZ* Tel (01885) 482438 E-mail sykes@quista.net

SYKES, Ian. b 44. Lon Univ DipTh Leic Univ DipEd. Bris Bapt Coll 64 Ripon Coll Cuddesdon 84. **d** 85 **p** 86. In Bapt Ch 64-84; C Headington *Ox* 85-88; TV Bourne Valley *Sarum* 88-97; R Peter Tavy, Mary Tavy, Lydford and Brent Tor *Ex* from 97. *The Rectory, Mary Tavy, Tavistock PL19 9PP* Tel (01822) 810516

SYKES, James Clement. b 42. Keble Coll Ox BA64 MA71. Westcott Ho Cam 65. **d** 67 **p** 68. C Bishop's Stortford St Mich *St Alb* 67-71; Chapl St Jo Sch Leatherhead 71-73; Bermuda 74-79; V Northaw *St Alb* 79-87; Chapl St Marg Sch Bushey 87-98; R Guernsey St Sampson *Win* from 99. *The Rectory, Grandes Maisons Road, St Sampsons, Guernsey GY2 4JS* Tel (01481) 244710 Mobile 07781-111459

SYKES, Miss Jean. b 45. Leeds Univ BA66 Bris Univ CertEd67. Ripon Coll Cuddesdon 86. **d** 88 **p** 94. C N Huddersfield *Wakef* 88-91; TD 91-93; TV Kippax w Allerton Bywater *Ripon* from 93. *The Vicarage, 134 Leeds Road, Allerton Bywater, Castleford WF10 2HB* Tel 0113-286 9415

SYKES, Jeremy Gordon. b 63. Hull Univ BA85. St Alb Minl Tr Scheme 92 Ripon Coll Cuddesdon 97. **d** 99 **p** 00. C Ipswich St Mary-le-Tower *St E* 99-02; P-in-c Briston w Burgh Parva and Melton Constable *Nor* from 02. *The Vicarage, 1 Grange Close, Briston, Melton Constable NR24 2LY* Tel (01263) 860280 E-mail jeremy@sykes-uk.com

SYKES, Jeremy Jonathan Nicholas. b 61. Girton Coll Cam BA83 MA86. Wycliffe Hall Ox BA88. **d** 89 **p** 90. C Knowle *Birm* 89-92; Asst Chapl Oakham Sch 92-98; Chapl Giggleswick Sch from 98; Lic to Offic *Bradf* from 98. *Giggleswick School, Giggleswick, Settle BD24 0DE* Tel (01729) 825856 Fax as telephone E-mail jemsykes@globalnet.co.uk

SYKES, Canon John. b 39. Man Univ BA62. Ripon Hall Ox 61. **d** 63 **p** 64. C Heywood St Luke *Man* 63-67; Chapl Bolton Colls of H&FE 67-71; C Bolton H Trin *Man* 67-71; R Reddish 71-78; V Saddleworth 78-87; TR Oldham from 87; Hon Can Man Cathl from 91; Chapl to The Queen from 95. *The Vicarage, 15 Grotton Hollow, Oldham OL4 4LN* Tel 0161-678 6767 or 624 4866 E-mail j.sykes@rdplus.net

✠**SYKES, The Rt Revd Stephen Whitefield.** b 39. St Jo Coll Cam BA61 MA65. Ripon Hall Ox 63. **d** 64 **p** 65 **c** 90. Fell and Dean St Jo Coll Cam 64-74; Asst Lect Div Cam Univ 64-68; Lect 68-74; Van Mildert Prof Div Dur Univ 74-85; Can Res Dur Cathl *Dur* 74-85; Regius Prof Div Cam Univ 85-90; Hon Can Ely Cathl *Ely* 85-90; Bp Ely 90-99; Perm to Offic *Ban* from 90; Prin St Jo Coll Dur from 99; Hon Asst Bp Dur from 99. *Ingleside, Whinney Hill, Durham DH1 3BE* Tel 0191-384 6465

SYKES, William George David. b 39. Ball Coll Ox BA63 MA68. Wycliffe Hall Ox 63. **d** 65 **p** 66. Chapl Bradf Cathl *Bradf* 65-69; Chapl Univ Coll *Lon* 69-78; Chapl Univ Coll Ox from 78. *The Senior Common Room, University College, Oxford OX1 4BH* Tel (01865) 276602

SYLVESTER, Jeremy Carl Edmund. b 56. Cape Town Univ BA78 HDipEd79. Coll of Resurr Mirfield 84. **d** 87 **p** 88. S Africa 87-96; P-in-c Stoke Newington St Olave *Lon* 96-98; TV Plymouth Em, St Paul Efford and St Aug *Ex* 98-01; CMS from 01. *CMS, Partnership House, 157 Waterloo Road, London SE1 8UU* Tel (020) 7928 8681

SYLVIA, Keith Lawrence Wilfred. b 63. Chich Th Coll 85. **d** 88 **p** 89. C Newbold w Dunston *Derby* 88-91; C Heston *Lon* 91-95; V Brighton St Matthias *Chich* 95-00; C Hove St Patr from 00. *The Vicarage, 30 Cambridge Road, Hove BN3 1DF* Tel (01273) 327242

SYMES, Collin. b 20. Birm Univ BA47 MA48. Bps' Coll Cheshunt 56. **d** 58 **p** 59. C Enfield St Mich *Lon* 58-60; C Brondesbury St Anne w Kilburn H Trin 60-62; R Maidwell w Draughton *Pet* 62-66; R Yardley Hastings 66-68; V Denton 66-68; Hon C Rusthall *Roch* 68-85; Chapl W Kent Coll of FE 68-73; Chapl Chapl RN Sch Haslemere 81-84; rtd 84; Chapl St Elphin's Sch Matlock 85-86; Perm to Offic *Chich* from 86 and *Roch* from 99. *5 Castle Mount, 40 Carlisle Road, Eastbourne BN20 7TD* Tel (01323) 721099

SYMES, Percy Peter. b 24. Leeds Univ BA50. Coll of Resurr Mirfield 50. **d** 52 **p** 53. C Ox St Barn *Ox* 52-54; C Headington 54-56; C Abingdon w Shippon 56-61; V Reading St Luke 61-81; V Drayton St Pet (Berks) 81-89; rtd 89; Perm to Offic *Ox* 94-02. *Merrileas, 23 Hollesley Road, Alderton, Woodbridge IP12 3BX* Tel (01394) 410452

SYMES-THOMPSON, Hugh Kynard. b 54. Peterho Cam BA76 MA81 St Jo Coll Dur DipTh79. **d** 79 **p** 80. C Summerfield *Birm* 79-82; C Harlow New Town w Lt Parndon *Chelmsf* 82-83; Australia 84-89; TV Dagenham *Chelmsf* 89-95; R Cranfield and

Hulcote w Salford *St Alb* from 95. *The Rectory, Court Road, Cranfield, Bedford MK43 0DR* Tel (01234) 750214 E-mail revhugh@symes-thom.freeserve.co.uk

SYMMONS, Roderic Paul. b 56. Chu Coll Cam BA77 MA81 Oak Hill Th Coll BA83 Fuller Th Sem California DMin90. d 83 p 84. C Ox St Aldate w St Matt *Ox* 83-88; Lic to Offic *LA* USA 89-90; R Ardingly *Chich* 90-99; RD Cuckfield 95-99; P-in-c Redland *Bris* from 99; Tutor Trin Coll Bris from 99. *Redland Vicarage, 151 Redland Road, Bristol BS6 6YE* Tel 0117-973 6863 Fax 946 6862 E-mail rod@redland.org.uk

SYMON, John Francis Walker. b 26. Edin Univ MA50. Edin Th Coll 50. d 52 p 53. C Edin St Cuth *Edin* 52-56; CF 56-59; R Forfar *St And* 59-68; R Dunblane 68-85; Can St Ninian's Cathl Perth 74-91; Chapl Trin Coll Glenalmond 85-91; rtd 91. *20 Cromlix Crescent, Dunblane FK15 9JQ* Tel (01786) 822449

SYMON, Canon Roger Hugh Crispin. b 34. St Jo Coll Cam BA59. Coll of Resurr Mirfield 59. d 61 p 62. C Westmr St Steph w St Jo *Lon* 61-66; P-in-c Hascombe *Guildf* 66-68; Chapl Surrey Univ 66-74; V Paddington Ch Ch *Lon* 74-78; V Paddington St Jas 78-79; USPG 80-87; Abp Cant's Acting Sec for Angl Communion Affairs 87-94; Can Res Cant Cathl *Cant* 94-02; rtd 02; Perm to Offic *Glouc* from 02. *5 Bath Parade, Cheltenham GL53 7HL* Tel (01242) 700645 E-mail rogersymon@blueyonder.co.uk

SYMONDS, Alan Jeffrey. b 56. Ridley Hall Cam CTM95. d 95 p 96. C Bath St Luke *B & W* 95-99; R Abbas and Templecombe w Horsington from 99. *The Rectory, 8 Church Hill, Templecombe BA8 0HG* Tel (01963) 370302 E-mail as@fish.co.uk

SYMONDS, Edward George. b 03. Launde Abbey 58. d 59 p 60. C Glen Parva and S Wigston *Leic* 59-64; V Leic All SS 64-74; rtd 74; Perm to Offic *Llan* from 74. *Skomer Residential Home, Marine Parade, Penarth CF64 3BG* Tel (029) 2070 5495

SYMONDS, James Henry. b 31. Ripon Hall Ox 67. d 69 p 70. C Southampton (City Cen) *Win* 69-71; CF 71-78; CF 79-90; P-in-c Arrington *Ely* 78-79; P-in-c Orwell 78-79; P-in-c Wimpole 78-79; P-in-c Croydon w Clopton 79-82; CF (R of O) 90-96; rtd 96; P-in-c Coughton, Spernall, Morton Bagot and Oldberrow *Cov* 99-02; Perm to Offic *Lich* from 00 and *Cov* from 02. *Thimble Cottage, Kings Coughton, Alcester B49 5QD* Tel (01789) 400814

SYMONS, Fernley Rundle. b 39. Peterho Cam BA61 MA71. St Steph Ho Ox 61. d 64 p 65. C Chesterton St Geo *Ely* 64-67; C Henleaze *Bris* 67-72; V Shirehampton 72-00; rtd 00; Perm to Offic *Bris* from 01. *The Glebe House, 1 Mclaren Road, Avonmouth, Bristol BS11 9FE* Tel 0117-908 6099 Fax as telephone E-mail fernleys@blueyonder.co.uk

SYMONS, James Edward. b 28. AKC57. d 58 p 59. C Benwell St Jas *Newc* 58-62; C Alnwick St Mich 62-65; C Prudhoe 65-67; V Mickley 67-95; Perm to Offic from 95; rtd 95. *14 Moor Road, Prudhoe NE42 5LH* Tel (01661) 832978

SYMONS, Stewart Burlace. b 31. Keble Coll Ox BA55 MA59. Clifton Th Coll 55. d 57 p 58. C Hornsey Rise St Mary *Lon* 57-60; C Gateshead St Geo *Dur* 60-61; C Patcham *Chich* 61-64; R Stretford St Bride *Man* 64-71; V Waterloo St Jo *Liv* 71-83; R Ardrossan *Glas* 83-96; C-in-c Irvine St Andr LEP 83-96; Miss to Seamen 83-96; rtd 96; Perm to Offic *Carl* from 96. *8 Carlingdale, Burneside, Kendal LA9 6PW* Tel (01539) 728750

SYMS, Richard Arthur. b 43. Ch Coll Cam BA66 MA71. Wycliffe Hall Ox 66. d 68 p 69. C New Eltham All SS *S'wark* 68-72; Chapl to Arts and Recreation *York* and *Dur* 72-73; C Hitchin St Mary *St Alb* 73-76; TV Hitchin 77-78; Perm to Offic 78-97; P-in-c Datchworth 97-03; rtd 03. *94 Pondcroft Road, Knebworth SG3 6DE* Tel (01438) 811933 E-mail syms94@faxvia.net

SYNNOTT, Alan Patrick Sutherland. b 59. d 85 p 86. C Lisburn Ch Ch *Conn* 85-88; CF 88-95; I Galloon w Drummully *Clogh* 95-01; I Monkstown *Conn* from 01. *22 Rosemount Avenue, Jordanstown, Newtonabbey BT37 0NH* Tel (028) 9080 1004 Fax 9085 3623

T

TABERN, James. b 23. St Aid Birkenhead 57. d 59 p 60. C Garston *Liv* 59-61; V Litherland St Paul Hatton Hill 61-72; V Gillingham St Mark *Roch* 72-79; V Lindow *Ches* 79-85; rtd 85; Perm to Offic *Liv* 86-91 and from 98; *Ches* from 97. *12 Dickinson Road, Formby, Liverpool L37 4BX* Tel (01704) 831131

TABERNACLE, Peter Aufrere. b 22. SSC. S'wark Ord Course 72. d 74 p 75. NSM Enfield St Geo *Lon* 74-80; C Corby Epiphany w St Jo *Pet* 80-83; V Wellingborough St Mark 83-88; P-in-c Wilby

83-88; rtd 88; Perm to Offic *Pet* from 88. *16 St Mary's Paddock, Wellingborough NN8 1HJ* Tel (01933) 228570 Fax as telephone E-mail petertab@btinternet.com

TABOR, John Tranham. b 30. Ball Coll Ox BA56 MA58. Ridley Hall Cam 55. d 58 p 59. C Lindfield *Chich* 58-62; Tutor Ridley Hall Cam 62-63; Chapl 63-68; Warden Scargill Ho 68-75; R Berkhamsted St Mary *St Alb* 75-96; rtd 96; Perm to Offic *St Alb* from 96; *Ox* 99-00. *2 Warwick Close, Aston Clinton, Aylesbury HP22 5JF* Tel (01296) 631562 Fax as telephone E-mail johnttabor@breathe.com

TABRAHAM, Canon Albert John. b 14. Birm Univ DipTh71. Coll of Resurr Mirfield 55. d 56 p 57. C Oldbury *Birm* 56-59; V Stockland Green 59-70; RD Aston 68-70; V Acocks Green 70-80; RD Yardley 74-77; Hon Can Birm Cathl 78-80; rtd 80; Hon C Duns *Edin* 80-01. *Woodville, 17 Cronwell Road, North Berwick EH39 4LZ* Tel (01620) 894829

TADMAN, John Christopher. b 33. Lon Coll of Div 54. d 58 p 59. C Blackheath St Jo *S'wark* 58-61; C Surbiton Hill Ch Ch 61-65; R Cratfield w Heveningham and Ubbeston *St E* 65-70; R Kelsale w Carlton 70-74; R Ashurst *Roch* 74-76; V Fordcombe 74-77; P-in-c Penshurst 76-77; R Penshurst and Fordcombe 77-85; V Felsted *Chelmsf* 85-93; Resource Min Brentwood 93-98; Chapl Warley Hosp Brentwood 93-98; rtd 98; Perm to Offic *Glouc* 99-01; Joint P-in-c Staverton w Boddington and Tredington etc from 01. *Fairways, Shaw Green Lane, Prestbury, Cheltenham GL52 3BP* Tel (01242) 582826

TADMAN-ROBINS, Christopher Rodney. b 47. JP82. Westmr Coll Ox BA91 MTh94 DipApTh93 Lon Inst of Educn PGCE69 GNSM68 LRAM68 ARCM68. Ox NSM Course 86. d 89 p 90. NSM Burford w Fulbrook and Taynton *Ox* 89-94; NSM Burford w Fulbrook, Taynton, Asthall etc 94-99; Perm to Offic from 00. *The Studio, The Old Barn, Idbury, Chipping Norton OX7 6RU* Tel (01993) 832094 E-mail chris@idbury.fsnet.co.uk

TAGGART, Canon Justin Paul. b 11. Linc Th Coll 32. d 34 p 35. C Spittlegate *Linc* 34-40; C Linc St Nic w St Jo Newport 40-45; V Morton w Hacconby 45-52; V Woodhall Spa and Kirkstead 52-76; R Langton w Woodhall 52-76; Can and Preb Linc Cathl 68-76; rtd 76; Perm to Offic *S & M* from 76. *Reedsbeck, Droghadfayle Road, Port Erin, Isle of Man IM9 6EE* Tel (01624) 834204

TAGGART, William Joseph. b 54. DipFD. DipTh. d 85 p 86. C Belfast St Mich *Conn* 85-90; Chmn Dioc Youth Coun 90-94; I Belfast St Kath from 90. *St Katharine's Rectory, 24 Lansdowne Road, Belfast BT15 4DB* Tel (028) 9077 7647 E-mail stkatharine@talk21.com

TAGUE, Russell. b 59. Aston Tr Scheme 90 Linc Th Coll 92. d 94 p 95. C Astley *Man* 94-97; Chapl HM YOI Swinfen Hall 97-00; Chapl HM Pris Risley from 00. *HM Prison, Warrington Road, Risley, Warrington WA3 6BP* Tel (01925) 763871 Fax 764103

TAILBY, Mark Kevan. b 36. K Coll Lon 60. d 64 p 65. C Newbold on Avon *Cov* 64-67; C Stratford-on-Avon w Bishopton 67-70; CF 70-76; P-in-c S Shoebury *Chelmsf* 76-79; P-in-c Stambridge 79-89; Chapl Rochford Gen Hosp 79-89; TV Dovercourt and Parkeston *Chelmsf* 89-93; P-in-c Colchester St Botolph w H Trin and St Giles 93-97; V 97-01; rtd 01; OCF from 93. *53 Jamaica Road, Malvern WR14 1TX* Tel (01684) 573869

TAILBY, Peter Alan. b 49. Chich Th Coll 83. d 85 p 86. C Stocking Farm *Leic* 85-88; C Knighton St Mary Magd 88-90; P-in-c Thurnby Lodge 90-98; P-in-c W Molesey *Guildf* from 98. *The Vicarage, 518 Walton Road, West Molesey KT8 0QF* Tel (020) 8979 3846 E-mail ptailby@netlineuk.net

TAINTON, Mrs Carol Anne. b 50. EMMTC 96. d 99 p 00. NSM Gamston and Bridgford *S'well* 99-03; P-in-c Lowdham w Caythorpe, and Gunthorpe from 03. *9 Roland Avenue, Wilford, Nottingham NG11 7AN* Tel 0115-981 3960

TAIT, James Laurence Jamieson. b 47. St Jo Coll Dur 78. d 80 p 81. C Heyside *Man* 80-81; C Westhoughton 81-84; R Aldingham and Dendron and Rampside *Carl* 84-88; V Flookburgh 88-92; New Zealand from 92. *3/323 Broadway Avenue, Palmerston North, New Zealand* Tel (0064) (6) 358 9134 or 358 5403 Fax 358 5403 E-mail stpeters@icon.nz

TAIT, Philip Leslie. b 52. Ex Univ BA73 Hull Univ PGCE74. NEOC 87. d 90 p 91. NSM Osbaldwick w Murton *York* 90-92; Chapl and Hd RS Berkhamsted Sch Herts 93-97; P-in-c Woodhorn w Newbiggin *Newc* 98; Chapl HM Pris Wolds 98-00; Chapl R Russell Sch Croydon from 00. *The Royal Russell School, Coombe Lane, Croydon CR9 5BY* Tel (020) 8657 4433 Fax 8657 9555

TAIT (née DAVIS), Ruth Elizabeth. b 39. St Andr Univ MA62 Moray Ho Coll of Educn DipEd63. Moray Ord Course 89. dss 90 d 94 p 95. Elgin w Lossiemouth *Mor* 90-94; C 94-96; NSM Dufftown *Ab* from 96; C Forres *Mor* 96-98; NSM Aberlour from 98. *30 Mayne Road, Elgin IV30 1PB* Tel (01343) 542919

TAIT, Ms Valerie Joan. b 60. Open Univ BA96 SRN82 RSCN82 DN88. Trin Coll Bris 99. d 01 p 02. C W Heref from 01. *79 Bridle Road, Hereford HR4 0PW* Tel (01432) 273708

TALBOT, Alan John. b 23. BNC Ox BA49 MA55. Coll of Resurr Mirfield 49. d 51 p 52. C Hackney Wick St Mary of Eton w

St Aug *Lon* 51-54; C Portsea St Sav *Portsm* 54-63; Tanganyika 63-64; Tanzania 64-68; V Stepney St Aug w St Phil *Lon* 69-78; V Twickenham All Hallows 78-86; rtd 88; Perm to Offic *S'wark* from 88. *46 Brandon Street, London SE17 1NL* Tel (020) 7703 0719

TALBOT, Derek Michael (Mike). b 55. St Jo Coll Dur BSc77 Nottm Univ DipTh85. St Jo Coll Nottm 84. **d** 87 **p** 88. C Rushden w Newton Bromswold *Pet* 87-90; C Barton Seagrave w Warkton 90-95; V Kettering Ch the King 95-02; V Northwood Em *Lon* from 02; AD Harrow from 02. *Emmanuel Vicarage, 3 Gatehill Road, Northwood HA6 3QB* Tel (01923) 828914 Mobile 07767-763715 E-mail mike.talbot@lineone.net

TALBOT (née THOMSON), Mrs Elizabeth Lucy (Libby). b 74. Lanc Univ BA96 Bris Univ BA00 MA01. Trin Coll Bris 98. **d** 01 **p** 02. C Bitterne *Win* from 01. *39 Whites Road, Bitterne, Southampton SO19 7NR* Tel (023) 8044 7929 Mobile 07977-115923 E-mail libby@thomson74.fslife.co.uk

TALBOT, George Brian. b 37. Qu Coll Birm 78. **d** 80 **p** 81. C Heref St Martin *Heref* 80-83; R Bishop's Frome w Castle Frome and Fromes Hill 83-90; P-in-c Acton Beauchamp and Evesbatch w Stanford Bishop 83-90; R Burstow *S'wark* 90-02; rtd 02. *Bellaluz 10 03, La Manga Club, 30385 Los Belones, Cartagena, Murcia, Spain* Tel (0034) (9) 6813 8103

TALBOT, John Herbert Boyle. b 30. TCD BA51 MA57. CITC 52. **d** 53 **p** 54. C Dublin St Pet *D & G* 53-57; Chan Vicar St Patrick's Cathl Dub 56-61; C Dublin Zion Ch 57-61; Chapl Asst St Thos Hosp Lon 61-64; Min Can and Sacr Cant Cathl *Cant* 64-67; R Brasted *Roch* 67-84; R Ightham 84-95; P-in-c Shipbourne 87-91; RD Shoreham 89-95; rtd 95; Perm to Offic *Roch* from 01. *12 Waterlakes, Edenbridge TN8 5BY* Tel (01732) 865729

TALBOT, John Michael. b 23. FRSM FRCPath68 Lon Univ MD52. S'wark Ord Course 75. **d** 78 **p** 79. NSM S Croydon Em *Cant* 78-81; Perm to Offic *Nor* 82-85 and from 96; NSM Hethersett w Canteloff w Lt and Gt Melton 85-96. *3 White Gates Close, Hethersett, Norwich NR9 3JG* Tel (01603) 811709

TALBOT, Mrs June Phyllis. b 46. Ripon Coll of Educn CertEd67. NEOC 88. **d** 91 **p** 94. NSM Cleadon *Dur* 91-97; Dioc Voc Adv from 94; NSM Bishopwearmouth St Gabr from 97. *66 Wheatall Drive, Whitburn, Sunderland SR6 7HQ* Tel 0191-529 2265

TALBOT (née KINGHAM), Canon Mair Josephine. b 59. Univ Coll Lon BA84. Ridley Hall Cam 85. **d** 88 **p** 94. C Gt Yarmouth *Nor* 88-94; Sen Asst P Raveningham Gp 94-99; Chapl Norfolk Mental Health Care NHS Trust 94-02; Bp's Adv for Women's Min *Nor* from 01; P-in-c Watton w Carbrooke and Ovington from 02; Hon Can Nor Cathl from 02. *St Mary's Vicarage, Norwich Road, Watton, Thetford IP25 6DB* Tel (01953) 881439 E-mail mair@mairtalbot.fsnet.co.uk

TALBOT, Mrs Marian. b 25. Qu Coll Birm 76. **dss** 78 **d** 87 **p** 94. Droitwich *Worc* 78-87; Par Dn Droitwich Spa 87-88; Chapl Droitwich Hosps 83-88; Asst Chapl Alexandra Hosp Redditch 88-98; Perm to Offic 88-98; rtd 98; Perm to Offic *Truro* from 00. *Noten, 10 The Fairway, Budock Vean, Mawnan Smith, Falmouth TO11 5LR* Tel (01326) 250035

TALBOT, Mike. *See* TALBOT, Derek Michael

TALBOT, Stephen Richard. b 52. BSc. Trin Coll Bris DipHE. **d** 84 **p** 85. C Tonbridge SS Pet and Paul *Roch* 84-89; P-in-c Hemingford Abbots *Ely* 89-96; P-in-c Hemingford Grey 89-01; P-in-c Ashburnham w Penhurst *Chich* from 01. *Agmerhurst Granary, Kitchenham Road, Ashburnham, Battle TN33 9NA* Tel (01424) 893605

TALBOT, Sister Susan Gabriel. b 46. Leeds Univ BA69 Man Poly CertEd70 Lon Univ DipTh72 Man Univ PhD00. N Ord Course 91. **d** 94 **p** 95. C Wythenshawe St Martin *Man* 94-98; P-in-c Cheetham St Jo 98-02; Lic Preacher from 02. *48 St Georges Road, Manchester M14 6SZ* Tel 0161-248 7297 E-mail susan@gabriel87.freeserve.co.uk

TALBOT-PONSONBY, Preb Andrew. b 44. Leeds Univ DipTh66. Coll of Resurr Mirfield 66. **d** 68 **p** 70. C Radlett *St Alb* 68-70; C Salisbury St Martin *Sarum* 70-73; P-in-c Acton Burnell w Pitchford *Heref* 73-80; P-in-c Frodesley 73-80; P-in-c Cound 73-80; Asst Dioc Youth Officer 73-80; P-in-c Bockleton w Leysters 80-81; V 81-92; P-in-c Kimbolton w Middleton-on-the-Hill 80-81; V Kimbolton w Hamnish and Middleton-on-the-Hill 81-92; P-in-c Wigmore Abbey 92-96; R 97-98; Preb Heref Cathl from 87; RD Leominster 97-98; Public Preacher from 98; Warden of Readers from 02. *Llan Retreat House, Twitchen, Clunbury, Craven Arms SY7 0HN* Tel (01588) 660417 E-mail llant-p@beeb.net

TALBOT-PONSONBY, Mrs Gillian. b 50. Sarum & Wells Th Coll 89. **d** 91 **p** 94. C Leominster *Heref* 91-92; NSM Wigmore Abbey 92-98; Public Preacher from 98; Asst Dioc Adv on Women in Min 99-03; Dioc Adv from 03. *Llan Retreat House, Twitchen, Clunbury, Craven Arms SY7 0HN* Tel (01588) 660417 E-mail llant-p@beeb.net

TALBOTT, Brian Hugh. b 34. RD78. St Pet Hall Ox BA57 MA64. Westcott Ho Cam. **d** 59 **p** 60. C Newc H Cross *Newc* 59-61; C Newc St Jo 61-64; Chapl RNR 63-91; Chapl Barnard Castle Sch

64-71; Chapl Bishop's Stortford Coll 71-96; Hon C Bishop's Stortford St Mich *St Alb* 71-96; rtd 96; Perm to Offic *B & W* from 96; Acting Chapl Wells Cathl Sch 97-98. *Four Seasons, Milton Lane, Wookey Hole, Wells BA5 1DG* Tel (01749) 679678

TALBOTT, Scott Malcolm. b 55. St Alb and Ox Min Course 00. **d** 03. C Watford St Andr *St Alb* from 03. *Elmhurst, 40 Berks Hill, Chorleywood, Rickmansworth WD3 5AH* Tel (01923) 282370 Mobile 07802-244877 E-mail scott.talbott@talk21.com

TALBOTT, Simon John. b 57. Pontifical Univ Maynooth BD81. **d** 81 **p** 82. In RC Ch 81-87; C Headingley *Ripon* 88-91; V Gt and Lt Ouseburn w Marton cum Grafton 91-97; Chapl Qu Ethelburga's Coll York 91-97; P-in-c Markington w S Stainley and Bishop Thornton *Ripon* 97-01; AD Ripon 97-01; P-in-c Epsom St Martin *Guildf* 01-02; V from 02. *35 Burgh Heath Road, Epsom KT17 4LP* Tel (01372) 743336 Fax 749193 E-mail s.talbott@virgin.net

TALING, Johannes Albert (Hans). b 59. St Jo Coll Nottm 93. EAMTC 00. **d** 02 **p** 03. C Littleborough *Man* from 02. *46 Petts Crescent, Littleborough OL15 8ED* Tel (01706) 376095 E-mail taling@onetel.net.uk

TALLANT, John. b 45. Edin Th Coll 86. **d** 88 **p** 89. C Cayton w Eastfield *York* 88-90; C N Hull St Mich 90-91; V Scarborough St Sav w All SS 91-93; V Fleetwood St Nic *Blackb* 93-99; P-in-c Sculcoates St Paul w Ch Ch and St Silas *York* 99-03; P-in-c Hull St Mary Sculcoates 99-03; P-in-c Hull St Steph Sculcoates 99-03; R Woldsburn from 03. *The New Rectory, West End, Bainton, Driffield YO25 9NR* Tel (01377) 217622

TALLON, Jonathan Robert Roe. b 66. Rob Coll Cam BA88 MA92. St Jo Coll Nottm BTh94. **d** 97 **p** 98. C Bury St Jo w St Mark *Man* 97-01; P-in-c Cadishead from 01. *St Mary's Vicarage, Penry Avenue, Cadishead, Manchester M44 5ZE* Tel 0161-775 2171

TAMBLING, Peter Francis. b 20. St Pet Hall Ox BA47. Westcott Ho Cam. **d** 49 **p** 50. C Stockport St Mary *Ches* 49-51; C Westbury *Sarum* 52-56; R Bishopstrow and Boreham 56-64; R Zeals and Stourton 64-73; P-in-c Bourton w Silton 71-73; R Upper Stour 73-74; R Glenfield *Leic* 74-85; RD Sparkenhoe III 76-81; rtd 85; Perm to Offic *B & W* 86-94. *20 Balsam Fields, Wincanton BA9 9HF* Tel (01963) 34237

TAMPLIN, Peter Harry. b 44. Sarum & Wells Th Coll 71. **d** 73 **p** 74. C Digswell *St Alb* 73-76; C Chesterton St Luke *Ely* 76-82; V Chesterton St Geo 82-95; R Durrington *Sarum* from 95. *The Rectory, Church Street, Durrington, Salisbury SP4 8AL* Tel (01980) 652229

TAMPLIN, Roger Ian. b 41. K Coll Lon BD63 AKC63. St Boniface Warminster 60. **d** 64 **p** 65. C St Helier *S'wark* 64-68; C Camberwell St Giles 68-72; C Tanga St Aug Tanzania 72-73; P-in-c Brent Pelham w Meesden *St Alb* 74-78; P-in-c Anstey 75-78; rtd 01. *31 Shackleton Spring, Stevenage SG2 9DF* Tel (01438) 316031 E-mail roger.tamplin@ic24.net

TAMS, Gordon Thomas Carl. b 37. Leeds Univ BA60 Newc Univ MLitt84 Reading Univ CertEd61 LLCM76. Edin Dioc NSM Course 83. **d** 90 **p** 91. NSM Kelso *Edin* 90-92; P-in-c Coldstream 92-02; rtd 02. *47 Lennel Mount, Coldstream TD12 4NS* Tel (01890) 882479 E-mail gordon.tams@dial.pipex.com

TAMS, Paul William. b 56. Huddersfield Poly CertEd77. EAMTC 87. **d** 90 **p** 91. NSM Mildenhall *St E* from 90. *38 Raven Close, Mildenhall, Bury St Edmunds IP28 7LF* Tel (01638) 715475 E-mail paultams@lineone.net

TANBURN, John Walter. b 30. Jes Coll Cam BA53 MA57. Clifton Th Coll 54. **d** 56 **p** 57. C Orpington Ch Ch *Roch* 56-59; C-in-c St Paul's Cray St Barn CD 59-64; V St Paul's Cray St Barn 64-67; Chapl Stowe Sch 67-72; R Morley *Nor* 72-82; Chapl Wymondham Coll 72-82; rtd 95. *Brook House, 49 Lower Road, Dover CT17 0QU* Tel (01304) 829098

TANKARD, Reginald Douglas Alan. b 37. Sarum Th Coll 60. **d** 62 **p** 63. C Howden *York* 62-65; C Heckmondwike *Wakef* 65-67; CF 67-70; C Thornbury *Bradf* 82-88; P-in-c Rockcliffe and Blackford *Carl* 88-90; V 90-03; rtd 03. *21 Northgate, Almondbury, Huddersfield HD5 8RX* Tel (01484) 514426

TANN, Canon David John. b 31. K Coll Lon BD57 AKC57. **d** 58 **p** 59. C Wandsworth St Anne *S'wark* 58-60; C Sholing *Win* 60-64; Asst Chapl Lon Univ 64-65; C Fulham All SS 65-68; Hon C 72-82; Lic to Offic 68-72; Teacher Godolphin and Latymer Sch Hammersmith 68-73; Ealing Boys Gr Sch 69-73; Hd of RE Green Sch Isleworth 73-82; V Dudley St Jas *Worc* 82-95; Chapl Burton Rd Hosp Dudley 83-95; Hon Can Worc Cathl *Worc* 90-95; RD Dudley 93-95; rtd 95; Perm to Offic *Lon* from 97. *75 Parkview Court, Fulham High Street, London SW6 3LL* Tel (020) 7736 6018

TANNER, Preb Alan John. b 25. OBE97. SS Coll Cam 43 Linc Coll Ox BA52 MA65. Coll of Resurr Mirfield 52. **d** 54 **p** 55. C Hendon St Mary *Lon* 54-58; V S Harrow St Paul 58-60; Dir Coun for Chr Stewardship 60-65; Dir Lay Tr 65-71; Sec Coun for Miss and Unity 65-80; V St Nic Cole Abbey 66-78; Sec Gtr Lon Chs' Coun 76-83; P-in-c St Ethelburga Bishopsgate 78-85; St Botolph without Bishopsgate 78-97; P-in-c All Hallows Lon Wall 80-97; Bp's Ecum Officer 81-97; AD The City 90-97; Preb St Paul's Cathl 91-97; P-in-c St Clem Eastcheap w St Martin Orgar 93-97;

P-in-c St Sepulchre w Ch Ch Greyfriars etc 93-97; P-in-c St Kath Cree 93-97; P-in-c Smithfield St Bart Gt 94-95; rtd 97; Preacher of the Charterhouse 73-00; Perm to Offic *Lon* from 00; *B & W* from 01; *Cant* from 03. *Cricklewood Cottage, 34 Convent Road, Broadstairs CT10 3BE*

TANNER, Canon Frank Hubert. b 38. St Aid Birkenhead 63. **d** 66 **p** 67. C Ipswich St Marg *St E* 66-69; C Mansfield St Pet *S'well* 69-72; V Huthwaite 72-79; Chapl to the Deaf 79-92; Hon Can S'well Minster 90-92; Chapl Northn and Rutland Miss to the Deaf 92-01; rtd 01. *The Tamarisks, Trenow Lane, Perranuthnoe, Penzance TR20 9NY* Tel (01736) 719426
E-mail franktanner@lineone.net

TANNER, Frederick James. b 24. **d** 64 **p** 65. Uganda 64-69; Hd Master Summerhill Jun Mixed Sch Bris from 69; Perm to Offic *Bris* 69-94; Hon C Chew Magna w Dundry *B & W* 81-86; Perm to Offic 86-94 and 97-00. *Orchard Cottage, Stocks Lane, North Wootton, Shepton Mallet BA4 4EP* Tel (01749) 890182

TANNER, John. **d** 03. C Taney *D & G* from 03. *Lisheen, Taney Park, Dundrum, Dublin 14, Irish Republic* Tel (00353) (1) 296 7106 *or* 298 5491 E-mail tanner1@eircom.net

TANNER, Mark Simon Austin. b 70. Ch Ch Ox BA92 MA96 St Jo Coll Dur BA98. Cranmer Hall Dur 95. **d** 98 **p** 99. C Upton (Overchurch) *Ches* 98-01; V Doncaster St Mary *Sheff* from 01. *St Mary's Vicarage, 59 St Mary's Road, Doncaster DN1 2NR* Tel (01302) 342565 E-mail mark.tanner@fish.co.uk

TANNER, Mark Stuart. b 59. Nottm Univ BA81. Sarum & Wells Th Coll. **d** 85 **p** 86. C Radcliffe-on-Trent *S'well* 85; C Radcliffe-on-Trent and Shelford etc 85-88; C Bestwood 88-89; TV 89-93; Bp's Research Officer 93-97; P-in-c S'well H Trin 93-98; V from 98; AD S'well from 01. *Holy Trinity Vicarage, Westhorpe, Southwell NG25 0NB* Tel (01636) 813243
E-mail mark.tanner@tesco.net

TANNER, Martin Philip. b 54. Univ Coll Lon BSc(Econ)75. Ridley Hall Lon 79. **d** 82 **p** 83. C Bitterne *Win* 82-85; C Weeke 85-88; V Long Buckby w Watford *Pet* 88-96; P-in-c Desborough 96-97; R Desborough, Brampton Ash, Dingley and Braybrooke from 97. *The Vicarage, Lower Street, Desborough, Kettering NN14 2NP* Tel (01536) 760324 Fax 760854
E-mail revmtanner@aol.com

TANSILL, Canon Derek Ernest Edward. b 36. Univ of Wales (Lamp) BA61. Ripon Hall Ox 61. **d** 63 **p** 64. C Chelsea St Luke *Lon* 63-67; C-in-c Saltdean CD *Chich* 67-69; V Saltdean 69-73; V Billingshurst 73-82; RD Horsham 77-82 and 85-93; Can and Preb Chich Cathl from 81; R Bexhill St Pet 82-85; RD Battle and Bexhill 84-86; V Horsham 85-86; TR from 86. *The Vicarage, The Causeway, Horsham RH12 1HE* Tel (01403) 272919 *or* 253762

TANZANIA, Archbishop of. *See* MTETEMELA, The Most Revd Donald Leo

TAPHOUSE, Bryan George. b 50. STETS DipTh98. **d** 98 **p** 99. NSM Romsey *Win* from 98. *2 Campion Drive, Romsey SO51 7RD* Tel (01794) 516022 Fax as telephone

TAPLIN, John. b 35. St Alb Minl Tr Scheme 78. **d** 81 **p** 82. NSM Knebworth *St Alb* 81-88; C Braughing, Lt Hadham, Albury, Furneux Pelham etc 88; R Lt Hadham w Albury 88-00; rtd 00; Perm to Offic *St E* from 00. *77 Hepworth Road, Stanton, Bury St Edmunds IP31 2UA* Tel (01359) 250212

TAPLIN, Kim. b 58. Lon Bible Coll BA79 Homerton Coll Cam PGCE84. S Dios Minl Tr Scheme 94. **d** 94 **p** 95. C Sholing *Win* 94-97; P-in-c Rendcomb *Glouc* 97-00; Chapl Rendcomb Coll Cirencester 97-00; Chapl Clifton Coll Bris from 01. *The Chaplaincy, Clifton College, 83B Pembroke Road, Clifton BS8 3EA* Tel 0117-315 7257 *or* 315 7258

TAPLIN, Stewart Tennent Eaton. b 46. Lanc Univ Dip Teaching91 Melbourne Univ BEd92 GradDipEd94 MEd97. ACT ThL69 DipYL71. **d** 72 **p** 73. V Altham w Clayton le Moors *Blackb* 74-76; Can Res Blackb Cathl 76-78; Lic to Offic *Carl* 76-78; Australia from 78. *2 Boston Street, Ashwood, Vic, Australia 3147* Tel (0061) (3) 9888 3328 *or* 9845 7777 Fax 9845 7710

TAPPER, John A'Court. b 42. FCA64. Sarum & Wells Th Coll 89. **d** 91 **p** 92. C Ashford *Cant* 91-94; P-in-c Folkestone H Trin w Ch Ch 94-96; V from 96; AD Elham from 00; P-in-c Sandgate St Paul w Folkestone St Geo from 01. *Holy Trinity Vicarage, 21 Manor Road, Folkestone CT20 2SA* Tel (01303) 253831
E-mail trinitybenefice@ic24.net

TARGETT, Kenneth. b 28. Qu Coll Birm 54. **d** 57 **p** 58. C Mansfield Woodhouse *S'well* 57-59; C Skipton Ch Ch *Bradf* 59-62; V Bradf St Jo 62-65; Perm to Offic 65-82; Australia 82-87; V Old Leake w Wrangle *Linc* 87-94; rtd 94; Perm to Offic *Linc* from 00. *The Sloop, Sea Lane, Old Leake, Boston PE22 9JA* Tel (01205) 871991 E-mail ken@thesloop.fsnet.co.uk

TARLETON, Canon Peter. b 46. TCD BA72 MA80 HDipEd77. TCD Div Sch Div Test 73. **d** 73 **p** 74. C Cork St Luke w St Ann *C, C & R* 73-75; C Dublin Drumcondra *D & G* 75-78; I Limerick City *L & K* 78-82; I Drumgoon w Dernakesh, Ashfield etc *K, E & A* 82-85; Chapl HM YOI Hindley 85-89; Chapl HM Pris Lindholme 89-99; Hon Can Sheff Cathl *Sheff* 98-99; Chapl HM Pris Leeds from 99; Perm to Offic *Sheff* from 99. *HM Prison, 2 Gloucester Terrace, Armley, Leeds LS12 2TJ* Tel 0113-263 6411 ext 325 Fax 279 9125

TARLING, Paul. b 53. Oak Hill Th Coll BA. **d** 85 **p** 86. C Old Hill H Trin *Worc* 85-89; V Walford w Bishopswood *Heref* 89-90; P-in-c Goodrich w Welsh Bicknor and Marstow 89-90; R Walford and St John w Bishopswood, Goodrich etc 90-96; RD Ross and Archenfield 95-96; P-in-c Kington w Huntington, Old Radnor, Kinnerton etc 96-00; R from 00; RD Kington and Weobley from 02. *The Vicarage, Church Road, Kington HR5 3AG* Tel (01544) 230525

TARPER, Miss Ann Jennifer. b 47. SRN71 Nottm Univ BCombStuds82. Linc Th Coll 79. **dss** 83 **d** 87 **p** 96. Stamford All SS w St Jo *Linc* 82-85; Witham *Chelmsf* 85-90; Par Dn 87-90; Min and Educn Adv to Newmarch Gp Min *Heref* 90-93; Perm to Offic 93-95; Dep Chapl HM Pris Dur 95-97; Chapl HM Pris Foston Hall 97-00; Perm to Offic *Lich* 97-02; C W End *Win* from 02. *Galilee, 1 Gatcombe Gardens, West End, Southampton SO18 3NA* Tel (023) 8047 4535

TARR, James Robert. b 39. Bps' Coll Cheshunt 64. **d** 67 **p** 68. C Wortley de Leeds *Ripon* 67-69; C Hunslet St Mary and Stourton St Andr 70-73; V Moorends *Sheff* 73-77; V Cross Stone *Wakef* 77-83; V Chilworth w N Baddesley *Win* 83-90; V Andover St Mich 90-93; V W Andover 93-00; Chapl Mojacar *Eur* 00-02; rtd 02. *Les Courades, Vieux Cerier, 16350 Charente, France* Tel (0033) (5) 45 30 00 39

TARRANT, Canon Ian Denis. b 57. G&C Coll Cam BA MA Nottm Univ DipTh. St Jo Coll Nottm 81. **d** 84 **p** 85. C Ealing St Mary *Lon* 84-87; CMS from 87; Republic of Congo 88-98; Can Boga from 97; Sen Angl Chapl Nottm Univ *S'well* from 98. *The Chaplaincy, University Park, Nottingham NG7 2RD* Tel 0115-951 3927 *or* 951 3378
E-mail ian.tarrant@nottingham.ac.uk

TARRANT, John Michael. b 38. St Jo Coll Cam BA59 MA63 Ball Coll Ox BA62 MA76. Ripon Hall Ox 60. **d** 62 **p** 63. C Chelsea All SS *Lon* 62-65; Chapl and Lect St Pet Coll Saltley 66-70; Belize 70-74; V Forest Row *Chich* 75-87; Perm to Offic *Heref* 93-99; NSM Ross 99-00; P-in-c Guilsborough w Hollowell and Cold Ashby *Pet* from 00; Jt P-in-c Cottesbrooke w Gt Creaton and Thornby from 00. *The Vicarage, 15 Church Mount, Guilsborough, Northampton NN6 8QA* Tel (01604) 743508

TARRANT, Paul John. b 57. Chich Th Coll. **d** 82 **p** 83. C Southgate Ch Ch *Lon* 82-85; C Hornsey St Mary w St Geo 85-90; USA 90-96; R Edin Old St Paul *Edin* 96-97. *Address temp unknown*

TARREN, Eileen. b 46. Cranmer Hall Dur. **d** 02 **p** 03. NSM Pittington, Shadforth and Sherburn *Dur* from 02. *14 Berwick Chase, Peterlee SR8 1NQ*

TARRIS, Canon Geoffrey John. b 27. Em Coll Cam BA50 MA55. Westcott Ho Cam 51. **d** 53 **p** 54. C Abbots Langley *St Alb* 53-55; Prec St E Cathl *St E* 55-59; V Bungay H Trin w St Mary 59-72; RD S Elmham 65-72; V Ipswich St Mary le Tower 72-78; Hon Can St E Cathl 74-82; V Ipswich St Mary le Tower w St Lawr and St Steph 78-82; Can Res St E Cathl 82-93; Dioc Dir of Lay Min and Warden of Readers 82-87; Dioc Dir of Ords 87-93; rtd 93; Perm to Offic *Nor* and *St E* from 93; Hon PV Nor Cathl *Nor* from 94. *53 The Close, Norwich NR1 4EG* Tel (01603) 622136

TARRY, Gordon Malcolm. b 54. Leeds Univ BSc75. Lon Bible Coll BA83 Ridley Hall Cam. **d** 85 **p** 86. C Gt Ilford St Andr *Chelmsf* 85-89; C Rainham 89-92; C Rainham w Wennington 92-93; V Gt Ilford St Jo from 93; AD Redbridge from 01. *St John's Vicarage, 2 Regent Gardens, Ilford IG3 8UL* Tel (020) 8590 5884 E-mail gordontarry@yahoo.co.uk

TASH, Stephen Ronald. b 56. Warw Univ BEd79. WMMTC 88. **d** 91 **p** 92. C Studley *Cov* 91-95; P-in-c Salford Priors from 95; Dioc Youth Officer 95-00; P-in-c Temple Grafton w Binton from 00; P-in-c Exhall w Wixford from 00. *The Vicarage, Station Road, Salford Priors, Evesham WR11 8UX* Tel (01789) 772445
E-mail stevetash@aol.com

TASKER, Harry Beverley. b 41. BA76. Wycliffe Hall Ox 64. **d** 67 **p** 68. C Withington St Paul *Man* 67-71; C Bingley All SS *Bradf* 71-72; Chapl RAF 72-76; R Publow w Pensford, Compton Dando and Chelwood *B & W* 76-84; V Long Ashton from 84; RD Portishead 86-91. *The Vicarage, 7 Church Lane, Long Ashton, Bristol BS41 9LU* Tel (01275) 393109

TASSELL, Canon Dudley Arnold. b 16. K Coll Lon BD49 AKC49. **d** 49 **p** 50. C New Eltham All SS *S'wark* 49-55; V Catford St Andr 55-63; R Rotherhithe St Mary w All SS 63-77; RD Bermondsey 69-76; Hon Can S'wark Cathl 72-76; V Spring Park *Cant* 76-84; RD Croydon Addington 81-84; V Spring Park All SS *S'wark* 85-86; rtd 86; Perm to Offic *Guildf* from 86. *72 Sandy Lane, Woking GU22 8BH* Tel (01483) 766154

TASSELL, Mrs Stella Venetia. b 39. RGN60 RNT63 RMN66 RHV72. Guildf Dioc Min Course 97. **d** 01 **p** 02. OLM Woodham *Guildf* from 01. *72 Sandy Lane, Woking GU22 8BH* Tel (01483) 762944 Mobile 07790-521567
E-mail tassell@fish.co.uk

TATE, Harold Richard. b 24. St Jo Coll Dur BA50. **d** 51 **p** 52. C Moss Side St Jas *Man* 51-54; C-in-c Langley St Aid CD 54-60; R Blackley St Pet 60-79; V Alsager Ch Ch *Ches* 79-89; rtd 89; Perm to Offic *Bradf* from 89. *c/o Mrs M E Beers, 4 Dene Drive, Middleton, Manchester M24 1QY*

TATE, Mrs Harriet Jane. b 62. Hull Univ BA84. Man OLM Scheme 99. **d** 02 **p** 03. OLM Heatons *Man* from 02. *70 Winchester Drive, Stockport SK4 2NU* Tel 0161-431 7051 E-mail harriettate@supanet.com

TATE, Henry Charles Osmond. b 13. K Coll Lon 64. **d** 65 **p** 66. C Boscombe St Andr *Win* 65-68; R Winfrith Newburgh w Chaldon Herring *Sarum* 68-78; V Chardstock *Ex* 78-82; rtd 82. *24 Ramsay Hall, 11-13 Byron Road, Worthing BN11 3HN* Tel (01903) 211360

TATE, James. b 56. DipAD80. Oak Hill Th Coll DipHE95. **d** 95 **p** 96. C Hammersmith St Simon *Lon* 95-98; C N Hammersmith St Kath 98-99; P-in-c from 99. *St Katherine's Vicarage, Westway, London W12 0SD* Tel (020) 8743 3951

TATE, John Robert. b 38. Dur Univ BA61 MA71. Cranmer Hall Dur DipTh69. **d** 70 **p** 71. C Bare *Blackb* 70-73; V Over Darwen St Jas 73-81; V Caton w Littledale 81-98; rtd 98; Perm to Offic *Blackb* from 98. *19 Clifton Drive, Morecambe LA4 6SR* Tel (01524) 832840

TATE, Robert John Ward. b 24. St Jo Coll Morpeth ThL48. **d** 49 **p** 50. Australia from 49; Chapl RN 53-79; QHC 76-79; rtd 79. *58 Skye Point Road, Carey Bay, NSW, Australia 2283* Tel (0061) (2) 4959 2921

TATHAM, Andrew Francis. b 49. Grey Coll Dur BA71 Southlands Coll Lon DAM80 K Coll Lon PhD84 AKC88 FBCartS96. S'wark Ord Course 89. **d** 92 **p** 93. NSM Headley w Box Hill *Guildf* 92-02; TV Ilminster and Distr *B & W* from 02. *The Rectory, Broadway, Ilminster TA19 9RE* Tel (01460) 52559

TATTERSALL, James. b 31. Sheff Univ BSc53 DipEd54. Linc Th Coll 81. **d** 82 **p** 83. C Boston *Linc* 82-84; C Tyldesley w Shakerley *Man* 84-85; TV Sutton *Liv* 89-94; rtd 94; Perm to Offic *Blackb* from 94. *111 Croston Road, Garstang, Preston PR3 1HQ* Tel (01995) 600083

TATTON-BROWN, Simon Charles. b 48. Qu Coll Cam BA70 MA78 Man Univ CQSW72. Coll of Resurr Mirfield 78. **d** 79 **p** 80. C Ashton St Mich *Man* 79-82; P-in-c Prestwich St Gabr 82-87; V 87-88; Bp's Dom Chapl 82-88; TR Westhoughton 88-96; TR Westhoughton and Wingates 97-00; V Chippenham St Andr w Tytherton Lucas *Bris* from 00; RD Chippenham from 03. *The Vicarage, 54A St Mary Street, Chippenham SN15 3JW* Tel (01249) 656834 E-mail stbrown@ukip.co.uk

TATTUM, Ian Stuart. b 58. N Lon Poly BA79 Lanc Univ DipRS86 Fitzw Coll Cam BA89. Westcott Ho Cam 87. **d** 90 **p** 91. C Beaconsfield *Ox* 90-94; C Bushey St Alb 94-96; P-in-c Pirton 96-01; P-in-c St Ippolyts from 00; P-in-c Gt and Lt Wymondley from 01. *The Vicarage, Stevenage Road, St Ippolyts, Hitchin SG4 7PE*

TAULTY, Mrs Eileen. **d** 03. OLM Pemberton St Mark Newtown *Liv* from 03. *38 Alexandra Crescent, Wigan WN5 9JP* Tel (01942) 208021

TAUNTON, Archdeacon of. *See* REED, The Ven John Peter Cyril
TAUNTON, Suffragan Bishop of. *See* RADFORD, The Rt Revd Andrew John

TAVERNOR (née LLOYD), Mrs Eileen. b 50. FIBMS74 Liv Poly HNC72. N Ord Course 88. **d** 91 **p** 94. C Heref St Martin w St Fran *Heref* 91-95; P-in-c Bucknell w Chapel Lawn, Llanfair Waterdine etc 95-01; V from 01. *The Vicarage, Bucknell SY7 0AD* Tel (01547) 530340

TAVERNOR, James Edward. b 23. Lich Th Coll 41 St D Coll Lamp BA49. **d** 50 **p** 51. C Monmouth *Mon* 50-52; C Prestbury *Glouc* 52-53; C Newbold w Dunston *Derby* 53-55; C Buxton 67-69; Perm to Offic *Derby* 70-75, *Heref* 75-83 and *St D* 83-91; rtd 88. *12 Beech Close, Ludlow SY8 2PD* Tel (01584) 876502

TAVERNOR, William Noel. b 16. Lich Th Coll 37. **d** 40 **p** 41. C Ledbury *Heref* 40-43; C Kidderminster St Mary *Worc* 43-46; V Bettws-y-Crwyn w Newcastle *Heref* 46-50; V Upton Bishop 50-57; V Aymestrey and Leinthall Earles 57-65; P-in-c Shobdon 58-65; V Canon Pyon w Kings Pyon and Birley 65-88; rtd 88; Perm to Offic *Heref* from 97. *Vine Cottage, Kingsland, Leominster HR6 9QS* Tel (01568) 708817

TAVINOR, The Very Revd Michael Edward. b 53. Univ Coll Dur BA75 Em Coll Cam CertEd76 K Coll Lon MMus77 AKC77 ARCO77. Ripon Coll Cuddesdon BA81 MA86. **d** 82 **p** 83. C Ealing St Pet Mt Park *Lon* 82-85; Min Can, Prec and Sacr Ely Cathl *Ely* 85-90; P-in-c Stuntney 87-90; V Tewkesbury w Walton Cardiff *Glouc* 90-99; P-in-c Twyning 99-99; V Tewkesbury w Walton Cardiff and Twyning 99-02; Hon Can Glouc Cathl 97-02; Dean Heref from 02. *The Deanery, Cathedral Close, Hereford HR1 2NG* Tel (01432) 374203 Fax 374220 E-mail dean@herefordcathedral.org

TAWN, Andrew Richard. b 61. Trin Coll Cam BA83 Ox Univ BA88. Ripon Coll Cuddesdon 86. **d** 89 **p** 90. C Dovecot *Liv* 89-93; TV Dorchester *Ox* 93-98; Student Supervisor Cuddesdon Coll 93-98; R Addingham *Bradf* from 98. *The Rectory, Low Mill Lane, Addingham, Ilkley LS29 0QP* Tel (01943) 830276 E-mail saintpeter@addinghamrectory.fsnet.co.uk

TAYLER, Raymond James. b 38. K Alfred's Coll Win TCert74. SW Minl Tr Course 98. **d** 01 **p** 02. NSM Malaga *Eur* from 01.

Casa Palomero, Oficina de Correos, 29714 Salares, Málaga, Spain Tel (0034) (95) 203 0461 E-mail rjtayler@yahoo.co.uk

TAYLOR, Alan Clive. b 48. Southn Univ BTh79. Sarum Th Coll 69. **d** 74 **p** 75. C Watford St Pet *St Alb* 74-78; C Broxbourne w Wormley 78-83; Chapl to the Deaf 83-91; V Shefford 83-91; R Portishead *B & W* 91-02; TR from 02. *66 Drakes Way, Portishead, Bristol BS20 6LD* Tel (01275) 842284 E-mail possetrector@aol.com

TAYLOR, Alan Gerald. b 33. Roch Th Coll 61 St Aid Birkenhead 61. **d** 63 **p** 64. C W Bridgford *S'well* 63-66; C E w W Barkwith *Linc* 66-69; V E Stockwith 69-76; V Morton 69-76; Countryside Officer 69-88; R Ulceby w Fordington 76-88; R Willoughby w Sloothby w Claxby 76-88; R Woolpit w Drinkstone *St E* 88-98; Rural Min Adv from 88; rtd 98. *5 Finch Close, Stowmarket IP14 5BQ* Tel (01449) 614078

TAYLOR, Canon Alan Leonard. b 43. Chich Th Coll 67. **d** 69 **p** 70. C Walton St Mary *Liv* 69-73; C Toxteth St Marg 73-75; V Stanley 75-83; V Leeds St Aid *Ripon* from 84; Hon Can Ripon Cathl from 97. *The Vicarage, Elford Place West, Leeds LS8 5QD* Tel 0113-248 6992 E-mail cllr.ala.taylor@leeds.gov.uk

TAYLOR, Andrew David. b 58. Regent's Park Coll Ox BA81 MA86 Toronto Univ MDiv92 K Coll Lon MTh95. Westcott Ho Cam 85. **d** 87 **p** 89. C Leckhampton SS Phil and Jas w Cheltenham St Jas *Glouc* 87-91; P-in-c Swindon w Uckington and Elmstone Hardwicke 92-93; C Highgate St Mich *Lon* 94-97; Chapl R Holloway and Bedf New Coll *Guildf* from 97. *10 Willow Walk, Egham TW20 0DQ* Tel (01784) 432025, 443070 or 443950 E-mail a.taylor@rhbnc.ac.uk

TAYLOR, Ann. *See* TAYLOR, Margaret Ann

TAYLOR, Ms Anne Elizabeth. b 68. Ulster Univ BSc91 MA99. CITC BTh94. **d** 94 **p** 95. C Dublin Rathfarnham *D & G* 94-01; Chapl Adelaide and Meath Hosp Dublin 01-03; Abp's Dom Chapl *D & G* from 03. *Rathfarnham Rectory, Rathfarnham Road, Terenure, Dublin 6W, Irish Republic* Tel (00353) (1) 490 5543 Fax as telephone E-mail sundayschoolsociety@ireland.anglican.org

TAYLOR, Arthur Alfred. b 42. Univ Coll Ox MA56. Ox NSM Course 80. **d** 83 **p** 84. NSM Monks Risborough *Ox* 83-96; NSM Aylesbury Deanery from 96. *9 Place Farm Way, Monks Risborough, Princes Risborough HP27 9JJ* Tel (01844) 347197

TAYLOR, Arthur John. b 17. Lon Univ BD39 BA55. ALCD39. **d** 40 **p** 41. C Walthamstow St Andr *Chelmsf* 40-42; C Hitchin H Sav *St Alb* 44-45; Asst Chapl Felsted Sch 45-46; Asst Master K Sch Ely 56-80; Perm to Offic *Ely* 56-85; rtd 80; Perm to Offic *Mon* from 86. *44 Homeforge House, Goldwire Lane, Monmouth NP25 5HA* Tel (01600) 716269

TAYLOR, Arthur Robert. b 26. ACIS59. Oak Hill Th Coll 67. **d** 68 **p** 69. C Wilmington *Roch* 68-71; C Polegate *Chich* 71-73; R Chesterton w Haddon *Ely* 73-80; P-in-c Alwalton 73-75; R 75-80; R Sawtry 80-91; rtd 91; Perm to Offic *Roch* from 92. *10 Faraday Ride, Tonbridge TN10 4RL* Tel (01732) 358694 E-mail bphaddon@talk21.com

TAYLOR, Miss Averil Mary. b 36. Sarum Dioc Tr Coll TCert56 Westmr Coll Ox TCert (Mus) 66. WEMTC 99. **d** 00 **p** 01. OLM Longden and Annscroft w Pulverbatch *Heref* from 00. *Sheaves, Lyth Bank, Lyth Hill, Shrewsbury SY3 0BE* Tel (01743) 872071 Fax as telephone

TAYLOR, Bernard Richmond Hartley. b 30. Reading Univ MEd. S Dios Minl Tr Scheme 82. **d** 85 **p** 86. NSM Englefield Green *Guildf* 85-90; NSM Lyddington w Stoke Dry and Seaton *Pet* 90-95; rtd 95; Perm to Offic *Guildf* from 96. *Middleton House, 40 Bond Street, Egham TW20 0PY* Tel (01784) 435886

TAYLOR, Brian. b 38. MBIM Bris Univ BA60 Liv Univ BA70 Southn Univ MA90. Ridley Hall Cam 60. **d** 66 **p** 66. Nigeria 66-72; Perm to Offic *Derby* 74-78; Chapl Newbury Coll 76-94; P-in-c Shaw cum Donnington *Ox* 89-90; R from 90. *The Rectory, Well Meadow, Shaw, Newbury RG14 2DS* Tel (01635) 40450 or 41155 E-mail bt@shawchurch.freeserve.co.uk

TAYLOR, Brian. b 42. St Deiniol's Hawarden 78. **d** 80 **p** 81. C Mold *St As* 80-84; V Bagillt from 84. *The Vicarage, Bryntirion Road, Bagillt CH6 6BZ* Tel (01352) 732732 Mobile 07803-305956 E-mail brian@prayers.freeserve.co.uk

TAYLOR, Brian. b 61. St Mich Coll Llan DipTh91. **d** 94 **p** 95. C Aberdare *Llan* 94-97; V Cwmparc from 97. *The Vicarage, Vicarage Terrace, Cwmparc, Treorchy CF42 6NA* Tel (01443) 773303

TAYLOR, Brian John Chatterton. b 30. Trin Hall Cam BA53 Kent Univ MA57 Melbourne Univ BEd66 Lon Univ MA78. Westcott Ho Cam 53. **d** 55 **p** 56. C Leigh St Jo *Man* 55-57; C Ashton Ch 57-58; Australia from 58; Miss to Seamen 58-60; Vic State High Schs 60-71; Sen Lect Toorak Teachers' Coll 72-80; Prin Lect Inst of Cath Educn 80-88; Co-ord RE Tintern Angl Girls' Gr Sch 89-93; Supernumerary Asst Redhill St Geo from 90. *RMB 6047, Merricks North, Vic, Australia 3926* Tel and fax (0061) (3) 5989 7564 Mobile 408-250630 E-mail sumptonv@surf.net

TAYLOR, Brian Valentine. b 34. St Deiniol's Hawarden 69. **d** 71 **p** 72. C Workington St Mich *Carl* 71-72; C Carl St Aid and Ch Ch 73-74; Chapl Rotterdam Miss to Seamen *Eur* 74-75; Asst Chapl Madrid 75-76; Chapl Marseille w St Raphaël, Aix-en-Provence etc 77-78; Chapl Alassio w Genoa and Rapallo 78-81; C Higher Broughton *Man* 82-83; P-in-c Cheetwood St Alb 83-84; Lic to Offic 84-85; rtd 85; Perm to Offic *Man* 85-97. *36A Station Road, Thornton-Cleveleys FY5 5HZ* Tel (01253) 827704

TAYLOR, Charles Derek. b 36. Trin Hall Cam BA59 MA62. Ripon Hall Ox 59. **d** 61 **p** 62. C Nottingham All SS *S'well* 61-64; C Binley *Cov* 64-67; C Stoke 67-70; R Purley *Ox* 70-74; V Milton *B & W* 74-93; RD Locking 86-87 and 90-93; V Wells St Cuth w Wookey Hole 93-98; rtd 98; Perm to Offic *Roch* from 00. *5 Banner Farm Road, Tunbridge Wells TN2 5EA* Tel (01892) 526825

TAYLOR, Canon Charles William. b 53. Selw Coll Cam BA74 MA78. Cuddesdon Coll 74. **d** 76 **p** 77. C Wolverhampton *Lich* 76-79; Chapl Westmr Abbey 79-84; V Stanmore *Win* 84-90; R N Stoneham 90-95; Can Res and Prec Lich Cathl *Lich* from 95. *23 The Close, Lichfield WS13 7LD* Tel (01543) 306140 *or* 306100 Fax 306109 E-mail charles.taylor@lichfield-cathedral.org

TAYLOR, Christopher Vincent. b 47. Cen Sch Speech & Drama DipDA71. Cranmer Hall Dur 94. **d** 96 **p** 97. C Kendal St Geo *Carl* 96-99; TV Wheatley *Ox* 99-03; TV Leeds City *Ripon* from 03. *28 Hawkswood Avenue, Leeds LS5 3PN* Tel 0113-259 0031

TAYLOR, Preb Clive Cavanagh. b 28. MBE91. Cranmer Hall Dur 61. **d** 63 **p** 64. C Wembley St Jo *Lon* 63-66; C Edmonton All SS 66-69; V Tottenham St Jo 69-76; RD E Haringey 73-76; Dir of Ords 76-85; Chapl Metrop Police Coll Hendon 76-93; Sen Chapl Metrop Police 78-93; V Temple Fortune St Barn 76-93; Preb St Paul's Cathl 78-93; AD W Barnet 79-85; rtd 93; Perm to Offic *Chich* from 93. *26 Wenthill Close, East Dean, Eastbourne BN20 0HT* Tel (01323) 422346

TAYLOR, Colin John. b 66. Witwatersrand Univ BCom87 HDipEd88 BTh94. Wycliffe Hall Ox MTh97. **d** 97 **p** 98. C Denton Holme *Carl* 97-01; Asst for Post-Ord Tr from 00; Bp's Dom Chapl from 01; Asst P Dalston w Cumdivock, Raughton Head and Wreay from 01. *The Vicarage, Wreay, Carlisle CA4 0RL* Tel (01697) 473883 *or* 476274
E-mail bishop.chaplain@carlislediocese.org.uk

TAYLOR, David. b 53. St Jo Coll Dur BA74 PGCE75. Sarum & Wells Th Coll DCM93. **d** 93 **p** 94. C Cheadle Hulme All SS *Ches* 93-97; V Macclesfield St Jo from 97; RD Macclesfield from 03. *St John's Vicarage, 25 Wilwick Lane, Macclesfield SK11 8RS* Tel (01625) 424185 Fax 612311
E-mail david.taylor937@ntlworld.com

TAYLOR, David Christopher Morgan. b 56. Leeds Univ BSc77 Univ Coll Lon PhD80 Univ Coll Ches MEd96 SOSc MIBiol. N Ord Course 91. **d** 94 **p** 95. Tutor Liv Univ *Liv* from 86; NSM Waterloo Ch Ch and St Mary 94-99; P-in-c Altcar 98-00; NSM Altcar and Hightown from 03. *20 Liverpool Road, Formby, Liverpool L37 4BW* Tel (01704) 833304 Fax 0151-794 5337 E-mail dcmt@liverpool.ac.uk

TAYLOR, Dennis James. b 31. ACIS62. Ripon Hall Ox 63. **d** 68 **p** 69. C Baswich *Lich* 68-77; P-in-c Hastings H Trin *Chich* 77-81; V 81-86; R Catsfield and Crowhurst 86-01; rtd 01; Perm to Offic *B & W* from 01. *17 Clifford Avenue, Taunton TA2 6DJ* Tel (01823) 275716

TAYLOR, Derek. *See* TAYLOR, Charles Derek

TAYLOR, The Very Revd Derek John. b 31. Univ of Wales (Lamp) BA52 Fitzw Ho Cam BA54 MA58 Ex Univ CertEd70 Birm Univ AdCertEd92. St Mich Coll Llan 54. **d** 55 **p** 56. C Newport St Paul *Mon* 55-59; CF (TA) 57-59 and 62-64; CF 59-62; V Bettws *Mon* 62-64; V Exminster *Ex* 64-70; Hd of RE Heathcote Sch Tiverton 70-71; W Germany 71-75; Chapl R Russell Sch Croydon 75-79; Chapl St Andr Sch Croydon 79-84; P-in-c Croydon St Andr *Cant* 79-81; V 81-84; Chapl Bromsgrove Sch 84-89; Provost St Chris Cathl Bahrain 90-97; Hon Chapl Miss to Seamen 90-97; NSM Droitwich Spa *Worc* 97-99; Asst P Finstall 99-00; P-in-c Milngavie *Glas* 00-03. *19 Warwick Hall Gardens, Bromsgrove B60 2AU* Tel (01527) 872144 Fax as telephone E-mail derekj.taylor@tesco.net

TAYLOR, Donald Alastair. b 26. Lon Univ BD Linc Coll Ox DPhil77. St Paul's Coll Mauritius. **d** 65 **p** 65. C Ware St Mary *St Alb* 65-66; Seychelles 66-78; SSJE from 68; Lect RS Middx Poly *Lon* 78-92. *74 Woodcote Road, Caversham, Reading RG4 7EX* Tel 0118-946 3965 Fax as telephone E-mail da.taylor3@ntlworld.com

TAYLOR, Edward Frank. b 23. Lon Univ BSc44. Chich Th Coll 50. **d** 52 **p** 53. C Manston *Ripon* 52-55; Chapl Chich Th Coll 55-59; PV Chich Cathl *Chich* 57-59; C Ifield 59-63; V Hangleton 63-73; V Wivelsfield 73-88; rtd 88; Perm to Offic *Bradf* 88-01. *8 Linkway, Westham, Pevensey BN24 5JB*

TAYLOR, Elizabeth. *See* TAYLOR, Mrs Mary Elizabeth

TAYLOR, Eric Hargreaves. b 21. Oak Hill Th Coll 47. **d** 51 **p** 52. C Tranmere St Cath *Ches* 51-54; V Constable Lee *Man* 54-62; V Camerton H Trin W Seaton *Carl* 62-71; V Ramsgate Ch Ch *Cant* 71-85; Chapl Ramsgate Gen Hosp 71-85; rtd 85; Perm to Offic *Cant* 85-90; *Blackb* 89-96; *Ches* from 96. *130 Ellesmere Road, Walton, Warrington WA4 6EF* Tel (01925) 268100

TAYLOR, Garry Kenneth. b 53. Edin Univ BMus75 Southn Univ BTh81 Ch Ch Coll Cant PGCE95. Sarum & Wells Th Coll 76. **d** 79 **p** 80. C Southsea H Spirit *Portsm* 79-82; C Croydon *Cant*

82-84; C Croydon St Jo *S'wark* 85-86; V Choral S'well Minster *S'well* 86-90; V Portsea St Alb *Portsm* 90-94; NSM Hamble le Rice *Win* 96-97; P-in-c Southampton St Jude from 97. *86 Shirley Avenue, Southampton SO15 5NJ* Tel (023) 8077 3940 E-mail garrykt@aol.com

TAYLOR, George Davidson. b 27. St Aid Birkenhead 60. **d** 62 **p** 63. C Urmston *Man* 62-65; V Shuttleworth 65-71; V Litherland St Phil *Liv* 71-85; rtd 85. *34 Beckwith Crescent, Harrogate HG2 0BQ* Tel (01423) 560023

TAYLOR, George James Trueman. b 36. Ripon Hall Ox 66. **d** 69 **p** 70. C Wavertree H Trin *Liv* 69-73; V Newton-le-Willows 73-79; V Stoneycroft All SS 79-83; V Haigh from 83; Jt P-in-c Aspull and New Springs 92-03. *The Vicarage, Copperas Lane, Haigh, Wigan WN2 1PA* Tel (01942) 831255

TAYLOR, Canon Godfrey Alan. b 36. Oak Hill Th Coll DipTh60. **d** 61 **p** 62. C Herne Bay Ch Ch *Cant* 61-64; C Tunbridge Wells St Jas *Roch* 64-68; V Guernsey H Trin *Win* 68-81; V Boscombe St Jo 81-03; Hon Can Win Cathl 96-03; AD Bournemouth 99-03; rtd 03. *Bosnoweth Vean, 21 Cullen View, Probus, Truro TR2 4NY* E-mail godfreyrev@aol.com

TAYLOR, Canon Gordon. b 46. AKC68. St Aug Coll Cant 69. **d** 70 **p** 71. C Rotherham *Sheff* 70-74; P-in-c Brightside St Thos 74-79; P-in-c Brightside St Marg 77-79; V Brightside St Thos and St Marg 79-82; R Kirk Sandall and Edenthorpe 82-91; V Beighton 91-96; V Goole 96-03; AD Snaith and Hatfield 98-03; V Tickhill w Stainton from 03; Hon Can Sheff Cathl from 93. *The Vicarage, 2 Sunderland Street, Tickhill, Doncaster DN11 9QJ* Tel (01302) 742224

TAYLOR, Gordon Clifford. b 15. VRD56 and Bars 66. FSA Ch Coll Cam BA37 MA41. Ripon Hall Ox 37. **d** 38 **p** 39. C Ealing St Steph Castle Hill *Lon* 38-40; Chapl RNVR 40-58; Asst Master Eton Coll 46-49; R St Giles-in-the-Fields *Lon* 49-99; RD Finsbury and Holborn 54-67; Chapl RNR 58-70; rtd 99. *4 King Street, Emsworth PO10 7AZ* Tel (01243) 379400

TAYLOR, Graham Peter. b 58. NEOC DipHE95. **d** 95 **p** 96. NSM Pickering *York* 95; NSM Pickering w Lockton and Levisham 95-96; C Whitby 96-98; C Whitby w Aislaby and Ruswarp 98-99; V Cloughton and Burniston w Ravenscar etc from 99. *The Vicarage, Mill Lane, Cloughton, Scarborough YO13 0AB* Tel (01723) 870270

✠**TAYLOR, The Rt Revd Humphrey Vincent.** b 38. Pemb Coll Cam BA61 MA66 Lon Univ MA70. Coll of Resurr Mirfield 61. **d** 63 **p** 64 **c** 91. C N Hammersmith St Kath *Lon* 63-64; C Notting Hill St Mark 64-66; USPG 67-71; Malawi 67-71; Chapl Bp Grosseteste Coll Linc 72-74; Sec Chapls in HE Gen Syn Bd of Educn 75-80; Gen Sec USPG 80-91; Sec Miss 80-91; Hon Can Bris Cathl *Bris* 86-91; Lic to Offic *S'wark* 89-91; Suff Bp Selby *York* 91-03; rtd 03. *10 High Street, Honeybourne, Evesham WR11 7PQ* Tel (01386) 834846

TAYLOR, Iain. b 03. OLM Cant St Pet w St Alphege and St Marg etc *Cant* from 03. *Address temp unknown*

TAYLOR, Ian. b 53. Saltley Tr Coll Birm CertEd75. LNSM course 92. **d** 95 **p** 96. OLM Heywood *Man* from 95. *818A Edenfield Road, Rochdale OL12 7RB* Tel (01706) 355738

TAYLOR, Jamie Alexander Franklyn (James). b 73. Kent Univ BA95. Westcott Ho Cam. **d** 98 **p** 99. C Walton-on-Thames *Guildf* 98-02; C St Peter-in-Thanet *Cant* from 02; Chapl E Kent Community NHS Trust from 03. *St Andrew's House, 29 Reading Street, Broadstairs CT10 3AZ* Tel (01843) 868923 Fax as telephone

TAYLOR, Jan William Karel. b 59. QUB BD82 MSocSc89 TCD DipTh84. **d** 84 **p** 85. C Belfast St Simon w St Phil *Conn* 84-87; I Belfast St Paul 87-92; Chapl RAF from 92; Perm to Offic *Ban* from 97. *Chaplaincy Services (RAF), HQ, Personnel and Training Command, RAF Innsworth, Gloucester GL3 1EZ* Tel (01452) 712612 ext 5164 Fax 510828

TAYLOR, Jane Suzanne. b 54. Ex Univ BA73. SEITE DipTM99. **d** 99 **p** 00. NSM Knaphill w Brookwood *Guildf* 99-00; C Frimley Green and Mytchett from 00. *49 Connaught Road, Brookwood, Woking GU24 0ES* Tel (01483) 472470 Fax 799026 E-mail janetaylor@brookwood99.freeserve.co.uk

TAYLOR, Mrs Janette Elizabeth. b 44. Glouc Sch of Min 89. **d** 92 **p** 94. C Glouc St Geo w Whaddon *Glouc* 92-96; R Woolaston w Alvington and Aylburton from 96. *The Rectory, Main Road, Alvington, Lydney GL15 6AT* Tel (01594) 529387

TAYLOR, Jason Victor. b 71. Lon Bible Coll BTh01 St Jo Coll Dur MA03. Cranmer Hall Dur 01. **d** 03. C Ripley *Derby* from 03. *31 Porterhouse Road, Ripley DE5 3FL* Tel 07773-352963 (mobile) E-mail jason_@talk21.com

TAYLOR, Miss Jean. b 37. Nottm Univ TCert58 Man Univ CertRS85. St Andr Coll Pampisford 62. **dss** 68 **d** 00 **p** 01. CSA 62-79; E Crompton *Man* 79-97; Chadderton St Luke 97-00; OLM from 00. *1A Crossley Street, Shaw, Oldham OL2 8EN* Tel (01706) 844061

TAYLOR, Mrs Jennifer Anne. b 53. Sussex Univ BEd75 Surrey Univ BA01. STETS 98. **d** 01 **p** 02. Chapl Salisbury Cathl Sch from 01; NSM Salisbury St Thos and St Edm *Sarum* from 01. *27 Viking Way, Salisbury SP2 8TA* Tel (01722) 503081 Fax as telephone E-mail geoffrey.taylor5@ntlworld.com

TAYLOR (née PATTERSON), Sister Jennifer Mary. b 41. CA Tr Coll IDC65. **dss** 77 **d** 87. CA from 65; Chapl Asst HM Pris Holloway 75-79; Ho Mistress Ch Hosp Sch Hertf 78-79; Chapl Asst RAChD 80-90; Germany 90-96; rtd 96; Perm to Offic *Eur* from 96. *Calle Arsenio Rodriguez 37, 38631 Las Galletas, Tenerife, Canary Islands* Tel (0034) (22) 732469

TAYLOR, John. b 58. Aston Tr Scheme 94 Ripon Coll Cuddesdon 96. **d** 98 **p** 99. C Southport Em *Liv* 98-03; V Hindley All SS from 03. *The Vicarage, 192 Atherton Road, Hindley, Wigan WN2 3XA* Tel (01942) 255175

TAYLOR, John Alexander. b 54. S Dios Minl Tr Scheme 89. **d** 92 **p** 93. NSM Abbotts Ann and Upper and Goodworth Clatford *Win* 92-99; Perm to Offic 99-00; NSM Hatherden w Tangley, Weyhill and Penton Mewsey 00-02; NSM W Andover from 02. *256 Weyhill Road, Andover SP10 3LR* Tel (01264) 359160

TAYLOR, Canon John Ambrose. b 19. K Coll Lon 45. Coll of Resurr Mirfield 49. **d** 50 **p** 51. C Helmsley *York* 50-55; V Nether w Upper Poppleton 55-63; V Ches St Oswald w Lt St Jo *Ches* 63-72; P-in-c Ches Lt St Jo 63-67; TV Ches 72-74; Hon Can Gib Cathl *Eur* 74-91; V Withyham St Jo *Chich* 74-88; RD Rotherfield 77-87; P-in-c Withyham St Mich 87; rtd 88; Perm to Offic *Chich* 88-00. *The College of St Barnabas, Blackberry Lane, Lingfield RH7 6NJ* Tel (01342) 870697

TAYLOR, Canon John Andrew. b 53. Linc Th Coll 86. **d** 88 **p** 89. C Stanley *Liv* 88-91; V Wigan St Jas w St Thos from 91; AD Wigan W from 99; Hon Can Liv Cathl from 03. *St James's Vicarage, Poolstock Lane, Wigan WN3 5HL* Tel (01942) 243896

✠**TAYLOR, The Rt Revd John Bernard.** b 29. KCVO97. Ch Coll Cam BA50 MA54 Jes Coll Cam 52 Hebrew Univ Jerusalem 54. Ridley Hall Cam 55. **d** 56 **p** 57 **c** 80. C Morden *S'wark* 56-59; V Henham *Chelmsf* 59-64; V Elsenham 59-64; Sen Tutor Oak Hill Th Coll 64-65; Vice-Prin 65-72; V Woodford Wells *Chelmsf* 72-75; Dioc Dir of Ords 72-80; Adn W Ham 75-80; Bp St Alb 80-95; High Almoner 88-95; rtd 95; Hon Asst Bp Ely from 95; Hon Asst Bp Eur from 98. *22 Conduit Head Road, Cambridge CB3 0EY* Tel (01223) 313783
E-mail jbt@camb6.freeserve.co.uk

TAYLOR, John Charles Browne. b 23. CEng58 MIEE58. Oak Hill Th Coll 81. **d** 82 **p** 83. NSM Havering-atte-Bower *Chelmsf* 82-85; NSM Collier Row St Jas and Havering-atte-Bower 86-89; rtd 89; Lic to Offic *Chelmsf* from 89. *Address temp unknown*

TAYLOR, John Denys. b 20. Leeds Univ BA49. Coll of Resurr Mirfield 49. **d** 51 **p** 52. C Leeds St Marg *Ripon* 51-54; India 54-59; C Gt Grimsby St Jas *Linc* 59-66; New Zealand from 66. *4A Brunton Place, Glenfield, Auckland 1310, New Zealand* Tel (0064) (9) 443 1671 Fax as telephone

TAYLOR, Canon John Frederick. b 20. St Chad's Coll Dur 39. Ely Th Coll 59. **d** 61 **p** 62. C Grangetown *York* 61-64; V Middlesbrough St Cuth 64-71; V Skipsea w Ulrome 71-79; P-in-c Barmston w Fraisthorpe 77-79; Can and Preb York Minster 79-85; R Skipsea w Ulrome and Barmston w Fraisthorpe 79-82; V Hemingbrough 82-85; rtd 85; Perm to Offic *York* from 85. *19 Willow Garth, Eastrington, Goole DN14 7QP* Tel (01430) 410647

TAYLOR, Canon John Michael. b 30. St Aid Birkenhead 56. **d** 59 **p** 60. C Chorley St Jas *Blackb* 59-62; C Broughton 62-64; Chapl St Boniface Coll Warminster 64-68; V Altham w Clayton le Moors *Blackb* 68-76; RD Accrington 71-76; Can Res Blackb Cathl 76-96; Tutor Carl and Blackb Dioc Tr Inst 88-96; rtd 96; Perm to Offic *Blackb* from 96. *Edenholme, 25 Gorse Road, Blackburn BB2 6LZ* Tel (01254) 693772

✠**TAYLOR, The Rt Revd John Mitchell.** b 32. Aber Univ MA54. Edin Th Coll 54. **d** 56 **p** 57 **c** 91. C Aberdeen St Marg *Ab* 56-58; R Glas H Cross *Glas* 58-64; R Glas St Ninian 64-73; R Dumfries 73-91; Chapl Dumfries and Galloway R Infirmary 73-91; Can St Mary's Cathl *Glas* 79-91; Bp Glas 91-98; rtd 98. *10 George Street, Castle Douglas DG7 1LN* Tel (01556) 502593 Fax as telephone

TAYLOR, John Porter. b 48. Ex Univ BA71 MA76. Cranmer Hall Dur 93. **d** 93 **p** 94. C Ossett cum Gawthorpe *Wakef* 93-96; R Crofton 96-02; Chapl Mid Yorks Hosps NHS Trust from 03. *Pinderfields General Hospital, Aberford Road, Wakefield WF1 4EE* Tel (01924) 201688

TAYLOR, John Ralph. b 48. St Jo Coll Nottm BTh74. **d** 74 **p** 75. C Clitheroe St Jas *Blackb* 74-77; C Kidsgrove *Lich* 77-79; C Hawkwell *Chelmsf* 79-82; V Linc St Geo Swallowbeck *Linc* 82-92; rtd 92. *The Gables, Beck Lane, South Hykeham, Lincoln LN6 9PQ* Tel (01522) 692043

TAYLOR, Canon John Rowland. b 29. OBE74. St Mich Coll Llan 57. **d** 58 **p** 59. C Caerau St Cynfelin *Llan* 58-59; C Aberdare 59-61; Miss to Seamen 61-88; Tanganyika 61-64; Tanzania 64-73; Adn Dar-es-Salaam 65-73; V-Gen 67-73; Thailand 73-84; Chapl Rotterdam w Schiedam *Eur* 84-88; V Warnham *Chich* 88-98; rtd 98; Perm to Offic *Chich* 98-00; P-in-c Streat w Westmeston from 00. *The Rectory, Streat Lane, Streat, Hassocks BN6 8RX* Tel (01273) 890607

TAYLOR, Joseph Robin Christopher. b 34. St Aid Birkenhead 58. **d** 61 **p** 62. C Aldershot St Mich *Guildf* 61-64; C Fleet 64-68; R Manaton *Ex* 69-74; R N Bovey 69-74; V Dawlish 74-87; P-in-c

Christow, Ashton, Trusham and Bridford 87-88; R 88-95; Perm to Offic *Ex* 95-98; *St E* from 98; rtd 99. *24 Edwin Panks Road, Hadleigh, Ipswich IP7 5JL* Tel (01473) 824262

TAYLOR, Kenneth Charles. b 24. St Deiniol's Hawarden 76. **d** 76 **p** 77. C Wilmslow *Ches* 76-79; V Whaldon 79-93; Chapl Clatterbridge Hosp Wirral 86-93; rtd 93; Perm to Offic *Ches* from 93. *9 Windsor Drive, Whitby, Ellesmere Port CH65 6SH* Tel 0151-356 2477

TAYLOR, Kingsley Graham. b 55. Univ of Wales (Cardiff) BD93. St Mich Coll Llan 90. **d** 93 **p** 94. C Llanelli *St D* 93-97; V Whitland w Cyffig and Henllan Amgoed etc from 97. *The Vicarage, North Road, Whitland SA34 0BH* Tel (01994) 240494 E-mail ktaylor559@aol.com

TAYLOR, Luke Alastare John. b 68. Brunel Univ BA97. Oak Hill Th Coll BA00. **d** 00 **p** 01. C Hanworth St Rich *Lon* from 00. *35 Oxford Way, Feltham TW13 6RY* Tel (020) 8755 2831

TAYLOR, Lyndon John. b 49. St Mich Coll Llan 92 DipMin93. **d** 95 **p** 96. NSM Swansea St Nic *S & B* 95-01; V Waunarllwydd from 01. *27 Gelli Gwyn Road, Morriston, Swansea SA6 7PP* Tel (01792) 775898

TAYLOR, Lynne. b 51. Sheff Univ BMet73 Salford Univ PhD80. Man OLM Scheme 98. **d** 01 **p** 02. OLM Turton Moorland Min *Man* from 01. *Meadow Barn Farm, Bradshaw Road, Bolton BL2 4JJ* Tel (01204) 300135 Fax as telephone

TAYLOR, Margaret Ann. b 46. LNSM course 96. **d** 98 **p** 99. OLM Newcastle w Butterton *Lich* from 98. *12 Silverton Close, Bradwell, Newcastle ST5 8LU* Tel (01782) 624476

TAYLOR, Marian Alexandra. b 62. Newc Univ BA85. Qu Coll Birm 89. **d** 91 **p** 96. C Earls Barton *Pet* 91-93; NSM Wellingborough St Barn 95-96; NSM Beaumont Leys *Leic* 96-97; NSM Kingsthorpe w Northampton St Dav *Pet* from 00. *75 Kentstone Close, Kingsthorpe, Northampton NN2 8UH* Tel (01604) 843471 E-mail marian@kingsthorpechurches.co.uk

TAYLOR, Mark Edward. b 54. St Jo Coll Auckland LTh. **d** 78 **p** 79. New Zealand 78-86 and from 90; Chapl RN 86-88; Chapl RNZN 90-94; Can Wellington 94-96; P-in-c Albany Greenhithe from 96. *PO Box 38, Albany Village 1331, New Zealand* Tel (0064) (9) 413 8364 or 415 8244 Fax 415 4428

TAYLOR, Mark Frederick. b 62. N Ireland Poly BA84 TCD DipTh87. **d** 87 **p** 88. C Ballymacarrett St Patr *D & D* 87-90; C Dundela St Mark 90-93; I Kilmore and Inch 93-02; I Whitehead and Islandmagee *Conn* from 02. *St Patrick's Rectory, 74 Cable Road, Whitehead, Carrickfergus BT38 9SJ* Tel (028) 9337 3300

TAYLOR, Mark John. b 73. St Andr Univ MTheol99. Coll of Resurr Mirfield 01. **d** 03. C N Meols *Liv* from 03. *28 Hoole Lane, Banks, Southport PR9 8BD* Tel (01704) 506037
E-mail mtaylor@mirfield.org.uk

TAYLOR, Martyn Andrew Nicholas. b 66. **d** 96 **p** 97. C Stamford St Geo w St Paul *Linc* 96-03; R from 03. *St George's Rectory, 16 St George's Square, Stamford PE9 2BN* Tel (01780) 757343 or 481800 E-mail associaterector@stgeorgeschurch.net

TAYLOR, Mrs Mary Elizabeth. b 39. Dioc OLM tr scheme 98. **d** 01 **p** 02. OLM Parr *Liv* from 01. *16 Hignett Avenue, Parr, St Helens WA9 2PJ* Tel (01744) 21086

TAYLOR, Mrs Maureen. b 36. Lon Bible Coll BTh90 MA94. **d** 98. NSM Borehamwood *St Alb* 97-00; NSM Radlett from 00. *57A Loom Lane, Radlett WD7 8NX* Tel (01923) 855197

TAYLOR, Michael Alan. b 47. Bris Univ CertEd70 Lon Univ BD85. Trin Coll Bris 72. **d** 76 **p** 77. C Chilwell *S'well* 76-79; Chapl RAF 79-87; New Zealand from 87. *1 Merton Place, Bryndwr, Christchurch 8005, New Zealand* Tel (0064) (3) 352 4788 or 355 6901 Fax 355 6908 E-mail strategic@chch.planet.org.nz

TAYLOR, Michael Allan. b 50. Nottm Univ BTh80. St Jo Coll Nottm 76. **d** 80 **p** 81. C Bowling St Jo *Bradf* 80-82; C Otley 82-85; P-in-c Low Moor St Mark 85-92; P-in-c Bris St Andr w St Bart *Bris* 92-96. *25 Cornfield Close, Bradley Stoke, Bristol BS32 9DN* Tel (01454) 618677

TAYLOR, Michael Andrew James. b 40. Univ Coll Ches BTh96. **d** 99 **p** 00. NSM Halliwell *Man* from 99. *123 Smithills Dean Road, Bolton BL1 6JX* Tel (01204) 491503

TAYLOR, Michael Barry. b 38. Bps' Coll Cheshunt 63. **d** 65 **p** 66. C Leeds St Cypr Harehills *Ripon* 65-68; C Stanningley St Thos 68-70; V Hunslet Moor St Pet and St Cuth 70-78; V Starbeck 78-00; rtd 00; Perm to Offic *Leic* from 00. *11 Aulton Crescent, Hinckley LE10 0XA* Tel (01455) 631866

TAYLOR, Michael Frank Chatterton. b 30. St Aid Birkenhead 59. **d** 61 **p** 62. C Knighton St Jo *Leic* 61-65; V Briningham *Nor* 65-86; R Melton Constable w Swanton Novers 65-86; P-in-c Thornage w Brinton w Hunworth and Stody 85-86; R Lyng w Sparham 86-90; R Elsing w Bylaugh 86-90; R Lyng, Sparham, Elsing and Bylaugh 90-95; RD Sparham 92-95; rtd 95; Perm to Offic *Portsm* from 95. *The Rhond, 33 Station Road, St Helens, Ryde PO33 1YF* Tel and fax (01983) 873531 Mobile 07989-274848 E-mail mfct@tesco.net

TAYLOR, Canon Michael Joseph. b 49. Gregorian Univ Rome STB72 PhL74 Birm Univ MA81. English Coll Rome 67. **d** 72 **p** 73. In RC Ch 72-83; Hon C Newport Pagnell w Lathbury *Ox* 83-86; TV Langley Marish 86-90; Vice Prin EMMTC *S'well* 90-97; Prin from 97; Hon Can S'well Minster from 00.

52 Parkside Gardens, Wollaton, Nottingham NG8 2PQ Tel 0115-928 3111 *or* 951 4854 Fax 951 4817
E-mail emmtc@nottingham.ac.uk

TAYLOR, Michael Laurence. b 43. ARCM68 Ch Coll Cam BA66 MA70 CertEd72 MPhil90. Cuddesdon Coll 66. **d** 68 **p** 69. C Westbury-on-Trym H Trin *Bris* 68-72; Asst Chapl Wellington Coll Berks 72-76; C St Helier *S'wark* 76-78; TV Bedminster *Bris* 78-82; P-in-c Chippenham St Andr w Tytherton Lucas 82-88; V 88-89; Dioc Ecum Officer *B & W* 89-90; P-in-c Rodney Stoke w Draycott 89-90. *21 Bath Road, Wells BA5 3HP* Tel (01749) 670348

TAYLOR, Michael Noel. b 40. Leeds Univ BSc62 PGCE63. EMMTC 95. **d** 98 **p** 99. NSM Woodthorpe *S'well* 98-02; NSM Gedling Deanery 02-03; NSM Epperstone from 03; NSM Gonalston from 03; NSM Oxton from 03; NSM Calverton from 03; NSM Woodborough from 03. *7 Highcroft, Woodthorpe, Nottingham NG3 5LP* Tel 0115-952 0295 Fax 952 4085
E-mail michael.taylor21@ntlworld.com

TAYLOR, Michael Stewart. b 58. Univ of Wales (Cardiff) DipTh90. St Mich Coll Llan BTh91. **d** 91 **p** 92. C Llangunnor w Cwmffrwd *St D* 91-94; V Llansantffraed and Llanbadarn Trefeglwys etc 94-97; P-in-c Jersey St Andr *Win* 97-99; V from 99. *The Vicarage, St Andrew's Road, First Tower, St Helier, Jersey JE2 3JG* Tel (01534) 734975 Fax as telephone
E-mail vicarmike@aol.com

TAYLOR, Nancy. b 49. SRN70 SCM72. Ox Min Course 88. **d** 91 **p** 94. Chapl Asst Stoke Mandeville Hosp Aylesbury 91-94; Asst Chapl Aylesbury Vale Community Healthcare NHS Trust 94-97; NSM Weston Turville *Ox* 91-99; Chapl Kneesworth Ho Hosp from 98. *Kneesworth House Hospital, Old North Road, Bassingbourn, Royston SG8 5JP* Tel (01763) 255700

TAYLOR, Neil Hamish. b 48. Open Univ BA00. Linc Th Coll 72. **d** 75 **p** 76. C Rotherham *Sheff* 75-78; C Doncaster St Geo 78-82; V Alston cum Garrigill w Nenthead and Kirkhaugh *Newc* 82-87; P-in-c Lambley w Knaresdale 82-87; TR Alston Team 87-88; V Maidstone St Paul *Cant* 88-98; OCF 89-94; Sen Chapl Mid Kent Healthcare NHS Trust 98-00; Sen Chapl Maidstone and Tunbridge Wells NHS Trust 00-01; Perm to Offic *Roch* 98-02; R Eynsford w Farningham and Lullingstone from 02. *The Rectory, Pollyhaugh, Eynsford, Dartford DA4 0HE* Tel (01322) 863050
E-mail neil_h_taylor@hotmail.com

TAYLOR, Canon Neville Patrick. b 40. Trin Coll Bris DipTh82. **d** 82 **p** 83. C Old Trafford St Jo *Man* 82-84; C Hurst 84-87; R Levenshulme St Mark from 87; Hon Can Man Cathl from 02. *St Mark's Rectory, 331 Mount Road, Levenshulme, Manchester M19 3HW* Tel 0161-224 9551

TAYLOR, Nicholas James. b 46. St Chad's Coll Dur BA67 DipTh68. **d** 69 **p** 70. C Beamish *Dur* 69-74; C Styvechale *Cov* 74-77; P-in-c Wilmcote w Billesley 77-79; P-in-c Aston Cantlow 77-79; V Aston Cantlow and Wilmcote w Billesley 79-87; V Cov St Fran N Radford 87-97; RD Cov N 93-97; TR Wilton *B & W* from 97. *The Vicarage, Fons George, Wilton, Taunton TA1 3JT* Tel (01823) 284253 E-mail church@ta13jt.freeserve.co.uk

TAYLOR, Nigel Thomas Wentworth. b 60. Bris Univ BA82 Ox Univ BA86. Wycliffe Hall Ox 84. **d** 87 **p** 88. C Ches Square St Mich w St Phil *Lon* 87-91; C Roxeth Ch Ch and Harrow St Pet 91-93; TV Roxeth 93-97; V S Mimms Ch Ch from 97. *Christ Church Vicarage, St Albans Road, Barnet EN5 4LA* Tel (020) 8449 0942 *or* 8449 0832
E-mail nigel.taylor@london.anglican.org

TAYLOR, Norman. b 26. CCC Cam BA49 MA52. Cuddesdon Coll 49. **d** 51 **p** 52. C Clitheroe St Mary *Blackb* 51-54; C Pontesbury I and II *Heref* 54-55; R Lt Wilbraham *Ely* 55-71; Chapl St Faith's Sch Cam 71-86; Perm to Offic *Ely* 87-91; rtd 91; Perm to Offic *Sarum* from 91; Perm to Offic *Ely* from 98. *Shire End West, Cobb Road, Lyme Regis DT7 3JP* Tel (01297) 442922

TAYLOR, Norman Adrian. b 48. St D Coll Lamp DipTh73. **d** 73 **p** 74. C Fleur-de-Lis *Mon* 73-75; C W Drayton *Lon* 75-79; C-in-c Hayes St Edm CD 79-85; V Hayes St Edm 85-87; V Pilton w Ashford *Ex* 87-89; V Sidley *Chich* 89-02; Chapl Hastings and Rother NHS Trust 00-02; V Durrington *Chich* from 02. *The Vicarage, Bramble Lane, Worthing BN13 3JE* Tel (01903) 505850
E-mail frnorman@bigfoot.com

TAYLOR, Norman Wyatt. b 23. Wells Th Coll 58. **d** 60 **p** 61. C Lawrence Weston *Bris* 60-63; V 63-69; V Bishop's Cannings *Sarum* 69-77; V Bishop's Cannings, All Cannings etc 77-80; V W Moors 80-87; rtd 88; Perm to Offic *Ex* 89-98. *3 Kits Close, Chudleigh, Newton Abbot TQ13 0LG* Tel (01626) 852733

TAYLOR, Patrick James. b 72. Magd Coll Cam BA96 MA99 MEng94. Ripon Coll Cuddesdon BA00. **d** 01 **p** 02. C Kenilworth St Nic *Cov* from 01. *St Barnabas' House, 145 Albion Street, Kenilworth CV8 2FY* Tel (01926) 858169
E-mail p.j.taylor@virgin.net

TAYLOR, Paul. b 63. RGN85. Sarum & Wells Th Coll 92 Linc Th Coll BTh95. **d** 95 **p** 96. C Boultham *Linc* 95-98; C Ditton St Mich w St Thos *Liv* 98-00; V Bickerstaffe and Melling from 00. *The Vicarage, Intake Lane, Bickerstaffe, Ormskirk L39 0EB* Tel (01695) 722304

TAYLOR, Paul Frank David. b 60. ARICS87 Leic Poly BSc84 MRICS01. Trin Coll Bris BA91. **d** 91 **p** 92. C Edin St Thos *Edin* 91-94; C Kempshott *Win* 94-98; C-in-c Hatch Warren CD 98-01; V Salisbury St Fran and Stratford sub Castle *Sarum* from 01. *The Vicarage, 52 Park Lane, Salisbury SP1 3NP* Tel (01722) 333762
E-mail paul@pfdt.freeserve.co.uk

TAYLOR, Paul Stanley. b 53. Ox Univ BEd MTh98. Westcott Ho Cam. **d** 84 **p** 85. C Bush Hill Park St Steph *Lon* 84-88; Asst Dir Post Ord Tr Edmonton Episc Area 87-94; Dir Post Ord Tr 94-00 and from 02; V Southgate St Andr 88-97; V Hendon St Mary 97-01; V Hendon St Mary and Ch Ch from 01; AD W Barnet from 00. *The Vicarage, 34 Parson Street, London NW4 1QR* Tel (020) 8203 2884 *or* 8202 4803 Fax 8203 6734 *or* 8203 4232
E-mail ptatstmarys@aol.com

TAYLOR, Peter. b 35. Sussex Univ MA72. Wells Th Coll 58. **d** 60 **p** 61. C Godalming *Guildf* 60-62; C Epsom St Martin 62-65; R E Clandon 65-75; R W Clandon 65-75; rtd 96; P-in-c Burpham *Chich* from 96. *The Vicarage, Burpham, Arundel BN18 9RJ* Tel (01903) 882948 Fax as telephone
E-mail pburpham@globalnet.co.uk

TAYLOR, Peter David. b 38. FCA. N Ord Course 77. **d** 80 **p** 81. C Penwortham St Mary *Blackb* 80-84; V Farington 84-92; V Euxton from 92. *The Vicarage, Wigan Road, Euxton, Chorley PR7 6JH* Tel (01257) 262102

TAYLOR, Canon Peter David. b 47. Liv Univ BEd74 Man Univ MEd78 Lanc Univ MA88. N Ord Course 78. **d** 81 **p** 82. C Formby H Trin *Liv* 81-84; V Stoneycroft All SS 84-91; Chapl St Kath Coll 91-96; Dioc RE Field Officer 91-96; Dioc Dir of Educn *Leic* from 96; Hon Can Leic Cathl from 98. *87 Main Street, Humberstone, Leicester LE5 1AE* Tel 0116-248 7450 Fax 251 1638 E-mail ptaylor@chouse.leicester.anglican.org

TAYLOR, The Ven Peter Flint. b 44. Qu Coll Cam BA65 MA69. Lon Coll of Div BD70. **d** 70 **p** 71. C Highbury New Park St Aug *Lon* 70-73; C Plymouth St Andr w St Paul and St Geo *Ex* 73-77; V Ironville *Derby* 77-83; P-in-c Riddings 82-83; R Rayleigh *Chelmsf* 83-96; Chapl HM YOI Bullwood Hall 85-90; RD Rochford *Chelmsf* 89-96; Adn Harlow from 96. *Glebe House, Church Lane, Sheering, Bishop's Stortford CM22 7NR* Tel (01279) 734524 Fax 734426
E-mail a.harlow@chelmsford.anglican.org

TAYLOR, Peter Graham. b 45. Liv Univ 86 TCert69 CQSW69. Local Minl Tr Course 91. **d** 94 **p** 95. NSM Holywell *St As* 94-97; C Llanrhos 97-02; rtd 02. *23 Merllyn Road, Rhyl LL18 4HG* Tel (01745) 336953 E-mail perunow@global.co.uk

TAYLOR, Peter John. b 40. Oak Hill Th Coll 62. **d** 65 **p** 66. C St Paul's Cray St Barn *Roch* 65-69; C Woking St Jo *Guildf* 69-77; R Necton w Holme Hale *Nor* 77-94; P-in-c N Pickenham w S Pickenham etc 94; R Necton, Holme Hale w N and S Pickenham from 95; RD Breckland 86-94; Hon Can Nor Cathl 98-03. *The Rectory, School Road, Necton, Swaffham PE37 8HT* Tel (01760) 722021

TAYLOR, Peter John. b 46. Tyndale Hall Bris 70. **d** 73 **p** 74. C Walshaw Ch Ch *Man* 73-75; C Rodbourne Cheney *Bris* 75-78; Asst Chapl HM Pris Pentonville 78-79; Chapl HM Borstal Roch 79-84; Chapl HM Pris Highpoint 84-90; Asst Chapl Gen of Pris from 90. *HM Prison Service Chaplaincy, PO Box 349, Stafford ST16 3DL* Tel (01785) 213456 Fax 227734

TAYLOR, Peter John. b 60. New Coll Edin LTh87. Edin Th Coll 83. **d** 87 **p** 88. C Edin SS Phil and Jas *Edin* 87-90; USA 90-92; R Glas St Oswald *Glas* 92-97; R Kirkcudbright from 97; R Gatehouse of Fleet from 97. *9 St Mary's Street, Kirkcudbright DG6 4AA* Tel (01557) 330146 Fax as telephone
E-mail ptkbt@aol.com

TAYLOR, Peter Joseph. b 41. Bps' Coll Cheshunt 66. **d** 68 **p** 69. C Wollaton *S'well* 68-71; C Cockington *Ex* 71-74; V Broadhembury 74-79; V Broadhembury w Payhembury 79-81; V Gt Staughton *Ely* 81-86; Chapl HM YOI Gaynes Hall 81-91; R Offord D'Arcy w Offord Cluny *Ely* 86-01; V Gt Paxton 86-01; rtd 01; Perm to Offic *Ely* from 01. *9 Park Way, Offord Cluny, St Neots PE18 9RW* Tel (01480) 811662

TAYLOR, Mrs Rachel Sara. b 60. Univ Coll Lon BA81. SEITE 01. **d** 01 **p** 02. C Wimbledon *S'wark* from 01. *40 Queens Road, Richmond TW10 6JF* Tel (020) 8286 6492

TAYLOR (or URMSON-TAYLOR), Ralph Urmson. Tulsa Univ MA72 Man Coll of Educn DipEd74 TCert82. Kelham Th Coll DipTh56. **d** 56 **p** 57. C Redcar *York* 57-59; C Bridlington Quay H Trin 59-62; C Sewerby w Marton 60-62; USA 62-02; Asst P Tulsa H Trin 62-65; Sacr 93-02; Chapl Holland Hall Sch 65-93; rtd 93. *Via Montecavallo 18, PG 06081 Assisi, Italy*

TAYLOR, Raymond. b 34. Lon Coll of Div 62. **d** 65 **p** 66. C Pennington *Man* 65-70; P-in-c Wombridge *Lich* 70-80; R S Normanton *Derby* 80-88; RD Alfreton 86-88; V Youlgreave, Middleton, Stanton-in-Peak etc 88-98; rtd 99; Perm to Offic *Derby* from 98. *4 Jeffries Avenue, Crich, Matlock DE4 5DU*

TAYLOR, Raymond Montgomery. b 43. Oak Hill Th Coll 77. **d** 80 **p** 81. Hon C Cricklewood St Pet *Lon* 80-85; Hon C Golders Green 85-87; V New Southgate St Paul 87-00; AD Cen Barnet 96-00; V Thaxted *Chelmsf* from 00. *The Vicarage, Watling Lane, Thaxted,*

Dunmow CM6 2QY Tel (01371) 830221 Fax as telephone
E-mail furor@scribendi.freeserve.co.uk

TAYLOR, Richard David. b 44. Worc Coll Ox BA67 MA70. Coll
of Resurr Mirfield 67. **d** 69 **p** 70. C Barrow St Geo w St Luke *Carl*
69-73; C Gosforth All SS *Newc* 73-80; TR Newc Epiphany 80-83;
V Tynemouth Priory 83-91; TR Benwell Team 91-98; P-in-c
Blyth St Cuth 98-01; V from 01. *The Vicarage, 29 Ridley Avenue,
Blyth NE24 3BA* Tel (01670) 352410
E-mail taylor@rev.taylor.totalserve.co.uk

TAYLOR, Richard Godfrey. b 73. Pemb Coll Cam MA99. Oak
Hill Th Coll BA00. **d** 00 **p** 01. C Brunswick *Man* from 00.
16 Condor Walk, Manchester M13 9RQ
E-mail fatboytaylor@hotmail.com

TAYLOR, Preb Richard John. b 21. Kelham Th Coll 38. **d** 45 **p** 46.
C Tunstall Ch Ch *Lich* 45-48; C Uttoxeter w Bramshall 48-52; V
Croxden 52-57; V Willenhall H Trin 57-68; R Edgmond 68-77;
Streetly 77-87; Preb Lich Cathl 78-87; rtd 87; Perm to Offic *Lich*
from 87. *15 Covey Close, Lichfield WS13 6BS* Tel (01543) 268558

TAYLOR, Richard John. b 46. Ripon Coll Cuddesdon 85. **d** 85
p 86. C Moseley St Mary *Birm* 85-87; V Kingsbury 87-91; TR
Hodge Hill from 91. *The Rectory, Hodge Hill Common,
Birmingham B36 8AG* Tel 0121-747 2094 *or* 747 9262

TAYLOR, Robert Stirling. b 62. Ball Coll Ox BA83 Leeds Univ
PhD88 Nottm Trent Univ PGCE93. Cranmer Hall Dur 00. **d** 02
p 03. C Mansfield St Jo *S'well* from 02. *8 Castle Street, Mansfield
NG18 5PP* Tel (01623) 620780

TAYLOR, Robin. *See* TAYLOR, Joseph Robin Christopher

TAYLOR, Roger. b 21. Birkbeck Coll Lon BA50 Leeds Univ
MA59 Essex Univ MPhil96. Oak Hill Th Coll 47. **d** 51 **p** 52. C
Chadderton Ch Ch *Man* 51-55; V Bowling St Steph *Bradf* 55-63;
SW Area Sec CPAS 63-68; V Felixstowe SS Pet and Paul *St E*
68-81; P-in-c Gt and Lt Thurlow w Lt Bradley 81-82; TV
Haverhill w Withersfield, the Wrattings etc 82-84; R Hopton,
Market Weston, Barningham etc 84-86; rtd 86; Perm to Offic
St E from 87. *Chapel House, Lindsey, Ipswich IP7 6QA* Tel
(01787) 211120

TAYLOR, Roger James Benedict. b 42. Glouc Sch of Min 89
WMMTC 95. **d** 96 **p** 97. OLM Cromhall w Tortworth and
Tytherington *Glouc* 96-99; P-in-c Wistanstow *Heref* 99-01; Min
Can Brecon Cathl *S & B* from 01. *The Almonry, Cathedral Close,
Brecon LD3 9DP* Tel (01874) 622972

TAYLOR, Canon Roland Haydn. b 29. St Chad's Coll Dur BA53
DipTh55. **d** 55 **p** 56. C N Gosforth *Newc* 55-58; C Barnsley
St Mary *Wakef* 58-61; V Brotherton 61-68; V Purston cum S
Featherstone 68-76; RD Pontefract 74-94; R Badsworth 76-97;
Hon Can Wakef Cathl 81-97; rtd 97. *57 Fairview, Carleton,
Pontefract WF8 3NU* Tel (01977) 796564

TAYLOR, Roy. b 63. Ex Coll Ox BA86 Ox Univ MA89 York Univ
PGCE87 Univ of Wales (Cardiff) BD97. St Mich Coll Llan 95.
d 97 **p** 98. C Guisborough *York* 97-99; Chapl Rossall Sch
Fleetwood 99-02; V Dolphinholme w Quernmore and Over
Wyresdale *Blackb* from 02. *The Vicarage, Dolphinholme,
Lancaster LA2 9AH* Tel (01524) 791300

TAYLOR, Roy Partington. b 33. Birm Univ BA54 PGCE55
MPhil87. St Alb and Ox Min Course 96. **d** 98 **p** 99. NSM Hurley
and Stubbings *Ox* 98-02; NSM Burchetts Green 02-03; Perm to
Offic from 03; rtd 03. *16 Highfield Road, Maidenhead SL6 5DF*
Tel (01628) 675220

TAYLOR, Roy William. b 37. Ch Coll Cam BA61 MA64. Clifton
Th Coll 61. **d** 63 **p** 64. C Blackb Sav *Blackb* 63-66; C
Hensingham *Carl* 66-68; CMS Taiwan 69-79; TV Bushbury *Lich*
79-85; OMF 85-93; Hon C Wolverhampton St Jude *Lich* 93-94;
P-in-c Torquay St Jo and Ellacombe *Ex* 94-99; R Instow and V
Westleigh 99-03; RD Hartland 01-03; rtd 03. *31 Shore Road,
Millisle, Newtownards BT22 2BT* Tel (028) 9186 2769

TAYLOR, Simon Dominic Kent. b 69. Surrey Univ BSc90
PGCE91 Sussex Univ MA(Ed)99 Birm Univ BA01. **d** 01 **p** 02. C
Southgate *Chich* from 01. *54 Dovedale Crescent, Crawley
RH11 8SG* Tel (01293) 552287

TAYLOR, Simon John. b 72. Worc Coll Ox BA94 MPhil96 MA99
DPhil00. St Mich Coll Llan 00 Ven English Coll Rome 01. **d** 02
p 03. C Cotham St Sav w St Mary and Clifton St Paul *Bris* from
02. *182 St Michael's Hill, Bristol BS2 8DE* Tel 0117-377 9591
E-mail taylor@fish.co.uk

TAYLOR, Mrs Stella Isabelle. b 31. S Dios Minl Tr Scheme 86.
d 89 **p** 94. NSM Haworth *Bradf* 89-91; Par Dn Keighley St Andr
92-94; C 94-96; rtd 97; Perm to Offic *Bradf* 97-00. *8 The Linkway,
Westham, Pevensey BN24 5JB*

TAYLOR, Stephen. b 65. City Univ BSc87 Lon Univ PGCE90.
NTMTC 95. **d** 98 **p** 99. NSM Enfield Chase St Mary *Lon* 98-02;
Perm to Offic *Eur* 02-03; C Hornsey St Mary w St Geo Lon from
03; Chapl Bp Stopford's Sch Enfield 98-02 and from 03. *145A
North View Road, London N8 7ND, or Bishop Stopford's School,
Brick Lane, Enfield EN1 3PU* Tel 07711-559107 (mobile)
E-mail revtaylor@wanadoo.fr

TAYLOR, Stephen Gordon. b 35. Bris Univ BA60. Ridley Hall
Cam 60. **d** 62 **p** 63. C Gt Baddow *Chelmsf* 62-65; C Portsdown
Portsm 65-69; P-in-c Elvedon *St E* 69-70; R 70-75; P-in-c
Eriswell 69-70; R 70-75; P-in-c Icklingham 69-70; R 70-75; Chapl

St Felix Sch Southwold 75-77; R Lt Shelford w Newton *Ely*
77-96; rtd 96; Perm to Offic *Ely* from 96. *15 Church Close,
Whittlesford, Cambridge CB2 4NY* Tel (01223) 830461

TAYLOR, Stephen James. b 48. Chich Th Coll 70. **d** 73 **p** 74. C
Tottenham St Paul *Lon* 73-76; St Vincent 78-85; Grenada 85-88;
C-in-c Hammersmith SS Mich and Geo White City Estate CD
Lon 88-96; AD Hammersmith 92-96; P-in-c Hammersmith
St Luke 94-96; USPG Brazil from 96. *Avenue Rio Branco
277/907, Cinelandia, 20047-900, Rio de Janeiro, RJ, Brazil*

TAYLOR, Canon Stephen Ronald. b 55. Dur Univ MA99.
Cranmer Hall Dur 80. **d** 83 **p** 84. C Chester le Street *Dur* 83-87; V
Newbottle 87-92; V Stranton 92-00; TR Sunderland from 00;
Hon Can Rift Valley Tanzania from 00. *6 Thornhill Terrace,
Sunderland SR2 7JL* Tel 0191-514 0447 *or* 565 4066
E-mail stephen.taylor@durham.anglican.org

TAYLOR, Stewart. b 51. St Jo Coll Dur 74. **d** 77 **p** 78. C Norwood
St Luke *S'wark* 77-81; C Surbiton Hill Ch Ch 81-91; V
Cambridge St Phil *Ely* from 91. *St Philip's Vicarage, 252 Mill
Road, Cambridge CB1 3NF* Tel (01223) 247652 *or* 414775

TAYLOR, Stuart Bryan. b 40. St Chad's Coll Dur BA64 DipTh66.
d 66 **p** 67. C Portsea N End St Mark *Portsm* 66-70; C Epsom
St Martin *Guildf* 70-76; Chapl Clifton Coll Bris 76-88; Dir
Bloxham Project 88-93; Chapl Giggleswick Sch 93-95; Bp's
Officer for Miss and Evang *Bris* 96-01; Bp's Adv for Past Care
for Clergy and Families from 01; Hon Min Can Bris Cathl from
02; Chapl Bris Cathl Sch from 01. *62 Providence Lane, Long
Ashton, Bristol BS41 9DN* Tel (01275) 393625

TAYLOR, Mrs Teresa Mary. b 53. SRN76 SCM78 HVCert80.
WEMTC 98. **d** 02 **p** 03. NSM Kingswood *Bris* from 02.
15 Hampton Street, Bristol BS15 1TP Tel 0117-373 2410
E-mail testaylor@blueyonder.co.uk

TAYLOR, Thomas. b 33. Sarum & Wells Th Coll 77. **d** 80 **p** 81.
NSM Heatherlands St Jo *Sarum* 80-82; TV Kinson 82-88; TV
Shaston 88-98; Chapl Westmr Memorial Hosp Shaftesbury
88-98; rtd 98; Perm to Offic *Sarum* from 98. *10 Hanover Lane,
Gillingham SP3 4TA* Tel (01747) 826569

TAYLOR, Thomas. b 42. St Jo Coll Dur BA64. Linc Th Coll 64.
d 66 **p** 67. C Clitheroe St Mary *Blackb* 66-69; C Skerton St Luke
69-71; C-in-c Penwortham St Leon CD 71-72; V Penwortham
St Leon 72-78; R Poulton-le-Sands 78-81; P-in-c Morecambe
St Lawr 78-81; R Poulton-le-Sands w Morecambe St Laur 81-85;
Chapl Ld Wandsworth Coll Hants 85-92; V Walton-le-Dale
Blackb 92-94; P-in-c Samlesbury 92-94; V Walton-le-Dale
St Leon w Samlesbury St Leon 95-96; RD Leyland 94-96; Hon C
Tarleton from 03. *52 Hesketh Lane, Tarleton, Preston PR4 6AQ*
Tel (01772) 813871

TAYLOR, Thomas Fish. b 13. Glas Univ MA46. Kelham Th Coll
30. **d** 36 **p** 37. C Millfield St Mary *Dur* 36-38; C Middlesbrough
All SS *York* 38-41; R Glas St Martin *Glas* 41-48; Chapl Priory of
Our Lady Burford 48-50; Lic to Offic *Roch* 50-52; Chapl Mount
Ephraim Distr Hosp Tunbridge Wells 50-52; V Chalford *Glouc*
52-58; R Over w Nether Compton and Trent *Sarum* 58-65; P-in-c
Poughill w Stockleigh English *Ex* 67-69; P-in-c Rattery 69-79; rtd
79; Perm to Offic *Ex* 79-92 and *Sarum* from 88. *Digby House,
40 Avenue Road, Wimborne BH21 1BT*

TAYLOR, Thomas Ronald Bennett. b 23. TCD BA46 MA54.
Div Test. **d** 47 **p** 48. C Larne and Inver *Conn* 47-49; Chapl RAF
49-65; I Narraghmore w Fontstown and Timolin *D & G* 65-68; I
Tynan w Middletown *Arm* 68-85; rtd 85. *34 Kernan Park,
Portadown BT63 5QY* Tel (028) 3833 7230

TAYLOR, Willam Goodacre Campbell. *See* CAMPBELL-
TAYLOR, William Goodacre

TAYLOR, William Austin. b 36. Linc Th Coll 65. **d** 67 **p** 68. C
Tyldesley w Shakerley *Man* 67-71; R Cheetham St Mark 71-79;
TR Peel 79-90; AD Farnworth 83-90; V Pelton *Dur* 90-96; rtd 96;
Perm to Offic *Man* from 96. *36 Tynesbank, Worsley, Manchester
M28 8SL* Tel 0161-790 5327

TAYLOR, William Henry. b 56. Kent Univ BA79 Lon Univ
MTh81 Lanc Univ MPhil87 FRAS80. Westcott Ho Cam. **d** 83
p 84. C Maidstone All SS and St Phil w Tovil *Cant* 83-86; Abp's
Adv on Orthodox Affairs 86-88; C St Marylebone All SS *Lon*
86-88; Chapl Guy's Hosp Lon 88; CMS Jordan 88-91; V Ealing
St Pet Mt Park Lon 91-00; AD Ealing 93-98; Dean Portsm 00-02;
P-in-c Notting Hill St Jo and St Pet *Lon* 02; V Notting Hill St Jo
from 03. *St John's Vicarage, 25 Ladbroke Road, London W11 3PD*
Tel (020) 7727 3439 *or* 7727 4262
E-mail vicar@stjohnsnottinghill.com

TAYLOR, William Richard de Carteret Martin. b 33. CCC Cam
MA57. Westcott Ho Cam 58. **d** 59 **p** 60. C Eastney *Portsm* 59-63;
Chapl RN 63-67 and 70-87; V Childe Okeford *Sarum* 67-70; V
Manston w Hamoon 67-70; Chapl from 83; TR Tisbury *Sarum*
87-89; Chapl Hatf Poly *St Alb* 89-92; Chapl Herts Univ 92-98;
rtd 98; Perm to Offic *Ely* from 00. *Lark Rise, 47A New Street,
St Neots, Huntingdon PE19 1AJ* Tel (01480) 475598

TAYLOR, Capt William Thomas. b 61. Rob Coll Cam BA83
BA90. Ridley Hall Cam 88. **d** 91 **p** 92. C Bromley Ch Ch *Roch*
91-95; C St Helen Bishopsgate w St Andr Undershaft etc *Lon*
95-98; V 98-02; R St Pet Cornhill from 01. *The Old Rectory,
Merrick Square, London SE1 4JB* Tel (020) 7378 8186

TEAGUE, Gaythorne Derrick. b 24. Bris Univ MB, ChB49 MRCGP53 DPH. **d** 74 **p** 75. NSM Bris St Andr Hartcliffe *Bris* 74-86; Perm to Offic *B & W* from 86. *Innisfree, Bell Square, Blagdon, Bristol BS40 7UB* Tel (01761) 462671

TEAGUE, Robert Hayden. b 15. Univ of Wales (Ban). Dorchester Miss Coll 36 St Deiniol's Hawarden. **d** 63 **p** 64. C Rhosddu *St As* 63-65; C Llanrhos 65-66; V Llangernyw, Gwytherin and Llanddewi 66-77; V Meliden and Gwaenysgor 77-83; rtd 83. *4 Ffordd Tanrallt, Melidan, Prestatyn LL19 8PR* Tel (01745) 857419

TEALE, Adrian. b 53. Univ of Wales (Abth) BA74 CertEd77 MA80 Univ of Wales (Cardiff) MTh89. Wycliffe Hall Ox 78. **d** 80 **p** 81. C Betws w Ammanford *St D* 80-84; V Brynaman w Cwmllynfell 84-01; RD Dyffryn Aman 95-01; V Betws w Ammanford from 01. *The Vicarage, College Street, Ammanford SA18 3AB* Tel (01269) 592084

TEAR, Jeremy Charles. b 67. Westmr Coll Ox BA89 Birm Univ MA99 N Lon Poly 90 GradIPM90 MIPD94. Aston Tr Scheme 95 Qu Coll Birm 97. **d** 99 **p** 00. C Timperley *Ches* 99-03; V Macclesfield St Paul from 03. *St Paul's Vicarage, Swallow Close, Macclesfield SK10 1QN* Tel (01625) 422910
E-mail revjtear@fish.co.uk

TEARE, Mrs Marie. b 46. Open Univ BA81 RSCN67. N Ord Course 95. **d** 98 **p** 99. C Brighouse and Clifton *Wakef* 98-01; V Waggoners *York* from 01; RD Harthill from 02. *The Vicarage, Pulham Lane, Wetwang, Driffield YO25 9XT* Tel (01377) 236410
E-mail marie.teare@lineone.net

TEARE, Canon Robert John Hugh. b 39. Bris Univ BSc62 Leeds Univ DipTh69. Coll of Resurr Mirfield 67. **d** 70 **p** 71. C Fareham SS Pet and Paul *Portsm* 70-73; Chapl K Alfred Coll *Win* 73-78; V Pokesdown St Jas 78-82; R Winnall from 82; RD Win 89-99; Hon Can Win Cathl from 92. *The Rectory, 22 St John's Street, Winchester SO23 0HF* Tel (01962) 863891
E-mail rjh.teare@btinternet.com

TEARNAN, John Herman Janson. b 37. Bris Univ BSc59. Kelham Th Coll 62. **d** 66 **p** 67. C Kettering SS Pet and Paul *Pet* 66-71; Lic to Offic 71-85; Perm to Offic *St Alb* 82-85; *Pet* 85-94; Chapl HM YOI Wellingborough 89-90; Chapl HM YOI Glen Parva 90-94; Guyana 94-03; rtd 03. *19 Rectory Walk, Barton Seagrave, Kettering NN15 6SP* Tel (01536) 514349

TEASDALE, Keith. b 56. Cranmer Hall Dur 86. **d** 88 **p** 89. C Crook *Dur* 88-92; V Dunston from 92; AD Gateshead W from 00. *St Nicholas' Vicarage, Willow Avenue, Dunston, Gateshead NE11 9UN* Tel 0191-460 0509 *or* fax and tel 460 9327 Mobile 07718-907660 E-mail stn@ukonline.co.uk

TEBBS, Richard Henry. b 52. Southn Univ BTh. Sarum & Wells Th Coll 75. **d** 78 **p** 79. C Cinderhill *S'well* 78-82; C Nor St Pet Mancroft *Nor* 82; C Nor St Pet Mancroft w St Jo Maddermarket 82-85; TV Bridport *Sarum* 85-94; TR Yelverton, Meavy, Sheepstor and Walkhampton *Ex* from 94. *The Rectory, St Paul's Church, Yelverton PL20 6AB* Tel (01822) 852362
E-mail tebbsfamily@rtebbs.fsnet.co.uk

TEBBUTT, Christopher Michael. b 55. St Jo Coll Nottm BA94. **d** 96 **p** 97. C Catherington and Clanfield *Portsm* 96-00; P-in-c Southbroom *Sarum* from 00. *Southbroom Vicarage, London Road, Devizes SN10 1LT* Tel (01380) 723891

TEBBUTT, Sandra Eileen. b 56. FBDO78. STETS 96. **d** 99 **p** 00. NSM Blendworth w Chalton w Idsworth *Portsm* 99-00; Chapl Wilts and Swindon Healthcare NHS Trust from 00; Lic to Offic *Sarum* from 00. *Southbroom Vicarage, London Road, Devizes SN10 1LT* Tel (01380) 723891

TEBBUTT, Simon Albert. b 27. Qu Coll Birm 88. **d** 89 **p** 90. NSM Northampton St Matt *Pet* 89-92; TV Duston Team 92-94; rtd 94; NSM Gt and Lt Houghton w Brafield on the Green *Pet* 94-96; NSM Cogenhoe and Gt and Lt Houghton w Brafield 96-97; Dioc Sec St Luke's Hosp for the Clergy from 00; Perm to Offic from 01. *Tanners, Moulton Lane, Boughton, Northampton NN2 8RF* Tel (01604) 843240

TEDD, Christopher Jonathan Richard. *See* HOWITZ, Christopher Jonathan Richard.

TEDMAN, Alfred. b 33. AKC59. **d** 60 **p** 61. C Newington St Mary *S'wark* 60-64; C Milton *Portsm* 64-68; R Bonchurch 68-98; RD E Wight 78-83; P-in-c Whitwell 79-82; P-in-c St Lawrence 82-84; V Wroxall 84-98; rtd 98. *Winfrith House, Blackgang Road, Niton, Ventnor PO38 2BW*

TEE, John. b 59. **d** 82 **p** 83. C Walworth *S'wark* 82-85; Chapl RAF 85-89; CF 89-03. *Address temp unknown*

TEGALLY, Narinder Jit Kaur. b 57. RGN93. St Alb and Ox Min Course 99. **d** 02. NSM Welwyn Garden City *St Alb* from 02. *31 Harvey Road, London Colney, St Albans AL2 1NA* Tel (01727) 769762

TEGGARTY, Samuel James Karl. b 53. Dundee Univ BSc77. CITC 98. **d** 01 **p** 02. NSM Newry *D & D* 01-03; NSM Kilkeel from 03. *79 Knockchree Avenue, Kilkeel, Newry BT34 4BP* Tel (028) 4176 9076 E-mail karl@teggarty.fsnet.co.uk

TEGGIN, John. b 26. **d** 83 **p** 84. NSM Dublin Sandford w Milltown *D & G* 84-93; Dir Leprosy Miss 86-96. *4 Temple Hill, Blackrock, Co Dublin, Irish Republic* Tel (00353) (1) 280 4008

TELFER, Andrew Julian. b 68. Essex Univ BA94. Wycliffe Hall Ox BTh97. **d** 97 **p** 98. C Skelmersdale St Paul *Liv* 97-01; C Ashton-in-Makerfield St Thos 01-03; V Whiston from 03. *The Vicarage, 90 Windy Arbor Road, Prescot L35 3SG* Tel 0151-426 6329

TELFER, Canon Frank Somerville. b 30. Trin Hall Cam BA53 MA58. Ely Th Coll 53. **d** 55 **p** 56. C Liv Our Lady and St Nic *Liv* 55-58; Chapl Down Coll Cam 58-62; Bp's Chapl *Nor* 62-65; Chapl Kent Univ *Cant* 65-73; Can Res Guildf Cathl *Guildf* 73-95; rtd 96; Perm to Offic *Nor* from 96. *Holbrook, Glandford, Holt NR25 7JP* Tel (01263) 740586

TELFORD, Alan. b 46. St Jo Coll Nottm. **d** 83 **p** 84. C Normanton *Derby* 83-86; TV N Wingfield, Pilsley and Tupton 86-90; TV N Wingfield, Clay Cross and Pilsley 90-92; P-in-c Oakwood 92-94; V Leic St Chris *Leic* from 94. *The Vicarage, 84A Marriott Road, Leicester LE2 6NT* Tel 0116-283 2679
E-mail alan@saffron84a.freeserve.co.uk

TELFORD, Richard Francis. b 46. K Coll Lon 65. **d** 69 **p** 70. C Barkingside H Trin *Chelmsf* 69-72; C Wickford 72-77; P-in-c Romford St Jo 77-80; V 80-82; Perm to Offic 93-96. *59 Hartswood Road, Brentwood CM14 5AG* Tel (01277) 214911

TELLINI, Canon Gianfranco. b 36. Gregorian Univ Rome DTh65. Franciscan Sem Trent 57. **d** 61 **p** 61. In RC Ch 61-66; C Mill Hill Jo Keble Ch *Lon* 66; C Roxbourne St Andr 66-67; Lect Sarum Th Coll 67-69; Sen Tutor 72-74; Vice-Prin Edin Th Coll 74-82; Lect Th Edin Univ from 74; R Pittenweem *St And* 82-85; R Elie and Earlsferry 82-85; R Dunblane 85-98; Can St Ninian's Cathl Perth from 90; rtd 99. *53 Buchan Drive, Dunblane FK15 9HW* Tel (01786) 823281 E-mail g.tellini@virgin.net

TEMBEY, David. b 51. **d** 96 **p** 97. NSM Whitehaven *Carl* 96-00; NSM Holme Cultram St Cuth 00-02; NSM Holme Cultram St Mary 00-02; NSM Bromfield w Waverton 00-02; TV Solway Plain from 02. *The Vicarage, Abbeytown, Wigton CA7 4SP* Tel (01697) 361246 E-mail tembey6@aol.com

TEMPERLEY, Robert Noble. b 29. JP. St Jo Coll York CertEd50 ACP52 Dur Univ DAES62. NEOC 85. **d** 88 **p** 88. NSM Ryhope *Dur* 88-97; rtd 98; Perm to Offic *Dur* from 98. *18 Withernsea Grove, Ryhope, Sunderland SR2 0BU* Tel 0191-521 1813

TEMPLE, Mrs Sylvia Mary. b 48. Ex Univ BA70 Univ of Wales (Abth) PGCE71. St D Dioc Tr Course 93. **d** 94 **p** 97. NSM Tenby *St D* 94-99; C 99-00; V Martletwy w Lawrenny and Minwear etc from 00. *St John's Rectory, Church Street, Templeton, Narberth SA67 8XX* Tel (01834) 861412

TEMPLEMAN, Peter Morton. b 49. Ch Ch Ox BA71 MA75 BTh75. Wycliffe Hall Ox 73. **d** 76 **p** 77. C Cheltenham St Mary, St Matt, St Paul and H Trin *Glouc* 76-79; Chapl St Jo Coll Cam 79-84; P-in-c Finchley St Paul Long Lane *Lon* 84-85; P-in-c Finchley St Luke 84-85; V Finchley St Paul and St Luke 85-99; V Peterlee *Dur* from 99. *The Vicarage, Manor Way, Peterlee SR8 5QW* Tel 0191-586 2630

TEMPLETON, Iain McAllister. b 57. HNC86. St Andr Coll Drygrange 80. **d** 85 **p** 86. In RC Ch 85-92; NSM Dornoch *Mor* 95; P-in-c Kirriemuir *St And* 95-99; R Eccleston *Blackb* from 99. *The Rectory, New Lane, Eccleston, Chorley PR7 6NA* Tel (01257) 451206 Fax as telephone E-mail fatheriain@aol.com *or* fatheriain@priest.com

TEN WOLDE, Christine Caroline. b 57. **d** 99 **p** 00. NSM Llanegryn w Aberdyfi w Tywyn *Ban* from 99. *Aber-groes, Abertafol, Aberdovey LL35 0RE* Tel (01654) 767047 Mobile 07977-108438 Fax 767572
E-mail admin@stpeterschurch.org.uk

TENNANT, Cyril Edwin George. b 37. Keble Coll Ox BA59 MA63 Lon Univ BD61. Clifton Th Coll 59. **d** 62 **p** 63. C Stapleford *S'well* 62-65; C Felixstowe SS Pet and Paul *St E* 65-69; V Gipsy Hill Ch Ch *S'wark* 69-84; V Lee St Mildred 84-90; V Ilfracombe SS Phil and Jas w W Down *Ex* 90-01; P-in-c Lundy Is 90-92; rtd 01. *23 Broadgate, Pilton, Barnstaple EX31 4AL* Tel (01271) 323517

TENNANT, Osmond Roy. b 21. Worc Ord Coll 62. **d** 63 **p** 64. C S Molton w Nymet St George *Ex* 63-67; V Escot 67-89; R Talaton 67-89; P-in-c Clyst Hydon and Clyst St Lawrence 74-87; rtd 89; Perm to Offic *Ex* from 89. *Rockleigh, 29 West Clyst, Exeter EX1 3TL* Tel (01392) 465515

TER BLANCHE, Harold Daniel. b 35. St Paul's Coll Grahamstown LTh85. **d** 63 **p** 64. S Africa 63-82; Chapl Miss to Seamen 82-84; Chapl Grimsby Distr Gen Hosp 84-94; Chapl NE Lincs NHS Trust 94-00; rtd 00; Perm to Offic *Linc* from 00. *25 Collingwood Crescent, Grimsby DN34 5RG* Tel (01472) 276624 Fax 313995

TERESA, Sister. *See* WHITE, Sister Teresa Joan

✠**TEROM, The Rt Revd Zechariah James.** b 41. St Columba's Coll Hazaribagh BA64 Ranchi Univ MA66. Bp's Coll Calcutta BD71. **d** 71 **c** 86. India from 71; C Hazaribagh 71-73; Par P Manoharpur 73-76; Bp Chotanagpur from 86; Moderator Ch of N India from 01. *Bishop's Lodge, PO Box 1, Church Road, Ranchi 834 001, Bihar, India* Tel (0091) (651) 311181 Fax 311184 *or* 314184

TERRANOVA, Jonathan Rossano (Ross). b 62. Sheff Poly BA85. Oak Hill Th Coll BA88. **d** 88 **p** 89. C Carl St Jo *Carl* 88-91; C

Stoughton *Guildf* 91-94; R Ditton *Roch* from 94; RD Malling from 02. *The Rectory, 2 The Stream, Ditton, Maidstone ME20 6AG* Tel (01732) 842027

TERRELL, Richard Charles Patridge. b 43. Wells Th Coll 69. **d** 71 **p** 72. C Shepton Mallet *B & W* 71-76; P-in-c Drayton 76-78; P-in-c Muchelney 76-78; TV Langport Area Chs 78-82; P-in-c Tatworth 82-89; V 89-96; R W Coker w Hardington Mandeville, E Chinnock etc from 96. *The Rectory, 7 Cedar Fields, West Coker, Yeovil BA22 9DB* Tel (01935) 862328

TERRETT, Mervyn Douglas. b 43. AKC65. **d** 66 **p** 67. C Pet St Mary Boongate *Pet* 66-69; C Sawbridgeworth *St Alb* 69-74; V Stevenage H Trin 74-85; Perm to Offic from 86. *Red Roofs, 20 Woodfield Road, Stevenage SG1 4BP* Tel (01438) 720152

TERRY, Christopher Laurence. b 51. FCA80. St Alb Minl Tr Scheme. **d** 83 **p** 84. Hon C Dunstable *St Alb* 83-89; C Abbots Langley 89-92; TV Chambersbury 92-99; Chapl Abbot's Hill Sch Herts 96-99; R Southwick St Mich *Chich* from 99; RD Hove from 00. *The Rectory, 22 Church Lane, Southwick, Brighton BN42 4GB* Tel (01273) 592389 E-mail tecrry@aol.com

TERRY, Colin Alfred. b 49. Trin Coll Bris. **d** 00 **p** 01. C Bexleyheath Ch Ch *Roch* 00-03; V Belvedere All SS from 03. *All Saints' Vicarage, Nuxley Road, Belvedere DA17 5JE* Tel (01322) 432169 E-mail colin@terry22.freeserve.co.uk

TERRY, Ms Helen Barbara. b 58. Keele Univ BA80 ATCL98. Ripon Coll Cuddesdon 01. **d** 03. C Cainscross w Selsley *Glouc* from 03. *48 Cashes Green Road, Cainscross, Stroud GL5 4LN* Tel (01453) 752792

TERRY, Ian Andrew. b 53. St Jo Coll Dur BA74 St Jo Coll York PGCE75 St Mary's Coll Twickenham MA99. Coll of Resurr Mirfield 78. **d** 80 **p** 81. C Beaconsfield *Ox* 80-83; C N Lynn w St Marg and St Nic *Nor* 83-84; Chapl and Hd RE Eliz Coll Guernsey 84-89; Chapl St Jo Sch Leatherhead 89-92; R Bisley and W End *Guildf* 92-02; Asst Chapl HM Pris Coldingley 99-02; Dioc Dir of Educn *Heref* from 02. *The Vicarage, Breinton, Hereford HR4 7PG* Tel (01432) 273447 *or* 357864
E-mail iaterry@attglobal.net
or education@diooffice.freeserve.co.uk

TERRY, James Richard. b 74. Linc Coll Ox BA95 ACA98. Oak Hill Th Coll BA03. **d** 03. C Harold Wood *Chelmsf* from 03. *48 Harold Court Road, Harold Wood, Romford RM3 0YX* Tel (01708) 344127 E-mail james_terry1@hotmail.com

TERRY, John Arthur. b 32. S'wark Ord Course. **d** 66 **p** 67. C Plumstead All SS *S'wark* 66-69; C Peckham St Mary Magd 69-72; V Streatham Vale H Redeemer 72-80; R Sternfield w Benhall and Snape *St E* 80-84; V Stevenage St Mary Shephall *St Alb* 84-86; V Stevenage St Mary Sheppall w Aston 86-90; V Cople w Willington 90-97; Chapl Shuttleworth Agric Coll 90-97; rtd 97; Perm to Offic *Nor* from 98. *2 Kestrel Drive, Brandon IP27 0UA* Tel (01842) 812055

TERRY, Justyn Charles. b 65. Keble Coll Ox BA86 St Jo Coll Dur BA95. Cranmer Hall Dur 92. **d** 95 **p** 96. C Paddington St Jo w St Mich *Lon* 95-99; V Kensington St Helen w H Trin from 99. *St Helen's Vicarage, St Helen's Gardens, London W10 6LP* Tel (020) 8968 7807 Fax 8969 5782
E-mail justyn.terry@london.anglican.org

TERRY, Stephen John. b 49. K Coll Lon BD72 AKC74. **d** 75 **p** 76. C Tokyngton St Mich *Lon* 75-78; C Hampstead St Steph w All Hallows 78-81; V Whetstone St Jo 81-89; TR Aldrington *Chich* from 89; OStJ from 89. *The Rectory, 77 New Church Road, Hove BN3 4BB* Tel (01273) 737915

TESTA, Luigi Richard Frederick. b 30. Nottm Univ Cert Th & Past Studies 85. **d** 85 **p** 86. NSM Castle Donington and Lockington cum Hemington *Leic* 85-95; Perm to Offic from 95. *40 Hillside, Castle Donington, Derby DE74 2NH* Tel (01332) 810823

TESTER, Clarence Albert. b 20. Qu Coll Birm 47. **d** 50 **p** 51. C Southmead *Bris* 50-53; C Knowle St Barn 53-55; Chapl Ham Green Hosp Bris 55-70; V Halberton *Ex* 70-85; rtd 85; Perm to Offic *B & W* 86-98. *Brays Batch, Chewton Mendip, Bath BA3 4LH* Tel (01761) 241218

TESTER, Canon Francis Edward. b 24. Leeds Univ BA46. Coll of Resurr Mirfield 45. **d** 47 **p** 48. C Lon Docks St Pet w Wapping St Jo *Lon* 47-51; C Pimlico St Mary Graham-street 51-57; V Acton Green St Pet 58-64; V Hockerill *St Alb* 64-71; Chapl High Wood and St Faith's Hosps Brentwood 71-89; V Brentwood St Thos *Chelmsf* 71-89; RD Brentwood 84-89; Hon Can Chelmsf Cathl 87-89; rtd 89; Perm to Offic *Chelmsf* 89-92; Perm to Offic *Nor* 89-91 and 94-98; P-in-c Toftrees w Shereford 91-94; P-in-c Hempton and Pudding Norton 91-94. *Wythe, Burnt Street, Wells-next-the-Sea NR23 1HW* Tel (01328) 711306

TETLEY, Brian. b 38. St Jo Coll Dur BA82 ACA62 FCA72. Cranmer Hall Dur 80. **d** 83 **p** 84. C Chipping Sodbury and Old Sodbury *Glouc* 83-86; Chapl and Succ Roch Cath *Roch* 86-89; R Gravesend H Family w Ifield 89-93; Tutor Westcott Ho Cam 93-94 and 95-96; Tutor Ridley Hall and Prec Ely Cathl *Ely* 95; C Duxford, Hinxton and Ickleton 97; Perm to Offic 98-99; NSM Worc Cathl *Worc* 00-03; rtd 03. *15B College Green, Worcester WR1 2LH* Tel (01905) 724157 Fax as telephone
E-mail btetley@cofe-worcester.org.uk

TETLEY, The Ven Joy Dawn. b 46. St Mary's Coll Dur BA68 Leeds Univ CertEd69 St Hugh's Coll Ox BA75 MA80 Dur Univ PhD88. NW Ord Course 77. **dss** 77 **d** 87 **p** 94. Bentley *Sheff* 77-79; Buttershaw St Aid *Bradf* 79-80; Dur Cathl *Dur* 80-83; Lect Trin Coll Bris 83-86; Chipping Sodbury and Old Sodbury *Glouc* 83-86; Dn Roch Cathl *Roch* 87-89; Hon Can Roch Cathl 90-93; Assoc Dir of Post Ord Tr 87-88; Dir Post Ord Tr 88-93; Hon Par Dn Gravesend H Family w Ifield 89-93; Prin EAMTC *Ely* 93-99; Adn Worc and Can Res Worc Cathl *Worc* from 99. *15B College Green, Worcester WR1 2LH* Tel (01905) 724157 Fax as telephone E-mail jtetley@cofe-worcester.org.uk

TETLEY, Matthew David. b 61. Bucks Coll of Educn BSc83. Sarum & Wells Th Coll BTh89. **d** 87 **p** 88. C Kirkby *Liv* 87-90; C Hindley St Pet 90-93; TV Whorlton *Newc* 93-96; V Newbiggin Hall 96-01; P-in-c Longhorsley and Hebron from 01; Chapl HM Pris Acklington from 01. *Address withheld by request*

TETLOW, John. b 46. St Steph Ho Ox 73. **d** 76 **p** 77. C Stanwell *Lon* 76-77; C Hanworth All SS 77-80; C Somers Town 80-83; TV Wickford and Runwell *Chelmsf* 83-90; P-in-c Walthamstow St Mich 90-96. *6A Bushwood, London E11 3AY* Tel (020) 8520 6328

TETLOW, Richard Jeremy. b 42. Trin Coll Cam MA66 Goldsmiths' Coll Lon CQSW74. Qu Coll Birm 81. **d** 83 **p** 84. C Birm St Martin *Birm* 83-85; C Birm St Martin w Bordesley St Andr 85-88; V Birm St Jo Ladywood 89-01; V Ladywood St Jo and St Pet from 01. *St John's Vicarage, Darnley Road, Birmingham B16 8TF* Tel 0121-454 0973

TETZLAFF, Silke. b 67. Friedrich Schiller Univ 87 K Coll Lon BA97 AKC97 Anglia Poly Univ MA01. Westcott Ho Cam 99. **d** 01 **p** 02. C Leagrave *St Alb* from 01. *St Luke's House, 39 Butely Road, Leagrave, Luton LU4 9EW* Tel (01582) 572054 E-mail silke.tetzlaff@ntlworld.com

TEWKESBURY, Suffragan Bishop of. *See* WENT, The Rt Revd John Stewart

THACKER, Ian David. b 59. DCR81 DRI84. Oak Hill Th Coll BA91. **d** 91 **p** 92. C Illogan *Truro* 91-94; C Eglwysilan *Llan* 94-96; TV Hornsey Rise Whitehall Park Team *Lon* 96-97; TV Upper Holloway 97-01; Chapl HM YOI Huntercombe and Finnamore from 01. *HM Young Offender Institution, Huntercombe Place, Nuffield, Henley-on-Thames RG9 5SB* Tel (01491) 641711 *or* 641715 Fax 641902
E-mail ithacker@talk21.com

THACKER, James Robert. b 40. W Virginia State Coll BA63 Nashotah Ho Wisconsin BD66 Cath Univ of America MSW76. **d** 66 **p** 66. USA 66-90; V War w Avondale and Keystone 66-68; R Wheeling w Bellaire and Martins Ferry 68-71; V Harpers Ferry 71-77; Assoc R Westhampton Beach 78-80; R Lynchburg 80-85; R Roanoke 85-90; R St Mark Bermuda 90-99; R St Alban Japan from 99. *3-6-25, Shiba-Koen, Minato-Ku, Tokyo 105-0011, Japan* Tel (0081) (3) 3431 8534 Fax 5472 4766
E-mail thacker_global@hotmail.com

THACKER, Jonathan William. b 53. Lon Univ BA74 Nottm Univ DipTh78. Linc Th Coll 76. **d** 79 **p** 80. C Bromyard *Heref* 79-82; C Penkridge w Stretton *Lich* 82-87; V Brothertoft Gp *Linc* 87-96; RD Holland W 92-95; P-in-c Crosby 96-01; V from 01; Chapl Scunthorpe and Goole Hosps NHS Trust 99-01; Chapl N Lincs and Goole Hosps NHS Trust 01. *St George's Vicarage, 87 Ferry Road, Scunthorpe DN15 8LY* Tel and fax (01724) 843328 *or* tel 843336 E-mail jon@han195.freeserve.co.uk

THACKER, Kenneth Ray. b 31. Open Univ BA73. Tyndale Hall Bris 56. **d** 59 **p** 60. C Penn Fields *Lich* 59-61; C Tipton St Martin 62-64; V Moxley 64-71; R Leigh 71-91; rtd 92; Perm to Offic *Lich* from 92. *24 Rugby Close, Newcastle ST5 3JN* Tel (01782) 617812

THACKER, Roger Ailwyn Mackintosh. b 46. CCC Cam BA68 MA73. Westcott Ho Cam 68. **d** 70 **p** 71. C St John's Wood *Lon* 70-74; P-in-c Hammersmith St Paul 74-79; V 79-99; rtd 00; Perm to Offic *St Alb* from 01. *The New Vicarage, 21 Lower Mall, London W6 9DJ* Tel (020) 7741 1860 *or* 7748 3855

THACKRAY, John Adrian. b 55. Southn Univ BSc76 ACIB84. Coll of Resurr Mirfield 81. **d** 84 **p** 85. C Loughton St Jo *Chelmsf* 84-87; Chapl Bancroft's Sch Woodford Green 87-92; Sen Chapl K Sch Cant 92-01; Chapl Abp's Sch Cant 01-02; Hon Min Can Cant Cathl *Cant* from 93; Sen Chapl K Sch Roch from 02; Hon PV Roch Cathl *Roch* from 02. *King's School, Rochester ME1 1TE* Tel (01634) 812306

THACKRAY, William Harry. b 44. Leeds Univ CertEd66. Chich Th Coll 70. **d** 73 **p** 74. C Sheff St Cuth *Sheff* 73-76; C Stocksbridge 76-78; P-in-c Newark St Leon *S'well* 79-80; TV Newark w Hawton, Cotham and Shelton 80-82; V Choral S'well Minster 82-85; V Bawtry w Austerfield 85; P-in-c Misson 85; V Bawtry w Austerfield and Misson 86-93; RD Bawtry 90-93; P-in-c Balderton 93-03; P-in-c Coddington w Barnby in the Willows 98-03; P-in-c Balderton and Barnby-in-the-Willows from 03. *The Vicarage, Main Street, Balderton, Newark NG24 3NN* Tel (01636) 704811

THAKE, Preb Terence. b 41. ALCD65. **d** 66 **p** 67. C Gt Faringdon w Lt Coxwell *Ox* 66-70; C Aldridge *Lich* 70-73; V Werrington 73-82; Chapl HM Det Cen Werrington Ho 73-82; TR Chell *Lich* 82-94; Chapl Westcliffe Hosp 82-94; RD Stoke N 91-94; Preb

Lich Cathl from 94; V Colwich w Gt Haywood 94-00; P-in-c Colton 95-00; R Colton, Colwich and Gt Haywood from 00; RD Rugeley from 98. *The Vicarage, Main Road, Little Haywood, Stafford ST18 0TS* Tel (01889) 881262 Fax as telephone E-mail terry.thake@btinternet.com

THAME, Miss Margaret Eve. b 31. SRN54 SCM55. Glouc Sch of Min 85. **d** 88 **p** 94. NSM Pittville All SS *Glouc* 88-94; NSM Cheltenham St Mich *Glouc* 94-02; Perm to Offic from 02. *13 Brighton Road, Cheltenham GL52 6BA* Tel (01242) 241228

THATCHER, Barbara Mary. b 25. Lon Univ BCom. **d** 90 **p** 94. NSM Helensburgh *Glas* from 90. *228 West Princes Street, Helensburgh G84 8HA* Tel (01436) 672003

THATCHER, Stephen Bert. b 58. Greenwich Univ PGCE03. St Jo Coll Nottm LTh87 ALCD87. **d** 87 **p** 88. C Bargoed and Deri w Brithdir *Llan* 87-89; C Llanishen and Lisvane 89-91; V Llanwnda, Goodwick w Manorowen and Llanstinan *St D* 91-95; P-in-c Coberley, Cowley, Colesbourne and Elkstone *Glouc* 95-96; Dioc Rural Adv 95-96; R New Radnor and Llanfihangel Nantmelan etc *S & B* 96-00; Dioc Tourism Officer 96-99; Dioc Chs and Tourism Rep 97-00; CF from 00. *c/o MOD Chaplains (Army)* Tel (01980) 615804 Fax 615800 E-mail stephen.thatcher2@btopenworld.com

THAWLEY, The Very Revd David Laurie. b 24. St Edm Hall Ox BA47 MA49. Cuddesdon Coll 49. **d** 51 **p** 52. C Bitterne Park *Win* 51-56; C-in-c Andover St Mich CD 56-60; Australia from 60; Can Res Brisbane 64-72; Dean Wangaratta 72-89; rtd 89. *Lavender Cottage, 2 Bond Street, North Caulfield, Vic, Australia 3161* Tel (0061) (3) 9571 0513 Mobile 407-811870 E-mail dthawley@bigpond.com

THAYER, Michael David. b 52. Sarum & Wells Th Coll 77. **d** 80 **p** 81. C Minehead *B & W* 80-85; Chapl RN 85-89; TV Lowestoft and Kirkley *Nor* 89-92; Chapl St Helena Hospice Colchester 92-97; Chapl HM Pris Acklington 99-01; Chapl HM Pris Erlestoke 01-03; R S Tawton and Belstone *Ex* from 03. *The Rectory, South Tawton, Okehampton EX20 2LQ* Tel (01837) 849048 E-mail michael.thayer@btopenworld.com

THEAKER, David Michael. b 41. **d** 68 **p** 69. C Folkingham w Laughton *Linc* 68-71; C New Cleethorpes 71-74; P-in-c Gt Grimsby St Andr and St Luke 74-77; P-in-c Thurlby 77-79; Perm to Offic *Ely* from 00. *11 Willow Way, Hauxton, Cambridge CB2 5JB* Tel (01223) 873132

THEAKSTON, Ms Sally Margaret. b 62. UEA BSc84 Ox Univ BA89 K Coll Lon MA94. Ripon Coll Cuddesdon 86. **d** 89 **p** 94. Par Dn Hackney *Lon* 89-93; Par Dn Putney St Mary *S'wark* 93-94; C 94-96; Chapl RN 96-02; TR Gaywood *Nor* from 02. *St Faith's Rectory, Gayton Road, King's Lynn PE30 4DZ* Tel and fax (01553) 774662 Mobile 07904-070654 E-mail stheakston@aol.com

THELWELL, The Ven John Berry. b 49. Univ of Wales (Ban) BD72. Qu Coll Birm 73. **d** 73 **p** 74. C Minera *St As* 73-80; Dioc Youth Chapl 78-86; V Gwernaffield and Llanferres 80-93; Chapl Clwyd Fire Service 88-94; RD Mold 91-93; TR Hawarden 93-02; Can Cursal St As Cathl 95-02; Prec 98-02; Adn Montgomery from 02; V Berriew from 03. *The Vicarage, Berriew, Welshpool SY21 8PL* Tel (01686) 640223 Fax as telephone

THEOBALD, Graham Fitzroy. b 43. ALCD67. **d** 67 **p** 68. C Crookham *Guildf* 67-71; C York Town St Mich 71-74; V Wrecclesham 74-83; Chapl Green Lane Hosp 74-81; R Frimley 83-85; Chapl Frimley Park Hosp 83-85; Perm to Offic *Ox* 90-92; C Easthampstead 92-97; Chapl E Berks NHS Trust from 92. *Chaplain's Office, E Berks NHS Trust, Church Hill House, Crowthorne Road, Bracknell RG12 7EP* Tel (01344) 823279 Mobile 07721-408740 E-mail graham.theobald@eberks-tr.anglox.nhs.uk

THEOBALD, Henry Charles. b 32. Lon Univ DRBS63. S'wark Ord Course 60. **d** 63 **p** 64. C Battersea St Phil *S'wark* 63-65; C Caterham 65-68; C Reigate St Luke S Park 68-73; Chapl S Lon Hosp for Women & St Jas Hosp Balham 73-83; Chapl St Mary's Hosp Portsm 83-95; rtd 93; Perm to Offic *Portsm* from 93; Chapl SSB 93-02. *141 Warren Avenue, Southsea PO4 8PP* Tel (023) 9281 7443

THEOBALD, John Walter. b 33. St Aid Birkenhead 62. **d** 65 **p** 66. C Hindley All SS *Liv* 65-68; C Beverley Minster *York* 68-71; R Loftus 71-86; P-in-c Carlin How w Skinningrove 73-86; Dep Chapl HM Pris Leeds 86-89; Chapl HM Pris Rudgate 89-93; Chapl HM Pris Thorp Arch 89-93; Chapl HM Pris Leeds 93-97; V Leeds St Cypr Harehills *Ripon* 97-01; rtd 01; P-in-c Swillington *Ripon* from 01. *The Rectory, Wakefield Road, Swillington, Leeds LS26 8DS* Tel 0113-286 0172

THEODOSIUS, Hugh John. b 32. Trin Coll Cam BA56 MA60. Cuddesdon Coll 56. **d** 58 **p** 59. C Milton *Win* 58-62; C Romsey 62-64; C Southampton Maybush St Pet 64-70; V Malden St Jo *S'wark* 70-81; V Billingborough *Linc* 81-94; V Horbling 81-94; V Sempringham w Pointon and Birthorpe 81-94; RD Aveland and Ness w Stamford 87-93; rtd 97; Perm to Offic *Linc* from 00; *Ely* from 01. *Sempringham House, East Bank, Sutton Bridge, Spalding PE12 9YN* Tel (01406) 351977

THEODOSIUS, Richard Francis. b 35. Fitzw Coll Cam BA59. Lich Th Coll 69. **d** 71 **p** 72. C Bloxwich *Lich* 71-73; Chapl Blue

Coat Comp Sch Walsall 71-73; Chapl Ranby Ho Sch Retford 73-96; P-in-c Norton Cuckney *S'well* 96-02; rtd 02. *Downlea, 51 Town Street, Lound, Retford DN22 8RT* Tel (01777) 818744

THETFORD, Suffragan Bishop of. See ATKINSON, The Rt Revd David John

THEWLIS, Andrew James. b 64. Man Univ BSc86. Cranmer Hall Dur 87. **d** 90 **p** 91. C Walshaw Ch Ch *Man* 90-95; P-in-c Jersey St Jo *Win* 95-98; R from 98. *The Rectory, La rue des Landes, St John, Jersey JE3 4AF* Tel (01534) 861677 Mobile 07797-723828 E-mail athewlis@itl.net

THEWLIS, Brian Jacob. b 24. Melbourne Univ BA49. Coll of Resurr Mirfield 52. **d** 53 **p** 54. C Wednesbury St Jas *Lich* 53-57; Chapl K Coll Auckland New Zealand 57-61; C Sidley *Chich* 59-60; Australia from 61; I Reservoir St Geo 61-68; I Malvern St Paul 68-82; I Beaumaris St Mich 82-87; I Frankston St Paul 87-94; rtd 94. *41 Sixth Street, Parkdale, Vic, Australia 3194* Tel (0061) (3) 9587 3095

THEWLIS, John Charles. b 49. Van Mildert Coll Dur BA70 PhD75. N Ord Course 78. **d** 81 **p** 82. NSM Hull St Mary Sculcoates *York* 81-83; C Spring Park *Cant* 83-84; C Spring Park All SS *S'wark* 85-86; V Eltham Park St Luke 86-01; R Carshalton from 01. *The Rectory, 2 Talbot Road, Carshalton SM5 3BS* Tel (020) 8647 2366 E-mail rector@jctclerk.demon.co.uk

THEWSEY, Robert Sydney. b 65. Ripon Coll Cuddesdon DipMin01. **d** 01 **p** 02. C Chorlton-cum-Hardy St Clem *Man* from 01. *94 Hardy Lane, Chorlton cum Hardy, Manchester M21 8DN* Tel 0161-881 9458 E-mail robert.thewsey@btinternet.com

THICKE, James Balliston. b 43. Sarum & Wells Th Coll 74. **d** 77 **p** 78. C Wareham *Sarum* 77-80; TV 80-83; Dioc Youth Adv *Dur* 83-87; C Portishead *B & W* 87-90; V Westfield from 90; RD Midsomer Norton from 98; Chapl Norton Radstock Coll of FE from 00. *Westfield Vicarage, Midsomer Norton, Bath BA3 4BJ* Tel (01761) 412105 Fax 419865

THIEDE, Prof Carsten Peter. b 52. KStJ87. Tech Univ Berlin MA75 Qu Coll Ox 76. EAMTC 99. **d** 99 **p** 00. Prof NT Hist Basel Th Coll Switzerland from 98; Dir Eur Office Ben-Gurion Univ of the Negev Beer-Sheva Israel from 98; OCF from 99; Lic to Offic *Eur* from 02. *Friedrich-Ebert-Strasse 52, 33102 Paderborn, Germany* Tel (0049) (5251) 31230 Fax 37646 E-mail c.p.thiede@t-online.de

THIEME, Paul Henri. b 22. Old Cath Sem Amersfoort 46. **d** 50 **p** 50. The Netherlands 50-57 and from 79; Perm to Offic *York* 58-59; C Newland St Aug 59-63; V Kingston upon Hull St Sav and St Mark 63-73; V Middlesbrough St Aid 73-79; rtd 79. *Haagweg 174, 2282 AY Rijswijk ZH, The Netherlands* Tel (0031) (70) 390 9296

✠**THIRD, The Rt Revd Richard Henry McPhail.** b 27. Em Coll Cam BA50 MA55 Kent Univ Hon DCL90. Linc Th Coll 50. **d** 52 **p** 53 **c** 76. C Mottingham St Andr *S'wark* 52-55; C Sanderstead All SS 55-59; V Sheerness H Trin w St Paul *Cant* 59-67; V Orpington All SS *Roch* 67-76; RD Orpington 73-76; Hon Can Roch Cathl 74-76; Suff Bp Maidstone *Cant* 76-80; Suff Bp Dover 80-92; rtd 92; Asst Bp B & W from 92. *25 Church Close, Martock TA12 6DS* Tel (01935) 825519

THIRTLE, Ms Lucy Rachel. b 62. Ex Univ BA85. Cranmer Hall Dur Dip Th & Min 99. **d** 99 **p** 00. C Basingstoke *Win* from 99. *1 The Glebe, Church Square, Basingstoke RG21 7QW* Tel (01256) 466694

THISELTON, Canon Prof Anthony Charles. b 37. Novi Testamenti Societas 75 Lon Univ BD59 K Coll Lon MTh64 Sheff Univ PhD77 Dur Univ DD93 Lambeth DD02. Oak Hill Th Coll 58. **d** 60 **p** 61. C Sydenham H Trin *S'wark* 60-63; Tutor Tyndale Hall Bris 63-67; Sen Tutor 67-70; Lect Bibl Studies Sheff Univ 70-79; Sen Lect 79-85; Prof Calvin Coll Grand Rapids 82-83; Special Lect Th Nottm Univ 86-88; Prin St Jo Coll Nottm 86-88; Prin St Jo Coll w Cranmer Hall Dur 88-92; Prof Chr Th Nottm Univ from 92; Can Th Leic Cathl *Leic* from 94. *Department of Theology, Nottingham University, University Park, Nottingham NG7 2RD* Tel 0115-951 5852 Fax 951 5887

THISTLETHWAITE, Canon Nicholas John. b 51. Selw Coll Cam BA73 MA77 PhD80. Ripon Coll Cuddesdon BA78 MA83. **d** 79 **p** 80. C Newc St Gabr *Newc* 79-82; Chapl G&C Coll Cam 82-90; Lic to Offic *Ely* 82-90; V Trumpington 90-99; Can Res and Prec Guildf Cathl *Guildf* from 99. *3 Cathedral Close, Guildford GU2 7TL* Tel and fax (01483) 569682 *or* tel 565287 E-mail precentor@guildford-cathedral.org

THISTLEWOOD, Michael John. b 31. Ch Coll Cam BA53 MA57. Linc Th Coll 54. **d** 56 **p** 57. C N Hull St Mich *York* 56-59; C Scarborough St Mary 59-61; V Kingston upon Hull St Jude w St Steph 61-67; V Newland St Aug 67-72; Asst Master Bemrose Sch Derby 72-80; V Derby St Andr w St Osmund *Derby* 80-82; Lic to Offic *Ox* 84-95; rtd 88; Perm to Offic *Carl* 88-98; *Derby* from 98. *1 Lincoln Green, Chellaston, Derby DE73 1QP* Tel (01332) 701995 E-mail michael@thistlewood4164.freeserve.co.uk

THODAY, Margaret Frances. b 38. **d** 03. *Flat 3, 4 Norwich Road, Cromer NR27 0AX* Tel (01263) 510945

THODY, Charles Michael Jackson. b 62. Linc Th Coll BTh94. **d** 94 **p** 95. C Immingham *Linc* 94-97; P-in-c Leasingham and

Cranwell 97-01; P-in-c Bishop Norton, Wadingham and Snitterby 01-03; Chapl Doncaster and S Humber Healthcare NHS Trust 01-03; Chapl Notts Healthcare NHS Trust from 03. *Rampton Hospital, Retford DN22 0PD* Tel (01777) 248321 E-mail charles@thody.freeserve.co.uk

THOM, Alastair George. b 60. ACA86 G&C Coll Cam BA81 MA84. Ridley Hall Cam 88. **d** 91 **p** 92. C Lindfield *Chich* 91-94; C Finchley St Paul and St Luke 94-98; P-in-c Paddington Em Harrow Road from 98; P-in-c W Kilburn St Luke w St Simon and St Jude from 98. *The Vicarage, 19 Macroom Road, London W9 3HY* Tel (020) 8962 0294 E-mail familythom@compuserve.com

THOM, Christopher Henry. d 03. NSM Loose *Cant* from 03. *Old Hill House, Old Loose Hill, Loose, Maidstone ME15 0BN* Tel (01622) 744833 E-mail chthom@ukonline.co.uk

THOM, James. b 31. St Chad's Coll Dur BA53 DipTh57. **d** 57 **p** 58. C Middlesbrough St Thos *York* 57-60; C Hornsea and Goxhill 60-62; C S Bank 62-63; V Copmanthorpe 63-75; V Coxwold 75-77; RD Easingwold 77-82; V Coxwold and Husthwaite 77-87; Abp's Adv for Spiritual Direction 86-93; P-in-c Topcliffe 87-93; rtd 93; Perm to Offic *Ripon* and *York* from 93. *34 Hellwath Grove, Ripon HG4 2JT* Tel (01765) 605083

THOM, Thomas Kennedy Dalziel. b 29. Pemb Coll Cam BA53 MA57. St Steph Ho Ox 60. **d** 61 **p** 62. C Colchester St Jas, All SS, St Nic and St Runwald *Chelmsf* 61-64; USPG 65-70; Ghana 65-70; SSJE 71-72; Chapl Essex Univ *Chelmsf* 73-80; Sec Chapls in HE Gen Syn Bd of Educn 81-87; Partnership Sec and Dep Gen Sec USPG 87-92; Chapl Burrswood Chr Cen *Roch* 93-94; rtd 95; Hon C Kennington St Jo w St Jas *S'wark* 95-00; Perm to Offic from 00. *24 South Island Place, London SW9 0DX* Tel (020) 7582 2798

THOMAS, Adrian Leighton. b 37. St D Coll Lamp BA62 DipTh. **d** 63 **p** 64. C Port Talbot St Theodore *Llan* 63-70; V Troedrhiwgarth 70-73; C Sandhurst *Ox* 73-77; V Streatley 77-84; P-in-c Moulsford 81-84; V Streatley w Moulsford 84-90; P-in-c Sutton Courtenay w Appleford 90-00; V 00-02; AD Abingdon 96-02; rtd 02; P-in-c Lugano *Eur* from 02. *Via Pola 8, 6932 Breganzona, Switzerland* Tel (0041) (91) 968 1149 E-mail leighton@leightonthomas.demon.co.uk

THOMAS, Alan. *See* THOMAS, Thomas Alan

THOMAS, Canon Alan. b 42. Univ of Wales (Cardiff) BA65. St Mich Coll Llan 65. **d** 67 **p** 68. C Fairwater *Llan* 67-69; C Llanishen and Lisvane 69-73; V Troedyrhiw w Merthyr Vale 73-77; V Pembroke Dock *St D* 77-93; P-in-c Cosheston w Nash and Upton 85-93; R 93; V Pembroke Dock 93-03; Chapl S Pembrokeshire Hosp 77-97; Chapl Pembrokeshire and Derwen NHS Trust 97-03; RD Castlemartin *St D* 83-03; Can St D Cathl 89-03; Treas 01-03; rtd 03. *The Vicarage, Church Street, Pembroke Dock SA72 6AR* Tel (01646) 682943

THOMAS, Alan William Charles. b 19. Liv Univ BA41. St Aid Birkenhead 42. **d** 43 **p** 44. C Everton Em *Liv* 43-45; C Fazakerley Em 45-50; V Everton St Benedict 50-56; V Tipton St Martin *Lich* 56-67; V Wolverhampton St Jude 67-87; rtd 87; Perm to Offic *Lich* 87-89 and from 01; *Ex* 89-98. *25 Chelston Drive, Wolverhampton WV6 0LQ* Tel (01902) 755083

THOMAS, Aled Huw. b 59. Univ of Wales (Abth) BD81 DPS83. St Mich Coll Llan 84. **d** 85 **p** 86. C Llandeilo Fawr and Taliaris *St D* 85-86; P-in-c Llangrannog and Llandysiliogogo 86-88; Chapl RAF 88-92; R Ystradgynlais *S & B* 92-94; CF from 94. *c/o MOD Chaplains (Army)* Tel (01980) 615804 Fax 615800

THOMAS, The Ven Alfred James Randolph. b 48. St D Coll Lamp DipTh71. **d** 71 **p** 72. C Cydweli and Llandyfaelog *St D* 71-74; C Carmarthen St Dav 74-76; TV Aberystwyth 76-81; V Betws w Ammanford 81-93; RD Dyffryn Aman 90-93; V Carmarthen St Pet 93-02; Can St D Cathl 96-02; V Bronllys w Llanfilo *S & B* from 02; Adn Brecon from 03. *The Vicarage, Bronllys, Brecon LD3 0HS* Tel (01874) 711200

THOMAS, Andrew Herbert Redding. b 41. Lon Coll of Div 66. **d** 69 **p** 70. C Cromer *Nor* 69-72; Holiday Chapl 72-76; R Grimston w Congham 76-83; R Roydon All SS 76-83; C-in-c Ewell St Paul Howell Hill CD *Guildf* 83-89; V Howell Hill 89-95; RD Epsom 93-95; TR Beccles St Mich *St E* from 95; P-in-c Worlingham w Barnby and N Cove 98-01. *The Rectory, 53 Cromwell Avenue, Beccles NR34 9XF* Tel (01502) 716017 Fax as telephone E-mail andrew@becclesteam.freeserve.co.uk

THOMAS, Anne. *See* THOMAS, Miss Eileen Anne Harwood

THOMAS, Arthur Norman. b 17. St Aid Birkenhead 54. **d** 56 **p** 57. C Chapel Allerton *Ripon* 56-59; V Wyther Ven Bede 59-65; R Seacroft 65-70; TR 70-76; R Thornton Watlass w Thornton Steward and E Witton 76-86; rtd 86; Perm to Offic *Ripon* from 86. *10 St Andrew's Meadow, Kirkby Malzeard, Ripon HG4 3SW* Tel (01765) 658884

THOMAS, Arun. *See* THOMAS, John Arun

THOMAS, Austin George. b 23. Open Univ BA75. Wells Th Coll 65. **d** 67 **p** 68. C Brislington St Luke *Bris* 67-73; P-in-c Bris St Geo 73-74; P-in-c Bris St Leon Redfield 74-75; TV E Bris 75-80; R Lyddington w Wanborough 80-88; rtd 88; Perm to Offic *Bris* from 88. *11 College Road, Bristol BS16 2HN* Tel 0117-958 3511

THOMAS, Barry Wilfred. b 41. Univ of Wales (Cardiff) BD75. St Mich Coll Llan 72. **d** 75 **p** 76. C Porthmadog *Ban* 75-78; V

Llanegryn and Llanfihangel-y-Pennant etc 78-82; Sec Dioc Coun for Miss and Unity 81-94; R Llanbeblig w Caernarfon and Betws Garmon etc 82-94; Can Ban Cathl 89-94; Chapl Monte Carlo *Eur* 95-00; V Llanfihangel Ystrad and Cilcennin w Trefilan etc 00 from 00. *The Vicarage, Felinfach, Lampeter SA48 8AE* Tel (01570) 471073

THOMAS, Bryan. b 36. Univ of Wales (Abth) BA59. St Deiniol's Hawarden 68. **d** 70 **p** 71. C Llangynwyd w Maesteg *Llan* 70-72; V Cwmllynfell *St D* 72-76; V Gors-las 76-82; R Yarnbury *Sarum* 82-97; TR Wylye and Till Valley 97-02; RD Wylye and Wilton 94-98; rtd 02. *11 Ebble Crescent, Warminster BA12 9PF* Tel (01985) 300519

THOMAS, Charles Moray Stewart Reid. b 53. BNC Ox BA74 MA79. Wycliffe Hall Ox 75. **d** 78 **p** 79. C Bradf Cathl *Bradf* 78-81; C Barnsbury St Andr and H Trin w All SS *Lon* 81-90; TV Barnsbury 90-99; Chapl Goodenough Trust from 99. *The London Goodenough Trust, London House, Mecklenburgh Square, London WC1N 2AB* Tel (020) 7837 8888 E-mail moray.thomas@dlondon.org.uk

THOMAS, Cheeramattathu John. b 25. Travanscore Univ BA46 BT49 Serampore Coll BD55 United Th Coll Bangalore MA66. Andover Newton Th Coll. **d** 55 **p** 57. Singapore 55-60; Sarawak 60-65; C Eastham *Ches* 66-74; V St Sutton 75-83; USA from 83; rtd 91. *301 Eagle Lakes Drive, Friendswood, TX 77546, USA* Tel (001) (281) 996 7797

THOMAS, Clive Alexander. b 49. St Luke's Coll Ex CertEd71 Open Univ BA77. STETS 94. **d** 97 **p** 99. NSM Southwick St Mich *Chich* 97-01; C Bridport *Sarum* from 01. *28 Watton Road, Bridport DT6 5NJ* Tel (01308) 420819 E-mail rev.cathomas@lineone.net

THOMAS, Colin Norman. b 41. Open Univ BA78. Trin Coll Bris 72. **d** 74 **p** 75. C Handforth *Ches* 74-77; C Bucknall and Bagnall *Lich* 77-80; TV 80-86; V Ogley Hay from 86; RD Lich from 99. *St James's Vicarage, 37 New Road, Brownhills, Walsall WS8 6AT* Tel (01543) 372187 or 373251 E-mail thomas@colnor.freeserve.co.uk

✠**THOMAS, The Rt Revd David.** b 42. Keble Coll Ox BA64 BA66 MA67. St Steph Ho Ox 64. **d** 67 **p** 68 **c** 96. C Hawarden *St As* 67-69; Tutor St Mich Coll Llan 69-70; Chapl 70-75; Sec Ch in Wales Liturg Commn 70-75; Vice-Prin St Steph Ho Ox 75-79; Prin 82-87; V Chepstow *Mon* 79-82; Lic to Offic *Ox* 82-87; Newton St Pet *S & B* 87-96; Can Brecon Cathl 94-96; RD Clyne 96; Prov Asst Bp from 96. *Bodfair, 3 White's Close, Belmont Road, Abergavenny NP7 5HZ* Tel (01873) 858780 Fax 858269 E-mail pab@churchinwales.org.uk

THOMAS, David Brian. b 45. MIEEE. St D Dioc Tr Course 82. **d** 85 **p** 86. NSM Llandysul *St D* 85-87; NSM Lampeter Pont Steffan w Silian 88-92; NSM Lampeter and Ultra-Aeron 92-96; P-in-c Llanfihangel Genau'r-glyn and Llangorwen 96-97; V from 97; RD Llanbadarn Fawr from 00. *The Vicarage, Maes y Garn, Bow Street SY24 5DS* Tel (01970) 828638

THOMAS, David Edward. b 60. Univ of Wales (Lamp) BA83 LTh85. St Mich Coll Llan DPS86. **d** 86 **p** 87. C Killay *S & B* 86-89; P-in-c Newbridge-on-Wye and Llanfihangel Brynpabuan 89-90; V 90-91; V Brecon St David w Llanspyddid and Llanilltyd from 91. *The Vicarage, 26 St David's Crescent, Ffrwdgrech Road, Brecon LD3 8DP* Tel (01874) 622707

THOMAS, Canon David Geoffrey. b 24. AKC48. **d** 49 **p** 50. C Milford Haven *St D* 49-52; Miss to Seamen 52-53 and 68-81; C Pembroke St Mary w St Mich 53-54; R Rhoscrowther and Pwllcrochan 54-68; V Milford Haven 68-89; Can St D Cathl 77-89; Treas 85-89; rtd 89. *49 Pill Lane, Milford Haven SA73 2LD* Tel (01646) 695792

THOMAS, David Geoffrey. b 37. Univ of Wales (Cardiff) BA58. Launde Abbey 70 Qu Coll Birm 71. **d** 71 **p** 72. Hon C Fenny Drayton *Leic* 71-75; Chapl Community of the H Family Baldslow Chich 75-77; Perm to Offic *Chich* 77-79; P-in-c Mill End and Heronsgate w W Hyde *St Alb* 79-81; Sen Lect Watford Coll 82-91; R Walgrave w Hannington and Wold and Scaldwell *Pet* 91-01; rtd 02. *1 Cypress Close, Desborough, Kettering NN14 2XU* Tel (01536) 763749 Fax as telephone

THOMAS, The Very Revd David Glynne. b 41. Dur Univ BSc63. Westcott Ho Cam 64. **d** 67 **p** 68. C St John's Wood *Lon* 67-70; Min Can St Alb 70-72; Chapl Wadh Coll Ox 72-75; C Ox St Mary V w St Cross and St Pet *Ox* 72-75; Bp's Dom Chapl 75-78; P-in-c Burnham 78-82; TR Burnham w Dropmore, Hitcham and Taplow 82-83; Australia 83-87 and from 99; Can Res Worc Cathl *Worc* 87-99; Dean Brisbane from 99. *The Deanery, PO Box 421, Brisbane, Qld, Australia 4001* Tel (0061) (7) 3835 2236 or 3835 2231 Fax 3832 3173 E-mail brisdean@anglicanbrisbane.org.au

THOMAS, David Godfrey. b 50. St Chad's Coll Dur BA71 Fitzw Coll Cam BA74 MA78. Westcott Ho Cam 72. **d** 75 **p** 76. C Kirkby *Liv* 75-78; TV Cov E *Cov* 78-88; TR Canvey Is *Chelmsf* 88-92; R Wivenhoe from 92. *The Rectory, 44 Belle Vue Road, Wivenhoe, Colchester CO7 9LD* Tel (01206) 825174

THOMAS, David John. b 34. Univ of Wales (Swansea) St D Coll Lamp. St D Dioc Tr Course 85. **d** 88 **p** 89. NSM Cwmaman *St D* 88-96; Public Preacher from 96. *9 New School Road, Garnant, Ammanford SA18 1LL* Tel (01269) 823936

THOMAS, David Richard. b 48. BNC Ox BA71 MA74 Fitzw Coll Cam BA75 MA80 Lanc Univ PhD83. Ridley Hall Cam 73 Qu Coll Birm 79. **d** 80 **p** 81. C Anfield St Columba *Liv* 80-83; C Liv Our Lady and St Nic w St Anne 83-85; Chapl CCC Cam 85-90; V Witton *Blackb* 90-93; Bp's Adv on Inter-Faith Relns 90-93; Dir Cen for Study of Islam and Chr-Muslim Relns Selly Oak from 93; Perm to Offic *Birm* from 94; Sen Lect Birm Univ from 99. *15 Appletree Close, Birmingham B31 2YP* Tel 0121-476 4983 *or* 415 2281 E-mail d.thomas.islam@sellyoak.ac.uk

THOMAS, David Ronald Holt. b 28. Lich Th Coll 55. **d** 58 **p** 59. C Uttoxeter w Bramshall *Lich* 58-61; C Hednesford 61-66; R Armitage from 66; RD Rugeley 88-94. *The Rectory, Hood Lane, Armitage, Rugeley WS15 4AG* Tel (01543) 490278

THOMAS, David Thomas. b 44. St Cath Coll Cam BA66 MA70 St Jo Coll Dur DipTh68. **d** 71 **p** 72. C Chorlton-cum-Hardy St Clem *Man* 71-74; Chapl Salford Tech Coll 74-79; P-in-c Pendleton St Thos *Man* 75-77; V 77-80; TR Gleadless *Sheff* 80-90; RD Attercliffe 86-90; V Benchill *Man* 90-99; TV Wythenshawe *Man* 99-00; AD Withington 99-00; P-in-c Stretford St Matt from 00. *St Matthew's Rectory, 39 Sandy Lane, Stretford, Manchester M32 9DB* Tel 0161-865 2535 E-mail tom-hil@talk21.com

THOMAS, Canon David William. b 17. Univ of Wales BA63 MA67. St D Coll Lamp BA38 St Mich Coll Llan 39. **d** 41 **p** 43. C Cynwyl Gaeo w Llansawel *St D* 41-46; C Llandysul 46-48; V Clydau and Penrhydd w Castellan 48-55; V Llanfihangel Genau'r Glyn 55-67; V Llangynfelyn 58-62; V Pontyberem 67-76; V Llanilar w Rhostie and Llangwyryfon etc 76-83; Hon Can St D Cathl 78-83; rtd 83. *Nantyddderwen, 138 Marged Street, Ammanford SA18 2NN* Tel (01269) 594986

THOMAS, David William Wallace. b 51. St Chad's Coll Dur BA72. St Mich Coll Llan 72. **d** 75 **p** 76. C Bargoed and Deri w Brithdir *Llan* 75-79; Hon C 79-81; V Nantymoel w Wyndham 81-84; Chapl RN from 84. *Royal Naval Chaplaincy Service, Room 203, Victory Building, HM Naval Base, Portsmouth PO1 3LS* Tel (023) 9272 7903 Fax 9272 7111

THOMAS, David Wynford. b 48. Univ of Wales (Abth) LLB70. Qu Coll Birm 76. **d** 79 **p** 80. C Swansea St Mary w H Trin and St Mark *S & B* 79-83; P-in-c Swansea St Mark 83-89; Lic to Offic 90. *74 Terrace Road, Swansea SA1 6HU*

THOMAS, Canon Dillwyn Morgan. b 26. Univ of Wales (Lamp) BA50. Qu Coll Birm 50. **d** 52 **p** 53. C Dowlais *Llan* 52-59; C Pontypridd St Cath 59-63; V Llanwynno 63-68; V Bargoed w Brithdir 68-74; V Bargoed and Deri w Brithdir 74-75; V Penarth All SS 75-88; Can Llan Cathl 86-88; rtd 88; Perm to Offic *Llan* from 88. *11 Baroness Place, Penarth CF64 3UL* Tel (029) 2025 1698

THOMAS, Dorothy Judith. b 47. **d** 03. NSM Wargrave w Knowl Hill *Ox* from 03. *The Vicarage, Knowl Hill Common, Reading RG10 9YD* E-mail djudthomas@hotmail.com

THOMAS (née THOMSON), Mrs Dorothy Lucille. b 39. Univ of Wales (Lamp). **d** 00. OLM Pontnewydd *Mon* from 00. *Raldoro, Mount Pleasant Road, Pontnewydd, Cwmbran NP44 1BD* Tel (01633) 771353

THOMAS, Edward. *See* THOMAS, The Ven Charles Edward

THOMAS, Edward Bernard Meredith. b 21. Leeds Univ BA44 Queensland Univ BEd68 BD72. Coll of Resurr Mirfield 47. **d** 49 **p** 50. C St Mary-at-Lambeth *S'wark* 49-54; C Portsea N End St Mark *Portsm* 54-56; V Portsea All SS 56-64; Australia from 64; rtd 92. *33 Highfield Street, Durack, Qld, Australia 4077* Tel (0061) (7) 3372 3517

THOMAS, Edward Walter Dennis. b 32. St Mich Coll Llan 61. **d** 63 **p** 64. C Loughor *S & B* 63-69; V Ystradfellte 69-74; V Dukinfield St Mark and St Luke *Ches* from 74; Chapl Gtr Man Police from 77; OCF from 88. *The Vicarage, 2 Church Square, Dukinfield SK16 4PX* Tel 0161-330 2783 E-mail revewdt@aol.com

THOMAS, Miss Eileen Anne Harwood. b 35. Univ of Wales (Swansea) BA59 Kent Univ MA80. Cant Sch of Min 80. **dss** 83 **d** 87 **p** 94. Mill Hill Jo Keble Ch *Lon* 83-86; The Lydiards *Bris* 86-92; Par Dn 87-92; C-in-c Woodgate Valley CD *Birm* 92-96; rtd 96; Perm to Offic *Truro* from 96. *2 Trelinnoe Gardens, South Petherwin, Launceston PL15 7TH* Tel (01566) 773380

THOMAS, Canon Eirwyn Wheldon. b 35. St Mich Coll Llan 58. **d** 61 **p** 62. C Glanadda *Ban* 61-67; R Llantrisant and Llandeusant 67-75; V Nefyn w Tudweiliog w Llandudwen w Edern 75-01; Can Ban Cathl 97-01; rtd 01. *11 Wenfro Road, Abergele LL22 7LE* Tel (01745) 823587

THOMAS (née REEVES), Mrs Elizabeth Anne. b 45. Sheff Univ BA67 PGCE75. SW Minl Tr Course 87. **d** 90 **p** 94. Par Dn Stoke Damerel *Ex* 90-93; Dioc Children's Adv *Bradf* 93-01; Par Dn Baildon 93-94; C 94-96; P-in-c Denholme Gate 96-01; P-in-c Tuxford w Weston and Markham Clinton *S'well* from 01. *The Vicarage, Lincoln Road, Tuxford, Newark NG22 0HP* Tel (01777) 870497 Fax as telephone

THOMAS, The Ven Elwyn Bernard. b 45. Univ of Wales (Swansea) BSc68. St Mich Coll Llan BD71. **d** 71 **p** 72. C Aberdare St Fagan *Llan* 71-74; C Merthyr Dyfan 74-76; R Dowlais 76-86; V Llangynwyd w Maesteg 86-00; Can Llan Cathl 98-00; R Llandyrnog and Llangwyfan *St As* from 00; Adn St As from 00. *The Rectory, Ffordd Las, Llandyrnog, Denbigh LL16 4LT* Tel (01824) 790777 Fax 790877 E-mail bernardthomas@bun.com

THOMAS, Canon Ernest Keith. b 49. Univ of Wales (Cardiff) DipTh76. St Mich Coll Llan 73. **d** 76 **p** 77. C Swansea St Gabr *S & B* 76-79; C Killay 79-81; S Africa 81-92 and from 96; Prec Kimberley Cathl 81-84; R Kimberley St Aug 84-92; R Kimberley St Alb 89-92; Can Kimberley Cathl 86-92; V Aberdare *Llan* 93-96; Sub-Dean Bloemfontein Cathl from 96. *PO Box 1523, Bloemfontein, 9300 South Africa* Tel (0027) (51) 447 5951

THOMAS, Canon Euros Lloyd. b 53. Bris Poly LLB75. St Mich Coll Llan DipTh79. **d** 79 **p** 80. C Llanelli *St D* 79-84; R Cilgerran w Bridell and Llantwyd from 84; RD Cemais and Sub-Aeron from 93; P-in-c Clydau from 00; Can St D Cathl from 03. *The Rectory, Cilgerran, Cardigan SA43 2RZ* Tel (01239) 614500

THOMAS, Frank Lowth. b 22. Lon Coll of Div 64. **d** 66 **p** 67. C Walthamstow St Mary *Chelmsf* 66-68; C Bickenhill w Elmdon *Birm* 68-71; R Carlton Colville *Nor* 71-81; R Smallburgh w Dilham w Honing and Crostwight 81-85; rtd 85; Perm to Offic *Nor* from 86. *7 Mill Close, Salhouse, Norwich NR13 6QB* Tel (01603) 720376

THOMAS, Geler Harries. b 28. St D Coll Lamp BA55. St Mich Coll Llan. **d** 57 **p** 58. C Llanelli Ch Ch *St D* 57-62; V Llandyssilio and Egremont 62-69; V Llanedy 69-79; V Llangennech and Hendy 79-88; V Llanegwad w Llanfynydd 88-92; RD Llangadog and Llandeilo 89-90; rtd 92. *14 Llys-y-Ferin, Pont-ar-Gothi, Nantgaredig, Carmarthen SA32 7NF* Tel (01267) 290516

THOMAS, Geoffrey Brynmor. b 34. K Coll Lon BA56 AKC56. Ridley Hall Cam 58. **d** 60 **p** 61. C Harlow New Town w Lt Parndon *Chelmsf* 60-65; V Leyton All SS 65-74; V Haley Hill *Wakef* 74-82; R The Winterbournes and Compton Valence *Sarum* 82-89; TV Cheltenham St Mark *Glouc* 89-92; P-in-c Dowdeswell and Andoversford w the Shiptons etc 92-95; RD Northleach 92-95; rtd 95; Perm to Offic *B & W* from 96. *48 Riverside Walk, Midsomer Norton, Bath BA3 2PD* Tel (01761) 414146

THOMAS, Geoffrey Charles. b 30. St Jo Coll Nottm LTh ALCD64. **d** 64 **p** 65. C York St Paul *York* 64-67; C Cheltenham Ch Ch *Glouc* 67-70; V Whitgift w Adlingfleet *Sheff* 70-74; P-in-c Eastoft 72-74; V Mortomley St Sav 74-88; R Middleton Cheney w Chacombe *Pet* 88-93; rtd 94; Perm to Offic *York* from 94. *77 Penyghent Avenue, York YO31 0QH* Tel (01904) 414082

THOMAS, Canon Geoffrey Heale. b 29. St Mich Coll Llan 58. **d** 60 **p** 61. C Llansamlet *S & B* 60-63; Nigeria 63-67; V Swansea St Nic *S & B* 67-80; CF (TA) 72; V Oystermouth *S & B* 80-98; Hon Can Brecon Cathl 92-96; Can 97-98; rtd 98. *19 Ffordd Dryden, Killay, Swansea SA2 7PA* Tel (01792) 206308

THOMAS, George. b 46. Leeds Univ BEd69. St Jo Coll Dur 75 Cranmer Hall Dur DipTh77. **d** 78 **p** 79. C Highfield *Liv* 78-83; V Chorley St Jas *Blackb* 83-02; P-in-c Blackb St Gabr from 02. *St Gabriel's Vicarage, 6 Charnwood Close, Blackburn BB2 7BT* Tel (01254) 581412 E-mail gt@fish.co.uk

THOMAS, Glyn. b 36. Lon Univ BPharm61. St Deiniol's Hawarden 80. **d** 82 **p** 83. C Rhyl w St Ann *St As* 83-85; R Llanycil w Bala and Frongoch and Llangower etc 85-03; RD Penllyn 96-03; rtd 03. *Blaen-y-Coed, 7 Lon Helyg, Abergele LL22 7JQ*

THOMAS, Gordon Herbert. b 43. Guildf Dioc Min Course 00. **d** 00 **p** 01. OLM Cove St Jo *Guildf* from 00. *13 Tay Close, Farnborough GU14 9NB* Tel (01252) 512347

THOMAS, Greville Stephen. b 64. Qu Coll Birm 94. **d** 96 **p** 97. C Hillingdon All SS *Lon* 96-99; C Acton Green from 99. *276 Osborne Road, London W3 8SR* Tel (020) 8993 3237 E-mail grev@totalise.co.uk

THOMAS, Gwilym Ivor. b 20. St D Coll Lamp BA41 Univ of Wales MPhil95. **d** 43 **p** 44. C Llansadwrn w Llanwrda *St D* 43-47; C Llanedy 47-53; V Ambleston w St Dogwells 53-62; V Llansantffraed 62-70; V Llansantffraed and Llanbadarn Trefeglwys 70-80; V Llansantffraed and Llanbadarn Trefeglwys etc 80-85; RD Glyn Aeron 78-85; rtd 85. *Stanley House, 9 Hill Street, New Quay SA45 9QD* Tel (01545) 560167

THOMAS, Harald Daniel. b 34. FInstTT. **d** 97. Par Dn Pontnewydd *Mon* from 97. *Raldoro, Mount Pleasant Road, Pontnewydd, Cwmbran NP44 1BD* Tel (01633) 771353

THOMAS, Herbert John. b 13. AKC42. **d** 42 **p** 43. C Hendford *B & W* 42-44; C Street 44-48; C-in-c Southdown St Barn CD 48-58; V Bath St Barn 58-62; V Bridgwater St Jo 62-73; R Compton Martin w Ubley 73-79; rtd 79; Perm to Offic *B & W* from 79. *39 Longleat Court, Park Road, Frome BA11 1ED* Tel (01373) 463762

THOMAS, Miss Hilary Faith. b 43. Ex Univ BA65 Southn Univ PGCE66. Trin Coll Bris DipHE92 DPS94. **d** 94 **p** 95. C Yeovil w Kingston Pitney *B & W* 94-98; V Brislington St Luke *Bris* from 98. *The Vicarage, St Luke's Gardens, Bristol BS4 4NW* Tel 0117-977 7633

THOMAS, Hugh. b 25. St D Coll Lamp BA50. **d** 51 **p** 52. C Penbre *St D* 51-55; P-in-c Moelgrove and Monington 55-63; V Llanfynydd 63-74; V Pontyates 74-80; V Pontyates and Llangyndeyrn 80-90; rtd 91. *90 Priory Street, Kidwelly SA17 4TY* Tel (01554) 890114

THOMAS, Canon Huw Glyn. b 42. Univ of Wales (Lamp) BA62 Linacre Coll Ox BA65 MA69. Wycliffe Hall Ox 62. **d** 65 **p** 66. C Oystermouth *S & B* 65-68; Asst Chapl Solihull Sch 68-69; Chapl 69-73; Selection Sec ACCM 73-78; C Loughton St Jo *Chelmsf* 74-77; V Bury St Jo *Man* 78-83; Dir of Ords 82-87; V Bury St Jo w St Mark 83-86; Can Res and Treas Liv Cathl *Liv* 87-95; Ethiopia from 95. *St Matthew's Church, PO Box 109, Addis Ababa, Ethiopia*

THOMAS, Ian Melville. b 50. Jes Coll Ox BA71 MA75. St Steph Ho Ox 71. **d** 73 **p** 74. PV St D Cathl *St D* 73-77; Chapl RAF 77-95; Command Chapl RAF 95-00; V Llanelli *St D* 01-02; TR from 02. *The Vicarage, 1 Cysgod y Llan, Llanelli SA15 3HD* Tel (01554) 772072

THOMAS, Ian William. b 53. Bedf Coll of Educn CertEd74. Ox Min Course 89. **d** 92 **p** 93. NSM Fenny Stratford *Ox* from 92. *5 Laburnum Grove, Bletchley, Milton Keynes MK2 2JW* Tel (01908) 644457

THOMAS, Canon Idris. b 48. St D Coll Lamp DipTh71. **d** 71 **p** 72. C Llanbeblig w Caernarfon and Betws Garmon etc *Ban* 71-75; P-in-c Llanaelhaiarn 75-77; R Llanaelhaearn w Clynnog Fawr from 77; RD Arfon 93-00; AD from 02; Hon Can Ban Cathl from 99. *Y Rheithordy, Trefor, Caernarfon LL54 5HN* Tel (01286) 660547

THOMAS, Mrs Iris. b 18. Univ of Wales (Abth) BA39 DipEd40. Llan Ord Course. **d** 80 **p** 91. Hon C Tylorstown *Llan* 80-84; Hon C Ferndale w Maerdy 84-85; rtd 85; Perm to Offic *Llan* from 86. *1 Maerdy Court, Maerdy Road, Ferndale CF3 4BT* Tel (01443) 755235

THOMAS, Jennifer Monica. b 58. Wilson Carlile Coll Dip Evang82 Sarum & Wells Th Coll DipMin93. **d** 93 **p** 94. Par Dn Wandsworth St Paul *S'wark* 93-94; C Forest Hill 97-02; V Mitcham Ascension from 02. *The Vicarage, Sherwood Park Road, Mitcham CR4 1NE* Tel (020) 8764 1258

THOMAS, John. *See* THOMAS, Cheeramattathu John

THOMAS, John Arun. b 47. Bombay Univ BA69 MA72 Nottm Univ CertEd80 Bombay Univ PhD84. Oak Hill Th Coll 84. **d** 88 **p** 89. C Liv Ch Ch Norris Green *Liv* 88-89; C Wavertree St Mary 89-93; V St Mary Cray and St Paul's Cray *Roch* 93-96; India 96-99; Prin Bombay Scottish Sch 97-99; Australia from 99. *7/26 Hillcrest Road, Quakers Hill, NSW, Australia 2763* E-mail arunn51@hotmail.com

THOMAS, Canon John Herbert Samuel. b 34. Pemb Coll Cam BA57 MA64. St Mich Coll Llan 57. **d** 58 **p** 59. C Port Talbot St Theodore *Llan* 58-60; C Llantwit Major and St Donat's 60-67; P-in-c Barry All SS 67-74; V Dinas w Penygraig 74-85; V Pontypridd St Cath 85-90; V Pontypridd St Cath w St Matt 90-99; RD Pontypridd 90-99; Can Llan Cathl from 95; rtd 99. *Ty Canon, Salisbury Road, Abercynon, Mountain Ash CF45 4NU* Tel (01443) 742577

THOMAS, John Roger. Trin Coll Carmarthen BA. St Mich Coll Llan. **d** 03. C Cardigan w Mwnt and Y Ferwig w Llangoedmor *St D* from 03. *8 Heol y Wern, North Park Estate, Cardigan SA43 1NE* Tel (01239) 613685

THOMAS, John Thurston. b 28. Univ of Wales (Swansea) BSc48 DipEd49 Leeds Univ PhD58 CChem FRSC65. Glouc Sch of Min 88. **d** 90 **p** 91. NSM S Cerney w Cerney Wick and Down Ampney *Glouc* 90-96; Perm to Offic *Glouc* 96-01; *S & B* from 01. *4 Nicholl Court, Mumbles, Swansea SA3 4LZ* Tel (01792) 360098

THOMAS, Judith. *See* THOMAS, Dorothy Judith

THOMAS, Julian Mark. b 48. SW Minl Tr Course 00. **d** 03. C Okehampton w Inwardleigh, Bratton Clovelly etc *Ex* from 03. *19 Fern Meadow, Okehampton EX20 1PB* Tel (01837) 54263 E-mail jmthomas@fish.co.uk

THOMAS, Mrs June Marion. b 31. Univ of Wales BA53 DipEd54. NEOC 83. **dss** 86 **d** 87 **p** 94. Stockton St Pet *Dur* 86-87; Hon Par Dn 87-89; NSM Stockton St Mark 89-94; P-in-c 94-01; rtd 01. *50 Brisbane Grove, Stockton-on-Tees TS18 5BP* Tel (01642) 582408

THOMAS, Keith. b 55. Southlands Coll Lon TCert80. N Ord Course 92. **d** 95 **p** 96. NSM Knuzden *Blackb* 95-98; NSM Darwen St Pet w Hoddlesden from 98; Tullyallan Sch Darwen from 99. *20 Duxbury Street, Darwen BB3 2LA* Tel (01254) 776484

THOMAS, Kenneth. *See* THOMAS, Canon William Kenneth

THOMAS, Leighton. *See* THOMAS, Adrian Leighton

THOMAS, Leslie Richard. b 45. Lon Coll of Div 65. **d** 69 **p** 70. C Knotty Ash St Jo *Liv* 69-72; C Sutton 72-74; TV 74-77; V Banks 77-82; V Gt Crosby All SS 82-92; P-in-c Marthall *Ches* 92-02; Chapl David Lewis Cen for Epilepsy 92-02; V Bickerton, Bickley,

Harthill and Burwardsley from 02. *The Vicarage, Harthill Road, Burwardsley, Chester CH3 9NU* Tel (01829) 770067

THOMAS, Ms Margaret. b 41. Bris Univ BSc63 Leeds Univ CertEd64 Ex Univ ADC70. Cranmer Hall Dur 81. **dss** 83 **d** 87 **p** 94. Maghull *Liv* 83-86; Asst Chapl Liv Univ 86-89; St Luke in the City 86-87; Par Dn 87-89; Chapl St Helen's and Knowsley HA 89-92; Chapl St Helen's and Knowsley Hosps Trust 92-02; rtd 02. *68 The Northern Road, Liverpool L23 2RQ* Tel 0151-931 5707

THOMAS, Mark Wilson. b 51. Dur Univ BA72 Hull Univ MA89. Ripon Coll Cuddesdon 76. **d** 78 **p** 79. C Chapelthorpe *Wakef* 78-81; C Seaford w Sutton *Chich* 81-84; V Gomersal *Wakef* 84-92; TR Almondbury w Farnley Tyas 92-01; RD Almondbury 93-01; Hon Can Wakef Cathl 99-01; P-in-c Shrewsbury St Chad w St Mary *Lich* from 01. *25 The Crescent, Town Walls, Shrewsbury SY1 1TH* Tel (01743) 343761 Fax as telephone E-mail saint.chads@ukonline.co.uk

THOMAS, Sister Mary Josephine. b 30. Ripon Dioc Tr Coll TCert50 Carl Dioc Tr Course 88. **d** 90 **p** 94. NSM Hawes Side *Blackb* 90-93; NSM St Annes St Marg 93-00; Perm to Offic from 00. *112 St Andrew's Road North, Lytham St Annes FY8 2JQ* Tel (01253) 728016

THOMAS, Michael Longdon Sanby. b 34. Trin Hall Cam BA55 MA60. Wells Th Coll 56. **d** 58 **p** 59. C Sandal St Helen *Wakef* 58-60; Chapl Portsm Cathl *Portsm* 60-64; V Shedfield 64-69; V Portchester 69-98; rtd 98. *188 Castle Street, Portchester, Fareham PO16 9QH* Tel (023) 9242 0416 Fax as telephone E-mail thomasfamily73@cwtv.net

THOMAS, Michael Rosser David. b 74. Kent Univ BA96. St Steph Ho Ox BTh02. **d** 02 **p** 03. C Aberavon *Llan* from 02. *The Parsonage, 9 James Street, Port Talbot SA13 1AR* Tel (01639) 680585 E-mail fr.michael@ntlworld.co.uk

THOMAS, Moray. *See* THOMAS, Charles Moray Stewart Reid

THOMAS, Nigel Bruce. b 63. St Jo Coll Nottm MA98. BD. **d** 97 **p** 98. C Millom *Carl* 97-02; R Bentham *Bradf* from 02. *The Vicarage, 27 Station Road, Bentham, Lancaster LA2 7LH* Tel (01524) 261321

THOMAS, Owen James. b 17. Univ of Wales BA38. Tyndale Hall Bris 38. **d** 40 **p** 41. C Wandsworth St Steph *S'wark* 40-43; C Dagenham *Chelmsf* 43-46; R Glas St Silas *Glas* 46-51; Tutor Lon Bible Coll 51-62; Chapl and Lect 62-76; P-in-c Woburn Square Ch Ch *Lon* 51-52; Aux Chapl US Airforce 66-68; Hon C Northwood Em *Lon* 70-76; V Canonbury St Steph 76-85; rtd 85; Perm to Offic *Chich* from 85. *22 Woodland Way, Fairlight, Hastings TN35 4AU* Tel (01424) 813613 E-mail oth83ogt@aol.com

THOMAS, Mrs Pamela Sybil. b 38. Ripon Coll Cuddesdon 88. **d** 90 **p** 94. Par Dn Preston w Sutton Poyntz and Osmington w Poxwell *Sarum* 90-94; C 94-96; P-in-c Weymouth St Edm from 96; P-in-c Abbotsbury, Portesham and Langton Herring from 97; Chapl Westhaven Hosp Weymouth from 96. *The Rectory, Portesham, Weymouth DT3 4HB* Tel (01305) 871217

THOMAS, Mrs Patricia Margaret. b 44. Hockerill Coll Cam TCert65. Sarum & Wells Th Coll 79. **dss** 82 **d** 87 **p** 94. Verwood *Sarum* 82-87; Hon Par Dn 87-88; Chapl Asst Friern Hosp Lon 88-90; Par Dn Upton cum Chalvey *Ox* 90-94; C 94-95; Perm to Offic *Portsm* from 95. *74 Fleet End Road, Warsash, Southampton SO31 9JE* Tel (01489) 583819 Fax as telephone E-mail patthomas@warsashcounselling.freeserve.co.uk

THOMAS, Canon Patrick Hungerford Bryan. b 52. St Cath Coll Cam BA73 MA77 Leeds Univ BA78 Univ of Wales PhD82. Coll of Resurr Mirfield 76. **d** 79 **p** 80. C Aberystwyth *St D* 79-81; C Carmarthen St Pet 81-82; R Llangeitho and Blaenpennal w Betws Leucu etc 82-84; Warden of Ords 83-86; R Brechfa w Abergorlech etc 84-01; V Carmarthen St Dav from 01; Can St D Cathl from 00. *St David's Vicarage, 4 Penllwyn Park, Carmarthen SA31 3BU* Tel (01267) 234183

THOMAS, Paul Richard. b 75. Univ of Wales (Cardiff) BA96 MA99. Ripon Coll Cuddesdon BA01. **d** 02 **p** 03. C Wanstead St Mary w Ch Ch *Chelmsf* from 02. *13 Wanstead Place, London E11 2SW* Tel (020) 8530 4970 E-mail paul@traditionalthomas.com

THOMAS, Canon Paul Robert. b 42. OBE02. N Ord Course. **d** 82 **p** 83. C Hull Newland St Jo *York* 82-84; P-in-c Rowley 84-87; Soc Resp Officer Hull 84-87; R Rowley w Skidby 87-88; TR Barking St Marg w St Patr *Chelmsf* 88-93; Gen Sec and Admin St Luke's Hosp for Clergy 93-98; Can and Preb Chich Cathl *Chich* from 98; P in O from 98; rtd 03. *St Luke's House, 11 Wells Road, Walsingham NR22 6DL* Tel (01328) 820433 Mobile 0778-987395

THOMAS, Paul Wyndham. b 55. Oriel Coll Ox BA76 BTh78 MA80. Wycliffe Hall Ox 77. **d** 79 **p** 80. C Llangynwyd w Maesteg *Llan* 79-85; TV Langport Area Chs *B & W* 85-90; P-in-c Thorp Arch w Walton *York* 90-93; Clergy Tr Officer from 90; V Nether w Upper Poppleton from 93. *The Vicarage, 15 Nether Way, Upper Poppleton, York YO26 6JQ* Tel (01904) 794744

THOMAS, Canon Peter George Hartley. b 38. AKC63. **d** 64 **p** 65. C Leigh Park St Fran CD *Portsm* 64-69; V Cosham 69-77; R

Hayes *Roch* 77-01; Hon Can Roch Cathl 00-01; rtd 01. *Somershey, 71 High Street, Church Stretton SY6 6BY* Tel (01694) 723125

THOMAS, Peter James. b 53. Lon Univ BSc75. Trin Coll Bris 77. **d** 80 **p** 81. C Hucclecote *Glouc* 80-84; C Loughborough Em *Leic* 84-85; TV Parr *Liv* 85-92; V Eckington *Worc* from 92; V Defford w Besford from 92; RD Pershore from 00. *The Vicarage, Drakes Bridge Road, Eckington, Pershore WR10 3BN* Tel (01386) 750203 Fax as telephone E-mail pthomas5@aol.com

THOMAS, Canon Peter Rhys. b 37. TCD BA59 MA72 MInstPkg MCIPD. **d** 72 **p** 73. C Cong *T, K & A* 73-75; I 75-77; C Bingley All SS *Bradf* 77-79; V Shelf 79-81; Producer Relig Broadcasting Viking Radio 81-84; P-in-c Croxton *Linc* 81-82; P-in-c Ulceby 81-82; P-in-c Wootton 81-82; P-in-c Ulceby Gp 82; V 82-84; R E and W Tilbury and Linford *Chelmsf* 84-89; I Celbridge w Straffan and Newcastle-Lyons *D & G* 89-93; I Youghal Union *C, C & R* 93-99; Dioc Communications Officer (Cork) 95-99; Can Cork Cathl 97-99; Preb Cloyne Cathl 97-99; rtd 99; Rep Leprosy Miss Munster from 00. *Abina Cottage, Ballykenneally, Ballymacoda, Co Cork, Irish Republic* Tel (00353) (24) 98082 E-mail prthomas@iol.ie

THOMAS, Peter Wilson. b 58. BD AKC. Ripon Coll Cuddesdon. **d** 82 **p** 83. C Stockton St Pet *Dur* 82-85; TV Solihull *Birm* 85-90; V Rednal from 90. *St Stephen's Vicarage, Edgewood Road, Rednal, Birmingham B45 8SG* Tel 0121-453 3347

THOMAS, Philip Harold Emlyn. b 41. Cant Univ (NZ) BA64 MA77 Dur Univ PhD82. Melbourne Coll of Div BD68. **d** 68 **p** 69. Australia 68-71; New Zealand 71-77; Fell and Chapl Univ Coll Dur 77-83; V Heighington *Dur* from 84; AD Darlington 94-00. *The Vicarage, 15 East Green, Heighington, Newton Aycliffe DL5 6PP* Tel (01325) 312134 Fax as telephone E-mail philip.thomas@durham.anglican.org

THOMAS, Philip John. b 52. Liv Poly BSc74 Leeds Poly 77. Trin Coll Bris 94. **d** 96 **p** 97. C Skelton w Upleatham *York* 96-97; C Acomb St Steph 97-01; V Woodthorpe *S'well* from 01; Chapl Mother's Union from 03. *St Mark's Vicarage, 37A Melbury Road, Nottingham NG5 4PG* Tel 0115-926 7859

THOMAS, Ralph Pilling. b 23. Univ of Wales (Lamp) BA49. Wycliffe Hall Ox 49. **d** 51 **p** 52. C S Shore H Trin *Blackb* 51-53; C Chorley St Geo 53-59; V Wellow *B & W* 59-63; V Hinton Charterhouse 59-63; R Coppull St Jo *Blackb* 63-68; Asst Chapl HM Pris Wandsworth 68-69; Chapl HM Pris Leeds 69-74; R Kirklington w Burneston and Wath *Ripon* 74-88; RD Wensley 85-88; rtd 88; Perm to Offic *St E* 88-99. *50 Firby Road, Bedale DL8 2BH* Tel (01677) 423019

THOMAS, Ramon Lorenzo. b 44. Victoria Univ Wellington BCA73 Mass Inst of Tech MSc80 CA73. Oak Hill Th Coll 89. **d** 97 **p** 98. NSM Yateley *Win* 97-99; Chairman Judah Trust from 99. *1 Dickens Way, Yateley GU46 6XX* Tel (01252) 682224 E-mail judahtrust@aol.com

THOMAS, Rhys. *See* THOMAS, Canon Peter Rhys

THOMAS, Richard. b 45. St D Coll Lamp 68. **d** 71 **p** 72. C Llanelli St Paul *St D* 71-74; Chapl RN 74-90; V St Ishmael's w Llan-saint and Ferryside *St D* 90-93; V Maindee *Mon* 93-95; V St Clears w Llangynin and Llanddowror etc *St D* from 95. *The Vicarage, High Street, St Clears, Carmarthen SA33 4EE* Tel (01994) 230266

THOMAS, Richard Frederick. b 24. Qu Coll Cam BA45 MA49. Ridley Hall Cam 47. **d** 49 **p** 50. C S Croydon Em *Cant* 49-51; Chapl and Ho Master Haileybury Coll 51-67; Jerusalem 67-74; Ho Master Bp Luffa Sch Chich 74-80; Lic to Offic Chich 75-77; Hon C Chich St Pancras and St Jo 78-80; R N Mundham w Hunston and Merston 80-89; Perm to Offic *Portsm* from 89; C Compton, the Mardens, Stoughton and Racton *Chich* 96-00; C Stansted 96-00; rtd 00; Perm to Offic *Chich* from 00. *16 Brent Court, Emsworth PO10 7JA* Tel (01243) 430613 Mobile 07947-518314 E-mail thomasrb@ntlworld.com

THOMAS, Richard Paul. b 50. MIPR. Wycliffe Hall Ox 74. **d** 76 **p** 77. C Abingdon w Shippon *Ox* 76-80; R Win All SS w Chilcomb and Chesil *Win* 80-88; Dioc Communications Officer 83-89; Dioc Communications Officer *Ox* from 89. *18 Eason Drive, Abingdon OX14 3YD* Tel (01235) 553360 *or* (01865) 244566 Pager 01893-703279 Fax (01865) 790470 E-mail communications@oxford.anglican.org

THOMAS, Robert Stanley. b 31. Lon Univ BD65 Man Univ MEd78. Sarum Th Coll 66. **d** 67 **p** 68. C Maltby *Sheff* 67-70; Lic to Offic *St Alb* 70-72; Man 72-79; *St As* 80-82; Dioc RE Adv *St As* 82-96; V Glyndyfrdwy and Llansantffraid Glyn Dyfrdwy 82-96; RD Edeirnion 88-96; rtd 96. *Lynward, 74 Middleton Road, Oswestry SY11 2LF* Tel (01691) 654326

THOMAS, Robin. b 27. Cen Sch of Art Lon NDD50. St Steph Ho Ox 89. **d** 89 **p** 90. NSM Clifton All SS w St Jo *Bris* 89-94; P-in-c Tintagel *Truro* 94-97; rtd 97; Perm to Offic *Truro* from 97. *22 Hendra Vean, Truro TR1 3TU* Tel (01872) 271276

THOMAS, Roderick Charles Howell. b 54. LSE BSc75. Wycliffe Hall Ox 91. **d** 93 **p** 94. C Plymouth St Andr w St Paul and St Geo *Ex* 93-95; C Plymouth St Andr and St Paul Stonehouse 95-99; P-in-c Elburton from 99. *St Matthew's Vicarage, 3 Sherford Road, Plymouth PL9 8DQ* Tel (01752) 402771 E-mail roderick.t@virgin.net

THOMAS, Roger. *See* THOMAS, John Roger

THOMAS, Ronald Buford. b 62. Memphis State Univ (USA) BA84 Emory Univ Atlanta MDiv88 Peterho Cam PhD02. Candler Sch of Th 84. **d** 93 **p** 94. USA 93-99; Asst P Salt Lake City St Paul 93-95; Assoc R 95-99; Perm to Offic *Ely* from 99. *Flat 2, 28 Parkside, Cambridge CB1 1JE* Tel (01223) 741432 E-mail rbt21@cam.ac.uk

THOMAS, Roy. *See* LUTHER THOMAS, The Ven Ilar Roy

THOMAS, Russen William. b 30. Univ of Wales (Lamp) BA55. St Mich Coll Llan 55. **d** 57 **p** 58. C Newport St Jo Bapt *Mon* 57-59; C Pembroke Dock *St D* 59-62; R St Florence and Redberth 62-69; V Newport St Julian *Mon* 69-79; V Stratton *Truro* 79-88; RD Stratton 83-88; V Lanteglos by Fowey 88-91; Miss to Seamen 88-97; rtd 92; Chapl Playa de Las Americas Tenerife *Eur* 93-97; Perm to Offic *Cov* from 97. *Porthkerry, 1 Beech Road, Oxhill, Warwick CV35 0QS*

THOMAS, Simon Jonathan Francklin. b 51. Sheff Univ BA72 Nottm Univ BA78 Open Univ MA02. St Jo Coll Nottm 76. **d** 80 **p** 80. SAMS Peru 80-82; C Camberwell All SS *S'wark* 82; SAMS Bolivia 83-95; C Ashtead *Guildf* from 96. *1 Oakfield Road, Ashtead KT21 2RE* Tel (01372) 813334 Fax 813352 E-mail simon@simonjfthomas.freeserve.co.uk

THOMAS, Preb Stephen Blayney. b 35. St D Coll Lamp BA62. Bp Burgess Hall Lamp DipTh63. **d** 63 **p** 64. C Ledbury *Heref* 63-67; C Bridgnorth w Tasley 67-68; C Clun w Chapel Lawn, Bettws-y-Crwyn and Newcastle 68-73; C Clungunford w Clunbury and Clunton, Bedstone etc 68-73; V Norbold 73-84; RD Bridgnorth 81-83; R Kingsland 84-96; P-in-c Aymestrey and Leinthall Earles w Wigmore etc 84-96; P-in-c Eardisland 84-96; Preb Heref Cathl 85-01; R Kingsland w Eardisland, Aymestrey etc 97-99; rtd 99; Perm to Offic *Heref* from 00; *Worc* from 00. *28 Castle Close, Burford, Tenbury Wells WR15 8AY* Tel (01584) 819642

THOMAS, Stuart Grahame. b 54. Pemb Coll Cam BA77 MA81 ATCL97. Ridley Hall Cam 85. **d** 87 **p** 88. C Guildf H Trin w St Mary *Guildf* 87-91; V Churt 91-94; V Ewell St Fran from 94; Dioc Ecum Officer from 99. *St Francis's Vicarage, 61 Ruxley Lane, Epsom KT19 0JG* Tel (020) 8393 5616 E-mail revstuart.thomas@virgin.net

THOMAS, Canon Sydney Robert. b 44. Univ of Wales (Swansea) BA65 MA83. St D Coll Lamp LTh67. **d** 67 **p** 68. C Llanelli *St D* 67-77; V Pontyberem 77-01; TR Cwm Gwendraeth from 01; RD Cydweli from 94; Can St D Cathl from 94; Chan 01-03; Treas from 03. *The Vicarage, 56 Llannon Road, Pontyberem, Llanelli SA15 5LY* Tel (01269) 870345

THOMAS, Theodore Eilir. b 36. Univ of Wales (Lamp) BA58. Sarum Th Coll 58. **d** 60 **p** 61. C Fenton *Lich* 60-63; C Stourport All SS and St Mich CD *Worc* 63-67; V Worc H Trin 67-74; P-in-c Dudley St Fran 74-79; V 79-83; R Plympton St Maurice *Ex* from 83. *St Maurice's Rectory, 31 Wain Park, Plympton, Plymouth PL7 3HX* Tel (01752) 346114

THOMAS, Thomas. b 68. Selw Coll Cam BA90. Wycliffe Hall Ox 91. **d** 93 **p** 94. C Much Woolton *Liv* 93-97; V Carr Mill from 97. *St David's Vicarage, 27 Erkdale Avenue, Carr Mill, St Helens WA11 7EN* Tel (01744) 732330

THOMAS, Thomas Alan. b 37. K Coll Lon BD60 AKC60. St Boniface Warminster 60. **d** 61 **p** 62. C Washington *Dur* 61-65; C Bishopwearmouth St Mary V w St Pet CD 65-70; V Ruishton w Thornfalcon *B & W* 70-82; R Hutton 82-94; V Frome Ch Ch 94-96; Chapl Victoria Hosp Frome 94-96; R Camerton w Dunkerton, Foxcote and Shoscombe *B & W* 96-00; rtd 00; Perm to Offic *B & W* from 00. *12 Farrington Way, Farrington Gurney, Bristol BS39 6US* Tel (01761) 453434

THOMAS, Thomas John Samuel. b 21. St D Coll Lamp BA48. **d** 49 **p** 50. C Dafen and Llwynhendy *St D* 49-50; Chapl RAF 52-77; QHC 73-85; V Horsham *Chich* 77-85; rtd 85; Perm to Offic *St D* from 85. *1 Glynhir Road, Llandybie, Ammanford SA18 2TA* Tel (01269) 850726

THOMAS, Canon Thomas Vernon. b 21. St D Coll Lamp BA42 Selw Coll Cam BA44 MA48. St Mich Coll Llan 44. **d** 45 **p** 46. C St Brides Minor *Llan* 45-47; Ripon Cathl *Ripon* 47-50; Min Can and Succ Ripon Cathl 47-50; C Leeds St Pet 50-55; V Beeston 55-77; Hon Can Ripon Cathl 75-89; R Spofforth w Kirk Deighton 77-89; rtd 89; Perm to Offic *Ripon* from 89. *The Lodge, Main Street, East Keswick, Leeds LS17 9DB* Tel (01937) 573033

THOMAS, Virginia Jacqueline. b 48. UEA BA70. Yale Div Sch MDiv97. **d** 00 **p** 01. NSM Chelsea St Luke and Ch Ch *Lon* from 00. *Flat 5, 15 Egerton Gardens, London SW3 2BW* Tel (020) 7589 0460 E-mail ginny_tea@aol.com

THOMAS, William George. b 29. JP. FRSA Birm Univ BA50 CertEd51. EAMTC 82. **d** 85 **p** 86. NSM Brampton *Ely* 85-87; NSM Bluntisham w Earith 87-89; P-in-c Foxton 89-95; rtd 95; Perm to Offic *Ely* from 95. *3 The Paddock, Bluntisham, Huntingdon PE17 3NR* Tel (01487) 842057

THOMAS, The Ven William Jordison. b 27. K Coll Cam BA50 MA55. Cuddesdon Coll 51. **d** 53 **p** 54. C Byker St Ant *Newc* 53-56; C Berwick H Trin 56-59; V Alwinton w Holystone and Alnham 59-70; V Alston cum Garrigill w Nenthead and Kirkhaugh 70-80; P-in-c Lambley w Knaresdale 72-80; RD

Bamburgh and Glendale 81-83; TR Glendale Gp 80-83; Adn Northd and Can Res Newc Cathl 83-92; rtd 92; Perm to Offic *Newc* from 92. *Wark Cottage, Whittingham, Alnwick NE66 4RB* Tel (01665) 574300

THOMAS, Canon William **Kenneth.** b 19. Mert Coll Ox BA40 MA44. Westcott Ho Cam 40. **d** 42 **p** 43. C Brislington St Luke *Bris* 42-47; C Westbury-on-Trym St Alb 47-52; CF 49-51; V Oldland and Longwell Green *Bris* 52-71; V Minety w Oaksey 71-82; P-in-c 82-84; RD Malmesbury 73-79; Hon Can Bris Cathl 77-84; P-in-c Crudwell w Ashley 82-84; rtd 84; Perm to Offic *Bris* 84-03. *1 Oaktree Court, Portland Drive, Willen, Milton Keynes MK15 9LP* Tel (01908) 660618

THOMAS, The Ven William **Phillip.** b 43. Lich Th Coll 68. **d** 70 **p** 71. C Llanilid w Pencoed *Llan* 70-74; C Pontypridd St Cath 74-76; V Tonyrefail 76-84; Youth Chapl 78-80; RD Rhondda 81-84; R Neath w Llantwit 84-98; Adn Llan from 97; V Caerau w Ely 98-00. *6 Rachel Close, Cardiff CF5 2SH* Tel (029) 2056 2991 Fax as telephone E-mail jeanclev@talk21.com

THOMAS, William **Rhys Ithel Phillips.** b 16. St Jo Coll Dur BA38 DipTh41 MA42. **d** 41 **p** 42. C Newport H Trin *Mon* 41-43; CF (EC) 43-48; C Usk *Mon* 48-49; V Llanishen w Trellech Grange 49-56; CF (TA) 49-56; CF 56-60; Area Sec (E Distr) Miss to Seamen 60-62; R Gt and Lt Saxham w Westley *St E* 62-68; Lic to Offic 68-78; Chapl Asst Addenbrooke's Hosp Cam 78-81; rtd 81; Perm to Offic *Ely* 85-00. *c/o P D Thomas Esq, Flat 2, Garden House, Napier Place, London W14 8LG*

THOMAS ANTHONY, Brother. *See* DE HOOP, Brother Thomas Anthony

THOMASSON, **Keith Duncan.** b 69. St Pet Coll Ox BA91 MA97 Lon Inst of Educn PGCE92. Ripon Coll Cuddesdon BA01 Bossey Ecum Inst Geneva. **d** 02 **p** 03. C Lancaster St Mary w St John and St Anne *Blackb* from 02. *25 Bishopdale Road, Lancaster LA1 5NF* Tel (01524) 844672 E-mail keiththomasson@hotmail.com

THOMPSON, **Andrew David.** b 68. Poly of Wales BSc90. Wycliffe Hall Ox 98. **d** 00 **p** 01. C Oakwood *Derby* from 00. *6 Cornflower Drive, Oakwood, Derby DE21 2SA* Tel (01332) 835739 E-mail navina@andy5.freeserve.co.uk

THOMPSON, Mrs **Angela Lorena Jennifer.** b 66. St Alb and Ox Min Course CBTS99. **d** 99 **p** 00. NSM Chalfont St Giles *Ox* from 99. *2 The Leys, Chesham Bois, Amersham HP6 5NP* Tel (01494) 726654 E-mail angelalj70@hotmail.com

THOMPSON, Canon **Anthony Edward.** b 38. Bris Univ BA61. Ridley Hall Cam 61. **d** 63 **p** 64. C Peckham St Mary Magd *S'wark* 63-66; SAMS Paraguay 67-72; C Otley *Bradf* 72-75; TV Woughton *Ox* 75-82; P-in-c Lower Nutfield *S'wark* 82-02; V S Nutfield w Outwood 02-03; RD Reigate 91-93; Local Min Adv Croydon Episc Area 93-03; Hon Can S'wark Cathl 03; rtd 03. *3 The Curlews, Shoreham-by-Sea BN43 5UQ* Tel (01273) 440183 E-mail cc@nutfield99.freeserve.co.uk

THOMPSON, **Athol James Patrick.** b 34. St Paul's Coll Grahamstown 72. **d** 74 **p** 75. S Africa 74-83; P-in-c Dewsbury St Matt and St Jo *Wakef* 84; TV Dewsbury 84-93; Chapl Staincliffe and Dewsbury Gen Hosps Wakef 84-90; Chapl Dewsbury and Distr Hosp 90-93; V Shiregreen St Jas and St Chris *Sheff* 93-99; rtd 99; Perm to Offic *Sheff* from 99. *109 Park Avenue, Chapeltown, Sheffield S35 1WH*

THOMPSON, **Barry Pearce.** b 40. St Andr Univ BSc63 Ball Coll Ox PhD66 Hull Univ MA82. NW Ord Course 76. **d** 79 **p** 80. C Cottingham *York* 79-82; V Swine 82-83; Lect Th Hull Univ 83-88; Ind Chapl *York* 83-85; Abp's Adv on Ind Issues 85-88; Can Res Chelmsf Cathl *Chelmsf* 88-98; Treas and Can Windsor 98-02; rtd 02; Perm to Offic *York* from 03. *44 Topcliffe Road, Sowerby, Thirsk YO7 1RB* Tel (01845) 525170 Mobile 07768-515790

THOMPSON, **Beverley Francis.** b 40. Bps' Coll Cheshunt 61. **d** 64 **p** 65. C St Ives *Truro* 64-67; Guyana 67-69; C Madron w Morvah *Truro* 69-72; R Mawgan w St Martin-in-Meneage 73-78; P-in-c Landulph 78-84; P-in-c St Dominic 78-84; P-in-c Crantock 84-89; P-in-c Newlyn St Newlyn 84-89; V Mullion 89-94; Miss to Seamen 89-94; RD Kerrier *Truro* 91-94; rtd 00; Perm to Offic *Truro* from 99. *8 Roscarrack Close, Falmouth TR11 4PJ* Tel (01326) 311589

THOMPSON, **Brian.** b 34. BSc. St Jo Coll Nottm. **d** 84 **p** 85. C Bletchley *Ox* 84-87; V Sneyd Green *Lich* 87-99; rtd 99; Perm to Offic *Lich* from 01. *7 Chapel Lane, Rode Heath, Stoke-on-Trent ST7 3SD* Tel (01270) 884025

THOMPSON, **David.** *See* THOMPSON, John David

THOMPSON, **David Arthur.** b 37. Clifton Th Coll. **d** 69 **p** 70. C Finchley Ch Ch *Lon* 69-72; C Barking St Marg w St Patr *Chelmsf* 72-75; TV 75-81; V Toxteth Park St Clem *Liv* 81-91; TR Parr 91-03; rtd 03. *Charis, 72 Harkwood Drive, Hamworthy, Poole BH15 4PE* Tel (01202) 668904

THOMPSON, **David Frank.** b 44. Hull Univ BA65 Nottm Univ PGCE66. St Steph Ho Ox 73. **d** 75 **p** 76. C Sidmouth, Woolbrook and Salcombe Regis *Ex* 75-78; C Lamorbey H Redeemer *Roch* 78-80; Chapl and Hd RS R Masonic Sch for Girls Rickmansworth 81-99; V Eastwood St Dav *Chelmsf* from 99. *St David's Vicarage, 400 Rayleigh Road, Leigh-on-Sea SS9 5PT*

Tel and fax (01702) 523126 Mobile 07801-951346 E-mail dthomp6310@aol.com

THOMPSON, **David John.** b 17. Selw Coll Cam BA48 MA52. Ridley Hall Cam 48. **d** 50 **p** 51. C Denton Holme *Carl* 50-53; V Fulham St Mary N End *Lon* 53-62; V Wallington H Trin *S'wark* 62-74; R Hambledon *Guildf* 74-84; rtd 84; Perm to Offic *Chich* from 85. *1 Pond Willow, North Trade Road, Battle TN33 0HU* Tel (01424) 773000

THOMPSON, **David John.** b 64. Cranmer Hall Dur Cert Th & Min 95. **d** 95 **p** 96. C Poulton-le-Sands w Morecambe St Laur *Blackb* 95-99; V Farington Moss 99-02; V Lea from 02. *45 Abingdon Drive, Ashton-on-Ribble, Preston PR2 1EY* Tel (01772) 729197

THOMPSON, Canon **Donald Frazer.** b 20. St Cath Coll Cam BA46 MA49. Coll of Resurr Mirfield 46. **d** 48 **p** 49. C Cheshunt *St Alb* 48-52; C Norton 52-56; V Wigan St Anne *Liv* 56-62; V Leeds St Aid *Ripon* 62-73; RD Allerton 70-73; R Adel 73-87; Hon Can Ripon Cathl 75-87; RD Headingley 85-87; rtd 87; Perm to Offic *Cov* from 87. *75 Cubbington Road, Leamington Spa CV32 7AQ* Tel (01926) 332935

THOMPSON, **Edward Ronald Charles.** b 25. AKC51. **d** 52 **p** 53. C Hinckley St Mary *Leic* 52-54; Jerusalem 54-55; Chapl St Boniface Coll Warminster 56-59; R Hawkchurch w Fishpond *Sarum* 59-63; V Camberwell St Mich w All So w Em *S'wark* 63-67; P-in-c St Mary le Strand w St Clem Danes *Lon* 67-74; R 74-93; rtd 93; Perm to Offic *S'wark* from 95. *3 Woodsyre, London SE26 6SS* Tel (020) 8670 8289

THOMPSON, **Frederick Robert.** b 15. Dur Univ LTh40. St Aug Coll Cant 37. **d** 40 **p** 41. C Northampton Ch Ch *Pet* 40-44; C Maidstone All SS *Cant* 44-46; India 46-57; Area Sec (Dios Birm and Lich) SPG 57-64; V Tutbury *Lich* 64-80; rtd 80; Perm to Offic *Sarum* from 80. *1 Panorama Road, Poole BH13 7RA* Tel (01202) 700735

THOMPSON, **Garry John.** b 49. Qu Coll Birm. **d** 96 **p** 97. C Wilnecote *Lich* 96-99; V Lapley w Wheaton Aston from 99; P-in-c Blymhill w Weston-under-Lizard from 99. *The Vicarage, Pinfold Lane, Wheaton Aston, Stafford ST19 9PD* Tel (01785) 840395 E-mail garrythompson@clergy.net

✓THOMPSON, The Rt Revd **Geoffrey Hewlett.** b 29. Trin Hall Cam BA52 MA56. Cuddesdon Coll 52. **d** 54 **p** 55 **c** 74. C Northampton St Matt *Pet* 54-59; V Wisbech St Aug *Ely* 59-66; V Folkestone St Sav *Cant* 66-74; Suff Bp Willesden *Lon* 74-79; Area Bp Willesden 79-85; Bp Ex 85-99; rtd 99; Hon Asst Bp Carl from 99. *Low Broomrigg, Warcop, Appleby-in-Westmorland CA16 6PT* Tel (01768) 341281

THOMPSON, **Geoffrey Peter.** b 58. St Pet Coll Ox BA80 MA82. SEITE 99. **d** 02. C Cheam *S'wark* from 02. *49 Brocks Drive, Sutton SM3 9UW* Tel (020) 8641 6535 E-mail gtchurch@dircon.co.uk

THOMPSON, **George Harry Packwood.** b 22. Qu Coll Ox BA48 MA48 BTh49. Qu Coll Birm 50. **d** 51 **p** 52. Lect Qu Coll Birm 51-53; C Coleshill *Birm* 51-53; Chapl and Lect Sarum Th Coll 53-55; Vice-Prin 55-64; V Combe *Ox* 64-85; Perm to Offic from 85; rtd 87. *12 Briar Thicket, Woodstock OX20 1NT* Tel (01993) 811915

THOMPSON, Preb **Gordon Henry Moorhouse.** b 41. Univ of Wales LLM95. K Coll Lon 63 St Boniface Warminster 66. **d** 67 **p** 68. C Leominster *Heref* 67-70; C Burford II w Greete and Hope Bagot 70-74; TV 74-89; C Burford III w Lt Heref 70-74; TV 74-89; C Tenbury 70-74; TV 74-89; TV Burford I 74-89; RD Ludlow 83-89; Preb Heref Cathl 85-97; rtd 89; Perm to Offic *Heref* from 89. *The Poplars, Bitterley Village, Ludlow SY8 3HQ* Tel (01584) 891093

THOMPSON, **Harold Anthony.** b 41. N Ord Course 84. **d** 87 **p** 88. C Leeds Belle Is St Jo and St Barn *Ripon* 87-90; V Leeds St Cypr Harehills 90-96; V Shadwell from 96. *The Vicarage, 2 Church Farm Garth, Leeds LS17 8HD* Tel 0113-273 7035

THOMPSON, **Ian Charles.** b 58. Wycliffe Hall Ox 80. **d** 83 **p** 84. C Knutsford St Jo and Toft *Ches* 83-86; C Birkenhead Ch Ch 86-88; V Balderstone *Man* 88-99; TR S Rochdale 00-01; AD Rochdale from 97; P-in-c Littleborough from 01. *The Vicarage, 19 Deardon Street, Littleborough OL15 9DZ* Tel (01706) 378334 E-mail ithompson9@aol.com

THOMPSON, **Ian David.** b 51. Hull Univ BSc72. N Ord Course 94. **d** 97 **p** 98. C Blackley St Andr *Man* 97-00; P-in-c from 00. *The Vicarage, Churchdale Road, Higher Blackley, Manchester M9 8NE* Tel 0161-740 2961

THOMPSON, **Ian George.** b 60. SEITE 99. **d** 02. NSM Walworth St Pet *S'wark* from 02. *223 Hollydale Road, London SE15 2AR* Tel (020) 7639 5015 Mobile 07985-582257

THOMPSON, **Ian Malcolm.** b 59. Wm Booth Memorial Coll CertEd79 Aber Univ BTh98 Selw Coll Cam MA02. Edin Th Coll CECM93. **d** 94 **p** 97. C Longside, Old Deer and Strichen *Ab* 94-96; R Aberdeen St Mary 96-99; Chapl and Dean of Chpl Selw Coll Cam from 99; Chapl Newnham Coll Cam from 99. *Selwyn College, Cambridge CB3 9DQ* Tel (01223) 335875 E-mail imt22@cam.ac.uk

THOMPSON, **James.** b 30. Dip Hypnotherapy 84 Nottm Univ DipEd65 DipTh65. Paton Congr Coll Nottm 61 Wycliffe Hall

Ox 66. **d** 66 **p** 67. C Woodlands *Sheff* 66-69; R Firbeck w Letwell 69-71; V Milnsbridge *Wakef* 71-80; Chapl St Luke's Hosp Huddersfield 71-80; NSM Dewsbury 80-84; Lect Huddersfield Coll FE 80-84; Dioc Chapl Aber Hosps 84-89; Dioc Supernumerary *Ab* 84-89; R Buckie 89-94; R Portsoy 89-94; rtd 95. *Peace Haven, Fron Park Road, Holywell, Flintwell CH8 7UY* Tel (01352) 712368

THOMPSON, James. b 37. Coll of Resurr Mirfield 64. **d** 67 **p** 68. C Shieldfield Ch Ch *Newc* 67-69; C Hendon *Dur* 69-74; V Gateshead St Chad Bensham 74-85; R Easington 85-90; Chapl Thorpe Hosp Easington 85-90; V Cassop cum Quarrington *Dur* from 90. *The Vicarage, Bowburn, Durham DH6 5DL* Tel 0191-377 0347

✠THOMPSON, The Rt Revd James Lawton. b 36. Em Coll Cam BA64 MA71 E Lon Poly Hon DLitt89 Ex Univ Hon DD95 ACA59 FCA70. Cuddesdon Coll 64. **d** 66 **p** 67 c 78. C E Ham St Geo *Chelmsf* 66-68; Chapl Cuddesdon Coll 68-71; Lic to Offic *S'wark* 71-72; TR Thamesmead 72-78; Suff Bp Stepney *Lon* 78-79; Area Bp Stepney 79-91; Bp B & W 91-01; rtd 02. *Watercombe House, Wheddon Cross, Minehead TA24 7BD*

THOMPSON, Jeremy James Thomas. b 58. Sunderland Univ BEd92. Cranmer Hall Dur 94. **d** 96 **p** 97. C Bedlington *Newc* 96-00; P-in-c Choppington 00-02; V from 02. *The Vicarage, Scotland Gate, Choppington NE62 5SX* Tel (01670) 822216 E-mail jeremy@jtthompson.fsnet.co.uk

THOMPSON, John **David**. b 40. Lon Univ BD65 Ch Ch Ox DPhil69. St Steph Ho Ox 65. **d** 67 **p** 68. C Solihull *Birm* 67-71; C Biddestone w Slaughterford *Bris* 71-73; Lect Wells Th Coll 71-72; C Yatton Keynell *Bris* 71-73; C Castle Combe 71-73; V Braughing *St Alb* 74-77; R Digswell 77-82; TR Digswell and Panshanger 82-98; rtd 00. *Rose of Sharon, PO Box 71, Skegness PE25 3WB* Tel (01754) 898912

THOMPSON, John Michael. b 47. Nottm Univ BTh77 Hull Univ Cert Local & Regional Hist 90. Linc Th Coll 73. **d** 77 **p** 78. C Old Brumby *Linc* 77-80; C Grantham 80-81; TV 81-84; V Holton-le-Clay 84-94; V Holton-le-Clay and Tetney 94-97; R Humshaugh w Simonburn and Wark *Newc* from 97. *The Vicarage, Humshaugh, Hexham NE46 4AA* Tel (01434) 681304

THOMPSON, John Turrell. b 57. Sheff Univ BA(Econ)79 Southn Univ BTh88. Sarum & Wells Th Coll 83. **d** 86 **p** 87. C Tavistock and Gulworthy *Ex* 86-90; TV Pinhoe and Broadclyst 90-95; P-in-c Northam w Westward Ho! and Appledore 95-96; TV Bideford, Northam, Westward Ho, Appledore etc 96-00; rtd 00. *Brambles Patch, 39 Westermore Drive, Roundswell, Barnstaple EX31 3XU*

THOMPSON, John Wilfred. b 44. CA Tr Coll 66 St Deiniol's Hawarden 84. **d** 85 **p** 86. C Rhyl w St Ann *St As* 85-87; R Fritwell w Souldern and Ardley w Fewcott *Ox* 87-97. *61 Blake Road, Bicester OX6 7HH*

THOMPSON (née LILLIE), Mrs Judith Virginia. b 44. LMH Ox BA66 Univ of E Africa DipEd67 Essex Univ MA73 Bris Univ Dip Counselling 92. Gilmore Course IDC82. dss 82 **d** 87 **p** 94. Lawrence Weston Bris 82-85; E Bris 85-95; Hon Par Dn 87-95; Chapl HM Rem Cen Pucklechurch 87-91; Chapl Asst Southmead Hosp Bris 91-95; C Knowle St Barn Bris 95-02; Bp's Adv for Past Care for Clergy and Families 97-00; Community Th St Mich Coll Llan from 00; Dir In-House Tr from 02. *St Michael's College, 54 Cardiff Road, Llandaff, Cardiff CF5 2YJ* Tel (02920) 563379

THOMPSON, Kenneth. b 31. St Deiniol's Hawarden 84. **d** 87 **p** 88. Hon Par Dn Upton (Overchurch) *Ches* 87-90; NSM Tranmere St Cath 90-95; rtd 96; Perm to Offic from 96. *33 Meadway, Upton, Wirral CH49 6JQ* Tel 0151-677 6433

THOMPSON, Kenneth (**Brother Nathanael**). b 29. St Deiniol's Hawarden 76. **d** 78 **p** 79. SSF from 62; C Llanbeblig w Caernarfon *Ban* 78-80; C Swansea St Gabr *S & B* 84-87; C Swansea St Mary w H Trin 87; C Dolgellau w Llanfachreth and Brithdir etc *Ban* 95-99; rtd 98. *Church House, Llanerchymedd LL71 8EG*

THOMPSON, Kevin. b 55. Sheff Univ BEd77. Oak Hill Th Coll DipHE89. **d** 89 **p** 90. C Brinsworth w Catcliffe *Sheff* 89-92; V Kimberworth Park 92-97; V Grenoside 97-98; Perm to Offic from 98. *Address temp unknown* E-mail kevin.thompson10@virgin.net

THOMPSON, Mark William. b 52. St Jo Coll Nottm 77. **d** 81 **p** 82. C Barnsbury St Andr and H Trin w All SS *Lon* 81-84; C Addiscombe St Mary *Cant* 84; C Addiscombe St Mary *S'wark* 85-87; V Thorpe Edge *Bradf* 87-94; Chapl Essex Rivers Healthcare NHS Trust from 94. *Colchester General Hospital, Turner Road, Colchester CO4 5JL* Tel (01206) 747474 E-mail mark.thompson@essexrivers.nhs.uk

THOMPSON, Martin Eric. b 52. FCCA. Trin Coll Bris 95. **d** 97 **p** 98. C Heref St Pet w St Owen and St Jas *Heref* 97-01; P-in-c Huntley and Longhope *Glouc* 01-02; R Huntley and Longhope, Churcham and Bulley from 03. *The Rectory, 56 Byfords Road, Huntley, Gloucester GL19 3EL* Tel (01452) 831735 E-mail revmartin@lineone.net

THOMPSON, Matthew. b 68. CCC Cam BA90 MA94 MPhil94. Ridley Hall Cam 91. **d** 94 **p** 95. C Hulme Ascension *Man* 94-97;

C Langley and Parkfield 97-98; TV 98-00; P-in-c Man Clayton St Cross w St Paul from 00. *The Rectory, 54 Clayton Hall Road, Manchester M11 4WH* Tel 0161-223 0766

THOMPSON, Mervyn Patrick. b 59. Wilson Carlile Coll 84 Coll of Resurr Mirfield 90. **d** 92 **p** 93. C Sheff St Cath Richmond Road *Sheff* 92-95; V Thurnscoe St Hilda from 95; P-in-c Thurnscoe St Helen from 99. *The Vicarage, Hanover Street, Thurnscoe, Rotherham S63 0HJ* Tel (01709) 893259

THOMPSON, Michael. b 49. NEOC 83. **d** 86 **p** 87. C Ashington *Newc* 86-88; C Ponteland 88-91; TV Newc Epiphany 91-98; P-in-c Choppington 98-99; P-in-c Woldingham *S'wark* 99-02; TV Caterham 02-03; TV Saffron Walden w Wendens Ambo, Littlebury etc *Chelmsf* from 03. *3 Bridge Cottages, Water End, Ashdon, Saffron Walden CB10 2NA* Tel (01799) 584171 E-mail rev-thompson@lineone.net

THOMPSON, Michael Bruce. b 53. N Carolina Univ BA75 Dallas Th Sem ThM79 Virginia Th Sem 79 Ch Coll Cam PhD88. **d** 80 **p** 81. Asst Min New Bern N Carolina 80-83; Chair Youth and Evang and Renewal in E Carolina 81-83; Lect Greek Cam Univ 87-88; Lect St Jo Coll Nottm 88-95; Lect NT and Dir of Studies Ridley Hall Cam from 95; Vice Prin from 00. *Dashwood House, Sidgwick Avenue, Cambridge CB3 9DA* Tel (01223) 741077 Fax 741081 E-mail mbt2@cam.ac.uk

THOMPSON, Michael James. b 55. St Andr Univ MTh78 Univ of Wales (Cardiff) DPS79 Dur Univ MA93. St Mich Coll Llan 78. **d** 79 **p** 80. C Aberavon *Llan* 79-81; C Kensington St Mary Abbots w St Geo *Lon* 81-85; Chapl Westmr Abbey 85-87; Sacrist 86-87; P-in-c Westmr St Marg 86-87; R Lowick w Sudborough and Slipton *Pet* 87-94; P-in-c Islip 87-94; Hon C Hampstead Ch Ch *Lon* 95-96; Hon C Smithfield St Bart Gt 95-96; V Sneinton St Steph w St Alb *S'well* 96-98; Perm to Offic *Lon* 98; R Stamford St Mary and St Martin *Linc* from 98. *The Rectory, Pinfold Lane, Stamford PE9 2LS* Tel (01780) 751233 E-mail rectorstam@aol.com

THOMPSON, Michael John. Cam Univ MA. **d** 00 **p** 01. OLM Badgeworth, Shurdington and Witcombe w Bentham *Glouc* from 00. *Cornerways, 1 Church Lane, Shurdington, Gloucester GL51 5TJ* Tel (01242) 862467 E-mail mthompson123@aol.com

THOMPSON, Neil Haughton. b 48. SS Hild & Bede Coll Dur BEd72 Leic Univ MA75. S'wark Ord Course 77 Ven English Coll Rome. **d** 80 **p** 81. C Merton St Mary *S'wark* 80-82; C Dulwich St Barn 82-84; V Shooters Hill Ch Ch 84-87; V S Dulwich St Steph 87-96; R Limpsfield and Titsey from 96. *The Rectory, Limpsfield, Oxted RH8 0DG* Tel (01883) 722812 or tel and fax 712512 E-mail neilthompson@houndofheaven.co.uk

THOMPSON, Patricia. b 60. SRN. NEOC 94. **d** 97 **p** 98. NSM Sunderland St Chad *Dur* from 97; Voc Adv from 99. *11 Friarsfield Close, Chapelgarth, Sunderland SR3 2RZ* Tel 0191-522 7911

THOMPSON, Patrick Arthur. b 36. Dur Univ BA59. Qu Coll Birm DipTh61. **d** 61 **p** 62. C W Wickham St Fran *Cant* 61-65; C Portchester *Portsm* 65-68; C Birchington w Acol *Cant* 68-71; V S Norwood St Mark 71-77; P-in-c Norbury St Oswald 77-81; V Norbury St Oswald *S'wark* 81-93; V Sutton New Town St Barn 93-00; rtd 00. *Rose Cottage, Market Street, Forres IV36 1EF* Tel (01309) 675917

THOMPSON, Paul. b 58. Ox Univ BA. Ripon Coll Cuddesdon 80. **d** 83 **p** 84. Chapl Fazakerley Hosp 83-86; C Kirkby *Liv* 83-86; TV 86-89; Ind Chapl 86-89; Chapl Kirkby Coll of FE 86-89; CF 89-01; Chapl Epsom Coll from 01. *Epsom College, Epsom KT17 4JQ* Tel (01372) 821288 E-mail schaplain@epsomcollege.org.uk

THOMPSON, Paul. b 65. TCD BA87. CITC 87. **d** 89 **p** 90. C Orangefield w Moneyreagh *D & D* 89-92; I Dromara w Garvaghy 92-97; I Ramoan w Ballycastle and Culfeightrin *Conn* 97-00; Dep Chapl HM Pris Liv 00-01; Chapl HM YOI Portland from 01. *HM Young Offender Institution, The Grove, Portland DT5 1DL* Tel (01305) 820301 Fax 823718

THOMPSON, Paul Noble. b 54. Univ of Wales (Cardiff) BMus77. Coll of Resurr Mirfield DipTh79. **d** 80 **p** 81. C Bargoed and Deri w Brithdir *Llan* 80-83; C Whitchurch 83-84; V Porth w Trealaw 84-89; V Llanharan w Peterston-super-Montem 89-97; C Barry All SS 97-01; Youth Chapl 97-01; V Lisvane from 01. *The Vicarage, 2 Llwyn-y-Pia Road, Lisvane, Cardiff CF14 0SY* Tel (029) 2075 3338

THOMPSON, Mrs Pauline. b 44. EMMTC 81. dss 84 **d** 87 **p** 94. Derby St Aug *Derby* 84-87; Par Dn 87-88; Par Dn Boulton 88-90; Par Dn Allestree 91-94; C 94-97; Sub-Chapl HM Pris Sudbury 92-94; P-in-c Hartington, Biggin and Earl Sterndale *Derby* 97-01; rtd 01; Perm to Offic *Derby* from 01. *46 Hawthorn Court, Kedleston Road, Derby DE22 1FY* Tel (01332) 210127

THOMPSON, Peter. **d** 03. C Clooney w Strathfoyle *D & R* from 03. *11 Mosley Park, Londonderry BT47 1HR* Tel (028) 7134 1966

THOMPSON, Peter Kerr. b 32. Kelham Th Coll. **d** 56 **p** 57. Solomon Is 56-76; Adn Malaita and Outer E Solomon 62-76; Adn N Melanesia 68-70; Australia from 76; R S Gulf 76-78; R Port Hedland 78-82; R Melville 85-88; R Childers 89-91; R Bundaberg W 91-92. *28 Saunders Street, Point Vernon, Qld, Australia 4655* Tel (0061) (7) 4124 3645

THOMPSON, Canon Peter Ross. b 26. St Jo Coll Cam BA47 MB, BChir50. Tyndale Hall Bris. **d** 60 **p** 61. C New Malden and Coombe *S'wark* 60-61; Burma 61-66; R Slaugham *Chich* 66-72; V Polegate 72-92; Can and Preb Chich Cathl 91-92; rtd 92; Perm to Offic *Guildf* from 92. *Tregenna, Barley Mow Lane, Knaphill, Woking GU21 2HX* Tel (01483) 480595

THOMPSON, Randolph. b 25. Lich Th Coll 63. **d** 65 **p** 66. C Boultham *Linc* 65-68; V Paddock *Wakef* 68-69; P-in-c Cornholme 69-71; V 71-72; Chapl Barnsley Hall & Lea Hosps Bromsgrove 72-84; V Hanley Castle, Hanley Swan and Welland *Worc* 84-89; rtd 89; Perm to Offic *Lich* from 90. *37 Hampton Fields, Oswestry SY11 1TL* Tel (01691) 658484

THOMPSON, Canon Raymond Craigmile. b 42. **d** 84 **p** 85. C Clooney *D & R* 84-86; I Urney w Sion Mills 86-92; I Derryvullen N w Castlearchdale *Clogh* from 92; Chapl to Bp Clogh from 02; Can Clogh Cathl from 03. *The Rectory, Enniskillen Road, Irvinestown BT94 1GW* Tel (028) 6662 1225 Fax as telephone

THOMPSON, Richard Brian. b 60. Sheff Poly BSc83. Ripon Coll Cuddesdon 86. **d** 89 **p** 90. C Thorpe Bay *Chelmsf* 89-92; V Rushmere *St E* 92-97; Dep Chapl HM Pris Nor 97-98; Chapl HM Pris Wayland 98-01; Chapl HM Pris and YOI Hollesley Bay from 01. *The Chaplain's Office, Hollesley Bay Colony, Hollesley, Woodbridge IP12 3JW* Tel (01394) 411741 ext 325 Fax 411071

THOMPSON, Robert. b 36. AKC61. **d** 62 **p** 63. C Cockerton *Dur* 62-65; C Dur St Marg 65-70; V Wallsend St Jo *Newc* 70-78; V Norham and Duddo 78-99; rtd 99; Perm to Offic *Ripon* from 99. *Southlands, Grainbeck Lane, Killinghall, Harrogate HG3 2AA* Tel (01423) 565743

THOMPSON, Robert Craig. b 72. Univ Coll Dur BA92. Westcott Ho Cam 94. **d** 96 **p** 97. C Wigan All SS *Liv* 96-00; P-in-c Ladybrook *S'well* from 00. *St Mary's Vicarage, Bancroft Lane, Mansfield NG18 5LZ* Tel (01623) 621709

THOMPSON, Robert George. b 71. K Coll Cam BA93 MA97. Ripon Coll Cuddesdon MTh95. **d** 97 **p** 98. C Ruislip St Martin *Lon* 97-01; Chapl Parkside Community NHS Trust Lon from 01. *Chaplain's Office, St Charles Community Hospital, Exmoor Street, London W10 6DZ* Tel (020) 8838 3996 or 8962 4390

THOMPSON, Roger Quintin. b 63. K Coll Lon BA85 AKC85 Nottm Univ PGCE86 MA96. Aston Tr Scheme 92 St Jo Coll Nottm 94. **d** 96. C Easton H Trin w St Gabr and St Lawr and St Jude *Bris* 96-00; C Lisburn Ch Ch Cathl *Conn* from 00. *82 Thornleigh Drive, Lisburn BT28 2DS* Tel (028) 9260 4483 E-mail roger@lisburncathedral.org.uk *or* rogfi@appleonline.net

THOMPSON, Ross Keith Arnold. b 53. Sussex Univ BA75 Bris Univ PhD82. Coll of Resurr Mirfield 80. **d** 82 **p** 83. C Knowle *Bris* 82-85; TV E Bris 85-94; V Bristol St Aid w St Geo 94-95; V Knowle St Barn and H Cross Inns Court 95-02; Tutor St Mich Coll Llan from 02. *St Michael's College, 54 Cardiff Road, Llandaff, Cardiff CF5 2YJ* Tel (02920) 563379

THOMPSON, Ruth Jean. *See* GOSTELOW, Mrs Ruth Jean

THOMPSON, Stephen Peter. b 45. Lon Univ BSc67 Lon Inst of Educn PGCE71 K Coll Lon BD77 AKC77 SOAS Lon BA82 Poona Univ MPhil85 PhD87 FRAS91. Ripon Coll Cuddesdon. **d** 00. NSM Bedford Park *Lon* 00-01; NSM Isleworth St Fran from 01. *18 Rostrevor Mansions, Rostrevor Road, London SW6 5AP* Tel (020) 7736 6809 Mobile 07713-252363 Fax (020) 7747 4947 E-mail drsthompson@usa.net

THOMPSON, Thomas Oliver. b 27. TCD 61. **d** 63 **p** 64. C Lisburn Ch Ch *Conn* 63-68; Chapl to Ch of Ireland Miss to Deaf and Dumb 68-76; I Glenavy w Tunny and Crumlin 77-92; rtd 92. *34 Strandview Avenue, Portstewart BT55 7LL* Tel (028) 7083 3267

THOMPSON, Canon Timothy. b 34. Fitzw Ho Cam BA59 MA64. Cuddesdon Coll 59. **d** 61 **p** 62. C Noel Park St Mark *Lon* 61-64; C Shrub End *Chelmsf* 64-67; New Zealand 67-70; R Tolleshunt Knights w Tiptree *Chelmsf* 70-81; R Colchester St Jas, All SS, St Nic and St Runwald 81-88; RD Colchester 84-88; Hon Can Chelmsf Cathl 85-88; Can Res Chelmsf Cathl 88-01; Vice-Provost 88-00; Vice-Dean 00-01; rtd 01. *44 Sixth Avenue, Chelmsford CM1 4ED* Tel (01245) 260382

THOMPSON, Timothy Charles. b 51. Lon Univ BSc73 AKC. Westcott Ho Cam 75. **d** 78 **p** 79. C Ipswich St Mary at Stoke w St Pet & St Mary Quay *St E* 78-81; Ind Chapl *Nor* 81-88; C Lowestoft and Kirkley 81-83; TV 83-88; V Coney Hill *Glouc* 88-94; P-in-c Caister *Nor* 94-00; R from 00. *The Rectory, Rectory Close, Caister-on-Sea, Great Yarmouth NR30 5EG* Tel (01493) 720287 E-mail tim.thompson@ukonline.co.uk

THOMPSON, Canon Timothy William. b 47. Bris Univ CertEd70 Open Univ BA78. EMMTC. **d** 88 **p** 89. C Scartho *Linc* 88-91; V Haxey 91-95; P-in-c Surfleet 95-00; Asst Local Min Officer 95-00; RD Elloe W 98-00; P-in-c Linc St Pet-at-Gowts and St Andr from 00; C P-in-c Linc St Botolph from 00; RD Christianity from 02; Can and Preb Linc Cathl from 02. *St Peter-at-Gowts Vicarage, 1 Sibthorp Street, Lincoln LN5 7SP* Tel (01522) 530256 Mobile 07885-238813 Fax (01522) 531040 E-mail tim.thompson@virgin.net

THOMPSON, Canon Tom Malcolm. b 38. Dur Univ BA60 Man Univ MPhil93. Bps' Coll Cheshunt 60. **d** 62 **p** 63. C Standish *Blackb* 62-65; C Lancaster St Mary 65-67; V Chorley All SS 67-72; V Barrowford 72-78; RD Pendle 75-78; R Northfield *Birm*

78-82; RD Kings Norton 79-82; V Longton *Blackb* 82-94; RD Leyland 89-94; V Nunthorpe *York* 94-03; Can and Preb York Minster 98-03; RD Stokesley 00-03; rtd 03. *Wainstones, 6 Greengate Crescent, Levens, Kendal LA8 8QB*

THOMPSON-McCAUSLAND, Marcus Perronet. b 31. Trin Coll Cam BA54 MA60. Coll of Resurr Mirfield 57. **d** 59 **p** 60. C Perry Barr *Birm* 59-65; V Rubery 65-72; R Cradley *Heref* 72-82; P-in-c Storridge 72-82; P-in-c Mathon 72-82; P-in-c Castle Frome 72-82; Hon C Camberwell St Giles *S'wark* 82-87; Hon C Lydbury N *Heref* 88-89; Hon C Lydbury N w Hopesay and Edgton 89-94; Hon C Wigmore Abbey from 95. *18 Watling Street, Leintwardine, Craven Arms SY7 0LW* Tel (01547) 540228

THOMPSON-VEAR, John Arthur. b 76. Sunderland Univ BA98. St Steph Ho Ox BA02. **d** 03. C Plymouth Crownhill Ascension *Ex* from 03. *45 Southwell Road, Plymouth PL6 5BG* Tel (01752) 706466

THOMPSTONE, Canon John Deaville. b 39. BNC Ox BA63 MA67. Ridley Hall Cam 63. **d** 65 **p** 66. C Hoole *Ches* 65-68; C Fulwood *Sheff* 68-71; V Skirbeck H Trin *Linc* 71-77; V Shipley St Pet *Bradf* 77-91; RD Airedale 82-88; V Poynton *Ches* from 91; Hon Can Ches Cathl from 02. *The Vicarage, 41 London Road North, Poynton, Stockport SK12 1AF* Tel (01625) 850524 *or* 872711 Fax 850510 E-mail john@thompstone.fsnet.co.uk

THOMSETT, Murray Richard. b 32. MBKSTS Kingston Tech Coll HND54. Oak Hill Th Coll 91. **d** 92 **p** 93. NSM Whitton SS Phil and Jas *Lon* 92-96; NSM Hampton All SS 96-02; Chapl Terminal 4 Heathrow Airport from 96. *27 Coombe Road, Hampton TW12 3PB* Tel (020) 8979 7549 or 8745 2700 E-mail murrayt@nildram.co.uk

THOMSON, Alexander Keith. b 38. Cranmer Hall Dur BA63. **d** 64 **p** 65. C Middleton *Man* 64-68; Chapl Rannoch Sch Perthshire 68-72; P-in-c Kinloch Rannoch *St And* 68-72; Asst Chapl Oundle Sch 72-94; Chapl Laxton Sch 88-94; Lic to Offic *Pet* 73-94; Perm to Offic 94-98; rtd 98. *Holly Lodge, Achurch Road, Thorpe Waterville, Kettering NN14 3ED*

THOMSON, Andrew Maitland. b 43. CA(Z)67 Univ Coll of Rhodesia & Nyasaland Dip Applied Economics 65. Westcott Ho Cam 78. **d** 80 **p** 81. Zimbabwe 80-92; P-in-c E w N and W Barsham *Nor* 92-95; P-in-c N and S Creake w Waterden 92-94; P-in-c Sculthorpe w Dunton and Doughton 92-94; R N and S Creake w Waterden, Syderstone etc from 95. *The Rectory, 18 Front Street, South Creake, Fakenham NR21 9PE* Tel (01328) 823433 E-mail rector@creake.surfaid.org

THOMSON, Canon Celia Stephana Margaret. b 55. LMH Ox MA83 Birkbeck Coll Lon MA87 K Coll Lon MA94. Sarum & Wells Th Coll 89. **d** 91 **p** 94. Par Dn Southfields St Barn *S'wark* 91-94; C 94-95; V W Wimbledon Ch Ch 95-03; Tutor SEITE 95-00; Voc Adv Lambeth Adnry 96-00; Can Res Glouc Cathl *Glouc* from 03. *3 Miller's Green, Gloucester GL1 2BN* Tel (01452) 415824 E-mail cthomson@church-of-england.org.uk

THOMSON, Preb Clarke Edward Leighton. b 19. TD65. Pemb Coll Ox BA41 MA45. Wycliffe Hall Ox 44. **d** 45 **p** 46. C Penge Lane H Trin *Roch* 45-47; Egypt 47-50; C Chelsea All SS *Lon* 50-51; V 51-92; CF (TA) 52-69; Preb St Paul's Cathl *Lon* 86-92; rtd 92; Perm to Offic *Lon* from 93. *15 Redburn Street, London SW3 4DA* Tel (020) 7351 5371

THOMSON, The Ven David. b 52. Keble Coll Ox MA78 DPhil78 Selw Coll Cam BA80 MA84. Westcott Ho Cam 78. **d** 81 **p** 82. C Maltby *Sheff* 81-84; Sec Par and People 84-94; TV Banbury *Ox* 84-94; TR Cockermouth w Embleton and Wythop *Carl* 94-02; Adn Carl and Can Res Carl Cathl from 02. *2 The Abbey, Carlisle CA3 8TZ* Tel (01228) 523026 Mobile 07771-864550 Fax (01228) 594899 E-mail archdeacon.north@carlislediocese.org.uk

THOMSON, Elizabeth Jane. b 64. Univ Coll Ox MA85 DPhil89 Trin Coll Cam BA02 Moray Ho Coll of Educn PGCE90. Westcott Ho Cam 00. **d** 03. C Pilton w Croscombe, N Wootton and Dinder *B & W* from 03. *Hill House, Fayreway, Croscombe, Wells BA5 3RA* Tel (01749) 343427 E-mail ejt@ecosse.net

THOMSON, Elizabeth Lucy. *See* TALBOT, Mrs Elizabeth Lucy

THOMSON, James Maclaren. b 69. Grey Coll Dur BA91 Univ Coll Lon MA93. Wycliffe Hall Ox BA99. **d** 00 **p** 01. C Oulton Broad *Nor* from 00. *3 Windward Way, Lowestoft NR33 9HF* Tel (01502) 502166 E-mail oxthomson@aol.com

THOMSON, Canon John Bromilow. b 59. York Univ BA81 Wycliffe Hall Ox BA84 MA91. **d** 85 **p** 86. C Ecclesall *Sheff* 85-89; S Africa 89-92; Tutor St Paul's Coll Grahamstown 89-92; Asst P Grahamstown St Bart 90-92; Asst Lect Rhodes Univ 91-92; V Doncaster St Mary *Sheff* 93-01; Dir Min from 01; Hon Can Sheff Cathl from 01. *15 Grange View, Balby, Doncaster DN4 0XL* Tel (01302) 570205 or 309143 E-mail john.thomson@sheffield-diocese.org.uk

THOMSON, Julian Harley. b 43. AKC70. St Aug Coll Cant 70. **d** 71 **p** 72. C Wellingborough All Hallows *Pet* 71-74; Min Can, Prec and Sacr Ely Cathl *Ely* 74-80; P-in-c Stuntney 76-80; V Arrington 80-91; R Croydon w Clopton 80-91; R Orwell 80-91; R Wimpole 80-91; V Linton 91-96; R Bartlow 91-96; P-in-c Castle Camps 91-96; TR Linton 96-01; RD Linton 99-01; rtd 01; Perm to Offic *Nor* from 01. *Lavender Cottage, 7 Abbey Road, Great Massingham, King's Lynn PE32 2HN* Tel (01485) 520721

THOMSON, Keith. *See* THOMSON, Alexander Keith

THOMSON, Matthew James. b 63. Nottm Univ BA92 Univ of Wales (Ban). St Jo Coll Nottm 92. **d** 95 **p** 96. C Cosham *Portsm* 95-98; C Nailsea Ch Ch w Tickenham *B & W* 98-01; V Congresbury w Puxton and Hewish St Ann from 01; Bp's Healing Adv from 01. *The Vicarage, Station Road, Congresbury, Bristol BS49 5DX* Tel (01934) 833126
E-mail mndjthomson@netscapeonline.co.uk

THOMSON, Peter Ashley. b 36. Ox Univ BA74 MA78 MACE77. Ridley Coll Melbourne ThL57. **d** 59 **p** 60. Australia 59-62, 64-96 and from 01; C Fen Ditton *Ely* 62-63; V Upwood w Gt and Lt Raveley 63-64; C W Holloway St Luke *Lon* 96-97; 2000 by 2000 (Millennium Projects) Officer 97-01; rtd 02. *PO Box 498, Mansfield, Vic, Australia 3722* Tel (0061) (3) 5777 5635

THOMSON, Peter Malcolm. b 44. Trin Coll Bris 75. **d** 78 **p** 79. C Tonbridge St Steph *Roch* 78-82; R Cobham w Luddesdowne and Dode 82-90; V Wythall *Birm* 90-02; rtd 02; Perm to Offic *Birm* from 02. *37 Northbrook Road, Shirley, Solihull B90 3NR* Tel 0121-745 9042

THOMSON, Canon Richard Irving. b 32. Oak Hill Th Coll 57. **d** 60 **p** 61. C Kingston upon Hull H Trin *York* 60-63; C S Croydon Em *Cant* 63-66; V Shoreditch St Leon *Lon* 66-73; Chapl Vevey w Château d'Oex and Villars *Eur* 73-78; V Reigate St Mary *S'wark* 78-97; Hon Can S'wark Cathl 90-97; rtd 97; Perm to Offic *Win* from 97. *Little Heathfield, Forest Front, Dibden Purlieu, Southampton SO45 3RG* Tel (023) 8084 9613

THOMSON, Richard William Byars. b 60. Birm Univ BA86. Ripon Coll Cuddesdon 86. **d** 88 **p** 89. C Moulsecoomb *Chich* 88-90; P-in-c Kirriemuir *St And* 90-94; P-in-c Piddletrenthide w Plush, Alton Pancras etc *Sarum* 94-02; P-in-c Milborne St Andrew w Dewlish 94-02; Chapl Milton Abbey Sch Dorset from 02. *Nether Fen, Milton Abbey, Blandford Forum DT11 0DA* Tel (01258) 881513

THOMSON, Robert Douglass. b 37. Lon Univ TCert61 Newc Univ DAES70 Dur Univ BEd75. NEOC 76. **d** 79 **p** 80. NSM Shincliffe *Dur* 79-98; Chapl St Aid Coll Dur 93-99. *11 Hill Meadows, High Shincliffe, Durham DH1 2PE* Tel 0191-386 3358

THOMSON, Robin Alexander Stewart. b 43. Ch Coll Cam MA69 K Coll Lon MTh72. SEITE 94. **d** 96 **p** 97. NSM Wimbledon Em Ridgway Prop Chpl *S'wark* 96-02; NSM Tooting Graveney St Nic from 02. *2 Coppice Close, London SW20 9AS* Tel (020) 8540 7748 *or* 8770 9717 Fax 8770 9747 E-mail 100126.3641@compuserve.com

THOMSON, Canon Ronald. b 24. Leeds Univ BA49. Coll of Resurr Mirfield 49. **d** 51 **p** 52. C Sunderland *Dur* 51-54; C Attercliffe w Carbrook *Sheff* 54-57; V Shiregreen St Hilda 57-73; RD Ecclesfield 72-73; V Worsbrough 73-88; RD Tankersley 75-85; Hon Can Sheff Cathl 77-88; rtd 88; Perm to Offic *Sheff* from 88. *4 St Mary's Garden, Worsbrough, Barnsley S70 5LU* Tel (01226) 203553

THOMSON, Ronald Arthur. b 29. G&C Coll Cam BA53 MA57. Ripon Hall Ox. **d** 57 **p** 58. C Sanderstead All SS *S'wark* 57-60; C Kidbrooke St Jas 60-62; Chapl RAF 62-68; C Amersham *Ox* 68; R Watton at Stone *St Alb* 68-94; rtd 94. *Ashby, 65 Edmonds Drive, Aston Brook, Stevenage SG2 9TJ* Tel (01438) 362192

THOMSON, Russell. b 39. AKC62. **d** 63 **p** 64. C Hackney *Lon* 63-66; C Plumstead Wm Temple Ch Abbey Wood CD *S'wark* 66-69; TV Strood Roch 69-75; V Gillingham St Mary 75-89; V Roch from 89; Chapl St Bart Hosp Roch 89-94; Chapl Medway NHS Trust from 94; Chapl Wisdom Hospice from 89. *The Vicarage, 138 Delce Road, Rochester ME1 2EH* Tel (01634) 845122 *or* 848900

THOMSON, Wendy Leigh. b 64. Trin W Univ Vancouver BA87. Wycliffe Hall Ox BTh99. **d** 00 **p** 01. C Oulton Broad *Nor* from 00. *3 Windward Way, Lowestoft NR33 9HF* Tel (01502) 502166 E-mail oxthomson@aol.com

THOMSON, Mrs Winifred Mary. b 35. St Mary's Coll Dur BA57 MA58 Lon Univ 86. Qu Coll Birm 79. **dss** 82 **d** 87 **p** 94. Leic H Spirit *Leic* 82; Oadby 86-87; Par Dn 87-92; rtd 93; Perm to Offic *Leic* 93-03. *140 Knighton Church Road, Leicester LE2 3JJ* Tel 0116-270 5863

THOMSON GIBSON, Thomas. *See* GIBSON, Thomas Thomson

THOMSON-GLOVER, Canon William Hugh. b 28. Trin Hall Cam BA52 MA56. Cuddesdon Coll 52. **d** 54 **p** 55. C Stepney St Dunstan and All SS *Lon* 54-58; C Tiverton St Andr *Ex* 58-60; P-in-c 60-63; Chapl Clifton Coll Bris 63-69; V Bris Lockleaze St Mary Magd w St Fran *Bris* 70-76; P-in-c Sherston Magna w Easton Grey 76-81; P-in-c Luckington w Alderton 76-81; V Sherston Magna, Easton Grey, Luckington etc 81-93; P-in-c Foxley w Bremilham 84-86; RD Malmesbury 88-93; Hon Can Bris Cathl 91-93; rtd 93; Perm to Offic *Ex* from 93. *Woodgate Farm House, Woodgate, Culmstock, Cullompton EX15 3HW* Tel (01884) 841465

THORBURN, Austin Noel. b 13. Trin Coll Cam BA36 MA40. Bps' Coll Cheshunt 36. **d** 38 **p** 39. C Hope St Jas *Man* 38-43; V Castleton All So 43-48; V Blackrod 48-52; SPG Pakistan 52-56; Lic to Offic *Glouc, Lich* and *Worc* 63-67; C Tettenhall Regis *Lich* 67-69; C Langley Marish *Ox* 71-76; TV 76-79; rtd 79; Perm to

Offic *Carl* 79-88; Perm to Offic *Ox* 88-98. *Lench's Trust, Flat 7, 231 Ladywood Middleway, Birmingham B16 8EU* Tel 0121-454 6376

THORBURN, Guy Douglas Anderson. b 50. Ridley Hall Cam. **d** 83 **p** 84. C Putney St Marg *S'wark* 83-87; R Moresby *Carl* 87-97; V Gt Clacton *Chelmsf* from 97. *St John's Vicarage, Valley Road, Clacton-on-Sea CO15 4AR* Tel (01255) 423435

THORBURN, Peter Hugh. b 17. Worc Coll Ox BA41 MA43. Wells Th Coll 46. **d** 47 **p** 48. C Mill Hill Jo Keble Ch *Lon* 47-51; Lon Dioc Home Missr Colindale St Matthias 51; V 51-54; V Wigan St Mich *Liv* 54-65; USA 65-68; V Chipping Sodbury and Old Sodbury *Glouc* 68-72; Chapl Withington Hosp Man 72-82; rtd 82; Perm to Offic *B & W* from 83; *Bris* from 85; and *Lon* 95-97; Warden Servants of Ch the K from 89. *8 Stoberry Crescent, Wells BA5 2TG* Tel (01749) 672919

THORBURN, Simon Godfrey. b 51. Newc Univ BSc73 Fitzw Coll Cam BA77 MA81. Westcott Ho Cam 75. **d** 78 **p** 79. C Stafford St Mary and St Chad *Lich* 78-79; C Stafford 79-82; C Tettenhall Regis 82-83; TV 83-90; Soc Resp Officer *S'wark* 90-97; V Edgbaston St Geo *Birm* from 97; AD Edgbaston from 03; Chapl St Geo Sch Edgbaston from 99. *St George's Vicarage, 3 Westbourne Road, Birmingham B15 3TH* Tel 0121-454 2303

THORESEN, Ms Alveen Fern. b 46. Avondale Coll NSW BA(Ed)69 Newc Univ Aus BA76 New England Univ NSW MA82. St Alb and Ox Min Course 96. **d** 01 **p** 02. NSM Caversham and Mapledurham *Ox* from 01. *1 Crescent Court, Crescent Road, Reading RG1 5SJ* Tel 0118-926 7119
E-mail alveen.thoresen@mon.bbc.co.uk

THORLEY, Barry. b 44. Westcott Ho Cam 70. **d** 73 **p** 74. C Camberwell St Giles *S'wark* 73-76; C Moseley St Mary *Birm* 76-78; V Birchfield 78-83; V Brixton St Matt *S'wark* 84-89; C Greenwich St Alfege 96-00; C Thamesmead 00-01; TR from 01. *6 Sorrel Close, London SE28 8ER* Tel (020) 8312 9770

THORLEY, Mrs Mary Kathleen. b 53. OBE00. Univ of Wales (Swansea) BA74 Glos Coll of Educn PGCE75. St Mich Coll Llan 99. **d** 02 **p** 03. NSM Carmarthen St Pet *St D* from 02. *35 Mryddin Crescent, Carmarthen SA31 1DH* Tel (01267) 235927

THORLEY-PAICE, Alan. *See* PAICE, Alan

THORN (formerly KINGS), Mrs Jean Alison. b 63. RGN85 Heythrop Coll Lon MTh. Cranmer Hall Dur BA90. **d** 91 **p** 93. Chapl Bris Poly *Bris* 91-92; Chapl UWE 92-95; Hon C Bris Lockleaze St Mary Magd w St Fran 91-95; C Fishponds All SS 95-96; Hon C 96-97; V Bris Ch the Servant Stockwood 97-01; Perm to Offic from 01. *The Vicarage, 780 Whitchurch Lane, Bristol BS14 0EU* Tel (01275) 832380

THORN, Peter. b 50. Man Poly BEd79. Ridley Hall Cam 82. **d** 84 **p** 85. C Aughton Ch Ch *Liv* 84-87; C Skelmersdale St Paul 87-90; Dioc Children's Officer 87-92; P-in-c Croft w Southworth 90-92; C Streatley *St Alb* 92-95; R Blofield w Hemblington *Nor* 95-96; P-in-c 96-99; Assoc Dioc Dir of Tr 97-99; V Sheff St Bart *Sheff* 99-01; P-in-c Shotley *St E* from 01. *The Vicarage, 2 Gate Farm Road, Shotley, Ipswich IP9 1QH* Tel (01473) 788166 Mobile 07810-363291 E-mail peterthorn15@hotmail.com

THORN, Robert Anthony D'Venning. b 54. AKC76. Chich Th Coll 75. **d** 77 **p** 78. C Bodmin *Truro* 77-80; TV N Hill w Altarnon, Bolventor and Lewannick 80-83; V Feock 83-90; Dioc Ecum Officer 83-90; Broadcasting Officer *Linc* 90-93; V Whitchurch *Bris* from 93. *The Vicarage, 780 Whitchurch Lane, Bristol BS14 0EU* Tel (01275) 832380

THORNBOROUGH (née O'MEARA), Ms Colette Margaret Mary. b 63. Univ of Wales (Abth) BA85. Moorlands Bible Coll DipTh90 DPS91. **d** 98 **p** 99. C Much Woolton *Liv* 98-02; V Blundellsands St Nic from 02. *St Nicholas' Vicarage, Nicholas Road, Blundellsands, Liverpool L23 6TS* Tel 0151-924 3551

THORNBURGH, Richard Hugh Perceval. b 52. Sarum & Wells Th Coll. **d** 84 **p** 85. C Broadstone *Sarum* 84-87; TV Beaminster Area 87-95; TV Hanley H Ev *Lich* 96-01; R S Elmham and Ilketshall *St E* from 01. *Parsonage House, Low Street, Ilketshall St Margaret, Bungay NR35 1QZ* Tel (01986) 781345 Fax as telephone E-mail richard.thornburgh@btinternet.com

THORNBURY, Peter Dawson. b 43. Open Univ BA84 TCD BTh93. CITC 90. **d** 93 **p** 94. C Annagh w Drumgoon, Ashfield etc *K, E & A* 93-96; I Clondehorkey w Cashel *D & R* 96-98; I Mevagh w Glenalla 96-98; Bp's C Kilsaran w Drumcar, Dunleer and Dunany *Arm* from 98. *Kilsaran Rectory, Dromisken Road, Castlebellingham, Dundalk, Co Louth, Irish Republic* Tel (00353) (42) 937 2699

THORNE, Mrs Anita Dawn. b 46. Trin Coll Bris 84. **dss** 86 **d** 87 **p** 94. Chapl Bris Poly *Bris* 86-88; Par Dn Olveston 88-94; P-in-c 94-96; P-in-c Portland All SS w St Pet *Sarum* from 96. *The Rectory, Straits, Easton, Portland DT5 1HG* Tel (01305) 861285 Fax 861431 E-mail anita@portland64.freeserve.co.uk

THORNE, Mrs Anne. b 55. Trin Minl Tr Course 95. **d** 98 **p** 99. C Crediton and Shobrooke *Ex* 98-01; C Crediton, Shobrooke and Sandford etc 01; C Beer and Branscombe 01-03; C Seaton and Beer from 03. *The Vicarage, Mare Lane, Beer, Seaton EX12 3NB* Tel (01297) 20996

THORNE, Mrs Marie Elizabeth. b 47. EMMTC 83. **dss** 86 **d** 87 **p** 94. Cleethorpes *Linc* 86-90; C 87-90; C Brigg 90-96; P-in-c New

Waltham 96-00; V from 00. *The Vicarage, 41 Dunbar Avenue, New Waltham, Grimsby DN36 4PY* Tel (01472) 589998
E-mail m.thorne2@ntlworld.com

THORNETT, Frederick Charles. b 34. Harris Coll CQSW68. LNSM course. **d** 85 **p** 86. OLM Skegness and Winthorpe *Linc* 85-90; C New Sleaford 90-92; P-in-c Harlaxton 92-95; R Harlaxton Gp 95-99; rtd 99; Perm to Offic *Linc* 99-02. *93 Boston Road, Spilsby PE23 5HH* Tel (01790) 754151

THORNEWILL, Canon Mark Lyon. b 25. ALCD56. **d** 56 **p** 58. C-in-c Bradf Cathl *Bradf* 56-59; C-in-c Otley 59-62; R Lifton *Ex* 62-66; R Kelly w Bradstone 62-66; USA from 66; Dir Past Care Norton Hosps Louisville KY 69-84; Hon Can Louisville Cathl from 70; rtd 90. *Soma House, 116 East Campbell Street, Frankfort, KY 40601, USA* Tel (001) (502) 696 9274
E-mail mthornewil@aol.com

THORNEYCROFT, Preb Pippa Hazel Jeanetta. b 44. Ex Univ BA65. Qu Coll Birm 85 WMMTC. **d** 88 **p** 94. NSM Albrighton *Lich* 88-90; NSM Beckbury, Badger, Kemberton, Ryton, Stockton etc 90-96; Dioc Adv for Women in Min from 93; P-in-c Shareshill from 96; Preb Lich Cathl from 99; RD Penkridge from 01. *The Vicarage, 11 Brookhouse Lane, Featherstone, Wolverhampton WV10 7AW* Tel and fax (01902) 727579 Mobile 07970-869011 E-mail pippa@thorneycroft.plus.com

THORNILEY, Richard James Gordon. b 56. Portsm Poly BA78. St Jo Coll Nottm MTh95. **d** 97 **p** 98. C Bowbrook S *Worc* 97-01; R Church Lench w Rous Lench and Abbots Morton etc from 01. *The Rectory, Station Road, Harvington, Evesham WR11 8NJ* Tel (01386) 870527 E-mail richard.gill@rthorniley.fsnet.co.uk

THORNLEY, Arthur Richard. b 15. VRD. Selw Coll Cam BA38. Westcott Ho Cam 38. **d** 39 **p** 40. C St Mary-at-Lambeth *S'wark* 39-44; Chapl RNVR 44-47; Chapl RN 47-58; Chapl Malvern Coll 58-65; USA 65-66; Chapl RN 66-70; Chapl Lon Ho 70-75; PV Truro Cathl *Truro* 75-80; Chapl Truro Cathl Sch 75-80; rtd 80; Hon PV Truro Cathl *Truro* from 80; Perm to Offic *Chich* from 92. *47 The Hawthorns, 4 Carew Road, Eastbourne BN21 2BF* Tel (01323) 647686

THORNLEY, David Howe. b 43. Wycliffe Hall Ox 77. **d** 79 **p** 80. C Burgess Hill St Andr *Chich* 79-83; P-in-c Amberley w N Stoke 83-84; P-in-c Parham and Wiggonholt w Greatham 83-84; V Amberley w N Stoke and Parham, Wiggonholt etc 84-92; P-in-c S w N Bersted from 92. *121 Victoria Drive, Bognor Regis PO21 2EH* Tel (01243) 862018

THORNLEY, Geoffrey Pearson. b 23. Pemb Coll Cam BA47 MA52. Cuddesdon Coll. **d** 50 **p** 51. C Stepney St Dunstan and All SS *Lon* 50-53; Chapl RN 53-73; Bp's Dom Chapl *Linc* 73-75; P-in-c Riseholme 73-78; P-in-c Scothern w Sudbrooke 77-78; V Dunholme 75-85; Hon PV Linc Cathl 75-85; rtd 85; Chapl Allnutt's Hosp Goring Heath 85-96. *18 Dolphin Court, Cliff Road, Meads, Eastbourne BN20 7XD* Tel (01323) 647115

THORNLEY, Canon Nicholas Andrew. b 56. St Jo Coll Nottm BTh81. **d** 81 **p** 84. C Frodingham *Linc* 81-84; P-in-c Belton 84-85; V 85-90; V Horncastle w Low Toynton 90-98; V High Toynton 98; R Greetham w Ashby Puerorum 98; RD Horncastle 94-98; TR Gainsborough and Morton from 98; Can and Preb Linc Cathl from 98. *Gainsborough Rectory, 32 Morton Terrace, Gainsborough DN21 1RQ* Tel (01427) 612965
E-mail nick@gains98.fsnet.co.uk

THORNS, Mrs Joanne. b 64. Sunderland Univ BSc86 MRPharmS. Cranmer Hall Dur DTM99. **d** 99 **p** 00. C Norton St Mary *Dur* from 99; C Stockton St Chad from 02. *St Chad's Vicarage, Ragpath Lane, Stockton-on-Tees TS19 9JN* Tel (01642) 674737 E-mail joanne.thorns@durham.anglican.org

THORNTON, Canon Cecil. b 26. Lon Univ BD PhD ThD. Tyndale Hall Bris 47. **d** 50 **p** 51. C Kilkeel *D & D* 50-51; C Dromore Cathl 51-54; I Magherahamlet 54-60; I Inniskeel *D & R* 60-65; I Fahan Lower and Upper 65-88; Can Raphoe Cathl 79-88; rtd 88; Perm to Offic *Conn* from 91. *Cluain-Fois, 38 Ballywillan Road, Portrush BT56 8JN* Tel (028) 7082 4669

THORNTON, Darren Thomas. b 68. Univ of Wales (Ban) BTh02. Wilson Carlile Coll 90 EAMTC 00. **d** 02 **p** 03. C E Dereham and Scarning *Nor* from 02. *15 George Eliot Way, Dereham NR19 1EX* Tel (01362) 851435
E-mail darrenthornton@hotmail.com

THORNTON, David John Dennis. b 32. Kelham Th Coll 52. **d** 56 **p** 57. C New Eltham All SS *S'wark* 56-58; C Stockwell Green St Andr 58-62; V Tollesbury *Chelmsf* 62-74; P-in-c Salcot Virley 72-74; V Kelvedon 74-00; rtd 00; Perm to Offic *Nor* from 01. *The Old Stable, 24 Pauls Lane, Overstrand, Cromer NR27 0PE* Tel (01263) 579279

THORNTON, Howard Deyes. b 52. Canadian Th Sem MA99. **d** 01 **p** 03. NSM Hanborough and Freeland *Ox* 01-02; C Luton St Mary *St Alb* from 02; Chapl Luton Univ from 02. *10 Trowbridge Gardens, Luton LU2 7JY* Tel (01582) 537050

THORNTON, John. b 26. St Edm Hall Ox BA53 MA57. Westcott Ho Cam 53. **d** 55 **p** 56. C Woodhall Spa *Linc* 55-58; C Glouc St Steph *Glouc* 58-60; C Wotton St Mary 60-62; P-in-c Gt Witcombe 62-63; R 63-91; Chapl HM Pris Glouc 82-91; rtd 91; Perm to Offic *Glouc* from 91. *24 Spencer Close, Hucclecote, Gloucester GL3 3EA* Tel (01452) 619775

THORNTON, Magdalen Mary. *See* SMITH, Mrs Magdalen Mary

THORNTON, Peter Stuart. b 36. St Pet Hall Ox BA59 MA67. Cuddesdon Coll 59. **d** 61 **p** 62. C E Coatham *York* 61-64; C Scarborough St Martin 64-67; R Seaton Ross w Everingham and Bielby and Harswell 67-81; RD Weighton 75-85; P-in-c Thornton w Allerthorpe 80-81; R Seaton Ross Gp of Par 81-85; V York St Lawr w St Nic 85-01; Asst Chapl York Health Services NHS Trust 93-02; rtd 01; Perm to Offic *York* from 01. *138 Lawrence Street, York YO10 3EB* Tel (01904) 423648

THORNTON, Timothy Charles Gordon. b 35. Ch Ch Ox BA58 MA61. Linc Th Coll 60. **d** 62 **p** 63. C Kirkholt CD *Man* 62-64; Tutor Linc Th Coll 64-68; Chapl 66-68; Fiji 69-73; Chapl Brasted Place Coll Westerham 73-74; Can Missr *Guildf* 74-79; P-in-c Hascombe 74-79; V Chobham w Valley End 79-84; V Spelsbury and Chadlington *Ox* 84-87; V Chadlington and Spelsbury, Ascott under Wychwood 87-00; rtd 00; Perm to Offic *Carl* from 01. *The Old Cottage, Warcop, Appleby-in-Westmorland CA16 6NX* Tel (01768) 341239

✠**THORNTON, The Rt Revd Timothy Martin.** b 57. Southn Univ BA78 K Coll Lon MA97. St Steph Ho Ox 78. **d** 80 **p** 81 **c** 01. C Todmorden *Wakef* 80-82; P-in-c Walsden 82-85; Lect Univ of Wales (Cardiff) *Llan* 85-87; Chapl 85-86; Sen Chapl 86-87; Bp's Chapl *Wakef* 87-91; Dir of Ords 88-91; Bp's Chapl *Lon* 91-94; Dep P in O 92-01; Prin NTMTC 94-98; V Kensington St Mary Abbots w St Geo *Lon* 98-01; AD Kensington 00-01; Area Bp Sherborne *Sarum* from 01. *Sherborne House, Tower Hill, Iwerne Minster, Blandford Forum DT11 8NH* Tel (01747) 812766 E-mail tim.thornton@talk21.com

THOROGOOD, John Martin. b 45. Birm Univ BA68 PGCE69. Ox NSM Course 82. **d** 85 **p** 86. NSM Sunningdale *Ox* 85-90; Chapl St Geo Sch Ascot 88-90; TV Camelot Par *B & W* 90-97; V Evercreech w Chesterblade and Milton Clevedon 97-03; RD Cary and Bruton 96-03; R Dulverton and Brushford from 03. *The Vicarage, High Street, Dulverton TA22 9DW* Tel (01398) 323425 E-mail rev@johnthevicar.freeserve.co.uk

THOROLD, John Robert Hayford. b 16. K Coll Cam BA43 MA45. Cuddesdon Coll 42. **d** 42 **p** 43. C Cheltenham St Mary *Glouc* 42-44; C Limehouse St Anne *Lon* 44-47; P-in-c Ripon Hall Ox 47-52; V Mitcham SS Pet and Paul *S'wark* 52-86; OGS from 53; rtd 87; Perm to Offic *Blackb* 87-96; Hon Fell St Deiniol's Lib Hawarden from 00. *St Deiniol's Library, Hawarden, Deeside CH5 3DF* Tel (01244) 532350

THOROLD, Canon John Stephen. b 35. Bps' Coll Cheshunt 61. **d** 63 **p** 64. C Cleethorpes *Linc* 63-70; V Cherry Willingham w Greetwell 70-77; P-in-c Firsby w Gt Steeping 77-79; R 79-86; R Aswardby w Sausthorpe 77-86; R Halton Holgate 77-86; R Langton w Sutterby 77-86; V Spilsby w Hundleby 77-86; R Lt Steeping 79-86; R Raithby 79-86; V New Sleaford 86-01; RD Lafford 87-96; Can and Preb Linc Cathl 98-01; rtd 01; Perm to Offic *Linc* from 01. *8 Ashwood Close, Horncastle LN9 5HA* Tel (01507) 526562

THOROLD, Trevor Neil. b 63. Hull Univ BA87. Ripon Coll Cuddesdon 87. **d** 89 **p** 90. C W Bromwich St Andr w Ch Ch *Lich* 89-93; Res Min Oswestry H Trin 93-94; Res Min Oswestry 94-97; Local Min Adv (Shrewsbury) from 97; P-in-c Petton w Cockshutt, Welshampton and Lyneal etc from 97; RD Ellesmere 98-02. *The Rectory, Cockshutt, Ellesmere SY12 0JQ* Tel (01939) 270211 Fax as telephone
E-mail trevor.thorold@lichfield.anglican.org

THORP, Adrian. b 55. Clare Coll Cam BA77 MA80 Lon Univ BD80. Trin Coll Bris 77. **d** 80 **p** 81. C Kendal St Thos *Carl* 80-83; C Handforth *Ches* 83-86; V Siddal *Wakef* 86-91; V Bishopwearmouth St Gabr *Dur* from 91. *The Vicarage, 1 St Gabriel's Avenue, Sunderland SR4 7TF* Tel 0191-567 5200

THORP, Catherine. b 57. St Luke's Coll Ex BEd79. Oak Hill Th Coll 93. **d** 96 **p** 02. NSM Watford Ch Ch *St Alb* 96-99; NSM Kings Langley from 99. *111 Barton Way, Croxley Green, Rickmansworth WD3 3PB* Tel (01923) 442713

THORP, Miss Eileen Margaret. b 31. **d** 95 **p** 96. NSM Daventry, Ashby St Ledgers, Braunston etc *Pet* 95-02; rtd 02; Perm to Offic *Pet* from 02. *Waterside, Dark Lane, Braunston, Daventry NN11 7HJ* Tel (01788) 890321

THORP, Mrs Helen Mary. b 54. Bris Univ BA75 MA(Theol)77 DipHE Dur Univ MA98. Trin Coll Bris 78. **d** 87 **p** 94. NSM Siddal *Wakef* 87-91; NSM Bishopwearmouth St Gabr *Dur* from 91; Voc Adv from 93. *The Vicarage, 1 St Gabriel's Avenue, Sunderland SR4 7TF* Tel 0191-567 5200

THORP, Mrs Maureen Sandra. b 47. Man OLM Scheme 92. **d** 95 **p** 96. OLM Heywood *Man* 95-01; P-in-c Shore from 01; P-in-c Calderbrook from 01. *The Vicarage, 4 Stansfield Hall, Littleborough OL15 9RH* Tel (01706) 378414
E-mail tel.mo@virgin.uk

THORP, Norman Arthur. b 29. DMA63. Tyndale Hall Bris 63. **d** 65 **p** 66. C Southsea St Jude *Portsm* 65-68; C Braintree *Chelmsf* 68-73; P-in-c Tolleshunt D'Arcy w Tolleshunt Major 73-75; V 75-83; R N Buckingham *Ox* 83-95; RD Buckingham 90-95; rtd 95; Perm to Offic *Ox* 97-00. *20 Swinbridge Lane, Furzton, Milton Keynes MK4 1JT* Tel (01908) 506342

THORP, Roderick Cheyne. b 44. Ch Ch Ox BA65 MA69. Ridley Hall Cam 66. d 69 p 70. C Reading Greyfriars Ox 69-73; C Kingston upon Hull St Martin York 73-76; C Heworth H Trin 76-79; C-in-c N Bletchley CD Ox 79-86; TV Washfield, Stoodleigh, Withleigh etc Ex 86-96; RD Tiverton 91-96; P-in-c Dolton 96-00; P-in-c Iddesleigh w Dowland 96-00; P-in-c Monkokehampton 96-00; rtd 00; P-in-c Etton w Dalton Holme York from 00. The Rectory, Etton, Beverley HU17 7PQ Tel (01430) 810375 E-mail aranjay@freeuk.com

THORP, Stephen Linton. b 62. Lon Bible Coll CertRS88 Trin Coll Bris BA92. d 92 p 93. C Knutsford St Jo and Toft Ches 92-96; TV Newton Tracey, Horwood, Alverdiscott etc Ex from 96. The Rectory, Beaford, Winkleigh EX19 8NN Tel (01805) 603213 E-mail slthorp@tworiversteam.co.uk

THORP, Timothy. b 65. St Steph Ho Ox BTh93. d 96 p 97. C Jarrow Dur 96-99; P-in-c N Hylton St Marg Castletown 99-02; C Felpham Chich from 02; Missr Arundel and Bognor from 02. 3 Byron Close, Bognor Regis PO22 6QU Tel (01243) 582511 E-mail fathertimt@bigfoot.com

THORPE, Christopher David Charles. b 60. Cov Poly BA83. Ripon Coll Cuddesdon 85. d 88 p 89. C Norton St Alb 88-92; TV Blakenall Heath Lich 92-99; TR Bilston from 99. St James's Vicarage, Dover Street, Bilston WV14 6AW Tel (01902) 491560 E-mail chris@christhorpe.org

THORPE, Donald Henry. b 34. St Aid Birkenhead 57. d 60 p 61. C Mexborough Sheff 60-64; C Doncaster St Leon and St Jude 64-67; V Doncaster Intake 67-74; V Millhouses H Trin 74-85; Prec Leic Cathl Leic 85-89; TR Melton Gt Framland 89-93; rtd 93; Perm to Offic Sheff and S'well from 93. 18 All Hallows Drive, Tickhill, Doncaster DN11 9PP Tel (01302) 743129

THORPE, John Wellburn. b 31. Lich Th Coll 55. d 58 p 59. C Heref St Martin Heref 58-61; C Dudley St Fran Worc 61-65; R Gt w Lt Witley 65-70; C Tuffley Glouc 70-72; P-in-c Blaisdon w Flaxley 73-76; P-in-c Westbury-on-Severn w Flaxley and Blaisdon 76-77; V 77-84; P-in-c Walton-on-Trent w Croxall etc Derby 84-94; rtd 94. 3 Standing Butts Close, Walton-on-Trent, Swadlincote DE12 8NJ

THORPE, Kerry Michael. b 51. Lon Univ BD78. Oak Hill Th Coll DipTh76. d 78 p 79. C Upton (Overchurch) Ches 78-81; C Chester le Street Dur 81-84; V Fatfield 84-93; V Margate H Trin Cant 93-98; C from 98. 1 Wealdhurst Park, St Peter's, Broadstairs CT10 2LD Tel (01843) 871183 E-mail kerrythorpe@harvestnac.freeserve.co.uk

THORPE, Lynne Gail. b 62. Dioc OLM tr scheme 99. d 02. OLM Ipswich St Jo St E from 02. 31 King Edward Road, Ipswich IP3 9AN Tel (01473) 717833

THORPE, Martin Xavier. b 66. Collingwood Coll Dur BSc87 Bris Univ MPhil00 GRSC87. Trin Coll Bris BA94. d 94 p 95. C Ravenhead Liv 94-98; TV Sutton 98-02; Asst Dir CME from 01; V Westbrook St Phil from 02. St Philip's Vicarage, 89 Westbrook Crescent, Warrington WA5 5TE Tel (01925) 654400 Fax as telephone E-mail martinpol.thorpe@talk21.com

THORPE, Michael William. b 42. Lich Th Coll 67. d 70 p 71. C Walthamstow St Mich Chelmsf 70-71; C Plaistow St Andr 71; P-in-c Plaistow St Mary 72-74; TV Gt Grimsby St Mary and St Jas Linc 74-78; Chapl Grimsby Distr Hosps 78-83; Chapl Roxbourne, Northwick Park and Harrow Hosps 83-87; Chapl St Geo Linc and Linc Co Hosps 87-92; Chapl Ipswich Hosp NHS Trust 92-00; rtd 00. Moselle Cottage, 68 Lacey Street, Ipswich IP4 2PH Tel (01473) 421850

THORPE, Richard Charles. b 65. Birm Univ BSc87. Wycliffe Hall Ox 93. d 96 p 97. C Brompton H Trin w Onslow Square St Paul Lon from 96. 3 Holy Trinity Church House, Brompton Road, London SW7 2RW Tel (020) 7590 8278 or 7581 8255

THORPE, Trevor Cecil. b 21. Em Coll Cam BA47 MA52. Ridley Hall Cam 48. d 50 p 51. C Farnborough Guildf 50-53; C W Ham All SS Chelmsf 53-57; V N Weald Bassett from 57. The Vicarage, Vicarage Lane, North Weald, Epping CM16 6AL Tel (01992) 522246

THRALL, Canon Margaret Eleanor. b 28. Girton Coll Cam BA50 MA54 PhD60 Cam Univ BA52. Ban Ord Course 81. d 82 p 97. Asst Chapl Univ of Wales (Ban) Ban 82-88; Lect Th Univ of Wales (Ban) 83-96; Hon Can Ban Cathl Ban 94-98; rtd 98; Perm to Offic Ban from 98. 25 Y Rhos, Bangor LL57 2LT Tel (01248) 364957

THREADGILL, Alan Roy. b 31. St Alb Minl Tr Scheme 77. d 80 p 81. NSM Bedford St Andr St Alb 80-83; Chapl RAD 83-86; C Melton Gt Framland Leic 86-89; R Wymondham w Edmondthorpe, Buckminster etc 89-95; rtd 95; Perm to Offic Leic 95-02 and Ox from 02. 16 Jessops Close, Headington, Oxford OX3 0NU Tel (01865) 423138

THRELFALL-HOLMES, Miranda. b 73. Ch Coll Cam BA95 MA00 Univ Coll Dur MA97 PhD00 St Jo Coll Dur BA02. Cranmer Hall Dur 00. d 03. C Newc St Gabr Newc from 03. 26 Coniscliffe Road, Heaton, Newcastle upon Tyne NE6 5QL Tel 0191-276 0215

THROSSELL, John Julian. b 30. Nottm Univ BSc53 Syracuse Univ PhD56. Oak Hill Th Coll 72. d 75 p 76. NSM

Wheathampstead St Alb 75-82; V Codicote 82-88; NSM Halesworth w Linstead, Chediston, Holton etc St E 89-95; rtd 91. 20 Dakings Drift, Halesworth IP19 8TQ Tel (01986) 874602

THROWER, Clive Alan. b 41. Sheff Univ BSc62 CEng90. EMMTC 76. d 79 p 80. C Derby Cathl Derby 79-86; C Spondon 86-91; Soc Resp Officer 86-91; Faith in the City Link Officer 88-91; Dioc Rural Officer 91; P-in-c Ashford w Sheldon 91; V Ashford w Sheldon and Longstone from 92; Dioc Rural and Tourism Officer from 96. The Vicarage, Church Lane, Great Longstone, Bakewell DE45 1TB Tel (01629) 640257 Fax 640657 E-mail clive@thrower.org.uk

THROWER, Martin Charles. b 61. EAMTC 95. d 98 p 99. NSM Ipswich St Bart St E 98-01; NSM Bury St Edmunds All SS w St Jo and St Geo 01-03; P-in-c Hawstead and Nowton w Stanningfield etc from 03; P-in-c Lawshall from 03. The Rectory, Harrow Green, Lawshall, Bury St Edmunds IP29 4PB Tel (01284) 830855 E-mail martin.thrower@btinternet.com

THROWER, Philip Edward. b 41. Kelham Th Coll 61. d 66 p 67. C Hayes St Mary Lon 66-69; C Yeovil B & W 69-71; C Shirley St Jo Cant 71-77; P-in-c S Norwood St Mark 77-81; V 81-84; V S Norwood St Mark S'wark 85-97; V Malden St Jas from 97. St James's Vicarage, 7 Bodley Road, New Malden KT3 5QD Tel (020) 8942 1860 or 8942 5070

THRUSH, Margaret. b 37. St Mary's Coll Dur BA60. Cranmer Hall Dur BA96 DMS97. d 97 p 98. NSM Houghton le Spring Dur from 97. 9 Brierville, Durham DH1 4QE Tel 0191-386 1958

THUBRON, Thomas William. b 33. Edin Th Coll 62. d 65 p 66. C Gateshead St Mary Dur 65-66; C Shildon 66-67; E Pakistan 68-71; Bangladesh 71-80; V Wheatley Hill Dur 80-87; V Dur St Giles 87-98; rtd 98. The Old Vicarage, Stoker Crescent, Wheatley Hill, Durham DH6 3RP Tel (01429) 823940

THURBURN-HUELIN, David Richard. b 47. St Chad's Coll Dur BA69 Ex Univ MA98. Westcott Ho Cam 69. d 71 p 72. C Poplar Lon 71-76; Chapl Liddon Ho Lon 76-80; R Harrold and Carlton w Chellington St Alb 81-88; V Goldington 88-95; Dir OLM Truro 95-00; P-in-c Shipston-on-Stour w Honington and Idlicote Cov from 01. Shipston Rectory, 8 Glen Close, Shipston-on-Stour CV36 4ED Tel (01608) 661724 E-mail thurburn@fish.co.uk

THURLOW, Ms Judith Mary Buller. b 44. Ch Ch Coll Cant CertEd63 Natal Univ DipEd78 BTh94 MTh00. d 95 p 96. S Africa 95-00; C Port Shepstone St Kath 95-98; C Durban St Paul 99-00; C Orpington All SS Roch 00-02; R Kingsdown from 02. The Rectory, School Lane, West Kingsdown, Sevenoaks TN15 6JL Tel and fax (01474) 852265 Mobile 07949-272106 E-mail judiththurlow@ukgateway.net

THURMER, Canon John Alfred. b 25. Oriel Coll Ox BA50 MA55 Ex Univ Hon DD91. Linc Th Coll 50. d 52 p 53. C Lt Ilford St Mich Chelmsf 52-55; Chapl and Lect Sarum Th Coll 55-64; Chapl Ex Univ Ex 64-73; Lect 64-85; Can Res and Chan Ex Cathl 73-91; rtd 91; Perm to Offic Ex from 91. 38 Velwell Road, Exeter EX4 4LD Tel (01392) 272277

THURSFIELD, John Anthony. b 21. Magd Coll Ox BA47 MA51. Cuddesdon Coll 47. d 49 p 50. V Basing Win 60-72; Chapl Bonn w Cologne Eur 72-75; R E Clandon Guildf 75-79; R W Clandon 75-79; V Reydon St E 79-83; Perm to Offic Heref 84-93 and from 96; rtd 86. Little Homend, The Homend, Ledbury HR8 1AR Tel (01531) 632935

THURSTON, Ian Charles. b 54. SS Hild & Bede Coll Dur CertEd78. S Dios Minl Tr Scheme 87. d 89 p 90. C St Chris Cathl Bahrain 89-91; C All Hallows by the Tower etc Lon 91-97; V Tottenham H Trin 97-00; R Cheadle w Freehay Lich from 00. The Rectory, Church Street, Cheadle, Stoke-on-Trent ST10 1HU Tel (01538) 753337

TIBBO, George Kenneth. b 29. Reading Univ BA50 MA54. Coll of Resurr Mirfield 55. d 57 p 58. C W Hartlepool St Aid Dur 57-61; V Darlington St Mark 61-74; V Darlington St Mark w St Paul 74-75; R Crook 75-80; V Stanley 76-80; V Oldham St Chad Limeside Man 80-87; V Hipswell Ripon 87-95; OCF 90-95; rtd 95; P-in-c Nidd Ripon 95-01. 4 The Almshouses, Nidd, Harrogate HG3 3BP Tel (01423) 770060

TIBBS, Canon John Andrew. b 29. AKC53. d 54 p 55. C Eastbourne St Mary Chich 54-57; S Africa 57-62; C Bourne Guildf 62-64; Swaziland 64-68; V Sompting Chich 69-73; R Ifield 73-78; TR 78-83; V Elstow St Alb 83-89; rtd 90; Chapl Bedf Gen Hosp 90-95; Hon Can St Alb 91-95; Perm to Offic from 00. 19 Adelaide Square, Bedford MK40 2RN Tel (01234) 359579

TICE, Richard Ian (Rico). b 66. Bris Univ BA88. Wycliffe Hall Ox BTh94. d 94 p 95. C Langham Place All So Lon from 94. Basement Flat, 141 Cleveland Street, London W1P 5PH Tel (020) 7388 3280 or 7580 3522 E-mail rico.tice@allsouls.org

TICKLE, Robert Peter. St Chad's Coll Dur BA74. St Steph Ho Ox 74. d 76 p 77. 5 Bramley Court, Orchard Lane, Harrold, Bedford MK43 7BG Tel (01234) 721417

TICKNER, Canon Colin de Fraine. b 37. Chich Th Coll. d 66 p 67. C Huddersfield St Pet and St Paul Wakef 66-68; C Dorking w Ranmore Guildf 68-74; V Shottermill 74-91; RD Godalming 89-91; R Ockley, Okewood and Forest Green 91-97; Hon Can Guildf Cathl 96-97; rtd 97; Adv for Past Care Guildf from 97;

Chapl St Cath Sch Bramley from 97. *11 Linersh Drive, Bramley, Guildford GU5 0EJ* Tel (01483) 898161

TICKNER, David Arthur. b 44. MBE89. AKC67. **d** 69 **p** 70. C Thornhill Lees *Wakef* 69-71; C Billingham St Aid *Dur* 71-74; TV 74-78; CF 78-98; Perm to Offic *Guildf* 96-98; R Heysham *Blackb* from 98. *The Rectory, Main Street, Heysham, Morecambe LA3 2RN* Tel (01524) 851422 Fax as telephone
E-mail david.tickner@tesco.net

TICKNER, Geoffrey John. b 55. BD. St Mich Coll Llan. **d** 82 **p** 83. C Bourne *Guildf* 82-85; C Grayswood 85-90; V New Haw 90-02; RD Runnymede 98-02; P-in-c Stevenage H Trin *St Alb* from 02. *Holy Trinity Vicarage, 18 Letchmore Road, Stevenage SG1 3JD* Tel (01438) 353229
E-mail vicar@holytrinity-stevenage.info.

TIDMARSH, Canon Peter Edwin. b 29. Keble Coll Ox BA52 MA56 DipEd. St Steph Ho Ox 52. **d** 54 **p** 55. C Stepney St Dunstan and All SS *Lon* 54-58; C Streatham St Pet *S'wark* 58-62; Chapl Shiplake Coll Henley 62-64; Hd Master All SS Choir Sch 64-68; C St Marylebone All SS *Lon* 64-68; V Cubert *Truro* from 68; Dir of Educn 69-85; Hon Can Truro Cathl from 73. *The Vicarage, St Cubert, Newquay TR8 5HA* Tel (01637) 830301 E-mail petwww@btinternet.com

TIDMARSH, Philip Reginald Wilton. b 14. G&C Coll Cam BA36 MA40. Ridley Hall Cam 46. **d** 48 **p** 49. V Odiham w S Warnborough *Win* 66-76; P-in-c Abbotts Ann 76-79; Perm to Offic *Heref* 79-98; rtd 86. *6B Shepherd's Mead, Dilton Marsh, Westbury BA13 4DX* Tel (01373) 865253

TIDSWELL, David Alan. b 42. CEng73 FIEE84. St Steph Ho Ox 99. **d** 00 **p** 01. NSM Forest Row *Chich* from 00. *Manapouri, Hammerwood Road, Ashurst Wood, East Grinstead RH19 3SA* Tel (01342) 822808 Mobile 07932-537410

TIDY, John Hylton. b 48. AKC72 St Aug Coll Cant 72. **d** 73 **p** 74. C Newton Aycliffe *Dur* 73-78; V Auckland St Pet 78-84; V Burley in Wharfedale *Bradf* 84-92; Dean Jerusalem 92-97; V Surbiton St Andr and St Mark *S'wark* from 97; RD Kingston from 00. *St Mark's Vicarage, 1 Church Hill Road, Surbiton KT6 4UG* Tel (020) 8399 6053 Fax 8390 4928
E-mail jhtidy@blueyonder.co.uk

TIERNAN, Paul Wilson. b 54. Man Univ BA76. Coll of Resurr Mirfield 77. **d** 79 **p** 80. C Lewisham St Mary *S'wark* 79-83; V Sydenham St Phil from 83. *St Philip's Vicarage, 122 Wells Park Road, London SE26 6AS* Tel (020) 8699 4930

TIGWELL, Brian Arthur. b 36. S'wark Ord Course 74. **d** 77 **p** 78. C Purley St Mark *S'wark* 77-80; TV Upper Kennet *Sarum* 80-85; V Devizes St Pet 85-99; Wilts Adnry Ecum Officer 88-99; RD Devizes 92-98; rtd 99; Perm to Offic *Sarum* from 01. *2 Lansdowne Court, Long Street, Devizes SN10 1NJ* Tel (01380) 726177

TILBY, Ms Angela Clare Wyatt. b 50. Girton Coll Cam BA72 MA76. Cranmer Hall Dur 77. **d** 97 **p** 98. Tutor Westcott Ho Cam 97-01; NSM Cherry Hinton St Jo *Ely* from 97; Vice-Prin Westcott Ho Cam from 01. *Westcott House, Jesus Lane, Cambridge CB5 8BP* Tel (01223) 741000
E-mail angelus@easynet.co.uk

TILDESLEY, Edward William David. b 56. SS Hild & Bede Coll Dur BEd79. St Alb and Ox Min Course 93. **d** 96 **p** 97. Chapl Shiplake Coll Henley 96-99; NSM Emmer Green *Ox* 96-99; Chapl Oakham Sch 99-00; TV Dorchester *Ox* from 00. *The Vicarage, Clifton Hampden, Abingdon OX14 3EF* Tel and fax (01865) 407784 E-mail etildesley@home.ab.com

TILL, Barry Dorn. b 23. Jes Coll Cam BA49 MA49. Westcott Ho Cam 48. **d** 50 **p** 51. C Bury St Mary *Man* 50-53; Fell Jes Coll Cam 53-60; Chapl 53-56; Dean 56-60; Lic to Offic *Ely* 53-60; Dean Hong Kong 60-64; Attached Ch Assembly 64-65; Prin Morley Coll Lon 66-87; Dir Baring Foundn 87-92; rtd 92. *44 Canonbury Square, London N1 2AW* Tel (020) 7359 0708

TILL, The Very Revd Michael Stanley. b 35. Linc Coll Ox BA60 MA67. Westcott Ho Cam. **d** 64 **p** 65. C St John's Wood *Lon* 64-67; Chapl K Coll Cam 67-70; Dean 70-80; AD Hammersmith *Lon* 81-86; V Fulham All SS 81-86; Adn Cant and Can Res Cant Cathl *Cant* 86-96; Dean Win from 96. *The Deanery, The Close, Winchester SO23 9LS* Tel and fax (01962) 853738 *or* 857203 E-mail michael.till@dial.pipex.com

TILLBROOK, Richard Ernest. b 50. St Mark & St Jo Coll Lon CertEd71 ACP76. NTMTC DipTh99. **d** 99 **p** 00. Hd RE Davenant Foundn Sch Loughton 71-03; NSM High Laver w Magdalen Laver and Lt Laver etc *Chelmsf* 99-03; V Colchester St Barn from 03. *St Barnabas' Vicarage, 13 Abbot's Road, Colchester CO2 8BE* Tel (01206) 797481 Mobile 07818-440530

TILLER, Edgar Henry. b 22. ACP71 Open Univ BA78. Wells Th Coll 57. **d** 59 **p** 60. C Weston-super-Mare St Jo *B & W* 59-62; V Stoke Lane 62-67; V Leigh upon Mendip 62-67; Perm to Offic *Ex* from 67; rtd 91. *3 Byron Close, Pilton, Barnstaple EX31 1QH* Tel (01271) 372483

TILLER, The Ven John. b 38. Ch Ch Ox BA60 MA64 Bris Univ MLitt72. Tyndale Hall Bris 60. **d** 62 **p** 63. C Bedford St Cuth *St Alb* 62-65; C Widcombe *B & W* 65-67; Tutor Tyndale Hall Bris 67-71; Chapl 67-71; Lect Trin Coll Bris 71-73; P-in-c Bedford Ch Ch *St Alb* 73-78; Chief Sec ACCM 78-84; Hon Can St Alb 79-84; Can Res Heref Cathl from 84; Chan 84-02; Dioc

Dir of Tr 91-00; Adn Heref from 02. *The Archdeacon's House, 3 St John Street, Hereford HR1 2NB* Tel (01432) 265659

TILLETT, Leslie Selwyn. b 54. Peterho Cam BA75 MA79 Leeds Univ BA80. Coll of Resurr Mirfield 78. **d** 81 **p** 82. C W Dulwich All SS and Em *S'wark* 81-85; R Purleigh, Cold Norton and Stow Maries *Chelmsf* 85-93; R Beddington *S'wark* from 93. *The Rectory, 18 Bloxworth Close, Wallington SM6 7NL* Tel (020) 8647 1973 Fax 8773 2383
E-mail selwyn@stmarysbeddington.org.uk

TILLETT, Michael John Arthur. b 57. Ridley Hall Cam 96. **d** 98 **p** 99. C Framlingham w Saxtead *St E* 98-01; P-in-c Stoke by Nayland w Leavenheath and Polstead 01-03; R from 03. *The Vicarage, Church Street, Stoke by Nayland, Colchester CO6 4QH* Tel (01206) 262248 Mobile 07703-794548
E-mail revtillett@aol.com

TILLETT, Miss Sarah Louise. b 59. Regent Coll Vancouver MCS00. Wycliffe Hall Ox 01. **d** 03. C Knowle *Birm* from 03. *St Anne's Cottage, 1713 High Street, Knowle, Solihull B93 0LN* Tel (01564) 775762 Mobile 07764-608796 Fax (01564) 779123 E-mail sarah.tillett@knowleparishchurch.org.uk

TILLEY, Canon David Robert. b 38. Kelham Th Coll 58. **d** 63 **p** 64. C Bournemouth St Fran *Win* 63-67; C Moulsecoomb *Chich* 67-70; C Ifield 70-75; TV Warwick *Cov* 76-85; P-in-c Alderminster 85-89; P-in-c Halford 85-89; Dioc Min Tr Adv from 85; CME Adv from 90; P-in-c Alderminster and Halford 90-96; Assoc Min Willenhall from 96; Hon Can Cov Cathl from 03. *6 Church Road, Baginton, Coventry CV8 3AR* Tel (024) 7630 2508 *or* 7667 4328 Fax 7630 2508 *or* 7669 1760
E-mail david.tilley@covdioc.org

TILLEY, James Stephen (Steve). b 55. St Jo Coll Nottm BTh84. **d** 84 **p** 85. C Nottingham St Jude *S'well* 84-88; C Chester le Street *Dur* 88-92; Tr and Ed CYFA (CPAS) 92-94; Hd from 94; Perm to Offic *Cov* 93-02; Hon C Leamington Priors St Paul from 02. *CPAS, Athena Drive, Tachbrook Park, Warwick CV34 6NG* Tel (01926) 334242 Fax 337613

TILLEY, Peter Robert. b 41. Bris Univ BA62. Sarum & Wells Th Coll 77. **d** 79 **p** 80. C Wandsworth St Paul *S'wark* 79-82; V Mitcham St Mark 82-91; RD Merton 89-91; R Walton St Mary *Liv* 91-92; TR Walton-on-the-Hill 92-98; rtd 98; P-in-c Ghent *Eur* from 98. *Coupure 908, 9000 Ghent, Belgium* Tel (0032) (9) 223 7691 Fax 225 4165 E-mail pt-ak-mts-gent@freegates.be

TILLIER, Jane Yvonne. b 59. New Hall Cam BA81 PhD85. Ripon Coll Cuddesdon BA90. **d** 91 **p** 94. Par Dn Sheff St Mark Broomhill *Sheff* 91-94; C 94-95; Chapl Glouc Cathl *Glouc* 95-97; P-in-c Madeley *Lich* 97-03. *Address temp unknown*
E-mail jane.tillier@cwcom.net

TILLMAN, Miss Mary Elizabeth. b 43. S Dios Minl Tr Scheme 86. **d** 89 **p** 95. NSM Bridgemary *Portsm* 89-93; NSM Portsea All SS from 93; Adv in Min to People w Disabilities from 93. *391 Fareham Road, Gosport PO13 0AD* Tel (01329) 232589

TILLOTSON, Simon Christopher. b 67. Lon Univ BA90 Trin Coll Cam BA93 MA96 Sarum Dioc Tr Coll CertHE00. Ridley Hall Cam 91. **d** 94 **p** 95. C Paddock Wood *Roch* 94-98; C Ormskirk *Liv* 98-00; V Aylesford *Roch* from 00. *The Vicarage, Vicarage Close, Aylesford ME20 7BB* Tel (01622) 717434 Mobile 07946-527471 E-mail sct@tillotsons.freeserve.co.uk

TILLYER, Desmond Benjamin. b 40. Ch Coll Cam BA63 MA67. Coll of Resurr Mirfield 64. **d** 66 **p** 67. C Hanworth All SS *Lon* 66-70; Chapl Liddon Ho Lon 70-74; V Pimlico St Pet w Westmr Ch Ch *Lon* from 74; AD Westmr St Marg 85-92. *1 St Peter's House, 119 Eaton Square, London SW1W 9AL* Tel (020) 7235 4242 Fax as telephone
E-mail vicar@stpetereatonsquare.co.uk

TILSON, Canon Alan Ernest. b 46. TCD. **d** 70 **p** 71. C Londonderry Ch Ch *D & R* 70-73; I Inver, Mountcharles and Killaghtee 73-79; I Leckpatrick w Dunnalong 79-89; Bermuda from 89; Hon Can Bermuda Cathl from 96. *Holy Trinity Rectory, PO Box CR 186, Hamilton Parish CR BX, Bermuda* Tel (001441) 293 1710 Fax 293 4363

TILSTON, Derek Reginald. b 27. NW Ord Course. **d** 73 **p** 74. NSM Bury St Mark *Man* 73-77; NSM Holcombe 77-82; NSM Bury St Jo 82-83; NSM Bury St Jo w St Mark 83-84; C Bramley *Ripon* 85-87; TV 87-90; R Tendring and Lt Bentley w Beaumont cum Moze *Chelmsf* 90-92; rtd 93; Perm to Offic *St E* from 93. *Cobbler's Croft, 19 The Street, Wissett, Halesworth IP19 0JE* Tel (01986) 874693

TILT, Dawn Caroline. b 59. Llan Ord Course. **d** 99 **p** 00. NSM Pyle w Kenfig *Llan* 99-00; NSM Ewenny w St Brides Major from 00. *The Lodge, Nottage Court, Porthcawl CF36 3TE* Tel (01656) 782546 E-mail thetilts@hotmail.com

TILTMAN, Alan Michael. b 48. Selw Coll Cam BA70 MA74. Cuddesdon Coll 71. **d** 73 **p** 74. C Chesterton Gd Shep *Ely* 73-77; C Preston St Jo *Blackb* 77-79; Chapl Lancs (Preston) Poly 77-79; TV Man Whitworth *Man* 79-86; Chapl Man Univ (UMIST) 79-86; V Urmston 86-99; Dir CME from 99; C Salford Sacred Trin 99-00; C Salford St Phil w St Steph 99-00; C Salford Sacred Trin and St Phil 00-02. *197A Lancaster Road, Salford M6 8NB, or Board of Ministry, 90 Deansgate, Manchester M3 2GJ* Tel and fax 0161-278 3391 *or* tel 832 5785 Fax 832 1466

E-mail atiltman@manchester.anglican.org
or a.tiltman@zoo.co.uk

TIMBERLAKE, Neil Christopher. b 26. Kelham Th Coll 47. **d** 51 **p** 52. C Ardwick St Benedict *Man* 51-54; C Moss Side Ch Ch 54-55; C Stockport St Alb Hall Street *Ches* 55-57; C Cov St Jo *Cov* 57-60; V Heath *Derby* 60-68; Australia 68-70; C Leyland St Ambrose *Blackb* 70-72; C Bilborough w Strelley *S'well* 72-74; V Langold 74-86; rtd 86. *7 Thirlmere Avenue, Colne BB8 7DD* Tel (01282) 863879

TIMBRELL, Keith Stewart. b 48. Edin Th Coll 72. **d** 74 **p** 75. C Chorley St Pet *Blackb* 74-77; C Altham w Clayton le Moors 77-79; Chapl Whittingham Hosp Preston 79-95; Trust Chapl Dorset Health Care NHS Trust from 95. *St Ann's Hospital, 69 Haven Road, Poole BH13 7LN* Tel (01202) 708881

TIMBRELL, Maxwell Keith. b 28. St Jo Coll Morpeth ThL51. **d** 51 **p** 52. Australia 51-58 and 64-82; C Hanworth All SS *Lon* 59-63; V Ingleby Greenhow w Bilsdale Priory *York* 83-85; P-in-c Kildale 83-85; V Ingleby Greenhow w Bilsdale Priory, Kildale etc 85-96; rtd 96; Perm to Offic *York* from 96. *Jasmine House, Nunnington, York YO65 5US* Tel (01439) 748319

TIMMINS, Susan Katherine. b 64. Leic Univ BScEng85 MICE91. St Jo Coll Nottm MTh94. **d** 96 **p** 97. C Iver *Ox* 96-00; P-in-c Pendlebury St Jo *Man* from 00. *St John's Vicarage, 27 Bolton Road, Pendlebury, Manchester M27 2XS* Tel 0161-925 0171 E-mail susanktimmins@aol.com

TIMMIS (née PITT), Mrs Karen Lesley Finella. b 62. Lon Univ BA84. Chich Th Coll BTh94. **d** 94 **p** 95. C Walton-on-the-Hill *Liv* 94-98; P-in-c Warrington St Barn 98-00; V from 00. *The Vicarage, 73 Loveley Lane, Warrington WA5 1TY* Tel (01925) 633556

TIMOTHY, Miss Bronwen Doris (Bonnie). b 57. Sheff City Poly BSc81 Univ of Wales (Cardiff) PGCE82. St Mich Coll Llan 99. **d** 02 **p** 03. C Tenby *St D* from 02. *The Vicarage, Penally, Tenby SA70 7PN* Tel (01834) 849141 Mobile 07773-645694

TIMS, Brian Anthony. b 43. Solicitor 64. STETS 95. **d** 98 **p** 99. NSM Whitchurch w Tufton and Litchfield *Win* 98-02; NSM Appleshaw, Kimpton, Thruxton, Fyfield etc from 02. *St Peter's Vicarage, High Street, Shipton Bellinger, Tidworth SP9 7UF* Tel (01980) 842244 E-mail brian@btims.freeserve.co.uk

TINGAY, Kevin Gilbert Xavier. b 43. Sussex Univ BA79. Chich Th Coll 79. **d** 80 **p** 81. C W Tarring *Chich* 80-83; TV Worth 83-90; R Bradford w Oake, Hillfarrance and Heathfield *B & W* 90-01; RD Tone 96-01; P-in-c Camerton w Dunkerton, Foxcote and Shoscombe from 01; Bp's Inter Faith Officer from 01; Bp's Adv for Regional Affairs from 01. *The Rectory, Skinners Hill, Camerton, Bath BA2 0PU* Tel (01761) 470249 Fax as telephone E-mail kgxt@compuserve.com

TINGLE, Michael Barton. b 31. Bps' Coll Cheshunt 65. **d** 67 **p** 68. C Totteridge *St Alb* 67-70; C Hitchin St Mary 70-73; V Gt Gaddesden 73-78; V Belmont *Lon* 78-86; V Burford w Fulbrook and Taynton *Ox* 86-94; V Burford w Fulbrook, Taynton, Asthall etc 94-97; rtd 97; Perm to Offic *St Alb* from 97. *10 Edenhall Close, Leverstock Green, Hemel Hempstead HP2 4ND* Tel (01442) 217674

TINKER, Preb Eric Franklin. b 20. OBE89. Ex Coll Ox BA42 MA46 City Univ Hon DD87 Lon Univ Hon DD89 Middx Univ Hon DD93. Linc Th Coll 42. **d** 44 **p** 45. C Gt Berkhamsted *St Alb* 44-46; C Rugby St Andr *Cov* 46-48; CF 48-49; Lon Sec SCM 49-51; Chapl Lon Univ *Lon* 51-55; V Handsworth St Jas *Birm* 55-65; V Enfield St Andr *Lon* 65-69; Preb St Paul's Cathl 69-90; Sen Chapl Lon Univs and Polys 69-90; Dir of Educn (Dios Lon and S'wark) 72-80; Gen Sec Lon Dioc Bd of Educn 80-82; rtd 90; Perm to Offic *Lon* from 90. *35 Theberton Street, London N1 0QY* Tel (020) 7359 4750

TINKER, Melvin. b 55. Hull Univ BSc Ox Univ MA. Wycliffe Hall Ox 80. **d** 83 **p** 84. C Wetherby *Ripon* 83-85; Chapl Keele Univ *Lich* 85-90; V Cheadle All Hallows *Ches* 90-94; V Hull Newland St Jo *York* from 94. *St John's Vicarage, Clough Road, Hull HU6 7PA* Tel (01482) 343658 E-mail melvin@tink.karoo.co.uk

TINNISWOOD, Robin Jeffries. b 41. K Coll Lon BScEng64 Bris Univ DipTh69. Wells Th Coll 67. **d** 70 **p** 71. C Yeovil St Mich *B & W* 70-72; C Gt Marlow *Ox* 72-74; C Christow, Ashton, Trusham and Bridford *Ex* 74-77; P-in-c Ex St Paul 77; TV Heavitree w Ex St Paul 78-79; TV Ifield *Chich* 79-85; Perm to Offic *S'wark* 98-01; P-in-c Cury and Gunwalloe w Mawgan *Truro* from 01. *Swift Cottage, Chymder, Cury Cross Lanes, Helston TR12 7BP* Tel (01326) 241596

TINSLEY, Bernard Murray. b 26. Nottm Univ BA51 Birm Univ DPS. Westcott Ho Cam 51. **d** 53 **p** 54. C Rotherham *Sheff* 53-56; C Goole 56-58; V Thorpe Hesley 58-61; R Alverdiscott w Huntshaw *Ex* 61-78; R Newton Tracey 61-78; R Beaford and Roborough 67-78; V St Giles in the Wood 67-78; V Yarnscombe 67-78; R Newton Tracey, Alverdiscott, Huntshaw etc 78-88; RD Torrington 81-86; rtd 88; Perm to Offic *Ex* from 88. *The Grange, Grange Road, Bideford EX39 4AS* Tel (01237) 471414

TINSLEY, Derek. b 31. ALCM65 BTh93 PhD97. NW Ord Course 73. **d** 76 **p** 77. C Gt Crosby St Faith *Liv* 76-80; V Wigan St Anne 80-85; V Colton w Satterthwaite and Rusland *Carl*

85-93; rtd 93; Perm to Offic *Liv* from 93. *Lyndale, 43 Renacres Lane, Ormskirk L39 8SG*

TINSLEY, Preb Derek Michael. b 35. Lon Coll of Div ALCD66 LTh. **d** 66 **p** 67. C Rainhill *Liv* 66-68; C Chalfont St Peter *Ox* 68-73; P-in-c Maids Moreton w Foxcote 73-74; P-in-c Akeley w Leckhampstead 73-74; P-in-c Lillingstone Dayrell w Lillingstone Lovell 73-74; R N Buckingham 74-82; RD Buckingham 78-82; P-in-c Alstonfield *Lich* 82-84; P-in-c Butterton 82-84; P-in-c Warslow and Elkstones 82-84; P-in-c Wetton 82-84; V Alstonfield, Butterton, Warslow w Elkstone etc 85-95; RD Alstonfield 82-95; Preb Lich Cathl 91-98; V Cheddleton 95-98; Chapl St Edw Hosp Cheddleton 96-98; rtd 98; Perm to Offic *Lich* and *Derby* from 98. *3 Windsor Close, Manor Green, Ashbourne DE6 1RJ* Tel (01335) 346226

TIPLADY, Peter. b 42. MRCGP72 FFPHM86 Dur Univ MB, BS65. Carl Dioc Tr Course 86. **d** 89 **p** 90. NSM Wetheral w Warwick *Carl* from 89. *Meadow Croft, Wetheral, Carlisle CA4 8JG* Tel (01228) 561611 *or* 603608 E-mail petertiplady@ncha.demon.co.uk

TIPP, Canon James Edward. b 45. Heythrop Coll Lon MA93. Oak Hill Th Coll 73. **d** 75 **p** 76. C St Mary Cray and St Paul's Cray *Roch* 75-78; C Southborough St Pet w Ch Ch and St Matt 78-82; R Snodland All SS w Ch Ch from 82; RD Cobham from 96; Hon Can Roch Cathl from 01. *The Vicarage, 11 St Katherine's Lane, Snodland ME6 5EH* Tel (01634) 240232 Fax as telephone E-mail jim@jtipp.freeserve.co.uk

TIPPER, Michael William. b 38. Hull Univ BSc59 MSc61. Em Coll Saskatoon 72. **d** 73 **p** 74. Canada 73-77, 79-80, 83-88 and from 91; R Amcotts *Linc* 77-79; V Aycliffe *Dur* 80-83; V Kneesall w Laxton and Wellow *S'well* 88-91; rtd 98. *106 Purdue Court West, Lethbridge AB, Canada, T1K 4R8*

TIPPING, Mrs Brenda Margaret. b 44. N Lon Univ CQSW85 Dur Univ MA96. St Alb and Ox Min Course 96. **d** 99 **p** 00. NSM Stevenage St Andr and St Geo *St Alb* from 99. *250 Grace Way, Stevenage SG1 5AJ* Tel (01438) 228467 Pager 01426-101670 Fax as telephone

TIPPING, John Woodman. b 42. AKC65. **d** 66 **p** 67. C Croydon St Sav *Cant* 66-70; C Plaistow St Mary *Roch* 70-72; V Brockley Hill St Sav *S'wark* 72-83; P-in-c Sittingbourne St Mary *Cant* 83-86; V 86-94; P-in-c Mersham w Hinxhill 94-03; P-in-c Mersham w Hinxhill and Sellindge from 03; P-in-c Sevington from 94; P-in-c Brabourne w Smeeth 95-00; AD N Lympne 95-02. *The Rectory, Bower Road, Mersham, Ashford TN25 6NN* Tel (01233) 502138 Fax as telephone E-mail jwtipping@talk21.com

TIRWOMWE, Stephen Warren. b 46. TCert73 Makerere Univ Kampala 81 Open Univ MA94 Leeds Univ MA01. Bp Tucker Coll Mukono DipTh82 BD88 All Nations Chr Coll 93. **d** 81 **p** 82. Uganda 87-97 and from 02; C Osmondthorpe St Phil *Ripon* 97-02; Dioc Miss Co-ord Kigezi from 02. *Abaho Ahurira, PO Box 1091, Kabale, Uganda* Tel (00256) (77) 870467 E-mail swtirwomwe@hotmail.com

TISANI, Canon Ezra Vuyisile Kenton. b 41. Nottm Univ BA. St Pet Coll Alice. **d** 68 **p** 69. S Africa 68-79 and from 82; Lic to Offic *S'well* 79-80; C Lowdham 80-82. *PO Box 6087, Grahamstown, 6140 South Africa* Tel (0027) (461) 22740

TISDALE, Mark-Aaron Buchanan. b 67. Pittsburgh Univ BA94. Westcott Ho Cam 00. **d** 02 **p** 03. C Norton *St Alb* from 02. *2 Common View, Letchworth Garden City SG6 1DA* Tel (01462) 672256 E-mail mabtisdale@yahoo.com

TITCOMB, Mrs Claire. b 35. St Alb and Ox Min Course 95. **d** 98 **p** 99. OLM Witney *Ox* from 98; Assoc P for Min Development from 01. *30 Beech Road, Witney OX8 5LW* Tel (01993) 771234 E-mail claireroyt@clara.net

TITCOMBE, Peter Charles. *See* JONES, Peter Charles

TITFORD, Richard Kimber. b 45. UEA BA67. Ripon Coll Cuddesdon 78. **d** 80 **p** 80. C Middleton *Man* 80-83; P-in-c Edwardstone w Groton and Lt Waldingfield *St E* 83-90; R 90-02; P-in-c Boxford 00-02; C Assington w Newton Green and Lt Cornard 00-02; R Boxford, Edwardstone, Groton etc 02-03; rtd 03; Perm to Offic *St E* from 03. *The Rectory, Willow Corner, Edwardstone, Sudbury CO10 5PG* Tel (01787) 211760 Fax 210825 E-mail titford@anglianet.co.uk

TITLEY, David Joseph. b 47. Ex Univ BSc Surrey Univ PhD. Wycliffe Hall Ox. **d** 82 **p** 83. C Stowmarket *St E* 82-85; C Bloxwich *Lich* 85-90; TV 90-95; V Prees 95-00; V Fauls 95-00; V Clacton St Paul *Chelmsf* from 00. *The Vicarage, 7 St Alban's Road, Clacton-on-Sea CO15 6BA* Tel (01255) 424760 E-mail titleys@supanet.com

TITLEY, Robert John. b 56. Ch Coll Cam BA78 MA82. Westcott Ho Cam DipTh83. **d** 85 **p** 86. C Lower Sydenham St Mich *S'wark* 85-88; C Sydenham All SS 85-88; Chapl Whitelands Coll of HE 88-94; V W Dulwich All SS from 94. *The Vicarage, 165 Rosendale Road, London SE21 8LN* Tel (020) 8670 0826

TIVEY, Nicholas. b 65. Liv Poly BSc89. Ridley Hall Cam CTM94. **d** 94 **p** 95. C Bromborough *Ches* 94-97; TV Walton H Trin *Ox* 97-01; Chapl HM Pris Wayland from 01. *The Chaplain's Office, HM Prison Wayland, Griston, Thetford IP25 6RL* Tel (01953) 858080

TIZZARD, David John. b 40. LRAM. Sarum Th Coll 65. **d** 68 **p** 69. C Foley Park *Worc* 68-70; Hon C Gravesend St Geo *Roch* 70-73; Miss to Seamen 70-72; PV Truro Cathl *Truro* 73-75; TV Bemerton *Sarum* 75-79; Soc Resp Adv 79-85; Chapl to the Deaf 79-85; Can and Preb Sarum Cathl 84-85; R S Hill w Callington *Truro* 85-87; P-in-c Linkinhorne 86-87; Relig Affairs Producer BBC Radio Solent 87-94; V Portswood St Denys *Win* 87-94; P-in-c Distington *Carl* 94-96; Soc Resp Officer 94-96; Hon Can Carl Cathl 94-96; TV Beaminster Area *Sarum* 96-99; rtd 99; Perm to Offic *Ex* from 99. *Chy Trevor, Lyme Road, Axminster EX13 5BL* Tel (01297) 32928

TIZZARD, Dudley Frank. b 19. Roch Th Coll 63. **d** 65 **p** 66. C Bearsted *Cant* 65-68; C Cant St Martin w St Paul 68-71; Chapl HM Pris Cant 68-71; V Petham w Waltham *Cant* 71-75; C Sevenoaks St Jo *Roch* 75-78; Perm to Offic *Cant* 78-84 and 87-01; rtd 84; Lic to Offic *Cant* 84-87. *96 Langlands Road, Cullompton EX15 1JB* Tel (01884) 38279

TIZZARD, Peter Francis. b 53. Oak Hill Th Coll DipHE88. **d** 90 **p** 91. C Letchworth St Paul w Willian *St Alb* 90-95; I Drumkeeran w Templecarne and Muckross *Clogh* 95-00; P-in-c Ramsgate Ch Ch *Cant* 00-02; V from 02. *24 St Mildred's Avenue, Ramsgate CT11 0HT* Tel (01843) 853732

TOAN, Robert Charles. b 50. Oak Hill Th Coll. **d** 84 **p** 85. C Upton (Overchurch) *Ches* 84-87; V Rock Ferry 87-99; RD Birkenhead 97-99; V Plas Newton from 99; P-in-c Ches Ch Ch from 03; RD Ches from 02. *St Michael's Vicarage, 22 Plas Newton Lane, Chester CH2 1PA* Tel (01244) 319677 *or* 315129 Fax 315129 E-mail bob.toan@xaltmail.com

TOBIN, Richard Francis. b 44. CertEd. Chich Th Coll 76. **d** 78 **p** 79. C W Leigh CD *Portsm* 78-79; C Halstead St Andr *Chelmsf* 79; C Halstead St Andr w H Trin 79; C Halstead St Andr w H Trin and Greenstead Green 79-87; Youth Chapl 82-87; V S Shields St Simon *Dur* from 87. *St Simon's Vicarage, Wenlock Road, South Shields NE34 9AL* Tel 0191-455 3164 *or* 424 0690 Fax 424 0689 E-mail ricktobin@btinternet.com

TODD, Alastair. b 20. CMG71. CCC Ox BA45 Lon Univ DipTh65. Sarum & Wells Th Coll 71. **d** 73 **p** 74. C Willingdon *Chich* 73-77; P-in-c Brighton St Aug 77-78; V Brighton St Aug and St Sav 78-86; rtd 86; Perm to Offic *Chich* from 86. *59 Park Avenue, Eastbourne BN21 2XH* Tel (01323) 505843

TODD, Canon Andrew John. b 61. Keble Coll Ox 80 Univ Coll Dur BA84 K Coll Lon MPhil98. Coll of Resurr Mirfield 85. **d** 87 **p** 88. C Thorpe *Nor* 87-91; Chapl K Alfred Coll *Win* 91-94; Sen Asst P E Dereham and Scarning *Nor* 94-97; Dir Studies EAMTC *Ely* 94-01; Vice-Prin 97-01; CME Officer *St E* from 01; Can Res St E Cathl from 01. *3 Crown Street, Bury St Edmunds IP33 1QX* Tel and fax (01284) 706813 Mobile 07785-560558 E-mail andrew.todd@stedmundsbury.anglican.org

TODD, Catherine Frances. b 61. Surrey Univ BSc84 Westmr Coll Ox BTh99 RGN84 RM86. EAMTC 96. **d** 99 **p** 00. NSM Sutton and Witcham w Mepal *Ely* 99-01; C Horringer *St E* from 01; R from 03. *3 Crown Street, Bury St Edmunds IP33 1QX* Tel (01284) 706813

TODD, Clive. b 57. Linc Th Coll 89. **d** 91 **p** 92. C Consett *Dur* 91-93; C Bensham 93-95; P-in-c S Hetton w Haswell 95-98; R Ebchester from 98; V Medomsley from 98. *The Rectory, Shaw Lane, Ebchester DH8 0PY* Tel (01207) 563348

TODD, Edward Peter. b 44. Cranmer Hall Dur 86. **d** 88 **p** 89. C Hindley All SS *Liv* 88-91; P-in-c Wigan St Steph 91-96; V 96-98; P-in-c N Meols from 98; P-in-c Banks from 99. *The Rectory, 20 Moss Lane, Churchtown, Southport PR9 7QR* Tel (01704) 225436

TODD, George Robert. b 21. Sarum & Wells Th Coll 74. **d** 76 **p** 77. Hon C Wellington and Distr *B & W* 76-86; Perm to Offic from 86. *15 John Grinter Way, Wellington TA21 9AR* Tel (01823) 662828

TODD, Jeremy Stephen Bevan (Jez). b 69. Kent Univ Dip Mgt96. Trin Coll Bris BA92. **d** 97 **p** 98. C Tufnell Park St Geo and All SS *Lon* from 97. *St George's Centre, Crayford Road, London N7 0ND* Tel (020) 7609 0121

TODD, Joy Gertrude. b 28. Ox Univ MTh99 Lon Univ DipRS94. LNSM course. **d** 90 **p** 94. OLM Guildf H Trin w St Mary *Guildf* 90-99; Perm to Offic from 99. *165 Stoke Road, Guildford GU1 1EY* Tel (01483) 567500

TODD, Michael Edward. b 62. Brighton Poly BA84 Surrey Univ PGCE85. Ven English Coll Rome 98 SEITE DTM99. **d** 99. C Farnham *Guildf* 99-00; Chapl Surrey Inst Art and Design 99-00; Development Officer Surrey Univ *Guildf* 00-02; Progr Manager and Lect Croydon Coll from 02. *De Pastorie, 10 Wincott Street, London SE11 4NT* Tel (020) 7735 8191 E-mail mikeytodd@hotmail.com

TODD, Nicholas Stewart. b 61. Huddersfield Poly HND84. Wycliffe Hall Ox 94. **d** 96 **p** 97. C Gt Wyrley *Lich* 96-99; V Leaton and Albrighton w Battlefield 99-02; R Holbrook, Stutton, Freston, Woolverstone etc *St E* from 02. *The Rectory, Fishponds Lane, Holbrook, Ipswich IP9 2QZ* Tel (01473) 327705 Mobile 07762-645174 E-mail nictodd@aol.com

TODD, Canon Norman Henry. b 19. PhC Lon Univ BPharm42 Fitzw Ho Cam BA50 MA55 Nottm Univ PhD78. Westcott Ho

---

Cam 50. **d** 52 **p** 53. C Aspley *S'well* 52-54; Chapl Westcott Ho Cam 55-58; V Arnold *S'well* 58-65; V Rolleston w Morton 65-69; Can Res S'well Minster 65-69; R Elston w Elston Chapelry 71-76; R E Stoke w Syerston 72-76; V Sibthorpe 72-76; Bp's Adv on Tr 76-83; C Averham w Kelham 76-80; V Rolleston w Morton 80-83; P-in-c Upton 80-83; V Rolleston w Fiskerton, Morton and Upton 83-88; Hon Can S'well Minster 82-88; rtd 88; Perm to Offic *S'well* from 88; Abps' Adv for Bps' Min 88-94. *39 Beacon Hill Road, Newark NG24 2JH* Tel (01636) 671857

TODD, William Colquhoun Duncan. b 26. AKC53 St Boniface Warminster 53. **d** 54 **p** 55. C Westmr St Steph w St Jo *Lon* 54-59; Win Coll Missr 60-72; C-in-c Leigh Park CD *Portsm* 59-69; V Leigh Park 69-72; R Bp's Hatfield *St Alb* 72-00; Angl Adv Southern TV 62-72; Thames TV 72-92; Carlton TV 93-00; rtd 00; Perm to Offic *St Alb* from 00. *15 Archway House, Park Street, Hatfield AL9 5BB* Tel (01707) 256268

TODD, Canon William Moorhouse. b 26. Lich Th Coll 54. **d** 57 **p** 58. C W Derby St Mary *Liv* 57-61; V Liv St Chris Norris Green 61-97; Hon Can Liv Cathl 92-97; rtd 97; Perm to Offic *Liv* from 97. *3 Haymans Grove, West Derby, Liverpool L12 7LD* Tel 0151-256 1712

TOFTS, Jack. b 31. Roch Th Coll 66. **d** 68 **p** 69. C Richmond *Ripon* 68-71; C Croydon *Cant* 71-74; P-in-c Welney *Ely* 74-78; P-in-c Upwell Ch Ch 74-79; V Gorefield 78-94; R Newton 78-94; R Tydd St Giles 78-94; rtd 96; Perm to Offic *Ely* from 96. *The Birches, Church Road, Walpole St Peter, Wisbech PE14 7NU* Tel (01945) 780455

TOLL, Brian Arthur. b 35. Ely Th Coll 62 Linc Th Coll 64. **d** 65 **p** 66. C Cleethorpes *Linc* 65-68; C Hadleigh w Layham and Shelley *St E* 68-72; R Claydon and Barham 72-86; P-in-c Capel w Lt Wenham 86-94; R Capel St Mary w Lt and Gt Wenham 94-96; P-in-c Ipswich St Mary at the Elms 96-01; P-in-c Holton St Mary w Gt Wenham 87-91; Bp's Adv on Deliverance and Exorcism 89-97; rtd 01; Perm to Offic *St E* from 01. *39 Derwent Road, Ipswich IP3 0QR* Tel (01473) 424305 E-mail batoll@ntlworld.com

TOLLEFSEN, Alida Thadden Maria (Alja). b 50. Utrecht Univ 89. St Steph Ho Ox 96. **d** 98 **p** 99. C Bramhall *Ches* 98-02; V Knutsford St Cross from 02. *The Vicarage, Mobberley Road, Knutsford WA16 8EL* Tel (01565) 632389 E-mail tollef@pncl.co.uk

TOLLER, Elizabeth Margery. b 53. Leeds Univ BA75. Ripon Coll Cuddesdon 84. **d** 87 **p** 00. Asst Chapl Leeds Gen Infirmary 87-90; Perm to Offic *Nor* 90-91; Chapl Lt Plumstead Hosp 92-93; Chapl Co-ord HM Pris Nor 93-95; Chapl Gt Yarmouth Coll 96-99; Perm to Offic *S'wark* 99-00; Hon C Wandsworth St Paul from 00. *116 Augustus Road, London SW19 6EW* Tel (020) 8788 2024 E-mail mtoller@gmx.de

TOLLER, Heinz Dieter. b 52. Bonn Univ DipTh77. NEOC 86. **d** 87 **p** 88. C Leeds Gipton Epiphany *Ripon* 87-90; R Coltishall w Gt Hautbois and Horstead *Nor* 90-99; V Wandsworth St Paul *S'wark* from 99. *116 Augustus Road, London SW19 6EW* Tel (020) 8788 2024 Mobile 07941-291120 Fax 0870-284 3237 E-mail htoller@gmx.de

TOLLERSON, Peter Joseph Moncrieff. b 65. Oak Hill Th Coll 99. **d** 01 **p** 02. C Ulverston St Mary w H Trin *Carl* from 01. *18 Church Walk, Ulverston LA12 7EN* Tel (01229) 586133 E-mail pedroandcarmen@yahoo.com

TOLLEY, Canon George. b 25. Lon Univ BSc45 MSc48 PhD52 Sheff Univ Hon DSc83 Open Univ Hon DUniv84 Hon DSc86 FRSC CBIM. Linc Th Coll 65. **d** 67 **p** 68. C Sharrow St Andr Sheff 67-90; Hon Can Sheff Cathl 76-98. *74 Furniss Avenue, Sheffield S17 3QP* Tel 0114-236 0538

TOLWORTHY, Canon Colin. b 37. Chich Th Coll 64. **d** 67 **p** 68. C Hulme St Phil *Man* 67-70; C Lawton Moor 70-71; C Hangleton *Chich* 71-76; V Eastbourne St Phil 76-87; V Hastings H Trin from 87; Can and Preb Chich Cathl from 03. *Holy Trinity Vicarage, 72 Priory Avenue, Hastings TN34 1UG* Tel (01424) 441766 E-mail colintolworthy@hotmail.com

TOMALIN, Stanley Joseph Edward. b 66. Oak Hill Th Coll BA93. **d** 96 **p** 97. C Bitterne *Win* 96-00; C Hailsham *Chich* 00; P-in-c Hawkswood CD from 01. *15 Howlett Drive, Hailsham BN27 1QW* Tel (01323) 846680 E-mail tomalinstan@aol.com

TOMBLING, Canon Arthur John. b 32. St Jo Coll Cam BA54 MA58. Ridley Hall Cam 55. **d** 57 **p** 58. C Rushden *Pet* 57-59; Asst Chapl Repton Sch Derby 59-61; C Reigate St Mary *S'wark* 61-64; V Battersea Park St Sav 64-87; P-in-c Battersea St Geo w St Andr 74-87; V Battersea St Sav and St Geo w St Andr 87-95; P-in-c Battersea Park All SS 89-95; RD Battersea 85-90; Hon Can S'wark Cathl 89-95; rtd 95; Perm to Offic *Pet* from 95. *5 William Steele Way, Higham Ferrers, Rushden NN10 8LS* Tel (01933) 418072

TOMBS, Kenneth Roberts. b 42. Open Univ BA84. S Dios Minl Tr Scheme 92. **d** 95 **p** 96. Dep Hd Twyford C of E High Sch Acton 86-97; Chapl from 98; NSM Ickenham *Lon* from 95. *91 Burns Avenue, Southall UB1 2LT* Tel (020) 8574 3738 E-mail ken.tombs@tesco.net

TOMKINS, Clive Anthony. b 47. Cant Sch of Min 85. **d** 88 **p** 89. C Eastry and Northbourne w Tilmanstone etc *Cant* 88-91; R

91-96; P-in-c 96-97; Chapl Eastry Hosp 91-93; Chapl Cant and Thanet Community Healthcare Trust 93-97; P-in-c Woodchurch *Cant* 97-01; P-in-c Maidstone St Martin from 01. *St Martin's Vicarage, Northumberland Road, Maidstone ME15 7LP* Tel (01622) 676282 E-mail clivetomkins@hotmail.com

TOMKINS, Ian James. b 60. Univ of Wales (Cardiff) LLB81 Aston Business Sch MBA90. Ridley Hall Cam. **d** 00 **p** 01. C Bourton-on-the-Water w Clapton *Glouc* from 00. *23 Roman Way, Bourton-on-the-Water, Cheltenham GL54 2EW* Tel (01451) 810608 E-mail ian-tomkins@lineone.net

TOMKINS, Jocelyn Rachel. *See* WALKER, Ms Jocelyn Rachel

TOMKINSON, Raymond David. b 47. RGN MSSCh. EAMTC 86. **d** 89 **p** 90. NSM Chesterton St Geo *Ely* 89-91; C Sawston 91-93; C Babraham 91-93; P-in-c Wimbotsham w Stow Bardolph and Stow Bridge etc 93-94; R 94-00; RD Fincham 94-97; Dir Old Alresford Place *Win* from 00; P-in-c Old Alresford and Bighton from 00. *The Rectory, Kiln Lane, Old Alresford, Alresford SO24 9DU* Tel (01962) 732780 E-mail raymond@tomkinson29.freeserve.co.uk

TOMLIN, Graham Stuart. b 58. Linc Coll Ox MA80 Ex Univ PhD96. Wycliffe Hall Ox BA85. **d** 86 **p** 87. C Ex St Leon w H Trin *Ex* 86-89; Tutor Wycliffe Hall Ox from 89; Vice-Prin from 98; Chapl Jes Coll Ox 89-94. *Wycliffe Hall, Oxford OX2 6PW* Tel (01865) 274210 Fax 274205 E-mail graham.tomlin@wycliffe.ox.ac.uk

TOMLIN, Keith Michael. b 53. Imp Coll Lon BSc75. Ridley Hall Cam 77. **d** 80 **p** 81. C Heywood St Jas *Man* 80-83; C Rochdale 83-84; TV 84-85; Chapl Rochdale Tech Coll 83-85; R Benington w Leverton *Linc* 85-99; R Leverton 99-01; Chapl HM Pris N Sea Camp 97-01; P-in-c Fotherby *Linc* from 01. *The Rectory, Peppin Lane, Fotherby, Louth LN11 0UG* Tel (01507) 602312

TOMLINE, Stephen Harrald. b 35. Dur Univ BA57. Cranmer Hall Dur DipTh61. **d** 61 **p** 62. C Blackley St Pet *Man* 61-66; V Audenshaw St Steph 66-90; V Newhey 90-01; rtd 01; Perm to Offic *Carl* from 01. *3 Humphrey Cottages, Stainton, Kendal LA8 0AD* Tel (01539) 560988

TOMLINSON, Anne Lovat. b 56. Edin Univ MA78 PhD85 MTh98. St Jo Coll Nottm CertCS87. **d** 93. Tutor TISEC from 93; Dir Past Studies from 98; Perm to Offic *Edin* from 93. *3 Bright's Crescent, Edinburgh EH9 2DB* Tel 0131-667 6224 Fax as telephone E-mail anniet@talk21.com

TOMLINSON, Arthur John Faulkner (Jack). b 20. Clare Coll Cam BA41 MA45. Ridley Hall Cam 46. **d** 48 **p** 49. C Hampstead Em W End *Lon* 48-50; C Kensington St Helen w H Trin 50-54; V Furneux Pelham w Stocking Pelham *St Alb* 54-62; R Sarratt 62-85; rtd 85; Perm to Offic *Nor* from 85. *5 Mead Close, Buxton, Norwich NR10 5EL* Tel (01603) 279470

TOMLINSON, Barry William. b 47. Reading Univ DipTh. Clifton Th Coll 72. **d** 72 **p** 73. C Pennington *Man* 72-76; SAMS 76-80; Chile 77-80; C-in-c Gorleston St Mary CD *Nor* 80; Chapl Jas Paget Hosp Gorleston 81-87; V Gorleston St Mary *Nor* 80-88; P-in-c Gt w Lt Plumstead 88-89; R Gt w Lt Plumstead and Witton 89-93; R Gt and Lt Plumstead w Thorpe End and Witton 93-98; Chapl Lt Plumstead Hosp 88-94; Chapl Norwich Community Health Partnership NHS Trust 94-95; RD Blofield *Nor* 96-98; R Roughton and Felbrigg, Metton, Sustead etc 99-02; V Margate H Trin *Cant* 98-99; rtd 02; Perm to Offic *Nor* from 02. *12 Heath Road, Sheringham NR26 8JH* Tel (01263) 820266 E-mail bwtomlinson@lineone.net

TOMLINSON, David Robert. b 60. Kent Univ BSc82 Chelsea Coll Lon PGCE83 Jes Coll Cam BA92 MA96. Ridley Hall Cam CTM93. **d** 93 **p** 94. C Godalming *Guildf* 93-98; V Grays North *Chelmsf* from 98; RD Thurrock from 03. *St John's Vicarage, 8A Victoria Avenue, Grays RM16 2RP* Tel (01375) 372101 E-mail djtgrays@btinternet.com

TOMLINSON, David William. b 48. Lon Bible Coll MA95 Westcott Ho Cam 97. **d** 97 **p** 98. NSM W Holloway St Luke *Lon* 97-00; P-in-c 00-01; V from 01. *St Luke's Vicarage, Penn Road, London N7 9RE* Tel (020) 7607 1504 Fax 7700 5262 E-mail revdavetomlinson@hotmail.com

TOMLINSON, Edward James. b 74. Homerton Coll Cam BEd96. Westcott Ho Cam 99. **d** 02 **p** 03. C Brentwood St Thos *Chelmsf* from 02. *Stokes House, St Thomas Road, Brentwood CM14 4DS* Tel (01277) 210323 Mobile 07788-855646 E-mail frtomlinson@yahoo.co.uk

TOMLINSON, Eric Joseph. b 45. Qu Coll Birm 70. **d** 73 **p** 74. C Cheadle *Lich* 73-76; C Sedgley All SS 77-79; V Ettingshall 79-94; P-in-c Longsdon 94; P-in-c Rushton 94; P-in-c Horton 94; V Horton, Lonsdon and Rushton Spencer from 94. *The Vicarage, Longsdon, Stoke-on-Trent ST9 9QF* Tel (01538) 385318

TOMLINSON, Frederick William. b 58. Glas Univ MA80 Edin Univ BD83. Edin Th Coll 80. **d** 83 **p** 84. C Cumbernauld *Glas* 83-86; C Glas St Mary 86-88; R Edin St Hilda *Edin* 88-01; R Edin St Fillan 88-01; R Edin St Pet from 01. *3 Bright's Crescent, Edinburgh EH9 2DB* Tel 0131-667 6224 Fax as telephone E-mail fred.tomlinson@talk21.com

TOMLINSON, Ian James. b 50. K Coll Lon AKC72 Hull Univ MA90 Ox Univ MTh01. St Aug Coll Cant 72. **d** 73 **p** 74. C Thirsk w S Kilvington and Carlton Miniott etc *York* 73-76; C

Harrogate St Wilfrid *Ripon* 76-79; R Appleshaw, Kimpton, Thruxton, Fyfield etc *Win* from 79; Dioc Adv in Past care and Counselling from 01. *The Rectory, Ragged Appleshaw, Andover SP11 9HX* Tel (01264) 772414 Fax 771302 E-mail ian@raggedappleshaw.freeserve.co.uk

TOMLINSON, Jack. *See* TOMLINSON, Arthur John Faulkner

TOMLINSON, Mrs Jean Mary. b 32. K Coll Lon CertRK53 BEd75. S Dios Minl Tr Scheme 84. **d** 87 **p** 94. Hon Par Dn Spring Park All SS *S'wark* 87-92; Chapl HM YOI Hatfield 92-98; Perm to Offic *S'well* from 92. *6 Cheyne Walk, Bawtry, Doncaster DN10 6RS* Tel (01302) 711281

TOMLINSON (née MILLS), Mrs Jennifer Clare. b 61. Trin Hall Cam BA82 MA86. Ridley Hall Cam 88. **d** 91 **p** 94. C Busbridge *Guildf* 91-95; C Godalming 95-97; NSM 97-98; NSM Grays North *Chelmsf* from 98. *St John's Vicarage, 8A Victoria Avenue, Grays RM16 2RP* Tel (01375) 372101 E-mail djtgrays@btinternet.com

TOMLINSON, Canon John Coombes. b 34. Nottm Univ DipEd76. Lich Th Coll 60. **d** 62 **p** 63. C Cheadle *Lich* 62-66; Warden Lich Dioc Tr Cen 66-73; C Alstonfield 66-68; P-in-c Ilam w Blore Ray and Okeover 68-73; Dioc Youth Tr Officer 68-73; Bp's Youth Chapl *Derby* 73-84; Dep Dir of Educn 78-79; Dir 79-84; TR Buxton w Burbage and King Sterndale 84-96; Dioc Adv Past Care and Counselling from 85; RD Buxton 91-96; Hon Can Derby Cathl 91-02; R Matlock 96-02; rtd 02; Perm to Offic *Derby* from 02. *Farriers, Ilam Moor Lane, Ilam, Ashbourne DE6 2BD* Tel (01335) 350385

TOMLINSON, John Howard. b 54. MICE83 Newc Univ BSc76. Chich Th Coll 91. **d** 93 **p** 94. C Blewbury, Hagbourne and Upton *Ox* 93-96; C Cowley St Jas 96-97; TV from 97. *St Francis's Vicarage, 2 Meyseys Close, Headington, Oxford OX3 7SF* Tel (01865) 748915 E-mail fj@care4free.net

TOMLINSON, John William Bruce. b 60. Univ of Wales (Abth) BA82 Man MA90. Hartley Victoria Coll 87 Mar Thoma Th Sem Kottayam 90 Linc Th Coll 91. **d** 92 **p** 93. In Methodist Ch 90-91; C Sawley *Derby* 92-95; P-in-c Man Victoria Park *Man* 95-98; Dioc CUF Officer 95-98; Chapl St Anselm Hall Man Univ 96-98; V Shelton and Oxon *Lich* from 98. *The Vicarage, 10A Shelton Gardens, Bicton Heath, Shrewsbury SY3 5AG* Tel (01743) 232774 E-mail pelican@supanet.com

TOMLINSON, Matthew Robert Edward. b 61. St Chad's Coll Dur BA83 Univ of Wales (Cardiff) BD94. St Mich Coll Llan 92. **d** 94 **p** 95. C Abergavenny St Mary w Llanwenarth Citra *Mon* 94-96; PV Llan Cathl and Chapl Llan Cathl Sch 96-00; V Edgbaston St Aug *Birm* from 00. *St Augustine's Vicarage, 44 Vernon Road, Birmingham B16 9SH* Tel and fax 0121-454 0127 Mobile 07989-915499 E-mail jm.tomlinson@virgin.net

TOMPKINS, David John. b 32. Oak Hill Th Coll 55. **d** 58 **p** 59. C Northampton St Giles *Pet* 58-61; C Heatherlands St Jo *Sarum* 61-63; V Selby St Jas *York* 63-73; V Wistow 63-73; V Retford St Sav *S'well* 73-87; P-in-c Clarborough w Hayton 84-87; V Kidsgrove *Lich* 87-90; V Tockwith and Bilton w Bickerton *York* 90-97; rtd 97; Perm to Offic *Pet* from 00. *49 Wentworth Drive, Oundle, Peterborough PE8 4QF* Tel (01832) 275176

TOMPKINS, Francis Alfred Howard. b 26. St Jo Coll Dur BA50 DipTh52. **d** 52 **p** 53. C Islington St Mary *Lon* 52-55; Argentina 55-61; Field Supt SAMS 61-65; V Donington *Linc* 65-79; RD Holland W 69-78; V Silloth *Carl* 79-91; rtd 91; Perm to Offic *Linc* 91-00; *York* from 01. *17 Southfield Drive, North Ferriby HU14 3DU* Tel (01482) 632483

TOMPKINS, Michael John Gordon. b 35. JP76. Man Univ BSc58 MPS59. N Ord Course 82. **d** 85 **p** 86. C Abington *Pet* 85-87; TV Daventry 87-92; P-in-c Braunston 87-92; TV Daventry, Ashby St Ledgers, Braunston etc 92-93; R Paston 93-98; Perm to Offic *Ches* from 98; rtd 00. *19 Clarendon Close, Chester CH4 9BL* Tel (01244) 659147

TOMPKINS, Peter Michael. b 58. Open Univ BA92 SS Hild & Bede Coll Dur CertEd79. St Jo Coll Nottm MA96. **d** 96 **p** 97. C Bromfield w Waverton *Carl* 96-99; R Woldsburn *York* 99-01; TV E Farnworth and Kearsley *Man* from 01. *The Vicarage, 93 Bradford Street, Farnworth, Bolton BL4 9JY* Tel (01204) 572819

TOMS, Sheila Patricia. b 33. Cam Univ TCert54 Univ of Wales (Cardiff) BEd77 Univ of Wales (Swansea) ADC74. Llan Ord Course 90. **dss** 91 **d** 94 **p** 97. Llan 94; NSM Peterston-super-Ely w St Brides-super-Ely 94-00; P-in-c Newport St Paul *Mon* from 00. *East Wing, Dingestow Court, Dingestow, Monmouth NP25 4DY* Tel (01600) 740262

TONBRIDGE, Archdeacon of. *See* MANSELL, The Ven Clive Neville Ross

TONBRIDGE, Suffragan Bishop of. *See* CASTLE, The Rt Revd Brian Colin

TONES, Kevin Edward. b 64. Hertf Coll Ox BA85. Ridley Hall Cam 88. **d** 91 **p** 92. C Warmsworth *Sheff* 91-92; C Thorne 92-96; V Greasbrough from 96. *The Vicarage, 16 Church Street, Greasbrough, Rotherham S61 4DX* Tel (01709) 551288 E-mail kevt@tesco.net

TONG, Canon Peter Laurence. b 29. Lon Univ BA50. Oak Hill Th Coll 52. **d** 54 **p** 55. C Everton St Chrys *Liv* 54-56; P-in-c Liv

St Sav 56-59; V Blackb Sav *Blackb* 59-65; Chapl Blackb R Infirmary 63-65; V Islington St Andr w St Thos and St Matthias *Lon* 65-75; V Welling *Roch* 75-82; TR Bedworth *Cov* 82-94; Hon Can Cov Cathl 88-94; Hon Can Chile from 89; rtd 94; Perm to Offic *Roch* from 94. *46 Bladindon Drive, Bexley DA5 3BP* Tel (020) 8303 0085

TONGE, Brian. b 36. St Chad's Coll Dur BA58. Ely Th Coll 59. **d** 61 **p** 62. C Fleetwood *Blackb* 61-65; Chapl Ranby Ho Sch Retford 65-69; Hon C Burnley St Andr w St Marg *Blackb* 69-97; rtd 97; Perm to Offic *Blackb* from 97. *50 Fountains Avenue, Simonstone, Burnley BB12 7PY* Tel (01282) 776518

TONGE, Lister. b 51. K Coll Lon AKC74 Man Univ Dip Counselling 92 Loyola Univ Chicago MPS95. St Aug Coll Cant 74. **d** 75 **p** 76. C Liv Our Lady and St Nic w St Anne *Liv* 75-78; S Africa 78-79; CR 79-91; Lic to Offic *Wakef* 83-91; Perm to Offic *Man* 89-94; USA 93-95; Perm to Offic *Liv* 95-96; Chapl Community of St Jo Bapt from 96. *Rowell House, 7 Woodstock Road East, Begbroke, Kidlington OX5 1RL* Tel (01865) 848940 Fax 08701-376624 E-mail listertonge@ntlworld.com

TONGE, Malcolm. b 53. Lancs Poly BA74 FCA77. NEOC 00. **d** 03. NSM Brookfield *York* from 03. *65 Belmont Avenue, Middlesbrough TS5 8EW* Tel (01642) 599209 E-mail malcolm.tonge@huntsman.com

TONGUE, Canon Paul. b 41. St Chad's Coll Dur BA63 DipTh64. **d** 64 **p** 65. C Dudley St Edm *Worc* 64-69; C Sedgley All SS *Lich* 69-70; V Amblecote *Worc* from 70; Hon Can Worc Cathl from 93; Chapl Dudley Gp of Hosps NHS Trust from 93; RD Stourbridge *Worc* 96-01. *The Vicarage, 14 The Holloway, Amblecote, Stourbridge DY8 4DL* Tel (01384) 394057 E-mail paul@amblecotevic.freeserve.co.uk

TONKIN, The Ven David Graeme. b 31. Univ of NZ LLB56 LLM57 Barrister-at-Law. Coll of Resurr Mirfield 57. **d** 59 **p** 60. C Hackney Wick St Mary of Eton w St Aug *Lon* 59-62; Chapl Worksop Coll Notts 62-68; Lic to Offic *S'well* 63-68; Jordan 68-74; New Zealand from 74; Can St Pet Cathl Waikato 88-89; Adn Waitomo 89-98; rtd 93. *Box 91, Owhango, New Zealand* Tel (0064) (7) 895 4738 Fax as telephone

TONKIN, Canon Richard John. b 28. Lon Coll of Div ALCD59 BD60. **d** 60 **p** 61. C Leic Martyrs *Leic* 60-63; C Keynsham *B & W* 63-66; V Hinckley H Trin *Leic* 66-74; R Oadby 74-84; Hon Can Leic Cathl 83-93; V Leic H Apostles 84-93; rtd 93; Perm to Offic *Leic* from 93. *39 Shackerdale Road, Wigston, Leicester LE8 1BQ* Tel 0116-281 2517

TONKINSON, Canon David Boyes. b 47. K Coll Lon BD71 AKC71. St Aug Coll Cant 71. **d** 72 **p** 73. C Surbiton St Andr *S'wark* 72-74; C Selsdon St Jo w St Fran *Cant* 75-81; V Croydon St Aug 81-84; V Croydon St Aug *S'wark* 85-89; C Easthampstead *Ox* 89-96; Ind Chapl 89-96; Chapl Bracknell Coll 93-96; Soc Resp Adv *Portsm* 96-02; Hon Can Portsm Cathl from 96; Ind Chapl *Win* from 02. *9 Grebe Close, Kempshott, Basingstoke RG22 5JU* Tel (01256) 810161 E-mail davidbanhim@aol.com

TOOBY, Anthony Albert. b 58. Sarum & Wells Th Coll 89. **d** 91 **p** 92. C Warsop *S'well* 91-95; C Ollerton w Boughton 95-98; V Girlington *Bradf* from 98. *The Vicarage, 27 Baslow Grove, Bradford BD9 5JA* Tel (01274) 544987

TOOGOOD, John Peter. b 73. Leeds Univ BA95. Ripon Coll Cuddesdon 98. **d** 00 **p** 01. C Sherborne w Castleton and Lillington *Sarum* from 00. *32 Abbots Way, Sherborne DT9 6DT* Tel (01935) 812086 Fax 812206 E-mail john@thetoogoods.fsnet.co.uk

TOOGOOD, Ms Melanie Lorraine. b 57. K Coll Lon BD78 AKC78. Cuddesdon Coll DipMin94. **d** 96 **p** 97. C Shepperton *Lon* 96-99; C Greenford H Cross from 99. *St Edward's House, Medway Drive, Greenford UB6 8LN* Tel (020) 8997 4953 E-mail melanietoogood@tesco.net

TOOGOOD, Noel Hare. b 32. Birm Univ BSc54. Wells Th Coll 59. **d** 61 **p** 62. C Rotherham *Sheff* 61-65; C Darlington St Jo *Dur* 65-70; V Burnopfield 70-81; P-in-c Roche *Truro* 81-84; P-in-c Withiel 81-84; R Roche and Withiel 84-91; RD St Austell 88-91; V Madron 91-96; rtd 96; Perm to Offic *Portsm* from 97. *Acorn Cottage, Oakhill Road, Seaview PO34 5AP*

TOOGOOD, Robert Charles. b 45. AKC70. St Aug Coll Cant 70. **d** 71 **p** 72. C Shepperton *Lon* 71-74; C Kirk Ella *York* 74-76; P-in-c Levisham w Lockton 76-81; P-in-c Ebberston w Allerston 76-81; R Kempsey and Severn Stoke w Croome d'Abitot *Worc* 81-92; V Bramley *Win* from 92. *The Vicarage, Bramley, Basingstoke RG26 5DQ* Tel (01256) 881373

TOOGOOD, Robert Frederick. b 43. St Paul's Cheltenham CertEd65 DipPE65 Open Univ BA74. Trin Coll Bris DipHE95. **d** 95 **p** 96. C Southbroom *Sarum* 95-99; TV Langport Area Chs *B & W* from 99. *The Vicarage, 1 New Street, Long Sutton, Langport TA10 9JW* Tel (01458) 241260 E-mail bob.toogood@ukonline.co.uk

TOOKE, Mrs Sheila. b 44. EAMTC 89. **d** 91 **p** 94. NSM March St Wendreda *Ely* 91-95; P-in-c Upwell Ch Ch 95-97; P-in-c Welney 95-97; P-in-c Manea 95-97; R Christchurch and Manea

and Welney 97-03; rtd 03. *The Haven, 21 Wisbech Road, March PE15 8ED* Tel (01354) 652844 E-mail stooke@c-m-w.fsnet.co.uk

TOOKEY, Preb Christopher Tom. b 41. AKC67. **d** 68 **p** 69. C Stockton St Pet *Dur* 68-71; C Burnham *B & W* 71-77; R Clutton w Cameley 77-81; V Wells St Thos w Horrington from 81; RD Shepton Mallet 86-95; Preb Wells Cathl from 90; Chapl Bath and West Community NHS Trust from 95. *The Vicarage, 94 St Thomas's Street, Wells BA5 2UZ* Tel (01749) 672193 E-mail christophertookey@hotmail.com

TOOLEY, Geoffrey Arnold. b 27. Lon Coll of Div 55. **d** 58 **p** 59. C Chalk *Roch* 58-60; C Meopham 60-62; P-in-c Snodland and Paddlesworth 62-68; P-in-c Burham 68-76; C Riverhead w Dunton Green 76-79; C S w N Bersted *Chich* 79-83; C-in-c N Bersted CD 83-96; rtd 97. *Hawksworth, Charnwood Road, Bognor Regis PO22 9DN*

TOOLEY, Norman Oliver. b 27. Roch Th Coll. **d** 65 **p** 66. C Gravesend St Mary *Roch* 65-68; C Ormskirk *Liv* 68-73; Chapl Merseyside Cen for the Deaf 73-78; C Bootle Ch Ch 78-80; C W Ham *Chelmsf* 80-86; Chapl RAD 86-92; rtd 92; Perm to Offic *Roch* 92-98. *6 Newton Terrace, Crown Lane, Bromley BR2 9PH* Tel (020) 8303 0085

TOON, John Samuel. b 30. Man Univ BA LTh. Bps' Coll Cheshunt 64. **d** 65 **p** 66. C Newark St Mary *S'well* 65-67; C Clewer St Andr *Ox* 67-69; Canada 70, 73-76 and from 78; R Osgathorpe *Leic* 70-72; C Maidstone All SS w St Phil and H Trin *Cant* 76-78; rtd 95; P-in-c N Peace Par from 92. *St Martin's Anglican Church, 10364-100 Street, Fort St John BC, Canada, V1J 3Z1* Tel (001) (250) 785 6471 E-mail achurch@awink.com

TOON, Peter. b 39. Lambeth STh65 K Coll Lon BD65 MTh67 Liv Univ MA72 Ch Ch Ox DPhil77. NW Ord Course 72. **d** 73 **p** 74. C Skelmersdale St Paul *Liv* 73-74; Lib Latimer Ho Ox 74-76; C Ox St Ebbe w St Pet *Ox* 74-76; Tutor Oak Hill Th Coll 76-82; Hon Lect St Giles-in-the-Fields *Lon* 76-82; Dir Post-Ord Tr *St E* 82-87; P-in-c Boxford 82-88; V Staindrop *Dur* 88-91; USA 91-01; P-in-c Biddulph Moor *Lich* from 01; P-in-c Brown Edge from 03. *The Rectory, Hot Lane, Biddulph Moor, Stoke-on-Trent ST8 7HP* Tel (01782) 513323 E-mail ptoon@ont.com

TOOP, Alan Neil. b 49. St Alb Minl Tr Scheme 79 Linc Th Coll 82. **d** 83 **p** 84. C Kempston Transfiguration *St Alb* 83-87; C Ludlow *Heref* 87-92; P-in-c Stokesay and Sibdon Carwood w Halford 92-01; P-in-c Acton Scott 96-01; RD Condover 96-00; V Minsterley from 01; R Habberley from 01. *The Vicarage, Minsterley, Shrewsbury SY5 0AA* Tel (01743) 791213

TOOP, William John. b 07. Lon Univ BSc27 K Coll Cam BA38 MA42. **d** 41 **p** 42. E Pakistan 41-44 and 46-47; Chapl Lahore Cathl 44; Ind Chapl *Man* 44-47; V Cofton *Ex* 48-52; R Torwood St Mark 52-79; P-in-c Torquay H Trin 74-79; R Torwood St Mark w H Trin 79; rtd 79; Lic to Offic *Ex* 79-95; Perm to Offic from 95. *Georgian House, Park Hill Road, Torquay TQ1 2DZ* Tel (01803) 201387

TOOTH, Nigel David. b 47. RMN69 Dip Counselling 96. Sarum & Wells Th Coll 71. **d** 74 **p** 75. C S Beddington St Mich *S'wark* 74-77; C Whitchurch *Bris* 77-83; TV Bedminster 83-87; Chapl Dorchester Hosps 87-94; Chapl Herrison Hosp Dorchester 87-94; Chapl W Dorset Gen Hosps NHS Trust from 94. *Dorset County Hospital, Williams's Avenue, Dorchester DT1 2JY* Tel (01305) 255198 *or* 889576

TOOVEY, Preb Kenneth Frank. b 26. K Coll Lon BD51 AKC51. **d** 52 **p** 53. C Munster Square St Mary Magd *Lon* 52-60; V Upper Teddington SS Pet and Paul 60-70; V Ruislip St Martin 70-81; RD Hillingdon 75-81; V Greenhill St Jo 81-91; Preb St Paul's Cathl 83-91; rtd 91; Perm to Offic *Lon* from 91. *10 Fort Road, Northolt UB5 5HH* Tel (020) 8842 2812

TOOZE, Margaret Elizabeth. b 27. St Mich Ho Ox 54. **dss** 83 **d** 89 **p** 94. Kenya 61-88; C Bath Walcot *B & W* 89-95; Perm to Offic from 95. *1 Victoria House, Weston Road, Bath BA1 2XY* Tel (01225) 465642

TOPALIAN, Berj. b 51. **d** 97 **p** 98. NSM Clifton Ch Ch w Em *Bris* 97-98; C Bris St Mich and St Paul 98-99; C Cotham St Sav w St Mary and Clifton St Paul 99-01; V Pilning w Compton Greenfield from 01. *The Vicarage, The Glebe, Pilning, Bristol BS35 4LE* Tel (01454) 633409 E-mail berjtopalian@hotmail.com

TOPHAM, Paul Raby. b 31. DipEd58 MIL66 Columbia Pacific Univ LTh80 MA81. SSC. **d** 85 **p** 86. Chapl St Paul's Prep Sch Barnes 85-91; Chapl Toulouse w Biarritz, Cahors and Pau *Eur* 91-94; Perm to Offic *Lon* 94-97; Perm to Offic *Eur* from 94; rtd 96; P-in-c St Margaret's-on-Thames *Lon* 97-00; Hon C Hounslow W Gd Shep from 00; Hon C Teddington SS Pet and Paul and Fulwell from 00. *5 Marlingdene Close, Hampton TW12 3BJ* Tel (020) 8979 4277 Mobile 07714-650980 E-mail rev@topham28.freeserve.co.uk

TOPPING, Kenneth Bryan Baldwin. b 27. Bps' Coll Cheshunt 58. **d** 59 **p** 60. C Fleetwood *Blackb* 59-63; V Ringley *Man* 63-70; V Cleator Moor w Cleator *Carl* 70-91; rtd 92; Perm to Offic *Blackb* from 92. *23 Harrow Avenue, Fleetwood FY7 7HD* Tel (01253) 681441

TOPPING, Norman. b 32. NW Ord Course 73. **d** 76 **p** 77. NSM Prenton *Ches* 76-79; C E Runcorn w Halton 79-80; C Halton 80;

P-in-c Newton Flowery Field 80-81; V 81-86; V Bredbury St Mark 86-96; rtd 96; Perm to Offic *Ches* from 96. *18 Wellbank, Sandbach CW11 0EP* Tel (01270) 764771

TOPPING, Roy William. b 37. MBE92. S Dios Minl Tr Scheme 91. **d** 92 **p** 93. Bahrain 89-94; Chapl Miss to Seamen Milford Haven 94-99; rtd 99; Perm to Offic *Sarum* from 00. *7 Lady Down View, Tisbury, Salisbury SP3 6LL* Tel (01747) 871909

TORDOFF, Donald William. b 45. Nottm Univ BA69. Qu Coll Birm 69. **d** 71 **p** 72. C High Harrogate Ch Ch *Ripon* 71-75; C Moor Allerton 75-80; V Bilton 80-92; R Spennithorne w Finghall and Hauxwell 92-01; rtd 01. *4 Weavers Green, Northallerton DL7 8FJ* Tel (01609) 760155
E-mail don@onetel.net.uk

TORDOFF (née PARKER), Mrs Margaret Grace. b 40. SRN65 SCM67 HVCert73. Cranmer Hall Dur 81. **dss** 83 **d** 87 **p** 94. Bilton *Ripon* 83-87; C 87-92; Chapl Spennithorne Hall 92; NSM Spennithorne w Finghall and Hauxwell 92-00; rtd 00; Perm to Offic *M & K* from 00. *4 Weavers Green, Northallerton DL7 8FJ* Tel (01609) 760155

TORODE, Brian Edward. b 41. FCollP93 St Paul's Cheltenham TCert63 Poitiers Univ Dip French Studies 62. WEMTC 90. **d** 93 **p** 94. Hd Master Elmfield Sch Cheltenham from 82; NSM Up Hatherley *Glouc* 93-94; NSM Cheltenham St Steph 93-95; NSM Cheltenham Em 94-95; NSM Cheltenham Em w St Steph from 95. *23 Arden Road, Leckhampton, Cheltenham GL53 0HG* Tel (01242) 231212

TORRENS, Marianne Rose. *See* ATKINSON, Mrs Marianne Rose

TORRENS, Robert Harrington. b 33. Trin Coll Cam BA56 MA61. Ridley Hall Cam 56. **d** 58 **p** 59. C Bromley SS Pet and Paul *Roch* 58-60; C Aylesbury *Ox* 60-63; V Eaton Socon *St Alb* 63-73; Lic to Offic 73-75; V Pittville All SS *Glouc* 75-84; Chapl Frenchay Hosp Bris 84-94; Chapl Manor Park Hosp Bris 84-94; Chapl St Pet Hospice Bris 94-98; P-in-c Chippenham *Ely* 98-01; P-in-c Snailwell 98-01; Perm to Offic *Ely* and *St E* from 01. *68 Barons Road, Bury St Edmunds IP33 2LW* Tel (01284) 752075

TORRY, Alan Kendall. b 33. Ex & Truro NSM Scheme. **d** 77 **p** 79. NSM Truro St Paul *Truro* 77-80; TV Probus, Ladock and Grampound w Creed and St Erme 80-84; P-in-c Gulval 84-88; V 88-99; P-in-c Marazion 85-88; V 88-99; rtd 99. *5 Chyandaunce Close, Gulval, Penzance TR18 3BZ* Tel (01736) 362944

TORRY, Malcolm Norman Alfred. b 55. St Jo Coll Cam BA76 MA80 K Coll Lon MTh79 LSE MSc96 Lon Univ BD78 PhD90 BA01. Cranmer Hall Dur 79. **d** 80 **p** 81. C S'wark H Trin w St Matt *S'wark* 80-83; C S'wark Ch Ch 83-88; Ind Chapl 83-88; V Hatcham St Cath 88-96; V E Greenwich Ch Ch w St Andr and St Mich 96-97; TR E Greenwich from 97; RD Greenwich Thameside 98-01. *St George's Vicarage, 89 Westcombe Park Road, London SE3 7RZ* Tel (020) 8858 3006 or 8305 2339 Fax 8305 1802 E-mail malcolm@mtorry.freeserve.co.uk

TOSTEVIN, Alan Edwin John. b 41. BA. Trin Coll Bris 83. **d** 86 **p** 87. C Hildenborough *Roch* 86-89; TV Ipsley *Worc* from 89. *29 Sheldon Road, Redditch B98 7QS* Tel (01527) 501092 E-mail alan@tostevin41.freeserve.co.uk

TOTNES, Archdeacon of. *See* GILPIN, The Ven Richard Thomas

TOTTEN, Andrew James. b 64. QUB BA87 TCD BTh90. CITC. **d** 90 **p** 91. C Newtownards *D & D* 90-94; CF from 94. *c/o MOD Chaplains (Army)* Tel (01980) 615804 Fax 615800

TOTTERDELL, Mrs Rebecca Helen. b 57. Lon Bible Coll BA80. Oak Hill Th Coll 88. **d** 91 **p** 94. Par Dn Broxbourne w Wormley *St Alb* 91-94; C 94-95; C Stevenage St Nic and Graveley 95-99; P-in-c Benington w Walkern from 99. *The Rectory, Church End, Walkern, Stevenage SG2 7PB* Tel (01438) 861322

TOTTLE, Mrs Nicola Rachael. b 72. Trin Coll Bris 98. **d** 01 **p** 02. C Bassaleg *Mon* from 01. *St Anne's Church House, 2 High Cross Drive, Rogerstone, Newport NP10 9AB* Tel (01633) 895441 E-mail nicola.tottle@ukgateway.net

TOUCHSTONE, Grady Russell. b 50. Cant Univ (NZ) BA72. St Jo Coll Nottm DipTh78 DPS80. **d** 80 **p** 81. C Hyson Green *S'well* 80-83; New Zealand from 83; C Cashmere 83-85; Chapl Christchurch Cathl 85-89; P-in-c Amuri 89-90; V 90-94; C Johnsonville and Churton Park 94-96; P-in-c Churton Park from 96. *13 Halswater Drive, Churton Park, Wellington, New Zealand* Tel (0064) (4) 478 4099 Fax 478 4087 E-mail john.tovey@xtra.co.nz

TOVEY, Phillip Noel. b 56. Lon Univ BA77 Trin Coll Bris DipHE82 Lon Bible Coll BA83 Nottm Univ MPhil88 Lambeth STh95. St Jo Coll Nottm 85. **d** 87 **p** 88. C Beaconsfield *Ox* 87-90; C Banbury 90-91; TV 91-95; Chapl Ox Brookes Univ 95-98; P-in-c Holton and Waterperry w Albury and Waterstock 95-97; TV Wheatley 97-98; Dioc Tr Officer from 98. *2 Ashcroft Close, Oxford OX2 9SE* Tel (01865) 863224 or 863680 E-mail phillip.tovey@virgin.net

TOVEY, Canon Ronald. b 27. AKC51. **d** 52 **p** 53. C Glossop *Derby* 52-55; C Chorlton upon Medlock *Man* 55-57; C Hulme St Phil 55-57; C Hulme St Jo 55-57; C Hulme H Trin 55-57; Malawi 57-69; Lesotho 69-85; Adn S Lesotho 77-85; Hon Can Lesotho 85-92; R Reddish *Man* 85-92; rtd 92; Perm to Offic *Pet* from 92; *Linc* 99-02. *86 Kings Road, Oakham LE15 6PD* Tel (01572) 770628 E-mail ronshir@tovey2.fsnet.co.uk

TOWELL, Alan. b 37. Sarum & Wells Th Coll 86 WMMTC 87. **d** 89 **p** 90. C Boultham *Linc* 89-93; P-in-c Scunthorpe Resurr 93-97; rtd 97. *154 Upper Eastern Green Lane, Coventry CV5 7DN* Tel (024) 7646 1881

TOWELL, Geoffrey Leonard. b 37. K Coll Lon BA59. Linc Th Coll 59. **d** 61 **p** 62. C Ashbourne w Mapleton *Derby* 61-65; C Claxby w Normanby-le-Wold *Linc* 65-67; V Alkborough w Whitton 67-80; R W Halton 68-80; P-in-c Winteringham 75-80; V Alkborough 81-85; Dioc Ecum Officer 85-91; rtd 91. *40 Lady Frances Drive, Market Rasen, Lincoln LN8 3JJ* Tel (01673) 843983

TOWERS, Canon David Francis. b 32. G&C Coll Cam BA56 MA60. Clifton Th Coll 56. **d** 58 **p** 59. C Gresley *Derby* 58-63; V Brixton St Paul *S'wark* 63-75; V Chatteris *Ely* 75-87; RD March 82-87; Hon Can Ely Cathl 85-87; R Burnley St Pet *Blackb* 87-97; rtd 97; Perm to Offic *Bradf* from 99. *9 West View, Langcliffe, Settle BD24 9EJ* Tel (01729) 825803

TOWERS, John Keble. b 19. Keble Coll Ox BA41 MA57. Edin Th Coll 41. **d** 43 **p** 44. Chapl Dundee St Paul *Bre* 43-47; India 47-62; R Edin Ch Ch-St Jas *Edin* 62-71; V Bradf St Oswald Chapel Green *Bradf* 71-78; P-in-c Holme Cultram St Mary *Carl* 78-80; V 80-85; rtd 85; Perm to Offic *Glas* 85-92; Hon C Moffat 92-00. *Flat 22/20, Croft-an-Righ, Edinburgh EH8 8ED* Tel 0131-557 1385

TOWERS, The Very Revd Patrick Leo. b 43. AKC68 Hull Univ CertEd69. **d** 74 **p** 75. Japan 74-81; TV Bourne Valley *Sarum* 81-83; Dioc Youth Officer 81-83; Chapl Oundle Sch 83-86; I Rathkeale w Askeaton and Kilcornan *L & K* 86-89; I Nenagh 89-00; Can Limerick, Killaloe and Clonfert Cathls 97-00; Provost Tuam *T, K & A* from 00; Can from 00; I Galway w Kilcummin from 00. *The Rectory, Taylor's Hill, Galway, Irish Republic* Tel (00353) (91) 521914 Fax as telephone E-mail kapnist@iol.ie

TOWERS, Terence John. b 33. AKC60. **d** 61 **p** 62. C Bishopwearmouth Gd Shep *Dur* 61-65; V Runham *Nor* 65-67; R Stokesby w Herringby 65-67; V Ushaw Moor *Dur* 67-93; rtd 93. *8 Beech Court, Langley Park, Durham DH7 9XL* Tel 0191-373 0210

TOWLER, Canon David George. b 42. Cranmer Hall Dur 73. **d** 76 **p** 77. C Newbarns w Hawcoat *Carl* 76-80; V Huyton St Geo *Liv* 80-98; V Newburgh w Westhead from 98; AD Ormskirk from 01; Hon Can Liv Cathl from 03. *The Vicarage, Back Lane, Newburgh, Wigan WN8 7XB* Tel (01257) 463267 Fax as telephone

TOWLER, John Frederick. b 42. Bps' Coll Cheshunt 62. **d** 66 **p** 67. C Lowestoft St Marg *Nor* 66-71; R Horstead 71-77; Warden Dioc Conf Ho Horstead 71-77; Prec Worc Cathl *Worc* 77-81; Min Can Worc Cathl 77-81; rtd 02. *42 Monks Road, Hyde, Winchester SO23 7EQ* Tel and fax (01962) 863451 Mobile 07787-504662 E-mail cjt@ptners.freeserve.co.uk

TOWLSON, George Eric. b 40. N Ord Course 80. **d** 83 **p** 84. NSM Wakef St Andr and St Mary *Wakef* 83-84; NSM Ox St Mich w St Martin and All SS *Ox* 84-86; Perm to Offic 86-87; NSM Hoar Cross w Newchurch *Lich* 87-93; C Wednesbury St Paul Wood Green 93-01; rtd 01; Perm to Offic *Lich* from 01. *58 Church Lane, Barton under Needwood, Burton-on-Trent DE13 8HX* Tel (01283) 713673

TOWNDROW, The Ven Frank Noel. b 11. K Coll Cam BA34 MA38. Coll of Resurr Mirfield 35. **d** 37 **p** 38. C Chingford SS Pet and Paul *Chelmsf* 37-40; Chapl RAFVR 40-47; P-in-c Grangemouth *Edin* 47-48; R 48-51; V Kirton in Lindsey *Linc* 51-53; R Manton 51-53; R Greenford H Cross *Lon* 53-62; V Haddon *Pet* 62-66; R Holdenby 62-66; V Ravensthorpe 63-66; Can Res Pet Cathl 66-77; Adn Oakham 67-77; Chapl to The Queen 75-81; rtd 77; Perm to Offic *Pet* 77-96. *17 Croake Hill, Swinstead, Grantham NG33 4PE* Tel (01476) 550478

TOWNEND, John Philip. b 52. Southn Univ BTh95. Sarum & Wells Th Coll 89. **d** 91 **p** 92. C Sherborne w Castleton and Lillington *Sarum* 91-95; P-in-c Wool and E Stoke 95-98; Sacr and Chapl Westmr Abbey 98-01; P-in-c Brightwalton w Catmore, Leckhampstead etc *Ox* from 01. *The Rectory, Main Street, Chaddleworth, Newbury RG20 7EW* Tel (01488) 638566 E-mail john@jptownend.freeserve.co.uk

TOWNEND, Lee Stuart. b 65. Cranmer Hall Dur DipTM98. **d** 98 **p** 99. C Buxton w Burbage and King Sterndale *Derby* 98-01; V

Loose *Cant* from 01. *The Vicarage, 17 Linton Road, Loose, Maidstone ME15 0AG* Tel (01622) 743513
E-mail leenliz@ukonline.co.uk

TOWNEND, Noel Alexander Fortescue. b 06. Selw Coll Cam BA28 MA32. Cuddesdon Coll 29. **d** 30 **p** 32. C Freemantle *Win* 30-34; Australia 34-40; Chapl RAFVR 40-47; R Week St Mary *Truro* 47-55; V Port Isaac 55-73; rtd 73; Hon C N Petherton w Northmoor Green *B & W* 73-95; Perm to Offic from 95. *4 Tappers Lane, North Petherton, Bridgwater TA6 6SH* Tel (01278) 663279

TOWNER, Colin David. b 39. St Pet Coll Ox BA61 MA65 Lon Univ BD63 ARCM72 LRAM73. Tyndale Hall Bris 61. **d** 64 **p** 65. C Southsea St Simon *Portsm* 64-67; C Penge St Jo *Roch* 67-70; V Leic St Chris *Leic* 70-74; Hon C Southsea St Jude *Portsm* 75-82; Perm to Offic 86-90 and 00-01; C Southsea St Pet 01-03; P-in-c from 03. *St Peter's Vicarage, Playfair Road, Southsea PO5 1EQ* Tel (023) 9229 7296 E-mail sctowner@yahoo.com

TOWNER, Preb Paul. b 51. Bris Univ BSc72 BTh81. Oak Hill Th Coll 78. **d** 81 **p** 82. C Aspley *S'well* 81-84; R Gt Hanwood *Heref* 84-99; RD Pontesbury 93-99; Preb Heref Cathl from 96; P-in-c Heref St Pet w St Owen and St Jas from 99. *The Vicarage, 102 Green Street, Hereford HR1 2QW* Tel (01432) 273676
E-mail preb.paul@ukgateway.net

TOWNLEY, Peter Kenneth. b 55. Sheff Univ BA78 Man Univ DSPT83. Ridley Hall Cam 78. **d** 80 **p** 81. C Ashton Ch Ch *Man* 80-83; C-in-c Holts CD 83-88; R Stretford All SS 88-96; V Ipswich St Mary-le-Tower *St E* from 96; RD Ipswich from 01. *St Mary le Tower Vicarage, 8 Fonnereau Road, Ipswich IP1 3JP* Tel (01473) 252770 Fax as telephone
E-mail peter.k.townley@btinternet.com

TOWNLEY, The Very Revd Robert Keith. b 44. St Jo Coll Auckland LTh67. **d** 67 **p** 68. New Zealand 67-70; C Lisburn Ch Ch *Conn* 71-74; C Portman Square St Paul *Lon* 75-80; Chan Cork Cathl *C, C & R* 82-94; Dean Ross 82-94; I Ross Union 82-94; Dean Kildare *M & K* from 95; Hon CF from 95; I Kildare w Kilmeague and Curragh *M & K* from 95; P-in-c Newbridge w Carnalway and Kilcullen 95-97; P-in-c Geashill w Killeigh and Ballycommon 00-01. *Dean's House, Curragh Camp, Co Kildare, Irish Republic* Tel (00353) (45) 441654 Fax as telephone

TOWNLEY, Roger. b 46. Man Univ BSc York Univ MSc. St Deiniol's Hawarden 82. **d** 84 **p** 85. C Longton *Blackb* 84-88; V Penwortham St Leon 88-92; V Wrightington from 92; Chapl Wrightington Hosp NHS Trust 92-01; Chapl Wrightington Wigan and Leigh NHS Trust from 01. *The Vicarage, Church Lane, Wrightington, Wigan WN6 9SL* Tel (01257) 451332
E-mail r.townley@talk21.com

TOWNROE, Canon Edward John. b 20. St Jo Coll Ox BA42 MA48 FKC59. Linc Th Coll 42. **d** 43 **p** 44. C Sunderland *Dur* 43-48; Chapl St Boniface Coll Warminster 48-56; Warden 56-69; Lic to Offic *Sarum* 48-93; Perm to Offic from 93; Can and Preb Sarum Cathl 69-93; rtd 85. *St Boniface Lodge, Church Street, Warminster BA12 8PG* Tel (01985) 212355

TOWNROE, Canon Michael Dakeyne. b 15. Linc Th Coll 35. **d** 38 **p** 39. C Grantham *Linc* 38-41; C W Grinstead *Chich* 41-44; C Pulborough 44-47; R Graffham w Woolavington 47-59; Chapl St Mich Sch Burton Park 47-59; RD Petworth *Chich* 56-59; R Bexhill St Pet 59-82; RD Battle and Bexhill 64-77; Can and Preb Chich Cathl 69-82; rtd 82; Perm to Offic *Chich* from 82. *Whitegates Retirement Home, Westfield Lane, Westfield, Hastings TN35 4SB* Tel (01424) 754865

TOWNSEND, Allan Harvey. b 43. WMMTC 89. **d** 92 **p** 93. NSM Fenton *Lich* 92-96; C Tividale 96-98; P-in-c Saltley and Shaw Hill *Birm* from 98; P-in-c Washwood Heath from 01. *The Clergy House, St Saviour's Road, Birmingham B8 1HW* Tel 0121-689 8897 Fax 246 4335 E-mail frallan@stsaviours98.freeserve.co.uk

TOWNSEND, Anne Jennifer. b 38. Lon Univ MB, BS60 MRCS60 LRCP60. S'wark Ord Course 88. **d** 91 **p** 94. NSM Wandsworth St Paul *S'wark* from 91; Chapl Asst St Geo Hosp Tooting 91-92; Dean MSE 93-99. *89E Victoria Drive, London SW19 6PT* Tel (020) 8785 7675 E-mail anne.townsend@gmx.net

TOWNSEND, Christopher Robin. b 47. St Jo Coll Nottm LTh74. **d** 74 **p** 75. C Gt Horton *Bradf* 74-77; C Heaton St Barn 77-78; C Wollaton *S'well* 78-80; V Slaithwaite w E Scammonden *Wakef* from 80. *The Vicarage, Station Road, Slaithwaite, Huddersfield HD7 5AW* Tel (01484) 842748

TOWNSEND, Derek William (Bill). b 52. Fitzw Coll Cam BA74 Man Univ PhD89. St Jo Coll Nottm 91. **d** 91 **p** 92. C Hazlemere *Ox* 91-95; TV Banbury 95-98; V Banbury St Paul 98-01. *Address temp unknown*

TOWNSEND, Mrs Diane Rosalind. b 45. Stockwell Coll of Educn CertEd66 K Alfred's Coll Win BEd88. Sarum Th Coll 93. **d** 96 **p** 97. NSM Botley *Portsm* 96-00; NSM Curdridge 96-00; NSM Durley 96-00; NSM Buriton from 00. *41 North Lane, Buriton, Petersfield GU31 5RS* Tel (01730) 269390

TOWNSEND, Gary. b 65. Trin Coll Bris. **d** 00 **p** 01. C Minster-in-Sheppey *Cant* from 00. *Queenborough Vicarage, North Road, Queenborough ME11 5HA* Tel (01795) 662648

TOWNSEND, Canon John Clifford. b 24. St Edm Hall Ox BA48 MA49. Wells Th Coll. **d** 50 **p** 51. C Machen *Mon* 50-51; C Usk and Monkswood w Glascoed Chpl and Gwehelog 51-55; R

Melbury Osmond w Melbury Sampford *Sarum* 55-60; Chapl RNVR 57-58; Chapl RNR 58-75; V Branksome St Aldhelm *Sarum* 60-70; R Melksham 70-73; TR 73-80; Can and Preb Sarum Cathl 72-90; RD Bradford 73-80; P-in-c Harnham 80-81; V 81-90; RD Salisbury 80-85; rtd 90; Perm to Offic *Sarum* from 90. *19 Wyke Oliver Close, Preston, Weymouth DT3 6DR* Tel (01305) 833641

TOWNSEND, John Elliott. b 39. ALCD63. **d** 64 **p** 65. C Harold Wood *Chelmsf* 64-68; C Walton *St E* 68-72; V Kensal Rise St Martin *Lon* 72-83; V Hornsey Ch Ch 83-98; V Forty Hill Jes Ch from 98. *The Vicarage, Forty Hill, Enfield EN2 9EU* Tel (020) 8363 1935 Fax as telephone
E-mail john@jesuschurch.freeserve.co.uk

TOWNSEND, John Errington. b 20. St Aug Coll Cant 64. **d** 65 **p** 66. C Alverstoke *Portsm* 65-69; R Droxford 69-74; Soc Work Org Sec 74-78; Perm to Offic 82-01; rtd 85. *2 Vigo Mews, Parkwood Road, Tavistock PL19 0RG* Tel (01822) 615912

TOWNSEND, Mark Timothy. b 67. Aston Tr Scheme 93 Cuddesdon Coll 93. **d** 96 **p** 97. C Ludlow, Ludford, Ashford Carbonell etc *Heref* 96-99; TV Leominster from 99. *1A School Road, Leominster HR6 8NJ* Tel (01568) 612124

TOWNSEND, Peter. b 35. AKC63. **d** 64 **p** 65. C Norbury St Oswald *Cant* 64-67; C New Romney w Hope 67-69; C Westborough *Guildf* 69-74; P-in-c Wicken *Pet* 74-87; R Paulerspury 74-84; P-in-c Whittlebury w Silverstone 82-84; V Whittlebury w Paulerspury 84-87; V Greetham and Thistleton w Stretton and Clipsham 87-01; rtd 01; Perm to Offic *Pet* from 01. *26 King's Road, Oakham LE15 6PD* Tel (01572) 757286

TOWNSEND, Peter. b 37. Open Univ BA87. Wells Th Coll 67. **d** 69 **p** 70. C Desborough *Pet* 69-72; C Bramley *Ripon* 72-75; C-in-c Newton Hall LEP *Dur* 75-80; P-in-c Newton Hall 80-81; V Hartlepool St Luke 81-03; rtd 03. *348 Stockton Road, Hartlepool TS25 2PW* Tel (01429) 291651
E-mail townsendfamgo@ntlworld.com

TOWNSEND, Philip Roger. b 51. Sheff Univ BA78. Trin Coll Bris 78. **d** 80 **p** 81. C W Streatham St Jas *S'wark* 80-85; C Ardsley *Sheff* 85-88; V Crookes St Tim from 88. *St Timothy's Vicarage, 152 Slinn Street, Sheffield S10 1NZ* Tel 0114-266 1745
E-mail st.tims@cwcom.net

TOWNSEND, Robert William. b 68. Univ of Wales (Ban) BA90. St Mich Coll Llan BTh93. **d** 93 **p** 95. C Dolgellau w Llanfachreth and Brithdir etc *Ban* 93-94; Min Can Ban Cathl 94-96; P-in-c Amlwch 96-97; R 97-99; R Llanfair-pwll and Llanddaniel-fab etc 99-03; P-in-c Llanilar w Rhostie and Llangwyryfon etc *St D* from 03; Dioc Schools Officer from 03. *The Vicarage, Llanilar, Aberystwyth SY23 4PD* Tel (01974) 241659 Mobile 07855-492006 E-mail robert@rectory.net

TOWNSEND, Robin. See TOWNSEND, Christopher Robin
TOWNSEND, William. See TOWNSEND, Derek William

TOWNSHEND, Charles Hume. b 41. St Pet Coll Ox BA64 MA69. Westcott Ho Cam 64. **d** 66 **p** 67. C Warlingham w Chelsham and Farleigh *S'wark* 66-75; R Old Cleeve, Leighland and Treborough *B & W* 75-85; R Bishops Lydeard w Bagborough and Cothelstone 85-95; V N Curry from 95. *The Vicarage, Moor Lane, North Curry, Taunton TA3 6JZ* Tel (01823) 490255
E-mail curryvic@fish.co.uk

TOWNSHEND, David William. b 57. Lon Univ PGCE80 Ox Univ MA85. Cranmer Hall Dur 81. **d** 84 **p** 85. C Barking St Marg w St Patr *Chelmsf* 84-87; Canada from 87. *Box 587, Westport ON, Canada, K0G 1X0* Tel (001) (613) 272 2664

TOWNSHEND, Edward George Hume. b 38. Pemb Coll Cam BA66 MA70. Westcott Ho Cam 68. **d** 70 **p** 71. C Hellesdon *Nor* 70-74; Ind Chapl 74-81; TV Lowestoft St Marg 74-79; TV Lowestoft and Kirkley 79-81; V Stafford St Jo *Lich* 81-85; P-in-c Tixall w Ingestre 81-85; V Stafford St Jo and Tixall w Ingestre 85-87; R Lich St Chad 87-99; RD Lich 94-99; P-in-c Hammerwich 96-99; C Hamstead St Paul *Birm* 99-02; Chapl Birm Airport from 00; Sen Ind Chapl from 02. *Hamstead Vicarage, 840 Walsall Road, Birmingham B42 1ES* Tel 0121-357 8941 Mobile 07931-928114 E-mail airport.chaplain@bhx.co.uk *or* dryfly57@hotmail.com

TOY, Elizabeth Margaret. b 37. NDAD59 CQSW77. Oak Hill NSM Course 83. **d** 88 **p** 94. NSM Hildenborough *Roch* from 88. *2 Francis Cottages, London Road, Hildenborough, Tonbridge TN11 8NQ* Tel (01732) 833886

TOY, Canon John. b 30. Hatf Coll Dur BA53 MA62 Leeds Univ PhD82. Wells Th Coll 53. **d** 55 **p** 56. C Newington St Paul *S'wark* 55-58; S Sec SCM 58-60; Chapl Ely Th Coll 60-64; Chapl Gothenburg w Halmstad and Jönköping *Eur* 65-69; Asst Chapl St Jo Coll York 69-72; Sen Lect 72-79; Prin Lect 79-83; Can Res and Chan York Minster *York* 83-99; rtd 99. *11 Westhorpe, Southwell NG25 0ND* Tel (01636) 812609 Fax as telephone
E-mail john.toy@virgin.net

TOZE, Ms Lissa Melanie. b 58. Birm Univ BA79. St Alb and Ox Min Course 94. **d** 01 **p** 02. C Risborough *Ox* from 01. *26 Summerleys Road, Princes Risborough HP27 9DT* Tel (01844) 345981 E-mail lissa.toze@tesco.net

TOZE, Stephen James. b 51. Birm Univ BA79. Qu Coll Birm 76 Westcott Ho Cam 93. **d** 93 **p** 94. C Leominster *Heref* 93-94; R Gt

Brickhill w Bow Brickhill and Lt Brickhill *Ox* 94-02; Rural Officer Buckm Adnry 95-02; V Wilshamstead and Houghton Conquest *St Alb* from 02. *The Vicarage, 15 Vicarage Lane, Wilstead, Bedford MK45 3EU* Tel (01234) 740423

TOZER, Frank William. b 21. Open Univ BSc94. Wells Th Coll 61. **d** 63 **p** 64. C Kemp Town St Mark *Chich* 63-65; C Crawley 65-73; V Heathfield 73-87; rtd 87; Perm to Offic *Chich* from 87. *30 Orchid Close, Eastbourne BN23 8DE* Tel (01323) 768270

TOZER, Reginald Ernest. b 25. St Aid Birkenhead 57. **d** 59 **p** 60. C Plaistow St Andr *Chelmsf* 59-62; P-in-c Clayton *Lich* 62-69; V E Ham w Upton Park *Chelmsf* 69-75; V Hatfield Peverel w Ulting 75-91; rtd 91; Perm to Offic *St E* from 91. *Basil's Place, 4 Church Road, Snape, Saxmundham IP17 1SZ* Tel (01728) 688895

TRAFFORD, Mrs Joyce. b 35. N Ord Course 84. **d** 87 **p** 94. Par Dn Chapelthorpe *Wakef* 87-94; C 94-98; rtd 98; Perm to Offic *Wakef* from 98. *1 Gillion Crescent, Durkar, Wakefield WF4 6PP* Tel (01924) 252033

TRAFFORD, Peter. b 39. Chich Th Coll. **d** 83 **p** 84. C Bath Bathwick *B & W* 83-86; Chapl RN 86-90; P-in-c Donnington *Chich* 90-99; V Jarvis Brook from 99. *The Vicarage, Tubwell Lane, Crowborough TN6 3RH* Tel (01892) 652639

TRAFFORD-ROBERTS, Rosamond Jane. b 40. Qu Coll Birm BA. **d** 95 **p** 96. C Ledbury *Heref* 95-00; Lect St Botolph Aldgate w H Trin Minories *Lon* from 00; Chapl Ho of St Barn-in-Soho from 03. *11 Linnell House, 50 Folgate Street, London E1 6UP* Tel (020) 7247 9704

TRAILL, Geoffrey Conway. b 58. Ridley Coll Melbourne BA82 BTh87. **d** 85 **p** 85. Australia 85-87 and from 88; C Shrub End *Chelmsf* 87-88. *1 Albert Street, Point Lonsdale, Vic, Australia 3225* Tel (0061) (3) 5258 4624 Mobile 412-381225 Fax 5258 4623 E-mail gtraill@optusnet.com.au

TRAINOR, Mrs Lynn Joanna. b 65. Bris Univ BSc87 Ex Univ PGCE89. St Alb and Ox Min Course 99. **d** 02. C Ascot Heath *Ox* from 02. *The Parsonage, King Edward's Road, Ascot SL5 8PD* Tel (01344) 883772 E-mail lynn@lynnie.co.uk

TRANTER, John. b 51. St Jo Coll Nottm. **d** 00 **p** 01. C Gt Wyrley *Lich* from 00. *6 Clover Ridge, Cheslyn Hay, Walsall WS6 7DP* Tel (01922) 419161

TRANTER, Stephen. b 61. Lanc Univ BA81 RGN87 RMN89. Trin Coll Bris BA99. **d** 99 **p** 00. C Blackpool St Thos *Blackb* 99-03; P-in-c Blackb St Jas from 03. *St James's Vicarage, Cromer Place, Blackburn BB1 8EL* Tel (01254) 56465 E-mail stranter@fish.co.uk

TRAPNELL, Canon Stephen Hallam. b 30. G&C Coll Cam BA53 MA57 Virginia Th Sem BD56 MDiv70 Hon DD02. Ridley Hall Cam 53. **d** 56 **p** 57. C Upper Tulse Hill St Matthias *S'wark* 56-59; C Reigate St Mary 59-61; V Richmond Ch Ch 61-72; P-in-c Sydenham H Trin 72-80; R Worting *Win* 80-92; Field Officer Decade of Evang 92-96; Can Shyogwe (Rwanda) from 93; rtd 96; Perm to Offic *Sarum* from 93; Perm to Offic *Win* from 96. *Downs Cottage, Rivar Road, Shalbourne, Marlborough SN8 3QE* Tel (01672) 870514 Fax 871439 E-mail stephen.trapnell@ukgateway.net

TRASK, Mrs Marion Elizabeth. b 54. Leic Univ BSc75 Brunel Univ PGCE76. Moorlands Bible Coll 82 Oak Hill Th Coll 93. **d** 96 **p** 97. C Bermondsey St Mary w St Olave, St Jo etc *S'wark* 96-00; C Peckham St Mary Magd from 00. *2 Wroxton Road, London SE15 2BN* Tel (020) 7635 0750

TRASLER, Graham Charles George. b 44. Ch Ch Ox BA65 MA69. Cuddesdon Coll 66. **d** 68 **p** 69. C Gateshead St Mary *Dur* 68-71; P-in-c Monkwearmouth St Pet 71-79; P-in-c Bentley *Guildf* 79; P-in-c Binsted *Win* 79; R Bentley and Binsted 80-84; R New Alresford w Ovington and Itchen Stoke 84-01; RD Alresford 99-01; P-in-c Stockbridge and Longstock and Leckford from 01. *The Rectory, 11 Trafalgar Way, Stockbridge SO20 6ET* Tel (01264) 810810 Fax as telephone E-mail gtrasler@aol.com

TRATHEN, Paul Kevin. b 69. York Univ BA91 MA93 Jordanhill Coll Glas PGCE94 Middx Univ BA03. NTMTC 00. **d** 03. C Wickford and Runwell *Chelmsf* from 03. *8 Honington Close, Wickford SS11 8XB* Tel 07711-287090 (mobile) E-mail paultrathen@aol.com

TRAVERS, Canon Colin James. b 49. St Pet Coll Ox BA70 MA74. Ridley Hall Cam 70. **d** 72 **p** 73. C Hornchurch St Andr *Chelmsf* 72-75; Youth Chapl 75-77; C Aldersbrook 75-77; V Barkingside St Laur 77-82; V Waltham Abbey 82-88; V S Weald 88-95; Co-ord NTMTC and Hon C Gt Warley and Ingrave St Nic 95-98; P-in-c Gt Canfield w High Roding and Aythorpe Roding 98-02; V Theydon Bois from 02; Hon Can Chelmsf Cathl from 01. *The Vicarage, 2 Piercing Hill, Theydon Bois, Epping CM16 7JN* Tel (01992) 814725 E-mail colin@revtravers.f9.co.uk

TRAVERS, John William. b 48. Open Univ BA84 Hull Univ MA86. Linc Th Coll 75. **d** 78 **p** 79. C Headingley *Ripon* 78-81; TV Louth *Linc* 81-89; P-in-c Shingay Gp of Par *Ely* 89; R 90-95; V Hamble le Rice *Win* from 95. *The Vicarage, Hamble, Southampton SO31 4JF* Tel (023) 8045 2148 Fax as telephone E-mail jtravers@mcmail.com

TRAVERSE, Ernest. b 28. Oak Hill Th Coll 73. **d** 75 **p** 76. C Roby *Liv* 75-76; C Rainhill 76-78; V Wigan St Barn Marsh Green 78-80; TV Bemerton *Sarum* 80-83; C Hednesford *Lich* 83-86; rtd 86; Perm to Offic *Liv* from 86. *20 Ashgrove Crescent, Billinge, Wigan WN5 7NH* Tel (01744) 894257

TRAVES, Stephen Charles. b 44. Sheff City Coll of Educn CertEd66 Open Univ BA79 Coll of Ripon & York St Jo DipTh99. N Ord Course 96. **d** 99 **p** 00. NSM Barnsley St Pet and St Jo *Wakef* from 99. *32 Osprey Avenue, Birdwell, Barnsley S70 5SH* Tel (01226) 280541 Mobile 07957-990361 E-mail stephen@traves2.demon.co.uk

TRAYNOR, Nigel Martin Arthur. b 58. St Jo Coll Nottm 94. **d** 96 **p** 97. C Wellington, All SS w Eyton *Lich* 96-00; P-in-c Pype Hayes *Birm* 00-02; TV Erdington from 02. *St Mary's Vicarage, 1162 Tyburn Road, Birmingham B24 0TB* Tel 0121-373 3534 E-mail nigelt6@msn.com

TREACY, Richard James. b 74. Aber Univ BD Univ of Wales (Cardiff) MTh99. **d** 98 **p** 99. C Hillsborough *D & D* 98-02. *17 Kinedale Cottages, Ballynahinch BT24 8YW* Tel (028) 9756 4960 E-mail rjt1@tesco.net

TREADGOLD, The Very Revd John David. b 31. LVO90. Nottm Univ BA58. Wells Th Coll 58. **d** 59 **p** 60. V Choral S'well Minster *S'well* 59-64; CF (TA) 62-67 and 74-78; R Wollaton *S'well* 64-74; V Darlington St Cuth w St Hilda *Dur* 74-81; Chapl to The Queen 81-89; Can Windsor 81-89; Chapl in Windsor Gt Park 81-89; Dean Chich 89-01; rtd 01. *43 Priors Acre, Boxgrove, Chichester PO18 0ER* Tel (01243) 782385

TREANOR, Canon Desmond Victor. b 28. St Jo Coll Dur BA53 DipTh54 MA59. **d** 54 **p** 55. C Oakwood St Thos *Lon* 54-57; C Sudbury St Andr 57-59; V Lansdown *B & W* 59-66; V Derby St Werburgh *Derby* 66-68; V Leic St Anne *Leic* 68-75; V Humberstone 75-86; Hon Can Leic Cathl 78-93; P-in-c Leic St Eliz Nether Hall 81-86; RD Christianity N 82-86; R Gt Bowden w Welham, Glooston and Cranoe 86-93; RD Gartree I 88-93; rtd 93; Perm to Offic *Leic* and *Pet* from 93. *5 Brookfield Way, Kibworth, Leicester LE8 0SA* Tel 0116-279 2750

TREANOR, Terence Gerald. b 29. St Jo Coll Ox BA52 MA56. Wycliffe Hall Ox 52. **d** 54 **p** 55. C Hornsey Ch Ch *Lon* 54-57; C Cambridge H Trin *Ely* 57-60; V Doncaster St Mary *Sheff* 60-66; Chapl Oakham Sch 66-94; rtd 94; Perm to Offic *Leic* 94-99; Perm to Offic *Linc* and *Pet* from 94. *35 Glebe Way, Oakham LE15 6LX* Tel (01572) 757495

TREASURE, Andrew Stephen. b 51. Oriel Coll Ox BA73 MA77. St Jo Coll Nottm BA76. **d** 77 **p** 78. C Beverley Minster *York* 77-81; C Cambridge H Trin *Ely* 81-84; C Cambridge H Trin w St Andr Gt 84-85; V Eccleshill *Bradf* 85-98; P-in-c Bradf St Oswald Chapel Green from 98; P-in-c Horton from 98. *St Oswald's Vicarage, Christopher Street, Bradford BD5 9DH* Tel (01274) 522717

TREASURE, Geoffrey. b 39. Hatf Coll Dur BA61 Univ of Wales (Cardiff) DipEd62. Oak Hill NSM Course 90. **d** 93 **p** 94. NSM Forty Hill Jes Ch *Lon* 93-95; Consultant SW England CPAS 95-02; Perm to Offic *B & W* from 95. *Gable Cottage, West Lyng, Taunton TA3 5AP* Tel (01823) 490458

TREASURE, Mrs Joy Elvira. b 23. St Anne's Coll Ox MA50 CertEd. S Dios Minl Tr Scheme 80. **dss** 82 **d** 87 **p** 94. Tisbury *Sarum* 82-87; Hon Par Dn 87-91; rtd 92; Perm to Offic *Sarum* from 92. *Friars Lodge, The Friary, Salisbury SP1 2HU* Tel (01722) 333741

TREASURE, Ronald Charles. b 24. Oriel Coll Ox BA48 MA52. Cuddesdon Coll. **d** 50 **p** 51. C Whitby *York* 50-54; C-in-c N Hull St Mich 54-58; V 58-62; V New Malton 62-80; RD Malton 63-75; rtd 89; Perm to Offic *York* from 89. *Castle Walls, Castlegate, Kirkbymoorside, York YO62 6BW* Tel (01751) 432916

TREBLE, Harry. b 06. Lon Univ BD55 BA61. AKC32. **d** 32 **p** 33. C Stamford Hill St Bart *Lon* 32-34; C S Hackney St Jo w Ch Ch 34-42; V Epping Upland *Chelmsf* 42-49; CF 43-46; Hon CF 46; P-in-c Barkingside St Cedd *Chelmsf* 49-61; V 61-83; rtd 83. *20 Linden Crescent, Woodford Green IG8 0DG* Tel (020) 8504 9482

TREBY, David Alan. b 47. FIBMS72 Bris Poly MSc90. St Jo Coll Nottm Dip Th Studies 94 MA95. **d** 95 **p** 96. C Camborne *Truro* 95-00; V Stoke Gabriel and Collaton *Ex* from 00. *The Vicarage, Stoke Gabriel, Totnes TQ9 6QX* Tel (01803) 782358 E-mail dave@treby.freeserve.co.uk

TREDENNICK, Angela Nicolette (Nicky). b 38. SRN62 SCM63 Lon Inst of Educn HVCert66. S'wark Ord Course 87. **d** 90 **p** 94. NSM Charlwood *S'wark* 90-92; Par Dn Roehampton H Trin 92-94; C 94-97; RD Wandsworth 95-97; V Redhill St Matt from 97; RD Reigate 00-03. *St Matthew's Vicarage, 27 Ridgeway Road, Redhill RH1 6PQ* Tel (01737) 761568

TREDWELL, Samantha Jane. b 69. Nottm Trent Univ BEd92. EMMTC 00. **d** 03. C Skegby w Teversal *S'well* from 03. *Teversal Parsonage, Fackley Road, Sutton-in-Ashfield NG17 3JA* Tel (01623) 550566 E-mail robert@sam.fsnet.co.uk

TREE, Robin Leslie. b 46. S Dios Minl Tr Scheme 89. **d** 92 **p** 93. NSM St Leonards Ch Ch and St Mary *Chich* 92-95; NSM Hastings H Trin 95-98; TV Bexhill St Pet 98-01; V Hampden

Park from 01. *St Mary's Vicarage, 60 Brassey Avenue, Eastbourne BN22 9QH* Tel (01323) 503166
E-mail frrobin@ltree.freeserve.co.uk

TREEBY, Stephen Frank. b 46. Man Univ LLB67 Nottm Univ DipTh69 Lambeth STh01. Cuddesdon Coll 69. **d** 71 **p** 72. C Ashbourne w Mapleton *Derby* 71-74; C Boulton 74-76; Chapl Trowbridge Coll *Sarum* 76-79; TV Melksham 79-87; V Dilton's-Marsh 87-01; Chapl Westbury Hosp 87-01; R Spetisbury w Charlton Marshall etc *Sarum* from 01. *The Rectory, Spetisbury, Blandford Forum DT11 9DF* Tel (01258) 453153

TREEN, Preb Robert Hayes Mortlock. b 19. New Coll Ox BA46 MA46. Westcott Ho Cam 45. **d** 47 **p** 48. C Bath Abbey w St Jas *B & W* 47-52; PC Pill 52-61; R Bath St Sav 61-76; Preb Wells Cathl from 74; V Bishops Hull 76-84; RD Taunton S 77-81; RD Taunton 81-84; rtd 84; Perm to Offic *B & W* from 84. *13 The Leat, Bishops Lydeard, Taunton TA4 3NY* Tel (01823) 433437

TREETOPS, Ms Jacqueline. b 47. NEOC 83. dss 86 **d** 87 **p** 94. Low Harrogate St Mary *Ripon* 86-87; C Roundhay St Edm 87-95; C Potternewton 95-97; rtd 97. *43 Lincombe Bank, Leeds LS8 1QG* Tel 0113-237 0474

TREFUSIS, Charles Rodolph. b 61. Hull Univ BA83. Wycliffe Hall Ox 85. **d** 90 **p** 91. C Blackheath St Jo *S'wark* 90-94; V Purley Ch Ch from 94. *The Vicarage, 38 Woodcote Valley Road, Purley CR8 3AJ* Tel (020) 8660 1790 E-mail ctrefusis@aol.com

TREGENZA, Matthew John. b 69. Univ of Wales (Lamp) BA92 SS Coll Cam PGCE93 Lon Univ MA01 FRGS96. Westcott Ho Cam 01. **d** 03. C Marnhull *Sarum* from 03. *2 Markstone Cottages, Duck Street, Child Okeford, Blandford Forum DT11 8ET* Tel (01258) 863629 E-mail matthew@tregenza.clara.co.uk

TREHARNE, David Owen. b 73. **d** 99. OLM Bassaleg *Mon* 99-00. *18 Hendre Close, Llandaff, Cardiff CF5 2HT* Tel (029) 2056 4655

TREHERNE, Canon Alan Thomas Evans. b 30. Univ of Wales (Lamp) BA53. Wycliffe Hall Ox. **d** 55 **p** 56. C Heref St Pet w St Owen *Heref* 55-57; India 57-72; C-in-c Netherley Ch Ch CD *Liv* 72-74; R Gateacre 74-75; TR 75-96; RD Farnworth 81-89; Hon Can Liv Cathl 94-96; rtd 96; Perm to Offic *Lich* 96-00; RD Oswestry 01-02. *19 Smale Rise, Oswestry SY11 2YL* Tel (01691) 671569 E-mail alan@treherne.co.uk

TRELLIS, Oswald Fitz-Burnell. b 35. Chich Th Coll 73. **d** 74 **p** 75. C Chelmsf All SS *Chelmsf* 74-78; C-in-c N Springfield CD 79-85; V Heybridge w Langford 85-94; Dean Georgetown Guyana 94-01; P-in-c Doddinghurst and Mountnessing *Chelmsf* from 01. *The Rectory, Church Lane, Doddinghurst, Brentwood CM15 0NJ* Tel (01277) 821366

TREMBATH, Martyn Anthony. b 65. Leeds Univ BA86. Ripon Coll Cuddesdon. **d** 90 **p** 91. C Bodmin w Lanhydrock and Lanivet *Truro* 90-91; C St Erth 92-96; C Phillack w Gwithian and Gwinear 94-96; C Hayle 94-96; Asst Chapl R Free Hampstead NHS Trust 96-98; Sen Chapl R Cornwall Hosps Trust from 98. *Royal Cornwall Hospital, Truro TR1 3LJ* Tel (01872) 252883 *or* 250000

TREMELLING, Peter Ian. b 53. Ex & Truro NSM Scheme 94. **d** 96 **p** 98. OLM St Illogan *Truro* from 96. *38 Wheal Agar, Pool, Redruth TR15 3QL* Tel (01209) 210625

TREMLETT, Andrew. b 64. Pemb Coll Cam BA86 MA90 Qu Coll Ox BA88 MA95 Ex Univ MPhil96 Liv Univ PGCE03. Wycliffe Hall Ox 86. **d** 89 **p** 90. C Torquay St Matthias, St Mark and H Trin *Ex* 89-92; Miss to Seamen 92-94; Asst Chapl Rotterdam *Eur* 92-94; Chapl 94-95; TV Fareham H Trin *Portsm* 95-98; Bp's Dom Chapl 98-03; V Goring-by-Sea *Chich* from 03. *The Vicarage, 12 Compton Avenue, Goring-by-Sea, Worthing BN12 4UJ* Tel (01903) 242525
E-mail a.tremlett@btopenworld.com

TREMLETT, The Ven Anthony Frank. b 37. Ex & Truro NSM Scheme 78. **d** 81 **p** 82. C Southway *Ex* 81-82; P-in-c 82-84; V 84-88; RD Plymouth Moorside 86-88; Adn Totnes 88-94; Adn Ex 94-02; rtd 02. *57 Great Berry Road, Crownhill, Plymouth PL6 5AY* Tel (01752) 240052 E-mail tremlettfa@aol.com

TRENCHARD, Hubert John. b 26. S Dios Minl Tr Scheme. **d** 83 **p** 84. NSM Sturminster Marshall *Sarum* 83-87; NSM Blandford Forum and Langton Long 87-96. *20 Chapel Gardens, Blandford Forum DT11 7UY* Tel (01258) 459576

TRENCHARD, Hugh. b 50. Dur Univ BD72. St Mich Coll Llan 72. **d** 75 **p** 76. C Caerleon *Mon* 75-80; Dioc Chapl GFS 78-86; Asst Chapl Mon Sch 80-84; V Llanarth w Clytha, Llansantffraed and Bryngwyn *Mon* 80-84; TV Cyncoed 84-93; Prov Officer for Soc Resp 94-96; V Caerwent w Dinham and Llanfair Discoed etc from 96. *The Vicarage, Vicarage Gardens, Caerwent, Newport NP26 5BF* Tel (01291) 424984

TRENCHARD, Paul Charles Herbert Anstiss. b 53. Liv Univ LLB76. St Steph Ho Ox 77. **d** 80 **p** 81. C Torquay St Martin Barton 80-84; R Ashprington, Cornworthy and Dittisham 84-92; R Barnwell w Tichmarsh, Thurning and Clapton *Pet* from 92. *The Rectory, Barnwell, Peterborough PE8 5PG* Tel (01832) 272374

TRENDALL, Peter John. b 43. Oak Hill Th Coll 66. **d** 69 **p** 70. C Beckenham Ch Ch *Roch* 69-73; C Bedworth *Cov* 73-76; C Hornsey Rise St Mary *Lon* 76-82; P-in-c Upper Holloway St Steph 80-82; V Hornsey Rise St Mary w St Steph 82-84; V Walthamstow St Mary w St Steph *Chelmsf* 84-85; TR 85-93; P-in-c Chigwell 93-94; TR Chigwell and Chigwell Row from 94. *The Rectory, 66 High Road, Chigwell IG7 6QB* Tel (020) 8500 3510 E-mail petertrendall@tesco.net

TRENDER, Lawrence. b 37. Bps' Coll Cheshunt 64. **d** 66 **p** 67. C Petersham *S'wark* 66-71; C Malden St Jo 71-73; R Thornham Magna w Thornham Parva *St E* 73-81; P-in-c Mellis 73-81; P-in-c Gislingham 73-81; R Thornhams Magna and Parva, Gislingham and Mellis 81-87; RD Hartismere 85-87; R Skipsea w Ulrome and Barmston w Fraisthorpe *York* 92-01; rtd 01; Perm to Offic *York* from 01. *Stone Cottage, 5 Far Lane, Bewholme, Driffield YO25 8EA* Tel (01964) 533020

TRESIDDER, Alistair Charles. b 65. Qu Coll Ox BA88. Cranmer Hall Dur 93. **d** 93 **p** 94. C Limehouse *Lon* 93-98; V W Hampstead St Luke from 98. *St Luke's Vicarage, 12 Kidderpore Avenue, London NW3 7SU* Tel (020) 7794 2634 *or* 7431 6317

TRETHEWEY, The Ven Frederick Martyn. b 49. Lon Univ BA70 DipTh77 Lambeth STh79. Oak Hill Th Coll 75. **d** 78 **p** 79. C Tollington Park St Mark w St Anne *Lon* 78-82; C Whitehall Park St Andr Hornsey Lane 82-87; TV Hornsey Rise Whitehall Park Team 87-88; V Brockmoor *Lich* 88-93; V Brockmoor *Worc* 93-01; Chapl Russells Hall Hosp Dudley 88-94; Chapl Dudley Gp of Hosps NHS Trust 94-01; RD Himley *Worc* 96-01; Hon Can Worc Cathl 99-01; Adn Dudley from 01. *15 Worcester Road, Droitwich WR9 8AA* Tel (01905) 773301
E-mail fred.trethewey@ntlworld.com

TRETHEWEY, Richard John. b 74. Jes Coll Ox MA02. Wycliffe Hall Ox BA02. **d** 02. C Biddulph *Lich* from 02. *48 Thames Drive, Biddulph, Stoke-on-Trent ST8 7HL* Tel 07759-650572 (mobile) E-mail richard@trethewey.org.uk

TRETT, Peter John. b 44. LNSM course 96. **d** 97 **p** 98. OLM High Oak, Hingham and Scoulton w Wood Rising *Nor* from 97. *Holly House, Plough Lane, Hardingham, Norwich NR9 4AE* Tel (01953) 850369

TREVELYAN, Preb James William Irvine. b 37. Selw Coll Cam BA64 MA67. Cuddesdon Coll 62. **d** 65 **p** 66. C Heston *Lon* 65-68; C Folkestone St Sav *Cant* 68-72; R Lenham w Boughton Malherbe 72-78; P-in-c Honiton, Gittisham and Combe Raleigh *Ex* 78-79; R Honiton, Gittisham, Combe Raleigh and Monkton 79-83; TR Honiton, Gittisham, Combe Raleigh, Monkton etc 83-00; Chapl Ex and Distr Community Health Service NHS Trust 78-00; P-in-c Farway w Northleigh and Southleigh *Ex* 84-86; Preb Ex Cathl 95-00; rtd 00; Perm to Offic *Carl* from 02. *Ash Meadow, Moorthwaite Lane, Barbon, Carnforth LA6 2LW* Tel (01524) 276530

TREVOR, Canon Charles Frederic. b 27. Sarum Th Coll 54. **d** 56 **p** 57. C Sutton in Ashfield St Mich *S'well* 56-58; C Birstall *Leic* 58-61; V Prestwold w Hoton 61-66; V Thornton in Lonsdale w Burton in Lonsdale *Bradf* 66-74; V Kirkby Malham 74-85; P-in-c Coniston Cold 81-85; Hon Can Bradf Cathl 85-92; V Sutton 85-92; RD S Craven 86-91; rtd 92; Perm to Offic *Bradf* from 92. *5 Brooklyn, Threshfield, Skipton BD23 5ER* Tel (01756) 752640

TREVOR-MORGAN, Canon Basil Henry. b 27. Univ of Wales (Lamp) BA51. Wells Th Coll 51. **d** 53 **p** 54. C Chepstow *Mon* 53-56; C Halesowen *Worc* 56-59; CF (TA) 59-92; V Stourbridge St Thos *Worc* 59-76; Chapl Christchurch Hosp 76-92; V Christchurch *Win* 76-92; Hon Can Win Cathl 84-92; rtd 93; Perm to Offic *Sarum* from 96. *31 West Walk, West Bay, Bridport DT6 4HT* Tel (01308) 456461

TREW, Mrs Ann Patricia. b 58. Ripon Coll Cuddesdon. **d** 00 **p** 01. C Hambleden Valley *Ox* from 00. *The Vicarage, Turville, Henley-on-Thames RG9 6QU* Tel (01491) 638240

TREW, Jeremy Charles. b 66. Univ of Wales (Abth) BSc89 Leeds Univ MSc92. St Jo Coll Nottm MA94. **d** 97 **p** 98. C Roundhay St Edm *Ripon* 97-01; P-in-c Spofforth w Kirk Deighton from 01. *The Rectory, Church Lane, Spofforth, Harrogate HG3 1AF* Tel (01937) 590251

TREW, Robin Nicholas. b 52. UWIST BSc74. St Jo Coll Nottm 87. **d** 89 **p** 90. C Cov H Trin *Cov* 89-93; V Snitterfield w Bearley 93-02; R Allesley from 02. *The Rectory, Rectory Lane, Allesley, Coventry CV5 9EQ* Tel (024) 7640 2006
E-mail robtrew@lineone.net

TREWEEKS, Mrs Angela Elizabeth. b 35. Gilmore Ho IDC59. dss 59 **d** 87 **p** 94. Chapl Asst St Nic Hosp Newc 85-87; Chapl 87; Hon C Newc St Geo *Newc* 87-89; Chapl St Mary's Hosp Stannington 92-95; Hon C Rothbury *Newc* from 94; rtd 95; Perm to Offic *Newc* from 96. *The Nook, Pondicherry, Rothbury, Morpeth NE65 7YS* Tel (01669) 620393

TRICKETT, Judith. b 50. St Jo Coll Nottm 89. **d** 91 **p** 94. Par Dn Kimberworth *Sheff* 91-93; Dn-in-c Worsbrough Common 93-94; V 94-01; V Herringthorpe from 01. *The Vicarage, 493 Herringthorpe Valley Road, Rotherham S60 4LB* Tel (01709) 836052

TRICKETT, Stanley Mervyn Wood. b 27. Lich Th Coll 64. **d** 66 **p** 67. C Kington w Huntington *Heref* 66-70; P-in-c Old Radnor 70-81; P-in-c Knill 70-81; V Shrewton *Sarum* 81-97; P-in-c Winterbourne Stoke 81-92; RD Wylye and Wilton 85-89; rtd 97;

Perm to Offic *Sarum* from 97. *3 Oakwood Grove, Alderbury, Salisbury SP5 3BN* Tel (01722) 710275

TRICKETT, Preb Susan. b 42. JP89. S Dios Minl Tr Scheme 91. **d** 94 **p** 95. NSM Combe Down w Monkton Combe and S Stoke *B & W* 94-99; V High Littleton from 99; Dean Women Clergy from 99; Preb Wells Cathl from 00. *Holy Trinity Vicarage, Church Hill, High Littleton, Bristol BS39 6HG* Tel (01761) 472097 E-mail susi.trickett@btinternet.com

TRICKEY, Christopher Jolyon. b 57. Barrister-at-Law 80 Jes Coll Cam BA79 MA83. Trin Coll Bris BA90. **d** 90 **p** 91. C Chesham Bois *Ox* 90-94; R Busbridge *Guildf* 94-98; P-in-c Hambledon 97-98; R Busbridge and Hambledon from 98; Chapl Godalming Coll from 01. *Busbridge Rectory, Brighton Road, Godalming GU7 1XA* Tel (01483) 418820 Fax 421267 E-mail rev_j_trickey@yahoo.co.uk

TRICKEY, The Very Revd Frederick Marc. b 35. Dur Univ BA62. Cranmer Hall Dur DipTh64. **d** 64 **p** 65. C Alton St Lawr *Win* 64-68; V Win St Jo cum Winnall 68-77; R Guernsey St Martin 77-02; Angl Adv Channel TV from 77; Dean Guernsey *Win* from 95; Hon Can Win Cathl from 95; P-in-c Sark from 02. *L'Esperance, La Route des Camps, St Martin, Guernsey GY4 6AD* Tel (01481) 238441

TRICKLEBANK, Steven. b 56. Nottm Univ BTh88. Linc Th Coll 85. **d** 88 **p** 89. C Ditton St Mich *Liv* 88-91; C Wigan All SS 91-93; Chapl Aintree Hosps NHS Trust *Liv* 93-97; C-in-c St Edm Anchorage Lane CD *Sheff* 97-00; Chapl Doncaster R Infirmary and Montagu Hosp NHS Trust *Sheff* from 00; V Stocksbridge *Sheff* from 00. *The Vicarage, Victoria Road, Stocksbridge, Sheffield S36 2FX* Tel 0114-288 6964

TRIFFITT, Jonathan Paul. b 74. St Jo Coll Nottm BA03. **d** 03. C W Kilburn St Luke w St Simon and St Jude *Lon* from 03; C Paddington Em Harrow Road from 03. *Flat 2, 228 Fernhead Road, London W9 3EH* Tel (020) 8968 8985 E-mail j.triffitt@btinternet.com

TRIGG, Jeremy Michael. b 51. Open Univ BA88. Ripon Coll Cuddesdon 80. **d** 81 **p** 82. C Harrogate St Edm *Ripon* 81-84; C Harrogate St Wilfrid and St Luke 84-87; TV Pocklington Team *York* 87-90; R Rowley w Skidby 90-97; TV Wolverton *Ox* 97-98; R from 98. *28 Harvester Close, Greenleys, Milton Keynes MK12 6LE* Tel (01908) 222802

TRIGG, John Alfred. b 29. Keble Coll Ox BA64 MA64. Ripon Hall Ox 64. **d** 65 **p** 66. C Dursley *Glouc* 65-67; C Glouc St Geo 67-68; C Swan *Ox* 68-72; P-in-c Stokenchurch and Cadmore End 72-76; V Stokenchurch and Ibstone 76-94; rtd 94; Perm to Offic *Sarum* from 94. *Medbury, Tisbury Row, Tisbury, Salisbury SP3 6RZ* Tel (01747) 870707

TRIGG, Jonathan David. b 49. Ex Coll Ox BA71 MA75 Dur Univ PhD92. Cranmer Hall Dur BA82. **d** 83 **p** 84. C Enfield St Andr *Lon* 83-87; V Oakwood St Thos 87-96; AD Enfield 92-96; V Highgate St Mich from 96; AD W Haringey from 00. *The Vicarage, 10 The Grove, London N6 6LB* Tel (020) 8347 5124 *or* 8340 7279 Fax 8347 5124 E-mail jaydene6@supanet.com

TRILL, Barry. b 42. Chich Th Coll 65. **d** 68 **p** 69. C W Hackney St Barn *Lon* 68-73; TV Is of Dogs Ch Ch and St Jo w St Luke 73-78; P-in-c Hastings All So *Chich* 78-79; V 79-99; rtd 99; Perm to Offic *Chich* from 01. *12 Heathlands, Westfield, Hastings TN35 4QZ* Tel (01424) 753595

TRILL, Victor Alfred Mansfield. b 21. St Deiniol's Hawarden. **d** 81 **p** 82. Hon C Prestbury *Ches* 81-83; Hon C Church Hulme 83-85; V Marbury 85-90; rtd 90; Perm to Offic *Ches* from 90. *5 Maisterson Court, Nantwich CW5 5TZ* Tel (01270) 628948

TRIMBLE, Mrs Anne Inman. b 40. Kenton Lodge Tr Coll CertEd60 Cam Univ DipRS84. NEOC 89. **d** 92 **p** 94. NSM Longnewton w Elton *Dur* 92-94; rtd 94; Perm to Offic *Dur* 94-98. *3 Queen Anne Terrace, Stockton-on-Tees TS18 5HS* Tel (01642) 581141

TRIMBLE, Canon John Alexander. b 33. Lon Univ BD65. Edin Th Coll 55. **d** 58 **p** 59. C Glas St Mary *Glas* 58-60; C Edin St Jo *Edin* 60-65; R Baillieston *Glas* 65-69; R Falkirk *Edin* 69-86; R Troon *Glas* 86-98; Can St Mary's Cathl 91-98; rtd 98; Perm to Offic *Newc* from 98. *4 Hencotes Mews, Hexham NE46 2DZ* Tel (01434) 603032

TRIMBLE, Thomas Henry. b 36. TCD DipTh82 BTh90. CITC 79. **d** 82 **p** 83. C Seapatrick *D & D* 82-85; I Magheracross *Clogh* 85-90; Bp's Appeal Sec 89-90; I Donegal w Killymard, Lough Eske and Laghey *D & R* 90-01; Can Raphoe Cathl 93-01; rtd 01. *Tyrone House, Tullycullion, Donegal, Irish Republic* Tel (00353) (74) 974 0706 E-mail harryandruby@utvinternet.com

TRIMBY, George Henry. b 44. DipTh. Trin Coll Bris 84. **d** 86 **p** 87. C Newtown w Llanllwchaiarn w Aberhafesp *St As* 86-88; P-in-c Llanfair DC, Derwen, Llanelidan and Efenechtyd 88-90; V 90-95; V Llanasa from 95; P-in-c Whitford 98-02. *The Vicarage, Llanasa Road, Gronant, Prestatyn LL19 9TL* Tel (01745) 888797

TRINDER, John Derek. b 28. Glouc Th Course 74. **d** 77 **p** 78. C Forest of Dean Ch Ch w English Bicknor *Glouc* 77; Hon C 77-79; Hon C Chepstow *Mon* 79-81; C Newport St Paul 81-82; V Dingestow and Llangovan w Penyclawdd and Tregaer 82-87; V Kirton in Holland *Linc* 87-93; rtd 93; Perm to Offic *Linc* 93-02.

3 Arkendale, Whittington College, London Road, Felbridge, East Grinstead RH19 2QU Tel (01342) 326413

TRIPLOW, Keith John. b 44. Selw Coll Cam BA66 MA70. Chich Th Coll 70. **d** 72 **p** 73. C Ipswich All Hallows *St E* 72-76; C Dartford H Trin *Roch* 76-78; V Fyfield w Tubney and Kingston Bagpuize *Ox* from 78. *The Vicarage, Fyfield, Abingdon OX13 5LR* Tel (01865) 390803

TRIST, Richard McLeod. b 55. Univ of NSW BSEd76. Ridley Coll Melbourne BTh86 DipMin86. **d** 87 **p** 87. Australia 87-96 and from 01; C Langham Place All So *Lon* 97-01; V Camberwell St Mark from 01. *1 Canterbury Road, Camberwell, Vic, Australia 3124* Tel (0061) (3) 9897 1532 *or* 9882 3776 Fax 9882 6514 E-mail richard.trist@bigpond.com *or* stmarksc@bigpond.com

TRISTRAM, Canon Catherine Elizabeth. b 31. Somerville Coll Ox BA53 MA57. dss 83 **d** 87 **p** 94. Holy Is *Newc* 84-87; Hon C 87-01; Hon Can Newc Cathl 94-01; Perm to Offic from 01. *4 Lewins Lane, Holy Island, Berwick-upon-Tweed TD15 2SB* Tel (01289) 389306

TRISTRAM, Geoffrey Robert. b 53. K Coll Lon BA76 Pemb Coll Cam BA78 MA80. Westcott Ho Cam 77. **d** 79 **p** 80. C Weymouth H Trin *Sarum* 79-82; C Gt Berkhamsted *St Alb* 83-85; OSB 85-99; Asst Chapl Oundle Sch 86-88; Sen Chapl 88-91; R Welwyn w Ayot St Peter *St Alb* 91-99; Chapl Qu Victoria Hosp and Danesbury Home 91-99; SSJE USA from 99. *Society of St John the Evangelist, 980 Memorial Drive, Cambridge, MA 02138, USA* Tel (001) (617) 876 3037

TRISTRAM, Canon Michael Anthony. b 50. Solicitor 76 Ch Coll Cam BA72 MA76. Ripon Coll Cuddesdon 79. **d** 82 **p** 83. C Stanmore *Win* 82-85; R Abbotts Ann and Upper and Goodworth Clatford 85-92; V Pershore w Pinvin, Wick and Birlingham *Worc* 92-03; Hon Can Worc Cathl 00-03; Can Res Portsm Cathl *Portsm* from 03. *51 High Street, Portsmouth PO1 2LU* Tel (023) 9273 1282 *or* 9234 7605 Fax 9229 5480 E-mail michael.tristram@ntlworld.com

TRIVASSE, Keith Malcolm. b 59. Man Univ BA81 CertEd82 MPhil90 Birm Univ DipTh86 Dur Univ MA98. Qu Coll Birm 84. **d** 86 **p** 87. C Prestwich St Marg *Man* 86-88; C Orford St Marg *Liv* 88-90; TV Sunderland *Dur* 90-91; P-in-c N Hylton St Marg Castletown 91-95; R Bothal and Pegswood w Longhirst *Newc* 95-97; P-in-c Bury Ch King *Man* from 01; P-in-c Bury St Paul from 01. *St Paul's Vicarage, Fir Street, Bury BL9 7QG* Tel 0161-761 6991 E-mail keith.trivasse@care4free.net

TRODDEN, Michael John. b 54. K Coll Lon BD77 AKC77 CertEd. Wycliffe Hall Ox 79. **d** 80 **p** 81. C Woodford St Mary w St Phil and St Jas *Chelmsf* 80-87; V Aldborough Hatch 87-96; R Ampthill w Millbrook and Steppingley *St Alb* from 96. *The Rectory, Rectory Lane, Ampthill, Bedford MK45 2EL* Tel (01525) 402320

TROLLOPE, David Harvey. b 41. BSc63. Lon Coll of Div 66. **d** 68 **p** 69. C Bermondsey St Jas w Ch Ch *S'wark* 68-71; Uganda 71-77; Kenya 77-82; V Gt Crosby St Luke *Liv* from 82. *St Luke's Vicarage, 71 Liverpool Road, Crosby, Liverpool L23 5SE* Tel 0151-924 1737

TROMANS, Kevin Stanley. b 57. St Martin's Coll Lanc BEd79. Aston Tr Scheme 90 Coll of Resurr Mirfield 92. **d** 94 **p** 95. C Rawdon *Bradf* 94-96; C Woodhall 96-98; V Liversedge w Hightown *Wakef* 98-02; V Bierley *Bradf* from 02. *St John's Vicarage, Bierley Lane, Bradford BD4 6AA* Tel (01274) 681397 Fax as telephone E-mail kevandkate@krtromans.freeserve.co.uk

TROMBETTI, Lynda Joan. b 52. Guildf Dioc Min Course 00. **d** 03. OLM Dorking w Ranmore *Guildf* from 03. *Mead Cottage, Pilgrims Way, Westhumble, Dorking RH5 6AP* Tel and fax (01306) 884360 Mobile 07968-629364 E-mail theflyingtrombettis@compuserve.com

TROOD, James William. b 68. Cov Poly BSc90 St Jo Coll Dur PGCE91. St Jo Coll Nottm MTh02. **d** 02 **p** 03. C Anchorsholme *Blackb* from 02. *2 Norman Close, Thornton-Cleveleys FY5 3UA* Tel (01253) 854376 Mobile 07713-139571 E-mail jimtrood@breathemail.net

TROTMAN, Anthony Edward Fiennes. b 11. Ex Coll Ox BA33 MA56. Wycliffe Hall Ox 46. **d** 48 **p** 49. C Ballymacarrett St Patr *D & D* 48-51; C Dundela St Mark 51-52; R Corsley *Sarum* 52-59; R Chilmark 59-76; P-in-c Teffont Evias and Teffont Magna 73-75; rtd 76; Perm to Offic *Sarum* from 76. *17 Estcourt Road, Salisbury SP1 3AP* Tel (01722) 324857

TROTT, Stephen. b 57. Hull Univ BA79 Fitzw Coll Cam BA83 MA87 Univ of Wales (Cardiff) LLM03 FRSA86. Westcott Ho Cam 81. **d** 84 **p** 85. C Hessle *York* 84-87; C Kingston upon Hull St Alb 87-88; R Pitsford w Boughton *Pet* from 88; Sec CME 88-93; Chapl Northants Gr Sch from 91. *The Rectory, Humfrey Lane, Boughton, Northampton NN2 8RQ* Tel (01604) 845655 Fax 08701-305526 E-mail strott@btinternet.com

TROTTER, Harold Barrington (Barry). b 33. Sarum Th Coll 64. **d** 66 **p** 67. C Salisbury St Fran *Sarum* 66-69; Dioc Youth Officer 69-72; V Horton and Chalbury 69-73; R Frenchay *Bris* 73-81; V Henbury 81-99; rtd 99; Perm to Offic *Ex* 00-02; Perm to Offic from 02. *14 Butlers Mead, Blakeney GL15 4EH* Tel (01594) 510176

TROUNSON, Ronald Charles. b 26. Em Coll Cam BA48 MA52. Ripon Hall Ox 54. **d** 56 **p** 57. C Plymouth St Gabr *Ex* 56-58;

Chapl Denstone Coll Uttoxeter 58-76; Bursar 76-78; Prin St Chad's Coll Dur 78-88; R Easton on the Hill, Collyweston w Duddington etc *Pet* 89-94; NSM 94-99; RD Barnack 91-94; rtd 94; Perm to Offic *Pet* from 99. *6 Western Avenue, Easton on the Hill, Stamford PE9 3NB* Tel (01780) 489030

TROUT, Keith. b 49. Trin Coll Bris DipHE92. **d** 92 **p** 93. C Pudsey St Lawr and St Paul *Bradf* 92-97; V Burley *Ripon* from 97. *St Matthias Vicarage, 271 Burley Road, Leeds LS4 2EL* Tel 0113-278 5872 *or* 230 4408 E-mail keithtrout@stmatthias.co.uk

TRUBY, Canon David Charles. b 57. BA79 Nottm Univ DipTh80. Linc Th Coll 79. **d** 82 **p** 83. C Stanley *Liv* 82-85; C Hindley St Pet 85-90; R Brimington *Derby* 90-98; Can Res Derby Cathl from 98. *22 Kedleston Road, Derby DE22 1GU* Tel (01332) 385552

TRUDGILL, Harry Keith. b 25. LCP54 Leeds Univ DipEd49 Lon Univ BD61. St Deiniol's Hawarden 76. **d** 76 **p** 76. In Methodist Ch 58-75; C Glas St Marg *Glas* 76-78; R Lenzie 78-86; rtd 86; Perm to Offic *Bradf* from 86. *10 Wharfe View, Grassington, Skipton BD23 5NL* Tel (01756) 752114

TRUEMAN, Reginald. b 24. K Coll Cam BA47 MA49 Man Univ BD53. St Jo Coll Winnipeg Hon DD58 Ely Th Coll 48 Union Th Sem (NY) STM50. **d** 50 **p** 51. C Bolton St Pet *Man* 50-53; Hong Kong 53-61; Prin Union Th Coll 57-61; Lect K Coll Lon 61-74; Sen Lect N Co Coll of Educn 75-78; Teacher Manor Park Sch Newc 78-82; Lesotho 84-86; rtd 92. *22 The Square, Petersfield GU32 3HS* Tel (01730) 261341

TRUMAN, Miss Catherine Jane. b 64. Coll of Ripon & York St Jo BEd88. St Jo Coll Nottm 01. **d** 03. C Owlerton *Sheff* from 03. *195 Walkley Lane, Sheffield S6 2PA* Tel 0114-281 3541 E-mail jane.truman@btinternet.com

TRUMAN, Miss Charlotte Jane. b 71. Birm Univ BPhil96. Westcott Ho Cam CTM99. **d** 99 **p** 00. C High Harrogate Ch Ch *Ripon* 99-03; P-in-c Oulton w Woodlesford from 03. *The Vicarage, 46 Holmsley Lane, Woodlesford, Leeds LS26 8RY* Tel 0113-282 0411
E-mail cjtruman@christchurch80.freeserve.co.uk

TRUMPER, Roger David. b 52. Ex Univ BSc74 K Coll Lon MSc75 Ox Univ BA80 MA85. Wycliffe Hall Ox 78. **d** 81 **p** 82. C Tunbridge Wells St Jo *Roch* 81-84; C Slough *Ox* 84-87; TV Shenley and Loughton 87-88; TV Watling Valley 88-93; R Byfleet *Guildf* from 93. *The Rectory, 81 Rectory Lane, West Byfleet KT14 7LX* Tel (01932) 342374

TRURO, Bishop of. *See* IND, The Rt Revd William

TRURO, Dean of. *See* MOXON, The Very Revd Michael Anthony

TRUSS, Canon Charles Richard. b 42. Reading Univ BA63 Linacre Coll Ox BA66 MA69 K Coll Lon MPhil79. Wycliffe Hall Ox 64. **d** 66 **p** 67. C Leic H Apostles *Leic* 66-69; C Hampstead St Jo *Lon* 69-72; V Belsize Park 72-79; V Wood Green St Mich 79-82; TR Wood Green St Mich w Bounds Green St Gabr etc 82-85; R Shepperton 85-94; V Waterloo St Jo w St Andr *S'wark* from 94; RD Lambeth from 95; Hon Can S'wark Cathl from 01. *St John's Vicarage, 1 Secker Street, London SE1 8UF* Tel and fax (020) 7928 4470 *or* tel 7633 9819
E-mail rtruss@stjohnswaterloo.co.uk

TRUSTRAM, Canon David Geoffrey. b 49. Pemb Coll Ox BA71 MA76 Qu Coll Cam BA73 MA77. Westcott Ho Cam 74. **d** 75 **p** 76. C Surbiton St Mark *S'wark* 75-77; C Surbiton St Andr and St Mark 77-78; C Richmond St Mary 78-79; C Richmond St Mary w St Matthias and St Jo 79; P-in-c Eastry *Cant* 82-88; R Eastry and Northbourne w Tilmanstone etc 88-90; Chapl Eastry Hosp 82-90; V Tenterden St Mildred w Smallhythe *Cant* from 90; Hon Can Cant Cathl from 96; AD Tenterden from 99. *The Vicarage, Church Road, Tenterden TN30 6AT* Tel (01580) 763118 Fax 761173 E-mail trustram@btinternet.com

TSANG, Wing Man. **d** 02 **p** 03. C Merthyr Tydfil Ch Ch *Llan* from 02. *17 Pembroke Close, Merthyr Tydfil CF48 1JF* Tel (01685) 388375

TSIPOURAS, John George. b 38. Trin Coll Bris 76. **d** 78 **p** 79. C Cheadle Hulme St Andr *Ches* 78-82; V Hurdsfield 82-03; rtd 03. *Address temp unknown* E-mail tsipouras@aol.com

TUAM, Archdeacon of. *See* PREVITE, The Ven Anthony Michael Allen

TUAM, Dean of. *See* GRIMASON, The Very Revd Alistair John

TUAM, KILLALA AND ACHONRY, Bishop of. *See* HENDERSON, The Rt Revd Richard Crosbie Aitken

TUAM, Provost of. *See* TOWERS, The Very Revd Patrick Leo

TUBBS, Preb Brian Ralph. b 44. AKC66. **d** 67 **p** 68. C Ex St Thos *Ex* 67-72; TV Sidmouth, Woolbrook and Salcombe Regis 72-77; R Ex St Jas 77-96; RD Christianity 89-95; Preb Ex Cathl from 95; V Paignton St Jo from 96; Chapl S Devon Healthcare NHS Trust from 96. *The Vicarage, Palace Place, Paignton TQ3 3AQ* Tel (01803) 559059 E-mail father_tubbs@compuserve.com

TUBBS, Canon Christopher Norman. b 25. G&C Coll Cam BA51 MA54. Wycliffe Hall Ox. **d** 52 **p** 53. C Neston *Ches* 52-55; C Nor St Pet Mancroft *Nor* 55-59; V Scalby *York* 59-68; V Scalby w Ravenscar and Staintondale 68-95; RD Scarborough 76-82; Can and Preb York Minster 85-96; rtd 95; Perm to Offic *York* from 96. *9 Mill Lane, West Ayton, Scarborough YO13 9JT* Tel (01723) 863211

TUBBS, Gary Andrew. b 59. Univ of Wales (Swansea) BA82 Bris Univ MSc84 Bris Poly PGCE84. Oak Hill Th Coll. **d** 00 **p** 01. C Stanwix *Carl* 00-02; C Carl H Trin and St Barn from 02. *St Barnabas' Rectory, Brookside, Carlisle CA2 7SU* Tel (01228) 515274 E-mail garytubbs@bigfoot.com

TUBBS, Mrs Margaret Amy. SW Minl Tr Course. **d** 01. OLM St Martin w Looe *Truro* from 01. *The Stables, Port Looe, Looe PL13 2HZ* Tel (01503) 265628
E-mail stablesretreat@onetel.co.uk

TUBBS, Peter Alfred. b 22. G&C Coll Cam BA48 MA53. Linc Th Coll 55. **d** 57 **p** 58. C Tettenhall Regis *Lich* 57-60; C Wellington Ch Ch 60-64; Asst Chapl Keele Univ 65-69; V Cardington *St Alb* 69-85; RD Elstow 77-82; C Sandy 85-89; rtd 89; Perm to Offic *St Alb* from 89. *1 Foster Grove, Sandy SG19 1HP* Tel (01767) 682803

TUCK, Andrew Kenneth. b 42. Kelham Th Coll 63. **d** 68 **p** 69. C Poplar *Lon* 68-74; TV 74-76; V Walsgrave on Sowe *Cov* 76-90; R Farnham *Guildf* from 90; Chapl Surrey Hants Borders NHS Trust from 90; RD Farnham *Guildf* from 00. *The Rectory, Upper Church Lane, Farnham GU9 7PW* Tel (01252) 715412
E-mail andrew@farnhamrectory.freeserve.co.uk

TUCK, David John. b 36. St Cath Coll Cam BA61 MA65. Cuddesdon Coll 61. **d** 63 **p** 64. C Kelling w Salthouse *Nor* 63-69; C Holt 63-69; Zambia 69-73; V Sprowston *Nor* 73-84; R Beeston St Andr 73-84; RD Nor N 81-84; V Pinner *Lon* 84-01; rtd 01. *119 High Street, Northwood HA6 1ED* Tel (01923) 824713
E-mail davidtuck@msn.com

TUCK, Gillian. b 40. SRN64 SCM66. Llan Dioc Tr Scheme 93. **d** 97 **p** 98. NSM Pontypridd St Cath w St Matt *Llan* 97-01; P-in-c Pontypridd St Matt and Cilfynydd from 01. *4 Maes Glas, Coed y Cwm, Pontypridd CF37 3EJ* Tel (01443) 791049

TUCK, Nigel Graham. b 57. Chich Th Coll 82. **d** 85 **p** 86. C Port Talbot St Theodore *Llan* 85-87; C Llantrisant 87-90; TV Duston Team *Pet* 90-95; C Aldwick *Chich* 95-98; C-in-c N Bersted CD 98-00; V N Bersted 01-02; rtd 02. *102 Wallace Avenue, Worthing BN11 5QA*

TUCK, Ralph Thomas. b 42. Worc Coll Ox BA64 Bris Univ CertEd66 Leeds Univ DipFE81. N Ord Course 87. **d** 90 **p** 91. NSM S Crosland *Wakef* 90-93; NSM Helme 90-93; Perm to Offic from 93. *5 Nields Road, Slaithwaite, Huddersfield HD7 5HT* Tel (01484) 843583

TUCK, Ronald James. b 47. S'wark Ord Course 75. **d** 78 **p** 79. C Upper Holloway St Pet *Lon* 78-79; C Upper Holloway St Pet w St Jo 79-81; P-in-c Scottow *Nor* 81-88; P-in-c Swanton Abbott w Skeyton 81-88; R Bradwell from 88. *The Rectory, Church Walk, Bradwell, Great Yarmouth NR31 8QQ* Tel (01493) 663219

TUCKER, Andrew Michael. b 64. K Coll Lon BD87. Wycliffe Hall Ox DipMin95. **d** 95 **p** 96. C Moreton *Ches* 95-96; C Poynton 96-99; C Polegate *Chich* 99-02; C-in-c Lower Willingdon St Wilfrid CD from 03. *St Wilfrid's House, 90 Broad Road, Lower Willingdon, Eastbourne BN20 9RA* Tel (01323) 482088

TUCKER, Anthony Ian. b 50. CYCW78. CA Tr Coll 73 S'wark Ord Course 81. **d** 85 **p** 86. NSM E Ham w Upton Park St Alb *Chelmsf* 85-86; NSM S'well Minster *S'well* 86-90; C Rolleston w Fiskerton, Morton and Upton 90-93; P-in-c Teversall 93-96; Chapl Sutton Cen 93-96; P-in-c Norwell w Ossington, Cromwell and Caunton from 96; Dioc Tourism Adv from 96; AD Newark from 00. *The Vicarage, Main Street, Norwell, Newark NG23 6JT* Tel (01636) 636329 Fax 636056
E-mail tony@horse-power.demon.co.uk

TUCKER, Desmond Robert. b 29. Bris Sch of Min 83. **d** 86 **p** 87. C Bris St Mich *Bris* 86-88; P-in-c 88-94; rtd 94; Perm to Offic *Bris* from 94. *94 Fremantle House, Dove Street, Bristol BS2 8LH* Tel 0117-924 6803

TUCKER, Douglas Greening. b 17. Lon Univ DipTh53. St Aid Birkenhead 49. **d** 52 **p** 53. C Jesmond Clayton Memorial *Newc* 52-56; C Fenham St Jas and St Basil 56-58; V Cowgate 58-62; V Elsham *Linc* 62-85; V Worlaby 62-85; V Bonby 73-85; rtd 85; Perm to Offic *Newc* 85-02. *Balintore, 4 Kilrymont Place, St Andrews KY16 8DH* Tel (01334) 476738

TUCKER, Harold George. b 21. St Aug Coll Cant 48 Sarum Th Coll 50. **d** 51 **p** 52. C S Molton w Nymet St George *Ex* 51-56; V Mariansleigh and Romansleigh w Meshaw 56-64; R Bratton Fleming 64-73; P-in-c Goodleigh 67-73; P-in-c Stoke Rivers 67-73; P-in-c Parracombe 69-73; P-in-c Martinhoe 69-73; R Whimple 73-86; rtd 86; Perm to Offic *Ex* and *Truro* from 86. *Lansdowne, The Crescent, Widemouth Bay, Bude EX23 0AE* Tel (01288) 361396

TUCKER, Ian Malcolm. b 46. Bris Coll HND69 ONC66. S Dios Minl Tr Scheme 86. **d** 89 **p** 90. NSM Pill w Easton in Gordano and Portbury *B & W* 89-95; C Frome St Jo and St Mary 95-99; TV Redruth w Lanner and Treleigh *Truro* from 99. *Pencoys Vicarage, Four Lanes, Redruth TR16 6LR* Tel (01209) 215035 E-mail iandm@btopenworld.com

TUCKER, John Yorke Raffles. b 24. Magd Coll Cam BA49 MA56. Westcott Ho Cam 49. **d** 51 **p** 52. C Shadwell St Paul w Ratcliffe St Jas *Lon* 51-54; C Preston Ascension 54-58; V S Hackney St Mich 58-67; V Belmont 67-78; V Sunbury 78-89; rtd

89; Perm to Offic *Ex* 89-93; Perm to Offic *B & W* from 93. *Tudor Cottage, Fivehead, Taunton TA3 6PJ* Tel (01460) 281330

TUCKER, Michael. b 33. MA. **d** 84 **p** 85. NSM Sawston *Ely* 84-87; C Ely 87-90; P-in-c Barton Bendish w Beachamwell and Shingham 90-98; P-in-c Wereham 90-98; rtd 98; Perm to Offic *Nor* from 99; *Ely* from 00. *20 Priory Lane, King's Lynn PE30 5DU* Tel (01553) 774707

TUCKER, Canon Michael Owen. b 42. Lon Univ BSc66 Surrey Univ PhD69. Glouc Sch of Min 81. **d** 84 **p** 85. NSM Uley w Owlpen and Nympsfield *Glouc* 84-92; P-in-c Amberley from 92; Dioc NSM Officer from 94; Hon Can Glouc Cathl from 98; RD Stonehouse from 99. *The Rectory, Amberley, Stroud GL5 5JG* Tel (01453) 878515 Fax 872914
E-mail mike@tucker1.free-online.co.uk

TUCKER, Nicholas Harold. b 41. Reading Univ BSc66. N Ord Course 90. **d** 93 **p** 94. NSM Ilkley All SS *Bradf* 93-98; P-in-c Uley w Owlpen and Nympsfield *Glouc* from 98. *The Rectory, The Green, Uley, Dursley GL11 5SN* Tel (01453) 860249 Fax 861184
E-mail nicktucker@lineonet.net

TUCKER, Richard Parish. b 51. Cam Univ BA72 MA76 Lon Univ BD83. Wycliffe Hall Ox 80. **d** 83 **p** 84. C Wellington w Eyton *Lich* 83-84; C Walsall 84-88; TV Dronfield *Derby* 88-90; TV Dronfield w Holmesfield 90-98; V Sutton Coldfield St Columba *Birm* from 98. *St Columba's Vicarage, 280 Chester Road North, Sutton Coldfield B73 6RR* Tel 0121-354 5873

TUCKER, Stephen Reid. b 51. New Coll Ox BA72 MA76 Lon Univ DipC&G96. Ripon Coll Cuddesdon DipTh76. **d** 77 **p** 78. C Hove All SS *Chich* 77-80; Lect Chich Th Coll 80-86; V Portsea St Alb *Portsm* 86-90; Chapl and Dean of Div New Coll Ox 90-95; P-in-c Ovingdean *Chich* 96-01; Bp's Adv on CME 96-01; V Hampstead St Jo *Lon* from 01. *The Vicarage, 14 Church Row, London NW3 6UU* Tel (020) 7435 0553 *or* 7794 5808

TUCKER, Mrs Susan. b 53. Stockwell Coll of Educn CertEd74. **d** 97 **p** 98. C Taunton St Andr *B & W* 97-01; V Bishops Hull from 01; Chapl St Marg Hospice from 01. *The Vicarage, Bishops Hull Hill, Bishops Hull, Taunton TA1 5EB* Tel (01823) 333032
E-mail suetucker@tuckers99.freeserve.co.uk

TUCKER, Vivian Clive Temple. b 39. Univ of Wales BSc60 DipEd61. St As Minl Tr Course 93. **d** 96 **p** 97. NSM Gresford *St As* 96-98. *8 Snowdon Drive, Ty Gwyn, Wrexham LL11 2UY* Tel (01978) 359226

TUCKETT, Christopher Mark. b 48. Qu Coll Cam MA71 Lanc Univ PhD79. Westcott Ho Cam 71. **d** 75 **p** 76. C Lancaster St Mary *Blackb* 75-77; Chapl and Fell Qu Coll Cam 77-79; Lect NT Man Univ 79-89; Sen Lect 89-91; Prof Bibl Studies 91-96; Lect NT Ox Univ from 96; Perm to Offic *Ches* from 93; *Derby* from 98. *Kidd Road Farm, Moorfield, Glossop SK13 7PN* Tel (01457) 860150

TUDBALL, Arthur James. b 28. AKC54. **d** 54 **p** 55. C Munster Square St Mary Magd *Lon* 54-56; Malaysia 63-73 and 75-79; Brunei 73-75; Singapore from 79; rtd 89. *Marine Parade Post Office, PO Box 529, Singapore 914401* Tel (0065) 3422258 Fax 3422259

TUDGE, Paul Quartus. b 55. Leeds Univ BEd78. Cranmer Hall Dur 84. **d** 87 **p** 88. C Roundhay St Edm *Ripon* 87-90; C Leeds City 91; V Woodside 91-99; Warden of Readers 96-99; V Ilkley All SS *Bradf* from 99; RD Otley from 02. *The Vicarage, 58 Curly Hill, Ilkley LS29 0BA* Tel (01943) 607537 *or* 816035 Fax 607058
E-mail paultudge@btinternet.com

TUDGEY, Stephen John. b 51. Nottm Univ BTh81 Westmr Coll Ox MTh00. St Jo Coll Nottm LTh81. **d** 81 **p** 82. C Grays Thurrock *Chelmsf* 81-84; C Madeley *Heref* 84-87; R Chilcompton w Downside and Stratton on the Fosse *B & W* from 87. *The Rectory, The Street, Chilcompton, Radstock BA3 4HN* Tel (01761) 232219

TUDOR, David Charles Frederick. b 42. Sarum Th Coll 70. **d** 73 **p** 74. C Plymouth St Pet *Ex* 73-75; C Reddish *Man* 75-78; P-in-c Hamer 78-80; V Goldenhill *Lich* 80-87; V Meir 87-91; Chapl Asst Nottm City Hosp 91-94; Chapl Cen Sheff Univ Hosps NHS Trust 94-96; V Nottingham St Geo w St Jo *S'well* from 96. *St George's Vicarage, Strome Close, Nottingham NG2 1HD* Tel 0115-986 4881 E-mail st.george@clara.net

TUDOR, David St Clair. b 55. K Coll Lon BD77 AKC77 K Coll Lon MTh89. Ripon Coll Cuddesdon 77. **d** 78 **p** 79. C Plumstead St Nic *S'wark* 78-80; C Redhill St Matt 80-83; C-in-c Reigate St Phil CD 83-87; Asst Sec Gen Syn Bd for Miss and Unity 87-88; Perm to Offic *S'wark* 94-97; TV Canvey Is *Chelmsf* 97-00; TR from 00. *St Nicholas House, 210 Long Road, Canvey Island SS8 0JR* Tel (01268) 682586 E-mail dstudor@tinyworld.co.uk

TUDOR, Malcolm George Henry Booth. b 36. Nottm Univ BA71. Linc Th Coll 72. **d** 60 **p** 61. In RC Ch 60-71; C Cinderhill *S'well* 72-74; P-in-c Broxtowe 74-78; Public Preacher from 75; P-in-c E Drayton w Stokeham 78-86; R E Markham and Askham 78-86; P-in-c Headon w Upton 78-86; V Llandinam w Trefeglwys w Penstrowed *Ban* 86-01; rtd 01; Perm to Offic *Ban* from 01. *14 Rhos-y-Maen Isaf, Llanidloes SY18 6LB* Tel (01686) 411192

TUFFEL, Kennedy Joseph. b 20. Worc Ord Coll 64. **d** 66 **p** 67. C Belmont *Lon* 66-68; C Goring-by-Sea *Chich* 68-72 and 81-89;

NSM 89-96; V Barnham 72-78; Hon C W Worthing St Jo 78-81; rtd 89; Perm to Offic *Chich* from 96. *15 Mill House Gardens, Mill Road, Worthing BN11 4NE* Tel (01903) 700671

TUFFIELD, Canon Basil Thomas. b 23. Fitzw Ho Cam BA49 MA54. Wells Th Coll 50. **d** 52 **p** 53. C Charlton St Luke w St Paul *S'wark* 52-58; C Carshalton 58-65; V Carshalton Beeches 65-79; P-in-c Cross Canonby *Carl* 79-82; V 82-90; P-in-c Allonby w W Newton 81-82; V Allonby 82-90; RD Solway 84-90; Hon Can Carl Cathl 87-90; rtd 90; Perm to Offic *Carl* from 90. *Hafod y Cwm, Llandernog Road, Nannerch, Mold CH7 5RP* Tel (01352) 741234

TUFFIN, Mrs Gillian Patricia. b 43. S Dios Minl Tr Scheme 91. **d** 94 **p** 95. C Gidea Park *Chelmsf* 94-98; TV Stoke-upon-Trent *Lich* 98-01; NSM Northolt Park St Barn *Lon* from 02. *76 Stowe Crescent, Ruislip HA4 7SS* Tel (01895) 631858
E-mail tuffins@bun.com

TUFFNELL, Nigel Owen. b 65. Teesside Poly BSc90. St Jo Coll Nottm 91. **d** 94 **p** 95. C Guisborough *York* 94-97; P-in-c Northwold *Ely* 97-98; P-in-c Stoke Ferry w Wretton 97-98; P-in-c Whittington 97-98; R Northwold and Wretton w Stoke Ferry etc 98-03; Bp's Adv on Environmental issues 02-03; P-in-c Kegworth *Leic* from 03; P-in-c Hathern, Long Whatton and Diseworth w Belton etc from 03. *The Rectory, 24 Nottingham Road, Kegworth, Derby DE74 2FH* Tel (01509) 672349
E-mail tuffnell@aol.com

TUFNELL, Edward Nicholas Pember. b 45. Chu Coll Cam MA68. St Jo Coll Nottm BA73. **d** 73 **p** 74. C Ealing St Mary *Lon* 73-76; BCMS 76-88; Tanzania 76-88; P-in-c Lt Thurrock St Jo *Chelmsf* 89-91; V Grays North 91-98; Chapl Thurrock Community Hosp Grays 89-98; P-in-c Bourton-on-the-Water w Clapton *Glouc* from 98. *The Rectory, School Hill, Bourton-on-the-Water, Cheltenham GL54 2AW* Tel (01451) 820386
E-mail edward@stlawbourton.freeserve.co.uk

TUFT, Preb Patrick Anthony. b 31. Selw Coll Cam BA56 MA60. Edin Th Coll 56. **d** 58 **p** 59. C Keighley *Bradf* 58-63; PV Chich Cathl *Chich* 63-68; Min Can St Paul's Cathl *Lon* 68-74; Hon Min Can St Paul's Cathl 74-94; V Chiswick St Nic w St Mary from 74; PV Westmr Abbey 74-79; AD Hounslow *Lon* 87-93; P-in-c Chiswick St Paul Grove Park 88-90; Preb St Paul's Cathl from 95. *Chiswick Vicarage, The Mall, London W4 2PJ* Tel (020) 8995 4717 Mobile 07768-892099
E-mail patrick@ptuft.freeserve.co.uk

TUGWELL, Elizabeth Ann. b 36. SW Minl Tr Course. **d** 94 **p** 95. NSM Ludgvan *Truro* 94-97; NSM St Hilary w Perranuthnoe 94-97; Perm to Offic from 99. *Boslasson, Enys Close, Carbis Bay, St Ives TR26 2SD* Tel (01736) 798551

TULL, Preb Christopher Stuart. b 36. Hertf Coll Ox BA60 MA64. Oak Hill Th Coll 60. **d** 62 **p** 63. C Stoodleigh *Ex* 62-71; C Washfield 62-71; TV Washfield, Stoodleigh, Withleigh etc 71-74; RD Tiverton 74-75; R Bishops Nympton w Rose Ash 75-77; V Mariansleigh 75-77; TR Bishopsnympton, Rose Ash, Mariansleigh etc 77-99; RD S Molton 80-87 and 95-99; Preb Ex Cathl 84-99; rtd 99. *The Old Smithy, Challacombe, Barnstaple EX31 4TU* Tel (01598) 763201

TULLETT, Peter Watts. b 46. Qu Coll Birm 92. **d** 94 **p** 95. C Worle *B & W* 94-96; Chapl HM YOI Portland 96-01. *Address temp unknown*

TULLOCH, Richard James Anthony. b 52. Wadh Coll Ox BA74 Selw Coll Cam BA79. Ridley Hall Cam 76. **d** 79 **p** 80. C Morden *S'wark* 79-83; C Jesmond Clayton Memorial *Newc* 83-94; V New Borough and Leigh *Sarum* from 94. *The Vicarage, 15 St John's Hill, Wimborne BH21 1BX* Tel (01202) 883490

TULLOCH, Walter Harold. b 16. AIMLS53 MRSH62. St Deiniol's Hawarden 79. **d** 79 **p** 80. NSM Maghull *Liv* 79-86; Hon C from 88; rtd 86; Perm to Offic *Liv* from 86. *8 Tailor's Lane, Maghull, Liverpool L31 3HD* Tel 0151-526 1936

TULLY, David John. b 56. St Jo Coll Dur BA77 Nottm Univ PGCE78. Ridley Hall Cam 81. **d** 84 **p** 85. C Gosforth St Nic *Newc* 84-86; C Newburn 86-90; TV Whorlton 90-96; V 96-00; R Gateshead Fell *Dur* from 00. *The Rectory, 45 Shotley Gardens, Low Fell, Gateshead NE9 5DP* Tel 0191-440 2190
E-mail david.tully@tesco.net

TULLY, Janet. **d** 03. OLM Margate St Jo *Cant* from 03. *Address temp unknown*

TUNBRIDGE, Canon Genny Louise. b 64. Clare Coll Cam BA85 St Cross Coll Ox DPhil93 Birm Univ BD95. Qu Coll Birm 93. **d** 96 **p** 97. C Boston *Linc* 96-00; Lect 00-01; Prec Chelmsf Cathl *Chelmsf* from 01; Can Res from 03. *The Precentor's House, 1B Rainsford Avenue, Chelmsford CM1 2PJ* Tel (01245) 257306 *or* 294482 Fax 294499
E-mail precentor@chelmsfordcathedral.org.uk

TUNBRIDGE, John Stephen. b 31. Keble Coll Ox BA54 MA59. Ely Th Coll 54. **d** 56 **p** 57. C Upper Norwood All SS w St Marg *Cant* 56-57; C Ramsgate St Geo 57-60; P-in-c 76-84; C Folkestone St Mary and St Eanswythe 60-62; R Gt Chart 62-67; V Womenswold 67-76; C-in-c Aylesham CD 67-76; R Harbledown 84-94; Perm to Offic *St D* from 94; rtd 96. *Ashdown, 11 Castle Road, St Ishmaels, Haverfordwest SA62 3SF* Tel (01646) 636584

TUNLEY, Timothy Mark. b 61. Oak Hill Th Coll DipHE84 Ridley Hall Cam CTM92. **d** 92 **p** 93. C Aldborough w Boroughbridge and Roecliffe *Ripon* 92-95; C Knaresborough 95-98; V Swaledale from 98. *Swaledale Vicarage, Reeth, Richmond DL11 6TR* Tel (01748) 884706
E-mail timtunley@tesco.net

TUNNICLIFFE, Mrs Jean Sarah. b 36. RGN69. Glouc Sch of Min 89. **d** 92 **p** 94. NSM Dixton *Heref* from 92. *Bryn Awelon, 21 Ridgeway, Wyesham, Monmouth NP25 3JX* Tel (01600) 714115

TUNNICLIFFE, Canon Martin Wyndham. b 31. Keele Univ BA56. Qu Coll Birm 59. **d** 60 **p** 61. C Castle Bromwich SS Mary and Marg *Birm* 60-65; V Shard End 65-73; R Over Whitacre w Shustoke 73-78; V Tanworth 78-98; RD Solihull 89-94; Hon Can Birm Cathl 91-98; rtd 98; Perm to Offic *Birm* from 98. *202 Ralph Road, Shirley, Solihull B90 3LE* Tel 0121-745 6522
E-mail martin@202rr.freeserve.co.uk

TUNNICLIFFE, Mrs Siv. b 33. Stockholm Univ MPhil58. St Alb and Ox Min Course 94. **d** 97 **p** 98. OLM Wingrave w Rowsham, Aston Abbotts and Cublington *Ox* from 97. *Baldway House, Wingrave, Aylesbury HP22 4PA* Tel (01296) 681374 Fax as telephone

TUNSTALL, Barry Anthony. b 29. Sarum Th Coll 53. **d** 55 **p** 56. C Croxley Green All SS *St Alb* 55-58; C Apsley End 58-63; V N Mymms 63-81; R Kirkby Overblow *Ripon* 81-94; rtd 94; Perm to Offic *B & W* from 01. *8 Lower Silk Mill, Darshill, Shepton Mallet BA4 5HF* Tel (01749) 344761

TUPLING, Mrs Catherine Louise. b 74. Westhill Coll Birm BTh96. Wycliffe Hall Ox 01. **d** 03. C Belper *Derby* from 03. *48 Arkwright Avenue, Belper DE56 0HY* Tel (01773) 599119
E-mail cltupling@tup-house.freeserve.co.uk

TUPPER, Michael Heathfield. b 20. St Edm Hall Ox BA41 MA46. Ridley Hall Cam 41. **d** 43 **p** 44. C Win Ch Ch *Win* 43-45; Chapl Monkton Combe Sch Bath 45-48; Asst Chapl Shrewsbury Sch 48-59 and 60-79; Kenya 59-60; Hon C Bayston Hill *Lich* 80-98; rtd 98; Perm to Offic *Lich* from 99. *9 Eric Lock Road, Bayston Hill, Shrewsbury SY3 0HQ* Tel (01743) 722674

TURAY, Prince Eddie Solomon. b 60. Sierra Leone Th Hall 82. **d** 85 **p** 87. Sierra Leone 85-91; Hon C Gt Cambridge Road St Jo and St Jas *Lon* 94-97; C Edmonton St Aldhelm 97-00; Perm to Offic from 00. *73 Haselbury Road, London N18 1PZ* Tel (020) 8372 5161

✠**TURNBULL, The Rt Revd Anthony Michael Arnold.** b 35. CBE03. Keble Coll Ox BA58 MA62 Hon DD03. Cranmer Hall Dur DipTh60. **d** 60 **p** 61 **c** 88. C Middleton *Man* 60-61; C Luton w E Hyde *St Alb* 61-65; Dir of Ords *York* 65-69; Abp's Dom Chapl 65-69; Chapl York Univ 69-76; V Heslington 69-76; Chief Sec CA 76-84; Can Res Roch Cathl *Roch* 84-88; Adn Roch 84-88; Bp Roch 88-94; Bp Dur 94-03; rtd 03; Hon Asst Bp Cant from 03. *67 Strand Street, Sandwich CT13 9HN* Tel (01304) 611389
E-mail bstmt@btopenworld.com

TURNBULL, Brian Robert. b 43. Chich Th Coll 71. **d** 74 **p** 75. C Norbury St Phil *Cant* 74-76; C Folkestone St Sav 76-77; Hon C Tong *Lich* 83-88; C Jarrow *Dur* 88-89; TV 89-94; P-in-c Hartlepool St Oswald 94-96; V from 96. *St Oswald's Clergy House, Brougham Terrace, Hartlepool TS24 8EY* Tel (01429) 273201 E-mail frbrian@turnbull23.freeserve.co.uk

TURNBULL, James Awty. b 28. Solicitor Bradf Univ HondLaws97. Cranmer Hall Dur 89. **d** 89 **p** 90. NSM Bolton Abbey *Bradf* 89-98; Perm to Offic from 98. *Deerstones Cottage, Deerstones, Skipton BD23 6JB*

TURNBULL, Michael. *See* TURNBULL, The Rt Revd Anthony Michael Arnold

TURNBULL, Michael Francis. b 62. Liv Univ BTh99. N Ord Course 95. **d** 98 **p** 99. C Birkenhead Ch Ch *Ches* 98-02; P-in-c Leasowe from 02. *St Chad's Vicarage, 70 Castleway North, Wirral CH46 1RW* Tel 0151-677 6889
E-mail mike@turnbull24.freeserve.co.uk
or mike@theturnbulls.info

TURNBULL, Peter Frederick. b 64. SS Mark & Jo Coll Plymouth BA85. Sarum & Wells Th Coll BTh91. **d** 91 **p** 92. C Upper Norwood All SS *S'wark* 91-95; Chapl HM Pris Dorchester 95-98; C Dorchester *Sarum* 95-98; NSM Melbury 98-99; C Maltby *Sheff* 99-02; TV from 02. *The Rectory, 69 Blyth Road, Maltby, Rotherham S66 7LF* Tel (01709) 812684
E-mail pturnbull@vicarage91.freeserve.co.uk

TURNBULL, Richard Duncan. b 60. Reading Univ BA82 MICAS85 Dur Univ PhD97. Cranmer Hall Dur BA92. **d** 94 **p** 95. C Portswood Ch Ch *Win* 94-98; V Chineham from 98. *The Vicarage, 1 Hartswood, Chineham, Basingstoke RG24 8SJ* Tel (01256) 474285 Fax 328912 E-mail rdturnbull@aol.com

TURNBULL, Stephen. b 40. Nottm Univ BTh74. Linc Th Coll 70. **d** 74 **p** 75. C Kirkstall *Ripon* 74-76; C Fairfield *Derby* 76-79; TV Seacroft *Ripon* 79-84; Chapl Derby City Hosp 84-94; Chapl Derbyshire Children's Hosp 84-94; Chapl Derby City Gen Hosp NHS Trust 94-98; Chapl S Derbyshire Acute Hosps NHS Trust 98-02; rtd 02. *6 Muswell Road, Derby DE22 4HP* Tel (01332) 521136

TURNBULL, William George. b 25. Lich Th Coll 63. **d** 65 **p** 66. C Nunhead St Silas *S'wark* 65-69; C Portishead *B & W* 69-73; C

Holsworthy w Cookbury *Ex* 73-76; P-in-c Bridgerule 76-79; P-in-c Pyworthy w Pancraswyke 77-79; P-in-c Pyworthy, Pancrasweek and Bridgerule 79-80; R 80-81; V Otterton and Colaton Raleigh 81-90; rtd 90; Chapl Convent Companions Jes Gd Shep W Ogwell 90-94; Lic to Offic *Ex* 90-94; Perm to Offic *Chich* from 94; Perm to Offic *S'wark* from 00. *College of St Barnabas, Blackberry Lane, Lingfield RH7 6NJ* Tel (01342) 870585

TURNER, Alan James. b 40. Oak Hill Th Coll BA81. **d** 81 **p** 82. C Bradley *Wakef* 81-84; C Sandal St Helen 84-86; P-in-c Sileby *Leic* 86-87; TR Sileby, Cossington and Seagrave 87-94; R Hollington St Leon *Chich* 94-01; R Frant w Eridge from 01. *The Rectory, Frant, Tunbridge Wells TN3 9DX* Tel (01892) 750638

TURNER, Alan Roy. b 51. Sheff Univ BA96 MA99. EMMTC. **d** 00 **p** 01. C Bladon w Woodstock *Ox* from 00; Chapl Cokethorpe Sch Witney from 01. *19 Park Close, Bladon, Woodstock OX20 1RN* Tel (01993) 812796
E-mail beverley@agathos.fs.net.uk

TURNER, Albert Edward. b 41. Glouc Sch of Min 83. **d** 89 **p** 90. C Woodford St Mary w St Phil and St Jas *Chelmsf* 89-91; R Greatworth and Marston St Lawrence etc *Pet* 91-99; R Somersham w Pidley and Oldhurst *Ely* 99-02; rtd 02. *19 Baines Coney, Haverhill CB9 7WU* Tel (01440) 706844
E-mail aet@care4.net

TURNER, Alison Joan. b 66. EAMTC. **d** 97 **p** 98. Perm to Offic *Chelmsf* 97-01. *The Rectory, 34 St Martin's Avenue, London E6 3DX* Tel 07958-276651 (mobile)

TURNER, Andrew John. b 52. St Jo Coll Nottm LTh. **d** 83 **p** 84. C Framlingham w Saxtead *St E* 83-86; P-in-c Badingham w Bruisyard and Cransford 86-88; P-in-c Dennington 86-88; R Badingham w Bruisyard, Cransford and Dennington 88-91; Chapl RAF from 91. *Chaplaincy Services (RAF), HQ, Personnel and Training Command, RAF Innsworth, Gloucester GL3 1EZ* Tel (01452) 712612 ext 5164 Fax 510828

TURNER, Ann. *See* TURNER, Mrs Patricia Ann

TURNER, Mrs Ann Elizabeth Hamer. b 38. Ex Univ BA59 PGCE60. Trin Coll Bris 84. **dss** 86 **d** 87 **p** 94. Bath St Luke *B & W* 86-87; Hon C 87-91; Chapl Dorothy Ho Foundn 89-91; C Bath Twerton-on-Avon 91-94; TV 94-96; rtd 98; Perm to Offic *Ex* from 00. *4 Beech Park, West Hill, Ottery St Mary EX11 1UH* Tel (01404) 813476

TURNER, Anthony John. b 49. DipMin. St Mich Coll Llan 89. **d** 91 **p** 92. C Coity w Nolton *Llan* 91-95; R Castlemartin w Warren and Angle etc *St D* from 95; OCF 95-01. *The Rectory, Angle, Pembroke SA71 5AN* Tel (01646) 641368

TURNER, The Ven Antony Hubert Michael. b 30. FCA63 Lon Univ DipTh56. Tyndale Hall Bris 54. **d** 56 **p** 57. C Nottingham St Ann *S'well* 56-58; C Cheadle *Ches* 58-62; PC Macclesfield Ch Ch 62-68; Lic to Offic *S'wark* 68-74; Home Sec BCMS 68-74; V Southsea St Jude *Portsm* 74-86; P-in-c Portsea St Luke 75-80; RD Portsm 79-84; Hon Can Portsm Cathl 85-86; Adn Is of Wight 86-96; rtd 96; Perm to Offic *Portsm* from 96. *15 Avenue Road, Hayling Island PO11 0LX* Tel (023) 9246 5881

TURNER, Benjamin John. b 45. Bolton Inst of Tech CEng MICE. N Ord Course 82. **d** 85 **p** 86. C Worsley *Man* 85-88; V Elton St Steph 88-95; Asst P Greystoke, Matterdale, Mungrisdale etc *Carl* 95-98; TV Gd Shep TM 98-01; Asst Chapl Leeds Teaching Hosps NHS Trust from 01. *St James's University Hospital, Beckett Street, Leeds LS9 7TF* Tel 0113-243 3144

TURNER, Mrs Beryl Rose. b 31. Nottm Univ CertEd75 BEd76. **dss** 84 **d** 87 **p** 94. Mortomley St Sav *Sheff* 84-86; Whitgift w Adlingfleet and Eastoft 86; The Marshland 86-87; Par Dn Goole 87-94; C 94; rtd 95; Perm to Offic *Sheff* from 95. *49 Colonel's Walk, Goole DN14 6HJ* Tel (01405) 769193

TURNER, Canon Carl Francis. b 60. St Chad's Coll Dur BA81. St Steph Ho 83. **d** 85 **p** 86. C Leigh-on-Sea St Marg *Chelmsf* 85-88; C Brentwood St Thos 88-90; TV Plaistow 90-95; P-in-c 95-96; TR Plaistow and N Canning Town 96-01; Prec and Can Res Ex Cathl *Ex* from 01. *6 Cathedral Close, Exeter EX1 1EZ* Tel (01392) 272498 E-mail precentor@exeter-cathedral.org.uk

TURNER, Charles Maurice Joseph. b 13. **d** 79 **p** 80. Hon C Brislington St Luke *Bris* 79-83; Hon C Bris Ch Ch w St Ewen and All SS 83-84; Hon C Bris St Steph w St Nic and St Leon 83-84; Hon C City of Bris 84-89; Perm to Offic 89-98. *31 Eagle Road, Bristol BS4 3LQ* Tel 0117-977 6329

TURNER, Mrs Christina Caroline. b 64. **d** 99 **p** 00. C Castle Church *Lich* 99-02; C Rugby St Andr *Cov* from 02. *63A Lower Hillmorton Road, Rugby CV21 3TQ* Tel (01788) 544381
E-mail tina.turner@tinyworld.co.uk

TURNER, Mrs Christine. b 42. EMMTC. **d** 94 **p** 95. Asst Chapl Qu Medical Cen Nottm Univ Hosp NHS Trust 94-97; NSM Hickling w Kinoulton and Broughton Sulney *S'well* 94-97; NSM Cotgrave 97-99; P-in-c Willoughby-on-the-Wolds w Wysall and Widmerpool from 99. *Bridge Farm, Hickling, Melton Mowbray LE14 3AH* Tel (01949) 81304
E-mail revd.christine@care4free.net

TURNER, Christopher Gilbert. b 29. New Coll Ox BA52 MA55. Ox Min Course 91. **d** 92 **p** 93. Hon C Hook Norton w Gt Rollright, Swerford etc *Ox* from 92. *Rosemullion, High Street, Great Rollright, Chipping Norton OX7 5RQ* Tel (01608) 737359

TURNER, Christopher James Shepherd. b 48. Ch Ch Ox BA70 MA74. Wycliffe Hall Ox 71. d 74 p 75. C Rusholme H Trin Man 74-78; C Chadderton Ch Ch 78-80; V 80-89; V Selly Park St Steph and St Wulstan Birm 89-99; P-in-c Locking B & W from 99; Chapl Weston Hospice from 99. The Vicarage, The Green, Locking, Weston-super-Mare BS24 8DA Tel (01934) 823556 Fax as telephone E-mail cjs.turner@cwcom.net

TURNER, Christopher Matthew. b 68. Brunel Univ BSc90. Cranmer Hall Dur 01. d 03. C Hykeham Linc from 03. 28 Sycamore Crescent, Lincoln LN6 0RR Tel (01522) 688274 E-mail c.turner@which.net

TURNER, Colin Peter John. b 42. Clifton Th Coll 63. d 66 p 67. C Kinson Sarum 66-68; C York St Paul York 68-72; Org Sec (SE Area) CPAS 73-78; TV Weymouth St Jo Sarum 78-87; TV Radipole and Melcombe Regis 78-87; R Radstock w Writhlington B & W from 90; R Kilmersdon w Babington from 90. The Rectory, 1 Bristol Road, Radstock, Bath BA3 3EF Tel (01761) 433182 E-mail stnicholasradstock@lineone.net

TURNER, David. b 40. St Andr Univ BSc63 Keele Univ 99. Ridley Hall Cam 63. d 65 p 66. C Bootle St Matt Liv 65-68; C Wigan St Barn Marsh Green 68-73; V Huyton St Geo 73-79; V Meltham Mills and Wilshaw Wakef 79-89; P-in-c Helme 81-85; P-in-c Meltham 85-89; V 89; V Gawber 89-95; Asst Chapl Wirral Hosp NHS Trust 91-99; rtd 01. 7 Fleetcroft Road, Wirral CH49 5LY Tel 0151-606 9242 Mobile 07816-261654

TURNER, Canon David Stanley. b 35. MISM69 MISE69 Lon Univ CertRK69 Westmr Coll Ox BA84. WMMTC 86. d 87 p 88. NSM Worc St Mich Worc 87-90; Min Shelfield St Mark CD Lich 90-95; C Walsall Wood 90-95; Min Can and Chapl St Woolos Cathl Mon 95-97; V Tredegar St Jas from 97; Hon Can St Bart's Cathl Barrackpore from 96. St James's Vicarage, Poplar Road, Tredegar NP22 4LH Tel (01495) 722510

TURNER, Derek John. b 54. Univ of Wales (Ban) BSc81 PhD86. St Jo Coll Nottm. d 87 p 88. C Pelsall Lich 87-91; C Stratford-on-Avon w Bishopton Cov 91-99; R Leire w Ashby Parva and Dunton Bassett Leic from 00. The Rectory, Dunton Road, Leire, Lutterworth LE17 5HD Tel (01455) 209421 Mobile 07713-832676 Fax 08707-060402 E-mail frderek@cesmail.net

TURNER, Donald. b 29. S'wark Ord Course. d 71 p 72. C Hounslow St Steph Lon 71-76; Hon C Isleworth St Jo 76-78; C Brighton St Pet w Chpl Royal Chich 78-80; C Brighton St Pet w Chpl Royal and St Jo 80-85; P-in-c St Leonards SS Pet and Paul 85-87; V 87-91; rtd 91; Hon C Malborough w S Huish, W Alvington and Churchstow Ex 93-98; Chapl Las Palmas Eur 98-01. 15 Coombe Meadows, Chillington, Kingsbridge TQ7 2JL Tel (01548) 531440

TURNER, Edgar. See TURNER, Canon Robert Edgar

TURNER, Canon Edward Robert. b 37. Em Coll Cam BA62 BTh66 MA67. Westcott Ho Cam 64. d 66 p 67. C Salford St Phil w St Steph Man 66-69; Chapl Tonbridge Sch 69-81; Adv for In-Service Tr Roch 81-89; Dir of Educn 81-96; Can Res Roch Cathl 81-00; Vice-Dean Roch Cathl 88-00; Dioc Adv on Community Affairs 90-00; Consultant Rochester 2000 Trust and Bp's Consultant on Public Affairs 00-02; Perm to Offic Nor from 01; rtd 02. Glebe House, Church Road, Neatishead, Norwich NR12 8BT Tel (01692) 631295

TURNER, Mrs Eileen Margaret. b 45. Goldsmiths' Coll Lon TCert66 Chester Coll of HE MTh02. N Ord Course 90. d 93 p 94. Par Dn Sandal St Cath Wakef 93-94; C 94-96; P-in-c Hammerwich Lich 96-02; Dir OLM Course 96-02; Dir Ext Studies St Jo Coll Nottm from 02. St John's College, Chilwell Lane, Bramcote, Beeston, Nottingham NG9 3DS Tel 0115-925 1114 Mobile 07774-623769 E-mail e.turner@stjohns-nottm.ac.uk

TURNER, Miss Elizabeth Jane. b 67. Leeds Univ BEng88. Trin Coll Bris 93. d 96 p 97. C Eccles Man 96-00; P-in-c Barrow Ches from 00; Dioc Ecum Officer from 00. The Rectory, Mill Lane, Great Barrow, Chester CH3 7JF Tel (01829) 740263

TURNER, Canon Francis Edwin. b 29. Sarum Th Coll 54. d 57 p 58. C Cheriton Street Cant 57-61; C Willesborough w Hinxhill 61-64; P-in-c Betteshanger w Ham 64-65; R Northbourne w Betteshanger and Ham 64-70; R Northbourne, Tilmanstone w Betteshanger and Ham 70-74; V Sittingbourne St Mich 74-94; RD Sittingbourne 78-84; Hon Can Cant Cathl 84-94; rtd 94. 6 Cherry Grove, Hungerford RG17 0HP Tel (01488) 682683

TURNER, Canon Frederick Glynne. b 30. Univ of Wales (Lamp) BA52. St Mich Coll Llan 52. d 54 p 55. C Aberaman Llan 54-60; C Oystermouth S & B 60-64; V Abercynon Llan 64-71; V Ton Pentre 71-73; TR Ystradyfodwg 73-77; R Caerphilly 77-82; V Whitchurch 82-96; Can Llan Cathl 84-96; Prec 95-96; rtd 96; Perm to Offic Llan from 96. 83 Newborough Avenue, Llanishen, Cardiff CF14 5DA Tel (029) 2075 4443

TURNER, Miss Gaynor. b 44. LNSM course 93. d 96 p 97. NSM Salford Sacred Trin Man 96-99; Asst Chapl to the Deaf from 96; Lic Preacher from 99. 19 Ellesmere Avenue, Worsley, Manchester M28 0AL

TURNER, Geoffrey. b 46. St Deiniol's Hawarden 85. d 87 p 88. C Loughor S & B 87-89; C Swansea St Pet 89-90; R New Radnor and Llanfihangel Nantmelan etc 90-96; V Ystalyfera from 96;

RD Cwmtawe from 00. The Vicarage, Ystalyfera, Swansea SA9 2EP Tel (01639) 842257

TURNER, Geoffrey. b 51. Selw Coll Cam BA75 PGCE75 MA78. N Ord Course 90. d 93 p 94. C E Crompton Man 93-96; C Heywood St Luke w All So 96-98; TV Heywood 98-01; TR from 01. St Luke's Vicarage, 26 Heywood Hall Road, Heywood OL10 4UU Tel (01706) 360182

TURNER, Geoffrey Edwin. b 45. Aston Univ BSc68 Newc Univ MSc69 PhD72. Cranmer Hall Dur BA74 DipTh75. d 75 p 76. C Wood End Cov 75-79; V Huyton Quarry Liv 79-86; Press and Communications Officer Ely 86-94; P-in-c Gt w Lt Abington 86-94; P-in-c Hildersham 86-94; V Letchworth St Paul w Willian St Alb 94-01; P-in-c Willingham Ely 01-02; P-in-c Rampton 01-02; R Willingham from 02; R Rampton from 02. The Rectory, 23 Rampton End, Willingham, Cambridge CB4 5ES Tel (01954) 261225 E-mail geoff@btinternet.com

✠TURNER, The Rt Revd Geoffrey Martin. b 34. Oak Hill Th Coll 60. d 63 p 64 c 94. C Tonbridge St Steph Roch 63-66; C Heatherlands St Jo Sarum 66-69; V Derby St Pet Derby 69-73; V Chadderton Ch Ch Man 73-79; R Bebington Ches 79-93; Hon Can Ches Cathl 89-93; RD Wirral N 89-93; Adn Ches 93-94; Suff Bp Stockport 94-00; rtd 00; Perm to Offic Ches from 00. 23 Lang Lane, West Kirby, Wirral CH48 5HG Tel 0151-625 8504

TURNER, Canon Gerald Garth. b 38. Univ of Wales (Lamp) BA61 St Edm Hall Ox BA63 MA67. St Steph Ho Ox 63. d 65 p 66. C Drayton in Hales Lich 65-68; Chapl Prebendal Sch Chich 68-70; PV Chich Cathl Chich 68-70; C Forest Row 70-72; V Hope Derby 72-78; Prec Man Cathl Man 78-86; Can Res 78-86; R Tattenhall and Handley Ches from 86. The Rectory, Tattenhall, Chester CH3 9QE Tel (01829) 770328 E-mail ggarthturner@hotmail.com

TURNER, Graham Colin. b 55. Bradf Univ BTech. Oak Hill Th Coll BA81. d 81 p 82. C Upper Armley Ripon 81-86; V Bordesley Green Birm from 86; AD Yardley and Bordesley from 00. The Vicarage, 405 Belcher's Lane, Bordesley Green, Birmingham B9 5SY Tel 0121-772 0418 or 753 0648 Fax 766 5401

TURNER, Mrs Heather Winifred. b 43. SRN65. Cant Sch of Min 89. d 90 p 94. Par Dn Orpington All SS Roch 90-93; Chapl to the Deaf 93-00; P-in-c Wrotham 95-01; TV E Dereham and Scarning Nor 01-02; rtd 02; Perm to Offic Nor from 02. 4 Church Farm Barns, Church Hill, Banham, Norwich NR16 2SX Tel (01953) 887972 E-mail heather-r@fish.co.uk

TURNER, Henry John Mansfield. b 24. Magd Coll Cam BA45 MA48 Man Univ PhD85. Westcott Ho Cam 48. d 50 p 51. C Crosby Linc 50-52; C Chorlton upon Medlock Man 52-55; Inter-Colleg Sec SCM (Man) 52-55; C Leigh St Mary Man 55-57; V Rochdale Gd Shep 57-62; India 63-67; V Becontree St Geo Chelmsf 67-71; R Weeley 71-79; Chapl St Deiniol's Lib Hawarden 79-80; Sub-Warden 80-86; Perm to Offic Chelmsf from 86; Hon C St Botolph without Bishopgate Lon from 87. Merrywood, 25 Fourth Avenue, Frinton-on-Sea CO13 9DU Tel (01255) 677554

TURNER, James Alfred. b 34. Ox Coll FE MCIPS76. Ox Min Course 91. d 94 p 95. NSM Kidlington w Hampton Poyle Ox from 94. 11 St Mary's Close, Kidlington, Oxford OX5 2AY Tel (01865) 375562

TURNER, James Henry. b 51. N Ord Course 99. d 02 p 03. NSM Middleton St Cross Ripon from 02. 38 Acre Crescent, Middleton, Leeds LS10 4DJ Tel 0113-277 2681 E-mail jamesjpturner@aol.com

TURNER, Jane. See TURNER, Miss Elizabeth Jane

TURNER, Canon Jessica Mary. b 60. SS Coll Cam BA81 PGCE82. Trin Coll Bris 88. d 91 p 94. Par Dn Preston Em Blackb 91-94; C Bamber Bridge St Aid 94-95; Chapl Preston Acute Hosps NHS Trust 95-98; Chapl Blackpool Victoria Hosp NHS Trust from 98; Hon Can Blackb Cathl Blackb from 02. Chaplaincy Office, Victoria Hospital, Whinney Heys Road, Blackpool FY3 8NR Tel (01253) 303876 or 899791 E-mail turner@exch.bvh-tr.nwest.nhs.uk

TURNER, John David Maurice. b 22. Keble Coll Ox BA45 MA48. Ripon Hall Ox 69. d 70 p 71. C Crowthorne Ox 70-73; V Cropredy w Gt Bourton 73-79; V Cropredy w Gt Bourton and Wardington 80-83; Perm to Offic Ox and Pet 83-03; rtd 87. 14 Stuart Court, High Street, Kibworth, Leicester LE8 0LR Tel (01858) 881378

TURNER, John William. b 43. Sheff Univ BSc73. Wycliffe Hall Ox 86. d 88 p 89. C Clayton Bradf 88-91; C Horton 91-92; V Bankfoot 92-01; V Holland-on-Sea Chelmsf from 01. The Vicarage, 297 Frinton Road, Holland-on-Sea, Clacton-on-Sea CO15 5SP Tel (01255) 812420 E-mail john.turner@virgin.net

TURNER, Canon Keith Howard. b 50. Southn Univ BA71. Wycliffe Hall Ox 72. d 75 p 76. C Enfield Ch Ch Trent Park Lon 75-79; C Chilwell S'well 79-83; P-in-c Linby w Papplewick 83-90; R from 90; Hon Can S'well Minster from 02. The Rectory, Main Street, Linby, Nottingham NG15 8AE Tel 0115-963 2346 E-mail k.h.turner@btopenworld.com

TURNER, Keith Stanley. b 51. ACIB80. NTMTC DTPS99. d 99 p 00. Par Dn S Hornchurch St Jo and St Matt Chelmsf 99-03; C from 99. *16 Wells Gardens, Rainham RM13 7LU* Tel (01708) 554274

TURNER, Kevin Louis Sinclair. b 60. St Jo Coll Nottm BA00. **d** 00 **p** 01. C Mount Pellon *Wakef* 00-03; P-in-c Sowerby from 03. *37 Hops Lane, Halifax HX3 5FB* Tel (01422) 362416 Fax as telephone E-mail kevin@kevinturner.freeserve.co.uk

TURNER, Lawrence John. b 43. Kelham Th Coll 65. **d** 70 **p** 71. C Lower Gornal *Lich* 70-73; C Wednesbury St Paul Wood Green 73-74; C Porthill 75-77; C Wilton *York* 77-80; P-in-c 80-82; R Jersey St Martin *Win* from 82; Chmn Jersey Miss to Seamen from 82. *The Rectory, La rue de la Croix au Maitre, St Martin, Jersey JE3 6HW* Tel (01534) 854294

TURNER, Leslie. b 29. NE Lon Poly BSc87. St Jo Coll Dur 50 St Aid Birkenhead 51. **d** 54 **p** 55. C Darwen St Cuth *Blackb* 54-56; C Haslingden w Grane and Stonefold 56-59; V Oswaldtwistle St Paul 59-65; Chapl Belmont and Henderson Hosps Sutton 65-71; St Ebba's Hosp Epsom 65-71; Qu Mary's Carshalton 67-71; Lic to Offic *Pet* 71-94; Chapl Princess Marina & St Crispin's Hosps 71-87; Chapl Northn Gen Hosp 87-94; Chapl Manfield Hosp Northn 87-94; Chapl St Edm Hosp Northn 87-94; rtd 94; Perm to Offic *Pet* from 94. *20 Banbury Close, Northampton NN4 9UA* Tel (01604) 769233

TURNER, Mrs Lorraine Elizabeth. b 67. Brunel Univ BSc90 Open Univ MA96. Cranmer Hall Dur 01. **d** 03. C Birchwood *Linc* from 03. *28 Sycamore Crescent, Lincoln LN6 0RR* Tel (01522) 688274 E-mail lorraine.t@which.net

TURNER, Mark. b 60. Aston Tr Scheme 87 Sarum & Wells Th Coll BTh92. **d** 92 **p** 93. C New Sleaford *Linc* 92-94; C Bottesford and Muston *Leic* 94-98; C Harby, Long Clawson and Hose 94-98; C Barkestone w Plungar, Redmile and Stathern 94-98; P-in-c Thurnby Lodge 98-00; C Aylestone Park CD 00-03; P-in-c Areley Kings *Worc* from 03. *14 Dunley Road, Stourport-on-Severn DY13 0AX* Tel (01299) 829557 E-mail rev.turner@compuserve.com

TURNER, Mark Richard Haythornthwaite. b 41. TCD MA67 Linc Coll Ox BA68. Wycliffe Hall Ox 65. **d** 68 **p** 69. C Birtley *Newc* 68-71; C Cambridge Gt St Mary w St Mich *Ely* 71-74; Chapl Loughb Univ *Leic* 74-79; P-in-c Keele *Lich* 80-85; Chapl Keele Univ 80-85; P-in-c Ashley 85-95; P-in-c Mucklestone 86-95; R Farnborough *Roch* 95-00; P-in-c Upper Tean *Lich* from 00; Local Min Adv (Stafford) from 00. *The Vicarage, Vicarage Road, Tean, Stoke-on-Trent ST10 4LE* Tel (01538) 722227

TURNER, Martin John. b 34. Trin Hall Cam BA55 MA59. Cuddesdon Coll 58. **d** 60 **p** 61. C Rugby St Andr *Cov* 60-65; C Cov Cathl 65-68; USA 68-70; V Rushmere St *E* 70-82; V Monkwearmouth St Pet *Dur* 82-90; V Bathford *B & W* 90-99; rtd 99; Perm to Offic *B & W* from 00. *The Vicarage, 35 Kewstoke Road, Kewstoke, Weston-super-Mare BS22 9YE* Tel (01934) 645654 Mobile 07929-231167 E-mail turnerschemanoff@aol.com

TURNER, Mrs Maureen. b 55. Leeds Univ BA78 MA01. St Jo Coll Nottm 84. **d** 87 **p** 94. Par Dn Darlaston St Lawr *Lich* 87-91; C Stratford-on-Avon w Bishopton *Cov* 91-98; Chapl Myton Hamlet Hospice 98-01; NSM Leire w Ashby Parva and Dunton Bassett *Leic* 00-01; Chapl Team Ldr Univ Hosps Leic NHS Trust from 01. *Leicester Royal Infirmary, Infirmary Square, Leicester LE1 5WW* Tel 0116-258 5487 E-mail maureen.turner@uhl-tr.nhs.uk

TURNER, Maurice. *See* TURNER, Charles Maurice Joseph

TURNER, Maurice William. b 27. Sarum Th Coll 53. **d** 56 **p** 57. C Thornhill *Wakef* 56-60; V Gawber 60-71; V Alverthorpe 71-74; V Shelton and Oxon *Lich* 74-81; P-in-c Battlefield w Albrighton 81-82; V Leaton 81-82; V Leaton and Albrighton w Battlefield 82-92; rtd 92; Perm to Offic *Lich* 93-96; Perm to Offic *Heref* from 96. *10 Melbourne Rise, Bicton Heath, Shrewsbury SY3 5DA* Tel (01743) 352667

TURNER, Michael Andrew. b 34. K Coll Cam BA59 MA62. Cuddesdon Coll 59. **d** 61 **p** 62. C Luton St Andr *St Alb* 61-64; V 70-77; C-in-c Northolt St Mary *Lon* 64-70; Perm to Offic *St Alb* 77-93; Dep Hd and Chapl Greycoat Hosp Sch 86-93; P-in-c Shilling Okeford *Sarum* 93-99; Chapl Croft Ho Sch Shillingstone 93-99; rtd 99; V of Close Sarum Cathl *Sarum* from 02. *12 Berkshire Road, Harnham, Salisbury SP2 8NY* Tel (01722) 504000

TURNER, Michael John Royce. b 43. St Jo Coll Dur BA65. Chich Th Coll 65. **d** 67 **p** 68. C Hodge Hill *Birm* 67-71; C Eling, Testwood and Marchwood *Win* 71-72; TV 72-77; R Kirkwall *Ab* 77-85; R Drumlithie *Bre* from 85; R Drumtochty from 85; R Fasque from 85; R Laurencekirk from 85. *Beattie Lodge, Laurencekirk AB30 1HJ* Tel (01561) 377380 Fax as telephone E-mail mjrturner@zoo.co.uk

TURNER, Canon Nicholas Anthony. b 51. Clare Coll Cam BA73 MA77 Keble Coll Ox BA77 MA81. Ripon Coll Cuddesdon 76. **d** 78 **p** 79. C Stretford St Matt *Man* 78-80; Tutor St Steph Ho Ox 80-84; V Leeds Richmond Hill *Ripon* 84-91; Ascension Is 91-96; Offg Chapl RAF 91-96; Can Th St Helena Cathl from 94; V Raynes Park St Sav *S'wark* 96-01; P-in-c Broughton, Marton and Thornton *Bradf* from 01. *The Rectory, Broughton, Skipton BD23 3AN* Tel (01282) 842332 E-mail the.wanderer@virgin.net

TURNER (née SYMINGTON), Mrs Patricia Ann. b 46. SRN68 RMN71 SCM72 Cam Univ DipRS82. St Steph Ho Ox 82. dss 84 **d** 87. Buttershaw St Aid *Bradf* 84-87; TD Manningham 87-91; Ascension Is 91-96; Par Dn Raynes Park St Sav *S'wark* 96-01; Par Dn Broughton, Marton and Thornton *Bradf* from 01. *The Rectory, Broughton, Skipton BD23 3AN* Tel (01282) 842332 E-mail the.wanderer@virgin.net

TURNER, Peter Carpenter. b 39. Oak Hill Th Coll 63. **d** 66 **p** 67. C Chadwell *Chelmsf* 66-69; C Braintree 69-73; R Fyfield 73-87; P-in-c Moreton 77-87; C-in-c Bobbingworth 82-87; P-in-c Willingale w Shellow and Berners Roding 84-87; V E Ham St Geo from 87. *The Vicarage, Buxton Road, London E6 3NB* Tel (020) 8472 2111 E-mail pet@btinternet.com

TURNER, The Ven Peter Robin. b 42. CB98. AKC65 St Luke's Coll Ex PGCE70 Open Univ BA79 Westmr Coll Ox MTh96. St Boniface Warminster 65. **d** 66 **p** 67. C Crediton *Ex* 66-69; Perm to Offic 69-70; Chapl RAF 70-88; Asst Chapl-in-Chief RAF 88-95; Chapl-in-Chief RAF 95-98; QHC 92-98; Can and Preb Linc Cathl *Linc* 95-98; Chapl Dulwich Coll 98-02; Bp's Dom Chapl *S'well* from 02; Hon Can S'well Minster from 02. *8 Raysmith Close, Southwell NG25 0BG* Tel and fax (01636) 816764 Mobile 07860-583475 E-mail pr.turner@lineone.net *or* chaplain@southwell.anglican.org

TURNER, Philip William. b 25. CM65. Worc Coll Ox BA50 MA62. Chich Th Coll 49. **d** 51 **p** 52. C Armley St Bart *Ripon* 51-56; P-in-c Crawley *Chich* 56-62; V Northampton St Matt *Pet* 62-66; Relig Broadcasting Org BBC Midl Region 66-71; Asst Master Brian Mill Sch Droitwich 71-73; Chapl Eton Coll 73-75; Chapl Malvern Coll 75-84; Chapl St Jas and Abbey Schs Malvern 84-86; rtd 90; Perm to Offic *Worc* from 90. *181 West Malvern Road, Malvern WR14 4AY* Tel (01684) 563852

TURNER, Canon Robert Edgar. b 20. TCD BA42 MA51. Linc Th Coll 44. **d** 45 **p** 46. C Kings Heath *Birm* 45-51; Min Can Belf Cathl 51-63; Dean of Res QUB 51-58; Bp's Dom Chapl *D & D* 56-67; I Belfast St Geo *Conn* 58-90; Can Belf Cathl 71-76; Preb Clonmethan St Patr Cathl Dublin 76-90; Dioc Registrar *Conn* from 82; rtd 90. *19 Cricklewood Park, Belfast BT9 5GU* Tel (028) 9066 3214 Fax 9058 6843 E-mail returner@nireland.com *or* registrar@connor.anglican.org

TURNER, Robin Edward. b 35. Selw Coll Cam BA57 MA63. Qu Coll Birm DipTh63. **d** 63 **p** 64. C Aveley *Chelmsf* 63-67; C Upminster 67-71; R Goldhanger w Lt Totham 71-80; R Lt Baddow 80-00; Hon Chapl New Hall Sch Essex 80-00; rtd 00; Perm to Offic *Nor* from 00. *29 Swann Grove, Holt NR25 6DP* Tel (01263) 711330

TURNER, Canon Roger Dyke. b 39. Trin Coll Bris 79. **d** 81 **p** 82. C Clevedon St Andr *B & W* 81-82; C Clevedon St Andr and Ch Ch 83-85; R Freshford, Limpley Stoke and Hinton Charterhouse 85-88; V Kenilworth St Jo *Cov* from 88; RD Kenilworth 90-98; Hon Can Cov Cathl from 00. *St John's Vicarage, Clarke's Avenue, Kenilworth CV8 1HX* Tel (01926) 779297 *or* 853203 E-mail stjohn.kenilworth@btinternet.com

TURNER, St John Alwin. b 31. Dur Univ BA57 MA61. Cranmer Hall Dur DipTh58. **d** 59 **p** 60. C W Hartlepool St Paul *Dur* 59-62; C S Shore H Trin *Blackb* 62-65; V Huncoat 65-67; Org Sec (Dios Ripon and York) CMS 67-72; V Harrogate St Mark *Ripon* 72-94; rtd 96; Perm to Offic *Linc* from 01. *2 The Tilney, Whaplode, Spalding PE12 6UW* Tel (01406) 371390

TURNER, Susan. b 58. Man Univ BA89. N Ord Course 89. **d** 92 **p** 94. NSM Balderstone *Man* 92-93; NSM E Crompton 93-94; Hon C 94-96; Chapl Man Coll of Arts and Tech 92-96; Asst Chapl S Man Univ Hosps NHS Trust 96-97; Chapl Burnley Health Care NHS Trust 97-03; Chapl Cen Man/Man Children's Univ Hosp NHS Trust from 02. *Chaplaincy Office, Manchester Royal Infirmary, Oxford Road, Manchester M13 9WL* Tel 0161-276 45824

TURNER (formerly BENBOW), Mrs Susan Catherine. b 47. Birm Univ BEd70. St Alb Minl Tr Scheme 82. dss 85 **d** 87 **p** 94. Gt Wyrley *Lich* 85-87; Par Dn 87-88; Par Dn Whitstable *Cant* 88-92; Par Dn Eastry and Northbourne w Tilmanstone etc 92-94; C 94-96; P-in-c Gt Mongeham w Ripple and Sutton by Dover 96-98; rtd 98; Perm to Offic *Nor* from 99. *Whitegates, The Crescent, Walcott, Norwich NR12 0NH*

TURNER, Sylvia Jean. b 46. Lon Univ 72 Open Univ BA77. Westcott Ho Cam CTM95. **d** 95 **p** 96. C Whitstable *Cant* 95-99; R Wigmore Abbey *Heref* from 99. *The Rectory, Watling Street, Leintwardine, Craven Arms SY7 0LL* Tel (01547) 540235 E-mail sylvia.turner@virgin.net

TURNER, Tina. b 60. St Jo Coll Nottm BA02. **d** 02 **p** 03. C Halifax All So and St Aug *Wakef* from 02. *37 Hops Lane, Halifax HX3 5FB* Tel (01422) 360758 E-mail tina@tturner.junglelink.co.uk

TURNER, Valerie Kay. b 50. Shp Paul & Mary Coll Cheltenham BEd72. WMMTC 97 Wycliffe Hall Ox DipTh00. **d** 00 **p** 01. C Cheltenham St Luke and St Jo *Glouc* from 00. *18 Eldon Road, Cheltenham GL52 6TU* Tel (01242) 253641 E-mail valmark@turner.tc

TURNER, Canon Walter John. b 29. Bris Univ BA53. Clifton Th Coll 49. **d** 54 **p** 55. C W Bromwich All SS *Lich* 54-58; C-in-c

Oxley 58-60; V 60-65; V Wednesfield St Thos 65-74; RD Shifnal 75-83; V Boningale 75-83; V Wednesfield St Thos 83-; Preb Lich Cathl 80-83; Can Res and Prec Lich Cathl 83-94; rtd 94; Perm to Offic *Lich* from 94. *9 Kestrel Close, Newport TF10 8QE* Tel (01952) 820758

TURNER, William Edward. b 41. Keble Coll Ox BA63 MA73. Linc Th Coll 76. **d** 78 **p** 79. C Lich St Chad *Lich* 78-80; Chapl Trent (Nottm) Poly *S'well* 80-89; Chapl Lancs (Preston) Poly *Blackb* 89-92; Chapl Cen Lancs Univ from 92. *10 Queens Road, Fulwood, Preston PR2 3EA* Tel (01772) 717791 *or* 892615 Fax 202073

TURNER-LOISEL, Mrs Elizabeth Anne. b 57. Lanc Univ BA79 MA80 York Univ PGCE81. EMMTC 96. **d** 99 **p** 00. C Eastwood *S'well* from 99; Chapl Nat Sch Hucknall from 99. *182 Nottingham Road, Selston, Nottingham NG16 6AB* Tel (01773) 780778 E-mail rev.liz@ntlworld.com

TURNOCK, Geoffrey. b 38. MSOSc Leeds Univ BSc61 PhD64. EMMTC 84. **d** 87 **p** 88. NSM Oadby *Leic* 87-00; NSM Okeford *Sarum* from 00. *The Rectory, Church Road, Shillingstone, Blandford Forum DT11 0SL* Tel (01258) 860261

TURP, Paul Robert. b 48. Oak Hill Th Coll BA79. **d** 79 **p** 80. C Southall Green St Jo *Lon* 79-83; V Shoreditch St Leon w St Mich 83-88 and from 00; TR Shoreditch St Leon and Hoxton St Jo 88-00. *The Vicarage, 36 Hoxton Square, London N1 6NN* Tel (020) 7739 2063

TURPIN, Canon John Richard. b 41. St D Coll Lamp BA63 Magd Coll Cam BA65 MA70. Cuddesdon Coll 65. **d** 66 **p** 67. C Tadley St Pet *Win* 66-71; V Southampton Thornhill St Chris 71-85; V Ringwood from 85; Hon Can Win Cathl from 99. *The Vicarage, 65 Southampton Road, Ringwood BH24 1HE* Tel (01425) 473219 E-mail johnturpin@ringwoodparish.org.uk

TURPIN, Raymond Gerald. b 35. LNSM course 94. **d** 97 **p** 98. OLM Brockley Hill St Sav *S'wark* from 97. *60 Bankhurst Road, London SE6 4XN* Tel (020) 8690 6877 *or* 8311 2000

TURRALL, Albert Thomas George. b 19. Linc Th Coll 64. **d** 66 **p** 67. C Rowley Regis *Birm* 66-69; V Astley *Worc* 69-74; V Montford w Shrawardine *Lich* 74-77; R Montford w Shrawardine and Fitz 77-84; rtd 84; Perm to Offic *Heref* 86-98; Perm to Offic *Lich* from 86. *15 Highbury Close, Shrewsbury SY2 6SN* Tel (01743) 249831

TURRELL, Peter Charles Morphett. b 47. Dioc OLM tr scheme 98. **d** 01 **p** 02. OLM Carshalton Beeches *S'wark* from 01. *62 Stanley Park Road, Carshalton SM5 3HW* Tel (020) 8669 0318

TURRELL, Stephen John. b 35. Lon Univ DipRS85. S'wark Ord Course. **d** 83 **p** 84. NSM W Wickham St Jo *Cant* 83-84; Chapl Guild of St Bride from 83; NSM Addington *S'wark* 85-92; NSM Blendworth w Chalton w Idsworth *Portsm* 92-97; Perm to Offic 97-01; Hon C Storrington *Chich* from 01. *9 Longland Avenue, Storrington, Pulborough RH20 4HY* Tel (01903) 741272

TURTON, Arthur Bickerstaffe. b 19. Oak Hill Th Coll 46. **d** 48 **p** 49. C Rawtenstall St Mary *Man* 48-51; C Islington St Mary *Lon* 51-52; V Lozells St Silas *Birm* 52-56; V Streatham Park St Alb *S'wark* 56-60; Org Sec CPAS Metrop Area 60-64; V Southborough St Pet *Roch* 64-68; P-in-c Southborough St Matt 67-68; V Southborough St Pet w Ch Ch and St Matt 68-76; V Histon *Ely* 76-82; rtd 84; Perm to Offic *Chich* 82-88; *Ely* 88-96. *1172 Greenwood Avenue, Victoria, BC, Canada, V9A 5M1* Tel (001) (250) 385 0062

TURTON, Douglas Walter. b 38. Kent Univ BA77 Surrey Univ MSc90. Oak Hill Th Coll 77. **d** 78 **p** 79. C Cant St Mary Bredin *Cant* 78-80; P-in-c Thornton Heath St Paul 80-81; V 81-84; V Thornton Heath St Paul *S'wark* 85-91; R Eastling w Ospringe and Stalisfield w Otterden *Cant* 91-00; rtd 00. *16 Weatherall Close, Dunkirk, Faversham ME13 9UL* Tel (01227) 752244

TURTON, Neil Christopher. b 45. Wycliffe Hall Ox 77. **d** 79 **p** 80. C Guildf Ch Ch *Guildf* 79-83; C Godalming 83-86; V Wyke 86-92; R Frimley 92-02; RD Surrey Heath 97-02; V All SS Bay Head NJ USA from 02. *All Saints Rectory, 509 Lake Avenue, Bay Head, NJ 08742, USA* E-mail neil.turton@virgin.net

TURTON, Paul Edward. b 26. St Pet Hall Ox BA50 MA55. Qu Coll Birm 50. **d** 52 **p** 53. C Selly Oak St Mary *Birm* 52-55; C Ward End 55-57; I Netherton CD *Liv* 57-64; V Brockley Hill St Sav *S'wark* 64-68; Perm to Offic 68-70; Dir of Educn *Nor* 70-75; Dep Dir Nat Soc Cen Camberwell 75-77; Dir Nat Soc RE Cen Kensington 78-84; C Eastbourne St Mary *Chich* 84-86; rtd 86; Perm to Offic *Chich* from 87. *32 Churchill Close, Eastbourne BN20 8AJ* Tel (01323) 638089

TUSCHLING, Miss Ruth Mary Magdalen. b 65. Freiburg Univ MA94. Westcott Ho Cam BA97. **d** 98 **p** 99. C Hampstead St Jo *Lon* 98-01; Perm to Offic *Ely* from 01. *Corpus Christi College, Cambridge CB2 1RH* Tel (01223) 306271

✠**TUSTIN, The Rt Revd David.** b 35. Magd Coll Cam BA57 MA61 Lambeth DD98. Cuddesdon Coll 58. **d** 60 **p** 61 **c** 79. C Stafford St Mary *Lich* 60-63; C St Dunstan in the West *Lon* 63-67; Asst Gen Sec C of E Coun on Foreign Relns 63-67; V Wednesbury St Paul Wood Green *Lich* 67-71; V Tettenhall Regis 71-79; RD Trysull 76-79; Suff Bp Grimsby *Linc* 79-00; Can and Preb Linc Cathl 79-00; rtd 00; Hon Asst Bp Linc from 01. *The*

Ashes, Tunnel Road, Wrawby, Brigg DN20 8SF Tel (01652) 655584 Fax as telephone E-mail tustindavid@hotmail.com

TUTTON, Canon John Knight. b 30. Man Univ BSc51. Ripon Hall Ox 53. **d** 55 **p** 56. C Tonge w Alkrington *Man* 55-57; C Bushbury *Lich* 57-59; R Blackley St Andr *Man* 59-67; R Denton Ch Ch 67-95; Hon Can Man Cathl 90-95; rtd 95; Hon C Exminster and Kenn *Ex* 96-01; Perm to Offic from 01. *2 Hescane Park, Cheriton Bishop, Exeter EX6 6JP* Tel (01647) 24651 E-mail johnktutton@onetel.net.uk

✠**TUTU, The Most Revd Desmond Mpilo.** b 31. UNISA BA K Coll Lon BD MTh FKC78. St Pet Rosettenville LTh. **d** 60 **p** 61 **c** 76. S Africa 60-62; C Golders Green St Alb *Lon* 62-65; C Bletchingley *S'wark* 65-66; S Africa 67-70; Lesotho 70-72; Assoc Dir Th Educn Fund WCC 72-75; C Lee St Aug *S'wark* 72-75; Dean Johannesburg 75-76; Bp Lesotho 76-78; Asst Bp Johannesburg 78-85; Bp Johannesburg 85-86; Abp Cape Town 86-96; rtd 96. *PO Box 3162, Cape Town, 8000 South Africa*

TWADDELL, Canon William Reginald. b 33. TCD Dip Bibl Studies 61. **d** 62 **p** 63. C Belfast Whiterock *Conn* 62-65; I Loughgilly w Clare *Arm* 65-71; I Milltown 71-84; I Portadown St Mark 84-01; Preb Arm Cathl 88-96; Treas 96-98; Prec 98-01; rtd 01. *Tea Cottage, 19 Birches Road, Portadown BT62 1LS* Tel (028) 3885 2520

TWEDDELL, Christopher Noel. b 66. Auckland Univ BA93. St Jo Coll Auckland. **d** 92 **p** 93. New Zealand 92-97; C Maindee *Mon* 97-98; Hong Kong from 98. *55A Seabird Lane, Discovery Bay, Lantau Island, Hong Kong*

TWEDDLE, David William Joseph. b 28. ATCL56 Dur Univ BSc50 Open Univ BA97. Wycliffe Hall Ox 54. **d** 56 **p** 57. C Darlington H Trin *Dur* 56-60; P-in-c Prestonpans *Edin* 60-63; PV Linc Cathl *Linc* 63-65; C Pet St Jo *Pet* 65-71; Hon Min Can Pet Cathl 68-93; V Southwick w Glapthorn 71-83; P-in-c Benefield 80-83; R Benefield and Southwick w Glapthorn 83-93; RD Oundle 84-89; rtd 94; Perm to Offic *Ely* and *Pet* from 94. *6 Barton Square, Ely CB7 4DF* Tel (01353) 614393

TWEED, Andrew. b 48. Univ of Wales (Cardiff) BA69 Trin Coll Carmarthen MA97. St Deiniol's Hawarden. **d** 81 **p** 84. NSM Llandrindod w Cefnllys *S & B* 81-87; NSM Llandrindod w Cefnllys and Disserth from 87. *Gwenallt, Wellington Road, Llandrindod Wells LD1 5NB* Tel (01597) 823671 E-mail andrewtweed1@aol.com

TWEEDIE-SMITH, Ian David. b 60. Newc Univ BA83. Wycliffe Hall Ox 83. **d** 85 **p** 86. C Hatcham St Jas *S'wark* 85-89; C Bury St Edmunds St Mary *St E* 89-02; TV Woking St Pet *Guildf* from 02. *The Vicarage, 66 Westfield Road, Woking GU22 9NG* Tel (01483) 770779 Fax 770786 E-mail iantweediesmith@waitrose.com

TWEEDY, Andrew Cyril Mark. b 61. Man Univ BA(Econ)81. St Alb and Ox Min Course 98. **d** 01 **p** 02. C Carterton *Ox* 01-03; C Carterton and Brize Norton from 03. *39 Bluebell Way, Carterton OX18 1JY* Tel (01993) 840320 Mobile 07870-549393 E-mail andrew@tweedy.psa-online.com

TWIDELL, Canon William James. b 30. St Mich Coll Llan 58. **d** 60 **p** 61. C Tonge w Alkrington *Man* 60-63; C High Wycombe All SS *Ox* 63-65; P-in-c Elkesley w Bothamsall *S'well* 65-66; V Bury St Thos *Man* 66-72; V Daisy Hill 72-84; R Flixton St Mich 84-00; AD Stretford 88-99; Hon Can Man Cathl 97-00; rtd 00; Perm to Offic *Man* and *Ches* from 00. *11 Mercer Way, Nantwich CW5 5YD* Tel (01270) 620328

TWINLEY, David Alan. b 66. Ox Univ BTh00. St Steph Ho Ox 97. **d** 00 **p** 01. C Saffron Walden w Wendens Ambo, Littlebury etc *Chelmsf* from 00. *42 De Vigier Avenue, Saffron Walden CB10 2BN* Tel (01799) 500194 E-mail davidtwinley@lineone.net

TWISLETON, John Fiennes. b 48. St Jo Coll Ox BA69 MA73 DPhil73. Coll of Resurr Mirfield DipTh75. **d** 76 **p** 77. C New Bentley *Sheff* 76-79; P-in-c Moorends 79-80; V 80-86; USPG 86-90; Coll of the Ascension Selly Oak 86-87; Prin Alan Knight Tr Cen Guyana 87-90; V Holbrooks *Cov* 90-96; Edmonton Area Missr *Lon* 96-01; Dioc Adv for Miss and Renewal *Chich* from 01; C Haywards Heath St Rich from 01. *27 Gatesmead, Haywards Heath RH16 1SN* Tel (01444) 414658 Fax as telephone E-mail john@twisleton.co.uk

TWISLETON, Peter. b 50. Linc Th Coll. **d** 84 **p** 85. C Bodmin w Lanhydrock and Lanivet *Truro* 84-87; C Par 87-90; R St Breoke and Egloshayle 90-93; R Bude Haven and Marhamchurch 93-97; V Horbury w Horbury Bridge *Wakef* from 98. *St Peter's Vicarage, Horbury, Wakefield WF4 6AS* Tel (01924) 273477

TWISLETON-WYKEHAM-FIENNES, Oliver William. *See* FIENNES, The Very Revd the Hon Oliver William

TWISS, Dorothy Elizabeth. Gilmore Ho 68 Linc Th Coll 70. **d** 87 **p** 94. Chapl Asst RAF 78-91; TV Pewsey *Sarum* 91-95; Chapl HM Pris Drake Hall 95-01; Chapl HM Pris Ford from 01. *The Chaplain's Office, HM Prison Ford, Arundel BN18 0BX* Tel (01903) 663085 Fax 663001

TWITTY, Miss Rosamond Jane. b 54. Univ of Wales (Ban) BSc75 CertEd76. Trin Coll Bris BA89. **d** 90 **p** 94. Par Dn Lt Thurrock St Jo *Chelmsf* 90-94; C 94-95; C Upper Armley *Ripon* from

95. *115A Heights Drive, Leeds LS12 3TG* Tel 0113-263 7240
E-mail janetwitty@supanet.com

TWOHIG, Brian Robert. b 48. La Trobe Univ Vic BA77 PhD86.
St Mich Th Coll Crafers 70. **d** 72 **p** 73. Australia 72-78 and 80-82;
C Leatherhead *Guildf* 78-80; ST New Windsor *Ox* 82-92; V
Sheff St Cuth *Sheff* 92-97; rtd 97; Perm to Offic *Chich* from 98.
26A Bloomsbury Street, Brighton BN2 1HQ

TWOMEY, Jeremiah Francis (Derry). b 50. Man Poly BA83 Univ
of Wales (Ban) PGCE85 Real Colegio de Escoceses Valladolid
Spain. NEOC 92. **d** 94 **p** 95. C Beverley St Nic *York* 94-96; V
Anlaby Common St Mark 96-99; Ind Chapl *Newc* from 99.
20 Tyndale Close, Wylam NE41 8EY Tel (01661) 853884

TWOMEY, Jeremiah Thomas Paul. b 46. CITC 87. **d** 87 **p** 88. C
Derryloran *Arm* 87-90; I Brackaville w Donaghendry and
Ballyclog 90-97; I Mohill w Farnaught, Aughavas, Oughteragh
etc *K, E & A* 97-00; Bp's C Belfast Whiterock *Conn* from 00.
8 Lyndhurstview Road, Lyndhurst Meadows, Belfast BT13 3XR
Tel (028) 9072 1134 E-mail ptwomey@esatclear.ie

TWYCROSS, Stephen Jervis. b 33. Nottm Univ BEd73 Leic Univ
MA85. Lambeth STh88 Kalk Bay Bible Inst S Africa 56 Wycliffe
Hall Ox 58. **d** 60 **p** 61. C Hinckley H Trin *Leic* 60-64; V
Barlestone 64-71; Wheat Dio Leic 71-87; P-in-c Stokesay *Heref*
87-91; P-in-c Sibdon Carwood w Halford 87-91; Chapl Utrecht
w Amersfoort, Harderwijk and Zwolle *Eur* 91-94; V Llanwddyn
and Llanfihangel-yng-Nghwynfa etc *St As* 94-96; rtd 96; Perm to
Offic *Ban* from 96. *1 Britannia Place, Porthmadog LL49 9LY* Tel
(01766) 514682

TWYFORD, Canon Arthur Russell. b 36. ALCD60. **d** 60 **p** 61. C
Speke All SS *Liv* 60-64; Asst Dioc Youth Officer *Ox* 64-70; R
Maids Moreton w Foxcote 64-72; P-in-c Lillingstone Dayrell w
Lillingstone Lovell 70-72; V Desborough *Pet* 72-88; P-in-c
Braybrook 73-77; P-in-c Brampton Ash w Dingley 73-77; R
Brampton Ash w Dingley and Braybrooke 77-88; RD Kettering
79-87; Can Pet Cathl 81-95; R Stanwick w Hargrave 88-95; rtd
95; Perm to Offic *Pet* from 95. *1 Laws Lane, Finedon,
Wellingborough NN9 5LU* Tel (01933) 682116

TYDEMAN, Canon Richard. b 16. St Jo Coll Ox BA39 MA43.
Ripon Hall Ox 38. **d** 39 **p** 40. C Langley St Mich *Birm* 39-41; C
Ipswich All SS *St E* 41-45; P-in-c Ipswich St Helen 45-46; V
Woodbridge St Jo 46-53; V Newmarket All SS 53-63; RD
Newmarket 54-63; Hon Can St Edm Cathl 59-63; R St Sepulchre w
Ch Ch Greyfriars etc *Lon* 63-81; Dep Min Can St Paul's Cathl
63-81; Preacher Lincoln's Inn 72-81; rtd 81; Perm to Offic *St E*
from 82. *10 Colneis Road, Felixstowe IP11 9HF* Tel (01394)
283214

TYDEMAN, Rosemary. *See* WILLIAMS, Mrs Rosemary

TYE, Eric John. b 37. St Alb Minl Tr Scheme 78. **d** 81 **p** 82. NSM
Rushden St Mary w Newton Bromswold *Pet* from 81. *31 Morris
Avenue, Rushden NN10 9PB* Tel (01933) 353274

TYE, John Raymond. b 31. Lambeth STh64 Linc Th Coll 66. **d** 68
p 69. C Crewe St Mich *Ches* 68-71; C Wednesfield St Thos *Lich*
71-76; P-in-c Petton w Cockshutt 76-79; P-in-c Hordley 79;
P-in-c Weston Lullingfield 79; R Petton w Cockshutt and
Weston Lullingfield etc 79-81; V Hadley 81-84; R Ightfield w
Calverhall 84-89; V Ash 84-89; R Calton, Cauldon, Grindon and
Waterfall 89-96; RD Alstonfield 95-96; rtd 96. *38 Aston Street,
Wem, Shrewsbury SY4 5AU*

TYERS, Canon Gerald Seymour. b 22. St Pet Hall Ox BA46
MA49. Linc Th Coll 47. **d** 49 **p** 50. C Perry Street *Roch* 49-52; C
Gillingham St Aug 52-53; V 60-67; V Orpington St Andr 53-60; V
Erith Ch Ch 67-82; Chapl Erith and Distr Hosp 67-82; RD Erith
79-82; R Foots Cray *Roch* 82-91; Hon Can Roch Cathl 82-91; rtd
91; Perm to Offic *Roch* from 91. *Yew Tree Cottage, Castle Hill,
Hartley, Dartford DA3 7BH* Tel (01474) 707923

TYERS, Canon John Haydn. b 33. Lon Univ BSc51 Open Univ
BA00. Ridley Hall Cam 53. **d** 55 **p** 56. C Nuneaton St Nic *Cov*
55-58; C Rugby St Andr 58-62; V Cov St Anne 62-71; V Keresley
and Coundon 71-78; V Atherstone 78-85; P-in-c Pleshey *Chelmsf*
85-91; Warden Pleshey Retreat Ho 85-91; Hon Can Chelmsf
Cathl *Chelmsf* 86-91; P-in-c Ash *Lich* 91-96; P-in-c Ightfield w
Calverhall 91-96; rtd 96; Perm to Offic *Heref* from 97. *7 Brook
Road, Pontesbury, Shrewsbury SY5 0QZ* Tel (01743) 790354

TYERS, Philip Nicolas. b 56. Nottm Univ BTh84. St Jo Coll
Nottm 80. **d** 84 **p** 85. C Rugby St Matt *Cov* 84-88; TV Cov E
88-95; P-in-c Preston St Matt *Blackb* 95-96; TR Preston Risen
Lord from 96. *St Matthew's Vicarage, 20 Fishwick View, Preston
PR1 4YA* Tel (01772) 794312 E-mail tyers-5@fish.co.uk

TYLDESLEY, Mrs Vera. b 47. Man Coll of Educn BEd80.
LNSM course 95. **d** 98 **p** 99. OLM Pendlebury St Jo *Man* from
98. *7 Kingsway, Swinton, Manchester M27 4JU* Tel 0161-736
3845

TYLER, Alan William. b 60. Univ of Wales (Ban) DipTh84.
Ridley Hall Cam 84. **d** 86 **p** 87. C Bedwellty *Mon* 86-89; C
St Mellons and Michaelston-y-Fedw 89-92; V Abersychan and
Garndiffaith 92-97; Chapl Glan Hafren NHS Trust 97-99; Sen
Chapl Gwent Healthcare NHS Trust from 99; Lic to Offic *Mon*
from 97. *The Royal Gwent Hospital, Cardiff Road, Newport
NP20 2UB* Tel (01633) 234234 or 871457

TYLER, Alison Ruth. b 51. Keele Univ BA74 Birm Univ
CQSW78. S'wark Ord Course 93. **d** 95 **p** 96. NSM Hatcham

St Cath *S'wark* 95-99; Dep Chapl HM Pris Brixton 99-02; Chapl
HM Pris Wormwood Scrubs from 02. *HM Prison Wormwood
Scrubs, Du Cane Road, London W12 0TU* Tel (020) 8588 3200 *or*
7207 0756 Fax 8749 5655 E-mail ar.tyler@ntlworld.com

TYLER, Andrew. b 57. Univ of Wales (Lamp) BA79 Warw Univ
MA80 Man Univ BD86. Coll of Resurr Mirfield 83. **d** 87 **p** 88. C
Glen Parva and S Wigston *Leic* 87-90; C Didcot All SS *Ox*
90-92; Asst Chapl Chu Hosp Ox 92-93; NSM Caversham
St Andr *Ox* 93-97; Co-ord Tr Portfolio (Berks) 96-97; P-in-c Nor
St Giles *Nor* 97-99; P-in-c Norwich St Mary Magd w St Jas 99-00;
V from 00. *St Mary's Vicarage, 10 Crome Road, Norwich
NR3 4RQ* Tel (01603) 661381 Fax as telephone
E-mail xatyler@aol.com

TYLER, Brian Sidney. b 32. MIPI79. Chich Th Coll 62. **d** 64 **p** 65.
C Brighton St Mich *Chich* 64-69; C-in-c Southwick St Pet 69-75;
Perm to Offic 80; NSM Brighton Resurr 93-94; Chapl
St Dunstan's Hosp Brighton 93-95; C Brighton St Matthias *Chich*
95-02; Hon C from 02; rtd 02. *318 Ditchling Road, Brighton
BN1 6JG* Tel (01273) 559292

TYLER, David Stuart. b 69. Hull Univ BSc91 ACA94. Wycliffe
Hall Ox 01. **d** 03. C Ashby-de-la-Zouch St Helen w Coleorton
Leic from 03. *5 Ullswater Crescent, Ashby-de-la-Zouch
LE65 1FH* Tel (01530) 413166
E-mail catherine@somervilletyler.freeserve.co.uk

TYLER (née FOSTER), Mrs Frances Elizabeth. b 55. Linc Th
Coll 81. **dss** 84 **d** 87 **p** 94. Hampton All SS *Lon* 84-87; Par Dn
Brentford 87-91; NSM Walsgrave on Sowe *Cov* from 91; Dioc
Adv for Women's Min from 97. *The Vicarage, 4 Farber Road,
Coventry CV2 2BG* Tel (024) 7661 5152
E-mail revftyler@aol.com

TYLER, Mrs Gaynor. b 46. Univ of Wales (Abth) BA68. S'wark
Ord Course 87. **d** 90 **p** 94. NSM Reigate St Luke S Park *S'wark*
90-97; Maelienydd *S & B* from 97. *Dyffryn Farm, Llanwrthwl,
Llandrindod Wells LD1 6NU* Tel (01597) 811017

TYLER, Graham Reginald. b 25. CEng65 Aber Univ CertCS95.
Moray Ord Course 90. **d** 95. Hon C Thurso *Mor* from 95. Hon C
Wick from 95. *11 Houston Terrace, Thurso KW14 8PX* Tel
(01847) 893876 E-mail grahamtyler@easicom.com

TYLER, John Arthur Preston. b 19. Em Coll Cam BA42 MA46.
Wycliffe Hall Ox 42. **d** 44 **p** 45. C Rodbourne Cheney *Bris* 44-47;
C Worthing Ch Ch *Chich* 48-50; C Streatham Park St Alb *S'wark*
50-59; R Wickhambreaux and Stodmarsh *Cant* 59-65; R
Ickham w Wickhambreaux and Stodmarsh 65-85; rtd 85; Perm
to Offic *Ox* 86-89; Perm to Offic *Cant* from 89. *Church Orchard,
Church Lane, Kingston, Canterbury CT4 6HY* Tel (01227)
830193

TYLER, John Thorne. b 46. Selw Coll Cam BA68 MA71 Ex Univ
DipEd70. Sarum & Wells Th Coll 70. **d** 72 **p** 73. C Frome St Jo
B & W 72-74; Chapl Huish Coll Taunton 74-93; Hon C Stoke
St Gregory w Burrowbridge and Lyng *B & W* 77-93; P-in-c
Shepton Beauchamp w Barrington, Stocklinch etc 93-94; TV
Ilminster and Distr 94-98; rtd 99; Hon C Quantock Towers
B & W 99-01; P-in-c Stogursey w Fiddington from 01. *The
Rectory, High Street, Stogursey, Bridgwater TA5 1PL* Tel (01278)
732884 E-mail tyleruk@hotmail.com

TYLER, The Ven Leonard George. b 20. Liv Univ BA41 Ch Coll
Cam BA46 MA50. Westcott Ho Cam. **d** 43 **p** 44. C Toxteth Park
Ch Ch *Liv* 43-44; Ceylon 46-50; R Bradford cum Beswick *Man*
50-55; V Leigh St Mary 55-66; RD Leigh 57-62; Adn Rochdale
62-66; Prin Wm Temple Coll 66-73; R Easthampstead *Ox* 73-85;
rtd 85; Perm to Offic *Ox* from 85. *11 Ashton Place, Kintbury,
Hungerford RG15 9XS* Tel (01488) 658510

TYLER, Malcolm. b 56. Kent Univ BSc77 Cam Univ BA84.
Ridley Hall Cam 82. **d** 85 **p** 86. C Twickenham St Mary *Lon*
85-88; C Acton St Mary 88-91; V Walsgrave on Sowe *Cov* from
91. *The Vicarage, 4 Farber Road, Coventry CV2 2BG* Tel (024)
7661 5152 *or* 7661 8845 E-mail stmaryssowe@aol.com

TYLER, Samuel John. b 32. Lon Univ BD57. Oak Hill Th Coll
57. **d** 58 **p** 59. C W Ham All SS *Chelmsf* 58-61; V Berechurch
61-64; R Aythorpe w High and Leaden Roding 64-72; Perm to
Offic 73-74; P-in-c Gt Ilford St Jo 74-76; V 76-92; rtd 92. *21 Ash
Green, Canewdon, Rochford SS4 3QN* Tel (01702) 258526

TYLER (née WAITE), Mrs Sheila Margaret. b 25. SRN47 Lon
Univ DipTh73. Trin Coll Bris 71. **dss** 79 **d** 87 **p** 94. Easton H Trin
w St Gabr and St Lawr *Bris* 79-80; Westbury-on-Trym St Alb
81-85; rtd 85; Hon Par Dn Henleaze *Bris* 87-94; Hon C 94-95;
Chapl Stoke Park and Purdown Hosps Stapleton 88-90; Perm to
Offic *Bris* from 95; *B & W* 95-00; *Chich* 01-02. *6 Gracey Court,
Woodland Road, Broadclyst, Exeter EX5 3GA* Tel (01392)
462872

TYLER, William Stanley. b 12. Ripon Hall Ox 54. **d** 55 **p** 56. C
Upton *Ex* 55-58; V E Stonehouse 58-68; R Woodleigh and
Loddiswell 68-76; rtd 76. *clo Miss D A Tyler, 26 Fairmile House,
30 Twickenham Rd, Teddington TW11 8BA*

TYMMS, Canon Wilfrid Widdas. b 18. Ch Coll Cam BA40 MA44.
Linc Th Coll 40. **d** 41 **p** 42. C Gateshead St Jas *Dur* 41-45; Cam
Staff Sec SCM 45-47; Hon C Cambridge St Benedict *Ely* 45-47; S
Africa 47-53; R Stella *Dur* 53-59; V Stockton St Pet 59-70; Chapl
Stockton and Thornaby Hosp 59-70; R Middleton St Geo

70-78; Hon Can Dur Cathl 72-78; Can Res Dur Cathl 78-83; rtd 83. *clo P B Tymms Esq, The Magnolias, Pittington Road, Rainton Gate, Houghton-le-Spring DH5 9RG*

TYNDALE-BISCOE, William Francis (Brother Francis). b 04. Trin Coll Cam BA25 MA29. Westcott Ho Cam 27. **d** 28 **p** 29. SSF from 37; Lic to Offic *Sarum* 45-62; Cen Africa 62-74; Australia 74-77 and 86-98; Melanesia 77-86; rtd 86; Perm to Offic *Worc* from 99. *The Friary, St Philip's Church, 115 Corn Wall Street, Annerly, Qld, Australia 4103* Tel (01300) 341345 Fax 341293

TYNDALL, Daniel Frank. b 61. Aston Tr Scheme 90 Sarum & Wells Th Coll BTh93. **d** 93 **p** 94. C Wolverhampton *Lich* 93-96; Assoc V Bris St Mary Redcliffe w Temple etc *Bris* 96-01; V Earley St Nic *Ox* from 01. *St Nicolas' Vicarage, 53 Sutcliffe Avenue, Reading RG6 7JN* Tel 0118-966 3563 Fax as telephone E-mail danieltyndall@bigfoot.com

TYNDALL, Mrs Elizabeth Mary. b 30. St Andr Univ MA51 Hughes Hall Cam CertEd52 Birm Univ DPS81. Qu Coll Birm 81. **dss** 83 **d** 87 **p** 94. Rugby St Andr *Cov* 83-87; Par Dn Feltham *Lon* 87-91; rtd 92; NSM Vale of White Horse Deanery *Ox* from 93. *4 Folly View Road, Faringdon SN7 7DH* Tel (01367) 240977

TYNDALL, Jeremy Hamilton. b 55. St Jo Coll Nottm BTh81 LTh81. **d** 81 **p** 82. C Oakwood St Thos *Lon* 81-84; C Upper Holloway St Pet w St Jo 84-87; TV Halewood *Liv* 87-96; P-in-c Yardley St Edburgha *Birm* 96-99; V 99-01; R Eugene St Thos USA from 01. *St Thomas's Episcopal Church, 1465 Coburg Road, Eugene, OR 97401, USA* Tel (001) (541) 343 5241

TYNDALL, Simon James. b 54. LSE BSc(Econ)77 Lon Univ PGCE82 Open Univ MA98. St Jo Coll Nottm 88. **d** 90 **p** 91. C Yeovil w Kingston Pitney *B & W* 90-94; V Rastrick St Jo *Wakef* 94-01; TR Chippenham St Paul w Hardenhuish etc *Bris* from 01. *The Rectory, 9 Greenway Park, Chippenham SN15 1QG* Tel (01249) 657216 E-mail sjt@fish.co.uk

TYNDALL, Canon Timothy Gardner. b 25. Jes Coll Cam BA50. Wells Th Coll 50. **d** 51 **p** 52. C Warsop *S'well* 51-55; R Newark St Leon 55-60; V Sherwood 60-75; P-in-c Bishopwearmouth St Mich w St Hilda *Dur* 75-85; RD Wearmouth 75-85; Hon Can Dur Cathl 83-90; Chief Sec ACCM 85-90; rtd 90; Perm to Offic *Lon* and *S'wark* from 90. *29 Kingswood Road, London W4 5EU* Tel (020) 8994 4516

TYNEY, Canon James Derrick. b 33. TCD. **d** 62 **p** 63. C Ballynafeigh St Jude *D & D* 62-64; C Bangor St Comgall 64-69; I Clonallon w Warrenpoint 69-75; I Groomsport 75-00; Can Belf Cathl 93-00; Dioc Registrar *D & D* 97-00; rtd 00. *27 Sandringham Drive, Bangor BT20 5NA* Tel (028) 9145 5670

TYRER, Ms Jayne Linda. b 59. Goldsmiths' Coll Lon BA81 CertEd82. Sarum & Wells Th Coll 85. **d** 87 **p** 95. C Rochdale *Man* 87-88; Par Dn Heywood St Luke w All So 88-91; Hon Par Dn Burneside *Carl* from 91; Chapl Kendal Hosps 91-94; Chapl Westmorland Hosps NHS Trust 94-98; Chapl Morecambe Bay Hosps NHS Trust from 98. *St Oswald's Vicarage, Burneside, Kendal LA9 6QX* Tel (01539) 722015 E-mail revd.j.tyler@btinternet.com

TYREUS, Per Jonas Waldemar (Peter). b 45. Uppsala Univ 66. **p** 71. Sweden 71-00; C Pelton *Dur* 00-03; C Chester le Street from 03. *The Vicarage, Church Road, Pelton, Chester le Street DH2 1XB* Tel 0191-370 2204 E-mail peter@petertyreus.plus.com

TYRREL, John Cockett. b 16. Qu Coll Cam BA38 MA42. Ridley Hall Cam 38. **d** 40 **p** 41. C Southall H Trin *Lon* 40-43; Chapl RNVR 43-46; S Africa 46-50; Australia from 50; rtd 81; Perm to Offic *Canberra and Goulburn* from 81. *20/58 Shackleton Circuit, Mawson, ACT, Australia 2607* Tel (0061) (2) 6286 1317

TYRRELL, The Very Revd Charles Robert. b 51. SRN73 Open Univ BA80. Oak Hill Th Coll 74. **d** 77 **p** 78. C Halewood *Liv* 77-80; C St Helens St Helen 80-83; V Banks 83-88; New Zealand from 88; Can Wellington 88-94; Dean Nelson from 94. *The Deanery, 365 Trafalgar Street, Nelson, New Zealand* Tel (0064) (3) 548 8574 *or* 548 1008 Fax 548 3264 E-mail charles.tyrell@clear.net.nz

TYRRELL, Frank Englefield (Peter). b 20. DSC44 VRD. Qu Coll Birm 70. **d** 72 **p** 73. C S Gillingham *Roch* 72-76; Chapl N Staffs R Infirmary Stoke-on-Trent 76-78; Chapl Stoke-on-Trent City Gen Hosp 76-78; rtd 86; Perm to Offic *Lich* from 00. *42 Leamington Gardens, Maybank, Newcastle ST5 0JX* Tel (01782) 632478

TYRRELL, John Patrick Hammond. b 42. Cranmer Hall Dur 62. **d** 65 **p** 66. C Edin St Jo *Edin* 65-68; Chapl RN 68-72; Hong Kong 72-74 and 79-82; R Westborough *Guildf* 74-78; C Yateley *Win* 82-83; C-in-c Darby Green CD 83-88; V Darby Green 88-96; V Chineham 96-97; rtd 02. *5 Blacksmith's Court, Metheringham, Lincoln LN4 3YQ* Tel (01526) 322147

TYRRELL, Stephen Jonathan. b 39. Sheff Univ BA62. Clifton Th Coll. **d** 65 **p** 66. C Rodbourne Cheney *Bris* 65-68; C Lillington *Cov* 68-72; P-in-c Bishop's Itchington 73-78; V 78-86; V Kingston upon Hull St Nic *York* 86-92; TV Cheltenham St Mary, St Matt, St Paul and H Trin *Glouc* from 92. *85 Brunswick Street, St Paul's, Cheltenham GL50 4HA* Tel (01242) 524572

TYSOE, James Raymond. b 19. Qu Coll Birm 70. **d** 75 **p** 76. NSM Cov E *Cov* 75-85; NSM Cov Cathl 85-87; Perm to Offic *Glouc*

from 87. *Wisma Mulia, Bridge Road, Frampton on Severn, Gloucester GL2 7HE* Tel (01452) 740890

TYSON, Mrs Nigella Jane. b 44. RGN66 Kent Univ BA95. SEITE 96. **d** 97 **p** 98. NSM Aylesham w Adisham, Nonington w Wymynswold and Goodnestone etc *Cant* 97-00; P-in-c Kingsland w Eardisland, Aymestrey etc *Heref* from 00. *The Rectory, Kingsland, Leominster HR6 9QW* Tel (01568) 708255 Fax 708062 *or* 08701-324310 E-mail nigella@kingslandgroup.org.uk

TYSON, Canon William Edward Porter. b 25. St Cath Coll Cam BA49 MA52. Ridley Hall Cam 49. **d** 51 **p** 52. C Wilmslow *Ches* 51-54; C Astbury 54-57; V Macclesfield St Pet 57-62; V Over Tabley 62-70; V High Legh 62-70; CF (TA) 64-91; V Church Hulme *Ches* 70-91; Chapl Cranage Hall Hosp 70-91; Hon Can Ches Cathl *Ches* 82-91; RD Congleton 85-90; rtd 91; Perm to Offic *Ches* and *Carl* from 91. *59 Kirkhead Road, Allithwaite, Grange-over-Sands LA11 7DD* Tel (01539) 535291

U

UCHIDA, Job Minoru. b 28. St Paul's Univ Tokyo BA51. Cen Th Coll Tokyo. **d** 54 **p** 55. Japan 54-56 and 59-89; SSM 56-58; Chapl to Japanese in UK 89-99; Hon C W Acton St Martin *Lon* 95-99; rtd 99. *9 Park View Way, Mansfield NG18 2RN* Tel (01623) 656947

UDAL, Miss Joanna Elizabeth Margaret. b 64. SS Hild & Bede Coll Dur BSc86. Ripon Coll Cuddesdon BTh94. **d** 97 **p** 98. C Whitton St Aug *Lon* 97-00; Asst to Abp Sudan from 00. *Provincial Office, Episc Ch of the Sudan, PO Box 604, Khartoum, Sudan* Tel (00249) (11) 485718 Fax 485717 E-mail ecsprovince@hotmail.com

UDDIN, Mohan. b 52. Sussex Univ BA74 Lon Bible Coll MA87 Brunel Univ PhD98 Cam Univ MA02 PGCE75. Ridley Hall Cam 99. **d** 03. C Hornchurch St Andr *Chelmsf* from 03. *55A Chelmsford Drive, Upminster RM14 2PH* Tel (01708) 452705 E-mail mohan.uddin@btopenworld.com

UDY, John Francis. b 24. ACA51 FCA61 ATII65. EMMTC 78. **d** 81 **p** 82. NSM Kirton in Holland *Linc* 81-89; NSM Sutterton w Fosdyke and Algarkirk 89-94; rtd 94; Perm to Offic *Linc* 99-02. *26 Grosvenor Road, Frampton, Boston PE20 1DB* Tel (01205) 722043

UFFINDELL, David Wilfred George. b 37. Qu Coll Birm 72. **d** 75 **p** 76. NSM Harlescott *Lich* from 75. *13 Kenley Avenue, Heath Farm, Shrewsbury SY1 3HA* Tel (01743) 352029 Fax as telephone E-mail revuffindell@aol.com

UFFINDELL, Harold David. b 61. Down Coll Cam MA87. Wycliffe Hall Ox BA86 MA91 Oak Hill Th Coll 86. **d** 87 **p** 88. C Kingston Hill St Paul *S'wark* 87-91; C Surbiton St Matt 91-98; V Sunningdale *Ox* from 98. *The Vicarage, Sidbury Close, Sunningdale, Ascot SL5 0PD* Tel (01344) 620061 E-mail david@htpcsunn.freeserve.co.uk

UGANDA, Archbishop of. *See* MPALANYI-NKOYOYO, The Most Revd Livingstone

UGWUNNA, Sydney Chukwunma. b 45. Nebraska Wesleyan Univ BSc67 Univ of Nebraska, Linc MSc70 Wayne State Univ PhD79. Virginia Th Sem MDiv96. **d** 96 **p** 97. USA 96-98; C Knaresborough *Ripon* 98-02; Nigeria from 02. *St Stephen's Cathedral, Umuahia, Nigeria*

ULLMANN, Clair. *See* FILBERT-ULLMANN, Mrs Clair

UMPLEBY, Mark Raymond. b 70. Trin Coll Bris BA99. **d** 99 **p** 00. C Birstall *Wakef* 99-02; TV N Huddersfield from 02. *The Vicarage, 8 Oakdean, Fixby, Huddersfield HD2 2FA* Tel (01484) 358194 E-mail markumpleby@hotmail.com

UMZIMVUBU, Bishop of. *See* DAVIES, The Rt Revd Geoffrey Francis

UNDERDOWN, Steven. Hull Univ BSc75 CertEd76. **d** 88. CSWG from 82; Lic to Offic *Chich* from 88. *The Monastery, Crawley Down, Crawley RH10 4LH* Tel (01342) 712074

UNDERHILL, Edward Mark Thomas. b 24. Univ Coll Dur BA50. St Aid Birkenhead 50. **d** 52 **p** 53. C Meopham *Roch* 52-54; Kenya 55-57; PC Gateshead St Geo *Dur* 57-68; V Gateshead St Geo from 68. *St George's Vicarage, 327 Durham Road, Gateshead NE9 5AJ* Tel 0191-487 5587

UNDERHILL, Robin. b 31. Marymount Coll California BA89 Woodbury Univ California BSc90. Claremont Sch of Th MA92. **d** 93 **p** 94. USA 93-01; Asst P Beverly Hills All SS 93-00; Pastor San Fernando St Simon 00-01; rtd 01; P-in-c Stranraer *Glas* from 01; P-in-c Portpatrick from 01. *The New Parsonage, 2 Meadowbank, Stranraer DG9 0HF* Tel (01776) 705053

UNDERHILL, Stanley Robert. b 27. Cant Sch of Min. **d** 82 **p** 83. C New Addington *Cant* 82-84; C Cannock *Lich* 84-86; TV 86-88;

R Dymchurch w Burmarsh and Newchurch *Cant* 88-92; rtd 92; Chapl Menorca *Eur* 92-94; Perm to Offic *Cant* from 94. *4 Charles Cobb Close, Dymchurch, Romney Marsh TN29 0JQ* Tel (01303) 874726

UNDERWOOD, Adrian Anthony. b 67. **d** 02. C Sparkhill w Greet and Sparkbrook *Birm* from 02. *132 Oakwood Road, Sparkhill, Birmingham B11 4HD* Tel 0121-777 6093 Mobile 07752-001698 E-mail stjohns-sparkhill@charis.co.uk

UNDERWOOD, Brian. b 35. Dur Univ BA57 Keble Coll Ox PGCE76 Dur Univ MA72. Clifton Th Coll 57. **d** 59 **p** 60. C Blackpool Ch Ch *Blackb* 59-61; C New Malden and Coombe *S'wark* 61-64; Travel Sec Pathfinders 64-68; Chapl Chantilly *Eur* 68-69; Home Sec CCCS 69-71; P-in-c Gatten St Paul *Portsm* 71-72; Chapl Lyon w Grenoble and Aix-les-Bains *Eur* 72-75; Asst Chapl Trent Coll Nottm 76-80; Chapl Qu Eliz Gr Sch Blackb 80-85; R Bentham St Jo *Bradf* 85-92; V St Alb Ch Ch *St Alb* 92-00; rtd 00; Perm to Offic *St Alb* from 00. *16 Mitford Close, Bedford MK41 8RF* Tel (01234) 407856

UNDERWOOD, Charles Brian. b 23. Leeds Univ BA48 CertEd. Coll of Resurr Mirfield 48. **d** 50 **p** 51. C Tilehurst St Mich *Ox* 50-53; C Leic St Paul *Leic* 53-54; Youth Chapl 54-61; V Leic St Geo 57-59; R Harby 59-61; New Zealand 61-62; Dioc Youth Chapl *Bradf* 63-72; R Carleton-in-Craven 63-76; V Twyning *Glouc* 76-88; RD Tewkesbury 81-88; rtd 88; Perm to Offic *Glouc* from 00. *9 Ellendene Drive, Pamington, Tewkesbury GL20 8LU* Tel (01684) 772504

UNDERWOOD, David Richard. b 47. AKC69 St Osyth Coll of Educn PGCE72. St Aug Coll Cant 69. **d** 70 **p** 92. C Witham *Chelmsf* 70-71; Teacher 71-82; Hd Teacher Gt Heath Sch Mildenhall 82-91; NSM Chevington w Hargrave and Whepstead w Brockley *St E* 82-91; Par Dn Haverhill w Withersfield, the Wrattings etc 91-92; TV 92-94; P-in-c Bury St Edmunds St Jo 94-99; RD Thingoe 95-99; P-in-c Bury St Edmunds St Geo 98-99; Dir of Educn from 99. *7 Farrows Close, Chevington, Bury St Edmunds IP29 5QJ* Tel and fax (01284) 850610 Mobile 07710-522074 E-mail david@stedmundsbury.anglican.org

UNDERWOOD, Jack Maurice. b 13. Leeds Univ BA36 Lon Univ BD41. Coll of Resurr Mirfield 36. **d** 38 **p** 39. C Kidderminster St Mary and All SS, Trimpley etc *Worc* 38-40; C Hornsey St Mary *Lon* 40-42; Chapl RAFVR 42-46; V Middleton *Birm* 50-53; Prin Stroud Court Ox 60-71; Perm to Offic *Eur* 73-78; rtd 78. *Willow Lea, Hatford, Faringdon SN7 8JF* Tel (01367) 710364

UNDERWOOD, John Alan. b 40. Glos Coll of Arts & Tech BSc88 Ox Poly CertEd84 MBCS74. St Alb and Ox Min Course 96. **d** 99 **p** 00. OLM Eynsham and Cassington *Ox* from 99. *17 Witney Road, Eynsham, Oxford OX29 4PH* Tel (01865) 881254 *or* 301305 Fax 301301 E-mail junderw549@aol.com

UNGOED-THOMAS, Peter. b 27. Pemb Coll Ox BA51 MA67. St Mich Coll Llan. **d** 60 **p** 61. C Llangeinor *Llan* 60-64; 1 Dublin Donnybrook *D & G* 64-67; RAChD 67-70; Chapl Leigh C of E Schs 70-74; C Leigh St Mary *Man* 70-74; Lect Warley Coll 74-86; Perm to Offic *Birm* and *St D* from 75; Lect Sandwell Coll of F&HE from 86; rtd 94. *93 Heol Felin-Foel, Llanelli SA15 3JQ*

UNITED STATES OF AMERICA, Presiding Bishop of. *See* GRISWOLD, The Most Revd Frank Tracy

✠**UNO, The Most Revd James Toru.** c 98. Bp Kita Kanto from 98; Primate of Nippon Seikokai from 02. *NSKK Provincial Office, 65 Yarai-cho, Shinjuku-ku, Tokyo, 162-0805, Japan* Tel (0081) (48) 642 2680 Fax 648 0358 *or* 476 7484

UNSWORTH, Philip James. b 41. UEA BEd82 Nottm Coll of Educn CertEd63 Nottm Univ DipEd72. EAMTC 94. **d** 97 **p** 98. NSM Hethersett w Canteloff w Lt and Gt Melton *Nor* 97-00; P-in-c Blofield w Hemblington from 00. *The Rectory, 10 Oakwood, Blofield, Norwich NR13 4JQ* Tel (01603) 713160

UNSWORTH, Thomas Foster. b 28. Lon Univ BA56. Lich Th Coll 60. **d** 62 **p** 63. C Northfield *Birm* 62-64; C The Lickey 64-66; V Forcett *Ripon* 66-68; V Leyburn 68-73; V Bellerby 68-73; Chapl Whittingham Hosp Preston 73-79; V Freckleton *Blackb* 79-83; V S Yardley St Mich *Birm* 83-86; V Sutton w Carlton and Normanton upon Trent etc *S'well* 86-90; rtd 90; Chapl St Raphaël *Eur* 90-97; Perm to Offic *Cant* from 99. *4 Elm House, Bartholomew Street, Hythe CT21 5BY*

UNWIN, Christopher Michael Fairclough. b 31. Dur Univ BA57. Linc Th Coll 65. **d** 67 **p** 68. C S Shields St Hilda w St Thos *Dur* 67-73; R Tatsfield *S'wark* 73-81; RE Adv to Ch Secondary Schs 73-81; V Newc St Gabr *Newc* 81-96; RD Newc E 96; rtd 96; Perm to Offic *Dur* and *Newc* from 96. *2 The Cottage, West Row, Greatham, Hartlepool TS25 2HW* Tel (01429) 872781

UNWIN, Lindsay Charles Philip. b 17. Magd Coll Cam BA39 MA63. Qu Coll Birm 39. **d** 40 **p** 41. C Benwell St Jas *Newc* 40-44; V 55-63; C Sugley 44-47; V Horton 47-55; Adn Northd and Can Res Newc Cathl 63-82; Perm to Offic from 82; rtd 82. *60 Sandringham Avenue, Benton, Newcastle upon Tyne NE12 8JX* Tel 0191-270 0418

UNWIN, The Ven Kenneth. b 26. St Edm Hall Ox BA48 MA52. Ely Th Coll 49. **d** 51 **p** 52. C Leeds All SS *Ripon* 51-55; C Dur St Marg *Dur* 55-59; V Dodworth *Wakef* 59-69; V Royston 69-73; V Wakef St Jo 73-82; Hon Can Wakef Cathl 80-82; RD Wakef

80-81; Adn Pontefract 82-92; rtd 92; Perm to Offic *Bradf* and *Wakef* from 92. *2 Rockwood Close, Skipton BD23 1UG* Tel (01756) 791323

UPCOTT, Derek Jarvis. b 26. CEng FIMechE FBIM. S'wark Ord Course 81. **d** 84 **p** 85. NSM Gt Chesham *Ox* from 84; Perm to Offic *St Alb* 90-99; Perm to Offic *Ox* from 99. *Bluff Cottage, Blackthorne Lane, Ballinger, Great Missenden HP16 9LN* Tel (01494) 837505

UPHILL, Ms Ann Carol. b 54. Westcott Ho Cam 95. **d** 97 **p** 98. C Strood St Nic w St Mary *Roch* 97-01; R Footscray w N Cray from 01. *The Rectory, Rectory Lane, Sidcup DA14 5BP* Tel and fax (020) 8300 7096 Mobile 07802-883121 E-mail annuphill@lineone.net

UPHILL, Keith Ivan. b 35. Keble Coll Ox BA70 MA74. Wycliffe Hall Ox 67. **d** 70 **p** 71. C Maghull *Liv* 70-73; V Wroxall *Portsm* 73-77; TV Fareham H Trin 77-82; C Havant 82-84; P-in-c Merton St Jo *S'wark* 84-85; V 85-95; rtd 95; Perm to Offic *Portsm* from 95. *20 Wilby Lane, Anchorage Park, Portsmouth PO3 5UF* Tel (023) 9266 6998

UPPER SHIRE, Bishop of. *See* MALANGO, The Most Revd Bernard Amos

UPRICHARD, Jervis. b 17. **d** 42 **p** 43. C Kilmegan w Maghera *D & D* 42-45; C Ballymacarrett St Patr 45-46; C Kilmegan 46-47; C Belfast St Aid *Conn* 48-50; I Naas w Killashee *M & K* 50-53; I Outeragh w Fenagh *K, E & A* 53-60; V Edgeside *Man* 60-66; rtd 82; Perm to Offic *Man* 82-91. *c/o Miss A Uprichard, 6 Murray Terrace, Ladywell, Motherwell ML1 3PZ*

UPTON, Anthony Arthur. b 30. Leic Univ MA97. Wells Th Coll 61. **d** 63 **p** 64. C Milton *Portsm* 63-67; Chapl RN 67-83; V Foleshill St Laur *Cov* 83-91; rtd 91; Perm to Offic *Cov* from 91. *Redlands Bungalow, Banbury Road, Lighthorne CV35 0AH*

UPTON, Ms Caroline Tracey. b 67. Lon Univ BMus90 Edin Univ BD94. Edin Th Coll 91. **d** 94 **p** 95. C Edin St Martin *Edin* 94-96; Hon C Edin St Pet 97-99; C 99-01; Chapl Lothian Univ Hosps NHS Trust from 99. *10 (3F1) Montagu Terrace, Edinburgh EH3 5QX* Tel 0131-552 0731 E-mail cu.olut@care4free.net

UPTON, Christopher Martin. b 53. Bp Grosseteste Coll CertEd74. EAMTC 94. **d** 97 **p** 98. NSM Gorleston St Andr *Nor* from 97. *27 Curlew Way, Bradwell, Great Yarmouth NR31 8QX* Tel (01493) 668184

UPTON, Clement Maurice. b 49. Linc Th Coll 88. **d** 90 **p** 91. C Northampton St Alb *Pet* 90-93; V Laxey *S & M* 93-96; V Lonan 93-96; V Hipswell *Ripon* 96-01; V Wellingborough St Andr *Pet* from 01. *St Andrew's Vicarage, Berrymoor Road, Wellingborough NN8 2HU* Tel (01933) 222692

UPTON, Donald George Stanley. b 16. Peterho Cam BA38 MA44. Westcott Ho Cam 39. **d** 40 **p** 41. C Ashbourne w Mapleton *Derby* 40-43; V Mackworth All SS 43-51; Chapl Bps' Coll Cheshunt 51-54; Chapl Haileybury Coll 54-58; Qu Eliz Gr Sch Barnet 59-60; Alleyne's Gr Sch Stevenage 60-69; Lic to Offic *St Alb* 69-97; Perm to Offic from 97; Chapl St Alb High Sch for Girls 69-73; Ch Hosp Sch Hertf 73-80; rtd 80. *2 The Square, Braughing, Ware SG11 2QS*

UPTON, Ms Julie. b 61. Ripon Coll Cuddesdon 87. **d** 88 **p** 94. C Kirkstall *Ripon* 88-91; Par Dn E Greenwich Ch Ch w St Andr and St Mich *S'wark* 91-94; C 94; Perm to Offic from 01; *St E* from 02. *29 Avondale Road, Shipley BD18 4QR* Tel 0113-278 3779

UPTON, Michael Gawthorne. b 29. AKC53. **d** 54 **p** 55. C Middleton *Man* 54-57; C Plymouth St Andr *Ex* 57-59; Dep Dir of Educn *Cant* 59-63; Hon C Riverhead *Roch* 63-70; Youth Chapl 63-70; Lic to Offic *Ex* 70-94; Chr Aid Area Sec (Devon and Cornwall) 70-94; Chr Aid SW Region Co-ord 73-89; rtd 94; Perm to Offic *Ex* from 94. *Otter Dell, Harpford, Sidmouth EX10 0NH* Tel (01395) 568448

UPTON, Mrs Susan Dorothy. b 53. Bp Grosseteste Coll CertEd74 Nottm Univ BEd75. EAMTC 99. **d** 02 **p** 03. NSM Bradwell *Nor* from 02. *27 Curlew Way, Bradwell, Great Yarmouth NR31 8QX* Tel (01493) 668184 E-mail sue-upton@talk21.com

UPTON-JONES, Peter John. b 38. Selw Coll Cam BA63 MA67 Liv Univ CertEd64. N Ord Course 90. **d** 92 **p** 93. NSM Formby H Trin *Liv* 92-00; P-in-c Lezayre St Olave Ramsey *S & M* from 00; P-in-c Kirkbride from 00. *The Rectory, Bride, Isle of Man IM7 4AT* Tel (01624) 880351

URMSON-TAYLOR, Ralph. *See* TAYLOR, Ralph Urmson

✠**URQUHART, The Rt Revd David Andrew.** b 52. Ealing Business Sch BA77. Wycliffe Hall Ox 82. **d** 84 **p** 85 **c** 00. C Kingston upon Hull St Nic *York* 84-87; TV Drypool 87-92; V Cov H Trin *Cov* 92-00; Hon Can Cov Cathl 99-00; Suff Bp Birkenhead *Ches* from 00. *Bishop's Lodge, 67 Bidston Road, Prenton CH43 6TR* Tel 0151-652 2741 Fax 651 2330 E-mail bpbirkenhead@chester.anglican.org

URQUHART, Canon Edmund Ross. b 39. Univ Coll Ox BA62 DipTh63 MA68. St Steph Ho Ox 62. **d** 64 **p** 65. C Millтом *Win* 64-69; C Norton *Derby* 69-73; V Bakewell from 73; RD Bakewell and Eyam from 95; Hon Can Derby Cathl from 02. *The Vicarage, South Church Street, Bakewell DE45 1FD* Tel (01629) 812256 Fax 814457

URQUHART, Ian Garnham. b 46. Univ Coll Lon LLB71 Univ Coll Ches 97. Wycliffe Hall Ox 98. **d** 99 **p** 00. NSM Barnston

Ches from 99. *5 St Peter's Close, Heswall, Wirral CH60 0DU* Tel and fax 0151-342 3588 Mobile 07770-823373 E-mail ian@papintalo.demon.co.uk

URSELL, David John. b 45. R Agric Coll Cirencester NDA70 MRAC70. SW Minl Tr Course 92. **d** 95 **p** 96. NSM Dolton *Ex* from 95; Rural Convenor from 95. *Aller Farm, Dolton, Winkleigh EX19 8PP* Tel (01805) 804414 *or* 804737

URSELL, Philip Elliott. b 42. Univ of Wales BA66 Ox Univ MA82. St Steph Ho Ox 66. **d** 68 **p** 69. C Newton Nottage *Llan* 68-71; Asst Chapl Univ of Wales (Cardiff) 71-77; Chapl Wales Poly 74-77; Lic to Offic *Llan* from 77; Chapl Em Coll Cam 77-82; Prin Pusey Ho Ox 82-02; Warden Ascot Priory from 85; Lic to Offic *Ox* from 82. *St Edward's, Ascot Priory, Priory Road, Ascot SL5 8RT* Tel (01344) 885157 Fax as telephone E-mail ascot.priory@ic24.net

✠**URWIN, The Rt Revd Lindsay Goodall.** b 55. Ripon Coll Cuddesdon 77. **d** 80 **p** 81 **c** 93. C Walworth *S'wark* 80-83; V N Dulwich St Faith 83-88; Dioc Missr *Chich* 88-93; OGS from 91; Can and Preb Chich Cathl *Chich* from 93; Area Bp Horsham from 94. *Bishop's House, 21 Guildford Road, Horsham RH12 1LU* Tel (01403) 211139 Fax 217349 E-mail bishhorsham@clara.net

URWIN, Preb Roger Talbot. b 22. Ex Coll Ox BA43 MA47. Sarum Th Coll 48. **d** 50 **p** 50. C Weymouth H Trin *Sarum* 50-53; V Netheravon w Fittleton 53-57; CF (R of O) 56-57; V Townstall w Dartmouth *Ex* 57-66; V Dartmouth St Petrox 58-66; RD Ipplepen 61-66; V Littleham w Exmouth 66-72; TR 72-87; RD Aylesbeare 69-73; P-in-c Withycombe Raleigh 72-74; Preb Ex Cathl 82-87; rtd 87; Perm to Offic *Truro* from 87. *Bishop's Lodge, Kelly Park, St Mabyn, Bodmin PL30 3RL* Tel (01208) 841606

USHER, George. b 30. Univ of Wales (Swansea) BSc51. St Deiniol's Hawarden 73. **d** 75 **p** 76. NSM Clun w Chapel Lawn *Heref* 75-78; NSM Clun w Chapel Lawn, Bettws-y-Crwyn and Newcastle 79-80; C Shrewsbury St Giles *Lich* 80-83; C Shrewsbury St Giles w Sutton and Atcham 83-84; R Credenhill w Brinsop and Wormsley etc *Heref* 84-98; rtd 98. *1 Trinity Court, The Esplanade, Sidmouth EX10 8BE* Tel (01395) 513889 E-mail georgeusher@clara.net

USHER, Graham Barham. b 70. Edin Univ BSc93 CCC Cam BA95 MA00. Westcott Ho Cam CTM96 St Nic Th Coll Ghana 96. **d** 96 **p** 97. C Nunthorpe *York* 96-99; V N Ormesby from 99. *The Vicarage, James Street, North Ormesby, Middlesbrough TS3 6LD* Tel (01642) 271814 E-mail gbu@compuserve.com

USHER, Robin Reginald. b 50. AKC74. St Aug Coll Cant 75. **d** 76 **p** 77. C Hulme Ascension *Man* 76-80; P-in-c Newall Green St Fran 80-85; C Atherton 85-87; TV 87-90; V Leigh St Jo 90-99; Chapl Wigan and Leigh Health Services NHS Trust 93-99; V Milnrow *Man* from 99. *The Vicarage, 40 Eafield Avenue, Milnrow, Rochdale OL16 3UN* Tel (01706) 642988

USHER-WILSON, Lucian Neville. b 36. Linc Coll Ox MA63 St Andr Univ DipEd64 Open Univ DipEd. St Steph Ho Ox 91. **d** 94 **p** 96. NSM Compton and Otterbourne *Win* 94-96; NSM Shill Valley and Broadshire *Ox* from 96. *The Tallat, Westwell, Burford OX18 4JT* Tel (01993) 822464

UTLEY, Canon Edward Jacob. b 24. AKC52. **d** 53 **p** 54. C Pontefract St Giles *Wakef* 53-56; C Bexhill St Pet *Chich* 56-60; Chapl Asst Bexhill Hosp 56-60; Chapl Dudley Road Hosp Birm 60-89; RD Birm City *Birm* 75-82; Hon Can Birm Cathl 80-89; rtd 89; Perm to Offic *Birm* from 89. *St Raphael, 50 Wheatsheaf Road, Edgbaston, Birmingham B16 0RY* Tel 0121-454 2666

UTTLEY, Mrs Valerie Gail. b 43. Man Univ BA64. N Ord Course 80. **dss** 83 **d** 87 **p** 94. Otley *Bradf* 83-87; Hon Par Dn 87-89; Par Dn Calverley 89-92; Ind Chapl *Ripon* 92-97; C Kirkstall 95-97; V Lofthouse from 97. *The Vicarage, 8 Church Farm Close, Lofthouse, Wakefield WF3 3SA* Tel (01924) 823286

V

VAIL, David William. b 30. Dur Univ BA56 Sheff Univ DipEd71. Oak Hill Th Coll 56. **d** 58 **p** 59. C Toxteth Park St Bede *Liv* 58-61; Kenya 61-77; Chapl Versailles *Eur* 77-82; Gen Sec Rwanda Miss 82-88; V Virginia Water *Guildf* 88-96; rtd 96; Perm to Offic *Ox* from 98. *36 Silverthorne Drive, Caversham, Reading RG4 7NS* Tel 0118-954 6667

VAIZEY, Martin John. b 37. AKC64. **d** 65 **p** 66. C Bishopwearmouth Gd Shep *Dur* 65-69; C Darlington H Trin 69-72; V Easington Colliery 72-80; C-in-c Bishopwearmouth St Mary V w St Pet CD 80-85; V Sunderland Springwell w Thorney Close 85-88; R Witton Gilbert 88-96; P-in-c Wingate Grange 96-99; V Wheatley Hill and Wingate w Hutton Henry from 99. *The Vicarage, North Road East, Wingate TS28 5BW* Tel (01429) 837968

VALE, Thomas Stanley George. b 52. Chich Th Coll 85. **d** 87 **p** 88. C Leic St Phil *Leic* 87-90; C Knighton St Mary Magd 90-93; P-in-c Leic St Chad 93-97; V 97-01; V Blackfordby and Woodville from 01. *11 Vicarage Close, Blackfordby, Swadlincote DE11 8AZ* Tel (01524) 219445 E-mail tvale@webleicester.co.uk

VALENTINE, Derek William. b 24. S'wark Ord Course 65. **d** 68 **p** 69. NSM Battersea St Luke *S'wark* 68-77; NSM Fenstanton *Ely* 77-88; Perm to Offic *Bradf* 88-96. *Address withheld by request*

VALENTINE, Hugh William James. b 56. Bradf Univ BA83 CQSW. S'wark Ord Course 86. **d** 89 **p** 90. NSM Stoke Newington Common St Mich *Lon* 89-92; NSM Westmr St Jas from 92. *12 Louisa Gardens, London E1 4NG* Tel (020) 7790 1884 E-mail hugh.valentine@dlondon.org.uk

VALENTINE, Jeremy Wilfred. b 38. NW Ord Course 76. **d** 79 **p** 80. C Cundall *Ripon* 79-82; TV Huntington *York* 82-87; V Sand Hutton from 87; RD Buckrose and Bulmer and Malton 98-02. *The Vicarage, Sand Hutton, York YO41 1LB* Tel (01904) 468443 Fax 468670 E-mail jeremyvalentine@tinyworld.co.uk

VALENTINE, John Harvey. b 63. Ch Ch Ox BA85 MA85. Ridley Hall Cam BA92. **d** 93 **p** 94. C Heigham H Trin *Nor* 93-97; C Ches Square St Mich w St Phil *Lon* 97-00; C Brompton H Trin w Onslow Square St Paul 00-02; P-in-c Holborn St Geo w H Trin and St Bart from 02. *7 Russell Square Mansions, 122 Southampton Row, London WC1B 5AE* Tel (020) 7404 9606 Mobile 07736-066091 Fax (020) 7831 0588 E-mail jhvalen@aol.com

VALIANT, Mrs Lesley Jean. b 51. Whitelands Coll Lon CertEd74 Univ Coll Chich BA99. STETS 99. **d** 01 **p** 02. NSM Bedhampton *Portsm* from 01. *14 Peacock Close, Fareham PO16 8YG* Tel (01329) 282995 Mobile 07751-168228 E-mail valiants@globalnet.co.uk

VALLINS, Canon Christopher. b 43. Lich Th Coll 63. **d** 66 **p** 67. C Cuddington *Guildf* 66-70; C Aldershot St Mich 70-73; V W Ewell 73-81; R Worplesdon 81-89; Chapl Merrist Wood Coll of Agric 81-89; RD Guildf 86-89; Chapl Epsom Health Care NHS Trust 89-99; Chapl Horton Hosp Epsom 95-98; Bp's Adv on Healing *Guildf* from 97; Hon Can Guildf Cathl from 01; Sen Chapl Epsom and St Helier NHS Trust from 99. *Little Watermead, Reigate Road, Hookwood, Horley RH6 0HD* Tel (01293) 824188 E-mail chrisvallins@yahoo.com

VALLIS, Brett Paul Stanley. b 72. G&C Coll Cam BA93 St Jo Coll Dur BA01. Cranmer Hall Dur 99. **d** 02 **p** 03. C Monkseaton St Mary *Newc* from 02. *89 Queen's Road, Monkseaton, Whitley Bay NE26 3AS* E-mail vallisbrett@yahoo.co.uk

VAN BEVEREN, Susan Margaret. b 64. **d** 96. NSM Amsterdam w Den Helder and Heiloo *Eur* 96-03; Officer for Miss in Work and Economic Life *Ox* from 03. *14 Elm Road, Reading RG6 5TS* Tel 0118-986 4718 E-mail susanvb@bevesconsulting.com

VAN CARRAPIETT, Timothy Michael James. b 39. Chich Th Coll 66. **d** 63 **p** 64. C Sugley *Newc* 63-65; C Newc St Fran 65-69; P-in-c Wrangbrook w N Elmsall CD *Wakef* 69-74; P-in-c Flushing *Truro* 74-75; P-in-c Mylor w Flushing 75-76; P-in-c St Day 76-82; R Aldrington *Chich* 82-87; V Bexhill St Barn 87-01; rtd 01; Perm to Offic *St E* from 01. *Bear-Wuff Cottage, 9 Tacon Road, Felixstowe IP11 2DT* Tel (01394) 271338

VAN CULIN, Canon Samuel. b 30. OBE. Princeton Univ AB52. Virginia Th Sem DB55 Hon DD77 Gen Th Sem NY Hon DD83. **d** 55 **p** 56. USA 55-83; Sec Gen ACC 83-94; Hon C All Hallows by the Tower etc *Lon* from 89; Hon Can Cathl *Cant* 83-94; Hon Can Ibadan from 83; Hon Can Jerusalem from 84; Hon Can S Africa from 89; Hon Can Honolulu from 91; rtd 94. *16A Burgate, Canterbury CT1 2HG* Tel (01227) 458018

VAN D'ARQUE, Christopher Simon Wayne. b 62. St Jo Coll Dur BA99. **d** 99 **p** 00. C Letchworth St Paul w Willian *St Alb* 99-02; C Westminster St Jas the Less *Lon* 02-03; V W Bessacarr *Sheff* from 03. *The Vicarage, 39 Sturton Close, Doncaster DN4 7JG* Tel (01302) 538487 E-mail clan.vandarque@virgin.net

VAN DE KASTEELE, Peter John. b 39. Magd Coll Cam BA61 MA65. Clifton Th Coll 61. **d** 63 **p** 64. C Eastbourne H Trin *Chich* 63-66; C N Pickenham w S Pickenham etc *Nor* 66-70; R Mursley w Swanbourne and Lt Horwood *Ox* 70-80; Admin Sec Clinical Th Assn from 83; Gen Dir 88-99; Perm to Offic *Glouc* from 83; Hon C Westcote w Icomb and Bledington 88-89; rtd 99. *St Mary's Home, Church Westcote, Chipping Norton OX7 6SF* Tel (01993) 830193

van de WEYER, Robert William Bates. b 50. Lanc Univ BA76. S'wark Ord Course 78. **d** 81 **p** 82. Warden Lt Gidding Community from 77; Hon C Gt w Lt Gidding and Steeple Gidding *Ely* 81-83; P-in-c 83-93; P-in-c Winwick 83-93; P-in-c Hamerton 83-93; P-in-c Upton and Copmanford 83-93; Perm to Offic from 93. *Woodend, Upton, Huntingdon PE28 5YF* Tel (01480) 890333

VAN DEN BERG, Jan Jacob. b 56. Sarum & Wells Th Coll 86. **d** 88 **p** 89. C Glouc St Aldate *Glouc* 88-91; C Ollerton w Boughton *S'well* 91-95; P-in-c Scrooby 95-00; P-in-c Blyth 97-00; C Brampton and Farlam and Castle Carrock w Cumrew *Carl* 00-02; TV Eden, Gelt and Irthing from 02. *The Vicarage, Hayton, Brampton CA8 9HR* Tel (01228) 670248 E-mail jan@vandenberg.fsnet.co.uk

VAN DEN BERGH, Victor Michael Cornelius. b 53. Lon Bible Coll ALBC92. Ridley Hall Cam 02. **d** 03. C Tamworth *Lich* from 03. *19 Perrycrofts Crescent, Tamworth B79 8UA* Tel (01827) 65926 Mobile 07770-900712 E-mail vic_vdb@btinternet.com

van den HOF, Ariadne Rolanda Magdalena. b 71. Univ of Wales (Cardiff) MTh96. Old Cath Sem Amersfoort 90 St Mich Coll Llan 98. **d** 99 **p** 00. C Dolgellau w Llanfachreth and Brithdir etc *Ban* 99-01; Min Can Ban Cathl 01-02; P-in-c Trefdraeth w Aberffraw, Llangadwaladr etc from 02. *The Rectory, 1 Maes Glas, Bethel, Bodorgan LL62 5NW* Tel (01407) 840190 E-mail ariadne@telco4u.net

van der LINDE, Herbert John. b 43. Rhodes Univ BA66. Coll of Resurr Mirfield. **d** 68 **p** 69. C Kingston St Luke *S'wark* 68-75; C Chipping Campden w Ebrington *Glouc* 75-78; V Cheltenham St Pet 78-84; V Bussage from 84. *St Michael's Vicarage, Bussage, Stroud GL6 8BB* Tel (01453) 883556

VAN DER PUMP, Charles Lyndon. b 25. FRCM. S'wark Ord Course 86. **d** 88 **p** 89. NSM Primrose Hill St Mary w Avenue Road St Paul *Lon* from 88. *48 Canfield Gardens, London NW6 3EB* Tel (020) 7624 4517 Fax as telephone

VAN DER TOORN, Mrs Stephne. b 53. Natal Univ BA73. **d** 93 **p** 95. NSM Pretoria St Mary S Africa 93-01; C Fawley *Win* from 01. *15 Long Lane Close, Holbury, Southampton SO45 2LE* Tel (023) 8089 1809 Mobile 07984-026897 E-mail vandertoorn@btinternet.com

van der VALK, Jesse. b 59. Nottm Univ BTh84 Birm Univ MPhil88 Avery Hill Coll PGCE85. St Jo Coll Nottm 81. **d** 88 **p** 89. C Droitwich Spa *Worc* 88-92; V Hartshead and Hightown *Wakef* 92-96; R Woolwich St Mary w St Mich *S'wark* from 96; USPG (Lon Volunteers and Co-workers Team) from 97. *The Rectory, 43 Rectory Place, London SE18 5DA* Tel (020) 8854 2302 E-mail jessevdvalk@aol.com

VAN KOEVERING, Mrs Helen Elizabeth Parsons. b 60. SS Hild & Bede Coll Dur BA82 Trin Coll Bris MPhil99. S Wales Ord Course 01. **d** 02 **p** 03. C Bettws *Mon* 02-03; Bp's Sec Niassa Mozambique from 03. *CP 264, Lichinga, Niassa, Mozambique* Tel (00258) 712 0735 Fax as telephone E-mail mark@koev.freeserve.co.uk *or* diocese.niassa@teledata.mz

✠**VAN KOEVERING, The Rt Revd Mark Allan.** b 57. Michigan State Univ BSc79 MSc85. Trin Coll Bris BA99. **d** 99 **p** 00 **c** 03. C Bettws *Mon* 99-01; P-in-c 01-03; Bp Niassa Mozambique from 03. *Diocese do Niassa, CP 264, Lichinga, Niassa, Mozambique* Tel (00258) 712 0735 Fax as telephone E-mail mark@koev.freeserve.co.uk *or* diocese.niassa@teledata.mz

VAN LEER, Samuel Wall. b 67. Virginia Univ BA90 California Univ MA91 St Jo Coll Dur BA01. Cranmer Hall Dur 99. **d** 02 **p** 03. C Berne w Neuchâtel *Eur* from 02. *St Ursula's Church, Jubiläumsplatz 2, CH-3005 Berne, Switzerland* Tel (0041) (31) 352 8567 Mobile (078) 726 4687 Fax (31) 351 0548

VAN LEEUWEN, Canon Dirk Willem. b 45. Utrecht Univ LLD71. Th Faculty Brussels 71 S'wark Ord Course 80. **d** 82 **p** 83. Asst Chapl Brussels Cathl *Eur* 82-84; Chapl Haarlem 84-93; Chapl Antwerp St Boniface from 94; Chapl Charleroi 94-00; P-in-c Ypres 97-99; P-in-c Leuven 98-99; Can Brussels Cathl from 96; Chapl Knokke from 01; P-in-c Ostend from 01; P-in-c Bruges 01-03; V Gen to Bp Eur from 02. *Grétrystraat 39, B-2018 Antwerp, Belgium* Tel (0032) (3) 239 3339 Fax 230 4797 E-mail dirk.vanleeuwen@pi.be

VAN STRAATEN, Christopher Jan. b 55. Bris Univ BA77 Natal Univ HDipEd78. Oak Hill Th Coll DipHE92. **d** 92 **p** 93. C Woodley *Ox* 92-96; V Gillingham St Aug *Roch* from 96. *St Augustine's Vicarage, Rock Avenue, Gillingham ME7 5PW* Tel (01634) 850288 E-mail chris.vanstraaten@sagk.org.uk

van WENGEN, Rosemary Margaret. b 38. Westf Coll Lon BA60 Univ of Leiden MA77 PhD81. SEITE 98. **d** 01 **p** 02. NSM Benenden *Cant* from 01. *Beach House, Grange Road, St Michaels, Tenterden TN30 6EF* Tel (01580) 764857 Fax 761405 E-mail rvanwengen@aol.com

VAN ZANDBERGEN, Karen. *See* BURNETT-HALL, Mrs Karen

VANDERSTOCK, Alan. b 31. St Jo Coll Dur BA57. Cranmer Hall Dur DipTh59. **d** 59 **p** 60. C Kersal Moor *Man* 59-62; C-in-c Lower Kersal CD 63-67; Lic Preacher *Cant* from 67; Sen Tutor Heath Clark High Sch Croydon 73-83; Dep Hd Teacher Norbury Manor High Sch Croydon 83-86; Sen Master Shirley High Sch Croydon 86-92; rtd 92. *17 Snowbell Road, Kingsnorth, Ashford TN23 3NF* Tel (01233) 503889

VANDYCK, Mrs Salli Diane Seymour. b 39. Grenoble Univ Dip French Studies 57 DipTT77 AIL75 CertFE93. S'wark Ord Course 93 SEITE 93. **d** 96 **p** 97. NSM Chertsey *Guildf* 96-98; NSM Ross *Heref* 98-03; rtd 03. *The Rectory, Linton, Ross-on-Wye HR9 7RX* Tel (01989) 720472

VANN, Ms Cherry Elizabeth. b 58. ARCM78 GRSM80. Westcott Ho Cam 86. **d** 89 **p** 94. Par Dn Flixton St Mich *Man* 89-92; Chapl Bolton Inst of F&HE 92-96; Par Dn Bolton St Pet 92-94; C

94-98; TV E Farnworth and Kearsley from 98; Chapl to the Deaf from 98. *195 Harrowby Street, Farnworth, Bolton BL4 9QU* Tel (01204) 572455 E-mail cvannskye@aol.com

VANN, Canon Paul. b 41. St D Coll Lamp DipTh65. **d** 65 **p** 66. C Griffithstown *Mon* 65-67; C Llanfrechfa All SS 67-71; Dioc Youth Chapl 69-74; Chapl St Woolos Cathl 71-72; P-in-c Llanrumney 72-76; V 76-97; Asst Chapl HM Pris Cardiff 75-78; RD Bassaleg *Mon* 90-99; R Machen from 97; Can St Woolos Cathl from 01. *The Rectory, Rectory Gardens, Chatham, Machen, Caerphilly CF83 8SU* Tel (01633) 440321

VANNERLEY, David van Krieken. b 50. Ch Ch Coll Cant CertEd71 Kent Univ BA78. SEITE 00. **d** 03. *34 Cherry Gardens, Herne Bay CT6 5QZ* Tel (01227) 369096 E-mail vannerley@aol.com

VANNOZZI, Peter. b 62. Lon Univ BA83. Ripon Coll Cuddesdon BA86 MA91 DipTh97. **d** 87 **p** 88. C Kenton *Lon* 87-90; C Fleet *Guildf* 90-93; V Northwood Hills St Edm *Lon* 93-97; AD Harrow 95-97; V S Dulwich St Steph *S'wark* from 97; RD Dulwich from 02. *St Stephen's Vicarage, College Road, London SE21 7HN* Tel (020) 8693 3797 Fax as telephone E-mail vicar@ststephensdulwich.org

VANSTON, The Ven William Francis Harley. b 24. TCD BA48 MA52. **d** 48 **p** 49. C Belfast St Mary *Conn* 48-51; C Dublin Rathfarnham *D & G* 51-58; I Narraghmore w Fontstown and Timolin 58-65; I Arklow 65-67; I Arklow w Inch 67-73; I Arklow w Inch and Kilbride 73-89; RD Rathdrum 77-89; Adn Glendalough 83-89; rtd 89. *31 Seabank Court, Sandycove, Dun Laoghaire, Co Dublin, Irish Republic* Tel (00353) (1) 280 4575

VANSTONE, Preb Walford David Frederick. b 38. Open Univ BA81. AKC69. **d** 70 **p** 71. C Feltham *Lon* 70-75; TV E Runcorn w Halton *Ches* 75-80; V Grange St Andr 80-82; V Hampton All SS *Lon* from 82; P-in-c Teddington SS Pet and Paul and Fulwell 99-00; AD Hampton 95-03; Preb St Paul's Cathl from 99. *All Saints' Vicarage, 40 The Avenue, Hampton TW12 3RS* Tel (020) 8979 2102 Fax 8255 6118 E-mail wvanstone@aol.com

VARAH, Preb Edward Chad. b 11. CH00 OBE69 CBE95. Keble Coll Ox BA33 MA46 Leic Univ Hon LLD79 St Andr Univ Hon LLD93 City Univ Hon DSc93. Linc Th Coll 34. **d** 35 **p** 36. C Linc St Giles *Linc* 35-38; C Putney St Mary *S'wark* 38-40; C Barrow St Jo *Carl* 40-42; V Blackb H Trin *Blackb* 42-49; V Battersea St Paul *S'wark* 49-53; P-in-c St Steph Walbrook and St Swithun etc *Lon* 53-54; R from 54; Founder The Samaritans 53; Dir 53-74; Preb St Paul's Cathl *Lon* from 75. *St Stephen's Vestry, 39 Walbrook, London EC4N 8BN* Tel (020) 7283 4444 *or* 7626 8242

VARAH, Paul Hugh. b 46. St Deiniol's Hawarden 83. **d** 85 **p** 86. C Prestatyn *St As* 85-87; P-in-c Hawarden 87-88; TV 88-89; V Esclusham 89-96; V Connah's Quay from 96. *The Vicarage, Church Hill, Connah's Quay, Deeside CH5 4AD* Tel (01244) 830224 Fax as telephone

VARGAS, Eric Arthur Dudley. b 27. BD. S Dios Minl Tr Scheme 81. **d** 83 **p** 84. C Farncombe *Guildf* 83-86; R Ockley, Okewood and Forest Green 86-90; V Kirdford *Chich* 90-93; rtd 93; Perm to Offic *Portsm* and *Chich* from 93. *5 Bath Road, Emsworth PO10 7EP* Tel (01243) 376284

VARGESON, Peter Andrew. b 53. Wycliffe Hall Ox 85. **d** 87 **p** 88. C Yateley *Win* 87-92; V Bursledon from 92; AD Eastleigh from 99. *The Vicarage, School Road, Bursledon, Southampton SO31 8BW* Tel (023) 8040 2821 E-mail peter.vargeson@ukgateway.net

VARLEY (née TRIM), Elizabeth Ann. b 52. Homerton Coll Cam BEd75 Van Mildert Coll Dur PhD85 St Jo Coll Dur BA96. NEOC 94. **d** 96 **p** 97. C Sedgefield *Dur* 96-99; Dir Post-Ord Tr (Stepney Area) *Lon* 99-02; V Hipswell *Ripon* from 02. *The Vicarage, 7 Forest Drive, Colburn, Catterick Garrison DL9 4PN* Tel (01748) 833320

VARLEY, Robert. b 36. St Jo Coll Cam BA57 MA64 Man Poly PGCE92. NW Ord Course 71. **d** 74 **p** 75. C Wallasey St Hilary *Ches* 74-77; V Rock Ferry 77-81; Perm to Offic *Man* 82-83; Hon C E Farnworth and Kearsley 83-86; Hon C Walkden Moor 86-87; C 87-89; V Lt Hulton 89-90; Perm to Offic from 97. *66 Normanby Road, Worsley, Manchester M28 7TS* Tel 0161-790 8420

VARNEY, Donald James. b 35. Chich Th Coll 84. **d** 86. Hon C Liss *Portsm* from 86. *12 Birch Close, Liss, Petersfield GU33 7HS* Tel (01730) 893945

VARNEY, Peter David. b 38. Univ Coll Dur BA61 MA64 Birm Univ DipTh63. Qu Coll Birm 61. **d** 64 **p** 65. C Newington St Paul *S'wark* 64-66; C Camberwell St Mich w All So w 64-66-67; Malaysia 67-68; Hon C Croxley Green All SS *St Alb* 69; Perm to Offic *Roch* 69-72 and 74-84; Asst Chapl CSJB 72-73; Asst Sec Chrs Abroad 74-79; Dir Bloxham Project 84-86; Perm to Offic *Cant* 84-85 and *S'wark* 85-86; P-in-c Thornage w Brinton w Hunworth and Stody *Nor* 87-88; P-in-c Briningham 87-88; P-in-c Melton Constable w Swanton Novers 87-88; Perm to Offic from 88; Chapl Yare and Norvic Clinics and St Andr Hosp Nor 90-95; rtd 03. *9 Coslany Street, Norwich NR3 3DT* Tel (01603) 462237 E-mail pv@onetel.net.uk

VARNEY, Stephen Clive. b 59. Qu Mary Coll Lon BSc80 Sussex Univ MSc82 Southn Univ BTh88. Sarum & Wells Th Coll 83. **d** 86 **p** 87. C Riverhead w Dunton Green *Roch* 86-91; V Bostall Heath 91-99; V Bromley St Mark from 99. *St Mark's Vicarage, 51 Hayes Road, Bromley BR2 9AE* Tel (020) 8460 6220 Mobile 07961-117578

VARNEY, Wilfred Davies. b 10. Sarum & Wells Th Coll 71. **d** 71 **p** 72. C Glouc St Paul *Glouc* 71-74; V Lydbrook 74-77; rtd 77; Hon C Felpham w Middleton *Chich* 77-80; Hon C Overbury w Alstone, Teddington and Lt Washbourne *Worc* 80-82; Perm to Offic *Nor* 82-87 and 91-93; P-in-c Nor St Andr 87-91; Perm to Offic *Guildf* 93-00. *11 Manormead, Tilford Road, Hindhead GU26 6RA* Tel (01428) 606652

VARNEY, William James Granville. b 22. St D Coll Lamp 62. **d** 65 **p** 66. C Burry Port and Pwll *St D* 65-68; V Strata Florida 68-71; V Llandyfriog, Llanfair Trelygen, Troedyraur etc 71-78; OCF 78; R Aberporth w Tremain and Blaenporth *St D* 78-87; P-in-c Penbryn and Betws Ifan w Bryngwyn 88-92; rtd 92. *Alma, Tan y Groes, Cardigan SA43 2JT* Tel (01239) 810217

VARNHAM, Gerald Stanley. b 29. Sarum & Wells Th Coll 74. **d** 77 **p** 78. Hon C Portchester *Portsm* 77-86; Perm to Offic from 88. *15 Southampton Road, Fareham PO16 7DZ* Tel (01329) 234182

VARNON, Nicholas Charles Harbord. b 45. St Luke's Coll Ex CertEd71 Open Univ BA83 BPhil91 MA94 Univ of Wales MPhil00. St Mich Coll Llan DipTh91. **d** 93 **p** 94. C Pontypridd St Cath w St Matt *Llan* 93-97; P-in-c Sutton St Nicholas w Sutton St Michael *Heref* from 97; P-in-c Withington w Westhide from 97; CF (ACF) from 00. *The Rectory, Sutton St Nicholas, Hereford HR1 3BA* Tel (01432) 880253

VARQUEZ, Leo Bacleon. b 61. St Andr Th Sem Manila LTh86. **d** 86 **p** 86. Philippines 86-97; P St Andr 86-91; P St Isidore 92-94; SSF 95-99; Asst Chapl Univ Hosp Birm NHS Trust 97-98; NSM Edin St Jo *Edin* 98-99; Chapl Assoc Edin Univ 99; NSM Mill End and Heronsgate w W Hyde *St Alb* 99-00; Asst Chapl HM Pris Featherstone 00-02; C Hednesford *Lich* from 00. *St Michael's Church House, 554 Littleworth Road, Rawnsley, Cannock WS12 1JD* Tel (01543) 871135
E-mail levar@onetel.net.uk

VARTY, John Eric. b 44. Tyndale Hall Bris 68. **d** 71 **p** 72. C Barrow St Mark *Carl* 71-74; C Cheadle *Ches* 74-82; V Cheadle All Hallows 82-89; V Alsager Ch Ch from 89. *Christ Church Vicarage, 43 Church Road, Alsager, Stoke-on-Trent ST7 2HS* Tel (01270) 873727 E-mail vartyj1j2@clara.co.uk

VARTY, Robert. b 46. LRAM. Sarum & Wells Th Coll 84. **d** 86 **p** 87. C Plympton St Mary *Ex* 86-89; TV Northam w Westward Ho! and Appledore 89-95; P-in-c Wigginton *St Alb* 95-00; TV Tring 95-00; rtd 00; Perm to Offic *Ex* from 01. *6 Shute Wood, Hollacombe, Chudleigh EX18 7QJ* Tel (01837) 83642

VASEY, Arthur Stuart. b 37. Qu Coll Birm 68. **d** 71 **p** 72. C Shelf *Bradf* 71-73; Australia 74-76; Chapl St Jo Hosp Linc 76-79; P-in-c Tanfield *Dur* 79-84; C Birtley 84-85; C Middlesbrough St Thos *York* 85-86; rtd 02. *Glen Esk, 3 Quarry Bank, Malton YO17 7HA*

VASEY-SAUNDERS, Mrs Leah Beverley. b 77. Huddersfield Univ BMus98. Cranmer Hall Dur 00. **d** 03. C Wharlton *Newc* from 03. *2 Grange Road, Ponteland, Newcastle upon Tyne NE20 9UL* Tel (01661) 860599 E-mail leahvasey@fish.co.uk

VAUGHAN, Andrew Christopher James. b 61. Univ of Wales (Lamp) BA82. Linc Th Coll 84. **d** 84 **p** 85. C Caerleon *Mon* 84-86; C Magor w Redwick and Undy 86-88; Ind Chapl 84-94; Linc Ind Miss *Linc* from 94. *4 Grange Close, Canwick, Lincoln LN4 2AH* Tel and fax (01522) 528266 Mobile 07702-468549 E-mail vaughanlim@tesco.net

VAUGHAN, Brian John. b 38. Lich Th Coll 65. **d** 68 **p** 69. C Fisherton Anger *Sarum* 68-70; C Wareham w Arne 70-73; Australia from 73; Asst P Mt Lawley 73; R Dalwallinu 73-76; R Morawa 75-78; Field Officer Bible Soc of W Australia 78-81; Assoc P Mt Lawley 81-86; R Pinjarra 86-96; R Manjimup 96-00; rtd 00. *Milborne, 6 Steeple Retreat, Busselton, W Australia 6280* Tel (0061) (8) 9751 1225 Fax 9751 2858
E-mail sherton@optusnet.com.au

VAUGHAN, Carole Ann. b 47. Leeds Univ CertEd68. STETS 95. **d** 98 **p** 99. NSM Oakley w Wootton St Lawrence *Win* from 98. *The Rectory, Glebe Lane, Worting, Basingstoke RG23 8QA* Tel (01256) 331531 E-mail carole@vaughan50.freeserve.co.uk

VAUGHAN, Charles Jeremy Marshall. b 52. Man Univ BSc75 LTh. St Jo Coll Nottm 83. **d** 85 **p** 86. C Epsom Common Ch Ch *Guildf* 85-88; C Woking Ch Ch 88-93; R Worting *Win* from 93. *The Rectory, Glebe Lane, Worting, Basingstoke RG23 8QA* Tel (01256) 331531
E-mail jeremy.vaughan@ukgateway.net

VAUGHAN, Idris Samuel. b 46. Sarum Th Coll 70. **d** 72 **p** 73. C Workington St Jo *Carl* 72-76; C Foley Park *Worc* 76-79; P-in-c Hayton St Mary *Carl* 79; V 79-85; Chapl Asst Univ Hosp Nottm 85-90; Chapl Asst Nottm Gen Hosp 85-90; Chapl Stafford Distr Gen Hosp 90-94; Chapl Chase Hosp Cannock 90-94; Chapl Mid Staffs Gen Hosps NHS Trust from 94. *The Chaplain's Office, Stafford District General Hospital, Weston Road, Stafford ST16 3RS* Tel (01785) 230930 *or* 257731 ext 4930

VAUGHAN, Jeffrey Charles. b 45. S'wark Ord Course 85. **d** 88 **p** 89. NSM Tottenham St Paul *Lon* 88-91; C Hendon St Alphage 91-95; V Enfield SS Pet and Paul from 95. *The Vicarage, 177 Ordnance Road, Enfield EN3 6AB* Tel (01992) 719770 Fax (020) 8292 8456

VAUGHAN, John. b 30. Sarum Th Coll 53. **d** 56 **p** 57. C Wigan St Andr *Liv* 56-59; Australia 59-64; P-in-c Riddings *Derby* 64-71; R Hasland 71-80; V Temple Normanton 71-80; TV Dronfield 80-86; V Bradwell 86-95; rtd 95; Perm to Offic *Derby* from 95. *11 Millstone Close, Dronfield Woodhouse, Dronfield S18 8ZL* Tel (01246) 415647

VAUGHAN, Patrick Handley. b 38. TCD BA60 BD65 Selw Coll Cam BA62 MA66 Nottm Univ PhD88. Ridley Hall Cam 61. **d** 63 **p** 64. Min Can Bradf Cathl *Bradf* 63-66; Uganda 67-73; P-in-c Slingsby *York* 74-77; Tutor NW Ord Course 74-77; P-in-c Hovingham *York* 74-77; Prin EMMTC *S'well* 77-90; Hon Can Leic Cathl *Leic* 87-90; Assoc Lect Open Univ from 94. *113 Upperthorpe Road, Sheffield S6 3EA* Tel 0114-272 2675

✠**VAUGHAN, The Rt Revd Peter St George.** b 30. Selw Coll Cam BA55 MA59 BNC Ox MA63. Ridley Hall Cam. **d** 57 **p** 58 **c** 89. C Birm St Martin *Birm* 57-63; Chapl Ox Pastorate 63-67; Asst Chapl BNC Ox 63-67; Ceylon 67-72; New Zealand 72-75; Prin Crowther Hall CMS Tr Coll Selly Oak 75-83; Adn Westmorland and Furness *Carl* 83-89; Hon Can Carl Cathl 83-89; Area Bp Ramsbury *Sarum* 89-98; Can and Preb Sarum Cathl 89-98; rtd 98; Hon Asst Bp Bradf 98-01; Hon Can Bradf Cathl from 98; Perm to Offic *Glouc* from 01; Hon Asst Bp Bris from 02. *Willowbrook, Downington, Lechlade GL7 3DL* Tel (01367) 252216

VAUGHAN, Preb Roger Maxwell. b 39. AKC62. **d** 63 **p** 64. C W Bromwich All SS *Lich* 63-65; C Wolverhampton 65-70; V Tunstall Ch Ch 70-79; V Tunstall 79-79; V Abbots Bromley 79-86; P-in-c Blithfield 85-86; V Abbots Bromley w Blithfield 86-93; V Stafford St Jo and Tixall w Ingestre from 93; Preb Lich Cathl from 99. *St John's Vicarage, Westhead Avenue, Stafford ST16 3RP* Tel (01785) 253493
E-mail salrog.vaughan@btinternet.com

VAUGHAN, Ronald Alfred. b 38. S'wark Ord Course 78. **d** 81 **p** 82. NSM Stepney St Pet w St Benet *Lon* 81-86; Asst P St Jo on Bethnal Green from 87; Dep Dioc Sec 90-95; Projects Officer (Stepney Area) from 95. *St Bartholomew's Vicarage, Buckhurst Street, London E1 5QT* Tel (020) 7247 8013 Fax as telephone
E-mail ron.vaughan@eggconnect.net

VAUGHAN, Trevor. b 41. TD91. Cen Lancs Univ BA91. Linc Th Coll 66. **d** 69 **p** 70. C Wyken *Cov* 69-72; C Stratford-on-Avon w Bishopton 72-73; P-in-c Monks Kirby w Withybrook and Copston Magna 73-75; P-in-c Wolvey, Burton Hastings and Stretton Baskerville 73-77; P-in-c Withybrook w Copston Magna 73-77; V Heyhouses *Blackb* 77-80; CF (TA) from 79; V Chorley St Geo *Blackb* 80-83; R Bolton by Bowland w Grindleton *Bradf* 83-89; V Settle 89-91; R Broughton, Marton and Thornton 91-00; V Morecambe St Barn *Blackb* 00-03; P-in-c Sabden and Pendleton from 03. *St Nicholas' Vicarage, Westley Street, Sabden, Clitheroe BB7 9EH* Tel (01282) 771384

VAUGHAN-JONES, Canon John Paschal. b 18. Keble Coll Ox BA39 MA43. St Steph Ho Ox 39. **d** 41 **p** 42. C Laindon w Basildon *Chelmsf* 41-43 and 47-49; CF 43-47; R Chipping Ongar *Chelmsf* 49-83; R Shelley 49-83; RD Ongar 72-82; Hon Can Chelmsf Cathl 78-83; rtd 83. *Armadale, 3 Great Lane, Malborough, Kingsbridge TQ7 3SA* Tel (01548) 562138

VAUGHAN-WILSON, Jane Elizabeth. b 61. Magd Coll Ox MA87. Cranmer Hall Dur. **d** 89 **p** 94. Par Dn Ormesby *York* 89-93; Dn-in-c Middlesbrough St Agnes 93-94; P-in-c 94-95; TV Basingstoke *Win* 95-03; Perm to Offic *Truro* from 03. *4 Tolver Road, Penzance TR18 2AG* Tel (01736) 351825

VAYRO, Mark Shaun. b 66. Aston Tr Scheme 88 Linc Th Coll BTh93. **d** 93 **p** 94. C Northampton St Mich w St Edm *Pet* 93-96; TV Duston Team 96-98; V Elm and Friday Bridge w Coldham *Ely* 98-01. *125 Spalding Road, Pinchbeck, Spalding LN11 3UE*

VEAZEY, Harry Christopher Hurford. b 11. Westcott Ho Cam 33. **d** 35 **p** 36. C Sutton New Town St Barn *S'wark* 35-38; C Newington St Mary 38-41; V Nunhead St Silas 41-57; V Doddington w Wychling *Cant* 57-80; V Newnham 57-80; RD Ospringe 78-80; V rtd 80; Perm to Offic *Cant* 80-02. *Five Oaks, Pluckley Road, Charing, Ashford TN27 0AJ* Tel (01233) 713009

VEEN, Keith Henry. b 46. Dioc OLM tr scheme 96. **d** 01 **p** 02. OLM Croydon St Pet *S'wark* from 01. *91 The Ridgeway, Croydon CR0 4AH* Tel (020) 8688 3565
E-mail keithveen@veenco.fsnet.co.uk

VELLACOTT, John Patrick Millner. b 29. Ox NSM Course 86. **d** 89 **p** 90. NSM Cholsey *Ox* 89-93; Chapl Nerja *Eur* 93-97; rtd 97; Perm to Offic *Truro* 97-00; *Glouc* 00-02; *Carl* from 03.

5 Stonycroft Drive, Arnside, Carnforth LA5 0EE Tel (01524) 762800

VELLACOTT, Peter Graham. b 38. Seale-Hayne Agric Coll NDA59. EAMTC 90. **d** 93 **p** 94. NSM Framlingham w Saxtead *St E* 93-95; NSM Brandeston w Kettleburgh 95-99; NSM Easton 95-99; P-in-c Brandeston w Kettleburgh and Easton from 99. *Soham House, Brandeston, Woodbridge IP13 7AX* Tel (01728) 685423

VENABLES, Dudley James. b 17. Cant Sch of Min 77. **d** 80 **p** 81. NSM Ramsgate H Trin *Cant* 80-82; Chapl Asst St Aug Hosp Cant 83-88; NSM Wye w Brook 83-88; Perm to Offic from 88; Chapl Cant and Thanet Mental Health Unit 93-98; Chapl E Kent Community NHS Trust from 98. *48 Abbots Walk, Wye, Ashford TN25 5ES* Tel (01233) 813000

✠**VENABLES, The Most Revd Gregory James.** b 49. Lon Univ CertEd74. **d** 84 **p** 84 **c** 93. SAMS from 77; Paraguay 78-90; C Rainham *Chelmsf* 90-92; C Rainham w Wennington 92-93; Aux Bp Peru and Bolivia 93-95; Bp Bolivia 95-00; Asst Primate of S Cone 95-02; Bp Coadjutor Argentina 00-02; Dioc Bp from 02; Presiding Bp of S Cone from 01. *Conesa 1925 1B, (1428) Belgrano, Capital Federal, Buenos Aires, Argentina* Tel (0054) (11) 4342 4618 *or* 4783 0272 Fax 4784 1277 E-mail bpgreg@ciudad.com.ar

VENABLES, Mrs Margaret Joy. b 37. Bp Otter Coll CertEd57 S Dios Minl Tr Scheme 86. **d** 89 **p** 94. NSM Wilton *B & W* 89-91; NSM Taunton St Andr 91-92; C 92-97; P-in-c Haynes *St Alb* 97-03; P-in-c Clophill 00-03; R Campton, Clophill and Haynes from 03; RD Shefford from 01. *The Vicarage, 4A North Lane, Haynes, Bedford MK45 3PW* Tel (01234) 381235 *or* (01727) 854532

VENABLES, Philip Richard Meredith. b 58. Magd Coll Ox BA79 CertEd80. Wycliffe Hall Ox 85. **d** 88 **p** 89. C Gillingham St Mark *Roch* 88-93; V Penge St Jo from 93. *The Vicarage, St John's Road, London SE20 7EQ* Tel (020) 8778 6176 E-mail philip@venables01.freeserve.co.uk

VENESS, Allan Barry. b 39. Lon Inst of Educn TCert60 Sussex Univ BEd81 Univ Coll Chich Dip Th & Min 99. Bp Otter Coll 94. **d** 97. NSM Felpham *Chich* 97-01; NSM Aldwick from 01. *95 Limmer Lane, Felpham, Bognor Regis PO22 7LP* Tel (01243) 583230 Fax 582471

VENEZUELA, Bishop of. *See* GUERRERO, The Rt Revd Orlando

✠**VENNER, The Rt Revd Stephen Squires.** b 44. Birm Univ BA65 Linacre Coll Ox BA67 MA71 Lon Univ PGCE72. St Steph Ho Ox 65. **d** 68 **p** 69 **c** 94. C Streatham St Pet *S'wark* 68-71; C Streatham Hill St Marg 71-72; C Balham Hill Ascension 72-74; Bp's Chapl to Overseas Students 74-76; V Clapham St Pet 74-76; P-in-c Studley *Sarum* 76; V 76-82; V Weymouth H Trin 82-94; RD Weymouth 88-93; Can and Preb Sarum Cathl 89-94; Suff Bp Middleton *Man* 94-99; Suff Bp Dover Cant from 99. *Upway, 52 St Martin's Hill, Canterbury CT1 1PR* Tel (01227) 464537 *or* 459382 Fax 450855 *or* 784485 E-mail bishop@bishcant.org

VENNING, Nigel Christopher. b 50. K Coll Lon BD75 AKC75. St Aug Coll Cant 75. **d** 76 **p** 77. C Minehead *B & W* 76-80; C Fawley *Win* 80-83; P-in-c Combe St Nicholas w Wambrook *B & W* 83-89; P-in-c Whitestaunton 83-89; R Staplegrove 89-01; P-in-c Norton Fitzwarren 00-01; R Staplegrove w Norton Fitzwarren 01-03; RD Taunton 96-01; P-in-c Pitminster w Corfe from 03; P-in-c Churchstanton, Buckland St Mary and Otterford from 03. *The Vicarage, Pitminster, Taunton TA3 7AZ* Tel (01823) 421232 Fax 352353 E-mail nigelvenning@lycos.co.uk

VERE HODGE, Preb Francis. b 19. MC43. Worc Coll Ox BA46 MA46. Cuddesdon Coll 46. **d** 48 **p** 49. C Battle *Chich* 48-54; R Iping 54-58; R Linch 54-58; V Kingswood *S'wark* 58-65; V Moorlinch w Stawell and Sutton Mallet *B & W* 65-79; R Greinton 68-79; RD Glastonbury 75-79; P-in-c Lydeard St Lawrence w Combe Florey and Tolland 79-84; Preb Wells Cathl 79-98; rtd 84; Perm to Offic *B & W* 84-99 and *Ex* from 99. *1 Gracey Court, Woodland Road, Broadclyst, Exeter EX5 3GA* Tel (01392) 469005

VERE NICOLL, Charles Fiennes. b 55. Solicitor 79. St Alb and Ox Min Course 96. **d** 99 **p** 00. NSM Basildon w Aldworth and Ashampstead *Ox* from 99. *Broadfield House, Yattendon, Thatcham RG18 0UH* Tel (01635) 203018 Mobile 07768-238128 E-mail cfvnicoll@aol.com

VEREKER, Jennifer Lesley. b 45. Totley Hall Coll CertEd66. WMMTC 96. **d** 99 **p** 00. NSM Rugby St Andr *Cov* 99-03; TV Gt and Lt Coates w Bradley *Linc* from 03. *St Nicolas' Vicarage, Great Coates Road, Great Coates, Grimsby DN37 9NS* Tel (01472) 882495 E-mail jenny@cjpvereker.freeserve.co.uk

✠**VERNEY, The Rt Revd Stephen Edmund.** b 19. MBE45. Ball Coll Ox BA48 MA48. **d** 50 **p** 51 **c** 77. C Gedling *S'well* 50-52; C-in-c Clifton CD 52-57; V Clifton St Fran 57-58; Dioc Missr *Cov* 58-64; V Leamington Hastings 58-64; Can Res Cov Cathl 64-70; Can Windsor 70-77; Suff Bp Repton *Derby* 77-85; Hon Can Derby Cathl 77-85; Dioc Dir of Post-Ord Tr 83-85; rtd 86;

Perm to Offic *Ox* 86-91; Asst Bp Ox from 91. *Charity School House, Church Road, Blewbury, Didcot OX11 9PY* Tel (01235) 850004

VERNON, Bryan Graham. b 50. Qu Coll Cam BA72 MA76. Qu Coll Birm DipTh74. **d** 75 **p** 76. C Newc St Gabr *Newc* 75-79; Chapl Newc Univ 79-91; Lect Health Care Ethics from 91; Chmn Newc Mental Health Trust 91-94; Perm to Offic from 94. *34 Queens Road, Jesmond, Newcastle upon Tyne NE2 2PQ* Tel 0191-281 3861 E-mail b.g.vernon@ncl.ac.uk

VERNON, John Christie. b 40. Lon Univ BScEng ACGI62. Linc Th Coll 63. **d** 65 **p** 66. C Barnard Castle *Dur* 65-69; CF 69-92; Chapl Ellesmere Coll Shropshire 92-99; rtd 99; Perm to Offic *Lich* 99-01; NSM Ellesmere Deanery from 01; RD Ellesmere from 02. *The Drift House, Lake House Mews, Grange Road, Ellesmere SY12 9DE* Tel (01691) 623765 Mobile 07778-312226 E-mail john.vernon@which.net

VERNON, Matthew James. b 71. Collingwood Coll Dur BSc93. Westcott Ho Cam BA96 CTM97. **d** 97 **p** 98. C Guildf H Trin w St Mary *Guildf* 97-01; Chapl St Jo Cathl Hong Kong from 01. *St John's Cathedral, Garden Road, Hong Kong* Tel (00852) 2523 4157 Fax 2521 7830 E-mail vernon@stjohnscathedral.org.uk

VERNON, Robert Leslie. b 47. Sarum & Wells Th Coll 73. **d** 76 **p** 77. C Hartlepool St Luke *Dur* 76-79; C Birm St Geo *Birm* 79-82; V Bordesley Green 82-86; Dioc Youth Officer *Carl* 86-89; P-in-c Holme 86-89; Dioc Youth Adv *Newc* 89-95; V Ulgham and Widdrington 95-01; P-in-c Pokesdown St Jas *Win* from 01. *St James's Vicarage, 12 Harewood Avenue, Bournemouth BH7 6NQ* Tel (01202) 425918

VESEY, Nicholas Ivo. b 54. Bris Univ BSc73 St Jo Coll Dur DipTh97. Cranmer Hall Dur 95. **d** 97 **p** 98. C Tunbridge Wells St Mark *Roch* 97-01; V New Catton St Luke w St Aug *Nor* from 01. *St Luke's Vicarage, 61 Aylsham Road, Norwich NR3 2HF* Tel (01603) 416973 E-mail nicholas.vesey@btopenworld.com

VESSEY, Andrew John. b 45. Bp Otter Coll CertEd67 Sarum & Wells Th Coll 84. **d** 86 **p** 87. C Framlingham w Saxtead *St E* 86-89; V Catshill and Dodford *Worc* 89-94; P-in-c Areley Kings 94-95; R 95-02; RD Stourport 00-02; TV Kidderminster St Jo and H Innocents from 02. *The Vicarage, 33 Lea Bank Avenue, Kidderminster DY11 6PA* Tel (01562) 824028 E-mail andrew@vessey.plus.com

VESSEY, Peter Allan Beaumont. b 36. R Agric Coll Cirencester Dip Estate Mgt 56. Lon Coll of Div ALCD65 LTh74. **d** 64 **p** 65. C Rayleigh *Chelmsf* 64-67; C Cambridge H Trin *Ely* 67-71; V Kingston upon Hull St Aid Southcoates *York* 71-80; V Swanwick and Pentrich *Derby* 80-94; Perm to Offic from 94; rtd 96. *2 Bakehouse Cottage, Scarthin, Cromford, Matlock DE4 3QF* Tel (01629) 825572 Fax 823988

VESTERGAARD, David Andrew. b 64. Reading Univ BSc86. Wycliffe Hall Ox 97. **d** 99 **p** 00. C Chadderton Ch Ch *Man* 99-02; V Wednesfield Heath *Lich* from 02. *Holy Trinity Vicarage, Bushbury Road, Wolverhampton WV10 0LY* Tel (01902) 738313 E-mail david@vestergaard.co.uk

VETTERS, Miss Shirley Jacqueline Margaret. b 34. S'wark Ord Course 85. **d** 88 **p** 94. NSM E Ham w Upton Park St Alb *Chelmsf* 88-91; C Birm St Martin w Bordesley St Andr *Birm* from 91; Chapl to the Markets from 91. *341 George Road, Erdington, Birmingham B23 7RY* Tel 0121-382 4109 *or* 643 5428

VEVAR, Canon John Harvard. b 14. Univ of Wales BA36. St Mich Coll Llan 37. **d** 38 **p** 40. C Llanfechell w Bodewryd, Rhosbeirio etc *Ban* 38-42; C Newtown w Llanllwchaiarn *St As* 42-46; P-in-c Llanfairynghornwy w Llanrhwydrys *Ban* 46-51; R Mellteyrn w Botwnnog 51-84; P-in-c Llandudwen 67-73; Can Ban Cathl 78-84; rtd 84; Perm to Offic *Ban* from 84. *Gwynant, Tudweiliog, Pwllheli LL53 8AJ* Tel (01758) 770270

VEVERS, Geoffrey Martin. b 51. Oak Hill Th Coll. **d** 82 **p** 83. C Wealdstone H Trin *Lon* 82-84; C Harrow Trin St Mich 84-88; V Wandsworth St Steph *S'wark* 88-96; V Battersea Fields from 96. *St Saviour's Vicarage, 351A Battersea Park Road, London SW11 4LH* Tel (020) 7498 1642

VIBERT (née GREEN), Imogen Elizabeth. b 73. Birm Univ BA96 Cam Univ BTh02. Westcott Ho Cam 99. **d** 02. C Poplar *Lon* from 02. *6 Mountague Place, London E14 0EX* E-mail imogengreen@supanet.com

VIBERT, Simon David Newman. b 63. Oak Hill Th Coll BA89. **d** 89 **p** 90. C Houghton *Carl* 89-92; C-in-c Buxton Trin Prop Chpl *Derby* 92-99; V Wimbledon Park St Luke *S'wark* from 99. *St Luke's Vicarage, 28 Farquhar Road, London SW19 8DA* Tel (020) 8946 3396 E-mail simon@wimbledonchurch.co.uk

VICARS, David. b 22. Leeds Univ BA48. Coll of Resurr Mirfield 48. **d** 50 **p** 51. C Newington St Paul *S'wark* 50-54; C Kingston St Luke 54-56; C Cirencester *Glouc* 56-59; Malaysia 59-66; Area Sec USPG *Llan, Mon, St D* and *S & B* 67-77; R Coychurch w Llangan and St Mary Hill *Llan* 77-90; rtd 90; Perm to Offic *Llan* from 90. *43 Bryn Rhedyn, Pencoed, Bridgend CF35 6TL* Tel (01656) 860920

VICARY, Canon Douglas Reginald. b 16. Trin Coll Ox BA38 BSc39 DipTh40 MA42. Wycliffe Hall Ox 39. **d** 40 **p** 41. Asst Chapl St Lawr Coll Ramsgate 40-45; C Collingtree w Courteenhall *Pet* 40-45; Tutor Wycliffe Hall Ox 45-47; Chapl 47-48; Chapl Hertf Coll Ox 45-48; Dir of Educn Roch 48-57; Min Can Roch Cathl 49-52; Can Res 52-57; Hon Can 57-75; Dir Post Ord Tr 52-57; Hd Master K Sch Roch 57-75; Can Res and Prec Wells Cathl *B & W* 75-88; Chapl to The Queen 77-87; rtd 88; Perm to Offic *B & W* from 88. *8 Tor Street, Wells BA5 2US* Tel (01749) 679137

VICK, Samuel Kenneth Lloyd. b 31. Univ of Wales (Lamp) BA53. Linc Th Coll. **d** 55 **p** 56. C Shotton *St As* 55-56; C Wrexham 56-61; C Knowle H Nativity *Bris* 61-67; V Mirfield Eastthorpe St Paul *Wakef* 67-78; V Altofts 78-98; rtd 98. *The Master's Lodge, Archbishop Holgate Hospital, Hemsworth, Pontefract WF96 4PP* Tel (01977) 610434

VICKERMAN, Canon John. b 42. Chich Th Coll 69. **d** 72 **p** 73. C Horbury *Wakef* 72-76; C Elland 76-78; V Glass Houghton 78-89; V Bruntcliffe 89-96; V King Cross from 96; RD Halifax from 00; Hon Can Wakef Cathl from 02. *The Vicarage, West Royd Avenue, Halifax HX1 3NU* Tel (01422) 352933

VICKERS, Dennis William George. b 30. RIBA72 York Univ MA91 IHBC99. Glouc Th Course 83. **d** 86 **p** 87. NSM Stokesay *Heref* 86-88; NSM Bucknell w Chapel Lawn, Llanfair Waterdine etc 88-92; NSM Wigmore Abbey from 93. *Reeves Holding, Reeves Lane, Stanage, Knighton LD7 1NA* Tel (01547) 530577 Fax 530773

VICKERS, Donald. Edge Hill Coll of HE DASE80 Univ of Wales (Ban) MEd87. N Ord Course 97. **d** 00 **p** 01. NSM Leigh St Mary *Man* from 00. *21 Broom Way, Westhoughton, Bolton BL5 3TZ* Tel (01942) 815193 Mobile 07768-492581 E-mail don@dvickers20.freeserve.co.uk

VICKERS, Mrs Janice Audrey Maureen. b 56. Guildf Dioc Min Course 93. **d** 96 **p** 97. OLM Woking Ch Ch *Guildf* from 96. *7 Langdale Close, Woking GU21 4RS* Tel (01483) 720873 E-mail rjvickers@aol.com

VICKERS, Mrs Mary Janet. b 57. Westmr Coll Ox MTh97. St Jo Coll Nottm BTh85. **dss** 83 **d** 87 **p** 99. World City St Paul and Old St Martin etc *Worc* 85-89; Par Dn 87-89; World Miss Officer *Worc* 89-92; USPG from 92; Lic to Offic *Eur* 95-99; Perm to Offic from 99; Perm to Offic Adnry of the Army from 97; NSM Cheswardine, Childs Ercall, Hales, Hinstock etc *Lich* 99-01; NSM Wrecclesham *Guildf* 01-02. *20 Keynston Down Road, Blandford Camp, Blandford Forum DT11 8AQ* Tel (01258) 456029 Fax as telephone E-mail revsvickers@tiscali.co.uk

VICKERS, Michael. b 60. Cranmer Hall Dur BA98. **d** 98 **p** 99. C Monkwearmouth *Dur* 98-00; Kowloon St Andr Hong Kong from 00. *5 Waldo Villas, 202 Wong Chuk Wan, Sai Kung, New Territories, Hong Kong* Tel (00852) 2792 1873

✠**VICKERS, The Rt Revd Michael Edwin.** b 29. Worc Coll Ox BA56 MA56 Dur Univ DipTh59. **d** 59 **p** 60. C Bexleyheath Ch Ch *Roch* 59-62; Chapl Lee Abbey 62-67; V Hull Newland St Jo *York* 67-81; AD Cen and N Hull 72-81; Can and Preb York Minster 81-88; Adn E Riding 81-88; Area Bp Colchester *Chelmsf* 88-94; rtd 94; Asst Bp Blackb from 94. *2 Collingham Park, Lancaster LA1 4PD* Tel (01524) 848492 E-mail michael.e.vickers@lineone.net

VICKERS, Peter. b 56. St Jo Coll Nottm LTh85. **d** 85 **p** 86. C Worc St Barn w Ch Ch *Worc* 85-88; TV Kidderminster St Mary and All SS w Trimpley etc 88-92; Ind Chapl 88-92; CF from 92. *c/o MOD Chaplains (Army)* Tel (01980) 615804 Fax 615800 E-mail revsvickers@msn.com

VICKERS, Peter George. b 41. Local Minl Tr Course 90. **d** 93 **p** 94. OLM Cobham *Guildf* from 93. *24 Station Road, Stoke D'Abernon, Cobham KT11 3BN* Tel (01932) 862497 E-mail revpetervickers@cobham82.fsnet.co.uk

VICKERS, Randolph. b 36. Newc Univ MA93 FCIM FInstD. St Alb Minl Tr Scheme 77. **d** 80 **p** 82. NSM Hitchin *St Alb* 80-87; NSM Luton Lewsey St Hugh 87-89; NSM Shotley *Newc* 89-01; rtd 01; Perm to Offic *Newc* from 01. *Beggar's Roost, 26 Painshawfield Road, Stocksfield NE43 7PF* Tel (01661) 842364 Fax as telephone E-mail rvickers@christian-healing.com

VICKERSTAFF, John Joseph. b 60. Westcott Ho Cam. **d** 97 **p** 98. C Halesworth w Linstead, Chediston, Holton *St E* 97-99; C Blyth Valley 99-01; TV Ch the King *Newc* from 00. *27 Polwarth Drive, Newcastle upon Tyne NE3 5NH* Tel 0191-236 3788

VICKERY, Charles William Bryan. b 38. Lich Th Coll 63. **d** 65 **p** 66. C Hove St Barn *Chich* 65-73; Chapl Hostel of God Clapham 73-76; P-in-c Kingston St Luke *S'wark* 76-82; V 82-94; rtd 98. *63 Connaught Road, Teddington TW11 0QF* Tel (020) 8977 8628

VICKERY, Jonathan Laurie. b 58. Bretton Hall Coll BEd80. Wycliffe Hall Ox 81. **d** 84 **p** 85. C Gorseinon *S & B* 84-86; P-in-c Whitton and Pilleth and Cascob etc 86-87; R 87-91; V Crickhowell w Cwmdu and Tretower 91-02; P-in-c Downend *Bris* from 02. *Christ Church Vicarage, Shrubbery Road, Bristol BS16 5TB* Tel 0117-908 9868 E-mail vicar@christchurchdownend.com

VICKERY, Robin Francis. b 48. K Coll Lon BD73 AKC73. **d** 74 **p** 75. C Clapham St Jo *S'wark* 74-77; C Clapham Ch Ch and St Jo 75-77; C Reigate St Luke S Park 77-79; Hon C Clapham H Spirit 80-87 and from 02; Hon C Clapham TM 87-01; Perm to Offic *Lon* from 99. *13 Chelsham Road, London SW4 6NR* Tel (020) 7622 4792

VIDAL-HALL, Roderic Mark. b 37. Sheff Univ BSc60 Birm Univ DPS70. Lich Th Coll 62. **d** 64 **p** 65. C Ilkeston St Mary *Derby* 64-67; C Nether and Over Seale 67-70; V Chellaston 70-84; C Stoneydelph w Marchington Woodlands *Lich* 84-97; C Kingstone w Gratwich 85-97; TV Uttoxeter Area 97-01; rtd 01. *Le Perhou, 22630 St Juuat, France* Tel (0033) (2) 96 88 16 34 E-mail mark@vidalhall.co.uk

VIGAR, Gilbert Leonard. b 12. Lon Univ BD46 BA50 MA52 Nottm Univ MPhil72. Kelham Th Coll 32. **d** 38 **p** 39. C Sheff St Cuth *Sheff* 38-42; P-in-c Herringthorpe 42-47; V Bradwell *Derby* 47-52; V Ault Hucknall 52-55; P-in-c Heath 52-55; V Winshill 55-57; V Madingley *Ely* 57-61; Asst Dir Educn 57-61; Prin Lect Bp Grosseteste Coll Linc 61-77; rtd 77; Hon C Win H Trin *Win* 79-85; Hon C Eastbourne St Sav and St Pet *Chich* 85-88; Perm to Offic from 88. *5 Chatsworth Gardens, Eastbourne BN20 7JP* Tel (01323) 644121

VIGARS, Anthony Roy. b 54. St Jo Coll Dur BA75. Trin Coll Bris 77. **d** 78 **p** 79. C Barking St Marg w St Patr *Chelmsf* 78-81; C Littleover *Derby* 81-84; C-in-c Stapenhill Immanuel CD 84-90; V Meltham *Wakef* 90-97; V Reading St Jo *Ox* from 97. *St John's Vicarage, 50 London Road, Reading RG1 5AS* Tel 0118-931 1012 E-mail vigars@lineone.net

VIGEON, Canon Owen George. b 28. Peterho Cam BA52 MA57. Ely Th Coll 52. **d** 54 **p** 55. C Barrow St Luke *Carl* 54-58; Chapl St Jo Coll York 58-61; V Burnley St Steph *Blackb* 61-69; V Bilsborrow 69-73; Asst Dir RE 69-73; V St Annes 74-85; RD Fylde 80-85; R Halton w Aughton 85-93; Hon Can Blackb Cathl 92-93; rtd 93; Perm to Offic *Worc* from 93. *19 Lynden Close, Bromsgrove B61 8PD* Tel (01527) 574520 Fax 570542 E-mail owen@vigeon.freeserve.co.uk

VIGERS, Neil Simon. b 62. K Coll Lon BD84 MTh87. Linc Th Coll 88. **d** 90 **p** 91. C Chelsea St Luke and Ch Ch *Lon* 90-93; C Staines St Mary and St Pet 93-96; P-in-c Hook *Win* 96-02; R from 02. *The Rectory, London Road, Hook RG27 9EG* Tel (01256) 762268 E-mail neil@stjohnhook.fsnet.co.uk

VIGERS, Patricia Anne. b 31. Lon Inst of Educn TCert53. OLM course 96. **d** 99 **p** 00. OLM Betchworth *S'wark* from 99; OLM Buckland from 99. *5 Normanton, Buckland Road, Reigate RH2 9RQ* Tel (01737) 243698

VIGOR, Ms Margaret Ann. b 45. Ripon Coll Cuddesdon 85. **d** 87 **p** 96. Chapl Asst All SS Convent Ox 87-89; Par Dn Basildon St Martin w Nevendon *Chelmsf* 89-91; NSM Billingham St Cuth *Dur* from 96. *15 Mitchell Street, Hartlepool TS26 9EZ* Tel (01429) 867458

VILLAGE, Andrew. b 54. Collingwood Coll Dur BSc75 Edin Univ PhD80. Trin Coll Bris BA92. **d** 92 **p** 93. C Northampton St Giles *Pet* 92-95; R Middleton Cheney w Chacombe from 95. *The Rectory, 3 High Street, Middleton Cheney, Banbury OX17 2PB* Tel (01295) 710254 E-mail andy@villages.fsnet.co.uk

VILLER, Canon Allan George Frederick. b 38. EAMTC 78. **d** 81 **p** 82. NSM Ely 81-85; V Emneth 85-92; V Littleport 92-03; RD Ely 98-03; Hon Can Ely Cathl 01-03; rtd 03; Hon C Barton Bendish w Beachamwell and Shingham *Ely* from 03; Hon C Fincham from 03; Hon C Marham from 03; Hon C Shouldham from 03; Hon C Shouldham Thorpe from 03. *The Rectory, High Street, Fincham, King's Lynn PE33 9EL* Tel (01366) 347491 E-mail allan@agfv.demon.co.uk

VILLIERS, Preb Tony. b 35. Lich Th Coll 59. **d** 62 **p** 63. C Shifnal *Lich* 62-65; C Wednesbury St Paul Wood Green 65-67; R Llanymynech 67-01; V Morton 72-01; P-in-c Llanyblodwel and Trefonen 00-01; RD Oswestry 82-87; Preb Lich Cathl 89-01; Wales and W Reg Chapl ATC 99-01; rtd 01. *Beach Mount, The Evergreens, Sheriffhales, Shifnal TF11 8SB* Tel (01952) 463586

VINCE, Mrs Barbara Mary Tudor. b 29. St Alb Minl Tr Scheme 79. **dss** 82 **d** 87 **p** 94. Northwood H Trin *Lon* 82-86; Belmont 86-89; Par Dn 87-89; rtd 90; Perm to Offic from 90. *22 St Mary's Avenue, Northwood HA6 3AZ* Tel (01923) 825730

VINCE, David Eric. b 59. Birm Univ BA81 Nottm Univ BCombStuds85 Goldsmiths' Coll Lon PGCE90. Linc Th Coll 82. **d** 85 **p** 86. C Gt Malvern St Mary *Worc* 85-88; C All Hallows by the Tower etc *Lon* 88-90; Min St Giles Cripplegate w St Bart Moor Lane etc 90-92; R Salwarpe and Hindlip w Martin Hussingtree *Worc* 92-97; R Willersey, Saintbury, Weston-sub-Edge etc *Glouc* 97-03; P-in-c Quinton 02-03; R Mickleton, Willersey, Saintbury etc from 03; RD Campden from 01. *The Rectory, Weston-sub-Edge, Chipping Campden GL55 6QH* Tel (01386) 840292 Fax as telephone E-mail dev@amserve.com

VINCE, Raymond Michael. b 45. Lon Univ BD69 Bris Univ MA72 K Coll Lon MTh80 LSE MSc83. Tyndale Hall Bris 66. **d** 71 **p** 72. C Southsea St Jude *Portsm* 71-75; Hon C Islington St Mary *Lon* 75-83; Chapl N Lon Poly 75-83; USA from 83. *906 South Orleans Drive, Tampa, FL 33606, USA*

VINCENT, Preb Alfred James. b 30. Bris Univ BA54 Lon Univ BD56. Tyndale Hall Bris 50. **d** 54 **p** 55. C Shrewsbury St Julian *Lich* 54-56; C Camborne *Truro* 56-59; V Kenwyn 59-68; Lic to Offic *St Alb* 68; Lect Qu Coll Birm 68-70; Lic to Offic *Birm* 68-70; V Bordesley St Oswald 70-76; V S Shields St Hilda w St Thos *Dur* 76-84; Hon Chapl Miss to Seafarers from 79; V Bude Haven *Truro* 84-89; R Bude Haven and Marhamchurch 89-92; RD Stratton 88-92; Preb St Endellion 90-95; rtd 92; P-in-c Chacewater *Truro* 92-95; Perm to Offic from 95. *5 Raymond Road, Redruth TR15 2HD* Tel (01209) 219263

VINCENT, Bruce Matthews. b 24. Univ of Wales (Swansea) Dip Youth Work 50 Open Univ BA76 Surrey Univ MPhil83. **d** 88 **p** 88. NSM Sidcup St Jo *Roch* 88-94; Perm to Offic from 94. *497 Footscray Road, London SE9 3UH* Tel (020) 8850 5450

VINCENT, Christopher Robin. b 30. Sarum Th Coll 57. **d** 60 **p** 61. C Frome St Jo *B & W* 60-64; V Puxton w Hewish St Ann and Wick St Lawrence 64-70; V Buckland Dinham w Elm 70-71; V Buckland Dinham w Elm, Orchardleigh etc 71-77; P-in-c Frome H Trin 77-90; Chapl St Adhelm's Hosp Frome 77-88; RD Frome *B & W* 85-89; V Kewstoke w Wick St Lawrence 90-94; rtd 94; Perm to Offic *B & W* from 94. *Willows Edge, 2 Westwood Close, Weston-super-Mare BS22 6JU* Tel (01934) 517425

VINCENT, David Cyril. b 37. Selw Coll Cam BA60 MA64. Coll of Resurr Mirfield 60. **d** 62 **p** 63. C Cheetwood St Alb *Man* 62-65; C Lawton Moor 65-67; V Wandsworth Common St Mary *S'wark* 67-84; RD Tooting 75-80; R Stoke D'Abernon *Guildf* 84-02; rtd 02. *29 North Street, Stoke-sub-Hamdon TA14 6QS*

VINCENT, George William Walter. b 13. ALCD40. **d** 40 **p** 41. C Hammersmith St Simon *Lon* 40-44; C Stowmarket *St E* 44-47; R Earl Stonham 47-55; R Alderton w Ramsholt and Bawdsey 55-86; rtd 86; Perm to Offic *St E* from 86. *c/o B Vincent Esq, Rectory House, Alderton, Woodbridge IP12 3BL* Tel (01394) 411306

VINCENT, Henry William Gordon. b 16. Leeds Univ BA42. Coll of Resurr Mirfield 42. **d** 44 **p** 45. C Bridgwater St Jo *B & W* 44-46; C Greenford H Cross *Lon* 46-52; C Teddington St Alb 52-55; V N Hammersmith St Kath 55-64; V Whitton St Aug 64-81; rtd 81; Perm to Offic *Sarum* from 81. *20 West Mills Road, Dorchester DT1 1SR* Tel (01305) 263933

VINCENT, John Leonard. b 61. Univ of Wales (Lamp) BA83 Southn Univ BTh87. Chich Th Coll 84. **d** 87 **p** 88. C Hampton All SS *Lon* 87-90; C Shepperton 90-95; V Whitton SS Phil and Jas from 95. *The Vicarage, 205 Kneller Road, Twickenham TW2 7DY* Tel (020) 8894 1932 E-mail pipnjim@aol.com

VINCENT, Michael Francis. b 48. CertEd70 Open Univ BA83. Sarum & Wells Th Coll 85. **d** 87 **p** 88. C Nuneaton St Mary *Cov* 87-90; C Stockingford 90-91; P-in-c 91-99; V from 99. *The Vicarage, Church Road, Stockingford, Nuneaton CV10 8LG* Tel (024) 7637 2089 Fax as telephone
E-mail mick@vincent4850.freeserve.co.uk

VINCENT, Canon Noel Thomas. b 36. Fitzw Ho Cam BA63 MA67. Ridley Hall Cam 60. **d** 63 **p** 64. C Fenham St Jas and St Basil *Newc* 63-67; C Prudhoe 67-70; V Holbrooke *Derby* 70-74; P-in-c Lt Eaton 72-74; P-in-c Osmaston w Edlaston 74-78; Hon C 78-85; Dioc Info Officer 74-78; Sen Producer Relig Progr BBC Man 82-91; Hon C Brailsford w Shirley and Osmaston w Edlaston *Derby* 85-86; Hon Can Derby Cathl 85-86; P-in-c Offic *Ches* 86-92; Chief Producer BBC Relig Progr Lon 91-93; Chief Asst to Hd BBC Relig Broadcasting 93-95; Hon C Twickenham St Mary *Lon* 92-95; Can Res and Treas Liv Cathl *Liv* 95-02; rtd 02. *45 Duke Street, Formby, Liverpool L37 4AP* Tel (01704) 875938

VINCENT, Robin. *See* VINCENT, Christopher Robin

VINCENT, Roy David. b 37. Univ of Wales (Swansea) Dip Youth Work. Chich Th Coll 81. **d** 83 **p** 84. C Atherton *Man* 83-86; V E Crompton 86-95; P-in-c Burwash *Chich* 95-00; R from 00. *The New Rectory, Rectory Close, Etchingham Road, Burwash, Etchingham TN19 7BH* Tel (01435) 882301

VINCER, Ms Louise Claire. b 69. Roehampton Inst BA90 Edin Univ MTh93. Westcott Ho Cam MA00. **d** 00 **p** 01. C Waltham H Cross *Chelmsf* from 00. *Abbey Lodge Upper, 5A Greenyard, Waltham Abbey EN9 1RD* Tel (01992) 701106
E-mail lcvincer@ukonline.co.uk

VINCER, Canon Michael. b 41. Sarum & Wells Th Coll 77. **d** 80 **p** 81. Hon C Littleham w Exmouth *Ex* 80-92; Miss to Seamen 80-92; Area Sec USPG *Ex* and *Truro* 86-92; Ind Chapl Gtr Man Ind Miss *Man* from 92; Chapl Man Airport from 92; Lic Preacher from 92; Perm to Offic *Ches* from 92; Hon Can Man Cathl *Man* from 02. *10 Highfield Crescent, Wilmslow SK9 2JL* Tel (01625) 525982 *or* 0161-489 2838 Fax 0161-489 3909
E-mail mike.vincer@ntlworld.com *or*
mike.vincer@manairport.co.uk

VINE, James David. b 67. Brighton Univ BSc95. St Steph Ho Ox. **d** 00 **p** 01. C Eastbourne St Mary *Chich* 00-03; V Stone Cross St Luke w N Langney from 03. *The Vicarage, 8 Culver Close, Eastbourne BN23 8EA* Tel (01323) 764473

VINE, John. b 24. Keble Coll Ox BA45 MA50. St Steph Ho Ox 45. **d** 48 **p** 49. C Hackney Wick St Mary of Eton w St Aug *Lon* 48-50; C Holborn St Alb w Saffron Hill St Pet 50-53; Chapl Ely Th Coll 53-56; Vice-Prin Ely Th Coll 56-60; Hon C St Leonards Ch Ch

Chich 60-62; Chapl Lich Th Coll 62-67; R Wrington *B & W* 67-69; V Earl's Court St Cuth w St Matthias *Lon* from 69. *St Cuthbert's Clergy House, 50 Philbeach Gardens, London SW5 9EB* Tel (020) 7370 3263

VINE, Michael Charles. b 51. Worc Coll Ox BA73 MA80. Cuddesdon Coll 73. **d** 76 **p** 77. C Wallsend St Luke *Newc* 76-79; C Denton 79-81; V Sugley 81-91; V Shiremoor 91-02; R Wallsend St Pet and St Luke from 02. *The Vicarage, 148 Park Road, Wallsend NE28 7QS* Tel 0191-262 3723
E-mail vinemichael@hotmail.com

VINE, Michael Derek. b 35. Ch Ch Ox BA58 MA63 Reading Univ PGCE. Ely Th Coll 58. **d** 60 **p** 61. C Syston *Leic* 60-63; C S Ascot *Ox* 63-66; Chapl RN 66-70; Perm to Offic *Portsm* 71-74; *Lon* 74-91; C Chepstow *Mon* 91-94; V Llantilio Pertholey w Bettws Chpl etc 94-00; rtd 00. *5 Chestnut Court, Abergavenny NP7 5JD*

VINE, Canon Neville Peter. b 54. K Coll Lon BD80 AKC80. Linc Th Coll 80. **d** 81 **p** 82. C Peterlee *Dur* 81-86; Chapl Peterlee Coll 84-86; V Auckland St Pet *Dur* 86-89; Perm to Offic 89-91; R Easington 91-99; R Easington, Easington Colliery and S Hetton 99-03; AD Easington 98-03; V Auckland St Andr and St Anne from 03; AD Auckland from 03; Hon Can Dur Cathl from 03. *4 Conway Grove, Bishop Auckland DL14 6AF*
E-mail neville.p.vine@lineone.net

VINER, Canon Leonard Edwin. b 20. Univ Coll Dur LTh41 BA43. St Aug Coll Cant 38. **d** 43 **p** 44. C W Molesey *Guildf* 43-45; Nyasaland 46-56 and 58-64; Malawi 64-71; C Roxbourne St Andr *Lon* 56-58; R Honing w Crostwight *Nor* 71-75; P-in-c E Ruston 71-73; V 73-75; P-in-c Witton w Ridlington 71-73; V 73-75; C Corby Epiphany w St Jo *Pet* 75-79; R Bystock w Stanion 79-86; rtd 86; Asst Chapl Lisbon *Eur* 86-87; Chapl Tangier 87-89; Perm to Offic *Pet* from 90. *8 Clive Close, Kettering NN15 5BQ* Tel (01536) 519734

VINEY, Arthur William. b 32. BEd. S Dios Minl Tr Scheme. **d** 82 **p** 83. NSM Clayton w Keymer *Chich* 82-86; NSM Streat w Westmeston 86-94; rtd 94; Perm to Offic *Chich* from 94. *3 The Almshouses of the Holy Name, Brighton Road, Hurstpierpoint, Hassocks BN6 9EF* Tel (01273) 832570

VINEY, Peter. b 43. Ox NSM Course. **d** 76 **p** 77. NSM High Wycombe *Ox* from 76. *76 Westmead, Princes Risborough HP27 9HS* Tel (01844) 275461

VIPOND, Canon John. b 17. Lon Univ BD48. ALCD48. **d** 48 **p** 49. C Roxeth Ch Ch *Lon* 48-51; V 51-56; V Pudsey St Lawr *Bradf* 56-73; Hon Can Bradf Cathl 67-73; V St Austell *Truro* 73-83; rtd 83; Perm to Offic *Truro* from 83. *Wisteria, 15 Coffeelake Meadow, Lostwithiel PL22 0LT* Tel (01208) 873141

VIRGO, Canon Leslie Gordon. b 25. Linc Th Coll 56. **d** 58 **p** 59. C Hatcham Park All SS *S'wark* 58-61; C Selsdon *Cant* 61-65; Chapl Warlingham Park Hosp Croydon 65-73; Dioc Adv on Past Care and Counselling from 74; R Chelsfield *Roch* from 74; Hon Can Roch Cathl from 83. *Chelsfield Rectory, Skibbs Lane, Orpington BR6 7RH* Tel (01689) 825749
E-mail leslie.virgo@tinyworld.co.uk

VIRJI, Elizabeth Jane. b 47. Win Sch of Art BA95. STETS 98. **d** 01 **p** 02. NSM Hale w Badshot Lea *Guildf* from 01; Chapl Surrey Inst Art and Design from 01. *Kiln Cottage, Pottery Lane, Wrecclesham, Farnham GU10 4QJ* Tel (01252) 721542 Fax 820248 E-mail jane@jvirji.freeserve.co.uk

VIRTUE, Thomas James. b 32. QUB BA56 TCD 58 Liv Univ DipRS80. **d** 58 **p** 59. C Belfast St Mich *Conn* 58-61; C Belfast St Bart 61-63; I Tempo *Clogh* 63-66; P-in-c Glynn w Raloo and Templecorran *Conn* 66-70; TV Ellesmere Port *Ches* 70-74; TV Ches Team 74-83; V Gt Sutton 83-97; rtd 97; Perm to Offic *Ches* from 97. *48 Saughall Road, Blacon, Chester CH1 5EY* Tel (01244) 399531

VIVASH, Peter Henry. b 57. Hockerill Coll of Educn CertEd78 Chelmer Inst of HE CQSW85. Cranmer Hall Dur 90. **d** 92 **p** 93. C Malpas *Mon* 92-95; R Bettws 95-01; P-in-c Thornthwaite cum Braithwaite, Newlands etc *Carl* from 01; Dioc Rep CMS from 01. *Thornthwaite Vicarage, Braithwaite, Keswick CA12 5RY* Tel (01768) 778243 E-mail vivash@pvivash.fsnet.co.uk

VIVIAN, Adrian John. b 42. K Coll Lon BD65 AKC66. St Denys Warminster 62. **d** 66 **p** 67. C Bromley St Andr *Roch* 66-69; C Egg Buckland *Ex* 69-73; Perm to Offic 73-84; P-in-c Newton Ferrers w Revelstoke 84-97. *4 Fell Close, Yealmpton, Plymouth PL8 2EG* Tel (01752) 873116

VIVIAN, Thomas Keith. b 27. St Jo Coll Cam BA48 MA52. St Deiniol's Hawarden 76. **d** 80 **p** 81. Hd Master Lucton Sch Leominster 62-85; Lic to Offic *Heref* 80-85; P-in-c Chew Stoke w Nempnett Thrubwell *B & W* 85-88; R 88-97; P-in-c Norton Malreward 85-88; R 88-97; RD Chew Magna 92-97; rtd 97; Perm to Offic *Sarum* and *B & W* from 97. *Timberley, Sidmouth Road, Lyme Regis DT7 3ES* Tel (01297) 443547

VIVIAN, Victor Ivan. b 38. Nottm Poly LLB87. EMMTC DTPS94. **d** 94 **p** 95. NSM Bestwood *S'well* 94-99; Korea 99-03; rtd 03. *12 Deepdale Road, Wollaton, Nottingham NG8 2FU* Tel 0115-928 3954

VOAKE, Andrew James Frederick. b 28. Dur Univ BA55. Oak Hill Th Coll 51. **d** 55 **p** 56. C Uxbridge St Marg *Lon* 55; C Fulham St Matt 55-58; C Hove Bp Hannington Memorial Ch *Chich* 58-61; V Kirkdale St Lawr *Liv* 61-63; Chapl Millfield Sch Somerset 63-71; R Bp Latimer Memorial Ch *Birm* 71-73; R Birm Bishop Latimer w All SS 73-80; V Crondall and Ewshot *Guildf* 80-90; rtd 90; Perm to Offic *B & W* from 90. *1 St Aubyns Avenue, Weston-super-Mare BS23 4UJ* Tel (01934) 620587

✠**VOBBE, The Rt Revd Joachim Gerhard.** b 47. Bonn Univ DipTh72. **p** 72 **c** 95. Chapl Cologne *Eur* 72-74; Chapl Düsseldorf 74-77; R Blumberg 77-82; R Offenbach 82-95; Bp Bonn from 95; Asst Bp Eur from 99. *Gregor-Mendel-Strasse 28, D-53115 Bonn, Germany* Tel (0049) (228) 232285 Fax 238314 E-mail ordinariat@alt-katholisch.de

VOCKINS, Michael David. b 44. OBE96. Univ of Wales (Abth) BSc69. Glouc Sch of Min 85. **d** 88 **p** 89. NSM Cradley w Mathon and Storridge *Heref* from 88; RD Ledbury from 02; Perm to Offic *Worc* from 88. *Birchwood Lodge, Birchwood, Storridge, Malvern WR13 5EZ* Tel (01886) 884366 *or* (01905) 748474

VODEN, Capt Raymond William Lang. b 35. CQSW74. SW Minl Tr Course 85. **d** 88 **p** 89. CA from 60; NSM Bideford *Ex* 88-94; C Northlew w Ashbury 94; C Bratton Clovelly w Germansweek 94; TV Okehampton w Inwardleigh, Bratton Clovelly etc 94-01; Chapl Ex and Distr Community Health Service NHS Trust 94-01; Bp's Adv for Child Protection *Ex* 96-01; Perm to Offic *Ex* from 99 and *Truro* from 01; rtd 01. *1 School Lane, Harrowbarrow, Callington PL17 8BS* Tel (01579) 350135 E-mail ray@northmoor67.freeserve.co.uk

VOGT, Charles William Derek. b 36. Cert Analytical Psychology 85. EMMTC 83. **d** 86 **p** 87. NSM Ilkeston H Trin *Derby* 86-87; C Derby St Anne and St Jo 87-90; TV Staveley and Barrow Hill 90-95; P-in-c Hasland 95-96; R 97-01; P-in-c Temple Normanton 95-96; V 97-01; rtd 01. *54 Old Bakery Close, Exwick, Exeter EX4 2UZ* Tel (01392) 271943

VOGT, Robert Anthony. b 25. Jes Coll Cam BA50 MA54. S'wark Ord Course 60. **d** 63 **p** 64. C Sutton New Town St Barn *S'wark* 63-67; C Kidbrooke St Jas 67-72; V Wood End *Cov* 72-80; RD Cov E 77-80; R Kidbrooke St Jas *S'wark* 80-85; TR 85-90; rtd 90; Perm to Offic *S'wark* from 90. *16 Tristan Square, London SE3 9UB* Tel (020) 8297 2361

VOLTZENLOGEL, Timothy John. b 60. St Jo Coll Dur BA81. Wycliffe Hall Ox BTh00. **d** 00 **p** 01. C Eastbourne All SS *Chich* from 00. *1F Grassington Road, Eastbourne BN20 7BP* Tel (01323) 721231 E-mail timvoltz@tinyworld.co.uk

VON BENZON, Charles Nicholas. b 54. Kent Univ BA78 Solicitor 79. S'wark Ord Course 82. **d** 85 **p** 86. NSM Bromley SS Pet and Paul *Roch* 85-87; Perm to Offic *Chich* 87-93; Ed *Newsletter among Ministers at Work* 89-93; Asst to RD Dallington 93-95; C The Deverills *Sarum* 95; TV Cley Hill Warminster 95-01; R Fladbury w Wyre Piddle and Moor etc *Worc* from 96. *The Rectory, Station Road, Fladbury, Pershore WR10 2QW* Tel (01386) 860356 E-mail nicholasvonbenzon@btinternet.com

VON MALAISE, Nicolas Christoph Axel. b 62. Univ Coll Ox BA84. Ripon Coll Cuddesdon BA86. **d** 87 **p** 88. C Oxhey St Matt *St Alb* 87-90; C Northfield *Birm* 90-92; Asst Chapl Win Coll from 92. *Winchester College, Winchester SO23 9LX* Tel (01962) 884056 *or* 860051

VONBERG, Canon Michael. b 27. Lon Univ BA51. Wells Th Coll 58. **d** 59 **p** 60. C Bournemouth St Andr *Win* 59-61; C Milton 61-64; V Camberwell St Geo *S'wark* 64-74; V Kenley 75-94; RD Croydon S 85-93; Hon Can S'wark Cathl 89-94; rtd 94; Perm to Offic *Guildf* from 94. *81 Christchurch Mount, Epsom KT19 8LP*

VOOGHT, Canon Michael George Peter. b 38. St Pet Hall Ox BA61 MA65. Chich Th Coll 61. **d** 63 **p** 64. C E Dulwich St Jo *S'wark* 63-66; C Prestbury *Glouc* 66-72; R Minchinhampton 72-85; RD Stonehouse 79-85; V Thornbury 85-02; Hon Can Glouc Cathl 86-02; rtd 02. *62 High Street, Thornbury, Bristol BS35 2AN* Tel (01454) 414915

VORLEY, Kenneth Arthur. b 27. Sarum Th Coll 65. **d** 67 **p** 68. C Ashbourne w Mapleton and Clifton *Derby* 67-71; R W Hallam and Mapperley 71-77; V Hemingford Grey *Ely* 78-88; rtd 88; Perm to Offic *Carl* 88-01. *The Old Manor, Little Braithwaite, Keswick CA12 5SR* Tel (01768?) 78535

VOSS, Mrs Philomena Ann. b 35. Edge Hill Coll of HE CertEd55. St Alb Minl Tr Scheme 87 EAMTC 95. **d** 96 **p** 97. NSM Tye Green w Netteswell *Chelmsf* 96-03; NSM Ware St Mary *St Alb* from 03. *21 Queen's Road, Hertford SG13 8AZ* Tel (01992) 554676 E-mail annvoss@tesco.net

VOUSDEN, Canon Alan Thomas. b 48. K Coll Lon BSc69. Qu Coll Birm DipTh71. **d** 72 **p** 73. C Orpington All SS *Roch* 72-76; C Belvedere All SS 76-80; R Cuxton and Halling 80-86; V Bromley St Mark 86-98; Chapl Bromley Hosp 86-94; Chapl Bromley Hosps NHS Trust 94-98; V Rainham *Roch* from 98; Hon Can Roch Cathl from 99; RD Gillingham from 00. *The Vicarage, 80 Broadview Avenue, Gillingham ME8 9DE* Tel (01634) 231538 Fax 362023 E-mail alan-vousden@rainhamvic-kent.freeserve.co.uk

VOUT, Victor Alan. b 25. Lon Univ BA53 Hull Univ BA56. Ripon Hall Ox 63. **d** 65 **p** 66. C Norton Woodseats St Paul *Sheff* 65-70; V Clifton St Jas 70-92; rtd 92; Perm to Offic *Sheff* from 92. *87 Spinneyfield, Moorgate, Rotherham S60 3LZ* Tel (01709) 839258

VOWLES, Miss Patricia. b 50. S'wark Ord Course 84. **d** 87 **p** 94. USPG 70-91; NSM Nunhead St Antony w St Silas *S'wark* 87-91; Par Dn Newington St Mary 91; Dn-in-c Camberwell St Mich w All So w Em 91; Par Dn 91-94; V from 94. *St Michael's Vicarage, 128 Bethwin Road, London SE5 0YY* Tel and fax (020) 7703 8686 *or* 7703 1491 Mobile 07741-174113 E-mail p.vowles@btinternet.com

VOWLES, Canon Peter John Henry. b 25. Magd Coll Ox BA50 MA55. Westcott Ho Cam 50. **d** 52 **p** 53. C Kings Heath *Birm* 52-56; C Huddersfield St Pet *Wakef* 56-57; PC Perry Beeches *Birm* 57-64; V 64-72; R Cottingham *York* 72-83; R Man St Ann *Man* 83-91; Hon Can Man Cathl 83-91; rtd 91; Perm to Offic *Man* from 91. *10 Redshaw Close, Fallowfield, Manchester M14 6JB* Tel 0161-257 2065

VYVYAN, John Philip. b 28. New Coll Ox BA51 MA59. Cuddesdon Coll 57. **d** 59 **p** 60. C Notting Hill St Mark *Lon* 59-61; USPG (Sarawak & Borneo) 61-64; V Adderbury w Milton *Ox* 64-93; rtd 93; Perm to Offic *Truro* from 93. *Forth Coth, Carnon Downs, Truro TR3 6LE* Tel (01872) 865740

W

WACKWITZ-MARSHALL, Alan John. b 48. Carl Dioc Tr Course. **d** 89 **p** 90. NSM Carl St Luke Morton *Carl* 89-92; NSM Carl H Trin and St Barn from 01. *3 Knowefield Avenue, Carlisle CA3 9BH* Tel (01228) 525338

WADDELL, Peter Matthew. b 75. Keble Coll Ox BA96 Fitzw Coll Cam MPhil98 PhD02. Westcott Ho Cam 98. **d** 02 **p** 03. C Oxton *Ches* from 02. *11 Spurstow Close, Prenton CH43 2NQ* Tel 0151-653 2148 E-mail peterwad@hotmail.com

WADDINGTON, Gary Richard. b 69. St Chad's Coll Dur BSc91. St Steph Ho Ox BTh93. **d** 96 **p** 97. C Southsea H Spirit *Portsm* 96-00; V Paulsgrove from 00. *St Michael's Vicarage, Hempsted Road, Portsmouth PO6 4AS* Tel (023) 9237 8808 Mobile 07778-402490 E-mail frgaryw@aol.com

WADDINGTON, The Very Revd Robert Murray. b 27. Selw Coll Cam BA51 MA55. Ely Th Coll 51. **d** 53 **p** 54. C Bethnal Green St Jo w St Simon *Lon* 53-56; Australia 56-59 and 61-71; C Chesterton St Luke *Ely* 59-61; OGS from 60; Can Res Carl Cathl *Carl* 72-77; Bp's Adv for Educn 72-77; Hon Can Carl Cathl 77-84; Gen Sec Gen Syn Bd of Educn 77-84; Gen Sec Nat Soc 77-84; Dean Man 84-93; rtd 93; Perm to Offic *York* from 93. *6 Waverley Street, York YO31 7QZ* Tel (01904) 670200

WADDINGTON-FEATHER, John Joseph. b 33. FRSA87 Leeds Univ BA54 Keele Univ PGCE74. St Deiniol's Hawarden 75. **d** 77 **p** 78. NSM Longden and Annscroft w Pulverbatch *Heref* 77-84 and from 85; Chapl Asst HM Pris Shrewsbury 77-84 and from 85; Sudan 84-85; Chapl Prestfelde Sch Shrewsbury 86-96; rtd 96; Perm to Offic *Lich* from 99. *Fair View, Old Coppice, Lyth Bank, Bayston Hill, Shrewsbury SY3 0BW* Tel (01743) 872177 Fax as telephone E-mail john@feather-books.com

WADDLE, William. b 31. Linc Th Coll 64. **d** 66 **p** 67. C Tynemouth Priory *Newc* 66-69; C Longbenton St Bart 69-75; V Denton 75-81; V Beadnell 81; V Beadnell w Ellingham 81-93; RD Bamburgh and Glendale 83-92; Perm to Offic 93-99; rtd 93. *7 Hillside Road, Belford NE70 7NB* Tel (01668) 219 070

WADDY, Canon Lawrence Heber. b 14. Ball Coll Ox BA37 MA45. Westcott Ho Cam 39. **d** 40 **p** 41. Asst Master Win Coll 38-42 and 46-49; Chapl RNVR 42-46; Hd Master Tonbridge Sch 49-62; Lic Preacher *Roch* 50-63; Hon Can Roch Cathl 61-63; Hon Bp's Chapl 63; USA from 63; Chapl Bps' Sch 63-67; Hd Master and Chapl Santa Maria Academy Chula Vista 67-69; Assoc Min Coronado Ch Ch 68-70; Lect California Univ San Diego 69-80; V San Diego Gd Samaritan 70-74; rtd 75; Hon Asst Min La Jolla St Jas-by-the-Sea from 75; Hon Can San Diego from 98. *5910 Camino de la Costa, La Jolla, CA 92037, USA* Tel (001) (858) 459 5221

WADDY, Richard Patteson Stacy. b 04. Ball Coll Ox BA26 MA30. Cuddesdon Coll 26. **d** 27 **p** 28. C Leic St Pet *Leic* 27-30; India 30-47; R Ampthill *St Alb* 47-52; RD Ampthill 51-52; Warden Coll of Ascension Selly Oak 52-59; Hon Can Birm Cathl *Birm* 54-59; R Morley *Derby* 59-67; Hon Can Derby Cathl 63-67; Chapl Qu Anne's Sch Caversham 67-72; rtd 72; Chapl

Community of All Hallows Ditchingham 72-79. *Manormead, Tilford Road, Hindhead GU26 6RA* Tel (01428) 604780

WADE, Andrew John. b 50. R Agric Coll Cirencester NDA72. Trin Coll Bris DipHE86. **d** 86 **p** 87. C St Keverne *Truro* 86-89; TV Probus, Ladock and Grampound w Creed and St Erme 89-92; V Constantine 92-00; P-in-c Ludgvan 00-01; P-in-c Marazion 00-01; P-in-c St Hilary w Perranuthnoe 00-01; R Ludgvan, Marazion, St Hilary and Perranuthnoe from 01; RD Penwith from 03. *The Rectory, Ludgvan, Penzance TR20 8EZ* Tel (01736) 740784 E-mail andrewatludgvan@aol.com

WADE, Christopher John. b 54. ARICS82 ACIArb88 Trent Poly BSc81 MRICS01. Aston Tr Scheme 88 Trin Coll Bris DipHE92. **d** 92 **p** 93. C Barnsley St Geo *Wakef* 92-95; C Whittle-le-Woods *Blackb* 95-99; P-in-c Bulwell St Jo *S'well* 99-03. *20 Westley Close, Whitley Bay NE26 4NR* Tel 08451-665277 Fax as telephone E-mail chris@heavenfire.org

WADE, David Peter. b 65. St Jo Coll Nottm LTh92 DCM92. **d** 92 **p** 93. C Victoria Docks Ascension *Chelmsf* 92-95; P-in-c Victoria Docks St Luke 95-97; V from 97. *The Vicarage, 16A Ruscoe Road, London E16 1JB* Tel (020) 7476 2076 E-mail davenicky@hotmail.com

WADE, Geoffrey Adrian. b 61. Ripon Coll Cuddesdon. **d** 01 **p** 02. C Worc City St Paul and Old St Martin etc *Worc* 01-02; C Wordsley from 02. *25 Middleway Avenue, Wordsley, Stourbridge DY8 5NB* Tel (01384) 293350

WADE, Walter. b 29. Oak Hill Th Coll 64. **d** 66 **p** 67. C Denton Holme *Carl* 66-69; V Jesmond H Trin *Newc* 69-78; R Moresby *Carl* 78-87; P-in-c Langdale 87-94; Member Rural Life and Agric Team 93-94; rtd 94; Perm to Offic *Carl* from 94. *Manor Cottage, Fellside, Caldbeck, Wigton CA7 8HA* Tel (01697) 478214

WADE-STUBBS, Edward Pomery Flood. b 17. St Jo Coll Dur LTh39 BA40. Tyndale Hall Bris 36. **d** 40 **p** 41. C Burslem St Jo *Lich* 40-42; C Handsworth St Jas *Birm* 42-44; C Hawkhurst *Cant* 44-46; C Cheltenham St Mark *Glouc* 51-53; R Gt Witcombe 53-62; Canada 62-63; R Sutton Veny *Sarum* 63-66; V Norton Bavant 63-66; rtd 69; Perm to Offic *Sarum* 90-95. *Millward House, 6 Madeira Park, Tunbridge Wells TN2 5SZ* Tel (01892) 528115

WADEY, Ms Rachel Susan. b 71. Lanc Univ BA94 Ox Univ BA98. St Steph Ho Ox 95. **d** 98 **p** 99. C Poulton-le-Fylde *Blackb* 98-01; C Blackpool H Cross from 01. *19 Windermere Road, Blackpool FY4 2BX* Tel (01253) 341231 E-mail rachel_28_uk@yahoo.co.uk

WADGE, Alan. b 46. Grey Coll Dur BA94 St Chad's Coll Dur DipTh69. **d** 70 **p** 71. C Cockerton *Dur* 70-74; C Whitworth w Spennymoor 74-75; P-in-c Shipton Moyne w Westonbirt and Lasborough *Glouc* 75-80; Chapl Westonbirt Sch 75-80; V Dean Forest H Trin *Glouc* 80-83; Chapl Gresham's Sch Holt 83-91; R Ridgeway *Ox* from 91; RD Wantage 95-01. *The Rectory, Letcombe Regis, Wantage OX12 9LD* Tel (01235) 763805

WADHAM, Philip Andrew. b 41. Bradf Univ MA92. Vancouver Sch of Th BTh80. **d** 80 **p** 80. Canada 80-82 and 85-88; Ecuador 82-85; Area Sec USPG *Wakef* and *Bradf* 88-92; Perm to Offic *Bradf* 88-93; Canada from 93. *600 Jarvis Street, Toronto ON, Canada, K0G 1X0*

WADLAND, Douglas Bryan. b 33. K Coll Dur BA61 CQSW62. Oak Hill Th Coll 90. **d** 91 **p** 92. NSM Cowley *Lon* 91-93; Asst Chapl Hillingdon Hosp NHS Trust 91-93; P-in-c Wembley St Jo *Lon* 93-00; Chapl Cen Middx Hosp NHS Trust 93-00; rtd 00; Hon C Alperton *Lon* from 03. *4 Selby Road, London W5 1LX* Tel (020) 8998 1839 E-mail wadland@lizbryan.freeserve.co.uk

WADMAN, Vera Margaret. b 51. EAMTC 97. **d** 00 **p** 01. NSM Burnham *Chelmsf* 00-02; NSM Creeksea w Althorne, Latchingdon and N Fambridge from 02. *Fernlea Cottage, 8 Fernlea Road, Burnham-on-Crouch CM0 8EJ* Tel (01621) 783963 E-mail verawadman@onetel.net.uk

WADSWORTH (née REID), Mrs Alison Margaret. b 36. Bris Univ CertEd57. LNSM course 95. **d** 97 **p** 98. OLM Cley Hill Warminster *Sarum* from 97. *2 Saxon's Acre, Warminster BA12 8HT* Tel (01985) 212510

WADSWORTH, Andrew James. b 56. St Jo Coll Dur BA79 Cam Univ CertEd80 Lambeth STh95 FRSA99. Sarum & Wells Th Coll 84 Chich Th Coll 86. **d** 87 **p** 88. NSM Forest Row *Chich* 87-89; NSM E Grinstead St Swithun 87-89; C Shrewsbury St Chad w St Mary *Lich* 89-91; TV Honiton, Gittisham, Combe Raleigh, Monkton etc *Ex* 91-97; V Bulkington w Shilton and Ansty *Cov* from 97. *The Vicarage, School Road, Bulkington, Nuneaton CV12 9JB* Tel (024) 7631 2396 E-mail rev.andrew@wadswortha.fsnet.co.uk

WADSWORTH, Andrew John. b 67. Reading Univ BSc88 ARICS90 MRICS01. Wycliffe Hall Ox 99. **d** 01 **p** 02. C Plymouth St Andr and St Paul Stonehouse *Ex* from 01. *18 Glenhurst Road, Plymouth PL3 5LT* Tel (01752) 267025 E-mail awadsworth@waddy20.freeserve.com

WADSWORTH, Jean. b 44. St Jo Coll Dur BA71. Cranmer Hall Dur 85. **d** 87 **p** 94. Par Dn Thamesmead *S'wark* 87-92; Par Dn Rotherhithe H Trin 92-94; C 94-98; V New Eltham All SS from 98; RD Eltham and Mottingham from 01. *All Saints' Vicarage, 22 Bercta Road, London SE9 3TZ* Tel (020) 8850 9894

WADSWORTH, Canon Michael Philip. b 43. Qu Coll Ox BA65 MA68 DPhil75 Cam Univ PhD78. Ripon Hall Ox 67. **d** 70 **p** 71. C Sutton St Mich *York* 70-73; Lect Sussex Univ *Chich* 73-78; Hon C Hove St Jo 75-78; Fell and Chapl SS Coll Cam 78-81; Dir Th Studies 79-81; CF (TA) from 80; C Ditton St Mich *Liv* 81; TV 82-84; Dioc Lay Tr Officer 83-89; V Orford St Marg 84-89; V Haddenham *Ely* 89-98; V Wilburton 89-98; RD Ely 94-98; Hon Can Ely Cathl 96-01; P-in-c Gt Shelford 98-01; Perm to Offic from 01; rtd 01; Perm to Offic *Linc* from 01. *6 Miller's Way, Heckington, Sleaford NG34 9JG* Tel (01529) 460879

WADSWORTH, Peter Richard. b 52. Qu Coll Ox BA73 MA77. Cuddesdon Coll 74 English Coll Rome 76. **d** 77 **p** 78. C High Wycombe *Ox* 77-81; C Farnham Royal w Hedgerley 81-84; Dioc Ecum Officer *Portsm* 84-90; V E Meon 84-96; V Langrish 84-96; V Elson from 96; RD Gosport 96-02. *St Thomas's Vicarage, 21 Elson Road, Gosport PO12 4BL* Tel (023) 9258 2824 Fax as telephone E-mail peter@hisstudy.freeserve.co.uk

WADSWORTH, Roy. b 37. NEOC 89. **d** 89 **p** 90. NSM Alne *York* from 89; Ind Chapl 94-03; rtd 02. *The Rosery, Tollerton, York YO61 1PX* Tel (01347) 838212

WAGGETT, Geoffrey James. b 49. Sarum & Wells Th Coll 83. **d** 85 **p** 86. C Newton Nottage *Llan* 85-88; TV Glyncorrwg w Afan Vale and Cymmer Afan 88-89; R 89-99; V Glyncorrwg and Upper Afan Valley 99-00; TR Ebbw Vale *Mon* from 00. *The Rectory, Eureka Place, Ebbw Vale NP23 6PN* Tel (01495) 301723

WAGHORN, Geoffrey Brian. b 28. St Aid Birkenhead 62. **d** 64 **p** 65. C Gillingham H Trin *Roch* 64-66; C St Mary Cray and St Paul's Cray 66-68; C Lenton w Ingoldsby *Linc* 68-70; V Messingham 70-77; R Fishtoft 77-85; R Durley *Portsm* 85-93; V Curdridge 85-93; rtd 93; Perm to Offic *Portsm* and *Win* from 93. *17 Waters Edge, Hedge End, Southampton SO30 4AE* Tel (01489) 782795

WAGSTAFF, Alan Robert Joseph. b 21. Lon Univ DipTh69. S'wark Ord Course 67. **d** 70 **p** 71. C St Paul's Cray St Barn *Roch* 70-76; V Southborough St Pet w Ch Ch and St Matt 76-86; RD Tunbridge Wells 83-86; rtd 86; Perm to Offic *Chich* and *Roch* from 86. *Mews Cottage, 27A The Green, St Leonards-on-Sea TN38 0SX* Tel (01424) 425895

WAGSTAFF, Mrs Alison. b 40. K Coll Dur BA63 Man Univ CertEd64 New Coll Edin DPS92. TISEC 95. **d** 98 **p** 99. C Edin St Cuth *Edin* from 98. *27 Cambridge Gardens, Edinburgh EH6 5DH* Tel 0131-554 6702 Fax 220 5150 E-mail alisonwags@aol.com

WAGSTAFF, Andrew Robert. b 56. K Coll Lon BD79 AKC79. Coll of Resurr Mirfield 81. **d** 83 **p** 84. C Newark w Hawton, Cotham and Shelton *S'well* 83-86; C Dublin St Bart w Leeson Park *D & G* 86-89; V Nottingham St Geo w St Jo *S'well* 89-95; TV Worksop Priory from 95. *The Vicarage, Cheapside, Worksop S80 2HX* Tel (01909) 472180

WAGSTAFF, The Ven Christopher John Harold. b 36. St D Coll Lamp BA62 DipTh63. **d** 63 **p** 64. C Queensbury All SS *Lon* 63-68; V Tokyngton St Mich 68-73; V Coleford w Staunton *Glouc* 73-83; RD Forest S 76-82; Adn Gloucester 83-00; Hon Can Glouc Cathl 83-00; Hon Can St Andr Cathl Njombe (Tanzania) from 93; rtd 00; Perm to Offic *Glouc* from 00. *Karibuni, Collafield, Littledean, Cinderford GL14 3LG* Tel (01594) 825282

WAGSTAFF, Miss Joan. b 33. Gilmore Ho. **dss** 75 **d** 87 **p** 94. Ellesmere Port *Ches* 86-87; Par Dn 87-93; rtd 93; Perm to Offic *Ches* from 93. *41 Heywood Road, Great Sutton, South Wirral CH66 3PS* Tel 0151-348 0884

WAGSTAFF, Michael. b 59. R Holloway Coll Lon BA81. Coll of Resurr Mirfield 86. **d** 89 **p** 90. C Worksop Priory *S'well* 89-92; C Ab Kettleby Gp *Leic* 92-94; TV Leic Resurr 94-00; Dioc Soc Resp Officer *Sheff* from 00. *27 The Copse, Bramley, Rotherham S66 3TB* Tel (01709) 703672 E-mail michael.wagstaff@sheffield-diocese.org.uk

WAGSTAFF, Robert William. b 36. Edin Th Coll 61. **d** 63 **p** 64. C Harringay St Paul *Lon* 63-64; C Mill Hill Jo Keble Ch 64-69; NSM N Lambeth *S'wark* 70-80; NSM Wilden, Hartlebury and Ombersley w Doverdale 80-97; C Shrawley, Witley, Astley and Abberley *Worc* 98-02; rtd 02. *The Red House, Quarry Bank, Hartlebury, Kidderminster DY11 7TE* Tel (01299) 250883

WAGSTAFFE, Eric Herbert. b 25. St Aid Birkenhead 55. **d** 57 **p** 58. C Harpurhey Ch Ch *Man* 57-60; R 60-69; V Pendlebury St Jo 69-84; V Hoghton *Blackb* 84-91; rtd 91; Perm to Offic *Blackb* from 91; Perm to Offic *Man* from 95. *3 Chelwood Close, Bolton BL1 7LN* Tel (01204) 596048

WAIN, Phillip. b 54. Aston Tr Scheme 89 Linc Th Coll 93. **d** 93 **p** 94. C Witton *Ches* 93-97; R Lea Gp *Linc* from 97. *The Rectory, 18 Gainsborough Road, Lea, Gainsborough DN21 5HZ* Tel (01427) 613188

WAINAINA, Francis Samson Kamoko. b 51. St Jo Coll Dur MA89. Oak Hill Th Coll BA84. **d** 84 **p** 85. Kenya 84-88; C Upton (Overchurch) *Ches* 89-92; V Ellesmere St Pet *Sheff* 92-95; C York St Mich-le-Belfrey *York* 95-01; V Starbeck *Ripon* from 01. *The Vicarage, 78 High Street, Harrogate HG2 7LW* Tel (01423) 546477 *or* 889162 E-mail francis.wainaina@ntlworld.com

✠WAINE, The Rt Revd John. b 30. KCVO96. Man Univ BA51. Ridley Hall Cam 53. **d** 55 **p** 56 **c** 75. C W Derby St Mary *Liv* 55-58; C Sutton 58-60; V Ditton St Mich 60-64; V Southport H Trin 64-69; V Kirkby 69-71; TR 71-75; Suff Bp Stafford *Lich* 75-78; Preb Lich Cathl 75-78; Bp St E 78-86; Bp Chelmsf 86-96; Clerk of the Closet 89-96; rtd 96; Perm to Offic *St E* from 96. *Broadmere, Ipswich Road, Grundisburgh, Woodbridge IP13 6TJ* Tel (01473) 738296

WAINE, Stephen John. b 59. Westcott Ho Cam 81. **d** 84 **p** 85. C Wolverhampton *Lich* 84-88; Min Can and Succ St Paul's Cathl *Lon* 88-93; V Romford St Edw *Chelmsf* from 93; P-in-c Romford St Jo from 02. *St Edward's Vicarage, 15 Oaklands Avenue, Romford RM1 4DB* Tel (01708) 740385
E-mail stephen@stephenwaine.freeserve.co.uk

WAINWRIGHT, Frank Alan. b 18. Leeds Univ BA39. Coll of Resurr Mirfield 39. **d** 41 **p** 42. C Glouc St Paul *Glouc* 41-46; C Perry Hill St Geo *S'wark* 46-47; V 47-57; V N Dulwich St Faith 57-64; Chapl Maudsley Hosp *Lon* 60-62; Chapl St Gabr Coll Camberwell 62-64; V Woodham *Guildf* 64-72; rtd 83; Perm to Offic *Truro* from 83. *Menhay, Pendoggett, St Kew, Bodmin PL30 3HH* Tel (01208) 880528

WAINWRIGHT, John Pounsberry. b 42. St Steph Ho Ox 64. **d** 66 **p** 67. C Palmers Green St Jo *Lon* 66-70; C Primrose Hill St Mary w Avenue Road St Paul 70-71; P-in-c St John's Wood All SS 71-73; V Hendon All SS Childs Hill from 73. *All Saints' Vicarage, Church Walk, London NW2 2TJ* Tel (020) 7435 3182

WAINWRIGHT, Joseph Allan. b 21. K Coll Lon BD50 AKC50 Columbia Pacific Univ PhD82 Sussex Univ DPhil85. **d** 50 **p** 51. C Boston *Linc* 50-53; Chapl St Paul's Coll Cheltenham 53-62; Educn Sec BCC 62-66; Lect Moray Ho Coll of Educn Edin 66-78; Perm to Offic *Chich* 79-88; rtd 86. *Beggar's Roost, Lewes BN7 1LX* Tel (01273) 477453

WAINWRIGHT, Kevin Frank. b 46. Linc Th Coll 73. **d** 75 **p** 76. C Stand *Man* 75-78; C Radcliffe St Thos and St Jo 78-80; V Kearsley Moor from 80. *St Stephen's Vicarage, Blair Street, Kearsley, Bolton BL4 8QP* Tel (01204) 572535

WAINWRIGHT, Malcolm Hugh. b 47. Man Univ BA68 Nottm Univ MA89. St Jo Coll Nottm CTM97 MA98. **d** 98 **p** 99. NSM Cotgrave *S'well* 98-01; NSM Owthorpe 98-01; P-in-c Plumtree from 01; P-in-c Tollerton from 01. *5 Wright's Orchard, Keyworth, Nottingham NG12 5RE* Tel 0115-937 4603
E-mail mwainw7761@aol.com

WAINWRIGHT, Mrs Margaret Gillian. b 45. Qu Mary Coll Lon BA68. EAMTC 00. **d** 03. NSM Combs and Lt Finborough *St E* from 03. *The Cottage, Elmswell Road, Wetherden, Stowmarket IP14 3LN* Tel (01359) 242653
E-mail margwain@btopenworld.com

WAINWRIGHT, Martin John. b 69. Loughb Univ BEng92. Trin Coll Bris BA98. **d** 98 **p** 99. C Chislehurst Ch Ch *Roch* 98-02; V Camberley St Mary *Guildf* from 02. *St Mary's House, 37 Park Road, Camberley GU15 2SP* Tel (01276) 22085 *or* 685167 Fax as telephone E-mail mjw@fish.co.uk

WAINWRIGHT, Maurice Sidney. b 30. Lon Univ BSc54. Bps' Coll Cheshunt 54. **d** 56 **p** 57. C Twickenham St Mary *Lon* 56-59; C Caversham *Ox* 59-61; Public Preacher *Chelmsf* 61-95; rtd 95. *60 Eastwood Road, London E18 1BU* Tel (020) 8989 1529

WAINWRIGHT, Miss Pauline Barbara. b 40. St Deiniol's Hawarden 83. **dss** 84 **d** 87 **p** 94. New Ferry *Ches* 84-90; Par Dn 87-90; Par Dn Hallwood 90-94; C 94-00; rtd 00; Perm to Offic *Ches* 00-03. *91 Sunny Bank Road, Griffithstown, Pontypool NP4 5LN* E-mail anamcara@btinternet.com

WAINWRIGHT, Raymond Laycock. b 25. Lon Univ BD60. Ho of Resurr Mirfield 55. **d** 56 **p** 57. C Bingley All SS *Bradf* 56-58; C Almondbury *Wakef* 58-60; V Gawthorpe and Chickenley Heath 60-74; V New Mill 74-89; V Thurstonland 74-89; TV Upper Holme Valley 89-91; rtd 91; Perm to Offic *Wakef* from 91. *7 Greenlaws Close, Upperthong, Holmfirth HD9 3HN* Tel (01484) 683779

WAINWRIGHT, Robert Neil. b 52. NEOC 99. **d** 02 **p** 03. NSM Barlby w Riccall *York* from 02; Perm to Offic *Lon* from 02. *33 Hillfield, Selby YO8 3ND* Tel 07768-390060 (mobile) Fax (01757) 706216 E-mail robbwain@yahoo.com

WAIT, Canon Alan Clifford. b 33. St Cath Soc Ox BA58 MA70. Coll of Resurr Mirfield. **d** 60 **p** 61. C Charlton St Luke w St Paul *S'wark* 60-67; C Caterham 67-72; V N Dulwich St Faith 72-83; RD Dulwich 78-83; V Purley St Barn 83-01; RD Croydon S 93-01; Hon Can S'wark Cathl 01; rtd 01; Perm to Offic *Cant* from 01. *Forgefield Oast, Church Hill, Bethersden, Ashford TN26 3AQ* Tel (01233) 820529

WAITE, John Langton (Tony). b 10. Solicitor 34 ACP37 Man Univ 30. Wycliffe Hall Ox 37. **d** 39 **p** 40. C Hove Bp Hannington Memorial Ch *Chich* 39-41; C Walcot *B & W* 41-42; V Blackheath St Jo *S'wark* 42-48; V Leeds St Geo *Ripon* 48-58; V Woking St Jo *Guildf* 58-76; rtd 76; Perm to Offic *Portsm* from 82. *11 The Crescent, Alverstoke, Gosport PO12 2DH* Tel (023) 9252 1458 Fax as telephone E-mail tonywaite@cwcom.net

WAITE, Julian Henry. b 47. Open Univ BA98. Brasted Th Coll 68 Ridley Hall Cam 70. **d** 72 **p** 73. C Wollaton *S'well* 72-76; C Herne Bay Ch Ch *Cant* 76-79; P-in-c Mersham 79-87; Chapl Wm

Harvey Hosp Ashford 79-87; Chapl R Cornwall Hosps Trust 79-87; R Mersham w Hinxhill *Cant* 87; V Marden 87-93; Chapl HM Pris Blantyre Ho 90-93; Chapl HM Pris Swaleside from 01. *HM Prison Swaleside, Eastchurch, Sheerness ME12 4AX* Tel (01795) 884042 Fax 884200

WAITE, Sheila Margaret. *See* TYLER, Mrs Sheila Margaret

WAIYAKI, Canon Jennie. b 34. MBE88. ALA64. NEOC 89. **d** 92 **p** 94. NSM Ulgham and Widdrington *Newc* 92-97; Chapl Northumbria Healthcare NHS Trust from 97; NSM Longhorsley and Hebron *Newc* from 97; Hon Can Newc Cathl from 02. *6 Woodburn Street, Stobswood, Morpeth NE61 5QD* Tel (01670) 791066

WAKE, Colin Walter. b 50. Oriel Coll Ox BA72 MA. Cuddesdon Coll 74. **d** 75 **p** 76. C Sandhurst *Ox* 75-78; C Faversham *Cant* 79-80; TV High Wycombe *Ox* 80-89; R Weston Favell *Pet* from 89; Chapl St Jo Hosp Weston Favell from 89. *The Rectory, Churchway, Weston Favell, Northampton NN3 3BX* Tel (01604) 784679 *or* 787117

WAKEFIELD, Allan. b 31. Qu Coll Birm 72. **d** 74 **p** 75. C Kingsthorpe w Northampton St Dav *Pet* 74-77; TV Clifton *S'well* 77-81; V Bilborough St Jo 81-85; R Bere Ferrers *Ex* 85-91; R Mevagissey and St Ewe *Truro* 91-96; rtd 96; Perm to Offic *Truro* 96-98; Hon C Malborough w S Huish, W Alvington and Churchstow *Ex* 98-02. *4 Eden Cottages, Exeter Road, Ivybridge PL21 0BL* Tel (01752) 698724

WAKEFIELD, Andrew Desmond. b 55. K Coll Lon BD77 AKC77. Coll of Resurr Mirfield 77. **d** 78 **p** 79. C Mitcham Ascension *S'wark* 78-81; C Putney St Mary 81-86; TV Wimbledon 86-91; Ind Chapl from 90; Dioc Urban Missr 91-97; P-in-c S Wimbledon St Andr 91-97; V from 97. *105 Hartfield Road, London SW19 3TJ* Tel (020) 8542 1794 Fax 8542 6566
E-mail wakefieldandrew@hotmail.com

WAKEFIELD, Anne Frances. b 58. St Aid Coll Dur BSc79 Sheff Univ PGCE80. NTMTC 97. **d** 97 **p** 98. NSM Danbury *Chelmsf* 97-98; NSM Sherburn w Pittington *Dur* 98-01; Asst Chapl HM Pris *Dur* 01-03; Chapl HM YOI Northallerton from 03. *HM Young Offender Institution, 15A East Road, Northallerton DL6 1NW* Tel (01609) 780078 Fax 779664

WAKEFIELD, David Geoffrey. b 43. AMIC90. S'wark Ord Course 84. **d** 87 **p** 88. C Addiscombe St Mildred *S'wark* 87-89; C Reigate St Luke S Park 89-93; Chapl HM Pris Bullingdon 93-96; Chapl HM Pris Ranby 96-99; P-in-c Flintham *S'well* from 99; P-in-c Car Colston w Screveton from 99; Chapl HM Pris Whatton from 99. *The Vicarage, Woods Lane, Flintham, Newark NG23 5LR* Tel (01636) 525750 Fax as telephone
E-mail david@thewakefields.freeserve.co.uk

WAKEFIELD, Gavin Tracy. b 57. Van Mildert Coll Dur BSc78 Sheff Univ CertEd80 Nottm Univ DipTh84 Kent Univ PhD98. St Jo Coll Nottm 83. **d** 86 **p** 87. C Anston *Sheff* 86-89; C Aston cum Aughton and Ulley 89-91; TV Billericay and Lt Burstead *Chelmsf* 91-98; Dir Miss & Past Studies Cranmer Hall Dur from 98. *7 Ferens Close, Durham DH1 1JX* Tel 0191-384 1229
E-mail gavin.wakefield@durham.ac.uk

WAKEFIELD, Kenneth. b 54. St Jo Coll Dur BA95. **d** 95 **p** 96. C E and W Leake, Stanford-on-Soar, Rempstone etc *S'well* 95-98; TV Launceston *Truro* 98-03; P-in-c Boyton, N Tamerton, Werrington etc from 03. *The Rectory, Werrington, Launceston PL15 8TP* Tel (01566) 773932

WAKEFIELD, Canon Kenneth Eyles. b 25. St Jo Coll Dur BA50 DipTh51 MA56. **d** 51 **p** 52. C Redhill H Trin *S'wark* 51-54; C Attenborough w Bramcote and Chilwell *S'well* 54-56; V Leyton St Edw *Chelmsf* 56-59; Chapl Bartlet Hosp Felixstowe 59-89; V Walton *St E* 59-88; Hon Chapl Miss to Seamen 64-88; RD Colneys *St E* 73-86; Hon Can St E Cathl 75-88; rtd 89; Perm to Offic *St E* from 89. *14 Fleetwood Road, Felixstowe IP11 7EQ* Tel (01394) 672113

WAKEFIELD, Peter. b 48. Nottm Univ BTh72 DipAdEd85. St Jo Coll Nottm 68 ALCD72. **d** 72 **p** 73. C Hinckley H Trin *Leic* 72-75; C Kirby Muxloe 75-78; V Barlestone 78-85; TV Padgate *Liv* 85-88; V Quinton w Marston Sicca *Glouc* 91-97; rtd 97. *18 Pampas Close, Stratford-upon-Avon CV37 0TM* Tel (01789) 267390

WAKEFIELD, Bishop of. *See* PLATTEN, The Rt Revd Stephen George

WAKEFIELD, Dean of. *See* NAIRN-BRIGGS, The Very Revd George Peter

WAKEHAM, Geoffrey. **d** 96 **p** 97. P-in-c Torrevieja *Eur* 96-00; Asst Chapl 00-01; rtd 01. *Calle Nervion 20, Torrejon Alto, 03180 Torrevieja, Alicante, Spain* Tel (0034) (6) 670 0135

WAKEHAM-DAWSON, Andrew Whistler. b 65. Wye Coll Lon BSc87 Open Univ PhD94. STETS 98. **d** 01 **p** 02. NSM Paddington St Sav *Lon* from 01. *Mill Laine Farm, Offham, Lewes BN7 3QB* Tel (01273) 473191

WAKELIN, Brian Roy. b 53. Westf Coll Lon BSc74. STETS DipHE99. **d** 99 **p** 00. NSM Win Ch Ch *Win* from 99. *11 Elm Court, Elm Road, Winchester SO22 5BA* Tel (01962) 866859

WAKELIN, Paul Edward. b 60. St Steph Ho Ox 90. **d** 92 **p** 93. C Sevenoaks St Jo *Roch* 92-96; V Perry Street from 96. *All Saints' Vicarage, Perry Street, Gravesend DA11 8RD* Tel (01474) 534398

WAKELING, Bruce. b 50. Lon Univ BA74. Westcott Ho Cam 74. **d** 77 **p** 78. C Weymouth H Trin *Sarum* 77-82; TV Oakdale 82-89; R Clopton w Otley, Swilland and Ashbocking *St E* 89-98; V Rushmere from 98. *The Vicarage, 253 Colchester Road, Rushmere, Ipswich IP4 4SH* Tel (01473) 270976

WAKELING, Hugh Michael. b 42. Cape Town Univ BSc63 CEng82 FIChemE94. Wycliffe Hall Ox 71. **d** 74 **p** 75. C Kennington St Mark *S'wark* 74-78; C Surbiton Hill Ch Ch 78-80; NSM Richmond H Trin and Ch Ch 80-84; NSM California *Ox* 85-89 and from 00; NSM Arborfield w Barkham 89-00. *Pine Lodge, 52 Pine Drive, Wokingham RG40 3LE* Tel 0118-973 4078 Fax as telephone

WAKELING, Mrs Joan. b 44. Hockerill Coll Cam CertEd65 Lon Univ DipTh79. S'wark Ord Course 76. **dss** 79 **d** 90 **p** 94. Subiton Hill Ch Ch *S'wark* 79-80; Richmond H Trin and Ch Ch 80-84; California *Ox* 84-89; Arborfield w Barkham 89-00; NSM 90-00; Chapl Luckley-Oakfield Sch Wokingham from 90; NSM Finchampstead *Ox* from 00. *Pine Lodge, 52 Pine Drive, Wokingham RG40 3LE* Tel 0118-973 4078 Fax as telephone E-mail jwakelin@fish.co.uk

✠**WAKELING, The Rt Revd John Denis.** b 18. MC45. St Cath Coll Cam BA40 MA44 Nottm Univ Hon DD84. Ridley Hall Cam 46. **d** 47 **p** 48 **c** 70. C Barwell w Potters Marston and Stapleton *Leic* 47-50; Chapl Clare Coll Cam 50-52; V Plymouth Em *Ex* 52-59; Preb Ex Cathl 57-59; V Barking St Marg *Chelmsf* 59-65; P-in-c Barking St Patr 60-65; Adn W Ham 65-70; Bp S'well 70-85; rtd 85. *26 Manormead, Tilford Road, Hindhead GU26 6RA*

WAKELING, Rayner Alan. b 58. Portsm Poly BSc79 Bris Univ PGCE80. St Steph Ho Ox. **d** 01 **p** 02. C Willesden Green St Andr and St Fran Lon from 01. *150 Ellesmere Road, London NW10 1JT* Tel (020) 8452 3999

WAKELY, Anthony Peter Robin. b 48. TCD BA71 Edin Univ PhD79 Milltown Inst Dub MA03. CITC 01. **d** 03. P-in-c Clones w Killeevan *Clogh* from 03. *The Rectory, Scotshouse, Clones, Co Monaghan, Irish Republic* E-mail r_wakely@hotmail.com

WAKELY, Marcus. b 40. Solicitor 62 FRSA88. EMMTC 84. **d** 87 **p** 88. NSM Carrington *S'well* 87-91; C Worksop Priory 91-95; V Sheff St Matt *Sheff* 95-01; rtd 01. *16 Park House Gates, Nottingham NG3 5LX* Tel 0115-960 9038

WAKELY, Roger. b 42. St Paul's Cheltenham CertEd. S'wark Ord Course 67. **d** 70 **p** 71. C Ealing St Mary *Lon* 70-76; Chapl Bp Wand Sch Sunbury-on-Thames 76-82; R Gaulby *Leic* 82-87; V Galleywood Common *Chelmsf* 87-95; Warden of Ords 89-95; rtd 95; Perm to Offic *Chelmsf* 95-99; Perm to Offic *Ex* from 99. *Linford, Broadway, Sidmouth EX10 8XH*

WAKELY, Simon Nicolas. b 66. K Alfred's Coll Win BA88. St Jo Coll Nottm Dip Th Studies 91 DipMM92. **d** 92 **p** 93. C Wymondham *Nor* 92-95; P-in-c Babbacombe *Ex* from 95. *Babbacombe Vicarage, Cary Park, Torquay TQ1 3NH* Tel (01803) 323002 E-mail simon.wakely@virgin.net

WAKEMAN, Canon Hilary Margaret. b 38. EAMTC. **dss** 85 **d** 87 **p** 94. Heigham St Thos *Nor* 85-90; C 87-90; C Nor St Mary Magd w St Jas 90-91; Dn-in-c Norwich-over-the-Water Colegate St Geo 90-91; TD Norwich Over-the-Water 91-94; TV 94-96; Hon Can Nor Cathl 94-96; I Kilmoe Union *C, C & R* 96-01; Dir of Ords 99-01; rtd 01. *Skeagh, Schull, Co Cork, Irish Republic* Tel (00353) (28) 28263 E-mail wakeman@iol.ie

WAKERELL, Richard Hinton. b 55. Qu Coll Birm 81. **d** 84 **p** 85. C Gillingham St Mary *Roch* 84-87; C Kingswinford St Mary *Lich* 87-93; V Rickerscote 93. *70 Truro Drive, Plymouth PL5 4PB*

✠**WALDEN, The Rt Revd Graham Howard.** b 31. Univ of Qld BA52 MA54 Ch Ox BLitt60 MLitt80. St Fran Coll Brisbane ThL54. **d** 54 **p** 55 **c** 81. C W Hackney St Barn *Lon* 54-56; C Poplar St Sav w St Gabr and St Steph 57-58; Perm to Offic *Ox* 55-59; Australia from 59; Adn Ballarat 70-89; Bp in Hamilton 81-84; Asst Bp Ballarat 84-89; Bp The Murray 89-01; rtd 01. *13 O'Connor Place, Dubbo, NSW, Australia 2830* Tel (0061) (2) 6884 0883

WALDEN, John Edward Frank. b 38. FInstSMM. Oak Hill Th Coll 67. **d** 69 **p** 70. C Rainham *Chelmsf* 69-73; P-in-c Bris H Cross Inns Court *Bris* 73-78; Conf and Publicity Sec SAMS 78-81; Hon C Southborough St Pet w Ch Ch and St Matt *Roch* 78-81; Exec Sec Spanish and Portuguese Ch Aid Soc 80-81; Hon C Tonbridge St Steph 81-84; R Earsham w Alburgh and Denton *Nor* 84-89; Perm to Offic from 01. *11 Hemmings Close, Norwich NR5 9EH*

WALDEN, Samuel. b 15. Richmond Th Coll 45. **d** 57 **p** 58. USA 57-71; R Blackley H Trin *Man* 71-74; Chapl Prestwich Hosp Man 74-80; rtd 80; Perm to Offic *Bradf* 90-02 and *York* from 02. *16 Dulverton Hall, The Esplanade, Scarborough YO11 2AR* Tel (01723) 340116

WALDRON, Laurence Charles. b 22. Bps' Coll Cheshunt 58. **d** 59 **p** 60. C Gravelly Hill *Birm* 59-63; C-in-c Lea Hall CD 63-66; V Lea Hall 66-77; V Wiggenhall St Mary Magd *Ely* 77-87; V Wiggenhall St Germans and Islington 77-87; rtd 87; Perm to Offic *Lich* 90-00. *16 Heath Gardens, Stone ST15 0AW* Tel (01785) 818237

WALES, David Neville. b 55. Rhodes Univ BA78 Open Univ BSc01 Dip Psych. Coll of Resurr Mirfield 80. **d** 82 **p** 83. Zimbabwe 82-88; C Linslade *Ox* 89-91; P-in-c Weston Turville from 91; Voc Adv from 99. *The Rectory, Church Walk, Weston Turville, Aylesbury HP22 5SH* Tel (01296) 613212 E-mail davidnwales@tiscali.co.uk

WALES, Archbishop of. *See* MORGAN, The Most Revd Barry Cennydd

WALFORD, Mrs Angela. b 44. Whitelands Coll Lon CertEd76. S Dios Minl Tr Scheme 85. **d** 92 **p** 94. NSM Boyatt Wood *Win* 92-99; Asst Chapl Epsom and St Helier NHS Trust from 99. *St Helier Hospital, Wrythe Lane, Carshalton SM5 1AA* Tel (020) 8296 2306 *or* 8644 4343 ext 2306

WALFORD, David. b 45. S'wark Ord Course 75. **d** 78 **p** 79. NSM Hackbridge and N Beddington *S'wark* 78-83; C Fawley *Win* 83-87; C-in-c Boyatt Wood CD 87-90; V Boyatt Wood 90-97; rtd 97; Perm to Offic *S'wark* from 98; Assoc P S Beddington St Mich from 00; Hon Chapl Epsom and St Helier NHS Trust 00-03; Asst Chapl from 03. *58 Wolseley Road, Mitcham Junction, Mitcham CR4 4JQ* Tel (020) 8646 2841 E-mail wols@tinyworld.co.uk

WALFORD, David John. b 47. St Luke's Coll Ex CertEd68 K Coll Lon AKC71. St Aug Coll Cant 71. **d** 72 **p** 73. C Oxton *Ches* 72-77; C Neston 77-80; Youth Chapl 80-81; V Backford 80-81; C Woodchurch 81; Chapl Fulbourn Hosp and Ida Darw Hosp Cam 82-83; Chapl N Man Gen Hosp 83-86; Distr Chapl in Mental Health *Ex* HA from 86; Chapl R Devon and Ex Hosp (Wonford) 86-94; Chapl R Devon and Ex Healthcare NHS Trust from 94; Chapl Ex and Distr Community Health Service NHS Trust 94-01; Chapl Mid Devon Primary Care Trust from 01. *Royal Devon and Exeter Hospital, Barrack Road, Exeter EX2 5DW* Tel (01392) 402024 *or* 411611

WALFORD, David Sanderson. b 23. BEM49. Chich Th Coll 78. **d** 79 **p** 80. Hon C Chich St Pet *Chich* 79-81; C Chich St Paul and St Pet 81-83; P-in-c Wisbech St Aug *Ely* 83-86; rtd 88. *Sibford, Church Hill, Marnhull, Sturminster Newton DT10 1PU* Tel (01258) 820201

WALFORD, Frank Roy. b 35. Birm Univ MB, ChB58. Qu Coll Birm 78. **d** 80 **p** 81. Hon C Walsall Pleck and Bescot *Lich* 80-85; Chr Healing Cen Bordon 85-88; Dep Medical Dir St Wilfrid's Hospice Chich from 88; Perm to Offic *Chich* from 88. *15 Grove Road, Chichester PO19 8AR* Tel (01243) 533947

WALFORD, Robin Peter. b 46. Qu Coll Birm 75. **d** 78 **p** 79. C Radcliffe-on-Trent *S'well* 78-81; TV Newark w Hawton, Cotham and Shelton 81-84; P-in-c Forest Town 84-92; Co-ord Chapl Leeds Community and Mental Health Services 92-97; Perm to Offic *Ripon* from 97. *2A Weetwood Lane, Leeds LS16 5LS* Tel 0113-278 9953

WALKER, Alan David. b 44. Bretton Hall Coll CertEd65. EAMTC 92. **d** 95 **p** 96. NSM Ashill w Saham Toney *Nor* 95-00; C Cockley Cley w Gooderstone 00-02; P-in-c from 02; C Gt and Lt Cressingham w Threxton 00-02; P-in-c from 02; C Didlington 00-02; P-in-c from 02; C Hilborough w Bodney 00-02; P-in-c from 02; C Oxborough w Foulden and Caldecote 00-02; P-in-c from 02; C Mundford w Lynford 00-02; C Ickburgh w Langford 00-02; C Cranwich 00-02. *Gooderstone Rectory, Foulden Road, Gooderstone, King's Lynn PE33 9DF* Tel (01366) 328856 E-mail alan@revwalker.freeserve.co.uk

WALKER, Alan Robert Glaister. b 52. K Coll Cam BA76 MA79 New Coll Ox MA84 Poly Cen Lon LLB91 Heythrop Coll Lon MTh93 Univ of Wales LLM96. St Steph Ho Ox 83. **d** 84 **p** 85. C St John's Wood *Lon* 84-86; Chapl Poly Cen Lon 87-92; Chapl Univ Westmr 92-94; Chapl Univ Ch Ch the K 87-94; V Hampstead Garden Suburb from 94. *The Vicarage, 1 Central Square, London NW11 7AH* Tel and fax (020) 8455 7206 Mobile 07956-491037 E-mail fatherwalker@aol.com

WALKER, Albert William John. b 14. Linc Th Coll 43. **d** 45 **p** 46. C Ches St Mary *Ches* 45-48; C Hoylake 48-51; V Lower Tranmere 51-56; V Plumstead St Nic *S'wark* 56-66; V Merton St Jas 66-67; V Kingston St Luke 67-74; V Mickleton *Glouc* 74-79; rtd 79; Chapl Convent of St Mary at the Cross Edgware 79-87; Lic to Offic *Lon* 79-87; Perm to Offic *Carl* 87-95 and *Truro* 95. *Shepherd's Fold, 4 Treza Road, Porthleven, Helston TR13 9HB* Tel (01326) 562104

WALKER, Allen Ross. b 46. Chich Th Coll 86. **d** 88. C Cosham *Portsm* 88-91; Chapl Portsm Mental Health Community 91-97; Dn Portsm Deanery 91-97; Community Chapl Burnham Deanery *Ox* from 97. *21 Palmerstone Avenue, Langley, Slough SL3 7PU* Tel (01753) 522807

WALKER, Alwyn. *See* WALKER, Ernest Alwyn

WALKER, Andrew Stephen. b 58. St Chad's Coll Dur BA80 Heythrop Coll Lon MA99. St Steph Ho Ox 83. **d** 85 **p** 86. C Fareham SS Pet and Paul *Portsm* 85-87; C St John's Wood *Lon* 87-93; V Streatham St Pet *S'wark* 93-98; Perm to Offic *Bris* and *S'wark* 98-00; R St Edm the King and St Mary Woolnoth etc *Lon* from 00. *St Mary Woolnoth Vestry, Lombard Street, London EC3V 9AN* Tel and fax (020) 7626 9701 Mobile 07931-745853 E-mail asw744216@aol.com

WALKER, Anthony Charles St John. b 55. Trin Coll Ox MA80. Wycliffe Hall Ox 78. **d** 81 **p** 82. C Bradf Cathl *Bradf* 81-84; C

Nottingham St Ann w Em *S'well* 84-88; V Retford St Sav 88-01; TR Retford from 02; AD Retford from 00. *St Saviour's Vicarage, 31 Richmond Road, Retford DN22 6SJ* Tel (01777) 703800 Fax as telephone E-mail tony@tonywalker.f9.co.uk

WALKER, Canon Arthur Keith. b 33. Dur Univ BSc57 Fitzw Ho Cam BA60 MA64 Leeds Univ PhD68 FRSA94. Lich Th Coll 62. **d** 63 **p** 64. C Slaithwaite w E Scammonden *Wakef* 63-66; V N Wootton *B & W* 66-71; Lect Wells Th Coll 66-71; Can Res and Prec Chich Cathl *Chich* 71-80; TV Basingstoke *Win* 81-87; Can Res Win Cathl 87-03; rtd 03. *29 Sussex Street, Winchester SO23 8TG* Tel (01962) 864751
E-mail keith.walker@winchester-cathedral.org.uk

WALKER, Barry Donovan. b 28. Linc Coll Ox BA52 MA56. Linc Th Coll 52. **d** 54 **p** 55. C Enfield St Mich *Lon* 54-58; C Hornsey St Mary 58-61; V Kensal Rise St Martin 61-71; V Palmers Green St Jo 71-83; R Takeley w Lt Canfield *Chelmsf* 83-88; rtd 88; Perm to Offic *Chelmsf* 88-01; *Lon* from 95. *122 Waterfall Road, London N14 7JN* Tel (020) 8886 1695

WALKER, Miss Bethany Helen. b 58. RGN80 DON80 Lon Univ DN83. Cranmer Hall Dur 86. **d** 89 **p** 94. C Newark *S'well* 89-93; rtd 93; Perm to Offic *S'well* from 93. *Julian House, 76 Peveril Road, Beeston, Nottingham NG9 2HU* Tel 0115-922 0672

WALKER, Brian Cecil. b 28. FCA62. Cranmer Hall Dur 68. **d** 70 **p** 71. C Heworth w Peasholme St Cuth *York* 70-73; C Attenborough w Chilwell *S'well* 73-75; C Chilwell 75-78; R Trowell 78-89; rtd 89; Perm to Offic *Worc* from 89; Perm to Offic *Birm* from 98. *1 Chaucer Road, Bromsgrove B60 2EE* Tel (01527) 579382

WALKER, Cameron. *See* WALKER, Canon John Cameron

WALKER, Christopher James Anthony. b 43. Sarum & Wells Th Coll 85. **d** 87 **p** 88. Hon C Durrington *Sarum* 87-89; CF 87-98; rtd 98. *c/o MOD Chaplains (Army)* Tel (01980) 615804 Fax 615800

WALKER, Christopher John. b 52. ALA74. Chich Th Coll 75. **d** 78 **p** 79. C Reading All SS Ox 78-82; C Stony Stratford 82-84; C Wokingham All SS 84-90; V Headington St Mary 90-98; R S w N Moreton, Aston Tirrold and Aston Upthorpe from 98. *The Rectory, Church Lane, South Moreton, Didcot OX11 9AF* Tel (01235) 812042 Fax as telephone
E-mail rwalker@brookes.ac.uk

WALKER, Christopher John Deville. b 42. St Jo Coll Dur BA69. Westcott Ho Cam 69. **d** 71 **p** 72. C Portsea St Mary *Portsm* 71-75; C Saffron Walden w Wendens Ambo and Littlebury *Chelmsf* 75-77; C St Martin-in-the-Fields *Lon* 77-80; V Riverhead w Dunton Green *Roch* 80-89; V Chatham St Steph 89-97; R Chislehurst St Nic from 97. *The Rectory, The Glebe, Chislehurst BR7 5PX* Tel (020) 8467 0196 Fax as telephone

WALKER, Canon David. b 48. Linc Th Coll 71. **d** 74 **p** 75. C Arnold *S'well* 74-77; C Crosby *Linc* 77-79; V Scrooby *S'well* 79-86; V Sutton in Ashfield St Mary 86-94; P-in-c Sutton in Ashfield St Mich 89-94; TR Birkenhead Priory *Ches* from 94; RD Birkenhead from 99; Hon Can Ches Cathl from 03. *St Anne's Vicarage, 29 Park Road West, Prenton CH43 1UR* Tel 0151-652 1309 Fax as telephone E-mail walker_david@onetel.net.uk

WALKER, Canon David Andrew. b 52. St Andr Univ MTh75 MA Hull Univ MPhil00. Linc Th Coll 79. **d** 81 **p** 82. C Hessle *York* 81-84; C N Hull St Mich 84-86; V from 86; AD Cen and N Hull from 99; RD Hull from 00; Can and Preb York Minster from 01. *St Michael's Vicarage, 214 Orchard Park Road, Hull HU6 9BX* Tel (01482) 803375

WALKER, Canon David Grant. b 23. FSA60 FRHistS62 Bris Univ BA49 Ball Coll Ox DPhil54. **d** 62 **p** 62. Hon C Swansea St Mary w H Trin *S & B* 62-86; Chapl and Lect Univ of Wales (Swansea) 62; Sen Lect 63-82; Dir Post-Ord Tr 65-93; Can Brecon Cathl from 72; Prec 79-90; Chan 90-93; Chapl Univ of Wales (Swansea) 75-76; Dir of In-Service Tr from 77; P-in-c Caereithin 86-87. *52 Eaton Crescent, Swansea SA1 4QN* Tel (01792) 472624

WALKER, David Ian. b 41. Dip Ch Music. Bernard Gilpin Soc Dur 64 Bps' Coll Cheshunt 65. **d** 68 **p** 69. C Todmorden *Wakef* 68-72; V Rastrick St Jo 72-77; V Crosland Moor 77-86; V Kirton in Lindsey *Linc* 86-98; R Manton 86-98; V Clee from 99; OCF from 88. *Old Clee Vicarage, 202 Clee Road, Grimsby DN32 8NG* Tel (01472) 691800

WALKER, David John. b 47. St Jo Coll Nottm 88. **d** 90 **p** 91. C Strood St Fran *Roch* 90-94; V Larkfield from 94. *The Vicarage, 206 New Hythe Lane, Larkfield, Maidstone ME20 6PT* Tel (01732) 843349 Fax as telephone
E-mail davidjwalker@challenge1.freeserve.co.uk

WALKER, The Rt Revd David Stuart. b 57. Cam Univ MA. Qu Coll Birm DipTh. **d** 83 **p** 84 **c** 00. C Handsworth *Sheff* 83-86; TV Maltby 86-91; Ind Chapl 86-91; V Bramley and Ravenfield 91-95; R Bramley and Ravenfield w Hooton Roberts etc 95-00; Hon Can Sheff Cathl 00; Suff Bp Dudley *Worc* from 00. *Bishop's House, Bishop's Walk, Cradley Heath B64 7RH* Tel 0121-550 3407 Fax 550 7340
E-mail bishop.david@cofe-worcester.org.uk

WALKER, Dennis Richard. b 25. Bp Gray Coll Cape Town LTh57. **d** 57 **p** 58. S Africa 57-73; V Catterick *Ripon* 73-78; V

Manston 78-86; rtd 86; Perm to Offic *York* from 90. *23 Promenade, Bridlington YO15 2QA* Tel (01262) 672131

WALKER, Derek Fred. b 46. Trin Coll Bris 71. **d** 74 **p** 75. C St Paul's Cray St Barn *Roch* 74-78; C Rushden w Newton Bromswold *Pet* 78-80; R Kirkby Thore w Temple Sowerby and Newbiggin *Carl* 80-83; V Coppull *Blackb* 83-87; V New Ferry *Ches* 87-96; R Akeman *Ox* from 96. *The Rectory, Alchester Road, Chesterton, Bicester OX26 1UW* Tel (01869) 369815 Fax as telephone E-mail akemanbenefice@yahoo.com

WALKER, Douglas. b 36. Lich Th Coll 61. **d** 63 **p** 64. C Bris St Ambrose Whitehall *Bris* 63-68; P-in-c Easton All Hallows 68-71; V Penhill 71-79; P-in-c Crundale w Godmersham *Cant* 79-83; P-in-c Elmsted w Hastingleigh 79-83; V Sheerness H Trin w St Paul 83-01; rtd 01. *21 Lower Ferry Lane, Callow End, Worcester WR2 4UN* Tel (01905) 831508

WALKER, Duncan Andrew. b 59. **d** 90 **p** 91. C Gorseinon *S & B* 90-91; C Morriston 92-94; V Llanelli Ch Ch *St D* 94-98; V Swansea St Jas *S & B* from 98. *St James's Vicarage, 1 Ffynone Drive, Swansea SA1 6DB* Tel (01792) 470532

✠**WALKER, The Rt Revd Edward William Murray (Dominic).** b 48. AKC73 Heythrop Coll Lon MA97 Brighton Univ Hon DLitt98. **d** 72 **p** 72 **c** 97. CGA 67-83; C Wandsworth St Faith *S'wark* 72-73; Bp's Dom Chapl 73-76; R Newington St Mary 76-85; RD S'wark and Newington 80-85; OGS from 83; Superior 90-96; V Brighton St Pet w Chpl Royal and St Jo *Chich* 85-86; P-in-c Brighton St Nic 85-86; TR Brighton St Pet and St Nic w Chpl Royal 86-97; RD Brighton 85-97; Can and Preb Chich Cathl 85-97; Area Bp Reading *Ox* 97-03; Bp Mon from 03. *Bishopstow, 91A Stow Hill, Newport NP9 4EA* Tel (01633) 263510 E-mail bishop.monmouth@churchinwales.org.uk

WALKER, Mrs Elizabeth. b 42. Sunderland Poly CQSW85. NEOC 91. **d** 94 **p** 00. NSM Stockton St Chad *Dur* from 94. *29 Bramble Road, Stockton-on-Tees TS19 0NQ* Tel (01642) 615332

WALKER, Mrs Elizabeth Margaret Rea. b 49. Ch Ch Coll Cant CertEd70. S'wark Ord Course 89. **d** 92 **p** 94. NSM Ash *Roch* 92-97; NSM Ridley 92-97; Chapl St Geo Sch Gravesend 92-97; P-in-c Burham and Wouldham *Roch* from 97; Assoc Dir of Ords from 97. *The Rectory, 266 Rochester Road, Burham, Rochester ME1 3RJ* Tel and fax (01634) 666862 Mobile 07931-356502

WALKER, Ernest Alwyn. b 18. Clifton Th Coll 54. **d** 56 **p** 57. C Brixton Road Ch Ch *S'wark* 56-59; V Kingston upon Hull St Barn *York* 59-70; V Shiptonthorpe w Hayton 70-77; V Daubhill *Man* 77-84; rtd 84. *34 Kemple View, Clitheroe BB7 2QD* Tel (01200) 427061

WALKER, Gavin Russell. b 43. FCA78. Coll of Resurr Mirfield 76. **d** 78 **p** 79. C Wakef St Jo *Wakef* 78-81; C Northallerton w Kirby Sigston *York* 81-83; V Whorlton w Carlton and Faceby 83-85; Chapl Pontefract Gen Infirmary 85-89; P-in-c Brotherton *Wakef* 85-89; V Earl's Heaton 89-97; TV Dewsbury 97-99; TV Egremont and Haile *Carl* from 99. *The Vicarage, 1 Bridge End Park, Egremont CA22 2RH* Tel (01946) 822051 Mobile 07986-505886 E-mail staffa@lineone.net

WALKER, Geoffrey. *See* WALKER, K Canon Philip Geoffrey

WALKER, Gerald Roger. b 41. K Coll Lon BD67 AKC67. **d** 68 **p** 69. C High Elswick St Phil *Newc* 68-70; C Goring-by-Sea *Chich* 70-75; R Selsey 75-81; V Hove St Andr Old Ch 81-91; V Copthorne 91-95; rtd 95; NSM Streat w Westmeston *Chich* 95-99; Perm to Offic *S'wark* from 00. *1 Glebe Cottages, Newdigate, Dorking RH5 5AA* Tel (01306) 631587

WALKER, Canon Graham. b 35. Ex Coll Ox BA58 BTh60 MA62 Leeds Univ MPhil80. Sarum Th Coll 60. **d** 61 **p** 62. C Guiseley *Bradf* 61-64; C Ingrow cum Hainworth 64-68; Lic to Offic 68-80; V Hellifield 80-01; RD Bowland 86-95; Hon Can Bradf Cathl 89-01; P-in-c Gisburn 94-01; rtd 01. *Shaw House, 3 Branstone Beck, High Bentham, Lancaster LA2 7LX* Tel (01524) 261125

WALKER, Canon Harvey William. b 26. Edin Univ MA52. St Steph Ho Ox 58. **d** 60 **p** 61. C Newc St Matt w St Mary *Newc* 60-64; V 64-94; Hon Can Newc Cathl 80-94; Perm to Offic from 95; rtd 95. *21 Grosvenor Drive, Whitley Bay NE26 2JP* Tel 0191-252 1858

WALKER, Mrs Hazel. b 47. N Ord Course MA01. **d** 00 **p** 01. C Crofton *Wakef* from 00. *30 Heron Drive, Sandal, Wakefield WF2 6SW* Tel (01924) 259687
E-mail allen@heron55.freeserve.co.uk

WALKER, Helen Margaret. *See* WALKER, Miss Bethany Helen

WALKER, Hugh. *See* WALKER, John Hugh

WALKER, Ian Richard Stevenson. b 51. Univ of Wales (Lamp) BA73. Qu Coll Birm DipTh75. **d** 76 **p** 77. C Stainton-in-Cleveland *York* 76-79; C Fulford 79-81; C Kidderminster St Mary *Worc* 81-82; TV Kidderminster St Mary and All SS, Trimpley etc 82-86; R Keyingham w Ottringham, Halsham and Sunk Is *York* 86-98; RD S Holderness 94-98; R Scartho *Linc* from 98. *St Giles's Rectory, 44 Waltham Road, Grimsby DN33 2LX* Tel (01472) 872728
E-mail irsw@stgilesrec.fsnet.co.uk

WALKER, Jack. b 21. Kelham Th Coll 37. **d** 45 **p** 46. C Tynemouth Ch Ch *Newc* 45-49; C Wallsend St Luke 49-51; C Linthorpe *York* 51-55; V Newbald 55-96; V Sancton 55-96; rtd

96. *10 Molescroft Avenue, Beverley HU17 7HH* Tel (01482) 864597

WALKER, Jill Dorothy Ann. b 36. RGN58 Westmr Coll Ox DipApTh93. St Alb Minl Tr Scheme 89. **d** 96 **p** 97. NSM E Barnet *St Alb* 96-99; Asst Chapl Barnet and Chase Farm Hosps NHS Trust from 99. *2 Dean's Gardens, St Albans AL4 9LS* Tel (01727) 834436

WALKER, Mrs Jillian Francesca. b 41. **d** 99 **p** 00. OLM Blackbourne *St E* from 99. *The Woolpack, Bury Road, Ixworth, Bury St Edmunds IP31 2HX* Tel (01359) 230776

WALKER (née TOMKINS), Ms Jocelyn Rachel. b 64. Univ of Wales (Ban) BA85 Man Univ PGCE86. N Ord Course 98. **d** 01 **p** 02. C Chadderton St Matt *Man* from 01. *1 St Luke's Court, Buckley Street, Chadderton, Oldham OL9 9HZ* Tel 0161-345 3361 E-mail joss.walker@tiscali.com

WALKER, John. *See* WALKER, Albert William John

WALKER, John. b 51. Aber Univ MA74 Edin Univ BD78. Edin Th Coll 75. **d** 78 **p** 79. C Broughty Ferry *Bre* 78-81; P-in-c Dundee St Jo 81-85; Ind Chapl 83-88; R Dundee St Luke 85-95; R Inverurie *Ab* from 95; P-in-c Kemnay from 95; I Alford from 95; R Auchindoir from 95. *The Rectory, St Mary's Place, Inverurie AB51 3NW* Tel (01467) 620470 Fax as telephone E-mail jbwalker@cwcom.net

WALKER, John Anthony Patrick. b 58. Man Metrop Univ PGCE97. Trin Coll Bris BA86. **d** 86 **p** 87. C Canford Magna *Sarum* 86-90; TV Glyncorrwg w Afan Vale and Cymmer Afan *Llan* 90-96; Hd of RE Whitworth High Sch Rochdale 96-00; Community Chapl and C Gorton St Phil *Man* from 00. *The Rectory, 195B Mount Road, Manchester M18 7GG* Tel 0161-223 0421 Mobile 07980-692813

WALKER, Canon John Cameron. b 31. St Andr Univ MA52. Edin Th Coll 63. **d** 65 **p** 66. C Edin H Cross *Edin* 65-67; C Perth St Jo *St And* 67-70; Chapl Angl Students Glas 70-74; Youth Chapl Warks Educn Cttee 75-77; Officer Gen Syn Bd of Educn 78-82; C W Hendon St Jo *Lon* 79-82; PV Westmr Abbey 82-84; Chapl Ghent w Ypres *Eur* 84-92; Chapl Ghent 92-98; Miss to Seamen 84-98; Can Brussels Cathl *Eur* 93-98; rtd 98. *Le Petit Clos, rue des Lilas, 11300 Bouriège, France* Tel (0033) (4) 68 31 17 04 Fax as telephone

WALKER, John David. b 44. St Jo Coll Dur BA76 DipTh77. **d** 77 **p** 78. C Heworth H Trin *York* 77-81; P-in-c Allerthorpe and Barmby on the Moor w Fangfoss 81-83; TV Pocklington Team 84-89; P-in-c Hovingham 89; TV Street 89-92; R Dunnington 92-99; V Thorne *Sheff* 99-03; rtd 03; Perm to Offic *York* from 03. *9 Bishop Blunt Close, Hessle HU13 9NJ* E-mail john.d.walker@bt.internet.com

WALKER, John Frank. b 53. Leeds Univ BEd76 Ripon Coll of Educn CertEd75. NW Ord Course 78. **d** 81 **p** 82. NSM Whitkirk *Ripon* 81-82; C 82-85; V Sutton Courtenay w Appleford *Ox* 85-90; Dioc Children's Adv *S'wark* 90-94; V Walworth St Jo from 94; Youth and Children's Officer Woolwich Episc Area 95-99. *St John's Vicarage, 18 Larcom Street, London SE17 1NQ* Tel (020) 7703 4375

WALKER, John Frederick. b 21. St Jo Coll Dur BA47 DipTh49 MA51. **d** 49 **p** 50. C Normanton *Wakef* 49-51; C Northowram 51-53; V Gawthorpe and Chickenley Heath 53-59; V Haley Hill 59-74; V Hampsthwaite *Ripon* 74-86; P-in-c Killinghall 76-86; rtd 86; Perm to Offic *Bradf* from 86. *36 Rockwood Drive, Skipton BD23 1UW* Tel (01756) 799835

WALKER, John Howard. b 47. Brasted Th Coll 67 Clifton Th Coll 69. **d** 72 **p** 73. C Upton (Overchurch) *Ches* 72-76; Asst Chapl Liv Univ *Liv* 76-79; V Everton St Chrys 79-82; C Parr Mt 83-86; SAMS 86-94; Area Sec (NE and E Midl) SAMS 86-89; Paraguay 89-94; V Calverley *Bradf* from 95. *The Vicarage, Town Gate, Calverley, Pudsey LS28 5NF* Tel 0113-257 7968

WALKER, John Hugh. b 36. K Coll Lon BD57 AKC57 K Coll Lon MTh75 MA85 Lon Inst of Educn PGCE68. St Boniface Warminster 57. **d** 58 **p** 59. C Southend St Alb *Chelmsf* 58-61; V Gt Ilford St Alb 61-67; Perm to Offic 67-68; Hon C Forest Gate St Edm 68-74; Perm to Offic *Cant* 75-82 and from 87; C Dymchurch w Burmarsh and Newchurch 82-87; rtd 94. *14 Danes Court, Dover CT16 2QE* Tel (01304) 202233

WALKER, John Michael. b 32. Qu Coll Birm. **d** 57 **p** 58. C Ruddington *S'well* 57-60; C Horsham *Chich* 60-64; C Sullington 64-70; C Storrington 64-70; V Peasmarsh 70-73; V Washington 73-77; R Ashington, Washington and Wiston w Buncton 77-98; rtd 98; Perm to Offic *Chich* from 98. *The Granary, Staplefield Farm, Horsham Road, Steyning BN44 3AA*

WALKER, Canon John Percival. b 45. CITC 68. **d** 71 **p** 72. C Belfast St Clem *D & D* 71-74; C Magheralumoney *Clogh* 74-78; C Lisburn St Paul *Conn* 78-81; I Belfast St Ninian 81-88; I Belfast St Mary 88-89; I Belfast St Mary w H Redeemer from 89; Preb Conn Cathl from 98. *St Mary's Rectory, 558 Crumlin Road, Belfast BT14 7GL* Tel and fax (028) 9058 4540 *or* tel 9074 8423 E-mail john.walker18@ntlworld.com

WALKER, John Robert. b 50. NE Lon Poly BSc74 K Coll Lon PhD77. Trin Coll Bris BA93 MA95. **d** 96 **p** 97. C Bushbury *Lich* 96-00; TV Dewsbury *Wakef* 00-01. *183 Queens Drive, Ossett WF5 0NP* Tel (01924) 273837 E-mail revdjrw@aol.com

WALKER, Keith. *See* WALKER, Canon Arthur Keith

WALKER, Keith. b 48. Linc Th Coll 82. **d** 84 **p** 85. C Whickham *Dur* 84-87; C Trimdon Station 87; P-in-c 87-89; V 89-90; R Penshaw 90-98; P-in-c Shiney Row 92-95; P-in-c Herrington 93-95; rtd 98; Hon C Jersey St Brelade *Win* from 01. *The Parsonage, la rue du Croquet, St Brelade, Jersey JE3 8BZ* Tel (01534) 746154

WALKER, Mrs Lesley Ann. b 53. Westmr Coll Ox PDATS96 MTh00. S Dios Minl Tr Scheme 85. **d** 88 **p** 94. Par Dn Oakdale *Sarum* 88-92; TD Bridgnorth, Tasley, Astley Abbotts, etc *Heref* 92-94; TV 94-03; Vice Prin Local Min Tr Scheme *Cant* from 03; Dir Min and Tr from 03. *32 Goodwood Avenue, Bridgnorth WV15 5BD* Tel (01746) 765874 *or* 767174

WALKER, Mrs Margaret Joy. b 44. Avery Hill Coll DipHE80 Newc Univ MA93. CA Tr Coll 80. **dss** 86 **d** 87 **p** 94. Scargill Ho 86-87; Hon Par Dn Monkwearmouth St Andr *Dur* 87; Hon Par Dn Chester le Street 87-93; NSM Wells Cathl *B & W* 94-01; Perm to Offic *Cant* from 02. *1 Ensigne Cottages, Shalmsford Street, Chartham, Canterbury CT4 7RF* Tel (01227) 738690

WALKER, Margaret (Sister Lucy Clare). b 37. Guildf Dioc Min Course 99. **d** 01 **p** 02. CSP from 88; NSM Aldershot St Mich *Guildf* from 01. *68 Bourne Court, Manor Road, Aldershot GU11 5DL* Tel (01252) 326396 Mobile 07951-368727

WALKER, Mark Robert Joseph George. b 66. Nottm Univ BA88 TCD PhD98. CITC 90. **d** 92 **p** 93. C Larne and Inver *Conn* 92-95; C Glynn w Raloo 92-95; Asst Chapl Royla Hosp Larne 92-94; Lect Th and C Hist Univ Coll Ches 95-00 and 00-01; Chapl NE Wales Inst of HE from 01; Dir Dioc Minl Tr Course *St As* from 01; C Wrexham from 01. *The Chaplaincy, Post Point 22, North East Wales Institute, Plas Coch College, Mold Road, Wrexham LL11 2AW* Tel (01978) 293336 Mobile 07798-483963 Fax (01978) 293254 E-mail m.walker@newi.ac.uk

WALKER, Preb Martin Frank. b 39. St Jo Coll Nottm 71. **d** 73 **p** 74. C Penn *Lich* 73-78; V Bentley 78-82; V Kinver 82-88; R Kinver and Enville 88-91; V Harlescott 91-02; P-in-c Standon and Cotes Heath 02; P-in-c Croxton w Broughton and Adbaston 02; Preb Lich Cathl from 00; R Broughton w Croxton and Cotes Heath w Standon from 02. *The Rectory, Station Road, Cotes Heath, Stafford ST21 6NR* Tel (01782) 791549 Fax as telephone E-mail martin.walker7@btinternet.com

WALKER, Martin John. b 52. Linc Coll Ox BA73 PGCE74 Château de Bossey Geneva Dip Ecum78. Cranmer Hall Dur BA78. **d** 79 **p** 80. C Harlow New Town w Lt Parndon *Chelmsf* 79-81; C Dorchester *Ox* 81-83; Chapl Bath Coll of HE 83-89; TV Southampton (City Cen) *Win* 89-91; Adv in RE and Resources *Sarum* 91-92; Hon C Northolt St Mary *Lon* 92-00; Chapl Bancroft's Sch Woodford Green 92-99; Chapl St Helen's Sch Northwood 99-00; Chapl Wellingborough Sch from 00; Perm to Offic *Lon* from 00. *Marsh House, Wellingborough School, Irthlingborough Road, Wellingborough NN8 2BX* Tel (01933) 222427 E-mail revjmwalker@yahoo.com

WALKER, Meuryn. **d** 00 **p** 01. NSM Wakef St Jo *Wakef* from 00. *188 Stanley Road, Wakefield WF1 4AE*

WALKER, Michael John. b 39. St D Coll Lamp BA61. St Aid Birkenhead 61. **d** 63 **p** 64. C Clifton *York* 63-66; C Marfleet 66-69; V Salterhebble St Jude *Wakef* 69-83; V Llangollen w Trevor and Llantysilio *St As* 83-93; RD Llangollen 87-93; V Kerry and Llanmerewig and Dolfor 93-01; RD Cedewain 97-01; rtd 01; Perm to Offic *Ban* from 01. *Sylfaen-y-Graig, 21 Garth Terrace, Porthmadog LL49 9BE* Tel (01766) 515192

WALKER, Canon Nigel Maynard. b 39. ALCD66 LTh80. **d** 67 **p** 68. C Southsea St Jude *Portsm* 67-70; S Africa 70-76; C Abingdon w Shippon *Ox* 76-80; V Upton (Overchurch) *Ches* 80-94; Chan Brussels Cathl *Eur* from 94; Chapl Brussels from 94; P-in-c Leuven from 02. *avenue Parmentier 240/4, B-1150 Brussels, Belgium* Tel (0032) (2) 770 7715 *or* 511 7183 Fax 511 1028 E-mail holy.trinity@arcasdis.com

WALKER, Mrs Pamela Sarah. b 52. Somerville Coll Ox BA73 MA77 St Jo Coll Dur BA78. Cranmer Hall Dur 76. **dss** 79 **d** 84 **p** 94. Harlow New Town w Lt Parndon *Chelmsf* 79-81; Dorchester *Sarum* 82-83; Bath St Bart *B & W* 85-88; Hon Par Dn 87-88; Par Dn Warmley *Bris* 88-89; Par Dn Bitton 88-89; Par Dn Southampton (City Cen) *Win* 89-92; Par Dn Northolt St Mary *Lon* 92-94; R from 94. *St Mary's Rectory, Ealing Road, Northolt UB5 6AA* Tel (020) 8841 5691 *or* 8575 7737

WALKER, Paul Gary. b 59. Lon Univ BD. St Jo Coll Nottm 82. **d** 84 **p** 85. C Bowling St Steph *Bradf* 84-87; C Tong 87-90; P-in-c Oakenshaw cum Woodlands 90-97; V Wrose from 97; RD Calverley from 01. *St Cuthbert's Vicarage, 71 Wrose Road, Bradford BD2 1LN* Tel (01274) 611631 E-mail sqwalker@netcom.ca

WALKER, Paul Laurence. b 63. St Chad's Coll Dur BA84. Chich Th Coll BTh90. **d** 88 **p** 89. C Shildon w Eldon *Dur* 88-91; C Barnard Castle w Whorlton 91-93; C Silksworth 93-96; C-in-c Moorside St Wilfrid CD 96-99; V Norton St Mary from 99. *2 Brambling Close, Norton, Stockton-on-Tees TS20 1TX* Tel (01642) 558888 E-mail paul.walker@durham.anglican.org *or* revpwalker@aol.com

WALKER, Pauline Ann. b 51. Open Univ BA87. St As Minl Tr Course 88. **d** 93 **p** 97. NSM Bistre *St As* 93-99; C Bistre from 99.

Mountain Farm, Foxes Lane, Alltami, Mold CH7 6RT Tel (01244) 550638

WALKER, Pauline Jean. b 49. St Hild Coll Dur BSc72 Homerton Coll Cam PGCE73 Nottm Univ MA96. All Nations Chr Coll 89 St Jo Coll Nottm 94. **d** 96 **p** 97. C Bitterne *Win* 96-01; CMS from 01. *CMS, Partnership House, 157 Waterloo Road, London SE1 8UU* Tel (020) 7928 8681

WALKER, Percival. *See* WALKER, Canon John Percival

WALKER, Peter Anthony. b 57. Pemb Coll Cam BA79 MA83 St Jo Coll Dur BA86. Cranmer Hall Dur 84. **d** 87 **p** 88. C Chesham Bois *Ox* 87-90; Chapl Bradf Cathl *Bradf* 90-93; TV W Swindon and the Lydiards *Bris* 93-99; V Keresley and Coundon Cov from 99. *Keresley Vicarage, 34 Tamworth Road, Coventry CV6 2EL* Tel (024) 7633 2717 Fax as telephone E-mail peter@st-thomas-keresley.org.uk

WALKER, Canon Peter Anthony Ashley. b 46. Chich Th Coll 67. **d** 70 **p** 71. C Stamford Hill St Thos *Lon* 70-74; C Bethnal Green St Matt 74-77; V Hackney Wick St Mary of Eton w St Aug 77-84; Warden Rydal Hall *Carl* 84-95; P-in-c Rydal 84-95; P-in-c Porthleven w Sithney *Truro* 95-01; RD Kerrier 96-01; Can Res Truro Cathl from 01. *The Vicarage, Feock, Truro TR3 6SD* Tel (01872) 862534

WALKER, Peter Jeffrey. b 46. Kelham Th Coll 65. **d** 70 **p** 71. C Middlesbrough All SS *York* 70-75 and 77-78; SSF 75-77; C-in-c Wrangbrook w N Elmsall CD *Wakef* 78-82; V Athersley 82-86; SSM 86-88; Perm to Offic *Dur* 88-89; V Hartlepool H Trin 89-95; Dep Chapl HM Pris Birm 95-96; Chapl HM Pris Moorland 96-01; Chapl HM Pris Full Sutton from 01. *HM Prison, Full Sutton, York YO41 1PS* Tel (01759) 375100 Fax 371206

✠**WALKER, The Rt Revd Peter Knight.** b 19. Qu Coll Ox BA47 MA47 Cam Univ Hon DD78. Westcott Ho Cam 53. **d** 54 **p** 55 **c** 72. Asst Master Merchant Taylors' Sch Lon 50-56; C Hemel Hempstead St Mary *St Alb* 56-58; Fell Dean and Lect Th CCC Cam 58-62; Asst Tutor 59-62; Prin Westcott Ho Cam 62-72; Hon Can Ely Cathl *Ely* 66-72; Suff Bp Dorchester *Ox* 72-77; Can Res Ch 72-77; Bp Ely 77-89; rtd 89; Hon Asst Bp Ox 89-95; Perm to Offic *Ely* from 95. *19 St Mark's Court, Barton Road, Cambridge CB3 9LE* Tel (01223) 363041

WALKER, Peter Sidney Caleb. b 50. St Mich Th Coll Crafers DipMin80. **d** 80 **p** 81. Australia 80-88; R Swallow *Linc* 88-94; R Selworthy and Timberscombe and Wootton Courtenay *B & W* 94-95; R Luccombe 94-95; R Selworthy, Timberscombe, Wootton Courtenay etc 95-01; Chapl Costa del Sol W *Eur* from 01. *Urb Beverly Hills C14, 29680 Estepona, Malaga, Spain* Tel (0034) (952) 808605 E-mail peterdiana@terra.es

WALKER, Peter Stanley. b 56. SRN RMN Nottm Univ BCombStuds. Linc Th Coll 80. **d** 83 **p** 84. C Woodford St Barn *Chelmsf* 83-86; C Brentwood St Thos 86-88; V Colchester St Barn 88-94; P-in-c Colchester St Jas, All SS, St Nic and St Runwald 94-96; R Colchester St Jas and St Paul w All SS etc from 96. *The Rectory, 76 East Hill, Colchester CO1 2QW* Tel (01206) 866802 Fax 799444 E-mail fatherpeter@walkerssc.freeserve.co.uk

WALKER, Peter William Leyland. b 61. CCC Cam BA82 MA86 PhD87 Ox Univ DPhil96. Wycliffe Hall Ox 87. **d** 89 **p** 90. C Tonbridge SS Pet and Paul *Roch* 89-93; Fell Tyndale Ho Cam 93-96; Tutor Wycliffe Hall Ox 96. *Wycliffe Hall, 54 Banbury Road, Oxford OX2 6PW* Tel (01865) 274214 E-mail peter.walker@wycliffe.ox.ac.uk

WALKER, Canon Philip Geoffrey. b 47. St Jo Coll Dur BA70 Oriel Coll Ox BA72 MA76 Newc Univ MA93 Bris Univ PhD01. Ripon Hall Ox 70. **d** 74 **p** 75. C Sheff St Geo *Sheff* 74-77; C Cambridge Gt St Mary w St Mich *Ely* 77-81; V Monkwearmouth St Andr *Dur* 81-87; R Chester le Street 87-93; RD Chester-le-Street 89-93; Dioc Missr *B & W* 93-01; Can Res Wells Cathl 94-01; Prin Local Min Tr Scheme *Cant* from 02. *1 Ensigne Cottages, Shalmsford Street, Chartham, Canterbury CT4 7RF* Tel (01227) 738690 E-mail pn72@dial.pipex.com

WALKER, Philip Kingsley. b 47. Ox Univ BA70 Univ of Wales DPS90. St Mich Coll Llan. **d** 90 **p** 91. C Maindee *Mon* 90-92; C Llanmartin 92-94; V Bishton 94-98; R Panteg from 98. *Panteg Rectory, The Highway, New Inn, Pontypool NP4 0PH* Tel (01495) 763724

WALKER, Raymond. b 28. Carl Dioc Tr Inst 83. **d** 86 **p** 87. NSM Gt Salkeld w Lazonby *Carl* 86-91; C Greystoke, Matterdale, Mungrisdale etc 91-92; TV 92-95; rtd 95. *Brackenrigg, Town Head, Lazonby, Penrith CA10 1AT* Tel (01768) 898314

WALKER, Richard David. b 45. Hull Univ BSc68. S Dios Minl Tr Scheme 92. **d** 95 **p** 96. NSM Horfield St Greg *Bris* 95-98; NSM Lawrence Weston and Avonmouth 98-00; Chapl HM Pris Leic 00-03. *Address temp unknown*

WALKER, Richard Mainprize. b 43. Keele Univ BA DipEd. Wycliffe Hall Ox 84. **d** 86 **p** 87. C Guildf Ch Ch *Guildf* 86-90; V Bradley St Martin *Lich* from 90. *St Martin's Vicarage, King Street, Bradley, Bilston WV14 8PQ* Tel (01902) 493109

WALKER, Richard Mark. b 63. York Univ BSc84. St Jo Coll Nottm MA00. **d** 00 **p** 01. C Ben Rhydding *Bradf* from 00. *21 Cardan Drive, Ben Rhydding, Ilkley LS29 8PH*

WALKER, Roger. *See* WALKER, Gerald Roger

WALKER, Ruth. b 51. Dioc OLM tr scheme. **d** 03. OLM Camberley St Mary *Guildf* from 03. *73 Verran Road, Camberley GU15 2ND* Tel (01276) 503551 E-mail trevorwalker@csma-netlink.co.uk

WALKER (née APPLETON), Mrs Ruth Elizabeth. b 58. St Jo Coll Dur BA79 Hughes Hall Cam PGCE80. St Jo Coll Nottm 86. **d** 88 **p** 94. Par Dn Princes Risborough w Ilmer *Ox* 88-90; C Congr Chapl Bradf Cathl *Bradf* 90-93; C The Lydiards *Bris* 93-94; NSM W Swindon and the Lydiards 94-96; C Swindon St Jo and St Andr 96-98; Perm to Offic 98-99; C Keresley and Coundon *Cov* from 99. *Keresley Vicarage, 34 Tamworth Road, Coventry CV6 2EL* Tel (024) 7633 2717 Fax as telephone E-mail ruth@st-thomas-keresley.org.uk

WALKER, Sharon Anne. b 60. Derby Univ BA99. St Jo Coll Nottm. **d** 02 **p** 03. C Greetham and Thistleton w Stretton and Clipsham *Pet* from 02; C Cottesmore and Barrow w Ashwell and Burley from 02. *The Vicarage, Church Lane, Greetham, Oakham LE15 7NF* Tel (01572) 812015

WALKER, Simon Patrick. b 71. Ch Ch Ox BA93. Wycliffe Hall Ox BTh94. **d** 97 **p** 98. C Abingdon *Ox* 97-01; Perm to Offic *Ches* from 01. *11 Nantwich Road, Middlewich CW10 9HE* Tel (01606) 832598 E-mail simon.walker@cin.org.uk

WALKER, Stanley Frederick. b 48. St Jo Coll Nottm. **d** 84 **p** 85. C Ellesmere Port *Ches* 84-89; V Seacombe 89-97; C Lache cum Saltney from 97. *89 Sandy Lane, Saltney, Chester CH4 8UA* Tel (01244) 629073 Mobile 07802-960430 Fax 677818 E-mail stanwalker@02.co.uk

WALKER, Canon Stephen. b 09. St Jo Coll Dur BA30 DipTh31 MA33. **d** 32 **p** 33. C Horsforth *Ripon* 32-35; C Upper Armley 35-36; V Birmingham St Barn *Birm* 36-40; V Monkwearmouth All SS *Dur* 40-43; V Bruntcliffe *Wakef* 43-50; V N Ferriby *York* 50-58; V Beverley St Mary 58-77; Chapl Westwood Hosp 59-77; RD Beverley 63-73; Can and Preb York Minster 64-77; rtd 77; Perm to Offic *Dur* from 77-98 and *York* 77-01. *clo the Revd M J Walker, Sylfaen-y-Graig, 21 Garth Terrace, Porthmadog LL49 9BE* Tel (01766) 515192

WALKER, Stephen Michael Maynard. b 62. St Jo Coll Dur BA84. Trin Coll Bris 86. **d** 88 **p** 89. C Eastwood *S'well* 88-92; CF 92-02; C Marple All SS *Ches* from 02. *125 Church Lane, Marple, Stockport SK6 7LD* Tel 0161-427 3841

WALKER, Stephen Patrick. b 62. York Univ BSc83 PGCE84. St Jo Coll Nottm DipTh89 DPS90. **d** 90 **p** 91. C Hull Newland St Jo *York* 90-94; Min Grove Green LEP *Cant* 94-98; Children's Min Adv 96-98; TV Drypool *York* 98-99; TR from 99. *The Vicarage, 139 Laburnum Avenue, Hull HU8 8PA* Tel (01482) 374257 E-mail stephen_walker@bigfoot.com

WALKER, Mrs Susan Joy. b 52. Univ of Wales (Lamp) BA73 Hull Univ MA91. Qu Coll Birm 75. **dss** 83 **d** 87 **p** 94. Kidderminster St Mary and All SS, Trimpley etc *Worc* 83-86; Keyingham w Ottringham, Halsham and Sunk Is *York* 86-87; Hon Par Dn 87-94; Hon C 94-98; Chapl Hull Coll of FE 89-98; Chapl N Lindsey Coll *Linc* from 98. *St Giles's Rectory, 44 Waltham Road, Grimsby DN33 2LX* Tel (01472) 872728 or 294034 E-mail sjwalker@leggott.ac.uk

WALKER, The Ven Thomas Overington. b 33. Keble Coll Ox BA58 MA61. Oak Hill Th Coll 58. **d** 60 **p** 61. C Woking St Paul *Guildf* 60-62; C St Leonards St Leon *Chich* 62-64; Travelling Sec IVF 64-67; Succ Birm Cathl *Birm* 67-70; V Harborne Heath 70-91; P-in-c Edgbaston St Germain 83-91; Hon Can Birm Cathl 80-91; RD Edgbaston 89-91; Adn Nottingham *S'well* 91-96; rtd 96; Perm to Offic *Heref* from 97. *6 Cornbrook, Clee Hill, Ludlow SY8 3QQ* Tel (01584) 890176

WALKER, Trevor John. b 51. Southn Univ BTh80. Sarum & Wells Th Coll 75. **d** 78 **p** 79. C Standish *Blackb* 78-81; P-in-c N Somercotes *Linc* 81-82; P-in-c S Somercotes 81-82; V Somercotes 82-85; R Binbrook Gp from 85. *The Rectory, Louth Road, Binbrook, Lincoln LN8 6BJ* Tel (01472) 398227 Fax 399547 E-mail priest1@compuserve.com

WALKER, Canon Walter Stanley. b 21. AKC42. Cuddesdon Coll 42. **d** 44 **p** 45. C Southport All SS *Liv* 44-47; Miss to Seamen 47-48; C-in-c Kelsall CD *Ches* 48-53; V Birkenhead St Mary w St Paul 53-61; Chapl Barony Hosp Nantwich 61-66; R Wistaston 61-66; R Bromborough 66-77; R Wallasey St Hilary 77-86; RD Wallasey 77-86; Hon Can Ches Cathl 80-86; rtd 86; Perm to Offic *Ches* from 86. *41 Seabank Road, Wirral CH60 4SN* Tel 0151-342 6543

WALKER, William. b 10. FCIM48. **d** 51 **p** 52. C Gotham *S'well* 51-58; Chapl, Lect and Tutor Stanford Hall Loughb 52-70; C-in-c Normanton on Soar 58-65; V Daybrook 70-80; rtd 80; Perm to Offic *S'well* 80-92. *278 Rutland Road, Nottingham NG2 5EB* Tel 0115-982 2632

WALKEY, Malcolm Gregory Taylor. b 44. Lon Univ DipTh68. Kelham Th Coll 63. **d** 68 **p** 69. C Oadby *Leic* 68-72; TV Corby SS Pet and Andr w Gt and Lt Oakley *Pet* 72-79; R Ashton w Hartwell 79-86; TR Halesworth w Linstead, Chediston, Holton etc *St E* 86-91; P-in-c Laxfield 93-01; rtd 01; Perm to Offic *St E* from 02. *4 Church View, Holton, Halesworth IP19 8PB* Tel (01986) 872594

WALKLATE, Keith. b 46. FCIB MIEx FRSA. Ox Min Course 92. **d** 95 **p** 96. NSM Wykeham *Ox* from 95; CME Adv 96-97. *Holly Tree House, 17 Old Glebe, Upper Tadmarton, Banbury OX15 5TH* Tel (01295) 780273 Fax 780834
E-mail keithwalklate@btinternet.com

WALL, Canon David Oliver. b 39. TD JP. OStJ. Bps' Coll Cheshunt 62. **d** 65 **p** 66. C Lt Ilford St Mich *Chelmsf* 65-68; CF 68-73; R Sudbourne w Orford *St E* 73-76; R Orford w Sudbourne and Chillesford w Butley 76-79; P-in-c Iken 76-79; R Drinkstone 79-82; R Rattlesden 79-82; R Chedburgh w Depden, Rede and Hawkedon 82-99; Sen Chapl ACF from 88; Chapl to Suffolk Fire Service *St E* 91-03; Hon Can St E Cathl 96-00; rtd 00; Perm to Offic *Ely* from 01. *Orford House, 43 Corsbie Close, Bury St Edmunds IP33 3ST* Tel (01284) 723232

WALL, Miss Elizabeth Anne. b 51. **d** 00 **p** 01. OLM Lich St Chad *Lich* from 00. *Gaia Cottage, 15 Gaia Lane, Lichfield WS13 7LW* Tel (01543) 254891 *or* 416595

✠**WALL, The Rt Revd Eric St Quintin.** b 15. BNC Ox BA37 MA46. Wells Th Coll 37. **d** 38 **p** 39 **c** 72. C Boston *Linc* 38-41; Chapl RAFVR 41-45; V Sherston Magna w Easton Grey *Bris* 44-53; RD Malmesbury 51-53; V Cricklade w Latton 53-60; Bp's Chapl and Dioc Adv in Chr Stewardship 60-66; Hon Can Bris Cathl 60-72; V Westbury-on-Trym St Alb 66-72; RD Clifton 67-72; Suff Bp Huntingdon and Can Res Ely Cathl *Ely* 72-80; rtd 80; Perm to Offic *Nor* from 80; *St E* from 81; *Ely* 86-00; Hon Asst Bp Glouc from 00. *Forest House, Cinderhill, Coleford GL16 8HQ* Tel (01594) 832424

WALL, John Caswallen. b 60. York Univ BA83 MA85 Ox Univ BA89. St Steph Ho Ox 86. **d** 89 **p** 90. C Ifield *Chich* 89-94; C Brighton St Pet and St Nic w Chpl Royal 94-97; C Brighton St Pet w Chpl Royal 97-98; TV Newbury *Ox* from 98. *St George's Vicarage, 206 Andover Road, Newbury RG14 6NU* Tel (01635) 41249 Fax 524994 E-mail stgeorge@easynet.co.uk

WALL, Martyn Philip Lucas. b 17. Hertf Coll Ox BA38 MA43 Open Univ BA95. Wells Th Coll 69. **d** 71 **p** 72. C Highworth w Sevenhampton and Inglesham etc *Bris* 71-74; R Wick w Doynton 74-85; rtd 85; Perm to Offic *Sarum* from 85. *9 Woburn Close, Trowbridge BA14 9TJ* Tel (01225) 754323

WALL, Nicholas John. b 46. Brasted Th Coll 69 Trin Coll Bris 71. **d** 73 **p** 74. C Moonee *S'wark* 73-78; R Dunkeswell and Dunkeswell Abbey *Ex* 78-83; V Sheldon 78-83; P-in-c Luppitt 81-83; V Dunkeswell, Sheldon and Luppitt 83-03; V Dunkeswell, Luppitt, Sheldon and Upottery from 03; CF(V) from 87. *The Rectory, Dunkeswell, Honiton EX14 0RE* Tel (01404) 891243

WALL, Mrs Pauline Ann. b 39. Bris Sch of Min 87. **dss** 85 **d** 87 **p** 94. Bris Ch the Servant Stockwood 85-99; Hon Par Dn 87-94; Hon C 94-99; Chapl St Brendan's Sixth Form Coll 90-99; rtd 99; Perm to Offic *Bris* from 99. *41 Ladman Road, Bristol BS14 8QD* Tel (01275) 833083

WALL, Richard David. b 78. Ch Ch Ox BA99. St Steph Ho Ox 00. **d** 02 **p** 03. C Bocking St Mary *Chelmsf* from 02. *3 Hadley Close, Braintree CM7 5LP* Tel (01376) 329571 Mobile 07952-381734 E-mail frrichardwall@aol.com

WALL, Robert William. b 52. Ex Coll Ox MA Ex Univ BPhil77. Trin Coll Bris 80. **d** 83 **p** 84. C Blackb Sav *Blackb* 83-86; C Edgware *Lon* 86-89; C Barnsbury 89-90; TV 90-99; V Dalston St Mark w St Bart from 99. *St Mark's Vicarage, Sandringham Road, London E8 2LL* Tel (020) 7254 4741

WALLACE, Preb Alastair Robert. b 50. St Cath Coll Cam BA71 MA75 Lon Univ BD75. Trin Coll Bris 72. **d** 75 **p** 76. C Ex St Leon w H Trin *Ex* 75-79; Chapl Ridley Hall Cam 79-80; R Bath St Mich w St Paul *B & W* 80-96; RD Bath 90-96; Sub-Dean Wells 96-99; Hon Asst Dioc Missr from 96; Preb Wells Cathl from 96; TR Ilminster and Distr from 99. *The Rectory, Court Barton, Ilminster TA19 0DU* Tel (01460) 52610
E-mail alastair.wallace@btinternet.com

WALLACE, Mrs Ann. b 29. CITC 92. **d** 95 **p** 96. Aux Min Abbeyleix w Old Church, Ballyroan etc *C & O* from 95. *Knapton, Abbeyleix, Portlaoise, Co Laois, Irish Republic* Tel (00353) (502) 31010

WALLACE, Mrs Brenda Claire. b 52. Linc Th Coll 73 S'wark Ord Course 78. **dss** 80 **d** 87 **p** 94. Sutton at Hone *Roch* 80-83; Borstal 83-87; Hon Par Dn 87-89; HM Pris Cookham Wood 83-89; Asst Chapl 87-89; NSM Stansted Mountfitchet *Chelmsf* 89-96; NSM Stansted Mountfitchet w Birchanger and Farnham 97; C Hutton from 97. *The Rectory, 175 Rayleigh Road, Hutton, Brentwood CM13 1LX* Tel (01277) 215115 Fax 263407
E-mail huttonchurch@zetnet.co.uk

WALLACE, David Alexander Rippon. b 39. CEng MIEE. Ox Min Course 94. **d** 96 **p** 97. NSM Haddenham w Cuddington, Kingsey etc *Ox* 96-97; NSM Worminghall w Ickford, Oakley and Shabbington from 97. *11 Station Road, Haddenham, Aylesbury HP17 8AN* Tel (01844) 290670
E-mail revd@wallaces.org

WALLACE, Derek George. b 33. Glas Univ MA55. Edin Th Coll 55. **d** 57 **p** 58. C Falkirk *Edin* 57-60; C Ayr *Glas* 60-62; Chapl Netherton Tr Sch Morpeth 62-67; V Oldham St Jo *Man* 67-70; R Burravoe *Ab* 70-78; R Lerwick 70-78; R Port Glas 78-94; Miss to

Seamen 78-94; rtd 94. *39 Coronation Crescent, Margate CT9 5PN* Tel (01843) 223869

WALLACE, Mrs Edwina Margaret. b 49. EMMTC 00. **d** 03. C Broughton Astley and Croft w Stoney Stanton *Leic* from 03. *1 Aland Gardens, Broughton Astley, Leicester LE9 6NE* Tel (01455) 283512 Mobile 07766-714261
E-mail em.wallace@btopenworld.com

WALLACE, Godfrey Everingham. *See* EVERINGHAM, Georgina Wendy

WALLACE, James Stephen. b 60. Plymouth Poly BSc81 St Martin's Coll Lanc 90. Westcott Ho Cam 96. **d** 98 **p** 99. C Newport Pagnell w Lathbury and Moulsoe *Ox* 98-02; USPG Sri Lanka from 02. *Devasarana Development Centre, Ibbagamuwa, Sri Lanka*

WALLACE, Julie Michele. b 58. Cam Univ DipRS82 Lon Univ Dip Counselling 88 Cert Counselling 92 DipApTh92 Ox Univ MTh93 Univ Coll Lon MSc02. CA Tr Coll 77. **d** 88 **p** 94. Chapl Middx Poly *Lon* 86-90; Voc Adv CA 90-92; Member CA Counselling Service 92-96; Hon C Bellingham St Dunstan *S'wark* 91-96; TV Kidbrooke St Jas 96-99; Perm to Offic 99-01; Hon C Croydon Woodside 01-03. *61 Cornmow Drive, London NW10 1BB* Tel (020) 8438 6605

✠**WALLACE, The Rt Revd Martin William.** b 48. K Coll Lon BD70 AKC70. St Aug Coll Cant 70. **d** 71 **p** 72 **c** 03. C Attercliffe *Sheff* 71-74; C New Malden and Coombe *S'wark* 74-77; V Forest Gate St Mark *Chelmsf* 77-93; RD Newham 82-91; P-in-c Forest Gate Em w Upton Cross 85-89; Hon Can Chelmsf Cathl 89-03; P-in-c Forest Gate All SS 91-93; Dioc ACUPA Link Officer 91-97; P-in-c Bradwell on Sea 93-97; P-in-c St Lawrence 93-97; Ind Chapl Maldon and Dengie Deanery 93-97; Adn Colchester 97-03; Bp's Adv for Hosp Chapl 97-03; Bp Selby *York* from 03. *10 Precentor's Court, York YO1 2EJ* Tel (01904) 656492 Fax 655671 E-mail bishselby@clara.net

WALLACE (née ALEXANDER), Mrs Nancy Joan. b 42. Roehampton Inst TCert64 N Lon Univ CertCC70 PQCSW97 Ox Brookes Univ BA97. St Alb and Ox Min Course CBTS95. **d** 98 **p** 99. NSM Worminghall w Ickford, Oakley and Shabbington *Ox* from 98. *11 Station Road, Haddenham, Aylesbury HP17 8AN* Tel (01844) 290670 Fax as telephone E-mail nancy@wallace.nildram.co.uk

WALLACE, Nicholas Robert. b 56. Trin Coll Bris DipHE95. **d** 95 **p** 96. C Fishponds St Jo *Bris* 95-98; P-in-c Barton Hill St Luke w Ch Ch 98-99; P-in-c Barton Hill St Luke w Ch Ch and Moorfields 99-00; R Binstead *Portsm* from 00; V Havenstreet St Pet from 00. *The Rectory, Pitts Lane, Ryde PO33 3SU* Tel (01983) 562890

WALLACE, Raymond Sherwood. b 28. Selw Coll Dunedin (NZ). **d** 52 **p** 54. New Zealand 52-58; C St Pancras H Cross w St Jude and St Pet *Lon* 58-64; C N Harrow St Alb 64-67; V Stroud Green H Trin 67-79; V Penwerris *Truro* 79-84; R Wymington w Podington *St Alb* 84-87; rtd 87; Perm to Offic *St Alb* from 87. *141 Dunsmore Road, Luton LU1 5JX* Tel (01582) 455882

WALLACE, Richard Colin. b 39. Mert Coll Ox BA61 MA64. St Chad's Coll Dur 69. **d** 71 **p** 72. Tutor St Chad's Coll Dur 71-72; P-in-c Kimblesworth *Dur* 72-74; Chapl Bradf Univ *Bradf* 74-79; C Bingley All SS 79-80; TV 80-89; V Earby from 89; P-in-c Kelbrook from 01; RD Skipton from 00. *The Vicarage, Skipton Road, Earby, Barnoldswick BB18 6JL* Tel (01282) 842291

WALLACE, Richard Ernest. b 35. Ridley Coll Melbourne ThL61 ACT 61. **d** 61 **p** 62. Australia 61-67 and from 69; C Balwyn St Barn 61-62; C S Yarra 62-64; C Bentleigh St Jo 64-65; I Northcote 65-66; C Ipswich St Fran *St E* 67-69; I Belgrave 69-77; Dir Angl Renewal Min 79-82; I Blackburn St Jo 83-92; I Syndal St Jas 92-95; Sen Assoc P Glen Waverley 95-97. *49 Patterson Street, Ringwood East, Vic, Australia 3155* Tel (0061) (3) 9870 1000 Mobile 0419-314060 Fax (3) 9870 1821
E-mail rwallace@melbpc.org.au

WALLACE, Richard John. b 56. Coll of Resurr Mirfield. **d** 82 **p** 83. C Catford St Laur *S'wark* 82-85; C Bellingham St Dunstan 85-87; V 87-95; TR Stanley *Dur* 95-99; V Cockerton from 99. *St Mary's Vicarage, Newton Lane, Cockerton, Darlington DL3 9EX* Tel (01325) 367092

WALLACE, Richard Samuel. b 17. TCD BA39 MA53. **d** 41 **p** 42. C Belfast St Steph *Conn* 41-43; C Hammersmith St Pet *Lon* 43-44; India 44-51; Perivale *Lon* 51-54; V Notting Hill St Mark 54-60; V Teddington St Mark 60-83; rtd 83; Perm to Offic *Ex* from 83. *St Christopher, 17 Hartley Road, Exmouth EX8 2SG* Tel (01395) 279595

WALLACE, Robert. b 52. Sussex Univ BSc73 Nottm Univ DipTh75. Linc Th Coll 73. **d** 76 **p** 77. C Plaistow St Mary *Roch* 76-79; C Dartford H Trin 79-83; V Borstal 83-89; Chapl The Foord Almshouses 83-89; Chapl HM Pris Cookham Wood 83-89; V Stansted Mountfitchet *Chelmsf* 89-96; P-in-c Farnham 89-96; R Stansted Mountfitchet w Birchanger and Farnham 97; R Hutton from 97. *The Rectory, 175 Rayleigh Road, Hutton, Brentwood CM13 1LX* Tel (01277) 215115 Fax 263407
E-mail huttonchurch@zetnet.co.uk

WALLER, David Arthur. b 61. Leeds Univ BA83. Chich Th Coll 89. **d** 91 **p** 92. C Aldwick *Chich* 91-95; TV Crawley 95-00; V

Walthamstow St Sav *Chelmsf* from 00. *41 Fraser Road, London E17 9DD* Tel (020) 8520 2036
E-mail d.a.waller@btinternet.com

WALLER, David James. b 58. Whitelands Coll Lon BA85 K Coll Lon MA95. Ripon Coll Cuddesdon 85. **d** 88 **p** 89. C Tettenhall Regis *Lich* 88-91; Chapl Univ of Greenwich *S'wark* 92-97; P-in-c Yiewsley *Lon* 97-01; TR Plymstock and Hooe *Ex* from 01. *The Rectory, 5 Cobb Lane, Plymstock, Plymouth PL9 9BQ* Tel (01752) 403126 E-mail david@waller2000.freeserve.co.uk

WALLER, Derek James Keith. b 54. Em Coll Cam BA75 PGCE76. Trin Coll Bris 88. **d** 91 **p** 92. C Church Stretton *Heref* 91-95; R Appleby Gp *Leic* from 95. *The Rectory, Rectory Lane, Appleby Magna, Swadlincote DE12 7BQ* Tel (01530) 270482 E-mail waller@leicester.anglican.org

WALLER, Ms Elizabeth Jean. b 58. Keswick Hall Coll BEd BTh. Linc Th Coll 84. **d** 87 **p** 94. Par Dn Mile End Old Town H Trin *Lon* 87-90; Manna Chr Cen 90-91; Chapl LSE *Lon* 91-96; Hon C Soho St Anne w St Thos and St Pet 91-96; CARA from 96; NSM Notting Dale St Clem w St Mark and St Jas *Lon* 96-99; Perm to Offic 99-00. *55 Browning Avenue, Hanwell W7 1AX* Tel (020) 8578 3827

WALLER, Gordon Robert. b 50. Dioc OLM tr scheme 00. **d** 03. OLM Tooting All SS *S'wark* from 03. *131 Ribblesdale Road, London SW16 6SP* Tel (020) 8769 6733
E-mail baldypevsner@yahoo.co.uk

WALLER, John. b 60. Man Univ BA84. St Jo Coll Nottm 85. **d** 87 **p** 88. C Chorlton-cum-Hardy St Clem *Man* 87-90; R Openshaw 90-95; Chapl Ancoats Hosp Man 93-95; TV Watling Valley *Ox* 95-96; TR 96-03; R Brickhills and Stoke Hammond from 03. *Kingswood, Pound Hill, Great Brickhill, Milton Keynes MK17 9AS* Tel (01525) 261062 E-mail john.waller1@virgin.net

WALLER, John Pretyman. b 41. Sarum Th Coll 68. **d** 71 **p** 72. C Ipswich St Jo *St E* 71-74; R Waldringfield w Hemley 74-78; P-in-c Newbourn 74-78; R Waldringfield w Hemley and Newbourn from 78. *The Rectory, Mill Road, Waldringfield, Woodbridge IP12 4PY* Tel (01473) 36247

✠**WALLER, The Rt Revd John Stevens.** b 24. Peterho Cam BA48 MA53. Wells Th Coll 48. **d** 50 **p** 51 **c** 79. C Hillingdon St Jo *Lon* 50-52; C Twerton *B & W* 52-55; C-in-c Weston-super-Mare St Andr Bournville CD 55-59; V Weston-super-Mare St Andr Bournville 59-60; R Yarlington 60-63; Youth Chapl 60-63; Tr Officer C of E Youth Coun 63-67; V Frindsbury w Upnor *Roch* 67-72; P-in-c Strood St Fran 67-72; P-in-c Strood St Mary 67-72; P-in-c Strood St Nic 67-72; TR Strood 72-73; RD Strood 67-73; R Harpenden St Nic *St Alb* 73-79; Suff Bp Stafford *Lich* 79-87; Asst Bp B & W from 87; P-in-c Long Sutton w Long Load 87-88; TV Langport Area Chs 88-89; rtd 89. *102 Harnham Road, Salisbury SP2 8JW* Tel (01722) 329739 Fax 411492

WALLER, Canon John Watson. b 35. Qu Mary Coll Lon BSc57 St Cath Soc Ox DipTh60. Wycliffe Hall Ox 58. **d** 61 **p** 62. C Pudsey St Lawr *Bradf* 61-65; V 74-82; V Mortomley St Sav *Sheff* 65-74; V Pudsey St Lawr and St Paul *Bradf* 82-88; Hon Can Bradf Cathl 84-88; RD Calverley 84-88; V Kingston upon Hull H Trin *York* 88-01; AD Cen and N Hull 94-99; Can and Preb York Minster from 95; RD Hull 96-00; rtd 01; Perm to Offic *York* from 01. *7 Seven Wells, Amotherby, Malton YO17 6TT* Tel (01653) 691388

WALLER, Orlando Alfred. b 12. St Aid Birkenhead 39. **d** 41 **p** 42. C Birkenhead St Pet *Ches* 41-42; C Crewe St Barn 42-45; C Gatley 45-49; Min Heald Green St Cath CD 49-51; V Haslington w Crewe Green 51-54; Australia 54-59; V Runcorn St Jo Weston *Ches* 59-63; V Merrington *Dur* 63-70; P-in-c Bearpark 70-71; V 71-76; rtd 77. *22 Thornley Close, Broom Park, Durham DH7 7NN*

WALLER, Philip Thomas. b 56. Ex Coll Ox BA78 MA88. St Jo Coll Dur BA87. **d** 88 **p** 89. C Enfield St Andr *Lon* 88-91; C Belper *Derby* 91-95; P-in-c Oakwood from 95. *The Vicarage, 239 Morley Road, Oakwood, Derby DE21 4TB* Tel (01332) 667803
E-mail waller.family@clara.co.uk

WALLES, Bruce Andrew. b 54. Coll of Resurr Mirfield 90. **d** 92 **p** 93. C Maidstone St Martin *Cant* 92-96; TV Banbury *Ox* 96-98; V Banbury St Leon from 98. *St Leonard's Vicarage, Middleton Road, Banbury OX16 4RG* Tel (01295) 262120 Fax as telephone
E-mail wallba@ntlworld.com

WALLEY, Peter Francis. b 60. Bris Univ BSc82 MICE89 CEng89. Trin Coll Bris DipTh98. **d** 98 **p** 99. C Ex St Jas *Ex* 98-01; Asst Chapl Brussels *Eur* from 01. *Allée de l'Aqueduc 23, 1410 Waterloo, Belgium* Tel (0032) (2) 354 5985 or 511 7183 E-mail peter.walley@belgacom.net

WALLING, Mrs Carolyn. b 47. Rolle Coll CertEd69. Episc Div Sch Cam Mass MDiv87. **d** 86 **p** 87. Saudi Arabia 89; USA 94-96; Par Dn Mottingham St Andr *S'wark* 90; Par Dn Battersea St Mary 91-94; C Lee Gd Shep w St Pet 96. *50 Queen of Denmark Court, Finland Street, London SE16 1TB* Tel (020) 7231 3873 Fax as telephone

WALLINGTON, Martin John. b 59. St Alb and Ox Min Course 95. **d** 98 **p** 99. NSM Chorleywood St Andr *St Alb* 98-03; P-in-c Wooburn *Ox* from 03. *Wooburn Vicarage, Windsor Hill, Wooburn Green, High Wycombe HP10 0EH* Tel (01628) 521209

WALLINGTON, Paul. b 62. Birm Univ BCom83 ACA86. Trin Coll Bris BA94. **d** 94 **p** 95. C Chorley St Laur *Blackb* 94-97; C

Darwen St Pet w Hoddlesden 97-98; TV 98-00; rtd 00. *551 Darwen Road, Dunscar, Bolton BL7 9RT* Tel (01204) 308637 E-mail thewallingtons@hotmail.com

WALLIS, Benjamin John. b 55. Wimbledon Sch of Art BA79. Chich Th Coll 92. **d** 94 **p** 95. C Battersea Ch Ch and St Steph *S'wark* 94-98; C Wood Green St Mich w Bounds Green St Gabr etc *Lon* 98-03; V Barkingside St Geo *Chelmsf* from 03. *St George's Vicarage, Woodford Avenue, Ilford IG2 6XQ* Tel (020) 8550 4149

WALLIS, David Peter. b 72. Ripon Coll Cuddesdon BTh03. **d** 03. C Eastbourne St Mary *Chich* from 03. *6 Bay Pond Road, Eastbourne BN21 1HX* Tel (01323) 733159

WALLIS, Ian George. b 57. Sheff Univ BA79 PhD92 St Edm Ho Cam MLitt87. Ridley Hall Cam 88. **d** 90 **p** 91. C Armthorpe *Sheff* 90-92; Chapl SS Coll Cam 92-95; Lic to Offic *Ely* 93-95; Hon C Chesterton Gd Shep 95; R Houghton le Spring *Dur* from 95. *The Rectory, Dairy Lane, Houghton le Spring DH4 5BH* Tel 0191-584 2198 Fax 512 1685

WALLIS, John Anthony. b 36. St Pet Coll Ox BA60 MA65. Clifton Th Coll 60. **d** 62 **p** 63. C Blackpool St Mark *Blackb* 62-65; C Leeds St Geo *Ripon* 65-69; Korea 69-74; Nat Sec (Scotland) OMF 75-78; Home Dir OMF 78-89; Hon C Sevenoaks St Nic *Roch* 78-89; Chapl The Hague *Eur* 89-95; V Northwood Em *Lon* 95-01; rtd 01; Perm to Offic *Nor* from 03. *Church Cottage, 61 Gayton Road, Grimston, King's Lynn PE32 1BG* Tel (01485) 600336 E-mail johna.wallis@virgin.net

WALLIS, Paul Anthony. b 65. Nottm Univ BTh90. St Jo Coll Nottm 87. **d** 90 **p** 91. C Somers Town *Lon* 90-93; P-in-c Southsea St Pet *Portsm* 93-94; Chapl Generation Min 95-00; Chapl-Gen from 02; R Kambah St Steph and Chapl Aus Nat Univ 00-02. *Jesus House, 26 Belmont Street, Southsea PO5 1ND* Tel (023) 9229 8019 E-mail ministry@paulwallis.com

WALLIS, Peter. b 42. K Coll Lon MB, BS68 MRCS AKC68. STETS 98. **d** 01. NSM Clymping and Yapton w Ford *Chich* from 01. *Chanters, 3 Second Avenue, Felpham, Bognor Regis PO22 7LJ* Tel (01243) 584080 Mobile 07885-542651
E-mail revdocpeterw@aol.com

WALLIS, Raymond Christopher. b 38. Lon Univ DipTh61 Moor Park Coll Farnham 62. Sarum Th Coll 63. **d** 66 **p** 67. C Allerton *Bradf* 66-68; C Langley Marish *Ox* 68-69; C Caister *Nor* 69-73; P-in-c E w W Bradenham 73-80; R Outwell *Ely* 80-84; R Upwell St Pet 80-84; V Bishopstone *Chich* 84-97; rtd 97; Perm to Offic *Chich* from 97. *The Moorings, Rattle Road, Westham, Pevensey BN24 5DS* Tel (01323) 766247

WALLIS, Roland Seabon. b 17. MBE44. Lon Univ BSc38 Ex Univ BSc57. St Aug Coll Cant 75. **d** 77 **p** 78. NSM Whitstable *Cant* 77-87; rtd 87; Perm to Offic *Cant* 87-01. *Aspen House, 33 Carlton Road, Littleover, Derby DE23 6HB*

WALLMAN-GIRDLESTONE, Jane Elizabeth. b 61. Homerton Coll Cam BEd83 Bell Educational Trust CertTESOL85 Open Univ AdDipEd88 Drama Studio Lon Dip Theatre88. St Steph Ho Ox 89 Sarum & Wells Th Coll BTh92. **d** 93 **p** 94. C Woodbridge St Mary *St E* 93-96; V Ipswich St Thos 96-00; Dir of Past Studies and Adv for Women's Min St Mich Coll Llandaff 00-02. *Isle View, The Clattach, Allanfearn, Inverness IV2 7HZ* Tel (01463) 230708 E-mail jane@sharing-space.co.uk

WALLS, Michael Peter. b 38. Cape Town Univ BA57 Lon Univ DipTh61. Wells Th Coll 59. **d** 61 **p** 62. C Morecambe St Barn *Blackb* 61-64; C Birm St Paul *Birm* 64-66; Ind Chapl 64-74; V Temple Balsall 66-74; Chapl Wroxall Abbey Sch 72-74; V Kings Heath *Birm* 74-76; Hon C Bordesley St Benedict 76-78; Sen Chapl Oakham Sch 78-83; P-in-c Leic St Sav *Leic* 83-85; P-in-c Knossington and Cold Overton 85-87; P-in-c Owston and Withcote 85-87; V Tilton w Lowesby 85-87; P-in-c 87; V Whatborough Gp of Par 87-90; Bp's Adv Relns w People of Other Faiths 89-93; Hon Can Leic Cathl 89-93; V Leic St Mary 90-93; rtd 93; Perm to Offic *Ban* from 02. *Gwynt y Mor, 1A Bro Cymerau, Pwllheli LL53 5PY* Tel (01758) 613495
E-mail michael.w@tinyworld.co.uk

WALLS, Roland Charles. b 17. CCC Cam BA48 MA52. Kelham Th Coll 34. **d** 40 **p** 41. C Manston *Ripon* 40-43; C Sheff Parson Cross St Cecilia *Sheff* 43-45; Perm to Offic *Ely* 45-48; Fell CCC Cam 48-62; Chapl 52-55; Dean of Chpl 55-58; Lect Kelham Th Coll 48-51; Bp's Dom Chapl *Ely* 51-52; Select Preacher Cam Univ 56; Select Preacher Ox Univ 77; Can Res Sheff Cathl *Sheff* 58-62; Hon C-in-c Roslin (Rosslyn Chpl) *Edin* 62-69; Lect Div Edin Univ 63-77; Community of the Transfiguration from 65. *23 Manse Road, Roslin EH25 9LF*

WALLS, Simon Conor. b 67. Dur Univ BA89 TCD MPhil90. **d** 91 **p** 92. C Castleknock and Mulhuddart, w Clonsilla *D & G* 91-93; Chapl Asst Maidstone Hosp 93-95; Chapl Brighton Health Care NHS Trust 95-96. *Address temp unknown*

WALMISLEY, Andrew John. b 55. Ex Univ BA75. Ridley Hall Cam 76. **d** 78 **p** 79. C W Brompton St Mary w St Pet *Lon* 78-81; USA from 81. *2601 Derby Street, Berkeley, CA 94705, USA* E-mail walmisley@aol.com

WALMSLEY, Derek. b 57. Oak Hill Th Coll DipHE91. **d** 91 **p** 92. C Bletchley *Ox* 91-95; C Utley *Bradf* 95-00; V from 00. *St Mark's Vicarage, Greenhead Road, Keighley BD20 6ED* Tel (01535) 607003

WALMSLEY, John William. b 37. Hull Univ BA71 MA73 PhD81. Wycliffe Hall Ox 71. **d** 72 **p** 73. C Clifton *York* 72-74; C Acomb St Steph 74-76; P-in-c Newton upon Ouse 76-81; P-in-c Shipton w Overton 76-81; V York St Thos w St Maurice 81-89; V Barkingside St Laur *Chelmsf* 89-92; Dir Children in Distress 92-01; rtd 01. *The Dolphin Hotel, Bridge Street, Whitby YO22 4BJ*

WALMSLEY, Patricia Jane. b 62. Bris Univ BSc83 PhD87 Trin Coll Cam BTh01. Ridley Hall Cam 99. **d** 01 **p** 02. C Bowdon *Ches* from 01. *Kilgowan, Vicarage Lane, Bowdon, Altrincham WA14 3AS* Tel 0161-928 7933
E-mail jane@walmsley92.freeserve.co.uk

WALMSLEY-McLEOD, Paul Albert. b 56. St Cuth Soc Dur BA82 Cam Univ CertEd83. Westcott Ho Cam 85. **d** 87 **p** 88. C Gt Bookham *Guildf* 87-90; Asst Chapl St Chris Hospice Lon 90-93; Soc Care Team Member Phoenix Ho Fountain Project 93-95; C Catford (Southend) and Downham *S'wark* 95-96; TV 96-99; P-in-c Downham St Barn 00-02; R Friern Barnet St Jas *Lon* from 02. *The Rectory, 147 Friern Barnet Lane, London N20 0NP* Tel (020) 8445 7844
E-mail p.w.mcleod@btinternet.com

WALNE, John Clifford. b 29. Wycliffe Hall Ox. **d** 87 **p** 88. NSM Hedsor and Bourne End *Ox* 87-88; Hon C Lezayre St Olave Ramsey *S & M* 88-92; Hon C Kirkbride 88-92; P-in-c Berrington w Betton Strange *Heref* 92-97; rtd 97. *2 Bell Close, Beaconsfield HP9 1AT* Tel (01494) 670120

WALROND-SKINNER, Susan Mary. *See* PARFITT, Susan Mary

WALSALL, Archdeacon of. *See* SADLER, The Ven Anthony Graham

WALSER, Emil Jonathan. b 16. St Jo Coll Dur LTh38 BA39 MA43. Oak Hill Th Coll 35. **d** 39 **p** 40. C Holloway St Mary Magd *Lon* 39-42; C Pudsey St Lawr *Bradf* 42-46; R Whalley Range St Edm *Man* 46-52; V Mackworth All SS *Derby* 52-65; P-in-c Kirk Langley St-59; R 59-65; V Baslow 65-82; RD Bakewell and Eyam 78-81; rtd 82; Perm to Offic *York* from 82. *2 Almond Grove, Filey YO14 9EH* Tel (01723) 515582

WALSER (née SHIELS), Mrs Rosalinde Cameron. b 47. Edin Univ MA68 Moray Ho Coll of Educn PGCE69. N Ord Course 92. **d** 95 **p** 97. NSM Scarborough St Mary w Ch ch and H Apostles *York* 95-97; Chapl St Cath Hospice Scarborough 95-97; Chapl Scarborough Coll 95-97; P-in-c E Ayton *York* from 97. *29 Sea Cliff Road, Scarborough YO11 2XU* Tel (01723) 372382

WALSH, Bertram William Nicholas. b 21. TCD BA44. CITC 46. **d** 46 **p** 47. C Dublin St Pet w St Matthias *D & G* 46-47; Min Can St Patr Cathl Dublin 47-49; C Dublin St Jas *D & G* 47-49; Res Preacher Cork Cathl *C, C & R* 49-52; C Dublin St Bart *D & G* 52-54; Clerical V Ch Ch Cathl Dublin 54-58; Chapl St Columba's Coll Dub 60-87; rtd 87. *130 Grange Road, Rathfarnham, Dublin 14, Irish Republic* Tel (00353) (1) 493 1229

WALSH, David Christopher. b 59. Warwick Univ BA81 St Jo Coll Nottm BA83. Ripon Coll Cuddesdon 00. **d** 02 **p** 03. C Greenwich St Alfege *S'wark* from 02. *88 Ashburnham Grove, London SE10 8UJ* Tel (020) 8333 9152 Mobile 07957-656643
E-mail david@david.walsh.name

✠**WALSH, The Rt Revd Geoffrey David Jeremy.** b 29. Pemb Coll Cam BA53 MA58. Linc Th Coll 53. **d** 55 **p** 56 **c** 86. C Southgate Ch Ch *Lon* 55-58; SCM Sec Cam 58-61; V Moorfields *Bris* 61-66; R Marlborough *Sarum* 66-76; Can and Preb Sarum Cathl 73-76; Adn Ipswich *St E* 76-86; R Elmsett w Aldham 76-80; Suff Bp Tewkesbury *Glouc* 86-95; rtd 95; Perm to Offic *St E* from 95. *6 Warren Lane, Martlesham Heath, Ipswich IP5 3SH* Tel (01473) 620797

WALSH, Geoffrey Malcolm. b 46. Sarum & Wells Th Coll 82. **d** 84 **p** 85. C Wellington and Distr *B & W* 84-87; TV Axminster, Chardstock, Combe Pyne and Rousdon *Ex* 87-90; Chapl RN 90-94; R Huntspill *B & W* from 94. *The Rectory, Church Road, West Huntspill, Highbridge TA9 3RN* Tel (01278) 793950 Fax as telephone E-mail g.walsh1@ntlworld.co.uk

WALSH, John Alan. b 37. Chich Th Coll 63. **d** 66 **p** 67. C Wigan St Anne *Liv* 66-69; C Newport w Longford *Lich* 69-73; V Dunstall 73-83; V Rangemore 73-83; P-in-c Tatenhill 77-83; R Dunstall w Rangemore and Tatenhill 83; V Hartshill from 83. *Holy Trinity Vicarage, Hartshill, Stoke-on-Trent ST4 7NJ* Tel (01782) 616965

WALSH, Peter. b 64. Liv Univ BA86 Nottm Univ BTh90. Linc Th Coll 87. **d** 90 **p** 91. C Cantley *Sheff* 90-93; C Poulton-le-Fylde *Blackb* 93-95; V Blackpool St Steph 95-03; TR Ches Team *Ches* from 03. *6 Elizabeth Crescent, Chester CH4 7AZ* Tel (01244) 683585

WALSHE, Canon Brian. b 28. AKC49. St Boniface Warminster. **d** 54 **p** 55. C Southsea St Pet *Portsm* 54-57; C Portsea St Jo Rudmore 57-58; Warden Wellington Coll Miss Walworth 58-62; V Chesterfield St Aug *Derby* 62-68; R Langley Marsh *Ox* 68-76; Chapl Manfield Hosp Northn 76-88; V Northampton St Alb *Pet* 76-88; Dir Mountbatten Community Trust from 76; Chief Exec Lon Youth Trust from 87; rtd 88; Perm to Offic *Pet* 88-93; Perm to Offic *Chich* from 93. *9/10 Warrior Court, 16 Warrior Way, St Leonards-on-Sea TN37 6BS*

WALSHE, Marie Sylvia. b 54. RGN RCNT. **d** 99 **p** 00. Aux Min Kilkeel *D & D* 99-00; Aux Min Down H Trin w Hollymount from 00; Aux Min Rathmullan w Tyrella from 00. *The Rectory, 10 Ballydonnell Road, Downpatrick BT30 8EN*
E-mail kwalshe@talk21.com

WALT, Canon Trevor William. b 52. MBE03. RMN74 RNT79. Ox NSM Course 83. **d** 86 **p** 87. NSM Crowthorne *Ox* 86-89; Chapl Asst Broadmoor Hosp Crowthorne 86-89; Chapl from 89; Hon Can Ch Ch *Ox* from 00. *Broadmoor Hospital, Crowthorne RG45 7EG* Tel (01344) 773111 ext 4450

WALTER, Christopher Stuart Radclyffe. b 47. Sarum & Wells Th Coll DipTh93. **d** 93 **p** 94. C Fakenham w Alethorpe *Nor* 93-96; P-in-c Buxton w Oxnead, Lammas and Brampton from 96; P-in-c Coltishall w Gt Hautbois and Horstead from 99. *The Vicarage, Back Lane, Buxton, Norwich NR10 5HD* Tel (01603) 279394

WALTER, Donald Alex. b 34. Ripon Hall Ox 57. **d** 60 **p** 61. C Ealing St Steph Castle Hill *Lon* 60-63; Jamaica 63-80; V Twickenham Common H Trin *Lon* 81-00; rtd 00. *Ebenezer, 23 Hawley Close, Hampton TW12 3XX* Tel (020) 8941 5193
E-mail alexandpamela@maperche.co.uk

WALTER, Giles Robert. b 54. Cam Univ MA76. Cranmer Hall Dur 78. **d** 82 **p** 83. C Finchley Ch Ch *Lon* 82-86; C Cambridge H Sepulchre w All SS *Ely* 86-92; C Cambridge H Sepulchre 92-93; P-in-c Tunbridge Wells St Jo *Roch* 93-95; V from 95. *St John's Vicarage, 1 Amherst Road, Tunbridge Wells TN4 9LG* Tel (01892) 521183

WALTER, Ian Edward. b 47. Edin Univ MA69 Keble Coll Ox BA71 MA78. Cuddesdon Coll 71. **d** 73 **p** 74. C Greenock *Glas* 73-76; C Glas St Mary 76-79; Chapl Angl Students Glas 76-79; R Paisley St Barn 79-84; P-in-c Bolton St Phil *Man* 84-86; V 86-91; Dioc Ecum Officer 88-94; V Elton All SS 91-98; V Stalybridge 98-01; R Hawick *Edin* from 01. *St Cuthbert's Rectory, Rectory Close, Liddlesdale Road, Hawick TD9 0ET* Tel (01450) 372043
E-mail ian.walter@amserve.net

WALTER, Michael. b 36. AKC62. **d** 63 **p** 64. C Middlesbrough St Jo the Ev *York* 63-65; C Sherborne *Win* 65-68; C Bournemouth St Fran 68-69; Prec Newc Cathl *Newc* 69-71; C Dur St Marg *Dur* 72-74; P-in-c Deaf Hill cum Langdale 74-77; V Newington w Dairycoates *York* 77-88; Perm to Offic 88-92; C Feltham *Lon* 92-96; Perm to Offic 96-03; rtd 01. *52 Royal Road, Teddington TW11 0SB* Tel (020) 8943 4212

WALTER, Noel. b 41. St D Coll Lamp DipTh66. **d** 66 **p** 67. C Mitcham Ascension *S'wark* 66-71; C Caterham 71-74; V Welling 74-82; C Warlingham w Chelsham and Farleigh 82-88; Chapl Warlingham Park Hosp Croydon 82-88; Chapl R Earlswood Hosp Redhill 88-90; Chapl Redhill Gen Hosp 88-91; Chapl E Surrey Hosp Redhill 88-96; Sen Chapl Gt Ormond Street Hosp for Children NHS Trust from 96; Perm to Offic *Ex* from 98. *Great Ormond Street Hospital, Great Ormond Street, London WC1N 3JH, or 3 Carleton Villas, London NW5 2QU* Tel (020) 7405 9200, 7813 8232 or 7482 2133

WALTER, Peter John. b 44. CEng MIGasE. Chich Th Coll 80. **d** 82 **p** 83. C Leominster *Heref* 82-85; P-in-c Brimfield 85-90; P-in-c Orleton 85-90; R Orleton w Brimfield 91-95. *Mews Corrage, 39 West Street, Leominster HR6 8EP*

WALTER, Robin. b 37. Univ Coll Dur BA63 MA90 Linacre Coll Ox BA65 MA69. St Steph Ho Ox 63. **d** 66 **p** 68. C Peckham St Jo *S'wark* 66-69; Chapl Univ *Lon* 69-70; C Dur St Marg *Dur* 70-74; R Burnmoor 74-79; Asst Master Barnard Castle Sch 79-97; Lic to Offic 79-82; Hon C Whorlton 82-88; NSM Barnard Castle Deanery 88-97; P-in-c Redmarshall 97-01; R 01-03; P-in-c Bishopton w Gt Stainton 97-01; V 01-03; rtd 03; Perm to Offic *York* from 03. *3 Yew Tree Mews, Osbaldwick, York YO10 3PQ* Tel (01904) 424045

WALTERS, Andrew Farrar. b 42. ACP67 St Luke's Coll Ex CertEd71. **d** 81 **p** 82. Hd Master and Warden St Mich Coll Tenbury 77-85; Chapl Ex Cathl Sch 85-87; Hd Master Homefield Sch Sutton 87-92; Hd Master Lich Cathl Sch 92-02; Hon C Sutton St Nic *S'wark* 87-92; Chan's V Lich Cathl *Lich* 93-02; rtd 02. *The Drey, Trallong, Brecon LD3 8HP* Tel (01874) 636374 Fax as telephone E-mail andrew.walter2@talk21.com

WALTERS, Christopher John Linley. b 24. St Pet Hall Ox BA47 MA49. Linc Th Coll 48. **d** 50 **p** 51. C Dartford Ch Ch *Roch* 50-53; C Oswestry St Oswald *Lich* 53-56; V Weston Rhyn 56-61; V Newcastle St Paul 61-70; V Pattingham 70-85; P-in-c Patshull 77-85; V Pattingham w Patshull 85-89; rtd 89; Perm to Offic *Heref* from 93. *Old School House, 19 Cardington, Church Stretton SY6 7JZ* Tel (01694) 771528

WALTERS, Christopher Rowland. b 47. Open Univ BA78 Univ of Wales PGCE94. **d** 02. Hd Master Mayflower Chr Sch Pontypool from 90; OLM Abergavenny H Trin *Mon* from 02. *Court Farm, Llanfihangel Pontymoel, Pontypool NP4 0JB* Tel (01495) 0740440 or 762323 Mobile 07967-945320
E-mail church@chriswalters.co.uk

WALTERS, David Michael Trenham. b 46. Open Univ BA86. St D Coll Lamp DipTh69. **d** 69 **p** 70. C Killay *S & B* 69-72; CF 72-89 and 91-01; Chapl Eagle Ho Prep Sch Crowthorne 89-91; P-in-c Llanyrnewydd *S & B* from 01. *Westwood Cottage, 65 Pennard Road, Pennard, Swansea SA3 2AD*

WALTERS, David Trevor. b 37. Ex Coll Ox BA58 MA62. St Steph Ho Ox 62. **d** 64 **p** 65. C Cardiff St Mary *Llan* 64-69; C Brecon w Battle *S & B* 69-73; Min Can Brecon Cathl 69-73; V Llanddew and Talachddu 73-78; V Cefncoed and Capel Nantddu 78-80; V Cefn Coed and Capel Nantddu w Vaynor etc 80-87; V Talgarth and Llanelieu from 87. *The Vicarage, 10 Bronant, Talgarth, Brecon LD3 0HF* Tel (01874) 711249

WALTERS, Mrs Felicity Ann. b 56. WEMTC. **d** 01 **p** 02. C Glouc St Geo w Whaddon *Glouc* from 01. *82 Bodiam Avenue, Tuffley, Gloucester GL4 0TL* Tel (01452) 383578
E-mail felicitywalters@posthaste88.freeserve.co.uk

WALTERS, Canon Francis Raymond. b 24. Ball Coll Ox BA49 MA54. Wycliffe Hall Ox 51. **d** 53 **p** 54. C Boulton *Derby* 53-56; Lect Qu Coll Birm 56-64; Succ Birm Cathl *Birm* 56-58; C Harborne St Pet 58-64; V Leic St Nic *Leic* 64-74; Chapl Leic Univ 64-74; R Appleby 74-77; Dioc Dir of Educn 77-89; Hon Can Leic Cathl 77-91; P-in-c Swithland 77-91; rtd 91; Perm to Offic *Nor* from 91. *2 Beeston Common, Sheringham NR26 8ES* Tel (01263) 824414

WALTERS, Ian Robert. b 51. ACA75 FCA81. LNSM course 80. **d** 85 **p** 86. OLM Ingoldsby *Linc* from 85. *Dairy Farmhouse, Westby, Grantham NG33 4EA* Tel (01476) 585542 Fax 585066 E-mail ianwalters@cirebase.freeserve.co.uk

WALTERS, Ms Jennifer Betty. b 56. Birm Univ BA77. STETS. **d** 00 **p** 01. NSM Freemantle *Win* from 00. *115B Millbrook Road East, Southampton SO15 1HP* Tel (023) 8033 2613

WALTERS, John Morgan. b 09. **d** 34 **p** 35. New Zealand 34-37; C Folke w Long Burton, N Wootton and Haydon *Sarum* 39; C Lt Bardfield *Chelmsf* 39-40; C Radlett *St Alb* 40-42; P-in-c Watford St Jas 42-43; V Dean w Shelton 43-48; V Hexton 48-52; R Higham Gobion 48-52; V High Wych 52-74; RD Bishop's Stortford 63-67; rtd 74; Perm to Offic *St E* from 75. *5 Canonfields, Bury St Edmunds IP33 1JX* Tel (01284) 761010

WALTERS, John Philip Hewitt. b 50. Coll of Resurr Mirfield 72. **d** 73 **p** 74. C Llangiwg *S & B* 73-76; Min Can Brecon Cathl 76-79; C Brecon w Battle 76-79; V Merthyr Cynog and Dyffryn Honddu etc 79-83; V Llandeilo Tal-y-bont from 83. *The Vicarage, 28 Bolgoed Road, Pontardulais, Swansea SA4 8JE* Tel (01792) 882468

WALTERS, Leslie Ernest Ward. b 27. Wadh Coll Ox BA51 MA55. Ridley Hall Cam 55. **d** 57 **p** 58. C Heref St Pet w St Owen *Heref* 57-59; C Morden *S'wark* 59-61; V Felbridge 61-68; V Streatham Immanuel w St Anselm 68-81; V Cotmanhay *Derby* 81-92; Chapl Ilkeston Gen Hosp 81-88; Chapl Ilkeston Community Hosp 88-92; rtd 92; Perm to Offic *Nor* from 93. *Rokeby, 18 Taverham Road, Felthorpe, Norwich NR10 4DR* Tel (01603) 755134

WALTERS, Canon Michael William. b 39. Dur Univ BSc61. Clifton Th Coll 61. **d** 63 **p** 64. C Aldershot H Trin *Guildf* 63-66; C Upper Armley *Ripon* 66-69; NE Area Sec CPAS 69-75; V Hyde St Geo *Ches* 75-82; V Knutsford St Jo and Toft 82-97; Hon Can Ches Cathl from 94; P-in-c Congleton St Pet 97-98; TR Congleton from 98. *The Rectory, 14 Chapel Street, Congleton CW12 4AB* Tel (01260) 273212 Fax as telephone E-mail michael@congletontp.freeserve.co.uk

WALTERS, Nicholas Humphrey. b 45. K Coll Lon BD67 AKC67. **d** 68 **p** 69. C Weston *Guildf* 68-71; Chapl and Lect NE Surrey Coll of Tech Ewell 71-77; Hon C Ewell 71-77; Warden Moor Park Coll Farnham 77-80; Tutor Surrey Univ *Guildf* from 80; Dir of Studies Guildf Inst from 82; Lic to Offic from 84. *9 Valley View, Godalming GU7 1RD* Tel (01483) 415106

WALTERS, Peter. b 27. Leeds Univ BSc48 Univ of Wales (Abth) MSc52. Ripon Coll Cuddesdon 78. **d** 79 **p** 80. C Kingswood *Bris* 79-82; R Stanton St Quintin, Hullavington, Grittleton etc 82-88; rtd 88; Perm to Offic *Glouc* 88-97. *Holly Tree House, 12 Bethany Lane, West Cross, Swansea SA3 5TL* Tel (01792) 405197

WALTERS, Mrs Sheila Ann Beatrice. b 37. Bris Univ DipEd58. EMMTC 85. **d** 89 **p** 94. Hon C Ashby-de-la-Zouch St Helen w Coleorton *Leic* 89-98; Perm to Offic 99-02; NSM Packington w Normanton-le-Heath from 02. *115 Loughborough Road, Coleorton, Coalville LE67 8HH* Tel (01530) 832267

WALTHEW, Mrs Nancy Jennifer. b 39. Leeds Inst of Educn CertEd59 Ripon Coll of Educn RTC59. N Ord Course 92. **d** 95 **p** 96. NSM Wilmslow *Ches* from 95. *Ashburn, 13 Priory Road, Wilmslow SK9 5PS* Tel (01625) 525462

WALTON, Mrs Alison Claire. b 59. Homerton Coll Cam BEd82. Lon Bible Coll DPS87 Oak Hill Th Coll DipHE89 BA90 MPhil92. **d** 92 **p** 98. C Bedford Ch Ch *St Alb* 92-94; Perm to Offic 94-95; Perm to Offic *S'well* 95-98; NSM Lenton Abbey 98-99; Assoc Lect St Jo Coll Nottm 97-99; C Thorley *St Alb* 00-03; V Croxley Green St Oswald from 03. *St Oswald's Vicarage, 159 Baldwins Lane, Croxley Green, Rickmansworth WD3 3LL* Tel (01923) 232387 E-mail ali.walton@macunlimited.net

WALTON, Mrs Ann Beverley. b 56. Huddersfield Poly BSc78 Sheff Poly MPhil84 Coll of Ripon & York St Jo MA97. N Ord Course 00. **d** 03. C Ecclesfield *Sheff* from 03. *15 Nursery Drive, Ecclesfield, Sheffield S35 9XU*
E-mail annbwalton@hotmail.com

WALTON, Brian. b 53. Sarum & Wells Th Coll 83. **d** 85 **p** 86. C Silksworth *Dur* 85-86; C Bishopwearmouth St Mich w St Hilda

86-88; Chapl RN 88-92; V Sugley *Newc* 92-95; Chapl Lemington Hosp 92-95; CF from 95. *c/o MOD Chaplains (Army)* Tel (01980) 615804 Fax 615800

WALTON, Mrs Camilla Iris. b 56. STETS 97. **d** 00 **p** 01. C Lyndhurst and Emery Down and Minstead *Win* from 00. *Blyth Cottage, North Lane, Nomansland, Salisbury SP5 2BU* Tel (01794) 390398 Fax 390936 E-mail camillawalton@aol.com

WALTON, The Ven Geoffrey Elmer. b 34. Dur Univ BA59. Qu Coll Birm DipTh61. **d** 61 **p** 62. C Warsop *S'well* 61-65; Dioc Youth Chapl 65-69; V Norwell 65-69; Recruitment Sec ACCM 69-75; V Weymouth H Trin *Sarum* 75-82; RD Weymouth 79-82; Can and Preb Sarum Cathl 81-00; Adn Dorset 82-00; P-in-c Witchampton and Hinton Parva, Long Crichel etc 82-96; V Witchampton, Stanbridge and Long Crichel etc 96-00; rtd 00; Perm to Offic *Sarum* from 01. *Priory Cottage, 6 Hibberds Field, Cranborne, Wimborne BH21 5QL* Tel (01725) 517167

WALTON, John Victor. b 45. Lon Univ BSc67. Linc Th Coll 79. **d** 81 **p** 82. C Stevenage St Mary Shephall *St Alb* 81-85; TV Bourne Valley *Sarum* 85-95; P-in-c Puddletown and Tolpuddle 95-02; R Puddletown, Tolpuddle and Milborne w Dewlish from 02. *The Vicarage, The Square, Puddletown, Dorchester DT2 8SL* Tel (01305) 848216 E-mail life@clara.co.uk

WALTON, Kevin Anthony. b 64. St Chad's Coll Dur BA87 Dur Univ PhD99. Trin Coll Bris BA91. **d** 92 **p** 93. C Stranton *Dur* 92-95; C Hartlepool H Trin 95-96; V Sunderland St Mary and St Pet from 96. *The Clergy House, Springwell Road, Sunderland SR3 4DY* Tel 0191-528 3754
E-mail kevin.walton@durham.anglican.org

WALTON, Luke. b 64. Leeds Univ LLB87. Cranmer Hall Dur BA94. **d** 97 **p** 98. C Didsbury St Jas and Em *Man* 97-02; C Clifton Ch Ch w Em *Bris* from 02. *62 Clifton Park Road, Bristol BS8 3HN* Tel 0117-973 2128 Mobile 07799-414199
E-mail luke.w@fish.co.uk

WALTON, Mrs Marjorie Sandra. b 46. WMMTC 97. **d** 00 **p** 01. NSM The Whitacres and Shustoke *Birm* from 00. *51 Station Road, Nether Whitacre, Coleshill, Birmingham B46 2JB* Tel (01675) 464641

WALTON, Maurice James. b 31. Liv Univ BArch53 MCD54 RIBA54 MRTPI55. Wycliffe Hall Ox 93. **d** 94 **p** 95. NSM Billing *Pet* 94-97; NSM Brington w Whilton and Norton etc 97-02; rtd 02. *10A Sutton Street, Flore, Northampton NN7 4LE*
E-mail wal.gill@virgin.net

WALTON, Reginald Arthur. b 40. St Jo Coll Nottm 80. **d** 81 **p** 82. C Woodthorpe *S'well* 81-84; P-in-c Nottingham St Andr 84-85; V 85-91; R Moreton *Ches* 91-01; P-in-c Whatton w Aslockton, Hawksworth, Scarrington etc *S'well* from 01. *The Vicarage, Main Street, Aslockton, Nottingham NG13 9AL* Tel (01949) 51040

WALTON, Stephen James. b 71. Mert Coll Ox BA92 MA97. Oak Hill Th Coll BA01. **d** 02 **p** 03. C Thurnby w Stoughton *Leic* from 02. *8 Sturrock Close, Thurnby, Leicester LE7 9QP* Tel 0116-241 9198 E-mail walton_stephen@hotmail.com

WALTON, Stephen John. b 55. Birm Univ BSc76 Fitzw Coll Cam BA79 MA82 Sheff Univ PhD97. Ridley Hall Cam 77. **d** 83 **p** 84. C Bebington Ches 83-86; Voc and Min Adv CPAS 86-92; Lic to Offic *St Alb* 86-94; Public Preacher from 00; Bp's Dom Chapl 94-95; Lect St Jo Coll Nottm 95-99; Lect Lon Bible Coll 99-03; Sen Lect from 03. *St Oswald's Vicarage, 159 Baldwins Lane, Croxley Green, Rickmansworth WD3 3LL* Tel (01923) 232387 *or* 456326 Fax 456327 E-mail s.walton@londonbiblecollege.ac.uk

WAMBUNYA, Timothy Livingstone (Amboko). b 66. Simon of Cyrene Th Inst 93 Oak Hill Th Coll DipHE94 BA94. **d** 97 **p** 98. C Southall Green St Jo *Lon* 97-00; TV Tollington from 00. *Emmanuel Vicarage, 145 Hornsey Road, London N7 6DU* Tel (020) 7700 7110 Mobile 07770-887232 Fax 7607 1737
E-mail t.wamb@virgin.net

WANDSWORTH, Archdeacon of. *See* GERRARD, The Ven David Keith Robin

WANJIE, Lukas Macharia. b 50. Fitzw Coll Cam BA79 MA83 Birkbeck Coll Lon MSc98. St Paul's Coll Limuru 72 Ridley Hall Cam 76. **d** 75 **p** 76. C Uthiru St Pet Kenya 75-76; C Mill End and Heronsgate w W Hyde *St Alb* 79; V Westlands St Mark Nairobi 80-84; Prin Trin Bible Coll Nairobi 85-91; C St Alb St Steph 91-94; Perm to Offic 94-95; Race Relations Adv Croydon *S'wark* 95-01; V Bermondsey St Kath w St Bart from 01. *St Katharine's Vicarage, 90 Eugenia Road, London SE16 2RA* Tel (020) 7237 3679 E-mail lukas.wanjie@dswark.org.uk

WANLISS, Hector. b 62. St Paul's Coll Grahamstown DipTh85. **d** 88 **p** 90. S Africa 88-97; P-in-c Aylesham w Adisham *Cant* 97-99; CF from 99. *c/o MOD Chaplains (Army)* Tel (01980) 615804 Fax 615800

WANN, Canon Denis Francis. b 27. TCD BA55 MA77 Div Test 56. **d** 56 **p** 57. C Belfast St Donard *D & D* 56-58; BCMS Tanzania 58-72; Hon Can Moro from 72; C Lurgan Ch the Redeemer *D & D* 72-73; Australia 73-91 and from 95; R Port Kembla 73-78; R Albion Park 78-84; RD Shoalhaven 79-82; Adn Wollongong and Camden 82-84; R Turramurra 84-91; I Bailieborough w Knockbride, Shercock and Mullagh *K, E & A* 91-95; rtd 95; Assoc Min Wollongong from 96. *4/28 Robertson Street, Coniston, NSW, Australia 2500* Tel (0061) (2) 4227 6906 Fax 4229 2144 E-mail dwann@telstra.easymail.com.au

WANSTALL, Noelle Margaret. *See* HALL, Canon Noelle Margaret

WARBRICK, Quentin David. b 66. Jes Coll Ox BA88. Cranmer Hall Dur 89. d 92 p 93. C Birm St Martin w Bordesley St Andr *Birm* 92-96; C Handsworth St Jas 96-00; V Packwood w Hockley Heath from 00. *The Vicarage, Nuthurst Lane, Hockley Heath, Solihull B94 5RP* Tel (01564) 783121
E-mail qd@dwarbrick.fsnet.co.uk

WARBURTON, Andrew James. b 44. Oak Hill Th Coll 64. d 69 p 70. C New Milverton *Cov* 69-72; C Fulham St Matt *Lon* 72-76; C Chesham St Mary *Ox* 76-80; TV Gt Chesham 80-94; Chapl Paris St Mich *Eur* 94-97; Asst Chapl Amsterdam w Heiloo 97-00. *Burnbrae Cottage, Riccarton, Newcastleton TD9 0SN*

WARBURTON, John Bryce. b 33. St Aid Birkenhead 64. d 66 p 67. C Padiham *Blackb* 66-69; C Burnley St Pet 69-70; V Tideswell *Derby* 70-81; V Bollington St Jo *Ches* 81-91; V Capesthorne w Siddington and Marton 91-98; rtd 98. *64 Friars Street, Sudbury CO10 2AG* Tel (01787) 371132

WARBURTON, Piers Eliot de Dutton. b 30. Cranmer Hall Dur BA65. d 65 p 66. C Grassendale *Liv* 65-68; Bermuda 68-71; R Sherborne *Win* 71-76; V Yateley 76-82; R Guernsey St Andr 82-89; V Hartley Wintney, Elvetham, Winchfield etc 89-98; rtd 98; Perm to Offic *Win* from 98. *Rowan Cottage, Station Road, Chilbolton, Stockbridge SO20 6AL* Tel (01264) 860275

WARBURTON, Walter George. b 16. Bede Coll Dur BA40 DipTh42 MA43. d 41 p 42. C Witton *Blackb* 41-45; C Accrington Ch Ch 45-46; V Bolton St Barn *Man* 46-52; V Haslingden St Jo Stonefold *Blackb* 52-60; V Gt Marsden 60-81; rtd 81; Perm to Offic *Blackb* from 81. *145 Halifax Road, Nelson BB9 0EL* Tel (01282) 697589

WARCHUS, Michael Edward George. b 37. Lon Univ DipTh67. Roch Th Coll 65. d 68 p 69. C Buckhurst Hill *Chelmsf* 68-71; C Stainton-in-Cleveland *York* 71-76; V Carlton and Drax 76-86; V Acomb St Steph 86-98; rtd 98; Perm to Offic *York* from 98. *12 Tentergate Gardens, Knaresborough HG5 9BL* Tel (01423) 862887

WARD, Alan William. b 56. Trin Coll Bris 80. d 81 p 82. C New Ferry *Ches* 81-86; Dioc Youth Officer 86-91; C Charlesworth and Dinting Vale *Derby* 91-96; V Mickleover All SS from 96. *All Saints' Vicarage, Etwall Road, Mickleover, Derby DE3 0DL* Tel (01332) 513793 E-mail alanward3@tesco.net

WARD, Alfred John. b 37. Coll of Resurr Mirfield. d 93 p 94. C Hendon St Mary *Lon* 93-00. *St John's House, 27 Highview Avenue, Edgware HA8 9TX*

WARD, Mrs Alisoun Mary. b 52. Univ of Wales BA74. Ridley Hall Cam 94. d 96 p 97. C S Woodham Ferrers *Chelmsf* 96-00; TV Southend 00-02. *160 Upper Fant Road, Maidstone ME16 8DJ* Tel (01622) 728202 E-mail rev_soun@hotmail.com

WARD, Andrew John. b 65. Cliff Th Coll 85 Trin Coll Bris BA99. d 99 p 00. C Belper *Derby* 99-03; TV Walbrook Epiphany from 03. *St James's Vicarage, 224 Osmaston Road, Derby DE23 8JX* Tel (01332) 265531 E-mail andyward@cwcom.net

WARD, Anthony Colin. b 55. Univ of Rhodesia BA76 Lambeth MA03. Wycliffe Hall Ox 78. d 80 p 81. Zimbabwe 80-85; S Africa 85-90; Asst P Leic H Trin w St Jo *Leic* 90-96; R Rainham w Wennington *Chelmsf* from 96. *The Vicarage, 73 Lake Avenue, Rainham RM13 9SG* Tel (01708) 522951 Fax 08700-940113
E-mail wards@nildram.co.uk

WARD, Anthony Peter. b 46. Bris Univ BSc67 Ox Univ DipEd68. St Jo Coll Nottm. d 82 p 83. C Hellesdon *Nor* 82-85; P-in-c Nor St Aug w St Mary 85-91; P-in-c Norwich-over-the-Water Colegate St Geo 85-90; Norfolk Churches' Radio Officer 85-95; TV Norwich Over-the-Water 91-95; V Gorleston St Andr from 95; RD Gt Yarmouth 98-02. *St Andrew's Vicarage, Duke Road, Gorleston, Great Yarmouth NR31 6LL* Tel (01493) 663477
E-mail tonyward@fish.co.uk

WARD, Arthur John. b 32. Lon Univ BD57. St Aid Birkenhead 57. d 57 p 58. C Ecclesfield *Sheff* 57-60; C Fulwood 60-63; Tutor St Aid Birkenhead 63-66; R Denton St Lawr *Man* 66-74; CMS 74-82; TV Wolverhampton *Lich* 82-90; V Edgbaston SS Mary and Ambrose *Birm* 90-96; rtd 96; Perm to Offic *Heref* from 97. *Bramble Cottage, 6 Lower Forge, Eardington, Bridgnorth WV16 5LQ* Tel (01746) 764758

WARD, Miss Beverley Jayne. b 61. Bolton Inst of Educn CertEd97. St Steph Ho Ox 00. d 02. C Standish *Blackb* from 02. *69 Churchlands Lane, Standish, Wigan WN6 0XU* Tel 07811-907274 (mobile)

WARD, Brett Ernest. b 62. ACT ThL86. d 89 p 89. Australia 89-97; C Forton *Portsm* 97-99; P-in-c from 99. *The Vicarage, 10 Spring Garden Lane, Gosport PO12 1HY* Tel (023) 9250 3140 E-mail fr.brett@hisdesk1.demon.co.uk

WARD, Canon Calvin. b 34. Univ of Wales BA57 DipEd60 Fitzw Ho Cam BA63 MA67. Westcott Ho Cam 61. d 64 p 65. C Handsworth St Mich *Birm* 64-66; C Shaw Hill 66-69; V Windhill *Bradf* 69-76; V Esholt 76-81; V Oakworth 81-91; V Allerton 91-99; Hon Can Bradf Cathl 94-99; rtd 99; Perm to Offic *Bradf* from 99. *47 Wheatlands Drive, Heaton, Bradford BD9 5JN*

WARD, Christopher John William. b 36. Bps' Coll Cheshunt 66 Qu Coll Birm 68. d 69 p 70. C Wednesbury St Bart *Lich* 69-73;

CF 73-93; rtd 93; Perm to Offic *Sarum* from 93. *6 Meadow View, Blandford Forum DT11 7JB* Tel (01258) 455140

WARD, David. b 40. St Jo Coll Nottm 83. d 85 p 86. C Aspley S'well 85-89; V from 89. *St Margaret's Vicarage, 319 Aspley Lane, Nottingham NG8 5GA* Tel 0115-929 2920 *or* tel and fax 929 8899 E-mail revd.d.ward@ic24.net

WARD, David Conisbee. b 33. St Jo Coll Cam BA54 MA59. S'wark Ord Course 77. d 80 p 81. NSM Surbiton St Matt S'wark 80-83; C Streatham Immanuel w St Anselm 83-84; P-in-c 84-87; V Hook 87-93; rtd 93; Perm to Offic S'wark and Chich from 94. *50 Elgar Avenue, Surbiton KT9 9JN* Tel (020) 8399 9679

WARD, Canon David Robert. b 51. Oak Hill Th Coll 74. d 77 p 78. C Kirkheaton *Wakef* 77-81; V Earl's Heaton 81-88; V Bradley from 88; Hon Can Wakef Cathl from 02. *The Vicarage, 3 St Thomas Gardens, Huddersfield HD2 1SL* Tel (01484) 427838

WARD, The Ven Edwin James Greenfield (Ted). b 19. LVO63. Ch Coll Cam BA46 MA48. Ridley Hall Cam 46. d 48 p 49. C E Dereham w Hoe *Nor* 48-50; V N Elmham w Billingford 50-55; Chapl to The Queen 55-90; Extra Chapl to The Queen from 90; R W Stafford w Frome Billet *Sarum* 67-84; Can and Preb Sarum Cathl 67-84; Adn Sherborne 67-84; rtd 85. *14 Arle Close, Alresford SO24 9BG* Tel (01962) 735501

WARD, Ms Frances Elizabeth Fearn. b 59. St Andr Univ MTh83 Jes Coll Cam DipTh89 Man Univ PhD00 Lon Hosp RGN87. Westcott Ho Cam 87. d 89 p 94. Par Dn Westhoughton *Man* 89-93; Tutor Practical Th N Coll Man 93-98; Hon C Bury St Pet 93-98; C Unsworth 98-99; V Bury St Pet from 99; Bp's Adv on Women in Min from 02. *St Peter's Vicarage, St Peter's Road, Bury BL9 9QZ* Tel 0161-764 1187
E-mail frankie@poward.fsnet.co.uk

WARD, Frank Neal. b 16. EAMTC 78. d 80 p 81. NSM Weybourne w Upper Sheringham *Nor* 80-84; NSM Kelling w Salthouse 80-84; NSM Briningham 84-92; NSM Brinton, Briningham, Hunworth, Stody etc 92-97; Perm to Offic from 97. *Newlands, The Street, Sharrington, Melton Constable NR24 2AB* Tel (01263) 860337

WARD, Frank Wyatt. b 30. Oak Hill NSM Course 84. d 92 p 94. NSM Paddington St Pet *Lon* from 92. *82 Hill Rise, Greenford UB6 8PE* Tel (020) 8575 5515

WARD, Garry William. b 67. RGN90 RM92. Qu Coll Birm 01. d 03. C Wednesfield *Lich* from 03. *18 Duke Street, Wednesfield, Wolverhampton WV11 1TH* Tel 07734-567860 (mobile)
E-mail garry@pundle.co.uk

WARD, Geoffrey Edward. b 30. Linc Th Coll 62. d 64 p 65. C Oundle *Pet* 64-68; C Weston Favell 68-70; TV 70-72; R Cottingham w E Carlton 72-95; rtd 95; Perm to Offic from 95. *4 Sovereigns Court, Saxonfields, Kettering NN16 9SS* Tel (01536) 520498

WARD, Graham John. b 55. Fitzw Coll Cam BA80 Selw Coll Cam MA83. Westcott Ho Cam 87. d 90 p 91. C Bris St Mary Redcliffe w Temple etc *Bris* 90-92; Chapl Ex Coll Ox 92-94; Dean Peterho Cam from 95; Perm to Offic *Ely* from 00. *Peterhouse, Cambridge CB2 1RD* Tel (01223) 338200 Fax 337578
E-mail gjw21@cam.ac.uk

WARD, Ian Stanley. b 62. K Coll Lon BD83. Cranmer Hall Dur 84. d 86 p 87. C Moreton *Ches* 86-89; Chapl RAF from 89. *Chaplaincy Services (RAF), HQ, Personnel and Training Command, RAF Innsworth, Gloucester GL3 1EZ* Tel (01452) 712612 ext 5164 Fax 510828

WARD, Jayne. *See* WARD, Miss Beverley Jayne

WARD, John. *See* WARD, Arthur John

WARD, John Frederick. b 55. St Mich Coll Llan 81. d 84 p 85. C Pembroke Dock *St D* 84-86; PV Llan Cathl *Llan* 86-89; R St Brides Minor w Bettws 89-97; V Shard End *Birm* from 97. *The Vicarage, 47 Shustoke Road, Birmingham B34 7BA* Tel 0121-747 3299

WARD, John Raymond. b 31. St Jo Coll Dur BA54 DipTh56. d 56 p 57. C Leeds St Pet *Ripon* 56-60; C Seacroft 60-63; V Kirkstall 63-75; V Bramhope 75-95; rtd 96. *94 Leeds Road, Bramhope, Leeds LS16 9AN* Tel 0113-230 0356

WARD, Prof John Stephen Keith. b 38. Univ of Wales (Cardiff) BA62 Linacre Coll Ox BLitt68 DD97 Trin Hall Cam MA72 DD97. Westcott Ho Cam 72. d 72 p 73. Lect Philosophy of Relig Lon Univ 71-75; Hon C Hampstead St Jo 72-75; Dean Trin Hall Cam 75-82; Prof Moral and Soc Th K Coll Lon 82-85; Prof Hist and Philosophy of Relig 85-91; Regius Prof Div Ox Univ from 91; Can Res Ch Ch *Ox* from 91. *Christ Church, Oxford OX1 1DP* Tel (01865) 276246
E-mail keith.ward@chch.ox.ac.uk

WARD, John Stewart. b 43. St Jo Coll Dur BA66. Ripon Coll Cuddesdon 77. d 79 p 80. C High Harrogate Ch Ch *Ripon* 79-82; V Ireland Wood 82-86; Chapl Wells Cathl Sch 86-88; V Menston w Woodhead *Bradf* 88-95; R Bolton Abbey from 95; RD Skipton from 98. *The Rectory, Bolton Abbey, Skipton BD23 6AL* Tel (01756) 710326 *or* 710238

WARD, Keith Raymond. b 37. Dur Univ BSc60. Chich Th Coll 63. d 65 p 66. C Wallsend St Luke *Newc* 65-68; C Wooler 68-74; V Dinnington 74-81; V Bedlington 81-93; V Stannington 93-99; rtd

99; Perm to Offic *Newc* from 00. *2 Ethel's Close, Gloster Meadows, Amble, Morpeth NE65 0GD* Tel (01665) 714357

WARD, Kenneth Arthur. b 22. St D Coll Lamp BA50 Chich Th Coll 50. **d** 52 **p** 53. C Wellingborough St Barn *Pet* 52-55; C Stevenage *St Alb* 55-58; R Daventry *Pet* 58-72; RD Daventry 68-76; R Daventry w Norton 73-79; R Daventry 79-82; V Pattishall w Cold Higham 82-88; rtd 88; Perm to Offic *Pet* from 89. *43 Inlands Rise, Daventry NN11 4DQ*

WARD, Kevin. b 47. Edin Univ MA69 Trin Coll Cam PhD76. **d** 78 **p** 79. CMS 75-92; Uganda 76-90; Qu Coll Birm 91; Perm to Offic *Birm* 91; C Halifax *Wakef* 91-92; P-in-c Charlestown 92-95; Lect Leeds Univ from 95. *8 North Grange Mews, Leeds LS26 2EW* Tel 0113-278 7801 E-mail trskw@leeds.ac.uk

WARD, Canon Leslie Alan James. b 38. K Coll Lon 58 St Boniface Warminster AKC61. **d** 62 **p** 63. C Earlham St Anne *Nor* 62-65; C Gt Yarmouth 65-70; R Belton 70-83; R Burgh Castle 71-83; Chapl Norfolk and Nor Hosp 83-94; Chapl W Norwich and Colman Hosp 83-94; Chapl Norfolk and Nor Univ Hosp NHS Trust 94-02; Hon Can Nor Cathl *Nor* 86-02; rtd 02; Perm to Offic *Nor* from 02. *32 Riverway Court, Norwich NR1 1BF* Tel (01603) 631537

WARD, Lionel Owen. b 37. Univ of Wales (Cardiff) BA58 Univ of Wales (Swansea) DipEd59 MA65 Lon Univ PhD70. St Mich Coll Llan 83. **d** 85 **p** 86. NSM Swansea St Mary w H Trin *S & B* 85-89; P-in-c Swansea St Matt w Greenhill 89-00; TV Cen Swansea 00-01; Dioc Dir of Educn 97-01; RD Swansea 98-01; rtd 02. *96 Glanbrydan Avenue, Uplands, Swansea SA2 0JH* Tel (01792) 521144

WARD, Louis Arthur. b 13. Ripon Hall Ox 72. **d** 73 **p** 74. C Corsham *Bris* 73-77; Bp's Chapl for the Arts 76-80; V Bitton 78-80; rtd 80; Perm to Offic *Bris* 80-95; Perm to Offic *Glouc* 86-96. *10 Orchard Close, Westbury-on-Trym, Bristol BS9 1AS* Tel 0117-962 8332

WARD, Mrs Marjorie. b 38. Univ of Wales (Abth) BA59 DipEd60. N Ord Course 83. **dss** 86 **d** 87 **p** 94. Keighley St Andr *Bradf* 86-88; Hon Par Dn 87-88; Hon Par Dn Oakworth 88-90; C Allerton 91-99; rtd 99; Perm to Offic *Bradf* from 00. *47 Wheatlands Drive, Heaton, Bradford BD9 5JN*

WARD, Mark. b 62. ACGI84 Imp Coll Lon BScEng84. Wycliffe Hall Ox BTh93. **d** 93 **p** 94. C Parkham, Alwington, Buckland Brewer etc *Ex* 93-96; C S Molton w Nymet St George, High Bray etc 96-97; TV from 97. *The Vicarage, East Street, South Molton EX36 3HX* Tel (01598) 740325
E-mail mark@thewards.fslife.co.uk

WARD, Matthew Alan James. b 69. Nottm Poly BSc91. Ridley Hall Cam 94. **d** 97 **p** 98. C Birchwood *Linc* 97-00; Chapl Cov Univ *Cov* from 00. *40 Spencer Avenue, Coventry CV5 6NP* Tel (024) 7667 5549 *or* 7688 8315 Fax 7688 8337
E-mail m.ward@coventry.ac.uk

WARD, Canon Michael Anthony. b 42. Sarum Th Coll 67. **d** 70 **p** 71. C Bridport *Sarum* 70-74; TV Swanborough 74-77; P-in-c Chute w Chute Forest 77-79; P-in-c Shalbourne w Ham 77-79; TR Wexcombe 79-86; V Southbroom 86-99; Can and Preb Sarum Cathl from 95; TR Alderbury Team 99-01; TR Clarendon from 01. *The Rectory, 5 The Copse, Alderbury, Salisbury SP5 3BL* Tel (01722) 710229

WARD, Michael Henry. b 42. St Martin's Coll Lanc BA02. **d** 03. NSM S Shore H Trin *Blackb* from 03. *509 Lytham Road, Blackpool FY4 1TE* Tel (01253) 404204

WARD, Michael Reginald. b 31. BNC Ox BA54 MA58. Tyndale Hall Bris 54. **d** 59 **p** 57. C Ealing St Mary *Lon* 56-59; C Morden *S'wark* 59-61; Area Sec (Midl and E Anglia) CCCS 61-66; V Chelsea St Jo *Lon* 66-73; P-in-c Chelsea St Andr 72-73; V Chelsea St Jo w St Andr 73-76; P-in-c Hawkesbury *Glouc* 76-80; P-in-c Alderley w Hillesley 79-80; P-in-c Bibury w Winson and Barnsley 80-85; V Barkby and Queniborough *Leic* 85-90; R Gunthorpe w Bale w Field Dalling, Saxlingham etc *Nor* 90-98; rtd 98; Perm to Offic *Heref* from 98; Perm to Offic *Glouc* from 00. *2 Rose Cottages, Victoria Road, Ledbury HR8 2DB* Tel (01531) 635515

WARD, Nigel Andrew. b 50. Peterho Cam BA72 MA76. Oak Hill NSM Course 89. **d** 92 **p** 93. NSM Frogmore *St Alb* from 92. *15 Park Street, St Albans AL2 2PE* Tel (01727) 872667

WARD, Patricia. b 43. QUB BA65. St Mich Coll Llan 89. **d** 91 **p** 97. NSM Swansea St Mary w H Trin *S & B* 91-98; C Glantawe 98-99; NSM 99-02; rtd 02. *96 Glanbrydan Avenue, Uplands, Swansea SA2 0JH* Tel (01792) 521144

WARD, Peter Garnet. b 28. GRSM51 LRAM. Ridley Hall Cam 59. **d** 61 **p** 62. C Maghull *Liv* 61-64; Kenya 64-73; Master St Leon Mayfield Sch Sussex 73-83; Perm to Offic *Chich* 74-75; P-in-c Coleman's Hatch 75-77; Lic to Offic 77-83; P-in-c Herstmonceux 83-84; P-in-c Wartling 83-84; R Herstmonceux and Wartling 84-94; rtd 94; Perm to Offic *Chich* from 94. *Old Jesolo, Cross Lane, Ticehurst, Wadhurst TN5 7HQ* Tel (01580) 201340

WARD, Canon Philip Paul Ben. b 35. Toronto Univ BA60. ALCD66. **d** 66 **p** 67. C Chenies and Lt Chalfont *Ox* 66-68; C Ardsley *Sheff* 68-70; C Finham *Cov* 70-73; V Terrington St Clement *Ely* 73-81; Canada from 81; Hon Can Ch Ch Cathl

Fredericton from 93; rtd 98. *4261 Heritage Drive, Tracy NB, Canada, E5L 1B2* Tel (001) (506) 368 9182
E-mail bethany@nbnet.nb.ca

WARD, Robert. b 60. Em Coll Cam BA81 MA85. Chich Th Coll. **d** 86 **p** 87. C Horfield H Trin *Bris* 86-90; C Stantonbury and Willen *Ox* 90; TV 90-96; V Knowle St Martin *Bris* from 96. *St Martin's Vicarage, 46 St Martin's Road, Bristol BS4 2NG* Tel 0117-977 6275 Fax as telephone
E-mail frrob@wardmail.fslife.co.uk

WARD, Robert Arthur Philip. b 53. Lon Univ BD82 Open Univ BA88. Qu Coll Birm 77. **d** 79 **p** 80. C Balsall Heath St Paul *Birm* 79-82; Chapl RAF 82-98; TR Blakenall Heath *Lich* 98-01. *St Winifred's Cottage, Maesbury Marsh, Oswestry SY10 8JA* Tel (01691) 679906

WARD, Robert Charles Irwin. b 48. Leic Univ LLB70 Called to the Bar (Inner Temple) 72. St Jo Coll Dur 78. **d** 80 **p** 81. C Byker St Mich w St Lawr *Newc* 80-85; Perm to Offic from 86; Dir Clarence Trust and NE Area Revival Min from 86; Asst Chapl HM Pris Frankland 91-95. *1 Hawthorn Villas, The Green, Wallsend NE28 7NT* Tel and fax 0191-234 3969 Mobile 07768-528181

WARD, Robin. b 66. Magd Coll Ox BA87 MA91 K Coll Lon PhD03. St Steph Ho Ox 88. **d** 91 **p** 92. C Romford St Andr *Chelmsf* 91-94; C Willesden Green St Andr and St Fran *Lon* 94-96; V Sevenoaks St Jo *Roch* from 96; Chapl Invicta Community Care NHS Trust from 97. *St John's Vicarage, 62 Quakers Hall Lane, Sevenoaks TN13 3TX* Tel (01732) 451710

WARD (née NIXSON), Mrs Rosemary Clare. b 57. Westf Coll Lon BA79 Liv Univ MA80 MPhil82. Aston Tr Scheme 89 Trin Coll Bris BA94. **d** 94 **p** 95. C E Bris 94; C Bris St Andr Hartcliffe 94-98; C Downend 98-02; C Broad Blunsdon 02; P-in-c from 02; C Highworth w Sevenhampton and Inglesham etc from 02; Dioc Lay Tr Adv from 02. *The Rectory, Churchway, Blunsdon, Swindon SN26 7DG* Tel (01793) 729592
E-mail rc@nixsonr.freeserve.co.uk

WARD, Mrs Sheena Mary. b 55. Newc Univ BA76 PGCE77. Dioc OLM tr scheme 98. **d** 00 **p** 01. OLM Cramlington *Newc* from 00. *17 Yarmouth Drive, Cramlington NE23 1TL* Tel (01670) 732211 E-mail sheena.ward@dsl.pipex.com

WARD, Simon William James. b 71. Dur Univ BA94 Westmr Coll Ox PGCE96. Ripon Coll Cuddesdon. **d** 00 **p** 01. C Aldershot St Mich *Guildf* 00-03; TV Sole Bay *St E* from 03. *The Rectory, 45 Wangford Road, Reydon, Southwold IP18 6PZ* Tel (01502) 722192 E-mail simonandgeorge@yahoo.ca

WARD, Stanley. b 34. NEOC. **d** 84 **p** 85. NSM Jarrow *Dur* 84-90; P-in-c Thornley 90-99; rtd 99. *4 Church Walk, Thornley, Durham DH6 3EN* Tel (01429) 821766 Fax as telephone

WARD, Stanley Gordon. b 21. Qu Coll Cam BA43 MA47. EMMTC 76. **d** 79 **p** 80. NSM Wollaton *S'well* 79-83; NSM Plympton St Mary *Ex* 84-88; Perm to Offic from 88. *60 Wain Park, Plympton, Plymouth PL7 2HX* Tel (01752) 344042

WARD, Mrs Susan Elizabeth. b 50. N Ord Course 92. **d** 95 **p** 96. NSM Heyside *Man* from 95. *45 Fold Green, Chadderton, Oldham OL9 9DX* Tel 0161-620 2839

WARD, Timothy James. b 67. CCC Ox BA90 MA95 Edin Univ PhD99. Oak Hill Th Coll BA95. **d** 99 **p** 00. C Crowborough *Chich* from 99. *1 Croft Cottages, Church Road, Crowborough TN6 1ED* Tel (01892) 662909 E-mail wardtmthy@aol.com

WARD, Timothy John Conisbee. b 62. New Coll Ox BA85 PGCE86. Wycliffe Hall Ox BA91. **d** 92 **p** 93. C Dorking St Paul *Guildf* 92-96; C Herne Hill *S'wark* 96-02; V Walberton w Binsted *Chich* from 02. *St Mary's Vicarage, The Street, Walberton, Arundel BN18 0PQ* Tel (01243) 551488

WARD, Timothy William. b 49. Open Univ BA74 Birm Univ BPhil(Ed)93. St Deiniol's Hawarden 78. **d** 79 **p** 80. Hon C Handsworth St Mary *Birm* 79-95; Perm to Offic from 95; Hon C Gt Barr *Lich* from 95. *3 Dale Close, Birmingham B43 6AS* Tel 0121-358 1880 *or* 248 7832
E-mail curate.greatbarr@btinternet.com

WARD, William Edward. b 48. FSAScot71. AKC71. **d** 72 **p** 73. C Heref St Martin *Heref* 72-77; C Blakenall Heath *Lich* 77-78; TV 78-82; V Astley, Clive, Grinshill and Hadnall 82-91; R Edgmond w Kynnersley and Preston Wealdmoors from 91; P-in-c Tibberton w Bolas Magna and Waters Upton from 02; Chapl Harper Adams Agric Coll from 96. *The Rectory, 37 High Street, Edgmond, Newport TF10 8JW*

WARD, William Francis. b 35. Ely Th Coll 61 Coll of Resurr Mirfield 64. **d** 64 **p** 65. C Byker St Ant *Newc* 64-67; C Glas St Marg *Glas* 67-69; R Glas Ascension 69-74; Chapl RNR 72-74; Chapl RN 74-78; R Arbroath *Bre* 78-99; Hon Chapl Miss to Seafarers from 78; P-in-c Auchmithie *Bre* 79-90; rtd 99. *1 Denholm Gardens, Letham, Angus DD8 2XT* Tel (01307) 818032 E-mail billward@letham.fsworld.co.uk

WARD-BODDINGTON, Canon Douglas. b 20. MBE97. S'wark Ord Course 69. **d** 72 **p** 73. C S'wark Ch Ch *S'wark* 72-77; Admin S Lon Ind Miss 72-77; Chapl Algarve *Eur* 77-80 and 83-89; V Gen to Bp Eur 80-83; Can Gib Cathl 80-97; rtd 89; Chapl Oporto *Eur* 89-97; Chapl CSP 98-02; Perm to Offic *S'wark* 97-98; *Eur* from 97; *Guildf* and *Chich* from 98. *The Warden's*

House, Hawley Green, Blackwater, Camberley GU17 9DN Tel (01276) 34872 Mobile 07730-147153
E-mail wardboddington@talk21.com

WARDALE, Harold William. b 40. BSc PhD. Wycliffe Hall Ox 83. **d** 85 **p** 86. C Bedminster St Mich *Bris* 85-89; C Bishopston 89; TV 89-96; V Lawrence Weston 96-98; V Lawrence Weston and Avonmouth from 99. *The Vicarage, 335 Long Cross, Bristol BS11 0NN* Tel 0117-982 5863

WARDALE, Robert Christopher. b 46. Newc Univ BA69. Coll of Resurr Mirfield 77. **d** 79 **p** 80. C Cockerton *Dur* 79-84; P-in-c Hedworth 84-87; V 87-92; V Darlington H Trin 92. *Holy Trinity Vicarage, 45 Milbank Road, Darlington DL3 9NL* Tel (01325) 480444 E-mail chris.wardale@durham.anglican.org

WARDELL, Stewart Francis. b 68. Chu Coll Cam BA89 Bris Univ MA95. Cuddesdon Coll BA98. **d** 98 **p** 99. C Brentwood St Thos *Chelmsf* 98-02; R Hawkinge w Acrise and Swingfield *Cant* from 02. *The Rectory, 78 Canterbury Road, Hawkinge, Folkestone CT18 7BP* Tel (01303) 892369

WARDEN, John Michael. b 41. Univ Coll Lon BA63 Trin Coll Ox BA65 MA. NEOC 80. **d** 82 **p** 83. NSM Osmotherley w E Harlsey and Ingleby Arncliffe *York* 82-86; V Kirkdale 86-97; V Kirkdale w Harome, Nunnington and Pockley from 98. *Kirkdale Vicarage, Main Road, Beadlam, Nawton, York YO62 7ST* Tel (01439) 771206

WARDEN, Richard James. b 57. Kent Univ BA79 K Coll Lon MTh86. Wycliffe Hall Ox 81. **d** 83 **p** 84. C Fulham St Mary N End *Lon* 83-85; CF 85-89; Chapl Wycombe Abbey Sch 89-01; Sen Chapl and Hd RS Wellington Coll Berks from 01. *9 Connaught Close, Wellington College, Crowthorne RG45 7QE* Tel (01344) 750346 E-mail revrjw@wellington-college.berks

WARDLE, Edward Christian. b 13. **d** 62 **p** 63. C Farnley *Ripon* 62-64; C Wortley de Leeds 64-66; R Llanwyddelan w Manafon *St As* 66-79; P-in-c Stottesdon *Heref* 79-82; Perm to Offic *Ripon* 82-92. *The Gables Nursing Home, Swinnow Road, Pudsey, Leeds LS28 9AP* Tel 0113-257 0123

WARDLE, Canon John Alexander. b 30. TD73. Lon Univ BA59 Man Univ MA81. Oak Hill Th Coll 53. **d** 57 **p** 58. C Blackpool St Mark *Blackb* 57-60; C Tunbridge Wells St Jo *Roch* 60-62; V Maidstone St Luke *Cant* 62-69; CF (TA) 62-73; V Hartford *Ches* 69-79; R Barton Seagrave w Warkton *Pet* 79-96; Can Pet Cathl 94-96; rtd 96; Perm to Offic *Eur* from 96; SAMS Spain 96-99; Perm to Offic *Leic* and *Pet* from 99. *17 Westmorland Drive, Desborough, Kettering NN14 2XB* Tel (01536) 762558 E-mail abywardle@yahoo.com

WARDLE, John Argyle. b 47. St Jo Coll Dur BA71 ARCM67 CertEd73. Cranmer Hall Dur DipTh72. **d** 73 **p** 74. C Mansfield St Pet *S'well* 73-77; Chapl St Felix Sch Southwold 77-87; TV Haverhill w Withersfield, the Wrattings etc *St E* 87-90; V Choral S'well Minster *S'well* 90-99; Bp's Adv on Healing 94-99; R Bridlington Priory *York* from 99; RD Bridlington from 03. *The Rectory, Church Green, Bridlington YO16 7JX* Tel (01262) 672221 or 601938 E-mail jawardle@fish.co.uk

WARDLE-HARPUR, Canon James. b 31. St Jo Coll Dur BA55. Wells Th Coll 55. **d** 56 **p** 57. C Sheff Parson Cross St Cecilia *Sheff* 56-59; C Maltby 59-61; V Doncaster St Jude 61-64; Pakistan 64-68; R Man Victoria Park *Man* 68-75; V Foxton w Gumley and Laughton *Leic* 75-79; V Foxton w Gumley and Laughton and Lubenham 79-82; TR Leic Resurr 82-88; V Burrough Hill Pars 88-94; Hon Can Leic Cathl 88-94; rtd 96. *Laburnum Cottage, 1 Coates Lane, Starbotton, Skipton BD23 5HZ* Tel (01756) 760401

WARDMAN, Carol Joy. b 56. Lon Univ BA79. Nor Ord Course 91. **d** 94 **p** 95. NSM Hebden Bridge *Wakef* 94-97; NSM Sowerby from 97. *25 Scarr Head Road, Sowerby Bridge HX6 3PU* Tel (01422) 316723 or 0161-832 5253

WARDROBE, Bevan. b 26. Harrf Coll Dur BA53. Cuddesdon Coll 53. **d** 54 **p** 55. C Southgate Ch Ch *Lon* 54-59; PV Lich Cathl *Lich* 59-67; Asst Master Cathl Sch 59-67; Hd Master York Minster Song Sch 67-85; V Choral York Minster *York* 67-85; Chapl Rome *Eur* 85-91; rtd 91; Chapl San Remo *Eur* 91-96; Perm to Offic *Glouc* from 96. *3 Regency Gardens, Sandford Road, Cheltenham GL53 7AJ* Tel (01242) 242355

WARE, Canon John Lawrence. b 37. Nottm Univ BA59. Ridley Hall Cam 62. **d** 62 **p** 63. C Attercliffe *Sheff* 62-66; C Ranmoor 66-68; R Liddington *Bris* 68-74; Soc and Ind Adv 74-79; P-in-c City of Bris 74-79; Hon Can Bris Cathl 76-01; V Kingswood 79-88; RD Bitton 85-87; P-in-c Broad Blunsdon 88-94; RD Cricklade 88-94; The Blunsdons 94-01; rtd 01; Perm to Offic *Bris* from 01. *26 Dongola Road, Bishopston, Bristol BS7 9HP* Tel 0117-924 1304

WARE, Ms Judith Marian. b 52. St Hugh's Coll Ox BA74 MA PGCE75. Carl and Blackb Dioc Tr Inst 00. **d** 02. NSM Windermere St Mary and Troutbeck *Carl* from 02. *1 Chris Law Lodge, Phoenix Way, Windermere LA23 1BB* Tel (01539) 447177

WARE, Stephen John. b 55. Univ of Wales (Lamp) BA76. Ripon Coll Cuddesdon 77. **d** 79 **p** 80. C Lighthorne *Cov* 79-82; Chapl RAF from 82. *Chaplaincy Services (RAF), HQ, Personnel and Training Command, RAF Innsworth, Gloucester GL3 1EZ* Tel (01452) 712612 ext 5164 Fax 510828

WAREHAM, Mrs Caroline. b 32. Lightfoot Ho Dur 55. **dss** 80 **d** 87 **p** 94. Stanwell *Lon* 80-88; Par Dn 87-88; C Epsom St Barn *Guildf* 88-95; C Aldershot St Mich 95-98; rtd 98; Perm to Offic *Sarum* from 00. *17 Homefield, Mere, Warminster BA12 6LT* Tel (01747) 861716

WAREHAM, Mrs Sheila. b 36. CertEd56. N Ord Course 85. **d** 88 **p** 94. NSM Lostock Hall *Blackb* 88-90; NSM Allithwaite *Carl* 90-91; NSM Windermere RD 91-94; P-in-c Colton 94-96; Perm to Offic from 97. *Lyng Nook, Church Road, Allithwaite, Grange-over-Sands LA11 7RD* Tel (01539) 535237

WARHAM, Mrs Jean. b 55. **d** 00 **p** 01. OLM Newcastle w Butterton *Lich* from 00. *166 High Street, Alsagers Bank, Stoke-on-Trent ST7 8BA* Tel (01782) 721505

WARHURST (née HART), Mrs Jane Elizabeth. b 56. Sheff Univ BA77 Man Poly DCG78. N Ord Course 98. **d** 01 **p** 02. C Edge Hill St Cypr w St Mary *Liv* from 01. *St Mary's Vicarage, Towerlands Street, Liverpool L7 8TT*

WARHURST, Richard. b 76. Univ Coll Chich BA99. St Steph Ho Ox 00. **d** 02 **p** 03. C New Shoreham *Chich* from 02; C Old Shoreham from 02. *17 Colvill Avenue, Shoreham-by-Sea BN43 5WN* Tel (01273) 464528

WARING, Graham George Albert. b 37. ACII62. Portsm Dioc Tr Course 86. **d** 87 **p** 02. Chapl Asst Qu Alexandra Hosp Portsm 87-92; NSM Portsea All SS *Portsm* 92-94; NSM Widley w Wymering 94-95; NSM Wisbech St Aug *Ely* 95-98; Chapl King's Lynn and Wisbech Hosps NHS Trust 96-00; NSM Leverington *Ely* 98-00; NSM Southea w Murrow and Parson Drove 98-00; Perm to Offic *York* 00-02; NSM Scarborough St Sav w All SS from 02. *28 Newby Farm Road, Newby, Scarborough YO12 6UN* E-mail graham.waring@virgin.net

WARING, Jeffery Edwin. b 53. Trin Coll Bris 80. **d** 83 **p** 84. C Harpurhey Ch Ch *Man* 83-86; TV Eccles 86-92; P-in-c Hamworthy *Sarum* from 92. *St Michael's Rectory, 1 St Michael's Close, Hamworthy, Poole BH15 4QT* Tel (01202) 674878

WARING, John Valentine. b 29. St Deiniol's Hawarden 65. **d** 67 **p** 68. C Bistre *St As* 67-71; C Blackpool St Thos *Blackb* 71-72; R Levenshulme St Pet *Man* 72-87; R Caerwys and Bodfari *St As* 87-94; rtd 94. *13 St Mellors Road, Southdown Park, Buckley CH7 2ND* Tel (01244) 547290

WARING, Mrs Margaret Ruth. b 44. Keele Univ CertEd65. SW Minl Tr Course 86. **d** 90 **p** 94. Par Dn Tavistock and Gulworthy *Ex* 90-94; C 94-96; TV Axminster, Chardstock, All Saints etc from 96. *The Vicarage, Chardstock, Axminster EX13 7BY* Tel (01460) 220005

WARING, Roger. b 32. ACP66 CertEd56 Open Univ BA74. SW Minl Tr Course 83. **d** 86 **p** 87. NSM Ex St Sidwell and St Matt *Ex* 86-90; NSM Tavistock and Gulworthy 90-96; NSM Axminster, Chardstock, All Saints etc 96-99; Perm to Offic from 99. *The Vicarage, Chardstock, Axminster EX13 7BY* Tel (01460) 220005

WARING, Mrs Sheila May. b 29. SS Paul & Mary Coll Cheltenham CertEd49. Oak Hill Th Coll 85. **dss** 86 **d** 87 **p** 94. Eastwood *Chelmsf* 86-92; NSM 87-92; Chapl Rochford Hosp 87-92; Chapl Southend Community Care Services NHS Trust 92-99; NSM Prittlewell St Pet *Chelmsf* 92-96; NSM Prittlewell w Westcliff 96-99; Perm to Offic from 99. *42 Manchester Drive, Leigh-on-Sea SS9 3HR* Tel (01702) 711046

WARKE, Alistair Samuel John. b 66. Ulster Univ BA89. CITC BTh92. **d** 92 **p** 93. C Arm St Mark *Arm* 92-95; I Killyman from 95; Hon V Choral Arm Cathl from 95. *St Andrew's Rectory, 85 Dungorman Road, Killyman, Dungannon BT71 6SE* Tel (028) 8772 2500 E-mail killyman@armagh.anglican.org

✠**WARKE, The Rt Revd Robert Alexander.** b 30. TCD BA52 BD60. Union Th Sem (NY) Dip Ecum60. **d** 53 **p** 54 **c** 88. C Newtownards *D & D* 53-56; C Dublin St Cath w St Victor *D & G* 56-58; C Dublin Rathfarnham 58-64; Min Can St Patr Cathl Dublin 59-64; I Dunlavin w Ballymore Eustace and Hollywood *D & G* 64-67; I Dublin Drumcondra w N Strand 67-71; I Dublin St Barn 67-71; I Dublin Zion Ch 71-88; Adn Dublin 80-88; Bp C, C & R 88-98; rtd 98. *6 Kerdiff Park, Monread Road, Naas, Co Kildare, Irish Republic* Tel (00353) (45) 898144 E-mail rawarke@eircom.net

WARLAND, Preb Cyril John. b 21. St Cath Soc Ox BA43 MA56. Cuddesdon Coll. **d** 44 **p** 45. C Bradf St Wilfrid Lidget Green *Bradf* 44-46; C Goldthorpe *Sheff* 47-56; R Mary Tavy *Ex* 56-88; RD Tavistock 77-88; P-in-c Walkhampton 80-83; Preb Ex Cathl 82-88; R Peter Tavy 82-88; rtd 88; Lic to Offic *Ex* 88-89; Perm to Offic from 89. *2 Rowantree Road, Newton Abbot TQ1 4LL* Tel (01626) 355369

WARLAND, Peter William. b 35. K Coll Lon 56. **d** 60 **p** 61. C Pemberton St Jo *Liv* 60-64; C Warrington St Elphin 64-66; V Farnworth All SS *Man* 66-71; Chapl RN 71-92; Hon Chapl to The Queen 88-92; Chapl Greenbank and Freedom Fields Hosps Ex 92-00; Chapl St Luke's Hospice Plymouth 94-00; rtd 00; Perm to Offic *Ex* from 00. *122 Wingfield Road, Stoke, Plymouth PL3 4ER* Tel (01752) 561381

WARMAN, Canon John Richard. b 37. Pemb Coll Ox BA61 MA. Ridley Hall Cam 61. **d** 63 **p** 64. C Huyton St Mich *Liv* 63-67; Asst Chapl Liv Univ 67-68; Chapl 68-74; P-in-c Holbrooke *Derby*

74-80; P-in-c Lt Eaton 74-80; R Sawley 80-96; RD Ilkeston 82-92; Hon Can Derby Cathl 91-02; V Allestree 96-02; rtd 02; Perm to Offic *Derby* from 02. *27 Swanmore Road, Littleover, Derby DE23 3SD* Tel (01332) 510089
E-mail jnp.warman@cwcom.net

WARMAN, Miss Marion Alice. b 20. Newnham Coll Cam BA43 MA50. S'wark Ord Course 76. **dss** 79 **d** 87 **p** 94. Spring Grove St Mary *Lon* 79-87; Hon Par Dn 87-94; Hon C from 94; Chapl Asst W Middx Hosp Isleworth 80-93; Chapl Asst Hounslow and Spelthorne NHS Trust from 93; Perm to Offic *Lon* from 93. *43 Thornbury Road, Isleworth TW7 4LE* Tel (020) 8560 5905

WARMAN, Philip Noel. b 64. Roehampton Inst BSc85 PGCE86. Ridley Hall Cam 99. **d** 01 **p** 02. C Burney Lane *Birm* from 01. *136 Burney Lane, Ward End, Birmingham B8 2AR* Tel 0121-783 7935

WARNE, Miss Susan Annette. b 39. Man Univ BSc61 Nottm Univ DipEd62. Dioc OLM tr scheme 97. **d** 00 **p** 01. OLM Kelsale-cum-Carlton, Middleton, Theberton etc *St E* from 00. *Wynkyns, 22 Oakwood Park, Yoxford, Saxmundham IP17 3JU* Tel (01728) 668410

WARNER, Alan Winston. b 51. Lon Univ BSc73 Leeds Univ DipTh75. Coll of Resurr Mirfield 73. **d** 76 **p** 77. C Willenhall St Anne *Lich* 76-78; C Baswich 78-81; V Wednesfield St Greg 81-87; Chapl Frimley Park Hosp 87-94; Chapl Frimley Park Hosp NHS Trust from 94; OCF from 95. *Frimley Park Hospital, Portsmouth Road, Frimley, Camberley GU16 5UJ* Tel (01276) 604604 E-mail alanwarner@igclick.net

WARNER, Canon Andrew Compton. b 35. Fitzw Ho Cam BA58 MA62. Westcott Ho Cam 59. **d** 60 **p** 61. C Addlestone *Guildf* 60-64; C-in-c Ash Vale CD 64-71; V Hinchley Wood 71-80; R Gt Bookham 80-00; RD Leatherhead 88-93; Hon Can Guildf Cathl 99-00; rtd 00; Perm to Offic *Win* from 00. *5 Pearman Drive, Andover SP10 2SB* Tel (01264) 391325
E-mail dandawarner@yahoo.co.uk

WARNER, Clifford Chorley. b 38. Hull Univ MA88. EMMTC 76. **d** 79 **p** 80. NSM Swanwick and Pentrich *Derby* 79-88; NSM Allestree 88-98; Perm to Offic from 98. *17 Amber Heights, Ripley DE5 3SP* Tel (01773) 745089

WARNER, David. b 40. AKC63. **d** 64 **p** 65. C Castleford All SS *Wakef* 64-68; Warden Hollowford Tr and Conf Cen Sheff 68-72; R Wombwell *Sheff* 72-83; V Wortley 83-84; V Wortley w Thurgoland 84-95; RD Tankersley 88-93; V Worsbrough 95-00; P-in-c Bildeston w Wattisham *St E* 00-02; P-in-c Whatfield w Semer, Nedging and Naughton 00-02; R Bildeston w Wattisham and Lindsey, Whatfield etc from 02. *The Rectory, Rectory Road, Whatfield, Ipswich IP7 6QU* Tel (01473) 822100

WARNER, David Leonard John. b 24. Kelham Th Coll 47. **d** 51 **p** 52. C Mill Hill St Mich *Lon* 51-54; C Pimlico St Sav 54-56; S Africa 56-68; V Bournemouth H Epiphany *Win* 68-78; V Whitchurch w Tufton and Litchfield 78-89; RD Whitchurch 79-89; rtd 89; Perm to Offic *Win* from 89; Hon Can Win Cathl from 97. *9 Sparkford Close, Winchester SO22 4NH* Tel (01962) 867343

WARNER, Dennis Vernon. b 46. Lon Univ BA68 K Coll Lon BD71. **d** 72 **p** 73. C W Bromwich All SS *Lich* 72-75; C Uttoxeter w Bramshall 75-79; NSM Stretton w Claymills from 79. *17 Shrewsbury Road, Stretton, Swadlincote DE13 0JF* Tel (01283) 548058 *or* (01543) 306030
E-mail dennis.warner@lichfield.anglican.org

WARNER, Canon George Francis. b 36. Trin Coll Ox BA60 MA64 Qu Coll Cam BA63. Westcott Ho Cam 61. **d** 63 **p** 64. C Birm St Geo *Birm* 63-66; C Maidstone All SS w St Phil and H Trin *Cant* 66-69; Chapl Wellington Coll Berks 69-78; TR Coventry Caludon *Cov* 78-95; Hon Can Cov Cathl 85-02; RD Cov E 89-95; P-in-c Leamington Priors All SS 92-02; P-in-c Leamington Spa H Trin and Old Milverton 95-02; rtd 02; Perm to Offic *Cov* from 02. *Coll Leys Edge, Fant Hill, Upper Brailes, Banbury OX15 5AY* Tel (01608) 685550

WARNER, James Morley. b 32. S'wark Ord Course 66. **d** 69 **p** 70. C S Mymms K Chas *Lon* 69-72; C Bush Hill Park St Steph 72-75; V W Hendon St Jo 75-98; rtd 98; Perm to Offic *Lon* 98-00; Hon C Wembley Park from 00. *46 Churchill Road, Kenton, Harrow HA3 0AY* Tel (020) 8907 8505

WARNER, John Philip. b 59. Keble Coll Ox BA80 MA85. St Steph Ho Ox. **d** 83 **p** 84. C Brighton Resurr *Chich* 83-87; C Paddington St Mary *Lon* 87-90; V Teddington St Mark and Hampton Wick St Jo 90-00; Chapl Belgrade *Eur* from 00. *British Interests Section (Belgrade), FCO, King Charles Street, London SW1A 2AH*

WARNER, Canon Martin Clive. b 58. St Chad's Coll Dur BA80 MA85. St Steph Ho Ox 82. **d** 84 **p** 85. C Plymouth St Pet *Ex* 84-88; TV Leic Resurr *Leic* 88-93; Admin Shrine of Our Lady of Walsingham 93-02; P-in-c Hempton and Pudding Norton *Nor* 98-00; Hon Can Nor Cathl 00-02; Can Res St Paul's Cathl *Lon* from 03. *3 Amen Court, London EC4M 7BU* Tel (020) 7248 2559 Fax as telephone E-mail pastor@stpaulscathedral.org.uk

WARNER, Mary. b 52. Univ of Wales (Swansea) BSc73 Aber Univ PhD77. NEOC 90. **d** 93 **p** 94. C Bensham *Dur* 93-96; Asst Chapl Newcastle upon Tyne Hosps NHS Trust 96-98; Chapl Hartlepool and E Durham NHS Trust 98-99; Chapl N Tees and

Hartlepool NHS Trust from 99. *General Hospital, Holdforth Road, Hartlepool TS24 9AH* Tel (01429) 266654 *or* 0191-522 6444 E-mail mary.warner@nth.northy.nhs.uk

WARNER, Canon Michael John William. b 41. Sarum Th Coll 68. **d** 71 **p** 72. C Plympton St Mary *Ex* 71-75; V St Goran w Caerhays *Truro* 75-78; V Bishops Tawton *Ex* 78-79; V Newport 78-79; Perm to Offic *Truro* 79-83; V St Stythians w Perranarworthal and Gwennap 83-93; Sec Dioc Adv Cttee 93-01; P-in-c Budock 93-97; P-in-c Tregony w St Cuby and Cornelly from 97; Hon Can Truro Cathl from 98; C Probus, Ladock and Grampound w Creed and St Erme from 02. *The Rectory, 18 Fore Street, Tregony, Truro TR2 5RN* Tel (01872) 530507 Fax 530850 E-mail m.j.w.w@btinternet.com

WARNER, Nigel Bruce. b 51. ALCM67 St Jo Coll Cam BA72 DipTh73 MA76. Wycliffe Hall Ox 75. **d** 77 **p** 78. C Luton St Mary *St Alb* 77-80; Prec Dur Cathl *Dur* 80-84; R St John Lee *Newc* 84-91; V Lamesley *Dur* 91-98; V Bishopwearmouth St Nic from 98; AD Wearmouth from 99. *St Nicholas' Vicarage, Queen Alexandra Road, Sunderland SR3 1XQ* Tel 0191-522 6444 *or* 520 2127 Fax nigel.warner@durham.anglican.org

WARNER, Canon Robert William. b 32. TCD BA54 MA65 BD65. TCD Div Sch Div Test56. **d** 56 **p** 57. C Wythenshawe St Martin CD *Man* 56-60; R Hulme St Steph w St Mark 60-66; R Droylsden St Mary 66-76; R Stand 76-97; AD Radcliffe and Prestwich 85-96; Hon Can Man Cathl 87-97; rtd 97; Perm to Offic *Man* from 99. *28 Cow Lees, Westhoughton, Bolton BL5 3EG* Tel (01942) 818823

WARNER, Terence. b 36. **d** 92 **p** 93. NSM Leek and Meerbrook *Lich* 92-98; NSM Odd Rode *Ches* from 98. *53 Heath Avenue, Rode Heath, Stoke-on-Trent ST7 3RY* Tel (01270) 872132

WARNES, Brian Leslie Stephen. b 40. Natal Univ BSocSc76. Kelham Th Coll 59. **d** 67 **p** 68. C Tonge Moor *Man* 67-71; S Africa 71-87; V Blean *Cant* 87-94; New Zealand from 94. *12 Chelsea Street, Linwood, Christchurch, New Zealand* Tel (0064) (3) 389 4331 *or* 343 0519 Fax 348 3827

WARNES, Miss Marjorie. b 32. Leeds Inst of Educn CertEd53. St Jo Coll Nottm 85. **d** 87 **p** 94. C Leamington Priors St Mary *Cov* 87-97; rtd 97; Perm to Offic *Cov* from 97. *78 Lewis Road, Radford Semele, Leamington Spa CV31 1UQ* Tel (01926) 420811

WARNES, Warren Hugh. b 23. St Barn Coll Adelaide ThL49. **d** 50 **p** 50. Australia 50-58 and 60-62; C Northolt St Mary *Lon* 58-60 and 62-64; V Kings Heath *Pet* 64-71; V Rockingham w Caldecote 71-73; V Gretton w Rockingham and Caldecote 73-83; V Marston St Lawrence w Warkworth and Thenford 83-89; rtd 89; Perm to Offic *Pet* from 89; Officer for Clergy Widows (Northampton) from 90. *17 Thorpe Road, Earls Barton, Northampton NN6 0PJ* Tel (01604) 812935

WARR, Timothy Gerald. b 59. Trin Coll Bris BA86. **d** 88 **p** 89. C Yateley *Win* 88-91; C Chapel Allerton *Ripon* 91-93; V Wortley de Leeds 93-01; TR Borehamwood *St Alb* from 01. *The Rectory, 94 Shenley Road, Borehamwood WD6 1EB* Tel (020) 8207 6603 E-mail tim.warr@btinternet.com

WARREN, The Very Revd Alan Christopher. b 32. CCC Cam BA56 MA60. Ridley Hall Cam 56. **d** 57 **p** 58. C Cliftonville *Cant* 57-59; C Plymouth St Andr *Ex* 59-62; Chapl Kelly Coll Tavistock 62-64; V Leic H Apostles *Leic* 64-72; Hon Can Cov Cathl *Cov* 72-78; Dioc Missr 72-78; Provost Leic 78-92; rtd 92; Perm to Offic *Nor* from 92. *9 Queen's Drive, Hunstanton PE36 6EY* Tel (01485) 534533

WARREN, Bunny. *See* WARREN, Gordon Lenham

✠**WARREN, The Rt Revd Cecil Allan.** b 24. Sydney Univ BA51 Qu Coll Ox BA56 MA59. ACT ThL52. **d** 50 **p** 51 **c** 65. Australia 50-83; Can Canberra and Goulburn 63-65; Asst Bp 65-72; Bp 72-83; Asst Bp Derby 83-89; TR Old Brampton and Loundsley Green 83-89; Hon Can Derby Cathl 83-89; rtd 89. *2119 Sidney Street, Toowoomba, Australia 4350* Tel (0061) (7) 4638 4487

WARREN, Clifford Frederick. b 32. Univ of Wales (Lamp) BA53. St Mich Coll Llan 54. **d** 56 **p** 57. C Whitchurch *Llan* 56-68; Lic to Offic 68-70; C Llanedeyrn *Mon* 70-76; R Machen 76-97; rtd 97; Lic to Offic *Mon* from 97. *1 Drury Close, Thornhill, Cardiff CF14 9BJ* Tel (029) 2076 5127

WARREN, David. b 39. S'wark Ord Course. **d** 87 **p** 88. NSM Mottingham St Andr *S'wark* from 87. *26 Longcroft, London SE9 3BQ* Tel (020) 8851 4824

WARREN, Desmond Benjamin Moore. b 22. TCD BA44 MA49. Bps' Coll Cheshunt 46. **d** 48 **p** 49. C Moulsham St Jo *Chelmsf* 48-52; C Colchester St Mary V 52-55; V Elmstead 55-63; R Sandy *St Alb* 63-78; P-in-c Gt Munden 78-79; P-in-c Westmill 78-79; R Westmill w Gt Munden 79-84; rtd 84; Lic to Offic (Lismore) *C & O* 84-90; Perm to Offic *C & R* from 91. *Dysert, Ardmore, Youghal, Co Cork, Irish Republic* Tel (00353) (24) 94110 E-mail dwarren@gofree.indigo.ie

WARREN, Eric Anthony. b 28. MBE. Ex & Truro NSM Scheme. **d** 83 **p** 84. NSM Chudleigh *Ex* 83-88; Perm to Offic from 88. *Lower Radway House, Bishopsteignton, Teignmouth TQ14 9SS* Tel (01626) 772131 *or* 779277

WARREN, Frederick Noel. b 30. TCD BA52 MA58 BD66 QUB PhD72. **d** 53 **p** 54. C Belfast St Matt *Conn* 53-56; C Belfast St Geo 56-59; I Castlewellan *D & D* 59-65; I Clonallon w Warrenpoint

65-69; I Newcastle 69-87; Can Belf Cathl 73-76; Preb Wicklow St Patr Cathl Dublin 76-88; I Dunfanaghy, Raymunterdoney and Tullaghbegley *D & R* 87-97; Preb Swords St Patr Cathl Dublin 89-97; rtd 97. *Runclevin, Dufanaghy, Letterkenny, Co Donegal, Irish Republic* Tel (00353) (74) 913 6635

WARREN, Geoffrey. *See* WARREN, Robert Geoffrey

WARREN, Geoffrey Richard. b 44. Middx Poly MA91. Bps' Coll Cheshunt 66 Qu Coll Birm 68. **d** 69 **p** 70. C Waltham Cross *St Alb* 69-73; C Radlett 73-78; C Tring 78-80; TV Tring 80-95; V Watford St Andr from 95. *St Andrew's Vicarage, 18 Park Road, Watford WD17 4QN* Tel (01923) 239265
E-mail geoffwarren@btinternet.com

WARREN, Mrs Gillian. b 53. Sheff Univ BA74 PGCE75. WMMTC 89. **d** 92 **p** 94. Par Dn Tettenhall Regis *Lich* 92-94; C 94-95; TV Bilston 95-00; R Lich St Chad 00-02; V Wednesbury St Paul Wood Green from 02. *St Paul's Vicarage, 68 Wood Green Road, Wednesbury WS10 9QT* Tel 0121-556 0687

WARREN, Gordon Lenham (Bunny). b 45. Wycliffe Hall Ox DipMin93. **d** 93 **p** 94. C Sunbury *Lon* 93-96; C Laleham 96-98; R Limehouse from 98. *Limehouse Rectory, 5 Newell Street, London E14 7HP* Tel (020) 7987 1502

WARREN, Preb Henry Fiennes. b 21. Keble Coll Ox BA42 MA47. Cuddesdon Coll 42. **d** 48 **p** 49. C Weston-super-Mare St Jo *B & W* 48-53; R Exford 53-75; RD Wiveliscombe 65-73; Preb Wells Cathl from 73; R W Monkton 75-86; rtd 86; Perm to Offic *B & W* from 86. *6 Brookside, Broadway, Ilminster TA19 9RT* Tel (01460) 57922

WARREN, James Randolph. b 54. St Paul's Cheltenham CertEd75 Bris Univ BEd76 Birm Univ MEd84. Ridley Hall Cam CTM92. **d** 92 **p** 93. C Boldmere *Birm* 92-95; V Torpoint *Truro* 95-01; Hon Chapl RN 98-01; V Shottery St Andr *Cov* from 01. *The Vicarage, Church Lane, Shottery, Stratford-upon-Avon CV37 9HQ* Tel (01789) 293381 Fax 296648

WARREN, Malcolm Clive. b 46. Open Univ Dip Applied Science 95. St D Coll Lamp DipTh74. **d** 74 **p** 75. C Newport St Andr *Mon* 74-78; C Risca 78-79; V St Hilary Greenway 79-84; TV Grantham *Linc* 84-90; Ind Chapl 87-90; Ind Chapl *Worc* from 90; P-in-c Dudley St Aug Holly Hall 95-96; Perm to Offic 96-97; TV Kidderminster St Mary and All SS w Trimpley etc from 97. *186 Birmingham Road, Kidderminster DY10 2SJ* Tel (01562) 820473 Fax as telephone

WARREN, Martin John. b 59. St Coll Cam BA81 MA85. St Jo Coll Nottm 83. **d** 86 **p** 87. C Littleover *Derby* 86-90; C Hermitage and Hampstead Norreys, Cold Ash etc *Ox* 90-91; TV 91-97; TV Hermitage 97-02; P-in-c Shebbear, Buckland Filleigh, Sheepwash etc *Ex* from 02. *The Rectory, Shebbear, Beaworthy EX21 5RU* Tel (01409) 281424 E-mail w.chara@fish.co.uk

WARREN, Michael John. b 40. Kelham Th Coll 59. **d** 64 **p** 65. C Withington St Chris *Man* 64-67; C Worsley 67-69; C Witney *Ox* 69-72; V S Hinksey 72-80; Canada 80-99 and from 02; C Verwood *Sarum* 99-00; rtd 00. *Apartment 3, 32 Lafayette Crescent, Lethbridge AB, Canada, T1K 4B6* Tel (001) (403) 317 0317

WARREN, Michael Philip. b 62. Nottm Univ GradDipPhys87. Oak Hill Th Coll BA91. **d** 94 **p** 95. C Tunbridge Wells St Jo *Roch* 94-98; Assoc Min Heydon, Gt and Lt Chishill, Chrishall etc *Chelmsf* from 98. *The Vicarage, Bury Lane, Elmdon, Saffron Walden CB11 4NQ* Tel (01763) 838893
E-mail elmdonvic@aol.com

WARREN, The Ven Norman Leonard. b 34. CCC Cam BA58 MA62. Ridley Hall Cam 58. **d** 60 **p** 61. C Bedworth *Cov* 60-63; V Leamington Priors St Paul 63-77; R Morden *S'wark* 77-88; TR 88-89; RD Merton 86-89; Adn Roch and Can Res Roch Cathl *Roch* 89-00; rtd 00; Perm to Offic *Roch* from 00. *1 Sandling Way, St Mary's Island, Chatham ME4 3AZ* Tel (01634) 891363

WARREN, Canon Paul Kenneth. b 41. Selw Coll Cam BA63 MA67. Cuddesdon Coll 64. **d** 67 **p** 68. C Lancaster St Mary *Blackb* 67-70; Chapl Lanc Univ 70-78; V Langho Billington 78-83; Bp's Dom Chapl 83-88; Chapl Whalley Abbey 83-88; R Standish 88-01; P-in-c Silverdale from 01; Hon Can Blackb Cathl from 91; RD Chorley 92-98. *The Vicarage, St John's Grove, Silverdale, Carnforth LA5 0RH* Tel (01524) 701268

WARREN, Peter. b 40. FCA64. Oak Hill Th Coll 77. **d** 79 **p** 80. C Newcastle w Butterton *Lich* 79-82; TV Sutton St Jas and Wawne *York* 82-87; V Ledsham w Fairburn 87-95; R Ainderby Steeple w Yafforth and Kirby Wiske etc *Ripon* 95-03; rtd 03. *Appletree House, 2 Harvest Close, York YO32 5SA*
E-mail rabbit@ainderbysteeple.fsnet.co.uk

WARREN, Peter John. b 55. CertEd76 BA86. Trin Coll Bris 83. **d** 86 **p** 87. C W Streatham St Jas *S'wark* 86-91; P-in-c Edin Clermiston Em *Edin* 91-98; P-in-c Blackpool Ch Ch w All SS *Blackb* 98-03; V from 03. *The Vicarage, 23A North Park Drive, Blackpool FY3 8LR* Tel (01253) 391235 Fax as telephone
E-mail revpwarren@blueyonder.co.uk

WARREN, Philip James. b 65. SS Paul & Mary Coll Cheltenham BA87 Hughes Hall Cam PGCE88 Kingston Univ MA93. St Jo Coll Nottm MA99. **d** 00 **p** 01. C Reigate St Mary *S'wark* from 00. *3 St Clair Close, Reigate RH2 0QB* Tel (01737) 242391 *or* 221100 E-mail pjwarren@ukonline.co.uk

WARREN, Canon Robert. b 54. TCD BA78 MA81. CITC 76. **d** 78 **p** 79. C Limerick City *L & K* 78-81; Dioc Youth Adv (Limerick) 79-86; I Adare w Kilpeacon and Croom 81-88; Bp's Dom Chapl 81-95; Dioc Registrar (Limerick) from 81; Dioc Registrar (Killaloe etc) from 86; I Tralee w Kilmoyley, Ballymacelligott etc from 88; Can Limerick, Killaloe and Clonfert Cathls 95-96; Chan from 97; Asst Dioc Sec *L & K* from 90. *St John's Rectory, Ashe Street, Tralee, Co Kerry, Irish Republic* Tel (00353) (66) 712 2245 *or* 712 4152 Mobile 087-252 1133 Fax 712 9004 E-mail rwarren@indigo.ie

WARREN, Robert Geoffrey. b 51. DipHE. Trin Coll Bris 79. **d** 82 **p** 83. C Felixstowe SS Pet and Paul *St E* 82-86; V Gazeley w Dalham, Moulton and Kentford 86-90; P-in-c Ipswich St Clem w St Luke and H Trin 90-98; C Gt Finborough w Onehouse and Harleston 98-00; rtd 01. *11 Homefield, Locking, Weston-super-Mare BS24 8ED* Tel (01934) 824408

WARREN, Robert Irving. b 38. Univ of BC BA58 Ox Univ MA73. Angl Th Coll (BC) LTh61. **d** 61 **p** 63. Canada 61-89; R Northfield *Birm* from 89. *The Rectory, Rectory Road, Birmingham B31 2NA* Tel 0121-477 3111 *or* 475 1518

WARREN, Canon Robert Peter Resker. b 39. Jes Coll Cam BA63 MA. ALCD65. **d** 65 **p** 66. C Rusholme H Trin *Man* 65-68; C Bushbury *Lich* 68-71; V Crookes St Thos *Sheff* 71-90; TR 90-93; RD Hallam 78-83; Hon Can Sheff Cathl 82-93; Can Th Sheff Cathl from 93; Nat Officer for Evang from 93; Springboard Missr from 98. *Willow Bank House, Borrage Lane, Ripon HG4 2PZ* Tel (01765) 602996 Fax 600446

WARREN, William Frederick. b 55. Sarum & Wells Th Coll 83. **d** 86 **p** 87. C E Greenwich Ch Ch w St Andr and St Mich *S'wark* 86-91; C Richmond St Mary w St Matthias and St Jo 91-95; TV 96-97; V Putney St Marg from 97. *St Margaret's Vicarage, 46 Luttrell Avenue, London SW15 6PE* Tel (020) 8788 5522 *or* 8789 5932 Fax as telephone E-mail wwarren@dircon.co.uk

WARRICK, Mark. b 54. Aston Univ BSc76 Nottm Univ BCombStuds83. Linc Th Coll 80. **d** 83 **p** 84. C Grantham *Linc* 83-87; C Cirencester *Glouc* 87-91; V Over *Ely* 91-97; V Deeping St James from 97. *The Vicarage, 16 Church Street, Deeping St James, Peterborough PE6 8HD* Tel (01778) 345890 Fax 345877 E-mail vicar@dsj.org.uk

WARRILLOW, Brian Ellis. b 39. Linc Th Coll 81. **d** 83 **p** 84. C Tunstall *Lich* 83-85; C Shrewsbury H Cross 86-87; P-in-c Tilstock 88; P-in-c Whixall 88; V Tilstock and Whixall 89-92; TV Hanley H Ev 92-94; rtd 94; Perm to Offic *Lich* from 01; P-in-c Menton *Eur* from 02. *Soleil de Menton, 2 Avenue du Pigautier, 06500 Menton, France*

WARRILOW, Mrs Christine. b 42. Lanc Univ BA86. N Ord Course 86. **d** 89 **p** 94. C Netherton *Liv* 89-92; C Cantril Farm 92-94; V 94-96; V Hindley Green 96-02; rtd 02. *10 Beacon View Drive, Upholland, Skelmersdale WN8 0HL*

WARRINER, Leonard. b 15. Ox NSM Course 76. **d** 79 **p** 80. NSM Chalfont St Peter *Ox* from 79. *Briar Rose, Winkers Lane, Chalfont St Peter, Gerrards Cross SL9 0AJ* Tel (01753) 884443

WARRINGTON, Gwynfa Lewis Jones. b 44. St D Coll Lamp 64. **d** 67 **p** 68. C Gorseinon *S & B* 67-70; C Pembroke Dock *St D* 70-74; V Rosemarket and Freystrop 74-78; R Llangwm and Freystrop 78-79; V Ystradfellte *S & B* 79-84; V Abercynon *Llan* 84-87; V Beguildy and Heyope *S & B* 87-98; V Llywel and Traean-glas w Llanulid 98-00; V Trallwng w Bettws Penpont w Aberyskir etc from 00. *The Vicarage, Trallong, Brecon LD3 8HP* Tel (01874) 636549

WARRINGTON, Mrs Irene. b 50. LNSM course 95. **d** 98 **p** 99. OLM Heywood *Man* from 98. *5 Byng Street, Heywood OL10 2JA* Tel (01706) 624328

WARRINGTON, Katherine Irene (Kay). b 44. Univ of Wales (Swansea) BSc67 DipEd68. St Mich Coll Llan 93. **d** 95. NSM Knighton and Norton *S & B* 95-98; Dioc Children's Officer from 96; NSM Llywel and Traean-glas w Llanulid 98-00; NSM Trallwng w Bettws Penpont w Aberyskir etc from 00. *The Vicarage, Trallong, Brecon LD3 8HP* Tel (01874) 636549

WARRINGTON, Archdeacon of. *See* BRADLEY, The Ven Peter David Douglas

WARRINGTON, Suffragan Bishop of. *See* JENNINGS, The Rt Revd David Willfred Michael

WARWICK, Gordon Melvin. b 31. N Ord Course 79. **d** 80 **p** 81. NSM Darrington *Wakef* 80-87; TV Almondbury w Farnley Tyas 87-95; rtd 95; Perm to Offic *Newc* from 95. *Andante, Christon Bank, Alnwick NE66 3EZ* Tel (01665) 576742

WARWICK, Hugh Johnston. b 39. ARCM63. St Alb and Ox Min Course 97. **d** 00 **p** 01. NSM Rotherfield Peppard *Ox* 00-02; NSM Rotherfield Peppard and Kidmore End etc from 02. *Middle Dale Cottage, 112 Shiplake Bottom, Peppard Common, Henley-on-Thames RG9 5HR* Tel 0118-972 3070 Fax as telephone E-mail hwarwick@cix.compulink.co.uk

WARWICK, Canon John Michael. b 37. Fitzw Ho Cam BA58 MA62. Ely Th Coll 58. **d** 60 **p** 61. C Towcester w Easton Neston *Pet* 60-63; C Leighton Buzzard *St Alb* 63-64; C Boston *Linc* 64-66; P-in-c Sutterton 66-72; V 72-74; V Sutton St Mary 74-84; V Bourne 84-02; Can and Preb Linc Cathl 89-02; RD Aveland and Ness w Stamford 93-00; Chapl Bourne Hosps *Lincs* 84-93;

Chapl NW Anglia Healthcare NHS Trust 93-98; rtd 02. *24 Hurst Park Road, Twyford, Reading RG10 0EY* Tel 0118-932 0649

WARWICK, Archdeacon of. *See* PAGET-WILKES, The Ven Michael Jocelyn James

WARWICK, Suffragan Bishop of. *See* PRIDDIS, The Rt Revd Anthony Martin

WASEY, Kim Alexandra Clare. b 77. Man Univ BA99. Qu Coll Birm 00. **d** 02 **p** 03. C Rochdale *Man* from 02. *10 Blenheim Street, Rochdale OL12 7DF* Tel (01706) 651368 Mobile 07944-155772 E-mail kim-wasey@supanet.com

WASH, John. b 46. CEng MIStructE70. **d** 81 **p** 83. OLM Newington St Mary *S'wark* from 81. *15 Canterbury Place, London SE17 3AD* Tel (020) 7582 9280

WASHINGTON, Nigel Leslie. b 50. St Paul's Cheltenham BEd73 Lon Univ MA83. St Alb and Ox Min Course 97. **d** 00 **p** 01. NSM Westoning w Tingrith *St Alb* from 00. *3 Avenue Mews, Flitwick, Bedford MK45 1BF* Tel (01525) 714442 E-mail nigelwash@hotmail.com

WASHINGTON, Canon Patrick Leonard. b 44. Nottm Univ BSc66. St Steph Ho Ox 65. **d** 68 **p** 69. C Fleet *Guildf* 68-71; C Farnham 71-74; TV Staveley and Barrow Hill *Derby* 74-83; V Norbury St Phil *Cant* 83-84; V Norbury St Phil *S'wark* from 85; RD Croydon N 90-99; Hon Can S'wark Cathl from 01. *St Philip's Vicarage, 66 Pollards Hill North, London SW16 4NY* Tel (020) 8764 1812

WASSALL, Canon Keith Leonard. b 45. Bede Coll Dur TCert67. Chich Th Coll 68. **d** 71 **p** 72. C Upper Gornal *Lich* 71-74; C Codsall 74-75; C Shelton 75-76; TV Hanley All SS 76-79; Bermuda 79-81 and from 99; V Rickerscote *Lich* 81-92; P-in-c Coven 92-99; Asst Chapl HM Pris Featherstone 92-99; Can Res Bermuda from 99. *PO Box HM 627, Hamilton HM CX, Bermuda* Tel (001441) 292 4033 *or* 292 0394 E-mail kwassall@hotmail.com *or* cathedral@northrock.bm

WASTELL, Canon Eric Morse. b 33. St Mich Coll Llan DipTh62. **d** 62 **p** 63. C Oystermouth *S & B* 62-65; Antigua 65-74; Hon Can Antigua 71-74; V Swansea St Gabr *S & B* 74-98; RD Clyne 88-96; Can Brecon Cathl from 90; rtd 98. *18 Belgrave Court, Walter Road, Uplands, Swansea SA1 4PY* Tel (01792) 466709

WASTIE, Canon David Vernon. b 37. Open Univ BA84. Chich Th Coll 79. **d** 81 **p** 82. C Bitterne Park *Win* 81-83; TV Chambersbury *St Alb* 83-87; V Jersey St Luke *Win* 87-95; P-in-c Jersey St Jas 87-93; V 93-95; V Southbourne St Kath 95-99; Hon Can Bukavu from 94; rtd 02. *8 Hazelby Road, Creswell, Worksop S80 4BB* Tel (01909) 720126 E-mail canonwastie@hotmail.com

WATCHORN, Canon Brian. b 39. Em Coll Cam BA61 MA65 Ex Coll Ox BA62. Ripon Hall Ox 61. **d** 63 **p** 64. C Bolton St Pet *Man* 63-66; Chapl G&C Coll Cam 66-74; V Chesterton St Geo *Ely* 75-82; Fell Dean and Chapl Pemb Coll Cam from 82; Lic to Offic *Ely* from 82; Hon Can Ely Cathl from 94. *Pembroke College, Cambridge CB2 1RF* Tel (01223) 338100 E-mail dean@pem.cam.ac.uk

WATERER, Anthony Tatham. b 14. ARCA38. Cuddesdon Coll 45. **d** 47 **p** 48. C Arundel w Tortington and S Stoke *Chich* 47-48; C Henfield 48-50; V Farnham *Ripon* 50-73; Asst Chapl Scotton Banks Sanatorium 50-51; R Staveley w Copgrove 53-73; R Rawreth w Rettendon *Chelmsf* 73-82; Chapl Rawreth Rehabilitation Cen 74-79; rtd 82; Hon C Clayton w Keymer *Chich* 83-94; Perm to Offic from 94. *9 Stafford Way, Hassocks BN6 8QG* Tel (01273) 844341

WATERFIELD, Janet Lyn. b 60. WMMTC 99. **d** 02. C Bilston *Lich* from 02. *6 Hodnet Close, Bilston WV14 0UF* Tel 07905-539111 (mobile) E-mail janetwaterfield@blueyonder.co.uk

WATERFORD, Dean of. *See* LESTER, The Very Revd Trevor Rashleigh

WATERHOUSE, Eric Thomas Benjamin. b 24. Lon Univ DipTh60. Kelham Th Coll 47 Qu Coll Birm 50. **d** 51 **p** 52. C Wolverhampton St Pet *Lich* 51-56; C Lower Gornal 56-57; V Walsall St Mark 57-60; R Kington w Dormston *Worc* 60-64; R Worc St Clem 64-77; P-in-c Abberton, Naunton Beauchamp and Bishampton etc 77-80; R 80-92; rtd 92; Perm to Offic *Worc* from 92. *7 Hazel Avenue, Evesham WR11 1XT* Tel (01386) 421312

WATERHOUSE, Canon Peter. b 46. Leeds Univ DipTh68. Linc Th Coll 68. **d** 70 **p** 71. C Consett *Dur* 70-73; C Heworth St Mary 73-76; V Stockton St Chad 76-83; V Lanchester from 83; AD Lanchester 90-99; Hon Can Dur Cathl from 03. *The Vicarage, 1 Lee Hill Court, Lanchester, Durham DH7 0QE* Tel (01207) 521170

WATERMAN, Canon Albert Thomas. b 33. Roch Th Coll 61. **d** 64 **p** 65. C Dartford St Alb *Roch* 64-67; V Ilkeston St Jo *Derby* 67-75; V Mackworth St Fran 75-79; V Dartford St Alb *Roch* 79-98; RD Dartford 84-97; Hon Can Roch Cathl 96-98; rtd 98. *19 Beachfield Road, Bembridge PO35 5TN* Tel (01983) 874286

WATERMAN, Mrs Jacqueline Mahalah. b 45. ALCM71. Cant Sch of Min 82. dss 85 **d** 87 **p** 94. Wavertree H Trin *Liv* 85-90; Par Dn 87-90; Par Dn Anfield St Columba 90-94; C 94; TV Speke St Aid 94-97; P-in-c Walton St Jo 97-99; V 99-01; C Baildon *Bradf* from 01. *93 Hoyle Court Road, Baildon, Shipley BD17 6EL* Tel (01274) 594456

WATERS, Arthur Brian. b 34. St Deiniol's Hawarden 71. **d** 73 **p** 74. C Bedwellty *Mon* 73-76; P-in-c Newport All SS 76-81; V Mynyddislwyn 81-91; C-in-c Maesglas Newport CD 91-95; V Maesglas and Duffryn 95-99; rtd 99. *3B Blaen-y-Pant Crescent, Blaen-y-Pant, Newport NP20 5QB*

WATERS, Brenda Mary. b 51. Bp Otter Coll. **d** 99. NSM Whyke w Rumboldswhyke and Portfield *Chich* from 99. *69 Chatsworth Road, Chichester PO19 7YA*

WATERS, Mrs Carolyn Anne. b 52. St Jo Coll Nottm BA02. **d** 00 **p** 01. NSM Frodsham *Ches* 00-02; C Penhill *Bris* from 02. *The Vicarage, Bremhill Close, Swindon SN2 5DS* Tel (01793) 721921 Mobile 07789-430317 E-mail caswaters@dsl.pipex.com

WATERS, David Keith. b 46. S Wales Bapt Coll DipTh73 DPS73 St Mich Coll Llan 93. **d** 93 **p** 94. In Bapt Ch 73-90; C Caerphilly *Llan* 93-97; TV Cwmbran *Mon* 97-99; R Gelligaer *Llan* from 99. *The Rectory, Church Road, Gelligaer, Hengoed CF82 8FW* Tel (01443) 830300

WATERS, Miss Jill Christine. b 43. CertEd64. Cranmer Hall Dur 82. dss 82 **d** 87 **p** 94. New Milverton *Cov* 82-86; Draycott-le-Moors w Forsbrook *Lich* 86-96; Par Dn 87-94; C 94-96; P-in-c Mow Cop from 96. *The Vicarage, 5 Congleton Road, Mow Cop, Stoke-on-Trent ST7 3PJ* Tel (01782) 515077

WATERS, John Michael. b 30. Qu Coll Cam BA53 MA58. Ridley Hall Cam 53. **d** 55 **p** 56. C Southport Ch Ch *Liv* 55-57; C Farnworth 57-62; V Blackb H Trin *Blackb* 63-70; Sec Birm Coun Chr Chs 70-77; Chapl Birm Cathl *Birm* 70-74; Dioc Ecum Officer 74-77; V Hednesford *Lich* 77-93; RD Rugeley 78-88; rtd 93; P-in-c Etton w Dalton Holme *York* 93-99; Perm to Offic from 00. *Blacksmith's Cottage, Middlewood Lane, Fylingthorpe, Whitby YO22 4UB* Tel (01947) 880422

WATERS, Mark. b 51. Southn Univ BTh85. Sarum & Wells Th Coll 79. **d** 82 **p** 83. C Clifton All SS w St Jo *Bris* 82-85; P-in-c Brislington St Anne 85-91; Dioc Soc Resp Officer *Sheff* 91-94; Community Org Citizen Organisation Foundn 94-00; NSM Rotherham 94-97; Hon C Gt Crosby St Faith and Waterloo Park St Mary *Liv* 97-00; TV Kirkby from 00. *30 Victoria Road West, Crosby, Liverpool L23 8UQ* Tel 0151-931 1031

WATERS, Nicholas Marshall Stephenson. b 35. Selw Coll Cam BA59 MA63. Wells Th Coll 59. **d** 61 **p** 62. C Eastbourne St Mary *Chich* 61-64; Asst Chapl Ardingly Coll 64-93; P-in-c Slindon, Eartham and Madehurst *Chich* 93-99; R 99-03; rtd 03. *Lyle House, School Lane, Fittleworth, Pulborough RH20 1JB* Tel (01798) 865778

WATERS, Stephen. b 49. Chich Th Coll 83. **d** 85 **p** 86. C Baildon *Bradf* 85-87; C Altrincham St Geo *Ches* 87-89; TV Ellesmere Port 89-91; P-in-c Crewe St Jo 91-93; V Mossley 93-98; TV Congleton 98-99; P-in-c Alvanley 99-02; V Penhill *Bris* from 02. *The Vicarage, Bremhill Close, Swindon SN2 5DS* Tel (01793) 721921 Mobile 07796-694139 E-mail frstephen.waters@dsl.pipex.com

WATERS, William Paul. b 52. Aston Tr Scheme 84 Chich Th Coll 86. **d** 88 **p** 89. C Tottenham St Paul *Lon* 88-91; C Stroud Green H Trin 91-95; TV Wickford and Runwell *Chelmsf* 95-98; Chapl Runwell Hosp Wickford 95-98; Chapl Qu Medical Cen Nottm Univ Hosp NHS Trust from 98. *Queen's Medical Centre University Hospital, Derby Road, Nottingham NG7 2UH* Tel 0115-924 9924 ext 43799 *or* 917 4412 Mobile 07711-721483 E-mail waterspalwat@aol.com

WATERSTONE, Canon Albert Thomas. b 23. TCD BA45 BD67. CITC 46. **d** 46 **p** 47. C Kilkenny St Canice Cathl *C & O* 46-50; P-in-c Borris-in-Ossory w Aghavoe 50-51; I 52-54; I Fiddown w Kilmacow 54-64; I Tullamore w Lynally and Rahan *M & K* 64-73; I Tullamore w Durrow, Newtownfertullagh, Rahan etc 73-90; Can Meath 81-90; rtd 90. *Lynally House, Mocklagh, Blue Ball, Tullamore, Co Offaly, Irish Republic* Tel (00353) (506) 21367

WATERSTREET, Canon John Donald. b 34. Trin Hall Cam BA58 MA62. Lich Th Coll 58. **d** 60 **p** 61. C Blackheath *Birm* 60-64; C Aston SS Pet and Paul 64-67; R Sheldon 67-77; RD Coleshill 75-77; V Selly Oak St Mary 77-89; RD Edgbaston 84-89; Hon Can Birm Cathl 86-00; R The Whitacres and Shustoke 89-97; C Acocks Green 97-00; rtd 00. *547 Fox Hollies Road, Hall Green, Birmingham B28 8RL* Tel 0121-602 2080

WATERTON, Dawn. b 46. WMMTC 95. **d** 98 **p** 99. NSM Nuneaton St Nic *Cov* from 98. *65 Main Street, Higham on the Hill, Nuneaton CV13 6AH* Tel (01455) 212861

WATES, John Norman. b 43. JP82. BNC Ox MA65 Solicitor 72 FRSA00. Dioc OLM tr scheme 99. **d** 02. OLM Chipstead *S'wark* from 02. *Elmore, High Road, Chipstead, Coulsdon CR5 3SB* Tel (01737) 557550 Fax 552918 E-mail john@jwates.com

WATHEN, Mark William Gerard. b 12. TD45. ACIB. K Coll Lon 31. **d** 82 **p** 82. Hon C Broadford *Arg* 82-91; Hon C Fort William 82-91; Hon C Portree 82-96; rtd 96. *Tollgate Cottage, Norwich Road, Marsham, Norwich NR10 5PX* Tel (01263) 732255

WATHEN, Sydney Gordon. Open Univ BA FRSA94. EMMTC. **d** 86 **p** 87. NSM W Hallam and Mapperley *Derby* 86-01; Perm to Offic from 01. *40 Station Road, West Hallam, Ilkeston DE7 6GW* Tel 0115-932 9255

WATHERSTON, Peter David. b 42. Lon Univ BSc69 FCA76. Ridley Hall Cam 75. **d** 77 **p** 78. C Barnsbury St Andr *Lon* 77-78;

C Barnsbury St Andr w H Trin 79-80; C Barnsbury St Andr and H Trin w All SS 81; Chapl Mayflower Family Cen Canning Town *Chelmsf* 81-96; Perm to Offic from 96; Co-ord First Fruit Charity from 97. *264 Plashet Grove, London E6 1DQ, or Latimer Hall, Cleves Road, London E6 1QF* Tel (020) 8470 6868 *or* 8548 4676 Fax 8548 4110 E-mail first.fruit@virgin.net

WATKIN, David William. b 42. FCA70. Qu Coll Birm 84. d 86 p 87. C Tunstall *Lich* 86-89; Camberwell Deanery Missr *S'wark* 89-95; V Trent Vale *Lich* 95-01; V Milton from 01. *The Vicarage, Baddeley Green Lane, Stoke-on-Trent ST2 7EY* Tel (01782) 534062

WATKIN, Prof Thomas Glyn. b 52. Pemb Coll Ox BA74 MA77 BCL75 Barrister-at-Law (Middle Temple) 76. Llan Dioc Tr Scheme 89. d 92 p 94. NSM Roath St Martin *Llan* from 92. *49 Cyncoed Road, Penylan, Cardiff CF23 5SB* Tel (029) 2049 5662

WATKINS, Alfred Felix Maceroni. b 20. Glouc Th Course 70. d 72 p 73. C Yate *Glouc* 72-75; V Parkend 75-90; rtd 90; Perm to Offic *Heref* from 93. *Leylines, 26 Southbank Road, Hereford HR1 2TJ* Tel (01432) 341014

WATKINS, Anthony John. b 42. St D Coll Lamp BA64 St Steph Ho Ox 64. d 66 p 67. C E Dulwich St Jo *S'wark* 66-71; C Tewkesbury w Walton Cardiff *Glouc* 71-75; Prec 75-81; Chapl Choral Ches Cathl *Ches* 75-81; V Brixworth w Holcot *Pet* from 81. *The Vicarage, Station Road, Brixworth, Northampton NN6 9DF* Tel (01604) 880286

WATKINS, Mrs Christine Dorothy (Sue). b 29. d 89 p 00. Deacon Port Macquarie Australia 89-95; Chapl Port Macquarie Gen Hosp 89-95; Perm to Offic *Chich* 97-00; NSM Crawley from 00. *2 Homethorne House, Oak Road, Crawley RH11 8AE* Tel (01293) 526055

WATKINS, Christopher. b 43. Sarum & Wells Th Coll 88. d 90 p 91. C Abergavenny St Mary w Llanwenarth Citra *Mon* 90-94; TV Cwmbran 94-96; TV Wordsley *Worc* from 00. *St Paul's House, Hawbush Road, Brierley Hill DY5 3NL* Tel (01384) 480693 E-mail chriswat@blueyonder.co.uk

WATKINS, David James Hier. b 39. Trin Coll Carmarthen CertEd60 Univ of Wales DipEd67 BEd76. St Mich Coll Llan. d 90 p 91. NSM Oystermouth *S & B* from 90; Dioc Youth Chapl from 91; Lect Gorseinon Coll from 92. *10 Lambswell Close, Langland, Swansea SA3 4HJ* Tel (01792) 369742

WATKINS, Gordon Derek. b 29. d 53 p 54. Australia 53-61; C Harrogate St Wilfrid *Ripon* 61-63; V Upton Park *Chelmsf* 63-67; V Gt and Lt Bentley 67-73; R Gt Canfield 73-78; Dioc Past Sec *Lon* 78-84; Sec Dioc Adv Cttee 84-94; PV Westmr Abbey 84-89; P-in-c St Martin Ludgate *Lon* 84-89; P in O 84-94; rtd 94. *21 Cramond Place, Dalgety Bay, Dunfermline KY11 9LS* Tel (01383) 822634

WATKINS (née ROBERTS), Mrs Gwyneth. b 35. Univ of Wales (Swansea) BA MEd. St Mich Coll Llan 90. d 91 p 97. C Llanbadarn Fawr w Capel Bangor and Goginan *S D* 91-94; P-in-c Maenordeifi and Capel Colman w Llanfihangel etc 94-97; R 97-98; rtd 98. *Wenllys, Waunfarlais Road, Llandybie, Ammanford SA18 3NG*

WATKINS, Mrs Hilary Odette. b 47. New Hall Cam MA73. St Alb and Ox Min Course 98. d 01 p 02. NSM Appleton *Ox* from 01; NSM Besselsleigh from 01. *3 Byron Close, Abingdon OX14 5PA* Tel (01235) 535847 E-mail hilarywatkins@beeb.net

WATKINS, Jonathan. b 58. Padgate Coll of Educn BEd79. Trin Coll Bris 90. d 92 p 93. C Wallington H Trin *S'wark* 92-97; C Hartley Wintney, Elvetham, Winchfield etc *Win* 97-99; Chapl K Alfred's Coll Win from 99. *King Alfred's College, Sparkford Road, Winchester SO22 4NR* Tel (01962) 827246 *or* 827410 E-mail jonathan.watkins@wkac.ac.uk

WATKINS, Miss Lorna Ann Francis Charles. b 59. Trin Coll Carmarthen BEd82. St Steph Ho Ox 82. d 84 p 97. C Tenby and Gumfreston *St D* 84-89; C Pembroke Dock 89-91; Dn-in-c Cosheston w Nash and Upton 91-92; C Manordeilo 92-94; C Mynyddislwyn 94-95; TV Mynyddislwyn 95-99; R Herbrandston and Hasguard w St Ishmael's *St D* from 99. *The Rectory, 5 Sandy Haven Drive, Herbrandston, Milford Haven SA73 3TS*

WATKINS, Michael Morris. b 32. MRCS60 LRCP60. St Jo Coll Nottm DPS78. d 81 p 81. C Hornchurch St Andr *Chelmsf* 81-84; P-in-c Snitterfield w Bearley *Cov* 84-90; V 90-92; rtd 93; Perm to Offic *Cov* from 93. *Glaslyn, Riverside, Tiddington Road, Stratford-upon-Avon CV37 7BD* Tel (01789) 298085 E-mail revdocmw@waitrose.com

WATKINS, Ms Betty Anne. See MOCKFORD, Mrs Betty Anne

WATKINS, Peter. b 51. Oak Hill Th Coll BA. d 82 p 83. C Whitnash *Cov* 82-86; V Wolston and Church Lawford 86-99; RD Rugby 94-99; V Finham from 99. *St Martin's Vicarage, 136 Green Lane South, Coventry CV3 6EA* Tel (024) 7641 8330 Fax as telephone E-mail st-martins@freeuk.com

WATKINS, Peter Gordon. b 34. St Pet Coll Ox BA57 MA61. Wycliffe Hall Ox 58. d 59 p 60. C Wolverhampton St Geo *Lich* 59-60; C Burton St Chad 60-61; C Westmr St Jas *Lon* 61-63; USA 63-65; V Ealing Common St Matt *Lon* from 67. *St Matthew's*

Vicarage, 7 North Common Road, London W5 2QA Tel (020) 8567 3820

WATKINS, Robert Henry. b 30. New Coll Ox BA54 MA60. Westcott Ho Cam 59. d 60 p 61. C Newc H Cross *Newc* 60-63; C Morpeth 63-67; V Delaval 67-80; V Lancercost w Kirkcambeck and Walton *Carl* 80-90; rtd 90; Perm to Offic *Carl* from 90. *Lowpark, Loweswater, Cockermouth CA13 0RU* Tel (01900) 85242

WATKINS, Sue. See WATKINS, Mrs Christine Dorothy

WATKINS, Susan Jane. b 58. Qu Coll Birm. d 01 p 02. C Edgbaston St Germain *Birm* from 01. *410 Gillott Road, Birmingham B16 9LP* Tel 0121-242 3059 E-mail sue-watkins@blueyonder.co.uk

WATKINS, Canon William Hywel. b 36. St D Coll Lamp BA58. Wycliffe Hall Ox 58. d 61 p 62. C Llanelli *St D* 61-68; V Llwynhendy 68-78; V Slebech and Uzmaston w Boulston 78-01; Asst Chapl OStJ 82-87; Sub-Chapl 87-99; Chapl from 99; RD Daugleddau *St D* 87-01; Hon Can St D Cathl 91-93; Can St D Cathl 93-01; rtd 01. *Nant-yr-Arian, Llanbadarn Fawr, Aberystwyth SY23 3SZ* Tel (01970) 623359 Fax as telephone

WATKINS-JONES, Arthur Basil. b 24. Sarum Th Coll 67. d 69 p 70. C Broadstone *Sarum* 69-73; P-in-c Winterbourne Stickland and Turnworth etc 73-76; R 76-78; P-in-c Lilliput 78-82; V 82-89; rtd 89; Perm to Offic *Sarum* from 89. *Oak Cottage, 31 Danecourt Road, Poole BH14 0PG* Tel (01202) 746074

WATKINS-WRIGHT, Richard Kenneth David. b 39. Westcott Ho Cam 66. d 70 p 71. C Bilton *Cov* 70-74; Asst Chapl St Geo Hosp Lon 74-75; Chapl Oakwood Hosp Maidstone 76-78; R Lt w Lt Gransden *Ely* 78-97; rtd 99; Perm to Offic *Ely* from 01. *Halsou, De Lisle Close, Papworth Everard, Cambridge CB3 8UT* Tel (01480) 830746

WATKINSON, Adam John McNicol. b 68. Keble Coll Ox BA89 MA93 St Martin's Coll Lanc PGCE90. N Ord Course 01. d 03. NSM Croston and Bretherton *Blackb* from 03; Chapl Ormskirk Sch from 03. *2 Brookdale, Sheep Hill Lane, New Longton, Preston PR4 4XL* Tel (01772) 619844 E-mail adamjwatkinson@aol.com

WATLING, His Honour Brian. b 35. QC79. K Coll Lon LLB56 Barrister 57. d 87 p 88. NSM Lavenham *St E* 87-90; NSM Nayland w Wiston from 90. *The Red House, Boxford, Sudbury CO10 5HH*

WATLING, Sister Rosemary Dawn. b 32. Newnham Coll Cam BA70 MA73. Gilmore Course 70. dss 85 d 87 p 94. CSA 79-90; Paddington St Mary *Lon* 85-86; E Bris 86-87; Hon Par Dn 87; Par Dn Clifton H Trin, St Andr and St Pet 87-94; C 94-95; rtd 95; NSM Wraxall *B & W* 96-02; Perm to Offic from 02. *32 St Andrew's Mews, Wells BA5 2LB* Tel (01749) 673675

WATSON, Canon Alan. b 34. Lon Univ LLB58. Linc Th Coll 58. d 60 p 61. C Spring Park *Cant* 60-63; C Sheerness H Trin w St Paul 63-68; R Allington 68-73; P-in-c Maidstone St Pet 73; R Allington and Maidstone St Pet 73-99; Hon Can Cant Cathl 85-99; RD Sutton 86-92; rtd 99; Perm to Offic *B & W* and *Sarum* from 00. *68 Southgate Drive, Wincanton BA9 9ET* Tel (01963) 34368 E-mail alan@watson.orbitalnet.co.uk

WATSON, Alan. b 41. AKC64. St Boniface Warminster. d 65 p 66. C Hendon *Dur* 65-68; C Sheff Parson Cross St Cecilia *Sheff* 68-70; C Harton Colliery *Dur* 70-72; TV 72-74; R Gorton St Mary and St Thos *Man* 74-82; R Swinton St Pet 82-87; TR Swinton and Pendlebury 87-89; R Rawmarsh w Parkgate *Sheff* 89-94; P-in-c Dunscroft St Edwin 96-99; V from 99. *The Vicarage, 162 Station Road, Dunscroft, Doncaster DN7 4JR* Tel (01302) 841328

WATSON, Albert Victor. b 44. Ridley Hall Cam 85. d 87 p 88. C Hornchurch St Andr *Chelmsf* 87-94; P-in-c Tye Green w Netteswell 94-95; R from 95; RD Harlow from 99. *The Rectory, Tawneys Road, Harlow CM18 6QR* Tel (01279) 425138 E-mail reval@ruraldean.fsnet.co.uk

WATSON, Alfred Keith. b 39. Birm Univ BSc61. Ox Min Course 93. d 96 p 97. NSM Aylesbury w Bierton and Hulcott *Ox* 96-01; NSM Ludgvan, Marazion, St Hilary and Perranuthnoe *Truro* from 01. *The Rectory, St Hilary, Churchtown, Penzance TR20 9DQ* Tel (01736) 710229

WATSON, Andrew John. b 61. CCC Cam BA82 MA90. Ridley Hall Cam 84. d 87 p 88. C Ipsley *Worc* 87-91; C Notting Hill St Jo and St Pet *Lon* 91-96; V E Twickenham St Steph from 96; AD Hampton from 03. *St Stephen's Vicarage, 21 Cambridge Park, Twickenham TW1 2JE* Tel (020) 8892 5258 E-mail andrewwatson@st-stephens.org.uk

WATSON, Anne-Marie Louise. See RENSHAW, Ms Anne-Marie Louise

WATSON, Basil Alderson. b 16. OBE65. Selw Coll Cam BA38 MA44. Westcott Ho Cam 39. d 40 p 41. C Cambridge H Trin *Ely* 40-41; C Sugley *Newc* 41-44; Chapl RNVR 44-46; Chapl RN 46-70; V St Lawr Jewry *Lon* 70-86; RD The City 76-79; rtd 86. *19 Straightsmouth, London SE10 9LB* Tel (020) 8853 0643

WATSON, Craig. b 60. Bath Univ BSc81 CertEd82. N Ord Course 00. d 03. NSM Thorpe Edge *Bradf* from 03. *22 Northlea Avenue, Thackley, Bradford BD10 8LJ* Tel (01274) 413962

WATSON, David. See WATSON, Canon Leonard Alexander David

WATSON, The Very Revd Derek Richard. b 38. Selw Coll Cam BA61 MA65. Cuddesdon Coll 62. **d** 64 **p** 65. C New Eltham All SS *S'wark* 64-66; Chapl Ch Coll Cam 66-70; Bp's Dom Chapl *S'wark* 70-73; V Surbiton St Mark 73-77; V Surbiton St Andr and St Mark 77-78; Can Res and Treas S'wark Cathl 78-82; Dioc Dir of Ords 78-82; P-in-c Chelsea St Luke *Lon* 82-85; R 85-87; P-in-c Chelsea Ch Ch 86-87; R Chelsea St Luke and Ch Ch 87-96; AD Chelsea 94-96; Dean Sarum 96-02; rtd 02. *Bede House, Paul's Mill, Penn, High Wycombe HP10 8NZ* Tel (01494) 816502

WATSON, Derek Stanley. b 54. NEOC DipHE95. **d** 95 **p** 96. C W Acklam *York* 95-98; C-in-c Ingleby Barwick CD 98-00; V Ingleby Barwick from 00. *St Francis's House, Barwick Way, Ingleby Barwick, Stockton-on-Tees TS17 0WD* Tel (01642) 760171 Fax as telephone E-mail derek@watson1954.freeserve.co.uk

WATSON, Mrs Diane Elsie. b 44. N Ord Course 92. **d** 95 **p** 96. C Grange St Andr *Ches* 95-00; C Runcorn H Trin 96-00; R Thurstaston from 00. *Thurstaston Rectory, Telegraph Road, Thurstaston, Wirral CH61 0HJ* Tel 0151-648 1816 E-mail diane.watson@virgin.net

WATSON, Preb Donald Wace. b 17. Qu Coll Cam BA39 MA43. Lich Th Coll 39. **d** 41 **p** 42. C W Bromwich St Andr *Lich* 41-43; C Fenton 43-47; C-in-c Birches Head CD 47-48; V Smethwick St Steph *Birm* 48-51; R Kingstone w Gratwich *Lich* 51-55; V Kinver 55-82; Preb Lich Cathl 78-82; rtd 82; Perm to Offic *Heref* from 89. *The Stables, King Street, Much Wenlock TF13 6BL* Tel (01952) 728364

WATSON, Mrs Elsada Beatrice (Elsie). b 30. Westhill Coll Birm CPS86. WMMTC. **d** 89 **p** 94. NSM Birm St Pet *Birm* 89-90; NSM Lozells St Paul and St Silas 90-93; Par Dn 93-94; C 94-96; Perm to Offic from 96; rtd 96. *4 Maidstone Road, Birmingham B20 3EH* Tel 0121-356 0626

WATSON, Geoffrey. b 48. Liv Univ BEd71. Linc Th Coll 81. **d** 83 **p** 84. C Hartlepool St Luke *Dur* 83-87; P-in-c Shadforth 87-94; Soc Resp Officer 87-94; Dioc Rural Development Adv 90-94; V Staveley, Ings and Kentmere *Carl* from 94. *The Vicarage, Kentmere Road, Staveley, Kendal LA8 9PA* Tel (01539) 821267 E-mail geof watson@lineone.net

WATSON, Gordon Mark Stewart. b 67. Wolv Poly BA90 DipEd. CITC BTh95. **d** 95 **p** 96. C Ballymoney w Finvoy and Rasharkin *Conn* 95-98; I Brackaville w Donaghendry and Ballyclog *Arm* from 98. *82 Dungannon Road, Coalisland, Dungannon BT71 4HT* Tel (028) 8774 0243 Mobile 07710-924660 E-mail h.t.brackville@talk21.com

WATSON, Graeme Campbell Hubert. b 35. Ch Ch Ox BA58 BA59 MA61. Coll of Resurr Mirfield 59. **d** 61 **p** 62. C Edin St Mary *Edin* 61-63; C Carrington *S'well* 63-67; Tanzania 67-77; Tutor St Cyprian's Coll Ngala 67-69; Vice-Prin St Mark's Th Coll Dar es Salaam 69-73; P-in-c Dar es Salaam St Alb 74-77; P-in-c Kingston St Mary w Broomfield *B & W* 77-80; V 80-81; R Kingston St Mary w Broomfield etc 81-95; P-in-c Feock *Truro* 95-00; Tutor SW Minl Tr Course 95-00; rtd 00; Perm to Offic *Truro* 00-02; *Lon* from 02. *75 Winston Road, London N16 9LN* Tel (020) 7249 8701 E-mail gralizwatson@btinternet.com

WATSON, Hartley Roger. b 40. K Coll Lon. **d** 64 **p** 65. C Noel Park St Mark *Lon* 64-67; C Munster Square St Mary Magd 67-68; C Stamford Hill St Jo 68-70; Chapl RAF 70-76; R St Breoke *Truro* 76-84; P-in-c Egloshayle 82-84; R Wittering w Thornhaugh and Wansford *Pet* 84-00; RD Barnack 98-00; R Brigstock w Stanion and Lowick and Sudborough from 00. *The Rectory, Church Street, Brigstock, Kettering NN14 3EX* Tel (01536) 373371

WATSON, Henry Stanley. b 36. **d** 72 **p** 74. Hon C Bethnal Green St Jas Less *Lon* 72-83; Hon C Old Ford St Paul w St Steph and St Mark 83-88; Hon C Bethnal Green St Jas Less 89-93; Hon C Scarborough St Mary w Ch Ch and H Apostles *York* 93-97; P-in-c Seamer from 97. *The Vicarage, 3 Stockhill, Seamer, Scarborough YO12 4QG* Tel (01723) 863102

WATSON, Canon Ian Leslie Stewart. b 50. Wycliffe Hall Ox 79. **d** 81 **p** 82. C Plymouth St Andr w St Paul and St Geo *Ex* 81-85; TV Ipsley *Worc* 85-90; V Woodley St Jo the Ev *Ox* 90-92; TR Woodley 92-95; Chapl Amsterdam w Den Helder and Heiloo *Eur* 95-01; Chief Executive Can Gib Cathl from 02; ICS from 01; Perm to Offic *Cov* 01-02. *Intercontinental Church Society, 1 Athena Drive, Tachbrook Park, Warwick CV34 6NL* Tel (01926) 430347 Fax 330238 E-mail ilwatson@ics-uk.org

WATSON, James Valentine John Giles. b 65. Newc Univ BA87 Ox Univ BA91 MA97. Ripon Coll Cuddesdon 89. **d** 92 **p** 93. C Newc St Geo *Newc* 92-95; TV Daventry, Ashby St Ledgers, Braunston etc *Pet* 95-00; V Woodplumpton *Blackb* from 00. *The Vicarage, Sandy Lane, Woodplumpton, Preston PR4 0RX* Tel (01772) 690355 E-mail james@jvrswatson.freeserve.co.uk

WATSON, The Ven Jeffrey John Seagrief. b 39. Em Coll Cam BA61 MA65. Clifton Th Coll 62. **d** 65 **p** 66. C Beckenham Ch Ch *Roch* 65-69; C Southsea St Jude *Portsm* 69-71; V Win Ch Ch *Win* 71-81; V Bitterne 81-93; RD Southn 83-93; Hon Can Win Cathl 91-93; Adn Ely from 93; Hon Can Ely Cathl from 93. *St Botolph's Rectory, 1A Summerfield, Cambridge CB3 9HE* Tel (01223) 515725 Fax 571322 E-mail archdeacon.ely@ely.anglican.org

WATSON, John. b 16. Oak Hill Th Coll 76. **d** 78 **p** 79. Hon C Lexden *Chelmsf* 78-81; Perm to Offic *Ches* 81-85 and from 90; Hon C Alsager St Mary *Ches* 85-90. *9 Woolaston Drive, Alsager, Stoke-on-Trent ST7 2PL* Tel (01270) 874565

WATSON, John. b 34. **d** 60 **p** 61. C Stockton St Pet *Dur* 60-64; C Darlington H Trin 64-66; V Swalwell 66-68; Perm to Offic *Dur* 68-69; *Leic* 69-74; *Man* 74-76; rtd 96. *16 Phippsville Court, St Matthews Parade, Northampton NN2 7JW* Tel (01604) 718040 E-mail john.moirawatson@btopenworld.com

WATSON, John Calum. b 69. Spurgeon's Coll BD96. Trin Coll Bris MA03. **d** 03. C Richmond H Trin and Ch Ch *S'wark* from 03. *23 Grena Road, Richmond TW9 1XU* Tel (020) 8948 4476 E-mail john@allyu.org.uk

WATSON, Canon John Derrick. b 35. K Coll Lon 56. Edin Th Coll 60. **d** 61 **p** 62. C Fulham St Etheldreda *Lon* 61-64; P-in-c Stevenage H Trin St Alb 64-71; V 71-74; V Leagrave 74-84; RD Luton 80-82; V Eaton Socon 84-98; Hon Can St Alb 93-98; RD Biggleswade 94-96; rtd 98; Perm to Office *Ely* and *St Alb* from 99. *14 Balmoral Way, Eynesbury, St Neots PE19 2RJ* Tel (01480) 404520

WATSON, Preb John Francis Wentworth. b 28. St Jo Coll Nottm LTh59. **d** 59 **p** 60. C Egham *Guildf* 59-62; C-in-c Ewell St Paul Howell Hill CD 62-66; R Ashtead 66-72; V Plymouth St Andr w St Paul and St Geo *Ex* 72-94; Angl Adv TV SW 83-93; Westcountry TV 93-94; Preb Ex Cathl 84-94; rtd 94; Perm to Offic *Ex* from 97. *Woodland House, Western Road, Ivybridge PL21 9AL* Tel (01752) 893735

WATSON, John Lionel. b 39. G&C Coll Cam BA61 MA65. Ridley Hall Cam 62. **d** 64 **p** 65. C Toxteth Park St Philemon w St Silas *Liv* 64-69; C Morden *S'wark* 69-73; C Cambridge St Phil *Ely* 73-74; Chapl Elstree Sch Woolhampton 74-77; R Woolhampton w Midgham *Ox* 77-81; R Woolhampton w Midgham and Beenham Valance 81-95; Perm to Offic *Win* from 97; rtd 00. *Westfield House, Littleton Road, Crawley, Winchester SO21 2QD* Tel (01962) 776892

WATSON, John Robertson Thomas. b 27. CITC 68. **d** 70 **p** 71. C Belfast St Steph *Conn* 71-73; Bp's C Swanlinbar w Templeport *K, E & A* 73-82; I Arvagh w Carrigallen, Gowna and Columbkille 82-97; Preb Kilmore Cathl 88-97; rtd 97. *75 Church Road, Dundonald, Belfast BT16 2LW* Tel (028) 9048 2520

WATSON, Jonathan Ramsay George. b 38. Oriel Coll Ox BA61 MA65 DipEd62. Ridley Hall Cam 88. **d** 90 **p** 91. C Locks Heath *Portsm* 90-94; V Erith St Paul *Roch* 94-01; rtd 01. *14 Park Crescent, Midhurst GU29 9ED* Tel (01730) 816145 E-mail jrgwatson@netscapeonline.co.uk

WATSON, Julie Sandra. b 59. Liv Poly BSc81 Teesside Poly PhD86. NEOC 99. **d** 02. NSM Redcar *York* from 02. *19 Abbey Court, Normanby, Middlesbrough TS6 9BU* Tel (01642) 456449 E-mail j.s.watson@tees.ac.uk

WATSON, Keith. *See* WATSON, Alfred Keith

WATSON, Kenneth Roy. b 27. CEng68 MIMechE68. EMMTC 83. **d** 86 **p** 87. NSM Ashby-de-la-Zouch St Helen w Coleorton *Leic* 86-90; R Breedon cum Isley Walton and Worthington 90-93; rtd 93; Perm to Offic *Leic* and *Derby* from 93. *2 Meadow Gardens, Atherstone Road, Measham, Swadlincote DE12 7EG* Tel (01530) 273263

WATSON, Laurence Leslie. b 31. Keble Coll Ox BA55 MA59. Ely Th Coll. **d** 57 **p** 58. C Solihull *Birm* 57-60; C Digswell *St Alb* 60-62; V Smethwick St Steph *Birm* 62-67; V Billesley Common 67-95; rtd 95; Perm to Offic *Cov* from 95. *10 Redwing Close, Bishopton, Stratford-upon-Avon CV37 9EX* Tel (01789) 294569

WATSON, Canon Leonard Alexander David. b 37. Man Univ BSc59. Coll of Resurr Mirfield 62. **d** 64 **p** 65. C Rawmarsh w Parkgate *Sheff* 64-68; C Empangeni S Africa 69-74; TV E Runcorn w Halton *Ches* 74-79; TV Sanderstead All SS *S'wark* 79-86; TR Selsdon St Jo w St Fran 86-98; RD Croydon Addington 90-95; P-in-c Horne and Outwood 98-02; Hon Can S'wark Cathl 02-03; rtd 02. *White Gables, Station Road, East Tisted, Alton GU34 3QX* Tel (01420) 588317 E-mail da.di.watson@tinyonline.co.uk

WATSON, Mark. *See* WATSON, Gordon Mark Stewart

WATSON, Michael Henry. b 44. Victoria Univ Wellington BA65 MA66. Wycliffe Hall Ox 75. **d** 77 **p** 78. C Farnborough *Roch* 77-81; New Zealand from 81. *PO Box 7023, Wellington South, New Zealand* Tel (0064) (4) 389 2760 or 389 9603 Fax 389 2109

WATSON, Michael Paul. b 58. Trin Coll Bris DipHE93. **d** 93 **p** 94. C Derby St Alkmund and St Werburgh *Derby* 93-99; USA from 00; Lt Rock St Andr 00-01; R Bridge Community Austin from 01. *10636 Floral Park Drive, Austin, TX 78759, USA* E-mail mike.bridgepoint@worldnet.att.net

WATSON, Nicholas Edgar. b 67. St Cath Coll Cam BA88 MA92. Wycliffe Hall Ox BA91. **d** 92 **p** 93. C Benfieldside *Dur* 92-95; C-in-c Stockton Green Vale H Trin CD 95-96; P-in-c Stockton H Trin 96-00; Chapl Ian Ramsey Sch Stockton 95-00; P-in-c Breadsall *Derby* from 00; Warden of Readers from 00. *The Rectory, 57 Rectory Lane, Breadsall, Derby DE21 5LL* Tel (01332) 831352 E-mail revnickw@derbyreaders.fsnet.co.uk

WATSON, Prof Paul Frederick. b 44. MRCVS69 RVC(Lon) BSc66 BVetMed69 Sydney Univ PhD73 Lon Univ DSc95. Oak

Hill NSM Course 86. **d** 88 **p** 89. NSM Muswell Hill St Jas w St Matt *Lon* 88-96; NSM Edmonton St Aldhelm 96-01; Perm to Offic from 01. *50 New Road, Ware SG12 7BY* Tel (01920) 466941 E-mail pwatson@rvc.ac.uk

WATSON, Paul R. b 66. St Andr Univ MA89 Glas Univ BD95 MTh00. **d** 00. C Glas St Ninian *Glas* from 00. *416 Paisley Road, Glasgow G51 1BE* Tel 0141-427 4205 E-mail paul.watson@iscs.org.uk

WATSON, Paul William. b 55. Huddersfield Poly BA. St Jo Coll Nottm. **d** 86 **p** 87. C Meltham Mills *Wakef* 86-89; C Meltham 89-90; TV Borehamwood *St Alb* 90-96; V Oswaldtwistle Immanuel and All SS *Blackb* from 96. *Immanuel Vicarage, New Lane, Oswaldtwistle, Accrington BB5 3QN* Tel (01254) 233962 *or* 382147 E-mail janet paul@lineone.net

WATSON, Philip. b 60. RGN83. Qu Coll Birm 86. **d** 89 **p** 90. C Ordsall *S'well* 89-93; TV Benwell Team *Newc* 93-99; V Stocking Farm *Leic* from 99. *St Luke's Vicarage, 97 Halifax Drive, Leicester LE4 2DP* Tel 0116-235 3206

WATSON, Richard Frederick. b 66. Avery Hill Coll BA87. Trin Coll Bris ADMT93. **d** 93 **p** 94. C Kempston Transfiguration *St Alb* 93-97; TV Dunstable 97-03; R E Barnet from 03. *The Rectory, 136 Church Hill Road, Barnet EN4 8XD* Tel (020) 8368 3840 *or* 8361 7524 E-mail rf.watson@btopenworld.com

WATSON, Richard Rydill. b 47. SSC. Sarum & Wells Th Coll 74. **d** 77 **p** 78. C Cayton w Eastfield *York* 77-80; C Howden 80-82; P-in-c Burton Pidsea and Humbleton w Elsternwick 82-83; V Dormanstown 83-87; V Cotehill and Cumwhinton *Carl* 87-89; Chapl Harrogate Distr and Gen Hosp 89-94; Chapl Harrogate Health Care NHS Trust 94-99; Asst Chapl Oldham NHS Trust from 99; P-in-c Shaw *Man* from 99. *The Vicarage, 13 Church Road, Shaw, Oldham OL2 7AT* Tel (01706) 847369

WATSON, Robert Bewley. b 34. Bris Univ BA59. Clifton Th Coll 56. **d** 61 **p** 62. C Bebington *Ches* 61-65; C Woking St Jo *Guildf* 65-68; V Knaphill 68-98; rtd 98; Perm to Offic *Guildf* from 98. *Endrise, 1 Wychelm Road, Lightwater GU18 5RT* Tel (01276) 453822

WATSON, Roger. *See* WATSON, Hartley Roger

WATSON, The Ven Sheila Anne. b 53. St Andr Univ MA75 MPhil80. Edin Th Coll 79. **dss** 79 **d** 87 **p** 94. Bridge of Allan *St And* 79-80; Alloa 79-80; Monkseaton St Mary *Newc* 80-84; Adult Educn Officer *Lon* 84-87; Hon C Chelsea St Luke and Ch Ch 87-96; Selection Sec ABM 92-93; Sen Selection Sec 93-96; Adv on CME *Sarum* 97-02; Dir of Min 98-02; Can and Preb Sarum Cathl 00-02; Adn Buckingham *Ox* from 02. *Bede House, Paul's Hill, Penn, High Wycombe HP10 8NZ* Tel (01494) 814571 Fax 817946 E-mail archdbuc@oxford.anglican.org

WATSON, Miss Stephanie Abigail. b 61. Heriot-Watt Univ BA84 Dur Univ CCSk90. Cranmer Hall Dur 86. **d** 90 **p** 94. C Bishop's Castle w Mainstone *Heref* 90-93; Dep Chapl HM Pris Dur 93-95; Chapl HM Rem Cen Low Newton 95-98; V Chilton and Cornforth *Dur* 98-02; Chapl Wrekin Coll Telford from 02. *Wrekin College, Wellington, Telford TF1 3BH* Tel (01952) 415059

WATSON, Terence David. b 38. Jes Coll Ox BA61 MA67. Chich Th Coll 73. **d** 74 **p** 75. C Sidley *Chich* 74-78; C Woodham *Guildf* 78-86; C Willesborough w Hinxhill *Cant* 86-87; C Willesborough 87-93; C Maidstone St Mich 93-94; C Clacton St Jas *Chelmsf* 94-98; rtd 98; Perm to Offic *Chelmsf* 98-00 and *Chich* from 01. *38 St Mary's Road, Eastbourne BN21 1QD* Tel (01323) 439647 E-mail tdw@bushinternet.com

WATSON, Thomas Anthony. b 23. Chich Th Coll 50. **d** 52 **p** 53. C Ashburton w Buckland-in-the-Moor *Ex* 52-54; C Bideford 54-57; V Bishops Nympton 57-59; R Rose Ash 57-59; N Rhodesia 59-64; Zambia 64-65; V Honicknowle *Ex* 65-72; R Butterleigh 72-90; R Silverton 72-90; rtd 90; Chapl Palermo w Taormina *Eur* 90-93; Perm to Offic *Ex* from 93. *13A Lower North Street, Exeter EX4 3ET* Tel (01392) 424423

WATSON, Timothy Patrick. b 38. ALCD66. **d** 66 **p** 67. C Northwood Em *Lon* 66-70; TV High Wycombe *Ox* 70-76; Gen Sec ICS 76-82; R Bath Weston All SS w N Stoke *B & W* 82-93; R Bath Weston All SS w N Stoke and Langridge 93-94; TR Cheltenham St Mary, St Matt, St Paul and H Trin *Glouc* from 94. *The Rectory, 18 Park Place, Cheltenham GL50 2QT* Tel (01242) 512208

WATSON, Miss Violet Hazel. b 29. SRN52 SCM54 RSCN59. Linc Th Coll 83. **dss** 85 **d** 87. Hammersmith SS Mich and Geo White City Estate CD *Lon* 85-86; Sunbury 86; Fulham St Dionis Parson's Green 86-87; Par Dn 87; Perm to Offic *St Alb* 88-90. *4 Hayes Terrace, Crown Lane, Shorne, Gravesend DA12 3DZ*

WATSON, William. b 36. Ripon Hall Ox 64. **d** 66 **p** 67. C Leamington Priors H Trin *Cov* 66-69; V Salford Priors 69-74; V Malin Bridge *Sheff* 74-79; Chapl Shrewsbury R Hosps 79-89; Chapl R Hallamshire Hosp Sheff 89-92; Chapl Cen Sheff Univ Hosps NHS Trust 92-93; P-in-c Alveley and Quatt *Heref* 93-96; Chapl N Gen Hosp NHS Trust Sheff 96-01; Chapl Weston Park Hosp Sheff 96-99; Chapl Cen Sheff Univ Hosps NHS Trust 99-01; rtd 96; Perm to Offic *Sheff* from 01. *396 Stannington Road, Stannington, Sheffield S6 5QQ* Tel 0114-232 4005

WATSON, William Lysander Rowan. b 26. TCD BA47 MA50 Clare Coll Cam MA52 St Pet Hall Ox MA57. **d** 49 **p** 50. C

Chapelizod and Kilmainham *D & G* 49-51; Tutor Ridley Hall Cam 51-55; Chapl 55-57; Chapl St Pet Coll Ox 57-93; Fell and Tutor 59-93; Sen Tutor 77-81; Vice Master 83-85; Lect Th Ox Univ 60-93; rtd 93. *Llandaff Barn, 11 Thames Street, Eynsham, Witney OX8 1HF* Tel (01865) 464198

WATSON WILLIAMS, Richard Hamilton Patrick. b 31. SS Coll Cam BA57 MA62. St Aug Coll Cant. **d** 59 **p** 60. C Dorking St Paul *Guildf* 59-63; C Portsea St Mary *Portsm* 63-66; V Culgaith *Carl* 66-71; V Kirkland 66-71; V Wigton 72-79; Warden Dioc Conf Ho Crawshawbooth *Man* 79-82; P-in-c Crawshawbooth 79-82; Master Lady Kath Leveson Hosp 82-98; P-in-c Temple Balsall *Birm* 82-84; V 84-98; rtd 98; Perm to Offic *Glouc* from 98. *16 Barton Mews, Barton Road, Tewkesbury GL20 5RL* Tel (01684) 290509 E-mail squaredws@beeb.net

WATT, The Very Revd Alfred Ian. b 34. FRSA95. Edin Th Coll 57. **d** 60 **p** 61. Chapl St Paul's Cathl Dundee *Bre* 60-63; Prec 63-66; P-in-c Dundee H Cross 64-66; R Arbroath 66-69; R Perth St Ninian *St And* 69-82; Provost St Ninian's Cathl Perth 69-82; Can St Ninian's Cathl Perth 82-98; R Kinross 82-95; Dean St Andr 89-98; rtd 98. *33 Stirling Road, Milnathort, Kinross KY13 9XS* Tel (01577) 865711

WATT, Prof William Montgomery. b 09. Edin Univ MA30 PhD44 Ball Coll Ox BA32 BLitt36 MA36 Aber Univ Hon DD66 Hamdard Univ Karachi Hon DLitt98. Cuddesdon Coll 38. **d** 39 **p** 40. C W Brompton St Mary *Lon* 39-41; C Edin Old St Paul *Edin* 41-43; Hon C 46-60; Jerusalem 43-46; Lect Edin Univ 46-53; Reader 53-64; Prof Arabic and Islamic Studies 64-79; Hon C Edin St Columba *Edin* 60-67; Hon C Dalkeith 80-93; Hon C Lasswade 80-93; rtd 93. *The Neuk, 2 Bridgend, Dalkeith EH22 1JT* Tel 0131-663 3197

WATT-WYNESS, Gordon. b 25. Cranmer Hall Dur 70 St Jo Coll Dur 70. **d** 72 **p** 73. C Scarborough St Mary w Ch Ch, St Paul and St Thos *York* 72-76; R Rossington *Sheff* 76-90; rtd 90; Perm to Offic *York* from 90. *15 Newton Court, Crescent Road, Filey YO14 4LL* Tel (01723) 516608

WATTERS, Mrs Kay. b 44. St Alb and Ox Min Course 98. **d** 01 **p** 02. OLM Prestwood and Gt Hampden *Ox* from 01. *7 Widmere Field, Prestwood, Great Missenden HP16 0SP* Tel (01494) 865468 Mobile 07714-220241 Fax (01494) 862552

WATTERSON, Mrs Susan Mary. b 50. S & M Dioc Inst 84. **d** 87 **p** 94. NSM Rushen *S & M* 87-89; Hon Par Dn Castletown 89-94; C 94-96; Dioc Youth Officer 87-91; Bp's Adv for Healing Min 91-94; Asst Chapl Bris Univ *Bris* 96-99; Hon C Bris St Mich and St Paul 96-99; Project Leader Galway Chr Tr Inst 99-00; I Youghal Union *C, C & R* from 00; RD NE Cork from 03. *Upper Strand, Youghal, Cork, Irish Republic* Tel (00353) (24) 92350

WATTHEY, Arthur Edward. b 20. St Cath Coll Cam BA45 MA48. St Aug Coll Cant 73. **d** 73 **p** 74. NSM Glen Magna w Stretton Magna *Leic* 73-76; NSM Carlton Curlieu, Illston on the Hill etc 76-81; Perm to Offic from 81; Perm to Offic *Pet* 85-96; Bp's Insp of Par Registers and Records *Leic* 90-94. *2 The Chase, Great Glen, Leicester LE8 9EQ* Tel 0116-259 2603

WATTLEY, Jeffery Richard. b 57. Univ of Wales (Abth) BSc(Econ)79. Trin Coll Bris BA92. **d** 92 **p** 93. C Reading Greyfriars *Ox* 92-96; V Wonersh *Guildf* 96-98; V Wonersh w Blackheath from 98. *The Vicarage, The Street, Wonersh, Guildford GU5 0PF* Tel (01483) 893131 E-mail jrwattley@aol.com

WATTON, Robert Newman Kingsley. b 45. Qu Coll Birm 72. **d** 74 **p** 75. C Madron w Morvah *Truro* 74-78; Dioc Adv in RE 78-81; P-in-c Lostwithiel 78-83; P-in-c Lanhydrock 81-83; P-in-c Lanivet 81-82; V Launceston 83-91; RD Trigg Major 89-91; R Kingston, Langton Matravers and Worth Matravers *Sarum* from 91. *The Rectory, St George's Close, Langton Matravers, Swanage BH19 3HZ* Tel (01929) 422559 E-mail robert.watton@virgin.net

WATTS, Canon Anthony George. b 46. K Coll Lon BD69 AKC69 Lon Univ CertEd70. Sarum & Wells Th Coll 82. **d** 84 **p** 85. C Wimborne Minster and Holt *Sarum* 84-87; P-in-c Shilling Okeford 87-92; Chapl Croft Ho Sch Shillingstone 87-92; R W Parley *Sarum* 92-00; RD Wimborne 98-00; TR Cley Hill Warminster from 00; Can and Preb Sarum Cathl from 00. *The Rectory, 5 Church Street, Warminster BA12 8PG* Tel (01985) 213456 Fax as telephone

WATTS, Anthony John. b 30. AKC59. **d** 60 **p** 61. C Whitburn *Dur* 60-63; C Croxdale 63-65; V Warrington St Pet *Liv* 65-70; V Peel *Man* 70-78; P-in-c Bury St Mark 78-81; V Davyhulme Ch Ch 81-99; Chapl Trafford Gen Hosp 89-94; Chapl Trafford Healthcare NHS Trust 94-99; rtd 99; Perm to Offic *Ches* from 00. *11 Brackenfield Way, Winsford CW7 2UX* Tel (01606) 590803

WATTS, David Henry. b 27. Ex Coll Ox BA50 MA55. Wells Th Coll 51. **d** 53 **p** 54. C Haslemere *Guildf* 53-55; C Chelmsf Cathl *Chelmsf* 55-58; Succ Chelmsf Cathl 55-58; V Chessington *Guildf* 58-62; Educn Officer Essex Educn Cttee 62-70; HMI of Schs 70-87; Hon C Wetherby *Ripon* 79-87; P-in-c Healaugh w Wighill, Bilbrough and Askham Richard *York* 87-89; Chapl HM Pris Askham Grange 87-96; rtd 89; Perm to Offic *York* from 98. *3 Westwood Way, Boston Spa, Wetherby LS23 6DX* Tel (01937) 845005

WATTS, Canon Frank Walter. b 30. St Boniface Warminster 53 K Coll Lon AKC54. d 54 p 55. C Llandough w Leckwith *Llan* 54-56; C Llanishen and Lisvane 56-59; C Gt Marlow *Ox* 59-60; R Black Bourton 60-63; V Carterton 60-63; C-in-c Brize Norton 61-63; V Brize Norton and Carterton 63-69; Australia from 69; Hon Can Perth from 78; rtd 95. *Villa 5, 178-180 Fern Road, Wilson, W Australia 6107* Tel and fax (0061) (8) 9258 4532 Mobile 408-094991 E-mail frawawa@southwest.com.au

WATTS, Fraser Norman. b 46. Magd Coll Ox BA68 MA74 K Coll Lon MSc70 PhD75 Magd Coll Cam DipTh90 CPsychol89 FBPsS80. Westcott Ho Cam 88. d 90 p 91. NSM Harston w Hauxton *Ely* 90-95; P-in-c 91-95; Fell Qu Coll Cam from 94; Lect Cam Univ from 94; Chapl Cam St Edw *Ely* from 95. *19 Grantchester Road, Cambridge CB3 9ED* Tel (01223) 359223 Fax 335577 E-mail fnw1001@hermes.cam.ac.uk

WATTS, Gordon Sidney Stewart. b 40. CITC 63. d 66 p 67. C Belfast St Steph *Conn* 66-69; CF 69-94; V Boldre w S Baddesley *Win* 94-96; P-in-c Warmfield *Wakef* 96-02; Sub Chapl HM Pris Wakef 97-02; Chapl Huggens Coll Northfleet from 02. *Chaplain's House, Huggens College, College Road, Northfleet DA11 9DL* Tel (01474) 352428 Fax 533091 E-mail gss.watts@virgin.net

WATTS, Graham Hadley Lundie. b 74. Man Metrop Univ BA95. Ridley Hall Cam 98. d 02 p 03. C Camberley St Paul *Guildf* from 02. *3 Upper Gordon Road, Camberley GU15 2HJ* Tel (01276) 504103 E-mail chefandkiller@yahoo.com

WATTS, Ian Charles. b 63. Hull Univ BA85. Linc Th Coll 86. d 88 p 89. C W Kirby St Bridget *Ches* 88-93; V High Lane 93-00; P-in-c Newton in Mottram from 00. *St Mary's Vicarage, 39 Bradley Green Road, Hyde SK14 4NA* Tel (0161) 368 1489

WATTS, Ian Harold. b 15. St Pet Coll Ox BA39 MA47. Wycliffe Hall Ox. d 65 p 66. Nigeria 65-68; Chapl Uppingham Sch Leics 68-73; Hon C Mirfield *Wakef* 73-79; Chapl Cannes *Eur* 80-87; rtd 87. *3 Golf Court, High Street, Aberlady, Longniddry EH32 0SQ* Tel (01875) 870681

WATTS, John Robert. b 39. Leeds Univ BSc60 MSc63 DipEd63. Oak Hill Th Coll 88. d 90 p 91. C Partington and Carrington *Ches* 90-93; P-in-c Tintwistle 93-98; V Hollingworth w Tintwistle from 98; RD Mottram from 99. *The Vicarage, 10 Church Street, Tintwistle, Glossop SK13 1JR* Tel (01457) 852575 E-mail revrob@jrwatts.fsnet.co.uk

WATTS, John Stanley. b 28. LCP62 Birm Univ DipEd65 MEd72 Nottm Univ MPhil83. Qu Coll Birm 83. d 86 p 87. Lect Wolverhampton Poly 77-90; Hon C Dudley St Fran *Worc* 86-91; Lect Wolverhampton Univ 90-93; Hon C Sedgley St Mary 91-98; Perm to Offic from 98. *5 Warren Drive, Sedgley, Dudley DY3 3RQ* Tel (01902) 661265

WATTS, Mrs Mary Kathleen. b 31. Lon Univ DipRS73 BA86. Gilmore Ho 73. dss 77 d 87 p 94. Lower Streatham St Andr *S'wark* 77-88; C 87-88; C Streatham Immanuel w St Anselm 87-88; C Streatham Immanuel and St Andr 90-91; rtd 91; Perm to Offic *S'wark* 91-94; Hon C Streatham St Oswald from 94. *2 Beaufort Gardens, London SW16 3BP* Tel (020) 8764 6165

WATTS, Paul George. b 43. Nottm Univ BA67. Wells Th Coll 67. d 69 p 70. C Sherwood *S'well* 69-74; Chapl Trent (Nottm) Poly 74-80; V Nottingham All SS 80-84; Public Preacher from 84. *16 Grosvenor Avenue, Nottingham NG5 3DX* Tel 0115-960 9964 *or* 915 0640 E-mail paul.watts@nottinghamcity.gov.uk

WATTS, Ms Rebecca Harriet. b 61. St Cath Coll Cam BA83 MA Welsh Coll of Music & Drama 84. Wycliffe Hall Ox 87. d 90 p 94. C Goldsworth Park *Guildf* 90-94; Chapl Wadh Coll Ox 94-97; C Ox St Mary V w St Cross and St Pet *Ox* 94-97; Chapl Somerville Coll Ox 97-98; Perm to Offic *Newc* 98-99 and from 02. *15 Woodbine Avenue, Gosforth, Newcastle upon Tyne NE3 4EU* Tel 0191-285 9840

WATTS, Robert. See WATTS, John Robert

WATTS, Roger Edward. b 39. S'wark Ord Course 85. d 88 p 89. C Belmont *S'wark* 88-92; R Godstone 92-97; R Godstone and Blindley Heath from 97. *The Rectory, 17 Ivy Mill Lane, Godstone RH9 8NK* Tel (01883) 742354

WATTS, Roger Mansfield. b 41. Univ of Wales (Cardiff) BSc63 CEng76 MIEE76. Chich Th Coll 89. d 91 p 92. C Chippenham St Andr w Tytherton Lucas *Bris* 91-93; C Henfield w Shermanbury and Woodmancote *Chich* 93-96; R Jedburgh *Edin* 96-99; R Wingerworth *Derby* from 99. *The Rectory, Longedge Lane, Wingerworth, Chesterfield S42 6PU* Tel (01246) 234242

WATTS, Ronald Horace. b 57. CITC DipTh92. d 92 p 93. C Sligo *K, E & A* 92-93; C Limerick City *L & K* 94-95; I Holmpatrick w Balbriggan and Kenure *D & G* 95-01; C Taney 01-03; Chapl Adelaide and Meath Hosp Dublin from 03. *26 Lakelands Avenue, Upper Kilmacud Road, Stillorgan, Co Dublin, Irish Republic* Tel (00353) 86-2518784 (mobile)

WATTS, Ms Samantha Alison Lundie. b 70. Birm Univ BA92 Cam Univ BA01. Ridley Hall Cam 99. d 02 p 03. C Camberley St Paul *Guildf* from 02. *3 Upper Gordon Road, Camberley GU15 2HJ* Tel (01276) 504103 E-mail chefandkiller@yahoo.com

WATTS, Scott Antony. b 67. FRMetS99 MCMI00. EAMTC 00. d 03. NSM Brampton *Ely* from 03. *10 Link Drive, Brampton,*

Huntingdon PE28 4FE Tel (01480) 411141 Mobile 07903-301417 E-mail rev.scott.watts@ntlworld.com

WATTS, Mrs Valerie Anne. b 44. UEA BEd79. EAMTC 90. d 93 p 94. NSM N Walsham w Antingham *Nor* from 93. *15 Millfield Road, North Walsham NR28 0EB* Tel (01692) 405119

WATTS, Wilfred Richard James. b 11. St Mich Coll Llan 64. d 66 p 66. C Coleford w Staunton *Glouc* 66-69; V Viney Hill 69-82; rtd 82; Perm to Offic *Glouc* 82-97. *c/o Mrs E M Sowerby, 22 Petvin Close, Street BA16 0SX*

WATTS, William Henry Norbury. b 51. CertEd. St Jo Coll Nottm 87. d 89 p 90. C S Molton w Nymet St George, High Bray etc *Ex* 89-93; TV Swanage and Studland *Sarum* from 93. *The Vicarage, School Lane, Studland, Swanage BH19 3AJ* Tel (01929) 450441 E-mail wiznrol@compuserve.com

WAUD, John David. b 31. N Ord Course 82. d 85 p 86. C Cayton w Eastfield *York* 85-88; R Brandesburton 88-93; R Beeford w Frodingham and Foston 93-99; rtd 99; Perm to Offic *York* from 00. *23 St Leonard Road, Molescroft, Beverley HU17 7HU* Tel (01482) 864726 E-mail jdw2@jdw2.karoo.co.uk

WAUDBY, Miss Christine. b 45. TCert66. Trin Coll Bris DipHE. d 90 p 94. C Weston-super-Mare Ch Ch *B & W* 90-94; C Blackheath *Birm* 94-99; Perm to Offic from 99. *c/o The Revd W Brown, St Boniface Vicarage, Quinton, Birmingham B32 2QD* Tel 0121-427 1939

WAUDE, Andrew Leslie. b 74. Leeds Univ BA02. Coll of Resurr Mirfield 99. d 02 p 03. C Swinton and Pendlebury *Man* from 02. *46 Townsend Road, Swinton, Manchester M27 6SH* Tel 0161-794 1808 Mobile 07715-787137 E-mail fr_andrew@lycos.co.uk

WAUGH, Ian William. b 52. Bede Coll Dur DipEd74 BEd75. NEOC 99. d 02 p 03. NSM Benfieldside *Dur* from 02. *36 Muirfield Close, Shotley Bridge, Consett DH8 5XE* Tel (01207) 591923 Mobile 07808-412953 E-mail ian-barbara-waugh@lineone.net

WAUGH, Mrs Jane Leitch. b 38. DMusEd60 CertEd61 Toronto Univ MDiv83. Trin Coll Toronto 80. d 84 p 94. Canada 84-87; Par Dn Dunnington *York* 88-90; Perm to Offic 90-93; NSM York St Olave w St Giles 93-96; Perm to Offic from 96; rtd 98. *Moonrakers, Rectory Corner, Brandsby, York YO61 4RJ* Tel (01347) 888637

WAUGH, Nigel John William. b 56. TCD BA78 MA81. CITC 76. d 79 p 80. C Ballymena *Conn* 79-82; C Ballyholme *D & D* 82-84; I Bunclody w Kildavin *C & O* 84-86; I Bunclody w Kildavin and Clonegal 86-91; I Bunclody w Kildavin, Clonegal and Kilrush 91-98; Preb Ferns Cathl 88-91; Treas 91-96; Radio Officer (Cashel) 90-91; (Ferns) 92-98; Dioc Info Officer (Ferns) 91-98; Prec Ferns Cathl 96-98; I Delgany *D & G* from 98. *The Rectory, 8 Elsinore, Delgany, Greystones, Co Wicklow, Irish Republic* Tel (00353) (1) 287 4515 Fax 287 7578 E-mail delgany@glendalough.anglican.org

WAXHAM, Derek Frank. b 33. Oak Hill Th Coll 76. d 79 p 80. Hon C Old Ford St Paul w St Steph *Lon* 79-82; Hon C Old Ford St Paul w St Steph and St Mark 82-89; NSM Bow w Bromley St Leon from 89. *39 Hewlett Road, London E3 5NA* Tel (020) 8980 1748

WAY, Albert James. b 27. St D Coll Lamp BA61 DipTh63. d 63 p 64. C Neath w Llantwit *Llan* 63-68; C Watford St Jo *St Alb* 68; R Clayhidon *Ex* 68-76; V Llanbadog and Llanllowell *Mon* 76-83; V Llanhilleth 83-98; rtd 98. *9 Berthon Road, Little Mill, Pontypool NP4 0HE* Tel (01495) 785724

WAY, Andrew Lindsay. b 43. Linc Th Coll 76. d 78 p 79. C Shenfield *Chelmsf* 78-82; C Waltham *Linc* 82-84; V New Waltham 84-89; R Duxford *Ely* 89-94; V Hinxton 89-94; V Ickleton 89-94; P-in-c Doddington w Benwick 94-97; P-in-c Wimblington 94-97; R Doddington w Benwick and Wimblington 97-98; R Eythorne and Elvington w Waldershare etc *Cant* from 98; AD Dover 00-03. *The Rectory, Barfreystone Road, Eythorne, Dover CT15 4AH* Tel (01304) 830241 Fax (08701) 255866 E-mail albeway@clara.co.uk

WAY, Anthony Hilton. b 21. ARIBA. Chich Th Coll 57. d 59 p 60. C Chich St Paul and St Bart *Chich* 59-61; C Hangleton 61-63; V Horam 63-70; V Ditchling 70-77; Asst Dioc Sec 77-83; Chapl Dioc Ch Ho 79-83; V Linchmere 83-91; rtd 91; Perm to Offic *Chich* from 91. *59 Finches Garden, Lindfield, Haywards Heath RH16 2PB* Tel (01444) 484584

WAY, Mrs Barbara Elizabeth. b 47. Open Univ BA82 Hull Univ PGCE86. Linc Th Coll IDC78. dss 78 d 87 p 94. Shenfield *Chelmsf* 78-82; Adult Educn Adv *Linc* 82-85; Dioc Lay Min Adv 85; New Waltham 82-89; Min 87-89; Tetney 86-89; Min 87-89; NSM Duxford *Ely* 89-94; NSM Ickleton 89-94; NSM Hinxton 89-94; Dir Past Studies EAMTC 91-94; Min Pampisford 92-94; P-in-c Coates 94-95; TV Whittlesey, Pondersbridge and Coates 95-98; Local Min Adv *Cant* 98-02; Dioc Dir of Reader Selection and Tr from 00; Dioc Adv in Women's Min from 02; P-in-c Whitfield w Guston from 02; Chapl E Kent Hosps NHS Trust from 02. *The Rectory, Barfreystone Road, Eythorne, Dover CT15 4AH* Tel (01304) 830241 Fax (08701) 255866 E-mail bway@diocant.clara.co.uk

WAY, Colin George. b 31. St Cath Coll Cam BA55 MA59 Lon Inst of Educn PGCE58. EAMTC. d 84 p 85. NSM Hempnall *Nor*

84-87; C Gaywood, Bawsey and Mintlyn 87-90; R Acle w Fishley and N Burlingham 90-96; RD Blofield 95-96; rtd 96; Perm to Offic *Nor* 96-97; P-in-c Pulham Market, Pulham St Mary and Starston 97-99; Hon C Eaton 99-02; Perm to Offic from 02. *347 Unthank Road, Norwich NR4 7QG* Tel (01603) 458363 E-mail cw@eatonparish.com

WAY, David. b 54. Pemb Coll Ox MA DPhil. Cranmer Hall Dur BA Cuddesdon Coll 83. **d** 85 **p** 86. C Chenies and Lt Chalfont *Ox* 85-87; C Chenies and Lt Chalfont, Latimer and Flaunden 87-88; Tutor and Dir Studies Sarum & Wells Th Coll 88-93; Selection Sec Min Division from 94; Sec Minl Educn Cttee from 94; Th Educn Sec Min Division from 99. *Ministry Division, Church House, Great Smith Street, London SW1P 3NZ* Tel (020) 7898 1405 Fax 7898 1421
E-mail david.way@mindiv.c-of-e.org.uk

WAY, David Charles. b 61. St Mich Coll Llan BTh94. **d** 97 **p** 98. C Cardiff St Mary and St Steph w St Dyfrig etc *Llan* 97-02; V Aberaman and Abercwmboi w Cwmaman from 02. *St Margaret's Vicarage, Gladstone Street, Aberaman, Aberdare CF44 6SA* Tel (01685) 872871 E-mail david.way@dtn.ntl.com

WAY, Lawrence William. b 32. St Mich Coll Llan 77. **d** 79 **p** 80. C Merthyr Dyfan *Llan* 79-82; V Abercynon 82-84; TV Cwmbran *Mon* 84-86; V Caerwent w Dinham and Llanfair Discoed etc 86-90; V Pontnewydd 90-93; rtd 93. *8 Ceredig Court, Llanyravon, Cwmbran NP44 8SA* Tel (01633) 865309 Fax 876830
E-mail frway.angelus@virgin.net

WAY, Michael David. b 57. K Coll Lon BD78 AKC78. St Steph Ho Ox 79. **d** 80 **p** 83. C Bideford *Ex* 80-81; Hon C Wembley Park St Aug *Lon* 81-84; C Kilburn St Aug w St Jo 84-89; V Earlsfield St Jo *S'wark* 89-92; Project Co-ord CARA 92-99; Consultant Cen Sch for Counselling and Therapy 99; Dir RADICLE *Lon* from 00. *14 St Peter's Gardens, London SE27 0PN* Tel (020) 8670 3439 *or* 7932 1129

WAYNE, Kenneth Hammond. b 31. Bps' Coll Cheshunt 58. **d** 61 **p** 62. C Eyres Monsell CD *Leic* 61-62; C Loughborough Em 62-65; C-in-c Staunton Harold 65-73; R Breedon w Isley Walton 65-73; V Leic St Phil 73-85; V Ault Hucknall *Derby* 85-95; rtd 95; Perm to Offic *Derby* 85-95. *The Haven, 3 Burton Walk, East Leake, Loughborough LE12 6LB* Tel (01509) 852848

WAYTE, Alleyn Robert. b 33. Trin Coll Ox BA56 MA60. Westcott Ho Cam 60. **d** 61 **p** 62. C Cannock *Lich* 61-66; P-in-c Dawley 66-75; V Stretton w Claymills 75-92; rtd 92; Perm to Offic *Derby* from 92. *2 Church Close, Willington, Derby DE65 6EN* Tel (01283) 701815

WAYTE, Christopher John. b 28. Lon Univ BSc54. Wells Th Coll 54. **d** 56 **p** 57. C Maidstone St Martin *Cant* 56-60; C W Wickham St Jo 60-61; C Birchington w Acol 61-64; C-in-c Buckland Valley CD 64-68; R Biddenden 68-80; Chapl ATC 71-86; P-in-c Boughton Monchelsea *Cant* 80-85; V St Margarets-at-Cliffe w Westcliffe etc 85-91; rtd 92; Perm to Offic *Cant* from 92. *9 St John's Road, Hythe CT21 4BE* Tel (01303) 263060
E-mail audrey@wayte93.freeserve.co.uk

WEALE, Colin Alexander. b 26. Univ of Wales (Lamp) BA49 Lon Univ DipRS77 Open Univ MPhil87 Middx Univ PhD96. Lambeth STh81 Sarum Th Coll 49. **d** 51 **p** 52. C Swansea St Mary and H Trin *S & B* 51-55; Min Can Brecon Cathl 55-59; C Brecon w Battle 55-59; V Llanbister and Llanbadarn Fynydd w Llananno 59-61; R Bengeo H Trin *St Alb* 61-69; R Bengeo 69-93; rtd 93; Perm to Offic *Nor* from 93. *1 Diana Way, Caister-on-Sea, Great Yarmouth NR30 5TP* Tel (01493) 377946

WEARMOUTH, Alan Wilfred. b 54. St Paul's Cheltenham CertEd75 Bris Univ BEd76. Glouc Sch of Min 85. **d** 88 **p** 89. NSM Coleford w Staunton *Glouc* from 88. *Windhover, Broadwell Bridge, Coleford GL16 7GA* Tel (01594) 832660

WEARN, William Frederick. b 51. S Dios Minl Tr Scheme. **d** 85 **p** 86. NSM Hythe St Martin 85-94; Asst Chapl HM Pris Liv 94-95; Chapl HM Pris Wakef 95-96; Chapl HM Pris Garth 96-97; rtd 97; Perm to Offic *Liv* from 97. *66 Sussex Road, Southport PR9 0SP*

WEATHERHEAD, The Very Revd Thomas Leslie. b 13. Hatf Coll Dur BA37 LTh37. St Aug Coll Cant 32. **d** 37 **p** 38. C Chesterton Hill H Spirit *Ripon* 37-40; C Wensley 40-42; Chapl RAFVR 42-47; C Leeds Halton St Wilfrid *Ripon* 47-48; V New Mills *Derby* 48-59; R Staveley 59-65; Dean and V-Gen Nassau 65-72; R Felmingham 72-79; P-in-c Suffield 72-74; R 74-79; P-in-c Colby w Banningham and Tuttington 72-74; R 74-79; RD Tunstead 76-79; rtd 79; Perm to Offic *Ripon* from 79. *St Nicholas' Lodge, 25 Bishopton Lane, Ripon HG4 2QN* Tel (01765) 600413

WEATHERILL, Stephen Robert. b 70. Roehampton Inst BA98 Nottm Univ MA00. St Jo Coll Nottm 98. **d** 00 **p** 02. C Bridlington Priory *York* 00-01; NSM Kendal St Thos *Carl* from 02. *35 Church Street, Milnthorpe LA7 7DX* Tel (01539) 565871 E-mail stephen@project-vision.co.uk

WEATHERLEY, Miss Mary Kathleen. b 36. SRN57 SCM59 Midwife Teacher's Dip 72. SW Minl Tr Course 78. **dss** 82 **d** 87 **p** 94. Littleham w Exmouth *Ex* 82-84; Heavitree w Ex St Paul 85-87; Hon Par Dn 87-88; Chapl Asst R Devon and Ex Hosp 85-93; Lic to Offic *Ex* 88-94; NSM Littleham w Exmouth 94-98;

Perm to Offic from 98. *38 Egremont Road, Exmouth EX8 1SA* Tel (01395) 265528

WEATHRALL, Ian Charles. b 22. OBE75. AKC47. **d** 47 **p** 48. C Southampton St Mary w H Trin *Win* 47-51; India from 51; Brotherhood of Ascension from 51; Hd 70-88; rtd 92. *7 Court Lane, Delhi 110 054, India* Tel (0091) (11) 396 8515

WEAVER, Alan William. b 63. Brighton Poly HNC88. Linc Th Coll 95. **d** 95 **p** 96. C Seaford w Sutton *Chich* 95-98; C Langney 98-01; P-in-c Haven CD from 02. *1 Columbus Drive, Eastbourne BN23 6RR* Tel (01323) 642897 Fax as telephone
E-mail angyalanweaver@mistral.co.uk

WEAVER, Ms Angela Mary. b 48. WMMTC 92. **d** 95 **p** 96. C Hill Birm 95-99; V Hamstead St Paul from 99. *Hamstead Vicarage, 840 Walsall Road, Birmingham B42 1ES* Tel 0121-357 8941 Mobile 07813-807853 E-mail angelamweaver@aol.com

WEAVER, Prof Arthur Kenneth (Ken). b 17. Trin Coll Cam BA30 MA44 MRAeS50. Ox NSM Course 81 Wycliffe Hall Ox 81. **d** 81 **p** 82. NSM Ashbury, Compton Beauchamp and Longcot w Fernham *Ox* 81-87; Perm to Offic from 87. *White Lodge, King's Lane, Longcot, Faringdon SN7 7SS* Tel (01793) 782364

WEAVER, Brian John. b 34. Oak Hill Th Coll 82. **d** 84 **p** 85. C Nailsea H Trin *B & W* 84-88; R Nettlebed w Bix and Highmore *Ox* 88-98; rtd 98; Hon C Warfield *Ox* from 99. *47 Walsh Avenue, Warfield, Bracknell RG42 3XZ* Tel (01344) 485379
E-mail bri_jac@onetel.net.uk

WEAVER, David Anthony. b 43. Hatf Coll Dur BSc65. Lich Th Coll 68. **d** 71 **p** 72. C Walsall Wood *Lich* 71-75; C Much Wenlock w Bourton *Heref* 75-76; Canada 76-79 and 82; V Mow Cop *Lich* 79-82; P-in-c Burntwood 82-00; V from 00; Chapl St Matt Hosp Burntwood 83-95. *The Vicarage, Church Road, Burntwood, Walsall WS7 9EA* Tel (01543) 675014

WEAVER, Duncan Charles. b 60. St Jo Coll Nottm BA99. St Jo Coll Nottm DipTh94. **d** 94 **p** 95. C Watford *St Alb* 94-98; TV Bourne Valley *Sarum* 98-01; CF from 01. *c/o MOD Chaplains (Army)* Tel (01980) 615804 Fax 615800
E-mail dweaver385@aol.com

WEAVER, Fiona Margaret. b 61. Westcott Ho Cam. **d** 00 **p** 01. C Islington St Jas w St Pet *Lon* from 00; Asst Chapl Univ of N Lon 00-02; Asst Chapl Lon Metrop Univ 01-03; Chapl from 03. *123 Calabria Road, London N5 1HS* Tel (020) 7704 9914
E-mail f.weaver@londonmet.ac.uk

WEAVER, Ian Douglas. b 65. Ridley Coll Melbourne BMin96. **d** 96 **p** 96. Australia 96-98 and from 03; TV Rushden St Mary w Newton Bromswold *Pet* 98-02; Dioc Youth Min Facilitator Melbourne from 03. *The Anglican Centre, 209 Flinders Lane, Melbourne, Vic, Australia 3000* Tel (0061) (3) 9653 4220 Mobile 409-604006 Fax (3) 9653 4268
E-mail iweaver@melbourne.anglican.com.au

WEAVER, Canon John. b 28. Ex Coll Ox BA51 MA55. St Steph Ho Ox 52. **d** 55 **p** 56. C Ex St Dav *Ex* 55-58; S Africa from 58; Hon Can St John's from 81; Adn Midl 84-95; Hon Can Pietermaritzburg from 95. *PO Box 56, Underberg, 3257 South Africa* Tel (0027) (33) 701 1124

WEAVER, Mrs Joyce Margaret. b 43. **d** 00 **p** 01. OLM Warrington St Ann *Liv* from 00. *71 Orford Avenue, Warrington WA2 8PQ* Tel (01925) 634993

WEAVER, Ken. *See* WEAVER, Prof Arthur Kenneth

WEAVER, Canon Michael Howard. b 39. Leeds Univ DipArch63 DipTh66 DLA69 Southn Univ MPhil95. Chich Th Coll 63. **d** 66 **p** 67. C Kidderminster St Jo *Worc* 66-69; Br Honduras 69-71; TV Droitwich *Worc* 71-76; V Arundel w Tortington and S Stoke *Chich* 76-96; Sub-Chapl HM Pris Ford 77-96; P-in-c Clymping *Chich* 84-87; RD Arundel and Bognor 88-93; Hon Can Enugu from 94; V Lymington *Win* from 96; Chapl Southampton Community Services NHS Trust from 96. *The Vicarage, Grove Road, Lymington SO41 3RF* Tel (01590) 673847
E-mail junovicarage@hotmail.com

WEAVER, Raymond Alexander. b 30. Bris Univ BA51 CertEd52. **d** 86 **p** 87. NSM Weymouth H Trin *Sarum* 86-96; Perm to Offic from 96. *10 Windsor Court, Westerhall Road, Weymouth DT4 7SZ* Tel (01305) 783681

WEAVER, Canon William. b 40. Man Univ BA63 BD65. **d** 74 **p** 75. Lect Th Leeds Univ 67-91; Hon C Clifford *York* 82-86; Chapl K Edw Sch Birm 91-94; Provost Woodard Schs (Midl Division) 94-03; Hon Can Derby Cathl *Derby* from 96; Perm to Offic from 96. *20 St Peter's Garth, Thorner, Leeds LS14 3EE* Tel 0113-289 3689

WEBB, Canon Albert. b 22. AKC49. **d** 50 **p** 51. C Warsop *S'well* 50-52; V Cleeve Prior *Worc* 52-59; V Foley Park 59-66; V Evesham 66-87; RD Evesham 73-79; Hon Can Worc Cathl 75-87; rtd 87; Perm to Offic *Worc* from 87. *2 Dolphin Close, Worcester WR2 6BG* Tel (01905) 422230

WEBB, Anthony John. b 24. Sarum & Wells Th Coll 79. **d** 81 **p** 82. C Yeovil *B & W* 81-84; P-in-c Cossington 84-87; P-in-c Woolavington 84-87; P-in-c Bawdrip 87; V Woolavington w Cossington and Bawdrip 87-91; rtd 91; Perm to Offic *B & W* from 91. *4 Brue Crescent, Burnham-on-Sea TA8 1LR* Tel (01278) 787483

WEBB, Arthur Robert. b 33. FRSA LCP67 Lanc Univ MA82. Wells Th Coll 69. **d** 70 **p** 70. C W Drayton *Lon* 70-72; Hd Master St Jas Cathl Sch Bury St Edmunds 72-86; Min Can St E Cathl *St E* 72-87; Succ St E Cathl 81-87; P-in-c Seend and Bulkington *Sarum* 87-88; V 88-91; R Heytesbury and Sutton Veny 91-96; rtd 96; Perm to Offic *B & W* from 96; *Sarum* from 98; and *Bris* from 00. *27 Marlborough Buildings, Bath BA1 2LY* Tel (01225) 484042

WEBB, Mrs Barbara Mary. b 39. Bedf Coll Lon BA60 Cam Univ PGCE61. Wycliffe Hall Ox 00. **d** 02. NSM Cumnor *Ox* from 02. *50 West St Helen Street, Abingdon OX14 5BP* Tel (01235) 202873 E-mail derry_barbara@msn.com

WEBB, Brenda Lynne. d 99 p 00. NSM Kelsale-cum-Carlton, Middleton, Theberton etc *St E* from 99. *The Rectory, Manor Gardens, Saxmundham IP17 1ET* Tel (01728) 604234 E-mail richard@saxrectory.freeserve.co.uk

WEBB, Christopher Scott. b 70. Univ of Wales (Abth) BSc. Trin Coll Bris BA96. **d** 96 **p** 97. C Dafen *St D* 96-98; C Cowbridge *Llan* 98-01; Officer for Renewal, Development and Local Ecum from 01. *3 Leoline Close, Cowbridge CF71 7BU* Tel (01446) 773515 *or* 772302 E-mail chris@webbsworld.freeserve.co.uk

WEBB, Cyril George. b 19. Roch Th Coll 64. **d** 66 **p** 67. C Bournemouth St Andr *Win* 66-71; V Micheldever 71-72; V Micheldever and E Stratton, Woodmancote etc 72-79; V Bubwith w Ellerton and Aughton *York* 79-83; I Tomregan w Drumlane *K, E & A* 83-86; rtd 86; Perm to Offic *Cant* 90-98. *62 Columbia Avenue, Whitstable CT5 4EH* Tel (01227) 264687

WEBB, David Basil. b 30. Ch Coll Cam BA54 MA58. Ripon Hall Ox 54. **d** 55 **p** 56. C Wimbledon *S'wark* 55-57; Chapl Em Coll Cam 57-60; V Langley Mill *Derby* 60-64; R Farnborough *Roch* 64-73; R Dunstable *St Alb* 73-78; TR 78-84; RD Dunstable 81-84; TR Bemerton *Sarum* 84-90; V Haslingden w Grane and Stonefold *Blackb* 90-96; RD Accrington 92-95; rtd 96; Perm to Offic *Bradf* from 96. *22 Thwaites Avenue, Ilkley LS29 8EH* Tel (01943) 609762

WEBB, David William. b 30. MRINA Kent Univ DipTh84. Cant Sch of Min 86. **d** 89 **p** 90. NSM Sittingbourne St Mary *Cant* 89-95; Hon C Iwade from 95. *16 School Lane, Iwade, Sittingbourne ME9 8SE* Tel (01795) 424502

WEBB, Mrs Diane. b 45. LNSM course 91. **d** 93 **p** 94. OLM Stowmarket *St E* from 93; RD Stowmarket from 00. *36 Wordsworth Road, Stowmarket IP14 1TT* Tel (01449) 677880

WEBB, Diane Silvia. Birm Univ BA66 Dur Univ MA93. N Ord Course 82. dss 85 **d** 03. Wyther Ven Bede *Ripon* 85-86; Perm to Offic *York* 95-99; rtd 03; NSM Bow Common *Lon* from 03. *17 Hanover Place, Brokesley Street, London E3 4QD* Tel (020) 8981 3174 E-mail diane@webb.lcbroadband.co.uk

WEBB, Dominic Mark. b 68. Oriel Coll Ox BA91. Wycliffe Hall Ox BA93. **d** 96 **p** 97. C Cradley *Worc* 96-99; C Leyton Ch Ch *Chelmsf* 99-02; P-in-c St Helier *S'wark* from 02. *St Peter's Vicarage, Bishopsford Road, Morden SM4 6BH* Tel (020) 8648 6050 Mobile 07736-927115 E-mail domwebb@talk21.com

WEBB, Frances Mary. See BATTIN, Mrs Frances Mary

WEBB, Mrs Gillian Anne. b 49. Whitelands Coll Lon CertEd71. St Alb Minl Tr Scheme 83. dss 86 **d** 87 **p** 94. Kempston Transfiguration *St Alb* 86-87; NSM 87-96; NSM Kempston from 96. *2 Hillson Close, Marston Moreteyne, Bedford MK43 0QN* Tel (01234) 767256

WEBB, Gregory John. b 55. Man Univ LLB77. Oak Hill Th Coll 89. **d** 91 **p** 92. C Bury St Edmunds St Geo *St E* 91-94; P-in-c Bury St Edmunds All SS 94-02; TR Bury St Edmunds All SS w St Jo and St Geo from 02; RD Thingoe from 01. *All Saints' Vicarage, 59 Bennett Avenue, Bury St Edmunds IP33 3JJ* Tel (01284) 701063

WEBB, Harold William. b 37. St Chad's Coll Dur BA59. St Steph Ho Ox 59. **d** 61 **p** 62. C Plumstead St Nic *S'wark* 61-65; S Africa 65-70; Sacr Wakef Cathl *Wakef* 71-72; P-in-c Lane End *Ox* 72-76; V Lane End w Cadmore End 76-84; Chapl to the Deaf *Guildf* 84-96; V Roade and Ashton w Hartwell *Pet* 96-02; rtd 02. *16 Harrow Drive, West Wittering, Chichester PO20 8EJ* Tel (01243) 673460

WEBB (née EDWARDS), Mrs Helen Glynne. b 57. SRN79 RMN81 Birkbeck Coll Lon MSc94. Wycliffe Hall Ox 88. **d** 90 **p** 94. Par Dn Clapham St Jas *S'wark* 90-94; Chapl Asst Southmead Health Services NHS Trust 94-97; Perm to Offic *Bris* from 97. *13 The Green, Olveston, Bristol BS35 4DN* Tel (01454) 615827 Fax as telephone

WEBB, Jason Stephen. b 72. Southlands Coll Lon BA93. St Steph Ho Ox DipMin95. **d** 95 **p** 96. C Leeds St Aid *Ripon* 95-99; Chapl Agnes Stewart C of E High Sch Leeds 97-99; P-in-c Toxteth Park St Agnes and St Pancras *Liv* from 99; Chapl St Hilda's Priory and Sch Whitby 99-03. *St Agnes's Vicarage, 1 Buckingham Avenue, Liverpool L17 3BA* Tel 0151-733 1742 Fax as telephone E-mail jswebbuk@aol.com

WEBB, Jennifer Rose. b 48. Leeds Univ BA70 Bedf Coll Lon CQSW72. LNSM course 93. **d** 96 **p** 97. OLM Ham St Rich *S'wark* from 96. *3 Locksmeade Road, Ham, Richmond TW10 7YT* Tel (020) 8948 0031 *or* 8547 6052

WEBB, John Christopher Richard. b 38. ACA63 FCA74. Wycliffe Hall Ox 64. **d** 67 **p** 68. C Hendon St Paul Mill Hill *Lon* 67-71; CF 71-93; R Bentworth and Shalden and Lasham *Win* 93-03; RD

Alton 98-02; rtd 03. *Lower Farm Cottage, Church Street, Podimore, Yeovil BA22 8JG* E-mail john.c.r.webb@ukgateway.net

WEBB, Kenneth Gordon. b 47. Lon Univ MB, BS71 DRCOG73. Trin Coll Bris BA92. **d** 93 **p** 94. C Cheltenham St Mark *Glouc* 93-97; Banchang Ch Ch Thailand 97-02; P-in-c Duns *Edin* from 02. *The Rectory, Wellfield, Duns TD11 3EH* Tel (01361) 882209

WEBB, Marjorie Valentine (Sister Elizabeth). b 31. Bedf Coll Lon Westmr Coll Ox MTh98. **d** 88 **p** 94. CSF from 55; Revd Mother 71-86; Lic to Bp Heref 86-90; Perm to Offic *Lon* 88-90; Lic to Offic *Lich* 90-91; *B & W* from 95; *Cant* 95-00; *Birm* 97-00; *Lich* from 00. *The Community of St Francis, 10 Halcrow Street, London E1 2EP* Tel (020) 7247 6233

WEBB, Martin George. b 46. SS Mark & Jo Coll Chelsea CertEd68 Leeds Univ MEd95. N Ord Course 82. **d** 85 **p** 86. NSM Brotherton *Wakef* 85-87; Perm to Offic *York* 95-98; NSM Bethnal Green St Barn *Lon* from 98. *17 Hanover Place, Brokesley Street, London E3 4QD* Tel (020) 8981 3174 E-mail martin@webb.lcbroadband.co.uk

WEBB, Michael David. b 59. K Coll Lon BD82 PGCE83. Ripon Coll Cuddesdon 88. **d** 90 **p** 91. C Broughton Astley *Leic* 90-93; C Hugglescote w Donington, Ellistown and Snibston 93-94; TV 94-98; R Castleford All SS and Whitwood *Wakef* 98-01; P-in-c Glass Houghton 98-01; TR Castleford 02; rtd 02. *7 St Peter's Close, Farndon, Newark NG24 3SN* Tel (01636) 702548 E-mail michael@webbs-web.co.uk

WEBB, Canon Michael John. b 49. Linc Coll Ox BA70 MA74. Linc Th Coll 70. **d** 72 **p** 73. C Tring *St Alb* 72-75; C Chipping Barnet 75-78; C Chipping Barnet w Arkley 78-82; TV Cullercoats St Geo *Newc* 82-87; V Newc H Cross 89-97; V Newc St Gabr from 97; AD Newc E from 97; Hon Can Newc Cathl from 02. *St Gabriel's Vicarage, 9 Holderness Road, Heaton, Newcastle upon Tyne NE6 5RH* Tel 0191-276 3957 *or* fax and tel 265 5843 E-mail ruraldeaneast@ukgateway.net

WEBB, Nikola. See MARSHALL, Pauline Nikola

WEBB, Peter Henry. b 55. Nottm Univ BA77 Sunderland Univ Dip Psychology 95. St Steph Ho Ox 77. **d** 79 **p** 80. C Lancing w Coombes *Chich* 79-82; C The Hydneye CD 82-84; C-in-c 84-86; Chapl Sunderland Distr Gen Hosp 86-94; Chapl City Hosps Sunderland NHS Trust from 94. *The Chaplain's Office, Sunderland Royal General Hospital, Kayll Road, Sunderland SR4 7TP* Tel 0191-565 6256 *or* 569 9180

WEBB, Rex Alexander Francis. b 32. Ely Th Coll 56. **d** 58 **p** 59. C Millbrook 58-60; Australia from 60; rtd 97. *54 Annaburoo Crescent, Tiwi, Darwin, NT, Australia 0810*

WEBB, Richard. b 38. Oak Hill NSM Course 91. **d** 94 **p** 95. NSM Hanwell St Mary w St Chris *Lon* from 94. *St Christopher's Vicarage, 4 Hillyard Road, London W7 1BH* Tel (020) 8578 2796

WEBB, Richard Frederick. b 42. Cant Sch of Min. **d** 84 **p** 85. C Ipswich St Clem w H Trin *St E* 84-87; R Rougham and Beyton w Hessett 87-91; R Rougham, Beyton w Hessett and Rushbrooke 91-92; P-in-c Woodbridge St Jo 92-98; P-in-c Saxmundham from 98; P-in-c Kelsale-cum-Carlton, Middleton, Theberton etc from 02. *The Rectory, Manor Gardens, Saxmundham IP17 1ET* Tel (01728) 604234

WEBB, Richard Lacey. b 09. ALCD30. **d** 32 **p** 33. C Keynsham *B & W* 32-35; R Wacton Magna w Parva *Nor* 36-41; V Castle Acre w Newton 41-49; R Garboldisham 49-66; R Blo' Norton 49-66; RD Rockland 63-66; V Lakenham St Alb 66-77; rtd 77; Hon C Nor St Andr *Nor* 83-86; Perm to Offic 86-87. *32 Ipswich Road, Norwich NR4 6QR* Tel (01603) 51348

WEBB, Robert. See WEBB, Arthur Robert

WEBB, Rowland James. b 33. Roch Th Coll 64. **d** 67 **p** 68. C Tavistock and Gulworthy *Ex* 67-70; Chapl RN 70-86; R Mundford w Lynford *Nor* 86-90; V Burnham *Chelmsf* 90-98; rtd 98; Perm to Offic *Chelmsf* from 98. *4 Pine Drive, Ingatestone CM4 9EF*

WEBB, Stephen. See WEBB, Jason Stephen

WEBB, Timothy Robert. b 57. Univ of Wales (Abth) BA79 CQSW89 Univ of Wales (Ban) BTh03. **d** 03. C Machynlleth w Llanwrin and Penegoes *Ban* from 03. *Y Rheithordy, Penegoes, Machynlleth SY20 8NH* Tel (01654) 703214 Mobile 07765-298575

WEBB, William John. b 43. Cuddesdon Coll 68. **d** 71 **p** 72. C Weston Favell *Pet* 71-73; C Newport w Longford *Lich* 74-77; C Baswich 77-79; P-in-c Stonnall 79-83; P-in-c Wall 79-83; V Fauls 83-95; V Prees 83-95; V St Martin's from 95. *The Vicarage, St Martins, Oswestry SY11 3AP* Tel (01691) 772295

WEBBER, David Price. b 39. Chich Th Coll 90. **d** 91 **p** 92. NSM Shoreham Beach *Chich* 91-93; NSM Hove St Patr 93-96; Turks and Caicos Is from 96. *PO Box 24, Grand Turk, Turks and Caicos Islands, BWI*

WEBBER, The Very Revd Eric Michael. b 16. Lon Univ BD54 ATh(SA)55 Univ of Tasmania MEd77 MHums85. AKC43. **d** 43 **p** 44. C Clapham H Spirit *S'wark* 43-47; C Wimbledon 47-50; S Africa 50-58; Australia from 58; Dean Hobart 59-71; Sen Lect Relig Studies Tasmanian Coll Adv Educn 71-81; rtd 94. *5B Kendrick Court, Dynnyrne, Tas, Australia 7005* Tel (0061) (3) 6223 6413

WEBBER, John Arthur. b 45. Keble Coll Ox BA67 MA71. Gen Th Sem (NY) STM85 Cuddesdon Coll 70. **d** 71 **p** 72. C Penarth All SS *Llan* 71-74; USPG Bangladesh 75-84 and 85-91; USA 84-85; Asst P Stepney St Dunstan and All SS *Lon* 91-97; Bp's Adv on Inter-Faith Relns from 91; P-in-c Bethnal Green St Barn 97-00; Dir of Ords from 00. *The Institute Flat, 24 Exmouth Market, London EC1R 4QE* Tel (020) 7278 0516 *or* 7247 1448

WEBBER, Lionel Frank. b 35. Kelham Th Coll St Mich Coll Llan. **d** 60 **p** 61. C Bolton Sav *Man* 60-63; C Aberavon *Llan* 63-65; R Salford Stowell Memorial *Man* 65-69; V Aberavon H Trin *Llan* 69-74; TV Stantonbury *Ox* 74-76; TR Basildon St Martin w H Cross and Laindon *Chelmsf* 76-79; P-in-c Nevendon 77-79; RD Basildon 79-89; R Basildon St Martin w Nevendon 79-95; R Basildon St Martin 95-01; Hon Can Chelmsf Cathl 84-01; Chapl to The Queen 94-01; rtd 01. *12 Ramblers Way, Burnham-on-Crouch CM0 8LR* Tel (01621) 785152

WEBBER, Michael Champneys Wilfred. b 48. Man Univ BA71 MA(Theol)78. Cuddesdon Coll 73. **d** 75 **p** 76. C Caterham *S'wark* 75-79; P-in-c Kidbrooke St Jas 79-84; TV 84-85; V Earls Barton *Pet* from 87; RD Wellingborough from 00. *The Vicarage, 7 High Street, Earls Barton, Northampton NN6 0JG* Tel (01604) 810447 Fax as telephone
E-mail michaelc.webber@btinternet.com

WEBBER, Peter Cecil. b 21. Lon Coll of Div ALCD55 LTh. **d** 55 **p** 56. C Wimbledon St Luke *S'wark* 55-58; V Beckenham St Jo *Roch* 58-67; V Foord St Jo *Cant* 67-86; RD Elham 80-83; rtd 86; Perm to Offic *Chich* from 86. *15 Goodwin Close, Hailsham BN27 3DE* Tel (01323) 848668

WEBBER, Raymond John. b 40. Lon Univ DipTh65. Linc Th Coll 84. **d** 85 **p** 86. C Helston *Truro* 85; C Helston and Wendron 85-90; TV 90-93; R Kenton, Mamhead, Powderham, Cofton and Starcross *Ex* 93-03; rtd 03. *1 Seton Gardens, Camborne TR14 7JS* Tel (01209) 711360

WEBBER, Thomas George Edward. b 63. LSE BSc84. Trin Coll Bris DipTh98. **d** 98 **p** 99. C Churchdown *Glouc* 98-02; TV Stoke Gifford *Bris* from 02. *The Vicarage, Mautravers Close, Bradley Stoke, Bristol BS32 8ED* Tel 0117-931 2222
E-mail tcwebber@lineone.net

WEBBER, Toby Roderic. b 75. St Jo Coll Dur BA96. Wycliffe Hall Ox BA01. **d** 02 **p** 03. C Chorley St Laur *Blackb* from 02. *57 Park Road, Chorley PR7 1QZ* Tel (01257) 274170 Fax 231374

WEBER, Douglas John Craig. b 20. Ex Coll Ox BA46 MA46. Sarum Th Coll. **d** 49 **p** 50. C Portsea N End St Mark *Portsm* 49-52; C Alverstoke 52-55; V Hook w Warsash 55-88; rtd 88; Perm to Offic *Portsm* from 88. *1 Trevose Way, Titchfield, Fareham PO14 4NG* Tel (01489) 583065

WEBLEY, Robin Bowen. b 32. Univ of Wales (Cardiff) DPS. St Mich Coll Llan 87. **d** 89 **p** 90. C St D Cathl *St D* 89-91; Min Can St D Cathl 89-91; R Castlemartin w Warren and Angle etc 91-94; Succ St D Cathl 94-00; rtd 00. *Whiteleys, Stepaside, Narberth SA67 8NS* Tel (01834) 813603

WEBSTER, The Very Revd Alan Brunskill. b 18. KCVO88. Qu Coll Ox BA39 MA43 BD54 City Univ Hon DD. Westcott Ho Cam 41. **d** 42 **p** 43. C Attercliffe w Carbrook *Sheff* 42-44; C Sheff Arbourthorne 44-46; Chapl and Lib Westcott Ho Cam 46-48; Vice-Prin 48-53; V Barnard Castle *Dur* 53-59; RD Barnard Castle 54-59; Warden Linc Th Coll 59-70; Can and Preb Linc Cathl *Linc* 64-70; Dean Nor 70-78; Dean St Paul's *Lon* 78-87; rtd 88; Perm to Offic *Nor* 88-01. *20 Beechbank, Norwich NR2 2AL* Tel (01603) 455833

WEBSTER, David Edward. b 39. K Coll Lon 60 Edin Th Coll 62. **d** 64 **p** 65. C Maghull *Liv* 64-69; R Wavertree St Mary 69-76; TV Greystoke, Matterdale and Mungrisdale *Carl* 76-81; R Lowton St Luke *Liv* 81-88; R Stoneleigh w Ashow and Baginton *Cov* 88-01; Chapl Nat Agric Cen 88-01; P-in-c Pennington and Lindal w Marton and Bardsea *Carl* from 01. *The Vicarage, Main Road, Swarthmoor, Ulverston LA12 0RZ* Tel (01229) 583174 Fax as telephone E-mail d.webster@ruralnet.org.uk

WEBSTER, David Leslie Holbarow. b 37. St Alb and Ox Min Course 00. **d** 02. NSM Hurst *Ox* from 02. *515 Reading Road, Winnersh, Wokingham RG41 5HL* Tel 0118-979 4568 Fax 961 9575 E-mail dlhwebster@supanet.com

WEBSTER, David Robert. b 32. Selw Coll Cam BA56 MA60. Linc Th Coll 56. **d** 58 **p** 59. C Billingham St Cuth *Dur* 58-61; C Doncaster St Geo *Sheff* 61-64; Chapl Doncaster R Infirmary 61-64; V Lumley *Dur* 64-76; V Belmont 76-93; rtd 93. *25 Eldon Grove, Hartlepool TS26 9LY* Tel (01429) 425915
E-mail david.webster6@ntlworld.com

WEBSTER, Dennis Eric. b 39. Fitzw Ho Cam BA60 MA64 Linacre Coll Ox MA70 Lon Univ CertEd61. Wycliffe Hall Ox 62. **d** 65 **p** 66. C Herne Bay Ch Ch *Cant* 65-68; C Tulse Hill H Trin *S'wark* 68-69; Missr Kenya 70-75; Chapl Pierrepont Sch Frensham 75-91; R Chiddingfold *Guildf* 91-02; rtd 02. *Sylvan Cottage, 24 Longdown Road, Lower Bourne, Farnham GU10 3JL* Tel (01252) 713919

WEBSTER, Derek Herbert. b 34. FRSA82 Hull Univ BA55 Lon Univ BD55 Leic Univ MEd68 PhD73. Lambeth STh67 Linc Th Coll 76. **d** 76 **p** 77. Lect Hull Univ from 72; Reader from 97;

NSM Cleethorpes *Linc* from 76. *60 Queen's Parade, Cleethorpes DN35 0DG* Tel (01472) 693786
E-mail dwebster@edrev.demon.co.uk

WEBSTER, Mrs Diane Margaret. b 43. Oak Hill NSM Course 91. **d** 94 **p** 95. NSM Welwyn Garden City *St Alb* 94-99; P-in-c Burley Ville *Win* from 99; RD Christchurch from 03. *The Vicarage, Church Corner, Burley, Ringwood BH24 4AP* Tel (01425) 402303 E-mail dwebster@fish.co.uk

WEBSTER, Geoffrey William. b 36. St Alb Minl Tr Scheme 77. **d** 80 **p** 81. NSM Harlington *St Alb* 80-82; C Belmont *Dur* 82-86; R Gateshead Fell 86-94; P-in-c Hamsterley 94-95; V Hamsterley and Witton-le-Wear 95-02; rtd 02. *38A Owton Manor Lane, Hartlepool TS25 3AE* Tel (01429) 265798

WEBSTER, Canon Glyn Hamilton. b 51. SRN73. Cranmer Hall Dur 74 St Jo Coll Dur 74. **d** 77 **p** 78. C Huntington *York* 77-81; V York St Luke 81-92; Chapl York Distr Hosp 81-92; Sen Chapl York Health Services NHS Trust 92-99; Can and Preb York Minster *York* 94-99; Can Res York Minster from 99; RD City of York from 99. *4 Minster Yard, York YO1 7JD* Tel (01904) 620877 Fax 557201 E-mail pastor@yorkminster.org

WEBSTER, Prof John Bainbridge. b 55. Clare Coll Cam MA81 PhD82. **d** 83 **p** 84. Chapl and Dep Sen Tutor St Jo Coll Dur 83-86; Hon C Bearpark *Dur* 83-86; Assoc Prof Systematic Th Wycliffe Coll Toronto 86-93; Prof Systematic Th 93-95; Ramsay Armitage Prof Systematic Th 95-96; Lady Marg Prof Div Ox Univ from 96; Can Res Ch Ch *Ox* from 96. *Christ Church, Oxford OX1 1DP* Tel (01865) 276247 Fax as telephone E-mail john.webster@christ-church.ox.ac.uk

WEBSTER, Canon Martin Duncan. b 52. Nottm Univ BSc74 DipTh76. Linc Th Coll 75. **d** 78 **p** 79. C Thundersley *Chelmsf* 78-81; C Canvey Is 81-82; TV 82-86; V Nazeing 86-99; RD Harlow 88-99; TR Waltham H Cross from 99; Hon Can Chelmsf Cathl from 00. *The Rectory, Highbridge Street, Waltham Abbey EN9 1DG* Tel (01992) 762115 Fax as telephone E-mail martin-webster@lineone.net

WEBSTER, Mrs Monica. b 39. DipCOT60. WMMTC 94. **d** 97 **p** 98. NSM Wolverton w Norton Lindsey and Langley *Cov* 97-01; Asst Chapl to the Deaf 97-01; NSM Stoneleigh w Ashow and Baginton 98-01; Chapl to the Deaf and Hard of Hearing *Carl* from 01; NSM Aldingham, Dendron, Rampside and Urswick from 02; NSM Pennington and Lindal w Marton and Bardsea from 02. *The Vicarage, Main Road, Trinkeld, Swarthmoor, Ulverston LA12 0RZ* Tel (01229) 583174 Fax as telephone E-mail revmonic@fish.co.uk

WEBSTER, Mrs Patricia Eileen. b 34. St Gabr Coll Lon TCert54. Gilmore Ho 56. **d** 87 **p** 94. Par Dn Belmont *Dur* 87-93; rtd 93. *25 Eldon Grove, Hartlepool TS26 9LY* Tel (01429) 425915 E-mail david.webster6@ntlworld.com

WEBSTER, Peter. b 26. MRICS FCIOB FASI. Cranmer Hall Dur 68. **d** 70 **p** 71. C Tickhill w Stainton *Sheff* 70-72; C Conisbrough 72-73; V Walkley 73-77; V Rawcliffe 77-84; V Barrow-on-Humber *Linc* 84; P-in-c Goxhill 84; V Barrow and Goxhill 84-91; rtd 91; Perm to Offic *Sheff* and *York* from 91. *1 Parsons Lane, Howden, Goole DN14 7BT* Tel (01430) 431637 E-mail cleric@fish.co.uk

WEBSTER, Ms Rosamond Mary. b 54. Coll of Ripon & York St Jo BEd90 MA01. Westcott Ho Cam 00. **d** 02 **p** 03. C Frodingham *Linc* from 02. *66 Church Lane, Scunthorpe DN15 7AF* Tel (01724) 848171 Mobile 07779-784320 E-mail roswebstera@onetel.net.uk

WEBSTER, Sarah Vernoy. b 38. Univ of Georgia BSc61. S'wark Ord Course 87. **d** 90 **p** 94. NSM Primrose Hill St Mary w Avenue Road St Paul *Lon* 90-01; Lic to Offic *Chelmsf* from 01; *Lon* from 01. *27 Meadowbank, London NW3 3AY*
E-mail revsallywebster@aol.com

WEBSTER, Mrs Sheila Mary. b 22. Bedf Coll Lon CertSS43. Gilmore Ho 69. dss 81 **d** 87. Patcham *Chich* 77-83; Hove All SS 84-90; Hon Par Dn 87-90; rtd 90; Perm to Offic *Chich* from 90. *108 Surrenden Road, Brighton BN1 6WB* Tel (01273) 561222

WEBSTER-SMITH, Preb Alfred William. b 10. St Chad's Coll Dur BA32 DipTh33 MA35. **d** 33 **p** 34. C Riddlesdown *S'wark* 33-36; Tanganyika 36-51; Gen Sec UMCA 51-59; Lic to Offic *S'wark* 51-59; Hon Can Masasi from 57; Zambia 59-66; Can N Rhodesia 60-62; R Pontesbury I and II *Heref* 66-76; RD Pontesbury 66-76; Preb Heref Cathl 73-81; rtd 76; Perm to Offic *S'wark* from 80. *The College of St Barnabas, Blackberry Lane, Lingfield RH7 6NJ* Tel (01342) 870609

WEDDERSPOON, The Very Revd Alexander Gillan. b 31. Jes Coll Ox BA54 MA61 Lon Univ BD62. Cuddesdon Coll. **d** 61 **p** 62. C Kingston All SS *S'wark* 61-63; Lect RE Lon Univ 63-66; Educn Adv C of E Sch Coun 66-70; Can Res Win Cathl *Win* 70-87; Treas 80-85; Vice-Dean 85-87; Dean Guildf 87-01; rtd 01. *1 Ellery Close, Cranleigh GU6 8DF* Tel (01483) 548586

WEDGBURY, John William. b 53. RMCS BSc78. St Jo Coll Nottm 84. **d** 87 **p** 88. C Foord St Jo *Cant* 87-91; V Mangotsfield *Bris* 91-92; NSM Manselton *S & B* 00-02; P-in-c Caereithin from 02. *Caereithin Vicarage, 64 Cheriton Close, Portmead, Swansea SA5 5LA* Tel (01792) 583646

WEDGEWORTH, Michael John. b 40. Nottm Univ BSc62. Wesley Ho Cam MA66. **d** 93 **p** 94. In Meth Ch 66-93; NSM

Feniscowles *Blackb* 93-96; Sec DBF from 95; Hon P Blackb Cathl from 95; Lic to Offic from 96. *46 Preston New Road, Blackburn BB2 6AH* Tel (01254) 260078 *or* 54421 Fax 699963 E-mail mike.wedgeworth@blackburn.anglican.org.uk

WEDGWOOD, Preb Charles Mervyn. b 16. Selw Coll Cam BA38 MA46. Wycliffe Hall Ox 38. **d** 40 **p** 41. C Melton Mowbray w Burton Lazars, Freeby etc *Leic* 40-46; Chapl RAFVR 42-46; V Copt Oak *Leic* 46-50; Chapl Towle Recovery Homes Woodhouse Eaves 46-50; R Kirby Muxloe 50-54; RD Sparkenhoe III 53-54; V Claughton cum Grange *Ches* 54-56; V Keynsham w Queen Charlton *B & W* 56-67; R Burnett 56-67; Chapl Keynsham Hosp 56-67; Preb Wells Cathl 63-81; V Wellington w W Buckland and Nynehead 67-72; Chapl Wellington Hosps 67-72; V Combe Down w Monkton Combe 73-81; V Combe Down w Monkton Combe and S Stoke 81; RD Bath 76-81; rtd 81; Perm to Offic *B & W* 81-97; Perm to Offic *Ex* 86-93. *Flat 5, Manormead, Tilford Road, Hindhead GU26 6RA* Tel (01428) 602556

WEDGWOOD, George Peter. b 26. St Jo Coll Dur BA51 DipTh52 MA56. **d** 52 **p** 53. C Barrow St Mark *Carl* 52-54; Chapl Sedbergh Sch 54-57; P-in-c Dur St Cuth *Dur* 57-63; Chapl Dur High Sch 58-63; Chapl, Hd of Div and Sen Lect St Kath Coll *Liv* 63-69; Prin Lect 69-83; Hd of Div Liv Coll of HE 84-86; P-in-c Kirkoswald, Renwick and Ainstable *Carl* 86-88; rtd 88; Perm to Offic *Carl* 88-92 and *Liv* 92-97; Hon C Hawick *Edin* from 02. *Cavers Manse Cottage, Hawick TD9 8LJ* Tel (01450) 370224

WEDGWOOD, Keith. b 20. Hertf Coll Ox BA42 MA46. Wycliffe Hall Ox 42. **d** 43 **p** 44. C Hartlebury *Worc* 43-46; C Worc St Martin 46-49; Succ Derby Cathl *Derby* 49-52; V Choral Sarum Cathl *Sarum* 52-68; Succ 55-68; Canada 68-72; P-in-c Osmington w Poxwell *Sarum* 72-77; TV The Iwernes and Sutton Waldron 77-78; P-in-c 78-81; V The Iwernes, Sutton Waldron and Fontmell Magna 81-85; rtd 85; Perm to Offic *Sarum* from 85. *18 Walton Road, Bournemouth BH10 4BJ* Tel (01202) 532116

WEDGWOOD GREENHOW, Stephen John Francis. b 57. Man Univ BA82. Edin Th Coll MTh84. **d** 84 **p** 85. C Wythenshawe Wm Temple Ch *Man* 84-87; USA from 87. *556 North George Washington Blvd, Yuba City, CA 95993, USA* Tel (001) (530) 822 0691

WEEDEN, Simon Andrew. b 55. York Univ BA79. Wycliffe Hall Ox 88. **d** 90 **p** 91. C Gt Chesham *Ox* 90-94; P-in-c Haversham w Lt Linford, Tyringham w Filgrave 94-97; R Lamp 97-99; P-in-c Bramshott and Liphook *Portsm* 99-00; R from 00. *The Rectory, 22 Portsmouth Road, Liphook GU30 7DJ* Tel (01428) 723119 Fax 725390 E-mail simon@weedens.freeserve.co.uk

WEEDING, Paul Stephen. b 62. Leic Poly BSc. Ripon Coll Cuddesdon 88. **d** 90 **p** 91. C Llanishen and Lisvane *Llan* 90-93; C Merthyr Tydfil Ch Ch 93-97; V Abercynon from 97. *The Vicarage, 67 Grovers Field, Abercynon, Mountain Ash CF45 4PQ* Tel (01443) 740207

✠**WEEKES, The Rt Revd Ambrose Walter Marcus.** b 19. CB70. AKC41 Linc Th Coll 41. **d** 42 **p** 43 **c** 77. C New Brompton St Luke *Roch* 42-44; Chapl RNVR 44; Chapl RN 46-69; Chapl of the Fleet and Adn for the RN 69-72; QHC from 69; Can Gib Cathl *Eur* 71-73; Chapl Tangier 72-73; Dean Gib 73-77; Aux Bp Eur 77-80; Suff Bp Eur 80-86; Dean Brussels 81-86; rtd 86; Asst Bp Roch 86-88; Asst Bp Eur from 89; Chapl Montreux w Gstaad *Eur* 89-92. *Charterhouse, Charterhouse Square, London EC1M 6AN* Tel (020) 7251 4201

WEEKES, Cecil William. b 31. CITC. **d** 78 **p** 79. NSM Glenageary *D & G* 78-80; Bp's V Kilkenny Cathl *C & O* 80-83; I Carlow w Urglin and Staplestown 83-90; Can Leighlin Cathl 88-96; Can Ossory Cathl 88-96; I Lismore w Cappoquin, Kilwatermoy, Dungarvan etc 90-96; Dean Lismore 90-96; Chan Cashel Cathl 90-96; Prec Waterford Cathl 90-96; rtd 96. *The Cottage, Danesfort Road, Bennettsbridge, Co Kilkenny, Irish Republic* Tel (00353) (56) 772 7711 E-mail cwweekes@eircom.net

WEEKES, David John. b 34. Magd Coll Cam BA59 MA68 Lon Univ PGCE68 Aber Univ MTh79. Clifton Th Coll 62. **d** 64 **p** 65. C Cheadle *Ches* 64-68; Uganda 69-73; Perm to Offic *St And* 73-74; Chapl and Hd of RE Fettes Coll Edin 74-94; Warden and Chapl Lee Abbey Internat Students' Club Kensington 94-01; rtd 01; Perm to Offic *Lon* from 94. *Loaning Hill House, Kilmany, Cupar KY15 4PT* Tel 07855-761970 (mobile) E-mail davidweekes@hotmail.com

WEEKES, Robin Alasdair Rutley. b 73. Peterho Cam MA94. Wycliffe Hall Ox BA98 MA98. **d** 99 **p** 00. C Wimbledon Em Ridgway Prop Chpl *S'wark* from 99. *25 Richmond Road, London SW20 0PG* Tel (020) 8947 2029

WEEKS, Ms Jane Anne. b 61. UEA BA00. Aston Tr Scheme 95 EAMTC. **d** 00 **p** 01. C Hadleigh *St E* 00-02; C Hadleigh, Layham and Shelley 02-03. *Bracken, 165 Lower Warren Road, Aylesford, Maidstone ME20 7EH* Tel (01634) 861775 E-mail weeks.clan@virgin.net

WEETMAN, Mrs Dorothy. b 41. Dioc OLM tr scheme 98. **d** 03. OLM Prudhoe *Newc* from 03. *Station Gate East, Eltringham Road, Prudhoe NE42 6LA* Tel (01661) 834538

WEETMAN, John Charles. b 66. Qu Coll Ox BA87 MA92. Trin Coll Bris BA91. **d** 91 **p** 92. C Hull Newland St Jo *York* 91-95; V Boosbeck w Moorsholm 95-02; V Redcar from 02; RD Guisborough from 99. *St Peter's Vicarage, 66 Aske Road, Redcar TS10 2BP* Tel (01642) 490700

WEIGHTMAN, Miss Andrea Frances. b 66. Sheff Univ BA87. Ridley Hall Cam 00. **d** 03. C Handforth *Ches* from 03. *61 Pickmere Road, Handforth, Wilmslow SK9 3TB* Tel (01625) 526207 Mobile 07974-946668

WEIL, Thomas James. b 53. K Coll Lon BSc74 PhD79 AKC74. S Tr Scheme 97. **d** 97 **p** 99. NSM Stoughton *Guildf* from 97. *17 Lyons Drive, Guildford GU2 9YP* Tel (01483) 234535

WEIR, Graham Francis. b 52. GSM LASI. N Ord Course 88. **d** 91 **p** 92. NSM High Crompton *Man* 91-92; NSM Heyside 92-94; Asst Chapl Bolton Hosps NHS Trust 94-96; Chapl from 96. *The Chaplain's Office, Royal Bolton Hospital, Minerva Road, Farnworth, Bolton BL4 0JR* Tel (01204) 390770 *or* 390390 E-mail chaplain@boltonh-tr.nwest.nhs.uk

WEIR, John Michael Vasavour. b 48. K Coll Lon BD72 AKC72 MA00. **d** 73 **p** 74. C Hatfield Hyde *St Alb* 73-76; C Watford St Mich 76-79; Asst Chapl Oslo St Edm *Eur* 80-81; V Bethnal Green St Pet w St Thos *Lon* from 81; Chapl Qu Eliz Hosp for Children Lon 81-98; Chapl Team Ldr Toc H from 01. *St Peter's Vicarage, St Peter's Close, London E2 7AE* Tel (020) 7739 2717 E-mail jweir91488@aol.com

WEIR, John William Moon. b 36. St Luke's Coll Ex CertEd69 Ex Univ BEd76. SW Minl Tr Course 82. **d** 85 **p** 86. NSM Meavy, Sheepstor and Walkhampton *Ex* 85-87; NSM Yelverton, Meavy, Sheepstor and Walkhampton from 87; Hd Master Princetown Primary Sch 86-94; Sub-Chapl HM Pris Dartmoor 86-94. *Goblin's Green, Dousland, Yelverton PL20 6ND* Tel (01822) 852671

WEIR, William Daniel Niall. b 57. UEA BA79. Ripon Coll Cuddesdon 80. **d** 83 **p** 84. C Chelsea St Luke *Lon* 83-87; PV Westmr Abbey 85-89; C Poplar *Lon* 87-88; TV 88-93; P-in-c Forest Gate Em w Upton Cross *Chelmsf* 93-97; V 97-99; Asst Chapl Southn Univ Hosps NHS Trust 99-00; Trust Chapl 00-03; R W Hackney St Barn *Lon* from 03. *The Rectory, 306 Amhurst Road, London N16 7UE* Tel (020) 7254 3235 E-mail niall.weir@bigfoot.com

WELANDER, Canon David Charles St Vincent. b 25. FSA. Lon Coll of Div BD47 ALCD47. **d** 48 **p** 49. C Heigham H Trin *Nor* 48-51; Tutor Oak Hill Th Coll 51-52; Chapl and Tutor Lon Coll of Div 52-56; V Iver *Ox* 56-63; V Cheltenham Ch Ch *Glouc* 63-75; RD Cheltenham 73-75; Can Res Glouc Cathl 75-91; rtd 91; Perm to Offic *Glouc* 91-98; Perm to Offic *Bris* from 91. *Willow Cottage, 1 Sandpits Lane, Sherston Magna, Malmesbury SN16 0NN* Tel (01666) 840180

WELBOURN, David Anthony. b 41. K Coll Lon BD63 AKC63 Sunderland Poly DMS77. St Boniface Warminster 63. **d** 64 **p** 65. C Stockton St Chad *Dur* 64-67; C S Westoe 69-74; Ind Chapl 69-80; Ind Chapl *Nor* 80-90; Ind and Commerce Officer *Guildf* from 90. *81 Collingwood Crescent, Guildford GU1 2NU* Tel (01483) 825541 Fax to telephone E-mail david@dwelbourn.freeserve.co.uk

WELBY, Canon Justin Portal. b 56. Trin Coll Cam BA78 MA90 St Jo Coll Dur BA91 Dip Minl Studies 92 MACT84. Cranmer Hall Dur 89. **d** 92 **p** 93. C Chilvers Coton w Astley *Cov* 92-95; R Southam 95-02; V Ufton 98-02; RD Southam 97-99; Can Res Cov Cathl from 02; Co-Dir Internat Min from 02. *35 Asthill Grove, Coventry CV3 6HN* Tel (024) 7650 5426 *or* 7626 7073 E-mail jwelby@coventrycathedral.org.uk

WELBY, Peter Edlin Brown. b 34. Open Univ BA75. St Jo Coll Dur 75. **d** 77 **p** 78. C Auckland St Andr and St Anne *Dur* 77-79; C S Westoe 79-81; V Tudhoe 81-93; R Croxdale and Tudhoe 93-99; rtd 99. *Blyth House, 9 Rhodes Terrace, Nevilles Cross, Durham DH1 4JW* Tel 0191-384 8295

WELBY, Richard Alexander Lyon (Alex). b 58. St Jo Coll Nottm BTh81 LTh Leeds Univ MA93. Ridley Hall Cam 83. **d** 84 **p** 85. C Stoke Bishop *Bris* 84-88; V Bowling St Steph *Bradf* 88-95; P-in-c Hatherleigh, Meeth, Exbourne and Jacobstowe *Ex* from 95. *The Rectory, Hatherleigh, Okehampton EX20 3JY* Tel (01837) 810314 Fax to telephone E-mail alex.welby@virgin.net

WELCH, David John. b 52. NTMTC 98. **d** 01 **p** 02. C Walthamstow *Chelmsf* from 01. *9 Church End, London E17 9RJ* Tel (020) 8509 3746 E-mail dwelch@fish.co.uk

WELCH, Derek. b 27. Keble Coll Ox BA51 MA57. Coll of Resurr Mirfield 51. **d** 53 **p** 54. C Middlesbrough St Jo the Ev *York* 53-58; C Oswaldtwistle Immanuel *Blackb* 58-59; V Accrington St Andr 59-65; V Salesbury 66-72; V Heyhouses on Sea 73-92; rtd 92; Perm to Offic *Blackb* from 92. *76 St Thomas's Road, Lytham St Annes FY8 1JR* Tel (01253) 781469

WELCH, Francis Hugh. b 16. Lon Univ BD67. S'wark Ord Course 67. **d** 70 **p** 71. Lic to Offic *St Alb* 70-71; C St Alb St Steph 71-75; P-in-c 75-80; Chapl St Alb City Hosp 80-90; Perm to Offic *Lon* 80-90; rtd 81; Perm to Offic *St Alb* 80-81 and 90-93; Hon C St Alb St Pet 81-89; Hon C St Alb St Mich 89-90; Perm to Offic *St D* from 93. *Bryntelor, Sarnau, Llandysul SA44 6QN* Tel (01239) 654573

WELCH, Gordon Joseph. b 47. Man Univ BSc68 PhD72. N Ord Course 84. **d** 87 **p** 88. NSM Upton Ascension *Ches* 87-98; Lic to Offic 99-00; NSM Backford and Capenhurst 00-02; NSM Ellesmere Port from 02; Hon Chapl ATC from 02. *6 St James's Avenue, Chester CH2 1NA* Tel (01244) 382196

WELCH, Canon Grant Keith. b 40. AKC63. **d** 64 **p** 65. C Nottingham St Mary *S'well* 64-68; V Cinderhill 68-73; Master St Jo Hosp Weston Favell 73-88; R Weston Favell *Pet* 73-88; Can Pet Cathl 83-88; P-in-c Gt Houghton 84-85; V Wymondham *Nor* 88; C Loughton St Jo *Chelmsf* 89-92; TR from 92; AD Epping Forest from 00. *The Rectory, Church Lane, Loughton IG10 1PD* Tel (020) 8508 1224

WELCH, Harold Gerald. b 16. St Cath Soc Ox BA48 MA53. Wycliffe Hall Ox 48. **d** 50 **p** 51. C Ipswich St Jo *St E* 50-53; V Offton, Nettlestead and Willisham 53-58; V Lozells St Paul *Birm* 58-66; V Austrey 66-83; V Warton 66-83; rtd 83; Perm to Offic *Lich* from 88 and *Birm* 88-00. *2 Clifford Close, Tamworth B77 2DD* Tel (01827) 53678

WELCH, Ian Michael. b 59. Warwick Univ BA81 Connecticut Univ MA84. Ripon Coll Cuddesdon 00. **d** 02 **p** 03. C Lee St Aug *S'wark* from 02. *38 Marvels Lane, London SE12 9PE* Tel (020) 8857 4810

WELCH, John Harry. b 52. Oak Hill Th Coll 85. **d** 87 **p** 88. C Parr *Liv* 87-90; V W Derby St Luke 90-00; V Eccleston Park from 00. *St James's Vicarage, 159A St Helen's Road, Prescot L34 2QB* Tel 0151-426 6421

WELCH, Canon Michael Robin. b 33. MBE81. St Chad's Coll Dur BSc55. Wells Th Coll 57. **d** 59 **p** 60. C S Shields St Hilda *Dur* 59-63; CF (R of O) 61-88; Warden and Tr Officer Dioc Youth Cen *Newc* 63-68; Soc and Ind Adv Portsm 69-96; V Portsea All SS 72-85; V Swanmore St Barn 85-96; RD Bishop's Waltham 88-93; Hon Can Portsm Cathl 92-96; rtd 96; Perm to Offic *Sarum* from 96. *Southwell, Church Street, Mere, Warminster BA12 6LS* Tel (01747) 860047

WELCH, Mrs Pamela Jean. b 47. Girton Coll Cam MA76 K Coll Lon BD79 AKC79. Qu Coll Birm 79. **dss** 80 **d** 87. Tottenham H Trin *Lon* 80-84; Asst Chapl Bryanston Sch 84-87; Perm to Offic *Chich* 87-94. *40 Maidenhead Lane, Borrowdale, Harare, Zimbabwe*

WELCH, Paul Baxter. b 47. Lanc Univ BEd74 MA75. St Alb Minl Tr Scheme 80. **d** 83 **p** 84. NSM Heath and Reach *St Alb* 83-84; Bp's Sch Adv *Win* 84-89; P-in-c Clungunford w Clunbury and Clunton, Bedstone etc *Heref* 89-93; V Wellingborough All SS *Pet* 93-01; R Pulborough *Chich* from 01. *The Rectory, 2 London Road, Pulborough RH20 1AP* Tel (01798) 875773 E-mail paul.welch@virgin.net

WELCH, Mrs Sally Ann. b 62. Pemb Coll Ox MA88. St Alb and Ox Min Course 96. **d** 99 **p** 00. NSM Abingdon *Ox* 99-01; P-in-c Kintbury w Avington from 01. *The Vicarage, Elizabeth Gardens, Kintbury, Hungerford RG17 9TB* Tel (01488) 658243 Mobile 07974-439630 E-mail sally.welch@virgin.net

WELCH, Stephan John. b 50. Hull Univ BA74 Lon Univ MTh98. Qu Coll Birm DipTh76. **d** 77 **p** 78. C Waltham Cross *St Alb* 77-80; P-in-c Reculver *Cant* 80-86; P-in-c Herne Bay St Bart 82-86; V Reculver and Herne Bay St Bart 86-92; V Hurley and Stubbings *Ox* 92-00; P-in-c Hammersmith St Pet *Lon* from 00; AD Hammersmith and Fulham from 01. *17 Ravenscourt Road, London W6 0UH* Tel (020) 8741 4848

WELCHMAN, Richard Neville de Beaufort. b 11. St Pet Hall Ox BA33 DipTh34 MA37. Wycliffe Hall Ox 33. **d** 34 **p** 35. C Plymouth St Andr *Ex* 34-40; CF 40-45; P-in-c Yelverton *Ex* 45-54; R Lifton 54-62; R Kelly w Bradstone 59-62; V Pinhoe 62-76; rtd 77; Lic to Offic *Ex* 77-95; Perm to Offic from 95. *8 Culvert Road, Stoke Canon, Exeter EX5 4BD* Tel (01392) 841503

WELDON, William Ernest. b 41. TCD BA62 MA66. **d** 64 **p** 65. C Belfast Trin Coll Miss *Conn* 64-67; C Carnmoney 67-71; Chapl RN 71-96; QHC 93-96; Hon C Holbeton *Ex* 96-01; Perm to Offic from 01. *4 Burrow Court, Tiverton EX16 4PS* Tel (01884) 855227

WELHAM, Clive Richard. b 54. **d** 80 **p** 81. C Bellingham St Dunstan *S'wark* 80-84; Chapl Goldsmiths' Coll Lon 84-95; V Plumstead Ascension from 95. *The Ascension Vicarage, Thornhill Avenue, London SE18 2HS* Tel (020) 8854 3395

WELLER, David Christopher. b 60. UWIST BSc83. St Jo Coll Nottm MA94. **d** 96 **p** 97. C Wednesfield Heath *Lich* 96-99; TV Glascote and Stonydelph from 99. *The Vicarage, 86 Bamford Street, Glascote, Tamworth B77 2AS* Tel (01827) 62612 E-mail david@weller220.freeserve.co.uk

WELLER, John Christopher. b 25. St Pet Hall Ox BA49 MA52 Nottm Univ BD57. Qu Coll Birm 50. **d** 51 **p** 52. C Nottingham All SS *S'well* 51-54; C-in-c Porchester St Jas CD 54-58; S Rhodesia 58-64; Zambia 64-71; V W Heath *Birm* 71-81; Warden and Chapl Resthaven Home Stroud 81-84; P-in-c Duddeston 84-85; Zimbabwe 85-90; Can Harare 87-90; rtd 90; P-in-c Ward End *Birm* 96-97; Perm to Offic from 97. *141 Yardley Fields Road, Birmingham B33 8RP* Tel 0121-784 0540

WELLER, Richard Morton. b 33. Selw Coll Cam BA57 MA61. Wells Th Coll 61. **d** 63 **p** 64. C Stockingford *Cov* 63-66; C Pontefract St Giles *Wakef* 66-68; C-in-c Stockton St Jas CD *Dur* 68-74; V E Ardsley *Wakef* 74-83; V Heckmondwike 83-91; V

Birstall 91-96; RD Birstall 92-96; V Gawber 96-01; rtd 01. *14 Callis Way, Penistone, Sheffield S36 6UH* Tel (01226) 379760

WELLER (née SPENCE), Susan Karen. b 65. Leeds Univ BSc86 Liv Univ PhD89. Wycliffe Hall Ox BA95 DipMin96. **d** 96 **p** 97. C Caverswall and Weston Coyney w Dilhorne *Lich* 96-00; C Wilnecote from 00; Dioc Adv for Women in Min from 00. *The Vicarage, 86 Bamford Street, Glascote, Tamworth B77 2AS* Tel (01827) 62612 or (01782)) 596783

WELLING, Anthony Wyndham. b 29. Ely Th Coll 55. **d** 58 **p** 83. C Coppenhall St Paul *Ches* 58-60; Lic to Offic *Ox* 82; Hon C Cookham from 83. *Broadway Barn, High Street, Ripley, Woking GU23 6AQ* Tel (01483) 225384

WELLINGTON, Bishop of. *See* BROWN, The Rt Revd Thomas John

WELLINGTON, Canon James Frederick. b 51. Leic Univ LLB72 Fitzw Coll Cam BA76. Ridley Hall Cam 74. **d** 77 **p** 78. C Mill Hill Jo Keble Ch *Lon* 77-80; C Wood Green St Mich 80-82; C Wood Green St Mich w Bounds Green St Gabr etc 82-83; V Stocking Farm *Leic* 83-90; V Gt Glen, Stretton Magna and Wistow etc 90-98; Warden of Readers 91-97; Hon Can Leic Cathl from 94; RD Gartree II 96-98; TR Syston from 98; RD Goscote from 00. *The Rectory, Upper Church Street, Syston, Leicester LE7 1HR* Tel 0116-260 8276 E-mail jhcwelli@leicester.anglican.org

WELLS, Adrian Mosedale. b 61. SW Minl Tr Course DTPS99. **d** 99 **p** 00. NSM Kingskerswell w Coffinswell *Ex* from 99. *1 St Bartholomew Way, Ogwell, Newton Abbot TQ12 6YW* Tel (01626) 331147 E-mail a.s.well@ic24.net

WELLS, Andrew Stuart. b 48. St Jo Coll Dur BA71. Cranmer Hall Dur DipTh75. **d** 74 **p** 75. C Walmsley *Man* 74-77; C Failsworth H Family 77-79; R Openshaw 79-90; V Hindsford 90-98. *1 Henry Street, Haslington, Crewe CW1 5PS* Tel (01270) 585303

WELLS, The Ven Anthony Martin Giffard. b 42. St Jo Coll Nottm 72. **d** 74 **p** 75. C Orpington Ch *Roch* 74-78; P-in-c Odell *St Alb* 78-82; R 82-86; P-in-c Pavenham 78-82; V 82-86; RD Sharnbrook 81-86; R Angmering *Chich* 86-98; RD Arundel and Bognor 93-98; Chapl Paris St Mich *Eur* from 98; Adn France from 02. *11 bis rue de Surene, 75008 Paris, France* Tel (0033) (1) 42 66 10 08 or 47 42 70 88 Fax 47 42 74 75 E-mail stmichaelsparis@free.fr

WELLS, Antony Ernest. b 36. Oak Hill Th Coll 58. **d** 61 **p** 62. C Bethnal Green St Jas Less *Lon* 61-64; SAMS Paraguay 64-69; V Kirkdale St Athanasius *Liv* 69-73; SAMS Argentina 73-75; V Warfield *Ox* 75-81; V Fairfield *Liv* 81-83; C Rainhill 83-85; TV Cheltenham St Mark *Glouc* 85-89; P-in-c Forest of Dean Ch Ch w English Bicknor 89-95; rtd 97; Assoc Min Pinhoe and Broadclyst *Ex* from 02. *The Vicarage, Broadclyst, Exeter EX5 3EW* Tel (01392) 461280

WELLS, Miss Cecilia Isabel. b 24. Bedf Coll Lon BA45. St Mich Ho Ox 56. **dss** 62 **d** 87. Chester le Street *Dur* 74-84; rtd 84; Perm to Offic *Ches* from 84. *12 Rectory Close, Nantwich CW5 5SW* Tel (01270) 627258

WELLS, Charles Francis. b 39. Oak Hill Th Coll DipHE. **d** 85 **p** 86. C Southend St Sav Westcliff *Chelmsf* 85-89; P-in-c E and W Horndon w Lt Warley 89-96; V E and W Horndon w Lt Warley and Childerditch 96-97; P-in-c Tillingham from 97. *Tillingham Vicarage, 6 Bakery Close, Southminster CM0 7TW* Tel (01621) 778017

WELLS, David. *See* WELLS, Canon William David Sandford

WELLS, David. b 63. **d** 00 **p** 01. C Sprowston w Beeston *Nor* from 00; P-in-c Drayton w Felthorpe from 03. *The Rectory, 46 School Road, Drayton, Norwich NR8 6EF* Tel (01603) 755124 E-mail david.wells@btinternet.com

WELLS, David Henry Nugent. b 20. St Chad's Coll Dur BA42 MA46 DipTh47. **d** 47 **p** 48. C Wednesbury St Paul Wood Green *Lich* 47-48; C Rugeley 48-50; C Hanley All SS 50-53; R Leigh 53-57; R Ashley 57-64; V Hales 57-64; V Alrewas 64-73; V Wychnor 64-73; R Upton Magna 73-81; V Withington 73-81; P-in-c Uffington 81; R Uffington, Upton Magna and Withington 81-85; rtd 85; Perm to Offic *Lich* 85-00. *13 Belvidere Avenue, Shrewsbury SY2 5PF* Tel (01743) 365822

WELLS, Canon Edward Arthur. b 23. MBE97. SRN. Oak Hill Th Coll. **d** 57 **p** 58. C Wednesfield Heath *Lich* 57-60; R Mettingham w Ilketshall St John *St E* 60-62; V Sproughton w Burstall 62-74; V Ipswich St Nic 74-80; Hon Can St E Cathl 80-88; Chapl Ipswich Hosp 80-90; rtd 88; Perm to Offic *St E* from 88. *74 Christchurch Street, Ipswich IP4 2DH* Tel (01473) 254046

WELLS, George Reginald. b 11. K Coll Cam BA33. Cuddesdon Coll 33. **d** 34 **p** 35. C Penistone w Midhope *Wakef* 34-37; India 38-61; V Hagbourne *Ox* 61-74; P-in-c Gt Coxwell 74-80; P-in-c Buscot 74-80; P-in-c Coleshill 74-80; P-in-c Eaton Hastings 74-80; rtd 80; Perm to Offic *Glas* from 80. *8 Greystone Avenue, Dumfries DG1 1PE* Tel (01387) 68294

WELLS, Jeremy Stephen. b 47. Nottm Univ BA69 Univ of Wales (Cardiff) DPS87 UWE MSc97. Chich Th Coll 72. **d** 73 **p** 74. C S Yardley St Mich *Birm* 73-76; C St Marychurch *Ex* 76-78; P-in-c Bridgwater H Trin *B & W* 78-82; P-in-c Brent Knoll 82-84; P-in-c E Brent w Lympsham 82-84; R Brent Knoll, E Brent and Lympsham 84-99. *Address temp unknown*

WELLS, Jo Bailey. b 65. CCC Cam BA87 MA90 Minnesota Univ MA90 St Jo Coll Dur BA92 Dip Minl Studies 93 PhD97. Cranmer Hall Dur. **d** 95 **p** 96. Chapl Clare Coll Cam 95-98; Dean 98-01; Perm to Offic *Nor* from 99; Tutor Ridley Hall Cam from 01. *Ridley Hall, Cambridge CB3 9HG* Tel (01223) 741078 E-mail jbw21@cam.ac.uk

WELLS, John Michael. b 35. Mert Coll Ox BA58 MA61. Westcott Ho Cam 60. **d** 62 **p** 63. C Hornchurch St Andr *Chelmsf* 62-64; C Barking St Marg 64-66; C Wanstead H Trin Hermon Hill 66-69; V Elm Park St Nic Hornchurch 69-76; Offg Chapl RAF 69-76; R Wakes Colne w Chappel *Chelmsf* 76-79; Project Officer Cathl Cen for Research and Tr 79-81; Hon Chapl Chelmsf Cathl 79-81; Area Sec CMS *Chelmsf* and *Ely* 81-88; E Cen Co-ord 85-91; Area Sec *Chelmsf* and *St E* 88-91; Public Preacher *Chelmsf* 82-91; V Hanging Heaton *Wakef* 92-96; rtd 00; Perm to Offic *Chelmsf* from 00. *2 Clarkesmead, Tiptree, Colchester CO5 0BX* Tel (01621) 819899

WELLS, John Rowse David. b 27. Kelham Th Coll 53. **d** 57 **p** 58. SSM from 57; Lic to Offic *S'well* 57-59; Australia 59-65 and from 97; Tutor St Mich Th Coll 61-65; Lesotho 65-96; R Mantsonyane St Jas 67-77; Can SS Mary and Jas Cathl Maseru 77-96; Adn Cen Lesotho 80-95. *St Michael's Priory, 75 Watsons Road, Diggers Rest, Vic, Australia 3427* Tel (0061) (3) 9740 1618 Fax 9740 0007 E-mail ssm.melbourne@bigpond.com

WELLS, Lydia Margaret. b 50. St Aid Coll Dur BA72 Sheff Univ MPhil92 Leeds Univ MA00. N Ord Course 97. **d** 00 **p** 01. C Adwick-le-Street w Skelbrooke *Sheff* 00-03; V Doncaster Intake from 03. *The Vicarage, Kingston Road, Intake, Doncaster DN2 6LS* Tel (01302) 343119 Mobile 07977-740813 E-mail lydwells@tesco.net

WELLS, Mark Wynne-Eyton. b 20. Peterho Cam BA48 MA54. Westcott Ho Cam 48. **d** 50 **p** 51. C Heene *Chich* 50-53; C Sullington 53-57; R Slinfold 57-59; R Rhodesia 59-62; V Stoke by Nayland w Leavenheath *St E* 62-88; RD Hadleigh 71-76 and 85-86; rtd 88; Perm to Offic *Nor* from 88. *Red House, The Street, Great Snoring, Fakenham NR21 0AH* Tel (01328) 820641

WELLS, Michael John. b 46. Solicitor 74 Univ Coll Ox BA68 MA73. S Dios Minl Tr Scheme 92. **d** 95 **p** 96. NSM Brighton St Pet w Chpl Royal *Chich* 95-98; Sen C from 99; NSM Brighton St Bart 98-99. *35 Park Crescent, Brighton BN2 3HB* Tel (01273) 600735

WELLS, Nicholas Anthony. b 60. Cranmer Hall Dur 88. **d** 91 **p** 92. C Accrington St Jo w Huncoat *Blackb* 91-94; C Douglas St Geo and St Barn *S & M* 94-95; C Douglas All SS and St Thos 95-97; V Onchan from 97. *The Vicarage, Church Road, Onchan, Isle of Man IM3 1BF* Tel (01624) 675797 E-mail naw@mcb.net

WELLS, Peter Robert. b 59. Wilson Carlile Coll 78 Sarum & Wells Th Coll 87. **d** 89 **p** 90. CA from 81; C Mortlake w E Sheen *S'wark* 89-93; Dir St Marylebone Healing and Counselling Cen 93-97; TV N Lambeth *S'wark* 97-00; Chapl Trin Hospice Lon from 97. *3 The Chase, London SW4 0NP* Tel (020) 7787 1000

WELLS, Philip Anthony. b 57. BA MPhil. Coll of Resurr Mirfield. **d** 84 **p** 85. C Wylde Green *Birm* 84-87; Chapl and Succ Birm Cathl 87-91; Bp's Dom Chapl 91-97; V Polesworth from 97. *The Vicarage, High Street, Polesworth, Tamworth B78 1DU* Tel (01827) 892340 E-mail polesworthabbey@aol.com

WELLS, Richard John. b 46. St Mich Coll Llan DipTh70 Cuddesdon Coll 70. **d** 71 **p** 72. C Kingston upon Hull St Alb *York* 71-75; C Addlestone *Guildf* 75-80; V Weston 80-88; V Milford 88-96; Chapl Milford Hosp Godalming 88-96; R Westbourne *Chich* from 96. *The New Rectory, Westbourne Road, Emsworth PO10 8UL* Tel (01243) 372867

WELLS, Robert Crosby. b 28. St Jo Coll Dur BA52. **d** 54 **p** 55. C S Shore H Trin *Blackb* 54-59; C-in-c Lang Ho 59-69; V Ribby w Wrea 69-93; rtd 93; Perm to Offic *Blackb* from 93. *4 Myra Road, Fairhaven, Lytham St Annes FY8 1EB* Tel (01253) 739851

WELLS, The Ven Roderick John. b 36. Dur Univ BA63 Hull Univ MA85. Cuddesdon Coll 63. **d** 65 **p** 66. C Lambeth St Mary the Less *S'wark* 65-68; P-in-c 68-71; R Skegness *Linc* 71-77; P-in-c Winthorpe 77; R Skegness and Winthorpe 77-78; TR Gt and Lt Coates w Bradley 78-89; RD Grimsby and Cleethorpes 83-89; Can and Preb Linc Cathl 86-01; Adn Stow 89-01; V Hackthorn w Cold Hanworth 89-93; P-in-c N w S Carlton 89-93; rtd 01; Perm to Offic *Linc* and *Pet* from 01. *2 Alsthorpe Road, Oakham LE15 6FD* Tel (01572) 756532 E-mail wells1@wells1.netlineuk.net

WELLS, Mrs Sally Ursula. b 40. St Mark's Coll Canberra BTh93 Ripon Coll Cuddesdon 96. **d** 97 **p** 98. Asst Chapl Vienna *Eur* 97-02; Perm to Offic from 02. *Fugbachgasse 12/19, A-1020 Vienna, Austria* Tel (0043) (1) 406 6354 Fax as telephone E-mail wellsvienna@nusurf.at

WELLS, Samuel Martin Bailey. b 65. Mert Coll Ox BA87 MA95 Edin Univ BD91 Dur Univ PhD96. Edin Th Coll 88. **d** 91 **p** 92. C Wallsend St Luke *Newc* 91-95; C Cherry Hinton St Andr *Ely* 95-97; C Teversham 95-97; P-in-c Earlham St Eliz *Nor* 97-03; RD Nor S 99-03; P-in-c Cambridge St Mark *Ely* from 03. *St Mark's Vicarage, Barton Road, Cambridge CB3 9JZ* Tel (01223) 363339 E-mail samwells@bigfoot.com

WELLS, Stephen Glossop. b 22. CCC Ox BA48 MA48. Westcott Ho Cam 48. **d** 50 **p** 51. C Poplar All SS w St Frideswide *Lon* 50-56; R Saltford *B & W* 56-80; P-in-c Corston w Newton St Loe 76-80; RD Chew Magna 80-85; R Saltford w Corston and Newton St Loe 80-87; TV Wellington and Distr 87-90; Preb Wells Cathl 84-90; rtd 90; Perm to Offic *St Alb* from 90. *57 Meadow Road, Berkhamsted HP4 1JL* Tel (01442) 870981

WELLS, Terry Roy John. b 45. EAMTC 89. **d** 92 **p** 93. C Martlesham w Brightwell *St E* 92-95; R Higham, Holton St Mary, Raydon and Stratford 95-00; TV Walton and Trimley from 00. *The Vicarage, Church Lane, Trimley St Martin, Felixstowe IP11 0SW* Tel (01394) 286388 E-mail terry.wells@tesco.net

WELLS, Canon William David Sandford. b 41. JP. Oriel Coll Ox BA64 MA66. Ridley Hall Cam 63. **d** 65 **p** 66. C Gt Malvern St Mary *Worc* 65-70; V Crowle 70-84; P-in-c Himbleton w Huddington 78-84; V E Bowbrook 84-89; Hon Can Worc Cathl from 84; RD Droitwich 84-96; R Bowbrook S from 89. *The Vicarage, Church Road, Crowle, Worcester WR7 4AT* Tel (01905) 381617 Fax 08701-623981 E-mail david@sandfordwells.freeserve.co.uk

WELLS, Archdeacon of. *See* ACWORTH, The Ven Richard Foote

WELLS, Dean of. *Vacant*

WELSBY, George Andrew. b 61. St Martin's Coll Lanc BA82 Leeds Univ BA98. Coll of Resurr Mirfield 96. **d** 98 **p** 99. C W Derby St Jo *Liv* 98-02; V Nuneaton St Mary *Cov* from 02. *St Mary's Abbey Vicarage, 99 Bottrill Street, Nuneaton CV11 5JB* Tel (024) 7638 2936

WELSH, Angus Alexander. b 30. Trin Coll Cam BA54 MA59 St Jo Coll Dur DipTh56. **d** 56 **p** 57. C Jesmond Clayton Memorial *Newc* 56-60; C Fenham St Jas and St Basil 60-62; V Bacup St Jo *Man* 62-68; Tristan da Cunha 68-71; St Vincent 72-78; R Heysham *Blackb* 78-88; V Blackb St Steph 88-96; rtd 96; Perm to Offic *Newc* from 96. *23 Low Stobhill, Morpeth NE61 2SF* Tel (01670) 513261

WELSH, Jennifer Ann. b 48. Univ Coll Lon BA. **d** 81 **p** 98. NSM Newport St Matt *Mon* 81-85; NSM Risca from 85. *470 Caerleon Road, Newport NP9 7LW* Tel (01633) 258287

WELSH, Jennifer Lee. b 59. Calgary Univ BSc81. Cam Episc Div Sch (USA) MDiv87. **d** 87 **p** 88. Canada 87-89; Asst Chapl HM Pris Linc 89-94; Perm to Offic *Win* 94-02. *The Vicarage, 21 Vincent Square, London SW1P 2NA* Tel (020) 7834 8981

WELSH, Miss Mary Elizabeth. b 22. St Hilda's Coll Ox BA44 MA48 Lon Univ DipEd45 BD50. Lambeth STh64. **dss** 68 **d** 87 **p** 94. Ex St Mark *Ex* 70-82; Lic to Offic 82-85; Yatton Moor *B & W* 85-87; Perm to Offic 87-01. *26 Rectory Way, Yatton, Bristol BS49 4JF* Tel (01934) 833329

WELSH, Maxwell Wilfred. b 29. Bp's Coll Calcutta 55. **d** 58 **p** 59. India 58-72; C Cannock *Lich* 73-76; C Wednesfield 76-79; V Milton 79-86; V Croxton w Broughton and Adbaston 86-00; rtd 00; Perm to Offic *Lich* from 01. *24 Churchfield Road, Eccleshall, Stafford ST21 6AG* Tel (01785) 850330

WELSH, Philip Peter. b 48. Keble Coll Ox BA69 MA73 Selw Coll Cam BA72 MA76. Westcott Ho Cam 71. **d** 73 **p** 74. C W Dulwich All SS and Em *S'wark* 73-76; C Surbiton St Andr and St Mark 76-79; Lect Steph Coll Delhi India 79-81; V Malden St Jo *S'wark* 81-87; Min Officer *Lich* 87-94; TR Basingstoke *Win* 94-02; V Westmr St Steph w St Jo *Lon* from 02. *The Vicarage, 21 Vincent Square, London SW1P 2NA* Tel (020) 7834 8981

WELSH, Robert Leslie. b 32. Sheff Univ BA54 St Jo Coll Dur DipTh58. **d** 58 **p** 59. C S Westoe *Dur* 58-62; C Darlington St Cuth 62-66; CF (TA) 64-67; V E Rainton *Dur* 66-85; R W Rainton 66-85; R Wolsingham and Thornley 85-97; rtd 97. *12 Lea Green, Wolsingham, Bishop Auckland DL13 3DU* Tel (01388) 528529

WELSMAN, Derek Brian. b 65. Trin Coll Bris DipTS99. **d** 99 **p** 00. C Ash *Guildf* 99-02; V Easebourne *Chich* from 02; Chapl K Edw VII Hosp Midhurst from 02. *The Priory, Easebourne, Midhurst GU29 0AJ* Tel (01730) 812655 or 813441

WELTERS, Mrs Elizabeth Ann. b 49. Bris Univ BSc70 Reading Univ PGCE71. St Alb and Ox Min Course 94. **d** 97 **p** 98. NSM Aylesbury w Bierton and Hulcott *Ox* 97-03; NSM Schorne from 03. *235 Bicester Road, Aylesbury HP19 9BE* Tel (01296) 421200

WELTON, Peter Abercrombie. b 62. Birm Univ BA84. Qu Coll Birm 84. **d** 86 **p** 87. C Walthamstow St Pet *Chelmsf* 86-89; Community Priest 89-93. *Address temp unknown*

WEMYSS, Gary. b 52. St Jo Coll Dur 79. **d** 80 **p** 81. C Blackb St Jas *Blackb* 80-83; C Padiham 83-86; V Stalmine 86-90; P-in-c Egton-cum-Newland and Lowick *Carl* 90-03; V Egton-cum-Newland and Lowick and Colton from 03. *The Vicarage, Penny Bridge, Ulverston LA12 7RQ* Tel (01229) 861285

WENHAM, David. b 45. MA PhD. Ridley Hall Cam. **d** 84 **p** 85. Lic to Offic *Ox* 84-96; Tutor Wycliffe Hall Ox from 84; NSM Shelswell *Ox* from 96. *Wycliffe Hall, 54 Banbury Road, Oxford OX2 6PW* Tel (01865) 274200/5/8 Fax 274215 E-mail david.wenham@wycliffe.ox.ac.uk

WENHAM, Michael Timothy. b 49. Pemb Coll Cam MA75. Wycliffe Hall Ox DipTh85. **d** 86 **p** 87. C Norbury *Ches* 86-89; V Stanford in the Vale w Goosey and Hatford *Ox* from 89. *The*

Vicarage, Stanford in the Vale, Faringdon SN7 8HU Tel (01367) 710267

WENHAM, Peter William. b 47. Pemb Coll Cam MA73 FRCS76 Cam Univ MD85. St Jo Coll Nottm 98. **d** 01 **p** 02. NSM Wollaton Park *S'well* from 01. *31 Sutton Passeys Crescent, Wollaton, Nottingham NG8 1BX* Tel 0115-970 2481

WENSLEY, Beryl Kathleen. *See* YATES, Mrs Beryl Kathleen

✠**WENT, The Rt Revd John Stewart.** b 44. CCC Cam BA66 MA70. Oak Hill Th Coll 67. **d** 69 **p** 70 **c** 96. C Northwood Em *Lon* 69-75; V Margate H Trin *Cant* 75-83; Vice-Prin Wycliffe Hall Ox 83-89; Adn Surrey *Guildf* 89-96; Chmn Dioc Coun for Unity and Miss 90-96; Suff Bp Tewkesbury *Glouc* from 96; Hon Can Glouc Cathl from 96. *Bishop's House, Church Road, Staverton, Cheltenham GL51 0TW* Tel (01242) 680188 Fax 680233 E-mail bshptewk@star.co.uk

WENZEL, Peggy Sylvia. STh. Gilmore Ho. **d** 88 **p** 94. Perm to Offic *Sarum* from 88; rtd 92. *Church Cottage, Church Street, Pewsey SN9 5DL* Tel (01672) 63834

WERNER, David Robert Edmund. b 33. Clifton Th Coll 61. **d** 63 **p** 64. C Holywell *St As* 63-68; C Llanrhos 68-70; R Tedburn St Mary *Ex* 71-91; RD Kenn 80-83; Perm to Offic from 92; rtd 98. *The Old Rectory, Church Lane, Tedburn St Mary, Exeter EX6 6EN* Tel (01647) 61253

WERNER, Canon Donald Kilgour. b 39. Univ of Wales BA61 Linacre Coll Ox BA64 MA67. Wycliffe Hall Ox 61. **d** 64 **p** 65. C Wrexham *St As* 64-69; Chapl Brasted Place Coll Westerham 69-73; Chapl Bris Univ *Bris* 73-76; Hon C Clifton St Paul 73-76; Chapl Keele Univ *Lich* 77-79; P-in-c Keele 77-79; C York St Mich-le-Belfrey *York* 79-83; Dir of Evang 79-83; R Holborn St Geo w H Trin and St Bart *Lon* 83-02; Hon Can Bujumbura from 99; Lect Light Univ from 03; Lic Preacher *Lon* from 02. *7 Minstrel Close, Hucknall NG15 7NZ* Tel 0115-963 1504 Mobile 07971-372147 E-mail wernerdonald@aol.com

WERRELL, Ralph Sidney. b 29. Hull Univ PhD02. Tyndale Hall Bris 54. **d** 56 **p** 57. C Penn Fields *Lich* 56-60; C Champion Hill St Sav *S'wark* 60-61; R Danby Wiske w Yafforth *Ripon* 61-65; P-in-c Hutton Bonville *York* 61-65; R Combs *St E* 65-75; V Bootle Ch Ch *Liv* 75-80; R Scole, Brockdish, Billingford, Thorpe Abbots etc *Nor* 80-83; R Southam w Stockton *Cov* 83-89; R Southam 89-94; rtd 95; Perm to Offic *Birm* and *Cov* from 95; *Lich* from 01. *Sameach, 2A Queens Road, Kenilworth CV8 1JQ* Tel (01926) 858677 Fax as telephone

WERRETT, Olivia Margaret. b 50. Bp Otter Coll 00. **d** 03. NSM Bexhill St Pet *Chich* from 03. *127 Pebsham Lane, Bexhill-on-Sea TN40 2RP* Tel (01424) 214144
E-mail olivia@1950werrett.freeserve.co.uk

WERWATH, Wolfgang Albert Richard Kurt. b 22. Ripon Hall Ox 54. **d** 56 **p** 57. C Hamer *Man* 56-58; C N Reddish 58-59; V Chadderton St Luke 59-67; V Whitfield *Derby* 67-75; V Bretby w Newton Solney 75-88; rtd 88; Perm to Offic *Derby* from 88; *S'well* from 90. *28 D'Ayncourt Walk, Farnsfield, Newark NG22 8DP* Tel (01623) 882635

WESSON, Preb John Graham. b 38. St Pet Coll Ox BA62 DipTh63 MA68. Clifton Th Coll 63. **d** 65 **p** 66. C Southport Ch Ch w St Andr *Liv* 65-68; C Ox St Ebbe w St Pet *Ox* 68-71; Chapl Poly Cen Lon 71-76; C-in-c Edin St Thos *Edin* 76-82; Dir Past Studies Trin Coll Bris 82-86; R Birm St Martin w Bordesley St Andr *Birm* 86-96; RD Birm City 88-95; Hon Can Birm Cathl 91-96; Dir Local Min Development *Lich* 96-98; Team Ldr Min Division 99-03; Team Ldr Bd of Min 99-03; C Lich St Mich w St Mary and Wall 96-03; Preb Lich Cathl 99-03; rtd 03. *11 Gordon Drive, Abingdon OX14 3SW* Tel (01235) 526088
E-mail john.wesson@lichfield.anglican.org

WEST, Alan David. b 61. Southn Univ BTh92 Thames Valley Univ MA97. Aston Tr Scheme 87 Sarum & Wells Th Coll 89. **d** 92 **p** 93. C S'wark St Geo the Martyr w St Jude *S'wark* 92-94; C S'wark St Geo the Martyr w St Alphege & St Jude 95-96; V Boscoppa *Truro* 96-02; Chapl Mt Edgcumbe Hospice from 02. *Mount Edgcumbe Hospice, Porthpean Road, St Austell PL26 6AB* Tel (01726) 65711 Fax 66421

WEST, Andrew Victor. b 59. Wycliffe Hall Ox 87. **d** 90 **p** 91. C Leyland St Andr *Blackb* 90-94; C Blackpool St Jo 94-96; TV Bedworth *Cov* 96-98; Chapl Glos Univ 98-03; C Carl St Jo *Carl* from 03; Chapl St Martin's Coll Carl from 03. *68 Greystone Road, Carlisle CA1 2DG* Tel (01228) 520893

WEST, Arthur. b 20. Linc Th Coll 59. **d** 60 **p** 61. C Cottingham *York* 60-64; V Ruswarp w Sneaton 64-68; V Nether w Upper Poppleton 68-85; RD Ainsty 77-85; rtd 85; Perm to Offic *York* from 85. *8 River View, Linton on Ouse, York YO30 2BJ* Tel (01347) 848463

WEST, Bernard Kenneth. b 31. Linc Th Coll. **d** 67 **p** 68. C E Ham St Geo *Chelmsf* 67-71; Australia from 71; rtd 89. *Lot 33, Mitchell Street, Wooroloo, W Australia 6558* Tel (0061) (8) 9573 1132

WEST, Bryan Edward. b 39. Avery Hill Coll CertEd69 BEd80 Kent Univ MA86. Cant Sch of Min 85. **d** 88 **p** 89. NSM Gravesend H Family w Ifield *Roch* 88-92; C Gravesend St Geo 92-95; NSM Hatcham Park All SS *S'wark* 95-98; Perm to Offic *Chelmsf* 95-98; NSM Ashingdon w S Fambridge 98-01; NSM Stambridge 98-01; NSM Canvey Is from 01; Chapl Southend

Health Care NHS Trust from 99. *St Anne's House, 51 St Anne's Road, Canvey Island SS8 7LS* Tel (01268) 514412
E-mail roadbuilder@fish.co.uk

WEST, Miss Caroline Elisabeth. b 61. RGN84. Wycliffe Hall Ox DipMin95. **d** 95. NSM Eastrop *Win* from 95. *19 Beaulieu Court, Riverdene, Basingstoke RG21 4DQ* Tel (01256) 350389
E-mail caroline.west@stmarys-basingstoke.org.uk

WEST, Mrs Christine Cecily. TCD BA60 MA63 HDipEd61. CITC 91. **d** 94 **p** 95. NSM Bray *D & G* 94-96; NSM Kilternan 96-99; Lic to Offic from 99. *55 Beech Park Road, Foxrock, Dublin 18, Irish Republic* Tel (00353) (1) 289 6374

WEST, Canon Clive. b 35. QUB BD75 Stranmillis Coll TCert57 TCD DBS63 Lon Univ DipTh68. CITC 62. **d** 64 **p** 65. C Lisburn Ch Ch Cathl *Conn* 64-68; Asst Master Lisnagarvey Sec Sch Lisburn 68-70; C Belfast All SS 70-71; I 84-00; Can Belf Cathl 95-00; I Mullabrack w Kilcluney *Arm* 76-84; rtd 00. *16 Stormont Park, Belfast BT4 3GX* Tel (028) 9041 9317

WEST, David Marshall. b 48. St Jo Coll Dur BA70. Qu Coll Birm DipTh72. **d** 73 **p** 74. C Wylde Green *Birm* 73-76; C Wokingham St Paul *Ox* 76-79; V Hurst 79-88; V Maidenhead St Luke 88-95; C Whitley Ch Ch 95-99; P-in-c Reading Ch Ch from 99. *Christ Church Vicarage, 4 Vicarage Road, Reading RG2 7AJ* Tel 0118-987 1250 E-mail revdmwest@hotmail.com

WEST, Derek Elvin. b 47. Hull Univ BA69. Westcott Ho Cam 71. **d** 73 **p** 74. C Walthamstow St Pet *Chelmsf* 73-77; C Chingford SS Pet and Paul 77-80; TV W Slough *Ox* 80-88; Slough Community Chapl 88-95; TV Upton cum Chalvey from 95. *St Peter's Vicarage, Montem Lane, Slough SL1 2QJ* Tel (01753) 520725

WEST, Mrs Elizabeth Maxine. b 47. Liv Univ BA69 Lon Inst of Educn PGCE70 K Coll Lon BA95 AKC. NTMTC. **d** 99 **p** 00. NSM Hornsey H Innocents *Lon* 99-00; NSM Highgate St Mich from 00. *West Villa, Inderwick Road, London N8 9JU* Tel (020) 8348 3042

WEST, Eric Edward. b 32. Leeds Univ BA60. Bps' Coll Cheshunt 63. **d** 64 **p** 65. C Biscot *St Alb* 64-71; V 71-02; rtd 03; Perm to Offic *St Alb* from 03. *134 Brompton Close, Luton LU3 3QU* Tel (01582) 581417

WEST, Eric Robert Glenn. b 55. QUB BA79 Man Univ DipEd80. CITC BTh92. **d** 92 **p** 93. C Enniskillen *Clogh* 92-95; I Lisbellaw 95-00; CF 00-03; I Annagh w Drumgoon, Ashfield etc *K, E & A* from 03. *4 Drumclay Park North, Enniskillen BT74 6ND* Tel 07803-885014 (mobile)

WEST, Gerald Eric. b 18. ACII48. St Deiniol's Hawarden. **d** 80 **p** 81. Hon C Bramhall *Ches* 80-82; C 82-87; rtd 87; Perm to Offic *Ches* from 87. *255 Bramhall Moor Lane, Hazel Grove, Stockport SK7 5JL* Tel 0161-439 3029

WEST, Harold Reginald. b 15. Dur Univ BA43 MA46. Coll of Resurr Mirfield 43. **d** 45 **p** 46. C Tynemouth H Trin W Town *Newc* 45-48; C Sugley 48-55; V Cresswell 55-61; V Newc St Luke 61-82; Perm to Offic from 82; rtd 82. *42 Linden Road, Gosforth, Newcastle upon Tyne NE3 4HB* Tel 0191-284 4291

WEST, Henry Cyrano. b 28. K Coll Lon. **d** 51 **p** 52. C Braunstone *Leic* 51-53; C Wandsworth St Anne *S'wark* 53-55; C Raynes Park St Sav 55-58; CF 58-63; V Sculcoates *York* 63-71; P-in-c Kingston upon Hull St Jude w St Steph 67-71; Lic to Offic *Cov* 71-75; Lic to Offic *Man* 75-87; Hon C Hulme Ascension 87-94; rtd 91; Perm to Offic *Man* from 91. *6 King's Drive, Middleton, Manchester M24 4PB* Tel 0161-643 4410

WEST, Keith. *See* RYDER-WEST, Keith

WEST (formerly WINDIATE), Mrs Mary Elizabeth. b 49. Linc Th Coll 94. **d** 94 **p** 95. C Loughton St Jo *Chelmsf* 94-98; P-in-c Ashingdon w S Fambridge 98-01; P-in-c Stambridge 98-01; TV Canvey Is from 01. *St Anne's House, 51 St Anne's Road, Canvey Island SS8 7LS* Tel (01268) 514412
E-mail maryandbryan@uk.online.co.uk

WEST, Canon Michael Brian. b 39. Bris Univ BSc60. Linc Th Coll 64. **d** 66 **p** 67. C Bp's Hatfield *St Alb* 66-69; Ind Chapl 69-81; Hon Can St Alb 78-81; Sen Ind Chapl *Sheff* 81-01; Hon Can Sheff Cathl 81-01; Perm to Offic from 02. *21 Endcliffe Rise Road, Sheffield S11 8RU* Tel 0114-266 1921

WEST, Canon Michael Frederick. b 50. Trin Coll Ox BA72 MA76 UEA PhD96. Westcott Ho Cam 72. **d** 74 **p** 75. C Wolverhampton *Lich* 74-78; C Hanley H Ev 78-79; TV 79-82; Dioc Youth Officer *St E* 83-88; V Ipswich St Thos 88-95; Prin OLM Scheme from 96; Hon Can St E Cathl from 96. *St Edmundsbury and Ipswich Diocesan Ministry Course, Churchgates House, Cutler Street, Ipswich IP1 1UQ* Tel (01473) 298552 Fax 298501

WEST, Michael John. b 33. Imp Coll Lon BScEng54 ARSM54 CEng60 FIMM68 FEng89 Hon FIMM96. S'wark Ord Course 85. **d** 88 **p** 89. NSM Caterham *S'wark* 88-98; Perm to Offic *Lon* from 96; *Chich* from 97; *S'wark* from 98. *Minstrels, The Causeway, Horsham RH12 1HE* Tel (01403) 263437 Fax 249604
E-mail goodshepherd@btinternet.com

WEST, Michael Oakley. b 31. Open Univ BA97 DipEurHum97. Bris Bapt Coll 53 Wells Th Coll 62. **d** 63 **p** 64. C Swindon Ch Ch *Bris* 63-66; Libya 66-68; R Lydiard Millicent w Lydiard Tregoz *Bris* 68-75; V Breage w Germoe *Truro* 75-82; CMS 82-91; Chapl Tel Aviv 82-89; Chapl Shiplake Coll Henley 91-94; Asst Chapl Bryanston Sch 94-95; Perm to Offic *Eur* 95-97; rtd 96; Perm to

Offic *Lon* 96-97; Lic to Offic Spokane USA from 97. *1932 East 25th Avenue, Spokane, WA 99203, USA*

WEST, Paul Leslie. b 57. OLM course 96. **d** 99 **p** 00. OLM Kinnerley w Melverley and Knockin w Maesbrook *Lich* from 99. *Braddan, Farm Hall, Kinnerley, Oswestry SY10 8EG* Tel (01691) 682600

WEST, Peter Harcourt. b 29. **d** 59 **p** 60. C Histon *Ely* 59-60; C Hampreston *Sarum* 60-61; C Braintree *Chelmsf* 61-63; Perm to Offic from 72; rtd 94. *Westgates, 139 Witham Road, Black Notley, Braintree CM77 8LR* Tel (01376) 323048

WEST, Canon Philip William. b 48. Magd Coll Ox BA70 MA78. St Jo Coll Nottm BA74 DPS75. **d** 75 **p** 76. C Rushden w Newton Bromswold *Pet* 75-79; C Pitsmoor w Ellesmere *Sheff* 79-83; V Attercliffe 83-89; Ind Chapl 85-90; P-in-c Darnall 86-89; V Stannington from 89; P-in-c Sheff St Bart from 02; AD Hallam from 96; Hon Can Sheff Cathl from 01. *The Vicarage, 214 Oldfield Road, Stannington, Sheffield S6 6DY* Tel 0114-234 5586 *or* 232 4490

WEST, Reginald Roy. b 28. St Deiniol's Hawarden 74. **d** 74 **p** 75. C Abergavenny St Mary w Llanwenarth Citra *Mon* 74-77; V Tredegar St Jas 77-96; rtd 96; Lic to Offic *Mon* from 96. *2 Croesonen Park, Abergavenny NP7 6PD* Tel (01873) 857043

WEST, Stephen Peter. b 52. Liv Univ CertEd74. Oak Hill Th Coll 87. **d** 89 **p** 90. C Gateacre *Liv* 89-92; V Liv All So Springwood 92-02; TV Teignmouth, Ideford w Luton, Ashcombe etc *Ex* from 02. *The Vicarage, 3 Moors Park, Bishopsteignton, Teignmouth TQ14 9RH* Tel (01626) 775247

WEST, Thomas Roderic. b 55. DipTh BTh90. TCD Div Sch. **d** 86 **p** 87. C Dromore Cathl *D & D* 86-89; I Carrowdore w Millisle 89-95; I Moira from 95. *1 Main Street, Moira, Craigavon BT67 0LE* Tel (028) 9261 1268

WEST, Timothy Ralph. b 53. Bath Univ BSc75. Ridley Hall Cam 82. **d** 85 **p** 86. C Mildenhall *St E* 85-88; TV Melbury *Sarum* 88-92; TR 92-98; TR Preston w Sutton Poyntz and Osmington w Poxwell from 98. *The Rectory, Sutton Road, Preston, Weymouth DT3 6BX* Tel (01305) 833142 Mobile 07000-785720

WEST AFRICA, Archbishop of. See OKINE, The Most Revd Robert Garshong Allotey

WEST CUMBERLAND, Archdeacon of. See DAVIS, The Ven Alan Norman

WEST HAM, Archdeacon of. See FOX, The Ven Michael John

WEST INDIES, Archbishop of. See GOMEZ, The Most Revd Drexel Wellington

WEST-LINDELL, Stein Erik. b 54. BA. Linc Th Coll 82. **d** 84 **p** 85. C Allington and Maidstone St Pet *Cant* 84-87; R Orlestone w Snave and Ruckinge w Warehorne 87-93; R Byfield w Boddington and Aston le Walls *Pet* 93-99; V Nor Lakenham St Alb and St Mark *Nor* from 99. *St Alban's Vicarage, Eleanor Road, Norwich NR1 2RE* Tel (01603) 621843

WESTALL, Jonathan Mark. b 67. Nottm Univ BSc88 K Coll Lon PGCE93 Dur Univ BA98. **d** 99 **p** 00. C St Helier *S'wark* 99-02; C Reading Greyfriars *Ox* from 02. *93 York Road, Reading RG1 8DU* Tel 0118-957 6436
E-mail jon@westall.clava.co.uk

✠**WESTALL, The Rt Revd Michael Robert.** b 39. Qu Coll Cam BA62 MA66. Cuddesdon Coll 63 Harvard Div Sch 65. **d** 66 **p** 67 **c** 01. C Heref St Martin *Heref* 66-70; India 70-83; Vice Prin Bp's Coll Calcutta 76-79; Prin 79-83; Tanzania 84-92 and from 01; Prin St Mark's Th Coll Dar-es-Salaam 84-92; R Alfrick, Lulsley, Suckley, Leigh and Bransford *Worc* 93-00; Bp SW Tanganyika from 01. *Bishop's House, PO Box 32, Njombe, Tanzania* Tel (00255) (26) 278 2012 Fax 278 2403
E-mail punitha@africaonline.co.tz

WESTBROOK, Canon Colin David. b 36. Oriel Coll Ox BA59. St Steph Ho Ox DipTh60 MA63. **d** 61 **p** 62. C Roath St Martin *Llan* 61-66; C Roath 66-74; V Llantarnam *Mon* 74-79; V Newport St Jo Bapt from 79; Hon Can St Woolos Cathl 88-91; Can St Woolos Cathl from 91; Warden of Ords 91-99. *St John's Vicarage, Oakfield Road, Newport NP20 4LP* Tel (01633) 265581

WESTBROOK (née REED), Mrs Ethel Patricia Ivy. b 42. Bris Univ CertEd63. Cant Sch of Min 80. **dss** 84 **d** 87 **p** 94. Fawkham and Hartley *Roch* 84-85; Asst Dir of Educn 84-86; Cliffe at Hoo w Cooling 85-86; Corby SS Pet and Andr w Gt and Lt Oakley *Pet* 86-90; Par Dn 87-90; Par Dn Roch Pet and 94-99; C Rainham 94-99; V Joydens Wood St Barn from 99; Dioc Chapl Mother's Union from 01. *The Vicarage, 6 Tile Kiln Lane, Bexley DA5 2BD* Tel (01322) 528923 Fax as telephone
E-mail patwestbrook@wipe.fsnet.co.uk

WESTBY, Martyn John. b 61. Leeds Univ BA83. Trin Coll Bris 96. **d** 98 **p** 99. C Drypool *York* 98-01; P-in-c Cherry Burton from 01; Chapl Bp Burton Coll York from 01. *The Rectory, Main Street, Cherry Burton, Beverley HU17 7RF* Tel (01964) 503036

WESTCOTT, James John. b 55. St Jo RC Sem Surrey 76. **d** 81 **p** 82. In RC Ch 81-93; C Westmr St Steph w St Jo *Lon* 93-96; P-in-c Haggerston St Chad 96-01; V from 01. *St Chad's Vicarage, Dunloe Street, London E2 8JR* Tel (020) 7613 2229

WESTERMANN-CHILDS, Miss Emma Jane. b 71. Univ of Wales (Ban) BA93 Ox Univ MTh99. Ripon Coll Cuddesdon 96. **d** 98 **p** 99. C Launceston *Truro* 98-01; P-in-c St Stephen in Brannel from 01. *The Rectory, 70 Fore Road, St Stephen, St Austell PL26 7RL* Tel (01726) 822236
E-mail reverendemma@benedictine.net

WESTERN, Canon Robert Geoffrey. b 37. Man Univ BSc60. Qu Coll Birm DipTh62. **d** 62 **p** 63. C Sedbergh *Bradf* 62-65; PV Linc Cathl *Linc* 65-73; Hd Master Linc Cathl Sch 74-96; Can and Preb Linc Cathl *Linc* 74-96; rtd 97. *2 Guldrey House, Guldrey Lane, Sedbergh LA10 5DS* Tel (01539) 621426

WESTHAVER, George Derrick. b 68. St Mary's Univ Halifax NS BA92. Wycliffe Coll Toronto MDiv98. **d** 97 **p** 98. C Teversham and Cherry Hinton St Andr *Ely* 97-00; TV The Ramseys and Upwood from 00. *The Vicarage, Thatchers Close, Upwood, Ramsey, Huntingdon PE26 2PN* Tel (01487) 814473
E-mail westhaver@classicfm.net

WESTLAKE, Michael Paul. b 34. Ex Coll Ox BA56 MA64. Wells Th Coll 59. **d** 61 **p** 62. C Southmead *Bris* 61-67; V Eastville St Thos 67-74; V Eastville St Thos w St Anne 74-83; P-in-c Easton St Mark 79-83; V Marshfield w Cold Ashton and Tormarton etc 83-01; rtd 01; Perm to Offic *Birm* from 03. *65 Duxford Road, Great Barr, Birmingham B42 2JD* Tel 0121-380 7030

WESTLAKE, Peter Alan Grant. b 19. CMG72 MC43. CCC Ox MA48 Univ of Wales (Ban) BD81 MSc81 FRAS. **d** 81 **p** 82. *53 Church Street, Beaumaris LL58 8AB* Tel (01248) 810114

WESTLAND, Richard Theodore. b 27. LNSM course. **d** 87 **p** 88. OLM Freiston w Butterwick *Linc* 87-97; rtd 97; Perm to Offic *Linc* from 97. *76 Brand End Road, Butterwick, Boston PE22 0JD* Tel (01205) 760572

WESTLEY, Stuart. b 24. Em Coll Cam BA48 MA52 Man Univ DASE84. Wells Th Coll 49. **d** 50 **p** 51. C Prestwich St Marg *Man* 50-53; C Tonge w Alkrington 53-55; C-in-c Oldham St Ambrose 55-58; Lic to Offic *Blackb* 58-70; Chapl Arnold Sch Blackpool 58-66; Asst Chapl Denstone Coll Uttoxeter 70-73; Chapl Ermysted's Gr Sch Skipton 73-85; Hon C Blackpool St Mich *Blackb* 75-77; Perm to Offic *Bradf* 77-78; Lic to Offic 78-85; C Padiham *Blackb* 85-89; rtd 89; Perm to Offic *Blackb* from 89. *20 Crichton Place, Blackpool FY4 1NS* Tel (01253) 347962
E-mail s.westley@amserve.net

WESTMINSTER, Archdeacon of. See HUTT, The Ven David Handley

WESTMINSTER, Dean of. See CARR, The Very Revd Arthur Wesley

WESTMORELAND, Mrs Diane Ruth. b 57. Man Univ BA78. NEOC 95. **d** 98 **p** 99. NSM Tadcaster w Newton Kyme *York* 98-99; C 99-02; P-in-c Stamford Bridge Gp of Par from 02. *The Rectory, 8 Viking Road, Stamford Bridge, York YO41 1BR* Tel (01759) 371353 Mobile 07870-745506
E-mail diane@dianewestmoreland.com

WESTMORLAND AND FURNESS, Archdeacon of. See HOWE, The Ven George Alexander

WESTNEY, Michael Edward William. b 29. Lich Th Coll 64. **d** 65 **p** 66. C Hughenden *Ox* 65-68; C Banbury 68-71; TV Trunch *Nor* 71-78; V Reading St Matt *Ox* 78-83; TV W Slough 83-88; TR 88-94; rtd 94; Perm to Offic *Ox* 97-00. *59 Portland Close, Burnham, Slough SL2 2LT* Tel (01628) 660052

WESTON, Christopher James. b 20. G&C Coll Cam BA46 MA49. Ridley Hall Cam 47. **d** 49 **p** 50. C Neasden cum Kingsbury St Cath *Lon* 49-53; Singapore 53-55; Chapl Cheltenham Coll 56-63; V Clifton St Jas *Sheff* 63-70; P-in-c Stevenage St Nic *St Alb* 70-71; V 71-87; rtd 87; Perm to Offic *Ely* 87-99. *6 Allen Court, Hauxton Road, Trumpington, Cambridge CB2 2LU* Tel (01223) 510926

WESTON, Canon David Wilfrid Valentine. b 37. Lanc Univ PhD93. **d** 67 **p** 68. OSB 60-84; Lic to Offic *Ox* 67-84; Prior Nashdom Abbey 71-74; Abbot 74-84; C Chorley St Pet *Blackb* 84-85; V Pilling 85-89; Bp's Dom Chapl *Carl* 89-94; Can Res Carl Cathl from 94; Lib from 95; Vice-Dean 00. *3 The Abbey, Carlisle CA3 8TZ* Tel (01228) 521834

WESTON, Frederick Victor Henry. b 41. Qu Coll Cam BA63 MA67. St D Coll Lamp LTh65. **d** 65 **p** 66. C Grangetown *Llan* 65-67; C Cwmmer w Abercregan CD 67-69; C Haverhill *St E* 69-74; R Gt and Lt Whelnetham 74-79; Perm to Offic 82-92; Chapl HM Pris Highpoint 92-98. *154 Southgate Street, Bury St Edmunds IP33 2AF*

WESTON, Ivan John. b 45. MBE88. Chich Th Coll 71. **d** 74 **p** 75. C Harlow St Mary Magd *Chelmsf* 74-77; Chapl RAF 77-00; Perm to Offic *Nor* 93-95; *Ely* from 00. *2 The Furlongs, Needingworth, St Ives PE27 4TX* Tel (01480) 462107

WESTON, John Oglivy. b 30. St Pet Coll Ox BA66 MA70. Linc Th Coll 71. **d** 71 **p** 72. Lect Trent (Nottm) Poly 66-82; Hon C Long Clawson and Hose *Leic* 71-82; Hon C Bingham *S'well* 82-85; Lic to Offic 85-91; rtd 91; Perm to Offic *Heref* 91-97. *Mowbray Lodge, Marshbrook, Church Stretton SY6 6QE* Tel (01694) 781288

WESTON, Mrs Judith. b 36. MSR56 Open Univ BA75. St Jo Coll Nottm 84. **dss** 85 **d** 87 **p** 94. Huddersfield H Trin *Wakef* 85-87;

Par Dn 87-91; Par Dn Wakef St Andr and St Mary 91-94; C 94-95; Chapl Huddersfield NHS Trust 95-98; rtd 96; Perm to Offic *Wakef* from 98. *Overcroft, 8A Newland Road, Huddersfield HD5 0QT* Tel (01484) 453591

WESTON, Canon Keith Aitken Astley. b 26. Trin Hall Cam BA51 MA55. Ridley Hall Cam 51. **d** 53 **p** 54. C Weston-super-Mare Ch Ch *B & W* 53-56; C Cheltenham St Mark *Glouc* 56-59; PC Clevedon Ch Ch *B & W* 59-64; R Ox St Ebbe w H Trin and St Pet *Ox* 64-85; RD Ox 71-76; Hon Can Ch Ch 81-85; Dir Post-Ord Tr *Nor* 85-90; Dioc Dir of Ords 85-91; P-in-c Nor St Steph 85-91; Hon Brigade Chapl Norfolk Co Fire Service 90-91; rtd 91; Hon C Thame *Ox* from 91. *18 Moor End Lane, Thame OX9 3BQ* Tel (01844) 215441

WESTON, Neil. b 51. Jes Coll Ox BA73 MA78. Ridley Hall Cam 74. **d** 76 **p** 77. C Ealing St Mary *Lon* 76-80; P-in-c Pertenhall w Swineshead *St Alb* 80-89; P-in-c Dean w Yelden, Melchbourne and Shelton 80-89; R The Stodden Churches 89-91; R Newhaven *Chich* 91-98; Miss to Seamen 91-98; P-in-c Radcliffe-on-Trent and Shelford etc *S'well* from 98. *The Rectory, 2 Vicarage Lane, Radcliffe-on-Trent, Nottingham NG12 2FB* Tel 0115-933 2203 Fax as telephone E-mail neilweston@aol.com

WESTON, Paul David Astley. b 57. Trin Hall Cam BA80 MA83 Westmr Coll Ox MPhil92 K Coll Lon PhD02. Wycliffe Hall Ox 83. **d** 85 **p** 86. C New Malden and Coombe *S'wark* 85-89; Lect Oak Hill Th Coll 89-97; Vice-Prin 97-00; Gen Sec UCCF 00-01; Assoc Lect Ridley Hall Cam 02-03; Tutor from 03; Perm to Offic *Ely* from 01. *31 Thornton Close, Girton, Cambridge CB3 0NF* Tel (01223) 710115 E-mail pdaw2@cam.ac.uk

WESTON, Ralph Edward Norman. b 30. Worc Ord Coll 67. **d** 69 **p** 70. C Harborne St Pet *Birm* 69-71; CF 71-75; Chapl Oswestry Sch 75-85; Chapl Rotherham Distr Gen Hosp 85-95; CF (ACF) 87-95; TV Thorverton, Cadbury, Upton Pyne etc *Ex* 95-99; rtd 95; Perm to Offic *Ex* from 99. *10 Rogers Close, Tiverton EX16 6UW* Tel (01884) 259622 Fax as telephone

WESTON, Stephen John Astley. b 55. Aston Univ BSc77. Ridley Hall Cam 78. **d** 81 **p** 82. C Gt Chesham *Ox* 81-85; C Southport Ch Ch *Liv* 85-87; P-in-c Gayhurst w Ravenstone, Stoke Goldington etc *Ox* 87-91; R 91-96; RD Newport 92-95; V Chipping Norton 96-01; TR from 01; AD Chipping Norton from 02. *The Vicarage, Church Street, Chipping Norton OX7 5NT* Tel (01608) 642688 E-mail revsweston@lineone.net

WESTON, Timothy Bernard Charles. b 48. **d** 03. OLM Watton w Carbrooke and Ovington *Nor* from 03. *The Oaks, Shipham Road, Carbrooke, Thetford IP25 6SX* Tel (01362) 820292

WESTON, Mrs Virginia Anne. b 58. UEA BSc79. Wycliffe Hall Ox 84. **d** 87 **p** 02. Par Dn New Malden and Coombe *S'wark* 87-89; Lic to Offic *Lon* 89-01; Lic to Offic *Ely* from 01; Chapl to People at Work in Cam from 02. *31 Thornton Close, Girton, Cambridge CB3 0NF* Tel (01223) 710115 *or* 276657 E-mail chaplain@htcambridge.org.uk *or* virginiaweston@yahoo.co.uk

WESTWOOD, Canon John Richard. b 55. Clare Coll Cam BA77 MA81 Lambeth DipTh93 MA98. Ripon Coll Cuddesdon 77. **d** 79 **p** 80. C Oakham w Hambleton and Egleton *Pet* 79-81; C Oakham, Hambleton, Egleton, Braunston and Brooke 81-83; V Gt w Lt Harrowden and Orlingbury 83-90; V Wellingborough St Andr 90-99; RD Wellingborough 92-97; Warden of Readers from 95; Can Pet Cathl from 97; R Irthlingborough from 99. *The Rectory, 79 Finedon Road, Irthlingborough, Wellingborough NN9 5TY* Tel (01933) 650278 E-mail john@john-westwood.fsnet.co.uk

WESTWOOD, Peter. b 38. Open Univ BA76. AKC65. **d** 65 **p** 66. C Acomb St Steph *York* 65-68; Chapl HM Youth Cust Cen Onley 69-73; Chapl HM Pris Leic 73-77; Chapl HM Pris Maidstone 77-81; Chapl HM Pris Dur 81-87; Chapl HM Pris Brixton 87-93; Chapl HM Pris Wormwood Scrubs 93-98; Perm to Offic *S'wark* from 98; rtd 99. *St Stephen's Church, College Road, London SE21 7HN* Tel (020) 8693 0082

WESTWOOD, Timothy. b 61. Wolv Poly DMS86 MBA91. WMMTC 95. **d** 98 **p** 99. NSM Sedgley St Mary *Worc* from 98. *5 Deborah Close, Wolverhampton WV2 3HS* Tel (01902) 831078 E-mail twestwood@cableinet.co.uk

WETHERALL, Canon Cecil Edward (Ted). b 29. St Jo Coll Dur 49. **d** 56 **p** 57. C Ipswich St Aug *St E* 56-59; R Hitcham 59-79; P-in-c Brettenham 61-63; P-in-c Kettlebaston 71-91; R Hitcham w Lt Finborough 79-91; Hon Can St E Cathl 83-93; Perm to Offic from 92; P-in-c Preston 85-91; rtd 92; Asst Chapl Athens w Kifissia, Patras, Thessaloniki etc *Eur* 92-96. *Kastraki, Tolo, Nafplio, 21056 Argolis, Greece*

WETHERALL, Nicholas Guy. b 52. Lon Univ BMus73 Ox Univ CertEd75. Chich Th Coll 82. **d** 84 **p** 85. C Cleobury Mortimer w Hopton Wafers *Heref* 84-87; TV Leominster 87-92; V Cuckfield *Chich* from 92; RD Cuckfield from 99. *The Vicarage, Broad Street, Cuckfield, Haywards Heath RH17 5LL* Tel (01444) 454007

WETHERELL, Ms Eileen Joyce. b 44. Westf Coll Lon BSc66. S Dios Minl Tr Scheme 89. **d** 92 **p** 94. Par Dn Southampton Maybush St Pet *Win* 92-94; C 94-96; TV Totton from 96; Dioc Adv for Women's Min from 02. *The Vicarage, Cooks Lane,*

Calmore, Southampton SO4O 2RU Tel (023) 8081 2702 Fax as telephone E-mail eileenwetherell@btinternet.com

WETHERELL, Philip Anthony. b 45. Leic Univ MPhil87. AKC72. **d** 73 **p** 74. C Walthamstow St Sav *Chelmsf* 73-75; Chapl and Tutor Namibia Internat Peace Cen 75-76; C Knighton St Mary Magd *Leic* 76-80; TV Southampton (City Cen) *Win* 80-84; Miss Personnel Sec USPG 84-96; Admin Coun for Educn in World Citizenship 97-98; Development Officer Kaloko Trust UK from 98. *Flat D, 14 Asylum Road, London SE15 2RL* Tel (020) 7732 1601

WETZ, Peter Joseph Patrick. b 37. **d** 62 **p** 62. C Hatfield Hyde *St Alb* 85; C Stevenage St Pet Broadwater 85-87; V Irlam *Man* 87-00; rtd 00. *9 Whitby Avenue, York YO31 0EU* Tel (01904) 422924

WEYMAN, John Derek Henry. b 31. Wells Th Coll 69. **d** 70 **p** 71. C Headley All SS *Guildf* 70-76; V Westcott 76-97; RD Dorking 84-89; rtd 97; Perm to Offic *Truro* from 99. *Kittiwake, Polurrian Cliff, Mullion, Helston TR12 7EW* Tel (01326) 240457

WEYMAN, Canon Richard Darrell George. b 46. Lon Univ BA Bris Univ PhD. Sarum & Wells Th Coll. **d** 84 **p** 85. C Sherborne w Castleton and Lillington *Sarum* 84-88; V Malden St Jo *S'wark* 88-92; P-in-c Marnhull *Sarum* from 92; Dir Post Ord Tr from 92; Can and Preb Sarum Cathl from 99. *The Rectory, Conyers Place, Marnhull, Sturminster Newton DT10 1PZ* Tel (01258) 821134

WEYMONT, Martin Eric. b 48. St Jo Coll Dur BA69 MA74 Fitzw Coll Cam PGCE73 Lon Inst of Educn PhD89 Open Univ BSc96. Westcott Ho Cam 71. **d** 73 **p** 74. C Blackheath *Birm* 73-76; Hon C Willesden St Matt *Lon* 76-77; Hon C Belmont 77-79; P-in-c W Twyford 79-85; NSM Cricklewood St Mich 85-88; Chapl St Pet Colleg Sch Wolv 88-91; Hon C Wolverhampton *Lich* 88-91; NSM Bickershaw *Liv* 91-97; P-in-c Mells w Buckland Dinham, Elm, Whatley etc *B & W* from 97. *The Rectory, Mells, Frome BA11 3PT* Tel (01373) 812320 Fax 813778

WHALE, Desmond Victor. b 35. Bris Sch of Min 81. **d** 84 **p** 85. Lic to Offic *Bris* 84-88; C Parr *Liv* 88-91; R Winfarthing w Shelfanger w Burston w Gissing etc *Nor* 91-00; RD Redenhall 97-99; rtd 00; Perm to Offic *Nor* from 00. *47 Cornbrash Rise, Hilperton, Trowbridge BA14 7TS* Tel 07887-717052 (mobile)

WHALE, Canon Jeffery Walter George. b 33. Lon Univ BSc60. Cuddesdon Coll 60. **d** 62 **p** 63. C Rugby St Andr *Cov* 62-68; C-in-c Britwell St Geo CD *Ox* 68-77; P-in-c Datchet 77-78; TR Riverside 78-88; RD Burnham 83-87; Hon Can Ch Ch 85-01; TR New Windsor 88-01; rtd 01; Hon C Chenies and Lt Chalfont, Latimer and Flaunden *Ox* from 01. *The Rectory, Latimer, Chesham HP5 1UA* Tel (01494) 762281 E-mail jeffery.whale@ukgateway.net

WHALE, Noel Raymond. b 41. Ox Univ 67. **d** 70 **p** 71. C Amersham *Ox* 70-73; Australia from 73; C Geelong 73-76; P-in-c Altona 76-79; I 79-85; I Ivanhoe 86-97; Prec/Min Can St Paul's Cathl 97-01; I Bundoora St Pet from 01. *12 Alma Road, PO Box 1225, Bundoora, Vic, Australia 3083* Tel (0061) (3) 9467 4442 *or* 9467 3769 Mobile 412-196127 Fax (3) 9467 6642 E-mail jonahnoel@hotmail.com

WHALE, Peter Richard. b 49. Auckland Univ BSc71 MA72 Down Coll Cam BA74 MA78 Otago Univ BD78 Ex Univ PhD89. St Jo Coll Auckland 75. **d** 77 **p** 78. New Zealand 77-85; TV Saltash *Truro* 85-90; Jt Dir SW Min Tr Course Truro 86-90; Preb St Endellion 89-90; Prin WMMTC 90-92. *6 Bluebell Walk, Coventry CV4 9XR* Tel (024) 7646 4894 E-mail petegray@btinternet.com

WHALES, Jeremy Michael. b 31. Bris Univ MA82. Lambeth STh72 Wycliffe Hall Ox 59. **d** 61 **p** 62. C W Wimbledon Ch Ch *S'wark* 61-64; Lect St Paul's Coll Cheltenham 64-67; Asst Chapl and Sen Lect 67-74; Chapl 74-78; Assoc Chapl and Sen Lect Coll of SS Paul and Mary Cheltenham 78-84; V Cheltenham St Luke and St Jo *Glouc* 85-92; rtd 92; Perm to Offic *Glouc* from 92; Clergy Widows Officer (Cheltenham Adnry) 96-99. *5 Robert Burns Avenue, Cheltenham GL51 6NU* Tel (01242) 527583

WHALEY, Stephen John. b 57. York Univ BA79. Cranmer Hall Dur BA85. **d** 86 **p** 87. C Selby Abbey *York* 86-90; V Derringham Bank from 90; AD W Hull 98-00. *110 Calvert Road, Hull HU5 5DH* Tel (01482) 352175

WHALLEY, Anthony Allen. b 41. Linc Th Coll 77. **d** 79 **p** 80. C Upton cum Chalvey *Ox* 79-83; R Newton Longville w Stoke Hammond and Whaddon 83-96; R Winslow w St Horwood and Addington from 99. *The Vicarage, Vicarage Road, Winslow, Buckingham MK18 3BJ* Tel (01296) 712564 E-mail stlaurence.winslow@btinternet.com

WHALLEY, Mrs Constance Mary. b 55. Carl and Blackb Dioc Tr Inst 99. **d** 02 **p** 03. NSM Garstang St Helen and St Michaels-on-Wyre *Blackb* from 02. *Brierfield, Stoney Lane, Goosnargh, Preston PR3 2WH* Tel (01995) 640652

WHALLEY, George Peter. b 40. LNSM course 82. **d** 86 **p** 86. NSM Ellon *Ab* from 86; NSM Cruden Bay from 86. *128 Braehead Drive, Cruden Bay, Peterhead AB42 0NW* Tel (01779) 812511 Fax 812771 E-mail pwhalley@compuserve.com

WHALLEY, Jonathan Peter Lambert. b 60. St Jo Coll Nottm BA95. **d** 97 **p** 98. C Hattersley *Ches* 97-01; V The Marshland

Sheff from 01. *The Vicarage, Kings Causeway, Swinefleet, Goole DN14 8DH* Tel (01405) 704643 E-mail tuvix@ntlworld.com

WHALLEY, Michael Thomas. b 30. AKC55. **d** 56 **p** 57. C Nottingham All SS *S'well* 56-58; C Clifton St Fran 58-60; C Mansfield St Pet 60; V N Wilford St Faith 60-66; Asst Chapl HM Pris Man 66-67; Chapl HM Youth Cust Cen Dover 67-69; Lic to Offic *Linc* 70-75; Chapl HM Pris Aylesbury 75-79; C Aylesbury *Ox* 79-83; P-in-c Bierton w Hulcott 83-89; TV Aylesbury w Bierton and Hulcott 89-95; rtd 95; Perm to Offic *Linc* from 97. *17 Willowfield Avenue, Nettleham, Lincoln LN2 2TH* Tel (01522) 595372

✠**WHALON, The Rt Revd Pierre Welté.** b 52. Boston Univ BMus74 Duquesne Univ MMus81. Virginia Th Sem MDiv85. **d** 85 **p** 85 **c** 01. USA 85-01; R N Versailles All So 85-91; R Philadelphia St Paul 91-93; R Fort Pierce St Andr 93-01; Bp in Charge Convocation of American Chs in Eur from 01; Hon Asst Bp Eur from 02. *23 Avenue George V, 75008 Paris, France* Tel (0033) (1) 53 23 84 04 *or* tel and fax 47 20 02 23 E-mail bppwhalon@aol.com *or* ecusa.eu@americancath.asso.fr

WHARTON, Christopher Joseph. b 33. Keble Coll Ox BA57 MA61. **d** 79 **p** 80. NSM Harpenden St Nic *St Alb* 79-93; R Kimpton w Ayot St Lawrence 93-00; Perm to Offic from 00. *97 Overstone Road, Harpenden AL5 5PL* Tel (01582) 761164

WHARTON, Ms Gillian Vera. b 66. TCD BTh93 MPhil99. CITC 90. **d** 93 **p** 94. C Glenageary *D & G* 93-96; PV Ch Ch Cathl Dublin 96-00; Dioc Youth Officer 96-00; C Lucan w Leixlip 96-00; Chapl Rathdown Sch from 00. *101 Stepaside Park, Stepaside, Co Dublin, Irish Republic* Tel and fax (00353) (1) 214 9858 Mobile 87-230 0767 E-mail gillwharton@hotmail.com

✠**WHARTON, The Rt Revd John Martin.** b 44. Van Mildert Coll Dur BA69 Linacre Coll Ox BTh71 MA76. Ripon Hall Ox 69. **d** 72 **p** 73 **c** 92. C Birm St Pet *Birm* 72-75; C Croydon *Cant* 76-77; Dir Past Studies Ripon Coll Cuddesdon 77-83; C Cuddesdon *Ox* 79-83; Sec to Bd of Min and Tr *Bradf* 83-92; Dir Post-Ord Tr 84-92; Hon Can Bradf Cathl 84-92; Can Res Bradf Cathl 92; Bp's Officer for Min and Tr 92; Area Bp Kingston *S'wark* 92-97; Bp Newc from 97. *The Bishop's House, 29 Moor Road South, Newcastle upon Tyne NE3 1PA* Tel 0191-285 2220 Fax 284 6933 E-mail bishop@newcastle.anglican.org

WHARTON, Richard Malcolm. b 69. Univ of Cen England in Birm BA91 PGCE92. Ripon Coll Cuddesdon BTh98. **d** 98 **p** 99. C Weoley Castle *Birm* 98-01; C Hall Green Ascension from 01; P-in-c Gospel Lane St Mich from 03. *4 Etwall Road, Hall Green, Birmingham B28 0LE* Tel 0121-777 3689 Mobile 07974-422207

WHARTON, Susan Jane. b 58. Leeds Univ BSc79 Coll of Ripon & York St Jo MA00. Nor Ord Course 96. **d** 99 **p** 00. NSM Bingley All SS *Bradf* 99-00; C from 00. *6 Woodvale Crescent, Bingley BD16 4AL* Tel (01274) 565789 E-mail wharton@nildram.co.uk

WHARTON, Thomas Anthony. b 21. Bps' Coll Cheshunt 49. **d** 52 **p** 53. C Beeston *S'well* 52-55; C Ambleside w Rydal *Carl* 55-58; V Northowram *Wakef* 58-65; V Chipping Norton *Ox* 65-86; Chapl Berne *Eur* 86-89; rtd 89; Perm to Offic *Glouc* from 89. *4 Bowling Green Crescent, Cirencester GL7 2HA* Tel (01285) 659043

WHATELEY, Thomas Roderick (Rod). b 52. St Jo Coll Nottm 94. **d** 96 **p** 97. C Willesborough *Cant* 96-99; P-in-c Cliftonville from 99. *St Paul's Vicarage, Northdown Road, Cliftonville, Margate CT9 2RD* Tel (01843) 220857 E-mail rod.whateley@tiscali.co.uk

WHATLEY, Lionel Frederick. b 50. Port Eliz Univ DipEd75 Rosebank Bible Coll DipTh83. St Paul's Coll Grahamstown 77. **d** 79 **p** 80. S Africa 79-99; R Ashington, Washington and Wiston w Buncton *Chich* from 99. *The Rectory, Mill Lane, Ashington, Pulborough RH20 3BH* Tel (01903) 893878 Fax 893886 E-mail whatley@onetel.net.uk

WHATLEY, Roger James. b 49. Chich Th Coll 94. **d** 96. NSM Newport St Jo *Portsm* from 96. *Beechcroft, 46 Trafalgar Road, Newport PO30 1QG* Tel (01983) 825938

WHATMORE, Michael John. b 30. Bris Univ BA51 St Cath Soc Ox BA53 MA54. Wycliffe Hall Ox 56. **d** 56 **p** 58. C Bexley St Mary *Roch* 56-57; C Keston 57-59; C Bromley St Mark 59-61; Distr Sec (GB) Bible Soc 61-64; R Stanningley St Thos *Ripon* 64-67; V Speke All SS *Liv* 67-70; Teacher & Sen Tutor Barton Peveril Coll 70-92; rtd 92; Perm to Offic *Win* from 92. *26 Grebe Close, Milford on Sea, Lymington SO41 0XA* Tel (01590) 644892

WHATMOUGH, Michael Anthony (Tony). b 50. ARCO71 Ex Univ BA72. Edin Th Coll BD81. **d** 81 **p** 82. C Edin St Hilda *Edin* 81-84; C Edin St Fillan 81-84; C Salisbury St Thos and St Edm *Sarum* 84-86; R 86-93; RD Salisbury 90-93; V Bris St Mary Redcliffe w Temple etc *Bris* from 93. *The Vicarage, 10 Redcliffe Parade West, Bristol BS1 6SP* Tel 0117-929 1962 *or* 929 1487 Fax 929 1541 E-mail tony.whatmough@bigfoot.com

WHATSON, Mark Edwin Chadwick. b 57. CEng83 MIMechE83 Southn Univ BSc79. N Ord Course 86. **d** 88 **p** 91. NSM Church Hulme *Ches* 88-91; NSM Goostrey 91-95; NSM Hardwicke, Quedgeley and Elmore w Longney *Glouc* 95-98; C Thornbury 98-01; Ind Chapl 99-01; R Freshwater *Portsm* from 01; R Yarmouth from 01. *The Rectory, Afton Road, Freshwater PO40 9TS* Tel (01983) 752010 Fax as telephone E-mail mark.whatson@bigfoot.com

WHATTON, Miss Joanna Nicola. b 72. Liv Univ BA93 Bris Univ BA00 Homerton Coll Cam PGCE95. Trin Coll Bris 98. **d** 01 **p** 02. C Chislehurst St Nic *Roch* from 01. *Southbeech, Old Perry Street, Chislehurst BR7 6PP* Tel (020) 8467 1170

WHAWELL, Arthur Michael. b 38. SRN59. Sarum & Wells Th Coll 74. **d** 76 **p** 77. C Cottingham *York* 76-79; P-in-c Bessingby 79-84; P-in-c Carnaby 79-84; V Birchencliffe *Wakef* 84-87; Chapl Huddersfield R Infirmary 84-87; V St Bart Less *Lon* 87-95; Chapl St Bart Hosp Lon 87-95; P-in-c Wormingford, Mt Bures and Lt Horkesley *Chelmsf* 95-00; V from 00. *The Vicarage, Church Road, Wormingford, Colchester CO6 3AZ* Tel (01787) 227398 E-mail michael@whawell.freeserve.co.uk

WHEALE, Alan Leon. b 43. HNC65 AKC69 Hull Univ MA92. St Aug Coll Cant 69 DipMin89. **d** 70 **p** 71. C Tamworth *Lich* 70-73; C Cheddleton 73-75; V Garretts Green *Birm* 75-78; V Perry Beeches 78-83; V Winshill *Derby* 83-84; Deputation Appeals Org (E Midl) CECS 84-86; C Arnold *S'well* 86-96; V Daybrook 88-96; R Clifton Campville w Edingale and Harlaston *Lich* 96-01; R Clifton Campville w Edingale and Harlaston from 96; P-in-c No Man's Heath 96-01; P-in-c Thorpe Constantine from 96; P-in-c Elford from 97. *The Rectory, Main Street, Clifton Campville, Tamworth B79 0AP* Tel (01827) 373257 E-mail alan-wheale@supanet.com

WHEALE, Sarah Ruth. *See* BULLOCK, Mrs Sarah Ruth

WHEAT, Charles Donald Edmund. b 37. Nottm Univ BA70 Sheff Univ MA76. Kelham Th Coll 57. **d** 62 **p** 63. C Sheff Arbourthorne *Sheff* 62-67; Lic to Offic *S'well* 67-70; SSM from 69; Chapl St Martin's Coll Lanc 70-73; Prior SSM Priory Sheff 73-75; Lic to Offic *Sheff* 73-97; C Ranmoor 75-77; Asst Chapl Sheff Univ 75-77; Chapl 77-80; Prov SSM in England 81-91; Dir 82-89; Lic to Offic *Blackb* 81-88; V Middlesbrough All SS *York* 88-95; Roehampton Inst *S'wark* 96-97; Chapl OHP 97-98; Prior St Antony's Priory Dur 98-01; V Middlesbrough St Thos *York* 01-03; rtd 03; Perm to Offic *York* from 03. *154 Carisbrooke Avenue, Thorntree, Middlesbrough TS3 9LS* Tel (01642) 210824 E-mail ssmmbro@aol.com

WHEATLEY, Canon Arthur. b 31. Edin Th Coll 68. **d** 70 **p** 70. C Dundee St Salvador *Bre* 70-71; C Dundee St Martin 70-71; P-in-c Dundee St Ninian 71-76; R Elgin H Trin *Mor* 76-80; R Lossiemouth 76-80; Can St Andr Cathl Inverness 78-80 and from 83; Provost 80-83; R Inverness St Andr 80-83; Chapl HM Pris Inverness from 80; P-in-c Rothiemurchus *Mor* 83-95; P-in-c Grantown-on-Spey 83-95; NSM from 96; rtd 95. *Wester Curr Cottage, Dulnain Bridge, Grantown-on-Spey PH26 3LX* Tel (01479) 851273

WHEATLEY, David. b 44. Dioc OLM tr scheme 00. **d** 02 **p** 03. OLM Castleford *Wakef* from 02. *124 Queens Park Drive, Castleford WF10 3AP* Tel (01977) 553885

WHEATLEY, Gordon Howard. b 29. Trin Coll Cam MA52. Lon Bible Coll DipTh58. **d** 90 **p** 91. C Cockley Cley w Gooderstone *Nor* 90-94; C Didlington 90-94; C Gt and Lt Cressingham w Threxton 90-94; C Hilborough w Bodney 90-94; C Oxborough w Foulden and Caldecote 90-94; P-in-c Mundford w Lynford 94-98; P-in-c Ickburgh w Langford 94-98; P-in-c Cranwich 94-98; rtd 98; Perm to Offic *Nor* from 98. *6 Mount Close, Swaffham PE37 7NQ* Tel (01760) 722450

WHEATLEY, Ian James. b 62. Chich Th Coll BTh94. **d** 94 **p** 95. C Braunton *Ex* 94-97; Chapl RN from 97. *Royal Naval Chaplaincy Service, Room 203, Victory Building, HM Naval Base, Portsmouth PO1 3LS* Tel (023) 9272 7903 Fax 9272 7111

WHEATLEY, John. b 14. **d** 77 **p** 78. NSM Cambois *Newc* 77-87; rtd 87; Perm to Offic *Newc* from 87. *20 Cypress Gardens, Blyth NE24 2LP* Tel (01670) 353353

WHEATLEY, The Ven Paul Charles. b 38. Dur Univ BA61. Linc Th Coll 61. **d** 63 **p** 64. C Bishopston *Bris* 63-68; Youth Chapl 68-73; V Swindon St Paul 73-77; TR Swindon Dorcan 77-79; R Ross *Heref* 79-81; P-in-c Brampton Abbotts 79-81; RD Ross and Archenfield 79-91; TR Ross w Brampton Abbotts, Bridstow and Peterstow 81-91; Preb Heref Cathl 87-91; Adn Sherborne *Sarum* 91-03; P-in-c W Stafford w Frome Billet 91-03; rtd 03. *The Farthings, Bridstow, Ross-on-Wye HR9 6QF* Tel (01305) 264637 E-mail 101543.3471@compuserve.com

✠**WHEATLEY, The Rt Revd Peter William.** b 47. Qu Coll Ox BA69 MA73 Pemb Coll Cam BA71 MA75. Ripon Hall Ox 72. **d** 73 **p** 74 **c** 99. C Fulham All SS *Lon* 73-78; V St Pancras H Cross w St Jude and St Pet 78-82; P-in-c Hampstead All So 82-90; P-in-c Kilburn St Mary 82-90; P-in-c Kilburn St Mary w All So 90-95; V W Hampstead St Jas 82-95; Dir Post-Ord Tr 85-95; AD N Camden 88-93; Adn Hampstead 95-99; Area Bp Edmonton from 99. *27 Thurlow Road, London NW3 5PP* Tel (020) 7435 5890 Fax 7435 6049 E-mail bishop.edmonton@london.anglican.org

WHEATLEY, Miss Sarah Jane. b 45. St Gabr Coll Lon Dip Teaching67. St Alb Minl Tr Scheme 77. **d** 96 **p** 97. NSM Meppershall w Campton and Stondon *St Alb* 96-99; P-in-c Shillington 99-03; V Gravenhurst, Shillington and Stondon from 03. *All Saints' Vicarage, Vicarage Close, Shillington, Hitchin SG5 3LS* Tel (01462) 713797 *or* 731170 E-mail jane.wheatley@talk21.com

WHEATLEY PRICE, Canon John. b 31. Em Coll Cam BA54 MA58. Ridley Hall Cam 54. **d** 56 **p** 57. C Drypool St Andr and St Pet *York* 56-59; CMS 59-76; Uganda 60-74; Adn Soroti 72-74; Hon Can Soroti 78-97; Adn N Maseno Kenya 74-76; V Clevedon St Andr *B & W* 76-82; V Clevedon St Andr and Ch Ch 82-87; Chapl Amsterdam *Eur* 87-92; P-in-c Cromford *Derby* 92-95; P-in-c Matlock Bath 92-95; V Matlock Bath and Cromford 95-96; rtd 96; Perm to Offic *Sarum* 96-01; *Birm* from 01. *2 Beausale Drive, Knowle, Solihull B93 0NS* Tel (01564) 730067 E-mail johnwheatleyprice@lineone.net

WHEATON, Christopher. b 49. St Jo Coll Nottm BTh80 LTh80. **d** 80 **p** 81. C Hatcham St Jas *S'wark* 80-83; C Warlingham w Chelsham and Farleigh 83-87; V Carshalton Beeches from 87. *The Vicarage, 38 Beeches Avenue, Carshalton SM5 3LW* Tel (020) 8647 6056 E-mail good.shepherd@btinternet.com

WHEATON, Canon David Harry. b 30. St Jo Coll Ox BA53 MA56 Lon Univ BD55. Oak Hill Th Coll 58. **d** 59 **p** 60. Tutor Oak Hill Th Coll 59-62; Prin 71-86; C Enfield Ch Ch Trent Park *Lon* 59-62; R Ludgershall *Ox* 62-66; V Onslow Square St Paul *Lon* 66-71; Chapl Brompton Hosp 69-71; Hon Can St Alb 76-96; V Ware Ch Ch 86-96; RD Hertford 88-91; Chapl to The Queen 90-00; rtd 96. *43 Rose Drive, Chesham HP5 1RR* Tel (01494) 783862

WHEATON, Canon Ralph Ernest. b 32. St Jo Coll Dur BA54. Cranmer Hall Dur DipTh58. **d** 58 **p** 59. C Evington *Leic* 58-63; V Bardon Hill 63-71; V Whitwick St Jo the Bapt 71-81; RD Akeley S 79-81; V Blyth *S'well* 81-96; P-in-c Scofton w Osberton 83-86; V 86-96; RD Worksop 83-93; Hon Can S'well Minster 86-96; P-in-c Langold 86-91; rtd 96; Perm to Offic *Linc* 99-02. *Petriburg, Main Street, Hayton, Retford DN22 9LL* Tel (01777) 705910

WHEBLE, Eric Clement. b 23. S'wark Ord Course 68. **d** 71 **p** 72. C Croydon H Trin *Cant* 71-78; Hon C Croydon St Sav 78-80; Hon C Norbury St Oswald 80-81; TV Selsdon St Jo w St Fran 81-84; TV Selsdon St Jo w St Fran *S'wark* 85-88; rtd 88; Perm to Offic *Portsm* from 96; *Win* from 01. *23 Holmesland Drive, Botley, Southampton SO30 2SH* Tel (01489) 798050

WHEELDON, John Graham. b 32. Sarum & Wells Th Coll 85. **d** 87 **p** 88. C Winchcombe, Gretton, Sudeley Manor etc *Glouc* 87-90; R Huntley and Longhope 90-91; rtd 91. *17 Mitton Way, Mitton, Tewkesbury GL20 8AW*

WHEELDON, William Dennis. b 25. Leeds Univ BA51. Coll of Resurr Mirfield 52. **d** 54 **p** 56. CR 55-76; Barbados 59-66; Prin Coll of Resurr Mirfield 66-75; P-in-c New Whittington *Derby* 83-87; P-in-c Belper Ch Ch and Milford 87-90; rtd 90; Perm to Offic *Bradf* from 90. *10 Brooklyn, Threshfield, Skipton BD23 5ER* Tel (01756) 753187

WHEELER, Preb Alexander Quintin Henry (Alastair). b 51. Lon Univ BA73 Nottm Univ DipTh75. St Jo Coll Nottm 74. **d** 77 **p** 78. C Kenilworth St Jo *Cov* 77-80; C Madeley *Heref* 80-83; P-in-c Draycott-le-Moors *Lich* 83-84; P-in-c Forsbrook 83-84; R Draycott-le-Moors w Forsbrook 84-91; V Nailsea Ch Ch *B & W* 91-96; R Nailsea Ch Ch w Tickenham from 96; RD Portishead 95-01; Preb Wells Cathl from 03. *The Rectory, 1 Christ Church Close, Nailsea, Bristol BS48 1RT* Tel (01275) 853187 E-mail aqhw@aol.com

WHEELER, Andrew Charles. b 48. CCC Cam BA69 MA72 Makerere Univ Kampala MA72 Leeds Univ PGCE72. Trin Coll Bris BA88. **d** 88 **p** 88. CMS from 76; C Whitton *Sarum* 88-89; Egypt 89-92; Sudan 92-00; Abp's Sec for Angl Communion Affairs *Cant* 00-01. *Address temp unknown* E-mail awheeler@maf-europe.org

WHEELER, Anthony William. b 28. NSM Shirehampton *Bris* 76-98; Chmn Avonmouth Miss to Seamen from 76; rtd 98; Perm to Offic *Bris* 98-00. *3 The Priory, Priory Gardens, Bristol BS11 0BZ* Tel 0117 982 2261

WHEELER, (née MILLAR), Mrs Christine. b 55. City of Lon Poly BSc76 DipCOT81. S Dios Minl Tr Scheme 84. **d** 87 **p** 94. NSM Kingston Buci *Chich* 87-89; Par Dn Merstham and Gatton *S'wark* 89-94; C 94-96; R Rockland St Mary w Hellington, Bramerton etc *Nor* from 96. *The Rectory, 2 Rectory Lane, Rockland St Mary, Norwich NR14 7EY* Tel (01508) 538619 E-mail rector@lineone.net

WHEELER, David Ian. b 49. Southn Univ BSc70 PhD78. N Ord Course 87. **d** 90 **p** 91. C Blackpool St Jo *Blackb* 90-94; R Old Trafford St Jo *Man* from 94. *St John's Rectory, Lindum Avenue, Old Trafford, Manchester M16 9NQ* Tel 0161-872 0500

WHEELER, David James. b 44. Leeds Univ MA95 LSE CQSW74. S Dios Minl Tr Scheme 87. **d** 90 **p** 91. C Hythe *Cant* 90-92; C Knaresborough *Ripon* 92-97; Asst Soc Resp Officer 94-97; P-in-c Gt and Lt Ouseburn w Marton cum Grafton etc 97-01; V from 01; AD Ripon from 00. *The Vicarage, Great Ouseburn, York YO26 9RQ* Tel (01423) 330928 Fax as telephone E-mail sacerdote@lineone.net

WHEELER, David Robert. b 62. Birm Univ BSc84. Oak Hill Th Coll BA95. **d** 95 **p** 96. C Lancaster St Thos *Blackb* 95-96. *Address temp unknown*

WHEELER, Sister Eileen Violet. b 28. TCert48 Newnham Coll Cam MA52. Chich Th Coll 85. **dss** 86 **d** 87 **p** 95. Bexhill St Pet

Chich 86-95; Hon Par Dn 87-90; Par Dn 90-94; NSM 94-95; rtd 94; Hon C Bexhill St Mark *Chich* 95-00; Perm to Offic 00-02; Hon C Horsham from 02. *1 The Briary, St Peter's Crescent, Bexhill-on-Sea TN40 2ET* Tel (01424) 215115

WHEELER, Graham John. b 39. St Mich Coll Llan DipTh66 BD78. **d** 66 **p** 67. C Roath St Martin *Llan* 66-71; C Cadoxton-juxta-Barry 71-75; Perm to Offic 75-79; C Highcliffe w Hinton Admiral *Win* 79-83; C Milton 83-90; P-in-c Bournemouth St Ambrose from 90. *St Ambrose Vicarage, 72 West Cliff Road, Bournemouth BH4 8BE* Tel (01202) 764957

WHEELER, James Albert. b 49. Sarum & Wells Th Coll 74. **d** 76 **p** 77. C Orpington All SS *Roch* 76-79; C Roch 79-81; C Bexley St Jo 81-84; V Penge Lane H Trin 84-93; P-in-c Tunbridge Wells St Luke 93-99; V from 99. *St Luke's Vicarage, 158 Upper Grosvenor Road, Tunbridge Wells TN1 2EQ* Tel (01892) 521374

WHEELER, John David. b 33. Selw Coll Cam BA54 MA58. Ely Th Coll 54. **d** 56 **p** 57. C Charlton St Luke w St Paul *S'wark* 56-60; C Northolt St Mary *Lon* 61-63; V Bush Hill Park St Mark 64-71; V Ealing St Pet Mt Park 71-74; V Truro St Paul *Truro* 74-79; V Truro St Paul and St Clem 79-80; P-in-c Hammersmith St Sav *Lon* 80-83; V Cobbold Road St Sav w St Mary 83-96; rtd 96; Perm to Offic *Heref* 96-01; *Chich* from 01. *49 Magdalen Road, St Leonards-on-Sea TN37 6EU* Tel (01424) 714371

WHEELER, Julian Aldous. b 48. Nottm Univ BTh74. Kelham Th Coll 70. **d** 75 **p** 76. C Bideford *Ex* 75-79; Lic to Offic 79-86; Hon C Parkham, Alwington, Buckland Brewer etc from 86. *Forge Cottage, Pump Lane, Abbotsham, Bideford EX39 5AZ* Tel (01237) 473948 E-mail jwheeler@connectfree.co.uk

WHEELER, Preb Madeleine. b 42. Gilmore Course 76. **dss** 78 **d** 87 **p** 94. Ruislip Manor St Paul *Lon* 78-92; Par Dn 87-91; TD 91-92; Chapl for Women's Min (Willesden Episc Area) 86-95; P-in-c N Greenford All Hallows 94-00; Preb St Paul's Cathl 95-00; rtd 00; Perm to Offic *St Alb* from 00. *178A Harefield Road, Uxbridge UB8 1PP* Tel (01895) 257274

WHEELER, Nicholas Charles. b 50. SEITE 00. **d** 03. NSM Blackheath St Jo *S'wark* from 03. *52 Oakways, London SE9 2PD* Tel (020) 8850 7819

WHEELER, Nicholas Gordon Timothy. b 59. BCombStuds84. Linc Th Coll. **d** 84 **p** 85. C Hendon St Alphage *Lon* 84-87; C Wood Green St Mich w Bounds Green St Gabr etc 87-89; TV 89-93; R Cranford 93-02; V Ruislip St Mary from 02. *St Mary's Vicarage, 9 The Fairway, Ruislip HA4 0SP* Tel (020) 8845 3485 Mobile 07946-111968 E-mail wheelernicholas@cs.com

WHEELER, Nicholas Paul. b 60. Ox Univ BA86 MA91. Wycliffe Hall Ox 83. **d** 87 **p** 88. C Wood Green St Mich w Bounds Green St Gabr etc *Lon* 87-91; Chapl to Bp Edmonton 91-96; P-in-c Somers Town 96-03; P-in-c Camden Town St Mich w All SS and St Thos St Matt 96-03; P-in-c Camden Town St Mich w All SS and St Thos 96-03; P-in-c Camden Square St Paul 96-03; TR Old St Pancras from 03. *The Vicarage, 191 St Pancras Way, London NW1 9NH* Tel (020) 7485 6837 or rel and fax 7424 0724

WHEELER, Richard Anthony (Tony). b 23. St Chad's Coll Dur BA46 MA48 DipTh48. **d** 48 **p** 49. C Kingswinford St Mary *Lich* 48-52; C Toxteth Park St Agnes *Liv* 52-54; V Upholland 54-64; R Dorchester H Trin w Frome Whitfield *Sarum* 64-73; TV Dorchester 73-87; rtd 87; Perm to Offic *Sarum* from 87. *30 Mountain Ash Road, Dorchester DT1 2PB* Tel (01305) 264811 E-mail peewheet@cix.compulink.co.uk

WHEELER, Canon Richard Roy. b 44. K Coll Lon BD72. St Aug Coll Cant. **d** 74 **p** 74. C Brixton St Matt *S'wark* 74-78; Dir St Matt Meeting Place Brixton 78-79; Sec BCC Community Work Resource Unit 79-82; TV Southampton (City Cen) *Win* 83-88; TR 88-98; Hon Can Win Cathl 94-98; Soc Resp Adv *St Alb* from 98; Can Res St Alb from 01. *Holywell Close, 43 Holywell Hill, St Albans AL1 1HE* Tel (01272) 856753 E-mail sro@stalbansdioc.org.uk

WHEELER, Mrs Sally Ann Violet. b 59. Westmr Coll Ox BEd81. St Alb and Ox Min Course 94. **d** 97 **p** 98. NSM Chippenham St Paul w Hardenhuish etc *Bris* 97-01; C Gtr Corsham and Lacock from 01. *The Vicarage, Folly Lane, Lacock, Chippenham SN15 2LL* Tel (01249) 730272 E-mail wheelers.7@btinternet.com

WHEELHOUSE, Brian Clifford Dunstan. b 69. St Steph Ho Ox BTh93. **d** 96 **p** 97. C Brighton Resurr *Chich* 96-99; C Hangleton 99-00; Perm to Offic 00-01; C Kingstanding St Luke *Birm* from 01. *79 Hawthorn Road, Kingstanding, Birmingham B44 8QT* Tel 0121-386 4168 Mobile 07941-717667

WHEELWRIGHT, Michael Harvey. b 39. Bps' Coll Cheshunt 64. **d** 67 **p** 68. C Glen Parva and S Wigston *Leic* 67-70; C Evington 70-74; V Leic St Eliz Nether Hall 74-79; Chapl Prudhoe Hosp Northd 79-99; Perm to Offic *Dur* from 95; *Newc* from 99; rtd 99. *6 Nunnykirk Close, Ovingham, Prudhoe NE42 6BP* Tel (01661) 835749

WHELAN, Canon John Bernard. b 17. Dur Univ LTh41. Oak Hill Th Coll 38. **d** 47 **p** 48. C Ambleside w Rydal *Carl* 47-49; C Barrow St Luke 49-54; Korea 54-66; Japan 66-67; C Bury St Mary *Man* 68-71; Asst Chapl Crumpsall Hosp *Man* 71-73; Chapl N Man Gen Hosp 73-82; rtd 82; Chapl Las Palmas *Eur* 82-84; Asst Chapl Valletta w Sliema 84-93; Can Malta Cathl 87-93. *8 Glynne Way, Hawarden, Deeside CH5 3NL* Tel (01244) 532751

WHELAN, Miss Patricia Jean. b 33. ACA55 FCA82. Dalton Ho Bris 58. dss 64 d 87 p 94. Stapleford *S'well* 62-69; Aylesbury *Ox* 69-75; Bushbury *Lich* 75-77; Patchway *Bris* 77-81; Trin Coll Bris 81-82; W Swindon LEP 82-86; High Wycombe *Ox* 86-87; Par Dn 87-91; Par Dn Ox St Ebbe w H Trin and St Pet 91-93; rtd 93. *81 Cogges Hill Road, Witney OX28 3XU* Tel (01993) 779099

WHELAN, Peter **Warwick** Armstrong. b 34. Southn Univ BTh80 Open Univ BA80 DipHSW94 S Bank Univ 97. Sarum Th Coll 69. d 71 p 72. C Salisbury St Mark *Sarum* 71-73; C Solihull *Birm* 73-77; TR Shirley 77-86; Chapl Whittington Hosp NHS Trust 86-99; Chapl Camden and Islington Community Health NHS Trust 86-98; Perm to Offic *Ex* from 98; rtd 99. *Olde Court Coach House, Higher Lincombe Road, Torquay TQ1 2EX* Tel (01803) 212483

WHELAN, Raymond Keith. b 40. Cant Sch of Min 85. d 88 p 91. C Eastbourne St Andr *Chich* 88-93; C-in-c Parklands St Wilfrid CD 93-95; TV Chich 95-00; V Chich St Wilfrid 00-01. *9 Ruislip Gardens, Aldwick, Bognor Regis PO21 4LB*

WHERLOCK, Mrs Evalene Prudence. b 50. WEMTC 98. d 01 p 02. NSM Bishopsworth and Bedminster Down *Bris* from 01. *63 Bridgwater Road, Bedminster Down, Bristol BS13 7AX* Tel 0117-964 1035 Mobile 07899-932763
E-mail evawherlock@ukonline.co.uk

WHERRY, Anthony Michael. b 44. Nottm Univ BA65 Univ Coll Lon DAA66. WMMTC 88. d 91 p 92. NSM Worc City St Paul and Old St Martin etc *Worc* 91-95; NSM Worc E Deanery 95-02; NSM Worc SE from 02. *2 Redfern Avenue, Worcester WR5 1PZ* Tel (01905) 358532 *or* 766350 Mobile 07770-435820 Fax 766363
E-mail twherry@lineone.net

WHETTEM, Canon John Curtiss. b 27. Peterho Cam BA50 MA55. Wycliffe Hall Ox 50. d 52 p 53. C Clifton Ch Ch *Bris* 52-55; C Wandsworth All SS *S'wark* 55-58; V Soundwell *Bris* 58-63; Youth Chapl 63-68; Chapl Bris Cathl 64-68; R N Mundham w Hunston *Chich* 68-80; P-in-c Oving w Merston 75-80; TR Swanborough *Sarum* 80-92; RD Pewsey 84-89; rtd 92; Perm to Offic *Sarum* from 92. *32 Hogshill Street, Beaminster DT8 3AA* Tel (01308) 863050

WHETTER, Michael Arnold. b 30. Bris Univ BA51. Wells Th Coll 53. d 55 p 56. C Dursley *Glouc* 55-58; C Coppenhall *Ches* 58-61; R Ches H Trin 61-71; V Stockport St Alb Hall Street 72-90; V Offerton 90-91; Chapl Cherry Tree Hosp Stockport 72-91; Chapl Offerton Hosp Stockport 72-91; V Bollington St Jo *Ches* 91-00; rtd 00; Perm to Offic *Glouc* from 00. *Knapp Cottage, Selsley West, Stroud GL5 5LJ* Tel (01453) 822920

WHETTINGSTEEL, Raymond Edward. b 44. S Dios Minl Tr Scheme 79. d 82 p 83. NSM Sholing *Win* 82-84; C Southampton Maybush St Pet 84-89; V Hatherden w Tangley, Weyhill and Penton Mewsey from 89. *The Rectory, Penton Mewsey, Andover SP11 0RD* Tel (01264) 773554

WHETTLETON, Timothy **John**. b 53. Univ of Wales (Swansea) BA74. St Mich Coll Llan DMS98 Dip Practical Th 99. d 99 p 00. C Llansamlet *S & B* 99-01; P-in-c Gowerton from 01. *The Vicarage, 14 Church Street, Gowerton, Swansea SA4 3EA* Tel (01792) 872266

WHETTON, Nicholas John. b 56. Open Univ BA94. St Jo Coll Nottm 83. d 86 p 87. C Hatfield *Sheff* 86-90; V Cornholme *Wakef* 90-96; P-in-c Livesey *Blackb* 96-99; V 99-03; P-in-c Ewood 96-97; Chapl HM Pris Hull from 03. *The Chaplain's Office, HM Prison Hull, Hedon Road, Hull HU9 5LS* Tel (01482) 282200

WHIFFEN, Canon William Timothy. b 25. SS Coll Cam BA50 MA54 FRSA94. Linc Th Coll. d 52 p 53. C Wigan St Mich *Liv* 52-56; India 57-69; V Clay Cross *Derby* 69-74; Sec (Overseas Division) USPG 74-79; TR Woughton *Ox* 79-85; P-in-c Seer Green and Jordans 85-91; Hon Can Ch *Ox* 91-92; rtd 91. *90 Booker Avenue, Bradwell Common, Milton Keynes MK13 8EF* Tel (01908) 677466

✠WHINNEY, The Rt Revd Michael Humphrey Dickens. b 30. Pemb Coll Cam BA55 MA59. Gen Th Sem (NY) STM90 Ridley Hall Cam 55. d 57 p 58 c 82. C Rainham *Chelmsf* 57-60; Hd Cam Univ Miss Bermondsey 60-67; Chapl 67-73; V Bermondsey St Jas w Ch Ch *S'wark* 67-73; Adn S'wark 73-82; Suff Bp Aston *Birm* 82-85; Bp S'well 85-88; Asst Bp Birm from 88; Can Res Birm Cathl 92-95; rtd 96. *3 Moor Green Lane, Moseley, Birmingham B13 8NE* Tel 0121-249 2856 Fax as telephone
E-mail michael.whinney@btinternet.com

WHINNEY, Nigel Patrick Maurice. b 43. Open Univ BA91. SW Minl Tr Course 95. d 97 p 98. NSM Ilminster and Distr *B & W* from 97; NSM Officer (Taunton Adnry) from 99; RD Crewkerne and Ilminster from 01. *The Monks Dairy, Isle Brewers, Taunton TA3 6QL* Tel (01460) 281975
E-mail pearls@harriet-whinney.co.uk

WHINTON, William Francis Ivan. b 35. N Ord Course 77. d 80 p 81. NSM Stockport St Mary *Ches* 80-87; Dudley 82-87; V Birtles 87-00; Dioc Officer for Disabled 89-00; rtd 00; Chapl for Deaf People *Ches* from 00. *Allmeadows Cottage, Wincle, Macclesfield SK11 0QJ* Tel (01260) 227278

WHIPP, Antony Douglas. b 46. Leeds Univ BSc68. Ripon Coll Cuddesdon 84. d 86 p 87. C Dalston *Carl* 86-89; V Holme Cultram St Mary 89-96; V Holme Cultram St Cuth 89-96; V Kells 96-00; V Hartlepool St Aid *Dur* from 00. *St Aidan's Vicarage, St Aidan's Street, Hartlepool TS25 1SN* Tel (01429) 273539 Fax 232604 E-mail tony.whipp@durham.anglican.org

WHIPP, Margaret Jane. b 55. LMH Ox BA76 Sheff Univ MB, ChB79 MRCP82 FRCR86. N Ord Course 87. d 90 p 94. NSM Wickersley *Sheff* 90-98; Tutor Cranmer Hall Dur from 98. *Westlands, 32 St Charles Road, Tudhoe Village, Spennymoor DL16 6JY* Tel (01388) 811461

WHITAKER, Anthony. b 50. SS Mark & Jo Coll Chelsea CertEd72 Middx Univ BA02 MCIPD. NTMTC 99. d 02 p 03. NSM Blackmore and Stondon Massey *Chelmsf* from 02. *3 Marks Avenue, Ongar CM5 9AY* Tel (01277) 363725 Mobile 07905-013017 E-mail whitaker tony@hotmail.com

WHITAKER, David Arthur Edward. b 27. New Coll Ox BA50 MA55. Wells Th Coll 51. d 53 p 54. C W Bridgford *S'well* 53-56; CF 56-58; V Clifton St Fran *S'well* 58-63; Basutoland 63-66; Lesotho 66-69; R Buckerell *Ex* 69-76; R Feniton 69-76; P-in-c Tiverton St Pet 76-79; R 79-92; rtd 92; Perm to Offic *Heref* from 92. *The Cottage, Hereford Road, Weobley, Hereford HR48 8SW* Tel (01544) 318669

WHITAKER, Irene Anne. b 57. Dioc OLM tr scheme 99. d 01 p 02. OLM Parr *Liv* from 01. *369 Elephant Lane, St Helens WA9 5HF* Tel (01744) 637207 Mobile 07748-435224

WHITAKER, Margaret Scott. b 45. d 03. OLM Eaton *Nor* from 03. *38 Judges Walk, Norwich NR4 7QF* Tel (01603) 461314

WHITAKER, Michael Benjamin. b 60. Nottm Univ BA83. Sarum & Wells Th Coll 85. d 87 p 88. C Gt Grimsby St Mary and St Jas *Linc* 87-91; C Abingdon *Ox* 91-95; Chapl to the Deaf *Sarum* 95-00; Perm to Offic *Win* 97-00; Asst Chapl Chapl to the Deaf *Ox* from 00. *87 Bagley Wood Road, Kennington, Oxford OX1 5LY*

WHITBY, Suffragan Bishop of. See LADDS, The Rt Revd Robert Sidney

WHITCROFT, Graham Frederick. b 42. Oak Hill Th Coll 64. d 66 p 92. C Cromer *Nor* 66-69; C Attercliffe *Sheff* 69-72; V Kimberworth Park 72-85; V Lepton *Wakef* from 85; RD Kirkburton from 98. *The Vicarage, 138 Wakefield Road, Lepton, Huddersfield HD8 0LU* Tel (01484) 602172

WHITE, Alan. b 18. Man Univ BSc39 MSc40 St Cath Soc Ox BA42 MA46 Leeds Univ MEd52. Ripon Hall Ox 40. d 42 p 43. C Leic St Marg *Leic* 42-45; Chapl and Asst Master Leeds Gr Sch 45-56; Lic to Offic *Worc* 56-89; Asst Master Bromsgrove Sch 56-72; Chapl 72-83; rtd 83; P-in-c Tardebigge *Worc* 89-00; Perm to Offic from 00. *25 Leadbetter Drive, Bromsgrove B61 7JG* Tel (01527) 877955

WHITE, Preb Alan. b 43. Ex Univ BA65. Chich Th Coll 65. d 68 p 69. C Upper Clapton St Matt *Lon* 68-72; C Southgate Ch Ch 72-76; P-in-c Friern Barnet St Pet le Poer 76-79; V 79-85; TR Ex St Thos and Em *Ex* from 85; RD Christianity from 99; Preb Ex Cathl from 03. *St Thomas's Vicarage, 57 Cowick Street, Exeter EX4 1HR* Tel (01392) 255219

WHITE, Mrs Alison Mary. b 56. St Aid Coll Dur BA78 Leeds Univ MA94. Cranmer Hall Dur 83. d 86 p 94. NSM Chester le Street *Dur* 86-89; Dioc Adv in Local Miss 89-93; Hon Par Dn Birtley 89-93; Dir Past Studies Cranmer Hall Dur 93-98; Dir of Ords *Dur* 98-00; Springboard Missr Dur 00-02; Springboard Missr *Pet* from 02. *4 The Avenue, Dallington, Northampton NN5 7AN* Tel (01604) 581400 Fax 750925
E-mail alison.m.white@ukgateway.net

WHITE, Canon Andrew Paul Bartholomew. b 64. MIOT85 ABIST85 St Thos Hosp Lon Dip Surgery84 DA84 CertMBiol84. Ridley Hall Cam 86. d 90 p 91. C Battersea Rise St Mark *S'wark* 90-93; P-in-c Balham Hill Ascension 93-97; V 97-98; Can Res Cov Cathl *Cov* from 98; Dir Internat Min from 98. *35 Morningside, Coventry CV5 6PD* Tel (024) 7667 5146 *or* 7622 7597 Fax 7655 2654 E-mail reconciliation@globalnet.co.uk

WHITE, Andrew Peter. b 65. Lon Univ BA87. Sarum & Wells Th Coll BTh94. d 94 p 95. C Croydon St Matt *S'wark* 94-96; C S Wimbledon H Trin and St Pet 96-98; TV Droitwich Spa *Worc* from 98; RD Droitwich from 02. *St Nicholas' Vicarage, Ombersley Close, Droitwich WR9 8JY* Tel (01905) 771516
E-mail andrew.white12@virgin.net

WHITE, Antony. See FELTHAM-WHITE, Antony James

WHITE, Canon Christopher Norman Hessler. b 32. TD76. St Cath Coll Cam BA56 MA60. Cuddesdon Coll 57. d 59 p 60. C Solihull *Birm* 59-62; C Leeds St Aid *Ripon* 62-65; V Aysgarth *Ripon* 65-74; R Richmond 74-76; P-in-c Hudswell w Downholme and Marske 75-76; R Richmond w Hudswell 76-97; RD Richmond 75-80 and 93-97; Hon Can Ripon Cathl 89-97; Chapl St Fran Xavier Sch Richmond 89-97; rtd 97; Perm to Offic *Ripon* from 97. *Orchard House, Aske, Richmond DL10 5HN* Tel (01748) 850968

WHITE, Colin Davidson. b 44. St And Dioc Tr Course 86 Coates Hall Edin 90. d 88 p 89. NSM Glenrothes *St And* 88-89; P-in-c 89-90; P-in-c Leven 90-92; R 92-95; V Grimethorpe *Wakef* 95-01; P-in-c Kellington w Whitley 01-02; TV Knottingley and Kellington w Whitley from 02. *The Vicarage, 1 Manor Farm Close, Kellington, Goole DN14 0PF* Tel (01977) 663728 Mobile 07973-795560 Fax (01977) 663671
E-mail cicol@whitefam67.fsnet.co.uk

WHITE, Crispin Michael. b 42. FRSA94 Southn Univ MA98. Bps' Coll Cheshunt 62. **d** 65 **p** 66. C S Harrow St Paul *Lon* 65-67; C Mill Hill St Mich 67-68; Canada 68-71; Toc H Padre (W Region) 71-75; (E Midl Region) 75-82; Ind Chapl *Portsm* 82-98; P-in-c Hatfield Broad Oak and Bush End *Chelmsf* from 98; Ind Chapl from 98. *The Vicarage, Feathers Hill, Hatfield Broad Oak, Bishop's Stortford CM22 7HD* Tel (01279) 718274 Fax 718097 E-mail crispin.white@eccr.org.uk

WHITE, David Christopher. b 51. Lon Univ LLB73. St Jo Coll Nottm 86. **d** 88 **p** 89. C Bulwell St Mary *S'well* 88-92; V Nottingham All SS 92-98; TR Clarendon Park St Jo w Knighton St Mich *Leic* from 98; Bp's NSM Officer from 02. *The Rectory, 9 Springfield Road, Leicester LE2 3BB* Tel 0116-270 6097 E-mail dwhite@ntlworld.com

WHITE, David John. b 26. Leeds Univ BA53. Coll of Resurr Mirfield 53. **d** 55 **p** 56. C Brighton St Pet *Chich* 55-58; C Wednesbury St Jas *Lich* 58-60; C Bishops Hull St Jo *B & W* 60-61; R Morton *Derby* 61-62; In RC Ch 62-73; Lect Whitelands Coll Lon 72-75; R Tregony w St Cuby and Cornelly *Truro* 75-79; R Castle Bromwich SS Mary and Marg *Birm* 79-83; V Plymouth St Simon *Ex* 83-88; R Lapford, Nymet Rowland and Coldridge 88-93; RD Chulmleigh 93; rtd 93; Perm to Offic *Ex* 94-99. *The Belvedere, Peak Hill Road, Sidmouth EX10 8RZ* Tel (01395) 513365

WHITE, David Paul. b 58. Oak Hill Th Coll. **d** 84 **p** 85. C Toxteth Park St Clem *Liv* 84-87; C Woodford Wells *Chelmsf* 87-89; C Woodside Park St Barn *Lon* 89-90; TV Canford Magna *Sarum* 90-93; V York St Mich-le-Belfrey *York* 93-99; V St Austell *Truro* from 99. *The Vicarage, 1 Carnsmerry Crescent, St Austell PL25 4NA* Tel (01726) 73839 E-mail david@st-michael-le-belfry.org

WHITE, Derek. b 35. MBE97. **d** 84 **p** 85. Hon C St Marylebone St Cypr *Lon* 84-87; C 87-96; Bp's Chapl for the Homeless 87-01; P-in-c St Mary le Strand w St Clem Danes 96-01; rtd 01. *80 Coleraine Road, London SE3 7BE* Tel (020) 8858 3622

WHITE, Derek James. Birm Univ BA56. Chich Th Coll 56. **d** 58 **p** 59. C Stanmer w Falmer and Moulsecoomb *Chich* 58-61; Asst Chapl Ardingly Coll 61-63; Chapl 63-72; C Glynde, W Firle and Beddingham *Chich* 72-73; R Bramber w Botolphs 73-87; V Upper Beeding 73-87; R Beeding and Bramber w Botolphs 87-98; rtd 98; Perm to Offic *Chich* from 98. *38 Beach Crescent, Littlehampton BN17 5NT* Tel (01903) 731076

WHITE, Douglas Richard Leon (Rick). b 49. Linc Th Coll 81. **d** 83 **p** 84. C Warsop *S'well* 83-88; V Kirkby in Ashfield St Thos 88-93; Asst Chapl Qu Medical Cen Nottm Univ Hosp NHS Trust 93-98; Chapl Cen Notts Healthcare NHS Trust 98-01; Chapl Notts Healthcare NHS Trust 01-02; Chapl Geo Eliot Hosp NHS Trust Nuneaton from 02; Chapl Mary Ann Evans Hospice from 02. *George Eliot Hospital, College Street, Nuneaton CV10 7DJ* Tel (024) 7635 1351

WHITE, Dudley William. b 33. Univ of Wales (Ban) BSc53. St Mich Coll Llan BD69. **d** 59 **p** 60. C Sketty *S & B* 59-66; R New Radnor and Llanfihangel Nantmelan 66-70; V Penyfai w Tondu *Llan* 70-77; V Swansea St Jude *S & B* 77-98; rtd 98. *37 Dunraven Road, Sketty, Swansea SA2 9LQ* Tel (01792) 201937

WHITE, Eric James. b 46. Man OLM Scheme. **d** 01 **p** 02. OLM Pennington from 01. *18 Clifton Road, Leigh WN7 3LS* Tel (01942) 678758

✠**WHITE, The Rt Revd Francis.** b 49. Univ of Wales (Cardiff) BSc(Econ)70 DSS71. St Jo Coll Nottm DipTh78. **d** 80 **p** 81 **c** 02. C Dur St Nic *Dur* 80-84; C Chester le Street 84-87; Chapl Dur and Ches le Street Hosps 87-89; V Birtley *Dur* 89-97; RD Chester-le-Street 93-97; Adn Sunderland and Hon Can Dur Cathl 97-02; Can Pet Cathl *Pet* from 02; Suff Bp Brixworth from 02. *4 The Avenue, Dallington, Northampton NN5 7AN* Tel (01604) 759423 Fax 750925 E-mail fw@bpofbrixworth.free-online.co.uk

WHITE, Frederick William Hartland. b 22. MBE62. Kelham Th Coll 39. **d** 45 **p** 46. C Newc St Jo *Newc* 45-50; CF 50-70; Asst Chapl Gen 70-74; QHC from 73; V Harrow St Mary *Lon* 74-87; rtd 87; Perm to Offic *Sarum* from 87. *Whitesfield House, 5 Seend Cleeve, Melksham SN12 6PS*

WHITE, Canon Gavin Donald. b 27. Toronto Univ BA49 Lon Univ PhD70. Trin Coll Toronto BD61 Gen Th Sem (NY) STM68 St Steph Ho Ox 51. **d** 53 **p** 54. Canada 53-58; Zanzibar 59-62; Kenya 62-66; C Hampstead St Steph *Lon* 68-70; Lect Glas Univ 71-92; Lic to Offic *Glas* 71-90; rtd 92; Hon Can St Mary's Cathl *Glas* from 92; Hon C St Andrews All SS *St And* from 94. *85D Market Street, St Andrews KY16 9NX* Tel (01334) 477338 E-mail 101502.2022@compuserve.com

WHITE, Geoffrey Brian. b 54. Jes Coll Ox BA76 MA80. St Steph Ho Ox 76. **d** 79 **p** 80. C Huddersfield St Pet *Wakef* 79-82; C Flixton St Mich *Man* 82-84; TV Westhoughton 84-91; V Stevenage St Mary Shephall w Aston *St Alb* from 91; RD Stevenage from 01. *St Mary's Vicarage, 148 Hydean Way, Sheppall, Stevenage SG2 9YA* Tel (01438) 351963

WHITE, Canon Geoffrey Gordon. b 28. Selw Coll Cam BA50 MA54. Cuddesdon Coll 51. **d** 53 **p** 54. C Bradford-on-Avon *Sarum* 53-56; C Kennington St Jo *S'wark* 56-61; V Leeds St Wilfrid *Ripon* 61-63; Chapl K Coll Hosp Lon 63-66; V

Aldwick *Chich* 66-76; V Brighton Gd Shep Preston 76-93; Can and Preb Chich Cathl 90-93; rtd 93; Hon C Stepney St Dunstan and All SS *Lon* from 94. *Flat 65, Telfords Yard, London E1 9BQ* Tel (020) 7480 6585

WHITE, Howard Christopher Graham. b 43. Leeds Univ BA65. Coll of Resurr Mirfield 67. **d** 67 **p** 68. C Friern Barnet St Jas *Lon* 67-71; P-in-c Uxbridge Moor 71-73; Asst Chapl RADD 73-77; Hon C Corringham *Chelmsf* 73-77; Team Ldr St Sav Cen for the Deaf Acton 77-84; Perm to Offic *Guildf* 86-94; Perm to Offic *Chich* from 94. *Chez Nous, St Saviour's Hill, St Saviour, Jersey JE2 7LF*

WHITE, Hugh Richard Bevis. b 55. New Coll Ox BA78 Ox Univ DPhil85. S'wark Ord Course 93. **d** 96 **p** 97. NSM Westcote Barton w Steeple Barton, Duns Tew etc *Ox* 96-99; NSM Ox St Mary V w St Cross and St Pet 99-01; V Deddington w Barford, Clifton and Hempton from 01. *28 Duns Tew, Bicester OX25 6JR* Tel (01869) 347889

WHITE, Ian Terence. b 56. CertEd. Ripon Coll Cuddesdon 83. **d** 86 **p** 87. C Maidstone St Martin *Cant* 86-89; C Earley St Pet *Ox* 89-91; TV Schorne 91-96; V St Osyth *Chelmsf* 96-00; V The Suttons w Tydd *Linc* from 00. *The Vicarage, 41 Chapelgate, Sutton St James, Spalding PE12 0EE* Tel (01945) 440457 E-mail reviewnhite@aol.com

WHITE, Jack Chapman. b 27. St Louis Univ BSc49 Univ of Cincinnati PhD82. **d** 54 **p** 55. USA 54-62 and 65-94; C St Louis H Trin 54-55; C St Louis Ascension 54-56; P-in-c 56-57; P-in-c St Louis St Andr 57; Chapl Utica Coll Syracuse Univ NY 57-58; Adv and Asst Chapl Barnard Coll Columbia Univ 58-62; Can Res American Cathl Paris 62-65; Chapl American Coll France 62-65; Chapl Howard Univ Washington DC 65-66; Dir Youth Services Piedmont 66-67; Assoc Min Washington DC St Thos 68-74; Tutor Gestalt Inst Gt Duck Is 75; Dir Speakers Bureau Nat Cathls Assn (NYC) from 78; Izmir (Smyrna) w Bornova *Eur* 95-96; rtd 96. *PK 148 Pasapor, Alfancak, Izmir, Turkey 35220*

WHITE, Miss Janice. b 49. Trin Coll Bris IDC76. **d** 91 **p** 94. C Claygate *Guildf* 91-98; Assoc Min Stanford-le-Hope w Mucking *Chelmsf* from 98. *Glebe House, Wharf Road, Stanford-le-Hope SS17 0BY* Tel (01375) 645542

WHITE, Jeremy Spencer. b 54. St Luke's Coll Ex BEd78. Wycliffe Hall Ox 81. **d** 84 **p** 85. C S Molton w Nymet St George, High Bray etc *Ex* 84-87; TV 87-95; V Sway *Win* 95-00; P-in-c Uplyme w Axmouth *Ex* 00-03; R from 03. *The Rectory, Rhode Lane, Uplyme, Lyme Regis DT7 3TX* Tel (01297) 443256

WHITE, Canon John Austin. b 42. Hull Univ BA64. Coll of Resurr Mirfield 64. **d** 66 **p** 67. C Leeds St Aid *Ripon* 66-69; Asst Chapl Leeds Univ 69-73; Chapl N Ord Course 73-82; Can and Prec Windsor from 82. *8 The Cloisters, Windsor Castle, Windsor SL4 1NJ* Tel (01753) 848787 E-mail j.white@stgeorges-windsor.org

WHITE, John Christopher. b 62. Keble Coll Ox BA84. Wycliffe Hall Ox 86. **d** 89 **p** 90. C Southway *Ex* 89-93; TV Plymouth Em, St Paul Efford and St Aug 93-99; Hon C Abbotskerswell from 99. *The Vicarage, Church Path, Abbotskerswell, Newton Abbot TQ12 5NY* Tel (01626) 334445 E-mail priscillawhite@fish.co.uk

WHITE, John Cooper. b 58. LTCL79 K Alfred's Coll Win BEd82 Lon Univ MA92 FRSA94. St Steph Ho Ox 86. **d** 89 **p** 90. C Christchurch *Win* 89-93; P-in-c Bournemouth St Alb 93-94; V 94-00; P-in-c Southbourne St Kath from 00. *St Katharine's Vicarage, 7 Wollaston Road, Bournemouth BH6 4AR* Tel (01202) 423986

WHITE, Canon John Francis. b 47. Qu Coll Cam BA69 MA73. Cuddesdon Coll 72. **d** 72 **p** 73. Sacr Wakef Cathl *Wakef* 72-73; Prec 73-76; V Thurlstone 76-82; P-in-c Hoyland Swaine 81-82; V Chapelthorpe from 82; RD Chevet from 96; Hon Can Wakef Cathl from 00. *The Vicarage, 3 Church Lane, Chapelthorpe, Wakefield WF4 3JF* Tel (01924) 255360 E-mail john@white3.demon.co.uk

WHITE, John Malcolm. b 54. Aston Univ BSc77. Trin Coll Bris BA87. **d** 87 **p** 88. C Harborne Heath *Birm* 87-91; C S Harrow St Paul *Lon* 91-93; TV Roxeth 93-96; V Derby St Alkmund and St Werburgh *Derby* from 96. *The Vicarage, 200 Duffield Road, Derby DE22 1BL* Tel (01332) 348339

WHITE, John McKelvey. b 57. QUB BA TCD DipTh82. **d** 82 **p** 83. C Clooney *D & R* 82-84; C Belfast H Trin *Conn* 84-86; I Kilcronaghan w Draperstown and Sixtowns *D & R* 86-94; I Ballybeen *D & D* from 94. *1 Grahamsbridge Road, Dundonald, Belfast BT16 0DB* Tel (028) 9048 9297

WHITE, Canon John Neville. b 41. Edin Univ MA63. Cranmer Hall Dur DipTh65. **d** 65 **p** 66. C Sedgefield *Dur* 65-68; C Stoke Cov 68-72; V Wrose *Bradf* 72-90; V Farsley from 90; RD Calverley 93-98; Hon Can Bradf Cathl from 96. *The Vicarage, 9 St John's Avenue, Farsley, Pudsey LS28 5DN* Tel 0113-257 4009

WHITE, John William. b 57. CEng71 MIMechE71. St Alb and Ox Min Course 98. **d** 01 **p** 02. NSM Sandhurst *Ox* from 01. *21 Broom Acres, Sandhurst GU47 8PN* Tel (01344) 774349

WHITE, Jonathan Roger. b 36. Lon Univ BSc61. Cuddesdon Coll 63. **d** 65 **p** 66. C Swinton St Pet *Man* 65-67; C Prestwich St Mary 67-70; R Salford Stowell Memorial 70-74; TV Swan *Ox* 74-78; P-in-c Monks Risborough 78-84; P-in-c Gt and Lt Kimble

78-84; P-in-c Prestwood 84-87; P-in-c Gt w Lt Hampden 85-87; P-in-c Prestwood and Gt Hampden 87-93; R 93-02; RD Wendover 89-94; rtd 02. *Fairlight, Mark Cross, Crowborough TN6 3PJ* Tel (01892) 852388

WHITE (née REDMAN), Mrs Julia Elizabeth Hithersay. b 43. St Alb Minl Tr Scheme 87 St Alb and Ox Min Course 99. **d** 99 **p** 00. NSM Harpenden St Jo *St Alb* from 99. *The Folly, 71 Station Road, Harpenden AL5 4RL* Tel (01582) 763869

WHITE, Mrs Julia Mary (Jo). b 52. N Ord Course. **d** 03. C Ashbourne w Mapleton *Derby* from 03. *12 Meynell Rise, Ashbourne DE6 1RU* Tel (01335) 346446

WHITE, Julian Edward Llewellyn. b 53. St D Coll Lamp BA79 Bp Burgess Hall Lamp 73 Chich Th Coll 79. **d** 79 **p** 80. C Newport St Mark *Mon* 79-83; TV Llanmartin 83-86; R Llandogo and Tintern 86-90 and 91-98; P-in-c St Paul and St Thos St Kitts-Nevis 90-91; V Mathern and Mounton w St Pierre from 98. *St Tewdric's Vicarage, Mathern, Chepstow NP16 6JA* Tel (01291) 622317

WHITE, Justin Michael. b 70. Keble Coll Ox MEng93 Warwick Univ MA94 Trin Coll Cam BA00. Westcott Ho Cam 98. **d** 01 **p** 02. C Chippenham St Andr w Tytherton Lucas *Bris* from 01. *20A St Mary Street, Chippenham SN15 3JP* Tel (01249) 443364 Mobile 07866-073023 E-mail jwhite9243@aol.com

WHITE, Keith. b 54. Liv Poly BA78 Lon Univ BD82. Wycliffe Hall Ox 78. **d** 81 **p** 82. C Edin St Thos *Edin* 81-84; C Fulwood *Sheff* 84-87; R Heigham H Trin *Nor* 87-95; Zimbabwe 95-97; V Ipswich St Jo *St E* from 97. *St John's Vicarage, Cauldwell Hall Road, Ipswich IP4 4QE* Tel (01473) 728034
E-mail keith@whites10.freeserve.co.uk

WHITE, Kenneth Charles. b 15. TD. FCIS FHSM. St Deiniol's Hawarden 76. **d** 77 **p** 78. Hon C Upton Ascension *Ches* 77-79; R Warburton 79-82; rtd 82; Perm to Offic *Ches* 82-99; Chapl Asst Countess of Ches Hosp 84-99. *Birch Heath Lodge, Christleton, Chester CH3 7AP* Tel (01244) 330025

WHITE, Kenneth Charles. b 26. Tyndale Hall Bris 48. **d** 54 **p** 56. Uganda 54-55; Kenya 55-57; C Morden *S'wark* 57-60; V Ramsey St Mary's w Ponds Bridge *Ely* 60-66; V Leyton Ch Ch *Chelmsf* 66-81; V Totland Bay *Portsm* 81-91; rtd 91; Perm to Offic *Llan* from 91. *30 Pendwyallt Road, Whitchurch, Cardiff CF14 7EG* Tel (029) 2061 1529

WHITE, Malcolm Robert. b 46. Man Univ BSc68. St Jo Coll Dur 74. **d** 77 **p** 78. C Innerhythe *York* 77-81; C Sutton St Jas and Wawne 81-83; V Upper Holloway St Pet w St Jo *Lon* 83-95; TV Burnham w Dropmore, Hitcham and Taplow *Ox* 95-00; CMS Jordan from 00. *CMS, Partnership House, 157 Waterloo Road, London SE1 8UU* Tel (020) 7803 3318 Fax 7401 3215
E-mail malcolm@sleepy-hollow.freeserve.co.uk

WHITE, Marilyn Jeanne. b 32. Avery Hill Coll CertEd69. WMMTC 85. **d** 88 **p** 94. NSM Westbury-on-Severn w Flaxley and Blaisdon *Glouc* 88-98; Perm to Offic *B & W* from 98. *4 Minster Way, Bath BA2 6RQ* Tel (01225) 464450

WHITE (née DUNCOMBE), Mrs Maureen Barbara. b 42. Bris Univ BA63 Ox Univ DipEd69. Oak Hill Th Coll 87. **d** 89 **p** 00. NSM Wallington H Trin *S'wark* 89-91; Perm to Offic *Win* 99-00; NSM Totton from 00. *Meadowsweet, 132 Woodlands Road, Ashurst, Southampton SO40 7AP* Tel (023) 8029 2309 Mobile 07712-418224 E-mail meadowsweet new.uk@excite.co.uk

WHITE, Michael Godfrey. b 46. St Alb and Ox Min Course 98. **d** 02. OLM Shelswell Ox from 02. *11 Hardwick, Bicester OX27 8SS* Tel (01869) 278157
E-mail mike.doreenwhite@ntlworld.com

WHITE, Nicolas John. b 54. BEd. Wycliffe Hall Ox. **d** 83 **p** 84. C Islington St Mary *Lon* 83-87; Chapl Univ Coll 87-89. *36 Castelnau, London SW13 9RU*

WHITE, Noel Louis. b 11. TCD BA45 MA58. CITC 46. **d** 46 **p** 47. C Ballymacarrett St Patr *D & D* 46-50; CMS Miss Sudan 50-59; C Lisburn St Paul *Conn* 60-62; V Derrnaughan 62-64; Asst Gen Sec CMS Ireland 71-81; Lic to Offic *D & D* 75-82; rtd 82; Hon C Newtownards *D & D* from 82. *Achlon, 90 Hamilton Road, Bangor BT20 4LG* Tel (028) 9145 0121 Fax 9127 4717

WHITE, Peter Francis. b 27. St Edm Hall Ox BA51 MA55. Ridley Hall Cam 51. **d** 53 **p** 54. C Drypool St Columba *York* 53-56; V Dartford St Edm *Roch* 56-62; CF 62-78; R Barming *Roch* 78-89; rtd 89; Perm to Offic *Wakef* 89-98. *Middleton House Cottage, Middleton on the Hill, Ludlow SY8 4BE* Tel (01568) 750454

WHITE, Peter John. b 26. St Aid Birkenhead 57. **d** 60 **p** 61. C Toxteth Park St Gabr *Liv* 60-62; C Huyton St Mich 62-63; V

Thornham w Gravel Hole *Man* 63-68; C Keighley *Bradf* 68-71; C Newington w Dairycoates *York* 71-75; C Frodingham *Linc* 75-80; R Mareham-le-Fen and Revesby 80-86; V Wrawby 86-91; V Melton Ross w New Barnetby 86-91; rtd 91; Perm to Offic *Linc* 91-95. *3 Park Avenue, Wakefield WF2 8DS* Tel (01924) 201438

WHITE, Philip Craston. b 59. York Univ BA81 Nottm Univ PGCE84. Trin Coll Bris DipTS99. **d** 99 **p** 00. C Countesthorpe w Foston *Leic* from 99. *7 Borrowcup Close, Countesthorpe, Leicester LE8 5XJ* Tel 0116-277 6066

WHITE, Philip William. b 53. Bede Coll Dur CertEd75 Coll of Ripon & York St Jo MA01. St Jo Coll Nottm DCM91. **d** 91 **p** 92. C Clifton *York* 91-95; TV Heworth H Trin 95-01; P-in-c Scarborough St Jas w H Trin from 01; Tr Officer E Riding from 01. *St James's Vicarage, 24 Seamer Road, Scarborough YO12 4DT* Tel (01723) 361469 Mobile 07720-010066
E-mail phil@vicarage.netkonect.co.uk

WHITE, Canon Phillip George. b 33. Univ of Wales (Lamp) BA54. St Mich Coll Llan 54. **d** 56 **p** 57. C Tongwynlais *Llan* 56-58; C Mountain Ash 58-60; C Aberavon 60-62; Area Sec (Middx) CMS 62-64; V Treherbert *Llan* 64-76; P-in-c Treorchy 75-76; V Treherbert w Treorchy 76-77; V Pyle w Kenfig 77-99; RD Margam 86-99; Can Llan Cathl from 91; rtd 99. *8 Heol Fair, Porthcawl CF36 5LA* Tel (01656) 786297

WHITE, Mrs Priscilla Audrey. b 62. St Hugh's Coll Ox BA84 MA88. Wycliffe Hall Ox 87. **d** 89 **p** 94. Par Dn Southway *Ex* 89-93; NSM Plymouth Em, St Paul Efford and St Aug 93-99; P-in-c Abbotskerswell from 99. *The Vicarage, Church Path, Abbotskerswell, Newton Abbot TQ12 5NY* Tel (01626) 334445
E-mail priscillawhite@fish.co.uk

WHITE, Richard Alfred. b 49. DipSW CQSW. St Jo Coll Nottm. **d** 90 **p** 91. C Leic St Phil *Leic* 90-95; C Old Dalby and Nether Broughton 95-98; R Ibstock w Heather from 98. *The Rectory, 2 Hinckley Road, Ibstock LE67 6PB* Tel (01530) 260246
E-mail rwhite@leicester.anglican.org

WHITE, Richard Allen. b 25. Open Univ BA78 Southn Univ MPhil88 MTh95. Sarum & Wells Th Coll 78. **d** 81 **p** 82. NSM Bursledon *Win* 81-85; C W End 85-90; C Fareham SS Pet and Paul *Portsm* 90-95; Chapl St Chris Hosp Fareham 92-98; rtd 96; Perm to Offic *Portsm* and *Win* from 96. *11 Quay Haven, Swanwick, Southampton SO31 7DE* Tel (01489) 576529

WHITE, Richard Stanley. b 70. Trin Coll Bris BA02. **d** 03. C Haydock St Mark *Liv* from 03. *303 Park Street, Haydock, St Helens WA11 0BG* Tel (01744) 634026
E-mail richardwhite@stmarkshaydock.org

WHITE, Rick. *See* WHITE, Douglas Richard Leon

WHITE, Canon Robert Bruce. b 42. Sarum & Wells Th Coll 71. **d** 73 **p** 74. C Woodford St Barn *Chelmsf* 73-75; Youth Chapl 75-79; C-in-c Sutton 75-78; P-in-c 78-79; C-in-c Shopland 75-78; P-in-c 78-79; TR Southend St Jo w St Mark, All SS w St Fran etc 79-82; P-in-c Southend St Alb 80-82; TR Southend 82-89; P-in-c Brentwood St Thos from 89; RD Brentwood from 93; Hon Can Chelmsf Cathl from 97; Chapl NE Lon Mental Health Tr from 97. *The Vicarage, 91 Queen's Road, Brentwood CM14 4EY* Tel (01277) 225700 E-mail pilgrimtravel@supanet.com

WHITE, Canon Robert Charles. b 61. Mansf Coll Ox BA83. St Steph Ho Ox 83. **d** 85 **p** 86. C Forton *Portsm* 85-88; C Portsea N End St Mark 88-92; V Warren Park 92-00; P-in-c Leigh Park 94-96; V 96-00; Hon Can Portsm Cathl from 97; RD Havant 98-00; V Portsea St Mary from 00. *St Mary's Vicarage, Fratton Road, Portsmouth PO1 5PA* Tel (023) 9282 2687 *or* 9282 2990 Fax 9235 9320 E-mail revrcwhite@aol.com

WHITE, The Ven Robin Edward Bantry. b 47. TCD BA70 BD79. CITC 72. **d** 72 **p** 73. C Dublin Zion Ch *D & G* 72-76; Min Can St Patr Cathl Dublin 76-79; C Taney Ch Ch *D & G* 76-79; I Abbeystrewry Union *C, C & R* 79-89; I Douglas Union w Frankfield from 89; Can Ross Cathl 89-93; Can Cork Cathl from 89; Adn Cork, Cloyne and Ross from 93. *The Rectory, Carrigaline Road, Douglas, Cork, Irish Republic* Tel and fax (00353) (21) 489 1539 Mobile 87-2862178
E-mail archdeacon@cork.anglican.org

WHITE, Roderick Harry. b 55. Trin Coll Bris BA86. **d** 86 **p** 87. C Northampton St Giles *Pet* 86-89; C Godley cum Newton Green *Ches* 89-93; P-in-c 93-99; R Northiam *Chich* from 99. *The Rectory, 24 High Meadow, Northiam, Rye TN31 6GA* Tel (01797) 253118

WHITE, Roger Charles. b 37. St Alb Minl Tr Scheme 77. **d** 80 **p** 81. NSM Wilshamstead and Houghton Conquest *St Alb* from 80. *30 Wood End Road, Kempston, Bedford MK43 9BB* Tel (01234) 743396

WHITE, Roger David. b 37. Univ of Wales (Cardiff) BTh91. St Mich Coll Llan DipTh66. **d** 66 **p** 67. C Mountain Ash *Llan* 66-71; C Port Talbot St Theodore 71-74; V Caerhun w Llangelynin *Ban* 74-85; R Llanbedrog w Llannor w Llanfihangel etc 85-88; V Llangeinor *Llan* 88-90; V Spittal w Trefgarn and Ambleston w St Dogwells *St D* 90-98; V Abergwili w Llanfihangel-uwch-Gwili etc 98-00; rtd 00. *4 Gathen Close, Llanelli SA15 2RW* Tel (01554) 754917

WHITE, Roger Ian Scott. b 41. Leeds Univ BA62 Culham Coll Ox PGCE70. Coll of Resurr Mirfield 62. **d** 64 **p** 65. C Wotton-under-Edge *Glouc* 64-69; NSM Rugby St Andr *Cov* 71-80; W Germany 80-82; P-in-c Brinklow *Cov* 82-86; R 86-90; P-in-c Harborough Magna 82-86; R 86-90; P-in-c Monks Kirby w Pailton and Stretton-under-Fosse 82-86; V 86-90; Germany 90-92; V Lydgate w Friezland *Man* 92-01; Chapl Hamburg *Eur* from 01. *Beim Grünen Jäger 16, 20359 Hamburg, Germany* Tel (0049) (40) 439 2334

✠WHITE, The Rt Revd Roger John. b 41. Kelham Th Coll. d 66 p 67 c 84. C Manston *Ripon* 66-69; USA from 69; Bp Milwaukee from 85. *3950 North Ridgefield Circle, Shorewood, WI 53211, USA* Tel (001) (414) 291 2883 Fax 272 7790
E-mail bishop@episcopalmilwaukee.org

WHITE, Ronald Henry. b 36. Bris Univ BSc58 Ox Univ DipEd59 Lon Univ DipTh64. SW Minl Tr Course 82. d 85 p 86. C Ivybridge *Ex* 85-87; C Ivybridge w Harford 87-88; V Blackawton and Stoke Fleming 88-95; V Stoke Fleming, Blackawton and Strete 95-00; RD Woodleigh 95-99; rtd 00. *17 Logan Way, Hemyock, Cullompton EX15 3RD* Tel (01823) 681020

WHITE, Canon Roy Sidney. b 34. Sarum Th Coll 62. d 65 p 66. C Selsdon *Cant* 65-68; C Ranmoor *Sheff* 68-72; V Croydon St Andr *Cant* 72-78; Dir Abp Coggan Tr Cen 78-85; Dir of Chr Stewardship *S'wark* 85-91; Hon Can S'wark Cathl 85-91; Can Res S'wark Cathl 91-99; Vice Provost S'wark 91-99; rtd 99; Perm to Offic *Cant* from 00. *11 Beach Avenue, Birchington CT7 9JS* Tel (01843) 843414

WHITE, Mrs Ruth Anna. b 45. Aoyama Gakuin Tokyo BA68 Grenoble Univ. Westmr Coll Cam 83 EAMTC 98. d 99 p 00. NSM Leyton St Mary w St Edw and St Luke *Chelmsf* 99-03; NSM Leytonstone St Jo from 03; Asst Chapl among Deaf and Deaf-blind people from 99. *18A Barclay Road, London E11 3DG* Tel and fax (020) 8558 5692 Mobile 07960-580837
E-mail ruth-white@lineone.net

WHITE, Mrs Sally Margaret. b 59. Univ of Wales (Cardiff) BTh01. St Mich Coll Llan 99. d 01 p 02. C Berkeley w Wick, Breadstone and Newport *Glouc* 01-02; C Berkeley w Wick, Breadstone, Newport, Stone etc from 02. *4 Crown Orchard, Stone, Berkeley GL13 9LE* Tel (01454) 260994

WHITE, Sandy Dulcie. b 44. LNSM course 95. d 98 p 99. OLM W Streatham St Jas *S'wark* from 98. *242 Mitcham Lane, London SW16 6NU* Tel (020) 8677 9487

WHITE, Simon Inigo Dexter. b 58. York Univ BA80 Nottm Univ PGCE81. St Jo Coll Nottm 87. d 90 p 91. C Chadkirk *Ches* 90-94; C Stockport St Geo 94; TV Stockport SW 94-99; Chapl Stockport Gr Sch 94-99; P-in-c W Hallam and Mapperley *Derby* 99-02; P-in-c Stanley 99-02; R W Hallam and Mapperley w Stanley from 02. *The Rectory, The Village, West Hallam, Ilkeston DE7 6GR* Tel 0115-932 4695

WHITE, Simon James Hithersay. b 65. St Jo Coll Nottm 01. d 03. C Alnwick *Newc* from 03. *65 Allerburn Lea, Alnwick NE66 2NQ* Tel (01665) 510677 E-mail simonjhwhite@breathemail.net

WHITE, The Very Revd Stephen Ross. b 58. Hull Univ BA79 QUB DPhil93. Ripon Coll Cuddesdon BA84. d 85 p 86. C Redcar *York* 85-88; P-in-c Gweedore, Carrickfin and Templecrone *D & R* 88-92; Bp's Dom Chapl 91-92; Dean Raphoe 92-02; I Raphoe w Raymochy and Clonleigh 93-01; Dean Killaloe and Clonfert *L & K* from 02. *The Deanery, Killaloe, Co Clare, Irish Republic* Tel (00353) (61) 376687
E-mail dean@killaloe.anglican.org

WHITE, Sister Teresa Joan. b 36. Wellesley Coll (USA) BA58 Harvard Univ STB61 Lon Univ CertEd74 Hon DD86. dss 75 d 87 p 94. CSA from 72; Teacher Burlington-Danes Sch 74-76; Lect Inst of Chr Studies Lon 76-78; Gen Sec World Congress of Faiths 77-81; Lect Dioc Readers' Course *S'wark* 81-89; Asst Abp's Sec for Ecum Affairs 81-82; Ed *Distinctive Diaconate* from 81; Ed *DIAKONIA News* from 87; Ed *Distinctive News of Women in Ministry* from 94; Lic to Offic *Lon* from 94. *St Andrew's House, 2 Tavistock Road, London W11 1BA* Tel (020) 7792 5993 Fax as telephone
E-mail sister.teresa@london.anglican.org

WHITE, Trevor John. b 37. St Pet Coll Ox BA61 MA65 Lon Univ BD92. Wycliffe Hall Ox 61. d 63 p 64. C Walsall *Lich* 63-67; V Greasbrough *Sheff* 67-73; Chapl Nat Nautical Sch Portishead 73-82; Chapl Bris Cathl Sch 82-00; rtd 00; Perm to Offic *B & W* from 02; *Bris* from 00. *4 Gardner Road, Portishead, Bristol BS20 7ER* Tel (01275) 847855

WHITE, Canon Vernon Philip. b 53. Clare Coll Cam BA75 MA79 Oriel Coll Ox MLitt80. Wycliffe Hall Ox DipTh76. d 77 p 78. Tutor Wycliffe Hall Ox 77-83; Chapl and Lect Ex Univ 83-87; R Wotton and Holmbury St Mary *Guildf* 87-93; Dir of Ords 87-93; Can Res and Chan Linc Cathl *Linc* 93-01; Dir STETS from 01. *19 The Close, Salisbury SP1 2EE* Tel (01722) 424804
E-mail vpwhite@stets.ac.uk

WHITE, William Frederick. b 30. St Jo Coll Nottm. d 02. NSM Hillingdon St Jo *Lon* from 02; Asst Chapl Hillingdon Hosp NHS Trust from 02. *31A Copperfield Avenue, Hillingdon, Uxbridge UB8 3NU* Tel (01895) 236746

WHITE, William John. b 54. BSc. Wycliffe Hall Ox. d 84 p 85. C Bowdon *Ches* 84-87; C Chadkirk 87-90; R Wistaston from 90;

RD Nantwich 98-01. *The Rectory, 44 Church Lane, Wistaston, Crewe CW2 8HA* Tel (01270) 665742 or 567119

WHITE SPUNNER, Mrs Jessie Janet. b 37. SRN59 SCM61. CITC 91. d 94 p 95. NSM Shinrone w Aghancon etc *L & K* from 94. *Milltown Park, Shinrone, Birr, Co Offaly, Irish Republic* Tel (00353) (505) 47035 Fax as telephone
E-mail shinrone@killaloe.anglican.org or janwspun@iol.ie

WHITEFIELD, Keith Russell. b 60. Aber Univ MA83 PhD91 Edin Univ BD91. Edin Th Coll 88. d 91 p 93. C Haddington *Edin* 91-94; C Dunbar 91-94; Miss P Wester Hailes St Luke from 94. *35/5 Wester Hailes Park, Edinburgh EH14 3AG*
E-mail keith.whitefield@cableinet.co.uk

WHITEHEAD, Alex. *See* WHITEHEAD, Matthew Alexander

WHITEHEAD, Barry. b 30. Oriel Coll Ox BA53 MA62. St Steph Ho Ox 53. d 55 p 56. C Edgehill St Dunstan *Liv* 55-58; C Upholland 58-61; Ind Chapl 61-90; CF (TA) 64-78; V Aspull *Liv* 77-96; rtd 96; Perm to Offic *Blackb* and *Liv* from 96; *Nor* from 01. *5 Sedgely, Standish, Wigan WN6 0BZ* Tel (01257) 427160

WHITEHEAD, Brian. b 36. SRN58. S'wark Ord Course DipTh75. d 75 p 77. C Croydon St Aug *Cant* 75-78; C St Marychurch *Ex* 78-80; V Devonport St Mark Ford 80-87; V Castle Donington and Lockington cum Hemington *Leic* 87-98; Chapl Asmara St Geo Eritrea 98-99; Vice Provost All SS Cathl Cairo 99-00; Assoc P Abu Dhabi 00-01; rtd 01; Perm to Offic *Nor* from 01. *10 Bluebell Gardens, Wells-next-the-Sea NR23 1JJ* Tel (01328) 711139 E-mail britone@uk.packardbell.org

WHITEHEAD, Christopher Martin Field. b 36. ALCD62. d 62 p 63. C Higher Openshaw *Man* 62-63; C Halliwell St Pet 64-66; V Owlerton *Sheff* 66-75; V Hunmanby w Muston *York* 75-95; RD Scarborough 91-94; R Lockington and Lund and Scorborough w Leconfield 95-01; rtd 01; Perm to Offic *York* from 01. *59 Cornelian Drive, Scarborough YO11 3AL* Tel (01723) 377837

WHITEHEAD, Canon Denys Gordon. b 22. Pemb Coll Ox BA50 MA55. Linc Th Coll 49. d 52 p 53. C Sheff St Swithun *Sheff* 52-54; C Rawmarsh 54-57; Man Sec SCM 57-60; C Chorlton upon Medlock *Man* 57-60; Zambia from 60; Adn S Zambia 80-89; rtd 89; Hon Can Zambia from 93. *PO Box 60648, Livingstone, Zambia* Tel (00260) (3) 323565

WHITEHEAD, Canon Derek. b 27. St Jo Coll Cam BA50 MA55 Lon Univ BD60 Lanc Univ PhD73. Wells Th Coll 55. d 56 p 57. C Lower Broughton Ascension *Man* 56-59; Chapl Highgate Sch Lon 63-65; Lect Div Preston Poly 65-79; Dir of Educn *Chich* 79-94; Can and Preb Chich Cathl 82-98; NSM Fletching from 93; rtd 94. *2 Sheffield Park House, Uckfield TN22 3QY* Tel (01825) 790734

WHITEHEAD, Frederick Keith. b 35. K Coll Lon BD58 AKC58. St Boniface Warminster 58. d 59 p 60. C S Shore H Trin *Blackb* 59-63; C Whitfield *Derby* 63-66; Lic to Offic 66-93; V Glossop 93-98; Chapl Shire Hill Hosp Glossop 93-99; rtd 99; Perm to Offic *Derby* from 98. *7 Badgers Way, Glossop SK13 6PP* Tel (01457) 852717

WHITEHEAD, Gordon James. b 42. Clifton Th Coll 66. d 73 p 74. Chile 73-87; C Coleraine *Conn* 87-94; I Errigle Keerogue w Ballygawley and Killeshil *Arm* 94-02; I Bright w Ballee and Killough *D & D* from 02. *Bright Rectory, 126 Killough Road, Downpatrick BT30 8LL* Tel (028) 4484 2229
E-mail whiteheads@bigfoot.com or bright@down.anglican.org

WHITEHEAD, Mrs Hazel. b 54. K Coll Lon BD76 AKC76 Lon Univ CertTESOL89 Lambeth MA97. Oak Hill Th Coll 93. d 94 p 95. Tutor Dioc Min Course *Guildf* 94-96; Prin from 96; NSM Oatlands 97; P-in-c from 99. *The Vicarage, 5 Burwood Road, Walton-on-Thames KT12 4AA* Tel (01932) 269343 Fax 230274
E-mail hazel@gdmc.screaming.net

WHITEHEAD, Ian Richard. b 63. St Jo Coll Nottm BA95. d 95 p 96. C Hillmorton *Cov* 95-97; C Whitnash 97-99; R Rolleston *Lich* from 99; V Anslow from 99. *The Rectory, Church Road, Rolleston-on-Dove, Burton-on-Trent DE13 9BE* Tel (01283) 810132 or 810151 E-mail revirwhite@aol.com

WHITEHEAD, Mrs Jennifer Jane. b 45. St Jo Coll York CertEd67. LNSM course 95. d 98 p 99. OLM Winterton Gp *Linc* from 98. *11 Queen Street, Winterton, Scunthorpe DN15 9TR* Tel (01724) 734027

WHITEHEAD, John Stanley. b 38. Jes Coll Cam BA63 MA67 MPhil. Westcott Ho Cam 63. d 64 p 65. C Batley All SS *Wakef* 64-67; C Mitcham St Mark *S'wark* 67-70; C Frindsbury w Upnor *Roch* 70-72; TV Strood 72-75; R Halstead 75-82; V Betley *Lich* 82-85; V Betley and Keele 85-01; Asst Chapl Keele Univ 82-01; rtd 01. *Paddock House, Longhill Lane, Hankelow, Crewe CW3 0JG* Tel (01270) 812607
E-mail john@whitehead400.freeserve.co.uk

WHITEHEAD, Matthew Alexander. b 44. Leeds Univ BA65 St Chad's Coll Dur DipEd66 Birm Univ MA75. Qu Coll Birm DipTh68. d 69 p 70. C Bingley All SS *Bradf* 69-72; C Keele *Lich* 72-74; Asst Chapl Keele Univ 72-74; Bp's Dom Chapl *Dur* 74-80; V Escomb 74-80; V Witton Park 74-80; V Birtley 80-89; RD Chester-le-Street 84-89; V Stockton St Pet 89-00; V The Trimdons 00-03; Hon Can Dur Cathl 96-03; P-in-c Stow Gp

Linc from 03. *The Rectory, Normanby Road, Stow, Lincoln LN1 2DF* Tel (01427) 788251
E-mail alexwhitehead@btopenworld.com

WHITEHEAD, Canon Michael Hutton. b 33. St Chad's Coll Dur 54. d 58 p 59. C Southwick St Columba *Dur* 58-64; V Hendon St Ignatius 64-70; P-in-c Sunderland 67-80; V Hendon 70-80; V Hendon and Sunderland 80-87; Hon Can Dur Cathl from 84; V Hartlepool St Aid 87-98; RD Hartlepool 91-95; rtd 98. *4 West Row, Greatham, Hartlepool TS25 2HW* Tel (01429) 872922

WHITEHEAD, Nicholas James. b 53. AIB Roehampton Inst DipMMin97. Ridley Hall Cam 86. d 88 p 89. C Bourne *Guildf* 88-92; V Hersham from 92. *The Vicarage, 5 Burwood Road, Hersham, Walton-on-Thames KT12 4AA* Tel (01932) 227445
E-mail nick@nickhaze.demon.co.uk

WHITEHEAD, Paul Conrad. b 60. St Jo Coll Nottm LTh92. d 92 p 93. C Mansfield Woodhouse *S'well* 92-96; C Carlton-in-the-Willows 96-02; C Colwick 96-02; CF (TA) from 96. *84 Hillside Road, Beeston, Nottingham NG9 3AT* Tel 0115-919 7031
E-mail paulkirsten@ntlworld.com

WHITEHEAD, Philip. b 34. Kelham Th Coll 55. d 59 p 60. C Sugley *Newc* 59-62; C Alnwick St Paul 62-63; C Newc St Gabr 63-66; C Gosforth All SS 66-67; V Kenton Ascension 67-75; V Spittal 75-88; P-in-c Scremerston 81-88; V Cresswell and Lynemouth 88-96; Perm to Offic from 96; rtd 96. *13 Abbey Gate, Morpeth NE61 2XL* Tel (01670) 514953

WHITEHEAD, Robin Lawson. b 53. Bris Univ BA76 Lon Univ MA96. St Steph Ho Ox 77. d 80 p 81. C Cheshunt *St Alb* 80-83; C E Grinstead St Swithun *Chich* 83-85; V Friern Barnet St Pet le Poer *Lon* 85-92; R Friern Barnet St Jas 92-95; C Wood Green St Mich w Bounds Green St Gabr etc 96-97; TR Leic Resurr *Leic* from 97. *St Matthew's Vicarage, Taylor Road, Leicester LE1 2JN* Tel 0116-262 3038 E-mail rwhitehead@leicester.anglican.org

WHITEHORN, Arthur Basil. b 24. Ox Univ MA50. WMMTC 81. d 84 p 85. NSM Bromsgrove St Jo *Worc* 84-94; Asst Chapl Bromsgrove and Redditch HA 84-89; Perm to Offic from 94. *15 Perry Lane, Bromsgrove B61 7JL* Tel (01527) 874857

WHITEHOUSE, Alan Edward. b 35. CEng66. Glouc Sch of Min 89. d 92 p 93. NSM Evesham *Worc* 92-96; NSM Evesham w Norton and Lenchwick from 96. *The Coppice, 56 Elm Road, Evesham WR11 3DW* Tel (01386) 442427 *or* tel and fax 442213

WHITEHOUSE, Nigel Andrew. b 57. St Mary's RC Sem Birm 75. d 80 p 81. In RC Ch 81-87; C Whittlesey and Pondersbridge *Ely* 92-94; P-in-c Newton 94-98; R 98-03; P-in-c Gorefield 94-98; V 98-03; P-in-c Tydd St Giles 94-98; R 98-03; TR Whittlesey, Pondersbridge and Coates from 03. *The Vicarage, St Mary's Street, Whittlesey, Peterborough PE7 1BG* Tel (01733) 203676
E-mail nigel.whitehouse@ntlworld.com

WHITEHOUSE, Canon Susan Clara. b 48. R Holloway Coll Lon BA70. Westcott Ho Cam 87. d 89 p 94. Par Dn Farnley *Ripon* 89-93; Dioc Development Rep from 92; C Bedale 93-96; C Thornton Watlass w Thornton Steward 93-96; V Aysgarth and Bolton cum Redmire from 96; Hon Can Ripon Cathl from 02; AD Wensley from 03. *The Vicarage, Carperby, Leyburn DL8 4DQ* Tel (01969) 663235

WHITELEY, Donal Royston. b 27. Qu Coll Birm 54. d 57 p 58. C Handsworth St Mary *Birm* 57-60; C Kingswinford St Mary *Lich* 60-63; R Norton Canes 63-71; V Wetley Rocks 71-96; rtd 96; Perm to Offic *Derby* from 97. *7 Balmoral Road, Burton-on-Trent DE15 0JN* Tel (01283) 548312

WHITELEY, Robert. b 36. Dur Univ BA67. Cranmer Hall Dur 62. d 67 p 68. C Maidstone All SS w St Phil and H Trin *Cant* 67-70; Asst Chapl K Sch Roch 70-71; Chapl 71-82; rtd 01. *5 Grange Farm, Little Woodham Lane, Gosport PO13 8AB* Tel (023) 9258 0813

WHITELEY, Canon Robert Louis. b 28. Leeds Univ BA48. Coll of Resurr Mirfield 50. d 52 p 53. C Hollinwood *Man* 52-55; Br Honduras 56-61; V Illingworth *Wakef* 61-68; V Westgate Common 68-75; Can Res Wakef Cathl 75-80; Hon Can Wakef Cathl 80-93; V Almondbury 80-82; TR Almondbury w Farnley Tyas 82-92; RD Almondbury 81-93; rtd 93; Perm to Offic *Wakef* from 93; *Ox* from 98. *2 Woodclyffe Almshouses, Wargrave Hill, Wargrave, Reading RG10 8JH* Tel 0118-940 3877

WHITELOCK, Alfred Theodore. b 33. Bris Univ BTh58. Chich Th Coll 58. d 60 p 61. C Bris St Andr w St Bart *Bris* 60-62; USA from 69. *3025 Ivyland Road, Roanoke, VA 24014, USA* Tel (001) (540) 427 5073 E-mail pateral@yahoo.com

WHITELOCK, Mrs Susan Karen. b 62. STETS 98. d 01. NSM Portsea N End St Mark *Portsm* from 01. *404 Copnor Road, Portsmouth PO3 5EW* Tel 07903-414029 (mobile)

WHITEMAN, Canon Cedric Henry. b 28. Lich Th Coll 59. d 61 p 62. C Abington *Pet* 61-63; V Kettering St Andr 64-79; RD Kettering 73-79; Can Pet Cathl 77-79; V Rotherham *Sheff* 79-87; RD Rotherham 79-86; Hon Can Sheff Cathl 85-98; Bp's Dom Chapl 86-99; V Wentworth 87-91; rtd 91; Perm to Offic *Sheff* from 99. *11 Thornbrook Close, Chapeltown, Sheffield S35 2BB* Tel 0114-245 7479

WHITEMAN, Christopher Henry Raymond. b 51. Portsm Poly BA73 Worc Coll of Educn PGCE74 Open Univ BSc97. St Jo Coll Nottm DipTh90 MA99. d 90 p 91. C Rockland St Mary w Hellington, Bramerton etc *Nor* 90-93; P-in-c Gillingham w

Geldeston, Stockton, Ellingham etc 93-94; R from 94. *The Rectory, The Street, Geldeston, Beccles NR34 0LN* Tel (01502) 712255

WHITEMAN, The Ven Rodney David Carter. b 40. Ely Th Coll 61. d 64 p 65. C Kings Heath *Birm* 64-70; V Rednal 70-79; V Erdington St Barn 79-89; RD Aston 81-86 and 88-89; Hon Can Birm Cathl 85-89; Adn Bodmin *Truro* 89-00; P-in-c Cardynham 89-94; P-in-c Helland 89-94; Hon Can Truro Cathl from 89; Adn Cornwall from 00. *Archdeacon's House, 3 Knights Hill, Kenwyn, Truro TR1 3UY* Tel (01872) 272866 Fax 242108
E-mail rodney@truro.anglican.org

WHITESIDE, Canon Peter George. b 30. St Cath Coll Cam BA55 MA61. Cuddesdon Coll 55. d 57 p 58. C Westmr St Steph w St Jo *Lon* 57-61; Chapl Clifton Coll Bris 61-70; Hd Master Linc Cathl Sch 71-73; Can and Preb Linc Cathl *Linc* 72-73; Australia 74-92; Prin and Chapl Wadhurst C of E Gr Sch 74-89; TV Brentford *Lon* 92-97; rtd 97. *c/o Mrs M Pretlove, 101 Camborne Road, Morden SM4 4JN*

WHITESIDE, Robert Henry. b 44. TCD BA67 MA71 HDipEd68. CITC 95. d 98 p 99. C Clonsast w Rathangan, Thomastown etc *M & K* 98-00; Chapl K Hosp Sch Dub from 00. *The King's Hospital, Palmerstown, Dublin 20, Irish Republic* Tel (00353) (1) 626 5933 Fax 623 0349

WHITFIELD, Charles. b 25. St Pet Hall Ox BA49 MA53. Ridley Hall Cam 49. d 51 p 52. C Ecclesfield *Sheff* 51-54; C Grassendale *Liv* 54-56; C Neasden cum Kingsbury St Cath *Lon* 56-58; C St Martin-in-the-Fields 58-59; V Bromley H Trin *Roch* 59-68; V Egg Buckland *Ex* 68-90; rtd 90; Perm to Offic *Ex* from 99. *23 Chapel Meadow, Buckland Monachorum, Yelverton PL20 7LR*

WHITFIELD, Joy Verity. See CHAPMAN, Mrs Joy Verity

WHITFIELD, Leslie Turnbull. b 43. Nottm Univ MA00 DipEE67 CEng72 MIEE72 DMS74 MCMI74. St Jo Coll Nottm. d 00 p 01. C Bottesford w Ashby *Linc* 00-03; P-in-c Mablethorpe w Trusthorpe from 03. *The Rectory, 88 Wellington Road, Mablethorpe LN12 1HT* Tel (01507) 473159
E-mail les.whitfield@ntlworld.com

WHITFIELD, Trevor. b 48. Bedf Coll Lon BSc71 Bris Univ PGCE73 Fitzw Coll Cam BA78 MA88. Ridley Hall Cam 76. d 79 p 80. C Battersea St Pet and St Paul *S'wark* 79-82; Chapl Stockholm w Uppsala *Eur* 82-83; C-in-c Roundshaw St Paul CD *S'wark* 83-89; Asst Chapl R Victoria Infirmary Newc 89-92; Asst Chapl Berne w Neuchâtel *Eur* 92-95; Chapl Utrecht w Amersfoort, Harderwijk and Zwolle 95-02; Chapl Maisons-Laffitte from 02. *15 avenue Carnot, 78600 Maisons-Laffitte, France* Tel (0033) (1) 39 63 34 97

WHITFORD, Judith. *See* POLLINGER, Mrs Judith

WHITFORD, William Laurence. b 56. Open Univ BA92 Liv Univ DipApTh96. N Ord Course 92. d 95 p 96. C Hindley All SS *Liv* 95-99; P-in-c E and W Tilbury and Linford *Chelmsf* from 99. *The Rectory, Princess Margaret Road, East Tilbury, Grays RM18 8PB* Tel (01375) 842220
E-mail laurence@whitfordw.freeserve.co.uk

WHITHAM, Ian Scott. b 66. Oak Hill Th Coll. d 01 p 02. C Yateley *Win* 01-03; C Yateley and Eversley from 03. *18 Hall Farm Crescent, Yateley GU46 7HT* Tel (01252) 661717 Mobile 07946-394467 E-mail ianwitham@yahoo.co.uk

WHITING, Antony Gerald Stroud. b 26. CITC 81. d 86 p 87. NSM Clonmel Union *C, C & R* 86-87; Cork St Fin Barre's Union 87-88; Lic to Offic 88-92; Bp's C Mallow Union 92-97; I 97-98; rtd 98. *Edgwater, Midleton, Co Cork, Irish Republic* Tel (00353) (21) 463 1876

WHITING, Graham James. b 58. Bris Univ BSc81. Chich Th Coll 83. d 86 p 88. C Portslade St Nic and St Andr *Chich* 86-87; C W Tarring 87-91; C Seaford w Sutton 91-94; P-in-c Bournemouth St Clem *Win* 94-02; V Findon Valley *Chich* from 02. *The Vicarage, 29 Central Avenue, Worthing BN14 0DS* Tel (01903) 872900 E-mail graham.whiting@lineone.net

WHITING, Joseph Alfred. b 41. Oak Hill Th Coll 82. d 85 p 86. Hon C Sidcup St Andr *Roch* 85-88; C Southborough St Pet w Ch Ch and St Matt 88-92; C Aldridge *Lich* 92-97; TV Rye *Chich* 97-02; rtd 02. *71 Ash Tree Drive, West Kingsdown, Sevenoaks TN15 6LW* Tel (01474) 853202
E-mail joebarb@westking1.fsnet.co.uk

WHITING, Mark Justin Robert. b 70. St Steph Ho Ox 99. d 01 p 02. C Sevenoaks St Jo *Roch* from 01. *14 Quakers Hall Lane, Sevenoaks TN13 3TR* Tel and fax (01732) 743127 Mobile 07951-589024 E-mail revmark.whiting@bushinternet

WHITLEY, Eric Keir. b 47. Salford Univ BSc68. Trin Coll Bris 77. d 79 p 80. C Nottingham St Ann w Em *S'well* 79-83; V Donisthorpe and Moira w Stretton-en-le-Field *Leic* 83-91; V Thorpe Acre w Dishley 91-00; V Loughb Gd Shep from 00. *21 Parklands Drive, Loughborough LE11 2SZ* Tel (01509) 211005

WHITLEY, John Duncan Rooke. b 29. Trin Coll Cam BA51 MA55 Jordan Hill Coll Glas CertEd82. Coll of Resurr Mirfield 52. d 54 p 55. C Ashington *Newc* 54-59; C Chiswick St Nic w St Mary *Lon* 59-61; V Ware St Mary *St Alb* 61-71; Can Missr St Mary's Cathl Edin 71-74; Chapl Edin R Infirmary 71-74; Dioc Educn Officer *Edin* 71-74; Lic to Offic from 74; Warrant from 90; Asst Chapl Lothian Primary Healthcare NHS Trust from 95.

114 Viewforth, Edinburgh EH10 4LN Tel 0131-229 0130 *or* 537 6368 Mobile 07803-581449 Fax 229 6528 *or* 537 6516
E-mail john.whitley@blueyonder.co.uk

WHITLEY, John William. b 46. TCD BA68. Cranmer Hall Dur BA71. **d** 71 **p** 72. C Belfast St Mary Magd *Conn* 71-73; C Toxteth St Philemon w St Gabr *Liv* 73-78; P-in-c Toxteth Park St Cleopas 78-88; TV Toxteth St Philemon w St Gabr and St Cleopas 89-95; P-in-c Litherland St Paul Hatton Hill 95-02; V from 02. *St Paul's Vicarage, Watling Avenue, Liverpool L21 9NU* Tel 0151-928 2705

WHITLEY (née ALLISON), Rosemary Jean. b 45. LTCL67. Trin Coll Bris 75 St Jo Coll Nottm 94. **d** 95 **p** 99. NSM Loughb Gd Shep *Leic* 95-98 and from 00; NSM Thorpe Acre w Dishley 98-00. *21 Parklands Drive, Loughborough LE11 2SZ* Tel (01501) 211005

WHITLOCK, Canon James Frederick. b 44. Ch Coll Cam BA75 MA78. Westcott Ho Cam 73. **d** 76 **p** 77. C Newquay *Truro* 76-79; P-in-c St Mawgan w St Ervan and St Eval 79-81; R 81; Bp's Dom Chapl 82-85; Dioc Dir of Ords 82-85; V Leagrave *St Alb* 85-89; TR Probus, Ladock and Grampound w Creed and St Erme *Truro* 89-95; V Penzance St Mary w St Paul 95-00; P-in-c Penzance St Jo 97-00; Hon Can Truro Cathl 98-00; rtd 00; Perm to Offic *Truro* from 00. *10 Barlandhu, Newlyn, Penzance TR18 5QT* Tel (01736) 330474

WHITMORE, Benjamin Nicholas. b 66. Imp Coll Lon BEng88. Cranmer Hall Dur 89. **d** 92 **p** 93. C Gt Wyrley *Lich* 92-95; C Hednesford 95-00; V Walsall Pleck and Bescot from 00. *St John's Vicarage, Vicarage Terrace, Walsall WS2 9HB* Tel (01922) 631989 E-mail bennyjo@vicres.fsnet.co.uk

WHITMORE, Edward James. b 36. Lon Univ BD66. Tyndale Hall Bris. **d** 68 **p** 69. Tanzania 68-76; Lic to Offic *Blackb* from 79. *74 Greencroft, Penwortham, Preston PR1 9LB* Tel (01772) 746522

WHITMORE, Miss Jane Frances. b 30. dss 79 **d** 87 **p** 94. Elloughton and Brough w Brantingham *York* 79-83; Foley Park *Worc* 83-87; C Frimley *Guildf* 87-96; rtd 96; Perm to Offic *Worc* from 96. *The Grange, 26 Middleton Road, Marlpool, Kidderminster DY11 5EY*

WHITMORE, Stephen Andrew. b 53. Sheff Univ BSc74. St Jo Coll Nottm 89. **d** 91 **p** 92. C Newbury *Ox* 91-95; TV High Wycombe from 95. *70 Marlow Road, High Wycombe HP11 1TH* Tel (01494) 438722 E-mail steve@stjohnschurch.freeserve.co.uk

WHITNALL, Robert Edward (Dominic). b 14. Magd Coll Ox BA37. Cuddesdon Coll 37. **d** 38 **p** 39. C Staveley *Derby* 38-44; S Africa 47-66; CR from 47; Hon C Battyeford *Wakef* from 68; rtd 84. *House of the Resurrection, Stocks Bank Road, Mirfield WF14 0BN* Tel (01924) 494318

WHITTA, Rex Alfred Rought. b 28. Leeds Inst of Educn CertEd52 Open Univ BA88 Lon Univ CertTESOL85. Qu Coll Birm DipTh63. **d** 63 **p** 64. C Newland St Aug *York* 63-66; V Elloughton 66-68; P-in-c Brantingham 66-68; V Elloughton and Brough w Brantingham 68-74; TR Redcar w Kirkleatham 74-78; V Redcar 78-81; V Bassenthwaite, Isel and Setmurthy *Carl* 84-86; P-in-c Cloughton *York* 86-88; P-in-c Hackness w Harwood Dale 86-88; rtd 89; Perm to Offic *York* from 89. *10 Betton Rise, East Ayton, Scarborough YO13 9HU* Tel (01723) 863493
E-mail rex.whitta1@btopenworld.com

WHITTAKER, Mrs Angela. b 68. Birm Univ BA89 St Martin's Coll Lanc PGCE91. NEOC 98. **d** 00 **p** 01. C Houghton le Spring *Dur* from 00. *Kepier Flat, Kepier, Church Street, Houghton le Spring DH4 4DN* Tel 0191-584 9449

WHITTAKER, Arthur. b 30. Oak Hill Th Coll. **d** 60 **p** 61. C Bispham *Blackb* 60-64; V Edge Hill St Cypr *Liv* 64-73; Area Sec CMS *Ban, St As, Ches* and *S & M* 73-74; C Maghull *Liv* 74-93; V Bilsborrow *Blackb* 74-96; rtd 96; Hon C Preesall *Blackb* from 98; Perm to Offic *Blackb* from 96 and *Carl* from 00. *16 Trinity Drive, Holme, Carnforth LA6 1QL* Tel (01524) 781208

WHITTAKER, Arthur George. b 14. MRIPHH38 LTCL57 Man Univ 48. **d** 60 **p** 61. C Ibstock *Leic* 60-62; C Leic St Phil 62-63; V Hadfield *Derby* 63-72; V Coldham *Ely* 72-81; V Friday Bridge 72-81; rtd 81; Perm to Offic *Glouc* 81-98. *27 Mosley Crescent, Cashes Green, Stroud GL5 4LT* Tel (01453) 763622

WHITTAKER, Barry Percival. b 29. AKC54. K Coll Lon BD54. **d** 55 **p** 57. C Benchill *Man* 55-59; C Atherton 59-60; Canada from 60. *54 Crescent Avenue, St Thomas ON, Canada, N5P 2K3* Tel (001) (519) 633 0884

WHITTAKER, Brian Lawrence. b 39. Clifton Th Coll 63. **d** 66 **p** 67. C Whitton and Thurleston w Akenham *St E* 66-69; C Normanton *Wakef* 69-74; P-in-c Castle Hall *Ches* 74-77; P-in-c Dukinfield Ch Ch 74-77; P-in-c Stalybridge H Trin and Ch Ch 74-77; V 77-83; TR Bucknall and Bagnall *Lich* 83-91; R Draycott-le-Moors w Forsbrook from 91. *The Rectory, 7 Cheadle Road, Blythe Bridge, Stoke-on-Trent ST11 9PW* Tel (01782) 392259

WHITTAKER, Bryan. b 58. Southn Univ BTh82. Chich Th Coll 82. **d** 84 **p** 85. C Whitleigh *Ex* 84-88; C Corringham *Chelmsf* 88-92; V Rush Green 92-94. *361 Dagenham Road, Romford RM7 0XX*

WHITTAKER, Derek. b 30. OBE85. Liv Univ BEng51 PhD58 CEng65. **d** 93 **p** 95. Zambia 93-96; NSM Broom Leys *Leic* 97-00;

rtd 00; Perm to Offic *Leic* from 00. *44 St David's Crescent, Coalville LE67 4SJ* Tel (01530) 831071

WHITTAKER, Edward Geoffrey. b 59. Birm Univ BSc82 Avery Hill Coll PGCE85 Dur Univ MA95. Westcott Ho Cam 97. **d** 99 **p** 00. C Neston *Ches* 99-02; V Rocester and Croxden w Hollington *Lich* from 02. *The Vicarage, Church Lane, Rocester, Uttoxeter ST14 5JZ* Tel (01889) 590424

WHITTAKER, Garry. b 59. St Jo Coll Nottm DCM91. **d** 91 **p** 92. C Denton Ch Ch *Man* 91-95; P-in-c Waterhead from 95. *Holy Trinity Vicarage, Church Street East, Waterhead, Oldham OL4 2JQ* Tel 0161-624 4011

WHITTAKER, James Rawstron. b 14. Worc Coll Ox BA38 MA46. Wells Th Coll 38. **d** 40 **p** 41. C York St Mary Bishophill Senior *York* 40-43; Hornsea w Bewholme 43-47; R Neen Sollars w Milson *Heref* 47-55; V Annscroft 55-70; R Pontesbury III 55-70; V Longden 55-70; V Almeley 70-80; P-in-c Kinnersley w Norton Canon 74-80; rtd 81; Perm to Offic *Heref* from 82. *Eign Gate House, 142 Eign Street, Hereford HR4 0AP* Tel (01432) 268961

WHITTAKER, Mrs Jennifer Margaret. b 43. Glas Univ MA64. St Alb and Ox Min Course 00. **d** 03. NSM Martley and Wichenford, Knightwick etc *Worc* from 03. *The Key Barn, Half Key, Malvern WR14 1UP* Tel (01886) 833897
E-mail jenniferwhittaker@virgin.net

WHITTAKER, Jeremy Paul. b 59. Ox Univ MA. Ripon Coll Cuddesdon 82. **d** 84 **p** 85. C Crowthorne *Ox* 84-87; C Westborough *Guildf* 87-88; V New Bury 88-91; Chapl Frensham 91-95; Perm to Offic *Guildf* from 95. *6 Springhaven Close, Guildford GU1 2JP*

WHITTAKER, Canon John. b 20. Ch Coll Cam BA47 MA49. Ridley Hall Cam 46. **d** 48 **p** 49. C Astley Bridge *Man* 48-51; C Kersal Moor 51-53; R Birch St Agnes 53-66; V New Bury 66-75; Hon Can Man Cathl 71-87; R Middleton 75-87; rtd 87; Perm to Offic *Man* from 87. *5 Farnborough Road, Bolton BL1 7HJ* Tel (01204) 595499

WHITTAKER, John. b 27. Oak Hill Th Coll 53. **d** 55 **p** 56. C Blackpool St Thos *Blackb* 55-57; C St Helens St Helen *Liv* 58-60; V Hensingham *Carl* 60-67; V Skelmersdale St Paul *Liv* 67-77; V Gt Faringdon w Lt Coxwell *Ox* 77-83; RD Vale of White Horse 80-83; rtd 83; Perm to Offic *Ox* 83-88; C Broughton Poggs w Filkins, Broadwell etc 88-95; C Shill Valley and Broadshire 95--96; Perm to Offic from 98. *26 The Pines, Faringdon SN7 8AU* Tel (01367) 241009

WHITTAKER, John. b 69. Leic Univ BA90 ACA93. Ripon Coll Cuddesdon BTh00. **d** 00 **p** 01. C Melton Mowbray *Leic* 00-03; P-in-c Barrow upon Soar w Walton le Wolds from 03. *27 Cotes Road, Barrow upon Soar, Loughborough LE12 8JP* Tel (01509) 621834 E-mail john.whittaker3@ntlworld.com

WHITTAKER, Karl Paul. b 55. ATL. CITC BTh95. **d** 95 **p** 96. C Killowen *D & R* 95-99; I Annaghmore *Arm* from 99. *54 Moss Road, Portadown BT62 1NB* Tel (028) 3885 1555
E-mail paul@revwhittaker.freeserve.co.uk

WHITTAKER, Canon Peter Harold. b 39. AKC62. **d** 63 **p** 64. C Walton St Mary *Liv* 63-67; C Ross *Heref* 67-70; R Bridgnorth St Mary 70-78; P-in-c Oldbury 70-78; TR Bridgnorth, Tasley, Astley Abbotts and Oldbury 78-81; RD Bridgnorth 78-81; Preb Heref Cathl 80-81; V Leighton Buzzard w Eggington, Hockliffe etc *St Alb* 81-92; RD Dunstable 84-85; R Barton-le-Cley w Higham Gobion and Hexton from 92; Hon Can St Alb from 92. *The Rectory, Church Road, Barton-le-Clay, Bedford MK45 4LA* Tel (01582) 881226

WHITTAKER, Robert Andrew. b 49. DipEd Open Univ BA75 Nottm Univ MA83. Linc Th Coll 85. **d** 87 **p** 88. C Mansfield Woodhouse *S'well* 87-90; V Norwell w Ossington, Cromwell and Caunton 90-95; Chapl Ranby Ho Sch Retford from 95. *East Lodge, Ranby House School, Ranby, Retford DN22 8HX* Tel (01777) 701455

WHITTAKER, William Paul. *See* STAFFORD-WHITTAKER, William Paul

WHITTAM, Canon Kenneth Michael. b 26. Ball Coll Ox BA50 MA54. Cuddesdon Coll 50. **d** 52 **p** 53. C Adlington *Blackb* 52-55; C St Annes 55-58; R Halton w Aughton 58-62; R Colne St Bart 62-66; Chapl Highgate Sch Lon 66-75; V Shotwick *Ches* 75-89; can Res Ches Cathl and Dioc Missr 75-85; Hon Can Ches Cathl 85-90; Clergy Study Officer 85-91; rtd 91; Perm to Offic *Ches* from 91. *22 Warwick Close, Little Neston, Neston CH64 0SR* Tel 0151-336 8541

WHITTINGHAM, Mrs Janet Irene. b 49. Man OLM Scheme. **d** 03. OLM Pendleton *Man* from 03. *24 Aylesbury Close, Salford M5 4FQ* Tel 0161-736 5878

WHITTINGHAM, Peter. b 58. Sheff Univ BA79. St Jo Coll Nottm 88. **d** 90 **p** 91. C Northowram *Wakef* 90-93; C Airedale w Fryston 93-96; V Wrenthorpe from 96; P-in-c Alverthorpe from 02. *The Vicarage, 121 Wrenthorpe Road, Wrenthorpe, Wakefield WF2 0JS* Tel (01924) 373758

WHITTINGHAM, Ronald Norman. b 43. Linc Coll Ox BA65 MA68. Coll of Resurr Mirfield 65. **d** 67 **p** 68. C Horninglow *Lich* 67-69; C Drayton in Hales 69-70; C Uttoxeter w Bramshall 71-75; P-in-c Burton St Paul 75-80; V Shareshill 80-83; V

Silverdale and Knutton Heath 83-89; P-in-c Alsagers Bank 83-89; V Silverdale and Alsagers Bank 89-92; V Honley *Wakef* 92-99; TV Hugglescote w Donington, Ellistown and Snibston *Leic* 99-02; TV Leic Presentation from 02. *St Chad's Clergy House, 145 Coleman Road, Leicester LE5 4LH* Tel 0116-276 6062

WHITTINGTON, Canon David John. b 45. OBE01. Qu Coll Ox BA67 MA71. Coll of Resurr Mirfield 69. **d** 71 **p** 72. Chapl St Woolos Cathl *Mon* 71-72; C Ox St Mary V w St Cross and St Pet *Ox* 72-76; Chapl Qu Coll Ox 72-76; V Stockton *Dur* 77-98; Hon Can Dur Cathl 93-98; Can Res Dur Cathl from 98; Dioc Dir of Educn from 98. *16A The College, Durham DH1 3EQ* Tel 0191-384 5489 *or* 374 6005 Fax 384 7529
E-mail david.whittington@durham.anglican.org

WHITTINGTON, Peter Graham. b 68. Ox Poly BA90. Trin Coll Bris BA95. **d** 95 **p** 96. C Gateacre *Liv* 95-99; V Huyton St Geo from 99. *St George's Vicarage, 1 St George's Road, Huyton, Liverpool L36 8BE* Tel 0151-489 1997 Fax as telephone
E-mail whitts01@surfaid.org

WHITTINGTON, Richard Hugh. b 47. MBE74. Sarum & Wells Th Coll DipTh93. **d** 93 **p** 94. C Enfield St Jas *Lon* 93-96; P-in-c Ightham *Roch* 96-97; R 97-01; Chapl R Hosp Chelsea from 01. *The Chaplaincy, The Royal Hospital Chelsea, Royal Hospital Road, London SW3 4SL* Tel (020) 7881 5234 *or* 7881 5260 Mobile 07979-360025 Fax (020) 7881 5463
E-mail roylhospch@aol.com

WHITTINGTON, Mrs Sharon Ann. b 56. Leeds Univ BA79 PGCE80. NEOC. **d** 00 **p** 01. NSM Street *York* 00-03; NSM York St Olave w St Giles from 03; P-in-c York St Thos w St Maurice from 03. *30 Marygate, York YO30 7BH* Tel (01904) 656859

WHITTLE, Alan. b 29. K Coll Lon BD52 AKC52. **d** 53 **p** 54. C Combe Down *B & W* 53-55; C Bath Twerton-on-Avon 55-57; Australia 57-66; R Aston Rowant w Crowell *Ox* 66-68; Lic to Offic *S'wark* 69-72; V Mitcham Ch Ch 72-92; rtd 92; Perm to Offic *S'wark* from 92. *117 May Cross Avenue, Morden SM4 4DF* Tel (020) 8540 0201

WHITTLE, Fred. b 17. Keble Coll Ox BA40 MA44. Cuddesdon Coll 40. **d** 41 **p** 42. C Northampton St Matt *Pet* 41-47; C W Molesey *Guildf* 47-49; C Isham *Pet* 49-51; V Warmington 51-58; R Orlingbury w Pytchley 58-71; R Gt w Lt Addington 71-82; rtd 82; Lic to Offic *Pet* 82-85; Perm to Offic from 85. *6 Coleman Street, Raunds, Wellingborough NN9 6NJ* Tel (01933) 624989

WHITTLE, Ian Christopher. b 60. Univ Coll Dur BA81 Fitzw Coll Cam BA88 MA91. Ridley Hall Cam 85. **d** 88 **p** 89. C S Petherton w the Seavingtons *B & W* 88-91; Asst Chapl The Hague *Eur* 91-97; P-in-c Gayton Gp of Par *Nor* 97-99; R Gayton, Gayton Thorpe, E Walton, E Winch etc from 99; RD Lynn from 02. *The Rectory, Grimston Road, Gayton, King's Lynn PE32 1QA* Tel (01553) 636227

WHITTLE, John William. b 46. Qu Mary Coll Lon BA68. Sarum & Wells Th Coll 84. **d** 86 **p** 87. C Blandford Forum and Langton Long etc *Sarum* 86-88. *The Cottage, Queens Road, Blandford Forum DT11 7JJ*

WHITTLE, Naomi Clare. b 54. Colchester Inst of Educn BA75 Lon Univ PGCE76 LGSM77 Kent Univ DipTM98 Middx Univ MA(Theol)99. SEITE 95. **d** 98 **p** 99. C Catford (Southend) and Downham *S'wark* 98-02; P-in-c Shooters Hill Ch Ch 02; V from 02. *Christ Church Vicarage, 1 Craigholm, Shooters Hill, London SE18 3RR* Tel (020) 8856 5858
E-mail naomi@whittle30.fsnet.co.uk

WHITTLE, Robin Jeffrey. b 51. Bris Univ BA72 Leic Univ CQSW75. Sarum & Wells Th Coll 85. **d** 87 **p** 88. C Henbury *Bris* 87-91; V Capel *Guildf* 91-96; Chapl among Deaf People from 96; Perm to Offic *S'wark* and *Roch* 97-01; P-in-c Walton-on-the-Hill *Guildf* from 99. *The Rectory, Breech Lane, Tadworth KT20 7SD* Tel (01737) 812105 Fax 814333
E-mail bob@whittle1.fsnet.co.uk

WHITTLE, Mrs Sheila Margaret. b 36. Glouc Th Course 83 NY Th Sem MA88 Vancouver Sch of Th. **d** 90 **p** 90. R Bulkley Valley Canada 90-93; C Dunbar St Phil 93; P-in-c Maple Ridge St Jo the Divine 93-95; Lethbridge St Mary the Virgin 95-97; NSM Portsea N End St Mark *Portsm* 97-98; P-in-c Lezant w Lawhitton and S Petherwin w Trewen *Truro* 98-02; rtd 02; Perm to Offic *Glouc* from 03. *5 Pennine Close, Walton Cardiff, Tewkesbury GL20 7PL* Tel (01684) 299981 E-mail whittle@beeb.net

WHITTOCK, Alida. STETS. **d** 03. NSM Weymouth H Trin *Sarum* from 03. *79 Clearmount Road, Weymouth DT4 9LE* Tel (01305) 786792

WHITTOCK, Michael Graham. b 47. Hull Univ BA69 Fitzw Coll Cam BA71 MA76. Westcott Ho Cam 69 Union Th Sem Virginia 71. **d** 72 **p** 73. C Kirkby *Liv* 72-76; C Prescot 76-79; R Methley w Mickletown *Ripon* 79-92; RD Whitkirk 88-92; V Morley St Pet w Churwell *Wakef* 92-01; R Gt Hanwood *Heref* from 01; R Longden and Annscroft w Pulverbatch from 01. *The Rectory, Plealey Lane, Longden, Shrewsbury SY5 8ET* Tel (01743) 861003 Fax 861237

WHITTOME, Donald Marshall. b 26. Cam Univ BA50 MA53. S Dios Minl Tr Scheme. **d** 84 **p** 85. NSM Henfield w Shermanbury and Woodmancote *Chich* 84-93; P-in-c Poynings w Edburton, Newtimber and Pyecombe 93-97; rtd 97; Perm to

Offic *Chich* from 97. *Quaker's Rest, 7 Dean Court Road, Rottingdean, Brighton BN2 7DE* Tel (01273) 705508 Fax 271475

WHITTON, Eric. b 33. N Lon Poly 78. Lon Coll of Div ALCD59 Western Th Sem Michigan 60. **d** 60 **p** 61. C Mortlake w E Sheen *S'wark* 60-64; C Surbiton St Matt 64-66; Youth Officer *Lon* 66-72; Tr Officer Gen Syn Bd of Educn 73-78; Visiting Lect Roehampton Inst of HE from 80; rtd 94. *31 Ovington Street, London SW3 2JA* Tel (020) 7584 8819

WHITTY, Gordon William. b 35. WMMTC. **d** 82 **p** 83. NSM Willenhall St Giles *Lich* 82-84; NSM Coseley Ch Ch 84-85; C 85-87; TV Hanley H Ev 87-91; P-in-c Meir 91-98; P-in-c Hanbury w Newborough and Rangemore 98-99; V from 99. *The New Vicarage, Church Lane, Hanbury, Burton-on-Trent DE13 8TF* Tel (01283) 813357
E-mail gordonwhitty@vinweb.co.uk

WHITTY, Harold George. b 41. TCD BA64 MA67. CITC Div Test65. **d** 65 **p** 66. C Willowfield *D & D* 65-68; C Lisburn Ch Ch *Conn* 68-71; Bp's Dom Chapl 70-71; Asst Dir Exhibitions CMJ 71-72; C Enfield Ch Ch Trent Park *Lon* 72-75; TV Washfield, Stoodleigh, Withleigh etc *Ex* 75-83; R Washfield, Stoodleigh, Withleigh etc 83-84; TR 84-93; RD Tiverton 82-84; P-in-c Allithwaite *Carl* 93-97; TV Cartmel Peninsula 97-02; Local Min Officer 99-02; P-in-c Aylesbeare, Rockbeare, Farringdon etc *Ex* from 02. *The Vicarage, Rockbeare, Exeter EX5 2EG* Tel (01404) 822569
E-mail harold.whitty@btinternet.com

WHITWAM, Miss Diana Morgan. b 28. MCSP54 Brighton Poly Dip Counselling 82. Local Minl Tr Course 88. **d** 93 **p** 94. OLM Stoke-next-Guildf 93-01; Perm to Offic from 02. *27 Acacia Road, Guildford GU1 1HL* Tel (01483) 822482

WHITWELL, Canon John Peter. b 36. Qu Coll Birm 62. **d** 65 **p** 66. C Stepney St Dunstan and All SS *Lon* 65-68; C Chingford SS Pet and Paul *Chelmsf* 68-71; V Walthamstow St Sav 71-78; P-in-c Lt Ilford St Mich 78-88; R 88-98; RD Newham 91-97; Hon Can Chelmsf Cathl 96-98; rtd 98; Perm to Offic *Ox* from 99. *152 Bath Road, Banbury OX16 0TT* Tel (01295) 266243

WHITWELL, Martin Corbett. b 32. Pemb Coll Ox BA55 MA59. Clifton Th Coll 55. **d** 57 **p** 58. C Wolverhampton St Jude *Lich* 57-60; C Aldridge 60-66; Chapl Sandbach Co Secondary Sch 68-74; C Chipping Campden *Glouc* 70-71; Perm to Offic *Chich* 74-75; *Bris* 75-76; C Tranmere St Cath *Ches* 76-80; V Lt Leigh and Lower Whitley 80-90; rtd 90; Perm to Offic *Ches* from 90; *Heref* and *Lich* from 93. *11 Hollies Drive, Bayston Hill, Shrewsbury SY3 0NN* Tel (01743) 874241

WHITWELL, Timothy John. b 72. Westmr Coll Ox BTh97 Leeds Univ MA00. Aston Tr Scheme 94 Coll of Resurr Mirfield 97. **d** 99 **p** 00. C Middlesbrough Ascension *York* 99-02; R Loftus and Carlin How w Skinningrove from 02. *The Rectory, 11 Micklow Lane, Loftus, Saltburn-by-the-Sea TS13 4JE*

WHITWORTH, Benjamin Charles Battams. b 49. CCC Ox BA71 MA85. Linc Th Coll 83. **d** 85 **p** 86. C Swanborough *Sarum* 85-88; C Sherborne w Castleton and Lillington 88-91; V Milborne Port w Goathill *B & W* 91-98; rtd 98; Perm to Offic *B & W* from 00. *13 The Avenue, Taunton TA1 1EA* Tel (01823) 272442

WHITWORTH, Canon Duncan. b 47. K Coll Lon BD69 AKC69. St Aug Coll Cant 69. **d** 70 **p** 71. C Tonge Moor *Man* 70-73; C Upper Norwood St Jo *Cant* 73-78; Asst Chapl Madrid *Eur* 78-82; Chapl Br Embassy Ankara 82-83; V Douglas St Matt *S & M* from 84; RD Douglas from 91; Can St German's Cathl from 96. *St Matthew's Vicarage, Alexander Drive, Douglas, Isle of Man IM2 3QN* Tel (01624) 676310

WHITWORTH, Canon Patrick John. b 51. Ch Ch Ox BA72 MA76 St Jo Coll Dur DipTh75 MA78. **d** 76 **p** 77. C York St Mich-le-Belfrey *York* 76-79; C Brompton H Trin w Onslow Square St Paul *Lon* 79-84; V Gipsy Hill Ch Ch *S'wark* 84-95; Hon Can Bauchi from 95; R Bath Weston All SS w N Stoke and Langridge *B & W* from 95; RD Bath from 03. *The Vicarage, Weston, Bath BA1 4BU* Tel (01225) 421159
E-mail pwhitworth1@compuserve.com

WHYBORN, Robert. b 42. Loughb Coll of Educn CSD69. N Ord Course 87. **d** 90 **p** 91. NSM Milnrow *Man* 90-97; NSM Greenfield 97-03; NSM Saddleworth from 03. *St Mary's Vicarage, 1 Park Lane, Greenfield, Oldham OL3 7DX* Tel (01457) 872346 Fax as telephone E-mail revrob8@aol.com

WHYBROW, Paul Andrew. b 58. Qu Coll Cam DipTheol BEd80. Oak Hill Th Coll DipMin89 DipTh90 BA90 Wycliffe Hall Ox 95. **d** 97 **p** 98. C Magor *Mon* 97-00; V Poughill *Truro* from 00. *The Vicarage, Poughill, Bude EX23 9ER* Tel (01288) 355183
E-mail pa.whybrow@btinternet.com

WHYMAN, Oliver. b 27. ALCM52 LCP57. S'wark Ord Course 60. **d** 63 **p** 64. C Streatham Ch Ch *S'wark* 63-68; Lic to Offic 68-87; NSM Sutton New Town St Barn 87-92; rtd 92; Perm to Offic *S'wark* 92-00. *37 Jubilee Court, London Road, Thornton Heath CR7 6JL* Tel (020) 8684 5320

WHYSALL, Mrs Joan. b 42. Lady Mabel Coll DipEd64 Nottm Univ MA01. EMMTC 98. **d** 01 **p** 02. NSM Trowell, Awsworth and Cossall *S'well* from 01. *55 Trowell Park Drive, Trowell,*

Nottingham NG9 3RA Tel 0115-875 2677 Mobile 07802-415036 Fax 08701-371114 E-mail joan.whysall@ntlworld.com
WHYTE, Alastair John. b 61. Coll of Ripon & York St Jo BA83 Lanc Univ MA95. Sarum & Wells Th Coll 83. **d** 85 **p** 86. C Chorley St Geo *Blackb* 85-88; C Poulton-le-Fylde 88-91; V Wesham 91-00; Chapl Wesham Park Hosp Preston 91-94; Chapl Blackpool, Wyre and Fylde Community NHS Trust 94-02; P-in-c Treales *Blackb* 98-00; V Garstang St Thos 00-02; AD Garstang 02. *Address withheld by request*
WHYTE, David. b 30. **d** 97 **p** 97. NSM Calne and Blackland *Sarum* 97-00; rtd 00; Perm to Offic *Sarum* from 01. *20 Castle Street, Calne SN11 0DX* Tel (01249) 817033
WHYTE, Duncan Macmillan. b 25. St Jo Coll Dur BA49 St Cath Soc Ox BA51 MA57. Wycliffe Hall Ox 49. **d** 51 **p** 53. C Garston *Liv* 51-56; C St Leonards St Leon *Chich* 56-59; V Southsea St Simon *Portsm* 59-66; Gen Sec Lon City Miss 66-92; Hon C Blackheath St Jo *S'wark* 66-92; rtd 92; Perm to Offic *Sarum* from 92. *1 The Meadows, Salisbury SP1 2SS* Tel (01722) 330528
WHYTE, Henry Lewis. b 38. Lon Coll of Div ALCD70 LTh74. **d** 70 **p** 71. C Crawley *Chich* 70-74; V Bermondsey St Jas w Ch Ch *S'wark* 74-82; V Kingston Hill St Paul 82-94; V Blackheath Park St Mich 94-02; rtd 02. *6 Horn Park Lane, London SE12 8UU* Tel (020) 8318 9837
WHYTE, Canon Herbert Blayney. b 21. TCD BA43 MA53. **d** 44 **p** 45. C Dublin Crumlin *D & G* 44-47; Succ St Patr Cathl Dublin 47-50; Dioc Registrar (Ossory, Ferns and Leighlin) *C & O* 50-58; Bp's V and Lib Kilkenny Cathl 50-58; Bp Ossory Dom Chapl 50-58; Preb Ossory Cathl 56-58; I Maryborough 58-68; Clerical V Ch Ch Cathl Dublin *D & G* 68-91; I Dublin Crumlin 68-91; Can Ch Ch Cathl Dublin 80-86; Chan 86-91; rtd 91. *238 Redford Park, Greystones, Co Wicklow, Irish Republic* Tel (00353) (1) 287 7264
WHYTE, Canon Malcolm Dorrance. b 29. Man Univ BA50 BD53. Wycliffe Hall Ox 57. **d** 57 **p** 58. C Roch St Pet w St Marg *Roch* 57-60; V Ravenhead *Liv* 60-67; V Southport Em 67-95; RD N Meols 78-89; AD 89-95; Hon Can Liv Cathl 91-96; rtd 96; Perm to Offic *Blackb* and *Liv* from 96. *13 Ruskin Close, Tarleton, Preston PR4 6XY* Tel (01772) 813017
WHYTE, Canon Robert Euan. b 44. St Pet Coll Ox BA67. Cuddesdon Coll 67. **d** 69 **p** 70. C Blackheath Ascension *S'wark* 69-73; BCC 73-87; NSM Lewisham St Swithun *S'wark* 73-76; NSM Heston *Lon* 76-77; NSM Rusthall *Roch* 77-87; C 87-88; V from 88; RD Tunbridge Wells 91-96; Hon Can Roch Cathl from 00. *The Vicarage, Bretland Road, Rusthall, Tunbridge Wells TN4 8PB* Tel (01892) 521357 Fax 537014
E-mail rewhyte@btinternet.com
WIBBERLEY, Anthony Norman. b 36. K Coll Lon BSc68 AKC58. Sarum & Wells Th Coll 76. **d** 79 **p** 80. Hon C Tavistock and Gulworthy *Ex* 79-86; R Hoby cum Rotherby w Brooksby, Ragdale & Thru'ton *Leic* 86-90; V Ingol *Blackb* 90-96; Perm to Offic *Ely* from 97; rtd 00. *13 Missleton Court, Cherry Hinton Road, Cambridge CB1 8BL*
WIBREW, Mrs Janet Anne. b 48. Win Sch of Art NDAD89. S Dios Minl Tr Scheme 89. **d** 92 **p** 94. NSM Basingstoke *Win* 92-95; Chapl N Hants Hosp 95-96; Asst Chapl Basingstoke Distr Hosp 97-99; NSM Cliddesden and Ellisfield w Farleigh Wallop etc *Win* 97-99. *High Meadows, Green Lane, Ellisfield, Basingstoke RG25 2QW* Tel (01256) 381387
WIBROE, Andrew Peter. b 56. K Coll Lon BD83 AKC83 Thames Poly PGCE91. Ripon Coll Cuddesdon 83. **d** 86 **p** 87. C Purley St Mark *S'wark* 86-88; C Boyne Hill *Ox* 89-90; Hon C Milton next Gravesend Ch Ch *Roch* from 90. *32 Ayelands, New Ash Green, Longfield DA3 8JN* Tel (01474) 879014
E-mail peterwibroe@aol.com
WICK, Patricia Anne. b 54. Lon Bible Coll BA80 Oak Hill Th Coll DipHE86. **dss** 86 **d** 87 **p** 94. Halliwell St Luke *Man* 86-87; Par Dn 87-91; Par Dn Drypool *York* 91-94; C 94-95; TV 95-97; Perm to Offic 98-99; CMS Uganda from 98. *PO Box 845, Arua, Uganda* E-mail t.wick@bushnet.net
WICKENS, Andrew Peter. b 63. St Jo Coll Dur BA85 Magd Coll Cam MEd97 PGCE95 ARCM84. Westcott Ho Cam. **d** 00 **p** 01. C Louth *Linc* 00-03; TV from 03; PV Linc Cathl from 01. *St Michael's Vicarage, Little Lane, Louth LN11 9DU*
E-mail apw@tonality.freeserve.co.uk
WICKENS, Andrew St Lawrence John. b 63. Mert Coll Ox BA85 Birm Univ MPhil94. Qu Coll Birm 89. **d** 92 **p** 93. C Birchfield *Birm* 92-96; Perm to Offic 96-97; Zambia 97-00; CMS Kenya from 01. *St Paul's United Theological College, PO Brivate Bag, Limuru, Kenya* Tel (00254) 72-887988 (mobile) Fax (00254) (154) 73033
WICKENS, John Philip. b 33. Open Univ BA76. K Coll Lon 57. **d** 61 **p** 62. C Hatcham Park All SS *S'wark* 61-64; USA 64-66; Tutor Richmond Fellowship Coll 66-95; Hon C Sutton Ch Ch *S'wark* 68-83; Hon C Benhilton 83-95; rtd 95; Perm to Offic *Worc* from 95. *West Villa, 196 West Malvern Road, Malvern WR14 4AZ* Tel (01684) 574043
WICKENS, Mrs Moira. b 56. S Dios Minl Tr Scheme 91. **d** 94. NSM Ifield *Chich* 94-96; C Saltdean 96-03; Schs Liaison Officer from 03; C Ovingdean from 03. *21 Ainsworth Avenue, Ovingdean, Brighton BN2 7BG* Tel (01273) 309546

WICKHAM, Mrs Jennifer Ruth. b 68. Univ of W Ontario BA91. Cranmer Hall Dur BA98. **d** 98 **p** 99. C Ponteland *Newc* 98-00; Assoc P Ottawa St Geo Canada from 01. *57A Tauvette Street, Ottawa ON, Canada, K1B 3A2* Tel (001) (613) 590 7921 *or* 235 1636 E-mail ajwickham@yahoo.com *or* revjw.stgeorge@cyberus.ca
WICKHAM, Lionel Ralph. b 32. St Cath Coll Cam BA57 MA61 PhD LRAM. Westcott Ho Cam 57. **d** 59 **p** 60. C Boston *Linc* 59-61; Tutor Cuddesdon Coll 61-63; V Cross Stone *Wakef* 63-67; Lect Th Southn Univ 67-78; Sen Lect 78-81; V Honley 81-87; Lect Cam Univ 87-00; NSM W Wratting *Ely* 89-00; NSM Weston Colville 89-00; rtd 00; Perm to Offic *Wakef* from 99. *19 Barrowstead, Skelmanthorpe, Huddersfield HD8 9UW* Tel (01484) 864185 E-mail lpatristic@aol.com
WICKHAM, Nicholas John. b 27. Trin Coll Cam BA51 MA56. Coll of Resurr Mirfield 54 Ox NSM Course 85. **d** 87 **p** 88. NSM Banbury *Ox* 87-92; rtd 92. *19 Britannia Wharf, Britannia Road, Banbury OX16 5DS* Tel (01295) 256537
WICKHAM, Canon Norman George. b 25. Kelham Th Coll 42. **d** 51 **p** 52. C Syston *Leic* 51-54; V Leic St Gabr 54-57; R Wingerworth *Derby* 57-69; TP Edin St Jo *Edin* 69-79; Can and Vice Provost St Mary's Cathl Edin 74-79; R Edin Ch Ch 79-88; Can St Mary's Cathl 86-91; rtd 88; Hon Can St Mary's Cathl *Edin* from 91. *The Coach House, 15 Spylaw Road, Edinburgh EH10 5BN* Tel 0131-447 1050
E-mail norman.wickham@btinternet.com
WICKHAM, Robert James. b 72. Grey Coll Dur BA94. Ridley Hall Cam 95. **d** 98 **p** 99. C Willesden St Mary *Lon* 98-01; C Somers Town 01-03; C Old St Pancras from 03. *St Mary's House, Eversholt Street, London NW1 1BN* Tel (020) 7387 7301
E-mail fr.rob@prayer.freeserve.co.uk
WICKINGS, Luke Iden. b 59. Sheff Poly BA81. Oak Hill Th Coll BA90. **d** 90 **p** 91. C Fulham St Mary N End *Lon* 90-94; C Bletchley *Ox* 94-00; V W Norwood St Luke *S'wark* from 00. *The Vicarage, 6 Chatsworth Way, London SE27 9HR* Tel (020) 8670 2706 *or* 8761 0068
WICKREMASINGHE, Rosemary Ethel. b 32. Reading Univ ATD52 K Coll Lon BD85 AKC85. St Alb and Ox Min Course 93. **d** 96 **p** 97. NSM Godrevy *Truro* from 96. *10 Glebe Row, Phillack, Hayle TR27 5AJ* Tel (01736) 757850
WICKS, Christopher Blair. b 59. BA. Oak Hill Th Coll 85. **d** 88 **p** 89. C Edmonton All SS w St Mich *Lon* 88-92; C Southborough St Pet w Ch Ch and St Matt etc *Roch* 92-96; TV from 96. *72 Powder Mill Lane, Southborough, Tunbridge Wells TN4 9EJ* Tel (01892) 529098 E-mail chriswicks@compuserve.com
WICKS, Mrs Susan Joyce. b 51. SEN80 CSS89. EMMTC 97. **d** 00 **p** 01. C Birstall and Wanlip *Leic* from 00. *33 Walker Road, Birstall, Leicester LE4 3BP* Tel 0116-267 7572 Mobile 07808-917164 E-mail sueterry.wicks@virgin.net
WICKS, Susan Lynn. b 66. Trin Coll Bris DipHE98. **d** 98 **p** 99. C Whitburn *Dur* 98-03; TV S Carl TM *Carl* from 03. *St Elisabeth's Vicarage, Arnside Road, Carlisle CA1 3QA* Tel (01228) 596427
WICKSTEAD, Gavin John. b 46. St Chad's Coll Dur BA67. Linc Th Coll 82. **d** 84 **p** 85. C Louth *Linc* 84-87; P-in-c E Markham and Askham *S'well* 87-89; P-in-c Headon w Upton 87-89; P-in-c Grove 87-89; R E Markham w Askham, Headon w Upton and Grove 90-92; P-in-c Skegness and Winthorpe *Linc* 92-97; R 97-01; V Holbeach from 01. *The Vicarage, 2 Church Walk, Holbeach, Spalding PE12 7DT* Tel (01406) 422185
E-mail wickstead@btopenworld.com
WIDDAS, Preb John Anderson. b 38. Kelham Th Coll 58. **d** 63 **p** 64. C Willenhall H Trin *Lich* 63-66; C Tamworth 66-69; V 86-96; V Chesterton 69-74; R Lich St Chad 74-86; RD Lich 77-86; Preb Lich Cathl 80-00; P-in-c Gentleshaw 80-82; P-in-c Farewell 80-82; RD Tamworth 91-95; V Walsall Wood 96-00; rtd 00; Chapl Burton Hosps NHS Trust 00-03. *90 Main Street, Alrewas, Burton-on-Trent DE13 7AE* Tel (01283) 792031
WIDDECOMBE, Canon Malcolm Murray. b 37. Tyndale Hall Bris 57. **d** 62 **p** 63. C Bris H Trin *Bris* 62-65; C Barton Hill St Luke w Ch Ch 65-67; P-in-c Bris St Phil and St Jacob w Em 67-74; V from 74; RD Bris City 79-85; Hon Can Bris Cathl from 86. *The Vicarage, 7 King's Drive, Bristol BS7 8JW* Tel and fax 0117-924 3169 *or* 929 3386 *or* tel 924 6299
E-mail wid.at.pipnjay@ukonline.co.uk
WIDDECOMBE, Roger James. b 70. Wycliffe Hall Ox 01. **d** 03. C Downend *Bris* from 03. *8 Farm Court, Bristol BS16 6DF*
WIDDESS, Mrs Margaret Jennifer. b 48. Bedf Coll Lon BA70 Clare Coll Cam PGCE75. EAMTC 94. **d** 97 **p** 98. NSM Cambridge St Botolph *Ely* from 97. *69 Gwydir Street, Cambridge CB1 2LG* Tel (01223) 313908
E-mail margaret.widdess@ukonline.co.uk
WIDDICOMBE, Peter John. b 52. Univ of Manitoba BA74 St Cath Coll Ox MPhil77 St Cross Coll Ox DPhil90. Wycliffe Coll Toronto MDiv81. **d** 81 **p** 82. Canada 81-84 and from 93; C Ox St Andr 84-86; Acting Chapl Trin Coll Ox 88; Linc Coll Ox 89; P-in-c Penn 90-93. *457 Northlake Drive, Waterloo ON, Canada, 2NV 2A4*
WIDDOWS, David Charles Roland. b 52. Hertf Coll Ox BA75 MA79. St Jo Coll Nottm BA77. **d** 79 **p** 80. C Blackley St Andr *Man* 79-83; P-in-c Rochdale Deeplish St Luke 83-84; V 84-92;

TR Stoke Gifford *Bris* from 92. *The Vicarage, 24 North Road, Stoke Gifford, Bristol BS34 8PB* Tel 0117-923 6395 *or* 969 2486

WIDDOWS, Edward John. b 45. ACertCM00. Lon Coll of Div 66. **d** 70 **p** 71. C Formby St Pet *Liv* 70-72; C Uckfield, Isfield and Lt Horsted *Chich* 72-73; C Babbacombe *Ex* 73-76; V Sithney *Truro* 76-78; RD Kerrier 77-78; V Bude Haven 78-84; P-in-c Laneast w St Clether and Tresmere 84-85; P-in-c N Hill w Altarnon, Bolventor and Lewannick 84-85; P-in-c Boyton w N Tamerton 84-85; P-in-c N Petherwin 84-85; R Collingham w S Scarle and Besthorpe and Darlton *S'well* 85-92; R Guernsey St Michel du Valle *Win* 92-99; R Compton and Otterbourne 99-02; rtd 02; Perm to Offic *Pet* from 02. *Glebe Cottage, 4 Spring Back Way, Uppingham, Oakham LE15 9TT* Tel (01572) 821980

WIDDOWS, Heather Susan. b 45. Open Univ BA76. Moray Ord Course 91. **d** 96 **p** 97. NSM Kishorn *Mor* from 96. *2 Fasaich, Gairloch IV21 2DB* Tel (01445) 712176 Fax as telephone

WIDDOWS, John Christopher (Kit). b 46. Trin Coll Cam BA69 MA72. Cuddesdon Coll 69. **d** 71 **p** 72. C Herrington *Dur* 71-76; Chapl Nat Exhibition Cen 76-80; TV Chelmsley Wood *Birm* 76-80; V Halifax St Hilda *Wakef* 80-95; RD Halifax 92-95; AD Newc Cen *Newc* from 95; Master Newc St Thos Prop Chpl from 95. *9 Chester Crescent, Newcastle upon Tyne NE2 1DH* Tel and fax 0191-232 9789 *or* tel 232 0842
E-mail kit@widdows-rev.fsnet.co.uk

WIDDOWSON, Charles Leonard. b 28. ALCD62. **d** 62 **p** 63. C Radcliffe-on-Trent *S'well* 62-66; R Newark Ch Ch 66-69; Australia from 69; rtd 93. *5 Sharrock Avenue, Cheltenham, Vic, Australia 3192* Tel (0061) (03) 9584 9004

WIDDOWSON, Robert William. b 47. Linc Th Coll 83. **d** 85 **p** 86. C Syston *Leic* 85-88; R Husbands Bosworth w Mowsley and Knaptoft etc 88-93; R Asfordby 93-98; P-in-c Ab Kettleby Gp 93-98; P-in-c Old Dalby and Nether Broughton 95-98; P-in-c Charlton Musgrove, Cucklington and Stoke Trister *B & W* from 98; Adv in Rural Affairs from 98. *The Rectory, Charlton Musgrove, Wincanton BA9 8HN* Tel (01963) 33233

WIFFEN, Richard Austin. b 58. St Pet Coll Ox BA80. Trin Coll Bris BA90. **d** 90 **p** 91. C Bowdon *Ches* 90-93; C Ellesmere Port 93-94; TV 94-02; Hon C from 02. *Lime Tree Farm, Stanney Lane, Little Stanney, Chester CH2 4HT* Tel 0151-355 1654

WIFFEN, Susan. b 38. Open Th Coll BA99. SEITE 99. **d** 01 **p** 02. NSM Canvey Is *Chelmsf* from 01. *40 Gladwyns, Basildon SS15 5JA* Tel (01268) 410492

WIFFIN, Susan Elizabeth. b 51. Edin Th Coll 93. **d** 96 **p** 97. NSM Jedburgh *Edin* 96-98; P-in-c Galashiels 98-01. *26 South Myrescroft, Ancrum, Jedburgh TD8 6XE* Tel (01835) 830298

WIGFIELD, Thomas Henry Paul. b 26. Edin Th Coll 46. **d** 49 **p** 50. C Seaham w Seaham Harbour *Dur* 49-52; C Dur St Marg 52-54; V Fatfield 54-63; Asst Dir Chs' TV Cen 63-79; Perm to Offic *Lon* 63-91; Perm to Offic *St Alb* 60-91; Hd of Services Foundn for Chr Communication 79-84; Chs' Liaison Officer 84-91; rtd 91; Perm to Offic *Ox* from 91. *16 Fishers Field, Buckingham MK18 1SF* Tel (01280) 817893

WIGGEN, Richard Martin. b 42. Open Univ BA78 Hull Univ MA86. Qu Coll Birm 64. **d** 67 **p** 68. C Penistone w Midhope *Wakef* 67-70; C Leeds St Pet *Ripon* 70-73; Asst Youth Chapl *Glouc* 73-76; Youth Officer *Liv* 76-80; V Kirkstall *Ripon* 80-90; V Meanwood from 90. *Meanwood Vicarage, 9 Parkside Green, Leeds LS6 4NY* Tel 0113-275 7885
E-mail wiggen@btopenworld.com

WIGGINS, Gillian Holt. b 33. Birm Univ MB, ChB56. **d** 03. NSM Ascot Heath *Ox* from 03. *Keren, 2 Kiln Lane, Winkfield, Windsor SL4 2DU* Tel (01344) 884008 E-mail gilliwig@aol.com

WIGGINS, Karl Patrick. b 38. ARICS64 FRICS87. Trin Coll Bris BD72. **d** 72 **p** 73. C Hildenborough *Roch* 72-76; Hon C Reading St Barn *Ox* 76-78; Hon C Chieveley w Winterbourne and Oare 78-80; Hon C Earley St Nic 80-83; Hon C Reading St Jo 83-88; Hon C Beech Hill, Grazeley and Spencers Wood 88-98; rtd 98; Perm to Offic *Ox* 99. *Willow Cottage, 37 New Road, Bradford-on-Avon BA15 1AP* Tel (01225) 867007
E-mail kk-wiggins@msn.com

WIGGINTON, Canon Peter Walpole. b 20. Dur Univ LTh44. Edin Th Coll 40. **d** 43 **p** 44. C Derby St Jas *Derby* 43-46; C Brimington 46; C Gedling *S'well* 46-49; PV S'well Minster 49-52; V Rolleston w Morton 52-56; R W Keal *Linc* 56-83; R E Keal 57-83; RD Bolingbroke 66-88; Can and Preb Linc Cathl 77-88; R E and W Keal 83-88; R Bolingbroke 83-88; R Toynton All Saints w Toynton St Peter 83-88; Chapl Trin Hosp Retford from 88; Perm to Offic *S'well* from 91. *The Rectory Farm, Rectory Road, Retford DN22 7AY* Tel (01777) 860352

WIGGLESWORTH, Mark. b 60. Clare Coll Cam BA82. St Jo Coll Nottm Dip Th Studies 91 DipMM92. **d** 92 **p** 93. C Brinsworth w Catcliffe *Sheff* 92-93; C Brinsworth w Catcliffe and Treeton 93-95; C Goole 95-96; V Askern from 96. *The Vicarage, Church Street, Askern, Doncaster DN6 0PH* Tel (01302) 700404 E-mail markandbethwig@yahoo.co.uk

WIGGS, Robert James. b 50. Pemb Coll Cam BA72 MA CertEd. Qu Coll Birm 78. **d** 80 **p** 81. C Stratford St Jo and Ch Ch w Forest

Gate St Jas *Chelmsf* 80-83; C E Ham w Upton Park St Alb 83-86; TV 86-91; TR Grays Thurrock 91-99; Perm to Offic from 99. *113 Moulsham Street, Chelmsford CM2 0JN* Tel (01245) 359138

WIGHT, Dennis Marley. b 53. Southn Univ BTh87. Sarum & Wells Th Coll 82. **d** 85 **p** 86. C Gillingham *Sarum* 85-87; Appeals Org CECS from 87; Perm to Offic *Birm* 89-90; V Coseley Ch Ch *Lich* 90-93; V Coseley Ch Ch *Worc* 93-94; R Stoke Prior, Wychbold and Upton Warren 94-02; RD Droitwich 96-99; V Dale and St Brides w Marloes *St D* from 02. *The Vicarage, Dale, Haverfordwest SA62 3RN* Tel (01646) 636255
E-mail dennis.wight@tesco.net

WIGHT (née JONES), Mrs Sian Hilary. b 54. CertEd75 Birm Univ BEd76 Southn Univ BTh87. Sarum & Wells Th Coll 82. **dss** 85 **d** 87 **p** 94. Ex St Sidwell and St Matt *Ex* 85-87; Par Dn 87-88; Perm to Offic *Lich* 89-90 and 93-96; Hon Par Dn Coseley Ch Ch 90-93; Hon Par Dn Coseley Ch Ch *Worc* 93-94; NSM Stoke Prior, Wychbold and Upton Warren 94-02; NSM Dale and St Brides w Marloes *St D* from 02. *The Vicarage, Dale, Haverfordwest SA62 3RN* Tel (01646) 636255

WIGHTMAN, William David. b 39. Birm Univ BA61. Wells Th Coll 61. **d** 63 **p** 64. C Rotherham *Sheff* 63-67; C Castle Church *Lich* 67-70; V Buttershaw St Aid *Bradf* 70-76; V Cullingworth 76-83; R Peterhead *Ab* 83-91; R Strichen, Old Deer and Longside 90-91; Provost St Andr Cathl 91-02; R Aberdeen St Andr 91-02; P-in-c Aberdeen St Ninian 91-02; Hon Can Ch Ch Cathl Connecticut from 91; rtd 02. *66 Wold Road, Pocklington, York YO42 2QG* Tel (01759) 301369
E-mail davidwightman@ntlworld.com

WIGLEY, Brian Arthur. b 31. Qu Coll Birm. **d** 82 **p** 83. C Houghton le Spring *Dur* 82-85; C Louth *Linc* 85-86; TV 86-89; Chapl City Hosp NHS Trust Birm 89-95; rtd 95; Perm to Offic *Ex* from 95. *3 Willows Close, Frogmore, Kingsbridge TQ7 2NY* Tel (01548) 531374

WIGLEY, Canon Harry Maxwell (Max). b 38. Oak Hill Th Coll 61. **d** 64 **p** 65. C Upton (Overchurch) *Ches* 64-67; C Gateacre *Liv* 67-69; C Chadderton Ch Ch *Man* 69-72; V Gt Horton *Bradf* 69-88; Hon Can Bradf Cathl from 85; V Pudsey St Lawr and St Paul 88-96; V Yeadon St Jo from 96. *20 Collier Lane, Baildon, Shipley BD17 5LN* E-mail hjwigley@nascr.net

WIGLEY, Ms Jennifer. b 53. Bris Univ BA74 Birm Univ MA75 Ox Univ CertEd76. Qu Coll Birm 86. **d** 87 **p** 97. C Llangollen w Trevor and Llantysilio *St As* 87-89; C Swansea St Jas *S & B* 89-94; NSM Aberystwyth *St D* 95-98; Tutor St Mich Coll Llan 98-00; C Sketty *S & B* 98-00; Chapl Univ of Wales (Swansea) 00-02; Chapl Univ of Wales (Cardiff) *Llan* 02; TV Cen Cardiff from 03. *17 Chargot Road, Llandaff, Cardiff CF5 1EW* E-mail jenny@wigleyrev.fsnet.co.uk

WIGNALL, Daniel Robert Phillip. b 65. Ox Poly BEd88. St Jo Coll Nottm MA98. **d** 98 **p** 99. C Fletchamstead *Cov* 98-01; C Abingdon *Ox* from 01. *102 Gibson Close, Abingdon OX14 1XT* Tel (01235) 539172 Fax 08701-377372
E-mail danny.wignall@ntlworld.com

WIGNALL, Paul Graham. b 49. Lanc Univ BA72 Qu Coll Cam BA74 MA78. Westcott Ho Cam 72. **d** 74 **p** 75. C Chesterton Gd Shep *Ely* 74-76; Min Can Dur Cathl *Dur* 76-79; Tutor Ripon Coll Cuddesdon 80-84; P-in-c Aston Rowant w Crowell *Ox* 81-83; C Shepherd's Bush St Steph w St Thos *Lon* 84-85; P-in-c St Just-in-Roseland and St Mawes *Truro* 99-01; Dir Tr and Development from 01; C St Agnes and Mithian w Mount Hawke from 01. *The Vicarage, Mount Hawke, Truro TR4 8DE* Tel (01209) 891516 *or* (01872) 270162
E-mail paulwignall@supanet.com *or* dtd@truro.anglican.org

WIGRAM, Andrew Oswald. b 39. Lon Univ BD64. Bps' Coll Cheshunt 61. **d** 64 **p** 65. C Marton-in-Cleveland *York* 64-69; Kenya 69-82; V Westcliff St Mich *Chelmsf* 82-95; RD Southend-on-Sea 89-94; R Cropwell Bishop w Colston Bassett, Granby etc *S'well* from 96. *The Vicarage, 2 Bingham Close, Cropwell Bishop, Nottingham NG12 3GR* Tel 0115-989 3172
E-mail andrew@wigram.fsnet.co.uk

WIGRAM, Miss Ruth Margaret. b 41. CertEd63. Cranmer Hall Dur 83. **dss** 84 **d** 87 **p** 94. Shipley St Paul and Frizinghall *Bradf* 84-87; Par Dn 87-90; Asst Dioc Dir of Ords 90-96; C Skipton H Trin 90-96; V Easby w Brompton on Swale and Bolton on Swale *Ripon* from 96. *The Vicarage, St Paul's Drive, Brompton on Swale, Richmond DL10 7HQ* Tel (01748) 811840
E-mail ruth.wigram@lineone.net

WIGSTON, Kenneth Edmund. b 28. Lich Th Coll 55. **d** 58 **p** 59. C Sharrow St Andr *Sheff* 58-61; C Kidlington *Ox* 61-68; R Airdrie *Glas* 68-78; R Gartcosh 68-78; R Glas St Oswald 78-85; R Onich *Arg* 85-94; R Glencoe 85-94; R Ballachulish 85-94; rtd 94; Perm to Offic *Arg* from 94. *Old Croft Cottage, 18 Tighphuirt, Glencoe, Ballachulish PA39 4HN* Tel (01855) 811503

WIKELEY, Canon John Roger Ian. b 41. AKC64. **d** 65 **p** 66. C Southport H Trin *Liv* 65-69; C Padgate Ch Ch 69-71; TV Padgate 71-73; R 73-74; TR 74-85; TR W Derby St Mary 85-98; V from 98; AD W Derby from 89; Hon Can Liv Cathl from 94. *The Rectory, West Derby, Liverpool L12 5EA* Tel 0151-256 6600 Fax 226 4343 E-mail jriw@wikeley.f9.co.uk

WIKNER, Richard Hugh. b 46. MSI. St Alb Minl Tr Scheme 79. **d** 94 **p** 95. NSM Lt Heath *St Alb* from 94. *Koinonia, 5 The Avenue, Potters Bar EN6 1EG* Tel (01707) 650437
E-mail hughwikner@lineone.net

WILBOURNE, David Jeffrey. b 55. Jes Coll Cam BA78 MA82. Westcott Ho Cam 79. **d** 81 **p** 82. C Stainton-in-Cleveland *York* 81-85; Chapl Asst Hemlington Hosp 81-85; R Monk Fryston and S Milford *York* 85-91; Abp's Dom Chapl 91-97; Dir of Ords 91-97; V Helmsley from 97. *Canons Garth, Helmsley, York YO62 5AQ* Tel (01439) 770236

WILBOURNE, Geoffrey Owen. b 29. Lich Th Coll 60. **d** 62 **p** 63. C Marfleet *York* 62-65; V Ellerton Priory w Aughton and E Cottingwith 65-70; TV Scalby w Ravenscar and Staintondale 70-73; V Kingston upon Hull St Nic 73-76; V Keyingham 76-85; V Hemingbrough 85-91; rtd 91; Perm to Offic *York* from 02. *40 Knight Point Drive, Scarborough YO11 3JT* Tel (01723) 355255

WILBRAHAM, David. b 59. Oak Hill Th Coll BA88. **d** 88 **p** 89. C Ince Ch Ch *Liv* 88-91; Min St Helens St Helen 91-93; Perm to Offic *Guildf* 96-99; NSM Hindhead 99-00; V 00-03; V Churt and Hindhead from 03. *The Vicarage, Wood Road, Hindhead GU26 6PX* Tel (01428) 605305 Mobile 07779-262302
E-mail davidwilbraham@lineone.net

WILBY, Mrs Jean (Sister Davina). b 38. Open Univ BA82. Wycliffe Hall Ox 83. **dss** 85 **d** 87 **p** 94. Maidenhead St Andr and St Mary *Ox* 85-87; C 87; TD Hermitage and Hampstead Norreys, Cold Ash etc 87-91; Lic to Offic 92-95; All SS Convent Ox 91-95; NSM Iffley *Ox* 94-95; C Denham 95-98; rtd 98; P-in-c Woolstone w Gotherington and Oxenton etc *Glouc* from 98. *The Rectory, 67 Mallerson Road, Gotherington, Cheltenham GL52 4EX* Tel (01242) 675559

WILBY, Timothy David. b 59. Univ Coll Dur BA80 MA87. Ripon Coll Cuddesdon 81. **d** 83 **p** 84. C Standish *Blackb* 83-86; CF 86-89; V Chorley All SS *Blackb* 89-95; V Penwortham St Leon 95-00; TR Fellside Team from 00. *The Vicarage, Goosnargh Lane, Goosnargh, Preston PR3 2BN* Tel (01772) 865274 E-mail timwilby@aol.com or fellsiddirector@aol.com

WILBY, Mrs Wendy Ann. b 49. ARCM69 LRAM72 St Hugh's Coll Ox BA71. NEOC 90. **d** 90 **p** 94. Par Dn Barwick in Elmet *Ripon* 90-93; C High Harrogate St Pet 93-94; P-in-c Birstwith 94-01; AD Harrogate 00-01; Chapl St Aid Sch Harrogate 94-01; V Halifax *Wakef* from 01. *The Vicarage, Kensington Road, Halifax HX3 0BX* Tel (01422) 365477
E-mail octave@wwilby.freeserve.co.uk

WILCOCK, Michael Jarvis. b 32. Dur Univ BA54. Tyndale Hall Bris 60. **d** 62 **p** 63. C Southport Ch Ch *Liv* 62-65; C St Marylebone All So w SS Pet and Jo *Lon* 65-69; V Maidstone St Faith *Cant* 69-77; Dir Past Studies Trin Coll Bris 77-82; V Dur St Nic *Dur* 82-98; rtd 98; Perm to Offic *Chich* from 98. *1 Tudor Court, 51 Carlisle Road, Eastbourne BN21 4JR* Tel (01323) 417170

WILCOCK, Paul Trevor. b 59. Bris Univ BA Leeds Univ MA93. Trin Coll Bris 83. **d** 87 **p** 88. C Kirkheaton *Wakef* 87-90; Chapl Huddersfield Poly 90-92; Chapl Huddersfield Univ 92-93; Dir Student Services from 93; NSM Huddersfield H Trin from 92. *25 Mendip Avenue, Huddersfield HD3 3QG* Tel (01484) 472675 Fax 473120 E-mail p.t.wilcock@hud.ac.uk

WILCOCK, Terence Granville. b 50. Open Univ BA82. EAMTC. **d** 02 **p** 03. NSM Oundle w Ashton and Benefield w Glapthorn Pet from 02. *Ash House, Main Street, Tansor, Peterborough PE8 5HS* Tel (01832) 226451 E-mail terryatash@aol.com

WILCOCKSON, Stephen Anthony. b 51. Nottm Univ BA73 Ox Univ BA75 MA81. Wycliffe Hall Ox 73. **d** 76 **p** 77. C Pudsey St Lawr *Bradf* 76-78; C Wandsworth All SS *S'wark* 78-81; V Rock Ferry *Ches* 81-86; V Lache cum Saltney 86-95; V Howell Hill *Guildf* from 95; RD Epsom from 00. *St Paul's Vicarage, 17 Northey Avenue, Cheam, Sutton SM2 7HS* Tel (020) 8224 9927
E-mail stevewilcockson@yahoo.com

WILCOX, Anthony Gordon. b 41. Lon Coll of Div LTh67 ALCD67. **d** 67 **p** 68. C Cheltenham Ch Ch *Glouc* 67-72; C Beccles St Mich *St E* 72-74; TV 74-81; V Ipswich All SS from 81. *All Saints' Vicarage, 264 Norwich Road, Ipswich IP1 4BT* Tel (01473) 252975

WILCOX, Brian Howard. b 46. Westcott Ho Cam 71. **d** 73 **p** 74. C Kettering SS Pet and Paul *Pet* 73-78; V Eye 78-82; R Clipston w Naseby and Haselbech w Kelmarsh 82-90; V Hornsea w Atwick *York* 90-97; RD N Holderness 95-97; R Uckfield *Chich* from 97; R Isfield from 97; R Lt Horsted from 97. *The Rectory, Belmont Road, Uckfield TN22 1BP* Tel (01825) 762251

WILCOX, Colin John. b 43. St Mich Coll Llan DipTh84. **d** 86 **p** 87. C Newport St Andr *Mon* 86-88; C Llanmartin 88-90; TV 90-92; V Griffithstown from 92. *St Hilda's Vicarage, 2 Sunnybank Road, Griffithstown, Pontypool NP4 5LT* Tel (01495) 763641

✠**WILCOX, The Rt Revd David Peter.** b 30. St Jo Coll Ox BA52 MA56. Linc Th Coll 52. **d** 54 **p** 55 **c** 86. C St Helier *S'wark* 54-56; C Ox St Mary V *Ox* 56-59; Tutor Linc Th Coll 59-60; Chapl 60-61; Sub-Warden 61-63; India 64-70; R Gt w Lt Gransden *Ely* 70-72; Can Res Derby Cathl *Derby* 72-77; Warden EMMTC 73-77; Prin Ripon Coll Cuddesdon 77-85; V Cuddesdon *Ox* 77-85; Suff Bp Dorking *Guildf* 86-95; rtd 95; Hon Asst Bp Chich

from 95. *4 The Court, Hoo Gardens, Willingdon, Eastbourne BN20 9AX* Tel (01323) 506108

WILCOX, David Thomas Richard. b 42. Down Coll Cam BA63 Regent's Park Coll Ox BA66 Tübingen Univ. **d** 95 **p** 96. C Bris St Mary Redcliffe w Temple etc *Bris* 95-97; TV Yate New Town 97-02; Hon C from 02; rtd 02. *The Vicarage, Shorthill Road, Westerleigh, Bristol BS37 8QN* Tel (01454) 312152

WILCOX, Graham James. b 43. Qu Coll Ox BA64 MA75 Lon Univ BD97. Ridley Hall Cam 64. **d** 66 **p** 67. C Edgbaston St Aug *Birm* 66-69; C Sheldon 69-72; Asst Chapl Wrekin Coll Telford 72-74; C Asterby w Goulceby *Linc* 74-77; R 77-81; R Benniworth w Market Stainton and Ranby 77-81; R Donington on Bain 77-81; R Stenigot 77-81; R Gayton le Wold w Biscarthorpe 77-81; V Scamblesby w Cawkwell 77-81; R Asterby Gp 81-88; V Sutton le Marsh 88-90; R Sutton, Huttoft and Anderby 90-98; R Fyfield, Moreton w Bobbingworth etc *Chelmsf* from 98. *The Rectory, Willingale Road, Fyfield, Ongar CM5 0SD* Tel (01277) 899255
E-mail gwilcox5@compuserve.com

WILCOX, Haydon Howard. b 56. Sarum & Wells Th Coll. **d** 82 **p** 83. C Fishponds St Jo *Bris* 82-85; TV Hucknall Torkard *S'well* 85-91; R Bilsthorpe 91-99; R Eakring 91-99; P-in-c Maplebeck 91-99; P-in-c Winkburn 91-99; P-in-c Aldershot St Mich *Guildf* 99-03; V from 03. *St Michael's Vicarage, 120 Church Lane East, Aldershot GU11 3SS* Tel (01252) 320108
E-mail 100600.331@compuserve.com

WILCOX, Canon Hugh Edwin. b 37. St Edm Hall Ox BA62 MA66. St Steph Ho Ox 62. **d** 64 **p** 65. C Colchester St Jas, All SS, St Nic and St Runwald *Chelmsf* 64-66; Hon C Clifton St Paul *Bris* 66-68; SCM 66-68; Sec Internat Dept BCC 68-74; Asst Gen Sec 74-76; V Ware St Mary *St Alb* from 76; Hon Can St Alb from 96. *The Vicarage, 31 Thundercourt, Milton Road, Ware SG12 0PT* Tel (01920) 464817
E-mail hwilcox@ware-vicarage.freeserve.co.uk

WILCOX, Jeffry Reed. b 40. K Coll Lon AKC65 BA78. **d** 66 **p** 67. C Ryhope *Dur* 66-69; C Cockerton 69-71; P-in-c Pallion 71-82; R Streatham St Leon *S'wark* from 82; RD Streatham 92-00. *The Rectory, 1 Becmead Avenue, London SW16 1UH* Tel (020) 8769 4366 or 8769 1216

WILCOX, John Bower. b 28. AKC55. **d** 58 **p** 59. C Orford St Marg *Liv* 58-60; C W Derby St Mary 60-63; Ind Chapl *Linc* 63-74; R Aisthorpe w W Thorpe and Scampton 63-74; R Brattleby 64-74; Ind Chapl *York* 74-89; P-in-c Middlesbrough St Cuth 89-93; Urban Development Officer 89-93; rtd 93; Perm to Offic *York* from 93. *5 Duncan Avenue, Redcar TS10 5BX* Tel (01642) 489683

WILCOX, Peter Jonathan. b 61. St Jo Coll Dur BA84 MA91 St Jo Coll Ox DPhil93. Ridley Hall Cam BA86. **d** 87 **p** 88. C Preston on Tees *Dur* 87-90; NSM Ox St Giles and SS Phil and Jas w St Marg *Ox* 90-93; TV Gateshead *Dur* 93-98; Dir Urban Miss Cen Cranmer Hall 93-98; P-in-c Walsall St Paul *Lich* from 98. *St Paul's Vicarage, 57 Mellish Road, Walsall WS4 2DG* Tel (01922) 624963 or 626817

WILD, Alan James. b 46. LNSM course 94. **d** 97 **p** 98. OLM Walworth St Pet *S'wark* from 97. *67 Liverpool Grove, London SE17 2HP* Tel (020) 7708 1216

WILD, Hilda Jean. b 48. Linc Th Coll 95. **d** 95 **p** 96. C Newark *S'well* 95-99; V Earlsdon *Cov* from 99. *St Barbara's Vicarage, 24 Rochester Road, Coventry CV5 6AG* Tel (024) 7667 4057

WILD, Roger Bedingham Barratt. b 40. Hull Univ MA94. ALCD64. **d** 65 **p** 66. C Shipley St Pet *Bradf* 65-68; C Pudsey St Lawr 68-71; P-in-c Rawthorpe *Wakef* 71-73; V 73-78; V Ripon H Trin *Ripon* 78-93; RD Ripon 86-93; R Barwick in Elmet 93-01; OCF 79-93; CMS from 01. *Trinity Theological College, 490 Upper Bukit Timar Road, Singapore 678093* Tel (0065) 6762 3714 E-mail rbbwild@hotmail.com.uk or roger@ttc.edu.sg

WILDE, David Wilson. b 37. Lon Coll of Div ALCD61 BD62. **d** 62 **p** 63. C Kirkheaton *Wakef* 62-66; C Attenborough w Chilwell *S'well* 66-72; P-in-c Bestwood Park 72-83; R Kimberley from 83. *The Rectory, 1 Eastwood Road, Kimberley, Nottingham NG16 2HX* Tel 0115-938 3565
E-mail cherryw@freenetname.co.uk

WILDEY, Canon Ian Edward. b 51. St Chad's Coll Dur BA72. Coll of Resurr Mirfield 72. **d** 74 **p** 75. C Westgate Common *Wakef* 74-77; C Barnsley St Mary 77-81; V Ravensthorpe 81-95; R Barnsley St Mary from 95; Dir of Educn from 96; Hon Can Wakef Cathl from 00. *The Rectory, 30 Victoria Road, Barnsley S70 2BU* Tel (01226) 282270 Fax as telephone
E-mail ian@ewildey.freeserve.co.uk

WILDING, Miss Anita Pamela. b 38. MBE02. Blackpool and Fylde Coll of Further Tech TCert61. CMS Tr Coll Chislehurst 65. **dss** 89 **d** 92 **p** 93. CMS from 87; Kenya from 87. *St Andrew's College, PO Box 6, Kerugoya, Kenya* Tel (00254) (163) 21025

WILDING, David. b 43. K Coll Lon BD67 AKC67. **d** 68 **p** 69. C Thornhill *Wakef* 68-72; C Halifax St Jo Bapt 70-72; V Scholes 72-79; V Lightcliffe 79-97; rtd 97; Perm to Offic *Wakef* from 97. *10 Stratton Park, Rastrick, Brighouse HD6 3SN*

WILDING, Joseph. b 14. Edin Th Coll 50. **d** 52 **p** 53. C Dumbarton *Glas* 52-56; R Alexandria 56-80; P-in-c 80-84; rtd 84; Perm to Offic *Blackb* from 84. *Ash House Farm, Ulnes Walton, Preston PR5 3LU*

WILDING, Michael Paul. b 57. Chich Th Coll 82. **d** 85 **p** 86. C Treboeth *S & B* 85-87; C Llangiwg 87-88; V Defynnog w Rhydybriw and Llandeilo'r-fan 88-00; V Defynnog, Llandilo'r Fan, Llanulid, Llywel etc from 00. *The Vicarage, Sennybank, Sennybridge, Brecon LD3 8PP* Tel (01874) 638927

WILDS, The Ven Anthony Ronald. b 43. Dur Univ BA64. Bps' Coll Cheshunt 64. **d** 66 **p** 67. C Newport Pagnell *Ox* 66-72; Zambia 72-75; V Chandler's Ford *Win* 75-85; V Andover w Foxcott 85-97; RD Andover 89-94; Hon Can Win Cathl 91-97; TR Solihull *Birm* 97-01; Hon Can Birm Cathl 00-01; Adn Plymouth *Ex* from 01. *33 Leat Walk, Roborough, Plymouth PL6 7AT* Tel (01752) 793397
E-mail archdeacon.of.plymouth@exeter.anglican.org

WILES, Prof Maurice Frank. b 23. Ch Coll Cam BA47 MA52 DD FKC72 FBA81. Ridley Hall Cam 48. **d** 50 **p** 51. C Stockport St Geo *Ches* 50-52; Chapl Ridley Hall Cam 52-55; Lect NT Studies Ibadan Nigeria 55-59; Dean Clare Coll Cam 59-67; Lect Div Cam Univ 59-67; Prof Chr Doctrine K Coll Lon 67-70; Regius Prof Div Ox Univ 70-91; Can and Canon Th Ch *Ox* 70-91; Bampton Lect Ox Univ 86; rtd 91. *11 Baytree Close, Oxford OX4 4DT* Tel (01865) 777091

WILES, Roger Kenneth. b 58. Witwatersrand Univ BA. St Paul's Coll Grahamstown DipTh. **d** 83 **p** 84. S Africa 83-99; C Johannesburg St Gab 83-84; C Belgravia St Jo 84-85; Chapl Jeppe Boys' High Sch 85-86; Chapl Witwatersrand Univ 86-93; R Edenvale Em 94-99; P-in-c Edin Clermiston Em *Edin* from 99. *127 Clermiston Road, Edinburgh EH12 6UR* Tel and fax 0131-316 4706 Mobile 07909-574169 E-mail roger@gam.co.za

WILFORD (formerly GIBSON), Laura Mary. b 50. N Ord Course 85. **d** 88 **p** 94. Par Dn Foley Park *Worc* 88-90; Par Dn Kidderminster St Jo and H Innocents 90-94; TV 94-96; P-in-c Mamble w Bayton, Rock w Heightington etc 96-99; TV Cartmel Peninsula *Carl* 99-01; Jt Dir of Ords 00-01; P-in-c Worminghall w Ickford, Oakley and Shabbington *Ox* from 01. *The Rectory, 32A The Avenue, Worminghall, Aylesbury HP18 9LE* Tel (01844) 338839 E-mail laura.wilford@virgin.net

WILKES, Jonathan Peter. b 66. Leic Poly BA88 Ripon Coll Cuddesdon BTh93. **d** 96 **p** 97. C Hackney *Lon* 96-00; P-in-c Paddington St Pet from 00. *St Peter's Vicarage, 59 Elgin Avenue, London W9 2DB* Tel (020) 7289 2011

WILKES, Mrs Penelope Ann Ross. b 49. Dioc OLM tr scheme 96. **d** 99 **p** 00. OLM Debenham w Aspall and Kenton *St E* from 99; OLM Helmingham w Framsden and Pettaugh w Winston from 99. *23 Moores Close, Debenham, Stowmarket IP14 6RU* Tel (01728) 860633

WILKES, Canon Robert Anthony. b 48. Trin Coll Ox BA70 MA73. Wycliffe Hall Ox 71. **d** 74 **p** 75. C Netherton *Liv* 74-77; V 77-81; Bp's Dom Chapl 81-85; CMS 85-98; Pakistan 85-86; Regional Sec Middle E and Pakistan 87-98; Perm to Offic *S'wark* 87-90; Perm to Offic *Ox* 90-98; P-in-c Mossley Hill St Matt and St Jas *Liv* from 98; Hon Can Liv Cathl from 03. *The Vicarage, Rose Lane, Mossley Hill, Liverpool L18 8DB* Tel 0151-724 2650 E-mail wilkesmh@surfaid.org

WILKIE, Alan James. b 17. Chich Th Coll 39. **d** 42 **p** 43. C Wednesbury St Paul Wood Green *Lich* 42-44; C Porthill 44-52; C Stoke-upon-Trent 52-54; Chapl Stoke-on-Trent City Gen Hosp 52-54; Lic to Offic *Guildf* 54-65; Lic to Offic *Nor* 66-68; Hd Badingham Coll Leatherhead 54-65; Wymondham 65-68; V Lindale *Carl* 69-71; P-in-c Field Broughton 71; V Lindale w Field Broughton 71-85; rtd 85; Perm to Offic *Carl* 85-99 and from 02. *Fernlea, Beckermet CA21 2YF* Tel (01946) 841284

WILKIE, Michael John David. b 65. Oak Hill Th Coll BA90 Ex Univ PGCE94. SW Minl Tr Course 98. **d** 00 **p** 01. NSM Combe Martin, Brayton*a*rbor, Lynton, Brendon etc *Ex* from 00. *The Terrace, Parracombe, Barnstaple EX31 4PE* Tel (01548) 763584

WILKIN, Kenneth. b 54. Open Univ BA97 Dip Environment & Development97. S'wark Ord Course 86 Wilson Carlile Coll. **d** 88 **p** 89. C Wolverhampton *Lich* 88-92; V W Bromwich St Andr w Ch Ch 92-98; Dep Chapl HM Pris Pentonville 98-00; Chapl HM Pris Holloway from 00. *HM Prison Holloway, 1 Parkhurst Road, London N7 0NU* Tel (020) 7607 6747 Fax 7697 8395

WILKIN, Paul John. b 56. Linc Th Coll 88. **d** 90 **p** 91. C Leavesden All SS *St Alb* 90-93; C Jersey St Brelade *Win* 93-97; V Squirrels Heath *Chelmsf* from 97. *The Vicarage, 36 Ardleigh Green Road, Hornchurch RM11 2LQ* Tel (01708) 446571 E-mail paulwilkin@iname.com

WILKIN, Rose Josephine. See HUDSON-WILKIN, Mrs Rose Josephine

WILKINS, Mrs Janice Joy. b 49. St D Coll Lamp 90. **d** 93 **p** 97. NSM Tredegar St Jas *Mon* 93-96; NSM Newbridge 96-97; C Mynyddislwyn 97-01; V Abercarn and Cwmcarn from 01. *The Vicarage, Twyn Road, Abercarn, Newport NP11 5GU* Tel (01495) 243919

WILKINS, Ralph Herbert. b 29. Lon Univ BD61. St Aug Coll Cant 72. **d** 73 **p** 74. C Epsom Common Ch Ch *Guildf* 73-76; C Haslemere 77-79; P-in-c Market Lavington and Easterton

Sarum 79-82; V 82-90; P-in-c Puddletown and Tolpuddle 90-94; P-in-c Milborne St Andrew w Dewlish 92-94; P-in-c Piddletrenthide w Plush, Alton Pancras etc 92-94; rtd 94; Perm to Offic *Ab* 94-01. *The Mill, Marton, Welshpool SY21 8JY* Tel (01938) 580566

WILKINS, Miss Susan Stafford. b 47. Dur Univ BA. Sarum Th Coll. **dss** 82 **d** 87 **p** 94. Redlynch and Morgan's Vale *Sarum* 82-88; Hon Par Dn 87-88; Hon Par Dn Bemerton 88-90; Par Dn Hilperton w Whaddon and Staverton etc 90-94; TV Worle *B & W* 94-99; P-in-c Hallwood *Ches* from 99. *The Vicarage, 6 Kirkstone Crescent, Runcorn WA7 3JQ* Tel (01928) 713101 E-mail suewilkins@hallwoodlep.fsnet.co.uk

WILKINS, Vernon Gregory. b 53. Trin Coll Cam MA74 Ox Univ BA88. Wycliffe Hall Ox 86. **d** 89 **p** 90. C Boscombe St Jo *Win* 89-91; C Bursledon 91-94; V Ramsgate St Luke *Cant* from 94. *St Luke's Vicarage, St Luke's Avenue, Ramsgate CT11 7JX* Tel (01843) 592562 E-mail vernon@vgwilkins.freeserve.co.uk

WILKINSON, Adrian Mark. b 68. TCD BA90 MA94 BTh94 NUI HDipEd91. CITC 91. **d** 94 **p** 95. C Douglas Union w Frankfield *C, C & R* 94-97; I Dunboyne Union *M & K* 97-02; Chapl NUI 97-02; Min Can St Patr Cathl Dublin 97-02; I Rathmolyon w Castlerickard, Rathcore and Agher *M & K* 01-02; I Douglas Union w Frankfield *C, C & R* from 02. *Lysander, Carr's Hill, Douglas, Cork, Irish Republic* E-mail amwilk@indigo.ie

WILKINSON, Canon Alan Bassindale. b 31. St Cath Coll Cam BA54 MA58 PhD59 DD97. Coll of Resurr Mirfield 57. **d** 59 **p** 60. C Kilburn St Aug *Lon* 59-61; Chapl St Cath Coll Cam 61-67; V Barrow Gurney *B & W* 67-70; Asst Chapl and Lect St Matthias's Coll Bris 67-70; Prin Chich Th Coll 70-74; Can and Preb Chich Cathl *Chich* 70-74; Warden Verulam Ho 74-75; Dir of Aux Min Tr *St Alb* 74-75; Sen Lect Crewe and Alsager Coll of HE 75-78; Hon C Alsager St Mary *Ches* 76-78; Dioc Dir of Tr *Ripon* 78-84; P-in-c Thornthwaite w Thruscross and Darley 84-88; Hon Can Ripon Cathl 84-88; Perm to Offic *Portsm* from 88; Hon P Portsm Cathl from 88; Hon Dioc Th 93-01; Hon Chapl Portsm Cathl 94-01; rtd 96; Visiting Lect Portsm Univ from 98. *29 Kings Road, Emsworth PO10 7HN* Tel (01243) 370457

WILKINSON, Alice Margaret Marion. See BISHOP, Mrs Alice Margaret Marion

WILKINSON, Andrew Wilfrid. b 66. Nottm Univ BTh96. Linc Th Coll 93. **d** 96 **p** 97. C Longridge *Blackb* 96-99; V Garstang St Helen and St Michaels-on-Wyre from 99; AD Garstang from 02. *St Helen's Vicarage, 6 Vicarage Lane, Churchtown, Preston PR3 0HW* Tel (01995) 602294 Fax as telephone E-mail vic.garstang@virgin.net

WILKINSON (née PHILPOTT), Barbara May. b 48. Leeds Univ BA69 CertEd70 MA90. N Ord Course 90. **d** 93 **p** 94. NSM Carleton and Lothersdale *Bradf* 93-96; C Steeton 96-00; Asst Chapl Airedale NHS Trust from 96. *37 Aire Valley Drive, Bradley, Keighley BD20 9HY* Tel (01535) 636339

WILKINSON, David Andrew. b 62. Edge Hill Coll of HE BA83. Oak Hill Th Coll BA85. **d** 88 **p** 89. C Upton (Overchurch) *Ches* 88-91; C Fulham St Matt *Lon* 91-94; V Duffield *Derby* 94-99; V Finchley St Paul and St Luke *Lon* 99-03. *Honeysuckle Cottage, 19 Church Street, Windermere LA23 1AQ* Tel (015394) 43069

WILKINSON, David Edward Paul. b 36. Univ of Wales (Swansea) BSc57. St Mich Coll Llan 57. **d** 59 **p** 60. C Brecon w Battle *S & B* 59-60; Min Can Brecon Cathl 60-66; R Llanelwedd w Llanfaredd, Cwmbach Llechryd etc 66-72; V Tycoch 72-74; Asst Master Churchmead Sch Datchet 75-82; TV Seacroft *Ripon* 82-01; rtd 01; Hon Min Can Ripon Cathl *Ripon* from 01. *The Vicarage, Knaresborough Road, Bishop Monkton, Harrogate HG3 3QQ* Tel (01765) 677372 Mobile 07909-961197 E-mail paulwilkinson4@aol.com

WILKINSON, Canon David James. b 45. St D Coll Lamp 65 Wycliffe Hall Ox 68. **d** 69 **p** 70. C Swansea St Thos and Kilvey *S & B* 69-73; C Clydach 73-76; R Llanbadarn Fawr, Llandegley and Llanfihangel etc 76-81; V Swansea St Nic 81-88; V Killay 88-94; V Ilston w Pennard from 94; RD N Gower from 99; Can Brecon Cathl from 99. *The Vicarage, 88 Pennard Road, Pennard, Swansea SA3 2AD* Tel (01792) 232928 Fax as telephone

WILKINSON, Edward. b 55. Cranmer Hall Dur 86. **d** 88 **p** 89. C Bishopwearmouth St Nic *Dur* 88-92; P-in-c Newbottle 92-96; V from 96. *The Vicarage, Newbottle, Houghton le Spring DH4 4EP* Tel 0191-584 3244

WILKINSON, Edwin. b 29. Oak Hill Th Coll 53. **d** 56 **p** 57. C Blackb Ch Ch *Blackb* 56-58; C Cheltenham St Mark *Glouc* 58-61; V Tiverton St Geo *Ex* 61-66; V Rye Harbour *Chich* 66-73; V Camber and E Guldeford 73-79; V Westfield 79-87; V Bexhill St Steph 87-93; rtd 93; Perm to Offic *Chich* from 93. *51 Anderida Road, Eastbourne BN22 0PZ* Tel (01323) 503083

WILKINSON, Geoffrey. See WILKINSON, Roy Geoffrey
WILKINSON, The Ven Guy Alexander. b 48. Magd Coll Cam BA69. Ripon Coll Cuddesdon 85. **d** 87 **p** 88. C Coventry

Caludon *Cov* 87-90; P-in-c Ockham w Hatchford *Guildf* 90-91; R 91-94; Bp's Dom Chapl 90-94; V Small Heath *Birm* 94-99; Adn Bradf from 99. *14 Park Cliffe Road, Bradford BD2 4NS* Tel and fax (01274) 641337 Mobile 07932-652315
E-mail guy@gwilkinson.org.uk

WILKINSON, James Daniel. b 73. Westmr Coll Ox BTh95. St Steph Ho Ox 97. **d** 99 **p** 00. C Wantage *Ox* 99-02; P-in-c S Hinksey from 02; P Sec to Bp Ebbsfleet from 02. *The Vicarage, 33 Vicarage Road, Oxford OX1 4RD* Tel (01865) 245879
E-mail frwilkinson@ukonline.co.uk

WILKINSON, John Andrew. b 59. Pemb Coll Ox BA83 MA87 St Jo Coll Dur BA86. Cranmer Hall Dur 84. **d** 87 **p** 88. C Broadheath *Ches* 87-91; TV Worthing Ch the King *Chich* 91-97; Chapl Chantilly *Eur* from 97. *7A avenue du Bouteiller, 60500 Chantilly, France* Tel (0033) (3) 44 57 52 00 *or* tel and fax 44 58 53 22 E-mail wilkstp@club-internet.fr

WILKINSON, John David. b 36. AKC59. **d** 60 **p** 61. C Wythenshawe Wm Temple Ch CD *Man* 60-63; C Morley St Pet w Churwell *Wakef* 63-65; V Robert Town 65-75; V Battyeford 75-88; V Airedale w Fryston 88-98; P-in-c Cawthorne from 98. *The Vicarage, 5 Church Lane, Cawthorne, Barnsley S75 4DW* Tel (01226) 790235 Fax as telephone
E-mail john@cawthornevicarage.fsnet.co.uk

WILKINSON, Canon John Donald. b 29. Mert Coll Ox BA54 MA56 Louvain Univ Belgium LTh59 Lon Univ PhD82 FSA80. Gen Th Sem (NY) Hon STD63 Cuddesdon Coll 54. **d** 56 **p** 57. C Stepney St Dunstan and All SS *Lon* 56-59; Jerusalem 61-63; Gen Ed USPG 63-69; Dean St Geo Coll Jerusalem 69-75; Can Jerusalem 73-75; P-in-c S Kensington H Trin w All SS *Lon* 75-78; Bp's Dir of Clergy Tr 75-79; Dir Br Sch of Archaeology Jerusalem 79-83; USA 83-91; NSM Kensington St Mary Abbots w St Geo *Lon* 91-94; rtd 94; Hon C St Marylebone St Cypr *Lon* 94-98; Perm to Offic from 98. *7 Tenniel Close, London W2 3LE* Tel (020) 7229 9205 Fax as telephone

WILKINSON, Canon John Lawrence. b 43. Ch Coll Cam BA65 MA69 Birm Univ MLitt91. Qu Coll Birm DipTh68 Gen Th Sem (NY) STB69. **d** 69 **p** 70. C Braunstone *Leic* 69-71; C Hodge Hill *Birm* 71-74; P-in-c Aston St Jas 75-84; Tutor Qu Coll Birm 85-95; Hon C Birm St Geo *Birm* 86-95; V Kings Heath from 95; Hon Can Birm Cathl from 99. *All Saints' Vicarage, 2 Vicarage Road, Birmingham B14 7RA* Tel 0121-444 1207
E-mail john-renate@jrwilkinson.freeserve.co.uk

WILKINSON, John Stoddart. b 47. Univ of Wales (Cardiff) CQSW83. St D Coll Lamp DipTh70. **d** 70 **p** 71. C Kells *Carl* 70-72; C Barrow St Geo w St Luke 72-74; Perm to Offic *Mon* 74-89; Sub-Chapl HM YOI Hewell Grange 89-90; Sub-Chapl HM Rem Cen Brockhill 89-90; rtd 02. *Seren y Mor, 11 Dunsany Park, Haverfordwest SA61 1UD* Tel (01437) 762364

WILKINSON, Jonathan Charles. b 61. Leeds Univ BA83. Wycliffe Hall Ox 85. **d** 87 **p** 88. C Plymouth St Andr w St Paul and St Geo *Ex* 87-90; C Oulton Broad *Nor* 90-93; V Hallwood *Ches* 93-99; TR Gateshead *Dur* from 99. *The Rectory, 91 Old Durham Road, Gateshead NE8 4BS* Tel 0191-477 3990
E-mail wilkinson@clara.net

WILKINSON, Mrs Joyce Aileen. b 29. BSc(Econ) MA. **d** 99 **p** 00. NSM Bredon w Bredon's Norton *Worc* from 99. *Bamford Cottage, High Street, Kemerton, Tewkesbury GL20 7HP* Tel (01386) 725549 E-mail joycewilkinson@lineone.net.uk

WILKINSON, Miss Julia Mary. b 52. Cam Inst of Educn CertEd73 Open Univ BA85 Univ of Wales (Ban) BD89. Linc Th Coll 92. **d** 92 **p** 94. Par Dn High Wycombe *Ox* 92-94; C 94-96; TV 96-01; Bp's Adv for Women in Ordained Min 97-01; P-in-c St Issey w St Petroc Minor *Truro* from 01; P-in-c St Merryn from 01; Co Dioc Dir of Ords from 01. *The Rectory, St Issey, Wadebridge PL27 7HJ* Tel (01841) 540314 Fax as telephone E-mail revjulia@stpetroc.fsnet.co.uk

WILKINSON, Canon Keith Howard. b 48. Hull Univ BA70 FRSA94 MCT99. Westcott Ho Cam 74. **d** 76 **p** 77. C Pet St Jude *Pet* 76-79; Chapl Eton Coll 79-84; Perm to Offic *Pet* 82-94; Chapl Malvern Coll 84-89; Hd Master Berkhamsted Sch Herts 89-96; Lic to Offic *St Alb* 89-96; Hd Master K Sch Cant from 96; Hon Can Cant Cathl *Cant* from 96. *The King's School, Canterbury CT1 2ES* Tel (01227) 595501
E-mail headmaster@kings-school.co.uk

WILKINSON, Kenneth Samuel. b 31. TCD BA60 MA69. CITC 60. **d** 60 **p** 61. C Dublin St Michan w St Paul *D & G* 60-63; Min Can St Patr Cathl Dublin 62-67; C Dublin Ch Ch Leeson Park *D & G* 63-67; I Killegney *C & O* 67-70; I Enniscorthy w Clone, Clonmore, Monart etc 70-02; Preb Ferns Cathl 83-88; Adn Ferns 88-02; Dioc Dir of Ords 94-02; rtd 02. *149 Hazelwood, Old Coach Road, Gorey, Co Wexford, Irish Republic*

WILKINSON, Margaret Anne. b 46. Lon Univ MB, BS70 MSc74 MRCPsych77. St Alb and Ox Min Course 95. **d** 98 **p** 99. NSM Heston *Lon* from 98. *33 Summerhouse Avenue, Hounslow TW5 9DJ* Tel (020) 8570 2831

WILKINSON, Miss Marlene Sandra. b 45. SRN71 Huddersfield Poly NDN86 Leeds Univ DipTh91 Sheff Univ Dip Bibl Studies 93. Trin Coll Bris IDC78. **dss** 78 **d** 93 **p** 94.

Wrose *Bradf* 78-82; Chapl St Luke's Hosp Bradf 78-82; Past Tutor Aston Tr Scheme 79-81; W Yorkshire CECS 82-84; Westgate Common *Wakef* 84-86; E Ardsley 86-92; Wakef St Jo 92-94; NSM 93-94; TV Barrow St Geo w St Luke *Carl* 94-00; TV Darwen St Pet w Hoddlesden *Blackb* 00-02; rtd 03. *4 Hopefield Court, East Ardsley, Wakefield WF3 2LL* Tel (01924) 872825

WILKINSON, Mrs Mary Frances. b 52. St As Minl Tr Course 99. **d** 03. NSM Shotton *St As* from 03. *10 Appleby Drive, Hawarden, Deeside CH5 3HN* Tel (01244) 534036

WILKINSON, Michael Alan. b 27. Selw Coll Cam BA51. Westcott Ho Cam 52. **d** 53 **p** 54. C Swindon Ch Ch *Bris* 53-57; C Knowle St Barn 57-59; C Eltham St Jo *S'wark* 59-65; C Sydenham St Bart 65-77; Perm to Offic *Ex* 77-84; P-in-c Yealmpton 84-91; P-in-c Brixton 87-91; V Yealmpton and Brixton 91-97; RD Ivybridge 91-93; rtd 97; Perm to Offic *Ex* from 97. *The Old Forge, Kingston, Kingsbridge TQ7 4PT* Tel (01548) 810424

WILKINSON, Paul. b 51. Sarum & Wells Th Coll 75. **d** 78 **p** 79. C Allerton *Bradf* 78-80; C Baildon 80-83; V Hengoed w Gobowen *Lich* 83-90; V Potterne w Worton and Marston *Sarum* from 90; Chapl Roundway Hosp Devizes from 92. *The Vicarage, 4 Rookes Lane, Potterne, Devizes SN10 5NF* Tel (01380) 723189
E-mail pwilkinson@vicarage79.fsnet.co.uk

WILKINSON, Paul Martin. b 56. Brunel Univ BSc. Wycliffe Hall Ox 83. **d** 86 **p** 87. C Hinckley H Trin *Leic* 86-90; V Newbold on Avon *Cov* from 90. *The Vicarage, Main Street, Newbold, Rugby CV21 1HH* Tel (01788) 543055 Fax 542458
E-mail paul.wilkinson4@tesco.net

WILKINSON, Peter David Lloyd. b 67. Trin Coll Ox BA89 MA93. Ridley Hall Cam BA94 CTM95. **d** 95 **p** 96. C Brampton St Thos *Derby* 95-98; C Tunbridge Wells St Jo *Roch* 98-02; C Ox St Ebbe w H Trin and St Pet *Ox* from 02. *10 Lincoln Road, Oxford OX1 4TB* Tel (01865) 728885
E-mail pete@peteandjules.freeserve.co.uk

WILKINSON, Peter Howarth. b 32. St Pet Hall Ox BA54 MA58. Ridley Hall Cam 56. **d** 58 **p** 59. C Cheadle *Ches* 58-62; V Nettlebed *Ox* 62-68; rtd 68; Hon C Cheadle *Ches* 69-82. *10 Norbreck Avenue, Cheadle SK8 2ET* Tel 0161-428 7699

WILKINSON, Robert. See WILKINSON, Walter Edward Robert

WILKINSON, Robert Ian. b 43. MIMunE73 MICE84 CEng73. Oak Hill NSM Course. **d** 88 **p** 89. NSM Hawkwell *Chelmsf* 88-89; NSM Thundersley 89-91; C New Thundersley 91-94; V Berechurch St Marg w St Mich from 94. *The Vicarage, 348 Mersea Road, Colchester CO2 8RA* Tel (01206) 576859
E-mail vicar@stmargcol.org.uk

WILKINSON, Robert John. b 66. Birkbeck Coll Lon BA98 Fitzw Coll Cam BA00 ACIB90. Westcott Ho Cam 98. **d** 01 **p** 02. C Southgate Ch Ch *Lon* from 01. *62 Oakfield Road, London N14 6LX* Tel (020) 8886 3346 Fax 08701-307538
E-mail robert.wilkinson@london.anglican.org

WILKINSON, Canon Robert Matthew. b 21. TCD BA46. TCD Div Sch 47. **d** 47 **p** 48. C Limerick St Lawr w H Trin and St Jo *L & K* 47-49; C Arm St Mark *Arm* 49-51; I Mullavilly 51-55; I Derryloran 55-73; Can Arm Cathl 67-73; I Ballymore 73-87; Treas Arm Cathl 73-75; Chan 75-83; Prec 83-87; rtd 87. *60 Coleraine Road, Portrush BT56 8HN* Tel (028) 7082 2758

WILKINSON, Robert Samuel. b 52. Wycliffe Hall Ox DipMin94. **d** 94 **p** 95. C Boughton Monchelsea *Cant* 94-96; C Parkwood CD 95-96; C Plymouth St Andr and St Paul Stonehouse *Ex* 96-01; P-in-c Whimple, Talaton and Clyst St Lawr from 01. *The Rectory, Grove Road, Whimple, Exeter EX5 2TP* Tel (01404) 822521
E-mail rob@standrewschurch.org.uk

WILKINSON, Roger. b 46. K Coll Lon BA68 AKC68 AKC72. St Aug Coll Cant 72. **d** 73 **p** 74. C Lt Stanmore St Lawr *Lon* 73-76; Asst Chapl St Geo Hosp Lon 76-78; Chapl Hounslow and Spelthorne HA 78-88; TV Langley and Parkfield *Man* 88-89; C Shelf and Buttershaw St Aid *Bradf* 89-90; Chapl Asst Ipswich Hosp NHS Trust 90-94; C Fingringhoe w E Donyland and Abberton etc *Chelmsf* 94-01; P-in-c Greensted-juxta-Ongar w Stanford Rivers from 01; P-in-c Stapleford Tawney w Theydon Mt from 01. *52 Epping Road, Toot Hill, Ongar CM5 9SQ* Tel (01992) 524005
E-mail rogerwilko@supanet.com

WILKINSON, Roy Geoffrey. b 42. Open Univ BSc93. Sarum Th Coll 67. **d** 70 **p** 71. C Belsize Park *Lon* 70-73; C Heston 73-75; C Hythe *Cant* 75-79; V Croydon Woodside 79-86; NSM Skegness and Winthorpe *Linc* 96-97; Asst Mental Health Chapl Linc Distr Healthcare NHS Trust 96-97; Mental Health Chapl from 97. *Witham Court EMI Unit, Fen Lane, North Hykeham, Lincoln LN6 8UZ* Tel (01522) 500690

WILKINSON, Simon Evelyn. b 49. Nottm Univ BA74. Cuddesdon Coll 74. **d** 76 **p** 77. C Cheam *S'wark* 76-78; P-in-c Warlingham w Chelsham and Farleigh 78-83; Hd RS Radley Coll 83-89; R Bishop's Waltham and Upham *Portsm* 89-97; TR Shaston *Sarum* 97-03; P-in-c Amesbury from 03. *The Vicarage, Church Street, Amesbury, Salisbury SP4 7EU* Tel (01980) 623145

WILKINSON, Walter Edward Robert. b 38. St Andr Univ MA60. Lon Coll of Div BD63 ALCD63. **d** 63 **p** 64. C High Wycombe *Ox* 63-70; PV, Succ and Sacr Roch Cathl *Roch* 70-73; P-in-c Asby w Ormside *Carl* 73-80; R Cherry Burton *York* 80-95; RD Beverley 88-94; P-in-c Grasmere *Carl* 95-03; rtd 03. *4 Heversham Gardens, Heversham, Milnthorpe LA7 7RA* Tel (01539) 564044 E-mail bob@carliol.clara.co.uk

WILKINSON, Canon Wilfred Badger. b 21. K Coll Lon BD50 AKC50. **d** 50 **p** 51. C Luton St Mary *St Alb* 50-53; C Gt Berkhamsted 53-57; C-in-c Wythenshawe Wm Temple Ch CD *Man* 57-65; R Clifton w Glapton *S'well* 65-71; TR Clifton 71-86; Hon Can S'well Minster 83-86; rtd 86; Perm to Offic *S'well* from 86. *Hazelford, Boat Lane, Bleasby, Nottingham NG14 7FT* Tel (01636) 831493

WILKS, Eric Percival. b 32. Wells Th Coll 67. **d** 68 **p** 69. C Fladbury w Throckmorton, Wyre Piddle and Moor *Worc* 68-70; Perm to Offic from 70. *4 Catherine Cottages, Droitwich Road, Hartlebury, Kidderminster DY10 4EL* Tel (01299) 251580

WILKS, Ernest Howard. b 26. Oak Hill Th Coll 64. **d** 66 **p** 67. C Slough *Ox* 66-69; R Gressenhall w Longham and Bittering Parva *Nor* 69-77; Area Sec CMS *St E* and *Nor* 77-83; P-in-c Deopham w Hackford *Nor* 83-84; P-in-c Morley 83-84; P-in-c Wicklewood and Crownthorpe 83-84; R Morley w Deopham, Hackford, Wicklewood etc 84-88; CMS Nigeria 89-91; rtd 91; Perm to Offic *Nor* from 91. *Corner Cottage, Carbrooke Road, Griston, Thetford IP25 6QE* Tel (01953) 881413

WILL, Nicholas James. b 53. Birm Univ LLB75. Qu Coll Birm 93. **d** 95 **p** 96. C Bridgnorth, Tasley, Astley Abbotts, etc *Heref* 95-00; R Raveningham Gp *Nor* from 00. *The Rectory, Church Road, Thurlton, Norwich NR14 6RN* Tel (01508) 548648

WILLANS, Jonathan Michael Arthur. b 60. QUB BD. CITC 83. **d** 85 **p** 86. C Larne and Inver *Conn* 85-88; R Hawick *Edin* 88-91; P-in-c Brockham Green *S'wark* from 91; P-in-c Leigh from 91. *The Vicarage, Clayhill Road, Leigh, Reigate RH2 8PD* Tel and fax (01306) 611224

WILLANS, William Richard Gore. b 48. Qu Coll Ox BA70 MA74 Ox Univ PGCE71. CITC 77. **d** 79 **p** 80. Canada 79-98; C Bonne Bay 79-80; P-in-c Bonne Bay N 80-82; R 82-87; R Thunder Bay St Thos 87-98; RD Thunder Bay 89-93 and 95-97; I Craigs w Dunaghy and Killagan *Conn* from 98. *Craigs Rectory, 95 Hillmount Road, Cullybackey, Ballymena BT42 1NZ* Tel (028) 2588 0248 *or* 2588 2225 E-mail willans@btinternet.com

WILLARD, John Fordham. b 38. K Coll Lon BD62 AKC62. **d** 63 **p** 64. C Balham Hill Ascension *S'wark* 63-67; C Leigh Park *Portsm* 67-73; C-in-c Leigh Park St Clare CD 73-75; R Bishop's Waltham 75-87; P-in-c Upham 78-79; R 79-87; V Dalston H Trin w St Phil *Lon* 87-97; P-in-c Haggerston All SS 90-97; P-in-c Fairford *Glouc* 97-98; V Fairford and Kempsford w Whelford from 98. *The Vicarage, The Croft, Fairford GL7 4BB* Tel (01285) 712467

WILLCOCK, Canon Richard William. b 39. Hertf Coll Ox BA62 MA66. Ripon Hall Ox 62. **d** 64 **p** 65. C Ashton St Mich *Man* 64-68; Bp's Dom Chapl 68-72; V Charlestown 72-73; V Charlestown 73-75; Chapl Casterton Sch Lancs 75-80; V Bamford *Man* 80-92; R Framlingham w Saxtead *St E* from 92; RD Loes 95-97; Warden of Readers 98-03; Hon Can St E Cathl from 00. *The Rectory, St Michael's Close, Framlingham, Woodbridge IP13 9BJ* Tel (01728) 621082 E-mail richardw@stedmundsbury.anglican.org

WILLCOX, Canon Frederick John. b 29. Kelham Th Coll 49. **d** 54 **p** 55. C Tranmere St Paul *Ches* 54-56; Lic to Offic *S'well* 57-61; S Africa 62-70; P-in-c Derby St Andr w St Osmund *Derby* 70-74; V 74-80; V Netherton St Andr *Worc* 80-94; Hon Can Worc Cathl 91-94; rtd 94; Perm to Offic *Worc* from 94. *48 Meadow Croft, West Hagley, Stourbridge DY9 0LJ* Tel (01562) 887255

WILLCOX, Ralph Arthur. b 32. Westhill Coll Birm CertYS59 Cranfield Inst of Tech MSc80. St Alb Minl Tr Scheme 86. **d** 89 **p** 90. NSM Aspley Guise w Husborne Crawley and Ridgmont *St Alb* 89-92; Chapl HM Pris Bedf 92-99; Asst Chapl 99-02; Lic to Offic *St Alb* 92-03; rtd 02; Perm to Offic *St Alb* from 03. *5 Church Road, Woburn Sands, Milton Keynes MK17 8TE* Tel (01908) 582510

WILLCOX, Richard John Michael. b 39. Birm Univ BSc62 PhD67. Qu Coll Birm 78. **d** 80 **p** 81. C Boldmere *Birm* 80-83; V Edgbaston SS Mary and Ambrose 83-89; V Evercreech w Chesterblade and Milton Clevedon *B & W* 89-97; Dioc Development Rep 90-01; V Bridgwater H Trin 97-01; rtd 01. *The Briars, Ledbury Road, Wellington Heath, Ledbury HR8 1NB* Tel (01531) 636191 E-mail rswillcox@aol.com

WILLCOX, Canon Sydney Harold. b 36. Univ of Wales (Lamp) BA58. St Mich Coll Llan. **d** 60 **p** 61. C Pwllheli *Ban* 60-62; C Llandegfan w Beaumaris and Llanfaes 62-65; R Llanenddwyn 65-70; R Dolgellau, Llanfachreth, Brithdir etc 70-76; TR Ridgeway *Sarum* 76-86; RD Marlborough 81-86; TR Cockermouth w Embleton and Wythop *Carl* 86-94; RD Derwent 89-94; Hon Can Carl Cathl 91-94; TR Chalke Valley *Sarum* 94-01; rtd 02. *7 Hillingdon, Bridport DT6 3DH* Tel (01308) 459139

WILLESDEN, Area Bishop of. *See* BROADBENT, The Rt Revd Peter Alan

WILLETT, Canon Allen Gardiner. b 20. Bris Univ BA51 Lon Univ BD54. Clifton Th Coll 47. **d** 54 **p** 55. C Rawtenstall St Mary *Man* 54-57; Nigeria 57-58; Tutor Clifton Th Coll 58-60; C Wallington H Trin *S'wark* 60-62; Tutor All Nations Miss Coll Taplow 62-63; V Bedminster St Luke w St Silas *Bris* 63-68; V Galleywood Common *Chelmsf* 68-87; RD Chelmsf 83-86; Hon Can Chelmsf Cathl 85-87; rtd 87; Perm to Offic *Pet* 87-00; *Linc* 90-99 and *Ely* 90-97; *Chelmsf* from 01. *61 Ashdown Way, Ipswich IP3 8RL* Tel (01473) 423751

WILLETT, Frank Edwin. b 45. Lon Univ DipTh68. Kelham Th Coll 64. **d** 68 **p** 69. C Oswestry H Trin *Lich* 68-71; C Bilston St Leon 71-74; USPG Coll of the Ascension Selly Oak 74-75; USPG 74-80; Zambia 75-80; V Curbar and Stoney Middleton *Derby* 80-88; Area Sec USPG *Derby* and *Leic* 88-91; V Chesterfield St Aug *Derby* 91-98; Chapl Walton Hosp 91-98; Ind Chapl *Derby* 98-03; P-in-c Brampton St Mark from 03; P-in-c Loundsley Green from 03. *The Vicarage, 15 St Mark's Road, Chesterfield S40 1DH* Tel (01246) 234015 E-mail f@willett85.freeserve.co.uk

WILLETT, Canon Geoffrey Thomas. b 38. Dur Univ BA59 MA82. Cranmer Hall Dur DipTh61. **d** 62 **p** 63. C Widnes St Paul *Liv* 62-65; C Harborne Heath *Birm* 65-68; V Wakef St Andr and St Mary *Wakef* 68-75; V Hinckley H Trin *Leic* 75-89; TR 89; RD Sparkenhoe II 84-87; RD Sparkenhoe W 87-89; Hon Can Leic Cathl from 87; P-in-c Markfield 89-90; R 90-99; P-in-c Thornton, Bagworth and Stanton 96-99; R Markfield, Thornton, Bagworth and Stanton etc from 99; RD Sparkenhoe E 91-99. *The Rectory, 3A The Nook, Markfield LE67 9WE* Tel (01530) 242844

WILLETT, Canon John Ivon. b 40. Ch Ch Ox BA63 MA65. Chich Th Coll 61. **d** 63 **p** 64. C Leic St Andr *Leic* 63-66; C Bordesley St Alb *Birm* 66-72; Min Can, Prec and Sacr Pet Cathl *Pet* 72-82; R Uppingham w Ayston and Wardley w Belton 82-99; Can Pet Cathl 97-99; V Cantley *Sheff* from 99. *St Wilfrid's Vicarage, 200 Cantley Lane, Doncaster DN4 6PA* Tel (01302) 535133

WILLETT, Michael John Farquhar. b 32. St Mich Coll Llan Dip Minl Studies 92. **d** 92 **p** 93. NSM Llangorse, Cathedine, Llanfihangel Talyllyn etc *S & B* 92-01; NSM Llyn Safaddan 01-02; Wales Reg Chapl Third Order SSF from 99. *Beaufort House, Llangynidr, Crickhowell NP8 1NT* Tel (01874) 730449

WILLETT, Stephen John. b 54. Ridley Hall Cam 88. **d** 90 **p** 91. C Chapeltown *Sheff* 90-94; V Hackenthorpe from 94. *The Vicarage, 63 Sheffield Road, Sheffield S12 4LR* Tel 0114-248 4486

WILLETTS, Alfred. b 15. **d** 62 **p** 63. C Canton St Jo *Llan* 62-65; V Afan Vale 65-67; R Man St Phil w St Mark *Man* 67-75; R Man Apostles 75-84; rtd 85; Perm to Offic *Ches* 85-91; Perm to Offic *Man* 85-97. *c/o Dr P Willetts, 25 Kings Way, Harrow HA1 1XT* Tel (020) 8427 0111

WILLETTS, Ms Mary Elizabeth Willetts. b 33. St Hild Coll Dur BA54 Hughes Hall Cam CertEd55. Cranmer Hall Dur 02. **d** 02 **p** 03. NSM Stockton-on-the-Forest w Holtby and Warthill *York* from 02. *Walnut Cottage, Warthill, York YO19 5XL* Tel (01904) 489874

WILLEY, David Geoffrey. b 53. Imp Coll Lon BSc74. Oak Hill Th Coll BA86. **d** 86 **p** 87. C Cromer *Nor* 86-90; R High Halstow w All Hallows and Hoo St Mary *Roch* 90-94; R Gravesend St Geo 94-02; TR N Farnborough *Guildf* from 02. *The Rectory, 66 Church Avenue, Farnborough GU14 7AP* Tel (01252) 544754 E-mail david.willey@btopenworld.com

WILLEY, Graham John. b 38. Moray Ord Course 91. **d** 93 **p** 94. NSM W Coast Jt Congregations *Mor* 93-99; NSM Stirling *St And* from 99. *Westerlea, 11 Deroran Place, Stirling FK8 2PG* Tel (01786) 473419

WILLIAMS (née TYDEMAN), Mrs Rosemary. b 47. Roehampton Inst TCert69. St Alb and Ox Min Course 97. **d** 00 **p** 01. NSM Walton H Trin *Ox* 00-03; NSM E and W Horndon w Lt Warley and Childerditch *Chelmsf* from 03. *The Rectory, 155 Thorndon Avenue, West Horndon, Brentwood CM13 3TR* Tel (01277) 811223 E-mail stevecgs@ukonline.co.uk

WILLIAMS, Alan Ronald Norman. b 60. RMN85. Linc Th Coll 95. **d** 95 **p** 96. C Malvern Link w Cowleigh *Worc* 95-99; TV from 99; V Risca *Mon* 99-03. *165 Leigh Sinton Road, Malvern WR14 1LB* Tel (01886) 833578 E-mail alan.r.williams@btinternet.com

WILLIAMS, Aled Jones. b 56. Univ of Wales (Ban) BA77 Univ of Wales (Cardiff) DipTh79. St Mich Coll Llan 77. **d** 79 **p** 80. C Conwy w Gyffin *Ban* 79-82; R Llanrug 82-86; R Machynlleth and Llanwrin 86-87; Member L'Arche Community 88-95; V Ynyscynhaearn w Penmorfa and Porthmadog 95-01; V Porthmadoc and Ynyscynhaearn and Dolbenmaen from 01. *The Vicarage, Ffordd Penamser, Porthmadog LL49 9PA* Tel (01766) 514951

WILLIAMS, Canon Aled Wyn. b 47. Univ of Wales (Abth) BA69. St Mich Coll Llan 69. **d** 71 **p** 72. C Llanelli *St D* 71-73;

WILLIAMS, P-in-c Capel Colman w Llanfihangel Penbedw etc 73-74; V 74-81; V Llanddewi Brefi w Llanbadarn Odwyn 81-84; V Llanddewi Brefi w Llanbadarn Odwyn, Cellan etc 84-01; V Lampeter and Llanddewibrefi Gp from 01; RD Lampeter and Ultra-Aeron from 96; Can St D Cathl from 97. *Y Ficerdy Newydd, Maes y Llan, Guilsfield, Welshpool SY21 9NF* Tel (01974) 298937

WILLIAMS, Alexander Ernest. b 14. Fitzw Ho Cam BA35 MA46 Regent's Park Coll Ox 35. Coll of Resurr Mirfield 79. **d** 79 **p** 80. Hon C Carshalton Beeches *S'wark* 79-87; rtd 87; Perm to Offic *S'wark* from 87. *34 Marlborough Court, Wallington SM6 9PG* Tel (020) 8647 8446

WILLIAMS, Alfred Donald. b 26. St Aid Birkenhead 57. **d** 59 **p** 60. C Ordsall *S'well* 59-62; V Ladybrook 62-70; P-in-c Newark Ch Ch 70-71; R Gotham 72-88; P-in-c W Leake w Kingston-on-Soar and Ratcliffe-on-Soar 72-81; rtd 88; Perm to Offic *Bradf* from 88. *20 Grassington Road, Skipton BD23 1LL* Tel (01756) 794496

WILLIAMS, Miss Alison Lindsay. b 47. Univ of Wales (Abth) BA69 PGCE70. Wycliffe Hall Ox 00. **d** 00 **p** 01. C Stratton St Margaret w S Marston etc *Bris* from 00. *29 Winchester Close, Stratton St Margaret, Swindon SN3 4HB* Tel (01793) 826534

WILLIAMS, Amanda Clare. See WILLIAMS-POTTER, Mrs Amanda Clare

WILLIAMS, Andrew Barrington. b 62. Ripon Coll Cuddesdon 96. **d** 98 **p** 99. C Oswaldtwistle Immanuel and All SS *Blackb* 98-01; C Whittle-le-Woods 01-02; P-in-c Hillock *Man* from 02. *St Andrew's Vicarage, Mersey Drive, Whitefield, Manchester M45 8LA* Tel 0161-766 1635 Fax 0871 242 1319 E-mail andyb.williams@lineone.net

WILLIAMS, Andrew David. b 67. Univ of Wales (Lamp) BA91. Linc Th Coll 93. **d** 93 **p** 94. C Perry Street *Roch* 93-96; C Ealing St Pet Mt Park *Lon* 96-00; R Finchley St Mary from 00. *St Mary's Rectory, Rectory Close, London N3 1TS* Tel (020) 8346 4600 Fax 8343 3174 E-mail awstmary@dialstart.net

WILLIAMS, Andrew Gibson. b 31. Edin Univ MA57. Edin Th Coll 56. **d** 59 **p** 60. C Todmorden *Wakef* 59-61; C Clitheroe St Mary *Blackb* 61-63; V Burnley St Jas 63-65; CF (TA) 64-65; CF 65-71; R Winterslow *Sarum* 71-84; P-in-c Condover *Heref* 84-88; P-in-c Acton Burnell w Pitchford 84-88; P-in-c Frodesley 84-88; R Condover w Frodesley, Acton Burnell etc 88-90; R Whimple, Talaton and Clyst St Lawr *Ex* 90-94; rtd 94; Perm to Offic *Ex* from 94. *14 Sharps Court, Exmouth EX8 1DT* Tel (01395) 271014

WILLIAMS, Andrew Joseph. b 55. St Jo Coll Nottm BTh81. **d** 81 **p** 82. C Hollington St Leon *Chich* 81-84; C Sutton Coldfield H Trin *Birm* 84-87; Perm to Offic from 87; Chapl Blue Coat Comp Sch Walsall 91-01; Chapl St Elphin's Sch Matlock from 01; Lic to Offic *Derby* from 01. *St Elphin's School, Darley Dale, Matlock DE4 2HA* Tel (01629) 732314 E-mail revandyw@aol.com

WILLIAMS, Andrew Thomas. b 66. Ex Univ LLB88 Solicitor 90. Trin Coll Bris BA00. **d** 00 **p** 01. C Whitchurch *Ex* from 00. *1 St Andrew's Road, Whitchurch, Tavistock PL19 9BY* Tel (01822) 611167 E-mail elena.w@virgin.net

WILLIAMS, Mrs Anthea Elizabeth. b 50. Trevelyan Coll Dur BA71 Kent Univ MA97 Middx Univ MSc00. Linc Th Coll 72. **dss** 79 **d** 87 **p** 94. St Marylebone Ch Ch *Lon* 79-84; Maidstone St Martin *Cant* 84-91; Par Dn 87-91; Dn-in-c Rolvenden 91-94; Chapl E Kent Community NHS Trust from 91; P-in-c Rolvenden *Cant* from 94; Asst Dir of Ords 98-03; P-in-c Newenden from 01. *The Vicarage, Rolvenden, Cranbrook TN17 4ND* Tel (01580) 241235 E-mail willtyd@aol.com

WILLIAMS, Anthony David. b 38. LRCP62 MRCS62 DRCOG65 Cert Family Planning 65 MRCGP68. S Dios Minl Tr Scheme 87. **d** 90 **p** 91. Hon C Jersey St Pet *Win* 90-92; NSM Jersey St Helier from 92. *Beau Vallon Ouest, Mont de la Rosiere, St Saviour, Jersey JE2 7HF* Tel (01534) 863859 E-mail tonyw@cinergy.co.uk

WILLIAMS, Anthony Francis. b 21. Trin Coll Ox BA49 MA53. Coll of Resurr Mirfield 49. **d** 51 **p** 52. C Paignton St Jo *Ex* 51-54; C Cov H Trin *Cov* 54-60; V Cov All SS 60-67; V Lindridge *Worc* 67-77; P-in-c Bluntisham w Earith *Ely* 77-79; R 79-88; rtd 88; Perm to Offic *Ely* from 88. *21 King's Hedges, St Ives PE27 3XU* Tel (01480) 467686

WILLIAMS, Canon Anthony Riley. b 36. Univ of Wales BA60. Chich Th Coll 57. **d** 59 **p** 60. C Llandinorwig *Ban* 59-61; C Llandegfan w Beaumaris and Llanfaes 61-64; R Ludchurch and Templeton *St D* 64-72; V Lamphey w Hodgeston 72-83; RD Castlemartin 75-83; V Llanelli 83-00; Can St D Cathl 86-00; Chan St D Cathl 93-00; Chapl Bryntirion Hosp Llanelli 90-94; Chapl Derwen NHS Trust W Wales 94-00; rtd 01. *66 Main Street, Pembroke SA71 4HH* Tel (01646) 685213

WILLIAMS, The Ven Arfon. b 58. Univ of Wales (Abth) BD83 Univ of Wales (Ban) MA84. Wycliffe Hall Ox 83. **d** 84 **p** 85. C Carmarthen St Dav *St D* 84-86; TV Aberystwyth 86-88; V Glanogwen *Ban* 88-94; Dir Oast Ho Retreat Cen *Chich* 95-98; Asst to RD Rye 95-98; C Ewhurst 95-98; Co-ord for Adult Educn (E Sussex Area) 97-98; I Jordanstown *Conn* 98-02; Adn Meirionnydd *Ban* from 02; R Dolgellau w Llanfachreth and Brithdir etc from 02. *The Rectory, Pencefn Road, Dolgellau LL40 2YW* Tel (01341) 422225 Fax 423761 E-mail arfon@williams-jordanstown.freeserve.co.uk

WILLIAMS, Preb Arthur Edwin. b 33. Leeds Univ BA57. Coll of Resurr Mirfield 57. **d** 59 **p** 60. C Wednesfield St Thos *Lich* 59-62; C Codsall 62-65; V 83-98; V Coseley St Chad 65-73; R Kingswinford H Trin 73-81; TR Wordsley 81-83; RD Himley 77-83; Preb Lich Cathl 82-98; RD Penkridge 89-94; rtd 98; Perm to Offic *Lich* from 01. *2 Campbell Close, Bridgnorth WV16 5PD* Tel (01746) 761344

WILLIAMS, Barrie. b 33. Em Coll Cam BA54 MA58 Bris Univ MLitt71. Lambeth STh75 Ripon Hall Ox 62. **d** 63 **p** 64. C Penwortham St Mary *Blackb* 63-65; then Precentor St Martin *Sarum* 65-77; Chapl St Edw K and Martyr Cam *Ely* 77-84; Chapl Trin Hall Cam 77-84; R Ashley w Weston by Welland and Sutton Bassett *Pet* 84-85; Asst Chapl St Hilda's Priory and Sch Whitby 85-97; rtd 98; Perm to Offic *York* from 98. *Flat 5, Crinkle Court, 9 Chubb Hill, Whitby YO21 1JU* Tel (01947) 600766

WILLIAMS, Benjamin Clive. b 24. Lon Univ BD59. Westcott Ho Cam 59. **d** 61 **p** 62. C Bury St Mark *Man* 61-63; C Christchurch *Win* 63-66; R Denton w S Heighton and Tarring Neville *Chich* 66-74; Dioc Stewardship Adv 74-81; P-in-c Clapham w Patching 76-81; V Ticehurst and Flimwell 81-89; rtd 89; Perm to Offic *Chich* from 89. *14 Lindfield Avenue, Seaford BN25 4DY* Tel (01323) 491019

WILLIAMS, Brian. See WILLIAMS, Herbert Brian

WILLIAMS, Brian. b 48. WMMTC. **d** 83 **p** 84. NSM Lich St Chad *Lich* from 83; Asst Chapl Sandwell Health Care NHS Trust 98; Angl Chapl 98-99; Chapl Burton Hosps NHS Trust from 99. *Queen's Hospital, Belvedere Road, Burton-on-Trent DE13 0RB* Tel (01283) 566333

WILLIAMS, Brian Frederick. b 55. Philippa Fawcett Coll CertEd77 BEd78. SEITE 98. **d** 01 **p** 02. NSM Folkestone St Mary and St Eanswythe *Cant* from 01. *79 Surrenden Road, Folkestone CT19 4EB* Tel (01303) 276242 E-mail brianwilliams@cheritonfolk.fsnet.co.uk

WILLIAMS, Brian Luke. b 54. AKC75. St Steph Ho Ox 76. **d** 77 **p** 78. C Kettering St Mary *Pet* 77-80; C Walsall St Gabr Fulbrook *Lich* 80-85; P-in-c Sneyd 83-85; V from 85; RD Stoke N 94-99. *Sneyd Vicarage, Hamil Road, Stoke-on-Trent ST6 1AP* Tel (01782) 825841 Fax as telephone

WILLIAMS, Bryan. **d** 01. OLM Fazeley *Lich* from 01. *47 Dama Road, Fazeley, Tamworth B78 3SU* Tel (01827) 289830

WILLIAMS, Ms Carol Jean Picknell. b 45. FCIPD89. Ox NSM Course 86. **d** 89 **p** 94. NSM High Wycombe *Ox* 89-97; P-in-c Penn 97-01; rtd 01. *Châtelaine House, Kinsham, Presteigne LD8 2HP* Tel (01544) 267067 E-mail caroljpwilliams@compuserve.com

WILLIAMS, Mrs Catherine Anne. b 65. Selw Coll Cam BA87 MA91. SEITE 98. **d** 00 **p** 01. C Chatham St Steph *Roch* 00-02; C Bishop's Cleeve *Glouc* from 03. *Abbey House, Church Street, Tewkesbury GL20 5SR* Tel (01684) 293333 E-mail catherine.williams0@talk21.com

WILLIAMS, Ms Catherine Lois. b 51. Swansea Coll of Educn CertEd74 Univ of Wales (Swansea) BEd80. St Mich Coll Llan. **d** 00 **p** 01. C Gorseinon *S & B* 00-02; C Cen Swansea from 03. *Christ Church Vicarage, 226 Oystermouth Road, Swansea SA1 3UH* Tel (01792) 652606

✠**WILLIAMS, The Rt Revd Cecil.** b 42. Punjab Univ MA(Ed)67 Peshawar Univ MA72. **d** 87 **p** 88 **c** 01. Pakistan 87-02; Asst Bp Peshawar 01-02; C Potternewton *Ripon* from 02. *8 Granton Road, Potternewton, Leeds LS7 3LZ* Tel 0113-262 6225

WILLIAMS, Cecil Augustus Baldwin. b 09. TCD BA31 MA39. CITC 32. **d** 32 **p** 33. C Belfast St Mary Magd *Conn* 32-35; BCMS Kapoeta Sudan 35-39; I Schull *C, C & R* 40-49; Sec Ch of Ireland Jews' Soc 49-54; I Dublin St Luke *D & G* 54-71; BCMS Sec 56-63; I Crinken 71-81; rtd 81. *3 St John's Close, Portstewart BT55 7HJ* Tel (028) 7083 4249 E-mail cabw@onetel.net.uk

WILLIAMS, Canon Cecil Peter. b 41. TCD BA63 MA67 Lon Univ BD67 PhD86 Bris Univ MLitt77. Clifton Th Coll 64. **d** 67 **p** 68. C Maghull *Liv* 67-70; Lic to Offic *Bris* 70-91; Tutor Clifton Th Coll 70-72; Tutor Trin Coll Bris 72-91; Lib 73-81; Course Ldr 81-85; Vice-Prin 85-91; V Ecclesall *Sheff* from 91; Hon Can Sheff Cathl from 01. *The Vicarage, Ringinglow Road, Sheffield S11 7PQ* Tel 0114-236 0084 *or* 268 7574 Mobile 07801-353786 Fax 0870-137 1003 E-mail peter.williams@ecclesall.parishchurch.org.uk

WILLIAMS, Preb Clive Gregory. b 45. Trin Coll Bris 83. **d** 85 **p** 86. C Bedhampton *Portsm* 85-88; V Highley w Billingsley, Glazeley etc *Heref* from 88; RD Bridgnorth from 96; Preb Heref Cathl from 99. *The Vicarage, Church Street, Highley, Bridgnorth WV16 6NA* Tel (01746) 861612 Mobile 07802-694663 E-mail clivewilliams@highley.clara.net

WILLIAMS, The Ven Colin Henry. b 52. Pemb Coll Ox BA73 MA78. St Steph Ho Ox BA80. **d** 81 **p** 82. C Liv St Paul Stoneycroft *Liv* 81-84; TV Walton St Mary 84-89; Chapl Walton Hosp Liv 86-89; Bp's Dom Chapl *Blackb* 89-94; Chapl Whalley Abbey 89-94; V Poulton-le-Fylde 94-99; Adn Lancaster from 99.

St Michael's House, Hall Lane, St Michael's-on-Wyre, Preston PR3 0TQ Tel (01995) 679242 Fax 679747
E-mail archdeacon.lancaster@ukonline.co.uk

WILLIAMS, David. b 19. **d** 66 **p** 67. Hon C Parkend *Glouc* 66-78; Hon C Coleford w Staunton 78-83; Perm to Offic from 83. *The Nook, Parkend Road, Bream, Lydney GL15 6JZ* Tel (01594) 562240

WILLIAMS, David. b 43. ACA65 FCA. K Coll Lon AKC69 BD69. **d** 70 **p** 71. C Walkden Moor *Man* 70-72; C Deane 72-75; V Horwich St Cath 75-81; Hon C Chorley All SS *Blackb* 84-86; P-in-c Weeton 86-87; V Singleton w Weeton 87-97; C Lancaster St Mary w St John and St Anne 98-00; Chapl HM Pris Lanc Castle 98-00; rtd 00; Perm to Offic *Man* from 02. *153 Crompton Way, Bolton BL2 2SQ* Tel (01524) 382362
E-mail goodfornowt@aol.com

WILLIAMS, Canon David. b 49. BTh Dip Tech Mining. **d** 88 **p** 89. C Lurgan etc w Ballymachugh, Kildrumferton etc *K, E & A* 88-91; I Kinsale Union *C, C & R* from 91; Miss to Seafarers from 91; Can Cork and Cloyne Cathls *C, C & R* 95-97; Treas Cork Cathl from 97; Preb Tymothan St Patr Cathl Dublin from 97. *St Multose Rectory, Abbey Court, Kinsale, Co Cork, Irish Republic* Tel (00353) (21) 477 2220

WILLIAMS, David Albert. b 15. St D Coll Lamp BA35. St Mich Coll Llan 36. **d** 38 **p** 39. C Penrhosgarnedd *Ban* 38-40; C Glanadda 38-40; C Llanbadarn Fawr *St D* 40-49; Chapl RAF 49-58; Perm to Offic *Birm* 58-59; Malaya 59-61; Perm to Offic *Heref* 61-69; Lic to Offic 69-80; rtd 80; Perm to Offic *St D* from 80. *London House, Llanwrda SA19 8AA*

WILLIAMS, David Alun. b 65. St Thos Hosp Lon MB, BS88. Wycliffe Hall Ox BTh94 All Nations Chr Coll MA98. **d** 94 **p** 95. C Ware Ch Ch *St Alb* 94-97; Crosslinks from 98; Kenya from 98; Perm to Offic *St Alb* 98-00. *PO Box 72584, Carlile College, Nairobi, Kenya* Tel (00254) (2) 715561

WILLIAMS, David Frank. b 48. S Dios Minl Tr Scheme 91. **d** 94 **p** 95. NSM Romsey *Win* from 94. *24 Feltham Close, Romsey SO51 8PB* Tel (01794) 524050

WILLIAMS, David Gareth. b 58. Lon Univ BD81. Ripon Coll Cuddesdon 82. **d** 84 **p** 85. C Chandler's Ford *Win* 84-88; C Alton St Lawr 88-90; R Crawley and Littleton and Sparsholt w Lainston 90-97; P-in-c Andover w Foxcott from 97. *St Mary's Vicarage, Church Close, Andover SP10 1DP* Tel (01264) 350344 or 352729

WILLIAMS, David Gerald Powell. b 35. St Mich Coll Llan DipTh62. **d** 62 **p** 63. C Canton St Jo *Llan* 62-64; Field Tr Officer Ch in Wales Prov Youth Coun 63-70; Prov Youth Chapl 65-70; V Treharris *Llan* 70-75; R Flemingston w Gileston and St Hilary 75-78; Warden of Ords 77-80; Dir Past Studies and Chapl St Mich Coll Llan 78-80; Sub-Warden 79-80; Dir Ch in Wales Publications and Communications 80-85; Prov Dir of Educn Ch in Wales 80-85; Dir of Miss Ch in Wales 85-87; Hon Can Llan Cathl *Llan* 84-93; V Pendoylan w Welsh St Donats 87-93; R Llandudno 93-95; Press Officer to Abp of Wales 93-00; rtd 00. *Wentworth Lodge, 9 Tydraw Road, Penylan, Cardiff CF23 5HA* Tel (029) 2048 8598

WILLIAMS, David Gordon. b 43. Selw Coll Cam BA65 MA69. Oak Hill Th Coll 66. **d** 68 **p** 69. C Maidstone St Luke *Cant* 68-71; C Rugby St Matt *Cov* 71-73; P-in-c Budbrooke 73-74; V 74-81; V Lenton *S'well* 81-87; TR Cheltenham St Mark *Glouc* 87-03; Hon Can Glouc Cathl 96-03; R Toodyay w Goomalling Australia from 03. *St Stephen's Church, PO Box 807, Toodyay, W Australia 6566*

WILLIAMS, David Grant. b 61. Bris Univ BSocSc83. Wycliffe Hall Ox 86. **d** 89 **p** 90. C Ecclesall *Sheff* 89-92; V Dore 92-02; RD Ecclesall 97-02; V Win Ch Ch *Win* from 02. *Christ Church Vicarage, Sleepers Hill, Winchester SO22 4ND* Tel (01962) 862414 Mobile 07889-547095 E-mail vicarccwinch@aol.com

WILLIAMS, David Henry. b 33. Trin Coll Cam BA56 MA60 PhD77. St D Coll Lamp 67. **d** 69 **p** 70. C Monmouth *Mon* 69-70; Chapl St Woolos Cathl 70-71; P-in-c Six Bells 71-76; Libya 76-79; P-in-c Crumlin *Mon* 79-80; R Llanddewi Skirrid w Llanvetherine etc 80-83; Perm to Offic 83-87; Guest Master Caldey Abbey 83-87; V Buttington and Pool Quay *St As* 87-95; Chapl Warsaw *Eur* 95-97; rtd 97. *33 Heol Aberwennol, Borth SY24 5NP* Tel (01970) 871822 Fax as telephone

WILLIAMS, Canon David Humphrey. b 23. Em Coll Cam BA49 MA54. St Steph Ho Ox 49. **d** 51 **p** 52. C Daybrook *S'well* 51-55; C-in-c Bilborough St Jo Bapt CD 55-62; V Bilborough St Jo 62-63; RD Bulwell 70-88; P-in-c Bestwood Park 71-78; R Hucknall Torkard 63-71; TR 71-88; Hon Can S'well Minster 75-88; rtd 88; Perm to Offic *S'well* from 88. *12 Wollaton Paddocks, Trowell Road, Nottingham NG8 2ED* Tel 0115-928 0639

WILLIAMS, David Ivan Ross. b 47. Imp Coll Lon BSc70 Leic Univ MSc72 ARCS70 FBIS. STETS 00. **d** 03. NSM Havant *Portsm* from 03. *9 St George's Road, Hayling Island PO11 0BS* Tel (023) 9246 7597 Mobile 07866-772025
E-mail david@dirw.demon.co.uk

WILLIAMS, David James. b 42. Chich Th Coll 67. **d** 70 **p** 71. C Charlton-by-Dover St Bart *Cant* 70-74; C Dorking w Ranmore *Guildf* 74-77; C Guildf H Trin w St Mary 77-78; P-in-c E Molesey

St Paul 78-88; V Burpham 88-94; rtd 95. *1 Taleworth Close, Ashtead KT21 2PU* Tel (01372) 278056

WILLIAMS, David John. b 30. Open Univ BA79. St D Coll Lamp 64. **d** 66 **p** 67. C Mold *St As* 66-69; C Llanrhos 69-71; R Llangynhafal and Llanbedr Dyffryn Clwyd 71-86; P-in-c Llanychan 77-86; RD Dyffryn Clwyd 86-95; R Ruthin w Llanrhydd 86-95; rtd 95. *16 The Park, Ruthin LL15 1PW* Tel (01824) 705746

WILLIAMS, Canon David John. b 38. AKC62. **d** 63 **p** 64. C Benchill *Man* 63-66; C Heywood St Jas 66-69; V Leesfield 69-73; Chapl TS Arethusa 73-74; TV Southend St Jo w St Mark, All SS w St Fran etc *Chelmsf* 74-80; V Horndon on the Hill 80-93; RD Thurrock 83-92; P-in-c Rochford 93-02; RD Rochford 96-02; P-in-c Sutton w Shopland 98-02; Hon Can Chelmsf Cathl 99-02; rtd 02. *29 Stonebeck Avenue, Harrogate HG1 2BN* Tel (01423) 522828

WILLIAMS, David John. b 43. Wadh Coll Ox BA64. St Jo Coll Nottm 73. **d** 75 **p** 76. C Newcastle w Butterton *Lich* 75-79; P-in-c Oulton 79-89; P-in-c Stone Ch Ch 84-89; V Stone Ch Ch and Oulton 89-96; P-in-c Ashley from 96; P-in-c Mucklestone from 96. *The Rectory, Charnes Road, Ashley, Market Drayton TF9 4LQ* Tel (01630) 672210

WILLIAMS, David John. b 52. N Ord Course 92. **d** 95 **p** 96. C Gt Crosby St Luke *Liv* 95-99; V W Derby St Jas from 99; Chapl Royal Liverpool Children's NHS Trust from 99. *St James's Vicarage, 2 Lansdowne, Liverpool L12 7LQ* Tel 0151-259 5767

WILLIAMS, Canon David Leslie. b 35. ALCD63. **d** 63 **p** 64. C Bexleyheath Ch Ch *Roch* 63-64; C Gt Faringdon w Lt Coxwell *Ox* 64-66; CMS 67-76; Uganda 67-73; C Shortlands *Roch* 73-74; Fiji 74-77; V Bromley H Trin *Roch* 77-86; R Meopham w Nurstead 86-96; RD Cobham 86-96; Chapl Thames Gateway NHS Trust 96-01; Hon Can Roch Cathl *Roch* 98-01. *107 Ploughmans Way, Gillingham ME8 8LT* Tel (01634) 372545

WILLIAMS, David Michael Rochfort. b 40. Hull Univ DipTh81. St Mich Coll Llan DipTh65. **d** 65 **p** 66. C Pembroke Dock *St D* 65-68; Chapl Miss to Seamen and Ind Chapl 68-71; P-in-c Walwyn's Castle w Robeston W 68-70; R 70-71; Ind Chapl *Mon* 71-74; Hon Chapl St Woolos Cathl 71-74; V Blaenavon w Capel Newydd 74-77; Ind Chapl *St As* 77-88; V Whitford 81-87; V Ruabon 87-92; TR Cen Telford *Lich* 92-00; R Burton and Rosemarket *St D* 00-02; Chapl Miss to Seafarers from 00; Milford Haven from 02; Southampton from 02. *Windrush, 13 Bassett Gardens, Southampton SO16 7EA* Tel (023) 8070 3256

WILLIAMS, David Norman. b 54. Lanc Univ BSc Leeds Univ BA. Coll of Resurr Mirfield. **d** 84 **p** 85. C Ireland Wood *Ripon* 84-87; C Beeston 87-91; V Cross Roads cum Lees *Bradf* 91-99; V Skipton Ch Ch from 99. *Christ Church Vicarage, Carleton Road, Skipton BD23 2BE* Tel (01756) 793612

WILLIAMS, David Paul. *See* HOWELL, David Paul

WILLIAMS, David Roger. b 49. Open Univ BA. St D Coll Lamp DipTh73. **d** 73 **p** 74. C Llansamlet *S & B* 73-76; C Oystermouth 76-79; V Aberedw w Llandeilo Graban and Llanbadarn etc 79-81; V Brynmawr 81-89; V Newport St Julian *Mon* from 89. *St Julian's Vicarage, 41 St Julians Avenue, Newport NP19 7JT* Tel (01633) 258046

WILLIAMS, Denise Laraine. b 50. Liv Univ TCert71. N Ord Course 00. **d** 03. C Padgate *Liv* from 03. *23 Kenilworth Drive, Padgate, Warrington WA1 3JT* E-mail dwill@fish.co.uk

WILLIAMS, Derek. b 27. Man Univ BSc49. St Deiniol's Hawarden 76. **d** 78 **p** 79. NSM Abergele *St As* 78-97; rtd 97; Perm to Offic *St As* from 97. *48 Eldon Drive, Abergele LL22 7DA* Tel (01745) 833479

WILLIAMS, Derek Lawrence. b 45. Lon Univ DipTh68. Tyndale Hall Bris 65. **d** 69 **p** 70. C Cant St Mary Bredin *Cant* 69-71; Gen Sec Inter-Coll Chr Fellowship 71-75; Lic to Offic *St Alb* 78-84; Lic to Offic *Bris* 85-92; Perm to Offic *Pet* 92-02; Par and Miss Co-ord Northampton St Giles 93-97; Dioc Millennium Officer 98-00; Dioc Communications Officer from 00; NSM Brington w Whilton and Norton etc from 02; Dioc Communications Officer *Eur* from 02. *The Rectory, Harlestone Road, Church Brampton, Northampton NN6 8AU* Tel (01604) 843881 Fax 843388
E-mail dl.williams@btopenworld.com

WILLIAMS, Derwyn Gavin. b 69. Trin Coll Cam BA89 MA93. Ripon Coll Cuddesdon DipMin94. **d** 94 **p** 95. C Harpenden St Nic *St Alb* 94-97; Bp's Dom Chapl 97-00; R Sandy from 00. *The Rectory, High Street, Sandy SG19 1AQ* Tel (01767) 680512

WILLIAMS, Diana Mary. b 36. Bris Univ CertEd56 Leeds Univ BSc57. Oak Hill Th Coll 86. **d** 87 **p** 94. C S Mymms K Chas *St Alb* 87-95; V 95-98; R Sandon, Wallington and Rushden w Clothall from 98; RD Buntingford from 01. *The Vicarage, Payne End, Sandon, Buntingford SG9 0QU* Tel (01763) 287256

WILLIAMS, Ms Diane Patricia. b 53. Dur Univ CertEd74 Liv Univ DipRE83 Lanc Univ MA84. Cranmer Hall Dur 84. **dss** 86 **d** 87 **p** 94. Clubmoor *Liv* 86-90; Par Dn 87-90; Dioc Lay Tr Officer 90-96; Par Dn Everton St Geo 90-94; Assoc P 94-96; Chapl Lanc Univ *Blackb* 96-00; Chapl Edin Univ *Edin* from 00. *Chaplaincy Centre, The University of Edinburgh, 1 Bristo Square, Edinburgh EH8 9AL* Tel 0131-650 2596/5 Fax 650 9111
E-mail e.u.chaplain@ed.ac.uk

WILLIAMS, Diane Ruth. b 52. Hull Univ BA80. Linc Th Coll. **d** 94 **p** 95. C Stokesley *York* 94-98; TV Louth *Linc* from 98; Chapl Linc and Louth NHS Trust 98-01; Chapl United Lincs Hosps NHS Trust from 01. *The Vicarage, 24 Grosvenor Road, Louth LN11 0JB* Tel (01507) 604573

WILLIAMS, Donald. *See* WILLIAMS, Alfred Donald

WILLIAMS, Mrs Donna Ann. b 64. St Jo Coll Nottm BA00. **d** 00 **p** 01. C Denton St Lawr *Man* from 00. *St Peter's Vicarage, Chester Square, Ashton-under-Lyne OL7 0LB* Tel 0161-343 3770 E-mail sweetpea@dwilliams11.freeserve.co.uk

WILLIAMS, Dorian George. b 26. Barrister-at-Law (Gray's Inn) 52. WMMTC 91. **d** 93 **p** 94. NSM Edvin Loach w Tedstone Delamere etc *Heref* 93-98; Perm to Offic from 98. *Howberry, Whitbourne, Worcester WR6 5RZ* Tel (01886) 821189

WILLIAMS, Dylan John. b 72. Univ of Wales (Ban) BTh97. Ripon Coll Cuddesdon 97. **d** 99 **p** 00. C Holyhead *Ban* 99-01; C Dolgellau w Llanfachreth and Brithdir etc 01-02; P-in-c Amlwch from 02. *The Rectory, Bull Bay Road, Amlwch LL68 9EA* Tel (01407) 830740 E-mail dylwilliams@lineone.net

WILLIAMS, The Ven Edward Bryan. b 36. Univ of Wales (Lamp) BA58. St Mich Coll Llan 58. **d** 60 **p** 61. C Rhyl w St Ann *St As* 60-68; Dioc Youth Chapl 66-78; V Dyserth and Trelawnyd and Cwm 68-77; R Denbigh 77-82; Can St As Cathl 81-87; R Denbigh and Nantglyn 82-87; Adn Wrexham 87-01; V Bwlchgwyn 87-01; rtd 01. *18 Caerphilly Road, Buckley CH7 8QT* Tel (01244) 541476

WILLIAMS, Edward Ffoulkes (Peter). b 34. Chich Th Coll 71. **d** 73 **p** 74. C Kidderminster St Geo *Worc* 73-78; TV Worc St Barn w Ch Ch 78-82; R Exhall w Wixford and V Temple Grafton w Binton *Cov* 82-00; rtd 00; Perm to Offic *Truro* from 00. *Penpons Cottage, Treviskey, Lanner, Redruth TR16 6AU* Tel (01209) 820230

WILLIAMS, Edward Heaton. b 18. St Aid Birkenhead 56. **d** 58 **p** 59. C Timperley *Ches* 58-62; V Macclesfield St Pet 62-66; Sec Dioc Miss Bd 63-67; R Wistaston 66-81; Dioc Bd for Miss and Unity 67-69; V Burton 81-85; rtd 85; Perm to Offic *Ox* 85-94; Perm to Offic *Pet* from 85. *4 Bowmens Lea, Aynho, Banbury OX17 3AG* Tel (01869) 810533

WILLIAMS, Prof Edward Sydney. b 23. FRCP FRCR K Coll Lon BSc PhD MB, BS MD AKC. Sarum & Wells Th Coll 84. **d** 87 **p** 88. NSM Bramley and Grafham *Guildf* 87-89; Hon C Shamley Green 89-94; Perm to Offic from 94. *Little Hollies, The Close, Wonersh, Guildford GU5 0PA* Tel (01483) 892591

WILLIAMS, Elfed Owain. b 24. Newc Univ DipAdEd74. St Deiniol's Hawarden 79. **d** 81 **p** 82. Hon C Whorlton *Newc* 81-82; Hon C Elham w Denton and Wootton *Cant* 82-86; R Barham w Bishopsbourne and Kingston 86-91; rtd 91; Perm to Offic *Newc* from 91. *Chusan, 31 Ryecroft Way, Wooler NE71 6DY* Tel (01668) 281253

WILLIAMS, Eric Rees. b 30. Roch Th Coll 60 St Deiniol's Hawarden 71. **d** 72 **p** 73. C Llanelli *St D* 72-75; P-in-c Tregaron 75-76; V 76-82; RD Lampeter and Ultra-Aeron 82-87; V Tregaron w Ystrad Meurig and Strata Florida 82-87; V St Dogmael's w Moylgrove and Monington 87-98; rtd 98. *Ty Elli, 1 Heol Derw, Cardigan SA43 1NH* Tel (01239) 612296

WILLIAMS, Evelyn Joyce. b 37. Cant Sch of Min 86. **d** 89 **p** 94. NSM Sittingbourne H Trin w Bobbing *Cant* from 89. *32 Rock Road, Sittingbourne ME10 1JF* Tel (01795) 470372

WILLIAMS, Frederick Errol. b 41. MBIM80. Sarum & Wells Th Coll 86. **d** 88 **p** 89. C Milton *Win* 88-91; P-in-c Chilbolton cum Wherwell 91-94; R from 94; RD Andover from 99. *The Rectory, Chilbolton, Stockbridge SO20 6BA* Tel (01264) 860258 E-mail errolw@compuserve.com

WILLIAMS, Gareth Wynn. b 67. St D Coll Lamp BA88 Hull Univ MA89. Westcott Ho Cam 89. **d** 91 **p** 92. C Mold *St As* 91-93; TV Hawarden 93-95; Ecum Chapl Glam Univ *Llan* 95-99; Lect Univ of Wales (Cardiff) from 99; Dir Academic Studies St Mich Coll Llan from 99; Vice-Prin from 02. *St Michael's Theological College, 54 Cardiff Road, Llandaff, Cardiff CF5 2YJ* Tel (029) 2056 3379 Fax 2057 6377

WILLIAMS, Gavin John. b 61. Down Coll Cam BA84 Wycliffe Hall Ox BA88 Barrister-at-Law 85. **d** 89 **p** 90. C Muswell Hill St Jas w St Matt *Lon* 89-92; Asst Chapl Shrewsbury Sch 92-95; Chapl 95-02; Chapl Westmr Sch from 02. *Westminster School, Little Dean's Yard, London SW1P 3PF* Tel (020) 7963 1128 E-mail gavin.williams@westminster.org.uk

WILLIAMS, Geoffrey Thomas. b 35. Ox NSM Course 77. **d** 80 **p** 81. NSM Earley St Bart *Ox* 80-82; NSM Reading St Luke 82-85; V Wembley Park St Aug *Lon* 85-86; C-in-c S Kenton Annunciation CD 86-90; V Streatham Hill St Marg *S'wark* from 90. *The Vicarage, 165 Barcombe Avenue, London SW2 3BH* Tel (020) 8674 7348

WILLIAMS, George Harold. b 20. Lon Univ BSc49. **d** 67 **p** 68. C Bishopsworth *Bris* 67-70; V Weston-super-Mare Ch Ch *B & W* 70-85; rtd 85; Perm to Offic *B & W* from 86. *15 Elmhurst Road, Hutton, Weston-super-Mare BS24 9RJ* Tel (01934) 813342

WILLIAMS, Preb George Maxwell Frazer. b 42. TCD BA65 MA69. Cuddesdon Coll 65. **d** 67 **p** 68. C Bolton St Jas w St Chrys *Bradf* 67-70; C Lich St Chad *Lich* 70-73; V Shawbury 73-79;

P-in-c Moreton Corbet 73-79; V Willenhall H Trin 79-86; TR 86-88; V Penn from 88; Preb Lich Cathl from 96; RD Trysull from 02. *St Bartholomew's Vicarage, 68 Church Hill, Penn, Wolverhampton WV4 5JD* Tel (01902) 341399 *or* 576809

WILLIAMS, George Melvin (Kim). b 24. Worc Ord Coll 64. **d** 66 **p** 67. C Holdenhurst *Win* 66-70; V Yateley 70-75; V St Leonards and St Ives 75-90; rtd 90; Perm to Offic *Win* from 90. *20 Hillside Drive, Christchurch BH23 4RU* Tel (01202) 484930

WILLIAMS, George Ola. b 55. Bradf Univ PhD90 Waterloo Lutheran Univ MA83. St Jo Coll Nottm Cert Th & Min 94 MTh95. **d** 96 **p** 97. C Enfield St Jas *Lon* 96-00; V Allerton *Bradf* from 00. *The Vicarage, Ley Top Lane, Allerton, Bradford BD15 7LT* Tel (01274) 541948

WILLIAMS, Canon Giles Peter. b 54. Lon Univ BA77 MA78. Trin Coll Bris 80. **d** 82 **p** 83. C Reading Greyfriars *Ox* 82-85; Rwanda Miss 85-90; Mid-Africa Min (CMS) 90-94; Can Kigali Cathl Rwanda from 90; V Woking St Jo *Guildf* from 95. *The Vicarage, St John's Hill Road, Woking GU21 7RQ* Tel (01483) 761253 E-mail giles@williams.dabs.net *or* vicar@stjohnswoking.org.uk

WILLIAMS, Glyn. b 54. K Coll Lon BD77 AKC77. Ripon Coll Cuddesdon 77. **d** 78 **p** 79. C Coppenhall *Ches* 78-81; C Northampton St Alb *Pet* 81-82; TV Birkenhead Priory *Ches* 82-85; Chapl RAF 85-90 and from 96; Dep Chapl HM Pris Wandsworth 90-91; Chapl HM Pris Elmley 91-95. *Chaplaincy Services (RAF), HQ, Personnel and Training Command, RAF Innsworth, Gloucester GL3 1EZ* Tel (01452) 712612 ext 5164 Fax 510828

WILLIAMS, Glyn Alun. b 17. St D Coll Lamp BA40. **d** 41 **p** 42. C Gors-las *St D* 41-46; C Llangyfelach and Morriston *S & B* 46-48; C Llansadwrn w Llanwrda *St D* 48-50; V Llandyssilio 50-57; V Llangynderyn 57-71; V Pencarreg and Llancrwys 71-73; rtd 73. *11 Tirwaun, Pwll, Llanelli SA15 4AY* Tel (01554) 759850

WILLIAMS, Graham Ivor. b 23. Jes Coll Ox BA48 MA48. Cuddesdon Coll 48. **d** 49 **p** 50. C Swansea St Mary and H Trin *S & B* 49-53; C Edgbaston St Bart *Birm* 53-55; R Nutfield *S'wark* from 55. *The Rectory, Blechingley Road, Nutfield, Redhill RH1 4HN* Tel (01737) 822286 E-mail revgiw@hotmail.com

WILLIAMS, Graham Parry. b 46. Bp Burgess Hall Lamp 67 St D Coll Lamp DipTh70. **d** 70 **p** 71. C Ebbw Vale *Mon* 70-73; C Trevethin 73-74; V Nantyglo 74-76; Chapl RN 76-85; R Northlew w Ashbury *Ex* 85-87; R Bratton Clovelly w Germansweek 85-87; TV Pontypool *Mon* 88-90; C Skegness and Winthorpe *Linc* 90-91; V Sutton Bridge 91-94; P-in-c Witham Gp 94-97; P-in-c Ruskington 97-01; R from 01; RD Lafford from 02. *The Rectory, All Saints' Close, Ruskington, Sleaford NG34 9ER* Tel (01526) 832463

WILLIAMS, Gwenllian. *See* GILES, Mrs Gwenllian

WILLIAMS, Gwilym Elfed. b 33. Univ of Wales (Lamp) BA53. St Mich Coll Llan 53. **d** 56 **p** 57. C Llandudno *Ban* 56-59; C Aberdare *Llan* 59-63; C Penarth All SS 63-65; R Eglwysilan 65-70; V Mountain Ash 70-81; V Llanblethian w Cowbridge and Llandough etc 81-93; P-in-c St Hilary 87-91; V Lisvane 93-00; rtd 00; Perm to Offic *Glouc* from 01. *2 Whitminster Lane, Frampton on Severn, Gloucester GL2 7HR* Tel (01452) 741442

WILLIAMS, The Ven Harold Edgar. b 17. Univ of Wales (Lamp) BA39. AKC42. **d** 42 **p** 43. C Leytonstone St Jo *Chelmsf* 42-45; C Barnes St Mary *S'wark* 45-46; Chapl RNVR 46-51 and 55-58; Chapl RN 51-55; C Swansea St Jude *S & B* 48-51; Bp's Messenger 55-56; R Llanhamlach and Llansantffraed-juxta-Usk 55-61; Dir of Ords 55-79; Dir Post-Ord Tr 56; V Hay 61-67; V Brynmawr 67-76; Can Brecon Cathl 72-83; Sec Prov Selection Bd for Ords 73-76; V Newton St Pet 76-87; Chan Brecon Cathl 79-83; Adn Gower 83-87; rtd 87. *10 Budehaven Terrace, Mumbles, Swansea SA3 5PY* Tel (01792) 540618

WILLIAMS, Harry Abbott. b 19. Trin Coll Cam BA41 MA45. Cuddesdon Coll 41. **d** 43 **p** 44. C Pimlico St Barn *Lon* 43-45; C St Marylebone All SS 45-48; Chapl and Tutor Westcott Ho Cam 48-51; Fell and Lect Trin Coll Cam 51-69; Dean of Chpl and Tutor 58-69; CR from 72; Lic to Offic *Wakef* from 80; rtd 89. *House of the Resurrection, Stocks Bank Road, Mirfield WF14 0BN* Tel (01924) 494318

WILLIAMS, Haydn Clifford. b 32. Univ of Wales (Abth) BA54 DipEd55. EMMTC 89. **d** 95 **p** 99. NSM Anstey *Leic* 95-01; NSM Broom Leys 01-03; rtd 03; Perm to Offic *Leic* from 03. *84 Blackwood, Coalville LE67 4RN* Tel (01530) 838403

WILLIAMS, Preb Heather Marilyn. b 42. Oak Hill Th Coll 82. dss 85 **d** 87 **p** 94. Taunton Lyngford *B & W* 85-87; Hon C 87-89; C Worle 89-94; V Weston-super-Mare St Andr Bournville from 94; Preb Wells Cathl from 02. *St Andrew's Vicarage, Coniston Crescent, Weston-super-Mare BS23 3RX* Tel (01934) 627818 E-mail williams.heather@btinternet.com

WILLIAMS, Helena Maria Alija. *See* CERMAKOVA, Helena Maria Alija

WILLIAMS, Henry Gordon. b 33. JP83. St Aid Birkenhead 57. **d** 60 **p** 61. C Radcliffe St Mary *Man* 60-63; Australia from 63. OStJ from 78; rtd 99. *36 Onslow Street, PO Box 259, Northampton, W Australia 6535* Tel (0061) (8) 9934 1259 Fax 9934 1507 E-mail hgw@wn.com.aiu

WILLIAMS, The Ven Henry Leslie. b 19. Univ of Wales (Lamp) BA41. St Mich Coll Llan 41. **d** 43 **p** 44. C Aberdovey *Ban* 43-45; C Ban Cathl Par 45-48; Chapl RN 48-49; C Ches St Mary *Ches* 49-53; V Barnston 53-84; CF (TA) 54-62; RD Wirral N *Ches* 67-75; Hon Can Ches Cathl 72-75; Adn Ches 75-88; rtd 88; Perm to Offic *Ches* from 88. *1 Bartholomew Way, Chester CH4 7RJ* Tel (01244) 675296

WILLIAMS, Herbert <u>Brian</u>. b 18. BNC Ox BA39 MA48. Linc Th Coll 80. **d** 81 **p** 82. NSM Asterby Gp *Linc* 81-94; rtd 88; Perm to Offic *Linc* 94-97. *55 Upgate, Louth LN11 9HD* Tel (01507) 608093

WILLIAMS, Mrs Hilary Susan. b 45. STETS 99. **d** 02 **p** 03. NSM Shottermill *Guildf* from 02. *Stacey's Farm Cottage, Thursley Road, Elstead, Godalming GU8 6DG* Tel (01252) 703217 E-mail staceyfc@hotmail.com

WILLIAMS, Canon Howard. b 08. Univ of Wales BA29 MA32 St Jo Coll Cam MLitt45 ALCM27. St Steph Ho Ox 30. **d** 31 **p** 32. C Aberystwyth St Mich *St D* 31-36; Perm to Offic *Ely* 36-38; V Llan-non *St D* 38-49; Dioc Insp of Schs 40-50; Lect Univ of Wales 49-50; V Betws w Ammanford 49-57; V Llanelli 57-75; Chapl Llanelli Hosps 57-75; Can St D Cathl 60-75; Treas 73-75; rtd 75. *Cwm Eithin, 53 Maes Hendre, Waunfawr, Aberystwyth SY23 3PS* Tel (01970) 615311

WILLIAMS, Howell Mark. b 56. Univ of Wales (Cardiff) BD87. St Mich Coll Llan 84. **d** 87 **p** 88. C Swansea St Thos and Kilvey *S & B* 87-89; TV Aberystwyth *St D* 89-93; V Hirwaun *Llan* 93-99; V Swansea St Pet *S & B* from 99. *St Peter's Vicarage, 59 Station Road, Fforestfach, Swansea SA5 5AU* Tel (01792) 581514 E-mail mark@swanseastpeters.freeserve.co.uk

WILLIAMS, Hugh Marshall. b 38. Lon Univ MB, BS62 Liv Univ MChOrth71 FRCS70. St Alb and Ox Min Course 95. **d** 97 **p** 98. NSM Lt Compton w Chastleton, Cornwell etc *Ox* 97-01; Team Min Chipping Norton from 01. *Wayside, Worcester Road, Salford, Chipping Norton OX7 5YJ* Tel (01608) 646933 Mobile 07889-343456 E-mail hmw@surfaid.org

WILLIAMS, Hugh Martin. b 45. AKC73. St Aug Coll Cant 73. **d** 74 **p** 75. C Heston *Lon* 74-78; Chapl City Univ 78-84; PV Westmr Abbey 82-84; V Newquay *Truro* 84-93; V Christchurch *Win* from 93. *The Priory Vicarage, Quay Road, Christchurch BH23 1BU* Tel (01202) 483102

WILLIAMS, Hugh Wynford. b 16. Selw Coll Cam BA40 MA44. St D Coll Lamp BA38 St Mich Coll Llan 41. **d** 41 **p** 42. C Kirkburton *Wakef* 41-43; C Skipton H Trin *Bradf* 43-44; Perm to Offic 44-51; Perm to Offic *Pet* 51-74; Chapl Oundle Sch 54-74; R Tichmarsh *Pet* 74-88; P-in-c Clapton 77-88; rtd 88; Perm to Offic *Pet* from 88. *28 Church Street, Tichmarsh, Kettering NN14 3DB* Tel (01832) 734529

WILLIAMS, Ian Kenneth. b 44. MMS83 MBIM87 Nottm Univ DipAE92 MEd94. EMMTC 84. **d** 87 **p** 88. NSM Corby Glen *Linc* 87-98; R Ingoldsby 98-00; NSM Edenham w Witham on the Hill and Swinstead from 00. *65 High Street, Corby Glen, Grantham NG33 4LU* Tel (01476) 550595 E-mail ikw2@tutor.open.ac.uk

WILLIAMS, Ian Withers. b 43. Linc Th Coll 68. **d** 69 **p** 70. C Burney Lane *Birm* 69-72; C Cleobury Mortimer w Hopton Wafers *Heref* 72-75; P-in-c Coreley and Doddington 75-79; V Knowbury 75-79; V Lich St Ch *Lich* from 79. *Christ Church Vicarage, Christ Church Lane, Lichfield WS13 8AL* Tel (01543) 305526 Mobile 07711-260521 Fax (01543) 305527 E-mail ian@christchurchlichfield.co.uk

WILLIAMS, Ieuan Merchant. b 13. St D Coll Lamp BA36. **d** 39 **p** 40. C Ardsley *Sheff* 39-42; C Wombwell 42-48; R N and S Wheatley w W Burton *S'well* 48-55; R W Leake w Kingston-on-Soar and Ratcliffe-on-Soar 55-59; V Burton Joyce w Bulcote 59-71; R Brightwell Baldwin *Ox* 71-80; R Cuxham w Easington 72-80; P-in-c Britwell Salome 76-80; P-in-c Ewelme 76-80; rtd 80; Perm to Offic *Ox* from 80. *5 The Cloisters, Ewelme, Oxford OX10 6HS* Tel (01491) 838897

WILLIAMS, Ifan. b 24. St D Coll Lamp 54. **d** 56 **p** 57. C Llangefni w Tregaean *Ban* 56-60; R Llanfachreth 60-67; Dioc Youth Officer 62-65; Area Sec (Merioneth) USPG 63-89; P-in-c Brithdir and Bryncoedifor *Ban* 65-67; V Ffestiniog w Blaenau Ffestiniog 67-89; RD Ardudwy 80-89; rtd 89; Perm to Offic *Ban* from 89. *Cil-y-Coed, 6 Stad Penrallt, Llanystumdwy, Criccieth LL52 0SR* Tel (01766) 522978

WILLIAMS, Jack. b 26. Univ of Wales (Ban) BSc50. St Mich Coll Llan 50. **d** 52 **p** 53. C Buckley *St As* 52-55; C Llanrhos 55-59; V Bronnington and Bettisfield 59-61; C Ripponden *Wakef* 61-65; Chapl Rishworth Sch Ripponden 65-68; Hd Master 68-86; V Halifax St Jo *Wakef* 86-89; rtd 89; Perm to Offic *Ban* from 89. *2 Pont-y-Rhyd, Llangoed, Beaumaris LL58 8NU* Tel (01248) 490732

WILLIAMS, James Llanfair Warren. b 48. St Mich Coll Llan 92. **d** 92 **p** 93. C Pembroke Dock *St D* 92-93; C Pembroke Dock w Cosheston w Nash and Upton 93-95; V Cwmaman 95-98; Chapl Costa Blanca *Eur* 98-00; V Meifod w Llangynyw w Pont Robert w Pont Dolanog *St As* from 01. *The Vicarage, Meifod SY22 6DH* Tel (01938) 500231

WILLIAMS, James Nicholas Owen (<u>Nick</u>). b 39. MBE. CEng DipTh. S'wark Ord Course. **d** 82 **p** 83. C Petersfield w Sheet *Portsm* 82-86; TV Droitwich *Worc* 86-87; TV Droitwich Spa 87-88; R Church Lench w Rous Lench and Abbots Morton 88-94; V Milton *B & W* from 94; RD Locking from 99. *St Peter's Vicarage, Baytree Road, Weston-super-Mare BS22 8HG* Tel (01934) 624247 E-mail jnowil@lineone.net

WILLIAMS, Janet Patricia. *See* FFRENCH, Mrs Janet Patricia

WILLIAMS, Jeffrey. *See* WILLIAMS, Robert Jeffrey Hopkin

WILLIAMS, Ms Jennifer Ruth. b 66. St Hugh's Coll Ox BA88 PGCE89. Wycliffe Hall Ox 98 N Ord Course 00. **d** 00 **p** 01. C Heaton Mersey *Man* 00-02; C Heatons from 02. *St Margaret's Rectory, 250 Burnage Lane, Manchester M19 1FL* Tel 0161-432 1844 E-mail jonandjenni0@tinyworld.co.uk

WILLIAMS, Canon John. b 31. AKC56. **d** 57 **p** 58. C Cockerton *Dur* 57-60; C Camberwell St Geo *S'wark* 60-62; C Stockton St Chad *Dur* 62-65; V 65-68; R Longnewton 68-83; Soc Resp Officer 68-83; Hon Can Dur Cathl 80-83; Bp's Officer for Min *Lich* 83-96; Preb Lich Cathl 83-96; C Lich St Mary w St Mich 95-96; rtd 96. *2 Fox Spring Rise, Edinburgh EH10 6NE* Tel 0131-445 2983 Fax as telephone E-mail jwilliams@quista.net

WILLIAMS, John Anthony. b 53. G&C Coll Cam BA75 MA79 St Jo Coll Dur BA83 PhD86. Cranmer Hall Dur 81. **d** 86 **p** 87. C Beverley Minster *York* 86-89; C Cloughton 89-90; P-in-c 90-93; Clergy Tr Officer E Riding 89-93; P-in-c Emley *Wakef* 93-98; Dioc Minl Tr Officer from 93; Min Scheme Officer from 98. *6 Stonecroft Gardens, Shepley, Huddersfield HD8 8EX* Tel (01484) 608703 Fax as telephone E-mail jwilwms@fish.co.uk

WILLIAMS, John Barrie. b 38. Lon Univ DSS68 Univ of Wales (Cardiff) MSc77 DipEd80 PhD91. St Mich Coll Llan 89. **d** 87 **p** 88. NSM Newcastle *Llan* 87-89; C Port Talbot St Theodore 89; Perm to Offic from 89. *Shorncliffe, 11 Priory Oak, Bridgend CF31 2HY* Tel (01656) 660369

WILLIAMS, John Beattie. b 42. Univ of Wales BA66. Cuddesdon Coll 67. **d** 69 **p** 69. C St Helier *S'wark* 69-70; C Yeovil H Trin *B & W* 70-76; P-in-c Ebbesbourne Wake w Fifield Bavant and Alvediston *Sarum* 76-78; Chapl to the Deaf 76-78; Chapl to the Deaf *B & W* 78-83; TV Fareham H Trin *Portsm* 83-94; R W Wittering and Birdham w Itchenor *Chich* from 94. *The Rectory, Pound Road, West Wittering, Chichester PO20 8AJ* Tel (01243) 514057

WILLIAMS, John David Anthony. b 55. St Steph Ho Ox 85. **d** 87 **p** 88. C Paignton St Jo *Ex* 87-90; C Heavitree w Ex St Paul 90-91; TV 91-01; P-in-c Exminster and Kenn from 01. *The Rectory, Milbury Lane, Exminster, Exeter EX6 8AD* Tel (01392) 824283

WILLIAMS, John Edward. b 31. Univ of Wales (Abth) DipTh55. St Deiniol's Hawarden 76. **d** 76 **p** 77. C Llansamlet *S & B* 76-78; V Aberffraw and Llangwyfan w Llangadwaladr *Ban* 78-83; rtd 83. *17 Pontwillim Estate, Brecon LD3 9BT* Tel (01874) 625375

WILLIAMS, John Elwyn Askew. b 09. St Jo Coll Cam BA32 MA36. Ridley Hall Cam 32. **d** 34 **p** 35. C Roch St Marg *Roch* 34-37; C Lenton *S'well* 37-40; CF (EC) 40-46; P-in-c Eakring *S'well* 46-47; R 47-55; V Winkburn 47-55; V Sutton on the Forest *York* 55-61; V Whitchurch w Creslow *Ox* 61-81; rtd 81; Perm to Offic *Ox* 81-02. *Badgeworth Court Care Home, Badgeworth, Cheltenham GL51 4UL* Tel (01452) 715015

WILLIAMS, John Francis Meyler. b 34. St Jo Coll Cam BA56 MA60. Sarum & Wells Th Coll 79. **d** 81 **p** 82. C Hadleigh w Layham and Shelley *St E* 81-84; P-in-c Parham w Hacheston 84-87; P-in-c Campsey Ashe and Marlesford 84-87; R Campsea Ashe w Marlesford, Parham and Hacheston 87-95; P-in-c Kedington 95-97; rtd 97; Chapl St Kath Convent Parmoor 97-98; Perm to Offic *Ox* from 01. *12 Dorchester Court, Ferry Pool Road, Oxford OX2 7DT* Tel (01865) 310395

WILLIAMS, Canon John Francis Oliver. b 15. TCD BA40 MA43. **d** 40 **p** 41. C Shankill *C & O* 40-42; C Oldcastle *M & K* 42-44; P-in-c Clonfadfornan w Castletown 44-46; I Athboy w Girley and Kildalkey 46-54; Sec Ch of Ireland Jews' Soc 54-56; I Dublin Irishtown *D & G* 56-73; I Dalkey St Patr 73-82; Can Ch Ch Cathl Dublin 81-82; rtd 82. *Wayside, Church Road, Greystones, Co Wicklow, Irish Republic* Tel (00353) (1) 287 4953

WILLIAMS, John Frederick Arthur. b 26. Lon Univ BSc50 Southn Univ PhD53. Ridley Hall Cam 63. **d** 65 **p** 66. C Cambridge H Sepulchre w All SS *Ely* 65-66; P-in-c Cambridge St Mark 66-67; V Portswood Ch Ch *Win* 67-90; Assoc V 90-93; C Win Ch Ch 93-96; rtd 96; Perm to Offic *Win* from 96. *120 Bellemoor Road, Southampton SO1 2QY* Tel (023) 8077 1482

WILLIAMS, John Gilbert. b 36. St Aid Birkenhead 64. **d** 67 **p** 68. C Bollington St Jo *Ches* 67-69; C Oxton 69-72; P-in-c Acton Beauchamp and Evesbatch 72-76; P-in-c Castle Frome *Heref* 72-76; P-in-c Bishop's Frome 72-76; R Kingsland 76-83; P-in-c Eardisland 77-83; P-in-c Aymestry and Leinthall Earles 82-83; R Cradley w Mathon and Storridge 83-94; R Norton St Philip w Hemington, Hardington etc *B & W* 94-01; rtd 01; Perm to Offic *St D* from 02. *Bronydd, Parc y Plas, Aberporth, Cardigan SA43 2BZ* Tel (01239) 810268 E-mail j.s@johngwilliams.fsnet.co.uk

WILLIAMS, Canon John Heard. b 35. Bris Univ BA58. Clifton Th Coll 59. **d** 59 **p** 60. C Tunbridge Wells Ch Ch *Roch* 59-65; V

Forest Gate St Sav *Chelmsf* 65-75; P-in-c W Ham St Matt 72-75; TR Forest Gate St Sav w W Ham St Matt from 75; Hon Can Chelmsf Cathl from 82. *St Saviour's Rectory, Sidney Road, London E7 0EF* Tel (020) 8534 6109

WILLIAMS, John Herbert. b 19. LVO89. St D Coll Lamp BA41 Sarum & Wells Th Coll 41. **d** 43 **p** 44. Chapl HM Pris Birm 57-64; Chapl HM Pris Wormwood Scrubs 64-71; SE Regional Chapl 71-74; Chapl HM Remand Cen Latchmere Ho 71-74; Dep Chapl Gen of Pris 74-83; P in O 79-83; Chapl RVO 83-89; Chapl to RVO and Qu Chpl of the Savoy 83-89; Chapl to The Queen 87-89; rtd 89. *75 Monks Drive, London W3 0ED* Tel (020) 8992 5206

WILLIAMS, Canon John James. b 20. TD61. Linc Coll Ox BA42 MA46. St Mich Coll Llan 42. **d** 44 **p** 45. C Rhosymedre *St As* 44-47; C Flint 47-50; CF 49-62; C Llanrhos *St As* 50-53; V Whixall *Lich* 53-57; V Prees 57-64; Sen CF (TA) 62-67; CF (TA) 67-68; V Powick *Worc* 64-85; Hon Can Worc Cathl 77-85; rtd 85; Perm to Offic *Worc* from 85. *9 St Nicholas's Road, Peopleton, Pershore WR10 2EN* Tel (01905) 840032

WILLIAMS, John Keith. b 63. MISM89. Ridley Hall Cam 95. **d** 97 **p** 98. C Potters Bar *St Alb* 97-99; C Bishop's Stortford St Mich 99-01; P-in-c Bishop's Stortford from 01. *Holy Trinity Vicarage, 69 Havers Lane, Bishop's Stortford CM23 3PA* Tel (01279) 656546 E-mail hetelfdegebod@netscapeonline.co.uk

WILLIAMS, Prof John Mark Gruffydd. b 52. St Pet Coll Ox BA73 MSc76 MA77 DPhil79 Ox Univ DSc FBPsS84. EAMTC 86. **d** 89 **p** 90. NSM Girton *Ely* 89-91; Perm to Offic *Ban* from 91. *Institute of Medical and Social Care Research, Wheldon Building, University of Wales, Bangor LL57 2UW* Tel (01248) 382628 Fax 383982 E-mail j.m.g.williams@bangor.ac.uk

WILLIAMS, John Michael. b 44. MBASW Univ of Wales (Cardiff) CQSW74. St Deiniol's Hawarden 80. **d** 83 **p** 84. NSM Llanrhos *St As* 83-94; P-in-c Brynymaen w Trofarth 94-95; V 95-99; V Llanrhaeadr-yng-Nghinmeirch w Prion and Nantglyn from 99. *The Vicarage, Llanrhaeadr, Denbigh LL16 4NN* Tel (01745) 890250 E-mail dyfnog@btinternet.com

WILLIAMS, Canon John Peter Philip. b 49. Univ of Wales (Ban) DipTh70 Open Univ BA84. Chich Th Coll 71. **d** 72 **p** 73. C Abergele *St As* 72-77; R Henllan and Llannefydd 77-82; R Henllan and Llannefydd and Bylchau from 82; RD Denbigh from 98; Hon Can St As Cathl from 01. *The Rectory, Henllan, Denbigh LL16 5BB* Tel (01745) 812628

WILLIAMS, John Richard. b 48. Rhodes Univ BA68 K Coll Lon BD72 AKC72. **d** 73 **p** 74. S Africa 73-76; C Addington *Cant* 77-80; C Minster-in-Sheppey 80-86; R Temple Ewell w Lydden 86-90; V Hound *Win* 90-94; V Highcliffe w Hinton Admiral 94-03; RD Christchurch 98-03; Chapl Montreux w Gstaad *Eur* from 03. *St John's House, 92 avenue de Chillon, CH-1820 Territet, Montreux, Switzerland* Tel (0041) (21) 963 4354 Fax 963 4391 E-mail montreux@anglican.ch

WILLIAMS, John Roger. b 31. Bris Univ BA55 Lon Univ BD57. Tyndale Hall Bris 57. **d** 57 **p** 58. C Islington H Trin Cloudesley Square *Lon* 57-60; Travelling Sec IVF 60-64; V Selly Hill St Steph *Birm* 64-74; P-in-c Chilwell *S'well* 74-75; V 75-90; Dioc Tourism Officer 90-95; P-in-c Perlethorpe 90-95; P-in-c Norton Cuckney 90-95; rtd 95; Perm to Offic *Derby* from 95. *Derwent Lights, 4 Wyntor Avenue, Winster, Matlock DE4 2DU* Tel (01629) 650142

WILLIAMS, Canon John Roger. b 37. Westmr Coll Ox MTh97. Lich Th Coll 60. **d** 63 **p** 64. C Wem *Lich* 63-66; C Wolverhampton St Pet 66-69; R Pudleston w Hatf *Heref* 69-74; P-in-c Stoke Prior and Ford w Humber 69-74; P-in-c Docklow 69-74; V Fenton *Lich* 74-81; R Shipston-on-Stour w Honington and Idlicote *Cov* 81-92; RD Shipston 83-90; Hon Can Cov Cathl 90-00; R Lighthorne 92-00; V Chesterton 92-00; V Newbold Pacey w Moreton Morrell 92-00; P-in-c Denstone w Ellastone and Stanton *Lich* from 00. *Denstone Vicarage, Main Road, Denstone, Uttoxeter ST14 5HF* Tel (01889) 590263

WILLIAMS, John Strettle. b 44. MBE00. DipEd73 BA84. N Ord Course 77. **d** 80 **p** 81. NSM Liv St Paul Stoneycroft *Liv* 80-83; Chapl Cen Liv Coll of FE from 80; Hon C Liv Our Lady and St Nic w St Anne from 83; Chapl RNR 84-90; Chapl City Coll of FE Liv from 85; CF (TA) from 95. *28 Brook Street, Whiston, Prescot L35 5AP* Tel 0151-426 9598

WILLIAMS, John Trefor. b 23. Worc Ord Coll 65. **d** 67 **p** 68. C Paignton St Jo *Ex* 67-72; V Winkleigh 72-80; P-in-c Ashreigney 73-79; R 79-80; P-in-c Brushford 75-79; V 79-80; R Broadwoodkelly 79-80; P-in-c Berrynarbor 80-81; P-in-c Combe Martin 80-81; R Combe Martin and Berrynarbor 81-92; rtd 92; Perm to Offic *Ex* from 92. *97 Littleham Road, Exmouth EX8 2RA* Tel (01395) 264460

WILLIAMS, Jonathan Anthony. b 65. Wycliffe Hall Ox BTh95. **d** 98 **p** 99. C Denton Ch Ch *Man* 98-02; R Burnage St Marg from 02. *St Margaret's Rectory, 250 Burnage Lane, Manchester M19 1FL* Tel 0161-432 1844 E-mail jonjenni@fish.co.uk

WILLIAMS, Jonathan Lane. b 59. Dorset Inst of HE 85. STETS 96. **d** 99 **p** 00. NSM Moordown *Win* from 99. *28 Queen Mary Avenue, Moordown, Bournemouth BH9 1TS* Tel and fax (01202) 531630 Mobile 07977-444186 E-mail jon.williams@ukgateway.net

WILLIAMS, Jonathan Simon. b 60. Univ of Wales (Cardiff) BSc81. Coll of Resurr Mirfield 83. **d** 86 **p** 87. C Gelligaer *Llan* 86-89; C Cwmbran *Mon* 89-90; TV 90-97; V Marshfield and Peterstone Wentloog etc 97-00; TR Bassaleg from 00; RD Bassaleg from 99. *The Vicarage, 1 Church View, Bassaleg, Newport NP10 8ND* Tel (01633) 893258 E-mail jonathan@williamsvicarage.freeserve.co.uk

WILLIAMS, Mrs Josephine Mary. b 47. Reading Univ BEd78 Hatfield Poly MEd87. St Alb and Ox Min Course 96. **d** 99 **p** 00. NSM Terriers *Ox* from 99; Chapl HM YOI Aylesbury from 02. *5 Firs View Road, Hazlemere, High Wycombe HP15 7TD* Tel (01494) 813059 E-mail mail@jowilliams.net

WILLIAMS, Miss Joy Margaret. b 30. Lon Univ BD69. Linc Th Coll 82. **dss** 83 **d** 87 **p** 94. Pershore w Pinvin, Wick and Birlingham *Worc* 83-87; Par Dn 87-88; Par Dn Dudley St Jo 88-90; rtd 90; Perm to Offic *Worc* from 90. *Pixie Cottage, 40 Ridge Street, Pershore WR10 1AT* Tel (01386) 556867

WILLIAMS, Julian Thomas. b 65. Clare Coll Cam BA87. Wycliffe Hall Ox BA90. **d** 91 **p** 92. Min Can St D Cathl *St D* 91-94; C St D Cathl 91-94; V Cil-y-Cwm and Ystrad-ffin w Rhandir-mwyn etc 94-00; R Nursling and Rownhams *Win* from 00. *The Vicarage, 27 Horns Drove, Rownhams, Southampton SO16 8AH* Tel (023) 8073 8293

WILLIAMS, Keith. b 37. St Jo Coll Nottm 83. **d** 85 **p** 86. C Holbeck *Ripon* 85-88; R Swillington 88-95; V Batley All SS *Wakef* 95-01; P-in-c Purlwell 95-00; rtd 01. *17 Kirkfield Drive, Colton, Leeds LS15 9DR* Tel 0113-225 5754 E-mail kwilliams000@btclick.com

WILLIAMS, Keith Douglas. b 41. EMMTC 86. **d** 89 **p** 90. NSM Netherfield w Colwick *S'well* from 89; NSM Gedling from 95; Chapl Notts Healthcare NHS Trust from 93. *19 Eastholme Croft, Nottingham NG2 4DZ* Tel 0115-961 4850

WILLIAMS, Keith Graham. b 38. ARICS62 Reading Univ MSc70 St Jo Coll Dur DipTh77 MRICS01. **d** 77 **p** 78. C Almondbury *Wakef* 77-81; C Chapelthorpe 81-82; V Ryhill 82-88; V E Ardsley 88-99; RD Wakef 96-99; rtd 03. *21 Cadogan Court, Grenville Road, Pevensey Bay, Pevensey BN24 6BS* Tel (01323) 764424

WILLIAMS, Kelvin George John. b 36. ALCD62. **d** 62 **p** 63. C Bath Abbey w St Jas *B & W* 62-65; CF (TA) 64-65 and 70-79; Chapl R Nat Hosp for Rheumatic Diseases Bath 64-65; CF 65-68; C Clevedon St Andr *B & W* 68-70; V Ston Easton w Farrington Gurney 70-74; P-in-c Bradford 74-75; R Bradford w Oake, Hillfarrance and Heathfield 75-76; NSM Puriton and Pawlett 89-91; V 92-02; NSM Bridgwater Deanery 91-92; rtd 02. *Highlands, Knowleyards Road, Middlezoy, Bridgwater TA7 0NY* Tel (01823) 698413

WILLIAMS, Kim. *See* WILLIAMS, George Melvin

WILLIAMS (née HANNAH), Mrs Kimberley Victoria. b 75. Bp Grosseteste Coll BSc98. Ripon Coll Cuddesdon BTh01. **d** 01 **p** 02. C Machynlleth w Llanwrin and Penegoes *Ban* 01-02; C Twrcelyn Deanery from 02. *The Rectory, Bull Bay Road, Amlwch LL68 9EA* Tel (01407) 831670 Fax as telephone E-mail kimwilliams@lineone.net

WILLIAMS, Lee Lawrence. b 75. St Steph Ho Ox 98. **d** 01 **p** 02. C Cowbridge *Llan* from 01. *3 Leoline Close, Cowbridge CF71 7BU* Tel (01446) 773515

WILLIAMS, Lloyd. b 43. Oak Hill Th Coll DPS74. **d** 74 **p** 75. C Laisterdyke *Bradf* 74-77; C Hoole *Ches* 77-80; V Rawthorpe *Wakef* 80-84; HM Pris Leeds 84-85; Chapl HM Pris Cardiff 85-88; R Aldington w Bonnington and Bilsington *Cant* 88-95; Chapl HM Pris Aldington 88-95; RD N Lympne *Cant* 94-95; P-in-c Tuen Mun Hong Kong 95-99; V Clayton *Bradf* 99-03; rtd 03. *Charters Garth, Hutton-le-Hole, York YO62 6UD* Tel (01751) 417032 Mobile 07866-604345 E-mail lloyd@healingtrust.fslife.co.uk

WILLIAMS, Lois. *See* WILLIAMS, Ms Catherine Lois

WILLIAMS, Mrs Louise Margaret. b 66. Lanc Univ BA87. St Jo Coll Nottm DPS91. **d** 91 **p** 94. Par Dn W Ham *Chelmsf* 91-94; C Harold Hill St Geo 94-95; NSM Southend St Sav Westcliff from 95; Chapl Asst Southend Health Care NHS Trust from 97. *St Saviour's Vicarage, 33 King's Road, Westcliff-on-Sea SS0 8LL* Tel (01702) 342920 E-mail stsaviorwest@aol.com

WILLIAMS, Malcolm Kendra. b 34. Lon Univ MB, BS59. Oak Hill NSM Course 84. **d** 85 **p** 86. NSM Margate H Trin *Cant* 85-87; P-in-c Austrey and Warton *Birm* 87-90; V Wonersh *Guildf* 90-95; R Banket Zimbabwe 96-99; rtd 99; Hon C Wittersham w Stone-in-Oxney and Ebony *Cant* 00; Perm to Offic from 01; Hon C Chipperfield St Paul *St Alb* from 02; Hon C Sarratt from 02. *The Vicarage, The Street, Chipperfield, Kings Langley WD4 9BJ* Tel (01923) 263054 E-mail williamsmnb@aol.com

WILLIAMS, Mark. b 64. St Mich Coll Llan BTh94. **d** 97 **p** 98. C Mountain Ash *Llan* 97; C Mountain Ash and Miskin 97-99; C Neath w Llantwit 99-01; C Neath 01-02; V Skewen from 02. *Skewen Vicarage, 41 Hill Road, Neath Abbey, Neath SA10 7NP* Tel (01792) 814116

WILLIAMS, Mark. b 73. Pemb Coll Cam BA94 MA98 Ox Univ BA98. Ripon Coll Cuddesdon 95 Ven English Coll Rome 97. **d** 98 **p** 99. C Caerphilly *Llan* 98-00; V Walworth St Chris *S'wark*

from 00; Warden Pemb Coll (Cam) Miss from 00. *45 Aldridge Street, London SE17 2RG* Tel (020) 7701 4162 *or* 7703 3803 E-mail fr_mark@yahoo.com

WILLIAMS, Mark John. b 66. St Martin's Coll Lanc BA88 PGCE93. Cranmer Hall Dur 98. **d** 00 **p** 01. C Hockerill *St Alb* 00-03; TV Chipping Barnet w Arkley from 03. *St Peter's Vicarage, Barnet Road, Barnet EN5 3JF* Tel (020) 8440 5797 E-mail mark.john.williams@lineone.net

WILLIAMS, Mark Naylor. b 28. CCC Cam BA52 MA56 CertEd. Ripon Hall Ox 58. **d** 59 **p** 60. C Dorchester *Ox* 59-65; R Gt and Lt Braxted *Chelmsf* 65-70; R E Kilbride *Glas* 70-74; R Norton *Sheff* 74-89; R Lt w Gt Ellingham w Rockland *Nor* 89-95; rtd 95; Perm to Offic *Chelmsf* from 95. *15 Olivia Drive, Leigh-on-Sea SS9 3EF* Tel (01702) 478734

WILLIAMS, Mark Robert. b 62. Spurgeon's Coll Lon BA83 Trin Coll Bris DipHE82 Univ Coll of Swansea PGCE84. Ripon Coll Cuddesdon. **d** 01. C Wellington and Distr *B & W* from 01. *19 Churchfields, Wellington TA21 8SD* Tel (01823) 664841 Mobile 07971-416318 E-mail blots@lineone.net.

WILLIAMS, The Ven Martin Inffeld. b 37. SS Coll Cam BA62 MA92. Chich Th Coll 62. **d** 64 **p** 65. C Greenford H Cross *Lon* 64-70; Tutor Chich Th Coll 70-75; Vice-Prin 75-77; V Roath St German *Llan* 77-92; Adn Margam 92-01; Adn Morgannwg from 02; Treas Llan Cathl from 92; V Penydarren from 92. *The Vicarage, Church Street, Penydarren, Merthyr Tydfil CF47 9HS* Tel (01685) 386258 Fax as telephone

WILLIAMS, Martin Jonathan. b 63. Birm Univ BA84. Trin Coll Bris DipHE96. **d** 98 **p** 99. C Bisley and W End *Guildf* 98-01; C Gerrards Cross and Fulmer *Ox* from 01. *Willowbrook, 54 The Uplands, Gerrards Cross SL9 7JG* Tel (01753) 892571 Mobile 07974-010703 E-mail williamsmartinj@cs.com

WILLIAMS, Mary Edith. b 50. Darlington Tr Coll BEd73. Cranmer Hall Dur 00. **d** 02 **p** 03. C Filey *York* from 02. *16A Willow Close, Filey YO14 9NY* Tel (01723) 515439 E-mail brmewilliams@supanet.com

WILLIAMS, Mervyn Rees. b 28. Univ of Wales (Swansea) BA49 Lon Univ PGCE54. St Deiniol's Hawarden 68. **d** 72 **p** 73. NSM Llangollen w Trevor and Llantysilio *St As* 72-94; rtd 94. *12 Wern Road, Llangollen LL20 8DU* Tel (01978) 860369

WILLIAMS, Meurig Llwyd. b 61. Univ of Wales (Abth) BA83 PGCE84 Univ of Wales (Cardiff) BD90. Westcott Ho Cam 90. **d** 92 **p** 93. C Holyhead w Rhoscolyn w Llanfair-yn-Neubwll *Ban* 92-95; P-in-c Denio w Abererch 95-96; V 96-99; V Cardiff Dewi Sant *Llan* from 99. *Hafod-Lon, 51 Heath Park Avenue, Cardiff CF14 3RF* Tel (029) 2075 1418 E-mail mllwyd@aol.com

WILLIAMS, Michael. *See* WILLIAMS, David Michael Rochfort

WILLIAMS, Michael. b 70. Nottm Univ BA98. St Jo Coll Nottm 95. **d** 98 **p** 99. C Shifnal *Lich* 98-01; TV Stafford from 01. *St Bertelin's Vicarage, 36 Holmcroft Road, Stafford ST16 1JB* Tel (01785) 252874

WILLIAMS, Michael Dermot Andrew. b 57. Ex Univ BA86. Ripon Coll Cuddesdon 90. **d** 92 **p** 93. NSM Christow, Ashton, Trusham and Bridford *Ex* 92-97; NSM Marston w Elsfield *Ox* 97-99; Chief Exec Radcliffe Infirmary NHS Trust 97-99; V Shipton-under-Wychwood w Milton, Fifield etc *Ox* 99-02; RD Chipping Norton 01-02; Exec Dir Thames Valley HA from 02. *10 Southcroft, Marston, Oxford OX3 0PF* Tel (01865) 242513 E-mail williamsmda@compuserve.com

WILLIAMS, Michael John. b 31. St Edm Hall Ox BA53 MA57. Wells Th Coll 53. **d** 55 **p** 56. C Wood Green St Mich *Lon* 55-59; C Bedminster St Aldhelm *Bris* 59-62; C Witney *Ox* 62-65; C Thatcham 66-70; Perm to Offic *Ex* 70-81; C Rainhill *Liv* 81-86; Chapl Whiston Hosp 83-86; rtd 86; Perm to Offic *Ex* from 86. *1 Bramble Lane, Crediton EX17 1DA* Tel (01363) 774005

WILLIAMS, Canon Michael Joseph. b 42. St Jo Coll Dur BA68. Bernard Gilpin Soc Dur 63 Cranmer Hall Dur 64. **d** 70 **p** 71. C Toxteth Park St Philemon *Liv* 70-75; TV Toxteth St Philemon w St Gabr 75-78; Dir Past Studies St Jo Coll Dur 78-88; Prin N Ord Course 89-99; Hon Can Liv Cathl *Liv* 92-99; P-in-c Bolton St Pet *Man* from 99; Hon Can Man Cathl from 00; AD Bolton from 02. *The Vicarage, Silverwell Street, Bolton BL1 1PS* Tel (01204) 533847 Fax as telephone E-mail vicar@boltonparishchurch.co.uk

WILLIAMS, Michael Robert John. b 41. Cranmer Hall Dur 67. **d** 70 **p** 71. C Middleton *Man* 70-73; C-in-c Blackley White Moss St Mark CD 73-79; R Blackley White Moss St Mark 79-86; R Gorton Em 86-96; R Gorton Em w St Jas from 96. *Emmanuel Rectory, 35 Blackwin Street, Manchester M12 5LD* Tel 0161-223 3510

WILLIAMS, Mrs Nia Catrin. b 69. Univ of Wales (Abth) DipTh94 Univ of Wales (Cardiff) BTh96. St As Minl Tr Course 97. **d** 98 **p** 99. C Llanrhos *St As* 98-02; C Colwyn 02-03; C Llanrwst and Llanddoget and Capel Garmon from 03. *The Rectory, Llanddoged Road, Llanrwst LL26 0DW* Tel (01492) 640223

WILLIAMS, Nicholas Jolyon. b 68. Univ of Wales (Swansea) BA89. Wycliffe Hall Ox BTh96. **d** 96 **p** 97. C Ditton *Roch* 96-99; C N Farnborough *Guildf* from 99. *64 Woburn Avenue, Farnborough GU14 7EQ* Tel (01252) 546093 E-mail nick@nwilliams75.fsnet.co.uk

WILLIAMS, Nick. *See* WILLIAMS, James Nicholas Owen

WILLIAMS, Nigel Howard. b 63. Llys Fasi Agric Coll NCA81. St Mich Coll Llan DipTh95. **d** 95 **p** 96. C Denbigh and Nantglyn *St As* 95-97; P-in-c Llanrwst and Llanddoget and Capel Garmon 97-98; R from 98. *The Rectory, Llanddoged Road, Llanrwst LL26 0DW* Tel (01492) 640223

WILLIAMS, Norman Ernest. b 23. IEng FIEEE AMIEE Cardiff Coll of Tech HNC. Llan Dioc Tr Scheme 78. **d** 82 **p** 83. NSM Llanblethian w Cowbridge and Llandough etc *Llan* 82-93; rtd 93; Perm to Offic *Llan* from 93. *The Poplars, Southgate, Cowbridge CF71 7BD* Tel (01446) 772107 E-mail normanewilliams@compuserve.com

WILLIAMS, Norman Leigh. b 26. Open Univ BA86 Trin Coll Carmarthen 83. **d** 85 **p** 86. NSM Loughor *S & B* 85-96; NSM Adnry Gower 87-96; rtd 96. *Gorwydd Villa, 13 The Woodlands, Gowerton, Swansea SA4 3DP* Tel (01792) 874853

WILLIAMS, Olivia Hazel. b 55. Dun Laoghaire Inst CertEd98 TCD BTh01. CITC 98. **d** 01 **p** 02. C Greystones *D & G* from 01; Abp's Dom Chapl from 03. *192 Heathervue, Greystones, Co Wicklow, Irish Republic* Tel (00353) (1) 287 1336 E-mail curate.greystones@glendalough.anglican.org

WILLIAMS, Owen David. b 38. S'wark Ord Course 72. **d** 75 **p** 76. NSM Tatsfield *S'wark* 75-80; C Maidstone All SS w St Phil and H Trin *Cant* 80-81; C Maidstone All SS and St Phil w Tovil 81-82; V St Nicholas at Wade w Sarre and Chislet w Hoath 82-92; TV Bruton and Distr *B & W* 92-98; R Kirkby Fleetham w Langton on Swale and Scruton *Ripon* 98-03; rtd 03; P-in-c Walford and St John w Bishopswood, Goodrich etc *Heref* from 03. *The Vicarage, Walford, Ross-on-Wye HR9 5QP* Tel (01989) 562703

WILLIAMS, Paul Andrew. b 62. Oak Hill Th Coll BA91. **d** 91 **p** 92. C Ware Ch Ch *St Alb* 91-94; C Harold Wood *Chelmsf* 94-99; C Langham Place All So *Lon* from 99. *12 De Walden Street, London W1M 7PH* Tel (020) 7935 9811 *or* 7580 3522 E-mail paul.williams@allsouls.org

WILLIAMS, Paul Gavin. b 68. Grey Coll Dur BA89. Wycliffe Hall Ox MPhil93. **d** 92 **p** 93. C Muswell Hill St Jas w St Matt *Lon* 92-96; C Clifton Ch Ch w Em *Bris* 96-99; R Gerrards Cross and Fulmer *Ox* from 99. *The Rectory, Oxford Road, Gerrards Cross SL9 7DJ* Tel (01753) 883301 Fax 892177

WILLIAMS, Paul Rhys. b 58. St Andr Univ MTh82. Westcott Ho Cam 83. **d** 86 **p** 87. Asst Chapl Selw Coll Cam 86-87; C Chatham St Steph *Roch* 87-90; V Gillingham St Aug 90-95; Bp's Dom Chapl 95-03; Hon Can Roch Cathl 01-03; V Tewkesbury w Walton Cardiff and Twyning *Glouc* from 03. *Abbey House, Church Street, Tewkesbury GL20 5SR* Tel (01684) 293333 Fax 273113 E-mail vicar@tewkesburyabbey.org.uk

WILLIAMS, Paul Robert. b 66. Huddersfield Poly BA88. Wycliffe Hall Ox DipMin99. **d** 99 **p** 00. C Roxeth *Lon* 99-03; C Harlow St Mary Magd *Chelmsf* from 03. *134 East Park, Harlow CM17 0SA* Tel (01279) 427357 Fax as telephone E-mail paul-w@xalt.co.uk

WILLIAMS, Mrs Pauline Mary. b 52. Univ of Wales (Cardiff) BD96 Trin Coll Carmarthen PGCE97. St Mich Coll Llan 00. **d** 02 **p** 03. C Coity w Nolton *Llan* from 02. *2 Fenwick Drive, Brackla, Bridgend CF31 2LD* Tel (01656) 659749 Mobile 07974-652211 E-mail williamspm89@hotmail.com

WILLIAMS, Canon Peris Llewelyn. b 39. Univ of Wales (Lamp) BA59. Qu Coll Birm 59. **d** 62 **p** 63. C Upton Ascension *Ches* 62-65; C Davenham 65-68; C Grange St Andr 68-73; TV E Runcorn w Halton 73-74; V Backford 74-80; Youth Chapl 74-80; V Witton 80-86; V Hoylake 86-93; R Ches H Trin 93-02; Hon Can Ches Cathl 98-02; rtd 02; Perm to Offic *Ches* from 02. *Padarn, 65 Long Lane, Chester CH2 2PG* Tel (01244) 341305

WILLIAMS, Peter. *See* WILLIAMS, Canon Cecil Peter

WILLIAMS, Peter. *See* WILLIAMS, Edward Ffoulkes

WILLIAMS, Peter Charles. b 50. SW Minl Tr Course 98. **d** 01 **p** 02. OLM Landrake w St Erney and Botus Fleming *Truro* from 01. *5 North Road, Landrake, Saltash PL12 5EL* Tel (01752) 851260 E-mail peterfreda@5northroad.fsnet.co.uk

WILLIAMS, Peter Hurrell. b 34. Keble Coll Ox BA58 MA61. Tyndale Hall Bris 62. **d** 64 **p** 65. C Sparkbrook Ch Ch *Birm* 64-67; C Rushden St Pet 67-70; P-in-c Clapham Park All SS *S'wark* 70-78; R Stanford-le-Hope w Mucking *Chelmsf* 78-92; P-in-c Gt Oakley w Wix 92-96; R Gt Oakley w Wix and Wrabness 96-97; rtd 97; Perm to Offic *Chelmsf* from 01. *3 Hillcrest Close, Horndon-on-the-Hill, Stanford-le-Hope SS17 8LS* Tel (01375) 643697

WILLIAMS, Peter John. b 55. Southn Univ BTh80 Univ of Wales (Swansea) DSS90. Chich Th Coll 76. **d** 80 **p** 81. C Chepstow *Mon* 80-84; C Morriston *S & B* 84-85; V Glantawe 85-88; R Reynoldston w Penrice and Llangennith from 88; Dioc Soc Resp Officer from 88. *The Vicarage, Llangennith, Swansea SA3 1HU* Tel (01792) 386391

WILLIAMS, Peter Rodney. b 22. Chich Th Coll 60. **d** 62 **p** 63. C Seaford w Sutton *Chich* 62-65; P-in-c Wivelsfield 65-72; V Eastbourne St Jo 72-87; rtd 87; Perm to Offic *Chich* from 87. *33 Park Gates, Chiswick Place, Eastbourne BN21 4BD* Tel (01323) 723359

WILLIAMS, Philip Allan. b 48. Bris Univ BSc69 CertEd74. Trin Coll Bris 86. **d** 88 **p** 89. C Heref St Pet w St Owen and St Jas *Heref* 88-93; R Peterchurch w Vowchurch, Turnastone and Dorstone 93-96; P-in-c Holmer w Huntington 96-01; V from 01. *The Vicarage, Holmer, Hereford HR4 9RG* Tel (01432) 273200 E-mail revphil@holmer.supanet.com

WILLIAMS, Philip Andrew. b 64. Sheff Univ BA86. St Jo Coll Dur 88. **d** 90 **p** 91. C Hillsborough and Wadsley Bridge *Sheff* 90-94; C Lenton Abbey *S'well* 94-96; P-in-c 96-02; C Wollaton Park 94-96; V Porchester from 02. *St James's Vicarage, Marshall Hill Drive, Nottingham NG3 6FY* Tel 0115-960 6185

WILLIAMS, Philip James. b 52. St Chad's Coll Dur BA73. Coll of Resurr Mirfield 74. **d** 76 **p** 77. C Stoke upon Trent *Lich* 76-80; TV 80; Chapl N Staffs Poly 80-84; TV Stoke-upon-Trent 80-84; R Shrewsbury St Giles w Sutton and Atcham from 84. *St Giles's Rectory, 127 Abbey Foregate, Shrewsbury SY2 6LY* Tel (01743) 356426 E-mail philipjwilliams@lineone.net

WILLIAMS, Ray. b 23. Birm City Tech Coll DipMechE41 Lon Univ DipEd46. St Aid Birkenhead 56. **d** 58 **p** 59. C Sparkhill St Jo *Birm* 58-60; Area Sec (Dios St Alb and Chelmsf) CMS 60-65; V Shenstone *Lich* 65-73; New Zealand from 73; Asst P Blenheim 73-78; V Wakefield and Tapawera 78-83; P-in-c Murchison 79-82; Asst P Nelson All SS 83-85; Asst P Havelock and the Sounds 92-96. *16 Limerick Grove, Ascot Park, Porirua 6006, New Zealand* Tel (0064) (4) 235 9912

WILLIAMS, Raymond Howel. b 27. St Jo Coll Cam BA49 MA51 Ball Coll Ox BLitt63. St Jo Coll Nottm 72 NW Ord Course 73. **d** 73 **p** 74. C Derby St Pet *Derby* 73-76; C Enfield Ch Ch Trent Park *Lon* 75-81; V S Mymms K Chas *St Alb* 81-94; NSM 94-95; rtd 94; Perm to Offic *St Alb* from 95. *The Vicarage, Payne End, Sandon, Buntingford SG9 0QU* Tel (01763) 287256

WILLIAMS, Richard Dennis. b 57. LTCL79. Coll of Resurr Mirfield 79. **d** 82 **p** 83. C Roath *Llan* 82-85; C Penarth w Lavernock 85-88; V Abertillery *Mon* 88-95; V Tredunnoc and Llantrisant w Llanhennock etc 95-01; V Hay w Llanigon and Capel-y-Ffin *S & B* from 01. *19 Gypsy Castle Lane, Hay-on-Wye, Hereford HR3 1XX* Tel (01497) 820448

WILLIAMS, Richard Elwyn. b 57. Hull Univ BA79. Coll of Resurr Mirfield 79. **d** 81 **p** 82. C Altrincham St Geo *Ches* 81-84; C Stockport St Thos 84-85; C Stockport St Thos w St Pet 86; R Withington St Crispin *Man* 86-95; V Alveston *Cov* from 95; RD Fosse from 99. *The Vicarage, Alveston, Stratford-upon-Avon CV37 7QB* Tel (01789) 292777 E-mail rrickvic@aol.com

WILLIAMS, Canon Richard Glyndwr. b 18. St D Coll Lamp BA39 BD50. **d** 41 **p** 42. C Kidwelly *St D* 41-46; C Llandudno *Ban* 46-52; R Trefriw 52-55; V Llandinorwig 55-62; Sec Dioc Coun for Educn 58-62; Warden Ch Hostel Ban 62-70; Chapl Univ of Wales (Ban) *Ban* 62-70; Dir of Ords 62-70 and 84-86; Prec Ban Cathl 68-88; Can from 68; R Llanbeblig w Caernarfon 70-71; R Llanbeblig w Caernarfon and Betws Garmon etc 71-81; V Llandysilio 81-88; RD Tindaethwy 82-88; rtd 88; Perm to Offic *Ban* from 88. *Borth, 9 Cae Cil Melyn, Penrhosgarnedd, Bangor LL57 2ND* Tel (01248) 362883

WILLIAMS, Canon Richard Henry Lowe. b 31. Liv Univ BA52. K Coll (NS) BD64 Ridley Hall Cam 54. **d** 56 **p** 57. C Drypool St Andr and St Pet *York* 56-59; Canada 59-64; V Kirkdale St Athanasius *Liv* 64-68; R Much Woolton 68-79; R Croft w Southworth 79-89; Dioc Communications Officer 79-97; Hon Can Liv Cathl 88-97; R Wavertree St Mary 89-97; rtd 97; Perm to Offic *Liv* from 97. *16 Childwall Crescent, Liverpool L16 7PQ* Tel 0151-722 7962

WILLIAMS, Richard Huw. b 63. Bradf and Ilkley Coll BA85. St Jo Coll Nottm LTh88 DPS89. **d** 89 **p** 90. C Forest Gate St Edm *Chelmsf* 89-90; C Plaistow 90-92; C Canning Town St Matthias 92-96; V Southend St Sav Westcliff from 96. *St Saviour's Vicarage, 33 King's Road, Westcliff-on-Sea SS0 8LL* Tel (01702) 342920 E-mail stsaviourwest@aol.com

WILLIAMS, Richard Lawrence. b 62. Warw Univ BSc83 ACA87. Wycliffe Hall Ox 95. **d** 97 **p** 98. C Wallington H Trin *S'wark* 97-00; V Addiscombe St Mary Magd w St Martin from 00. *The Vicarage, Canning Road, Addiscombe CR0 6QD* Tel and fax (020) 8654 3459 *or* 8656 3457 E-mail richard@rlwilliams.fsnet.co.uk

WILLIAMS, Robert. b 49. **d** 97 **p** 98. C W Derby St Mary *Liv* 97-01; R Golborne from 01. *The Rectory, Church Street, Golborne, Warrington WA3 3TH* Tel (01942) 728305

WILLIAMS, Robert David. b 05. St D Coll Lamp BA32. **d** 33 **p** 34. C Llandinorwig *Ban* 33-38; C Meyllteyrn 38-42; R Llanddona w Llaniestyn 42-48; V Llanerchymedd w Rhodogeidio and Gwredog 48-57; V Dolwyddelan 57-62; V Llandysilio 62-75; rtd 75; Perm to Offic *Ban* from 75. *7 Park Road, Llanfairfechan LL33 0AE* Tel (01248) 680102

WILLIAMS, Robert Edward. b 42. Ex Univ BA63. Lich Th Coll. **d** 65 **p** 66. C Wednesbury St Paul Wood Green *Lich* 65-67; C Whitchurch 67-69; P-in-c Whixall 69-72; P-in-c Edstaston 69-72; CF 72-91; R Cheriton w Tichborne and Beauworth *Win* 91-01; R Upper Itchen 01-02; rtd 02. *84 Portway, Warminster BA12 8QE*

WILLIAMS, Robert Edward. b 50. Univ of Wales (Ban) DipTh71. St Mich Coll Llan BD74 CertEd79. **d** 74 **p** 75. C Flint *St As* 74-77; Asst Chapl Sandbach Sch 79-80; Chapl and Hd RE 80-88; Perm to Offic *Ches* 86-88; Perm to Offic *St As* 87-88; CF from 88. *c/o MOD Chaplains (Army)* Tel (01980) 615804 Fax 615800

WILLIAMS, Robert Ellis Greenleaf. b 12. St D Coll Lamp BA34 Lich Th Coll 34. **d** 36 **p** 37. C S Banbury *Ox* 36-39; Australia 39-54; R Croydon w Clopton *Ely* 54-58; V Tadlow w E Hatley 54-58; V Hatley 54-58; V Oldham St Ambrose *Man* 58-66; V Rochdale St Aid 66-75; TV Weston-super-Mare Cen Par *B & W* 75-78; P-in-c Castleton All So *Man* 78-80; rtd 80; Perm to Offic *Man* 81-96. *18 Barrowdale Drive, Rochdale OL11 3JZ* Tel (01706) 356582

WILLIAMS, Robert George Dibdin. b 20. St Mich Coll Llan 56. **d** 58 **p** 59. C Welshpool *St As* 58-63; R Nannerch 63-68; V Cilcain and Nannerch 68-75; V Gwersyllt 75-85; rtd 85. *30 Ffordd y Gaer, Bradley, Wrexham LL11 4BW* Tel (01978) 754007

WILLIAMS, Robert Jeffrey Hopkin. b 62. ALAM Univ of Wales (Abth) BA84. Chich Th Coll BTh90. **d** 90 **p** 91. C Eastbourne St Mary *Chich* 90-94; R Upper St Leonards St Jo 94-02; V Twickenham St Mary *Lon* from 02. *37 Arragon Road, Twickenham TW1 3NG* Tel (020) 8892 2319

WILLIAMS, The Ven Robert John. b 51. Cartrefle Coll of Educn CertEd72 Univ of Wales (Ban) BEd73 MA92. St Mich Coll Llan BD76. **d** 76 **p** 77. C Swansea St Mary and H Trin *S & B* 76-78; Chapl Univ of Wales (Swansea) 78-84; Children's Adv 81-88; Asst Dir of Educn 81-88; Bp's Chapl for Th Educn 83-88; R Reynoldston w Penrice and Llangennith 84-88; R Denbigh and Nantglyn *St As* 88-94; V Sketty *S & B* 94-99; Dir of Ords 94-99; P-in-c Port Eynon w Rhosili and Llanddewi and Knelston from 99; Can Brecon Cathl 95-00; Adn Gower from 00. *The Rectory, Port Eynon, Swansea SA3 1NL* Tel (01792) 390456

WILLIAMS, Roger. See WILLIAMS, David Roger

WILLIAMS, Roger. See WILLIAMS, Canon John Roger

WILLIAMS, Roger Anthony. b 54. Univ of Wales (Lamp) BA76. Bp Burgess Hall Lamp 72 Qu Coll Birm 76. **d** 78 **p** 79. C Llanelli *St D* 78-82; V Monkton 82-86; Chapl to the Deaf *B & W* 86-90; Chapl to the Deaf *Ox* from 90. *Denchworth House, Denchworth, Wantage OX12 0DX* Tel (01235) 868248 (Minicom) *or* 868442

WILLIAMS, Roger Stewart. b 54. Qu Coll Cam BA75 MA79. Wycliffe Hall Ox BA78 MA82. **d** 79 **p** 80. C Hamstead St Paul *Birm* 79-82; C Barking St Marg w St Patr *Chelmsf* 82-85; V Mildmay Grove St Jude and St Paul *Lon* 85-95; P-in-c Charles w Plymouth St Matthias *Ex* from 95; Chapl Plymouth Univ from 95. *The Vicarage, 6 St Lawrence Road, Plymouth PL4 6HN* Tel (01752) 665640 E-mail rswilliams@supanet.com

WILLIAMS, Roger Thomas. b 54. Man Univ BSc76 Birm Univ MSc78 PhD83 Pemb Coll Cam PGCE92. Ridley Hall Cam 00. **d** 02 **p** 03. C Cambridge St Martin *Ely* from 02. *4 Tenison Court, Tenison Road, Cambridge CB1 2EF* Tel and fax (01223) 321585 Mobile 07751-601066 E-mail rogertw11@hotmail.com

WILLIAMS, Ronald Hywel. b 35. St D Coll Lamp BA62. **d** 63 **p** 64. C Machynlleth and Llanwrin *Ban* 63-66; C Llanaber 66-69; C Hawarden *St As* 69-73; R Llansantffraid Glan Conwy and Eglwysbach 73-77; V Rhosllannerchrugog 77-88; R Cilcain and Nannerch and Rhyd-y-mwyn 88-92; V Llanbadarn Fawr w Capel Bangor and Goginan *St D* 92-95; V Llanbadarn Fawr 95-00; RD Llanbadarn Fawr 94-00; rtd 00. *15 Maes y Garn, Bow Street SY24 5DS* Tel (01970) 820247

✠**WILLIAMS, The Most Revd and Rt Hon Rowan Douglas.** b 50. Ch Coll Cam BA71 MA75 Wadh Coll Ox DPhil75 DD89 Erlangen Hon DrTheol99 FBA90 Hon FGMS00. Coll of Resurr Mirfield 75. **d** 77 **p** 78 **c** 92. Tutor Westcott Ho Cam 77-80; Hon C Chesterton St Geo *Ely* 80-83; Lect Div Cam Univ 80-86; Dean Clare Coll Cam 84-86; Can Th Leic Cathl *Leic* 81-92; Lady Marg Prof Div Ox Univ 86-92; Can Res Ch Ch *Ox* 86-92; Bp Mon 92-02; Abp Wales 99-02; Abp Cant from 02. *Lambeth Palace, London SE1 7JU,* or *The Old Palace, Canterbury CT1 2EE* Tel (020) 7898 1200 *or* (01227) 459401 Fax (020) 7261 9836

WILLIAMS, Canon Roy. b 28. Lon Univ DipTh60. Ely Th Coll 58. **d** 60 **p** 61. C Daybrook *S'well* 60-63; V Bilborough St Jo 63-73; V Arnold 73-92; Hon Can S'well Minster 85-92; rtd 92; Perm to Offic *S'well* from 92. *10 Maris Drive, Burton Joyce, Nottingham NG14 5AJ* Tel 0115-931 2030

WILLIAMS, Mrs Sarah Ann. b 59. **d** 03. C Warmley, Syston and Bitton *Bris* from 03. *19 Ipswich Grove, Norwich NR2 2LU*

WILLIAMS, (née CROSLAND), Mrs Sarah Rosita. b 50. St Mary's Coll Cheltenham CertEd71 BEd72. EAMTC 01. **d** 03. C Warmley, Syston and Bitton *Bris* from 03. *25 Poplar Road, Warmley, Bristol BS30 5JX* Tel 0117-960 9969 E-mail sarah.williams@skynet.com

WILLIAMS, Shamus Frank Charles. b 57. St Cath Coll Cam BA79 MA83. Ripon Coll Cuddesdon 81. **d** 84 **p** 85. C Swanage and Studland *Sarum* 84-87; C St Alb St Pet *St Alb* 87-90; TV Saffron Walden w Wendens Ambo and Littlebury *Chelmsf* 90-95; R Shingay Gp of Par *Ely* from 95; RD Shingay from 97.

The Vicarage, Church Street, Guilden Morden, Royston SG8 0JD Tel (01763) 853067

WILLIAMS, Stephen Clark. b 47. Univ of Wales (Cardiff) BSc(Econ)69 Warw Univ MSc70. Wycliffe Hall Ox DipMin93. **d** 93 **p** 94. C High Wycombe *Ox* 93-96; C Walton H Trin 96-97; TV from 97; Acting TR from 01; P-in-c E and W Horndon w Lt Warley and Childerditch *Chelmsf* from 03. *The Rectory, 155 Thorndon Avenue, West Horndon, Brentwood CM13 3TR* Tel (01277) 811223 E-mail stevecgs@ukonline.co.uk

WILLIAMS, Stephen Geoffrey. b 54. St Jo Coll Nottm BTh79 LTh79. **d** 79 **p** 80. C Skelmersdale St Paul *Liv* 79-81; C Burley *Ripon* 81-86. *24 Coronation Drive, Penketh, Warrington WA5 2DD* Tel (01925) 723599

WILLIAMS, Stephen Grant. b 51. K Coll Lon BD73 AKC73. **d** 75 **p** 76. C Paddington Ch Ch *Lon* 75-78; C Paddington St Jas 78-80; Chapl LSE 80-91; Chapl (Sen) Lon Univs from 91. *15 Wilmington Square, London WC1X 0ER* Tel (020) 7837 1782 *or* 7387 0670 Fax (020) 7387 4373 E-mail chaplaincy@lon.ac.uk

WILLIAMS, The Ven Stephen Heath. b 51. LTh DipRE DipMin. **d** 74 **p** 75. Australia 74-76 and from 78; C Leigh Park *Portsm* 76-78; Adn SW 89-98; I Newton All SS 98-00. *Gwandalan, Malabar Road, Holbrook, NSW, Australia 2644* Tel (0061) (2) 6036 3603

WILLIAMS, Stephen James. b 52. Lon Univ BSc73. Ridley Hall Cam 73. **d** 78 **p** 79. C Waltham Abbey *Chelmsf* 78-82; C Bedford St Paul *St Alb* 82-86; P-in-c Chalgrave 86-88; V Harlington from 86. *The Vicarage, Church Road, Harlington, Dunstable LU5 6LE* Tel (01525) 872413 Fax 753683 E-mail revdstevewilliams@harlingtonchurch.org.uk

WILLIAMS, The Very Revd Stephen John. b 49. Univ of NSW BA73 DipEd73 Cam Univ BA77 MA81 Macquarie Univ (NSW) MA92. Ridley Hall Cam 75. **d** 78 **p** 79. Lect Th Bp Tucker Coll Uganda 78; C Brompton H Trin w Onslow Square St Paul *Lon* 79-82; Australia from 82; C Shenton Park St Matt 82-83; Chapl Blue Mountains Gr Sch 84-90; R W Lindfield 91-01; Dean Armidale from 02. *PO Box 749, Armidale, NSW, Australia 2350* Tel (0061) (2) 6772 2269 Fax 6772 0188

WILLIAMS, Stephen Lionel. b 48. St Kath Coll Liv CertEd74 Open Univ BA77. N Ord Course 93. **d** 96 **p** 97. NSM Hough Green St Basil and All SS *Liv* 96-99; C Padgate 99-02; V Walton St Jo from 02. *St John's Vicarage, 472 Rice Lane, Walton, Liverpool L9 2BW* Tel 0151-525 3458

WILLIAMS, Stephen Stuart. b 60. Magd Coll Ox BA82 Dur Univ BA88. Cranmer Hall Dur 86. **d** 89 **p** 90. C W Derby Gd Shep *Liv* 89-93; Relig Affairs Producer BBC Radio Merseyside 92-00; TV Liv Our Lady and St Nic w St Anne *Liv* 93-01; P-in-c Prestwich St Gabr *Man* from 01; Bp's Dom Chapl from 01. *St Gabriel's Vicarage, 8 Bishops Road, Prestwich, Manchester M25 8HT* Tel 0161-773 8839 *or* 792 2096 Mobile 07813-436170

WILLIAMS, Susan. b 50. Swansea Coll of Educn CertEd72. Ban Ord Course 94. **d** 97 **p** 98. NSM Criccieth w Treflys *Ban* 97-00; P-in-c 00-01; P-in-c Criccieth and Treflys w Llanystumdwy etc 01-02; R from 02. *Taleifion, High Street, Criccieth LL52 0RN* Tel (01766) 523222 *or* (01248) 354999 Fax 523183 E-mail sue.williams2@ntlworld.com

WILLIAMS, Ms Susan Jean. b 54. Chester Coll of HE MTh00 Lanc Univ MA02. N Ord Course 95. **d** 98 **p** 99. C Prescot *Liv* 98-01; Perm to Offic *Blackb* 01-02; C Scotforth from 02. *10 Lawnswood Avenue, Lancaster LA1 4NZ* Tel (01524) 847278 Mobile 07904-076864 E-mail rev_sue@lineone.net

WILLIAMS, Mrs Susan Merrilyn Marsh. b 62. Ban Ord Course 00. **d** 03. NSM Botwnnog w Bryncroes *Ban* from 03. *Tyddyn Mawr, Tudweiliog, Pwllheli LL53 8PB* Tel (01758) 770208 E-mail smw4tmawr@aol.com

WILLIAMS, Terence. b 36. Univ of Wales (Abth) BSc57 Univ of Wales (Cardiff) MA67 Aston Univ PhD71. Glouc Sch of Min 78. **d** 81 **p** 81. NSM Deerhurst, Apperley w Forthampton and Chaceley *Glouc* 81-87; NSM Tarrington w Stoke Edith, Aylton, Pixley etc *Heref* 87-88; P-in-c Upper and Lower Slaughter w Eyford and Naunton *Glouc* 88-91; P-in-c Redmarley D'Abitot, Bromesberrow w Pauntley etc 91-95; R 95-99; RD Forest N 95-99; rtd 99; Perm to Offic *Glouc* 99-02; P-in-c Hasfield w Tirley and Ashleworth from 02. *Lyne Cottage, Ledbury Road, Newent, Gloucester GL18 1DL* Tel (01531) 820439

WILLIAMS, Terence John. b 36. Univ of Wales BSc62. St Deiniol's Hawarden 85. **d** 86 **p** 87. C Llangyfelach *S & B* 86-88; C Morriston 88-89; V Llanwrtyd w Llanddulas in Tir Abad etc 89-91; V Llanedi w Tycroes and Saron *St D* 91-00; rtd 01. *Coedmawr, 50 Swansea Road, Penllergaer, Swansea SA4 9AQ* Tel (01792) 892110

WILLIAMS, Thomas Bruce. b 41. Oak Hill Th Coll 74 DipPS76. **d** 76 **p** 77. C Liskeard w St Keyne and St Pinnock *Truro* 76-79; Australia from 79; rtd 99. *21 McClure Street, Bendigo, Vic, Australia 3550* Tel (0061) (3) 5444 1485

WILLIAMS, Timothy John. b 54. BEd83. Trin Coll Carmarthen. **d** 89 **p** 90. NSM Llansamlet *S & B* 89-97; P-in-c Bryngwyn and Newchurch and Llanbedr etc 97-01; V Aberedw w Llandeilo Graban and Llanbadarn etc from 01. *The Vicarage, Aberedw, Builth Wells LD2 3UW* Tel (01982) 560359

WILLIAMS, Timothy John. b 64. Kent Univ BA86. St Mich Coll Llan BD89. **d** 89 **p** 90. C Killay *S & B* 89-91; C Llwynderw

91-94; V Knighton and Norton 94-00; P-in-c Whitton w Pilleth w Cascob 99-00; V Killay from 00. *The Vicarage, Church Street, Knighton LD7 1AG* Tel (01547) 528566

WILLIAMS, Tom David. b 19. St D Coll Lamp BA41 St Mich Coll Llan 41. **d** 43 **p** 45. C Llanbeblig *Ban* 43-47; C Aberdovey 47-49; C Llanengan and Llangian 49; C Llandegai 49-53; R Llangybi w Llanarmon 53-60; V Llanidloes 60-75; P-in-c Llangurig 66-72; V 72-75; RD Arwystli 73-75; R Criccieth w Treflys 75-82; V Llanfihangel Ysgeifiog and Llanffinan etc 82-84; rtd 84; Perm to Offic *Ban* from 84. *Trefri Fach, Llangaffo, Gaerwen LL60 6LT* Tel (01248) 440687

WILLIAMS, Canon Trevor Russell. b 48. TCD BA71. St Jo Coll Nottm BA73. **d** 74 **p** 75. C Maidenhead St Andr and St Mary *Ox* 74-77; Asst Chapl QUB 78-80; Relig Broadcasting Producer BBC 81-88; I Newcastle *D & D* 88-93; Ldr Corrymeela Community 93-03; I Belfast H Trin and St Silas *Conn* from 03; Preb Rathmichael St Patr Cathl Dublin from 02. *The Rectory, 313 Ballysillan Road, Belfast BT14 6RD* Tel (028) 9071 3958 E-mail belfast@corrymeela.org.uk *or* www.corrymeela.org.uk

WILLIAMS, Canon Trevor Stanley Morlais. b 38. Jes Coll Ox BA63 Univ of E Africa MA67. Westcott Ho Cam BA67. **d** 67 **p** 68. C Clifton St Paul *Bris* 67-70; Asst Chapl Bris Univ 67-70; Chapl and Fell Trin Coll Ox from 70; Hon Can Ch Ch *Ox* from 95. *Trinity College, Oxford OX1 3BH* Tel (01865) 279886 E-mail trevor.williams@trinity.ox.ac.uk

WILLIAMS, Valerie Jane. b 53. Dioc OLM tr scheme 00. **d** 03. OLM Merstham and Gatton *S'wark* from 03. *Merstham Lodge, Harps Oak Lane, Merstham, Redhill RH1 3AN* Tel (01737) 644850 E-mail valwilliams@vwilliams99.freeserve.co.uk

WILLIAMS, Vincent Handley. b 24. LRAM LLCM ARCM CertEd. St Deiniol's Hawarden 76. **d** 78 **p** 79. Hon C Barrow *Ches* 78-81; C Dodleston 81-83; V Lostock Gralam 83-90; rtd 90; Perm to Offic *Ches* from 90. *2 Springfield Close, Higher Kinnerton, Chester CH4 9BU* Tel (01244) 660983

WILLIAMS, Walter Haydn. b 31. Univ of Wales (Lamp) BA53 Selw Coll Cam BA56 MA60. St Mich Coll Llan 53. **d** 54 **p** 55. C Denbigh *St As* 56-58; V Choral St As Cathl 58-61; C St As 58-61; R Llanfyllin 61-68; V Northop 68-73; V Mold 73-86; RD Mold 79-86; Can St As Cathl 77-82; Prec 81-82; Preb and Chan 82-86; R Overton and Erbistock and Penley 86-94; Chmn Ch of Wales Liturg Cttee 86-94; rtd 94. *2 Park Lane, Craig y Don, Llandudno LL30 1PQ* Tel (01492) 877294

WILLIAMS, William David Brynmor. b 48. Univ of Wales (Swansea) DipTh71 Open Univ BA89. St D Coll Lamp 71. **d** 72 **p** 73. C Killay *S & B* 72-74; C Wokingham All SS *Ox* 74-75; CF 75-77; C Spilsby w Hundleby *Linc* 83-87; R Meppershall w Campton and Stondon *St Alb* 87-90; V Hemsby *Nor* 90-96; P-in-c Winterton w E and W Somerton and Horsey 94-96; rtd 96. *The Old School, 14 Weekley, Kettering NN16 9UW* Tel (01536) 417612

WILLIAMS, William John. b 23. Fitzw Ho Cam BA50 MA55. Wycliffe Hall Ox. **d** 54 **p** 55. V Cholsey *Ox* 69-73; rtd 88. *3 Lon-y-Bugail, Bridgend CF31 4UE* Tel (01656) 663453

WILLIAMS-HUNTER, Ian Roy. b 44. Trin Coll Bris 71. **d** 73 **p** 74. C Redhill H Trin *S'wark* 73-75; C Deane *Man* 76-80; R Hartshorne *Derby* 80-02; P-in-c Bretby w Newton Solney 01-02; R Hartshorne and Bretby from 02. *The Rectory, 74 Woodville Road, Hartshorne, Swadlincote DE11 7ET* Tel (01283) 217866

WILLIAMS-POTTER, Mrs Amanda Clare. b 69. Univ of Wales (Ban) BD90. Westcott Ho Cam CTM92. **d** 92 **p** 97. C Carmarthen St Dav *St D* 92-94; Chapl Trin Coll Carmarthen 94-99; V Llan-non *St D* 99-01; TV Cwm Gwendraeth from 01. *The Vicarage, 32A Heol y Bryn, Upper Tumble, Llanelli SA14 6DN* Tel (01269) 841358 E-mail mandy.williams-potter@barclays.net

WILLIAMSON, Alfred Michael. b 28. Kelham Th Coll 53. **d** 58 **p** 59. C Nottingham St Geo w St Jo *S'well* 58-64; SSM 60-64; V Kenwyn St Geo *Truro* 64-73; V St Agnes 73-87; Australia from 87; R Beverley and Brookton 87-93; rtd 93. *19 Lakeview Crescent, Forster, NSW, Australia 2428* Tel (0061) (2) 6554 2239 E-mail coomba@ozemail.com.au

WILLIAMSON, Andrew John. b 39. MRPharmS. St Alb Minl Tr Scheme 82. **d** 85 **p** 86. NSM Oxhey All SS *St Alb* 85-88; NSM Bricket Wood 88-97; NSM Campbeltown *Arg* from 97. *36B Longrow, Campbeltown PA28 6DD* Tel (01586) 551478

WILLIAMSON, Canon Anthony William. b 33. OBE77 DL98. Trin Coll Ox BA56 MA60. Cuddesdon Coll 56. **d** 60 **p** 61. Hon C Cowley St Jas *Ox* 60-79; TV 79-89; Dir of Educn (Schs) 89-00; Hon Can Ch Ch 94-00; rtd 00. *9 The Goggs, Watlington OX49 5JX* Tel (01491) 612143 E-mail tony_williamson@lineone.net

WILLIAMSON, Barry. See WILLIAMSON, Peter Barry Martin

WILLIAMSON, Brian. See WILLIAMSON, John Brian Peter

WILLIAMSON, David Barry. b 56. St Jo Coll Nottm 80. **d** 83 **p** 84. C N Mymms *St Alb* 83-86; C Burley *Ripon* 86-92; Project Worker CECS 92-96; Youth and Children's Adv *B & W* from 96. *Education Department, The Old Deanery, Wells BA5 2UG* Tel (01458) 446435 *or* (01749) 670777 Fax (01749) 674240 E-mail david.williamson@bathwells.anglican.org

WILLIAMSON, Edward McDonald. b 42. CITC 67. **d** 69 **p** 70. C Limerick St Mary *L & K* 69-70; CF 70-73; C Penzance St Mary w St Paul *Truro* 73-76; V Mullion 76-81; rtd 81; Perm to Offic *Truro* from 81. *Hazelmere, The Commons, Mullion, Helston TR12 7HZ* Tel (01326) 240865

WILLIAMSON, Henry Lyttle (Ray). b 47. Lon Bible Coll DipTh91. **d** 95 **p** 96. NSM Edin St Marg *Edin* 96-98; P-in-c from 98. *44/9 Restalrig Drive, Edinburgh EH7 6JF* Tel 0131-652 0111

WILLIAMSON, Ivan Alister. b 63. TCD BTh90 Ulster Univ HNC87. CITC 87. **d** 90 **p** 91. C Lisburn St Paul *Conn* 90-95; C Roxbourne St Andr *Lon* 95-99; Lect QUB from 95; Bp's C Ematris w Rockcorry, Aghabog and Aughnamullan *Clogh* 99-01. *48 Willesden Park, Belfast BT9 5GY* Tel (028) 9066 0705

WILLIAMSON, Mrs Jennifer Irene. b 44. Glas Univ MA66 Sunderland Poly Dip Teaching79. NEOC 89. **d** 92 **p** 94. NSM Easby w Brompton on Swale and Bolton on Swale *Ripon* 92-95; P-in-c Gilling and Kirkby Ravensworth from 95. *The Vicarage, Gilling West, Richmond DL10 5JG* Tel (01748) 824466

WILLIAMSON, John. b 33. Bede Coll Dur. NEOC 81. **d** 84 **p** 85. NSM Beamish *Dur* 84-85; C Sedgefield 85-88; P-in-c Trimdon 88-89; V 89-94; rtd 94. *9 Beamish View, Stanley DH9 0XB* Tel (01207) 237380 E-mail john.williamson@durham.anglican.org

WILLIAMSON, John Brian Peter. b 30. Selw Coll Cam PhD55 CEng EurIng FIMechE FIEE FInstP FWeldI. WMMTC. **d** 84 **p** 87. NSM Malvern H Trin and St Jas *Worc* 84-94; Perm to Offic from 94. *Monkfield House, Newland, Malvern WR13 5BB* Tel (01905) 830522

WILLIAMSON, John Mark. b 43. FCP87 Birm Univ BA65 Univ of Wales (Cardiff) MEd75 MA82. St D Coll Lamp LTh67. **d** 67 **p** 68. C Shepton Mallet *B & W* 67-70; Hon C Dinder 70-71; Chapl Clifton Coll Bris 71-75; Lect All SS Bris 75-78; Chapl Bris Cathl *Bris* 77-78; Perm to Offic *Pet* 78-84; Perm to Offic *B & W* 84-97. *11 Aldborough Court, 21 Douglas Avenue, Exmouth EX8 2HA* Tel (01395) 265784

WILLIAMSON, Mrs Kathleen Lyndsay. b 50. **d** 03. NSM Stretton and Appleton Thorn *Ches* from 03. *39 Thirlmere Close, Frodsham, Warrington WA6 7NA* Tel 07899-664068 (mobile)

WILLIAMSON, Michael. *See* WILLIAMSON, Alfred Michael

WILLIAMSON, Canon Michael John. b 39. ALCD63. **d** 64 **p** 65. C Pennington 64-67; C Higher Openshaw 67-69; P-in-c Man St Jerome w Ardwick St Silas 69-72; C-in-c Holts CD 72-77; R Droylsden St Mary from 77; Hon Can Man Cathl from 97. *The Rectory, Dunkirk Street, Droylsden, Manchester M43 7FB* Tel 0161-370 1569

WILLIAMSON, Olwen Joan. b 43. Dioc OLM tr scheme 00. **d** 03. OLM Mortlake w E Sheen *S'wark* from 03. *25 Christchurch Road, London SW14 7AB* Tel (020) 8876 7183 E-mail olwenontour@hotmail.com

WILLIAMSON, Paul Nicholas. b 55. Univ of Otago BTh79 Nottm Univ MPhil93. St Jo Coll Auckland 80. **d** 80 **p** 81. New Zealand 80-86 and from 88; C Selston *S'well* 86-88. *94 Hamilton Road, Hataitai, Wellington 3, New Zealand* Tel (0064) (4) 386 2140 *or* 386 3042 Fax 386 4231 E-mail allsaint@ihug.co.nz

WILLIAMSON, Paul Stewart. b 48. K Coll Lon BD71 AKC71. **d** 72 **p** 73. C Deptford St Paul *S'wark* 72-75; Hon C Kennington St Jo 76-77; C Hoxton H Trin w St Mary *Lon* 78-83; C St Marylebone All SS 83-84; C Willesden St Mary 84-85; Perm to Offic 86-89; C Hanworth St Geo 89-92; P-in-c from 92. *The Rectory, 7 Blakewood Close, Feltham TW13 7NL* Tel (020) 8844 0457

WILLIAMSON, Peter Barry Martin. b 21. Wycliffe Hall Ox 61. **d** 62 **p** 63. C Billericay St Mary *Chelmsf* 62-68; V Bentley Common 68-77; V Lt Thurrock St Jo 77-86; rtd 86; Perm to Offic *St E* from 86. *Corner Cottage, The Street, Kelsale, Saxmundham IP17 2PB* Tel (01728) 602963

WILLIAMSON, Ralph James. b 62. LSE BSc(Econ)84. Ripon Coll Cuddesdon BA89 MA97. **d** 90 **p** 91. C Southgate St Andr *Lon* 90-93; TV Ross w Brampton Abbotts, Bridstow, Peterstow etc *Heref* 93-97; Chapl Ch Ch Ox from 97. *Christ Church, Oxford OX1 1DP* Tel (01865) 276236

WILLIAMSON, Robert Harvey (Robin). b 45. DMA75. Dioc OLM tr scheme 99. **d** 02 **p** 03. OLM Maidstone St Luke *Cant* from 02. *Holly Bank, Bower Mount Road, Maidstone ME16 8AU* Tel (01622) 682959 E-mail robin.helen@tesco.net

WILLIAMSON, Robert John. b 55. K Coll Lon BA77. Coll of Resurr Mirfield 78. **d** 79 **p** 80. C Kirkby *Liv* 79-82; C Warrington St Elphin 82-84; P-in-c Burneside *Carl* 84-90; V Walney Is 90-00; V Darlington St Cuth *Dur* from 00. *The Vicarage, 26 Upsall Drive, Darlington DL3 8RB* Tel (01325) 358911

✠**WILLIAMSON, The Rt Revd Robert Kerr (Roy).** b 32. Kingston Univ DEd98. Oak Hill Th Coll 61. **d** 63 **p** 64 c 84. C Crowborough *Chich* 63-66; V Hyson Green *S'well* 66-72; V Nottingham St Ann w Em 72-76; V Bramcote 76-79; Adn Nottingham 78-84; Bp Bradf 84-91; Bp S'wark 91-98; rtd 98; Hon Asst Bp S'well from 98. *30 Sidney Road, Beeston, Nottingham NG9 1AN* Tel 0115-925 4901 Fax as telephone E-mail roywilliamson@waitrose.com

WILLIAMSON, Roger Brian. b 38. Imp Coll Lon BSc59 MIEE61. St Steph Ho Ox 01. **d** 02 **p** 03. NSM Harting w Elsted and Treyford cum Didling *Chich* from 02. *Rock Cottage, Nursted, Petersfield GU31 5RD* Tel (01730) 262316 Mobile 07767-266031 E-mail williamsonroger@aol.com

WILLIAMSON, Mrs Sheilagh Catherine. b 54. Dur Inst of Educn CertEd76 St Martin's Coll Lanc MA00. Carl and Blackb Dioc Tr Inst 97. **d** 00 **p** 01. C Darlington St Hilda and St Columba *Dur* 00-03; P-in-c from 03. *The Vicarage, 26 Upsall Drive, Darlington DL3 8RB* Tel (01325) 358911

WILLIAMSON, Canon Thomas George. b 33. AKC57. **d** 58 **p** 59. C Winshill *Derby* 58-61; C Hykeham *Linc* 61-64; V Brauncewell w Dunsby 64-78; R S w N Leasingham 64-78; RD Lafford 78-87; V Cranwell 78-80; R Leasingham 78-80; V Billinghay 80-87; V Gosberton, Gosberton Clough and Quadring 97-98; Can and Preb Linc Cathl 94-98; rtd 98; Perm to Offic *Linc* 98-01. *10 Newton Way, Woolsthorpe, Grantham NG33 5NR* Tel (01476) 861749 E-mail thomas.williamson1@btinternet.com

WILLIE, Canon Andrew Robert. b 43. Bris Univ BA65 Fitzw Coll Cam BA73 MA77. Ridley Hall Cam 71. **d** 74 **p** 75. Chapl St Woolos Cathl *Mon* 74-79; Chapl St Woolos Hosp Newport 75-79; V Newbridge *Mon* 79-85; V Mathern and Mounton w St Pierre 85-98; Post-Ord Tr Officer 85-98; Warden of Readers from 91; V Newport St Mark from 98; Can St Woolos Cathl from 02. *The Vicarage, 7 Gold Tops, Newport NP20 4PH* Tel (01633) 263321

WILLIMENT, Paul. b 47. Leeds Univ BSc68. St Steph Ho Ox 70. **d** 73 **p** 74. C Guiseley *Bradf* 73-76; C Northampton St Mary *Pet* 76-79; Malaysia from 80. *Box 347, Kuching, Sarawak, Malaysia*

WILLINK, Simon Wakefield. b 29. Magd Coll Cam BA52 MA55. Cuddesdon Coll 52. **d** 54 **p** 55. C Thornbury *Glouc* 54-57; C Tetbury w Beverston 57-60; R Siddington w Preston 60-64; New Zealand 65-71; C Kelburn St Mich 65; V Takapau 65-70; Lic to Offic Waiapu 70-80; Perm to Offic *Ex* 90-92; Hon C Sidmouth, Woolbrook, Salcombe Regis, Sidbury etc from 92; rtd 95. *Coombe Cottage, Cotford, Sidbury, Sidmouth EX10 0SH* Tel (01395) 597545

WILLIS, Andrew Lyn. b 48. Univ of Wales (Lamp) BA73. **d** 74 **p** 75. C Swansea St Mary w H Trin and St Mark *S & B* 74-81; V Glasbury and Llowes 81-83; Chapl RAF 83-02; Perm to Offic *Ban* 83-96. *Address temp unknown*

WILLIS, Anthony David. b 40. Sarum & Wells Th Coll 87. **d** 89 **p** 90. C Ivybridge w Harford *Ex* 89-92; C Catherington and Clanfield *Portsm* 92-94; R Ellesborough, The Kimbles and Stoke Mandeville *Ox* from 94. *28A Risborough Road, Stoke Mandeville, Aylesbury HP22 5UT* Tel (01296) 612855

WILLIS, Canon Anthony John. b 38. MBE00. Univ of Wales (Lamp) BA62. Qu Coll Birm DipTh74. **d** 64 **p** 65. C Kidderminster St Jo *Worc* 64-68; C Dunstable *St Alb* 68-72; V Rubery *Birm* 72-80; R Salwarpe and Hindlip w Martin Hussingtree *Worc* 80-92; Chapl to Agric and Rural Life from 85; Hon Can Worc Cathl from 99. *Glebe House, Grafton Flyford, Worcester WR7 4PG* Tel (01905) 381460 Fax 381110 E-mail carlagchap@aol.com *or* jwillis@cofe-worcester.org.uk

WILLIS, Christopher Charles Billopp. b 32. MCIPD. Bps' Coll Cheshunt 58. **d** 59 **p** 60. C Golders Green St Alb *Lon* 59-61; C N Harrow St Alb 61-64; V Shaw and Whitley *Sarum* 64-69; Ind Chapl *Ex* 69-77; Lic to Offic 77-92; Chapl W Buckland Sch Barnstaple 77-92; rtd 97; Perm to Offic *Ex* from 97. *Rose Cottage, Chittlehampton, Umberleigh EX37 9QL* Tel (01769) 540289

WILLIS, David George. b 45. Oak Hill Th Coll BA79. **d** 79 **p** 80. C Wallington H Trin *S'wark* 79-84; V Ramsgate St Mark *Cant* 84-89; Hon C Woodnesborough w Worth and Staple 94-02; Hon C Eastry and Northbourne w Tilmanstone etc from 02. *75 Poulders Gardens, Sandwich CT13 0AJ* Tel (01304) 611959

WILLIS, Geoffrey Stephen Murrell. b 58. Sussex Univ BA80. Wycliffe Hall Ox 83. **d** 86 **p** 87. C Ashtead *Guildf* 86-89; Chapl Lee Abbey 89-94; Lic to Offic *Ex* 89-94; R Dunsfold *Guildf* 94-01; R Dunsfold and Hascombe from 01. *The Rectory, Church Green, Dunsfold, Godalming GU8 4LT* Tel (01483) 200207 E-mail geoffrey@rod.demon.co.uk

WILLIS, Hugh. b 39. Bris Univ BDS63 MGDSRCSEng82 FRSH87. LNSM course 97. **d** 98 **p** 99. OLM Charminster and Stinsford *Sarum* from 98. *Glebe Farmhouse, West Hill, Charminster, Dorchester DT2 9RD* Tel (01305) 262940 Fax as telephone E-mail tournai@aol.com

WILLIS, Joyce Muriel. b 42. CQSW73 Open Univ BA86. EAMTC 86. **d** 89 **p** 94. NSM Hadleigh *St E* 89-02; NSM Hadleigh, Layham and Shelley from 02. *26 Ramsey Road, Hadleigh, Ipswich IP7 6AN* Tel (01473) 823165

WILLIS, Mrs Marilyn Lesley. b 47. EAMTC 99. **d** 02 **p** 03. NSM Irthlingborough *Pet* from 02. *4 Lime Street, Rushden NN10 6DY* Tel (01933) 355965 Mobile 07947-020044 E-mail willis_marilyn@hotmail.com

WILLIS, Mrs Patricia. b 50. RGN85 Brunel Univ BSc95 Ox Brookes Univ PGDE98. St Alb and Ox Min Course 96. **d** 99 **p** 00. C Warmley, Syston and Bitton *Bris* 99-03; V Hanham from 03. *The Vicarage, 30 Church Road, Bristol BS15 3AE* Tel and fax 0117-967 3580 Mobile 07932-654833 E-mail revpatwillis@aol.com

WILLIS, Peter Ambrose Duncan. b 34. Kelham Th Coll 55 Lich Th Coll 58. **d** 59 **p** 60. C Sevenoaks St Jo *Roch* 59-63; Trinidad and Tobago 63-68; P-in-c Diptford *Ex* 68-69; R 69-85; P-in-c N Huish 68-69; R 69-85; R Diptford, N Huish, Harberton and Harbertonford 85-96; rtd 99. *Sun Cottage, Church Street, Modbury, Ivybridge PL21 0QR* Tel (01548) 830541

WILLIS, The Very Revd Robert Andrew. b 47. Warw Univ BA68 Worc Coll Ox DipTh71. Cuddesdon Coll 70. **d** 72 **p** 73. C Shrewsbury St Chad *Lich* 72-75; V Choral Sarum Cathl *Sarum* 75-78; TR Tisbury 78-87; RD Chalke 82-87; V Sherborne w Castleton and Lillington 87-92; Can and Preb Sarum Cathl 88-92; RD Sherborne 91-92; Chapl Cranborne Chase Sch 78-92; Dean Heref 92-01; P-in-c Heref St Jo 92-01; Dean Cant from 01. *The Deanery, The Precincts, Canterbury CT1 2EP* Tel (01227) 865264 *or* 762862 E-mail dean@canterbury-cathedral.org

WILLIS, Mrs Rosemary Ann. b 39. LNSM course 89. **d** 93 **p** 96. OLM Fressingfield, Mendham etc *St E* from 93. *Priory House, Fressingfield, Eye IP21 5PH* Tel (01379) 586254

WILLIS, Thomas Charles. b 30. Bps' Coll Cheshunt 55. **d** 58 **p** 59. C Anlaby Common St Mark *York* 58-61; C Middlesbrough St Martin 61-63; V Kingston upon Hull St Paul w Sculcoates Ch Ch 63-69; P-in-c Sculcoates St Silas 67-69; V Sculcoates St Paul w Ch Ch and St Silas 69-80; V Bridlington H Trin and Sewerby w Marton 80-96; rtd 96; Perm to Offic *York* from 96. *23 Hillcrest Drive, Beverley HU17 7JL* Tel (01482) 888511

WILLMINGTON, John Martin Vanderlure. b 45. St D Coll Lamp BA69. St Steph Ho Ox 69. **d** 71 **p** 72. C Upper Teddington SS Pet and Paul *Lon* 71-75; C Kensington St Mary Abbots w St Geo 75-83; R Perivale 83-91; V Acton Green from 91. *206 St Alban's Avenue, London W4 5JU* Tel (020) 8994 5735 E-mail willmington@actongreen.demon.co.uk

WILLMONT, Anthony Vernon. b 35. Lich Th Coll 62. **d** 63 **p** 64. C Yardley St Edburgha *Birm* 63-65; C Smethwick H Trin w St Alb 65-68; V Ropley w W Tisted *Win* 68-77; V Ipswich St Aug *St E* 77-84; R King's Worthy *Win* 84-90; R Headbourne Worthy 84-90; R Lapworth *Birm* 90-99; R Baddesley Clinton 90-99; P-in-c Thornton in Lonsdale w Burton in Lonsdale *Bradf* 99-02; rtd 02; Perm to Offic *Bradf* from 02. *9 Lowcroft, Butts Lane, Bentham, Lancaster LA2 2FD* Tel (01524) 261655

WILLMOTT, Robert Owen Noel. b 41. Lich Th Coll 65. **d** 68 **p** 69. C Perry Hill St Geo *S'wark* 68-71; C Denham *Ox* 71-76; P-in-c Tingewick w Water Stratford 76-77; P-in-c Radclive 76-77; R Tingewick w Water Stratford, Radclive etc 77-89; R Wingrave w Rowsham, Aston Abbotts and Cublington from 89. *The Rectory, Leighton Road, Wingrave, Aylesbury HP22 4PA* Tel (01296) 681623 E-mail wingravebob@yahoo.com

✠**WILLMOTT, The Rt Revd Trevor.** b 50. St Pet Coll Ox BA71 MA74. Westcott Ho Cam DipTh73. **d** 74 **p** 75 **c** 02. C Norton *St Alb* 74-77; Asst Chapl Oslo w Bergen, Trondheim and Stavanger *Eur* 78-79; Chapl Naples w Sorrento, Capri and Bari 79-83; R Ecton *Pet* 83-89; Warden Ecton Ho 83-89; Dioc Dir of Ords and Dir Post-Ord Tr *Pet* 86-97; Can Res, Prec and Sacr Pet Cathl 89-97; Adn Dur and Can Res Dur Cathl *Dur* 97-02; Suff Bp Basingstoke *Win* from 02. *Bishopswood End, Kingswood Rise, Four Marks, Alton GU34 5BD* Tel (01420) 562925 Fax 561251 E-mail vicky.wilson@dial.pipex.com

WILLOUGHBY, Francis Edward John. b 38. St Jo Coll Nottm. **d** 83 **p** 84. C Tonbridge SS Pet and Paul *Roch* 83-87; V Sutton at Hone 87-02; P-in-c Horton Kirby 00-02; rtd 03. *23 Mountjoy, Battle TN33 0EQ* Tel (01424) 775234

WILLOUGHBY, The Ven George Charles. b 20. TCD BA43 MA46. CITC Div Test 44. **d** 44 **p** 45. C Conwall *D & R* 44-47; C Derry Cathl 47-51; I Clooney 59-85; Dioc Dir of Ords 62-72; Adn Derry 79-85; rtd 85. *21 Tyler Avenue, Limavady BT49 0DT* Tel (028) 7176 5382

✠**WILLOUGHBY, The Rt Revd Noel Vincent.** b 26. TCD BA48 MA52. TCD Div Sch Div Test48. **d** 50 **p** 51 **c** 80. C Drumglass *Arm* 50-53; C Dublin St Cath *D & G* 53-55; C Bray Ch Ch 55-59; I Delgany 59-69; I Glenageary 69-80; Treas St Patr Cathl Dublin 77-80; Adn Dublin *D & G* 78-80; Bp *C & O* 80-97; rtd 97. *Dromingle, Belmont, Newtown Road, Wexford, Irish Republic* Tel (00353) (53) 20008

WILLOUGHBY, Canon Paul Moore. b 60. DipTh BA. **d** 86 **p** 87. C Dublin St Patr Cathl Gp *D & G* 86-90; C Glenageary 90-92; I Dublin Booterstown 92-94; I Kilmocomogue Union *C, C & R* from 94; Can Cork and Ross Cathls from 00. *The Rectory, Durrus, Bantry, Co Cork, Irish Republic* Tel (00353) (27) 61011 Fax 61608 E-mail bantry@cork.anglican.org

WILLOUGHBY, Mrs Serena Louise. b 72. Oak Hill Th Coll BA93. **d** 96 **p** 97. C St Paul's Cray St Barn *Roch* 96-99; C Hildenborough 99-00; C Tonbridge St Steph 03. *20 Judd Road, Tonbridge TN9 2NH* Tel (01732) 505296 Mobile 07788-428010 E-mail johnser@20judd.fsnet.co.uk

WILLOWS, David Keith. b 70. St Jo Coll Dur BA90 K Coll Lon MA94 PhD99. Wycliffe Hall Ox. **d** 95 **p** 96. C Ox St Mary V w St Cross and St Pet *Ox* 95-97; Asst Chapl Oxon Mental Healthcare NHS Trust 97-00; P-in-c St Martin Ludgate *Lon* 00-01; Reseach Dir Paternoster Cen from 00. *104C Camden Street, London NW1 0HY* Tel (020) 7248 6233 E-mail david.willows@paternostercentre.com

WILLOWS, Michael John. b 35. Sarum & Wells Th Coll 70. **d** 72 **p** 73. C Pershore w Wick *Worc* 72-75; P-in-c Astley 75-81; Ind Chapl 75-88; P-in-c Hallow 81-85; V 85-88; V Wollaston from 88. *The Vicarage, 46 Vicarage Road, Wollaston, Stourbridge DY8 4NP* Tel (01384) 395674

WILLOX, Peter. b 63. Sunderland Poly BSc85. St Jo Coll Dur 86. **d** 89 **p** 90. C Bradley *Wakef* 89-92; C Utley *Bradf* 92-95; TV Bingley All SS 95-02; C Ambleside w Brathay *Carl* from 02. *Hazeldene, Nook Lane, Ambleside LA22 9BJ* Tel (01539) 430303

WILLS, David. b 58. Oak Hill Th Coll DipHE94. **d** 94 **p** 95. C Chadwell *Chelmsf* 94-99; P-in-c Darlaston St Lawr *Lich* from 99; C Darlaston All SS from 99. *The Rectory, 1 Victoria Road, Darlaston, Wednesbury WS10 8AA* Tel 0121-526 2240

WILLS, David Ernest. b 37. St Jo Coll Cam BA58 MA62. Ridley Hall Cam 58. **d** 60 **p** 61. C Kenilworth St Jo *Cov* 60-63; C Northwood Em *Lon* 63-66; V Huyton St Geo *Liv* 66-73; V Littleover *Derby* 73-84; V Mossley Hill St Matt and St Jas *Liv* 84-97; TR Walbrook Epiphany *Derby* 97-02; RD Derby S 99-02; rtd 02; Perm to Offic *Derby* from 02. *90 Chesterfield Road, Holmewood, Chesterfield S42 5TE* Tel (01246) 856625

WILLS, Preb David Stuart Ralph. b 36. Chich Th Coll 64. **d** 66 **p** 67. C Bodmin *Truro* 66-70; V Bude Haven 70-78; TV Banbury *Ox* 78-83; Accredited Cllr from 81; V Launceston St Steph w St Thos *Truro* 83-88; P-in-c Kenwyn St Geo 88-93; V Truro St Geo and St Jo 93-96; Preb St Endellion 95-01; rtd 96. *Garden Cottage, Penwinnick Road, St Agnes TR5 0LA* Tel (01872) 553020 Mobile 07773-402109 Fax (01872) 553121 E-mail david.wills@cht.swest.nhs.uk

WILLS, Herbert Ashton Peter. b 24. St Edm Hall Ox BA46 MA50. Qu Coll Birm 60. **d** 60 **p** 61. C Stocksbridge *Sheff* 60-63; Chapl Repton Sch Derby 64-69; Chapl St Matthias's Coll Bris 69-78; Asst Chapl Sheff Univ *Sheff* 78-80; Chapl 80-84; R Flax Bourton *B & W* 84-92; V Barrow Gurney 84-92; rtd 92; Perm to Offic *Glouc* 92-97. *clo W R Wills, 4 Whirlowdale Close, Sheffield S11 9NQ*

WILLS, Ian Leslie. b 49. Wycliffe Hall Ox 77. **d** 80 **p** 81. C Henbury *Bris* 80; C Gtr Corsham 80-83; C Whitchurch 83-86; Chapl HM Rem Cen Pucklechurch 86-96; P-in-c Pucklechurch and Abson w Dyrham *Bris* 86-87; V Pucklechurch and Abson 87-99; V Soundwell Vicarage, 46 Sweets Road, Bristol BS15 1XQ* Tel 0117-967 1511 E-mail ianwills49@aol.com

WILLS, Morley. b 35. Ex & Truro NSM Scheme. **d** 80 **p** 81. NSM St Enoder *Truro* 80-82; NSM Kenwyn St Geo 82-85; NSM Truro St Paul and St Clem 85-88; P-in-c Crantock from 89. *81 Vyvyan Drive, Quintrell Downs, Newquay TR8 4NF* Tel (01637) 872648

WILLS, Nicholas Richard. b 71. Birm Univ BA93. Cranmer Hall Dur DMS99. **d** 99 **p** 00. C Boldmere *Birm* from 99. *19 Southam Drive, Sutton Coldfield B73 5PD* Tel 0121-354 8432 E-mail nickandbecky@nbwills.freeserve.co.uk

WILLSON, Andrew William. b 64. Oriel Coll Ox BA85 Nottm Univ BTh90 MA98. Linc Th Coll 87. **d** 90 **p** 91. C Northampton St Mary *Pet* 90-93; C Cov E *Cov* 93-96; Perm to Offic 96-01; Chapl Solihull Sixth Form Coll 98-01; Chapl Imp Coll *Lon* from 01; Chapl R Coll of Art from 01. *1 Porchester Gardens, London W2 3LA* Tel (020) 7229 6359 E-mail mary-andrew@clarkewillson.fsnet.co.uk

WILLSON, Stephen Geoffrey. b 63. Nottm Univ BTh90. St Jo Coll Nottm. **d** 90 **p** 91. C Newport St Andr *Mon* 90-92; C Risca 92-94; TV Cyncoed 94-96; Dioc Youth Chapl 94-99; Lay Past Asst 96-98; TV Cyncoed 98-01; TR from 01. *The Rectory, 256 Cyncoed Road, Cardiff CF23 6RU* Tel (029) 2075 2138

WILLSON, Stuart Leslie. b 61. Nottm Univ BA83. Sarum & Wells Th Coll 83. **d** 84 **p** 85. C Llandrindod w Cefnllys *S & B* 84-85; Chapl Angl Students Univ of Wales (Swansea) 85-88; C Llwynderw 85-88; Ind Chapl Gatwick Airport *Chich* 88-95; Nene Coll of HE Northn 95-98; Dir Fundraising and Communication CUF from 98. *1D Northstead Cottage, Northstead Road, Leamington Spa NN22 3JN* Tel (020) 8674 3146 E-mail stuart@willso.freeserve.co.uk

WILMAN, Arthur Garth. b 37. EAMTC 84. **d** 87 **p** 88. NSM Swavesey *Ely* 87-90; NSM Fen Drayton w Conington 87-90; NSM Hardwick 90-98; NSM Toft w Caldecote and Childerley 90-98; Perm to Offic from 98. *37 Prentice Close, Longstanton, Cambridge CB4 5DY* Tel (01954) 781400

WILMAN, Mrs Dorothy Ann Jane. b 38. Reading Univ BSc60 Lon Univ DipTh67. Westcott Ho Cam 89. **d** 90 **p** 94. NSM Toft w Caldecote and Childerley *Ely* 90-93; Dean's Asst Trin Hall Cam 92-98; Asst Chapl Cam St Edw *Ely* 93-98; P-in-c Hemingford Abbots 98-02; P-in-c Houghton w Wyton 98-02; rtd 02; Perm to Offic *Ely* from 02. *37 Prentice Close, Longstanton, Cambridge CB4 5DY* Tel (01954) 781400

WILMAN, Leslie Alan. b 37. Selw Coll Cam BA61 MA65. Ridley Hall Cam 61. **d** 63 **p** 64. C Skipton H Trin *Bradf* 63-67; C Guiseley 67-69; V Morton St Luke 69-79; R Swanton Morley w Worthing *Nor* 79-82; P-in-c E Bilney w Beetley 79-82; P-in-c Hoe 80-82; R Swanton Morley w Worthing, E Bilney, Beetley etc 82-89; R Swanton Morley w Beetley w E Bilney and Hoe 89-00; RD Brisley and Elmham 87-93; rtd 00; Perm to Offic *Nor* from 00. *Last House, Chapel Lane, Foulsham, Dereham NR20 5RA* Tel (01362) 684109

WILMER, John Watts. b 26. Lich Th Coll 56. **d** 58 **p** 59. C Wolverhampton Ch Ch *Lich* 58-60; C Fenton 60-63; V Dresden 63-76; TV Sutton St Jas and Wawne *York* 76-80; R Bishop Wilton w Full Sutton 80; P-in-c Kirby Underdale w Bugthorpe 80; R Bishop Wilton w Full Sutton, Kirby Underdale etc 80-87; V York St Hilda 87-91; rtd 92; Perm to Offic *York* from 92. *27 Hunters Way, Dringhouses, York YO24 1JL* Tel (01904) 709591

WILMOT, David Mark Baty. b 60. Liv Univ BA82. Sarum & Wells Th Coll 84. **d** 87 **p** 88. C Penrith w Newton Reigny and Plumpton Wall *Carl* 87-91; C St Alb St Pet *St Alb* 91-93; Chapl City Coll St Alb 92-93; V Milton *Lich* 93-01; RD Leek 96-01; V Windermere St Mary and Troutbeck *Carl* from 01. *St Mary's Vicarage, Ambleside Road, Windermere LA23 1BA* Tel (01539) 443032 E-mail dwilmot@fish.co.uk

WILMOT, Jonathan Anthony de Burgh. b 48. St Jo Coll Nottm LTh73 BTh74. **d** 74 **p** 75. C Cambridge St Martin *Ely* 74-77; Chapl Chantilly *Eur* 77-82; Asst Chapl Paris St Mich 80-82; Chapl Versailles 82-87; V Blackheath St Jo *S'wark* 88-95; V Reading Greyfriars *Ox* from 95. *Greyfriars Vicarage, 64 Friar Street, Reading RG1 1EH* Tel 0118-951 6707
E-mail jonathan.wilmot@greyfriars.org.uk

WILMOT, Stuart Leslie. b 42. Oak Hill Th Coll 64. **d** 68 **p** 69. C Spitalfields Ch Ch w All SS *Lon* 68-71; C Islington St Mary 71-74; P-in-c Brixton St Paul *S'wark* 75-81; R Mursley w Swanbourne and Lt Horwood *Ox* 81-91; P-in-c Bermondsey St Jas w Ch Ch *S'wark* 91-96; V 96-99; V Bermondsey St Jas w Ch Ch and St Crispin 99-02; P-in-c Bermondsey St Anne 91-93; P-in-c Bermondsey St Anne and St Aug 93-96; V 96-02; RD Bermondsey 96-00; rtd 02. *Amberlea, College, East Chinnock, Yeovil BA22 9DY*

✠**WILSON, The Rt Revd Alan Thomas Lawrence.** b 55. St Jo Coll Cam BA77 MA81 Ball Coll Ox DPhil89. Wycliffe Hall Ox 77. **d** 79 **p** 80 **c** 03. Hon C Eynsham *Ox* 79-81; C 81-82; C Caversham St Pet and Mapledurham etc 82-89; V Caversham St Jo 89-92; R Sandhurst 92-03; RD Sonning 98-03; Hon Can Ch Ch 02-03; Bp Buckingham *Ox* from 03. *Sheridan, Grimms Hill, Great Missenden HP16 9BD* Tel (01494) 8862173 Fax 852333
E-mail bishopbucks@oxford.anglican.org

WILSON, Canon Alfred Michael Sykes. b 32. Jes Coll Cam BA56 MA61. Ridley Hall Cam 56. **d** 58 **p** 59. C Fulwood *Sheff* 58-63; V Gt Horton *Bradf* 63-69; R Rushden w Newton Bromswold *Pet* 69-76; RD Higham 75-83; P-in-c Rushden St Pet 75-77; R Rushden w Newton Bromswold 77-83; Can Pet Cathl 77-97; R Preston and Ridlington w Wing and Pilton 83-97; RD Rutland 85-95; rtd 97; Perm to Offic *Nor* from 98. *Swallow Cottage, 2 Little Lane, Blakeney, Holt NR25 7NH* Tel (01263) 740975

WILSON, Andrew. *See* WILSON, James Andrew Christopher

WILSON, Andrew Alan. b 47. Nottm Univ BA68. St Steph Ho Ox 68. **d** 71 **p** 72. C Streatham St Paul *S'wark* 71-75; TV Catford (Southend) and Downham 75-80; V Malden St Jas 80-89; Chapl Croydon Community Mental Health Unit 89-94; Chapl Bethlem and Maudsley NHS Trust Lon 94-99; Chapl S Lon and Maudsley NHS Trust from 99; Mental Health Chapl (Croydon) from 00. *The Maudsley Hospital, London SE5 8AZ* Tel (020) 7919 2815 Fax as telephone

WILSON, Andrew Kenneth. b 62. Cert Journalism. Oak Hill Th Coll BA91. **d** 91 **p** 92. C Springfield H Trin *Chelmsf* 91-96; V Sidcup Ch Ch *Roch* from 96. *The Vicarage, 16 Christchurch Road, Sidcup DA15 7HE* Tel (020) 8308 0835 E-mail akw@fish.co.uk

WILSON, Andrew Marcus William. b 69. Ex Coll Ox BA91 CCC Cam BA93 K Coll Lon MA99. Westcott Ho Cam CTM94. **d** 94 **p** 95. C Forest Gate Em w Upton Cross *Chelmsf* 94-99; TV Poplar *Lon* from 99. *St Nicholas' Vicarage, Dee Street, London E14 0PT* Tel (020) 7515 8405 Fax as telephone
E-mail andrewwilson@bigfoot.com

WILSON, Andrew Martin. b 60. Bris Univ BSc82. Trin Coll Bris DipHE99. **d** 99 **p** 00. C Broadwater St Mary *Chich* from 99. *26 Rectory Gardens, Worthing BN14 7TE* Tel (01903) 237685 E-mail andy@wilsons933.netscapeonline.co.uk

WILSON, Antony Charles. b 69. Em Coll Cam MA92 PGCE92. Wycliffe Hall Ox 01. **d** 03. C Bath Walcot *B & W* from 03. *5 The Linleys, Bath BA1 2XE* Tel (01225) 316572
E-mail curate@walcotchurch.org.uk

WILSON, Arthur Guy Ross. b 28. St Aid Birkenhead 58. **d** 59 **p** 60. C Bexley St Mary *Roch* 59-63; C Gravesend St Geo 63-66; V Belvedere All SS 66-70; V Brighton St Matthias *Chich* 70-77; V Bradf St Clem *Bradf* 77-84; Lic to Offic 84-87; C Baildon 87-88; V Skirwith, Ousby and Melmerby w Kirkland *Carl* 88-93; C Menston w Woodhead *Bradf* 93-96; Chapl High Royds Hosp Menston 93-96; rtd 96; Perm to Offic *Derby* 96-99. *43 Borough Road, Tamworth B79 8AW* Tel (01827) 310224

WILSON, Ashley Peter. b 58. Edin Univ BSc81 BVM&S83 St Jo Coll Dur BA99. Cranmer Hall Dur. **d** 00 **p** 01. C Nunthorpe *York* from 00. *15 Ripon Road, Nunthorpe, Middlesbrough TS7 0HX* Tel (01642) 310834 E-mail ashley@dunelm.org.uk

WILSON, Mrs Barbara Joyce. b 51. Carl and Blackb Dioc Tr Inst 98. **d** 01 **p** 02. OLM Leyland St Jo *Blackb* from 01. *43 Hall Lane, Leyland PR25 3YD* Tel (01772) 435340
E-mail barbara.j.wilson@btinternet.com

WILSON, Barry Frank. b 58. Man Metrop Univ BA89 MPhil94 MTh99 Keele Univ PGCE90. N Ord Course 94. **d** 97 **p** 98. C Stone St Mich w Aston St Sav *Lich* 97-99; Chapl St Mary and St Anne's Sch Abbots Bromley from 00. *St Mary and St Anne's School, High Street, Abbots Bromley, Rugeley WS15 3BW* Tel (01283) 840726

WILSON, Barry Richard. b 46. WMMTC 88. **d** 91 **p** 92. NSM Leek and Meerbrook *Lich* 91-93; C Styvechale *Cov* 93-98; V Chesterton *Lich* from 98. *The Vicarage, Church Street, Chesterton, Newcastle ST5 7HJ* Tel (01782) 562479
E-mail barry-hazel@breathemail.net

WILSON, Bernard Martin. b 40. St Jo Coll Cam BA63 MA68 Lon Univ CertEd67. Ripon Hall Ox 72. **d** 73 **p** 74. C Bilton *Cov* 73-77; Dioc Development Officer *Birm* 78-83; Soc Resp Officer *Derby* 83-90; V Darley Abbey 83-90; Chapl Derbyshire R Infirmary 88-90; Educn Unit Dir Traidcraft Exchange 91; V Mickleover St Jo *Derby* 92-98; Adv to Bd of Miss and Soc Resp *Leic* from 98. *74 Station Road, Wigston, Leicester LE18 2DJ* Tel 0116-288 1051 or 273 3893 Fax 273 7849
E-mail martin@idbmsr.leicester.anglican.org

WILSON, Brian Arthur. b 37. Portsm Dioc Tr Course 84 Chich Th Coll. **d** 85. NSM S w N Hayling *Portsm* 85-88; Chapl Asst RN 88-97; rtd 97; NSM Bedhampton *Portsm* 98-01. *6 Sunwood Road, Havant PO9 4DJ* Tel (023) 9247 2182

WILSON, Canon Cecil Henry. b 40. CITC 67. **d** 69 **p** 70. C Lurgan St Jo *D & D* 69-72; Min Can Dromore Cathl 72-75; Youth Sec CMS Ireland 75-80; Nat Sec from 87; Gen Sec from 87; Can Belf Cathl from 00. *20 Knockbreda Road, Belfast BT6 0JA* Tel (028) 9064 4011 *or* 9032 4581 Fax 9032 1756

WILSON, Charles Roy. b 30. Brasted Place Coll 56. St Aid Birkenhead 57. **d** 59 **p** 60. C Kirkdale St Paul N Shore *Liv* 59-62; C St Helens St Mark 62-66; V Wolverhampton St Matt *Lich* 66-74; V Ripley *Derby* 74-88; V Willington 88-95; V Findern 88-95; rtd 95; Perm to Offic *Derby* from 95. *Jubilate, 12 Oak Tree Close, Swanwick, Alfreton DE55 1FG* Tel (01773) 541822

WILSON (née BRAVERY), Mrs Christine Louise. b 58. STETS 94. **d** 97 **p** 98. NSM Henfield w Shermanbury and Woodmancote *Chich* 97-99; C 99-02; TV Hove from 02. *The Vicarage, 119 Holland Road, Hove BN3 1JS* Tel (01273) 721176 *or* 728895 E-mail revchristine@talk21.com

WILSON, Christopher Harry. b 59. Man Univ MusB80 Ox Univ MTh01. Wycliffe Hall Ox 88. **d** 91 **p** 92. C S Lafford *Linc* 91-95; P-in-c Billingborough 95-96; P-in-c Sempringham w Pointon and Birthorpe 95-96; P-in-c Horbling 95-96; P-in-c Aslackby and Dowsby 95-96; V Billingborough Gp 96-03; P-in-c Leamington Priors All SS *Cov* from 03; Jt P-in-c Leamington Spa H Trin and Old Milverton from 03. *Clive House, Kenilworth Road, Leamington Spa CV32 5TL* Tel (01926) 424016
E-mail wilson@fish.co.uk

WILSON, Mrs Claire Frances. b 43. Hull Univ BA65. SW Minl Tr Course 85. **d** 87 **p** 94. Par Dn Belsize Park *Lon* 87-94; C 94-97; C Chingford SS Pet and Paul *Chelmsf* from 97. *Old Church House, Priory Avenue, London E4 8AA* Tel (020) 8529 0110

WILSON, Colin Edward. b 63. Ripon Coll Cuddesdon BTh94. **d** 94 **p** 95. C High Wycombe *Ox* 94-98; P-in-c Broadwell, Evenlode, Oddington and Adlestrop *Glouc* 98-00; P-in-c Westcote w Icomb and Bledington 98-00; R Broadwell, Evenlode, Oddington, Adlestrop etc from 00. *The Rectory, Broadwell, Moreton-in-Marsh GL56 0TU* Tel (01451) 831866

WILSON, David. b 67. Univ of Northumbria at Newc BSc94 St Jo Coll Dur BA00. Cranmer Hall Dur 97. **d** 00 **p** 01. C Nantwich *Ches* from 00. *22 Beatty Road, Nantwich CW5 5JP* Tel (01270) 623620 Mobile 07760-378085
E-mail dywilson@tinyworld.co.uk

WILSON, David Brian. b 47. QUB BA68. CITC 71. **d** 71 **p** 72. C Ballyholme *D & D* 71-74; C Guildf Ch Ch *Guildf* 74-78; I Arvagh w Carrigallen, Gowna and Columbkille *K, E & A* 78-81; R Clogherny w Seskinore and Drumnakilly *Arm* 81-95; I Caledon w Brantry from 95. *The Rectory, 36 Church Hill Road, Caledon BT68 4UY* Tel (028) 3756 8205

WILSON, Preb David Gordon. b 40. Man Univ BSc61 Clare Coll Cam BA63 MA68. Ridley Hall Cam 63. **d** 65 **p** 66. C Clapham Common St Barn *S'wark* 65-69; C Onslow Square St Paul *Lon* 69-73; V Leic H Apostles *Leic* 73-84; V Spring Grove St Mary *Lon* from 84; Chapl Brunel Univ 90-02; AD Hounslow 97-02; P-in-c Isleworth St Fran from 00; Preb St Paul's Cathl from 02. *St Mary's Vicarage, Osterley Road, Isleworth TW7 4PW* Tel (020) 8560 3555 Fax 8847 4001
E-mail david@gwilson20.freeserve.co.uk

WILSON, David Mark. b 53. Lon Univ BSc75. Wycliffe Hall Ox BA77 MA82. **d** 78 **p** 79. C Romford Gd Shep Collier Row *Chelmsf* 78-81; C Cheadle Hulme St Andr *Ches* 81-85; V Huntington 85-95; Chapl Bp's Blue Coat C of E High Sch 85-95; V Birkenhead Ch Ch *Ches* from 95. *Christ Church Vicarage, 7 Palm Grove, Prenton CH43 1TE* Tel and fax 0151-652 5647 *or* tel 652 3990 E-mail the.vicar@btinternet.com

WILSON, David Merritt. b 26. S'wark Ord Course 61. **d** 64 **p** 65. C Brixton St Paul *S'wark* 64-69; Lic to Offic from 69; rtd 97. *18 Calais Street, London SE5 9LP* Tel (020) 7274 5707

WILSON, Derrick. b 33. Oak Hill Th Coll 69. **d** 71 **p** 72. C Lurgan Ch the Redeemer *D & D* 71-74; C Willowfield 74-75; I 83-88; I Knocknamuckley 75-83; I Tullylish 88-98; rtd 98. *Hollycroft, 6 Thornhill Crescent, Tandragee, Craigavon BT62 2NZ* Tel (028) 3884 9900

WILSON, Mrs Dorothy Jean. b 35. St Mary's Coll Dur BA57 DipEd58 Newc Poly LLB78. NEOC 86. **d** 88 **p** 96. NSM Dur St Giles *Dur* from 88; Perm to Offic *Newc* 88-96; Chapl Univ of Northumbria at Newc 94-96; Chapl N Dur Healthcare NHS Trust from 97. *The Chaplaincy, Dryburn Hospital, North Road, Durham DH1 5TW, or 86 Gilesgate, Durham DH1 1HY* Tel 0191-333 2333 *or* 386 5016

WILSON, Duncan Thomas. b 31. **d** 00. NSM Chickerell w Fleet *Sarum* 00-01; rtd 01. *Sleepy Hollow, 19 Mohune Way, Chickerell, Weymouth DT3 4NG* Tel (01305) 781420

WILSON, Edith Yvonne. b 43. St Martin's Coll Lanc MA98. Carl and Blackb Dioc Tr Inst 97. **d** 97 **p** 98. NSM Skerton St Chad *Blackb* from 97. *7 Edenvale Road, Lancaster LA1 2NN* Tel (01524) 60534 E-mail yvonne@ywilson7.freeserve.co.uk

WILSON, Edward Thomas. b 48. Southn Univ BTh82. Chich Th Coll 78. **d** 82 **p** 83. C Cardiff St Jo *Llan* 82-86; V Aberavon H Trin 86-92; R St Nicholas w Bonvilston and St George-super-Ely from 92. *The Rectory, 8 Ger-y-Llan, St Nicholas, Cardiff CF5 6SY* Tel (01446) 760728

WILSON, Erik. b 51. Lanc Univ BA72. Trin Coll Bris 83. **d** 85 **p** 86. C Linthorpe *York* 85-89; V Hull St Martin w Transfiguration 89-98; AD W Hull 96-98; V Linthorpe from 98. *St Barnabas' Vicarage, 5 Park Road South, Middlesbrough TS5 6LD* Tel (01642) 817306 E-mail erik.wilson@ntlworld.com

WILSON, Frances Mary. b 61. Leeds Univ BA98. Westcott Ho Cam. **d** 00 **p** 01. C Rothwell *Ripon* from 00. *37 Haigh Road, Rothwell, Leeds LS26 0LW* Tel 0113-393 4595

WILSON, Francis. b 34. ACP67. Cuddesdon Coll 71. **d** 73 **p** 74. C Newc St Fran *Newc* 73-79; V Wallsend St Jo 79-99; rtd 99; Perm to Offic *Newc* from 99. *65 Bede Close, Holystone, Newcastle upon Tyne NE12 9SP*

WILSON, Frederick John. b 25. Lon Univ BScEng45. Oak Hill Th Coll 68. **d** 70 **p** 71. C Wandsworth All SS *S'wark* 70-75; P-in-c Garsdon w Lea and Cleverton *Bris* 75-84; P-in-c Charlton w Brokenborough and Hankerton 80-84; Chapl Barn Fellowship Whatcombe Ho 84-87; C Corby Epiphany w St Jo *Pet* 87-92; rtd 92; Perm to Offic *Pet* from 93; *Linc* 93-02. *2 Thorseby Close, Netherton, Peterborough PE3 9QS* Tel (01733) 263386

WILSON, Geoffrey. b 42. LNSM course 96. **d** 97 **p** 98. OLM Gunton St Pet *Nor* from 97. *7 Monet Square, Gunton, Lowestoft NR32 4LZ* Tel (01502) 564064

WILSON, Geoffrey Samuel Alan. b 46. TCD BA69 QUB DipEd90 TCD MA72. CITC BTh93. **d** 96 **p** 97. C Glendermott *D & R* 96-99; I Camus-juxta-Mourne from 99. *The Rectory, Newtown Street, Strabane BT82 8DW* Tel (028) 7188 2314

WILSON, George Thomas. b 47. Carl and Blackb Dioc Tr Inst 97. **d** 00 **p** 01. OLM Newbarns w Hawcoat *Carl* from 00. *21 Furness Park Road, Barrow-in-Furness LA14 5PH* Tel (01229) 820168

✠**WILSON, The Rt Revd Godfrey Edward Armstrong.** b 26. Linc Th Coll. **d** 54 **p** 55 **c** 80. C Sheff St Geo and St Steph *Sheff* 54-57; New Zealand from 58; C Masterton 58-59; V Aramoho 59-62; V St Pet Wellington 62-78; Min Tr Officer Waiapu Dio 78-80; Asst Bp Auckland 80-91; rtd 91. *30 Maryland Street, Point Chevalier, Auckland 1002, New Zealand* Tel (0064) (9) 846 4669

WILSON, Graham Whitelaw. b 46. Glas Sch of Art DA70 Leeds Univ CertEd77 Birm Univ MPhil00. EMMTC DTPS95. **d** 95 **p** 96. NSM Burbage w Aston Flamville *Leic* 95-97; C 97-01; C Stoke Golding w Dadlington 01-02; C Higham-on-the-Hill w Fenny Drayton and Witherley 01-02; C Fenn Lanes Gp from 02. *The Rectory, Old Forge Road, Fenny Drayton, Nuneaton CV13 6BD* Tel (01827) 711259 E-mail gwwilson@btinternet.com

WILSON, Canon Harold. b 29. St Jo Coll Ox BA53 MA57. Ridley Hall Cam 57. **d** 59 **p** 60. C Leamington Priors St Mary *Cov* 59-61; C Walsgrave on Sowe 61-64; V Potters Green 64-67; Chapl Barcelona *Eur* 67-73; V Bursledon *Win* 73-83; RD Eastleigh 75-83; V Yateley 83-94; RD Oldham 85-88; Hon Can Win Cathl 87-94; rtd 94; Perm to Offic *Win* from 94. *11 Hill Meadow, Overton, Basingstoke RG25 3JD* Tel (01256) 771825

WILSON, Harold Marcus. b 32. St Jo Coll Dur BA55 DipTh57. **d** 57 **p** 58. C Adlington *Blackb* 57-60; Miss to Seamen 60-81; Basrah, Iraq 60-63; Kobe, Japan 63-67; Tyne and Blyth 67-77; Tyne and Wear 70-77; Port of Spain, Trinidad and Tobago 77-81; P-in-c Crowfield w Stonham Aspal and Mickfield *St E* 81-97; rtd 97; Perm to Offic *Pet* 98-03. *8 Patticroft, Glemsford, Sudbury CO10 7UJ* Tel (01787) 281088

WILSON, Mrs Heather Clarissa. b 49. Hull Univ BA71 Leic Univ PGCE72. EAMTC 01. **d** 03. NSM Duston Team *Pet* from 03. *12 Ardens Grove, Rothersthorpe, Northampton NN7 3JJ* Tel (01604) 832200 Mobile 07702-033727 E-mail heather@wilson1214.freeserve.co.uk

WILSON, Hewitt. *See* WILSON, Canon John Hewitt

WILSON, Ian Andrew. b 57. Nottm Univ BTh89. Linc Th Coll 86. **d** 89 **p** 90. C Whitton and Thurleston w Akenham *St E* 89-93; P-in-c Elmsett w Aldham 93-02; R Elmsett w Aldham,

Hintlesham, Chattisham etc 02; Chapl Woodbridge Sch from 03. *12 Moorfield Road, Woodbridge IP12 4JN* Tel (01394) 384573

WILSON, James. b 65. St Steph Ho Ox. **d** 01 **p** 02. C Whitchurch *Bris* from 01. *127 Bristol Road, Whitchurch, Bristol BS14 0PU* Tel (01275) 834992 E-mail revjameswilson@aol.com

WILSON, James Andrew Christopher. b 48. Ex & Truro NSM Scheme. **d** 82 **p** 83. NSM Plymouth Crownhill Ascension *Ex* 82-83; NSM Yelverton 83-85; C Plymstock 85-87; R Lifton 87-92; R Kelly w Bradstone 87-92; V Broadwoodwidger 87-92; R Calstock *Truro* from 92; RD E Wivelshire from 00. *The Rectory, Sand Lane, Calstock PL18 9QX* Tel (01822) 832518 E-mail andrew.wilson@virgin.net

WILSON, James Charles. TCD BA82 MLL82 MA84 DipTh85 BD87. **d** 85 **p** 86. C Bangor Abbey *D & D* 85-88; C Dublin Rathfarnham *D & G* 88-91; I Desertcreat *Arm* 91-95; Bp's C Rathmolyon w Castlerickard, Rathcore and Agher *M & K* 95-00; Asst P Mullingar, Portnashangan, Moyliscar, Kilbixy etc 00-03; P-in-c Ardclinis and Tickmacrevan w Layde and Cushendun *Conn* from 03. *St Mary's Rectory, 76 Largy Road, Carnlough, Ballymena BT44 0JJ* Tel (028) 2888 5593 Fax as telephone E-mail diomeath@hotmail.com

WILSON, James Kenneth. b 47. **d** 88 **p** 89. C Holyhead w Rhoscolyn w Llanfair-yn-Neubwll *Ban* 88-91; Chapl RAF from 91. *Chaplaincy Services (RAF), HQ Personnel and Training Command, RAF Innsworth, Gloucester GL3 1EZ* Tel (01452) 712612 ext 5164 Fax 510828

WILSON, James Lewis. b 39. TCD BA62 HDipEd63 MA65 BD71. TCD Div Sch Div Test74. **d** 74 **p** 75. C Enniskillen *Clogh* 74-76; C Belfast St Matt *Conn* 76-79; I Killeshandra w Killegar *K, E & A* 79-81; I Derrylane 79-81; I Loughgilly w Clare *Arm* from 81. *The Rectory, 124 Gosford Road, Loughgilly, Armagh BT60 2DE* Tel (028) 3750 7265

WILSON, Lt Col James Phillip Maclean. b 31. RMA 52 MBIM75. Glouc Sch of Min 89. **d** 91 **p** 92. NSM Quinton w Marston Sicca *Glouc* 91-97; P-in-c 97-01. *The Old Bakery, Upper Quinton, Stratford-upon-Avon CV37 8SX* Tel (01789) 720224

WILSON, Canon James Robert. b 36. CITC. **d** 66 **p** 67. C Ballywillan *Conn* 67-73; I Drummaul 73-79; I Drummaul w Duneane and Ballyscullion 79-01; Preb Conn Cathl 96; Treas 96-98; Chan 98-01; rtd 01. *90 Killycowan Road, Glarryford, Ballymena BT44 9HL*

WILSON, Miss Jane Jennifer. b 43. Ch Ch Coll Cant TCert65 Open Univ BA84. Wycliffe Hall Ox 89. **d** 91 **p** 94. Par Dn Northwood Em *Lon* 91-94; C 94-98; TV Blythburgh w Reydon *St E* 98; TV Sole Bay 98-02; TR from 02; RD Halesworth from 01. *The Vicarage, Gardner Road, Southwold IP18 6HJ* Tel (01502) 722397

WILSON, Janet Mary. b 44. Dioc OLM tr scheme 00. **d** 03. OLM S Croydon Em *S'wark* from 03. *Elmwood, 2 Weybourne Place, Sanderstead CR2 0RZ* Tel (020) 8688 6676 E-mail janwilson@emmanuelcroydon.org.uk

WILSON, John Anthony. b 34. Linc Th Coll. **d** 83 **p** 84. C Nunthorpe *York* 83-85; V Whorlton w Carlton and Faceby 85-94; V E Coatham 94-99; rtd 99; Perm to Offic *York* from 00. *52 South Parade, Northallerton DL7 8SL* Tel (01609) 778814

WILSON, Canon John Christopher Heathcote. b 13. Qu Coll Ox BA39 MA41. Cuddesdon Coll 40. **d** 41 **p** 42. C Bradf St Wilfrid Lidget Green *Bradf* 41-44; C Skipton H Trin 44-47; CF 47-50; V Kingston upon Hull St Nic *York* 50-59; V Kirk Ella 59-68; AD W Hull 72-79; Can and Preb York Minster 79-95; rtd 88; Perm to Offic *York* from 95. *14 Tremayne Avenue, Brough HU15 1BL* Tel (01482) 668481

WILSON, John Clifford. b 32. AKC56. **d** 57 **p** 58. C Bordesley St Andr *Birm* 57-59; C Kings Norton 59-61; Somalia and Aden 61-63; V Lydbrook *Glouc* 64-67; TV Bow w Bromley St Leon *Lon* 69-73; P-in-c Stepney St Pet w St Benet 73-80; P-in-c Long Marton w Dufton and w Milburn *Carl* 80-81; R 81-87; V Annesley Our Lady and All SS *S'well* 87-95; V Annesley w Newstead 95-97; rtd 97; Perm to Offic *Heref* from 98. *Cwm Well Cottage, Upper Cwm, Little Dewchurch, Hereford HR2 6PS* Tel (01432) 840559

WILSON, John Frederick. b 33. Qu Coll Birm 58. **d** 61 **p** 62. C Jarrow St Paul *Dur* 61-65; C Monkwearmouth All SS 65-68; Br Honduras 68-71; V Scunthorpe Resurr *Linc* 71-90; Chapl Divine Healing Miss Crowhurst 90-91; V Terrington St Clement *Ely* 91-99; rtd 99; Perm to Offic *Ely* from 99. *7 Oakleigh Crescent, Godmanchester, Huntingdon PE29 2JJ* Tel (01480) 392791

WILSON, Canon John Hamilton. b 29. St Chad's Coll Dur BA53. Sarum Th Coll 53. **d** 55 **p** 56. C W End *Win* 55-59; C Fishponds St Mary *Bris* 59-64; V Bedminster St Fran 64-73; RD Bedminster 68-73; R Horfield H Trin 73-96; Hon Can Bris Cathl 77-96; rtd 96; Perm to Offic *Bris* from 96. *2 West Croft, Bristol BS9 4PQ* Tel 0117-962 9204 Fax as telephone

WILSON, Canon John Hewitt. b 24. CB77. TCD BA46 Div Test47 MA61. **d** 47 **p** 48. C Dublin St Geo *D & G* 47-50; Chapl RAF 50-73; Chapl-in-Chief RAF 73-80; QHC 73-80; Can and Preb Linc Cathl *Linc* 74-80; R The Heyfords w Rousham and Somerton *Ox* 81-93; rtd 93. *Glencree, Philcote Street, Deddington, Oxford OX15 0TB* Tel (01869) 38903

WILSON, John Lake. b 34. Linc Th Coll 74. **d** 76 **p** 77. C N Lynn w St Marg and St Nic *Nor* 76-80; V Narborough w Narford 80-85; R Pentney St Mary Magd w W Bilney 80-85; V Lakenham St Mark 85-93; P-in-c Trowse 92-93; V Lakenham St Mark w Trowse 93-98; Chapl Whitlingham Hosp 93-98; rtd 98; Perm to Offic *Nor* from 98. *Slinmoor, Warham Road, Wells-next-the-Sea NR23 1NE* Tel (01328) 711035

WILSON, Canon John Walter. b 25. St Jo Coll Dur BA67 Hatf Coll Dur MSc74. Cranmer Hall Dur. **d** 67 **p** 68. C Auckland St Helen *Dur* 67-69; V S Hetton 69-75; Lect Sunderland Poly 75-82; V Ormesby w Scratby *Nor* 82-92; RD Flegg (Gt Yarmouth) 89-92; Hon Can Nor Cathl 91-92; rtd 92; Perm to Offic *Nor* from 92; Bp's Officer for Rtd Clergy and Widows 95-99. *4 Rectory Lane, Chedgrave, Norwich NR14 6NE* Tel (01508) 520259

WILSON, Joseph William Sidney. b 23. St Aid Birkenhead 62. **d** 64 **p** 65. C Gt Sankey *Liv* 64-66; Chapl Rotterdam w Schiedam etc *Eur* 67-68; C Birkdale St Jo *Liv* 68-71; V Eppleton *Dur* 71-78; V Riccall *York* 78-84; V Freckleton *Blackb* 84-87; rtd 87; Perm to Offic *Ches* from 87. *27 Sandy Lane, Wallasey CH45 3JY* Tel 0151-639 9083

WILSON, Miss Judith Anne. b 48. Keele Univ BA71 Leic Univ PGCE72. S Dios Minl Tr Scheme 92. **d** 95 **p** 96. NSM Slaugham *Chich* 95-96; Sub Chapl HM Pris Wandsworth 95-96; Chapl HM Pris and YOI Hollesley Bay 96-01; Chapl HM Pris Nor from 01. *HM Prison, Knox Road, Norwich NR1 4LU* Tel (01603) 437531 E-mail judith.wilson@virgin.net

WILSON, Kenneth. b 59. Selw Coll Cam BA82 MA82 Birm Univ MPhil95 Birkbeck Coll Lon DipRS88 ARICS84 MRICS01. S'wark Ord Course 86. **d** 89 **p** 90. C Walthamstow St Pet *Chelmsf* 89-92; TV Wolverhampton *Lich* 92-97; Perm to Offic from 00. *6 Westland Road, Wolverhampton WV3 9NY* Tel (01902) 561485 Fax as telephone E-mail kw@soulofindia.com

WILSON, Malcolm Richard Milburn. b 30. Edin Th Coll 57. **d** 59 **p** 60. C Dumbarton *Glas* 59-61; India 62-63; C Dunfermline *St And* 63-65; R Newport-on-Tay 65-70; R Tayport 65-70; R Baillieston *Glas* 70-74; R Milngavie 74-84; R Bearsden 74-84; R Dalbeattie 84-88; R Gourock 88-94; rtd 94. *20 Dougalston Gardens North, Milngavie, Glasgow G62 6HN* Tel 0141-956 4138

WILSON, Marjorie Jayne. *See* SHIPTON, Mrs Marjorie Jayne

WILSON, Mark Anthony John. b 56. TCD BA80. CITC 75. **d** 80 **p** 81. C Dublin Rathfarnham *D & G* 80-83; Bp's C Dublin Finglas 83-85; I Celbridge w Straffan and Newcastle-Lyons 85-88; CF 88-93; I Dundalk w Heynestown *Arm* from 93. *The Rectory, Old Golf Links Road, Blackrock, Co Louth, Irish Republic* Tel (00353) (42) 932 1402 Fax as telephone E-mail dundalk@armagh.anglican.org

WILSON, The Ven Mark John Crichton. b 46. Clare Coll Cam BA67 MA70. Ridley Hall Cam 67. **d** 69 **p** 70. C Luton w E Hyde *St Alb* 69-72; C Ashtead *Guildf* 72-77; Chapl Epsom Coll 77-81; V Epsom Common Ch Ch *Guildf* 81-96; RD Epsom 87-91; Adn Dorking from 96; Hon Can Guildf Cathl from 96. *The Rectory, Parsonage Way, Frimley, Camberley GU16 8HZ* Tel (01276) 62820 E-mail archdeacon@mjcwilson.plus.com

WILSON, Martin. *See* WILSON, Bernard Martin

WILSON, Canon Mavis Kirby. b 42. Ex Univ BA64 Cam Univ CertEd71. S Dios Minl Tr Scheme 82. **dss** 84 **d** 87 **p** 94. Chessington *Guildf* 84-85; Epsom St Martin 85-86; Epsom Common Ch Ch 86-87; C 87-96; Dioc Adv in Miss, Evang, and Par Development 90-02; R Frimley from 02; Hon Can Guildf Cathl from 94. *The Rectory, Parsonage Way, Frimley, Camberley GU16 8HZ* Tel (01276) 23309 E-mail mavis@frimrec.fsnet.co.uk

WILSON, Mervyn Raynold Alwyn. b 33. Qu Coll Cam BA57 MA61. Ripon Hall Ox 57. **d** 59 **p** 60. C Rubery *Birm* 59-62; C Kings Norton 62-63; V Hamstead St Bernard 63-69; R Bermondsey St Mary w St Olave, St Jo etc *S'wark* 69-78; R Bulwick, Blatherwycke w Harringworth and Laxton *Pet* 78-03; rtd 03. *The Red Post House, Fivehead, Taunton TA3 6PX* Tel (01460) 281555 E-mail mervyn@ratilova.freeserve.co.uk

WILSON, The Very Revd Mervyn Robert. b 22. Bris Univ BA51 Lon Univ BD58. Tyndale Hall Bris 52. **d** 52 **p** 53. C Ballymacarrett St Patr *D & D* 52-56; C Donaghcloney 56-59; C Newtownards 59-61; I Ballyphilip w Ardquin 61-70; I Newry St Patr 70-92; Preb Dromore Cathl 83-85; Can Belf Cathl 85-89; Dean Dromore *D & D* 90-92; rtd 92. *31 Manor Drive, Lisburn BT28 1JH* Tel (028) 9266 6361

WILSON, Michael. *See* WILSON, Canon Alfred Michael Sykes

WILSON, Michael. b 13. Trin Coll Cam BA35 MA39. Westcott Ho Cam 37. **d** 38 **p** 39. C Eastleigh *Win* 38-41; CF (EC) 41-46; V St Mary Bourne w Litchfield *Win* 45-52; N Rhodesia 52-61; R Kingsland *Heref* 61-65; Zambia 66-68; C Bournemouth St Clem w St Mary *Win* 68-73; V Appleshaw 73-78; rtd 78. *St Cross Grange, 140 St Cross Road, Winchester SO23 9RJ* Tel (01962) 860172

WILSON, Canon Michael. b 44. Liv Univ BA66 Fitzw Coll Cam BA68 MA73. Westcott Ho Cam. **d** 69 **p** 70. C Worksop Priory *S'well* 69-71; C Gt Malvern St Mary *Worc* 71-75; V Leic St Anne *Leic* 75-85; TR Leic Ascension 85-88; Hon Can Leic Cathl

85-88; Can Res and Treas from 88. *39 Meadowcourt Road, Leicester LE2 2PD* Tel 0116-272 0041 Fax 272 2315 E-mail mwilson@leicester.anglican.org

WILSON, Neil. b 61. Newc Univ BA83. Ripon Coll Cuddesdon 85. **d** 88 **p** 89. C Wallsend St Luke *Newc* 88-91; C Monkseaton St Pet 91-93; V Earsdon and Backworth from 93. *Earsdon Vicarage, 5 Front Street, Whitley Bay NE25 9JU* Tel 0191-252 9393 E-mail frneilwilson@aol.com

WILSON, Paul David. b 64. Cranmer Hall Dur 96. **d** 98 **p** 99. C Bramley and Ravenfield w Hooton Roberts etc *Sheff* 98-01; V Hatfield from 01. *The Vicarage, High Street, Hatfield, Doncaster DN7 6RS* Tel (01302) 840280

WILSON, Paul Edward. b 43. Ridley Hall Cam 81. **d** 83 **p** 84. C Brighstone and Brooke w Mottistone *Portsm* 83-86; C Shorwell w Kingston 83-86; TV Tring *St Alb* 86-90; P-in-c Renhold 90-91; Chapl HM Pris Bedf 90-91; V Buckfastleigh w Dean Prior *Ex* 91-96; P-in-c Stockland, Dalwood, Kilmington and Shute 96-00; TR Melbury *Sarum* 00-03; rtd 03. *April Cottage, Braishfield Road, Braishfield, Romsey SO51 0PQ* Tel (01794) 368089 E-mail revpwilson@ntlworld.com

WILSON, Paul Hugh. b 26. Glouc Sch of Min 80. **d** 83 **p** 84. NSM Much Birch w Lt Birch, Much Dewchurch etc *Heref* 83-86; C 86-92; rtd 92; Perm to Offic *Heref* from 92. *Cherry Lyn, Staunton-on-Wye, Hereford HR4 7LR* Tel (01981) 500231

WILSON, Paul Thomas Wardley. b 43. AKC67. St Aug Coll Cant. **d** 70 **p** 71. C Tokyngton St Mich *Lon* 70-74; Soc Community Worker *Roch* 74-81; Perm to Offic 81-90; Lic to Offic *Cant* 83-88; Sen Adv Coun for Soc Resp from 83; Chief Exec Carr Gomm Soc from 88. *Carr Gomm Society, 6-12 Tabard Street, London SE1 4JU* Tel (020) 7397 5300

WILSON, Peter Dennis. b 51. Dioc OLM tr scheme. **d** 03. OLM Benwell Team *Newc* from 03. *34 Bennwell Lane, Benwell, Newcastle upon Tyne NE15 6RR* Tel 0191-273 2856

WILSON, Peter John. b 43. CertEd76 BEd84. Linc Th Coll. **d** 71 **p** 72. C Stretford St Matt *Man* 71-73; C Rugby St Andr *Cov* 73-76; TV 76-92; Hon C Bilton 76-79; Asst Dir of Educn *Blackb* 79-81; P-in-c Accrington St Paul 79-81; Dioc Officer for Stewardship *Carl* 92-02; P-in-c Dacre 95-02; Hon Can Carl Cathl 98-02; R Stone St Mich and St Wulfad w Aston St Sav *Lich* from 02. *11 Farrier Close, Stone ST15 8XP* Tel (01785) 812747 E-mail ptrwln@lineone.net

WILSON, Canon Peter Sheppard. b 39. TCD BA61. CITC 62. **d** 62 **p** 63. C Killowen *D & R* 62-68; C Portadown St Columba *Arm* 68-70; I Convoy w Monellan and Donaghmore *D & R* 70-78; P-in-c Castletown *S & M* 78; V 78-83; R Kilmacolm *Glas* 83-85; R Bridge of Weir 83-85; I Camus-juxta-Bann *D & R* 85-92; Bp's Dom Chapl 90-92; I Maguiresbridge w Derrybrusk *Clogh* from 92; Chapl to Bp Clogh 98-00; Can Clogh Cathl from 00. *9 Drumgoon Road, Maguiresbridge BT94 4PJ* Tel (028) 6672 1250

WILSON, Quentin Harcourt. b 45. FTCL75 K Coll Lon AKC68 BD76. St Aug Coll Cant 69. **d** 70 **p** 71. C Is of Dogs Ch Ch and St Jo w St Luke *Lon* 70-72; C Muswell Hill St Jas 72-77; Succ and Sacr Ex Cathl *Ex* 77-81; Min Can Windsor 81-84; V Langho Billington *Blackb* 84-97; Chapl Brockhall Hosp Blackb 85-97; RD Whalley *Blackb* 89-95; P-in-c Burnley St Pet 97-98; R 98-02; rtd 02; Perm to Offic *York* from 03. *Chanting Hill Farmhouse, Welburn, York YO60 7EF* Tel (01653) 619590 E-mail qhwilson@bushinternet.com

WILSON, Mrs Rachel Elizabeth. b 56. Keswick Hall Coll BEd77. N Ord Course 00. **d** 03. NSM Slaidburn *Bradf* from 03; NSM Long Preston w Tosside from 03. *The Vicarage, 7 Station Road, Long Preston, Skipton BD23 4NH* Tel (01729) 840513

WILSON, Richard Graham. b 67. Bris Univ BSc91 BA01 DipSW93. Trin Coll Bris 99. **d** 01 **p** 02. C Wandsworth St Mich *S'wark* from 01. *St Michael's Vicarage, 73 Wimbledon Park Road, London SW18 5TT* Tel (020) 8874 7682

WILSON, Robert Brian. b 29. AKC55. **d** 56 **p** 57. C Wortley de Leeds *Ripon* 56-60; C Chapel Allerton 60-63; V Hunslet Moor St Pet and St Cuth 63-70; V Bilton 70-80; V Gt and Lt Ouseburn w Marton cum Grafton 80-90; rtd 90. *56 Church Avenue, Harrogate HG1 4HG* Tel (01423) 504398

WILSON, Canon Robert Malcolm (Robin). b 35. St Andr Univ MA59. ALCD62. **d** 62 **p** 63. C Wallington H Trin *S'wark* 62-66; C Dur St Nic *Dur* 66-70; V Colchester St Pet *Chelmsf* 70-01; RD Colchester 93-98; Hon Can Chelmsf Cathl 94-01; rtd 01; Perm to Offic *St E* and *Chelmsf* from 01. *Hawthorns, Melton Road, Melton, Woodbridge IP12 1NH* Tel (01394) 383514

WILSON, Robert Stoker. b 39. Dur Univ BSc62. Oak Hill Th Coll 62. **d** 64 **p** 65. C High Elswick St Paul *Newc* 64-68; C Kirkheaton 68-70; Youth Chapl *Liv* 70-73; P-in-c S Shields St Steph *Dur* 73-78; R 78-83; Youth Chapl 73-77; P-in-c S Shields St Aid 81-83; V Greenside 83-94; P-in-c Fatfield 94-98; P-in-c Coniscliffe from 98; Dioc Adv for IT from 98. *76 Merrybent, Darlington DL2 2LE* Tel (01325) 374510 Mobile 07808-911928 Fax 374124 E-mail stoker.wilson@durham.anglican.org

WILSON, Canon Ronald. b 11. St Aid Birkenhead. **d** 51 **p** 52. C Lenton *S'well* 51-53; C Worksop St Anne 53-55; V Lenton Abbey 55-63; V Pinchbeck *Linc* 63-78; Can and Preb Linc Cathl 72-78;

rtd 78; Perm to Offic *Ox* from 01. *14 Windermere Gardens, Linslade, Leighton Buzzard LU7 7QP* Tel (01525) 379676

WILSON, Mrs Rosamund Cynthia. b 54. Univ of Wales MSc94 MCSP75. Trin Coll Bris. **d** 01 **p** 02. NSM Stoke Bishop *Bris* from 01. *10 Druid Stoke Avenue, Bristol BS9 1DD* Tel 0117-968 7554 Mobile 07855-998520 Fax 0117-959 3645 E-mail roswilson@vicar.co.uk

WILSON, Simon Anthony. b 67. Portsm Poly BA88. Cranmer Hall Dur 96. **d** 99 **p** 00. NSM Barnham Broom *Nor* 99-00; NSM Barnham Broom and Upper Yare 00-02; NSM Hellesdon from 02; Public Preacher from 03. *50 Wensum Valley Close, Norwich NR6 5DJ* Tel (01603) 483790 E-mail vswilson@btinternet.com

WILSON, Stephen Charles. b 51. Newc Univ BA73 Cam Univ MA82. Westcott Ho Cam BA78. **d** 79 **p** 80. C Fulham All SS *Lon* 79-82; C W Hampstead St Jas 82-85; P-in-c Alexandra Park St Sav 85-93; V Preston next Faversham, Goodnestone and Graveney *Cant* from 93; Hon Min Can Cant Cathl from 98. *The Vicarage, Preston Lane, Faversham ME13 8LG* Tel (01795) 536801

WILSON, Stephen John. b 45. Bradf Univ BTech69. Trin Coll Bris DipHE92. **d** 92 **p** 93. C Marple All SS *Ches* 92-96; P-in-c Moulton 96-01; Chapl Mid Cheshire Hosps Trust 96-99; V Hyde St Geo *Ches* from 01. *The Vicarage, 85 Edna Street, Hyde SK14 1DR* Tel 0161-367 8787 E-mail hydes@fish.co.uk

WILSON, Stuart Arnold. b 47. NDA68. SW Minl Tr Course 94. **d** 97 **p** 98. NSM Okehampton w Inwardleigh, Bratton Clovelly etc *Ex* 97-02; TV from 02. *The Vicarage, Northlew, Okehampton EX20 3NJ* Tel (01409) 221714 Mobile 07779-471245 E-mail revsawil@aol.com

WILSON, Susan Annette. b 60. Bath Univ BPharm81 PhD86 MRPharmS82. Westcott Ho Cam. **d** 00 **p** 01. C Newc St Geo *Newc* from 00. *Tower House, St George's Close, Newcastle upon Tyne NE2 2TF* Tel 0191-281 3871 E-mail susan.wilson@tinyworld.co.uk

WILSON, Miss Susan Elizabeth. b 52. Lady Spencer Chu Coll of Educn CertEd74 BEd75. WEMTC DipApTh99. **d** 99 **p** 00. NSM Saltford w Corston and Newton St Loe *B & W* from 99. *Glendale, 7 Leighton Road, Bath BA1 4NF* Tel (01225) 330587

WILSON, Thomas Irven. b 30. TCD BA51 Div Test 52 MA58. **d** 53 **p** 54. C Ballymena *Conn* 53-56; Chapl RAF 56-85; Asst Chapl-in-Chief 73-85; QHC from 80; rtd 85. *Rathclaren House, Kilbrittain, Co Cork, Irish Republic* Tel (00353) (23) 49689

WILSON, Canon Thomas Roderick. b 26. St Pet Hall Ox BA50 MA55. Sarum Th Coll 50. **d** 52 **p** 53. C Poulton-le-Sands *Blackb* 52-56; C Altham w Clayton le Moors 56-58; V Habergham Eaves H Trin 58-78; RD Burnley 70-78; Hon Can Blackb Cathl 75-89; V Bare 78-81; P-in-c Accrington St Jas 81-82; P-in-c Accrington St Paul 81-82; V Accrington St Jas w St Paul 82-89; rtd 89; Perm to Offic *Blackb* from 89. *33 Nook Terrace, Cherry Tree, Blackburn BB2 4SW* Tel (01254) 209390

WILSON, Timothy Charles. b 62. Oak Hill Th Coll BA90. **d** 90 **p** 91. C Highley *Heref* 90-94; C Margate H Trin *Cant* 94-98; P-in-c Margate St Phil 98-02; V 02-03; P-in-c Gt Chart from 03. *The Rectory, The Street, Great Chart, Ashford TN23 3AY* Tel (01233) 620371 E-mail tandcwilson@lineone.net

WILSON, Timothy John. b 56. St Pet Coll Ox MA80. Trin Coll Bris 81. **d** 83 **p** 84. C Gt Horton *Bradf* 83-86; C Handforth *Ches* 86-90; V Halifax All SS *Wakef* from 90. *All Saints' Vicarage, Greenroyd Avenue, Halifax HX3 0LP* Tel (01422) 365805 Fax as telephone E-mail wilsons@domini.org

WILSON (née NICHOLSON), Mrs Veronica Mary. b 66. Nene Coll Northampton BSc88 Chester Coll of HE PGCE90. Cranmer Hall Dur DMS99. **d** 99 **p** 00. C Barnham Broom *Nor* 99-00; C Barnham Broom and Upper Yare 00-02; C Hellesdon from 02. *50 Wensum Valley Close, Norwich NR6 5DJ* Tel (01603) 483790 E-mail vswilson@btinternet.com

WILSON, Walter. b 33. Wm Temple Coll Rugby 55. **d** 59 **p** 60. C Sheff St Swithun *Sheff* 59-63; Ind Chapl 63-66; C Attercliffe 63-66; R Swallow w Cabourn *Linc* 66-72; Dioc Youth Officer *Heref* 72-77; Chapl Ipswich Sch 77-94; rtd 94; Perm to Offic *St E* from 94. *Riverside Cottage, Mendlesham Green, Stowmarket IP14 5RF* Tel (01449) 766198

WILSON, William Adam. b 53. Sheff Univ BA74 St Jo Coll Dur BA84. Cranmer Hall Dur 82. **d** 85 **p** 86. C S Croydon Em *S'wark* 85-89; C Wandsworth All SS 89-93; Chapl Fontainebleau *Eur* 93-00; V S Lambeth St Steph *S'wark* from 00. *The Vicarage, St Stephen's Terrace, London SW8 1DH* Tel (020) 7564 1930 *or* 7735 8461 Fax (020) 7735 7737 E-mail vicar@ststephenssouthlambeth.org.uk

WILSON, William Gerard. b 42. St Chad's Coll Dur BA65 DipHE67. **d** 67 **p** 68. C Hollinwood *Man* 67-71; V Oldham St Jas 71-79; R Birch w Fallowfield 79-93; V Paddington St Jas *Lon* from 93; AD Westmr Paddington from 97. *6 Gloucester Terrace, London W2 3DD* Tel (020) 7723 8119 *or* 7262 9976 Mobile 07976-363480 E-mail synaxis52@hotmail.com

WILSON, William John. b 26. CEng MIEE MRTvS. S Dios Minl Tr Scheme 79. **d** 82 **p** 83. NSM Weeke *Win* 82-88; NSM Win St Barn 89-95; Hon Chapl R Hants Co Hosp Win from 89; rtd 95; Perm to Offic *Win* from 95. *23 Buriton Road, Winchester SO22 6JE* Tel (01962) 881904

WILSON, Yvonne. See WILSON, Edith Yvonne

WILSON-BARKER, Mrs Carol Amanda. b 64. SW Minl Tr Course 00. **d** 03. C Godrevy *Truro* from 03. *Godrevy House, Penpol Avenue, Hayle TR27 4NQ* Tel (01736) 757259 E-mail carolw953@aol.com

WILSON-BROWN, Nigel Hugh. b 65. Goldsmiths' Coll Lon BSc87. Wycliffe Hall Ox DipMin95. **d** 97 **p** 98. C Wimbledon Em Ridgway Prop Chpl *S'wark* 97-00; Chapl K Sch Bruton from 00. *King's School, Plox, Bruton BA10 0ED* Tel (01749) 814200

WILTON, Albert Edward. b 10. St Paul's Coll Grahamstown 69. **d** 67 **p** 68. Rhodesia 67-68; S Africa 69-77; rtd 77; Perm to Offic *St E* 77-86; Perm to Offic *Chich* from 92. *College of St Barnabas, Blackberry Lane, Lingfield RH7 6NJ* Tel (01342) 870522

WILTON, Mrs Carlyn Zena. b 54. R Holloway Coll Lon BA75 Southn Univ PGCE76. SW Minl Tr Course 99. **d** 02 **p** 03. NSM Carbis Bay w Lelant *Truro* from 02. *Venton Ellway, 61 Queensway, Hayle TR27 4NL* Tel (01736) 752863 E-mail ventonellway@thefreeinternet.com

WILTON, Christopher. b 52. Lon Univ LLB75 Solicitor 79. NEOC 97. **d** 00 **p** 01. NSM Sherburn in Elmet w Saxton *York* from 00. *Charnwood, Nanny Lane, Church Fenton, Tadcaster LS24 9RL* Tel (01937) 558006 Mobile 07968-268622 Fax (01977) 600343 E-mail cwilton@hartley-worstenholme.co.uk

WILTON, Gary Ian. b 60. Bath Univ BSc83. Trin Coll Bris MA93 Wycliffe Hall Ox 85. **d** 88 **p** 89. C Clevedon St Andr and Ch Ch *B & W* 88-92; Lect Univ of the W of England, Bris 92-93; TV Bath Twerton-on-Avon *B & W* 93-97; Dir Studies and Lect Wilson Carlile Coll of Evang from 98. *74 Montgomery Road, Nether Edge, Sheffield S7 1LR* Tel 0114-255 1863 *or* 278 7020 Fax 279 5863

WILTON (née ADAMS), Mrs Gillian Linda. b 57. SRN79 SCM81. Trin Coll Bris DipHE84 DPS85. **dss** 85 **d** 87 **p** 94. Easton H Trin w St Gabr and St Lawr and St Jude *Bris* 85-91; Par Dn 87-91; Regional Adv (Dios B & W and Bris) CMJ 91-97; Perm to Offic *B & W* 92-93; NSM Bath Twerton-on-Avon 93-97; Chapl Sheff Children's Hosp NHS Trust from 98. *74 Montgomery Road, Nether Edge, Sheffield S7 1LR* Tel 0114-255 1863 *or* 271 7000

WILTON, Glenn Warner Paul. b 33. Miami Univ Ohio BSc55 Cath Univ of America 69 Univ of Washington Seattle MSW76. Pontifical Beda Coll Rome 66 Ch Div Sch of the Pacific (USA) 77. **d** 65 **p** 66. In RC Ch 65-72; NSM Seattle USA 77-81; Chapl Pastures Hosp Derby 82-88; Chapl St Martin's Hosp Cant 89-93; Chapl St Aug Hosp Cant 89-93; Chapl E Kent Community NHS Trust 93-03; rtd 03; Perm to Offic *Cant* from 03. *10 Lichfield Avenue, Canterbury CT1 3YA* Tel (01227) 454230 E-mail paul@wilton25.freeserve.co.uk

WILTON, Harry Owens. b 22. St Aid Birkenhead 43. **d** 46 **p** 47. C Edge Hill St Cypr *Liv* 49-51; C Kingston upon Hull H Trin *York* 49-51; Area Sec (NW England) CCCS 51-53; V Southport All So *Liv* 53-56; Perm to Offic *C, C & R* from 99. *Crantock, Mansfield's Land, Kinsale, Co Cork, Irish Republic* Tel (00353) (21) 773417 Fax 773418

WILTSE, Joseph August Jean Paul. b 41. Leeds Univ BA64. Coll of Resurr Mirfield 64. **d** 66 **p** 67. C Airedale w Fryston *Wakef* 66-70; Canada from 70. *6983 Richmond Street, Powell River BC, Canada, V8A 1H7*

WILTSHIRE, Albert. b 19. Qu Coll Birm 49. **d** 51 **p** 52. C Stockton St Jo *Dur* 51-55; C Brandon 55-57; PC Monkwearmouth Ven Bede 57-59; V Carlinghow *Wakef* 59-63; V Woodhorn w Newbiggin *Newc* 63-71; V Chatton w Chillingham 71-75; Chapl OHP 75-77; P-in-c Felton *Newc* 77-80; V Cornhill w Carham 80-85; V Branxton 80-85; Perm to Offic from 85; rtd 85. *The Levers, Yeavering, Wooler NE71 6HG* Tel (01668) 216427

WILTSHIRE, John Herbert Arthur. b 27. S'wark Ord Course 63. **d** 66 **p** 67. C Lee Gd Shep w St Pet *S'wark* 66-69; Min W Dulwich Em CD 69-79; R Coulsdon St Jo 79-93; rtd 93; Perm to Offic *Ches* from 94. *26 Meadow Lane, Willaston, Neston CH64 2TZ* Tel 0151-327 6668

WILTSHIRE, Robert Michael. b 50. WMMTC. **d** 89 **p** 90. NSM Droitwich Spa *Worc* 89-93; Asst Chapl HM Pris Wormwood Scrubs 93-94; Chapl HM Pris Standford Hill 94-97; Chapl HM Pris Whitemoor 97-99; Asst Chapl Gen of Pris from 99. *The Home Office, 54 Gaol Road, Stafford ST16 3AW* Tel (01785) 213456 Fax 227734

WILTSHIRE, Archdeacon of. See HOPKINSON, The Ven Barnabas John

WIMBUSH, Canon Timothy. b 44. JP. St Steph Ho Ox. **d** 68 **p** 69. C Hobs Moat *Birm* 68-71; C W Wycombe *Ox* 71-76; R Wykeham from 76; RD Deddington 86-00; Hon Can Ch Ch from 95. *The Rectory, Sibford Gower, Banbury OX15 5RW* Tel (01295) 780555

WIMMER, Michael John. b 41. Natal Univ BA64. Coll of Resurr Mirfield 65. **d** 67 **p** 68. S Africa 67-86; Miss to Seamen Canada from 86. *401 East Waterfront Road, Vancouver BC, Canada, V6A 4G9*

WIMSETT, Paul. b 58. Univ of Wales (Abth) BSc(Econ)79 Hull Univ MA86. St Jo Coll Nottm DipTh83. **d** 85 **p** 86. C Nuneaton

St Nic *Cov* 85-89; C Loughborough Em *Leic* 89-92; TV Totnes, Bridgetown and Berry Pomeroy etc *Ex* 92-99; V Chudleigh w Chudleigh Knighton and Trusham from 99. *The Vicarage, Parade, Chudleigh, Newton Abbot TQ13 0JF* Tel (01626) 853241 E-mail wimsett@eurobell.co.uk

WIMSHURST, Michael Alexander. b 33. St Jo Coll Ox BA58. Westcott Ho Cam 59. **d** 60 **p** 61. C Lewisham St Mary *S'wark* 60-65; India 66-70; V Battersea St Pet *S'wark* 71-73; V Battersea St Pet and St Paul 73-97; rtd 97; Perm to Offic *Cant* from 98. *50 Broad Street, Canterbury CT1 2LS* Tel (01227) 457889

WINBOLT LEWIS, Martin John. b 46. Fitzw Coll Cam BA69 MA72. St Jo Coll Nottm LTh75. **d** 75 **p** 76. C Highbury Ch Ch *Lon* 75-78; C Nottingham St Nic *S'well* 79-82; R Carlton Colville *Nor* 82-83; R Carlton Colville w Mutford and Rushmere 83-88; V Burley *Ripon* 88-96; Asst Chapl Pinderfields and Pontefract Hosps NHS Trust 96-99; Chapl 99-00; Lead Chapl 00-02; Lead Chapl Mid Yorks Hosps NHS Trust from 02. *27 Arncliffe Road, West Park, Leeds LS16 5AP* Tel (01924) 814677 E-mail martin.winbolt-lewis@panp-tr.northy.nhs.uk

WINCH, Victor Edward. b 17. AIB41 Selw Coll Cam BA47 MA52. Ridley Hall Cam. **d** 48 **p** 49. C Gt Baddow *Chelmsf* 48-50; SW Area Sec CPAS 50-54; V Hastings Em *Chich* 54-69; V Hastings St Mary in the Castle 54-69; Chapl Buchanan Hosp 59-69; V Kirdford 69-82; rtd 82; Perm to Offic *Heref* 83-97; Perm to Offic *Ex* from 97. *26 Gracey Court, Woodland Road, Broadclyst, Exeter EX5 3GA* Tel (01392) 469650

WINCHESTER, Gordon Law. b 50. DRSAMD71. Trin Coll Bris. **d** 82 **p** 83. C Cheadle *Ches* 82-84; Asst Chapl Amsterdam *Eur* 84-88; C Hove Bp Hannington Memorial Ch *Chich* 88-96; V Wandsworth All SS *S'wark* from 96. *Wandsworth Vicarage, 11 Rusholme Road, London SW15 3JX* Tel (020) 8788 7400 E-mail vicar@wandsworthparish.co.uk

WINCHESTER, Paul. b 44. St Pet Coll Ox BA66 MA70. Ridley Hall Cam 67. **d** 69 **p** 70. C Wednesfield Heath *Lich* 69-72; Perm to Offic *Sarum* 73-84; R Tushingham and Whitewell *Ches* 84-02; Perm to Offic *Ox* from 02. *12 The Pines, Faringdon SN7 8AU*

WINCHESTER, Paul Marc. b 53. Univ of Wales (Lamp) BA80 DipTh. St Mich Coll Llan 82. **d** 84 **p** 85. C Bedwellty *Mon* 84-86; C Chepstow 86-89; V Cwmcarn 89-93; V Fleur-de-Lis 93-98; R Bedwas and Rudry from 98. *The Rectory, Bryn Golea, Bedwas, Newport CF83 8AU* Tel (029) 2088 5220

WINCHESTER, Archdeacon of. *See* GUILLE, The Ven John Arthur

WINCHESTER, Bishop of. *See* SCOTT-JOYNT, The Rt Revd Michael Charles

WINCHESTER, Dean of. *See* TILL, The Very Revd Michael Stanley

WINDEBANK, Clive Leonard. b 41. New Coll Ox BA62 MA85. Ox NSM Course 75. **d** 78 **p** 79. Kuwait 78-83; NSM Brompton H Trin w Onslow Square St Paul *Lon* 83-84; NSM Basildon w Aldworth and Ashampstead *Ox* 85-88; NSM Streatley w Moulsford 88-00; NSM Wallingford from 00. *The Coombe House, The Coombe, Streatley, Reading RG8 9QL* Tel (01491) 872174

WINDER, John William. b 15. SS Coll Cam BA37 MA41. Ridley Hall Cam 37. **d** 39 **p** 40. C Huddersfield H Trin *Wakef* 39-43; C Sowerby Bridge w Norland 43-48; V Stainland 48-53; V Manningham St Paul *Bradf* 53-66; R Bolton by Bowland 66-81; rtd 81; Perm to Offic *Bradf* from 81. *2 Croft Rise, Menston, Ilkley LS29 6LU* Tel (01943) 872084

WINDIATE, Mary Elizabeth. *See* WEST, Mrs Mary Elizabeth

WINDLE, Mrs Catherine Elizabeth. b 72. Hatf Coll Dur BA95 Homerton Coll Cam PGCE96 St Jo Coll Dur MTh02. Cranmer Hall Dur 00. **d** 03. C Hucknall Torkard *S'well* from 03. *149 Beardall Street, Hucknall, Nottingham NG15 7HA* Tel 0115-964 0683

WINDLE, Christopher Rodney. b 45. Univ of Wales (Lamp) BA66. Qu Coll Birm DipTh68. **d** 70 **p** 71. C Lache cum Saltney *Ches* 70-73; C Stockton Heath 73-76; P-in-c Bredbury St Barn 76-83; V from 83. *St Barnabas' Vicarage, Osborne Street, Stockport SK6 2DA* Tel 0161-406 6569

WINDLEY, Caroline Judith. b 62. Trent Poly BA84 CQSW84 Nottm Univ MA97. St Jo Coll Nottm MA96. **d** 97 **p** 98. C Kidderminster St Geo *Worc* 97-01; P-in-c Quarry Bank from 01. *The Vicarage, Maughan Street, Brierley Hill DY5 2DN* Tel (01384) 565480

WINDMILL, Roy Stanley. b 17. Sarum Th Coll. **d** 54 **p** 55. C Wells St Cuth w Coxley and Wookey Hole *B & W* 54-58; R Honiley *Cov* 58-64; PC Wroxall 58-64; V Meriden 64-66; C Cov H Trin 66-70; P-in-c Kineton 70-75; P-in-c Combroke w Compton Verney 70-75; C Wraxall *B & W* 76-78; P-in-c Holton 78-82; rtd 82; Perm to Offic *B & W* 82-97; Perm to Offic *Ex* 82-98. *21 Rectory Drive, Burnham-on-Sea TA8 2DT* Tel (01278) 782715

WINDON, Gary. b 62. N Staffs Poly BSc85. Qu Coll Birm 98. **d** 00 **p** 01. C Penn *Lich* from 00. *105 Brenton Road, Penn, Wolverhampton WV4 5NS* Tel (01902) 335439 E-mail gwindon@bigfoot.com

WINDRIDGE, Michael Harry. b 47. Sarum & Wells Th Coll DCM93. **d** 93 **p** 94. C Hempnall *Nor* 93-96; NSM Twickenham St Mary *Lon* 96-97; Perm to Offic *Nor* from 98. *Fritton Cottage, The Common, Fritton, Norwich NR15 2QS* Tel (01508) 498577

WINDRIDGE, Peter William Roland. b 23. ACGI MIMechE BScEng. Sarum & Wells Th Coll 82. **d** 84 **p** 85. NSM Shirley St Jo *Cant* 84; NSM Shirley St Jo *S'wark* 85-86; NSM New Addington 86-95; rtd 95; Perm to Offic *S'wark* from 95. *83 Orchard Avenue, Croydon CR0 7NF* Tel (020) 8655 0872

WINDROSS, Andrew. b 49. Univ of Wales (Ban) BA71. Cuddesdon Coll 71. **d** 74 **p** 75. C Wakef St Jo *Wakef* 74-78; C Bromley All Hallows *Lon* 78-83; V De Beauvoir Town St Pet 83-02; AD Hackney 89-94; Bp's Officer for Ordained Min Stepney Area from 02; Hon C S Hackney St Mich w Haggerston St Paul from 02. *31 Lavender Grove, London E8 3LU*

WINDROSS, Anthony Michael. b 50. CCC Cam BA72 MA75 Birm Univ PGCE73. S Dios Minl Tr Scheme 90. **d** 93 **p** 94. NSM Eastbourne St Mary *Chich* 93-97; C E Grinstead St Swithun 97-99; V Sheringham *Nor* from 99. *The Vicarage, 10 North Street, Sheringham NR26 8LW* Tel (01263) 822089 E-mail amw@telinco.co.uk

WINDSLOW, Miss Kathryn Alison. b 62. Southn Univ BTh83 K Coll Lon MPhil01. Linc Th Coll 84. **dss** 86 **d** 87 **p** 94. Littlehampton and Wick *Chich* 86-89; Par Dn 87-89; Dn-in-c Scotton w Northorpe *Linc* 89-94; P-in-c 94-97; Asst Local Min Officer 89-97; Local Min Officer and Prin OLM Course 97-02; V Graffoe Gp from 02. *The Rectory, Vicarage Lane, Wellingore, Lincoln LN5 0JF* Tel (01522) 810246 E-mail kathryn@kwindslow.freeserve.co.uk

WINDSOR, Graham. b 35. G&C Coll Cam BA57 MA64 PhD67 Lon Univ BD60. Clifton Th Coll 58 Trin Coll Bris 79. **d** 79 **p** 80. C Rainham *Chelmsf* 79-82; rtd 00. *369 Pump Lane, Gillingham ME8 7TJ* Tel (01634) 388567 E-mail graham_windsor@hotmail.com

WINDSOR, Julie Fiona. b 59. Ridley Hall Cam. **d** 00 **p** 01. C Chertsey *Guildf* from 00. *25 Abbey Road, Chertsey KT16 8AL* Tel (01932) 563255 E-mail jfwindsor@hotmail.co.uk

WINDSOR, Dean of. *See* CONNER, The Rt Revd David John

WINFIELD, Canon Flora Jane Louise. b 64. Univ of Wales (Lamp) BA85 DipApTh97 FRSA98. Ripon Coll Cuddesdon 87. **d** 89 **p** 94. Par Dn Stantonbury and Willen *Ox* 89-92; Co Ecum Officer *Glouc* 92-94; Chapl Mansf Coll Ox 94-97; Local Unity Sec Coun for Chr Unity 97-02; CF (TA) from 97; Can Res Win Cathl *Win* from 02. *5A The Close, Winchester SO23 9LS* Tel (01962) 857239 Fax 857201 E-mail flora.winfield@winchester-cathedral.org.uk

WINFIELD, Miss June Mary. b 29. Gilmore Ho 57. **dss** 66 **d** 87 **p** 94. H Dogs Ch Ch and St Jo w St Luke *Lon* 66-68; Bracknell *Ox* 68-74; Dean of Women's Min 74-80; St Marylebone w H Trin *Lon* 80-82; Ind Chapl 82-89; rtd 89; NSM Ealing St Steph Castle Hill *Lon* 89-97; Asst Dioc Dir Ords Willesden Area 94-97; Perm to Offic from 97. *25 Trinity Road, Marlow SL7 3AN* Tel (01628) 484317

WING, Miss Myra Susan (Sue). b 45. Cranmer Hall Dur 92. **d** 94 **p** 95. C Appledore w Brookland, Fairfield, Brenzett etc *Cant* 94-98; Hon C Wittersham w Stone-in-Oxney and Ebony 95-98; V Grayshott *Guildf* from 98. *The Vicarage, 10 Vicarage Gardens, Grayshott, Hindhead GU26 6NH* Tel (01428) 604540 E-mail susan@wing63.fsnet.co.uk

WINGATE, Canon Andrew David Carlile. b 44. Worc Coll Ox BA66 MA71 MPhil68 Birm Univ PhD95. Linc Th Coll 70. **d** 72 **p** 73. C Halesowen *Worc* 72-75; Lect Tamilnadu Th Sem India 76-82; Prin WMMTC 82-90; Prin United Coll of Ascension Selly Oak 90-00; Hon Can Birm Cathl *Birm* 97-00; Dir Min and Tr *Leic* from 00; Can Th Leic Cathl from 00. *23 Roundhill Road, Leicester LE5 5RJ* Tel 0116-221 6146 *or* 273 6363 Mobile 07808-586259 E-mail awingate@leicester.anglican.org

WINGATE, Canon David Hugh. b 22. Qu Coll Cam BA48 MA53. Qu Coll Birm 47. **d** 49 **p** 50. C Cov St Mary *Cov* 49-52; V Wolston 52-56; V Cov All SS 56-60; R Patterdale *Carl* 60-66; Chapl United Leeds Hosp 66-71; Chapl Garlands Cumberland and Westmoreland Hosps 71-86; V Cotehill and Cumwhinton *Carl* 72-86; Hon Can Carl Cathl 85-86; rtd 87; Perm to Offic *Carl* from 87-01 and *Bradf* from 02. *Flat 3, 30 Manor Street, Otley LS21 1AX* Tel (01943) 463710

WINGFIELD, Christoper Laurence. b 57. Westmr Coll Ox BTh99. Ripon Coll Cuddesdon DipMin95. **d** 95 **p** 96. C Hadleigh w Layham and Shelley *St E* 95-98; C Hadleigh 98-99; P-in-c Melton 99-00; R 00-01; R Sproughton w Burstall, Copdock w Washbrook etc from 01. *The Rectory, Glebe Close, Sproughton, Ipswich IP8 3BQ* Tel (01473) 241078 Mobile 07703-814022 E-mail chris.wingfield@stedmundsbury.anglican.org

WINGFIELD, Eric John. b 16. Queensland Univ BA51. ACT ThL43 St Fran Coll Brisbane. **d** 44 **p** 44. Australia 44-57; C Westmr St Matt *Lon* 57-58; R Wadingham w Snitterby *Linc* 59-77; V Cowbit 77-78; P-in-c Moulton St Jas 77-78; P-in-c Weston 78; V Cowbit (united benefice) 78-81; rtd 81. *1A Fallowfield, Luton LU3 1UL* Tel (01582) 592208

WINGFIELD DIGBY, Andrew Richard. b 50. Keble Coll Ox BA72. Wycliffe Hall Ox 74. **d** 77 **p** 78. C Cockfosters Ch Ch CD *Lon* 77-80; C Hadley Wood St Paul Prop Chpl 80-84; Dir Chrs in Sport 84-02; V Ox St Andr *Ox* from 02; Six Preacher Cant Cathl *Cant* from 97. *337 Woodstock Road, Oxford OX2 7NX* Tel (01865) 310370 Mobile 07768-611232
E-mail andrew.wingfield.digby@standrewsoxford.org.uk

WINGFIELD DIGBY, The Very Revd Richard Shuttleworth. b 11. Ch Coll Cam BA35 MA39. Westcott Ho Cam 35. **d** 36 **p** 37. C Rugby St Andr *Cov* 36-46; CF (EC) 40-45; V Newmarket All SS *St E* 46-53; R Bury St Mary *Man* 53-66; RD Bury 62-66; Hon Can Man Cathl 65-66; Dean Pet 66-80; rtd 80; Perm to Offic *B & W* from 81. *Byways, Higher Holton, Wincanton BA9 8AP* Tel (01963) 32137

WINKETT, Miss Lucy Clare. b 68. Selw Coll Cam BA90 MA94 ARCM92. Qu Coll Birm BD94. **d** 95 **p** 96. C Lt Ilford St Mich *Chelmsf* 95-97; Min Can and Chapl St Paul's Cathl *Lon* from 97. *7B Amen Court, London EC4M 7BU* Tel (020) 7236 3871 *or* 7246 8323 Fax 7246 8336
E-mail chaplain@stpaulscathedral.org.uk

WINKS, Paul David. b 45. Ex Univ BA67. Cuddesdon Coll 68. **d** 70 **p** 71. C Rickerscote *Lich* 70-73; Chapl RAF 73-75; C Yate *Bris* 76-77; TV Yate New Town 77-83; P-in-c Leigh upon Mendip w Stoke St Michael *B & W* 83-84; V from 84. *The Vicarage, Leigh Street, Leigh upon Mendip, Radstock BA3 5QP* Tel (01373) 812559

WINN, Alan John. b 42. **d** 01 **p** 02. OLM Ringwould w Kingsdown *Cant* from 01. *Chilterns, Back Street, Ringwould, Deal CT14 8HL* Tel (01304) 361030 E-mail johnwinn@beeb.net

WINN, Mrs Jean Elizabeth. b 58. Man Univ BSc80. Wycliffe Hall Ox 85. **d** 88 **p** 98. C W Derby St Luke *Liv* 88-89; Perm to Offic from 97. *St Margaret's Vicarage, Rocky Lane, Liverpool L6 4BA* Tel 0151-264 9669

WINN, Paul William James. b 44. Liv Univ BSc66. EMMTC 86. **d** 89 **p** 90. NSM Spalding St Paul *Linc* 89-98; Perm to Offic 98-00; P-in-c Cowbit 00-01; V from 01. *The Vicarage, 2 Small Drove, Weston, Spalding PE12 6HS* Tel (01406) 373630

WINN, Peter Anthony. b 60. Worc Coll Ox BA82 MA86. Wycliffe Hall Ox 83. **d** 86 **p** 87. C W Derby Gd Shep *Liv* 86-89; V Seaforth 89-02; P-in-c Anfield St Marg from 02. *St Margaret's Vicarage, Rocky Lane, Liverpool L6 4BA* Tel 0151-264 9669

WINN, Simon Reynolds. b 66. Bris Univ BA88. Trin Coll Bris 96. **d** 98 **p** 99. C Portswood Ch Ch *Win* 98-02; V Northolt W End St Jos *Lon* from 02. *St Joseph's Vicarage, 430 Yeading Lane, Northolt UB5 6JS* Tel (020) 8845 6161
E-mail simon.winn@ukgateway.net

WINNARD, Jack. b 30. Oak Hill Th Coll 79. **d** 81 **p** 82. C Skelmersdale St Paul *Liv* 81-84; C Goose Green 84-85; V Wigan St Barn Marsh Green 85-98; rtd 99; Perm to Offic *Liv* from 00. *Maranatha, 11 Beech Walk, Winstanley, Wigan WN3 6DH* Tel (01942) 222339

WINNINGTON-INGRAM, David Robert. b 59. Hertf Coll Ox BA82 MA85 K Coll Cam BA89. Westcott Ho Cam 87. **d** 90 **p** 91. C Bishop's Cleeve *Glouc* 90-94; TV Colyton, Southleigh, Offwell, Widworthy etc *Ex* 94-00; V S Brent and Rattery from 00. *The Vicarage, Firswood, South Brent TQ10 9AN* Tel (01364) 649070

WINSLADE, Richard Clive. b 69. Aston Tr Scheme 91 Linc Th Coll BTh93. **d** 96 **p** 97. C Waltham Cross *St Alb* 96-99; C Leavesden All SS 99-03; R Maulden from 03. *The Rectory, Clophill Road, Maulden, Bedford MK45 2AA* Tel (01525) 403139
E-mail richardjo@rwinslade.fsnet.co.uk

WINSOR, Anthony Geoffrey. b 56. Nottm Univ BTh87 Middx Univ MA92 PhD97. Linc Th Coll 84. **d** 87. C Cobbold Road St Sav w St Mary *Lon* 87-88; Barnardo's CANDL Project 88-89. *2 The Bench, Ham Street, Richmond TW10 7HX* Tel (020) 8940 9978 E-mail tony.winsor@btinternet.com

WINSPER, Arthur William (Brother Benedict). b 46. Glas NSM Course 89. **d** 91 **p** 92. SSF from 70; NSM Barrowfield *Glas* 91-96; P-in-c St Aug Miss Penhalonga Zimbabwe 96-98; Perm to Offic *Worc* from 98. *Society of St Francis, Glasshampton, Shrawley, Worcester WR6 6TQ* Tel (01299) 896345

✠**WINSTANLEY, The Rt Revd Alan Leslie.** b 49. Nottm Univ BTh72. St Jo Coll Nottm 68 ALCD72. **d** 72 **p** 73 **c** 88. C Livesey *Blackb* 72-75; C Gd Sankey *Liv* 75-77; C-in-c Penketh 75-77; V 78-81; SAMS 81-93; Peru 88-93; Bp Bolivia and Peru 88-93; V Eastham *Ches* from 94; Asst Bp Ches from 94. *The Vicarage, Ferry Road, Eastham, Wirral CH62 0AJ* Tel 0151-327 2182 Fax as telephone E-mail bpalan.winstanley@ic24.net

WINSTANLEY, John Graham. b 47. K Coll Lon 67. **d** 71 **p** 72. C Wandsworth St Paul *S'wark* 71-74; Chapl Salford Univ *Man* 75-79; R Kersal Moor 79-87. *14 Lyndhurst Avenue, Prestwich, Manchester M25 0GF* Tel 0161-740 2715 Fax 720 6916
E-mail john@blots.co.uk

WINSTON, Canon Jeremy Hugh. b 54. Trin Coll Carmarthen BEd76 BA CertEd. St Steph Ho Ox 78. **d** 79 **p** 80. C Bassaleg *Mon* 79-83; Dioc Children's Adv 79-89; V Itton and St Arvans w Penterry and Kilgwrrwg etc 83-93; V Abergavenny St Mary w Llanwenarth Citra from 93; RD Abergavenny from 02; Can

St Woolos Cathl from 02. *St Mary's Vicarage, Monk Street, Abergavenny NP7 5ND* Tel (01873) 853168
E-mail jeremy.winston@virgin.net

WINSTONE, Canon Peter John. b 30. Jes Coll Ox BA52 MA56. Ridley Hall Cam 53. **d** 55 **p** 56. C Bitterne *Win* 55-58; C Keighley *Bradf* 58-60; PC Fairweather Green 60-67; V Clapham 67-84; R Leathley w Farnley, Fewston and Blubberhouses 84-95; Hon Can Bradf Cathl 89-95; rtd 95; Perm to Offic *Worc* from 95. *7 Kingfisher Close, Worcester WR5 3RY* Tel (01905) 763114

WINTER, Anthony Cathcart. b 28. FCA. Ridley Hall Cam 54. **d** 56 **p** 57. C Childwall St Dav *Liv* 56-58; C Hackney St Jo *Lon* 58-63; V Newmarket All SS *St E* 63-73; Lic to Offic 74-81; Perm to Offic *Lon* 78-81 and 99; Hon C St Andr-by-the-Wardrobe w St Ann, Blackfriars 81-86; Hon C Smithfield St Bart Gt 86-95; Chapl S'wark Cathl *S'wark* from 99. *25 Bowater House, Fann Street, London EC1Y 0RJ* Tel (020) 7490 5765 Fax 7490 1064

WINTER, Dagmar. b 63. Heidelberg Univ DrTheol96. Herborn Th Sem 93. **d** 96 **p** 97. C Bromley St Mark *Roch* 96-99; C Hexham *Newc* from 99. *3 Dipton Close, Hexham NE46 1UG* Tel (01434) 604935 Fax as telephone
E-mail dagmar@winternet.freeserve.co.uk

WINTER, Canon David Brian. b 29. K Coll Lon BA53 CertEd54. Oak Hill NSM Course. **d** 87 **p** 88. NSM Finchley St Paul and St Luke *Lon* 87-89; Hd of Relig Broadcasting BBC 87-89; Bp's Officer for Evang *Ox* 89-95; P-in-c Ducklington 89-95; Hon Can Ch Ch 95; rtd 95; Hon C Hermitage *Ox* 95-00; Perm to Offic 00-02; Hon C Dorchester from 02. *6 Courtiers Green, Clifton Hampden, Abingdon OX14 3EN* Tel (01865) 407237 Fax as telephone E-mail david_winter@onetel.net.uk

WINTER, Canon Dennis Graham St Leger. b 33. K Coll Lon BSc54 AKC54. Tyndale Hall Bris BD62. **d** 61 **p** 62. C Pennycross *Ex* 61-64; C Maidstone St Faith *Cant* 64-66; V Paddock Wood *Roch* 66-99; RD Tonbridge 89-95; RD Paddock Wood 95-99; Hon Can Roch Cathl 90-99; rtd 99; Perm to Offic *Newc* from 00. *4 Oaky Balks, Alnwick NE66 2QE* Tel (01665) 602658

WINTER, Ernest Philip. b 18. Bris Univ BA49 St Cath Coll Ox BLitt54 MA56. Worc Ord Coll 57. **d** 58 **p** 59. C Worc St Barn w Ch Ch *Worc* 58-61; V Reddal Hill St Luke 61-79; P-in-c Upper Arley 79-86; P-in-c Wribbenhall 81-83; rtd 86; Perm to Offic *Worc* from 86; Perm to Offic *Heref* from 87. *4 Summit Road, Clows Top, Kidderminster DY14 9HN* Tel (01299) 832342

WINTER, Mrs Fiona Helen. b 64. Sheff Univ BSc87. NEOC 97. **d** 00. NSM Gt Ayton w Easby and Newton in Cleveland *York* 00-02. *9 The Acres, Stokesley, Middlesbrough TS9 5QA* Tel (01642) 713146

WINTER, Henry David. b 24. Sarum Th Coll 51. **d** 53 **p** 54. C Hope St Jas *Man* 53-55; C Heywood St Luke 55-58; R Hulme St Mich 58-63; Chapl Essex Co Hosp Colchester 63-85; V Colchester St Paul *Chelmsf* 63-95; rtd 95; Perm to Offic *Chelmsf* from 95. *24 Valley Crescent, West Bergholt, Colchester CO6 3ED* Tel (01206) 242455

WINTER, Jonathan Gay. b 37. Lon Inst of Educn DipEd84. AKC64. **d** 65 **p** 66. C W Dulwich All SS and Em *S'wark* 65-69; Asst Master Kidbrooke Sch 69-77; Norwood Sch 77-80; Dep Hd Lewisham Sch 80-89; Hon C Dulwich St Barn from 90; Chapl Dulwich Coll 95-98; Cllr from 98; Dean of MSE (Woolwich) from 00. *160 Turney Road, London SE21 7JJ* Tel and fax (020) 7274 3060 Mobile 07811-529503
E-mail jonathanwinter@btinternet.com

WINTER, Nichola Jane. b 58. Trevelyan Coll Dur BA79. Dioc OLM tr scheme 99. **d** 02. OLM Aldeburgh w Hazlewood *St E* from 02. *Threeways, Donkey Lane, Friston, Saxmundham IP17 1PL* Tel (01728) 688979 E-mail njwinter@lineone.net

WINTER, Raymond McMahon. b 23. FSA73 Selw Coll Cam BA52 MA60. Wycliffe Hall Ox 59. **d** 61 **p** 62. C Gaywood, Bawsey and Mintlyn *Nor* 61-64; P-in-c Horstead w Frettenham w Stanninghall 64-71; Youth Chapl 64-71; Warden Dioc Conf Ho 64-71; Chapl Loretto Sch Musselburgh 71-74; P-in-c Latchingdon w Mundon and N Fambridge *Chelmsf* 74-75; P-in-c Brettenham w Rushford *Nor* 75-83; P-in-c Riddlesworth w Gasthorpe and Knettishall 76-83; P-in-c Garboldisham w Blo' Norton 77-83; Chapl Bedgebury Sch Kent 83-91; Hon C Kilndown *Cant* 83-87; Hon C Goudhurst w Kilndown 87-91; Warden Coll of St Barn Lingfield 88-94; rtd 91; Perm to Offic *Nor* from 94. *27 Breydon Road, Norwich NR7 8EF* Tel (01602) 484489

WINTER, Stephen Christopher. b 55. Southn Univ BA76. Trin Coll Bris 85. **d** 88 **p** 89. C Birm St Luke *Birm* 88-92; TV Kings Norton 92-98; Ind Chapl *Worc* from 98. *1 Marlborough Avenue, Bromsgrove B60 2PG* Tel (01527) 575737
E-mail stephen@winter5.fsnet.co.uk

WINTER, Thomas Andrew. b 24. Wadh Coll Ox BA51 MA63. Ely Th Coll 51. **d** 53 **p** 54. C Horninglow *Lich* 53-56; S Africa 56-83; R Woodston *Ely* 83-90; rtd 90; Perm to Offic *Ely* 90-97; *Chich* from 90. *6 The Close, Shoreham-by-Sea BN43 5AH* Tel (01273) 452606

WINTERBOTHAM, Canon Anthony James Marshall. b 27. Magd Coll Cam BA51 MA55. Wells Th Coll 55. **d** 57 **p** 58. C Portsea St Mary *Portsm* 57-63; Asst Chapl Wellington Coll Berks 63-67; Hon Chapl Portsm Cathl *Portsm* from 67; Hon Can

90-91; Chapl and Hd of RE Portsm Gr Sch 67-91; rtd 92; Perm to Offic *Portsm* from 92. *4 Poynings Place, St Nicholas Street, Portsmouth PO1 2PB* Tel (023) 9282 5068 Mobile 07761-222375 E-mail tonywinterbotham@compuserve.com

WINTERBOTTOM, Canon Ian Edmund. b 42. St Andr Univ MA66 Nottm Univ DipTh68. Linc Th Coll 66. **d** 68 **p** 69. C Blackb St Steph *Blackb* 68-71; C Wingerworth *Derby* 71-73; P-in-c Brimington 73-77; R 77-89; RD Bolsover and Staveley 86-93; R Pleasley 89-94; P-in-c Shirebrook 92-94; TR E Scarsdale 94-00; Hon Can Derby Cathl from 95; Ind Chapl from 00. *The Vicarage, Barrow-on-Trent, Derby DE72 1HA* Tel (01332) 703350 E-mail ianwinterbottom@compuserve.com

WINTERBOURNE, George. b 20. ERD61. S'wark Ord Course 64. **d** 67 **p** 68. C Cove St Jo *Guildf* 67-71; Perm to Offic 72; Hon C Aldershot St Mich 73-78; Perm to Offic *B & W* 79-80; Lic to Offic 80-87; rtd 87; Perm to Offic *Glouc* 87-99. *4 Lawn Crescent, Shurdington, Cheltenham GL51 5UR* Tel (01242) 862671

WINTERBURN, Derek Neil. b 60. Bris Univ BSc63 Ox Univ BA85. Wycliffe Hall Ox 83. **d** 86 **p** 87. C Mildmay Grove St Jude and St Paul *Lon* 86-89; C Hackney Marsh 89-91; TV 91-96; V Hampton St Mary from 96. *St Mary's Vicarage, Church Street, Hampton TW12 2EB* Tel (020) 8979 3071 Fax 8941 7221 E-mail stmary@bigfoot.com

WINTERBURN, Ieuan Thomas. b 16. Univ of Wales BA37 Univ of S Africa BA48 Witwatersrand Univ MA52. K Coll Lon 37. **d** 39 **p** 40. C Llanelli *St D* 39-44; S Africa 44-59 and 70-72; C Cheam *S'wark* 59-60; V Champion Hill *S'wark* 60-64; Seychelles 64-68; Adn Seychelles 64-68; Dean Mahe 66-68; Deputations Sec USPG *Win* 68-69; Rhodesia 72-80; Zimbabwe 80-81; V Borth and Eglwys-fach w Llangynfelyn *St D* 81-85; rtd 85. *Moorhavens Home of the Aged, PO Box 31, Winkelspruit, South Africa*

WINTERBURN, Maurice. b 14. Oak Hill Th Coll 61. **d** 62 **p** 63. C Bethnal Green St Jas Less *Lon* 62-65; C Ealing St Mary 65-68; V Stambermill *Worc* 68-79; P-in-c The Lye 74-79; rtd 79; Perm to Offic *Worc* from 79. *36 Whittingham Road, Halesowen B63 3TF* Tel 0121-550 0434

WINTLE, Anthony Robert. b 44. K Coll Lon 64. St Mich Coll Llan DipTh68. **d** 68 **p** 69. C Llandaff N *Llan* 68-70; C Baglan 70-75; V Treharris 75-86; V Treharris w Bedlinog 86-90; R St Fagans w Michaelston-super-Ely from 90. *The Rectory, Greenwood Lane, St Fagans, Cardiff CF5 6EL* Tel (029) 2056 5869

WINTLE, David Robert. b 56. Open Univ BA84. Qu Coll Birm 93. **d** 95 **p** 96. C Cov St Mary *Cov* 95-00; P-in-c Baginton w Bubbenhall and Ryton-on-Dunsmore from 00; P-in-c Baginton from 02. *The Vicarage, Church Road, Ryton on Dunsmore, Coventry CV8 3ET* Tel (024) 7630 1283 E-mail david@wintled.fsnet.co.uk

WINTLE, Graham. b 52. Bris Univ BSc73. Oak Hill Th Coll BA86. **d** 86 **p** 87. C Southgate *Chich* 86-89; C New Malden and Coombe *S'wark* 89-92; V Surbiton Hill Ch Ch from 92. *Christ Church Vicarage, 7 Christ Church Road, Surbiton KT5 8JJ* Tel (020) 8399 3444 *or* 8390 7215 E-mail gwintle@blueyonder.co.uk

WINTLE, Canon Ruth Elizabeth. b 31. Westf Coll Lon BA53 St Hugh's Coll Ox BA67 MA74. St Mich Ho Ox 63. **dss** 72 **d** 87 **p** 94. Tutor St Jo Coll Dur 72-74; Selection Sec ACCM 74-83; St Jo in Bedwardine *Worc* 83-87; Par Dn 87-94; Dir of Ords 84-92; Hon Can Worc Cathl 87-97; rtd 95; Bp's Adv on Women's Min *Worc* 95-97; Perm to Offic from 98. *Westwood, Claphill Lane, Rushwick, Worcester WR2 5TP* Tel (01905) 422841

WINTON, Alan Peter. b 58. Sheff Univ BA83 PhD87. Linc Th Coll 91. **d** 91 **p** 92. C Southgate Ch Ch *Lon* 91-95; P-in-c St Paul's Walden *St Alb* 95-99; Dioc CME Officer 95-02; R Welwyn w Ayot St Peter from 99. *The Rectory, 2 Ottway Walk, Welwyn AL6 9DS* Tel (01438) 714150 E-mail rector@welwyn.org.uk

WINTON, Ms Philippa Mary. b 56. Nottm Univ BA78. Trin Coll Bris DipHE82. **dss** 83 **d** 87 **p** 94. Sheff St Jo *Sheff* 83-86; Sheff Gillcar St Silas 86-87; Chapl Asst R Hallamshire Hosp Sheff 87; Hon Par Dn Linc St Faith and St Martin w St Pet *Linc* 90-92; Chapl Asst W Middx Univ Hosp Isleworth 92-93; Perm to Offic *Lon* 93-95; Perm to Offic *St Alb* from 95. *The Rectory, 2 Ottway Walk, Welwyn AL6 9DS* Tel (01438) 714150

WINTON, Stanley Wootton. b 30. Sarum & Wells Th Coll 70. **d** 72 **p** 73. C Birkenhead St Jas w St Bede *Ches* 72-75; V 75-79; TR Ellesmere Port 79-88; Chapl Ellesmere Port and Manor Hosps 79-95; R Delamere *Ches* 88-95; rtd 95; Perm to Offic *Ches* from 95. *26 Wimborne Avenue, Thingwall, Wirral CH61 7UL* Tel 0151-648 0176

WINWARD, Stuart James. b 36. Open Univ BA85. Lich Th Coll 65. **d** 68 **p** 69. C Lytham St Cuth *Blackb* 68-71; C Padiham 71-73; V Musbury 73-84; R Old Trafford St Hilda *Man* 84-89; V Davyhulme St Mary 89-98; rtd 98; Perm to Offic *Ches* from 99. *1 Walnut Grove, Sale M33 6AJ* Tel 0161-905 1039

WIPPELL, David Stanley. b 46. Queensland Univ BSc67 Selw Coll Cam BA77 MA. Westcott Ho Cam 76. **d** 78 **p** 79. C Wolvercote w Summertown *Ox* 78-80; Asst Chapl St Edw Sch Ox 78-00; Chapl from 00; Housemaster 85-97; Chapl St Hugh's Coll Ox 80-85. *St Edward's School, Woodstock Road, Oxford OX2 7NN* Tel (01865) 319271 Fax 319206 E-mail wippell@aol.com

WISBECH, Archdeacon of. *See* BEER, The Ven John Stuart

WISE, David Reginald. b 46. Glas Univ BSc68 QUB PhD74 LRAM67. Edin Th Coll 72. **d** 74 **p** 75. Chapl St Andr Cathl *Ab* 74-75; C Ayr *Glas* 75-78; R Airdrie 78-81; P-in-c Gartcosh 78-81; P-in-c Leic St Nic *Leic* 81-82; Chapl Leic Univ 81-89; TV Leic H Spirit 82-89; Chapl St Hilda's Priory and Sch Whitby 89-96; TV Louth *Linc* 96-98; V Mexborough *Sheff* from 98. *The Vicarage, Church Street, Mexborough S64 0ER* Tel (01709) 582321

WISE, Ms Pamela Margaret. b 51. CertEd73 BA79. Ripon Coll Cuddesdon 89. **d** 91 **p** 94. Par Dn Tokyngton St Mich *Lon* 91-94; C N Greenford All Hallows 94; C Bedford All SS *St Alb* 94-97; TV Hitchin from 97. *St Faith's Vicarage, 31 Meadowbank, Hitchin SG4 0HY* Tel (01462) 432179 E-mail pamelawise@dtn.ntl.com

WISE, Richard Edmund. b 67. Clare Coll Cam BA88 MusB89 LRAM91. Cranmer Hall Dur 01. **d** 03. C Stanmore *Win* from 03. *St Mark's House, Oliver's Battery Crescent, Winchester SO22 4EU* Tel (01962) 861970 E-mail rwise@fish.co.uk

WISEMAN, David John. b 51. Lon Univ BD80 Birm Univ Dip Islam87. Cranmer Hall Dur 77. **d** 80 **p** 81. C Bilston *Lich* 80-84; P-in-c W Bromwich St Phil 84-86; V 86-89; P-in-c Cheetham St Mark *Man* 89-94; Dioc Community Relns Officer 89-96; P-in-c Ashton H Trin 94-99; TR Ashton from 00; Chapl Tameside Coll from 94. *Holy Trinity Vicarage, Dean Street, Ashton-under-Lyne OL6 7HD* Tel 0161-344 0075 E-mail david@wiseman50.freeserve.co.uk

WISEMAN, John. b 56. Sarum & Wells Th Coll 80. **d** 83 **p** 84. C Swinton St Pet *Man* 83-87; C Swinton and Pendlebury 87-88; TV Atherton 88-93; V Bedford Leigh 93-02; V Lt Lever from 02. *The Vicarage, Market Street, Little Lever, Bolton BL3 1HH* Tel (01204) 700936

WISHART, Michael Leslie. b 45. St Mich Coll Llan DipTh73. **d** 73 **p** 74. C Llangyfelach *S & B* 73-76; Chapl RN 77-80 and 85-96; Chapl RNR 80-85; V Beguildy and Heyope *S & B* 80-84; V Gowerton 84-85; R Dowlais *Llan* from 97. *The Rectory, Gwernllwyn Road, Dowlais, Merthyr Tydfil CF48 3NA* Tel (01685) 722118

WISKEN, Canon Brian Leonard. b 34. Dur Univ BA58. Linc Th Coll 58. **d** 60 **p** 61. C Lobley Hill *Dur* 60-63; C Ipswich All Hallows *St E* 63-65; P-in-c Scunthorpe All SS *Linc* 65-69; V 69-71; Dioc Stewardship Adv 70-75; R Panton w Wragby 71-75; V Langton by Wragby 71-75; R Cleethorpes 75-77; TR 77-89; V Linc St Nic w St Jo Newport 89-99; Can and Preb Linc Cathl 88-00; rtd 99; Perm to Offic *Nor* and *St E* from 99. *49 Gainsborough Drive, Lowestoft NR32 4NJ* Tel (01502) 512378 E-mail brian@wisken.fslife.co.uk

WISKEN, Robert Daniel. b 30. ACT. **d** 60 **p** 60. C N Rockhampton St Barn Australia 60; V N Rockhampton St Matt 61-63; V Winton *Man* 63-65; R Luddington w Hemington and Thurning *Pet* 65-69; P-in-c Clopton *St E* 66-69; V Ipswich All SS 69-73; V Sompting *Chich* 74-78; Org Sec (SW England) CECS 78-80; R Edmundbyers w Muggleswick *Dur* 80-83; R Wexham *Ox* 83-86; Australia 86-03; rtd 95. *19C Park Road, Exmouth EX8 1TN*

WITCHELL, David William. b 47. St Jo Coll Nottm BTh75 LTh75. **d** 75 **p** 76. C Northampton St Mary *Pet* 75-78; C Oakham w Hambleton and Egleton 78-81; C Oakham, Hambleton, Egleton, Braunston and Brooke 81-82; V Weedon Bec w Everdon 82-90; V Wellingborough St Barn 90-00; RD Wellingborough 98-00; P-in-c Paignton St Paul Preston *Ex* 00-02; V Paignton Ch Ch and Preston St Paul from 03; RD Torbay from 03. *St Paul's Vicarage, Locarno Avenue, Paignton TQ3 2DH* Tel (01803) 522872

WITCHELL, Derek William Frederick. b 49. Ox Poly DipArch78. St Alb and Ox Min Course 00. **d** 03. *8 Onslow Drive, Thame OX9 3YX* Tel (01844) 212064 Fax as telephone E-mail derek@witchell.psa-online.com

WITCHER, Ian. b 49. CertEd93 Lon Inst of Educn Lic97. **d** 97 **p** 98. NSM Shaston *Sarum* from 97. *7 Old Boundary Road, Shaftesbury SP7 8ND* Tel (01747) 854878

WITCOMBE, John Julian. b 59. Cam Univ MA84 Nottm Univ MPhil91. St Jo Coll Nottm BA83 DPS84. **d** 84 **p** 85. C Birtley *Dur* 84-87; C Chilwell *S'well* 87-91; V Lodge Moor St Luke *Sheff* 91-95; TR Uxbridge *Lon* 95-98; Dean St Jo Coll Nottm from 98; Public Preacher *S'well* from 98. *7 Peache Way, Chilwell Lane, Beeston, Nottingham NG9 3DX* Tel 0115-922 4046

WITCOMBE, Michael David. b 53. Univ of Wales (Lamp) BA76. Qu Coll Birm 76. **d** 78 **p** 79. C Neath w Llantwit *Llan* 78-80; C Whitchurch 80-83; V Newcastle 83-02; P-in-c Ewenny 84-86; V Llanishen from 02. *The Vicarage, 2 The Rise, Llanishen, Cardiff CF14 0RA* Tel (029) 2075 2545

WITCOMBE, Ricarda Jane. b 64. Ch Coll Cam BA86 MA90 Nottm Univ MA(TS)99. St Jo Coll Nottm 98. **d** 01 **p** 02. C Wilford *S'well* from 01. *7 Peache Way, Chilwell Lane, Beeston, Nottingham NG9 3DX* Tel 0115-922 4046 E-mail ricarda@ricarda.fsnet.co.uk

WITCOMBE, Simon Christopher. b 61. Dundee Univ MA83 PGCE84 Dur Univ BA90. St Jo Coll Dur 88. **d** 91 **p** 92. C Earlham St Anne *Nor* 91-95; Assoc P Skegness and Winthorpe *Linc* 95-98; Gen Preacher 95-98; R Woodhall Spa Gp from 98.

The Vicarage, Alverston Avenue, Woodhall Spa LN10 6SN Tel (01526) 353856 E-mail witcombe@tinyonline.co.uk

WITHERIDGE, John Stephen. b 53. Kent Univ BA76 Ch Coll Cam BA78 MA82 FRSA98. Ridley Hall Cam 78. **d** 79 **p** 80. C Luton St Mary *St Alb* 79-82; Asst Chapl Marlborough Coll 82-84; Abp's Chapl *Cant* 84-87; Conduct Eton Coll 87-96; Hd Charterhouse Sch Godalming from 96; Perm to Offic *Guildf* from 96. *Charterhouse, Godalming, Surrey GU7 2DJ* Tel (01483) 291600 Fax 291647

WITHERS, Mrs Christine Mary. b 37. ALA60. Gilmore Ho DipRS81. **dss** 81 **d** 87 **p** 94. Chorleywood Ch Ch *St Alb* 81-86; Darley *Derby* 86-92; C 87-92; Chapl HM Pris Drake Hall 92-95; P-in-c Standon and Cotes Heath *Lich* 96-98; rtd 02. *St Mary's Close, Westbury, Shrewsbury SY5 9QX* Tel (01743) 885038

WITHERS, Geoffrey Edward. b 68. QUB BSc90 TCD BTh93. CITC 90. **d** 93 **p** 94. C Ballymena w Ballyclug *Conn* 93-97; I Monkstown 97-01; Chapl RAF from 01. *Chaplaincy Services (RAF), HQ, Personnel and Training Command, RAF Innsworth, Gloucester GL3 1EZ* Tel (01452) 712612 ext 5164 Fax 510828 E-mail geoffwithers@bigfoot.com

WITHERS, Gillian. b 58. BEd80. **d** 97 **p** 98. NSM Mossley *Conn* 97-03; C Bangor St Comgall *D & D* from 03. *17 Grange Road, Bangor BT20 3QQ* Tel (028) 9145 6638 E-mail vicarofdibley4@hotmail.com

WITHERS, John Geoffrey. b 39. St Jo Coll Dur BA61 Birm Univ CertEd63 Reading Univ Dip Educn Guidance 70 CQSW72. SW Minl Tr Course 84. **d** 87 **p** 88. NSM Drewsteignton *Ex* 87-99; P-in-c 99-01; Sub Chapl HM Pris Ex from 96; P-in-c Hittisleigh and Spreyton *Ex* 99-01; P-in-c Chagford, Drewsteignton, Hittisleigh etc 01; C from 01. *St Levan, Broomhill, Chagford, Newton Abbot TQ13 8DD* Tel (01647) 432340

WITHERS, Michael. b 41. TCD BA66 Edin Univ BD70 QUB MTh83 Birm Univ PGCE67. Union Th Sem (NY) STM71. **d** 71 **p** 73. C Seagoe *D & D* 71-77; C Seapatrick 77-80; I Belfast St Chris 80-89; I Movilla 89-96; rtd 96. *11 Earlswood Road, Belfast BT4 3DY* Tel (028) 9047 1037

WITHERS, Michael Selby. b 36. Sheff Univ BA61 PGCE62 Univ of Wales (Swansea) 75. St Alb and Ox Min Course 93. **d** 96 **p** 97. NSM Bletchley *Ox* 96-97; NSM Ellesborough, The Kimbles and Stoke Mandeville 97-01; NSM Risborough from 01. *Penjarrick House, Main Road, Lacey Green, Princes Risborough HP27 0QU* Tel (01844) 274424

WITHERS GREEN, Timothy. b 30. K Coll Lon 51. **d** 55 **p** 56. C Greenhill St Jo *Lon* 55-58; C St Helier *S'wark* 58-61; V Belmont 61-79; CF (TA) 71-79; R Hexham *Newc* 79-84; R Weldon w Deene *Pet* 84-95; rtd 95; Perm to Offic *Pet* from 95. *2 Benefield Road, Oundle, Peterborough PE8 4ET* Tel (01832) 273957

WITHEY, Michael John. b 45. Open Univ BA80 Ox Univ MTh98. Oak Hill Th Coll 71. **d** 74 **p** 75. C St Alb St Paul *St Alb* 74-76; C Luton St Mary 77; C Luton St Fran 77-80; V Woodside w E Hyde 80-87; CF (TA) 83-87; Dioc Stewardship Adv *Ox* 87-89; Chapl HM YOI Onley 89-91; V Hengoed w Gobowen *Lich* 91-95; Chapl Robert Jones and Agnes Hunt Orthopaedic Hosp 91-95; P-in-c Chasetown *Lich* 95-00; V 00-02; V Stroud H Trin *Glouc* from 02; Chapl Cotswold and Vale Primary Care Trust from 02; Chapl Glos Partnership Trust from 02. *Holy Trinity Vicarage, 10 Bowbridge Lane, Stroud GL5 2JW* Tel (01453) 764551

WITHINGTON, Brian James. b 54. Sheff Poly CQSW76 Leic Univ MSc01. EAMTC 94. **d** 97 **p** 98. NSM Pet St Jo *Pet* from 97. *8 Livermore Green, Werrington, Peterborough PE4 5DG* Tel (01733) 322918 E-mail brian@bwithington.freeserve.co.uk

WITHINGTON, George Kenneth. b 37. Birm Univ BA59. Wells Th Coll 59. **d** 61 **p** 62. C Hartcliffe St Andr CD *Bris* 61-65; V Swindon St Jo 65-73; V Cricklade w Latton 73-97; RD Cricklade 94-97; rtd 97; Perm to Offic *Heref* and *Worc* from 97. *19 Oak Drive, Colwall, Malvern WR13 6RA* Tel (01684) 541899

WITHINGTON, Canon Keith. b 32. Univ of Wales (Lamp) BA55. Qu Coll Birm 55. **d** 57 **p** 58. C Bournville *Birm* 57-61; V 61-00; RD Moseley 81-91; Hon Can Birm Cathl 83-00; rtd 00; Perm to Offic *Birm* and *Worc* from 00. *44 Dugard Way, Droitwich WR9 8UX* Tel (01905) 795847 E-mail kw1000@bushinternet.com

WITHINGTON, Paul Martin. b 60. Kent Univ BSc86. Trin Coll Bris 01. **d** 03. C Elworth and Warmingham *Ches* from 03. *80 Abbey Road, Sandbach CW11 3HB* Tel (01270) 764014

WITHNELL, Roderick David. b 55. Leic Univ Cert Th & Past Studies 89. EMMTC 86 Ridley Hall Cam 89. **d** 90 **p** 91. C Shenfield *Chelmsf* 90-94; C Woodleigh and Loddiswell *Ex* 94-95; TV Modbury, Bigbury, Ringmore w Kingston etc 95-00; Canada 00-01; TR Burrington, Chawleigh, Cheldon, Chulmleigh etc *Ex* from 01. *The Rectory, Chulmleigh EX18 7BY* Tel (01769) 580537

WITHY, John Daniel Forster. b 38. Bible Tr Inst Glas CertRK61 ALCD64. **d** 64 **p** 65. C Belfast St Aid *Conn* 64-68; Dir Chr Conf Cen Sion Mills from 68. *Zion House, 120 Melmont Road, Strabane BT82 9ET* Tel (028) 8165 8672

WITT, Bryan Douglas. b 52. St Mich Coll Llan BD84. **d** 84 **p** 85. C Betws w Ammanford *St D* 84-87; V Llanllwni 87-91; V

Llangennech and Hendy from 91. *The Vicarage, Mwrwg Road, Llangennech, Llanelli SA14 8UA* Tel (01554) 820324

WITTER, Mrs Tania Judy Ingram. b 37. Girton Coll Cam BA58 MA63. St Jo Coll Nottm Dip Past Counselling 95 Oak Hill Th Coll 94. **d** 95 **p** 96. NSM Highbury Ch Ch w St Jo and St Sav Lon from 95. *27 Arvon Road, London N5 1PL* Tel (020) 7607 3156 Fax as telephone

WITTS, Donald Roger. b 47. Cranmer Hall Dur 86. **d** 88 **p** 89. C Leyland St Ambrose *Blackb* 88-90; C Staines St Mary and St Pet *Lon* 90-93; Ind Missr *Man* 93-95; Dioc Communications Officer *Cant* 95-00; P-in-c Blean 95-01; P-in-c Birchington w Acol and Minnis Bay 01-03; V from 03. *All Saints' Vicarage, 15 Minnis Road, Birchington CT7 9SE* Tel (01843) 841117 E-mail don.witts@ukonline.co.uk

WITTS, Graham Robert. b 53. Newc Univ BEd Bris Univ MA01. Linc Th Coll 79. **d** 82 **p** 83. C Horncastle w Low Toynton *Linc* 82-85; TV Gt Grimsby St Mary and St Jas 85-89; TR Yelverton, Meavy, Sheepstor and Walkhampton *Ex* 89-93; C Glastonbury w Meare *B & W* 93-03; RD Glastonbury 00-03; V Burnham from 03. *The Vicarage, Rectory Road, Burnham-on-Sea TA8 2BZ* Tel (01278) 782991 E-mail thewittsonweb@hotmail.com

WITTS, Paul Michael. b 58. Man Univ MA(Theol)95 Sheff Poly BN86 Sheff Univ MSc88 RMN79 RGN86 DipEd83 DN92. St Steph Ho Ox 94. **d** 96 **p** 97. C Bamber Bridge St Aid *Blackb* 96-98; C Halifax *Wakef* 98-01; Spirituality and Soc Exclusion Adv 98-01; V S Elmsall from 01. *St Mary's Vicarage, Doncaster Road, South Elmsall, Pontefract WF9 2HS* Tel (01977) 642861 Fax as telephone E-mail kbs64@dial.pipex.com

WIXON, Jack. b 44. Lich Th Coll 68. **d** 71 **p** 72. C Adlington *Blackb* 71-74; C St Annes 74-76; V Chorley St Jas 76-82; V Preston Em 82-94; V Ribby w Wrea from 94. *The Vicarage, 1 Vicarage Close, Wrea Green, Preston PR4 2PQ* Tel (01772) 687644

WOADDEN, Christopher Martyn. b 56. St Jo Coll Nottm LTh. **d** 87 **p** 88. C Mickleover All SS *Derby* 87-90; C Wirksworth w Alderwasley, Carsington etc 90-92; C Wirksworth 92; TV Gt and Lt Coates w Bradley *Linc* 92-98; V Holton-le-Clay and Tetney from 98. *The Vicarage, Church Walk, Holton-le-Clay, Grimsby DN36 5AN* Tel (01472) 824082

WOAN, Miss Susan Ann. b 52. Univ of Wales (Abth) BSc71 Ch Ch Coll Cant MA91 Rob Coll Cam BA95. Ridley Hall Cam BA93 CTM93. **d** 96 **p** 97. C Histon *Ely* 96-97; C Radipole and Melcombe Regis *Sarum* 97-00; Chapl Bournemouth and Poole Coll of FE *Win* from 00; Hon C Bournemouth St Jo w St Mich from 00; Perm to Offic *Sarum* from 00. *1 Gervis Road, Bournemouth BH1 3ED* Tel (01202) 291289

WODEHOUSE, Armine Boyle. b 24. Oak Hill Th Coll 83. **d** 86 **p** 86. NSM Gt Parndon *Chelmsf* 86-92; Perm to Offic *Eur* 89-92; Chapl Menton 92-99; rtd 99. *Flat 12, 105 Onslow Square, London SW7 3LU* Tel (020) 7584 4845

WODEHOUSE, Carol Lylie. See KIMBERLEY, Countess of

WODEMAN, Cyril Peter Guy. b 28. Qu Coll Cam BA50 MA55 ARCO54 LRAM58 ARCM58. Cranmer Hall Dur 72. **d** 73 **p** 74. C Penwortham St Mary *Blackb* 73-77; V Burnley St Steph 77-85; V Hornby w Claughton 85-93; rtd 93; Perm to Offic *Blackb* and *Carl* from 93. *5 Harling Bank, Kirkby Lonsdale, Carnforth LA6 2DJ* Tel (01524) 272474

WOFFENDEN (née HANCOCK), Mrs Dorothy Myfanwy. b 41. N Ord Course 01. **d** 03. NSM Brinnington w Portwood *Ches* from 03. *8 Churchill Crescent, Marple, Stockport SK6 6HJ* Tel 0161-427 6839 E-mail dwoffenden@smartone.co.uk

WOLFE, Canon Michael Matheson. b 27. Pemb Coll Ox BA49 MA53. Cuddesdon Coll 51. **d** 53 **p** 54. C Moorfields *Bris* 53-57; P-in-c Fochabers *Mor* 57-58; Sub-Warden Aberlour Orphanage 58-59; V Southport St Paul *Liv* 59-65; V Upholland 65-73; TR 73-82; RD Ormskirk 78-82; Hon Can Liv Cathl 78-82; Can Res Liv Cathl 82-96; Merseyside Ecum Officer 82-96; AD Toxteth and Wavertree 89-96; rtd 96; Perm to Offic *Liv* from 97; Hon Chapl Liv Cathl from 97. *23 Hunters Lane, Liverpool L15 8HL* Tel 0151-733 1541

WOLFENDEN, Peter Graham. b 40. St Pet Coll Ox BA63 MA66. Linc Th Coll 62. **d** 64 **p** 65. C Adlington *Blackb* 64-66; Asst Master Barton Peveril Gr Sch 66-69; Chapl Bp Wordsworth Sch Salisbury 69-72; Hon C Bishopstoke *Win* 66-72; Hon C Ponteland *Newc* 72-02; Hd Master Richard Coates Middle Sch Ponteland 78-01; Chapl Malta and Gozo *Eur* from 02. *75 Rodolphe Street, Sliema SLM14, Malta GC* Tel (00356) 2133 0575 Fax 2133 4677

WOLLASTON, Canon Barbara Kathleen. b 30. LSE BSc(Soc)64. Gilmore Ho 51. **d** 87 **p** 94. Dir Past Studies Qu Coll Birm 80-89; Dioc Dir of Ords *S'wark* 89-94; rtd 94. *21 Chapel Street, Wem, Shrewsbury SY4 5ER* Tel (01939) 232229

WOLLEY, John. BSc. **d** 85 **p** 86. Hon C Croydon St Aug *S'wark* 85-89; Perm to Offic *Linc* 89-01. *7 Royal Oak Court, Upgate, Louth LN11 9JA* Tel (01507) 601614

WOLLEY, Richard. b 33. Ox Univ MA. S Dios Minl Tr Scheme 82. **d** 85 **p** 86. NSM Brighton Resurr *Chich* 85-88; C 88-89; C Brighton St Geo w St Anne and St Mark 89-91; R Buxted and

Hadlow Down 91-98; rtd 98. *35 Scarletts Close, Uckfield TN22 2BA* Tel (01825) 761042

WOLSTENCROFT, The Ven Alan. b 37. Cuddesdon Coll. **d** 69 **p** 70. C Halliwell St Thos *Man* 69-71; C Stand 71-73; V Wythenshawe St Martin 73-80; AD Withington 78-91; Chapl Wythenshawe Hosp Man 80-89; V Baguley *Man* 80-91; V Bolton St Pet 91-98; Hon Can Man Cathl 86-98; Can Res Man Cathl from 98; Adn Man from 98. *2 The Walled Garden, Swinton, Manchester M27 0FR* Tel 0161-794 2401 Fax 794 2411 E-mail archdeaconalan@wolstencrofta.fsnet.co.uk

WOLSTENHULME, Arthur James. b 20. Leeds Univ BA42. Coll of Resurr Mirfield 42. **d** 44 **p** 46. C Tonge Moor *Man* 44-45; C Hollinwood 45-48; C Walsall St Mary and All SS Palfrey *Lich* 48-52; V Cov St Pet *Cov* 52-56; V New Bilton 56-66; R Kingsthorpe *Pet* 66-73; TR Kingsthorpe w Northampton St Dav 73-86; rtd 86; Perm to Offic *Pet* from 86. *2 Springbanks Way, Northampton NN4 0QA* Tel (01604) 766405 Fax as telephone

WOLVERHAMPTON, Area Bishop of. *See* BOURKE, The Rt Revd Michael Gay

WOLVERSON, Marc Ali Morad. b 68. Univ of Kansas BA91. Ripon Coll Cuddesdon DipMin96. **d** 96 **p** 97. C Nantwich *Ches* 96-99; Baton Rouge St Luke USA 99-00; Assoc V Bramhall *Ches* from 00. *17 Syddal Road, Bramhall, Stockport SK7 1AB* Tel 0161-439 0994 E-mail frmarc@onetel.net.uk

WOOD, Mrs Ann Rene. b 49. St Deiniol's Hawarden 87. **d** 90 **p** 94. Par Dn Bamber Bridge St Aid *Blackb* 90-93; C W Burnley 93-95; V Marton Moss 95-00; Hon Can Blackb Cathl 98-00; R Whiston *Sheff* from 00. *The Rectory, Doles Lane, Whiston, Rotherham S60 4JA* Tel (01709) 364430 E-mail ann.wood@ukonline.co.uk

WOOD (née BLACKBURN), Mrs Anne Dorothy. b 54. Keele Univ BA76 Huddersfield Univ DPSE89 Bradf Univ MSc90. N Ord Course 95. **d** 98 **p** 99. NSM Batley St Thos *Wakef* 98-00; Jt P-in-c Morley St Paul 01-02; C Bruntcliffe 01-02; C Morley 02-03; TV from 03. *St Paul's Vicarage, 2 Bridge Court, Morley, Leeds LS27 0BD* Tel 0113-238 1037 Mobile 07769-503147 E-mail anne.d.wood@talk21.com

WOOD, Anthony James. b 38. Kelham Th Coll 58. **d** 63 **p** 64. C Shrewsbury St Alkmund *Lich* 63; C Harlescott 63-66; C Porthill 66-70; P-in-c Priorslee 70-76; Chapl Telford Town Cen 73-74; V Barton-under-Needwood 76-97; V Barton under Needwood w Dunstall from 97; RD Tutbury from 02. *The Vicarage, 3 Church Lane, Barton under Needwood, Burton-on-Trent DE13 8HU* Tel (01283) 712359

WOOD, The Ven Arnold. b 18. Clifton Th Coll 66. **d** 65 **p** 66. C Kirkheaton *Wakef* 65-67; V Mount Pellon 67-73; R Lanreath *Truro* 73-81; V Pelynt 73-81; RD W Wivelshire 76-81; Lib Truro Cathl 81-88; Can Res Truro Cathl 81-88; Adn Cornwall 81-88; Warden Community of the Epiphany Truro 85-00; rtd 88; Perm to Offic *Truro* from 00. *13 Groveville, Northedge Lane, Hipperholme, Halifax HX3 8LD* Tel (01422) 207014 E-mail awood.cobblers@virgin.net

WOOD, Barbara Ann. b 49. St Mich Coll Llan 00. **d** 02 **p** 03. C Glan Ely *Llan* from 02. *12 Mansell Avenue, Cardiff CF5 4TB* Tel (029) 2084 3242 E-mail babswood01@hotmail.com

WOOD, Barry. b 56. CQSW81 CYCW81 Open Univ BA87 Sheff Univ MMin01. St Steph Ho Ox 87. **d** 89 **p** 90. C Tranmere St Paul w St Luke *Ches* 89-92; TV Ches Team 92-94; P-in-c S Tawton and Belstone *Ex* 94-00; R 00-02; RD Okehampton 98-02; TR Wylye and Till Valley *Sarum* 02-03; rtd 03. *77 Slade Close, Ottery St Mary EX11 1SY* Tel (01404) 814953

WOOD, Beresford Donald Richard. b 32. Leeds Univ BA58. Cant Sch of Min 91. **d** 94 **p** 95. Chapl St Mary's Sch Westbrook from 94; NSM Folkestone St Mary and St Eanswythe *Cant* 94-02; Perm to Offic from 02. *St Katherine's Cottage, Pound Lane, Elham, Canterbury CT4 6TS* Tel (01303) 840817

WOOD, Miss Beryl Jean. b 54. Linc Th Coll 85. **d** 87 **p** 94. C Gaywood, Bawsey and Mintlyn *Nor* 87-92; C Gaywood 92-93; Asst Chapl Univ Hosp Nottm 93-95; R Shipdham w E and W Bradenham *Nor* from 95; RD Dereham in Mitford 00-03. *The Rectory, Church Close, Shipdham, Thetford IP25 7LX* Tel (01362) 820234

WOOD, Mrs Brenda. b 46. Eliz Gaskell Coll Man TCert67 Leeds Metrop Univ BEd94. N Ord Course 00. **d** 03. NSM Kirkstall *Ripon* from 03. *18 Wentworth Crescent, Leeds LS17 7TW* Tel 0113-226 7991 E-mail bwood@ntlworld.com

WOOD, Canon Brian Frederick. b 31. Leeds Univ BA52. Coll of Resurr Mirfield 55. **d** 57 **p** 58. C Wigan St Anne *Liv* 57-60; C Elland *Wakef* 60-63; V Carlinghow 63-73; V Drighlington 73-94; RD Birstall 83-92; Hon Can Wakef Cathl 89-94; rtd 94; Perm to Offic *Bradf* and *Wakef* from 94. *10 Grove Road, Menston, Ilkley LS29 6JD* Tel (01943) 872820

WOOD, Catherine Rosemary. b 54. Melbourne Coll of Div 82 St Jo Coll Auckland 83. **d** 83 **p** 84. New Zealand 83-01; C Howick 83-87; C Auckland St Paul 88; P-in-c Mangere E 89-90; Co-ord Environmental Educn 90-95; N Fieldworker Chr World Service 96-01; Hon C Glen Eden 90-97; NSM Auckland Cathl 98-01; Perm to Offic *S'wark* 01-02; P-in-c Tatsfield from 02; C Limpsfield and Titsey from 02. *The Rectory, Ricketts Hill Road,*

Tatsfield, Westerham TN16 2NA Tel (01959) 577289 Mobile 07960-088873 E-mail catswhiskers@ukonline.co.uk

WOOD, Christopher William. b 44. Rhodes Univ BA66 Univ of S Africa BTh82. St Bede's Coll Umtata 79. **d** 80 **p** 82. S Africa 80-87; C Houghton Regis *St Alb* 87-00; C Milton *Portsm* 00-03 *27 Penton Walk, Stoke-on-Trent ST3 3DG*

WOOD, Colin Arthur. b 41. CEng MICE68 MIStructE68. S'wark Ord Course 86. **d** 89 **p** 90. C Tadworth *S'wark* 89-93; TV Morden from 93. *49 Cambourne Road, Morden SM4 4JL* Tel (020) 8542 2966

WOOD, David Arthur. b 30. Man Univ BA51. Lich Th Coll 59. **d** 61 **p** 62. C Ashton Ch Ch *Man* 61-64; C Elton All SS 64-68; Dioc Youth Adv *Newc* 68-72; R Cramlington 72-73; TR 73-83; V Wylam 83-86; TV Egremont and Haile *Carl* 86-94; rtd 94; Perm to Offic *Carl* from 94. *6 John Street, Maryport CA15 6JT* Tel (01900) 816706

WOOD, David Christopher. b 52. Oak Hill Th Coll DipHE91. **d** 91 **p** 92. C Kendal St Thos *Carl* 91-95; P-in-c Crosby Ravensworth from 95; P-in-c Asby from 95; P-in-c Bolton from 95. *The Vicarage, Crosby Ravensworth, Penrith CA10 3JJ* Tel (01931) 715226 E-mail revddavidcwood@hotmail.com

WOOD, David John. b 48. Newc Univ BSc70 PGCE71 Open Univ MA91. Dioc OLM tr scheme 99. **d** 01 **p** 02. OLM Bedlington *Newc* from 01. *7 East Riggs, Bedlington NE22 5SH* Tel (01670) 825200 E-mail davwd50@hotmail.com

WOOD, David Michael. b 39. Chich Th Coll. **d** 82 **p** 83. C Epping St Jo *Chelmsf* 82-85; C Totton *Win* 85-88; V Southway *Ex* 88-97; P-in-c Black Torrington, Bradf w Cookbury etc 97-01; R from 01. *The Rectory, Black Torrington, Beaworthy EX21 5PU* Tel (01409) 231279

WOOD, Dennis William. b 28. Qu Mary Coll Lon BSc53 Glas Univ PhD57. NEOC 82. **d** 85 **p** 85. NSM Stanhope *Dur* 85-86; NSM Stanhope w Frosterley 86-94; NSM Eastgate w Rookhope 86-94; NSM Melrose *Edin* from 94. *Gordonlee, Ormiston Terrace, Melrose TD6 9SP* Tel (01896) 823835

WOOD, Donald. b 40. **d** 95 **p** 96. NSM Caldicot *Mon* 95-99; P-in-c Llangwm Uchaf and Llangwm Isaf w Gwernesney etc from 99. *The Rectory, Gwernesney, Usk NP15 1HF* Tel (01291) 672518

WOOD, Edward Berryman. b 33. Ely Th Coll 54. **d** 57 **p** 58. C Aldershot St Mich *Guildf* 57-60; C Worplesdon 60-62; V Littleport St Matt *Ely* 62-64; V Balham St Jo Bedf Hill *S'wark* 64-71; V New Eltham All SS 71-84; RD Eltham (Sub-Deanery) 79-82; P-in-c Woldingham 84-98; rtd 98; Perm to Offic *Chich* from 99. *5 The Mount, 45 Meads Road, Eastbourne BN20 7PX* Tel (01323) 730501

WOOD, Edward Francis. b 28. Chich Th Coll 56. **d** 58 **p** 59. C Newc St Fran *Newc* 58-62; C High Elswick St Phil 62-64; C Delaval 64-67; C-in-c Shiremoor CD 67-68; Dioc Broadcasting Adv 68-78; V Shiremoor 68-78; C Newc St Geo 78-82; C Newc Epiphany 82-93; Perm to Offic from 93; rtd 93. *52 Albemarle Avenue, Jesmond, Newcastle upon Tyne NE2 3NQ* Tel 0191-284 5338 E-mail francis@fwood11.fsnet.co.uk

WOOD, Elaine Mary. *See* RICHARDSON, Elaine Mary

WOOD, Mrs Elizabeth Jane. b 51. Ch Ch Coll Cant DipEd73. NEOC 98. **d** 01 **p** 02. C Denton *Newc* from 01. *32 The Drive, East Denton, Newcastle upon Tyne NE5 2AD* Tel 0191-275 3723

WOOD, Elizabeth Lucy. b 35. WMMTC 89. **d** 92 **p** 94. NSM Wellingborough St Mark *Pet* 92-95; P-in-c Stanwick w Hargrave 95-00; Perm to Offic from 00. *21 Meadow Way, Irthlingborough, Wellingborough NN9 5RS*

WOOD, Eric Basil. b 25. St Edm Hall Ox BA50 MA50. Cuddesdon Coll 50. **d** 51 **p** 52. C Cheshunt *St Alb* 51-54; C St Pancras w St Jas and Ch Ch *Lon* 54-57; C Leatherhead *Guildf* 57-62; V Mapledurham *Ox* 62-68; P-in-c Drayton St Pet (Berks) 68-72; V 72-81; P-in-c Buckland 81-84; V 84-88; P-in-c Littleworth 81-84; V 84-88; P-in-c Pusey 81-84; R 84-88; Master Hugh Sexey's Hosp Bruton 88-95; rtd 89. *2 Bedwardine House, Henwick Road, Worcester WR2 5NT* Tel (01905) 748207

WOOD, Frederick Leonard. b 29. BEM59. Worc Ord Coll. **d** 64 **p** 65. C Paignton St Paul Preston *Ex* 64-68; V Charles w Plymouth St Matthias 68-81; rtd 82; Perm to Offic *B & W* 85-92 and *Ox* from 93. *Oaklands, 1 Windrush Heights, Sandhurst GU47 8ET* Tel (01344) 762368

WOOD, Geoffrey. b 39. Tyndale Hall Bris 56. **d** 61 **p** 62. C Tranmere St Cath *Ches* 61-64; C Newburn *Newc* 64-68; R Gt Smeaton w Appleton upon Wiske *Ripon* 69-79; P-in-c Cowton w Birkby 73-79; P-in-c Danby Wiske w Yafforth and Hutton Bonville 76-79; R Gt Smeaton w Appleton Wiske and Birkby etc 79-89; R Fressingfield, Mendham etc *St E* 92-98; rtd 98; Perm to Offic *Dur* from 98. *9 Gordon Bank, Eggleston, Barnard Castle DL12 0AS* Tel (01833) 650146

WOOD, Geoffrey James. b 47. N Ord Course 88. **d** 91 **p** 92. C Stainton-in-Cleveland *York* 91-94; V Middlesbrough St Oswald 94-99; V Eskdaleside w Ugglebarnby and Sneaton from 99. *The Vicarage, 22 Eskdaleside, Sleights, Whitby YO22 5EP* Tel (01947) 810349 E-mail frgeoffwood@supanet.com

WOOD, George Albert. b 22. St Paul's Coll Grahamstown. **d** 54 **p** 55. S Africa 54-60 and 63-77; C Cheam *S'wark* 60-63; Area Sec USPG *Chich* from 78; TV Littlehampton and Wick *Chich* 86-88;

rtd 88; Perm to Offic *Chich* from 88. *3 Orchard Gardens, Rustington, Littlehampton BN16 3HS* Tel (01903) 787746

WOOD, George Robert. b 26. Em Coll Cam BA52. Oak Hill Th Coll 52. **d** 53 **p** 54. C Denton Holme *Carl* 53-56; V Cambridge St Matt *Ely* 56-60; NW Area Sec CPAS 60-61; R Watermillock *Carl* 61-74; V Holme Eden 74-76; Chapl Lindley Lodge 76-78; C Kingston upon Hull H Trin *York* 78-80; V Chipping *Blackb* 80-81; P-in-c Whitewell 80-81; V Chipping and Whitewell 82-83; R Bunwell w Carleton Rode and Tibenham *Nor* 83-88; P-in-c Wray w Tatham Fells *Blackb* 88-89; rtd 89; Perm to Offic *Carl* 89-99. *11 Woodlands, Bridge Lane, Penrith CA11 8GW* Tel (01768) 210194

WOOD, Miss Helen Ruth. b 54. Bedf Coll Lon BA75. Glouc Sch of Min 87. **d** 91 **p** 94. NSM Up Hatherley *Glouc* 91-94; NSM Cheltenham Em w St Steph from 94; Asst Chapl Cheltenham Ladies' Coll from 91. *9 Southfield Manor Park, Sandy Lane, Charlton Kings, Cheltenham GL53 9DJ* Tel (01242) 242793

WOOD, Mrs Jennifer Sarah. b 40. Sarum Dioc Tr Coll CertEd60. Oak Hill Th Coll DipHE94. **d** 94 **p** 95. C St Illogan *Truro* 94-98; R Heanton Punchardon w Marwood *Ex* from 98. *The Rectory, Heanton, Barnstaple EX31 4DG* Tel (01271) 812249 Fax as telephone E-mail sarah@heanton-marwood.freeserve.co.uk

WOOD, John. b 37. LNSM course 75. **d** 77 **p** 79. NSM Dunbar *Edin* from 77; NSM Haddington from 77. *7 Herdmanflatt, Haddington EH41 3LN* Tel (01620) 822838

WOOD, John Andrew Scriven. b 48. Leeds Univ BSc70. St Jo Coll Nottm 76. **d** 79 **p** 80. C Colwich *Lich* 79-82; C W Bridgford *S'well* 82-90; V Gamston and Bridgford 90-95; Chapl Kings Mill Cen NHS Trust from 95. *The King's Mill Centre, Mansfield Road, Sutton in Ashfield NG17 4JL* Tel (01623) 622515 ext 4137 or 0115-982 0969

WOOD, John Arthur. b 23. Roch Th Coll 68. **d** 70 **p** 71. C Wetherby *Ripon* 70-71; P-in-c Sheff Arbourthorne *Sheff* 71-75; TV Sheff Manor 75-81; R Rodney Stoke w Draycott *B & W* 81-88; rtd 88; Perm to Offic *Sheff* from 88. *Flat 36, The Glen, Endcliffe Vale Road, Sheffield S10 3FN* Tel 0114-266 5173

WOOD, John Maurice. b 58. Qu Coll Cam BA80 MA83. Wycliffe Hall Ox BA87. **d** 87 **p** 88. C Northwood Em *Lon* 87-91; C Muswell Hill St Jas w St Matt 91-94; P-in-c S Tottenham St Ann 94-01; V from 01. *St Ann's Vicarage, South Grove, London N15 5QG* Tel and fax (020) 8800 3506 Mobile 07771-867359 E-mail johnwood@stanns.fsnet.co.uk

WOOD, John Samuel. b 47. Lanchester Poly BSc69 Sheff Univ DipEd. Westcott Ho Cam 72. **d** 81 **p** 82. NSM Haverhill *St E* 81-83; C Whitton and Thurleston w Akenham 83-86; P-in-c Walsham le Willows 86-88; P-in-c Finningham w Westhorpe 86-88; R Walsham le Willows and Finningham w Westhorpe 88-94; Min Can St E Cathl 89-94; TR Whitstable *Cant* 94-02; Hon Min Can Cant Cathl 96-02; TR Swanage and Studland *Sarum* from 02. *The Rectory, 12 Church Hill, Swanage BH19 1HU* Tel (01929) 422916 E-mail john.s.wood@btinternet.com

WOOD, Keith. b 49. St Steph Ho Ox 76. **d** 78 **p** 79. C Bognor *Chich* 78-81; C Hangleton 81-83; R W Blatchington 83-87; V Worthing St Jo 87-96; R Winchelsea and Icklesham 96-00; rtd 00. *12 Boveway Drive, Liskeard PL14 3UH* Tel (01579) 349080

WOOD, Canon Keith Ernest. b 33. Qu Coll Ox BA55 BCL56 DipTh57 MA70. Wycliffe Hall Ox 56. **d** 58 **p** 59. C Barking St Marg *Chelmsf* 58-61; Min Basildon St Andr ED 61-70; V Brampton Bierlow *Sheff* 70-82; R Grasmere *Carl* 82-94; RD Windermere 89-94; Hon Can Carl Cathl 91-94 and 98-01; Bp's Dom Chapl 94-01; rtd 01; Perm to Offic *Carl* from 01. *The Old Tower, Brackenburgh, Calthwaite CA11 9PW* Tel (01768) 894273 Fax 894019

WOOD, Laurence Henry. b 27. Kelham Th Coll 47. **d** 52 **p** 53. C Ravensthorpe *Wakef* 52-55; C Almondbury 55-58; V Linthwaite 58-64; R Bonsall *Derby* 64-70; V Cromford 64-70; V Longwood *Wakef* 70-76; V Liversedge 76-92; rtd 92; Perm to Offic *Wakef* from 92. *203 The Rock, Gillroyd Lane, Linthwaite, Huddersfield HD7 5SR* Tel (01484) 843499

WOOD, Mrs Lorna. b 43. EAMTC 85. **d** 88 **p** 94. NSM Sprowston *Nor* 88-90; NSM Sprowston w Beeston 90-95; P-in-c Nor St Helen 95-01; Chapl Gt Hosp Nor 95-99; NSM Coltishall w Gt Hautbois and Horstead *Nor* from 01. *The Rectory, Rectory Road, Coltishall, Norwich NR12 7HL* Tel (01603) 737255

WOOD, Mark. *See* WOOD, The Rt Revd Stanley Mark

WOOD, Martin Robert. b 65. Birm Univ BSc86. Trin Coll Bris. **d** 00 **p** 01. C Wells St Cuth w Wookey Hole *B & W* from 00. *46 Goodymoor Avenue, Wells BA5 2JJ* Tel (01749) 679440 E-mail mrwood@breathemail.net

✠**WOOD, The Rt Revd Maurice Arthur Ponsonby.** b 16. DSC44. Qu Coll Cam BA38 MA42. Ridley Hall Cam 40. **d** 40 **p** 41 **c** 71. C Portman Square St Paul *Lon* 40-43; Chapl RNVR 43-47; Hon Chapl Commando Assn from 47; R Ox St Ebbe *Ox* 47-52; V Islington St Mary *Lon* 52-61; RD Islington 52-61; Prin Oak Hill Th Coll 61-71; Preb St Paul's Cathl *Lon* 69-71; Bp Nor 71-85; Chapl RNR from 71; rtd 85; Perm to Offic *Nor* from 85; Hon Asst Bp Lon from 85; Res P Englefield *Ox* 87-94; Hon Asst Bp Ox 89-94. *30 Stuart Court, High Street, Kibworth, Leicester LE8 0LR* Tel 0116-279 1194

WOOD, Michael Edmund. b 46. Dur Univ BA PGCE. Coll of Resurr Mirfield 94. **d** 96 **p** 97. NSM Battyeford *Wakef* from 96; Asst Chapl Kirkwood Hospice Huddersfield 96-97; Chapl from 97. *9 Dorchester Road, Fixby, Huddersfield HD2 2JZ* Tel (01484) 536496 E-mail mike@revwood.freeserve.co.uk

WOOD, Michael Frank. b 55. Nottm Univ BCombStuds. Linc Th Coll. **d** 84 **p** 85. C Marton *Blackb* 84-88; TV Ribbleton 88-93; V Blackpool St Mary 93-00; P-in-c S Shore St Pet 98-00; RD Blackpool 96-00; TR Brighouse and Clifton *Wakef* from 00. *The Rectory, 56 Bracken Road, Brighouse HD6 2HXJ* Tel (01484) 714032 Fax as telephone E-mail fr-m-wood@brighouse71.fsnet.co.uk

WOOD, Mrs Michaela. b 67. **d** 01 **p** 02. NSM Sunbury *Lon* from 01. *The Vicarage, 1 Byechurch End, Teddington TW11 8PS* Tel (020) 8977 3330

WOOD, Canon Nicholas Martin. b 51. AKC74. **d** 75 **p** 76. C E Ham w Upton Park St Alb *Chelmsf* 75-78; C Leyton St Luke 78-81; V Rush Green 81-91; Chapl Barking Tech Coll 81-91; TR Elland *Wakef* from 91; RD Brighouse and Elland from 96; Hon Can Wakef Cathl from 00. *Elland Rectory, 50 Victoria Road, Elland HX5 0QA* Tel (01422) 256088 Fax as telephone E-mail martin@phyll.force9.co.uk

WOOD, Paul Dominic. b 52. R Agric Coll Cirencester DipAgr74 Tasmania Coll of Ad Educn DipEd80. Ridley Coll Melbourne BTh87. **d** 87 **p** 88. Australia 87-92 and from 95; C Newtown St Jas 87-89; C Launceston St Jo 89-91; TV Ifield *Chich* 92-95; P-in-c Lancefield w Romsey 96-97; I 97-00; R Mansfield from 01. *St John's Rectory, 43 Highett Street, PO Box 261, Mansfield, Vic, Australia 3722* Tel and fax (0061) (3) 5775 2036 E-mail qwoodies@bigpond.com

WOOD, Preb Peter Thomas. b 31. Clifton Th Coll 57. **d** 60 **p** 61. C Woodford Wells *Chelmsf* 60-63; SAMS 63-72; Chile 63-72; V Clevedon Ch Ch *B & W* 72-82; Chapl St Brandon's Sch Clevedon 72-82; Chapl Heref Gen Hosp 82-93; V Heref St Pet w St Owen and St Jas *Heref* 82-98; Police Chapl 86-98; RD Heref City 90-96; Preb Heref Cathl 91-98; P-in-c Chilton Cantelo, Ashington, Mudford, Rimpton etc *B & W* 98-01; Hon P-in-c from 01; rtd 01. *The Vicarage, Camel Street, Marston Magna, Yeovil BA22 8DD* Tel (01935) 850536 E-mail ptwood@breathemail.net

WOOD, Philip Hervey. b 42. Sarum & Wells Th Coll 73. **d** 74 **p** 75. C Cov H Trin *Cov* 74-75; C Finham 75-77; C Wandsworth Common St Mary *S'wark* 78-81; R Bodiam *Chich* 81-87; R Ewhurst 81-87; Dep Chapl HM Pris Wandsworth 88-90; Chapl HM Rem Cen Latchmere Ho 88-90; Lic to Offic *Chich* from 90; Chapl Hastings and Rother NHS Trust 90-99. *24 Knebworth Road, Bexhill-on-Sea TN39 4JJ* Tel (01424) 730031

WOOD, Philip James. b 48. Bris Univ BSc65 Westmr Coll Ox MTh93. Oak Hill Th Coll 71. **d** 74 **p** 75. C Islington St Mary *Lon* 74-77; C Stapenhill w Cauldwell *Derby* 77-80; V Walthamstow St Luke *Chelmsf* 80-94; AD Waltham Forest 89-94; Can Chelmsf Cathl 93-94; NSM Hackney Wick St Mary of Eton w St Aug *Lon* 01-02; TV Becontree W *Chelmsf* from 02. *St Thomas's Vicarage, Burnside Road, Dagenham RM8 2JN* Tel (020) 8590 6190

WOOD, Philip Norman. b 52. EMMTC 97. **d** 00 **p** 01. NSM Pleasley Hill *S'well* from 00; NSM Mansfield St Aug from 00; NSM Ladybrook from 00. *St Augustine's Vicarage, 46 Abbott Road, Mansfield NG19 6DD* Tel (01623) 621247

WOOD, Ms Rachel Astrid. b 71. Birm Univ BA92 MA99. Qu Coll Birm BD98. **d** 99 **p** 00. C Attercliffe, Darnall and Tinsley *Sheff* 99-01; C Roundhay St Edm *Ripon* from 01. *1 Gledhow Grange View, Leeds LS8 1PH* Tel 0113-266 8212 E-mail raw@fish.co.uk

WOOD, Raymond John Lee. b 28. ACII55 ACIArb. Linc Th Coll 66. **d** 68 **p** 69. C Beaconsfield *Ox* 68-72; CF 70-72; V Wath-upon-Dearne w Adwick-upon-Dearne *Sheff* 72-77; R St Tudy w Michaelstow *Truro* 78-86; P-in-c St Mabyn 82-86; R St Tudy w St Mabyn and Michaelstow 86-95; Chapl Bodmin Fire Brigade from 91; rtd 95; Perm to Offic *Truro* from 96. *1 Wesley Chapel, Harewood Road, Calstock PL18 9QN* Tel (01822) 835918 E-mail rjlwood@tesco.net

WOOD, Reginald John. b 16. Worc Ord Coll 61. **d** 63 **p** 64. C Weston-super-Mare St Jo *B & W* 63-65; C Radstock 65-68; V The Seavingtons w Lopen 68-80; rtd 81; Perm to Offic *Ex* from 82. *Downside, 11 Station Road, Budleigh Salterton EX9 6RW* Tel (01395) 442389

WOOD, Richard. *See* WOOD, Beresford Donald Richard

✠**WOOD, The Rt Revd Richard James.** b 20. Wells Th Coll 51. **d** 52 **p** 53 **c** 73. C Calne *Sarum* 52-55; S Africa 55-73; Namibia 73-77; Suff Bp Damaraland 73-77; V Kingston upon Hull St Mary *York* 77-79; Chapl Hull Coll of HE 77-79; Tanzania 79-85; rtd 85; Asst Bp York 79 and 85-99. *Flat 3, Plough Steep, Itchen Abbas, Winchester SO21 1BQ* Tel (01962) 779400 E-mail cwood20498@aol.com

WOOD, Roger Graham. b 49. K Coll Lon BD. Chich Th Coll 74. **d** 76 **p** 77. C Skipton H Trin *Bradf* 76-79; Dioc Youth Chapl 79-87; V Queensbury 87-96; P-in-c Langcliffe w Stainforth and Horton 96-01; V from 01. *The Vicarage, Stainforth, Settle BD24 9PG* Tel (01729) 823010

WOOD, Roger William. b 43. Leeds Univ BA65 MA67 Fitzw Coll Cam BA69 MA75. Westcott Ho Cam 67. **d** 70 **p** 71. C Bishop's Stortford St Mich *St Alb* 70-74; C Sundon w Streatley 75-79; V Streatley from 80. *17 Sundon Road, Streatley, Luton LU3 3PL* Tel (01582) 882780

WOOD, Ronald Ernest. b 49. Sarum & Wells Th Coll 79. **d** 81 **p** 82. C Weston-super-Mare Cen Par *B & W* 81-84; C Forest of Dean Ch Ch w English Bicknor *Glouc* 84-88; R Sixpenny Handley w Gussage St Andrew etc *Sarum* from 88. *The Vicarage, 60 High Street, Sixpenny Handley, Salisbury SP5 5ND* Tel (01725) 552608

WOOD, Sarah. *See* WOOD, Mrs Jennifer Sarah

WOOD, Shane Grant Lindsay. b 60. Southn Univ BTh91. St Steph Ho Ox 95. **d** 97 **p** 98. C Parkstone St Pet w Branksea and St Osmund *Sarum* 97-00; V Teddington SS Pet and Paul and Fulwell *Lon* from 00. *The Vicarage, 1 Bychurch End, Teddington TW11 8PS* Tel (020) 8977 3330

WOOD, Stanley Charles. b 26. Glouc Th Course 80. **d** 83 **p** 84. NSM Lower Cam w Coaley *Glouc* 83-87; P-in-c Shipton Moyne w Westonbirt and Lasborough 87-91; rtd 92; Perm to Offic *Glouc* from 92. *8 The Vennings, Cam, Dursley GL11 5NQ* Tel (01453) 544873

✠**WOOD, The Rt Revd Stanley Mark.** b 19. Univ of Wales BA40. Coll of Resurr Mirfield 40. **d** 42 **p** 43 **c** 71. C Cardiff St Mary *Llan* 42-45; S Africa 45-55; S Rhodesia 55-65; Rhodesia 65-77; Can Mashonaland 61-65; Dean Salisbury 65-71; Bp Matabeleland 71-77; Asst Bp Heref 77-81; Preb Heref Cathl 77-87; Suff Bp Ludlow 81-87; Adn Ludlow 82-83; rtd 87; Perm to Offic *Llan* from 87. *College of St Barnabas, Blackberry Lane, Lingfield RH7 6NJ* Tel (01342) 871556
E-mail markwood@talk21.com

WOOD, Stella Margaret. b 70. Trin Coll Ox BA91 MA DPhil95. STETS 95. **d** 97 **p** 98. NSM Mere w W Knoyle and Maiden Bradley *Sarum* from 97. *19 Church Street, Maiden Bradley, Warminster BA12 7HW* Tel (01985) 844456

WOOD, Stuart Hughes. b 32. ACIB64. Guildf Dioc Min Course 93. **d** 95 **p** 96. OLM Camberley St Martin Old Dean *Guildf* 95-02; OLM Camberley St Paul 99-02; OLM Camberley St Mich Yorktown 99-02; rtd 02; Perm to Offic *Guildf* from 02. *42 Roundway, Camberley GU15 1NS* Tel (01276) 22115
E-mail s.wood@twg.co.uk *or* stuart.wood1@tesco.net

WOOD, Sylvia Marian. *See* CHAPMAN, Canon Sylvia Marian

WOOD, Thomas Henry. Glassboro Coll (USA) BEcon84. St D Coll Lamp 57. **d** 60 **p** 61. C Pontnewynydd *Mon* 60-62; C Middlesbrough All SS *York* 64-69; C Fleetwood *Blackb* 69-73; V Ferndale *Llan* 73-77; C Sheff Parson Cross St Cecilia *Sheff* 88-93; V St Hilary Greenway *Mon* 93-01; rtd 01. *Brousse Pave, 50140 St Clement-Rancourdray, France*

WOOD, Thomas Patrick Scarborough. b 19. TCD BA41 BD54. **d** 42 **p** 43. C Portarlington w Ballykean and Cloneyhurke *M & K* 42-44; C Dublin St Geo *D & G* 44-46; I Rathaspick w Russagh and Streete *K, E & A* 46-56; P-in-c Ballysumaghan 46-49; I Calry 56-94; Preb Elphin Cathl 67-83; Preb Mulhuddart St Patr Cathl Dublin 83-94; rtd 94. *7 Glenmullen Court, Church Street, Sligo, Irish Republic* Tel (00353) (71) 914 2656

WOOD, Timothy Robert. b 55. Dioc OLM tr scheme 99. **d** 02 **p** 03. OLM Maidstone St Paul *Cant* from 02. *7 The Hedges, Maidstone ME14 2JW* Tel (01622) 753982
E-mail jane_wood@lineone.net

✠**WOOD, The Rt Revd Wilfred Denniston.** b 36. KA00. Lambeth DipTh62 Gen Th Sem NY Hon DD86 FRSA93. Codrington Coll Barbados 57. **d** 61 **p** 62 **c** 85. C Hammersmith St Steph *Lon* 62-63; C Shepherd's Bush St Steph w St Thos 63-74; Bp's Chapl for Community Relns 67-74; V Catford St Laur *S'wark* 74-82; Hon Can S'wark Cathl 77-82; RD E Lewisham 77-82; Borough Dean S'wark 82-85; Adn S'wark 82-85; Suff Bp Croydon 85-91; Area Bp Croydon 91-02; rtd 02. *69 Pegwell Gardens, Christ Church, Barbados* Tel (001) (246) 420 1822 Fax 420 3426

WOOD, William George. b 31. Oak Hill Th Coll 61. **d** 63 **p** 64. C Woking St Jo *Guildf* 63-69; V Camberwell All SS *S'wark* 69-88; R Horne 88-97; P-in-c Outwood 88-97; rtd 97. *43 Kingston Way, Seaford BN25 4NG* Tel (01323) 490572

WOODALL, David Paul. b 59. Chester Coll of HE BTh03. N Ord Course 00. **d** 03. C Darwen St Pet w Hoddlesden *Blackb* from 03. *44 Minster Crescent, Darwen, Blackburn BB3 3PY* Tel (01254) 703796 Fax as telephone

WOODALL, Reginald Homer. b 38. Univ of Wales DipTh59. St Mich Coll Llan 59. **d** 61 **p** 62. C Newtown w Llanllwchaiarn w Aberhafesp *St As* 61-65; C Rhosddu 65-66; C Hawarden 66-70; CF 70-74; C Thornton Heath St Jude *Cant* 74-77; TV Cannock *Lich* 77-79; TV Basildon St Martin w H Cross and Laindon etc *Chelmsf* 79-84; P-in-c Canning Town St Cedd 84-93; rtd 93. *64 Stephens Road, London E15 3JL*

WOODBRIDGE, Trevor Geoffrey. b 31. Lon Univ BSc52. ALCD57. **d** 58 **p** 59. C Bitterne *Win* 58-61; C Ilkeston St Mary *Derby* 61-65; Area Sec CMS *Ex* and *Truro* 65-81; SW Regional Sec 70-81; TV Clyst St George, Aylesbeare, Clyst Honiton etc *Ex* 82-84; V Aylesbeare, Rockbeare, Farringdon etc 85-95; rtd 95;

Perm to Offic *Ex* from 95. *19 Marlborough Road, Exeter EX2 4TJ*

WOODCOCK, Carolyn. b 47. N Ord Course BTh98. **d** 98 **p** 99. NSM Laneside *Blackb* 98-00; Chapl HM Pris Lanc Castle from 00. *HM Prison Lancaster, The Castle, Lancaster LA1 1YL* Tel (01524) 385100

WOODCOCK, Edward Marsden. b 47. Hull Univ MSc01. Coll of Resurr Mirfield 01. **d** 03. C Wrenthorpe *Wakef* from 03; C Alverthorpe from 03. *11 Aldbury Close, Carlton, Barnsley S71 2BW* Tel (01226) 247755
E-mail edward@thewoodcocks.plus.com

WOODCOCK, John Charles Gerard. b 31. Kelham Th Coll 52. **d** 56 **p** 57. SSM 56-88; S Africa 56-62 and 76-83; Lesotho 62-76; Chapl Bede Ho Staplehurst 83-87; C Auckland St Andr and St Anne *Dur* 87-88. *3 Helena Terrace, Cockton Hill, Bishop Auckland DL14 6BP* Tel (01388) 604956

WOODCOCK, Michael David. b 67. Avery Hill Coll BEd91. Wycliffe Hall Ox BTh96. **d** 96 **p** 97. C Orpington Ch Ch *Roch* 96-99; R Knockholt w Halstead from 99. *The Rectory, Church Road, Halstead, Sevenoaks TN14 7HQ* Tel (01959) 532133
E-mail meesh@fish.co.uk

WOODCOCK, Michael Paul. b 71. Univ of Greenwich BA93. St Jo Coll Nottm MA98 DipTM99. **d** 99 **p** 00. C Brinsley w Underwood *S'well* 99-02; C New Malden and Coombe *S'wark* from 02. *2 California Road, New Malden KT3 3RU* Tel (020) 8942 0544

WOODCOCK, Nicholas Ethelbert. b 46. Abps' Cert in Ch Music 74 FRSA90. Cant Sch of Min 80. **d** 90 **p** 91. Chief Exec and Co Sec Keston Coll Kent 89-92; NSM Clerkenwell H Redeemer w St Phil *Lon* 90-92; NSM Clerkenwell H Redeemer and St Mark 92-93; Chapl RN 93-01; Prec and Sacr Ely Cathl *Ely* from 01; Min Can Ely Cathl from 01. *Precentor's House, 32 High Street, Ely CB7 4JU* Tel (01353) 660335 *or* 667735 Fax 665658
E-mail ely.precentor@cathedral.ely.anglican.org

WOODERSON, Mrs Marguerite Ann. b 44. RGN SCM. Qu Coll Birm 86. **d** 89 **p** 94. Par Dn Stoneydelph St Martin CD *Lich* 89-90; Par Dn Glascote and Stonydelph 90-91; Par Dn Chasetown 91-94; C 94; I Celbridge w Straffan and Newcastle-Lyons *D & G* from 98. *The Rectory, Maynooth Road, Celbridge, Co Kildare, Irish Republic* Tel (00353) (1) 628 8231 Mobile 86-851 2557 Fax (45) 897206
E-mail annwooderson@eircom.net

WOODERSON, Preb Michael George. b 39. Southn Univ BA61. Lon Coll of Div BD69. **d** 69 **p** 70. C Morden *S'wark* 69-73; C Aldridge *Lich* 73-81; V Chasetown 81-94; RD Lich 86-94; Preb Lich Cathl 89-94; P-in-c Hammerwich 91-94; I Naas w Kill and Rathmore *M & K* from 94. *The Rectory, 15 Spring Gardens, Naas, Co Kildare, Irish Republic* Tel (00353) (45) 897206

WOODGATE, Mrs Elizabeth Mary. b 66. W Sussex Inst of HE BEd87. St Jo Coll Nottm MTh02. **d** 02. C Crofton *Portsm* 02-03; C Lee-on-the-Solent from 03. *85 Seymour Road, Lee-on-the-Solent PO13 9EQ* Tel (01329) 668089
E-mail bethpoppy@hotmail.com

WOODGATES, Mrs Margaret. b 47. St D Coll Lamp BA67. WMMTC 00. **d** 03. NSM Redditch, The Ridge *Worc* from 03. *18 Warwick Hall Gardens, Bromsgrove B60 2AU* Tel (01527) 577785

WOODGER, John McRae. b 36. Tyndale Hall Bris 60. **d** 63 **p** 64. C Heref St Pet w St Owen *Heref* 63-66; C Macclesfield St Mich *Ches* 66-69; V Llangarron w Llangrove *Heref* 69-74; P-in-c Garway 70-74; R Church Stretton 74-84; Preb Heref Cathl 82-84; V Watford *St Alb* 84-01; rtd 01. *36 Bronte Drive, Ledbury HR8 2FZ* Tel (01531) 636745 E-mail woodger@fish.co.uk

WOODGER, John Page. b 30. Master Mariner 56 Lon Univ DipTh58. St Aid Birkenhead 56. **d** 59 **p** 60. C Kimberworth *Sheff* 59-62; Chapl HM Borstal Pollington 62-70; C Goole *Sheff* 62-63; V Balne 63-70; C Halesowen *Worc* 70-74; V Cookley 74-81; TV Droitwich 81-85; TV Bedminster *Bris* 85-93; rtd 93; Perm to Offic *Bris* 93-97; Perm to Offic *Worc* from 98. *1 Barbel Crescent, Worcester WR5 3QU* Tel (01905) 769065

WOODGER, Richard William. b 50. Sarum & Wells Th Coll 76. **d** 79 **p** 80. C Chessington *Guildf* 79-82; C Frimley 82-85; C Frimley Green 82-85; P-in-c Hollmwood 85-90; TR Headley All SS 90-98; TR Penrith w Newton Reigny and Plumpton Wall *Carl* from 98. *The Rectory, 3 Lamley Gardens, Graham Street, Penrith CA11 9LR* Tel (01768) 863000 *or* 862867

WOODHALL, Peter. b 32. Edin Th Coll 57. **d** 60 **p** 61. C Carl St Barn *Carl* 60-63; Hon Chapl Estoril *Eur* 63-65; Chapl RN 66-82; TR Is of Scilly *Truro* 82-90; V Mithian w Mount Hawke 90-95; rtd 97. *Tregarth, 4 Peverell Road, Porthleven, Helston TR13 9DH*

WOODHAM, Richard Medley Swift. b 43. Master Mariner 70 DipTh. S'wark Ord Course 71. **d** 73 **p** 74. C Gravesend St Aid *Roch* 73-75; C Chessington *Guildf* 75-78; Warden Dioc Conf Ho Horstead *Nor* 78-87; R Horstead 78-87; Youth Chapl 78-88; V Nor St Mary Magd w St Jas 87-91; TR Norwich Over-the-Water 91-98; P-in-c Lakenham St Jo 98-99; V Nor Lakenham St Jo and All SS and Tuckswood from 99; RD Nor E from 02. *The Vicarage, Harwood Road, Norwich NR1 2NG* Tel (01603) 625678
E-mail rich1w@aol.com

WOODHAMS, Kathryn Asma Patricia. d 02. NSM S Mimms Ch Ch *Lon* from 02. *28 Station Road, London N21 3RB* Tel (020) 8364 2945

WOODHAMS, Raymond John. b 40. Garnett Coll Lon CertEd68 IEng. STETS 98. **d** 01. NSM E Blatchington *Chich* from 01. *The Old Parsonage, West Dean, Seaford BN25 4AL* Tel (01323) 870432 Fax as telephone
E-mail raymondj.woodhams@virgin.net

WOODHAMS, Roy Owen. b 57. ARCM76 GRSM78 Lon Inst of Educn TCert79. Ripon Coll Cuddesdon DipMin93. **d** 93 **p** 94. C Deal St Leon and St Rich and Sholden *Cant* 93-97; P-in-c Cherbury *Ox* 97-02; P-in-c Gainfield 99-02; R Cherbury w Gainfield from 02; AD Vale of White Horse from 01. *The Rectory, Church Lane, Longworth, Abingdon OX13 5DX* Tel (01865) 820213 E-mail roy@longworthrectory.freeserve.co.uk

WOODHAMS, Mrs Sophie Harriet. b 27. Cranmer Hall Dur 66. **dss** 80 **d** 87. Raveningham *Nor* 80-81; Henleaze *Bris* 81-87; rtd 87. *12 Hanover House, Hyde Valley, Welwyn Garden City AL7 4DA* Tel (01707) 890944

WOODHEAD, Mrs Bernice. b 45. Man OLM Scheme 98. **d** 01 **p** 02. OLM Shore *Man* from 01; OLM Calderbrook from 01. *2 Mount Avenue, Littleborough OL15 9JP* Tel (01706) 379517

WOODHEAD, Christopher Godfrey. b 26. Pemb Coll Cam BA50 MA55. Ely Th Coll 50. **d** 52 **p** 53. C Barnsley St Edw *Wakef* 52-54; C Mill Hill St Mich *Lon* 54-58; C Sandridge *St Alb* 58-66; R Earl Stonham *St E* 66-72; V Hoo St Werburgh *Roch* 72-88; C Cheam *S'wark* 88-91; rtd 91; Perm to Offic *Cant* from 91. *4 Eastgate Close, Herne Bay CT6 7ER* Tel (01227) 374137

WOODHEAD, Miss Helen Mary. b 35. Bedf Coll Lon BA57. Westcott Ho Cam 86. **d** 87 **p** 94. Par Dn Daventry *Pet* 87-90; C Godalming *Guildf* 90-95; Asst Dioc Dir of Ords 90-00; C Worplesdon 95-00; rtd 00; Perm to Offic *Lich* from 00. *12 Barley Croft, Whittington, Lichfield WS14 9LY* Tel (01543) 432345

WOODHEAD, Michael. b 51. St Jo Coll Nottm 88. **d** 90 **p** 91. C Stannington *Sheff* 90-93; V Deepcar 93-01; TV Crookes St Thos from 01. *79 Glebe Road, Sheffield S10 1FB*

WOODHEAD, Mrs Sandra Buchanan. b 42. Man Poly BA82 Man Univ BD85. St Deiniol's Hawarden. **dss** 86 **d** 87 **p** 94. High Lane *Ches* 86-90; Hon Par Dn 87-90; C Brinnington w Portwood 91-94; V 94-00; R Withington St Paul *Man* from 00. *Withington Rectory, 491 Wilmslow Road, Manchester M20 9AW* Tel 0161-445 3781

WOODHEAD-KEITH-DIXON, James Addison. b 25. St Aid Birkenhead 44. **d** 48 **p** 49. C Upperby St Jo *Carl* 48-50; C Dalton-in-Furness 50-52; V Blawith w Lowick 52-59; V Lorton 59-80; Chapl Puerto de la Cruz Tenerife *Eur* 80-82; TV Bellingham/Otterburn Gp *Newc* 82-83; TR 83-91; TR N Tyne and Redesdale Team 91-92; rtd 92. *Culpee House, Creebridge, Newton Stewart DG8 6NR*

WOODHOUSE, Canon Alison Ruth. b 43. Bedf Coll of Educn CertEd64 Lon Univ DipTh70. Dalton Ho Bris 68. **dss** 79 **d** 87 **p** 94. Bayston Hill *Lich* 79-81; W Derby St Luke *Liv* 81-86; Burscough Bridge 86-95; Par Dn 87-94; C 94-95; V Formby St Luke from 95; AD Sefton from 00; Hon Can Liv Cathl from 02. *St Luke's Vicarage, St Luke's Church Road, Formby, Liverpool L37 2DE* Tel (01704) 877655

WOODHOUSE, The Ven Andrew Henry. b 23. DSC45. Qu Coll Ox BA48 MA49. Linc Th Coll 48. **d** 50 **p** 51. C Poplar All SS w St Frideswide *Lon* 50-56; V W Drayton 56-70; RD Hillingdon 67-70; Adn Ludlow *Heref* 70-82; R Wistanstow 70-82; P-in-c Acton Scott 70-73; Can Res Heref Cathl 82-91; Treas 82-85; Adn Heref 82-91; rtd 91; Perm to Offic *Guildf* from 91. *Orchard Cottage, Bracken Close, Woking GU22 7HD* Tel (01483) 760671

WOODHOUSE, Andrew Laurence. b 40. Leeds Univ NDD63 ATCL64 Nottm Univ DipEd72. NW Ord Course. **d** 82 **p** 83. NSM Bedale *Ripon* 82-02; NSM Bedale and Leeming from 03; P-in-c Thornton Watlass from 99. *The Rectory, Thornton Watlass, Ripon HG4 4AH* Tel (01677) 422737

WOODHOUSE, The Ven Charles David Stewart. b 34. Kelham Th Coll 55. **d** 59 **p** 60. C Leeds Halton St Wilfrid *Ripon* 59-63; Youth Chapl *Liv* 63-66; Bermuda 66-69; Asst Gen Sec CEMS 69-70; Gen Sec 70-76; Bp's Dom Chapl *Ex* 76-81; R Ideford, Luton and Ashcombe 76-81; V Hindley St Pet *Liv* 81-92; Adn Warrington 81-01; Hon Can Liv Cathl 83-01; rtd 01. *9 Rob Lane, Newton-le-Willows WA12 0DR*

WOODHOUSE, David Edwin. b 45. Lon Univ BSc68. Cuddesdon Coll 68. **d** 71 **p** 72. C E Dulwich St Jo *S'wark* 71-74; Lic to Offic 74-77; Perm to Offic *Bris* 77-79; Lic to Offic 79-98. *Kingsbury Hall, The Green, Calne SN11 8DG* Tel (01249) 821521 Fax 817246 E-mail kingsburyhallcd@aol.com

WOODHOUSE, David Maurice. b 40. Lon Univ BA62. Clifton Th Coll 63. **d** 65 **p** 66. C Wellington w Eyton *Lich* 65-68; C Meole Brace 68-71; V Colwich 71-82; P-in-c Gt Haywood 78-82; R Clitheroe St Jas *Blackb* 82-88; Ellel Grange Chr Healing Cen 88-91; V The Lye and Stambermill *Worc* 91-99; Chapl Acorn Chr Healing Trust 99-02; Dioc Healing Adv *Guildf* 00-02; rtd 02. *1 Lilac Avenue, Penwortham, Preston PR1 9PB* Tel (01772) 742088 E-mail david.woodhouse@classicfm.net

WOODHOUSE, Hugh Frederic. b 12. TCD BA34 BD37 DD52. **d** 37 **p** 38. C Belfast St Donard *D & D* 37-39; C Bangor 40-44; I Aghalee 44-46; I Newtownards 46-51; Canada 51-63; Regius Prof Div TCD 63-82; rtd 82. *4591 West 16th Avenue, Vancouver BC, Canada, V6R 3E8* Tel (001) (604) 224 4812

WOODHOUSE, Canon Keith Ian. b 33. K Coll Lon 54. **d** 58 **p** 59. C Stockton St Chad CD *Dur* 58-61; C Man St Aid *Man* 61-64; V Peterlee *Dur* 64-99; AD Easington 72-98; Hon Can Dur Cathl 79-99; rtd 99; Dioc Pensions and Widows Officer *Dur* from 00. *85 Baulkham Hills, Penshaw, Houghton le Spring DH4 7RZ* Tel 0191-584 3977 Fax as telephone
E-mail keithianwoodhouse@excite.com

WOODHOUSE, Canon Patrick Henry Forbes. b 47. Ch Ch Ox BA69 MA81. St Jo Coll Nottm 69 Lon Coll of Div ALCD71 LTh71. **d** 72 **p** 73. C Birm St Martin *Birm* 72-74; C Whitchurch *Bris* 75-76; C Harpenden St Nic *St Alb* 76-80; Tanzania 80-81; Soc Resp Officer *Carl* 81-85; P-in-c Dean 81-85; Dir Soc Resp *Win* 85-90; V Chippenham St Andr w Tytherton Lucas *Bris* 90-00; Can Res and Prec Wells Cathl *B & W* from 00. *4 The Liberty, Wells BA5 2SU* Tel (01749) 673188 Fax as telephone
E-mail pwoodhouse@liberty4.fsnet.co.uk

WOODHOUSE, Thomas Mark Bews. b 66. Cheltenham & Glouc Coll of HE BA98. Aston Tr Scheme 90 Westcott Ho Cam CTM95. **d** 95 **p** 96. C Cainscross w Selsley *Glouc* 95-98; V Hardwicke and Elmore w Longney from 98. *Church House, Cornfield Drive, Hardwicke, Gloucester GL2 4QJ* Tel (01452) 720015 E-mail thomas.woodhouse@tesco.net

WOODING JONES, Andrew David. b 61. Oak Hill Th Coll BA91. **d** 91 **p** 92. C Welling *Roch* 91-95; TV Crookes St Thos *Sheff* 95-00; Resident Dir Ashburnham Trust from 00; NSM Ashburnham w Penhurst *Chich* from 01. *Ashburnham Christian Trust, Ashburnham Place, Battle TN33 9NF* Tel (01424) 892244 Fax 894200 E-mail andrewwj@ashburnham.org.uk

WOODLAND, Robert Alan. b 29. Bps' Coll Cheshunt 59. **d** 61 **p** 62. C Cheshunt *St Alb* 61-66; V Oxhey All SS 66-76; V Hainault *Chelmsf* 76-81; R Bicknoller w Crowcombe and Sampford Brett *B & W* 81-89; rtd 90; Perm to Offic *B & W* from 90. *74 Paganel Road, Minehead TA24 5EY* Tel (01643) 702118

WOODLEY, David James. b 38. K Coll Lon BD61 AKC61 Open Univ BA98. **d** 62 **p** 63. C Lancing St Jas *Chich* 62-64; C St Alb St Pet *St Alb* 64-67; Malaysia 67-70; Lic to Offic *Linc* 71-72; V Westoning w Tingrith *St Alb* 72-77; Asst Chapl HM Pris Wormwood Scrubs 77-78; Chapl HM Pris Cardiff 78-84; Chapl HM Rem Cen Risley 84-92; Chapl HM Pris Styal 92-98; rtd 98; Perm to Offic *Ches* from 98. *36 Brock Street, Macclesfield SK10 1DL* Tel (01625) 615222

WOODLEY, Canon John Francis Chapman. b 33. Univ of Wales (Lamp) BA58. Edin Th Coll 58. **d** 60 **p** 61. C Edin All SS *Edin* 60-65; Chapl St Andr Cathl *Ab* 65-67; Prec 67-71; R Glas St Oswald *Glas* 71-77; P-in-c Cumbernauld 77-82; Can St Mary's Cathl 82-99; CSG from 82; R Dalbeattie *Glas* 93-99; rtd 99; Hon Can St Mary's Cathl *Glas* from 99; Dioc Supernumerary from 99. *3 Highburgh Drive, Rutherglen, Glasgow G73 3RR*

WOODLEY, The Ven Ronald John. b 25. Bps' Coll Cheshunt 50. **d** 53 **p** 54. C Middlesbrough St Martin *York* 53-58; C Whitby 58-61; C-in-c Middlesbrough Berwick Hills CD 61-66; V Middlesbrough Ascension 66-71; R Stokesley 71-85; RD Stokesley 77-85; Can and Preb York Minster 82-00; Adn Cleveland 85-91; rtd 91; Perm to Offic *Ripon* from 91; Perm to Offic *York* from 00. *2A Minster Court, York YO1 7JJ* Tel (01904) 679675

WOODLEY, Simon Andrew. b 66. Liv Univ BA88 Univ of Cen England in Birm 96. Ridley Hall Cam BTh00. **d** 00 **p** 01. C Birm St Martin w Bordesley St Andr *Birm* from 00. *175 St Andrew's Road, Birmingham B9 4NB* Tel 0121-688 6708

WOODMAN, Brian Baldwin. b 35. Leeds Univ BA57 PhD73. N Ord Course 84. **d** 87 **p** 88. C Guiseley w Esholt *Bradf* 87-90; TV Bingley All SS 90-94; P-in-c St Merryn *Truro* 94-00; rtd 00; Perm to Offic *Truro* from 00. *Penty an Garth, Trevance, St Issey, Wadebridge PL27 7QF* Tel (01841) 541387

WOODMAN, Christopher James. b 65. Chich Th Coll BTh93. **d** 93 **p** 94. C Leigh-on-Sea St Marg *Chelmsf* 93-97; TV Canvey Is 97-00; TV Moulsecoomb *Chich* 00-03; C Brighton St Mich from 03. *Basement Flat, St Michael's Vicarage, 6 Montpelier Villas, Brighton BN1 3DH* Tel (01273) 703525
E-mail cjw@btinternet.com

WOODMAN, Oliver Nigel. b 47. FCIPD. Sarum Th Coll 67. **d** 70 **p** 82. C Stepney St Dunstan and All SS *Lon* 70-71; NSM Ovingdean w Rottingdean and Woodingdean *Chich* 81-87; NSM Eastbourne St Sav and St Pet 88-93; Asst to RD Eastbourne 93-98; NSM Eastbourne St Sav and St Pet 98-01; NSM Stanmore *Win* from 02. *48 Old Kennels Lane, Winchester SO22 4JS* Tel (01962) 878937 Fax 842018
E-mail o.woodman@btinternet.com *or* oliver@seemp.co.uk

WOODMAN, The Ven Peter Wilfred. b 36. Univ of Wales (Lamp) BA58. Wycliffe Hall Ox 58. **d** 60 **p** 61. C New Tredegar *Mon* 60-61; C Newport St Paul 61-64; C Llanfrechfa All SS 64-66; Abp of Wales's Messenger 66-67; V Llantilio Pertholey w Bettws Chpl etc *Mon* 67-74; V Bassaleg 74-90; Can St Woolos

Cathl 84-01; V Caerwent w Dinham and Llanfair Discoed etc 90-96; Adn Mon 93-01; R Mamhilad and Llanfihangel Pontymoile 96-01; rtd 01. *Glaslyn, 40 Longhouse Barn, Penpertleni, Pontypool NP4 0BD* Tel (01873) 881322

WOODMANSEY, Michael Balfour. b 55. Leic Univ BSc. Ridley Hall Cam. d 83 p 84. C St Paul's Cray St Barn *Roch* 83-89; C S Shoebury *Chelmsf* 89-93; R Stifford 93-01; TR Heworth H Trin *York* from 01. *Heworth Rectory, Melrosegate, York YO31 0RP* Tel (01904) 422958
E-mail michael@mwoodmansey.freeserve.co.uk

WOODMORE, Mrs Dilys Mary. b 44. St Alb and Ox Min Course 98. d 01 p 02. NSM Dedworth *Ox* from 01. *59 Terrington Hill, Marlow SL7 2RE* Tel (01628) 486274

WOODROFFE, Ian Gordon. b 46. Edin Th Coll 69. d 72 p 73. C Soham *Ely* 72-75; P-in-c Swaffham Bulbeck 75-80; Youth Chapl 75-80; V Cambridge St Jas 80-87; Chapl Mayday Univ Hosp Thornton Heath 87-94; Chapl Mayday Healthcare NHS Trust Thornton Heath 94-97; Perm to Offic *S'wark* from 97; Staff Counsellor Epsom and St Helier NHS Trust from 97. *Epsom and St Helier NHS Trust, Wrythe Lane, Carshalton SM5 1AA* Tel (020) 8296 2769

WOODS, The Very Revd Alan Geoffrey. b 42. TD93. ACCA65 FCCA80. Sarum Th Coll 67. d 70 p 71. C Bedminster St Fran *Bris* 70-73; Youth Chapl 73-76; Warden Legge Ho Res Youth Cen 73-76; P-in-c Neston 76-79; TV Gtr Corsham 79-81; CF (TA) 80-94; P-in-c Charminster *Sarum* 81-83; V Charminster and Stinsford 83-90; RD Dorchester 85-90; Chapl Dorchester Hosps 86-87; V Calne and Blackland *Sarum* 90-96; RD Calne 90-96; Chapl St Mary's Sch Calne 90-96; Can and Preb Sarum Cathl *Sarum* 92-96; Sen Chapl Malta and Gozo *Eur* 96-03; Chan Malta Cathl 96-03; Dean Gib from 03. *The Deanery, Bomb House Lane, Gibraltar* Tel (00350) 78377 Fax 78463
E-mail anglicangib@gibnynex.gi

WOODS, Albert. b 12. St Paul's Coll Burgh St Chad's Coll Regina LTh47. d 41 p 42. Canada 41-50; C Huyton Quarry *Liv* 50-51; V Litherland St Andr 51-56; Chapl Whiston Co Hosp Prescot 50-51; CF (TA) 50-78; V Rainbow Hill St Barn *Worc* 56-61; P-in-c Tolladine 58-61; V Elmley Castle w Netherton and Bricklehampton 61-63; Dioc Adv on Chr Stewardship 58-63; Dir Chr Stewardship 63-66; V Hampton 66-71; V Upper w Nether Swell *Glouc* 71-78; rtd 78; Perm to Offic *Liv* 85-91; *Worc* 91-02. *3 Abbey Lodge, Church Street, Tewkesbury GL20 5RZ*

WOODS, Allan Campbell. b 32. MIEH59. Ox NSM Course 85. d 89 p 90. NSM W Wycombe w Bledlow Ridge, Bradenham and Radnage *Ox* 89-97; NSM Terriers 97-98; Perm to Offic from 98. *4 Pitcher's Cottages, Bennett End, Radnage, High Wycombe HP14 4EF* Tel (01494) 482083
E-mail allanwoods@email.msn.com

WOODS, Charles William. b 31. Lich Th Coll 55. d 58 p 59. C Hednesford *Lich* 58-62; V Wilnecote 62-67; V Basford 67-76; V Chasetown 76-81; P-in-c Donington 81-83; V 83-96; V Boningale 83-96; RD Shifnal 84-89; rtd 96; Perm to Offic *Lich* from 96. *17 Campion Drive, Telford TF2 7RH* Tel (01952) 677134

WOODS, Christopher Guy Alistair. b 35. Dur Univ BA60. Clifton Th Coll 60. d 62 p 63. C Rainham *Chelmsf* 62-65; C Edin St Thos *Edin* 65-69; Sec Spanish and Portuguese Ch Aid Soc 69-79; C Willesborough w Hinxhill *Cant* 74-80; P-in-c Murston w Bapchild and Tonge 80-87; R 87-90; R Gt Horkesley *Chelmsf* 90-98; RD Dedham and Tey 91-98; rtd 98; P-in-c Tenerife Sur *Eur* 99-00; Perm to Offic *Chelmsf* from 00. *Blue Bonnet, Mill Lane, Bradfield, Manningtree CO11 2UT* Tel (01255) 870411

WOODS, Canon Christopher Samuel. b 43. Cant Univ (NZ) BA. Qu Coll Birm 75. d 76 p 77. C Childwall All SS *Liv* 76-79; V Parr Mt 79-00; TV Parr from 01; AD St Helens from 00; Hon Can Liv Cathl from 03. *The Vicarage, Traverse Street, St Helens WA9 1BW* Tel (01744) 22778
E-mail csw@gasworksview.freeserve.co.uk

WOODS, David Arthur. b 28. Bris Univ BA52. Tyndale Hall Bris 48. d 53 p 54. C Camborne *Truro* 53-56; C Bromley Ch Ch *Roch* 56-58; V Tewkesbury H Trin *Glouc* 58-66; V Stapleford *S'well* 66-70; Miss to Seamen 70-93; Hon Chapl Miss to Seamen 70's; V Fowey *Truro* 70-93; RD St Austell 80-88; rtd 93; Perm to Offic *Truro* from 93. *Linden, 3 Richmond Road, Pelynt, Looe PL13 2NH* Tel (01503) 220374

WOODS, David Benjamin. b 42. Linc Th Coll 88. d 90 p 91. C Louth *Linc* 90-93; P-in-c Ingoldmells w Addlethorpe 93-97; R 97-01; P-in-c Sutton Bridge from 01. *The Vicarage, 79 Bridge Road, Sutton Bridge, Spalding PE12 9SD* Tel (01406) 351503

WOODS, David Edward. b 36. City Univ FBCO61 FSMC61. SW Minl Tr Course 83 S Dios Minl Tr Scheme 94. d 95 p 96. NSM Bemerton *Sarum* 95-98; NSM Salisbury St Martin 98-00; NSM Laverstock 98-00; NSM Salisbury St Martin and Laverstock from 00. *13B Bower Gardens, Salisbury SP1 2RL* Tel (01722) 334482

WOODS, Edward Christopher John. b 44. NUI BA67. CITC 66. d 67 p 68. C Drumglass *Arm* 67-70; C Belfast St Mark *Conn* 70-73; I Kilcolman *L & K* 73-78; I Portarlington w Cloneyhurke and Lea *M & K* 78-84; Chan Kildare Cathl 81-84; I Killiney Ballybrack *D & G* 85-92; I Dublin Rathfarnham from 93; Dir of

Ords (Dub) from 98. *Rathfarnham Rectory, Rathfarnham, Terenure, Dublin 6 W, Irish Republic* Tel (00353) (1) 490 5543 Fax as telephone E-mail anneted@gofree.indigo.ie

WOODS, Canon Eric John. b 51. Magd Coll Ox BA72 MA77 Trin Coll Cam BA77 MA83 FRSA94. Westcott Ho Cam 75. d 78 p 79. C Bris St Mary Redcliffe w Temple etc *Bris* 78-81; Hon C Clifton St Paul 81-83; Asst Chapl Bris Univ 81-83; V Wroughton 83-93; RD Wroughton 88-93; V Sherborne w Castleton and Lillington *Sarum* from 93; Chapl Sherborne Sch for Girls from 93; RD Sherborne *Sarum* from 96; Can and Preb Sarum Cathl from 98; Chapl Dorset Community NHS Trust 93-00; Chapl SW Dorset Primary Care Trust from 01. *The Vicarage, Abbey Close, Sherborne DT9 3LQ* Tel (01935) 812452 Fax 812206 E-mail abbey@sherborne.netkonect.co.uk

WOODS, Frederick James. b 45. Southn Univ BA66 MPhil74 Fitzw Coll Cam BA76 MA79. Ridley Hall Cam 74. d 77 p 78. C Stratford-on-Avon w Bishopton *Cov* 77-81; V Warminster Ch Ch *Sarum* 81-96; RD Heytesbury 95-96; TR Woodley *Ox* 96-01; V Colchester St Pet and St Botolph *Chelmsf* from 01. *St Peter's Vicarage, Balkerne Close, Colchester CO1 1NZ* Tel (01206) 572641 E-mail fredjwoods@hotmail.com

WOODS, Geoffrey Edward. b 49. Lon Univ BD70 K Coll Lon MA94. Tyndale Hall Bris 67. d 73 p 74. C Gipsy Hill Ch Ch *S'wark* 73-76; C Uphill *B & W* 76-79; R Swainswick w Langridge and Woolley 79-84; Perm to Offic *Bris* 84-96; NSM Colerne w N Wraxall from 96. *22 Watergates, Colerne, Chippenham SN14 8DR* Tel (01225) 743675

WOODS, Canon John Mawhinney. b 19. Edin Th Coll 55. d 58 p 59. C Kirkcaldy *St And* 58-60; R Walpole St Peter *Ely* 60-75; R Inverness St Andr *Mor* 75-80; Provost St Andr Cathl Inverness 75-80; Hon Can St Andr Cathl Inverness from 80; V The Suttons w Tydd *Linc* 80-85; rtd 85; Perm to Offic *Nor* from 85. *24 Queen Street, King's Lynn PE30 1HT* Tel (01553) 762569

WOODS, John William Ashburnham. b 22. Reading Univ BSc50. NW Ord Course 73 St Jo Coll Lusaka 69. d 71 p 74. Zambia 71-72; C Goole *Sheff* 73-75; P-in-c Firbeck w Letwell 75-76; R 76-82; P-in-c Woodsetts 75-76; V 76-82; Bp's Rural Adv 80-92; R Barnburgh w Melton on the Hill 82-92; RD Wath 86-92; rtd 92; NSM Birdsall w Langton *York* 93-96; P-in-c Settrington w N Grimston, Birdsall w Langton 96-98; Perm to Offic from 00. *The Vicarage, 2 Cromarty Cottages, Birdsall, Malton YO17 9NN* Tel (01944) 768374 E-mail revjwoods@btinternet.com

WOODS, Joseph Richard Vernon. b 31. Solicitor 57. Cuddesdon Coll 58. d 60 p 61. C Newc St Gabr *Newc* 60-63; Trinidad and Tobago 63-67; Chapl Long Grove Hosp Epsom 67-76; P-in-c Ewell St Fran *Guildf* 76-79; V 79-87; V Englefield Green 87-96; rtd 96; Perm to Offic *Win* from 97. *8 Wren Close, Christchurch BH23 4BD* Tel (01425) 270799

WOODS, Michael. b 57. Ripon Coll Cuddesdon. d 01 p 02. C Bamber Bridge St Aid *Blackb* from 01. *6 Bluebell Way, Bamber Bridge, Preston PR5 6XQ* Tel (01772) 311073
E-mail woodsfamily@cuddesdon.fsnet.co.uk

WOODS, Canon Michael Spencer. b 44. K Coll Lon BD66 AKC66 Hull Univ DipMin88 Sheff Univ MMinTheol99. d 67 p 68. C Sprowston *Nor* 67-70; Malaysia 70-74; TV Hempnall *Nor* 74-79; TV Halesworth w Linstead, Chediston, Holton etc *St E* 79-85; TR Braunstone *Leic* 85-92; RD Sparkenhoe E 89-91; TR Gt Yarmouth *Nor* from 92; Hon Can Nor Cathl from 96. *The Rectory, 1 Osborne Avenue, Great Yarmouth NR30 4EE* Tel (01493) 850666 E-mail michael.woods@rjt.co.uk

WOODS, Canon Norman Harman. b 35. K Coll Lon BD62 AKC62. d 63 p 64. C Poplar All SS w St Frideswide *Lon* 63-68; C-in-c W Leigh CD *Portsm* 68-76; V Hythe *Cant* 76-01; RD Elham 83-89; Hon Can Cant Cathl 90-01; rtd 01; Perm to Offic *Cant* from 01. *36 Abbey Gardens, Canterbury CT2 7EU* Tel (01227) 470957 E-mail norman.woods@tesco.net

WOODS, Richard Thomas Evelyn Brownrigg. b 51. St Steph Ho Ox 83. d 85 p 86. C Southgate Ch Ch *Lon* 85-88; C Northampton All SS w St Kath *Pet* 88-89; V Maybridge *Chich* 89-99; R Singleton from 99; V E Dean from 99; V W Dean from 99. *The Rectory, Singleton, Chichester PO18 0EZ* Tel (01243) 811213 Fax as telephone E-mail rector_singleton@hotmail.com

WOODS, Roger Andrew. b 60. Southn Univ BSc81. Oak Hill Th Coll DipHE97 BA01. d 98 p 99. C Audley *Lich* 98-02; TV Leek and Meerbrook from 02. *St Luke's Vicarage, Novi Lane, Leek ST13 6NR* Tel (01538) 386109

WOODS, The Ven Samuel Edward. b 10. Trin Coll Cam BA34 MA37. Westcott Ho Cam 35. d 36 p 37. New Zealand 36-46 and from 55; V Southport H Trin *Liv* 46-50; R Bp's Hatfield *St Alb* 50-55; Adn Rangiora and Westland 55-59 and 63-68; Adn Sumner 59-63; Adn Timaru 68-71; Adn Akaroa and Asburton 74-77. *18 Wren Street, Parkwood, Waikanae, New Zealand* Tel (0064) (4) 293 1035

WOODS, Tanya Joy. b 73. CITC 99. d 02. NSM Killesher *K, E & A* from 02. *Cornacrea, Cavan, Irish Republic* Tel (00353) (49) 433 2188 Mobile 87-686 0074
E-mail tanyawoods@eircom.net

WOODS, Theodore Frank Spreull. b 37. Cam Univ BA58 DipEd80. Wells Th Coll 60. d 62 p 63. C Stocking Farm CD *Leic*

62-67; Papua New Guinea 67-77; V Knighton St Jo *Leic* 77-80; Australia from 80; Chapl Angl Ch Gr Sch Brisbane 80-88; Chapl Hillbrook Angl Sch from 89; rtd 03. *44 Merle Street, Carina, Qld, Australia 4152* Tel (0061) (7) 3398 4437 *or* 3354 3422 Fax 3354 1057

WOODS, Timothy James. b 52. Poly Cen Lon BA78 MSc79 Ex Univ MA96 AIB75 PACTA88. Qu Coll Birm 81. **d** 83 **p** 84. C Brierley Hill *Lich* 83-86; C Stoneydelph St Martin CD 86-88; World Development Officer 86-88; Chr Aid Area Sec (SE Lon) 88-91; V Estover *Ex* 91-97; TR Brixham w Churston Ferrers and Kingswear 97-00; Dir Bd of Ch and Soc *Sarum* from 00. *The Vicarage, 14 Church Road, Laverstock, Salisbury SP1 1QX* Tel (01722) 349152 *or* 411966 Fax 411990
E-mail tim.woods@salisbury.anglican.org

WOODS, Mrs Valerie Irene. b 44. Trin Coll Bris DipHE84. **dss** 84 **d** 87 **p** 94. Coleford w Staunton *Glouc* 84-88; C 87-88; TD Bedminster *Bris* 88-94; TV 94-95; Chapl HM Rem Cen Pucklechurch 95-96; Chapl HM Pris Eastwood Park 96-00; V Wood End *Cov* from 01. *St Chad's Vicarage, Hillmorton Road, Coventry CV2 1FY* Tel (024) 7661 2909
E-mail val.woods@btinternet.com

WOODSFORD, Canon Andrew Norman. b 43. Nottm Univ BA65. Ridley Hall Cam 65. **d** 67 **p** 68. C Radcliffe-on-Trent *S'well* 67-70; P-in-c Ladybrook 70-73; P-in-c Barton in Fabis 73-81; P-in-c Thrumpton 73-81; R Gamston w Eaton and W Drayton 81-88; Chapl Bramcote Sch Notts 81-93; Warden of Readers *S'well* from 88; Hon Can S'well Minster from 93; RD Retford 93-00. *The Rectory, Gamston, Retford DN22 0QB* Tel (01777) 838706 E-mail woodsford@email.msn.com

WOODSFORD, Martyn Paul. b 64. Oak Hill Th Coll 01. **d** 03. C Southover *Chich* from 03. *4 Elm Grove, Lewes BN7 1UL* Tel (01273) 471435 Mobile 07904-239842

WOODSIDE, David. b 60. St Jo Coll Dur BA81. Cranmer Hall Dur 87. **d** 90 **p** 91. C Stoke Newington St Mary *Lon* 90-92. *Address temp unknown*

WOODWARD, Andrew John. b 59. ACIB85. SEITE DipTM99. **d** 99 **p** 00. NSM Weybridge *Guildf* from 99. *9 Sandy Close, Maybury, Woking GU22 8BQ* Tel (01483) 771331
E-mail 106217.1777@compuserve.com

WOODWARD, Anthony John. b 50. Salford Univ BSc78. St Jo Coll Nottm DipTh79. **d** 81 **p** 82. C Deane *Man* 81-84; CF 84-87; R Norris Bank *Man* 87-90; V Lostock St Thos and St Jo 92-96; Perm to Offic 96-01; C Halliwell 01-02; TV from 02. *St Paul's Vicarage, Vicarage Road, Bolton BL1 8BP* Tel (01204) 495038

WOODWARD, Arthur Robert Harry (Bob). b 28. **d** 76 **p** 77. Rhodesia 76-80; Zimbabwe 80-87; Adn E Harare 82-87; R Wymington w Podington *St Alb* 87-97; RD Sharnbrook 89-97; rtd 97; Perm to Offic *Portsm* from 97. *9 Briarfield Gardens, Horndean, Waterlooville PO8 9HX* Tel (023) 9259 6983
E-mail woodward@bushinternet.com

WOODWARD, Ian. b 44. OLM course 96. **d** 97 **p** 98. OLM Queen Thorne *Sarum* 97-99; Adv to Bd of Ch and Soc 97-00; NSM Wilton w Netherhampton and Fugglestone 00-02; R Bere Regis and Affpuddle w Turnerspuddle from 02. *The Vicarage, West Street, Bere Regis, Wareham BH20 7HQ* Tel (01929) 471262 Mobile 07973-318866 E-mail revianw@btinternet.com

WOODWARD, James Welford. b 61. K Coll Lon BD82 AKC82 Lambeth STh85 Birm Univ MPhil91 Open Univ PhD99. Westcott Ho Cam 83. **d** 85 **p** 86. C Consett *Dur* 85-87; Bp's Dom Chapl *Ox* 87-90; Chapl Qu Eliz Hosp Birm 90-96; Distr Chapl Co-ord S Birm HA 90-96; Chapl Manager Univ Hosp Birm NHS Trust 92-96; P-in-c Middleton *Birm* 96-98; P-in-c Wishaw 96-98; Bp's Adv on Health and Soc Care from 96; V Temple Balsall from 98; Master Foundn and Hosp of Lady Katherine Leveson from 98; Dir Leveson Cen for the Study of Ageing, Spirituality and Soc Policy from 00. *The Master's House, Temple Balsall, Knowle, Solihull B93 0AL* Tel (01564) 772415 Fax 778432 E-mail james.w.woodward@btinternet.com

WOODWARD, Canon John Clive. b 35. Univ of Wales (Lamp) BA56. St Jo Coll Dur 56. **d** 58 **p** 59. C Risca *Mon* 58-63; C Chepstow 63-66; V Ynysddu 66-74; V Newport Ch Ch 74-84; Can St Woolos Cathl 82-00; TR Cyncoed 84-00; rtd 00. *17 Carisbrooke Way, Cyncoed, Cardiff CF23 9HS* Tel (029) 2048 4448

WOODWARD, Mark Christian. b 73. Univ of Wales (Lamp) BA95 Trin Coll Carmarthen PGCE97. Trin Coll Bris MA02. **d** 02 **p** 03. C Egham *Guildf* from 02. *33 Grange Road, Egham TW20 9QP* Tel (01784) 434137 Mobile 07949-630031
E-mail markcwoodwarduk@yahoo.co.uk

WOODWARD, Matthew Thomas. b 75. Brunel Univ BA97 K Coll Lon MA99 Anglia Poly Univ MA01. Westcott Ho Cam 99. **d** 01 **p** 02. C Hampstead St Jo *Lon* from 01. *1 Holly Bush Vale, London NW3 6TX* Tel (020) 7794 6838 Mobile 07971-573734
E-mail matthewwoodward@mac.com

WOODWARD, Maurice George. b 29. Selw Coll Cam BA56 MA58. Wells Th Coll 56. **d** 58 **p** 59. C Gedling *S'well* 58-61; Succ Leic Cathl *Leic* 61-64; Chapl Leic R Infirmary 62-64; CF (R of O) 63-94; V Barrow upon Soar *Leic* 64-77; Hon Chapl Leic Cathl 64-77; V Clare w Poslingford *St E* 77-85; P-in-c Stoke by Clare w

Wixoe 84-85; R How Caple w Sollarshope, Sellack etc *Heref* 85-94; rtd 94; Perm to Offic *Glouc* 95-01; Hon C Northleach w Hampnett and Farmington etc from 01. *3 Bank Villas, West End, Northleach, Cheltenham GL54 3HG* Tel (01451) 860971

WOODWARD, Canon Peter Cavell. b 36. St Cath Coll Cam BA58 MA62. Bps' Coll Cheshunt 58. **d** 60 **p** 61. C Chingford St Anne *Chelmsf* 60-63; Madagascar 63-75; V Weedon Bec *Pet* 75-76; P-in-c Everdon 75-76; V Weedon Bec w Everdon 76-81; RD Daventry 79-81; Can Pet Cathl 81-02; V Brackley St Pet w St Jas 81-02; Chapl Brackley Cottage Hosp 81-02; RD Brackley 82-88; rtd 02; Perm to Offic *Pet* from 02. *7 Glastonbury Road, Northampton NN4 8BB* Tel (01604) 660679
E-mail pcwoodward@lineone.net

WOODWARD, Reginald Charles Huphnill. b 19. Lon Univ BA41 DipEd FRGS FRAS. Wells Th Coll 41. **d** 43 **p** 44. C Linc St Giles *Linc* 43-46; Succ St Mary's Cathl *Edin* 46-51; Hd Master St Mary's Cathl Choir Sch Edin 47-53; Lic to Offic *Linc* 53-95; Teacher K Sch Grantham 53-74; Hd Master K Lower Sch Grantham 74-79; rtd 79. *104 Harrowby Road, Grantham NG31 9DS* Tel (01476) 571912

WOODWARD, Richard Tharby. b 39. Man Univ BA60. Chich Th Coll 60. **d** 62 **p** 63. C Mansfield St Mark *S'well* 62-65; Chapl Liddon Ho Lon 65-69; C-in-c Beaconsfield St Mich CD *Ox* 69-76; TV Beaconsfield 76-94; rtd 94; Perm to Offic *Ox* 97-00. *10 Baring Crescent, Beaconsfield HP9 2NG* Tel (01494) 670690

WOODWARD, Robert. See WOODWARD, Arthur Robert Harry

WOODWARD, Roger David. b 38. WMMTC 87. **d** 90 **p** 91. C Castle Bromwich SS Mary and Marg *Birm* 90-93; C Kingstanding St Luke from 93; C Kingstanding St Mark from 93. *77 Bannersgate Road, Sutton Coldfield B73 6TY* Tel 0121-355 8497

WOODWARDS, David George. b 36. K Coll Lon BD62 MTh73. Oak Hill Th Coll 62. **d** 64 **p** 65. C Heworth H Trin *York* 64-66; Nigeria 67-71; V Edwardstone w Groton *St E* 72-82; RD Sudbury 81-88; R Glemsford 82-88; P-in-c Stanstead w Shimplingthorne and Alpheton 85-86; P-in-c Lawshall 85-86; P-in-c Hartest w Boxted, Somerton and Stanstead 86-88; Hon Can St E Cathl 87-94; R Thorndon w Rishangles, Stoke Ash, Thwaite etc 88-94; RD Hartismere 88-93; rtd 94. *4 Cricketers Close, Sudbury CO10 2AL* Tel (01787) 374160 Fax 883312

WOOKEY, Mrs Frances Anne. b 52. ACII73. WEMTC 94. **d** 97 **p** 98. C Glouc St Jas and All SS *Glouc* 97-01; V Hanley Castle, Hanley Swan and Welland *Worc* from 01. *The Vicarage, 5 Westmere, Hanley Swan, Worcester WR8 0DG* Tel (01684) 310321 E-mail fwookey@fides.demon.co.uk

WOOKEY, Stephen Mark. b 54. Em Coll Cam BA76 MA80. Wycliffe Hall Ox 77. **d** 80 **p** 81. C Enfield Ch Trent Park *Lon* 80-84; Asst Chapl Paris St Mich *Eur* 84-87; C Langham Place All So *Lon* 87-96; R Moreton-in-Marsh w Batsford, Todenham etc *Glouc* from 96; RD Stow from 99. *The Rectory, Bourton Road, Moreton-in-Marsh GL56 0BG* Tel (01608) 652680
E-mail stephen_wookey@talk21.com

WOOLCOCK, Mrs Annette Elisabeth. b 56. Qu Coll Birm BTheol94. **d** 94 **p** 95. C Hethersett w Canteloff w Lt and Gt Melton *Nor* 94-96; C Stourport and Wilden *Worc* 96-00; P-in-c The Ampneys w Driffield and Poulton *Glouc* from 00. *The Rectory, Ampney Crucis, Cirencester GL7 5RY* Tel (01285) 851240

WOOLCOCK, Christine Ann. See FROUDE, Canon Christine Ann

WOOLCOCK, John. b 47. DipRK70 Open Univ BA82 BA86. Wm Temple Coll Rugby 69 Sarum & Wells Th Coll 70. **d** 72 **p** 73. C Kells *Carl* 72-76; C Barrow St Matt 76-78; R Distington 78-86; V Staveley w Kentmere 86-93; V Staveley, Ings and Kentmere 93; Soc Resp Officer 89-93; Hon Can Carl Cathl 91-93; TR Egremont and Haile from 93. *The Rectory, Grove Road, Egremont CA22 2LU* Tel (01946) 820268

WOOLDRIDGE, Derek Robert. b 33. Nottm Univ BA57. Oak Hill Th Coll. **d** 59 **p** 60. C Chesterfield H Trin *Derby* 59-63; C Heworth w Peasholme St Cuth *York* 63-70; R York St Paul 70-00; rtd 01; Perm to Offic *York* from 01. *80 Grantham Drive, York YO26 4TZ* Tel (01904) 798393
E-mail drw@100york.freeserve.co.uk

WOOLDRIDGE, John Bellamy. b 27. Tyndale Hall Bris 54. **d** 56 **p** 57. C Norbury *Ches* 56-58; C Bramcote *S'well* 58-60; R Eccleston *Ches* 60-66; NW Area Sec CPAS 66-68; P-in-c Knutsford St Jo *Ches* 68-71; V Knutsford St Jo and Toft 71-79; V Gt Clacton *Chelmsf* 79-82; V Disley *Ches* 82-88; Min Buxton Trin Prop Chpl *Derby* 88-92; rtd 92; Lic to Offic *S'well* from 92; Perm to Offic *Derby* from 92. *227 Bramcote Lane, Nottingham NG8 2QA* Tel 0115-928 8332

WOOLHOUSE, Kenneth. b 38. BNC Ox BA61 MA65. Cuddesdon Coll 61. **d** 64 **p** 65. C Old Brumby *Linc* 64-67; W Germany 67-68; Chapl Cov Cathl *Cov* 68-75; C-in-c Hammersmith SS Mich and Geo White City Estate CD *Lon* 75-81; Dir Past Studies Chich Th Coll 81-86; P-in-c Birdham w W Itchenor *Chich* 81-86; Chapl W Sussex Inst of HE 86-95; TV

N Lambeth *S'wark* 95-01; rtd 01; Perm to Offic *S'wark* from 01. *15 Tavistock Tower, Russell Place, London SE16 7PQ* Tel (020) 7237 8147

WOOLHOUSE, Miss Linda June. b 49. ACP76 CertEd70. WMMTC 85. **d** 88 **p** 94. Hon Par Dn Old Swinford Stourbridge *Worc* 88-92; Par Dn 93-94; Community Chapl 92-93; C Old Swinford Stourbridge 94-96; Black Country Urban Ind Miss *Lich* 96-01; Res Min W Bromwich All SS 96-01; V Pensnett *Worc* from 01. *St Mark's Vicarage, Vicarage Lane, Pensnett, Brierley Hill DY5 4JH* Tel (01384) 262666
E-mail linda@woolhousel.freeserve.co.uk

WOOLLARD, Miss Bridget Marianne. b 56. K Coll Cam BA77 MA80 Sheff Univ PGCE78 St Jo Coll Dur BA81 Birm Univ MPhil87. Cranmer Hall Dur 79. **dss** 82 **d** 87 **p** 94. Battersea St Pet and St Paul *S'wark* 82-84; Chapl Southn Univ *Win* 84-89; Tutor Past Th and Dir Past Studies Qu Coll Birm 89-92; Telford Chr Coun Officer for Ind and Commerce *Lich* 92-97; Perm to Offic *Heref* 92-97; Lect in Past Th Trin Coll Melbourne Australia 97-98; Chapl Addenbrooke's NHS Trust from 98; Perm to Offic *Lich* from 98; *Ely* from 01. *19 Mere Grove, Shawbirch, Telford TF5 0NR* Tel (01952) 243205 *or* (01223) 217769

WOOLLARD, David John. b 39. Leic Univ BSc62. Trin Coll Bris DipHE88. **d** 88 **p** 89. C Clifton *York* 88-91; C York St Luke 91-94; V Selby St Jas from 94; V Wistow 94-96. *St James's Vicarage, 14 Leeds Road, Selby YO8 4HX* Tel (01757) 702861

WOOLLASTON, Brian. b 53. CertEd76 DipTh83. St Paul's Coll Grahamstown 81. **d** 83 **p** 84. C Kington w Huntington, Old Radnor, Kinnerton etc *Heref* 88-89; C Tupsley 89-91; V Newbridge-on-Wye and Llanfihangel Brynpabuan etc *S & B* 91-98; CF from 98. *c/o MOD Chaplains (Army)* Tel (01980) 615804 Fax 615800

WOOLLCOMBE (née DEARMER), Mrs Juliet. b 38. St Mary's Coll Dur BA60 Hughes Hall Cam DipEd61. Gilmore Course 74. **dss** 77 **d** 87 **p** 94. St Marylebone Ch Ch *Lon* 77-80; Dean of Women's Min (Lon Area) 87-89; Dn-in-c Upton Snodsbury and Broughton Hackett etc *Worc* 89-94; NSM Pershore w Pinvin, Wick and Birlingham 94-98; rtd 98; Perm to Offic *Worc* from 98. *19 Ashdale Avenue, Pershore WR10 1PL* Tel (01386) 556550

✠**WOOLLCOMBE, The Rt Revd Kenneth John.** b 24. St Jo Coll Ox BA49 MA53 S Sewanee Univ STD63 Trin Coll Hartford (USA) Hon DD75. Westcott Ho Cam 49. **d** 51 **p** 52 **c** 71. C Gt Grimsby St Jas *Linc* 51-53; Fell Chapl and Lect St Jo Coll Ox 53-60; Tutor St Jo Coll Ox 56-60; USA 60-63; Prof Dogmatic Th Gen Th Sem NY 60-63; Prin Edin Th Coll 63-71; Can St Mary's Cathl *Edin* 63-71; Bp Ox 71-78; Asst Bp Lon 78-81; Can Res and Prec St Paul's Cathl 81-89; rtd 89; Asst Bp Worc from 89; Perm to Offic from 89. *19 Ashdale Avenue, Pershore WR10 1PL* Tel (01386) 556550

WOOLLEY, Canon Christopher Andrew Lempriere. b 15. Ch Ch Ox BA37 MA70. Ely Th Coll 37. **d** 39 **p** 40. C Kilburn St Aug *Lon* 39-46; Tanganyika 46-64; Tanzania 64-70; Adn Njombe 64-70; Can Liuli 65-70; Hon Can from 70; P-in-c Hanwell *Ox* 70-84; V Horley w Hornton 70-84; rtd 84; Perm to Offic *B & W* 86-91. *Springfield, Street Road, Glastonbury BA6 9EG* Tel (01458) 835175

WOOLLEY, Francis Bertram Hopkinson. b 43. Sarum & Wells Th Coll 75. **d** 78 **p** 79. C Halesowen *Worc* 78-81; TV Droitwich 81-86; TV Cambridge Ascension *Ely* 86-92; R Leverington 92-01; P-in-c Wisbech St Mary 92-98; P-in-c Southea w Murrow and Parson Drove 98-01; P-in-c Balsham 01-02; P-in-c W Wickham 01-02; P-in-c Weston Colville 01-02; P-in-c W Wratting 01-02; R Balsham, Weston Colville, W Wickham etc from 02. *The Rectory, 19 West Wratting Road, Balsham, Cambridge CB1 6DX* Tel (01223) 894010
E-mail francis.woolley@tesco.net

WOOLLEY, John Alexander. b 28. St Deiniol's Hawarden 61. **d** 63 **p** 64. C Garston *Liv* 63-65; C-in-c Gt Crosby St Luke 65-71; R Croft w Southworth 71-75; Chapl Cherry Knowle & Ryhope Hosps Sunderland 75-83; Chapl Cell Barnes Hosp St Alb 83-93; Chapl Hill End Hosp St Alb 83-93; rtd 93; NSM Niton *Portsm* 95-97; NSM Whitwell 95-97; NSM St Lawrence 95-97. *39 Falkland Road, Southport PR8 6LG*

WOOLLEY, Miss Susan Margaret. b 41. Hockerill Coll of Educn TCert63. Dioc OLM tr scheme 97. **d** 00 **p** 01. NSM Catford (Southend) and Downham *S'wark* from 00. *195 Conisborough Crescent, London SE6 2SF* Tel (020) 8698 4437

WOOLMER, John Shirley Thursby. b 42. Wadh Coll Ox BA63 MA69. St Jo Coll Nottm 70. **d** 72 **p** 73. Asst Chapl Win Coll 72-75; C Ox St Aldate w H Trin *Ox* 75-82; R Shepton Mallet w Doulting *B & W* 82-02; Chapl Bath and West Community NHS Trust 97-01; Preb Wells Cathl *B & W* 00-02; NSM Leic H Trin w St Jo *Leic* from 02; Par Evang from 02. *Fig Tree Cottage, Hall Gates, Cropston, Leicester LE7 7GQ1* Tel 0116-235 3569

WOOLMER, Kelvin Frederick. b 55. EAMTC 98. **d** 01 **p** 02. NSM Squirrels Heath *Chelmsf* from 01. *228 Pettits Lane North, Romford RM1 4PB* Tel (01708) 509913
E-mail kelvinwoolmer@aol.com

WOOLNOUGH, Jeffrey Ralph. b 59. MCSD88. Coll of Resurr Mirfield 00. **d** 02 **p** 03. C Gt Ilford St Mary *Chelmsf* from 02. *5 Regents Gardens, Ilford IG3 8UL* Tel (020) 8597 7443
E-mail jeff76@btinternet.com

WOOLSTENHOLMES, Cyril Esmond. b 16. Bede Coll Dur BA37 MA41 DipTh38. **d** 39 **p** 40. C Leadgate *Dur* 39-44; C Darlington St Cuth 44-46; C W Hartlepool St Paul 46-50; V Tudhoe Grange 50-67; R Shadforth 67-82; rtd 82. *12 Wearside Drive, The Sands, Durham DH1 1LE* Tel 0191-384 3763

WOOLVEN, Ronald. b 36. Oak Hill Th Coll 60. **d** 63 **p** 64. C Romford Gd Shep Collier Row *Chelmsf* 63-68; C Widford 68-73; P-in-c Barling w Lt Wakering 73-84; V from 84. *154 Little Wakering Road, Great Wakering, Southend-on-Sea SS3 0JN* Tel (01702) 219200

WOOLVERIDGE, Gordon Hubert. b 27. Barrister-at-Law 52 CCC Cam BA51 MA55. S Dios Minl Tr Scheme 81. **d** 84 **p** 85. NSM St Edm the King w St Nic Acons etc *Lon* 84-85; NSM Chich St Paul and St Pet *Chich* 85-88; P-in-c Greatham w Empshott *Portsm* 88-90; P-in-c Hawkley w Prior's Dean 88-90; P-in-c Greatham w Empshott and Hawkley w Prior's Dean 90-92; rtd 92; Perm to Offic *Sarum* from 93. *Brook House, Winfrith Newburgh, Dorchester DT2 8JH* Tel (01305) 853633

WOOLWAY, Joanne. *See* GRENFELL, Joanne Woolway

WOOLWICH, Area Bishop of. *See* BUCHANAN, The Rt Revd Colin Ogilvie

WOON, Edward Charles. b 43. SW Minl Tr Course 94. **d** 96 **p** 97. OLM Tuckingmill *Truro* 96-02; P-in-c from 02. *All Saints' Vicarage, 35 Roskear, Camborne TR14 8DG* Tel (01209) 715910 Mobile 07974-431863

WOOSTER, Patrick Charles Francis. b 38. Qu Coll Birm 63. **d** 65 **p** 66. C Chippenham St Andr w Tytherton Lucas *Bris* 65-70; C Cockington *Ex* 70-72; V Stone w Woodford *Glouc* 72-73; P-in-c Hill 72-73; V Stone w Woodford and Hill 73-99; rtd 99; Perm to Offic *Worc* from 99. *20 Hylton Road, Hampton, Evesham WR11 2QB* Tel (01386) 45907

WOOSTER, Mrs Ruth Mary. b 45. St Alb and Ox Min Course 95. **d** 98 **p** 99. OLM High Wycombe *Ox* from 98. *Homewood, 45 New Road, Sands, High Wycombe HP12 4LH* Tel (01494) 530087
E-mail ruth@woosies.freeserve.co.uk

WOOTTON, Philip Charles. b 63. Hatf Coll Dur BA85 Dur Inst of Educn DipTM00. **d** 00 **p** 01. C Meopham w Nurstead *Roch* from 00. *38 Evenden Road, Meopham DA13 0HA* Tel (01474) 812569

WORCESTER, Archdeacon of. *See* TETLEY, The Ven Joy Dawn

WORCESTER, Bishop of. *See* SELBY, The Rt Revd Peter Stephen Maurice

WORCESTER, Dean of. *See* MARSHALL, The Very Revd Peter Jerome

WORDSWORTH, Jeremy Nathaniel. b 30. Clare Coll Cam BA54 MA58. Ridley Hall Cam 54. **d** 56 **p** 57. C Gt Baddow *Chelmsf* 56-59; Chapl Felsted Sch 59-63; Chapl Sherborne Sch 63-71; PV and Succ S'wark Cathl *S'wark* 71-73; P-in-c Stone *Worc* 73-77; V Malvern St Andr 77-82; V Combe Down w Monkton Combe and S Stoke *B & W* 82-95; rtd 95. *4 The Glebe, Hinton Charterhouse, Bath BA2 7SB* Tel (01225) 722520
E-mail hintonwordys@ukonline.co.uk

WORDSWORTH, Paul. b 42. Birm Univ BA64 Hull Univ DipMin89. Wells Th Coll 64. **d** 66 **p** 67. C Anlaby St Pet *York* 66-71; C Marfleet 71-72; TV 72-77; V Sowerby 77-90; P-in-c Sessay 77-90; V York St Thos w St Maurice 90-01; Dioc Community Miss Project Ldr from 90; Abp's Miss Adv 96-00; Miss Strategy Development Officer from 01; Abp's Officer for Miss and Evang from 01. *12 Muncastergate, Heworth, York YO31 9LA* Tel (01904) 427035 Fax 427034

WORGAN, Maurice William. b 40. Ely Th Coll 62 Sarum Th Coll 64. **d** 65 **p** 66. C Cranbrook *Cant* 65-69; C Maidstone St Martin 69-72; P-in-c Stanford w Postling and Radegund 72-73; R Lyminge w Paddlesworth 72-73; R Lyminge w Paddlesworth, Stanford w Postling etc 73-88; V Cant St Dunstan w H Cross from 88. *St Dunstan's Vicarage, 5 Harkness Drive, Canterbury CT2 7RW* Tel (01227) 463654 Fax as telephone
E-mail maurice@maurice-worgan.co.uk

WORKMAN, David Andrew. b 22. MICS49 AMBIM78 FBIM80. Arm Aux Min Course 87. **d** 90 **p** 91. C Dundalk w Heynestown *Arm* 90-97; rtd 97; Perm to Offic *Arm* from 97. *Dunbeag, Togher, Drogheda, Co Louth, Irish Republic* Tel (00353) (41) 685 2171

WORKMAN, John Lewis. b 26. St Deiniol's Hawarden 82. **d** 83 **p** 84. C Swansea St Mary and Battle w Llanddew *S & B* 83-86; Min Can Brecon Cathl 83-86; P-in-c Swansea St Luke 86-87; V 87-95; rtd 95. *12 Grove House, Clyne Close, Mayals, Swansea SA3 5HL* Tel (01792) 405674

WORLEDGE, Paul Robert. b 70. Hertf Coll Ox BA91 Lon Inst of Educn PGCE92. Oak Hill Th Coll BA00. **d** 00 **p** 01. C Boscombe St Jo *Win* from 00. *167 Southcote Road, Boscombe, Bournemouth BH1 3SP* Tel (01202) 397691
E-mail worledge@bigfoot.com

WORLEY, William. b 37. TD89. Cranmer Hall Dur 69. **d** 72 **p** 73. C Consett *Dur* 72-76; V Seaton Carew from 76; CF (TA) from 77. *The Vicarage, 11 Ruswarp Grove, Seaton Carew, Hartlepool TS25 2BA* Tel (01429) 262463

WORMALD, Roy Henry. b 42. Chich Th Coll 64. **d** 67 **p** 68. C Walthamstow St Mich *Chelmsf* 67-69; C Cov St Thos *Cov* 69-72; C Cov St Jo 69-72; C Wood Green St Mich *Lon* 72-77; P-in-c Hanwell St Mellitus 77-80; V Hanwell St Mellitus w St Mark 80-95; C Hillingdon St Jo 95-99; R Kirkley St Pet and St Jo *Nor* from 99. *St Peter's Rectory, Rectory Road, Lowestoft NR33 0ED* Tel (01502) 502155

WORN, Nigel John. b 56. Sarum & Wells Th Coll. **d** 84 **p** 85. C Walworth St Jo *S'wark* 84-88; Succ S'wark Cathl 88-92; V Mitcham Ascension 92-01; RD Merton 97; V Kew from 01. *The Vicarage, 278 Kew Road, Kew, Richmond TW9 3EE* Tel (020) 8940 4616 E-mail nigel.worn@which.net

WORRALL, Frederick Rowland. b 27. **d** 86 **p** 87. NSM Chellaston *Derby* 86-93; NSM Barrow-on-Trent w Twyford and Swarkestone 94-97; Perm to Offic from 97. *37 St Peter's Road, Chellaston, Derby DE73 1UU* Tel (01332) 701890

WORRALL, Peter Henry. b 62. CA Tr Coll Dip Evang88 WMMTC 93. **d** 95 **p** 96. C Bromsgrove St Jo *Worc* 95-99; P-in-c Hartlebury from 99. *Church Rise, Quarry Bank, Hartlebury, Kidderminster DY11 7TE* Tel (01299) 251535

WORRALL, Suzanne. *See* SHERIFF, Canon Suzanne

WORSDALL, John Robin. b 33. Dur Univ BA57. Linc Th Coll 62. **d** 63 **p** 64. C Manthorpe w Londonthorpe *Linc* 63-66; C Folkingham w Laughton 66-68; V New Bolingbroke w Carrington 68-74; P-in-c S Somercotes 74-80; V N Somercotes 74-80; P-in-c Stickney 80-82; P-in-c E Ville w Mid Ville 80-82; P-in-c Stickford 80-82; R Stickney Gp 82-98; rtd 98. *2 Streathers Court, Raunds, Wellingborough NN9 6DR* Tel (01933) 460078

WORSDELL, William Charles. b 35. AKC59. **d** 60 **p** 61. C Glouc St Aldate *Glouc* 60-66; V Devonport St Barn *Ex* 66-72; R Uplyme 72-77; R Withington and Compton Abdale w Haselton *Glouc* 77-87; V Badgeworth w Shurdington 87-95; rtd 95; Perm to Offic *Ex* 97-99; *Pet* 00-02. *Fairhaven, 13 Spriggs Close, Clapham, Bedford MK41 6GD* Tel (01234) 211990

WORSFOLD, Ms Caroline Jayne. b 61. St Steph Ho Ox. **d** 88 **p** 94. Chapl Asst Leic R Infirmary 88-90; C Sunderland Pennywell St Thos *Dur* 90-91; Sunderland HA Chapl 90-94; Chapl Priority Healthcare Wearside NHS Trust from 94. *Cherry Knowle Hospital, Ryhope, Sunderland SR2 0NB* Tel 0191-565 6256 ext 43370 *or* 522 7347

WORSFOLD, John. b 24. Keble Coll Ox BA50 MA50. Cuddesdon Coll 50. **d** 51 **p** 52. C Clapham H Spirit *S'wark* 51-62; C Richmond St Mary w St Matthias and St Jo 62-63; C Shirley St Geo *Cant* 63-80; C Croydon H Sav 80-84; C Croydon H Sav *S'wark* 85-89; rtd 90; Perm to Offic *S'wark* from 90. *26 Links Road, West Wickham BR4 0QW* Tel (020) 8777 7463

WORSFOLD, Richard Vernon. b 64. Ex Univ LLB86. Cranmer Hall Dur BA94 DMS95. **d** 95 **p** 96. C Countesthorpe w Foston *Leic* 95-99; TV Bradgate Team 99-01; TR from 01. *The Vicarage, 15 Groby Road, Ratby, Leicester LE6 0LJ* Tel (01509) 214553 E-mail rworsfold@leicester.anglican.org

WORSLEY, Mrs Christine Anne. b 52. Hull Univ BA73 Bris Univ CertEd74 Birm Univ MPhil94. WMMTC 82. **dss** 84 **d** 87 **p** 94. Smethwick St Mary *Birm* 84-87; Par Dn 87; Par Dn Smethwick H Trin w St Alb 87-89; Par Dn Coventry Caludon *Cov* 89-91; Chapl Myton Hamlet Hospice 92-95; Tutor WMMTC from 95; Perm to Offic *Birm* 95-98; *Cov* from 98; Lic to Offic *Birm* from 98. *41 Brays Lane, Coventry CV2 4DT* Tel (024) 7645 5099 *or* 0121-454 1527 E-mail christine@worsleyc.fsnet.co.uk

WORSLEY, Howard John. b 61. Man Univ BA83 Leeds Univ PGCE85 Birm Univ PhD00. St Jo Coll Nottm Dip Th Studies 92 MA93. **d** 93 **p** 94. C Huthwaite *S'well* 93-96; V Radford St Pet 96-01; Dir Studies St Jo Coll Nottm from 02. *The Vicarage, 18 Russell Road, Nottingham NG7 6HB* Tel 0115-978 7473 E-mail howard.worsley@talk21.com

WORSLEY, Malcolm. b 37. Carl Dioc Tr Inst 94. **d** 96 **p** 97. NSM Hawes Side *Blackb* 96-98 and from 01; NSM Lt Thornton 98-01. *14 Winslow Avenue, Carleton, Poulton-le-Fylde FY6 7PQ* Tel (01253) 882208 *or* 621859 Fax 751156 E-mail philippi@dial.pipex.com *or* m worsley@dial.pipex.com

WORSLEY, Richard John. b 52. Qu Coll Cam BA74 MA78 Univ of Wales CertEd76 Birm Univ MPhil91 Warwick Univ MA96. Qu Coll Birm DipTh79. **d** 80 **p** 81. C Styvechale *Cov* 80-84; V Smethwick H Trin w St Alb *Birm* 84-89; TV Coventry Caludon *Cov* 89-96; Hon C Binley from 97. *41 Brays Lane, Coventry CV2 4DT* Tel (024) 7645 5099

WORSLEY, Mrs Ruth Elizabeth. b 62. **d** 96 **p** 97. C Basford w Hyson Green *S'well* 96-99; C Hyson Green and Forest Fields 99-01; P-in-c from 01. *The Vicarage, 18 Russell Road, Nottingham NG7 6HB* Tel 0115-978 7473 E-mail howard.worsley@talk21.com

WORSNIP, Harry. b 29. Oldham Tech Coll HNC50. St Alb Minl Tr Scheme 89. **d** 92 **p** 93. NSM Arlesey w Astwick *St Alb* 92-96; NSM Goldington 96-99; Perm to Offic from 00. *28 Milburn Road, Bedford MK41 0NZ* Tel (01234) 266422

WORSSAM, Richard Mark. b 61. St Jo Coll Dur BA83 Selw Coll Cam BA92. Ridley Hall Cam CTM93. **d** 93 **p** 94. C Green Street Green and Pratts Bottom *Roch* 93-97; R Fawkham and Hartley

from 97. *The Rectory, 3 St John's Lane, Hartley, Longfield DA3 8ET* Tel (01474) 703819

WORT, Gavin. b 78. K Alfred's Coll Win BTh99. Westcott Ho Cam 00. **d** 02 **p** 03. C Eastleigh *Win* from 02. *St Francis House, Nightingale Avenue, Eastleigh SO50 9JB* Tel (023) 8061 9949 E-mail gwort@hotmail.com

WORTH, Preb Frederick Stuart. b 30. Oak Hill Th Coll 60. **d** 62 **p** 63. C Okehampton w Inwardleigh *Ex* 62-68; R Dunkeswell and Dunkeswell Abbey 68-78; P-in-c Luppitt 69-72; P-in-c Upottery 72-76; V Sheldon 73-78; RD Honiton 77-84 and 86-90; R Uplyme 78-86; R Uplyme w Axmouth 86-00; Preb Ex Cathl 96-00; rtd 00; Perm to Offic *Ex* and *Sarum* from 00. *Yarrow, 3 Westcliff Road, Charmouth, Bridport DT6 6BG* Tel (01297) 560194

WORTHEN, Jeremy Frederick. b 65. Rob Coll Cam BA86 MPhil88 Toronto Univ PhD92. Ripon Coll Cuddesdon DipTh93 DipMin94. **d** 94 **p** 95. C Bromley SS Pet and Paul *Roch* 94-97; Tutor SEITE from 97. *SEITE, Ground Floor Offices, Sun Pier House, Medway Street, Chatham ME4 4HF* Tel (01634) 832299

WORTHINGTON, George. b 35. AKC60. **d** 61 **p** 62. C Stockton St Pet *Dur* 61-65; C Poulton-le-Fylde *Blackb* 65-67; V Trawden 67-76; P-in-c Gressingham 76-78; P-in-c Arkholme 76-78; P-in-c Whittington 77-78; V Whittington w Arkholme and Gressingham 78-91; V Warton St Paul 91-00; rtd 00; Perm to Offic *Blackb* from 00 and *Carl* from 02. *4 Cavendish Gardens, Kirby Lonsdale, Carnforth LA6 3BW* Tel (01524) 271699

WORTHINGTON, Mark. b 55. Solicitor 80 Leeds Poly BA77. Cranmer Hall Dur 93. **d** 93 **p** 94. C Monkwearmouth St Andr *Dur* 93-96; C Chester le Street 96-00; V Harlow Green and Lamesley from 00. *The Vicarage, Lamesley, Gateshead NE11 0EU* Tel 0191-487 6490 E-mail mark.worthington@durham.anglican.org

WORTLEY, Prof John Trevor. b 34. Dur Univ BA57 MA60 DD86 Lon Univ PhD69 FRHistS. Edin Th Coll 57. **d** 59 **p** 60. C Huddersfield St Jo *Wakef* 59-64; Canada from 64; Prof Medical Hist Manitoba Univ from 69; Visiting Prof Sorbonne Univ from 99. *298 Yale Avenue, Winnipeg MB, Canada, R3M 0M1, or Manitoba University, Winnipeg MB, Canada, R3T 2N2* Tel (001) (204) 284 7554 *or* 474 9830 E-mail wortley@cc.umanitoba.ca

WORTLEY, Mrs Lyn Sharon. b 59. Open Univ BA94 MA98. N Ord Course 95. **d** 98 **p** 99. C Greasbrough *Sheff* 98-01; P-in-c Bramley and Ravenfield w Hooton Roberts etc from 01. *The Vicarage, 88 Main Street, Bramley, Rotherham S66 2SQ* Tel (01709) 702828 E-mail lyn@thewortleys.freeserve.co.uk

WORTON, David Reginald (Brother Paschal). b 56. St Steph Ho Ox 88. **d** 90 **p** 90. SSF from 77; NSM Anfield St Columba *Liv* 90-92; Zimbabwe 92-94; Asst P Harare Cathl 92-93; Asst P St Aug Miss Penhalonga 93-94; Lic to Offic *Newc* from 94. *The Friary, Alnmouth, Alnwick NE66 3NJ* Tel (01665) 830213

WOSTENHOLM, David Kenneth. b 56. Edin Univ BSc77 MB, ChB80 Southn Univ BTh88. Chich Th Coll 82. **d** 85 **p** 86. C Leytonstone St Marg w St Columba *Chelmsf* 85-90; V Brighton Annunciation *Chich* 90-01; TR Hove from 01. *The Vicarage, Wilbury Road, Hove BN3 3PB* Tel (01273) 681341 E-mail david@glitterage.f9.co.uk

WOTHERSPOON, David Colin. b 36. Portsm Coll of Tech CEng65 MIMechE65. St Jo Coll Dur 76. **d** 78 **p** 79. C Blackb St Gabr *Blackb* 78-81; V Witton 81-90; Chapl Berne w Neuchâtel *Eur* 90-01; rtd 01; Perm to Offic *Blackb* from 01. *300 Pleckgate Road, Blackburn BB1 8QU* Tel (01254) 249743

WOTTON, David Ashley. b 44. Chich Th Coll 71. **d** 74 **p** 75. C Allington and Maidstone St Pet *Cant* 74-77; C Ham St Andr *S'wark* 78-79; Chapl HM Rem Cen Latchmere Ho 78-79; C Tattenham Corner and Burgh Heath *Guildf* 85-88; P-in-c E Molesey St Mary 88-93; R Headley w Box Hill from 93; Offg Chapl RAF from 93. *The Rectory, Headley, Epsom KT18 6LE* Tel (01372) 377327

WOULDHAM, Ralph Douglas Astley. b 19. Leeds Univ BA48. Coll of Resurr Mirfield 48. **d** 50 **p** 51. C Leeds Halton St Wilfrid *Ripon* 50-53; Perm to Offic *Newc* 53-56; V Bolam 56-62; TR Usworth *Dur* 62-69; V Cleadon 69-79; V Lowick and Kyloe w Ancroft *Newc* 79-84; rtd 84. *10 Bank Hill, Berwick-upon-Tweed TD15 1BE*

WRAGG, Christopher William. b 60. SEITE. **d** 00 **p** 01. C Gt Warley Ch Ch *Chelmsf* 00-01; C Warley Ch Ch and Gt Warley St Mary from 01. *35 Conifer Drive, Warley, Brentwood CM14 5TZ* Tel (01277) 222863 Mobile 07714-507147 E-mail chris wragg@lineone.net

WRAGG, Peter Robert. b 60. Lon Univ BSc68. Sarum & Wells Th Coll 71. **d** 74 **p** 75. C Feltham *Lon* 74-79; TV Hackney 79-85; P-in-c Isleworth St Mary 85-94; V Feltham from 94. *The Vicarage, Cardinal Road, Feltham TW13 5AL* Tel (020) 8890 6681 *or* 8890 2011 E-mail office@parish-of-feltham.fsnet.co.uk

WRAIGHT, John Radford. b 38. St Chad's Coll Dur BA62 DipTh64. **d** 64 **p** 65. C Shildon *Dur* 64-67; C Newton Aycliffe 67-70; C Darlington St Jo 70-75; P-in-c Livingston LEP *Edin* 75-80; TV Carl H Trin and St Barn *Carl* 80-85; P-in-c Lindale w Field Broughton 85-95; R Middleton Tyas w Croft and

Eryholme *Ripon* from 95; rtd 03. *14 Colorado Grove, Darlington DL1 2YW* Tel (01325) 354613 E-mail j.r.wraight@amserve.net

WRAKE, John. b 28. RMA. Clifton Th Coll 56. **d** 59 **p** 60. C Gt Baddow *Chelmsf* 59-62; CF 62-66; V Tilton w Lowesby *Leic* 66-73; R Maresfield *Chich* 73-79; rtd 93. *Parkfield, Batts Ridge Road, Maresfield, Uckfield TN22 2HJ* Tel (01825) 762727

WRAPSON, Donald. b 36. St Aid Birkenhead 60. **d** 65 **p** 66. C Bacup St Sav *Man* 65-68; C Wolverhampton St Matt *Lich* 68-72; C Normanton *Derby* 72-78; V Dordon *Birm* 78-82; Chapl Birm Accident Hosp 82-92; Chapl Selly Oak Hosp Birm 82-92; Chapl Trauma Unit Birm Gen Hosp 92-95; Chapl S Birm Community Health NHS Trust 95-01; rtd 01; Perm to Offic *Birm* from 01. *37 Walkers Heath Road, Birmingham B38 0AB* Tel 0121-458 2995

WRATTEN, Martyn Stephen. b 34. AKC58 St Boniface Warminster 58. **d** 59 **p** 60. C Wandsworth Common St Mary *S'wark* 59-62; C Putney St Mary 62-65; C Pembury *Roch* 65-70; R Stone 70-76; Chapl Joyce Green Hosp Dartford 70-73; Stone Ho Hosp Kent 73-76; Hillcrest Hosp and Netherne Hosp Coulsdon 76-87; Hon C Netherne St Luke CD *S'wark* 76-87; V Gt Doddington *Pet* 87-88; V Gt Doddington and Wilby 88-95; Hon C N Petherton w Northmoor Green *B & W* 95-96; rtd 95; Perm to Offic *B & W* from 96. *1 Baymead Close, North Petherton, Bridgwater TA6 6QZ* Tel (01278) 662873

WRAW, Canon John Michael. b 59. Linc Coll Ox BA81 Fitzw Ho Cam BA84. Ridley Hall Cam 82. **d** 85 **p** 86. C Bromyard *Heref* 85-88; TV Sheff Manor *Sheff* 88-92; V Clifton St Jas 92-01; AD Rotherham from 98; Hon Can Sheff Cathl from 01; P-in-c Wickersley from 01. *The Rectory, Church Lane, Wickersley, Rotherham S66 1ES* Tel (01709) 543111
E-mail john@wraw.freeserve.co.uk

WRAY, Christopher. b 48. Hull Univ BA70 New Coll Ox DipTh73. Cuddesdon Coll 70. **d** 73 **p** 74. C Brighouse *Wakef* 73-76; C Almondbury 76-78; C Tong *Bradf* 78-80; V Ingleton w Chapel le Dale 80-86; R Brompton Regis w Upton and Skilgate *B & W* 86-91; V Yoxford and Peasenhall w Sibton *St E* 91-94; Perm to Offic *Carl* 94-97; R Brough w Stainmore, Musgrave and Warcop 97-02; R Walkingham Hill *Ripon* from 02. *The Rectory, Main Street, Staveley, Knaresborough HG5 9LD* Tel (01423) 340275

WRAY, Christopher Brownlow. b 46. Open Univ BA91. Oak Hill Th Coll 86. **d** 88 **p** 89. C Quidenham *Nor* 88-91; TV Chippenham St Paul w Hardenhuish etc *Bris* 91-97; P-in-c Chipping Sodbury and Old Sodbury *Glouc* from 97. *The Vicarage, Horse Shoe Lane, Chipping Sodbury, Bristol BS37 6ET* Tel (01454) 313159

WRAY, Karl. b 51. St And Coll Greystoke 72 Ian Ramsey Coll 74 Coll of Resurr Mirfield 75. **d** 78 **p** 79. C Salford St Phil w St Steph *Man* 78-83; CF 83-86 and 89-92; V Sculcoates St Paul w Ch Ch and St Silas *York* 86-89; V Carl St Luke Morton *Carl* from 92. *St Luke's Vicarage, Brownrigg Drive, Carlisle CA2 6PA* Tel (01228) 515693 E-mail karlwray@ukonline.co.uk

WRAY, Kenneth Martin. b 43. Linc Th Coll 72. **d** 75 **p** 76. C Shipley St Paul *Bradf* 75-79; V Edlington *Sheff* 79-85; V Nether Hoyland St Pet 85-97; V Up Hatherley *Glouc* from 97. *The Vicarage, Hatherley Road, Up Hatherley, Cheltenham GL51 6HX* Tel (01242) 236979 E-mail martin@wray111.fsnet.co.uk

WRAY, Martin John. b 51. St Steph Ho Ox 86. **d** 88 **p** 89. C E Boldon *Dur* 88-90; C Seaham w Seaham Harbour 90-92; P-in-c Chopwell 92-95; V 95-97; C Shildon 98-00; C Croxdale and Tudhoe from 00. *21 Four Villas, Tudhoe Village, Spennymoor DL16 6LP* Tel (01388) 818418

WRAY, Michael. b 49. Univ of Wales (Cardiff) BSc(Econ)77 Keele Univ PGCE78 RGN87. Ripon Coll Cuddesdon 80. **d** 82 **p** 83. C Blackpool St Steph *Blackb* 82-83; C Torrisholme 83-84; NSM Headington Quarry *Ox* 93-95; C Kennington *Cant* 95-99; CF (TA) 95-99; P-in-c Isham w Pytchley *Pet* from 99; Chapl Rockingham Forest NHS Trust 99-01; Chapl Northants Healthcare NHS Trust from 01. *The Rectory, Kettering Road, Isham, Kettering NN14 1UJ* Tel (01536) 722371
E-mail revmray.aeiou@virgin.net

WRAYFORD, Geoffrey John. b 38. Ex Coll Ox BA61 MA65. Linc Th Coll 61. **d** 63 **p** 64. C Cirencester *Glouc* 63-69; Chapl Chelmsf Cathl *Chelmsf* 69-74; V 70-74; V Canvey Is 74-76; TR 76-80; P-in-c Woodlands *B & W* 80-88; V 89-92; P-in-c Frome St Jo 80-88; P-in-c Frome Ch Ch 80-85; P-in-c Frome St Mary 85-88; V Frome St Jo and St Mary 89-92; V Minehead from 92; Chapl Taunton and Somerset NHS Trust from 92. *The Vicarage, 7 Paganel Road, Minehead TA24 5ET* Tel (01643) 703530
E-mail g.wrayford@breathemail.net

WREN, Christopher John. b 54. Dur Univ BEd76 MA85. St Steph Ho Ox 77. **d** 79 **p** 80. C Stockton St Pet *Dur* 79-82; C Newton Aycliffe 82-85; V Gateshead St Chad Bensham 85-91; TR Bensham 91-98; V Marton *Blackb* from 98. *St Paul's Vicarage, 55 Vicarage Lane, Marton, Blackpool FY4 4EF* Tel (01253) 762679 Fax 318791 E-mail wthenest@cs.com *or* wthenest@aol.com

WREN, Douglas Peter. b 59. Lanc Univ BA82. Trin Coll Bris BA88. **d** 88 **p** 89. C Nantwich *Ches* 88-91; C Chatham St Phil and St Jas *Roch* 91-94; R Kingsdown 94-02; R Speldhurst w

Groombridge and Ashurst from 02. *The Rectory, Southfields, Speldhurst, Tunbridge Wells TN3 0PD* Tel (01892) 862821
E-mail douglas.wren@diocese-rochester.org

WREN, John Aubrey. b 46. St Chad's Coll Dur BA69. Cuddesdon Coll 72. **d** 74 **p** 75. C Fenny Stratford and Water Eaton *Ox* 74-77; TV Brighton Resurr *Chich* 77-84; V Eastbourne St Andr 84-92; V Hove St Barn and St Agnes 92-96. *24 Marlborough Road, Lowestoft NR32 3BU* Tel (01502) 539274

WREN, Mrs Kathleen Ann. b 50. St Steph Ho Ox 83. **dss** 85 **d** 87. Gateshead St Cuth w St Paul *Dur* 85-86; Gateshead St Chad Bensham 86-91; Par Dn 87-91; Adv for Women's Min 90-98; Par Dn Bensham 91-94; C 94-98; Hon Can Dur Cathl 93-98; C Marton *Blackb* from 98. *St Paul's Vicarage, 55 Vicarage Lane, Marton, Blackpool FY4 4EF* Tel (01253) 762679 Fax 318791 E-mail wthenest@cs.com *or* wthenest@aol.com

WREN, Comdr Richard. b 35. S Dios Minl Tr Scheme 88. **d** 90 **p** 91. NSM Tisbury *Sarum* 90-01; TV 95-01; TV Nadder Valley from 01. *Gaston House, Tisbury, Salisbury SP3 6LG* Tel (01747) 870674

WRENBURY, The Revd and Rt Hon Lord (John Burton Buckley). b 27. Solicitor 52 K Coll Cam BA48. S'wark Ord Course 87. **d** 90 **p** 91. NSM Brightling, Dallington, Mountfield etc *Chich* from 90. *Oldcastle, Dallington, Heathfield TN21 9JP* Tel (01435) 830400

WRENN, Peter Henry. b 34. Lon Univ BA56. Qu Coll Birm 58. **d** 60 **p** 61. C Dronfield *Derby* 60-64; C Hessle *York* 64-65; V Loscoe *Derby* 65-70; Asst Chapl Solihull Sch 71-77; Chapl 77-97; rtd 97; Perm to Offic *Birm* from 97. *63 Shakespeare Drive, Shirley, Solihull B90 2AN* Tel 0121-744 3941

WREXHAM, Archdeacon of. *See* SQUIRES, The Ven Malcolm

WRIGHT, Alan James. b 38. Chich Th Coll 63. **d** 66 **p** 67. C Edgehill St Dunstan *Liv* 66-69; Swaziland 69-71; P-in-c Seaforth *Liv* 71-76; V Taunton All SS *B & W* 76-95; rtd 99. *Bethel, Langford Lane, Norton Fitzwarren, Taunton TA2 6NZ* Tel (01823) 326558

WRIGHT, Alan Richard. b 31. LNSM course 95. **d** 96 **p** 97. OLM Quidenham Gp *Nor* from 96. *Upgate Farm, Carleton Rode, Norwich NR16 1NJ* Tel (01953) 860300

WRIGHT, Alan William. b 44. AMusTCL71 Hull Univ BA66 Bris Univ PGCE67. Local Minl Tr Course 87. **d** 95 **p** 96. OLM Barton upon Humber *Linc* from 95. *1 Birchdale, Barton-upon-Humber DN18 5ED* Tel (01652) 632364
E-mail wrightherewrightnow@hotmail.com

WRIGHT, Alfred John. b 22. Wycliffe Hall Ox 66. **d** 66 **p** 67. C Newbury St Jo *Ox* 66-71; V E Challow 71-91; Chapl Community of St Mary V Wantage 75-89; rtd 91; Perm to Offic *Ox* from 92. *3 Latton Close, Southmoor, Abingdon OX13 5AE* Tel (01865) 820625 E-mail sheba@eggconnect.net

WRIGHT, Andrew David Gibson. b 58. St Andr Univ MTheol81. Ridley Hall Cam. **d** 83 **p** 84. C W Derby Gd Shep *Liv* 83-86; C Carl H Trin and St Barn *Carl* 86-88; V Wigan St Jas w St Thos *Liv* 88-91; Chapl St Edw Sch Ox 91-97; Ho Master from 97. *St Edward's School, Oxford OX2 7NN* Tel (01865) 319252 *or* 319204

WRIGHT, Anna Chang. b 55. **d** 02. OLM Blyth Valley *St E* from 02. *Rose End, Back Road, Wenhaston, Halesworth IP19 9DY* Tel (01502) 478411

WRIGHT, Miss Anne. b 39. Dalton Ho Bris 67. **dss** 76 **d** 87 **p** 94. BCMS 71-88; Uganda 71-77; N Area Sec BCMS 78-88; Pudsey St Lawr and St Paul *Bradf* 82-87; Hon Par Dn 87-88; Par Dn Kingston upon Hull H Trin *York* 88-93; Hd of Min amongst Women CPAS 93-02; CPAS Consultant (W Midl) 96-02; Regional Consultant (Midl) CPAS 99-02; Perm to Offic *Cov* from 93; rtd 02. *48 Falstaff Close, Nuneaton CV11 6FB* Tel (024) 7635 2290 E-mail jacquelinewright@btopenworld.com

WRIGHT, Anthony. *See* WRIGHT, Derek Anthony

WRIGHT, Anthony John. b 47. ACA70 FCA77 Ex Univ MA99. Ripon Coll Cuddesdon 86. **d** 88 **p** 89. C Kidderminster St Mary and All SS w Trimpley etc *Worc* 88-91; P-in-c Offenham and Bretforton 91-96; R Backwell w Chelvey and Brockley *B & W* 96-02; RD Portishead 01-02; P-in-c Tetbury w Beverston *Glouc* 02-03; R from 03; P-in-c Shipton Moyne w Westonbirt and Lasborough 02-03; V Shipton Moyne from 03. *The Rectory, Church Lane, Shipton Moyne, Tetbury GL8 8PW* Tel (01666) 880132 E-mail sheba.wright@virgin.net

WRIGHT, Canon Anthony Robert. b 49. Lanchester Poly BA70. St Steph Ho Ox 70. **d** 73 **p** 74. C Amersham on the Hill *Ox* 73-76; C Reading St Giles 76-78; P-in-c Prestwood 78-84; P-in-c Wantage 84-87; V 87-92; RD Wantage 84-92; P-in-c W w E Hanney 88-91; V Portsea St Mary *Portsm* 92-98; Hon Can Portsm Cathl 96-98; R Westmr St Marg from 98; Chapl to Speaker of Ho of Commons from 98; Can Westmr Abbey from 98. *2 Little Cloister, London SW1P 3PL* Tel (020) 7654 4806 Fax 7654 4821

WRIGHT, Antony John. b 31. St Pet Coll Saltley CertEd53. Chan Sch Truro. **d** 79 **p** 80. NSM St Breoke *Truro* 79-84; TV Probus, Ladock and Grampound w Creed and St Erme 84-89; V Perranzabuloe 89-95; rtd 96; Perm to Offic *Truro* from 96. *Nansmoor Cottage, Hendrawna Lane, Bolingey, Perranporth TR6 0DF* Tel (01872) 572850

WRIGHT, Canon Barry Owen. b 38. S'wark Ord Course 66. **d** 69 **p** 70. C Plumstead Ascension *S'wark* 69-74; Hon C Welling 74-89; Hon Can S'wark Cathl 79-89; Sen Chapl W Midl Police *Birm* 89-93; Sen Chapl Metrop Police *Lon* from 93; V Mill Hill St Mich from 02. *St Michael's Vicarage, 9 Flower Lane, London NW7 2JA* Tel (020) 8959 1449 Fax 8906 1857
E-mail bwrg8@aol.com

WRIGHT, Catherine Jane. b 62. Bris Univ BA84 MA92 Selw Coll Cam BA96. Ridley Hall Cam 94. **d** 97 **p** 98. C Highworth w Sevenhampton and Inglesham etc *Bris* 97-00; Perm to Offic *Ex* 99-01; NSM Stoke St Gregory w Burrowbridge and Lyng *B & W* from 01; Dioc Voc Adv from 02; Asst Dir of Ords from 02. *The Rectory, West Monkton, Taunton TA2 8QT* Tel (01823) 412226
E-mail cjwright@onetel.net.uk

WRIGHT, Charles Frederick Peter. b 16. Qu Coll Ox BA39 MA42. Westcott Ho Cam 40. **d** 41 **p** 42. C Stocksbridge *Sheff* 41-43; C Goole 43-47; C Ecclesall 47-50; R Brown and Chilton Candover w Northington etc *Win* 50-54; V Long Sutton 54-61; V Welton *Linc* 61-69; Lect Linc Th Coll 61-63; Lic to Offic *Linc* 69-99; rtd 81. *9 Bromley College, London Road, Bromley BR1 1PE* Tel (020) 8460 9461

WRIGHT, Charles Kenneth (Ken). b 38. CEng73 MIMechE73 MBIM91. Sarum & Wells Th Coll DCM93. **d** 93 **p** 94. C Bridgwater St Mary, Chilton Trinity and Durleigh *B & W* 93-96; Chapl Workington *Carl* 96-03; C Camerton, Seaton and W Seaton 96-03; Chapl W Cumbria Health Care NHS Trust from 96; rtd 03. *Naemair, 72 Ruskin Close, High Harrington, Workington CA14 4LS* Tel (01946) 833536
E-mail kenwright@fish.co.uk

WRIGHT, Christopher Joseph Herbert. b 47. St Cath Coll Cam BA69 MA73 PhD77. Ridley Hall Cam 75. **d** 77 **p** 78. C Tonbridge SS Pet and Paul *Roch* 77-81; Perm to Offic *St Alb* 82-01; BCMS India 83-88; Tutor and Dir Studies All Nations Chr Coll Ware 88-93; Prin from 93; Public Preacher *Lon* from 01. *All Nations Christian College, Easneye, Ware SG12 8LX* Tel (01920) 461243 Fax 462997

WRIGHT, Christopher Nigel. b 39. Kelham Th Coll 60. **d** 65 **p** 66. C Ellesmere Port *Ches* 65-69; C Latchford Ch Ch 69-72; C Gt Budworth 72-75; C Wigan St Andr *Liv* 75-76; V New Springs 77-82; C Dovecot 82-85; C Rainford 85-89; rtd 89; Perm to Offic *Liv* from 89. *105 Ilfracombe Road, Sutton Leach, St Helens WA9 4NN* Tel (01744) 821199

WRIGHT, Clifford. See WRIGHT, The Rt Revd Royston Clifford

WRIGHT, Canon Clifford Nelson. b 35. K Coll Lon BD59 AKC59. **d** 60 **p** 61. C Stevenage *St Alb* 60-67; V Camberwell St Luke *S'wark* 67-81; RD Camberwell 75-80; Hon Can S'wark Cathl 79-80; TR Basingstoke *Win* 81-93; RD Basingstoke 84-93; Hon Can Win Cathl 89-00; R Win St Matt 93-00; rtd 00. *1 Valley Dene, Dibden Purlieu, Southampton SO45 4NG* Tel (023) 8084 5898

WRIGHT, David Evan Cross. b 35. K Coll Lon BD64 AKC64. **d** 65 **p** 66. C Morpeth *Newc* 65-69; C Benwell St Jas 69-70; C Bushey *St Alb* 70-74; V High Wych 74-77; R High Wych and Gilston w Eastwick 77-80; V St Alb St Mary Marshalswick 80-89; P-in-c Sandridge 87-89; R Lenham w Boughton Malherbe *Cant* 89-00; rtd 00; P-in-c Fuengirola St Andr *Eur* from 01; Perm to Offic *Chich* from 01. *Calle Paulino Uzcudun 16, 29640 Torreblanca, Fuengirola, Malaga, Spain* Tel (0034) (5) 247 2140 Fax as telephone

WRIGHT, David Henry. b 23. Keble Coll Ox BA48. St Steph Ho Ox 52. **d** 54 **p** 55. C Penton Street St Silas w All SS *Lon* 54-57; V Barnsbury St Clem 57-66; V Wandsworth St Anne *S'wark* 66-73; P-in-c Stanley *St And* 73-75; R Dunkeld 73-92; R Strathtay 75-92; rtd 92. *79 Don Street, Woodside, Aberdeen AB24 2RX*

WRIGHT, David William. b 63. Barrister 86 Liv Univ LLB85 Fitzw Coll Cam BA92 Cam Univ MA96 Univ of Wales (Cardiff) LLM99. Westcott Ho Cam 90. **d** 93 **p** 94. C Chorlton-cum-Hardy St Clem *Man* 93-97; P-in-c Donnington Wood *Lich* 97-99; V from 99. *The Vicarage, St George's Road, Donnington Wood, Telford TF2 7NJ* Tel and fax (01952) 604239 Mobile 07977-543735 E-mail david.wright@lichfield.anglican.org

WRIGHT, Denise Ann. b 42. **d** 98. Par Dn Machen *Mon* from 98. *56 St David's Drive, Machen, Newport CF83 8RH* Tel (029) 2088 5655

WRIGHT, Derek Anthony. b 35. ACP66 Lon Univ CertEd57. Cranmer Hall Dur 80. **d** 81 **p** 82. C Auckland St Andr and St Anne *Dur* 81-83; V Cornforth 83-87; P-in-c Thornley 87-88; R Gt and Lt Glemham, Blaxhall etc *St E* 88-90; V Evenwood *Dur* 90-93; P-in-c Satley and Tow Law 93-95; V 95-99; rtd 99. *39 Hilltop Road, Bearpark, Durham DH7 7TA*

WRIGHT, Edward Maurice. b 54. **d** 88 **p** 91. C Maidstone St Luke *Cant* 88-93; R Cliffe at Hoo w Cooling *Roch* from 93. *St Helen's Rectory, Church Street, Cliffe, Rochester ME3 7PY* Tel (01634) 220220

WRIGHT, Edward Michael. b 37. St Cath Soc Ox BA61 MA65. Cuddesdon Coll DipTh63. **d** 64 **p** 65. C Willesden St Andr *Lon* 64-68; Bahamas 68-71; V Lewisham St Steph and St Mark *S'wark* 72-80; V Ox St Barn and St Paul *Ox* from 80. *St Barnabas' Vicarage, St Barnabas Street, Oxford OX2 6BG* Tel (01865) 557530 Fax as telephone E-mail michaelwright@cwcom.net

WRIGHT, Frank Albert. b 51. Portsm Univ MA02. Sarum & Wells Th Coll 80. **d** 83 **p** 84. C Buckingham *Ox* 83-86; C Newport Pagnell w Lathbury and Moulsoe 86-89; TV W Slough 89-95; TR 95-99; TR Fareham H Trin *Portsm* from 99; Dioc Interfaith Adv from 01. *The Rectory, 9 Brook Meadow, Fareham PO15 5JH* Tel and fax (01329) 280180 Fax 232688
E-mail wrightfa@compuserve.com

WRIGHT, Frederic Ian. b 64. City Univ BSc85. Wycliffe Hall Ox BTh94. **d** 94 **p** 95. C Carl St Jo *Carl* 94-98; C Bassenthwaite, Isel and Setmurthy 98-02; TV Binsey from 02. *The Vicarage, Bassenthwaite, Keswick CA12 4QH* Tel (01768) 776198
E-mail iwright@bassenthwaite.fsbusiness.co.uk

WRIGHT, Frederick John. b 15. AKC42. **d** 42 **p** 43. C Brierley Hill *Lich* 42-45; C Walsall Pleck and Bescot 45-49; V W Bromwich Gd Shep 49-54; R Headless Cross *Worc* 54-67; R Romsley 67-80; rtd 80; Perm to Offic *Ely* from 80. *Rosevear, 3 Dury Lane, Colne, Huntingdon PE28 3NB* Tel (01487) 840518

WRIGHT, Gerald Grattan. b 32. Delaware State Coll BSc72. Ripon Hall Ox 73. **d** 76 **p** 77. NSM Wolvercote w Summertown *Ox* 76-87 and 88-97; C Ox St Mich w St Martin and All SS 87-88; NSM Yarnton w Begbroke and Shipton on Cherwell from 97. *28 Davenant Road, Oxford OX2 8BX* Tel (01865) 552617

WRIGHT, Graham. b 50. Oak Hill Th Coll 73. **d** 76 **p** 77. C Northampton St Giles *Pet* 76-79; C Man Resurr *Man* 79-82; V Barkingside St Laur *Chelmsf* 82-88; Chapl K Geo V Hosp Ilford 82-88; P-in-c Yoxford *St E* 88-90; Chapl Suffolk Constabulary 88-90. *8-10 Dixons Fold, North Walsham Road, Norwich NR6 7QD* Tel (01603) 459960

WRIGHT, Graham Ewen. b 44. Lon Univ DipRS. S'wark Ord Course 86. **d** 89 **p** 90. NSM Aveley and Purfleet *Chelmsf* 89-95. *2 Palmers, Corringham, Stanford-le-Hope SS17 7JA* Tel (01375) 671747

WRIGHT, Mrs Heather Margaret. b 47. EAMTC 93. **d** 96 **p** 97. NSM Heigham St Thos *Nor* 96-99; Hon Asst Dioc Chapl among Deaf and Deafblind People from 99; NSM Sprowston w Beeston from 03. *133 Moore Avenue, Norwich NR6 7LQ* Tel and minicom (01603) 404194

WRIGHT, Howard John Douglas. b 64. BA85. Trin Coll Bris BA94. **d** 96 **p** 97. C Ipswich St Matt *St E* 96-00; V Four Marks *Win* from 00. *The Vicarage, 22 Lymington Bottom, Four Marks, Alton GU34 5AA* Tel (01420) 563344
E-mail howardwright@lineone.net

WRIGHT, Hugh Edward. b 57. BNC Ox BA79 MA87 Ex Univ CertEd81. Sarum & Wells Th Coll 85. **d** 87 **p** 88. C Hobs Moat *Birm* 87-90; C W Drayton *Lon* 90-92; V Oakfield St Jo *Portsm* from 92; RD E Wight from 00. *St John's Vicarage, Victoria Crescent, Ryde PO33 1DQ* Tel (01983) 562863
E-mail hewright@stjohnsryde.freeserve.co.uk

WRIGHT, Ian. See WRIGHT, Frederic Ian

WRIGHT, Ian. b 65. SSC. Coll of Resurr Mirfield 97. **d** 99 **p** 00. C S Lafford *Linc* 99-01; C Hawley H Trin *Guildf* 01-03; Chapl Bonn w Cologne *Eur* from 03. *Altenrather Strasse 156, 53797 Lohmar, Germany*

WRIGHT, Mrs Jean. b 41. Man Univ BA63 CertEd64. Carl Dioc Tr Inst 88. **d** 91 **p** 94. NSM Kirkby Stephen w Mallerstang etc *Carl* from 91. *Mains View, Crosby Garrett, Kirkby Stephen CA17 4PR* Tel (01768) 371457

WRIGHT, John. See WRIGHT, Nicholas John

WRIGHT, John. See WRIGHT, Alfred John

WRIGHT, John. See WRIGHT, Anthony John

WRIGHT, John Alastair. b 30. FRSA72. Cranmer Hall Dur 62. **d** 64 **p** 65. C Thornton-le-Fylde *Blackb* 64-67; Miss to Seamen 67-72; V Darlington St Luke *Dur* 72-78; Community Chapl Darlington 78-89; rtd 89. *4 Grasmere, Agar Nook, Coalville LE67 4SH* Tel (01530) 837390

WRIGHT, John Douglas. b 42. Birm Univ BSc64 CertEd66. St Steph Ho Ox 69. **d** 69 **p** 70. C Swanley St Mary *Roch* 69-74; C Stockwell Green St Andr *S'wark* 74-79; V Leigh St Jo *Man* 79-82; P-in-c Whitehawk *Chich* from 82. *St Cuthman's Vicarage, 1 St Cuthman's Close, Whitehawk, Brighton BN2 5LJ* Tel (01273) 699424 Mobile 07944-419007
E-mail jonwrightscuthmans@amserve.net

WRIGHT, Canon John Harold. b 36. ATCL Dur Univ BA58 ACertCM. Ely Th Coll 58. **d** 62 **p** 63. C Boston *Linc* 61-64; C Willesborough w Hinxhill *Cant* 64-68; V Westwell 68-75; R Eastwell w Boughton Aluph 68-75; V Rolvenden 75-84; R Cheriton 84-01; Hon Can Cant Cathl 97-01; rtd 01; Perm to Offic *Cant* from 01. *1 Cliff Road, Hythe CT21 5XA* Tel (01303) 265303

WRIGHT, Miss Julia Mary. b 64. Reading Univ BA88. Trin Coll Bris DipTh98. **d** 98 **p** 99. C Woodley *Ox* 98-03; TV Aylesbury w Bierton and Hulcott from 03. *4 Cubb Field, Aylesbury HP19 7SH* Tel (01296) 423218 E-mail jwrightstjohn@aol.com

WRIGHT, Ken. See WRIGHT, Charles Kenneth

WRIGHT, Canon Kenneth William. b 13. Coll of Resurr Mirfield 37. **d** 39 **p** 40. C Clerkenwell H Redeemer w St Phil *Lon* 39-42; C Acton Green St Pet 42-45; C Boyne Hill *Ox* 45-50; V Stony Stratford St Mary 50-57; R Fenny Stratford 54-74; TR Fenny Stratford and Water Eaton 74-79; P-in-c Lt Brickhill 57-58; RD

Bletchley 63-70; P-in-c Simpson w Woughton on the Green 69-72; RD Milton Keynes 70-72; Hon Can Ch 70-79; rtd 80; Perm to Offic *S'well* from 80. *Garden Flat B, St Katharine's House, Ormond Road, Wantage OX12 8EA* Tel (01235) 768030

WRIGHT, Canon Kenyon Edward. b 32. CBE99. Glas Univ MA53 Fitzw Coll Cam BA55 Serampore Coll MTh61. Wesley Ho Cam 53. **d** 71 **p** 71. In Meth Ch India 57-71; Dir Urban Min Cov Cathl *Cov* 71-81; Dir of Internat Min and Can Res 72-81; Public Preacher 72-74; Gen Sec Scottish Chs Coun 81-90; Dir Scottish Chs Ho Dunblane 81-90; Dir Kairos Trust 90-92; Hon C Knightswood H Cross Miss *Glas* 91-92; rtd 92; P-in-c Glencarse *Bre* 94-00. *4 Katrine Crescent, Callander FK17 8JS* Tel (01877) 330464 Fax as telephone E-mail kenyon@which.net

WRIGHT, Lawrence Charles. b 57. Hull Univ MA94. EMMTC 93. **d** 96 **p** 96. Australia 96-98; C Penzance St Jo *Truro* 98-02; TV Penzance St Mary w St Paul and St Jo from 02. *The Vicarage, 1 Empress Avenue, Penzance TR18 2UQ* Tel (01736) 333187 E-mail lwright@fish.co.uk

WRIGHT, Leslie Vandernoll. b 24. Trin Hall Cam MA50. Ridley Hall Cam 49. **d** 51 **p** 52. C Aldershot H Trin *Guildf* 51-53; C Cambridge H Trin *Ely* 53-57; V Marston *Ox* 57-59; Asst Master Castle Ct Sch Parkstone 59-61; Asst Chapl Stowe Sch 61-64; Hd Master St Mich Prep Sch Five Oaks Jersey 64-66; Chapl Windlesham Ho Sch Sussex 66-68; Chapl Vevey *Eur* 68-73; Hd St Geo Sch Clarens 73-89; rtd 89; Chapl Lugano *Eur* 89-92. *18 avenue Schubert, Domine de Tournon, 83440 Montauroux, France* Tel (0033) (4) 94 47 6 43

WRIGHT, Mrs Louisa Mary (Lisa). b 33. S'wark Ord Course. **d** 87 **p** 94. NSM Streatham Hill St Marg *S'wark* 87-95; Hon C Streatham St Leon 95-02; rtd 02; Perm to Offic *S'wark* from 02. *19 Hillside Road, London SW2 3HL* Tel (020) 8671 8037

WRIGHT, Marion Jane. b 47. Whitelands Coll Lon CertEd69. Cranmer Hall Dur 73. **d** 00 **p** 02. NSM Scalby *York* from 00. *3 East Park Road, Scalby, Scarborough YO13 0PZ* Tel (01723) 350208 E-mail chrisw@springbankyo.13.freeserve.co.uk

WRIGHT, Martin. b 48. Avery Hill Coll BEd81 K Alfred's Coll Win CertEd69 LRAM76. St Alb and Ox Min Course CBTS98. **d** 98 **p** 99. NSM St Alb St Mary Marshalswick *St Alb* 98-01; C Gt Berkhamsted from 02. *All Saints' House, Shrublands Road, Berkhamsted HP4 3HY* Tel (01442) 866161 Mobile 07774-923550 E-mail m.wright@c-of-e.freeserve.co.uk

WRIGHT, Canon Martin Neave. b 37. AKC61 Leic Univ DSRS67. St Boniface Warminster. **d** 62 **p** 63. C Corby St Columba *Pet* 62-65; Ind Chapl 65-71; Nigeria 71-75; P-in-c Honiley *Cov* 75-84; P-in-c Wroxall 75-84; Ind Chapl 75-84; Soc Resp Officer 84-96; Hon Can Cov Cathl 95-96; Bp's Chapl and Past Asst *B & W* 96-02; Preb Wells Cathl 96-02; Sub-Dean Wells 00-02; rtd 02. *2 Honiwell Close, Harbury, Leamington Spa CV33 9LY* Tel (01926) 613699

WRIGHT, Michael. *See* WRIGHT, Edward Michael

WRIGHT, Canon Michael. b 30. St Chad's Coll Dur BA55 DipTh56. **d** 56 **p** 57. C New Cleethorpes *Linc* 56-59; C Skegness 59-62; V Louth St Mich 62-73; R Stewton 62-73; R Warmsworth *Sheff* 73-86; Warden Dioc Readers' Assn 81-86; Hon Can Sheff Cathl 82-95; V Wath-upon-Dearne w Adwick-upon-Dearne 86-94; V Wath-upon-Dearne 94-95; RD Wath 92-95; rtd 95; Perm to Offic *Linc* from 01. *17 Ashfield Road, Sleaford NG34 7DZ* Tel (01529) 415698

WRIGHT, Michael Christopher. b 44. Leeds Univ BA65 CertEd67 MSc75 FRSA95. Wells Th Coll 65. **d** 67 **p** 68. C Dormanstown *York* 67-69; Perm to Offic *Linc* 69-88; Perm to Offic *Sheff* 71-95; Hd Master Eastmoor High Sch Wakef 84-87; Hd Master Carleton High Sch Pontefract 87-95; C-in-c St Edm Anchorage Lane CD 95-96; Chapl Doncaster R Infirmary and Montagu Hosp NHS Trust 95-01; Chapl Doncaster and Bassetlaw Hosps NHS Trust from 01. *Doncaster Royal Infirmary, Armthorpe Road, Doncaster DN2 5LT* Tel (01302) 366666 ext 3616 E-mail mcw@tcseuro.co.uk

WRIGHT, Michael John. b 38. Dur Univ MA91 DipTM84 Cert Cllr Supervision 94. Chich Th Coll 59. **d** 62 **p** 63. C Yate *Glouc* 62-65; C Kirby Moorside w Gillamoor *York* 65-68; V 68-72; V Bransdale cum Farndale 68-72; V Kirkbymoorside w Gillamoor, Farndale etc 72-73; Dioc Communications Officer 72-74; V Ormesby 74-80; P-in-c Middlesbrough St Cuth 81-88; Perm to Offic 88-99; NSM W Acklam 91-97; Chapl Butterwick Hospice Stockton-on-Tees 97-99; Chapl S Dur Hospice Bp Auckland 97-99. *25 Thornfield Road, Middlesbrough TS5 5DD* Tel (01642) 851919 E-mail mjw@careatwork.fsnet.co.uk

WRIGHT, Nicholas John. b 65. Liv Univ BA87. Wycliffe Hall Ox 89. **d** 92 **p** 93. C Burley *Ripon* 92-95; C Brightside w Wincobank *Sheff* 95-97; TV Sheff Manor 97-03; Perm to Offic from 03. *22 Norfolk Road, Sheffield S2 2SX*

WRIGHT, Nicholas Mark. b 59. Loughb Univ BSc80. Qu Coll Birm 82. **d** 85 **p** 86. C Coney Hill *Glouc* 85-89; C Rotherham *Sheff* 89-91; TV Worc SE *Worc* 91-98; R Inkberrow w Cookhill and Kington w Dormston from 98. *The Vicarage, High Street, Inkberrow, Worcester WR7 4DU* Tel (01386) 792122 E-mail ncbjmswright@btinternet.com

⊹**WRIGHT, The Rt Revd Nicholas Thomas.** b 48. Ex Coll Ox BA71 MA75 DPhil81 DD00. Wycliffe Hall Ox BA73. **d** 75 **p** 76 **c** 03. Fell Mert Coll Ox 75-78; Chapl 76-78; Chapl and Fell Down Coll Cam 78-81; Asst Prof NT Studies McGill Univ Montreal 81-86; Chapl and Fell Worc Coll Ox and Univ Lect Th 86-93; Dean Lich 93-99; Can Th Cov Cathl *Cov* 92-99; Lector Theologiae and Can Westmr Abbey 00-03; Bp Dur from 03. *Auckland Castle, Bishop Auckland DL14 7NR* Tel (01388) 602576 Fax 605264 E-mail bishop.of.durham@durham.anglican.org

WRIGHT, Ms Pamela Anne. b 45. Open Univ BSc00. St As Minl Tr Course 01. **d** 03. NSM Llanrhos *St As* from 03. *Brackenrigg, Bryn Pydew Road, Bryn Pydew, Llandudno Junction LL31 9JH* Tel (01492) 541552 Mobile 07850-180420 Fax (01492) 541652 E-mail pamscot45@aol.com

WRIGHT, Miss Pamela Jean. b 38. ALA63. NTMTC 02. **d** 03. NSM Harrow Trin St Mich *Lon* from 03. *71 Curzon Avenue, Stanmore HA7 2AL* Tel (020) 8863 0597 E-mail pamwright@tstmichaels.fsnet.co.uk

WRIGHT, Patricia. b 46. SRN68 DN68 DipHV69. S'wark Ord Course 80. **dss** 85 **d** 89. Chapl R Lon Hosp (Mile End) 83-89; Bethnal Green St Matt w St Jas the Gt *Lon* 85-87; St Botolph Aldgate w H Trin Minories 88-89; Hon C from 89. *8 Royal Mint Street, London E1 8LG* Tel (020) 7283 1670

WRIGHT, Canon Paul. b 54. K Coll Lon BD78 AKC78 Heythrop Coll Lon MTh80. Ripon Coll Cuddesdon 78. **d** 79 **p** 80. C Beckenham St Geo *Roch* 79-83; Chapl Ch Sch Richmond 83-85; C Richmond St Mary w St Matthias and St Jo *S'wark* 83-85; V Gillingham St Aug *Roch* 85-90; R Crayford 90-99; RD Erith 93-97; Hon Can Roch Cathl from 98; V Sidcup St Jo from 99. *St John's Vicarage, 13 Church Avenue, Sidcup DA14 6BU* Tel (020) 8300 0383 Mobile 07811-147219 E-mail canonpaul@rochdlc.freeserve.co.uk

WRIGHT, Paul Stephen. b 66. Cen Lancs Univ BA88 Liv Univ MA96. Westcott Ho Cam 90. **d** 93 **p** 94. C Upholland *Liv* 93-96; CF from 96. *c/o MOD Chaplains (Army)* Tel (01980) 615804 Fax 615800

WRIGHT, Peter. *See* WRIGHT, Charles Frederick Peter

WRIGHT, Canon Peter. b 35. K Coll Lon AKC61 Hull Univ MA86. St Boniface Warminster 61. **d** 62 **p** 63. C Goole *Sheff* 62-67; V Norton Woodseats St Chad 67-80; R Aston cum Aughton 80-84; P-in-c Ulley 80-84; Chapl Rotherham Priority Health Services NHS Trust 80-84; R Aston cum Aughton and Ulley *Sheff* 84-93; TR Aston cum Aughton w Swallownest, Todwick etc 93-00; RD Laughton 85-93; Chapter Clerk and Hon Can Sheff Cathl 92-00; rtd 00; Perm to Offic *Sheff* from 01. *40 Chancet Wood Drive, Sheffield S8 7TR* Tel 0114-274 7218 Fax as telephone E-mail allsaints.pw@talk21.com

WRIGHT, Peter Gordon. b 27. St Aid Birkenhead 55. **d** 57 **p** 58. C Mansfield Woodhouse *S'well* 57-61; V Coddington w Barnby in the Willows 61-97; rtd 97. *1 Southfield, Balderton, Newark NG24 3QB*

WRIGHT, Peter Reginald. b 34. St Chad's Coll Dur BA60. Linc Th Coll 60. **d** 62 **p** 63. C Lt Ilford St Mich *Chelmsf* 62-65; C Billingham St Aid *Dur* 65-68; TV 68-71; TR 71-76; Chapl Portsm Poly *Portsm* 76-87; Sec Chapls in HE Gen Syn Bd of Educn 88-95; rtd 95; Perm to Offic *Portsm* from 95. *6 Garden Lane, Southsea PO5 3DP* Tel (023) 9273 6651

WRIGHT, Peter Westrope. b 24. Kelham Th Coll 43. **d** 48 **p** 49. C Pimlico St Barn *Lon* 48-50; C Sidley *Chich* 50-59; R E Blatchington 59-73; P-in-c Lewes St Mich 73-75; TV Lewes All SS, St Anne, St Mich and St Thos 75-84; TR 84-87; rtd 89; Perm to Offic *Chich* from 89. *17 South Street, Lewes BN7 2BT* Tel (01273) 473332

WRIGHT, Philip. b 32. G&C Coll Cam BA53 MA57. Wells Th Coll 56. **d** 57 **p** 58. C Barnard Castle *Dur* 57-60; C Heworth St Mary 60-64; V Tow Law 64-70; V Tanfield 70-78; V Gateshead Ch Ch 78-02; rtd 02. *Meldon, High Heworth Lane, Gateshead NE10 0PB* Tel 0191-469 2161

WRIGHT, Phillip. b 35. Kelham Th Coll 57 St Aid Birkenhead 59. **d** 61 **p** 62. C Goldthorpe *Sheff* 61-65; V Doncaster St Jude 65-71; V Kettering All SS *Pet* 71-82; V S Kirkby *Wakef* 82-94; rtd 98. *2 The Grove, Wickersley, Rotherham S66 2BP* Tel (01709) 543922 E-mail thegrove@onetel.net.uk

WRIGHT, Robert. *See* WRIGHT, Canon Anthony Robert

WRIGHT, Robert Charles. b 31. Roch Th Coll 65. **d** 67 **p** 68. C Manston *Ripon* 67-70; C Moor Allerton 70-74; P-in-c Terrington St John *Ely* 74-79; P-in-c Walpole St Andrew 74-75; P-in-c Tilney All Saints w Tilney St Lawrence 74-79; V Terrington St John 80-91; V Tilney St Lawrence 80-91; V Tilney All Saints 80-91; R Stiffkey and Cockthorpe w Morston, Langham etc *Nor* 91-96; rtd 96; Perm to Offic *Nor* from 96. *Glenfinnan, 83 Childs Way, Sheringham NR26 8TX* Tel (01263) 822535

WRIGHT, Canon Robert Doogan. b 24. TCD BA46 MA. TCD Div Sch Div Test 47. **d** 47 **p** 48. C Carnmoney *Conn* 47-49; C Belfast St Jas 49-51; C Belfast St Matt 51-53; P-in-c Belfast Whiterock 53-57; I Magheragall 57-64; I Belfast St Mark 64-70; I Carrickfergus 70-82; Can Conn Cathl 79-86; I Killead w Gartree

82-86; Chan Conn Cathl 83-86; rtd 86. *123 Station Road, Greenisland, Carrickfergus BT38 8UN* Tel (028) 9086 2779

WRIGHT, Robert James. b 74. St Chad's Coll Dur BA96 K Coll Lon MA98. St Steph Ho Ox 00. **d** 02. C Ilfracombe, Lee, Woolacombe, Bittadon etc *Ex* from 02. *St Peter's Clergy House, Highfield Road, Ilfracombe EX34 9LH* Tel (01271) 879372 Mobile 07905-321004 E-mail robwri99@hotmail.com

WRIGHT, Robert John. b 47. St Jo Coll Dur BA70. SEITE 00. **d** 03. NSM Notting Hill St Jo *Lon* from 03; NSM Notting Hill St Pet from 03. *93 Peel Street, London W8 7PB* Tel (020) 7221 4399 Mobile 07010-701332 Fax (020) 7460 2736 E-mail church@robert-wright.com

✠**WRIGHT, The Rt Revd Royston Clifford.** b 22. Univ of Wales BA42. St Steph Ho Ox 43. **d** 45 **p** 46 **c** 86. C Bedwas *Mon* 45-47; C Newport St Jo Bapt 47-49; C Walton St Mary *Liv* 49-51; Chapl RNVR 50-51; Chapl RN 51-68; V Blaenavon w Capel Newydd *Mon* 68-74; RD Pontypool 73-74; TR Ebbw Vale 74-77; Can St Woolos Cathl 74-77; Adn Mon 77-88; Adn Newport 77-86; Bp Mon 86-91; rtd 91; Lic to Offic *Mon* from 91. *23 Rupert Brooke Drive, Newport NP20 3HP* Tel (01633) 250770

WRIGHT (née PRECIOUS), Sally Joanne. b 75. Hatf Coll Dur BA97 Cam Univ MA03. Westcott Ho Cam 00. **d** 02 **p** 03. C Chich St Paul and Westhampnett *Chich* from 02. *37 Somerstown, Chichester PO19 6AL* Tel (01243) 775199 or 533403 E-mail sallyprecious@yahoo.com

WRIGHT, Samuel. *See* WRIGHT, William Samuel

WRIGHT, Sarah Jane. b 64. Nottm Trent Univ BA99. Ripon Coll Cuddesdon DipMin01. **d** 01 **p** 02. C Clarendon Park St Jo w Knighton St Mich *Leic* from 01. *St Michael's House, 12 Scott Street, Leicester LE2 6DW* Tel 0116-270 0964 Mobile 07790-342728 E-mail sarah@squeaks.co.uk

WRIGHT, Simon Christopher. b 44. AKC67. **d** 68 **p** 69. C Bitterne Park *Win* 68-72; C Kirkby 72-74; V Wigan St Anne *Liv* 74-79; Abp's Dom Chapl *York* 79-84; Dir of Ords 79-84; V W Acklam 84-00; RD Middlesbrough 87-98; Can and Preb York Minster 94-00; V Dartmouth *Ex* from 00. *The Vicarage, Northford Road, Dartmouth TQ6 9EP* Tel (01803) 835543

WRIGHT, Stephen Irwin. b 58. Ex Coll Ox BA80 MA84 Selw Coll Cam BA85 MA90 Lanc Univ MA92 St Jo Coll Dur PhD97. Ridley Hall Cam 83. **d** 86 **p** 87. C Newbarns w Hawcoat *Carl* 86-90; C Burton and Holme 90-94; NSM Esh *Dur* 94-97; NSM Hamsteels 94-97; C Consett 97-98; Dir Coll of Preachers from 98; Perm to Offic *S'wark* from 99. *Spurgeon's College, 189 South Norwood Hill, London SE25 6DJ* Tel (020) 8653 0850 or 8768 0878 ext 233 Fax 8711 0959 E-mail s.wright@spurgeons.ac.uk

WRIGHT, Canon Stephen Mark. b 60. Keele Univ BA83. Trin Coll Bris 86. **d** 89 **p** 90. C Thorne *Sheff* 89-92; CMS from 92; Nigeria 93-98; Hon Can Asaba from 98; Chapl Ahmadi St Paul Kuwait from 99. *St Paul's Church, PO Box 9999, Ahmadi 61010, Kuwait* Tel (00965) 398 5929 Fax as telephone E-mail stpaulq8@kems.net

WRIGHT, Stuart. *See* WRIGHT, William Charles Stewart

WRIGHT, Thomas Stephen. b 31. Fitzw Ho Cam BA54 MA58. Bps' Coll Cheshunt 56. **d** 57 **p** 58. C Bishop's Stortford St Mich *St Alb* 57-61; C St E Cathl *St E* 61-64; R Hartest w Boxted 64-82; Chapl RAF 64-71; RD Sudbury *St E* 70-81; P-in-c Somerton 71-82; P-in-c Stansfield 82-91; V Denston w Stradishall and Stansfield 91-97; Min Can St E Cathl 92-98. *21 Manderville Road, Bury St Edmunds IP33 2BJ* Tel (01284) 765287

WRIGHT, Tim Stanley. b 63. Derby Coll of Educn BEd86. St Jo Coll Dur 89. **d** 92 **p** 93. C Eccleshill *Bradf* 92-96; TV Southend *Chelmsf* 96-00; V Boulton *Derby* from 00. *The Vicarage, 1 St Mary's Close, Alvaston, Derby DE24 0GF* Tel (01332) 571296

WRIGHT, Timothy. b 63. NUU BSc85. Cranmer Hall Dur 86. **d** 89 **p** 90. C Bramcote *S'well* 89-93; I Glenavy w Tunny and Crumlin *Conn* 93-98; Chapl RAF from 98; Perm to Offic *Lich* from 01. *Chaplaincy Services (RAF), HQ, Personnel and Training Command, RAF Innsworth, Gloucester GL3 1EZ* Tel (01452) 712612 ext 5164 Fax 510828

WRIGHT, Timothy John. b 41. K Coll Lon BD63 AKC63. **d** 64 **p** 65. C Highfield *Ox* 64-68; Asst Chapl Worksop Coll Notts 68-71; Chapl Malvern Coll 71-77; Ho Master 77-86; Hd Master Jo Lyon Sch Harrow 86-01; rtd 01. *Beech House, Colwall Green, Malvern WR13 6DX* Tel (01684) 541102

WRIGHT, Timothy John. b 54. Nottm Univ BA76. Ripon Coll Cuddesdon 90. **d** 92 **p** 93. C Dawlish *Ex* 92-95; TV Teignmouth, Ideford w Luton, Ashcombe etc 95-01; Chapl Wycombe Abbey Sch from 01. *Wycombe Abbey School, Abbey Way, High Wycombe HP11 1PE* Tel (01494) 520381

WRIGHT, Toby Christopher. b 75. New Coll Ox BA98 MA01 Leeds Univ MA01. Coll of Resurr Mirfield 99. **d** 01 **p** 02. C Petersfield *Portsm* from 01. *3 Larcombe Road, Petersfield GU32 3LS* Tel (01730) 268176 E-mail tobyc.wright@virgin.net

WRIGHT, Tom. *See* WRIGHT, The Rt Revd Nicholas Thomas

WRIGHT, Mrs Vyvienne Mary. b 59. S Dios Minl Tr Scheme 80. dss 83 **d** 87 **p** 94. Martock w Ash *B & W* 83-00; Hon C 87-00; Perm to Offic from 00. *29 North Street, Martock TA12 6DH* Tel (01935) 823292

WRIGHT, William Charles Stewart. b 53. Ulster Poly BSc81. CITC BTh95. **d** 95 **p** 96. C Ballyholme *D & D* 95-98; I Conwal Union w Gartan *D & R* from 98. *Conwal Rectory, New Line Road, Letterkenny, Co Donegal, Irish Republic* Tel (00353) (74) 912 2573

WRIGHT, William Easton. b 20. Linc Th Coll 52. **d** 53 **p** 54. C Petrockstowe w Peters Marland *Ex* 53-56; R Farway w Northleigh and Southleigh 56-69; RD Honiton 65-68; R Offwell w Widworthy 69-72; P-in-c Cotleigh 69-72; R Offwell, Widworthy, Cotleigh, Farway etc 72-85; rtd 85; Perm to Offic *Ex* from 85. *17 North Street, Ottery St Mary EX11 1DR* Tel (01404) 813744

WRIGHT, Canon William Hutchinson. b 27. St Jo Coll Dur BA50 DipTh52. **d** 55 **p** 56. C Kimberworth *Sheff* 55-59; Ind Chapl *Dur* 59-92; Hon Can Dur Cathl 72-92; rtd 92. *109 Bishopton Road, Stockton-on-Tees TS18 4PL* Tel (01642) 678817

WRIGHT, William Samuel. b 59. TCD DipTh87 BTh89 MA90. **d** 87 **p** 88. C Belfast St Aid *Conn* 87-91; Sec Dioc Bd of Miss 90-91; I Cleenish w Mullaghdun *Clogh* 91-99; I Lisburn Ch Ch Cathl *Conn* from 99; Can and Preb Conn Cathl from 01. *Cathedral Rectory, Clonevin Park, Lisburn BT28 3BL* Tel (028) 9266 2865 *or* 9260 2400 E-mail sam@rector.fsnet.co.uk *or* cathedral@connor.anglican.org

WRIGHTSON, Bernard. b 25. CertEd50 Leeds Univ DipSC60 ACP65. Linc Th Coll 83. **d** 83 **p** 84. Hon C Alford w Rigsby *Linc* 83-86; Perm to Offic 86-89; NSM Mablethorpe w Trusthorpe 89-94; Perm to Offic from 94. *Pipits Acre, 64 Church Lane, Mablethorpe LN12 2NU* Tel (01507) 472394

WRISDALE, Jean May. b 40. LNSM course. **d** 90 **p** 94. OLM Fotherby *Linc* from 90. *The Meadows, Livesey Road, Ludborough, Grimsby DN36 5SQ* Tel (01472) 840474

WRIST-KNUDSEN, Svend Michael. b 61. Copenhagen Univ DipTh87. St Jo Coll Dur BA91. **d** 91 **p** 92. C Newton Aycliffe *Dur* 91-95; P-in-c Penzance St Jo *Truro* 95-97. *71 Canterbury Park, Liverpool L18 9XP*

WROE, Mark. b 69. Surrey Univ BA92. Ridley Hall Cam 94. **d** 96 **p** 97. C Chilvers Coton w Astley *Cov* 96-00; P-in-c Heworth St Alb *Dur* 00-03; V from 03. *The Vicarage, Coldwell Park Drive, Felling, Gateshead NE10 9BY* Tel 0191-438 1720 E-mail revdocwroe@supanet.com

WYARD, Peter Joseph. b 54. Pemb Coll Cam MA76 Sussex Univ MSc80 Brunel Univ MSc88. EAMTC 99. **d** 02 **p** 03. C Framlingham w Saxtead *St E* from 02. *17 Fulchers Field, Framlingham, Woodbridge IP13 9HT* Tel (01728) 622042 E-mail peter.wyard@btinternet.com

WYATT, Colin. b 27. Ex Coll Ox BA54 MA55 Lon Univ BD62. Tyndale Hall Bris 60. **d** 63 **p** 64. C Radipole *Sarum* 63-66; C Southborough St Pet *Roch* 66-67; V Tetsworth *Ox* 67-72; Lect Bible Tr Inst Glas 72-74; R Hurworth *Dur* 74-79; P-in-c Dinsdale w Sockburn 74-76; R 76-79; R Seaham *Dur* 79-84; R Bacton w Wyverstone and Cotton *St E* 84-92; rtd 92; Perm to Offic *Ripon* from 92. *20 Harrogate Road, Ripon HG4 1SR* Tel (01765) 606810

WYATT, Canon David Stanley Chadwick. b 36. Fitzw Ho Cam BA59 MA71. Ely Th Coll 59. **d** 61 **p** 62. C Rochdale *Man* 61-63; Bp's Dom Chapl 63-68; R Salford St Paul w Ch Ch from 68; Hon Can Man Cathl from 82; P-in-c Salford Ordsall St Clem 91-96; AD Salford 97. *St Paul's Church House, Broadwalk, Salford M6 5AN* Tel 0161-736 8868

WYATT, Peter John. b 38. Kelham Th Coll 58. **d** 64 **p** 65. C N Stoneham *Win* 64-68; C Brixham *Ex* 68-69; Dominica 69-75; Zambia 76-78; P-in-c Ettington *Cov* 78-79; V Butlers Marston and the Pillertons w Ettington 79-86; V Codnor and Loscoe *Derby* 86-91; Chapl for Deaf People from 91; rtd 03. *16 Cae Melyn, Tregynon, Newtown SY16 3EF* Tel (01686) 650368

WYATT, Richard Norman. b 21. LVCM. **d** 84 **p** 85. C Puttenham and Wanborough *Guildf* 84-90; Perm to Offic *Chich* 91-93 and from 97; P-in-c Stedham w Iping 93-97; rtd 97; RD Midhurst *Chich* 98-99. *Trenethick, June Lane, Midhurst GU29 9EL* Tel (01730) 813447 E-mail normanwyatt@midhurst0.demon.co.uk

WYATT, Royston Dennis. b 36. FRICS67. Sarum & Wells Th Coll 74. **d** 77 **p** 78. NSM Canford Magna *Sarum* 77-82; V Abbotsbury, Portesham and Langton Herring 82-88; Dioc Missr *Linc* 88-95; R Welford w Weston *Glouc* from 95; RD Campden 96-01. *The Rectory, Church Lane, Welford on Avon, Stratford-upon-Avon CV37 8EL* Tel (01789) 750808 E-mail revrdw@btinternet.com

WYATT (née OWEN), Mrs Susan Elizabeth. b 53. Bris Univ BSc75 Bath Univ PGCE78. EAMTC 97. **d** 00 **p** 01. Asst Dioc Adv in Miss and Evang *Ely* from 00; C Over from 00; C Long Stanton w St Mich from 02. *The Vicarage, High Street, Longstanton, Cambridge CB4 5BP* Tel (01954) 201853 *or* 204529 Mobile 07713-241261 E-mail suzywyatt@aol.com *or* sue.wyatt@ely.anglican.org

WYATT, Trevor. b 60. Keele Univ BSc81. SEITE. **d** 00 **p** 01. NSM Wilmington *Roch* from 00. *216 Birchwood Road, Wilmington, Dartford DA2 7HA* Tel (01322) 666521 Mobile 07860-306746 E-mail trevor.wyatt@bt.com

WYBREW, Canon Hugh Malcolm. b 34. Qu Coll Ox BA58 MA. Linc Th Coll 59. **d** 60 **p** 61. C E Dulwich St Jo *S'wark* 60-64; Tutor St Steph Ho Ox 65-71; Chapl Bucharest *Eur* 71-73; V Pinner *Lon* 73-83; Sec Fellowship of SS Alb and Sergius 84-86; Dean Jerusalem 86-89; V Ox St Mary Magd *Ox* from 89; Hon Can Gib Cathl *Eur* from 89; Hon Can Ch Ch *Ox* from 01. *15 Beaumont Street, Oxford OX1 2NA* Tel (01865) 247836 Fax 245073 E-mail hugh.wybrew@theology.ox.ac.uk

WYER, Keith George. b 45. St Paul's Cheltenham CertEd66 K Coll Lon BD71 AKC71. St Aug Coll Cant 71. **d** 72 **p** 73. C Moseley St Mary *Birm* 72-76; Chapl RNR 73-92; C Walsall *Lich* 76-77; Min Walsall St Martin 77-79; Chapl Colston's Sch Bris 79-86; Chapl Kelly Coll Tavistock 86-92; R Combe Martin and Berrynarbor *Ex* 92-95; TR Combe Martin, Berrynarbor, Lynton, Brendon etc from 96; RD Shirwell 95-01. *The Rectory, Rectory Road, Combe Martin, Ilfracombe EX34 0NS* Tel (01271) 883203 E-mail keith@kgw.eurobell.co.uk

WYKES, Peter. b 44. Lon Univ MB, BS68. Ban & St As Minl Tr Course 97. **d** 00 **p** 01. NSM Trefnant w Tremeirchion *St As* 00-01; NSM Cefn w Trefnant w Tremeirchion from 01. *Clattwm, 1 Plas Chambres Road, Denbigh LL16 5UP* Tel (01745) 730263

WYLAM, John. b 43. AKC66 FE TCert75. **d** 67 **p** 68. C Derby St Bart *Derby* 67-70; SSF 70-73; C Seaton Hirst *Newc* 74-77; V Byker St Silas 77-83; V Alwinton w Holystone and Alnham 83-98; R Chollerton w Birtley and Thockrington from 98. *The Vicarage, Chollerton, Hexham NE46 4TF* Tel (01434) 681721 E-mail johnwylam@btopenworld.com

WYLD, Kevin Andrew. b 58. St Cath Coll Ox BA79 MA85 Univ Coll Dur MSc83 Edin Univ BD85. Edin Th Coll 82. **d** 85 **p** 86. C Winlaton *Dur* 85-87; C Houghton le Spring 87-90; V Medomsley 90-95; V High Spen and Rowlands Gill 95-00; R Cen Florida St Rich USA from 00. *St Richard's Episcopal Church, 5151 Lake Howell Road, Winter Park, FL 32792, USA* Tel (001) (407) 671 4211 Fax 671 2028

WYLIE, Alan. b 47. Is of Man Tr Inst 88. **d** 92 **p** 93. NSM Douglas St Geo and St Barn *S & M* 92-96; NSM Challoch *Glas* from 97. *19 St John Street, Creetown, Newton Stewart DG8 7JA* Tel (01671) 820628

WYLIE, Clive George. b 64. QUB BSc86 TCD BTh90 MA93. CITC 97. **d** 90 **p** 91. C Drumglass w Moygashel *Arm* 90-93; I Tynan, Aghavilly and Middletown 93-98; Hon V Choral Arm Cathl 93-98; Team P Glas E End *Glas* from 98; Miss 21 Co-ord from 98. *011 Park View, 780 Tollcross Road, Glasgow G32 8TY* Tel 0141-764 0628 *or* tel and fax 764 0891 Mobile 07887-676705 E-mail mission21@glasgow.anglican.org

WYLIE, David Victor. b 61. ACA86 LSE BSc(Econ)82 Leeds Univ BA91. Coll of Resurr Mirfield 89. **d** 92 **p** 93. C Kilburn St Aug w St Jo *Lon* 92-95; C Heston 95-98; Chapl RN from 98. *Royal Naval Chaplaincy Service, Room 203, Victory Building, HM Naval Base, Portsmouth PO1 3LS* Tel (023) 9272 7903 Fax 9272 7111

WYLIE, Nigel Bruce. b 62. Trin Coll Bris 88. **d** 91 **p** 92. C Selly Park St Steph and St Wulstan *Birm* 91-94. *Address temp unknown*

WYLIE-SMITH, Ms Megan Judith. b 52. BD74. S'wark Ord Course 88. **d** 91 **p** 94. C Greenstead *Chelmsf* 91-94; C W Ham 94-97; TV Becontree S 97-01; rtd 01; Perm to Offic *Chelmsf* from 01. *67 Gordon Road, London E11 2RA* Tel (020) 8530 6434 E-mail megan@wylie-smith.freeserve.co.uk

WYNBURNE, John Paterson Barry. b 48. St Jo Coll Dur BA70. Wycliffe Coll Toronto MDiv72 Ridley Hall Cam 72. **d** 73 **p** 74. C Gt Stanmore *Lon* 73-76; Chapl Bucharest w Sofia *Eur* 76-77; C Dorking w Ranmore *Guildf* 77-80; V Send 80-88; V York Town St Mich 88-93; V Camberley St Mich Yorktown 93-95; TR Beaconsfield *Ox* from 95. *The Rectory, Wycombe End, Beaconsfield HP9 1NB* Tel (01494) 677058 *or* 673949 E-mail jwynburne@aol.com

WYNES, Michael John. b 33. AKC57. **d** 58 **p** 59. C Gt Berkhamsted *St Alb* 58-62; C Silverhill St Matt *Chich* 62-65; C Wilton *B & W* 65-68; R Berkley w Rodden 68-77; V Priddy 77-86; V Westbury sub Mendip w Easton 77-86; C Milton 86-93; rtd 93; Perm to Offic *B & W* from 95. *23A Fairways, Wells BA5 2DF* Tel (01749) 673778

WYNGARD, Canon Ernest Clive. b 30. Leeds Univ BA52. Coll of Resurr Mirfield 52. **d** 54 **p** 55. C Bishopwearmouth St Mich *Dur* 54-59; C Winlaton 59-61; V Castleside 61-67; V Beamish 67-80; RD Lanchester 78-80; V Dur St Giles 80-87; Hon Can Dur Cathl from 83; V Greatham 87-94; Master Greatham Hosp 87-94; rtd 94. *20 Chichester Close, Hartlepool TS25 2QT* Tel (01429) 297261

WYNN, Edward Laurence. b 65. Leeds Metrop Univ BSc96 Leeds Univ MA02 RGN88. N Ord Course 98. **d** 01 **p** 02. C Emley *Wakef* from 01; C Flockton cum Denby Grange from 01. *3 St Michael's Gardens, Emley, Huddersfield HD8 9TH* Tel (01924) 840423 E-mail eddie@wynn11.freeserve.co.uk

WYNN, Richard David. b 44. Univ Coll of Rhodesia & Nyasaland Inst of Educn TCert65. St Paul's Coll Grahamstown 86. **d** 88 **p** 89. S Africa 88-02; C Kirby-Hilton Ascension 88-91; R

Ixopo St Jo 91-99; R Richmond-cum-Byrne St Mary 99-02; P-in-c Cinderford St Steph w Littledean *Glouc* from 02. *The Vicarage, St Annal's Road, Cinderford GL14 2AS* Tel (01594) 822286 Fax as telephone E-mail rswynn@cinderschurch.fsnet.co.uk

WYNN-EVANS, Canon James Naylor. b 34. Magd Coll Ox BA55 MA59. Linc Th Coll 57. **d** 59 **p** 60. C Goole *Sheff* 59-62; C Hatfield 62-63; Chapl HM Borstal Hatf 62-67; C-in-c Dunscroft CD *Sheff* 63-67; Bp's Dom Chapl *Edin* 67-75; C Edin St Columba 67-69; R Edin St Marg 69-85; P-in-c Edin SS Phil and Jas 76-85; P-in-c Edin St Dav 85-97; Info Officer Scottish Episc Ch 97-99; Can St Mary's Cathl 86-95; Hon Can St Mary's Cathl from 98. *1 Gayfield Place, Edinburgh EH7 4AB* Tel 0131-556 1566 E-mail wynn-evans@supanet.com

WYNNE, Preb Alan John. b 46. St Luke's Coll Ex CertEd71. St Steph Ho Ox BA71 MA75. **d** 71 **p** 72. C Watford St Pet *St Alb* 71-74; Chapl Liddon Ho Lon 74-75; Chapl Abp Tenison's Sch Kennington 75-86; Hon C St Marylebone Annunciation Bryanston Street *Lon* 81-86; V Hoxton St Anne w St Columba 86-94; TR Poplar from 94; Preb St Paul's Cathl from 01; AD Tower Hamlets from 01. *Poplar Rectory, Newby Place, London E14 0EY* Tel (020) 7987 3133 *or* tel and fax 7538 9198 E-mail alan@poplar22.fsnet.co.uk

WYNNE, Canon Frederick John Gordon. b 44. Chu Coll Cam BA66 MA70. CITC DipTh84. **d** 84 **p** 85. C Dublin St Patr Cathl Gp *D & G* 84-86; C Romsey *Win* 86-89; R Broughton, Bossington, Houghton and Mottisfont 89-97; I Dunleckney w Nurney, Lorum and Kiltennel *C & O* from 97; Chan Ossory Cathl from 00; Chan Leighlin Cathl from 00. *The Rectory, Dunleckney, Muine Bheag, Co Carlow, Irish Republic* Tel (00353) (59) 972 1570

WYNNE, Preb Geoffrey. b 41. K Coll Lon BD64 AKC64 Lon Univ BSc(Soc)75 Heythrop Coll Lon MTh86. **d** 66 **p** 67. C Wolverhampton St Pet *Lich* 66-70; Chapl Wolv Poly 66-79; Sen Chapl 79-92; Sen Chapl Wolv Univ from 92; Dir of Ords 76-83; Preb Lich Cathl from 83; AD Wolverhampton from 03. *The Chaplain's House, 1 Compton Park, Wolverhampton WV3 9DU* Tel (01902) 712051 *or* 322904 E-mail g.wynne@wlv.ac.uk

WYNNE, James Arthur Hill. b 13. BSP45. **d** 47 **p** 48. C Kilmore w Drumsnatt *Clogh* 47-50; C Tydavnet 47-50; C Darlington St Hilda *Dur* 50-52; V S Shields St Oswin 52-67; V Coundon 67-82; rtd 82; Perm to Offic *Dur* and *Newc* 82-02. *5 Old Kilmore Road, Moira, Craigavon BT67 0LZ* Tel (028) 9261 1363

WYNNE, Jean. b 02. Lic to Offic *M & K* from 02. *Ballinure House, Rathangan, Co Kildare, Irish Republic* Tel (00353) (46) 973 0098 Mobile 86-356 4590

WYNNE, Canon Ronald Charles. b 16. Selw Coll Cam BA38 MA42 Cape Town Univ MA79. Bp's Coll Calcutta 41. **d** 42 **p** 43. Ceylon 42-45; C Basingstoke *Win* 46-50; C Fleet *Guildf* 50-56; V Lockerley w E Dean *Win* 56-61; St Vincent 61-67; Botswana 68-82; rtd 82; Perm to Offic *Glouc* from 83. *19 Ricardo Road, Minchinhampton, Stroud GL6 9BY* Tel (01453) 883372

WYNNE, Trefor. b 35. St Mich Coll Llan 72. **d** 74 **p** 75. C Llangynwyd w Maesteg *Llan* 74-77; V Trealaw 77-83; R Llanbeulan w Llanfaelog and Tal-y-Llyn *Ban* 83-96; RD Llifon and Talybolion 93-96; rtd 96; Perm to Offic *Llan* from 96. *3 St John's Drive, Ton Pentre, Pentre CF41 7EU* Tel (01443) 433660

WYNNE-GREEN, Roy Rowland. b 36. SSC90 Westmr Coll Ox DipPh99. Chich Th Coll 67. **d** 70 **p** 71. C Fleetwood *Blackb* 70-73; C Cen Torquay *Ex* 73-75; Chapl SW Hosp and Chapl Asst St Thos Hosp Lon 75-85; Chapl R Surrey Co Hosp Guildf 85-94; Chapl R Surrey Co Hosp NHS Trust 94-01; Chapl Heathlands Mental Health Trust Surrey 94-98; Chapl Surrey Hants Borders NHS Trust 98-01; rtd 01; Perm to Offic *Guildf* from 02. *St Benedict's House, 6 Lawn Road, Guildford GU2 5DE* Tel (01483) 574582

WYNNE-JONES, Dyfed. b 56. St Mich Coll Llan DipTh79. **d** 79 **p** 80. C Porthmadog *Ban* 79-82; R Llangelynnin w Rhoslefain 82-86; Dioc Youth Officer 82-88; V Llanllechid 86-88; Chapl RAF from 88; P-in-c Lyneham w Bradenstoke *Sarum* 99-01. *Chaplaincy Services (RAF), HQ, Personnel and Training Command, RAF Innsworth, Gloucester GL3 1EZ* Tel (01452) 712612 ext 5164 Fax 510828

WYNNE-JONES, Nicholas Winder. b 45. Jes Coll Ox BA67 MA72 Selw Coll Cam 71. Oak Hill Th Coll 69. **d** 72 **p** 73. C St Marylebone All So w SS Pet and Jo *Lon* 72-75; Chapl Stowe Sch 75-83; V Gt Clacton *Chelmsf* 83-95; V Beckenham Ch Ch *Roch* from 95; RD Beckenham from 00. *Christ Church Vicarage, 18 Court Downs Road, Beckenham BR3 6LR* Tel (020) 8650 3847 Fax 8658 9532 E-mail vicar@ccb.org.uk

WYNTER, Michael Pallant. b 48. Ripon Coll Cuddesdon DipMin95. **d** 95 **p** 96. C Hughenden *Ox* 95-98; P-in-c Norton sub Hamdon, W Chinnock, Chiselborough etc *B & W* 98-01; R from 01; RD Ivelchester from 01. *The Rectory, Cat Street, Chiselborough, Stoke-sub-Hamdon TA14 6TT* Tel (01935) 881202

Y

YABBACOME, David Wallace. b 55. Bp Otter Coll BEd Linc Th Coll DipTh. **d** 83 **p** 84. C Egham Hythe *Guildf* 83-86; C Cen Telford *Lich* 86-87; TV 87-92; R Cheadle w Freehay 92-00; V Linc St Nic w St Jo Newport *Linc* from 00. *St Nicholas' Vicarage, 103 Newport, Lincoln LN1 3EE* Tel (01522) 525653 Mobile 07779-557541 E-mail revyabb@ntlworld.com

YABSLEY, Mrs Janet. b 42. St Alb Minl Tr Scheme 81. **dss** 84 **d** 87 **p** 94. Luton St Andr *St Alb* 84-87; NSM Luton St Aug Limbury 87-00; NSM Luton All SS w St Pet from 00. *11 Dale Road, Dunstable LU5 4PY* Tel (01582) 661480

YACOMENI, Peter Frederick. b 34. Worc Coll Ox BA58 MA61. Wycliffe Hall Ox 58. **d** 60 **p** 61. C New Malden and Coombe *S'wark* 60-64; C Bethnal Green St Jas Less *Lon* 64-68; V Barton Hill St Luke w Ch Ch *Bris* 68-75; V Bishopsworth 75-86; RD Bedminster 84-86; P-in-c Wick w Doynton 86-87; V Wick w Doynton and Dyrham 87-98; RD Bitton 95-98; Chapl Wilts and Swindon Healthcare NHS Trust from 98; rtd 98; Perm to Offic *Bris* from 98. *15 Orwell Close, Malmesbury SN16 9UB* Tel (01666) 826628

YALLOP, John. b 47. BA79. Oak Hill Th Coll 79. **d** 79 **p** 80. C Brinsworth w Catcliffe *Sheff* 79-81; C Heeley 81-83; C Pitsmoor Ch Ch 83-86; V Ellesmere St Pet 86-88; C Worksop St Jo *S'well* 90-94; P-in-c Cliftonville *Cant* 94-99. *47 Beatrice Road, Margate CT9 5SW* Tel (01843) 229872

YAM, David Tong Kho. See HAOKIP, David Tongkhoyam

YANGON, Bishop of. See SAN SI HTAY, The Most Revd Samuel

YAP, Thomas Fook Piau. b 75. Leeds Univ BA98 MA99. St Jo Coll Nottm MTh02. **d** 03. C Starbeck *Ripon* from 03. *41 Pearl Street, Harrogate HG1 4QW* Tel (01423) 889162 E-mail admin@andysonline.org.uk

YATES, Alan John Richard. b 38. Lon Univ LDS62. LNSM course 98. **d** 99 **p** 00. OLM Cley Hill Warminster *Sarum* from 99. *212 Pottle Street, Horningsham, Warminster BA12 7LX* Tel and fax (01985) 844374 Mobile 07970-864714

YATES, Andrew Martin. b 55. St Chad's Coll Dur BA77. Linc Th Coll 78. **d** 80 **p** 81. C Brightside St Thos and St Marg *Sheff* 80-83; TV Haverhill w Withersfield, the Wrattings etc *St E* 84-90; Ind Chapl 84-90; R Aylesham w Adisham *Cant* 90-96; P-in-c Dudley St Aug Holly Hall *Worc* from 96; Chapl Merry Hill Shopping Cen from 96. *St James's Vicarage, The Parade, Dudley DY1 3JA* Tel (01384) 253570 E-mail yatesasb@aol.com

YATES, Anthony Hugh. b 39. Univ of Wales BA62. Wycliffe Hall Ox 62. **d** 65 **p** 66. C Withington St Crispin *Man* 65-68; C Sheff Parson Cross St Cecilia *Sheff* 68-73; V Middlesbrough St Thos *York* 73-82; V Fenton *Lich* 82-95; V Kilburn St Aug w St Jo *Lon* from 95. *St Augustine's House, Kilburn Park Road, London NW6 5XB* Tel (020) 7624 1637 E-mail saint@augustine93.freeserve.co.uk

YATES (formerly WENSLEY), Mrs Beryl Kathleen. b 29. CertRK55. Selly Oak Coll 53. **dss** 76 **d** 87 **p** 94. Raynes Park St Sav *S'wark* 76-83; Chapl Asst St Geo Hosp Lon 83-89; Chapl Win HA 89-94; rtd 94. *15 Abbotts Ann Road, Harestock, Winchester SO22 6ND* Tel (01962) 882854

YATES, Francis Edmund. b 49. Ox Univ BEd72 Sheff Univ MEd88. Linc Th Coll 95. **d** 95 **p** 96. C Chesterfield St Mary and All SS *Derby* 95-98; P-in-c Newlyn St Newlyn *Truro* 98-03; Dioc Adv for Schs and RE 98-03; P-in-c Tideswell *Derby* from 03. *The Vicarage, 6 Pursglove Drive, Tideswell, Buxton SK17 8PA* Tel (01298) 871317 E-mail fryates@msn.com

YATES, James Ainsworth. b 21. Bps' Coll Cheshunt 56. **d** 58 **p** 59. C Dunstable *St Alb* 58-60; V Shillington 60-79; V Upper Gravenhurst 62-72; R Lower Gravenhurst 62-72; RD Shefford 69-79; V Upper w Lower Gravenhurst 72-79; V Sandon and Wallington w Rushden 79; R Sandon, Wallington and Rushden w Clothall 79-87; rtd 87; Perm to Offic *St Alb* 87-00. *97 Grove Road, Hitchin SG5 1SQ* Tel (01462) 434959

YATES, Miss Joanna Mary. b 49. St Anne's Coll Ox BA71 MA74 K Coll Lon PGCE72. S'wark Ord Course 89. **d** 91 **p** 94. Promotions and Publications Officer Nat Soc 85-95; Chapl Ch Ho Westmr 91-95; C Regent's Park St Mark *Lon* 91-95; C Finchley St Mary 95-01; TV Leeds City *Ripon* from 01. *St Peter's Vicarage, 15 Parkside Green, Leeds LS6 4NY* Tel 0113-278 7449 or 256 2036 Mobile 07904-440152 Fax 0113-243 9731

✠**YATES, The Rt Revd John.** b 25. Jes Coll Cam BA49 MA52 Cheltenham & Glouc Coll of HE Hon DLitt92. Linc Th Coll 49. **d** 51 **p** 52 **c** 72. C Southgate Ch Ch *Lon* 51-54; Lic to Offic *Linc* 54-59; Tutor Linc Th Coll 54-59; Chapl 56-59; V Bottesford *Linc* 59-65; Prin Lich Th Coll 66-72; Preb Lich Cathl 72; Lic to Offic 66-72; Suff Bp Whitby *York* 72-75; Bp Glouc 75-91; Bp at Lambeth (Hd of Staff) *Cant* 91-94; rtd 94. *15 Abbotts Ann Road, Harestock, Winchester SO22 6ND* Tel (01962) 882854

YATES, Keith Leonard. b 36. K Coll Lon BD AKC61 Nottm Univ MPhil79. Wells Th Coll. **d** 69 **p** 70. C Luton Ch Ch *St Alb* 69-73; Hon C Luton St Andr 73-76; R Grimoldby w Manby *Linc* 76-80; P-in-c Yarburgh 76-78; R 78-80; P-in-c Alvingham w N and S

Cockerington 76-78; V 78-80; P-in-c Gt w Lt Carlton 77-78; R 78-80; Lect Sarum & Wells Th Coll 80-87; R Upper Chelsea H Trin w St Jude *Lon* 87-96; rtd 96; Perm to Offic *Sarum* from 97. *4 Redlands Lane, Broadwindsor, Beaminster DT8 3ST* Tel (01308) 868892

YATES, Kenneth. b 44. Leeds Univ CQSW80. Kelham Th Coll 65. **d** 70 **p** 71. C Leeds City *Ripon* 70-74; C Worksop Priory *S'well* 74-75; Hon C Bawtry w Austerfield 75-78; Hon C Cantley *Sheff* 80-83; Hon C Doncaster St Jude 83-86; Hon C Ashford St Matt *Lon* 86-88; TV Brighton Resurr *Chich* 88-95; R E Blatchington from 95. *The Rectory, 86 Belgrave Road, Seaford BN25 2HE* Tel (01323) 892964

YATES, Lindsay Anne. See ADAM, Mrs Lindsay Anne

YATES, Michael Anthony. b 48. Oak Hill Th Coll. **d** 82 **p** 83. C Hebburn St Jo *Dur* 82-85; C Sheldon *Birm* 85-87; V Lea Hall 87-92; TV Old Brampton and Loundsley Green *Derby* 92-98; V Loundsley Green 98-01; V Riddings and Ironville from 01. *The Vicarage, Vicarage Lane, Ironville, Nottingham NG16 5PT* Tel (01773) 602241

YATES, Michael Peter. b 47. Leeds Univ BA69 MA70 MPhil85 Sheff Univ DCouns95. Coll of Resurr Mirfield 69. **d** 71 **p** 72. C Crewe St Andr *Ches* 71-76; V Wheelock 76-79; Chapl Rainhill Hosp Liv 79-89; Chapl Barnsley Distr Gen Hosp 89-94; Chapl Barnsley Distr Gen Hosp NHS Trust from 94. *The Chaplain's Office, Barnsley Hospital, Gawber Road, Barnsley S75 2EP* Tel (01226) 730000 Fax 202859

YATES, Paul David. b 47. Sussex Univ BA73 DPhil80. Sarum & Wells Th Coll 88. **d** 91 **p** 92. NSM Lewes All SS, St Anne, St Mich and St Thos *Chich* 91-00; NSM Lewes St Mich and St Thos at Cliffe w All SS from 00. *17 St Swithun's Terrace, Lewes BN7 1UJ* Tel (01273) 473463

YATES, Peter Francis. b 47. Sheff Univ BA69 Nottm Univ DipTh71. Kelham Th Coll 69. **d** 74 **p** 75. C Mexborough *Sheff* 74-78; C Sevenoaks St Jo *Roch* 78-81; CSWG from 81; Lic to Offic *Chich* from 86. *The Monastery, Crawley Down, Crawley RH10 4LH* Tel (01342) 712074

YATES, Raymond Paul. b 55. Oak Hill Th Coll BA88. **d** 88 **p** 89. C Bootle St Mary w St Paul *Liv* 88-91; C Drypool *York* 91-92; TV 92-97; C Orpington All SS *Roch* 97-00; R Beeford w Frodingham and Foston *York* from 00; RD N Holderness from 02; Chapl HM Pris Hull from 01. *The Rectory, 10 Glebe Gardens, Beeford, Driffield YO25 8BF* Tel (01262) 488042

YATES, Canon Roger Alan. b 47. MRCP77 Trin Coll Cam BA68 MB71 BChir71 MA72 Bris Univ PhD75. N Ord Course 84. **d** 87 **p** 88. NSM Wilmslow *Ches* from 87; Hon Can Ches Cathl from 99. *3 Racecourse Park, Wilmslow SK9 5LU* Tel (01625) 520246 E-mail roger.yates@astrazeneca.com

YATES, Mrs Rosamund. b 63. Rob Coll Cam BA84 MA88. Oak Hill Th Coll BA93. **d** 93. C Holloway St Mary Magd *Lon* 93-95; NSM Tervuren w Liège *Eur* 95-97; NSM W Ealing St Jo w St Jas *Lon* from 01. *98 Cumberland Road, London W7 2EB* Tel (020) 8621 5332

YATES, Mrs Sîan. b 57. Univ of Wales (Ban) Westmr Coll Ox MTh91. Linc Th Coll 78. **d** 80 **p** 94. C Risca *Mon* 80-83; Chapl Ch Hosp Horsham 83-85; TD Haverhill w Withersfield, the Wrattings etc *St E* 85-90; Dioc Youth Chapl *Cant* 90-93; Assoc Min Cant St Martin and St Paul 93-96; Educn Chapl *Worc* from 96; P-in-c Dudley St Jas from 96; P-in-c Dudley St Barn 01-02. *St James's Vicarage, The Parade, Dudley DY1 3JA* Tel (01384) 253570 E-mail yatesasb@aol.com

YATES, Canon Timothy Edward. b 35. Magd Coll Cam BA59 MA62 Uppsala Univ DTh78. Ridley Hall Cam 58. **d** 60 **p** 61. C Tonbridge SS Pet and Paul *Roch* 60-63; Tutor St Jo Coll Dur 63-71; Warden Cranmer Hall Dur 71-79; P-in-c Darley w S Darley *Derby* 79-82; R Darley 82-90; Dioc Dir of Ords 85-95; Hon Can Derby Cathl 89-00; C Ashford w Sheldon and Longstone 90-00; rtd 00; Perm to Offic *Derby* from 01. *Holly House, South Church Street, Bakewell DE45 1FD* Tel (01629) 812686

YATES, Warwick John (Ricky). b 52. Univ of Wales (Lamp) BA78. Wycliffe Hall St 87. **d** 89 **p** 90. C Hoddesdon *St Alb* 89-93; R Finmere w Mixbury, Cottisford, Hardwick etc *Ox* 93-95; R Shelswell from 95. *The Rectory, Water Stratford Road, Finmere, Buckingham MK18 4AT* Tel (01280) 847184 Fax as telephone E-mail rickyyates@supanet.com

YATES, William Herbert. b 35. Man Univ BA59. Chich Th Coll 60. **d** 61 **p** 62. C Blackpool St Steph *Blackb* 61-65; C Wednesbury St Jo *Lich* 65-69; V Porthill 69-78; R Norton in the Moors 78-84; R Church Aston 84-00; rtd 00; Perm to Offic *Lich* from 01. *83 Stallington Road, Blythe Bridge, Stoke-on-Trent ST11 9PD* Tel (01782) 397182

YATES-ROUND, Joseph Laurence John. b 25. S'wark Ord Course 75. **d** 76 **p** 77. NSM Tonbridge SS Pet and Paul *Roch* 76-83; Chapl Palma and Balearic Is w Ibiza etc *Eur* 83-90; rtd 90; Perm to Offic *Ches* from 90. *5 Willowtree Grove, Alsager, Stoke-on-Trent ST7 3TE* Tel (01270) 883425

YEATS, Charles. b 56. Natal Univ BCom77 Witwatersrand Univ MBA79 Ball Coll Ox MA85 K Coll Lon MTh90 Dur Univ PhD99. Wycliffe Hall Ox 85. **d** 87 **p** 88. C Islington St Mary *Lon* 87-90; Research Fell Whitefield Inst Ox 90-92; Chapl and Fell

Univ Coll Dur 92-00; Perm to Offic *Dur* from 00. *58 Archery Rise, Durham DH1 4LA* Tel 0191-384 0606
YEATS, Peter Derek. b 62. Leeds Univ BA84. Cranmer Hall Dur 85. **d** 87 **p** 88. C Tynemouth Cullercoats St Paul *Newc* 87-90; USPG 90-00; Miss to Seafarers Port Chapl Kobe Japan from 00. *USPG, Partnership House, 157 Waterloo Road, London SE1 8XA* Tel (020) 7928 8681 Fax 7928 2371
YELDHAM, Anthony Paul Richard. See KYRIAKIDES-YELDHAM, Anthony Paul Richard
YELLAND, Jeffrey Charles. b 46. CEng MIStructE72. STETS 98. **d** 01 **p** 02. NSM Effingham w Lt Bookham *Guildf* from 01. *32 Hookfield, Epsom KT19 8JG* Tel and fax (01372) 807096 Mobile 07802-781836 E-mail jeff.yelland@cwcom.net
YENDALL, John Edward Thomas. b 52. St Jo Coll Dur BA88. Cranmer Hall Dur 84. **d** 88 **p** 89. C Bangor *Ban* 89-90; C Botwnnog 90-91; R Trefdraeth w Aberffraw etc 91-01; RD Malltraeth 97-01; V Llanwddyn and Llanfihangel-yng-Nghwynfa etc *St As* from 01. *The Vicarage, Llanwddyn, Oswestry SY10 0LX* Tel (01691) 870663
YEO (née HARRISSON), Mrs Jennifer Marjorie. b 40. SRN62. Cant Sch of Min 87. **d** 90 **p** 97. NSM Kemsing w Woodlands *Roch* 90-91; Chapl Stone Ho Hosp Kent 90-91; NSM Totnes, Bridgetown and Berry Pomeroy etc *Ex* 95-97; NSM Ashprington, Cornworthy and Dittisham 97-98; Perm to Offic from 98. *Skaigh, 45 Glanvill Way, Honiton EX14 2GD* Tel (01404) 549537
YEO, Richard Ellery. b 25. Ex Coll Ox MA49 DipEd49. Cant Sch of Min 86. **d** 89 **p** 90. NSM Broadstairs *Cant* 89-92; Perm to Offic *Ex* from 95. *Skaigh, 45 Glanvill Way, Honiton EX14 2GD* Tel (01404) 549537
YEOMAN, Canon David. b 44. Univ of Wales DipTh69. St Mich Coll Llan 66. **d** 70 **p** 71. C Cardiff St Jo *Llan* 70-72; C Caerphilly 72-76; V Ystrad Rhondda w Ynyscynon 76-81; V Mountain Ash 81-96; R Coity w Nolton from 96; Can Llan Cathl from 00. *Nolton Rectory, Merthyr Mawr Road North, Bridgend CF31 3NH* Tel (01656) 652247 *or* 667690 Mobile 07971-926631 E-mail david@calon.freeserve.co.uk
YEOMAN, Douglas. b 35. ACII63. **d** 77 **p** 78. NSM Edin St Martin *Edin* 77-96; NSM Edin St Luke 79-90; Chapl Edinburgh Healthcare NHS Trust from 95; NSM Edin St Cuth *Edin* from 96. *6 Craiglockhart Crescent, Edinburgh EH14 1EY* Tel 0131-443 5449 E-mail d.yeoman@currantbun.com
YEOMAN, Miss Ruth Jane. b 60. Sheff Univ BSc82 MSc85 Dur Univ PGCE83. Ripon Coll Cuddesdon BA90 MA94. **d** 91 **p** 94. C Coleshill *Birm* 91-95; C Hodge Hill 95-01; Bp's Adv for Children's Work 95-01; L'Arche Lambeth Community 01-03; Perm to Offic *S'wark* 01-03 and *Birm* 03; V Menston w Woodhead *Bradf* from 03. *The Vicarage, 12 Fairfax Gardens, Menston, Ilkley LS29 6ET* Tel (01943) 877739 Mobile 07752-912646 E-mail ruthjyeoman@hotmail.com
YEOMANS, Robert John. b 44. AKC66. **d** 67 **p** 68. C Pontesbury I and II *Heref* 67-70; Asst Youth Officer *St Alb* 70-72; Project Officer (Dio St Alb) Gen Syn Bd of Educn 73-77; V Is of Dogs Ch Ch and St Jo w St Luke *Lon* 77-87; V Waterloo St Jo w St Andr *S'wark* 87-93; Chapl United Bris Healthcare NHS Trust 93-02; Chapl Ex Hospiscare from 02. *5 Valley Path, Newton Abbot TQ12 1YQ* Tel (01626) 208065
YERBURGH, Canon David Savile. b 34. Magd Coll Cam BA57 MA61. Wells Th Coll 57. **d** 59 **p** 60. C Cirencester *Glouc* 59-63; C Bitterne Park *Win* 63-67; V Churchdown St Jo *Glouc* 67-74; RD Glouc N 73-74; V Charlton Kings St Mary 74-85; R Minchinhampton 85-95; Hon Can Glouc Cathl 86-95; rtd 95; Perm to Offic *Sarum* from 95. *2 Mill Race Close, Mill Road, Salisbury SP2 7RX* Tel (01722) 320064
YERBURGH, Peter Charles. b 31. Magd Coll Cam BA53 MA57. Wells Th Coll 53. **d** 55 **p** 56. C Southbroom *Sarum* 55-58; Chapl Wells Cathl Sch 58-71; Chapl Durlston Court Sch Barton on Sea 71-91; rtd 91. *2 Mill Race Close, Mill Road, Salisbury SP2 7RX* Tel (01722) 327796
YERBURY, Gregory Howard. b 67. Trin Coll Bris BA93. St Jo Coll Nottm 94. **d** 96 **p** 97. C Crofton *Portsm* 96-00; P-in-c Bolton St Jo *Man* from 00. *St John's Vicarage, 7 Alford Close, Bolton BL2 6NR* Tel (01204) 389044 E-mail greg@stjohns.arbonne.co.uk
YEWDALL, Mrs Mary Doreen. b 23. Nottm Univ DipEd71 BTh85. EMMTC 76. **dss** 79 **d** 87 **p** 94. Kirkby in Ashfield St Thos *S'well* 79-81; Daybrook 81-87; Par Dn 87-89; rtd 89; Hon Par Dn Bilsthorpe *S'well* 89-91; Hon Par Dn Eakring 89-91; Hon Par Dn Winkburn 89-91; Hon Par Dn Maplebeck 89-91; NSM Norton juxta Malton *York* 92-95; NSM Whitwell w Crambe, Flaxton, Foston etc 95-98; Perm to Offic from 98. *West Croft, The Rise, Thornton Dale, Pickering YO18 7TG* Tel (01751) 477757
YIEND, Paul Martin. b 57. UEA BA80. St Jo Coll Nottm Dip Th Studies 92 MA96. **d** 92 **p** 94. C Bushbury *Lich* 92-95; Asst Chapl Brussels *Eur* 99-00; P-in-c Charleroi w Liège from 00. *rue Basse des Canes 11, 5300 Andenne, Belgium* Tel (0032) (85) 844482 Fax as telephone E-mail paul.yiend@skynet.be
YIN, Canon Roy Henry Bowyer. b 10. K Coll Cam BA32 MA36. Cuddesdon Coll 32. **d** 33 **p** 34. C Cambridge St Giles w St Pet *Ely* 33-37; Chapl K Coll Cam 33-37; Chapl Hurstpierpoint Coll

37-46; Ceylon 46-62; Singapore from 64; rtd 75; Hon Can Singapore from 80. *114-A Newton Road, Singapore 307980* Tel (0065) 253 4080
YODER, John Henry. b 36. **d** 76 **p** 77. USA 76-79 and from 80; C Wolverhampton *Lich* 79-80. *6233 West Washington Boulevard, Las Vegas, NV 89107, USA*
✠YONG, The Most Revd Datuk Ping Chung. b 41. Memorial Univ Newfoundland BA68. Qu Coll Newfoundland LTh69. **d** 69 **p** 70 **c** 90. Malaysia 69-84 and from 90; P Sabah 69-77; Adn Sabah 77-84; Chairman ACC 84-90; Bp Sabah from 90; Abp SE Asia from 00. *PO Box 10811, 88809 Kota Kinabalu, Sabah, Malaysia* Tel (0060) (88) 245846 *or* 249296 Fax 245942 E-mail pcyong@pc.jaring.my
YONGE, James Mohun (Brother Amos). b 47. Keele Univ BA71. WMMTC 91. **d** 94 **p** 95. SSF from 76. *The Society of St Francis, 16 Dalserf Street, Glasgow G31 4AS* Tel 0141-550 1202
✠YOON, The Rt Revd Paul Hwan. b 38. **d** 67 **c** 87. Bp Taejon 87-02; Presiding Bp Korea 00-02; rtd 02. *PO Box 22, Taejon 300-600, Republic of Korea* Tel (0082) (42) 256 9987 Fax 255 8918
YORK, Canon Humphrey Bowmar. b 28. St Chad's Coll Dur BA54. **d** 55 **p** 56. C Beamish *Dur* 55-57; C Tettenhall Regis *Lich* 57-62; P-in-c Lansallos w Pelynt *Truro* 62-63; R Lanreath 62-67; V Pelynt 63-67; P-in-c Lanlivery 67-74; P-in-c Luxulyan 67-74; P-in-c Lanlivery w Luxulyan 74-83; RD Bodmin 76-82; R Antony w Sheviock 83-93; Hon Can Truro Cathl 90-93; rtd 93; Perm to Offic *Truro* and *Sarum* from 93. *8 Huntingdon Street, Bradford-on-Avon BA15 1RF*
YORK, Archbishop of. See HOPE, The Most Revd and Rt Hon David Michael
YORK, Archdeacon of. See SEED, The Ven Richard Murray Crosland
YORK, Dean of. See FURNELL, The Very Revd Raymond
YORKE, John Andrew. b 47. Cranmer Hall Dur 70. **d** 73 **p** 74. C Spitalfields Ch Ch w All SS *Lon* 73-78; Canada 78-92; V Totland Bay *Portsm* from 92; V Thorley from 95. *The Vicarage, Alum Bay New Road, Totland Bay PO39 0ES* Tel (01983) 752031 E-mail andy.yorke@lineone.net
YORKE, The Very Revd Michael Leslie. b 39. Magd Coll Cam BA62 MA66. Cuddesdon Coll 62. **d** 64 **p** 65. C Croydon *Cant* 64-68; Succ Chelmsf Cathl *Chelmsf* 68-69; Prec and Chapl 69-73; Dep Dir Cathl Cen for Research and Tr 72-74; P-in-c Ashdon w Hadstock 74-76; R 76-78; Can Res Chelmsf Cathl 78-88; Vice-Provost 84-88; P-in-c N Lynn w St Marg and St Nic *Nor* 88-92; P-in-c King's Lynn St Marg w St Nic 92-94; Chmn Dioc Adv Bd for Min 90-94; Hon Can Nor Cathl 93-94; Provost Portsm 94-99; Dean Lich from 99. *The Deanery, 16 The Close, Lichfield WS13 7LD* Tel (01543) 306250 *or* 306294 Fax 306251 E-mail michael.yorke@lichfieldcathedral.org
YORKSTONE, Peter. b 48. Loughb Univ BTech72. Oak Hill Th Coll 79. **d** 81 **p** 82. C Blackpool St Thos *Blackb* 81-85; V Copp 85-00; P-in-c Giggleswick and Rathmell w Wigglesworth *Bradf* from 00. *The Vicarage, Bankwell Road, Giggleswick, Settle BD24 0AP* Tel (01729) 822425 E-mail peter@pyorkstone.freeserve.co.uk
YOUATT, Jennifer Alison. See MONTGOMERY, Mrs Jennifer Alison
YOUDE, Paul Crosland. b 47. Birm Univ LLB68. WEMTC 93. **d** 96 **p** 97. NSM Cheltenham St Luke and St Jo *Glouc* 96-99; C Cirencester 99-03; P-in-c Lydney from 03. *5 Raglan Gardens, Lydney GL15 5GZ* Tel (01594) 842321 Fax as telephone E-mail paul@pyoude.freeserve.co.uk
YOUENS, Edward. See MONTAGUE-YOUENS, Canon Hubert Edward
YOUINGS, Adrian. b 65. Ex Univ BSc86 Bath Univ PhD90. Wycliffe Hall Ox 93. **d** 96 **p** 97. C Dorking St Paul *Guildf* 96-99; C S Croydon Em *S'wark* from 99. *12 Hurst View Road, South Croydon CR2 7AG* Tel (020) 8681 5653 E-mail adrian@emmanuelcroydon.org.uk
YOULD, Guy Martin. b 37. FSAScot75 Keble Coll Ox BA61 DipTh62 MA65 Magd Coll Ox BD68 Hull Univ PhD80. Lambeth STh75 St Steph Ho Ox 61. **d** 63 **p** 64. C Middlesbrough St Jo the Ev *York* 63-65; Chapl Magd Coll Ox 65-68; C Cowley St Jo *Ox* 65-68; Asst Chapl Radley Coll 68-71; C W Kirby St Bridget *Ches* 71-74; Chapl Loretto Sch Musselburgh 74; V Liscard St Mary w St Columba *Ches* 74-78; St Barn Coll Belair Australia 78-80; C Doncaster St Leon and St Jude *Sheff* 80-81; C Brodsworth w Hooton Pagnell, Frickley etc 81-87; Chapl St Mary's Sch Wantage 87-93; R Chapel Chorlton, Maer and Whitmore *Lich* 93-98; P-in-c Altarnon w Bolventor, Laneast and St Clether *Truro* 98-02; P-in-c Lezant 98-02; rtd 02; C Gt and Lt Torrington and Frithelstock *Ex* from 03. *St Giles' House, Little Torrington, Torrington EX38 8PS* Tel (01805) 622497
YOUNG, Andrew Charles. b 54. FIBMS83. N Ord Course 98. **d** 01 **p** 02. C Heywood *Man* from 01. *16 Chesham Avenue, Castleton, Rochdale OL11 2YB* Tel (01706) 718578 E-mail andrewyoung3@hotmail.com
YOUNG, Andrew John. b 50. St Jo Coll Dur BA73. Westcott Ho Cam 73. **d** 75 **p** 89. C Nailsworth *Glouc* 75-76; NSM Yeovil w Kingston Pitney *B & W* 89-93; NSM Tintinhull w Chilthorne Domer, Yeovil Marsh etc from 95. *15 Cook Avenue, Chard TA20 2JR*

894

YOUNG, Arthur. b 65. Belf Bible Coll BTh92. CITC 99. **d** 01 **p** 02. C Donaghadee *D & D* from 01. *7 Rosepark Avenue, Donaghadee BT21 0BW* Tel (028) 9188 2495

YOUNG, Canon Brian Thomas. b 42. Linc Th Coll 67. **d** 70 **p** 71. C Monkseaton St Mary *Newc* 70-73; C Berwick H Trin 73-77; P-in-c Gt Broughton *Carl* 77-80; V Gt Broughton and Broughton Moor 80-83; V Chorley *Ches* 83-90; V Alderley Edge from 90; RD Knutsford from 96; Hon Can Ches Cathl from 97. *The Vicarage, Church Lane, Alderley Edge SK9 7UZ* Tel (01625) 583249

YOUNG, Canon Charles John. b 24. GIMechE50 Open Univ BA98. Qu Coll Birm 52. **d** 55 **p** 56. C Dudley St Thos *Worc* 55-58; C Beeston *S'well* 58-61; V Lady Bay 61-66; R Kirkby in Ashfield 66-75; V Balderton 75-92; RD Newark 82-90; Hon Can S'well Minster 84-92; rtd 92; Bp's Chapl for Rtd Clergy *S'well* from 92. *9 The Paddocks, London Road, Newark NG24 1SS* Tel (01636) 613445

YOUNG, Christopher Terence. b 53. Cape Town Univ BA76 Univ of S Africa BTh80. St Bede's Coll Umtata 79. **d** 80 **p** 81. S Africa 80-86 and from 88; C Rainham *Chelmsf* 86-88. *11B Coniston Road, Rondebosch, 7700 South Africa* Tel (0027) (21) 685 6868 or 689 2087

✠**YOUNG, The Rt Revd Clive.** b 48. St Jo Coll Dur BA70. Ridley Hall Cam 70. **d** 72 **p** 73 **c** 99. C Neasden cum Kingsbury St Cath *Lon* 72-75; C Hammersmith St Paul 75-79; P-in-c Old Ford St Paul w St Steph 79-82; V Old Ford St Paul w St Steph and St Mark 82-92; AD Tower Hamlets 88-92; Adn Hackney 92-99; V St Andr Holborn 92-99; Suff Bp Dunwich *St E* from 99. *28 Westerfield Road, Ipswich IP4 2UJ* Tel (01473) 222276 Fax 210303 E-mail bishop.clive@stedmundsbury.anglican.org

YOUNG, Daniel George Harding. b 52. New Coll Ox BA73 MA83. Cranmer Hall Dur 77. **d** 80 **p** 81. C Bushbury *Lich* 80-83; Chapl Dean Close Sch Cheltenham from 83. *6 Tyfield, Sherborne St John, Basingstoke RG24 9HZ* Tel (01256) 850397

YOUNG, David. b 37. NDTJ61 Open Univ PhD89. **d** 61 **p** 68. C Crofton *Wakef* 67-68; C Heckmondwike 68-71; V Stainland 71-76; R Patrington w Winestead *York* 76-80; Chapl Winestead Hosp 76-80; Gen Preacher *Linc* from 80; Chapl St Jo Hosp Linc 80-90; Chapl N Lincs Mental Health Unit 90-93; Chapl Linc Distr Healthcare NHS Trust 93-97; Dep Chapl from 98. *Westview, Aisthorpe, Lincoln LN1 2SG* Tel (01522) 730912

YOUNG, David Charles. b 44. Oriel Coll Ox BA66 MA70. S'wark Ord Course 74. **d** 77 **p** 78. C Harborne St Pet *Birm* 77-81; P-in-c Edgbaston St Germain 81-83; P-in-c Birm St Paul 83-85; Perm to Offic *St Alb* from 85; *Ox* 91-00. *18 Tamar Walk, Leighton Buzzard LU7 8DD* Tel (01525) 382881 E-mail david.young@dial.pipex.com

YOUNG, Canon David John. b 43. Nottm Univ BA64 MPhil89 Lambeth STh87. Coll of Resurr Mirfield 64. **d** 66 **p** 67. C Warsop *S'well* 66-68; C Harworth 68-71; P-in-c Hackenthorpe Ch Ch *Derby* 71-73; TV Frecheville and Hackenthorpe 73-75; V Chaddesden St Phil 75-83; R Narborough and Huncote *Leic* 83-89; RD Guthlaxton I 87-90; Chapl Leic Univ 90-95; V Eyres Monsell 95-98; Perm to Offic 98-99; rtd 03. *50 Threadgold Close, Leicester LE4 1BY* Tel 0116-236 5634

✠**YOUNG, The Rt Revd David Nigel de Lorentz.** b 31. CBE00. Ball Coll Ox BA54 MA58. Wycliffe Hall Ox 57. **d** 59 **p** 60 **c** 77. C Allerton *Liv* 59-62; C St Marylebone St Mark Hamilton Terrace *Lon* 62-63; CMS 63-67; Lect Man Univ 67-70; V Burwell *Ely* 70-75; Hon Can Ely Cathl 75-77; Adn Huntingdon 75-77; V Gt w Lt Gidding and Steeple Gidding 75-77; R Hemingford Abbots 77; Bp Ripon 77-99; Hon Asst Bp Bradf from 00. *Chapel House, Lawkland, Austwick, Lancaster LA2 8AT* Tel (01524) 251209

YOUNG, Derek John. b 42. St D Coll Lamp DipTh73. **d** 73 **p** 74. C Griffithstown *Mon* 73-76; C Ebbw Vale 76-77; V Penmaen 77-81; V Penmaen and Crumlin 81-87; Chapl Oakdale Hosp Gwent 83-87; V New Tredegar *Mon* 87-99; V Llanfihangel Crucorney w Oldcastle etc from 99. *The Vicarage, Llanfihangel Crucorney, Abergavenny NP7 8DH* Tel (01873) 890349

YOUNG, Desmond Terence. b 17. TCD BA40. **d** 41 **p** 42. C Hadfield *Derby* 41-44; C Derby St Werburgh 44-47; CF 47-55; I Fertagh *C & O* 55-62; I Inistioge w the Rower 62-74; P-in-c Thomastown 62-74; C Roundhay St Edm *Ripon* 74-77; V Leeds Gipton Epiphany 77-83; rtd 83; Perm to Offic *Guildf* 83-94. *c/o T D Young Esq, Carden House, Rectory Lane, Gedney, Spalding PE12 0BU*

YOUNG, George William. b 31. Lon Coll of Div ALCD55 LTh74. **d** 56 **p** 57. C Everton Em *Liv* 56-57; C Halliwell St Pet *Man* 58-61; V Newburn *Newc* 61-67; P-in-c Tylers Green *Ox* 67-69; V 69-80; Lic to Offic 80-84; Area Sec (W England) SAMS 80-84; Hon C Purley Ch Ch *S'wark* 84-87; V Beckenham St Jo *Roch* 87-92; rtd 92; Perm to Offic *S'wark* from 92. *9 Shortacres, High Street, Nutfield, Redhill RH1 4HJ* Tel (01737) 822363

YOUNG, Henry Lawrence. b 19. TCD BA40 MA46. **d** 47 **p** 48. C Ballywillan *Conn* 47-49; C Urney w Denn and Derryheen *K, E & A* 49-50; I 50-51; CF 51-60; I Donegal w Killymard, Lough Eske and Laghey *D & R* 60-64; R Gt and Lt Casterton w

Pickworth and Tickencote *Pet* 64-70; rtd 70; Hon C Perth St Jo *St And* from 70. *19 Servite House, Corrie Place, Perth PH2 6QE* Tel (01738) 553573

YOUNG, Hilary Antoinette Francesca. d 01 p 02. NSM Thorne *Sheff* from 01. *The Vicarage, Stainforth Road, Barnby Dun, Doncaster DN3 1AA* Tel (01302) 882835

YOUNG, Hyacinth Loretta. b 49. NTMTC 95. **d** 98 **p** 99. NSM Harlesden All So *Lon* 98-00; TV Wembley Park from 00. *194 Windermere Avenue, Wembley HA9 8QT*

YOUNG, Iain Clavering. b 56. Newc Poly BA79. Coll of Resurr Mirfield 80. **d** 83 **p** 84. C Wallsend St Luke *Newc* 83-86; C Horton 86-87; V 87-92; V Friern Barnet St Pet le Poer *Lon* 92-95; C Holborn St Alb w Saffron Hill St Pet 96-97; P-in-c Hoxton H Trin w St Mary 97-02; V from 02; Chapl Moorfields Eye Hosp NHS Trust from 97. *Holy Trinity Vicarage, 3 Bletchley Street, London N1 7QG* Tel (020) 7253 4796

YOUNG, Jeremy Michael. b 54. Ch Coll Cam BA76 MA80 Lon Univ MTh94. Coll of Resurr Mirfield 78. **d** 80 **p** 81. C Whitworth w Spennymoor *Dur* 80-83; C Boxmoor St Jo *St Alb* 83-86; V Croxley Green St Oswald 86-94; Dir Theol CITC 94-99; Lic to Offic *D & G* from 99. *27 Rostrevor Road, Rathgar, Dublin 6, Irish Republic* Tel (00353) (1) 497 0331

YOUNG, John. See YOUNG, David John

YOUNG, Canon John David. b 37. DLC60 Lon Univ BD65 Sussex Univ MA77. Clifton Th Coll 62. **d** 65 **p** 66. C Plymouth St Jude *Ex* 65-68; Hd of RE Northgate Sch Ipswich 68-71; Chapl and Sen Lect Bp Otter Coll Chich 71-81; Chapl and Sen Lect W Sussex Inst of HE 77-81; Chapl and Sen Lect Coll of Ripon and York St Jo 81-87; C York St Paul *York* 87-88; Dioc Ev 88-02; Can and Preb York Minster 92-03; Miss Strategy Development Officer 00-02; rtd 02; Lic to Offic *York* from 02. *72 Middlethorpe Grove, York YO24 1JY* Tel (01904) 704195 Fax as telephone E-mail johnyoung@stpaulsyork.org.uk

YOUNG, John Kenneth. Edin Th Coll 62. **d** 64 **p** 65. C Gosforth All SS *Newc* 64-67; C Newc St Gabr 67-69; R Bowers Gifford *Chelmsf* 69-72; R Bowers Gifford w N Benfleet 72-75; P-in-c Kirkwhelpington *Newc* 75-79; P-in-c Kirkharle 77-79; P-in-c Kirkheaton 75-79; P-in-c Cambo 77-79; V Kirkwhelpington, Kirkharle, Kirkheaton and Cambo 79-82; V Gosforth St Nic 82-92; V Healey and Slaley 92-97; rtd 97; Perm to Offic *Newc* from 97. *20 Mitford Way, Dinnington, Newcastle upon Tyne NE13 7LW* Tel (01661) 821050

YOUNG, John Robert. b 43. SSM 63. **d** 68 **p** 69. Australia 68-72; C Ch Ch Cathl Darwin 68-70; C Murrumbeena 70-72; C Stocking Farm *Leic* 72-74; Australia from 74; P-in-c W Reservoir 75-78; I Montmorency 78-85; I E Burwood 85-96; R Warracknabeal from 96. *21 Regent Street, PO Box 78, Port Fairy, Vic, Australia 3284* Tel (0061) (3) 5568 1028 Fax as telephone

YOUNG, Canon Jonathan Frederick. b 25. Univ of Wales (Lamp) BA51 Birm Univ MA81. St Mich Coll Llan 51. **d** 53 **p** 54. C Roath St Martin *Llan* 53-59; Lic to Offic *Ox* 59-74; SSJE 62-71; Bp's Chapl for Community Relns *Birm* 71-74; Chapl Coun for Soc Resp 74-85; Hon Can Birm Cathl 84-85; USA from 85; rtd 90. *52 Harvard Road, Belmont, MA 02478, USA* Tel (001) (617) 484 9439 E-mail youngmj@aol.com

YOUNG, Canon Jonathan Priestland. b 44. AKC68. **d** 69 **p** 70. C Clapham H Trin *S'wark* 69-73; C Mitcham St Mark 73-74; V Godmanchester *Ely* 74-82; P-in-c Cambridge St Giles w St Pet 82; Chapl St Jo Coll Sch Cam 88-93; P-in-c Ellington *Ely* 01-02; P-in-c Chesterton St Luke 82; TR Cambridge Ascension 82-01; P-in-c Grafham 01-02; P-in-c Easton 01-02; P-in-c Spaldwick w Barham and Woolley 01-02; R E Leightonstone from 02; Hon Can Ely Cathl from 01; RD Leightonstone from 02. *The Rectory, Parson's Drive, Ellington, Huntingdon PE28 0AU* Tel (01480) 891695 Fax as telephone

YOUNG, Kathleen Margaret. See BROWN, Canon Kathleen Margaret

YOUNG, Mark Gilbert Campbell. b 60. Mert Coll Ox BA88. Wycliffe Hall Ox 86. **d** 91 **p** 92. C Holborn St Geo w H Trin and St Bart *Lon* 91-95; C St Pancras w St Jas and Ch Ch 95-99; V W Hampstead Trin from 99; P-in-c W Hampstead St Cuth from 01. *1A Akenside Road, London NW3 5BS* Tel (020) 7794 2975

YOUNG, Martin Edward. b 20. Oriel Coll Ox BA41 MA45. Cuddesdon Coll 41. **d** 43 **p** 44. C Newbury *Ox* 43-45; C Wymondham *Nor* 45-49; C Gt Berkhamsted *St Alb* 49-51; V Littlemore *Ox* 51-64; R Wootton w Quinton *Pet* 64-72; R Wootton w Quinton and Preston Deanery 72-78; V Welford w Sibbertoft 78-82; V Welford w Sibbertoft and Marston Trussell 82-88; rtd 88; Perm to Offic *Pet* 2 *Knutsford Lane, Long Buckby, Northampton NN6 7RL* Tel (01327) 843929

YOUNG, Martin John. b 72. Univ Coll Lon BSc93 Oak Hill Th Coll BA01. **d** 01 **p** 02. C Heigham H Trin *Nor* from 01. *14 Trinity Street, Norwich NR2 2BQ* Tel (01603) 614231 E-mail martin@holytrinity.nch.clara.co.uk

YOUNG, Norman Keith. b 35. EAMTC 85. **d** 87 **p** 88. C Burwell *Ely* 87-91; V Swaffham Bulbeck and Swaffham Prior w Reach 91-92; V Barnby Dun *Sheff* from 92; Ind Chapl from 92; AD Doncaster from 98. *The Vicarage, Stainforth Road, Barnby Dun, Doncaster DN3 1AA* Tel (01302) 882835 Fax 880029 E-mail norman@youngvic.u-net.com

YOUNG, Peter John. b 26. Pemb Coll Cam BA49 MA54. Ridley Hall Cam 49. **d** 51 **p** 52. C Cheadle *Ches* 51-54; Malaya 54-63; Malaysia from 63; rtd 92. *247 Jalan 5/48, 46000 Petaling Jaya, Selangor, Malaysia* Tel (0060) (3) 7782 9269 Fax 7783 0849

YOUNG, Canon Raymond Grant. b 11. MBE81. **d** 43 **p** 44. C Ince Ch Ch *Liv* 43-45; C Pemberton St Jo 46; Chapl to Deaf *Win* and *Portsm* 46-49; Perm to Offic *Portsm* 48-59; V Marchwood *Win* 59-70; Chapl to Deaf *Win* and *Portsm* 70-81; Hon Can Win Cathl *Win* 77-81; rtd 81; Perm to Offic *Win* 81-95. *66 Chalvington Road, Eastleigh SO53 3DT* Tel (023) 8026 1519

YOUNG, Richard Michael. b 63. **d** 96 **p** 97. NSM Brunswick *Man* from 96. *2 Birch Grove, Rusholme, Manchester M14 5JY* Tel 0161-225 0884 Mobile 07778-817784 E-mail richard_young@3igroup.com

YOUNG, Canon Roger Edward. b 40. Dur Univ BSc62. Cuddesdon Coll 64. **d** 66 **p** 67. C Eglwysilan *Llan* 66-68; C Llanishen and Lisvane 68-74; C-in-c Rhydyfelin *CD* 74-78; TR Ystradyfodwg 78-81; R 81-88; Chapl Tyntyla, Llwynypia and Porth and Distr Hosps 81-88; R Peterston-super-Ely w St Brides-super-Ely *Llan* from 88; Prin Llandaff NSM Ord Course 86-98; Dir NSM Tr from 98; Can Llan Cathl from 02. *The Rectory, Peterston-super-Ely, Cardiff CF5 6LH* Tel (01446) 760297

YOUNG, Simon Robert. b 72. Trevelyan Coll Dur BSc94 Fitzw Coll Cam BA98. Westcott Ho Cam BA98 CTM99. **d** 99. C Plaistow St Mary *Roch* 99-00. *Address temp unknown*

YOUNG, Canon Stanley. b 14. St Jo Coll Dur BA36. Ely Th Coll 36. **d** 37 **p** 38. C Camberwell St Luke *S'wark* 37-40; Min Can Carl Cathl *Carl* 40-45; Warden St Anne's Ch Ho Soho 45-48; C Pimlico St Mary Graham-street *Lon* 48-50; Warden Pemb Coll Miss Walworth *S'wark* 50-53; V Aldermaston w Wasing *Ox* 53-69; RD Bradfield 63-68; V Long Crendon 70-80; P-in-c Chearsley w Nether Winchendon 77-80; V Long Crendon w Chearsley and Nether Winchendon 80-94; Hon Can Ch Ch 81-94; rtd 94. *clo J Neil Esq, Springs Medley, Shupps Lane, Chearsley, Aylesbury HP18 0DE* Tel (01844) 201087

YOUNG, Stephen. b 33. St Edm Hall Ox MA61. St Jo Coll Nottm 75 ALCD77. **d** 77 **p** 78. C Crofton *Portsm* 77-81; C Rainham *Chelmsf* 81-87; V Ramsgate Ch Ch and St Luke 87-98; rtd 98; Perm to Offic *Cant* from 98. *9 Egerton Drive, Cliftonville, Margate CT9 9YE* Tel (01843) 223071

YOUNG, Stephen Edward. b 52. K Coll Lon BD73 AKC73 Ch Ch Coll Cant CertEd74. **d** 75 **p** 76. C Walton St Mary *Liv* 75-79; C St Marylebone All SS *Lon* 83; C Pimlico St Gabr 83-85; Chapl Whitelands Coll of HE *S'wark* 85-88; Asst Chapl St Paul's Sch Barnes 88-91; Chapl 91-02; P in O from 91; Hon C Pimlico St Mary Bourne Street *Lon* from 94; Chapl Dulwich Coll from 02. *Dulwich College, Dulwich Common, London SE21 7LD* Tel (020) 8299 9218

YOUNG, Stuart Kincaid. b 59. **d** 95 **p** 96. C Letchworth St Paul w Willian *St Alb* 95-00; V Pucklechurch and Abson *Bris* from 00. *The Vicarage, Westerleigh Road, Pucklechurch, Bristol BS16 9RD* Tel 0117-937 2260

YOUNG, Walter Howlett. b 08. Clifton Th Coll 32. **d** 34 **p** 35. C Bath St Sav *B & W* 34-37; C Bath Abbey w St Jas 37-38; R Hinton Blewett 38-43; Chapl RNVR 43-46; Chapl HM Pris Leyhill 46-50; C Wraxall *B & W* 50-67; V Compton Dando 67-73; R Chelwood 67-73; rtd 73; Perm to Offic *B & W* 73-94. *Abbeyfield Extra Care House, 224 Redland Road, Bristol BS6 6YR* Tel 0117-973 5923

YOUNG, William Maurice. b 32. St Jo Coll Nottm 80. **d** 81 **p** 82. C Harlescott *Lich* 81-84; V Hadley 84-94; rtd 94; Perm to Offic *Heref* from 94. *Old Chapel School, Newport Street, Clun, Craven Arms SY7 8JZ* Tel (01588) 640846

YOUNGER, Jeremy Andrew. b 46. Nottm Univ BA68 Bris Univ MA71. Wells Th Coll 68. **d** 70 **p** 71. C Basingstoke *Win* 70-74; C Harpenden St Nic *St Alb* 74-76; Dir Communications 77-81; Chapl Sarum & Wells Th Coll 77-81; V Clifton All SS w St Jo *Bris* 81-84; Relig Affairs Producer BBC Radio Nottm *S'well* 84-86; C Bow w Bromley St Leon *Lon* 86-88; Projects and Min Manager Westmr St Jas 89-93; Hon C St Marylebone All SS 89-93; New Zealand from 93. *3 Punga Street, Mount Eden, Auckland 1003, New Zealand* Tel (0064) (9) 630 7867 or 379 0625 Fax 303 1302

YOUNGSON, David Thoms. b 38. Cuddesdon Coll 71. **d** 73 **p** 74. C Norton St Mary *Dur* 73-76; C Hartlepool St Paul 76-79; P-in-c Stockton St Jo *CD* 79-84; V Stockton St Jo 84-86; V Owton Manor 86-90; rtd 90; Perm to Offic *Dur* 90-99. *35 Buxton Gardens, Billingham TS22 5AJ*

YULE, John David. b 49. G&C Coll Cam BA70 MA74 PhD76. Westcott Ho Cam 79. **d** 81 **p** 82. C Cherry Hinton St Andr *Ely* 81-84; C Almondbury w Farnley Tyas *Wakef* 84-87; V Swavesey *Ely* 87-95; V Fen Drayton w Conington 87-95; R Fen Drayton w Conington and Lolworth etc from 95. *The Vicarage, Honey Hill, Fen Drayton, Cambridge CB4 5SF* Tel (01954) 231903 E-mail jdyule@argonet.co.uk

YULE, Robert White. b 49. FCMA81. St Jo Coll Nottm LTh88. **d** 88 **p** 89. C Wilford *S'well* 88-91; TV Bestwood 91-96; P-in-c Selston 96-98; V 98-00; C Watford St Pet *St Alb* from 00. *68 Tudor Avenue, Watford WD2 4NX* Tel (01923) 337002 or 337000

Z

ZACHAU, Eric. b 31. AKC57. **d** 58 **p** 59. C Bishopwearmouth St Mich *Dur* 58-62; C Ryhope 62-63; V Beadnell *Newc* 63-69; V Earsdon 69-81; V Bamburgh and Lucker 81-95; V Bamburgh and Beadnell 95-01; RD Bamburgh and Glendale 92-97; rtd 01; Perm to Offic *Newc* from 01. *Flat 4, Beadnell Hall, Beadnell, Chathill NE67 5AT* Tel (01665) 721802

ZAIR, Richard George. b 52. Newc Univ BSc74. Trin Coll Bris 75 St Jo Coll Dur 79. **d** 80 **p** 81. C Bishopsworth *Bris* 80-83; C New Malden and Coombe *S'wark* 83-91; Dir of Evang CPAS 91-99; Regional Dir from 99; Perm to Offic *Cov* from 91. *64 Kingsway, Leamington Spa CV31 3LE* Tel (01926) 424634 Fax 458459 E-mail rzair@cpas.org.uk

ZAMMIT, Mark Timothy Paul. b 60. Aston Tr Scheme 90 Sarum & Wells Th Coll 94. **d** 94 **p** 95. C Bitterne Park *Win* 94-98; TV Shaston *Sarum* 98-03; TR from 03; RD Blackmore Vale from 01; Chapl Port Regis Prep Sch from 99. *The Vicarage, Bittles Green, Motcombe, Shaftesbury SP7 9NX* Tel (01747) 851442 Fax as telephone E-mail markzammit@beeb.net

ZANDSTRA-HOUGH, Wendy Lorraine. **d** 00 **p** 01. C The Hague *Eur* 00-03. *Address temp unknown*

ZAPHIRIOU, Paul Victor. b 49. Hamilton Coll (NY) BA73. Wycliffe Hall Ox 00. **d** 02 **p** 03. C Holborn St Geo w H Trin and St Bart *Lon* from 02. *Flat 12, 95 Elm Park Gardens, London SW10 9QW* Tel (020) 7352 9235 Mobile 07899-796409 E-mail pzaphiriou@hotmail.com

ZAREK, Jennifer Hilary. b 51. Southn Univ MSc73 Newnham Coll Cam MA76 Southn Univ PhD78 Ox Univ BTh98 Garnett Coll Lon CertEd83 Lon Univ Dip Educn Mgt 87 Birkbeck Coll Lon DipRS91. St Steph Ho Ox 95. **d** 97 **p** 98. C Caterham *S'wark* 97-00; V Hutton Cranswick w Skerne, Watton and Beswick *York* from 00. *The Vicarage, 5 Howl Lane, Hutton Cranswick, Driffield YO25 9QA* Tel (01377) 270402 E-mail jzaek@beeb.net

ZASS-OGILVIE, Ian David. b 38. ARICS72 FRICS80. AKC65 St Boniface Warminster 65. **d** 66 **p** 67. C Washington *Dur* 66-70; Bp's Soc and Ind Adv for N Dur 70-73; Hon C Newc St Jo *Newc* 73-75; V Tynemouth St Jo 75-78; Hon C St Marylebone St Mary *Lon* 78-81; V Bromley St Jo *Roch* 81-84; R Keith *Mor* 84-88; R Huntly 84-88; R Aberchirder 84-88; R Edin St Pet *Edin* 88-00; Dir Churches' Regional Commn in the NE *Newc & Dur* from 00. *Ushaw College, Durham DH7 9RH* Tel 0191-373 5453 E-mail idzo@ricsonline.org or idzo.crcne@btinternet.com

ZEAL, Stanley Allan. b 33. Leeds Univ BA55. Coll of Resurr Mirfield. **d** 57 **p** 58. C Perry Hill St Geo *S'wark* 57-61; C Cobham *Guildf* 61-64; V Ash Vale 64-69; R Ash 64-69; Chapl Northfield Hosp Aldershot 69-98; V Aldershot St Mich *Guildf* 69-98; rtd 98. *68 Church Road, Seven Sisters, Neath SA10 9DT* Tel (01439) 700726

ZIETSMAN, Sheila. **d** 90 **p** 91. C Geashill w Killeigh and Ballycommon *M & K* 90-91; C Mullingar, Portnashangan, Moyliscar, Kilbixy etc 91-96; Chapl Wilson's Hosp Sch Multyfarnham 91-96; Chapl E Glendalough Sch from 96. *The Old Forge, Glanmore, Ashford, Co Wicklow, Irish Republic* Tel (00353) (404) 42878 Fax as telephone

ZIHNI, Andrew Stephen. b 77. Mert Coll Ox BA99. St Steph Ho Ox BA01. **d** 02 **p** 03. C Goldthorpe w Hickleton *Sheff* from 02. *Church House, 3 West Street, Goldthorpe, Rotherham S63 9JU* Tel (01709) 881468 Mobile 07967-390010 E-mail father_andrew_zihni@oratorium.zzn.com

ZIPFEL, Marilyn Ellen. b 48. **d** 03. OLM Oulton Broad *Nor* from 03. *Rozel, Station Road, Lowestoft NR32 4QF*

ZORAB, Mark Elston. b 53. FRICS77 MRAC75. Mon Dioc Tr Scheme 92. **d** 94. NSM Itton and St Arvans w Penterry and Kilgwrrwg etc *Mon* from 94. *Oak Cottage, Itton Road, Chepstow NP16 6BQ* Tel (01291) 626222 or 672138

ZOTOV, Mrs Carolyn Ann. b 47. Lady Mabel Coll CertEd68 Open Univ 78 Nottm Univ Dip Special Educn 86. EMMTC 91. **d** 92 **p** 94. NSM Hykeham *Linc* 92-94; NSM Aisthorpe w Scampton w Thorpe le Fallows etc 94; C Ingham w Cammeringham w Fillingham 94-97; C Linc Minster Gp 97-01; rtd 01; Assoc P Nettleham *Linc* from 01. *Greenleaves, 1 The Drive, Church Lane, Lincoln LN2 1QR* Tel (01522) 525435 E-mail caz@greenleaves.fsnet.co.uk

ZUCCA, Peter Rennie. b 43. **d** 96 **p** 97. NSM Spotland *Man* 96-99; NSM Bamford from 99; NSM Rochdale St Geo w St Alb from 99. *19 Judith Street, Rochdale OL12 7HS* Tel (01706) 359327

ZWALF, Willem Anthony Louis (Wim). b 46. AKC68. **d** 71 **p** 72. C Fulham St Etheldreda w St Clem *Lon* 71-74; Chapl City Univ 74-78; R Coalbrookdale, Iron-Bridge and Lt Wenlock *Heref* 78-90; V Wisbech SS Pet and Paul *Ely* from 90; P-in-c Wisbech St Aug from 03; RD Wisbech Lynn Marshland from 02. *The Vicarage, Love Lane, Wisbech PE13 1HP* Tel (01945) 583559 or 582508 Fax 466686 E-mail wimzwalf@cwcom.net or wimzwalf@aol.com

DEACONESSES

The biographies of women clergy are to be found in the preceding section.

BENNETT, Miss Doreen. b 29. St Mich Ho Ox 60. **dss** 79. Moreton *Ches* 79-80; Dewsbury Moor *Wakef* 80-86; Germany 86-91; rtd 89; Perm to Offic *Blackb* 95-02. *15 Stuart Court, High Street, Kibworth, Leicester LE8 0LR* Tel 0116-279 6885

BLACKBURN, Mary Paterson. b 16. St Chris Coll Blackheath 45 Wm Temple Coll Rugby 59. **dss** 76. Sawston *Ely* 74-78; rtd 78. *3 Stuart Court, High Street, Kibworth, Leicester LE8 0LR* Tel 0116-279 6324

BRIERLY, Margaret Ann. b 32. Dalton Ho Bris 54. **dss** 85. Wreningham *Nor* 85-86; Tetsworth, Adwell w S Weston, Lewknor etc *Ox* 86-95; rtd 95; Perm to Offic *Blackb* from 03. *13 Pinewood Avenue, Brookhouse, Lancaster LA2 9NU*

BUTLER, Miss Ann. b 41. St Mich Ho Ox 67 Dalton Ho Bris IDC69. **dss** 82. Bucknall and Bagnall *Lich* 82-87; Leyton St Mary w St Edw *Chelmsf* 89-97; Leyton St Mary w St Edw and St Luke 97-02; rtd 02. *40 Lichfield Street, Stone ST15 8NB* Tel (01785) 818160

BYATT, Margaret Nelly. b 18. Bedf Coll Lon BA40. Lon Bible Coll DipTh50 Gilmore Ho 59. **dss** 62. Chelsea St Luke *Lon* 60-63; St Helier *S'wark* 63-66; Lee Gd Shep w St Pet 66-78; rtd 78. *41 Woodlands, Overton, Basingstoke RG25 3HW* Tel (01256) 770347

COOPER, Janet Pamela. b 46. Glos Coll of Educn TCert67 Ox Poly CETD79. Trin Coll Bris DipHE83. **dss** 83. Patchway *Bris* 83-88; Perm to Offic *Glouc* 90-96. *Ephraim Cottage, Kington Mead Farm, Kington Road, Thornbury, Bristol BS35 1PQ* Tel (01454) 414202

DEE, Mary. b 21. St Chris Coll Blackheath 55. **dss** 64. Shottermill *Guildf* 63-66; Bishop's Waltham *Portsm* 66-72; Cumnor *Ox* 75-81; rtd 81. *Flat 4, 45 Oxford Avenue, Bournemouth BH6 5HT* Tel (01202) 424240

DOROTHY, Sister. *See* WARR, Sister Dorothy Lilian Patricia

DUCKERING, Alice Muriel. b 07. Gilmore Ho 43. **dss** 46. USPG 45-70; Kegworth *Leic* 71-77; rtd 77. *23 Stuart Court, High Street, Kibworth, Leicester LE8 0LR*

ESSAM, Susan Catherine. b 46. Southn Univ BA67 CertEd68. Linc Th Coll DipTh74. **dss** 80. Pershore w Pinvin, Wick and Birlingham *Worc* 78-82; CMS Nigeria from 83. *Bishopscourt, PO Box 6283, Jos, Plateau State, Nigeria* Tel (00234) (73) 612221 E-mail jos@anglican.skannet.com.ng

EVANS (née CHERRETT), Mrs Diana. b 59. Somerville Coll Ox BA81 MA85 Warwick Univ CertEd96. St Steph Ho Ox 81. **dss** 84. Sherborne w Castleton and Lillington *Sarum* 84-88; Northampton St Paul *Pet* 93-98; Sec Dioc Adv Cttee from 94; Lic to Offic from 98. *The Rectory, London Road, Uppingham, Oakham LE15 9TJ* Tel (01572) 823381 E-mail diana.evans@peterborough-diocese.org.uk

FINDER, Miss Patricia Constance. b 30. Dalton Ho Bris 63. **dss** 71. Clapham St Jas *S'wark* 79-90; rtd 90. *5 Castle Gate, Ilkley LS29 8DF* Tel (01943) 607023

FISH, Margaret. b 18. St Mich Ho Ox 49. **dss** 77. Perm to Offic *Nor* 78-89. *35 Ashwell Court, Norwich NR5 9BS* Tel (01603) 746123

FROST, Constance Mary. b 09. Gilmore Ho 34. **dss** 37. Walworth St Jo *S'wark* 36-40; Fenton *Lich* 41-47; St Wyrley 47-49; Bilston 49-73; rtd 73; Perm to Offic *Chich* from 73. *17 Church Way, Worthing BN13 1HD* Tel (01903) 201596

GOUGH, Mrs Janet Ainley. b 46. SRN RSCN SCM Lon Univ CertRK73. Trin Coll Bris 70. **dss** 76. Leic H Apostles *Leic* 73-80; USA 80-81; Perm to Offic *Leic* 81-96. *410 Hinckley Road, Leicester LE3 0WA* Tel 0116-285 4284 Fax as telephone

GREAVES, Dorothea Mary. b 16. St Denys Warminster 39. **dss** 62. Willesden St Andr *Lon* 63-76; rtd 76; Perm to Offic *Chich* from 76. *St Peter's Grange, 24 Maze Hill, St Leonards-on-Sea TN37 6HZ*

GRIERSON, Miss Janet. b 13. Westf Coll Lon BA34. Lambeth STh37 MA82 Greyladies Coll 34 K Coll Lon 34. **dss** 48. Vice-Prin Gilmore Ho 48-55; Prin 55-60; Lect Div St Mary's Coll Ban 62-63; Prin Lect RE Summerfield Coll Kidderminster 63-75; rtd 75; Perm to Offic *Worc* from 75. *8 Parkview, Abbey Road, Malvern WR14 3HG* Tel (01684) 569341

HAMBLY, Miss Winifred Kathleen. b 18. Lambeth DipTh55 Gilmore Ho 54. **dss** 55. Cricklewood St Pet *Lon* 55-78; Eastbourne St Mich *Chich* from 78. *4 Tutts Barn Court, Tutts Barn Lane, Eastbourne BN22 8XP* Tel (01323) 640735

HAMILTON, Miss Pamela Moorhead. b 43. SRN64 SCM66. Trin Coll Bris DipTh75. **dss** 77. Derby St Pet and Ch Ch w H Trin *Derby* 77-84; Bedworth *Cov* from 85; rtd 03. *10 William Street, Bedworth, Nuneaton CV12 9QN* Tel 024 7649 1608

HARRIS, Audrey Margaret. *See* STOKES, Audrey Margaret

HARRISON, Mrs Ann. b 55. Ex Univ BSc77. Linc Th Coll DipHE81. **dss** 82. Acomb H Redeemer *York* 82-83; Lic to Offic

Wakef 83-91. *The Vicarage, Church Hill, Easingwold, York YO61 3JT* Tel (01347) 821394

HEWITT, Miss Joyce Evelyn. b 30. SRN51 SCM55. St Mich Ho Ox IDC61. **dss** 67. Spitalfields Ch Ch w All SS *Lon* 67-70; CMJ 71-73; Canonbury St Steph *Lon* 73-75; Chorleywood RNIB Coll for Blind Girls 75-80; rtd 90. *38 Ashridge Court, Station Road, Newbury RG14 7LL* Tel (01635) 47829

HIDER, Ms Margaret Joyce Barbara. b 25. St Mich Ho Ox 52. **dss** 77. Bris H Cross Inns Court *Bris* 77-84; Uphill *B & W* 84-89; rtd 89; Perm to Offic *B & W* from 89. *Bethany, 8 Uphill Way, Weston-super-Mare BS23 4TH* Tel (01934) 414191

HINDE, Miss Mavis Mary. b 29. Lightfoot Ho Dur. **dss** 65. Hitchin St Mary *St Alb* 65-68; Ensbury *Sarum* 69-70; Portsea St Alb *Portsm* 70-76; Houghton Regis *St Alb* 77-85; Eaton Socon 85-94; rtd 94; Perm to Offic *Ely* from 94. *8 Burnt Close, Eynesbury, St Neots PE19 2LZ* Tel (01480) 218219

HORNBY-NORTHCOTE, Mrs Vivien Sheena. b 42. Birkbeck Coll Lon BA91 Warwick Univ MA96. Gilmore Course 74. **dss** 79. Mitcham St Olave *S'wark* 79-81; St Dunstan in the West *Lon* 82-86; St Marg Lothbury and St Steph Coleman Street etc 86; rtd 98. *3 Priory Mews, Sidney Street, Cheltenham GL52 6DJ* Tel (01242) 525659

HOWARD, Jean Elizabeth. b 37. Man Univ BA59 Univ of Wales (Cardiff) TDip61 Lon Univ DipTh BD86. St Mich Ho Ox 61. **dss** 82. Hanger Lane St Ann *Lon* 82-84; Dagenham *Chelmsf* 88-90; Perm to Offic from 90; rtd 97. *99 Kitchener Road, London E17 4LJ* Tel (020) 8527 3013

KELLY, Miss Philippa. b 14. St Chris Coll Blackheath 37. **dss** 61. Malaya 61-63; Singapore 63-64; Sheldon *Birm* 64-69; Jamaica 69-71; Kidderminster St Mary *Worc* 72-75; rtd 75. *Dulverton Hall, St Martin's Square, Scarborough YO11 2DB* Tel (01723) 501806

MacCORMACK, Mrs June Elizabeth. b 45. LNSM course 82 St Jo Coll Nottm 85. **dss** 86. Bieldside *Ab* from 86. *5 Overton Park, Dyce, Aberdeen AB21 7FT* Tel (01224) 722691 Fax as telephone E-mail jadm1@aol.com

MOORE (née STOWE), Mrs Ann Jessica Margaret. b 41. St Mich Ho Ox. **dss** 87. Watford *St Alb* 87-88; Spitalfields Ch Ch w All SS *Lon* 88-89; rtd 89. *168 Thorpe Road, Kirby Cross, Frinton-on-Sea CO13 0NQ* Tel (01255) 851933

MOORHOUSE, Olga Marian. b 28. Dalton Ho Bris 54. **dss** 63. Wolverhampton St Matt *Lich* 62-68; Fazakerley Em *Liv* 68-70; Huyton St Geo 70-76; Blurton *Lich* 76-88; rtd 88. *37 Rosalind Grove, Wednesfield, Wolverhampton WV11 3RZ* Tel (01902) 630128

MORGAN, Beryl. b 19. Dalton Ho Bris 47. **dss** 77. Princess Marg Hosp Swindon 69-79; rtd 79. *Ty Clyd, 120 Beacons Park, Brecon LD3 9BP* Tel (01874) 622398

MULLER, Louise Irmgard. b 12. **dss** 64. Prestonville St Luke *Chich* 65-72; rtd 73; Perm to Offic *Chich* from 73. *24 Clifton Road, Worthing BN11 4DP* Tel (01903) 206541

NORTHCOTE, Vivien. *See* HORNBY-NORTHCOTE, Mrs Vivien Sheena

OBEE, Sister Monica May. b 37. **dss** 82. Radford *Cov* 82-97; rtd 97. *14 The Hill, Walsingham NR22 6DF* Tel (01328) 821033

OLIVER, Miss Kathleen Joyce. b 44. Man Univ BA65. N Ord Course 80. **dss** 83. Littleborough *Man* from 83. *Littleborough Christian Centre, Todmorden Road, Littleborough OL15 9EA* Tel (01706) 376477 Fax 375520

OLPHIN, Miss Maureen Rose. b 30. Lon Univ BSc Sheff Univ DipEd Man Univ DipTh. **dss** 84. Sheff St Barn and St Mary *Sheff* 84-90; rtd 90. *41A Queen Street, Mosborough, Sheffield S20 5BP* Tel 0114-247 3009

PATRICK, Ruby Olivia. b 16. Gilmore Ho 69. **dss** 72. E Ham w Upton Park *Chelmsf* 72-74; Becontree St Elisabeth 74-75; Trinidad and Tobago 75-82; rtd 82. *41A New River Crescent, London N13 5RD* Tel (020) 8882 5146

PIERSON, Mrs Valerie Susan (Sue). b 44. CertEd65. Trin Coll Bris 76. **dss** 79. Fulham St Matt *Lon* from 79. *48 Peterborough Road, London SW6 3EB* Tel (020) 7731 6544 Fax 7731 1858 E-mail lance@pierson69.freeserve.co.uk

PLATT, Marjorie. b 18. Qu Coll Birm 76. **dss** 78. Hinckley St Mary *Leic* 78-91; Burbage w Aston Flamville from 91. *216 Brookside, Burbage, Hinckley LE10 2TW* Tel (01455) 233928

POLLARD, Shirley Ann. b 27. Wm Temple Coll Rugby 67 Cranmer Hall Dur 69. **dss** 84. Cramlington *Newc* 78-85; rtd 85; Perm to Offic *Worc* from 85. *3 Buttermere Drive, Worcester WR4 9HX* Tel (01905) 610724

PRICE, Mrs Patricia Kate Lunn. *See* SCHMIEGELOW, Patricia Kate Lunn

RAINEY, Miss Irene May. b 14. RSCN36 SCM38. Gilmore Ho 69. **dss** 72. Filton *Bris* 70-74; Crowthorne *Ox* 74-79; rtd 79;

897

Perm to Offic *Ely* from 80. *12 Stevens Close, Cottenham, Cambridge CB4 8TT* Tel (01954) 251634

ROBINSON, Philippa. b 09. R Holloway Coll Lon BA31 Nottm Univ Cert Th & Past Studies 76. **dss** 75. Branksome St Aldhelm *Sarum* 76-83; Lic to Offic from 83; Tutor Bp's Cert 84-86. *6 Lindum Court, Poole Road, Branksome BH12 1AS* Tel (01202) 769493

SAMPSON, Miss Hazel. b 35. Lightfoot Ho Dur 58. **dss** 64. Fenton *Lich* 64-67; Gt Wyrley 67-69; Chapl Asst Manor Hosp Walsall 69-76; Lich St Mary w St Mich 76-95; rtd 95; Perm to Offic *Lich* from 95. *107 Walsall Road, Lichfield WS13 8DD* Tel (01543) 419664

SCHMIEGELOW, Patricia Kate Lunn. b 37. St Mich Ho Ox IDC65. **dss** 86. The Hague *Eur* 86-89; Perm to Offic *Glouc* from 90; Gen Sec ICS 92-97; rtd 97. *Waterside, Coln St Aldwyns, Cirencester GL7 5AJ* Tel (01285) 750218 Fax as telephone

SELWOOD, Miss Eveline Mary. b 34. **dss** 76. Huddersfield St Jo *Wakef* 76-79; King Cross 79-85; rtd 94; Perm to Offic *Wakef* from 94. *27 Alverthorpe Road, Wakefield WF2 9NW* Tel (01924) 378364

SILL, Grace Mary. b 11. St Chris Coll Blackheath 53. **dss** 62. Lawrence Weston *Bris* 55-63; Southmead Hosp Bris 63-77; rtd 77; Perm to Offic *Bris* 77-87. *10 Tyndale Court, Chertsey Road, Bristol BS6 6NF* Tel 0117-973 2903

SKINNER, Elizabeth Alice. b 53. **dss** 82. Bourne *Guildf* 82-84. *The Manse, 27 King's Road, Fleet GU13 9AF* Tel (01252) 615903

SPROSON, Doreen. b 31. St Mich Ho Ox IDC58. **dss** 70. Wandsworth St Mich *S'wark* 68-71; Women's Sec CMS 71-74; Goole *Sheff* 74-76; Kirby Muxloe *Leic* 76-77; Perm to Offic *S'wark* 85-97; rtd 91. *20 Huggens' College, College Road, Northfleet, Gravesend DA11 9LL* Tel (01474) 325262

STOKES, Audrey Margaret. b 39. Dalton Ho Bris 68. **dss** 82. Collier Row St Jas *Chelmsf* 82-85; Woking St Mary *Guildf* 85-95; rtd 95. *1 Greet Park Close, Southwell NG25 0EE*

STOWE, Ann Jessica Margaret. *See* MOORE, Mrs Ann Jessica Margaret

SYMES, Miss Annabel. b 41. AIMLS68. S Dios Minl Tr Scheme 79. **dss** 85. Chapl Asst Salisbury Health Care NHS Trust from 85; Barford St Martin, Dinton, Baverstock etc *Sarum* 89-01; Nadder Valley from 01. *7 Shaftesbury Road, Barford St Martin, Salisbury SP3 4BL* Tel (01722) 744110

TAYLOR, Muriel. b 28. CA Tr Coll 48. **dss** 76. Gateshead Fell *Dur* 76-86; Gateshead Harlow Green 86-88; rtd 88. *18 Beechwood Avenue, Gateshead NE9 6PP* Tel 0191-487 6902

THUMWOOD, Janet Elizabeth. b 30. STh60 DipRE61. Trin Coll Toronto 58. **dss** 62. Canada 62-63; Mile End Old Town H Trin *Lon* 63-65; CSF 66-77; rtd 90. *66 Headley Grove, Tadworth KT20 5JF* Tel (01737) 371076

TURNER, Miss Rosie (Poppy). b 22. St Mich Ho Ox 56. **dss** 61. Hornsey Rise St Mary *Lon* 61-62; Wealdstone H Trin 62-70; CMJ 71-72; CMS 73-74; Dss Ho Hindhead 74-76; Sutton Ch Ch *S'wark* 77-80; rtd 80. *Bungalow 16, Huggens' College, College Road, Northfleet, Gravesend DA11 9DL* Tel (01474) 357722

WARR, Sister Dorothy Lilian Patricia. b 14. Selly Oak Coll 38. **dss** 53. St Etheldreda's Children's Home Bedf 51-59; CSA from 53; Goldington *St Alb* 54-59; S'wark St Sav w All Hallows *S'wark* 59-65; St Mich Convalescent Home Westgate-on-Sea 65-74; rtd 75. *37 Spinners Court, Queen Street, Lancaster LA1 1RY* Tel (01524) 845613

WEBB, Sybil Janet. b 20. SRN42 SCM43. Gilmore Course 69. **dss** 77. Worthing St Geo *Chich* 77-80; rtd 80; Perm to Offic *Chich* from 80. *42 Ham Road, Worthing BN11 2QX* Tel (01903) 202997

WRIGHT, Edith Mary. b 22. St Hugh's Coll Ox MA46 DipEd46. Gilmore Ho STh58. **dss** 61. St Marylebone St Mary *Lon* 58-71; Lect Linc Th Coll 71-73; Oatlands *Guildf* 73-76; Roehampton H Trin *S'wark* 76-82; rtd 82. *26 Hazelwood Close, Harrow HA2 6HD* Tel 0181-863 7320

WRIGHT, Gloria Mary. b 40. **dss** 83. Smethwick St Matt w St Chad *Birm* 83-84; Tottenham H Trin *Lon* 84-86; rtd 00. *21 St Stephens Hill, Launceston PL15 8HN* Tel (01566) 776691

DIOCESAN, AREA, SUFFRAGAN AND ASSISTANT BISHOPS AND PROVINCIAL EPISCOPAL VISITORS IN ENGLAND, WALES, SCOTLAND AND IRELAND

BATH AND WELLS
Bishop of Bath and Wells — P B PRICE
Honorary Assistant Bishops — J R G NEALE
W M D PERSSON
R H M THIRD
J S WALLER
P E BARBER
B ROGERSON
R F SAINSBURY
Suffragan Bishop of Taunton — A J RADFORD

BIRMINGHAM
Bishop of Birmingham — J M SENTAMU
Honorary Assistant Bishops — A C DUMPER
A P HALL
M H D WHINNEY
M SANTER
M W SINCLAIR
Suffragan Bishop of Aston — J M AUSTIN

BLACKBURN
Bishop of Blackburn — A D CHESTERS
Honorary Assistant Bishop — M E VICKERS
Suffragan Bishop of Burnley — J W GODDARD
Suffragan Bishop of Lancaster — G S PEDLEY

BRADFORD
Bishop of Bradford — D C JAMES
Honorary Assistant Bishops — M W JARRETT
D N DE L YOUNG

BRISTOL
Bishop of Bristol — M A HILL
Honorary Assistant Bishops — J R G NEALE
P ST G VAUGHAN
Suffragan Bishop of Swindon — M D DOE

CANTERBURY
Archbishop of Canterbury, Primate — R D WILLIAMS
of All England and Metropolitan
Honorary Assistant Bishops — M F GEAR
R D SAY
A M A TURNBULL
Suffragan Bishop of Dover — S S VENNER
Suffragan Bishop of Maidstone — G A CRAY
Suffragan Bishop of Ebbsfleet — A BURNHAM
(Provincial Episcopal Visitor)
Suffragan Bishop of Richborough — K NEWTON
(Provincial Episcopal Visitor)

CARLISLE
Bishop of Carlisle — G G DOW
Honorary Assistant Bishops — I M GRIGGS
G L HACKER
G H THOMPSON
Suffragan Bishop of Penrith — J W S NEWCOME

CHELMSFORD
Bishop of Chelmsford — J W GLADWIN
Honorary Assistant Bishops — J M BALL
J N JOHNSON
Area Bishop of Barking — D J L HAWKINS
Area Bishop of Bradwell — L A GREEN
Area Bishop of Colchester — C H MORGAN

CHESTER
Bishop of Chester — P R FORSTER
Honorary Assistant Bishops — W A PWAISIHO
A L WINSTANLEY
C F BAZLEY
D S SHEPPARD
Suffragan Bishop of Birkenhead — D A URQUHART
Suffragan Bishop of Stockport — W N STOCK

CHICHESTER
Bishop of Chichester — J W HIND
Honorary Assistant Bishops — C C LUXMOORE
M GREEN
M H ST J MADDOCKS
M E ADIE
M R J MANKTELOW
M E MARSHALL
D P WILCOX
Area Bishop of Horsham — L G URWIN
Area Bishop of Lewes — W P BENN

COVENTRY
Bishop of Coventry — C J BENNETTS
Honorary Assistant Bishop — D R J EVANS
Suffragan Bishop of Warwick — A M PRIDDIS

DERBY
Bishop of Derby — J S BAILEY
Honorary Assistant Bishop — R M C BEAK
Suffragan Bishop of Repton — D C HAWTIN

DURHAM
Bishop of Durham — N T WRIGHT
Honorary Assistant Bishop — S W SYKES
Suffragan Bishop of Jarrow — J L PRITCHARD

ELY
Bishop of Ely — A J RUSSELL
Honorary Assistant Bishops — R L FISHER
S BARRINGTON-WARD
P S DAWES
J B TAYLOR
Suffragan Bishop of Huntingdon — J G INGE

EXETER
Bishop of Exeter — M L LANGRISH
Honorary Assistant Bishops — R F CARTWRIGHT
I C DOCKER
Suffragan Bishop of Crediton — R S HAWKINS
Suffragan Bishop of Plymouth — J H GARTON

GLOUCESTER
Bishop of Gloucester — D E BENTLEY
Honorary Assistant Bishops — M A MANN
J R G NEALE
E ST Q WALL
Suffragan Bishop of Tewkesbury — J S WENT

GUILDFORD
Bishop of Guildford — J W GLADWIN
Suffragan Bishop of Dorking — I J BRACKLEY

HEREFORD
Bishop of Hereford — J K OLIVER
Suffragan Bishop of Ludlow — M W HOOPER

LEICESTER
Bishop of Leicester — T J STEVENS

LICHFIELD
Bishop of Lichfield — J M GLEDHILL
Honorary Assistant Bishop — R O BOWLBY
Area Bishop of Shrewsbury — A G C SMITH
Area Bishop of Stafford — C J HILL
Area Bishop of Wolverhampton — M G BOURKE

LINCOLN
Bishop of Lincoln — J C SAXBEE
Honorary Assistant Bishops — J E BROWN
P B HARRIS
D G SNELGROVE
D TUSTIN
Suffragan Bishop of Grantham — A L J REDFERN
Suffragan Bishop of Grimsby — D D J ROSSDALE

LIVERPOOL
Bishop of Liverpool — J S JONES
Honorary Assistant Bishops — J W ROXBURGH
I C STUART
Suffragan Bishop of Warrington — D W M JENNINGS

LONDON
Bishop of London — R J C CHARTRES
Honorary Assistant Bishops — D S ARDEN
M A BAUGHEN
E HOLLAND
M E MARSHALL
M A P WOOD
Area Bishop of Edmonton — P W WHEATLEY
Suffragan Bishop of Fulham — J C BROADHURST
Area Bishop of Kensington — M J COLCLOUGH
Area Bishop of Stepney — S J OLIVER
Area Bishop of Willesden — P A BROADBENT

MANCHESTER
Bishop of Manchester — N S MCCULLOCH
Suffragan Bishop of Hulme — S R LOWE

Suffragan Bishop of Middleton	M A O LEWIS
Suffragan Bishop of Bolton	D K GILLETT

NEWCASTLE
Bishop of Newcastle	J M WHARTON
Assistant Bishops	P RICHARDSON
	K E GILL

NORWICH
Bishop of Norwich	G R JAMES
Honorary Assistant Bishops	E N DEVENPORT
	D LEAKE
	M J MENIN
Suffragan Bishop of Lynn	A C FOOTTIT
Suffragan Bishop of Thetford	D J ATKINSON

OXFORD
Bishop of Oxford	R D HARRIES
Honorary Assistant Bishops	A R M GORDON
	S E VERNEY
	A K CRAGG
	J F E BONE
	W J D DOWN
Area Bishop of Buckingham	A T L WILSON
Area Bishop of Dorchester	C W FLETCHER
Area Bishop of Reading	*vacant*

PETERBOROUGH
Bishop of Peterborough	I P M CUNDY
Honorary Assistant Bishop	J R FLACK
Suffragan Bishop of Brixworth	F WHITE

PORTSMOUTH
Bishop of Portsmouth	K W STEVENSON
Honorary Assistant Bishops	M E ADIE
	H D HALSEY

RIPON AND LEEDS
Bishop of Ripon and Leeds	J R PACKER
Honorary Assistant Bishops	R EMMERSON
	D E JENKINS
Suffragan Bishop of Knaresborough	*vacant*

ROCHESTER
Bishop of Rochester	M J NAZIR-ALI
Honorary Assistant Bishop	M F GEAR
Suffragan Bishop of Tonbridge	B C CASTLE

ST ALBANS
Bishop of St Albans	C W HERBERT
Honorary Assistant Bishops	D J FARMBROUGH
	R J N SMITH
Suffragan Bishop of Bedford	R N INWOOD
Suffragan Bishop of Hertford	C R J FOSTER

ST EDMUNDSBURY AND IPSWICH
Bishop of St Edmundsbury and Ipswich	J H R LEWIS
Suffragan Bishop of Dunwich	C YOUNG

SALISBURY
Bishop of Salisbury	D S STANCLIFFE
Honorary Assistant Bishops	J K CAVELL
	J D G KIRKHAM
Area Bishop of Ramsbury	P F HULLAH
Area Bishop of Sherborne	T M THORNTON

SHEFFIELD
Bishop of Sheffield	J NICHOLLS
Honorary Assistant Bishops	D M HALLATT
	K H PILLAR
Suffragan Bishop of Doncaster	C G ASHTON

SODOR AND MAN
Bishop of Sodor and Man	*vacant*

SOUTHWARK
Bishop of Southwark	T F BUTLER
Honorary Assistant Bishops	H W MONTEFIORE
	M K RUMALSHAH
Area Bishop of Kingston-upon-Thames	R I CHEETHAM
Area Bishop of Woolwich	C O BUCHANAN
Area Bishop of Croydon	N BAINES

SOUTHWELL
Bishop of Southwell	G H CASSIDY
Honorary Assistant Bishops	R J MILNER
	J T FINNEY
	J W H FLAGG
	R K WILLIAMSON
Suffragan Bishop of Sherwood	A W MORGAN

TRURO
Bishop of Truro	W IND
Suffragan Bishop of St Germans	R SCREECH

WAKEFIELD
Bishop of Wakefield	S G PLATTEN
Honorary Assistant Bishop	R A M GENDERS
Suffragan Bishop of Pontefract	A W ROBINSON

WINCHESTER
Bishop of Winchester	M C SCOTT-JOYNT
Honorary Assistant Bishops	H B DEHQANI-TAFTI
	L L REES
	E R BARNES
Suffragan Bishop of Basingstoke	T WILLMOTT
Suffragan Bishop of Southampton	J M GLEDHILL

WORCESTER
Bishop of Worcester	P S M SELBY
Honorary Assistant Bishop	K J WOOLLCOMBE
Suffragan Bishop of Dudley	D S WALKER

YORK
Archbishop of York, Primate of England and Metropolitan	D M HOPE
Honorary Assistant Bishops	C C BARKER
	R G G FOLEY
	D G GALLIFORD
	M HENSHALL
	N D JONES
	D R LUNN
	D J SMITH
Suffragan Bishop of Hull	R M C FRITH
Suffragan Bishop of Selby	*vacant*
Suffragan Bishop of Whitby	R S LADDS
Suffragan Bishop of Beverley (Provincial Episcopal Visitor)	M W JARRETT

EUROPE
Bishop of Gibraltar in Europe	D G ROWELL
Suffragan Bishop in Europe	D HAMID
Honorary Assistant Bishops	J W ROWTHORN
	J G VOBBE
	A W M WEEKES
	D P dos S de PINA CABRAL
	R GARRARD
	I HARLAND
	P B HARRIS
	E HOLLAND
	C LOPEZ LOZANO
	M R J MANKTELOW
	A F B ROGERS
	A SANCHEZ
	F P SARGEANT
	D J SMITH
	F L SOARES
	J B TAYLOR
	P W WHALON
	H F de WAAL

CHURCH IN WALES

ST ASAPH
Bishop of St Asaph — J S DAVIES

BANGOR
Bishop of Bangor — F J S DAVIES

ST DAVIDS
Bishop of St Davids — C N COOPER

LLANDAFF
Bishop of Llandaff and Archbishop of Wales — B C MORGAN

MONMOUTH
Bishop of Monmouth — E W M WALKER

SWANSEA AND BRECON
Bishop of Swansea and Brecon — A E PIERCE

SCOTTISH EPISCOPAL CHURCH

ABERDEEN AND ORKNEY
Bishop of Aberdeen and Orkney and Primus — A B CAMERON

ARGYLL AND THE ISLES
Bishop of Argyll and the Isles — D M CAMERON

BRECHIN
Bishop of Brechin — N CHAMBERLAIN

EDINBURGH
Bishop of Edinburgh — B A SMITH
Honorary Assistant Bishop

GLASGOW AND GALLOWAY
Bishop of Glasgow and Galloway — I JONES

MORAY, ROSS AND CAITHNESS
Bishop of Moray, Ross and Caithness — J M CROOK

ST ANDREWS, DUNKELD AND DUNBLANE
Bishop of St Andrews, Dunkeld and Dunblane — M H G HENLEY

CHURCH OF IRELAND

ARMAGH
Archbishop of Armagh and Primate of All Ireland and Metropolitan — R H A EAMES

CASHEL AND OSSORY
Bishop of Cashel and Ossory — P F BARRETT

CLOGHER
Bishop of Clogher — M G ST A JACKSON

CONNOR
Bishop of Connor — A E T HARPER

CORK, CLOYNE AND ROSS
Bishop of Cork, Cloyne and Ross — W P COLTON

DERRY AND RAPHOE
Bishop of Derry and Raphoe — K R GOOD

DOWN AND DROMORE
Bishop of Down and Dromore — H C MILLER

DUBLIN AND GLENDALOUGH
Archbishop of Dublin, Bishop of Glendalough, Primate of Ireland and Metropolitan — J R W NEILL

KILMORE, ELPHIN AND ARDAGH
Bishop of Kilmore, Elphin and Ardagh — K H CLARKE

LIMERICK AND KILLALOE
Bishop of Limerick and Killaloe — M H G MAYES

MEATH AND KILDARE
Bishop of Meath and Kildare — R L CLARKE

TUAM, KILLALA AND ACHONRY
Bishop of Tuam, Killala and Achonry — R C A HENDERSON

BISHOPS IN THE HOUSE OF LORDS

The Archbishops of Canterbury and York, and the Bishops of London, Durham and Winchester always have seats in the House of Lords. Twenty-one of the remaining Diocesan Bishops also sit in the Upper House, and they do so according to their dates of seniority. When a vacancy arises, it is filled by the senior Diocesan Bishop without a seat. Translation of a Bishop from one See to another does not affect his right to sit in the House of Lords.

The Bishop of Sodor and Man and the Bishop of Gibraltar in Europe are not eligible to sit in the House of Lords, but the former has a seat in the Upper House of the Tynwald, Isle of Man.

ARCHBISHOPS

	Enthroned	Entered House of Lords
CANTERBURY	2003	2003
YORK	1995	1990

BISHOPS SITTING IN THE HOUSE OF LORDS
(as at 1 December 2003)

	Became Diocesan Bishop	Entered House of Lords
LONDON	1995	1996
DURHAM	2003	2003
WINCHESTER	1995	1996
OXFORD	1987	1993
SOUTHWARK	1991	1997
MANCHESTER	1992	1997
SALISBURY	1993	1998
ROCHESTER	1994	1999
CHELMSFORD	1994	1999
PORTSMOUTH	1995	1999
DERBY	1995	1999
ST ALBANS	1995	1999
PETERBOROUGH	1996	2001
CHESTER	1996	2001
ST EDMUNDSBURY AND IPSWICH	1997	2002
TRURO	1997	2002
WORCESTER	1997	2002
NEWCASTLE	1997	2003
SHEFFIELD	1997	2003
COVENTRY	1998	2003
LIVERPOOL	1998	2003
LEICESTER	1999	2003
SOUTHWELL	1999	2003
NORWICH	1999	awaiting introduction

BISHOPS AWAITING SEATS IN THE HOUSE OF LORDS
(in order of seniority)

	Became Diocesan Bishop
EXETER	2000
RIPON AND LEEDS	2000
ELY	2000
CARLISLE	2000
CHICHESTER	2001
LINCOLN	2001
BATH AND WELLS	2002
BIRMINGHAM	2002
BRADFORD	2002
BRISTOL	2003
WAKEFIELD	2003
LICHFIELD	2003
GUILDFORD	*vacant*
BLACKBURN	*vacant*
GLOUCESTER	*vacant*
HEREFORD	*vacant*

HISTORICAL SUCCESSION OF ARCHBISHOPS AND BISHOPS

In a number of dioceses, especially for the mediaeval period, the dating of some episcopal appointments is not known for certain. For ease of reference, the date of consecration is given when known, or, in the case of more modern appointments, the date of confirmation of election. More information on the dates of individual bishops can be found in the Royal Historical Society's *Handbook of British Chronology*.

ENGLAND

PROVINCE OF CANTERBURY

Canterbury

Description of arms. Azure, an archiepiscopal cross in pale or surmounted by a pall proper charged with four crosses patée fitchée sable.

597 Augustine
604 Laurentius
619 Mellitus
624 Justus
627 Honorius
655 Deusdedit
668 Theodorus
693 Berhtwald
731 Tatwine
735 Nothelm
740 Cuthbert
761 Bregowine
765 Jaenberht
793 Æthelheard
805 Wulfred
832 Feologild
833 Ceolnoth
870 Æthelred
890 Plegmund
914 Æthelhelm
923 Wulfhelm
942 Oda
959 Ælfsige
959 Byrhthelm
960 Dunstan
*c.*988 Athelgar
990 Sigeric Serio
995 Ælfric
1005 Ælfheah
1013 Lyfing [Ælfstan]
1020 Æthelnoth
1038 Eadsige
1051 Robert of Jumièges
1052 Stigand
1070 Lanfranc
1093 Anselm
1114 Ralph d'Escures
1123 William de Corbeil
1139 Theobald of Bec
1162 Thomas Becket
1174 Richard [of Dover]
1184 Baldwin
1193 Hubert Walter
1207 Stephen Langton

1229 Richard le Grant
1234 Edmund Rich
1245 Boniface of Savoy
1273 Robert Kilwardby
1279 John Pecham
1294 Robert Winchelsey
1313 Walter Reynolds
1328 Simon Mepham
1333 John Stratford
1349 Thomas Bradwardine
1349 Simon Islip
1366 Simon Langham
1368 William Whittlesey
1375 Simon Sudbury
1381 William Courtenay
1396 Thomas Arundel[1]
1398 Roger Walden
1414 Henry Chichele
1443 John Stafford
1452 John Kempe
1454 Thomas Bourgchier
1486 John Morton
1501 Henry Deane
1503 William Warham
1533 Thomas Cranmer
1556 Reginald Pole
1559 Matthew Parker
1576 Edmund Grindal
1583 John Whitgift
1604 Richard Bancroft
1611 George Abbot
1633 William Laud
1660 William Juxon
1663 Gilbert Sheldon
1678 William Sancroft
1691 John Tillotson
1695 Thomas Tenison
1716 William Wake
1737 John Potter
1747 Thomas Herring
1757 Matthew Hutton
1758 Thomas Secker
1768 Frederick Cornwallis
1783 John Moore
1805 Charles Manners Sutton
1828 William Howley
1848 John Bird Sumner
1862 Charles Thomas Longley
1868 Archibald Campbell Tait
1883 Edward White Benson
1896 Frederick Temple
1903 Randall Thomas Davidson
1928 Cosmo Gordon Lang
1942 William Temple
1945 Geoffrey Francis Fisher
1961 Arthur Michael Ramsey
1974 Frederick Donald Coggan
1980 Robert Alexander Kennedy Runcie
1991 George Leonard Carey
2002 Rowan Douglas Williams

London

Description of arms. Gules, two swords in saltire argent hilts and pommels or.

Theanus
Eluanus
Cadar
Obinus
Conanus
Palladius
Stephanus
Iltutus
Theodwinus
Theodredus
Hilarius
314 Restitutus
Guitelinus
Fastidius
Vodinus
Theonus
*c.*604 Mellitus
664 Cedd[2]
666 Wini
675 Eorcenwald
693 Waldhere
716 Ingwald
745 Ecgwulf
772 Wigheah
782 Eadbeorht
789 Eadgar
793 Coenwalh
796 Eadbald
798 Heathoberht
803 Osmund
*c.*811 Æthelnoth
824 Ceolberht
862 Deorwulf
898 Swithwulf
898 Heahstan
900 Wulfsige
*c.*926 Æthelweard
926 Leofstan
926 Theodred
— Wulfstan I
953 Brihthelm
959 Dunstan
964 Ælfstan
996 Wulfstan II
1004 Ælfhun
1014 Ælfwig

[1] On 19 October 1399 Boniface IX annulled Arundel's translation to St Andrew and confirmed him in the See of Canterbury.
[2] See vacant for a term of years.

1035 Ælfweard
1044 Robert of Jumièges
1051 William
1075 Hugh of Orival
1086 Maurice
1108 Richard de Belmeis
1128 Gilbert [the Universal]
1141 Robert de Sigillo
1152 Richard de Belmeis II
1163 Gilbert Foliot
1189 Richard Fitz Neal
1199 William of Ste-Mere-Eglise
1221 Eustace de Fauconberg
1229 Roger Niger
1244 Fulk Basset
1260 Henry Wingham
1263 Henry of Sandwich
1274 John Chishull
1280 Richard Gravesend
1306 Ralph Baldock
1313 Gilbert Segrave
1317 Richard Newport
1319 Stephen Gravesend
1338 Richard Bintworth
1355 Michael Northburgh
1362 Simon Sudbury
1375 William Courtenay
1382 Robert Braybrooke
1404 Roger Walden
1406 Nicholas Bubwith
1407 Richard Clifford
1421 John Kempe
1426 William Gray
1431 Robert Fitz-Hugh
1436 Robert Gilbert
1450 Thomas Kempe
1489 Richard Hill
1496 Thomas Savage
1502 William Warham
1504 William Barons [Barnes]
1506 Richard Fitz-James
1522 Cuthbert Tunstall [Tonstall]
1530 John Stokesley
1540 Edmund Bonner
1550 Nicholas Ridley
1553 Edmund Bonner (restored)
1559 Edmund Grindal
1570 Edwin Sandys
1577 John Aylmer
1595 Richard Fletcher
1597 Richard Bancroft
1604 Richard Vaughan
1607 Thomas Ravis
1610 George Abbot
1611 John King
1621 George Monteigne [Mountain]
1628 William Laud
1633 William Juxon
1660 Gilbert Sheldon
1663 Humfrey Henchman
1676 Henry Compton
1714 John Robinson
1723 Edmund Gibson
1748 Thomas Sherlock
1761 Thomas Hayter
1762 Richard Osbaldeston
1764 Richard Terrick
1778 Robert Lowth
1787 Beilby Porteus
1809 John Randolph
1813 William Howley
1828 Charles James Blomfield
1856 Archibald Campbell Tait
1869 John Jackson
1885 Frederick Temple
1897 Mandell Creighton
1901 Arthur Foley Winnington-Ingram

1939 Geoffrey Francis Fisher
1945 John William Charles Wand
1956 Henry Colville Montgomery Campbell
1961 Robert Wright Stopford
1973 Gerald Alexander Ellison
1981 Graham Douglas Leonard
1991 David Michael Hope
1995 Richard John Carew Chartres

†Westminster

1540 Thomas Thirlby

Winchester

Description of arms. Gules, two keys endorsed and conjoined at the bows in bend, the upper or, the lower argent, between which a sword in bend sinister of the third, hilt and pommel gold.

BISHOPS OF THE WEST SAXONS
634 Birinus
650 Ægilberht

BISHOPS OF WINCHESTER
660 Wine
670 Leutherius
676 Haedde
705 Daniel
744 Hunfrith
756 Cyneheard
778 Æthelheard
778 Ecbald
785 Dudd
c.785 Cyneberht
803 Eahlmund
814 Wigthegn
825 Herefrith[1]
838 Eadmund
c.838 Eadhun
839 Helmstan
852 Swithhun
867 Ealhferth
877 Tunberht
879 Denewulf
909 Frithestan
931 Byrnstan
934 Ælfheah I
951 Ælfsige I
960 Brihthelm
963 Æthelwold I
984 Ælfheah II
1006 Cenwulf
1006 Æthelwold II
c.1014 Ælfsige II
1032 Ælfwine
1043 Stigand
   Ælfsige III?
1070 Walkelin
1107 William Giffard
1129 Henry of Blois
1174 Richard of Ilchester (Toclyve)
1189 Godfrey de Lucy
1205 Peter des Roches
1244 Will. de Raleigh

1260 Aymer de Valance [of Lusignan]
1262 John Gervaise
1268 Nicholas of Ely
1282 John of Pontoise
1305 Henry Merewell [or Woodlock]
1316 John Sandale
1320 Rigaud of Assier
1323 John Stratford
1333 Adam Orleton
1346 William Edendon [Edington]
1367 William of Wykeham
1404 Henry Beaufort
1447 William of Waynflete
1487 Peter Courtenay
1493 Thomas Langton
1501 Richard Fox
1529 Thomas Wolsey
1531 Stephen Gardiner (deposed)
1551 John Ponet [Poynet]
1553 Stephen Gardiner (restored)
1556 John White (deposed)
1561 Robert Horne
1580 John Watson
1584 Thomas Cowper [Cooper]
1595 William Wickham [Wykeham]
1596 William Day
1597 Thomas Bilson
1616 James Montague
1619 Lancelot Andrewes
1628 Richard Neile
1632 Walter Curll
1660 Brian Duppa
1662 George Morley
1684 Peter Mews
1707 Jonathan Trelawney
1721 Charles Trimnell
1723 Richard Willis
1734 Benjamin Hoadly
1761 John Thomas
1781 Brownlow North
1820 George Pretyman Tomline
1827 Charles Richard Sumner
1869 Samuel Wilberforce
1873 Edward Harold Browne
1891 Anthony Wilson Thorold
1895 Randall Thomas Davidson
1903 Herbert Edward Ryle
1911 Edward Stuart Talbot
1923 Frank Theodore Woods
1932 Cyril Forster Garbett
1942 Mervyn George Haigh
1952 Alwyn Terrell Petre Williams
1961 Sherard Falkner Allison
1975 John Vernon Taylor
1985 Colin Clement Walter James
1995 Michael Charles Scott-Joynt

Bath and Wells

Description of arms. Azure, a saltire per saltire quarterly counterchanged or and argent.

BISHOPS OF WELLS
909 Athelm
925 Wulfhelm I

---

† Indicates a diocese no longer extant, or united with another diocese.
[1] Never signed without Wigthegn.

928 Ælfheah
938 Wulfhelm II
956 Byrhthelm
974 Cyneweard
979 Sigegar
997 Ælfwine
999 Lyfing
1013 Æthelwine (ejected)
1013 Beorhtwine (deposed)
  Æthelwine (restored)
  Beorhtwine (restored)
1024 Brihtwig [also Merehwit]
1033 Duduc
1061 Gisa
1088 John of Tours [de Villula]

BISHOPS OF BATH

1090 John of Tours [de Villula]
1123 Godfrey
1136 Robert
1174 Reg. Fitz Jocelin
1192 Savaric FitzGeldewin

BATH AND GLASTONBURY

1206 Jocelin of Wells

BATH AND WELLS

1244 Roger of Salisbury
1248 William Bitton I
1265 Walter Giffard
1267 William Bitton II
1275 Robert Burnell
1293 William of March
1302 Walter Hasleshaw
1309 John Droxford
1329 Ralph of Shrewsbury
1364 John Barnet
1367 John Harewell
1386 Walter Skirlaw
1388 Ralph Erghum
1401 Henry Bowet
1407 Nicholas Bubwith
1425 John Stafford
1443 Thomas Beckington
1466 Robert Stillington
1492 Richard Fox
1495 Oliver King
1504 Adriano de Castello [di
  Corneto]
1518 Thomas Wolsey
1523 John Clerk
1541 William Knight
1548 William Barlow
1554 Gilbert Bourne
1560 Gilbert Berkeley
1584 Thomas Godwin
1593 John Still
1608 James Montague
1616 Arthur Lake
1626 William Laud
1628 Leonard Mawe
1629 Walter Curll
1632 William Piers
1670 Robert Creighton
1673 Peter Mews
1685 Thomas Ken (deposed)
1691 Richard Kidder
1704 George Hooper
1727 John Wynne
1743 Edward Willes
1774 Charles Moss
1802 Richard Beadon
1824 George Henry Law
1845 Richard Bagot
1854 Robert John Eden, Lord
  Auckland
1869 Arthur Charles Hervey
1894 George Wyndham Kennion
1921 St John Basil Wynne Wilson
1937 Francis Underhill

1943 John William Charles Wand
1946 Harold William Bradfield
1960 Edward Barry Henderson
1975 John Monier Bickersteth
1987 George Leonard Carey
1991 James Lawton Thompson
2002 Peter Bryan Price

Birmingham

Description of arms. Per pale indented or and gules, five roundels, two, two, and one, and in chief two crosses patée all counterchanged.

1905 Charles Gore
1911 Henry Russell Wakefield
1924 Ernest William Barnes
1953 John Leonard Wilson
1969 Laurence Ambrose Brown
1978 Hugh William Montefiore
1987 Mark Santer
2002 John Mugabi Sentamu

Bristol

Description of arms. Sable, three ducal coronets in pale or.

1542 Paul Bush
1554 John Holyman
1562 Richard Cheyney
1581 John Bullingham (held
  Gloucester and Bristol
  1586–9)
1589 Richard Fletcher
  [See vacant for ten years]
1603 John Thornborough
1617 Nicholas Felton
1619 Rowland Searchfield
1623 Robert Wright
1633 George Coke
1637 Robert Skinner
1642 Thomas Westfield
1644 Thomas Howell
1661 Gilbert Ironside
1672 Guy Carleton
1679 William Gulston
1684 John Lake
1685 Jonathan Trelawney
1689 Gilbert Ironside
1691 John Hall
1710 John Robinson
1714 George Smalridge
1719 Hugh Boulter
1724 William Bradshaw
1733 Charles Cecil
1735 Thomas Secker

1737 Thomas Gooch
1738 Joseph Butler
1750 John Conybeare
1756 John Hume
1758 Philip Yonge
1761 Thomas Newton
1782 Lewis Bagot
1783 Christopher Wilson
1792 Spencer Madan
1794 Henry Reginald Courtenay
1797 Ffolliott Herbert Walker
  Cornewall
1803 George Pelham
1807 John Luxmoore
1808 William Lort Mansel
1820 John Kaye
1827 Robert Gray
1834 Joseph Allen
[1836 to 1897 united with
  Gloucester]
1897 George Forrest Browne
1914 George Nickson
1933 Clifford Salisbury Woodward
1946 Frederick Arthur Cockin
1959 Oliver Stratford Tomkins
1976 Ernest John Tinsley
1985 Barry Rogerson
2003 Michael Arthur Hill

Chelmsford

Description of arms. Or, on a saltire gules a pastoral staff of the first and a sword argent, hilt and pommel gold.

1914 John Edwin Watts-Ditchfield
1923 Frederic Sumpter Guy Warman
1929 Henry Albert Wilson
1951 Sherard Falkner Allison
1962 John Gerhard Tiarks
1971 Albert John Trillo
1986 John Waine
1996 John Freeman Perry
2003 John Warren Gladwin

Chichester

Description of arms. Azure, our blessed Lord in judgement seated in His throne, His dexter hand upraised or, His sinister hand holding an open book proper, and issuant from His mouth a two-edged sword point to the sinister gules.

BISHOPS OF SELSEY
681 Wilfrid
716 Eadberht

731 Eolla
733 Sigga [Sigeferth]
765 Aaluberht
c.765 Oswald [Osa]
780 Gislhere
786 Tota
c.789 Withhun
c.811 Æthelwulf
824 Cynered
845 Guthheard
900 Wighelm
909 Beornheah
931 Wulfhun
943 Ælfred
955 Daniel
956 Brihthelm
963 Eadhelm
980 Æthelgar
990 Ordbriht
1009 Ælfmaer
1032 Æthelric I
1039 Grimketel
1047 Heca
1058 Æthelric II
1070 Stigand

BISHOPS OF CHICHESTER
1075 Stigand
1088 Godfrey
1091 Ralph Luffa
1125 Seffrid I [d'Escures Pelochin]
1147 Hilary
1174 John Greenford
1180 Seffrid II
1204 Simon FitzRobert
1215 Richard Poore
1218 Ranulf of Wareham
1224 Ralph Nevill
1245 Richard Wich
1254 John Climping
1262 Stephen Bersted [or Pagham]
1288 Gilbert de St Leofard
1305 John Langton
1337 Robert Stratford
1362 William Lenn
1369 William Reade
1386 Thomas Rushock
1390 Richard Mitford
1396 Robert Waldby
1397 Robert Reade
1417 Stephen Patrington
1418 Henry de la Ware
1421 John Kempe
1421 Thomas Polton
1426 John Rickingale
1431 Simon Sydenham
1438 Richard Praty
1446 Adam de Moleyns
1450 Reginald Pecock
1459 John Arundel
1478 Edward Story
1504 Richard Fitz-James
1508 Robert Sherburne
1536 Richard Sampson
1543 George Day (deposed)
1552 John Scory
1553 George Day (restored)
1557 John Christopherson
1559 William Barlow
1570 Richard Curtis
1586 Thomas Bickley
1596 Anthony Watson
1605 Lancelot Andrewes
1609 Samuel Harsnett
1619 George Carleton
1628 Richard Montague
1638 Brian Duppa
1642 Henry King

1670 Peter Gunning
1675 Ralph Brideoake
1679 Guy Carleton
1685 John Lake
1689 Simon Patrick
1691 Robert Grove
1696 John Williams
1709 Thomas Manningham
1722 Thomas Bowers
1724 Edward Waddington
1731 Francis Hare
1740 Matthias Mawson
1754 William Ashburnham
1798 John Buckner
1824 Robert James Carr
1831 Edward Maltby
1836 William Otter
1840 Philip Nicholas Shuttleworth
1842 Ashurst Turner Gilbert
1870 Richard Durnford
1896 Ernest Roland Wilberforce
1908 Charles John Ridgeway
1919 Winfrid Oldfield Burrows
1929 George Kennedy Allen Bell
1958 Roger Plumpton Wilson
1974 Eric Waldram Kemp
2001 John William Hind

Coventry

Description of arms. Gules, within a bordure argent charged with eight torteaux, a cross potent quadrate of the second.

1918 Huyshe Wolcott Yeatman-
       Biggs
1922 Charles Lisle Carr
1931 Mervyn George Haigh
1943 Neville Vincent Gorton
1956 Cuthbert Killick Norman
       Bardsley
1976 John Gibbs
1985 Simon Barrington-Ward
1998 Colin James Bennetts

Derby

Description of arms. Purpure, a cross of St Chad argent beneath three fountains in chief.

1927 Edmund Courtenay Pearce
1936 Alfred Edward John
       Rawlinson
1959 Geoffrey Francis Allen
1969 Cyril William Johnston Bowles

1988 Peter Spencer Dawes
1995 Jonathan Sansbury Bailey

Dorchester[1]

634 Birinus
650 Agilbert
c.660 Ætla
c.888 Ahlheard

Ely

Description of arms. Gules, three ducal coronets or.

1109 Hervey
1133 Nigel
1174 Geoffrey Ridel
1189 William Longchamp
1198 Eustace
1220 John of Fountains
1225 Geoffrey de Burgo
1229 Hugh of Northwold
1255 William of Kilkenny
1258 Hugh of Balsham
1286 John of Kirkby
1290 William of Louth
1299 Ralph Walpole
1303 Robert Orford
1310 John Ketton
1316 John Hotham
1337 Simon Montacute
1345 Thomas de Lisle
1362 Simon Langham
1367 John Barnet
1374 Thomas Arundel
1388 John Fordham
1426 Philip Morgan
1438 Lewis of Luxembourg
1444 Thomas Bourgchier
1454 William Grey
1479 John Morton
1486 John Alcock
1501 Richard Redman
1506 James Stanley
1515 Nicholas West
1534 Thomas Goodrich
1555 Thomas Thirlby
1559 Richard Cox
1600 Martin Heton
1609 Lancelot Andrewes
1619 Nicolas Felton
1628 John Buckeridge
1631 Francis White
1638 Matthew Wren
1667 Benjamin Laney
1675 Peter Gunning
1684 Francis Turner
1691 Simon Patrick
1707 John Moore
1714 William Fleetwood
1723 Thomas Greene
1738 Robert Butts
1748 Thomas Gooch
1754 Matthias Mawson
1771 Edmund Keene
1781 James Yorke
1808 Thomas Dampier

[1] Originally a West Saxon, after Ahlheard's time a Mercian, bishopric. See transferred to Lincoln 1077.

1812 Bowyer Edward Sparke
1836 Joseph Allen
1845 Thomas Turton
1864 Edward Harold Browne
1873 James Russell Woodford
1886 Alwyne Frederick Compton
1905 Frederick Henry Chase
1924 Leonard Jauncey White-
      Thomson
1934 Bernard Oliver Francis
      Heywood
1941 Harold Edward Wynn
1957 Noel Baring Hudson
1964 Edward James Keymer
      Roberts
1977 Peter Knight Walker
1990 Stephen Whitefield Sykes
2000 Anthony John Russell

Exeter

Description of arms. Gules, a sword erect in pale argent hilt or surmounted by two keys addorsed in saltire gold.

BISHOPS OF CORNWALL

870 Kenstec
893 Asser
931 Conan
950 Æthelge[ard]
*c.*955 Daniel
963 Wulfsige Comoere
990 Ealdred
1009 Æthelsige
1018 Buruhwold
1027 Lyfing, Bishop of Crediton
      Cornwall and Worcester
1046 Leofric Bishop of Crediton
      and Cornwall
[See transferred to Exeter 1050]

BISHOPS OF CREDITON

909 Eadwulf
934 Æthelgar
953 Ælfwold I
973 Sideman
979 Ælfric
987 Ælfwold II
1008 Ælfwold III
1015 Eadnoth
1027 Lyfing
1046 Leofric[1]

BISHOPS OF EXETER

1050 Leofric
1072 Osbern Fitz-Osbern
1107 Will. Warelwast
1138 Robert Warelwast
1155 Robert II of Chichester
1161 Bartholomew
1186 John the Chanter
1194 Henry Marshall
1214 Simon of Apulia
1224 William Brewer
1245 Richard Blund
1258 Walter Bronescombe
1280 Peter Quinel [Wyvill]

1292 Thomas Bitton
1308 Walter Stapeldon
1327 James Berkeley
1328 John Grandisson
1370 Thomas Brantingham
1395 Edmund Stafford
1419 John Catterick
1420 Edmund Lacy
1458 George Nevill
1465 John Booth
1478 Peter Courtenay
1487 Richard Fox
1493 Oliver King
1496 Richard Redman
1502 John Arundel
1505 Hugh Oldham
1519 John Veysey (resigned)
1551 Miles Coverdale
1553 John Veysey (restored)
1555 James Turberville
1560 William Alley [or Allei]
1571 William Bradbridge
1579 John Woolton
1595 Gervase Babington
1598 William Cotton
1621 Valentine Carey
1627 Joseph Hall
1642 Ralph Brownrigg
1660 John Gauden
1662 Seth Ward
1667 Anthony Sparrow
1676 Thomas Lamplugh
1689 Jonathan Trelawney
1708 Offspring Blackall
1717 Lancelot Blackburn
1724 Stephen Weston
1742 Nicholas Claget
1747 George Lavington
1762 Frederick Keppel
1778 John Ross
1792 William Buller
1797 Henry Reginald Courtenay
1803 John Fisher
1807 George Pelham
1820 William Carey
1830 Christopher Bethell
1831 Henry Phillpotts
1869 Frederick Temple
1885 Edward Henry Bickersteth
1901 Herbert Edward Ryle
1903 Archibald Robertson
1916 Rupert Ernest William
      Gascoyne Cecil
1936 Charles Edward Curzon
1949 Robert Cecil Mortimer
1973 Eric Arthur John Mercer
1985 Geoffrey Hewlett Thompson
1999 Michael Laurence Langrish

Gloucester

Description of arms. Azure, two keys addorsed in saltire the wards upwards or.

1541 John Wakeman *alias* Wiche
1551 John Hooper

1554 James Brooks
1562 Richard Cheyney[2]
1581 John Bullingham[3]
1598 Godfrey Goldsborough
1605 Thomas Ravis
1607 Henry Parry
1611 Giles Thompson
1612 Miles Smith
1625 Godfrey Goodman
1661 William Nicolson
1672 John Pritchett
1681 Robert Frampton
1691 Edward Fowler
1715 Richard Willis
1721 Joseph Wilcocks
1731 Elias Sydall
1735 Martin Benson
1752 James Johnson
1760 William Warburton
1779 James Yorke
1781 Samuel Hallifax
1789 Richard Beadon
1802 George Isaac Huntingford
1815 Henry Ryder
1824 Christopher Bethell
1830 James Henry Monk
[1836 to 1897, united with Bristol]

BISHOPS OF GLOUCESTER AND
BRISTOL

1836 James Henry Monk
1856 Charles Baring
1861 William Thomson
1863 Charles John Ellicott[4]

BISHOPS OF GLOUCESTER

1897 Charles John Ellicott
1905 Edgar Charles Sumner Gibson
1923 Arthur Cayley Headlam
1946 Clifford Salisbury Woodward
1954 Wilfred Marcus Askwith
1962 Basil Tudor Guy
1975 John Yates
1992 Peter John Ball
1993 David Edward Bentley

Guildford

Description of arms. Gules, two keys conjoined wards outwards in bend, the uppermost or, the other argent, interposed between them in bend sinister a sword of the third, hilt and pommel gold, all within a bordure azure charged with ten wool-packs argent.

1927 John Harold Greig
1934 John Victor Macmillan
1949 Henry Colville Montgomery
      Campbell
1956 Ivor Stanley Watkins
1961 George Edmund Reindorp
1973 David Alan Brown
1983 Michael Edgar Adie
1994 John Warren Gladwin

[1] Removed See from Crediton.   [2] Also Bishop of Bristol.   [3] Held Gloucester and Bristol 1581-9.   [4] Gloucester only from 1897.

Hereford

Description of arms. Gules, three
leopards' faces jessant-de-lis reversed
or.

676	Putta
688	Tyrhtel
710	Torhthere
c.731	Wahistod
736	Cuthberht
741	Podda
c.758	Acca
c.770	Headda
777	Aldberht
786	Esne
c.788	Ceolmund
c.798	Utel
801	Wulfheard
824	Beonna
c.832	Eadwulf
c.839	Cuthwulf
866	Mucel
c.866	Deorlaf
888	Cynemund
890	EadBar
c.931	Tidhelm
940	Wulfhelm
c.940	Ælfric
971	Æthelwulf
1016	Æthelstan
1056	Leofgar
1056	Ealdred, Bishop of Hereford and Worcester
1060	Walter
1079	Robert Losinga
1096	Gerard
1107	Reinhelm
1115	Geoffrey de Clive
1121	Richard de Capella
1131	Robert de Bethune
1148	Gilbert Foliot
1163	Robert of Melun
1174	Robert Foliot
1186	William de Vere
1200	Giles de Braose
1216	Hugh of Mapenore
1219	Hugh Foliot
1234	Ralph Maidstone
1240	Peter d'Aigueblanche
1269	John Breton
1275	Thomas Cantilupe
1283	Richard Swinfeld
1317	Adam Orleton
1327	Thomas Chariton
1344	John Trilleck
1361	Lewis Charleton
1370	William Courtenay
1375	John Gilbert
1389	John Trefnant
1404	Robert Mascall
1417	Edmund Lacy
1420	Thomas Polton

1422	Thomas Spofford
1449	Richard Beauchamp
1451	Reginald Boulers
1453	John Stanbury
1474	Thomas Milling
1492	Edmund Audley
1502	Adriano de Castello [di Corneto]
1504	Richard Mayeu
1516	Charles Booth
1535	Edward Fox
1539	John Skip
1553	John Harley
1554	Robert Parfew or Wharton
1559	John Scory
1586	Herbert Westfaling
1603	Robert Bennett
1617	Francis Godwin
1634	Augustine Lindsell
1635	Matthew Wren
1635	Theophilus Field
1636	George Coke
1661	Nicolas Monk
1662	Herbert Croft
1691	Gilbert Ironside
1701	Humphrey Humphries
1713	Philip Bisse
1721	Benjamin Hoadly
1724	Henry Egerton
1746	James Beauclerk
1787	John Harley
1788	John Butler
1803	Ffolliott Herbert Walker Cornewall
1808	John Luxmoore
1815	George Isaac Huntingford
1832	Edward Grey
1837	Thomas Musgrave
1848	Renn Dickson Hampden
1868	James Atlay
1895	John Percival
1918	Herbert Hensley Henson
1920	Martin Linton Smith
1931	Charles Lisle Carr
1941	Richard Godfrey Parsons
1949	Tom Longworth
1961	Mark Allin Hodson
1974	John Richard Gordon Eastaugh
1990	John Keith Oliver

Leicester

see also under Lincoln

Description of arms. Gules, a pierced
cinquefoil ermine, in chief a lion
passant guardant grasping in the dexter
forepaw a cross crosslet fitchée or.

NEW FOUNDATION

1927	Cyril Charles Bowman Bardsley

1940	Guy Vernon Smith
1953	Ronald Ralph Williams
1979	Cecil Richard Rutt
1991	Thomas Frederick Butler
1999	Timothy John Stevens

Lichfield

Description of arms. Per pale gules and
argent, a cross potent quadrate in the
centre per pale argent and or between
four crosses patée those to the dexter
argent and those to the sinister gold.

BISHOPS OF MERCIA

656	Diuma[1]
658	Ceollach
659	Trumhere
662	Jaruman

BISHOPS OF LICHFIELD

669	Chad[2]
672	Winfrith
676	Seaxwulf
691	Headda[3]
731	Aldwine
737	Hwita
757	Hemele
765	Cuthfrith
769	Berhthun
779	Hygeberht[4]
801	Aldwulf
816	Herewine
818	Æthelwald
830	Hunberht
836	Cyneferth
845	Tunberht
869	Eadberht
883	Wulfred
900	Wigmund or Wilferth
915	Ælfwine
941	Wulfgar
949	Cynesige
964	Wynsige
975	Ælfheah
1004	Godwine
1020	Leofgar
1026	Brihtmaer
1039	Wulfsige
1053	Leofwine
1072	Peter

BISHOPS OF LICHFIELD,
CHESTER, AND COVENTRY[5]

1075	Peter
1086	Robert de Limesey[5]
1121	Robert Peche
1129	Roger de Clinton
1149	Walter Durdent
1161	Richard Peche
1183	Gerard La Pucelle
1188	Hugh Nonant

[1] Archbishop of the Mercians, the Lindisfari, and the Middle Angles.
[2] Bishop of the Mercians and the Lindisfari.
[3] Archbishop of Lichfield after 787.
[4] Bishop of Lichfield and Leicester.
[5] 1102 Robert de Limesey, Bishop of Lichfield, moved the See to Coventry. Succeeding Bishops are usually termed *of Coventry* until 1228. Then *Coventry and Lichfield* was the habitual title until the Reformation. *Chester* was used by some 12th-century Bishops, and popularly afterwards. After the Reformation *Lichfield and Coventry* was used until 1846.

1198 Geoffrey Muschamp
1215 William Cornhill
1224 Alex. Stavensby
1240 Hugh Pattishall
1246 Roger Weseham
1258 Roger Longespee
1296 Walter Langton
1322 Roger Northburgh
1360 Robert Stretton
1386 Walter Skirlaw
1386 Richard le Scrope
1398 John Burghill
1415 John Catterick
1420 William Heyworth
1447 William Booth
1452 Nicholas Close
1453 Reginald Boulers
1459 John Hales
1493 William Smith
1496 John Arundel
1503 Geoffrey Blyth
1534 Rowland Lee
1541 [Chester formed as a bishopric]
1543 Richard Sampson
1554 Ralph Baynes
1560 Thomas Bentham
1580 William Overton
1609 George Abbot
1610 Richard Neile
1614 John Overall
1619 Thomas Morton
1632 Robert Wright
1644 Accepted Frewen
1661 John Hackett
1671 Thomas Wood
1692 William Lloyd
1699 John Hough
1717 Edward Chandler
1731 Richard Smalbroke
1750 Fred. Cornwallis
1768 John Egerton
1771 Brownlow North
1775 Richard Hurd
1781 James Cornwallis [4th Earl
        Cornwallis]
1824 Henry Ryder
1836 [Coventry transferred to
        Worcester diocese]
1836 Samuel Butler
1840 James Bowstead
1843 John Lonsdale
1868 George Augustus Selwyn
1878 William Dalrymple Maclagan
1891 Augustus Legge
1913 John Augustine Kempthorne
1937 Edward Sydney Woods
1953 Arthur Stretton Reeve
1975 Kenneth John Fraser Skelton
1984 Keith Norman Sutton
2003 Jonathan Michael Gledhill

Lincoln

Description of arms. Gules, two lions
passant guardant or, on a chief azure,
the Virgin ducally crowned sitting

on a throne issuant from the chief, on
her dexter arm the infant Jesus, and in
her sinister hand a sceptre all gold.

BISHOPS OF LINDSEY
634 Birinus
650 Agilbert
660 Aetlai
678 Eadhaed
680 Æthelwine
693 (?)Edgar
731 (?)Cyneberht
733 Alwig
750 Aldwulf
767 Ceolwulf
796 Eadwulf
839 Beorhtred
869 Burgheard
933 Ælfred
953 Leofwine
996 Sigefrith

BISHOPS OF LEICESTER
664 Wilfrid, translated from York
679 Cuthwine
691 Headda[1] (founder of Lichfield
        Cathedral 705–37)
727 Aldwine
737 Torhthelm
764 Eadberht
785 Unwona
803 Wernberht
816 Raethhun
840 Ealdred
844 Ceolred
874 [See of Leicester removed to
        Dorchester]

BISHOPS OF DORCHESTER
(after it became a Mercian See)
c.888 Ahlheard
900 Wigmund or Wilferth
909 Cenwulf
925 Wynsige
c.951 Osketel
953 Leofwine
975 Ælfnoth
979 Æscwig
1002 Ælfheln
1006 Eadnoth I
1016 Æthelric
1034 Eadnoth II
1049 Ulf
1053 Wulfwig
1067 Remigius

BISHOPS OF LINCOLN
1072 Remigius
1094 Robert Bloett
1123 Alexander
1148 Robert de Chesney
1183 Walter de Coutances
1186 Hugh of Avalon
1203 William of Blois
1209 Hugh of Wells
1235 Robert Grosseteste
1254 Henry Lexington [Sutton]
1258 Richard Gravesend
1280 Oliver Sutton [Lexington]
1300 John Dalderby
1320 Henry Burghersh
1342 Thomas Bek
1347 John Gynewell
1363 John Bokyngham
        [Buckingham]
1398 Henry Beaufort
1405 Philip Repingdon

1420 Richard Fleming
1431 William Gray
1436 William Alnwick
1450 Marmaduke Lumley
1452 John Chedworth
1472 Thomas Rotherham [Scott]
1480 John Russell
1495 William Smith
1514 Thomas Wolsey
1514 William Atwater
1521 John Longland
1547 Henry Holbeach [Rands]
1552 John Taylor
1554 John White
1557 Thomas Watson
1560 Nicholas Bullingham
1571 Thomas Cooper
1584 William Wickham
1595 William Chaderton
1608 William Barlow
1614 Richard Neile
1617 George Monteigne [Mountain]
1621 John Williams
1642 Thomas Winniffe
1660 Robt. Sanderson
1663 Benjamin Laney
1667 William Fuller
1675 Thomas Barlow
1692 Thomas Tenison
1695 James Gardiner
1705 William Wake
1716 Edmund Gibson
1723 Richard Reynolds
1744 John Thomas
1761 John Green
1779 Thomas Thurlow
1787 George Pretyman [Pretyman
        Tomline after June 1803]
1820 George Pelham
1827 John Kaye
1853 John Jackson
1869 Christopher Wordsworth
1885 Edward King
1910 Edward Lee Hicks
1920 William Shuckburgh Swayne
1933 Frederick Cyril Nugent Hicks
1942 Henry Aylmer Skelton
1946 Leslie Owen
1947 Maurice Henry Harland
1956 Kenneth Riches
1975 Simon Wilton Phipps
1987 Robert Maynard Hardy
2001 John Charles Saxbee

Norwich

Description of arms. Azure, three
labelled mitres or.

BISHOPS OF DUNWICH
631 Felix
648 Thomas
c.653 Berhtgils [Boniface]
c.670 Bisi
c.673 Æcce
693 Alric (?)
716 Eardred

---

[1] Bishop of Leicester and Lichfield.

731 Aldbeorht I
747 Æscwulf
747 Eardwulf
775 Cuthwine
775 Aldbeorht II
781 Ecglaf
781 Heardred
793 Ælfhun
798 Tidferth
824 Waermund[1]
825 Wilred
836 Husa
870 Æthelwold

BISHOPS OF ELMHAM
673 Beaduwine
706 Nothberht
c.731 Heathulac
736 Æthelfrith
758 Eanfrith
c.781 Æthelwulf
c.785 Alhheard
814 Sibba
824 Hunferth
824 Hunbeorht
836 Cunda[2]
c.933 Ælfred[3]
c.945 Æthelweald
956 Eadwulf
970 Ælfric I
974 Theodred I
982 Theodred II
997 Æthelstan
1001 Ælfgar
1021 Ælfwine
1038 Ælfric II
1039 Ælfric III
1043 Stigand[4]
1043 Grimketel[5]
1044 Stigand (restored)
1047 Æthelmaer

BISHOPS OF THETFORD
1070 Herfast
1086 William de Beaufai
1091 Herbert Losinga

BISHOPS OF NORWICH
1091 Herbert Losinga
1121 Everard of Montgomery
1146 William de Turbe
1175 John of Oxford
1200 John de Gray
1222 Pandulf Masca
1226 Thomas Blundeville
1239 William Raleigh
1245 Walter Suffield or Calthorp
1258 Simon Walton
1266 Roger Skerning
1278 William Middleton
1289 Ralph Walpole
1299 John Salmon
1325 [Robert de Baldock]
1325 William Ayermine
1337 Anthony Bek
1344 William of Norwich [Bateman]
1356 Thomas Percy
1370 Henry Spencer [Dispenser]
1407 Alexander Tottington
1413 Richard Courtenay
1416 John Wakeryng
1426 William Ainwick
1436 Thomas Brown

1446 Walter Lyhert [le Hart]
1472 James Goldwell
1499 Thomas Jane
1501 Richard Nykke
1536 William Reppes [Rugge]
1550 Thomas Thirlby
1554 John Hopton
1560 John Parkhurst
1575 Edmund Freke
1585 Edmund Scambler
1595 William Redman
1603 John Jegon
1618 John Overall
1619 Samuel Harsnett
1629 Francis White
1632 Richard Corbet
1635 Matthew Wren
1638 Richard Montagu
1641 Joseph Hall
1661 Edward Reynolds
1676 Antony Sparrow
1685 William Lloyd
1691 John Moore
1708 Charles Trimnell
1721 Thomas Green
1723 John Leng
1727 William Baker
1733 Robert Butts
1738 Thomas Gooch
1748 Samuel Lisle
1749 Thomas Hayter
1761 Philip Yonge
1783 Lewis Bagot
1790 George Horne
1792 Charles Manners Sutton
1805 Henry Bathurst
1837 Edward Stanley
1849 Samuel Hinds
1857 John Thomas Pelham
1893 John Sheepshanks
1910 Bertram Pollock
1942 Percy Mark Herbert
1959 William Launcelot Scott Fleming
1971 Maurice Arthur Ponsonby Wood
1985 Peter John Nott
1999 Graham Richard James

Oxford

Description of arms. Sable, a fess argent, in chief three demi-ladies couped at the waist heads affrontée proper crowned or arrayed and veiled of the second, in base an ox of the last, horned and hoofed gold, passing a ford barry wavy of six azure and argent.

1542 Robert King[6]
1558 [Thomas Goldwell]
1567 Hugh Curen [Curwen]

1589 John Underhill
1604 John Bridges
1619 John Howson
1628 Richard Corbet
1632 John Bancroft
1641 Robert Skinner
1663 William Paul
1665 Walter Blandford
1671 Nathaniel Crewe [Lord Crewe]
1674 Henry Compton
1676 John Fell
1686 Samuel Parker
1688 Timothy Hall
1690 John Hough
1699 William Talbot
1715 John Potter
1737 Thomas Secker
1758 John Hume
1766 Robert Lowth
1777 John Butler
1788 Edward Smallwell
1799 John Randolph
1807 Charles Moss
1812 William Jackson
1816 Edward Legge
1827 Charles Lloyd
1829 Richard Bagot
1845 Samuel Wilberforce
1870 John Fielder Mackarness
1889 William Stubbs
1901 Francis Paget
1911 Charles Gore
1919 Hubert Murray Burge
1925 Thomas Banks Strong
1937 Kenneth Escott Kirk
1955 Harry James Carpenter
1971 Kenneth John Woollcombe
1978 Patrick Campbell Rodger
1987 Richard Douglas Harries

Peterborough

Description of arms. Gules, two keys in saltire the wards upwards between four cross crosslets fitchée or.

1541 John Chamber
1557 David Pole
1561 Edmund Scambler
1585 Richard Howland
1601 Thomas Dove
1630 William Piers
1633 Augustine Lindsell
1634 Francis Dee
1639 John Towers
1660 Benjamin Laney
1663 Joseph Henshaw
1679 William Lloyd
1685 Thomas White
1691 Richard Cumberland
1718 White Kennett
1729 Robert Clavering
1747 John Thomas
1757 Richard Terrick

[1] Bishop of Dunwich or Elmham.
[2] Bishop of Elmham or Dunwich.
[3] Bishop of Elmham or Lindsey.
[4] Deposed before conseration.
[5] Bishop of Selsey and Elmham.
[6] Bishop Rheon. in partibus. Of Oseney 1542-5. See transferred to Oxford 1545.

1764 Robert Lambe
1769 John Hinchliffe
1794 Spencer Madan
1813 John Parsons
1819 Herbert Marsh
1839 George Davys
1864 Francis Jeune
1868 William Connor Magee
1891 Mandell Creighton
1897 Edward Carr Glyn
1916 Frank Theodore Woods
1924 Cyril Charles Bowman
     Bardsley
1927 Claude Martin Blagden
1949 Spencer Stottisbury Gwatkin
     Leeson
1956 Robert Wright Stopford
1961 Cyril Eastaugh
1972 Douglas Russell Feaver
1984 William John Westwood
1996 Ian Patrick Martyn Cundy

Portsmouth

Description of arms. Per fess or and
gules, in chief upon waves of the sea
proper a lymphad sable, and in base
two keys conjoined wards outwards in
bend, the uppermost or, the other
argent, interposed between them in
bend sinister a sword also argent, hilt
and pommel gold.

1927 Ernest Neville Lovett
1936 Frank Partridge
1942 William Louis Anderson
1949 William Launcelot Scott
     Fleming
1960 John Henry Lawrence Phillips
1975 Archibald Ronald McDonald
     Gordon
1985 Timothy John Bavin
1995 Kenneth William Stevenson

Rochester

Description of arms. Argent, on a
saltire gules an escallop or.

604 Justus
624 Romanus
633 Paulinus
644 Ithamar
664 Damianus
669 Putta
676 Cwichelm
678 Gebmund
716 Tobias
727 Aldwulf

741 Dunn
747 Eardwulf
772 Diora
785 Waermund I
805 Beornmod
844 Tatnoth
868 Badenoth
868 Waermund II
868 Cuthwulf
880 Swithwulf
900 Ceolmund
c.926 Cyneferth
c.934 Burhric
949 Beorhtsige
955 [Daniel?] Rochester or Selsey
964 Ælfstan
995 Godwine I
1046 Godwine II
1058 Siward
1076 Arnost
1077 Gundulf
1108 Ralph d'Escures
1115 Ernulf
1125 John
1137 John II
1142 Ascelin
1148 Walter
1182 Waleran
1185 Gilbert Glanvill
1215 Benedict of Sausetun
     [Sawston]
1227 Henry Sandford
1238 Richard Wendene
1251 Lawrence of St Martin
1274 Walter Merton
1278 John Bradfield
1283 Thomas Ingoldsthorpe
1292 Thomas of Wouldham
1319 Hamo Hethe
1353 John Sheppey
1362 William of Whittlesey
1364 Thomas Trilleck
1373 Thomas Brinton
1389 William Bottlesham
     [Bottisham]
1400 John Bottlesham
1404 Richard Young
1419 John Kempe
1422 John Langdon
1435 Thomas Brouns
1437 William Wells
1444 John Low
1468 Thomas Rotherham
     [otherwise Scott]
1472 John Alcock
1476 John Russell
1480 Edmund Audley
1493 Thomas Savage
1497 Richard Fitz-James
1504 John Fisher
1535 John Hilsey [Hildesleigh]
1540 Nicolas Heath
1544 Henry Holbeach
1547 Nicholas Ridley
1550 John Ponet [Poynet]
1551 John Scory
1554 Maurice Griffith
1560 Edmund Gheast [Guest]
1572 Edmund Freke
1576 John Piers
1578 John Young
1605 William Barlow
1608 Richard Neile
1611 John Buckeridge
1628 Walter Curil
1630 John Bowle
1638 John Warner
1666 John Dolben
1683 Francis Turner
1684 Thomas Sprat

1713 Francis Atterbury
1723 Samuel Bradford
1731 Joseph Wilcocks
1756 Zachary Pearce
1774 John Thomas
1793 Samuel Horsley
1802 Thomas Dampier
1809 Walker King
1827 Hugh Percy
1827 George Murray
1860 Joseph Cotton Wigram
1867 Thomas Legh Claughton
1877 Anthony Wilson Thorold
1891 Randall Thomas Davidson
1895 Edward Stuart Talbot
1905 John Reginald Harmer
1930 Martin Linton Smith
1940 Christopher Maude Chavasse
1961 Richard David Say
1988 Anthony Michael Arnold
     Turnbull
1994 Michael James Nazir-Ali

St Albans

Description of arms. Azure, a saltire or,
overall a sword erect in pale proper,
hilt and pommel gold, in chief a
celestial crown of the same.

1877 Thomas Legh Claughton
1890 John Wogan Festing
1903 Edgar Jacob
1920 Michael Bolton Furse
1944 Philip Henry Loyd
1950 Edward Michael Gresford
     Jones
1970 Robert Alexander Kennedy
     Runcie
1980 John Bernard Taylor
1995 Christopher William Herbert

St Edmundsbury and Ipswich

Description of arms. Per pale gules and
azure, between three ducal coronets a
demi-lion passant guardant conjoined
to the demi-hulk of an ancient ship or.

1914 Henry Bernard Hodgson
1921 Albert Augustus David
1923 Walter Godfrey Whittingham
1940 Richard Brook
1954 Arthur Harold Morris
1966 Leslie Wilfrid Brown
1978 John Waine
1986 John Dennis
1997 John Hubert Richard Lewis

Salisbury

Description of arms. Azure, our Lady crowned, holding in her dexter arm the infant Jesus, and in her sinister arm a sceptre all or, round both the heads circles of glory gold.

BISHOPS OF SHERBORNE

705 Ealdhelm
709 Forthhere
736 Herewaeld
774 Æthelmod
793 Denefrith
801 Wigberht
825 Ealhstan
868 Heahmund
877 Æthelheah
889 Wulfsige I
900 Asser
c.909 Æthelweard
c.909 Waerstan
925 Æthelbald
925 Sigehelm
934 Ælfred
943 Wulfsige II
958 Ælfwold I
979 Æthelsige I
992 Wulfsige III
1002 Æthelric
1012 Æthelsige II
1017 Brihtwine I
1017 Ælfmaer
1023 Brihtwine II
1045 Ælfwold II
1058 Hereman, Bishop of Ramsbury

BISHOPS OF RAMSBURY

909 Æthelstan
927 Oda
949 Ælfric I
951 Osulf
970 Ælfstan
981 Wulfgar
986 Sigeric
993 Ælfric II
1005 Brihtwold
1045 Hereman[1]

BISHOPS OF SALISBURY

1078 Osmund Osmer
1107 Roger
1142 Jocelin de Bohun
1189 Hubert Walter
1194 Herbert Poore
1217 Richard Poore
1229 Robert Bingham
1247 William of York
1257 Giles of Bridport
1263 Walter de la Wyle
1274 Robert Wickhampton
1284 Walter Scammel
1287 Henry Brandeston
1289 William de la Corner
1292 Nicholas Longespee
1297 Simon of Ghent
1315 Roger de Mortival
1330 Robert Wyville

1375 Ralph Erghum
1388 John Waltham
1395 Richard Mitford
1407 Nicholas Bubwith
1407 Robert Hallum
1417 John Chaundler
1427 Robert Nevill
1438 William Aiscough
1450 Richard Beauchamp
1482 Lionel Woodville
1485 Thomas Langton
1494 John Blythe
1500 Henry Deane
1502 Edmund Audley
1525 Lorenzo Campeggio
1535 Nicholas Shaxton
1539 John Salcot [Capon]
1560 John Jewell
1571 Edmund Gheast [Guest]
1577 John Piers
1591 John Coldwell
1598 Henry Cotton
1615 Robert Abbot
1618 Martin Fotherby
1620 Robert Townson [Toulson]
1621 John Davenant
1641 Brian Duppa
1660 Humfrey Henchman
1663 John Earle
1665 Alexander Hyde
1667 Seth Ward
1689 Gilbert Burnet
1715 William Talbot
1721 Richard Wilis
1723 Benjamin Hoadly
1734 Thomas Sherlock
1748 John Gilbert
1757 John Thomas
1761 Robert Hay Drummond
1761 John Thomas
1766 John Hume
1782 Shute Barrington
1791 John Douglas
1807 John Fisher
1825 Thomas Burgess
1837 Edward Denison
1854 Walter Kerr Hamilton
1869 George Moberly
1885 John Wordsworth
1911 Frederic Edward Ridgeway
1921 St Clair George Alfred Donaldson
1936 Ernest Neville Lovett
1946 Geoffrey Charles Lester Lunt
1949 William Louis Anderson
1963 Joseph Edward Fison
1973 George Edmund Reindorp
1982 John Austin Baker
1993 David Staffurth Stancliffe

Southwark

Description of arms. Argent, eleven fusils in cross conjoined, seven in pale fesswise, four in fess palewise, in the dexter chief a mitre all gules.

1905 Edward Stuart Talbot
1911 Hubert Murray Burge

1919 Cyril Forster Garbett
1932 Richard Godfrey Parsons
1942 Bertram Fitzgerald Simpson
1959 Arthur Mervyn Stockwood
1980 Ronald Oliver Bowlby
1991 Robert Kerr Williamson
1998 Thomas Frederick Butler

Truro

Description of arms. Argent, on a saltire gules a sword and key or and in base a fleur-de-lis sable all within a bordure of the last charged with fifteen besants.

1877 Edward White Benson
1883 George Howard Wilkinson
1891 John Gott
1906 Charles William Stubbs
1912 Winfrid Oldfield Burrows
1919 Frederic Sumpter Guy Warman
1923 Walter Howard Frere
1935 Joseph Wellington Hunkin
1951 Edmund Robert Morgan
1960 John Maurice Key
1973 Graham Douglas Leonard
1981 Peter Mumford
1990 Michael Thomas Ball
1997 William Ind

Worcester

Description of arms. Argent, ten torteaux, four, three, two, and one.

680 Bosel
691 Oftfor
693 Ecgwine
718 Wilfrid I
745 Milred
775 Waermund
777 Tilhere
781 Heathured
798 Deneberht
822 Heahberht
845 Alhhun
873 Waerferth
915 Æthelhun
922 Wilferth II
929 Cenwald
957 Dunstan
961 Oswald
992 Ealdwulf
1002 Wulfstan I
1016 Leofsige
1027 Lyfing
1033 Brihtheah

[1] Ramsbury was added to Sherbourne in 1058 when Hereman became Bishop of Sherbourne. The See was moved to Salisbury in 1078.

912

1040 Æltric Puttoc, Bishop of York and Worcester	1362 John Barnet	1641 John Prideaux
1041 Lyfing (restored)	1364 William of Whittlesey	1660 George Morley
1046 Ealdred Bishop of Hereford and Worcester 1056–60	1369 William Lenn	1662 John Gauden
1062 Wulfstan II	1375 Henry Wakefield	1662 John Earle
1096 Samson	1396 Robert Tideman of Winchcomb	1663 Robert Skinner
1115 Theulf	1401 Richard Clifford	1671 Walter Blandford
1125 Simon	1407 Thomas Peverel	1675 James Fleetwood
1151 John of Pagham	1419 Philip Morgan	1683 William Thomas
1158 Aldred	1426 Thomas Polton	1689 Edward Stillingfleet
1164 Roger of Gloucester	1435 Thomas Bourgchier	1699 William Lloyd
1180 Baldwin	1444 John Carpenter	1717 John Hough
1186 William of Northolt	1476 John Alcock	1743 Isaac Maddox
1191 Robert Fitz Ralph	1487 Robert Morton	1759 James Johnson
1193 Henry de Sully	1497 Giovanni de' Gigli	1774 Brownlow North
1196 John of Coutances	1499 Silvestro de' Gigli	1781 Richard Hurd
1200 Mauger	1521 Julius de Medici Guilio de Medici (administrator)	1808 Ffoliott Herbert Walker Cornewall
1214 Walter de Gray	1523 Geronimo Ghinucci	1831 Robert James Carr
1216 Silvester of Evesham	1535 Hugh Latimer	1841 Henry Pepys
1218 William of Blois	1539 John Bell	1861 Henry Philpott
1237 Walter Cantilupe	1544 Nicholas Heath (deposed)	1891 John James Stewart Perowne
1266 Nicolas of Ely	1552 John Hooper	1902 Charles Gore
1268 Godfrey Giffard	1554 Nicholas Heath (restored)	1905 Huyshe Wolcott Yeatman-Biggs
1302 Walter Gainsborough	1555 Richard Pates	1919 Ernest Harold Pearce
1308 Walter Reynolds	1559 Edwin Sandys	1931 Arthur William Thomson Perowne
1313 Walter Maidstone	1571 Nicholas Bullingham	
1317 Thomas Cobham	1577 John Whitgift	1941 William Wilson Cash
1327 Adam Orleton	1584 Edmund Freke	1956 Lewis Mervyn Charles-Edwards
1334 Simon Montacute	1593 Richard Fletcher	
1337 Thomas Hempnall	1596 Thomas Bilson	1971 Robert Wylmer Woods
1339 Wulstan Bransford	1597 Gervase Babington	1982 Philip Harold Ernest Goodrich
1350 John Thoresby	1610 Henry Parry	
1353 Reginald Brian	1617 John Thornborough	1997 Peter Stephen Maurice Selby

PROVINCE OF YORK

York

Description of arms. Gules, two keys in saltire argent, in chief a regal crown proper.

BISHOPS

314 Eborius
625 Paulinus
    [Vacancy 633–64]
664 Cedda
664 Wilfrid I
678 Bosa (retired)
686 Bosa (restored)
691 Wilfrith (restored)
706 John of Beverley
718 Wilfrid II

ARCHBISHOPS

734 Egberht
767 Æthelberht
780 Eanbald I
796 Eanbald II
808 Wulfsige
837 Wigmund
854 Wulfhere
900 Æthelbald
c.928 Hrothweard
931 Wulfstan I
956 Osketel

971 Oswald	1514 Thomas Wolsey
971 Edwald	1531 Edward Lee
992 Ealdwulf [1]	1545 Robert Holgate
1003 Wulfstan II	1555 Nicholas Heath
1023 Ælfric Puttoc	1561 Thomas Young
1041 Æthelric	1570 Edmund Grindal
1051 Cynesige	1577 Edwin Sandys
1061 Ealdred	1589 John Piers
1070 Thomas I of Bayeux	1595 Matthew Hutton
1100 Gerard	1606 Tobias Matthew
1109 Thomas II	1628 George Monteigne [Mountain]
1119 Thurstan	1629 Samuel Harsnett
1143 William Fitzherbert	1632 Richard Neile
1147 Henry Murdac	1641 John Williams
1153 William Fitzherbert (restored)	1660 Accepted Frewen
1154 Roger of Pont l'Eveque	1664 Richard Sterne
1191 Geoffrey Plantagenet	1683 John Dolben
1215 Walter de Gray	1688 Thomas Lamplugh
1256 Sewal de Bovill	1691 John Sharp
1258 Godfrey Ludham [Kineton]	1714 William Dawes
1266 Walter Giffard	1724 Lancelot Blackburn
1279 William Wickwane	1743 Thomas Herring
1286 John Romanus [le Romeyn]	1747 Matthew Hutton
1298 Henry Newark	1757 John Gilbert
1300 Thomas Corbridge	1761 Roben Hay Drummond
1306 William Greenfield	1777 William Markham
1317 William Melton	1808 Edward Venables Vernon Harcourt
1342 William de la Zouche	1847 Thomas Musgrave
1352 John Thoresby	1860 Charles Thomas Longley
1374 Alexander Neville	1863 William Thomson
1388 Thomas Arundel	1891 William Connor Magee
1396 Robert Waldby	1891 William Dalrymple Maclagan
1398 Richard le Scrope	1909 Cosmo Gordon Lang
1407 Henry Bowet	1929 William Temple
1426 John Kempe	1942 Cyril Forster Garbett
1452 William Booth	1956 Arthur Michael Ramsey
1464 George Nevill	1961 Frederick Donald Coggan
1476 Lawrence Booth	1975 Stuart Yarworth Blanch
1480 Thomas Rotherham [Scott]	1983 John Stapylton Habgood
1501 Thomas Savage	1995 David Michael Hope
1508 Christopher Bainbridge	

[1] Ealdwulf and Wulfstan II held the Sees of York and Worcester together, Ælfric Puttoc held both 1040-41 and Ealdred 1060-61.

Durham

Description of arms. Azure, a cross or between four lions rampant argent.

BISHOPS OF LINDISFARNE[1]

635 Aidan
651 Finan
661 Colman
664 Tuda
    [Complications involving
    Wilfrid and Chad]
681 Eata
685 Cuthberht
    [Vacancy during which Wilfrid
    administered the See]
688 Eadberht
698 Eadfenh
731 Æthelweald
740 Cynewulf
781 Higbald
803 Ecgberht
821 Heathwred
830 Ecgred
845 Eanberht
854 Eardwulf

BISHOPS OF HEXHAM

664 Wilfrith
678 Eata
681 Tunberht
684 Cuthbert
685 Eata (restored)
687 John of Beverley
709 Acca
734 Frithoberht
767 Ahimund
781 Tilberht
789 Æthelberht
797 Heardred
800 Eanberht
813 Tidferth

BISHOPS OF CHESTER-LE-STREET[2]

899 Eardwulf
899 Cutheard
915 Tilred
925 Wigred
944 Uhtred
944 Seaxhelm
944 Ealdred
968 Ælfsige
990 Aldhun

BISHOPS OF DURHAM

990 Aldhun d. 1018
    [See vacant 1018–1020]
1020 Edmund
c.1040 Eadred
1041 Æthelric
1056 Æthelwine
1071 Walcher
1081 William of Saint Calais
1099 Ralph [Ranulf] Flambard
1133 Geoffrey Rufus
1143 William of Sainte-Barbe
1153 Hugh of le Puiset
1197 Philip of Poitiers

1217 Richard Marsh
1228 Richard Poore
1241 Nicholas Farnham
1249 Walter Kirkham
1261 Robert Stichill
1274 Robert of Holy Island
1284 Anthony Bek
1311 Richard Kellaw
1318 Lewis de Beaumont
1333 Richard of Bury
1345 Thomas Hatfield
1382 John Fordham
1388 Walter Skirlaw
1406 Thomas Langley
1438 Robert Nevill
1457 Lawrence Booth
1476 William Dudley
1485 John Shirwood
1494 Richard Fox
1502 William Senhouse [Sever]
1507 Christopher Bainbridge
1509 Thomas Ruthall
1523 Thomas Wolsey
1530 Cuthbert Tunstall
1561 James Pilkington
1577 Richard Barnes
1589 Matthew Hutton
1595 Tobias Matthew
1606 William James
1617 Richard Neile
1628 George Monteigne [Mountain]
1628 John Howson
1632 Thomas Morton
1660 John Cosin
1674 Nathaniel Crew [Lord Crew]
1721 William Talbot
1730 Edward Chandler
1750 Joseph Butler
1752 Richard Trevor
1771 John Egerton
1787 Thomas Thurlow
1791 Shute Barrington
1826 William Van Mildert
1836 Edward Maltby
1856 Charles Thomas Longley
1860 Henry Montagu Villiers
1861 Charles Baring
1879 Joseph Barber Lightfoot
1890 Brooke Foss Westcott
1901 Handley Carr Glyn Moule
1920 Herbert Hensley Henson
1939 Alwyn Terrell Petre Williams
1952 Arthur Michael Ramsey
1956 Maurice Henry Harland
1966 Ian Thomas Ramsey
1973 John Stapylton Habgood
1984 David Edward Jenkins
1994 Anthony Michael Arnold
    Turnbull
2003 Nicholas Thomas Wright

Blackburn

Description of arms. Per fess gules and or, in chief two keys in saltire wards downwards argent, in base a rose of the first barbed and seeded proper.

1926 Percy Mark Herbert
1942 Wilfred Marcus Askwith
1954 Walter Hubert Baddeley
1960 Charles Robert Claxton
1972 Robert Arnold Schürhoff
    Martineau
1982 David Stewart Cross
1989 Alan David Chesters

Bradford

Description of arms. Azure, two keys in saltire or, in chief a woolpack proper corded gold.

1920 Arthur William Thomson
    Perowne
1931 Alfred Walter Frank Blunt
1956 Frederick Donald Coggan
1961 Clement George St Michael
    Parker
1972 Ross Sydney Hook
1981 Geoffrey John Paul
1984 Robert Kerr Williamson
1992 David James Smith
2002 David Charles James

Carlisle

Description of arms. Argent, on a cross sable a labelled mitre or.

1133 Æthelwulf
1203 Bernard
1219 Hugh of Beaulieu
1224 Walter Mauclerc
1247 Silvester Everdon
1255 Thomas Vipont
1258 Robert de Chause
1280 Ralph Ireton
1292 John of Halton
1325 John Ross
1332 John Kirkby
1353 Gilbert Welton
1363 Thomas Appleby
1396 Robert Reade
1397 Thomas Merks
1400 William Strickland
1420 Roger Whelpdale
1424 William Barrow
1430 Marmaduke Lumley
1450 Nicholas Close
1452 William Percy
1462 John Kingscote
1464 Richard le Scrope
1468 Edward Story
1478 Richard Bell

---

[1] See transferred to Chester-le-Street 883.   [2] See transferred to Durham 995.

1496 William Senhouse [Sever]
1504 Roger Layburne
1508 John Penny
1521 John Kite
1537 Robert Aldrich
1556 Owen Oglethorpe
1561 John Best
1570 Richard Barnes
1577 John May
1598 Henry Robinson
1616 Robert Snowden
1621 Richard Milbourne
1624 Richard Senhouse
1626 Francis White
1629 Barnabas Potter
1642 James Ussher
1660 Richard Sterne
1664 Edward Rainbowe
1684 Thomas Smith
1702 William Nicolson
1718 Samuel Bradford
1723 John Waugh
1735 George Fleming
1747 Richard Osbaldeston
1762 Charles Lyttleton
1769 Edmund Law
1787 John Douglas
1791 Edward Venables Vernon
        [Harcourt]
1808 Samuel Goodenough
1827 Hugh Percy
1856 Henry Montagu Villiers
1860 Samuel Waldegrave
1869 Harvey Goodwin
1892 John Wareing Bardsley
1905 John William Diggle
1920 Henry Herbert Williams
1946 Thomas Bloomer
1966 Sydney Cyril Bulley
1972 Henry David Halsey
1989 Ian Harland
2000 Geoffrey Graham Dow

Chester

Description of arms. Gules, three labelled mitres or.

1541 John Bird
1554 George Cotes
1556 Cuthbert Scott
1561 William Downham
1579 William Chaderton
1595 Hugh Bellott
1597 Richard Vaughan
1604 George Lloyd
1616 Thomas Morton
1619 John Bridgeman
1660 Brian Walton
1662 Henry Ferne
1662 George Hall
1668 John Wilkins
1673 John Pearson
1686 Thomas Cartwright
1689 Nicolas Stratford
1708 William Dawes
1714 Francis Gastrell
1726 Samuel Peploe
1752 Edmund Keene
1771 William Markham

1777 Beilby Porteus
1788 William Cleaver
1800 Henry William Majendie
1810 Bowyer Edward Sparke
1812 George Henry Law
1824 Charles James Blomfield
1828 John Bird Sumner
1848 John Graham
1865 William Jacobson
1884 William Stubbs
1889 Francis John Jayne
1919 Henry Luke Paget
1932 Geoffrey Francis Fisher
1939 Douglas Henry Crick
1955 Gerald Alexander Ellison
1974 Hubert Victor Whitsey
1982 Michael Alfred Baughen
1996 Peter Robert Forster

Liverpool

Description of arms. Argent, an eagle with wings expanded sable, holding in its dexter claw an ancient inkhorn proper, around its head a nimbus or, a chief paly azure and gules, the dexter charged with an open book or, inscribed with the words 'Thy Word is Truth', the sinister charged with a lymphad gold.

1880 John Charles Ryle
1900 Francis James Chavasse
1923 Albert Augustus David
1944 Clifford Arthur Martin
1966 Stuart Yarworth Blanch
1975 David Stuart Sheppard
1998 James Stuart Jones

Manchester

Description of arms. Or, on a pale engrailed gules three mitres of the first, on a canton of the second three bendlets enhanced gold.

1848 James Prince Lee
1870 James Fraser
1886 James Moorhouse
1903 Edmund Arbuthnott Knox
1921 William Temple
1929 Frederic Sumpter Guy Warman
1947 William Derrick Lindsay Greer
1970 Patrick Campbell Rodger
1979 Stanley Eric Francis Booth-
        Clibborn
1993 Christopher John Mayfield
2002 Nigel Simeon McCulloch

Newcastle

Description of arms. Gules, a cross between four lions rampant or, on a chief gold three triple-towered castles of the first.

1882 Ernest Roland Wilberforce
1896 Edgar Jacob
1903 Arthur Thomas Lloyd
1907 Norman Dumenil John Straton
1915 Herbert Louis Wild
1927 Harold Ernest Bilbrough
1941 Noel Baring Hudson
1957 Hugh Edward Ashdown
1973 Ronald Oliver Bowlby
1981 Andrew Alexander Kenny
        Graham
1997 John Martin Wharton

Ripon and Leeds
(Ripon until 1999)

Description of arms. Argent, on a saltire gules two keys wards upwards or, on a chief of the second a Holy Lamb proper.

*c.*678 Eadheath

NEW FOUNDATION

1836 Charles Thomas Longley
1857 Robert Bickersteth
1884 William Boyd Carpenter
1912 Thomas Wortley Drury
1920 Thomas Banks Strong
1926 Edward Arthur Burroughs
1935 Geoffrey Charles Lester Lunt
1946 George Armitage Chase
1959 John Richard Humpidge
        Moorman
1975 Stuart Hetley Price
1977 David Nigel de Lorentz Young
2000 John Richard Packer

Sheffield

Description of arms. Azure, a crosier in pale ensigned by a fleur-de-lis vert,

between in fess a key surmounted by a
sword in saltire to the dexter, and to the
sinister eight arrows interlaced and
banded saltirewise, all or.

1914 Leonard Hedley Burrows
1939 Leslie Stannard Hunter
1962 Francis John Taylor
1971 William Gordon Fallows
1980 David Ramsay Lunn
1997 John Nicholls

Sodor and Man[1]

Description of arms. Argent, upon a
pedestal between two coronetted
pillars the Virgin Mary with arms
extended, in her dexter hand a church
proper and in base upon an
escutcheon, surmounted by a mitre,
the arms of Man – viz. gules, three legs
in armour conjoined at the thigh and
flexed at the knee.

 447 Germanus
     Conindrius
     Romulus
     Machutus
     Conanus
     Contentus
     Baldus
     Malchus
     Torkinus
     Brendanus
[Before 1080 Roolwer]
     William
     Hamond
1113 Wimund
1151 John
1160 Gamaliel
     Ragnald
     Christian of Argyle
     Michael
1203 Nicholas de Meaux
     Nicholas II
1217 Reginald
1226 John
1229 Simon of Argyle
1252 Richard
1275 Mark of Galloway
1305 Alan
1321 Gilbert Maclelan
1329 Bernard de Linton
1334 Thomas
1348 William Russell
1387 John Donegan
1387 Michael
1392 John Sproten
1402 Conrad
1402 Theodore Bloc
1429 Richard Messing Andrew
1435 John Seyre
1455 Thomas Burton
1458 Thomas Kirklam

1472 Angus
1478 Richard Oldham
1487 Hugh Blackleach
1513 Hugh Hesketh
1523 John Howden
1546 Henry Man
1556 Thomas Stanley
1570 John Salisbury
1576 John Meyrick
1600 George Lloyd
1605 John Philips
1634 William Forster
1635 Richard Parr
1661 Samuel Rutter
1663 Isaac Barrow
1671 Henry Bridgman
1683 John Lake
1685 Baptist Levinz
1698 Thomas Wilson
1755 Mark Hildesley
1773 Richard Richmond
1780 George Mason
1784 Claudius Crigan
1814 George Murray
1828 William Ward
1838 James Bowstead
1840 Henry Pepys
1841 Thomas Vowler Short
1847 Walter Augustus Shirley
1847 Robert John Eden
1854 Horatio Powys
1877 Rowley Hill
1887 John Wareing Bardsley
1892 Norman Dumenil John Straton
1907 Thomas Wortley Drury
1912 James Denton Thompson
1925 Charles Leonard Thornton-
     Duesbery
1928 William Stanton Jones
1943 John Ralph Strickland Taylor
1954 Benjamin Pollard
1966 George Eric Gordon
1974 Vernon Sampson Nicholls
1983 Arthur Henry Attwell
1989 Noël Debroy Jones

Southwell

Description of arms. Sable, three
fountains proper, on a chief or a pale
azure, charged with a representation
of the Virgin Mary seated bearing the
Infant Christ or between a stag lodged
proper and two staves raguly crossed
vert.

1884 George Ridding
1904 Edwyn Hoskyns
1926 Bernard Oliver Francis
     Heywood
1928 Henry Mosley
1941 Frank Russell Barry
1964 Gordon David Savage
1970 John Denis Wakeling

1985 Michael Humphrey Dickens
     Whinney
1988 Patrick Burnet Harris
1999 George Henry Cassidy

Wakefield

Description of arms. Or, a fleur-de-lis
azure, on a chief of the last three
celestial crowns gold.

1888 William Walsham How
1897 George Rodney Eden
1928 James Buchanan Seaton
1938 Campbell Richard Hone
1946 Henry McGowan
1949 Roger Plumpton Wilson
1958 John Alexander Ramsbotham
1968 Eric Treacy
1977 Colin Clement Walter James
1985 David Michael Hope
1992 Nigel Simeon McCulloch
2003 Stephen George Platten

Gibraltar in Europe

Description of arms. Argent, in base
rising out of the waves of the sea a
rock proper, thereon a lion guardant
or supporting a passion cross erect
gules, on a chief engrailed of the last a
crosier in bend dexter and a key in
bend sinister or surmounted by a
Maltese cross argent fimbriated gold.

BISHOPS OF GIBRALTAR

1842 George Tomlinson
1863 Walter John Trower
1868 Charles Amyand Harris
1874 Charles Waldegrave Sandford
1904 William Edward Collins
1911 Henry Joseph Corbett Knight
1921 John Harold Greig
1927 Frederick Cyril Nugent Hicks
1933 Harold Jocelyn Buxton
1947 Cecil Douglas Horsley
1953 Frederick William Thomas
     Craske
1960 Stanley Albert Hallam Eley
1970 John Richard Satterthwaite[2]

BISHOPS OF GIBRALTAR IN
EUROPE

1980 John Richard Satterthwaite
1993 John William Hind
2001 Douglas Geoffrey Rowell

[1] Included in the province of York by Act of Parliament 1542. Prior to Richard Oldham there is some uncertainty as to several names and
dates. From 1425 to 1553 there was an English and Scottish succession. It is not easy to say which claimant was Bishop either *de jure* or *de facto*.
[2] Bishop of Fulham and Gibraltar from 1970 to 1980.

BISHOPS SUFFRAGAN IN ENGLAND

Aston (Birmingham)

1954 Clement George St Michael
Parker
1962 David Brownfield Porter
1972 Mark Green
1982 Michael Humphrey Dickens
Whinney
1985 Colin Ogilvie Buchanan
1989–92 *no appointment*
1992 John Michael Austin

Barking (Chelmsford)

[in St Albans diocese to 1914]
1901 Thomas Stevens
1919 James Theodore Inskip
1948 Hugh Rowlands Gough
1959 William Frank Percival
Chadwick
1975 Albert James Adams
1983 James William Roxburgh
1991 Roger Frederick Sainsbury
2002 David John Leader Hawkins

Barrow-in-Furness (Carlisle)

1889 Henry Ware
1909 Campbell West-Watson
1926 Henry Sidney Pelham
1944 *in abeyance*

Basingstoke (Winchester)

1973 Colin Clement Walter James
1977 Michael Richard John
Manktelow
1994 Douglas Geoffrey Rowell
2002 Trevor Willmott

Bedford (St Albans)

1537 John Hodgkins[1]
1560–1879 *in abeyance*
1879 William Walsham How[2]
1888 Robert Claudius Billing[3]
1898–1935 *in abeyance*
1935 James Lumsden Barkway
1939 Aylmer Skelton
1948 Claude Thomas Thellusson
Wood
1953 Angus Campbell MacInnes
1957 Basil Tudor Guy
1963 Albert John Trillo
1968 John Tyrrell Holmes Hare
1977 Andrew Alexander Kenny
Graham
1981 David John Farmbrough
1994 John Henry Richardson
2003 Richard Neil Inwood

Berwick (Durham)

1536 Thomas Sparke
1572 *in abeyance*

Beverley (York)

1889 Robert Jarratt Crosthwaite
1923–94 *in abeyance*
1994 John Scott Gaisford
2000 Martyn William Jarrett

Birkenhead (Chester)

1965 Eric Arthur John Mercer
1974 Ronald Brown
1993 Michael Laurence Langrish
2000 David Andrew Urquhart

Bolton (Manchester)

1984 David George Galliford
1991 David Bonser
1999 David Keith Gillett

Bradwell (Chelmsford)

1968 William Neville Welch
1973 John Gibbs
1976 Charles Derek Bond
1993 Laurence Alexander Green

Bristol (Worcester)

1538 Henry Holbeach [Rands]
1542 *became diocesan see*

Brixworth (Peterborough)

1989 Paul Everard Barber
2002 Francis White

Buckingham (Oxford)

1914 Edward Domett Shaw
1921 Philip Herbert Eliot
1944 Robert Milton Hay
1960 Gordon David Savage
1964 George Christopher Cutts
Pepys
1974 Simon Hedley Burrows
1994 Colin James Bennetts
1998 Michael Arthur Hill
2003 Alan Thomas Lawrence
Wilson

Burnley (Blackburn)

[in Manchester diocese to 1926]
1901 Edwyn Hoskyns
1905 Alfred Pearson
1909 Henry Henn
1931 Edgar Priestley Swain
1950 Charles Keith Kipling Prosser
1955 George Edward Holderness
1970 Richard Charles Challinor
Watson
1988 Ronald James Milner
1994 Martyn William Jarrett
2000 John William Goddard

Colchester (Chelmsford)

[in London diocese to 1845
in Rochester diocese to 1877
in St Albans diocese 1877–1914]
1536 William More
1541–91 *in abeyance*
1592 John Sterne
1608–1882 *in abeyance*
1882 Alfred Blomfield
1894 Henry Frank Johnson
1909 Robert Henry Whitcombe
1922 Thomas Alfred Chapman
1933 Charles Henry Ridsdale
1946 Frederick Dudley Vaughan
Narborough
1966 Roderic Norman Coote
1988 Michael Edwin Vickers
1995 Edward Holland
2001 Christopher Heudebourck
Morgan

Coventry (Worcester)

see also under Lichfield
1891 Henry Bond Bowlby
1894 Edmund Arbuthnott Knox
1903–18 *no appointment*
1918 *became diocesan see*

Crediton (Exeter)

1897 Robert Edward Trefusis
1930 William Frederick Surtees
1954 Wilfred Arthur Edmund
Westall
1974 Philip John Pasterfield
1984 Peter Everard Coleman
1996 Richard Stephen Hawkins

Croydon (Southwark)

(in Canterbury diocese to 1985)
1904 Henry Horace Pereira
1924–30 *no appointment*
1930 Edward Sydney Woods
1937 William Louis Anderson
1942 Maurice Henry Harland
1947 Cuthbert Killick Norman
Bardsley
1957 John Taylor Hughes
1977 Geoffrey Stuart Snell
1985 Wilfred Denniston Wood
2003 Nicholas Baines

Derby (Southwell)

1889 Edward Ash Were
1909 Charles Thomas Abraham
1927 *became diocesan see*

Doncaster (Sheffield)

1972 Stuart Hetley Price
1976 David Stewart Cross
1982 William Michael Dermot
Persson
1993 Michael Frederick Gear
2000 Cyril Guy Ashton

Dorchester (Oxford)

see also under Dorchester (*diocesan
see*) *and* Lincoln
1939 Gerald Burton Allen
1952 Kenneth Riches
1957 David Goodwin Loveday
1972 Peter Knight Walker
1979 Conrad John Eustace Meyer
1988 Anthony John Russell
2000 Colin William Fletcher

Dorking (Guildford)

[in Winchester diocese to 1927]
1905 Cecil Henry Boutflower
1909–68 *in abeyance*
1968 Kenneth Dawson Evans
1986 David Peter Wilcox
1996 Ian James Brackley

Dover (Canterbury)

1537 Richard Yngworth
1545 Richard Thornden
1557–69 *no appointment*
1569 Richard Rogers
1597–1870 *in abeyance*
1870 Edward Parry
1890 George Rodney Eden
1898 William Walsh
1916 Harold Ernest Bilbrough
1927 John Victor Macmillan
1935 Alfred Careywollaston Rose
1957 Lewis Evan Meredith
1964 Anthony Paul Tremlett
1980 Richard Henry McPhail Third

---

[1] Appointed for the diocese of London.   [2] Appointed for the diocese of London.
[3] Appointed for the diocese of London, and retained title after resigning his suffragan duties in 1895.

1992 John Richard Allan Llewellin
1999 Stephen Squires Venner

Dudley (Worcester)

1974 Michael Ashley Mann
1977 Anthony Charles Dumper
1993 Rupert William Noel Hoare
2000 David Stuart Walker

Dunwich (St Edmundsbury and Ipswich)

see also under Norwich

1934 Maxwell Homfray Maxwell-
        Gumbleton
1945 Clement Mallory Ricketts
1955 Thomas Herbert Cashmore
1967 David Rokeby Maddock
1977 William Johnston
1980 Eric Nash Devenport
1992 Jonathan Sansbury Bailey
1995 Timothy John Stevens
1999 Clive Young

Ebbsfleet (Canterbury)

1994 John Richards
1998 Michael Alan Houghton
2000 Andrew Burnham

Edmonton (London)

1970 Alan Francis Bright Rogers
1975 William John Westwood
1985 Brian John Masters
1999 Peter William Wheatley

Europe (Europe)

1980 Ambrose Walter Marcus
        Weekes
1986 Edward Holland
1995 Henry William Scriven
2002 David Hamid

Fulham (London)[1]

1926 Basil Staunton Batty
1947 William Marshall Selwyn
1949 George Ernest Ingle
1955 Robert Wright Stopford
1957 Roderic Norman Coote
1966 Alan Francis Bright Rogers
1970 John Richard Satterthwaite[2]
1980–1982 *no appointment*
1982 Brian John Masters
1985 Charles John Klyberg
1996 John Charles Broadhurst

Grantham (Lincoln)

1905 Welbore MacCarthy
1920 John Edward Hine
1930 Ernest Morell Blackie
1935 Arthur Ivan Greaves
1937 Algernon Augustus Markham
1949 Anthony Otter
1965 Ross Sydney Hook
1972 Dennis Gascoyne Hawker
1987 William Ind
1997 Alastair Llewellyn John Redfern

Grimsby (Lincoln)

1935 Ernest Morell Blackie
1937 Anhur Ivan Greaves
1958 Kenneth Healey
1966 Gerald Fitzmaurice Colin
1979 David Tustin
2000 David Douglas James Rossdale

Guildford (Winchester)

1874 John Sutton Utterton
1888 George Henry Sumner
1909 John Hugh Granville
        Randolph
1927 *became diocesan see*

Hertford (St Albans)

1968 Albert John Trillo
1971 Hubert Victor Whitsey
1974 Peter Mumford
1982 Kenneth Harold Pillar
1990 Robin Jonathan Norman
        Smith
2001 Christopher Richard James
        Foster

Horsham (Chichester)

1968 Simon Wilton Phipps
1975 Ivor Colin Docker
1991 John William Hind
1993 Lindsay Goodall Urwin

Hull (York)

1538 Robert Sylvester (Pursglove)
1579–1891 *in abeyance*
1891 Richard Frederick Lefevre
        Blunt
1910 John Augustus Kempthome
1913 Francis Gurdon
1929–31 *no appointment*
1931 Bemard Oliver Francis
        Heywood
1934 Henry Townsend Vodden
1957 George Frednck Townley
1965 Hubert Laurence Higgs
1977 Geoffrey John Paul
1981 Donald George Snelgrove
1994 James Stuart Jones
1998 Richard Michael Cockayne
        Frith

Hulme (Manchester)

1924 John Charles Hill
1930 Thomas Sherwood Jones
1945 Hugh Leycester Homby
1953 Kenneth Venner Ramsey
1975 David George Galliford
1984 Colin John Fraser Scott
1999 Stephen Richard Lowe

Huntingdon (Ely)

1966 Robert Amold Schürhoff
        Martineau
1972 Eric St Quintin Wall
1980 William Gordon Roe
1997 John Robert Flack
2003 John Geoffrey Inge

Ipswich (Norwich)

1536 Thomas Manning[3]
?–1899 *in abeyance*[4]
1899 George Carnac Fisher
1906 Henry Luke Paget
1909 *no appointment*
1914 *became diocesan see with*
        St Edmundsbury

Islington (London)

1898 Charles Henry Turner
1923 *in abeyance*

Jarrow (Durham)

1906 George Nickson

1914 John Nathaniel Quirk
1924 Samuel Kirshbaum Knight
1932 James Geoffrey Gordon
1939 Leslie Owen
1944 David Colin Dunlop
1950 John Alexander Ramsbotham
1958 Mervyn Armstrong
1965 Alexander Kenneth Hamilton
1980 Michael Thomas Ball
1990 Alan Smithson
2002 John Lawrence Pritchard

Kensington (London)

1901 Frederic Edward Ridgeway
1911 John Primatt Maud
1932 Bertram Fitzgerald Simpson
1942 Henry Colville Montgomery
        Campbell
1949 Cyril Eastaugh
1962 Edward James Keymer
        Roberts
1964 Ronald Cedric Osbourne
        Goodchild
1981 Mark Santer
1987 John George Hughes
1994–96 *no appointment*
1996 Michael John Colclough

Kingston-upon-Thames (Southwark)

1905 Cecil Hook
1915 Samuel Mumford Taylor
1922 Percy Mark Herbert
1927 Frederick Ochterlony Taylor
        Hawkes
1952 William Percy Gilpin
1970 Hugh William Montefiore
1978 Keith Norman Sutton
1984 Peter Stephen Maurice Selby
1992 John Martin Wharton
1997 Peter Bryan Price
2002 Richard Ian Cheetham

Knaresborough (Ripon)

1905 Lucius Frederick Moses
        Bottomley Smith
1934 Paul Fulcrand Dalacour de
        Labilliere
1938 John Norman Bateman-
        Champain
1948 Henry Handley Vully de
        Candole
1965 John Howard Cruse
1972 Ralph Emmerson
1979 John Dennis
1986 Malcolm James Menin
1997 Frank Valentine Weston

Lancaster (Blackburn)

1936 Benjamin Pollard
1955 Anthony Leigh Egerton
        Hoskyns-Abrahall
1975 Dennis Fountain Page
1985 Ian Harland
1990 John Nicholls
1998 Geoffrey Stephen Pedley

Leicester (Peterborough)

see also under Lichfield *and* Lincoln

1888 Francis Henry Thicknesse
1903 Lewis Clayton
1913 Norman MacLeod Lang
1927 *became diocesan see*

---

[1] From 1926 to 1980 exercised the Bishop of London's extra-diocesan jurisdiction over chaplaincies in Northern and Central Europe. Since 1996 has assisted the Diocesan Bishop in all matters not delegated to the Areas, and in pastoral care of parishes operating under the London Plan.
[2] Bishop of Fulham and Gibraltar.
[3] Manning does not appear to have acted as a suffragan bishop in the diocese of Norwich.
[4] The date of Manning's death is not known.

Lewes (Chichester)

1909 Leonard Hedley Burrows
1914 Herbert Edward Jones
1920 Henry Kemble Southwell
1926 Thomas William Cook
1929 William Champion Streatfield
1929 Hugh Maudsley Hordern
1946 Geoffrey Hodgson Warde
1959 James Herbert Lloyd Morrell
1977 Peter John Ball
1992 Ian Patrick Martyn Cundy
1997 Wallace Parke Benn

Ludlow (Hereford)

1981 Stanley Mark Wood
1987 Ian Macdonald Griggs
1994 John Charles Saxbee
2002 Michael Wrenford Hooper

Lynn (Norwich)

1963 William Somers Llewellyn
1972 William Aubrey Aitken
1986 David Edward Bentley
1994 David John Conner
1999 Anthony Charles Foottit

Maidstone (Canterbury)

1944 Leslie Owen
1946–56 *no appointment*
1956 Stanley Woodley Betts
1966–69 *no appointment*
1969 Geoffrey Lewis Tiarks
1976 Richard Henry McPhail Third
1980 Robert Maynard Hardy
1987 David James Smith
1992 Gavin Hunter Reid
2001 Graham Alan Cray

Malmesbury (Bristol)

1927 Ronald Erskine Ramsay
1946 Ivor Stanley Watkins
1956 Edward James Keymer
     Roberts
1962 Clifford Leofric Purdy Bishop
1973 Frederick Stephen Temple
1983 Peter James Firth
1994 *renamed* Swindon

Marlborough

1537 Thomas Morley (Bickley)[1]
c1561–1888 *in abeyance*
1888 Alfred Earle[2]
1919 *in abeyance*

Middleton (Manchester)

1927 Richard Godfrey Parsons
1932 Cecil Wilfred Wilson
1938 Arthur Fawssett Alston
1943 Edward Worsfold Mowll
1952 Frank Woods
1958 Robert Nelson
1959 Edward Ralph Wickham
1982 Donald Alexander Tytler
1994 Stephen Squires Venner
1999 Michael Augustine Owen
     Lewis

Nottingham (Lincoln)

[in York diocese to 1837]
1567 Richard Barnes
1570–1870 *in abeyance*

1870 Henry Mackenzie
1877 Edward Trollope
1893 *in abeyance*

Penrith (Carlisle)

see also under Richmond

1537 John Bird[3]
1539–1888 *in abeyance*
1888 John James Pulleine[4]
1939 Grandage Edwards Powell
1944 Herbert Victor Turner
1959 Sydney Cyril Bulley
1967 Reginald Foskett
1970 William Edward Augustus
     Pugh
1979 George Lanyon Hacker
1994 Richard Garrard
2002 James William Scobie
     Newcome

Plymouth (Exeter)

1923 John Howard Bertram
     Masterman
1934 Francis Whitfield Daukes
1950 Norman Harry Clarke
1962 Wilfred Guy Sanderson
1972 Richard Fox Cartwright
1982 Kenneth Albert Newing
1988 Richard Stephen Hawkins
1996 John Henry Garton

Pontefract (Wakefield)

1931 Campbell Richard Hone
1939 Tom Longworth
1949 Arthur Harold Morris
1954 George William Clarkson
1961 Eric Treacy
1968 William Gordon Fallows
1971 Thomas Richard Hare
1993 John Thornley Finney
1998 David Charles James
2002 Anthony William Robinson

Ramsbury (Salisbury)

see also under Salisbury

1974 John Robert Geoffrey Neale
1989 Peter St George Vaughan
1999 Peter Fearnley Hullah

Reading (Oxford)

1889 James Leslie Randall
1909–42 *in abeyance*
1942 Arthur Groom Parham
1954 Eric Henry Knell
1972 Eric Wild
1982 Ronald Graham Gregory
     Foley
1989 John Frank Ewan Bone
1997 Edward William Murray
     Walker

Repton (Derby)

1965 William Warren Hunt
1977 Stephen Edmund Verney
1986 Francis Henry Arthur
     Richmond
1999 David Christopher Hawtin

Richborough (Canterbury)

1995 Edwin Ronald Barnes
2002 Keith Newton

Richmond (Ripon)

1889 John James Pulleine[5]
1913 Francis Charles Kilner
1921 *in abeyance*

St Germans (Truro)

1905 John Rundle Cornish
1918–74 *in abeyance*
1974 Cecil Richard Rutt
1979 Reginald Lindsay Fisher
1985 John Richard Allan Llewellin
1993 Graham Richard James
2000 Royden Screech

Selby (York)

1939 Henry St John Stirling
     Woollcombe
1941 Carey Frederick Knyvett
1962 Douglas Noel Sargent
1972 Morris Henry St John
     Maddocks
1983 Clifford Conder Barker
1991 Humphrey Vincent Taylor

Shaftesbury (Salisbury)

[in Bristol diocese 1542–1836]
1539 John Bradley
? *in abeyance*[6]

Sheffield (York)

1901 John Nathaniel Quirk
1914 *became diocesan see*

Sherborne (Salisbury)

1925 Robert Crowther Abbott
1928 Gerald Burton Allen
1936 Harold Nickinson Rodgers
1947 John Maurice Key
1960 Victor Joseph Pike
1976 John Dudley Galtrey Kirkham
2001 Timothy Martin Thornton

Sherwood (Southwell)

1965 Kenneth George Thompson
1975 Harold Richard Darby
1989 Alan Wyndham Morgan

Shrewsbury (Lichfield)

1537 Lewis Thomas[7]
1561–1888 *in abeyance*
1888 Sir Lovelace Tomlinson
     Stamer
1905–40 *in abeyance*
1940 Eric Knightley Chetwode
     Hamilton
1944 Robert Leighton Hodson
1959 William Alonzo Parker
1970 Francis William Cocks
1980 Leslie Lloyd Rees
1987 John Dudley Davies
1994 David Marrison Hallatt
2001 Alan Gregory Clayton Smith

Southampton (Winchester)

1895 William Awdry
1896 George Carnac Fisher
1898 The Hon Arthur Temple
     Lyttelton

---

[1] Appointed for the diocese of London.
[2] Appointed for the diocese of London, but retained the title while Dean of Exeter 1900-18.
[3] Appointed for the diocese of Lichfield.
[4] Appointed for the diocese of Ripon.
[5] His suffragan title was changed from Penrith to Richmond by Royal Warrant.
[6] The date of Bradley's death is not known.
[7] Not appointed for Lichfield, but probably for Llandaff.

1903 James Macarthur
1921 Cecil Henry Boutflower
1933 Arthur Baillie Lumsdaine
     Karney
1943 Edmund Robert Morgan
1951 Kenneth Edward Norman
     Lamplugh
1972 John Kingsmill Cavell
1984 Edward David Cartwright
1989 John Freeman Perry
1996 Jonathan Michael Gledhill

Southwark (Rochester)

1891 Huyshe Wolcott Yeatman-
     Biggs
1905 *became diocesan see*

Stafford (Lichfield)

1909 Edward Ash Were
1915 Lionel Payne Crawfurd
1934 Douglas Henry Crick
1938 Lemprière Durell Hammond
1958 Richard George Clitherow
1975 John Waine
1979 John Stevens Waller
1987 Michael Charles Scott-Joynt
1996 Christopher John Hill

Stepney (London)

1895 George Forrest Browne
1897 Arthur Foley Winnington-
     Ingram
1901 Cosmo Gordon Lang
1909 Henry Luke Paget
1919 Henry Mosley
1928 Charles Edward Curzon
1936 Robert Hamilton Moberly
1952 Joost de Blank
1957 Francis Evered Lunt
1968 Ernest Urban Trevor
     Huddleston
1978 James Lawton Thompson
1992 Richard John Carew Chartres
1996 John Mugabi Sentamu
2003 Stephen John Oliver

Stockport (Chester)

1949 Frank Jackson Okell
1951 David Henry Saunders
     Saunders-Davies
1965 Rupert Gordon Strutt
1984 Frank Pilkington Sargeant
1994 Geoffrey Martin Turner
2000 William Nigel Stock

Swindon (Bristol)

1994 Michael David Doe

Taunton (Bath and Wells)

1538 William Finch
1559–1911 *in abeyance*
1911 Charles Fane de Salis
1931 George Arthur Hollis
1945 Harry Thomas
1955 Mark Allin Hodson
1962 Francis Horner West
1977 Peter John Nott
1986 Nigel Simeon McCulloch
1992 John Hubert Richard Lewis
1997 William Allen Stewart
1998 Andrew John Radford

Tewkesbury (Gloucester)

1938 Augustine John Hodson
1955 Edward Barry Henderson
1960 Forbes Trevor Horan
1973 Thomas Carlyle Joseph Robert
     Hamish Deakin
1986 Geoffrey David Jeremy Walsh
1996 John Stewart Went

Thetford (Norwich)

see also under Norwich
1536 John Salisbury
1570–1894 *in abeyance*
1894 Arthur Thomas Lloyd
1903 John Philips Alcott Bowers
1926–45 *no appointment*
1945 John Walker Woodhouse
1953 Manin Patrick Grainge
     Leonard
1963 Eric William Bradley Cordingly
1977 Hugh Charles Blackburne
1981 Timothy Dudley-Smith
1992 Hugo Ferdinand de Waal
2001 David John Atkinson

Tonbridge (Rochester)

1959 Russell Berridge White
1968 Henry David Halsey
1973 Philip Harold Ernest Goodrich
1982 David Henry Bartleet
1993 Brian Arthur Smith
2002 Brian Colin Castle

Warrington (Liverpool)

1918 Martin Linton Smith
1920 Edwin Hone Kempson
1927 Herbert Gresford Jones
1946 Charles Robert Claxton
1960 Laurence Ambrose Brown
1970 John Monier Bickersteth
1976 Michael Henshall
1996 John Richard Packer
2000 David Wilfred Michael
     Jennings

Warwick (Coventry)

1980 Keith Appleby Arnold
1990 Clive Handford
1996 Anthony Martin Priddis

Whalley (Blackburn)

[in Manchester diocese to 1926]
1909 Atherton Gwillym Rawstorne
1936 *in abeyance*

Whitby (York)

1923 Harry St John Stirling
     Woollcombe
1939 Harold Evelyn Hubbard
1947 Walter Hubert Baddeley
1954 Philip William Wheeldon
1961 George D'Oyly Snow
1972 John Yates
1976 Clifford Conder Barker
1983 Gordon Bates
1999 Robert Sidney Ladds

Willesden (London)

1911 William Willcox Perrin
1929 Guy Vernon Smith
1940 Henry Colville Montgomery
     Campbell
1942 Edward Michael Gresford
     Jones
1950 Gerald Alexander Ellison
1955 George Ernest Ingle
1964 Graham Douglas Leonard
1974 Geoffrey Hewlett Thompson
1985 Thomas Frederick Butler
1992 Geoffrey Graham Dow
2001 Peter Alan Broadbent

Wolverhampton (Lichfield)

1979 Barry Rogerson
1985 Christopher John Mayfield
1994 Michael Gay Bourke

Woolwich (Southwark)

1905 John Cox Leeke
1918 William Woodcock Hough
1932 Arthur Llewellyn Preston
1936 Leslie Hamilton Lang
1947 Robert William Stannard
1959 John Arthur Thomas
     Robinson
1969 David Stuart Sheppard
1975 Michael Eric Marshall
1984 Albert Peter Hall
1996 Colin Ogilvie Buchanan

WALES

Archbishops of Wales

1920 Alfred George Edwards (St Asaph 1889–1934)
1934 Charles Alfred Howell Green (Bangor 1928–44)
1944 David Lewis Prosser (St Davids 1927–50)
1949 John Morgan (Llandaff 1939–57)
1957 Alfred Edwin Morris (Monmouth 1945–67)
1968 William Glyn Hughes Simon (Llandaff 1957–71)
1971 Gwilym Owen Williams (Bangor 1957–82)
1983 Derrick Greenslade Childs (Monmouth 1972–87)
1987 George Noakes (St Davids 1982–91)
1991 Alwyn Rice Jones (St Asaph 1982–99)
1999 Rowan Douglas Williams (Monmouth 1992–2002)
2003 Barry Cennydd Morgan (Llandaff 1999–)

Bangor[1]

c.550 Deiniol [Daniel]
c.775 Elfod [Elbodugen]
1092 Herve
[Vacancy 1109–20]
1120 David the Scot
1140 Maurice (Meurig)
[Vacancy 1161–77]
1177 Guy Rufus [Gwion Goch]
[Vacancy c1190–95]
1195 Alan [Alban]
1197 Robert of Shrewsbury
[Vacancy 1212–15]
1215 Cadwgan
1237 Richard
1267 Anian [or Einion]
1307 Gruflydd ab Iowerth
1309 Anian [Einion] Sais
1328 Matthew de Englefield
1357 Thomas de Ringstead
1366 Gervase de Castro
1371 Hywel ap Gronwy
1372 John Gilbert
1376 John Swaffham
1400 Richard Young
[Vacancy c1404–8]
1408 Benedict Nicolls
1418 William Barrow
1425 John Cliderow
1436 Thomas Cheriton
1448 John Stanbury
1453 James Blakedon
1465 Richard Edenham
1495 Henry Dean
1500 Thomas Pigot
1505 Thomas Penny
1509 Thomas Skevington
1534 John Salcot [or Capon]
1539 John Bird
1542 Arthur Bulkeley
1555 William Glynn
1559 Rowland Meyrick
1566 Nicholas Robinson
1586 Hugh Bellot
1596 Richard Vaughan

1598 Henry Rowlands
1616 Lewis Bayly
1632 David Dolben
1634 Edmund Griffith
1637 William Roberts
1666 Robert Morgan
1673 Humphrey Lloyd
1689 Humphrey Humphreys
1702 John Evans
1716 Benjamin Hoadley
1721 Richard Reynolds
1723 William Baker
1728 Thomas Sherlock
1734 Charles Cecil
1738 Thomas Herring
1743 Matthew Hutton
1748 Zachary Pearce
1756 John Egerton
1769 John Ewer
1775 John Moore
1783 John Warren
1800 William Cleaver
1807 John Randolph
1809 Henry William Majendie
1830 Christopher Bethell
1859 James Colquhoun Campbell
1890 Daniel Lewis Lloyd
1899 Watkin Herbert Williams
1925 Daniel Davies
1928 Charles Alfred Howell Green (Archbishop of Wales 1934)
1944 David Edwardes Davies
1949 John Charles Jones
1957 Gwilym Owen Williams (Archbishop of Wales 1971)
1982 John Cledan Mears
1993 Barry Cennydd Morgan
1999 Francis James Saunders Davies

Llandaff[2]

c.550 Teiliau
c.872 Cyfeiliag
c.880 Libiau
c.940 Marchlwys
982 Gwyzan
c.995 Bledri
1027 Joseph
1056 Herewald
1107 Urban
[Vacancy of six years]
1140 Uchtryd
1148 Nicolas ap Gwrgant
[Vacancy of two years]
1186 William Saltmarsh
1193 Henry of Abergavenny
1219 William of Goldcliff
1230 Elias of Radnor
1245 William de Burgh
1254 John de Ware
1257 William of Radnor
1266 Willam de Breuse [or Brus]
1297 John of Monmouth
1323 John of Eaglescliffe
1344 John Paschal
1361 Roger Cradock
1383 Thomas Rushook
1386 William Bottesham
1389 Edmund Bromfield
1393 Tideman de Winchcomb
1395 Andrew Barret
1396 John Burghill
1398 Thomas Peverel
1408 John de la Zouch [Fulford]

1425 John Wells
1441 Nicholas Ashby
1458 John Hunden
1476 John Smith
1478 John Marshall
1496 John Ingleby
1500 Miles Salley
1517 George de Athequa
1537 Robert Holdgate [or Holgate]
1545 Anthony Kitchin
1567 Hugh Jones
1575 William Blethin
1591 Gervase Babington
1595 William Morgan
1601 Francis Godwin
1618 George Carleton
1619 Theophilus Field
1627 William Murray
1640 Morgan Owen
1660 Hugh Lloyd
1667 Francis Davies
1675 William Lloyd
1679 William Beaw
1706 John Tyler
1725 Robert Clavering
1729 John Harris
1739 Matthias Mawson
1740 John Gilbert
1749 Edward Cressett
1755 Richard Newcome
1761 John Ewer
1769 Jonathan Shipley
1769 Shute Barrington
1782 Richard Watson
1816 Herbert Marsh
1819 William Van Mildert
1826 Charles Richard Sumner
1828 Edward Copleston
1849 Alfred Ollivant
1883 Richard Lewis
1905 Joshua Pritchard Hughes
1931 Timothy Rees
1939 John Morgan (Archbishop of Wales 1949)
1957 William Glyn Hughes Simon (Archbishop of Wales 1968)
1971 Eryl Stephen Thomas
1975 John Richard Worthington Poole-Hughes
1985 Roy Thomas Davies
1999 Barry Cennydd Morgan (Archbishop of Wales 2003)

Monmouth

1921 Charles Alfred Howell Green
1928 Gilbert Cunningham Joyce
1940 Alfred Edwin Monahan
1945 Alfred Edwin Morris (Archbishop of Wales 1957)
1968 Eryl Stephen Thomas
1972 Derrick Greenslade Childs (Archbishop of Wales 1983)
1986 Royston Clifford Wright
1992 Rowan Douglas Williams (Archbishop of Wales 1999)
2003 Edward William Murray Walker

St Asaph[3]

c.560 Kentigern
c.573 Asaph
1143 Gilbert

[1] Very few of the names of the Celtic bishops have been preserved.
[2] The traditional list of bishops of the Celtic Church has little historical foundation. But the names of the following, prior to Urban, may be regarded as fairly trustworthy, though the dates are very uncertain.
[3] Prior to the Norman period there is considerable uncertainty as to names and dates.

1152 Geoffrey of Monmouth
1154 Richard
1160 Godfrey
1175 Adam
1183 John I
1186 Reiner
1225 Abraham
1235 Hugh
1242 Hywel Ab Ednyfed
1249 Anian I [or Einion]
1267 John II
1268 Anian II
1293 Llywelyn de Bromfield
1315 Dafydd ap Bleddyn
1346 John Trevor I
1357 Llywelyn ap Madoc ab Ellis
1377 William de Spridlington
1382 Lawrence Child
1390 Alexander Bache
1395 John Trevor II
1411 Robert de Lancaster
1433 John Lowe
1444 Reginald Pecock
1451 Thomas Bird *alias* Knight
1471 Richard Redman
1496 Michael Deacon
1500 Dafydd ab Iorwerth
1504 Dafydd ab Owain
1513 Edmund Birkhead
1518 Henry Standish
1536 Robert Warton [or Parfew]
1555 Thomas Goldwell
1560 Richard Davies
1561 Thomas Davies
1573 William Hughes
1601 William Morgan
1604 Richard Parry
1624 John Hanmer
1629 John Owen
1660 George Griffith
1667 Henry Glemham
1670 Isaac Barrow
1680 William Lloyd
1692 Edward Jones
1703 George Hooper
1704 William Beveridge
1708 Will. Fleetwood
1715 John Wynne
1727 Francis Hare
1732 Thomas Tanner
1736 Isaac Maddox
1744 Samuel Lisle
1748 Robert Hay Drummond
1761 Richard Newcome
1769 Jonathan Shipley
1789 Samuel Hallifax
1790 Lewis Bagot
1802 Samuel Horsley
1806 William Cleaver
1815 John Luxmore
1830 William Carey
1846 Thomas Vowler Short
1870 Joshua Hughes
1889 Alfred George Edwards
    (Archbishop of Wales 1920)
1934 William Thomas Havard

1950 David Daniel Bartlett
1971 Harold John Charles
1982 Alwyn Rice Jones (Archbishop
    of Wales 1991–99)
1999 John Stewart Davies

St Davids[1]

c.601 David
c.606 Cynog
831 Sadyrnfyw
    Meurig
c.840 Novis
    ?Idwal
c.906 Asser
    Llunwerth
944 Eneuris
c.961 Rhydderch
c.999 Morgeneu
1023 Morgeneu
1023 Erwyn
1039 Tramerin
1061 Joseph
1061 Bleddud
1072 Sulien
1078 Abraham
1080 Sulien
1085 Wilfrid
1115 Bernard
1148 David Fitz-Gerald
1176 Peter de Leia
1203 Geoffrey de Henlaw
1215 Gervase [Iorwerth]
1231 Anselm le Gras
1248 Thomas le Waleys
1256 Richard de Carew
1280 Thomas Bek
1296 David Martin
1328 Henry Gower
1347 John Thoresby
1350 Reginald Brian
1352 Thomas Fastolf
1362 Adam Houghton
1389 John Gilbert
1397 Guy de Mohne
1408 Henry Chichele
1414 John Catterick
1415 Stephen Patrington
1418 Benedict Nichols
1434 Thomas Rodburn [Rudborne]
1442 William Lindwood
1447 John Langton
1447 John de la Bere
1460 Robert Tully
1482 Richard Martin
1483 Thomas Langton
1485 Hugh Pavy
1496 John Morgan [Young]
1505 Robert Sherborn
1509 Edward Vaughan
1523 Richard Rawlins
1536 William Barlow
1548 Robert Ferrar
1554 Henry Morgan
1560 Thomas Young

1561 Richard Davies
1582 Marmaduke Middleton
1594 Anthony Rudd
1615 Richard Milbourne
1621 William Laud
1627 Theophilus Field
1636 Roger Mainwaring
1660 William Lucy
1678 William Thomas
1683 Laurence Womock
1686 John Lloyd
1687 Thomas Watson
[*Vacancy* 1699–1705]
1705 George Bull
1710 Philip Bisse
1713 Adam Ottley
1724 Richard Smallbrooke
1731 Elias Sydall
1732 Nicholas Claggett
1743 Edward Willes
1744 Richard Trevor
1753 Anthony Ellis
1761 Samuel Squire
1766 Robert Lowth
1766 Charles Moss
1774 James Yorke
1779 John Warren
1783 Edward Smallwell
1788 Samuel Horsley
1794 William Stewart
1801 George Murray
1803 Thomas Burgess
1825 John Banks Jenkinson
1840 Connop Thirlwall
1874 William Basil Tickell Jones
1897 John Owen
1927 David Lewis Prosser
    (Archbishop of Wales 1944)
1950 William Thomas Havard
1956 John Richards Richards
1971 Eric Matthias Roberts
1982 George Noakes (Archbishop
    of Wales 1987)
1991 John Ivor Rees
1996 David Huw Jones
2002 Carl Norman Cooper

Swansea and Brecon

1923 Edward Latham Bevan
1934 John Morgan
1939 Edward William Williamson
1953 William Glyn Hughes Simon
1958 John James Absalom Thomas
1976 Benjamin Noel Young
    Vaughan
1988 Dewi Morris Bridges
1999 Anthony Edward Pierce

Provincial Assistant Bishops

1996 David Thomas

---

[1] The following names occur in early records though the dates given cannot always be reconciled.

SCOTLAND

Sources: Bp Dowden's *The Bishops of Scotland* (Glasgow 1912), for all the sees up to the Reformation, and for Aberdeen and Moray to the present time.

For bishops after the Reformation (and for a few of the earliest ones before Queen Margaret) – Grub, *Ecclesiastical History of Scotland* (Edinburgh 1861, 4 Vols.) and Bp Keith and Bp Russel, *Scottish Bishops* (2nd ed. Edinburgh 1824).

Scottish episcopal elections became subject immediately to Roman confirmation in 1192. The subordination of the Scottish Church to York became less direct in 1165, and its independence was recognized in a bill of Celestine III in 1192. St Andrews was raised to metropolitan rank on 17 August 1472 and the Archbishop became primate of all Scotland with the same legative rights as the Archbishop of Canterbury on 27 March 1487.

The dates in the margin are those of the consecration or translation to the particular see of the bishops named; or in the case of bishops elect, who are not known to have been consecrated, they are those of the election; or in the case of titular bishops, of the date of their appointment.

The date of the death has been given where there was a long interregnum, or where there is dislocation (as at the Reformation and at the Revolution), or for some special reason to make the history intelligible.

The extra information in the list of College Bishops is given for the reason just stated.

St Andrews

St Andrews, Dunkeld and Dunblane

906 Cellach I
915(?) Fothad I
955 Malisius I
963 Maelbridge
970 Cellach II
996(?) Malasius II
(?) Malmore
1025 Alwyn
1028 Maelduin
1055 Tuthald or Tuadal
1059 Fothad II
1077 Gregory (elect)
to   Catharas (elect)
1107   Edmarus (elect)
    Godricus (elect)
1109 Turgot
1120 Eadmer (elect)
1127 Robert
1159 Waldeve (elect)
1160 Ernald
1165 Richard
1178 Hugh
1180 John the Scot
1198 Roger de Beaumon
1202 William Malveisin
1238 Geoffrey (elect)
1240 David de Bernham
1253 Robert de Stuteville (elect)
1254 Abel de Golin
1255 Gamelin
1273 William Wischard
1280 William Fraser
1298 William de Lamberton
1328 James Bennet
1342 William de Laundels
1385 Stephen de Pay (elect)
1386(?) Walter Trayl
1388 Alexander de Neville
1398 Thomas de Arundel
1401 Thomas Stewart (elect)
1402 Walter de Danielston (elect)
1403(?) Gilbert Greenlaw
1403 Henry Wardlaw
1408 John Trevor
1440 James Kennedy

ARCHBISHOPS

1465 Patrick Graham
1478 William Scheves
1497 James Stewart (elect)
1504 Alexander Stewart (elect)
1513 John Hepburn (elect)
1513 Innocenzo Cibo (elect)
1514 Andrew Forman
1522 James Betoun
1538 David Betoun [coadjutor]
1547 John Hamilton

1551 Gavin Hamilton [coadjutor] died 1571
1572 John Douglas (titular)
1576 Patrick Adamson (titular) died 1592
1611 George Gladstanes
1615 John Spottiswoode, died 1639
1661 James Sharp
1679 Alexander Burnet
1684 Arthur Rose, died 1704

BISHOPS OF FIFE

[1704–26 See vacant]
1726 James Rose
1733 Robert Keith
1743 Robert White
1761 Henry Edgar

BISHOPS OF ST ANDREWS

1842 Patrick Torry
1853 Charles Wordsworth
1893 George Howard Wilkinson
1908 Charles Edward Plumb
1931 Edward Thomas Scott Reid
1938 James Lumsden Barkway
1949 Arnold Brian Burrowes
1955 John William Alexander Howe
1969 Michael Geoffrey Hare Duke
1995 Michael Harry George Henley

†Dunkeld

849(?) Tuathal
865(?) Flaithbertach
1114 Cormac
1147 Gregory
1170 Richard I
1178 Walter de Bidun (elect)
1183(?) John I, the Scot
1203 Richard II, de Prebenda
1212(?) John II, de Leycester
1214(?) Hugh de Sigillo
1229 Matthew Scot (elect)
1229 Gilbert
1236(?) Geoffrey de Liberatione
1252 Richard III, of Inverkeithing
1273(?) Robert de Stuteville
1283(?) Hugh de Strivelin [Stirling] (elect)
1283 William
1288 Matthew de Crambeth
1309 John de Leek (elect)
1312 William Sinclair
1337 Malcolm de Innerpeffray (elect)
1344 Richard de Pilmor
1347 Robert de Den (elect)
1347(?) Duncan de Strathearn
1355 John Luce
1370 John de Carrick (elect)
1371(?) Michael de Monymusk
1377(?) Andrew Umfray (elect)

1379 John de Peblys [? of Peebles]
1379 Robert de Derling
1390(?) Nicholas Duffield
1391 Robert Sinclair
1398(?) Robert de Cardeny
1430 William Gunwardby
1437 Donald MacNaughton (elect)
1438 James Kennedy
1440(?) Thomas Livingston
1440 Alexander de Lawedre [Lauder] (elect)
1442 James de Brois [Brewhous]
1447 William Turnbull (elect)
1448 John Ralston
1452(?) Thomas Lauder
1476 James Livingston
1483 Alexander Inglis (elect)
1484 George Brown
1515 Andrew Stewart (elect)
1516 Gavin Douglas
1524 Robert Cockburn
1526(?) George Crichton
1546 John Hamilton
1552 Robert Crichton
1572 James Paton (titular)
1585 Peter Rollock (titular)
1607 James Nicolson (titular)
1611(?) Alexander Lindsay (deposed 1638)
1662 George Haliburton
1665 Henry Guthrie
1677 William Lindsay
1679 Andrew Bruce
1686 John Hamilton
1717 Thomas Rattray
1743 John Alexander
1776(?) Charles Rose
1792 Jonathan Watson
1808 Patrick Torry
1842 Held with St Andrews

†Dunblane

1162 Laurence
c.1180 Symon
1196 W[illelmus]
1198 Jonathan
1215 Abraham
1225 Ralph (elect)
1227 Osbert
1233 Clement
1259 Robert de Prebenda
1284 William I
1296 Alpin
1301 Nicholas
1307 Nicholas de Balmyle
1318(?) Roger de Balnebrich (elect)
1322 Maurice
c.1347 William II
c.1361 Walter de Coventre
c.1372 Andrew
c.1380 Dougal

† Indicates a diocese no longer extant, or united with another diocese.

1403(?) Finlay or Dermoch
1419 William Stephen
1430 Michael Ochiltree
1447(?) Robert Lauder
1468 John Hepburn
1487 James Chisolm
1527 William Chisolm I
1561 William Chisom II [coadjutor]
1575 Andrew Graham (titular)
1611 George Graham
1616 Adam Bellenden
1636 James Wedderburn
1661 Robert Leighton
1673 James Ramsay
1684 Robert Douglas
[1716–31 See vacant]
1731 John Gillan
1735 Robert White
1744 Thomas Ogilvie (elect)
1774 Charles Rose, died 1791
1776 Held with Dunkeld

Edinburgh

1634 William Forbes
1634 David Lindsay
1662 George Wishart
1672 Alexander Young
1679 John Paterson
1687 Alexander Rose
1720 John Fullarton
1727 Arthur Millar
1727 Andrew Lumsden
1733 David Freebairn
[1739–76 See vacant]
1776 William Falconer
1787 William Abernethy
      Drummond
1806 Daniel Sandford
1830 James Walker
1841 Charles Hughes Terrot
1872 Henry Cotterill
1886 John Dowden
1910 George Henry Somerset
      Walpole
1929 Harry Seymour Reid
1939 Ernest Denny Logie Danson
1947 Kenneth Charles Harman
      Warner
1961 Kenneth Moir Carey
1975 Alastair Iain Macdonald
      Haggart
1986 Richard Frederick Holloway
2001 Brian Arthur Smith

Aberdeen

Aberdeen and Orkney

BISHOPS AT MURTHLAC

(?) Beyn [Beanus]
(?) Donort
(?) Cormac

BISHOPS AT ABERDEEN

1132   Nechtan
c.1150 Edward
c.1172 Matthew
c.1201 John
c.1208 Adam de Kalder
1228   Matthew Scot (elect)
1230   Gilbert de Strivelyn
1240   Radulf de Lamley
1247   Peter de Ramsey
1258   Richard de Pottun
1272   Hugh de Bennum
1282   Henry le Chene
1329   Walter Herok (elect)
1329   Alexander I, de Kyninmund
1344   William de Deyn
1351   John de Rate

1356   Alexander II, de Kyninmund
1380   Adam de Tynyngham
1391   Gilbert de Grenlaw
1422   Henry de Lychton [Leighton]
c.1441 Ingram de Lindsay
1458   Thomas Spens
1480   Robert Blackadder (elect)
1488   William Elphinstone
1515   Robert Forman (elect)
1516   Alexander Gordon
1519   Gavin Dunbar
1529   George Learmonth [coadjutor]
1533   William Stewart
1547   William Gordon
1577   David Cunningham (elect)
1611   Peter Blackburn
1616   Alexander Forbes
1618   Patrick Forbes of Corse
1635   Adam Bellenden [Bannatyne]
1662   David Mitchell
1663   Alexander Burnet
1664   Patrick Scougal
1682   George Halyburton
[1715–21 See vacant]
1721   Archibald Campbell
1724   James Gadderar
1733   William Dunbar
1746   Andrew Gerard
1768   Robert Kilgour
1786   John Skinner
1816   William Skinner
1857   Thomas George Spink Suther
1883   Arthur Gascoigne Douglas
1906   Rowland Ellis
1912   Anthony Mitchell
1917   Frederic Llewellyn Deane
1943   Herbert William Hall
1956   Edward Frederick Easson
1973   Ian Forbes Begg
1978   Frederick Charles Darwent
1992   Andrew Bruce Cameron

†Orkney

1035   Henry
1050   Turolf
1072   John I
1072   Adalbert
1073   Radulf
1102   William I, 'the Old'
1108   Roger
1114   Radulf Novell
1168(?) William II
1188(?) Bjarni
1224   Jofreyrr
1248   Henry I
1270   Peter
1286   Dolgfinn
1310   William III
c.1369 William IV
c.1384 Robert Sinclair
.1384(?) John
1394   Henry II
1396(?) John Pak
1407   Alexander Vaus (elect)
1415   William Stephenson
1420   Thomas Tulloch
1461   William Tulloch
1477   Andrew Painter
1500   Edward Stewart
1524   John Benston [coadjutor]
1526(?) Robert Maxwell
1541   Robert Reid
1559   Adam Bothwell
1611   James Law
1615   George Graham
1639   Robert Barron (elect)
1661   Thomas Sydserf
1664   Andrew Honeyman
1677   Murdo Mackenzie

1688   Andrew Bruce, See afterwards
       administered with Caithness
1857   Held with Aberdeen

Brechin

1153(?) Samson
1178   Turpin
1202   Radulf
1215   Hugh
1218   Gregory
1246   Albin
1269(?) William de Crachin (elect)
1275   William Comyn
1296   Nicholas
1298   John de Kyninmund
1328   Adam de Moravia
1350   Philip Wilde
1351   Patrick de Locrys [Leuchars]
1383   Stephen de Cellario
1411   Walter Forrester
1426   John de Crannach
1455   George Schoriswood
1464   Patrick Graham
1465   John Balfour
1489   William Meldrum
1523   John Hepburn
1557   Donald Campbell (elect)
1565(?) John Sinclair (elect)
1566   Alexander Campbell (titular)
1610   Andrew Lamb
1619   David Lindsay
1634   Thomas Sydserf
1635   Walter Whitford
1662   David Strachan
1672   Robert Laurie
1678   George Haliburton
1682   Robert Douglas
1684   Alexander Cairncross
1684   James Drummond
1695–1709 Held with Edinburgh
1709   John Falconar
1724   Robert Norrie
1726   John Ochterlonie
1742   James Rait
1778   George Innes
1787   William Abernethy Drummond
1788   John Strachan
1810   George Gleig
1840   David Moir
1847   Alexander Penrose Forbes
1876   Hugh Willoughby Jermyn
1904   Walter John Forbes Robberds
1935   Kenneth Donald Mackenzie
1944   Eric Graham
1959   John Chappell Sprott
1975   Lawrence Edward Luscombe
1990   Robert Taylor Halliday
1997   Neville Chamberlain

Moray

Moray, Ross and Caithness

1114   Gregory
1153(?) William
1164   Felix
1172   Simon de Tonei
1187   Richard de Lincoln
1203   Brice de Douglas
1224(?) Andrew de Moravia
1244(?) Simon
1251   Radulf de Leycester (elect)
1253   Archibald
1299   David de Moravia
1326   John de Pilmor
1363   Alexander Bur
1397   William de Spyny
1407   John de Innes
1415   Henry Leighton
1422   Columba de Dunbar
1437   John de Winchester
1460(?) James Stewart

924

1463 David Stewart
1477 William de Tulloch
1487 Andrew Stewart
1501(?) Andrew Forman
1516(?) James Hepburn
1525 Robert Shaw
1532(?) Alexander Stewart
1538(?) Patrick Hepburn
1574 George Douglas
1611 Alexander Douglas
1623 John Guthrie
1662 Murdo Mackenzie
1677 James Aitken
1680 Colin Falconer
1687 Alexander Rose
1688 William Hay
1707 Held with Edinburgh
1725 Held with Aberdeen
1727 William Dunbar
1737 George Hay (elect)
1742 William Falconar
1777 Arthur Petrie
1787 Andrew Macfarlane
1798 Alexander Jolly
1838 Held with Ross
1851 Robert Eden
1886 James Butler Knill Kelly
1904 Arthur John Maclean
1943 Piers Holt Wilson
1953 Duncan Macinnes
1970 George Minshull Sessford
1994 Gregor Macgregor
1999 John Michael Crook

†Ross

1131(?) Macbeth
1150(?) Simon
1161 Gregory
1195 Reginald
1213 Andrew de Moravia (elect)
1215(?) Robert I
1250 Robert II
1272 Matthew
1275(?) Robert II de Fyvin
1295(?) Adam de Derlingtun (elect)
1297(?) Thomas de Dundee
1325 Roger
1351 Alexander Stewart
1372 Alexander de Kylwos
1398(?) Alexander de Waghorn
1418 Thomas Lyell (elect)
Griffin Yonge (elect)
1420 John Bulloch
1441(?) Andrew de Munro (elect)
1441(?) Thomas Tulloch
1464(?) Henry Cockburn
1478 John Wodman
1481 William Elphinstone (elect)
1483 Thomas Hay
1492 John Guthrie
1498 John Frisel [Fraser]
c.1507 Robert Cockburn
1525 James Hay
c.1539 Robert Cairncross
1552 David Painter
1561(?) Henry Sinclair
1566 John Lesley
1575 Alexander Hepburn
1611 David Lindsay
1613 Patrick Lindsay
1633 John Maxwell
1662 John Paterson
1679 Alexander Young
1684 James Ramsay
1696 See vacant or held with
  Caithness until 1727

1727 Held with Moray
1742 Held with Caithness
1762 Robert Forbes
1777 Held with Moray
1819 David Low
1851 Held with Moray

†Caithness

c.1146 Andrew
c.1187 John
1214 Adam
1223(?) Gilbert de Moravia
1250(?) William
1263 Walter de Baltrodin
1273(?) Nicholas (elect)
1275 Archibald Herok
1278 Richard (elect)
1279(?) Hervey de Dundee (elect)
1282 Alan de St Edmund
1295 John or James (elect)
1296 Adam de Derlingtun
1297 Andrew
1306 Fercard Belegaumbe
1328(?) David
1341 Alan de Moravia
1343 Thomas de Fingask
1370 Malcolm de Dumbrek
1381 Alexander Man
1414 Alexander Vaus
1425 John de Crannach
1428 Robert Strabrok
1446 John Innes
1448 William Mudy
1478(?) Prospero Camogli de Medici
1484(?) John Sinclair (elect)
1502 Andrew Stewart I
1517(?) Andrew Stewart II
1542 Robert Stewart (elect)
1600 George Gledstanes (elect)
1611 Alexander Forbes
1616 John Abernethy
1662 Patrick Forbes
1680 Andrew Wood
[1695 See vacant]
1731 Robert Keith
1741 Wm. Falconas
1762 Held with Ross
[1742 See Vacant]
1777 Held with Moray

Glasgow

Glasgow and Galloway

550(?) Kentigern or Mungo (no
  record of his successors)
1114(?) (Michael)
1118(?) John
1147 Herbert
1164 Ingram
1175 Jocelin
1199 Hugh de Roxburgh (elect)
1200 William Malveisin
1202 Florence (elect)
1208 Walter de St Albans
1233 William de Bondington
1259 Nicholas de Moffat (elect)
1259 John de Cheam
1268 Nicholas de Moffat (elect)
1271 William Wischard (elect)
1273 Robert Wischard
1317 Stephen de Donydouer (elect)
1318 John de Egglescliffe
1323 John de Lindsay
1337 John Wischard
1339 William Rae
1367 Walter Wardlaw
1388 Matthew de Glendonwyn

1391 John Framisden (titular)
1408 William Lauder
1427 John Cameron
1447 James de Brois [Brewhouse]
1448 William Turnbull
1456 Andrew de Durrisdeer
1475 John Laing
1483 George Carmichael (elect)

ARCHBISHOPS

1483 Robert Blackadder
  (Archbishop 9 Jan 1492)
1509 James Betoun I
1525 Gavin Dunbar
1551 Alexander Gordon
1552 James Betoun II (restored
  1587)
1571 John Porterfield (titular)
1573 James Boyd (titular)
1581 Robert Montgomery (titular)
1585 William Erskine (titular)
1610 John Spottiswoode
1615 James Law
1633 Patrick Lindsay
1661 Andrew Fairfoul
1664 Alexander Burnet (restored
  1674)
1671 Robert Leighton, died 1684
  (resigned 1674)
1679 Arthur Rose
1684 Alexander Cairncross, died
  1701
1687 John Paterson,[1] died 1708
[1708 Vacant]

BISHOPS

1731 Alexander Duncan, died 1733
[1733 Vacant]
1787 Held with Edinburgh
1805 William Abernethy
  Drummond
1809–37 Held with Edinburgh
1837 Michael Russell
1848 Walter John Trower
1859 William Scott Wilson
1888 William Thomas Harrison
1904 Archibald Ean Campbell
1921 Edward Thomas Scott Reid
1931 John Russell Darbyshire
1938 John Charles Halland How
1952 Francis Hamilton Moncreiff
1974 Frederick Goldie
1981 Derek Alec Rawcliffe
1991 John Mitchell Taylor
1998 Idris Jones

†Galloway or Candida Casa or Whithorn[2]

Ninian, died 432(?)
(?) Octa
681 Trumwine
731 Penthelm, died 735(?)
735 Frithowald, died 764
763 Pehtwine, died 776
777 Ethelbert
791 Beadwulf
1140 Gilla-Aldan
1154 Christian
1189 John
1214 Walter
1235 Odo Ydonc (elect)
1235 Gilbert
1255 Henry
1294 Thomas de Kircudbright [de
  Daltoun]
1327 Simon de Wedale
1355 Michael Malconhalgh

---

[1] After the deposition of John Paterson at the Revolution the See ceased to be Archiepiscopal.
[2] The traditional founder of the See is St Ninian, but nothing authentic is known of the bishops prior to the accession of Gilla-Aldan between 1133 and 1140.

1359(?) Thomas Macdowell (elect)
1359 Thomas
1364 Adam de Lanark
  (?) David Douglas, died 1373
  (?) James Carron (resigned 1373)
1378 Ingram de Kethnis (elect)
1379 Oswald
1380 Thomas de Rossy
  (?) Francis Ramsay, died 1402
1406 Elisaeus Adougan
1414(?) Gilbert Cavan (elect)
1415 Thomas de Butil
1422 Alexander Vaus
1451 Thomas Spens
1457(?) Thomas Vaus (elect)
1459 Ninian Spot
1482(?) George Vaus
1508(?) James Betoun (elect)
1509(?) David Arnot
1526 Henry Wemyss
1541(?) Andrew Dury
1559(?) Alexander Gordon
1610 Gavin Hamilton
1612(?) William Couper
1619 Andrew Lamb
1635 Thomas Sydserf
1661 James Hamilton
1675 John Paterson
1679 Arthur Rose
1680 James Aitken
1688 John Gordon, died 1726
1697 Held with Edinburgh
1837 Held with Glasgow

Argyll or Lismore

Argyll and The Isles

1193 Harald
1240 William
1253 Alan
1268 Laurence de Erganis
1300 Andrew
1342 Angusde Ergadia (elect)
1344 Martinde Ergaill
1387 John Dugaldi
1397(?) Bean Johannis
1420(?) Finlay de Albany
1428 George Lauder
1476 Robert Colquhoun
1504 David Hamilton
1532 Robert Montgomery
1539(?) William Cunningham (elect)
1553(?) James Hamilton (elect)
1580 Neil Campbell (titular)
1611 John Campbell (titular)
1613 Andrew Boyd
1637 James Fairlie
1662 David Fletcher
1665 John Young (elect)
1666 William Scroggie
1675 Arthur Rose
1679 Colin Falconer
1680 Hector Maclean
1688 Alexander Monro (elect)
Held with Ross
1847 Alexander Ewing
1874 George Mackarness
1883 James Robert Alexander
    Chinnery-Haldane
1907 Kenneth Mackenzie
1942 Thomas Hannay
1963 Richard Knyvet Wimbush
1977 George Kennedy Buchanan
    Henderson
1993 Douglas MacLean Cameron

†The Isles

900 Patrick
1080 Roolwer

1080 William
1095 Hamundr
1138 Wimund
1152 John I
1152(?) Ragnald
1154 Gamaliel
1170 Christian
1194 Michael
1210 Nicholas I
1219 Nicholas II of Meaux
1226(?) Reginald
1226 Simon
1249 Laurence (elect)
1253 Richard
1275 Gilbert (elect)
1275 Mark
1305 Alan
1324 Gilbert Maclelan
1328 Bernard de Linton
1331 Thomas de Rossy
1349 William Russell
1374 John Donkan
1387 Michael
1392 John Sproten (Man) (titular)
1402(?) Conrad (Man) (titular)
1402(?) Theodore Bloc (Man)
    (titular)
1410 Richard Messing (Man)
1422 Michael Anchire
1425(?) John Burgherlinus (Man)
1428 Angus I
1441(?) John Hectoris [McCachane]
    Macgilleon
1472 Angus II
1487 John Campbell
1511 George Hepburn
1514 John Campbell (elect)
1530(?) Ferchar MacEachan (elect)
1550(?) Roderick Maclean
1553(?) Alexander Gordon
1567 John Carswell (titular)
1573 John Campbell
1605 Andrew Knox
1619 Thomas Knox
1628 John Leslie
1634 Neil Campbell
1662 Robert Wallace
1677 Andrew Wood
1680 Archibald Graham [or
    McIlvernock]
Held with Orkney and
    Caithness
1819 Held with Argyll

College Bishops, Consecrated without Sees

1705 John Sage, died 1711
1705 John Fullarton (Edinburgh
    1720), died 1727
1709 Henry Christie, died 1718
1709 John Falconer (Fife 1720),
    died 1723
1711 Archibald Campbell
    (Aberdeen 1721), died 1744
1712 James Gadderar (Aberdeen
    1725, Moray 1725), died
    1733
1718 Arthur Millar (Edinburgh
    1727), died 1727
1718 William Irvine, died 1725
1722 Andrew Cant, died 1730
1722 David Freebairn (Edinburgh
    1733)
1726 John Ochterlonie (Brechin
    1731), died 1742
1726 James Ross (Fife 1731), died
    1733

1727 John Gillan (Dunblane 1731),
    died 1735
1727 David Ranken, died 1728

Bishops who have held the Office of Primus

1704 Alexander Rose (Edinburgh
    1704–20)
1720 John Fullarton (Edinburgh
    1720–27)
1727 Arthur Millar (Edinburgh
    1727)
1727 Andrew Lumsden (Edinburgh
    1727–33)
1731 David Freebairn (Edinburgh
    1733–39)
1738 Thomas Rattray (Dunkeld
    1727–43)
1743 Robert Keith (Caithness
    1731–41)
1757 Robert White (Dunblane
    1735–43, St Andrews
    1743–61)
1762 William Falconar (Orkney and
    Caithness 1741–62)
1782 Robert Kilgour (Aberdeen
    1768–86)
1788 John Skinner (Aberdeen
    1786–1816)
1816 George Gleig (Brechin
    1810–40)
1837 James Walker (Edinburgh
    1880–41)
1841 William Skinner (Aberdeen
    1816–57)
1857 Charles Hughes Terrot
    (Edinburgh 1841–72)
1862 Robert Eden (Moray, Ross,
    and Caithness 1851–86)
1886 Hugh Willoughby Jermyn
    (Brechin 1875–1903)
1901 James Butler Knill Kelly
    (Moray, Ross, and Caithness
    1886–1904)
1904 George Howard Wilkinson (St
    Andrews, Dunkeld, and
    Dunblane 1893–1907)
1908 Walter John Forbes Robberds
    (Brechin 1904–34)
1935 Arthur John Maclean (Moray,
    Ross, and Caithness
    1904–43)
1943 Ernest Denny Logie Danson
    (Edinburgh 1939–46)
1946 John Charles Halland How
    (Glasgow and Galloway
    1938–52)
1952 Thomas Hannay (Argyll and
    The Isles 1942–62)
1962 Francis Hamilton Moncreiff
    (Glasgow and Galloway
    1952–74)
1974 Richard Knyvet Wimbush
    (Argyll and The Isles
    1963–77)
1977 Alastair Iain Macdonald
    Haggart (Edinburgh
    1975–85)
1985 Lawrence Edward Luscombe
    (Brechin 1975–90)
1990 George Kennedy Buchanan
    Henderson (Argyll and The
    Isles 1977–92)
1992 Richard Frederick Holloway
    (Edinburgh 1986–2000)
2000 Andrew Bruce Cameron
    (Aberdeen 1992–)

IRELAND

PROVINCE OF ARMAGH

†Achonry

BISHOPS

- *c.*558 Cathfuidh
- 1152 Mael Ruanaid ua Ruadain
- 1159 Gille na Naehm O Ruadain [Gelasius]
- 1208 Clemens O Sniadaig
- 1220 Connmach O Torpaig [Carus]
- 1226 Gilla Isu O Cleirig [Gelasius]
- 1237 Tomas O Ruadhan
- 1238 Oengus O Clumain [Elias]
- 1251 Tomas O Maicin
- 1266 Tomas O Miadachain [Dionysus]
- 1286 Benedict O Bracain
- 1312 David of Kilheny
- 1348 David II
- 1348 Nicol Alias Muircheartach O hEadhra
- 1374 William Andrew
- 1385 Simon
- *c.*1390 Tomas mac Muirgheasa MacDonn-chadha
- 1401 Brian mac Seaain O hEadhra
- 1410 Maghnus O h Eadhra
- 1424 Donatus
- 1424 Richard Belmer
- 1436 Tadhg O Dalaigh
- 1442 James Blakedon
- 1449 Cornelius O Mochain
- 1463 Brian O hEasdhra [Benedictus]
- 1470 Nicholas Forden
- 1475 Robert Wellys
- 1484 Thomas fitzRichard
- 1484 Tomas O Conghalain
- 1489 John Bustamente
- 1492 Thomas Ford
- 1508 Eugenius O Flannagain

- 1522 Cormac O Snighe
- 1547 Thomas O Fihilly
- 1562 Eugene O'Harte
- 1613 Miler Magrath (with Cashel) United to Killala 1622

†Annadown

BISHOPS

- 1189 Conn ua Mellaig [Concors]
- 1202 Murchad ua Flaithbertaig
- 1242 Tomas O Mellaig
- 1251 Conchobar [Concors]
- 1283 John de Ufford
- 1308 Gilbert O Tigernaig
- 1323 Jacobus O Cethernaig
- 1326 Robert Petit
- 1328 Albertus
- 1329 Tomas O Mellaig
- 1359 Dionysius
- 1393 Johannes
- 1394 Henry Trillow
- 1402 John Bryt
- 1408 John Wynn
- 1421 John Boner [Camere]
- 1425 Seean Mac Braddaigh
- 1428 Seamus O Lonnghargain
- 1431 Donatus O Madagain
- 1446 Thomas Salscot

- 1450 Redmund Bermingham
- 1458 Thomas Barrett
- 1496 Francis Brunand
- 1540 John Moore United to Tuam *c.*1555

†Ardagh

- 454 Mel
- *c.*670 Erard
- 874 Faelghus
- Cele 1048
- 1152 Mac Raith ua Morain
- 1172 Gilla Crist O hEothaig [Christianus]
- O'Tirlenain 1187
- ua hEislinnen
- Annud O Muiredaig 1216
- 1217 Robert
- 1224 M.
- 1228 Loseph mac Teichthechain
- 1229 Mac Raith Mac Serraig
- 1232 Gilla Isu mac in Scelaige O Tormaid [Gelasius]
- 1232 Iocelinus
- 1238 Brendan Mac Teichthechain
- 1256 Milo of Dunstable
- 1290 Matha O'h-Eothaig [Mattheus]
- 1323 Robert Wirsop (did not get possession)
- 1324 Mac Eoaighseoan
- 1347 Eoghan O Ferghail [Audovenus]
- 1368 William Mac Carmaic
- 1373 Cairbre O'Ferghail [Charles]
- 1373 John Aubrey
- 1392 Henry Nony (did not get possession)
- 1396 Comedinus Mac Bradaigh [Gilbert]
- 1400 Adam Leyns
- 1419 Conchobar O'Ferghail [Cornelius]
- 1425 Risdeard O'Ferghail
- [1444 O'Murtry, not consecrated resigned]
- 1445 Cormac Mac Shamhradhain
- 1462 Seaan O'Ferghail
- 1467 Donatus O'Ferghail
- 1482 William O'Ferghail
- 1517 Ruaidri O'Maoileoin
- 1517 Rory O'Mallone [Roger O Melleine]
- 1541 Richard O'Ferrall
- 1553 Patrick MacMahon
- [1572 John Garvey, not consecrated]
- 1583 Lysach O'Ferrall
- 1604 Robert Draper
- 1613 Thomas Moigne
- 1679 William Bedell
- 1633 John Richardson
- 1661 Robert Maxwell
- 1673 Francis Marsh
- 1682 William Sheridan
- 1692 Ulysses Burgh
- 1604–33, 1661–92 and 1692–1751 Held by the Bishops of Kilmore

- 1751–1839 Held by the Archbishops of Tuam United to Kilmore 1839

Armagh

BISHOPS

- 444 Patrick
- Benignus 467
- Jarlath 481
- Cormac 497
- Dubthach 513
- Ailill I 526
- Ailill II 536
- David O'Faranan 551
- Carlaen 588
- MacLaisre 623
- −640 Thomian MacRonan
- Segeni 688
- Suibhne 730
- −732 Congusa
- Affinth 794
- −811 Nundha
- −818 Artri
- 835 Forannan
- Mael Patraic I 862
- Fethgna 875
- Cathasach MacRobartach 883
- Mochta 893
- 900 Maelaithghin
- Cellach
- Mael Ciarain 915
- Joseph 936
- Mael Patraic II 936
- Cathasach MacDolgen 966
- Maelmiure 994
- Airindach 1000
- Maeltuile 1032
- 1032 Hugh O'Ferris
- Mael Patraic III 1096
- 1099 Caincomrac O'Boyle

ARCHBISHOPS

- 1105 Cellach mac Aeda meic Mael Isu [Celsus]
- 1132 Mael maedoc Ua Morgair [Malachais]
- 1137 Gilla Meic Liac mac Diarmata meic Ruaidri [Gelasius]
- 1174 Conchobar O Conchaille [Concors]
- 1175 Gille in Coimhedh O Caran [Gilbertus]
- 1180 Tomaltach O Conchobair [Thomas]
- 1184 Mael Isu Ua Cerbaill [Malachias]
- 1202 Echdonn mac Gilla Uidir [Eugenius]
- 1217 Lucas Neterville
- 1227 Donatus O Fidabra
- 1240 Albert Suebeer of Cologne
- 1247 Reginald
- 1258 Abraham O'Conallain
- 1261 Mael Patraic O Scannail
- 1270 Nicol Mac Mael Isu
- 1303 Michael MacLochlainn (not confirmed)

---

† Indicates a diocese no longer extant, or united with another diocese.

1304 Dionysius (not confirmed)
1306 John Taaffe
1307 Walter Jorz
1311 Roland Jorz
1324 Stephen Segrave
1334 David Mag Oireachtaigh
1347 Richard FitzRalph
1362 Milo Sweetman
1383 John Colton
1404 Nicholas Fleming
1418 John Swayne
1439 John Prene
1444 John Mey
1457 John Bole [Bull]
1471 John Foxhalls or Foxholes
1475 Edmund Connesburgh
1480 Ottaviano Spinelli [de Palatio]
1513 John Kite
1521 George Cromer
1543 George Dowdall
1552 Hugh Goodacre
1553 George Dowdall (again)
[1560 Donat MacTeague, not
       recognized by the Crown,
       1562]
1563 Adam Loftus
1568 Thomas Lancaster
1584 John Long
1589 John Garvey
1595 Henry Ussher
1613 Christopher Hampton
1625 James Ussher
[Interregnum 1656–61]
1661 John Bramhall
1663 James Margetson
1679 Michael Boyle
1703 Narcissus Marsh
1714 Thomas Lindsay
1724 Hugh Boulter
1742 John Hoadly
1747 George Stone
1765 Richard Robinson [afterwards
       Baron Rokeby]
1795 William Newcome
1800 William Stuart
1822 John George Beresford
United to Clogher 1850–86
1862 Marcus Gervais Beresford
1886 Robert Bentknox
1893 Robert Samuel Gregg
1896 William Alexander
1911 John Baptist Crozier
1920 Charles Frederick D'Arcy
1938 John Godfrey FitzMaurice Day
1939 John Allen Fitzgerald Gregg
1959 James McCann
1969 George Otto Simms
1980 John Ward Armstrong
1986 Robert Henry Alexander
       Eames

Clogher

c.493 MacCarthinn or
       Ferdachrioch
       Ailill 869
1135 Cinaeth O Baigill
1135 Gilla Crist O Morgair
       [Christianus] (moved his see
       to Louth)

BISHOPS OF LOUTH
1135 Gilla Crist O Morgair
       [Christianus]
1138 Aed O Ceallaide [Edanus]
1178 Mael Isu O Cerbaill
       [Malachias]
1187 Gilla Crist O Mucaran
       [Christinus]

1194 Mael Isu Ua Mael
       Chiarain
1197 Gilla Tigernaig Mac Gilla
       Ronain [Thomas]

BISHOPS OF CLOGHER
1218 Donatus O Fidabra
1228 Nehemias
1245 David O Bracain
1268 Michael Mac an tSair
1287 Matthew Mac Cathasaigh I
–1310 Henricus
1316 Gelasius O Banain
1320 Nicholas Mac Cathasaigh
1356 Brian Mac Cathmaoil
       [Bernard]
1362 Matthew Mac Cathasaigh II
—   Aodh O hEothaigh [alias O
       Neill]
1373 John O Corcrain
       [Wurzburg]
1390 Art Mac Cathmhail
1433 Piaras Mag Uidhir [Petrus]
1450 Rossa mac Tomais Oig Mag
       Uidhir [Rogerius]
1475 Florence Woolley
[1484 Niall mac Seamuis Mac
       Mathghamna]
1484 John Edmund de Courci
1494 Seamus Mac Pilip Mac
       Mathghamna
1500 Andreas
1502 Nehemias O Cluainin
1504 Giolla Padraig O Conalaigh
       [Patrick]
1505 Eoghan Mac Cathmhail
       [Eugenius]
1517 Padraig O Cuilin
1535 Aodh O Cearbhalain [Odo]
1517 Patrick O'Cullen
1535 Hugh O'Carolan
1570 Miler Magrath
1605 George Montgomery
1621 James Spottiswood
1645 Henry Jones
1661 John Leslie
1671 Robert Leslie
1672 Roger Boyle
1691 Richard Tennison
1697 St George Ashe
1717 John Stearne
1745 Robert Clayton
1758 John Garnett
1782 John Hotham
1796 William Foster
1797 John Porter
1819 John George Beresford
1820 Percy Jocelyn
1822 Robert Ponsonby Tottenham
       Luftus
United to Armagh 1850–86
1886 Charles Maurice Stack
1903 Charles Frederick D'Arcy
1908 Maurice Day
1923 James MacManaway
1944 Richard Tyner
1958 Alan Alexander Buchanan
1970 Richard Patrick Crosland
       Hanson
1973 Robert William Heavener
1980 Gordon McMullan
1986 Brian Desmond Anthony
       Hannon
2002 Michael Geoffrey St Aubyn
       Jackson

Connor

506 Oengus MacNessa 514
       Lughadh 543

640 Dimma Dubh [the Black]
       Duchonna the Pious 725
       Cunnen or Cuinden 1038
       Flann O'Sculu 1117
1124 Mael Maedoc Ua Morgair
       [Malachias]
–1152 MaelPatraic O'Banain
1172 Nehemias
1178 Reginaldus
1226 Eustacius
1242 Adam
1245 Isaac de Newcastle-on-Tyne
1258 William de Portroyal
1261 William de Hay [or la Haye]
1263 Robert de Flanders
1275 Peter de Dunach
1293 Johannes
1320 Richard
1321 James de Couplith
1323 John de Eglecliff
1323 Robert Wirsop
1324 Jacabus O Cethernaig
1353 William Mercier
1374 Paulus
1389 Johannes
[1420 Seaan O Luachrain, not
       consecrated]
1423 Eoghan O'Domhnaill
1429 Domhnall O'Meraich
1431 John Fossade [Festade]
1459 Patricius
1459 Simon Elvington
United to Down 1441
1945 Charles King Irwin
1956 Robert Cyril Hamilton Glover
       Elliott
1969 Arthur Hamilton Butler
1981 William John McCappin
1987 Samuel Greenfield Poyntz
1995 James Edward Moore
2002 Alan Edwin Thomas Harper

Derry

Derry and Raphoe
       Caencomhrac 927
–937 Finachta MacKellach
–949 Mael Finnen

BISHOPS OF MAGHERA
(Where the See was in the twelfth
and the thirteenth centuries)
1107 Mael Coluim O Brolchain
—   Mael Brigte O Brolchain
1152 O Gormgaile Muiredach O
       Cobthaig [Mauricius]
1173 Amhlaim O Muirethaig
1185 Fogartach O Cerballain
       [Florentius]
c.1230 Gilla in Coimhded O
       Cerballain [Germanus]
c.1280 Fogartach O
       Cerballain II [Florentius]

BISHOPS OF DERRY
(Where the See was resettled)
1295 Enri Mac Airechtaig
       [O'Reghly] [of Ardagh]
1297 Gofraid MacLochlainn
       [Godfrey]
1316 Aed O Neill [Odo]
1319 Michael Mac Lochlainn
       [Maurice]
1349 Simon
1391 Johannes
1391 John Dongan
1394 Seoan O Mochain
1398 Aodh [Hugo]
1401 Seoan O Flannabhra
1415 Domhnall Mac Cathmhail

1419 Domhnall O Mearaich
1429 Eoghan O Domhnaill
    [Eugenius]
1433 John Oguguin
[1456 John Bole, appointment not
    completed, translated to
    Armagh]
1458 Bartholomew O Flannagain
c.1464 Johannes
1467 Nicholas Weston
1485 Domhnall O Fallamhain
1501 Seamus mac Pilip Mac
    Mathghamna [MacMahon]
1520 Ruaidhri O Domhnaill
1520 Rory O'Donnell
1554 Eugene O'Doherty
1568 F. [doubtful authority]
1569 Redmond O'Gallagher
[1603 Denis Campbell, not
    consecrated]
1605 George Montgomery
1610 Brutus Babington
[1611 Christopher Hampton,
    consecrated]
1613 John Tanner
1617 George Downham
1634 John Bramhall
1661 George Wild
1666 Robert Mossom
1680 Michael Ward
1681 Ezekiel Hopkins
1691 William King
1703 Charles Hickman
1714 John Hartstonge
1717 St George Ashe
1718 William Nicolson
1727 Henry Downes
1735 Thomas Rundle
1743 Carew Reynell
1745 George Stone
1747 William Barnard
1768 Frederick Augustus Hervey
    [afterwards Earl of
    Bristol]
1803 William Knox
1831 Richard Ponsonby
Raphoe united to Derry from 1834
1853 William Higgin
1867 William Alexander
1896 George Alexander Chadwick
    (resigned)
1916 Joseph Irvine Peacocke
1945 Robert M'Neil Boyd
1958 Charles John Tyndall
1970 Cuthbert Irvine Peacocke
1975 Robert Henry Alexander
    Eames
1980 James Mehaffey
2002 Kenneth Raymond Good

Down

Down and Dromore
    Fergus 584
    Suibhne 825
    Graithene 956
    Finghin 964
    Flaithbertach 1043
    MaelKevin 1086
— Mael Muire 1117
    Oengus Ua Gormain 1123
— [Anonymous]
c.1124 Mael Maedoc O Morgair
    [Malachias]
1152 Mael Isu mac in Chleirig
    Chuirr [Malachias]
1175 Gilla Domangairt Mac
    Cormaic
c.1176 Echmilid [Malachias]

c.1202 Radulfus
1224 Thomas
1251 Randulphus
1258 Reginaldus
1265 Thomas Lydel
1277 Nicholas le Blund
1305 Thomas Ketel
1314 Thomas Bright
1328 John of Baliconingham
1329 Ralph of Kilmessan
1353 Richard Calf I
1365 Robert of Aketon
1367 William White
1369 Richard Calf [II]
1386 John Ross
1394 John Dongan
1413 John Cely [or Sely]
1445 Ralph Alderle

BISHOPS OF DOWN AND CONNOR

1441 John Fossard
1447 Thomas Pollard
1451 Richard Wolsey
1456 Thomas Knight
1469 Tadhg O Muirgheasa
    [Thaddaeus]
1489 Tiberio Ugolino
1520 Robert Blyth
1542 Eugene Magennis
1565 James MacCawell
1569 John Merriman
1572 Hugh Allen
1593 Edward Edgeworth
1596 John Charden
1602 Roben Humpston
1607 John Todd (resigned)
1612 James Dundas
1613 Robert Echlin
1635 Henry Leslie
1661 Jeremy Taylor
1667 Roger Boyle
1672 Thomas Hacket
1694 Samuel Foley
1695 Edward Walkington
1699 Edward Smyth
1721 Francis Hutchinson
1739 Carew Reynell
1743 John Ryder
1752 John Whitcombe
1752 Robert Downes
1753 Arthur Smyth
1765 James Traill
1784 William Dickson
1804 Nathaniel Alexander
1823 Richard Mant

BISHOPS OF DOWN, CONNOR AND
DROMORE

1849 Robert Bent Knox
1886 William Reeves
1892 Thomas James Welland
1907 John Baptist Crozier
1911 Charles Frederick D'Arcy
1919 Charles Thornton Primrose
    Grierson
1934 John Frederick McNeice
1942 Charles King Irwin

BISHOPS OF DOWN AND
DROMORE

1945 William Shaw Kerr
1955 Frederick Julian Mitchell
1970 George Alderson Quin
1980 Robert Henry Alexander
    Eames
1986 Gordon McMullan
1997 Harold Creeth Miller

†Dromore

    Mael Brighde 974
    Riagan 1101
1197 Ua Ruanada
1227 Geraldus
1245 Andreas
1284 Tigernach I
1290 Gervasius
— Tigernach II
1309 Florentius Mac Donnocain
1351 Anonymous
1366 Milo
1369 Christophorus Cornelius 1382
1382 John O'Lannoy
1398 Thomas Orwell
1400 John Waltham
1402 Roger Appleby
1408 Richard Payl
1410 Marcus
1411 John Chourles
1414 Seaan O Ruanadha
1419 Nicholas Wartre
1429 Thomas Rackelf
1431 William
1431 David Chirbury
1450 Thomas Scrope [Bradley]
1450 Thomas Radcliff
1456 Donatus O h-Anluain
    [Ohendua]
1457 Richard Messing
1463 William Egremond
— Aonghus [Aeneas] 1476
1476 Robert Kirke
1480 Yvo Guillen
1483 George Braua
1511 Tadhg O Raghallaigh
    [Thaddeus]
1536 Quintin O Quigley [Cogley]
1539 Roger McHugh
1540 Arthur Magennis
1607 John Todd
[1613 John Tanner, not
    consecrated]
1613 Theophilus Buckworth
1661 Robert Leslie
1661 Jeremy Taylor (administered
    the diocese)
1667 George Rust
1671 Essex Digby
1683 Capel Wiseman
1695 Tobias Pullein
1713 John Stearne
1717 Ralph Lambert
1727 Charles Cobbe
1732 Henry Maule
1744 Thomas Fletcher
1745 Jemmett Browne
1745 George Marlay
1763 John Oswald
1763 Edward Young
1765 Henry Maxwell
1766 William Newcome
1775 James Hawkins
1780 William de la Poer Beresford
1782 Thomas Percy
1811 George Hall
1812 John Leslie
1819 James Saurin
United to Down since 1842

†Elphin

    Domnall mac Flannacain Ua
    Dubhthaig 1136
    Muiredach O Dubhthaig 1150
1152 Mael Isu O Connachtain
    Flannacan O Dubhthaig 1168
c.1177 Tomaltach mac Aeda
    Ua Conchobhair [Thomas]

c.1180 Florint Ua Riacain Ui Maelrvanaid
1206 Ardgar O Conchobhair
1226 Dionysius O Mordha
c.1230 Alanus
1231 Donnchad mac Fingein O Conchobhair [Dionysius Donatus]
1245 Eoin O Mugroin
1247 Tomaltach macToirrdelbaig O Conchobhair [Thomas]
1260 Mael Sechlainn O Conchobhair [Milo]
1262 Tomas mac Fergail mac Diarmata
1266 Muiris O Conchobhair
[1285 Amiaim O Tommaltaig, not consecrated]
1285 Gilla Isu mac in Liathana O Conchobhair
1297 Maelsechlainn mac Briain [Malachias]
1303 Donnchad O Flannacain, [Donatus]
1307 Cathal O Conchobhair
1310 Mael Sechlainn Mac Aedha
1313 Lurint O Lachtnain [Laurence]
1326 Sean O Finnachta
1355 Carolus
1357 Gregory O Mochain
1372 Thomas Barrett
1383 Seoan O Mochain
1407 Seaan O Grada
1405 Gerald Caneton
1412 Thomas Colby
1418 Robert Fosten
1421 Edmund Barrett
1427 Johannes
1429 Laurence O Beolain
1429 William O hEidighean
1448 Conchobhar O Maolalaidh
1458 Nicholas O Flanagan
1487 Hugo Arward
1492 Rlocard mac Briain O gCuanach
1499 George Brana
1501 Cornelius O Flannagain
1508 Christopher Fisher
1525 John Maxey
1539 William Maginn 1541(?)
1539 Gabriel de Sancto Serio
1541 Conach or Con O'Negall or O'Shyagall
1552 Roland Burke [de Burgo]
1582 Thomas Chester
1583 John Lynch
1611 Edward King
1639 Henry Tilson
1661 John Parker
1667 John Hodson
1691 Simon Digby
1720 Henry Downes
1724 Theophilus Bolton
1730 Robert Howard
1740 Edward Synge
1762 William Gore
1772 Jemmett Browne
1775 Charles Dodgson
1795 John Law
1810 Power le Poer Trench
1819 John Leslie 1854
United to Kilmore and Ardagh on the death of Bishop Beresford in 1841, when Bishop Leslie became Bishop of the united dioceses.

†Killala

Muiredach
Kellach

O Maolfogmair I 1137
O Maolfogmair II 1151
Imar O Ruaidhin 1176
1179 O Maolfogmair III
1199 Domnall Ua Becdha
1207 Cormac O'Tarpy O'Kelly 1214
1226 Aengus O Maolfogmair [Elias] Gille Cellaig O Ruaidhin
1253 Seoan O Laidlg
1281 Donnchad O Flaithbertaig [Donatus]
1307 John Tankard Sean O Flaithim 1343
1344 James Bermingham
1347 William O DusucBhda
1351 Robert Elyot
1381 Thomas Lodowys
1383 Conchobar O Coineoil [Cornelius]
1390 Thomas Horwell [Orwell]
1400 Thomas Barrett
1403 Muircheartach Cleirach mac Donnchadha O DusucBhda Connor O'Connell 1423
1427 Fergal Mac Martain
1431 Thaddaeus Mac Creagh
1432 Brian O Coneoil
1447 Robert Barrett
1452 Ruaidhri Bairead [Barrett]
1453 Thomas
1459 Richard Viel Miler O'Connell
1461 Donatus O Conchobhair
1470 Tomas Bairead [Barrett]
1487 John de Tuderto [Seaan O Caissin]
1500 Thomas Clerke
1508 Malachias O Clumhain
1513 Risdeard Bairead
1545 Redmond O'Gallagher
1570 Donat O'Gallagher
1580 John O'Casey
1592 Owen O'Conor
1613 Miler Magrath
Achonry united to Killala 1622
1623 Archibald Hamilton
1630 Archibald Adair (deposed, but subsequently restored)
164? John Maxwell
1661 Henry Hall
1664 Thomas Bayly
1671 Thomas Otway
1680 John Smith
1681 William Smyth
1682 Richard Tennison
1691 William Lloyd
1717 Henry Downes
1720 Charles Cobbe
1727 Robert Howard
1730 Robert Clayton
173? Mordecai Cary
175? Richard Robinson [afterwards Baron Rokeby]
1759 Samuel Hutchinson
1781 William Cecil Pery
1784 William Preston
1787 John Law
1795 John Porter
1798 Joseph Stock
1810 James Verschoyle
United to Tuam since 1834

Kilmore

Kilmore, Elphin and Ardagh
— Aed Ua Finn 1136
— Muirchenach Ua Maelmoeherge 1149

1152 Tuathal Ua Connachtaig [Thadeus]
1202 Mi Ua Dobailen
— Flann O Connachtaig [Florentius] 1231
1237 Congalach Mac Idneoil
1251 Simon O Ruairc
1286 Mauricius
— Matha Mac Duibne 1314
1320 Padraig O Cridecain
— Conchobhar Mac Conshnamha [Ford] 1355
1356 Richard O Raghilligh
1373 Johannes
1388 Thomas Rushook
1392 Sean O Raghilligh I [John]
1398 Nicol Mac Bradaigh
1401 Sean O'Raghilligh II
1407 John Stokes
1409 David O'Fairchellaigh
1422 Domhnall O Gabhann
1445 Aindrias Mac Bradaigh
1455 Fear Sithe Mag Dhuibhne
1465 Sean O Raghilligh II
1476 Cormac Mag Shamhradhain
1480 Tomas MacBradaigh
1512 Diarmaid O Raghilligh
1530 Edmund Nugent
1540 Sean Mac Bradaigh
1585 John Garvey
1604 Robert Draper
1613 Thomas Moigne
1629 William Bedell
1643 Robert Maxwell
1673 Francis Marsh
1682 William Sheridan
1693 William Smyth
1699 Edward Wetenhall
1715 Timothy Godwin
1727 Josiah Hort
1742 Joseph Story
1757 John Cradock
1772 Denison Cumberland
1775 George Lewis Jones
1790 William Foster
1796 Charles Broderick
1802 George de la Poer Beresford
Ardagh united to Kilmore 1839
Elphin united to Kilmore 1841
1841 John Leslie
1854 Marcus Gervais Beresford
1862 Hamilton Verschoyle
1870 Charles Leslie
1870 Thomas Carson
1874 John Richard Darley
1884 Samuel Shone
1897 Alfred George Elliott
1915 William Richard Moore
1930 Arthur William Barton
1939 Albert Edward Hughes
1950 Frederick Julian Mitchell
1956 Charles John Tyndall
1959 Edward Francis Butler Moore
1981 William Gilbert Wilson
1993 Michael Hugh Gunton Mayes
2001 Kenneth Harbert Clarke

†Mayo

Gerald 732
Muiredach [or Murray]
Mcinracht 732
Aidan 773
1172 Gilla Isu Ua Mailin Cele O Dubhthaigh 1210
1210 ?Patricius
1428 William Prendergast
1430 Nicholas 'Wogmay'
1439 Odo O h-Uiginn

1432	Martin Campania
1457	Simon de Duren
1493	John Bel
1541	Eugenius Macan Brehon
	United to Tuam 1559

†Raphoe

	Sean O Gairedain
	Donell O Garvan
	Felemy O Syda
	Oengus O'Lappin 959
1150	Muiredhach O'Cofley
1156	Gille in Coimhded Ua Carain [Gilbertus]
—	Anonymous
1204	Mael Isu Ua Doirig
—	Anonymous
1253	Mael Padraig O Scannail [Patricius]
1263	John de Alneto
1265	Cairpre O Scuapa
1275	Fergal O Firghil [Florentius]
1306	Enri Mac-in-Chrossain [Henricus]
1319	Tomas Mac Carmaic Ui Domhnaill
1363	Padraig Mac Maonghail
1367	Conchobar Mac Carmaic Ui Domhnaill [Cornelius]
1397	Seoan MacMenmain
1400	Eoin MacCarmaic [Johannes]
-1413	Anthony
-1414	Robert Rubire
1416	John McCormic
1420	Lochlainn O Gallchobhair I [Laurentius]
1440	Cornelius Mac Giolla Brighde
1443	Lochlainn O Gallchobhair II [Laurentius]
1479	John de Rogeriis
1482	Meanma Mac Carmail [Menclaus Mac Carmacain]
1514	Conn O Cathain [Cornelius]
1534	Eamonn O Gallchobhair
1547	Arthur o'Gallagher
1563	Donnell Magonigle [or McCongail]
[1603	Denis Campbell, not consecrated]
1605	George Montgomery
1611	Andrew Knox
1633	John Leslie

†Ardfert

BISHOPS

	Anmchad O h-Anmchada 1117
1152	Mael Brenain Ua Ronain
	Gilla Mac Aiblen O'Anmehadha 1166
	Domnall O Connairche 1193
1200	David Ua Duibdithrib
	Anonymous 1217
1218	John
1218	Gilbertus
1237	Brendan
1253	Christianus
1257	Philippus
1265	Johannes
1286	Nicolaus
1288	Nicol O Samradain

1661	Robert Leslie
1671	Ezekiel Hopkins
1682	William Smyth
1693	Alexander Cairncross
1701	Robert Huntington
1702	John Pooley
1713	Thomas Lindsay
1714	Edward Synge
1716	Nicholas Forster
1744	William Barnard
1747	Philip Twysden
1753	Robert Downes
1763	John Oswald
1780	James Hawkins
1807	John George Beresford
1819	William Magee
1822	William Bissett
	United to Derry since 1834

Tuam

Tuam, Killala and Achonry

BISHOPS

	Murrough O'Nioc 1032
	Hugh O'Hessian 1085
	Cathusach Ua Conaill 1117
	O Clerig 1137
	Muiredach Ua Dubhthaigh 1150

ARCHBISHOPS

1152	Aed Ua h-Oisin [Edanus]
1167	Cadhla Ua Dubhthaig [Catholicus]
1202	Felix Ua Ruanada
1236	Mael Muire O Lachtain [Marianus]
1250	Flann Mac Flainn [Florentius]
[1256	James O'Laghtnan, not confirmed or consecrated]
1257	Walter de Salerno
1258	Tomaltach O Conchobar [Thomas]
1286	Stephen de Fulbourn
1289	William de Bermingham
1312	Mael Sechlainn Mac Aeda
1348	Tomas MacCerbhaill [MacCarwill]
1364	Eoin O Grada
1372	Gregory O Mochain I
1384	Gregory O Mochain II
1387	William O Cormacain

PROVINCE OF DUBLIN

1336	Ailin O hEichthighirn
1331	Edmund of Caermaerthen
1348	John de Valle
1372	Cornelius O Tigernach
1380	William Bull
1411	Nicholas FitzMaurice
1404	Nicholas Ball
1405	Tomas O Ceallaigh
1409	John Attilburgh [Artilburch]
1450	Maurice Stack
1452	Maurice O Conchobair
1461	John Stack
1461	John Pigge
1473	Philip Stack
1495	John FitzGerald
[See vacant in 1534]	
1536	James FitzMaurice
1588	Nicholas Kenan
1600	John Crosbie
1622	John Steere

1393	Muirchertach mac Pilb O Cellaigh
1410	John Babingle
1411	Cornelius
1430	John Bermingham [Winfield]
1438	Tomas mac Muirchearthaigh O Cellaigh
1441	John de Burgo
1452	Donatus O Muiredaigh
1485	William Seoighe [Joyce]
1503	Philip Pinson
1506	Muiris O Fithcheallaigh
1514	Tomas O Maolalaidh
1537	Christopher Bodkin
1573	William O'Mullally [or Lealy]
	Annadown united to Tuam c.1555
	Mayo united to Tuam 1559
1595	Nehemiah Donnellan
1609	William O'Donnell [or Daniel]
1629	Randolph or Ralph Barlow
1638	Richard Boyle
1645	John Maxwell
1661	Samuel Pullen
1667	John Parker
1679	John Vesey
1716	Edward Synge
1742	Josiah Hort
1752	John Ryder
1775	Jemmett Browne
1782	Joseph Dean Bourke [afterwards Earl of Mayo]
1794	William Beresford [afterwards Baron Decies]
1819	Power le Poer Trench
	Killala united to Tuam from 1834

BISHOPS

1839	Thomas Plunket [afterwards Baron Plunket]
1867	Charles Brodrick Bernard
1890	James O'Sullivan
1913	Benjamin John Plunket
1920	Arthur Edwin Ross
1923	John Ort
1928	John Mason Harden
1932	William Hardy Holmes
1939	John Winthrop Crozier
1958	Arthur Hamilton Butler
1970	John Coote Duggan
1986	John Robert Winder Neill
1998	Richard Crosbie Aitken Henderson

1628	William Steere
1641	Thomas Fulwar
	United to Limerick 1661

†Ardmore

1153	Eugenius
	Incorporated with Lismore 1192

Cashel

Cashel, Waterford, Lismore, Ossory, Ferns and Leighlin

BISHOPS

	Cormac MacCuillenan 908
	Donnell O'Heney 1096 *or* 1098

ARCHBISHOPS

c.1111 Mael los Ua h-Ainmire
     Mael Iosa Ua Fogludha
     [Mauricius] 1131
     Domnall Ua Conaing 1137
     Gilla Naomh O'Marty 1149
–1152 Donat O'Lonergan I
–c.1160 M.
1172 Domnall O h-Ualla-chain
     [Donatus]
1186 Muirghes O h-Enna [Matheus]
c.1208 Donnchad Ua
     Longargain I [Donatus]
1216 Donnchad Ua Longargain II
     [Donatus]
1224 Mairin O Briain [Marianus]
1238 David mac Ceallaig [O'Kelly]
1254 David Mac Cearbaill [Mac
     Carwill]
1290 Stiamna O Bracain
1303 Maurice Mac Cearbaill
1317 William FitzJohn
1327 Seoan Mac Cerbaill
1329 Walter le Rede
1332 Eoin O Grada
1346 Radulphus O Cellaigh [Kelly]
1362 George Roche [de Rupe]
1365 Tomas Mac Cearbhaill
1374 Philip of Torrington
1382 Michael
1384 Peter Hackett
1406 Richard O Hedian
1442 John Cantwell I
1452 John Cantwell II
1484 David Creagh
1504 Maurice FitzGerald
1525 Edmund Butler
1553 Roland Baron or FitzGerald
1567 James MacCawell
Emly united to Cashel 1569
1571 Miler Magrath (Bishop of
     Cashel and Waterford from
     1582)
1623 Malcolm Hamilton
1630 Archibald Hamilton
1661 Thomas Fulwar
1667 Thomas Price
[See vacant 1685–91]
1691 Narcissus Marsh
1694 William Palliser
[1727 William Nicolson, not
     enthroned]
1727 Timothy Goodwin
1730 Theophilus Bolton
1744 Arthur Price
1752 John Whitcombe
1754 Michael Cox
1779 Charles Agar
1801 Charles Brodrick
1822 Richard Laurence
Waterford and Lismore united to
Cashel from 1833; on the death of
Abp Laurence in 1838 the province
was united to Dublin and the see
ceased to be an Archbishopric

BISHOPS

1839 Stephen Creagh Sandes
1843 Robert Daly
1872 Maurice FitzGerald
     Day
1900 Henry Stewart O'Hara
1919 Robert Miller
1931 John Frederick McNeice
1935 Thomas Arnold Harvey
1958 William Cecil De Pauley
1968 John Ward Armstrong
Ossory united to Cashel 1977
1980 Noel Vincent Willoughby

1997 John Robert Winder
     Neill
2003 Peter Francis Barrett

†Clonfert

Moena, or Moynean, or
     Moeinend 572
Cummin the Tall 662
Ceannfaeladh 807
Laithbheartach 822
Ruthnel or Ruthme 826
Cormac MacEdain 922
Ciaran O'Gabbla 953
Cathal 963
Eochu 1031
O'Corcoran 1095
Muiredach Ua h-Enlainge 1117
Gille Patraic Ua Ailcinned
     1149
c.1152 Petrus Ua Mordha
1172 Mail Isu mac in Baird
1179 Celechair Ua h-Armedaig
     Muirchertach Ua'Maeluidir
     1187
     Domnall Ua Finn 1195
     Muirchertach Ua Carmacain
     1204
1205 Mael Brigte Ua hErurain
1224 Cormac O Luimlin [Carus]
1248 Thomas
1259 Tomas mac Domnaill Moire O
     Cellaig
1266 Johannes de Alatre
1296 Robert
c.1302 John
1308 Gregorius O Brocaig
1320 Robert Le Petit
1322 Seoan O Leaain
1347 Tomas mac Gilbert O Cellaigh I
1378 Muircheartach mac Pilib O
     Cellaigh [Maurice]
1393 William O Cormacain
1398 David Corre
1398 Enri O Conmaigh
1405 Tomasi O Cellaigh II
1410 Cobhthach O Madagain
1438 Seaan O hEidin
1441 John White
1447 Conchobhar O Maolalaidh
1448 Cornelius O Cuinnlis
1463 Matthaeus Mag Raith
1508 David de Burgo
1509 Dionysius O'Mordha
1534 Roland de Burgo
1536 Richard Nangle
1580 Hugh
1582 Stephen Kirwan
1602 Roland Lynch
1627 Robert Dawson
1644 William Baily
1665 Edward Wolley
1691 William FitzGerald
1722 Theophilus Bolton
1724 Arthur Price
1730 Edward Synye
1732 Mordecai Cary
1716 John Whitcombe
1752 Arthur Smyth
1753 William Carmichael
1758 William Gote
1762 John Oswald
1763 Denison Cumberland
1772 Walter Cope
1782 John Law
1787 Richard Marlay
1795 Charles Broderick
1796 Hugh Hamilton
1798 Matthew Young
1801 George de la l'oer Beresford

1802 Nathaniel Alexander
1804 Christopher Butson
United to Killaloe since 1834

†Clonmacnoise

–663 Baitan O'Cormac
–839 Joseph [of Rossmore]
     Maclodhar 890
     Cairbre Crom 904
     Loingsech 919
–940 Donough I
–953 Donough II
–966 Cormae O Cillin
     Maenach 971
     Conaing O'Cosgraigh 998
     Male Poil 1001
     Flaithbertach 1038
     Celechar 1067
     O'Mallaen 1093
     Christian Aherne 1104
?1111 Domnall mac Flannacain Ua
     Dubthaig
1152 Muirchertach Ua Maeluidir
Cathal Ua Maeileoin 1207
c.1207 Muirchertach Ua Muiricen
1214 Aed O Maeileoin I
1227 Aed O Maeileoin II [Elias]
1236 Thomas Fitzpatrick
1252 Tomas O Cuinn
1280 Anonymous
1282 Gilbert (not consecrated)
1290 William O Dubhthaig
1298 William O Finnein
1303 Domnall O Braein
1324 Lughaid O Dalaigh
1337 Henricus
1349 Simon
1369 Richard [Braybroke]
1371 Hugo
1388 Philippus O Maoil
1389 Milo Corr
1397 O'Gallagher
1397 Philip Nangle
1423 David Prendergast
1426 Cormac Mac Cochlain
     [Cornelius]
1444 Sean O Dalaigh
1449 Thomas
1458 Robertus
1458 William
1459 John
1487 Walter Blake
1509 Tomas O Maolalaidh
1516 Quintin O h-Uiginn
1539 Richard O'Hogan
1539 Florence Kirwan
1556 Peter Wall [Wale]
United to Meath 1569

†Cloyne

     Reachtaidh 887
1148 Gilla na Naem O Muirchertaig
     [Nehemias]
     Ua Dubcroin 1159
     Ua Flannacain 1167
1177 Matthaeus Ua Mongaig
1201 Laurence Ua Suilleabain
1205 C.
1281 Luke
c.1224 Florence
1226 Daniel
1237 David mac Cellaig [O'Kelly]
1240 Ailinn O Suilleabain
1247 Daniel
1265 Reginaldus
1275 Alan O Longain
1284 Nicholas of Effingham

1323 Maurice O Solchain
1333 John Brid
1351 John Whitekot
1363 John Swaffham
1376 Richard Wye
1394 Gerard Caneton
1413 Adam Payn
United to Cork 1418–1638
1638 George Synge
1661–78 Held by the Bishops of Cork
1679 Patrick Sheridan
1683 Edward Jones
1693 William Palliser
1694 Tobias Pullein
1695 St George Ashe
1697 John Pooley
1702 Charles Crow
1726 Henry Maule
1732 Edward Synge
1734 George Berkeley
1753 James Stopford
1759 Robert Johnson
1767 Frederick Augustus Hervery
1768 Charles Agar
1780 George Chinnery
1781 Richard Woodward
1794 William Bennett
1820 Charles Mongan Warhurton
1826 John Brinkley
United to Cork on the death of Bp
Brinkley in 1835

Cork

Cork, Cloyne and Ross
    Donnell 876
    Soer Bhreatach 892
    DusucBhdhurn O'Stefam 959
    Cathmogh 969
    Mugron O'Mutan 1057
1138 Gregory
   ? Ua Menngorain 1147
1148 Gilla Aedha Ua Maigin
1174 [Gregorius] O h-Aedha [O
    Hea]
*c.*1182 Reginaldus I
1187 Aicher
1192 Murchad Ua h-Aedha
    Anonymous 1214
1215 Mairin Ua Briain [Marianus]
1225 Gilbertus
1248 Laurentius
1265 William of Jerpoint
1267 Reginaldus
1277 Robert Mac Donnchada
1302 Seoan Mac Cearbaill [Mac
    Carwill]
1321 Philip of Slane
1327 Walter le Rede
1330 John of Ballyconingham
1347 John Roche
1359 Gerald de Barri
1396 Roger Ellesmere
1406 Richard Kynmoure
1409 Patrick Fox
1409 Milo fitzJohn
1425 John Paston
1418 Adam Payn
1429 Jordan Purcell
1463 Gerald FitzGerald
1472 William Roche (Coadjutor)
1490 Tadhg Mac Carthaigh
1499 John FitzEdmund FitzGerald
1499 Patrick Cant
1523 John Benet
1536 Dominic Tyrre [Tirrey]
1562 Roger Skiddy
1570 Richard Dyxon
1572 Matthew Sheyn

Ross united to Cork 1583
1583 William Lyon
1618 John Boyle
1620 Richard Boyle
1638 William Chappell
1661 Michael Boyle
1663 Edward Synge
1679 Edward Wetenhall
1699 Dive Downes
1710 Peter Browne
1735 Robert Clayton
1745 Jemmett Browne
1772 Isaac Mann
1789 Euseby Cleaver
1789 William Foster
1790 William Bennet
1794 Thomas Stopford
1805 John George Beresford
1807 Thomas St Laurence
1831 Samuel Kyle
Cloyne united to Cork from 1835
1848 James Wilson
1857 William FitzGerald
1862 John Gregg
1878 Robert Samuel Gregg
1894 William Edward Meade
1912 Charles Benjamin Dowse
1933 William Edward Flewett
1938 Robert Thomas Hearn
1952 George Otto Sims
1957 Richard Gordon Perdue
1978 Samuel Greenfield Poyntz
1988 Robert Alexander Warke
1999 William Paul Colton

Dublin

Dublin and Glendalough

BISHOPS
    Sinhail 790
*c.*1028 Dunan [Donatus]
1074 Gilla Patraic
1085 Donngus
1096 Samuel Ua'h-Aingliu

ARCHBISHOPS
1121 Grene [Gregorius]
1162 Lorcan Ua'Tuathail
    [Laurentius]
1182 John Cumin
1213 Henry de Loundres
Glendalough united to Dublin
1230 Luke
125? Fulk de Sandford
1279 John de Derlington
1286 John de Sandford
1295 Thomas de Chadworth
1296 William de Hotham
1299 Richard de Ferings
[1307 Richard de Havering, not
    consecrated]
1311 John de Leche
1317 Alexander de Bicknor
1349 John de St Paul
1363 Thomas Minot
1376 Robert de Wikeford
1391 Robert Waldeby
1396 Richard Northalis
1397 Thomas Cranley
1418 Richard Talbot
1451 Michael Tregury
1472 John Walton
1484 Walter Fitzsimons
1512 William Rokeby
1521 Hugh Inge
1529 John Alan
1535 George Browne
1555 Hugh Curwin

1567 Adam Loftus
1605 Thomas Jones
1619 Lancelot Bulkeley
1661 James Margetson
1663 Michael Boyle
1679 John Parker
1682 Francis Marsh
1694 Narcissus Marsh
1703 William King
1730 John Hoadly
1743 Charles Cobbe
1765 William Carmichael
1766 Arthur Smyth
1772 John Cradock
1779 Robert Fowler
1801 Charles Agar [Earl of
    Normanton]
1809 Euseby Cleaver
1820 John George Beresford
1822 William Magee
1831 Richard Whately
Kildare united to Dublin 1846
1864 Richard Chenevix Trench
    (resigned)
1885 William Conyngham [Lord
    Plunket]
1897 Joseph Ferguson Peacocke
1915 John Henry Bernard
1919 Charles Frederick D'Arcy
1920 John Allen Fitzgerald Gregg
1939 Arthur William Barton
1956 George Otto Simms
1969 Alan Alexander Buchanan
1977 Henry Robert McAdoo
1985 Donald Arthur Richard Caird
1996 Walton Newcome Francis
    Empey
2002 John Robert Winder Neill

†Emly

    Raidghil 881
    Ua Ruaich 953
    Faelan 980
    MaelFinan 1030
    Diarmait Ua Flainnchua 1114
1152 Gilla in Choimhded Ua h-
    Ardmhail Mael Isu Ua
    Laigenain 1163
1172 Ua Meic Stia
1177 Charles O'Buacalla
1177 Isaac O'Hamery
1192 Ragnall Ua Flainnchua
1205 M.
1209 William
1212 Henry
1227 John Collingham
1238 Daniel
1238 Christianus
1251 Gilbert O'Doverty
1266 Florence or Laurence O'hAirt
1272 Matthew MacGormain
1275 David O Cossaig
1286 William de Clifford
1306 Thomas Cantock [Quantock]
1309 William Roughead
1335 Richard le Walleys
1353 John Esmond
1363 David Penlyn [Foynlyn]
1363 William
1405 Nicholas Ball
1421 John Rishberry
1422 Robert Windell
1428 Thomas de Burgo
1428 Robert Portland
1445 Cornelius O Cuinnlis
1444 Robert
1448 Cornelius O Maolalaidh
1449 William O Hetigan

1476 Pilib O Cathail
1494 Donatus Mac Briain
1498 Cinneidigh Mac Briain
1507 Tomas O hUrthaille
1543 Angus O'Hernan
1551 Raymond de Burgo
United to Cashel 1569
Transferred to Limerick 1976

†Ferns

−598 Edar [or Maedoc or Hugh]
     Maeldogair 676
     Coman 678
     Diratus 693
     Cillenius 715
     Cairbre O'Kearney 1095
     Ceallach Ua Colmain 1117
     Mael Eoin Ua Dunacain 1125
     Ua Cattain 1135
1178 Loseph Ua h-Aeda
1186 Ailbe Ua Maelmuaid [Albinus]
1224 John of St John
1254 Geoffrey of St John
1258 Hugh of Lamport
1283 Richard of Northampton
1304 Simon of Evesham
1305 Robert Walrand
1312 Adam of Northampton
1347 Hugh de Saltu [of Leixlip]
1347 Geoffrey Grandfeld
1349 John Esmond
1350 William Charnells
1363 Thomas Dene
1400 Patrick Barret
1418 Robert Whittey
1453 Tadhg O Beirn
1457 John Purcell I
1479 Laurence Nevill
1505 Edmund Comerford
1510 Nicholas Comyn
1519 John Purcell II
1539 Alexander Devereux
1566 John Devereux
1582 Hugh Allen
Leighlin united to Ferns 1597
1600 Robert Grave
1601 Nicholas Statford
1605 Thomas Ram
1635 George Andrews
1661 Robert Price
1667 Richard Boyle
1683 Narcissus Marsh
1691 Bartholomew Vigors
1722 Josiah Hort
1727 John Hoadly
1730 Arthur Price
1734 Edward Synge
1740 George Stone
1743 William Cottrell
1744 Robert Downes
1752 John Garnet
1758 William Carmichael
1758 Thomas Salmon
1759 Richard Robinson
1761 Charles Jackson
1765 Edward Young
1772 Joseph Deane Bourke
1782 Walter Cope
1787 William Preston
1789 Euseby Cleaver
1809 Percy Jocelyn
1820 Robert Ponsonby Tottenham
     Loftus
1822 Thomas Elrington
United to Ossory 1835

†Glendalough

Dairchell 678
Eterscel 814

Dungal 904
Cormac 927
Nuadha 920 [or Neva]
Gilda Na Naomh
     c.1080
Cormac O'Mail 1101
Aed Ua Modain 1126
1140 Anonymous
1152 Gilla na Naem
1157 Cinaed O Ronain [Celestinus]
1176 Maelcallann Ua Cleirchen
     [Malchus]
1186 Macrobius
1192 William Piro
1214 Robert de Bedford
United to Dublin
After the union with Dublin some
rival bishops appear
c.1216 Bricheus
1468 John
1475 Michael
1481 Denis White John 1494
1494 Ivo Ruffi
1495 John
1500 Francis Fitzjohn of Corduba

†Iniscattery (Scattery Island)

861 Aidan
959 Cinaeda O'Chommind
973 Scandlam O'Lenz
     O'Bruil 1069
     O'Bruil II 1081
     Dermot O Lennain 1119
     Aed Ua Bechain I 1188
     Cearbhal Ua'h-Enna
     [Carolus]
1193
1360 Tomas Mac Mathghamhna
1392 John Donkan
1414 Richard Belmer
     Dionysius 1447
1447 John Grene
Incorporated with Limerick

†Kells

Mael Finnen 968
c.1152 Tuathal Ua Connachtarg
1185 Anonymous
1202 M. Ua Dobailen
Incorporated with Meath

†Kildare

Conlaedh 520
Hugh [or Hed] the Black 639
Maeldoborcon 709
Eutigern 762
Lomthiull 787
Snedbran 787
Tuatchar 834
Orthanach 840
Aedgene Britt 864
Macnghal 870
Lachtnan 875
Suibhne 881
Scannal 885
Lergus 888
Mael Findan 950
Annchadh 981
Murrough McFlan 986
1030 MaelMartain
     MaelBrighde 1042
     Finn 1085
     MaelBrighde O Brolchan
     1097
     Hugh [Heremon] 1100
     Ferdomnach 1101

Cormac O Cathassaig 1146
Ua Duibhin 1148
1152 Finn mac Mael Muire Mac
     Cianain
     Fin mac Gussain Ua
     Gormain
1161 Malachias Ua Brain
1177 Nehemias
1206 Cornelius Mac Fealain
1223 Ralph of Bristol
1233 John of Taunton
1258 Simon of Kilkenny
1280 Nicholas Cusack
1300 Walter Calf [de Veel]
1333 Richard Houlot
1352 Thomas Giffard
1366 Robert of Aketon
     [Acton]
1404 John Madock
1431 William fitzEdward
1449 Geoffrey Hereford
1456 John Bole [Bull]
1464 Richard Lang
1474 David Cone
1475 James Wall
     William Barret
1480 Edward Lane
1526 Thomas Dillon
1529 Walter Wellesley
1540 William Miagh
1550 Thomas Lancaster
1555 Thomas Leverous
1560 Alexander Craik
1564 Robert Daly
1583 Daniel Neylan
1604 William Pilsworth
1636 Robert Ussher
1644 William Golborne
1661 Thomas Price
1667 Ambrose Jones
1679 Anthony Dopping
1682 William Moreton
1705 Welbore Ellis
1731 Charles Cobbe
1743 George Stone
1745 Thomas Fletcher
1761 Richard Robinson
1765 Charles Jackson
1790 George Lewis Jones
1804 Charles Lindsay
United to Dublin after the death of
     Bp Lindsay in 1846
1976 Separated from Dublin and
     united to Meath

†Kilfenora

1172 Anonymous
1205 F.
1224 Johannes
1254 Christianus
     Anonymous 1264
1266 Mauricius
1273 Florentius O Tigernaig
1281 Congalach [O Lochlainn]
1291 G.
1299 Simon O Cuirrin
1303 Maurice O Briain
1323 Risdeard O Lochlainn
c.1355 Dionysius
1372 Henricus
     Cornelius
1390 Patricius
1421 Feidhlimidh mac
     Mathghamhna O Lochlainn
     [Florentius]
1433 Fearghal
1434 Dionysius O Connmhaigh
1447 John Greni
1476 [? Denis] O Tombaigh

1491 Muircheartach mac
        Murchadha O Briain
        [Mauricius]
1514 Maurice O'Kelly
1541 John O'Neylan
-1585 Daniel, bishop-elect
1606 Bernard Adams [with
        Limerick q.v.]
1617 John Steere
1622 William Murray
[1628 Richard Betts, not
        consecrated]
1630 James Heygate
1638 Robert Sibthorp
1661–1741 Held by the Archbishops
        of Tuam
1742–52 Held by the Bishop of
        Clonfert
United to Killaloe 1752

†Killaloe

BISHOPS

        O'Gerruidher 1054
        Domnall Ua hEnna 1098
        Mael Muire O Dunain 1117
        Domnall Ua Conaing 1131
        Domnall Ua Longargain 1137
        Tadg Ua Longargain 1161
        Donnchad mac Diarmata Ua
        Briain 1164
1179 Constantin mac Toirrdelbaig
        Ua Briain
1194 Diarmait Ua Conaing
1201 Conchobhar Ua h-Enna
        [Cornelius]
1217 Robert Travers
1221 Domnall Ua h-Enna
        [Donatus]
1231 Domnall O Cenneitig
        [Donatus]
1253 Isoc O Cormacain [Isaac]
1268 Mathgamain O h-Ocain [O
        Hogan]
1281 Maurice O h-Ocain
1299 David Mac Mathghamna
        [Mac Mahon]
1317 Tomas O Cormacain I
1323 Brian O Cosgraig
1326 David Mac Briain [David of
        Emly]
?1326 Natus O Heime
1343 Tomas O h-Ogain
1355 Tomas O Cormacain II
1389 Mathghamain Mag Raith
1400 Donatus Mag Raith
1409 Robert Mulfield
1418 Eugenius O Faolain
1423 Thadeus Mag Raith I
1429 Seamus O Lonnghargain
1443 Donnchadh mac
        Toirdhealbhaigh O Briain
1460 Thadeus Mag Raith II
1463 Matthaeus O Griobhtha
1483 Toirdhealbhach mac
        Mathghamhna O Briain
        [Theodoricus]
1523 Thadeus
1526 Seamus O Cuirrin
1546 Cornelius O Dea
1554 Turlough [or Terence]
        O'Brien II
1570 Maurice [or Murtagh]
        O'Brien-Arra
1613 John Rider
1633 Lewis Jones
1647 Edward Parry
1661 Edward Worth
1669 Daniel Wytter

1675 John Roan
1693 Henry Ryder
1696 Thomas Lindsay
1713 Thomas Vesey
1714 Nicholas Forster
1716 Charles Carr
1740 Joseph Story
1742 John Ryder
1743 Jemmet Browne
1745 Richard Chenevix
1746 Nicholas Synge
Kilfenora united to Killaloe 1752
1771 Robert Fowler
1779 George Chinnery
1780 Thomas Barnard
1794 William Knox
1803 Charles Dalrymple Lindsay
1804 Nathaniel Alexander
1804 Robert Ponsonby Tottenham
        Loftus
1820 Richard Mant
1823 Alexander Arbuthnot
1828 Richard Ponsonby
1831 Edmund Knox [with Clonfert]
Clonfert united to Killaloe 1834
Kilmacduagh united to Killaloe
        1834
1834 Christopher Butson
1836 Stephen Crengh Sandes
1839 Ludlow Tonson [afterwards
        Baron Riversdale]
1862 William FitzGerald
1884 William Bennet Chester
1893 Frederick Richards Wynne
1897 Mervyn Archdall
1912 Charles Benjamin Dowse
1913 Thomas Sterling Berry
        (resigned)
1924 Henry Edmund Patton
1943 Robert M'Neil Boyd
1945 Hedley Webster
1953 Richard Gordon Perdue
1957 Henry Arthur Stanistreet
1972 Edwin Owen
1976 United to Limerick

†Kilmacduagh

    ? Ua Cleirig 1137
        Imar Ua Ruaidin 1176
        Rugnad O'Rowan 1178
1179 Mac Gilla Cellaig Ua Ruaidin
1206 Ua Cellaig
        Mael Muire O Connmaig
        1224
1227 Aed [Odo]
        Conchobhar O Muiredaig
        1247
1248 Gilla Cellaig O Ruaidin
        [Gilbertus]
1249 David yFredrakern
1254 Mauricius O Leaain
1284 David O Setachain
1290 Luirint O Lachtnain
        [Laurentius]
1307 Lucas
1326 Johannes
1360 Nicol O Leaain
1394 Gregory O Leaain
1405 Enri O Connmhaigh
1409 Dionysius
1409 Eugene O Faolain
1418 Diarmaid O Donnchadha
1419 Nicol O Duibhghiolla
1419 Seaan O Connmhaigh
1441 Dionysius O Donnchadha
1479 Cornelius O Mullony
1503 Matthaeus O Briain
1533 Christopher Bodkin
1573 Stephen O'Kirwan

[1584 Thomas Burke, not
        consecrated]
1587 Roland Lynch
1627–1836 Held in commendam by
        the Bishops of Clonfert
United to Killaloe since 1834

†Leighlin

-633 Laserian or Molaise
-865 Mainchin
-940 Conella McDonegan Daniel
        969
        Cleitic O'Muinic 1050
c.1096 Ferdomnac
        Mael Eoin Ua Dunacain 1125
        Sluaigedach Ua Cathain 1145
1152 Dungal O Caellaide
1192 Johannes
1197 Johannes
1202 Herlewin
1217 Richard [Fleming]
1228 William le Chauniver
1252 Thomas
1275 Nicholas Chever
1309 Maurice de Blanchville
1321 Meiler le Poer
1344 Radulphus O Ceallaigh
1349 Thomas of Brakenberg
1360 Johannes
1362 William (not consecrated)
1363 John Young
1371 Philip FitzPeter
1385 John Griffin
1398 Thomas Peverell
1400 Richard Bocomb
1419 John Mulgan
1432 Thomas Fleming
   — Diarmaid 1464
1464 Milo Roche
1490 Nicholas Magwyr
1513 Thomas Halsey
1524 Mauricius O Deoradhain
1527 Matthew Sanders
1550 Robert Travers
1555 Thomas O'Fihelly
1567 Donnell or Daniel Cavanagh
1589 Richard Meredith
United to Ferns since 1597 on the
        death of Bp Meredith

Limerick

*Limerick, Ardfert, Aghadoe, Killaloe,
Kilfenora, Clonfert, Kilmacduagh and
Emly*
-1106 Gilli alias Gilla Espaic
1140 Patricius
1150 Erolb [? = Harold]
1152 Torgesius
1179 Brictius
1203 Donnchad Ua'Briain
        [Donatus]
1207 Geoffrey
-1215 Edmund
1223 Hubert de Burgo
1252 Robert de Emly or Neil
1273 Gerald [or Miles] de Mareshall
1302 Robert de Dundonald
1312 Eustace de Aqua or de l'Eau
1336 Maurice de Rochfort
1354 Stephen Lawless
1360 Stephen Wall [de Valle]
1369 Peter Curragh
1399 Bernardus O Conchobhair
1400 Conchobhar O Deadhaidh
1426 John Mothel (resigned)
Iniscattery incorporated with
        Limerick

1456 Thomas Leger
1458 William Russel, *alias* Creagh
1463 Thomas Arthur
[1486 Richard Stakpoll, not
    consecrated]
1486 John Dunowe
1489 John O'Phelan [Folan]
1524 Sean O Cuinn
1551 William Casey
1557 Hugh de Lacey or Lees
    (deposed)
1571 William Casey
1594 John Thornburgh
1604 Bernard Adams
1626 Francis Gough
1634 George Webb
1643 Robert Sibthorp
Ardfert united to Limerick 1661
1661 Edward Synge
1664 William Fuller
1667 Francis Marsh
1673 John Vesey
1679 Simon Digby
1692 Nathaniel Wilson
1695 Thomas Smyth
1725 William Burscough
1755 James Leslie
1771 James Averill
1772 William Gore
1784 William Cecil Pery
1794 Thomas Barnard
1806 Charles Morgan Warburton
1820 Thomas Elrington
1823 John Jebb
1834 Edmund Knox
1849 William Higgin
1854 Henry Griffin
1866 Charles Graves
1899 Thomas Bunbury
1907 Raymond D'Audemra Orpen
1921 Harry Vere White
1934 Charles King Irwin
1942 Evelyn Charles Hodges
1961 Robert Wyse Jackson
1970 Donald Arthur Richard Caird
Killaloe united to Limerick 1976
Emly transferred to Limerick 1976
1976 Edwin Owen
1981 Walton Newcome Francis
    Empey
1985 Edward Flewett Darling
2000 Michael Hugh Gunton Mayes

†Lismore

Ronan 764
Cormac MacCuillenan 918
–999 Cinneda O'Chonmind
Niall mac Meic Aedacain
    1113
Ua Daightig 1119
1121 Mael Isu Ua h-Ainmere
Mael Muire Ua Loingsig 1150
1151 Gilla Crist Ua Connairche
    [Christianus]
1179 Felix
Ardmore incorporated with Lismore
    1192
1203 Malachias, O'Heda or
    O'Danus
1216 Thomas
1219 Robert of Bedford
1228 Griffin Christopher
1248 Ailinn O Suilleabain
1253 Thomas
1270 John Roche
1280 Richard Corre
1309 William Fleming
1310 R.
1322 John Leynagh

1356 Roger Cradock, provision
    annulled
1358 Thomas le Reve
United to Waterford 1363

Meath

Meath and Kildare

BISHOPS OF THE SEE OF CLONARD

Senach 588
–640 Colman 654
DusucBhduin O'Phelan 718
Tole 738
–778 Fulartach 779
Clothcu 796
Clemens 826
Cormac MacSuibhne
Cumsuth 858
Suarlech 870
Ruman MacCathasaid 922
Colman MacAilild 926
Tuathal O'Dubhamaigh 1028

BISHOPS OF MEATH

1096 Mael Muire Ua Dunain
1128 Eochaid O Cellaig
1151 Etru Ua Miadacain
    [Eleuzerius]
1177 Echtigern mac Mael Chiarain
    [Eugenius]
1192 Simon Rochfort
(The See was transferred from
    Clonard to Newtown near
    Trim, 1202)
Kells incorporated with Meath
1224 Donan De [Deodatus] (not
    consecrated)
1227 Ralph Petit
1231 Richard de la Corner
1253 Geoffrey Cusack
1255 Hugo de Taghmon
1283 Walter de Fulburn
1287 Thomas St Leger
1322 Seoan Mac Cerbaill [John
    MacCarwill]
1327 William de Paul
1350 William St Leger
1353 Nicholas [Allen]
1369 Stephen de Valle [Wall]
1380 William Andrew
1385 Alexander Petit [or de Balscot]
1401 Robert Montayne
1412 Edward Dantesey
[1430 Thomas Scurlog, apparently
    not consecrated]
1430 William Hadsor
1435 William Silk
1450 Edmund Ouldhall
1460 William Shirwood
1483 John Payne
1507 William Rokeby
1512 Hugh Inge
1523 Richard Wilson
1529 Edward Staples
1554 William Walsh
1563 Hugh Brady
Clonmacnoise united to Meath 1569
1584 Thomas Jones
1605 Roger Dod
1612 George Montgomery
1621 James Usher
1625 Anthony Martin
[Interregnum 1650–61]
1661 Henry Leslie
1661 Henry Jones
1682 Anthony Dopping
1697 Richard Tennison
1705 William Moreton

1716 John Evans
1724 Henry Downes
1727 Ralph Lambert
1732 Welbore Ellis
1734 Arthur Price
1744 Henry Maule
1758 William Carmichael
1765 Richard Pococke
1765 Arthur Smyth
1766 Henry Maxwell
1798 Thomas Lewis O'Beirne
1823 Nathaniel Alexander
1840 Charles Dickinson
1842 Edward Stopford
1850 Thomas Stewart Townsend
1852 James Henderson Singer
1866 Samuel Butcher
1876 William Conyngham [Lord
    Plunket]
1885 Charles Parsons Reichel
1894 Joseph Ferguson Peacocke
1897 James Bennett Keene
1919 Benjamin John Plunket
1926 Thomas Gibson George
    Collins
1927 John Orr
1938 William Hardy Holmes
1945 James McCann
1959 Robert Bonsall Pike
Kildare united to Meath 1976
1976 Donald Arthur Richard Caird
1985 Walton Newcome Francis
    Empey
1996 Richard Lionel Clarke

†Ossory

Dermot 973
1152 Domnall Ua Fogartaig
1180 Felix Ua Duib Slaine
1202 Hugo de Rous [Hugo Rufus]
1220 Peter Mauveisin
1231 William of Kilkenny
1233 Walter de Brackley
1245 Geoffrey de Turville
1251 Hugh de Mapilton
1260 Geoffrey St Leger
1287 Roger of Wexford
1289 Michael d'Exeter
1303 William FitzJohn
1317 Richard Ledred
1361 John de Tatenhale
1366 William
  — John of Oxford
1371 Alexander Petit [de Balscot]
1387 Richard Northalis
1396 Thomas Peverell
1399 John Waltham
1400 John Griffin
1400 John
1401 Roger Appleby
1402 John Waltham
1407 Thomas Snell
1417 Patrick Foxe
1421 Dionysius O Deadhaidh
1427 Thomas Barry
1460 David Hacket
1479 Seaan O hEidigheain
1487 Oliver Cantwell
1528 Milo Baron [or FitzGerald]
1553 John Bale
1554 John Tonory
1567 Christopher Gaffney
1577 Nicholas Walsh
1586 John Horsfall
1610 Richard Deane
1613 Jonas Wheeler
1641 Griffith Williams
1672 John Parry

1678 Benjamin Parry
1678 Michael Ward
1680 Thomas Otway
1693 John Hartstonge
1714 Thomas Vesey
1731 Edward Tennison
1736 Charles Este
1741 Anthony Dopping
1743 Michael Cox
1754 Edward Maurice
1755 Richard Pococke
1765 Charles Dodgson
1775 William Newcome
1779 John Hotham
1782 William Heresford
1795 Thomas Lewis O'Beirne
1799 Hugh Hamilton
1806 John Kearney
1813 Robert Fowler
Ferns united to Ossory 1835
1842 James Thomas O'Brien
1874 Robert Samuel Gregg
1878 William Fakenham Walsh
1897 John Baptist Crozier
1907 Charles Frederick D'Arcy
1911 John Henry Bernard
1915 John Allen Fitzgerald Gregg
1920 John Godfrey FitzMaurice
     Day
1938 Ford Tichbourne
1940 John Percy Phair
1962 Henry Robert McAdoo
United to Cashel 1977

†Ross

Nechtan MacNechtain 1160
Isaac O'Cowen 1161
O'Carroll 1168
1177 Benedictus
1192 Mauricius
1198 Daniel
1224 Fineen O Clothna [Florentius]
c.1250 Malachy
1254 Mauricius
1269 Walter O Mithigein
1275 Peter O h-Uallachain
     [? Patrick]
1291 Laurentius
1310 Matthaeus O Finn
1331 Laurentius O h-Uallachain
1336 Dionysius

1379 Bernard O Conchobhair
1399 Peter Curragh
1400 Thadeus O Ceallaigh
1401 Mac Raith O hEidirsgeoil
     [Macrobius]
1402 Stephen Brown
1403 Matthew
1418 Walter Formay
1424 John Bloxworth
1426 Conchobhar Mac
     Fhaolchadha [Cornelius]
     Maurice Brown 1431
1431 Walter of Leicester
1434 Richard Clerk
1448 Domhnall O Donnobhain
     John 1460
1460 Robert Colynson
–1464 Thomas
1464 John Hornse *alias* Skipton
1473 Aodh O hEidirsgeoil [Odo]
1482 Tadhg Mac Carthaigh
1494 John Edmund Courci
1517 Seaan O Muirthile
1519 Tadgh O Raghallaigh
     [Thaddeus]
1523 Bonaventura
1526 Diarmaid Mac Carthaigh
1544 Dermot McDonnell
1551 John
1554 Maurice O'Fihelly
1559 Maurice O'Hea
1561 Thomas O'Herlihy
1582 William Lyon [with Cork and
     Cloyne after 1581]
United to Cork 1583

†Waterford

1096 Mael lus Ua h-Ainmere
1152 Toistius
1175 Augustinus Ua Selbaig
     Anonymous 1199
1200 Robert I
1204 David the Welshman
1210 Robert II [Breathnach]
1223 William Wace
1227 Walter
1232 Stephen
1250 Henry
1252 Philip
1255 Walter de Southwell
1274 Stephen de Fulbourn

1286 Walter de Fulbourn
1308 Matthew
1323 Nicholas Welifed
1338 Richard Francis
1349 Robert Elyot
1350 Roger Cradock
Lismore united to Waterford
     1363
1363 Thomas le Reve
1394 Robert Read
1396 Thomas Sparklord
1397 John Deping
1400 Thomas Snell
1407 Roger of Appleby (*see under*
     Ossory)
1409 John Geese
1414 Thomas Colby
1421 John Geese
1426 Richard Cantwell
1446 Robert Poer
1473 Richard Martin
1475 John Bulcomb
1480 Nicol O hAonghusa
1483 Thomas Purcell
1519 Nicholas Comyn
1551 Patrick Walsh
1579 Marmaduke Middleton
1582 Miler Magrath (Bishop
     of Cashel and
     Waterford)
1589 Thomas Wetherhead [or
     Walley]
1592 Miler Magrath
1608 John Lancaster
1619 Michael Boyle
1636 John Atherton
1641 Archibald Adair
1661 George Baker
1666 Hugh Gore
1691 Nathaniel Foy
1708 Thomas Mills
1740 Charles Este
1746 Richard Chenevix
1779 William Newcome
1795 Richard Marlay
1802 Power le Poer Trench
1810 Joseph Stock
1813 Richard Bourke
United to Cashel under Church
     Temporalities Act 1833

CATHEDRALS
CHURCH OF ENGLAND

(BATH AND) WELLS (St Andrew) **Dean** *vacant,*
Cans Res THE VEN R F ACWORTH, M W MATTHEWS,
P H F WOODHOUSE, **Sub-Dean** N A SULLIVAN,
PV A J KEEP
BIRMINGHAM (St Philip) **Dean** A G MURSELL,
Cans Res G O'NEILL, D J LEE, **NSM** T J CLARKE
BLACKBURN (St Mary) **Dean** C J ARMSTRONG,
Cans Res A D HINDLEY, G D S GALILEE, A CLITHEROW,
Hon P M J WEDGEWORTH
BRADFORD (St Peter) **Dean** C D HANCOCK,
Cans Res D R JACKSON, D J BRIERLEY,
Can Th K N MEDHURST, **Hon Chapl** M P SHORT
BRISTOL (Holy Trinity) **Dean** R W GRIMLEY,
Cans Res P F JOHNSON, D R HOLT, B D CLOVER,
Hon Min Cans R C LUNN, R A SEARLE, S B TAYLOR
CANTERBURY (Christ) **Dean** R A WILLIS,
Cans Res M J CHANDLER, R ST J J MARSH,
THE VEN P A S EVANS, E F CONDRY **Prec** K I GOSS
CARLISLE (Holy Trinity) **Dean** G P KNOWLES,
Cans Res R A CHAPMAN, D W V WESTON, C HILL,
THE VEN D THOMSON
CHELMSFORD (St Mary, St Peter and St Cedd)
Dean P S M JUDD, **Cans Res** A W A KNOWLES, W R KING,
G L TUNBRIDGE
CHESTER (Christ and Blessed Virgin Mary)
Dean G F MCPHATE, **Cans Res** T J DENNIS, J M ROFF,
C P BURKETT, J M HUNT, **Can Th** L C A ALEXANDER
CHICHESTER (Holy Trinity) **Dean** N A FRAYLING,
Cans Res J F FORD, P C KEFFORD, P G ATKINSON,
PV D NASON, **Chapl** S J DAVIES
COVENTRY (St Michael) **Dean** J D IRVINE,
Cans Res A P B WHITE, S A BEAKE, J P WELBY,
A M DAFFERN, **Cans Th** C A LAMB, T J DAKIN,
Chapl A E DARBY
DERBY (All Saints) **Dean** M F
PERHAM, **Cans Res** G A CHESTERMAN, D C TRUBY,
B V GAUGE, N J HENSHALL, **Can Th** A BROWN,
Chapl A E HOLLINGHURST
DURHAM (Christ and Blessed Virgin Mary)
Dean M SADGROVE, **Cans Res** D W BROWN,
D J WHITTINGTON, M KITCHEN, D J KENNEDY,
Min Can G M MYERS
ELY (Holy Trinity) **Dean** *vacant,*
Cans Res P M SILLS,
Prec and Sacr N E WOODCOCK
EXETER (St Peter) **Dean** K B JONES,
Cans Res D J ISON, N COLLINGS, C F TURNER,
M J RYLANDS
GLOUCESTER (St Peter and Holy Trinity)
Dean N A S BURY, **Cans Res** N C HEAVISIDES, D M HOYLE,
G S BRIDGEWATER, C S M THOMSON
GUILDFORD (Holy Spirit) **Dean** V A STOCK, **Cans Res**
M F PALMER, N J THISTLETHWAITE, J R H HUBBARD, J H FROST,
Hon C D M MACMILLAN
HEREFORD (Blessed Virgin Mary and St Ethelbert)
Dean M E TAVINOR, **Cans Res** J TILLER, V HAMER, A PIPER
LEICESTER (St Martin) **Dean** V F FAULL,
Cans Res M WILSON, J B NAYLOR, J N CRAIG,
Chapl J S PARKIN
LICHFIELD (Blessed Virgin Mary and St Chad)
Dean M L YORKE, **Cans Res** A N BARNARD, C W TAYLOR,
C F LILEY, **Dean's V** P LOCKETT, **Chan's V** P L HOLLIDAY
LINCOLN (Blessed Virgin Mary) **Dean** A F KNIGHT,
Cans Res A H NUGENT, G J KIRK,
Succ P V A ADKINS
LIVERPOOL (Christ) **Dean** R W N HOARE,
Cans Res M C BOYLING, A B HAWLEY,
Cans Th R J ELFORD, J C POLKINGHORNE,
Chapl J CALDWELL, **Hon Chapl** M M WOLFE
LONDON (St Paul) **Dean** J H MOSES,
Cans Res P J W BUCKLER, E J NEWELL, M C WARNER
Min Cans A C COLES, L C WINKETT, S A REYNOLDS,
Dep Min Can THE VEN B A C KIRK-DUNCAN,
Hon Min Cans D J L BEAN, **Hon Assoc P** S E GENT

MANCHESTER (St Mary, St Denys and St George)
Dean K J RILEY, **Cans Res** J R ATHERTON, P DENBY,
THE VEN A WOLSTENCROFT, **Can Ev** R P GAMBLE
NEWCASTLE (St Nicholas) **Dean** C C DALLISTON,
Cans Res P R STRANGE, THE VEN P ELLIOTT, G V MILLER,
D J ELKINGTON
NORWICH (Holy Trinity) **Dean** *vacant,*
Cans Res C J OFFER, R J HANMER, M A KITCHENER,
Prec J M HASELOCK, **Chapl** A R LONG
OXFORD (Christ Church) **Dean** J H DRURY,
Cans Res O M T O'DONOVAN, J S K WARD, J B WEBSTER,
THE VEN J A MORRISON, M M PARRY,
THE VERY REVD N G COULTON, **Prec** M E BIDE
PETERBOROUGH (St Peter, St Paul and St Andrew)
Dean M BUNKER, **Cans Res** W S CROFT, S G COTTRELL
PORTSMOUTH (St Thomas of Canterbury)
Dean D C BRINDLEY, **Cans Res** D T ISAAC, G J KIRK,
M A TRISTRAM
RIPON (St Peter and St Wilfrid) **Dean** J A R METHUEN,
Cans Res M R GLANVILLE-SMITH, K PUNSHON,
Min Cans E D MURFET, P M DRIVER, **NSM** K E CROSSLEY
ROCHESTER (Christ and Blessed Virgin Mary)
Dean *vacant,* **Cans Res** C J MEYRICK, P H D´A LOCK,
R C GODSALL
ST ALBANS (St Alban) **Dean** C A LEWIS,
Cans Res M C SANSOM, I R LANE, R R WHEELER, D L STAMPS,
Prec B T HUISH, **Assoc Min** D C FITZGERALD CLARK
ST EDMUNDSBURY (St James) **Dean** J E ATWELL,
Cans Res A M SHAW, A J TODD, P BARHAM
SALISBURY (Blessed Virgin Mary) **Dean** *vacant,*
Cans Res D J C DAVIES, D M K DURSTON, J OSBORNE
SHEFFIELD (St Peter and St Paul) **Dean** *vacant,*
Cans Res THE VEN R F BLACKBURN, A P SHACKERLEY,
N S HOWE, H I J SUCH, **NSM** N M JOHNSON
SODOR AND MAN (St German) **Dean** THE BISHOP,
Can Prec B H KELLY
SOUTHWARK (St Saviour and St Mary Overie)
Dean C B SLEE, **Cans Res** J P H JOHN, B A SAUNDERS,
A P NUNN, S J ROBERTS, **Succ** J A D BUXTON,
Chapl A C WINTER, H PETTERSSON, N P GODFREY,
Hon C W S ROBINS
SOUTHWELL (Blessed Virgin Mary) **Dean** D LEANING,
Cans Res R H DAVEY, J D JONES, **PV** M L SHACKLEY
TRURO (St Mary) **Dean** M A MOXON, **Cans Res** P R GAY,
K P MELLOR, P A A WALKER
WAKEFIELD (All Saints) **Dean** G P NAIRN-BRIGGS,
Cans Res R CAPPER, R E GAGE, I M GASKELL,
Can Missr J R HOLMES
**WINCHESTER (Holy Trinity, St Peter, St Paul and St
Swithun)** **Dean** M STILL, **Cans Res** C STEWART, J A GUILLE,
F J L WINFIELD, K E ANDERSON, **Past Asst** J A BROWNING
WORCESTER (Christ and Blessed Virgin Mary)
Dean P J MARSHALL, **Cans Res** R B RUDDOCK,
THE VEN J D TETLEY, A L PETTERSEN,
Min Cans M R DORSETT
YORK (St Peter) **Dean** R FURNELL, **Cans Res** E R NORMAN,
G H WEBSTER, J L DRAPER, J J FLETCHER

Collegiate Churches
WESTMINSTER ABBEY
ST GEORGE'S CHAPEL, WINDSOR *See Royal
Peculiars, p. 941.*

Diocese in Europe
GIBRALTAR (Holy Trinity) **Dean** A G WOODS
MALTA Valletta (St Paul) **Pro-Cathedral** *vacant*
BRUSSELS (Holy Trinity) **Pro-Cathedral**
Chan N M WALKER

CHURCH IN WALES

The name of the Dean is given, together with other clergy holding full-time appointments.

BANGOR (St Deiniol) **Dean** T O EVANS,
 Min Can D T MORGAN
LLANDAFF (St Peter and St Paul) **Dean** J T LEWIS,
 Min Cans M A R HILL, G W A HOLCOMBE
MONMOUTH Newport **(St Woolos)**
 Dean R D FENWICK, **Min Cans** L T IRVINE-CAPEL,
 G P HOWELL

ST ASAPH (St Asaph) **Dean** C N L POTTER,
 Prec H J LLOYD, **PV** A C SULLY, **Chapl** M K R STALLARD
ST DAVIDS (St David and St Andrew) **Dean** J W EVANS,
 Min Can R P DAVIES, **Chapl** J S BENNETT
**(SWANSEA AND) BRECON (St John the
 Evangelist)** **Dean** J D E DAVIES, **Min Cans** R J B TAYLOR,
 J A I BROWN

SCOTTISH EPISCOPAL CHURCH

For the members of the chapter the *Scottish Episcopal Church Directory* should be consulted.

Aberdeen and Orkney
ABERDEEN (St Andrew) **Provost** R E KILGOUR

Argyll and The Isles
OBAN (St John) **Provost** A M MACLEAN
CUMBRAE (Holy Spirit) **Cathedral of The Isles**
Provost D M CAMERON *Bishop of Argyll and The Isles*

Brechin
DUNDEE (St Paul) **Provost** M A F BYRNE

Edinburgh
EDINBURGH (St Mary) **Provost** G J T FORBES

Glasgow and Galloway
GLASGOW (St Mary) **Provost** P J DINES

Moray, Ross and Caithness
INVERNESS (St Andrew) **Provost** M F HICKFORD

St Andrews, Dunkeld and Dunblane
PERTH (St Ninian) **Provost** H B FARQUHARSON

CHURCH OF IRELAND

Most cathedrals are parish churches, and the dean is usually, but not always, the incumbent. For the members of the chapter the *Church of Ireland Directory* should be consulted. The name of the dean is given, together with those of other clergy holding full-time appointments.

NATIONAL CATHEDRAL OF ST PATRICK, Dublin **Dean** R B MacCARTHY, **Dean's V** M D GARDNER
CATHEDRAL OF ST ANNE, Belfast R S J H MCKELVEY (St Anne's is a cathedral of the dioceses of Down and Dromore
 and of Connor)

Province of Armagh

Armagh
ARMAGH (St Patrick) H CASSIDY

Clogher
CLOGHER (St Macartan) T R MOORE
ENNISKILLEN (St Macartin) T R MOORE *Dean of Clogher*

Derry and Raphoe
DERRY (St Columb) W W MORTON
RAPHOE (St Eunan) J HAY

Down and Dromore
DOWN (Holy and Undivided Trinity) J F DINNEN
DROMORE (Christ the Redeemer) S H LOWRY

Connor
LISBURN (Christ) *(Dean of Connor)* J F A BOND,
 I W S WRIGHT

Kilmore, Elphin and Ardagh
KILMORE (St Fethlimidh) D S G GODFREY
SLIGO (St Mary and St John the Baptist) D GRISCOME

Tuam, Killala and Achonry
TUAM (St Mary) A J GRIMASON
KILLALA (St Patrick) *vacant*
ACHONRY (St Crumnathy) *vacant*

Province of Dublin

Dublin and Glendalough
DUBLIN (Holy Trinity) **Christ Church** J T F PATERSON

Meath and Kildare
TRIM (St Patrick) R W JONES *Dean of Clonmacnoise*
KILDARE (St Brigid) R K TOWNLEY

Cashel and Ossory
CASHEL (St John the Baptist) P J KNOWLES
WATERFORD (Blessed Trinity) **Christ Church**
 T R LESTER
LISMORE (St Carthage) W BEARE
KILKENNY (St Canice) N N LYNAS *Dean of Ossory*
LEIGHLIN (St Laserian) C A FAULL
FERNS (St Edan) L D A FORREST

Cork, Cloyne and Ross
CORK (St Fin Barr) M A J BURROWS
CLOYNE (St Colman) A G MARLEY
ROSS (St Fachtna) C L PETERS

Limerick and Killaloe
LIMERICK (St Mary) J M G SIRR
KILLALOE (St Flannan) S R WHITE

ROYAL PECULIARS, CLERGY OF THE QUEEN'S HOUSEHOLD, ETC.

Royal Peculiars

Collegiate Church of St Peter Westminster
(Westminster Abbey) Dean A W CARR,
Cans THE VEN D H HUTT, M J MIDDLETON, A R WRIGHT
Prec C M CHIVERS,   **PVs** J G PEDLAR, R G HOLLOWAY,
P A E CHESTER, P J COWELL, P F BRADSHAW, T H MORDECAI,
P MCGEARY, D A PETERS, A R BODDY
Queen's Free Chapel of St George Windsor Castle
(St George's Chapel)
Dean THE RT REVD D J CONNER,
Cans J A WHITE, L F P GUNNER, J A OVENDEN,
Min Cans E J CARTER, G S P C NAPIER

The Queen's Household

Royal Almonry

High Almoner THE RT REVD N S MCCULLOCH (Bishop of
Manchester)
Sub-Almoner W J BOOTH

The College of Chaplains

Clerk of the Closet THE RT REVD J S BAILEY (Bishop of
Derby)
Deputy Clerk of the Closet W J BOOTH

Chaplains to The Queen

J D A ADAMS	R S CLARKE	M E MINGINS
D L BARTLES-SMITH	R T COOPER	G MOFFAT
F W H BENTLEY	A S CRAIG	J W R MOWLL
M J BENTON	C M FARRINGTON	B C OSBORNE
R A BOWDEN	D FLEMING	J C PRIESTLEY
R V BRAZIER	R G GILBERT	H I L RUSSELL
D J BURGESS	D C GRAY	C W J SAMUELS
J V BYRNE	G R HALL	W S SCOTT
P N CALVERT	G JONES	I G SMITH-CAMERON
R A CHAPMAN	G I KOVOOR	J SYKES
G A CHESTERMAN	W A MATTHEWS	L F WEBBER

Extra Chaplains to The Queen

A D CAESAR	J G M W MURPHY	J R W STOTT
E A JAMES	J P ROBSON	E J G WARD

Chapels Royal

Dean of the Chapels Royal THE BISHOP OF LONDON
Sub-Dean of the Chapels Royal W J BOOTH
Priests in Ordinary R D E BOLTON, S E YOUNG, P R THOMAS
Deputy Priests in Ordinary A H MEAD, M D OAKLEY,
P R C ABRAM, D R MULLINER
Domestic Chaplain, Buckingham Palace W J BOOTH
Domestic Chaplain, Windsor Castle THE DEAN OF
WINDSOR
Domestic Chaplain, Sandringham J B V RIVIERE
Chaplain, Royal Chapel, Windsor Great Park
J A OVENDEN
Chaplain, Hampton Court Palace D R MULLINER
Chaplain, HM Tower of London P R C ABRAM

The Queen's Chapel of the Savoy

Chaplain W S SCOTT

Royal Memorial Chapel, Sandhurst

Chaplain S ROBBINS

Royal Foundation of St Katharine in Ratcliffe

Master R F SWAN

DIOCESAN OFFICES

CHURCH OF ENGLAND

BATH AND WELLS
Diocesan Office, The Old Deanery, Wells BA5 2UG
Tel (01749) 670777   Fax 674240   E-mail general@bathwells.anglican.org
Web www.bathwells.anglican.org

BIRMINGHAM
Diocesan Office, 175 Harborne Park Road, Birmingham B17 0BH
Tel 0121–426 0400   Fax 428 1114   E-mail reception@birmingham.anglican.org
Web www.birmingham.anglican.org

BLACKBURN
Church House, Cathedral Close, Blackburn BB1 5AA
Tel (01254) 54421   Fax 667309   E-mail diocese@blackburn.anglican.org
Web www.blackburn.anglican.org

BRADFORD
Kadugli House, Elmsley Street, Steeton, Keighley BD20 6SE
Tel (01535) 650555   Fax 650550   Web www.bradford.anglican.org

BRISTOL
Diocesan Church House, 23 Great George Street, Bristol BS1 5QZ
Tel 0117–906 0100   Fax 925 0460   E-mail any.name@bristoldiocese.org
Web www.bristol.anglican.org

CANTERBURY
Diocesan House, Lady Wootton's Green, Canterbury CT1 1NQ
Tel (01227) 459401   Fax 450964   E-mail reception@diocant.org
Web www.canterbury.anglican.org

CARLISLE
Church House, West Walls, Carlisle CA3 8UE
Tel (01228) 522573   Fax 815400   E-mail enquiries@carlislediocese.org.uk
Web www.carlisle.anglican.org.uk

CHELMSFORD
Diocesan Office, 53 New Street, Chelmsford CM1 1AT
Tel (01245) 294400   Fax 294477   E-mail mail@chelmsford.anglican.org
Web www.chelmsford.anglican.org

CHESTER
Church House, Lower Lane, Aldford, Chester CH3 6HP
Tel (01244) 620444   Fax 620456   E-mail churchhouse@chester.anglican.org
Web www.chester.anglican.org

CHICHESTER
Diocesan Church House, 211 New Church Road, Hove BN3 4ED
Tel (01273) 421021   Fax 421041   E-mail admin@diochi.org.uk
Web www.diochi.org.uk

COVENTRY
Church House, Palmerston Road, Coventry CV5 6FJ
Tel (024) 7667 4328   Fax 7669 1760   E-mail isobel.chapman@covdioc.org
Web www.coventry.anglican.org

DERBY
Derby Church House, Full Street, Derby DE1 3DR
Tel (01332) 382233   Fax 292969   E-mail ddbf@talk21.com
Web www.derby.anglican.org

DURHAM
Diocesan Office, Auckland Castle, Market Place, Bishop Auckland DL14 7QJ
Tel (01388) 604515   Fax 603695   E-mail diocesan.secretary@durham.anglican.org
Web www.durham.anglican.org

ELY
Diocesan Office, Bishop Woodford House, Barton Road, Ely CB7 4DX
Tel (01353) 652701   Fax 652700   E-mail d.secretary@office.ely.anglican.org
Web www.ely.anglican.org

EUROPE
Diocesan Office, 14 Tufton Street, London SW1P 3QZ
Tel (020) 7898 1155   Fax 7898 1166   E-mail diocesan.office@europe.c-of-e.org.uk
Web www.europe.anglican.org

EXETER
Diocesan House, Palace Gate, Exeter EX1 1HX
Tel (01392) 272686   Fax 499594   E-mail admin@exeter.anglican.org
Web www.exeter.anglican.org

GLOUCESTER
Church House, College Green, Gloucester GL1 2LY
Tel (01452) 410022   Fax 308324   E-mail church.house@glosdioc.org.uk
Web www.doma.demon.co.uk/glosdioc.htm

GUILDFORD	Diocesan House, Quarry Street, Guildford GU1 3XG Tel (01483) 571826 Fax 790333 E-mail reception.diocese@guildford.org.uk Web www.guildford.anglican.org
HEREFORD	Diocesan Office, The Palace, Hereford HR4 9BL Tel (01432) 373300 Fax 352952 E-mail diooffice@hereford.anglican.org Web www.hereford.anglican.org
LEICESTER	Church House, 3–5 St Martin's East, Leicester LE1 5FX Tel 0116–248 7400 Fax 253 2889 E-mail chouse@leicester.anglican.org Web www.leicester.anglican.org
LICHFIELD	St Mary's House, The Close, Lichfield WS13 7LD Tel (01543) 306030 Fax 306039 E-mail info@lichfield.anglican.org Web www.lichfield.anglican.org
LINCOLN	Diocesan Office, Church House, Lincoln LN2 1PU Tel (01522) 529241 Fax 512717 E-mail phil.hamlyn-williams@lincoln.anglican.org Web www.lincoln.anglican.org
LIVERPOOL	Church House, 1 Hanover Street, Liverpool L1 3DW Tel 0151–709 9722 Fax 709 2885 Web www.liverpool.anglican.org
LONDON	Diocesan House, 36 Causton Street, London SW1P 4AU Tel (020) 7932 1100 Fax 7932 1112 E-mail keith.robinson@london.anglican.org Web www.london.anglican.org
MANCHESTER	Diocesan Church House, 90 Deansgate, Manchester M3 2GH Tel 0161–833 9521 Fax 833 2751 E-mail manchesterdbf@manchester.anglican.org Web www.manchester.anglican.org
NEWCASTLE	Church House, St John's Terrace, North Shields NE29 6HS Tel 0191–270 4100 Fax 270 4101 E-mail church_house@newcastle.anglican.org Web www.newcastle.anglican.org
NORWICH	Diocesan House, 109 Dereham Road, Easton, Norwich NR9 5ES Tel (01603) 880853 Fax 881083 E-mail diocesanhouse@norwich.anglican.org Web www.norwich.anglican.org
OXFORD	Diocesan Church House, North Hinksey Lane, Botley, Oxford OX2 0NB Tel (01865) 208200 Fax 790470 E-mail diosec@oxford.anglican.org Web www.oxford.anglican.org
PETERBOROUGH	The Palace, Peterborough PE1 1YB Tel (01733) 887000 Fax 555271 E-mail office@peterborough-diocese.org.uk Web www.peterborough-diocese.org.uk
PORTSMOUTH	Cathedral House, St Thomas's Street, Portsmouth PO1 2HA Tel (023) 9282 5731 Fax 9229 3423 E-mail admin@portsmouth.anglican.org Web www.portsmouth.anglican.org
RIPON AND LEEDS	Ripon and Leeds Diocesan Office, St Mary's Street, Leeds LS9 7DP Tel 0113–200 0540 Fax 249 1129 E-mail philipa@riponleeds-diocese.org.uk Web www.ripon.anglican.org
ROCHESTER	St Nicholas' Church, Boley Hill, Rochester ME1 1SL Tel (01634) 830333 Fax 829463 E-mail dio.off@rochester.anglican.org Web www.rochester.anglican.org
ST ALBANS	Holywell Lodge, 41 Holywell Hill, St Albans AL1 1HE Tel (01727) 854532 Fax 844469 E-mail mail@stalbansdioc.org.uk Web www.stalbansdioc.org.uk
ST EDMUNDSBURY AND IPSWICH	Churchgates House, Cutler Street, Ipswich IP1 1UQ Tel (01473) 298500 Fax 298501 E-mail dbf@stedmundsbury.anglican.org Web www.stedmundsbury.anglican.org
SALISBURY	Church House, Crane Street, Salisbury SP1 2QB Tel (01722) 411922 Fax 411990 E-mail enquiries@salisbury.anglican.org Web www.salisbury.anglican.org
SHEFFIELD	Diocesan Church House, 95/99 Effingham Street, Rotherham S65 1BL Tel (01709) 309100 Fax 512550 E-mail sheffield.diocese@ukonline.co.uk Web web.ukonline.co.uk/trafic

SODOR AND MAN	Holly Cottage, Ballaughton Meadows, Douglas IM2 1JG Tel (01624) 626994 Fax as telephone E-mail dsec-sodor@mcb.net Web www.sodorman.anglican.org
SOUTHWARK	Trinity House, 4 Chapel Court, Borough High Street, London SE1 1HW Tel (020) 7939 9400 Fax 7939 9468 E-mail trinity@dswark.org.uk Web www.dswark.org
SOUTHWELL	Dunham House, Westgate, Southwell NG25 0JL Tel (01636) 817226 *or* 817229 Fax 815084 E-mail mail@southwell.anglican.org Web www.southwell.anglican.org
TRURO	Diocesan House, Kenwyn, Truro TR1 1JQ Tel (01872) 274351 Fax 222510 E-mail info@truro.anglican.org Web www.truro.anglican.org
WAKEFIELD	Church House, 1 South Parade, Wakefield WF1 1LP Tel (01924) 371802 Fax 364834 E-mail church.house@wakefield.anglican.org
WINCHESTER	Church House, 9 The Close, Winchester SO23 9LS Tel (01962) 844644 Fax 841815 E-mail chsewinchester@clara.net Web www.win.diocese.org.uk
WORCESTER	The Old Palace, Deansway, Worcester WR1 2JE Tel (01905) 20537 Fax 612302 Web www.cofe-worcester.org.uk
YORK	Diocesan House, Aviator Court, Clifton Moor, York YO30 4WJ Tel (01904) 699500 Fax 699501 E-mail yorkdbf@yorkdiocese.org Web www.dioceseofyork.org.uk

CHURCH IN WALES

BANGOR	Diocesan Centre, Cathedral Close, Bangor LL57 1RL Tel (01248) 354999 Fax 353882
LLANDAFF	Llandaff Diocesan Board of Finance, Heol Fair, Llandaff, Cardiff CF5 2EE Tel (029) 2057 8899 Fax 2057 6198
MONMOUTH	Diocesan Office, 64 Caerau Road, Newport NP9 4HJ Tel (01633) 267490 Fax 265586
ST ASAPH	St Asaph Diocesan Board of Finance, High Street, St Asaph LL17 0RD Tel (01745) 582245 Fax 583556
ST DAVIDS	Diocesan Office, Abergwili, Carmarthen SA31 2JG Tel (01267) 236145 Fax 223046
SWANSEA AND BRECON	Swansea and Brecon Diocesan Board of Finance Ltd, Swansea and Brecon Diocesan Centre, Cathedral Close, Brecon LD3 9DP Tel (01874) 623716 Fax as telephone

SCOTTISH EPISCOPAL CHURCH

ABERDEEN AND ORKNEY	Diocesan Centre, 39 King's Crescent, Aberdeen AB24 3HP Tel (01224) 636653 Fax 636186
ARGYLL AND THE ISLES	The Pines, Ardconnel Road, Oban, Argyll PA34 5DR Tel (01631) 566912 Fax as telephone E-mail office@argyll.anglican.org
BRECHIN	The Bishop's Room, St Paul's Cathedral, 1 High Street, Dundee DD1 1TD Tel (01382) 229230 (mornings only) Fax 203446
EDINBURGH	Diocesan Centre, 21A Grosvenor Crescent, Edinburgh EH12 5EL Tel 0131–538 7033 Fax 538 7088
GLASGOW AND GALLOWAY	Diocesan Office, 5 St Vincent Place, Glasgow G1 2DH Tel 0141–221 5720 *or* 221 2694 Fax 221 7014
MORAY AND CAITHNESS	Diocesan Office, 11 Kenneth Street, Inverness IV3 5NR Tel (01463) 226255 (mornings only) Fax as telephone
ST ANDREWS, DUNKELD AND DUNBLANE	Perth Diocesan Centre, 28A Balhousie Street, Perth PH1 5HJ Tel (01738) 443173 Fax 443174

CHURCH OF IRELAND

PROVINCE OF ARMAGH

ARMAGH
Church House, 46 Abbey Street, Armagh BT61 7DZ
Tel (028) 3752 2858   Fax 3751 0596

CLOGHER
The Deanery, 10 Augher Road, Clogher BT76 0AD
Tel (028) 8554 8235   Fax as telephone   E-mail dean@clogher.anglican.org

CONNOR
Diocesan Office, Church of Ireland House, 61/67 Donegall Street, Belfast
BT1 2QH
Tel (028) 9032 2268 *or* 9032 3188   Fax 9032 1635

DERRY AND
RAPHOE
Diocesan Office, London Street, Londonderry BT48 6RQ
Tel (028) 7126 2440   Fax 7137 2100

DOWN AND
DROMORE
Diocesan Office, Church of Ireland House, 61/67 Donegall Street, Belfast BT1 2QH
Tel (028) 9032 2268 *or* 9032 3188   Fax 9032 1635

KILMORE
Kilmore Diocesan Office, Whitestar Complex, Market Street, Cootehill,
Co Cavan, Irish Republic
Tel (00353) (49) 555 9954   Fax 555 9957   E-mail secretary@kilmore.anglican.org

ELPHIN AND
ARDAGH
Calry Rectory, The Mall, Sligo, Irish Republic

TUAM, KILLALA
AND ACHONRY
Stonehall House, Ballisodare, Co Sligo, Irish Republic
Tel (00353) (71) 67280   Fax 30264   E-mail hsherlock@iolfree.ie

PROVINCE OF DUBLIN

CASHEL AND
OSSORY
Diocesan Office, St Canice's Library, Kilkenny, Irish Republic
Tel (00353) (56) 61910 *or* 27248   Fax 51813   E-mail dco@cashel.anglican.org

CORK, CLOYNE
AND ROSS
St Nicholas House, 14 Cove Street, Cork, Irish Republic
Tel (00353) (21) 427 2262   Fax 496 8467   E-mail office@cork.anglican.org

DUBLIN AND
GLENDALOUGH
Diocesan Office, Church of Ireland House, Church Avenue, Rathmines,
Dublin 6, Irish Republic
Tel (00353) (1) 496 6981   Fax 497 2865   E-mail office@dublin.anglican.org

LIMERICK,
KILLALOE AND
ARDFERT
St Cronan's Rectory, Roscrea, Co Tipperary, Irish Republic
Tel (00353) (505) 21725   Fax 21993   E-mail condell@iol.ie

MEATH AND
KILDARE
Meath and Kildare Diocesan Centre, Moyglare, Maynooth, Co Kildare, Irish
Republic
Tel (00353) (1) 629 2163   Fax 629 2153   E-mail diomeath@iol.ie
or office@meath.anglican.org

ARCHDEACONRIES, DEANERIES AND RURAL DEANS OF THE CHURCH OF ENGLAND AND THE CHURCH IN WALES

The numbers given to the deaneries below correspond to those given in the benefice entries in the combined benefice and church index for England (p. 953) and for Wales (p. 1130). Where an archdeacony comes within the jurisdiction of a suffragan or area bishop under an established scheme, the respective bishop is indicated.

Some dioceses use the title Area Dean.

CHURCH OF ENGLAND

BATH AND WELLS

ARCHDEACONRY OF WELLS

1. AXBRIDGE   M P LEE
2. BRUTON   S LOW
3. CARY   S LOW
4. FROME   P N RAPSEY
5. GLASTONBURY JURISDICTION   W B GRAHAM
6. IVELCHESTER   M P WYNTER
7. MERSTON   M D ELLIS
8. SHEPTON MALLET   D R OSBORNE

ARCHDEACONRY OF BATH

9. BATH   P J WHITWORTH
10. CHEW MAGNA   T J DAPLYN
11. LOCKING   J N O WILLIAMS
12. MIDSOMER NORTON   J B THICKE
13. PORTISHEAD   I M HUBBARD

ARCHDEACONRY OF TAUNTON

14. SEDGEMOOR   P MARTIN
15. CREWKERNE AND ILMINSTER   N P M WHINNEY
16. EXMOOR   B E PRIORY
17. QUANTOCK   P DENISON
18. TAUNTON   C F E ROWLEY
19. TONE   A D NORRIS

BIRMINGHAM

ARCHDEACONRY OF BIRMINGHAM

1. BIRMINGHAM CITY CENTRE   I D GOW
2. EDGBASTON   S G THORBURN
3. HANDSWORTH   B A HALL
4. KINGS NORTON   R S FIELDSON
5. MOSELEY   S P CORBETT
6. SHIRLEY   J A STEVENS
7. WARLEY   M R DUNK

ARCHDEACONRY OF ASTON

8. ASTON   C M FEAK
9. COLESHILL   S T MAYES
10. POLESWORTH   S J BANKS
11. SOLIHULL   D A LEAHY
12. SUTTON COLDFIELD   J H LANGSTAFF
13. YARDLEY AND BORDESLEY   G C TURNER

BLACKBURN

ARCHDEACONRY OF BLACKBURN

1. ACCRINGTON   T R SMITH
2. BLACKBURN AND DARWEN   A RAYNES
3. BURNLEY   P J PIKE
4. CHORLEY   D F C MORGAN
5. LEYLAND   A HOLLIDAY
6. PENDLE   E A SAVILLE
7. WHALLEY   J W HARTLEY

ARCHDEACONRY OF LANCASTER

8. BLACKPOOL   R G RAINFORD
9. GARSTANG   A W WILKINSON
10. KIRKHAM   G I HIRST
11. LANCASTER   G S INGRAM
12. POULTON   P R F CLEMENCE
13. PRESTON   D H JENKINS
14. TUNSTALL   T J L MAIDMENT

BRADFORD

ARCHDEACONRY OF BRADFORD

1. AIREDALE   A J CLARKE
2. BOWLING AND HORTON   P M BILTON
3. CALVERLEY   P G WALKER
4. OTLEY   P Q TUDGE

ARCHDEACONRY OF CRAVEN

5. BOWLAND   D W MEWIS
6. EWECROSS   A W FELL
7. SKIPTON   J S WARD
8. SOUTH CRAVEN   B GRAINGER

BRISTOL

ARCHDEACONRY OF BRISTOL

1. BRISTOL SOUTH   R V HEADING
2. BRISTOL WEST   P W ROWE
3. CITY DEANERY   D C SELF

ARCHDEACONRY OF MALMESBURY

4. CHIPPENHAM   S C TATTON-BROWN
5. KINGSWOOD AND SOUTH GLOUCESTERSHIRE   V J HOWLETT
6. NORTH WILTSHIRE   B RAVEN
7. SWINDON   M A JOHNSON

CANTERBURY

ARCHDEACONRY OF CANTERBURY

1. EAST BRIDGE   D J ROPER
2. WEST BRIDGE   J S RICHARDSON
3. CANTERBURY   S W JONES
4. DOVER   S J BOWRING
5. ELHAM   J C TAPPER
6. OSPRINGE   A C OEHRING
7. RECULVER   P D SALES
8. SANDWICH   J M A ROBERTS
9. THANET   A J HOUSTON

ARCHDEACONRY OF MAIDSTONE

10. ASHFORD   B CHALMERS
11. CRANBROOK   B BARNES
13. ROMNEY   R H ELLIS
14. MAIDSTONE   K M GORHAM
15. NORTH DOWNS   R M GILL
16. SITTINGBOURNE   G H SPENCER
17. TENTERDEN   D G TRUSTRAM

CARLISLE

ARCHDEACONRY OF CARLISLE

1. APPLEBY   P E P NORTON
2. BRAMPTON   C J MORRIS
3. CARLISLE   P J BYE
4. PENRITH   D M FOWLER

ARCHDEACONRY OF WEST CUMBERLAND

5. CALDER   A D EDWARDS
6. DERWENT   B SMITH
7. SOLWAY   B ROWE

ARCHDEACONRY OF WESTMORLAND AND FURNESS

8. BARROW   P E MANN
9. FURNESS   D SANDERSON
10. KENDAL   T S EVANS
11. WINDERMERE   J A H CLEGG

CHELMSFORD

ARCHDEACONRY OF WEST HAM
(BISHOP OF BARKING)

1. BARKING AND DAGENHAM   J B PARSONS
2. HAVERING   H R DIBBENS
3. NEWHAM   A R EASTER
4. REDBRIDGE   G M TARRY
5. WALTHAM FOREST   P R BUTLER

ARCHDEACONRY OF SOUTHEND
(BISHOP OF BRADWELL)

6. BASILDON   E E MCCAFFERTY
7. BRENTWOOD   R B WHITE
8. CHELMSFORD NORTH   J MANN
9. CHELMSFORD SOUTH   M G BLYTH
10. HADLEIGH   R H S EASTOE
11. MALDON AND DENGIE   E H BEAVAN
12. ROCHFORD   D W PARROTT
13. SOUTHEND-ON-SEA   M J HARRIS
14. THURROCK   D R TOMLINSON

ARCHDEACONRY OF COLCHESTER
(BISHOP OF COLCHESTER)

15. BRAINTREE   P A NEED
16. COLCHESTER   S CARTER
17. DEDHAM AND TEY   C HORSEMAN
18. DUNMOW   L BOND
19. HINCKFORD   J F BLORE
20. HARWICH   S HARDIE
21. NEWPORT AND STANSTED   C BISHOP
22. SAFFRON WALDEN   D MAUDLIN
23. ST OSYTH   W B METCALFE
24. WITHAM   J M HALL

ARCHDEACONRY OF HARLOW
(BISHOP OF BARKING)

25. EPPING FOREST   R A D ENEVER
26. HARLOW   A V WATSON
27. ONGAR   P T C MASHEDER

CHESTER

ARCHDEACONRY OF CHESTER

1. BIRKENHEAD   D WALKER
2. CHESTER   R C TOAN
3. FRODSHAM   R J GILPIN
4. GREAT BUDWORTH   J T OWEN
5. MALPAS   D A BOYD
6. MIDDLEWICH   M L RIDLEY
7. WALLASEY   A J MANNINGS
8. WIRRAL NORTH   G P BENSON
9. WIRRAL SOUTH   H J ALDRIDGE

ARCHDEACONRY OF MACCLESFIELD

10. BOWDON   J SUTTON
11. CONGLETON   R N W ELBOURNE
12. KNUTSFORD   B T YOUNG
13. MACCLESFIELD   D TAYLOR
14. MOTTRAM   J R WATTS
15. NANTWICH   G D GEDDES
16. CHADKIRK   B S PERCIVAL
17. CHEADLE   H B EALES
18. STOCKPORT   R E READ

CHICHESTER

ARCHDEACONRY OF CHICHESTER

1. ARUNDEL AND BOGNOR   R D HARRIS
2. BRIGHTON   N E D MILMINE
3. CHICHESTER   D L PARKER
4. HOVE   C L TERRY
5. WORTHING   R G RUSSELL

ARCHDEACONRY OF HORSHAM

6. CUCKFIELD   N G WETHERALL
7. EAST GRINSTEAD   G BOND
8. HORSHAM   P H JONES
9. HURST   I G PRIOR
10. MIDHURST   A T CUNNINGTON
11. PETWORTH   D S POLLARD
12. STORRINGTON   P M RAMPTON
13. WESTBOURNE   B R COOK

ARCHDEACONRY OF LEWES AND HASTINGS

14. BATTLE AND BEXHILL   E F P BRYANT
15. DALLINGTON   R G H PORTHOUSE
16. EASTBOURNE   G T RIDEOUT
17. HASTINGS   *Vacant*
18. LEWES AND SEAFORD   C H ATHERSTONE
19. ROTHERFIELD   A C J CORNES
20. RYE   *Vacant*
21. UCKFIELD   *Vacant*

COVENTRY

ARCHDEACONRY OF COVENTRY

1. COVENTRY EAST   R W HARE
2. COVENTRY NORTH   G J MARCER
3. COVENTRY SOUTH   C H KNOWLES
4. KENILWORTH   R W E AWRE
5. NUNEATON   D JONES
6. RUGBY   E C LYONS

ARCHDEACONRY OF WARWICK

7. ALCESTER   S R BURCH
8. FOSSE   R E WILLIAMS
9. SHIPSTON   B MERRINGTON
10. SOUTHAM   D R PATTERSON
11. WARWICK AND LEAMINGTON   T M H BOYNS

DERBY

ARCHDEACONRY OF CHESTERFIELD

1. ALFRETON   H J DOBBIN
2. BAKEWELL AND EYAM   E R URQUHART
3. BOLSOVER AND STAVELEY   N R HARVEY
4. BUXTON   J O GOLDSMITH
5. CHESTERFIELD   N V JOHNSON
6. GLOSSOP   D M ROWLEY
7. WIRKSWORTH   S I MITCHELL

ARCHDEACONRY OF DERBY

8. ASHBOURNE   C D HARRISON
9. DERBY NORTH   S B BARBY
10. DERBY SOUTH   P R SANDFORD
11. DUFFIELD   D PERKINS
12. HEANOR   C L HUGHES
13. EREWASH   I E GOODING
14. LONGFORD   D MILNER
15. MELBOURNE   M G ALEXANDER
16. REPTON   D J HORSFALL

DURHAM

ARCHDEACONRY OF DURHAM

1. DURHAM   D J BELL
2. EASINGTON   A MILNE
3. HARTLEPOOL   M R GILBERTSON
4. LANCHESTER   M JACKSON
5. SEDGEFIELD   A KELHAM

ARCHDEACONRY OF AUCKLAND

6. AUCKLAND   N P VINE
7. BARNARD CASTLE   J E G CLARK
8. DARLINGTON   J R DOBSON
9. STANHOPE   P A GREENHALGH
10. STOCKTON   T J D OLLIER

ARCHDEACONRY OF SUNDERLAND

11. CHESTER-LE-STREET   B J ABBOTT
12. GATESHEAD   *Vacant*
13. GATESHEAD WEST   K TEASDALE
14. HOUGHTON-LE-SPRING   M L BECK
15. JARROW   G BUTTERY
16. WEARMOUTH   N B WARNER

ELY
ARCHDEACONRY OF ELY

1. BOURN   J C B PEMBERTON
2. CAMBRIDGE   M L DIAMOND
3. FORDHAM AND QUY   S G F EARL
4. LINTON   C A SINDALL
5. NORTH STOWE   H K MCCURDY
6. SHELFORD   K F M FISHER
7. SHINGAY   S F C WILLIAMS

ARCHDEACONRY OF HUNTINGDON

8. HUNTINGDON   M R GREENFIELD
9. LEIGHTONSTONE   J P YOUNG
10. ST IVES   R A DARMODY
11. ST NEOTS   R H W ARGUILE
12. YAXLEY   R LONGFOOT

ARCHDEACONRY OF WISBECH

13. ELY   *Vacant*
14. FELTWELL   D J KIGHTLEY
15. FINCHAM   D J KIGHTLEY
16. MARCH   P BAXANDALL
17. WISBECH LYNN MARSHLAND   W A L ZWALF

EXETER
ARCHDEACONRY OF EXETER

1. AYLESBEARE   R W C JEFFERY
2. CADBURY   S G C SMITH
3. CHRISTIANITY   A WHITE
4. CULLOMPTON   D L D ROBOTTOM
5. HONITON   N T SCHOFIELD
6. KENN   P G LUFF
7. OTTERY   N CLARKE
8. TIVERTON   D M FLETCHER

ARCHDEACONRY OF TOTNES

9. HOLSWORTHY   R B DORRINGTON
10. MORETON   D J STANTON
11. NEWTON ABBOT AND IPPLEPEN   C H BENSON
12. OKEHAMPTON   A E GEERING
13. TORBAY   D W WITCHELL
14. TOTNES   S E ROBERTS
15. WOODLEIGH   T W BRIGHTON

ARCHDEACONRY OF BARNSTAPLE

16. BARNSTAPLE   R P REEVE
17. HARTLAND   A J RICHARDSON
18. SHIRWELL   P BOWERS
19. SOUTH MOLTON   J HANNA
20. TORRINGTON   A S GRAESSER

ARCHDEACONRY OF PLYMOUTH

21. IVYBRIDGE   D ARNOTT
22. PLYMOUTH DEVONPORT   R M SIGRIST
23. PLYMOUTH MOORSIDE   T R J DICKENS
24. PLYMOUTH SUTTON   N H P MCKINNEL
25. TAVISTOCK   S G MAY

GLOUCESTER
ARCHDEACONRY OF GLOUCESTER

1. BISLEY   B C E COKER
2. DURSLEY   W J BOON
3. FOREST NORTH   R G STURMAN
4. FOREST SOUTH   A N JAMES
5. GLOUCESTER CITY   G D OSBORNE
6. GLOUCESTER NORTH   T E MASON
7. HAWKESBURY   P M LYES-WILSDON
8. STONEHOUSE   M O TUCKER

ARCHDEACONRY OF CHELTENHAM

9. CHELTENHAM   S S GREGORY
10. CAMPDEN   D E VINCE
11. CIRENCESTER   M A M ST JOHN-CHANNELL
12. FAIRFORD   A M ROSS
13. NORTHLEACH   D C NYE

14. STOW   S M WOOKEY
15. TETBURY   N C J MULHOLLAND
16. TEWKESBURY AND WINCHCOMBE   I F CALDER

GUILDFORD
ARCHDEACONRY OF SURREY

1. ALDERSHOT   D HOLT
2. CRANLEIGH   N P NICHOLSON
3. FARNHAM   A K TUCK
4. GODALMING   N JONES
5. GUILDFORD   C J MATTHEWS
6. SURREY HEATH   B NICOLE

ARCHDEACONRY OF DORKING

7. DORKING   M S KING
8. EMLY   W A J ALLBERRY
9. EPSOM   S A WILCOCKSON
10. LEATHERHEAD   B J PARADISE
11. RUNNYMEDE   R HAY
12. WOKING   R J N COOK

HEREFORD
ARCHDEACONRY OF HEREFORD

1. ABBEYDORE   J F BUTTERWORTH
2. BROMYARD   C I FLETCHER
3. HEREFORD CITY   A P MOTTRAM
4. HEREFORD RURAL   D J BOWEN
5. KINGTON AND WEOBLEY   P TARLING
6. LEDBURY   M D VOCKINS
7. LEOMINSTER   P J SWAIN
8. ROSS AND ARCHENFIELD   J B HUNNISETT

ARCHDEACONRY OF LUDLOW

9. BRIDGNORTH   C G WILLIAMS
10. CLUN FOREST   R T SHAW
11. CONDOVER   G H EARNEY
12. LUDLOW   A G SEABROOK
13. PONTESBURY   P D HARRATT
14. TELFORD SEVERN GORGE   V C SWEET

LEICESTER
ARCHDEACONRY OF LEICESTER

1. CHRISTIANITY (LEICESTER) NORTH   J J LEONARD
2. CHRISTIANITY (LEICESTER) SOUTH   H A S COCKS
3. FRAMLAND (Melton)   H M FLINT
4. GARTREE FIRST DEANERY (Harborough)   I W Y GEMMELL
5. GARTREE SECOND DEANERY (Wigston)   M F RUSK
6. GOSCOTE   J F WELLINGTON

ARCHDEACONRY OF LOUGHBOROUGH

7. AKELEY EAST (Loughborough)   D M F NEWMAN
8. AKELEY SOUTH (Coalville)   S P MOULT
9. AKELEY WEST (Ashby)   A J BURGESS
10. GUTHLAXTON FIRST DEANERY (Blaby)   G T RIMMINGTON
11. GUTHLAXTON SECOND DEANERY (Lutterworth)   M H W COUSSENS
12. SPARKENHOE EAST   *Vacant*
13. SPARKENHOE WEST (Hinckley and Bosworth)   M J NORMAN

LICHFIELD
ARCHDEACONRY OF LICHFIELD

1. LICHFIELD   C N THOMAS
2. PENKRIDGE   P H J THORNEYCROFT
3. RUGELEY   T THAKE
4. TAMWORTH   A BARRETT

ARCHDEACONRY OF STOKE-ON-TRENT

5. ALSTONFIELD   A J BURTON
6. CHEADLE   L R PRICE
7. ECCLESHALL   N A CLEMAS
8. LEEK   M F LEIGH
9. NEWCASTLE   W G H GARDINER

10. STAFFORD   M R METCALF
11. STOKE NORTH   W E SLATER
12. STOKE   M K ELLOR
13. TRENTHAM   B J BREWER
14. TUTBURY   A J WOOD
15. UTTOXETER   D V EVANS

ARCHDEACONRY OF SALOP

16. EDGMOND AND SHIFNAL   D J BUTTERFIELD
17. ELLESMERE   J C VERNON
18. HODNET   M G W HAYES
19. OSWESTRY   D R NORTH
20. SHREWSBURY   K T ROBERTS
21. TELFORD   V C SWEET
22. WEM AND WHITCHURCH   A R RIDLEY
23. WROCKWARDINE   G HORNER

ARCHDEACONRY OF WALSALL

24. TRYSULL   G M F WILLIAMS
25. WALSALL   D P LINGWOOD
26. WEDNESBURY   A R BOYD-WILLIAMS
27. WEST BROMWICH   P G GREEN
28. WOLVERHAMPTON   M R GILBERT

LINCOLN

ARCHDEACONRY OF STOW

1. AXHOLME, ISLE OF   J D BROWN
2. CORRINGHAM   R PROSSER
3. LAWRES   K N JAMES
4. MANLAKE   M P COONEY
5. WEST WOLD   I ROBINSON
6. YARBOROUGH   C H LILLEY

ARCHDEACONRY OF LINDSEY

7. BOLINGBROKE   P F COATES
8. CALCEWAITHE AND CANDLESHOE   I S PARTRIDGE
9. GRIMSBY AND CLEETHORPES   J E BROWN
10. HAVERSTOE   I R SHELTON
11. HORNCASTLE   M E BURSON-THOMAS
12. LOUTHESK   S D HOLDAWAY

ARCHDEACONRY OF LINCOLN

13. AVELAND AND NESS WITH STAMFORD   N RUSSELL
14. BELTISLOE   A T HAWES
15. CHRISTIANITY   T W THOMPSON
16. ELLOE EAST   D F BRATLEY
17. ELLOE WEST   T R BARKER
18. GRAFFOE   R S EYRE
19. GRANTHAM   P HOPKINS
20. HOLLAND EAST   M A R COOPER
21. HOLLAND WEST   M A BARSLEY
22. LAFFORD   G P WILLIAMS
23. LOVEDEN   J R HAWKINS

LIVERPOOL

ARCHDEACONRY OF LIVERPOOL

1. BOOTLE   D A PARRY
2. HUYTON   G S PEARSON
3. LIVERPOOL NORTH   H CORBETT
4. LIVERPOOL SOUTH   G J BUTLAND
5. SEFTON   A R WOODHOUSE
6. TOXTETH AND WAVERTREE   F R CAIN
7. WALTON   R S BRIDSON
8. WEST DERBY   J R I WIKELEY

ARCHDEACONRY OF WARRINGTON

9. NORTH MEOLS   C POPE
10. ST HELENS   C S WOODS
11. ORMSKIRK   D G TOWLER
12. WARRINGTON   M RAYNOR
13. WIDNES   G C ELSMORE
14. WIGAN EAST   D W LONG
15. WIGAN WEST   J A TAYLOR
16. WINWICK   R G LEWIS

LONDON

ARCHDEACONRY OF LONDON

1. THE CITY   J D M PATON

ARCHDEACONRY OF CHARING CROSS

2. WESTMINSTER PADDINGTON   W G WILSON
3. WESTMINSTER ST MARGARET   W S SCOTT
4. WESTMINSTER ST MARYLEBONE   L A MOSES

ARCHDEACONRY OF HACKNEY
(BISHOP OF STEPNEY)

5. HACKNEY   E J JONES
6. ISLINGTON   D SILVESTER
7. TOWER HAMLETS   A J WYNNE

ARCHDEACONRY OF MIDDLESEX
(BISHOP OF KENSINGTON)

8. CHELSEA   G C BEAUCHAMP
9. HAMMERSMITH AND FULHAM   S J WELCH
10. HAMPTON   A J WATSON
11. HOUNSLOW   D J SIMPSON
12. KENSINGTON   H D J RAYMENT-PICKARD
13. SPELTHORNE   C J SWIFT

ARCHDEACONRY OF HAMPSTEAD
(BISHOP OF EDMONTON)

14. BARNET, CENTRAL   D J NASH
15. BARNET, WEST   P S TAYLOR
16. CAMDEN, NORTH (Hampstead)   P J GALLOWAY
17. CAMDEN, SOUTH (Holborn and St Pancras)   R N ARNOLD
18. ENFIELD   T G CLEMENT
19. HARINGEY, EAST   A K DANGERFIELD
20. HARINGEY, WEST   G B SEABROOK

ARCHDEACONRY OF NORTHOLT
(BISHOP OF WILLESDEN)

21. BRENT   P W STONE
22. EALING   A R CORSIE
23. HARROW   D M TALBOT
24. HILLINGDON   O J FIELD

MANCHESTER

ARCHDEACONRY OF MANCHESTER

1. ARDWICK   P N CLARK
2. ECCLES   M R AINSWORTH
3. HEATON   M H MAXWELL
4. HULME   S J T GATENBY
5. MANCHESTER, NORTH   M D ASHCROFT
6. SALFORD   D J PALMER
7. STRETFORD   P J RAWLINGS
8. WITHINGTON   D M HUGHES

ARCHDEACONRY OF BOLTON

9. BOLTON   M J WILLIAMS
10. BURY   I M ROGERSON
11. DEANE   W P BREW
12. FARNWORTH   B HARTLEY
13. LEIGH   W BALDWIN
14. RADCLIFFE AND PRESTWICH   C J C HEWITT
15. ROSSENDALE   C H ELLIS
16. WALMSLEY   A J LINDOP

ARCHDEACONRY OF ROCHDALE

17. ASHTON-UNDER-LYNE   P R DIXON
18. HEYWOOD AND MIDDLETON   N J FEIST
19. OLDHAM   P B MCEVITT
20. ROCHDALE   I C THOMPSON
21. SADDLEWORTH   R W HAWKINS
22. TANDLE   R MORRIS

NEWCASTLE
ARCHDEACONRY OF NORTHUMBERLAND

1. BEDLINGTON   P J BRYARS
2. BELLINGHAM   C S PRICE
3. CORBRIDGE   M NELSON
4. HEXHAM   R BEST
5. NEWCASTLE CENTRAL   *Vacant*
6. NEWCASTLE EAST   M J WEBB
7. NEWCASTLE WEST   M J JACKSON
8. TYNEMOUTH   J A ROBERTSON

ARCHDEACONRY OF LINDISFARNE

9. ALNWICK   B COWEN
10. BAMBURGH AND GLENDALE   A J HUGHES
11. MORPETH   R A FERGUSON
12. NORHAM   A S ADAMSON

NORWICH
ARCHDEACONRY OF NORWICH

1. NORWICH EAST   R M S WOODHAM
2. NORWICH NORTH   M H STAGG
3. NORWICH SOUTH   N J H GARRARD

ARCHDEACONRY OF NORFOLK

4. BLOFIELD   V M ELPHICK
5. DEPWADE   H D POTTS
6. GREAT YARMOUTH   M G KICHENSIDE
7. HUMBLEYARD   D J CHAMBERLIN
8. LODDON   P M KNIGHT
9. LOTHINGLAND   J B SIMPSON
10. REDENHALL   J B SCOTT
11. THETFORD AND ROCKLAND   C J HALL
12. ST BENET AT WAXHAM AND TUNSTEAD   A D PARSONS

ARCHDEACONRY OF LYNN

13. BRECKLAND   S J SMITH
14. BRISLEY AND ELMHAM   B R A COLE
15. BURNHAM AND WALSINGHAM   J CHARLES
16. HEACHAM AND RISING   L H CAMPBELL
17. DEREHAM IN MITFORD   R AMES-LEWIS
18. HOLT   P G F NORWOOD
19. INGWORTH   R D BRANSON
20. LYNN   I C WHITTLE
21. REPPS   A H J LANE
22. SPARHAM   M D W PADDISON

OXFORD
ARCHDEACONRY OF OXFORD
(BISHOP OF DORCHESTER)

1. ASTON AND CUDDESDON   A R HAWKEN
2. BICESTER AND ISLIP   P J BALL
3. CHIPPING NORTON   S J A WESTON
4. COWLEY   E B BARDWELL
5. DEDDINGTON   J R A STROYAN
6. HENLEY   D R B CARTER
7. OXFORD   J S W CHORLTON
8. WITNEY   C J BUTLAND
9. WOODSTOCK   R J HUMPHREYS

ARCHDEACONRY OF BERKSHIRE
(BISHOP OF READING)

10. ABINGDON   J N COOPER
11. BRACKNELL   D S JONES
12. BRADFIELD   R B HOWELL
13. MAIDENHEAD   L S RAYFIELD
14. NEWBURY   N T MOFFATT
15. READING   B SHENTON
16. SONNING   G R HAMBORG
17. VALE OF WHITE HORSE   R O WOODHAMS
18. WALLINGFORD   E G CLEMENTS
19. WANTAGE   J L SALTER

ARCHDEACONRY (AND BISHOP) OF BUCKINGHAM

20. AMERSHAM   R J SALISBURY
21. AYLESBURY   T J HIGGINS
22. BUCKINGHAM   R H KENT
23. BURNHAM AND SLOUGH   D K MIELL

24. CLAYDON   D A HISCOCK
25. MILTON KEYNES   R M CATTLEY
26. MURSLEY   C J DYER
27. NEWPORT   M C STANTON-SARINGER
28. WENDOVER   A W BENNETT
29. WYCOMBE   C D BULL

PETERBOROUGH
ARCHDEACONRY OF NORTHAMPTON

1. BRACKLEY   T C OAKLEY
2. BRIXWORTH   C R EVANS
3. DAVENTRY   O R PAGE
4. NORTHAMPTON   S P ADAMS
5. TOWCESTER   M R H BAKER
6. WELLINGBOROUGH   M C W WEBBER
7. WOOTTON   R B STAINER

ARCHDEACONRY OF OAKHAM

8. BARNACK   P J C CLEMENTS
9. CORBY   J M COLLINS
10. HIGHAM   G L BROCKHOUSE
11. KETTERING   R T COOK
12. OUNDLE   J A ROSE
13. PETERBOROUGH   D J DUNCANSON
14. RUTLAND   M W R COVINGTON

PORTSMOUTH
ARCHDEACONRY OF THE MEON

1. BISHOP'S WALTHAM   P H KELLY
2. FAREHAM   M S COOPER
3. GOSPORT   I G BOOTH
4. PETERSFIELD   A D RICHARDS

ARCHDEACONRY OF PORTSDOWN

5. HAVANT   R I P COUTTS
6. PORTSMOUTH   J V BYRNE

ARCHDEACONRY OF ISLE OF WIGHT

7. WIGHT, EAST   H E WRIGHT
8. WIGHT, WEST   R J EMBLIN

RIPON AND LEEDS
ARCHDEACONRY OF RICHMOND

1. HARROGATE   J E COLSTON
2. RICHMOND   P S MIDWOOD
3. RIPON   D J WHEELER
4. WENSLEY   D G PATON-WILLIAMS

ARCHDEACONRY OF LEEDS

5. ALLERTON   S JARRATT
6. ARMLEY   T W LIPSCOMB
7. HEADINGLEY   M A CROSS
8. WHITKIRK   A F BUNDOCK

ROCHESTER
ARCHDEACONRY OF ROCHESTER

1. COBHAM   J E TIPP
2. DARTFORD   D B KITLEY
3. GILLINGHAM   A T VOUSDEN
4. GRAVESEND   C D GOBLE
5. ROCHESTER   P T KERR
6. STROOD   J F SOUTHWARD

ARCHDEACONRY OF TONBRIDGE

7. MALLING   J R TERRANOVA
8. PADDOCK WOOD   C J REED
9. SEVENOAKS   S R JONES
10. SHOREHAM   S M RAMSARAN
11. TONBRIDGE   *Vacant*
12. TUNBRIDGE WELLS   J P STEWART

ARCHDEACONRY OF BROMLEY AND BEXLEY

13. BECKENHAM   N W WYNNE-JONES
14. BROMLEY   S D BURTON-JONES
15. ERITH   D F SPRINGTHORPE
16. ORPINGTON   G C DAY
17. SIDCUP   N I KERR

ST ALBANS

ARCHDEACONRY OF ST ALBANS

1. ALDENHAM   G FELLOWS
2. BERKHAMSTED   R CLARKSON
3. HEMEL HEMPSTEAD   P J COTTON
4. HITCHIN   J N LUSCOMBE
5. RICKMANSWORTH   T J MARSHALL
6. ST ALBANS   A R HURLE
7. WATFORD   J KIDDLE
8. WHEATHAMPSTEAD   J P SMITH

ARCHDEACONRY OF BEDFORD

9. AMPTHILL   N JEFFERY
10. BEDFORD   T MAINES
11. BIGGLESWADE   V W BEYNON
12. DUNSTABLE   G H NEWTON
13. ELSTOW   N P MORRELL
14. LUTON   R C H FRANKLIN
15. SHARNBROOK   I W ARTHUR
16. SHEFFORD   M J VENABLES

ARCHDEACONRY OF HERTFORD

17. BARNET   C P HUITSON
18. BISHOP'S STORTFORD   D L HUMPHREY
19. BUNTINGFORD   D M WILLIAMS
20. CHESHUNT   M J BANISTER
21. WELWYN HATFIELD   C GARNER
22. HERTFORD AND WARE   R W BOWEN
23. STEVENAGE   G B WHITE

ST EDMUNDSBURY AND IPSWICH

ARCHDEACONRY OF IPSWICH

1. BOSMERE   P R DALTRY
2. COLNEYS   G L GRANT
3. HADLEIGH   D A C STRANACK
4. IPSWICH   P K TOWNLEY
5. SAMFORD   S J SWAIN
6. STOWMARKET   D J PARMENTER
7. WOODBRIDGE   R W CLIFTON

ARCHDEACONRY OF SUDBURY

8. CLARE   E J BETTS
9. IXWORTH   I HOOPER
10. LAVENHAM   R B COOK
11. MILDENHALL   S PETTITT
12. SUDBURY   L R PIZZEY
13. THINGOE   G J WEBB

ARCHDEACONRY OF SUFFOLK

14. BECCLES AND SOUTH ELMHAM   P J NELSON
15. HALESWORTH   J J WILSON
16. HARTISMERE   *Vacant*
17. HOXNE   D W FINCH
18. LOES   G E NOBLE
19. SAXMUNDHAM   R S SMITH

SALISBURY

ARCHDEACONRY OF SHERBORNE

1. DORCHESTER   P C LAMBERT
2. LYME BAY   J D ATKINSON
3. SHERBORNE   E J WOODS
4. WEYMOUTH   K A HUGO

ARCHDEACONRY OF DORSET

5. BLACKMORE VALE   M T P ZAMMIT
6. MILTON AND BLANDFORD   S F EVERETT
7. POOLE   N J C LLOYD
8. PURBECK   R J NAYLOR
9. WIMBORNE   P H LAWRENCE

ARCHDEACONRY OF SARUM

10. ALDERBURY   C ALLSOPP
11. CHALKE   H I J SOUTHERN
12. SALISBURY   K ROBINSON
13. STONEHENGE   P F SMITH

ARCHDEACONRY OF WILTS

14. BRADFORD   D G SMITH
15. CALNE   P M O GILES
16. DEVIZES   J RECORD
17. HEYTESBURY   H G HOSKINS
18. MARLBOROUGH   G M MACKICHAN
19. PEWSEY   N A LEIGH-HUNT

SHEFFIELD

ARCHDEACONRY OF SHEFFIELD

1. ATTERCLIFFE   M J CAMERON
2. ECCLESALL   J C SULLIVAN
3. ECCLESFIELD   E MITCHELL
4. HALLAM   P W WEST
5. LAUGHTON   S K PROCTOR
6. ROTHERHAM   J M WRAW

ARCHDEACONRY OF DONCASTER

7. ADWICK-LE-STREET   P A INGRAM
8. DONCASTER   N K YOUNG
9. DONCASTER, WEST   A J GILBERT
10. SNAITH AND HATFIELD   C ROBERTS
11. TANKERSLEY   J G FAIRHURST
12. WATH   A J DELVES

SODOR AND MAN

1. CASTLETOWN AND PEEL   B H KELLY
2. DOUGLAS   D WHITWORTH
3. RAMSEY   D J GREEN

SOUTHWARK

ARCHDEACONRY OF LEWISHAM
(BISHOP OF WOOLWICH)

1. CHARLTON   M D MARSHALL
2. DEPTFORD   W G CORNECK
3. ELTHAM AND MOTTINGHAM   J WADSWORTH
4. LEWISHAM, EAST   P D BUTLER
5. LEWISHAM, WEST   J O ARDLEY
6. PLUMSTEAD   H D OWEN

ARCHDEACONRY OF SOUTHWARK
(BISHOP OF WOOLWICH)

7. BERMONDSEY   A M DOYLE
8. CAMBERWELL   J D JELLEY
9. DULWICH   P VANNOZZI
10. SOUTHWARK AND NEWINGTON   G W GODDARD

ARCHDEACONRY OF LAMBETH
(BISHOP OF KINGSTON)

11. BRIXTON   M H CLARK
12. CLAPHAM   B F J GOODWIN
13. LAMBETH   C R TRUSS
14. MERTON   T G LEARY
15. STREATHAM   S BUTLER

ARCHDEACONRY OF WANDSWORTH
(BISHOP OF KINGSTON)

16. BATTERSEA   J M SHEPHERD
17. KINGSTON   P A HOLMES
18. RICHMOND AND BARNES   F A JACKSON
19. TOOTING   G G HOWARD
20. WANDSWORTH   B M D OLIVIER

ARCHDEACONRY (AND BISHOP) OF CROYDON

21. CROYDON ADDINGTON   A H R QUINN
22. CROYDON CENTRAL   G S DERRIMAN
23. CROYDON SOUTH   C J SKILTON
24. CROYDON NORTH   C E BLANKENSHIP
25. SUTTON   J B GOULD

ARCHDEACONRY OF REIGATE
(BISHOP OF CROYDON)

26. CATERHAM   M A HART
27. GODSTONE   D C EDWARDS
28. REIGATE   D CONNOLLY

SOUTHWELL
ARCHDEACONRY OF NEWARK

1. BAWTRY   J N GREEN
2. MANSFIELD   G K KNOTT
3. NEWARK   A I TUCKER
4. NEWSTEAD   A N EVANS
5. RETFORD   A C ST J WALKER
6. WORKSOP   A J COOPER

ARCHDEACONRY OF NOTTINGHAM

7. BEESTON   J P SMITHURST
8. EAST BINGHAM   D L HARPER
9. WEST BINGHAM   G J PIGOTT
10. GEDLING   J A FISHER
12. NOTTINGHAM NORTH   C J RATTENBERRY
13. NOTTINGHAM CENTRAL *Vacant*
14. SOUTHWELL   M S TANNER

TRURO
ARCHDEACONRY OF CORNWALL

1. ST AUSTELL   F M BOWERS
2. CARNMARTH NORTH   R C BUSH
3. CARNMARTH SOUTH   J HARRIS
4. KERRIER   D J STEVENS
5. PENWITH   A J WADE
6. POWDER   I H MORRIS
7. PYDAR   P A ROBSON

ARCHDEACONRY OF BODMIN

8. STRATTON   R N STRANACK
9. TRIGG MAJOR   A J M BROWNRIDGE
10. TRIGG MINOR AND BODMIN   S L BRYAN
11. WIVELSHIRE, EAST   J A C WILSON
12. WIVELSHIRE, WEST   B A MCQUILLEN

WAKEFIELD
ARCHDEACONRY OF HALIFAX

1. ALMONDBURY   J AUSTIN
2. BRIGHOUSE AND ELLAND   N M WOOD
3. CALDER VALLEY   P N CALVERT
4. HALIFAX   J VICKERMAN
5. HUDDERSFIELD   R M F CROMPTON
6. KIRKBURTON   G F WHITCROFT

ARCHDEACONRY OF PONTEFRACT

7. BARNSLEY   J L HUDSON
8. BIRSTALL   D E CRAIG-WILD
9. CHEVET   J F WHITE
10. DEWSBURY   L C DEW
11. PONTEFRACT   M DAVIES
12. WAKEFIELD   A S MACPHERSON

WINCHESTER
ARCHDEACONRY OF WINCHESTER

1. ALRESFORD   J G CRUICKSHANK
2. ALTON   J M CAMPBELL
3. ANDOVER   F E WILLIAMS
4. BASINGSTOKE   C L HAWKINS
5. ODIHAM   N D BEAMER
6. WHITCHURCH   M S KENNING
7. WINCHESTER   N P SEAL

ARCHDEACONRY OF BOURNEMOUTH

8. BOURNEMOUTH   R D PETERS
9. CHRISTCHURCH   D M WEBSTER
10. EASTLEIGH   P A VARGESON
11. LYNDHURST   P BAYES
12. ROMSEY   D B KINGTON
13. SOUTHAMPTON   N BOAKES

ARCHDEACONRY OF THE CHANNEL ISLANDS

14. GUERNSEY   F M TRICKEY
15. JERSEY   J N SEAFORD

WORCESTER
ARCHDEACONRY OF WORCESTER

1. EVESHAM   R N ARMITAGE
2. MALVERN   M J A BARR
3. MARTLEY AND WORCESTER WEST   G T M NOTT
4. PERSHORE   P J THOMAS
5. UPTON   C G HARDWICK
6. WORCESTER EAST   R G JONES

ARCHDEACONRY OF DUDLEY

7. BROMSGROVE   D ROGERS
8. DROITWICH   A P WHITE
9. DUDLEY   M N PREVETT
10. HIMLEY   D A PICKEN
11. KIDDERMINSTER   N J W BARKER
12. STOURBRIDGE   G S CROSS
13. STOURPORT   B GILBERT

YORK
ARCHDEACONRY OF YORK
(BISHOP OF SELBY)

1. AINSTY, NEW   R P BURTON
2. DERWENT   R M KIRKMAN
3. EASINGWOLD   M HARRISON
4. SELBY   D G RICHARDSON
5. SOUTH WOLD   V P HEWETSON
6. SOUTHERN RYEDALE   N N JONES
7. YORK, CITY OF   G H WEBSTER

ARCHDEACONRY OF EAST RIDING
(BISHOP OF HULL)

8. BEVERLEY   D W HOSKIN
9. BRIDLINGTON   J A WARDLE
10. HARTHILL   M TEARE
11. HOLDERNESS, NORTH   R P YATES
12. HOLDERNESS, SOUTH   S ROBINSON
13. HOWDEN   S FOSTER
14. HULL   D A WALKER
15. SCARBOROUGH   C W HUMPHRIES

ARCHDEACONRY OF CLEVELAND
(BISHOP OF WHITBY)

16. GUISBOROUGH   J C WEETMAN
17. HELMSLEY   J D PURDY
18. MIDDLESBROUGH   D G HODGSON
19. MOWBRAY   *Vacant*
20. PICKERING   F J A HEWITT
21. STOKESLEY   W J FORD
22. WHITBY   R LEWIS

CHURCHES IN WALES

ST ASAPH

ARCHDEACONRY OF ST ASAPH

1. ST ASAPH   R W ROWLAND
2. DENBIGH   J P P WILLIAMS
3. DYFFRYN CLWYD   J B DAVIES
4. HOLYWELL   *Vacant*
5. LLANRWST   R H GRIFFITHS
6. RHOS   *Vacant*

ARCHDEACONRY OF MONTGOMERY

7. CEDEWAIN   A T W REYNOLDS
8. CAEREINION   D E B FRANCIS
9. LLANFYLLIN   C F CARTER
10. POOL   R L BROWN

ARCHDEACONRY OF WREXHAM

11. BANGOR ISYCOED   M V JONES
12. EDEIRNION   S BRUSH
13. GRESFORD   D GRIFFITHS
14. LLANGOLLEN   W L JONES
15. MINERA   J G CANHAM
16. MOLD   J T HUGHES
17. PENLLYN   *Vacant*
18. WREXHAM   G O MARSHALL

BANGOR

ARCHDEACONRY OF BANGOR

1. ARFON   I THOMAS
2. ARLLECHWEDD   P R JONES
3. LLIFON AND TALYBOLION   J E NICE
4. MALLTRAETH   *Vacant*
5. OGWEN   L J PERRY
6. TINDAETHWY   R L NEWALL
7. TWRCELYN   G W EDWARDS

ARCHDEACONRY OF MEIRIONNYDD

8. ARDUDWY   R A BEACON
9. ARWYSTLI   K FERGUSON
10. CYFEILIOG AND MAWDDWY   E W ROWLANDS
11. LLYN AND EIFIONYDD   A JONES
12. YSTUMANER   J M RILEY

ST DAVIDS

ARCHDEACONRY OF ST DAVIDS

1. CASTLEMARTIN   V F MILLGATE
2. DAUGLEDDAU   G D GWYTHER
3. DEWISLAND AND FISHGUARD   R GRIFFITHS
4. NARBERTH   M BUTLER
5. ROOSE   D EVANS

ARCHDEACONRY OF CARDIGAN

6. CEMAIS AND SUB-AERON   E L THOMAS
7. EMLYN   J H A JAMES
8. GLYN AERON   C L BOLTON
9. LAMPETER AND ULTRA-AERON   A W WILLIAMS
10. LLANBADARN FAWR   D B THOMAS

ARCHDEACONRY OF CARMARTHEN

11. CARMARTHEN   S E JONES
12. CYDWELI   S R THOMAS
13. DYFFRYN AMAN   J H GRAVELL
14. LLANGADOG AND LLANDEILO   B T RICE
15. ST CLEARS   K T LITTLER

LLANDAFF

ARCHDEACONRY OF LLANDAFF

1. CAERPHILLY   M J SHORT
2. CARDIFF   A RABJOHNS
3. LLANDAFF   W G BARLOW
4. LLANTWIT MAJOR AND COWBRIDGE   P M LEONARD
5. PENARTH AND BARRY   E B DOWDING

ARCHDEACONRY OF MARGAM

6. BRIDGEND   E J EVANS
7. MARGAM   P R MASSON
8. NEATH   N HADFIELD

ARCHDEACONRY OF MORGANNWG

9. CYNON VALLEY   R E DAVIES
10. MERTHYR TYDFIL   S S MORGAN
11. PONTYPRIDD   M K JONES
12. RHONDDA   P N COLEMAN

MONMOUTH

ARCHDEACONRY OF MONMOUTH

1. ABERGAVENNY   J H WINSTON
2. CHEPSTOW   *Vacant*
3. MONMOUTH   J P W REES
4. NETHERWENT   D J JONES
5. RAGLAN-USK   S L GUEST

ARCHDEACONRY OF NEWPORT

6. BASSALEG   J S WILLIAMS
7. BEDWELLTY   R J SUMMERS
8. BLAENAU GWENT   M J BEASLEY
9. NEWPORT   A J EDWARDS
10. PONTYPOOL   B R PIPPEN

SWANSEA AND BRECON

ARCHDEACONRY OF BRECON

1. BRECON   B H JOHN
2. BUILTH   I B BESSANT
3. CRICKHOWELL   K RICHARDS
4. HAY   R T EDWARDS
5. MAELIENYDD   L A MARSHALL

ARCHDEACONRY OF GOWER

6. CLYNE   G E BENNETT
7. CWMTAWE   G TURNER
8. WEST GOWER   D J WILKINSON
9. LLWCHWR   D H E MOSFORD
10. PENDERI   T H JONES
11. SWANSEA   J W GRIFFIN

ENGLISH BENEFICES AND CHURCHES

An index of benefices, conventional districts, local ecumenical projects, and proprietary chapels (shown in bold type), together with entries for churches and other licensed places of worship listed on the Parish Index of the Central Board of Finance. Where the church name is the same as that of the benefice (or as that of the place whose name forms the beginning of the benefice name), the church entry is omitted. Church dedications are indicated in brackets.

The benefice entry gives the full legal name, followed by the diocese, its deanery number (p. 945), the patron(s), and the name(s) and appointment(s) of clergy serving there (if there ane none, the telephone number of the parsonage house is given). The following are the main abbreviations used; for others see the full list of abbreviations.

C	Curate	P	Patron(s)
C-in-c	Curate-in-charge	P-in-c	Priest-in-charge
Dn-in-c	Deacon-in-charge	Par Dn	Parish Deacon
Dss	Deaconess	R	Rector
Hon C	Honorary Curate	TM	Team Minister
Hon Par Dn	Honorary Parish Deacon	TR	Team Rector
Min	Minister	TV	Team Vicar
NSM	Non-stipendiary Minister	V	Vicar

Listed below are the elements in place names which are not normally treated as substantive in the index:

CENTRAL	HIGHER	MUCH	OVER
EAST	LITTLE	NETHER	SOUTH
GREAT	LOW	NEW	THE
GREATER	LOWER	NORTH	UPPER
HIGH	MIDDLE	OLD	WEST

Thus WEST WIMBLEDON (Christ Church) appears as **WIMBLEDON, WEST (Christ church)** and CENTRAL TELFORD as **TELFORD, CENTRAL**. The only exception occurs where the second element of the place name is a common noun thus, NEW LANE remains as **NEW LANE**, and WEST TOWN as **WEST TOWN**.

AB KETTLEBY (St James) and Holwell w Asfordby *Leic 3*
P *DBP, MMCET and V Rothley (jt)* R vacant (01664) 812327
ABBAS and Templecombe w Horsington *B & W 2* P *Bp and Ch Trust Fund (jt)* R A J SYMONDS
ABBERLEY (St Mary) *see* Shrawley, Witley, Astley and Abberley *Worc*
ABBERLEY (St Michael) *as above Worc*
ABBERTON (St Andrew) *see* Fingringhoe w E Donyland and Abberton etc *Chelmsf*
ABBERTON (St Edburga), The Flyfords, Naunton Beauchamp and Bishampton w Throckmorton *Worc 4* P *Bp and Croome Estate Trustees (1 turn), and Ld Chan (1 turn)* R D E HASSELL
ABBESS RODING (St Edmund King and Martyr) *see* Leaden Roding and Abbess Roding etc *Chelmsf*
ABBEY CHAPEL (St Mary) *see* Annesley w Newstead *S'well*
ABBEY HEY (St George) *Man 1* P *Bp* R vacant 0161-223 1624
ABBEY HULTON (St John) *see* Bucknall and Bagnall *Lich*
ABBEY WOOD (St Michael and All Angels) *S'wark 3* P *Bp* V D A SHERRATT, NSM D C ROBINSON
ABBEY WOOD (William Temple) *see* Thamesmead *S'wark*
ABBEYDALE *see* Sheff Abbeydale St Pet *Sheff*
ABBEYDALE (St John the Evangelist) *Sheff 2* P *Mrs C Longworth, Sir Samuel Roberts Bt, K B Jones, and J A Goodwin Esq* V J FILER
ABBEYDORE (St Mary) *see* Ewyas Harold w Dulas, Kenderchurch etc *Heref*
ABBEYSTEAD (Christ Church) *see* Dolphinholme w Quernmore and Over Wyresdale *Blackb*
ABBOTS BICKINGTON (St James) *see* Bradworthy, Sutcombe, Putford etc *Ex*
ABBOTS BROMLEY (St Nicholas) w Blithfield *Lich 3* P *Bp and D&C (jt)* P-in-c S C DAVIS
ABBOTS LANGLEY (St Lawrence) *St Alb 7* P *Bp* V B K ANDREWS, C A R MATTHEWS
ABBOTS LEIGH (Holy Trinity) w Leigh Woods *Bris 2* P *Bp* P-in-c D J SMITH
ABBOTS MORTON (St Peter) *see* Church Lench w Rous Lench and Abbots Morton etc *Worc*
ABBOTS RIPTON (St Andrew) w Wood Walton *Ely 8* P *Lord de Ramsey (2 turns), D&C (1 turn)* R vacant (01767) 80538
ABBOTSBURY (St Mary) *see* Highweek and Teigngrace *Ex*
ABBOTSBURY (St Nicholas), Portesham and Langton Herring *Sarum 4* P *The Hon C A Townshend and Bp (alt)* P-in-c P S THOMAS
ABBOTSHAM (St Helen) *see* Parkham, Alwington, Buckland Brewer etc *Ex*
ABBOTSKERSWELL (Blessed Virgin Mary) *Ex 11* P *Ld Chan* P-in-c P A WHITE, Hon C J C WHITE
ABBOTSLEY (St Margaret) *see* Gt Gransden and Abbotsley and Lt Gransden etc *Ely*
ABBOTSWOOD (St Nicholas Family Centre) *see* Yate New Town *Bris*
ABBOTTS ANN (St Mary) and Upper Clatford and Goodworth Clatford *Win 3* P *Exors T P de Paravicini Esq and Bp (jt)* R D N A BROAD, NSM N J JUDD

ABDON (St Margaret) *Heref 12* P *Bp* R I E GIBBS
ABENHALL (St Michael) w Mitcheldean *Glouc 3* P *DBP* R R G STURMAN
ABERFORD (St Ricarius) *see* Aberford w Micklefield *York*
ABERFORD (St Ricarius) w Micklefield *York 4* P *Abp and Oriel Coll Ox (jt)* V D G MOORE
ABINGDON (Christ Church) (St Helen) (St Michael and All Angels) (St Nicholas) *Ox 10* P *Patr Bd* TR M A J GOODE, TV P M DOLL, T C DAVIS, C A C ATHERSTONE, D R P WIGNALL, NSM C M MANSHIP, M C SAMS, T W HEWES
ABINGER (St James) cum Coldharbour *Guildf 7* P *Ch Patr Trust and J P M H Evelyn Esq (alt)* R A N BERRY
ABINGTON (St Peter and St Paul) *Pet 4* P *Bp* R S P ADAMS, C G C SCOTT
ABINGTON, GREAT (St Mary the Virgin) w LITTLE (St Mary) *Ely 4* P *MMCET* P-in-c J B MYNORS
ABINGTON PIGOTTS (St Michael and All Angels) *see* Shingay Gp of Par *Ely*
ABNEY (Mission Room) *see* Hope, Castleton and Bradwell *Derby*
ABRAM (St John) *Liv 14* P *R Wigan* V J L STEVENTON
ABRIDGE (Holy Trinity) *see* Lambourne w Abridge and Stapleford Abbotts *Chelmsf*
ABSON (St James the Great) *see* Pucklechurch and Abson *Bris*
ABTHORPE (St John the Baptist) *see* Silverstone and Abthorpe w Slapton etc *Pet*
ACASTER MALBIS (Holy Trinity) *York 1* P *R A G Raimes Esq* V C I COATES
ACASTER SELBY (St John) *see* Appleton Roebuck w Acaster Selby *York*
ACCRINGTON (Christ Church) *Blackb 1* P *Bp and V S Shore H Trin (jt)* V K LOGAN
ACCRINGTON Christ the King (St James) (St Paul) (St Andrew) (St Peter) (St Clement) (St Mary Magdalen) *Blackb 1* P *Patr Bd* TR A D LYON, TV S D MANSFIELD, L W CARSON-FEATHAM
ACCRINGTON (St John) w Huncoat (St Augustine) *Blackb 1* P *Bp and V Accrington St Jas w St Paul (jt)* V I H ROBERTSON
ACKLAM (St John the Baptist) *see* W Buckrose *York*
ACKLAM, WEST (St Mary) *York 18* P *Trustees* V J H HEARN
ACKLETON (Mission Room) *see* Worfield *Heref*
ACKLINGTON (St John the Divine) *see* Warkworth and Acklington *Newc*
ACKWORTH (All Saints) (St Cuthbert) *Wakef 11* P *Duchy of Lanc* R P HARTLEY
ACLE (St Edmund) w Fishley; North Burlingham; Beighton w Moulton *Nor 4* P *Bp and Ch Soc Trust (jt)* R D C CASSON
ACOCKS GREEN (St Mary) *Birm 13* P *Trustees* P-in-c A T BULLOCK
ACOL (St Mildred) *see* Birchington w Acol and Minnis Bay *Cant*
ACOMB (Holy Redeemer) *York 7* P *The Crown* V M A HAND
ACOMB (St Stephen) *York 7* P *Trustees* V D J ERRIDGE, C P A HORSLEY
ACOMB MOOR (James the Deacon) *York 7* P *Abp* V A A HORSMAN

ACRISE (St Martin)   *see* Hawkinge w Acrise and Swingfield *Cant*

ACTON (All Saints) w Great Waldingfield *St E 12* P *Bp*
V J W S FIELDGATE

ACTON (St Mary) *Lon 22* P *Bp* R J F FOX,
C D H K HILBORN, NSM P M SMEDLEY

ACTON (St Mary) and Worleston, Church Minshull and Wettenhall *Ches 15* P *Bp, V Over St Chad, and R C Roundell Esq (jt)* V D P BROCKBANK, C H F CHANTRY

ACTON, EAST (St Dunstan w St Thomas) *Lon 22* P *Bp*
V N J BLANDFORD-BAKER, NSM M K DAVIDGE-SMITH

ACTON, NORTH (St Gabriel) *Lon 22* P *Bp* V K A ROBUS

ACTON, WEST (St Martin) *Lon 22* P *Bp*
V N P HENDERSON, Hon C A GRIFFITHS

ACTON BEAUCHAMP (St Giles) and Evesbatch w Stanford Bishop *Heref 2* P *Bp and MMCET (alt)* P-in-c J A DAVIES

ACTON BURNELL (St Mary) *see* Condover w Frodesley, Acton Burnell etc *Heref*

ACTON GREEN (St Alban) *see* Oak Tree Angl Fellowship *Lon*

ACTON GREEN (St Peter) (All Saints) *Lon 22* P *Bp*
V J M V WILLMINGTON, C G S THOMAS

ACTON ROUND (St Mary) *Heref 9* P *DBP*
Hon C H J PATTERSON

ACTON SCOTT (St Margaret) *Heref 11* P *DBP*
P-in-c M L COPE

ACTON TRUSSELL (St James) *see* Penkridge Team *Lich*

ACTON TURVILLE (St Mary) *see* Badminton w Lt Badminton, Acton Turville etc *Glouc*

ADBASTON (St Michael and All Angels), High Offley, Knightley, Norbury and Woodseaves *Lich 7* P *Bp*
R P M FREEMAN

ADDERBURY (St Mary) w Milton *Ox 5* P *New Coll Ox*
V S W FLETCHER, C H A SCARR

ADDERLEY (St Peter), Ash, Calverhall, Ightfield and Moreton Say *Lich 18* P C C Corbet Esq, A E H Heber-Percy Esq, T C Heywood-Lonsdale Esq, and R Whitchurch (jt)
R R J ANDERS

ADDINGHAM (St Michael), Edenhall, Langwathby and Culgaith *Carl 4* P *D&C* V R A MOATT

ADDINGHAM (St Peter) *Bradf 4* P *J R Thompson-Ashby Esq*
R A R TAWN

ADDINGTON (St Margaret) *see* Birling, Addington, Ryarsh and Trottiscliffe *Roch*

ADDINGTON (St Mary) *see* Winslow w Gt Horwood and Addington *Ox*

ADDINGTON (St Mary) *S'wark 22* P *Abp* C J M MALES

ADDINGTON, GREAT (All Saints) w LITTLE (St Mary the Virgin) and Woodford *Pet 10* P *Bp and DBP (alt)*
P-in-c J A STOBART

ADDINGTON, NEW (St Edward) *S'wark 22* P *Bp*
C A P DODD

ADDISCOMBE (St Mary Magdalene) *S'wark 23* P *Trustees*
V R L WILLIAMS, C M T POWLEY, NSM A H BARRON

ADDISCOMBE (St Mildred) *S'wark 23* P *Bp* V *vacant* (020) 8654 3569

ADDLESTONE (St Augustine) (St Paul) *Guildf 11* P *Bp*
V R HAY, OLM A G BARDELL

ADDLETHORPE (St Nicholas) *see* Ingoldmells w Addlethorpe *Linc*

ADEL (St John the Baptist) *Ripon 7* P *Brig R G Lewthwaite, D R Lewthwaite Esq, and J V Lewthwaite Esq (jt)* R T C GILL

ADEYFIELD (St Barnabas) *see* Hemel Hempstead *St Alb*

ADFORTON (St Andrew) *see* Wigmore Abbey *Heref*

ADISHAM (Holy Innocents) *see* Aylesham w Adisham *Cant*

ADLESTROP (St Mary Magdalene) *see* Broadwell, Evenlode, Oddington, Adlestrop etc *Glouc*

ADLINGFLEET (All Saints) *see* The Marshland *Sheff*

ADLINGTON (St John's Mission Church) *see* Prestbury *Ches*

ADLINGTON (St Paul) *Blackb 4* P *Bp* V D F C MORGAN

ADSTOCK (St Cecilia) *see* Lenborough *Ox*

ADSTONE (All Saints) *see* Blakesley w Adstone and Maidford etc *Pet*

ADSWOOD (St Gabriel's Mission Church) *see* Stockport SW *Ches*

ADVENT (St Adwena) *see* Lanteglos by Camelford w Advent *Truro*

ADWELL (St Mary) *see* Thame *Ox*

ADWICK-LE-STREET (St Laurence) w Skelbrooke *Sheff 7*
P *Mrs P N Fullerton and Bp (jt)* P R A INGRAM

ADWICK-UPON-DEARNE (St John the Baptist)
see Barnburgh w Melton on the Hill etc *Sheff*

AFFPUDDLE (St Lawrence) *see* Bere Regis and Affpuddle w Turnerspuddle *Sarum*

AIGBURTH (St Anne) *Liv 4* P *Trustees* V G G AMEY

AIKTON (St Andrew) *see* Barony of Burgh *Carl*

AINDERBY STEEPLE (St Helen) w Yafforth and Kirby Wiske w Maunby *Ripon 4* P *Bp and Duke of Northd (jt)* R *vacant* (01609) 773346

AINSDALE (St John) *Liv 9* P *R Walton, Bp, and Adn (jt)*
V A OVEREND, C J FLETCHER

AINSTABLE (St Michael and All Angels) *Carl 4*
P *E P Ecroyd Esq* NSM J J H SMITH

AINSWORTH (Christ Church) *Man 14* P *Bp*
P-in-c D B GRIFFITHS

AINTREE (St Giles) w St Peter *Liv 7* P *Bp* V *vacant* 0151-526 7908

AIREDALE (Holy Cross) w Fryston *Wakef 11* P *Bp*
V J W KNILL-JONES, C L J COLLYER

AIRMYN (St David), Hook and Rawcliffe *Sheff 10* P *Bp and Ch Soc Trust (jt)* V G HOLLINGSWORTH

AISHOLT (All Saints) *see* Spaxton w Charlynch, Goathurst, Enmore etc *B & W*

AISLABY (St Margaret) *see* Whitby w Aislaby and Ruswarp *York*

AISTHORPE (St Peter) w Scampton w Thorpe le Fallows w Brattleby *Linc 3* P *DBP and J M Wright Esq (jt)* R *vacant*

AKELEY (St James) *see* N Buckingham *Ox*

AKEMAN *Ox 2* P *New Coll and Ch Ch (1 turn), Qu Coll, St Jo Coll, and Period and Country Houses Ltd (1 turn)*
R D F WALKER, C A J P GARROW

ALBERBURY (St Michael and All Angels) w Cardeston *Heref 13*
P *Bp and Sir Michael Leighton Bt (alt)* V A B STRATFORD

ALBOURNE (St Bartholomew) w Sayers Common and Twineham *Chich 9* P *Bp (2 turns), Ex Coll Ox (1 turn)*
R D M SWYER

ALBRIGHTON (St John the Baptist) *see* Leaton and Albrighton w Battlefield *Lich*

ALBRIGHTON (St Mary Magdalene) *Lich 16*
P *Haberdashers' Co and Ch Hosp Horsham (alt)* V R B BALKWILL

ALBURGH (All Saints) *see* Earsham w Alburgh and Denton *Nor*

ALBURY (St Helen) Tiddington *see* Wheatley *Ox*

ALBURY (St Mary) *see* Lt Hadham w Albury *St Alb*

ALBURY (St Peter and St Paul) *see* Shere, Albury and Chilworth *Guildf*

ALBY (St Ethelbert) *see* Erpingham w Calthorpe, Ingworth, Aldborough etc *Nor*

ALCESTER (St Nicholas) and Arrow w Oversley and Weethley *Cov 7* P *Marquess of Hertf* R D C CAPRON,
NSM R F DOBELL

ALCISTON (not known) *see* Berwick w Selmeston and Alciston *Chich*

ALCOMBE (St Michael the Archangel) *B & W 16* P *Bp*
V S STUCKES

ALCONBURY (St Peter and St Paul) w Alconbury Weston *Ely 8*
P *D&C Westmr* Hon C W N C GIRARD

ALDBOROUGH (St Andrew) w Boroughbridge and Roecliffe *Ripon 3* P *D&C York and Bp (alt)* V P J SMITH

ALDBOROUGH (St Mary) *see* Erpingham w Calthorpe, Ingworth, Aldborough etc *Nor*

ALDBOROUGH HATCH (St Peter) *Chelmsf 4* P *The Crown*
V *vacant* (020) 8599 0524

ALDBOURNE (St Michael) *see* Whitton *Sarum*

ALDBROUGH (St Bartholomew) and Mappleton w Goxhill and Withernwick *York 11* P *Ld Chan, Abp, and Adn E Riding (by turn)* P-in-c A MAKEL

ALDBROUGH (St Paul) *see* Forcett and Aldbrough and Melsonby *Ripon*

ALDBURY (St John the Baptist) *see* Tring *St Alb*

ALDEBURGH (St Peter and St Paul) w Hazlewood *St E 19*
P *Mrs A C V Wentworth* P-in-c P C ROBINSON,
OLM N J WINTER

ALDEBY (St Mary) *see* Raveningham Gp *Nor*

ALDENHAM (St John the Baptist) *St Alb 1* P *Lord Aldenham*
P-in-c R A FLETCHER

ALDERBROOK (St Richard) *see* Crowborough *Chich*

ALDERBURY (St Mary the Virgin) *see* Clarendon *Sarum*

ALDERCAR (St John) *see* Langley Mill *Derby*

ALDERFORD (St John the Baptist) w Attlebridge and Swannington *Nor 22* P *Bp and D&C (alt)*
P-in-c J P P ILLINGWORTH

ALDERHOLT (St James) *Sarum 9* P *DBP* V P J MARTIN

ALDERLEY (St Kenelm) *see* Wotton-under-Edge w Ozleworth, N Nibley etc *Glouc*

ALDERLEY (St Mary) w Birtles *Ches 12* P *Trustees and Bp (alt)* R W G BOWNESS

ALDERLEY EDGE (St Philip) *Ches 12* P *Trustees*
V B T YOUNG, NSM L C A ALEXANDER

ALDERMASTON (St Mary the Virgin) w Wasing and Brimpton *Ox 12* P *Bp, DBP, Sir William Mount Bt, and Worc Coll Ox (jt)* P-in-c P G STEELE

ALDERMINSTER (St Mary and Holy Cross) and Halford
Cov 9 **P** *Bp and SMF (jt)* **P-in-c** A J ADAMS,
Hon C D R J EVANS
ALDERNEY (St Anne) *Win 14* **P** *The Crown*
P-in-c S M MASTERS
ALDERSBROOK (St Gabriel) *Chelmsf 4* **P** *DBP*
V P H SMITH
ALDERSHOT (Holy Trinity) *Guildf 1* **P** *CPAS*
V G P H NEWTON
ALDERSHOT (St Augustine) *Guildf 1* **P** *Bp* **V** K M HODGES,
OLM J W A HARVEY
ALDERSHOT (St Michael the Archangel) (Ascension) *Guildf 1*
P *Bp* **V** H H WILCOX, **C** A J K MACKENZIE,
NSM M WALKER
ALDERSLEY (Christ the King) *see* Tettenhall Regis *Lich*
ALDERTON (St Andrew) *see* Wilford Peninsula *St E*
ALDERTON (St Giles) *see* Sherston Magna, Easton Grey,
Luckington etc *Bris*
ALDERTON (St Margaret) *see* Blisworth and Stoke Bruerne w
Grafton Regis etc *Pet*
**ALDERTON (St Margaret of Antioch), Great Washbourne,
Dumbleton and Wormington** *Glouc 16* **P** *M A E Casey Esq
(1 Turn), Bp (2 turns), and Hon S K L Evetts (1 turn)*
P-in-c C G POOLE
ALDERWASLEY (All Saints) *see* Wirksworth *Derby*
ALDFIELD (St Lawrence) *see* Fountains Gp *Ripon*
ALDFORD (St John the Baptist) and Bruera *Ches 5* **P** *Duke of
Westmr and D&C (alt)* **P-in-c** C J REES
ALDHAM (St Margaret and St Catherine) *see* Marks Tey and
Aldham *Chelmsf*
ALDHAM (St Mary) *see* Elmsett w Aldham, Hintlesham,
Chattisham etc *St E*
**ALDINGBOURNE (St Mary the Virgin), Barnham and
Eastergate** *Chich 1* **P** *Bp and D&C (jt)* **R** S P HOLLAND,
NSM C R S HARDING
**ALDINGHAM (St Cuthbert) and Dendron and Rampside and
Urswick** *Carl 9* **P** *Prime Min (1 turn), V Dalton-in-Furness
and Resident Landowners of Urswick (1 turn)* **R** C R HONOUR,
NSM M WEBSTER
**ALDINGTON (St Martin) w Bonnington and Bilsington and
Lympne w West Hythe** *Cant 13* **P** *Abp* **P-in-c** R A LOVE
ALDRIDGE (St Mary the Virgin) (St Thomas) *Lich 25*
P *MMCET* **C** R J CORNFIELD, **OLM** S E QUIBELL
**ALDRINGHAM (St Andrew) w Thorpe, Knodishall w Buxlow
and Friston** *St E 19* **P** *Mrs A C V Wentworth, Ch Patr Trust,
and Ch Soc Trust (by turn)* **P-in-c** C E BROOKS,
C J M SIMPSON
ALDRINGTON (St Leonard) *Chich 4* **P** *Bp* **TR** S J TERRY,
TV J A L HARRISSON
ALDSWORTH (St Bartholomew) *see* Sherborne, Windrush, the
Barringtons etc *Glouc*
ALDWARK (St Stephen) *see* Alne *York*
ALDWICK (St Richard) *Chich 1* **P** *Bp* **V** L C J NAGEL,
NSM A B VENESS
**ALDWINCLE (St Peter) w Thorpe Achurch and Pilton w
Wadenhoe and Stoke Doyle** *Pet 12* **P** *Soc Merchant Venturers
Bris (2 turns), G C Capron Esq (1 turn), and Wadenhoe Trust
(1 turn)* **R** J A ROSE
ALDWORTH (St Mary the Virgin) *see* Basildon w Aldworth
and Ashampstead *Ox*
ALEXANDRA PARK (St Andrew) *Lon 20* **P** *Bp*
V A F PYBUS, **Hon C** B W BRIDGEWOOD
ALFINGTON (St James and St Anne) *see* Ottery St Mary,
Alfington, W Hill, Tipton etc *Ex*
ALFOLD (St Nicholas) and Loxwood *Guildf 2* **P** *Bp and
CPAS (jt)* **R** J R J BURLEY
ALFORD (All Saints) *see* Six Pilgrims *B & W*
ALFORD (St Wilfrid) w Rigsby *Linc 8* **P** *Bp* **V** R H IRESON
ALFRETON (St Martin) *Derby 1* **P** *Bp* **V** H J DOBBIN,
NSM A M V ROOME
**ALFRICK (St Mary Magdalene) and Lulsley and Suckley and
Leigh and Bransford** *Worc 3* **P** *Prime Min and Bp (alt)*
P-in-c A B BULLOCK, **Hon C** J M OAKES
**ALFRISTON (St Andrew) w Lullington, Litlington and West
Dean** *Chich 18* **P** *Ld Chan (3 turns), R A Brown Esq (1 turn),
and Duke of Devonshire (1 turn)* **R** F J FOX-WILSON
ALGARKIRK (St Peter and St Paul) *see* Sutterton, Fosdyke,
Algarkirk and Wigtoft *Linc*
ALHAMPTON (Mission Church) *see* Fosse Trinity *B & W*
ALKBOROUGH (St John the Baptist) *Linc 4* **P** *Em Coll Cam
and Bp (alt)* **V** A F PLEDGER
ALKERTON (St Michael and All Angels) *see* Ironstone *Ox*
ALKHAM (St Anthony) w Capel le Ferne and Hougham *Cant 4*
P *Abp* **V** K A MEPHAM, **OLM** K G PILGRIM
**ALKMONTON (St John), Cubley, Marston, Montgomery and
Yeaveley** *Derby 14* **P** *Bp (3 turns), V Shirley (1 turn)*
V M G HUGGETT

ALL CANNINGS (All Saints) *see* Bishop's Cannings, All
Cannings etc *Sarum*
ALL SAINTS *see* Highertown and Baldhu *Truro*
ALL SAINTS (All Saints) *see* Axminster, Chardstock, All
Saints etc *Ex*
ALL STRETTON (St Michael and All Angels) *see* Church
Stretton *Heref*
ALLENDALE (St Cuthbert) w Whitfield *Newc 4* **P** *Viscount
Allendale and J C Blackett-Ord Esq (alt)* **R** J E HAMPSON
ALLENS CROSS (St Bartholomew) *Birm 4* **P** *Bp*
V D W JAMES
ALLENS GREEN (Mission Church) *see* High Wych and
Gilston w Eastwick *St Alb*
ALLEN'S ROUGH (Worship Centre) *see* Willenhall H Trin
Lich
ALLENSMORE (St Andrew) *see* Kingstone w Clehonger,
Eaton Bishop etc *Heref*
ALLENTON (St Edmund) and Shelton Lock *Derby 15* **P** *Bp*
V M J FENTON
ALLER (St Andrew) *see* Langport Area Chs *B & W*
ALLERSTON (St John) *see* Thornton Dale w Allerston,
Ebberston etc *York*
ALLERTHORPE (St Botolph) *see* Barmby Moor Gp *York*
ALLERTON (All Hallows) *Liv 4* **P** *J Bibby Esq*
V G J BUTLAND
ALLERTON (not known) *see* Mark w Allerton *B & W*
ALLERTON (St Peter) (St Francis of Assisi) *Bradf 1* **P** *Bp*
V G O WILLIAMS
ALLERTON BYWATER (St Mary) *see* Kippax w Allerton
Bywater *Ripon*
ALLESLEY (All Saints) *Cov 2* **P** *J R W Thomson-Bree Esq*
R R N TREW
ALLESLEY PARK (St Christopher) and Whoberley *Cov 3*
P *Bp* **V** G L PRINGLE, **C** D M FARMER
ALLESTREE (St Edmund King and Martyr) *Derby 11* **P** *Bp*
V E C PIERCY
ALLESTREE (St Nicholas) *Derby 11* **P** *Bp* **V** W F BATES,
NSM S M BAILEY
ALLHALLOWS (All Saints) *see* Binsey *Carl*
ALLINGTON (St John the Baptist) *see* Bourne Valley *Sarum*
ALLINGTON (St Nicholas) and Maidstone St Peter *Cant 14*
P *Abp* **R** J E PERRYMAN
ALLINGTON (St Swithin) *see* Bridport *Sarum*
ALLINGTON, EAST (St Andrew) *see* Modbury, Bigbury,
Ringmore w Kingston etc *Ex*
ALLINGTON, WEST (Holy Trinity) *see* Saxonwell *Linc*
ALLITHWAITE (St Mary) *see* Cartmel Peninsula *Carl*
ALLONBY (Christ Church), Cross Canonby and Dearham
Carl 7 **P** *TR Solway Plain, D&C, and Bp (jt)* **V** M E DAY,
NSM S M MCKENDRY
ALMELEY (St Mary) *see* Eardisley w Bollingham, Willersley,
Brilley etc *Heref*
ALMER (St Mary) *see* Red Post *Sarum*
**ALMONDBURY (St Michael and St Helen) (St Mary)
(All Hallows) w Farnley Tyas** *Wakef 1* **P** *DBP*
TR S FOULKES, **TV** A J SMITH
ALMONDSBURY (St Mary the Virgin) and Olveston *Bris 2*
P *Bp and D&C (jt)* **V** P W ROWE
ALNE (St Mary) *York 3* **P** *CPAS and MMCET (alt)*
P-in-c J S COLE, **NSM** R WADSWORTH
ALNE, GREAT (St Mary Magdalene) *see* Kinwarton w Gt
Alne and Haselor *Cov*
ALNHAM (St Michael and All Angels) *see* Alwinton w
Holystone and Alnham *Newc*
ALNMOUTH (St John the Baptist) *see* Lesbury w Alnmouth
Newc
ALNWICK (St Michael and St Paul) *Newc 9* **P** *Duke of Northd*
V M N F HAIG, **C** S J H WHITE
ALPERTON (St James) *Lon 21* **P** *CPAS* **V** J B ROOT,
Hon C D B WADLAND, **NSM** A S JACOB
ALPHAMSTONE (not known) *see* N Hinckford *Chelmsf*
ALPHETON (St Peter and St Paul) *see* Chadbrook *St E*
ALPHINGTON (St Michael and All Angels) *Ex 3* **P** *DBP*
P-in-c S L BESSENT
ALRESFORD (St Andrew) *Chelmsf 23* **P** *Bp*
P-in-c C J A HARVEY, **NSM** J R PANTRY
**ALRESFORD, NEW (St John the Baptist) w Ovington and
Itchen Stoke** *Win 1* **P** *Bp* **R** P H N COLLINS,
NSM J A BROWNING
ALRESFORD, OLD (St Mary) and Bighton *Win 1* **P** *Bp*
P-in-c R D TOMKINSON
ALREWAS (All Saints) *Lich 1* **P** *Bp* **V** J W ALLAN,
NSM P A L MADDOCK
ALSAGER (Christ Church) *Ches 11* **P** *Bp* **V** J E VARTY
ALSAGER (St Mary Magdalene) (St Patrick's Mission Church)
Ches 11 **P** *Bp* **V** R J ISHERWOOD, **NSM** J GLEAVES

ALSAGERS BANK (St John) *Lich 9* **P** *Bp* **V** P G HOUGH
ALSOP-EN-LE-DALE (St Michael and All Angels) *see* Fenny
Bentley, Thorpe, Tissington, Parwich etc *Derby*
ALSTON MOOR (St Augustine) *Newc 4* **P** *Bp* **R** J C HARDY
ALSTONE (St Margaret) *see* Overbury w Teddington, Alstone
etc *Worc*
ALSTONFIELD (St Peter), Butterton, Ilam, Warslow w
Elkstone and Wetton *Lich 5* **P** *Bp, DBP, V Mayfield, and
Sir Peter Walker-Okeover Bt (jt)* **V** M E JACKSON
ALSWEAR (not known) *see* Bishopsnympton, Rose Ash,
Mariansleigh etc *Ex*
ALTARNON (St Nonna) w Bolventor, Laneast and St Clether
Truro 9 **P** *Bp, D&C, and SMF (jt)* **P-in-c** B STAMFORD
ALTCAR (St Michael and All Angels) and Hightown *Liv 5*
P *Bp* **V** J C BAKER, **NSM** D C M TAYLOR
ALTHAM (St James) w Clayton le Moors *Blackb 1* **P** *DBP and
Trustees (alt)* **V** vacant (01254) 384321
ALTHORNE (St Andrew) *see* Creeksea w Althorne,
Latchingdon and N Fambridge *Chelmsf*
ALTHORPE (St Oswald) *see* Belton Gp *Linc*
ALTOFTS (St Mary Magdalene) *Wakef 9* **P** *Meynall Ingram
Trustees* **V** K RYDER-WEST
ALTON (All Saints) *Win 2* **P** *Bp* **P-in-c** P A BARLOW
ALTON (St Lawrence) *Win 2* **P** *D&C* **P-in-c** P G H DOORES,
C K E HUTCHINSON
ALTON (St Peter) w Bradley-le-Moors and Oakamoor w Cotton
Lich 6 **P** *Earl of Shrewsbury and Talbot, DBP, and
R Cheadle (jt)* **V** M L E LAST
ALTON BARNES (St Mary the Virgin) *see* Pewsey and
Swanborough *Sarum*
ALTON COMMON (Mission Room) *see* Alton w
Bradley-le-Moors and Oakamoor w Cotton *Lich*
ALTON PANCRAS (St Pancras) *see* Piddletrenthide w Plush,
Alton Pancras etc *Sarum*
ALTRINCHAM (St George) *Ches 10* **P** *V Bowdon*
V B R MCCONNELL, **C** J M HEDLEY
ALTRINCHAM (St John the Evangelist) *Ches 10* **P** *Bp*
P-in-c J R HEATON
ALVANLEY (St John the Evangelist) *Ches 3* **P** *Bp* **V** vacant
(01928) 722012
ALVASTON (St Michael and All Angels) *Derby 15* **P** *PCC*
V C J C FRITH
ALVECHURCH (St Lawrence) *Worc 7* **P** *Bp* **R** D H MARTIN
ALVEDISTON (St Mary) *see* Chalke Valley *Sarum*
ALVELEY (St Mary the Virgin) and Quatt *Heref 9*
P *J W H Thompson Esq and Lady Labouchere (jt)*
R N P ARMSTRONG
ALVERDISCOTT (All Saints) *see* Newton Tracey, Horwood,
Alverdiscott etc *Ex*
ALVERSTOKE (St Faith) (St Francis) (St Mary) *Portsm 3*
P *Bp* **R** E A GOODYER, **NSM** R A FORSE
ALVERSTONE (Church Hall) *see* Brading w Yaverland *Portsm*
ALVERTHORPE (St Paul) *Wakef 12* **P** *Bp*
P-in-c P WHITTINGHAM, **C** E M WOODCOCK
ALVESCOT (St Peter) *see* Shill Valley and Broadshire *Ox*
ALVESTON (St Helen) and Littleton-on-Severn w Elberton
Bris 2 **P** *Bp and D&C (jt)* **V** D J POLE
ALVESTON (St James) *Cov 8* **P** *R Hampton Lucy w
Charlecote and Loxley* **R** E WILLIAMS
ALVINGHAM (St Adelwold) *see* Mid Marsh Gp *Linc*
ALVINGTON (St Andrew) *see* Woolaston w Alvington and
Aylburton *Glouc*
ALVINGTON, WEST (All Saints) *see* Thurlestone, S Milton, W
Alvington etc *Ex*
ALWALTON (St Andrew) *see* The Ortons, Alwalton and
Chesterton *Ely*
ALWINGTON (St Andrew) *see* Parkham, Alwington,
Buckland Brewer etc *Ex*
ALWINTON (St Michael and All Angels) w Holystone and
Alnham *Newc 9* **P** *Ld Chan and Duke of Northd (alt)*
P-in-c J R GLOVER
ALWOODLEY (St Barnabas) *see* Moor Allerton *Ripon*
AMBERGATE (St Anne) and Heage *Derby 11* **P** *V Duffield
and Exors M A T Johnson Esq* **P-in-c** R J I PAGET
AMBERLEY (Holy Trinity) *Glouc 8* **P** *DBP*
P-in-c M O TUCKER, **NSM** A V M MORRIS
AMBERLEY (no dedication) *see* Marden w Amberley and
Wisteston *Heref*
AMBERLEY (St Michael) w North Stoke and Parham,
Wiggonholt and Greatham *Chich 12* **P** *Bp and Parham Estate
Trustees (jt)* **P-in-c** R D SILK
AMBLE (St Cuthbert) *Newc 9* **P** *Bp* **V** G HARWOOD
AMBLECOTE (Holy Trinity) *Worc 12* **P** *Bp* **V** P TONGUE
AMBLESIDE (St Mary) w Brathay *Carl 11* **P** *DBP*
V W R F COKE, **C** P WILLOX
AMBROSDEN (St Mary the Virgin) *see* Ray Valley *Ox*

AMCOTTS (St Mark) *see* Belton Gp *Linc*
AMERSHAM (St Mary the Virgin) *Ox 20* **P** *Capt
F Tyrwhitt Drake* **R** T J L HARPER, **NSM** D C CARR,
OLM E A NORMAN
AMERSHAM ON THE HILL (St Michael and All Angels)
Ox 20 **P** *Bp* **V** P D RODERICK, **C** J-S S GALLANT,
NSM P R BINNS
AMESBURY (St Mary and St Melor) *Sarum 13* **P** *D&C
Windsor* **P-in-c** S E WILKINSON, **C** S M LANGDON
AMINGTON (St Editha) *Birm 10* **P** *Bp* **V** M A HARRIS
AMOTHERBY (St Helen) *see* Street *York*
AMPFIELD (St Mark) *see* Hursley and Ampfield *Win*
AMPLEFORTH (St Hilda) w Oswaldkirk, Gilling East and
Stonegrave *York 17* **P** *Abp, Trin Coll Cam, and Prime Min
(by turn)* **V** W M CARTWRIGHT
AMPNEYS (St Mary) (St Peter) (Holy Rood) w Driffield and
Poulton, The *Glouc 12* **P** *Bp and Col Sir Piers Bengough (jt)*
P-in-c A E WOOLCOCK
AMPORT (St Mary), Grateley, Monxton and Quarley *Win 3*
P *D&C Chich, Exors T P de Paravicini Esq, Mrs C E Land, Bp,
and R Foundn of St Kath (jt)* **P-in-c** C F PETTET
AMPTHILL (St Andrew) w Millbrook and Steppingley *St Alb 9*
P *Ld Chan* **R** M J TRODDEN, **NSM** C D POWELL
AMPTON (St Peter) *see* Blackbourne *St E*
AMWELL, GREAT (St John the Baptist) w St Margaret's and
Stanstead Abbots *St Alb 22* **P** *Bp, Peache Trustees, and
Haileybury Coll (jt)* **V** E A DONALDSON, **NSM** W J CHURCH
AMWELL, LITTLE (Holy Trinity) *St Alb 22* **P** *Ch Patr Trust*
V R W BOWEN
ANCASTER (St Martin) *see* Ancaster Wilsford Gp *Linc*
ANCASTER WILSFORD Group, The *Linc 23* **P** *Bp (2 turns),
DBP (1 turn), and Mrs G V Hoare (1 turn)* **R** J R HAWKINS,
OLM J E COULTHURST
ANCHORSHOLME (All Saints) *Blackb 8* **P** *Bp, V Bispham,
and Ch Soc Trust (jt)* **P-in-c** T R NUNN, **C** J W TROOD
ANCOATS (All Souls) *see* Manchester Gd Shep and St Barn
Man
ANCROFT (St Anne) *see* Lowick and Kyloe w Ancroft *Newc*
ANDERBY (St Andrew) *see* Sutton, Huttoft and Anderby *Linc*
ANDOVER (St Mary the Virgin) (St Thomas) w Foxcott *Win 3*
P *St Mary's Coll Win* **P-in-c** D G WILLIAMS, **C** J L ASTON,
J M BENTALL
ANDOVER, WEST (St Michael and All Angels) *Win 3* **P** *Bp*
P-in-c C B RANKINE, **NSM** J A TAYLOR
ANDREAS (St Andrew) *S & M 3* **P** *The Crown* **R** vacant
ANDREAS (St Jude Chapelry) *S & M 3* **P** *R Andreas*
V vacant
ANERLEY Christ Church *Roch 13* **P** *CPAS* **V** M E PORTER
ANERLEY (St Paul) *Roch 13* **P** *Ch Patr Trust* **V** M M JONES
ANFIELD (St Columba) *Liv 7* **P** *Bp* **V** R S BRIDSON,
C J R STOTT, **NSM** K L MILLER
ANFIELD (St Margaret) *Liv 3* **P** *Bp* **P-in-c** P A WINN
ANGELL TOWN (St John the Evangelist) *S'wark 11* **P** *Bp*
V M H CLARK
ANGERSLEIGH (St Michael) *see* Trull w Angersleigh *B & W*
ANGLESEY Group, The *Ely 3* **P** *Trin Coll Cam and Bp (jt)*
P-in-c D H LEWIS, **NSM** D J KETTLE
ANGMERING (St Margaret) *Chich 1* **P** *J F P Somerset Esq
and Ch Patr Trust (jt)* **R** M J STANDEN, **C** M C PAYNE
ANLABY (St Peter) *York 14* **P** *Trustees* **V** N D BARNES,
NSM D J W BATH
ANLABY COMMON (St Mark) Hull *York 14* **P** *Abp*
V vacant (01482) 351977
ANMER (St Mary) *see* Dersingham w Anmer and Shernborne
Nor
ANNESLEY (Our Lady and All Saints) w Newstead *S'well 4*
P *Exors Major R P Chaworth-Musters* **V** vacant (01623)
759606
ANNFIELD PLAIN (St Aidan) *see* Collierley w Annfield Plain
Dur
ANNSCROFT (Christ Church) *see* Longden and Annscroft w
Pulverbatch *Heref*
ANSFORD (St Andrew) *see* Castle Cary w Ansford *B & W*
ANSLEY (St Lawrence) and Arley *Cov 5* **P** *Ch Patr Trust,
N W H Sylvester Esq, and A C D'O Ransom Esq (jt)*
P-in-c P B ALLAN
ANSLOW (Holy Trinity) *Lich 14* **P** *MMCET*
V I R WHITEHEAD
ANSTEY (St George) *see* Hormead, Wyddial, Anstey, Brent
Pelham etc *St Alb*
ANSTEY (St Mary) *Leic 12* **P** *R Thurcaston* **R** S J D FOSTER
ANSTEY, EAST (St Michael) *see* Bishopsnympton, Rose Ash,
Mariansleigh etc *Ex*
ANSTEY, WEST (St Petrock) *as above Ex*
ANSTON (St James) *Sheff 5* **P** *Bp* **V** P J COGHLAN
ANSTY (St James) *see* Bulkington w Shilton and Ansty *Cov*

ANSTY (St James)   *see* Nadder Valley *Sarum*
ANSTY (St John)   *see* Cuckfield *Chich*
ANTINGHAM (St Mary)   *see* Trunch *Nor*
ANTONY (St James the Great) w Sheviock   *Truro 11*   P *Bp and Col Sir John Carew-Pole Bt (alt)*   P-in-c B A ANDERSON
ANTROBUS (St Mark), Aston by Sutton, Little Leigh and Lower Whitley   *Ches 4*   P *Bp, V Gt Budworth, Lord Daresbury, and B H Talbot Esq (jt)*   P-in-c D J JOHNSON
ANWICK (St Edith)   *see* Kirkby Laythorpe *Linc*
APETHORPE (St Leonard)   *Pet 12*   P *Lord Brassey*   V *vacant*
APLEY (St Andrew)   *see* Bardney *Linc*
APPERLEY (Holy Trinity)   *see* Deerhurst, Apperley w Forthampton and Chaceley *Glouc*
APPLEBY Group, The   *Leic 9*   P *DBP, MMCET, Bp, and Ld Chan (by turn)*   R D J K WALLER,   NSM S C POLASHEK, L S BIRTWISTLE
APPLEBY (St Bartholomew)   *see* Winterton Gp *Linc*
APPLEBY (St Lawrence)   *Carl 1*   P *D&C and Bp (jt)*   V P E P NORTON,   NSM R A COLLINSON
APPLEBY MAGNA (St Michael and All Angels)   *see* Appleby Gp *Leic*
APPLEDORE (St Mary)   *see* Bideford, Northam, Westward Ho!, Appledore etc *Ex*
APPLEDORE (St Peter and St Paul) w Brookland and Fairfield and Brenzett w Snargate   *Cant 13*   P *Abp*   V L J HAMMOND,   C A A DUGUID,   NSM S J BODY
APPLEDRAM (St Mary the Virgin)   *Chich 3*   P *D&C*   P-in-c C A ASHLEY
APPLEFORD (St Peter and St Paul)   *see* Sutton Courtenay w Appleford *Ox*
APPLESHAW (St Peter) Kimpton, Thruxton, Fyfield and Shipton Bellinger   *Win 3*   P *Bp (1 turn), and Bp, D&C, and M H Routh Esq (1 turn)*   R I J TOMLINSON,   NSM A E MCKENZIE, B A TIMS
APPLETHWAITE (St Mary)   *see* Windermere St Mary and Troutbeck *Carl*
APPLETON (All Saints)   *see* Street *York*
APPLETON (St Lawrence)   *Ox 10*   P *Magd Coll Ox*   P-in-c R G PENMAN,   NSM H O WATKINS
APPLETON (St Mary Magdalene)   *see* Stockton Heath *Ches*
APPLETON-LE-MOORS (Christ Church)   *see* Lastingham w Appleton-le-Moors, Rosedale etc *York*
APPLETON ROEBUCK (All Saints) w Acaster Selby   *York 1*   P *Abp*   P-in-c J M RODEN
APPLETON THORN (St Cross)   *see* Stretton and Appleton Thorn *Ches*
APPLETON WISKE (St Mary)   *see* Gt Smeaton w Appleton Wiske and Birkby etc *Ripon*
APPLETREEWICK (St John the Baptist)   *see* Burnsall w Rylstone *Bradf*
APPLEY BRIDGE (All Saints)   *Blackb 4*   P *Bp*   V I J J DEWAR
APSLEY END (St Mary)   *see* Chambersbury *St Alb*
APULDRAM (St Mary the Virgin)   *see* Appledram *Chich*
ARBORFIELD (St Bartholomew) w Barkham   *Ox 16*   P *DBP*   R E P BICKERSTETH,   C T J SILK
ARBORY (St Columba)   *S & M 1*   P *The Crown*   V C A QUINE,   NSM C L BARRY
ARBOURTHORNE (St Paul) and Norfolk Park   *Sheff 1*   P *Bp and V Sheffield (jt)*   V *vacant* 0114-239 8533
ARDELEY (St Lawrence)   *St Alb 19*   P *D&C St Paul's*   P-in-c M CAPEL-EDWARDS
ARDINGLY (St Peter)   *Chich 6*   P *MMCET*   R S A K ALLABY,   NSM P N MORGAN
ARDINGTON (Holy Trinity)   *see* Wantage Downs *Ox*
ARDLEIGH (St Mary the Virgin) and Bromleys, The   *Chelmsf 20*   P *Ld Chan (2 turns), CR (1 turn), Wadh Coll Ox (1 turn)*   R N SPICER
ARDLEIGH GREEN (All Saints)   *see* Squirrels Heath *Chelmsf*
ARDLEY (St Mary)   *see* Fritwell w Souldern and Ardley w Fewcott *Ox*
ARDSLEY (Christ Church)   *Sheff 12*   P *R Darfield*   V R G R EVANS
ARDSLEY, EAST (St Gabriel) (St Michael)   *Wakef 12*   P E C S J G *Brudenell Esq*   V A R ROWE
ARDSLEY, WEST   *Wakef 8*   P E C S J G *Brudenell Esq*   V *vacant* (01924) 472375
ARDWICK (St Benedict)   *see* Longsight St Luke *Man*
ARDWICK (St Jerome and St Silas)   *see* Manchester Gd Shep and St Barn *Man*
ARELEY KINGS (St Bartholomew)   *Worc 13*   P *R Martley*   P-in-c M TURNER
ARKENDALE (St Bartholomew)   *see* Walkingham Hill *Ripon*
ARKENGARTHDALE (St Mary)   *see* Swaledale *Ripon*
ARKESDEN (St Mary the Virgin)   *see* Clavering w Langley and Arkesden *Chelmsf*
ARKHOLME (St John the Baptist)   *see* Hornby w Claughton and Whittington etc *Blackb*

ARKLEY (St Peter)   *see* Chipping Barnet w Arkley *St Alb*
ARKSEY (All Saints)   *Sheff 7*   P *DBP*   P-in-c J E ASHTON
ARLECDON (St Michael)   *see* Crosslacon *Carl*
ARLESEY (St Andrew) (St Peter) w Astwick   *St Alb 16*   P *DBP*   V S D EDWARDS
ARLEY (St Michael)   *see* Ansley and Arley *Cov*
ARLEY (St Wilfred)   *as above Cov*
ARLEY, UPPER (St Peter)   *see* Kidderminster St Mary and All SS w Trimpley etc *Worc*
ARLINGHAM (St Mary the Virgin)   *see* Frampton on Severn, Arlingham, Saul etc *Glouc*
ARLINGTON (St James)   *see* Shirwell, Loxhore, Kentisbury, Arlington, etc *Ex*
ARLINGTON (St Pancras), Folkington and Wilmington   *Chich 18*   P *Bp Lon, Mrs M P Gwynne-Longland, and Duke of Devonshire (by turn)*   R *vacant* (01323) 870268
ARMATHWAITE (Christ and St Mary)   *see* Hesket-in-the-Forest and Armathwaite *Carl*
ARMINGHALL (St Mary)   *see* Stoke H Cross w Dunston, Arminghall etc *Nor*
ARMITAGE (Holy Trinity) (St John the Baptist)   *Lich 3*   P *Bp*   R D R H THOMAS
ARMITAGE BRIDGE (St Paul)   *see* Em TM *Wakef*
ARMLEY (St Bartholomew) w New Wortley   *Ripon 6*   P *Bp, DBP, and Hyndman Trustees (jt)*   V T W LIPSCOMB,   C K HANSON
ARMLEY, UPPER (Christ Church)   *Ripon 6*   P *Ch Patr Trust*   V A G KAYE,   C R J TWITTY
ARMLEY HEIGHTS (Church of the Ascension)   *see* Upper Armley *Ripon*
ARMTHORPE (St Leonard and St Mary)   *Sheff 8*   P *Bp*   R R LANDALL
ARNCLIFFE (St Oswald)   *see* Kettlewell w Conistone, Hubberholme etc *Bradf*
ARNE (St Nicholas)   *see* Wareham *Sarum*
ARNESBY (St Peter) w Shearsby and Bruntingthorpe   *Leic 10*   P *Bp*   P-in-c B STANTON
ARNOLD (Emmanuel)   *see* Bestwood Em w St Mark *S'well*
ARNOLD (St Mary)   *S'well 10*   P *Bp*   V *vacant* 0115-926 2946
ARNSIDE (St James)   *Carl 10*   P *Bp*   P-in-c L J SHUTT,   OLM J S BROCKBANK
ARRETON (St George)   *Portsm 7*   P *Bp*   V P H FORD
ARRINGTON (St Nicholas)   *see* Orwell Gp *Ely*
ARROW (Holy Trinity)   *see* Alcester and Arrow w Oversley and Weethley *Cov*
ARTHINGTON (St Peter)   *see* Lower Wharfedale *Ripon*
ARTHINGWORTH (St Andrew) w Oxendon and East Farndon   *Pet 2*   P *St Jo Coll Cam (2 turns), E G Nugee Esq (2 turns), and Bp (1 turn)*   P-in-c D J P ISIORHO
ARTHURET (St Michael and All Angels)   *Carl 2*   P *Sir James Graham Bt*   P-in-c E C ROBINSON
ARUNDEL (St Nicholas) w Tortington and South Stoke   *Chich 1*   P *Bp (2 turns), Duke of Norfolk (1 turn)*   V K D RICHARDS,   NSM A-M CROSSE
ASBY (St Peter)   *Carl 1*   P *Bp*   P-in-c D C WOOD
ASCENSION Team Ministry, The   *Leic 1*   P *Patr Bd*   TR G J JOHNSON,   NSM A T HELM
ASCOT, NORTH (St Mary and St John)   *see* Ascot Heath *Ox*
ASCOT, SOUTH (All Souls)   *Ox 11*   P *Bp*   V D S JONES,   NSM S J JONES
ASCOT HEATH (All Saints)   *Ox 11*   P *Bp*   P-in-c A P LURY,   C L J TRAINOR,   NSM G H WIGGINS
ASCOTT UNDER WYCHWOOD (Holy Trinity)   *Ox 3*   P *Bp*   P-in-c M E J ABREY
ASFORDBY (All Saints)   *see* Ab Kettleby and Holwell w Asfordby *Leic*
ASGARBY (St Andrew)   *see* Kirkby Laythorpe *Linc*
ASH (Christ Church)   *see* Adderley, Ash, Calverhall, Ightfield etc *Lich*
ASH (Holy Trinity)   *see* Martock w Ash *B & W*
ASH (St Nicholas) w Westmarsh   *Cant 1*   P *Abp*   V J SWEATMAN
ASH (St Peter)   *Guildf 1*   P *Win Coll*   R K R M BRISTOW
ASH (St Peter and St Paul)   *Roch 1*   P J R A B *Scott Esq*   R J A PEAL
ASH (Thomas Chapel)   *see* Sampford Peverell, Uplowman, Holcombe Rogus etc *Ex*
ASH PRIORS (Holy Trinity)   *see* Lydeard St Lawrence w Brompton Ralph etc *B & W*
ASH VALE (St Mary)   *Guildf 1*   P *Bp*   P-in-c C M BRENNAND,   NSM S M R CUMMING-LATTEY
ASHAMPSTEAD (St Clement)   *see* Basildon w Aldworth and Ashampstead *Ox*
ASHBOCKING (All Saints)   *see* Clopton w Otley, Swilland and Ashbocking *St E*

ASHBOURNE (St John the Baptist) *Derby 8* **P** *Wright Trustees* **V** *vacant*

ASHBOURNE (St Oswald) w Mapleton *Derby 8* **P** *Bp*
V M SMITH, **C** J M WHITE

ASHBRITTLE (St John the Baptist) *see* Wellington and Distr *B & W*

ASHBURNHAM (St Peter) w Penhurst *Chich 14*
P *Ashburnham Chr Trust* **P-in-c** S R TALBOT,
NSM A D WOODING JONES

ASHBURTON (St Andrew) w Buckland in the Moor and Bickington *Ex 10* **P** *D&C* **V** P W DARBY

ASHBURY (St Mary the Virgin) *see* Shrivenham and Ashbury *Ox*

ASHBY (St Catherine) *see* Bottesford w Ashby *Linc*

ASHBY (St Mary) *see* Somerleyton, Ashby, Fritton, Herringfleet etc *Nor*

ASHBY (St Mary) *see* Thurton *Nor*

ASHBY (St Paul) *see* Bottesford w Ashby *Linc*

ASHBY, WEST (All Saints) *see* Hemingby *Linc*

ASHBY-BY-PARTNEY (St Helen) *see* Partney Gp *Linc*

ASHBY-CUM-FENBY (St Peter) *see* Laceby and Ravendale Gp *Linc*

ASHBY DE LA LAUNDE (St Hibald) *see* Digby Gp *Linc*

ASHBY-DE-LA-ZOUCH (Holy Trinity) *Leic 9* **P** *Bp*
V L A DUTTON, **NSM** D FLOWER

ASHBY-DE-LA-ZOUCH (St Helen) w Coleorton *Leic 9*
P D A G Shields Esq **P-in-c** B A ROBERTSON, **C** D S TYLER,
K A L DENNIS

ASHBY FOLVILLE (St Mary) *see* S Croxton Gp *Leic*

ASHBY MAGNA (St Mary) *see* Willoughby Waterleys, Peatling Magna etc *Leic*

ASHBY PARVA (St Peter) *see* Leire w Ashby Parva and Dunton Bassett *Leic*

ASHBY PUERORUM (St Andrew) *see* Greetham w Ashby Puerorum *Linc*

ASHBY ST LEDGERS (St Mary) *see* Daventry, Ashby St Ledgers, Braunston etc *Pet*

ASHCHURCH (St Nicholas) *Glouc 16* **P** *K Storey Esq*
R R E ROBERTS

ASHCOMBE (St Nectan) *see* Teignmouth, Ideford w Luton, Ashcombe etc *Ex*

ASHCOTT (All Saints) *see* Shapwick w Ashcott and Burtle *B & W*

ASHDON (All Saints) *see* Saffron Walden w Wendens Ambo, Littlebury etc *Chelmsf*

ASHE (Holy Trinity and St Andrew) *see* N Waltham and Steventon, Ashe and Deane *Win*

ASHEN (St Augustine) *see* Ridgewell w Ashen, Birdbrook and Sturmer *Chelmsf*

ASHENDON (St Mary) *see* Bernwode *Ox*

ASHFIELD, GREAT (All Saints) *see* Badwell and Walsham *St E*

ASHFIELD CUM THORPE (St Mary) *see* Earl Soham w Cretingham and Ashfield *St E*

ASHFORD (St Hilda) *Lon 13* **P** *Bp* **V** C A ROGERS

ASHFORD (St Mary the Virgin) *Cant 10* **P** *Abp*
NSM P A ROWE

ASHFORD (St Matthew) *Lon 13* **P** *Ld Chan* **V** R E HORTON

ASHFORD (St Peter) *see* Barnstaple *Ex*

ASHFORD, SOUTH (Christ Church) *Cant 10* **P** *Abp*
P-in-c A D KIRKWOOD

ASHFORD, SOUTH (St Francis of Assisi) *Cant 10* **P** *Abp*
P-in-c I L GARRETT, **NSM** C J GARRETT

ASHFORD BOWDLER (St Andrew) *see* Ludlow, Ludford, Ashford Carbonell etc *Heref*

ASHFORD CARBONELL (St Mary) *as above Heref*

ASHFORD COMMON (St Benedict) *see* Upper Sunbury St Sav *Lon*

ASHFORD HILL (St Paul) w Headley *Win 6* **P** *V Kingsclere*
V *vacant* (01635) 268217

ASHFORD IN THE WATER (Holy Trinity) w Sheldon and Great Longstone *Derby 2* **P** *V Bakewell* **V** C A THROWER

ASHILL (Blessed Virgin Mary) *see* Ilminster and Distr *B & W*

ASHILL (St Nicholas) w Saham Toney *Nor 13* **P** *Bp and New Coll Ox (alt)* **OLM** S D H MAWDITT

ASHILL (St Stephen) *see* Cullompton, Willand, Uffculme, Kentisbeare etc *Ex*

ASHINGDON (St Andrew) w South Fambridge *Chelmsf 12*
P *CCC Cam* **P-in-c** T F CLAY

ASHINGTON (Holy Sepulchre) *Newc 11* **P** *Bp* **V** E J NOBLE,
NSM L BEADLE

ASHINGTON (St Matthew) *see* Canford Magna *Sarum*

ASHINGTON (St Peter and St Paul), Washington and Wiston w Buncton *Chich 12* **P** *Bp and R H Goring Esq (alt)*
R L F WHATLEY

ASHINGTON (St Vincent) *see* Chilton Cantelo, Ashington, Mudford, Rimpton etc *B & W*

ASHLEWORTH (St Bartholomew) *see* Hasfield w Tirley and Ashleworth *Glouc*

ASHLEY (St Elizabeth) *see* Hale and Ashley *Ches*

ASHLEY (St James), Crudwell, Hankerton, Long Newnton and Oaksey *Bris 6* **P** *Trustees* **R** B RAVEN

ASHLEY (St John the Baptist) *Lich 7* **P** *Meynell Ch Trustees*
P-in-c D J WILLIAMS

ASHLEY (St Mary the Virgin) *see* Stoke Albany w Wilbarston and Ashley etc *Pet*

ASHLEY (St Mary) w Silverley *Ely 4* **P** *Bp and DBP (alt)*
R C A SINDALL, **Hon C** L M BROUGHTON

ASHLEY (St Peter and St Paul) *see* Somborne w Ashley *Win*

ASHLEY GREEN (St John the Evangelist) *see* Gt Chesham *Ox*

ASHMANHAUGH (St Swithin), Barton Turf, Beeston St Laurence, Horning, Irstead and Neatishead *Nor 12* **P** *Bp and Sir Ronald Preston Bt (jt)* **R** M C R CRIPPS,
C J A CRAFER, **NSM** J S PEEL

ASHMANSWORTH (St James) *see* Highclere and Ashmansworth w Crux Easton *Win*

ASHMORE (St Nicholas) *see* Iwerne Valley *Sarum*

ASHMORE PARK (St Alban) *see* Wednesfield *Lich*

ASHOVER (All Saints) and Brackenfield w Wessington *Derby 5*
P *Exors Revd J J C Nodder, Duke of Devonshire, V Crich and S Wingfield, and DBF (jt)* **NSM** R SMITH

ASHOW (Assumption of Our Lady) *see* Stoneleigh w Ashow *Cov*

ASHPERTON (St Bartholomew) *see* Ledbury *Heref*

ASHPRINGTON (St David), Cornworthy and Dittisham *Ex 13*
P *Bp* **P-in-c** S E ROBERTS

ASHREIGNEY (St James) *Ex 19* **P** *DBP* **R** P J NORMAN

ASHTEAD (St George) (St Giles) *Guildf 10* **P** *Bp*
R R J KITELEY, **C** R M COATES, S J F THOMAS,
OLM P R DAWSON, R M N HOOKER

ASHTON (Annunciation) *see* Breage w Germoe and Godolphin *Truro*

ASHTON (Holy Trinity) (St James) (St Michael and All Angels) (St Gabriel) (Queen Victoria Memorial Church) *Man 17*
P *Patr Bd* **TR** D J WISEMAN, **TV** R FARNWORTH,
H T NICOL, **C** A S MITCHELL

ASHTON (St John the Baptist) *see* Christow, Ashton and Bridford *Ex*

ASHTON (St Michael and All Angels) *see* Roade and Ashton w Hartwell *Pet*

ASHTON, WEST (St John) *see* Trowbridge St Thos and W Ashton *Sarum*

ASHTON GATE (St Francis) *see* Bedminster *Bris*

ASHTON HAYES (St John the Evangelist) *Ches 2* **P** *Keble Coll Ox* **P-in-c** B R K PERKES

ASHTON-IN-MAKERFIELD (Holy Trinity) *Liv 15* **P** *Bp*
R D R ABBOTT

ASHTON-IN-MAKERFIELD (St Thomas) *Liv 15*
P *R Ashton-in-Makerfield w Trin* **V** H E GREENWOOD

ASHTON KEYNES (Holy Cross), Leigh and Minety *Bris 6*
P *Bp* **V** P E H SELLEY, **NSM** V N JAMES

ASHTON-ON-RIBBLE (St Andrew) *Blackb 13* **P** *Trustees*
V C J ENTWISTLE

ASHTON-ON-RIBBLE (St Michael and All Angels) w Preston St Mark *Blackb 13* **P** *Bp* **V** *vacant* (01772) 726157

ASHTON UNDER HILL (St Barbara) *see* Overbury w Teddington, Alstone etc *Worc*

ASHTON-UNDER-LYNE (Christ Church) *Man 17* **P** *Bp*
V J S HOLLAND

ASHTON-UNDER-LYNE (St Peter) *Man 17*
P *R Ashton-under-Lyne St Mich* **P-in-c** H T NICOL

ASHTON-UPON-MERSEY (St Martin) *Ches 10* **P** *SMF*
R R J E CLACK, **NSM** D R LAW

ASHTON-UPON-MERSEY (St Mary Magdalene) *Ches 10*
P *Trustees* **V** G J SKINNER, **C** S B RANKIN

ASHURST (St James) *Chich 12* **P** *MMCET*
R P M RAMPTON

ASHURST (St Martin of Tours) *see* Speldhurst w Groombridge and Ashurst *Roch*

ASHURST WOOD (St Dunstan) *see* Forest Row *Chich*

ASHWATER (St Peter ad Vincula), Halwill, Beaworthy, Clawton and Tetcott w Luffincott *Ex 9* **P** *Ld Chan (1 turn), Major L J Melhuish, Lt-Col Sir John Molesworth-St Aubyn Bt, and Bp (jt) (2 turns)* **R** *vacant* (01409) 211205

ASHWELL (St Mary) *see* Cottesmore and Barrow w Ashwell and Burley *Pet*

ASHWELL (St Mary the Virgin) w Hinxworth and Newnham St Alb 19* **P *Bp, R Smyth Esq, and N J A Farr Esq (jt) (1 turn), Bp (3 turns)* **R** J A BIRDSEYE

ASHWELLTHORPE (All Saints), Forncett, Fundenhall, Hapton, Tacolneston and Wreningham *Nor 7* **P** *Bp, Keble Coll Ox, Ch Coll Cam, and MMCET (by turn)* **V** C W J STYLES

ASHWICK (St James) w Oakhill and Binegar *B & W 8* **P** *Bp*
R *vacant* (01749) 841341
ASHWICKEN (All Saints) *see* Gayton, Gayton Thorpe, E
Walton, E Winch etc *Nor*
ASHWORTH (St James) *see* Norden w Ashworth *Man*
ASKAM (Church Centre) *see* Dalton-in-Furness and
Ireleth-with-Askam *Carl*
ASKAM (St Peter) *as above Carl*
ASKERN (St Peter) *Sheff 7* **P** *Bp* **V** M WIGGLESWORTH
ASKERSWELL (St Michael), Loders and Powerstock *Sarum 2*
P *Ld Chan, Lady Laskey, Bp, and D&C (by turn)*
P-in-c M N A JONES
ASKHAM (St Nicholas) *see* E Markham w Askham, Headon w
Upton and Grove *S'well*
ASKHAM (St Peter) *see* Lowther and Askham and Clifton and
Brougham *Carl*
ASKHAM BRYAN (St Nicholas) *York 1* **P** *Abp*
P-in-c D S COOK
ASKHAM RICHARD (St Mary) *see* Healaugh w Wighill,
Bilbrough and Askham Richard *York*
ASKRIGG (St Oswald) w Stallingbusk *Ripon 4* **P** *V Aysgarth*
P-in-c A B CHAPMAN
ASLACKBY (St James) *see* Billingborough Gp *Linc*
ASLACTON (St Michael) *see* Bunwell, Carleton Rode,
Tibenham, Gt Moulton etc *Nor*
ASLOCKTON (St Thomas) *see* Whatton w Aslockton,
Hawksworth, Scarrington etc *S'well*
ASPALL (St Mary of Grace) *see* Debenham w Aspall and
Kenton *St E*
ASPATRIA (St Kentigern) w Hayton and Gilcrux *Carl 7* **P** *Bp*
V *vacant* (01697) 320398
ASPENDEN (St Mary), Buntingford and Westmill *St Alb 19*
P *CPAS, MCET, and K Coll Lon (jt)* **R** N J RICHARDS,
NSM G HOWDLE
ASPLEY (St Margaret) *S'well 13* **P** *Trustees* **V** D WARD
ASPLEY GUISE (St Botolph) w Husborne Crawley and
Ridgmont *St Alb 9* **P** *Ld Chan (1 turn), Trustees Bedf Estates
(1 turn), and Bp (2 turns)* **R** G BRADSHAW
ASPULL (St Elizabeth) *Liv 14* **P** *Trustees* **OLM** M L PERRIN
ASSINGTON (St Edmund) *see* Bures w Assington and Lt
Cornard *St E*
ASTBURY (St Mary) and Smallwood *Ches 11* **P** *Sir Richard
Baker Wilbraham Bt* **R** J C CUTTELL
ASTERBY Group, The *Linc 11* **P** *Bp, DBP, J N Heneage Esq,
F Smith Esq, and Mrs J Fox (jt)* **R** I D MCGRATH
ASTHALL (St Nicholas) *see* Burford w Fulbrook, Taynton,
Asthall etc *Ox*
ASTLEY (St Mary the Virgin) *see* Chilvers Coton w Astley *Cov*
ASTLEY (St Mary), Clive, Grinshill and Hadnall *Lich 22*
P *D R B Thompson Esq* **P-in-c** R R HAARHOFF
ASTLEY (St Peter) *see* Shrawley, Witley, Astley and Abberley
Worc
ASTLEY (St Stephen) *Man 13* **P** *V Leigh St Mary*
P-in-c R J CARMYLLIE, **OLM** A J DAND
ASTLEY ABBOTTS (St Calixtus) *see* Bridgnorth, Tasley,
Astley Abbotts, etc *Heref*
ASTLEY BRIDGE (St Paul) *Man 16* **P** *The Crown*
V A J LINDOP, **C** J P T HINDLEY
ASTON (St Giles) *see* Wigmore Abbey *Heref*
ASTON (St Mary) *see* Woore and Norton in Hales *Lich*
ASTON (St Mary) *see* Stevenage St Mary Sheppall w Aston
St Alb
ASTON (St Peter) *see* Antrobus, Aston by Sutton, Lt Leigh etc
Ches
ASTON (St Saviour) *see* Stone St Mich and St Wulfad w Aston
St Sav *Lich*
ASTON, LITTLE (St Peter) *Lich 1* **P** *Patr Bd* **V** S HUYTON
ASTON, NORTH (St Mary the Virgin) *see* Steeple Aston w N
Aston and Tackley *Ox*
ASTON ABBOTS (St James the Great) *see* Wingrave w
Rowsham, Aston Abbotts and Cublington *Ox*
ASTON BOTTERELL (St Michael and All Angels) *see* Ditton
Priors w Neenton, Burwarton etc *Heref*
ASTON CANTLOW (St John the Baptist) and Wilmcote w
Billesley *Cov 7* **P** *SMF* **P-in-c** D B ADDLEY
ASTON CLINTON (St Michael and All Angels) w Buckland and
Drayton Beauchamp *Ox 22* **P** *Exors Major S W Jenney, Jes
Coll Ox, and Bp (by turn)* **R** A W BENNETT
ASTON CUM AUGHTON (All Saints) w Swallownest and Ulley
Sheff 5 **P** *Bp* **TR** S K PROCTOR, **TV** J M HOFFMANN,
C S A CASH, J D PARKER
ASTON EYRE (not known) *see* Morville w Aston Eyre *Heref*
ASTON FLAMVILLE (St Peter) *see* Burbage w Aston
Flamville *Leic*
ASTON INGHAM (St John the Baptist) *see* Ross *Heref*
ASTON JUXTA BIRMINGHAM (St James) *Birm 8*
P *V Aston* **V** E J FURNESS

ASTON JUXTA BIRMINGHAM (St Peter and St Paul) *Birm 8*
P *Aston Trustees* **V** A J JOLLEY, **C** J A ARNOLD
ASTON LE WALLS (St Leonard) *see* Byfield w Boddington
and Aston le Walls *Pet*
ASTON ON TRENT (All Saints), Elvaston, Weston on Trent and
Shardlow *Derby 15* **P** *Bp, Earl of Harrington, and DBP
(by turn)* **R** A LUKE
ASTON ROWANT (St Peter and St Paul) *see* Chinnor w
Emmington and Sydenham etc *Ox*
ASTON SANDFORD (St Michael and All Angels)
see Haddenham w Cuddington, Kingsey etc *Ox*
ASTON SOMERVILLE (St Mary) *see* Childswyckham w
Aston Somerville, Buckland etc *Glouc*
ASTON-SUB-EDGE (St Andrew) *see* Mickleton, Willersey,
Saintbury etc *Glouc*
ASTON TIRROLD (St Michael) *see* S w N Moreton, Aston
Tirrold and Aston Upthorpe *Ox*
ASTON UPTHORPE (All Saints) *as above Ox*
ASTWICK (St Guthlac) *see* Arlesey w Astwick *St Alb*
ASTWOOD (St Peter) *see* Sherington w Chicheley, N Crawley,
Astwood etc *Ox*
ASTWOOD BANK (St Matthias and St George) *Worc 7*
P *DBP* **P-in-c** P G HARRISON, **C** C D I REES
ASWARBY (St Denys) *see* S Lafford *Linc*
ASWARDBY (St Helen) *see* Partney Gp *Linc*
ATCHAM (St Eata) *see* Shrewsbury St Giles w Sutton and
Atcham *Lich*
ATHELINGTON (St Peter) *see* Stradbroke, Horham,
Athelington and Redlingfield *St E*
ATHERINGTON (St Mary) *see* Newton Tracey, Horwood,
Alverdiscott etc *Ex*
ATHERSLEY (St Helen) *Wakef 7* **P** *Bp*
P-in-c R H MARSHALL
ATHERSTONE (St Mary) *Cov 5* **P** *V Mancetter*
V P I HARRIS
ATHERTON (St John the Baptist) (St George) (St Philip) and
Hindsford w Howe Bridge *Man 13* **P** *DBP* **TV** W BALDWIN,
T P HUMPHRY, **OLM** D SIMPSON, K BAINES
ATLOW (St Philip and St James) *see* Hulland, Atlow, Kniveton,
Bradley and Hognaston *Derby*
ATTENBOROUGH (St Mary the Virgin) *S'well 7* **P** *CPAS*
P-in-c S M HEMSLEY, **C** M F CHATFIELD,
NSM J P SMITHURST
ATTERCLIFFE (Hill Top Chapel) *see* Nine o'clock
Community *Sheff*
ATTERCLIFFE (St Alban), Darnall and Tinsley *Sheff 1*
P *Patr Bd* **TR** M L FUDGER, **TV** M J LUNT
ATTLEBOROUGH (Assumption of the Blessed Virgin Mary) w
Besthorpe *Nor 11* **P** *CR and Mrs S P J Scully (jt)*
R M AISBITT, **C** N P KINSELLA, **OLM** J I MAY
ATTLEBOROUGH (Holy Trinity) *Cov 5* **P** *V Nuneaton*
V C JONES, **NSM** B J JACQUES
ATTLEBRIDGE (St Andrew) *see* Alderford w Attlebridge and
Swannington *Nor*
ATWICK (St Lawrence) *see* Hornsea w Atwick *York*
ATWORTH (St Michael and All Angels) w Shaw and Whitley
Sarum 14 **P** *D&C Bris and R Melksham (alt)*
P-in-c G R J FORCE-JONES
AUBOURN (St Peter) *see* Bassingham Gp *Linc*
AUCKLAND (St Andrew) (St Anne) *Dur 6* **P** *Bp* **V** N P VINE
AUCKLAND (St Helen) *Dur 6* **P** *Bp* **V** R I MCTEER
AUCKLAND (St Peter) *Dur 6* **P** *The Crown* **V** P K LEE
AUCKLEY (St Saviour) *see* Finningley w Auckley *S'well*
AUDENSHAW (St Hilda) *Man 17* **P** *Bp* **V** J H KERSHAW
AUDENSHAW (St Stephen) *Man 17* **P** *Bp* **V** P R DIXON
AUDLEM (St James the Great) *Ches 15* **P** *Bp* **V** D ROSTRON
AUDLEY (St James the Great) *Lich 9* **P** *Ch Soc Trust*
V P T W DAVIES, **NSM** K M BURGESS
AUGHTON (All Saints) *see* Bubwith w Skipwith *York*
AUGHTON (Christ Church) *Liv 11* **P** *R Aughton St Mich*
V R MOUGHTIN, **C** M S FOLLIN
AUGHTON (St Michael) *Liv 11* **P** *Bp* **R** M P ADAMS
AUGHTON (St Saviour) *see* Halton w Aughton *Blackb*
AUKBOROUGH (St John the Baptist) *see* Alkborough *Linc*
AUKBOROUGH (St John the Baptist) *as above Linc*
AULT HUCKNALL (St John the Baptist) and Scarcliffe *Derby 3*
P *Bp and Duke of Devonshire (alt)* **V** A L BELL
AUNSBY (St Thomas of Canterbury) *see* S Lafford *Linc*
AUST (not known) *see* Almondsbury and Olveston *Bris*
AUSTERFIELD (St Helen) *see* Bawtry w Austerfield and
Misson *S'well*
AUSTREY (St Nicholas) and Warton (Holy Trinity) *Birm 10*
P *Ld Chan and V Polesworth St Editha (alt)* **P-in-c** S J BANKS,
C A E MANN
AUSTWICK (Epiphany) *see* Clapham-with-Keasden and
Austwick *Bradf*

AVEBURY (St James)   *see* Upper Kennet *Sarum*
AVELEY (St Michael) and Purfleet *Chelmsf 14*   **P** *Bp*
P-in-c V J ROCKALL,   **C** A M OVERTON-BENGE
AVENING (Holy Cross) w Cherington *Glouc 15*
P *E A Tarlton Esq (1 turn), D&C (2 turns)*   **NSM** C CARTER
AVERHAM (St Michael and All Angels) w Kelham *S'well 3*
P *DBP*   **P-in-c** I A LAMBERT
AVETON GIFFORD (St Andrew)   *see* Modbury, Bigbury,
Ringmore w Kingston etc *Ex*
AVINGTON (St Mary)   *see* Itchen Valley *Win*
AVON DASSETT (St Peter and St Clare) w Farnborough and
Fenny Compton *Cov 8*   **P** *G V L Holbech Esq and Mrs
A D Seyfried (jt), CCC Ox, and Bp(alt)*   **R** D P PYM
AVON-SWIFT Group Team   *see* Gilmorton, Peatling Parva,
Kimcote etc *Leic*
AVON VALLEY *Sarum 13*   **P** *Bp (3 turns), MOD (2 turns),
and Ch Hosp (1 turn)*   **P-in-c** C G FOX
AVONMOUTH (St Andrew)   *see* Lawrence Weston and
Avonmouth *Bris*
AWBRIDGE (All Saints)   *see* Michelmersh and Awbridge and
Braishfield etc *Win*
AWLISCOMBE (St Michael and All Angels)   *see* Honiton,
Gittisham, Combe Raleigh, Monkton etc *Ex*
AWRE (St Andrew)   *see* Newnham w Awre and Blakeney *Glouc*
AWSWORTH (St Peter)   *see* Trowell, Awsworth and Cossall
S'well
AXBRIDGE (St John the Baptist) w Shipham and Rowberrow
B & W 1   **P** *Bp and D&C (alt)*   **R** D J RICHARDS,
NSM P R ROGERS
AXFORD (St Michael)   *see* Whitton *Sarum*
AXMINSTER (St Mary), Chardstock, All Saints, Combpyne w
Rousdon and Membury *Ex 5*   **P** *Bp*   **TR** J H GOOD,
TV M R WARING
AXMOUTH (St Michael)   *see* Uplyme w Axmouth *Ex*
AYCLIFFE (Church Centre)   *see* Dover St Mary *Cant*
AYCLIFFE, GREAT (St Andrew) (St Clare) *Dur 5*   **P** *Patr Bd*
TR W E L BROAD,   **TV** M D ALLSOPP,   **C** M E ANDERSON
AYLBURTON (St Mary)   *see* Woolaston w Alvington and
Aylburton *Glouc*
AYLBURTON COMMON (Mission Church)   *see* Lydney *Glouc*
AYLESBEARE (Blessed Virgin Mary), Rockbeare, Farringdon,
Clyst Honiton and Sowton *Ex 1*   **P** *Bp and D&C (jt)*
P-in-c H G WHITTY
AYLESBURY (St Mary the Virgin) w Bierton and Hulcott *Ox 21*
P *Bp and Patr Bd (jt)*   **TR** T J HIGGINS,   **TV** P C FAULKNER,
P D ATKINSON, J M WRIGHT,   **C** D M GLOVER,
NSM A E FAULKNER
AYLESBY (St Lawrence)   *see* Keelby Gp *Linc*
AYLESFORD (St Peter and St Paul) *Roch 7*   **P** *D&C*
V S C TILLOTSON,   **NSM** C M HAYDON
AYLESHAM (St Peter) w Adisham *Cant 1*   **P** *Abp*
P-in-c T F BARNFATHER,   **Hon C** H D CONNOLL,
NSM E R G HOPTHROW
AYLESTONE (St Andrew) w St James *Leic 2*   **P** *Bp*
R A RACE
AYLESTONE PARK (Church of the Nativity) Conventional
District *Leic 2 vacant*
AYLMERTON (St John the Baptist); Runton; Beeston Regis;
Gresham *Nor 21*   **P** *Bp and Guild of All So (2 turns), Duchy of
Lanc (1 turn)*   **R** *vacant* (01263) 837279
AYLSHAM (St Michael) *Nor 19*   **P** *D&C Cant*
V R D BRANSON
AYLTON (not known)   *see* Ledbury *Heref*
AYMESTREY (St John the Baptist and St Alkmund)
see Kingsland w Eardisland, Aymestrey etc *Heref*
AYNHO (St Michael) and Croughton w Evenley and Farthinghoe
and Hinton-in-the-Hedges w Steane *Pet 1*   **P** *Bp (2 turns),
Mrs E A J Cartwright-Hignett (1 turn), Magd Coll Ox (1 turn),
and Ld Chan (1 turn)*   **R** P A M GOMPERTZ,   **C** J A HOBSON
AYOT ST LAWRENCE (St Lawrence)   *see* Kimpton w Ayot St
Lawrence *St Alb*
AYOT ST PETER (St Peter)   *see* Welwyn w Ayot St Peter *St Alb*
AYSGARTH (St Andrew) and Bolton cum Redmire *Ripon 4*
P *R Wensley and Trin Coll Cam (jt)*   **V** S C WHITEHOUSE,
C M RIMMER,   **Hon C** J RICHARDSON
AYSTON (St Mary the Virgin)   *see* Uppingham w Ayston and
Wardley w Belton *Pet*
AYTHORPE RODING (St Mary)   *see* Gt Canfield w High
Roding and Aythorpe Roding *Chelmsf*
AYTON, EAST (St John the Baptist) *York 15*   **P** *Abp*
P-in-c R C WALSER
AYTON, GREAT (All Saints) (Christ Church) w Easby and
Newton in Cleveland *York 21*   **P** *Abp*   **V** P H PEVERELL,
NSM G S JAQUES
BABBACOMBE (All Saints) *Ex 10*   **P** *V St Marychurch*
P-in-c S N WAKELY

BABCARY (Holy Cross)   *see* Six Pilgrims *B & W*
BABRAHAM (St Peter) *Ely 6*   **P** H R T *Adeane Esq*
P-in-c G KENDALL
BABWORTH (All Saints) w Sutton-cum-Lound and Scofton w
Osberton *S'well 5*   **P** *Bp, G M T Foljambe Esq, and Sir John
Whitaker Bt (jt)*   **R** H R SMITH
BACKFORD (St Oswald) and Capenhurst *Ches 9*   **P** *Bp*
R S M SOUTHGATE
BACKWELL (St Andrew) w Chelvey and Brockley *B & W 13*
P *DBP*   **R** S J HILL,   **C** J R EASTELL
BACKWORTH (St John)   *see* Earsdon and Backworth *Newc*
BACONSTHORPE (St Mary)   *see* Barningham w Matlaske w
Baconsthorpe etc *Nor*
BACTON (St Andrew) w Edingthorpe w Witton and Ridlington
Nor 12   **P** *Duchy of Lanc (1 turn), Bp and Earl of Kimberley
(1 turn)*   **V** I D FARLEY
BACTON (St Faith)   *see* Ewyas Harold w Dulas, Kenderchurch
etc *Heref*
BACTON (St Mary the Virgin) w Wyverstone, Cotton and Old
Newton, and Wickham Skeith *St E 6*   **P** *Patr Bd (2 turns),
Ld Chan (1 turn)*   **R** R W JACK,   **NSM** B B BILSTON
BACUP (Christ Church) *Man 15*   **P** *Trustees*   **OLM** D ALLEN
BACUP (St John the Evangelist) *Man 15*   **P** *Wm Hulme
Trustees*   **V** M HOLT
BACUP (St Saviour) *Man 15*   **P** *Ch Soc Trust*
P-in-c S E BROOK
BADBY (St Mary) w Newnham and Charwelton w Fawsley and
Preston Capes *Pet 3*   **P** *Bp*   **R** M D PETITT
BADDESLEY, NORTH (All Saints' Mission Church)
see Chilworth w N Baddesley *Win*
BADDESLEY, NORTH (St John the Baptist)   *as above Win*
BADDESLEY, SOUTH (St Mary the Virgin)   *see* Boldre w S
Baddesley *Win*
BADDESLEY CLINTON (St Michael) *Birm 6*
P *T W Ferrers-Walker Esq*   **R** M J MORGAN
BADDESLEY ENSOR (St Nicholas) w Grendon *Birm 10*
P *Bp, V Polesworth, and PCC (jt)*   **V** K HODSON
BADDILEY (St Michael) and Wrenbury w Burleydam *Ches 15*
P *V Acton and Bp (alt)*   **NSM** R M HARRISON
BADDOW, GREAT (Meadgate Church Centre) (St Mary the
Virgin) (St Paul) *Chelmsf 9*   **P** *Patr Bd*   **TR** A D MCGREGOR,
TV M A FARAH, T V ROBERTS,   **Hon C** R C MATTHEWS,
NSM P F ROBERTS
BADDOW, LITTLE (St Mary the Virgin) *Chelmsf 9*   **P** *Bp*
Hon C C A MCCAFFERTY
BADGER (St Giles)   *see* Beckbury, Badger, Kemberton, Ryton,
Stockton etc *Lich*
BADGEWORTH (Holy Trinity), Shurdington and Witcombe w
Bentham *Glouc 6*   **P** *Bp and F D Hicks Beach Esq (jt)*
OLM M J THOMPSON
BADGWORTH (St Congar)   *see* Crook Peak *B & W*
BADINGHAM (St John the Baptist) w Bruisyard, Cransford and
Dennington *St E 18*   **P** *R C Rous Esq (1 turn), DBP (2 turns)*
P-in-c J P T OLANCZUK
BADLESMERE (St Leonard)   *see* Selling w Throwley,
Sheldwich w Badlesmere etc *Cant*
BADMINTON (St Michael and All Angels) w Little Badminton,
Acton Turville and Hawkesbury *Glouc 7*   **P** *Duke of Beaufort*
P-in-c P R BERROW,   **NSM** G H EDWARDS
BADMINTON, LITTLE (St Michael and All Angels)
see Badminton w Lt Badminton, Acton Turville etc *Glouc*
BADSEY (St James) w Aldington and Offenham and Bretforton
Worc 1   **P** *Bp and Ch Ch Ox (jt)*   **V** A M HOUGH,
NSM M J SHEPHERD
BADSHOT LEA (St George)   *see* Hale w Badshot Lea *Guildf*
BADSWORTH (St Mary the Virgin) *Wakef 11*   **P** *DBP*
R D MATHERS
BADWELL (St Mary) and Walsham *St E 9*   **P** *Bp, DBP,
R M Martineau Esq, and Soc of the Faith (jt)*   **R** M G CLARKE
BAG ENDERBY (St Margaret)   *see* Ormsby Gp *Linc*
BAGBOROUGH (St Pancras)   *see* Bishops Lydeard w
Bagborough and Cothelstone *B & W*
BAGBY (St Mary)   *see* Thirkleby w Kilburn and Bagby *York*
BAGENDON (St Margaret)   *see* Stratton, N Cerney, Baunton
and Bagendon *Glouc*
BAGINTON (St John the Baptist) w Bubbenhall and
Ryton-on-Dunsmore *Cov 6*   **P** *D&C (2 turns), Bp (1 turn),
Lord Leigh and Bp (1 turn)*   **P-in-c** D R WINTLE
BAGNALL (St Chad)   *see* Bucknall and Bagnall *Lich*
BAGSHOT (Good Shepherd)   *see* Savernake *Sarum*
BAGSHOT (St Anne) *Guildf 6*   **P** *Ld Chan*   **V** S F BRIAN
BAGULEY (St John the Divine) Brooklands *Man 8*   **P** *Bp and
A W Hargreaves Esq (jt)*   **V** I MCVEETY,   **NSM** E SHORT
BAGWORTH (The Holy Rood)   *see* Markfield, Thornton,
Bagworth and Stanton etc *Leic*

BAILDON (St John the Evangelist) (St Hugh Mission Church) (St James) *Bradf 1* **P** S H K Butcher Esq **V** J D NOWELL, C J M WATERMAN, **NSM** K N MEDHURST

BAINTON (St Andrew) *see* Woldsburn *York*

BAINTON (St Mary) *see* Barnack w Ufford and Bainton *Pet*

BAKEWELL (All Saints) *Derby 2* **P** *D&C Lich* **V** E R URQUHART, **NSM** L E ELLSWORTH, A H COX

BALBY (St John the Evangelist) *Sheff 9* **P** *Bp* **V** B J INSTON

BALCOMBE (St Mary) *Chich 6* **P** *P A D Secretan Esq* **R** M S MALKINSON

BALDERSBY (St James) *see* Topcliffe, Baldersby w Dishforth, Dalton etc *York*

BALDERSTONE (St Leonard) *Blackb 7* **P** *V Blackb* **P-in-c** J R GARRARD

BALDERSTONE (St Mary) *see* S Rochdale *Man*

BALDERTON (St Giles) and Barnby-in-the-Willows *S'well 3* **P** *Bp and Ld Chan (alt)* **P-in-c** W H THACKRAY

BALDHU (St Michael) *see* Highertown and Baldhu *Truro*

BALDOCK (St Mary the Virgin) w Bygrave *St Alb 23* **P** *Marquess of Salisbury and Bp (alt)* **C** L KLIMAS

BALDWIN (St Luke) *see* Marown *S & M*

BALE (All Saints) *see* Gunthorpe w Bale w Field Dalling, Saxlingham etc *Nor*

BALHAM (St Mary and St John the Divine) *S'wark 19* **P** *Bp and Keble Coll Ox (jt)* **V** D A NICHOLSON, **NSM** J B SMITH, **OLM** R E SERBUTT

BALHAM HILL (Ascension) *S'wark 19* **P** *Bp* **V** S J HANCE, C N J GROARKE, **NSM** D V PENNIECOOKE

BALKWELL (St Peter) *Newc 8* **P** *Bp* **V** P S MCCONNELL

BALLAM (St Matthew) *see* Ribby w Wrea *Blackb*

BALLAUGH (St Mary) (St Mary Old Church) *S & M 3* **P** *The Crown* **R** C D ROGERS

BALLIDON (All Saints) *see* Wirksworth *Derby*

BALLINGER (St Mary Mission Hall) *see* Gt Missenden w Ballinger and Lt Hampden *Ox*

BALLINGHAM (St Dubricius) *see* Heref S Wye *Heref*

BALSALL COMMON (St Peter) *Birm 11* **P** *Bp* **V** A S MONTGOMERIE

BALSALL HEATH (St Barnabas) *see* Sparkbrook St Agatha w Balsall Heath St Barn *Birm*

BALSALL HEATH (St Paul) *Birm 5* **P** *Bp* **V** *vacant* 0121-440 2219

BALSCOTE (St Mary Magdalene) *see* Ironstone *Ox*

BALSHAM (Holy Trinity), Weston Colville, W Wickham and W Wratting *Ely 4* **P** *Bp, D&C, and Charterhouse (jt)* **R** F B H WOOLLEY, **NSM** M C BANNER

BALTERLEY (All Saints' Memorial Church) *see* Barthomley *Ches*

BALTONSBOROUGH (St Dunstan) w Butleigh, West Bradley and West Pennard *B & W 5* **P** *Bp* **V** B A M GILLETT, **NSM** C M DONKERSLEY

BAMBER BRIDGE (St Aidan) *Blackb 5* **P** *Bp* **V** G PIPER, C M WOODS

BAMBER BRIDGE (St Saviour) *Blackb 5* **P** *V Blackb* **V** W T BARNES

BAMBURGH (St Aidan) *Newc 10* **P** *Exors Lady Armstrong* **V** E M MCLEAN

BAMFORD (St John the Baptist) *see* Hathersage w Bamford and Derwent *Derby*

BAMFORD (St Michael) *Man 20* **P** *Bp* **V** S B GREY, **NSM** P R ZUCCA, L O RUDEN

BAMFURLONG (Good Shepherd) *see* Abram *Liv*

BAMPTON (Holy Trinity) (St James) (St Mary) w Clanfield *Ox 8* **P** *Bp, DBP, St Jo Coll Ox, D&C Ex, and B Babington-Smith Esq (jt)* **V** D J LLOYD

BAMPTON (St Michael and All Angels), Morebath, Clayhanger and Petton *Ex 8* **P** *DBP and D&C (jt)* **P-in-c** A J STONE

BAMPTON (St Patrick) *see* Shap w Swindale and Bampton w Mardale *Carl*

BAMPTON ASTON (St James) *see* Bampton w Clanfield *Ox*

BAMPTON LEW (Holy Trinity) *as above Ox*

BAMPTON PROPER (St Mary) *as above Ox*

BANBURY (St Francis) *Ox 5* **P** *Bp* **V** *vacant* (01295) 275449

BANBURY (St Hugh) *Ox 5* **P** *Bp* **V** D JACKSON

BANBURY (St Leonard) *Ox 5* **P** *Bp* **V** B A WALLES

BANBURY (St Mary) *Ox 5* **P** *Bp* **P-in-c** J E CHAPMAN

BANBURY (St Paul) *Ox 5* **P** *Bp* **P-in-c** E N COOMBS

BANHAM (St Mary) *see* Quidenham Gp *Nor*

BANKFOOT (St Matthew) *Bradf 2* **P** *Bp* **V** A I G SNOWDEN

BANKS (St Stephen in the Banks) *Liv 9* **P** *R N Meols* **P-in-c** E P TODD

BANNINGHAM (St Botolph) *see* King's Beck *Nor*

BANSFIELD *St E 8* **P** *DBP, Mrs G S M Slater, and Ld Chan (by turn)* **R** I M FINN

BANSTEAD (All Saints) *Guildf 9* **P** *Bp* **V** D N CHANCE, **Hon C** J P JENNINGS

BANWELL (St Andrew) *B & W 11* **P** *D&C Bris* **V** D R G LOCKYER

BAPCHILD (St Lawrence) *see* Murston w Bapchild and Tonge *Cant*

BAR HILL (not known) *Ely 5* **P** *Bp* **P-in-c** G J RENISON, C P A RUSH

BARBON (St Bartholomew) *see* Kirkby Lonsdale *Carl*

BARBOURNE (St Stephen) *Worc 6* **P** *Bp* **V** S W CURRIE, C T A DAVIES

BARBROOK (St Bartholomew) *see* Combe Martin, Berrynarbor, Lynton, Brendon etc *Ex*

BARBY (St Mary) w Kilsby *Pet 3* **P** *Bp* **R** P M DE LA P BERESFORD

BARCHESTON (St Martin) *Cov 9* **P** *Bp* **P-in-c** R K SMITH, C H C W PARBURY

BARCOMBE (St Francis) (St Mary the Virgin) *Chich 18* **P** *Ld Chan* **R** J W HOLLINGSWORTH, **NSM** A MOORE

BARDFIELD (St Peter and St Paul) *see* Gt and Lt Bardfield w Gt and Lt Saling *Chelmsf*

BARDFIELD, GREAT (St Mary the Virgin) and LITTLE (St Katherine) w Great and Little (Bardfield) Saling *Chelmsf 18* **P** *Soc of the Faith and Bp (jt)* **P-in-c** R W F BEAKEN

BARDNEY (St Laurence) *Linc 11* **P** *DBP (1 turn), Bp (2 turns), and St Jo Coll Cam (1 turn)* **R** J M PRATT

BARDON HILL (St Peter) *see* Coalville and Bardon Hill *Leic*

BARDSEA (Holy Trinity) *see* Pennington and Lindal w Marton and Bardsea *Carl*

BARDSEY (All Hallows) *Ripon 1* **P** *G L Fox Esq* **V** R J PEARSON

BARDSLEY (Holy Trinity) *Man 17* **P** *Wm Hulme Trustees* **P-in-c** G D GARRETT, **C** E M POPE, **OLM** E M LOWE

BARDWELL (St Peter and St Paul) *see* Blackbourne *St E*

BARE (St Christopher) *Blackb 11* **P** *Bp* **V** D L HEAP

BARFORD (St Botolph) *see* Barnham Broom and Upper Yare *Nor*

BARFORD (St John) *see* Deddington w Barford, Clifton and Hempton *Ox*

BARFORD (St Martin) *see* Nadder Valley *Sarum*

BARFORD (St Michael) *see* Deddington w Barford, Clifton and Hempton *Ox*

BARFORD (St Peter) w Wasperton and Sherbourne *Cov 8* **P** *Major J M Mills, R Hampton Lucy, and Lady Jeryl Smith-Ryland (jt)* **P-in-c** D C JESSETT

BARFORD, GREAT (All Saints) *see* Blunham, Gt Barford, Roxton and Tempsford etc *St Alb*

BARFREYSTONE (St Nicholas) *see* Eythorne and Elvington w Waldershare etc *Cant*

BARHAM (St Giles) *see* E Leightonstone *Ely*

BARHAM (St John the Baptist) w Bishopsbourne and Kingston *Cant 1* **P** *Abp* **R** D J ROPER, **C** L LLEWELLYN-MACDUFF

BARHAM (St Mary) *see* Claydon and Barham *St E*

BARHOLME (St Martin) *see* Uffington Gp *Linc*

BARKBY (St Mary) *see* Syston *Leic*

BARKESTONE (St Peter and St Paul) *see* Vale of Belvoir Par *Leic*

BARKHAM (St James) *see* Arborfield w Barkham *Ox*

BARKING (St Erkenwald) *Chelmsf 1* **P** *Bp* **V** C N POOLEY

BARKING (St Margaret) (St Patrick) *Chelmsf 1* **P** *Patr Bd* **TR** J B PARSONS, **TV** F M HINTON, G M BARLEY, C J A H EVENS

BARKING (St Mary) *see* Ringshall w Battisford, Barking w Darmsden etc *St E*

BARKINGSIDE (Holy Trinity) *Chelmsf 4* **P** *V Gt Ilford* **V** E A J CARGILL THOMPSON

BARKINGSIDE (St Cedd) *Chelmsf 4* **P** *Bp* **V** S G O O OLUKANMI

BARKINGSIDE (St Francis of Assisi) *Chelmsf 4* **P** *Bp* **V** M JENNINGS

BARKINGSIDE (St George) *Chelmsf 4* **P** *Bp* **V** B J WALLIS

BARKINGSIDE (St Laurence) *Chelmsf 4* **P** *Bp* **V** G R LOCK

BARKISLAND (Christ Church) w West Scammonden *Wakef 4* **P** *V Halifax* **V** D F HANDLEY

BARKSTON (St Nicholas) and Hough Group, The *Linc 23* **P** *Sir Oliver Thorold Bt; the Revd J R H Thorold and J R Thorold Esq; Lord Brownlow; and Sir Lyonel Tollemache Bt (by turn)* **R** A J FIDDYMENT, **NSM** S J HADLEY

BARKSTON ASH (Holy Trinity) *see* Sherburn in Elmet w Saxton *York*

BARKWAY (St Mary Magdalene), Reed and Buckland w Barley *St Alb 19* **P** *The Crown and DBP (alt)* **R** B KNIGHT

BARKWITH Group, The *Linc 5* **P** *D&C, J N Heneage Esq, K Coll Lon, and DBP (by turn)* **R** *vacant* (01673) 858291

BARKWITH, EAST (St Mary) *see* Barkwith Gp *Linc*

BARLASTON (St John the Baptist) *Lich 13* **P** *Countess of Sutherland* **P-in-c** W H SMITH

BARLAVINGTON (St Mary), Burton w Coates and Sutton w Bignor *Chich 11* **P** *Lord Egremont and Miss J B Courtauld (jt)* **P-in-c** W ELLIOT

BARLBOROUGH (St James) and Renishaw *Derby 3* **P** *Prime Min and Sir Reresby Sitwell Bt (alt)* **R** A J DAVIES

BARLBY (All Saints) w Riccall *York 2* **P** *Abp and V Hemingbrough (jt)* **V** I J FOX, **NSM** F LOFTUS, R N WAINWRIGHT

BARLESTONE (St Giles) *Leic 13* **P** *Bp* **P-in-c** G M DALLOW

BARLEY (St Margaret of Antioch) *see* Barkway, Reed and Buckland w Barley *St Alb*

BARLING (All Saints) w Little Wakering *Chelmsf 12* **P** *D&C St Paul's and Bp (alt)* **V** R WOOLVEN

BARLING MAGNA (All Saints) *see* Barling w Lt Wakering *Chelmsf*

BARLINGS (St Edward) *Linc 3* **P** *DBP (2 turns), Earl of Scarborough (1 turn)* **V** R G SPAIGHT

BARLOW (not known) *see* Brayton *York*

BARLOW, GREAT (St Lawrence) *Derby 5* **P** *TR Staveley and Barrow Hill* **V** *vacant*

BARLOW MOOR (Emmanuel) *see* Didsbury St Jas and Em *Man*

BARMBY MARSH (St Helen) *see* Howden *York*

BARMBY MOOR Group, The (St Catherine) *York 5* **P** *Abp (1 turn), Abp and Trustees Duke of Norfolk's Settlement Everingham Fund (2 turns)* **V** V P HEWETSON, **NSM** J H DAWKINS

BARMING (St Margaret of Antioch) w West Barming *Roch 7* **P** *Ld Chan* **R** *vacant (01622) 726263*

BARMING HEATH (St Andrew) *Cant 14* **P** *Abp* **V** B REED

BARMSTON (All Saints) *see* Skipsea w Ulrome and Barmston w Fraisthorpe *York*

BARNACK (St John the Baptist) w Ufford and Bainton *Pet 8* **P** *Bp and St Jo Coll Cam (alt)* **R** *vacant (01780) 740234*

BARNACRE (All Saints) *see* Scorton and Barnacre and Calder Vale *Blackb*

BARNARD CASTLE (St Mary) w Whorlton *Dur 7* **P** *Trin Coll Cam* **V** A J HARDING, **C** F J GRIEVE

BARNARDISTON (All Saints) *see* Stourhead *St E*

BARNBURGH (St Peter) w Melton on the Hill and Aldwick-upon-Dearne *Sheff 12* **P** *Ld Chan (2 turns), Bp (1 turn)* **R** *vacant (01709) 892598*

BARNBY (St John the Baptist) *see* Worlingham w Barnby and N Cove *St E*

BARNBY, EAST (Mission Chapel) *see* Lythe w Ugthorpe *York*

BARNBY DUN (St Peter and St Paul) *Sheff 8* **P** *Bp* **V** N K YOUNG

BARNBY IN THE WILLOWS (All Saints) *see* Balderton and Barnby-in-the-Willows *S'well*

BARNEHURST (St Martin) *Roch 15* **P** *Bp* **V** D F SPRINGTHORPE

BARNES Team Ministry, The (St Mary) (Holy Trinity) (St Michael and All Angels) *S'wark 18* **P** *Patr Bd* **TR** R N F COLLINS, **Hon C** G W HOLMES, **NSM** A J ROBERTS, G HOLDSTOCK

BARNET (Christ Church) *see* S Mimms Ch Ch *Lon*

BARNET (St Stephen) *see* Chipping Barnet w Arkley *St Alb*

BARNET, EAST (St Mary the Virgin) *St Alb 17* **P** *The Crown* **R** R F WATSON

BARNET, NEW (St James) *St Alb 17* **P** *Ch Patr Trust* **V** B R PENFOLD, **C** M D CRAWFORD

BARNET VALE (St Mark) *St Alb 17* **P** *Bp* **V** *vacant (020) 8449 4265*

BARNETBY LE WOLD (St Barnabas) *see* N Wolds Gp *Linc*

BARNEY (St Mary), Fulmodeston w Croxton, Hindringham, Thursford, Great and Little Snoring w Kettlestone and Pensthorpe *Nor 15* **P** *Lord Hastings, St Jo Coll Cam, D&C, DBP, and CCC Cam (by turn)* **R** C A MITCHELL

BARNHAM (St Gregory) *see* Blackbourne *St E*

BARNHAM (St Mary) *see* Aldingbourne, Barnham and Eastergate *Chich*

BARNHAM BROOM (St Peter and St Paul) and Upper Yare *Nor 17* **P** *Patr Bd* **TR** C H MILFORD, **TV** D K ALEXANDER

BARNINGHAM (St Andrew) *see* Hopton, Market Weston, Barningham etc *St E*

BARNINGHAM (St Mary the Virgin) w Matlaske w Baconsthorpe w Plumstead w Hempstead *Nor 18* **P** *Duchy of Lanc (1 turn), Lady Mott-Radclyffe, CPAS, and D&C (jt) (1 turn)* **P-in-c** J M L BANKS

BARNINGHAM (St Michael and All Angels) w Hutton Magna and Wycliffe *Ripon 2* **P** *Bp and V Gilling and Kirkby Ravensworth (jt)* **R** C H COWPER

BARNINGHAM, LITTLE (St Andrew), Blickling, Edgefield, Itteringham w Mannington, Oulton w Irmingland, Saxthorpe w Corpusty and Wickmere w Wolterton *Nor 19* **P** *Bp, Lord Walpole, SMF, MMCET (2 turns), and Pemb Coll Cam (1 turn)* **R** D R W HARES

BARNINGHAM WINTER (St Mary the Virgin) *see* Barningham w Matlaske w Baconsthorpe etc *Nor*

BARNOLDBY LE BECK (St Helen) *Linc 10* **P** *Ld Chan* **R** I R SHELTON, **NSM** A HUNDLEBY

BARNOLDSWICK (Holy Trinity) (St Mary le Gill) w Bracewell *Bradf 7* **P** *Bp* **V** J R LANCASTER

BARNSBURY (St Andrew) *Lon 6* **P** *Patr Bd* **TR** M W LEARMOUTH, **TV** M L J SAUNDERS

BARNSLEY Old Town (St Paul) *see* Barnsley St Mary *Wakef*

BARNSLEY (St Edward the Confessor) *Wakef 7* **P** *Bp* **V** H HALL

BARNSLEY (St George's Parish Church Centre) *Wakef 7* **P** *Bp* **V** D P J MUNBY

BARNSLEY (St Mary) *see* Bibury w Winson and Barnsley *Glouc*

BARNSLEY (St Mary) *Wakef 7* **P** *Bp* **R** I E WILDEY

BARNSLEY (St Peter and St John the Baptist) *Wakef 7* **P** *Bp* **V** A BRISCOE, **NSM** S C TRAVES

BARNSTAPLE (St Peter and St Mary Magdalene) (Holy Trinity) *Ex 15* **P** *Patr Bd (4 turns), Ld Chan (1 turn)* **TR** V ROSS, **TV** J P BENSON, G CHAVE-COX, M J PEARSON, M D D JONES, K A ELLIOTT, **C** J H CRUTCHLEY, **NSM** P D PILDITCH

BARNSTON (Christ Church) *Ches 8* **P** *Bp* **V** G P BENSON, **C** P D BASKERVILLE, **NSM** I G URQUHART

BARNSTON (not known) *see* Gt Dunmow and Barnston *Chelmsf*

BARNSTONE (St Mary Mission Room) *see* Cropwell Bishop w Colston Bassett, Granby etc *S'well*

BARNT GREEN (St Andrew) *see* Cofton Hackett w Barnt Green *Birm*

BARNTON (Christ Church) *Ches 4* **P** *Bp* **P-in-c** K M FRASER-SMITH

BARNWELL (All Saints) (St Andrew) w Tichmarsh, Thurning and Clapton *Pet 12* **P** *Soc of Merchant Venturers, MMCET, Em Coll Cam, and DBP (by turn)* **R** P C H A TRENCHARD

BARNWOOD (St Lawrence) *Glouc 5* **P** *D&C* **V** R C COATES, **C** S B MORRIS

BARONY OF BURGH, The (St Michael) *Carl 3* **P** *Patr Bd* **R** G M HART, **NSM** E A BLACK

BARR, GREAT (St Margaret) *Lich 25* **P** *M D S Farnham* **V** M C RUTTER, **Hon C** T W WARD

BARRINGTON (All Saints) *see* Orwell Gp *Ely*

BARRINGTON (Blessed Virgin Mary) *see* Ilminster and Distr *B & W*

BARRINGTON, GREAT (St Mary) *see* Sherborne, Windrush, the Barringtons etc *Glouc*

BARRINGTON, LITTLE (St Peter) *as above Glouc*

BARROW (All Saints) w Denham St Mary and Higham Green *St E 13* **P** *Bp, St Jo Coll Cam, and D W Barclay Esq (by turn)* **R** *vacant (01284) 810279*

BARROW and Goxhill *Linc 6* **P** *Ld Chan* **V** J C GIRTCHEN

BARROW (St Bartholomew) *Ches 2* **P** *D Okell Esq* **P-in-c** E J TURNER

BARROW (St Giles) *see* Broseley w Benthall, Jackfield, Linley etc *Heref*

BARROW, NORTH (St Nicholas) *see* Six Pilgrims *B & W*

BARROW, SOUTH (St Peter) *as above B & W*

BARROW GURNEY (Blessed Virgin Mary and St Edward King and Martyr) *B & W 13* **P** *Major M A Gibbs* **P-in-c** A SARGENT, **NSM** V L BARKLEY

BARROW HILL (St Andrew) *see* Staveley and Barrow Hill *Derby*

BARROW-IN-FURNESS (St Aidan) *Carl 8* **P** *Bp* **P-in-c** P E MANN, **C** E J NATTRASS, **NSM** H GRAINGER

BARROW-IN-FURNESS (St George) (St Luke) *Carl 8* **P** *Bp* **TR** P E MANN, **TV** C E FARRER

BARROW-IN-FURNESS (St James the Great) *Carl 8* **P** *DBP* **V** *vacant (01229) 821475*

BARROW-IN-FURNESS (St John the Evangelist) *Carl 8* **P** *DBP* **P-in-c** M D HERVEY

BARROW-IN-FURNESS (St Mark) *Carl 8* **P** *Bp* **V** I K HOOK

BARROW-IN-FURNESS (St Mary the Virgin) *see* Walney Is *Carl*

BARROW-IN-FURNESS (St Matthew) *Carl 8* **P** *Patr Bd* **TR** D G KENNEDY, **TV** M A EDWARDS

BARROW-IN-FURNESS (St Paul) *see* Newbarns w Hawcoat *Carl*

BARROW-ON-HUMBER (Holy Trinity) *see* Barrow and Goxhill *Linc*

BARROW-ON-TRENT (St Wilfrid) *see* Ticknall, Smisby and Stanton by Bridge etc *Derby*

BARROW UPON SOAR (Holy Trinity) w Walton le Wolds *Leic 7* **P** *St Jo Coll Cam and DBP (jt)* **P-in-c** J WHITTAKER

BARROWBY (All Saints) and Gonerby, Great *Linc 19*
P *R Grantham, and Duke of Devonshire (by turn)*
R P HOPKINS

BARROWDEN (St Peter) and Wakerley w South Luffenham and Morcott w Duddington and Tixover *Pet 8* **P** *Burghley Ho Preservation Trust, P W Rowley Esq, and Bp (3 turns), Ball Coll Ox (1 turn)* **R** P J C CLEMENTS

BARROWFORD (St Thomas) and Newchurch-in-Pendle *Blackb 6* **P** *Ld Chan and trustees (alt)* **V** J M HALLOWS

BARSHAM (Holy Trinity) *see Wainford St E*

BARSHAM, EAST (All Saints) *see Walsingham, Houghton and Barsham Nor*

BARSHAM, NORTH (All Saints) *as above Nor*

BARSHAM, WEST (The Assumption of the Blessed Virgin Mary) *as above Nor*

BARSTON (St Swithin) *Birm 11* **P** MMCET
P-in-c E W RUSSELL

BARTHOMLEY (St Bertoline) *Ches 11* **P** *Lord O'Neill*
P-in-c D C SPEEDY

BARTLEY (Mission Church) *see Copythorne Win*

BARTLEY GREEN (St Michael and All Angels) *Birm 2* **P** *Bp*
V C E MANSLEY, **C** S H MARSHALL

BARTLOW (St Mary) *see Linton Ely*

BARTON (St Cuthbert w St Mary) and Manfield and Cleasby w Stapleton *Ripon 2* **P** *Bp, D&C, and V Forcett and Stanwick w Aldbrough (jt)* **V** A L GLASBY

BARTON (St Lawrence) *see Fellside Team Blackb*

BARTON (St Mark's Chapel) w Peel Green (St Michael and All Angels) (St Catherine) *Man 2* **P** *Bp and TR Eccles*
P-in-c B LAMB

BARTON (St Martin) *see Torquay St Martin Barton Ex*

BARTON (St Michael), Pooley Bridge and Martindale *Carl 4* **P** *Bp and Earl of Lonsdale (jt)* **P-in-c** R J GLOVER

BARTON (St Paul) *Portsm 8* **P** *R Whippingham*
V P E PIMENTEL

BARTON (St Peter) *Ely 1* **P** *Ld Chan* **P-in-c** C A COLLINS

BARTON, GREAT (Holy Innocents) *St E 13* **P** *Sir Michael Bunbury Bt* **P-in-c** S J ABBOTT

BARTON BENDISH (St Andrew) w Beachamwell and Shingham *Ely 15* **P** *Bp and DBP (alt)* **P-in-c** D J POMERY,
Hon C A G F VILLER

BARTON HARTSHORN (St James) *see Swan Ox*

BARTON HILL (St Luke w Ch Ch) and Moorfields St Matthew *Bris 3* **P** *Bp, CPAS, and V Bris St Phil and St Jacob w Em (jt)*
P-in-c D HOLMYARD

BARTON IN FABIS (St George) *S'well 9* **P** *Ld Chan*
P-in-c S W OSMAN

BARTON-LE-CLEY (St Nicholas) w Higham Gobion and Hexton *St Alb 9* **P** *The Crown (3 turns), Mrs F A A Cooper (1 turn)* **R** P H WHITTAKER, **NSM** M M PARRETT

BARTON-LE-STREET (St Michael) *see Street York*

BARTON MILLS (St Mary) *see Mildenhall St E*

BARTON-ON-THE-HEATH (St Lawrence) *see Long Compton, Whichford and Barton-on-the-Heath Cov*

BARTON SEAGRAVE (St Botolph) w Warkton *Pet 11*
P *Ch Soc Trust (2 turns), Duke of Buccleuch (1 turn)*
R J M PERRIS, **C** L GATISS

BARTON ST DAVID (St David) *see Wheathill Priory Gp of Par B & W*

BARTON STACEY (All Saints) *see Lower Dever Valley Win*

BARTON TURF (St Michael) *see Ashmanhaugh, Barton Turf etc Nor*

BARTON UNDER NEEDWOOD (St James) w Dunstall *Lich 14* **P** *Bp and Sir Rupert Hardy Bt (jt)* **V** A J WOOD

BARTON UPON HUMBER (St Mary) *Linc 6* **P** *Bp*
V E J P HEPWORTH, **OLM** A W WRIGHT

BARTON UPON IRWELL (St Catherine) *see Barton w Peel Green Man*

BARWELL (St Mary) w Potters Marston and Stapleton *Leic 13*
P *R J W Titley Esq* **R** A C DEEGAN, **NSM** P HEBDEN

BARWICK (St Mary Magdalene) *see Yeovil H Trin w Barwick B & W*

BARWICK IN ELMET (All Saints) *Ripon 8* **P** *Duchy of Lanc*
R B H G JAMES

BASCHURCH (All Saints) and Weston Lullingfield w Hordley *Lich 17* **P** *Ch Patr Trust and Bp (jt)* **R** M P HOBBS

BASCOTE HEATH (Chapel) *see Radford Semele Cov*

BASEGREEN (St Peter) *see Gleadless Sheff*

BASFORD (St Aidan) *S'well 12* **P** *Bp* **P-in-c** P HEMSTOCK

BASFORD (St Leodegarius) *S'well 12* **P** *Bp*
P-in-c M A SKIDMORE, **NSM** R HALLETT

BASFORD (St Mark) *Lich 9* **P** *Bp* **P-in-c** R B READE

BASFORD, NEW (St Augustine) *see Basford St Leodegarius S'well*

BASHLEY (St John) *see Milton Win*

BASILDON (St Andrew) (Holy Cross) *Chelmsf 6* **P** *Bp*
V J R CARR

BASILDON (St Martin of Tours) *Chelmsf 6* **P** *Bp*
R E E MCCAFFERTY, **C** D S GILMORE, **NSM** I J E SWIFT

BASILDON (St Stephen) w Aldworth and Ashampstead *Ox 12*
P *St Jo Coll Cam, Simeon's Trustees, and DBF (by turn)*
Hon C A P FOTHERGILL, **NSM** C F VERE NICOLL,
OLM A KIGGELL

BASING (St Mary) *Win 4* **P** *Magd Coll Ox* **V** A S BISHOP,
NSM K O'LOUGHLIN

BASINGSTOKE (All Saints) (St Michael) *Win 4* **P** *Patr Bd*
TR J M STOKER, **TV** R J SIMMONDS, S P V CADE,
M A PHILLIPS, **C** L R THIRTLE, **NSM** E A GEORGE

BASINGSTOKE Brighton Hill (Christ the King)
see Basingstoke Win

BASINGSTOKE Popley (Bethlehem Chapel) *as above Win*

BASINGSTOKE South Ham (St Peter) *as above Win*

BASLOW (St Anne) w Curbar and Stoney Middleton *Derby 2*
P *Duke of Devonshire and V Hathersage (jt)* **V** G R ORCHARD

BASSENTHWAITE (St Bega) *see Binsey Carl*

BASSENTHWAITE (St John) *as above Carl*

BASSETT (St Michael and All Angels) *see N Stoneham Win*

BASSETT GREEN (St Christopher) *as above Win*

BASSINGBOURN (St Peter and St Paul) *Ely 7*
P *D&C Westmr* **V** J E ARMSTRONG

BASSINGHAM Group, The (St Michael and All Angels) *Linc 18*
P *Lady Jean Nevile, CCC Ox, Lord Middleton, Bp, and W R S Brown Esq (jt)* **P-in-c** J NEWTON

BASSINGTHORPE (St Thomas à Becket) *see Ingoldsby Linc*

BASTON (St John the Baptist) *see Ness Gp Linc*

BASWICH or Berkswich (Holy Trinity) *Lich 10* **P** *Bp*
V P A GRAYSMITH

BATCOMBE (Blessed Virgin Mary) *see Bruton and Distr B & W*

BATCOMBE (St Mary) *see Wriggle Valley Sarum*

BATH Abbey (St Peter and St Paul) w St James *B & W 9*
P *Simeon's Trustees* **R** S J OBERST, **C** D M DEWES,
T C OSMOND

BATH Bathwick (St John the Baptist) (Blessed Virgin Mary)
B & W 9 **P** *Bp* **R** D J PROTHERO, **C** N A BEARDSLEY

BATH (Christ Church) Proprietary Chapel *B & W 11*
P *R Walcot* **Min** A A J CLARIDGE, **NSM** C R BURROWS

BATH (Holy Trinity) *B & W 9* **P** *SMF* **R** G OAKES

BATH Odd Down (St Philip and St James) w Combe Hay
B & W 9 **P** *Simeon's Trustees* **V** A BAIN, **NSM** M JOYCE

BATH (St Barnabas) w Englishcombe *B & W 9* **P** *Bp*
V D J BURLEIGH

BATH (St Bartholomew) *B & W 9* **P** *Simeon's Trustees*
V I R LEWIS

BATH (St Luke) *B & W 9* **P** *Simeon's Trustees*
V D F PERRYMAN

BATH (St Mary Magdalene) Holloway, Extra-parochial Chapelry *B & W 11* **P** *Bath Municipal Charities for Ld Chan*
Min W G BURMAN

BATH (St Michael) w St Paul *B & W 9* **P** *CPAS*
R M C LLOYD WILLIAMS, **NSM** H J LATTY

BATH (St Saviour) w Swainswick and Woolley *B & W 9*
P *Ch Patr Trust and Or Coll Ox (jt)* **R** M J NORMAN,
NSM J R BULLAMORE

BATH (St Stephen) *see Charlcombe w Bath St Steph B & W*

BATH Twerton-on-Avon (Ascension) (St Michael) *B & W 9*
P *Patr Bd* **TR** K L SHILL, **TV** E C BROWN, R J PIMM

BATH Walcot (St Andrew) (St Swithin) *B & W 9* **P** *Simeon's Trustees* **R** H KOPSCH, **C** A C WILSON

BATH Weston (All Saints) w North Stoke and Langridge
B & W 9 **P** *Ld Chan* **R** P J WHITWORTH, **C** M H SALMON,
NSM J N RAWLINSON, P J NORMAN

BATH Weston (St John the Evangelist) (Emmanuel) w Kelston
B & W 9 **P** *Ld Chan* **R** C R GARRETT

BATH Widcombe (St Matthew) (St Thomas à Becket) *B & W 9*
P *Simeon's Trustees* **P-in-c** P J BETTS

BATHAMPTON (St Nicholas) w Claverton *B & W 9*
P *D&C Bris and Personal Reps R L D Skrine Esq (jt)*
R P BURDEN, **C** C D NORTH

BATHEALTON (St Bartholomew) *see Wellington and Distr B & W*

BATHEASTON (St John the Baptist) (St Catherine) *B & W 9*
P *Ch Ch Ox* **V** A J FRY

BATHFORD (St Swithun) *B & W 9* **P** *D&C Bris* **V** T C LING

BATHWICK (Blessed Virgin Mary) *see Bath Bathwick B & W*

BATHWICK (St John the Baptist) *as above B & W*

BATLEY (All Saints) and Purlwell *Wakef 10*
P *E C S J G Brudenell Esq, Trustees D Stubley Esq, and Bp (jt)*
V A P JOHNSON

BATLEY (St Thomas) *Wakef 10* **P** *V Batley* **V** P L BENSON

BATLEY CARR (Holy Trinity) *see Dewsbury Wakef*

BATSFORD (St Mary) *see Moreton-in-Marsh w Batsford, Todenham etc Glouc*

BATTERSEA (Christ Church and St Stephen) *S'wark 16*   **P** *Bp and V Battersea St Mary (alt)*   **V** P CLARK
BATTERSEA (St George)   *see* Battersea Fields *S'wark*
BATTERSEA (St Luke) *S'wark 16*   **P** *Bp*   **V** J M SHEPHERD, C S LEADER,   **Hon C** J A BAKER,   **OLM** J DEVERILL
BATTERSEA (St Mary) *S'wark 16*   **P** *Earl Spencer*   **V** J P KENNINGTON
BATTERSEA (St Michael) Wandsworth Common *S'wark 16*   **P** *V Battersea St Mary*   **P-in-c** A H STEVENS
BATTERSEA (St Peter) (St Paul) *S'wark 16*   **P** *V Battersea St Mary*   **P-in-c** P J S PERKIN
BATTERSEA (St Philip w St Bartholomew)   *see* Lavender Hill Ascension etc *S'wark*
BATTERSEA FIELDS (St Saviour) (All Saints) (St George) *S'wark 16*   **P** *Bp, CPAS, and Ch Patr Trust (jt)*   **V** G M VEVERS,   **C** A J GADD,   **Hon C** I G SMITH-CAMERON, **NSM** S E MULLALLY
BATTERSEA PARK (All Saints)   *see* Battersea Fields *S'wark*
BATTERSEA PARK (St Saviour)   *as above S'wark*
BATTERSEA RISE (St Mark) *S'wark 16*   **P** *V Battersea St Mary*   **V** P J S PERKIN,   **C** T J J MAYFIELD, **NSM** I G C DURIE
BATTISFORD (St Mary)   *see* Ringshall w Battisford, Barking w Darmsden etc *St E*
BATTLE (Church of the Ascension) (St Mary the Virgin) *Chich 14*   **P** *The Crown*   **V** A V CUMMINGS
BATTLE HILL (Good Shepherd)   *see* Willington Team *Newc*
BATTLESDEN (St Peter and All Saints)   *see* Woburn w Eversholt, Milton Bryan, Battlesden etc *St Alb*
BATTYEFORD (Christ the King) *Wakef 10*   **P** *V Mirfield*   **V** R A CLEMENTS,   **Hon C** R E WHITNALL,   **NSM** M E WOOD
BAUGHURST (St Stephen) and Ramsdell and Wolverton w Ewhurst and Hannington *Win 4*   **P** *Ld Chan, Duke of Wellington, and Bp (by turn)*   **R** A E BARTON
BAULKING (St Nicholas)   *see* Uffington, Shellingford, Woolstone and Baulking *Ox*
BAUMBER (St Swithin)   *see* Hemingby *Linc*
BAUNTON (St Mary Magdalene)   *see* Stratton, N Cerney, Baunton and Bagendon *Glouc*
BAVERSTOCK (St Editha)   *see* Nadder Valley *Sarum*
BAWBURGH (St Mary and St Walstan)   *see* Easton, Colton, Marlingford and Bawburgh *Nor*
BAWDESWELL (All Saints)   *see* Lyng, Sparham, Elsing, Bylaugh, Bawdeswell etc *Nor*
BAWDRIP (St Michael and All Angels)   *see* Woolavington w Cossington and Bawdrip *B & W*
BAWDSEY (St Mary)   *see* Wilford Peninsula *St E*
BAWTRY (St Nicholas) w Austerfield and Misson *S'well 1*   **P** *Bp*   **V** J N GREEN
BAXENDEN (St John) *Blackb 1*   **P** *Bp*   **V** S LEES
BAXTERGATE (St Ninian)   *see* Whitby w Aislaby and Ruswarp *York*
BAXTERLEY (not known) w Hurley and Wood End and Merevale w Bentley *Birm 10*   **P** *Ld Chan (1 turn), Bp and Sir William Dugdale Bt (1 turn)*   **R** J E GASPER
BAYDON (St Nicholas)   *see* Whitton *Sarum*
BAYFORD (Mission Room)   *see* Charlton Musgrove, Cucklington and Stoke Trister *B & W*
BAYFORD (St Mary)   *see* Lt Berkhamsted and Bayford, Essendon etc *St Alb*
BAYLHAM (St Peter)   *see* Gt and Lt Blakenham w Baylham and Nettlestead *St E*
BAYSTON HILL (Christ Church) *Lich 20*   **P** *V Shrewsbury H Trin w St Julian*   **V** R M GOLDENBERG,   **C** A G STONE
BAYSWATER (St Matthew) *Lon 2*   **P** *Exors Dame Jewell Magnus-Allcroft*   **V** G M EVANS
BAYTON (St Bartholomew)   *see* Mamble w Bayton, Rock w Heightington etc *Worc*
BEACHAMPTON (Assumption of the Blessed Virgin Mary) *see* Buckingham *Ox*
BEACHAMWELL (St Mary)   *see* Barton Bendish w Beachamwell and Shingham *Ely*
BEACON Parishes   *see* Painswick, Sheepscombe, Cranham, The Edge etc *Glouc*
BEACONSFIELD (St Mary and All Saints) (St Michael and All Angels) *Ox 20*   **P** *Patr Bd*   **TR** J P B WYNBURNE, **TV** R A CADDELL,   **C** R J GRAYSON,   **NSM** W T EVANS, A M CAW, R P SPICER
BEADLAM (St Hilda)   *see* Kirkdale w Harome, Nunnington and Pockley *York*
BEADNELL (St Ebba) *Newc 10*   **P** *Newc Dioc Soc*   **V** vacant
BEAFORD (All Saints)   *see* Newton Tracey, Horwood, Alverdiscott etc *Ex*
BEALINGS, GREAT (St Mary) and LITTLE (All Saints) w Playford and Culpho *St E 7*   **P** *Lord Cranworth (1 turn), Bp (3 turns)*   **P-in-c** P C E STENTIFORD

BEAMINSTER AREA (St Mary of the Annunciation) *Sarum 2*   **P** *Patr Bd*   **TR** K L MASTERS,   **TV** S A SMITH
BEAMISH (St Andrew)   *see* Ch the K *Dur*
BEARD (St James the Less)   *see* New Mills *Derby*
BEARLEY (St Mary the Virgin)   *see* Snitterfield w Bearley *Cov*
BEARPARK (St Edmund) and Ushaw Moor *Dur 1*   **P** *D&C and Bp (alt)*   **V** L G BARRON
BEARSTED (Holy Cross) w Thurnham *Cant 15*   **P** *Abp*   **V** J CORBYN,   **C** C J RYALLS
BEARWOOD (St Catherine) *Ox 16*   **P** *Bp*   **R** H D ETCHES
BEARWOOD (St Mary the Virgin) *Birm 7*   **P** *V Smethwick*   **V** A H PERRY,   **NSM** L GRANNER
BEAUCHAMP RODING (St Botolph)   *see* Leaden Roding and Abbess Roding etc *Chelmsf*
BEAUDESERT (St Nicholas) and Henley-in-Arden w Ullenhall *Cov 7*   **P** *MMCET, Bp, and High Bailiff of Henley-in-Arden (jt)*   **R** J F GANJAVI
BEAULIEU (Blessed Virgin and Holy Child) and Exbury and East Boldre *Win 11*   **P** *Bp and Lord Montagu of Beaulieu (jt)*   **V** D T P ABERNETHY
BEAUMONT CUM MOZE (St Leonard and St Mary) *see* Tendring and Lt Bentley w Beaumont cum Moze *Chelmsf*
BEAUMONT LEYS (Christ the King) *Leic 2*   **P** *Bp*   **V** C R OXLEY,   **C** P J OXLEY
BEAUWORTH (St James)   *see* Upper Itchen *Win*
BEAUXFIELD (St Peter)   *see* Whitfield w Guston *Cant*
BEAWORTHY (St Alban)   *see* Ashwater, Halwill, Beaworthy, Clawton etc *Ex*
BEBINGTON (St Andrew) *Ches 8*   **P** *M C Saunders-Griffiths Esq*   **R** S L JAMES, **C** S J BURMESTER, D M HALL
BEBINGTON, HIGHER (Christ Church) *Ches 8*   **P** *C J C Saunders-Griffiths Esq*   **V** A E SAMUELS
BECCLES (St Michael the Archangel) (St Luke's Church Centre) *St E 14*   **P** *Patr Bd*   **TR** A H R THOMAS, **TV** J N BEAUCHAMP,   **C** B E DAVIS
BECK ROW (St John)   *see* Mildenhall *St E*
BECKBURY (St Milburga), Badger, Kemberton, Ryton, Stockton and Sutton Maddock *Lich 16*   **P** *Lord Hamilton of Dalzell, Or Coll Ox, and MMCET (2 turns), Ld Chan (1 turn)*   **R** D F CHANTREY
BECKENHAM (Christ Church) *Roch 13*   **P** *Ch Trust Fund Trust*   **V** N W WYNNE-JONES,   **C** A M BOUSFIELD, **Hon C** J T ANSCOMBE
BECKENHAM (Holy Trinity)   *see* Penge Lane H Trin *Roch*
BECKENHAM (St Barnabas) *Roch 13*   **P** *Keble Coll Ox*   **V** P MARR
BECKENHAM (St George) *Roch 13*   **P** *Bp*   **R** M J HANCOCK
BECKENHAM (St James) Elmers End *Roch 13*   **P** *Bp*   **V** L C CARBERRY
BECKENHAM (St John the Baptist) Eden Park *Roch 13*   **P** *Ch Trust Fund Trust, Bp and Adn Bromley (jt)*   **V** N LANG, **NSM** N G READ
BECKENHAM (St Michael and All Angels) w St Augustine *Roch 13*   **P** *SMF and Bp (jt)*   **V** C M SMITH
BECKENHAM, NEW (St Paul) *Roch 13*   **P** *Bp*   **V** B W ROWLAND,   **Hon C** N E BAINES
BECKERMET (St Bridget) (St Bridget Old Church) (St John) w Ponsonby *Carl 5*   **P** *Bp, Adn W Cumberland, P Stanley Esq, and PCCs of Beckermet St Jo and St Bridget (jt)*   **P-in-c** W D MAHONEY
BECKFORD (St John the Baptist)   *see* Overbury w Teddington, Alstone etc *Worc*
BECKHAM, WEST (St Helen and All Saints)   *see* Weybourne Gp *Nor*
BECKINGHAM (All Saints)   *see* Brant Broughton and Beckingham *Linc*
BECKINGHAM (All Saints) w Walkeringham and Gringley-on-the-Hill *S'well 1*   **P** *Bp and Ld Chan (alt)*   **V** D HOLLIS
BECKINGTON (St George) w Standerwick, Berkley, Rodden, Lullington and Orchardleigh *B & W 4*   **P** *Bp (3 turns), Ch Soc Trust (1 turn), and Exors A Duckworth Esq*   **R** A F HOGARTH
BECKLEY (All Saints) and Peasmarsh *Chich 20*   **P** *Univ Coll Ox and SS Coll Cam (alt)*   **R** C F HOPKINS
BECKLEY (Assumption of the Blessed Virgin Mary) *see* Wheatley *Ox*
BECKTON (St Mark) *Chelmsf 3*   **P** *Bp*   **V** vacant (020) 7476 0618
BECKWITHSHAW (St Michael and All Angels)   *see* Pannal w Beckwithshaw *Ripon*
BECONTREE (St Elisabeth) *Chelmsf 1*   **P** *Bp*   **P-in-c** N JOHN
BECONTREE (St George) *Chelmsf 1*   **P** *Bp*   **V** S L SMALLWOOD
BECONTREE (St Mary) *Chelmsf 1*   **P** *CPAS*   **V** R HERBERT, **C** P D MACKAY

BECONTREE SOUTH (St Alban) (St John the Divine) (St Martin) *Chelmsf 1* **P** *Patr Bd* **TR** G A CLARKE, **TV** J SAXTON, **NSM** V D DRURY, B M HULL

BECONTREE WEST (St Cedd) (St Thomas) *Chelmsf 1* **P** *DBP* **TR** S A LAW, **TV** T D HULL, P J WOOD

BEDALE (St Gregory) and Leeming *Ripon 4* **P** *Sir Henry Beresford-Peirse Bt and R Kirklington w Burnestonetc (jt)* **R** D G PATON-WILLIAMS, **C** J BALL, **NSM** A L WOODHOUSE

BEDDINGHAM (St Andrew) *see Glynde, W Firle and Beddingham Chich*

BEDDINGTON (St Francis' Church Hall) *see S Beddington St Mich S'wark*

BEDDINGTON (St Mary) *S'wark 25* **P** *Lady Nairne* **R** L S TILLETT

BEDDINGTON, SOUTH (St Michael and All Angels) *S'wark 25* **P** *Bp* **V** P I D GRANT, **Hon C** D WALFORD

BEDFIELD (St Nicholas) *see Worlingworth, Southolt, Tannington, Bedfield etc St E*

BEDFONT, EAST (St Mary the Virgin) *Lon 11* **P** *Ld Chan* **V** P G HUTTON

BEDFORD (All Saints) *St Alb 10* **P** *Bp* **P-in-c** J M MACLEOD

BEDFORD (Christ Church) *St Alb 10* **P** *Bp* **V** R C HIBBERT, **C** T S ROBB

BEDFORD (St Andrew) *St Alb 10* **P** *Ld Chan* **V** C M DENT, **C** P E F CUDBY, **NSM** M D ROBINSON

BEDFORD (St John the Baptist) (St Leonard) *St Alb 10* **P** *MMCET* **R** N COOPER, **C** J M HANCOCK

BEDFORD (St Mark) *St Alb 10* **P** *Bp* **V** C ROYDEN, **C** J W CROSSLEY, **NSM** G R CAPPLEMAN, P J LITTLEFORD

BEDFORD (St Martin) *St Alb 10* **P** *Bp* **P-in-c** R S STOKES

BEDFORD (St Michael and All Angels) *St Alb 10* **P** *Bp* **V** vacant (01234) 266920

BEDFORD (St Paul) *St Alb 10* **P** *Bp* **V** J G PEDLAR

BEDFORD (St Peter de Merton) w St Cuthbert *St Alb 10* **P** *Ld Chan* **R** G E W BUCKLER, **Hon C** A S BURROW

BEDFORD LEIGH (St Thomas) (All Saints' Mission) *Man 13* **P** *V Leigh St Mary* **V** vacant (01942) 673519

BEDFORD PARK (St Michael and All Angels) *Lon 11* **P** *Bp* **V** K J MORRIS, **NSM** N V STANLEY, G MORGAN

BEDGROVE (Holy Spirit) *Ox 21* **P** *DBP* **V** vacant (01296) 22214

BEDHAMPTON (St Nicholas's Mission Church) (St Thomas) *Portsm 5* **P** *Bp* **R** J A RISDON, **C** C W MACLAY, **NSM** L J VALIANT

BEDINGFIELD (St Mary) *see Eye St E*

BEDINGHAM (St Andrew) *see Hempnall Nor*

BEDLINGTON (St Cuthbert) *Newc 1* **P** *D&C Dur* **V** M D J SAVAGE, **OLM** D J WOOD

BEDMINSTER (St Aldhelm) (St Paul) *Bris 1* **P** *Bp* **TR** R V HEADING, **TV** M F JEFFERY, C J PEARCE

BEDMINSTER (St Michael and All Angels) *Bris 1* **P** *Bp* **V** D S MOSS

BEDMINSTER DOWN (St Oswald) *see Bishopsworth and Bedminster Down Bris*

BEDMONT (Ascension) *see Abbots Langley St Alb*

BEDNALL (All Saints) *see Penkridge Team Lich*

BEDSTONE (St Mary) *see Clungunford w Clunbury and Clunton, Bedstone etc Heref*

BEDWORTH (All Saints) *Cov 5* **P** *Patr Bd* **TR** N P DENHAM, **TV** T E BENNETT, **Dss** P M HAMILTON

BEDWYN, GREAT (St Mary) *see Savernake Sarum*

BEDWYN, LITTLE (St Michael) *as above Sarum*

BEECH (St Peter) *see Alton St Lawr Win*

BEECH, HIGH (Holy Innocents) *see Waltham H Cross Chelmsf*

BEECH HILL (St Mary the Virgin), Grazeley and Spencers Wood *Ox 15* **P** *Bp* **P-in-c** J R HICKS, **NSM** M M DEVINE

BEECHDALE ESTATE (St Chad) *see Blakenall Heath Lich*

BEECHINGSTOKE (St Stephen) *see Pewsey and Swanborough Sarum*

BEEDING (St Peter) and Bramber w Botolphs *Chich 12* **P** *Bp* **R** T J N L'ESTRANGE

BEEDING, LOWER (Holy Trinity) (St John the Evangelist) *Chich 8* **P** *Bp* **P-in-c** S GALLAGHER

BEEDON (St Nicholas) and Peasemore w West Ilsley and Farnborough *Ox 14* **P** *Bp* **R** A L CRETNEY, **NSM** T R ASTIN, D F BROWN

BEEFORD (St Leonard) w Frodingham and Foston *York 11* **P** *Abp and Ch Soc Trust (jt)* **R** R P YATES

BEELEY (St Anne) and Edensor *Derby 2* **P** *Duke of Devonshire* **P-in-c** J D SLYFIELD

BEELSBY (St Andrew) *see Laceby and Ravendale Gp Linc*

BEENHAM VALENCE (St Mary) *see Woolhampton w Midgham and Beenham Valance Ox*

BEER (St Michael) *see Seaton and Beer Ex*

BEER HACKETT (St Michael) *see Bradford Abbas and Thornford w Beer Hackett Sarum*

BEERCROCOMBE (St James) *see Beercrocombe w Curry Mallet, Hatch Beauchamp etc B & W*

BEERCROCOMBE (St James) w Curry Mallet, Hatch Beauchamp, Orchard Portman, Staple Fitzpaine, Stoke St Mary w Thurlbear and West Hatch *B & W 18* **P** *Bp, Ch Trust Fund Trust, and D&C (4 turns), Duchy of Cornwall (1 turn)* **R** J K L POWELL, **NSM** M J PRAGNELL

BEESANDS (St Andrew) *see Stokenham w Sherford and Beesands, and Slapton Ex*

BEESBY (St Andrew) *see Saleby w Beesby and Maltby Linc*

BEESTON (St Andrew) *see Sprowston w Beeston Nor*

BEESTON (St John the Baptist) *S'well 7* **P** *Duke of Devonshire* **V** G B BARRODALE, **C** A J CARTWRIGHT

BEESTON (St Mary the Virgin) *Ripon 6* **P** *Patr Bd* **TR** P J BRINDLE, **TV** R BROOKE

BEESTON HILL (Holy Spirit) *Ripon 6* **P** *V Leeds St Pet* **P-in-c** R W SHAW

BEESTON NEXT MILEHAM (St Mary the Virgin) *see Litcham w Kempston, E and W Lexham, Mileham etc Nor*

BEESTON REGIS (All Saints) *see Aylmerton, Runton, Beeston Regis and Gresham Nor*

BEESTON RYLANDS (St Mary) *see Beeston S'well*

BEESTON ST LAURENCE (St Laurence) *see Ashmanhaugh, Barton Turf etc Nor*

BEETHAM (St Michael and All Angels) *Carl 10* **P** *Bp* **P-in-c** I DAVIES

BEETLEY (St Mary) *see Swanton Morley w Beetley w E Bilney and Hoe Nor*

BEGBROKE (St Michael) *see Yarnton w Begbroke and Shipton on Cherwell Ox*

BEIGHTON (All Saints) *see Acle w Fishley, N Burlingham, Beighton w Moulton Nor*

BEIGHTON (St Mary the Virgin) *Sheff 1* **P** *Bp* **V** M J CAMERON, **C** M MOSSMAN

BEKESBOURNE (St Peter) *see Patrixbourne w Bridge and Bekesbourne Cant*

BELAUGH (St Peter) *see Wroxham w Hoveton and Belaugh Nor*

BELBROUGHTON (Holy Trinity) w Fairfield and Clent *Worc 12* **P** *Ld Chan and St Jo Coll Ox (alt)* **R** B J MAPLEY

BELCHALWELL (St Aldheim) *see Hazelbury Bryan and the Hillside Par Sarum*

BELCHAMP (St Paul and St Andrew) *see N Hinckford Chelmsf*

BELCHAMP OTTEN (St Ethelbert and All Saints) *as above Chelmsf*

BELCHAMP WALTER (St Mary the Virgin) *as above Chelmsf*

BELCHFORD (St Peter and St Paul) *Linc 11* **P** *Ld Chan* **R** vacant

BELFIELD (St Ann) *Man 20* **P** *Bp* **V** C G KETLEY

BELFORD (St Mary) and Lucker *Newc 10* **P** *V Bamburgh and Beadnell and Bp (alt)* **V** A J HUGHES

BELGRAVE (St Gabriel) *see Leic Resurr Leic*

BELGRAVE (St Michael and All Angels) *as above Leic*

BELGRAVE (St Paul) *see Wilnecote Lich*

BELGRAVE (St Peter) *see Leic Resurr Leic*

BELHUS PARK (All Saints) *see S Ockendon and Belhus Park Chelmsf*

BELLE GREEN (Mission) *see Ince Ch Ch Liv*

BELLE ISLE (St John and St Barnabas) *see Leeds Belle Is St Jo and St Barn Ripon*

BELLEAU (St John the Baptist) *see Legbourne and Wold Marsh Linc*

BELLERBY (St John) *see Leyburn w Bellerby Ripon*

BELLFIELD (St Mark) *see Sutton St Jas and Wawne York*

BELLINGDON (St John the Evangelist) *see Gt Chesham Ox*

BELLINGHAM (St Cuthbert) *see N Tyne and Redesdale Team Newc*

BELLINGHAM (St Dunstan) *S'wark 4* **P** *Bp* **V** P D BUTLER, **C** A P DAVISON, **NSM** D L RILEY

BELMONT (St Anselm) *Lon 23* **P** *Bp* **V** W M DAVIES

BELMONT (St John) *S'wark 25* **P** *R Cheam* **V** E C PROBERT

BELMONT (St Mary Magdalene) *Dur 1* **P** *The Crown* **V** R N INNES, **C** J L MOBERLY

BELMONT (St Peter) *see Turton Moorland Min Man*

BELPER (Christ Church) (St Faith's Mission Church) w Turnditch *Derby 11* **P** *Bp* **V** D PERKINS

BELPER (St Peter) *Derby 11* **P** *V Duffield* **V** R M PARSONS, **C** D E KERR, C L TUPLING

BELSIZE PARK (St Peter) *Lon 16* **P** *D&C Westmr* **V** J P F HARRIS

BELSTEAD (St Mary the Virgin) *see Sproughton w Burstall, Copdock w Washbrook etc St E*

BELSTONE (St Mary) *see S Tawton and Belstone Ex*

BELTINGHAM (St Cuthbert) *see Haydon Bridge and Beltingham w Henshaw Newc*

BELTON (All Saints) and Burgh Castle *Nor 6* **P** *Bp and Ld Chan (alt)* **R** J J QUINN

BELTON Group, The (All Saints) *Linc 1* **P** *Bp and Prime Min (alt)* **V** T D BUCKLEY

BELTON (St John the Baptist) *see* Hathern, Long Whatton and Diseworth w Belton etc *Leic*

BELTON (St Peter) *see* Uppingham w Ayston and Wardley w Belton *Pet*

BELTON (St Peter and St Paul) *see* Barkston and Hough Gp *Linc*

BELVEDERE (All Saints) *Roch 15* **P** *DBP* **V** C A TERRY

BELVEDERE (St Augustine) *Roch 15* **P** *Bp* **P-in-c** C W JONES

BEMBRIDGE (Holy Trinity) (St Luke's Mission Church) *Portsm 7* **P** *V Brading* **V** A P MENNISS

BEMERTON (St Andrew) (St John the Evangelist) (St Michael and All Angels) *Sarum 12* **P** *Prime Min (2 turns) and Bp (1 turn)* **NSM** P D NEWTON

BEMPTON (St Michael) w Flamborough, Reighton w Speeton *York 9* **P** *Patr Bd* **V** *vacant* (01262) 850336

BEN RHYDDING (St John the Evangelist) *Bradf 4* **P** *V Ilkey* **V** B GREGORY, **C** R M WALKER

BENCHILL (St Luke the Physician) *see* Wythenshawe *Man*

BENEFIELD (St Mary the Virgin) *see* Oundle w Ashton and Benefield w Glapthorn *Pet*

BENENDEN (St George and St Margaret) *Cant 17* **P** *Abp* **V** C F SMITH, **NSM** R M VAN WENGEN

BENFIELDSIDE (St Cuthbert) *Dur 4* **P** *Bp* **V** M JACKSON, **NSM** I W WAUGH

BENFLEET, SOUTH (St Mary the Virgin) *Chelmsf 10* **P** *D&C Westmr* **V** M E GALLOWAY

BENGEO (Holy Trinity) (St Leonard) and Christ Church *St Alb 22* **P** *R M A Smith Esq* **R** I PEARSON

BENGEWORTH (St Peter) *Worc 1* **P** *Bp* **V** B D COLLINS

BENHALL (St Mary) *see* Sternfield w Benhall and Snape *St E*

BENHILTON (All Saints) *S'wark 25* **P** *Bp* **V** M A J OADES

BENINGTON (All Saints) *see* Freiston w Butterwick and Benington *Linc*

BENINGTON (St Peter) w Walkern *St Alb 23* **P** *Trustees Ripon Coll Ox and K Coll Cam (alt), and Bp* **P-in-c** R H TOTTERDELL

BENNETTS END (St Benedict) *see* Chambersbury *St Alb*

BENNIWORTH (St Julian) *see* Asterby Gp *Linc*

BENSHAM (St Chad) *Dur 12* **P** *Bp* **TR** C L V ATKINSON, **TV** M R PALMER, B M C BROGGIO

BENSINGTON (St Helen) *see* Benson *Ox*

BENSON (St Helen) *Ox 1* **P** *Ch Ch Ox* **V** A R HAWKEN

BENTHALL (St Bartholomew) *see* Broseley w Benthall, Jackfield, Linley etc *Heref*

BENTHAM (St John the Baptist) (St Margaret) *Bradf 6* **P** *Bp* **R** N B THOMAS

BENTILEE (St Stephen) *see* Bucknall and Bagnall *Lich*

BENTLEY (Emmanuel) *Lich 28* **P** *Bp, Mrs H G Jenkins, and A D Owen Esq (jt)* **V** N J CARTER, **NSM** J FORD

BENTLEY (St Mary) *see* Sproughton w Burstall, Copdock w Washbrook etc *St E*

BENTLEY (St Mary) and Binsted *Win 2* **P** *Adn Surrey and D&C (jt)* **R** J M CAMPBELL

BENTLEY (St Peter) *Sheff 7* **P** *Bp* **V** D R FOUNTAIN

BENTLEY (St Peter) *see* Rowley w Skidby *York*

BENTLEY, GREAT (St Mary the Virgin) and Frating w Thorrington *Chelmsf 23* **P** *St Jo Coll Cam and Bp (alt)* **R** W B METCALFE

BENTLEY, LITTLE (St Mary) *see* Tendring and Lt Bentley w Beaumont cum Moze *Chelmsf*

BENTLEY, LOWER (St Mary) *see* Tardebigge *Worc*

BENTLEY, NEW (St Philip and St James) *Sheff 7* **P** *Bp* **V** S P DICKINSON

BENTLEY COMMON (St Paul), Kelvedon Hatch and Navestock *Chelmsf 7* **P** *Bp* **R** R A L ROSE

BENTLEY HEATH (St James) *see* Dorridge *Birm*

BENTWORTH (St Mary) and Shalden and Lasham *Win 2* **P** *J L Jervoise Esq* **R** *vacant* (01420) 563218

BENWELL Team, The (St James) (St John) (Venerable Bede) *Newc 7* **P** *Bp* **TR** A PATTISON, **TV** J C HARDY, **OLM** P D WILSON

BEOLEY (St Leonard) (St Andrew's Church Centre) *Worc 7* **P** *Patr Bd* **V** D ROGERS, **C** L D MACHELL

BEPTON (St Mary) *see* Cocking, Bepton and W Lavington *Chich*

BERDEN (St Nicholas) *see* Manuden w Berden *Chelmsf*

BERE ALSTON (Holy Trinity) *see* Bere Ferrers *Ex*

BERE FERRERS (St Andrew) *Ex 24* **P** *DBP* **R** N C LAW

BERE REGIS (St John the Baptist) and Affpuddle w Turnerspuddle *Sarum 6* **P** *Ball Coll Ox (2 turns), Bp (1 turn)* **R** I WOODWARD

BERECHURCH (St Margaret w St Michael) *Chelmsf 16* **P** *Bp* **V** R I WILKINSON

BERGH APTON (St Peter and St Paul) *see* Thurton *Nor*

BERGHOLT, EAST (St Mary the Virgin) and Brantham *St E 5* **P** *Em Coll Cam* **R** S J SWAIN, **OLM** D W SEARLE

BERGHOLT, WEST (St Mary the Virgin) and Great Horkesley *Chelmsf 17* **P** *Bp and Ball Coll Ox (alt)* **R** C HORSEMAN

BERINSFIELD (St Mary and St Berin) *see* Dorchester *Ox*

BERKELEY (St Mary the Virgin) w Wick, Breadstone, Newport, Stone, Woodford and Hill *Glouc 2* **P** *Bp, Berkeley Will Trustees, and Mrs J D Jenner-Fust (jt)* **V** S G RICHARDS, **C** S M WHITE, **NSM** R P CHIDLAW

BERKHAMSTED (St Mary) *St Alb 2* **P** *Duchy of Cornwall* **R** P W HART

BERKHAMSTED, GREAT (All Saints) (St Peter) *St Alb 2* **P** *Bp* **R** M P J BONNEY, **C** M WRIGHT, **NSM** L GEOGHEGAN

BERKHAMSTED, LITTLE (St Andrew) and Bayford, Essendon and Ponsbourne *St Alb 22* **P** *Marquess of Salisbury (2 turns), CPAS (1 turn), and Bp (1 turn)* **P-in-c** P M HIGHAM, **NSM** J COPE

BERKHAMSYTCH (St Mary and St John) *see* Ipstones w Berkhamsytch and Onecote w Bradnop *Lich*

BERKLEY (Blessed Virgin Mary) *see* Beckington w Standerwick, Berkley, Rodden etc *B & W*

BERKSWELL (St John the Baptist) *Cov 4* **P** *Trustees Col C J H Wheatley* **P-in-c** P P HUGHES

BERKSWICH (Holy Trinity) *see* Baswich *Lich*

BERMONDSEY (St Anne) and St Augustine *S'wark 7* **P** *Bp and F W Smith Esq (alt)* **V** S J R HARTLEY, **C** M M MILLER

BERMONDSEY (St Hugh) Charterhouse Mission Conventional District *S'wark 5 vacant*

BERMONDSEY (St James w Christ Church) and St Crispin *S'wark 7* **P** *The Crown, Bp, and R Bermondsey St Mary (by turn)* **V** S J R HARTLEY, **OLM** W F GARLICK, S C CATTON

BERMONDSEY (St Katharine) w St Bartholomew *S'wark 7* **P** *Bp and R Rotherhithe St Mary w All SS (jt)* **V** L M WANJIE

BERMONDSEY (St Mary Magdalen w St Olave, St John and St Luke) *S'wark 7* **P** *Ch Patr Soc (2 turns), Ld Chan (1 turn), and Bp (1 turn)* **R** C D MOORE, **OLM** P E HOPPER

BERNEY, GREAT (St John) *see* Langdon Hills *Chelmsf*

BERNWODE *Ox 21* **P** *Bp, CPAS, Earl Temple of Stowe, and Sir Henry Aubrey-Fletcher Bt (jt)* **R** C D STIRLING, **C** A J FELTHAM-WHITE

BERRICK SALOME (St Helen) *see* Chalgrove w Berrick Salome *Ox*

BERRINGTON (All Saints) *see* Wenlock *Heref*

BERROW (Blessed Virgin Mary) and Breane *B & W 1* **P** *Adn Wells* **R** S F LACY

BERROW (St Faith) w Pendock, Eldersfield, Hollybush and Birtsmorton *Worc 5* **P** *Bp, D&C, and Sir Berwick Lechmere Bt (jt)* **R** A CUNNINGHAM, **NSM** E J BIRKIN

BERRY POMEROY (St Mary) *see* Totnes w Bridgetown, Berry Pomeroy etc *Ex*

BERRYNARBOR (St Peter) *see* Combe Martin, Berrynarbor, Lynton, Brendon etc *Ex*

BERSTED, NORTH (Holy Cross) *Chich 1* **P** *Abp* **V** *vacant* (01243) 823800

BERSTED, SOUTH (St Mary Magdalene) w NORTH (St Peter) *Chich 1* **P** *Abp* **P-in-c** D H THORNLEY

BERWICK (Holy Trinity) (St Mary) *Newc 12* **P** *Bp (2 turns), D&C Dur (1 turn)* **V** A HUGHES

BERWICK (St John) *see* Chalke Valley *Sarum*

BERWICK (St Michael and All Angels) w Selmeston and Alciston *Chich 18* **P** *Miss I M Newson and Mrs A Fitzherbert (1 turn), D&C (1 turn)* **P-in-c** P M BLEE

BERWICK PARK (Good Shepherd) *see* Wood Green St Mich w Bounds Green St Gabr etc *Lon*

BERWICK ST JAMES (St James) *see* Wylye and Till Valley *Sarum*

BESFORD (St Peter's Chapelry) *see* Defford w Besford *Worc*

BESSACARR, WEST (St Francis of Assisi) *Sheff 8* **P** *Bp* **V** C S W VAN D'ARQUE

BESSELSLEIGH (St Lawrence) *Ox 10* **P** *Ox Ch Trust* **P-in-c** R G PENMAN, **NSM** H O WATKINS

BESSINGBY (St Magnus) (St Mark) *York 9* **P** *G W J H Wright Esq* **V** *vacant*

BESSINGHAM (St Mary) *see* Roughton and Felbrigg, Metton, Sustead etc *Nor*

BESTHORPE (All Saints) *see* Attleborough w Besthorpe *Nor*

BESTHORPE (Holy Trinity) *see* Collingham w S Scarle and Besthorpe and Girton *S'well*

BESTWOOD (Emmanuel) (St Mark) *S'well 12* **P** *Bp and Ch Patr Trust (jt)* **V** B A STARK, **C** D GRAY

BESTWOOD (St Matthew on the Hill) (St Philip) *S'well 12* **P** *Bp and Ch Patr Trust (jt)* **V** A R HUMPHRIES

BESTWOOD/RISE PARK Local Ecumenical Project *S'well 9 vacant*

BESTWOOD PARK (no dedication) w Rise Park *S'well 12*
  P *Bp and Ch Patr Trust (jt)*   **V** P H REISS,   **NSM** B J NEILL
BESWICK (St Margaret)   *see* Hutton Cranswick w Skerne,
  Watton and Beswick *York*
BETCHWORTH (St Michael and All Angels) *S'wark 27*
  P *D&C Windsor*   **V** S J BAILEY,   **OLM** P A VIGERS
BETHERSDEN (St Margaret) w High Halden *Cant 17*   **P** *Abp*
  V D W FLEWKER
BETHESDA (Shared Church)   *see* Hallwood *Ches*
BETHNAL GREEN (St Barnabas) *Lon 7*   **P** *D&C Cant*
  V B C RALPH,   **NSM** M G WEBB
BETHNAL GREEN (St James the Less) *Lon 7*   **P** *CPAS*
  V R MONTGOMERY
BETHNAL GREEN (St John)   *see* St Jo on Bethnal Green *Lon*
BETHNAL GREEN (St Matthew w St James the Great) *Lon 7*
  P *Bp*   **R** K J SCULLY
BETHNAL GREEN (St Peter) (St Thomas) *Lon 7*   **P** *City Corp*
  V J M V WEIR
BETLEY (St Margaret) and Keele *Lich 9*
  P *T G H Howard-Sneyd Esq and DBP (jt)*   **OLM** P LANE
BETTISCOMBE (St Stephen)   *see* Golden Cap Team *Sarum*
BETTON STRANGE (St Margaret)   *see* Wenlock *Heref*
BETTWS-Y-CRWYN (St Mary)   *see* Clun w Bettws-y-Crwyn
  and Newcastle *Heref*
BEVENDEAN (Holy Nativity)   *see* Moulsecoomb *Chich*
BEVERLEY (St Mary) *York 8*   **P** *Abp*   **V** D W HOSKIN
BEVERLEY (St Nicholas) *York 8*   **P** *Abp*   **V** J A EVANS,
  NSM R MERRYWEATHER
BEVERLEY MINSTER (St John and St Martin) *York 8*
  P *Simeon's Trustees*   **V** D C BAILEY,   **C** N J Q DRAYSON,
  H A BENNETT
BEVERSTON (St Mary the Virgin)   *see* Tetbury w Beverston
  Glouc
BEWBUSH (Community Centre)   *see* Ifield *Chich*
**BEWCASTLE (St Cuthbert), Stapleton and Kirklinton w
  Hethersgill** *Carl 2*   **P** *Bp, D&C, and DBP (jt)*
  R A T BARTLAM
BEWDLEY (St Anne)   *see* Ribbesford w Bewdley and Dowles
  Worc
BEWERLEY GRANGE (Chapel)   *see* Upper Nidderdale *Ripon*
BEWHOLME (St John the Baptist)   *see* Sigglesthorne and Rise
  w Nunkeeling and Bewholme *York*
BEWICK, OLD (Holy Trinity)   *see* Glendale Gp *Newc*
BEXHILL (All Saints)   *see* Sidley *Chich*
BEXHILL (St Augustine) *Chich 14*   **P** *Bp*   **V** R COATES,
  Hon C P A FROSTICK
BEXHILL (St Barnabas) *Chich 14*   **P** *Bp*   **V** C I PRITCHARD
BEXHILL (St Mark) *Chich 14*   **P** *Bp*   **R** J W EDMONDSON
BEXHILL (St Peter) (St Michael) (Good Shepherd) (St Andrew)
  Chich 14   **P** *Bp*   **TR** E F P BRYANT,   **TV** D J KING,
  C M A BRYDON,   **Hon C** M CAMPLING,   **NSM** O M WERRETT
BEXHILL (St Stephen) *Chich 14*   **P** *Bp*   **V** D R FROST
BEXLEY (St John the Evangelist) *Roch 17*   **P** *The Crown*
  V V J LAMONT
BEXLEY (St Mary) *Roch 17*   **P** *Bp*   **V** C E POTTER
BEXLEYHEATH (Christ Church) *Roch 15*   **P** *Bp*
  C R M JOHNSON,   C A TERRY
BEXLEYHEATH (St Peter) *Roch 15*   **P** *Bp*
  V M H C LUMGAIR
BEXWELL (St Mary)   *see* Denver and Ryston w Roxham and W
  Dereham etc *Ely*
BEYTON (All Saints)   *see* Rougham, Beyton w Hessett and
  Rushbrooke *St E*
BIBURY (St Mary) w Winson and Barnsley *Glouc 12*   **P** *Bp and
  W H Wykeham-Musgrave Esq (alt)*   **P-in-c** G R MARTIN
BICESTER (St Edburg) w Bucknell, Caversfield and Launton
  Ox 2   **P** *Patr Bd*   **TR** P J BALL,   **TV** M MULLINS,
  D W BOUSKILL,   **C** C A BOYCE,   **NSM** R B ATKINS
BICKENHILL (St Peter) *Birm 11*   **P** *Birm Dioc Trustees*
  P-in-c C J G BARTON
BICKER (St Swithin) *Linc 21*   **P** *D&C*   **V** *vacant*
BICKERSHAW (St James and St Elizabeth) *Liv 14*   **P** *Bp*
  V J L STEVENTON
BICKERSTAFFE Four Lane Ends (not known)
  see Bickerstaffe and Melling *Liv*
BICKERSTAFFE (Holy Trinity) and Melling *Liv 11*   **P** *Earl of
  Derby and R Halsall (jt)*   **V** P TAYLOR
BICKERTON (Holy Trinity), Bickley, Harthill and Burwardsley
  Ches 5   **P** *Bp, Adn Ches, DBP, Dowager Marchioness of
  Cholmondeley, and A G Barbour Esq (jt)*   **V** L R THOMAS
BICKINGTON (St Andrew)   *see* Fremington *Ex*
BICKINGTON (St Mary the Virgin)   *see* Ashburton w
  Buckland in the Moor and Bickington *Ex*
BICKINGTON, HIGH (St Mary)   *see* Newton Tracey,
  Horwood, Alverdiscott etc *Ex*
BICKLEIGH Roborough (St Mary the Virgin) and Shaugh Prior
  Ex 20   **P** *Patr Bd*   **TR** R J CARLTON,   **C** M T MESLEY

BICKLEIGH (St Mary)   *see* Silverton, Butterleigh, Bickleigh
  and Cadeleigh *Ex*
BICKLEIGH DOWN (School)   *see* Bickleigh and Shaugh Prior
  Ex
BICKLEY (St George) *Roch 14*   **P** *SMF*   **V** D A S HERBERT,
  Hon C B W SHARPE
BICKLEY (St Wenefrede)   *see* Bickerton, Bickley, Harthill and
  Burwardsley *Ches*
BICKNACRE (St Andrew)   *see* Woodham Ferrers and
  Bicknacre *Chelmsf*
BICKNOLLER (St George)   *see* Quantock Towers *B & W*
BICKNOR (St James)   *see* Bredgar w Bicknor and Frinsted w
  Wormshill etc *Cant*
BICTON (Holy Trinity), Montford w Shrawardine and Fitz
  Lich 20   **P** *Earl of Powis, N E E Stephens Esq, and
  J G O Wingfield Esq (jt)*   **P-in-c** M R GODSON
BICTON (St Mary)   *see* E Budleigh w Bicton and Otterton *Ex*
BIDBOROUGH (St Lawrence)   *see* Southborough St Pet w Ch
  Ch and St Matt etc *Roch*
BIDDENDEN (All Saints) and Smarden *Cant 17*   **P** *Abp*
  R P G COX,   **Hon C** P A ANDERSON,   **NSM** J A MUXLOW
BIDDENHAM (St James) *St Alb 10*   **P** *Bp*
  P-in-c R J SUTTON,   **Hon C** G SMITH
BIDDESTONE (St Nicholas)   *see* By Brook *Bris*
BIDDISHAM (St John the Baptist)   *see* Crook Peak *B & W*
BIDDLESDEN (St Margaret)   *see* W Buckingham *Ox*
BIDDULPH (St Lawrence) *Lich 8*   **P** *MMCET*
  V M S J CANNAM,   **C** R J TRETHEWEY
BIDDULPH MOOR (Christ Church) *Lich 8*   **P** *MMCET*
  P-in-c P TOON
**BIDEFORD (St Mary) (St Peter East the Water), Northam,
  Westward Ho!, Appledore, Weare Giffard, Littleham,
  Landcross and Monkleigh** *Ex 16*   **P** *Patr Bd*   **TR** M EDSON,
  TV S R PIRRIE,   R J FROST,   J EWINGTON,   **C** P J DOBBIN,
  NSM A GLOVER,   C M LOW
BIDFORD-ON-AVON (St Laurence) *Cov 7*   **P** *Bp*
  V D A HALL
BIDSTON (St Oswald) *Ches 1*   **P** *Bp*   **V** *vacant* 0151-652 4852
  or 653 4584
BIELBY (St Giles)   *see* Holme and Seaton Ross Gp *York*
BIERLEY (St John the Evangelist) *Bradf 2*   **P** *DBP*
  V K S TROMANS
BIERLEY, EAST (St Luke)   *see* Birkenshaw w Hunsworth
  Wakef
BIERTON (St James the Great)   *see* Aylesbury w Bierton and
  Hulcott *Ox*
BIGBURY (St Lawrence)   *see* Modbury, Bigbury, Ringmore w
  Kingston etc *Ex*
BIGBY (All Saints)   *see* N Wolds Gp *Linc*
BIGGIN (St Thomas)   *see* Hartington, Biggin and Earl
  Sterndale *Derby*
BIGGIN HILL (St Mark) *Roch 14*   **P** *Bp*   **V** C W KITCHENER,
  NSM E C KITCHENER
BIGGLESWADE (St Andrew) *St Alb 11*   **P** *Bp*
  C S G CUTMORE
BIGHTON (All Saints)   *see* Old Alresford and Bighton *Win*
BIGNOR (Holy Cross)   *see* Barlavington, Burton w Coates,
  Sutton and Bignor *Chich*
BIGRIGG (St John)   *see* Egremont and Haile *Carl*
BILBOROUGH (St John the Baptist) *S'well 13*   **P** *Bp*
  P-in-c J E D CAVE
BILBOROUGH (St Martin) w Strelley *S'well 13*   **P** *SMF*
  P-in-c J E D CAVE
BILBROOK (Holy Cross)   *see* Codsall *Lich*
BILBROUGH (St James)   *see* Healaugh w Wighill, Bilbrough
  and Askham Richard *York*
**BILDESTON (St Mary Magdalene) w Wattisham and Lindsey,
  Whatfield w Semer, Nedging and Naughton** *St E 3*   **P** *Abp, Bp,
  CPAS, Jes Coll Cam, and Reformation Ch Trust (jt)*
  R D WARNER
BILHAM *Sheff 12*   **P** *Bp, Major W Warde-Aldam,
  W G A Warde-Norbury Esq, and Mrs S Grant-Dalton (jt)*
  P-in-c C D LETHBRIDGE
**BILLERICAY (Christ Church) (Emmanuel) (St John the Divine)
  (St Mary Magdalen) and Little Burstead** *Chelmsf 6*   **P** *Bp*
  TR E W COCKETT,   **TV** P F HINCKLEY,   D BARLOW,
  C C S BALDWIN
BILLESDON (St John the Baptist)   *see* Church Langton cum
  Tur Langton etc *Leic*
BILLESLEY COMMON (Holy Cross) *Birm 5*   **P** *Bp*
  V G L HODKINSON
BILLING, GREAT (St Andrew) w LITTLE (All Saints) *Pet 4*
  P *BNC Ox and Bp (alt)*   **R** S R PALMER,   **C** M J NEWITT,
  NSM J H CRAIG
BILLINGBOROUGH Group, The (St Andrew) *Linc 13*
  P *Prime Min (2 turns), Bp and St Jo Coll Dur (1 turn)*
  OLM J G SPREADBURY

BILLINGE (St Aidan) *Liv 15* P *R Wigan* V S C PRATT
BILLINGFORD (St Leonard) *see* Scole, Brockdish, Billingford, Thorpe Abbots etc *Nor*
BILLINGFORD (St Peter) *see* N Elmham w Billingford and Worthing *Nor*
BILLINGHAM (St Aidan) *Dur 10* P *D&C* V *vacant* (01642) 531740
BILLINGHAM (St Cuthbert) *Dur 10* P *D&C* V R I SMITH, NSM M A VIGOR
BILLINGHAM (St Luke) *Dur 10* P *D&C* V T P PARKER
BILLINGHAM (St Mary Magdalene) *Dur 10* P *D&C* V *vacant*
BILLINGHAM (St Mary Magdalene) *see* Grindon, Stillington and Wolviston *Dur*
BILLINGHAY (St Michael) *see* Carr Dyke Gp *Linc*
BILLINGSHURST (St Mary the Virgin) *Chich 8* P *Bp* V D C PAIN
BILLINGSLEY (St Mary) *see* Highley w Billingsley, Glazeley etc *Heref*
BILLINGTON (St Michael and All Angels) *see* Leighton Buzzard w Eggington, Hockliffe etc *St Alb*
BILLOCKBY (All Saints) *see* S Trin Broads *Nor*
BILLY MILL (St Aidan) *see* Cullercoats St Geo *Newc*
BILNEY, EAST (St Mary) *see* Swanton Morley w Beetley w E Bilney and Hoe *Nor*
BILSBORROW (St Hilda) *see* Fellside Team *Blackb*
BILSBY (Holy Trinity) w Farlesthorpe *Linc 8* P *Bp* V R H IRESON
BILSDALE MIDCABLE (St John) *see* Upper Ryedale *York*
BILSDALE PRIORY (St Hilda) *see* Ingleby Greenhow w Bilsdale Priory, Kildale etc *York*
BILSINGTON (St Peter and St Paul) *see* Aldington w Bonnington and Bilsington etc *Cant*
BILSON (Mission Church) *see* Cinderford St Steph w Littledean *Glouc*
BILSTHORPE (St Margaret) *S'well 14* P *DBP* P-in-c E F CULLY, NSM M A GROVES
BILSTON (St Leonard) (St Chad) (St Mary the Virgin) *Lich 28* P *Patr Bd* TR C D C THORPE, TV M R GILBERT, B M LEACH, C J L WATERFIELD, I D HOUGHTON, OLM C E DAVIES
BILTON (St John the Evangelist) and St Luke *Ripon 1* P *Bp* TR L BENTLEY, C P T ASKEW, NSM K A FITZSIMONS, G P CORNISH
BILTON (St Mark) *Cov 6* P *N M Assheton Esq* C C E MIER
BILTON, NEW (St Oswald) *Cov 6* P *Dioc Trustees* P-in-c G J HARDWICK, NSM P R GOULD
BILTON-IN-AINSTY (St Helen) *see* Tockwith and Bilton w Bickerton *York*
BILTON IN HOLDERNESS (St Peter) *York 12* P *Abp* V R J E MAJOR
BINBROOK Group, The (St Mary) *Linc 10* P *Ld Chan, DBP and G F Sleight Esq (alt)* R T J WALKER
BINCOMBE (Holy Trinity) w Broadwey, Upwey and Buckland Ripers *Sarum 4* P *G&C Coll Cam (2 turns), Miss M B F Frampton (1 turn), and Bp (1 turn)* R R A C SIMMONS, OLM P A JONES
BINEGAR (Holy Trinity) *see* Ashwick w Oakhill and Binegar *B & W*
BINFIELD (All Saints) (St Mark) *Ox 11* P *Ld Chan* R W J MEYER
BINGFIELD (St Mary) *see* St Oswald in Lee w Bingfield *Newc*
BINGHAM (St Mary and All Saints) *S'well 8* P *The Crown* R D L HARPER
BINGLEY (All Saints) *Bradf 1* P *Bp* TV H FIELDEN, C S J WHARTON
BINGLEY (Holy Trinity) *Bradf 1* P *Bp* V A J CLARKE, C C J ANDREW, NSM J JACKSON
BINHAM (St Mary) *see* Stiffkey and Cockthorpe w Morston, Langham etc *Nor*
BINLEY (St Bartholomew) *Cov 1* P *Bp* V D J HOWARD, C G P SMITH, Hon C R J WORSLEY
BINLEY WOODS Local Ecumenical Project *Cov 1* Min J CHEVERTON
BINSEY (St Margaret) *see* Ox St Thos w St Frideswide and Binsey *Ox*
BINSEY Team Ministry *Carl 7* P *Patr Bd* TR C S SIMS, TV F I WRIGHT, C J M FEARNLEY
BINSTEAD (Holy Cross) *Portsm 7* P *Bp* R N R WALLACE, NSM K R ADLAM
BINSTED (Holy Cross) *see* Bentley and Binsted *Win*
BINSTED (St Mary) *see* Walberton w Binsted *Chich*
BINTON (St Peter) *see* Temple Grafton w Binton *Cov*
BINTREE (St Swithin) *see* Twyford, Guist, Bintree, Themelthorpe etc *Nor*
BIRCH (St James) w Fallowfield *Man 4* P *Bp* R W G RAINES
BIRCH (St Mary) *see* Rhodes *Man*

BIRCH-IN-RUSHOLME (St Agnes) w Longsight St John w St Cyprian *Man 3* P *Prime Min and Bp (alt)* P-in-c S M EDWARDS
BIRCHAM, GREAT (St Mary the Virgin) *see* Docking, the Birchams, Stanhoe and Sedgeford *Nor*
BIRCHAM NEWTON (All Saints) *as above Nor*
BIRCHANGER (St Mary the Virgin) *see* Stansted Mountfitchet w Birchanger and Farnham *Chelmsf*
BIRCHENCLIFFE (St Philip the Apostle) *Wakef 5* P *V Lindley* P-in-c J A LAWSON, C C NIGHTINGALE
BIRCHES HEAD (St Matthew) *see* Hanley H Ev *Lich*
BIRCHFIELD (Holy Trinity) *Birm 3* P *Bp* V D J G BOWEN
BIRCHILLS, THE (St Andrew) *see* Walsall St Andr *Lich*
BIRCHIN COPPICE (St Peter) *see* Kidderminster St Jo and H Innocents *Worc*
BIRCHINGTON (All Saints) w Acol and Minnis Bay *Cant 9* P *Abp* V D R WITTS, OLM R E STAGG
BIRCHMOOR (St John) *see* Polesworth *Birm*
BIRCHOVER (St Michael) *see* Youlgreave, Middleton, Stanton-in-Peak etc *Derby*
BIRCHWOOD (Mission Church) *see* Blackdown *B & W*
BIRCHWOOD (St Luke) *Linc 15* P *Bp* V J B PAVEY, C L E TURNER
BIRCHWOOD (Transfiguration) *Liv 12* P *Bp, Adn, and R Warrington (jt)* V R C HARDCASTLE
BIRCLE (St John the Baptist) *Man 10* P *R Middleton St Leon* V A R BROCKBANK
BIRDBROOK (St Augustine) *see* Ridgewell w Ashen, Birdbrook and Sturmer *Chelmsf*
BIRDHAM (St James) *see* W Wittering and Birdham w Itchenor *Chich*
BIRDINGBURY (St Leonards) *see* Leam Valley *Cov*
BIRDLIP (St Mary in Hamlet) *see* Brimpsfield w Birdlip, Syde, Daglingworth etc *Glouc*
BIRDSALL (St Mary) *see* W Buckrose *York*
BIRKBY (St Peter) *see* Gt Smeaton w Appleton Wiske and Birkby etc *Ripon*
BIRKDALE Carr Lane (St Mary) *see* Birkdale St Jo *Liv*
BIRKDALE (St James) *Liv 9* P *Trustees* V J S BELLAMY
BIRKDALE (St John) *Liv 9* P *Trustees* V P C CATON
BIRKDALE (St Peter) *Liv 9* P *Trustees* V M I STOCKLEY, OLM S CALVELEY
BIRKENHEAD (Christ Church) *Ches 1* P *Bp* V D M WILSON
BIRKENHEAD (St James) w St Bede *Ches 1* P *Trustees* V D A LAMB
BIRKENHEAD (St Winifred) Welsh Church *Ches 1 vacant*
BIRKENHEAD PRIORY (Christ the King) *Ches 1* P *Bp, Simeon's Trustees, and Ch Patr Trust (jt)* TR D WALKER, TV D J AYLING
BIRKENSHAW (St Paul) w Hunsworth *Wakef 8* P *V Birstall* V S MITCHELL, NSM D S ANDREW, OLM R DAVIDSON
BIRKIN (St Mary) *see* Haddlesey w Hambleton and Birkin *York*
BIRLEY (St Peter) *see* Canon Pyon w Kings Pyon and Birley *Heref*
BIRLING (All Saints), Addington, Ryarsh and Trottiscliffe *Roch 7* P *Bp* R J B CROSS
BIRLING, LOWER (Christ Church) *see* Snodland All SS w Ch Ch *Roch*
BIRLINGHAM (St James the Great) *see* Pershore w Pinvin, Wick and Birlingham *Worc*
BIRMINGHAM (Bishop Latimer w All Saints) *Birm 3* P *St Martin's Trustees* R R F BASHFORD
BIRMINGHAM (St George) *Birm 8* P *St Martin's Trustees* P-in-c R K JOHNSON
BIRMINGHAM (St John the Evangelist) *see* Ladywood St Jo and St Pet *Birm*
BIRMINGHAM (St Luke) *Birm 1* P *Trustees* V A G LENOX-CONYNGHAM, NSM J R L MOXON
BIRMINGHAM (St Martin-in-the-Bull-Ring) w Bordesley St Andrew *Birm 1* P *St Martin's Trustees* R A NEWMAN, C I D GOW, S A WOODLEY, S J M VETTERS
BIRMINGHAM (St Paul) *Birm 1* P *St Martin's Trustees* V T F PYKE, C G P LANHAM
BIRSTALL (St James the Greater) and Wanlip *Leic 6* P *Bp and C A Palmer-Tomkinson Esq (jt)* V M E LAMBERT, C S J WICKS, NSM J N N ANAND
BIRSTALL (St Peter) *Wakef 8* P *Bp* V P J KNIGHT
BIRSTWITH (St James) *Ripon 1* P *Miss S J Greenwood* V *vacant* (01423) 772315
BIRTLES (St Catherine) *see* Alderley w Birtles *Ches*
BIRTLEY (St Giles) *see* Chollerton w Birtley and Thockrington *Newc*
BIRTLEY (St John the Evangelist) *Dur 11* P *R Chester le Street* V E G LLOYD
BIRTSMORTON (St Peter and St Paul) *see* Berrow w Pendock, Eldersfield, Hollybush etc *Worc*

BISBROOKE (St John the Baptist)   *see* Lyddington w Stoke Dry and Seaton etc *Pet*

BISCATHORPE (St Helen)   *see* Asterby Gp *Linc*

BISCOT (Holy Trinity)   *St Alb 14*   **P** *Bp*   **V** *vacant (01582) 573421*

BISHAM (All Saints)   *see* Gt Marlow w Marlow Bottom, Lt Marlow and Bisham *Ox*

BISHAMPTON (St James)   *see* Abberton, The Flyfords, Naunton Beauchamp etc *Worc*

BISHOP AUCKLAND (St Andrew) (St Anne)   *see* Auckland St Andr and St Anne *Dur*

BISHOP AUCKLAND (St Peter)   *see* Auckland St Pet *Dur*

BISHOP AUCKLAND Woodhouse Close Area of Ecumenical Experiment (Conventional District)   *Dur 10*   **C-in-c** V T FENTON

BISHOP BURTON (All Saints) w Walkington   *York 8*   **P** *Abp and DBP (alt)*   **R** D G KIRBY

BISHOP CAUNDLE (not known)   *see* The Caundles w Folke and Holwell *Sarum*

BISHOP MIDDLEHAM (St Michael)   *Dur 5*   **P** *Ld Chan*   **P-in-c** A KELHAM

BISHOP MONKTON (St John the Baptist)   *see* Ripon Cathl *Ripon*

BISHOP NORTON (St Peter), Waddingham and Snitterby   *Linc 6*   **P** *Bp and The Crown (alt)*   **R** *vacant (01673) 818551*

BISHOP SUTTON (Holy Trinity) and Stanton Drew and Stowey   *B & W 10*   **P** *Bp and Adn Bath (alt)*   **V** J HIGGINS

BISHOP THORNTON (St John the Evangelist)   *see* Markington w S Stainley and Bishop Thornton *Ripon*

BISHOP WILTON (St Edith)   *see* Garrowby Hill *York*

BISHOPDALE (Mission Room)   *see* Aysgarth and Bolton cum Redmire *Ripon*

BISHOPHILL JUNIOR (St Mary)   *see* Micklegate H Trin and Bishophill Junior St Mary *York*

BISHOP'S CANNINGS (St Mary the Virgin), All Cannings and Etchilhampton   *Sarum 16*   **P** *DBP*   **P-in-c** S ATTWATER

BISHOP'S CASTLE (St John the Baptist) w Mainstone, Lydbury North and Edgton   *Heref 10*   **P** *Earl of Powis (3 turns), Ld Chan (1 turn), and Mrs R E Bell (1 turn)*   **P-in-c** P D A COLLINS,   **C** J M READ

BISHOP'S CLEEVE (St Michael and All Angels)   *Glouc 16*   **P** *DBP*   **R** I F CALDER,   **C** A J ROBINSON, C A WILLIAMS

BISHOP'S FROME (St Mary the Virgin) w Castle Frome and Fromes Hill   *Heref 2*   **P** *Bp*   **P-in-c** J A DAVIES

BISHOPS GREEN (Community Church)   *see* Burghclere w Newtown and Ecchinswell w Sydmonton *Win*

BISHOP'S HATFIELD (St Etheldreda) (St John) (St Michael and All Angels) (St Luke)   *St Alb 21*   **P** *Marquess of Salisbury*   **TR** R E PYKE,   **TV** J A STOBART, J R CROCKER,   **C** V A HATHAWAY,   **NSM** S E MARSH

BISHOP'S HULL (St John the Evangelist)   *see* Taunton St Jo *B & W*

BISHOPS HULL (St Peter and St Paul)   *B & W 18*   **P** *Adn Taunton*   **V** S TUCKER

BISHOP'S ITCHINGTON (St Michael)   *Cov 10*   **P** *Bp*   **P-in-c** M C GREEN

BISHOP'S LAVINGTON (All Saints)   *see* The Lavingtons, Cheverells, and Easterton *Sarum*

BISHOPS LYDEARD (Blessed Virgin Mary) w Bagborough and Cothelstone   *B & W 18*   **P** *D&C (3 turns), Ms P M G Mitford (1 turn)*   **R** *vacant (01823) 432414*

BISHOPS NORTON (St John the Evangelist)   *see* Twigworth, Down Hatherley, Norton, The Leigh etc *Glouc*

BISHOP'S STORTFORD (Holy Trinity)   *St Alb 18*   **P** *Bp*   **P-in-c** J K WILLIAMS

BISHOP'S STORTFORD (St Michael)   *St Alb 18*   **P** *Bp*   **V** R A V MARCHAND,   **C** S E DAVENPORT,   **NSM** D C HINGE,   J E KNIGHT

BISHOP'S SUTTON (St Nicholas) and Ropley and West Tisted   *Win 1*   **P** *Peache Trustees*   **R** R J SUCH

BISHOP'S TACHBROOK (St Chad)   *Cov 10*   **P** *Bp*   **P-in-c** K M ROBERTS,   **NSM** R C PANTLING

BISHOPS TAWTON (St John the Baptist)   *see* Barnstaple *Ex*

BISHOP'S WALTHAM (St Peter)   *Portsm 1*   **P** *Bp*   **R** A G DAVIS,   **C** J M HEMMINGS

BISHOP'S WOOD (St Mary)   *see* Hartlebury *Worc*

BISHOPSBOURNE (St Mary)   *see* Barham w Bishopsbourne and Kingston *Cant*

BISHOPSNYMPTON (St Mary the Virgin), Rose Ash, Mariansleigh, Molland, Knowstone, East Anstey and West Anstey   *Ex 18*   **P** *DBP*   **R** J R KEELEY,   **P-in-c** A C JONES

BISHOPSTEIGNTON (St John the Evangelist)   *see* Teignmouth, Ideford w Luton, Ashcombe etc *Ex*

BISHOPSTOKE (St Mary) (St Paul)   *Win 10*   **P** *Bp*   **R** D J COTTRILL

BISHOPSTON (Church of the Good Shepherd)   *see* Bishopston and St Andrews *Bris*

BISHOPSTON (St Michael and All Angels)   *as above Bris*

BISHOPSTON (St Michael and All Angels) (Church of the Good Shepherd) and St Andrews   *Bris 3*   **P** *Patr Bd*   **TR** P R BAILEY,   **TV** R J BURBRIDGE

BISHOPSTONE (St Andrew)   *Chich 18*   **P** *Bp Lon*   **V** J E LLOYD-JAMES

BISHOPSTONE (St John the Baptist)   *see* Chalke Valley *Sarum*

BISHOPSTONE (St Lawrence)   *see* Credenhill w Brinsop and Wormsley etc *Heref*

BISHOPSTROW (St Aldhelm) and Boreham   *Sarum 17*   **P** *DBP*   **R** D R A BRETT,   **OLM** D M HAMMOND

BISHOPSWOOD (All Saints)   *see* Walford and St John w Bishopswood, Goodrich etc *Heref*

BISHOPSWOOD (St John the Evangelist)   *Lich 2*   **P** *V Brewood*   **V** *vacant*

BISHOPSWORTH (St Peter) and Bedminster Down   *Bris 1*   **P** *Bp*   **TR** T R J GODDEN,   **TV** J M LEWIS,   **NSM** E P WHERLOCK, R A LANE

BISHOPTHORPE (St Andrew)   *York 1*   **P** *Abp*   **V** C I COATES

BISHOPTON (St Peter) w Great Stainton   *Dur 10*   **P** *Ld Chan*   **V** *vacant*

BISHOPWEARMOUTH (Good Shepherd)   *Dur 16*   **P** *Bp*   **V** *vacant 0191-565 6870*

BISHOPWEARMOUTH (St Gabriel)   *Dur 16*   **P** *V Sunderland*   **V** A THORP,   **C** B G MAGORRIAN,   **NSM** H M THORP,   J P TALBOT

BISHOPWEARMOUTH (St Luke Pallion)   *see* Millfield St Mark and Pallion St Luke *Dur*

BISHOPWEARMOUTH (St Mary)   *see* Millfield St Mary *Dur*

BISHOPWEARMOUTH (St Nicholas) (Christ Church)   *Dur 16*   **P** *Bp*   **V** N B WARNER

BISLEY (All Saints), Oakridge, Miserden and Edgeworth   *Glouc 1*   **P** *Major M T N H Wills, Ld Chan, and Bp (by turn)*   **V** I E D FARROW

BISLEY (St John the Baptist) and West End (Holy Trinity)   *Guildf 6*   **P** *Bp*   **NSM** D H ROBINSON

BISPHAM (All Hallows)   *Blackb 8*   **P** *Ch Soc Trust*   **R** S J COX,   **C** G A POLLITT, P T DARLINGTON

BISTERNE (St Paul)   *see* Ringwood *Win*

BITCHFIELD (St Mary Magdalene)   *see* Ingoldsby *Linc*

BITTADON (St Peter)   *see* Ilfracombe, Lee, Woolacombe, Bittadon etc *Ex*

BITTERING PARVA (St Peter and St Paul)   *see* Gressenhall w Longham w Wendling etc *Nor*

BITTERLEY (St Mary) w Middleton, Stoke St Milborough w The Heath and Hopton Cangeford, Clee St Margaret and Cold Weston   *Heref 12*   **P** *Bp, DBP, Walcott Trustees, and Miss M F Rouse-Boughton (jt)*   **R** A G SEABROOK

BITTERNE (Holy Saviour)   *Win 13*   **P** *Bp*   **V** W G CHALLIS,   **C** F C DE ROBECK, E L TALBOT

BITTERNE PARK (All Hallows) (Ascension)   *Win 13*   **P** *Bp*   **V** S J CHAPMAN,   **C** M J A NEWTON

BITTESWELL (St Mary)   *see* Lutterworth w Cotesbach and Bitteswell *Leic*

BITTON (St Mary)   *see* Warmley, Syston and Bitton *Bris*

BIX (St James)   *see* Nettlebed w Bix, Highmoor, Pishill etc *Ox*

BLABY (All Saints)   *Leic 10*   **P** *Bp*   **P-in-c** J G GIBBINS

BLACK BOURTON (St Mary the Virgin)   *see* Shill Valley and Broadshire *Ox*

BLACK NOTLEY (St Peter and St Paul)   *Chelmsf 15*   **P** *St Jo Coll Cam*   **R** A G MORRISON

BLACK TORRINGTON (St Mary), Bradford w Cookbury, Thornbury and Highampton   *Ex 9*   **P** *DBP*   **R** D M WOOD

BLACKAWTON (St Michael)   *see* Stoke Fleming, Blackawton and Strete *Ex*

BLACKBIRD LEYS (Holy Family)   *Ox 4*   **P** *Bp*   **V** D T N PARRY,   **C** A BINDOFF,   **NSM** D R KABOLEH

BLACKBOURNE   *St E 9*   **P** *Patr Bd*   **TR** P M OLIVER,   **TV** E S FOGDEN,   **OLM** D A NEUPERT, S M NUTT, J F WALKER

BLACKBROOK (St Paul)   *see* Parr *Liv*

BLACKBURN (Christ Church w St Matthew)   *Blackb 2*   **P** *Bp*   **V** A RAYNES

BLACKBURN (Church of the Redeemer)   *Blackb 2*   **P** *Bp*   **V** *vacant (01254) 52782*

BLACKBURN (Saviour)   *Blackb 2*   **P** *CPAS*   **V** *vacant (01254) 55344*

BLACKBURN (St Aidan)   *Blackb 2*   **P** *Bp*   **V** *vacant (01254) 253519*

BLACKBURN (St Andrew)   *see* Livesey *Blackb*

BLACKBURN (St Barnabas)   *Blackb 2*   **P** *Bp*   **V** H H DANIEL

BLACKBURN (St Bartholomew)   *see* Ewood *Blackb*

BLACKBURN (St Gabriel)   *Blackb 2*   **P** *Bp*   **P-in-c** G THOMAS,   **C** R JACKSON

BLACKBURN (St James)   *Blackb 2*   **P** *Bp*   **P-in-c** S TRANTER

BLACKBURN (St Luke) w St Philip   *Blackb 2*   **P** *Bp*   **V** *vacant (01254) 581402*

BLACKBURN (St Michael and All Angels) (Holy Trinity Worship Centre) w St John the Evangelist *Blackb 2*
P *V Blackb*   **P-in-c** C R SCHAEFER
BLACKBURN (St Silas) *Blackb 2*   **P** *Trustees*
P-in-c A F RANSON
BLACKBURN (St Stephen) *Blackb 2*   **P** *Trustees*
P-in-c J E C PERCIVAL
BLACKBURN St Thomas (St Jude) *Blackb 2*   **P** *Bp and Trustees (alt)*   **V** C R SCHAEFER
BLACKDOWN Benefice, The *B & W 18*   **P** *DBP (4 turns), Pitminster PCC and Corfe PCC (1 turn)*   **NSM** P E DUFOUR
BLACKDOWN (Holy Trinity) *see* Beaminster Area *Sarum*
BLACKFEN (Good Shepherd) *see* Lamorbey H Redeemer *Roch*
BLACKFORD (Holy Trinity) *see* Wedmore w Theale and Blackford *B & W*
BLACKFORD (St John the Baptist) *see* Rockcliffe and Blackford *Carl*
BLACKFORD (St Michael) *see* Camelot Par *B & W*
BLACKFORDBY (St Margaret) and Woodville *Leic 9*   **P** *Bp*
V T S G VALE
BLACKHALL (St Andrew), Castle Eden and Monkhesleden *Dur 2*   **R** *Bp*   **R** *vacant* 0191-586 4202
BLACKHAM (All Saints) *see* Withyham St Mich *Chich*
BLACKHEATH (All Saints) *S'wark 4*   **P** *V Lewisham St Mary*
V N W S CRANFIELD,   **OLM** T W CHATTERTON
BLACKHEATH (Ascension) *S'wark 4*   **P** *V Lewisham St Mary*
P-in-c D J FUDGER,   **Hon C** E R NEWNHAM
BLACKHEATH (St John the Evangelist) *S'wark 3*   **P** *CPAS*
V M D MARSHALL,   **Hon C** J MCALLEN,
NSM A M BESWETHERICK
BLACKHEATH (St Martin) *see* Wonersh w Blackheath *Guildf*
BLACKHEATH (St Paul) *Birm 7*   **P** *Bp*   **V** M J SERMON,
C M S PRASADAM
BLACKHEATH PARK (St Michael and All Angels) *S'wark 3*
P *Bp*   **V** A R CHRISTIE,   **NSM** A SCOTT, M J CALLAGHAN
BLACKLAND (St Peter) *see* Calne and Blackland *Sarum*
BLACKLANDS Hastings (Christchurch and St Andrew) *Chich 17*   **P** *Ch Patr Trust*   **V** D F FENTIMAN
BLACKLEY (Holy Trinity) *Man 5*   **P** *Bp*   **R** P A STAMP
BLACKLEY (St Andrew) *Man 5*   **P** *Bp*   **P-in-c** I D THOMPSON
BLACKLEY (St Paul) *Man 5*   **P** *Bp*   **P-in-c** J L CLEGG
BLACKLEY (St Peter) *Man 5*   **P** *D&C*   **R** *vacant* 0161-740 2124
BLACKLEY White Moss (St Mark) *Man 5*   **P** *D&C*   **R** *vacant* 0161-740 7558
BLACKMOOR (St Matthew) and Whitehill *Portsm 4*   **P** *Earl of Selborne*   **V** A D RICHARDS
BLACKMORE (St Laurence) and Stondon Massey *Chelmsf 27*
P *Bp*   **V** I E CRAWFORD,   **NSM** A WHITAKER
BLACKPOOL (Christ Church w All Saints) (St Andrew)
Blackb 8   **P** *Bp and Trustees (jt)*   **V** P J WARREN
BLACKPOOL (Holy Cross) South Shore *Blackb 8*   **P** *Bp*
V S EDWARDS,   **C** R S WADEY
BLACKPOOL (Holy Trinity) *see* S Shore H Trin *Blackb*
BLACKPOOL (St John) *Blackb 8*   **P** *Trustees*
V M A MANLEY,   **C** S A PURVIS
BLACKPOOL (St Mark) *Blackb 8*   **P** *CPAS*   **NSM** J FISHER
BLACKPOOL (St Mary) South Shore *Blackb 8*   **P** *Bp*
P-in-c C G LORD
BLACKPOOL (St Michael and All Angels) *Blackb 8*   **P** *Bp*
V N J HEALE
BLACKPOOL (St Paul) Marton *see* Marton *Blackb*
BLACKPOOL (St Paul's Worship Centre) *Blackb 8*   **P** *Trustees*
P-in-c J E SHAW
BLACKPOOL (St Peter) *see* S Shore St Pet *Blackb*
BLACKPOOL (Stephen on the Cliffs) *Blackb 8*   **P** *Bp,
R Bispham All Hallows, and Ch Wardens (jt)*   **V** *vacant* (01253) 351484
BLACKPOOL (St Thomas) *Blackb 8*   **P** *CPAS*   **V** G A FISHER,
C P J NESBITT
BLACKPOOL (St Wilfrid) Mereside *Blackb 8*   **P** *Bp*
V P H HUDSON
BLACKROD (St Catherine) (Scot Lane School) *Man 11*
P *V Bolton-le-Moors St Pet*   **V** R C COOPER,
OLM C MCCABE
BLACKTOFT (Holy Trinity) *see* Howden *York*
BLACKWATER (St Barnabas) *see* Arreton *Portsm*
BLACKWELL (All Saints) and Salutation *Dur 8*   **P** *Bp*
V J R DOBSON,   **NSM** L G PEALL
BLACKWELL (St Catherine) *see* The Lickey *Birm*
BLACKWELL (St Werburgh) w Tibshelf *Derby 1*   **P** *Bp and MMCET (jt)*   **V** J CRANE
BLACON (Holy Trinity) *see* Ches H Trin *Ches*
BLADON (St Martin) w Woodstock *Ox 9*
P *Duke of Marlborough*   **R** R J HUMPHREYS,   **C** A R TURNER,
NSM C A W SANDERS, E J JOHNSON

BLAGDON (St Andrew) w Compton Martin and Ubley
B & W 10   **P** *Bp and Sir John Wills Bt (jt)*   **R** V E S GOODMAN
BLAGREAVES (St Andrew) *Derby 10*   **P** *Bp, Churchwardens, and CPAS (jt)*   **V** P G BYSOUTH
BLAISDON (St Michael and All Angels)
see Westbury-on-Severn w Flaxley, Blaisdon etc *Glouc*
BLAKEDOWN (St James the Great) *see* Churchill-in-Halfshire w Blakedown and Broome *Worc*
BLAKEMERE (St Leonard) *see* Cusop w Blakemere, Bredwardine w Brobury etc *Heref*
BLAKENALL HEATH (Christ Church) *Lich 25*   **P** *Patr Bd*
TR J C BARNES,   **TV** B D SIMS,   **C** J D DEAKIN
BLAKENEY (All Saints) *see* Newnham w Awre and Blakeney *Glouc*
BLAKENEY (St Nicholas w St Mary and St Thomas) w Cley, Wiveton, Glandford and Letheringsett *Nor 18*   **P** *Bp and Keble Coll Ox (jt)*   **R** P G F NORWOOD
BLAKENHALL (St Luke) *see* Wolverhampton St Luke *Lich*
BLAKENHAM, GREAT (St Mary) and LITTLE (St Mary) w Baylham and Nettlestead *St E 1*   **P** *Bp and MMCET (jt)*
R *vacant* (01473) 623840
BLAKESLEY (St Mary) w Adstone and Maidford and Farthingstone *Pet 5*   **P** *Sons of Clergy Corp, Bp, Hertf Coll Ox, and Capt R Grant-Renwick (by turn)*   **P-in-c** J T P HALL
BLANCHLAND (St Mary's Abbey) w Hunstanworth and Edmundbyers and Muggleswick *Newc 3*
P *D E Scott-Harden Esq, Lord Crewe's Trustees and D&C (alt)*
P-in-c D J IRVINE,   **NSM** J LYNCH
BLANDFORD FORUM (St Peter and St Paul) and Langton Long *Sarum 6*   **P** *Bp*   **R** T STOREY
BLANDFORD ST MARY (St Mary) *see* Spetisbury w Charlton Marshall etc *Sarum*
BLANKNEY (St Oswald) *see* Metheringham w Blankney and Dunston *Linc*
BLASTON (St Giles) *see* Six Saints circa Holt *Leic*
BLATCHINGTON, EAST (St John the Evangelist) (St Peter)
Chich 19   **P** *Bp*   **R** K YATES,   **NSM** R J WOODHAMS
BLATCHINGTON, WEST (St Peter) *Chich 4*   **P** *Bp*
R R T A FARROW
BLAXHALL (St Peter) *see* Gt and Lt Glemham, Blaxhall etc *St E*
BLEADON (St Peter and St Paul) *B & W 11*   **P** *Guild of All So*
R D T PARKINSON
BLEAN (St Cosmus and St Damian) *Cant 3*   **P** *Master of Eastbridge Hosp*   **P-in-c** D M H HAYES
BLEASBY (St Mary) *see* Thurgarton w Hoveringham and Bleasby etc *S'well*
BLEASDALE (St Eadmor) *see* Fellside Team *Blackb*
BLEATARN (Chapel of Ease) *see* Brough w Stainmore, Musgrave and Warcop *Carl*
BLEDINGTON (St Leonard) *see* Broadwell, Evenlode, Oddington, Adlestrop etc *Glouc*
BLEDLOW (Holy Trinity) *see* Risborough *Ox*
BLEDLOW RIDGE (St Paul) *see* W Wycombe w Bledlow Ridge, Bradenham and Radnage *Ox*
BLENDON (St James the Great) *Roch 17*   **P** *The Crown*
V A KEELER
BLENDWORTH (Holy Trinity) w Chalton w Idsworth *Portsm 5*
P *Bp*   **P-in-c** T A J READER,   **NSM** P FLETCHER, B R SMITH,
R A DONALD
BLETCHINGDON (St Giles) *see* Akeman *Ox*
BLETCHINGLEY (St Andrew) (St Mary) *S'wark 26*
P *Em Coll Cam*   **R** D C EDWARDS
BLETCHLEY (St Mary) *Ox 25*   **P** *DBP*   **P-in-c** M J ARCHER,
C C BUTT,   J M A ADAMS
BLETCHLEY, NORTH (Whaddon Way Church) Conventional District *Ox 25*   **NSM** J M LAWRENCE
BLETSOE (St Mary) *see* Riseley w Bletsoe *St Alb*
BLEWBURY (St Michael and All Angels), Hagbourne and Upton *Ox 18*   **P** *Bp*   **R** E G CLEMENTS,   **C** R J E DEWHURST
BLICKLING (St Andrew) *see* Lt Barningham, Blickling, Edgefield etc *Nor*
BLIDWORTH (St Mary of the Purification) w Rainworth
S'well 2   **P** *DBP and Ld Chan (alt)*   **V** R GOODHAND,
NSM B A ALLSOP
BLIDWORTH, NEW (St Andrew) *see* Blidworth w Rainworth *S'well*
BLINDLEY HEATH (St John the Evangelist) *see* Godstone and Blindley Heath *S'wark*
BLISLAND (St Protus and St Hyacinth) w St Breward *Truro 10*
P *SMF and D&C (alt)*   **P-in-c** D R CARRIVICK
BLISWORTH (St John the Baptist) and Stoke Bruerne w Grafton Regis and Alderton *Pet 5*   **P** *BNC Ox and MMCET (2 turns), Ld Chan (1 turn)*   **R** R MELLOR
BLITHFIELD (St Leonard) *see* Abbots Bromley w Blithfield *Lich*

BLO' NORTON (St Andrew) *see* Guiltcross *Nor*

BLOCKLEY (St Peter and St Paul) w Aston Magna and Bourton on the Hill *Glouc 9* P *Lord Dulverton and DBP (jt)* P-in-c G L HUMPHRIES

BLOFIELD (St Andrew) w Hemblington *Nor 4* P *G&C Coll Cam* P-in-c P J UNSWORTH

BLOOMSBURY (St George) w Woburn Square (Christ Church) *Lon 17* P *Ld Chan* R *P A BUTLER,* Hon C R I T JARRETT

BLORE RAY (St Bartholomew) *see* Calton, Cauldon, Grindon, Waterfall etc *Lich*

BLOXHAM (Our Lady of Bloxham) w Milcombe and South Newington *Ox 5* P *Ex Coll Ox and Eton Coll (jt)* V J R A STROYAN

BLOXHOLME (St Mary) *see* Digby Gp *Linc*

BLOXWICH (All Saints) (Holy Ascension) *Lich 25* P *Patr Bd* TR S C RAWLING, TV M H HAWKSWORTH

BLOXWORTH (St Andrew) *see* Red Post *Sarum*

BLUBBERHOUSES (St Andrew) *see* Leathley w Farnley, Fewston and Blubberhouses *Bradf*

BLUCHER (St Cuthbert) *see* Newburn *Newc*

BLUE BELL HILL (St Alban) *see* S Chatham H Trin *Roch*

BLUNDELLSANDS (St Michael) *Liv 5* P *Trustees* P-in-c M C FREEMAN

BLUNDELLSANDS (St Nicholas) *Liv 5* P *Trustees* V C M M THORNBOROUGH

BLUNDESTON (St Mary) *see* Somerleyton, Ashby, Fritton, Herringfleet etc *Nor*

BLUNHAM (St Edmund King and Martyr and St James), Great Barford, Roxton and Tempsford w Little Barford *St Alb 11* P *Prime Min, Trin Coll Cam (2 turns), and Ball Coll Ox (by turn)* R B EBELING, NSM D C QUIN

BLUNSDON (St Andrew) *see* N Swindon St Andr *Bris*

BLUNTISHAM (St Mary) cum Earith w Colne and Woodhurst *Ely 10* P *Ch Ch Ox* R C BACKHOUSE

BLURTON (St Bartholomew) (St Alban) *Lich 13* P *Bp* V P J MOCKFORD, C M R CHARMLEY, Hon C D A HEWITSON, OLM H T ADAMS

BLYBOROUGH (St Alkmund) *see* Glentworth Gp *Linc*

BLYFORD (All Saints) *see* Blyth Valley *St E*

BLYMHILL (St Mary) w Weston-under-Lizard *Lich 2* P *W H C Montgomery Esq, Sir Brooke Boothby Bt, and Viscount Boyne (jt)* P-in-c G J THOMPSON, NSM M G SIMS

BLYTH (St Cuthbert) *Newc 1* P *Bp* V R D TAYLOR

BLYTH (St Mary) *Newc 1* P *Bp* V B BENISON

BLYTH (St Mary and St Martin) and Scrooby w Ranskill *S'well 1* P *Bp and Trin Coll Cam (jt)* V R A SPRAY

BLYTH VALLEY Team Ministry, The *St E 15* P *Patr Bd* TR E L RENNARD, TV A B NORTON, A S DOTCHIN, C J B BYRNE, OLM A G DEERING, J E A BAILEY, M T JOEL, T SAVEGE, A C WRIGHT

BLYTHBURGH (Holy Trinity) *see* Sole Bay *St E*

BLYTON (St Martin) *see* Corringham and Blyton Gp *Linc*

BOARHUNT (St Nicholas) *see* Southwick w Boarhunt *Portsm*

BOARSTALL (St James) *see* Bernwode *Ox*

BOBBING (St Bartholomew) *see* Sittingbourne H Trin w Bobbing *Cant*

BOBBINGTON (Holy Cross) *see* Smestow Vale *Lich*

BOBBINGWORTH (St Germain) *see* Fyfield, Moreton w Bobbingworth etc *Chelmsf*

BOCKING (St Mary) *Chelmsf 15* P *Abp Cant* R P A NEED, C R D WALL

BOCKING (St Peter) *Chelmsf 15* P *Abp Cant* V T C DIAPER

BOCKLETON (St Michael) *see* Leominster *Heref*

BOCONNOC (not known) *see* Lostwithiel, St Winnow w St Nectan's Chpl etc *Truro*

BODDINGTON (St John the Baptist) *see* Byfield w Boddington and Aston le Walls *Pet*

BODDINGTON (St Mary Magdalene) *see* Staverton w Boddington and Tredington etc *Glouc*

BODENHAM (St Michael and All Angels) w Hope-under-Dinmore, Felton and Preston Wynne *Heref 4* P *Bp* P-in-c C M HILL

BODHAM (All Saints) *see* Weybourne Gp *Nor*

BODIAM (St Giles) *Chich 20* P *All So Coll Ox* R R K BAKER

BODICOTE (St John the Baptist) *Ox 5* P *New Coll Ox* V B L M PHILLIPS

BODINNICK (St John) *see* Lanteglos by Fowey *Truro*

BODLE STREET GREEN (St John the Evangelist) *see* Warbleton and Bodle Street Green *Chich*

BODMIN (St Leonard) (St Petroc) w Lanhydrock and Lanivet *Truro 10* P *DBP* TR G G C MINORS, C A B SHAW, Hon C J MARSHALL, NSM F B J COOMBES

BODNEY (St Mary) *see* Hilborough w Bodney *Nor*

BOGNOR (St Wilfrid) *Chich 1* P *Abp* V R P CALDER, C W G BULLOCH

BOLAM (St Andrew) *see* Heighington *Dur*

BOLAM (St Andrew) w Whalton and Hartburn w Meldon *Newc 11* P *Ld Chan (2 turns), J I K Walker Esq (1 turn), and D&C Dur (1 turn)* R G F REVETT

BOLAS MAGNA (St John the Baptist) *see* Tibberton w Bolas Magna and Waters Upton *Lich*

BOLDMERE (St Michael) *Birm 12* P *Birm Dioc Trustees* V P HOWELL-JONES, C N R WILLS, E G A DAVIS

BOLDON (St Nicholas) *Dur 15* P *Bp* R *vacant* 0191-536 7370

BOLDON, EAST (St George) *Dur 15* P *Bp* V E G STEPHENSON, NSM S BUYERS, M R DEVINE

BOLDRE (St John the Baptist) w South Baddesley *Win 11* P *Bp and Lord Teynham (jt)* V M L RICHES

BOLDRE, EAST (St Paul) *see* Beaulieu and Exbury and E Boldre *Win*

BOLDRON (Mission Room) *see* Startforth and Bowes and Rokeby w Brignall *Ripon*

BOLE (St Martin) *see* N Wheatley, W Burton, Bole, Saundby, Sturton etc *S'well*

BOLINGBROKE (St Peter and St Paul) *see* Marden Hill Gp *Linc*

BOLINGBROKE, NEW (St Peter) *see* Sibsey w Frithville *Linc*

BOLLINGHAM (St Silas) *see* Eardisley w Bollingham, Willersley, Brilley etc *Heref*

BOLLINGTON (Holy Trinity) *see* Rostherne w Bollington *Ches*

BOLLINGTON (St John the Baptist) *Ches 13* P *V Prestbury* V S R MARSH

BOLLINGTON CROSS (St Oswald) *see* Bollington St Jo *Ches*

BOLNEY (St Mary Magdalene) *Chich 6* P *K Coll Lon* P-in-c F MITCHINSON

BOLNHURST (St Dunstan) *see* Keysoe w Bolnhurst and Lt Staughton *St Alb*

BOLSOVER (St Mary and St Laurence) *Derby 3* P *Bp* V W T HICKS, C M SHAW

BOLSTERSTONE (St Mary) *Sheff 3* P *R B Rimington Wilson Esq* V K J BARNARD, C C E BARNARD

BOLTBY (Holy Trinity) *see* Felixkirk w Boltby *York*

BOLTON (All Saints) *see* Binsey *Carl*

BOLTON (All Saints) *Carl 1* P *V Morland w Thrimby etc* P-in-c D C WOOD

BOLTON Breightmet (St James) *Man 16* P *The Crown* P-in-c S C EDWARDS, NSM A PIERCE

BOLTON Chapel (unknown) *see* Whittingham and Edlingham w Bolton Chapel *Newc*

BOLTON (St Chad) *see* Tonge Fold *Man*

BOLTON (St James w St Chrysostom) *Bradf 3* P *Bp* V D J SWALES, C C B LLOYD

BOLTON (St John the Evangelist) Top o' th' Moss *Man 16* P *The Crown* P-in-c G H YERBURY

BOLTON (St Matthew w St Barnabas) *see* Halliwell *Man*

BOLTON (St Paul) *as above Man*

BOLTON (St Thomas the Apostle) *as above Man*

BOLTON ABBEY (St Mary and St Cuthbert) *Bradf 7* P *Duke of Devonshire* R J S WARD

BOLTON BY BOWLAND (St Peter and St Paul) w Grindleton *Bradf 5* P *Bp and V Hurst Green and Mitton (jt)* R D W MEWIS

BOLTON LE MOORS (St Bede) *Man 11* P *Bp* P-in-c A BORSBEY

BOLTON LE MOORS (St Paul) (Emmanuel) *Man 9* P *Patr Bd* P-in-c R J HORROCKS, C J A M BARNETT

BOLTON LE MOORS (St Peter) *Man 9* P *Bp* P-in-c M J WILLIAMS, C D A PLUMMER, NSM K G C NEWPORT

BOLTON LE MOORS (St Philip) *Man 9* P *Bp and Hulme Trustees (alt)* V *vacant* (01204) 61533

BOLTON LE MOORS (St Simon and St Jude) *Man 9* P *Trustees* P-in-c G BUSH

BOLTON-LE-SANDS (Holy Trinity) *Blackb 14* P *Bp* V T J L MAIDMENT, NSM B C JONES, L MACLUSKIE

BOLTON ON SWALE (St Mary) *see* Easby w Brompton on Swale and Bolton on Swale *Ripon*

BOLTON PERCY (All Saints) *York 1* P *Abp* P-in-c F A R MINAY

BOLTON-UPON-DEARNE (St Andrew the Apostle) *Sheff 12* P *Meynall Ch Trust* V D G STAFFORD

BOLTONS, THE *see* W Brompton St Mary w St Pet *Lon*

BOLVENTOR (Holy Trinity) *see* Altarnon w Bolventor, Laneast and St Clether *Truro*

BOMERE HEATH (Mission Room) *see* Leaton and Albrighton w Battlefield *Lich*

BONBY (St Andrew) *Linc 6* P *DBP* V G A PLUMB

BONCHURCH (St Boniface) (St Boniface Old Church) *Portsm 7* P *Ch Patr Trust* P-in-c D H LAURIE, NSM C A DAVIES

BONDLEIGH (St James the Apostle)   *see* N Tawton, Bondleigh, Sampford Courtenay etc *Ex*

BONEY HAY   *see* Chase Terrace *Lich*

BONINGALE (St Chad)   *Lich 16*   **P** *MMCET*
P-in-c R B BALKWILL

BONNINGTON (St Rumwold)   *see* Aldington w Bonnington and Bilsington etc *Cant*

BONSALL (St James the Apostle)   *see* Wirksworth *Derby*

BOOKER (St Birinus' Mission Church)   *see* High Wycombe *Ox*

BOOKHAM, GREAT (St Nicholas) *Guildf 10*   **P** *Bp*
R P R FLEMING,   **C** A E EVANS

BOOKHAM, LITTLE (not known)   *see* Effingham w Lt Bookham *Guildf*

BOONGATE (St Mary)   *see* Pet St Mary Boongate *Pet*

BOOSBECK (St Aidan) w Moorsholm *York 16*   **P** *Abp*
V E R NORRIS

BOOTHBY GRAFFOE (St Andrew)   *see* Graffoe Gp *Linc*

BOOTHBY PAGNELL (St Andrew)   *see* Ingoldsby *Linc*

BOOTHSTOWN (St Andrew's Church Institute)   *see* Worsley *Man*

BOOTLE (Christ Church) *Liv 1*   **P** *Bp*   **V** T RICH

BOOTLE (St Leonard) *Liv 1*   **P** Simeon's Trustees
P-in-c R J DRIVER

BOOTLE (St Mary w St Paul) *Liv 1*   **P** *Bp and Trustees (jt)*
V *vacant* 0151-922 1315

BOOTLE (St Matthew) *Liv 1*   **P** *Bp*   **P-in-c** R J DRIVER

BOOTLE (St Michael and All Angels), Corney, Whicham and Whitbeck *Carl 5*   **P** Earl of Lonsdale   **P-in-c** A D CORDINER

BORASTON (not known)   *see* Burford I *Heref*

BORDEN (St Peter and St Paul) *Cant 16*   **P** *SMF*
NSM C S JOHNSON

BORDERLINK PARISHES   *see* Cusop w Blakemere, Bredwardine w Brobury etc *Heref*

BORDESLEY (St Alban and St Patrick)   *see* Highgate *Birm*

BORDESLEY (St Benedict) *Birm 13*   **P** Keble Coll *Ox*
V M O C JOY,   **C** R J PRESTON

BORDESLEY GREEN (St Paul) *Birm 13*   **P** The Crown
V G C TURNER

BORDON (St Mark) *Guildf 3*   **P** *Bp*   **V** H O'SULLIVAN

BOREHAM (St Andrew) *Chelmsf 9*   **P** *Bp*   **P-in-c** A J ROSE

BOREHAM (St John the Evangelist)   *see* Bishopstrow and Boreham *Sarum*

BOREHAMWOOD (All Saints) (Holy Cross) (St Michael and All Angels) *St Alb 1*   **P** Patr Bd   **TR** T G WARR,
TV R C A LESLIE, A-M L RENSHAW

BORLEY (not known)   *see* N Hinckford *Chelmsf*

BOROUGH GREEN (Good Shepherd) *Roch 10*   **P** *Bp*
V A J POWELL

BOROUGHBRIDGE (St James)   *see* Aldborough w Boroughbridge and Roecliffe *Ripon*

BORROWASH (St Stephen's Chapel)   *see* Ockbrook *Derby*

BORROWDALE (St Andrew)   *see* Thornthwaite cum Braithwaite, Newlands etc *Carl*

BORSTAL (St Matthew) *Roch 5*   **P** V Rochester St Marg
P-in-c J E G DASH

BORWICK (St Mary)   *see* Warton St Oswald w Yealand Conyers *Blackb*

BOSBURY (Holy Trinity)   *see* Ledbury *Heref*

BOSCASTLE w Davidstow *Truro 10*   **P** Duchy of Cornwall *(1 turn), DBP (2 turns)*   **P-in-c** C MUSSER

BOSCOMBE (St Andrew)   *see* Bourne Valley *Sarum*

BOSCOMBE (St Andrew) *Win 8*   **P** *Bp*   **V** N A CARTER

BOSCOMBE (St John the Evangelist) *Win 8*
P Peache Trustees   **C** P R WORLEDGE,   **NSM** N S LEGRAND

BOSCOPPA *Truro 1*   **P** Prime Min   **P-in-c** K P ARTHUR

BOSHAM (Holy Trinity) *Chich 13*   **P** *Bp*   **V** T J INMAN,
NSM J V EMERSON

BOSLEY (St Mary the Virgin) and North Rode (St Michael) w Wincle (St Michael) and Wildboarclough (St Saviour) *Ches 13*
P Bp, V Prestbury, and Earl of Derby (jt)   **V** D W MOIR

BOSSALL (St Botolph)   *see* Sand Hutton *York*

BOSSINGTON (St James)   *see* Broughton, Bossington, Houghton and Mottisfont *Win*

BOSTALL HEATH (St Andrew) *Roch 15*   **P** *DBP*
V S SHOOTER

BOSTON (Holy Trinity)   *see* Skirbeck H Trin *Linc*

BOSTON (St Botolph) (St Christopher) *Linc 20*   **P** *Bp*
C P N MARSHALL, C H BROWN

BOSTON (St Nicholas)   *see* Skirbeck St Nic *Linc*

BOSTON (St Thomas)   *see* Skirbeck Quarter *Linc*

BOSTON SPA (St Mary) *York 1*   **P** Ch Ch *Ox*
V P E BRISTOW,   **C** A S G PIKE,   **NSM** M C PARKIN,
S H ROLLINGS

BOSWORTH (St Peter) and Sheepy Group *Leic 13*   **P** Patr Bd *(2 turns), Ld Chan (1 turn)*   **TR** J F PLANT,
TV B CAMPBELL, A S REED,   **NSM** A C HOLDSTOCK

BOTCHERBY (St Andrew)   *see* Carl St Aid and Ch Ch *Carl*

BOTESDALE (St Botolph)   *see* Redgrave cum Botesdale w Rickinghall *St E*

BOTHAL (St Andrew) and Pegswood w Longhirst *Newc 11*
P *Bp*   **R** S J LIDDLE,   **OLM** J J BECKWITH

BOTHAMSALL (Our Lady and St Peter)   *see* Elkesley w Bothamsall *S'well*

BOTHENHAMPTON (Holy Trinity)   *see* Bridport *Sarum*

BOTLEY (All Saints) *Portsm 1*   **P** *Bp*   **R** I G COOMBER,
C G M W KEITH,   **NSM** E A GROVES

BOTLEY (St Peter and St Paul)   *see* N Hinksey and Wytham *Ox*

BOTLEYS and Lyne (Holy Trinity) *Guildf 11*   **P** *Bp*
V A B OLSEN,   **NSM** D GODDARD

BOTOLPHS (St Botolph)   *see* Beeding and Bramber w Botolphs *Chich*

BOTTESFORD (St Mary the Virgin)   *see* Vale of Belvoir Par *Leic*

BOTTESFORD (St Peter) w Ashby *Linc 4*   **P** Patr Bd
TV P J LILEY, G M LINES,   **C** L T WHITFIELD

BOTTISHAM (Holy Trinity)   *see* Anglesey Gp *Ely*

BOTUS FLEMING (St Mary)   *see* Landrake w St Erney and Botus Fleming *Truro*

BOUGHTON (All Saints) *Ely 15*   **P** *Bp*   **R** *vacant*

BOUGHTON (St John the Baptist)   *see* Pitsford w Boughton *Pet*

BOUGHTON (St Matthew)   *see* Ollerton w Boughton *S'well*

BOUGHTON ALUPH (All Saints)   *see* Westwell, Hothfield, Eastwell and Boughton Aluph *Cant*

BOUGHTON ALUPH (St Christopher)   *as above Cant*

BOUGHTON MALHERBE (St Nicholas)   *see* Len Valley *Cant*

BOUGHTON MONCHELSEA (St Augustine) (St Peter)
Cant 15   **P** *Abp*   **V** R G DAVIS

BOUGHTON UNDER BLEAN (St Barnabas) (St Peter and St Paul) w Dunkirk and Hernhill *Cant 6*   **P** *Abp*
V J W R MOWLL

BOULGE (St Michael) w Burgh, Grundisburgh and Hasketon
St E 7   **P** Bp and DBP (jt)   **R** N DAVIS

BOULMER (St Andrew)   *see* Longhoughton w Howick *Newc*

BOULTHAM (Holy Cross) (St Helen) (St Mary Magdalene) (St Matthew) *Linc 15*   **P** *DBP*   **R** D J OSBOURNE,
C C M THACKER

BOULTON (St Mary the Virgin) *Derby 15*   **P** *Bp*
V T S WRIGHT,   **C** D BISHOP

BOUNDSTONE (Mission Church)   *see* Wrecclesham *Guildf*

BOURN (St Helena and St Mary)   *see* Papworth *Ely*

BOURNE (St Peter and St Paul) *Linc 13*   **P** *DBP*
V C J ATKINSON

BOURNE, The (St Thomas) and Tilford *Guildf 3*   **P** Bp and Adn Surrey (alt)   **V** J T L STILL,   **C** D E CROSBY,
Hon C J W BELL,   **NSM** J D A ADAMS, M E JACKSON

BOURNE, LOWER (St Martin)   *see* The Bourne and Tilford *Guildf*

BOURNE END (St John)   *see* Sunnyside w Bourne End *St Alb*

BOURNE END (St Mark)   *see* Hedsor and Bourne End *Ox*

BOURNE STREET (St Mary)   *see* Pimlico St Mary Bourne Street *Lon*

BOURNE VALLEY *Sarum 10*   **P** Patr Bd   **TR** C ALLSOPP,
TV S S BURNS,   **C** R V GOODBODY,   **NSM** T E GOODBODY

BOURNEMOUTH (All Saints)   *see* Pokesdown All SS *Win*

BOURNEMOUTH (Christ Church)   *see* Westbourne Ch Ch CD *Win*

BOURNEMOUTH (Holy Epiphany) *Win 8*   **P** *Bp*
P-in-c K V BATT

BOURNEMOUTH (St Alban) *Win 8*   **P** *Bp*   **P-in-c** R L NASH

BOURNEMOUTH (St Ambrose) *Win 8*   **P** *Bp*
P-in-c G J WHEELER

BOURNEMOUTH (St Andrew) Bennett Road *Win 8*
P Trustees   **P-in-c** G M ROBERTS

BOURNEMOUTH (St Augustine) *Win 8*   **P** *Bp*
P-in-c J J RICHARDSON

BOURNEMOUTH (St Barnabas) Queen's Park
see Holdenhurst and Iford *Win*

BOURNEMOUTH (St Clement) *Win 8*   **P** *DBP*   **V** *vacant* (01202) 392851

BOURNEMOUTH (St Francis) *Win 8*   **P** *CR*
V P G BERRETT,   **NSM** A J JORDAN

BOURNEMOUTH (St James)   *see* Pokesdown St Jas *Win*

BOURNEMOUTH (St John) (St Michael and All Angels) *Win 8*
P Bp and S R Willcox Esq (jt)   **P-in-c** R D BALDOCK,
Hon C S A WOAN

BOURNEMOUTH (St John the Evangelist)   *see* Boscombe St Jo *Win*

BOURNEMOUTH (St Luke) *Win 8*   **P** *Bp*   **V** S HOLMES

BOURNEMOUTH (St Peter) (St Stephen) w St Swithun and Holy Trinity *Win 8*   **P** Patr Bd   **TR** J J RICHARDSON,
TV R C N HARGER,   H G JAMES

BOURNVILLE (St Andrew)   *see* Weston-super-Mare St Andr Bournville *B & W*

BOURNVILLE (St Francis) *Birm 5* **P** *Bp* **V** P G BABINGTON,
NSM P L CADOGAN
BOURTON (Holy Trinity) *see* Wenlock *Heref*
BOURTON (St George) *see* Upper Stour *Sarum*
BOURTON (St James) *see* Shrivenham and Ashbury *Ox*
BOURTON (St Peter) w Frankton and Stretton on Dunsmore w
Princethorpe *Cov 6* **P** *Bp (2 turns), Simeon's Trustees*
(1 turn), and Mrs J H Shaw-Fox (1 turn) **P-in-c** C B POLLARD
BOURTON, GREAT (All Saints) *see* Shires' Edge *Ox*
BOURTON ON THE HILL (St Lawrence) *see* Blockley w
Aston Magna and Bourton on the Hill *Glouc*
BOURTON-ON-THE-WATER (St Lawrence) w Clapton
Glouc 14 **P** *Wadh Coll Ox* **P-in-c** E N P TUFNELL,
C I J TOMKINS, **NSM** T LOCKWOOD
BOVEY, NORTH (St John the Baptist) *see* Moretonhampstead,
Manaton, N Bovey and Lustleigh *Ex*
BOVEY TRACEY (St John the Evangelist) w Heathfield *Ex 10*
P *Guild of All So* **V** D J STANTON
BOVEY TRACEY (St Peter and St Paul and St Thomas of
Canterbury) w Hennock *Ex 10* **P** *Prime Min (2 turns),*
MMCET (1 turn) **V** W G HAMILTON, **Hon C** J E SPENCER
BOVINGDON (St Lawrence) *St Alb 5* **P** *Ch Soc Trust*
V T J MARSHALL, **Hon C** R H METCALFE
BOW (All Hallows) *see* Bromley by Bow All Hallows *Lon*
BOW (St Bartholomew) w Broad Nymet *Ex 2* **P** *DBP*
R J C HALL
BOW (St Mary) w Bromley (St Leonard) *Lon 7* **P** *Bp*
R G W GARNER, **NSM** D F WAXHAM
BOW BRICKHILL (All Saints) *see* Brickhills and Stoke
Hammond *Ox*
BOW COMMON (St Paul) *Lon 7* **P** *Bp* **V** D G ROSS,
C I C CZERNIAWSKA EDGCUMBE, **NSM** D S WEBB
BOWBROOK NORTH: Feckenham and Hanbury and Stock and
Bradley *Worc 8* **P** *Bp and D&C (jt)* **R** A J FULLER
BOWBROOK SOUTH: Crowle w Bredicot and Hadzor w
Oddingley and Tibberton and Himbleton and Huddington
Worc 8 **P** *Bp, D&C, R J G Berkeley Esq, and*
J F Bennett Esq (jt) **R** W D S WELLS
BOWBURN (Christ the King) *see* Cassop cum Quarrington
Dur
BOWDEN, GREAT (St Peter and St Paul) w Welham, Glooston
and Cranoe and Stonton Wyville *Leic 4* **P** *Bp,*
E Brudenell Esq, and MMCET (jt) **R** I W Y GEMMELL,
C S K BURNS
BOWDEN, LITTLE (St Hugh) *see* Market Harborough and
The Transfiguration etc *Leic*
BOWDEN, LITTLE (St Nicholas) *as above Leic*
BOWDEN HILL (St Anne) *see* Gtr Corsham and Lacock *Bris*
BOWDON (St Luke) (St Mary the Virgin) *Ches 10* **P** *Bp*
V K E HINE, **C** P J WALMSLEY
BOWERCHALKE (Holy Trinity) *see* Chalke Valley *Sarum*
BOWERS GIFFORD (St John) (St Margaret) w North Benfleet
Chelmsf 6 **P** *Em Coll Cam and Brig R H C Bryhers CBE (alt)*
C B C R JOHNSON
BOWES (St Giles) *see* Startforth and Bowes and Rokeby w
Brignall *Ripon*
BOWES PARK (St Michael-at-Bowes) *see* Wood Green St Mich
w Bounds Green St Gabr etc *Lon*
BOWLEE (St Thomas) *see* Rhodes *Man*
BOWLING (St John) *Bradf 2* **P** *V Bradford* **V** H K ASTIN,
C J SALMON
BOWLING (St Stephen) *Bradf 2* **P** *CPAS* **V** C W W BARBER
BOWNESS-ON-SOLWAY (St Michael), Kirkbride and Newton
Arlosh *Carl 3* **P** *Earl of Lonsdale (2 turns), V Holme Cultram*
(1 turn) **R** R P BLACKETT
BOWTHORPE (St Michael) *Nor 3* **P** *Bp and CPAS (jt)*
TV S D GODDARD
BOX (St Barnabas) *see* Minchinhampton *Glouc*
BOX (St Thomas à Becket) w Hazlebury and Ditteridge *Bris 4*
P *Bp* **R** R J SNOW, **NSM** J AYERS
BOX HILL (St Andrew) *see* Headley w Box Hill *Guildf*
BOX RIVER *see* Boxford, Edwardstone, Groton etc *St E*
BOXFORD (St Andrew) *see* Welford w Wickham and Gt
Shefford, Boxford etc *Ox*
BOXFORD (St Mary), Edwardstone, Groton, Little Waldingfield
and Newton *St E 12* **P** *DBP and The Hon Thomas Lindsay*
(1 turn), Ld Chan (2 turns), Peterho Cam (1 turn)
R D W MATTHEWS
BOXGROVE (St Mary and St Blaise) *Chich 3* **P** *Duke of*
Richmond and Gordon **P-in-c** I M FORRESTER
BOXLEY (St Mary the Virgin and All Saints) w Detling *Cant 15*
P *Abp* **P-in-c** R G GAMBLE, **NSM** E A ATTAWAY
BOXMOOR (St John the Evangelist) *St Alb 3* **P** *Bp*
V P V HUGHES, **C** L J BURGESS, **NSM** G A J ADAM
BOXTED (Holy Trinity) *see* Glem Valley United Benefice *St E*
BOXTED (St Peter) *see* Langham w Boxted *Chelmsf*

BOXWELL (St Mary the Virgin), Leighterton, Didmarton,
Oldbury-on-the-Hill and Sopworth *Glouc 15* **P** *Duke of*
Beaufort and J A Hutley Esq (alt) **R** N C J MULHOLLAND
BOXWORTH (St Peter) *see* Papworth *Ely*
BOYATT WOOD (St Peter) *Win 10* **P** *Bp* **V** P M GILKS,
NSM V A CORCORAN
BOYLESTONE (St John the Baptist), Church Broughton,
Dalbury, Longford, Long Lane, Radbourne, Sutton on the Hill
and Trusley *Derby 14* **P** *Patr Bd* **R** P M BISHOP
BOYNE HILL (All Saints) *Ox 13* **P** *Bp* **V** N J BROWN,
C R LANGTON
BOYNTON (St Andrew) *see* Rudston w Boynton, Carnaby and
Kilham *York*
BOYTHORPE (St Francis) *see* Chesterfield St Aug *Derby*
BOYTON (Holy Name), North Tamerton, Werrington w
St Giles-in-the-Heath and Virginstow *Truro 9* **P** *Duke*
of Cornwall, MMCET, Ld Chan, and R Williams Esq (by turn)
P-in-c K WAKEFIELD
BOYTON (St Andrew) *see* Wilford Peninsula *St E*
BOYTON (St Mary the Virgin) *see* Upper Wylye Valley *Sarum*
BOZEAT (St Mary) w Easton Maudit *Pet 6* **P** *Bp and*
Marquess of Northn (alt) **V** *vacant* (01933) 663216
BRABOURNE (St Mary the Blessed Virgin) *see* Smeeth w
Monks Horton and Stowting and Brabourne *Cant*
BRACEBOROUGH (St Margaret) *see* Uffington Gp *Linc*
BRACEBRIDGE (All Saints) *Linc 15*
P *Mrs B M Ellison-Lendrum* **V** J D DUCKETT,
OLM S E KIDDLE
BRACEBRIDGE HEATH (St John the Evangelist) *Linc 15*
P *Bp* **V** H C MIDDLETON
BRACEBY (St Margaret) *see* Sapperton w Braceby *Linc*
BRACEWELL (St Michael) *see* Barnoldswick w Bracewell
Bradf
BRACKENFIELD (Holy Trinity) *see* Ashover and
Brackenfield w Wessington *Derby*
BRACKLEY (St Peter w St James) *Pet 1* **P** *Bp* **V** N J GANDY,
C L BOND
BRACKNELL (Holy Trinity) *Ox 11* **P** *Bp* **TR** D R OSBORN,
TV C BLUNDELL, J M HARRIS, **Hon C** M G CLARKE,
NSM I N JAMES
BRACON ASH (St Nicholas) *see* Mulbarton w Bracon Ash,
Hethel and Flordon *Nor*
BRADBOURNE (All Saints) *see* Wirksworth *Derby*
BRADDAN (St Brendan) *S & M 2* **P** *Bp* **V** P S FREAR
BRADDEN (St Michael) *see* Greens Norton w Bradden and
Lichborough *Pet*
BRADELEY (St Mary and All Saints), Church Eaton and
Moreton *Lich 10* **P** *Bp and V Gnosall (jt)* **R** T W B FOX
BRADENHAM (St Botolph) *see* W Wycombe w Bledlow
Ridge, Bradenham and Radnage *Ox*
BRADENHAM, WEST (St Andrew) *see* Shipdham w E and W
Bradenham *Nor*
BRADENSTOKE (St Mary) *see* Lyneham w Bradenstoke
Sarum
BRADFIELD (St Andrew) and Stanford Dingley *Ox 12*
P *Ch Soc Trust* **R** H W ELLIS, **OLM** R S GREEN
BRADFIELD (St Clare) *see* Cockfield w Bradfield St Clare,
Felsham etc *St E*
BRADFIELD (St Giles) *see* Trunch *Nor*
BRADFIELD (St Lawrence) *see* Mistley w Manningtree and
Bradfield *Chelmsf*
BRADFIELD (St Nicholas) *Sheff 3* **P** *V Ecclesfield*
R T M PAGE
BRADFIELD COMBUST (All Saints) *see* Hawstead and
Nowton w Stanningfield etc *St E*
BRADFIELD ST GEORGE (St George) *see* Gt and Lt
Whelnetham w Bradfield St George *St E*
BRADFORD (All Saints) *see* Black Torrington, Bradf w
Cookbury etc *Ex*
BRADFORD (St Augustine) Undercliffe *Bradf 3* **P** *V Bradf*
V D J POOLE, **C** A BOWERMAN
BRADFORD (St Clement) *Bradf 3* **P** *Bp (2 turns) and Trustees*
(1 turn) **V** J E BAVINGTON
BRADFORD (St Columba w St Andrew) *Bradf 2* **P** *Bp*
P-in-c P M BILTON
BRADFORD (St Giles) w Oake, Hillfarrance and Heathfield
B & W 19 **P** *Bp and M V Spurway Esq (jt)* **P-in-c** A NORRIS
BRADFORD (St Oswald) Chapel Green *Bradf 2* **P** *Bp*
P-in-c A S TREASURE, **NSM** M M MALEK
BRADFORD (St Saviour) *see* Fairweather Green *Bradf*
BRADFORD (St Wilfrid) Lidget Green *Bradf 2* **P** *Bp*
V P M BILTON, **NSM** G A BRIGHOUSE
BRADFORD, WEST (St Catherine) *see* Waddington *Bradf*
BRADFORD ABBAS (St Mary the Virgin) and Thornford w
Beer Hackett *Sarum 3* **P** *J K Wingfield Digby Esq and Win*
Coll (alt) **R** J A EVANS

BRADFORD-ON-AVON (Christ Church) *Sarum 14*
P *V Bradf H Trin*   **P-in-c** R M LOWRIE,   **NSM** B F CHAPMAN
BRADFORD-ON-AVON (Holy Trinity) *Sarum 14*   **P** *D&C*
V   W A MATTHEWS,   **NSM** A A ONIONS
BRADFORD ON TONE (St Giles)   *see* Bradford w Oake,
Hillfarrance and Heathfield *B & W*
BRADFORD PEVERELL (Church of the Assumption),
Stratton, Frampton and Sydling St Nicholas *Sarum 1*   **P** *Win*
Coll and Bp (alt)   **R** K J SCOTT,   **OLM** P A STEAR
BRADGATE TEAM, The - Ratby cum Groby w Newton Linford
Leic 12   **P** *Patr Bd*   **TR** R V WORSFOLD,   **TV** L D CORKE,
NSM S LEIGHTON
BRADING (St Mary the Virgin) w Yaverland *Portsm 7*
P *Hon Mrs I S T Monck and Trin Coll Cam (jt)*
R D J B ABINGTON
BRADLEY (All Saints)   *see* Hulland, Atlow, Kniveton, Bradley
and Hognaston *Derby*
BRADLEY (All Saints)   *see* The Candover Valley *Win*
BRADLEY (St George)   *see* Gt and Lt Coates w Bradley *Linc*
BRADLEY (St John the Baptist)   *see* Bowbrook N *Worc*
BRADLEY (St Martin) *Lich 28*   **P** *Baldwin Pugh Trustees*
V R M WALKER
BRADLEY (St Mary)   *see* Cononley w Bradley *Bradf*
BRADLEY (St Thomas) *Wakef 5*   **P** *Bp*   **V** D R WARD
BRADLEY, GREAT (St Mary the Virgin)   *see* Stourhead *St E*
BRADLEY, LITTLE (All Saints)   *as above St E*
BRADLEY, NORTH (St Nicholas) Southwick and Heywood
Sarum 14   **P** *Win Coll*   **V** J R PARKER
BRADLEY, WEST (not known)   *see* Baltonsborough w
Butleigh, W Bradley etc *B & W*
BRADLEY-LE-MOORS (St Leonard)   *see* Alton w
Bradley-le-Moors and Oakamoor w Cotton *Lich*
BRADLEY STOKE (Christ the King) *see* Stoke Gifford *Bris*
BRADLEY STOKE NORTH (Holy Trinity) Conventional
District *Bris 5*   **C-in-c** P J PETERSON
BRADMORE (Mission Room)   *see* Keyworth and
Stanton-on-the-Wolds and Bunny etc *S'well*
BRADNINCH (St Denis) and Clyst Hydon *Ex 4*   **P** *D&C and*
D&C Windsor (jt)   **R** D L D ROBOTTOM
BRADNOP (Mission Church)   *see* Ipstones w Berkhamsytch
and Onecote w Bradnop *Lich*
BRADOC (Blessed Virgin Mary)   *see* Lanreath, Pelynt and
Bradoc *Truro*
BRADPOLE (Holy Trinity)   *see* Bridport *Sarum*
BRADSHAW (St John the Evangelist) and Holmfield *Wakef 4*
P *Bp*   **V** A DICK,   **C** S E W SHRINE
BRADSHAW (St Maxentius)   *see* Turton Moorland Min *Man*
BRADWELL (Holy Trinity) *see* Cressing w Stisted and
Bradwell etc *Chelmsf*
BRADWELL (St Barnabas)   *see* Hope, Castleton and Bradwell
Derby
BRADWELL (St Barnabas)   *see* Wolstanton *Lich*
BRADWELL (St Laurence and Methodist United)
see Stantonbury and Willen *Ox*
BRADWELL (St Nicholas) *Nor 6*   **P** *Bp*   **R** R J TUCK,
NSM S D UPTON
BRADWELL, NEW (St James)   *see* Stantonbury and Willen *Ox*
BRADWELL ON SEA (St Thomas) (St Peter-on-the-Wall)
Chelmsf 11   **P** *Bp*   **P-in-c** E H BEAVAN,   **NSM** K I DUNSTAN
BRADWORTHY (St John the Baptist), Sutcombe, Putford,
Abbots Bickington and Bulkworthy *Ex 9*   **P** *Prime Min and Bp*
(alt)   **R** R B DORRINGTON
BRAFFERTON (St Peter) w Pilmoor, Myton on Swale and
Thormanby w Raskelf *York 3*   **P** *Abp and Sir Anthony Milnes*
Coates Bt (jt)   **P-in-c** J S COLE
BRAFIELD ON THE GREEN (St Laurence)   *see* Cogenhoe
and Gt and Lt Houghton w Brafield *Pet*
BRAILES (St George) *Cov 9*   **P** *D&C*   **V** N J MORGAN,
NSM J W ROLFE
BRAILSFORD (All Saints) w Shirley and Osmaston w Edlaston
Derby 8   **P** *Bp, Earl Ferrers, and Sir Peter Walker-Okeover Bt*
(by turn)   **R** I ALDERSLEY,   **Hon C** W M RUMBALL,
NSM C L JOHNSON
BRAINTREE (St Michael) *Chelmsf 15*   **P** *Ch Trust Fund Trust*
V C O MASON,   **C** M J PETERS
BRAINTREE (St Paul) *Chelmsf 15*   **P** *Ch Trust Fund Trust*
V R W SEWELL
BRAISHFIELD (All Saints)   *see* Michelmersh and Awbridge
and Braishfield etc *Win*
BRAITHWAITE (St Herbert)   *see* Thornthwaite cum
Braithwaite, Newlands etc *Carl*
BRAITHWELL (St James)   *see* Bramley and Ravenfield w
Hooton Roberts etc *Sheff*
BRAMBER (St Nicholas)   *see* Beeding and Bramber w Botolphs
Chich
BRAMBLETON (not known)   *see* The Bourne and Tilford
Guildf

BRAMCOTE (St Michael and All Angels) *S'well 7*   **P** *CPAS*
V N C STYLES,   **C** J R PRANCE
BRAMDEAN (St Simon and St Jude)   *see* Upper Itchen *Win*
BRAMDEAN COMMON (Church in the Wood)   *as above Win*
BRAMERTON (St Peter)   *see* Rockland St Mary w Hellington,
Bramerton etc *Nor*
BRAMFIELD (St Andrew)   *see* Blyth Valley *St E*
BRAMFIELD (St Andrew), Stapleford, Waterford and
Watton-at-Stone *St Alb 22*   **P** *R M A Smith Esq (3 turns),*
Grocers' Co (1 turn)   **NSM** R A MARTIN
BRAMFORD (St Mary the Virgin) *St E 1*   **P** *D&C Cant*
P-in-c R J DEDMAN
BRAMHALL (St Michael and All Angels) (Hall Chapel) *Ches 17*
P *Trustees*   **C** M A M WOLVERSON,   **NSM** L M DADSON,
P HARDMAN
BRAMHAM (All Saints) *York 1*   **P** *G Lane Fox Esq*
P-in-c H N LAWRANCE
BRAMHOPE (St Giles) *Ripon 7*   **P** *Trustees*
V D M ROBINSON
BRAMLEY (Holy Trinity) and Grafham *Guildf 2*   **P** *Ld Chan*
V J N E BUNDOCK,   **NSM** R J HEYES
BRAMLEY (St Francis) and Ravenfield w Hooton Roberts and
Braithwell *Sheff 6*   **P** *Patr Bd*   **TV** M GREENLAND,
P-in-c L S WORTLEY
BRAMLEY (St James) *Win 4*   **P** *Qu Coll Ox*   **V** R C TOOGOOD
BRAMLEY (St Peter) *Ripon 6*   **P** *DBP*   **V** I T RODLEY
BRAMPFORD SPEKE (St Peter)   *see* Thorverton, Cadbury,
Upton Pyne etc *Ex*
BRAMPTON (St Mark) *Derby 5*   **P** *Bp*   **P-in-c** F E WILLETT
BRAMPTON (St Martin)   *see* Eden, Gelt and Irthing *Carl*
BRAMPTON (St Mary Magdalene) *Ely 8*   **P** *Bp*
R M R GREENFIELD,   **NSM** S A WATTS
BRAMPTON (St Peter)   *see* Buxton w Oxnead, Lammas and
Brampton *Nor*
BRAMPTON (St Peter)   *see* Hundred River *St E*
BRAMPTON (St Thomas the Martyr) *Derby 5*   **P** *Bp*
P-in-c D P MOUNCER
BRAMPTON, OLD (St Peter and St Paul) (Cutthorpe Institute)
Derby 5   **P** *Bp*   **P-in-c** A P KAUNHOVEN
BRAMPTON ABBOTTS (St Michael)   *see* Ross *Heref*
BRAMPTON ASH (St Mary)   *see* Desborough, Brampton Ash,
Dingley and Braybrooke *Pet*
BRAMPTON BIERLOW (Christ Church) *Sheff 12*
P *V Wath-upon-Dearne*   **P-in-c** P E BOLD
BRAMPTON BRYAN (St Barnabas)   *see* Wigmore Abbey
Heref
BRAMSHALL (St Laurence)   *see* Uttoxeter Area *Lich*
BRAMSHAW (St Peter) and Landford w Plaitford *Sarum 10*
P *Bp and D&C (alt)*   **R** D P CLACEY
BRAMSHILL (Mission Church)   *see* Yateley and Eversley *Win*
BRAMSHOTT (St Mary the Virgin) and Liphook *Portsm 4*
P *Qu Coll Ox*   **R** S A WEEDEN,   **C** A I FORDYCE
BRANCASTER (St Mary the Virgin)   *see* Hunstanton St Mary
w Ringstead Parva etc *Nor*
BRANCEPETH (St Brandon) *Dur 1*   **P** *Bp*
P-in-c D C COULING
BRANCEPETH, NEW (St Catherine)   *see* Brandon *Dur*
BRANDESBURTON (St Mary) and Leven w Catwick *York 11*
P *St Jo Coll Cam, Exors Sir Henry Strickland-Constable Bt, and*
Simeon's Trustees (jt)   **C** I B KITCHEN
BRANDESTON (All Saints) w Kettleburgh and Easton *St E 18*
P *J Austin Esq, Capt J L Round-Turner, and MMCET (jt)*
P-in-c P G VELLACOTT
BRANDLESHOLME (St Francis House Chapel)   *see* Elton All
SS *Man*
BRANDON (Chapel)   *see* Barkston and Hough Gp *Linc*
BRANDON (St John the Evangelist) *Dur 1*   **P** *R Brancepeth*
V D B GODSELL,   **C** P BROWN
BRANDON (St Peter) and Santon Downham w Elveden *St E 11*
P *Exors Earl of Iveagh*   **P-in-c** R N LEACH,
OLM A S I BUTTREY
BRANDON PARVA (All Saints)   *see* Barnham Broom and
Upper Yare *Nor*
BRANDSBY (All Saints)   *see* Crayke w Brandsby and Yearsley
York
BRANDWOOD (St Bede) *Birm 5*   **P** *Bp*   **V** A M DELMEGE,
NSM R J REYNOLDS
BRANKSEA ISLAND (St Mary)   *see* Parkstone St Pet and St
Osmund w Branksea *Sarum*
BRANKSOME (St Aldhelm) (St Francis) *Sarum 7*   **P** *Bp*
V S R BATTY,   **C** S D METZNER,   **NSM** I M DOWLEN
BRANKSOME (St Clement) (St Barnabas) *Sarum 8*
P *MMCET*   **V** J G V FOSTER,   **C** S C L DIMES
BRANKSOME PARK (All Saints) *Sarum 7*   **P** *MMCET*
V C M DAY
BRANSCOMBE (St Winifred)   *see* Colyton, Musbury,
Southleigh and Branscombe *Ex*

BRANSDALE (St Nicholas)   *see* Kirkbymoorside w Gillamoor, Farndale etc *York*
BRANSFORD (St John the Baptist)   *see* Alfrick, Lulsley, Suckley, Leigh and Bransford *Worc*
BRANSGORE (St Mary the Virgin)   *Win 9*
   P *P W J Jesson Esq*   **V** *P C ELKINS*,   **NSM** *H M GRIFFISS*
BRANSHOLME (St John)   *see* Sutton St Jas and Wawne *York*
BRANSTON (All Saints) w Nocton and Potterhanworth   *Linc 18*
   P *Stowe Sch (2 turns), Ld Chan (1 turn), and Nocton Ltd (1 turn)*   **R** *D F REAGON*
BRANSTON (St Saviour) w Tatenhill   *Lich 14*   **P** *Bp and Simeon's Trustees (jt)*   **V** *vacant* (01283) 568926
BRANSTON BY BELVOIR (St Guthlac)   *see* High Framland Par *Leic*
BRANT BROUGHTON (St Helen) and Beckingham   *Linc 23*
   P *Bp and Sir Richard Sutton Bt (alt)*   **R** *A J MEGAHEY*
BRANT ROAD (Church Centre)   *see* Bracebridge *Linc*
BRANTHAM (St Michael and All Angels)   *see* E Bergholt and Brantham *St E*
BRANTINGHAM (All Saints)   *see* Elloughton and Brough w Brantingham *York*
BRANXTON (St Paul)   *Newc 12*   **P** *Abp*   **P-in-c** *M J GILLHAM*,   **C** *D F BROOKE*
BRASSINGTON (St James)   *see* Wirksworth *Derby*
BRASTED (St Martin)   *Roch 9*   **P** *Abp*   **R** *vacant* (01959) 563491
BRATHAY (Holy Trinity)   *see* Ambleside w Brathay *Carl*
BRATOFT (St Peter and St Paul) w Irby-in-the-Marsh   *Linc 8*
   P *Bp*   **R** *T STEELE*
BRATTLEBY (St Cuthbert)   *see* Aisthorpe w Scampton w Thorpe le Fallows etc *Linc*
BRATTON (St James the Great) (Oratory), Edington and Imber, Erlestoke and Coulston   *Sarum 16*   **P** *Bp and V Westbury (jt)*   **Hon C** *J M HALL*
BRATTON CLOVELLY (St Mary the Virgin)   *see* Okehampton w Inwardleigh, Bratton Clovelly etc *Ex*
BRATTON FLEMING (St Peter)   *see* Shirwell, Loxhore, Kentisbury, Arlington, etc *Ex*
BRATTON ST MAUR (St Nicholas)   *see* Bruton and Distr *B & W*
BRAUGHING (St Mary the Virgin) w Furneux Pelham and Stocking Pelham   *St Alb 18*   **P** *Bp and Lord Hamilton (alt)*   **R** *R H NOKES*
BRAUNSTON (All Saints)   *see* Daventry, Ashby St Ledgers, Braunston etc *Pet*
BRAUNSTON (All Saints)   *see* Oakham, Hambleton, Egleton, Braunston and Brooke *Pet*
BRAUNSTONE (St Crispin)   *Leic 12*   **P** *Bp*
   P-in-c *S R STEVENSON*,   **NSM** *F M KNIGHT*
BRAUNSTONE PARK (St Peter) Conventional District   *Leic 12*
   C-in-c *J C BURCH*,   **C** *R R SOUTER*
BRAUNTON (St Brannock)   *Ex 15*   **P** *Bp*   **V** *R P REEVE*,   **C** *P A JARVIS*,   **Hon C** *L A BUTTLE*
BRAXTED, GREAT (All Saints)   *see* Tolleshunt Knights w Tiptree and Gt Braxted *Chelmsf*
BRAXTED, LITTLE (St Nicholas)   *see* Wickham Bishops w Lt Braxted *Chelmsf*
BRAY (St Michael) and Braywood   *Ox 13*   **P** *Bp*
   V *G D REPATH*
BRAY, HIGH (All Saints)   *see* S Molton w Nymet St George, High Bray etc *Ex*
BRAYBROOKE (All Saints)   *see* Desborough, Brampton Ash, Dingley and Braybrooke *Pet*
BRAYDESTON (St Michael)   *see* Brundall w Braydeston and Postwick *Nor*
BRAYTON (St Wilfrid)   *York 4*   **P** *Abp*   **TR** *D H REYNOLDS*
BREADSALL (All Saints)   *Derby 9*   **P** *Miss A I M Harpur-Crewe*   **P-in-c** *N E WATSON*
BREADSTONE (St Michael and All Angels)   *see* Berkeley w Wick, Breadstone, Newport, Stone etc *Glouc*
BREAGE (St Breaca) w Germoe and Godolphin   *Truro 4*   **P** *Bp and Ld Chan (alt)*   **P-in-c** *P A STEVENS*
BREAM (St James)   *Glouc 4*   **P** *Bp*   **V** *A G KENDALL*,   **NSM** *M M HALE*
BREAMORE (St Mary)   *see* Fordingbridge and Breamore and Hale etc *Win*
BREAN (St Bridget)   *see* Berrow and Breane *B & W*
BREARTON (St John the Baptist)   *see* Knaresborough *Ripon*
BREASTON (St Michael)   *see* Wilne and Draycott w Breaston *Derby*
BRECKLES (St Margaret)   *see* Caston, Griston, Merton, Thompson etc *Nor*
BREDBURY (St Barnabas)   *Ches 16*   **P** *V Bredbury St Mark*
   V *C R WINDLE*
BREDBURY (St Mark)   *Ches 16*   **P** *Bp*   **V** *A R GARNER*
BREDE (St George) w Udimore   *Chich 20*   **P** *Bp and Mrs M E Crook (alt)*   **R** *D G LLOYD-JAMES*

BREDENBURY (St Andrew) w Grendon Bishop and Wacton, Edwyn Ralph, Collington, Thornbury, Pencombe and Marston Stannett and Little Cowarne   *Heref 2*   **P** *DBP, V Bromyard, and Lt-Col H H Barneby (jt)*   **R** *C I FLETCHER*
BREDFIELD (St Andrew)   *see* Woodbridge St Jo and Bredfield *St E*
BREDGAR (St John the Baptist) w Bicknor and Frinsted w Wormshill and Milsted   *Cant 16*   **P** *Abp, Lord Kingsdown, M Nightingale Esq, and S McCandlish Esq (jt)*
   P-in-c *S F AUSTIN*
BREDHURST (St Peter)   *see* S Gillingham *Roch*
BREDICOT (St James the Less)   *see* Bowbrook S *Worc*
BREDON (St Giles) w Bredon's Norton   *Worc 4*   **P** *Bp*
   R *M T C BAYNES*,   **NSM** *J A WILKINSON*
BREDON'S NORTON (not known)   *see* Bredon w Bredon's Norton *Worc*
BREDWARDINE (St Andrew)   *see* Cusop w Blakemere, Bredwardine w Brobury etc *Heref*
BREDY, LITTLE (St Michael and All Angels)   *see* Bride Valley *Sarum*
BREEDON-ON-THE-HILL (St Mary and St Hardulph) cum Isley Walton and Worthington   *Leic 9*   **P** *D A G Shields Esq and Ch Coll Cam (alt)*   **C** *K A L DENNIS*,   **NSM** *J W A DAWSON*
BREIGHTMET (St James)   *see* Bolton Breightmet St Jas *Man*
BREIGHTMET Top o' th' Moss (St John the Evangelist)   *see* Bolton St Jo *Man*
BREINTON (St Michael) (Mission Hall)   *Heref 3*   **P** *Bp*
   V *R NORTH*
BREMHILL (St Martin)   *see* Derry Hill w Bremhill and Foxham *Sarum*
BRENCHLEY (All Saints)   *Roch 8*   **P** *D&C Cant*
   V *R C PAGET*
BRENDON (St Brendon)   *see* Combe Martin, Berrynarbor, Lynton, Brendon etc *Ex*
BRENT, EAST (The Blessed Virgin Mary)   *see* Brent Knoll, E Brent and Lympsham *B & W*
BRENT, SOUTH (St Petroc) and Rattery   *Ex 13*   **P** *Bp and Sir Rivers Carew Bt (jt)*   **V** *D R WINNINGTON-INGRAM*,   **Hon C** *D G H HAMBLIN*
BRENT ELEIGH (St Mary)   *see* Monks Eleigh w Chelsworth and Brent Eleigh etc *St E*
BRENT KNOLL (St Michael) and East Brent and Lympsham   *B & W 1*   **P** *Adn Wells (1 turn), Bp (2 turns)*   **R** *M P LEE*
BRENT PELHAM (St Mary the Virgin)   *see* Hormead, Wyddial, Anstey, Brent Pelham etc *St Alb*
BRENT TOR (Christ Church)   *see* Peter Tavy, Mary Tavy, Lydford and Brent Tor *Ex*
BRENT TOR (St Michael)   *as above Ex*
BRENTFORD (St Paul w St Lawrence and St George) (St Faith)   *Lon 11*   **P** *Bp*   **TR** *D J SIMPSON*,   **TV** *R C HOAD*,   **C** *A L BROOKER*
BRENTRY (St Mark)   *see* Henbury *Bris*
BRENTS and Davington w Oare and Luddenham, The   *Cant 6*
   P *Abp and Ld Chan (alt)*   **P-in-c** *A C OEHRING*,   **C** *J HESS*
BRENTWOOD (St George the Martyr)   *Chelmsf 7*   **P** *DBP*
   V *G F JENKINS*
BRENTWOOD (St Thomas)   *Chelmsf 7*   **P** *DBP*
   P-in-c *R B WHITE*,   **C** *E J TOMLINSON*
BRENZETT (St Eanswith)   *see* Appledore w Brookland, Fairfield, Brenzett etc *Cant*
BRERETON (St Michael)   *Lich 3*   **P** *R Rugeley*
   P-in-c *W H HEATH*
BRERETON (St Oswald) w Swettenham   *Ches 11*   **P** *DBP and MMCET (jt)*   **P-in-c** *C M KEMP*
BRESSINGHAM (St John the Baptist) w North and South Lopham and Fersfield   *Nor 10*   **P** *R D A Woode Esq, MMCET, and St Jo Coll Cam (by turn)*   **P-in-c** *R J MELLOWSHIP*
BRETBY (St Wystan)   *see* Hartshorne and Bretby *Derby*
BRETFORTON (St Leonard)   *see* Badsey w Aldington and Offenham and Bretforton *Worc*
BRETHERTON (St John the Baptist)   *see* Croston and Bretherton *Blackb*
BRETTENHAM (St Andrew)   *see* E w W Harling, Bridgham w Roudham, Larling etc *Nor*
BRETTENHAM (St Mary)   *see* Rattlesden w Thorpe Morieux, Brettenham etc *St E*
BRETTON (Holy Spirit)   *see* Pet H Spirit Bretton *Pet*
BRETTON PARK (St Bartholomew)   *see* Woolley *Wakef*
BREWHAM, SOUTH (St John the Baptist)   *see* Bruton and Distr *B & W*
BREWOOD (St Mary and St Chad)   *Lich 2*   **P** *Bp*   **V** *vacant* (01902) 850368
BRICETT, GREAT (St Mary and St Lawrence)   *see* Ringshall w Battisford, Barking w Darmsden etc *St E*
BRICKENDON (Holy Cross and St Alban)   *see* Lt Berkhamsted and Bayford, Essendon etc *St Alb*

BRICKET WOOD (St Luke) *St Alb 1* **P** *CPAS*
V M RAJKOVIC
BRICKHILL, GREAT (St Mary) *see* Brickhills and Stoke Hammond *Ox*
BRICKHILL, LITTLE (St Mary Magdalene) *as above Ox*
BRICKHILL, NORTH (St Mark) *see* Bedf St Mark *St Alb*
BRICKHILLS and Stoke Hammond, The *Ox 26* **P** *Bp, Major Sir Philip Pauncefort-Duncombe Bt, St Edw Sch Ox, and Cam Univ (jt)* **R** J WALLER
BRICKLEHAMPTON (St Michael) *see* Elmley Castle w Bricklehampton and Combertons *Worc*
BRIDE (St Bridget) *see* Kirkbride *S & M*
BRIDE VALLEY *Sarum 2* **P** *Patr Bd* **TR** J D ATKINSON, **TV** A J ASHWELL
BRIDEKIRK (St Bridget) *Carl 6* **P** *Trustees* **P-in-c** L FRASER
BRIDESTOWE (St Bridget) *see* Okehampton w Inwardleigh, Bratton Clovelly etc *Ex*
BRIDFORD (St Thomas à Becket) *see* Christow, Ashton and Bridford *Ex*
BRIDGE (St Peter) *see* Patrixbourne w Bridge and Bekesbourne *Cant*
BRIDGE SOLLARS (St Andrew) *see* Credenhill w Brinsop and Wormsley etc *Heref*
BRIDGEMARY (St Matthew) *Portsm 3* **P** *Bp* **V** *vacant* (01329) 235288
BRIDGERULE (St Bridget) *see* Pyworthy, Pancrasweek and Bridgerule *Ex*
BRIDGETOWN (St John the Evangelist) *see* Totnes w Bridgetown, Berry Pomeroy etc *Ex*
BRIDGFORD, EAST (St Peter) and Kneeton *S'well 8* **P** *Magd Coll Ox (2 turns), C G Neale Esq (1 turn)* **R** A HAYDOCK
BRIDGFORD, WEST (St Giles) (St Luke) *S'well 9* **P** *Waddington Trustees* **R** S J L CANSDALE, **C** J H CURRAN
BRIDGHAM (St Mary) *see* E w W Harling, Bridgham w Roudham, Larling etc *Nor*
BRIDGNORTH (St Mary Magdalene) (St Leonard) (St James), Tasley, Astley Abbotts, Oldbury and Quatford *Heref 9* **P** *DBP (3 turns) and Ld Chan (1 turn)* **TR** A A ROBERTS, **TV** M J KNEEN, **C** W NESBITT, **OLM** A ROGERS, T O'BRIEN
BRIDGWATER (Holy Trinity) *B & W 14* **P** *Bp* **P-in-c** M S MCCREADY
BRIDGWATER (St Francis of Assisi) *B & W 14* **P** *Bp* **P-in-c** B D JOY
BRIDGWATER (St John the Baptist) *B & W 14* **P** *Bp* **P-in-c** G M KIRK
BRIDGWATER (St Mary) and Chilton Trinity and Durleigh *B & W 14* **P** *Ld Chan* **V** C J P CHADWICK, **C** J M MUNNS
BRIDLINGTON (Emmanuel) *York 9* **P** *Trustees* **V** L C MUNT, **C** G O MITCHELL
BRIDLINGTON (Holy Trinity) and Sewerby w Marton *York 9* **P** *Abp* **V** D J MATHER
BRIDLINGTON (St Mary's Priory Church) *York 9* **P** *Simeon's Trustees* **R** J A WARDLE, **C** P LAMB, **NSM** P J ARTLEY
BRIDLINGTON QUAY (Christ Church) *York 9* **P** *R Bridlington Priory* **V** J G COUPER
BRIDPORT (St Mary) *Sarum 2* **P** *Patr Bd (2 turns) and Ld Chan (1 turn)* **TR** T N STUBBS, **TV** M A ALLCHIN, **S** GUISE, **C** C A THOMAS, **OLM** D E CAMPLING
BRIDSTOW (St Bridget) *see* Ross *Heref*
BRIERCLIFFE (St James) *Blackb 3* **P** *Hulme Trustees* **V** P J PIKE, **C** H HORNBY
BRIERFIELD (St Luke) *Blackb 6* **P** *Bp* **V** E A SAVILLE, **NSM** R D SHOOTER
BRIERLEY (St Paul) *see* Felkirk w Brierley *Wakef*
BRIERLEY HILL (St Michael) (St Paul) *Worc 10* **P** *TR Wordsley* **R** C S MINCHIN
BRIGG (St John the Evangelist), Wrawby and Cadney cum Howsham *Linc 6* **P** *Bp* **V** M J SILLEY
BRIGHAM (St Bridget) *Carl 7* **P** *Earl of Lonsdale* **P-in-c** J V HINE, **C** J MORGAN
BRIGHOUSE (St Martin) (St Chad) and Clifton *Wakef 2* **P** *Bp* **TR** M F WOOD, **TV** S J LORD
BRIGHSTONE (St Mary the Virgin) and Brooke w Mottistone *Portsm 8* **P** *Bp (2 turns), D&C St Paul's (1 turn)* **R** T W EADY
BRIGHTLING (St Thomas of Canterbury), Dallington, Mountfield and Netherfield *Chich 15* **P** *Bp, Adn Lewes and Hastings, H C Grissell Esq, Mrs A Egerton, and Mrs L A Fraser (jt)* **R** S BAKER, **NSM** J B B WRENBURY
BRIGHTLINGSEA (All Saints) (St James) *Chelmsf 23* **P** *Ld Chan* **V** R M SALENIUS
BRIGHTON (Annunciation) *Chich 2* **P** *Wagner Trustees* **P-in-c** D HAWTHORN
BRIGHTON (Good Shepherd) Preston *Chich 2* **P** *Bp* **V** J D F GREENER, **NSM** S J DATE

BRIGHTON (Resurrection) (St Alban) (St Luke) (St Martin w St Wilfrid) *Chich 2* **P** *Patr Bd* **TR** B L BRANDIE, **TV** K G PERKINTON, **C** S J HEANS
BRIGHTON (St Bartholomew) *Chich 2* **P** *Wagner Trustees* **V** V W HOUSE, **NSM** C J F BARBER
BRIGHTON (St Cuthman) *see* Whitehawk *Chich*
BRIGHTON (St George w St Anne and St Mark) *Chich 2* **P** *Bp and V Brighton (jt)* **V** A H MANSON-BRAILSFORD
BRIGHTON (St John) *see* Preston St Jo w Brighton St Aug and St Sav *Chich*
BRIGHTON (St Mary the Virgin) *see* Kemp Town St Mary *Chich*
BRIGHTON (St Matthias) *Chich 2* **P** *V Preston* **P-in-c** E J POLLARD, **Hon C** B S TYLER
BRIGHTON (St Michael and All Angels) *Chich 2* **P** *V Brighton* **V** R S FAYERS, **C** B A NORTH, C J WOODMAN, **NSM** D G HEWETSON
BRIGHTON (St Nicholas) *Chich 2* **P** *Bp* **V** D F MOODY, **C** P S J RITCHIE
BRIGHTON (St Paul) *Chich 2* **P** *Wagner Trustees* **Hon C** J N BALDRY
BRIGHTON (St Peter) (Chapel Royal) *Chich 2* **P** *Bp* **P-in-c** D J BIGGS, **C** M J WELLS, **NSM** J NEWSON
BRIGHTON, NEW (All Saints) *Ches 7* **P** *DBP* **V** *vacant* 0151-639 2748
BRIGHTON, NEW (St James) (Emmanuel) *Ches 7* **P** *Bp* **C** M LEWIS
BRIGHTSIDE (St Thomas and St Margaret) w Wincobank *Sheff 3* **P** *The Crown and Sheff Ch Burgesses (alt)* **V** M V GILBERT, **C** H M BENT
BRIGHTWALTON (All Saints) w Catmore, Leckhampstead, Chaddleworth and Fawley *Ox 14* **P** *Bp, P L Wroughton Esq, and D&C Westmr (jt)* **P-in-c** J P TOWNEND
BRIGHTWELL (St Agatha) *see* Wallingford *Ox*
BRIGHTWELL (St John the Baptist) *see* Martlesham w Brightwell *St E*
BRIGHTWELL BALDWIN (St Bartholomew) *see* Ewelme, Brightwell Baldwin, Cuxham w Easington *Ox*
BRIGNALL (St Mary) *see* Startforth and Bowes and Rokeby w Brignall *Ripon*
BRIGSLEY (St Helen) *see* Laceby and Ravendale Gp *Linc*
BRIGSTOCK (St Andrew) w Stanion and Lowick and Sudborough *Pet 9* **P** *Bp (2 turns), L G Stopford Sackville Esq (1 turn)* **R** H R WATSON
BRILL (All Saints) *see* Bernwode *Ox*
BRILLEY (St Mary) *see* Eardisley w Bollingham, Willersley, Brilley etc *Heref*
BRIMFIELD (St Michael) *see* Leominster *Heref*
BRIMINGTON (St Michael) *Derby 3* **P** *V Chesterfield* **NSM** H GUEST
BRIMPSFIELD (St Michael) w Birdlip, Syde, Daglingworth, the Duntisbournes and Winstone *Glouc 11* **P** *Ld Chan, Bp, DBP, and CCC Ox (by turn)* **P-in-c** J E JESSOP, **NSM** P NEWING
BRIMPTON (St Peter) *see* Aldermaston w Wasing and Brimpton *Ox*
BRIMSCOMBE (Holy Trinity) *see* Woodchester and Brimscombe *Glouc*
BRINDLE (St James) *Blackb 4* **P** *Trustees* **P-in-c** M H CANNON
BRINGHURST (St Nicholas) *see* Six Saints circa Holt *Leic*
BRINGTON (All Saints) w Molesworth and Old Weston *Ely 9* **P** *Bp* **P-in-c** C M FURLONG
BRINGTON (St Mary w St John) w Whilton and Norton and Church Brampton w Chapel Brampton and Harlestone and East Haddon and Holdenby *Pet 2* **P** *Patr Bd (5 turns), Prime Min (1 turn)* **R** C GOBLE, **C** D L WILLIAMS
BRININGHAM (St Maurice) *see* Brinton, Briningham, Hunworth, Stody etc *Nor*
BRINKBURN (not known) *see* Longframlington w Brinkburn *Newc*
BRINKHILL (St Philip) *see* S Ormsby Gp *Linc*
BRINKLEY (St Mary) *see* Raddesley Gp *Ely*
BRINKLOW (St John the Baptist) *Cov 6* **P** *Ld Chan* **R** P S RUSSELL
BRINKWORTH (St Michael and All Angels) w Dauntsey *Bris 6* **P** *Bp* **R** D ORMSTON
BRINNINGTON (St Luke) w Portwood St Paul *Ches 18* **P** *Bp* **V** R ATTLEY, **NSM** D M WOFFENDEN
BRINSCALL (St Luke) *see* Heapey St Barnabas and Withnell St Paul *Blackb*
BRINSLEY (St James the Great) w Underwood *S'well 4* **P** *Bp* **P-in-c** R B MURRAY
BRINSOP (St George) *see* Credenhill w Brinsop and Wormsley etc *Heref*
BRINSWORTH (St Andrew) w Catcliffe and Treeton *Sheff 6* **P** *Patr Bd* **TR** D M BENT, **TV** A T ISAACSON, **C** S J GARDNER

BRINTON (St Andrew), Briningham, Hunworth, Stody, Swanton Novers and Thornage *Nor 18*   **P** *J S Howlett Esq, Lord Hastings, and DBP (by turn)*   **P-in-c** R J MARSDEN

BRISLEY (St Bartholomew)   *see* Colkirk w Oxwick w Pattesley, Whissonsett etc *Nor*

BRISLINGTON (St Anne) *Bris 1*   **P** *Bp*   **V** S A HAWKINS

BRISLINGTON (St Christopher) (St Cuthbert) *Bris 1*   **P** *Bp and Simeon's Trustees (jt)*   **V** N HAWKINS, **NSM** V A ABBOTT

BRISLINGTON (St Luke) *Bris 1*   **P** *Bp*   **V** H F THOMAS, **C** G E ANDERSON

BRISTOL (Christ the Servant) Stockwood *Bris 1*   **P** *Bp* **V** D G OWEN

BRISTOL Lockleaze (St Mary Magdalene w St Francis) *Bris 3* **P** *Bp*   **V** J J HASLER

BRISTOL St Aidan w St George *Bris 3*   **P** *Bp and SMF* **V** *vacant* 0117-967 7812

BRISTOL (St Andrew) Hartcliffe *Bris 1*   **P** *Bp* **V** R H MARTIN,   **C** J A LOW

BRISTOL (St Andrew w St Bartholomew)   *see* Bishopston and St Andrews *Bris*

BRISTOL (St Leonard) Redfield   *see* E Bris St Ambrose and St Leon *Bris*

BRISTOL (St Mary the Virgin) Redcliffe w Temple and Bedminster St John the Baptist *Bris 1*   **P** *Bp* **V** M A WHATMOUGH,   **C** R D DODGE,   **NSM** W C BEAVER

BRISTOL (St Matthew and St Nathanael) (St Katharine) *Bris 3* **P** *Bp and CPAS (jt)*   **V** R V BRAZIER

BRISTOL St Paul's (St Agnes) *Bris 3*   **P** *Ld Chan and Patr Bd (alt)*   **TR** D C SELF,   **C** C L JONES,   **NSM** P BARTLE-JENKINS

BRISTOL (St Philip and St Jacob w Emmanuel) *Bris 3* **P** *Trustees*   **V** M M WIDDECOMBE

BRISTOL, The City of (Christ Church w St George) (St James w St Peter) (St Stephen w St James and St John the Baptist) *Bris 3*   **P** *Ld Chan (1 turn), Trustees (2 turns)*   **R** P CRICK

BRISTOL, EAST (St Aidan)   *see* Bristol St Aid w St Geo *Bris* **BRISTOL, EAST (St Ambrose) (St Leonard)** *Bris 3*   **P** *Bp* **V** R D JAMES

BRISTOL, EAST (St George)   *see* Bristol St Aid w St Geo *Bris* **BRISTON (All Saints) w Burgh Parva and Melton Constable** *Nor 18*   **P** *Bp and Lord Hastings (jt)*   **P-in-c** J G SYKES

BRITFORD (St Peter)   *see* Chalke Valley *Sarum*

BRITWELL SALOME (St Nicholas)   *see* Icknield *Ox*

BRIXHAM (St Mary) (All Saints) w Churston Ferrers and Kingswear *Ex 10*   **P** *The Crown*   **TR** A S ALLEN, **TV** A M BURDEN,   D F LAMBERT

BRIXTON (St Mary)   *see* Yealmpton and Brixton *Ex*

BRIXTON (St Matthew) (St Jude) *S'wark 11*   **P** *Abp and Ch Soc Trust (jt)*   **V** S M SICHEL

BRIXTON (St Paul) *S'wark 11*   **P** *Ch Soc Trust* **P-in-c** J M MCLAREN

BRIXTON, NORTH (Christ Church)   *see* Brixton Road Ch Ch *S'wark*

BRIXTON DEVERILL (St Michael)   *see* Cley Hill Warminster *Sarum*

BRIXTON HILL (St Saviour) *S'wark 11*   **P** *Ch Soc Trust* **V** *vacant*

BRIXTON ROAD (Christ Church) *S'wark 11*   **P** *CPAS* **V** D J B HAZLEHURST

BRIXWORTH (All Saints) w Holcot *Pet 2*   **P** *Bp* **V** A J WATKINS

BRIZE NORTON (St Britius)   *see* Carterton and Brize Norton *Ox*

BROAD BLUNSDON (St Leonard)   *see* Broad Blunsdon *Bris* **BROAD BLUNSDON (St Leonard)** *Bris 7*   **P** *Bp* **P-in-c** R C WARD

BROAD CAMPDEN (St Michael and All Angels)   *see* Chipping Campden w Ebrington *Glouc*

BROAD HINTON (St Peter ad Vincula)   *see* Upper Kennet *Sarum*

BROAD LANE (Licensed Room)   *see* Wybunbury w Doddington *Ches*

BROAD OAK (St George)   *see* Heathfield *Chich*

BROAD TOWN (Christ Church), Clyffe Pypard, Hilmarton and Tockenham *Sarum 15*   **P** *Ld Chan, DBP, and Prime Min (by turns)*   **R** M J FLIGHT

BROADBOTTOM (St Mary Magdalene)   *see* Mottram in Longdendale *Ches*

BROADBRIDGE HEATH (St John)   *see* Horsham *Chich*

BROADCHALKE (All Saints)   *see* Chalke Valley *Sarum*

BROADCLYST (St John the Baptist)   *see* Pinhoe and Broadclyst *Ex*

BROADFIELD (Christ the Lord)   *see* Southgate *Chich*

BROADHEATH (Christ Church), Crown East and Rushwick *Worc 3*   **P** *Bp and D&C (jt)*   **V** G T M NOTT

BROADHEATH (St Alban) *Ches 10*   **P** *Bp*   **V** J BEANEY

BROADHEMBURY (St Andrew the Apostle and Martyr), Payhembury and Plymtree *Ex 7*   **P** *W Drewe Esq, Ex Coll Ox, and Or Coll Ox (by turn)*   **R** A M ROBERTS

BROADHEMPSTON (St Peter and St Paul), Woodland, Staverton w Landscove and Littlehempston *Ex 13*   **P** *Prime Min (1 turn), D&C and Bp (1 turn)*   **R** N R C PEARKES

BROADMAYNE (St Martin)   *see* Watercombe *Sarum*

BROADOAK (St Paul)   *see* Symondsbury *Sarum*

BROADSTAIRS (Holy Trinity) *Cant 9*   **P** *V St Peter-in-Thanet* **R** M W HAYTON

BROADSTAIRS (St Andrew)   *see* St Peter-in-Thanet *Cant*

BROADSTONE (not known)   *see* Diddlebury w Munslow, Holdgate and Tugford *Heref*

BROADSTONE (St John the Baptist) *Sarum 7*   **P** *Bp* **V** M FREDRIKSEN,   **NSM** G A J SMITH

BROADWAS (St Mary Magdalene)   *see* Martley and Wichenford, Knightwick etc *Worc*

BROADWATER (St Mary) (St Stephen) *Chich 5*   **P** *Patr Bd* **TR** J BERRY,   **TV** S C COUPLAND,   D A STEVENSON, **C** A M WILSON,   R J EDWARDS

BROADWATER DOWN   *see* Tunbridge Wells St Mark *Roch*

BROADWATERS (St Oswald)   *see* Kidderminster St Mary and All SS w Trimpley etc *Worc*

BROADWAY (St Aldhem and St Eadburga)   *see* Ilminster and Distr *B & W*

BROADWAY (St Eadburgha) (St Michael and All Angels) w Wickhamford *Worc 1*   **P** *Peache Trustees and Ch Ch Ox (jt)* **V** *vacant* (01386) 852352

BROADWELL (Good Shepherd)   *see* Coleford w Staunton *Glouc*

BROADWELL (St Paul), Evenlode, Oddington, Adlestrop and Westcote w Icomb and Bledington *Glouc 14* **P** *Bp, Ch Soc Trust, Lord Leigh and DBP (1 turn), and Ch Ch Ox and D&C Worc (1 turn)*   **R** C E WILSON, **Hon C** B P DE W GOODWIN HUDSON

BROADWELL (St Peter and St Paul)   *see* Shill Valley and Broadshire *Ox*

BROADWEY (St Nicholas)   *see* Bincombe w Broadwey, Upwey and Buckland Ripers *Sarum*

BROADWINDSOR (St John the Baptist)   *see* Beaminster Area *Sarum*

BROADWOODKELLY (All Saints) *Ex 19*   **P** *DBP* **R** P J NORMAN

BROADWOODWIDGER (St Nicholas)   *see* Lifton, Broadwoodwidger, Stowford etc *Ex*

BROCKDISH (St Peter and St Paul)   *see* Scole, Brockdish, Billingford, Thorpe Abbots etc *Nor*

BROCKENHURST (St Nicholas) (St Saviour) *Win 11* **P** *E J F Morant Esq*   **P-in-c** F R CUMBERLEGE, **Hon C** R DROWN

BROCKHALL (St Peter and St Paul)   *see* Heyford w Stowe Nine Churches and Flore etc *Pet*

BROCKHAM GREEN (Christ Church) *S'wark 27* **P** *Hon J L Hamilton*   **P-in-c** J M A WILLANS, **OLM** F G LEHANEY

BROCKHAMPTON (All Saints)   *see* Fownhope w Mordiford, Brockhampton etc *Heref*

BROCKHAMPTON (Chapel)   *see* Bromyard *Heref*

BROCKHOLES (St George)   *see* Honley *Wakef*

BROCKLESBY PARK (All Saints) *Linc 6*   **P** *Earl of Yarborough*   **V** S PHILLIPS,   **Hon C** S W ANDREW

BROCKLEY (St Andrew)   *see* Horringer *St E*

BROCKLEY HILL (St Saviour) *S'wark 5*   **P** *V Forest Hill Ch Ch*   **V** A S PEBERDY,   **OLM** R G TURPIN

BROCKMOOR (St John) *Worc 10*   **P** *Prime Min* **P-in-c** G E P NATHANIEL

BROCKWORTH (St George) *Glouc 6*   **P** *DBP*   **V** M M ENNIS

BROCTON (All Saints)   *see* Baswich *Lich*

BRODSWORTH (St Michael and All Angels)   *see* Bilham *Sheff*

BROKENBOROUGH (St John the Baptist)   *see* Malmesbury w Westport and Brokenborough *Bris*

BROKERS WOOD (All Saints)   *see* White Horse *Sarum*

BROMBOROUGH (St Barnabas) *Ches 9*   **P** *D&C* **R** W J HOGG,   **C** I M ARCH,   **NSM** A G HOGG

BROME (St Mary)   *see* N Hartismere *St E*

BROMESWELL (St Edmund)   *see* Wilford Peninsula *St E*

BROMFIELD (St Mary the Virgin)   *see* Culmington w Onibury, Bromfield etc *Heref*

BROMFIELD (St Mungo)   *see* Solway Plain *Carl*

BROMFORD FIRS (not Known)   *see* Hodge Hill *Birm*

BROMHAM (St Nicholas)   *see* Rowde and Bromham *Sarum*

BROMHAM (St Owen) w Oakley and Stagsden *St Alb 13* **P** *Bp*   **C** S T SMITH,   **NSM** D J HARPHAM

BROMLEY (Christ Church) *Roch 14*   **P** *CPAS* **V** I J BROOMFIELD,   **C** N R T HISCOCKS,   **NSM** A SAVILLE, E J A SAVILLE

BROMLEY (Holy Trinity Mission Church) *see* Pennsett *Worc*
BROMLEY (St Andrew) *Roch 14* **P** *Bp* **V** H A ATHERTON,
  NSM E J DAVIS, A M KING
BROMLEY (St John the Evangelist) *Roch 14* **P** *Bp*
  V H P C BROADBENT
BROMLEY (St Mark) *Roch 14* **P** *V Bromley SS Pet & Paul*
  V S C VARNEY, **C** K W CLARK
BROMLEY (St Mary) *see* Plaistow St Mary *Roch*
BROMLEY (St Peter and St Paul) *Roch 14* **P** *Bp*
  V M M CAMP, **C** A M NEWMAN
BROMLEY, GREAT (St George) *see* Ardleigh and The
  Bromleys *Chelmsf*
BROMLEY BY BOW (All Hallows) *Lon 7* **P** *Bp and Grocers'*
  Co (jt) **R** *vacant*
BROMLEY COMMON (Holy Trinity) *Roch 14* **P** *The Crown*
  V R BRISTOW
BROMLEY COMMON (St Augustine) *Roch 14* **P** *Bp*
  V E H HESELWOOD
BROMLEY COMMON (St Luke) *Roch 14* **P** *Bp*
  V M G P INSLEY
BROMLEY CROSS (St Andrew's Mission Church) *see* Turton
  Moorland Min *Man*
BROMPTON (Holy Trinity) w Onslow Square St Paul *Lon 8*
  P *Bp and MMCET (jt)* **V** J A K MILLAR, **C** N G P GUMBEL,
  P W COWLEY, N K LEE, R C THORPE, J P B BARNES
BROMPTON (St Thomas) w Deighton *York 19* **P** *D&C Dur*
  V M S SNOWBALL
BROMPTON, NEW (St Luke) *Roch 3* **P** *Bp*
  P-in-c R L FEATHERSTONE
BROMPTON, WEST (St Mary) (St Peter) *Lon 8* **P** *Bp*
  V G C BEAUCHAMP
BROMPTON BY SAWDON (All Saints) w Hutton Buscel,
  Snainton and Wykeham *York 20* **P** *Viscount Downe (1 turn),*
  Sir Philip Naylor-Leyland (Bt) (1 turn), Abp (2 turns)
  V P E JARAM
BROMPTON ON SWALE (St Paul) *see* Easby w Brompton on
  Swale and Bolton on Swale *Ripon*
BROMPTON RALPH (The Blessed Virgin Mary) *see* Lydeard
  St Lawrence w Brompton Ralph etc *B & W*
BROMPTON REGIS (Blessed Virgin Mary) w Upton and
  Skilgate *B & W 16* **P** *Bp, Em Coll Cam, and Keble Coll*
  Ox (jt) **R** *vacant (01398) 371438*
BROMSBERROW (St Mary the Virgin) *see* Redmarley
  D'Abitot, Bromesberrow, Pauntley etc *Glouc*
BROMSGROVE (All Saints) *Worc 7* **P** *V Bromsgrove St Jo*
  V W MOORE
BROMSGROVE (St John the Baptist) *Worc 7* **P** *D&C*
  V N G MARNS, **C** M A ROGERS
BROMWICH, WEST (All Saints) (St Mary Magdalene)
  Lich 27 **P** *Bp* **V** M MORETON, **C** J D BREADON,
  P J COWPER, **OLM** A M BIRD, E A BROWN
BROMWICH, WEST (Good Shepherd w St John) *Lich 27*
  P *Bp* **V** P O OKECHI, **C** M A SMALLMAN, **NSM** M BEDEAU
BROMWICH, WEST (Holy Trinity) *Lich 27* **P** *Peache*
  Trustees **P-in-c** M A SMALLMAN
BROMWICH, WEST (St Andrew) (Christ Church) *Lich 27*
  P *Bp and V W Bromwich All SS (jt)* **V** M J CLARIDGE
BROMWICH, WEST (St Francis of Assisi) *Lich 27* **P** *Bp*
  V P G GREEN
BROMWICH, WEST (St James) (St Paul) *Lich 27* **P** *Bp and*
  V Tipton St Martin and St Paul **C** D HART
BROMWICH, WEST (St Peter) *Lich 27* **P** *Bp*
  P-in-c J W M C MOULDER
BROMWICH, WEST (St Philip) *Lich 27* **P** *Bp* **V** R C DESON
BROMYARD (St Peter) *Heref 2* **P** *Bp* **V** G T G SYKES,
  C F M BINDING, **NSM** C M SYKES, D B HYETT, C A STOKES
BROMYARD DOWNS (Mission Church) *see* Bromyard *Heref*
BRONDESBURY (Christ Church) (St Laurence) *Lon 21*
  P *Ld Chan* **V** D E NENO
BRONDESBURY St Anne w Kilburn (Holy Trinity) *Lon 21*
  P *Bp and Ch Patr Soc (alt)* **V** F B CAPIE
BROOK (St Mary) *see* Wye w Brook *Cant*
BROOKE (St Mary the Virgin) *see* Brighstone and Brooke w
  Mottistone *Portsm*
BROOKE (St Peter) *see* Oakham, Hambleton, Egleton,
  Braunston and Brooke *Pet*
BROOKE (St Peter), Kirstead, Mundham w Seething and
  Thwaite *Nor 5* **P** *G&C Coll Cam, Gt Hosp and Countess*
  Ferrers, and Ld Chan (by turn) **R** *vacant (01508) 550378*
BROOKE STREET (St Alban the Martyr) *see* Holborn St Alb
  w Saffron Hill St Pet *Lon*
BROOKEND (Mission Room) *see* Sharpness, Purton,
  Brookend and Slimbridge *Glouc*
BROOKFIELD (St Anne), Highgate Rise *Lon 17* **P** *Bp*
  V A J B MELDRUM
BROOKFIELD (St Margaret) *York 21* **P** *Abp* **V** R W SMITH,
  NSM M TONGE

BROOKFIELD (St Mary) *Lon 17* **P** *Bp* **V** C G POPE
BROOKHOUSE (St Paul) *see* Caton w Littledale *Blackb*
BROOKHURST (St Peter's Chapel) *see* Eastham *Ches*
BROOKING (St Barnabas) *see* Totnes w Bridgetown, Berry
  Pomeroy etc *Ex*
BROOKLAND (St Augustine) *see* Appledore w Brookland,
  Fairfield, Brenzett etc *Cant*
BROOKLANDS *see* Baguley *Man*
BROOKMANS PARK (St Michael) *see* N Mymms *St Alb*
BROOKSBY (St Michael and All Angels) *see* Upper Wreake
  Leic
BROOKSIDE (Pastoral Centre) *see* Cen Telford *Lich*
BROOKWOOD (St Saviour) *see* Knaphill w Brookwood
  Guildf
BROOM (St Matthew) *see* Bidford-on-Avon *Cov*
BROOM LEYS (St David) *Leic 8* **P** *Bp* **V** J W STEVENSON
BROOM VALLEY (St Barnabas) *see* Rotherham *Sheff*
BROOME (St Michael) *see* Ditchingham, Hedenham and
  Broome *Nor*
BROOME (St Peter) *see* Churchill-in-Halfshire w Blakedown
  and Broome *Worc*
BROOMFIELD (St Margaret) *see* Hollingbourne and Hucking
  w Leeds and Broomfield *Cant*
BROOMFIELD (St Mary and All Saints) *see* Kingston St Mary
  w Broomfield etc *B & W*
BROOMFIELD (St Mary w St Leonard) *Chelmsf 8* **P** *Bp*
  P-in-c P E BALL
BROOMFLEET (St Mary) *see* S Cave and Ellerker w
  Broomfleet *York*
BROOMHILL (St Mark) *see* Sheff St Mark Broomhill *Sheff*
BROSELEY (All Saints) w Benthall, Jackfield, Linley, Willey and
  Barrow *Heref 14* **P** *Patr Bd* **R** M A KINNA,
  NSM B D SHINTON
BROTHERTOFT Group, The (Christ Church) (St Gilbert of
  Sempringham) *Linc 21* **P** *Bp (2 turns), V Algarkirk (1 turn)*
  P-in-c B R DUFFUS
BROTHERTON (St Edward the Confessor) *Wakef 11* **P** *D&C*
  York **V** *vacant (01977) 672370*
BROTTON PARVA (St Margaret) *York 16* **P** *Abp*
  R B HARRISON
BROUGH (All Saints) *see* Elloughton and Brough w
  Brantingham *York*
BROUGH (St Michael) w Stainmore, Musgrave and Warcop
  Carl 1 **P** *Bp (2 turns) and Lord Hothfield (1 turn)* **R** *vacant*
  (01768) 341238
BROUGHAM (St Wilfrid Chapel) *see* Lowther and Askham
  and Clifton and Brougham *Carl*
BROUGHTON (All Saints) *see* Warboys w Broughton and
  Bury w Wistow *Ely*
BROUGHTON (All Saints), Marton and Thornton *Bradf 7*
  P *Ch Ch Ox and Exors Dame Harriet Nelson (jt)*
  P-in-c N A TURNER, **C** P A TURNER
BROUGHTON (St Andrew) w Loddington and Cransley and
  Thorpe Malsor *Pet 11* **P** *Ld Chan (1 turn), Bp (2 turns), and*
  Keble Coll Ox (1 turn) **R** *vacant (01536) 791373*
BROUGHTON (St James) (St Clement and St Matthias)
  (St John the Baptist) *Man 6* **P** *Patr Bd* **TR** H R F MARTIN,
  TV I C FELLOWS, **OLM** J S CORRIE
BROUGHTON (St John the Baptist) *Blackb 13* **P** *Trustees*
  V D H JENKINS, **C** R C HOLLIS, S J S KATO,
  NSM T B SCHOLZ, J T RICHARDSON
BROUGHTON (St Mary) *Lich 22* **P** *D R B Thompson Esq*
  P-in-c D T W PRICE
BROUGHTON (St Mary) *Linc 6* **P** *MMCET*
  R J W COTTON
BROUGHTON (St Mary Magdalene) (Holy Innocents) and
  Duddon *Carl 9* **P** *V Millom, Lt-Col D A S Pennefather, and*
  Ch Patr Trust (by turn) **P-in-c** S N PAUL, **C** E POW
BROUGHTON (St Mary the Virgin) *see* Wykeham *Ox*
BROUGHTON (St Mary) w Bossington and Houghton and
  Mottisfont *Win 12* **P** *Ld Chan (1 turn), Mr and Mrs*
  R G L Pugh, A Humbert Esq and Miss R A Humbert (jt)
  (2 turns) **P-in-c** R A CORNE
BROUGHTON (St Peter) w Croxton and Cotes Heath w Standon
  Lich 7 **P** *Bp, V Eccleshall, and T A J Hall Esq (jt)*
  R M F WALKER
BROUGHTON, GREAT (Christ Church) and Broughton Moor
  Carl 7 **P** *Bp* **P-in-c** D R KING, **C** J MORGAN
BROUGHTON, LOWER (Ascension) *Man 6* **P** *Trustees*
  P-in-c R A FARRELL
BROUGHTON, NETHER (St Mary the Virgin) *see* Old Dalby,
  Nether Broughton, Saxelbye etc *Leic*
BROUGHTON, UPPER (St Luke) *see* Hickling w Kinoulton
  and Broughton Sulney *S'well*
BROUGHTON ASTLEY (St Mary) and Croft w Stoney Stanton
  Leic 10 **P** *Patr Bd* **TR** D T SHAW, **C** E M WALLACE

BROUGHTON GIFFORD (St Mary the Virgin), Great Chalfield and Holt St Katharine *Sarum 14* **P** *D&C Bris (3 turns), Ld Chan (2 turns), and R C Floyd Esq (1 turn)* **R** *R G HART*, **OLM** *E A FIELDEN*

BROUGHTON HACKETT (St Leonard) *see* Peopleton and White Ladies Aston w Churchill etc *Worc*

BROUGHTON IN FURNESS (St Mary Magdalene) *see* Broughton and Duddon *Carl*

BROUGHTON MILLS (Holy Innocents) *as above Carl*

BROUGHTON MOOR (St Columba) *see* Gt Broughton and Broughton Moor *Carl*

BROUGHTON POGGS (St Peter) *see* Shill Valley and Broadshire *Ox*

BROWN CANDOVER (St Peter) *see* The Candover Valley *Win*

BROWN EDGE (St Anne) *Lich 8* **P** *Bp* **P-in-c** *P TOON*

BROWNHILL (St Saviour) *Wakef 8* **P** *V Batley* **V** *P N A SENIOR*

BROWNSOVER (Christ Church) *Cov 6* **P** *Bp* **V** *E C LYONS*

BROWNSWOOD PARK (St John the Evangelist) *Lon 5* **P** *City Corp* **P-in-c** *G S GAKURU*, **NSM** *S BISASO-SEKITOLEKO*

BROXBOURNE (St Augustine) w Wormley *St Alb 20* **P** *Bp and Peace Trustees (jt)* **P-in-c** *J H HORNER*

BROXHOLME (All Saints) *see* Saxilby Gp *Linc*

BROXTED (St Mary the Virgin) w Chickney and Tilty and Great and Little Easton *Chelmsf 18* **P** *Mrs F Spurrier (2 turns), DBP (1 turn), and MMCET (1 turn)* **R** *G C GREENSLADE*

BROXTOWE (St Martha) *S'well 13* **P** *Bp* **C** *K PADLEY*

BRUERA (St Mary) *see* Aldford and Bruera *Ches*

BRUISYARD (St Peter) *see* Badingham w Bruisyard, Cransford and Dennington *St E*

BRUMBY (St Hugh) (All Saints) *Linc 4* **P** *Bp* **TV** *D M BROWN*, **OLM** *A K PEAT*

BRUNDALL (St Lawrence) w Braydeston and Postwick *Nor 4* **P** *Bp and MMCET (jt)* **R** *R M BAKER*, **C** *R A K LAW*, **NSM** *P A ATKINSON*

BRUNDISH (St Lawrence) *see* Wilby w Brundish *St E*

BRUNSTEAD (St Peter) *see* Stalham, E Ruston, Brunstead, Sutton and Ingham *Nor*

BRUNSWICK (Christ Church) *Man 4* **P** *Ch Soc Trust* **R** *S J T GATENBY*, **C** *R G TAYLOR*, **NSM** *R M YOUNG*

BRUNSWICK (St Cuthbert) *see* Ch the King *Newc*

BRUNTCLIFFE (St Andrew) *see* Morley *Wakef*

BRUNTINGTHORPE (St Mary) *see* Arnesby w Shearsby and Bruntingthorpe *Leic*

BRUNTON PARK (St Aidan) *see* Ch the King *Newc*

BRUSHFORD (St Mary the Virgin) *Ex 19* **P** *D&C* **V** *P J NORMAN*

BRUSHFORD (St Nicholas) *see* Dulverton and Brushford *B & W*

BRUTON (Blessed Virgin Mary) and District *B & W 2* **P** *Patr Bd* **TR** *S F BOULD*, **C** *M B BROWN*, **NSM** *A C PARFITT*

BRYANSTON SQUARE (St Mary) w St Marylebone (St Mark) *Lon 4* **P** *The Crown* **P-in-c** *J P T PETERS*, **C** *J A J SOPER*, *B J KISSELL*, *M C L NORRIS*

BRYANSTON STREET (Annunciation) *see* St Marylebone Annunciation Bryanston Street *Lon*

BRYHER (All Saints) *see* Is of Scilly *Truro*

BRYMPTON (St Andrew) *see* Odcombe, Brympton, Lufton and Montacute *B & W*

BRYN (St Chad) *see* Clun w Bettws-y-Crwyn and Newcastle *Heref*

BRYN (St Peter) *Liv 15* **P** *Bp* **V** *D J HOOTON*

BUBBENHALL (St Giles) *see* Baginton w Bubbenhall and Ryton-on-Dunsmore *Cov*

BUBWITH (All Saints) w Skipwith *York 2* **P** *Abp and D&C, and Ld Chan (alt)* **V** *B EVES*

BUCKDEN (St Mary) *Ely 13* **P** *Bp* **P-in-c** *M E SMITH*

BUCKENHAM, NEW (St Martin) *see* Quidenham Gp *Nor*

BUCKENHAM, OLD (All Saints) *as above Nor*

BUCKERELL (St Mary and St Giles) *see* Feniton, Buckerell and Escot *Ex*

BUCKFAST SANCTUARY (not known) *see* Buckfastleigh w Dean Prior *Ex*

BUCKFASTLEIGH (Holy Trinity) (St Luke's Mission) w Dean Prior *Ex 14* **P** *D&C (2 turns), DBP (1 turn)* **V** *D J ROWLAND*, **NSM** *J N C IRWIN*

BUCKHORN WESTON (St John the Baptist) *see* Gillingham *Sarum*

BUCKHURST HILL (St Elisabeth) (St John the Baptist) (St Stephen) *Chelmsf 25* **P** *Patr Bd* **TR** *I D FARLEY*, **C** *C J BRIXTON*

BUCKINGHAM (St Peter and St Paul) *Ox 22* **P** *Bp, Adn Buckm, Mrs S A J Doulton, G&C Coll Cam, New Coll Ox, and Exors R J Dalziel Smith Esq (jt)* **R** *K P ASHBY*, **C** *P HARDY*, *M MORTON*

BUCKINGHAM, NORTH *Ox 22* **P** *Ch Soc Trust, Mrs J M Williams, and D J Robarts Esq (by turn)* **R** *R H KENT*, **OLM** *J A PRICE*

BUCKINGHAM, WEST *Ox 22* **P** *Bp, D&C Westmr, G Purefoy Esq, and R L Randall Esq (1 turn), New Coll Ox (1 turn), and DBP (1 turn)* **P-in-c** *E A SIMPSON*

BUCKLAND (All Saints) *see* Aston Clinton w Buckland and Drayton Beauchamp *Ox*

BUCKLAND (St Mary the Virgin) *see* Cherbury w Gainfield *Ox*

BUCKLAND (St Mary the Virgin) *S'wark 27* **P** *All So Coll Ox* **R** *S J BAILEY*, **OLM** *P A VIGERS*

BUCKLAND (St Michael) *see* Childswyckham w Aston Somerville, Buckland etc *Glouc*

BUCKLAND, EAST (St Michael) *see* S Molton w Nymet St George, High Bray etc *Ex*

BUCKLAND, WEST (Blessed Virgin Mary) *see* Wellington and Distr *B & W*

BUCKLAND, WEST (St Peter) *see* Swimbridge w W Buckland and Landkey *Ex*

BUCKLAND BREWER (St Mary and St Benedict) *see* Parkham, Alwington, Buckland Brewer etc *Ex*

BUCKLAND DINHAM (St Michael and All Angels) *see* Mells w Buckland Dinham, Elm, Whatley etc *B & W*

BUCKLAND FILLEIGH (St Mary and Holy Trinity) *see* Shebbear, Buckland Filleigh, Sheepwash etc *Ex*

BUCKLAND IN DOVER (St Andrew) w Buckland Valley (St Nicholas) *Cant 4* **P** *Abp* **R** *T FOREMAN*

BUCKLAND IN THE MOOR (St Peter) *see* Ashburton w Buckland in the Moor and Bickington *Ex*

BUCKLAND MONACHORUM (St Andrew) *Ex 24* **P** *Bp* **V** *G M COTTER*

BUCKLAND NEWTON (Holy Rood), Cerne Abbas, Godmanstone and Minterne Magna *Sarum 1* **P** *Adn Sherborne, Lord Digby, D H C Batten Esq, G E H Gallia Esq, and Col J L Yeatman (jt)* **V** *K S CURNOCK*

BUCKLAND RIPERS (St Nicholas) *see* Bincombe w Broadwey, Upwey and Buckland Ripers *Sarum*

BUCKLAND ST MARY (Blessed Virgin Mary) *see* Blackdown *B & W*

BUCKLAND TOUT SAINTS (St Peter) *see* Charleton w Buckland Tout Saints etc *Ex*

BUCKLAND VALLEY (St Nicholas) *see* Buckland in Dover w Buckland Valley *Cant*

BUCKLEBURY (St Mary) w Marlston *Ox 14* **P** *C J Pratt Esq* **P-in-c** *E MARQUEZ*

BUCKLEBURY, UPPER (All Saints) *see* Bucklebury w Marlston *Ox*

BUCKLERS HARD (St Mary) *see* Beaulieu and Exbury and E Boldre *Win*

BUCKLESHAM (St Mary) *see* Nacton and Levington w Bucklesham and Foxhall *St E*

BUCKMINSTER (St John the Baptist) *see* Wymondham w Edmondthorpe, Buckminster etc *Leic*

BUCKNALL (St Margaret) *see* Woodhall Spa Gp *Linc*

BUCKNALL (St Mary the Virgin) and Bagnall *Lich 12* **P** *Patr Bd* **TR** *M K ELLOR*, **TV** *C S LAKER*, *W E DUDLEY*

BUCKNELL (St Mary) w Chapel Lawn, Llanfair Waterdine and Stowe *Heref 10* **P** *Earl of Powis, Grocers' Co, and J Coltman Rogers Esq (jt)* **V** *E TAVERNOR*

BUCKNELL (St Peter) *see* Bicester w Bucknell, Caversfield and Launton *Ox*

BUCKROSE, WEST *York 6* **P** *Ld Chan (1 turn), Lord Middleton and Abp (3 turns)* **P-in-c** *M D B SINCLAIR*, **C** *A M SHARPE*

BUCKROSE CARRS *York 6* **P** *Prime Min, Major G R H Cholmley, Sir Philip Naylor-Leyland Bt, and D&C (by turn)* **R** *C J HAYES*, **C** *J M OLIVER*

BUCKS MILLS (St Anne) *see* Parkham, Alwington, Buckland Brewer etc *Ex*

BUCKWORTH (All Saints) *Ely 8* **P** *Bp* **Hon C** *W N C GIRARD*

BUDBROOKE (St Michael) *Cov 4* **P** *MMCET* **P-in-c** *A D BRADLEY*

BUDE HAVEN (St Michael and All Angels) and Marhamchurch *Truro 8* **P** *Bp and PCC (jt)* **R** *C M SCOTT*, **OLM** *P JUDSON*

BUDLEIGH, EAST (All Saints) w Bicton and Otterton *Ex 1* **P** *Lord Clinton* **P-in-c** *J S CACKETT*

BUDLEIGH SALTERTON (St Peter) *Ex 1* **P** *Lord Clinton* **V** *R S J CHARLES*

BUDOCK (St Budock) *Truro 3* **P** *Bp* **V** *G K BENNETT*

BUDWORTH, GREAT (St Mary and All Saints) *Ches 4* **P** *Ch Ch Ox* **V** *A G BROWN*

BUDWORTH, LITTLE (St Peter) *see* Whitegate w Lt Budworth *Ches*

BUGBROOKE (St Michael and All Angels) w Rothersthorpe
Pet 3   **P** *Exors E W Harrison (2 turns), DBP (1 turn)*
R T R PARTRIDGE
BUGLAWTON (St John the Evangelist)   *see* Congleton *Ches*
BUGTHORPE (St Andrew)   *see* Garrowby Hill *York*
BUILDWAS (Holy Trinity)   *see* Wrockwardine Deanery *Lich*
BULCOTE (Holy Trinity)   *see* Burton Joyce w Bulcote and Stoke
Bardolph *S'well*
BULFORD (St Leonard)   *see* Avon Valley *Sarum*
BULKELEY (All Saints)   *see* Bickerton, Bickley, Harthill and
Burwardsley *Ches*
BULKINGTON (Christ Church)   *see* Seend, Bulkington and
Poulshot *Sarum*
BULKINGTON (St James) w Shilton and Ansty *Cov 5*
P *Ld Chan*   **V** A J WADSWORTH,   **NSM** N W STEVENS
BULKWORTHY (St Michael)   *see* Bradworthy, Sutcombe,
Putford etc *Ex*
BULLEY (St Michael and All Angels)   *see* Huntley and
Longhope, Churcham and Bulley *Glouc*
BULLINGHOPE, UPPER (St Peter)   *see* Heref S Wye *Heref*
BULLINGTON (St Michael and All Angels)   *see* Lower Dever
Valley *Win*
BULMER (St Andrew)   *see* N Hinckford *Chelmsf*
BULMER (St Martin)   *see* Howardian Gp *York*
BULPHAN (St Mary the Virgin)   *see* Orsett and Bulphan and
Horndon on the Hill *Chelmsf*
BULWELL (St John the Divine) *S'well 12*   **P** *Bp*   **V** *vacant*
0115-927 8025
BULWELL (St Mary the Virgin and All Souls) *S'well 12*   **P** *Bp*
R C GALE
**BULWICK (St Nicholas) and Blatherwycke w Harringworth and
Laxton** *Pet 8*   **P** *G T G Conant Esq (3 turns),*
F & A George Ltd (1 turn)   **R** *vacant* (01780) 285249
BUNBURY (St Boniface) and Tilstone Fearnall *Ches 5*
P *Haberdashers' Co*   **V** R J GATES,   **NSM** E T DAVIES
BUNCTON (All Saints)   *see* Ashington, Washington and Wiston
w Buncton *Chich*
BUNGAY (Holy Trinity) w St Mary *St E 14*   **P** *DBP*
V I S MORGAN,   **OLM** R C B ALLEN
BUNNY (St Mary the Virgin)   *see* Keyworth and
Stanton-on-the-Wolds and Bunny etc *S'well*
**BUNWELL (St Michael and All Angels), Carleton Rode,
Tibenham, Great Moulton and Aslacton** *Nor 5*   **P** *Bp and DBP*
(alt)   **R** H D POTTS
BURBAGE (All Saints)   *see* Savernake *Sarum*
BURBAGE (Christ Church)   *see* Buxton w Burbage and King
Sterndale *Derby*
BURBAGE (St Catherine) w Aston Flamville *Leic 13*
P *Ball Coll Ox*   **R** F D JENNINGS,   **C** N C A SCOTT,
Dss M PLATT
BURCHETTS GREEN *Ox 13*   **P** *DBP and Bp (jt)*
V T A SCOTT
BURCOMBE (St John the Baptist)   *see* Nadder Valley *Sarum*
BURES (St Mary the Virgin) w Assington and Lt Cornard
St E 12   **P** *DBP and Bp (jt)*   **V** R L C KING,
NSM K M KING,   **OLM** J L GOYMOUR
BURFORD First Portion *Heref 12*   **P** *DBP, Bp Birm, Bp, and*
J J C Caldwell Esq (jt)   **R** *vacant*
BURFORD Second Portion (St Mary) w Greete and Hope Bagot
Heref 12   **P** *DBP*   **R** *vacant*
**BURFORD (St John the Baptist) w Fulbrook, Taynton, Asthall,
Swinbrook and Widford** *Ox 8*   **P** *Bp and*
Capt D Mackinnon (jt)   **V** R M COOMBS,   **C** S P ALLEN,
Hon C T S FARRELL
BURFORD Third Portion (St Mary) w Little Hereford *Heref 12*
P *DBP and Bp Birm (jt)*   **R** *vacant*
BURGATE (St Mary)   *see* N Hartismere *St E*
BURGESS HILL (St Andrew) *Chich 9*   **P** *Bp*   **V** I G PRIOR,
C S C M MCLARNON
BURGESS HILL (St Edward) *Chich 9*   **P** *Bp Chich, Bp
Horsham, and R Clayton w Keymer (jt)*   **V** T L PESKETT,
NSM S S MACCARTHY
BURGESS HILL (St John the Evangelist) *Chich 9*   **P** *Bp Chich,
Bp Horsham, and R Clayton w Keymer (jt)*   **V** M C KNOWLES
BURGH (St Botolph)   *see* Boulge w Burgh, Grundisburgh and
Hasketon *St E*
BURGH (St Margaret and St Mary)   *see* S Trin Broads *Nor*
BURGH (St Peter)   *see* Raveningham Gp *Nor*
BURGH-BY-SANDS (St Michael)   *see* Barony of Burgh *Carl*
BURGH CASTLE (St Peter and St Paul)   *see* Belton and Burgh
Castle *Nor*
BURGH HEATH (St Mary the Virgin)   *see* Tattenham Corner
and Burgh Heath *Guildf*
BURGH LE MARSH (St Peter and St Paul) *Linc 8*   **P** *Bp*
V T STEELE
BURGH-NEXT-AYLSHAM (St Mary)   *see* Marsham w
Burgh-next-Aylsham *Nor*

BURGH-ON-BAIN (St Helen)   *see* Asterby Gp *Linc*
BURGH PARVA (St Mary)   *see* Briston w Burgh Parva and
Melton Constable *Nor*
**BURGHCLERE (Ascension) (All Saints) w Newtown and
Ecchinswell w Sydmonton** *Win 6*   **P** *Earl of Carnarvon*
R D G BARTHOLOMEW
BURGHFIELD (St Mary the Virgin) *Ox 12*   **P** *Earl of
Shrewsbury*   **P-in-c** J M H LOVERIDGE
BURGHILL (St Mary the Virgin) *Heref 4*   **P** *DBP*
V J W R MORRISON
BURGHWALLIS (St Helen) and Campsall *Sheff 7*   **P** *Bp*
(2 turns), Mrs E H I Ellison-Anne (1 turn)   **R** M G JOHNSON
BURHAM (Methodist Church) and Wouldham *Roch 5*   **P** *Bp
and Ld Chan (jt)*   **P-in-c** E M R WALKER
BURITON (St Mary the Virgin) *Portsm 4*   **P** *Bp*
R W G HARRIS-EVANS,   **NSM** J C GRACE, D R TOWNSEND
BURLESCOMBE (St Mary)   *see* Sampford Peverell,
Uplowman, Holcombe Rogus etc *Ex*
BURLEY (St Matthias) *Ripon 7*   **P** *G M Bedford Esq,
J C Yeadon Esq, E Beety Esq, Mrs M E Dunham, and
Mrs L M Rawse (jt)*   **V** K TROUT
BURLEY IN WHARFEDALE (St Mary the Virgin) *Bradf 4*
P *Bp*   **C** R J BROOKS
BURLEY VILLE (St John the Baptist) *Win 9*   **P** *V Ringwood*
P-in-c D M WEBSTER
BURLEYDAM (St Mary and St Michael)   *see* Baddiley and
Wrenbury w Burleydam *Ches*
BURLINGHAM (St Andrew)   *see* Acle w Fishley, N
Burlingham, Beighton w Moulton *Nor*
**BURLINGHAM (St Edmund King and Martyr) w Lingwood,
Strumpshaw w Hassingham and Buckenham** *Nor 4*   **P** *Ch Soc
Trust, MMCET, and Bp (jt)*   **P-in-c** V M ELPHICK,
C R J KNOWLES
BURLTON (St Anne)   *see* Loppington w Newtown *Lich*
BURMANTOFTS (St Stephen and St Agnes) *Ripon 5*
P *Ch Trust Fund Trust*   **V** *vacant* 0113-248 2648
BURMARSH (All Saints)   *see* Dymchurch w Burmarsh and
Newchurch *Cant*
BURMINGTON (St Nicholas and St Barnabas)   *see* Wolford w
Burmington *Cov*
BURNAGE (St Margaret) *Man 3*   **P** *Bp*   **R** J A WILLIAMS
BURNAGE (St Nicholas) *Man 8*   **P** *Trustees*
NSM A-M HUMPHREYS
BURNBY (St Giles) *York 5*   **P** *Trustees*   **P-in-c** J F HUDGHTON
BURNESIDE (St Oswald) *Carl 10*   **P** *J A Cropper Esq,
Mrs E Bingham, and Mrs B Baines (jt)*   **V** N L DAVIES,
Hon Par Dn J L TYRER
BURNESTON (St Lambert)   *see* Kirklington w Burneston and
Wath and Pickhill *Ripon*
BURNETT (St Michael)   *see* Keynsham *B & W*
BURNEY LANE (Christ Church) *Birm 13*   **P** *Bp*
V P H SMITH,   **C** P N WARMAN
BURNHAM (St Andrew) *B & W 1*   **P** *D&C*   **V** G R WITTS
BURNHAM (St Mary the Virgin) *Chelmsf 11*
P *N D Beckett Esq and Walsingham Coll Trust (jt)*
V R A LOCKE
BURNHAM (St Peter) w Dropmore, Hitcham and Taplow *Ox 23*
P *Patr Bd*   **TR** S N D BROWN,   **TV** A C DIBDEN, T R HEWSON,
O J GRAHAM,   **NSM** G M EDEN
BURNHAM DEEPDALE (St Mary)   *see* Hunstanton St Mary
w Ringstead Parva etc *Nor*
BURNHAM NORTON (St Margaret)   *see* Burnham Gp of Par
Nor
BURNHAM-ON-CROUCH (St Mary the Virgin)   *see* Burnham
Chelmsf
BURNHAM-ON-SEA (St Andrew)   *as above B & W*
BURNHAM OVERY (St Clement)   *see* Burnham Gp of Par *Nor*
BURNHAM THORPE (All Saints)   *as above Nor*
BURNHAM ULPH (All Saints)   *as above Nor*
**BURNHAM WESTGATE (St Mary), Burnham Norton,
Burnham Overy, Burnham Thorpe, and Burnham Sutton w Ulph
(The Burnham Group of Parishes)** *Nor 15*   **P** *Ch Coll Cam
(1 turn), Ld Chan (2 turns), and DBP (1 turn)*
P-in-c J CHARLES
BURNLEY (St Andrew) w St Margaret and Burnley St James
Blackb 3   **P** *Prime Min and R Burnley St Pet (alt)*
V P R HAPGOOD-STRICKLAND,   **C** C J PETER
BURNLEY (St Catherine) (St Alban) and St Paul *Blackb 3*
P *R Burnley*   **V** R T D PARKER
BURNLEY (St Cuthbert) *Blackb 3*   **P** *R Burnley*
V T J COOPER
BURNLEY (St Mark) *Blackb 3*   **P** *Bp*   **V** J G HAIGH
**BURNLEY (St Matthew the Apostle) Habergham Eaves w Holy
Trinity** *Blackb 3*   **P** *R Burnley*   **P-in-c** I S MOSSLEY
BURNLEY (St Peter) *Blackb 3*   **P** *Bp*   **R** *vacant* (01282)
413599

BURNLEY (St Stephen) *Blackb 3* **P** *R Burnley*
V P V F CHEW
BURNLEY, WEST (All Saints) *Blackb 3* **P** *Bp and R Burnley*
(jt) **V** P K HARRISON
BURNMOOR (St Barnabas) *Dur 14* **P** *Lord Lambton*
P-in-c N A CHAMBERLAIN
BURNOPFIELD (St James) *Dur 4* **P** *Bp* **V** R G BIRCHALL
BURNSALL (St Wilfrid) w Rylstone *Bradf 7* **P** *Exors Earl of Craven and CPAS (jt)* **P-in-c** C J HAYWARD, **C** A HODGE
BURNT OAK (St Alphage) *see* Hendon St Alphage *Lon*
BURNT YATES (St Andrew) *see* Ripley *Ripon*
BURNTWOOD (Christ Church) *Lich 1* **P** *D&C*
V D A WEAVER, **C** E SNOWDEN, **OLM** C J LATIMER
BURPHAM (St Luke) Guildford *Guildf 5* **P** *Bp*
V C J MATTHEWS, **C** J H MCCABE, **P** M S ROSS-MCCABE
BURPHAM (St Mary the Virgin) *Chich 1* **P** *D&C*
P-in-c T PAYLOR
BURRADON (Good Shepherd) *see* Weetslade *Newc*
BURRILL (Mission Church) *see* Bedale and Leeming *Ripon*
BURRINGTON (Holy Trinity) and Churchill *B & W 11*
P *D&C Bris and Burrington PCC (jt)* **V** J C ABDY
BURRINGTON (Holy Trinity), Chawleigh, Cheldon, Chulmleigh, Meshaw, Thelbridge, Wembworthy, Witheridge and the Worlingtons *Ex 19* **P** *Patr Bd* **TR** R D WITHNELL, **TV** J HANNA, **C** J ROBERTS
BURRINGTON (St George) *see* Wigmore Abbey *Heref*
BURROUGH GREEN (St Augustine of Canterbury)
see Raddesley Gp *Ely*
BURROUGH HILL Parishes, The: Burrough on the Hill, Great Dalby, Little Dalby, Pickwell and Somerby *Leic 3* **P** *Bp, DBP, and Mrs M Burdett Fisher (jt)* **V** *vacant* (01664) 454318
BURROUGH ON THE HILL (St Mary the Virgin)
see Burrough Hill Pars *Leic*
BURROWBRIDGE (St Michael) *see* Stoke St Gregory w Burrowbridge and Lyng *B & W*
BURRSVILLE (St Mark) *see* Gt Clacton *Chelmsf*
BURSCOUGH BRIDGE (St John) (St Andrew) (St Cyprian) *Liv 11* **P** *V Ormskirk* **V** N R SHORT, **C** W D PETTY, **OLM** B ABRAHAM
BURSDON MOOR (St Martin) *see* Parkham, Alwington, Buckland Brewer etc *Ex*
BURSEA (Chapel) *see* Holme and Seaton Ross Gp *York*
BURSLEDON Pilands Wood (St Paul) *see* Bursledon *Win*
BURSLEDON (St Leonard) *Win 10* **P** *Bp* **V** P A VARGESON, **C** J PAWSON
BURSLEM (St John the Baptist) (St Paul) *Lich 11* **P** *Bp and MMCET (jt)* **R** C R JOHNSON
BURSLEM (St Werburgh) *Lich 11* **P** *Bp* **V** K L ROUND
BURSTALL (St Mary the Virgin) *see* Sproughton w Burstall, Copdock w Washbrook etc *St E*
BURSTEAD, GREAT (St Mary Magdalene) *Chelmsf 6* **P** *Bp*
V S SWIFT, **NSM** J M BARHAM
BURSTEAD, LITTLE (St Mary) *see* Billericay and Lt Burstead *Chelmsf*
BURSTOCK (St Andrew) *see* Beaminster Area *Sarum*
BURSTON (St Mary) *see* Winfarthing w Shelfanger w Burston w Gissing etc *Nor*
BURSTON (St Rufin) *see* Mid Trent *Lich*
BURSTOW (St Bartholomew) w Horne *S'wark 27* **P** *Ld Chan and Bp (alt)* **R** P G ATKINSON
BURSTWICK (St Elmo's) w Thorngumbald *York 12* **P** *Abp*
V *vacant* (01964) 626509
BURTLE (St Philip and St James) *see* Shapwick w Ashcott and Burtle *B & W*
BURTON (All Saints) w Christ Church *Lich 14* **P** *CPAS and Ch Soc Trust (jt)* **V** N R IRONS, **C** G N CROWE
BURTON (St James) and Holme *Carl 10* **P** *Simeon's Trustees*
P-in-c P G BAXENDALE
BURTON (St Luke) and Sopley *Win 9* **P** *Bp and D&C Cant (alt)* **P-in-c** M C SURMAN
BURTON (St Nicholas) and Shotwick *Ches 9* **P** *D&C (1 turn) and St Jo Hosp Lich (2 turns)* **V** H J ALDRIDGE
BURTON w COATES (St Agatha) *see* Barlavington, Burton w Coates, Sutton and Bignor *Chich*
BURTON AGNES (St Martin) w Harpham and Lowthorpe w Ruston Parva *York 10* **P** *Ld Chan (2 turns), C T Legard Esq (1 turn)* **P-in-c** C J ASTILL
BURTON BRADSTOCK (St Mary) *see* Bride Valley *Sarum*
BURTON BY LINCOLN (St Vincent) *Linc 2* **P** *Lord Monson*
R *vacant*
BURTON COGGLES (St Thomas à Becket) *see* Ingoldsby *Linc*
BURTON DASSETT (All Saints) *Cov 8* **P** *Bp* **V** P T FRANCIS
BURTON FLEMING (St Cuthbert) w Fordon, Grindale and Wold Newton *York 9* **P** *Abp and MMCET (jt)*
P-in-c S V COPE
BURTON GREEN (Chapel of Ease) *see* Kenilworth St Nic *Cov*

BURTON HASTINGS (St Botolph) *see* Wolvey w Burton Hastings, Copston Magna etc *Cov*
BURTON IN LONSDALE (All Saints) *see* Thornton in Lonsdale w Burton in Lonsdale *Bradf*
BURTON JOYCE (St Helen) w Bulcote and Stoke Bardolph *S'well 10* **P** *MMCET* **V** J A FISHER, **NSM** E C KIRK
BURTON LATIMER (St Mary the Virgin) *Pet 11* **P** *Bp*
R *vacant* (01536) 722959
BURTON LAZARS (St James) *see* Melton Mowbray *Leic*
BURTON LEONARD (St Leonard) *see* Ripon Cathl *Ripon*
BURTON-ON-TRENT (All Saints) *see* Burton All SS w Ch Ch *Lich*
BURTON-ON-TRENT (St Aidan) *see* Shobnall *Lich*
BURTON-ON-TRENT (St Chad) *Lich 14* **P** *Bp*
V M P SKILLINGS, **OLM** H FERGUSON-STUART, P J ORTON
BURTON-ON-TRENT (St Modwen) (St Paul) *Lich 14* **P** *Bp and Lord Burton (jt)* **P-in-c** P A FARTHING
BURTON OVERY (St Andrew) *see* Glen Magna cum Stretton Magna etc *Leic*
BURTON PEDWARDINE (St Andrew and the Blessed Virgin Mary and St Nicholas) *see* Helpringham w Hale *Linc*
BURTON PIDSEA (St Peter) and Humbleton w Elsternwick *York 12* **P** *Ld Chan and D&C (alt)* **V** J L CAMPBELL
BURTON UPON STATHER (St Andrew) *see* Flixborough w Burton upon Stather *Linc*
BURTONWOOD (St Michael) *Liv 16* **P** *R Warrington*
V R S NAYLOR, **Hon C** F H BOARDMAN
BURWARDSLEY (St John) *see* Bickerton, Bickley, Harthill and Burwardsley *Ches*
BURWASH (St Bartholomew) *Chich 14* **P** *BNC Ox*
R R D VINCENT
BURWASH WEALD (St Philip) *Chich 15* **P** *Bp*
P-in-c M N FULLAGAR
BURWELL (St Andrew) (St Mary) *Ely 3* **P** *DBP*
V S G F EARL, **NSM** P M DEBENHAM
BURY (Christ the King) *Man 10* **P** *Patr Bd*
P-in-c K M TRIVASSE
BURY (Holy Cross) *see* Warboys w Broughton and Bury w Wistow *Ely*
BURY (Holy Trinity) *Man 10* **P** *Patr Bd* **P-in-c** D A HAILES
BURY (St John the Evangelist) w Houghton and Coldwaltham and Hardham *Chich 11* **P** *Pemb Coll Ox, D&C, and Col Sir Brian Barttelot Bt (jt)* **NSM** C S STRIDE
BURY (St John w St Mark) *Man 10* **P** *R Bury St Mary*
V I J STAMP, **C** K F A GABBADON, J F J O'DWYER
BURY (St Mary the Virgin) *Man 10* **P** *Earl of Derby*
P-in-c J C FINDON
BURY St Paul *Man 10* **P** *Trustees* **P-in-c** K M TRIVASSE, **C** B A HARRISON
BURY (St Peter) *Man 10* **P** *R Bury St Mary* **V** F E F WARD, **NSM** J M SMITH
BURY (St Stephen) *see* Elton St Steph *Man*
BURY, NEW (St James) *Man 12* **P** *Bp* **TR** B HARTLEY, **TV** P D GULLY, **C** G KENNEDY, **OLM** D N BIRD, A COMBER, N A COWELL
BURY ST EDMUNDS (All Saints) (St John the Evangelist) (St George) *St E 13* **P** *Patr Bd* **TR** J WEBB, **TV** J R ELLIS, **C** M R FARRELL, **NSM** A J REDMAN
BURY ST EDMUNDS (Cathedral of St James) District *St E 13*
V *vacant*
BURY ST EDMUNDS (Christ Church) Moreton Hall *St E 13*
P *Bp, V Bury St Edm St Jas, and V Bury St Edm St Mary (jt)*
V J L ALDERTON-FORD, **NSM** N T CORWIN
BURY ST EDMUNDS (St Mary) (St Peter's District Church) *St E 13* **P** *Hyndman Trustees* **V** J D HAYDEN, **OLM** D T CROFTS, W J SUNDERLAND, G A BROWN
BURYTHORPE (All Saints) *see* W Buckrose *York*
BUSBRIDGE (St John the Baptist) and Hambledon *Guildf 4*
P *Patr Bd* **R** C J TRICKEY, **C** J E POSTILL
BUSCOT (St Mary) *see* Gt Coxwell w Buscot, Coleshill etc *Ox*
BUSH END (St John the Evangelist) *see* Hatfield Broad Oak and Bush End *Chelmsf*
BUSH HILL PARK (St Mark) *Lon 18* **P** *Bp*
V P C ATHERTON
BUSH HILL PARK (St Stephen) *Lon 18* **P** *V Edmonton All SS*
V R J ANNIS
BUSHBURY (St Mary) *Lich 28* **P** *Patr Bd* **TR** P H SMITH, **TV** R A M EAGER, P I DENNISON
BUSHEY (Holy Trinity) (St James) (St Paul) *St Alb 1* **P** *Bp*
R I C COOPER, **C** T S MOORE, **Hon C** W A PENNEY
BUSHEY HEATH (St Peter) *St Alb 1* **P** *Bp* **V** *vacant* (020) 8950 1424
BUSHLEY (St Peter) *see* Longdon, Castlemorton, Bushley, Queenhill etc *Worc*
BUSHMEAD Conventional District *St Alb 20* **C-in-c** S P DUST
BUSSAGE (St Michael and All Angels) *Glouc 1* **P** *Bp*
V H J VAN DER LINDE

BUTCOMBE (St Michael and All Angels) *see* Wrington w Butcombe *B & W*

BUTLEIGH (St Leonard) *see* Baltonsborough w Butleigh, W Bradley etc *B & W*

BUTLERS MARSTON (St Peter and St Paul) and the Pillertons w Ettington *Cov 9* **P** *Ch Ch Ox (1 turn), Bp, Major and Mrs J E Shirley, and Miss M L P Shirley (1 turn), and Mr and Mrs G Howell (1 turn)* **P-in-c** A J ADAMS, **Hon C** D R J EVANS

BUTLEY (St John the Baptist) *see* Wilford Peninsula *St E*

BUTTERCRAMBE (St John the Evangelist) *see* Sand Hutton *York*

BUTTERLEIGH (St Matthew) *see* Silverton, Butterleigh, Bickleigh and Cadeleigh *Ex*

BUTTERMERE (St James) *see* Lorton and Loweswater w Buttermere *Carl*

BUTTERMERE (St James the Great) *see* Savernake *Sarum*

BUTTERSHAW (St Aidan) *see* Shelf St Mich w Buttershaw St Aid *Bradf*

BUTTERSHAW (St Paul) *Bradf 2* **P** *Bp* **V** D J GRIFFITHS, **C** S A GRIFFITHS

BUTTERTON (St Bartholomew) *see* Alstonfield, Butterton, Ilam etc *Lich*

BUTTERTON (St Thomas) *see* Newcastle w Butterton *Lich*

BUTTERWICK (Mission Chapel) *see* Street *York*

BUTTERWICK (St Andrew) *see* Freiston w Butterwick and Benington *Linc*

BUTTERWICK (St Nicholas) *see* Langtoft w Foxholes, Butterwick, Cottam etc *York*

BUTTERWICK, EAST (St Andrew) *see* Messingham *Linc*

BUTTERWICK, WEST (St Mary the Virgin) *see* Epworth Gp *Linc*

BUTTSBURY (St Mary) *see* Ingatestone w Buttsbury *Chelmsf*

BUXHALL (St Mary) *see* Gt Finborough w Onehouse, Harleston, Buxhall etc *St E*

BUXTED (St Margaret the Queen) (St Mary) and Hadlow Down *Chich 21* **P** *Abp, Bp, and Wagner Trustees (jt)* **R** *vacant* (01825) 733103

BUXTON (St Andrew) w Oxnead, Lammas and Brampton *Nor 19* **P** *Bp* **P-in-c** C S R WALTER

BUXTON (St Anne) (St John the Baptist) (St Mary the Virgin) w Burbage and King Sterndale *Derby 4* **P** *Patr Bd* **TV** P FREETH

BUXTON (Trinity Chapel) Proprietary Chapel *Derby 4* **C-in-c** R MARSDEN

BUXWORTH (St James) *see* Hayfield and Chinley w Buxworth *Derby*

BY BROOK *Bris 4* **P** *Patr Bd* **TR** A C ASHCROFT, **TV** W D L HAWLEY

BYERS GREEN (St Peter) *Dur 6* **P** *Bp* **P-in-c** P T ALLINSON

BYFIELD (Holy Cross) w Boddington and Aston le Walls *Pet 1* **P** *Bp, CCC Ox, and Em Coll Cam (by turn)* **R** L L RANDALL

BYFLEET (St Mary) *Guildf 12* **P** *Ld Chan* **R** R D TRUMPER

BYFLEET, WEST (St John) *Guildf 12* **P** *Bp* **V** A B ELKINS, **NSM** J K ELKINS

BYFORD (St John the Baptist) *see* Letton w Staunton, Byford, Mansel Gamage etc *Heref*

BYGRAVE (St Margaret of Antioch) *see* Baldock w Bygrave *St Alb*

BYKER (St Anthony) *Newc 6* **P** *Bp* **V** J N CLARK-KING

BYKER St Mark and Walkergate (St Oswald) *Newc 6* **P** *Bp and Ch Trust Fund Trust (jt)* **V** K MOULDER

BYKER (St Martin) Newcastle upon Tyne *Newc 6* **P** *Bp* **P-in-c** P J A ROBINSON

BYKER (St Michael w St Lawrence) *Newc 6* **P** *Bp* **P-in-c** P J A ROBINSON

BYKER (St Silas) *Newc 6* **P** *Bp* **P-in-c** S A FAULKNER

BYLAND, OLD (All Saints) *see* Upper Ryedale *York*

BYLAUGH (St Mary) *see* Lyng, Sparham, Elsing, Bylaugh, Bawdeswell etc *Nor*

BYLEY CUM LEES (St John the Evangelist) *see* Middlewich w Byley *Ches*

BYRNESS (St Francis) *see* N Tyne and Redesdale Team *Newc*

BYTHAM, LITTLE (St Medardus) *see* Castle Bytham w Creeton *Linc*

BYTHORN (St Lawrence) *see* Keyston and Bythorn *Ely*

BYTON (St Mary) *see* Pembridge w Moor Court, Shobdon, Staunton etc *Heref*

BYWELL (St Peter) *Newc 3* **P** *Adn Northd* **V** T EMMETT

BYWORTH (St Francis) *see* Farnham *Guildf*

CABLE STREET (St Mary) *see* St Geo-in-the-East St Mary *Lon*

CABOURN (St Nicholas) *see* Swallow *Linc*

CADBURY (St Michael and All Angels) *see* Thorverton, Cadbury, Upton Pyne etc *Ex*

CADBURY, NORTH (St Michael the Archangel) *see* Camelot Par *B & W*

CADBURY, SOUTH (St Thomas à Becket) *as above B & W*

CADDINGTON (All Saints) *St Alb 14* **P** *D&C St Paul's* **V** A J D SMITH

CADEBY (All Saints) *see* Bosworth and Sheepy Gp *Leic*

CADELEIGH (St Bartholomew) *see* Silverton, Butterleigh, Bickleigh and Cadeleigh *Ex*

CADGWITH (St Mary) *see* St Ruan w St Grade and Landewednack *Truro*

CADISHEAD (St Mary the Virgin) *Man 2* **P** *Bp* **P-in-c** J R R TALLON

CADMORE END (St Mary le Moor) *see* Lane End w Cadmore End *Ox*

CADNEY (All Saints) *see* Brigg, Wrawby and Cadney cum Howsham *Linc*

CADOGAN SQUARE (St Simon Zelotes) *see* Upper Chelsea *Lon*

CAERHAYS (St Michael) *see* St Goran w Caerhays *Truro*

CAGE GREEN (Church Hall) *see* Tonbridge SS Pet and Paul *Roch*

CAINSCROSS (St Matthew) w Selsley *Glouc 8* **P** *Bp and Sir Charles Marling Bt (alt)* **V** C D SUTCH, **C** H B TERRY

CAISTER NEXT YARMOUTH (Holy Trinity) (St Edmund) *Nor 6* **P** *SMF* **R** T C THOMPSON

CAISTOR Group, The (St Peter and St Paul) *Linc 5* **P** *Bp and D&C (jt)* **V** I ROBINSON

CAISTOR ST EDMUNDS (St Edmund) *see* Stoke H Cross w Dunston, Arminghall etc *Nor*

CALBOURNE (All Saints) w Newtown *Portsm 8* **P** *Bp* **V** D J BEVINGTON, **NSM** H M WAKELING

CALCOT (St Birinus) *Ox 15* **P** *Magd Coll Ox* **V** A D BARNES

CALDBECK (St Mungo) (Fellside), Castle Sowerby and Sebergham *Carl 3* **P** *Bp and D&C (alt)* **R** S K PRIOR, **C** R E HIND

CALDECOTE (All Saints), Northill and Old Warden *St Alb 11* **P** *Grocers' Co (2 turns), R O Shuttleworth Remembrance Trust (1 turn)* **V** F COLEMAN

CALDECOTE (St Michael and All Angels) *see* Toft w Caldecote and Childerley *Ely*

CALDECOTE (St Theobald and St Chad) *see* Weddington and Caldecote *Cov*

CALDECOTT (St John the Evangelist) *see* Lyddington w Stoke Dry and Seaton etc *Pet*

CALDER GROVE (St John the Divine) *see* Chapelthorpe *Wakef*

CALDER VALE (Mission) *see* Scorton and Barnacre and Calder Vale *Blackb*

CALDER VALE (St John the Evangelist) *as above Blackb*

CALDERBROOK (St James the Great) *Man 20* **P** *Bp* **P-in-c** M S THORP, **OLM** B WOODHEAD

CALDMORE (St Michael and All Angels) w All Saints Palfrey *Lich 25* **P** *Bp* **V** F R MILLER, **C** T R H COYNE

CALDWELL (Chapel) *see* Forcett and Aldbrough and Melsonby *Ripon*

CALDWELL (St Giles) *see* Stapenhill w Cauldwell *Derby*

CALDY (Church of the Resurrection and All Saints) *see* W Kirby St Bridget *Ches*

CALEDONIAN ROAD (All Saints Hall) *see* Barnsbury *Lon*

CALIFORNIA (St Mary and St John) *Ox 16* **P** *DBP* **P-in-c** C R EDWARDS, **NSM** H M WAKELING, J R EDWARDS

CALLINGTON (St Mary) *see* S Hill w Callington *Truro*

CALLOW END (St James) *see* Powick and Guarlford and Madresfield w Newland *Worc*

CALMORE (St Anne) *see* Totton *Win*

CALNE (Holy Trinity) (St Mary the Virgin) and Blackland *Sarum 15* **P** *Bp* **V** R A KENWAY, **C** P A BROMILEY

CALOW (St Peter) and Sutton cum Duckmanton *Derby 3* **P** *Bp and V Chesterfield (jt)* **R** M H CHAMPNEYS

CALSHOT (St George) *see* Fawley *Win*

CALSTOCK (St Andrew) *Truro 11* **P** *Duchy of Cornwall* **R** J A C WILSON, **NSM** R MUNRO

CALSTONE WELLINGTON (St Mary the Virgin) *see* Oldbury *Sarum*

CALTHORPE (Our Lady w St Margaret) *see* Erpingham w Calthorpe, Ingworth, Aldborough etc *Nor*

CALTHWAITE (All Saints) *see* Hesket-in-the-Forest and Armathwaite *Carl*

CALTON (St Mary the Virgin), Cauldon, Grindon, Waterfall and Blore Ray w Okeover *Lich 5* **P** *Bp and Sir Peter Walker-Okeover Bt (jt)* **R** A J BURTON

CALUDON *see* Coventry Caludon *Cov*

CALVELEY CHURCH (not known) *see* Bunbury and Tilstone Fearnall *Ches*

CALVERHALL or CORRA (Holy Trinity) *see* Adderley, Ash, Calverhall, Ightfield etc *Lich*

CALVERLEIGH (St Mary the Virgin) *see* Washfield, Stoodleigh, Withleigh etc *Ex*

CALVERLEY (St Wilfrid) *Bradf 3* **P** *Bp* **V** J H WALKER
CALVERTON (All Saints) *Ox 25* **P** *DBP* **R** R NORTHING,
C G A PINNOCK
CALVERTON (St Wilfrid) *S'well 14* **P** *Bp* **P-in-c** P HILL,
C J E DRAYCOTT, **NSM** M N TAYLOR
CAM (St George) w Stinchcombe *Glouc 2* **P** *Bp* **V** J S KNEE
CAM, LOWER (St Bartholomew) w Coaley *Glouc 2* **P** *Bp*
V I A ROBB
CAMBER (St Thomas) *see* Rye *Chich*
CAMBERLEY (St Martin) Old Dean *Guildf 6* **P** *Bp*
V P A DOBSON
CAMBERLEY (St Mary) *Guildf 6* **P** *Bp* **V** M J WAINWRIGHT,
OLM R WALKER
CAMBERLEY (St Michael) Yorktown *Guildf 6* **P** *Bp*
V B NICOLE, **NSM** R S CROSSLEY, S BOWIE
CAMBERLEY (St Paul) (St Mary) *Guildf 6* **P** *Bp*
V M CHESTER, **C** G H L WATTS, S A L WATTS,
Hon C A C LONG, **OLM** S H STEPHENS
CAMBERLEY HEATHERSIDE (Community Centre) *Guildf 6*
P *Bp* **V** P J DYKES
CAMBERWELL (All Saints) Blenheim Grove *S'wark 8*
P *Ch Trust Fund Trust* **V** F I L ORR-EWING, **C** D L MOORE
CAMBERWELL (Christ Church) *S'wark 8* **P** *Trustees*
V H R BALFOUR
CAMBERWELL (St George) *S'wark 8* **P** *Bp and Trin Coll*
Cam (jt) **V** N J ELDER, **C** D J LAMBERT
CAMBERWELL (St Giles) (St Matthew) *S'wark 8* **P** *Bp*
V N P GEORGE, **Hon C** M S KEEN, **NSM** H D POTTER,
OLM P A ALDEN
CAMBERWELL (St Luke) *S'wark 8* **P** *Bp* **V** J D JELLEY
CAMBERWELL (St Matthew) *see* Herne Hill *S'wark*
CAMBERWELL (St Michael and All Angels w All Souls w
Emmanuel) *S'wark 10* **P** *DBP* **V** P VOWLES
CAMBERWELL (St Philip) and St Mark *S'wark 7*
P *The Crown* **V** N A W DAVIS
CAMBO (Holy Trinity) *see* Kirkwhelpington, Kirkharle,
Kirkheaton and Cambo *Newc*
CAMBOIS (St Peter) (St Andrew's Mission Church) and
Sleekburn *Newc 1* **P** *D&C* **V** J BLAKESLEY
CAMBORNE (St Martin and St Meriadoc) *Truro 2* **P** *Ch Soc*
Trust **R** W R STUART-WHITE, **C** G F SHIELD,
NSM D E HARVEY
CAMBOURNE Local Ecumenical Project *Ely 1 vacant*
CAMBRIDGE Ascension (St Giles) (St Luke the Evangelist)
(St Augustine of Canterbury) (All Souls Chapel) *Ely 2* **P** *Bp*
TR P A KING, **C** K R PEACOCK,
NSM O R SPENCER-THOMAS
CAMBRIDGE (Holy Cross) *Ely 2* **P** *Bp* **V** A L HARGRAVE,
NSM J E KEILLER, A C RIGELSFORD
CAMBRIDGE (Holy Sepulchre) (St Andrew the Great) *Ely 2*
P *PCC* **V** M H ASHTON, **C** G R WALTER, S J SCOTT,
C E SANDOM, S N MIDGLEY
CAMBRIDGE (Holy Trinity) *Ely 2* **P** *D&C and Peache*
Trustees (jt) **V** R A CHARKHAM, **C** W P OLHAUSEN,
C J SMITH
CAMBRIDGE (St Andrew the Less) (Christ Church) *Ely 2*
P *Ch Trust Fund Trust* **V** M L DIAMOND
CAMBRIDGE (St Barnabas) *Ely 2* **P** *V Cam St Paul*
V N M LADD, **C** C S BROOKES
CAMBRIDGE (St Benedict) *Ely 2* **P** *CCC Cam*
V R S DOUBLE, **NSM** D P FORD
CAMBRIDGE (St Botolph) *Ely 2* **P** *Qu Coll Cam*
P-in-c W HORBURY, **NSM** M J WIDDESS
CAMBRIDGE (St Clement) *Ely 2* **P** *Jes Coll Cam*
P-in-c G I R MCMAHON
CAMBRIDGE (St Edward King and Martyr) Proprietary Chapel
Ely 2, F N WATTS
CAMBRIDGE (St James) *Ely 2* **P** *Bp* **V** D G DEBOYS,
C J T W RIGNEY
CAMBRIDGE (St John the Evangelist) *see* Cherry Hinton St Jo
Ely
CAMBRIDGE (St Mark) *Ely 2* **P** *DBP* **P-in-c** S M B WELLS,
Hon C M M G ROBERTS
CAMBRIDGE (St Martin) (St Thomas) *Ely 2* **P** *V Cam*
St Paul **V** S O LEEKE, **C** R T WILLIAMS
CAMBRIDGE (St Mary the Great) w St Michael *Ely 2* **P** *Trin*
Coll Cam **V** J R BINNS, **C** K RAMSAY, B P MOSS
CAMBRIDGE (St Mary the Less) *Ely 2* **P** *Peterho Cam*
V R A H GREANY, **NSM** M A BISHOP
CAMBRIDGE (St Matthew) *Ely 2* **P** *V Cam St Andr the Less*
V E P J FOSTER
CAMBRIDGE (St Paul) *Ely 2* **P** *Ch Trust Fund Trust*
V M S BECKETT, **NSM** C J ROSE
CAMBRIDGE (St Philip) (St Stephen) *Ely 2* **P** *Ch Trust Fund*
Trust **V** S TAYLOR, **NSM** J M GLOVER
CAMDEN SQUARE (St Paul) *see* Old St Pancras *Lon*

CAMDEN TOWN (St Michael) *as above Lon*
CAMEL, WEST (All Saints) *see* Queen Camel w W Camel,
Corton Denham etc *B & W*
CAMELFORD (St Julitta) *see* Lanteglos by Camelford w
Advent *Truro*
CAMELFORD (St Thomas of Canterbury) *as above Truro*
CAMELOT Parishes, The *B & W 3* **P** *Patr Bd*
R J E G ANGLE, **NSM** R A HOSKINS
CAMELSDALE (St Paul) *see* Lynchmere and Camelsdale
Chich
CAMERTON (St Peter) w Dunkerton, Foxcote and Shoscombe
B & W 12 **P** *Bp* **P-in-c** K G X TINGAY
CAMERTON (St Peter), Seaton and West Seaton *Carl 7*
P *D&C and Ch Trust Fund Trust (jt)* **V** I GRAINGER
CAMMERINGHAM (St Michael) *see* Ingham w
Cammeringham w Fillingham *Linc*
CAMP HILL (St Mary and St John) w Galley Common *Cov 5*
P *Bp* **V** S D SNEATH
CAMPBELL ROOMS (not known) *see* Parr *Liv*
CAMPSALL (St Mary Magdalene) *see* Burghwallis and
Campsall *Sheff*
CAMPSEA ASHE (St John the Baptist) w Marlesford, Parham
and Hacheston *St E 18* **P** *Prime Min, Ch Soc Trust, and*
J S Schreiber Esq (by turn) **R** H V EDWARDS
CAMPTON (All Saints), Clophill and Haynes *St Alb 16* **P** *Bp*
and Ball Coll Ox (alt) **R** M J VENABLES
CANDLESBY (St Benedict) *see* Partney Gp *Linc*
CANDOVER VALLEY, The *Win 1* **P** *D&C and Lord*
Ashburton (jt) **P-in-c** D J KEIGHLEY
CANEWDON (St Nicholas) w Paglesham *Chelmsf 12* **P** *D&C*
Westmr and Hyndman Trustees (jt) **V** vacant (01702) 258217
CANFIELD, GREAT (St Mary) w High Roding and Aythorpe
Roding *Chelmsf 18* **P** *A Sainthill Esq, Ch Soc Trust, and Bp*
(by turn) **P-in-c** E J SIBSON
CANFIELD, LITTLE (All Saints) *see* Takeley w Lt Canfield
Chelmsf
CANFORD CLIFFS (Transfiguration) and Sandbanks *Sarum 7*
P *Bp* **V** J C OAKES
CANFORD HEATH (St Paul) *see* Oakdale *Sarum*
CANFORD MAGNA (Bearwood) (The Lantern) *Sarum 9*
P *Patr Bd* **TR** P H LAWRENCE, **TV** D J BETTS, G BOLAND,
NSM A SIMPSON, A D PHILLIPS, M G COATES, A A GEE,
OLM C CLARK, A J CORKE, B S PROBERT
CANLEY (St Stephen) *Cov 3* **P** *Bp* **V** A NEWTON
CANNING TOWN (St Matthias) *see* Plaistow and N Canning
Town *Chelmsf*
CANNINGTON (Blessed Virgin Mary), Otterhampton,
Combwich and Stockland *B & W 14* **P** *Bp* **R** P MARTIN
CANNOCK (St Luke) *Lich 3* **P** *Patr Bd* **TR** A R OSBORNE,
TV D E HEBBLEWHITE, R I O'CONNOR, **C** H SEARS,
NSM L J FARRINGTON
CANON FROME (St James) *see* Ledbury *Heref*
CANON PYON (St Lawrence) w Kings Pyon and Birley *Heref 7*
P *Bp and D&C (alt)* **P-in-c** M C CLUETT
CANONBURY (St Stephen) *Lon 6* **P** *V Islington St Mary*
V D J P MOORE, **NSM** M E EVANS
CANTERBURY (All Saints) *Cant 3* **P** *Abp* **P-in-c** S W JONES,
NSM M J STACE
CANTERBURY (St Dunstan w Holy Cross) *Cant 3* **P** *Abp*
V M W WORGAN
CANTERBURY (St Martin) (St Paul) *Cant 3* **P** *Abp*
R N M HALL
CANTERBURY (St Mary Bredin) *Cant 3* **P** *Simeon's Trustees*
V A T C PEMBERTON, **C** M R SEARLE
CANTERBURY (St Peter w St Alphege) (St Mildred) and
St Margaret w St Mary de Castro *Cant 3* **P** *The Crown*
R D M H HAYES, **Hon C** P E S DAVIE
CANTERBURY (St Stephen) *see* Hackington *Cant*
CANTLEY (St Margaret) *see* Freethorpe, Wickhampton,
Halvergate etc *Nor*
CANTLEY (St Wilfrid) *Sheff 8* **P** *Guild of All So*
V J I WILLETT, **C** R I T-A RAVEN
CANTLEY, NEW (St Hugh of Lincoln) *Sheff 8* **P** *Guild of*
All So **V** K SMITH
CANTRIL FARM (St Jude) *see* Stockbridge Village *Liv*
CANVEY ISLAND (St Anne) (St Katherine's Worship Centre)
(St Nicholas) *Chelmsf 10* **P** *Bp and Patr Bd (jt)*
TR D ST C TUDOR, **TV** M E WEST, J M ALLWRIGHT,
NSM B E WEST, R WIFFEN
CANWELL (St Mary, St Giles and All Saints) *Lich 4* **P** *Bp*
V H J BAKER
CANWICK (All Saints) *see* Washingborough w Heighington
and Canwick *Linc*
CAPEL (St John the Baptist) *see* Surrey Weald *Guildf*
CAPEL (St Thomas à Becket) *see* Tudeley cum Capel w Five
Oak Green *Roch*

CAPEL LE FERNE (St Radigund)   see Alkham w Capel le
Ferne and Hougham Cant
CAPEL ST MARY (St Mary) w Little Wenham and Great
Wenham   St E 5   P Bp and SMF (jt)   R vacant (01473)
310236
CAPENHURST (Holy Trinity)   see Backford and Capenhurst
Ches
CAPESTHORNE (Holy Trinity) w Siddington and Marton
Ches 13   P W A B Davenport Esq   P-in-c P O MOULTON
CAR COLSTON (St Mary) w Screveton   S'well 8
P H S Blagg Esq   P-in-c D G WAKEFIELD
CARBIS BAY (St Anta and All Saints) w Lelant (St Uny)   Truro 5
P Bp   P-in-c P A PULLEN,   NSM C Z WILTON
CARBROOKE (St Peter and St Paul)   see Watton w Carbrooke
and Ovington Nor
CARBURTON (St Giles)   see Worksop Priory S'well
CARDESTON (St Michael)   see Alberbury w Cardeston Heref
CARDINGTON (St James)   Heref 11   P Rt Hon Sir Frederick
Corfield   P-in-c J GROVES
CARDINGTON (St Mary)   St Alb 13   P S C Whitbread Esq
V N P MORRELL
CARDYNHAM (St Mewbud)   see St Neot and Warleggan w
Cardynham Truro
CAREBY (St Stephen)   see Castle Bytham w Creeton Linc
CARHAM (St Cuthbert)   see Cornhill w Carham Newc
CARHAMPTON (St John the Baptist)   see Dunster,
Carhampton and Withycombe w Rodhuish B & W
CARHARRACK (St Piran's Mission Church)   see Chacewater
w St Day and Carharrack Truro
CARISBROOKE (St John the Baptist)   see Newport St Jo
Portsm
CARISBROOKE (St Mary the Virgin)   Portsm 8   P Qu Coll Ox
V M A J EXELL
CARISBROOKE St Nicholas in the Castle   Portsm 8   P Qu Coll
Ox   V M A J EXELL
CARLBY (St Stephen)   see Ryhall w Essendine and Carlby Pet
CARLECOATES (St Anne)   see Penistone and Thurlstone
Wakef
CARLETON (St Mary the Virgin) and Lothersdale   Bradf 7
P Ch Ch Ox   R vacant (01756) 792789
CARLETON (St Michael) and E Hardwick   Wakef 11
P V Pontefract and Cawood Trustees (jt)   V S A STACEY
CARLETON (St Peter)   see Rockland St Mary w Hellington,
Bramerton etc Nor
CARLETON, EAST (St Mary)   see Swardeston w E Carleton,
Intwood, Keswick etc Nor
CARLETON IN CRAVEN   see Carleton and Lothersdale Bradf
CARLETON RODE (All Saints)   see Bunwell, Carleton Rode,
Tibenham, Gt Moulton etc Nor
CARLIN HOW (St Helen)   see Loftus and Carlin How w
Skinningrove York
CARLINGHOW (St John the Evangelist)   see Staincliffe and
Carlinghow Wakef
CARLISLE Belah (St Mark)   see Stanwix Carl
CARLISLE (Holy Trinity) (St Barnabas)   Carl 3   P Patr Bd
TR H J CARTER,   C N N STEADMAN, G A TUBBS,
NSM A J WACKWITZ-MARSHALL
CARLISLE (St Aidan) and Christ Church   Carl 3   P Bp
V R J OAKLEY
CARLISLE (St Cuthbert)   Carl 3   P D&C   P-in-c R D PRATT
CARLISLE (St Herbert) w St Stephen   Carl 3   P Bp   V vacant
(01228) 523375
CARLISLE (St James)   see Denton Holme Carl
CARLISLE (St John the Evangelist)   Carl 3   P CPAS
V P J BYE,   C A V WEST
CARLISLE (St Luke) Morton   Carl 3   P Bp   V K WRAY
CARLISLE Stanwix (St Michael)   see Stanwix Carl
CARLISLE, SOUTH Team Ministry (St John the Baptist)
(St Elisabeth)   Carl 3   P Patr Bd   TR T J HYSLOP,
TV S L WICKS,   C C G Y HYSLOP
CARLTON (St Aidan)   see Helmsley York
CARLTON (St Andrew)   see Nailstone and Carlton w
Shackerstone Leic
CARLTON (St Bartholomew)   see Guiseley w Esholt Bradf
CARLTON (St Botolph)   see Whorlton w Carlton and Faceby
York
CARLTON (St John the Baptist)   S'well 10   P Bp
V A M LUCKCUCK
CARLTON (St John the Evangelist)   Wakef 7   P DBP
P-in-c J L HUDSON
CARLTON (St Mary)   see Harrold and Carlton w Chellington
St Alb
CARLTON (St Peter)   see Raddesley Gp Ely
CARLTON (St Peter)   see Kelsale-cum-Carlton, Middleton,
Theberton etc St E
CARLTON, EAST (St Peter)   see Gretton w Rockingham and
Cottingham w E Carlton Pet

CARLTON, GREAT (St John the Baptist)   see Mid Marsh Gp
Linc
CARLTON, NORTH (St Luke) w SOUTH (St John the Baptist)
Linc 3   P Lord Monson   V vacant
CARLTON BY SNAITH (St Mary) and Drax   York 4   P Abp
and Ch Trust Fund Trust (jt)   P-in-c J H MDUMULLA
CARLTON COLVILLE (St Peter) and Mutford   Nor 9
P Simeon's Trustees and G&C Coll Cam (jt)   V S BISHOP
CARLTON CURLIEU (St Mary the Virgin)   see Glen Magna
cum Stretton Magna etc Leic
CARLTON FOREHOE (St Mary)   see Barnham Broom and
Upper Yare Nor
CARLTON HUSTHWAITE (St Mary)   see Coxwold and
Husthwaite York
CARLTON-IN-LINDRICK (St John the Evangelist) and
Langold w Oldcotes   S'well 6   P Bp and Ld Chan (alt)
R S E CLARK
CARLTON-IN-THE-WILLOWS (St Paul)   S'well 10
P MMCET   R vacant 0115-961 6169
CARLTON-LE-MOORLAND (St Mary)   see Bassingham Gp
Linc
CARLTON MINIOTT (St Lawrence)   see Thirsk York
CARLTON-ON-TRENT (St Mary)   see Sutton w Carlton and
Normanton upon Trent etc S'well
CARLTON SCROOP (St Nicholas)   see Caythorpe Linc
CARNABY (St John the Baptist)   see Rudston w Boynton,
Carnaby and Kilham York
CARNFORTH (Christ Church)   Blackb 14   P Bp   V S L JONES
CARNFORTH (Holy Trinity)   see Bolton-le-Sands Blackb
CARPENTER'S ARMS, The   see Deal, The Carpenter's Arms
Cant
CARR CLOUGH (St Andrew)   see Kersal Moor Man
CARR DYKE GROUP, The   Linc 22   P Sir Philip
Naylor-Leyland Bt and Ld Chan (alt)   V M K NICHOLAS
CARR MILL (St David)   Liv 10   P V St Helens St Mark and
Bp (jt)   V T THOMAS,   NSM S A GLYNN
CARRINGTON (St John the Evangelist)   S'well 12   P Bp
V J M MACGILLIVRAY,   C E J R MARTIN,   NSM A C DE ALWIS
CARRINGTON (St Paul)   see Sibsey w Frithville Linc
CARSHALTON (All Saints)   S'wark 25   P Bp   R J C THEWLIS
CARSHALTON BEECHES (Good Shepherd)   S'wark 25   P Bp
V C WHEATON,   Hon C J C JEFFERSON,   NSM T A BRYAN,
OLM P C M TURRELL
CARSINGTON (St Margaret)   see Wirksworth Derby
CARTERTON (St John the Evangelist) and Brize Norton   Ox 8
P Patr Bd   TR R K BILLINGS,   C A C M TWEEDY
CARTMEL FELL (St Anthony)   Carl 10   P Bp
P-in-c W F GREETHAM
CARTMEL PENINSULA Team Ministry, The (St Mary and
St Michael)   Carl 11   P Patr Bd   TR J A H CLEGG,
TV J E CROSSLEY, R A LATHAM, R W BAILEY,   C R J CROSSLEY,
NSM A BAKER, D C ELLIS, D S SIMON
CASSINGTON (St Peter)   see Eynsham and Cassington Ox
CASSOP CUM QUARRINTON   Dur 5   P Bp
V J THOMPSON
CASTERTON (Holy Trinity)   see Kirkby Lonsdale Carl
CASTERTON, GREAT (St Peter and St Paul) and LITTLE (All
Saints) w Pickworth and Tickencote   Pet 8   P Burghley Ho
Preservation Trust (2 turns), Lord Chesham (1 turn), and Bp
(1 turn)   P-in-c P STREET,   NSM J M SAUNDERS
CASTLE ACRE (St James)   see Castleacre, Newton, Westacre
and Southacre Nor
CASTLE ASHBY (St Mary Magdalene)   see Yardley Hastings,
Denton and Grendon etc Pet
CASTLE BOLTON (St Oswald)   see Aysgarth and Bolton cum
Redmire Ripon
CASTLE BROMWICH (St Clement)   Birm 9   P Bp
V W J SANDS
CASTLE BROMWICH (St Mary and St Margaret)   Birm 9
P Earl of Bradf   R M A SEARS
CASTLE BYTHAM (St James) w Creeton   Linc 14   P D&C, Bp,
Ld Chan, and DBP (by turn)   R B J BENNETT,
NSM M A E BARTON
CASTLE CAMPS (All Saints)   see Linton Ely
CASTLE CARROCK (St Peter)   see Eden, Gelt and Irthing Carl
CASTLE CARY (All Saints) w Ansford   B & W 3   P Bp
V J G PESCOD,   C A HILLIER
CASTLE CHURCH (St Mary)   Lich 10   P Bp   V J T H PYE
CASTLE COMBE (St Andrew)   see By Brook Bris
CASTLE DONINGTON (St Edward the King and Martyr) and
Lockington cum Hemington   Leic 7   P Lady Gretton and
C H C Coaker Esq (jt)   V vacant (01332) 810364
CASTLE EATON (St Mary the Virgin)   see Meysey Hampton w
Marston Meysey and Castle Eaton Glouc
CASTLE EDEN (St James)   see Blackhall, Castle Eden and
Monkhesleden Dur

CASTLE FROME (St Michael)   *see* Bishop's Frome w Castle
Frome and Fromes Hill *Heref*
CASTLE HEDINGHAM (St Nicholas)   *see* Sible Hedingham w
Castle Hedingham *Chelmsf*
CASTLE HILL (St Philip)   *see* Hindley All SS *Liv*
CASTLE RISING (St Lawrence) *Nor 16*   **P** *G Howard Esq*
P-in-c J B V RIVIERE
CASTLE SOWERBY (St Kentigern)   *see* Caldbeck, Castle
Sowerby and Sebergham *Carl*
CASTLE TOWN (St Thomas and St Andrew) *Lich 10*
P *Hyndman Trustees*   **P-in-c** H C OSMOND,
Hon C D M OSMOND
CASTLE VALE (St Cuthbert of Lindisfarne) *Birm 12*   **P** *Bp*
V D N MILLER,   **NSM** R M SHEPPARD
CASTLE VIEW ESTATE (St Francis)   *see* Langley Marish *Ox*
**CASTLEACRE (St James), Newton-by-Castleacre, Westacre
and Southacre** *Nor 13*   **P** *Bp, Earl of Leicester, and Capt
H Birkbeck (jt)*   **P-in-c** S R NAIRN
CASTLECROFT (The Good Shepherd)   *see* Tettenhall Wood
and Perton *Lich*
CASTLEFIELDS (All Saints and St Michael)   *see* Shrewsbury
All SS w St Mich *Lich*
CASTLEFORD (St Michael and All Angels)   *see* Smawthorpe
St Mich *Wakef*
CASTLEFORD Team Parish (All Saints) *Wakef 11*   **P** *Duchy
of Lanc and Bp (alt)*   **TR** S BINDOFF,   **C** M J A CARPENTER,
Hon C M C E BOOTES,   **OLM** D WHEATLEY
CASTLEMORTON (St Gregory)   *see* Longdon, Castlemorton,
Bushley, Queenhill etc *Worc*
CASTLESIDE (St John the Evangelist) *Dur 4*   **P** *Bp*
P-in-c L POTTER
CASTLETHORPE (St Simon and St Jude)   *see* Hanslope w
Castlethorpe *Ox*
CASTLETON (St Edmund)   *see* Hope, Castleton and Bradwell
Derby
CASTLETON (St Mary Magdalene)   *see* Sherborne w Castleton
and Lillington *Sarum*
CASTLETON (St Michael and St George)   *see* Danby *York*
CASTLETON MOOR (St Martin) *Man 18*   **P** *Bp*
P-in-c I E BUTTERWORTH,   **C** G C DOBBS
CASTLETOWN (St Margaret)   *see* N Hylton St Marg
Castletown *Dur*
CASTLETOWN (St Mary) *S & M 1*   **P** *Bp*   **V** S T M R DEAN,
NSM J R GULLAND
**CASTON (St Cross), Griston, Merton, Thompson, Stow Bedon,
Breckles and Great Hockham** *Nor 13*   **P** *Bp and DBP (jt)*
R *vacant* (01953) 483222
CASTOR (St Kyneburgha) w Sutton and Upton w Marholm
Pet 13   **P** *Sir Stephen Hastings (2 turns), Mrs V S V Gunnery
(1 turn)*   **R** W S D BURKE
CATCLIFFE (St Mary)   *see* Brinsworth w Catcliffe and Treeton
Sheff
CATCOTT (St Peter)   *see* W Poldens *B & W*
CATERHAM (St Mary the Virgin) (St Laurence) (St Paul)
S'wark 25   **P** *Bp*   **TR** M A HART,   **TV** G P REEVES,
C M POWELL,   **NSM** F M LONG, F M BALDWIN, A-M GARTON
CATERHAM VALLEY (St John the Evangelist) *S'wark 25*
P *Bp*   **P-in-c** J GARTON,   **NSM** S J ELLISON
CATESBY (St Mary)   *see* Daventry, Ashby St Ledgers,
Braunston etc *Pet*
CATFIELD (All Saints)   *see* Ludham, Potter Heigham, Hickling
and Catfield *Nor*
CATFORD (St Andrew) *S'wark 4*   **P** *Bp*   **V** R B JORDAN
CATFORD (St John) and Downham *S'wark 4*   **P** *Bp*
TR A H BORTHWICK,   **TV** M B HUSTON,   **NSM** F M NEAL,
S M WOOLLEY
CATFORD (St Laurence) *S'wark 4*   **P** *Bp*   **V** C F PICKSTONE
CATHERINGTON (All Saints) and Clanfield *Portsm 5*   **P** *Bp*
V G B HILL,   **C** J F O'SHAUGHNESSY,   **NSM** M S HOLLOWAY,
A C L JOHNSON
CATHERSTON LEWESTON (St Mary)   *see* Golden Cap Team
Sarum
CATON (St Paul) w Littledale *Blackb 11*   **P** *V Lanc*
V S C SPENCER,   **NSM** S E EVANS
CATSFIELD (St Laurence) and Crowhurst *Chich 14*   **P** *Bp and
J P Papillon (alt)*   **R** J W BESWICK
CATSHILL (Christ Church) and Dodford *Worc 7*   **P** *Bp*
V *vacant* (01527) 579619
CATTERICK (St Anne) *Ripon 2*   **P** *Bp*   **V** *vacant* (01748)
811462
CATTHORPE (St Thomas)   *see* Gilmorton, Peatling Parva,
Kimcote etc *Leic*
CATTISTOCK (St Peter and St Paul)   *see* Melbury *Sarum*
CATTON (All Saints)   *see* Stamford Bridge Gp of Par *York*
CATTON (St Nicholas and the Blessed Virgin Mary)
see Walton-on-Trent w Croxall, Rosliston etc *Derby*

CATTON, NEW (Christ Church) *Nor 2*   **P** *Bp*
V K G CROCKER,   **OLM** J EASTON
CATTON, NEW (St Luke) w St Augustine *Nor 2*   **P** *Bp, D&C,
and CPAS (jt)*   **V** N I VESEY,   **C** P G GODDARD
CATTON, OLD (St Margaret) *Nor 2*   **P** *D&C*   **V** S J BETTS,
C T G KEMP,   **OLM** T I PATIENT
CATWICK (St Michael)   *see* Brandesburton and Leven w
Catwick *York*
CATWORTH, GREAT   *see* Catworth Magna *Ely*
CATWORTH MAGNA (St Leonard) *Ely 9*   **P** *BNC Ox*
P-in-c S P MEWS,   **NSM** J RAWLINSON
CAULDON (St Mary and St Laurence)   *see* Calton, Cauldon,
Grindon, Waterfall etc *Lich*
CAUNDLE MARSH (St Peter and St Paul)   *see* The Caundles w
Folke and Holwell *Sarum*
CAUNDLES w Folke and Holwell, The *Sarum 3*
P *J K Wingfield Digby Esq, Bp, and D&C (jt)*
P-in-c J H P HAMILTON
CAUNTON (St Andrew)   *see* Norwell w Ossington, Cromwell
and Caunton *S'well*
CAUSEWAY HEAD (St Paul)   *see* Solway Plain *Carl*
CAUTLEY (St Mark)   *see* Sedbergh, Cautley and Garsdale *Bradf*
CAVENDISH (St Mary)   *see* Clare w Poslingford, Cavendish etc
St E
CAVENHAM (St Andrew)   *see* Mildenhall *St E*
CAVERSFIELD (St Laurence)   *see* Bicester w Bucknell,
Caversfield and Launton *Ox*
CAVERSHAM (Park Church)   *see* Emmer Green w Caversham
Park *Ox*
CAVERSHAM (St Andrew) *Ox 15*   **P** *Bp*   **V** K KINNAIRD
CAVERSHAM (St John the Baptist) *Ox 15*   **P** *Bp*
V P A DALLAWAY,   **OLM** S M COUSINS
CAVERSHAM (St Peter) and Mapledurham *Ox 15*   **P** *Eton
Coll and Ch Ch Ox (jt)*   **R** R J KINGSBURY,   **C** H F SERJEANT,
NSM A F THORESEN,   **OLM** K F KNEE-ROBINSON
CAVERSHAM HEIGHTS (St Andrew)   *see* Caversham St Andr
Ox
CAVERSHAM PARK Local Ecumenical Project *Ox 15 vacant*
CAVERSWALL (St Peter) and Weston Coyney w Dilhorne
Lich 6   **P** *D&C*   **C** P H GREENLAND
CAWOOD (All Saints) w Ryther and Wistow *York 4*   **P** *Abp and
Ld Chan (alt)*   **R** A STOKER
CAWSAND (St Andrew's Mission Church)   *see* Maker w Rame
Truro
**CAWSTON (St Agnes) w Booton and Brandiston, Haveringland
and Heydon** *Nor 19*   **P** *Pemb Coll Cam (3 turns), DBP (1 turn)*
P-in-c T W HARRIS
CAWTHORNE (All Saints) *Wakef 7*   **P** *S W Fraser Esq*
P-in-c J D WILKINSON
CAXTON (St Andrew)   *see* Papworth *Ely*
CAYNHAM (St Mary)   *see* Ludlow, Ludford, Ashford
Carbonell etc *Heref*
CAYTHORPE (St Aidan)   *see* Lowdham w Caythorpe, and
Gunthorpe *S'well*
CAYTHORPE (St Vincent) *Linc 23*   **P** *Bp, J F Fane Esq, and
S J Packe-Drury-Lowe Esq (by turn)*   **R** B H LUCAS,
NSM B HANCOCK
CAYTON (St John the Baptist) w Eastfield *York 15*   **P** *Abp*
V A CAMPBELL-WILSON
CENTRAL   *see under substantive place names*
CERNE ABBAS (St Mary)   *see* Buckland Newton, Cerne
Abbas, Godmanstone etc *Sarum*
CERNEY, NORTH (All Saints)   *see* Stratton, N Cerney,
Baunton and Bagendon *Glouc*
**CERNEY, SOUTH (All Hallows) w Cerney Wick and Down
Ampney** *Glouc 12*   **P** *Bp and Ch Ch Ox (alt)*   **V** J R CALVERT,
OLM R H GEORGE
CERNEY WICK (Holy Trinity)   *see* S Cerney w Cerney Wick
and Down Ampney *Glouc*
CHACELEY (St John the Baptist)   *see* Deerhurst, Apperley w
Forthampton and Chaceley *Glouc*
CHACEWATER (St Paul) w St Day and Carharrack *Truro 2*
P *D&C and R Kenwyn w St Allen (jt)*   **V** A S GOUGH,
NSM I D T LITTLE
CHACOMBE (St Peter and St Paul)   *see* Middleton Cheney w
Chacombe *Pet*
CHADBROOK *St E 12*   **P** *Bp and DBP (jt)*   **R** I M G FRIARS
CHADDERTON (Christ Church) (St Saviour) *Man 22*
P *Trustees*   **V** S DONALD
CHADDERTON (Emmanuel) (St George) *Man 22*   **P** *Trustees*
V G DARVILL
CHADDERTON (St Luke) *Man 22*   **P** *Bp*   **P-in-c** A L OWENS,
OLM J TAYLOR,   R W A REECE
CHADDERTON (St Mark) *Man 22*   **P** *The Crown*
V A COOKE
CHADDERTON (St Matthew) *Man 22*   **P** *The Crown*
P-in-c A L OWENS,   **C** J R WALKER

985

CHADDESDEN (St Mary) *Derby 9*   **P** *MMCET*
  V W A STILLWELL
CHADDESDEN (St Philip) *Derby 9*   **P** *Bp*   **V** J M PAGE
CHADDESLEY CORBETT (St Cassian) and Stone *Worc 11*
  P *Ld Chan*   **V** J A COX
CHADDLEWORTH (St Andrew) *see* Brightwalton w Catmore,
  Leckhampstead etc *Ox*
CHADKIRK (St Chad) *Ches 16*   **P** *R Stockport St Mary*
  V T D BARLOW,   **C** T R PARKER
CHADLINGTON (St Nicholas) *see* Chase *Ox*
CHADSMOOR (St Aidan) *see* Cannock *Lich*
CHADSMOOR (St Chad) *as above Lich*
CHADWELL (Emmanuel) (St Mary) *Chelmsf 14*
  P *Ch Soc Trust*   **R** N T B DEANE
CHADWELL HEATH (St Chad) *Chelmsf 1*   **P** *Vs Dagenham*
  and Ilford (alt)   **V** P A CARR
CHAFFCOMBE (St Michael and All Angels) *see* Chard and
  Distr *B & W*
CHAGFORD (St Michael), Drewsteignton, Hittisleigh, Spreyton,
  Gidleigh, and Throwleigh *Ex 12*   **P** *Bp, Guild of All So,*
  Personal reps Sir George Hayter-Hames, and Exors B Drew Esq
  R A E GEERING,   **C** J G WITHERS
CHAILEY (St Peter) *Chich 21*   **P** *J P B Tillard Esq*
  R G A LAY,   **NSM** J-H D BOWDEN
CHALBURY (All Saints) *see* Horton, Chalbury, Hinton Martel
  and Holt St Jas *Sarum*
CHALDON (St Peter and St Paul) *see* Caterham *S'wark*
CHALDON HERRING (St Nicholas) *see* The Lulworths,
  Winfrith Newburgh and Chaldon *Sarum*
CHALE (St Andrew) *Portsm 8*   **P** *Keble Coll Ox*
  R J W RUSSELL,   **Hon C** M R HODGE,   **NSM** L M HUNTER
CHALFIELD, GREAT (All Saints) *see* Broughton Gifford, Gt
  Chalfield and Holt *Sarum*
CHALFONT, LITTLE (St George) *see* Chenies and Lt
  Chalfont, Latimer and Flaunden *Ox*
CHALFONT ST GILES (St Giles) *Ox 20*   **P** *Bp*
  P-in-c T A STACEY,   **NSM** A L J THOMPSON
CHALFONT ST PETER (St Peter) *Ox 20*   **P** *St Jo Coll Ox*
  R J K GREASLEY,   **C** M R EWBANK,   **NSM** L WARRINER,
  OLM W GRAHAM
CHALFORD (Christ Church) and France Lynch *Glouc 1*
  P *Adn Glouc and DBP (jt)*   **V** P R KESLAKE
CHALGRAVE (All Saints) *St Alb 12*   **P** *DBP*   **V** *vacant*
CHALGROVE (St Mary) w Berrick Salome *Ox 1*   **P** *Ch Ch Ox*
  V I G H COHEN
CHALK (St Mary) *Roch 4*   **P** *R Milton*   **V** N I BOURNE
CHALKE VALLEY (Team Ministry) *Sarum 11*   **P** *Bp, DBP,*
  and K Coll Cam (by turn)   **TR** D E HENLEY,
  TV R C REDDING, G SOUTHGATE,   **NSM** S W T COLE,
  K D N ROSSLYN SMITH
CHALLACOMBE (Holy Trinity) *see* Shirwell, Loxhore,
  Kentisbury, Arlington, etc *Ex*
CHALLOCK (St Cosmas and St Damian) *see* Chilham w
  Challock and Molash *Cant*
CHALLOW, EAST (St Nicolas) *see* Hanney, Denchworth and E
  Challow *Ox*
CHALLOW, WEST (St Laurence) *see* Ridgeway *Ox*
CHALTON (St Michael and All Angels) *see* Blendworth w
  Chalton w Idsworth *Portsm*
CHALVEY (St Peter) *see* Upton cum Chalvey *Ox*
CHALVINGTON (St Bartholomew) *see* Laughton w Ripe and
  Chalvington *Chich*
CHAMBERSBURY Hemel Hempstead (Holy Trinity) (St Mary)
  (St Benedict) *St Alb 3*   **P** *DBP*   **TV** J C NEALE, D M LAWSON,
  Hon C D A BUTLER
CHANDLER'S FORD (St Boniface) (St Martin in the Wood)
  Win 10   **P** *Bp*   **V** M HARLEY,   **C** J S KRONENBERG,
  S ARMITAGE
CHANTRY (Holy Trinity) *see* Mells w Buckland Dinham, Elm,
  Whatley etc *B & W*
CHAPEL ALLERTON (St Matthew) *Ripon 5*   **P** *V Leeds*
  St Pet   **V** S JARRATT,   **C** M D BENNET
CHAPEL CHORLTON (St Laurence), Maer and Whitmore
  Lich 7   **P** *Bp and G Cavenagh-Mainwaring Esq (jt)*
  R N A CLEMAS
CHAPEL-EN-LE-FRITH (St Thomas à Becket) *Derby 4*
  P *PCC*   **V** N R BRALESFORD
CHAPEL HOUSE (Holy Nativity) *Newc 7*   **P** *Bp*
  P-in-c W RIGBY,   **NSM** A E MARR,   **OLM** D P MARR
CHAPEL LAWN (St Mary) *see* Bucknell w Chapel Lawn,
  Llanfair Waterdine etc *Heref*
CHAPEL LE DALE (St Leonard) *see* Ingleton w Chapel le Dale
  Bradf
CHAPEL PLAISTER (not known) *see* Box w Hazlebury and
  Ditteridge *Bris*
CHAPEL ST LEONARDS (St Leonard) w Hogsthorpe *Linc 8*
  P *V Willoughby St Helen*   **V** *vacant* (01754) 872666

CHAPELTHORPE (St James) *Wakef 9*   **P** *V Sandal*
  V J F WHITE
CHAPELTOWN (St John the Baptist) *Sheff 3*   **P** *Bp*
  V R A STORDY
CHAPMANSLADE (St Philip and St James) *see* Cley Hill
  Warminster *Sarum*
CHAPPEL (St Barnabas) *see* Gt and Lt Tey w Wakes Colne and
  Chappel *Chelmsf*
CHARBOROUGH (St Mary) *see* Red Post *Sarum*
CHARD (Blessed Virgin Mary) and District *B & W 15*
  P *Patr Bd*   **TR** M S KIVETT,   **TV** M M MASLEN,   **C** FURNESS,
  NSM E A J CHIVERS
CHARDSTOCK (All Saints) *see* Axminster, Chardstock, All
  Saints etc *Ex*
CHARDSTOCK (St Andrew) *as above Ex*
CHARFIELD (St John) and Kingswood *Glouc 7*   **P** *Bp, DBP*
  and R W Neeld Esq (jt)   **R** R C PESTELL
CHARFORD (St Andrew) *see* Bromsgrove St Jo *Worc*
CHARING (St Peter and St Paul) w Charing Heath (Holy
  Trinity) and Little Chart *Cant 10*   **P** *Abp and D&C (jt)*
  V B CHALMERS,   **OLM** P G COX
CHARLBURY (St Mary the Virgin) w Shorthampton *Ox 3*
  P *St Jo Coll Ox*   **V** J K FRENCH
CHARLCOMBE (Blessed Virgin Mary) w Bath (St Stephen)
  B & W 9   **P** *DBP and Simeon's Trustees (jt)*   **R** R OSBORNE,
  C L N O'NEILL
CHARLECOTE (St Leonard) *see* Hampton Lucy w Charlecote
  and Loxley *Cov*
CHARLES (St John the Baptist) *see* S Molton w Nymet
  St George, High Bray etc *Ex*
CHARLES w Plymouth St Matthias *Ex 23*   **P** *Ch Patr Trust*
  P-in-c R S WILLIAMS,   **C** T M CROOK
CHARLESTOWN (St George) *see* Pendleton *Man*
CHARLESTOWN (St Paul) *Truro 1*   **P** *The Crown*
  V J C GREATBATCH,   **Hon C** A D J JAGO
CHARLESTOWN (St Thomas the Apostle) *see* Southowram
  and Claremount *Wakef*
CHARLESWORTH (St John the Evangelist) and Dinting Vale
  Derby 6   **P** *The Crown (2 turns), Bp (1 turn)*
  NSM S M MCLEOD, R G ALLARD
CHARLETON (St Mary) w Buckland Tout Saints, East
  Portlemouth, South Pool and Chivelstone *Ex 14*   **P** *Ld Chan*
  (2 turns), E Roberts Esq, S Tyler Esq and N Tyler Esq (1 turn),
  Bp (1 turn), and DBP (1 turn)   **P-in-c** T W BRIGHTON
CHARLTON (All Saints) *see* Chalke Valley *Sarum*
CHARLTON (Holy Trinity) *see* Wantage *Ox*
CHARLTON (St John) *see* Fladbury w Wyre Piddle and Moor
  etc *Worc*
CHARLTON (St John the Baptist) *see* Garsdon, Lea and
  Cleverton and Charlton *Bris*
CHARLTON (St John the Baptist) *see* The Donheads *Sarum*
CHARLTON (St Luke w Holy Trinity) (St Richard) (St Thomas)
  S'wark 1   **P** *Bp and Viscount Gough (jt)*   **R** J G HESKINS,
  C E CRANMER,   **Hon C** J P LEE,   **NSM** M R HOUSE
CHARLTON (St Peter) *see* Upavon w Rushall and Charlton
  Sarum
CHARLTON (St Thomas the Apostle) *see* Andover w Foxcott
  Win
CHARLTON, SOUTH (St James) *see* Glendale Gp *Newc*
CHARLTON ABBOTS (St Martin) *see* Sevenhampton w
  Charlton Abbots, Hawling etc *Glouc*
CHARLTON ADAM (St Peter and St Paul) *see* Somerton w
  Compton Dundon, the Charltons etc *B & W*
CHARLTON HORETHORNE (St Peter and St Paul)
  see Henstridge and Charlton Horethorne w Stowell *B & W*
CHARLTON-IN-DOVER (St Peter and St Paul) *Cant 4*
  P *Keble Coll Ox*   **R** *vacant* (01304) 201143
CHARLTON KINGS (Holy Apostles) *Glouc 13*
  P *R Cheltenham*   **P-in-c** R J PATERSON
CHARLTON KINGS (St Mary) *Glouc 10*   **P** *Bp*
  V M GARLAND
CHARLTON MACKRELL (Blessed Virgin Mary)
  see Somerton w Compton Dundon, the Charltons etc *B & W*
CHARLTON MARSHALL (St Mary the Virgin)
  see Spetisbury w Charlton Marshall etc *Sarum*
CHARLTON MUSGROVE (St John) (St Stephen), Cucklington
  and Stoke Trister *B & W 2*   **P** *Bp*   **P-in-c** R W WIDDOWSON
CHARLTON ON OTMOOR (St Mary) *see* Ray Valley *Ox*
CHARLWOOD (St Nicholas) *S'wark 27*   **P** *DBF*
  R W G CAMPEN
CHARMINSTER (St Mary the Virgin) and Stinsford *Sarum 1*
  P *The Hon C A Townshend and Bp (alt)*   **V** P J SMITH,
  OLM H WILLIS
CHARMOUTH (St Andrew) *see* Golden Cap Team *Sarum*
CHARNEY BASSETT (St Peter) *see* Cherbury w Gainfield *Ox*
CHARNOCK RICHARD (Christ Church) *Blackb 4*   **P** *DBF*
  P-in-c N J P HAYTON

CHARSFIELD w Debach (St Peter), Monewden, Hoo, Dallinghoo and Letheringham *St E 18* **P** *MMCET and CPAS, Ld Chan, and Ch Patr Trust (by turn)* **P-in-c** B A MOCKFORD
CHART, GREAT (St Mary) *Cant 10* **P** *Abp*
P-in-c T C WILSON
CHART, LITTLE (St Mary) *see* Charing w Charing Heath and Lt Chart *Cant*
CHART SUTTON (St Michael) *see* Sutton Valence w E Sutton and Chart Sutton *Cant*
CHARTERHOUSE-ON-MENDIP (St Hugh) *see* Blagdon w Compton Martin and Ubley *B & W*
CHARTHAM (St Mary) *Cant 2* **P** *Abp* **R** C C BARLOW
CHARWELTON (Holy Trinity) *see* Badby w Newham and Charwelton w Fawsley etc *Pet*
CHASE *Ox 3* **P** *Bp and D&C Ch Ch (jt)* **P-in-c** M E J ABREY, C N A R HAWKES
CHASE *Sarum 7* **P** *Bp, Adn Dorset, Ch Soc Trust, Pemb Coll Cam, Univ Coll Ox, J P C Bourke Esq (4 turns), Ld Chan (1 turn)* **R** M J FOSTER, **Hon C** W H G JOHNSTONE, **OLM** S J EVANS
CHASE TERRACE (St John) *Lich 1* **P** *Bp* **V** D B LEAKE
CHASETOWN (St Anne) *Lich 1* **P** *V Burntwood*
V D J DITCH, **OLM** R V BAGLEY
CHASETOWN (St John) *see* Chase Terrace *Lich*
CHASTLETON (St Mary the Virgin) *see* Chipping Norton *Ox*
CHATBURN (Christ Church) and Downham *Blackb 7*
P *Hulme Trustees and Lord Clitheroe (jt)* **P-in-c** R NICHOLSON
CHATHAM (Christ the King) *see* Prince's Park CD *Roch*
CHATHAM (St Mary and St John) *Roch 5* **P** *D&C*
P-in-c B P ADAMS
CHATHAM (St Paul w All Saints) *Roch 5* **P** *Bp*
V B T KNAPP, **C** R A KNAPP
CHATHAM (St Philip and St James) *Roch 5* **P** *Ch Soc Trust*
V G J ACKERLEY, **C** R H SMITH, **NSM** S C SPENCER
CHATHAM (St Stephen) *Roch 5* **P** *Bp* **V** P J HESKETH, **NSM** P A SPREADBRIDGE
CHATHAM, SOUTH Holy Trinity (St William) (St Alban) (St David) *Roch 5* **P** *Bp* **TR** M ILYAS, **TV** J S CURRIE
CHATTERIS (St Peter and St Paul) *Ely 12* **P** *G&C Coll Cam*
V *vacant* (01354) 692173
CHATTISHAM (All Saints and St Margaret) *see* Elmsett w Aldham, Hintlesham, Chattisham etc *St E*
CHATTON (Holy Cross) *see* Glendale Gp *Newc*
CHAULDEN (St Stephen) *see* Hemel Hempstead *St Alb*
CHAVEY DOWN (St Martin) *see* Winkfield and Cranbourne *Ox*
CHAWLEIGH (St James) *see* Burrington, Chawleigh, Cheldon, Chulmleigh etc *Ex*
CHAWTON (St Nicholas) and Farringdon *Win 2* **P** *Bp*
P-in-c A JARDINE
CHEADLE (All Hallows) (St Philip's Mission Church) *Ches 17*
P *R Cheadle* **V** R I MCLAREN, **C** R G IVESON
CHEADLE (St Cuthbert) (St Mary) *Ches 17* **P** *Ch Soc Trust*
C J E M NEWMAN, P J KEYMER, **NSM** N C HALL
CHEADLE (St Giles) w Freehay *Lich 6* **P** *DBP*
R I C THURSTON
CHEADLE HEATH (St Augustine) *Ches 18* **P** *Bp* **V** *vacant* 0161-477 3541
CHEADLE HULME (All Saints) *Ches 17* **P** *Bp*
V H B EALES, **C** D A PARKER
CHEADLE HULME (Emmanuel) Conventional District
Ches 17 vacant
CHEADLE HULME (St Andrew) *Ches 17* **P** *R Cheadle*
V D W GUEST
CHEAM (St Dunstan) (St Alban the Martyr) (St Oswald)
S'wark 25 **P** *St Jo Coll Ox* **R** C A FRENCH,
C G P THOMPSON, R T LAWSON, **OLM** D W F BRICE
CHEAM COMMON (St Philip) *see* Worcester Park Ch Ch w St Phil *S'wark*
CHEARSLEY (St Nicholas) *see* Long Crendon w Chearsley and Nether Winchendon *Ox*
CHEBSEY (All Saints), Ellenhall and Seighford-with-Creswell
Lich 7 **P** *D&C, Trustees Earl of Lich, Personal Reps Major C Eld, and Qu Eliz Grant Trustees (jt)*
P-in-c A HETHERINGTON
CHECKENDON (St Peter and St Paul) *see* Langtree *Ox*
CHECKLEY (Mission Room) *see* Fownhope w Mordiford, Brockhampton etc *Heref*
CHECKLEY (St Mary and All Saints) *see* Uttoxeter Area *Lich*
CHEDBURGH (All Saints) *see* Chevington w Hargrave, Chedburgh w Depden etc *St E*
CHEDDAR (St Andrew) *B & W 1* **P** *D&C* **V** V L DALEY, **NSM** R D H BURSELL
CHEDDINGTON (St Giles) w Mentmore and Marsworth *Ox 26*
P *Bp and Earl of Rosebery (jt)* **R** R A HALE,
OLM M HANCE

CHEDDLETON (St Edward the Confessor) *Lich 8* **P** *Bp*
V M F LEIGH, **NSM** P A BECKETT
CHEDDON FITZPAINE (The Blessed Virgin Mary)
see Kingston St Mary w Broomfield etc *B & W*
CHEDGRAVE (All Saints) *see* Loddon, Sisland, Chedgrave, Hardley and Langley *Nor*
CHEDISTON (St Mary) *see* Blyth Valley *St E*
CHEDWORTH (St Andrew), Yanworth and Stowell, Coln Rogers and Coln St Denys *Glouc 13* **P** *Ld Chan (2 turns), Qu Coll Ox (1 turn)* **P-in-c** D G MITCHELL
CHEDZOY (The Blessed Virgin Mary) *see* Weston Zoyland w Chedzoy *B & W*
CHEETHAM (St John the Evangelist) *Man 5* **P** *Patr Bd*
P-in-c D J A BURTON
CHEETHAM (St Mark) *see* Lower Crumpsall w Cheetham St Mark *Man*
CHELBOROUGH, EAST (St James) *see* Melbury *Sarum*
CHELBOROUGH, WEST (St Andrew) *as above Sarum*
CHELDON (St Mary) *see* Burrington, Chawleigh, Cheldon, Chulmleigh etc *Ex*
CHELFORD (St John the Evangelist) w Lower Withington
Ches 12 **P** *J M Dixon Esq* **V** I SPARKS
CHELL (St Michael) *Lich 11* **P** *Patr Bd* **TR** J REID, **TV** S S PRATT, **C** J D FAGAN
CHELL HEATH (Saviour) *see* Chell *Lich*
CHELLASTON (St Peter) *Derby 15* **P** *Bp* **C** A R GILES
CHELLS (St Hugh) *see* Stevenage St Hugh and St Jo *St Alb*
CHELLS (St John) *as above St Alb*
CHELMARSH (St Peter) *see* Highley w Billingsley, Glazeley etc *Heref*
CHELMONDISTON (St Andrew) and Erwarton w Harkstead
St E 5 **P** *Ld Chan (1 turn), Bp (2 turns)* **R** R D NEWTON,
NSM W R FREEMAN
CHELMORTON AND FLAGG (St John the Baptist)
see Taddington, Chelmorton and Flagg, and Monyash *Derby*
CHELMSFORD (All Saints) (St Michael's Church Centre)
Chelmsf 8 **P** *Bp* **V** M CHESHER, **C** S F GARWOOD
CHELMSFORD (Ascension) *Chelmsf 8* **P** *Bp* **V** I L MORRIS
CHELMSFORD (St Andrew) *Chelmsf 8* **P** *Bp*
NSM C I HAMPTON
CHELMSLEY WOOD (St Andrew) *Birm 9* **P** *Bp*
R J M FATHERS
CHELSEA (All Saints) (Old Church) *Lon 8* **P** *R Chelsea St Luke and Earl Cadogan (jt)* **V** P D ELVY
CHELSEA (St John w St Andrew) (St John) *Lon 8* **P** *CPAS and Lon Coll of Div (jt)* **V** J R M COOK, **NSM** D C FRETT
CHELSEA (St Luke) (Christ Church) *Lon 8* **P** *Earl Cadogan*
R C C KEVILL-DAVIES, **C** J B MOFFATT, **NSM** V J THOMAS
CHELSEA, UPPER (Holy Trinity) (St Jude) *Lon 8* **P** *Earl Cadogan* **R** M E MARSHALL, **C** J V SIMPSON
CHELSEA, UPPER (St Saviour) (St Simon Zelotes) *Lon 8*
P *R Upper Chelsea H Trin w St Jude and Hyndman's Trustees (jt)* **V** R A GILLION
CHELSFIELD (St Martin of Tours) *Roch 16* **P** *All So Coll Ox*
R L G VIRGO
CHELSHAM (St Christopher) *see* Warlingham w Chelsham and Farleigh *S'wark*
CHELSHAM (St Leonard) *as above S'wark*
CHELSTON (St Peter) *see* Cockington *Ex*
CHELSWORTH (All Saints) *see* Monks Eleigh w Chelsworth and Brent Eleigh etc *St E*
CHELTENHAM (All Saints) *see* Prestbury and All SS *Glouc*
CHELTENHAM (Christ Church) *Glouc 10* **P** *Simeon's Trustees* **C** S J N GRAY
CHELTENHAM (Emmanuel) (St Stephen) *Glouc 9* **P** *Bp*
P-in-c P H NAYLOR, **NSM** H R WOOD, B E TORODE
CHELTENHAM (St Luke and St John) *Glouc 10*
P *R Cheltenham and Simeon's Trustees (alt)*
P-in-c M J LODGE, **C** V K TURNER
CHELTENHAM (St Mark) (St Barnabas) (St Aidan) (Emmanuel) *Glouc 10* **P** *Patr Bd* **TV** R J AVERY, M ALLEN, **OLM** B E HORNE, M L D HORNE
CHELTENHAM (St Mary) (St Matthew) (St Paul) (Holy Trinity) *Glouc 10* **P** *Patr Bd* **TR** T P WATSON,
TV M R BAILEY, S J TYRRELL, **C** P D SMITH, A M OSMOND
CHELTENHAM (St Michael) *Glouc 10* **P** *Bp*
V D I LAWRENCE
CHELTENHAM (St Peter) *Glouc 10* **P** *DBP*
P-in-c S W ELDRIDGE, **NSM** M J FRENCH
CHELTENHAM, WEST Team Ministry *see* Cheltenham St Mark *Glouc*
CHELVESTON (St John the Baptist) *see* Higham Ferrers w Chelveston *Pet*
CHELVEY (St Bridget) *see* Backwell w Chelvey and Brockley *B & W*
CHELWOOD (St Leonard) *see* Publow w Pensford, Compton Dando and Chelwood *B & W*

CHELWOOD GATE (not known) *see* Danehill *Chich*
CHENIES (St Michael) and Little Chalfont, Latimer and Flaunden *Ox 23* **P** *Bedf Estates Trustees and Lord Chesham (jt)* **P-in-c** D G ALLSOP, **Hon C** P SWART-RUSSELL, J W G WHALE
CHEQUERBENT (St Thomas) *see* Westhoughton and Wingates *Man*
CHEQUERFIELD (St Mary) *see* Pontefract St Giles *Wakef*
CHERBURY w Gainford *Ox 17* **P** *Bp, DBP, Jes Coll, Oriel Coll, and Worc Coll Ox (jt)* **R** R O WOODHAMS, NSM J HANCE
CHERHILL (St James the Great) *see* Oldbury *Sarum*
CHERINGTON (St John the Baptist) w Stourton *Cov 9* **P** *Bp* **P-in-c** R K SMITH, **C** H C W PARBURY
CHERINGTON (St Nicholas) *see* Avening w Cherington *Glouc*
CHERITON (All Souls) w Newington *Cant 5* **P** *Abp* **V** A G RICHARDS
CHERITON (St Martin) *Cant 5* **P** *Abp* **R** H C JONES
CHERITON (St Michael and All Angels) *see* Upper Itchen *Win*
CHERITON, NORTH (St John the Baptist) *see* Camelot Par *B & W*
CHERITON BISHOP (St Mary) *see* Tedburn St Mary, Whitestone, Oldridge etc *Ex*
CHERITON FITZPAINE (St Matthew) *see* N Creedy *Ex*
CHERRY BURTON (St Michael) *York 8* **P** R H Burton Esq **P-in-c** M J WESTBY
CHERRY HINTON (St Andrew) *Ely 2* **P** *Peterho Cam* **V** C D BOULTON, **C** J L MEADER
CHERRY HINTON (St John the Evangelist) *Ely 2* **P** *Bp* **V** D P E REINDORP, **Hon C** P S HESLAM, **NSM** A C W TILBY
CHERRY WILLINGHAM (St Peter and St Paul) *see* S Lawres Gp *Linc*
CHERTSEY (St Peter w All Saints) *Guildf 11* **P** *Haberdashers' Co* **V** T J HILLIER, **C** J F WINDSOR
CHESELBORNE (St Martin) *see* Milton Abbas, Hilton w Cheselbourne etc *Sarum*
CHESHAM, GREAT (Christ Church) (Emmanuel) (St Mary the Virgin) *Ox 20* **P** *Patr Bd* **TR** R J SALISBURY, **TV** R S HARRIS, W M C STILEMAN, **C** P T J CHADDER, **NSM** A DAVIS, D J UPCOTT
CHESHAM BOIS (St Leonard) *Ox 20* **P** *Peache Trustees* **R** G C ROWLANDSON, **NSM** D J BUTLER, C CLARE
CHESHUNT (St Mary the Virgin) *St Alb 20* **P** *Marquess of Salisbury* **V** B M BLACKSHAW, **C** M C H JONES
CHESSINGTON (St Mary the Virgin) *Guildf 9* **P** *Mert Coll Ox* **V** P M FLYNN
CHESTER (Christ Church) *Ches 2* **P** *Bp* **P-in-c** R C TOAN, **C** A D BUCHANAN
CHESTER (Holy Trinity without the Walls) *Ches 2* **P** *Bp* **R** J A STONE
CHESTER (St Mary on the Hill) *Ches 2* **P** *Duke of Westmr* **R** C W J SAMUELS
CHESTER (St Paul) *Ches 2* **P** R Ches **V** S T PENDLEBURY
CHESTER Team, The (St Barnabas) (St John the Baptist) (St Peter) (St Thomas of Canterbury) *Ches 2* **P** *DBP* **TR** P WALSH, **TV** B E STATHAM
CHESTER LE STREET (St Mary and St Cuthbert) *Dur 11* **P** *St Jo Coll Dur* **R** K H DUNNE, **C** P J W TYREUS, P S D NEVILLE, A ANDERSON
CHESTER SQUARE (St Michael) (St Philip) *Lon 3* **P** *Duke of Westmr* **V** C C MARNHAM, **C** M P L SHEA
CHESTERBLADE (The Blessed Virgin Mary) *see* Evercreech w Chesterblade and Milton Clevedon *B & W*
CHESTERFIELD (Holy Trinity) (Christ Church) *Derby 5* **P** *CPAS* **P-in-c** C J W JACKSON
CHESTERFIELD (St Augustine) *Derby 5* **P** *Bp* **V** I A DAVIS
CHESTERFIELD (St Mary and All Saints) *Derby 5* **P** *Bp* **V** M R KNIGHT, **C** R CHARLES
CHESTERFORD, GREAT (All Saints) w LITTLE (St Mary the Virgin) *Chelmsf 22* **P** *Bp* **V** A KEMP
CHESTERTON (Good Shepherd) *Ely 2* **P** *Bp* **V** A R MCKEARNEY, **C** S ROTHWELL
CHESTERTON (Holy Trinity) (St Chad) *Lich 9* **P** *Prime Min* **V** B R WILSON
CHESTERTON (St Andrew) *Ely 2* **P** *Trin Coll Cam* **V** J T D GARDOM, **C** H E DAWES
CHESTERTON (St George) *Ely 2* **P** *Bp* **V** P K REED, **NSM** R NICHOLLS
CHESTERTON (St Giles) *Cov 8* **P** *Lady Willoughby de Broke* **V** G J BURRELL, **C** R C FLOATE
CHESTERTON (St Lawrence) *see* Cirencester *Glouc*
CHESTERTON (St Michael) *see* The Ortons, Alwalton and Chesterton *Ely*
CHESTERTON, GREAT (St Mary) *see* Akeman *Ox*
CHESWARDINE (St Swithun), Childs Ercall, Hales, Hinstock, Sambrook and Stoke on Tern *Lich 18* **P** *Patr Bd* **TR** P S DAVIES

CHET VALLEY Benefice, The *see* Loddon, Sisland, Chedgrave, Hardley and Langley *Nor*
CHETNOLE (St Peter) *see* Wriggle Valley *Sarum*
CHETTISHAM (St Michael and All Angels) *see* Ely *Ely*
CHETTLE (St Mary) *see* Chase *Sarum*
CHETTON (St Giles) *see* Ditton Priors w Neenton, Burwarton etc *Heref*
CHETWODE (St Mary and St Nicholas) *see* Swan *Ox*
CHETWYND (St Michael and All Angels) *see* Newport w Longford, Chetwynd and Forton *Lich*
CHEVELEY (St Mary) *Ely 4* **P** *DBP and Mrs D A Bowlby (alt)* **R** C A SINDALL, **Hon C** L M BROUGHTON
CHEVENING (St Botolph) *Roch 9* **P** *Abp* **R** C F JOHNSON
CHEVERELL, GREAT (St Peter) *see* The Lavingtons, Cheverells, and Easterton *Sarum*
CHEVERELL, LITTLE (St Peter) *as above Sarum*
CHEVINGTON (All Saints) w Hargrave, Chedburgh w Depden, Rede and Hawkedon *St E 8* **P** *Guild of All So (1 turn), Ld Chan (2 turns), Bp and DBP (1 turn)* **R** vacant (01284) 89342
CHEVINGTON (St John the Divine) *Newc 9* **P** *Bp* **P-in-c** E M DIXON
CHEVITHORNE (St Thomas) *see* Tiverton St Pet and Chevithorne w Cove *Ex*
CHEW MAGNA (St Andrew) w Dundry and Norton Malreward *B & W 10* **P** *Bp* **R** C R M ROBERTS, **NSM** E HICKS
CHEW STOKE (St Andrew) w Nempnett Thrubwell *B & W 10* **P** *Bp and SMF (jt)* **P-in-c** C R M ROBERTS, **C** J R EASTELL
CHEWTON (Mission Church) *see* Keynsham *B & W*
CHEWTON MENDIP (St Mary Magdalene) w Ston Easton, Litton and Emborough *B & W 8* **P** *Earl Waldegrave (2 turns), Bp (1 turn)* **P-in-c** V S ROBERTS
CHEYLESMORE (Christ Church) *Cov 3* **P** *Ch Trust Fund Trust* **C** F P SELDON
CHICHELEY (St Laurence) *see* Sherington w Chicheley, N Crawley, Astwood etc *Ox*
CHICHESTER (St Pancras and St John) *Chich 3* **P** *Simeon's Trustees (2 turns), St Jo Chpl Trustees (1 turn)* **R** R B M GRIFFITHS
CHICHESTER (St Paul) and Westhampnett St Peter *Chich 3* **P** *Bp and D&C (jt)* **R** R W HUNT, **C** S J WRIGHT, F P A MASCARENHAS, **Hon C** M G STONE
CHICHESTER (St Wilfrid) *Chich 3* **P** *Bp* **V** S J ATKINSON
CHICKERELL (St Mary) w Fleet *Sarum 4* **P** *Bp* **P-in-c** R J PRESS
CHICKLADE (All Saints) *see* Nadder Valley *Sarum*
CHIDDINGFOLD (St Mary) *Guildf 4* **P** *Ld Chan* **R** S A CROWLE
CHIDDINGLY (not known) w East Hoathly *Chich 21* **P** *Bp* **R** P CLARK, **P-in-c** P A HODGINS
CHIDDINGSTONE (St Mary) w Chiddingstone Causeway *Roch 11* **P** *Abp and Bp (jt)* **P-in-c** I D HARRISON, **NSM** E J LORIMER
CHIDDINGSTONE CAUSEWAY (St Luke) *see* Chiddingstone w Chiddingstone Causeway *Roch*
CHIDEOCK (St Giles) *see* Golden Cap Team *Sarum*
CHIDHAM (St Mary) *Chich 13* **P** *Bp* **V** B R COOK
CHIEVELEY (St Mary the Virgin) w Winterbourne and Oare *Ox 14* **P** *Adn Berks* **V** vacant (01635) 248341
CHIGNAL SMEALEY (St Nicholas) *see* The Chignals w Mashbury *Chelmsf*
CHIGNALS w Mashbury, The *Chelmsf 8* **P** *CPAS (2 turns), Bp (1 turn)* **R** vacant
CHIGWELL (St Mary) (St Winifred) and Chigwell Row *Chelmsf 25* **P** *The Crown and Patr Bd (alt)* **TR** P J TRENDALL, **TV** A J NEALE, A SMITH
CHIGWELL ROW (All Saints) *see* Chigwell and Chigwell Row *Chelmsf*
CHILBOLTON (St Mary) cum Wherwell *Win 3* **P** *Bp and Marquess of Camden (alt)* **R** F E WILLIAMS
CHILCOMB (St Andrew) *see* Win All SS w Chilcomb and Chesil *Win*
CHILCOMBE (not known) *see* Bride Valley *Sarum*
CHILCOMPTON (St John the Baptist) w Downside and Stratton on the Fosse *B & W 12* **P** *Bp, MMCET, and V Midsomer Norton (jt)* **R** S J TUDGEY
CHILCOTE (St Matthew's Chapel) *see* Clifton Campville w Edingale and Harlaston *Lich*
CHILDE OKEFORD (St Nicholas) *see* Okeford *Sarum*
CHILDERDITCH (All Saints and St Faith) *see* E and W Horndon w Lt Warley and Childerditch *Chelmsf*
CHILDREY (St Mary the Virgin) *see* Ridgeway *Ox*
CHILDS ERCALL (St Michael and All Angels) *see* Cheswardine, Childs Ercall, Hales, Hinstock etc *Lich*
CHILDS HILL (All Saints) *see* Hendon All SS Childs Hill *Lon*

CHILDSWYCKHAM (St Mary the Virgin) w Aston Somerville, Buckland and Snowshill *Glouc 16* **P** *Bp*
P-in-c J A NEWCOMBE

CHILDWALL (All Saints) *Liv 4* **P** *Bp* **V** E BRAMHALL, C E J DURHAM

CHILDWALL (St David) *Liv 4* **P** *Bp* **V** S W C GOUGH, **NSM** G R NISBET

CHILDWALL VALLEY (St Mark) *see* Gateacre *Liv*

CHILDWICK (St Mary) *see* St Alb St Mich *St Alb*

CHILFROME (Holy Trinity) *see* Melbury *Sarum*

CHILHAM (St Mary) w Challock and Molash *Cant 2* **P** *Abp and Viscount Massereene and Ferrard (jt)* **V** C R DUNCAN

CHILLENDEN (All Saints) *see* Nonington w Wymynswold and Goodnestone etc *Cant*

CHILLESFORD (St Peter) *see* Wilford Peninsula *St E*

CHILLINGHAM (St Peter) *see* Glendale Gp *Newc*

CHILLINGTON (St James) *see* Ilminster and Distr *B & W*

CHILMARK (St Margaret of Antioch) *see* Nadder Valley *Sarum*

CHILTHORNE DOMER (Blessed Virgin Mary) *see* Tintinhull w Chilthorne Domer, Yeovil Marsh etc *B & W*

CHILTINGTON, EAST (not known) *see* Plumpton w E Chiltington cum Novington *Chich*

CHILTINGTON, WEST (St Mary) *Chich 12* **P** *Bp*
R K G O'DONNELL

CHILTON (All Saints) *see* Harwell w Chilton *Ox*

CHILTON (St Aidan) *Dur 5* **P** *Bp* **P-in-c** W E L BROAD

CHILTON (St Mary) *see* Bernwode *Ox*

CHILTON CANTELO (St James) w Ashington, Mudford, Rimpton and Marston Magna *B & W 7* **P** *DBP and D&C, D&C Bris, and Bp Lon (by turn)* **P-in-c** P T WOOD

CHILTON FOLIAT (St Mary) *see* Whitton *Sarum*

CHILTON MOOR (St Andrew) *Dur 14* **P** *Bp* **V** P D DAVEY

CHILTON POLDEN (St Edward) *see* W Poldens *B & W*

CHILTON TRINITY (Holy Trinity) *see* Bridgwater St Mary, Chilton Trinity and Durleigh *B & W*

CHILVERS COTON (All Saints) w Astley *Cov 5* **P** *Viscount Daventry* **V** P BROWN

CHILWELL (Christ Church) *S'well 7* **P** *CPAS*
P-in-c A S W CULLIS, **C** B H CAMBRIDGE, G A O JESSON, **NSM** L HEPTINSTALL

CHILWORTH (St Denys) w North Baddesley *Win 12*
P *Mrs P M A T Chamberlayne-Macdonald*
V P B C SALISBURY, **C** P S SHERWOOD

CHILWORTH (St Thomas) *see* Shere, Albury and Chilworth *Guildf*

CHINEHAM (Christ Church) *Win 4* **P** *Bp* **V** R D TURNBULL, **C** P J J PLYMING

CHINESE CONGREGATION *see* St Martin-in-the-Fields *Lon*

CHINGFORD (All Saints) (St Peter and St Paul) *Chelmsf 5*
P *Bp* **R** N J EDWARDS, **C** C F WILSON, B J LINNEY

CHINGFORD (St Anne) *Chelmsf 5* **P** *Bp* **V** G W ELLIS

CHINGFORD (St Edmund) *Chelmsf 5* **P** *Bp* **V** C L OWENS

CHINLEY (St Mary) *see* Hayfield and Chinley w Buxworth *Derby*

CHINNOCK, EAST (Blessed Virgin Mary) *see* W Coker w Hardington Mandeville, E Chinnock etc *B & W*

CHINNOCK, MIDDLE (St Margaret) *see* Norton sub Hamdon, W Chinnock, Chiselborough etc *B & W*

CHINNOCK, WEST (Blessed Virgin Mary) *as above B & W*

CHINNOR (St Andrew) w Emmington and Sydenham and Aston Rowant w Crowell *Ox 1* **P** *Bp, DBP, and Peache Trustees (jt)*
R M L LANGE-SMITH, **OLM** J M DEVAL, S Q HUTTON

CHIPPENHAM (St Andrew) w Tytherton Lucas *Bris 4*
P *Ch Ch Ox* **V** S C TATTON-BROWN, **C** J M WHITE

CHIPPENHAM (St Margaret) *Ely 3* **P** *Mrs A Crawley*
NSM M G BANYARD

CHIPPENHAM (St Paul) w Hardenhuish and Langley Burrell *Bris 4* **P** *Patr Bd* **TR** S J TYNDALL, **C** A D ROBINSON

CHIPPENHAM (St Peter) *Bris 4* **P** *Bp* **V** A D FENSOME, **C** R C LUNN

CHIPPERFIELD (St Paul) *St Alb 5* **P** *Trustees*
P-in-c J P HART, **Hon C** M K WILLIAMS

CHIPPING (St Bartholomew) and Whitewell (St Michael) *Blackb 7* **P** *Bp and Hulme Trustees (jt)* **V** A SIDDALL

CHIPPING BARNET (St John the Baptist) w Arkley *St Alb 17*
P *The Crown* **TR** S H SPEERS, **TV** M J WILLIAMS,
C S D MILLAR, **NSM** M J A LINDSAY

CHIPPING CAMPDEN (St James) w Ebrington *Glouc 9*
P *Peache Trustees (1 turn), Earl of Harrowby (2 turns)*
P-in-c D C M COOK, **NSM** M J ABSOLON

CHIPPING NORTON (St Mary the Virgin) *Ox 3* **P** *Patr Bd*
TR S J A WESTON, **TV** T A CANNON, **C** T NORMAN,
NSM S A HAYES, H M WILLIAMS, R D MANDERSON, J FIELDEN

CHIPPING ONGAR (St Martin) w Shelley *Chelmsf 27*
P *Guild of All So and Keble Coll Ox* **R** B J PYKE,
NSM G FRITH

CHIPPING SODBURY (St John the Baptist) and Old Sodbury *Glouc 7* **P** *D&C Worc* **P-in-c** C B WRAY, **C** H RUNDLE

CHIPPING WARDEN (St Peter and St Paul) *see* Culworth w Sulgrave and Thorpe Mandeville etc *Pet*

CHIPSTABLE (All Saints) *see* Wiveliscombe w Chipstable, Huish Champflower etc *B & W*

CHIPSTEAD (Good Shepherd) *see* Chevening *Roch*

CHIPSTEAD (St Margaret of Antioch) *S'wark 27* **P** *Abp*
R J M P GOODDEN, **OLM** J N WATES

CHIRBURY (St Michael) *Heref 13* **P** *Sir David Wakeman Bt and Bp (alt)* **V** P D HARRATT

CHIRTON (St John the Baptist) *see* Redhorn *Sarum*

CHISELBOROUGH (St Peter and St Paul) *see* Norton sub Hamdon, W Chinnock, Chiselborough etc *B & W*

CHISHILL, GREAT (St Swithun) *see* Heydon, Gt and Lt Chishill, Chrishall etc *Chelmsf*

CHISHILL, LITTLE (St Nicholas) *as above Chelmsf*

CHISLEDON (Holy Cross) *see* Ridgeway *Sarum*

CHISLEHURST (Annunciation) *Roch 14* **P** *Keble Coll*
V W B BEER

CHISLEHURST (Christ Church) *Roch 14* **P** *CPAS*
V J M ADAMS, **C** T J MILLS

CHISLEHURST (St Nicholas) *Roch 14* **P** *Bp*
R C J D WALKER, **C** J N WHATTON, **NSM** J B HURN

CHISLET (St Mary the Virgin) *see* St Nicholas at Wade w Sarre and Chislet w Hoath *Cant*

CHISWICK (St Michael) *Lon 11* **P** *V St Martin-in-the-Fields*
P-in-c N C FINCHAM

CHISWICK (St Michael and All Angels) *see* Bedford Park *Lon*

CHISWICK (St Nicholas w St Mary Magdalene) *Lon 11*
P *D&C St Paul's* **V** P A TUFT

CHISWICK (St Paul) Grove Park *Lon 11* **P** *V Chiswick*
V M C RILEY

CHITHURST (St Mary) *see* Rogate w Terwick and Trotton w Chithurst *Chich*

CHITTERNE (All Saints and St Mary) *see* Wylye and Till Valley *Sarum*

CHITTERNE (St Mary) *as above Sarum*

CHITTLEHAMHOLT (St John) *see* S Molton w Nymet St George, High Bray etc *Ex*

CHITTLEHAMPTON (St Hieritha) *as above Ex*

CHITTS HILL (St Cuthbert) *Lon 19* **P** *CPAS* **V** D M DALEY

CHIVELSTONE (St Sylvester) *see* Charleton w Buckland Tout Saints etc *Ex*

CHOBHAM (St Lawrence) w Valley End *Guildf 6* **P** *Bp and Brig R W Acworth (alt)* **V** A BODY

CHOLDERTON (St Nicholas) *see* Bourne Valley *Sarum*

CHOLESBURY (St Lawrence) *see* Hawridge w Cholesbury and St Leonard *Ox*

CHOLLERTON w Birtley and Thockrington *Newc 2*
P *Mrs P I Enderby (2 turns), Newc Dioc Soc (1 turn)*
R J WYLAM

CHOLSEY (St Mary) *Ox 18* **P** *Ld Chan* **V** A M PETIT

CHOPPARDS (Mission Room) *see* Upper Holme Valley *Wakef*

CHOPPINGTON (St Paul the Apostle) *Newc 1* **P** *D&C*
V J J T THOMPSON

CHOPWELL (St John the Evangelist) *Dur 13* **P** *Bp*
P-in-c P R MURRAY

CHORLEY (All Saints) *Blackb 4* **P** *Bp* **V** E N STRASZAK

CHORLEY (St George) *Blackb 4* **P** *R Chorley* **V** K BARRETT

CHORLEY (St James) *Blackb 4* **P** *R Chorley* **V** K HOWLES

CHORLEY (St Laurence) *Blackb 4* **P** *Bp* **R** J R CREE,
C T R WEBBER

CHORLEY (St Peter) *Blackb 4* **P** *R Chorley*
V L T ATHERTON

CHORLEY (St Philip) *see* Alderley Edge *Ches*

CHORLEYWOOD (Christ Church) *St Alb 5* **P** *CPAS*
V G A COLLINS

CHORLEYWOOD (St Andrew) *St Alb 5* **P** *Bp*
V M W G STIBBE, **C** M O KNIGHT, **Hon C** M S MCCRUM

CHORLTON-CUM-HARDY (St Clement) (St Barnabas) *Man 4* **P** *D&C* **R** H J BARBER, **C** R S THEWSEY

CHORLTON-CUM-HARDY (St Werburgh) *Man 4* **P** *Bp*
R A P JOHNSON, **OLM** M J CLEALL-HILL, **R J DIGGLE

CHRISHALL (Holy Trinity) *see* Heydon, Gt and Lt Chishill, Chrishall etc *Chelmsf*

CHRIST THE KING comprising the parishes of Tanfield, Stanley and South Moor *Dur 4* **P** *Bp (4 turns), Prime Min (1 turn)* **TR** A JOHNSTON, **TV** G J SIMMONS, I GROSU, **C** J O M CRAIG

CHRIST THE KING in the Diocese of Newcastle *Newc 5*
P *Patr Bd* **TR** R K KENNEDY, **TV** J J VICKERSTAFF,
M S JONES

CHRISTCHURCH (Christ Church) and Manea and Welney *Ely 16* **P** *Bp and R T Townley Esq (jt)* **R** *vacant* (01354) 638379

CHRISTCHURCH (Holy Trinity) *Win 9* **P** *Bp*
V H M WILLIAMS, **C** A M SMITH, A V SAUNDERS, J E F JASPER
CHRISTCHURCH Stourvale (St George) *see* Christchurch *Win*
CHRISTIAN MALFORD (All Saints) *see* Draycot Bris
CHRISTLETON (St James) *Ches 2* **P** *Bp* **R** K P LEE
CHRISTON (Blessed Virgin Mary) *see* Crook Peak *B & W*
CHRISTOW (St James), Ashton and Bridford *Ex 6* **P** *SMF, MMCET, Viscount Exmouth, Bp, and E A Beard Esq (jt)*
P-in-c G K MAYER
CHUDLEIGH (St Mary and St Martin) w Chudleigh Knighton and Trusham *Ex 10* **P** *Patr Bd* **V** P WIMSETT
CHUDLEIGH KNIGHTON (St Paul) *see* Chudleigh w Chudleigh Knighton and Trusham *Ex*
CHULMLEIGH (St Mary Magdalene) *see* Burrington, Chawleigh, Cheldon, Chulmleigh etc *Ex*
CHURCH ASTON (St Andrew) *Lich 16* **P** *R Edgmond*
P-in-c J C COWBURN
CHURCH BRAMPTON (St Botolph) *see* Brington w Whilton and Norton etc *Pet*
CHURCH BROUGHTON (St Michael) *see* Boylestone, Church Broughton, Dalbury, etc *Derby*
CHURCH CONISTON (St Andrew) *Carl 9* **P** *Peache Trustees*
P-in-c M R EAST
CHURCH EATON (St Editha) *see* Bradeley, Church Eaton and Moreton *Lich*
CHURCH HONEYBOURNE (St Ecgwyn) *see* Pebworth, Dorsington, Honeybourne etc *Glouc*
CHURCH HULME (St Luke) *Ches 11* **P** *V Sandbach*
V *vacant* (01477) 533124
CHURCH IN THE WOOD *see* Hollington St Leon *Chich*
CHURCH KIRK (St James) *Blackb 1* **P** *Hulme Trustees*
R N A ASHTON
CHURCH KNOWLE (St Peter) *see* Corfe Castle, Church Knowle, Kimmeridge etc *Sarum*
CHURCH LANGLEY (Church and Community Centre)
Chelmsf 26 **P** *V Harlow* **V** M J HAMPSON
CHURCH LANGTON (St Peter) cum Tur Langton, Thorpe Langton and Shangton, Billesdon cum Goadby and Rolleston and Skeffington *Leic 4* **P** *Bp, E Brudenell Esq, and MMCET (jt)* **R** B M KNIGHT, **NSM** A J ROBERTS
CHURCH LAWFORD (St Peter) *see* Wolston and Church Lawford *Cov*
CHURCH LAWTON (All Saints) *Ches 11* **P** *Mrs I L Lawton*
R G L JOYCE
CHURCH LENCH (All Saints) w Rous Lench and Abbots Morton and Harvington *Worc 1* **P** *Bp and D&C (jt)*
R R J G THORNILEY
CHURCH MINSHULL (St Bartholomew) *see* Acton and Worleston, Church Minshull etc *Ches*
CHURCH OAKLEY (St Leonard) *see* Oakley w Wootton St Lawrence *Win*
CHURCH PREEN (St John the Baptist) *see* Wenlock *Heref*
CHURCH STRETTON (St Laurence) *Heref 11* **P** *Ch Patr Trust* **R** J N MILLARD, **C** J G HUTCHINSON
CHURCH LAWFORD (St Peter) *see* Wolston and Church Lawford *Cov*
CHURCHAM (St Andrew) *see* Huntley and Longhope, Churcham and Bulley *Glouc*
CHURCHDOWN (St Andrew) (St Bartholomew) *Glouc 6*
P *D&C* **V** T E MASON, **C** M A BALFOUR
CHURCHDOWN (St John the Evangelist) *Glouc 6* **P** *Bp*
V K I MORGAN, **C** A MORRIS
CHURCHILL (All Saints) *see* Chipping Norton *Ox*
CHURCHILL (St John the Baptist) *see* Burrington and Churchill *B & W*
CHURCHILL-IN-HALFSHIRE (St James) w Blakedown and Broome *Worc 12* **P** *Viscount Cobham and N A Bourne Esq (alt)* **R** N J DAVIS
CHURCHOVER (Holy Trinity) w Willey *Cov 6* **P** *Bp*
Hon C C S HARPER
CHURCHSTANTON (St Peter and St Paul) *see* Blackdown *B & W*
CHURCHSTOKE (St Nicholas) w Hyssington and Sarn
Heref 10 **P** *The Crown (1 turn), Earl of Powis (2 turns)*
V W T BRYAN, **NSM** I R BALL
CHURCHSTOW (St Mary) *see* Thurlestone, S Milton, W Alvington etc *Ex*
CHURCHTOWN (St Helen) *see* Garstang St Helen and St Michaels-on-Wyre *Blackb*
CHURSTON FERRERS (St Mary the Vigin) *see* Brixham w Churston Ferrers and Kingswear *Ex*
CHURT (St John the Evangelist) and Hindhead *Guildf 3*
P *Adn Surrey* **V** D WILBRAHAM, **Hon C** S R JELLEY, **NSM** J D STRAIN
CHURWELL (All Saints) *see* Morley *Wakef*
CHUTE (St Nicholas) *see* Savernake *Sarum*
CHYNGTON (St Luke) *see* Seaford w Sutton *Chich*

CINDERFORD (St John the Evangelist) *Glouc 4* **P** *The Crown*
V J W HOLDER
CINDERFORD (St Stephen) w Littledean *Glouc 4* **P** *Ch Patr Trust* **P-in-c** R D WYNN
CINDERHILL (Christ Church) *S'well 13* **P** *Bp*
P-in-c K BATTE, **NSM** L P B O'BOYLE
CINNAMON BROW (Resurrection) *Liv 12* **P** *Bp, Adn, and R Warrington (jt)* **V** S W ELSTOB
CIPPENHAM (St Andrew) *see* W Slough *Ox*
CIRENCESTER (St John the Baptist) *Glouc 11* **P** *Bp*
V M A M ST JOHN-CHANNELL, **C** M R BIRCH, C A MCCLURE, **NSM** J A GARDNER
CLACTON, GREAT (St John the Baptist) *Chelmsf 23*
P *Ch Patr Trust* **V** G D A THORBURN, **C** I BAKER
CLACTON, LITTLE (St James) *see* Weeley and Lt Clacton *Chelmsf*
CLACTON-ON-SEA (St Christopher) (St James) *Chelmsf 23*
P *Bp* **V** A P D SPOONER
CLACTON-ON-SEA (St Paul) *Chelmsf 23* **P** *Ch Patr Trust*
V D J TITLEY, **NSM** D W HART
CLAINES (St George w St Mary Magdalene) *see* Worc St Geo w St Mary Magd *Worc*
CLAINES (St John the Baptist) *Worc 6* **P** *Bp* **V** S M AGNEW
CLANDON, EAST (St Thomas of Canterbury) and WEST
(St Peter and St Paul) *Guildf 5* **P** *Earl of Onslow and Bp (alt)*
R *vacant* (01483) 222573
CLANFIELD (St James) *see* Catherington and Clanfield *Portsm*
CLANFIELD (St Stephen) *see* Bampton w Clanfield *Ox*
CLANNABOROUGH (St Petrock) *see* N Creedy *Ex*
CLAPHAM (Christ Church) (St John the Evangelist) *S'wark 12*
P *Bp* **V** P J ROSE-CASEMORE, **NSM** S MOSS, S PEAKE
CLAPHAM (Holy Spirit) *S'wark 12* **P** *Bp* **V** J A BLUNDEN, **Hon C** R F VICKERY
CLAPHAM (Holy Trinity) (St Peter) *S'wark 12* **P** *DBP*
V D O ISHERWOOD, **C** A V CINNAMOND, **NSM** C A CLARKE, M P STRANGE
CLAPHAM (St James) *S'wark 12* **P** *CPAS* **V** C A COTTON, **Hon C** J MARSHALL
CLAPHAM (St Mary the Virgin) *see* Findon w Clapham and Patching *Chich*
CLAPHAM (St Paul) *S'wark 12* **P** *Bp* **V** J P H ALLAIN CHAPMAN, **NSM** R E LLOYD MORGAN
CLAPHAM (St Thomas of Canterbury) *St Alb 13* **P** *MMCET*
V S J LILEY
CLAPHAM COMMON (St Barnabas) *S'wark 16* **P** *Ch Trust Fund Trust* **V** D PAGE
CLAPHAM PARK (All Saints) *S'wark 12* **P** *CPAS*
V B F J GOODWIN
CLAPHAM PARK (St Stephen) *S'wark 13* **P** *Trustees*
V S P GATES, **C** P M PULLINGER
CLAPHAM-WITH-KEASDEN (St James) and Austwick
Bradf 6 **P** *Bp* **V** *vacant* (01524) 251313
CLAPTON (St James) *see* Bourton-on-the-Water w Clapton *Glouc*
CLAPTON (St James) *Lon 5* **P** *Bp* **V** R BROWN
CLAPTON (St Peter) *see* Barnwell w Tichmarsh, Thurning and Clapton *Pet*
CLAPTON, UPPER (St Matthew) *Lon 5* **P** *D&C Cant*
NSM R A FARLEY
CLARBOROUGH (St John the Baptist) w Hayton *S'well 5*
P *Bp* **P-in-c** M W BRIGGS
CLARE (St Peter and St Paul) w Poslingford, Cavendish, Stoke by Clare w Wixoe *St E 8* **P** *Lady Loch* **R** W J A RANKIN, **C** J E BAXTER
CLAREMOUNT (St Thomas the Apostle) *see* Southowram and Claremount *Wakef*
CLARENCE GATE GARDENS (St Cyprian) *see* St Marylebone St Cypr *Lon*
CLARENDON (Team Ministry) *Sarum 11* **P** *Team Coun*
TR M A WARD, **TV** M I CLUTTERBUCK, N H S BERSWEDEN, **Hon C** L M CATER, **NSM** D L SANDERS
CLARENDON PARK (St John the Baptist) w Knighton St Michael and All Angels *Leic 2* **P** *Bp* **TR** D C WHITE, **C** S J WRIGHT
CLATFORD, UPPER (All Saints) *see* Abbotts Ann and Upper and Goodworth Clatford *Win*
CLATWORTHY (St Mary Magdalene) *see* Wiveliscombe w Chipstable, Huish Champflower etc *B & W*
CLAUGHTON VILLAGE (St Bede) *see* Birkenhead St Jas w St Bede *Ches*
CLAVERDON (St Michael and All Angels) w Preston Bagot
Cov 7 **P** *Bp* **P-in-c** L G MORTIMER
CLAVERHAM (St Barnabas) *see* Yatton Moor *B & W*
CLAVERING (St Mary and St Clement) w Langley and Arkesden
Chelmsf 21 **P** *Ch Hosp and Keble Coll Ox (alt)*
V D S MCGUFFIE

CLAVERLEY (All Saints) w Tuckhill *Heref 9* **P** *Bp and E M A Thompson Esq (jt)* **V** S H CAWDELL, **NSM** S H L CAWDELL

CLAVERTON (Blessed Virgin Mary) *see Bathampton w Claverton B & W*

CLAVERTON DOWN (St Hugh) *as above B & W*

CLAWTON (St Leonard) *see Ashwater, Halwill, Beaworthy, Clawton etc Ex*

CLAXBY (St Mary) *see Walesby Linc*

CLAXTON (St Andrew) *see Rockland St Mary w Hellington, Bramerton etc Nor*

CLAY CROSS (St Bartholomew) *see N Wingfield, Clay Cross and Pilsley Derby*

CLAY HILL (St John the Baptist) (St Luke) *Lon 18* **P** *V Enfield St Andr and Bp (jt)* **V** L S DRAKE

CLAYBROOKE (St Peter) cum Wibtoft and Frolesworth *Leic 11* **P** *The Crown and Adn Loughb (by turn)* **V** J M BRADSHAW

CLAYDON and Barham *St E 1* **P** *G R Drury Esq* **P-in-c** T W BROADBENT, **NSM** S M EVANS, **OLM**-C B AUSTIN, J V ABLETT

CLAYDON (St James the Great) *see Shires' Edge Ox*

CLAYDONS, The (St Mary) (All Saints) *Ox 24* **P** *Sir Ralph Verney Bt* **P-in-c** R D HOLDER

CLAYGATE (Holy Trinity) *Guildf 8* **P** *Ch Patr Trust* **V** J T HENDERSON, **C** D M KING, **NSM** L M MORGAN

CLAYHANGER (St Peter) *see Bampton, Morebath, Clayhanger and Petton Ex*

CLAYHIDON (St Andrew) *see Hemyock w Culm Davy, Clayhidon and Culmstock Ex*

CLAYPOLE (St Peter) *Linc 23* **P** *DBP (2 turns), The Revd J R H Thorold and J R Thorold Esq (1 turn)* **R** G MUNN, **NSM** C C MUNN

CLAYTON (St Cross w St Paul) *see Man Clayton St Cross w St Paul Man*

CLAYTON (St James the Great) *Lich 9* **P** *Bp* **V** N M EDWARDS

CLAYTON (St John the Baptist) *Bradf 2* **P** *V Bradf* **V** K O DUNNETT

CLAYTON (St John the Baptist) w Keymer *Chich 9* **P** *BNC Ox* **R** *vacant (01273) 843570*

CLAYTON BROOK (Community Church) *see Whittle-le-Woods Blackb*

CLAYTON LE MOORS (All Saints) *see Altham w Clayton le Moors Blackb*

CLAYTON LE MOORS (St James) *as above Blackb*

CLAYTON WEST w HIGH HOYLAND (All Saints) *see High Hoyland, Scissett and Clayton W Wakef*

CLAYWORTH (St Peter) *see Everton and Mattersey w Clayworth S'well*

CLEADON (All Saints) *Dur 15* **P** *R Whitburn* **V** R A NIXON

CLEADON PARK (St Mark and St Cuthbert) *Dur 15* **P** *Bp* **V** R J A ALDERSON

CLEARWELL (St Peter) *see Newland and Redbrook w Clearwell Glouc*

CLEASBY (St Peter) *see Barton and Manfield and Cleasby w Stapleton Ripon*

CLEATOR (St Leonard) *see Crosslacon Carl*

CLEATOR MOOR (St John) *as above Carl*

CLECKHEATON (St John the Evangelist) *Wakef 8* **P** *V Birstall* **V** J BARKER

CLECKHEATON (St Luke) (Whitechapel) *Wakef 8* **P** *Bp and Sir Martin Wilson (jt)* **P-in-c** M A MCLEAN

CLEDFORD (Mission Room) *see Middlewich w Byley Ches*

CLEE, NEW (St John the Evangelist) (St Stephen) *Linc 9* **P** *Bp* **V** J W ELLIS

CLEE, OLD (Holy Trinity and St Mary the Virgin) *Linc 9* **P** *Bp* **V** D I WALKER

CLEE HILL (St Peter's Mission Room) *see Wigmore Abbey Heref*

CLEE ST MARGARET (St Margaret) *see Bitterley w Middleton, Stoke St Milborough etc Heref*

CLEETHORPE (Christ Church) *see Clee Linc*

CLEETHORPES St Aidan *Linc 9* **P** *Bp* **V** *vacant (01472) 692989*

CLEETHORPES (St Francis) Conventional District *Linc 9 vacant*

CLEETHORPES (St Peter) *Linc 9* **P** *Bp* **R** D C PEACOCK, **C** A P ISON, **NSM** D H WEBSTER

CLEETON (St Mary) *see Stottesdon w Farlow, Cleeton St Mary, etc Heref*

CLEEVE (Holy Trinity) *see Yatton Moor B & W*

CLEEVE, OLD (St Andrew), Leighland and Treborough *B & W 16* **P** *Selw Coll Cam (2 turns), Personal Reps G R Wolseley Esq (1 turn)* **R** *vacant (01984) 640576*

CLEEVE HILL (St Peter) *see Bishop's Cleeve Glouc*

CLEEVE PRIOR (St Andrew) and The Littletons *Worc 1* **P** *D&C and Ch Ch Ox (alt)* **V** D R EVANS

CLEHONGER (All Saints) *see Kingstone w Clehonger, Eaton Bishop etc Heref*

CLENCHWARTON (St Margaret) and West Lynn *Ely 17* **P** *DBP* **R** A J DAVEY

CLENT (St Leonard) *see Belbroughton w Fairfield and Clent Worc*

CLEOBURY MORTIMER (St Mary the Virgin) w Hopton Wafers, Neen Sollars and Milson, Neen Savage w Kinlet *Heref 12* **P** *Patr Bd (2 turns), Ld Chan (1 turn)* **R** W A BUCK

CLEOBURY NORTH (St Peter and St Paul) *see Ditton Priors w Neenton, Burwarton etc Heref*

CLERKENWELL (Our Most Holy Redeemer) *Lon 6* **P** *Trustees* **V** P A BAGOTT, **C** R M MACKLEY

CLERKENWELL (St James and St John) (St Peter) *Lon 6* **P** *Ch Patr Trust and PCC (jt)* **V** A J BAUGHEN

CLERKENWELL (St Mark) *Lon 6* **P** *City Corp* **V** P A BAGOTT, **C** R M MACKLEY

CLEVEDON (St Andrew) (Christ Church) (St Peter) *B & W 13* **P** *Simeon's Trustees (1 turn), Ld Chan (2 turns)* **V** T J BAILLIE, **C** C J JENNINGS

CLEVEDON (St John the Evangelist) *B & W 13* **P** *SMF* **V** D S M SMITH, **C** N W M LEGGETT

CLEVEDON, EAST (All Saints) w Clapton in Gordano, Walton Clevedon, Walton in Gordano and Weston in Gordano *B & W 13* **P** *Bp and SMF (jt)* **R** N A HECTOR, **C** S J CONSTABLE

CLEVELEYS (St Andrew) *Blackb 12* **P** *Trustees* **V** D E REEVES

CLEWER (St Andrew) *Ox 13* **P** *Eton Coll* **P-in-c** I N RANDALL

CLEWER (St Stephen) *see New Windsor Ox*

CLEY (St Margaret) *see Blakeney w Cley, Wiveton, Glandford etc Nor*

CLEY HILL Warminster (Team Ministry) *Sarum 17* **P** *Patr Bd* **TR** A G WATTS, **TV** R G ASKEW, **C** W P M HUGHES, **NSM** C J OWEN, N PAYNE, **OLM** A M WADSWORTH, A J R YATES

CLIBURN (St Cuthbert) *see Morland, Thrimby, Gt Strickland and Cliburn Carl*

CLIDDESDEN (St Leonard) and Ellisfield w Farleigh Wallop and Dummer *Win 1* **P** *Earl of Portsm and DBP (jt)* **P-in-c** C PARNELL-HOPKINSON

CLIFFE (St Andrew) *see Hemingbrough York*

CLIFFE, SOUTH (St John) *see N Cave w Cliffe York*

CLIFFE AT HOO (St Helen) w Cooling *Roch 6* **P** *D&C* **R** E M WRIGHT

CLIFFE VALE (St Stephen) *see Hartshill Lich*

CLIFFORD (St Luke) *York 1* **P** *G Lane-Fox Esq* **P-in-c** H N LAWRANCE

CLIFFORD (St Mary the Virgin) *see Cusop w Blakemere, Bredwardine w Brobury etc Heref*

CLIFFORD CHAMBERS (St Helen) *see Stratford-upon-Avon, Luddington etc Cov*

CLIFFORDS MESNE (St Peter) *see Newent and Gorsley w Cliffords Mesne Glouc*

CLIFFSEND (St Mary the Virgin) *see St Laur in Thanet Cant*

CLIFTON (All Saints) and Southill *St Alb 16* **P** *Bp and S C Whitbread Esq (jt)* **R** J K DIXON, **NSM** C T TOPLEY

CLIFTON (All Saints w St John) *Bris 2* **P** *Bp* **NSM** R DURBIN, J H J PATRICK

CLIFTON (Christ Church w Emmanuel) *Bris 2* **P** *Simeon's Trustees* **V** A J M DOW, **C** M C CAIN, L WALTON

CLIFTON (Holy Trinity) *Derby 8* **P** *Mrs M F Stanton, T W Clowes Esq, and V Ashbourne (by turn)* **V** *vacant (01335) 342199*

CLIFTON (Holy Trinity, St Andrew the Less and St Peter) *Bris 2* **P** *Simeon's Trustees* **V** B J DUCKETT, **NSM** I A BAILEY

CLIFTON (Mission Church) *see Conisbrough Sheff*

CLIFTON (St Anne) (St Thomas) *Man 2* **P** *Bp* **V** P J BARNETT, **OLM** M SOFIELD

CLIFTON (St Cuthbert) *see Lowther and Askham and Clifton and Brougham Carl*

CLIFTON (St Francis) (St Mary the Virgin) *S'well 9* **P** *DBP* **TR** E P FORSHAW, **TV** W D MILNER, D M R PALMER, **NSM** G CLEAVER

CLIFTON (St James) *Sheff 6* **P** *Bp* **V** J H RICHARDSON

CLIFTON (St John the Evangelist) *see Lund Blackb*

CLIFTON (St John the Evangelist) *see Brighouse and Clifton Wakef*

CLIFTON (St Luke) *Carl 4* **P** *R Workington* **P-in-c** K KITCHIN

CLIFTON (St Paul) *see Cotham St Sav w St Mary and Clifton St Paul Bris*

CLIFTON (St Philip and St James) *York 7* **P** *Trustees* **V** D O CASSWELL, **C** R J FACER, **NSM** R A HIRST

CLIFTON, NEW (Holy Trinity) *see Clifton S'well*

CLIFTON, NORTH (St George)   *see* Harby w Thorney and N and S Clifton *S'well*

CLIFTON CAMPVILLE (St Andrew) w Edingale and Harlaston *Lich 4*   **P** *Bp and Major F C Pipe-Wolferstan (jt)*   **R** A L WHEALE,   **Hon C** C M J IBALL

CLIFTON HAMPDEN (St Michael and All Angels) *see Dorchester Ox*

CLIFTON-ON-TEME (St Kenelm), Lower Sapey and the Shelsleys *Worc 3*   **P** *Bp and A F Evans Esq (jt)*   **P-in-c** G GILES

CLIFTON REYNES (St Mary the Virgin)   *see* Lavendon w Cold Brayfield, Clifton Reynes etc *Ox*

CLIFTON UPON DUNSMORE (St Mary) and Newton *Cov 6*   **P** *H A F W Boughton Leigh Esq*   **P-in-c** D M CHARLES-EDWARDS

CLIFTONVILLE (St Paul) *Cant 9*   **P** *Ch Patr Trust*   **P-in-c** T R WHATELEY,   **NSM** G B GRIFFITHS

CLIPPESBY (St Peter)   *see* Martham and Repps with Bastwick, Thurne etc *Nor*

CLIPSHAM (St Mary)   *see* Greetham and Thistleton w Stretton and Clipsham *Pet*

CLIPSTON (All Saints) w Naseby and Haselbech w Kelmarsh *Pet 2*   **P** *Ch Coll Cam, DBP, Mrs M F Harris, Exors Miss C V Lancaster (by turn)*   **R** D W FAULKS

CLIPSTONE (All Saints) *S'well 2*   **P** *Bp*   **P-in-c** M J GARRATT

CLITHEROE (St James) *Blackb 7*   **P** *Trustees*   **R** M W L PICKETT

CLITHEROE (St Mary Magdalene) *Blackb 7*   **P** *J R Peel Esq*   **V** P H DEARDEN,   **NSM** P W SHEPHERD

CLITHEROE (St Paul) Low Moor *Blackb 7*   **P** *Bp*   **V** R NICHOLSON

CLIVE (All Saints)   *see* Astley, Clive, Grinshill and Hadnall *Lich*

CLIVE VALE (All Souls)   *see* Hastings All So *Chich*

CLODOCK (St Clydog) and Longtown w Craswall, Llanveynoe, St Margaret's, Michaelchurch Escley and Newton *Heref 1*   **P** *DBP (2 turns), MMCET (1 turn)*   **V** F E RODGERS

CLOFORD (St Mary)   *see* Nunney and Witham Friary, Marston Bigot etc *B & W*

CLOPHILL (St Mary the Virgin)   *see* Campton, Clophill and Haynes *St Alb*

CLOPTON (St Mary) w Otley, Swilland and Ashbocking *St E 7*   **P** *Ld Chan and Bp (alt)*   **P-in-c** J N RAPLEY

CLOSWORTH (All Saints)   *see* E Coker w Sutton Bingham and Closworth *B & W*

CLOTHALL (St Mary Virgin)   *see* Sandon, Wallington and Rushden w Clothall *St Alb*

CLOUGHTON (St Mary) and Burniston w Ravenscar and Staintondale *York 15*   **P** *Abp*   **V** G P TAYLOR

CLOVELLY (All Saints)   *see* Parkham, Alwington, Buckland Brewer etc *Ex*

CLOVELLY (St Peter)   *as above Ex*

CLOWNE (St John the Baptist) *Derby 3*   **P** *Ld Chan*   **R** L R R HARRIS

CLOWS TOP (Mission Room)   *see* Mamble w Bayton, Rock w Heightington etc *Worc*

CLUBMOOR (St Andrew) *Liv 8*   **P** *Bp*   **V** S MCGANITY,   **OLM** S J JAMIESON

CLUMBER PARK (St Mary the Virgin)   *see* Worksop Priory *S'well*

CLUN (St George) w Bettws-y-Crwyn and Newcastle *Heref 10*   **P** *Earl of Powis*   **V** R T SHAW

CLUNBURY (St Swithin)   *see* Clungunford w Clunbury and Clunton, Bedstone etc *Heref*

CLUNGUNFORD (St Cuthbert) w Clunbury and Clunton, Bedstone and Hopton Castle *Heref 9*   **P** *Earl of Powis, Mrs S B Rocke, M S C Brown Esq, and Sir Hugh Ripley Bt (jt)*   **R** S B BELL

CLUNTON (St Mary)   *see* Clungunford w Clunbury and Clunton, Bedstone etc *Heref*

CLUTTON (St Augustine of Hippo) w Cameley *B & W 10*   **P** *Earl of Warw (2 turns), Exors J P Hippisley Esq (1 turn)*   **R** T J DAPLYN

CLYFFE PYPARD (St Peter)   *see* Broad Town, Clyffe Pypard, Hilmarton etc *Sarum*

CLYMPING (St Mary the Virgin) and Yapton w Ford *Chich 1*   **P** *Bp (2 turns), Ld Chan (1 turn)*   **R** R H HAYES,   **NSM** P WALLIS

CLYST HONITON (St Michael and All Angels)   *see* Aylesbeare, Rockbeare, Farringdon etc *Ex*

CLYST HYDON (St Andrew)   *see* Bradninch and Clyst Hydon *Ex*

CLYST ST GEORGE (St George)   *see* Clyst St Mary, Clyst St George etc *Ex*

CLYST ST LAWRENCE (St Lawrence)   *see* Whimple, Talaton and Clyst St Lawr *Ex*

CLYST ST MARY (St Mary), Clyst St George and Woodbury Salterton *Ex 1*   **P** *Lord Wraxall, D&C, and S Radcliffe (jt)*   **R** G L ROWE

COALBROOKDALE (Holy Trinity), Iron-Bridge and Little Wenlock *Heref 14*   **P** *Bp, Lord Forester, V Madeley, and V Much Wenlock (jt)*   **R** S H CARTER,   **NSM** J M EDWARDS

COALEY (St Bartholomew)   *see* Lower Cam w Coaley *Glouc*

COALPIT HEATH (St Saviour) *Bris 5*   **P** *Bp*   **V** C P LUNT

COALVILLE (Christ Church) and Bardon Hill *Leic 8*   **P** *Simeon's Trustees and R Hugglescote (jt)*   **V** T L RINGLAND,   **NSM** L FOOT

COATES (Holy Trinity)   *see* Whittlesey, Pondersbridge and Coates *Ely*

COATES (St Edith)   *see* Stow Gp *Linc*

COATES (St Matthew), Rodmarton and Sapperton w Frampton Mansell *Glouc 11*   **P** *Bp, Lord Bathurst, and Guild of All So (jt)*   **R** R A BOWDEN

COATES, GREAT (St Nicholas) and LITTLE (Bishop Edward King Church) (St Michael) w Bradley *Linc 9*   **P** *Patr Bd*   **TR** P M MULLINS,   **TV** J L VEREKER,   **C** A I MCCORMICK,   **NSM** C L BOGGIS

COATES, NORTH (St Nicholas)   *see* The North-Chapel Parishes *Linc*

COATHAM (Christ Church) and Dormanstown *York 16*   **P** *Trustees*   **V** J RICHARDSON,   **NSM** E SCRIVENS

COBBOLD ROAD (St Saviour) (St Mary) *Lon 9*   **P** *Bp*   **V** M J BULMAN,   **C** N F SHEHADI

COBERLEY (St Giles), Cowley, Colesbourne and Elkstone *Glouc 11*   **P** *H W G Elwes Esq (2 turns), Ld Chan (1 turn), and WlCdr H T Price (1 turn)*   **P-in-c** D N GREEN

COBHAM Sole Street (St Mary's Church Room)   *see* Cobham w Luddesdowne and Dode *Roch*

COBHAM (St Andrew) (St John the Divine) *Guildf 10*   **P** *D C H Combe Esq*   **V** B L PREECE,   **OLM** P G VICKERS

COBHAM (St Mary Magdalene) w Luddesdowne and Dode *Roch 1*   **P** *Earl of Darnley and CPAS (alt)*   **R** S P DAVIE,   **NSM** A E BEETY

COBO (St Matthew)   *see* Guernsey St Matt *Win*

COBRIDGE (Christ Church)   *see* Hanley H Ev *Lich*

COCKAYNE HATLEY (St John the Baptist)   *see* Potton w Sutton and Cockayne Hatley *St Alb*

COCKERHAM (St Michael) w Winmarleigh St Luke and Glasson Christ Church *Blackb 11*   **P** *Bp (2 turns), Trustees (1 turn)*   **R** M B ROBERTS

COCKERINGTON, SOUTH (St Leonard)   *see* Mid Marsh Gp *Linc*

COCKERMOUTH (All Saints) (Christ Church) w Embleton and Wythop *Carl 6*   **P** *Patr Bd*   **TR** W E SANDERS,   **TV** I M RUMSEY,   **C** B G PHILLIPS,   **NSM** M GODDARD

COCKERNHOE (St Hugh)   *see* Luton St Fran *St Alb*

COCKERTON (St Mary) *Dur 8*   **P** *Bp*   **V** R J WALLACE,   **C** R A GREEN

COCKFIELD (St Mary) *Dur 7*   **P** *Bp*   **R** M J SHEARING

COCKFIELD (St Peter) w Bradfield St Clare, Felsham and Gedding *St E 10*   **P** *St Jo Coll Cam (3 turns), Bp (2 turns), and Lt-Col J G Aldous (1 turn)*   **P-in-c** S G HILL

COCKFOSTERS (Christ Church) Trent Park   *see* Enfield Ch Ch Trent Park *Lon*

COCKING (not known), Bepton and West Lavington *Chich 10*   **P** *Ld Chan, and Bp, Rathbone Trust Co and Cowdray Trust (alt)*   **P-in-c** C J BRADLEY

COCKINGTON (St George and St Mary) (St Matthew) *Ex 10*   **P** *Bp*   **V** A K F MACEY

COCKLEY CLEY (All Saints) w Gooderstone *Nor 13*   **P** *Bp*   **P-in-c** A D WALKER

COCKSHUTT (St Simon and St Jude)   *see* Petton w Cockshutt, Welshampton and Lyneal etc *Lich*

COCKYARD (Church Hall)   *see* Chapel-en-le-Frith *Derby*

CODDENHAM (St Mary) w Gosbeck and Hemingstone w Henley *St E 1*   **P** *Pemb Coll Cam (2 turns), Lord de Saumarez (1 turn)*   **P-in-c** R W HOWE

CODDINGTON (All Saints)   *see* Colwall w Upper Colwall and Coddington *Heref*

CODDINGTON (All Saints) and Winthorpe and Langford w Holme *S'well 3*   **P** *Keble Coll Ox and Bp (jt)*   **R** J C HEALEY

CODDINGTON (St Mary)   *see* Farndon and Coddington *Ches*

CODFORD (St Mary)   *see* Upper Wylye Valley *Sarum*

CODFORD (St Peter)   *as above Sarum*

CODICOTE (St Giles) *St Alb 21*   **P** *Abp*   **V** L J BIGGS

CODNOR (St James) *Derby 12*   **P** *The Crown*   **V** M M MOOKERJI

CODSALL (St Nicholas) *Lich 2*   **P** *Bp and Lady Wrottesley (jt)*   **V** A P HARPER,   **C** D C BAKER

CODSALL WOOD (St Peter)   *see* Codsall *Lich*

COFFEEHALL (Community Church)   *see* Woughton *Ox*

COFFINSWELL (St Bartholomew)   *see* Kingskerswell w Coffinswell *Ex*

COFTON (St Mary)   *see* Kenton, Mamhead, Powderham, Cofton and Starcross *Ex*

COFTON HACKETT (St Michael) w Barnt Green   *Birm 4*   P *Bp*   V R S FIELDSON

COGENHOE (St Peter) and Great Houghton and Little Houghton w Brafield on the Green   *Pet 7*   P C G V Davidge Esq, Mrs A C Usher, Magd Coll Ox, and DBP (jt)   R R B STAINER

COGGES (St Mary) and South Leigh   *Ox 8*   P *Bp and Payne Trustees (jt)*   V A J SWEENEY,   C J E HOWSON,   NSM T P EDGE

COGGESHALL (St Peter ad Vincula) w Markshall   *Chelmsf 17*   P *Bp (2 turns), SMF (1 turn)*   V P C BANKS

COGGESHALL, LITTLE (St Nicholas)   *see* Coggeshall w Markshall *Chelmsf*

COKER, EAST (St Michael and All Angels) w Sutton Bingham and Closworth   *B & W 7*   P *D&C Ex*   P-in-c R M BURT

COKER, WEST (St Martin of Tours) w Hardington Mandeville, East Chinnock and Pendomer   *B & W 7*   P *MMCET and Ox Chs Trust, and DBP (alt)*   R R C P TERRELL

COLATON RALEIGH (St John the Baptist)   *see* Ottery St Mary, Alfington, W Hill, Tipton etc *Ex*

COLBURN (St Cuthbert)   *see* Hipswell *Ripon*

COLBURY (Christ Church)   *Win 11*   P *Mrs A V Barker-Mill*   P-in-c T M JOHNS

COLBY (Belle Abbey Church)   *see* Arbory *S & M*

COLBY (St Giles)   *see* King's Beck *Nor*

COLCHESTER (Christ Church w St Mary at the Walls)   *Chelmsf 16*   P *Bp*   R P R NORRINGTON

COLCHESTER (St Anne)   *see* Greenstead w Colchester St Anne *Chelmsf*

COLCHESTER (St Barnabas) Old Heath   *Chelmsf 16*   P *Bp*   V R E TILLBROOK

COLCHESTER (St James)   *see* Colchester St Jas and St Paul w All SS etc *Chelmsf*

COLCHESTER (St James) and St Paul w All Saints, St Nicholas and St Runwald   *Chelmsf 16*   P *Bp*   R P S WALKER

COLCHESTER (St John the Evangelist)   *Chelmsf 16*   P *Adn Colchester*   V R P FULLER,   C P J COOK,   NSM P H ADAMS

COLCHESTER (St Michael) Myland   *Chelmsf 16*   P *Ball Coll Ox*   R G A CATCHPOLE

COLCHESTER (St Peter) (St Botolph)   *Chelmsf 16*   P *Bp and Simeon's Trustees (jt)*   V F J WOODS

COLCHESTER (St Stephen)   *see* Colchester, New Town and The Hythe *Chelmsf*

COLCHESTER, New Town and The Hythe (St Stephen, St Mary Magdalen and St Leonard)   *Chelmsf 16*   P *Ball Coll Ox (2 turns), Ld Chan (1 turn)*   R I A HILTON

COLD ASH (St Mark)   *see* Hermitage *Ox*

COLD ASHBY (St Denys)   *see* Guilsborough w Hollowell and Cold Ashby *Pet*

COLD ASHTON (Holy Trinity)   *see* Marshfield w Cold Ashton and Tormarton etc *Bris*

COLD ASTON (St Andrew)   *see* Northleach w Hampnett and Farmington etc *Glouc*

COLD BRAYFIELD (St Mary)   *see* Lavendon w Cold Brayfield, Clifton Reynes etc *Ox*

COLD HIGHAM (St Luke)   *see* Pattishall w Cold Higham and Gayton w Tiffield *Pet*

COLD KIRBY (St Michael)   *see* Upper Ryedale *York*

COLD NORTON (St Stephen)   *see* Purleigh, Cold Norton and Stow Maries *Chelmsf*

COLD OVERTON (St John the Baptist)   *see* Whatborough Gp of Par *Leic*

COLD SALPERTON (All Saints)   *see* Sevenhampton w Charlton Abbots, Hawling etc *Glouc*

COLDEAN (St Mary Magdalene)   *see* Moulsecoomb *Chich*

COLDEN (Holy Trinity)   *Win 10*   P *V Twyford*   V A C MILLAR

COLDHAM (St Etheldreda)   *see* Elm and Friday Bridge w Coldham *Ely*

COLDHARBOUR (Christ Church)   *see* Abinger cum Coldharbour *Guildf*

COLDHARBOUR (St Alban Mission Church)   *see* Mottingham St Andr *S'wark*

COLDHURST (Holy Trinity)   *see* Oldham *Man*

COLDRED (St Pancras)   *see* Eythorne and Elvington w Waldershare etc *Cant*

COLDRIDGE (St Matthew)   *see* N Creedy *Ex*

COLDWALTHAM (St Giles)   *see* Bury w Houghton and Coldwaltham and Hardham *Chich*

COLEBROOKE (St Andrew)   *Ex 2*   P *D&C*   V J C HALL

COLEBY (All Saints)   *see* Graffoe Gp *Linc*

COLEFORD (Holy Trinity) w Holcombe   *B & W 12*   P *Bp and V Kilmersdon (jt)*   P-in-c V BONHAM

COLEFORD (St John the Evangelist) w Staunton   *Glouc 4*   P *Bp*   V P W SEMPLE,   Hon C P J COX,   NSM A W WEARMOUTH

COLEGATE (St George)   *see* Norwich St Geo Colegate *Nor*

COLEHILL (St Michael and All Angels)   *Sarum 9*   P *Wimborne Minster Sch*   V J W GOODALL

COLEMAN'S HATCH (Holy Trinity)   *see* Hartfield w Coleman's Hatch *Chich*

COLEORTON (St Mary the Virgin)   *see* Ashby-de-la-Zouch St Helen w Coleorton *Leic*

COLERNE (St John the Baptist) w North Wraxall   *Bris 4*   P *New Coll and Oriel Coll Ox (alt)*   R A V I BERNERS-WILSON,   NSM G E WOODS

COLESBOURNE (St James)   *see* Coberley, Cowley, Colesbourne and Elkstone *Glouc*

COLESHILL (All Saints)   *see* Amersham *Ox*

COLESHILL (All Saints)   *see* Gt Coxwell w Buscot, Coleshill etc *Ox*

COLESHILL (St Peter and St Paul)   *Birm 9*   P J K Wingfield Digby Esq   V R G BOLLARD

COLEY Norwood Green (St George)   *see* Coley *Wakef*

COLEY (St John the Baptist)   *Wakef 2*   P *V Halifax*   V M K MADELEY,   Hon C R C DOWSON

COLGATE (St Saviour)   *see* Rusper w Colgate *Chich*

COLINDALE (St Matthias)   *Lon 15*   P *Bp*   V M R POOLE

COLKIRK (St Mary) w Oxwick w Pattesley, Whissonsett, Horningtoft and Brisley   *Nor 15*   P *DBP, Ch Coll Cam, and C S P D Lane Esq (jt)*   P-in-c P S INMAN

COLLATON (St Mary the Virgin)   *see* Stoke Gabriel and Collaton *Ex*

COLLIER ROW (Ascension)   *see* Romford Ascension Collier Row *Chelmsf*

COLLIER ROW (Good Shepherd)   *see* Romford Gd Shep Collier Row *Chelmsf*

COLLIER ROW (St James) and Havering-atte-Bower   *Chelmsf 2*   P *CPAS and Bp (jt)*   V R J GARNETT

COLLIER STREET (St Margaret)   *see* Yalding w Collier Street *Roch*

COLLIERLEY (St Thomas) w Annfield Plain   *Dur 4*   P *Bp and The Crown (alt)*   V G H LAWES

COLLIERS END (St Mary)   *see* High Cross *St Alb*

COLLIERS WOOD (Christ Church)   *S'wark 14*   P *Bp*   P-in-c S A ROBERTS,   NSM M J HANCOCK

COLLINGBOURNE DUCIS (St Andrew)   *see* Savernake *Sarum*

COLLINGBOURNE KINGSTON (St Mary)   *as above Sarum*

COLLINGHAM (All Saints) (St John the Baptist) w South Scarle and Besthorpe and Girton   *S'well 3*   P *Ld Chan and D&C Pet (alt)*   R vacant (01636) 892317

COLLINGHAM (St Oswald) w Harewood   *Ripon 1*   P *Earl of Harewood and G H H Wheler Esq (jt)*   P-in-c M PALLIS

COLLINGTON (St Mary)   *see* Bredenbury w Grendon Bishop and Wacton etc *Heref*

COLLINGTREE (St Columba) w Courteenhall and Milton Malsor   *Pet 7*   P *Major Sir Hereward Wake Bt, G Phipps-Walker Esq, and Hyndman Trustees (by turn)*   P-in-c T J JOHNSON,   C C H FF NOBBS

COLLYHURST (The Saviour)   *Man 5*   P *Bp and Trustees (jt)*   R M A DONALDSON,   OLM M B ROGERS

COLLYWESTON (St Andrew)   *see* Ketton, Collyweston, Easton-on-the-Hill etc *Pet*

COLMWORTH (St Denys)   *see* Wilden w Colmworth and Ravensden *St Alb*

COLN ROGERS (St Andrew)   *see* Chedworth, Yanworth and Stowell, Coln Rogers etc *Glouc*

COLN ST ALDWYNS (St John the Baptist), Hatherop, Quenington, Eastleach and Southrop   *Glouc 12*   P *Earl St Aldwyn, D&C, Wadh Coll Ox, and DBP (jt)*   V A M ROSS,   NSM C J FINLAY

COLN ST DENYS (St James the Great)   *see* Chedworth, Yanworth and Stowell, Coln Rogers etc *Glouc*

COLNBROOK (St Thomas)   *see* Riverside *Ox*

COLNE (Christ Church) (Holy Trinity) (St Bartholomew) and Villages   *Blackb 6*   P *Patr Bd*   TR M L HARTLEY,   TV A W RINDL,   C M F SIBANDA,   NSM K ALLEN,   R L ALLEN

COLNE (St Helen)   *see* Bluntisham cum Earith w Colne and Woodhurst *Ely*

COLNE, THE UPPER, Parishes of Great Yeldham, Little Yeldham, Stambourne, Tilbury-juxta-Clare and Toppesfield   *Chelmsf 19*   P *Prime Min, Ld Chan, Bp, Duchy of Lancaster, and Trustees of the late Miss W M N Brett (by turn)*   R K G HOLLOWAY

COLNE ENGAINE (St Andrew)   *see* Earls Colne w White Colne and Colne Engaine *Chelmsf*

COLNEY (St Andrew)   *see* Cringleford and Colney *Nor*

COLNEY (St Peter)   *see* London Colney St Pet *St Alb*

993

COLNEY HEATH (St Mark) *St Alb 21*   **P** *Trustees*
V H J SPANNER,   **NSM** B R MCMAHON
COLSTERWORTH Group, The (St John the Baptist) *Linc 14*
  P *Bp (2 turns), Mrs R S McCorquodale, The*
  Revd J R H Thorold and J R Thorold Esq (1 turn)
  R D A CARNEY,   **OLM** P C HOLLINGSHEAD
COLSTON BASSETT (St John the Divine) *see Cropwell Bishop*
  w Colston Bassett, Granby etc S'well
COLTISHALL (St John the Baptist) w Great Hautbois and
  Horstead *Nor 19*   **P** *D&C and K Coll Cam (jt)*
  P-in-c C S R WALTER,   **NSM** L WOOD
COLTON (Holy Trinity) *see Egton-cum-Newland and Lowick*
  and Colton Carl
COLTON (St Andrew) *see Easton, Colton, Marlingford and*
  Bawburgh Nor
COLTON (St Mary the Virgin) *see Colton, Colwich and Gt*
  Haywood Lich
COLTON (St Michael and All Angels), Colwich and Great
  Haywood *Lich 3*   **P** *Bp and Earl of Lichfield's Trustees (jt)*
  R T THAKE,   **C** J LEONARDI
COLTON (St Paul) *see Bolton Percy York*
COLWALL (St Crispin's Chapel) (St James the Great) w Upper
  Colwall (Good Shepherd) and Coddington *Heref 6*   **P** *Bp*
  R C N H ATTWOOD
COLWALL, UPPER (Good Shepherd) *see Colwall w Upper*
  Colwall and Coddington Heref
COLWICK (St John the Baptist) *S'well 10*   **P** *DBP*   **R** *vacant*
COLYFORD (St Michael) *see Colyton, Musbury, Southleigh*
  and Branscombe Ex
COLYTON (St Andrew), Musbury, Southleigh and Branscombe
  Ex 5   **P** *D&C*   **NSM** M N ALLSO
COMBE (St Lawrence) *see Stonesfield w Combe Longa Ox*
COMBE (St Swithin) *see W Woodhay w Enborne, Hampstead*
  Marshall etc Ox
COMBE DOWN (Holy Trinity) (St Andrew) w Monkton Combe
  and South Stoke *B & W 9*   **P** *R Bath, Ox Chs Trust, and*
  Comdr H R Salmer (jt)   **V** P J LANGHAM,   **C** M G STREET
COMBE FLOREY (St Peter and St Paul) *see Lydeard St*
  Lawrence w Brompton Ralph etc B & W
COMBE HAY (not known) *see Bath Odd Down w Combe Hay*
  B & W
COMBE MARTIN (St Peter ad Vincula), Berrynarbor, Lynton,
  Brendon, Countisbury, Parracombe, Martinhoe and Trentishoe
  Ex 17   **P** *Patr Bd*   **TR** K G WYER,   **NSM** M J D WILKIE
COMBE PYNE (St Mary the Virgin) *see Axminster,*
  Chardstock, All Saints etc Ex
COMBE RALEIGH (St Nicholas) *see Honiton, Gittisham,*
  Combe Raleigh, Monkton etc Ex
COMBE ST NICHOLAS (St Nicholas) w Wambrook *B & W 15*
  P *Bp and T V D Eames Esq (jt)*   **V** P REGAN
COMBEINTEIGNHEAD (All Saints) *see Shaldon,*
  Stokeinteignhead, Combeinteignhead etc Ex
COMBERFORD (St Mary and St George) *see Wigginton Lich*
COMBERTON (St Mary) *Ely 1*   **P** *Jes Coll Cam*
  V R STEPHENSON
COMBERTON, GREAT (St Michael) *see Elmley Castle w*
  Bricklehampton and Combertons Worc
COMBERTON, LITTLE (St Peter) *as above Worc*
COMBROKE (St Mary and St Margaret) w Compton Verney
  Cov 8   **P** *Bp*   **V** C A HOST
COMBS (St Mary) and Little Finborough *St E 6*   **P** *Bp and*
  Pemb Coll Ox (jt)   **R** A L FOWLER,   **C** J K B FOWLER,
  NSM M G WAINWRIGHT
COMBWICH (St Peter) *see Cannington, Otterhampton,*
  Combwich and Stockland B & W
COMER GARDENS (St David) *see Worc St Clem Worc*
COMMONDALE (St Peter) *see Danby York*
COMPSTALL (St Paul) *see Werneth Ches*
COMPTON (All Saints) and Otterbourne *Win 7*   **P** *Bp and*
  Mrs P M A T Chamberlayne-Macdonald (jt)   **R** *vacant (01962)*
  713400
COMPTON (St Mary) *see Farnham Guildf*
COMPTON (St Mary and St Nicholas) *see Hermitage Ox*
COMPTON (St Mary), the Mardens, Stoughton and Racton
  Chich 13   **P** *Bp Lon (1 turn), Bp (2 turns)*   **P-in-c** A N STAMP
COMPTON (St Nicholas) w Shackleford and Peper Harow
  Guildf 4   **P** *Bp and Major J R More-Molyneux (jt)*
  R J M FELLOWS,   **NSM** J J SWANTON
COMPTON, LITTLE (St Denys) *see Chipping Norton Ox*
COMPTON, NETHER (St Nicholas) *see Queen Thorne Sarum*
COMPTON, OVER (St Michael) *as above Sarum*
COMPTON ABBAS (St Mary the Virgin) *see Shaston Sarum*
COMPTON ABDALE (St Oswald) *see Northleach w*
  Hampnett and Farmington etc Glouc
COMPTON BASSETT (St Swithin) *see Oldbury Sarum*
COMPTON BEAUCHAMP (St Swithun) *see Shrivenham and*
  Ashbury Ox

COMPTON BISHOP (St Andrew) *see Crook Peak B & W*
COMPTON CHAMBERLAYNE (St Michael) *see Fovant,*
  Sutton Mandeville and Teffont Evias etc Sarum
COMPTON DANDO (Blessed Virgin Mary) *see Publow w*
  Pensford, Compton Dando and Chelwood B & W
COMPTON DUNDON (St Andrew) *see Somerton w Compton*
  Dundon, the Charltons etc B & W
COMPTON GREENFIELD (All Saints) *see Pilning w*
  Compton Greenfield Bris
COMPTON MARTIN (St Michael) *see Blagdon w Compton*
  Martin and Ubley B & W
COMPTON PAUNCEFOOT (Blessed Virgin Mary)
  see Camelot Par B & W
COMPTON VALENCE (St Thomas à Beckett) *see The*
  Winterbournes and Compton Valence Sarum
CONCHAN (St Peter) *see Onchan S & M*
CONDICOTE (St Nicholas) *see Stow on the Wold, Condicote*
  and The Swells Glouc
CONDOVER (St Andrew and St Mary) w Frodesley, Acton
  Burnell and Pitchford *Heref 11*   **P** *Bp, Revd E W Serjeantson,*
  and Mrs C R Colthurst (jt)   **R** J C W ROSE,
  NSM M G GILLIONS
CONEY HILL (St Oswald) *Glouc 5*   **P** *The Crown*
  V L HOLLAND
CONEY WESTON (St Mary) *see Hopton, Market Weston,*
  Barningham etc St E
CONEYSTHORPE (Chapel) *see Street York*
CONGERSTONE (St Mary the Virgin) *see Bosworth and*
  Sheepy Gp Leic
CONGHAM (St Andrew) *see Grimston, Congham and Roydon*
  Nor
CONGLETON (St James) *Ches 11*   **P** *Bp*
  P-in-c R N W ELBOURNE
CONGLETON (St Peter) (St Stephen) *Ches 11*   **P** *Patr Bd*
  TR M W WALTERS,   **TV** M L EAMAN,   D J HYNDMAN
CONGRESBURY (St Andrew) w Puxton and Hewish St Ann
  B & W 11   **P** *MMCET*   **V** M J THOMSON
CONINGSBY (St Michael) w Tattershall *Linc 11*   **P** *DBP and*
  Baroness Willoughby de Eresby (alt)   **R** J R MOORE,
  OLM M DONE,   T R BARDELL
CONINGTON (St Mary) *see Fen Drayton w Conington and*
  Lolworth etc Ely
CONISBROUGH (St Peter) *Sheff 9*   **P** *Bp*   **V** A C GRIFFITHS
CONISCLIFFE (St Edwin) *Dur 8*   **P** *Bp*   **P-in-c** R S WILSON
CONISHOLME (St Peter) *see Somercotes and Grainthorpe w*
  Conisholme Linc
CONISTON (St Andrew) *see Church Coniston Carl*
CONISTON COLD (St Peter) *see Kirkby-in-Malhamdale w*
  Coniston Cold Bradf
CONISTONE (St Mary) *see Kettlewell w Conistone,*
  Hubberholme etc Bradf
CONONLEY (St John the Evangelist) w Bradley *Bradf 8*   **P** *Bp*
  V J C PEET
CONSETT (Christ Church) *Dur 4*   **P** *Bp*   **P-in-c** P SINCLAIR,
  C S BENNETT
CONSTABLE LEE (St Paul) *Man 15*   **P** *CPAS*
  P-in-c G D PARKIN
CONSTANTINE (St Constantine) *Truro 4*   **P** *D&C*
  P-in-c D J STEVENS
COOKBURY (St John the Baptist and the Seven Maccabes)
  see Black Torrington, Bradf w Cookbury etc Ex
COOKHAM (Holy Trinity) *Ox 13*   **P** *Mrs K E Rogers*
  P-in-c M D SMITH,   **Hon C** A W WELLING,
  OLM T J ROBINSON
COOKHAM DEAN (St John the Baptist) *Ox 13*
  P *V Cookham*   **V** *vacant (01628) 483342*
COOKHILL (St Paul) *see Inkberrow w Cookhill and Kington w*
  Dormston Worc
COOKLEY (St Michael and All Angels) *see Cratfield w*
  Heveningham and Ubbeston etc St E
COOKLEY (St Peter) *see Wolverley and Cookley Worc*
COOKRIDGE (Holy Trinity) *Ripon 7*   **P** *R Adel*
  V J F HAMILTON
COOMBE (Christ Church) *see New Malden and Coombe*
  S'wark
COOMBE BISSET (St Michael and All Angels) *see Chalke*
  Valley Sarum
COOMBES (not known) *see Lancing w Coombes Chich*
COOMBS WOOD (St Ambrose) *see Blackheath Birm*
COOPERSALE (St Alban) *see Epping Distr Chelmsf*
COPDOCK (St Peter) *see Sproughton w Burstall, Copdock w*
  Washbrook etc St E
COPFORD (St Michael and All Angels) w Easthorpe and
  Messing w Inworth *Chelmsf 24*   **P** *Ld Chan, Duchy of Lanc,*
  and DBP (by turn)   **R** C J GARLAND
COPGROVE (St Michael) *see Walkingham Hill Ripon*

COPLE (All Saints), Moggerhanger and Willington *St Alb 11*
P *Bp (2 turns)*, Ch Ch Ox *(1 turn)* **V** N T MACNEILL
COPLESTON CENTRE *see* Peckham St Sav *S'wark*
COPLEY *Wakef 4* **P** *V Halifax* **V** *vacant* (01422) 652964
COPMANTHORPE (St Giles) *York 1* **P** *R Micklegate H Trin*
V D S COOK
COPNOR (St Alban) *see* Portsea St Alb *Portsm*
COPNOR (St Cuthbert) *see* Portsea St Cuth *Portsm*
COPP (St Anne) w Inskip *Blackb 9* **P** *V Garstang St Helen and
St Michaels-on-Wyre* **V** D GASKELL
COPPENHALL (All Saints and St Paul) *see* Crewe All SS and
St Paul *Ches*
COPPENHALL (St Laurence) *see* Penkridge Team *Lich*
COPPENHALL (St Michael) *Ches 15* **P** *Bp* **R** C H RAZZALL
COPPULL (not known) *Blackb 4* **P** *R Standish* **V** J HUDSON
COPPULL (St John) *Blackb 4* **P** *R Standish* **R** J STEWART
COPSTON MAGNA (St John) *see* Wolvey w Burton Hastings,
Copston Magna etc *Cov*
COPT OAK (St Peter) *see* Markfield, Thornton, Bagworth and
Stanton etc *Leic*
COPTHORNE (St John the Evangelist) *Chich 7* **P** *Bp*
V A M CUTTING, **NSM** P SMITH
COPYTHORNE (St Mary) *Win 11* **P** *Bp Liv*
P-in-c N P JACOB
CORBRIDGE w Halton (St Andrew) and Newton Hall *Newc 3*
P *D&C Carl* **V** M J MORPHY, **NSM** J KINNAIRD
CORBY (Epiphany) (St John the Baptist) *Pet 9*
P *E Brudenell Esq* **P-in-c** M J ASQUITH
CORBY (St Columba and the Northern Saints) *Pet 9* **P** *Bp*
V *vacant* (01536) 204158 *or* 261436
CORBY (St Peter and St Andrew) (Kingswood Church) *Pet 9*
P *Bp* **V** M A CRAGGS
CORBY GLEN (St John the Evangelist) *Linc 14* **P** *Ld Chan
(2 turns)*, Sir Simon Benton Jones Bt *(1 turn)* **V** *vacant*
CORELEY (St Peter) and Doddington *Heref 12* **P** *DBP and
Mrs R C Woodward (jt)* **R** *vacant* (01584) 890129
CORFE (St Nicholas) *see* Blackdown *B & W*
**CORFE CASTLE (St Edward the Martyr), Church Knowle,
Kimmeridge Steeple w Tyneham** *Sarum 8* **P** *Major
M J A Bond and Major J C Mansel (jt)* **R** M A STRIKE
CORFE MULLEN (St Hubert) *Sarum 9* **P** *Bp* **R** *vacant*
(01202) 692129
CORHAMPTON (not known) *see* Meonstoke w Corhampton
cum Exton *Portsm*
CORLEY (not known) *see* Fillongley and Corley *Cov*
CORNARD, GREAT (St Andrew) *St E 12* **P** *Bp* **V** N J COLE,
OLM L BANNISTER
CORNARD, LITTLE (All Saints) *see* Bures w Assington and
Lt Cornard *St E*
CORNELLY (St Cornelius) *see* Tregony w St Cuby and
Cornelly *Truro*
CORNEY (St John the Baptist) *see* Bootle, Corney, Whicham
and Whitbeck *Carl*
CORNFORTH (Holy Trinity) *Dur 5* **P** *Bp*
P-in-c K LUMSDON
CORNHILL (St Helen) w Carham *Newc 12* **P** *Abp (2 turns)*,
E M Straker-Smith Esq *(1 turn)* **P-in-c** M J GILLHAM,
C D F BROOKE
CORNHOLME (St Michael and All Angels) and Walsden
Wakef 3 **P** *Bp and DBP (jt)* **V** P J JEFFERY,
OLM I M GREENMAN
CORNISH HALL END (St John the Evangelist)
see Finchingfield and Cornish Hall End etc *Chelmsf*
CORNWELL (St Peter) *see* Chipping Norton *Ox*
CORNWOOD (St Michael and All Angels) *Ex 20* **P** *Bp*
P-in-c F G DENMAN
CORNWORTHY (St Peter) *see* Ashprington, Cornworthy and
Dittisham *Ex*
CORONATION SQUARE (St Aidan) *see* Cheltenham St Mark
Glouc
CORRA (Holy Trinity) *see* Adderley, Ash, Calverhall, Ightfield
etc *Lich*
CORRINGHAM (St John the Evangelist) (St Mary the Virgin)
Chelmsf 14 **P** *SMF* **P-in-c** M HUME
CORRINGHAM (St Lawrence) and Blyton Group, The *Linc 2*
P *Ld Chan (2 turns)*, *Bp (1 turn)*, Meynell Ch Trustees *(1 turn)*
V *vacant* (01427) 628216
CORSCOMBE (St Mary the Virgin) *see* Melbury *Sarum*
CORSE (St Margaret) *see* Hartpury w Corse and Staunton
Glouc
CORSENSIDE (All Saints) *see* N Tyne and Redesdale Team
Newc
CORSENSIDE (St Cuthbert) *as above Newc*
CORSHAM, GREATER (St Bartholomew) and Lacock *Bris 4*
P *Patr Bd* **TR** R G CLIFTON, **TV** R M HOVEY,
C S A V WHEELER

CORSLEY (St Mary the Virgin) *see* Cley Hill Warminster
Sarum
CORSLEY (St Mary the Virgin) *as above Sarum*
CORSTON (All Saints) *see* Saltford w Corston and Newton
St Loe *B & W*
CORSTON (All Saints) *see* Gt Somerford, Lt Somerford,
Seagry, Corston etc *Bris*
CORTON (St Bartholomew) *see* Hopton w Corton *Nor*
CORTON (St Bartholomew) *see* Abbotsbury, Portesham and
Langton Herring *Sarum*
CORTON DENHAM (St Andrew) *see* Queen Camel w W
Camel, Corton Denham etc *B & W*
CORYTON (St Andrew) *see* Milton Abbot, Dunterton,
Lamerton etc *Ex*
COSBY (St Michael and All Angels) *Leic 10* **P** *Bp*
P-in-c P J HARBORD
COSELEY (Christ Church) (St Cuthbert) *Worc 10* **P** *Bp*
V H M HUMPHREY, **C** S G AXTELL
COSELEY (St Chad) *Worc 10* **P** *Bp* **V** A HOWES
COSGROVE (St Peter and St Paul) *see* Potterspury w Furtho
and Yardley Gobion etc *Pet*
COSHAM (St Philip) *Portsm 6* **P** *Bp* **P-in-c** G J SMITH
COSSALL (St Catherine) *see* Trowell, Awsworth and Cossall
S'well
COSSINGTON (All Saints) *see* Sileby, Cossington and Seagrave
Leic
COSSINGTON (Blessed Virgin Mary) *see* Woolavington w
Cossington and Bawdrip *B & W*
COSTESSEY (St Edmund) *Nor 3* **P** *Gt Hosp Nor*
V N J S PARRY
COSTESSEY, NEW (St Helen) *see* Costessey *Nor*
COSTOCK (St Giles) *see* E and W Leake, Stanford-on-Soar,
Rempstone etc *S'well*
COSTON (St Andrew) *see* Wymondham w Edmondthorpe,
Buckminster etc *Leic*
COTEBROOKE (St John and Holy Cross) *see* Tarporley *Ches*
COTEHELE HOUSE (Chapel) *see* Calstock *Truro*
COTEHILL (St John the Evangelist) *see* Scotby and Cotehill w
Cumwhinton *Carl*
COTES HEATH (St James) *see* Broughton w Croxton and
Cotes Heath w Standon *Lich*
COTESBACH (St Mary) *see* Lutterworth w Cotesbach and
Bitteswell *Leic*
COTGRAVE (All Saints) *S'well 8* **P** *DBP* **R** P D S MASSEY
COTHAM (St Saviour w St Mary) and Clifton St Paul *Bris 3*
P *Bp* **R** P J ROBERTS, **C** A F STUART, S J TAYLOR,
Hon C B W SILVERMAN
COTHELSTONE (St Thomas of Canterbury) *see* Bishops
Lydeard w Bagborough and Cothelstone *B & W*
COTHERIDGE (St Leonard) *see* Martley and Wichenford,
Knightwick etc *Worc*
COTHERSTONE (St Cuthbert) *see* Romaldkirk w Laithkirk
Ripon
COTLEIGH (St Michael and All Angels) *see* Offwell,
Northleigh, Farway, Cotleigh etc *Ex*
COTMANHAY (Christ Church) *Derby 13* **P** *Bp* **V** *vacant*
0115-932 5670
COTON (St Peter) *Ely 1* **P** *St Cath Coll Cam*
P-in-c C A COLLINS
COTON-IN-THE-ELMS (St Mary) *see* Seale and Lullington w
Coton in the Elms *Derby*
COTTAM (Holy Trinity) *see* Rampton w Laneham, Treswell,
Cottam and Stokeham *S'well*
COTTENHAM (All Saints) *Ely 5* **P** *Bp* **R** M J HORE
COTTERED (St John the Baptist) w Broadfield and Throcking
St Alb 19 **P** *Bp* **P-in-c** M CAPEL-EDWARDS
COTTERIDGE (St Agnes) *Birm 4* **P** *R Kings Norton*
V M W BLOOD, **NSM** R R COLLINS
COTTERSTOCK (St Andrew) *see* Warmington, Tansor and
Cotterstock etc *Pet*
COTTESBROOKE (All Saints) w Great Creaton and Thornby
Pet 2 **P** *Bp (2 turns)*, MacDonald-Buchanan Trustees *(1 turn)*
Jt P-in-c B LEE, J M TARRANT
COTTESMORE (St Nicholas) and Barrow w Ashwell and Burley
Pet 14 **P** *E R Hanbury Esq, Viscount Downe, and DBP
(by turn)* **R** M H W ROGERS, **V** S A WALKER
COTTIMORE (St John) *see* Walton-on-Thames *Guildf*
COTTINGHAM (St Mary) *York 14* **P** *Abp* **R** T G GRIGG
COTTINGHAM (St Mary Magdalene) *see* Gretton w
Rockingham and Cottingham w E Carlton *Pet*
COTTINGLEY (St Michael and All Angels) *Bradf 1* **P** *Bp*
V S J PINNINGTON
COTTINGWITH, EAST (St Mary) *see* Elvington w Sutton on
Derwent and E Cottingwith *York*
COTTISFORD (St Mary the Virgin) *see* Shelswell *Ox*
COTTON (St Andrew) *see* Bacton w Wyverstone, Cotton and
Old Newton etc *St E*

COTTON (St John the Baptist)   *see* Alton w Bradley-le-Moors and Oakamoor w Cotton *Lich*
COTTON MILL (St Julian)   *see* St Alb St Steph *St Alb*
COUGHTON (St Peter)   *Cov 7*   **P** *Bp*   **P-in-c** S R BURCH
COULSDON (St Andrew)   *S'wark 24*   **P** *Bp*   **V** M R GOODLAD, **NSM** P D JONES
COULSDON (St John)   *S'wark 24*   **P** *Abp*   **OLM** G A GREGSON
COULSTON, EAST (St Thomas of Canterbury)   *see* Bratton, Edington and Imber, Erlestoke etc *Sarum*
COUND (St Peter)   *see* Wenlock *Heref*
COUNDON (St James) and Eldon   *Dur 6*   **P** *Bp and Prime Min (alt)*   **P-in-c** G NICHOLSON
COUNTESS WEAR (St Luke)   *Ex 3*   **P** *V Topsham*   **V** P J S CROCKETT
COUNTESTHORPE (St Andrew) w Foston   *Leic 10*   **P** *DBP and Bp (alt)*   **V** A W JOHNSON, **C** P C WHITE, **NSM** M D GILLESPIE
COUNTISBURY (St John the Evangelist)   *see* Combe Martin, Berrynarbor, Lynton, Brendon etc *Ex*
COURTEENHALL (St Peter and St Paul)   *see* Collingtree w Courteenhall and Milton Malsor *Pet*
COVE (St John the Baptist) (St Christopher)   *Guildf 1*   **P** *Bp*   **TR** I M SCOTT-THOMPSON, **TV** J HILLMAN, B APPLETON, **OLM** G H THOMAS
COVEHITHE (St Andrew)   *see* Sole Bay *St E*
COVEN (St Paul)   *Lich 2*   **P** *V Brewood*   **V** *vacant* (01902) 790230 *or* 790991
COVEN HEATH (Mission Church)   *see* Bushbury *Lich*
COVENEY (St Peter ad Vincula)   *Ely 13*   **P** *Bp*   **P-in-c** M T COOPER
COVENHAM (Annunciation of the Blessed Virgin Mary)   *see* Fotherby *Linc*
COVENT GARDEN (St Paul)   *Lon 3*   **P** *Bp*   **P-in-c** M D OAKLEY
COVENTRY Caludon   *Cov 1*   **P** *Bp and Ld Chan (alt)*   **TR** J M FRANCIS, **TV** R W HARE, D T PETTIFOR
COVENTRY Holbrooks (St Luke)   *see* Holbrooks *Cov*
COVENTRY (Holy Trinity)   *Cov 2*   **P** *Ld Chan*   **V** G K SINCLAIR, **C** H E A JOHNSTON, **NSM** A M IRVINE
COVENTRY (St Francis of Assisi) North Radford   *Cov 2*   **P** *Bp*   **V** T C BROOKE
COVENTRY (St George)   *Cov 2*   **P** *Bp*   **V** L N JANICKER
COVENTRY (St John the Baptist)   *Cov 2*   **P** *Trustees*   **R** P N SUCH
COVENTRY (St Mary Magdalen)   *Cov 3*   **P** *Bp*   **V** C H KNOWLES, **NSM** D HISCOX
COVENTRY (St Nicholas)   *see* Radford *Cov*
COVENTRY EAST (St Anne and All Saints) (St Margaret) (St Peter)   *Cov 1*   **P** *Patr Bd*   **TR** C M GREGORY, **TV** L D JOHNSON, L A HUMPHREYS, **C** K R GOLDIE
COVERACK (St Peter)   *see* St Keverne *Truro*
COVERDALE (St Botolph)   *see* Middleham w Coverdale and E Witton etc *Ripon*
COVINGHAM (St Paul)   *see* Swindon Dorcan *Bris*
COVINGTON (All Saints)   *Ely 9*   **P** *Sir Stephen Hastings*   **P-in-c** S P MEWS, **NSM** J RAWLINSON
COWARNE, LITTLE (not known)   *see* Bredenbury w Grendon Bishop and Wacton etc *Heref*
COWARNE, MUCH (St Mary the Virgin)   *see* Stoke Lacy, Moreton Jeffries w Much Cowarne etc *Heref*
COWBIT (St Mary)   *Linc 17*   **P** *Ld Chan and DBP (alt)*   **V** P W J WINN
COWCLIFFE (St Hilda)   *see* N Huddersfield *Wakef*
COWDEN (St Mary Magdalene) w Hammerwood   *Chich 7*   **P** *Ch Soc Trust*   **P-in-c** P D F HORNER
COWES (Holy Trinity) (St Mary the Virgin)   *Portsm 8*   **P** *Trustees and V Carisbrooke St Mary (jt)*   **V** R J EMBLIN, **C** A-L ALDER, **NSM** K H G MORRIS
COWES (St Faith)   *Portsm 8*   **P** *Bp*   **P-in-c** M D H JOHNSTON, **NSM** R S NETHERWAY
COWES, EAST (St James)   *see* Whippingham w E Cowes *Portsm*
COWESBY (St Michael)   *York 19*   **P** *Abp*   **P-in-c** P R A R HOARE, **NSM** E A HOARE
COWFOLD (St Peter)   *Chich 9*   **P** *Bp Lon*   **V** G L DRIVER
COWGATE (St Peter)   *Newc 7*   **P** *Bp*   **V** *vacant* 0191-286 9913
COWGILL (St John the Evangelist)   *see* Dent w Cowgill *Bradf*
COWICK (Holy Trinity)   *see* Gt Snaith *Sheff*
COWLAM (St Mary)   *see* Waggoners *York*
COWLEIGH (St Peter)   *see* Malvern Link w Cowleigh *Worc*
COWLEY (St James) (St Francis)   *Ox 4*   **P** *Patr Bd*   **TR** S W M HARTLEY, **TV** J H TOMLINSON, **C** M J HARRIS, **NSM** W CHAND, M E A MCALISTER
COWLEY (St John) (St Alban) (St Bartholomew) (St Mary and St John)   *Ox 4*   **P** *St Steph Ho Ox*   **V** A J A ROMANIS, **C** M K BLAMEY, **NSM** A L FORBES, K H LAMDIN

COWLEY (St Laurence)   *Lon 24*   **P** *Bp*   **R** S M HARDWICKE
COWLEY (St Mary)   *see* Coberley, Cowley, Colesbourne and Elkstone *Glouc*
COWLEY CHAPEL (St Antony)   *see* Thorverton, Cadbury, Upton Pyne etc *Ex*
COWLING (Holy Trinity)   *Bradf 8*   **P** *Bp*   **P-in-c** J R PRICE
COWLINGE (St Margaret)   *see* Bansfield *St E*
COWPEN (St Benedict)   *see* Horton *Newc*
COWPLAIN (St Wilfrid)   *Portsm 5*   **P** *Bp*   **V** P H MOORE, **C** B J DUGMORE
COWTONS, The (All Saints) (St Luke's Pastoral Centre)   *Ripon 2*   **P** *V Gilling (1 turn), DBP (2 turns)*   **V** *vacant* (01325) 378230
COX GREEN (Good Shepherd)   *Ox 13*   **P** *Bp*   **P-in-c** V J BROOKS
COXFORD Group, The   *see* E w W Rudham, Helhoughton etc *Nor*
COXHEATH (Holy Trinity), East Farleigh, Hunton, Linton and West Farleigh   *Roch 7*   **P** *Ld Chan (1 turn), Abp, Lord Cornwallis, and D&C (1 turn)*   **R** R J CASTLE, **C** R A BIERBAUM, **NSM** D W JONES
COXHOE (St Mary)   *see* Kelloe and Coxhoe *Dur*
COXLEY (Christ Church) w Godney, Henton and Wookey   *B & W 8*   **P** *Bp*   **V** R R B PLOWMAN
COXWELL, GREAT (St Giles) w Buscot, Coleshill and Eaton Hastings   *Ox 17*   **P** *Bp and Lord Faringdon (jt)*   **P-in-c** J H NODDINGS
COXWELL, LITTLE (St Mary)   *see* Gt Faringdon w Lt Coxwell *Ox*
COXWOLD (St Michael) and Husthwaite   *York 3*   **P** *Abp*   **V** *vacant* (01347) 868301
CRABBS CROSS (St Peter)   *see* Redditch, The Ridge *Worc*
CRADLEY (St James) w Mathon and Storridge   *Heref 6*   **P** *Bp and D&C Westmr (jt)*   **R** S R ASHTON, **NSM** M D VOCKINS
CRADLEY (St Peter) (St Katherine's Mission Church)   *Worc 9*   **P** *R Halesowen*   **P-in-c** A J COOTE
CRADLEY HEATH (St Luke)   *see* Reddal Hill St Luke *Worc*
CRAGG VALE (St John the Baptist in the Wilderness)   *see* Erringden *Wakef*
CRAKEHALL (St Gregory)   *Ripon 4*   **P** *Sir Henry Beresford-Peirse Bt*   **V** D J CHRISTIE
CRAMBE (St Michael)   *see* Whitwell w Crambe, Flaxton and Foston *York*
CRAMLINGTON (St Nicholas)   *Newc 1*   **P** *Bp*   **TR** J A MACNAUGHTON, **TV** R G BATEMAN, H L SAVAGE, **OLM** S M WARD
CRAMPMOOR (St Swithun)   *see* Romsey *Win*
CRANBORNE (St Mary and St Bartholomew) w Boveridge, Edmondsham, Wimborne St Giles and Woodlands   *Sarum 9*   **P** *Viscount Cranborne, Earl of Shaftesbury, and Mrs J E Smith (jt)*   **R** D J PASKINS
CRANBOURNE (St Peter)   *see* Winkfield and Cranbourne *Ox*
CRANBROOK (St Dunstan)   *Cant 11*   **P** *Abp*   **V** M J BURRELL, **NSM** S M COX
CRANFIELD (St Peter and St Paul) and Hulcote w Salford   *St Alb 13*   **P** *MMCET*   **R** H K SYMES-THOMPSON
CRANFORD (Holy Angels) (St Dunstan)   *Lon 11*   **P** *R J G Berkeley Esq and Sir Hugo Huntington-Whiteley Bt (jt)*   **R** *vacant* (020) 8897 8836
CRANFORD (St John the Baptist) w Grafton Underwood and Twywell   *Pet 11*   **P** *Boughton Estates, DBP, and Sir John Robinson Bt (by turn)*   **R** D H P FOOT
CRANHAM (All Saints)   *Chelmsf 2*   **P** *St Jo Coll Ox*   **P-in-c** T W PAGE, **C** M A H FINCH, **NSM** G K ARBER
CRANHAM (St James the Great)   *see* Painswick, Sheepscombe, Cranham, The Edge etc *Glouc*
CRANHAM PARK Moor Lane (not known)   *see* Cranham Park *Chelmsf*
CRANHAM PARK (St Luke)   *Chelmsf 2*   **P** *Bp*   **V** J F DUNNETT, **C** M BARKER, R S FRANK
CRANLEIGH (St Nicolas)   *Guildf 2*   **P** *Bp*   **R** N P NICHOLSON, **C** S D GRIFFITHS
CRANMER Group   *see* Whatton w Aslockton, Hawksworth, Scarrington etc *S'well*
CRANMORE, WEST (St Bartholomew)   *see* Shepton Mallet w Doulting *B & W*
CRANOE (St Michael)   *see* Gt Bowden w Welham, Glooston and Cranoe etc *Leic*
CRANSFORD (St Peter)   *see* Badingham w Bruisyard, Cransford and Dennington *St E*
CRANSLEY (St Andrew)   *see* Broughton w Loddington and Cransley etc *Pet*
CRANTOCK (St Carantoc)   *Truro 7*   **P** *SMF*   **P-in-c** M WILLS

CRANWELL (St Andrew) *Linc 22* **P** *DBP*
P-in-c A J LITTLEWOOD

CRANWICH (St Mary) *Nor 13* **P** *CPAS* **P-in-c** P M FARROW

CRANWORTH (St Mary the Virgin) *see Barnham Broom and Upper Yare Nor*

CRASSWALL (St Mary) *see Clodock and Longtown w Craswall, Llanveynoe etc Heref*

CRASTER (Mission Church) *see Embleton w Rennington and Rock Newc*

CRATFIELD (St Mary) w Heveningham and Ubbeston w Huntingfield and Cookley *St E 15* **P** *Hon Mrs S Peel and Simeon's Trustees (alt)* **R** *vacant* (01986) 798564

CRATHORNE (All Saints) *York 21* **P** *Lord Crathorne, Hon David Dugdale, and J Southern Esq (jt)*
P-in-c P KITCHING

CRAWCROOK (Church of the Holy Spirit) *see Greenside Dur*

CRAWFORD (District Church) *see Upholland Liv*

CRAWLEY (St John the Baptist) *Chich 7* **P** *Bp*
TR M D LILES, **TV** F J M POLE, A R HARCUS, J BROWN,
C J M BALDWIN, **NSM** C D WATKINS

CRAWLEY (St Mary) and Littleton and Sparsholt w Lainston *Win 7* **P** *Ld Chan and DBP (alt)* **P-in-c** J MONTAGUE,
C S DAVIES

CRAWLEY, NORTH (St Firmin) *see Sherington w Chicheley, N Crawley, Astwood etc Ox*

CRAWLEY DOWN (All Saints) *Chich 7* **P** *R Worth*
V A J HALE

CRAWSHAWBOOTH (St John) *see Goodshaw and Crawshawbooth Man*

CRAY (St Barnabas) *see St Paul's Cray St Barn Roch*

CRAY (St Mary and St Paulinus) *see St Mary Cray and St Paul's Cray Roch*

CRAY, NORTH (St James) *see Footscray w N Cray Roch*

CRAYFORD (St Paulinus) *Roch 15* **P** *Bp* **R** A K LANE,
C J A EVANS

CRAYKE (St Cuthbert) w Brandsby and Yearsley *York 3*
P *The Crown and Abp (alt)* **R** *vacant*

CRAZIES HILL (Mission Room) *see Wargrave w Knowl Hill Ox*

CREAKE, NORTH (St Mary) and SOUTH (St Mary) w Waterden, Syderstone w Barmer and Sculthorpe *Nor 15* **P** *Bp, Earl Spencer, Earl of Leicester, Guild of All So, J Labouchere Esq, Mrs M E Russell, and DBP (jt)*
R A M THOMSON

CREATON, GREAT (St Michael and All Angels)
see Cottesbrooke w Gt Creaton and Thornby Pet

CREDENHILL (St Mary) Brinsop and Wormsley, Mansel Lacy and Yazor, Kenchester, Bridge Sollers and Bishopstone *Heref 4*
P *R M Ecroyd Esq, Major D J C Davenport and Bp (3 turns), Ld Chan (1 turn)* **P-in-c** A C E KNIGHT

CREDITON (Holy Cross) (St Lawrence) Shobrooke and Sandford w Upton Hellions *Ex 2* **P** *12 Govs of Crediton Ch*
R N GUTHRIE, **C** K M ROBERTS, W P JACKSON

CREECH ST MICHAEL (St Michael) *B & W 18* **P** *MMCET*
V D G MANNING

CREED (St Crida) *see Probus, Ladock and Grampound w Creed and St Erme Truro*

CREEDY, NORTH: Cheriton Fitzpaine, Woolfardisworthy, Kennerley, Washford Pyne, Puddington, Poughill, Stockleigh English, Morchard Bishop, Stockleigh Pomeroy, Down St Mary, Clannaborough, Lapford, Nymet Rowland, and Coldridge *Ex 2*
P *Ld Chan (1 turn), Patr Bd (5 turns)* **TR** B SHILLINGFORD,
TV S G C SMITH, M A HALL, **NSM** W A MCCAFFERTY,
J E LUCAS

CREEKMOOR (Christ Church) *see Oakdale Sarum*

CREEKSEA (All Saints) w Althorne and Latchingdon w North Fambridge *Chelmsf 11* **P** *Bp, Abp and Ld Chan (by turn)*
V S A ROBERTSON, **NSM** V M WADMAN

CREETING (St Peter) *see Creeting St Mary, Creeting St Peter etc St E*

CREETING ST MARY (St Mary), Creeting St Peter and Earl Stonham w Stonham Parva *St E 1* **P** *DBP (2 turns), Pemb Coll Cam (1 turn)* **P-in-c** C M EVERETT

CREETON (St Peter) *see Castle Bytham w Creeton Linc*

CREGNEISH (St Peter) *see Rushen S & M*

CRESSAGE (Christ Church) *see Wenlock Heref*

CRESSBROOK (St John the Evangelist) *see Tideswell Derby*

CRESSING (All Saints) w Stisted and Bradwell-juxt-Coggeshall and Pattiswick *Chelmsf 15* **P** *Bp, Exors Mrs D E G Keen, and Abp (by turn)* **R** J R CORBYN

CRESSINGHAM, GREAT (St Michael) and LITTLE (St Andrew), w Threxton *Nor 13* **P** *Bp and Sec of State for Defence* **P-in-c** A D WALKER

CRESSWELL (St Bartholomew) and Lynemouth *Newc 11*
P *Bp* **P-in-c** A E SIMPSON

CRESWELL (St Mary Magdalene) *see Elmton Derby*

CRETINGHAM (St Peter) *see Earl Soham w Cretingham and Ashfield St E*

CREWE (All Saints and St Paul) *Ches 15* **P** *Bp* **V** M SAVILLE

CREWE (Christ Church) (St Peter) *Ches 15* **P** *Bp*
V W C W FOSS

CREWE (St Andrew w St John the Baptist) *Ches 15* **P** *Bp*
V W J BAKER

CREWE (St Barnabas) *Ches 15* **P** *Bp* **V** R D POWELL

CREWE GREEN (St Michael and All Angels) *see Haslington w Crewe Green Ches*

CREWKERNE (St Bartholomew) w Wayford *B & W 15*
P *Ld Chan* **R** M C GALLAGHER, **M** E GOODLAND

CREWTON (St Peter) *see Boulton Derby*

CRICH (St Mary) and South Wingfield *Derby 1* **P** *Ch Trust Fund Trust and Duke of Devonshire (jt)* **V** P D BROOKS,
C T A DAVIS, **NSM** D HIGGON

CRICKET ST THOMAS (St Thomas) *as above B & W*

CRICK (St Margaret) and Yelvertoft w Clay Coton and Lilbourne *Pet 2* **P** *MMCET and St Jo Coll Cam (jt)* **R** R M BARLOW

CRICKET MALHERBIE (St Mary Magdalene) *see Chard and Distr B & W*

CRICKLADE (St Sampson) w Latton *Bris 6* **P** *D&C, Bp, and Hon P N Eliot (by turn)* **V** S J ORAM

CRICKLEWOOD (St Gabriel) and St Michael *Lon 21* **P** *Bp*
V M R ALDRIDGE, **C** J M W BOWCOTT, J M ITUMU

CRICKLEWOOD (St Peter) *Lon 15* **P** *Bp* **V** P D RABIN

CRIFTINS (St Matthew) w Dudleston and Welsh Frankton *Lich 17* **P** *Bp and V Ellesmere (jt)* **P-in-c** A C NETHERWOOD

CRIMPLESHAM (St Mary) *see Downham Market and Crimplesham w Stradsett Ely*

CRINGLEFORD (St Peter) and Colney *Nor 7* **P** *Exors E H Barclay Esq and Gt Hosp Nor (alt)* **R** A J BRADDOCK

CROCKENHILL (All Souls) *Roch 2* **P** *Bp* **P-in-c** C CROOK

CROCKERNWELL (Holy Trinity) *see Tedburn St Mary, Whitestone, Oldridge etc Ex*

CROCKHAM HILL (Holy Trinity) *Roch 11*
P *J St A Warde Esq* **P-in-c** S A J MITCHELL, **C** R JONES

CROFT (All Saints) *see The Wainfleet Gp Linc*

CROFT (Christ Church) *see Newchurch w Croft Liv*

CROFT (St Michael and All Angels) *see Leominster Heref*

CROFT (St Michael and All Angels) *see Broughton Astley and Croft w Stoney Stanton Leic*

CROFT (St Peter) *see Middleton Tyas w Croft and Eryholme Ripon*

CROFTON (All Saints) *Wakef 9* **P** *Duchy of Lanc*
C H WALKER, **OLM** A JORDAN

CROFTON (Holy Rood) (St Edmund) *Portsm 2* **P** *Bp*
V S P GIRLING

CROFTON (St Paul) *Roch 16* **P** *V Orpington*
V B A ABAYOMI-COLE

CROFTON PARK (St Hilda w St Cyprian) *S'wark 5*
P *V Lewisham St Mary* **V** S G BATES

CROGLIN (St John the Baptist) *Carl 2* **P** *D&C*
P-in-c C A RANDALL, **C** K S CAPELIN-JONES

CROMER (St Peter and St Paul) *Nor 21* **P** *CPAS*
V D E COURT, **C** I BRADY

CROMFORD (St Mary) *see Matlock Bath and Cromford Derby*

CROMHALL (St Andrew) w Tortworth and Tytherington *Glouc 7* **P** *Earl of Ducie, Or Coll Ox, and MMCET (jt)*
P-in-c P M LYES-WILSDON

CROMPTON, EAST (St James) *Man 22* **P** *Bp* **V** D PEEL,
C M D CARLISLE

CROMPTON, HIGH (St Mary) *Man 22* **P** *Bp*
P-in-c A BUTLER

CROMPTON FOLD (St Saviour) *see E Crompton Man*

CROMWELL (St Giles) *see Norwell w Ossington, Cromwell and Caunton S'well*

CRONDALL (All Saints) and Ewshot *Guildf 3* **P** *Bp*
V P M RICH, **NSM** B D BURBIDGE

CROOK (St Catherine) *Carl 10* **P** *CPAS* **V** *vacant*

CROOK (St Catherine) *Dur 9* **P** *R Brancepeth*
R J V HALLETT

CROOK PEAK *B & W 1* **P** *Ld Chan, Bp, Bp Lon, and R M Dod Esq (by turn)* **P-in-c** K R BROWN

CROOKES (St Thomas) *Sheff 4* **P** *Patr Bd* **TR** M J BREEN,
TV M WOODHEAD, **C** A F MACLAURIN, **NSM** R J G HOPKINS

CROOKES (St Timothy) *Sheff 4* **P** *Sheff Ch Burgesses*
V P R TOWNSEND

CROOKHAM (Christ Church) *Guildf 1* **P** *V Crondall and Ewshot* **P-in-c** M S NICHOLLS, **NSM** N C FORD

CROOKHORN (Good Shepherd) *Portsm 5* **P** *Simeon's Trustees* **V** A M RIMMER

CROPREDY (St Mary the Virgin) *see Shires' Edge Ox*

CROPTHORNE (St Michael) *see Fladbury w Wyre Piddle and Moor etc Worc*

CROPTON (St Gregory) *see* Lastingham w Appleton-le-Moors, Rosedale etc *York*

CROPWELL BISHOP (St Giles) w Colston Bassett, Granby w Elton, Langar cum Barnstone and Tythby w Cropwell Butler
S'well 8 **P** *CPAS and Bp, Ld Chan (alt)* **R** A O WIGRAM, **NSM** C T DOLBY

CROSBY (St George) (St Michael) *Linc 4* **P** *Sir Reginald Sheffield Bt* **V** J W THACKER

CROSBY, GREAT (All Saints) *Liv 5* **P** *R Sefton, Bp, V St Luke, and CPAS (jt)* **V** N J PATTERSON

CROSBY, GREAT (St Faith) and Waterloo Park St Mary the Virgin *Liv 1* **P** *St Chad's Coll Dur and Trustees (jt)*
V N G KELLEY, **Hon C** D A SMITH

CROSBY, GREAT (St Luke) *Liv 5* **P** *R Sefton*
V D H TROLLOPE, **OLM** B A CHAMBERS, M G QUAYLE

CROSBY GARRETT (St Andrew) *see* Kirkby Stephen w Mallerstang etc *Carl*

CROSBY-ON-EDEN (St John the Evangelist) *see* Eden, Gelt and Irthing *Carl*

CROSBY RAVENSWORTH (St Lawrence) *Carl 1* **P** *DBP*
P-in-c D C WOOD

CROSCOMBE (Blessed Virgin Mary) *see* Pilton w Croscombe, N Wootton and Dinder *B & W*

CROSLAND, SOUTH (Holy Trinity) *see* Em TM *Wakef*

CROSLAND MOOR (St Barnabas) *Wakef 5* **P** *Bp*
V M STOREY

CROSS CANONBY (St John the Evangelist) *see* Allonby, Cross Canonby and Dearham *Carl*

CROSS GREEN (St Hilda) *see* Leeds Richmond Hill *Ripon*

CROSS GREEN (St Saviour) *as above Ripon*

CROSS HEATH (St Michael and All Angels) *Lich 9* **P** *Bp*
P-in-c N B JAMIESON-HARVEY

CROSS IN HAND (St Bartholomew) *see* Waldron *Chich*

CROSS ROADS cum Lees (St James) *Bradf 8* **P** *Bp*
P-in-c E M CANNON

CROSS STONE (St Paul) *see* Todmorden *Wakef*

CROSS TOWN (St Cross) *see* Knutsford St Cross *Ches*

CROSSCRAKE (St Thomas) and Preston Patrick *Carl 10*
P *Bp and V Heversham and Milnthorpe (jt)* **V** *vacant* (01539) 560333

CROSSENS (St John) *Liv 9* **P** *Trustees* **P-in-c** P C GREEN

CROSSFLATTS (St Aidan) *see* Bingley All SS *Bradf*

CROSSLACON Team Ministry *Carl 5* **P** *Patr Bd*
TV A M GRANGE

CROSSPOOL (St Columba) *Sheff 4* **P** *Bp* **V** E HOPE, **NSM** L A FURBEY

CROSTHWAITE (St Kentigern) Keswick *Carl 6* **P** *Bp*
V A S E PENNY

CROSTHWAITE (St Mary) Kendal *Carl 10* **P** *DBP*
P-in-c W F GREETHAM

CROSTON (St Michael and All Angels) and Bretherton *Blackb 4*
P *M G Rawstorne Esq* **R** R J BRUNSWICK, **NSM** A J M WATKINSON

CROSTWICK (St Peter) *see* Spixworth w Crostwick and Frettenham *Nor*

CROSTWIGHT (All Saints) *see* Smallburgh w Dilham w Honing and Crostwight *Nor*

CROUCH END HILL (Christ Church) *see* Hornsey Ch Ch *Lon*

CROUGHTON (All Saints) *see* Aynho and Croughton w Evenley etc *Pet*

CROWAN (St Crewenna) and Treslothan *Truro 2*
P *D L C Roberts Esq and Mrs J W A Pendarves (jt)*
V P DOUGLASS, **C** M L PASCOE

CROWBOROUGH (All Saints) *Chich 19* **P** *Ld Chan*
V A C J CORNES, **C** T J WARD, **NSM** J A HOBBS

CROWBOROUGH (St John the Evangelist) *Chich 19* **P** *Guild of All So* **P-in-c** P A NAYLOR

CROWCOMBE (Holy Ghost) *see* Quantock Towers *B & W*

CROWELL (Nativity of the Blessed Virgin Mary) *see* Chinnor w Emmington and Sydenham etc *Ox*

CROWFIELD (All Saints) w Stonham Aspal and Mickfield
St E 1 **P** *DBP, Bp, and Lord de Saumarez (alt)* **R** *vacant* (01449) 711409

CROWHURST (St George) *see* Catsfield and Crowhurst *Chich*

CROWHURST (St George) *see* Lingfield and Crowhurst *S'wark*

CROWLAND (St Mary and St Bartholomew and St Guthlac)
Linc 17 **P** *Earl of Normanton* **R** F A GORDON-KERR, **C** C PENNOCK

CROWLE Group, The (St Oswald) *Linc 1* **P** *Bp (2 turns), Prime Min (1 turn)* **V** D SCHOFIELD

CROWLE (St John the Baptist) *see* Bowbrook S *Worc*

CROWMARSH GIFFORD (St Mary Magdalene)
see Wallingford *Ox*

CROWN EAST AND RUSHWICK (St Thomas)
see Broadheath, Crown East and Rushwick *Worc*

CROWNHILL (Ascension) *see* Plymouth Crownhill Ascension *Ex*

CROWTHORNE (St John the Baptist) *Ox 16* **P** *Bp*
V B R SPENCE

CROWTON (Christ Church) *see* Norley, Crowton and Kingsley *Ches*

CROXALL-CUM-OAKLEY (St John the Baptist)
see Walton-on-Trent w Croxall, Rosliston etc *Derby*

CROXBY (All Saints) *see* Swallow *Linc*

CROXDALE (St Bartholomew) and Tudhoe *Dur 6* **P** *D&C*
C M J WRAY

CROXDEN (St Giles) *see* Rocester and Croxden w Hollington *Lich*

CROXLEY GREEN (All Saints) *St Alb 5* **P** *V Rickmansworth*
V L G-H LEE

CROXLEY GREEN (St Oswald) *St Alb 5* **P** *Bp*
V A C WALTON, **NSM** C M CLARK

CROXTETH (St Paul) *Liv 8* **P** *R W Derby and Bp (jt)*
V I G BROOKS, **NSM** R MARSH

CROXTETH PARK (St Cuthbert) *Liv 8* **P** *Bp* **V** D R LESLIE

CROXTON (All Saints) *see* Thetford *Nor*

CROXTON Group, The SOUTH (St John the Baptist) *Leic 3*
P *DBP, Ch Soc Trust, and MMCET (jt)* **R** D A G G DOLMAN

CROXTON (St James) *see* Papworth *Ely*

CROXTON (St John the Evangelist) *Linc 6* **P** *Ld Chan*
R S PHILLIPS, **Hon C** S W ANDREW

CROXTON (St Paul) *see* Broughton w Croxton and Cotes Heath w Standon *Lich*

CROXTON KERRIAL (St Botolph and St John the Baptist)
see High Framland Par *Leic*

CROYDE (St Mary Magdalene) *see* Georgeham *Ex*

CROYDON (All Saints) *see* Orwell Gp *Ely*

CROYDON (Christ Church) Broad Green *S'wark 23*
P *Simeon's Trustees* **P-in-c** W MUNCEY, **OLM** J K EYNON

CROYDON (Holy Saviour) *S'wark 25* **P** *Bp*
V X SOOSAINAYAGAM, **NSM** P L GIBBS

CROYDON (St Andrew) *S'wark 23* **P** *Trustees* **V** *vacant* (020) 8688 6011

CROYDON (St Augustine) *S'wark 23* **P** *Bp* **V** G S DERRIMAN

CROYDON (St John the Baptist) *S'wark 23* **P** *Abp*
V C J L BOSWELL, **C** N J COLEMAN, T J JEFFREYS, P W HOLLAND, **OLM** P D F SMITH

CROYDON (St Mary Magdalene) *see* Addiscombe St Mary Magd w St Martin *S'wark*

CROYDON (St Matthew) *S'wark 23* **P** *V Croydon*
V P J BROWN, **C** R RATCLIFFE

CROYDON (St Michael and All Angels w St James) *S'wark 23*
P *Trustees* **V** D P MINCHEW, **C** P H SMITH

CROYDON (St Peter) *S'wark 23* **P** *V Croydon*
V S J KNOWERS, **OLM** R C IVES, K H VEEN

CROYDON Woodside (St Luke) *S'wark 25* **P** *Bp*
P-in-c N C GOLDING

CROYDON, SOUTH (Emmanuel) *S'wark 24* **P** *Ch Trust Fund Trust* **V** T A MAPSTONE, **C** A YOUINGS, **NSM** D J RICHARDSON, D A HUNTLEY

CROYDON, SOUTH (St Augustine) *see* Croydon St Aug *S'wark*

CROYLAND (St Mary and St Bartholomew and St Guthlac)
see Crowland *Linc*

CRUDGINGTON (St Mary Mission Church)
see Wrockwardine Deanery *Lich*

CRUDWELL (All Saints) *see* Ashley, Crudwell, Hankerton, Long Newnton etc *Bris*

CRUMPSALL (St Matthew w St Mary) *Man 5* **P** *Bp*
R *vacant* 0161-795 4376

CRUMPSALL, LOWER (St Thomas) w Cheetham St Mark
Man 5 **P** *Bp* **V** *vacant* 0161-205 3342

CRUNDALE (St Mary the Blessed Virgin) w Godmersham
Cant 2 **P** *Abp* **P-in-c** I G CAMPBELL

CRUWYS MORCHARD (Holy Cross) *see* Washfield, Stoodleigh, Withleigh etc *Ex*

CRUX EASTON (St Michael and All Angels) *see* Highclere and Ashmansworth w Crux Easton *Win*

CUBBINGTON (St Mary) *Cov 11* **P** *Bp* **V** K LINDOP

CUBERT (St Cubert) *Truro 7* **P** *DBP* **V** P E TIDMARSH

CUBLEY (St Andrew) *see* Alkmonton, Cubley, Marston, Montgomery etc *Derby*

CUBLINGTON (St Nicholas) *see* Wingrave w Rowsham, Aston Abbotts and Cublington *Ox*

CUCKFIELD (Holy Trinity) *Chich 6* **P** *Bp*
V N G WETHERALL, **NSM** J SEDGLEY

CUCKLINGTON (St Lawrence) *see* Charlton Musgrove, Cucklington and Stoke Trister *B & W*

CUDDESDON (All Saints) *see* Wheatley *Ox*

CUDDINGTON (St Mary) *Guildf 9* **P** *Bp*
P-in-c R G HARVEY, **NSM** S P AYLING

CUDDINGTON (St Nicholas) *see* Haddenham w Cuddington, Kingsey etc *Ox*

CUDHAM (St Peter and St Paul) and Downe *Roch 16*
  P *Ch Soc Trust and Bp (jt)*   **V** T R HATWELL,
  NSM N K HINTON

CUDWORTH (St John) *Wakef 7*   **P** *Bp*   **P-in-c** D NICHOLSON

CUDWORTH (St Michael) *see* Ilminster and Distr *B & W*

CUFFLEY (St Andrew) *see* Northaw and Cuffley *St Alb*

CULBONE (St Beuno) *see* Oare w Culbone *B & W*

CULFORD (St Mary) *see* Lark Valley *St E*

CULGAITH (All Saints) *see* Addingham, Edenhall,
  Langwathby and Culgaith *Carl*

CULHAM (St Paul) *see* Dorchester *Ox*

CULLERCOATS (St George) *Newc 8*   **P** *Patr Bd*
  TR M SLACK,   **TV** A J CAVANAGH,   R A E KENT,
  NSM A B BEESTON

CULLERCOATS (St Paul) *see* Tynemouth Cullercoats St Paul
  Newc

CULLINGWORTH (St John the Evangelist) *Bradf 8*   **P** *Bp*
  P-in-c D P HALLIDAY

**CULLOMPTON (St Andrew) (Langford Chapel), Willand,
  Uffculme, Kentisbeare, and Blackborough** *Ex 4*   **P** *Patr Bd*
  TR P J SOURBUT,   **TV** K HORSFALL,   A R DODDS,
  C A E NORMAN-WALKER,   **NSM** L M BARLEY

CULM DAVY (St Mary's Chapel) *see* Hemyock w Culm Davy,
  Clayhidon and Culmstock *Ex*

CULM VALLEY *see* Cullompton, Willand, Uffculme,
  Kentisbeare etc *Ex*

**CULMINGTON (All Saints) w Onibury, Bromfield and Stanton
  Lacy** *Heref 12*   **P** O T M Rogers-Coltman (1 turn), Earl of
  Plymouth (2 turns)   **P-in-c** M J STEWART

CULMSTOCK (All Saints) *see* Hemyock w Culm Davy,
  Clayhidon and Culmstock *Ex*

CULPHO (St Botolph) *see* Gt and Lt Bealings w Playford and
  Culpho *St E*

**CULWORTH (St Mary the Virgin) w Sulgrave and Thorpe
  Mandeville and Chipping Warden w Edgcote** *Pet 1*   **P** *Ch Patr
  Trust (1 turn), T M Sergison-Brooke Esq (1 turn), DBP
  (2 turns), and D L P Humfrey Esq (1 turn)*   **R** B M EAVES,
  NSM P J ALLEN

CUMBERWORTH (St Helen) *see* Sutton, Huttoft and Anderby
  Linc

CUMBERWORTH (St Nicholas), Denby and Denby Dale
  Wakef 6   **P** *Bp and V Penistone (jt)*   **P-in-c** T L ROBINS

CUMDIVOCK (St John) *see* Dalston w Cumdivock, Raughton
  Head and Wreay *Carl*

CUMMERSDALE (St James) *see* Denton Holme *Carl*

CUMNOR (St Michael) *Ox 10*   **P** *St Pet Coll Ox*
  V C B GARDNER,   **NSM** B M WEBB

CUMREW (St Mary the Virgin) *see* Eden, Gelt and Irthing *Carl*

CUMWHINTON (St John's Hall) *see* Scotby and Cotehill w
  Cumwhinton *Carl*

CUMWHITTON (St Mary the Virgin) *see* Eden, Gelt and
  Irthing *Carl*

CUNDALL (St Mary and All Saints) *see* Kirby-on-the-Moor,
  Cundall w Norton-le-Clay etc *Ripon*

CURBAR (All Saints) *see* Baslow w Curbar and Stoney
  Middleton *Derby*

CURBRIDGE (St Barnabas) *see* Sarisbury *Portsm*

CURBRIDGE (St John the Baptist) *see* Witney *Ox*

CURDRIDGE (St Peter) *Portsm 1*   **P** *D&C Win*
  V I G COOMBER,   **C** G M W KEITH,   **NSM** E A GROVES

**CURDWORTH (St Nicholas and St Peter ad Vincula)
  (St George)** *Birm 12*   **P** *Bp and Lord Norton (jt)*   **R** *vacant*
  (01675) 470384

CURRY, NORTH (St Peter and St Paul) *B & W 18*   **P** *D&C*
  V C H TOWNSHEND

CURRY MALLET (All Saints) *see* Beercrocombe w Curry
  Mallet, Hatch Beauchamp etc *B & W*

CURRY RIVEL (St Andrew) w Fivehead and Swell *B & W 15*
  P *D&C Bris (1 turn), P G H Speke Esq (2 turns)*
  R J M LANGDOWN

CURY (St Corentine) and Gunwalloe w St Mawgan-in-Meneage
  Truro 4   **P** *Bp*   **P-in-c** E B L BROWNING,   R J TINNISWOOD

**CUSOP (St Mary) w Blakemere, Bredwardine w Brobury,
  Clifford, Dorstone, Hardwicke, Moccas and Preston-on-Wye**
  Heref 1   **P** *Bp, D&C, CPAS, MMCET, P M I S Trumper Esq,
  S Penoyre Esq, and Mrs P Chester-Master (jt)*   **R** R M JAMES,
  Hon **C** S F BARNES,   **NSM** M K E MORGAN,   **OLM** C P STUTZ

CUTCOMBE (St John the Evangelist) *see* Exton and Winsford
  and Cutcombe w Luxborough *B & W*

CUTSDEAN (St James) *see* The Guitings, Cutsdean, Farmcote
  etc *Glouc*

CUXHAM (Holy Rood) *see* Ewelme, Brightwell Baldwin,
  Cuxham w Easington *Ox*

CUXTON (St Michael and All Angels) and Halling *Roch 6*
  P *Bp and D&C (jt)*   **R** R I KNIGHT

CUXWOLD (St Nicholas) *see* Swallow *Linc*

CWM HEAD (St Michael) *see* Wistanstow *Heref*

DACRE (Holy Trinity) w Hartwith and Darley w Thornthwaite
  Ripon 3   **P** *Bp, D&C, V Masham and Healey, and
  Mrs K A Dunbar (jt)*   **P-in-c** M S EVANS

DACRE (St Andrew) *Carl 4*   **P** *Trustees*   **P-in-c** A M MULLER

DADLINGTON (St James) *see* Fenn Lanes Gp *Leic*

DAGENHAM (St Martin) *see* Becontree S *Chelmsf*

DAGENHAM (St Peter and St Paul) *Chelmsf 1*   **P** *Ch Soc Trust*
  V R M REITH,   **C** S HANNA

DAGLINGWORTH (Holy Rood) *see* Brimpsfield w Birdlip,
  Syde, Daglingworth etc *Glouc*

DAGNALL (All Saints) *see* Kensworth, Studham and
  Whipsnade *St Alb*

DAISY HILL (St James) *Man 11*   **P** *Bp*   **V** R COWARD

DALBURY (All Saints) *see* Boylestone, Church Broughton,
  Dalbury, etc *Derby*

DALBY (St James) *see* Patrick *S & M*

DALBY (St Lawrence and Blessed Edward King) *see* Partney
  Gp *Linc*

DALBY (St Peter) *see* Howardian Gp *York*

DALBY, GREAT (St Swithun) *see* Burrough Hill Pars *Leic*

DALBY, LITTLE (St James) *as above Leic*

**DALBY, OLD (St John the Baptist), Nether Broughton, Saxelbye
  w Shoby, Grimston and Wartnaby** *Leic 3*   **P** *Bp, MMCET,
  V Rothley, and Personal Reps K J M Madocks-Wright Esq (jt)*
  V *vacant* (01664) 820064

DALE ABBEY (All Saints) *see* Stanton-by-Dale w Dale Abbey
  and Risley *Derby*

DALE HEAD (St James) *see* Long Preston w Tosside *Bradf*

DALHAM (St Mary) *see* Gazeley w Dalham, Moulton and
  Kentford *St E*

DALLAM (St Mark) *Liv 12*   **P** *R Warrington and Bp (jt)*
  V P J MARSHALL

DALLINGHOO (St Mary) *see* Charsfield w Debach,
  Monewden, Hoo etc *St E*

DALLINGTON (St Giles) *see* Brightling, Dallington,
  Mountfield etc *Chich*

DALLINGTON (St Mary) *Pet 7*   **P** *Earl Spencer*
  V A E PANTON

DALLOWGILL (St Peter) *see* Fountains Gp *Ripon*

DALSTON (Holy Trinity) w St Philip and Haggerston All Saints
  Lon 5   **P** *Ld Chan and Bp (alt)*   **V** R J HUDSON-WILKIN,
  C A R L PIGGOT

DALSTON (St Mark w St Bartholomew) *Lon 5*   **P** *Ch Patr
  Trust*   **V** R W WALL

**DALSTON (St Michael) w Cumdivock, Raughton Head and
  Wreay** *Carl 3*   **P** *Bp, DBP, and D&C (jt)*   **V** N J ASH,
  C C J TAYLOR

DALTON (Holy Trinity) *see* Newburn *Newc*

DALTON (Holy Trinity) *Sheff 6*   **P** *Bp*   **V** *vacant* (01709)
  850377

DALTON (St James) *see* Gilling and Kirkby Ravensworth *Ripon*

DALTON (St John the Evangelist) *see* Topcliffe, Baldersby w
  Dishforth, Dalton etc *York*

DALTON (St Michael and All Angels) *Liv 11*   **P** *Bp*
  V T C BARTON

DALTON, NORTH (All Saints) *see* Woldsburn *York*

DALTON, SOUTH *see* Dalton le Dale *Dur*

DALTON HOLME (St Mary) *see* Etton w Dalton Holme *York*

DALTON-IN-FURNESS (St Mary) and Ireleth-with-Askam
  Carl 9   **P** *Bp*   **V** A MITCHELL,   **C** D SANDERSON

DALTON LE DALE (Holy Trinity) (St Andrew) *Dur 2*   **P** *D&C*
  V A MILNE

DALWOOD (St Peter) *see* Kilmington, Stockland, Dalwood,
  Yarcombe etc *Ex*

DAMERHAM (St George) *see* W Downland *Sarum*

DANBURY (St John the Baptist) *Chelmsf 9*   **P** *Lord Fitzwalter*
  P-in-c M G BLYTH

DANBY (St Hilda) *York 22*   **P** *Viscount Downe*   **V** R LEWIS

DANBY WISKE (not known) *see* Gt Smeaton w Appleton
  Wiske and Birkby etc *Ripon*

DANEHILL (All Saints) *Chich 21*   **P** *Ch Soc Trust*   **V** *vacant*
  (01825) 790269

DANESMOOR (St Barnabas) *see* N Wingfield, Clay Cross and
  Pilsley *Derby*

DARBY END (St Peter) *Worc 9*   **P** *Bp*   **V** *vacant* (01384)
  637662

DARBY GREEN (St Barnabas) *Win 5*   **P** *Bp*   **V** J L H PAGE

DARENTH (St Margaret) *Roch 2*   **P** *D&C*
  P-in-c K D MATHERS,   **NSM** K E W MATHERS

DARESBURY (All Saints) *Ches 4*   **P** *D G Greenhall Esq*
  V D R FELIX,   **NSM** W P POVEY

DARFIELD (All Saints) *Sheff 12*   **P** *MMCET*
  R J G BLAKELEY

DARLASTON (All Saints) *Lich 26*   **P** *Simeon's Trustees*
  P-in-c N D PERKINSON,   **C** D WILLS,   R E INGLESBY

DARLASTON (St Lawrence) *Lich 26*   **P** *Bp and Simeon's Trustees (jt)*   **P-in-c** D WILLS,   **C** R E INGLESBY

DARLEY (Christ Church)   *see* Dacre w Hartwith and Darley w Thornthwaite *Ripon*

DARLEY (St Helen) *Derby 7*   **P** *Bp*   **R** R E QUARTON

DARLEY, SOUTH (St Mary the Virgin), Elton and Winster *Derby 7*   **P** *Bp and DBF (jt)*   **P-in-c** R E QUARTON

DARLEY ABBEY (St Matthew) *Derby 11*   **P** *DBP*   **V** D MOWBRAY,   **P-in-c** S M FRANCE

DARLINGSCOTT (St George)   *see* Tredington and Darlingscott w Newbold on Stour *Cov*

DARLINGTON (All Saints)   *see* Blackwell All SS and Salutation *Dur*

DARLINGTON (Holy Trinity) *Dur 8*   **P** *Adn Dur*   **V** R C WARDALE

DARLINGTON (St Cuthbert) *Dur 8*   **P** *Lord Barnard*   **V** R J WILLIAMSON,   **NSM** P M SINCLAIR

DARLINGTON St Hilda and (St Columba) *Dur 8*   **P** *Bp*   **P-in-c** S C WILLIAMSON

DARLINGTON (St James) *Dur 8*   **P** *The Crown*   **V** I L GRIEVES

DARLINGTON (St Mark) w St Paul *Dur 8*   **P** *Bp and St Jo Coll Dur*   **V** *vacant* (01325) 382400

DARLINGTON (St Matthew) and St Luke *Dur 8*   **P** *Bp*   **V** B HOLMES

DARLINGTON, EAST (St John) (St Herbert) *Dur 8*   **P** *The Crown*   **TV** C M BLAKESLEY

DARLTON (St Giles)   *see* Dunham-on-Trent w Darlton, Ragnall etc *S'well*

DARNALL (Church of Christ)   *see* Attercliffe, Darnall and Tinsley *Sheff*

DARRINGTON (St Luke and All Saints)   *see* Went Valley *Wakef*

DARSHAM (All Saints) *St E 19*   **P** *Exors Earl of Stradbroke*   **V** R J GINN,   **C** R S SMITH,   **OLM** E A MORRIS

DARTFORD (Christ Church) *Roch 2*   **V** *Dartford H Trin*   **V** D B KITLEY,   **C** A R ANGEL

DARTFORD (Holy Trinity) *Roch 2*   **P** *Bp*   **V** M J HENWOOD

DARTFORD (St Alban) *Roch 2*   **P** *V Dartford H Trin*   **P-in-c** D G BACON

DARTFORD (St Edmund the King and Martyr) *Roch 2*   **P** *Bp*   **V** R P CALLAGHAN,   **C** S C BREWER

DARTINGTON (Old St Mary's Church Tower)   *see* Totnes w Bridgetown, Berry Pomeroy etc *Ex*

DARTINGTON (St Mary)   *as above Ex*

DARTMOUTH (St Petrox) (St Saviour) *Ex 13*   **P** *DBP and Sir John Seale Bt (jt)*   **V** S C WRIGHT,   **C** P A STAPLE

DARTON (All Saints) *Wakef 7*   **P** *Bp*   **V** W R PLIMMER

DARWEN (St Barnabas) *Blackb 2*   **P** *Bp*   **V** L R COLLINSON

DARWEN (St Cuthbert) w Tockholes St Stephen *Blackb 2*   **P** *Bp*   **C** N E DAVIS

DARWEN (St Peter) w Hoddlesden St Paul *Blackb 2*   **P** *V Blackburn and DBP (jt)*   **TR** K P ARKELL,   **TV** G R MUMFORD,   **C** D P WOODALL,   **NSM** K THOMAS

DARWEN, LOWER (St James) *Blackb 2*   **P** *V Blackb*   **P-in-c** G M DYER,   **OLM** J R H CRAWFORD

DARWEN, OVER (St James) *Blackb 2*   **P** *V Blackb*   **P-in-c** T N DYER

DASSETT MAGNA (All Saints)   *see* Burton Dassett *Cov*

DATCHET (St Mary the Virgin)   *see* Riverside *Ox*

DATCHWORTH (All Saints) *St Alb 5*   **P** *Bp*   **R** *vacant* (01438) 813067

DAUBHILL (St George the Martyr) *Man 9*   **P** *Trustees*   **V** S J ABRAM

DAUNTSEY (St James Great)   *see* Brinkworth w Dauntsey *Bris*

DAVENHAM (St Wilfrid) *Ches 6*   **P** *Bp*   **R** R S MUNRO,   **C** A Q GREENHOUGH

DAVENTRY (Holy Cross), Ashby St Ledgers, Braunston, Catesby, Hellidon, Staverton and Welton *Pet 3*   **P** *Patr Bd*   **TR** O R PAGE,   **TV** C P ROSE-CASEMORE, A SLATER, E M COWLEY,   **C** G ANGELL

DAVIDSTOW (St David)   *see* Boscastle w Davidstow *Truro*

DAVINGTON (St Mary Magdalene)   *see* The Brents and Davington w Oare and Luddenham *Cant*

DAVYHULME (Christ Church) *Man 7*   **P** *Bp*   **P-in-c** H M EVANS

DAVYHULME (St Mary) *Man 7*   **P** *Bp*   **P-in-c** N W DAWSON

DAWDON (St Hild and St Helen) *Dur 2*   **P** *Bp*   **V** J C G POLLOCK

DAWLEY (Holy Trinity)   *see* Cen Telford *Lich*

DAWLEY (St Jerome) *Lon 24*   **P** *Hyndman Trustees*   **P-in-c** I W JONES

DAWLISH (St Gregory) *Ex 6*   **P** *D&C*   **P-in-c** J P BIRD,   **C** C S PEER

DAWLISH WARREN (Church Hall)   *see* Kenton, Mamhead, Powderham, Cofton and Starcross *Ex*

DAYBROOK (St Paul) *S'well 12*   **P** *Bp*   **P-in-c** C J RATTENBERRY,   **C** R B CHAPMAN

DAYLESFORD (St Peter)   *see* Chipping Norton *Ox*

DE BEAUVOIR TOWN (St Peter) *Lon 5*   **P** *Bp*   **V** J F PORTER-PRYCE,   **Hon C** C J BRICE

DEAL (St Andrew) *Cant 8*   **P** *Abp*   **R** *vacant* (01304) 374354

DEAL (St George the Martyr) *Cant 8*   **P** *Abp*   **V** C G SPENCER,   **C** S PORTER

DEAL (St Leonard) (St Richard) and Sholden *Cant 8*   **P** *Abp*   **R** G D KENDREW,   **C** G F SMALL,   **NSM** M W FISHLOCK,   **OLM** M A J GILLIBRAND

DEAL The Carpenter's Arms (extra-parochial place) *Cant 8*   **C-in-c** M J SCHORAH

DEAN (All Hallows)   *see* The Stodden Churches *St Alb*

DEAN (St Oswald) *Carl 6*   **P** *Trustees the late A R Sherwen Esq and R Workington (jt)*   **P-in-c** K KITCHIN

DEAN, EAST (St Simon and St Jude) w Friston and Jevington *Chich 16*   **P** *Duke of Devonshire (1 turn), D&C (2 turns)*   **R** *vacant* (01323) 423266

DEAN, EAST (St Winifred)   *see* Lockerley and E Dean w E and W Tytherley *Win*

DEAN, WEST (All Saints)   *see* Alfriston w Lullington, Litlington and W Dean *Chich*

DEAN, WEST (St Mary)   *see* Clarendon *Sarum*

DEAN COURT (St Andrew)   *see* Cumnor *Ox*

DEAN FOREST (Christ Church)   *see* Forest of Dean Ch Ch w English Bicknor *Glouc*

DEAN FOREST (Holy Trinity) *Glouc 4*   **P** *The Crown*   **V** A N JAMES

DEAN FOREST (St Paul)   *see* Parkend and Viney Hill *Glouc*

DEAN PRIOR (St George the Martyr)   *see* Buckfastleigh w Dean Prior *Ex*

DEANE (All Saints)   *see* N Waltham and Steventon, Ashe and Deane *Win*

DEANE (St Mary the Virgin) *Man 11*   **P** *Patr Bd*   **TR** I G MAINEY,   **TV** P ELLIS

DEANSHANGER (Holy Trinity)   *see* Passenham *Pet*

DEARHAM (St Mungo)   *see* Allonby, Cross Canonby and Dearham *Carl*

DEARNLEY (St Andrew) *Man 20*   **P** *Bp*   **P-in-c** P F DAVEY

DEBDEN (St Mary the Virgin) and Wimbish w Thunderley *Chelmsf 22*   **P** *Bp*   **R** A K GAIR

DEBENHAM (St Mary Magdalene) w Aspall and Kenton *St E 18*   **P** *Lord Henniker (2 turns), Bp (1 turn)*   **P-in-c** G E NOBLE,   **OLM** P A R WILKES, J E BUFTON

DEDDINGTON (St Peter and St Paul) Barford, Clifton and Hempton *Ox 5*   **P** *D&C Windsor and Bp (jt)*   **V** H R B WHITE

DEDHAM (St Mary the Virgin) *Chelmsf 17*   **P** *Duchy of Lanc and Lectureship Trustees (alt)*   **V** G G MOATE,   **C** R G GIBBS

DEDWORTH (All Saints) *Ox 13*   **P** *Bp*   **P-in-c** L M BROWN,   **NSM** D M WOODMORE

DEEPCAR (St John the Evangelist) *Sheff 3*   **P** *Bp*   **V** J P RAFFAY,   **NSM** T S GREGORY

DEEPING, WEST (St Andrew)   *see* Uffington Gp *Linc*

DEEPING ST JAMES (St James) *Linc 13*   **P** *Burghley Ho Preservation Trust*   **V** M WARRICK,   **NSM** S M C MARSHALL

DEEPING ST NICHOLAS (St Nicholas)   *see* Spalding St Jo w Deeping St Nicholas *Linc*

DEEPLISH (St Luke)   *see* S Rochdale *Man*

DEERHURST (St Mary) and Apperley w Forthampton and Chaceley *Glouc 16*   **P** *Bp, Exors G J Yorke Esq, and V Longdon (jt)*   **P-in-c** D BOWERS

DEFFORD (St James) w Besford *Worc 4*   **P** *D&C Westmr*   **V** P J THOMAS

DEIGHTON (All Saints)   *see* Brompton w Deighton *York*

DELABOLE (St John the Evangelist)   *see* St Teath *Truro*

DELAMERE (St Peter) *Ches 6*   **P** *The Crown*   **P-in-c** B R K PERKES

DELAVAL (Our Lady) *Newc 1*   **P** *Lord Hastings*   **V** P J BRYARS

DEMBLEBY (St Lucia)   *see* S Lafford *Linc*

DENABY, OLD (Mission Church)   *see* Mexborough *Sheff*

DENABY MAIN (All Saints) *Sheff 7*   **P** *Bp*   **V** R C DAVIES

DENBURY (St Mary the Virgin)   *see* Ipplepen, Torbryan and Denbury *Ex*

DENBY (St John the Evangelist)   *see* Cumberworth, Denby and Denby Dale *Wakef*

DENBY (St Mary the Virgin)   *see* Horsley and Denby *Derby*

DENBY DALE (Holy Trinity)   *see* Cumberworth, Denby and Denby Dale *Wakef*

DENCHWORTH (St James)   *see* Hanney, Denchworth and E Challow *Ox*

DENDRON (St Matthew)   *see* Aldingham, Dendron, Rampside and Urswick *Carl*

DENESIDE (All Saints)   *see* Seaham *Dur*

DENFORD (Holy Trinity) w Ringstead *Pet 10*   **P** *L Stopford-Sackville Esq*   **V** *vacant* (01933) 624627

DENGIE (St James) w Asheldham *Chelmsf 11* **P** *Bp* **R** *vacant*

DENHAM (St John the Baptist) *see* Hoxne w Denham, Syleham and Wingfield *St E*

DENHAM (St Mark) (St Mary the Virgin) *Ox 20* **P** *L J Way Esq* **R** J A HIRST, **NSM** C E L SMITH

DENHAM (St Mary) *see* Barrow w Denham St Mary and Higham Green *St E*

DENHAM, NEW (St Francis) *see* Denham *Ox*

DENHOLME *Bradf 8* **P** *Bp* **V** *vacant* (01274) 832813

DENMARK PARK (St Saviour) *see* Peckham St Sav *S'wark*

DENMEAD (All Saints) *Portsm 5* **P** *Ld Chan* **V** A W H ASHDOWN, **NSM** S M EDWARDS

DENNINGTON (St Mary) *see* Badingham w Bruisyard, Cransford and Dennington *St E*

DENSHAW (Christ Church) *Man 21* **P** *Bp* **V** S C L CLAYTON

DENSTON (St Nicholas) *see* Bansfield *St E*

DENSTONE (All Saints) w Ellastone and Stanton *Lich 15* **P** *Bp and Col Sir Walter Bromley-Davenport (jt)* **P-in-c** J R WILLIAMS

DENT (St Andrew) w Cowgill *Bradf 6* **P** *Bp and Sidesmen of Dent (alt)* **P** J BOYLES

DENTON (Christ Church) *Man 17* **P** *Bp* **P-in-c** D J COX

DENTON Dane Bank (St George) *see* Denton Ch Ch *Man*

DENTON (Holy Spirit) *Newc 7* **P** *Bp* **C** E J WOOD

DENTON (St Andrew) *see* Harlaxton Gp *Linc*

DENTON (St Helen) *see* Weston w Denton *Bradf*

DENTON (St Lawrence) *Man 17* **P** *Earl of Wilton* **R** R CASSIDY, **C** D A WILLIAMS

DENTON (St Leonard) w South Heighton and Tarring Neville *Chich 18* **P** *MMCET and Bp (alt)* **R** N A MANNING

DENTON (St Margaret) *see* Yardley Hastings, Denton and Grendon etc *Pet*

DENTON (St Mary) *see* Earsham w Alburgh and Denton *Nor*

DENTON (St Mary Magdalene) *see* Elham w Denton and Wootton *Cant*

DENTON, NETHER (St Cuthbert) *see* Lanercost, Walton, Gilsland and Nether Denton *Carl*

DENTON HOLME (St James) *Carl 3* **P** *Trustees* **V** J R LIBBY, **C** M C C NODDER

DENVER (St Mary) and Ryston w Roxham and West Dereham and Bexwell *Ely 15* **P** *G&C Coll Cam and Bp (jt)* **R** J K ISAACS

DENVILLE (Christchurch Centre) *see* Havant *Portsm*

DEOPHAM (St Andrew) *see* High Oak, Hingham and Scoulton w Wood Rising *Nor*

DEPDEN (St Mary the Virgin) *see* Chevington w Hargrave, Chedburgh w Depden etc *St E*

DEPTFORD Brockley (St Peter) *S'wark 3* **P** *Bp* **V** C M E G TOURNAY

DEPTFORD (St John) (Holy Trinity) *S'wark 3* **P** *Peache Trustees and Ch Trust Fund Trust (jt)* **P-in-c** C S BAINBRIDGE, **C** D A LAWTON, **OLM** P K M SOER

DEPTFORD (St Nicholas) (St Luke) *S'wark 3* **P** *MMCET, Peache Trustees, and CPAS (jt)* **V** W G CORNECK

DEPTFORD (St Paul) *S'wark 3* **P** *Bp* **R** P W FELLOWS

DERBY (St Alkmund and St Werburgh) *Derby 9* **P** *Simeon's Trustees* **V** J M WHITE, **C** D G HONOUR, B J DE LA T DE BERRY, **NSM** C A PRICE

DERBY (St Andrew w St Osmund) *Derby 10* **P** *Bp* **V** D C MACDONALD, R HOWORTH, M J MORGAN

DERBY (St Anne) (St John the Evangelist) *Derby 9* **P** *Bp* **V** C M G BRINKWORTH, **NSM** R L BOYLE

DERBY (St Augustine) *see* Walbrook Epiphany *Derby*

DERBY (St Barnabas) *Derby 9* **P** *Bp* **V** R J ELGAR, **NSM** A L MARTIN

DERBY (St Bartholomew) *Derby 10* **P** *Bp* **V** A G MESSOM

DERBY (St Luke) *Derby 9* **P** *Bp* **V** *vacant* (01332) 345720

DERBY (St Mark) *Derby 9* **P** *Bp* **V** L N CHILDS, **Hon C** M R FUTERS, **NSM** D L SCHOFIELD

DERBY (St Paul) *Derby 9* **P** *Bp* **V** *vacant* (01332) 362668

DERBY (St Peter and Christ Church w Holy Trinity) *Derby 10* **P** *CPAS* **V** *vacant* (01332) 347821

DERBY (St Thomas) *see* Walbrook Epiphany *Derby*

DERBY, WEST (Good Shepherd) *Liv 8* **P** *Bp and R W Derby (jt)* **C** K DAGGER

DERBY, WEST (St James) *Liv 8* **P** *Trustees* **V** D J WILLIAMS

DERBY, WEST (St John) *Liv 8* **P** *Trustees* **V** T P E NENER, **C** T B SHERRING, **Hon C** M S O B FISHER

DERBY, WEST (St Luke) *Liv 2* **P** *Bp* **P-in-c** S NICHOLSON

DERBY, WEST (St Mary) *Liv 8* **P** *Bp* **V** J R I WIKELEY, **C** G H CAPON, J E BOWEN

DERBYHAVEN (Chapel) *see* Malew *S & M*

DERBYSHIRE HILL (St Philip) *see* Parr *Liv*

DEREHAM, EAST (St Nicholas) and Scarning *Nor 17* **P** *Ld Chan* **TR** R AMES-LEWIS, **TV** B A HILL, **C** D T THORNTON

DEREHAM, WEST (St Andrew) *see* Denver and Ryston w Roxham and W Dereham etc *Ely*

DERRINGHAM BANK (Ascension) (St Thomas) *York 14* **P** *Abp* **V** S J WHALEY

DERRINGTON (St Matthew), Haughton and Ranton *Lich 10* **P** *Bp, Mrs M N Nutt, and Trustees Earl of Lichfield (jt)* **R** *vacant* (01785) 780181

DERRY Hill (Christ Church) w Bremhill and Foxham *Sarum 15* **P** *Prime Min and V Calne and Blackland* **V** D C FROST, **NSM** J W SCOTT

DERSINGHAM (St Nicholas) w Anmer and Shernborne *Nor 16* **P** *Ld Chan* **R** R P C ELVERSON

DESBOROUGH (St Giles), Brampton Ash, Dingley and Braybrooke *Pet 11* **P** *Bp, Earl Spencer, and DBP (by turn)* **R** M P TANNER, **C** M Y GARBUTT, **NSM** N M CLARKE

DESFORD (St Martin) and Peckleton w Tooley *Leic 12* **P** *Ld Chan* **R** R G SHARPE

DETHICK (St John the Baptist) *see* Tansley, Dethick, Lea and Holloway *Derby*

DETLING (St Martin) *see* Boxley w Detling *Cant*

DEVER VALLEY, LOWER *Win 7* **P** *Bp and D&C (jt)* **R** C FINCH, **NSM** R C CLARKSON

DEVIZES (St John) (St Mary) *Sarum 16* **P** *Ld Chan* **P-in-c** J RECORD, **C** D A GILL

DEVIZES (St Peter) *Sarum 16* **P** *Bp* **P-in-c** J RECORD

DEVONPORT (St Aubyn) *Ex 21* **P** *The Crown and R Stoke Damerel (alt)* **C** G M HOCKEY

DEVONPORT (St Bartholomew) *Ex 21* **P** *Bp* **V** R M SIGRIST

DEVONPORT (St Boniface) *see* Devonport St Boniface and St Phil *Ex*

DEVONPORT (St Boniface) (St Philip) *Ex 21* **P** *Bp* **TR** P J LOW, **C** D R DAVIS

DEVONPORT (St Budeaux) *Ex 21* **P** *V Plymouth St Andr w St Paul and St Geo* **V** S J BEACH

DEVONPORT (St Mark) Ford *Ex 21* **P** *Trustees* **V** A E APPLEGARTH

DEVONPORT (St Michael) (St Barnabas) *Ex 21* **P** *Bp and R Stoke Damerel (alt)* **P-in-c** T J BUCKLEY

DEVONPORT, NORTH *see* Devonport St Boniface and St Phil *Ex*

DEVORAN (St John the Evangelist and St Petroc) *Truro 6* **P** *Bp* **V** R SELLERS

DEWCHURCH, LITTLE (St David) *see* Heref S Wye *Heref*

DEWCHURCH, MUCH (St David) *see* Much Birch w Lt Birch, Much Dewchurch etc *Heref*

DEWLISH (All Saints) *see* Puddletown, Tolpuddle and Milborne w Dewlish *Sarum*

DEWSALL (St Michael) *see* Heref S Wye *Heref*

DEWSBURY (All Saints) (St Mark) (St Matthew and St John the Baptist) *Wakef 11* **P** *Bp, Adn Pontefract, RD Dewsbury, and Lay Chmn Dewsbury Deanery Syn (jt)* **TR** K PARTINGTON, **TV** P A CRABB, V R SMITH, **NSM** A E LEE, R H BAILEY

DEWSBURY (St Matthew and St John the Baptist) *see* Dewsbury *Wakef*

DEWSBURY (All Saints) *as above Wakef*

DEWSBURY (St Mark) *as above Wakef*

DEWSBURY MOOR (St John the Evangelist) *as above Wakef*

DHOON (Christ Church) *see* Maughold *S & M*

DIBDEN (All Saints) *Win 11* **P** *MMCET* **R** J D ALDERMAN, **C** R G LLOYD

DIBDEN PURLIEU (St Andrew) *see* Dibden *Win*

DICKER, UPPER (Holy Trinity) *see* Hellingly and Upper Dicker *Chich*

DICKLEBURGH (All Saints) and The Pulhams *Nor 10* **P** *Ld Chan (1 turn), Patr Bd (2 turns), Prime Min (1 turn)* **R** J B SCOTT, **OLM** P D SCHWIER

DIDBROOK (St George) *see* Toddington, Stanton, Didbrook w Hailes etc *Glouc*

DIDCOT (All Saints) *Ox 18* **P** *BNC Ox* **P-in-c** A M COLEBY, **C** J I MIDWINTER, **NSM** A J EDWARDS

DIDCOT (St Peter) *Ox 18* **P** *Bp* **V** N J GANDY, **NSM** P A GORDON

DIDDINGTON (St Laurence) *Ely 13* **P** *G E P Thornhill Esq* **P-in-c** N MORGAN

DIDDLEBURY (St Peter) w Munslow, Holdgate and Tugford *Heref 12* **P** *Bp (3 turns), D&C (1 turn)* **R** I E GIBBS

DIDLINGTON (St Michael) *Nor 13* **P** *CPAS* **P-in-c** A D WALKER

DIDMARTON (St Lawrence) *see* Boxwell, Leighterton, Didmarton, Oldbury etc *Glouc*

DIDSBURY (Christ Church) Barlow Moor Road *Man 8* **P** *Trustees* **P-in-c** R M GOVENDER

DIDSBURY (St James) (Emmanuel) *Man 8* **P** *Patr Bd* **TR** D M HUGHES, **TV** A R BRADLEY, **C** C J PARK

DIGBY GROUP, The (St Thomas of Canterbury) *Linc 22* **P** *Mrs H E Gillatt, Ld Chan, and DBP (by turn)* **P-in-c** J A BLANCHARD

DIGMOOR (Christ the Servant) *see* Upholland *Liv*

DIGSWELL (St John the Evangelist) (Christ the King) and Panshanger *St Alb 21* **P** *Patr Bd* **TV** S SHAHZAD, **P-in-c** C GARNER, **NSM** K E SUCKLING, S V BECK

DILHAM (St Nicholas) *see* Smallburgh w Dilham w Honing and Crostwight *Nor*

DILHORNE (All Saints) *see* Caverswall and Weston Coyney w Dilhorne *Lich*

DILSTON (St Mary Magdalene) *see* Corbridge w Halton and Newton Hall *Newc*

DILTON or LEIGH (Holy Saviour) *see* White Horse *Sarum*

DILTON MARSH (Holy Trinity) *as above Sarum*

DILWYN AND STRETFORD (St Mary the Virgin) *see* Leominster *Heref*

DINDER (St Michael and All Angels) *see* Pilton w Croscombe, N Wootton and Dinder *B & W*

DINEDOR (St Andrew) *see* Heref S Wye *Heref*

DINES GREEN (St Michael) *see* Worc St Mich *Worc*

DINGLEY (All Saints) *see* Desborough, Brampton Ash, Dingley and Braybrooke *Pet*

DINNINGTON (St Leonard) *Sheff 5* **P** *J C Athorpe Esq* **P-in-c** J E BOLTON

DINNINGTON (St Matthew) *see* Ch the King *Newc*

DINNINGTON (St Nicholas) *see* Merriott w Hinton, Dinnington and Lopen *B & W*

DINSDALE (St John the Baptist) w Sockburn *Dur 8* **P** *D&C and Sherburn Hosp (alt)* **R** *vacant*

DINTING VALE (Holy Trinity) *see* Charlesworth and Dinting Vale *Derby*

DINTON (St Mary) *see* Nadder Valley *Sarum*

DINTON (St Peter and St Paul) *see* Stone w Dinton and Hartwell *Ox*

DIPTFORD (St Mary the Virgin), North Huish, Harberton, Harbertonford, Halwell and Moreleigh *Ex 14* **P** *Bp and D&C (jt)* **R** J C OUGH, **C** H G POLLOCK, **Hon C** J E SPENCE, B PETTY

DIPTON (St John the Evangelist) and Leadgate *Dur 4* **P** *Bp* **V** D G HERON

DISCOED (St Michael) *see* Presteigne w Discoed, Kinsham, Lingen and Knill *Heref*

DISEWORTH (St Michael and All Angels) *see* Hathern, Long Whatton and Diseworth w Belton etc *Leic*

DISHLEY (All Saints) *see* Thorpe Acre w Dishley *Leic*

DISLEY (St Mary the Virgin) *Ches 16* **P** *Lord Newton* **V** P S DANIEL

DISS Heywood (St James the Great) *see* Diss *Nor*

DISS (St Mary) *Nor 10* **P** *Bp* **R** A C BILLETT, **C** S M OAKLAND

DISTINGTON (Holy Spirit) *Carl 7* **P** *Earl of Lonsdale* **P-in-c** J M STAGG

DITCHINGHAM (St Mary), Hedenham and Broome *Nor 5* **P** *Countess Ferrers and Bp (jt)* **R** I R BENTLEY

DITCHLING (St Margaret) *Chich 9* **P** *Bp* **V** J S CLARKE

DITTERIDGE (St Christopher) *see* Box w Hazlebury and Ditteridge *Bris*

DITTISHAM (St George) *see* Ashprington, Cornworthy and Dittisham *Ex*

DITTON (St Basil and All Saints) *see* Hough Green St Basil and All SS *Liv*

DITTON (St Michael) (St Thomas) *Liv 13* **P** *Bp* **OLM** J I CLARKE, D STRATFORD, L MOSS

DITTON (St Peter ad Vincula) *Roch 7* **P** *Ch Trust Fund Trust* **R** J R TERRANOVA

DITTON PRIORS (St John the Baptist) w Neenton, Burwarton, Cleobury North, Aston Botterell, Wheathill and Loughton and Chetton *Heref 9* **P** *Bp, Princess Josephine zu Loewenstein, and Exors Viscount Boyne (jt)* **P-in-c** J N ROWLAND

DIXTON (St Peter) *Heref 8* **P** *DBP* **P-in-c** J F M MILES, **NSM** J S TUNNICLIFFE

DOBCROSS (Holy Trinity) *see* Saddleworth *Man*

DOBWALLS (St Peter) *see* Liskeard and St Keyne *Truro*

DOCCOMBE (Chapel) *see* Moretonhampstead, Manaton, N Bovey and Lustleigh *Ex*

DOCK (Mission Church) *see* Immingham *Linc*

DOCKENFIELD (Church of the Good Shepherd) *see* Rowledge and Frensham *Guildf*

DOCKING (St Mary), the Birchams, Stanhoe and Sedgeford *Nor 16* **P** *Bp, D&C, and Mrs A J Ralli (3 turns), The Crown (1 turn)* **V** A J BUTCHER

DOCKLOW (St Bartholomew) *see* Leominster *Heref*

DODBROOKE (St Thomas à Beckett) *see* Kingsbridge and Dodbrooke *Ex*

DODDERHILL (St Augustine) *see* Droitwich Spa *Worc*

DODDINGHURST (All Saints) and Mountnessing *Chelmsf 7* **P** *Bp* **P-in-c** O F TRELLIS, **NSM** S M GRIDLEY

DODDINGTON (All Saints) *see* Quantoxhead *B & W*

DODDINGTON (St John) *see* Wybunbury w Doddington *Ches*

DODDINGTON (St John the Baptist) *see* Coreley and Doddington *Heref*

DODDINGTON (St John the Baptist), Newnham and Wychling *Cant 6* **P** *Abp, Adn, and Exors Sir John Croft Bt (jt)* **V** *vacant* (01795) 886265

DODDINGTON (St Mary and St Michael) *see* Glendale Gp *Newc*

DODDINGTON (St Mary) w Benwick and Wimblington *Ely 16* **P** *Bp, St Jo Coll Dur, and R Raynar Esq (jt)* **R** G COGGINS

DODDINGTON (St Peter) *see* Skellingthorpe w Doddington *Linc*

DODDINGTON, GREAT (St Nicholas) and Wilby *Pet 6* **P** *Exors Lt-Col H C M Stockdale and Ld Chan (alt)* **P-in-c** J PEARSON

DODDISCOMBSLEIGH (St Michael) *see* Tedburn St Mary, Whitestone, Oldridge etc *Ex*

DODFORD (Holy Trinity and St Mary) *see* Catshill and Dodford *Worc*

DODFORD (St Mary the Virgin) *see* Weedon Bec w Everdon and Dodford *Pet*

DODLESTON (St Mary) *Ches 2* **P** *D&C* **P-in-c** J A KENDALL

DODWORTH (St John the Baptist) *Wakef 7* **P** *V Silkstone* **V** A J HUDSON

DOGMERSFIELD (All Saints) *see* Hartley Wintney, Elvetham, Winchfield etc *Win*

DOLPHINHOLME (St Mark) w Quernmore and Over Wyresdale *Blackb 11* **P** *Bp and V Lanc (jt)* **V** R TAYLOR

DOLTON (St Edmund King and Martyr) *Ex 19* **P** *Ch Soc Trust* **P-in-c** A S GRAESSER, **NSM** D J URSELL

DONCASTER Holy Trinity *Sheff 8* **P** *SMF* **V** *vacant* (01302) 349684

DONCASTER Intake (All Saints) *Sheff 8* **P** *Bp* **V** L M WELLS

DONCASTER (St George) (St Edmund's Church Centre) *Sheff 8* **P** *Bp* **V** C M SMITH

DONCASTER (St James) *Sheff 9* **P** *Hyndman's Trustees* **V** A MURRAY

DONCASTER (St Jude) *Sheff 9* **P** *Bp* **V** A J GILBERT

DONCASTER (St Leonard and St Jude) *Sheff 7* **P** *The Crown* **V** N J PAY

DONCASTER (St Mary) *Sheff 8* **P** *Hyndman's Trustees* **V** M S A TANNER

DONHEAD ST ANDREW (St Andrew) *see* The Donheads *Sarum*

DONHEAD ST MARY (St Mary the Virgin) *as above Sarum*

DONHEADS, The *Sarum 11* **P** *DBP and New Coll Ox (alt)* **P-in-c** T C CURRY

DONINGTON (St Cuthbert) *Lich 16* **P** *MMCET* **P-in-c** J B HALL

DONINGTON (St Mary and the Holy Rood) *Linc 21* **P** *Simeon's Trustees* **V** *vacant* (01775) 822355

DONINGTON-ON-BAIN (St Andrew) *see* Asterby Gp *Linc*

DONISTHORPE (St John) and Moira w Stretton-en-le-Field *Leic 9* **P** *Ch Soc Trust (1 turn), and Bp (3 turns)* **V** A J BURGESS

DONNINGTON (St George) *Chich 3* **P** *Bp* **P-in-c** C R BEARD

DONNINGTON WOOD (St Matthew) *Lich 21* **P** *Bp* **V** D W WRIGHT

DONNISON (School) *see* Sunderland *Dur*

DONYATT (The Blessed Virgin Mary) *see* Ilminster and Distr *B & W*

DONYLAND, EAST (St Lawrence) *see* Fingringhoe w E Donyland and Abberton etc *Chelmsf*

DORCHESTER (St George) (St Mary the Virgin) (St Peter, Holy Trinity and All Saints) *Sarum 1* **P** *Patr Bd (3 turns), Ld Chan (1 turn)* **TR** P C LAMBERT, **TV** D L DENNIS, R A BETTS, **C** D J SMITH

DORCHESTER (St Peter and St Paul) *Ox 1* **P** *Patr Bd* **TR** J Y CROWE, **TV** S E BOOYS, E W D TILDESLEY, **Hon C** M C R BRAYBROOKE, D B WINTER, **NSM** R M GODFREY, **OLM** J R HILES

DORDON (St Leonard) *Birm 10* **P** *V Polesworth* **P-in-c** V J HICKS

DORE (Christ Church) *Sheff 2* **P** *Sir Philip Naylor-Leyland Bt* **V** M J HUNTER

DORKING (St Martin) w Ranmore *Guildf 7* **P** *Bp* **V** M S KING, **P** SHAYLER-WEBB, **OLM** L J TROMBETTI

DORKING (St Paul) *Guildf 7* **P** *Ch Patr Trust* **V** P D BRYER

DORMANSLAND (St John) *S'wark 26* **P** *Bp* **V** G PADDICK

DORMANSTOWN (All Saints) *see* Coatham and Dormanstown *York*

DORMINGTON (St Peter) *see* Fownhope w Mordiford, Brockhampton etc *Heref*

DORMSTON (St Nicholas)   *see* Inkberrow w Cookhill and Kington w Dormston *Worc*
DORNEY (St James the Less)   *see* Riverside *Ox*
DORRIDGE (St Philip) *Birm 6*   **P** *Bp*   **V** J A STEVENS, **C** M G GREENSTREET
DORRINGTON (St Edward) w Leebotwood, Longnor, Stapleton, Smethcote and Woolstaston *Heref 11*   **P** *DBP and J J C Coldwell Esq (jt)*   **R** R S PAYNE
DORRINGTON (St James)   *see* Digby Gp *Linc*
DORSINGTON (St Peter)   *see* Pebworth, Dorsington, Honeybourne etc *Glouc*
DORSTONE (St Faith)   *see* Cusop w Blakemere, Bredwardine w Brobury etc *Heref*
DORTON (St John the Baptist)   *see* Bernwode *Ox*
DOSTHILL (St Paul) *Birm 10*   **P** *Bp*   **V** A W MOORE
DOTTERY (St Saviour)   *see* Askerswell, Loders and Powerstock *Sarum*
DOUGLAS (All Saints) (St Thomas the Apostle) *S & M 2*   **P** *Bp*   **V** E T PETTENGELL,   **OLM** S A FERRIS
DOUGLAS (Christ Church) *Blackb 4*   **P** *Bp*   **V** B E HARDING
DOUGLAS (St George) *S & M 2*   **P** *Bp*   **V** B H PARTINGTON, **NSM** R HARPER
DOUGLAS (St Matthew the Apostle) *S & M 2*   **P** *Bp*   **V** D WHITWORTH,   **NSM** N PILLING
DOUGLAS (St Ninian) *S & M 2*   **P** *CPAS*   **V** B DARBYSHIRE, **NSM** B QUINN
DOUGLAS-IN-PARBOLD (Christ Church)   *see* Douglas *Blackb*
DOULTING (St Aldhelm)   *see* Shepton Mallet w Doulting *B & W*
DOVE HOLES (St Paul)   *see* Wormhill, Peak Forest w Peak Dale and Dove Holes *Derby*
DOVECOT (Holy Spirit) *Liv 2*   **P** *Bp*   **V** D G R BEARDSLEY
DOVECOT Buckland Valley (St Nicholas)   *see* Buckland in Dover w Buckland Valley *Cant*
DOVER (St Martin) *Cant 4*   **P** *CPAS*   **V** K G GARRETT
DOVER (St Mary the Virgin) *Cant 4*   **P** *Abp, Ld Warden of Cinque Ports, and Ld Lt of Kent (jt)*   **V** D G RIDLEY
DOVER (St Peter and St Paul)   *see* Charlton-in-Dover *Cant*
DOVERCOURT (All Saints) and Parkeston w Harwich *Chelmsf 20*   **P** *Bp and DBP (alt)*   **R** S HARDIE, **C** E G BUCHANAN, R J MARTIN
DOVERDALE (St Mary)   *see* Ombersley w Doverdale *Worc*
DOVERIDGE (St Cuthbert), Scropton, Sudbury and Somersal Herbert *Derby 14*   **P** *Duke of Devonshire*   **R** D MILNER, **NSM** P R JONES
DOVERSGREEN (St Peter) Conventional District *S'wark 26*   *vacant*
DOWDESWELL (St Michael)   *see* Sevenhampton w Charlton Abbots, Hawling etc *Glouc*
DOWLAND (not known)   *see* Iddesleigh w Dowland *Ex*
DOWLES Button Oak (St Andrew)   *see* Ribbesford w Bewdley and Dowles *Worc*
DOWLISHWAKE (St Andrew)   *see* Ilminster and Distr *B & W*
DOWN, East (St John the Baptist)   *see* Shirwell, Loxhore, Kentisbury, Arlington, etc *Ex*
DOWN AMPNEY (All Saints)   *see* S Cerney w Cerney Wick and Down Ampney *Glouc*
DOWN HATHERLEY (St Mary and Corpus Christi)   *see* Twigworth, Down Hatherley, Norton, The Leigh etc *Glouc*
DOWN ST MARY (St Mary the Virgin)   *see* N Creedy *Ex*
DOWNDERRY (St Nicholas)   *see* St Germans *Truro*
DOWNE (St Mary Magdalene)   *see* Cudham and Downe *Roch*
DOWNEND (Christ Church) (Church Centre) *Bris 5*   **P** *Peache Trustees*   **P-in-c** J L VICKERY,   **C** M A C ANDREWS, R J WIDDECOMBE
DOWNHAM (St Barnabas) *S'wark 4*   **P** *Bp*   **V** *vacant* (020) 8698 4851
DOWNHAM (St Leonard)   *see* Chatburn and Downham *Blackb*
DOWNHAM (St Leonard) *Ely 13*   **P** *Bp* **P-in-c** M J M HUGHES
DOWNHAM (St Luke)   *see* Catford (Southend) and Downham *S'wark*
DOWNHAM (St Margaret) w South Hanningfield *Chelmsf 9*   **P** *Bp*   **R** M E PERCIVAL
DOWNHAM, NORTH (St Mark)   *see* Catford (Southend) and Downham *S'wark*
DOWNHAM MARKET (St Edmund) and Crimplesham w Stradsett *Ely 15*   **P** *Bp*   **R** J W MATHER
DOWNHEAD (All Saints)   *see* Leigh upon Mendip w Stoke St Michael *B & W*
DOWNHOLME (St Michael and All Angels) and Marske *Ripon 2*   **P** *Bp*   **P-in-c** J K BALL
DOWNLEY (St James the Great)   *see* High Wycombe *Ox*
DOWNS BARN and NEAT HILL (Community Church)   *see* Stantonbury and Willen *Ox*

DOWNSHIRE HILL (St John)   *see* Hampstead St Jo Downshire Hill Prop Chpl *Lon*
DOWNSIDE (St Michael's Chapel)   *see* E Horsley and Ockham w Hatchford and Downside *Guildf*
DOWNSWAY (All Souls Worship Centre)   *see* Southwick St Mich *Chich*
DOWNTON (St Giles)   *see* Wigmore Abbey *Heref*
DOWNTON (St Lawrence) *Sarum 10*   **P** *Win Coll* **P-in-c** F H GIMSON
DOWSBY (St Andrew)   *see* Billingborough Gp *Linc*
DOXEY (St Thomas and St Andrew)   *see* Castle Town *Lich*
DOXFORD (St Wilfrid) *Dur 16*   **P** *Bp*   **V** *vacant*
DOYNTON (Holy Trinity)   *see* Wick w Doynton and Dyrham *Bris*
DRAKES BROUGHTON (St Barnabas)   *see* Stoulton w Drake's Broughton and Pirton etc *Worc*
DRAUGHTON (St Augustine)   *see* Skipton H Trin *Bradf*
DRAUGHTON (St Catherine)   *see* Maidwell w Draughton, Lamport w Faxton *Pet*
DRAX (St Peter and St Paul)   *see* Carlton and Drax *York*
DRAYCOT *Bris 6*   **P** *Bp, D&C Sarum, and R W Neeld Esq (jt)* **P-in-c** G W HEWITT
DRAYCOTT (St Mary)   *see* Wilne and Draycott w Breaston *Derby*
DRAYCOTT (St Peter)   *see* Rodney Stoke w Draycott *B & W*
DRAYCOTT IN THE CLAY (St Augustine)   *see* Hanbury w Newborough and Rangemore *Lich*
DRAYCOTT-LE-MOORS (St Margaret) w Forsbrook *Lich 6*   **P** *Bp*   **R** B L WHITTAKER,   **C** N M RUSSELL
DRAYTON (Iron Mission Room)   *see* Chaddesley Corbett and Stone *Worc*
DRAYTON (St Catherine)   *see* Langport Area Chs *B & W*
DRAYTON (St Leonard and St Catherine)   *see* Dorchester *Ox*
DRAYTON (St Margaret) w Felthorpe *Nor 2*   **P** *Bp* **P-in-c** D WELLS
DRAYTON (St Peter)   *see* Ironstone *Ox*
DRAYTON (St Peter) Berks *Ox 10*   **P** *Bp* **NSM** D M DERRICK
DRAYTON, EAST (St Peter)   *see* Dunham-on-Trent w Darlton, Ragnall etc *S'well*
DRAYTON, LITTLE (Christ Church) *Lich 18*   **P** *V Drayton in Hales*   **V** C J D PROBERT
DRAYTON, WEST (St Martin) *Lon 24*   **P** *Bp*   **V** O J FIELD, **NSM** A BISWAS
DRAYTON, WEST (St Paul)   *see* Gamston w Eaton and W Drayton *S'well*
DRAYTON BASSETT (St Peter) *Lich 4*   **P** *Bp*   **R** H J BAKER
DRAYTON-BEAUCHAMP (St Mary the Virgin)   *see* Aston Clinton w Buckland and Drayton Beauchamp *Ox*
DRAYTON IN HALES (St Mary) *Lich 18*   **P** *C C Corbet Esq* **P-in-c** M G W HAYES,   **C** J F HALL
DRAYTON PARSLOW (Holy Trinity)   *see* Stewkley w Soulbury and Drayton Parslow *Ox*
DRESDEN (Resurrection) *Lich 12*   **P** *V Blurton*   **V** *vacant* (01782) 321257
DREWSTEIGNTON (Holy Trinity)   *see* Chagford, Drewsteignton, Hittisleigh etc *Ex*
DRIFFIELD (St Mary)   *see* The Ampneys w Driffield and Poulton *Glouc*
DRIFFIELD, GREAT (All Saints) and LITTLE (St Peter) *York 10*   **P** *Abp*   **V** *vacant* (01377) 253394
DRIGG (St Peter)   *see* Seascale and Drigg *Carl*
DRIGHLINGTON (St Paul) *Wakef 8*   **P** *Bp* **P-in-c** S M ASKEY
DRIMPTON (St Mary)   *see* Beaminster Area *Sarum*
DRINGHOUSES (St Edward the Confessor) *York 7*   **P** *Abp* **V** C W M BALLOCK,   **NSM** S M COLLIER
DRINKSTONE (All Saints)   *see* Woolpit w Drinkstone *St E*
DROITWICH SPA (St Andrew w St Mary de Witton) (St Nicholas) (St Peter) (St Richard) *Worc 8*   **P** *Bp* **TR** S K BANYARD,   **TV** A P WHITE,   D A CHAPLIN, **C** K CLARINGBULL,   **NSM** R HOLDEN
DRONFIELD (St John the Baptist) w Holmesfield *Derby 5*   **P** *Ld Chan*   **TR** B GREEN,   **TV** W R EARDLEY, **NSM** R DOVE
DROPMORE (St Anne)   *see* Burnham w Dropmore, Hitcham and Taplow *Ox*
DROXFORD (St Mary and All Saints) *Portsm 1*   **P** *Bp* **P-in-c** J F FOLEY
DROYLSDEN (St Andrew) *Man 17*   **P** *Bp*   **R** I BLAY, **OLM** J A HEMSWORTH
DROYLSDEN (St Martin) *Man 17*   **P** *Bp*   **V** *vacant* 0161-370 9833
DROYLSDEN (St Mary) (St John) *Man 17*   **P** *Bp* **R** M J WILLIAMSON

DRY DODDINGTON (St James) *see* Claypole *Linc*
DRY DRAYTON (St Peter and St Paul) *Ely 5* **P** *MMCET*
  P-in-c C A COLLINS
DRY SANDFORD (St Helen) *see* Besselsleigh *Ox*
DRYBROOK (Holy Trinity) *see* Dean Forest H Trin *Glouc*
DRYPOOL (St Columba) (St John) *York 14* **P** *Patr Bd*
  TR S P WALKER, **TV** P A BICKNELL, M I BENNETT,
  C D J MCCLINTOCK
DUCKLINGTON (St Bartholomew) *Ox 8* **P** *DBP*
  P-in-c R J EDY
DUCKMANTON (St Peter and St Paul) *see* Calow and Sutton
  cum Duckmanton *Derby*
DUDDENHOE END (The Hamlet Church) *see* Heydon, Gt
  and Lt Chishill, Chrishall etc *Chelmsf*
DUDDESTON (St Matthew) *see* Nechells *Birm*
DUDDINGTON (St Mary) *see* Barrowden and Wakerley w S
  Luffenham etc *Pet*
DUDDO (All Saints) *see* Norham and Duddo *Newc*
DUDDON (St Peter) *see* Tarvin *Ches*
DUDLESTON (St Mary) *see* Criftins w Dudleston and Welsh
  Frankton *Lich*
DUDLEY (St Andrew) *see* Netherton St Andr *Worc*
DUDLEY (St Augustine) Holly Hall *Worc 9* **P** *V Dudley*
  P-in-c A M YATES
DUDLEY (St Barnabas) *Worc 9* **P** *Bp* **V** *vacant* (01384)
  256680
DUDLEY (St Edmund King and Martyr) *Worc 9* **P** *V Dudley*
  V M C BRAIN
DUDLEY (St Francis) *Worc 9* **P** *Bp* **P-in-c** G S JOHNSTON
DUDLEY (St James the Great) Eve Hill *Worc 9* **P** *V Dudley*
  P-in-c S YATES
DUDLEY (St John) Kate's Hill *Worc 9* **P** *V Dudley*
  P-in-c J K D FULLJAMES
DUDLEY (St Paul) *see* Weetslade *Newc*
DUDLEY (St Thomas and St Luke) *Worc 9* **P** *Bp*
  P-in-c J K D FULLJAMES
DUDLEY WOOD (St John) *Worc 9* **P** *V Netherton*
  P-in-c J A OLIVER
DUFFIELD (St Alkmund) *Derby 11* **P** *Ch Soc Trust*
  P-in-c M A PICKLES, **C** R C J HOPKINS
DUFTON (St Cuthbert) *see* Long Marton w Dufton and w
  Milburn *Carl*
DUKINFIELD (St John) (St Alban Mission Church) *Ches 14*
  P *R Stockport St Mary* **V** T J HAYES
DUKINFIELD (St Mark) (St Luke) *Ches 14* **P** *Bp*
  V E W D THOMAS
DULAS (St Michael) *see* Ewyas Harold w Dulas, Kenderchurch
  etc *Heref*
DULCOTE (All Saints) *see* Wells St Cuth w Wookey Hole
  B & W
DULLINGHAM (St Mary) *see* Raddesley Gp *Ely*
DULOE (St Cuby), Herodsfoot, Morval and St Pinnock *Truro 12*
  P *Ld Chan, Ch Soc Trust, and Ball Coll Ox (by turn)*
  P-in-c C D NEWELL, **NSM** G LONSDALE
DULVERTON (All Saints) and Brushford *B & W 16* **P** *D&C*
  and Bp (jt) **R** J M THOROGOOD
DULWICH (St Barnabas) *S'wark 9* **P** *Bp* **V** D L GWILLIAMS,
  Hon C J H JONES, J G WINTER, **NSM** J BROTHWOOD
DULWICH (St Clement) St Peter *S'wark 9* **P** *Bp*
  V M E A COULTER
DULWICH, EAST (St John the Evangelist) *S'wark 9* **P** *Ripon*
  Coll Cuddesdon **V** C L J RICHARDSON, **Hon C** R A SHAW,
  J M W SEDGWICK, **NSM** R C ANDREWS
DULWICH, NORTH (St Faith) *S'wark 9* **P** *Bp*
  V H W DAWES
DULWICH, SOUTH (St Stephen) *S'wark 9* **P** *Dulwich Coll*
  V P VANNOZZI, **C** E J OGLESBY, **NSM** A D W DUPUY
DULWICH, WEST (All Saints) *S'wark 15* **P** *Bp*
  V R J TITLEY, **OLM** R J SHAFTO
DULWICH, WEST (Emmanuel) *S'wark 15* **P** *Bp*
  V K G A ANSAH, **OLM** H O KIMBER
DUMBLETON (St Peter) *see* Alderton, Gt Washbourne,
  Dumbleton etc *Glouc*
DUMMER (All Saints) *see* Cliddesden and Ellisfield w Farleigh
  Wallop etc *Win*
**DUNCHIDEOCK (St Michael and All Angels) and Shillingford
  St George w Ide** *Ex 6* **P** *D&C and Mrs J M Michelmore (alt)*
  P-in-c G K MAYER
DUNCHURCH (St Peter) *Cov 6* **P** *Bp* **V** E M DYKE
DUNCTON (Holy Trinity) *Chich 11* **P** *Lord Egremont*
  P-in-c R A STAVELEY-WADHAM
DUNDRY (St Michael) *see* Chew Magna w Dundry and
  Norton Malreward *B & W*
DUNGEON HILL *Sarum 3* **P** *DBP and N G Halsey Esq (jt)*
  P-in-c J H P HAMILTON

**DUNHAM, GREAT (St Andrew) and LITTLE (St Margaret), w
  Great and Little Fransham and Sporle** *Nor 14* **P** *Hertf Coll
  Ox, Ch Soc Trust, Magd Coll Cam, and DBP (by turn)*
  P-in-c B R A COLE, **C** S J SMITH
DUNHAM MASSEY (St Margaret) (St Mark) (All Saints)
  Ches 10 **P** *J G Turnbull Esq* **V** J J E SUTTON
DUNHAM-ON-THE-HILL (St Luke) *see* Helsby and
  Dunham-on-the-Hill *Ches*
**DUNHAM-ON-TRENT (St Oswald) w Darlton, Ragnall,
  Fledborough and East Drayton** *S'well 5* **P** *Bp (2 turns),
  D&C York (1 turn)* **P-in-c** J CALVERT
DUNHOLME (St Chad) *see* Welton and Dunholme w Scothern
  Linc
DUNKERTON (All Saints) *see* Camerton w Dunkerton,
  Foxcote and Shoscombe *B & W*
**DUNKESWELL (Holy Trinity) (St Nicholas), Luppitt, Sheldon
  and Upottery** *Ex 5* **P** *MMCET, Bp, and D&C (jt)*
  V N J WALL
DUNMOW, GREAT (St Mary the Virgin) and Barnston
  Chelmsf 18 **P** *Ld Chan (2 turns), CPAS (1 turn)*
  R D S AINGE, **NSM** R DREW
DUNMOW, LITTLE (St Mary the Virgin) *see* Felsted and Lt
  Dunmow *Chelmsf*
DUNNINGTON (not known) *see* Salford Priors *Cov*
DUNNINGTON (St Nicholas) *see* Beeford w Frodingham and
  Foston *York*
DUNNINGTON (St Nicholas) *York 2* **P** *Abp* **R** M W SEARLE
DUNS TEW (St Mary Magdalene) *see* Westcote Barton w
  Steeple Barton, Duns Tew etc *Ox*
DUNSBY (All Saints) *see* Ringstone in Aveland Gp *Linc*
DUNSCROFT (St Edwin) *Sheff 10* **P** *Bp* **V** A WATSON
DUNSDEN (All Saints) *see* Shiplake w Dunsden and Harpsden
  Ox
DUNSFOLD (St Mary and All Saints) and Hascombe *Guildf 2*
  P *Bp and SMF (jt)* **R** G S M WILLIS
DUNSFORD (St Mary) *see* Tedburn St Mary, Whitestone,
  Oldridge etc *Ex*
DUNSFORTH (St Mary) *see* Aldborough w Boroughbridge
  and Roecliffe *Ripon*
DUNSLAND (Mission Church) *see* Ashwater, Halwill,
  Beaworthy, Clawton etc *Ex*
DUNSLEY (Mission Room) *see* Whitby w Aislaby and
  Ruswarp *York*
DUNSMORE (Chapel of the Ressurection) *see* Ellesborough,
  The Kimbles and Stoke Mandeville *Ox*
DUNSOP BRIDGE (St George) *see* Slaidburn *Bradf*
**DUNSTABLE (St Augustine of Canterbury) (St Fremund the
  Martyr) (St Peter)** *St Alb 12* **P** *Bp* **TR** G H NEWTON,
  TV E M CONSTANTINE, N D JONES, **C** K J SAYERS
DUNSTALL (St Mary) *see* Barton under Needwood w Dunstall
  Lich
DUNSTAN (St Leonard) *see* Penkridge Team *Lich*
DUNSTAN (St Peter) *see* Metheringham w Blankney and
  Dunston *Linc*
**DUNSTER (St George), Carhampton and Withycombe w
  Rodhuish** *B & W 16* **P** *Bp* **R** M P GRANTHAM
DUNSTON (Church House) *see* Newbold w Dunston *Derby*
DUNSTON (St Nicholas) w (Christ Church) *Dur 13* **P** *Bp*
  V K TEASDALE
DUNSTON (St Remigius) *see* Stoke H Cross w Dunston,
  Arminghall etc *Nor*
DUNSWELL (St Faith's Mission Church) *see* Hull Newland
  St Jo *York*
DUNTERTON (All Saints) *see* Milton Abbot, Dunterton,
  Lamerton etc *Ex*
DUNTISBOURNE ABBOTS (St Peter) *see* Brimpsfield w
  Birdlip, Syde, Daglingworth etc *Glouc*
DUNTISBOURNE ROUS (St Michael and All Angels)
  as above Glouc
DUNTON (St Martin) *see* Schorne *Ox*
DUNTON (St Mary Magdalene) w Wrestlingworth and Eyeworth
  St Alb 11 **P** *Ld Chan and DBP (alt)* **P-in-c** A MANNING
DUNTON BASSETT (All Saints) *see* Leire w Ashby Parva and
  Dunton Bassett *Leic*
DUNWICH (St James) *see* Westleton w Dunwich *St E*
DURHAM (St Giles) *Dur 1* **P** *D&C* **V** R I DAVISON,
  NSM D J WILSON
DURHAM (St Margaret of Antioch) and Neville's Cross St John
  Dur 1 **P** *D&C* **R** D C GLOVER, **NSM** S C BARTON
DURHAM (St Nicholas) *Dur 1* **P** *CPAS* **V** D R HANSON,
  C A R BALDOCK, **NSM** D V DAY, P S JOHNSON
DURHAM (St Oswald King and Martyr) *Dur 1* **P** *D&C*
  vacant
DURHAM NORTH (St Cuthbert) *Dur 1* **P** *Patr Bd*
  TR D J BELL, **TV** J D PICKERING, S J BAMBER, **C** R KALUS
DURLEIGH (not known) *see* Bridgwater St Mary, Chilton
  Trinity and Durleigh *B & W*

DURLEY (Holy Cross) *Portsm 1*   **P** *Ld Chan*   **R** I G COOMBER, **C** G M W KEITH,   **NSM** E A GROVES

DURNFORD (St Andrew)   *see* Woodford Valley *Sarum*

DURRINGTON (All Saints) *Sarum 13*   **P** *D&C Win*   **R** P H TAMPLIN,   **NSM** R A BUSSEY

DURRINGTON (St Symphorian) *Chich 5*   **P** *Bp*   **V** N A TAYLOR,   **C** S J DAVIES

DURSLEY (St James the Great) *Glouc 2*   **P** *Bp*   **R** J C G BROMLEY

DURSTON (St John the Baptist)   *see* N Newton w St Michaelchurch, Thurloxton etc *B & W*

DURWESTON (St Nicholas)   *see* Pimperne, Stourpaine, Durweston and Bryanston *Sarum*

DUSTON Team, The (St Francis) (St Luke) *Pet 7*   **P** *Bp*   **TR** N PURVEY-TYRER,   **TV** S J M READING, A Q MICKLETHWAITE,   **NSM** H C WILSON

DUSTON, NEW (Mission Church)   *see* Duston Team *Pet*

DUTTON (Licensed Room)   *see* Antrobus, Aston by Sutton, Lt Leigh etc *Ches*

DUXFORD (St Peter) w St John *Ely 6*   **P** *Bp*   **R** J E E CHARMAN

DYMCHURCH (St Peter and St Paul) w Burmarsh and Newchurch *Cant 13*   **P** *Abp*   **P-in-c** R H ELLIS, **NSM** P B SNARE

DYMOCK (St Mary the Virgin)   *see* Redmarley D'Abitot, Bromesberrow, Pauntley etc *Glouc*

DYRHAM (St Peter)   *see* Wick w Doynton and Dyrham *Bris*

EAGLE (All Saints)   *see* Swinderby *Linc*

EAKRING (St Andrew) *S'well 14*   **P** *DBP*   **P-in-c** E F CULLY

EALING (All Saints) *Lon 22*   **P** *Bp*   **V** N P HENDERSON, **C** D J BRAMMER,   **Hon C** A GRIFFITHS

EALING (Ascension)   *see* Hanger Hill Ascension and W Twyford St Mary *Lon*

EALING (Christ the Saviour) *Lon 22*   **P** *Bp*   **V** A F DAVIS

EALING (St Barnabas) *Lon 22*   **P** *Bp*   **V** N D R NICHOLLS

EALING (St Mary) *Lon 22*   **P** *Bp*   **V** S D PAYNTER, **C** P J NOTT,   **NSM** A L POULSON

EALING (St Paul) *Lon 22*   **P** *Bp*   **V** M P MELLUISH, **C** C J COLLINGTON

EALING (St Peter) Mount Park *Lon 22*   **P** *Bp*   **V** M POWELL, **NSM** M J JOACHIM, J O A CHOUFAR

EALING (St Stephen) Castle Hill *Lon 22*   **P** *D&C St Paul's*   **V** J E CLARK,   **C** J T HODGES

EALING, WEST (St John) w St James *Lon 22*   **P** *Bp*   **V** W R DONALDSON,   **TV** D E SMITH,   **C** J B CHAPMAN, **NSM** R YATES

EALING COMMON (St Matthew) *Lon 22*   **P** *Bp*   **V** P G WATKINS

EARBY (All Saints) *Bradf 7*   **P** *Bp*   **V** R C WALLACE

EARDISLAND (St Mary the Virgin)   *see* Kingsland w Eardisland, Aymestrey etc *Heref*

EARDISLEY (St Mary Magdalene) w Bollingham, Willersley, Brilley, Michaelchurch, Whitney, Winforton, Almeley and Kinnersley *Heref 5*   **P** *Patr Bd*   **R** J S POLLOCK

EARL SHILTON (St Simon and St Jude) w Elmesthorpe *Leic 13*   **P** *Bp*   **V** G GITTINGS

EARL SOHAM (St Mary) w Cretingham and Ashfield cum Thorpe *St E 18*   **P** *Lord Henniker, Ld Chan, and Wadh Coll Ox (by turn)*   **P-in-c** H C SANDERS

EARL STERNDALE (St Michael and All Angels)   *see* Hartington, Biggin and Earl Sterndale *Derby*

EARL STONHAM (St Mary)   *see* Creeting St Mary, Creeting St Peter etc *St E*

EARLESFIELD (The Epiphany)   *see* Grantham, Earlesfield *Linc*

EARLEY (St Nicolas) *Ox 15*   **P** *DBP*   **V** D F TYNDALL

EARLEY (St Peter) *Ox 15*   **P** *DBP*   **V** R R D SPEARS, **C** R E RUTHERFORD

EARLEY Trinity *Ox 15*   **P** *DBP*   **P-in-c** S C HOWARD

EARLEY, LOWER Trinity Church Local Ecumenical Project *Ox 15 vacant*

EARLHAM (St Anne) *Nor 3*   **P** *Bp*   **P-in-c** P C BAKER

EARLHAM (St Elizabeth) *Nor 3*   **P** *Bp*   **OLM** R M A HOUGHTON

EARLHAM (St Mary) *Nor 3*   **P** *Trustees*   **P-in-c** P C BAKER

EARLS BARTON (All Saints) *Pet 6*   **P** *DBP*   **V** M C W WEBBER,   **C** S M BELL

EARLS COLNE (St Andrew) w White Colne and Colne Engaine *Chelmsf 19*   **P** *DBP, Ch Hosp, and Keble Coll Ox (by turn)*   **P-in-c** J R BROOKS

EARL'S COURT (St Cuthbert) (St Matthias) *Lon 12*   **P** *Trustees*   **V** J VINE

EARL'S COURT (St Philip)   *see* Kensington St Phil Earl's Court *Lon*

EARLS CROOME (St Nicholas)   *see* Upton-on-Severn, Ripple, Earls Croome etc *Worc*

EARL'S HEATON   *see* Dewsbury *Wakef*

EARL'S HEATON (St Peter)   *as above Wakef*

EARLSDON (St Barbara) *Cov 3*   **P** *Bp*   **V** H J WILD

EARLSFIELD (St Andrew) *S'wark 20*   **P** *Bp*   **V** C W PRITCHARD,   **NSM** V A HACKETT

EARLSFIELD (St John the Divine) *S'wark 20*   **P** *Bp*   **V** C E ROBERTS

EARLY (St Bartholomew)   *see* Reading St Luke w St Bart *Ox*

EARNLEY (not known) and East Wittering *Chich 3*   **P** *Bp (2 turns), Bp Lon (1 turn)*   **R** J H LYON

EARNSHAW BRIDGE (St John)   *see* Leyland St Jo *Blackb*

EARSDON (St Alban) and Backworth *Newc 8*   **P** *Bp*   **V** N WILSON

EARSHAM (All Saints) w Alburgh and Denton *Nor 10*   **P** *Abp, J M Meade Esq, and St Jo Coll Cam (by turn)*   **R** I R BENTLEY

EARSWICK, NEW (St Andrew)   *see* Huntington *York*

EARTHAM (St Margaret)   *see* Slindon, Eartham and Madehurst *Chich*

EASBY (Chapel)   *see* Gt Ayton w Easby and Newton in Cleveland *York*

EASBY (St Agatha) w Brompton on Swale and Bolton on Swale *Ripon 2*   **P** *Bp*   **V** R M WIGRAM

EASEBOURNE (St Mary) *Chich 10*   **P** *Rathbone Trust Co and Cowdray Trust (jt)*   **V** D B WELSMAN

EASINGTON (All Saints) w Liverton *York 16*   **P** *Ld Chan*   **R** P F LANGFORD

EASINGTON (All Saints) w Skeffling, Kilnsea and Holmpton *York 12*   **P** *Ld Chan*   **R** W J G HEALE

EASINGTON (St Hugh)   *see* Banbury St Hugh *Ox*

EASINGTON (St Mary), Easington Colliery and South Hetton *Dur 2*   **P** *Bp*   **C** P T LUCAS

EASINGTON (St Peter)   *see* Ewelme, Brightwell Baldwin, Cuxham w Easington *Ox*

EASINGTON COLLIERY (The Ascension)   *see* Easington, Easington Colliery and S Hetton *Dur*

EASINGWOLD (St John the Baptist and All Saints) w Raskelfe *York 3*   **P** *Abp*   **V** J HARRISON

EAST   *see also under substantive place name*

EAST DEAN (All Saints) *Chich 13*   **P** *Bp*   **V** R T E B WOODS

EAST FERRY (St Mary the Virgin)   *see* Scotter w E Ferry *Linc*

EAST HAM (St Bartholomew) (St Mary Magdalene) w Upton Park *Chelmsf 3*   **P** *Patr Bd*   **TV** Q B D PEPPIATT, **NSM** J D HALLIDAY

EAST HAM (St George and St Ethelbert) *Chelmsf 3*   **P** *Bp*   **V** P C TURNER

EAST HAM (St Paul) *Chelmsf 3*   **P** *Ch Patr Trust*   **V** J R ALLCOCK,   **C** A M BAKER

EAST LANE (St Mary)   *see* W Horsley *Guildf*

EAST MARSHLAND *Ely 17*   **P** *Bp and MMCET (1 turn), Pemb Coll Cam (2 turns), Prime Min (1 turn), and Ld Chan (1 turn)*   **V** R C BENDING

EAST ORCHARD (St Thomas)   *see* Shaston *Sarum*

EAST WINCH (All Saints)   *see* Gayton, Gayton Thorpe, E Walton, E Winch etc *Nor*

EASTBOURNE (All Saints) *Chich 16*   **P** *Trustees*   **V** G T RIDEOUT,   **C** T J VOLTZENLOGEL

EASTBOURNE (All Souls) *Chich 16*   **P** *Ch Soc Trust and J H Cordle Esq (jt)*   **V** N H GREEN,   **C** R J R PAICE, P-J GUY

EASTBOURNE (Christ Church) *Chich 16*   **P** *V Eastbourne*   **V** N P CHATFIELD

EASTBOURNE Haven   *see* Haven CD *Chich*

EASTBOURNE (Holy Trinity) *Chich 16*   **P** *V Eastbourne*   **V** J A CHEESEMAN,   **C** W A STILLWELL, J G HOBSON

EASTBOURNE (St Andrew) *Chich 16*   **P** *Bp*   **V** A F STONE, **C** A J LANE

EASTBOURNE St Elizabeth (Church Hall) *Chich 16*   **P** *Bp*   **P-in-c** D J GILLARD

EASTBOURNE (St John) Meads *Chich 16*   **P** *Trustees*   **V** G T DAINTREE,   **NSM** K C LEFROY

EASTBOURNE (St Mary) *Chich 16*   **P** *Bp*   **V** C R LANSDALE, **C** B J KING, D P WALLIS

EASTBOURNE (St Michael and All Angels) Ocklynge *Chich 16*   **P** *V Eastbourne*   **V** J R HOUGHTON,   **Dss** W K HAMBLY

EASTBOURNE (St Philip) *Chich 16*   **P** *Bp*   **V** M A CUMING

EASTBOURNE (St Richard of Chichester)   *see* Langney *Chich*

EASTBOURNE (St Saviour and St Peter) *Chich 16*   **P** *Keble Coll Ox*   **V** D MOTTERSHEAD

EASTBURY (St James the Great) and East Garston *Ox 14*   **P** *Bp and Ch Ch Ox (alt)*   **P-in-c** W J STEWART

EASTCHURCH (All Saints) w Leysdown and Harty *Cant 16*   **P** *Abp and Keble Coll Ox (jt)*   **P-in-c** F R SEARLE

EASTCOMBE (St Augustine)   *see* Bussage *Glouc*

EASTCOTE (St Lawrence) *Lon 24*   **P** *Bp*   **V** D COLEMAN, **C** R M LAMPARD,   **Hon C** A V COLEMAN,   **NSM** L C F HILLEL

EASTER, HIGH (St Mary the Virgin) and Good Easter w Margaret Roding *Chelmsf 18* **P** *Bp Lon, Trustees R K Shepherd Esq, and D&C St Paul's (by turn)* **P-in-c** E J SIBSON

EASTERGATE (St George) *see* Aldingbourne, Barnham and Eastergate *Chich*

EASTERN GREEN (St Andrew) *Cov 3* **P** *R Allesley* **V** J A DAVIES

EASTERTON (St Barnabas) *see* The Lavingtons, Cheverells, and Easterton *Sarum*

EASTFIELD (Holy Nativity) *see* Cayton w Eastfield *York*

EASTGATE (All Saints) w Rookhope *Dur 9* **P** *Bp and Ld Chan (alt)* **P-in-c** P A GREENHALGH

EASTHAM (St Mary the Blessed Virgin) (St Peter's Chapel) (Chapel of the Holy Spirit) *Ches 9* **P** *D&C*

EASTHAM (St Peter and St Paul) *see* Teme Valley S *Worc*

EASTHAMPSTEAD (St Michael and St Mary Magdalene) *Ox 11* **P** *Ch Ch Ox* **R** G S COLE, **C** B L PEARSON

EASTHOPE (St Peter) *see* Wenlock *Heref*

EASTHORPE (St Mary the Virgin) *see* Copford w Easthorpe and Messing w Inworth *Chelmsf*

EASTINGTON (St Michael and All Angels), Frocester, Haresfield, Moreton Valence, Standish and Whitminster *Glouc 8* **P** *Bp and Col Sir Piers Bengough (1 turn), DBP and Exors Lady Mary Cooper (1 turn)* **R** R J R AMYS, **OLM** A L REEDER

EASTLEACH (St Andrew) *see* Coln St Aldwyns, Hatherop, Quenington etc *Glouc*

EASTLEIGH (All Saints) *Win 10* **P** *Bp* **V** R P DAVIES, **C** G WORT

EASTLEIGH Nightingale Avenue (St Francis) *see* Eastleigh *Win*

EASTLING (St Mary) w Ospringe and Stalisfield w Otterden *Cant 6* **P** *The Crown* **P-in-c** P A FENTON, **NSM** P J POLLARD

EASTMOORS (St Mary Magdalene) *see* Helmsley *York*

EASTNEY (St Margaret) *Portsm 6* **P** *Bp* **P-in-c** J J GILL

EASTNOR (St John the Baptist) *see* Ledbury *Heref*

EASTOFT (St Bartholomew) *see* The Marshland *Sheff*

EASTOKE (St Andrew) *see* Hayling Is St Andr *Portsm*

EASTON (All Hallows) *Bris 3* **P** *R Bris St Steph* **P-in-c** J M BROWN, **C** W P G HAZLEWOOD, **NSM** J F HOUSE

EASTON (All Saints) *see* Brandeston w Kettleburgh and Easton *St E*

EASTON (Holy Trinity w St Gabriel and St Lawrence and St Jude) *Bris 3* **P** *Trustees* **V** C G ROBINSON

EASTON (St Mary) *see* Itchen Valley *Win*

EASTON (St Paul) *see* Westbury sub Mendip w Easton *B & W*

EASTON (St Peter) *see* E Leightonstone *Ely*

EASTON (St Peter), Colton, Marlingford and Bawburgh *Nor 17* **P** *Bp, D&C, Adn, and Sir Edward Evans-Lombe (jt)* **P-in-c** A H REYNOLDS

EASTON, GREAT (St Andrew) *see* Six Saints circa Holt *Leic*

EASTON, GREAT (St John and St Giles) *see* Broxted w Chickney and Tilty etc *Chelmsf*

EASTON, LITTLE (not known) *as above Chelmsf*

EASTON GREY (not known) *see* Sherston Magna, Easton Grey, Luckington etc *Bris*

EASTON IN GORDANO (St George) *see* Pill w Easton in Gordano and Portbury *B & W*

EASTON MAUDIT (St Peter and St Paul) *see* Bozeat w Easton Maudit *Pet*

EASTON NESTON (St Mary) *see* Towcester w Easton Neston *Pet*

EASTON ON THE HILL (All Saints) *see* Ketton, Collyweston, Easton-on-the-Hill etc *Pet*

EASTON ROYAL (Holy Trinity) *see* Pewsey and Swanborough *Sarum*

EASTOVER (St John the Baptist) *see* Bridgwater St Jo *B & W*

EASTRINGTON (St Michael) *see* Howden *York*

EASTROP (St Mary) *Win 4* **P** *CPAS* **R** C L HAWKINS, **C** C D E MOLL, **NSM** C E WEST

EASTRY (St Mary Blessed Virgin) and Northbourne w Tilmanstone and Betteshanger w Ham *Cant 8* **P** *Abp and Lord Northbourne (jt)* **P-in-c** N M GENDERS, **Hon C** D G WILLIS

EASTTHORPE (St Paul) and Upper Hopton *Wakef 10* **P** *V Mirfield* **P-in-c** P J CRAIG-WILD

EASTVILLE (St Anne w St Mark and St Thomas) *Bris 3* **P** *Bp* **V** P J HAYWARD

EASTVILLE (St Paul) *see* Stickney Gp *Linc*

EASTWELL (St Michael) *see* Scalford w Goadby Marwood and Wycombe etc *Leic*

EASTWICK (St Botolph) *see* High Wych and Gilston w Eastwick *St Alb*

EASTWOOD (St David) *Chelmsf 10* **P** *Bp* **V** D F THOMPSON

EASTWOOD (St Laurence and All Saints) *Chelmsf 10* **P** *Ld Chan* **V** N L RANSOM

EASTWOOD (St Mary) *S'well 4* **P** *J N Plumptre Esq* **R** E A C CARDWELL, **C** E A TURNER-LOISEL

EATON (All Saints) *see* Gamston w Eaton and W Drayton *S'well*

EATON (Christ Church) and Hulme Walfield *Ches 11* **P** *Bp and R Astbury (alt)* **V** R B ROBERTS

EATON (Christ Church) (St Andrew) *Nor 3* **P** *D&C* **V** A BEARDSMORE, **C** P D BURR

EATON (St Denys) *see* Scalford w Goadby Marwood and Wycombe etc *Leic*

EATON (St Thomas) *see* Tarporley *Ches*

EATON, LITTLE (St Paul) *see* Holbrook and Lt Eaton *Derby*

EATON BISHOP (St Michael and All Angels) *see* Kingstone w Clehonger, Eaton Bishop etc *Heref*

EATON BRAY (St Mary the Virgin) w Edlesborough *St Alb 12* **P** *DBP* **V** M E GRANT

EATON HASTINGS (St Michael and All Angels) *see* Gt Coxwell w Buscot, Coleshill etc *Ox*

EATON SOCON (St Mary) *St Alb 11* **P** *E W Harper Esq* **V** K P FITZGIBBON

EATON SQUARE (St Peter) *see* Pimlico St Pet w Westmr Ch Ch *Lon*

EATON-UNDER-HEYWOOD (St Edith) *see* Hope Bowdler w Eaton-under-Heywood *Heref*

EBBERSTON (St Mary) *see* Thornton Dale w Allerston, Ebberston etc *York*

EBBESBOURNE WAKE (St John the Baptist) *see* Chalke Valley *Sarum*

EBCHESTER (St Ebba) *Dur 4* **P** *Bp* **R** C TODD

EBERNOE (Holy Trinity) *see* N Chapel w Ebernoe *Chich*

EBONY (St Mary the Virgin) *see* Wittersham w Stone-in-Oxney and Ebony *Cant*

EBREY WOOD (Mission Chapel) *see* Wrockwardine Deanery *Lich*

EBRINGTON (St Eadburgha) *see* Chipping Campden w Ebrington *Glouc*

ECCHINSWELL (St Lawrence) *see* Burghclere w Newtown and Ecchinswell w Sydmonton *Win*

ECCLES (St Mary the Virgin) *see* Quidenham Gp *Nor*

ECCLES (St Mary the Virgin) (St Andrew) *Man 2* **P** *Patr Bd* **TR** E A CROFTON, **TV** J R BAXENDALE, **NSM** L J READING

ECCLESALL (St Gabriel) *see* Greystones *Sheff*

ECCLESALL BIERLOW (All Saints) *Sheff 2* **P** *Dean* **V** C P WILLIAMS, **C** R J FILLINGHAM

ECCLESFIELD (St Mary the Virgin) *Sheff 3* **P** *DBF* **V** P I IMPEY, **C** A B WALTON

ECCLESFIELD (St Paul) *see* Sheff St Paul *Sheff*

ECCLESHALL (Holy Trinity) *Lich 7* **P** *Bp* **V** J H GRAHAM

ECCLESHILL (St Luke) *Bradf 3* **P** *V Bradf* **V** J P HARTLEY, **C** M HARGREAVES

ECCLESTON (Christ Church) *Liv 10* **P** *F Webster Esq, Lord Blanch, Canon J A Lawton, Revd D G Mellors, and Bp (jt)* **V** C D HENDRICKSE, **OLM** B PARKER, D E ANDERTON

ECCLESTON (St Luke) *Liv 10* **P** *Trustees* **V** P G DAY

ECCLESTON (St Mary the Virgin) *Blackb 4* **P** *DBP* **R** I M TEMPLETON

ECCLESTON (St Mary the Virgin) and Pulford *Ches 2* **P** *Duke of Westmr* **R** J B LUMBY

ECCLESTON (St Thomas) *Liv 10* **P** *Bp* **P-in-c** P H BURMAN

ECCLESTON, GREAT *see* Copp w Inskip *Blackb*

ECCLESTON PARK (St James) *Liv 10* **P** *Bp* **V** J H WELCH

ECKINGTON (Holy Trinity) *Worc 4* **P** *D&C Westmr* **V** P J THOMAS, **NSM** F B KINGS

ECKINGTON (St Peter and St Paul) and Ridgeway *Derby 3* **P** *The Crown and Patr Bd (alt)* **R** N R HARVEY, **C** B DALE, **G** MANLEY

ECKINGTON, UPPER (St Luke) *see* Eckington and Ridgeway *Derby*

ECTON (St Mary Magdalene) *Pet 6* **P** *The Crown* **P-in-c** J A PARKIN

EDALE (Holy and Undivided Trinity) *Derby 2* **P** *Rep Landowners* **P-in-c** A J G MURRAY-LESLIE

EDBURTON (St Andrew) *see* Poynings w Edburton, Newtimber and Pyecombe *Chich*

EDEN, Gelt and Irthing Team Ministry, The *Carl 2* **P** *Patr Bd* **TR** P K BARBER, **TV** J J VAN DEN BERG, C J LAXON, **NSM** D B MILLS, **OLM** E GOUGH

EDEN PARK (St John the Baptist) *see* Beckenham St Jo *Roch*

EDENBRIDGE (St Peter and St Paul) *Roch 11* **P** *Bp* **V** S A J MITCHELL, **C** R JONES

EDENFIELD (not known) and Stubbins *Man 10* **P** *Bp* **V** G N HIGHAM

EDENHALL (St Cuthbert) *see* Addingham, Edenhall, Langwathby and Culgaith *Carl*

EDENHAM (St Michael) w Witham on the Hill and Swinstead *Linc 14* **P** *Baroness Willoughby de Eresby, Ld Chan, and Bp (by turn)* **V** A T HAWES, **NSM** I K WILLIAMS

EDENSOR (St Paul) *Lich 12* **P** *Prime Min* **V** D S HEYWOOD, **OLM** P J BARBER
EDENSOR (St Peter) *see* Beeley and Edensor *Derby*
EDGBASTON (St Augustine) *Birm 2* **P** *Bp*
V M R E TOMLINSON
EDGBASTON (St Bartholomew) *Birm 2* **P** *Sir Euan Anstruther-Gough-Calthorpe Bt* **V** E D COOMBES
EDGBASTON (St George w St Michael) (St Michael's Hall) *Birm 2* **P** *Sir Euan Anstruther-Gough-Calthorpe Bt*
V S G THORBURN, **NSM** D D HANNAH
EDGBASTON (St Germain) *Birm 2* **P** *Trustees*
V H A SCRIVEN, **C** S J WATKINS
EDGBASTON (St Mary and St Ambrose) *Birm 5* **P** *Bp and Sir Euan Anstruther-Gough-Calthorpe Bt (jt)* **V** *vacant*
0121-440 2196
EDGCOTE (St James) *see* Culworth w Sulgrave and Thorpe Mandeville etc *Pet*
EDGCOTT (St Michael) *see* Swan *Ox*
EDGE, THE (St John the Baptist) *see* Painswick, Sheepscombe, Cranham, The Edge etc *Glouc*
EDGE HILL (St Cyprian) (St Mary) *Liv 3* **P** *Simeon's Trustees and Bp (jt)* **V** D A LEWIS, **C** J E WARHURST, **OLM** D F LARKEY
EDGE HILL (St Dunstan) *see* St Luke in the City *Liv*
EDGE HILL (St Mary) *see* Edge Hill St Cypr w St Mary *Liv*
EDGEFIELD (St Peter and St Paul) *see* Lt Barningham, Blickling, Edgefield etc *Nor*
EDGEFIELD (School Room) *see* Worsley *Man*
EDGELEY (St Mark) *see* Stockport SW *Ches*
EDGELEY (St Matthew) *see* Stockport St Matt *Ches*
EDGESIDE (St Anne) *see* Rossendale Middle Valley *Man*
EDGEWORTH (St Mary) *see* Bisley, Oakridge, Miserden and Edgeworth *Glouc*
EDGMOND (St Peter) w Kynnersley and Preston Wealdmoors *Lich 16* **P** *Bp, Adn Salop, Chan Lich, MMCET, and Preston Trust Homes Trustees (jt)* **R** W E WARD, **C** M C V NASH-WILLIAMS
EDGTON (St Michael the Archangel) *see* Bishop's Castle w Mainstone, Lydbury N etc *Heref*
EDGWARE (St Alphage) *see* Hendon St Alphage *Lon*
EDGWARE (St Andrew) (St Margaret) *Lon 15* **P** *MMCET* **TR** M D CLARK, **TV** R T BODLE, **C** P T COOPER
EDINGALE (Holy Trinity) *see* Clifton Campville w Edingale and Harlaston *Lich*
EDINGLEY (St Giles) w Halam *S'well 14* **P** *Bp* **P-in-c** D LEANING
EDINGTHORPE (All Saints) *see* Bacton w Edingthorpe w Witton and Ridlington *Nor*
EDINGTON (St George) *see* W Poldens *B & W*
EDINGTON (St Mary, St Katharine and All Saints) *see* Bratton, Edington and Imber, Erlestoke etc *Sarum*
EDITH WESTON (St Mary) w North Luffenham and Lyndon w Manton *Pet 14* **P** *Baroness Willoughby de Eresby, Sir John Conant Bt, and Em Coll Cam (by turn)* **R** B A NICHOLLS
EDITHMEAD (Mission) *see* Burnham *B & W*
EDLASTON (St James) *see* Brailsford w Shirley and Osmaston w Edlaston *Derby*
EDLINGHAM (St John the Baptist w Bolton Chapel) *see* Whittingham and Edlingham w Bolton Chapel *Newc*
EDLINGTON (St Helen) *see* Hemingby *Linc*
EDLINGTON (St John the Baptist) *Sheff 9* **P** *Bp*
V W J STOKOE
EDMONDSHAM (St Nicholas) *see* Cranborne w Boveridge, Edmondsham etc *Sarum*
EDMONTON (All Saints) (St Michael) *Lon 18*
P *D&C St Paul's* **V** B G KYRIACOU, **NSM** J E MARKBY
EDMONTON (St Aldhelm) *Lon 18* **P** *V Edmonton All SS*
V D R BOLSTER
EDMONTON (St Alphege) *Lon 18* **P** *Bp* **V** T G CLEMENT, **C** S P J CLARK
EDMONTON (St Mary w St John) (St Mary's Centre) *Lon 18*
P *D&C St Paul's* **P-in-c** A K DANGERFIELD, **C** J R FOX
EDMONTON (St Matthew) *see* Ponders End St Matt *Lon*
EDMONTON (St Peter w St Martin) *Lon 18* **P** *Bp*
V B M SMITH
EDMUNDBYERS (St Edmund) *see* Blanchland w Hunstanworth and Edmundbyers etc *Newc*
EDSTASTON (St Mary the Virgin) *see* Tilstock, Edstaston and Whixall *Lich*
EDSTON (St Michael) *see* Kirby Misperton w Normanby, Edston and Salton *York*
EDVIN LOACH (St Mary) w Tedstone Delamere, Tedstone Wafer, Upper Sapey, Wolferlow and Whitbourne *Heref 2* **P** *Bp, BNC Ox, Sir Francis Winnington Bt, and D P Barneby Esq (jt)* **P-in-c** D P HOWELL

EDWALTON (Holy Rood) *S'well 8* **P** *Exors Major R P Chaworth-Musters* **V** D C BIGNELL, **NSM** P A EDWARDS
EDWARDSTONE (St Mary the Virgin) *see* Boxford, Edwardstone, Groton etc *St E*
EDWINSTOWE (St Mary) *S'well 6* **P** *Earl Manvers' Trustees* **P-in-c** A J COOPER, **C** N J CARNALL
EDWYN RALPH (St Michael) *see* Bredenbury w Grendon Bishop and Wacton etc *Heref*
EFFINGHAM (St Lawrence) w Little Bookham *Guildf 10* **P** *Keble Coll Ox* **V** C A E LAWRENCE, **NSM** R A MILLER, J C YELLAND
EFFORD (St Paul) *see* Plymouth Em, St Paul Efford and St Aug *Ex*
EGDEAN (St Bartholomew) *Chich 11* **P** *Bp* **R** *vacant*
EGERTON (St James) w Pluckley *Cant 10* **P** *Abp* **R** M J HIGGS
EGG BUCKLAND (St Edward) *Ex 22* **P** *Ld Chan* **V** T R J DICKENS
EGGESFORD (All Saints) *see* Burrington, Chawleigh, Cheldon, Chulmleigh etc *Ex*
EGGINTON (St Michael) *see* Leighton Buzzard w Eggington, Hockliffe etc *St Alb*
EGGINTON (St Wilfrid) *see* Etwall w Egginton *Derby*
EGGLESCLIFFE (St John the Baptist) *Dur 10* **P** *Bp* **R** T J D OLLIER
EGGLESTON (Holy Trinity) *Dur 7* **P** *The Crown* **V** J E G CLARK
EGHAM (St John the Baptist) *Guildf 11* **P** *Ch Soc Trust* **V** J G PERKIN, **C** M C WOODWARD, **Hon C** J H GOODING
EGHAM HYTHE (St Paul) *Guildf 11* **P** *Bp* **V** G D KING, **NSM** S M LOVEDAY
EGLETON (St Edmund) *see* Oakham, Hambleton, Egleton, Braunston and Brooke *Pet*
EGLINGHAM (St Maurice) *see* Glendale Gp *Newc*
EGLOSHAYLE (St Petroc) *see* St Breoke and Egloshayle *Truro*
EGLOSKERRY (St Petrock and St Keri), North Petherwin, Tremaine and Tresmere *Truro 9* **P** *Duchy of Cornwall and Bp (alt)* **V** G PENGELLY
EGMANTON (Our Lady of Egmanton) *S'well 3* **P** *SMF* **V** C C LEVY
EGREMONT (St John) *Ches 7* **P** *Bp* **P-in-c** A J MANNINGS
EGREMONT (St Mary and St Michael) and Haile *Carl 5* **P** *Patr Bd* **TR** J WOOLCOCK, **TV** G R WALKER, **NSM** B J JEAPES
EGTON (St Hilda) *see* Middle Esk Moor *York*
EGTON-CUM-NEWLAND (St Mary the Virgin) and Lowick and Colton *Carl 9* **P** *Patr Bd* **V** G WEMYSS
EIGHT ASH GREEN (All Saints) *see* Fordham *Chelmsf*
EIGHTON BANKS (St Thomas) *Dur 12* **P** *Bp* **P-in-c** R L FERGUSON
ELBERTON (St John) *see* Alveston and Littleton-on-Severn w Elberton *Bris*
ELBURTON (St Matthew) *Ex 23* **P** *CPAS* **P-in-c** R C H THOMAS
ELDENE (not known) *see* Swindon Dorcan *Bris*
ELDERSFIELD (St John the Baptist) *see* Berrow w Pendock, Eldersfield, Hollybush etc *Worc*
ELDON (St Mark) *see* Coundon and Eldon *Dur*
ELDWICK (St Lawrence) *see* Bingley All SS *Bradf*
ELFORD (St Peter) *Lich 4* **P** *Bp* **P-in-c** A L WHEALE, **Hon C** J R FAGAN
ELHAM (St Mary the Virgin) w Denton and Wootton *Cant 5* **P** *Abp and Mert Coll Ox (jt)* **V** J V H RUSSELL
ELING (St Mary) *see* Totton *Win*
ELING, NORTH (St Mary) *see* Copythorne *Win*
ELKESLEY (St Giles) w Bothamsall *S'well 5* **P** *SMF* **P-in-c** C F ANDREWS
ELKINGTON, SOUTH (All Saints) *see* Louth *Linc*
ELKSTONE (St John the Baptist) *see* Alstonfield, Butterton, Ilam etc *Lich*
ELKSTONE (St John the Evangelist) *see* Coberley, Cowley, Colesbourne and Elkstone *Glouc*
ELLACOMBE (Christ Church) *see* Torquay St Jo and Ellacombe *Ex*
ELLAND (All Saints) (St Mary the Virgin) *Wakef 2* **P** *Bp, Adn Halifax, and V Halifax (jt)* **TR** N M WOOD, **TV** D BURROWS
ELLASTONE (St Peter) *see* Denstone w Ellastone and Stanton *Lich*
ELLEL (St John the Evangelist) w Shireshead *Blackb 11* **P** *V Cockerham w Winmarleigh and Glasson* **V** E W GRAY
ELLENBROOK (St Mary's Chapel) *see* Worsley *Man*
ELLENHALL (St Mary) *see* Chebsey, Ellenhall and Seighford-with-Creswell *Lich*
ELLERBURN (St Hilda) *see* Thornton Dale w Allerston, Ebberston etc *York*
ELLERBY (St James) *see* Swine *York*

ELLERKER (not known)   *see* S Cave and Ellerker w Broomfleet *York*

ELLESBOROUGH (St Peter and St Paul), The Kimbles and Stoke Mandeville   *Ox 28*   P *Chequers Trustees, The Hon I Hope-Morley, and D&C Linc (by turn)*   R A D WILLIS

ELLESMERE (St Mary)   *Lich 17*   P *Bp*   V P J EDGE, Hon C M W H GRAY

ELLESMERE (St Peter)   *Sheff 3*   P *Bp*   V vacant 0114-276 2555

ELLESMERE PORT   *Ches 9*   P *Bp*   TR G B MCGUINNESS, TV N R KING,   Hon C R A WIFFEN,   NSM G J WELCH

ELLINGHAM (St Mary)   *see* Gillingham w Geldeston, Stockton, Ellingham etc *Nor*

ELLINGHAM (St Mary and All Saints) and Harbridge and Hyde w Ibsley   *Win 9*   P *Earl of Normanton and Keble Coll Ox (jt)*   V vacant (01425) 653216

ELLINGHAM (St Maurice)   *Newc 10*   P *D&C Dur*   V E M MCLEAN

ELLINGHAM, GREAT (St James), LITTLE (St Peter), Rockland All Saints, Rockland St Peter and Shropham w Snetterton   *Nor 11*   P *Bp, Major E H C Garnier, and CCC Cam (jt)*   R vacant (01953) 453200

ELLINGTON (All Saints)   *see* E Leightonstone *Ely*

ELLISFIELD (St Martin)   *see* Cliddesden and Ellisfield w Farleigh Wallop etc *Win*

ELLISTOWN (St Christopher)   *see* Hugglescote w Donington, Ellistown and Snibston *Leic*

ELLOUGHTON (St Mary) and Brough w Brantingham   *York 13*   P *Abp and D&C Dur (jt)*   V P CUBITT

ELM (All Saints) and Friday Bridge w Coldham   *Ely 17*   P *Bp*   V vacant (01945) 860382

ELM (St Mary Magdalene)   *see* Mells w Buckland Dinham, Elm, Whatley etc *B & W*

ELM PARK (St Nicholas) Hornchurch   *Chelmsf 2*   P *Bp*   V R W FINCH,   NSM R MORTON

ELMBRIDGE (St Mary)   *see* Elmley Lovett w Hampton Lovett and Elmbridge etc *Worc*

ELMDON (St Nicholas)   *see* Heydon, Gt and Lt Chishill, Chrishall etc *Chelmsf*

ELMDON (St Nicholas) (St Stephen's Church Centre) (St Nicholas' Hall)   *Birm 11*   P *Ch Trust Fund Trust*   R P R CARTER,   NSM C L CARTER

ELMDON HEATH (St Francis of Assisi)   *see* Solihull *Birm*

ELMESTHORPE (St Mary)   *see* Earl Shilton w Elmesthorpe *Leic*

ELMHAM, NORTH (St Mary) w Billingford and Worthing   *Nor 14*   P *Bp (1 turn), Viscount Coke (2 turns), and G & C Coll Cam (1 turn)*   P-in-c D SIXSMITH

ELMHAM, SOUTH (St Cross) (St James) (St Margaret) (St Peter) (St Michael and All Angels) and Ilketshall   *St E 14*   P *Bp (3 turns), Ld Chan (1 turn), and Duke of Norfolk (1 turn)*   R R H P THORNBURGH,   NSM C S LEE,   OLM R A FINCH

ELMHURST (Mission Room)   *see* Lich St Chad *Lich*

ELMLEY   *see* Emley *Wakef*

ELMLEY CASTLE (St Mary) w Bricklehampton and the Combertons   *Worc 4*   P *Bp*   R T J HENDERSON

ELMLEY LOVETT (St Michael) w Hampton Lovett and Elmbridge w Rushdock   *Worc 8*   P *Bp and Ch Coll Cam (alt)*   P-in-c J READER

ELMORE (St John the Baptist)   *see* Hardwicke and Elmore w Longney *Glouc*

ELMSALL, NORTH (St Margaret)   *see* Badsworth *Wakef*

ELMSALL, SOUTH (St Mary the Virgin)   *Wakef 11*   P *Bp*   V P M WITTS

ELMSETT (St Peter) w Aldham, Hintlesham, Chattisham and Kersey   *St E 3*   P *Bp, MMCET, and St Chad's Coll Dur (jt)*   R vacant (01473) 658219

ELMSTEAD (St Anne and St Laurence)   *Chelmsf 20*   P *Jes Coll Cam*   Hon C M H GREEN

ELMSTED (St James the Great) w Hastingleigh   *Cant 2*   P *Abp*   P-in-c D W J HOUSTON

ELMSTONE (not known)   *see* Wingham w Elmstone and Preston w Stourmouth *Cant*

ELMSTONE HARDWICKE (St Mary Magdalene)   *see* Swindon w Uckington and Elmstone Hardwicke *Glouc*

ELMSWELL (St John)   *St E 10*   P *MMCET*   R M I MCNAMARA

ELMTON (St Peter)   *Derby 3*   P *Bp*   V D J HULL

ELSDON (St Cuthbert)   *see* N Tyne and Redesdale Team *Newc*

ELSECAR (Holy Trinity)   *Sheff 11*   P *Sir Philip Naylor-Leyland Bt*   V J G FAIRHURST

ELSENHAM (St Mary the Virgin)   *see* Henham and Elsenham w Ugley *Chelmsf*

ELSFIELD (St Thomas of Canterbury)   *see* Marston w Elsfield *Ox*

ELSHAM (All Saints)   *see* N Wolds Gp *Linc*

ELSING (St Mary)   *see* Lyng, Sparham, Elsing, Bylaugh, Bawdeswell etc *Nor*

ELSON (St Thomas)   *Portsm 3*   P *DBP*   V P R WADSWORTH

ELSTEAD (St James)   *Guildf 4*   P *Adn Surrey*   R W D LANG

ELSTED (St Paul)   *see* Harting w Elsted and Treyford cum Didling *Chich*

ELSTERNWICK (St Laurence)   *see* Burton Pidsea and Humbleton w Elsternwick *York*

ELSTON (All Saints) w Elston Chapelry   *S'well 3*   P *J C S Darwin Esq*   R G A FIRTH

ELSTOW (St Mary and St Helena)   *St Alb 13*   P *S C Whitbread Esq*   V R W HUBAND,   NSM M RAILTON-CROWDER

ELSTREE (St Nicholas)   *St Alb 1*   P *Ld Chan*   R vacant (020) 8953 1411

ELSWICK, HIGH (St Paul)   *Newc 7*   P *Trustees*   P-in-c G R CURRY

ELSWICK, HIGH (St Philip)   *see* Newc St Phil and St Aug and St Matt w St Mary *Newc*

ELSWICK, LOW (St Stephen)   *Newc 7*   P *Ch Soc Trust*   V G R CURRY

ELSWORTH (Holy Trinity)   *see* Papworth *Ely*

ELTHAM (Holy Trinity)   *S'wark 3*   P *Bp*   V M R HARRISON, C S G LEE,   NSM T N ALEXANDER-YATES

ELTHAM (St Barnabas)   *S'wark 3*   P *Bp*   P-in-c S COOK, Hon C G E STEVENSON

ELTHAM (St John the Baptist)   *S'wark 3*   P *DBP*   V J E NEAL

ELTHAM (St Saviour)   *S'wark 3*   P *Bp*   P-in-c W J SAUNDERS

ELTHAM, NEW (All Saints)   *S'wark 3*   P *Bp*   V J WADSWORTH,   OLM G S LYONS

ELTHAM PARK (St Luke)   *S'wark 3*   P *Bp*   Hon C P A KEOGH,   NSM M J MABBS, I NASH

ELTISLEY (St Pandionia and St John the Baptist)   *see* Papworth *Ely*

ELTON (All Saints)   *see* S Darley, Elton and Winster *Derby*

ELTON All Saints   *Man 10*   P *R Bury St Mary*   P-in-c S MILLINGTON,   C A J EDWARDS,   Hon C P J BEDDINGTON

ELTON (All Saints) w Stibbington and Water Newton   *Ely 12*   P *Sir Peter Proby Bt, Sir Philip Naylor-Leyland Bt, and Keble Coll Ox (jt)*   R vacant (01832) 280222

ELTON (no dedication)   *see* Longnewton w Elton *Dur*

ELTON (St Mary the Virgin)   *see* Wigmore Abbey *Heref*

ELTON (St Stephen)   *Man 10*   V Elton All SS   P-in-c E A JUMP,   OLM A M BULCOCK

ELTON-ON-THE-HILL (St Michael)   *see* Cropwell Bishop w Colston Bassett, Granby etc *S'well*

ELVASTON (St Bartholomew)   *see* Aston on Trent, Elvaston, Weston on Trent etc *Derby*

ELVEDEN (St Andrew and St Patrick)   *see* Brandon and Santon Downham w Elveden *St E*

ELVETHAM HEATH Local Ecumenical Project   *Guildf 1*   Min D G M PRICE

ELVINGTON (Holy Trinity) w Sutton on Derwent and East Cottingwith   *York 2*   P *Lt Col J Darlington*   R vacant (01904) 608462

ELWICK HALL (St Peter)   *see* Hart w Elwick Hall *Dur*

ELWORTH (St Peter) and Warmingham   *Ches 11*   P *V Sandbach, Q H Crewe Esq and J C Crewe Esq (alt)*   R D J PAGE,   C P M WITHINGTON

ELY (Holy Trinity w St Mary) (St Peter)   *Ely 13*   P *Patr Bd*   TR F J KILNER,   TV J R SANSOM, A C PARTRIDGE,   NSM V J KILNER, E A HUBBARD

EMBERTON (All Saints)   *see* Lamp *Ox*

EMBLETON (Holy Trinity) w Rennington and Rock   *Newc 9*   P *Mert Coll Ox*   V J M MOUNTNEY

EMBLETON (St Cuthbert)   *see* Cockermouth w Embleton and Wythop *Carl*

EMBROOK (Community of St Nicholas)   *see* Wokingham St Paul *Ox*

EMBSAY (St Mary the Virgin) w Eastby   *Bradf 7*   P *R Skipton H Trin*   P-in-c J A HOLFORD

EMERY DOWN (Christ Church)   *see* Lyndhurst and Emery Down and Minstead *Win*

EMLEY (St Michael the Archangel)   *Wakef 6*   P *Lord Savile*   P-in-c C E BULLIMORE,   C E L WYNN,   OLM L BROOKES

EMMANUEL Team Ministry, The   *Wakef 1*   P *Patr Bd*   TR I JACKSON,   TV I SHAW,   NSM D KENT

EMMER GREEN (St Barnabas) w Caversham Park   *Ox 15*   P *Bp and Ch Ch Ox (jt)*   R D E CHANDLER,   OLM M L DIMMICK

EMNETH (St Edmund) and Marshland St James   *Ely 17*   P *Bp*   V D L MASON

EMPINGHAM (St Peter) and Exton w Horn w Whitwell   *Pet 14*   P *Bp and Earl of Gainsborough (alt)*   P-in-c B A NICHOLLS, P STREET

EMPSHOTT (Holy Rood) *see* Greatham w Empshott and Hawkley w Prior's Dean *Portsm*

EMSCOTE (All Saints) *see* Warwick *Cov*

EMSWORTH (St James) *see* Warblington w Emsworth *Portsm*

ENBORNE (St Michael and All Angels) *see* W Woodhay w Enborne, Hampstead Marshall etc *Ox*

ENDCLIFFE (St Augustine) *Sheff 2* P *Ch Burgesses*
V S SHAKESPEARE, C N R RAO

ENDERBY (St John the Baptist) w Lubbesthorpe and Thurlaston *Leic 10* P *Bp and F B Drummond Esq* P-in-c S J DAVIES

ENDON (St Luke) w Stanley *Lich 8* P *R Leek and Meerbrook*
P-in-c A J BETTS

ENFIELD (Christ Church) Trent Park *Lon 18* P *Ch Trust Fund Trust* V R D JAMES, C E M C BOWES-SMITH

ENFIELD (St Andrew) *Lon 18* P *Trin Coll Cam*
V M M EDGE, C A RAWDING, Hon C O R COPE

ENFIELD (St George) *Lon 18* P *Bp* V T R BONIWELL

ENFIELD (St James) (St Barnabas) *Lon 18* P *V Enfield*
V J M BOWERS, C C G SKINGLEY

ENFIELD (St John the Baptist) *see* Clay Hill St Jo and St Luke *Lon*

ENFIELD (St Luke) *as above Lon*

ENFIELD (St Mark) *see* Bush Hill Park St Mark *Lon*

ENFIELD (St Matthew) *see* Ponders End St Matt *Lon*

ENFIELD (St Michael and All Angels) *Lon 18* P *V Enfield*
P-in-c A J F MANSFIELD

ENFIELD (St Peter and St Paul) *Lon 18* P *Bp*
V J C VAUGHAN

ENFIELD (St Stephen) *see* Bush Hill Park St Steph *Lon*

ENFIELD CHASE (St Mary Magdalene) *Lon 18* P *Bp*
V G J GILES

ENFORD (All Saints) *see* Avon Valley *Sarum*

ENGLEFIELD (St Mark) *see* Theale and Englefield *Ox*

ENGLEFIELD GREEN (St Jude) *Guildf 11* P *Bp*
V L C SMITH

ENGLISH BICKNOR (St Mary) *see* Forest of Dean Ch Ch w English Bicknor *Glouc*

ENGLISHCOMBE (St Peter) *see* Bath St Barn w Englishcombe *B & W*

ENHAM ALAMEIN (St George) *see* Smannell w Enham Alamein *Win*

ENMORE (St Michael) *see* Spaxton w Charlynch, Goathurst, Enmore etc *B & W*

ENMORE GREEN (St John the Evangelist) *see* Shaston *Sarum*

ENNERDALE (St Mary) *see* Lamplugh w Ennerdale *Carl*

ENSBURY PARK (St Thomas) *Sarum 7* P *Bp* V E FARROW

ENSTONE (St Kenelm) *see* Chase *Ox*

ENVILLE (St Mary the Virgin) *see* Kinver and Enville *Lich*

EPPERSTONE (Holy Cross) *S'well 10* P *Bp, Ld Chan, and C P L Francklin Esq (by turn)* R M J BROCK,
C J E DRAYCOTT, NSM M N TAYLOR

EPPING DISTRICT (All Saints) (St John the Baptist) *Chelmsf 25*
P *Patr Bd* TR G CONNOR, TV C F J BARD, J H LAWSON,
C B C MORRISON

EPPLETON (All Saints) and Hetton le Hole *Dur 14*
P *Prime Min and Bp (alt)* R M L BECK, C J M PERKINS,
NSM G M BECK

EPSOM (St Barnabas) *Guildf 9* P *Bp* V M C PRESTON,
NSM S H BULL

EPSOM (St Martin) (St Stephen on the Downs) *Guildf 9* P *Bp*
V S J TALBOTT, C C S BOURNE, NSM M E MARSH

EPSOM COMMON (Christ Church) *Guildf 9* P *Bp*
V A J FACEY, C D M AYRES

EPWELL (St Anne) *see* Wykeham *Ox*

EPWORTH Group, The (St Andrew) *Linc 1* P *Prime Min (2 turns), Ld Chan (1 turn)* R J D BROWN

ERCALL, HIGH (St Michael and All Angels)
see Wrockwardine Deanery *Lich*

ERDINGTON Team Ministry, The (St Barnabas) (St Chad)
Birm 8 P *Patr Bd* TR P R SPENCER, TV N M A TRAYNOR,
K D N CHANDRA, NSM A J CLUCAS, E M BLAIR-CHAPPELL

ERIDGE GREEN (Holy Trinity) *see* Frant w Eridge *Chich*

ERISWELL (St Laurence and St Peter) *see* Mildenhall *St E*

ERITH (Christ Church) *Roch 15* P *Bp* V J DRAYCOTT

ERITH (St John the Baptist) *Roch 15* P *Bp* V vacant (01322) 432555

ERITH (St Paul) Northumberland Heath *Roch 15* P *CPAS*
V J C ROSS

ERLESTOKE (Holy Saviour) *see* Bratton, Edington and Imber, Erlestoke etc *Sarum*

ERMINE (St John) *see* Linc St Jo *Linc*

ERMINGTON (St Peter and St Paul) and Ugborough *Ex 20*
P *Prime Min (1 turn), Bp and Grocers' Co (3 turns)*
V N M HUNT

ERNESETTLE (St Aidan) *Ex 21* P *Bp* P-in-c G J SMITH

ERPINGHAM (St Mary) w Calthorpe, Ingworth, Aldborough, Thurgarton and Alby w Thwaite *Nor 19* P *Bp, Lord Walpole, Gt Hosp Nor, Mrs S M Lilly, and DBP (by turn)*
R B T FAULKNER, NSM J W SMITH

ERRINGDEN *Wakef 3* P *Bp and V Halifax (jt)*
V J T ALLISON, NSM A MAUDE

ERWARTON (St Mary the Virgin) *see* Chelmondiston and Erwarton w Harkstead *St E*

ERYHOLME (St Mary) *see* Middleton Tyas w Croft and Eryholme *Ripon*

ESCOMB (no dedication) *Dur 6* P *Bp* V M L DENT

ESCOT (St Philip and St James) *see* Feniton, Buckerell and Escot *Ex*

ESCRICK (St Helen) and Stillingfleet w Naburn *York 2* P *Abp, D&C, and N C Forbes Adam Esq (jt)* R R M KIRKMAN

ESH (St Michael and All Angels) *Dur 1* P *Prime Min*
V M J PEERS, C T E HUBBLE, NSM C K ROBERTSON

ESHER (Christ Church) (St George) *Guildf 8* P *Wadh Coll Ox*
R W A J ALLBERRY

ESHOLT (St Paul) *see* Guiseley w Esholt *Bradf*

ESK MOOR, MIDDLE *York 22* P *Abp* V D C KING

ESKDALE (St Catherine) (St Bega's Mission), Irton, Muncaster and Waberthwaite *Carl 5* P *Bp, adn W Cumberland, Mrs P Gordon-Duff-Pennington, and P Stanley Esq (jt)*
V G M STONESTREET, NSM I M HALL

ESKDALESIDE (St John) w Ugglebarnby and Sneaton *York 22*
P *Abp* V G J WOOD

ESSENDINE (St Mary the Virgin) *see* Ryhall w Essendine and Carlby *Pet*

ESSENDON (St Mary the Virgin) *see* Lt Berkhamsted and Bayford, Essendon etc *St Alb*

ESSINGTON (St John the Evangelist) *Lich 2* P *Bp, R Bushbury, R Wednesfield, and Simeon's Trustees (jt)*
V N S ATKINS

ESTON (Christ Church) w Normanby *York 18* P *Abp*
TV L N CAVAN

ESTOVER (Christ Church) *Ex 22* P *Bp* V vacant (01752) 703713

ETAL (St Mary the Virgin) *see* Ford and Etal *Newc*

ETCHILHAMPTON (St Andrew) *see* Bishop's Cannings, All Cannings etc *Sarum*

ETCHING HILL (The Holy Spirit) *see* Rugeley *Lich*

ETCHINGHAM (Assumption and St Nicholas) *Chich 15* P *Bp*
R R DIXON

ETHERLEY (St Cuthbert) *Dur 6* P *Bp* R M L DENT

ETON (St John the Evangelist) *see* Riverside *Ox*

ETON WICK (St John the Baptist) *as above Ox*

ETTINGSHALL (Holy Trinity) *Lich 28* P *Bp* V A J JONES

ETTINGTON (Holy Trinity and St Thomas of Canterbury)
see Butlers Marston and the Pillertons w Ettington *Cov*

ETTON (St Mary) w Dalton Holme *York 8* P *Lord Hotham*
P-in-c R C THORP

ETTON (St Stephen) w Helpston and Maxey *Pet 13*
P *Sir Stephen Hastings (2 turns), D&C (1 turn)*
P-in-c L M ELLIOTT

ETWALL (St Helen) w Egginton *Derby 14* P *Bp, Sir Henry Every Bt, Major J W Chandos-Pole, and DBP (by turn)*
R S L RAYNER, NSM P A SHORT

EUSTON (St Genevieve) *see* Blackbourne *St E*

EUXTON (not known) *Blackb 4* P *Bp* V P D TAYLOR

EVE HILL (St James the Great) *see* Dudley St Jas *Worc*

EVEDON (St Mary) *see* Kirkby Laythorpe *Linc*

EVENLEY (St George) *see* Aynho and Croughton w Evenley etc *Pet*

EVENLODE (St Edward King and Martyr) *see* Broadwell, Evenlode, Oddington, Adlestrop etc *Glouc*

EVENWOOD (St Paul) *Dur 7* P *Bp* V G LIDDLE

EVERCREECH (St Peter) w Chesterblade and Milton Clevedon *B & W 2* P *DBP* V vacant (01749) 830322

EVERDON (St Mary) *see* Weedon Bec w Everdon and Dodford *Pet*

EVERINGHAM (St Everilda) *see* Holme and Seaton Ross Gp *York*

EVERSDEN, GREAT (St Mary) *see* Haslingfield w Harlton and Gt and Lt Eversden *Ely*

EVERSDEN, LITTLE (St Helen) *as above Ely*

EVERSHOLT (St John the Baptist) *see* Woburn w Eversholt, Milton Bryan, Battlesden etc *St Alb*

EVERSHOT (St Osmund) *see* Melbury *Sarum*

EVERSLEY (St Mary) *see* Yateley and Eversley *Win*

EVERTON (Holy Trinity) and Mattersey w Clayworth *S'well 1*
P *Ld Chan (2 turns), Bp (2 turns)* R S J STEVENS

EVERTON (St George) *Liv 3* P *Bp* V P H SPIERS,
NSM I D CASSIDY, OLM S LITTLE

EVERTON (St Mary) *see* Gamlingay and Everton *Ely*

EVERTON (St Mary) *see* Milford *Win*

EVERTON (St Peter) (St John Chrysostom) (Emmanuel) *Liv 3*
  P *Patr Bd* **R** H CORBETT, **OLM** D H STATTER
EVESBATCH (St Andrew) *see* Acton Beauchamp and
  Evesbatch w Stanford Bishop *Heref*
EVESHAM (All Saints w St Lawrence) w Norton and Lenchwick
  Worc 1 **P** *Bp and D&C (jt)* **V** R N ARMITAGE,
  NSM A E WHITEHOUSE, C W PARR
EVINGTON (St Denys) *Leic 1* **P** *Bp* **V** S B HEYGATE,
  C V J JUPP, D P JOHNSON
EVINGTON (St Stephen) *see* Twigworth, Down Hatherley,
  Norton, The Leigh etc *Glouc*
EVINGTON, NORTH (St Stephen) *Leic 1* **P** *Bp*
  P-in-c I ST C RICHARDS, **NSM** L M HUGHES
EWELL (St Francis of Assisi) Ruxley Lane *Guildf 9* **P** *Bp*
  V S G THOMAS, **NSM** L CHAPMAN
EWELL (St Mary the Virgin) *Guildf 9* **P** *Bp*
  V W R HANFORD
EWELL, WEST (All Saints) *Guildf 9* **P** *Bp* **V** A J HURD
EWELME (St Mary the Virgin), Brightwell Baldwin, Cuxham w
  Easington *Ox 1* **P** F D *Wright Esq and Mert Coll Ox,*
  Prime Min (alt) **R** M W GARNER
EWERBY (St Andrew) *see* Kirkby Laythorpe *Linc*
EWHURST (St James the Great) *Chich 20* **P** K *Coll Cam*
  R R K BAKER
EWHURST (St Peter and St Paul) *Guildf 2* **P** *Ld Chan*
  R *vacant* (01483) 277584
EWOOD (St Bartholomew) *Blackb 2* **P** *Bp* **C** A S CORNESS,
  NSM D C DICKINSON
EWSHOT (St Mary the Virgin) *see* Crondall and Ewshot *Guildf*
EWYAS HAROLD (St Michael and All Angels) w Dulas,
  Kenderchurch, Abbeydore, Bacton, Kentchurch, Llangua,
  Rowlestone, Llancillo, Walterstone, Kilpeck, St Devereux and
  Wormbridge *Heref 1* **P** *Patr Bd* **P-in-c** J F BUTTERWORTH,
  NSM J D MONGER
EXBOURNE (St Mary the Virgin) *see* Hatherleigh, Meeth,
  Exbourne and Jacobstowe *Ex*
EXBURY (St Katherine) *see* Beaulieu and Exbury and E Boldre
  Win
EXE, WEST (St Paul) *see* Tiverton St Geo and St Paul *Ex*
EXE VALLEY *see* Washfield, Stoodleigh, Withleigh etc *Ex*
EXETER (St David) (St Michael and All Angels) *Ex 3* **P** *D&C*
  V J M HENTON, **Hon C** P A LEE
EXETER (St James) *Ex 3* **P** *D&C* **C** P R SHARPE
EXETER (St Leonard w Holy Trinity) *Ex 3* **P** *CPAS*
  R D R HARRIS, **C** J P A ELVIN, D P AP G MEIRION-JONES
EXETER (St Mark) (St Matthew) (St Sidwell) *Ex 3* **P** *Bp and*
  D&C (jt) **R** S CROFT
EXETER (St Mary Steps) *see* Heavitree and St Mary Steps *Ex*
EXETER (St Paul) *as above Ex*
EXETER (St Thomas the Apostle) (Emmanuel) (St Andrew)
  (St Philip) *Ex 3* **P** *Bp* **TR** A WHITE, **TV** D B M GILL,
  C P BARRETT, **C** G A M RAWLINGS
EXETER, CENTRAL (St Martin) (St Mary Arches) (St Olave)
  (St Pancras) (St Petrock) (St Stephen) *Ex 3* **P** *Patr Bd*
  P-in-c A R BEEVER, **NSM** A A HALL
EXFORD (St Mary Magdalene), Exmoor, Hawkridge and
  Withypool *B & W 16* **P** *Bp (1 turn), Peterho Cam (2 turns)*
  R R J RAY
EXHALL (St Giles) *Cov 5* **P** *Bp* **V** W M SMITH
EXHALL (St Giles) w Wixford *Cov 7* **P** *Bp* **P-in-c** S R TASH,
  NSM L E DAVIES, L MUDD
EXMINSTER (St Martin) and Kenn *Ex 6* **P** *Mrs M P L Bate*
  and 12 Govs of Crediton Ch (jt) **P-in-c** J D A WILLIAMS
EXMOOR (St Luke) *see* Exford, Exmoor, Hawkridge and
  Withypool *B & W*
EXMOUTH (All Saints) *see* Withycombe Raleigh *Ex*
EXMOUTH (Holy Trinity) *see* Littleham w Exmouth *Ex*
EXMOUTH (St Andrew) *as above Ex*
EXMOUTH (St John in the Wilderness) *see* Withycombe
  Raleigh *Ex*
EXMOUTH (St John the Evangelist) *as above Ex*
EXMOUTH (St Saviour) *see* Littleham w Exmouth *Ex*
EXNING (St Agnes) *see* Newmarket St Mary w Exning St
  Agnes *St E*
EXNING (St Martin) (St Philip) w Landwade *St E 11* **P** *D&C*
  Cant **V** S PETTITT, **C** M C MARSHALL, **NSM** C T MCCARTY
EXTON (St Andrew) *see* Lympstone and Woodbury w Exton *Ex*
EXTON (St Peter and St Paul) *see* Empingham and Exton w
  Horn w Whitwell *Pet*
EXTON (St Peter and St Paul) *see* Meonstoke w Corhampton
  cum Exton *Portsm*
EXTON (St Peter) and Winsford and Cutcombe w Luxborough
  B & W 16 **P** *Ld Chan (2 turns), Em Coll Cam (1 turn), and*
  G A Warren Esq and D M Warren Esq (1 turn) **R** T M STAPLES
EXWICK (St Andrew) *Ex 3* **P** *Lord Wraxall*
  V J FAIRWEATHER
EYAM (St Lawrence) *Derby 2* **P** *Earl Temple* **R** D G SHAW
EYDON (St Nicholas) *see* Woodford Halse w Eydon *Pet*

EYE (St Matthew) *Pet 13* **P** *Bp* **V** A W BAINES
EYE (St Peter and St Paul) *see* Leominster *Heref*
EYE (St Peter and St Paul) *St E 16* **P** *Bp, SMF, and Lt Comdr*
  G C Marshall (jt) **R** *vacant* (01379) 870277
EYEWORTH (All Saints) *see* Dunton w Wrestlingworth and
  Eyeworth *St Alb*
EYKE (All Saints) *see* Wilford Peninsula *St E*
EYNESBURY (St Mary) *Ely 13* **P** *Bp* **R** T J MCCABE
EYNSFORD (St Martin) w Farningham and Lullingstone
  Roch 10 **P** *D&C* **R** N H TAYLOR, **NSM** C H SALMON
EYNSHAM (St Leonard) and Cassington *Ox 9* **P** *Wycliffe Hall*
  Ox and Ch Ch Ox (alt) **V** I R BENTLEY,
  OLM J A UNDERWOOD, R ASTON
EYPE (St Peter) *see* Symondsbury *Sarum*
EYRES MONSELL (St Hugh) *Leic 2* **P** *Bp* **V** D H P BROWN
EYTHORNE (St Peter and St Paul) and Elvington w
  Waldershare and Barfreystone w Sherdswell and Coldred
  Cant 4 **P** *Abp, St Jo Coll Ox, and Earl of Guilford (jt)*
  R A L WAY, **C** H M BURN, **NSM** M M MOWER
EYTON (All Saints) *see* Leominster *Heref*
EYTON (St Catherine) *see* Wellington, All SS w Eyton *Lich*
FACCOMBE (St Barnabas) *see* Hurstbourne Tarrant,
  Faccombe, Vernham Dean etc *Win*
FACEBY (St Mary Magdalene) *see* Whorlton w Carlton and
  Faceby *York*
FACIT (St John the Evangelist) *see* Whitworth w Facit *Man*
FACIT (St Michael the Archangel) *as above Man*
FAILAND (St Bartholomew) *see* Wraxall *B & W*
FAILSWORTH (Holy Family) *Man 19* **P** *Bp*
  P-in-c P B MCEVITT
FAILSWORTH (Holy Trinity) *Man 19* **P** *The Crown*
  R *vacant* 0161-682 7901
FAILSWORTH (St John) (St John the Evangelist) *Man 19*
  P *Bp* **R** A J MATTHEWS
FAIR OAK (St Thomas) *Win 10* **P** *Bp* **V** D S SNUGGS,
  C W M PIDGEON
FAIRBURN (St James) *see* Ledsham w Fairburn *York*
FAIRFIELD (St John the Divine) *Liv 3* **P** *MMCET*
  P-in-c J R SKINNER
FAIRFIELD (St Mark) *see* Belbroughton w Fairfield and Clent
  Worc
FAIRFIELD (St Matthew) *Linc 9* **P** *Bp* **V** D P ROWETT
FAIRFIELD (St Peter) *Derby 4* **P** *Ch Govs* **V** *vacant* (01298)
  23629
FAIRFIELD (St Thomas à Becket) *see* Appledore w Brookland,
  Fairfield, Brenzett etc *Cant*
FAIRFORD (St Mary the Virgin) and Kempsford w Whelford
  Glouc 12 **P** *D&C, Bp, and Mercers' Co (jt)* **V** J F WILLARD,
  Hon C M B COLE
FAIRHAVEN (St Paul) *Blackb 10* **P** *J C Hilton Esq*
  V G ROUSE
FAIRLIGHT, Guestling and Pett *Chich 20* **P** *Patr Bd*
  R B E CROSBY
FAIRSEAT (Holy Innocents) *see* Stansted w Fairseat and Vigo
  Roch
FAIRSTEAD (St Mary) w Terling and White Notley w
  Faulkbourne *Chelmsf 24* **P** *Bp, Exors Lord Rayleigh, and*
  C W O Parker Esq (by turn) **R** J M HALL
FAIRWARP (Christ Church) *Chich 21* **P** *Bp*
  P-in-c M COXHEAD, **NSM** I GIBSON
FAIRWEATHER GREEN (St Saviour) *Bradf 1* **P** *Bp*
  V P J CLEMENT
FAKENHAM (St Peter and St Paul) w Alethorpe *Nor 15*
  P *Trin Coll Cam* **R** A C BELL
FAKENHAM MAGNA (St Peter) *see* Blackbourne *St E*
FALCONWOOD (Bishop Ridley Church) *Roch 15* **P** *Bp*
  V I F DURNDELL
FALDINGWORTH (All Saints) *see* Middle Rasen Gp *Linc*
FALFIELD (St George) w Rockhampton *Glouc 7* **P** *Bp,*
  V Thornbury w Oldbury etc, Adn, and J Leigh Esq (jt)
  P-in-c P M LYES-WILSDON
FALINGE (St Edmund) *see* Rochdale *Man*
FALKENHAM (St Ethelbert) *see* Kirton w Falkenham *St E*
FALLOWFIELD (St Crispin) *see* Withington St Crispin *Man*
FALMER (St Laurence) *see* Stanmer w Falmer *Chich*
FALMOUTH (All Saints) *Truro 3* **P** *Bp*
  P-in-c S R F DRAKELEY
FALMOUTH (King Charles the Martyr) *Truro 3* **P** *Bp*
  NSM J B BENNETTS
FALSTONE (St Peter) *see* N Tyne and Redesdale Team *Newc*
FAMBRIDGE, NORTH (Holy Trinity) *see* Creeksea w
  Althorne, Latchingdon and N Fambridge *Chelmsf*
FAMBRIDGE, SOUTH (All Saints) *see* Ashingdon w S
  Fambridge *Chelmsf*
FANGFOSS (St Martin) *see* Barmby Moor Gp *York*
FAR FOREST (Holy Trinity) *see* Mamble w Bayton, Rock w
  Heightington etc *Worc*

FAR HEADINGLEY St Chad (St Oswald) *Ripon 7* **P** *Lord Grimthorpe* **V** B M OVEREND, **C** A CLAYTON
FARCET (St Mary) *Ely 12* **P** *Em Coll Cam* **V** D W SPENCER
FAREHAM (Holy Trinity) (St Columba) *Portsm 2* **P** *Bp* **TR** F A WRIGHT, **TV** J N J C DUSSEK, **C** M F PYE, **Hon C** A P BURR, **NSM** D M JACKSON
FAREHAM (St John the Evangelist) *Portsm 2* **P** *CPAS* **V** P D HALL
FAREHAM (St Peter and St Paul) *Portsm 2* **P** *Bp* **V** A W MARKS, **NSM** D J BUTCHER
FAREWELL (St Bartholomew) *Lich 1* **P** *MMCET* **P-in-c** M J BUTT, **NSM** M R AUSTIN
FARFORTH (St Peter) *see S Ormsby Gp Linc*
FARINGDON, GREAT (All Saints) w Little Coxwell *Ox 17* **P** *Simeon's Trustees* **P-in-c** C J DRAPER
FARINGDON, LITTLE (St Margaret of England) *see Shill Valley and Broadshire Ox*
FARINGTON MOSS (St Paul) *Blackb 5* **P** *V Penwortham* **P-in-c** P D HALLETT, **NSM** F KENDALL
FARLAM (St Thomas à Becket) *see Eden, Gelt and Irthing Carl*
FARLEIGH (St Mary) *see Warlingham w Chelsham and Farleigh S'wark*
FARLEIGH, EAST (not known) *see Coxheath w E Farleigh, Hunton and Linton Roch*
FARLEIGH, WEST (All Saints) *as above*
FARLEIGH HUNGERFORD (St Leonard) *see Hardington Vale B & W*
FARLEIGH WALLOP (St Andrew) *see Cliddesden and Ellisfield w Farleigh Wallop etc Win*
FARLESTHORPE (St Andrew) *see Bilsby w Farlesthorpe Linc*
FARLEY (All Saints) *see Clarendon Sarum*
FARLEY CHAMBERLAYNE (St John) *see Michelmersh and Awbridge and Braishfield etc Win*
FARLEY GREEN (St Michael) *see Shere, Albury and Chilworth Guildf*
FARLEY HILL (St John the Baptist) *St Alb 14* **P** *Bp* **V** R E MERRY
FARLEY HILL (St John the Evangelist) *see Swallowfield Ox*
FARLINGTON (St Andrew) (Church of the Resurrection) *Portsm 6* **P** *Mrs S J Wynter-Bee and E G Nugee Esq (jt)* **R** S B SUMMERS, **NSM** J L FELLOWS
FARLINGTON (St Leonard) *see Sheriff Hutton, Farlington, Stillington etc York*
FARLOW (St Giles) *see Stottesdon w Farlow, Cleeton St Mary, etc Heref*
FARMBOROUGH (All Saints) and Marksbury and Stanton Prior *B & W 10* **P** *MMCET (3 turns), Duchy of Cornwall (1 turn), and DBF (1 turn)* **R** J P KNOTT, **Hon C** J J HARRIES
FARMCOTE (St Faith) *see The Guitings, Cutsdean, Farmcote etc Glouc*
FARMINGTON (St Peter) *see Northleach w Hampnett and Farmington etc Glouc*
FARMOOR (St Mary) *see Cumnor Ox*
FARNBOROUGH (All Saints) *see Beedon and Peasemore w W Ilsley and Farnborough Ox*
FARNBOROUGH (St Botolph) *see Avon Dassett w Farnborough and Fenny Compton Cov*
FARNBOROUGH (St Giles) (St Nicholas) *Roch 16* **P** *Em Coll Cam* **R** M J HUGHES, **C** M HIRST
FARNBOROUGH, NORTH (St Peter) (Good Shepherd) *Guildf 1* **P** *Patr Bd* **TR** D G WILLEY, **TV** N L SHARP, **C** N J WILLIAMS, **NSM** S J CRABTREE, **OLM** J M JAMES
FARNBOROUGH, SOUTH (St Mark) *Guildf 1* **P** *Bp* **V** I C HEDGES
FARNCOMBE (St John the Evangelist) *Guildf 4* **P** *Bp* **P-in-c** M BLAKE, **C** N M ARTHY
FARNDALE (St Mary) *see Kirkbymoorside w Gillamoor, Farndale etc York*
FARNDON (St Chad) and Coddington *Ches 5* **P** *Duke of Westmr and D&C (jt)* **V** D A BOYD
FARNDON (St Peter) w Thorpe, Hawton and Cotham *S'well 3* **P** *Ld Chan* **R** J B QUARRELL
FARNDON, EAST (St John the Baptist) *see Arthingworth, Harrington w Oxendon and E Farndon Pet*
FARNHAM (St Andrew) *Guildf 3* **P** *Bp* **R** A K TUCK, **C** R M ROBERTS, **Hon C** J F W ANDERSON, **NSM** J M LIEVESLEY
FARNHAM (St Laurence) *see Chase Sarum*
FARNHAM (St Mary) *see Gt and Lt Glemham, Blaxhall etc St E*
FARNHAM (St Mary the Virgin) *see Stansted Mountfitchet w Birchanger and Farnham Chelmsf*
FARNHAM (St Oswald) *see Walkingham Hill Ripon*
FARNHAM COMMON (St John the Evangelist) *see Farnham Royal w Hedgerley Ox*

FARNHAM ROYAL (St Mary the Virgin) w Hedgerley *Ox 23* **P** *Bp and Eton Coll (jt)* **P-in-c** G H SAUNDERS, **NSM** S F BEDWELL, **OLM** G J BRIGGS
FARNHAM ROYAL SOUTH (St Michael) *see W Slough Ox*
FARNINGHAM (St Peter and St Paul) *see Eynsford w Farningham and Lullingstone Roch*
FARNLEY (All Saints) *see Leathley w Farnley, Fewston and Blubberhouses Bradf*
FARNLEY (St Michael) *Ripon 6* **P** *Bp* **P-in-c** D H RANDOLPH-HORN
FARNLEY, NEW (St James) *see Farnley Ripon*
FARNLEY TYAS (St Lucias) *see Almondbury w Farnley Tyas Wakef*
FARNSFIELD (St Michael) *S'well 14* **P** *Bp* **P-in-c** E F CULLY, **NSM** M A GROVES
FARNWORTH (St George) *see New Bury Man*
FARNWORTH (St Luke) (Bold Mission) (Cronton Mission) *Liv 13* **P** *V Prescot St Mary* **C** P MAKIN
FARNWORTH, EAST (All Saints) (St John) (St Peter) (St Thomas) and Kearsley *Man 12* **P** *Bp (2 turns), Ld Chan (1 turn)* **TR** F M SHAW, **TV** P M TOMPKINS, **C** E VANN, **OLM** P S CASTLE
FARRINGDON (All Saints) *see Chawton and Farringdon Win*
FARRINGDON (St Petrock and St Barnabas) *see Aylesbeare, Rockbeare, Farringdon etc Ex*
FARRINGTON GURNEY (St John the Baptist) *B & W 12* **P** *Bp* **P-in-c** E F CULLY, **NSM** M A GROVES
FARSLEY (St John the Evangelist) *Bradf 3* **P** *V Calverley* **V** J N WHITE
FARTHINGHOE (St Michael and All Angels) *see Aynho and Croughton w Evenley etc Pet*
FARTHINGSTONE (St Mary the Virgin) *see Blakesley w Adstone and Maidford etc Pet*
FARWAY (St Michael and All Angels) *see Offwell, Northleigh, Farway, Cotleigh etc Ex*
FATFIELD (St George) *Dur 11* **P** *Lord Lambton* **P-in-c** T M MALONEY, **C** F E MALONEY
FAULKBOURNE (St Germanus) *see Fairstead w Terling and White Notley etc Chelmsf*
FAULS (Holy Emmanuel) *Lich 22* **P** *V Prees* **V** *vacant*
FAVERSHAM (St Mary of Charity) *Cant 6* **P** *D&C* **P-in-c** A C OEHRING, **C** W J HORNSBY
FAWDON (St Mary the Virgin) *Newc 5* **P** *Bp* **P-in-c** P INGHAM
FAWKENHURST *Cant 12* **P** *DBP* **R** *vacant*
FAWKHAM (St Mary) and Hartley *Roch 1* **P** *Bp and D&C (jt)* **R** R M WORSSAM
FAWLEY (All Saints) *Win 11* **P** *Bp* **R** B P JAMES, **C** S VAN DER TOORN
FAWLEY (St Mary) *see Brightwalton w Catmore, Leckhampstead etc Ox*
FAWLEY (St Mary the Virgin) *see Hambleden Valley Ox*
FAWSLEY (St Mary the Virgin) *see Badby w Newham and Charwelton w Fawsley etc Pet*
FAZAKERLEY (Emmanuel) (St Paul) *Liv 7* **P** *Patr Bd* **TR** W FORSTER, **TV** M SIMMONS
FAZAKERLEY (St Nathanael) *see Walton-on-the-Hill Liv*
FAZELEY (St Paul) (St Barnabas) *Lich 4* **P** *Bp* **V** H J BAKER, **OLM** S ROWLEY, B WILLIAMS
FEATHERSTONE (All Saints) *Wakef 11* **P** *Ch Ch Ox* **V** N CLEWS
FEATHERSTONE (School Chapel) *see Haltwhistle and Greenhead Newc*
FECKENHAM (St John the Baptist) *see Bowbrook N Worc*
FEERING (All Saints) *see Kelvedon and Feering Chelmsf*
FELBRIDGE (St John) *S'wark 26* **P** *DBP* **V** S G BOWEN
FELBRIGG (St Margaret) *see Roughton and Felbrigg, Metton, Sustead etc Nor*
FELIXKIRK (St Felix) w Boltby *York 19* **P** *Abp* **P-in-c** P R A R HOARE, **NSM** E A HOARE
FELIXSTOWE (St John the Baptist) (St Edmund) *St E 2* **P** *Bp* **P-in-c** D C LOWE, **C** G J S HAYHOE
FELIXSTOWE (St Peter and St Paul) (St Andrew) (St Nicholas) *St E 2* **P** *Ch Trust Fund Trust* **V** *vacant (01394) 284135*
FELKIRK (St Peter) w Brierley *Wakef 7* **P** *Bp* **V** J BASKERVILLE
FELLING (Christ Church) *Dur 12* **P** *CPAS* **V** T J DAVIDSON
FELLISCLIFFE (Mission Church) *see Hampsthwaite and Killinghall Ripon*
FELLSIDE TEAM, The *Blackb 9* **P** *Patr Bd* **TR** T D WILBY, **TV** J M FINCH, **NSM** M A SHERDLEY
FELMERSHAM (St Mary) *St Alb 15* **P** *Bp* **P-in-c** D G MASON
FELMINGHAM (St Andrew) *see King's Beck Nor*
FELPHAM (St Mary the Virgin) *Chich 1* **P** *D&C* **R** R D HARRIS, **C** T THORP

FELSHAM (St Peter) *see* Cockfield w Bradfield St Clare, Felsham etc *St E*

FELSTED (Holy Cross) and Little Dunmow *Chelmsf 18* **P** *CPAS* **V** J C CHANDLER

FELTHAM (Christ Church) (St Dunstan) *Lon 11* **P** *Bp* **V** P R WRAGG

FELTHORPE (St Margaret) *see* Drayton w Felthorpe *Nor*

FELTON (St Katharine and the Noble Army of Martyrs) *see* Winford w Felton Common Hill *B & W*

FELTON (St Michael and All Angels) *Newc 9* **P** *Bp* **V** P A G ETTERLEY

FELTON (St Michael the Archangel) *see* Bodenham w Hope-under-Dinmore, Felton etc *Heref*

FELTON, WEST (St Michael) *Lich 19* **P** *Bp* **P-in-c** D R NORTH, **Hon C** B R W HAYES

FELTWELL (St Mary) and Methwold *Ely 14* **P** *Bp* **R** D J KIGHTLEY

FEN DITTON (Holy Cross) (St Mary Magdalene) (St Mary the Virgin) *Ely 3* **P** *Bp* **P-in-c** M C BOWERS

FEN DRAYTON (St Mary the Virgin) w Conington and Lolworth and Swavesey *Ely 5* **P** *The Crown, Jes Coll Cam, SMF, and Ch Coll Cam (by turn)* **R** J D YULE

FENCE-IN-PENDLE (St Anne) and Higham *Blackb 6* **P** *Bp and Ld Chan (alt)* **V** R J ADAMS

FENCOTE (St Andrew) *see* Kirkby Fleetham w Langton on Swale and Scruton *Ripon*

FENHAM (Holy Cross) *see* Newc H Cross *Newc*

FENHAM (St James and St Basil) *Newc 7* **P** *Bp* **C** A JONES

FENISCLIFFE (St Francis) *Blackb 2* **P** *Bp* **V** J G O'CONNOR

FENISCOWLES (Immanuel) *Blackb 2* **P** *V Blackb* **P-in-c** P A DAVISON

FENITON (St Andrew), Buckerell and Escot *Ex 7* **P** *DBP, D&C and J M Kennaway Esq (jt)* **P-in-c** R J GORDON

FENN LANES Group, The *Leic 13* **P** *Bp, D&C, and Lord O'Neill (jt)* **R** C M HEBDEN, **C** G W WILSON, **NSM** J E ATKINS

FENNY BENTLEY (St Edmund King and Martyr), Thorpe, Tissington, Parwich and Alsop-en-le-Dale *Derby 8* **P** *Bp, D A G Shields Esq, and Sir Richard FitzHerbert Bt (jt)* **R** C D HARRISON

FENNY DRAYTON (St Michael and All Angels) *see* Fenn Lanes Gp *Leic*

FENNY STRATFORD (St Martin) *Ox 25* **P** *Bp* **V** J A BULLOCK, **NSM** I W THOMAS

FENSTANTON (St Peter and St Paul) *Ely 8* **P** *Bp* **V** M A GUITE

FENTON (All Saints) *see* Claypole *Linc*

FENTON (Christ Church) *Lich 12* **P** *R Stoke-on-Trent* **V** D A CAMERON

FENWICK and MOSS (St John) *see* Fishlake w Sykehouse and Kirk Bramwith etc *Sheff*

FEOCK (St Feock) *Truro 6* **P** *Bp* **P-in-c** P A A WALKER, **NSM** B J HESELTINE

FERHAM PARK (St Paul) *see* Masbrough *Sheff*

FERNDOWN (St Mary) *see* Hampreston *Sarum*

FERNHAM (St John the Evangelist) *see* Shrivenham and Ashbury *Ox*

FERNHURST (St Margaret) *Chich 10* **P** *Rathbone Trust Co and Cowdray Trust (jt)* **V** A R ROAKE

FERNILEE (Holy Trinity) *see* Whaley Bridge *Ches*

FERRIBY, NORTH (All Saints) *York 14* **P** *H Trin Hull and Distr Ch Patr Soc Ltd* **V** A BASH

FERRIBY, SOUTH (St Nicholas) *Linc 6* **P** *Bp* **R** G A PLUMB

FERRING (St Andrew) *Chich 5* **P** *D&C* **V** T S STRATFORD

FERRYBRIDGE (St Andrew) *Wakef 11* **P** *D&C York* **V** *vacant (01977) 672772*

FERRYHILL (St Luke) (St Martha and St Mary) *Dur 5* **P** *D&C* **V** K LUMSDON

FERSFIELD (St Andrew) *see* Bressingham w N and S Lopham and Fersfield *Nor*

FETCHAM (St Mary) *Guildf 10* **P** *Bp* **R** P H BOUGHTON, **NSM** E M V BOUGHTON

FEWSTON (St Michael and St Lawrence) *see* Leathley w Farnley, Fewston and Blubberhouses *Bradf*

FIDDINGTON (St Martin) *see* Stogursey w Fiddington *B & W*

FIELD BROUGHTON (St Peter) *see* Cartmel Peninsula *Carl*

FIELD DALLING (St Andrew) *see* Gunthorpe w Bale w Field Dalling, Saxlingham etc *Nor*

FIFEHEAD MAGDALEN (St Mary Magdalene) *see* Gillingham *Sarum*

FIFEHEAD NEVILLE (All Saints) *see* Hazelbury Bryan and the Hillside Par *Sarum*

FIFIELD (St John the Baptist) *see* Shipton-under-Wychwood w Milton, Fifield etc *Ox*

FIFIELD BAVANT (St Martin) *see* Chalke Valley *Sarum*

FIGHELDEAN (St Michael and All Angels) *see* Avon Valley *Sarum*

FILBY (All Saints) *see* S Trin Broads *Nor*

FILEY (St John) (St Oswald) *York 15* **P** *PCC* **V** C W HUMPHRIES, **C** M E WILLIAMS

FILKINS (St Peter) *see* Shill Valley and Broadshire *Ox*

FILLEIGH (St Paul) *see* S Molton w Nymet St George, High Bray etc *Ex*

FILLINGHAM (St Andrew) *see* Ingham w Cammeringham w Fillingham *Linc*

FILLONGLEY (St Mary and All Saints) and Corley *Cov 5* **P** *Bp and Ch Soc Trust (jt)* **V** N J CLARKE, **NSM** J CLOSE

FILTON (St Peter) *Bris 5* **P** *Bp* **R** B R ARMAN, **NSM** E M DESMOND

FIMBER (St Mary) *see* Waggoners *York*

FINBOROUGH, GREAT (St Andrew) w Onehouse, Harleston, Buxhall and Shelland *St E 6* **P** *Bp* **P-in-c** N J HARTLEY

FINBOROUGH, LITTLE (St Mary) *see* Combs and Lt Finborough *St E*

FINCHAM (St Martin) *Ely 15* **P** *Bp* **P-in-c** D J POMERY, **Hon C** A G F VILLER

FINCHAMPSTEAD (St James) *Ox 16* **P** *DBP* **NSM** J WAKELING

FINCHFIELD (St Thomas) *see* Tettenhall Wood and Perton *Lich*

FINCHINGFIELD (St John the Baptist) and Cornish Hall End and Wethersfield w Shalford *Chelmsf 15* **P** *Mrs E M Bishop and Bp (alt)* **V** J F H SHEAD

FINCHLEY (Christ Church) *Lon 14* **P** *Ch Patr Trust* **V** T D ATKINS

FINCHLEY (Holy Trinity) *Lon 16* **P** *Bp* **V** L B HILL

FINCHLEY (St Barnabas) *see* Woodside Park St Barn *Lon*

FINCHLEY (St Mary) *Lon 14* **P** *Bp* **R** A D WILLIAMS, **NSM** J KRAFT

FINCHLEY (St Paul) (St Luke) *Lon 14* **P** *Simeon Trustees and Ch Patr Trust (jt)* **V** N R PYE

FINCHLEY, EAST (All Saints) *Lon 14* **P** *Bp* **V** C R HARDY

FINDERN (All Saints) *Derby 16* **P** *Bp* **V** *vacant*

FINDON (St John the Baptist) w Clapham and Patching *Chich 5* **P** *Abp, Bp, and J E P Somerset Esq (jt)* **V** S J GURR

FINDON VALLEY (All Saints) *Chich 5* **P** *Bp* **V** G J WHITING

FINEDON (St Mary the Virgin) *Pet 10* **P** *Bp* **V** J HUMPHRIES

FINGEST (St Bartholomew) *see* Hambleden Valley *Ox*

FINGHALL (St Andrew) *see* Spennithorne w Finghall and Hauxwell *Ripon*

FINGRINGHOE (St Andrew) w East Donyland and Abberton w Langenhoe *Chelmsf 16* **P** *Bp (3 turns), Ld Chan (1 turn)* **R** *vacant (01206) 729383*

FINHAM (St Martin in the Fields) *Cov 3* **P** *Bp* **V** P WATKINS

FINMERE (St Michael) *see* Shelswell *Ox*

FINNINGHAM (St Bartholomew) *see* Badwell and Walsham *St E*

FINNINGLEY (Holy Trinity and St Oswald) w Auckley *S'well 1* **P** *DBP* **P-in-c** D OTTEWELL

FINSBURY (St Clement) (St Barnabas) (St Matthew) *Lon 5* **P** *D&C St Paul's* **V** D E ALLEN

FINSBURY PARK (St Thomas) *Lon 5* **P** *Abp* **V** S R COLES, **NSM** V R ATTA-BAFFOE, B E F PEARSON

FINSTALL (St Godwald) *Worc 7* **P** *V Stoke Prior* **V** *vacant (01527) 872459*

FINSTHWAITE (St Peter) *see* Leven Valley *Carl*

FIR TREE (St Mary the Virgin) *see* Howden-le-Wear and Hunwick *Dur*

FIR VALE (St Cuthbert) *see* Sheff St Cuth *Sheff*

FIRBANK (St John the Evangelist), Howgill and Killington *Bradf 6* **P** *Ld Chan and V Sedbergh (alt)* **P-in-c** B A PITT, **Hon C** A W FELL

FIRBECK (St Martin) w Letwell *Sheff 5* **P** *Bp* **R** A P FEREADY

FIRLE, WEST (St Peter) *see* Glynde, W Firle and Beddingham *Chich*

FIRSBY (St Andrew) *see* Spilsby Gp *Linc*

FIRSWOOD (St Hilda) and Gorse Hill *Man 7* **P** *Prime Min* **P-in-c** T R MALKIN

FISH HALL (Mission Church) *see* Tonbridge SS Pet and Paul *Roch*

FISHBOURNE, NEW (St Peter and St Mary) *Chich 3* **P** *Ld Chan* **R** C A ASHLEY

FISHBURN (St Catherine) *see* Sedgefield *Dur*

FISHERMEAD (Trinity Church) *see* Woughton *Ox*

FISHERTON ANGER (St Paul) *Sarum 12* **P** *Ch Patr Trust* **R** R A CHARKHAM, **C** J D BIRCHALL

FISHLAKE (St Cuthbert) w Sykehouse and Kirk Bramwith w Fenwick and Moss *Sheff 10* **P** *Duchy of Lanc (1 turn), D&C Dur (2 turns), and Bp (1 turn)* **P-in-c** E S ATHERFOLD

FISHLEY (St Mary) *see* Acle w Fishley, N Burlingham, Beighton w Moulton *Nor*

FISHPOND (St John the Baptist)   see Golden Cap Team *Sarum*
FISHPONDS (All Saints) *Bris 3*   **P** *Bp*   **V** B E PEARCE
FISHPONDS (St John) *Bris 3*   **P** *Bp*   **V** J G BRAY
FISHPONDS (St Mary) *Bris 3*   **P** *Bp*   **V** R G MINSON
FISHTOFT (St Guthlac) *Linc 20*   **P** *DBP*   **R** M A R COOPER
FISKERTON (St Clement)   see S Lawres Gp *Linc*
FITTLETON (All Saints)   see Avon Valley *Sarum*
FITTLEWORTH (St Mary the Virgin)   see Stopham and
    Fittleworth *Chich*
FITTON HILL (St Cuthbert)   see Bardsley *Man*
FITZ (St Peter and St Paul)   see Bicton, Montford w
    Shrawardine and Fitz *Lich*
FITZHEAD (St James)   see Milverton w Halse and Fitzhead
    B & W
FITZWILLIAM (St Maurice)   see Kinsley w Wragby *Wakef*
FIVE ASHES (Church of the Good Shepherd)   see Mayfield
    Chich
FIVE OAK GREEN (St Luke)   see Tudeley cum Capel w Five
    Oak Green *Roch*
FIVEHEAD (St Martin)   see Curry Rivel w Fivehead and Swell
    B & W
FIXBY (St Francis)   see N Huddersfield *Wakef*
FLACKWELL HEATH (Christ Church) *Ox 29*   **P** *DBP*
    V C D BULL,   **NSM** G FOSTER,   **OLM** M H COURTNEY
FLADBURY (St John the Baptist) w Wyre Piddle and Moor and
    Cropthorne w Charlton *Worc 4*   **P** *Bp and D&C (jt)*
    R C N VON BENZON,   **C** J H GREEN
FLAGG (School Mission Room)   see Taddington, Chelmorton
    and Flagg, and Monyash *Derby*
FLAMBOROUGH (St Oswald)   see Bempton w Flamborough,
    Reighton w Speeton *York*
FLAMSTEAD (St Leonard) *St Alb 8*   **P** *Univ Coll Ox*
    P-in-c J F H GREEN
FLAUNDEN (St Mary Magdalene)   see Chenies and Lt
    Chalfont, Latimer and Flaunden *Ox*
FLAWBOROUGH (St Peter)   see Staunton w Flawborough
    S'well
FLAX BOURTON (St Michael and All Angels) *B & W 13*
    P *Lord Wraxall*   **P-in-c** A SARGENT,   **NSM** V L BARLEY
FLAXLEY (St Mary the Virgin)   see Westbury-on-Severn w
    Flaxley, Blaisdon etc *Glouc*
FLAXTON (St Lawrence)   see Whitwell w Crambe, Flaxton and
    Foston *York*
FLECKNEY (St Nicholas)   see Wistow *Leic*
FLECKNOE (St Mark)   see Leam Valley *Cov*
FLEET (All Saints) (St Philip and St James) *Guildf 1*   **P** *Bp*
    V D HOLT,   **C** J GOULD
FLEET (Holy Trinity)   see Chickerell w Fleet *Sarum*
FLEET (Old Church)   as above *Sarum*
FLEET (St Mary Magdalene) w Gedney *Linc 16*   **P** *The Crown*
    and DBP (alt)   **R** D F BRATLEY
FLEETWOOD (St David) *Blackb 12*   **P** *Bp and Meynell*
    Trustees (jt)   **V** E K SILLIS
FLEETWOOD (St Nicholas) *Blackb 12*   **P** *Bp and Meynell*
    Trustees (jt)   **V** P J BENFIELD,   **C** E A ALP
FLEETWOOD (St Peter) *Blackb 12*   **P** *Meynell Trustees*
    V A J GWILLIM
FLEGG COASTAL Benefice, The: Hemsby, Winterton, East and
    West Somerton and Horsey *Nor 6*   **P** *Bp, D&C, SMF, and*
    Major R A Ferrier (jt)   **R** M G KICHENSIDE,
    NSM A T CADMORE
FLEMPTON (St Catherine of Alexandria)   see Lark Valley *St E*
FLETCHAMSTEAD (St James) *Cov 3*   **P** *Bp*   **V** R J COOKE,
    C M A HEADING
FLETCHING (St Mary and St Andrew) *Chich 21*   **P** *Abp*
    NSM D WHITEHEAD
FLETTON (St Margaret) *Ely 12*   **P** *Sir Stephen Hastings*
    P-in-c W P L GAMMON
FLIMBY (St Nicholas) *Carl 7*   **P** *Bp*   **V** *vacant* (01900) 812386
FLIMWELL (St Augustine of Canterbury)   see Ticehurst and
    Flimwell *Chich*
FLINTHAM (St Augustine of Canterbury) *S'well 8*
    P M T *Hildyard Esq*   **P-in-c** D G WAKEFIELD
FLITCHAM (St Mary the Virgin)   see Sandringham w W
    Newton and Appleton etc *Nor*
FLITTON (St John the Baptist)   see Silsoe, Pulloxhill and Flitton
    St Alb
FLITWICK (St Andrew) (St Peter and St Paul) *St Alb 9*
    P *DBP*   **V** M F J BRADLEY
FLIXBOROUGH (All Saints) w Burton upon Stather *Linc 4*
    P *Sir Reginald Sheffield Bt*   **V** P W DADD
FLIXTON (St John) *Man 7*   **P** *Bp*   **V** K J MASSEY,
    OLM R W GREEN, B R CORKE, J N EDGE
FLIXTON (St Mary)   see S Elmham and Ilketshall *St E*
FLIXTON (St Michael) *Man 7*   **P** *Bp*   **P-in-c** S J SMITH,
    OLM A H CLEPHANE

FLOCKTON (St James the Great) cum Denby Grange *Wakef 6*
    P R *Carter's Trustees*   **P-in-c** C E BULLIMORE,   **C** E L WYNN,
    OLM L BROOKES
FLOOKBURGH (St John the Baptist)   see Cartmel Peninsula
    Carl
FLORDON (St Michael)   see Mulbarton w Bracon Ash, Hethel
    and Flordon *Nor*
FLORE (All Saints)   see Heyford w Stowe Nine Churches and
    Flore etc *Pet*
FLOWTON (St Mary)   see Somersham w Flowton and Offton w
    Willisham *St E*
FLUSHING (St Peter)   see Mylor w Flushing *Truro*
FLYFORD FLAVELL (St Peter)   see Abberton, The Flyfords,
    Naunton Beauchamp etc *Worc*
FOBBING (St Michael) *Chelmsf 14*   **P** *The Crown*
    P-in-c L R SMITH
FOLESHILL (St Laurence) *Cov 2*   **P** *Ld Chan*
    V M R CLEVELAND
FOLESHILL (St Paul) *Cov 2*   **P** *Ld Chan*   **V** A J CANNING,
    C L J BLAY
FOLEY PARK (Holy Innocents)   see Kidderminster St Jo and H
    Innocents *Worc*
FOLKE (St Lawrence)   see The Caundles w Folke and Holwell
    Sarum
FOLKESTONE (Holy Trinity w Christ Church) *Cant 5*   **P** *Abp*
    V J C TAPPER,   **NSM** C B HILL,   **OLM** D HADFIELD,
    J A ROBERTSON
FOLKESTONE (St Augustine) Conventional District
    Cant 5 vacant (01303) 245807
FOLKESTONE (St Augustine) (St Mary and St Eanswythe)
    Cant 5   **P** *Abp*   **V** D J ADLINGTON,   **NSM** B F WILLIAMS
FOLKESTONE (St George)   see Sandgate St Paul w Folkestone
    St Geo *Cant*
FOLKESTONE (St John the Baptist)   see Foord St Jo *Cant*
FOLKESTONE (St John the Baptist)   as above *Cant*
FOLKESTONE (St Peter) *Cant 5*   **P** *Trustees*
    V J A B PADDOCK
FOLKESTONE (St Saviour) *Cant 5*   **P** *Abp*
    P-in-c B M LLEWELLYN
FOLKESWORTH (St Helen)   see Stilton w Denton and
    Caldecote etc *Ely*
FOLKINGHAM (St Andrew)   see S Lafford *Linc*
FOLKINGTON (St Peter ad Vincula)   see Arlington,
    Folkington and Wilmington *Chich*
FOLKTON (St John)   see Willerby w Ganton and Folkton *York*
FOLLIFOOT (St Joseph and St James)   see Spofforth w Kirk
    Deighton *Ripon*
FONTHILL BISHOP (All Saints)   see Nadder Valley *Sarum*
FONTHILL GIFFORD (Holy Trinity)   as above *Sarum*
FONTMELL MAGNA (St Andrew)   see Iwerne Valley *Sarum*
FOOLOW (St Hugh)   see Eyam *Derby*
FOORD (St John the Baptist) *Cant 5*   **P** *CPAS*
    V A G BUCKLEY,   **C** R P GRINSELL,   **NSM** R A BIRCH
FOOTSCRAY (All Saints) w North Cray *Roch 17*   **P** *Bp and*
    Ld Chan (alt)   **R** A C UPHILL
FORCETT (St Cuthbert) and Aldbrough and Melsonby *Ripon 2*
    P *DBP and Univ Coll Ox (alt)*   **P-in-c** S R HAWORTH
FORD (St Andrew)   see Clymping and Yapton w Ford *Chich*
FORD (St John of Jerusalem)   see Leominster *Heref*
FORD (St John the Evangelist)   see Colerne w N Wraxall *Bris*
FORD (St Mark)   see Devonport St Mark Ford *Ex*
FORD (St Michael) *Heref 13*   **P** *Bp*   **V** A B STRATFORD
FORD (St Michael and All Angels) and Etal *Newc 12*   **P** *Lord*
    Joicey   **R** S T DICKINSON
FORD END (St John the Evangelist)   see Gt Waltham w Ford
    End *Chelmsf*
FORDCOMBE (St Peter)   see Penshurst and Fordcombe *Roch*
FORDHAM (All Saints) *Chelmsf 17*   **P** *Reformation Ch Trust,*
    Ball Coll Ox (alt)   **R** M R J NEVILLE
FORDHAM (St Peter and St Mary Magdalene) *Ely 3*
    P *Jes Coll Cam*   **V** A HASELHURST
FORDHOUSES (St James)   see Bushbury *Lich*
FORDINGBRIDGE (St Mary) and Breamore and Hale with the
    Charfords *Win 9*   **P** *Patr Bd*   **TR** T E DAYKIN,
    TV S T HORNE,   **Hon C** M L ASHTON, P D ASHTON,
    NSM C E ROLFE
FORDON (St James)   see Burton Fleming w Fordon, Grindale
    etc *York*
FOREBRIDGE (St Paul)   see Stafford St Paul Forebridge *Lich*
FOREMARK (St Saviour) and Repton w Newton Solney
    Derby 16   **P** *Bp and DBP (jt)*   **V** J R P BARKER
FOREST (St Stephen)   see Rainow w Saltersford and Forest
    Ches
FOREST GATE (All Saints) (St Edmund) *Chelmsf 3*   **P** *Bp*
    P-in-c B K SHIPSIDES,   **C** N A B MATLOOB
FOREST GATE (Emmanuel w St Peter) Upton Cross *Chelmsf 3*
    P *Bp*   **V** V W HYDON

FOREST GATE (St James) *see* Stratford St Jo w Ch Ch and St Jas *Chelmsf*

FOREST GATE (St Mark) *Chelmsf 3* **P** *Ch Patr Trust* **V** P J STOW

FOREST GATE (St Saviour) w West Ham St Matthew *Chelmsf 3* **P** *Patr Bd* **TR** J H WILLIAMS, **TV** M OKELLO

FOREST GREEN (Holy Trinity) *see* Ockley, Okewood and Forest Green *Guildf*

FOREST HILL (Christ Church) (St Paul) *S'wark 5* **P** *Bp and Earl of Dartmouth (jt)* **P-in-c** J R W ACKLAND, **NSM** T G BURMAN

FOREST HILL (St Augustine) Honor Oak Park *S'wark 5* **P** *Bp* **P-in-c** A S PEBERDY, S A LASKEY, **OLM** K G SIMS

FOREST HILL (St Nicholas) *see* Wheatley *Ox*

FOREST-IN-TEESDALE (St Mary the Virgin) *see* Middleton-in-Teesdale w Forest and Frith *Dur*

FOREST OF DEAN (Christ Church) w English Bicknor *Glouc 4* **P** *The Crown (3 turns), SMF (1 turn)* **V** *vacant* (01594) 832334

FOREST OF DEAN (Holy Trinity) *see* Dean Forest H Trin *Glouc*

FOREST ROW (Holy Trinity) *Chich 7* **P** *V E Grinstead* **NSM** D A TIDSWELL

FOREST TOWN (St Alban) *S'well 2* **P** *Bp* **P-in-c** P J STEAD, **NSM** J DEWHIRST

FORESTSIDE (Christ Church) *see* Stansted *Chich*

FORMBY (Holy Trinity) *Liv 5* **P** *Trustees* **V** K E JONES, **C** J M COLLIER

FORMBY (St Luke) *Liv 5* **P** *Bp* **V** A R WOODHOUSE

FORMBY (St Peter) *Liv 5* **P** *R Walton* **V** P W ORMROD

FORNCETT (St Peter) *see* Ashwellthorpe, Forncett, Fundenhall, Hapton etc *Nor*

FORNCETT END (St Edmund) *as above Nor*

FORNHAM ALL SAINTS (All Saints) *see* Lark Valley *St E*

FORNHAM ST MARTIN (St Martin) *as above St E*

FORRABURY (St Symphorian) *see* Boscastle w Davidstow *Truro*

FORSBROOK (St Peter) *see* Draycott-le-Moors w Forsbrook *Lich*

FORTHAMPTON (St Mary) *see* Deerhurst, Apperley w Forthampton and Chaceley *Glouc*

FORTON (All Saints) *see* Newport w Longford, Chetwynd and Forton *Lich*

FORTON (St James) *see* Ellel w Shireshead *Blackb*

FORTON (St John the Evangelist) *Portsm 3* **P** *DBP* **P-in-c** B E WARD

FORTY HILL (Jesus Church) *Lon 18* **P** *V Enfield* **V** J E TOWNSEND

FOSDYKE (All Saints) *see* Sutterton, Fosdyke, Algarkirk and Wigtoft *Linc*

FOSSE TRINITY *B & W 8* **P** *Bp and Canon D S Salter (jt)* **NSM** J M D SWAYNE

FOSTON (All Saints) *see* Whitwell w Crambe, Flaxton and Foston *York*

FOSTON (St Bartholomew) *see* Countesthorpe w Foston *Leic*

FOSTON (St Peter) *see* Saxonwell *Linc*

FOSTON-ON-THE-WOLDS (St Andrew) *see* Beeford w Frodingham and Foston *York*

FOTHERBY (St Mary) *Linc 12* **P** *Ld Chan (1 turn), DBP, MMCET and G F Sleight Esq (1 turn), and Bp (1 turn)* **P-in-c** K M TOMLIN, **OLM** J M WRISDALE

FOTHERINGHAY (St Mary and All Saints) *see* Warmington, Tansor and Cotterstock etc *Pet*

FOULDEN (All Saints) *see* Oxborough w Foulden and Caldecote *Nor*

FOULNESS (St Mary the Virgin) *see* Gt Wakering w Foulness *Chelmsf*

FOULRIDGE (St Michael and All Angels) *see* Colne and Villages *Blackb*

FOULSHAM (Holy Innocents) Hindolveston and Guestwick *Nor 22* **P** *Lord Hastings, Mrs M E E Bulwer-Long and D&C (alt)* **P-in-c** D SIXSMITH

FOUNTAINS Group, The *Ripon 3* **P** *D&C* **R** *vacant* (01765) 658260

FOUR ELMS (St Paul) *see* Hever, Four Elms and Mark Beech *Roch*

FOUR MARKS (Good Shepherd) *Win 2* **P** *Bp* **V** H J D WRIGHT, **C** T J FLETCHER

FOUR OAKS (All Saints) *Birm 12* **P** *Bp* **V** T C PLATTS, **C** C A PAILING, R F PAILING

FOURSTONES (St Aidan) *see* Warden w Newbrough *Newc*

FOVANT (St George), Sutton Mandeville and Teffont Evias w Teffont Magna and Compton Chamberlayne *Sarum 11* **P** *Reformation Ch Trust, Bp, and Ch Soc Trust (jt)* **R** J C EADE

FOWEY (St Fimbarrus) *Truro 1* **P** *Ch Soc Trust* **P-in-c** P DE GREY-WARTER

FOWLMERE (St Mary), Foxton, Shepreth and Thriplow *Ely 7* **P** *Bp* **C** P STRONG

FOWNHOPE (St Mary) w Mordiford, Brockhampton and Fawley and Woolhope *Heref 4* **P** *D&C (4 turns), and Major R J Hereford (1 turn)* **R** W R PRIDIE, **NSM** M M DEES

FOXCOTE (St James the Less) *see* Camerton w Dunkerton, Foxcote and Shoscombe *B & W*

FOXDALE (St Paul) *S & M 1* **P** *The Crown and Bp (alt)* **V** G M BREFFITT

FOXEARTH (St Peter and St Paul) *see* N Hinckford *Chelmsf*

FOXHAM (St John the Baptist) *see* Derry Hill w Bremhill and Foxham *Sarum*

FOXHILL (Chapel) *see* Frodsham *Ches*

FOXHOLE (St Boniface) *see* Paignton St Jo *Ex*

FOXHOLES (St Mary) *see* Langtoft w Foxholes, Butterwick, Cottam etc *York*

FOXLEY (not known) *see* Sherston Magna, Easton Grey, Luckington etc *Bris*

FOXLEY (St Thomas) *see* Lyng, Sparham, Elsing, Bylaugh, Bawdeswell etc *Nor*

FOXT (St Mark the Evangelist) *see* Kingsley and Foxt-w-Whiston *Lich*

FOXTON (St Andrew) w Gumley and Laughton *Leic 4* **P** *Bp Leic and D&C Linc (alt)* **P-in-c** I L JOHNSON

FOXTON (St Laurence) *see* Fowlmere, Foxton, Shepreth and Thriplow *Ely*

FOY (St Mary) *see* How Caple w Sollarshope, Sellack etc *Heref*

FRADLEY (St Stephen) *see* Alrewas *Lich*

FRADSWELL (St James the Less) *see* Mid Trent *Lich*

FRAISTHORPE (St Edmund King and Martyr) *see* Skipsea w Ulrome and Barmston w Fraisthorpe *York*

FRAMFIELD (St Thomas à Becket) *Chich 21* **P** *Mrs E R Wix* **V** E G DORE

FRAMILODE (St Peter) *see* Frampton on Severn, Arlingham, Saul etc *Glouc*

FRAMINGHAM EARL (St Andrew) *see* Poringland *Nor*

FRAMINGHAM PIGOT (St Andrew) *see* Thurton *Nor*

FRAMLAND Parishes, The HIGH *Leic 3* **P** *Duke of Rutland and Sir Lyonel Tollemache Bt (jt)* **P-in-c** P L BOTTING

FRAMLINGHAM (St Michael) w Saxtead *St E 18* **P** *Pemb Coll Cam* **R** R W WILLCOCK, **C** P J WYARD, **NSM** R L COURT

FRAMPTON (St Mary) *see* Bradford Peverell, Stratton, Frampton etc *Sarum*

FRAMPTON (St Mary) (St Michael) *Linc 21* **P** *Trustees* **V** A M HUGHES

FRAMPTON COTTERELL (St Peter) *Bris 5* **P** *SMF* **P-in-c** S E RUSHTON

FRAMPTON MANSELL (St Luke) *see* Coates, Rodmarton and Sapperton etc *Glouc*

FRAMPTON ON SEVERN (St Mary), Arlingham, Saul, Fretherne and Framilode *Glouc 8* **P** *DBP, V Standish w Haresfield etc, Brig Sir Jeffrey Darell Bt, and Bp (jt)* **V** P CHEESMAN

FRAMSDEN (St Mary) *see* Helmingham w Framsden and Pettaugh w Winston *St E*

FRAMWELLGATE MOOR (St Aidan) *see* Dur N *Dur*

FRANCE LYNCH (St John the Baptist) *see* Chalford and France Lynch *Glouc*

FRANCHE (St Barnabas) *see* Kidderminster St Mary and All SS w Trimpley etc *Worc*

FRANKBY (St John the Divine) w Greasby St Nicholas *Ches 8* **P** *D&C* **V** K P OWEN

FRANKLEY (St Leonard) *Birm 4* **P** *Bp* **R** M T DENNY

FRANKTON (St Nicholas) *see* Bourton w Frankton and Stretton on Dunsmore etc *Cov*

FRANSHAM, GREAT (All Saints) *see* Gt and Lt Dunham w Gt and Lt Fransham and Sporle *Nor*

FRANSHAM, LITTLE (St Mary) *as above Nor*

FRANT (St Alban) w Eridge *Chich 19* **P** *Bp and Marquess of Abergavenny (jt)* **R** A J TURNER

FREASLEY (St Mary) *see* Dordon *Birm*

FRECHEVILLE (St Cyprian) *Sheff 2* **P** *Bp* **R** M J GILLINGHAM

FRECKENHAM (St Andrew) *see* Mildenhall *St E*

FRECKLETON (Holy Trinity) *Blackb 10* **P** *Bp* **V** *vacant* (01772) 632209

FREEBY (St Mary) *see* Melton Mowbray *Leic*

FREEHAY (St Chad) *see* Cheadle w Freehay *Lich*

FREELAND (St Mary the Virgin) *see* Hanborough and Freeland *Ox*

FREEMANTLE (Christ Church) *Win 13* **P** *Bp* **R** N J COATES, **NSM** J B WALTERS

FREETHORPE (All Saints), Wickhampton, Halvergate w Tunstall, Reedham, Cantley and Limpenhoe w Southwood *Nor 4* **P** *Patr Bd* **R** C R DUXBURY

FREISTON (St James) w Butterwick and Benington *Linc 20*
R T STOTT, **NSM** L HALL
FREMINGTON (St Peter) *Ex 15* P *MMCET*
V P H HOCKEY, **NSM** D A ELLACOTT
FRENCHAY (St John the Baptist) and Winterbourne Down
Bris 5 P *St Jo Coll Ox and SMF (jt)* R *vacant* 0117-956 7616
FRENSHAM (St Mary the Virgin) *see* Rowledge and Frensham
Guildf
FRESHFORD (St Peter) w Limpley Stoke and Hinton
Charterhouse *B & W 9* P *Simeon's Trustees and V Norton*
St Phil (jt) R D J CLARK
FRESHWATER (All Saints) (St Agnes) *Portsm 8* P *St Jo Coll*
Cam R M E C WHATSON, **Hon C** D L GAMBLE,
NSM D K BELLAMY, G M HURT
FRESSINGFIELD (St Peter and St Paul), Mendham, Metfield,
Weybread and Withersdale *St E 17* P *Bp, Em Coll Cam,*
Ch Soc Trust, and SMF (jt) P-in-c D W FINCH, C C D KEYS,
NSM P A SCHWIER, **OLM** R A WILLIS
FRESTON (St Peter) *see* Holbrook, Stutton, Freston,
Woolverstone etc *St E*
FRETHERNE (St Mary the Virgin) *see* Frampton on Severn,
Arlingham, Saul etc *Glouc*
FRETTENHAM (St Swithin) *see* Spixworth w Crostwick and
Frettenham *Nor*
FRIAR PARK (St Francis of Assisi) *see* W Bromwich St Fran
Lich
FRIARMERE (St Thomas) *see* Saddleworth *Man*
FRICKLEY (All Saints) *see* Bilham *Sheff*
FRIDAY BRIDGE (St Mark) *see* Elm and Friday Bridge w
Coldham *Ely*
FRIDAYTHORPE (St Mary) *see* Waggoners *York*
FRIERN BARNET (All Saints) *Lon 14* P *Bp*
V A V BENJAMIN
FRIERN BARNET (St James the Great) (St John the Evangelist)
Lon 14 P *D&C St Paul's* R P A WALMSLEY-MCLEOD
FRIERN BARNET (St Peter le Poer) *Lon 14* P *D&C St Paul's*
V G J GILES
FRIESTHORPE (St Peter) *see* Middle Rasen Gp *Linc*
FRIETH (St John the Baptist) *see* Hambleden Valley *Ox*
FRIEZLAND (Christ Church) *see* Saddleworth *Man*
FRILSHAM (St Frideswide) *see* Hermitage *Ox*
FRIMLEY (St Francis) (St Peter) *Guildf 6* P *R Ash*
R M K WILSON, C W K PUGH
FRIMLEY GREEN (St Andrew) and Mytchett *Guildf 6* P *Bp*
C J S TAYLOR
FRINDSBURY (All Saints) w Upnor (St Phillip and St James)
Roch 6 P *Bp* V S R DYER, **NSM** D G S JOHNSTON
FRING (All Saints) *see* Snettisham w Ingoldisthorpe and Fring
Nor
FRINGFORD (St Michael) *see* Shelswell *Ox*
FRINSTED (St Dunstan) *see* Bredgar w Bicknor and Frinsted
w Wormshill etc *Cant*
FRINTON (St Mary Magdalene) (St Mary the Virgin Old
Church) *Chelmsf 23* P *CPAS* R A D ROSE, C S D GILL
FRISBY-ON-THE-WREAKE (St Thomas of Canterbury)
see Upper Wreake *Leic*
FRISKNEY (All Saints) *Linc 8* P *Bp* P-in-c J DUMAT
FRISTON (St Mary Magdalene) *see* Aldringham w Thorpe,
Knodishall w Buxlow etc *St E*
FRISTON (St Mary the Virgin) *see* E Dean w Friston and
Jevington *Chich*
FRITCHLEY (Mission Room) *see* Crich and S Wingfield *Derby*
FRITHELSTOCK (St Mary and St Gregory) *see* Gt and Lt
Torrington and Frithelstock *Ex*
FRITHVILLE (St Peter) *see* Sibsey w Frithville *Linc*
FRITTENDEN (St Mary) *see* Sissinghurst w Frittenden *Cant*
FRITTON (St Catherine) *see* Hempnall *Nor*
FRITTON (St Edmund) *see* Somerleyton, Ashby, Fritton,
Herringfleet etc *Nor*
FRITWELL (St Olave) w Souldern and Ardley w Fewcott *Ox 2*
P *DBP, St Jo Coll Cam, and Wadh Coll Ox (by turn)*
P-in-c P E HUNT
FRIZINGHALL (St Margaret) *Bradf 1* P *Bp*
P-in-c S P HACKING
FRIZINGTON (St Paul) *see* Crosslacon *Carl*
FROCESTER (St Andrew) *see* Eastington, Frocester, Haresfield
etc *Glouc*
FRODESLEY (St Mark) *see* Condover w Frodesley, Acton
Burnell etc *Heref*
FRODINGHAM (St Lawrence) *Linc 4* P *Lord St Oswald*
V M P COONEY, C E M WEBSTER, **NSM** M DUNFORD
FRODINGHAM, NORTH (St Elgin) *see* Beeford w
Frodingham and Foston *York*
FRODSHAM (St Lawrence) *Ches 3* P *Ch Ch Ox*
V M H MILLS
FROGMORE (Holy Trinity) *St Alb 1* P *CPAS*
V D R HEATH-WHYTE, **NSM** N A WARD

FROLESWORTH (St Nicholas) *see* Claybrooke cum Wibtoft
and Frolesworth *Leic*
FROME (Christ Church) *B & W 4* P *Bp* V P N RAPSEY
FROME (Holy Trinity) *B & W 4* P *Bp* V R D M MARTIN,
C W H H LANE
FROME (St John the Baptist) *B & W 4* P *DBP* V C ALSBURY
FROME (St Mary the Virgin) *B & W 4* P *Bp* V D R BARGE
FROME ST QUINTON (St Mary) *see* Melbury *Sarum*
FROME VAUCHURCH (St Mary) *as above Sarum*
FROMES HILL (St Matthew) *see* Bishop's Frome w Castle
Frome and Fromes Hill *Heref*
FROSTENDEN (All Saints) *see* Sole Bay *St E*
FROSTERLEY (St Michael and All Angels) *see* Stanhope w
Frosterley *Dur*
FROXFIELD (All Saints) *see* Whitton *Sarum*
FROXFIELD (St Peter) *see* Steep and Froxfield w Privett
Portsm
FROXFIELD (St Peter on the Green) *as above Portsm*
FROYLE (Assumption of the Blessed Virgin Mary) and
Holybourne *Win 2* P *Guild of All So and D&C (jt)*
V J S CROFT
FRYERNING (St Mary the Virgin) w Margaretting *Chelmsf 7*
P *Wadh Coll Ox* V *vacant* (01277) 355692
FRYSTON (St Peter) *see* Airedale w Fryston *Wakef*
FUGGLESTONE (St Peter) *see* Wilton w Netherhampton and
Fugglestone *Sarum*
FULBECK (St Nicholas) *see* Caythorpe *Linc*
FULBOURN (St Vigor w All Saints) *Ely 3* P *St Jo Coll Cam*
C R M NANCARROW
FULBROOK (St Gabriel) *see* Walsall St Gabr Fulbrook *Lich*
FULBROOK (St James the Great) *see* Burford w Fulbrook,
Taynton, Asthall etc *Ox*
FULFORD (St Oswald) *York 7* P *Abp* V D J GOODHEW
FULFORD-IN-STONE (St Nicholas) w Hilderstone *Lich 13*
P *D&C* P-in-c P D DAKIN, **NSM** C E DAKIN
FULHAM (All Saints) *Lon 9* P *Bp* V J P HAWES,
C E A MORSE, **NSM** L A PERRY
FULHAM (Christ Church) *Lon 9* P *CPAS* V S C R LEES,
C R P MALONE
FULHAM (St Alban) (St Augustine) *Lon 9* P *Bp and City*
Corp (jt) P-in-c J P MAPLE
FULHAM (St Andrew) Fulham Fields *Lon 9* P *Bp*
P-in-c G R KNIGHT
FULHAM (St Dionis) Parson's Green *Lon 9* P *Bp*
V A S ATKINS
FULHAM (St Etheldreda) (St Clement) *Lon 9* P *Bp*
P-in-c J F H HENLEY
FULHAM (St Mary) North End *Lon 9* P *Ch Soc Trust*
V R W CURL
FULHAM (St Matthew) *Lon 9* P *Ch Patr Trust*
V G Q D PIPER, **Dss** V S PIERSON
FULHAM (St Peter) *Lon 9* P *Bp* P-in-c J F GANGA
FULKING (Good Shepherd) *see* Poynings w Edburton,
Newtimber and Pyecombe *Chich*
FULL SUTTON (St Mary) *see* Garrowby Hill *York*
FULLETBY (St Andrew) *Linc 11* P *Keble Coll Ox* V *vacant*
FULMER (St James) *see* Gerrards Cross and Fulmer *Ox*
FULMODESTON (Christ Church) *see* Barney, Fulmodeston w
Croxton, Hindringham etc *Nor*
FULSHAW (St Anne) *see* Wilmslow *Ches*
FULSTOW (St Laurence) *see* Fotherby *Linc*
FULWOOD (Christ Church) *Blackb 13* P *V Lanc*
V E J BURNS
FULWOOD (Christ Church) *Sheff 4* P *CPAS* V H PALMER,
C T R DAVIES, J P CLARKE
FULWOOD Lodge Moor (St Luke) *see* Lodge Moor St Luke
Sheff
FULWOOD (St Cuthbert) *see* Preston St Cuth *Blackb*
FUNDENHALL (St Nicholas) *see* Ashwellthorpe, Forncett,
Fundenhall, Hapton etc *Nor*
FUNTINGTON (St Mary) and Sennicotts *Chich 13* P *Bp*
V J J HOLLIMAN
FUNTLEY (St Francis) *see* Fareham SS Pet and Paul *Portsm*
FURNACE GREEN (St Andrew) *see* Southgate *Chich*
FURNESS VALE (St John) *see* Disley *Ches*
FURNEUX PELHAM (St Mary the Virgin) *see* Braughing w
Furneux Pelham and Stocking Pelham *St Alb*
FURNHAM (Good Shepherd) *see* Chard and Distr *B & W*
FURTHO (St Bartholomew) *see* Potterspury w Furtho and
Yardley Gobion etc *Pet*
FURZE PLATT (St Peter) *Ox 13* P *Bp* P-in-c L S RAYFIELD
FURZEBANK (Worship Centre) *see* Willenhall H Trin *Lich*
FURZTON (not known) *see* Watling Valley *Ox*
FYFIELD (St Nicholas) *see* Upper Kennet *Sarum*
FYFIELD (St Nicholas) *see* Appleshaw, Kimpton, Thruxton,
Fyfield etc *Win*

FYFIELD (St Nicholas) w Tubney and Kingston Bagpuize *Ox 10*
P *St Jo Coll Ox*   **V** K J TRIPLOW
FYFIELD (St Nicholas), Moreton w Bobbingworth and Willingale w Shellow and Berners Roding *Chelmsf 27*
P *Ld Chan, St Jo Coll Cam, MMCET, and Major G N Capel-Cure (by turn)*   **R** G J WILCOX
FYLINGDALES (St Stephen) and Hawsker cum Stainsacre *York 22*   **P** *Abp*   **P-in-c** D W SMITH
GADDESBY (St Luke) *see* S Croxton Gp *Leic*
GADDESDEN, GREAT (St John the Baptist) and LITTLE (St Peter and St Paul) *St Alb 2* **P** *N G Halsey Esq and Bp (jt)*   **R** R P HOLLINGSHURST
GADEBRIDGE (St Peter) *see* Hemel Hempstead *St Alb*
GAINFORD (St Mary) *Dur 7* **P** *Trin Coll Cam*
P-in-c M ALDERSON
GAINSBOROUGH (All Saints) (St George) and Morton *Linc 2*
P *Bp* **TR** N A THORNLEY, **TV** L M MAGNUSSON, C P SMITH
GALLEY COMMON (St Peter) *see* Camp Hill w Galley Common *Cov*
GALLEYWOOD (Junior School Worship Centre)
see Galleywood Common *Chelmsf*
GALLEYWOOD COMMON (St Michael and All Angels) *Chelmsf 9* **P** *CPAS* **V** S BAILEY
GALMINGTON (St Michael) *see* Wilton *B & W*
GALMPTON (Chapel of The Good Shepherd) *see* Brixham w Churston Ferrers and Kingswear *Ex*
GAMESLEY (Bishop Geoffrey Allen Church and County Centre) *see* Charlesworth and Dinting Vale *Derby*
GAMLINGAY (St Mary the Virgin) and Everton *Ely 13* **P** *Bp, Clare Coll Cam, and Down Coll Cam (by turn)*
R C J-B HAMMOND
GAMLINGAY HEATH (St Sylvester) *see* Gamlingay and Everton *Ely*
GAMSTON and Bridgford *S'well 5* **P** *DBP* **V** S D SILVESTER
GAMSTON (St Peter) w Eaton and West Drayton *S'well 5*
P *D&C York and Bp (alt)* **R** C F ANDREWS
GANAREW (St Swithin) *see* Llangarron w Llangrove, Whitchurch and Ganarew *Heref*
GANTON (St Nicholas) *see* Willerby w Ganton and Folkton *York*
GARBOLDISHAM (St John the Baptist) *see* Guiltcross *Nor*
GARFORD (St Luke) *see* Marcham w Garford *Ox*
GARFORTH (St Mary the Virgin) *Ripon 8* **P** *DBP*
R R G N PLANT
GARGRAVE (St Andrew) *Bradf 5* **P** *Bp* **P-in-c** R C GEDDES
GARRETTS GREEN (St Thomas) *Birm 9* **P** *Bp* **V** vacant 0121-628 5394
GARRIGILL (St John) *see* Alston Moor *Newc*
GARROWBY HILL *York 5* **P** *Ld Chan (1 turn), Abp, D&C, and Earl of Halifax (3 turns)* **R** J C FINNEMORE
GARSDALE (St John the Baptist) *see* Sedbergh, Cautley and Garsdale *Bradf*
GARSDON (All Saints), Lea and Cleverton and Charlton *Bris 6* **P** *Ch Soc Trust and Bp (jt)* **R** R K EAST
GARSINGTON (St Mary) *see* Wheatley *Ox*
GARSTANG (St Helen) Churchtown and St Michaels-on-Wyre *Blackb 9* **P** *Dr I R H Jackson and R P Hornby Esq (jt)*
V A W WILKINSON, **NSM** C M WHALLEY
GARSTANG (St Thomas) *Blackb 9* **P** *V Churchtown St Helen*
V M A GISBOURNE
GARSTON (St Michael) *Liv 4* **P** *Trustees* **V** W N LETHEREN
GARSTON, EAST (All Saints) *see* Eastbury and E Garston *Ox*
GARSWOOD (St Andrew) *see* Ashton-in-Makerfield H Trin *Liv*
GARTHORPE (St Mary) *see* Crowle Gp *Linc*
GARTON IN HOLDERNESS (St Michael) *see* Roos and Garton in Holderness w Tunstall etc *York*
GARTON-ON-THE-WOLDS (St Michael and All Angels) *see* Woldsburn *York*
GARVESTON (St Margaret) *see* Barnham Broom and Upper Yare *Nor*
GARWAY (St Michael) *see* St Weonards w Orcop, Garway, Tretire etc *Heref*
GASTARD (St John the Baptist) *see* Gtr Corsham and Lacock *Bris*
GATCOMBE (St Olave) *Portsm 8* **P** *Qu Coll Ox*
R J W RUSSELL, **Hon C** M R HODGE, **NSM** L M HUNTER
GATE BURTON (St Helen) *see* Lea Gp *Linc*
GATE HELMSLEY (St Mary) *see* Sand Hutton *York*
GATEACRE (St Stephen) *Liv 4* **P** *Bp* **TR** P H JANVIER,
TV J L MCKELVEY, M NORRIS, **C** R K LYALL
GATEFORTH (St Mary's Mission Room) *see* Haddlesey w Hambleton and Birkin *York*
GATELEY (St Helen) *see* Gt and Lt Ryburgh w Gateley and Testerton *Nor*
GATESHEAD (Christ Church) *see* Bensham *Dur*

GATESHEAD Lobley Hill (All Saints) *see* Lobley Hill *Dur*
GATESHEAD (St Chad) *see* Bensham *Dur*
GATESHEAD (St Edmund's Chapel w Holy Trinity) (Venerable Bede) *Dur 12* **P** *Bp and The Crown (alt)*
TR J C WILKINSON, **TV** D M JOHNSON, **NSM** E CARR
GATESHEAD (St George) *Dur 12* **P** *Trustees*
GATESHEAD (St Helen) *Dur 12* **P** *Bp* **V** B M HARRISON
GATESHEAD (St Ninian) Harlow Green *see* Harlow Green and Lamesley *Dur*
GATESHEAD FELL (St John) *Dur 12* **P** *Bp* **R** D J TULLY
GATLEY (St James) *Ches 17* **P** *R Stockport St Thos*
V D S FISHER
GATTEN (St Paul) *Portsm 7* **P** *Ch Patr Trust* **V** P G ALLEN
GATTON (St Andrew) *see* Merstham and Gatton *S'wark*
GAULBY (St Peter) *Leic 5* **P** *Ch Soc Trust*
V A F B CHEESMAN
GAUTBY (All Saints) *see* Bardney *Linc*
GAWBER (St Thomas) *Wakef 7* **P** *V Darton* **V** A PRITCHETT,
NSM B BENFORD
GAWCOTT (Holy Trinity) *see* Lenborough *Ox*
GAWSWORTH (St James) *Ches 13* **P** *T R R Richards Esq*
R W A PWAISIHO
GAYDON (St Giles) w Chadshunt *Cov 8* **P** *Bp* **V** P T FRANCIS
GAYHURST (St Peter) w Ravenstone, Stoke Goldington and Weston Underwood *Ox 27* **P** *Bp and Lord Hesketh (jt)*
R A E D MURDOCH
GAYTON (St Mary) *see* Pattishall w Cold Higham and Gayton w Tiffield *Pet*
GAYTON (St Nicholas), Gayton Thorpe, East Walton, East Winch w West Bilney, Ashwicken w Leziate and Bawsey *Nor 20*
P *Bp, Capt H Birkbeck, and W O Lancaster Esq (jt)*
R I C WHITTLE
GAYTON (St Peter) *see* Mid Trent *Lich*
GAYTON LE WOLD (St Peter) *see* Asterby Gp *Linc*
GAYTON THORPE (St Mary) *see* Gayton, Gayton Thorpe, E Walton, E Winch etc *Nor*
GAYWOOD (St Faith) King's Lynn *Nor 20* **P** *Patr Bd*
TR S M THEAKSTON, **C** L A HUMPHREYS, K L BRANT,
OLM H E BERRY
GAZELEY (All Saints) w Dalham, Moulton and Kentford *St E 11* **P** *Bp (2 turns), Personal Reps Major the Hon J P Philipps (1 turn), and Ch Coll Cam (1 turn)*
P-in-c S J MITCHELL
GEDDING (St Mary the Virgin) *see* Cockfield w Bradfield St Clare, Felsham etc *St E*
GEDDINGTON (St Mary Magdalene) w Weekley *Pet 11*
P *Boughton Estates* **R** F G GODBER
GEDLING (All Hallows) *S'well 10* **P** *DBP* **R** D J STOTER,
C S A BAYLIS, **NSM** K D WILLIAMS
GEDNEY (St Mary Magdalene) *see* Fleet w Gedney *Linc*
GEDNEY DROVE END (Christ Church) *see* Lutton w Gedney Drove End, Dawsmere *Linc*
GEDNEY HILL (Holy Trinity) (St Polycarp) *Linc 16* **P** *Bp*
V R J MORRISON
GEE CROSS (Holy Trinity) (St Philip's Mission Room) *Ches 14*
P *V Werneth* **V** G D OSGOOD
GELDESTON (St Michael) *see* Gillingham w Geldeston, Stockton, Ellingham etc *Nor*
GENTLESHAW (Christ Church) *Lich 1* **P** *MMCET*
P-in-c M J BUTT, **NSM** M R AUSTIN
GEORGEHAM (St George) *Ex 15* **P** *MMCET*
NSM B STRANGE
GERMAN (St German) *S & M 1* **P** *Bp* **V** B H KELLY
GERMAN (St John the Baptist) *S & M 1* **P** *Bp*
V G M BREFFITT
GERMANSWEEK (St German) *see* Okehampton w Inwardleigh, Bratton Clovelly etc *Ex*
GERMOE (St Germoe) *see* Breage w Germoe and Godolphin *Truro*
GERRANS (St Gerran) w St Anthony-in-Roseland and Philleigh *Truro 6* **P** *Bp and MMCET (jt)* **P-in-c** J B SEWELL
GERRARDS CROSS (St James) and Fulmer *Ox 20* **P** *Bp and Simeon's Trustees (jt)* **R** P G WILLIAMS, **C** M J WILLIAMS, N D SCHLUTER, **NSM** J A KING, M R L BEEBEE
GESTINGTHORPE (St Mary) *see* Knights and Hospitallers Par *Chelmsf*
GIDDING, GREAT (St Michael) w LITTLE (St John) and Steeple Gidding *Ely 9* **P** *Sir Stephen Hastings and Bp (alt)*
P-in-c C M FURLONG
GIDEA PARK (St Michael) *Chelmsf 2* **P** *Bp*
V E R PILKINGTON
GIDLEIGH (Holy Trinity) *see* Chagford, Drewsteignton, Hittisleigh etc *Ex*
GIGGETTY LANE (The Venerable Bede) *see* Smestow Vale *Lich*

GIGGLESWICK (St Alkelda) and Rathmell w Wigglesworth
Bradf 5 **P** *Bp and Ch Trust Fund Trust (jt)*
P-in-c P YORKSTONE
GILCRUX (St Mary) *see* Aspatria w Hayton and Gilcrux *Carl*
GILDERSOME (St Peter) *Wakef 8* **P** *V Batley*
V A F LAWSON
GILLAMOOR (St Aidan) *see* Kirkbymoorside w Gillamoor,
Farndale etc *York*
GILLING (St Agatha) and Kirkby Ravensworth *Ripon 2* **P** *Bp
and A C P Wharton Esq (jt)* **P-in-c** J I WILLIAMSON
GILLING EAST (Holy Cross) *see* Ampleforth w Oswaldkirk,
Gilling E etc *York*
GILLINGHAM (Holy Trinity) *Roch 3* **P** *Bp* **V** G E TOVAR,
NSM H J CONNELL
GILLINGHAM (St Augustine) *Roch 3* **P** *Bp* **V** C J VAN
STRAATEN, **NSM** P MATTHIAS
GILLINGHAM (St Barnabas) *Roch 3* **P** *Bp* **V** K B BEST
GILLINGHAM (St Luke) *see* New Brompton St Luke *Roch*
GILLINGHAM (St Mark) *Roch 3* **P** *Hyndman Trustees*
V J M SAUNDERS
GILLINGHAM (St Mary Magdalene) *Roch 3* **P** *DBP*
V K R HAYES
GILLINGHAM (St Mary the Virgin) *Sarum 5* **P** *Bp*
TR A G GILL, **TV** J E SALTER, **NSM** J R HEDGES
**GILLINGHAM (St Mary) w Geldeston w Stockton w Ellingham
St Mary and Kirby Cane** *Nor 8* **P** *Ld Chan (1 turn), Bp,
MMCET and Ch Trust Fund Trust (1 turn)*
R C H R WHITEMAN, **OLM** W G JENNER
GILLINGHAM, SOUTH (St Matthew) *Roch 3* **P** *Patr Bd*
TR C M BUTT, **TV** R A LEE, A D JENKINS, **NSM** A L LEE,
G R LEWIS
GILLOW HEATH (Mission Room) *see* Biddulph *Lich*
**GILMORTON (All Saints), Peatling Parva, Kimcote cum
Walton, North Kilworth, South Kilworth, Misterton, Swinford,
Catthorpe, Shawell and Stanford** *Leic 11* **P** *Patr Bd (5 turns),
Ld Chan (1 turn)* **TR** K W BAKER
GILSLAND (St Mary Magdalene) *see* Lanercost, Walton,
Gilsland and Nether Denton *Carl*
GILSTEAD (St Wilfrid) *see* Bingley H Trin *Bradf*
GILSTON (St Mary) *see* High Wych and Gilston w Eastwick
St Alb
GIMINGHAM (All Saints) *see* Trunch *Nor*
GIPPING (Chapel of St Nicholas) *see* Haughley w Wetherden
and Stowupland *St E*
GIPSY HILL (Christ Church) *S'wark 15* **P** *CPAS*
V A P RUMSEY, **NSM** B ALLEN
GIPTON (Church of the Epiphany) *see* Leeds Gipton Epiphany
Ripon
GIRLINGTON (St Philip) *Bradf 1* **P** *Simeon's Trustees*
V A A TOOBY
GIRTON (St Andrew) *Ely 5* **P** *Ld Chan* **P-in-c** W J ADAM
GIRTON (St Cecilia) *see* Collingham w S Scarle and Besthorpe
and Girton *S'well*
GISBURN (St Mary the Virgin) *Bradf 5* **P** *Bp*
P-in-c E A KYTE, **Hon C** K J PHILLIPS
GISLEHAM (Holy Trinity) *see* Kessingland, Gisleham and
Rushmere *Nor*
GISLINGHAM (St Mary) and Thorndon *St E 16* **P** *Bp, Comdr
F P Brooke-Popham, MMCET, Ch Soc Trust, SMF, and Lord
Henniker (jt)* **R** D E CLAYDEN, **C** A K E SORENSEN
GISSING (St Mary the Virgin) *see* Winfarthing w Shelfanger w
Burston w Gissing etc *Nor*
GITTISHAM (St Michael) *see* Honiton, Gittisham, Combe
Raleigh, Monkton etc *Ex*
GIVENDALE, GREAT (St Ethelberga) *see* Pocklington and
Owsthorpe and Kilnwick Percy etc *York*
GLAISDALE (St Thomas) *see* Middle Esk Moor *York*
GLANDFORD (St Martin) *see* Blakeney w Cley, Wiveton,
Glandford etc *Nor*
GLANTON (St Peter) *see* Whittingham and Edlingham w
Bolton Chapel *Newc*
GLAPTHORN (St Leonard) *see* Oundle w Ashton and
Benefield w Glapthorn *Pet*
GLAPWELL (St Andrew) *see* Ault Hucknall and Scarcliffe
Derby
GLASCOTE (St George) and Stonydelph *Lich 4* **P** *Patr Bd*
TR I H MURRAY, **TV** D C WELLER, D S MCDONOUGH,
C E A LANDER, **OLM** M R LE-WORTHY, D BURGESS,
R LOCKWOOD
GLASSHOUGHTON (St Paul) *see* Castleford *Wakef*
GLASSON (Christ Church) *see* Cockerham w Winmarleigh and
Glasson *Blackb*
GLASTON (St Andrew) *see* Lyddington w Stoke Dry and
Seaton etc *Pet*
GLASTONBURY (St John the Baptist) (St Benedict) w Meare
B & W 5 **P** *Bp* **P-in-c** M D MARSH, **C** J G SUMNER,
Hon C M B MUDIE

GLATTON (St Nicholas) *see* Sawtry and Glatton *Ely*
GLAZEBURY (All Saints) w Hollinfare *Liv 16* **P** *Bp and
R Warrington (jt)* **NSM** P L GRAY
GLAZELEY (St Bartholomew) *see* Highley w Billingsley,
Glazeley etc *Heref*
GLEADLESS (Christ Church) *Sheff 1* **P** *DBP*
TR H A JOWETT, **TV** M CAUNT, **NSM** S D HOLDAWAY
GLEADLESS VALLEY (Holy Cross) *see* Heeley and Gleadless
Valley *Sheff*
**GLEMHAM, GREAT (All Saints) and LITTLE (St Andrew),
Blaxhall, Stratford St Andrew and Farnham** *St E 19* **P** *Earl of
Guilford, C J V Hope Johnstone Esq, and P M Cobbold Esq
(1 turn), and DBP (1 turn)* **P-in-c** C E BROOKS,
C B J SLATTER
**GLEMSFORD (St Mary the Virgin), Hartest w Boxted,
Somerton and Stanstead (Glem Valley United Benefice)** *St E 12*
P *Bp, Prime Min, and Ch Soc Trust (by turn)* **R** P J PRIGG
GLEN AULDYN (Mission Church) *see* Lezayre *S & M*
GLEN GROUP, The *Linc 17* **P** *Bp* **V** M A HARVEY
**GLEN MAGNA (St Cuthbert) cum Stretton Magna w Carlton
Curlieu and Burton Overy** *Leic 5* **P** *Bp, Dr A Llewelyn, and
Sir Geoffrey Palmer Bt (jt)* **V** G L SPENCER
GLEN PARVA and South Wigston *Leic 5* **P** *Bp* **V** P DAY
GLENDALE Group, The *Newc 10* **P** *Patr Bd (4 turns),
Ld Chan (1 turn)* **TR** R B S BURSTON, **TV** B C HURST,
G R KELSEY, **NSM** T R ROCHESTER
GLENFIELD (St Peter) *Leic 12* **P** *Bp* **R** J E SHARPE,
C O A ADAMS, **Hon C** P B HARVEY
GLENHOLT (St Anne) *see* Bickleigh and Shaugh Prior *Ex*
GLENTHAM (St Peter) *see* Owmby Gp *Linc*
GLENTWORTH Group, The (St Michael) *Linc 2* **P** *Bp,
MMCET, and Ch Soc Trust (jt)* **V** M DAWSON
GLINTON (St Benedict) *see* Peakirk w Glinton and
Northborough *Pet*
GLODWICK (St Mark w Christ Church) *Man 19* **P** *Bp*
V A R HEYES
GLOOSTON (St John the Baptist) *see* Gt Bowden w Welham,
Glooston and Cranoe etc *Leic*
GLOSSOP (All Saints) *Derby 6* **P** *Patr Bd* **V** D M ROWLEY
GLOUCESTER (St Aldate) Finlay Road *Glouc 5* **P** *Bp*
P-in-c K C JONES
GLOUCESTER (St Barnabas) *see* Tuffley *Glouc*
GLOUCESTER (St Catharine) *Glouc 5* **P** *Bp*
V G D OSBORNE, **C** J S J GROVES
GLOUCESTER (St George) w Whaddon *Glouc 5* **P** *Bp*
C F A WALTERS, **NSM** R M BRYANT
GLOUCESTER (St James and All Saints) *Glouc 5* **P** *Bp*
V M W BUTLER, **NSM** J M HOWARD
**GLOUCESTER (St Mark) (St Mary de Crypt) (St John the
Baptist) (Christ Church) (St Mary de Lode and St Nicholas)**
Glouc 5 **P** *D&C (1 turn), Bp (3 turns), Ld Chan (1 turn)*
R J L MARSHALL, **NSM** V J KERNER
GLOUCESTER (St Michael) *see* Tuffley *Glouc*
GLOUCESTER (St Oswald) *see* Coney Hill *Glouc*
GLOUCESTER (St Paul) *Glouc 5* **P** *Bp* **V** R C KEY,
NSM J R MURPHY
GLOUCESTER (St Stephen) *Glouc 5* **P** *Bp*
P-in-c J A L B CATERER
GLOUCESTER DOCKS Mariners' Church Proprietary Chapel
Glouc 5 **P** *Ch Soc Trust vacant*
GLOUCESTER ROAD (St Stephen) *see* S Kensington St Steph
Lon
GLUSBURN (All Saints) *see* Sutton *Bradf*
GLYMPTON (St Mary) *see* Wootton w Glympton and
Kiddington *Ox*
GLYNDE (St Mary), West Firle and Beddingham *Chich 18*
P *Bp and D&C Windsor (alt)* **V** *vacant* (01273) 858227
GNOSALL (St Lawrence) *Lich 7* **P** *Bp* **V** C M CASE,
C C M PLANT
GOADBY (St John the Baptist) *see* Church Langton cum Tur
Langton etc *Leic*
GOADBY MARWOOD (St Denys) *see* Scalford w Goadby
Marwood and Wycombe etc *Leic*
GOATHILL (St Peter) *see* Milborne Port w Goathill *B & W*
GOATHLAND (St Mary) *see* Middle Esk Moor *York*
GOATHURST (St Edward the King and Martyr) *see* Spaxton w
Charlynch, Goathurst, Enmore etc *B & W*
GOBOWEN (All Saints) *see* Hengoed w Gobowen *Lich*
GOBOWEN ROAD (Mission Room) *see* Oswestry *Lich*
GODALMING (St Peter and St Paul) *Guildf 4* **P** *Bp*
TR F J ASHE, **TV** I P BUSSELL, **NSM** M E HOBROUGH,
OLM D S MACE, P C K O'FERRALL
GODINGTON (Holy Trinity) *see* Shelswell *Ox*
GODLEY cum Newton Green (St John the Baptist) *Ches 14*
P *R Cheadle* **P-in-c** M D HARRIES
GODMANCHESTER (St Mary) *Ely 8* **P** *D&C Westmr*
V P J MOGER, **C** E B ATLING, A M BARRETT

GODMANSTONE (Holy Trinity)   *see* Buckland Newton, Cerne Abbas, Godmanstone etc *Sarum*
GODMERSHAM (St Lawrence the Martyr)   *see* Crundale w Godmersham *Cant*
GODREVY   *Truro 5*   **P** *Patr Bd*   **TR** A T NEAL,
TV L T ATTWOOD,   **C** C A WILSON-BARKER,
NSM R E WICKREMASINGHE, J B FOX, P C JOHNSON
GODSHILL (All Saints)   *Portsm 7*   **P** *Guild of All So*
V J M RYDER,   **NSM** M M K KAY
GODSHILL (St Giles)   *see* Fordingbridge and Breamore and Hale etc *Win*
GODSTONE (St Nicholas) and Blindley Heath   *S'wark 27*
P *Bp and C K G Hoare Esq (jt)*   **R** R E WATTS,
C S M SOKOLOWSKI,   **OLM** D G E HARDING
GOFF'S OAK (St James)   *St Alb 20*   **P** *V Cheshunt*
V J W BRIDSTRUP
GOLBORNE (St Thomas)   *Liv 16*   **P** *Bp*   **R** R WILLIAMS
GOLCAR (St John the Evangelist)   *Wakef 5*   **P** *V Huddersfield*
V R M F CROMPTON
GOLDEN CAP TEAM (Team Ministry)   *Sarum 2*   **P** *Patr Bd*
TR R H FAIRBROTHER,   **TV** J G W ANDREWS, A-M L STUART,
NSM T E C SHARPE, F A KEEGAN
GOLDEN GREEN (Mission)   *see* Hadlow *Roch*
GOLDEN VALLEY (St Matthias)   *see* Riddings and Ironville *Derby*
GOLDENHILL (St John the Evangelist)   *Lich 11*   **P** *Bp*
P-in-c K P SCOTT
GOLDERS GREEN (St Alban the Martyr and St Michael)
Lon 15   **P** *Bp*   **V** T E A PARK
GOLDHANGER (St Peter)   *see* Gt and Lt Totham w Goldhanger *Chelmsf*
GOLDINGTON (St Mary the Virgin)   *St Alb 10*   **P** *Bp*
V T MAINES,   **C** J M CAPPLEMAN
GOLDS HILL (St Paul)   *see* W Bromwich St Jas w St Paul *Lich*
GOLDSBOROUGH (St Mary)   *see* Knaresborough *Ripon*
GOLDSWORTH PARK (St Andrew)   *Guildf 12*   **P** *Bp*
V R J N COOK,   **C** J L BLAIR, C J BLAIR,
NSM C A HARRISON,   **OLM** P R B DONAGHY
GOLDTHORPE (St John the Evangelist and St Mary Magdalene) w Hickleton   *Sheff 12*   **P** *CR (2 turns), Earl of Halifax (1 turn)*   **V** A J DELVES,   **C** A S ZIHNI
GOMERSAL (St Mary)   *Wakef 8*   **P** *Bp*   **V** M G RAWSON,
NSM R M CAVE
GONALSTON (St Laurence)   *S'well 10*   **P** *C P L Francklin Esq, Bp, and Ld Chan (by turn)*   **R** M J BROCK,   **C** J E DRAYCOTT,
NSM M N TAYLOR
GONERBY, GREAT (St Sebastian)   *see* Barrowby and Gt Gonerby *Linc*
GOOD EASTER (St Andrew)   *see* High and Gd Easter w Margaret Roding *Chelmsf*
GOOD SHEPHERD TEAM MINISTRY, The   *Carl 4*
P *Patr Bd*   **TR** M A HOUSTON,   **TV** H M K BRETT YOUNG
GOODERSTONE (St George)   *see* Cockley Cley w Gooderstone *Nor*
GOODLEIGH (St Gregory)   *see* Barnstaple *Ex*
GOODMANHAM (All Saints)   *York 5*   **P** *Abp*
R P P OCKFORD
GOODMAYES (All Saints)   *Chelmsf 4*   **P** *Hyndman Trustees*
V C R KEATING
GOODMAYES (St Paul)   *Chelmsf 4*   **P** *Bp*   **V** B J RUTT-FIELD
GOODNESTONE (Holy Cross)   *see* Nonington w Wymynswold and Goodnestone etc *Cant*
GOODRICH (St Giles)   *see* Walford and St John w Bishopswood, Goodrich etc *Heref*
GOODRINGTON (St George)   *Ex 10*   **P** *Bp*
V B D PROTHERO,   **C** R H MASKELL
GOODSHAW (St Mary and All Saints) and Crawshawbooth
Man 15   **P** *Bp and Wm Hulme Trustees (jt)*
P-in-c W L OLIVER
GOODWORTH CLATFORD (St Peter)   *see* Abbotts Ann and Upper and Goodworth Clatford *Win*
GOOLE (St John the Evangelist) (St Mary) (Mariners' Club and Chapel)   *Sheff 10*   **P** *Bp*   **C** I SMITH
GOOSE GREEN (St Paul)   *Liv 15*   **P** *Bp*   **V** K BOLTON
GOOSEY (All Saints)   *see* Stanford in the Vale w Goosey and Hatford *Ox*
GOOSNARGH (St Mary the Virgin)   *see* Fellside Team *Blackb*
GOOSTREY (St Luke)   *Ches 11*   **P** *V Sandbach*
NSM A SARGEANT
GORAN HAVEN (St Just)   *see* St Goran w Caerhays *Truro*
GORDON HILL (St Michael and All Angels)   *see* Enfield St Mich *Lon*
GOREFIELD (St Paul)   *Ely 17*   **P** *Bp*   **V** *vacant*
GORING (St Thomas of Canterbury) w South Stoke   *Ox 6*
P *Ch Ch Ox*   **V** P E NIXON,   **C** H A CAMPBELL
GORING-BY-SEA (St Mary) (St Laurence)   *Chich 4*   **P** *Bp*
V A TREMLETT,   **C** D A BURT,   **NSM** P MATTHEWS

GORLESTON (St Andrew)   *Nor 6*   **P** *Ch Trust Fund Trust*
V A P WARD,   **C** J B SHAW,   **NSM** C M UPTON
GORLESTON (St Mary Magdalene)   *Nor 6*   **P** *Bp and Ch Trust Fund Trust (jt)*   **V** T W RIESS
GORNAL, LOWER (St James the Great)   *Worc 10*   **P** *Bp*
V J W MOTT
GORNAL, UPPER (St Peter)   *Worc 10*   **P** *V Sedgley All SS*
V M K BATE
GORSLEY (Christ Church)   *see* Newent and Gorsley w Cliffords Mesne *Glouc*
GORTON (Emmanuel) (St James)   *Man 1*   **P** *Bp and D&C (jt)*
R M R J WILLIAMS,   **OLM** D C GRAY
GORTON (St Philip)   *Man 1*   **P** *The Crown*
P-in-c S SCHOFIELD,   **C** J A P WALKER
GOSBECK (St Mary)   *see* Coddenham w Gosbeck and Hemingstone w Henley *St E*
GOSBERTON (St Peter and St Paul), Gosberton Clough and Quadring   *Linc 17*   **P** *Bp and D&C (jt)*   **V** J W FURST
GOSBERTON CLOUGH (St Gilbert and St Hugh)
see Gosberton, Gosberton Clough and Quadring *Linc*
GOSCOTE, EAST (St Hilda)   *see* Syston *Leic*
GOSFIELD (St Katherine)   *Chelmsf 19*   **P** *Mrs G M Lowe and Mrs M A Wilson (jt)*   **V** *vacant (01787) 473857*
GOSFORTH (All Saints)   *Newc 5*   **P** *Bp*   **R** B HILL,
C C R PICKFORD
GOSFORTH (St Hugh)   *Newc 5*   **P** *Bp*   **P-in-c** P KENNEY
GOSFORTH (St Mary) w Nether Wasdale and Wasdale Head
Carl 5   **P** *Bp, Earl of Lonsdale, V St Bees, and PCCs (jt)*
R C B GALLOWAY
GOSFORTH (St Nicholas)   *Newc 5*   **P** *Bp*
V P J CUNNINGHAM
GOSFORTH, NORTH (St Columba)   *see* Ch the King *Newc*
GOSFORTH VALLEY (St Andrew)   *see* Dronfield w Holmesfield *Derby*
GOSPEL END (St Barnabas)   *see* Sedgley All SS w *Worc*
GOSPEL LANE (St Michael)   *Birm 6*   **P** *Bp*
P-in-c R M WHARTON
GOSPEL OAK (All Hallows)   *see* Hampstead St Steph w All Hallows *Lon*
GOSPEL OAK (St Martin)   *see* Kentish Town St Martin w St Andr *Lon*
GOSPORT (Christ Church)   *Portsm 3*   **P** *Bp*
P-in-c J A GORDON
GOSPORT (Holy Trinity)   *Portsm 3*   **P** *DBP*
P-in-c I G BOOTH
GOSSOPS GREEN (St Alban)   *see* Ifield *Chich*
GOTHAM (St Lawrence)   *S'well 9*   **P** *Bp*   **P-in-c** S W OSMAN
GOUDHURST (St Mary the Virgin) w Kilndown   *Cant 11*
P *Abp and Prime Min (alt)*   **V** P T MACKENZIE
GOULCEBY (All Saints)   *see* Asterby Gp *Linc*
GOXHILL (All Saints)   *see* Barrow and Goxhill *Linc*
GOXHILL (St Giles)   *see* Aldbrough, Mappleton w Goxhill and Withernwick *York*
GRADE (St Grada and the Holy Cross)   *see* St Ruan w St Grade and Landewednack *Truro*
GRAFFHAM (St Giles) w Woolavington   *Chich 11*   **P** *Bp*
P-in-c P M GILBERT
GRAFFOE Group   *Linc 18*   **P** *Ch Coll Cam, D&C and DBP, Viscountess Chaplin, Oriel Coll Ox, and Mrs P N Fullerton (by turn)*   **V** K A WINDSLOW
GRAFHAM (All Saints)   *see* E Leightonstone *Ely*
GRAFHAM (St Andrew)   *see* Bramley and Grafham *Guildf*
GRAFTON, EAST (St Nicholas)   *see* Savernake *Sarum*
GRAFTON FLYFORD (St John the Baptist)   *see* Abberton, The Flyfords, Naunton Beauchamp etc *Worc*
GRAFTON REGIS (St Mary)   *see* Blisworth and Stoke Bruerne w Grafton Regis etc *Pet*
GRAFTON UNDERWOOD (St James the Apostle)
see Cranford w Grafton Underwood and Twywell *Pet*
GRAHAME PARK (St Augustine) Conventional District   *Lon 15*
C-in-c D C BATLEY-GLADDEN
GRAIN (St James) w Stoke   *Roch 6*   **P** *DBP*   **V** G F BARKER
GRAINSBY (St Nicholas)   *see* The North-Chapel Parishes *Linc*
GRAINTHORPE (St Clement)   *see* Somercotes and Grainthorpe w Conisholme *Linc*
GRAMPOUND (St Nun)   *see* Probus, Ladock and Grampound w Creed and St Erme *Truro*
GRAMPOUND ROAD Mission Church   *as above Truro*
GRANBOROUGH (St John the Baptist)   *see* Schorne *Ox*
GRANBY (All Saints)   *see* Cropwell Bishop w Colston Bassett, Granby etc *S'well*
GRANDBOROUGH (St Peter)   *see* Leam Valley *Cov*
GRANGE (Holy Trinity)   *see* Thornthwaite cum Braithwaite, Newlands etc *Carl*
GRANGE (St Andrew)   *Ches 3*   **P** *Bp*
P-in-c E W LAUTENBACH,   **C** N M REDEYOFF

GRANGE FELL (not known) *see* Cartmel Peninsula *Carl*
GRANGE MOOR (St Bartholomew) *see* Kirkheaton *Wakef*
GRANGE-OVER-SANDS (St Paul) *see* Cartmel Peninsula *Carl*
GRANGE PARK (St Peter) *Lon 18* **P** *Bp* **V** E G GREER
GRANGE VILLA (St Columba) *see* W Pelton *Dur*
GRANGETOWN (St Aidan) *Dur 16* **P** *V Ryhope*
V C COLLINS
GRANGETOWN (St Hilda of Whitby) *York 18* **P** *Abp*
V I M GRAHAM
GRANSDEN, GREAT (St Bartholomew) and Abbotsley and Lt Gransden and Waresley *Ely 13* **P** *Pemb Coll Cam (1 turn), Clare Coll Cam (2 turns), and Ball Coll Ox (1 turn)*
R B CURRY
GRANSDEN, LITTLE (St Peter and St Paul) *see* Gt Gransden and Abbotsley and Lt Gransden etc *Ely*
GRANTCHESTER (St Andrew and St Mary) *Ely 6* **P** *CCC Cam* **P-in-c** K F M FISHER
GRANTHAM Earlesfield *Linc 19* **P** *Bp* **V** S G ROWLAND
GRANTHAM Harrowby w Londonthorpe *Linc 19* **P** *Bp*
V *vacant* (01526) 861746
GRANTHAM Manthorpe *Linc 19* **P** *Bp*
P-in-c M R SAUNDERS
GRANTHAM (St Anne) New Somerby and St John Spitalgate *Linc 19* **P** *Bp and R Grantham (jt)* **V** F H LONG
GRANTHAM (St John the Evangelist) *see* Grantham, Manthorpe *Linc*
GRANTHAM (St Wulfram) *Linc 19* **P** *Bp* **R** C P ANDREWS,
C V L SIMS, **NSM** J T FARLEY
GRANTHAM (The Ascension) *see* Grantham, Harrowby w Londonthorpe *Linc*
GRANTHAM (The Epiphany) *see* Grantham, Earlesfield *Linc*
GRANVILLES WOOTTON (St Mary the Virgin) *see* Dungeon Hill *Sarum*
GRAPPENHALL (St Wilfrid) *Ches 4* **P** *P G Greenall Esq*
R M B KELLY
GRASBY (All Saints) *see* Caistor Gp *Linc*
GRASMERE (St Oswald) *Carl 11* **P** *Qu Coll Ox* **R** *vacant* (01539) 435326
GRASSENDALE (St Mary) *Liv 4* **P** *Trustees*
V J H ROBINSON
GRATELEY (St Leonard) *see* Amport, Grateley, Monxton and Quarley *Win*
GRATWICH (St Mary the Virgin) *see* Uttoxeter Area *Lich*
GRAVELEY (St Botolph) *see* Papworth *Ely*
GRAVELEY (St Mary) *see* Stevenage St Nic and Graveley St Alb
GRAVELLY HILL (All Saints) *Birm 8* **P** *Bp*
V G R MENSINGH
GRAVENEY (All Saints) *see* Preston next Faversham, Goodnestone and Graveney *Cant*
GRAVENHURST (St Giles), Shillington and Stondon *St Alb 16*
P *Bp* **V** S J WHEATLEY, **NSM** C M EAGGER
GRAVESEND (Holy Family) w Ifield *Roch 4* **P** *Bp and Lt-Col F B Edmeades (jt)* **R** J L FIELD
GRAVESEND (St Aidan) *Roch 4* **P** *Bp* **V** P G RICH,
NSM J P LITTLEWARD
GRAVESEND (St George) *Roch 4* **P** *Bp* **R** *vacant* (01474) 534965
GRAVESEND (St Mary) *Roch 4* **P** *R Gravesend* **V** *vacant* (01474) 352162
GRAYINGHAM (St Radegunda) *Linc 6* **P** *Bp* **R** S J FOSTER
GRAYRIGG (St John the Evangelist), Old Hutton and New Hutton *Carl 10* **P** *V Kendal* **P-in-c** B PEDDER
GRAYS NORTH (St John the Evangelist) *Chelmsf 14* **P** *Bp*
V D R TOMLINSON, **NSM** J C TOMLINSON
GRAYS THURROCK (St Peter and St Paul) *Chelmsf 14*
P *DBP* **TR** J C HASSELL, **TV** L H LEE, P M A PEELING,
C M E FAULKNER, **NSM** J K EDWARDS
GRAYSHOTT (St Luke) *Guildf 3* **P** *Bp* **V** M S WING
GRAYSWOOD (All Saints) *see* Haslemere and Grayswood *Guildf*
GRAYTHWAITE (Mission Room) *see* Hawkshead and Low Wray w Sawrey and Rusland etc *Carl*
GRAZELEY (Holy Trinity) *see* Beech Hill, Grazeley and Spencers Wood *Ox*
GREASBROUGH (St Mary) *Sheff 6* **P** *Sir Philip Naylor-Leyland Bt* **V** K E TONES
GREASBY (St Nicholas) *see* Frankby w Greasby *Ches*
GREASLEY (St Mary) *S'well 4* **P** *Bp* **P-in-c** D A MARVIN
GREAT *see also under substantive place name*
GREAT CAMBRIDGE ROAD (St John the Baptist and St James) *Lon 19* **P** *D&C St Paul's* **V** P B LYONS
GREAT GLEN (St Cuthbert) *see* Glen Magna cum Stretton Magna etc *Leic*
GREAT MOOR (St Saviour) *see* Stockport St Sav *Ches*

GREATER *see under substantive place name*
GREATFORD (St Thomas à Becket) *see* Uffington Gp *Linc*
GREATHAM (not known) *see* Amberley w N Stoke and Parham, Wiggonholt etc *Chich*
GREATHAM (St John the Baptist) *Dur 3* **P** *Trustees*
P-in-c R A COLLINS
GREATHAM w Empshott and Hawkley w Prior's Dean *Portsm 4*
P *DBP* **R** D H HEATLEY, **NSM** D C STICKLAND
GREATSTONE (St Peter) *see* Lydd *Cant*
GREATWORTH (St Peter) and Marston St Lawrence w Warkorth and Thenford *Pet 1* **P** *Bp (2 turns), The Crown (1 turn)* **P-in-c** M G BULL
GREAVE FOLD (Holy Innocents) *see* Chadkirk *Ches*
GREEN HAMMERTON (St Thomas) *see* Gt and Lt Ouseburn w Marton cum Grafton etc *Ripon*
GREEN HAWORTH (St Clement) *see* Accrington Ch the King *Blackb*
GREEN HEATH (St Saviour) *see* Hednesford *Lich*
GREEN STREET GREEN (St Mary) and Pratts Bottom *Roch 16* **P** *Bp* **V** P MILLER, K A CARPANI, **C** P J AVANN
GREEN VALE (Holy Trinity) *see* Stockton H Trin *Dur*
GREENFIELD *see* Bridgwater H Trin *B & W*
GREENFIELD (St Mary) *see* Saddleworth *Man*
GREENFIELDS (United Church) *see* Shrewsbury St Geo w Greenfields *Lich*
GREENFORD (Holy Cross) (St Edward the Confessor) *Lon 22*
P *K Coll Cam* **R** N RICHARDSON, **C** M L TOOGOOD
GREENFORD, NORTH (All Hallows) *Lon 22* **P** *Bp*
P-in-c P B DENTON, **NSM** D C DAVIS, P F HEAZELL
GREENGATES (St John the Evangelist) *Bradf 3* **P** *D&C*
V T COLLIN
GREENHAM (St Mary the Virgin) *Ox 14* **P** *Bp*
V J P H CLARKE
GREENHAM (St Peter) *see* Wellington and Distr *B & W*
GREENHEAD (St Cuthbert) *see* Haltwhistle and Greenhead *Newc*
GREENHILL (St John the Baptist) *Lon 23* **P** *Bp, Adn, and V Harrow St Mary (jt)* **V** J F SPINKS
GREENHILL (St Peter) *Sheff 2* **P** *Bp* **V** L C JENKINS
GREENHITHE (St Mary) *Roch 2* **P** *Ch Soc Trust and Canon T L Livermore (jt)* **R** R D BARRON
GREENHOW HILL (St Mary) *see* Upper Nidderdale *Ripon*
GREENLANDS (St Anne) *Blackb 8* **P** *Bp and V Blackpool St Steph (jt)* **V** A M BARTLETT
GREENLANDS (St John the Evangelist) *see* Ipsley *Worc*
GREENS NORTON (St Bartholomew) w Bradden and Lichborough *Pet 5* **P** *J E Grant-Ives Esq (1 turn), The Crown (3 turns), and Melanesian Miss Trust (1 turn)*
P-in-c J F A M KNIGHT
GREENSIDE (St John) *Dur 13* **P** *R Ryton w Hedgefield*
V P D SADDINGTON
GREENSTEAD (St Andrew) (St Matthew) w Colchester St Anne *Chelmsf 16* **P** *Patr Bd and Ld Chan (alt)* **TR** B S RAWLINGS, **TV** M A COHEN,
C A M PARKER, R M ROBERTS
GREENSTEAD GREEN (St James Apostle) *see* Halstead St Andr w H Trin and Greenstead Green *Chelmsf*
GREENSTED-JUXTA-ONGAR (St Andrew) w Stanford Rivers *Chelmsf 27* **P** *Bp Lon and Duchy of Lanc (alt)*
P-in-c R WILKINSON
GREENWICH (St Alfege) *S'wark 3* **P** *The Crown*
V G HARCOURT, **C** D C WALSH, **Hon C** S J DAVIES
GREENWICH, EAST (Christ Church) (St Andrew w St Michael) *S'wark 3* **P** *Patr Bd*
TR M N A TORRY, **TV** C J MORGAN
GREETE (St James) *see* Burford II w Greete and Hope Bagot *Heref*
GREETHAM (All Saints) w Ashby Puerorum *Linc 11* **P** *D&C*
R M E BURSON-THOMAS, **C** A C V HARVEY, **NSM** A C FORD
GREETHAM (St Mary the Virgin) and Thistleton w Stretton and Clipsham *Pet 14* **P** *Bp and Sir David Davenport-Handley (alt)*
C M H W ROGERS, S A WALKER
GREETLAND (St Thomas) and West Vale *Wakef 2*
P *V Halifax* **V** S GOTT
GREETWELL (All Saints) *see* S Lawres Gp *Linc*
GREINTON (St Michael and All Angels) *B & W 5* **P** *Bp*
R *vacant*
GRENDON (All Saints) *see* Baddesley Ensor w Grendon *Birm*
GRENDON (St Mary) *see* Yardley Hastings, Denton and Grendon etc *Pet*
GRENDON BISHOP (St John the Baptist) *see* Bredenbury w Grendon Bishop and Wacton etc *Heref*
GRENDON UNDERWOOD (St Leonard) *see* Swan *Ox*
GRENOSIDE (St Mark) *Sheff 3* **P** *Bp and V Ecclesfield (jt)*
V M J CAREY
GRESHAM (All Saints) *see* Aylmerton, Runton, Beeston Regis and Gresham *Nor*

GRESLEY (St George and St Mary) *Derby 16*   **P** *Simeon's Trustees*   **V** J A MUSTON,   **C** J A BURGESS
GRESSENHALL (Assumption of the Blessed Virgin Mary) w Longham w Wendling and Bittering Parva *Nor 14*   **P** *Ld Chan (1 turn), CPAS (2 turns)*   **R** J E BELHAM,   **NSM** K D BLOGG
GRESSINGHAM (St John the Evangelist)   *see* Hornby w Claughton and Whittington etc *Blackb*
GRETTON (Christ Church)   *see* Winchcombe, Gretton, Sudeley Manor etc *Glouc*
GRETTON (St James the Great) w Rockingham and Cottingham w East Carlton *Pet 9*   **P** *Bp, Comdr L M M Saunders Watson, Sir Geoffrey Palmer Bt, and BNC Ox (jt)*   **V** M FALLA,   **NSM** S L HUGHES
GREWELTHORPE (St James)   *see* Fountains Gp *Ripon*
GREYSTOKE (St Andrew)   *see* Gd Shep TM *Carl*
GREYSTONES (St Gabriel) *Sheff 2*   **P** *Dean*   **V** P W BECKLEY
GREYWELL (St Mary)   *see* Newnham w Nately Scures w Mapledurwell etc *Win*
GRIMEHILLS (St Mary)   *see* Darwen St Barn *Blackb*
GRIMETHORPE (St Luke) *Wakef 7*   **P** *Bp*   **P-in-c** P D NEEDHAM
GRIMLEY (St Bartholomew)   *see* Hallow and Grimley w Holt *Worc*
GRIMOLDBY (St Edith)   *see* Mid Marsh Gp *Linc*
GRIMSARGH (St Michael) *Blackb 13*   **P** *R Preston*   **V** G R LOXHAM
GRIMSBURY (St Leonard)   *see* Banbury St Leon *Ox*
GRIMSBY (St Augustine of Hippo) *Linc 9*   **P** *TR Gt Grimsby SS Mary and Jas*   **V** S W JONES
GRIMSBY, GREAT (St Andrew w St Luke and All Saints) *Linc 9*   **P** *Bp*   **P-in-c** T H ATKINSON
GRIMSBY, GREAT (St Mary and St James) (St Hugh) (St Mark) (St Martin) *Linc 9*   **P** *Bp*   **TR** M O HUNTER,   **C** D J SUDRON,   **NSM** J MCMANN
GRIMSBY, LITTLE (St Edith)   *see* Fotherby *Linc*
GRIMSBY WEST   *see* Gt and Lt Coates w Bradley *Linc*
GRIMSTEAD, EAST (Holy Trinity)   *see* Clarendon *Sarum*
GRIMSTEAD, WEST (St John)   *as above Sarum*
GRIMSTON (St Botolph), Congham and Roydon *Nor 20*   **P** *Qu Coll Cam, Bp, and G Howard Esq (jt)*   **R** W A HOWARD
GRIMSTON (St John the Baptist)   *see* Old Dalby, Nether Broughton, Saxelbye etc *Leic*
GRIMSTON, NORTH (St Nicholas)   *see* W Buckrose *York*
GRINDALE (St Nicholas)   *see* Burton Fleming w Fordon, Grindale etc *York*
GRINDLEFORD (St Helen)   *see* Eyam *Derby*
GRINDLETON (St Ambrose)   *see* Bolton by Bowland w Grindleton *Bradf*
GRINDON (All Saints)   *see* Calton, Cauldon, Grindon, Waterfall etc *Lich*
GRINDON (St James), Stillington and Wolviston *Dur 10*   **P** *Bp (2 turns), D&C (1 turn)*   **R** *vacant* (01740) 630549
GRINDON (St Oswald)   *see* Sunderland Pennywell St Thos *Dur*
GRINGLEY-ON-THE-HILL (St Peter and St Paul)   *see* Beckingham w Walkeringham and Gringley *S'well*
GRINSDALE (St Kentigern)   *see* Barony of Burgh *Carl*
GRINSHILL (All Saints)   *see* Astley, Clive, Grinshill and Hadnall *Lich*
GRINSTEAD, EAST (St Mary the Virgin) *Chich 7*   **P** *Bp*   **V** G BOND
GRINSTEAD, EAST (St Swithun) *Chich 7*   **P** *Bp*   **V** C EVERETT-ALLEN,   **C** R J S CATCHPOLE,   N H LAMB,   **NSM** J K PEATY
GRINSTEAD, WEST (St George) *Chich 8*   **P** *Bp*   **R** W E M HARRIS
GRINTON (St Andrew)   *see* Swaledale *Ripon*
GRISTHORPE (St Thomas)   *see* Filey *York*
GRISTON (St Peter and St Paul)   *see* Caston, Griston, Merton, Thompson etc *Nor*
GRITTLETON (St Mary the Virgin)   *see* By Brook *Bris*
GRIZEBECK (The Good Shepherd)   *see* Kirkby Ireleth *Carl*
GROBY (St Philip and St James)   *see* Bradgate Team *Leic*
GROOMBRIDGE (St John the Evangelist)   *see* Speldhurst w Groombridge and Ashurst *Roch*
GROOMBRIDGE, NEW (St Thomas) *Chich 19*   **P** *R Withyham*   **P-in-c** A B GREEN
GROSMONT (St Matthew)   *see* Middle Esk Moor *York*
GROSVENOR CHAPEL (no dedication) Chapel of Ease in the parish of Hanover Square St George w St Mark *Lon 3*   **C-in-c** S J HOBBS,   **Hon C** S D DEWEY
GROTON (St Bartholomew)   *see* Boxford, Edwardstone, Groton etc *St E*
GROVE (St Helen)   *see* E Markham w Askham, Headon w Upton and Grove *S'well*
GROVE (St John the Baptist) *Ox 19*   **P** *D&C Windsor*   **V** J C ROBERTSON,   **C** M R HODSON

GROVE GREEN (St John) Local Ecumenical Project *Cant 15*   **Min** D P MOUNCER
GROVE PARK (St Augustine)   *see* Lee St Aug *S'wark*
GROVEHILL (Resurrection)   *see* Hemel Hempstead *St Alb*
GRUNDISBURGH (St Mary the Virgin)   *see* Boulge w Burgh, Grundisburgh and Hasketon *St E*
GUARLFORD (St Mary)   *see* Powick and Guarlford and Madresfield w Newland *Worc*
GUERNSEY (Holy Trinity) *Win 14*   **P** *Trustees*   **V** G C A STOREY
GUERNSEY L'Islet (St Mary)   *see* Guernsey St Sampson *Win*
GUERNSEY (St Andrew de la Pommeraye) *Win 14*   **P** *The Crown*   **R** C R SMITH
GUERNSEY (St John the Evangelist) *Win 14*   **P** *Trustees*   **V** A T SHARP,   **NSM** J LE BILLON
GUERNSEY (St Marguerite de la Foret) *Win 14*   **P** *The Crown*   **NSM** L S LE VASSEUR
GUERNSEY (St Martin) *Win 14*   **P** *The Crown*   **R** M R KEIRLE,   **NSM** R G BELLINGER
GUERNSEY (St Matthew) *Win 14*   **P** *R Ste Marie du Castel*   **V** C E SELIM
GUERNSEY (St Michel du Valle) *Win 14*   **P** *The Crown*   **R** K C NORTHOVER
GUERNSEY (St Peter Port) *Win 14*   **P** *The Crown*   **R** *vacant* (01481) 720036
GUERNSEY (St Philippe de Torteval) *Win 14*   **P** *The Crown*   **R** *vacant*
GUERNSEY (St Pierre du Bois) *Win 14*   **P** *The Crown*   **R** *vacant* (01481) 263544
GUERNSEY (St Sampson) *Win 14*   **P** *The Crown*   **R** J C SYKES
GUERNSEY (St Saviour) (Chapel of St Apolline) *Win 14*   **P** *The Crown*   **R** W A PRESCOTT,   **NSM** L S LE VASSEUR
GUERNSEY (St Stephen) *Win 14*   **P** *R St Peter Port*   **V** M C MILLARD
GUERNSEY (Ste Marie du Castel) *Win 14*   **P** *The Crown*   **R** C E SELIM
GUESTLING (St Lawrence)   *see* Fairlight, Guestling and Pett *Chich*
GUESTWICK (St Peter)   *see* Foulsham w Hindolveston and Guestwick *Nor*
GUILDEN MORDEN (St Mary)   *see* Shingay Gp of Par *Ely*
GUILDEN SUTTON (St John the Baptist)   *see* Plemstall w Guilden Sutton *Ches*
GUILDFORD (All Saints) *Guildf 5*   **P** *Bp*   **V** B L MESSHAM,   **NSM** R D S SANDERS
GUILDFORD (Christ Church) (St Martha-on-the-Hill) *Guildf 5*   **P** *Simeon's Trustees and Duke Northd (jt)*   **V** S R SANDERS,   **NSM** R D S SANDERS,   **OLM** S J CAVALIER
GUILDFORD (Holy Spirit)   *see* Burpham *Guildf*
GUILDFORD (Holy Trinity) (St Mary the Virgin) (St Michael) *Guildf 5*   **P** *Bp*   **R** R L COTTON,   **C** A E DIXON,   **OLM** B D ROBERTS
GUILDFORD (St Clare)   *see* Westborough *Guildf*
GUILDFORD (St Francis)   *as above Guildf*
GUILDFORD (St Luke)   *see* Burpham *Guildf*
GUILDFORD (St Nicolas) *Guildf 5*   **P** *Bp*   **R** A H NORMAN
GUILDFORD (St Saviour) *Guildf 5*   **P** *Simeon's Trustees*   **R** D J BRACEWELL,   **C** S G HOLLAND,   **NSM** P J LEVELL
GUILSBOROUGH (St Ethelreda) w Hollowell and Cold Ashby *Pet 2*   **P** *J L Lowther Esq (2 turns) and Bp (1 turn)*   **P-in-c** J M TARRANT
GUILTCROSS *Nor 11*   **P** *Bp, Mrs C Noel, Exors C P B Goldson, and DBP (jt)*   **P-in-c** K A HAWKES
GUISBOROUGH (St Nicholas) *York 16*   **P** *Abp*   **R** P L BISHOP
GUISELEY (St Oswald King and Martyr) w Esholt *Bradf 4*   **P** *Patr Bd*   **TR** G B ATHERTON,   **TV** C NORMAN,   **NSM** T H BAXTER
GUIST (St Andrew)   *see* Twyford, Guist, Bintree, Themelthorpe etc *Nor*
GUITING POWER (St Michael)   *see* The Guitings, Cutsdean, Farmcote etc *Glouc*
GUITINGS, Cutsdean, Farmcote, Upper and Lower Slaughter w Eyford and Naunton, The *Glouc 14*   **P** *Bp, Ch Ch Ox, Guiting Manor Amenity Trust, and F E B Witts Esq (jt)*   **NSM** H J GARDNER
GULDEFORD, EAST (St Mary)   *see* Rye *Chich*
GULVAL (St Gulval) and Madron *Truro 5*   **P** *Ld Chan and Bp (jt)*   **P-in-c** D J PHIPPS,   **OLM** P A T HORDER
GULWORTHY (St Paul)   *see* Tavistock and Gulworthy *Ex*
GUMLEY (St Helen)   *see* Foxton w Gumley and Laughton *Leic*
GUNBY (St Nicholas)   *see* Witham Gp *Linc*
GUNBY (St Peter)   *see* Welton-le-Marsh w Gunby *Linc*
GUNHOUSE (St Barnabas)   *see* Trentside E *Linc*
GUNN CHAPEL (Holy Name)   *see* Swimbridge w W Buckland and Landkey *Ex*

GUNNERTON (St Christopher)   *see* Chollerton w Birtley and Thockrington *Newc*
GUNNESS (St Barnabas)   *see* Trentside E *Linc*
GUNNISLAKE (St Anne)   *see* Calstock *Truro*
GUNTHORPE (St John the Baptist)   *see* Lowdham w Caythorpe, and Gunthorpe *S'well*
GUNTHORPE (St Mary) w Bale w Field Dalling, Saxlingham and Sharrington *Nor 18*   **P** *Keble Coll Ox, MMCET, Bp, and DBP (by turn)*   **P-in-c** E J PENNY
GUNTON St Peter (St Benedict) *Nor 9*   **P** CPAS   **R** J A FAIRBAIRN,   **OLM** G WILSON
GUNWALLOE (St Winwalloe)   *see* Cury and Gunwalloe w Mawgan *Truro*
GURNARD (All Saints) *Portsm 8*   **P** *Bp*   **V** G E MORRIS,   **NSM** D M NETHERWAY
GUSSAGE (St Andrew)   *see* Sixpenny Handley w Gussage St Andrew etc *Sarum*
GUSSAGE ALL SAINTS (All Saints)   *see* Chase *Sarum*
GUSSAGE ST MICHAEL (St Michael)   *as above Sarum*
GUSTARD WOOD (St Peter)   *see* Wheathampstead *St Alb*
GUSTON (St Martin of Tours)   *see* Whitfield w Guston *Cant*
GUYHIRN (St Mary Magdalene) w Ring's End *Ely 17*   **P** *Bp*   **P-in-c** C HURST
GWEEK (Mission Church)   *see* Constantine *Truro*
GWENNAP (St Weneppa)   *see* St Stythians w Perranarworthal and Gwennap *Truro*
GWINEAR (St Winnear)   *see* Godrevy *Truro*
GWITHIAN (St Gwithian)   *as above Truro*
HABBERLEY (St Mary) *Heref 13*   **P** *Bp*   **R** A N TOOP
HABERGHAM (All Saints)   *see* W Burnley *Blackb*
HABERGHAM EAVES (St Matthew the Apostle)   *see* Burnley St Matt w H Trin *Blackb*
HABROUGH Group, The (St Margaret) *Linc 10*   **P** DBP   **P-in-c** M W PAGE-CHESTNEY,   **NSM** S V PAGE-CHESTNEY
HABTON, GREAT (St Chad)   *see* Kirby Misperton w Normanby, Edston and Salton *York*
HACCOMBE (St Blaise)   *see* Shaldon, Stokeinteignhead, Combeinteignhead etc *Ex*
HACCONBY (St Andrew)   *see* Ringstone in Aveland Gp *Linc*
HACHESTON (St Andrew)   *see* Campsea Ashe w Marlesford, Parham and Hacheston *St E*
HACKBRIDGE and Beddington Corner (All Saints) *S'wark 25*   **P** *Bp*   **P-in-c** A O ROLAND
HACKENTHORPE (Christ Church) *Sheff 2*   **P** *Bp*   **V** S J WILLETT
HACKFORD (St Mary the Virgin)   *see* High Oak, Hingham and Scoulton w Wood Rising *Nor*
HACKINGTON (St Stephen) *Cant 3*   **P** *Adn Cant*   **R** J G LEWIS-ANTHONY,   **C** D A DEER
HACKNESS (St Peter) w Harwood Dale *York 15*   **P** *Lord Derwent*   **V** J W BAKER
HACKNEY Mount Pleasant Lane (St Matthew)   *see* Upper Clapton St Matt *Lon*
HACKNEY (St James)   *see* Clapton St Jas *Lon*
HACKNEY (St John)   *see* St John-at-Hackney *Lon*
HACKNEY (St Luke) Homerton Terrace   *see* Homerton St Luke *Lon*
HACKNEY (St Thomas)   *see* Stamford Hill St Thos *Lon*
HACKNEY, OVER (Mission Room)   *see* Darley *Derby*
HACKNEY, SOUTH (St John of Jerusalem) (Christ Church) *Lon 5*   **P** *Lord Amherst*   **R** N R J FUNNELL,   **C** S M CONNELL,   **NSM** P L BAILEY
HACKNEY, SOUTH (St Michael and All Angels) London Fields w Haggerston (St Paul) *Lon 5*   **P** *R S Hackney St Jo w Ch Ch*   **V** A N EVERETT,   **Hon C** A WINDROSS
HACKNEY, WEST St Barnabas (St Paul) *Lon 5*   **P** *Bp*   **R** W D N WEIR
HACKNEY MARSH (All Souls) *Lon 5*   **P** *Patr Bd*   **TR** D J SAVILLE,   **TV** G L CLAYDON, J A G POPP,   **NSM** T A HALEY
HACKNEY WICK (St Mary of Eton) (St Augustine) *Lon 5*   **P** *Eton Coll*   **V** E J JONES,   **C** G H MAUDE,   **NSM** C T OLADUJI
HACKTHORN (St Michael and All Angels)   *see* Owmby Gp *Linc*
HADDENHAM (Holy Trinity) *Ely 13*   **P** *Adn Ely*   **V** F E G BRAMPTON
HADDENHAM (St Mary the Virgin) w Cuddington, Kingsey and Aston Sandford *Ox 20*   **P** *D&C Roch*   **V** A C DENHAM,   **OLM** J A RACE
HADDESLEY (St John the Baptist)   *see* Haddlesey w Hambleton and Birkin *York*
HADDISCOE (St Mary)   *see* Raveningham Gp *Nor*
HADDLESEY w Hambleton and Birkin *York 4*   **P** *Abp and Simeon's Trustees (jt)*   **P-in-c** S J MURRAY
HADDON (St Mary)   *see* Stilton w Denton and Caldecote etc *Ely*

HADDON, EAST (St Mary the Virgin)   *see* Brington w Whilton and Norton etc *Pet*
HADDON, OVER (St Anne)   *see* Bakewell *Derby*
HADDON, WEST (All Saints) w Winwick and Ravensthorpe *Pet 2*   **P** DBP   **P-in-c** C R EVANS,   **C** A M LORD
HADFIELD (St Andrew) *Derby 6*   **P** *Bp*   **V** *vacant* (01457) 852431
HADHAM, LITTLE (St Cecilia) w Albury *St Alb 18*   **P** *Bp Lon*   **P-in-c** T RAVEN
HADHAM, MUCH (St Andrew) *St Alb 18*   **P** *Bp Lon*   **P-in-c** C P SLAUGHTER
HADLEIGH (St Barnabas) *Chelmsf 10*   **P** *Bp*   **V** S J HOLMES
HADLEIGH (St James the Less) *Chelmsf 10*   **P** *Dr P W M Copeman*   **R** M J KETLEY
HADLEIGH (St Mary), Layham and Shelley *St E 3*   **P** *St Jo Coll Cam and Abp (alt)*   **V** D A C STRANACK,   **NSM** J M WILLIS
HADLEY (Holy Trinity) *Lich 21*   **P** *Bp, Adn Salop, V Wrockwardine, R Kynnersley, and V Wellington w Eyton (jt)*   **V** V C SWEET,   **C** T B BLOOR
HADLEY WOOD (St Paul) Proprietary Chapel *Lon 18*   **Min** A G PURSER
HADLOW (St Mary) *Roch 8*   **P** *Exors Miss I N King*   **V** G A SMITH
HADLOW DOWN (St Mark)   *see* Buxted and Hadlow Down *Chich*
HADNALL (St Mary Magdalene)   *see* Astley, Clive, Grinshill and Hadnall *Lich*
HADSTOCK (St Botolph)   *see* Saffron Walden w Wendens Ambo, Littlebury etc *Chelmsf*
HADZOR w Oddingley (St James)   *see* Bowbrook S *Worc*
HAGBOURNE (St Andrew)   *see* Blewbury, Hagbourne and Upton *Ox*
HAGGERSTON (St Chad) *Lon 5*   **P** *The Crown*   **V** J J WESTCOTT
HAGLEY (St John the Baptist) *Worc 12*   **P** *Viscount Cobham*   **R** R J C NEWTON
HAGLEY, WEST (St Saviour)   *see* Hagley *Worc*
HAGNABY (St Andrew)   *see* Marden Hill Gp *Linc*
HAGWORTHINGHAM (Holy Trinity)   *as above Linc*
HAIGH (St David) *Liv 14*   **P** *R Wigan*   **V** G J T TAYLOR
HAIL WESTON (St Nicholas) *Ely 13*   **P** *Mert Coll Ox*   **V** *vacant*
HAILE (not known)   *see* Egremont and Haile *Carl*
HAILES (Chapel)   *see* Toddington, Stanton, Didbrook w Hailes etc *Glouc*
HAILEY (St John the Evangelist)   *see* Witney *Ox*
HAILSHAM (St Mary) *Chich 16*   **P** *Ch Soc Trust*   **V** R G H PORTHOUSE,   **C** C B T CARLSON
HAINAULT (St Paul) *Chelmsf 4*   **P** *Bp*   **V** C S T CANT,   **NSM** H PRADELLA
HAINFORD (All Saints)   *see* Hevingham w Hainford and Stratton Strawless *Nor*
HAINTON (St Mary)   *see* Barkwith Gp *Linc*
HALA (St Paul's Centre)   *see* Scotforth *Blackb*
HALAM (St Michael)   *see* Edingley w Halam *S'well*
HALAS Team Ministry *Worc 9*   **P** *Patr Bd*   **TR** J C EVEREST,   **TV** M N PREVETT, R S HALL,   **C** S EDWARDS
HALBERTON (St Andrew)   *see* Sampford Peverell, Uplowman, Holcombe Rogus etc *Ex*
HALCON   *see* Taunton All SS *B & W*
HALDEN, HIGH (St Mary the Virgin)   *see* Bethersden w High Halden *Cant*
HALDENS (Christ the King)   *see* Digswell and Panshanger *St Alb*
HALDON   *see* Teignmouth, Ideford w Luton, Ashcombe etc *Ex*
HALE (St David)   *see* Timperley *Ches*
HALE (St John the Evangelist) w Badshot Lea *Guildf 3*   **P** *Patr Bd*   **TR** J J PAGE,   **TV** D HENLEY,   **C** D J SCOTT-BROMLEY,   **NSM** E J VIRJI
HALE (St Mary) *Liv 13*   **P** *Trustees*   **P-in-c** J D ENGEL
HALE (St Mary)   *see* Fordingbridge and Breamore and Hale etc *Win*
HALE (St Peter) and Ashley *Ches 10*   **P** *V Bowdon*   **V** M J ROBINSON
HALE, GREAT (St John the Baptist)   *see* Helpringham w Hale *Linc*
HALE, UPPER (St Mark)   *see* Hale w Badshot Lea *Guildf*
HALEBANK (St Mary Mission)   *see* Hale *Liv*
HALES (St Mary)   *see* Cheswardine, Childs Ercall, Hales, Hinstock etc *Lich*
HALESOWEN (St John the Baptist)   *see* Halas *Worc*
HALESWORTH (St Mary)   *see* Blyth Valley *St E*
HALEWOOD (St Nicholas) (St Mary) *Liv 4*   **P** *Bp*   **TR** A D J JEWELL,   **TV** S ERRINGTON,   **NSM** C CRITCHLEY

HALEY HILL (All Souls) *see* Halifax All So and St Aug *Wakef*
HALFORD (Our Blessed Lady) *see* Alderminster and Halford *Cov*
HALFORD (St Thomas) *see* Sibdon Carwood w Halford *Heref*
HALFWAY (St Peter) *see* Minster-in-Sheppey *Cant*
HALIFAX (All Saints) *Wakef 4* **P** *Ch Trust Fund Trust*
V T J WILSON, **NSM** J C K FREEBORN
HALIFAX (All Souls) (St Augustine) *Wakef 4* **P** *Simeon's Trustees and local trustees (jt)* **V** D J CHILLMAN, **C** T TURNER
HALIFAX (Holy Trinity) (St Jude) *Wakef 4* **P** *Bp, V Halifax, and trustees (jt)* **V** M C RUSSELL
HALIFAX (St Anne-in-the-Grove) *see* Southowram and Claremount *Wakef*
HALIFAX (St Hilda) *Wakef 4* **P** *Bp* **P-in-c** P F MILLWARD
HALIFAX (St John the Baptist) *Wakef 4* **P** *The Crown*
V W A WILBY, **C** E V DANDO
HALL GREEN (Church of the Ascension) *Birm 6* **P** *Bp, V Yardley, and Vice-Chmn of PCC (jt)* **V** D J SENIOR, **C** R M WHARTON
HALL GREEN (St Peter) *Birm 6* **P** *Bp* **V** M W STEPHENSON, **C** C A GRYLLS
HALL STREET (St Andrew) *see* Stockport St Mary *Ches*
HALLAM, WEST (St Wilfred) and Mapperley w Stanley *Derby 13* **P** *Bp* **R** S I D WHITE, **C** M I JACQUES, **NSM** P J OWEN-JONES
HALLATON (St Michael and All Angels) w Horninghold and Allexton; Tugby; East Norton; and Slawston *Leic 4* **P** *Bp, DBP, and E Brudenell Esq (jt)* **R** D M FISHER
HALLING (St John the Baptist) *see* Cuxton and Halling *Roch*
HALLINGBURY, GREAT (St Giles) (St Andrew) and LITTLE (St Mary the Virgin) *Chelmsf 26* **P** *Bp and Charterhouse (jt)* **P-in-c** M CHAPMAN
HALLIWELL (St Luke) *Man 9* **P** *MMCET* **V** A BROWN, **C** S M DNISTRIANSKYJ, **OLM** L ALLMARK
HALLIWELL (St Margaret) *Man 9* **P** *Trustees* **P-in-c** D J FRENCH
HALLIWELL (St Matthew w St Barnabas) (St Paul) (St Thomas the Apostle) *Man 9* **P** *Patr Bd* **TR** D R OTTLEY, **TV** A J WOODWARD, **NSM** M A J TAYLOR, **OLM** J M SHEPHERD
HALLIWELL (St Peter) (Barrow Bridge Mission) (St Andrew's Mission Church) *Man 9* **P** *Trustees* **V** R F OLDFIELD, **C** A M BAILIE
HALLOUGHTON (St James) *see* Thurgarton w Hoveringham and Bleasby etc *S'well*
HALLOW (St Philip and St James) and Grimley w Holt *Worc 3* **P** *Bp* **R** R N LATHAM, **NSM** D C L EVE
HALLWOOD (St Mark) *Ches 3* **P** *DBP* **P-in-c** S S WILKINS, **C** K PATTIMORE
HALSALL (St Cuthbert) *Liv 11* **P** *Brig D H Blundell-Hollinshead-Blundell* **R** *vacant* (01704) 841202
HALSE (Mission Church) *see* Brackley St Pet w St Jas *Pet*
HALSE (St James) *see* Milverton w Halse and Fitzhead *B & W*
HALSETOWN (St John's in the Fields) *Truro 5* **P** *D&C* **P-in-c** A N COUCH, **C** C H CLEMENTS
HALSHAM (All Saints) *see* Keyingham w Ottringham, Halsham and Sunk Is *York*
HALSTEAD (St Andrew) w Holy Trinity and Greenstead Green *Chelmsf 19* **P** *Bp* **P-in-c** J F BLORE, **C** W N E NEWMAN
HALSTEAD (St Margaret) *see* Knockholt w Halstead *Roch*
HALSTOCK (St Mary) *see* Melbury *Sarum*
HALSTOW, HIGH (St Margaret) (All Hallows) and Hoo St Mary *Roch 6* **P** *MMCET and Ch Soc Trust (jt)* **R** S G GWILT
HALSTOW, LOWER (St Margaret) *see* Upchurch w Lower Halstow *Cant*
HALTER DEVIL (Mission Room) *see* Mugginton and Kedleston *Derby*
HALTON (St Andrew) *see* Corbridge w Halton and Newton Hall *Newc*
HALTON (St Mary) *Ches 3* **P** *Bp* **C** I HUGHES
HALTON (St Michael and All Angels) *see* Wendover and Halton *Ox*
HALTON (St Oswald and St Cuthbert and King Alfwald) *see* Corbridge w Halton and Newton Hall *Newc*
HALTON (St Wilfred) w Aughton *Blackb 14* **P** *Exors of R T Sanderson Esq* **P-in-c** D RAITT
HALTON (St Wilfrid) *see* Leeds Halton St Wilfrid *Ripon*
HALTON, EAST (St Peter) *see* Habrough Gp *Linc*
HALTON, WEST (St Etheldreda) *see* Alkborough *Linc*
HALTON HOLGATE (St Andrew) *see* Spilsby Gp *Linc*
HALTON QUAY (St Indract's Chapel) *see* St Dominic, Landulph and St Mellion w Pillaton *Truro*
HALTON WEST (Mission Church) *see* Hellifield *Bradf*
HALTWHISTLE (Holy Cross) and Greenhead *Newc 4* **P** *Bp*
V R BEST, **NSM** R D BOS

HALVERGATE (St Peter and St Paul) *see* Freethorpe, Wickhampton, Halvergate etc *Nor*
HALWELL (St Leonard) *see* Diptford, N Huish, Harberton, Harbertonford etc *Ex*
HALWILL (St Peter and St James) *see* Ashwater, Halwill, Beaworthy, Clawton etc *Ex*
HAM (All Saints) *see* Savernake *Sarum*
HAM (St Andrew) *S'wark 17* **P** *K Coll Cam*
V S BROCKLEHURST, **Hon C** D S MARKWELL, **NSM** F M FORWARD
HAM (St Barnabas Mission Church) *see* Combe St Nicholas w Wambrook *B & W*
HAM (St James the Less) *see* Plymouth St Jas Ham *Ex*
HAM (St Richard) *S'wark 18* **P** *Bp* **V** P J H DUNN, **OLM** J R WEBB
HAMBLE LE RICE (St Andrew) *Win 10* **P** *St Mary's Coll Win*
V J W TRAVERS
HAMBLEDEN VALLEY (St Mary the Virgin) *Ox 29* **P** *Bp, Viscount Hambleden, and Miss M Mackenzie (jt)* **R** W M MACNAUGHTON, **C** A P TREW
HAMBLEDON (St Peter) *see* Busbridge and Hambledon *Guildf*
HAMBLEDON (St Peter and St Paul) *Portsm 1* **P** *Ld Chan* **P-in-c** R H G BRAND
HAMBLETON (Blessed Virgin Mary) w Out Rawcliffe *Blackb 9* **P** *V Kirkham and V St Michaels-on-Wyre (jt)* **V** J E PEERS
HAMBLETON (St Andrew) *see* Oakham, Hambleton, Egleton, Braunston and Brooke *Pet*
HAMBLETON (St Mary) *see* Haddlesey w Hambleton and Birkin *York*
HAMBRIDGE (St James the Less) *see* Kingsbury Episcopi w E Lambrook, Hambridge etc *B & W*
HAMER (All Saints) *Man 20* **P** *Bp* **V** M JONES
HAMERINGHAM (All Saints) w Scrafield and Winceby *Linc 11* **P** *DBP* **OLM** K A BUSH
HAMERTON (All Saints) *Ely 9* **P** *G R Petherick Esq* **R** *vacant*
HAMILTON TERRACE (St Mark) *see* St Marylebone St Mark Hamilton Terrace *Lon*
HAMMER (St Michael) *see* Lynchmere and Camelsdale *Chich*
HAMMERFIELD (St Francis of Assisi) *see* Boxmoor St Jo *St Alb*
HAMMERSMITH (Holy Innocents) *Lon 9* **P** *Bp* **P-in-c** D W G MATTHEWS
HAMMERSMITH (St John the Evangelist) *Lon 9* **P** *V Hammersmith St Paul* **P-in-c** M P ANDREW, **NSM** A H MEAD
HAMMERSMITH (St Luke) *Lon 9* **P** *Bp* **V** *vacant* (020) 8749 7523
HAMMERSMITH (St Matthew) *Lon 9* **P** *Trustees* **V** G H CHIPLIN
HAMMERSMITH (St Michael and St George) White City Estate Conventional District *Lon 9* *vacant* (020) 8743 7100
HAMMERSMITH (St Paul) *Lon 9* **P** *Bp* **P-in-c** S G DOWNHAM, **C** T J STILWELL, **NSM** P E BATES
HAMMERSMITH (St Peter) *Lon 9* **P** *Bp* **P-in-c** S J WELCH
HAMMERSMITH (St Saviour) *see* Cobbold Road St Sav w St Mary *Lon*
HAMMERSMITH (St Simon) *Lon 9* **P** *Simeon's Trustees*
V J J CLARK, **C** S M ARNOLD
HAMMERSMITH, NORTH (St Katherine) *Lon 9* **P** *Bp* **P-in-c** J TATE
HAMMERWICH (St John the Baptist) *Lich 1* **P** *Hammerwich Ch Lands Trustees* **P-in-c** M J BUTT, **NSM** M R AUSTIN
HAMMERWOOD (St Stephen) *see* Cowden w Hammerwood *Chich*
HAMMOON (St Paul) *see* Okeford *Sarum*
HAMNISH (St Dubricius and All Saints) *see* Leominster *Heref*
HAMPDEN, GREAT (St Mary Magdalene) *see* Prestwood and Gt Hampden *Ox*
HAMPDEN, LITTLE (not known) *see* Gt Missenden w Ballinger and Lt Hampden *Ox*
HAMPDEN PARK (St Mary-in-the-Park) *Chich 16* **P** *Bp*
V R L TREE
HAMPNETT (St George) *see* Northleach w Hampnett and Farmington etc *Glouc*
HAMPRESTON (All Saints) *Sarum 9* **P** *Patr Bd*
TR R G L LUTHER, **TV** L S CLOW, M L KIRKBRIDE
HAMPSTEAD Belsize Park (St Peter) *see* Belsize Park *Lon*
HAMPSTEAD (Christ Church) *Lon 16* **P** *Trustees*
V P D CONRAD
HAMPSTEAD (Emmanuel) West End *Lon 16* **P** *Trustees*
V P J GALLOWAY, **NSM** D W JOHN
HAMPSTEAD (St James) *see* Kilburn St Mary w All So and W Hampstead St Jas *Lon*
HAMPSTEAD (St John) *Lon 16* **P** *DBP* **V** S R TUCKER, **C** T J BELL, M T WOODWARD

HAMPSTEAD (St John) Downshire Hill Proprietary Chapel
Lon 16 **Min** J G L GOULD
HAMPSTEAD St Stephen w (All Hallows) *Lon 16* **P** *DBP and D&C Cant (jt)* **V** D N C HOULDING
HAMPSTEAD, SOUTH (St Saviour) *Lon 16* **P** *V Hampstead St Jo* **V** A C PAVLIBEYI
HAMPSTEAD, WEST (Holy Trinity) *Lon 16* **P** *MMCET*
V M G C YOUNG
HAMPSTEAD, WEST (St Cuthbert) *Lon 16* **P** *Ch Trust Fund Trust* **P-in-c** M G C YOUNG, **Hon C** D H HUBBARD
HAMPSTEAD, WEST (St Luke) *Lon 16* **P** *CPAS*
V A C TRESIDDER, **Hon C** R B C STANDRING
HAMPSTEAD GARDEN SUBURB (St Jude on the Hill)
Lon 15 **P** *Bp* **V** A R G WALKER
HAMPSTEAD NORREYS (St Mary) *see* Hermitage *Ox*
HAMPSTHWAITE (St Thomas à Becket) and Killinghall
Ripon 1 **P** *Sir James Aykroyd Bt, Sir Thomas Ingilby Bt, and Bp (jt)* **V** G A F HINCHCLIFFE
HAMPTON (All Saints) *Lon 10* **P** *Ld Chan*
V W D F VANSTONE, **C** L K ROBERTS
HAMPTON (St Andrew) *see* Herne Bay Ch Ch *Cant*
HAMPTON (St Andrew) w Sedgeberrow and
Hinton-on-the-Green *Worc 1* **P** *Ch Ch Ox, D&C Worc, and Laslett's Charity (jt)* **R** J R N J BOMYER
HAMPTON (St Mary the Virgin) *Lon 10* **P** *The Crown*
V D N WINTERBURN, **Hon C** G CLARKSON,
NSM Y L MURPHY
HAMPTON, GREAT AND LITTLE (St Andrew)
see Hampton w Sedgeberrow and Hinton-on-the-Green *Worc*
HAMPTON BISHOP (St Andrew) *see* Tupsley w Hampton Bishop *Heref*
HAMPTON GAY (St Giles) *see* Akeman *Ox*
HAMPTON HILL (St James) *Lon 10* **P** *V Hampton St Mary*
V B LEATHARD, **C** J A GITTOES, **NSM** B STEWART
HAMPTON IN ARDEN (St Mary and St Bartholomew)
Birm 11 **P** *Guild of All So* **P-in-c** J DE WIT
HAMPTON LOVETT (St Mary and All Saints) *see* Elmley Lovett w Hampton Lovett and Elmbridge etc *Worc*
HAMPTON LUCY (St Peter ad Vincula) w Charlecote and Loxley *Cov 8* **P** *Sir Edmund Fairfax-Lucy Bt (3 turns), Col A M H Gregory-Hood (1 turn)* **P-in-c** S A EDMONDS
HAMPTON POYLE (St Mary the Virgin) *see* Kidlington w Hampton Poyle *Ox*
HAMPTON WICK (St John the Baptist) *see* Teddington St Mark and Hampton Wick St Jo *Lon*
HAMSEY (St Peter) *Chich 18* **P** *Bp* **P-in-c** D BASTIDE
HAMSTALL RIDWARE (St Michael and All Angels) *see* The Ridwares and Kings Bromley *Lich*
HAMSTEAD (St Bernard) *Birm 3* **P** *Bp* **V** *vacant* 0121-358 1286
HAMSTEAD (St Paul) *Birm 3* **P** *Bp* **V** A M WEAVER,
C A J DUNNING, **NSM** A F M GOODMAN
HAMSTEAD MARSHALL (St Mary) *see* W Woodhay w Enborne, Hampstead Marshall etc *Ox*
HAMSTEELS (St John the Baptist) *Dur 1* **P** *The Crown*
V M J PEERS, **C** T E HUBBLE
HAMSTERLEY (St James) and Witton-le-Wear *Dur 6* **P** *Bp and The Crown (alt)* **V** *vacant* (01388) 488418
HAMWORTHY (St Gabriel) (St Michael) *Sarum 7*
P *MMCET* **P-in-c** J E WARING
HANBOROUGH (St Peter and St Paul) and Freeland *Ox 9*
P *St Jo Coll Ox* **R** T J N NAISH
HANBURY (St Mary the Virgin) *see* Bowbrook N *Worc*
HANBURY (St Werburgh) w Newborough and Rangemore
Lich 14 **P** *DBP and Lord Burton (jt)* **V** G W WHITTY
HANCHURCH (Chapel of Ease) *see* Trentham *Lich*
HANDCROSS (All Saints) *see* Slaugham *Chich*
HANDFORTH (St Chad) *Ches 17* **P** *R Cheadle*
V P F REYNOLDS, **C** A F WEIGHTMAN
HANDLEY (All Saints) *see* Tattenhall and Handley *Ches*
HANDLEY (St John the Baptist) *see* Eckington and Ridgeway *Derby*
HANDLEY (St Mark) *see* N Wingfield, Clay Cross and Pilsley *Derby*
HANDSACRE (St Luke) *see* Armitage *Lich*
HANDSWORTH (St Andrew) *Birm 3* **P** *Bp* **V** P R FRENCH,
C J AUSTEN
HANDSWORTH (St James) *Birm 3* **P** *Bp* **V** P J HIBBERT,
NSM M FARR
HANDSWORTH (St Mary) *Sheff 1* **P** *DBP* **R** I HOLLIN
HANDSWORTH (St Mary) (Epiphany) *Birm 3* **P** *Bp*
R B A HALL, **C** E A JOHNSEN
HANDSWORTH (St Michael) (St Peter) *Birm 3* **P** *Bp*
P-in-c I E PHILLIP
HANDSWORTH WOODHOUSE (St James) *see* Woodhouse St Jas *Sheff*

HANFORD (St Matthias) *Lich 13* **P** *Bp* **V** N A DI CASTIGLIONE, **C** R M D ORAM, G R ETHERTON
HANGER HILL (Ascension) and West Twyford *Lon 22* **P** *Bp and DBP (jt)* **V** S J REED, **Hon C** H M JEFFERY
HANGER LANE (St Ann) *see* S Tottenham St Ann *Lon*
HANGING HEATON (St Paul) *Wakef 10* **P** *R Dewsbury*
P-in-c C A GILL
HANGLETON (St Helen) (St Richard) *Chich 4* **P** *Bp*
V A G SAGE, **C** P BENNETT
HANHAM (Christ Church) (St George) *Bris 5* **P** *Bp*
V P WILLIS
HANKERTON (Holy Cross) *see* Ashley, Crudwell, Hankerton, Long Newnton etc *Bris*
HANLEY (All Saints) *see* Stoke-upon-Trent *Lich*
HANLEY Holy Evangelists (St Luke) *Lich 11* **P** *Bp*
TR K R HAYWOOD, **TV** P R CLARK, G E CHARLES,
NSM C LOWNDES
HANLEY (St Chad) *see* Hanley H Ev *Lich*
HANLEY CASTLE (St Mary), Hanley Swan and Welland
Worc 5 **P** *Ld Chan and Sir Berwick Lechmere Bt (alt)*
V F A WOOKEY
HANLEY CHILD (St Michael and All Angels) *see* Teme Valley S *Worc*
HANLEY SWAN (St Gabriel) *see* Hanley Castle, Hanley Swan and Welland *Worc*
HANLEY WILLIAM (All Saints) *see* Teme Valley S *Worc*
HANNAH (St Andrew) cum Hagnaby w Markby *Linc 8* **P** *Bp and Mrs A M Johnson (alt)* **R** R H IRESON
HANNEY (St James the Great), Denchworth and East Challow
Ox 19 **P** *Bp (2 turns), Worc Coll Ox (1 turn)* **V** A HOGG
HANNINGFIELD, EAST (All Saints) *Chelmsf 9* **P** *CPAS*
P-in-c K R PLAISTER
HANNINGFIELD, WEST (St Mary and St Edward) *Chelmsf 9*
P *DBP* **P-in-c** R V GOODWIN
HANNINGTON (All Saints) *see* Baughurst, Ramsdell, Wolverton w Ewhurst etc *Win*
HANNINGTON (St John the Baptist) *see* Highworth w Sevenhampton and Inglesham etc *Bris*
HANNINGTON (St Peter and St Paul) *see* Walgrave w Hannington and Wold and Scaldwell *Pet*
HANOVER SQUARE (St George) (St Mark) *Lon 3* **P** *Bp*
P-in-c J SLATER, **C** S J HOBBS
HANSLOPE (St James the Great) w Castlethorpe *Ox 27* **P** *Bp*
P-in-c G E ECCLESTONE
HANWELL (St Mary) (St Christopher) *Lon 22* **P** *Bp*
R M R GRAYSHON, **NSM** R WEBB
HANWELL (St Mellitus w St Mark) *Lon 22* **P** *Bp*
P-in-c J O HEREWARD
HANWELL (St Peter) *see* Ironstone *Ox*
HANWELL (St Thomas) *Lon 22* **P** *The Crown*
V P A ANDREWS
HANWOOD, GREAT (St Thomas) *Heref 13* **P** *Lt-Col H de Grey-Warter* **R** M G WHITTOCK
HANWORTH (All Saints) *Lon 11* **P** *Bp* **V** L T MCKENNA,
NSM R L HOLLANDS
HANWORTH (St Bartholomew) *see* Roughton and Felbrigg, Metton, Sustead etc *Nor*
HANWORTH (St George) *Lon 11* **P** *Lee Abbey Trust*
P-in-c P S WILLIAMSON
HANWORTH (St Richard of Chichester) *Lon 11* **P** *Bp*
V A JACKSON, **C** L A J TAYLOR
HAPPISBURGH (St Mary the Virgin), Walcott, Hempstead w Eccles and Sea Palling w Waxham *Nor 12* **P** *Bp (3 turns), K Coll Cam (2 turns), E C Evans-Lombe Esq and Bp (1 turn)*
R R A HINES, **C** S K BARTER, **OLM** E M MELLERUP
HAPTON (St Margaret) *see* Padiham w Hapton and Padiham Green *Blackb*
HAPTON (St Margaret) *see* Ashwellthorpe, Forncett, Fundenhall, Hapton etc *Nor*
HARBERTON (St Andrew) *see* Diptford, N Huish, Harberton, Harbertonford etc *Ex*
HARBERTONFORD (St Peter) *as above Ex*
HARBLEDOWN (St Michael and All Angels) *Cant 3* **P** *Abp*
R M A MORRIS
HARBORNE (St Faith and St Laurence) *Birm 2* **P** *Bp*
V I M MICHAEL
HARBORNE (St Peter) *Birm 2* **P** *Bp* **V** C J EVANS,
C L K COLLINS
HARBORNE HEATH (St John the Baptist) *Birm 2* **P** *Ch Soc Trust* **V** J P HUGHES, **C** J E GRIER, R I MERCHANT,
T L R MERCHANT
HARBOROUGH MAGNA (All Saints) *Cov 6* **P** *A H F W Boughton-Leigh Esq* **R** P S RUSSELL
HARBRIDGE (All Saints) *see* Ellingham and Harbridge and Hyde w Ibsley *Win*
HARBURY (All Saints) and Ladbroke *Cov 10* **P** *Bp*
R P R BROWN

HARBY (All Saints) w Thorney and North and South Clifton
S'well 3   **P** *Ld Chan and Bp (alt)*   **P-in-c** K B POTTER
HARBY (St Mary the Virgin)   *see* Vale of Belvoir Par *Leic*
HARDEN (St Saviour) and Wilsden *Bradf 8*   **P** *Bp, Adn,*
V Bradf, and R Bingley Esq (jt)   **V** *vacant* (01535) 272344
HARDENHUISH (St Nicholas)   *see* Chippenham St Paul w
Hardenhuish etc *Bris*
HARDHAM (St Botolph)   *see* Bury w Houghton and
Coldwaltham and Hardham *Chich*
HARDINGHAM (St George)   *see* Barnham Broom and Upper
Yare *Nor*
HARDINGSTONE (St Edmund) and Horton and Piddington
Pet 7   **P** *Bp*   **V** B H STEVENS
HARDINGTON MANDEVILLE (Blessed Virgin Mary)
see W Coker w Hardington Mandeville, E Chinnock etc *B & W*
HARDINGTON VALE *B & W 4*   **P** *Bp and*
J B Owen-Jones Esq (jt)   **R** N A DONE,   **C** T V COOK
HARDLEY (St Margaret)   *see* Loddon, Sisland, Chedgrave,
Hardley and Langley *Nor*
HARDMEAD (St Mary)   *see* Sherington w Chicheley, N
Crawley, Astwood etc *Ox*
HARDRAW (St Mary and St John)   *see* Hawes and Hardraw
Ripon
HARDRES, LOWER (St Mary)   *see* Petham and Waltham w
Lower Hardres etc *Cant*
HARDRES, UPPER (St Peter and St Paul)   *as above Cant*
HARDSTOFT (St Peter)   *see* Ault Hucknall and Scarcliffe *Derby*
HARDWICK (St James)   *see* Stockton St Jas *Dur*
HARDWICK (St Leonard)   *see* Mears Ashby and Hardwick
and Sywell etc *Pet*
HARDWICK (St Margaret)   *see* Hempnall *Nor*
HARDWICK (St Mary) *Ely 1*   **P** *Bp*   **P-in-c** K J BROWNING
HARDWICK, EAST (St Stephen)   *see* Carleton and E
Hardwick *Wakef*
HARDWICK-CUM-TUSMORE (St Mary)   *see* Shelswell *Ox*
HARDWICKE (Holy Trinity)   *see* Cusop w Blakemere,
Bredwardine w Brobury etc *Heref*
HARDWICKE (St Mary the Virgin)   *see* Schorne *Ox*
HARDWICKE (St Nicholas) and Elmore w Longney *Glouc 8*
P *Adn Glouc and Ld Chan (alt)*   **V** T M B WOODHOUSE
HAREBY (St Peter and St Paul)   *see* Marden Hill Gp *Linc*
HAREFIELD (St Mary the Virgin) *Lon 24*   **P** *The Hon*
J E F Newdegate   **V** A J R GANDON,   **NSM** A F ILSLEY
HAREHILLS (St Cyprian and St James)   *see* Leeds St Cypr
Harehills *Ripon*
HARESCOMBE (St John the Baptist)   *see* Painswick,
Sheepscombe, Cranham, The Edge etc *Glouc*
HARESFIELD (St Peter)   *see* Eastington, Frocester, Haresfield
etc *Glouc*
HAREWOOD (Methodist Chapel)   *see* Collingham w
Harewood *Ripon*
HARFORD (St Petroc)   *see* Ivybridge w Harford *Ex*
HARGRAVE (All Saints)   *see* Stanwick w Hargrave *Pet*
HARGRAVE (St Edmund King and Martyr)   *see* Chevington w
Hargrave, Chedburgh w Depden etc *St E*
HARGRAVE (St Peter) *Ches 5*   **P** *Bp*   **P-in-c** R M POWLEY
HARKSTEAD (St Mary)   *see* Chelmondiston and Erwarton w
Harkstead *St E*
HARLASTON (St Matthew)   *see* Clifton Campville w Edingale
and Harlaston *Lich*
HARLAXTON Group, The (St Mary and St Peter) *Linc 19*
P *Bp, DBP, Sir Richard Welby Bt, D&C, and Duke of*
Rutland (jt)   **P-in-c** G P POND
HARLESCOTT (Holy Spirit) *Lich 20*   **P** *Bp*   **C** J DAVIES,
I M BROTHERSTON,   **NSM** D W G UFFINDELL,
OLM W L STONEHOLD
HARLESDEN (All Souls) *Lon 21*   **P** *The Crown*
V M D MOORHEAD
HARLESDEN (St Mark)   *see* Kensal Rise St Mark and St
Martin *Lon*
HARLESTON (St Augustine)   *see* Gt Finborough w Onehouse,
Harleston, Buxhall etc *St E*
HARLESTON (St John the Baptist)   *see* Redenhall, Harleston,
Wortwell and Needham *Nor*
HARLESTONE (St Andrew)   *see* Brington w Whilton and
Norton etc *Pet*
HARLEY (St Mary)   *see* Wenlock *Heref*
HARLING, EAST (St Peter and St Paul) w West, Bridgham w
Roudham, Larling, Brettenham and Rushford *Nor 11*
P *Ld Chan (1 turn), DBP, Sir Robin Nugent Bt,*
C D F Musker Esq, Major E H C Garnier, and Exors Sir John
Musker (3 turns)   **R** J HANDLEY
HARLINGTON (Christ Church) Waltham Avenue Conventional
District *Lon 24*   **C-in-c** I W JONES,   **C** D M NICKLAS-CARTER
HARLINGTON (St Mary the Virgin) *St Alb 12*   **P** *Bp*
V S J WILLIAMS

HARLINGTON (St Peter and St Paul) *Lon 24*   **P** *Bp*
P-in-c M E SMITH
HARLOW (St Mary and St Hugh w St John the Baptist)
Chelmsf 26   **P** *Simeon's Trustees and Bp (alt)*
V S P E MOURANT,   **NSM** J C MOURANT
HARLOW (St Mary Magdalene) *Chelmsf 26*   **P** *V Harlow*
St Mary and St Hugh etc   **V** C P M PATTERSON,
C P R WILLIAMS,   **Hon C** G R NEAVE
HARLOW Town Centre (St Paul) w Little Parndon *Chelmsf 26*
P *Patr Bd*   **TR** D C KIRKWOOD,   **TV** A E MELANIPHY,
C M J T JOSS
HARLOW GREEN (St Ninian) and Lamesley *Dur 12*   **P** *Bp*
V M WORTHINGTON
HARLOW HILL (All Saints)   *see* Low Harrogate St Mary *Ripon*
HARLSEY, EAST (St Oswald)   *see* Osmotherley w Harlsey and
Ingleby Arncliffe *York*
HARLTON (Assumption of the Blessed Virgin Mary)
see Haslingfield w Harlton and Gt and Lt Eversden *Ely*
HARMANSWATER (St Paul)   *see* Bracknell *Ox*
HARMER HILL (St Andrew)   *see* Myddle *Lich*
HARMONDSWORTH (St Mary) *Lon 24*   **P** *DBP*
C P G J HUGHES
HARMSTON (All Saints)   *see* Graffoe Gp *Linc*
HARNHAM (St George) (All Saints) *Sarum 12*   **P** *Bp (1 turn),*
V Britford (2 turns)   **V** D P SCRACE,   **NSM** P A CLEGG,
J G POPPLETON
HARNHILL (St Michael and All Angels)   *see* The Ampneys w
Driffield and Poulton *Glouc*
HAROLD HILL (St George) *Chelmsf 2*   **P** *Bp*   **V** P A BROWN
HAROLD HILL (St Paul) *Chelmsf 2*   **P** *Bp*   **V** R D MOUL
HAROLD WOOD (St Peter) *Chelmsf 2*   **P** *New Coll Ox*
V D P BANTING,   **C** J R TERRY,   P H C KINGMAN
HAROME (St Saviour)   *see* Kirkdale w Harome, Nunnington
and Pockley *York*
HARPENDEN (St John the Baptist) *St Alb 8*   **P** *DBP*
V J P SMITH,   **NSM** J E H WHITE,   M MONK
HARPENDEN (St Nicholas) (All Saints) *St Alb 8*   **P** *Ld Chan*
R C D FUTCHER,   **C** E F INALL,   J S REVELEY,   P D SWINN
HARPFORD (St Gregory the Great)   *see* Ottery St Mary,
Alfington, W Hill, Tipton etc *Ex*
HARPHAM (St John of Beverley)   *see* Burton Agnes w
Harpham and Lowthorpe etc *York*
HARPLEY (St Lawrence)   *see* Gt w Lt Massingham, Harpley,
Rougham etc *Nor*
HARPOLE (All Saints)   *see* Kislingbury and Harpole *Pet*
HARPSDEN (St Margaret)   *see* Shiplake w Dunsden and
Harpsden *Ox*
HARPSWELL (St Chad)   *see* Glentworth Gp *Linc*
HARPTREE, EAST (St Laurence) w WEST (Blessed Virgin
Mary) and Hinton Blewett *B & W 10*   **P** *Duchy of Cornwall*
R *vacant* (01761) 221239
HARPUR HILL (St James)   *see* Buxton w Burbage and King
Sterndale *Derby*
HARPURHEY cum Moston (Christ Church) *Man 5*   **P** *Bp,*
Dean, K Greenwood Esq, Ms A Greenhalgh, and
V Morley Esq (jt)   **R** M D ASHCROFT,   **C** C J R HOWITZ
HARPURHEY (St Stephen) *Man 5*   **P** *Bp*   **R** M D ASHCROFT
HARRABY (St Elisabeth)   *see* S Carl TM *Carl*
HARRIETSHAM (St John the Baptist)   *see* Len Valley *Cant*
HARRINGAY (St Paul) *Lon 19*   **P** *Bp*   **V** R P P MARTIN
HARRINGTON (St Mary) *Carl 7*   **P** *Mrs E H S Thornely*
R J S DIXON
HARRINGTON (St Mary)   *see* S Ormsby Gp *Linc*
HARRINGTON (St Peter and St Paul)   *see* Arthingworth,
Harrington w Oxendon and E Farndon *Pet*
HARRINGWORTH (St John the Baptist)   *see* Bulwick,
Blatherwycke w Harringworth and Laxton *Pet*
HARROGATE (St Mark) *Ripon 1*   **P** *Peache Trustees*
V P D G HOOPER,   **C** J A BECKETT
HARROGATE (St Wilfrid) *Ripon 1*   **P** *Bp*   **V** M C R SOWERBY,
Hon C P A BALDWIN,   **NSM** T J BUCKINGHAM
HARROGATE, HIGH (Christ Church) *Ripon 1*   **P** *Bp*
V J E COLSTON
HARROGATE, HIGH (St Peter) *Ripon 1*   **P** *Ch Patr Trust*
V A M SHEPHERD,   **NSM** T J HURREN
HARROGATE, LOW (St Mary) *Ripon 4*   **P** *Peache Trustees*
V M W SOAR
HARROLD (St Peter and All Saints) and Carlton w Chellington
St Alb 15   **P** *Bp*   **P-in-c** J BURROWS
HARROW (Church of the Holy Spirit)   *see* Kenton *Lon*
HARROW (Holy Trinity) (St Michael) *Lon 23*   **P** *Bp*
C G E HEWLETT,   N R PYE,   **NSM** P J WRIGHT
HARROW (St John the Baptist)   *see* Greenhill St Jo *Lon*
HARROW (St Peter)   *see* Roxeth *Lon*
HARROW, NORTH (St Alban) *Lon 23*   **P** *Bp*   **V** J A FOSTER,
Hon C D S ARDEN,   **NSM** P BAGULEY

HARROW, SOUTH (St Paul) *Lon 23* **P** *R St Bride Fleet Street w Bridewell and Trin Gough Square* **V** A J HULME
HARROW GREEN (Holy Trinity and St Augustine of Hippo) *see* Leytonstone H Trin Harrow Green *Chelmsf*
HARROW ON THE HILL (St Mary) *Lon 23* **P** *Bp, Adn, and Hd Master Harrow Sch (jt)* **V** T J GOSDEN
HARROW WEALD (All Saints) *Lon 23* **P** *Bp, Adn, V Harrow St Mary, and R Bushey (jt)* **V** F D JAKEMAN
HARROWBARROW (All Saints) *see* Calstock *Truro*
HARROWBY (The Ascension) *see* Grantham, Harrowby w Londonthorpe *Linc*
HARROWDEN, GREAT (All Saints) w LITTLE (St Mary the Virgin) and Orlingbury *Pet 6* **P** *Sir Stephen Hastings and Bp (alt)* **P-in-c** S P DOMMETT
HARSTON (All Saints) w Hauxton and Newton *Ely 6* **P** *Bp (2 turns), D&C (1 turn)* **NSM** R G HOWELLS
HARSTON (St Michael and All Angels) *see* High Framland Par *Leic*
HARSWELL (St Peter) *see* Holme and Seaton Ross Gp *York*
HART (St Mary Magdalene) w Elwick Hall *Dur 3* **P** *Bp and DBP (alt)* **V** J E LUND
HART COMMON (not known) *see* Westhoughton and Wingates *Man*
HARTBURN (All Saints) *see* Stockton St Pet *Dur*
HARTBURN (St Andrew) *see* Bolam w Whalton and Hartburn w Meldon *Newc*
HARTCLIFFE (St Andrew) *see* Bris St Andr Hartcliffe *Bris*
HARTEST (All Saints) *see* Glem Valley United Benefice *St E*
HARTFIELD (St Mary) w Coleman's Hatch *Chich 19* **P** *Bp and Earl De la Warr (jt)* **R** P E P BRICE, **NSM** N T LEVISEUR
HARTFORD (All Saints) *see* Huntingdon *Ely*
HARTFORD (All Souls) *see* Hartley Wintney, Elvetham, Winchfield etc *Win*
HARTFORD (St John the Baptist) *Ches 6* **P** *Ch Soc Trust* **C** M I A SMITH, **NSM** G AGAR
HARTHILL (All Hallows) and Thorpe Salvin *Sheff 5* **P** *Bp* **P-in-c** P L CHAMBERS
HARTING (St Mary and St Gabriel) w Elsted and Treyford cum Didling *Chich 10* **P** *Bp* **R** D R C GIBBONS, **NSM** R B WILLIAMSON
HARTINGTON (St Giles), Biggin and Earl Sterndale *Derby 4* **P** *Duke of Devonshire* **P-in-c** J O GOLDSMITH, **Hon C** J H LISTER
HARTISMERE, NORTH *St E 16* **P** *MMCET, K Coll Cam, Bp, and DBP (jt)* **R** R H AXFORD, **NSM** C R AXFORD
HARTLAND (St Nectan) *see* Parkham, Alwington, Buckland Brewer etc *Ex*
HARTLAND COAST *as above Ex*
HARTLEBURY (St James) *Worc 13* **P** *Bp* **P-in-c** P H WORRALL
HARTLEPOOL (Holy Trinity) (St Mark's Centre) *Dur 3* **P** *Bp* **V** J L SMITH, **C** J A FRANCE
HARTLEPOOL (St Aidan) (St Columba) *Dur 3* **P** *Bp* **V** A D WHIPP
HARTLEPOOL (St Hilda) *Dur 3* **P** *Bp* **R** P Z KASHOURIS
HARTLEPOOL (St Luke) *Dur 3* **P** *Bp* **V** *vacant (01429) 272893*
HARTLEPOOL (St Oswald) *Dur 3* **P** *Bp* **V** B R TURNBULL
HARTLEPOOL (St Paul) *Dur 3* **P** *Bp* **V** R E MASSHEDAR
HARTLEY (All Saints) *see* Fawkham and Hartley *Roch*
HARTLEY, NEW (St Michael and All Angels) *see* Delaval *Newc*
HARTLEY BROOK (Mission Hall) *see* Becontree St Mary *Chelmsf*
HARTLEY MAUDITT (St Leonard) *see* E and W Worldham, Hartley Mauditt w Kingsley etc *Win*
HARTLEY WESPALL (St Mary) *see* Sherfield-on-Loddon and Stratfield Saye etc *Win*
HARTLEY WINTNEY (St John the Evangelist), Elvetham, Winchfield and Dogmersfield *Win 5* **P** *Bp and Sir Euan Anstruther-Gough-Calthorpe Bt (jt)* **V** R A EWBANK, **C** A BOTHAM
HARTLIP (St Michael and All Angels) *see* Newington w Hartlip and Stockbury *Cant*
HARTOFT (Mission Room) *see* Lastingham w Appleton-le-Moors, Rosedale etc *York*
HARTON (St Peter) (St Lawrence) *Dur 15* **P** *D&C* **V** R O DICK, **C** C A DICK
HARTPLAIN (not known) *Portsm 5* **P** *DBP* **P-in-c** T E JESSIMAN
HARTPURY (St Mary the Virgin) w Corse and Staunton *Glouc 6* **P** *Bp (2 turns), DBP (1 turn)* **P-in-c** J G EVANS, **NSM** P A HAMER
HARTSHEAD (St Peter) *see* Roberttown w Hartshead *Wakef*
HARTSHILL (Holy Trinity) *Cov 5* **P** *V Mancetter* **P-in-c** L P BEARD

HARTSHILL (Holy Trinity) *Lich 12* **P** *Bp* **V** J A WALSH
HARTSHORNE (St Peter) and Bretby *Derby 16* **P** *Bp and MMCET (jt)* **R** I R WILLIAMS-HUNTER
HARTWELL (St John the Baptist) *see* Roade and Ashton w Hartwell *Pet*
HARTWITH (St Jude) *see* Dacre w Hartwith and Darley w Thornthwaite *Ripon*
HARTY (St Thomas Apostle) *see* Eastchurch w Leysdown and Harty *Cant*
HARVINGTON (St James) *see* Church Lench w Rous Lench and Abbots Morton etc *Worc*
HARWELL (St Matthew) w Chilton *Ox 18* **P** *DBP and CPAS (jt)* **R** C J STOTT, **NSM** J V BARTON
HARWICH (St Nicholas) *see* Dovercourt and Parkeston w Harwich *Chelmsf*
HARWOOD (Christ Church) *Man 16* **P** *DBP* **V** A R HAZLEHURST, **OLM** H MOLLOY, M J FROST
HARWOOD, GREAT (St Bartholomew) *Blackb 7* **P** *V Blackb* **V** J HEIL, **C** L MCGREGOR
HARWOOD, GREAT (St John) *Blackb 7* **P** *Bp and V Gt Harwood St Bart (jt)* **P-in-c** J HEIL, **C** L MCGREGOR
HARWOOD DALE (St Margaret) *see* Hackness w Harwood Dale *York*
HARWORTH (All Saints) *S'well 1* **P** *Sir John Whitaker Bt* **V** D L ANDERSON
HASBURY (St Margaret) *see* Halas *Worc*
HASCOMBE (St Peter) *see* Dunsfold and Hascombe *Guildf*
HASELBECH (St Michael) *see* Clipston w Naseby and Haselbech w Kelmarsh *Pet*
HASELBURY PLUCKNETT (St Michael and All Angels), Misterton and North Perrott *B & W 15* **P** *Ld Chan (2 turns), Bp (2 turns), and H W F Hoskyns Esq (1 turn)* **P-in-c** J M FREE
HASELEY (St Mary) *see* Hatton w Haseley, Rowington w Lowsonford etc *Cov*
HASELEY, GREAT (St Peter) *see* Gt w Lt Milton and Gt Haseley *Ox*
HASELOR (St Mary and All Saints) *see* Kinwarton w Gt Alne and Haselor *Cov*
HASELTON (St Andrew) *see* Northleach w Hampnett and Farmington etc *Glouc*
HASFIELD (St Mary) w Tirley and Ashleworth *Glouc 6* **P** *W G F Meath-Baker Esq, Ld Chan, and Bp (by turn)* **P-in-c** T WILLIAMS
HASKETON (St Andrew) *see* Boulge w Burgh, Grundisburgh and Hasketon *St E*
HASLAND (St Paul) *Derby 5* **P** *V Chesterfield* **R** M R AINSCOUGH
HASLEMERE (St Bartholomew) (St Christopher) and Grayswood *Guildf 4* **P** *Ld Chan* **R** N JONES, **C** M L PLAYLE
HASLINGDEN (St James) w Grane and Stonefold *Blackb 1* **P** *Bp and Hulme Trustees (jt)* **V** T R SMITH
HASLINGDEN (St Peter) *see* Laneside *Blackb*
HASLINGDEN (St Thomas) *see* Musbury *Blackb*
HASLINGFIELD (All Saints) w Harlton and Great and Little Eversden *Ely 1* **P** *Qu Coll Cam, Ld Chan, Jes Coll Cam (by turn)* **R** P C OWEN-JONES, **NSM** D C R MCFADYEN
HASLINGTON (St Matthew) w Crewe Green St Michael *Ches 15* **P** *Bp* **V** P H GEDDES
HASSALL GREEN (St Philip) *see* Sandbach Heath w Wheelock *Ches*
HASSINGHAM (St Mary) *see* Burlingham St Edmund w Lingwood, Strumpshaw etc *Nor*
HASTINGLEIGH (St Mary the Virgin) *see* Elmsted w Hastingleigh *Cant*
HASTINGS (All Souls) Clive Vale *Chich 17* **P** *R Upper St Leon* **V** *vacant (01424) 421445*
HASTINGS (Christ Church and St Andrew) *see* Blacklands Hastings Ch Ch and St Andr *Chich*
HASTINGS (Emmanuel and St Mary in the Castle) *Chich 17* **P** *MMCET and Hyndman Trustees (alt)* **V** P J COEKIN
HASTINGS (Holy Trinity) *Chich 17* **P** *Bp* **V** C TOLWORTHY
HASTINGS (St Clement) (All Saints) *Chich 17* **P** *Bp* **R** I E MORRISON
HASWELL (St Paul), Shotton and Thornley *Dur 2* **P** *Bp* **V** J F MASSHEDAR
HATCH, WEST (St Andrew) *see* Beercrocombe w Curry Mallet, Hatch Beauchamp etc *B & W*
HATCH BEAUCHAMP (St John the Baptist) *as above B & W*
HATCH END (St Anselm) *Lon 23* **P** *Bp* **V** C PEARCE
HATCH WARREN (Church hall) Conventional District *Win 4 vacant*
HATCHAM (St Catherine) *S'wark 3* **P** *Haberdashers' Co* **V** F J MAKAMBWE, **NSM** J M L L BOGLE, **OLM** A C OBIORA
HATCHAM (St James) (St George) (St Michael) *S'wark 3* **P** *Ch Patr Soc* **P-in-c** C LITTLE, **NSM** E BOGLE

HATCHAM PARK (All Saints) *S'wark 3* **P** *Hyndman Trustees (2 turns), Haberdashers' Co (1 turn)* **V** O J BEAMENT, **OLM** J FRANCIS
HATCLIFFE (St Mary) *see* Laceby and Ravendale Gp *Linc*
HATFIELD *see* Bp's Hatfield *St Alb*
HATFIELD (St Lawrence) *Sheff 10* **P** *Bp* **V** P D WILSON, **NSM** G BECKETT
HATFIELD (St Leonard) *see* Leominster *Heref*
HATFIELD BROAD OAK (St Mary the Virgin) and Bush End *Chelmsf 26* **P** *Bp* **P-in-c** C M WHITE
HATFIELD HEATH (Holy Trinity) and Sheering *Chelmsf 26* **P** *Ch Ch Ox and V Hatfield Broad Oak (alt)* **R** T J POTTER, **NSM** B L SURTEES
HATFIELD HYDE (St Mary Magdalene) *St Alb 21* **P** *Marquess of Salisbury* **P-in-c** D L MUNCHIN, **C** G J RICHARDSON
HATFIELD PEVEREL (St Andrew) w Ulting *Chelmsf 24* **P** *Bp* **V** S R NORTHFIELD
HATFIELD REGIS *see* Hatfield Broad Oak and Bush End *Chelmsf*
HATHERDEN (Christ Church) w Tangley and Weyhill and Penton Mewsey *Win 3* **P** *Bp and Qu Coll Ox (jt)* **V** R E WHETTINGSTEEL
HATHERLEIGH (St John the Baptist) Meeth, Exbourne and Jacobstowe *Ex 12* **P** *CPAS, Lord Clinton, DBP, and Keble Coll Ox (jt)* **P-in-c** R A L WELBY
HATHERN (St Peter and St Paul), Long Whatton and Diseworth w Belton and Osgathorpe *Leic 7* **P** *Ld Chan, Haberdashers' Co, and Bp (by turn)* **P-in-c** N O TUFFNELL
HATHEROP (St Nicholas) *see* Coln St Aldwyns, Hatherop, Quenington etc *Glouc*
HATHERSAGE (St Michael and All Angels) w Bamford and Derwent *Derby 2* **P** *Duke of Devonshire and A C H Barnes Esq (jt)* **R** D C PICKERING
HATHERTON (St Saviour) *Lich 3* **P** *A R W Littleton Esq* **V** A R OSBORNE
HATLEY ST GEORGE (St George) *see* Gamlingay and Everton *Ely*
HATTERS LANE (St Andrew) *see* High Wycombe *Ox*
HATTERSLEY (St Barnabas) *Ches 14* **P** *Bp* **V** D A AKKER, **C** V L SCHOFIELD
HATTON (All Saints) *Derby 14* **P** *Bp and N J M Spurrier Esq (jt)* **P-in-c** S BAXTER
HATTON (Chapel of Ease) *see* E Bedfont *Lon*
HATTON (Holy Trinity) w Haseley, Rowington w Lowsonford and Honiley and Wroxall *Cov 4* **P** *Bp* **R** K J MOBBERLEY, **NSM** S MOBBERLEY
HATTON (St Stephen) *see* Hemingby *Linc*
HAUGH (St Leonard) *see* S Ormsby Gp *Linc*
HAUGHLEY (St Mary the Virgin) w Wetherden and Stowupland *St E 6* **P** *Ld Chan, Bp, and DBP (by turn)* **V** D J PARMENTER, **C** D K MAY, **NSM** A M BAIRD
HAUGHTON (Mission Room) *see* Bunbury and Tilstone Fearnall *Ches*
HAUGHTON (St Anne) *Man 17* **P** *DBP* **NSM** P A CLARK
HAUGHTON (St Chad) *see* W Felton *Lich*
HAUGHTON (St Giles) *see* Derrington, Haughton and Ranton *Lich*
HAUGHTON (St Mary the Virgin) *Man 17* **P** *Bp* **R** M J DOWLAND
HAUGHTON LE SKERNE (St Andrew) *Dur 8* **P** *Bp* **R** D J BRYAN, **C** D M KEEN
HAUTBOIS, GREAT (Holy Trinity) *see* Coltishall w Gt Hautbois and Horstead *Nor*
HAUXTON (St Edmund) *see* Harston w Hauxton and Newton *Ely*
HAUXWELL (St Oswald) *see* Spennithorne w Finghall and Hauxwell *Ripon*
HAVANT (St Faith) *Portsm 5* **P** *Bp* **R** D A GIBBONS, **C** C E KEAY, **NSM** D I R WILLIAMS
HAVEN Conventional District *Chich 16* **C-in-c** A W WEAVER
HAVENSTREET (St Peter) *Portsm 7* **P** *SMF* **V** N R WALLACE, **NSM** K R ALLDAY
HAVERHILL (St Mary the Virgin) w Withersfield *St E 8* **P** *Bp* **V** E J BETTS, **NSM** S A BAREHAM
HAVERIGG (St Luke) *see* Millom *Carl*
HAVERING-ATTE-BOWER (St John) *see* Collier Row St Jas and Havering-atte-Bower *Chelmsf*
HAVERINGLAND (St Peter) *see* Cawston w Booton and Brandiston etc *Nor*
HAVERSHAM (St Mary) *see* Lamp *Ox*
HAVERSTOCK HILL (Holy Trinity) *see* Kentish Town St Silas and H Trin w St Barn *Lon*
HAVERTHWAITE (St Anne) *see* Leven Valley *Carl*
HAWES (St Margaret) and Hardraw *Ripon 4* **P** *Bp, V Aysgarth and Bolton cum Redmire, Mrs R Metcalfe, and W H Willan Esq (jt)* **V** W M SIMMS

HAWES SIDE (St Christopher) *Blackb 8* **P** *Bp* **V** R G RAINFORD, **NSM** M WORSLEY
HAWKCHURCH (St John the Baptist) *see* Golden Cap Team *Sarum*
HAWKEDON (St Mary) *see* Chevington w Hargrave, Chedburgh w Depden etc *St E*
HAWKESBURY (St Mary) *see* Badminton w Lt Badminton, Acton Turville etc *Glouc*
HAWKHURST (St Laurance) *Cant 11* **P** *Ch Ch Ox* **V** R G DREYER
HAWKINGE (St Luke) w Acrise and Swingfield *Cant 5* **P** *Abp* **R** S F WARDELL
HAWKLEY (St Peter and St Paul) *see* Greatham w Empshott and Hawkley w Prior's Dean *Portsm*
HAWKRIDGE (St Giles) *see* Exford, Exmoor, Hawkridge and Withypool *B & W*
HAWKSHAW LANE (St Mary) *Man 10* **P** *F Whowell Esq* **P-in-c** G J ARMSTRONG
HAWKSHEAD (St Michael and All Angels) and Low Wray w Sawrey and Rusland and Satterthwaite *Carl 11* **P** *Bp* **V** A S PYE
HAWKSWOOD (Emmanuel) Conventional District *Chich 16* **C-in-c** S J E TOMALIN
HAWKSWORTH (St Mary and All Saints) *see* Whatton w Aslockton, Hawksworth, Scarrington etc *S'well*
HAWKSWORTH WOOD (St Mary) *Ripon 7* **P** *Patrons Leeds St Pet* **V** A J PEARSON
HAWKWELL (Emmanuel) (St Mary the Virgin) *Chelmsf 12* **P** *CPAS* **R** P A CORRIE, **C** P S HAMILTON
HAWKWOOD (St Francis) *see* Chingford SS Pet and Paul *Chelmsf*
HAWLEY (Holy Trinity) *Guildf 1* **P** *Keble Coll Ox* **V** M W NEALE, **C** I WRIGHT
HAWLEY, SOUTH (All Saints) *see* Hawley H Trin *Guildf*
HAWLING (St Edward) *see* Sevenhampton w Charlton Abbots, Hawling etc *Glouc*
HAWNBY (All Saints) *see* Upper Ryedale *York*
HAWORTH (St Michael and All Angels) *Bradf 8* **P** *V Bradf and Haworth Ch Lands Trust (jt)* **R** J A SAVAGE
HAWRIDGE (St Mary) w Cholesbury and St Leonard *Ox 28* **P** *Bp, Chpl Trust, and Neale's Charity (jt)* **P-in-c** D J BURGESS, **NSM** I CORNISH, G M ROWELL
HAWSKER (All Saints) *see* Fylingdales and Hawsker cum Stainsacre *York*
HAWSTEAD (All Saints) and Nowton w Stanningfield and Bradfield Combust *St E 13* **P** *Mrs J Oakes (2 turns), Bp (3 turns)* **P-in-c** M C THROWER
HAWTHORN (St Michael and All Angels) *Dur 2* **P** *I Pemberton Esq* **R** A MILNE
HAWTON (All Saints) *see* Farndon w Thorpe, Hawton and Cotham *S'well*
HAXBY (St Mary) w Wigginton *York 7* **P** *Abp and Ld Chan (alt)* **TR** M GREEN
HAXEY (St Nicholas) *Linc 1* **P** *Ld Chan* **V** J STAFF
HAY MILL (St Cyprian) *see* Yardley St Cypr Hay Mill *Birm*
HAYDOCK (St James) *Liv 18* **P** *R Ashton-in-Makerfield* **V** R MIDDLETON, **C** R W HART, **NSM** G J HARDMAN
HAYDOCK (St Mark) *Liv 10* **P** *MMCET* **V** P POTTER, **C** R S WHITE
HAYDON BRIDGE (St Cuthbert) and Beltingham w Henshaw *Newc 4* **P** *Bp and V Haltwhistle and Greenhead (jt)* **V** V G ASHWIN, **NSM** A R CURRIE
HAYDON WICK (St John) *Bris 7* **P** *CPAS* **V** R W ADAMS
HAYES (St Anselm) *Lon 24* **P** *Bp* **P-in-c** P L DE S HOMEWOOD
HAYES (St Edmund of Canterbury) *Lon 24* **P** *Bp* **V** R M REEVE
HAYES (St Mary) *Lon 24* **P** *Keble Coll Ox* **R** P L DE S HOMEWOOD
HAYES (St Mary the Virgin) *Roch 14* **P** *D&C* **R** G D GRAHAM
HAYES (St Nicholas) Raynton Drive Conventional District *Lon 24* **C-in-c** A K SILLIS
HAYFIELD (St Matthew) and Chinley w Buxworth *Derby 6* **P** *Bp and Resident Freeholders (jt)* **V** H A EDGERTON
HAYLE (St Elwyn) *see* Godrevy *Truro*
HAYLING, NORTH (St Peter) *Portsm 5* **P** *DBP* **NSM** H V HAWKES
HAYLING, SOUTH (St Mary) *Portsm 5* **P** *DBP* **V** P M J GINEVER, **NSM** C MEATYARD
HAYLING ISLAND (St Andrew) Eastoke *Portsm 5* **P** *DBP* **NSM** H V HAWKES
HAYNES (Mission Room) *see* Campton, Clophill and Haynes *St Alb*

HAYNES (St Mary)   *as above St Alb*
HAYTON (St James)   *see Aspatria w Hayton and Gilcrux Carl*
HAYTON (St Martin)   *see Shiptonthorpe and Hayton York*
HAYTON (St Mary Magdalene)   *see Eden, Gelt and Irthing Carl*
HAYTON (St Peter)   *see Clarborough w Hayton S'well*
HAYWARDS HEATH (St Richard) *Chich 6*   **P** *Bp*
   V I N CHANDLER,   **C** J F TWISLETON,   **Hon C** L D POODHUN
HAYWARDS HEATH (St Wilfrid) (Church of the Ascension)
   (Church of the Good Shepherd) (Church of the Presentation)
   Chich 6   **P** *Bp*   **TR** R C W SMITH,   **TV** T J STEAD,
   D F COOMBES
HAYWOOD, GREAT (St Stephen)   *see Colton, Colwich and Gt*
   Haywood Lich
HAZELBURY BRYAN (St Mary and St James) and the Hillside
   Parishes *Sarum 5*   **P** *Duke of Northd (2 turns),*
   M J Scott-Williams Esq, G A L-F Pitt-Rivers Esq, Exors
   F N Kent Esq, and Bp (1 turn each)   **P-in-c** D JONES
HAZELWELL (St Mary Magdalen) *Birm 5*   **P** *Bp*
   V A C PRIESTLEY
HAZLEMERE (Holy Trinity) *Ox 29*   **P** *Peache Trustees*
   V P C COLLIER,   **C** W F MASON, D MUNOZ-TRIVINO
HAZLEWOOD (St John the Evangelist) and Milford *Derby 11*
   P *Bp*   **P-in-c** R J HARRIS
HEACHAM (St Mary) *Nor 16*   **P** *Bp*   **V** P B FOREMAN,
   OLM D LOXLEY
HEADBOURNE WORTHY (St Swithun) *Win 7*   **P** *Univ Coll*
   Ox and Lord Northbrook (alt)   **R** A W GORDON
HEADCORN (St Peter and St Paul) *Cant 15*   **P** *Abp*
   V B E LANGMAN
HEADINGLEY (St Chad)   *see Far Headingley St Chad Ripon*
HEADINGLEY (St Michael and All Angels) *Ripon 7*
   P *V Leeds St Pet*   **V** M A CROSS,   **NSM** D W PEAT
HEADINGLEY (St Oswald)   *see Far Headingley St Chad Ripon*
HEADINGTON (St Andrew) *Ox 4*   **P** *Keble Coll Ox*
   V W M BREWIN
HEADINGTON (St Mary) *Ox 4*   **P** *Bp*   **P-in-c** J W SEWELL,
   Hon C S C BULLOCK
HEADINGTON QUARRY (Holy Trinity) *Ox 4*   **P** *Bp*
   P-in-c T D HONEY
HEADLESS CROSS (St Luke)   *see Redditch, The Ridge Worc*
HEADLEY (All Saints) *Guildf 3*   **P** *Qu Coll Ox*
   V H M SEMPLE,   **C** A E GELL
HEADLEY (St Mary the Virgin) w Box Hill (St Andrew)
   Guildf 9   **P** *Bp*   **R** D A WOTTON
HEADLEY (St Peter)   *see Ashford Hill w Headley Win*
HEADON (St Peter)   *see E Markham w Askham, Headon w*
   Upton and Grove S'well
HEADSTONE (St George) *Lon 23*   **P** *Bp*   **V** S R KEEBLE
HEAGE (St Luke)   *see Ambergate and Heage Derby*
HEALAUGH (St John the Baptist) w Wighill, Bilbrough and
   Askham Richard *York 1*   **P** *Abp (3 turns), A G Wailes*
   Fairburn Esq (1 turn)   **P-in-c** J A RENDALL,   **NSM** B H FRAY
HEALD GREEN (St Catherine) *Ches 17*   **P** *Bp*
   V G D C LANE,   **C** G W LAMB,   **NSM** S C JOHNSON
HEALEY (Christ Church) *Man 20*   **P** *Bp*   **P-in-c** J D QUANCE
HEALEY (St John) *Newc 3*   **P** *V Bywell St Pet*
   P-in-c D J IRVINE,   **NSM** J LYNCH
HEALEY (St Paul)   *see Masham and Healey Ripon*
HEALEY (War Memorial Mission)   *see S Ossett Wakef*
HEALING (St Peter and St Paul)   *see Keelby Gp Linc*
HEAMOOR (St Thomas)   *see Gulval and Madron Truro*
HEANOR (St Laurence) *Derby 12*   **P** *Wright Trustees*
   P-in-c I N PALLETT,   **C** J W BYATT
HEAP BRIDGE (St Thomas and St George)   *see Bury Ch King*
   Man
HEAPEY (St Barnabas) and Withnell *Blackb 4*   **P** *V Leyland*
   V K HOWARD
HEAPHAM (All Saints)   *see Lea Gp Linc*
HEARTSEASE (St Francis)   *see Nor Heartsease St Fran Nor*
HEATH (All Saints) *Derby 5*   **P** *Duke of Devonshire and*
   Simeon's Trustees (jt)   **V** A LOVE,   **NSM** M GUEST
HEATH (Mission Church)   *see Uttoxeter Area Lich*
HEATH, LITTLE (Christ Church) *St Alb 17*   **P** *Ch Patr Trust*
   V I D BROWN,   **NSM** R H WIKNER
HEATH, THE (not known)   *see Bitterley w Middleton, Stoke*
   St Milborough etc Heref
HEATH AND REACH (St Leonard) *St Alb 12*   **P** *V Leighton*
   Buzzard   **V** G A NEALE
HEATH HAYES (St John)   *see Cannock Lich*
HEATH TOWN (Holy Trinity)   *see Wednesfield Heath Lich*
HEATHER (St John the Baptist)   *see Ibstock w Heather Leic*
HEATHERLANDS (St John) *Sarum 7*   **P** *MMCET*
   V G A G LOUGHLIN

HEATHERYCLEUGH (St Thomas) *Dur 9*   **P** *Bp*
   P-in-c P A GREENHALGH
HEATHFIELD (All Saints) *Chich 15*   **P** *Bp*   **V** G C PICKERING
HEATHFIELD (St Catherine)   *see Bovey Tracey St Jo w*
   Heathfield Ex
HEATHFIELD (St John the Baptist)   *see Bradford w Oake,*
   Hillfarrance and Heathfield B & W
HEATHFIELD (St Richard) *Chich 15*   **P** *Bp*   **V** R S CRITTALL
HEATON (Christ Church) *Man 9*   **P** *R Deane St Mary*
   NSM M E MAYOH
HEATON (St Barnabas) *Bradf 1*   **P** *Trustees*   **V** R S ANDERSON
HEATON (St Gabriel)   *see Newc St Gabr Newc*
HEATON (St Martin) *Bradf 1*   **P** *Bp*   **V** A J BURNISTON
HEATON, HIGH (St Francis)   *see Newc St Fran Newc*
HEATON CHAPEL (St Thomas)   *see Heatons Man*
HEATON MERSEY (St John the Baptist)   *as above Man*
HEATON MOOR (St Paul)   *as above Man*
HEATON NORRIS (Christ w All Saints)   *as above Man*
HEATON REDDISH (St Mary) *Man 3*   **P** *Trustees*
   R W J MCKAE
HEATONS *Man 3*   **P** *Patr Bd (4 turns), Prime Min (1 turn)*
   TR M H MAXWELL,   **TV** S E W GUY, P G STANNARD,
   R I MECHANIC,   **C** J R WILLIAMS, T E BIDDINGTON,
   OLM H J TATE
HEAVITREE (St Michael and All Angels) (St Lawrence)
   (St Loye) and St Mary Steps *Ex 3*   **P** *Patr Bd*   **TR** M S HART,
   TV J F SEWARD, L M BATE,   **C** J FLETCHER, P R MORRELL
HEBBURN (St Cuthbert) *Dur 15*   **P** *TR Jarrow*
   P-in-c J B HUNT
HEBBURN (St John) *Dur 15*   **P** *Bp*   **P-in-c** D T OSMAN,
   C J P ROY
HEBBURN (St Oswald) *Dur 15*   **P** *The Crown*
   P-in-c J B HUNT
HEBDEN (St Peter)   *see Linton in Craven Bradf*
HEBDEN BRIDGE (St James) and Heptonstall *Wakef 3*
   P *V Halifax*   **V** H PASK
HEBRON (St Cuthbert)   *see Longhorsley and Hebron Newc*
HECK (St John the Baptist)   *see Gt Snaith Sheff*
HECKFIELD (St Michael) w Mattingley and Rotherwick *Win 5*
   P *New Coll Ox (2 turns), Bp (1 turn)*   **V** A F J CHAMBERS
HECKINGTON (St Andrew) *Linc 22*   **P** *Bp*
   P-in-c D F BOUTLE
HECKMONDWIKE (All Souls) (St James) *Wakef 8*
   P *V Birstall*   **V** P SWALES
HEDDINGTON (St Andrew)   *see Oldbury Sarum*
HEDDON-ON-THE-WALL (St Andrew) *Newc 3*   **P** *Ld Chan*
   P-in-c K M EMERY
HEDENHAM (St Peter)   *see Ditchingham, Hedenham and*
   Broome Nor
HEDGE END (St John the Evangelist) *Win 10*   **P** *Bp*
   V C J BANNISTER,   **NSM** S E LITJENS
HEDGE END (St Luke) *Win 10*   **P** *Bp*   **V** M R POWIS
HEDGEFIELD (St Hilda)   *see Ryton w Hedgefield Dur*
HEDGERLEY (St Mary the Virgin)   *see Farnham Royal w*
   Hedgerley Ox
HEDNESFORD (St Peter) *Lich 3*   **P** *Bp*   **C** L B VARQUEZ
HEDON (St Augustine) w Paull *York 12*   **P** *Abp*
   V I R HOWITT
HEDSOR (St Nicholas) and Bourne End *Ox 29*   **P** *Bp*
   R *vacant (01628) 523046*
HEDWORTH (St Nicholas) *Dur 15*   **P** *The Crown*
   P-in-c J S BAIN,   **Hon C** D M DUKE
HEELEY (Christ Church) and Gleadless Valley *Sheff 1*   **P** *DBP*
   and Prime Min (alt)   **TR** J M STRIDE,   **TV** A PATTERSON
HEENE (St Botolph) *Chich 5*   **P** *D&C*   **R** P R ROBERTS,
   C C G H KASSELL
HEIGHAM (Holy Trinity) *Nor 3*   **P** *Ch Trust Fund Trust*
   R A M STRANGE,   **C** M J YOUNG
HEIGHAM (St Barnabas) (St Bartholomew) *Nor 3*   **P** *Bp*
   P-in-c E HUTCHEON
HEIGHAM (St Thomas) *Nor 3*   **P** *Bp*   **V** N J H GARRARD,
   C D ROGERS
HEIGHINGTON (not known)   *see Washingborough w*
   Heighington and Canwick Linc
HEIGHINGTON (St Michael) *Dur 8*   **P** *D&C*
   V P H E THOMAS,   **NSM** M D M FERGUSON
HEIGHTINGTON (St Giles)   *see Mamble w Bayton, Rock w*
   Heightington etc Worc
HELFORD (St Paul's Mission Church)   *see Manaccan w*
   St Anthony-in-Meneage and St Martin Truro
HELHOUGHTON (All Saints)   *see E w W Rudham,*
   Helhoughton etc Nor
HELIDON (St John the Baptist)   *see Daventry, Ashby*
   St Ledgers, Braunston etc Pet
HELIONS BUMPSTEAD (St Andrew)   *see Steeple Bumpstead*
   and Helions Bumpstead Chelmsf

HELLAND (St Helena) *Truro 10* **P** *MMCET*
P-in-c D R CARRIVICK

HELLESDON (St Mary) (St Paul and St Michael) *Nor 2* **P** *Bp*
V P E GRIFFITHS, **C** V M WILSON, **NSM** S A WILSON,
OLM E O JONES-BLACKETT

HELLIFIELD (St Aidan) *Bradf 5* **P** *Ch Ch Ox*
P-in-c E A KYTE, **Hon C** K J PHILLIPS

HELLINGLY (St Peter and St Paul) and Upper Dicker *Chich 15*
P *Abp and Bp (jt)* **NSM** S J MORGAN

HELMDON (St Mary Magdalene) w Stuchbury and Radstone
and Syresham w Whitfield *Pet 1* **P** *Ox Univ, Mert Coll Ox, and
Worc Coll Ox (3 turns), Bp (1 turn), and DBP (1 turn)*
P-in-c J H ROBERTS, **NSM** W T ADAMS, D E MICKLETHWAITE

HELME (Christ Church) *see* Meltham *Wakef*

HELMINGHAM (St Mary) w Framsden and Pettaugh w
Winston *St E 18* **P** *Ld Chan, MMCET, and Lord Tollemache
(by turn)* **P-in-c** G E NOBLE, **OLM** P A R WILKES,
J E BUFTON

HELMSHORE (St Thomas) *see* Musbury *Blackb*

HELMSLEY (All Saints) *York 17* **P** *Lord Feversham*
V D J WILBOURNE

HELMSLEY, UPPER (St Peter) *see* Sand Hutton *York*

HELPERTHORPE (St Peter) *see* Weaverthorpe w
Helperthorpe, Luttons Ambo etc *York*

HELPRINGHAM (St Andrew) w Hale *Linc 22* **P** *Ld Chan
(2 turns), D&C (1 turn), DBP (1 turn), and the Rt Revd A C
Foottit (1 turn)* **P-in-c** S SAMUEL

HELPSTON (St Botolph) *see* Etton w Helpston and Maxey *Pet*

HELSBY (St Paul) and Dunham-on-the-Hill *Ches 3* **P** *Bp*
P-in-c R W CROOK

HELSINGTON (St John the Baptist) *Carl 10* **P** *V Kendal
H Trin* **V** *vacant*

HELSTON (St Michael) and Wendron *Truro 4* **P** *Patr Bd*
TR D G MILLER, **OLM** D NOAKES

HEMBLINGTON (All Saints) *see* Blofield w Hemblington *Nor*

HEMEL HEMPSTEAD (Holy Trinity) Leverstock Green
see Chambersbury *St Alb*

HEMEL HEMPSTEAD (St Benedict) Bennetts End *as above
St Alb*

HEMEL HEMPSTEAD (St Mary) *St Alb 3* **P** *Ld Chan*
TR P J COTTON, **TV** G R PATCHELL, S R ALLEN, S R J FRENCH,
D J MIDDLEBROOK, **NSM** T J BARTON, H J SMITH, D SPINK

HEMEL HEMPSTEAD (St Mary) Apsley End
see Chambersbury *St Alb*

HEMINGBROUGH (St Mary the Virgin) *York 2* **P** *Abp*
P-in-c M A PASKETT

HEMINGBY (St Margaret) *Linc 11* **P** *Bp (2 turns), Ld Chan
(2 turns), and DBP (1 turn)* **R** *vacant*

HEMINGFORD ABBOTS (St Margaret of Antioch) *Ely 8*
P *Lord Hemingford* **R** *vacant (01480) 698856*

HEMINGFORD GREY (St James) *Ely 8* **P** *Mrs G A Scott*
P-in-c P H CUNLIFFE

HEMINGSTONE (St Gregory) *see* Coddenham w Gosbeck
and Hemingstone w Henley *St E*

HEMINGTON (St Peter and St Paul) *see* Polebrook and Lutton
w Hemington and Luddington *Pet*

HEMINGTON (The Blessed Virgin Mary) *see* Hardington Vale
B & W

HEMLEY (All Saints) *see* Waldringfield w Hemley and
Newbourn *St E*

HEMLINGTON (St Timothy) *York 21* **P** *Abp* **V** A HOWARD

HEMPNALL (St Margaret) *Nor 5* **P** *Ld Chan (1 turn),
Patr Bd (5 turns)* **TR** C M MAHONY, **TV** E BILLETT

HEMPSTEAD (All Saints) *see* Barningham w Matlaske w
Baconsthorpe etc *Nor*

HEMPSTEAD (All Saints) *see* S Gillingham *Roch*

HEMPSTEAD (St Andrew) *see* The Sampfords and Radwinter
w Hempstead *Chelmsf*

HEMPSTEAD (St Andrew) *see* Happisburgh, Walcott,
Hempstead w Eccles etc *Nor*

HEMPSTED (St Swithun) *Glouc 5* **P** *Bp* **P-in-c** A M BUTLER

HEMPTON (Holy Trinity) and Pudding Norton *Nor 15*
P *The Crown* **P-in-c** P F KEELING

HEMPTON (St John the Evangelist) *see* Deddington w Barford,
Clifton and Hempton *Ox*

HEMSBY (St Mary) *see* Flegg Coastal Benefice *Nor*

HEMSWELL (All Saints) *see* Glentworth Gp *Linc*

HEMSWORTH (St Helen) *Wakef 11* **P** *Bp* **R** M DAVIES,
C L BENNETT

HEMYOCK (St Mary) w Culm Davy, Clayhidon and Culmstock
Ex 4 **P** *DBP, SMF, and D&C (jt)* **R** *vacant (01823) 681189*

HENBURY (St Mary the Virgin) *Bris 2* **P** *Lord Middleton
(1 turn), Bp (3 turns)* **V** D P LLOYD, **C** J K NICHOLSON

HENBURY (St Thomas) *Ches 13* **P** *Bp* **V** D S HARRISON

HENDFORD (Holy Trinity) *see* Yeovil H Trin w Barwick
B & W

HENDFORD (St Mary the Virgin and All Saints) *as above
B & W*

HENDON (All Saints) Childs Hill *Lon 15* **P** *Bp*
V J P WAINWRIGHT

HENDON (St Alphage) *Lon 15* **P** *Bp* **V** H D MOORE,
C C CRAWSHAW

HENDON (St Ignatius) *Dur 16* **P** *Bp* **R** A C JONES

HENDON (St Mary) (Christ Church) *Lon 15* **P** *Bp*
V P S TAYLOR, **C** S J OWEN, **NSM** R G CORP

HENDON (St Paul) Mill Hill *Lon 15* **P** *Bp* **V** A J SHAW,
C J E LOWE

HENDON, WEST (St John) *Lon 15* **P** *Bp* **V** J E I HAWKINS

HENDRED, EAST (St Augustine of Canterbury) *see* Wantage
Downs *Ox*

HENDRED, WEST (Holy Trinity) *as above Ox*

HENFIELD (St Peter) w Shermanbury and Woodmancote
Chich 9 **P** *Bp* **V** C J COLLISON, **C** J H GOULSTON

HENGOED w Gobowen *Lich 19* **P** *R Selattyn*
P-in-c A R BAILEY

HENGROVE (Christ Church) *Bris 1* **P** *Bp and Simeon's
Trustees (alt)* **V** N LAYTON

HENHAM (St Mary the Virgin) and Elsenham w Ugley
Chelmsf 21 **P** *Ch Hosp, Ch Soc Trust, and Bp (jt)*
P-in-c R W FARR, **C** J P RICHARDSON

HENLEAZE (St Peter) *Bris 2* **P** *Bp* **V** C M PILGRIM,
NSM B J PULLAN

HENLEY on Thames w Remenham *Ox 6* **P** *Bp and Jes Coll
Ox (jt)* **R** D P PRITCHARD, **C** E LOZADA-UZURIAGA

HENLEY (St Peter) *see* Coddenham w Gosbeck and
Hemingstone w Henley *St E*

HENLEY IN ARDEN (St John the Baptist) *see* Beaudesert and
Henley-in-Arden w Ullenhall *Cov*

HENLEY-ON-THAMES (Holy Trinity) *Ox 6* **P** *R Rotherfield
Greys St Nich* **V** D R B CARTER

HENLOW (St Mary the Virgin) and Langford *St Alb 16*
P *Ld Chan* **V** J MORLEY

HENNOCK (St Mary) *see* Bovey Tracey SS Pet, Paul and Thos
w Hennock *Ex*

HENNY, GREAT (St Mary) *see* N Hinckford *Chelmsf*

HENSALL (St Paul) *see* Gt Snaith *Sheff*

HENSHAW (All Hallows) *see* Haydon Bridge and Beltingham
w Henshaw *Newc*

HENSINGHAM (St John) (Keekle Mission) *Carl 5* **P** *Trustees*
V F T PEARSON

HENSTEAD (St Mary) *see* Sole Bay *St E*

HENSTRIDGE (St Nicholas) and Charlton Horethorne w
Stowell *B & W 2* **P** *Bp (2 turns), K S D Wingfield Digby Esq
(1 turn)* **R** P HALLETT

HENTLAND (St Dubricius) *see* How Caple w Sollarshope,
Sellack etc *Heref*

HENTON (Christ Church) *see* Coxley w Godney, Henton and
Wookey *B & W*

HEPPLE (Christ Church) *see* Rothbury *Newc*

HEPTONSTALL (St Thomas à Becket and St Thomas the
Apostle) *see* Hebden Bridge and Heptonstall *Wakef*

HEPWORTH (Holy Trinity) *see* Upper Holme Valley *Wakef*

HEPWORTH (St Peter) w Hinderclay, Wattisfield and
Thelnetham *St E 9* **P** *Bp, K Coll Cam, MMCET, and
P J Holt-Wilson Esq (jt)* **R** J W FULTON

HEREFORD (All Saints) (St Barnabas Church Centre) *Heref 3*
P *D&C Windsor* **P-in-c** A P MOTTRAM

HEREFORD (Holy Trinity) *Heref 3* **P** *Bp* **V** R NORTH

HEREFORD (St Francis) *see* Heref S Wye *Heref*

HEREFORD (St John the Baptist) *Heref 3* **P** *D&C* **V** *vacant*

HEREFORD (St Martin) *see* Heref S Wye *Heref*

HEREFORD (St Paul) *see* Tupsley w Hampton Bishop *Heref*

HEREFORD (St Peter w St Owen) (St James) *Heref 3*
P *Simeon's Trustees* **P-in-c** P TOWNER, **C** J J MERCER,
NSM A P CHEATLE, P W MASSEY, **OLM** S A ELSON

HEREFORD, LITTLE (St Mary Magdalene) *see* Burford III w
Lt Heref *Heref*

HEREFORD, WEST Team Ministry (St Nicholas) *Heref 3*
P *Ld Chan* **TR** R NORTH, **TV** B P CHAVE, **C** V J TAIT,
NSM S GREEN

HEREFORD SOUTH WYE (St Francis) (St Martin) *Heref 3*
P *Patr Bd* **TR** P G HADDLETON, **TV** M JOHNSON, **C** H M SHO—
R C GREEN, **OLM** C R EVANS

HERMITAGE (Holy Trinity) *Ox 14* **P** *Patr Bd*
TR J K COOMBS, **TV** A H LYNN, **C** T WARD,
NSM J L C HERRICK

HERMITAGE (St Mary) *see* Wriggle Valley *Sarum*

HERNE (St Martin) *Cant 7* **P** *Abp* **OLM** J L HADLOW,
J A BAKER

HERNE BAY (Christ Church) (St Andrew's Church and Centre)
Cant 7 **P** *Simeon's Trustees* **V** A W EVERETT,
Hon C S A MUST

HERNE BAY (St Bartholomew)   *see* Reculver and Herne Bay
St Bart *Cant*

HERNE HILL (St Paul) (St Saviour) *S'wark 9*   P *Bp and
Simeon's Trustees (jt)*   V C T BARKER,   C S POWNALL

HERNER (Chapel)   *see* Barnstaple *Ex*

HERNHILL (St Michael)   *see* Boughton under Blean w
Dunkirk and Hernhill *Cant*

HERODSFOOT (All Saints)   *see* Duloe, Herodsfoot, Morval
and St Pinnock *Truro*

HERONSGATE (St John the Evangelist)   *see* Mill End and
Heronsgate w W Hyde *St Alb*

HERRIARD (St Mary) w Winslade and Long Sutton and South
Warnborough and Tunworth and Upton Grey and Weston
Patrick *Win 5*   P *Bp, Qu Coll Ox, St Jo Coll Ox, Exors
Viscount Camrose, and J L Jervoise Esq (jt)*   NSM J E LEESE

HERRINGFLEET (St Margaret)   *see* Somerleyton, Ashby,
Fritton, Herringfleet etc *Nor*

HERRINGSWELL (St Ethelbert)   *see* Mildenhall *St E*

HERRINGTHORPE (St Cuthbert) *Sheff 6*   P *Bp*
V J TRICKETT

HERRINGTON *Dur 14*   P *Bp*   P-in-c P M HOOD,
NSM M S GOURLEY

HERSHAM (St Peter) *Guildf 8*   P *Bp*   V N J WHITEHEAD

HERSTMONCEUX (All Saints) and Wartling *Chich 15*   P *Bp*
P-in-c S L PANTER MARSHALL

HERSTON (St Mark)   *see* Swanage and Studland *Sarum*

HERTFORD (All Saints) *St Alb 22*   P *Ld Chan and Marquess
Townshend (alt)*   V W ST J KEMM

HERTFORD (St Andrew) *St Alb 22*   P *Duchy of Lanc*
R G C EDWARDS

HERTFORD HEATH (Holy Trinity)   *see* Lt Amwell *St Alb*

HERTINGFORDBURY (St Mary) *St Alb 22*   P *The Crown*
P-in-c R A CARUANA

HESKET-IN-THE-FOREST (St Mary the Virgin) and
Armathwaite *Carl 4*   P *D&C and E P Ecroyd Esq (jt)*
P-in-c E M SMITH,   C R C PATTINSON,   NSM J J H SMITH

HESKETH (All Saints) w Becconsall *Blackb 5*   P *Trustees*
R R PLANT

HESLERTON, EAST (St Andrew)   *see* Buckrose Carrs *York*

HESLERTON, WEST (All Saints)   *as above York*

HESLINGTON (St Paul) *York 2*   P *Abp*   V N E ECKERSLEY

HESSAY (St John the Baptist)   *see* Rufforth w Moor Monkton
and Hessay *York*

HESSENFORD (St Anne)   *see* St Germans *Truro*

HESSETT (St Ethelbert)   *see* Rougham, Beyton w Hessett and
Rushbrooke *St E*

HESSLE (All Saints) *York 14*   P *Ld Chan*   V K A DAVID,
C K L BURGESS

HESTER WAY LANE (St Silas)   *see* Cheltenham St Mark *Glouc*

HESTON (All Saints) (St Leonard) *Lon 11*   P *Bp*
V R CRANKSHAW,   C J SCOTT,   NSM M A WILKINSON

HESWALL (Church of the Good Shepherd) (St Peter) *Ches 8*
P *W A B Davenport Esq*   R J R GIBBS,   C A C HOWARD,
S M MANSFIELD

HETHE (St Edmund King and Martyr and St George)
see Shelswell *Ox*

HETHEL (All Saints)   *see* Mulbarton w Bracon Ash, Hethel and
Flordon *Nor*

HETHERSETT (St Remigius) w Canteloff w Little Melton and
Great Melton *Nor 7*   P *G&C Coll Cam,
E C Evans-Lombe Esq, and Em Coll Cam (by turn)*
R D B LAMMAS,   C J H ROBSON,   NSM J C MALLETT

HETHERSGILL (St Mary)   *see* Bewcastle, Stapleton and
Kirklinton etc *Carl*

HETTON, SOUTH (Holy Trinity)   *see* Easington, Easington
Colliery and S Hetton *Dur*

HETTON-LE-HOLE (St Nicholas)   *see* Eppleton and Hetton le
Hole *Dur*

HEVENINGHAM (St Margaret)   *see* Cratfield w Heveningham
and Ubbeston etc *St E*

HEVER (St Peter), Four Elms and Mark Beech *Roch 11*   P *Bp
and C Talbot Esq (jt)*   P-in-c M G RIBBLE,   NSM W J IZOD

HEVERSHAM (St Peter) and Milnthorpe *Carl 10*
P *Trin Coll Cam*   V J C HANCOCK,   NSM R RUTTER

HEVINGHAM (St Mary and St Botolph) w Hainford and
Stratton Strawless *Nor 19*   P *Bp and Sir Thomas
Beevor Bt (jt)*   P-in-c C J ENGELSEN

HEWELSFIELD (St Mary Magdalene)   *see* St Briavels w
Hewelsfield *Glouc*

HEWISH (Good Shepherd)   *see* Crewkerne w Wayford *B & W*

HEWORTH (Christ Church) *York 7*   P *Ch Trust Fund Trust*
V T MCDONOUGH,   NSM M D P NOKES

HEWORTH (Holy Trinity) (St Wulstan) *York 7*   P *Patr Bd*
TR M B WOODMANSEY,   NSM C M A RUTT

HEWORTH (St Alban) *Dur 12*   P *V Heworth St Mary*
V M WROE

HEWORTH (St Mary) *Dur 12*   P *Bp*   V V SHEDDEN,
NSM D M SNOWBALL

HEXHAM (St Andrew) *Newc 4*   P *Mercers' Co and Viscount
Allendale (alt)*   C D WINTER

HEXTABLE (St Peter)   *see* Swanley St Paul *Roch*

HEXTHORPE (St Jude)   *see* Doncaster St Jude *Sheff*

HEXTON (St Faith)   *see* Barton-le-Cley w Higham Gobion and
Hexton *St Alb*

HEY (St John the Baptist) *Man 21*   P *R Aston-under-Lyne
St Mich*   P-in-c R W HAWKINS,   C D R PENNY

HEYBRIDGE (St Andrew) (St George) w Langford *Chelmsf 11*
P *D&C St Paul's and Lord Byron (alt)*   V S E MCCARTHY

HEYBROOK BAY (Holy Nativity)   *see* Wembury *Ex*

HEYDON (Holy Trinity), Great Chishill and Little Chishill,
Chrishall, Elmdon w Wenden Lofts and Strethall *Chelmsf 22*
P *Patr Bd*   R J G SIMMONS,   C M P WARREN,
NSM E H G FISHER

HEYDON (St Peter and St Paul)   *see* Cawston w Booton and
Brandiston etc *Nor*

HEYDOUR (St Michael and All Angels)   *see* Ancaster Wilsford
Gp *Linc*

HEYFORD (St Peter and St Paul) w Stowe Nine Churches and
Flore w Brockhall *Pet 3*   P *The Revd S Hope, Ch Ch Ox, DPB
and Bp (by turn)*   R S L GOBLE

HEYFORD, LOWER (St Mary)   *see* The Heyfords w Rousham
and Somerton *Ox*

HEYFORD, UPPER (St Mary)   *as above Ox*

HEYFORDS w Rousham and Somerton, The *Ox 2*   P *New Coll
Ox, CCC Ox, C Cottrell-Dormer Esq, and P W G Barnes Esq
(by turn)*   R *vacant* (01869) 340733

HEYHOUSES (St Nicholas)   *see* Sabden and Pendleton *Blackb*

HEYHOUSES ON SEA (St Anne) *Blackb 10*   P J C Hilton Esq
V D M PORTER,   C K J FENTON

HEYSHAM (St Peter) (St Andrew) (St James) *Blackb 11*
P C E C Royds Esq   R A TICKNER

HEYSHOTT (St James) *Chich 10*   P *Bp*   P-in-c C BOXLEY

HEYSIDE (St Mark) *Man 22*   P *Trustees*   V R MORRIS,
NSM S E WARD

HEYTESBURY (St Peter and St Paul)   *see* Upper Wylye Valley
Sarum

HEYTHROP (St Nicholas)   *see* Chase *Ox*

HEYWOOD (All Souls) (St Luke) (St Margaret) *Man 18*
P *Patr Bd*   TR G TURNER,   TV M E READ, M E DICKER,
C A C YOUNG,   OLM A BROWN, I TAYLOR, R A J MILLER,
I WARRINGTON

HEYWOOD (St James) *Man 18*   P *Bp*   V S A EVASON

HIBALDSTOW (St Hibald)   *see* Scawby, Redbourne and
Hibaldstow *Linc*

HICKLETON (St Wilfrid)   *see* Goldthorpe w Hickleton *Sheff*

HICKLING (St Luke) w Kinoulton and Broughton Sulney (Upper
Broughton) *S'well 8*   P *Prime Min, Qu Coll Cam, and Bp
(by turn)*   R S B FAHIE

HICKLING (St Mary)   *see* Ludham, Potter Heigham, Hickling
and Catfield *Nor*

HIGH   *see also under substantive place name*

HIGH CROSS (St John the Evangelist) *St Alb 22*   P *DBP*
V H J SHARMAN

HIGH GREEN (St Saviour)   *see* Mortomley St Sav High Green
Sheff

HIGH HAM (St Andrew)   *see* Langport Area Chs *B & W*

HIGH LANE (St Thomas) *Ches 16*   P *R Stockport*
V K G LOWE

HIGH OAK, Hingham and Scoulton w Wood Rising *Nor 7*
P *Patr Bd*   TR P J STEPHENS,   TV S G STEPHENSON,
OLM P J TRETT, S A HOLT, J-J S AIDLEY

HIGHAM (St John the Evangelist)   *see* Fence-in-Pendle and
Higham *Blackb*

HIGHAM (St John the Evangelist) and Merston *Roch 6*
P *St Jo Coll Cam*   V J F SOUTHWARD

HIGHAM (St Mary), Holton St Mary, Raydon and Stratford
St Mary *St E 3*   P *Duchy of Lanc, Reformation Ch Trust, and
Mrs S E F Holden*   R C A GARRARD

HIGHAM FERRERS (St Mary the Virgin) w Chelveston *Pet 10*
P *Bp*   V G L BROCKHOUSE,   NSM P R NEEDLE

HIGHAM GOBION (St Margaret)   *see* Barton-le-Cley w
Higham Gobion and Hexton *St Alb*

HIGHAM GREEN (St Stephen)   *see* Barrow w Denham
St Mary and Higham Green *St E*

HIGHAM HILL (St Andrew)   *see* Walthamstow St Andr
Chelmsf

HIGHAM-ON-THE-HILL (St Peter)   *see* Fenn Lanes Gp *Leic*

HIGHAMPTON (Holy Cross)   *see* Black Torrington, Bradf w
Cookbury etc *Ex*

HIGHAMS PARK (All Saints) Hale End *Chelmsf 5*   P *Bp*
V C A MCGHIE

HIGHBRIDGE (St John the Evangelist) *B & W 1*   P *Bp*
V R P LODGE,   NSM S J HARTREE

HIGHBROOK (All Saints) and West Hoathly *Chich 6*
P *Ld Chan*   **V** A C CARR
HIGHBURY (Christ Church) (St John) (St Saviour) *Lon 6*
P *Ch Trust Fund Trust and Islington Ch Trust (jt)*
V J D BREWSTER,   **NSM** T J I WITTER
HIGHBURY NEW PARK (St Augustine) *Lon 6*   **P** *Trustees*
V C T MAIN
**HIGHCLERE (St Michael and All Angels) and Ashmansworth w
Crux Easton** *Win 6*   **P** *Earl of Carnarvon*   **R** T F HORSINGTON
HIGHCLIFFE (St Mark) w Hinton Admiral *Win 9*
P *Sir George Tapps-Gervis-Meyrick Bt and Bp (alt)*
C J H WATSON
HIGHER   *see also under substantive place name*
HIGHER FOLD Leigh (St Matthew)   *see* Bedford Leigh *Man*
HIGHERTOWN (St Paul) and Baldhu *Truro 6*   **P** *Bp and
Viscount Falmouth (alt)*   **V** G W SMYTH,
NSM A J STEVENSON
HIGHFIELD (All Saints) *Ox 4*   **P** *Bp*   **V** J E COCKE
HIGHFIELD (Christ Church)   *see* Portswood Ch Ch *Win*
HIGHFIELD (St Catherine)   *see* New Bury *Man*
HIGHFIELD (St Mary)   *see* Sheff St Mary Bramall Lane *Sheff*
HIGHFIELD (St Matthew) *Liv 15*   **P** *Trustees*
V R L PEARSON
HIGHFIELD (St Paul)   *see* Hemel Hempstead *St Alb*
HIGHGATE (All Saints) *Lon 20*   **P** *Bp*   **P-in-c** P STORR
VENTER
HIGHGATE (St Alban and St Patrick) *Birm 13*   **P** *Keble Coll
Ox*   **V** J G PENDORF
HIGHGATE (St Augustine) *Lon 20*   **P** *Bp*   **V** T BUGBY
HIGHGATE (St Michael) *Lon 20*   **P** *Bp*   **V** J D TRIGG,
C N J LITTLE,   **NSM** E M WEST
HIGHGATE CENTRE   *see* Bredbury St Barn *Ches*
HIGHGATE RISE (St Anne)   *see* Brookfield St Anne, Highgate
Rise *Lon*
**HIGHLEY (St Mary) w Billingsley, Glazeley and Deuxhill and
Chelmarsh** *Heref 9*   **P** *MMCET*   **C** C G WILLIAMS,
C D N H CHISLETT
HIGHMORE (St Paul)   *see* Nettlebed w Bix, Highmoor, Pishill
etc *Ox*
**HIGHNAM (Holy Innocents), Lassington, Rudford, Tibberton
and Taynton** *Glouc 3*   **P** *D&C, T J Fenton Esq, and
A E Woolley (jt)*   **P-in-c** M S RILEY,   **Hon C** G N CRAGO,
OLM G R W PARFITT
HIGHTERS HEATH (Immanuel) *Birm 5*   **P** *Bp*   **V** E I PITTS
HIGHTOWN (All Saints)   *see* Castleford *Wakef*
HIGHTOWN (St Barnabas)   *see* Liversedge w Hightown *Wakef*
HIGHTOWN (St Stephen)   *see* Altcar and Hightown *Liv*
HIGHWEEK (All Saints) (St Mary) and Teigngrace *Ex 11*
P *Bp*   **R** C R KNOTT
**HIGHWORTH (St Michael) w Sevenhampton and Inglesham and
Hannington** *Bris 7*   **P** *Bp (4 turns), Mrs M G Hussey-Freke
(1 turn)*   **V** G D SOWDEN,   **C** R C WARD
HILBOROUGH (All Saints) w Bodney *Nor 13*   **P** *DBP*
P-in-c A D WALKER
HILDENBOROUGH (St John the Evangelist) *Roch 11*
P *V Tonbridge*   **V** R J BAWTREE,   **C** P MEIER,   **NSM** E M TOY
HILDERSHAM (Holy Trinity) *Ely 4*   **P** *Trustees*
P-in-c J B MYNORS
HILDERSTONE (Christ Church)   *see* Fulford w Hilderstone
Lich
HILFIELD (St Nicholas)   *see* Wriggle Valley *Sarum*
HILGAY (All Saints) *Ely 15*   **P** *Hertf Coll Ox*   **R** D J EVANS
HILL (St James) *Birm 12*   **P** *Bp*   **V** R D HINDLEY,
C P OGILVIE
HILL (St Michael)   *see* Berkeley w Wick, Breadstone, Newport,
Stone etc *Glouc*
HILL CROOME (St Mary)   *see* Upton-on-Severn, Ripple, Earls
Croome etc *Worc*
HILL TOP (Mission Room)   *see* Greasley *S'well*
HILL TOP (St James)   *see* W Bromwich St Jas w St Paul *Lich*
HILLESDEN (All Saints)   *see* Lenborough *Ox*
HILLESLEY (St Giles)   *see* Wickwar, Rangeworthy and
Hillesley *Glouc*
HILLFARRANCE (Holy Cross)   *see* Bradford w Oake,
Hillfarrance and Heathfield *B & W*
HILLINGDON (All Saints) *Lon 24*   **P** *Bp*   **V** P C HULLYER,
C L FAWNS,   **Hon C** L C STOCK
HILLINGDON (St John the Baptist) *Lon 24*   **P** *Bp*
V R W HARRISON,   **NSM** G PINNELL,   **W F** WHITE
HILLINGTON (St Mary the Virgin) *Nor 16*
P *E W Dawnay Esq*   **R** *vacant*
HILLMORTON (St John the Baptist) *Cov 6*   **P** *Bp and
TR Rugby*   **V** A P HAINES
HILLOCK (St Andrew) *Man 14*   **P** *Bp and R Stand All SS*
P-in-c A B WILLIAMS
HILLSBOROUGH and Wadsley Bridge (Christ Church) *Sheff 4*
P *Ch Patr Trust*   **V** J E COUSANS

HILLTOP (Mission Room)   *see* Endon w Stanley *Lich*
HILMARTON (St Lawrence)   *see* Broad Town, Cliffe Pypard,
Hilmarton etc *Sarum*
**HILPERTON (St Michael and All Angels) w Whaddon and
Staverton w Hilperton Marsh** *Sarum 14*   **P** *R Trowbridge
St Jas and Viscount Long (alt)*   **P-in-c** R J H MAGILL
HILPERTON MARSH (St Mary Magdalen)   *see* Hilperton w
Whaddon and Staverton etc *Sarum*
HILSTON (St Margaret)   *see* Roos and Garton in Holderness w
Tunstall etc *York*
HILTON (All Saints)   *see* Milton Abbas, Hilton w Cheselbourne
etc *Sarum*
HILTON (St Mary Magdalene) *Ely 8*   **P** *Bp*   **V** M A GUITE
HILTON (St Peter)   *see* Stainton w Hilton *York*
HILTON w Marston-on-Dove *Derby 14*   **P** *N J M Spurrier Esq*
V A G MURPHIE,   **NSM** S K MATSON DE LAURIER
HIMBLETON (St Mary Magdalen)   *see* Bowbrook S *Worc*
HIMLEY (St Michael and All Angels)   *see* Smestow Vale *Lich*
HINCASTER (Mission Room)   *see* Heversham and Milnthorpe
Carl
HINCHLEY WOOD (St Christopher) *Guildf 8*   **P** *Bp*
V T A DONNELLY
HINCKFORD, NORTH *Chelmsf 19*   **P** *Patr Bd (4 turns),
Ld Chan (1 turn)*   **TR** *vacant (01787) 277210*
**HINCKLEY (Assumption of St Mary the Virgin) (St Francis)
(St Paul)** *Leic 13*   **P** *Bp*   **V** B DAVIS
HINCKLEY (Holy Trinity) (St John the Evangelist) *Leic 13*
P *DBP*   **TR** G D HAYLES,   **TV** J C MCGINLEY,   **C** F L PRICE
HINDERCLAY (St Mary)   *see* Hepworth, Hinderclay,
Wattisfield and Thelnetham *St E*
HINDERWELL (St Hilda) w Roxby *York 22*   **P** *Abp*
P-in-c J M E COOPER
HINDHEAD (St Alban)   *see* Churt and Hindhead *Guildf*
HINDLEY (All Saints) *Liv 14*   **P** *R Wigan*   **V** J TAYLOR
HINDLEY (St Peter) *Liv 14*   **P** *St Pet Coll Ox*   **V** S A MATHER,
NSM C A CLOSE
HINDLEY GREEN (St John) *Liv 14*   **P** *Bp*   **V** M J SHERWIN
HINDOLVESTON (St George)   *see* Foulsham w Hindolveston
and Guestwick *Nor*
HINDON (St John the Baptist)   *see* Nadder Valley *Sarum*
HINDRINGHAM (St Martin)   *see* Barney, Fulmodeston w
Croxton, Hindringham etc *Nor*
HINGHAM (St Andrew)   *see* High Oak, Hingham and Scoulton
w Wood Rising *Nor*
HINKSEY, NEW (St John the Evangelist)   *see* S Hinksey *Ox*
HINKSEY, NORTH (St Lawrence) and Wytham *Ox 7*   **P** *Bp*
P-in-c R E H BATES
HINKSEY, SOUTH (St Lawrence) *Ox 7*   **P** *Bp*
P-in-c J D WILKINSON,   **Hon C** B SINGH,   M P M STEWART
HINSTOCK (St Oswald)   *see* Cheswardine, Childs Ercall, Hales,
Hinstock etc *Lich*
HINTLESHAM (St Nicholas)   *see* Elmsett w Aldham,
Hintlesham, Chattisham etc *St E*
HINTON ADMIRAL (St Michael and All Angels)
see Highcliffe w Hinton Admiral *Win*
HINTON AMPNER (All Saints)   *see* Upper Itchen *Win*
HINTON BLEWETT (St Margaret)   *see* E w W Harptree and
Hinton Blewett *B & W*
HINTON CHARTERHOUSE (St John the Baptist)
see Freshford, Limpley Stoke and Hinton Charterhouse *B & W*
HINTON-IN-THE-HEDGES (Holy Trinity)   *see* Aynho and
Croughton w Evenley etc *Pet*
HINTON MARTEL (St John the Evangelist)   *see* Horton,
Chalbury, Hinton Martel and Holt St Jas *Sarum*
HINTON-ON-THE-GREEN (St Peter)   *see* Hampton w
Sedgeberrow and Hinton-on-the-Green *Worc*
HINTON PARVA (St Swithun)   *see* Lyddington and
Wanborough and Bishopstone etc *Bris*
HINTON ST GEORGE (St George)   *see* Merriott w Hinton,
Dinnington and Lopen *B & W*
HINTON ST MARY (St Mary)   *see* Sturminster Newton,
Hinton St Mary and Lydlinch *Sarum*
HINTON WALDRIST (St Margaret)   *see* Cherbury w Gainfield
Ox
HINTS (St Bartholomew) *Lich 4*   **P** *Personal Reps
A E Jones Esq*   **P-in-c** H J BAKER
HINXHILL (St Mary)   *see* Mersham w Hinxhill and Sellindge
Cant
HINXTON (St Mary and St John) *Ely 6*   **P** *Jes Coll Cam*
V J E E CHARMAN
HINXWORTH (St Nicholas)   *see* Ashwell w Hinxworth and
Newnham *St Alb*
HIPSWELL (St John the Evangelist) *Ripon 2*   **P** *Bp*
V E A VARLEY
HISTON (St Andrew) *Ely 5*   **P** *MMCET*   **V** H K MCCURDY,
C K A HODGINS,   **NSM** R J BEWLEY

HITCHAM (All Saints) *see* Rattlesden w Thorpe Morieux, Brettenham etc *St E*

HITCHAM (St Mary) *see* Burnham w Dropmore, Hitcham and Taplow *Ox*

HITCHIN (Holy Saviour) (St Faith) (St Mark) (St Mary) *St Alb 4* **P** *Patr Bd* **TR** M A H RODEN, **TV** J FOX, J F LANKSHEAR, P M WISE, **C** C C M SABEY-CORKINDALE

HITTISLEIGH (St Andrew) *see* Chagford, Drewsteignton, Hittisleigh etc *Ex*

HIXON (St Peter) *see* Mid Trent *Lich*

HOAR CROSS (Holy Angels) w Newchurch *Lich 14* **P** *Bp and Meynell Ch Trustees* **V** *vacant*

HOARWITHY (St Catherine) *see* How Caple w Sollarshope, Sellack etc *Heref*

HOATH (Holy Cross) *see* St Nicholas at Wade w Sarre and Chislet w Hoath *Cant*

HOATHLY, EAST (not known) *see* Chiddingly w E Hoathly *Chich*

HOATHLY, WEST (St Margaret) *see* Highbrook and W Hoathly *Chich*

HOBS MOAT (St Mary) *Birm 11* **P** *Bp* **V** D A LEAHY

HOBY (All Saints) *see* Upper Wreake *Leic*

HOCKERILL (All Saints) *St Alb 18* **P** *Bp Lon* **V** *vacant* (01279) 834407

HOCKERING (St Michael), Honingham, East Tuddenham and North Tuddenham *Nor 17* **P** J V *Berney Esq (1 turn), DBP (2 turns)* **R** *vacant* (01603) 880121

HOCKERTON (St Nicholas) *see* Kirklington w Hockerton *S'well*

HOCKHAM, GREAT (Holy Trinity) *see* Caston, Griston, Merton, Thompson etc *Nor*

HOCKLEY (St Matthew) *see* Wilnecote *Lich*

HOCKLEY (St Peter and St Paul) *Chelmsf 12* **P** *Wadh Coll Ox* **V** R A SEABROOK

HOCKLIFFE (St Nicholas) *see* Leighton Buzzard w Eggington, Hockliffe etc *St Alb*

HOCKWOLD (St James) w Wilton *Ely 14* **P** *G&C Coll Cam* **R** S BETSON

HOCKWORTHY (St Simon and St Jude) *see* Sampford Peverell, Uplowman, Holcombe Rogus etc *Ex*

HODDESDON (St Catherine and St Paul) *St Alb 20* **P** *Peache Trustees* **P-in-c** J P BROOKS, **NSM** D A MOORE BROOKS

HODDESDON (St Cuthbert) *see* Rye Park St Cuth *St Alb*

HODDLESDEN (St Paul) *see* Darwen St Pet w Hoddlesden *Blackb*

HODGE HILL (St Philip and St James) *Birm 9* **P** *Bp* **TR** R J TAYLOR

HODNET (St Luke) w Weston under Redcastle *Lich 18* **P** A E H *Heber-Percy Esq* **R** H A MATTHEWS

HODTHORPE (St Martin) *see* Whitwell *Derby*

HOE (St Andrew) *see* Swanton Morley w Beetley w E Bilney and Hoe *Nor*

HOE, WEST (St Michael) *see* Plymouth St Andr and St Paul Stonehouse *Ex*

HOE BENHAM (not known) *see* Welford w Wickham and Gt Shefford, Boxford etc *Ox*

HOGGESTON (Holy Cross) *see* Schorne *Ox*

HOGHTON (Holy Trinity) *Blackb 5* **P** V *Leyland* **P-in-c** M SAWLE

HOGNASTON (St Bartholomew) *see* Hulland, Atlow, Kniveton, Bradley and Hognaston *Derby*

HOGSTHORPE (St Mary) *see* Chapel St Leonards w Hogsthorpe *Linc*

HOLBEACH (All Saints) *Linc 16* **P** *Bp* **V** G J WICKSTEAD, **Hon C** G SPENCER

HOLBEACH FEN (St John) *Linc 16* **P** *Bp* **V** *vacant*

HOLBEACH MARSH (St Luke) (St Mark) (St Martin) *Linc 16* **P** V *Holbeach* **P-in-c** M J NOTLEY

HOLBECK (St Luke the Evangelist) *Ripon 6* **P** *Bp, V Leeds St Pet, and Meynell Ch Trust (jt)* **V** P JACKSON

HOLBETON (All Saints) *Ex 20* **P** *The Crown* **P-in-c** T R DEACON

HOLBORN (St Alban the Martyr) w Saffron Hill St Peter *Lon 1* **P** *D&C St Paul's* **V** H LEVETT, **Hon C** A C LEE

HOLBORN (St George the Martyr) Queen Square (Holy Trinity) (St Bartholomew) Grays Inn Road *Lon 1* **P** *Ch Soc Trust* **P-in-c** J H VALENTINE, **C** P V ZAPHIRIOU

HOLBORN (St Giles-in-the-Fields) *see* St Giles-in-the-Fields *Lon*

HOLBROOK (All Saints), Stutton, Freston, Woolverstone and Wherstead *St E 5* **P** R N S TODD, **OLM** A J MARSHALL, C A MARSHALL

HOLBROOK (St Michael) and Little Eaton *Derby 11* **P** *DBP* **V** *vacant* (01332) 880254

HOLBROOK ROAD (St Swithin) *see* Belper *Derby*

HOLBROOKS (St Luke) *Cov 2* **P** *Bp* **V** C DUNKLEY, **C** P CALVERT

HOLBURY (Good Shepherd) *see* Fawley *Win*

HOLCOMBE (Emmanuel) (Canon Lewis Hall) *Man 10* **P** R *Bury St Mary* **P-in-c** J G ARMSTRONG, **NSM** D ALTHAM, **OLM** R W AIREY

HOLCOMBE (St Andrew) *see* Coleford w Holcombe *B & W*

HOLCOMBE (St George) *see* Dawlish *Ex*

HOLCOMBE BURNELL (St John the Baptist) *see* Tedburn St Mary, Whitestone, Oldridge etc *Ex*

HOLCOMBE ROGUS (All Saints) *see* Sampford Peverell, Uplowman, Holcombe Rogus etc *Ex*

HOLCOT (St Mary and All Saints) *see* Brixworth w Holcot *Pet*

HOLDENHURST (St John the Evangelist) and Iford *Win 8* **P** *Bp* **V** A L MCPHERSON, **C** J M ROBERTSON, **NSM** N M BENCE, J M SEARE

HOLDGATE (Holy Trinity) *see* Diddlebury w Munslow, Holdgate and Tugford *Heref*

HOLFORD (St Mary the Virgin) *see* Quantoxhead *B & W*

HOLKHAM (St Withiburga) w Egmere w Warham, Wells-next-the-Sea and Wighton *Nor 15* **P** *Viscount Coke (2 turns), M J Beddard Esq (2 turns), and D&C(1 turn)* **R** A V DOUGLAS

HOLLACOMBE (St Petroc) *see* Holsworthy w Hollacombe and Milton Damerel *Ex*

HOLLAND, GREAT (All Saints) *see* Kirby-le-Soken w Gt Holland *Chelmsf*

HOLLAND, NEW (Christ Church) *see* Barrow and Goxhill *Linc*

HOLLAND FEN (All Saints) *see* Brothertoft Gp *Linc*

HOLLAND-ON-SEA (St Bartholomew) *Chelmsf 23* **P** *Ch Patr Trust* **V** J W TURNER

HOLLAND ROAD (St John the Baptist) *see* Kensington St Jo *Lon*

HOLLESLEY (All Saints) *see* Wilford Peninsula *St E*

HOLLINFARE (St Helen) *see* Glazebury w Hollinfare *Liv*

HOLLINGBOURNE (All Saints) and Hucking w Leeds and Broomfield *Cant 15* **P** *Abp* **V** D C BROOKES, **P-in-c** R M GILL, **NSM** N FRY

HOLLINGDEAN (St Richard) *see* Brighton St Matthias *Chich*

HOLLINGTON (St John the Evangelist) *see* Rocester and Croxden w Hollington *Lich*

HOLLINGTON (St John the Evangelist) (St Peter and St Paul) *Chich 17* **P** *Ch Patr Trust* **P-in-c** C D REDKNAP

HOLLINGTON (St Leonard) (St Anne) *Chich 17* **P** E G *Brabazon Esq* **R** J G KENNEDY, **C** L A HARDING

HOLLINGWOOD (St Francis) *see* Staveley and Barrow Hill *Derby*

HOLLINGWORTH (St Hilda) *see* Milnrow *Man*

HOLLINGWORTH (St Mary) w Tintwistle *Ches 14* **P** *Patr Bd* **V** J R WATTS, **C** S A LAWSON

HOLLINSWOOD (not known) *see* Cen Telford *Lich*

HOLLINWOOD (St Margaret) and Limeside *Man 19* **P** *Bp and V Prestwich (jt)* **V** *vacant* 0161-681 4541

HOLLOWAY (Emmanuel) *see* Tollington *Lon*

HOLLOWAY Hanley Road (St Saviour) *as above Lon*

HOLLOWAY (St Francis of Assisi) *see* W Holloway St Luke *Lon*

HOLLOWAY (St Mary Magdalene) *Lon 6* **P** *Bp and V Islington St Mary (jt)* **V** M D ROGERS, **C** J K RUST, E C M K JONES

HOLLOWAY, UPPER (All Saints) *see* Tufnell Park St Geo and All SS *Lon*

HOLLOWAY, UPPER (St Andrew) (St John) (St Mary) (St Peter) *Lon 6* **P** *Patr Bd* **TR** S J W COX, **TV** S J COUVELA, W K DORGU, **C** J B MURRAY

HOLLOWAY, WEST (St Luke) *Lon 6* **P** *Lon Coll Div Trustees* **V** D W TOMLINSON

HOLLOWELL (St James) *see* Guilsborough w Hollowell and Cold Ashby *Pet*

HOLLY HALL (St Augustine) *see* Dudley St Aug Holly Hall *Worc*

HOLLY HILL (Church Centre) *see* Frankley *Birm*

HOLLYBUSH (All Saints) *see* Berrow w Pendock, Eldersfield, Hollybush etc *Worc*

HOLLYM (St Nicholas) *see* Patrington w Hollym, Welwick and Winestead *York*

HOLMBRIDGE (St David) *see* Upper Holme Valley *Wakef*

HOLMBURY ST MARY (St Mary the Virgin) *see* Wotton and Holmbury St Mary *Guildf*

HOLMCROFT (St Bertelin) *see* Stafford *Lich*

HOLME (All Saints) and Seaton Ross Group, The *York 5* **P** *St Jo Coll Cam and Ld Chan (alt)* **P-in-c** N T B STRAFFORD, **NSM** J H ANDERSON

HOLME (Holy Trinity) *see* Burton and Holme *Carl*

HOLME (St Giles) *see* Yaxley and Holme w Conington *Ely*

HOLME (St Giles) *see* Coddington and Winthorpe and Langford w Holme *S'well*

HOLME, EAST (St John the Evangelist)   *see* Wareham *Sarum*
HOLME CULTRAM (St Cuthbert)   *see* Solway Plain *Carl*
HOLME CULTRAM (St Mary)   *as above Carl*
HOLME EDEN (St Paul) *Carl 2*   **P** *DBP*
P-in-c C A RANDALL,   **C** K S CAPELIN-JONES
HOLME HALE (St Andrew)   *see* Necton, Holme Hale w N and
S Pickenham *Nor*
HOLME-IN-CLIVIGER (St John) w Worsthorne *Blackb 3*
P *Patr Bd*   **V** L LAYCOCK,   **NSM** J E HOLT
HOLME-NEXT-THE-SEA (St Mary)   *see* Hunstanton St Mary
w Ringstead Parva etc *Nor*
HOLME-ON-SPALDING-MOOR (All Saints)   *see* Holme and
Seaton Ross Gp *York*
HOLME-ON-SPALDING-MOOR (Old School Mission Room)
as above York
HOLME PIERREPONT (St Edmund King and Martyr)
see Radcliffe-on-Trent and Shelford etc *S'well*
**HOLME RUNCTON (St James) w South Runcton and
Wallington** *Ely 15*   **P** *Bp*   **R** J C W NOLAN
HOLME VALLEY, The UPPER *Wakef 6*   **P** *Patr Bd*
TR J S ROBERTSHAW,   **TV** K GRIFFIN, G A BANKS,
NSM M D ELLERTON,   **OLM** G B BAMFORD, G SMITH
HOLME WOOD (St Christopher)   *see* Tong *Bradf*
HOLMER (St Bartholomew) (St Mary) w Huntington *Heref 3*
P *D&C*   **V** P A WILLIAMS
HOLMER GREEN (Christ Church)   *see* Penn Street *Ox*
HOLMES CHAPEL (St Luke)   *see* Church Hulme *Ches*
HOLMESDALE (St Philip)   *see* Dronfield w Holmesfield *Derby*
HOLMESFIELD (St Swithin)   *as above Derby*
HOLMEWOOD (St Alban Mission)   *see* Heath *Derby*
HOLMFIELD (St Andrew)   *see* Bradshaw and Holmfield *Wakef*
HOLMFIRTH (Holy Trinity)   *see* Upper Holme Valley *Wakef*
HOLMPTON (St Nicholas)   *see* Easington w Skeffling, Kilnsea
and Holmpton *York*
HOLMSIDE (St John the Evangelist) *Dur 4*   **P** *The Crown*
V *vacant* (01207) 529274
HOLMWOOD (St Mary Magdalene)   *see* Surrey Weald *Guildf*
HOLMWOOD, NORTH (St John the Evangelist) *Guildf 12*
P *Bp*   **P-in-c** C A CORRY
HOLNE (St Mary the Virgin)   *see* Widecombe-in-the-Moor,
Leusdon, Princetown etc *Ex*
HOLNEST (Church of the Assumption)   *see* Dungeon Hill
Sarum
**HOLSWORTHY (St Peter and St Paul) w Hollacombe and
Milton Damerel** *Ex 9*   **P** *DBP and Mrs F M Palmer (jt)*
R R M REYNOLDS
HOLT (St Andrew) w High Kelling *Nor 18*   **P** *St Jo Coll Cam*
R H C STOKER
HOLT (St James)   *see* Horton, Chalbury, Hinton Martel and
Holt St Jas *Sarum*
HOLT (St Katharine)   *see* Broughton Gifford, Gt Chalfield and
Holt *Sarum*
HOLT (St Martin)   *see* Hallow and Grimley w Holt *Worc*
HOLTBY (Holy Trinity)   *see* Stockton-on-the-Forest w Holtby
and Warthill *York*
HOLTON (St Bartholomew)   *see* Wheatley *Ox*
HOLTON (St Nicholas)   *see* Camelot Par *B & W*
HOLTON (St Peter)   *see* Blyth Valley *St E*
HOLTON-CUM-BECKERING (All Saints)   *see* Wragby Gp
Linc
HOLTON-LE-CLAY (St Peter) and Tetney *Linc 10*   **P** *Ld Chan*
(2 turns), Bp (1 turn)   **V** C M WOADDEN
HOLTON-LE-MOOR (St Luke)   *see* Kelsey Gp *Linc*
HOLTON ST MARY (St Mary)   *see* Higham, Holton St Mary,
Raydon and Stratford *St E*
HOLTS (St Hugh) Conventional District *Man 18 vacant* 0161--
620 1646
HOLTSPUR (St Thomas)   *see* Beaconsfield *Ox*
HOLTYE (St Peter)   *see* Cowden w Hammerwood *Chich*
HOLWELL (St Laurence)   *see* The Caundles w Folke and
Holwell *Sarum*
HOLWELL (St Leonard)   *see* Ab Kettleby and Holwell w
Asfordby *Leic*
HOLWELL (St Mary the Virgin)   *see* Shill Valley and Broadshire
Ox
HOLWELL (St Peter)   *see* Ickleford w Holwell *St Alb*
HOLWORTH (St Catherine by the Sea)   *see* Watercombe *Sarum*
HOLY ISLAND (St Mary the Virgin) *Newc 12*   **P** *Bp*
V R J KIRKPATRICK
HOLYBOURNE (Holy Rood)   *see* Froyle and Holybourne *Win*
HOLYMOORSIDE (St Peter)   *see* Brampton St Thos *Derby*
HOLYSTONE (St Mary the Virgin)   *see* Alwinton w Holystone
and Alnham *Newc*
HOLYWELL (St Cross)   *see* Ox St Mary V w St Cross and St Pet
Ox
HOLYWELL (St John the Baptist) w Needingworth *Ely 10*
P *Bp*   **P-in-c** E J G STRICKLAND

HOLYWELL (St Mary)   *see* Seghill *Newc*
HOMERSFIELD (St Mary)   *see* S Elmham and Ilketshall *St E*
HOMERTON (Christ Church on the Mead)   *see* Hackney
Marsh *Lon*
HOMERTON (St Barnabas w St Paul)   *as above Lon*
HOMERTON (St Luke) *Lon 5*   **P** *St Olave Hart Street Trustees*
V I HARPER
HOMINGTON (St Mary the Virgin)   *see* Chalke Valley *Sarum*
HONEYCHURCH (St Mary)   *see* N Tawton, Bondleigh,
Sampford Courtenay etc *Ex*
HONICKNOWLE (St Francis) *Ex 22*   **P** *Ld Chan*
V P J MORGAN
HONILEY (St John the Baptist)   *see* Hatton w Haseley,
Rowington w Lowsonford etc *Cov*
HONING (St Peter and St Paul)   *see* Smallburgh w Dilham w
Honing and Crostwight *Nor*
HONINGHAM (St Andrew)   *see* Hockering, Honingham, E
and N Tuddenham *Nor*
HONINGTON (All Saints)   *see* Shipston-on-Stour w
Honington and Idlicote *Cov*
HONINGTON (All Saints)   *see* Blackbourne *St E*
HONINGTON (St Wilfred)   *see* Barkston and Hough Gp *Linc*
**HONITON (St Michael) (St Paul), Gittisham, Combe Raleigh,
Monkton and Awliscombe** *Ex 5*   **P** *DBP*   **TR** J B HEDGES,
C A E J POLLINGTON, A P SHEATH,   **Hon C** R C H SAUNDERS
HONLEY (St Mary) *Wakef 1*   **P** *R Almondbury*
V D K BARNES
HOO (All Hallows)   *see* High Halstow w All Hallows and Hoo
St Mary *Roch*
HOO (St Andrew and St Eustachius)   *see* Charsfield w Debach,
Monewden, Hoo etc *St E*
HOO (St Werburgh) *Roch 6*   **P** *D&C*   **V** A B HARDING
HOOBROOK (St Cecilia)   *see* Kidderminster St Geo *Worc*
HOOE (St John the Evangelist)   *see* Plymstock and Hooe *Ex*
HOOE (St Oswald) *Chich 14*   **P** *Bp*   **V** S R EARL,
NSM P J DOODES
HOOK (St John the Evangelist) *Win 5*   **P** *Bp*   **R** N S VIGERS
HOOK (St Mary the Virgin)   *see* Airmyn, Hook and Rawcliffe
Sheff
HOOK (St Mary) w Warsash *Portsm 2*   **P** *Bp*   **V** A P NORRIS
HOOK (St Paul) *S'wark 17*   **P** *The Crown*
OLM D E HEATHER
HOOK COMMON (Good Shepherd)   *see* Upton-on-Severn,
Ripple, Earls Croome etc *Worc*
**HOOK NORTON (St Peter) w Great Rollright, Swerford and
Wigginton** *Ox 3*   **P** *Bp, DBP, BNC Ox, and Jes Coll Ox (jt)*
R J ACREMAN,   **Hon C** C G TURNER
HOOKE (St Giles)   *see* Beaminster Area *Sarum*
HOOLE (All Saints) *Ches 3*   **P** *Simeon's Trustees*
V R J KIRKLAND
HOOLE (St Michael) *Blackb 5*   **P** *Reps of Mrs E A Dunne and
Mrs D Downes (jt)*   **P-in-c** S P HUGHES
HOOLEY (Mission Hall)   *see* Redhill St Jo *S'wark*
HOOTON (St Paul) *Ches 9*   **P** *Trustees*   **V** D G SARGENT,
C A M DI CHIARA
HOOTON PAGNELL (All Saints)   *see* Bilham *Sheff*
HOOTON ROBERTS (St John)   *see* Bramley and Ravenfield w
Hooton Roberts etc *Sheff*
HOPE (Holy Trinity) w Shelve *Heref 13*   **P** *New Coll Ox*
(3 turns), J J C Coldwell Esq (1 turn)   **P-in-c** A KNIGHT
HOPE (St James) *Man 6*   **P** *Trustees*   **V** D SHARPLES
HOPE (St Peter), Castleton and Bradwell *Derby 2*   **P** *Bp and
D&C Lich (jt)*   **V** P J BOWLES
HOPE BAGOT (St John the Baptist)   *see* Burford II w Greete
and Hope Bagot *Heref*
HOPE BOWDLER (St Andrew) w Eaton-under-Heywood
Heref 11   **P** *DBP, Bp Birm, and Mrs R Bell (jt)*
P-in-c J GROVES
HOPE COVE (St Clements)   *see* Salcombe and Malborough w S
Huish *Ex*
HOPE MANSEL (St Michael)   *see* Ross *Heref*
HOPE-UNDER-DINMORE (St Mary the Virgin)
see Bodenham w Hope-under-Dinmore, Felton etc *Heref*
HOPESAY (St Mary the Virgin)   *see* Hopesay *Heref*
HOPESAY (St Mary the Virgin) *Heref 10*   **P** *Earl of Powis
(3 turns), Mrs R E Bell (1 turn)*   **P-in-c** R T SHAW
**HOPTON (All Saints), Market Weston, Barningham and Coney
Weston** *St E 9*   **P** *Ld Chan and Bp (alt)*   **P-in-c** M J HANSEN
HOPTON (St Peter)   *see* Mid Trent *Lich*
HOPTON w Corton *Nor 9*   **P** *Ld Chan and D&C (alt)*
V R A KEY
HOPTON, UPPER (St John the Evangelist)   *see* Eastthorpe and
Upper Hopton *Wakef*
HOPTON CASTLE (St Edward)   *see* Clungunford w Clunbury
and Clunton, Bedstone etc *Heref*
HOPTON WAFERS (St Michael and All Angels)   *see* Cleobury
Mortimer w Hopton Wafers etc *Heref*

HOPWAS (St Chad)   *see* Tamworth *Lich*
HOPWOOD (St John)   *see* Heywood *Man*
HORAM (Christ Church) (St James)   *Chich 15*   **P** *Bp*
   V M D REDHOUSE
HORBLING (St Andrew)   *see* Billingborough Gp *Linc*
HORBURY (St Peter and St Leonard) w Horbury Bridge
   (St John)   *Wakef 12*   **P** *Dean*   **V** P TWISLETON
HORBURY JUNCTION (St Mary)   *Wakef 12*   **P** *DBP*
   P-in-c A S MACPHERSON
HORDEN (St Mary)   *Dur 2*   **P** *Bp*   **V** *vacant* 0191-586 4423
HORDLE (All Saints)   *Win 11*   **P** *Bp*   **V** M G ANDERSON,
   C J E GRAINGER-SMITH,   **NSM** A C PETTS
HORDLEY (St Mary the Virgin)   *see* Baschurch and Weston
   Lullingfield w Hordley *Lich*
HORFIELD (Holy Trinity)   *Bris 3*   **P** *Bp*   **P-in-c** J S F HADLEY,
   C E L L BAUGHAN
HORFIELD (St Gregory)   *Bris 3*   **P** *Bp*   **V** R A SEARLE
HORHAM (St Mary)   *see* Stradbroke, Horham, Athelington
   and Redlingfield *St E*
HORKESLEY, GREAT (All Saints)   *see* W Bergholt and Gt
   Horkesley *Chelmsf*
HORKESLEY, GREAT (St John)   *as above Chelmsf*
HORKESLEY, LITTLE (St Peter and St Paul)
   see Wormingford, Mt Bures and Lt Horkesley *Chelmsf*
HORKSTOW (St Maurice)   *Linc 6*   **P** *DBP*   **V** G A PLUMB
HORLEY (St Bartholomew) (St Francis) (St Wilfrid)   *S'wark 27*
   P *Patr Bd*   **TV** S A HOLLOWAY
HORLEY (St Etheldreda)   *see* Ironstone *Ox*
HORLEY ROW (St Wilfrid)   *see* Horley *S'wark*
HORMEAD (St Nicholas), Wyddial, Anstey, Brent Pelham and
   Meesden   *St Alb 19*   **P** *St Jo Coll Cam, Ch Coll Cam, and Bp*
   (by turn)   **P-in-c** C L KIMBERLEY
HORN HILL (St Paul)   *see* Chalfont St Peter *Ox*
HORN PARK (St Francis)   *see* Eltham St Jo *S'wark*
HORNBLOTTON (St Peter)   *see* Six Pilgrims *B & W*
HORNBY (St Margaret) w Claughton and Whittington w
   Arkholme and Gressingham   *Blackb 14*   **P** *Patr Bd*
   V I H RENNIE
HORNBY (St Mary)   *Ripon 4*   **P** *D&C York*   **V** D J CHRISTIE
HORNCASTLE (St Mary the Virgin) w Low Toynton   *Linc 11*
   P *Bp (2 turns), Baroness Willoughby de Eresby (1 turn)*
   V M E BURSON-THOMAS,   **C** A C V HARVEY,
   NSM J F PARKIN, A C FORD
HORNCHURCH Elm Park (St Nicholas)   *see* Elm Park St Nic
   Hornchurch *Chelmsf*
HORNCHURCH (Holy Cross)   *Chelmsf 2*   **P** *Bp and*
   New Coll Ox (alt)   **V** R B N HAYCRAFT
HORNCHURCH (St Andrew) (St George) (St Matthew and
   St John)   *Chelmsf 2*   **P** *New Coll Ox*   **V** H R DIBBENS,
   C A C A PARRY, M UDDIN,   **NSM** S M PAPWORTH
HORNCHURCH, SOUTH (St John and St Matthew)   *Chelmsf 2*
   P *MMCET*   **V** R LOVE,   **C** K S TURNER,   **NSM** K D NORRIS
HORNDALE (St Francis)   *see* Gt Aycliffe *Dur*
HORNDON EAST (St Francis) and West Horndon w Little
   Warley and Childerditch   *Chelmsf 7*   **P** *Sir Antony Browne's*
   Sch and Bp (by turn)   **P-in-c** S C WILLIAMS,
   NSM R WILLIAMS
HORNDON ON THE HILL (St Peter and St Paul)   *see* Orsett
   and Bulphan and Horndon on the Hill *Chelmsf*
HORNE (St Mary)   *see* Burstow w Horne *S'wark*
HORNING (St Benedict)   *see* Ashmanhaugh, Barton Turf etc
   Nor
HORNINGHOLD (St Peter)   *see* Hallaton w Horninghold and
   Allexton, Tugby etc *Leic*
HORNINGLOW (St John the Divine)   *Lich 14*   **P** *Trustees*
   V M R FREEMAN,   **C** I NEWTON
HORNINGSEA (St Peter)   *Ely 3*   **P** *St Jo Coll Cam*
   P-in-c M C BOWERS
HORNINGSHAM (St John the Baptist)   *see* Cley Hill
   Warminster *Sarum*
HORNINGTOFT (St Edmund)   *see* Colkirk w Oxwick w
   Pattesley, Whissonsett etc *Nor*
HORNSEA (St Nicholas) w Atwick   *York 11*   **P** *Ld Chan*
   V J R RICE-OXLEY
HORNSEY (Christ Church)   *Lon 20*   **P** *Bp*   **V** D O AGBELUSI
HORNSEY (Holy Innocents)   *Lon 20*   **P** *Bp*
   P-in-c N H ASBRIDGE,   **C** P J HENDERSON
HORNSEY (St Mary) (St George)   *Lon 20*   **P** *Bp*
   R G B SEABROOK,   **C** S TAYLOR,   **NSM** C L FRANSELLA
HORNSEY RISE (St Mary)   *see* Upper Holloway *Lon*
HORNTON (St John the Baptist)   *see* Ironstone *Ox*
HORRABRIDGE (St John the Baptist)   *see* Sampford Spiney w
   Horrabridge *Ex*
HORRINGER (St Leonard)   *St E 13*   **P** *Bp and DBP (jt)*
   C C F TODD
HORSEHEATH (All Saints)   *see* Linton *Ely*

HORSELL (St Mary the Virgin)   *Guildf 12*   **P** *Bp*   **V** R JONES,
   C C A COSLETT,   **NSM** B ASHLEY
HORSENDON (St Michael and All Angels)   *see* Risborough *Ox*
HORSEY (All Saints)   *see* Flegg Coastal Benefice *Nor*
HORSFORD (All Saints) and Horsham w Newton St Faith   *Nor 2*
   P *Bp*   **V** P W BUTCHER
HORSFORTH (St Margaret)   *Ripon 7*   **P** *Bp*   **V** R E HAYES,
   C D L STEVENS
HORSHAM (Holy Trinity) (St Leonard) (St Mary the Virgin)
   (St Peter in the Causeway)   *Chich 8*   **P** *Patr Bd*
   TR D E E TANSILL,   **TV** W E L SOUTER,   M J BROADLEY,
   A G LOW,   P J APTED,   **C** S F E NEWHAM,   K D LITTLEJOHN,
   Hon C E V WHEELER,   **NSM** B SINTON
HORSHAM ST FAITH (St Mary and Andrew)   *see* Horsford
   and Horsham w Newton St Faith *Nor*
HORSINGTON (All Saints)   *see* Woodhall Spa Gp *Linc*
HORSINGTON (St John the Baptist)   *see* Abbas and
   Templecombe w Horsington *B & W*
HORSLEY (Holy Trinity)   *see* N Tyne and Redesdale Team
   Newc
HORSLEY (St Clement) and Denby   *Derby 12*   **P** *Bp and*
   Mrs L B Palmer (jt)   **V** K W HORLESTON,   **NSM** D C BEECH
HORSLEY (St Martin)   *see* Nailsworth w Shortwood, Horsley
   etc *Glouc*
HORSLEY, EAST (St Martin) and Ockham w Hatchford and
   Downside   *Guildf 10*   **P** *D&C Cant and Bp (jt)*
   R B J PARADISE,   **Hon C** R D C STEELE-PERKINS
HORSLEY, WEST (St Mary)   *Guildf 10*   **P** *Col A R N Weston*
   R A DELANEY
HORSLEY HILL (St Lawrence the Martyr) South Shields
   Dur 15   **P** *D&C*   **V** G BUTTERY
HORSLEY WOODHOUSE (St Susanna)   *see* Morley w
   Smalley and Horsley Woodhouse *Derby*
HORSMONDEN (St Margaret)   *Roch 8*   **P** *Bp*   **R** *vacant*
   (01892) 722521
HORSPATH (St Giles)   *see* Wheatley *Ox*
HORSTEAD (All Saints)   *see* Coltishall w Gt Hautbois and
   Horstead *Nor*
HORSTED, LITTLE (St Michael and All Angels)   *Chich 21*
   P *Rt Revd P J Ball*   **R** B H WILCOX,   **NSM** C HOWARTH
HORSTED KEYNES (St Giles)   *Chich 6*   **P** *Bp*
   R T D RAWDON-MOGG
HORTON (All Saints)   *Bradf 2*   **P** *J F Bardsley Esq*
   P-in-c A S TREASURE,   **NSM** M M MALEK
HORTON (St James the Elder) and Little Sodbury   *Glouc 7*
   P *Duke of Beaufort (1 turn), CPAS (2 turns)*   **R** *vacant* (01454)
   313256
HORTON (St Mary Magdalene)   *see* Hardingstone and Horton
   and Piddington *Pet*
HORTON (St Mary the Virgin)   *Newc 1*   **P** *V Woodhorn w*
   Newbiggin   **V** B T B BELL
HORTON (St Michael and All Angels)   *see* Riverside *Ox*
HORTON (St Michael), Lonsdon and Rushton Spencer   *Lich 8*
   P *Bp and R Leek and Meerbrook (jt)*   **V** E J TOMLINSON
HORTON (St Peter)   *see* Ilminster and Distr *B & W*
HORTON (St Wolfrida), Chalbury, Hinton Martel and Holt
   St James   *Sarum 9*   **P** *Earl of Shaftesbury and Qu Eliz Free*
   Gr Sch (jt)   **P-in-c** J R SINGLETON
HORTON, GREAT (St John the Evangelist)   *Bradf 2*   **P** *V Bradf*
   V N G JONES,   **NSM** L J SLOW
HORTON-CUM-STUDLEY (St Barnabas)   *see* Wheatley *Ox*
HORTON-IN-RIBBLESDALE (St Oswald)   *see* Langcliffe w
   Stainforth and Horton *Bradf*
HORTON KIRBY (St Mary)   *Roch 2*   **P** *Bp*   **V** *vacant* (01322)
   862201
HORWICH (Holy Trinity) (St Catherine) (St Elizabeth) and
   Rivington   *Man 11*   **P** *Patr Bd*   **TR** S FLETCHER,
   TV G C BURROWS,   M C BEHREND,   P E BERRY,
   C S H FOSTER-CLARK,   **OLM** T LITHERLAND
HORWOOD (St Michael)   *see* Newton Tracey, Horwood,
   Alverdiscott etc *Ex*
HORWOOD, GREAT (St James)   *see* Winslow w Gt Horwood
   and Addington *Ox*
HORWOOD, LITTLE (St Nicholas)   *see* Newton Longville and
   Mursley w Swanbourne etc *Ox*
HOSE (St Michael)   *see* Vale of Belvoir Par *Leic*
HOTHAM (St Oswald)   *York 13*   **P** *Ld Chan*
   P-in-c C H GOULDER
HOTHFIELD (St Margaret)   *see* Westwell, Hothfield, Eastwell
   and Boughton Aluph *Cant*
HOUGH GREEN (St Basil and All Saints)   *Liv 13*   **P** *Bp*
   V G C ELSMORE
HOUGH-ON-THE-HILL (All Saints)   *see* Barkston and Hough
   Gp *Linc*
HOUGHAM (All Saints)   *as above Linc*
HOUGHAM (St Laurence)   *see* Alkham w Capel le Ferne and
   Hougham *Cant*

HOUGHTON (All Saints) *see* Broughton, Bossington, Houghton and Mottisfont *Win*
HOUGHTON (St Giles) *see* Walsingham, Houghton and Barsham *Nor*
HOUGHTON (St John the Evangelist) (St Peter) *Carl 3* **P** *Trustees* **V** S N AUSTEN, **C** M P KENDALL
HOUGHTON (St Martin) *see* E w W Rudham, Helhoughton etc *Nor*
HOUGHTON (St Mary) w Wyton *Ely 8* **P** *Bp* **R** *vacant* (01480) 462499
HOUGHTON (St Nicholas) *see* Bury w Houghton and Coldwaltham and Hardham *Chich*
HOUGHTON, GREAT (St Mary) *see* Cogenhoe and Gt and Lt Houghton w Brafield *Pet*
HOUGHTON, GREAT (St Michael and All Angels) Conventional District *Sheff 12* **C-in-c** J P MILTON-THOMPSON
HOUGHTON, LITTLE (St Mary the Blessed Virgin) *see* Cogenhoe and Gt and Lt Houghton w Brafield *Pet*
HOUGHTON, NEW (Christ Church) *see* E Scarsdale *Derby*
HOUGHTON CONQUEST (All Saints) *see* Wilshamstead and Houghton Conquest *St Alb*
HOUGHTON LE SPRING (St Michael and All Angels) *Dur 14* **P** *Bp* **R** I G WALLIS, **C** A WHITTAKER, **NSM** M THRUSH
HOUGHTON-ON-THE-HILL (St Catharine) Keyham and Hungarton *Leic 5* **P** *Bp* **P-in-c** P M HOLLINGSWORTH
HOUGHTON REGIS (All Saints) (St Thomas) *St Alb 12* **P** *DBP* **C** T B SINGH
HOUND (St Edward the Confessor) (St Mary the Virgin) *Win 10* **P** *St Mary's Coll Win* **V** R W GOODHEW
HOUNSLOW (Holy Trinity) (St Paul) *Lon 11* **P** *Bp* **V** O C M ROSS, **C** D J MAHER, **NSM** N LAWRENCE
HOUNSLOW (St Stephen) *Lon 11* **P** *Bp* **V** R L RAMSDEN
HOUNSLOW WEST (Good Shepherd) *Lon 11* **P** *Bp* **V** C S P DOUGLAS LANE, **Hon C** P R TOPHAM
HOVE (All Saints) (St Andrew Old Church) (St John the Baptist) (Holy Trinity) *Chich 4* **P** *Bp* **TR** D K WOSTENHOLM, **TV** C L WILSON, H H D PRYSE, C G SPINKS, **C** J R PHILLIPS, D A GUEST, **NSM** R C GOULDTHORPE
HOVE (Bishop Hannington Memorial Church) (Holy Cross) *Chich 4* **P** *Trustees* **C** C M CHAMBERS, J DUDLEY-SMITH
HOVE (St Barnabas) and St Agnes *Chich 4* **P** *Bp and V Hove (alt)* **V** A R REED, **NSM** T J MACDONALD
HOVE St Patrick *Chich 4* **P** *Bp, V Hove, and V Brighton (jt)* **V** A B SHARPE, **C** K L W SYLVIA
HOVE (St Philip) *see* Aldrington *Chich*
HOVERINGHAM (St Michael) *see* Thurgarton w Hoveringham and Bleasby etc *S'well*
HOVETON (St John) *see* Wroxham w Hoveton and Belaugh *Nor*
HOVETON (St Peter) *as above Nor*
HOVINGHAM (All Saints) *see* Street *York*
HOW CAPLE (St Andrew and St Mary) w Sollarshope, Sellack, Kings Caple, Foy, Hentland and Hoarwithy *Heref 8* **P** *Bp, D&C, and Brig A F L Clive (jt)* **R** *vacant* (01432) 840485
HOWARDIAN GROUP, The *York 6* **P** *Abp and Hon S B G Howard (jt)* **R** C C ELLIS
HOWDEN Team Ministry, The (St Peter) *York 13* **P** *Abp (4 turns), Ld Chan (1 turn)* **TR** I M W ELLERY, **TV** M S POSKITT, S FOSTER, **C** M J BOAG
HOWDEN-LE-WEAR and Hunwick *Dur 9* **P** *Bp and V Auckland St Andr (alt)* **V** S IRWIN
HOWE (St Mary the Virgin) *see* Poringland *Nor*
HOWE BRIDGE (St Michael and All Angels) *see* Atherton and Hindsford w Howe Bridge *Man*
HOWELL (St Oswald) *see* Heckington *Linc*
HOWELL HILL (St Paul) *Guildf 9* **P** *Bp* **V** S A WILCOCKSON, **C** I M BLAKE, **NSM** B W RICHARDS
HOWGILL (Holy Trinity) *see* Firbank, Howgill and Killington *Bradf*
HOWICK (St Michael and All Angels) *see* Longhoughton w Howick *Newc*
HOWLE HILL (St John the Evangelist) *see* Walford and St John w Bishopswood, Goodrich etc *Heref*
HOWSHAM (St John) *see* Sand Hutton *York*
HOXNE (St Peter and St Paul) w Denham, Syleham and Wingfield *St E 17* **P** *Bp and DBP (jt)* **R** A R LOWE, **NSM** R J CLARK
HOXTON (Holy Trinity) (St Mary) *Lon 5* **P** *Bp* **V** I C YOUNG
HOXTON (St Anne) (St Columba) *Lon 5* **P** *The Crown* **V** *vacant* (020) 7729 1243
HOXTON (St John the Baptist) w Ch Ch *Lon 5* **P** *Haberdashers' Co and Adn (jt)* **V** A I KEECH
HOYLAKE (Holy Trinity and St Hildeburgh) *Ches 8* **P** *Bp* **V** A HEZEL, **Hon C** D K CHESTER
HOYLAND (St Peter) (St Andrew) *Sheff 11* **P** *Bp and Sir Stephen Hastings (jt)* **V** N P HOLMES

HOYLAND, HIGH (All Saints), Scissett and Clayton West *Wakef 6* **P** *Bp* **P-in-c** J HELLEWELL
HOYLANDSWAINE (St John the Evangelist) and Silkstone w Stainborough *Wakef 7* **P** *Bp* **V** S A MOOR
HUBBERHOLME (St Michael and All Angels) *see* Kettlewell w Conistone, Hubberholme etc *Bradf*
HUCCABY (St Raphael) *see* Widecombe-in-the-Moor, Leusdon, Princetown etc *Ex*
HUCCLECOTE (St Philip and St James) *Glouc 5* **P** *Bp* **V** M R BURKE, **NSM** M J NOAH
HUCKING (St Margaret) *see* Hollingbourne and Hucking w Leeds and Broomfield *Cant*
HUCKLOW, GREAT (Mission Room) *see* Hope, Castleton and Bradwell *Derby*
HUCKNALL TORKARD (St Mary Magdalene) (St Peter and St Paul) (St John's Mission Church) *S'well 4* **P** *Bp* **TR** L A CHURCH, **TV** S W BATTEN, **C** C E WINDLE
HUDDERSFIELD All Saints (St Thomas) *Wakef 5* **P** *DBP* **V** *vacant*
HUDDERSFIELD (Holy Trinity) *Wakef 5* **P** *Simeon's Trustees* **V** E O ROBERTS, **C** J M LAWSON, **NSM** R C SWINDELL, P T WILCOCK
HUDDERSFIELD (St John the Evangelist) *see* N Huddersfield *Wakef*
HUDDERSFIELD (St Peter) *Wakef 5* **P** *DBP* **V** C OGLE, **C** M R POLLARD
HUDDERSFIELD, NORTH (St Cuthbert) *Wakef 5* **P** *DBP* **TR** M J LOWLES, **TV** M R UMPLEBY, **NSM** G M DODD
HUDDINGTON (St James) *see* Bowbrook S *Worc*
HUDSWELL (St Michael and All Angels) *see* Richmond w Hudswell *Ripon*
HUGGATE (St Mary) *see* Nunburnholme and Warter and Huggate *York*
HUGGLESCOTE (St John the Baptist) w Donington, Ellistown and Snibston *Leic 8* **P** *Bp* **TR** J E HALL, **TV** V T GOODMAN
HUGHENDEN (St Michael) *Ox 29* **P** *DBP* **V** S N CRONK, **NSM** F J FRIEND
HUGHLEY (St John the Baptist) *see* Wenlock *Heref*
HUISH (St James the Less) *see* Shebbear, Buckland Filleigh, Sheepwash etc *Ex*
HUISH (St Nicholas) *see* Pewsey and Swanborough *Sarum*
HUISH, SOUTH (Holy Trinity) *see* Salcombe and Malborough w S Huish *Ex*
HUISH CHAMPFLOWER (St Peter) *see* Wiveliscombe w Chipstable, Huish Champflower etc *B & W*
HUISH EPISCOPI (Blessed Virgin Mary) *see* Langport Area Chs *B & W*
HULCOTE (St Nicholas) *see* Cranfield and Hulcote w Salford *St Alb*
HULCOTT (All Saints) *see* Aylesbury w Bierton and Hulcott *Ox*
HULL (Ascension) *see* Derringham Bank *York*
HULL (Holy Apostles) *see* Kingston upon Hull H Trin *York*
HULL (Most Holy and Undivided Trinity) *as above York*
HULL Newland (St John) *York 14* **P** *Abp* **V** M TINKER, **C** N J BUTTERY, M C BRAILSFORD
HULL (St Aidan) Southcoates *see* Kingston upon Hull St Aid Southcoates *York*
HULL (St Alban) *see* Kingston upon Hull St Alb *York*
HULL (St Cuthbert) *York 14* **P** *Abp* **V** A M LAIRD
HULL (St George) *see* Marfleet *York*
HULL (St Giles) *as above York*
HULL (St Hilda) *as above York*
HULL (St John the Baptist) *see* Newington w Dairycoates *York*
HULL (St Martin) w The Transfiguration *York 14* **P** *Abp* **V** S R J ELLIOTT, **NSM** J O OGADA
HULL (St Mary) Sculcoates *York 14* **P** *V Sculcoates* **Hon C** J G LEEMAN
HULL (St Mary the Virgin) Lowgate *see* Kingston upon Hull St Mary *York*
HULL (St Matthew w St Barnabas) *see* Kingston upon Hull St Matt w St Barn *York*
HULL (St Nicholas) *see* Kingston upon Hull St Nic *York*
HULL (St Paul) *see* Sculcoates St Paul w Ch Ch and St Silas *York*
HULL (St Philip) *see* Marfleet *York*
HULL (St Stephen) Sculcoates *York 14* **P** *Ld Chan (2 turns), V Hull H Trin (1 turn), and Abp (1 turn)* **Hon C** J G LEEMAN
HULL (St Thomas) *see* Derringham Bank *York*
HULL, NORTH (St Michael and All Angels) *York 14* **P** *Abp* **V** D A WALKER, **C** D P BLACK, M J LEIGH
HULLAND (Christ Church), Atlow, Kniveton, Bradley and Hognaston *Derby 8* **P** *Patr Bd* **R** C A MITCHELL
HULLAVINGTON (St Mary Magdalene), Norton and Stanton St Quintin *Bris 6* **P** *Bp, Eton Coll, and R W Neeld Esq (jt)* **R** A EVANS

HULLBRIDGE (St Thomas of Canterbury) *Chelmsf 12* **P** *Bp*
V W H REED, **NSM** S ADAMS
HULME (Ascension) *Man 4* **P** *Trustees* **P-in-c** A J SERVANT,
C K FLOOD
HULME WALFIELD (St Michael) *see* Eaton and Hulme
Walfield *Ches*
HULTON, LITTLE (St John the Baptist) *see* Walkden and Lt
Hulton *Man*
HULTON, OVER (St Andrew) *see* Deane *Man*
HUMBER (St Mary the Virgin) *see* Leominster *Heref*
HUMBERSTON (St Peter) *Linc 10* **P** *Bp* **V** B V EAST
HUMBERSTONE (St Mary) *see* Ascension TM *Leic*
HUMBERSTONE, NEW (St Barnabas) *see* Leic Presentation
Leic
HUMBLE, WEST (St Michael) *see* Leatherhead and
Mickleham *Guildf*
HUMBLETON (St Peter) *see* Burton Pidsea and Humbleton w
Elsternwick *York*
HUMPHREY PARK (St Clement) *see* Urmston *Man*
HUMSHAUGH (St Peter) w Simonburn and Wark *Newc 2*
P *Bp* **R** J M THOMPSON
HUNCOAT (St Augustine) *see* Accrington St Jo w Huncoat
Blackb
HUNCOTE (St James the Greater) *see* Narborough and
Huncote *Leic*
HUNDLEBY (St Mary) *see* Spilsby Gp *Linc*
HUNDON (All Saints) *St E 8* **P** *Jes Coll Cam*
P-in-c A R GEORGE, **NSM** S A BAREHAM
HUNDRED RIVER Benefice, The *St E 14* **P** *DBP,*
Shadingfield Properties Ltd, Bp, Miss to Seamen, and
F D L Barnes Esq (by turn) **R** P J NELSON,
OLM J M LOFTUS, S K NEAL
HUNGARTON (St John the Baptist)
see Houghton-on-the-Hill, Keyham and Hungarton *Leic*
HUNGERFORD (St Lawrence) and Denford *Ox 14*
P *D&C Windsor* **V** A W SAWYER
HUNMANBY (All Saints) w Muston *York 15* **P** *MMCET*
V J W R HATTAN
HUNNINGHAM (St Margaret) *Cov 10* **P** *Ld Chan*
P-in-c J T H BRITTON, **C** D R PATTERSON
HUNSDON (St Dunstan) (St Francis) w Widford and Wareside
St Alb 22 **P** *DBP* **R** J RISBY
HUNSINGORE (St John the Baptist) *see* Lower Nidderdale
Ripon
HUNSLET (St Mary) *Ripon 6* **P** *Bp (2 turns) and V Leeds*
St Pet (1 turn) **P-in-c** P ANDERTON
HUNSLET MOOR (St Peter) and St Cuthbert *Ripon 6* **P** *Bp*
P-in-c R W SHAW
HUNSLEY (St Peter) *see* Rowley w Skidby *York*
HUNSTANTON (St Edmund) w Ringstead *Nor 16*
P *H Le Strange Esq* **V** J S BLOOMFIELD, **NSM** R L EASEMAN
HUNSTANTON (St Mary) w Ringstead Parva,
Holme-next-the-Sea, Thornham, Brancaster, Burnham
Deepdale and Titchwell *Nor 16* **P** *Bp, Exors of the late H le*
Strange Esq, and Exors of the late H S N Simms-Adams Esq (jt)
R L H CAMPBELL, **C** S A PYE
HUNSTANWORTH (St James) *see* Blanchland w
Hunstanworth and Edmundbyers etc *Newc*
HUNSTON (St Leodegar) *see* N Mundham w Hunston and
Merston *Chich*
HUNSTON (St Michael) *see* Badwell and Walsham *St E*
HUNTINGDON (All Saints w St John the Baptist) (St Barnabas)
(St Mary) *Ely 8* **P** *Bp* **TR** A J MILTON, **TV** J M SAVAGE,
C R E JONES
HUNTINGFIELD (St Mary) *see* Cratfield w Heveningham and
Ubbeston etc *St E*
HUNTINGTON (All Saints) *York 7* **P** *Patr Bd*
TR K J DAVIES, **C** F R SCOTT
HUNTINGTON (St Luke) *Ches 2* **P** *Bp* **V** I J HUTCHINGS
HUNTINGTON (St Mary Magdalene) *see* Holmer w
Huntington *Heref*
HUNTINGTON (St Thomas) *see* Cannock *Lich*
HUNTINGTON (St Thomas à Becket) *see* Kington w
Huntington, Old Radnor, Kinnerton etc *Heref*
HUNTLEY (St John the Baptist) and Longhope, Churcham and
Bulley *Glouc 3* **P** *Bp and D&C (jt)* **R** M E THOMPSON
HUNTON (St James) *see* Lower Dever Valley *Win*
HUNTON (St Mary) *see* Coxheath w E Farleigh, Hunton and
Linton *Roch*
HUNTS CROSS (St Hilda) *Liv 4* **P** *Bp* **V** G A PERERA
HUNTSHAM (All Saints) *see* Sampford Peverell, Uplowman,
Holcombe Rogus etc *Ex*
HUNTSHAW (St Mary Magdalene) *see* Newton Tracey,
Horwood, Alverdiscott etc *Ex*
HUNTSPILL (St Peter and All Hallows) *B & W 1* **P** *Ball Coll*
Ox **R** G M WALSH

HUNWICK (St Paul) *see* Howden-le-Wear and Hunwick *Dur*
HUNWORTH (St Lawrence) *see* Brinton, Briningham,
Hunworth, Stody etc *Nor*
HURDSFIELD (Holy Trinity) *Ches 13* **P** *Hyndman Trustees*
V J G TSIPOURAS, **NSM** M J OWENS
HURLEY (Resurrection) *see* Baxterley w Hurley and Wood
End and Merevale etc *Birm*
HURLEY (St Mary the Virgin) *see* Burchetts Green *Ox*
HURSLEY (All Saints) and Ampfield *Win 12* **P** *T H Faber Esq*
and Lord Lifford (jt) **V** R B EDWARDS,
NSM L M ROBERTSON
HURST *see* Fawkenhurst *Cant*
HURST (St John the Evangelist) *Man 17* **P** *The Crown*
V I ST J FISHER, **OLM** A G LEES
HURST (St Nicholas) *Ox 16* **P** *Bp* **Hon C** C SMITH,
NSM D L H WEBSTER
HURST GREEN (Holy Trinity) *Chich 15* **P** *Bp* **V** R DIXON
HURST GREEN (St John the Evangelist) *S'wark 26* **P** *Bp*
V D F G BUTLIN, **NSM** M J SELLER
HURST GREEN (St John the Evangelist) and Mitton *Bradf 5*
P *Bp and J E R Aspinall Esq (jt)* **V** vacant (01254) 826686
HURSTBOURNE PRIORS (St Andrew), Longparish, St Mary
Bourne and Woodcott *Win 6* **P** *Bp and J C Woodcock Esq (jt)*
V M A COPPEN, **NSM** N M HARRISON, D M MARSDEN
HURSTBOURNE TARRANT (St Peter) and Faccombe and
Vernham Dean and Linkenholt *Win 3* **P** *Bp* **V** A T R GOODE,
NSM P A MILLS
HURSTPIERPOINT (Holy Trinity) (St George) *Chich 9*
P *Hurstpierpoint Coll* **R** J B A JOYCE
HURSTWOOD, HIGH (Holy Trinity) *Chich 21* **P** *Abp*
P-in-c M COXHEAD
HURWORTH (All Saints) *Dur 8* **P** *Ch Soc Trust* **R** vacant
(01325) 720362
HUSBANDS BOSWORTH (All Saints) w Mowsley and
Knaptoft and Theddingworth *Leic 4* **P** *DBP (2 turns), Bp*
(1 turn) **P-in-c** B STANTON
HUSBORNE CRAWLEY (St Mary Magdalene or St James)
see Aspley Guise w Husborne Crawley and Ridgmont *St Alb*
HUSTHWAITE (St Nicholas) *see* Coxwold and Husthwaite
York
HUTHWAITE (All Saints) *S'well 4* **P** *V Sutton-in-Ashfield*
P-in-c C A K MAIDEN, **NSM** J L ALLEN
HUTTOFT (St Margaret) *see* Sutton, Huttoft and Anderby
Linc
HUTTON (All Saints) (St Peter) *Chelmsf 7* **P** *D&C St Paul's*
R R WALLACE, **C** B C WALLACE
HUTTON (Blessed Virgin Mary) *B & W 11* **P** *DBP*
R B N STEVENSON
HUTTON, NEW (St Stephen) *see* Grayrigg, Old Hutton and
New Hutton *Carl*
HUTTON, OLD (St John the Evangelist) *as above Carl*
HUTTON BONVILLE (St Laurence) *see* Gt Smeaton w
Appleton Wiske and Birkby etc *Ripon*
HUTTON BUSCEL (St Matthew) *see* Brompton by Sawdon w
Hutton Buscel, Snainton etc *York*
HUTTON CRANSWICK (St Peter) w Skerne, Watton and
Beswick *York 10* **P** *Abp* **V** J H ZAREK
HUTTON HENRY (St Francis) *see* Wheatley Hill and Wingate
w Hutton Henry *Dur*
HUTTON-IN-THE-FOREST (St James) *see* Skelton and
Hutton-in-the-Forest w Ivegill *Carl*
HUTTON-LE-HOLE (St Chad) *see* Lastingham w
Appleton-le-Moors, Rosedale etc *York*
HUTTON MAGNA (St Mary) *see* Barningham w Hutton
Magna and Wycliffe *Ripon*
HUTTON ROOF (St John the Divine) *see* Kirkby Lonsdale
Carl
HUTTON RUDBY (All Saints) *see* Rudby in Cleveland w
Middleton *York*
HUTTONS AMBO (St Margaret) *see* Howardian Gp *York*
HUXHAM (St Mary the Virgin) *see* Stoke Canon, Poltimore w
Huxham and Rewe etc *Ex*
HUXLEY (St Andrew) *see* Hargrave *Ches*
HUYTON (St George) *Liv 2* **P** *Bp* **V** P G WHITTINGTON,
C D A GREEN
HUYTON (St Michael) *Liv 2* **P** *Earl of Derby* **V** J A STANLEY
HUYTON QUARRY (St Gabriel) *Liv 2* **V** *Huyton St Mich*
V M K ROGERS
HYDE (Holy Ascension) *see* Ellingham and Harbridge and
Hyde w Ibsley *Win*
HYDE (Holy Trinity) Gee Cross *see* Gee Cross *Ches*
HYDE (St George) *Ches 14* **P** *R Stockport St Mary*
V S J WILSON, **C** A BROWN, J BROWN
HYDE (St John the Baptist) Godley cum Newton Green
see Godley cum Newton Green *Ches*
HYDE (St Mary) Newton in Mottram *see* Newton in Mottram
Ches

HYDE (St Stephen) Newton Flowery Field   *see* Newton Flowery
Field *Ches*
HYDE (St Thomas) *Ches 14*   **P** *Bp*   **P-in-c** P O BENNISON
HYDE, EAST (Holy Trinity)   *see* Woodside w E Hyde *St Alb*
HYDE, WEST (St Thomas)   *see* Mill End and Heronsgate w W
Hyde *St Alb*
HYDE HEATH (Mission Church)   *see* Lt Missenden *Ox*
HYDE PARK CRESCENT (St John)   *see* Paddington St Jo w
St Mich *Lon*
HYDNEYE, THE (St Peter) *Chich 16*   **P** *Bp*   **V** C R GORING,
NSM J MANN
HYKEHAM (All Saints) (St Hugh) (St Michael and All Angels)
Linc 18   **P** *Ld Chan and Bp (alt)*   **TR** R S EYRE,
TV J FREEBAIRN-SMITH,   **C** C M TURNER,   **NSM** G F REID
HYLTON, NORTH (St Margaret) Castletown *Dur 16*   **P** *Bp*
V *vacant* 0191-516 8421
HYLTON, SOUTH (St Mary) *Dur 16*   **P** *Bp*   **V** J E RUSCOE
HYSON GREEN (St Stephen) and Forest Fields *S'well 12*
P *CPAS*   **P-in-c** R E WORSLEY,   **C** G J BURTON, C J COOKE
HYSSINGTON (St Etheldreda)   *see* Churchstoke w Hyssington
and Sarn *Heref*
HYTHE Butts Ash (St Anne)   *see* Hythe *Win*
HYTHE (St John the Baptist) *Win 11*   **P** *Bp*   **V** P D BAIRD,
NSM L R MEAD
HYTHE (St Leonard) (St Michael and All Angels) *Cant 5*
P R Saltwood   **V** B BARNES,   **C** E M RICHARDSON,
NSM P F HILL
HYTHE, WEST (St Mary)   *see* Aldington w Bonnington and
Bilsington etc *Cant*
IBBERTON (St Eustace)   *see* Hazelbury Bryan and the Hillside
Par *Sarum*
IBSTOCK (St Denys) w Heather *Leic 8*   **P** *Bp and*
MMCET (jt)   **R** R A WHITE
IBSTONE (St Nicholas)   *see* Stokenchurch and Ibstone *Ox*
ICKBURGH (St Peter) w Langford *Nor 13*   **P** *Bp*
P-in-c P M FARROW
ICKENHAM (St Giles) *Lon 24*   **P** *Eton Coll*
P-in-c P ROBINSON,   **C** A M GUTHRIE,   **NSM** K R TOMBS
ICKFORD (St Nicholas)   *see* Worminghall w Ickford, Oakley
and Shabbington *Ox*
ICKHAM (St John the Evangelist)   *see* Littlebourne and Ickham
w Wickhambreaux etc *Cant*
ICKLEFORD (St Katherine) w Holwell *St Alb 4*   **P** *DBP*
P-in-c J A S PAYNE COOK
ICKLESHAM (St Nicolas)   *see* Winchelsea and Icklesham
Chich
ICKLETON (St Mary Magdalene) *Ely 6*   **P** *Ld Chan*
V J E E CHARMAN
ICKLINGHAM (All Saints w St James)   *see* Mildenhall *St E*
ICKNIELD *Ox 1*   **P** *Ld Chan (1 turn), Ch Ch Ox (1 turn), Bp*
and Earl of Macclesfield (1 turn)   **R** C I EVANS,
NSM A M PATERSON
ICOMB (St Mary)   *see* Broadwell, Evenlode, Oddington,
Adlestrop etc *Glouc*
IDBURY (St Nicholas)   *see* Shipton-under-Wychwood w
Milton, Fifield etc *Ox*
IDDESLEIGH (St James) w Dowland *Ex 19*   **P** *Bp*
P-in-c A S GRAESSER
IDE (St Ida)   *see* Dunchideock and Shillingford St George w Ide
Ex
IDE HILL (St Mary the Virgin)   *see* Sundridge w Ide Hill
Roch
IDEFORD (St Mary the Virgin)   *see* Teignmouth, Ideford w
Luton, Ashcombe etc *Ex*
IDEN (All Saints)   *see* Rye *Chich*
IDLE (Holy Trinity) *Bradf 3*   **P** *V Calverley*   **V** D A JOHNSON
IDLICOTE (St James the Great)   *see* Shipston-on-Stour w
Honington and Idlicote *Cov*
IDRIDGEHAY (St James)   *see* Wirksworth *Derby*
IDSWORTH (St Hubert)   *see* Blendworth w Chalton w Idsworth
Portsm
IFFLEY (St Mary the Virgin) *Ox 4*   **P** *Ch Ch Ox*   **V** R J R LEA,
C K J EYEONS,   **NSM** D G S BARTON
IFIELD (St Margaret) *Chich 7*   **P** *Bp*   **TR** L W DOOLAN,
TV D G STANIFORD, S J PATCH,   **C** J W A CHALLIS,
NSM D M GOODWIN
IFIELD (St Margaret)   *see* Gravesend H Family w Ifield *Roch*
IFORD (St Nicholas) w Kingston and Rodmell *Chich 18*   **P** *Bp*
V G M DAW
IFORD (St Saviour)   *see* Holdenhurst and Iford *Win*
IGHTFIELD (St John the Baptist)   *see* Adderley, Ash,
Calverhall, Ightfield etc *Lich*
IGHTHAM (St Peter) *Roch 10*   **P** *C B Winnifrith Esq*
P-in-c P D MCGRATH
IKEN (St Botolph)   *see* Wilford Peninsula *St E*
ILAM (Holy Cross)   *see* Alstonfield, Butterton, Ilam etc *Lich*

ILCHESTER (St Mary Major) w Northover, Limington,
Yeovilton and Podimore *B & W 6*   **P** *Bp Lon (7 turns), Bp*
(1 turn), and Wadh Coll Ox (1 turn)   **R** C F H SUTCLIFFE
ILDERTON (St Michael)   *see* Glendale Gp *Newc*
ILFORD, GREAT (St Alban) *Chelmsf 4*   **P** *Bp*   **V** D I MILNES
ILFORD, GREAT (St Andrew) *Chelmsf 4*   **P** *Bp*
V R A D ENEVER,   **NSM** J W ENEVER
ILFORD, GREAT (St John the Evangelist) *Chelmsf 4*   **P** *Bp*
V G M TARRY,   **C** E A GUEST,   **NSM** A C OKWUOSA
ILFORD, GREAT (St Luke) *Chelmsf 4*   **P** *Bp*
P-in-c J BROWN
ILFORD, GREAT (St Margaret of Antioch) (St Clement)
Chelmsf 4   **P** *Patr Bd*   **V** S G PUGH
ILFORD, GREAT (St Mary) *Chelmsf 4*   **P** *V Gt Ilford*
V J G F KESTER,   **C** J R WOOLNOUGH
ILFORD, LITTLE (St Barnabas) *Chelmsf 3*   **P** *Bp*   **V** *vacant*
(020) 8472 2777
ILFORD, LITTLE (St Michael and All Angels) *Chelmsf 3*
P *Hertf Coll Ox*   **R** B J LEWIS,   **C** J R BULLOCK,
K L A FARRELL
ILFRACOMBE (Holy Trinity) (St Peter), Lee, Woolacombe,
Bittadon and Mortehoe *Ex 15*   **P** *Patr Bd*
TR N JACKSON-STEVENS,   **TV** G A B KING-SMITH,
C R J WRIGHT
ILFRACOMBE (St Philip and St James) w West Down *Ex 15*
P *Bp and Ch Trust Fund Trust (jt)*   **P-in-c** J J CLARK
ILKESTON (Holy Trinity) *Derby 13*   **P** *Bp*   **V** A M COLE
ILKESTON (St John the Evangelist) *Derby 13*   **P** *V Ilkeston*
St Mary   **V** E A PALMER,   **C** A J FISHER
ILKESTON (St Mary the Virgin) *Derby 13*   **P** *Bp*
V A J BROWN,   **C** D FERGUS,   **NSM** G L HALLIDAY
ILKETSHALL ST ANDREW (St Andrew)   *see* Wainford *St E*
ILKETSHALL ST JOHN (St John the Baptist)   *see* S Elmham
and Ilketshall *St E*
ILKETSHALL ST LAWRENCE (St Lawrence)   *as above St E*
ILKETSHALL ST MARGARET (St Margaret)   *as above St E*
ILKLEY (All Saints) *Bradf 4*   **P** *Hyndman Trustees*
V P Q TUDGE,   **Hon C** G D N SMITH
ILKLEY (St Margaret) *Bradf 4*   **P** *CR*   **V** R D HOYAL,
NSM A G BROWN
ILLINGWORTH (St Mary) *Wakef 4*   **P** *V Halifax*
V S DANDO
ILLOGAN (St Illogan)   *see* St Illogan *Truro*
ILLSTON (St Michael and All Angels)   *see* Gaulby *Leic*
ILMER (St Peter)   *see* Risborough *Ox*
ILMINGTON (St Mary) and Stretton-on-Fosse and Ditchford w
Preston-on-Stour w Whitchurch and Atherstone-on-Stour
Cov 9   **P** *Bp, MMCET, and Ms C A Alston-Roberts-West (jt)*
R B MERRINGTON
ILMINSTER (Blessed Virgin Mary) and District *B & W 15*
P *Patr Bd*   **TR** A R WALLACE,   **TV** A F TATHAM,
C E J SCOTT,   **NSM** N P M WHINNEY
ILSINGTON (St Michael) *Ex 10*   **P** *D&C Windsor*
P-in-c C J L CURD
ILSLEY, EAST (St Mary)   *see* Hermitage *Ox*
ILSLEY, WEST (All Saints)   *see* Beedon and Peasemore w W
Ilsley and Farnborough *Ox*
ILTON (St Peter)   *see* Ilminster and Distr *B & W*
IMMINGHAM (St Andrew) *Linc 10*   **P** *DBP*
P-in-c M W PAGE-CHESTNEY,   **NSM** S V PAGE-CHESTNEY
IMPINGTON (St Andrew) *Ely 5*   **P** *Adn Ely*
P-in-c H K MCCURDY,   **C** K A HODGINS,   **NSM** R J BEWLEY
INCE (St James)   *see* Thornton-le-Moors w Ince and Elton *Ches*
INCE IN MAKERFIELD (Christ Church) (St Christopher)
Liv 14   **P** *Simeon's Trustees*   **V** C J CROOKS,   **C** L RILEY
INCE IN MAKERFIELD (St Mary) *Liv 14*   **P** *Simeon's*
Trustees   **V** D W LONG
INDIAN QUEEN (St Francis)   *see* St Enoder *Truro*
INGATESTONE (St Edmund and St Mary) w Buttsbury
Chelmsf 7   **P** *Bp*   **P-in-c** P SHERRING
INGESTRE (St Mary the Virgin)   *see* Stafford St Jo and Tixall w
Ingestre *Lich*
INGHAM (All Saints) w Cammeringham w Fillingham *Linc 3*
P *Bp and Ball Coll Ox (jt)*   **Hon C** D J PRYOR
INGHAM (Holy Trinity)   *see* Stalham, E Ruston, Brunstead,
Sutton and Ingham *Nor*
INGHAM (St Bartholomew)   *see* Blackbourne *St E*
INGLEBY ARNCLIFFE (All Saints)   *see* Osmotherley w
Harlsey and Ingleby Arncliffe *York*
INGLEBY BARWICK (St Francis) *York 21*   **P** *Abp*
V D S WATSON,   **C** P E SEYMOUR
INGLEBY GREENHOW (St Andrew) w Bilsdale Priory, Kildale
and Westerdale *York 21*   **P** *Abp, Adn Cleveland, Bp Whitby,*
Viscount de l'Isle, R G Beckett Esq, and A H W Sutcliffe Esq (jt)
V *vacant* (01642) 723947
INGLETON (St John the Evangelist) *Dur 8*   **P** *Lord Barnard*
P-in-c D J ELLEANOR

INGLETON (St Mary the Virgin) w Chapel le Dale *Bradf 6*
　P *Bp*　**V** vacant (01524) 241440
INGOL (St Margaret) *Blackb 13*　**P** *Bp*　**V** M S HATTON
INGOLDISTHORPE (St Michael) *see* Snettisham w
　Ingoldisthorpe and Fring *Nor*
INGOLDMELLS (St Peter and St Paul) w Addlethorpe *Linc 8*
　P *Ld Chan and DBP (alt)*　**P-in-c** C M FRANCE
INGOLDSBY (St Bartholomew) *Linc 14*　**P** *Ch Coll Cam,*
　Sir Lyonel Tollemache Bt, D&C, Bp, and DBP (by turn)
　R M H SABELL,　**OLM** I R WALTERS
INGRAM (St Michael) *see* Glendale Gp *Newc*
INGRAVE (St Nicholas) (St Stephen) *Chelmsf 7*　**P** *Bp and Ch*
　Patr Trust (jt)　**V** A P PARSONS
INGRAVE (St Stephen) Conventional District *Chelmsf 7*
　NSM J A SEDANO
INGROW (St John the Evangelist) cum Hainworth *Bradf 8*
　P *Bp*　**V** C H KIRKE
INGS (St Anne) *see* Staveley, Ings and Kentmere *Carl*
INGWORTH (St Lawrence) *see* Erpingham w Calthorpe,
　Ingworth, Aldborough etc *Nor*
INHAM NOOK (St Barnabas) *see* Chilwell *S'well*
INKBERROW (St Peter) w Cookhill and Kington w Dormston
　Worc 1　**P** *Bp*　**R** N M WRIGHT,　**C** D GEORGE
INKERSALL (St Columba) *see* Staveley and Barrow Hill *Derby*
INKPEN (St Michael) *see* W Woodhay w Enborne, Hampstead
　Marshall etc *Ox*
INNS COURT (Holy Cross) *Bris 1*　**P** *Bris Ch Trustees*
　V B P LUCK
INSKIP (St Peter) *see* Copp w Inskip *Blackb*
INSTOW (All Saints Chapel) (St John the Baptist) *Ex 16*
　P *Christie Trustees*　**P-in-c** C A C COOPER
INTAKE (All Saints) *see* Doncaster Intake *Sheff*
INTWOOD (All Saints) *see* Swardeston w E Carleton, Intwood,
　Keswick etc *Nor*
INWARDLEIGH (St Petroc) *see* Okehampton w Inwardleigh,
　Bratton Clovelly etc *Ex*
INWORTH (All Saints) *see* Copford w Easthorpe and Messing
　w Inworth *Chelmsf*
IPING (St Mary) *see* Stedham w Iping *Chich*
IPPLEPEN (St Andrew), Torbryan and Denbury *Ex 11*　**P** *D&C*
　Windsor and SMF (jt)　**V** I C EGLIN
IPSDEN (St Mary the Virgin) *see* Langtree *Ox*
IPSLEY (St Peter) *Worc 7*　**P** *Patr Bd*　**TV** A J KELSO,
　A E J TOSTEVIN,　**C** A W PORTER,　**NSM** J W DAVEY
IPSTONES (St Leonard) w Berkhamsytch and Onecote w
　Bradnop *Lich 6*　**P** *Bp and R Leek and Meerbrook (jt)*
　V C M SCARGILL
IPSWICH (All Hallows) *St E 4*　**P** *Bp*　**V** vacant (01473)
　727467
IPSWICH (All Saints) *St E 4*　**P** *Bp*　**V** A G WILCOX
IPSWICH (St Andrew) *St E 4*　**P** *Bp*　**V** S R LLOYD
IPSWICH (St Augustine of Hippo) *St E 4*　**P** *Bp*
　V L F SIMPKINS,　**C** K C MORRISON
IPSWICH (St Bartholomew) *St E 4*　**P** *Bp*　**V** vacant (01473)
　727441
IPSWICH (St Helen) (Holy Trinity) (St Clement w St Luke)
　St E 4　**P** *Ch Patr Trust*　**R** G D G PRICE
IPSWICH (St John the Baptist) *St E 4*　**P** *Simeon's Trustees*
　V K WHITE,　**C** D J MIDDLETON,　**NSM** M GREEN,
　OLM L G THORPE
IPSWICH (St Margaret) *St E 4*　**P** *Simeon's Trustees*
　V D CUTTS,　**C** I S NAYLOR
IPSWICH (St Mary at Stoke) (St Peter) (St Francis) (St Clare's
　Church Centre) *St E 4*　**P** *Bp*　**TR** I D J MORGAN,
　TV C G G EVERETT, M S G MORGAN
IPSWICH (St Mary at the Elms) *St E 4*　**P** *PCC*
　P-in-c J H DOSSOR
IPSWICH (St Mary-le-Tower) (St Nicholas) *St E 4*　**P** *Bp*
　(3 turns), Ch Patr Trust (1 turn)　**V** P K TOWNLEY
IPSWICH (St Matthew) *St E 4*　**P** *Ld Chan*
　R P D HARDINGHAM,　**C** M K SIMM
IPSWICH (St Thomas) *St E 4*　**P** *Bp*　**V** P BOURNER,
　OLM B F ROSE
IRBY (St Chad's Mission Church) *see* Thurstaston *Ches*
IRBY-IN-THE-MARSH (All Saints) *see* Bratoft w
　Irby-in-the-Marsh *Linc*
IRBY ON HUMBER (St Andrew) *see* Laceby and Ravendale
　Gp *Linc*
IRCHESTER (St Katharine) *Pet 10*　**P** *Bp*　**V** J SIMMONS
IRCHESTER, LITTLE (St John) *see* Irchester *Pet*
IREBY (St James) *see* Binsey *Carl*
IRELAND WOOD (St Paul) *Ripon 7*　**P** *R Adel*
　V C R CORNWELL,　**Hon C** R A M T QUICK
IRLAM (St John the Baptist) *Man 2*　**P** *Trustees*
　P-in-c A J HARDY,　**OLM** J DODD, J STEPHENS
IRNHAM (St Andrew) *see* Corby Glen *Linc*

IRON ACTON (St James the Less) *Bris 5*　**P** *Ch Ch Ox*
　P-in-c S E RUSHTON
IRON-BRIDGE (St Luke) *see* Coalbrookdale, Iron-Bridge and
　Lt Wenlock *Heref*
IRONSTONE: Drayton, Hanwell, Horley, Hornton, Shenington
　w Alkerton, and Wroxton w Balscote *Ox 5*　**P** *Ld Chan*
　(1 turn), Bp, Earl De la Warr, and DBP (1 turn)　**R** R J CHARD,
　NSM P C SMITH
IRONVILLE (Christ Church) *see* Riddings and Ironville *Derby*
IRSTEAD (St Michael) *see* Ashmanhaugh, Barton Turf etc *Nor*
IRTHINGTON (St Kentigern) *see* Eden, Gelt and Irthing *Carl*
IRTHLINGBOROUGH (St Peter) *Pet 10*　**P** *Sir Stephen*
　Hastings　**R** J R WESTWOOD,　**NSM** M L WILLIS
IRTON (St Paul) *see* Eskdale, Irton, Muncaster and
　Waberthwaite *Carl*
ISEL (St Michael) *see* Binsey *Carl*
ISFIELD (St Margaret) *Chich 21*　**P** *Abp*　**R** B H WILCOX,
　Hon C B K MELBOURNE,　**NSM** C HOWARTH
ISHAM (St Peter) w Pytchley *Pet 11*　**P** *Bp*　**P-in-c** M WRAY
ISLE ABBOTTS (Blessed Virgin Mary) *see* Ilminster and Distr
　B & W
ISLE BREWERS (All Saints) *as above B & W*
ISLE OF DOGS (Christ Church and St John) (St Luke) *Lon 7*
　P *Bp*　**V** M A SEELEY,　**C** M J HAWKES, C P PENNINGTON
ISLEHAM (St Andrew) *Ely 3*　**P** *Ld Chan*
　P-in-c C W H GOODWINS
ISLES OF SCILLY: St Mary's, St Agnes, St Martin's, Bryher
　and Tresco *Truro 6*　**P** *Duchy of Cornwall*　**R** J C OULD
ISLEWORTH (All Saints) *Lon 11*　**P** *D&C Windsor*
　V W J MORGAN
ISLEWORTH (St Francis of Assisi) *Lon 11*　**P** *Bp*
　P-in-c D G WILSON,　**NSM** L P SMITH, S P THOMPSON
ISLEWORTH (St John the Baptist) *Lon 11*
　P *V Isleworth All SS*　**P-in-c** P R MYLES
ISLEWORTH (St Luke) *see* Spring Grove St Mary *Lon*
ISLEWORTH (St Mary) Osterley Road *as above Lon*
ISLEWORTH (St Mary the Virgin) *see* Hounslow H Trin w St
　Paul *Lon*
ISLEY WALTON (All Saints) *see* Breedon cum Isley Walton
　and Worthington *Leic*
ISLINGTON (St James the Apostle) (St Peter) *Lon 6*　**P** *Bp*
　V E H JONES,　**C** F M WEAVER
ISLINGTON (St Jude and St Paul) *see* Mildmay Grove St Jude
　and St Paul *Lon*
ISLINGTON (St Mary) *Lon 6*　**P** *CPAS*　**V** G R KINGS,
　C J S SWIFT,　**NSM** E W LOVERIDGE
ISLINGTON (St Mary Magdalene) *see* Holloway St Mary
　Magd *Lon*
ISLIP (St Nicholas) *see* Ray Valley *Ox*
ISLIP (St Nicholas) *Pet 10*　**P** *L G Stopford-Sackville Esq*
　R vacant
ISTEAD RISE (St Barnabas) *Roch 4*　**P** *Bp*　**V** V C SHORT
ITCHEN ABBAS (St John the Baptist) *see* Itchen Valley *Win*
ITCHEN VALLEY, The *Win 1*　**P** *Ld Chan*
　R J G CRUICKSHANK
ITCHENOR, WEST (St Nicholas) *see* W Wittering and
　Birdham w Itchenor *Chich*
ITCHINGFIELD (St Nicholas) w Slinfold *Chich 7*　**P** *Bp*
　R D M BEAL
IVEGILL (Christ Church) *see* Skelton and
　Hutton-in-the-Forest w Ivegill *Carl*
IVER (St Peter) *Ox 23*　**P** *Trustees*　**V** B A SKINNER,
　C A D R HOLMES
IVER HEATH (St Margaret) *Ox 23*　**P** *Trustees*　**R** vacant
　(01753) 654470
IVINGHOE (St Mary the Virgin) w Pitstone and Slapton *Ox 26*
　P *Bp and Ch Ch Ox (jt)*　**V** vacant (01296) 668260
IVINGTON (St John) *see* Leominster *Heref*
IVY HATCH (not known) *see* Ightham *Roch*
IVY ROW (Mission Room) *see* Roos and Garton in Holderness
　w Tunstall etc *York*
IVYBRIDGE (St John the Evangelist) w Harford *Ex 20*　**P** *Bp*
　V C H OSBORNE,　**C** M J W BENTON-EVANS
IVYCHURCH (St George) *see* St Mary's Bay w St
　Mary-in-the-Marsh etc *Cant*
IWADE (All Saints) *Cant 16*　**P** *Adn Maidstone*
　P-in-c J P LEFROY,　**Hon C** D W WEBB
IWERNE COURTNEY (St Mary) *see* Iwerne Valley *Sarum*
IWERNE MINSTER (St Mary) *as above Sarum*
IWERNE VALLEY *Sarum 7*　**P** *D&C Windsor, DBP,*
　G A L F Pitt-Rivers Esq, and A C L Sturge Esq (jt)
　V S F EVERETT,　**NSM** J H SIMMONS
IXWORTH (St Mary) *see* Blackbourne *St E*
IXWORTH THORPE (All Saints) *as above St E*
JACKFIELD (St Mary) *see* Broseley w Benthall, Jackfield,
　Linley etc *Heref*

JACOBSTOW (St James)   *see* St Gennys, Jacobstow w Warbstow and Treneglos *Truro*

JACOBSTOWE (St James)   *see* Hatherleigh, Meeth, Exbourne and Jacobstowe *Ex*

JARROW (St John the Baptist) (St Mark) (St Paul) (St Peter)   *Dur 15*   **P** *Bp*   **TR** W E BRAVINER,   **TV** J S CURRY, C I D AQUILINA,   **NSM** A RAINE

JARROW GRANGE (Christ Church)   *Dur 15*   **P** *Lord Northbourne*   **P-in-c** D T OSMAN,   **C** J P ROY

JARVIS BROOK (St Michael and All Angels)   *Chich 19*   **P** *Bp*   **V** P TRAFFORD,   **NSM** P K BURNETT

JERSEY (All Saints)   *Win 15*   **P** *R St Helier, Bp, and The Crown (by turn)*   **V** G J HOUGHTON

JERSEY Gouray (St Martin)   *Win 15*   **P** *Bp and The Crown (alt)*   **Hon C** L W MATTHEWS

JERSEY Greve d'Azette (St Nicholas)   *see* Jersey St Clem *Win*

JERSEY (Holy Trinity)   *Win 15*   **P** *The Crown*   **R** A KEOGH

JERSEY Millbrook (St Matthew)   *Win 15*   **P** *The Crown*   **V** *vacant* (01534) 617918 *or* 720934

JERSEY (St Andrew)   *Win 15*   **P** *Dean of Jersey*   **V** M S TAYLOR

JERSEY (St Brelade) (Communicare Chapel) (St Aubin)   *Win 15*   **P** *The Crown*   **R** M F W BOND,   **Par Dn** J M GURDON,   **Hon C** K WALKER,   **NSM** G GREEN

JERSEY (St Clement)   *Win 15*   **P** *The Crown*   **R** D M SHAW

JERSEY (St Helier)   *Win 15*   **P** *The Crown*   **R** J N SEAFORD,   **C** C PRICE,   **NSM** A D WILLIAMS

JERSEY (St James)   *Win 15*   **P** *Bp*   **V** D R D JONES,   **NSM** A F PEARCE

JERSEY (St John)   *Win 15*   **P** *The Crown*   **R** A J THEWLIS

JERSEY (St Lawrence)   *Win 15*   **P** *The Crown*   **R** *vacant* (01534) 20934

JERSEY (St Luke)   *Win 15*   **P** *Bp and The Crown (alt)*   **V** D R D JONES,   **NSM** A F PEARCE

JERSEY (St Mark)   *Win 15*   **P** *Bp*   **V** C I BUCKLEY

JERSEY (St Martin)   *Win 15*   **P** *The Crown*   **R** L J TURNER

JERSEY (St Mary)   *Win 15*   **P** *The Crown*   **R** D R D JONES

JERSEY (St Ouen) (St George)   *Win 15*   **P** *The Crown*   **R** J P HARKIN

JERSEY (St Paul) Proprietary Chapel   *Win 15*   **Min** P J BROOKS,   **Hon C** S R BROUGHTON

JERSEY (St Peter)   *Win 15*   **P** *The Crown*   **R** M R POOLTON

JERSEY (St Saviour)   *Win 15*   **P** *The Crown*   **R** A C SWINDELL,   **NSM** J J ILTON

JERSEY (St Simon)   *Win 15*   **P** *R St Helier, Bp, and The Crown (by turn)*   **V** G J HOUGHTON

JERSEY DE GROUVILLE (St Martin) (St Peter la Roque)   *Win 15*   **P** *The Crown*   **R** F R A MASON

JESMOND (Clayton Memorial Church)   *Newc 5*   **P** *Trustees*   **V** D R J HOLLOWAY,   **C** J J S PRYKE

JESMOND (Holy Trinity)   *Newc 5*   **P** *Trustees*   **P-in-c** R L SIMPSON,   **C** T E F ROSE,   **NSM** C SMITH, A F MUNDEN

JESMOND (St George)   *see* Newc St Geo *Newc*

JESMOND (St Hilda)   *see* Newc St Hilda *Newc*

JEVINGTON (St Andrew)   *see* E Dean w Friston and Jevington *Chich*

JOYDENS WOOD (St Barnabas)   *Roch 17*   **P** *Bp*   **V** E P I WESTBROOK

JURBY (St Patrick)   *S & M 3*   **P** *Bp*   **V** *vacant*

KATE'S HILL (St John)   *see* Dudley St Jo *Worc*

KEA (All Hallows) (Old Church)   *Truro 6*   **P** *V St Clement*   **V** H A HALLETT

KEAL, EAST (St Helen)   *see* Marden Hill Gp *Linc*

KEAL, WEST (St Helen)   *as above Linc*

KEARSLEY MOOR (St Stephen)   *Man 6*   **P** *R E Farnworth and Kearsley*   **V** K F WAINWRIGHT

KEASDEN (St Matthew)   *see* Clapham-with-Keasden and Austwick *Bradf*

KEDDINGTON (St Margaret)   *see* Louth *Linc*

KEDINGTON (St Peter and St Paul)   *see* Stourhead *St E*

KEEDWELL HILL (Ascension)   *see* Long Ashton *B & W*

KEELBY Group, The (St Bartholomew)   *Linc 10*   **P** *J E Spilman Esq and DBP (1 turn), Bp (1 turn)*   **R** R W GROSSE

KEELE (St John the Baptist)   *see* Betley and Keele *Lich*

KEEVIL (St Leonard)   *see* Steeple Ashton w Semington and Keevil *Sarum*

KEGWORTH (St Andrew)   *Leic 7*   **P** *Ch Coll Cam*   **P-in-c** N O TUFFNELL

KEIGHLEY (All Saints)   *Bradf 8*   **P** *Bp and R Keighley St Andr*   **V** N DANIELS,   **Hon C** C P HUTCHINSON

KEIGHLEY (St Andrew)   *Bradf 8*   **P** *Bp*   **P-in-c** P J MOTT

KEINTON MANDEVILLE (St Mary Magdalene)   *see* Wheathill Priory Gp of Par *B & W*

KELBROOK (St Mary)   *Bradf 7*   **P** *Bp*   **P-in-c** R C WALLACE

KELBY (St Andrew)   *see* Ancaster Wilsford Gp *Linc*

KELHAM (St Wilfrid)   *see* Averham w Kelham *S'well*

KELLAWAYS (St Giles)   *see* Draycot *Bris*

KELLET, NETHER (St Mark)   *see* Bolton-le-Sands *Blackb*

KELLET, OVER (St Cuthbert)   *Blackb 14*   **P** *Reformation Ch Trust*   **V** K CLAPHAM

KELLING (St Mary)   *see* Weybourne Gp *Nor*

KELLINGTON (St Edmund)   *see* Knottingley and Kellington w Whitley *Wakef*

KELLOE (St Helen) and Coxhoe   *Dur 5*   **P** *Bp*   **V** M J COOKE

KELLS (St Peter)   *Carl 5*   **P** *Bp*   **P-in-c** J D KELLY,   **OLM** A J BANKS

KELLY (St Mary the Virgin)   *see* Lifton, Broadwoodwidger, Stowford etc *Ex*

KELMARSH (St Denys)   *see* Clipston w Naseby and Haselbech w Kelmarsh *Pet*

KELMSCOTT (St George)   *see* Shill Valley and Broadshire *Ox*

KELSALE (St Peter)   *see* Kelsale-cum-Carlton, Middleton, Theberton etc *St E*

KELSALE-CUM-CARLTON, Middleton-cum-Fordley and Theberton w Eastbridge   *St E 19*   **P** *DBP, Prime Min, and Ch Patr Trust (by turn)*   **P-in-c** R F WEBB,   **C** R S SMITH,   **NSM** B L WEBB,   **OLM** S A WARNE

KELSALL (St Philip)   *Ches 2*   **P** *V Tarvin*   **P-in-c** I P ENTICOTT

KELSEY Group, The   *Linc 5*   **P** *Bp (3 turns), J M B Young Esq and S B Young Esq (1 turn)*   **R** P J GREEN

KELSEY, NORTH (All Hallows)   *see* Kelsey Gp *Linc*

KELSEY, SOUTH (St Mary)   *as above Linc*

KELSHALL (St Faith)   *see* Therfield w Kelshall *St Alb*

KELSTERN (St Faith)   *see* Binbrook Gp *Linc*

KELSTON (St Nicholas)   *see* Bath Weston St Jo w Kelston *B & W*

KELVEDON (St Mary the Virgin) and Feering   *Chelmsf 24*   **P** *Bp*   **V** D S REYNISH

KELVEDON HATCH (St Nicholas)   *see* Bentley Common, Kelvedon Hatch and Navestock *Chelmsf*

KEMBERTON (St Andrew)   *see* Beckbury, Badger, Kemberton, Ryton, Stockton etc *Lich*

KEMBLE (All Saints), Poole Keynes, Somerford Keynes and Sharncote   *Glouc 11*   **P** *DBP, Duchy of Lanc, and Mrs L R Rank (by turn)*   **P-in-c** C K RACE

KEMERTON (St Nicholas)   *see* Woolstone w Gotherington and Oxenton etc *Glouc*

KEMP TOWN (St Mary)   *Chich 2*   **P** *Bp, Mrs R A Hinton, A C R Elliott Esq, T J Elliott Esq, and the Revd Canon D H McKittrick (jt)*   **V** N J MASON

KEMPSEY (St Mary the Virgin) and Severn Stoke w Croome d'Abitot   *Worc 5*   **P** *D&C and Croome Estate Trustees (alt)*   **R** P R HOLZAPFEL

KEMPSFORD (St Mary)   *see* Fairford and Kempsford w Whelford *Glouc*

KEMPSHOTT (St Mark)   *Win 4*   **P** *Bp*   **V** D J STRATHIE

KEMPSTON (All Saints)   *St Alb 10*   **P** *Bp*   **P-in-c** R J SUTTON,   **NSM** G A WEBB

KEMPSTON (Transfiguration)   *St Alb 10*   **P** *Bp*   **V** N S D GIBSON,   **NSM** V E HOLLIS

KEMSING (St Mary the Virgin) w Woodlands   *Roch 10*   **P** *DBP*   **V** J N ASHWORTH

KENARDINGTON (St Mary)   *see* Orlestone w Snave and Ruckinge w Warehorne etc *Cant*

KENCHESTER (St Michael)   *see* Credenhill w Brinsop and Wormsley etc *Heref*

KENCOT (St George)   *see* Shill Valley and Broadshire *Ox*

KENDAL (Holy Trinity) (All Hallows Chapel)   *Carl 10*   **P** *Trin Coll Cam*   **V** R METCALFE,   **C** E M SHEARCROFT,   **NSM** P SMITH

KENDAL (St George)   *Carl 10*   **P** *V Kendal H Trin*   **V** A R BILLINGS,   **OLM** J F RADLEY

KENDAL (St Thomas)   *Carl 10*   **P** *CPAS*   **V** T R MONTGOMERY,   **C** T S MAY,   **NSM** S R WEATHERILL

KENDERCHURCH (St Mary)   *see* Ewyas Harold w Dulas, Kenderchurch etc *Heref*

KENDRAY (St Andrew)   *Sheff 12*   **P** *V Ardsley*   **V** *vacant* (01226) 203906

KENILWORTH (St John)   *Cov 4*   **P** *Simeon's Trustees*   **V** R D TURNER,   **NSM** Y L RICHMOND

KENILWORTH (St Nicholas) (St Barnabas)   *Cov 4*   **P** *Ld Chan*   **V** R W E AWRE,   **C** P J TAYLOR

KENLEY (All Saints)   *S'wark 24*   **P** *Abp*   **V** R C HAGON,   **NSM** S C CONWAY, D C HADLEY

KENLEY (St John the Baptist)   *see* Wenlock *Heref*

KENN (St Andrew)   *see* Exminster and Kenn *Ex*

KENN (St John the Evangelist)   *see* Yatton Moor *B & W*

KENN, NORTH   *see* Tedburn St Mary, Whitestone, Oldridge etc *Ex*

KENNERLEIGH (St John the Baptist)   *see* N Creedy *Ex*

KENNET, EAST (Christ Church)   *see* Upper Kennet *Sarum*

KENNET, UPPER *Sarum 18* **P** *Bp* **TR** W J SELLERS, **NSM** G M MACKICHAN

KENNETT (St Nicholas) *Ely 3* **P** *Mrs M F de Packh* **P-in-c** A HASELHURST

KENNINGHALL (St Mary) *see* Guiltcross *Nor*

KENNINGTON (St John the Divine w St James the Apostle) *S'wark 11* **P** *Ripon Coll Cuddesdon and Bp (jt)* **V** D M BRADSHAW, **C** L P DARRANT

KENNINGTON (St Mark) *S'wark 13* **P** *Abp* **V** R D DE BERRY, **C** C P BAKER

KENNINGTON (St Mary) *Cant 10* **P** *Abp* **V** C G PREECE

KENNINGTON (St Swithun) *Ox 10* **P** *Bp* **V** T SMITH, **Hon C** E A JOHNSON

KENNINGTON CROSS (St Anselm) *see* N Lambeth *S'wark*

KENNINGTON PARK (St Agnes) *S'wark 10* **P** *Trustees* **V** C I PEARSON

KENNY HILL (St James) *see* Mildenhall *St E*

KENSAL GREEN (St John) *Lon 2* **P** *Bp* **V** R D BEAL

KENSAL RISE (St Mark) (St Martin) *Lon 21* **P** *St Olave Hart Street Trustees and Bp (jt)* **V** P W STONE, **C** G P NOYCE, P D HILLAS, **Hon C** J BARRATT

KENSAL TOWN (St Thomas) (St Andrew) (St Philip) *Lon 12* **P** *Hyndman Trustees* **V** D FLETCHER

KENSINGTON (St Barnabas) *Lon 12* **P** *V Kensington St Mary Abbots w St Geo and Ch Ch* **V** T M HUMPHREY, **C** W KEMP

KENSINGTON (St Clement) *see* Notting Dale St Clem w St Mark and St Jas *Lon*

KENSINGTON (St Helen) (Holy Trinity) *Lon 12* **P** *Bp* **V** J C TERRY, **C** I P DOWSETT

KENSINGTON (St James) *see* Notting Dale St Clem w St Mark and St Jas *Lon*

KENSINGTON (St John the Baptist) *Lon 12* **P** *Trustees* **V** G F BRIGHT, **NSM** A E SPEAKMAN

KENSINGTON (St Mary Abbots) w St George (Christ Church) *Lon 12* **P** *Bp* **V** G W CRAIG, **C** A G C PEARSON, W J M GIBBS, M G FULLER

KENSINGTON (St Philip) Earl's Court *Lon 12* **P** *Bp* **V** M B E FORREST

KENSINGTON, NORTH (St Michael and All Angels) *see* Notting Hill St Mich and Ch Ch *Lon*

KENSINGTON, SOUTH (Holy Trinity w All Saints) *Lon 3* **P** *D&C Westmr* **P-in-c** J A CAVE BERGQUIST

KENSINGTON, SOUTH (St Augustine) *Lon 12* **P** *Keble Coll Ox* **P-in-c** C E SARGENT

KENSINGTON, SOUTH (St Jude) *Lon 8* **P** *Sir Laurence Magnus Bt* **V** *vacant* (020) 7370 1360

KENSINGTON, SOUTH (St Luke) *Lon 8* **P** *Ch Patr Trust* **V** W R HEALD

KENSINGTON, SOUTH (St Stephen) *Lon 12* **P** *Guild of All So* **V** R F BUSHAU

KENSINGTON, WEST (St Andrew) *see* Fulham St Andr Fulham Fields *Lon*

KENSINGTON, WEST (St Mary) *see* Fulham St Mary N End *Lon*

KENSINGTON, WEST (St Mary) The Boltons *see* W Brompton St Mary w St Pet *Lon*

KENSWORTH (St Mary the Virgin), Studham and Whipsnade *St Alb 12* **P** *Ld Chan and D&C St Paul's (alt)* **V** *vacant* (01582) 872223

KENT TOWN *see* E Molesey St Paul *Guildf*

KENTCHURCH (St Mary) *see* Ewyas Harold w Dulas, Kenderchurch etc *Heref*

KENTFORD (St Mary) *see* Gazeley w Dalham, Moulton and Kentford *St E*

KENTISBEARE (St Mary) *see* Cullompton, Willand, Uffculme, Kentisbeare etc *Ex*

KENTISBURY (St Thomas) *see* Shirwell, Loxhore, Kentisbury, Arlington, etc *Ex*

KENTISH TOWN (St Benet and All Saints) (St Luke) *Lon 17* **P** *Prime Min and D&C St Paul's (alt)* **V** R N ARNOLD

KENTISH TOWN (St Martin) (St Andrew) *Lon 17* **P** *Exors Dame Jewell Magnus-Allcroft* **V** J A HAYWARD

KENTISH TOWN (St Silas) and (Holy Trinity) w St Barnabas *Lon 17* **P** *Bp and D&C St Paul's (jt)* **V** G C ROWLANDS

KENTMERE (St Cuthbert) *see* Staveley, Ings and Kentmere *Carl*

KENTON (All Saints) *see* Debenham w Aspall and Kenton *St E*

KENTON (All Saints), Mamhead, Powderham, Cofton and Starcross *Ex 6* **P** *Earl of Devon, D&C Ex, D&C Sarum, and SMF (jt)* **Hon C** P DAWKES, P J SPACKMAN

KENTON (Ascension) *Newc 5* **P** *Bp* **P-in-c** A C RUSSELL

KENTON (St Mary the Virgin) *Lon 23* **P** *Bp* **V** D J SHERWOOD

KENTON, SOUTH (Annunciation) *see* Wembley Park *Lon*

KENWYN (St Keyne) w St Allen *Truro 6* **P** *Bp* **R** P D SAYLE, **OLM** R W HUMPHRIES, R F NICHOLLS

KERESLEY (St Thomas) and Coundon *Cov 2* **P** *Bp* **V** P A WALKER, **C** R E WALKER

KERESLEY END (Church of the Ascension) *see* Keresley and Coundon *Cov*

KERRIDGE (Holy Trinity) *see* Bollington St Jo *Ches*

KERSAL, LOWER (St Aidan) *Man 6* **P** *Bp* **V** G D MORRIS

KERSAL MOOR (St Paul) *Man 6* **P** *Trustees* **R** L K BATTYE

KERSEY (St Mary) *see* Elmsett w Aldham, Hintlesham, Chattisham etc *St E*

KERSWELL GREEN (St John the Baptist) *see* Kempsey and Severn Stoke w Croome d'Abitot *Worc*

KESGRAVE (All Saints) *St E 4* **P** *Bp* **V** R SPITTLE

KESSINGLAND (St Edmund), Gisleham and Rushmere *Nor 9* **P** *Ld Chan (1 turns) and Bp (2 turns)* **R** S J COLLIER, **OLM** J W ODDY

KESTON (not known) (St Audrey) *Roch 14* **P** *D&C* **R** *vacant* (01689) 853186

KESWICK (All Saints) *see* Swardeston w E Carleton, Intwood, Keswick etc *Nor*

KESWICK (St John) *Carl 6* **P** *Trustees* **V** B SMITH, **NSM** M COWAN

KESWICK, EAST (St Mary Magdalene) *see* Bardsey *Ripon*

KETLEY (St Mary the Virgin) and Oakengates *Lich 21* **P** *Bp* **V** *vacant* (01952) 612926

KETTERING (All Saints) *Pet 11* **P** *SMF* **V** R T COOK

KETTERING (Christ the King) *Pet 11* **P** *R Barton Seagrave w Warkton* **V** S M BENOY, **C** A I MORTON

KETTERING (St Andrew) *Pet 11* **P** *Bp* **V** *vacant* (01536) 513858

KETTERING (St Mary the Virgin) (St John the Evangelist) *Pet 11* **P** *SMF* **V** S J RAINE

KETTERING (St Peter and St Paul) (St Michael and All Angels) *Pet 11* **P** *Comdr L M M Saunders Watson* **P-in-c** D M J BARRINGTON, **NSM** A R G DUTTON

KETTERINGHAM (St Peter) *see* Swardeston w E Carleton, Intwood, Keswick etc *Nor*

KETTLEBASTON (St Mary) *see* Monks Eleigh w Chelsworth and Brent Eleigh etc *St E*

KETTLEBROOK (St Andrew) *see* Tamworth *Lich*

KETTLEBURGH (St Andrew) *see* Brandeston w Kettleburgh and Easton *St E*

KETTLENESS (St John the Baptist) *see* Lythe w Ugthorpe *York*

KETTLESTONE (All Saints) *see* Barney, Fulmodeston w Croxton, Hindringham etc *Nor*

KETTLETHORPE (St Peter and St Paul) *see* Saxilby Gp *Linc*

KETTLEWELL (St Mary) w Conistone, Hubberholme and Arncliff w Halton Gill *Bradf 7* **P** *Bp, Mrs A M Harries and W R G Bell Esq (jt)* **V** M A HESLOP

KETTON (St Mary the Virgin), Collyweston, Easton-on-the-Hill, Tinwell and Wittering *Pet 8* **P** *Burghley Ho Preservation Trust, Bp, and Ld Chan (by turn)* **R** D G EVERETT, **Hon C** D B SIMMONDS

KEW (St Anne) *S'wark 18* **P** *The Crown* **V** N J WORN

KEW (St Francis of Assisi) *Liv 9* **P** *Bp, Adn Warrington, and V Southport All SS and All So (jt)* **V** A P J GALBRAITH

KEW (St Philip and All Saints) (St Luke) *S'wark 18* **P** *Bp* **V** N P DARBY, **Hon C** G S SMITH

KEWSTOKE (St Paul) w Wick St Lawrence *B & W 11* **P** *Ld Chan* **V** N A SCHEMANOFF

KEXBY (St Paul) w Wilberfoss *York 5* **P** *Viscount de Vesci and Lord Egremont (alt)* **P-in-c** B S BOWES

KEYHAM (All Saints) *see* Houghton-on-the-Hill, Keyham and Hungarton *Leic*

KEYHAM, NORTH (St Thomas) *Ex 21* **P** *Bp* **V** *vacant* (01752) 51102

KEYINGHAM (St Nicholas) w Ottringham, Halsham and Sunk Island *York 12* **P** *Abp (3 turns), DBP (1 turn)* **R** R HOWARD

KEYMER (St Cosmas and St Damian) *see* Clayton w Keymer *Chich*

KEYMER (St Francis of Assisi) *as above Chich*

KEYNSHAM (St Francis) (St John the Baptist) *B & W 10* **P** *Patr Bd* **TR** J F SAMWAYS, **TV** A D JUDGE, A-M C BIRD, **NSM** M A SNOOK

KEYSOE (St Mary the Virgin) w Bolnhurst and Little Staughton *St Alb 15* **P** *CCC Ox (1 turn), Bp (2 turns)* **V** *vacant* (01234) 708251

KEYSTON (St John the Baptist) and Bythorn *Ely 9* **P** *Sir Stephen Hastings (2 turns), Bp (1 turn)* **P-in-c** S P MEWS, **NSM** J RAWLINSON

KEYWORTH (St Mary Magdalene) and Stanton-on-the-Wolds and Bunny w Bradmore *S'well 8* **P** *Bp and Ld Chan (alt)* **R** T SISSON, **NSM** T H KIRKMAN, S M OLDROYD

KIBWORTH (St Wilfrid) and Smeeton Westerby and Saddington *Leic 5* **P** *Mert Coll Ox and Bp (jt)* **R** S M LEE
KIDBROOKE (St James) (Holy Spirit) *S'wark 3* **P** *Patr Bd* **R** K W HITCH, **NSM** K F SITCH
KIDBROOKE (St Nicholas) *S'wark 1* **P** *Bp and Simeon's Trustees (jt)* **V** T M LINKENS
KIDDERMINSTER (St George) (St Chad) (St John the Baptist Church Hall) *Worc 11* **P** *Patr Bd* **TR** N J W BARKER, **TV** H A BURTON, **C** P A HUXTABLE
KIDDERMINSTER (St John the Baptist) (Holy Innocents) *Worc 11* **P** *Patr Bd* **TR** H F GODDARD, **TV** A J VESSEY, J R STEWART
KIDDERMINSTER (St Mary and All Saints) w Trimpley, Franche, Broadwaters and Upper Arley *Worc 11* **P** *Bp* **TR** D O BELL, **TV** F H HAWORTH, M C WARREN, **C** A A GOODMAN, **NSM** C L ALLEN
KIDDERMINSTER WEST *see* Kidderminster St Jo and H Innocents *Worc*
KIDDINGTON (St Nicholas) *see* Wootton w Glympton and Kiddington *Ox*
KIDLINGTON (St Mary the Virgin) w Hampton Poyle *Ox 7* **P** *Patr Bd* **TR** J A ELLIS, **TV** R G COPPEN, **C** J F JACKSON, **NSM** B DOUBTFIRE, J A TURNER
KIDLINGTON, SOUTH (St John the Baptist) *see* Kidlington w Hampton Poyle *Ox*
KIDMORE END (St John the Baptist) *see* Rotherfield Peppard and Kidmore End etc *Ox*
KIDSGROVE (St Thomas) *Lich 9* **P** *MMCET* **V** *vacant* (01782) 772895 or 771727
KILBURN (Mission Room) *see* Horsley and Denby *Derby*
KILBURN (St Augustine) (St John) *Lon 2* **P** *SMF* **V** A H YATES, **C** D R HUMPHREYS, **NSM** H R F O'GARRO
KILBURN (St Mary) *see* Thirkleby w Kilburn and Bagby *York*
KILBURN (St Mary w All Souls) Priory Road and W Hampstead St James *Lon 16* **P** *Bp, Ch Patr Trust, and trustees (jt)* **V** A D CAIN, **C** C E ROBSON
KILBURN, WEST (St Luke) (St Simon) (St Jude) *Lon 2* **P** *CPAS* **P-in-c** A G THOM, **C** A R SALISBURY, J P TRIFFITT
KILBY (St Mary Magdalene) *see* Wistow *Leic*
KILDALE (St Cuthbert) *see* Ingleby Greenhow w Bilsdale Priory, Kildale etc *York*
KILDWICK (St Andrew) *Bradf 8* **P** *Ch Ch Ox* **V** R A R FIGG
KILHAM (All Saints) *see* Rudston w Boynton, Carnaby and Kilham *York*
KILKHAMPTON (St James the Great) w Morwenstow *Truro 8* **P** *DBP and Bp (jt)* **R** P J ABELL
KILLAMARSH (St Giles) *Derby 3* **P** *The Crown* **R** R J BRADSHAW
KILLERTON (Holy Evangelist) *see* Pinhoe and Broadclyst *Ex*
KILLINGHALL (St Thomas the Apostle) *see* Hampsthwaite and Killinghall *Ripon*
KILLINGHOLME, NORTH AND SOUTH (St Denys) *see* Habrough Gp *Linc*
KILLINGTON (All Saints) *see* Firbank, Howgill and Killington *Bradf*
KILLINGWORTH (St John) *Newc 1* **P** *V Longbenton St Bart* **V** M L MALLESON
KILMERSDON (St Peter and St Paul) w Babington *B & W 12* **P** *Lord Hylton* **R** C P J TURNER
KILMESTON (St Andrew) *see* Upper Itchen *Win*
KILMINGTON (St Giles) *see* Kilmington, Stockland, Dalwood, Yarcombe etc *Ex*
KILMINGTON (St Giles), Stockland, Dalwood, Yarcombe and Shute *Ex 5* **P** *Bp and D&C (2 turns), Prime Min (1 turn)* **V** N H FREATHY, **C** G S GIBSON, **NSM** L A MILLS
KILMINGTON (St Mary the Virgin) *see* Upper Stour *Sarum*
KILNDOWN (Christ Church) *see* Goudhurst w Kilndown *Cant*
KILNGREEN (Diggle Mission Church) *see* Saddleworth *Man*
KILNHURST (St Thomas) *Sheff 12* **P** *Ld Chan* **V** N H ELLIOTT, **C** D E BARNSLEY
KILNWICK (All Saints) *see* Woldsburn *York*
KILNWICK PERCY (St Helen) *see* Pocklington and Owsthorpe and Kilnwick Percy etc *York*
KILPECK (St Mary and St David) *see* Ewyas Harold w Dulas, Kenderchurch etc *Heref*
KILSBY (St Faith) *see* Barby w Kilsby *Pet*
KILTON (St Nicholas) *see* Quantoxhead *B & W*
KILVERSTONE (St Andrew) *see* Thetford *Nor*
KILVINGTON (St Mary) *S'well 3* **P** *E G Staunton Esq* **P-in-c** J H BATESON
KILVINGTON, SOUTH (St Wilfrid) *see* Thirsk *York*
KILWORTH, NORTH (St Andrew) *see* Gilmorton, Peatling Parva, Kimcote etc *Leic*
KILWORTH, SOUTH (St Nicholas) *as above Leic*
KIMBERLEY (Holy Trinity) *S'well 7* **P** *Bp* **R** D W WILDE
KIMBERLEY (St Peter) *see* Barnham Broom and Upper Yare *Nor*

KIMBERWORTH (St Thomas) (St Mark) *Sheff 6* **P** *Bp* **V** P J HUGHES, **NSM** J M FODEN
KIMBERWORTH PARK (St John) *Sheff 6* **P** *Bp* **V** S G MILLWOOD
KIMBLE, GREAT (St Nicholas) *see* Ellesborough, The Kimbles and Stoke Mandeville *Ox*
KIMBLE, LITTLE (All Saints) *as above Ox*
KIMBLESWORTH (St Philip and St James) *see* Dur N *Dur*
KIMBOLTON (St Andrew) *Ely 9* **P** *Trustees Duke of Manchester* **V** R A FROST
KIMBOLTON (St James the Great) *see* Leominster *Heref*
KIMCOTE (All Saints) *see* Gilmorton, Peatling Parva, Kimcote etc *Leic*
KIMMERIDGE (St Nicholas of Myra) *see* Corfe Castle, Church Knowle, Kimmeridge etc *Sarum*
KIMPTON (St Peter and St Paul) *see* Appleshaw, Kimpton, Thruxton, Fyfield etc *Win*
KIMPTON (St Peter and St Paul) w Ayot St Lawrence *St Alb 8* **P** *Bp* **P-in-c** K A BUCKLER
KINETON (St Peter) *Cov 8* **P** *Lady Willoughby de Broke* **V** C A HOST, **C** P A LILLICRAP
KING CROSS (St Paul) *Wakef 4* **P** *Bp* **V** J VICKERMAN
KING STERNDALE (Christ Church) *see* Buxton w Burbage and King Sterndale *Derby*
KINGHAM (St Andrew) *see* Chipping Norton *Ox*
KINGMOOR (St Peter) *see* Houghton *Carl*
KING'S BECK *Nor 12* **P** *Bp, D&C, P H C Barber Esq, and J T D Shaw Esq (jt)* **R** S A SMITH
KINGS BROMLEY (All Saints) *see* The Ridwares and Kings Bromley *Lich*
KING'S CAPLE (St John the Baptist) *see* How Caple w Sollarshope, Sellack etc *Heref*
KING'S CLIFFE (All Saints) *Pet 8* **P** *Bp* **P-in-c** P J DAVIES
KINGS HEATH (All Saints) *Birm 5* **P** *V Moseley St Mary* **V** J L WILKINSON, **C** R A DONOVAN
KINGS HEATH (St Augustine) *Pet 7* **P** *Bp* **V** L MATHIAS, **NSM** J C MICKLETHWAITE
KING'S HILL (St Andrew) *see* Wednesbury St Bart *Lich*
KINGS LANGLEY (All Saints) *St Alb 2* **P** *Abp* **V** P R STEARN, **NSM** C THORP
KING'S LYNN (All Saints) *see* S Lynn *Nor*
KING'S LYNN (St John the Evangelist) *Nor 20* **P** *Bp* **P-in-c** S C STOKES
KING'S LYNN (St Margaret) (St Edmund) w St Nicholas *Nor 20* **P** *D&C* **R** C J IVORY, **C** M C JACKSON
KING'S LYNN (St Peter) *see* Clenchwarton and W Lynn *Ely*
KING'S NORTON (St John the Baptist) *see* Gaulby *Leic*
KINGS NORTON (St Nicolas) *Birm 4* **P** *Patr Bd* **TR** R J MORRIS, **TV** H M FLACK, R J FARMAN, **NSM** R FARMAN
KING'S PYON (St Mary the Virgin) *see* Canon Pyon w Kings Pyon and Birley *Heref*
KINGS RIPTON (St Peter) *Ely 8* **P** *Lord de Ramsey* **R** *vacant*
KING'S STANLEY (St George) *see* The Stanleys *Glouc*
KING'S SUTTON (St Peter and St Paul) and Newbottle and Charlton *Pet 1* **P** *SMF and Lady Townsend (jt)* **P-in-c** M R H BELLAMY
KING'S WALDEN (St Mary) and Offley w Lilley *St Alb 4* **P** *Sir Thomas Pilkington Bt (2 turns), St Jo Coll Cam (1 turn), D K C Salusbury-Hughes Esq and Mrs P A L McGrath (2 turns)* **V** J SCHILD
KING'S WORTHY (St Mary) (St Mary's Chapel) *Win 7* **P** *Univ Coll Ox and Lord Northbrook (alt)* **R** A W GORDON
KINGSBRIDGE (St Edmund the King and Martyr) and Dodbrooke *Ex 14* **P** *Bp* **R** C C ROBINS
KINGSBURY (Holy Innocents) *Lon 21* **P** *D&C St Paul's* **V** C F MORTON, **NSM** A J HOPKINS
KINGSBURY (St Andrew) *Lon 21* **P** *The Crown* **V** J T SMITH
KINGSBURY (St Peter and St Paul) *Birm 10* **P** *Bp* **V** *vacant* (01827) 873500
KINGSBURY EPISCOPI (St Martin) w East Lambrook, Hambridge and Earnshill *B & W 15* **P** *Bp (2 turns), D&C (1 turn)* **A** D A BURTON, A R ELWOOD
KINGSCLERE (St Mary) *Win 6* **P** *Bp* **V** *vacant* (01635) 298272
KINGSCLERE WOODLANDS (St Paul) *see* Ashford Hill w Headley *Win*
KINGSCOTE (St John the Baptist) *see* Nailsworth w Shortwood, Horsley etc *Glouc*
KINGSDON (All Saints) *see* Somerton w Compton Dundon, the Charltons etc *B & W*
KINGSDOWN (St Edmund the King and Martyr) *Roch 10* **P** *D&C* **R** J M B THURLOW
KINGSDOWN (St John the Evangelist) *see* Ringwould w Kingsdown *Cant*

KINGSEY (St Nicholas) see Haddenham w Cuddington, Kingsey etc *Ox*

KINGSHURST (St Barnabas) *Birm 9* **P** *Bp* **V** F C EVANS

KINGSKERSWELL (St Mary) w Coffinswell *Ex 11*
P *V St Marychurch* **V** J F LEONARD, **NSM** A M WELLS

KINGSLAND (St Michael and All Angels) w Eardisland, Aymestrey and Leinthall Earles *Heref 7* **P** *DBP (2 turns), Ld Chan (1 turn)* **P-in-c** N J TYSON

KINGSLEY (All Saints) see E and W Worldham, Hartley Mauditt w Kingsley etc *Win*

KINGSLEY (St John the Evangelist) see Norley, Crowton and Kingsley *Ches*

KINGSLEY (St Werburgh) and Foxt-with-Whiston *Lich 6*
P *Mrs N A Faulkner* **R** L R PRICE

KINGSLEY MOOR (St John the Baptist) see Kingsley and Foxt-w-Whiston *Lich*

KINGSNORTH (St Michael and All Angels) and Shadoxhurst *Cant 10* **P** *Abp* **P-in-c** S E MCLACHLAN, **C** T P HALL

KINGSNYMPTON (St James) see S Molton w Nymet St George, High Bray etc *Ex*

KINGSTAG (not known) see Sturminster Newton, Hinton St Mary and Lydlinch *Sarum*

KINGSTANDING (St Luke) *Birm 3* **P** *Bp* **V** D J A SMITH,
C R D WOODWARD, B C D WHEELHOUSE

KINGSTANDING (St Mark) *Birm 3* **P** *Bp* **V** D S COSSLETT,
C R D WOODWARD, **Hon C** A BARTLETT,
NSM S M L BARNES

KINGSTEIGNTON (St Michael) *Ex 11* **P** *Bp*
V C H BENSON, **NSM** R W BAMBERG

KINGSTHORPE (St John the Baptist) w Northampton St David *Pet 4* **P** *Patr Bd* **TR** J T SHORT, **TV** R MELLOR,
C J J E ROWLEY, **NSM** M A TAYLOR

KINGSTON (All Saints and St Andrew) see Papworth *Ely*

KINGSTON (St Giles) see Barham w Bishopsbourne and Kingston *Cant*

KINGSTON (St James) see Modbury, Bigbury, Ringmore w Kingston etc *Ex*

KINGSTON (St James) see Shorwell w Kingston *Portsm*

KINGSTON (St James), Langton Matravers and Worth Matravers *Sarum 8* **P** *Bp, D E Scott Esq, and R Swanage and Studland (jt)* **R** R N K WATTON

KINGSTON (St Pancras) see Iford w Kingston and Rodmell *Chich*

KINGSTON (St Winifred) and Ratcliffe-on-Soar *S'well 9*
P *D&C* **P-in-c** S W OSMAN

KINGSTON BAGPUIZE (St John the Baptist) see Fyfield w Tubney and Kingston Bagpuize *Ox*

KINGSTON BUCI (St Julian) *Chich 4* **P** *Lord Egremont*
R D M REEVE

KINGSTON DEVERILL (St Mary) see Cley Hill Warminster *Sarum*

KINGSTON HILL (St Paul) *S'wark 17* **P** *DBP*
V R M de VIAL, **NSM** F M M de QUIDT

KINGSTON LACY (St Stephen) see Sturminster Marshall, Kingston Lacy and Shapwick *Sarum*

KINGSTON LISLE (St John the Baptist) see Ridgeway *Ox*

KINGSTON PARK (not known) *Newc 5* **P** *Bp* **V** R C MILLS

KINGSTON SEYMOUR (All Saints) see Yatton Moor *B & W*

KINGSTON ST MARY (Blessed Virgin Mary) Broomfield and Cheddon Fitzpaine *B & W 18* **P** *D&C Bris and Bp (alt)*
R R J EDWARDS, **NSM** M M T DOBLE

KINGSTON UPON HULL (Ascension) see Derringham Bank *York*

KINGSTON UPON HULL (Most Holy and Undivided Trinity) *York 14* **P** *H Trin Hull & Distr Ch Patr Soc Ltd*
V J O FORRESTER, **C** P J BALL, M E BALL

KINGSTON UPON HULL (St Aidan) Southcoates *York 14*
P *Simeon's Trustees* **V** M A FRYER, **C** L J MCWILLIAMS

KINGSTON UPON HULL (St Alban) *York 14* **P** *Abp*
V E T FORWARD

KINGSTON UPON HULL (St Cuthbert) see Hull St Cuth *York*

KINGSTON UPON HULL (St John the Baptist)
see Newington w Dairycoates *York*

KINGSTON UPON HULL (St Martin) see Hull St Martin w Transfiguration *York*

KINGSTON UPON HULL (St Mary) Sculcoates see Hull St Mary Sculcoates *York*

KINGSTON UPON HULL (St Mary the Virgin) *York 14*
P *Abp* **P-in-c** P A BURKITT

KINGSTON UPON HULL (St Matthew w St Barnabas)
York 14 **P** *V Hull H Trin* **V** J A BAGSHAWE

KINGSTON UPON HULL (St Nicholas) *York 14* **P** *Abp*
V R A SCRIVENER, **NSM** T A COTSON

KINGSTON UPON HULL (St Paul) see Sculcoates St Paul w Ch Ch and St Silas *York*

KINGSTON UPON HULL (St Stephen) see Hull St Steph Sculcoates *York*

KINGSTON UPON HULL (St Thomas) see Derringham Bank *York*

KINGSTON UPON THAMES (All Saints) (St John the Evangelist) *S'wark 17* **P** *K Coll Cam* **V** J BATES,
C E J RICHARDSON, **NSM** S A CRAGG, R P RITCHIE

KINGSTON UPON THAMES (St Luke) *S'wark 17* **P** *Bp*
P-in-c M G HISLOP

KINGSTON VALE (St John the Baptist) *S'wark 17* **P** *Bp*
P-in-c A R BECK

KINGSTONE (St John and All Saints) see Ilminster and Distr *B & W*

KINGSTONE (St John the Baptist) see Uttoxeter Area *Lich*

KINGSTONE (St Michael and All Angels) w Clehonger, Eaton Bishop, Allensmore and Thruxton *Heref 1* **P** *Bp (2 turns), Prime Min (1 turn)* **R** F J BALLINGER

KINGSWEAR (St Thomas of Canterbury) see Brixham w Churston Ferrers and Kingswear *Ex*

KINGSWINFORD (St Mary) *Worc 10* **P** *Patr Bd*
TR J S LUNGLEY, **TV** D J HOSKIN

KINGSWOOD (Church of the Ascension) (Holy Trinity) *Bris 5*
P *Patr Bd* **TR** P G HUZZEY, **TV** A J HEAGERTY,
C R A DRURY, **NSM** T M TAYLOR

KINGSWOOD (St Andrew) *S'wark 27* **P** *Bp and R&S Ch Trust (jt)* **P-in-c** G A BARBER,
NSM A G F BOWYER

KINGSWOOD (St Mary the Virgin) see Charfield and Kingswood *Glouc*

KINGSWOOD, LOWER (Wisdom of God) see Kingswood *S'wark*

KINGTON (St James) see Inkberrow w Cookhill and Kington w Dormston *Worc*

KINGTON (St Mary) w Huntington, Old Radnor, Kinnerton and Titley *Heref 5* **P** *Patr Bd* **R** P TARLING, **C** A F EVANS,
NSM P J BUCKINGHAM

KINGTON, WEST (St Mary the Virgin) see By Brook *Bris*

KINGTON LANGLEY (St Peter) see Draycot *Bris*

KINGTON MAGNA (All Saints) see Gillingham *Sarum*

KINGTON ST MICHAEL (St Michael) *Bris 4* **P** *Patr Bd*
C A D ROBINSON

KINGWESTON (All Saints) see Wheathill Priory Gp of Par *B & W*

KINLET (St John the Baptist) see Cleobury Mortimer w Hopton Wafers etc *Heref*

KINNERLEY (St Mary) w Melverley and Knockin w Maesbrook *Lich 19* **P** *W H C Montgomery Esq, Sir Brooke Boothby Bt, and Viscount Boyne (jt)* **P-in-c** R A L MOWAT,
OLM P L WEST

KINNERSLEY (St James) see Eardisley w Bollingham, Willersley, Brilley etc *Heref*

KINNERTON (St Mary the Virgin) see Kington w Huntington, Old Radnor, Kinnerton etc *Heref*

KINNERTON, HIGHER (All Saints) see Dodleston *Ches*

KINNINVIE (Mission Room) see Barnard Castle w Whorlton *Dur*

KINOULTON (St Luke) see Hickling w Kinoulton and Broughton Sulney *S'well*

KINSBOURNE GREEN (St Mary) see Harpenden St Nic *St Alb*

KINSHAM (All Saints) see Presteigne w Discoed, Kinsham, Lingen and Knill *Heref*

KINSLEY (Resurrection) Wragby *Wakef 11* **P** *Bp and Lord St Oswald (jt)* **V** J HADJIOANNOU, **NSM** S J BAKER

KINSON (St Andrew) (St Philip) *Sarum 7* **P** *Patr Bd*
TR R G SAUNDERS, **TV** M J A HOWARD, **C** J D ANDERSON,
T F GOMM, **NSM** L G NORTON, **OLM** B J KENT

KINTBURY (St Mary the Virgin) w Avington *Ox 14* **P** *DBP (2 turns), Bp (1 turn)* **P-in-c** S A WELCH

KINVER (St Peter) and Enville *Lich 24* **P** *Bp, Mrs A D Williams, and DBP (jt)* **R** D J BLACKBURN,
Hon C M MORRIS, **NSM** E B DAVIES, R A LAWLEY

KINWARTON (St Mary the Virgin) w Great Alne and Haselor *Cov 7* **P** *Bp* **R** S R BURCH

KIPPAX (St Mary the Virgin) w Allerton Bywater *Ripon 8*
P *Bp* **TR** W P B CARLIN, **TV** J SYKES, **C** M C CRABTREE

KIPPINGTON (St Mary) *Roch 9* **P** *DBP* **V** S R JONES

KIRBY, WEST (St Andrew) *Ches 8* **P** *D&C*
P-in-c D M DIXON

KIRBY, WEST (St Bridget) *Ches 8* **P** *D&C* **R** R D CLARKE

KIRBY BEDON (St Andrew) see Rockland St Mary w Hellington, Bramerton etc *Nor*

KIRBY BELLARS (St Peter) see Upper Wreake *Leic*

KIRBY CANE (All Saints) see Gillingham w Geldeston, Stockton, Ellingham etc *Nor*

KIRBY GRINDALYTHE (St Andrew) see Weaverthorpe w Helperthorpe, Luttons Ambo etc *York*

KIRBY KNOWLE (St Wilfrid) *York 19* **P** *Abp*
P-in-c P R A R HOARE, **NSM** E A HOARE
KIRBY-LE-SOKEN (St Michael) w Great Holland *Chelmsf 23*
P *Bp and CPAS (jt)* **R** P L COLEY
KIRBY MISPERTON (St Laurence) w Normanby, Edston and
Salton *York 20* **P** *Lady Clarissa Collin, Abp, and St Jo Coll*
Cam (by turn) **R** *vacant* (01751) 431288
KIRBY MUXLOE (St Bartholomew) *Leic 12* **P** *Bp*
TR G H SUART, **NSM** A M MCCULLOUGH
KIRBY-ON-THE-MOOR (All Saints), Cundall w
Norton-le-Clay and Skelton-cum-Newby *Ripon 3* **P** *Bp,*
Sir Arthur Collins, and R E J Compton Esq (jt)
V J N O HORTON
KIRBY SIGSTON (St Lawrence) *see* Northallerton w Kirby
Sigston *York*
KIRBY UNDERDALE (All Saints) *see* Garrowby Hill *York*
KIRBY WISKE (St John the Baptist) *see* Ainderby Steeple w
Yafforth and Kirby Wiske etc *Ripon*
KIRDFORD (St John the Baptist) *Chich 11* **P** *Lord Egremont*
V S C KERSLEY
KIRK BRAMWITH (St Mary) *see* Fishlake w Sykehouse and
Kirk Bramwith etc *Sheff*
KIRK DEIGHTON (All Saints) *see* Spofforth w Kirk Deighton
Ripon
KIRK ELLA (St Andrew) *York 14* **P** *Patr Bd* **TR** J S JUCKES,
TV A M SAVAGE, **C** P J SOWERBUTTS
KIRK FENTON (St Mary) w Kirkby Wharfe and Ulleskelfe
York 1 **P** *Abp, J Fielden Esq, and T E Fielden Esq (jt)*
V R A CLEGG
KIRK HALLAM (All Saints) *Derby 13* **P** *Bp* **V** *vacant* 0115--
932 2402
KIRK HAMMERTON (St John the Baptist) *see* Lower
Nidderdale *Ripon*
KIRK IRETON (Holy Trinity) *see* Wirksworth *Derby*
KIRK LANGLEY (St Michael) *Derby 11* **P** *G Meynell Esq and*
J M Clark-Maxwell Esq (alt) **NSM** H M MEYNELL
KIRK MAUGHOLD (St Maughold) *see* Maughold *S & M*
KIRK PATRICK (Holy Trinity) *see* Patrick *S & M*
KIRK SANDALL and Edenthorpe (Good Shepherd) *Sheff 8*
P *Ld Chan* **R** J H MARTIN
KIRK SMEATON (St Peter) *see* Went Valley *Wakef*
KIRKANDREWS ON EDEN (St Mary) *see* Barony of Burgh
Carl
KIRKANDREWS ON ESK (St Andrew) *see* Nicholforest and
Kirkandrews on Esk *Carl*
KIRKBAMPTON (St Peter) *see* Barony of Burgh *Carl*
KIRKBRIDE (St Bride) *see* Bowness-on-Solway, Kirkbride and
Newton Arlosh *Carl*
KIRKBRIDE (St Bridget) *S & M 3* **P** *The Crown*
P-in-c J P UPTON-JONES
KIRKBURN (St Mary) *see* Woldsburn *York*
KIRKBURTON (All Hallows) *Wakef 6* **P** *Bp*
V G S HODGSON
KIRKBY (St Andrew) *see* Kelsey Gp *Linc*
KIRKBY (St Chad) (St Mark) (St Martin) (St Andrew) *Liv 7*
P *Patr Bd* **TR** T R STRATFORD, **TV** A J HEBER, M WATERS
KIRKBY, SOUTH (All Saints) *Wakef 11* **P** *Guild of All So*
V T H KAYE
KIRKBY FLEETHAM (St Mary) w Langton on Swale and
Scruton *Ripon 4* **P** *Bp Ripon and D&C York (jt)* **R** *vacant*
(01609) 748245
KIRKBY GREEN (Holy Cross) *see* Digby Gp *Linc*
KIRKBY IN ASHFIELD (St Thomas) *S'well 4* **P** *Bp*
V M EVANS
KIRKBY IN ASHFIELD (St Wilfrid) *S'well 4* **P** *Bp*
R A BUTT
KIRKBY-IN-CLEVELAND (St Augustine) *York 21* **P** *Abp*
V D J BOASE
KIRKBY-IN-MALHAMDALE (St Michael the Archangel) w
Coniston Cold *Bradf 5* **P** *Bp and D&C (jt)*
P-in-c F M I'ANSON
KIRKBY IRELETH (St Cuthbert) *Carl 9* **P** *D&C York*
V G MURFET
KIRKBY KNOWLE (St Wilfrid) *see* Kirby Knowle *York*
KIRKBY LAYTHORPE (St Denys) *Linc 22* **P** *Bp and DBP*
(alt) **R** R J ABRAHAM
KIRKBY LONSDALE (St Mary the Virgin) Team Ministry
Carl 10 **P** *Patr Bd* **TR** W G BETTRIDGE,
TV R J A MITCHELL, **C** S A LUNN, **NSM** P S ATKINSON,
M PILKINGTON
KIRKBY MALHAM (St Michael the Archangel)
see Kirkby-in-Malhamdale w Coniston Cold *Bradf*
KIRKBY MALLORY (All Saints) *see* Newbold de Verdun and
Kirkby Mallory *Leic*
KIRKBY MALZEARD (St Andrew) *see* Fountains Gp *Ripon*
KIRKBY-ON-BAIN (St Mary) *see* Thornton Gp *Linc*

KIRKBY OVERBLOW (All Saints) *see* Lower Wharfedale
Ripon
KIRKBY RAVENSWORTH (St Peter and St Felix) *see* Gilling
and Kirkby Ravensworth *Ripon*
KIRKBY STEPHEN (not known) w Mallerstang and Crosby
Garrett w Soulby *Carl 1* **P** *Bp, Earl of Lonsdale, and Lord*
Hothfield (jt) **R** R P PAUL, **NSM** J WRIGHT
KIRKBY THORE (St Michael) w Temple Sowerby and
Newbiggin *Carl 1* **P** *Lord Hothfield (3 turns), Major and Mrs*
Sawrey-Cookson (1 turn) **P-in-c** P E P NORTON
KIRKBY UNDERWOOD (St Mary and All Saints)
see Ringstone in Aveland Gp *Linc*
KIRKBY WHARFE (St John the Baptist) *see* Kirk Fenton w
Kirkby Wharfe and Ulleskelfe *York*
KIRKBY WOODHOUSE (St John the Evangelist) *S'well 4*
P *Bp* **V** M J MACDONALD
KIRKBYMOORSIDE (All Saints) w Gillamoor, Farndale and
Bransdale *York 17* **P** *Countess Feversham* **V** J D PURDY
KIRKDALE (St Gregory) w Harome, Nunnington and Pockley
York 17 **P** *Abp, Adn Cleveland, and Lady Clarissa Collin*
(2 turns), Ox Univ (1 turn) **V** J M WARDEN
KIRKDALE (St Lawrence) *Liv 3* **P** *CPAS* **P-in-c** M GRIFFIN,
OLM J GARNER
KIRKDALE (St Mary and St Athanasius) *Liv 3* **P** *Simeon's*
Trustees **V** *vacant* 0151-933 6860
KIRKDALE (St Paul) *see* Bootle St Mary w St Paul *Liv*
KIRKHAM (St Michael) *Blackb 10* **P** *Ch Ch Ox*
V J K BROCKBANK
KIRKHAUGH (Holy Paraclete) *see* Alston Moor *Newc*
KIRKHEATON (St Bartholomew) *see* Kirkwhelpington,
Kirkharle, Kirkheaton and Cambo *Newc*
KIRKHEATON (St John the Baptist) *Wakef 1* **P** *Ch Trust*
Fund Trust **R** W L HALLING, **C** K M SINGLETON
KIRKHOLT (St Thomas) *Man 20* **P** *Bp*
P-in-c B A HARRISON
KIRKLAND (Mission Church) *see* Lamplugh w Ennerdale
Carl
KIRKLAND (St Lawrence) *see* Skirwith, Ousby and Melmerby
w Kirkland *Carl*
KIRKLEATHAM (St Cuthbert) (St Hilda) *York 16* **P** *Abp*
V C GREENWELL, **C** L M SHIPP, **NSM** M E GARDNER
KIRKLEVINGTON (St Martin) *York 21* **P** *Abp* **V** *vacant*
(01642) 782439
KIRKLEY (St Peter and St John) *Nor 9* **P** *Bp and DBP (jt)*
R R H WORMALD
KIRKLINGTON (St Michael) w Burneston and Wath and
Pickhill *Ripon 4* **P** *Ch Soc Trust, Mrs M St B Anderson,*
G W Prior-Wandesforde Esq, and DBP (jt) **R** *vacant* (01892)
520660
KIRKLINGTON (St Swithin) w Hockerton *S'well 14* **P** *Bp*
P-in-c E F CULLY
KIRKLINTON (St Cuthbert) *see* Bewcastle, Stapleton and
Kirklinton etc *Carl*
KIRKNEWTON (St Gregory) *see* Glendale Gp *Newc*
KIRKOSWALD (St Oswald), Renwick, Great Salkeld and
Lazonby *Carl 4* **P** *Bp* **R** D M FOWLER
KIRKSTALL (St Stephen) *Ripon 7* **P** *Patrons Leeds St Pet*
V C A JAMES, **NSM** B WOOD
KIRKSTEAD (St Leonard) *see* Woodhall Spa Gp *Linc*
KIRKTHORPE (St Peter) *see* Warmfield *Wakef*
KIRKWHELPINGTON (St Bartholomew) w Kirkharle,
Kirkheaton and Cambo *Newc 11* **P** *Ld Chan (2 turns),*
J P P Anderson Esq (1 turn), and Bp (1 turn)
V R A FERGUSON
KIRMINGTON (St Helen) *see* Brocklesby Park *Linc*
KIRMOND-LE-MIRE (St Martin) *see* Walesby *Linc*
KIRSTEAD (St Margaret) *see* Brooke, Kirstead, Mundham w
Seething and Thwaite *Nor*
KIRTLING (All Saints) *Ely 4* **P** *Mrs D A Bowlby and Countess*
Ellesmere (alt) **V** C A SINDALL, **Hon C** L M BROUGHTON
KIRTLINGTON (St Mary the Virgin) *see* Akeman *Ox*
KIRTON (Holy Trinity) *S'well 3* **P** *SMF* **C** C C LEVY
KIRTON (St Mary and St Martin) w Falkenham *St E 2*
P *Ld Chan* **P-in-c** G L GRANT
KIRTON HOLME (Christ Church) *see* Brothertoft Gp *Linc*
KIRTON IN HOLLAND (St Peter and St Paul) *Linc 21*
P *Mercers' Co* **V** E HORNER
KIRTON IN LINDSEY (St Andrew) w Manton *Linc 6* **P** *Bp*
R S J FOSTER
KISLINGBURY (St Luke) and Harpole *Pet 3* **P** *Bp and*
Sir Stephen Hastings (alt) **R** D G BOND
KITT GREEN (St Francis of Assisi) *see* Pemberton St Fran
Kitt Green *Liv*
KITTISFORD (St Nicholas) *see* Wellington and Distr *B & W*
KLIVE (Blessed Virgin Mary) *see* Quantoxhead *B & W*
KNAITH (St Mary) *see* Lea Gp *Linc*

KNAPHILL (Holy Trinity) w Brookwood *Guildf 12* **P** *CPAS*
V N D GREW, **C** D A MINNS
KNAPTON (St Peter) *see* Trunch *Nor*
KNAPWELL (All Saints) *see* Papworth *Ely*
KNARESBOROUGH (Holy Trinity) (St John the Baptist)
Ripon 1 **P** *Bp and Earl of Harewood (jt)* **TR** A C BETTS,
TV A CALLAN-TRAVIS, **Hon C** D J FORD
KNARESDALE (St Jude) *see* Alston Moor *Newc*
KNEBWORTH (St Martin) (St Mary the Virgin and St Thomas
of Canterbury) *St Alb 23* **P** *Hon D A Fromanteel* **R** *vacant*
(01438) 224102
KNEESALL w Laxton and Wellow *S'well 3* **P** *DBP and Bp (jt)*
V *vacant* (01623) 835820
KNEETON (St Helen) *see* E Bridgford and Kneeton *S'well*
KNIGHTLEY (Christ Church) *see* Adbaston, High Offley,
Knightley, Norbury etc *Lich*
KNIGHTON (St John the Baptist) *see* Clarendon Park St Jo w
Knighton St Mich *Leic*
KNIGHTON (St Mary Magdalene) (St Guthlac) *Leic 2* **P** *Bp*
V C D ALLEN, **C** H E DEARNLEY, J M SHARP,
NSM M R SEDEN, R J BONNEY
KNIGHTON (Village Hall) *see* Mucklestone *Lich*
KNIGHTON, WEST (St Peter) *see* Watercombe *Sarum*
KNIGHTON-ON-TEME (St Michael and All Angels)
see Teme Valley N *Worc*
KNIGHTS AND HOSPITALLERS PARISHES, The
Chelmsf 19 **P** *Hosp of St Jo of Jerusalem, Bp, and Earl of*
Verulam (jt) **V** J E DONALDSON
KNIGHTS ENHAM (St Michael and All Angels) (St Paul's
Church Centre) *Win 3* **P** *Bp* **P-in-c** B L COX, **C** B ROSTILL
KNIGHTSBRIDGE (St Paul) Wilton Place *see* Wilton Place
St Paul *Lon*
KNILL (St Michael and All Angels) *see* Presteigne w Discoed,
Kinsham, Lingen and Knill *Heref*
KNIPTON (All Saints) *see* High Framland Par *Leic*
KNIVETON (St Michael and All Angels) *see* Hulland, Atlow,
Kniveton, Bradley and Hognaston *Derby*
KNOCKHOLT (St Katharine) w Halstead *Roch 9* **P** *D&C*
R M D WOODCOCK
KNOCKIN (St Mary) *see* Kinnerley w Melverley and Knockin
w Maesbrook *Lich*
KNODISHALL (St Lawrence) *see* Aldringham w Thorpe,
Knodishall w Buxlow etc *St E*
KNOOK (St Margaret) *see* Upper Wylye Valley *Sarum*
KNOSSINGTON (St Peter) *see* Whatborough Gp of Par *Leic*
KNOTTING (St Margaret) *see* Sharnbrook and Knotting w
Souldrop *St Alb*
KNOTTINGLEY (St Botolph) and Kellington w Whitley
Wakef 11 **P** *Patr Bd* **TR** C A FLATTERS, **TV** C D WHITE
KNOTTY ASH (St John) *Liv 2* **P** *R W Derby*
V J G M ROOKE
KNOWBURY (St Paul) w Clee Hill *Heref 12* **P** *Bp* **V** *vacant*
KNOWBURY (St Peter's Mission Room) Clee Hill *see* Wigmore
Abbey *Heref*
KNOWL HILL (St Peter) *see* Wargrave w Knowl Hill *Ox*
KNOWLE (Holy Nativity) *Bris 1* **P** *Bp* **V** J M BROWN,
C W P G HAZLEWOOD, **NSM** J F HOUSE
KNOWLE (Mission Room) *see* Coreley and Doddington *Heref*
KNOWLE (St Barnabas) *Bris 1* **P** *Bp* **V** A G PALMER
KNOWLE (St Boniface) *see* Crediton, Shobrooke and Sandford
etc *Ex*
KNOWLE (St John) *see* E Budleigh w Bicton and Otterton *Ex*
KNOWLE (St John the Baptist) (St Lawrence and St Anne)
Birm 11 **P** *Bp* **V** M J PARKER, **C** E W RUSSELL, J R LEACH,
S L TILLETT
KNOWLE (St Martin) *Bris 1* **P** *Bp* **V** R WARD
KNOWLE, WEST (Holy Cross) *see* Inns Court H Cross *Bris*
KNOWSLEY (St Mary) *Liv 2* **P** *Earl of Derby* **V** C DOWDLE,
NSM S C LEDBETTER
KNOWSTONE (St Peter) *see* Bishopsnympton, Rose Ash,
Mariansleigh etc *Ex*
KNOYLE, EAST (St Mary the Virgin), Semley and Sedgehill
Sarum 11 **P** *Bp and Ch Ch Ox* **P-in-c** P J RIDLEY
KNOYLE, WEST (St Mary the Virgin) *see* Mere w W Knoyle
and Maiden Bradley *Sarum*
KNUTSFORD (St Cross) Cross Town *Ches 12* **P** *Mrs J Singer*
V A T M TOLLEFSEN
KNUTSFORD (St John the Baptist) and Toft *Ches 12* **P** *Bp*
(3 turns), Mrs L M Anderson (1 turn) **V** N T ATKINSON,
C R MACKAY
KNUTTON (St Mary) *Lich 9* **P** *Sir Beville Stanier Bt and*
T H G Howard-Sneyd Esq (alt) **V** P G HOUGH,
NSM K R STABLES
KNUZDEN (St Oswald) *Blackb 2* **P** *Bp* **V** M A MORRIS
KNYPERSLEY (St John the Evangelist) *Lich 8* **P** *CPAS*
V J A DAWSWELL

KYME, NORTH (St Luke) *see* Kirkby Laythorpe *Linc*
KYME, SOUTH (St Mary and All Saints) *as above Linc*
KYNNERSLEY (St Chad) *see* Edgmond w Kynnersley and
Preston Wealdmoors *Lich*
KYRE WYARD (St Mary) *see* Teme Valley S *Worc*
LACEBY (St Margaret) and Ravendale Group, The *Linc 10*
P *D Parkinson Settled Estates, Ridley Hall Cam, and Earl of*
Yarborough (jt), Bp, and Ld Chan (by turn) **R** *vacant* (01472)
870884
LACEY GREEN (Church Hall) *see* Wilmslow *Ches*
LACEY GREEN (St John the Evangelist) *see* Risborough *Ox*
LACH DENNIS (All Saints) *see* Lostock Gralam *Ches*
LACHE (St Mark) cum Saltney *Ches 2* **P** *Bp* **V** T G N GREEN,
C R E IVESON, S F WALKER
LACKFORD (St Lawrence) *see* Lark Valley *St E*
LACOCK (St Cyriac) *see* Gtr Corsham and Lacock *Bris*
LADBROKE (All Saints) *see* Harbury and Ladbroke *Cov*
LADBROKE GROVE (St Michael and All Angels) *see* Notting
Hill St Mich and Ch Ch *Lon*
LADDINGFORD (St Mary) *see* Yalding w Collier Street *Roch*
LADOCK (St Ladoca) *see* Probus, Ladock and Grampound w
Creed and St Erme *Truro*
LADY BAY (All Hallows) *S'well 9* **P** *Bp* **V** R W BRECKLES
LADYBARN (St Chad) *Man 8* **P** *Bp* **R** D K PRYCE
LADYBROOK (St Mary the Virgin) *S'well 2* **P** *Bp*
P-in-c R C THOMPSON, **NSM** P N WOOD
LADYWOOD (St John the Evangelist) (St Peter) *Birm 2*
P *Trustees* **V** R J TETLOW, **C** J M MASON
LAFFORD, SOUTH *Linc 22* **P** *G Heathcote Esq, Bp,*
J Wilson Esq, D&C, DBP, N Playne Esq, Sir Bruno Welby Bt,
and Lady Willoughby de Eresby (by turn) **C** C P ROBERTSON
LAINDON (St Martin of Tours) *see* Basildon St Martin
Chelmsf
LAINDON (St Nicholas) w Dunton *Chelmsf 6* **P** *Bp*
R N C PAUL
LAIRA (St Augustine) *see* Plymouth Em, St Paul Efford and
St Aug *Ex*
LAIRA (St Mary the Virgin) *see* Plymouth St Simon and St
Mary *Ex*
LAISTERDYKE (St Mary) *Bradf 3* **P** *Simeon's Trustees*
V P DEO
LAITHKIRK (not known) *see* Romaldkirk w Laithkirk *Ripon*
LAKE (Good Shepherd) *Portsm 7* **P** *Bp* **V** R M SMITH,
NSM B M DOWNER
LAKENHAM (St Alban) *see* Nor Lakenham St Alb and St
Mark *Nor*
LAKENHAM (St John the Baptist and All Saints) *see* Nor
Lakenham St Jo and All SS and Tuckswood *Nor*
LAKENHAM (St Mark) *see* Nor Lakenham St Alb and St
Mark *Nor*
LAKENHEATH (St Mary) *St E 11* **P** *D&C Ely*
P-in-c R N LEACH, **OLM** A S I BUTTREY
LALEHAM (All Saints) *Lon 13* **P** *Earl of Lucan*
V P R BROWN
LAMARSH (Holy Innocents) *see* N Hinckford *Chelmsf*
LAMBERHURST (St Mary) and Matfield *Roch 8* **P** *D&C and*
V Brenchley (jt) **V** D M BOURNE
LAMBETH (St Andrew) *see* Waterloo St Jo w St Andr *S'wark*
LAMBETH (St John the Evangelist) *as above S'wark*
LAMBETH, NORTH (St Anselm) (St Mary's Mission)
(St Peter) *S'wark 13* **P** *The Crown (1 turn), Patr Bd (2 turns)*
TR A R AAGAARD, **TV** W ROEST, **NSM** M A K HILBORN
LAMBETH, SOUTH (St Anne and All Saints) *S'wark 13*
P *Abp and Bp* **V** A B NEWBY
LAMBETH, SOUTH (St Stephen) *S'wark 13* **P** *CPAS*
V W A WILSON
LAMBLEY (Holy Trinity) *S'well 10* **P** *Revd W J Gull*
P-in-c K A PAYNE
LAMBLEY (St Mary and St Patrick) *see* Alston Moor *Newc*
LAMBOURN (St Michael and All Angels) *Ox 14* **P** *Bp*
V W J STEWART
LAMBOURNE (St Mary and All Saints) w Abridge and
Stapleford Abbotts *Chelmsf 25* **P** *CCC Cam and*
Ld Chan (alt) **P-in-c** R J HOARE
LAMBROOK, EAST (St James) *see* Kingsbury Episcopi w
E Lambrook, Hambridge etc *B & W*
LAMERTON (St Peter) *see* Milton Abbot, Dunterton,
Lamerton etc *Ex*
LAMESLEY (St Andrew) *see* Harlow Green and Lamesley *Dur*
LAMMAS (St Andrew) *see* Buxton w Oxnead, Lammas and
Brampton *Nor*
LAMORBEY (Holy Redeemer) *Roch 17* **P** *Bp* **V** N I KERR
LAMORBEY (Holy Trinity) *Roch 17* **P** *Mrs H K L Whittow*
V *vacant* (020) 8300 8231
LAMORRAN (Holy Trinity) and Merther *Truro 6* **P** *Viscount*
Falmouth **R** *vacant* (01872) 52431

LAMP *Ox 27* **P** *CPAS* **P-in-c** I J PUSEY,
OLM H J LOWNDES
LAMPLUGH (St Michael) w Ennerdale *Carl 5* **P** *Trustees*
R J P SIMPSON
LAMPORT (All Saints) *see* Maidwell w Draughton, Lamport w
Faxton *Pet*
LAMYATT (St Mary and St John) *see* Bruton and Distr *B & W*
LANCASTER (Christ Church) (Christ Church Worship Centre)
Blackb 11 **P** *V Lanc and Trustees (alt)* **V** P S G HUDD,
C A PARKINSON, **NSM** B K HARDING
LANCASTER (St Chad) *see* Skerton St Chad *Blackb*
LANCASTER (St Luke) *see* Skerton St Luke *Blackb*
LANCASTER (St Mary) w St John and St Anne *Blackb 11*
P *Trustees* **V** P B CAVANAGH, **C** F E GREEN,
K D THOMASSON, S MCMAHON
LANCASTER (St Paul) *see* Scotforth *Blackb*
LANCASTER (St Thomas) *Blackb 11* **P** *CPAS*
V P G GUINNESS, **C** G A CROWTHER, D A PEATMAN
LANCHESTER (All Saints) *Dur 4* **P** *Ld Chan*
V P WATERHOUSE
LANCING (St James the Less) w Coombes *Chich 5* **P** *Bp Lon*
R R G RUSSELL, **C** C M D LINDLAR
LANCING (St Michael and All Angels) *Chich 5* **P** *Bp*
V B G CARTER
LANDBEACH (All Saints) *Ely 5* **P** *CCC Cam* **R** N I MOIR
LANDCROSS (Holy Trinity) *see* Bideford, Northam, Westward
Ho!, Appledore etc *Ex*
LANDEWEDNACK (St Wynwallow) *see* St Ruan w St Grade
and Landewednack *Truro*
LANDFORD (St Andrew) *see* Bramshaw and Landford w
Plaitford *Sarum*
LANDKEY (St Paul) *see* Swimbridge w W Buckland and
Landkey *Ex*
LANDRAKE (St Michael) w St Erney and Botus Fleming
Truro 11 **P** *Bp and MMCET (jt)* **V** M GRIFFITHS,
OLM P C WILLIAMS
LANDSCOVE (St Matthew) *see* Broadhempston, Woodland,
Staverton etc *Ex*
LANDULPH (St Leonard and St Dilpe) *see* St Dominic,
Landulph and St Mellion w Pillaton *Truro*
LANDYWOOD (St Andrew) *see* St Gt Wyrley *Lich*
LANE END (Holy Trinity) w Cadmore End *Ox 29* **P** *Bp*
V R H JENNINGS
LANEAST (St Sidwell and St Gulvat) *see* Altarnon w Bolventor,
Laneast and St Clether *Truro*
LANEHAM (St Peter) *see* Rampton w Laneham, Treswell,
Cottam and Stokeham *S'well*
LANERCOST (St Mary Magdalene), Walton, Gilsland and
Nether Denton *Carl 2* **P** *Bp, Adn, and the Hon*
P C W Howard (jt) **R** C J MORRIS, **NSM** M JENKINSON
LANESIDE (St Peter) *Blackb 1* **P** *V Haslingden St Jas*
V S C BROWN
LANGAR (St Andrew) *see* Cropwell Bishop w Colston Bassett,
Granby etc *S'well*
LANGCLIFFE (St John the Evangelist) w Stainforth and
Horton-in-Ribblesdale *Bradf 5* **P** *Bp, Adn Craven,*
W R G Bell Esq, N Caton Esq, and Churchwardens of
Horton-in-Ribblesdale (jt) **V** R G WOOD
LANGDALE (Holy Trinity) (Mission Chapel) *Carl 11*
P *R Grasmere* **P-in-c** W R F COKE, **NSM** A J FOLKS
LANGDALE END (St Peter) *see* Brompton by Sawdon w
Hutton Buscel, Snainton etc *York*
LANGDON, EAST (St Augustine) *see* St Margarets-at-Cliffe w
Westcliffe etc *Cant*
LANGDON, WEST (St Mary the Virgin) *as above Cant*
LANGDON HILLS (St Mary and All Saints) *Chelmsf 6*
P *D&C St Paul's* **R** C E HOPKINSON, **C** M A SHAW
LANGFORD (Blessed Virgin Mary) *see* Burrington and
Churchill *B & W*
LANGFORD (St Andrew) *see* Henlow and Langford *St Alb*
LANGFORD (St Bartholomew) *see* Coddington and
Winthorpe and Langford w Holme *S'well*
LANGFORD (St Giles) *see* Heybridge w Langford *Chelmsf*
LANGFORD (St Matthew) *see* Shill Valley and Broadshire *Ox*
LANGFORD, LITTLE (St Nicholas of Mira) *see* Wylye and
Till Valley *Sarum*
LANGFORD BUDVILLE (St Peter) *see* Wellington and Distr
B & W
LANGHAM (not known) *see* Gillingham *Sarum*
LANGHAM (St Mary the Virgin) *see* Badwell and Walsham
St E
LANGHAM (St Mary the Virgin) w Boxted *Chelmsf 17* **P** *Bp*
and Duchy of Lanc (alt) **P-in-c** T M BULL
LANGHAM (St Peter and St Paul) *Pet 14* **P** *Bp*
P-in-c M W R COVINGTON
LANGHAM EPISCOPI (St Andrew and St Mary) *see* Stiffkey
and Cockthorpe w Morston, Langham etc *Nor*

LANGHAM PLACE (All Souls) *Lon 4* **P** *The Crown*
R R T BEWES, **C** P A WILLIAMS, R A HIGGINS, A RIDER,
P BLACKHAM, R I TICE, **Hon C** J R W STOTT,
NSM M R E REEVES
LANGHO BILLINGTON (St Leonard) *Blackb 7* **P** *V Blackb*
P-in-c D NOBLET
LANGLEY (All Saints and Martyrs) and Parkfield *Man 18*
P *Patr Bd* **TR** P H MILLER, **TV** A I GALLAGHER,
C J BEBBINGTON
LANGLEY (St Francis) *see* Fawley *Win*
LANGLEY (St John) *Birm 7* **P** *Bp* **P-in-c** J R BARNETT
LANGLEY (St John the Evangelist) *see* Clavering w Langley
and Arkesden *Chelmsf*
LANGLEY (St Mary) *see* Otham w Langley *Cant*
LANGLEY (St Mary the Virgin) *see* Wolverton w Norton
Lindsey and Langley *Cov*
LANGLEY (St Michael) *see* Loddon, Sisland, Chedgrave,
Hardley and Langley *Nor*
LANGLEY (St Michael and All Angels) *Birm 7* **P** *The Crown*
P-in-c J R BARNETT
LANGLEY BURRELL (St Peter) *see* Chippenham St Paul w
Hardenhuish etc *Bris*
LANGLEY GREEN (St Leonard) *see* Ifield *Chich*
LANGLEY MARISH (St Mary the Virgin) *Ox 23* **P** *Patr Bd*
TR J R HURST, **TV** B H RUSSELL, C HANSON,
OLM R HOWELL
LANGLEY MARSH (St Luke Mission Church)
see Wiveliscombe w Chipstable, Huish Champflower etc *B & W*
LANGLEY MILL (St Andrew) *Derby 12* **P** *V Heanor*
P-in-c C L HUGHES
LANGLEY PARK (All Saints) *Dur 1* **P** *Prime Min*
V M J PEERS, **C** T E HUBBLE
LANGLEY PARK (St Peter's Church Hall) *see* Beckenham
St Barn *Roch*
LANGLEY STREET (Mission Room) *see* Derby St Barn
Derby
LANGLEYBURY (St Paul) *St Alb 7* **P** *D W A Loyd Esq*
V *vacant* (01923) 270634
LANGNEY (St Richard of Chichester) *Chich 16* **P** *Bp*
V D ASHTON, **NSM** I R BENGE
LANGOLD (St Luke) *see* Carlton-in-Lindrick and Langold w
Oldcotes *S'well*
LANGPORT Area Churches, The *B & W 6* **P** *Patr Bd*
TV R F TOOGOOD, **C** C C BARNES
LANGRICK (St Margaret of Scotland) *see* Brothertoft Gp *Linc*
LANGRIDGE (St Mary Magdalene) *see* Bath Weston All SS w
N Stoke and Langridge *B & W*
LANGRISH (St John the Evangelist) *Portsm 4* **P** *Bp*
V T E LOUDEN, **NSM** A M GOTHARD
LANGSTONE (St Nicholas) *see* Havant *Portsm*
LANGTOFT (St Michael) *see* Ness Gp *Linc*
LANGTOFT (St Peter) w Foxholes, Butterwick, Cottam and
Thwing *York 12* **P** *Abp and Keble Coll Ox (2 turns), Ld Chan*
(1 turn) **P-in-c** R SELWOOD, **NSM** C A ACONLEY
LANGTON (St Andrew) *see* W Buckrose *York*
LANGTON (St Margaret) *see* Woodhall Spa Gp *Linc*
LANGTON (St Peter) *as above Linc*
LANGTON, GREAT (St Wilfrid) *see* Kirkby Fleetham w
Langton on Swale and Scruton *Ripon*
LANGTON, GREAT (The Good Shepherd) *as above Ripon*
LANGTON BY PARTNEY (St Peter and St Paul) *see* Partney
Gp *Linc*
LANGTON-BY-WRAGBY (St Giles) *see* Wragby Gp *Linc*
LANGTON GREEN (All Saints) *Roch 12* **P** *R Speldhurst*
V M J GENTRY
LANGTON HERRING (St Peter) *see* Abbotsbury, Portesham
and Langton Herring *Sarum*
LANGTON LONG (All Saints) *see* Blandford Forum and
Langton Long *Sarum*
LANGTON MATRAVERS (St George) *see* Kingston, Langton
Matravers and Worth Matravers *Sarum*
LANGTON ON SWALE (St Wilfrid) *see* Kirkby Fleetham w
Langton on Swale and Scruton *Ripon*
LANGTREE *Ox 6* **P** *Patr Bd* **TR** K G DAVIES,
TV N E MOSS, **Hon C** J L EVANS, **NSM** A M LINTON,
P J R STEDDON
LANGTREE (not known) *see* Shebbear, Buckland Filleigh,
Sheepwash etc *Ex*
LANGWATHBY (St Peter) *see* Addingham, Edenhall,
Langwathby and Culgaith *Carl*
LANGWITH, UPPER (Holy Cross) *see* E Scarsdale *Derby*
LANGWORTH (St Hugh) *see* Barlings *Linc*
LANHYDROCK (St Hydrock) *see* Bodmin w Lanhydrock and
Lanivet *Truro*
LANIVET (St Ia) *as above Truro*
LANLIVERY (St Brevita) w Luxulyan *Truro 10* **P** *Bp (1 turn),*
Adn Bodmin (1 turn), and DBP (2 turns) **P-in-c** F M BOWERS

LANNER (Christ Church)   *see* Redruth w Lanner and Treleigh *Truro*
LANREATH (St Marnarck), Pelynt and Bradoc *Truro 12*
  P *A D G Fortescue Esq, J B Kitson Esq, and*
  H M Parker Esq (jt)   **R** D J A POLLARD
LANSALLOS (St Ildierna) *Truro 12*   **P** *DBP and*
  W Gundry-Mills Esq (alt)   **P-in-c** C D NEWELL,
  NSM G LONSDALE
LANSDOWN (St Stephen)   *see* Charlcombe w Bath St Steph *B & W*
LANTEGLOS BY CAMELFORD (St Julitta) w Advent
  Truro 10   **P** *Duchy of Cornwall*   **P-in-c** B J BERRIMAN,
  OLM R J STRATFIELD
LANTEGLOS BY FOWEY (St Wyllow) *Truro 12*   **P** *D&C*
  P-in-c J S HALKES
LAPAL (St Peter)   *see* Halas *Worc*
LAPFORD (St Thomas of Canterbury)   *see* N Creedy *Ex*
LAPLEY (All Saints) w Wheaton Aston *Lich 2*   **P** *Keble Coll Ox*
  V G J THOMPSON,   **OLM** G P ELLIS
LAPWORTH (St Mary the Virgin) *Birm 6*   **P** *Mert Coll Ox*
  R M J MORGAN
LARCHFIELD (St George)   *see* Boyne Hill *Ox*
LARK VALLEY Benefice, The *St E 13*   **P** *R W Gough Esq*
  (1 turn), Bp (2 turns)   **R** D P BURRELL,   **NSM** E M ELLIOTT
LARKFIELD (Holy Trinity) *Roch 7*   **P** *DBP*   **V** D J WALKER
LARLING (St Ethelbert)   *see* E w W Harling, Bridgham w
  Roudham, Larling etc *Nor*
LASBOROUGH (St Mary)   *see* Westonbirt and Lasborough *Glouc*
LASHAM (St Mary)   *see* Bentworth and Shalden and Lasham *Win*
LASHBROOK (Mission Room)   *see* Shiplake w Dunsden and
  Harpsden *Ox*
LASTINGHAM (St Mary) w Appleton-le-Moors, Rosedale and
  Cropton *York 17*   **P** *Abp (2 turns), Ld Chan (1 turn)*
  V A S FERGUSON
LATCHFORD (Christ Church) *Ches 4*   **P** *R Grappenhall*
  V J L GOODE
LATCHFORD (St James) (St Hilda) *Ches 4*   **P** *R Grappenhall*
  V J T OWEN,   **C** J E HARRIES
LATCHINGDON (Christ Church)   *see* Creeksea w Althorne,
  Latchingdon and N Fambridge *Chelmsf*
LATHBURY (All Saints)   *see* Newport Pagnell w Lathbury and
  Moulsoe *Ox*
LATHOM PARK (St John)   *see* Ormskirk *Liv*
LATIMER (St Mary Magdalene)   *see* Chenies and Lt Chalfont,
  Latimer and Flaunden *Ox*
LATTON (St John the Baptist)   *see* Cricklade w Latton *Bris*
LAUGHTON (All Saints)   *see* Corringham and Blyton Gp *Linc*
LAUGHTON (All Saints) w Ripe and Chalvington *Chich 18*
  P *Bp (2 turns), Hertf Coll Ox (1 turn)*   **R** D M FAREY
LAUGHTON (St Luke)   *see* Foxton w Gumley and Laughton *Leic*
LAUGHTON-EN-LE-MORTHEN (All Saints) w Throapham
  Sheff 5   **P** *Bp*   **P-in-c** J E BOLTON
LAUNCELLS (St Andrew and St Swithin)   *see* Stratton and
  Launcells *Truro*
LAUNCESTON (St Mary Magdalene) (St Thomas the Apostle)
  (St Stephen) *Truro 9*   **P** *Patr Bd*   **TR** T J G NEWCOMBE,
  C C R CARLYON
LAUNTON (Assumption of the Blessed Virgin Mary)
  see Bicester w Bucknell, Caversfield and Launton *Ox*
LAVANT (St Mary) (St Nicholas) *Chich 3*   **P** *Earl of March and*
  Kinrara   **R** D L PARKER
LAVENDER HILL (The Ascension) and Battersea St Philip w
  St Bartholomew *S'wark 16*   **P** *Bp and Keble Coll Ox (jt)*
  V P C B ALLEN,   **Hon C** A C SALMON
LAVENDON (St Michael) w Cold Brayfield, Clifton Reynes and
  Newton Blossomville *Ox 27*   **P** *T V Sutthery Esq, The Revd*
  S F Hamill-Stewart, Exors M E Farrer Esq, and Bp (jt)
  P-in-c C E CERRATTI
LAVENHAM (St Peter and St Paul) w Preston *St E 10*
  P *G&C Coll Cam, and Em Coll Cam (by turn)*   **R** *vacant*
  (01787) 247244
LAVENHAM (St Peter and St Paul)   *see* Lavenham w Preston *St E*
LAVER, HIGH (All Saints) w Magdalen Laver and Little Laver
  and Matching *Chelmsf 27*   **P** *Bp*   **R** P T C MASHEDER
LAVER, LITTLE (St Mary the Virgin)   *see* High Laver w
  Magdalen Laver and Lt Laver etc *Chelmsf*
LAVERSTOCK (St Andrew)   *see* Salisbury St Martin and
  Laverstock *Sarum*
LAVERSTOKE (St Mary)   *see* Overton w Laverstoke and
  Freefolk *Win*
LAVERTON (The Blessed Virgin Mary)   *see* Hardington Vale *B & W*

LAVINGTON, WEST (St Mary Magdalene)   *see* Cocking,
  Bepton and W Lavington *Chich*
LAVINGTONS, Cheverells, and Easterton, The *Sarum 16*
  P *Bp and Ch Ch Ox (jt)*   **R** H W B STEPHENS,
  Hon C P F SMITH
LAWFORD (St Mary) *Chelmsf 20*   **P** *St Jo Coll Cam*
  R P C M PRESTNEY
LAWHITTON (St Michael)   *see* Lezant w Lawhitton and S
  Petherwin w Trewen *Truro*
LAWLEY (St John the Evangelist)   *see* Cen Telford *Lich*
LAWRENCE WESTON (St Peter) and Avonmouth *Bris 2*
  P *Bp*   **V** H W WARDALE
LAWRES Group, The SOUTH *Linc 3*   **P** *D&C Linc, D&C Pet,*
  and Mercers' Co (jt)   **R** K N JAMES,   **C** M MCBRIDE
LAWSHALL (All Saints) *St E 12*   **P** *Lord de Saumarez*
  P-in-c M C THROWER
LAWTON (All Saints)   *see* Church Lawton *Ches*
LAWTON MOOR (St Michael and All Angels) *Man 8*   **P** *Bp*
  V P D ROLFE,   **OLM** I V SMITH
LAXEY (Christ Church) *S & M 2*   **P** *Bp*   **V** W H MARTIN,
  OLM J E GUILFORD
LAXFIELD (All Saints) *St E 17*   **P** *Simeon's Trustees*
  P-in-c F O NEWTON
LAXTON (All Saints)   *see* Bulwick, Blatherwycke w
  Harringworth and Laxton *Pet*
LAXTON (St Michael)   *see* Kneesall w Laxton and Wellow *S'well*
LAXTON (St Peter)   *see* Howden *York*
LAYER BRETON (St Mary the Virgin)   *see* Layer de la Haye
  and Layer Breton w Birch etc *Chelmsf*
LAYER DE LA HAYE (St John the Baptist) and Layer Breton w
  Birch and Layer Marney *Chelmsf 24*   **P** *Bp, Col J G Round,*
  and N S Charrington Esq (by turn)   **R** M H CLARKE
LAYER MARNEY (St Mary the Virgin)   *see* Layer de la Haye
  and Layer Breton w Birch etc *Chelmsf*
LAYHAM (St Andrew)   *see* Hadleigh, Layham and Shelley *St E*
LAYSTON W BUNTINGFORD (St Peter)   *see* Aspenden,
  Buntingford and Westmill *St Alb*
LAYTON, EAST (Christ Church)   *see* Forcett and Aldbrough
  and Melsonby *Ripon*
LAZONBY (St Nicholas)   *see* Kirkoswald, Renwick, Gt Salkeld
  and Lazonby *Carl*
LEA Group, The (St Helen) *Linc 2*   **P** *Bp, DBP, and Exors Lt Col*
  J E W G Sandars (jt)   **R** P WAIN
LEA (St Christopher) (St Barnabas) *Blackb 13*   **P** *Bp*
  V D J THOMPSON
LEA (St Giles)   *see* Garsdon, Lea and Cleverton and Charlton *Bris*
LEA, THE (St John the Baptist)   *see* Ross *Heref*
LEA AND HOLLOWAY (Christ Church)   *see* Tansley, Dethick,
  Lea and Holloway *Derby*
LEA CROSS (St Anne)   *see* Pontesbury I and II *Heref*
LEA HALL (St Richard) *Birm 9*   **P** *Bp*   **V** P M BRACHER
LEA MARSTON (St John the Baptist)   *see* The Whitacres and
  Shustoke *Birm*
LEADEN RODING (St Michael) and Abbess Roding and
  Beauchamp Roding w White Roding *Chelmsf 18*   **P** *Ld Chan,*
  Bp, and Viscount Gough (by turn)   **R** T J PIGREM
LEADENHAM (St Swithin) *Linc 23*   **P** *P R Reeve Esq*
  R A J MEGAHEY
LEADGATE (St Ives)   *see* Dipton and Leadgate *Dur*
LEAFIELD (St Michael and All Angels)   *see* Ramsden,
  Finstock and Fawler, Leafield etc *Ox*
LEAGRAVE (St Luke) *St Alb 14*   **P** *Bp*   **V** S PURVIS,
  C S TETZLAFF
LEAHOLM (St James's Chapel)   *see* Middle Esk Moor *York*
LEAKE (St Mary) w Over and Nether Silton and Kepwick
  York 19   **P** *Abp*   **P-in-c** P R A R HOARE,   **NSM** E A HOARE
LEAKE, EAST (St Mary), WEST (St Helena),
  Stanford-on-Soar, Rempstone and Costock *S'well 9*   **P** *Bp,*
  DBP, Lord Belper, and SS Coll Cam (jt)
  R G C HETHERINGTON,   **NSM** M R ESSEX
LEAKE, NEW (St Jude)   *see* Stickney Gp *Linc*
LEAKE, OLD (St Mary) w Wrangle *Linc 20*   **P** *Bp and DBP*
  (alt)   **Hon C** J F GLEADALL
LEAM LANE (St Andrew) *Dur 12*   **P** *Bp*   **V** P J A KENNEDY
LEAM VALLEY *Cov 6*   **P** *Bp (2 turns), Mrs H M O Lodder*
  (1 turn)   **V** E A SMITH,   **NSM** W T G GRIFFITHS
LEAMINGTON, SOUTH (St John the Baptist) *Cov 11*   **P** *Bp*
  V D W LAWSON
LEAMINGTON HASTINGS (All Saints)   *see* Leam Valley *Cov*
LEAMINGTON PRIORS (All Saints) *Cov 11*   **P** *Bp*
  P-in-c C H WILSON
LEAMINGTON PRIORS (St Mary) *Cov 11*   **P** *Ch Patr Trust*
  V M RODHAM,   **C** A M ATTWOOD
LEAMINGTON PRIORS (St Paul) *Cov 11*   **P** *Ch Patr Trust*
  V J N JEE,   **C** S F BETTERIDGE,   **Hon C** J S TILLEY

LEAMINGTON SPA (Holy Trinity) and Old Milverton *Cov 11*
  P *Bp and M Heber-Percy Esq (jt)*   **C** K LINDOP, C H WILSON,
  NSM F A SMITH
LEAMINGTON SPA (St Mark New Milverton) *see* New
  Milverton *Cov*
LEAMORE (St Aidan) *see* Blakenall Heath *Lich*
LEASINGHAM (St Andrew) *Linc 22*   **P** *DBP*
  P-in-c A J LITTLEWOOD
LEASOWE (St Chad) *Ches 7*   **P** *Bp*   **P-in-c** M F TURNBULL
LEATHERHEAD (All Saints) (St Mary and St Nicholas) and
  Mickleham *Guildf 10*   **P** *Bp Guildf and D&C Roch (jt)*
  R D J EATON,   **C** B STEADMAN-ALLEN, B J MARTIN,
  NSM D A IRELAND
LEATHLEY (St Oswald) w Farnley, Fewston and Blubberhouses
  Bradf 4   **P** *Bp and G N le G Horton-Fawkes Esq*
  NSM M F CLEVERLEY
LEATON (Holy Trinity) and Albrighton w Battlefield *Lich 20*
  P *Mrs J M Jagger*   **P-in-c** N C M SALTER
LEAVELAND (St Laurence) *see* Selling w Throwley, Sheldwich
  w Badlesmere etc *Cant*
LEAVENHEATH (St Matthew) *see* Stoke by Nayland w
  Leavenheath and Polstead *St E*
LEAVENING (not known) *see* W Buckrose *York*
LEAVESDEN (All Saints) *St Alb 7*   **P** *Bp*   **V** P R S BOLTON,
  C J M M SPREADBURY,   **NSM** A R ROSS, C DRURY
LECHLADE (St Lawrence) *Glouc 12*   **P** *Em Coll Cam*
  V *vacant* (01367) 252262
LECK (St Peter) *see* E Lonsdale *Blackb*
LECKFORD (St Nicholas) *see* Stockbridge and Longstock and
  Leckford *Win*
LECKHAMPSTEAD (Assumption of the Blessed Virgin Mary)
  see N Buckingham *Ox*
LECKHAMPSTEAD (St James) *see* Brightwalton w Catmore,
  Leckhampstead etc *Ox*
LECKHAMPTON (St Christopher) *see* Leckhampton SS Phil
  and Jas w Cheltenham St Jas *Glouc*
LECKHAMPTON (St Peter) *Glouc 10*   **P** *Bp*
  NSM F M BAYNE
LECKHAMPTON (St Philip and St James) w Cheltenham
  (St James) *Glouc 9*   **P** *Bp*   **V** P L CHICKEN,   **C** M J INGHAM,
  M G ROWLEY-BROOKE
LECONFIELD (St Catherine) *see* Lockington and Lund and
  Scorborough w Leconfield *York*
LEDBURY Team Ministry, The (St Michael and All Angels)
  (St Katherine's Chapel *Heref 6*   **P** *Patr Bd*   **TR** C L BEEVERS,
  TV H J MAYELL, S STRUTT,   **C** P A R HAMMERSLEY,
  NSM E C REED, H K NICHOLS, E M NICHOLS
LEDGEMOOR (Mission Room) *see* Canon Pyon w Kings
  Pyon and Birley *Heref*
LEDSHAM (All Saints) w Fairburn *York 4*
  P *G H H Wheler Esq*   **V** W F R BATSON
LEDSTON LUCK (Mission Church) *see* Ledsham w Fairburn
  York
LEE (Good Shepherd) (St Peter) *S'wark 4*   **P** *R Lee St Marg*
  V R D BAINBRIDGE,   **Hon C** A E HOAD
LEE (St Augustine) Grove Park *S'wark 4*   **P** *Bp*
  V G A BERRIMAN,   **C** I M WELCH
LEE (St Margaret) *S'wark 4*   **P** *Ld Chan*   **R** D S GATLIFFE,
  C J MIDDLEMISS,   **Hon C** E E W MARTIN
LEE (St Matthew) *see* Ilfracombe, Lee, Woolacombe, Bittadon
  etc *Ex*
LEE (St Mildred) Burnt Ash Hill *S'wark 4*   **P** *Bp*   **V** M C HILL,
  Hon C A D HILL
LEE (St Oswald) *see* St Oswald in Lee w Bingfield *Newc*
LEE, THE (St John the Baptist) *Ox 28*   **P** *Bp*
  P-in-c D J BURGESS,   **NSM** I CORNISH, G M ROWELL
LEE BROCKHURST (St Peter) *Lich 22*   **P** *Lord Barnard*
  P-in-c C S COOKE
LEE MOOR (Mission Church) *see* Bickleigh and Shaugh Prior
  Ex
LEE-ON-THE-SOLENT (St Faith) *Portsm 3*   **P** *Bp*
  V P A SUTTON,   **C** E M WOODGATE,   **NSM** K R SCHMIDT
LEEBOTWOOD (St Mary) *see* Dorrington w Leebotwood,
  Longnor, Stapleton etc *Heref*
LEEDS (All Hallows) *Ripon 7*   **P** *Bp and DBP (jt)*
  V R G GASTON
LEEDS (All Souls) *Ripon 7*   **P** *V Leeds St Pet, Simeon's*
  Trustees, and DBP (jt)   **V** D B EMMOTT
LEEDS Belle Isle (St John and St Barnabas) *Ripon 6*   **P** *Bp*
  V I W RUTHERFORD,   **C** P M MEADOWS
LEEDS Emmanuel *Ripon 7*   **P** *Trustees*   **P-in-c** S J ROBINSON
LEEDS Gipton (Church of the Epiphany) *Ripon 5*   **P** *Bp*
  C J E HEIGHTON
LEEDS Halton (St Wilfrid) *Ripon 5*   **P** *Bp*   **V** M D G HEATHER
LEEDS (Parish Church) *see* Leeds City *Ripon*
LEEDS Richmond Hill (All Saints) (St Hilda) (St Saviour)
  Ripon 8   **P** *Bp and Keble Coll Ox (jt)*   **V** *vacant* 0113-248 0971

LEEDS (St Aidan) *Ripon 5*   **P** *V Leeds St Pet*   **V** A L TAYLOR,
  NSM C T RAWLINS
LEEDS (St Cyprian and St James) Harehills *Ripon 5*   **P** *Bp*
  V *vacant* 0113-249 3746
LEEDS (St Edmund King and Martyr) *see* Roundhay St Edm
  Ripon
LEEDS (St George) *Ripon 7*   **P** *Simeon's Trustees*
  TV C C PRENTIS,   **C** J E MORRIS, C J HEWLETT
LEEDS (St John the Evangelist) *see* Roundhay St Jo *Ripon*
LEEDS (St Nicholas) *see* Hollingbourne and Hucking w Leeds
  and Broomfield *Cant*
LEEDS (St Wilfrid) *Ripon 5*   **P** *Bp*   **V** J HILTON
LEEDS CITY (St Peter) (Holy Trinity) *Ripon 5*   **P** *DBP*
  TR G C M SMITH,   **TV** J M YATES, C V TAYLOR,
  Hon C D G RHODES
LEEDSTOWN (St James's Mission Church) *see* Crowan and
  Treslothan *Truro*
LEEK (All Saints) (St Edward the Confessor) (St John the
  Evangelist) (St Luke) (St Paul) and Meerbrook *Lich 8*
  P *Patr Bd*   **TR** M J PARKER,   **TV** C R PETERS, R A WOODS,
  C E J FAIRLESS,   **NSM** S GOODWIN
LEEK WOOTTON (All Saints) *Cov 4*   **P** *Lord Leigh*
  P-in-c B W PEARSON
LEEMING (St John the Baptist) *see* Bedale and Leeming *Ripon*
LEEMING BAR (St Augustine) *as above Ripon*
LEES HILL (Mission Hall) *see* Lanercost, Walton, Gilsland and
  Nether Denton *Carl*
LEESFIELD Knoll's Lane (St Agnes) *see* Leesfield *Man*
LEESFIELD (St Thomas) *Man 19*   **P** *Bp*   **V** H G SMITH,
  C K L GRESHAM
LEFTWICH (Farm of the Good Shepherd) *see* Davenham *Ches*
LEGBOURNE (All Saints) and Wold Marsh *Linc 12*
  P *Ld Chan (1 turn), Bp, Viscountess Chaplin, Ch Trust Fund*
  Trust, D&C, and DBP (1 turn), Duchy of Lanc (1 turn)
  V T A REDFEARN
LEGBURTHWAITE (Mission Church) *see* St
  John's-in-the-Vale, Threlkeld and Wythburn *Carl*
LEGH, HIGH (St John) *see* Over Tabley and High Legh *Ches*
LEGSBY (St Thomas) *Linc 5*   **P** *Bp*   **V** M J CARTWRIGHT,
  NSM D L INKPIN
LEICESTER (Holy Apostles) *Leic 2*   **P** *DBP and*
  Ridley Hall Cam (jt)   **NSM** P R BERRY
LEICESTER (Holy Spirit) (St Andrew) (St Nicholas) *Leic 2*
  P *Bp*   **TV** E MATTHEWS-LOYDALL, J D CURTIS, D L CAWLEY,
  C J B NAYLOR
LEICESTER (Holy Trinity w St John the Divine) *Leic 2*
  P *Peache Trustees*   **V** R W MORGAN,   **C** S MENON,
  T L PHILLIPS,   **NSM** A J MORGAN, J S T WOOLMER
LEICESTER (Martyrs) *Leic 2*   **P** *Bp*   **V** A P HOBSON,
  C A M ROCHE
LEICESTER Presentation of Christ (St Barnabas) (St Peter)
  (St Saviour) *Leic 1*   **P** *Bp*   **TV** R N WHITTINGHAM,
  C C M KING,   **Hon C** M G IPGRAVE
LEICESTER Resurrection (St Alban) *Leic 1*   **P** *Bp*
  TR R L WHITEHEAD,   **TV** M J CATTERICK,   **C** A K FORD,
  J S A ASIR
LEICESTER (St Aidan) *Leic 2*   **P** *Bp*   **V** H A S COCKS,
  C D ROLLINS
LEICESTER (St Alban) *see* Leic Resurr *Leic*
LEICESTER (St Anne) *Leic 2*   **P** *Bp*   **V** I W HARRISON
LEICESTER (St Chad) *Leic 1*   **P** *Bp*   **V** *vacant* 0116-276 6062
LEICESTER (St Christopher) *Leic 2*   **P** *MMCET*
  V A TELFORD
LEICESTER (St James the Greater) *Leic 2*   **P** *Bp*
  V G RICHERBY,   **C** D H CLARK
LEICESTER (St John the Baptist) *see* Clarendon Park St Jo w
  Knighton St Mich *Leic*
LEICESTER St Leonard Conventional District *Leic 2*
  C-in-c R W MORGAN
LEICESTER (St Mary de Castro) *Leic 2*   **P** *Bp*
  V D L CAWLEY
LEICESTER (St Paul) *Leic 2*   **P** *Bp*   **P-in-c** R R POWELL
LEICESTER (St Philip) *Leic 1*   **P** *Adn Leic, V Evington, V Leic*
  H Trin, G A Cooling Esq, and A S Price Esq (jt)
  P-in-c S B HEYGATE,   **C** D P JOHNSON
LEICESTER (St Stephen) *see* N Evington *Leic*
LEICESTER (St Theodore of Canterbury) *Leic 1*   **P** *Bp*
  V J J LEONARD
LEICESTER, The Abbey (St Augustine) (St Margaret and All
  Saints) *Leic 2*   **P** *Bp*   **TV** R R POWELL,   **C** J B NAYLOR
LEICESTER FOREST EAST (St Andrew) *see* Kirby Muxloe
  Leic
LEIGH (All Saints) *see* Ashton Keynes, Leigh and Minety *Bris*
LEIGH (All Saints) *see* Uttoxeter Area *Lich*
LEIGH (All Saints' Mission) *see* Bedford Leigh *Man*
LEIGH (Holy Saviour) *see* White Horse *Sarum*

LEIGH or Wimborne (St John the Evangelist)   *see* New Borough and Leigh *Sarum*
LEIGH (St Andrew)   *see* Wriggle Valley *Sarum*
LEIGH (St Bartholomew) *S'wark 27*   **P** *N J Charrington Esq*   **P-in-c** J M A WILLANS,   **OLM** F G LEHANEY
LEIGH (St Catherine)   *see* Twigworth, Down Hatherley, Norton, The Leigh etc *Glouc*
LEIGH (St Clement) *Chelmsf 10*   **P** *Bp*   **R** K R HAVEY
LEIGH (St Edburga)   *see* Alfrick, Lulsley, Suckley, Leigh and Bransford *Worc*
LEIGH (St John the Evangelist) *Man 13*   **P** *Bp*   **V** vacant (01942) 672868
LEIGH (St Mary) *Roch 11*   **P** *Ch Trust Fund Trust*   **P-in-c** L W G KEVIS
LEIGH (St Mary the Virgin) *Man 13*   **P** *Bp*   **NSM** D VICKERS
LEIGH, LITTLE (St Michael and All Angels)   *see* Antrobus, Aston by Sutton, Lt Leigh etc *Ches*
LEIGH, NORTH (St Mary) *Ox 9*   **P** *Ld Chan*   **P-in-c** S G KIRKHAM
LEIGH, SOUTH (St James the Great)   *see* Cogges and S Leigh *Ox*
LEIGH, WEST (St Alban) *Portsm 5*   **P** *Bp*   **V** M J SHEFFIELD,   **C** S W CRADDUCK
LEIGH-ON-SEA (St Aidan) the Fairway *Chelmsf 10*   **P** *Bp*   **V** T BARNES
LEIGH-ON-SEA (St James) *Chelmsf 10*   **P** *Bp*   **V** B J SCHOOLING,   **Hon Par Dn** E J A INGRAM
LEIGH-ON-SEA (St Margaret) *Chelmsf 10*   **P** *Bp*   **V** R H S EASTOE,   **C** B BATSTONE
LEIGH PARK (St Francis) *Portsm 5*   **P** *Bp*   **V** J G P JEFFERY,   **C** J M B HONNOR, S HEWITT,   **NSM** M S HARPER, W P KENNEDY
LEIGH UPON MENDIP (St Giles) w Stoke St Michael *B & W 4*   **P** *DBP and V Doulting (jt)*   **V** P D WINKS
LEIGH WOODS (St Mary the Virgin)   *see* Abbots Leigh w Leigh Woods *Bris*
LEIGHLAND (St Giles)   *see* Old Cleeve, Leighland and Treborough *B & W*
LEIGHS, GREAT (St Mary the Virgin) *Chelmsf 8*   **P** *Linc Coll Ox*   **P-in-c** C J ELLIOTT
LEIGHS, LITTLE (St John) *Chelmsf 8*   **P** *Reformation Ch Trust*   **P-in-c** C J ELLIOTT
LEIGHTERTON (St Andrew)   *see* Boxwell, Leighterton, Didmarton, Oldbury etc *Glouc*
LEIGHTON (Holy Trinity)   *see* Trelystan *Heref*
LEIGHTON (St Mary)   *see* Wrockwardine Deanery *Lich*
LEIGHTON BROMSWOLD (St Mary) *Ely 9*   **P** *Bp*   **P-in-c** C M FURLONG
LEIGHTON BUZZARD (All Saints) w Eggington, Hockliffe and Billington *St Alb 12*   **P** *Bp*   **C** N Y LENTHALL, P D ANDREWS
LEIGHTON-CUM-MINSHULL VERNON (St Peter) *Ches 15*   **P** *Bp*   **V** G D GEDDES
LEIGHTONSTONE, EAST *Ely 9*   **P** *Bp (2 turns), Peterho Cam (1 turn)*   **R** J P YOUNG,   **C** J MUGGLETON,   **NSM** M J HARE
LEINTHALL EARLES (St Andrew)   *see* Kingsland w Eardisland, Aymestrey etc *Heref*
LEINTHALL STARKES (St Mary Magdalene)   *see* Wigmore Abbey *Heref*
LEINTWARDINE (St Andrew) Adforton   *as above Heref*
LEINTWARDINE (St Mary Magdalene)   *as above Heref*
LEIRE (St Peter) w Ashby Parva and Dunton Bassett *Leic 11*   **P** *Ball Coll Ox, Exors Major T G F Paget, and Adn Loughb (by turn)*   **R** D J TURNER
LEISTON (St Margaret) *St E 19*   **P** *Haberdashers' Co*   **V** M PICKERING,   **OLM** M R ELLIS
LELANT (St Uny)   *see* Carbis Bay w Lelant *Truro*
LEMINGTON, LOWER (St Leonard)   *see* Moreton-in-Marsh w Batsford, Todenham etc *Glouc*
LEMSFORD (St John the Evangelist) *St Alb 21*   **P** *Lord Brocket*   **P-in-c** E C CARDALE
LEN VALLEY, The *Cant 15*   **P** *Abp, All So Coll Ox, Viscount Chilston, and Lord Cornwallis (jt)*   **R** D A IRVINE,   **C** A P SADLER
LENBOROUGH *Ox 23*   **P** *Ch Ch Ox, Cam Univ, and New Coll Ox (2 turns), Ld Chan (1 turn)*   **OLM** J J SHIELDS
LENHAM (St Mary)   *see* Len Valley *Cant*
LENTON (Holy Trinity) (Priory Church of St Anthony) *S'well 13*   **P** *CPAS*   **V** W R LOVATT,   **NSM** J D LEEMING
LENTON (St Peter)   *see* Ingoldsby *Linc*
LENTON ABBEY (St Barnabas) *S'well 13*   **P** *CPAS*   **P-in-c** V L FLANAGAN,   **NSM** R A SHOCK
LENWADE (All Saints)   *see* Weston Longville w Morton and the Witchinghams *Nor*

LEOMINSTER (St Peter and St Paul) *Heref 7*   **P** *Patr Bd*   **TR** P J SWAIN,   **TV** G L JONES, J T MIDDLEMISS, M T TOWNSEND,   **C** E C GODDARD,   **NSM** P J PRIVETT,   **OLM** P C REES, P SMITH, C P REES
LEONARD STANLEY (St Swithun)   *see* The Stanleys *Glouc*
LEPTON (St John) *Wakef 6*   **P** *R Kirkheaton*   **V** G F WHITCROFT
LESBURY (St Mary) w Alnmouth   *Newc 9*   **P** *Dioc Soc*   **V** B COWEN,   **C** M J PENFOLD
LESNEWTH (St Michael and All Angels)   *see* Boscastle w Davidstow *Truro*
LESSINGHAM (All Saints)   *see* Happisburgh, Walcott, Hempstead w Eccles etc *Nor*
LETCHWORTH (St Mary the Virgin) (St Michael) *St Alb 4*   **P** *Guild of All So*   **R** N M SETTERFIELD
LETCHWORTH (St Paul) w Willian *St Alb 4*   **P** *Bp*   **V** A M LOVEGROVE,   **NSM** M P DACK, A J FERRIS
LETCOMBE BASSETT (St Michael and All Angels)   *see* Ridgeway *Ox*
LETCOMBE REGIS (St Andrew)   *as above Ox*
LETHERINGHAM (St Mary)   *see* Charsfield w Debach, Monewden, Hoo etc *St E*
LETHERINGSETT (St Andrew)   *see* Blakeney w Cley, Wiveton, Glandford etc *Nor*
LETTON (St John the Baptist) w Staunton, Byford, Mansel Gamage and Monnington *Heref 5*   **P** *Sir John Cotterell Bt (2 turns), Exors Mrs Dew (1 turn), Ch Ch Ox (3 turns), and DBP (1 turn)*   **P-in-c** R D KING,   **C** N R SPENCER
LETWELL (St Peter)   *see* Firbeck w Letwell *Sheff*
LEUSDON (St John the Baptist)   *see* Widecombe-in-the-Moor, Leusdon, Princetown etc *Ex*
LEVEDALE (Mission Church)   *see* Penkridge Team *Lich*
LEVEN (Holy Trinity)   *see* Brandesburton and Leven w Catwick *York*
LEVEN VALLEY *Carl 11*   **P** *Mrs C M Chaplin, V Colton, and Bp (jt)*   **P-in-c** D G GODDARD
LEVENS (St John the Evangelist) *Carl 10*   **P** *Trustees*   **V** vacant (01539) 560233
LEVENSHULME (St Andrew) (St Peter) *Man 3*   **P** *Bp and trustees (jt)*   **R** L S IRELAND,   **C** L A IRELAND
LEVENSHULME (St Mark) *Man 3*   **P** *Bp*   **R** N P TAYLOR
LEVER, GREAT (St Michael w St Bartholomew) *Man 12*   **P** *Bp*   **R** vacant (01204) 526510
LEVER, LITTLE (St Matthew) *Man 12*   **P** *V Bolton-le-Moors St Pet*   **V** J WISEMAN,   **NSM** I C ANTHONY
LEVER BRIDGE (St Stephen and All Martyrs) *Man 9*   **P** *The Crown*   **P-in-c** B SAGAR
LEVERINGTON (St Leonard) *Ely 17*   **P** *Bp*   **R** S K GARDNER
LEVERSTOCK GREEN (Holy Trinity)   *see* Chambersbury *St Alb*
LEVERTON (St Helena) *Linc 20*   **P** *Ld Chan*   **P-in-c** T STOTT
LEVERTON, NORTH and SOUTH (St Martin) (All Saints) *S'well 5*   **P** *Bp*   **P-in-c** M J LEATON,   **NSM** I CARTER
LEVINGTON (St Peter)   *see* Nacton and Levington w Bucklesham and Foxhall *St E*
LEVISHAM (St John the Baptist)   *see* Pickering w Lockton and Levisham *York*
LEWANNICK (St Martin)   *see* North Hill and Lewannick *Truro*
LEWES (St Anne) *Chich 18*   **P** *Bp and SMF (jt), and Ld Chan*   **R** P R C HAMILTON MANON,   **NSM** J R LOWERSON
LEWES (St John sub Castro) *Chich 18*   **P** *Bp*   **R** M J SULLY
LEWES (St John the Baptist)   *see* Southover *Chich*
LEWES (St Mary)   *see* Lewes St Anne *Chich*
LEWES (St Michael) (St Thomas at Cliffe) w All Saints *Chich 18*   **P** *Bp and SMF (jt), and Ld Chan*   **R** C K CHANNER,   **NSM** P D YATES
LEWISHAM (St Mary) *S'wark 4*   **P** *Earl of Dartmouth*   **V** D GARLICK
LEWISHAM (St Stephen) and St Mark *S'wark 4*   **P** *Keble Coll Ox*   **V** G KIRK,   **Hon C** F D GARDOM
LEWISHAM (St Swithun) Hither Green *S'wark 4*   **P** *V Lewisham St Mary*   **V** R DANIELL
LEWKNOR (St Margaret)   *see* Thame *Ox*
LEWSEY (St Hugh)   *see* Luton Lewsey St Hugh *St Alb*
LEWTRENCHARD (St Peter)   *see* Lifton, Broadwoodwidger, Stowford etc *Ex*
LEXDEN (St Leonard) *Chelmsf 16*   **P** *Bp*   **R** S CARTER,   **NSM** W J L HOWES
LEXHAM, EAST (St Andrew)   *see* Litcham w Kempston, E and W Lexham, Mileham etc *Nor*
LEXHAM, WEST (St Nicholas)   *as above Nor*
LEYBOURNE (St Peter and St Paul) *Roch 7*   **P** *Major Sir David Hawley Bt*   **R** C D DENCH
LEYBURN (St Matthew) w Bellerby *Ripon 4*   **P** *Lord Bolton and Mrs M E Scragg (alt)*   **P-in-c** C R HUGGETT
LEYFIELDS (St Francis)   *see* Tamworth *Lich*

LEYLAND (St Ambrose) *Blackb 5*   **P** *V Leyland*
   V P C BATTERSBY
LEYLAND (St Andrew) *Blackb 5*   **P** *CPAS*   **V** D R A GIBB,
   C M L SIMPSON
LEYLAND (St James) *Blackb 5*   **P** *Sir Henry Farington Bt*
   V A HOLLIDAY,   **NSM** M H PENMAN
LEYLAND (St John) *Blackb 5*   **P** *V Leyland St Andr and*
   CPAS (jt)   **V** A McHAFFIE,   **OLM** B J WILSON
LEYSTERS (St Andrew)   *see Leominster Heref*
LEYTON (All Saints) *Chelmsf 5*   **P** *V St Mary's Leyton*
   V M I HOLMDEN
LEYTON (Christ Church) *Chelmsf 5*   **P** *Ch Trust Fund Trust*
   V M E BURKILL,   **C** D N GIBBS
LEYTON (Emmanuel) *Chelmsf 5*   **P** *Bp*   **V** A ADEMOLA
LEYTON (St Catherine) (St Paul) *Chelmsf 5*
   P *V Leyton St Mary w St Edw*   **V** P A REILY,   **C** G J BOWEN
LEYTON (St Mary w St Edward) and St Luke *Chelmsf 5*
   P *Simeon's Trustees*   **C** D P J MELDRUM
LEYTONSTONE (Holy Trinity) Harrow Green *Chelmsf 5*
   P *Bp*   **V** I HARKER
LEYTONSTONE (St Andrew) *Chelmsf 5*   **P** *Bp*
   P-in-c D J DALAIS
LEYTONSTONE (St John the Baptist) *Chelmsf 5*   **P** *Bp*
   V R J DRAPER,   **NSM** R A WHITE
LEYTONSTONE (St Margaret w St Columba) *Chelmsf 5*
   P *Bp*   **V** R W C PAGE
LEZANT (St Briochus)   *see Stoke Climsland Truro*
LEZANT (St Briochus) w Lawhitton and South Petherwin w
   Trewen *Truro 9*   **P** *Bp and Ox Univ (jt)*   **R** *vacant (01566)*
   773782
LEZAYRE (Holy Trinity) *S & M 3*   **P** *The Crown*   **V** *vacant*
   (01624) 812500
LEZAYRE (St Olave) Ramsey *S & M 3*   **P** *The Crown and Bp*
   (alt)   **P-in-c** P J UPTON-JONES
LICHBOROUGH (St Martin)   *see Greens Norton w Bradden*
   and Lichborough Pet
LICHFIELD (Christ Church) *Lich 1*   **P** *Bp*   **V** I W WILLIAMS
LICHFIELD (St Chad) *Lich 1*   **P** *D&C*   **R** R D BULL,
   C H M MORBY,   **NSM** B WILLIAMS, D J SHERIDAN,
   OLM E A WALL, J HEELEY
LICHFIELD (St John's Hospital) Proprietary Chapel *Lich 1*
   P *Bp*   **Master** J R HARGREAVES
LICHFIELD (St Michael) (St Mary) and Wall St John *Lich 1*
   P *D&C*   **R** D K BEEDON,   **C** K A LOWTHER, M D GELDARD,
   C POLHILL,   **NSM** J ANKETELL, C J BAKER
LICKEY, THE (Holy Trinity) *Birm 4*   **P** *V Bromsgrove*
   V P D SWAN
LIDEN (St Timothy)   *see Swindon Dorcan Bris*
LIDLINGTON (St Margaret)   *see Marston Morteyne w*
   Lidlington St Alb
LIFTON (St Mary), Broadwoodwidger, Stowford, Lewtrenchard,
   Thrushelton and Kelly w Bradstone *Ex 25*   **P** *Bp, Mrs A M*
   Baring-Gould Almond, W F Kelly Esq, and
   J B Wollocombe Esq (jt)   **V** J H HEATH,   **C** J W HUNWICKE
LIGHTBOWNE (St Luke) *Man 5*   **P** *D&C*   **R** A J L LEWIS
LIGHTCLIFFE (St Matthew) *Wakef 2*   **P** *V Halifax*
   V R G COOPER,   **C** S J PITCHER
LIGHTHORNE (St Laurence) *Cov 8*   **P** *Lady Willoughby*
   de Broke   **R** G J BURRELL,   **C** R C FLOATE
LIGHTWATER (All Saints) *Guildf 6*   **P** *Ld Chan and Bp (alt)*
   V M J HORTON,   **OLM** R D BROWNING
LILBOURNE (All Saints)   *see Crick and Yelvertoft w Clay*
   Coton and Lilbourne Pet
LILLESHALL (St John the Evangelist) (St Michael and All
   Angels), Muxton and Sheriffhales *Lich 16*   **P** *Bp*
   V D J BUTTERFIELD,   **C** D M LAKE,   **OLM** J EVANS
LILLEY (St Peter)   *see King's Walden and Offley w Lilley St Alb*
LILLINGSTONE DAYRELL (St Nicholas)   *see N Buckingham*
   Ox
LILLINGSTONE LOVELL (Assumption of the Blessed Virgin
   Mary)   *as above Ox*
LILLINGTON (St Martin)   *see Sherborne w Castleton and*
   Lillington Sarum
LILLINGTON (St Mary Magdalene) *Cov 11*   **P** *Bp*
   V T M H BOYNS,   **C** J S MCCOACH
LILLIPUT (Holy Angels) *Sarum 7*   **P** *Bp*   **P-in-c** I J MAYO
LIMBER, GREAT (St Peter)   *see Brocklesby Park Linc*
LIMEHOUSE (St Anne) (St Peter) *Lon 7*   **P** *BNC Ox*
   R G L WARREN
LIMESIDE (St Chad)   *see Hollinwood and Limeside Man*
LIMINGTON (The Blessed Virgin Mary)   *see Ilchester w*
   Northover, Limington, Yeovilton etc B & W
LIMPENHOE (St Botolph)   *see Freethorpe, Wickhampton,*
   Halvergate etc Nor
LIMPLEY STOKE (St Mary)   *see Freshford, Limpley Stoke and*
   Hinton Charterhouse B & W

LIMPSFIELD (St Peter) and Titsey *S'wark 26*   **P** *Bp*
   R N H THOMPSON,   **C** C R WOOD,   **NSM** G G MOORGAS,
   J M FARMAN,   **OLM** R P RAINBIRD
LIMPSFIELD CHART (St Andrew) Conventional District
   S'wark 26 vacant
LINBY (St Michael) w Papplewick *S'well 4*
   P *T W A Cundy Esq*   **R** K H TURNER
LINCH (St Luke)   *see Lynch w Iping Marsh and Milland Chich*
LINCHMERE (St Peter)   *see Lynchmere and Camelsdale Chich*
LINCOLN (All Saints) *Linc 15*   **P** *Bp*   **V** A J KERSWILL
LINCOLN Minster Group, The (St Mary Magdalene)
   (St Michael on the Mount) (St Peter in Eastgate) *Linc 15*
   P *Adn Linc, D&C, and Bp (by turn)*   **R** *vacant (01522) 525741*
LINCOLN (St Botolph by Bargate) *Linc 15*   **P** *Bp*
   P-in-c T W THOMPSON,   **C** E W HANSON
LINCOLN (St Faith) (St Martin) (St Peter-at-Arches) *Linc 15*
   P *Bp*   **P-in-c** L C ACKLAM,   **C** H P GEISOW
LINCOLN (St George) Swallowbeck *Linc 15*   **P** *Bp and*
   V Skellingthorpe (jt)   **V** I G SILK
LINCOLN (St Giles) *Linc 15*   **P** *Bp*   **V** M J O'CONNELL
LINCOLN (St John the Baptist) (St John the Evangelist) *Linc 15*
   P *Bp*   **V** S A HOY
LINCOLN (St Mary-le-Wigford) (St Benedict) (St Mark)
   Linc 15   **P** *Bp*   **V** *vacant (01522) 29364*
LINCOLN (St Nicholas) (St John) Newport *Linc 15*   **P** *Bp and*
   D&C (alt)   **V** D W YABBACOME,   **C** R J GODDARD,
   NSM M F BAYNHAM
LINCOLN (St Peter-at-Gowts) (St Andrew) *Linc 15*   **P** *Bp*
   P-in-c T W THOMPSON,   **C** E W HANSON
LINCOLN (St Swithin) *Linc 15*   **P** *Bp*   **P-in-c** D EDGAR
LINDAL IN MARTON (St Peter)   *see Pennington and Lindal w*
   Marton and Bardsea Carl
LINDALE (St Paul)   *see Cartmel Peninsula Carl*
LINDFIELD (All Saints) *Chich 6*   **P** *Ch Soc Trust*
   V D J CLARKE,   **C** J N A HOBBS, N B B DILL
LINDLEY (St Stephen) *Wakef 5*   **P** *V Huddersfield*
   V G MANN
LINDOW (St John) *Ches 12*   **P** *Bp*   **V** S R GALES
LINDRIDGE (St Lawrence)   *see Teme Valley N Worc*
LINDSELL (St Mary the Virgin)   *see Stebbing w Lindsell*
   Chelmsf
LINDSEY (St Peter)   *see Bildeston w Wattisham and Lindsey,*
   Whatfield etc St E
LINFORD (St Francis)   *see E and W Tilbury and Linford*
   Chelmsf
LINFORD, GREAT (St Andrew)   *see Stantonbury and Willen Ox*
LINFORD, LITTLE (St Leonard)   *see Lamp Ox*
LINGDALE (Mission Room)   *see Boosbeck w Moorsholm York*
LINGEN (St Michael and All Angels)   *see Presteigne w Discoed,*
   Kinsham, Lingen and Knill Heref
LINGFIELD (St Peter and St Paul) and Crowhurst *S'wark 26*
   P *Bp*   **V** S M GENDALL,   **OLM** M W CARTER
LINGWOOD (St Peter)   *see Burlingham St Edmund w*
   Lingwood, Strumpshaw etc Nor
LINKENHOLT (St Peter)   *see Hurstbourne Tarrant, Faccombe,*
   Vernham Dean etc Win
LINKINHORNE (St Mellor) *Truro 12*   **P** *DBP*
   P-in-c A R INGLEBY
LINLEY (St Leonard)   *see Broseley w Benthall, Jackfield, Linley*
   etc Heref
LINLEY GREEN (not known)   *see Acton Beauchamp and*
   Evesbatch w Stanford Bishop Heref
LINSLADE (St Barnabas) (St Mary) *Ox 26*   **P** *Bp*
   P-in-c C J DYER,   **OLM** W JONES
LINSTEAD PARVA (St Margaret)   *see Blyth Valley St E*
LINTHORPE (St Barnabas) *York 18*   **P** *Abp*   **V** E WILSON,
   NSM R A MORRIS
LINTHWAITE (Christ Church) *Wakef 5*   **P** *R Almondbury*
   V T MORLEY
LINTON (Christ Church)   *see Walton-on-Trent w Croxall,*
   Rosliston etc Derby
LINTON (St Aidan)   *see Ashington Newc*
LINTON (St Mary) *Ely 4*   **P** *Patr Bd*
   TR M O M MILLS-POWELL,   **TV** B M SMITH
LINTON (St Mary the Virgin)   *see Ross Heref*
LINTON (St Nicholas)   *see Coxheath w E Farleigh, Hunton and*
   Linton Roch
LINTON IN CRAVEN (St Michael) *Bradf 7*   **P** *D&C*
   R C J HAYWARD,   **C** A HODGE
LINWOOD (St Cornelius) *Linc 5*   **P** *MMCET*
   R M J CARTWRIGHT,   **NSM** D L INKPIN
LIPHOOK (Church Centre)   *see Bramshott and Liphook*
   Portsm
LISCARD (St John)   *see Egremont St Jo Ches*
LISCARD (St Mary w St Columba) *Ches 7*   **P** *Bp*
   P-in-c A J MANNINGS,   **NSM** M A D HASTED

LISCARD (St Thomas) *Ches 7* **P** *Bp* **P-in-c** R T NELSON
LISKEARD (St Martin) and St Keyne *Truro 12* **P** *Simeon's Trustees* **V** M G SELLIX
LISS (St Mary) (St Peter) (St Saviour) *Portsm 4* **P** *Bp* R J R PINDER, **Hon C** D J VARNEY, **NSM** W N MALLAS
LISSET (St James of Compostella) *see* Beeford w Frodingham and Foston *York*
LISSINGTON (St John the Baptist) *see* Lissington *Linc*
LISSINGTON (St John the Baptist) *Linc 5* **P** *D&C York* **V** M J CARTWRIGHT
LISTON (not known) *see* N Hinckford *Chelmsf*
LITCHAM (All Saints) w Kempston, East and West Lexham, Mileham, Beeston-next-Mileham, Stanfield, Tittleshall and Godwick *Nor 14* **P** *Bp, Earl of Leic, Ch Soc Tr, DBP, Mrs E M Olesen, and N W D Foster Esq (jt)* **P-in-c** J B BOSTON
LITCHFIELD (St James the Less) *see* Whitchurch w Tufton and Litchfield *Win*
LITHERLAND (St Andrew) *Liv 1* **P** *Bp* **P-in-c** R J DRIVER, **C** J C M BISSEX
LITHERLAND (St John and St James) *see* Orrell Hey St Jo and St Jas *Liv*
LITHERLAND (St Paul) Hatton Hill *Liv 1* **P** *Bp* **V** J W WHITLEY
LITHERLAND (St Philip) *Liv 1* **P** *Trustees* **V** D A PARRY, **C** J L C DUFF
LITLINGTON (St Catherine) *see* Shingay Gp of Par *Ely*
LITLINGTON (St Michael the Archangel) *see* Alfriston w Lullington, Litlington and W Dean *Chich*
LITTLE *see also under substantive place name*
LITTLE BIRCH (St Mary) *see* Much Birch w Lt Birch, Much Dewchurch etc *Heref*
LITTLE COMMON *see* Bexhill St Mark *Chich*
LITTLE DART Team Ministry *see* Burrington, Chawleigh, Cheldon, Chulmleigh etc *Ex*
LITTLEBOROUGH (Holy Trinity) *Man 20* **P** *TR Rochdale* **P-in-c** I C THOMPSON, **C** J A TALING, **Dss** K J OLIVER
LITTLEBOURNE (St Vincent) and Ickham w Wickhambreaux and Stodmarsh *Cant 1* **P** *Abp, D&C, Ch Trust Fund Trust, and Adn Cant (jt)* **R** A J ALLAN
LITTLEBURY (Holy Trinity) *see* Saffron Walden w Wendens Ambo, Littlebury etc *Chelmsf*
LITTLEBURY GREEN (St Peter) *as above Chelmsf*
LITTLEDEAN (St Ethelbert) *see* Cinderford St Steph w Littledean *Glouc*
LITTLEHAM (St Margaret) w Exmouth *Ex 1* **P** *Patr Bd* **TR** I C MORTER, **TV** I W MACKENZIE
LITTLEHAM (St Swithin) *see* Bideford, Northam, Westward Ho!, Appledore etc *Ex*
LITTLEHAMPTON (St James) (St Mary) and Wick *Chich 1* **P** *Bp* **TR** R J CASWELL, **TV** J S A HUDSON, M J LANE, **C** S R MERRIMAN, **NSM** E A CARVER
LITTLEHEMPSTON (St John the Baptist) *see* Broadhempston, Woodland, Staverton etc *Ex*
LITTLEMOOR (St Francis of Assisi) *see* Preston w Sutton Poyntz and Osmington w Poxwell *Sarum*
LITTLEMORE (St Mary the Virgin and St Nicholas) *Ox 4* **P** *Or Coll Ox* **P-in-c** B G SCHUNEMANN, **Hon C** S A COAKLEY, **NSM** J B MUDDIMAN, T J MORGAN
LITTLEOVER (St Peter) *Derby 10* **P** *PCC* **P-in-c** J A SEARLE
LITTLEPORT (St George) *Ely 13* **P** *Bp* **V** A G F VILLER
LITTLETON (St Catherine of Alexandria) *see* Crawley and Littleton and Sparsholt w Lainston *Win*
LITTLETON (St Mary Magdalene) *Lon 13* **P** *C W L Barratt Esq* **P-in-c** P G MCAVOY
LITTLETON, HIGH (Holy Trinity) *B & W 12* **P** *Hyndman Trustees* **V** S TRICKETT
LITTLETON, NORTH (St Nicholas) *see* Cleeve Prior and The Littletons *Worc*
LITTLETON, SOUTH (St Michael the Archangel) *as above Worc*
LITTLETON DREW (All Saints) *see* By Brook *Bris*
LITTLETON-ON-SEVERN (St Mary of Malmesbury) *see* Alveston and Littleton-on-Severn w Elberton *Bris*
LITTLEWICK (St John the Evangelist) *see* Burchetts Green *Ox*
LITTLEWICK (St Thomas) *see* Horsell *Guildf*
LITTLEWORTH (Holy Ascension) *see* Cherbury w Gainfield *Ox*
LITTON (Christ Church) *see* Tideswell *Derby*
LITTON (St Mary the Virgin) *see* Chewton Mendip w Ston Easton, Litton etc *B & W*
LITTON CHENEY (St Mary) *see* Bride Valley *Sarum*
LIVERMERE, GREAT (St Peter) *see* Blackbourne *St E*
LIVERPOOL (All Souls) Springwood *Liv 4* **P** *The Crown* **P-in-c** A J COLMER

LIVERPOOL (Christ Church) Norris Green *Liv 8* **P** *Bp* **V** P W DAWKIN
LIVERPOOL (Our Lady and St Nicholas w St Anne) *Liv 3* **P** *Patr Bd* **TV** D E EMMOTT, **P-in-c** S D BROOKES, **Hon C** J S WILLIAMS
LIVERPOOL (St Anne) *see* Stanley *Liv*
LIVERPOOL (St Christopher) Norris Green *Liv 8* **P** *Bp* **P-in-c** J M COLEMAN
LIVERPOOL (St Luke in the City) (St Bride w St Saviour) (St Michael in the City) (St Stephen w St Catherine) *Liv 6* **P** *Patr Bd* **TR** N BLACK, **TV** S M STARKEY, M J FRY, **C** P R SKIRROW, **OLM** A Y CHEUNG
LIVERPOOL (St Paul) Stoneycroft *Liv 8* **P** *St Chad's Coll Dur* **V** *vacant* 0151-228 1041
LIVERPOOL (St Philip w St David) *Liv 3* **P** *Bp* **P-in-c** J A GARNETT
LIVERSEDGE (Christ Church) w Hightown *Wakef 8* **P** *Bp and V Birstall (jt)* **NSM** S M HOLT
LIVERTON (St Martin) *see* Easington w Liverton *York*
LIVERTON MINES (St Hilda) *as above York*
LIVESEY (St Andrew) *Blackb 2* **P** *Trustees* **V** *vacant* (01254) 259422
LLANCILLO (St Peter) *see* Ewyas Harold w Dulas, Kenderchurch etc *Heref*
LLANDINABO (St Junabius) *see* Much Birch w Lt Birch, Much Dewchurch etc *Heref*
LLANFAIR WATERDINE (St Mary) *see* Bucknell w Chapel Lawn, Llanfair Waterdine etc *Heref*
LLANGARRON (St Deinst) w Llangrove, Whitchurch and Ganarew *Heref 8* **P** *Bp, DBP, and D&C (jt)* **P-in-c** M A KELK
LLANGROVE (Christ Church) *see* Llangarron w Llangrove, Whitchurch and Ganarew *Heref*
LLANGUA (St James) *see* Ewyas Harold w Dulas, Kenderchurch etc *Heref*
LLANVEYNOE (St Beuno and St Peter) *see* Clodock and Longtown w Craswall, Llanveynoe etc *Heref*
LLANWARNE (Christ Church) *see* Much Birch w Lt Birch, Much Dewchurch etc *Heref*
LLANYBLODWELL (St Michael) and Trefonen *Lich 19* **P** *Bp and Earl of Powis (jt)* **Hon C** E OSMAN
LLANYMYNECH (St Agatha) *Lich 19* **P** *Bp* **R** *vacant* (01691) 830446
LOBLEY HILL (All Saints) *Dur 13* **P** *Bp* **V** R K HOPPER
LOCKERLEY (St John) and East Dean w East and West Tytherley *Win 12* **P** *DBP (1 turn), H B G Dalgety Esq (2 turns)* **P-in-c** J M PITKIN
LOCKING (St Augustine) *B & W 11* **P** *MMCET* **P-in-c** C J S TURNER
LOCKING CASTLE (no church) Conventional District *B & W 11* **C-in-c** J BOLTON
LOCKINGE (All Saints) *see* Wantage Downs *Ox*
LOCKINGE, WEST (All Souls) *as above Ox*
LOCKINGTON (St Mary) and Lund and Scorborough w Leconfield *York 8* **P** *Abp* **R** P MOATE
LOCKINGTON (St Nicholas) *see* Castle Donington and Lockington cum Hemington *Leic*
LOCKLEAZE (St Mary Magdalene w St Francis) *see* Bris Lockleaze St Mary Magd w St Fran *Bris*
LOCKS HEATH (St John the Baptist) *Portsm 2* **P** *Bp* **V** P D INGRAMS, **NSM** P A BOGGUST, M A ATKINSON
LOCKTON (St Giles) *see* Pickering w Lockton and Levisham *York*
LODDINGTON (St Leonard) *see* Broughton w Loddington and Cransley etc *Pet*
LODDINGTON (St Michael and All Angels) *Leic 3* **P** *Bp* **P-in-c** A J BOYD
LODDISWELL (St Michael and All Angels) *see* Modbury, Bigbury, Ringmore w Kingston etc *Ex*
LODDON (Holy Trinity), Sisland, Chedgrave, Hardley and Langley *Nor 8* **P** *Bp, E G Gilbert Esq, Gt Hosp, and Sir Christopher Beauchamp Bt (jt)* **V** C R CHAPMAN, **C** L E RICKETTS
LODE (St James) *see* Anglesey Gp *Ely*
LODERS (St Mary Magdalene) *see* Askerswell, Loders and Powerstock *Sarum*
LODGE, THE (St John) *see* Weston Rhyn and Selattyn *Lich*
LODGE MOOR (St Luke) *Sheff 4* **P** *CPAS* **V** J D STRIDE
LODSWORTH (St Peter) *see* Lurgashall, Lodsworth and Selham *Chich*
LOFTHOUSE (Christ Church) *Ripon 8* **P** *DBP* **V** V G UTTLEY
LOFTUS-IN-CLEVELAND (St Leonard) and Carlin How w Skinningrove *York 16* **P** *Ld Chan (2 turns), Abp (1 turn)* **R** T J WHITWELL
LOLWORTH (All Saints) *see* Fen Drayton w Conington and Lolworth etc *Ely*

LONAN (All Saints) *S & M 2*   **P** *The Crown*   **V** W H MARTIN, **OLM** J E GUILFORD

LONDESBOROUGH (All Saints) *York 5*   **P** *R F Ashwin Esq* **P-in-c** J F HUGHTON

LONDON, LITTLE (St Stephen)   *see* Bramley *Win*

LONDON CITY CHURCHES:

All Hallows Berkynchirche-by-the-Tower w St Dunstan-in-the-East *Lon 1*   **P** *Abp*   **V** P A DELANEY, C D DRISCOLL,   **Hon C** G R de MELLO, S VAN CULIN, S D HAINES

St Andrew-by-the-Wardrobe w St Ann, Blackfriars *Lon 1*   **P** *PCC and Mercers' Co (jt)*   **R** A H F GRIFFIN, **NSM** D HITCHCOCK, E GRIFFITHS

St Bartholomew the Great, Smithfield *Lon 1*   **P** *D&C Westmr*   **R** M R DUDLEY

St Bartholomew the Less, Smithfield Gate *Lon 1*   **P** *St Bart's Hosp*   **V** M J STEVENS,   **NSM** N J GOULDING

St Botolph Aldgate w Holy Trinity Minories *Lon 1*   **P** *Bp*   **V** B J LEE,   **Hon C** P WRIGHT, K LEECH,   **NSM** J PEIRCE, R J TRAFFORD-ROBERTS

St Botolph without Bishopgate *Lon 1*   **P** *D&C St Paul's*   **P-in-c** J D M PATON,   **Hon C** H J M TURNER

St Bride Fleet Street w Bridewell and Trinity Gough Square *Lon 1*   **P** *D&C Westmr*   **R** D G MEARA

St Clement Eastcheap w St Martin Orgar *Lon 1*   **P** *D&C St Paul's*   **P-in-c** K H GIBBONS,   **Hon C** M B KIDDLE

St Edmund the King and St Mary Woolnoth w St Nicholas Acons, All Hallows Lombard Street, St Benet Gracechurch, St Leonard Eastcheap, St Dionis Backchurch and St Mary Woolchurch, Haw *Lon 1*   **P** *The Crown (3 turns), D&C Cant (1 turn), Bp (1 turn), and Abp (1 turn)*   **R** A S WALKER

St Giles Cripplegate w St Bartholomew Moor Lane and St Alphage London Wall and St Luke Old Street w St Mary Charterhouse and St Paul Clerkenwell *Lon 1*   **P** *D&C St Paul's*   **R** K M RUMENS

St Helen, Bishopsgate w St Andrew Undershaft and St Ethelburga, Bishopsgate and St Martin Outwich and St Mary Axe *Lon 1*   **P** *Merchant Taylors' Co* **C** N D BEYNON, B C COOPER, A JONES, S M C DOWDY, J P DE COSTOBADIE, C W D SKRINE

St James Garlickhythe w St Michael Queenhithe and Holy Trinity-the-Less *Lon 1*   **P** *D&C St Paul's*   **R** A H F GRIFFIN, **NSM** D HITCHCOCK

St Magnus the Martyr w St Margaret New Fish Street and St Michael Crooked Lane *Lon 1*   **P** *DBP* **P-in-c** K H GIBBONS

St Margaret Lothbury and St Stephen Coleman Street w St Christopher-le-Stocks, St Bartholomew-by-the-Exchange, St Olave Old Jewry, St Martin Pomeroy, St Mildred Poultry and St Mary Colechurch *Lon 1*   **P** *Simeon's Trustees*   **R** W J H CROSSLEY,   **NSM** B W RICKARDS

St Mary at Hill w St Andrew Hubbard, St George Botolph Lane and St Botolph by Billingsgate *Lon 1*   **P** *Ball Coll Ox (2 turns), PCC (1 turn), and Abp (1 turn)*   **R** B A C KIRK-DUNCAN

St Mary le Bow w St Pancras Soper Lane, All Hallows Honey Lane, All Hallows Bread Street, St John the Evangelist Watling Street, St Augustine w St Faith under St Paul's and St Mildred Bread Street w St Margaret Moyses *Lon 1*   **P** *Grocers' Co (1 turn), Abp (2 turns)*   **R** G R BUSH

St Michael Cornhill w St Peter le Poer and St Benet Fink *Lon 1*   **P** *Drapers' Co*   **P-in-c** P J MULLEN

St Olave Hart Street w All Hallows Staining and St Catherine Coleman *Lon 1*   **P** *Trustees*   **R** J F COWLING

St Peter Cornhill *Lon 1*   **P** *City Corp*   **R** W T TAYLOR

St Sepulchre w Christ Church Greyfriars and St Leonard Foster Lane *Lon 1*   **P** *St Jo Coll Ox*   **P-in-c** P J MULLEN

St Stephen Walbrook and St Swithun London Stone w St Benet Sherehog and St Mary Bothaw w St Laurence Pountney *Lon 1*   **P** *Grocers' Co and Magd Coll Cam (alt)*   **R** E C VARAH

St Vedast w St Michael-le-Querne, St Matthew Friday Street, St Peter Cheap, St Alban Wood Street, St Olave Silver Street, St Michael Wood Street, St Mary Staining, St Anne and St Agnes and St John Zachary Gresham Street *Lon 1*   **P** *D&C St Paul's*   **P-in-c** J D M PATON

LONDON COLNEY (St Peter) *St Alb 1*   **P** *Bp*   **V** *vacant* (01727) 769797

LONDON DOCKS (St Peter) w Wapping St John *Lon 7*   **P** *Bp*   **R** T E JONES,   **C** I C ROGERS

LONDON GUILD CHURCHES:

All Hallows London Wall *Lon 1*   **P** *Ld Chan*   **V** G B HEWITT

St Andrew Holborn *Lon 1*   **P** *Bp*   **V** L DENNEN, **NSM** W C BEAVER

St Benet Paul's Wharf *Lon 1*   **P** *Bp*   **V** *vacant* (020) 7723 3104 or 7489 8754

St Botolph without Aldersgate *Lon 1*   **P** *Bp* **P-in-c** S M C DOWDY

St Dunstan in the West *Lon 1*   **P** *Abp*   **P-in-c** W D F GULLIFORD

St Katharine Cree *Lon 1*   **P** *Bp*   **P-in-c** J F COWLING

St Lawrence Jewry *Lon 1*   **P** *City Corp*   **V** D J BURGESS

St Margaret Pattens *Lon 1*   **P** *Ld Chan*   **P-in-c** A G C PEARSON

St Martin Ludgate *Lon 1*   **P** *D&C St Paul's* **P-in-c** A J MORLEY

St Mary Abchurch *Lon 1*   **P** *CCC Cam*   **P-in-c** O R CLARKE

St Mary Aldermary *Lon 1*   **P** *The Crown and Ld Chan (alt)* **P-in-c** J R MOTHERSOLE

St Michael Paternoster Royal *Lon 1*   **P** *Bp* **V** R J CHRISTIANSON,   **Hon C** K PETERS

LONDONDERRY (St Mark) (Holy Trinity) *Birm 7*   **P** *Bp* **V** *vacant* 0121-429 1149

LONDONTHORPE (St John the Baptist)   *see* Grantham, Harrowby w Londonthorpe *Linc*

LONG ASHTON (All Saints) *B & W 13*   **P** *Bp*   **V** H B TASKER

LONG BENNINGTON (St Swithin)   *see* Saxonwell *Linc*

LONG BENTON (St Bartholomew) *Newc 6*   **P** *Ball Coll Ox* **V** P S RAMSDEN,   **C** A E STARKIE

LONG BENTON (St Mary Magdalene) *Newc 6*   **P** *Ball Coll Ox*   **V** D M GRAY

LONG BREDY (St Peter)   *see* Bride Valley *Sarum*

LONG BUCKBY (St Lawrence) w Watford *Pet 2*   **P** *Bp and Ld Chan (alt)*   **V** C R EVANS,   **C** A M LORD

LONG BURTON (St James)   *see* Dungeon Hill *Sarum*

LONG CLAWSON (St Remigius)   *see* Vale of Belvoir Par *Leic*

LONG COMPTON (St Peter and St Mary), Whichford and Barton-on-the-Heath *Cov 9*   **P** *Bp, Trin Coll Ox, and Ch Ch Ox (by turn)*   **P-in-c** R K SMITH,   **C** H C W PARBURY

LONG CRENDON (St Mary the Virgin) w Chearsley and Nether Winchendon *Ox 21*   **P** *Bp and R V Spencer-Bernard Esq (jt)* **V** R JACKSON

LONG CROSS (Christ Church) *Guildf 11*   **P** *J D Tringham Esq* **V** A B OLSEN,   **NSM** D GODDARD

LONG DITTON (St Mary) *Guildf 8*   **P** *Bp S'wark* **R** S A COOPER

LONG EATON (St John) *Derby 13*   **P** *Bp*   **V** S E DYAS, **C** P J DAVEY

LONG EATON (St Laurence) *Derby 13*   **P** *Bp*   **V** S D ELLIS

LONG HANBOROUGH (Christ Church)   *see* Hanborough and Freeland *Ox*

LONG ITCHINGTON (Holy Trinity) and Marton *Cov 10* **P** *Bp*   **P-in-c** J T H BRITTON,   **C** D R PATTERSON

LONG LANE (Christ Church)   *see* Boylestone, Church Broughton, Dalbury, etc *Derby*

LONG LOAD (Christ Church)   *see* Langport Area Chs *B & W*

LONG MARSTON (All Saints)   *see* Tring *St Alb*

LONG MARSTON (All Saints) *York 1*   **P** *Col E C York* **R** J A RENDALL,   **NSM** H FRAY

LONG MARTON (St Margaret and St James) w Dufton and w Milburn *Carl 1*   **P** *Lord Hothfield*   **P-in-c** M S LANGLEY

LONG MELFORD (Holy Trinity)   *see* Chadbrook *St E*

LONG MELFORD (St Catherine)   *as above St E*

LONG NEWNTON (Holy Trinity)   *see* Ashley, Crudwell, Hankerton, Long Newnton etc *Bris*

LONG PRESTON (St Mary the Virgin) w Tosside *Bradf 5* **P** *D&C Ch Ch Ox and V Gisburn (alt)* **P-in-c** M R RUSSELL-SMITH,   **NSM** R E WILSON

LONG RISTON (St Margaret)   *see* Skirlaugh w Long Riston *York*

LONG STANTON (All Saints) w St Michael *Ely 5*   **P** *Magd Coll Cam and Bp (alt)*   **P-in-c** M E RABY,   **C** S E WYATT

LONG STANTON (St Michael and All Angels)   *see* Wenlock *Heref*

LONG SUTTON (All Saints)   *see* Herriard w Winslade and Long Sutton etc *Win*

LONG SUTTON (Holy Trinity)   *see* Langport Area Chs *B & W*

LONG SUTTON (St Mary)   *see* Sutton St Mary *Linc*

LONG WHATTON (All Saints)   *see* Hathern, Long Whatton and Diseworth w Belton etc *Leic*

LONG WITTENHAM (St Mary the Virgin)   *see* Dorchester *Ox*

LONGBOROUGH (St James)   *see* Moreton-in-Marsh w Batsford, Todenham etc *Glouc*

LONGBRIDGE (St John the Baptist) *Birm 4*   **P** *Bp* **V** C J CORKE,   **C** J L C SHAW

LONGBRIDGE DEVERILL (St Peter and St Paul)   *see* Cley Hill Warminster *Sarum*

LONGCOT (St Mary the Virgin)   *see* Shrivenham and Ashbury *Ox*

LONGDEN (St Ruthen) and Annscroft w Pulverbatch *Heref 13* **P** *Bp and MMCET (jt)*   **R** M G WHITTOCK, **NSM** J J WADDINGHAM-FEATHER, **OLM** O S DAWSON-CAMPBELL, A M TAYLOR

LONGDON (St James) *Lich 1*   **P** *Bp*   **P-in-c** M W JEFFERSON, **NSM** R J BELLAMY

LONGDON (St Mary), Castlemorton, Bushley, Queenhill w Holdfast *Worc 5* **P** *Bp, D&C Westmr, and Soc of the Faith (jt)*
V C A MOSS
LONGDON-UPON-TERN (St Bartholomew)
see Wrockwardine Deanery *Lich*
LONGFIELD (Mission Room) (St Mary Magdalene) *Roch 1*
P *Ld Chan* **R** K C BARNES
LONGFLEET (St Mary) *Sarum 7* **P** *MMCET* **V** A N PERRY,
C P D SAINSBURY, **NSM** I B PAUL
LONGFORD (St Chad) *see* Boylestone, Church Broughton,
Dalbury, etc *Derby*
LONGFORD (St Thomas) *Cov 2* **P** *Bp* **V** G BUCKBY
LONGFRAMLINGTON (St Mary the Virgin) w Brinkburn
Newc 9 **P** *Bp* **V** P A G ETTERLEY
LONGHAM (St Andrew and St Peter) *see* Gressenhall w
Longham w Wendling etc *Nor*
LONGHILL (St Margaret) *see* Sutton St Mich *York*
LONGHIRST (St John the Evangelist) *see* Bothal and
Pegswood w Longhirst *Newc*
LONGHOPE (All Saints) *see* Huntley and Longhope,
Churcham and Bulley *Glouc*
LONGHORSLEY (St Helen) and Hebron *Newc 11* **P** *Ld Chan*
P-in-c M D TETLEY, **NSM** J WAIYAKI, **OLM** R M DORANS
**LONGHOUGHTON (St Peter and St Paul) (including Boulmer)
w Howick** *Newc 9* **P** *Duke of Northd and Bp (alt)*
V B COWEN, **C** M J PENFOLD
LONGLEVENS (Holy Trinity) *see* Wotton St Mary *Glouc*
LONGNEWTON (St Mary) w Elton *Dur 10* **P** *Bp and
St Chad's Coll Dur (alt)* **R** *vacant (01642) 581251*
LONGNEY (St Lawrence) *see* Hardwicke and Elmore w
Longney *Glouc*
LONGNOR (St Bartholomew), Quarnford and Sheen *Lich 5*
P *Bp, V Alstonfield, and DBP (jt)* **V** D C NICOL,
OLM M J EVANS
LONGNOR (St Mary) *see* Dorrington w Leebotwood,
Longnor, Stapleton etc *Heref*
LONGPARISH (St Nicholas) *see* Hurstbourne Priors,
Longparish etc *Win*
LONGRIDGE (St Lawrence) (St Paul) *Blackb 13* **P** *Trustees*
V S M AIKEN, **C** S JOHNSON
LONGSDON (St Chad) *see* Horton, Lonsdon and Rushton
Spencer *Lich*
LONGSIGHT (St Luke) *Man 1* **P** *D&C and Trustees (jt)*
R P N CLARK
LONGSLEDDALE (St Mary) *see* Skelsmergh w Selside and
Longsleddale *Carl*
LONGSOLE (Mission Room) *see* Barming *Roch*
LONGSTOCK (St Mary) *see* Stockbridge and Longstock and
Leckford *Win*
LONGSTONE, GREAT (St Giles) *see* Ashford w Sheldon and
Longstone *Derby*
LONGSTOWE (St Mary) *see* Papworth *Ely*
LONGTHORPE (St Botolph) *Pet 13* **P** *Sir Stephen Hastings*
NSM B G HOWITT
LONGTON (St Andrew) *Blackb 5* **P** *A F Rawstorne Esq*
V A PARKINSON
LONGTON (St James and St John) *Lich 12* **P** *Bp* **R** *vacant
(01782) 342187*
LONGTON (St Mark) *see* Edensor *Lich*
LONGTON (St Mary and St Chad) *Lich 12* **P** *Bp*
V P LOCKETT
LONGTON, NEW (All Saints) *Blackb 5* **P** *Bp*
V D M ROGERS
LONGWELL GREEN (All Saints) *Bris 5* **P** *Bp*
V D J A ADAMS
LONGWOOD (St Mark) *Wakef 5* **P** *V Huddersfield*
V J A HUNT
LONGWORTH (St Mary) *see* Cherbury w Gainfield *Ox*
LONSDALE, EAST *Blackb 14* **P** *Patr Bd* **V** R N HAMBLIN,
Hon C R HANNAFORD
LOOE, WEST (St Nicholas) *see* St Martin w Looe *Truro*
LOOSE (All Saints) *Cant 14* **P** *Abp* **V** L S TOWNEND
LOPEN (All Saints) *see* Merriott w Hinton, Dinnington and
Lopen *B & W*
LOPHAM NORTH (St Nicholas) *see* Bressingham w N and S
Lopham and Fersfield *Nor*
LOPHAM SOUTH (St Andrew) *as above Nor*
LOPPINGTON (St Michael and All Angels) w Newtown *Lich 22*
P *Bp and R Wem (jt)* **P-in-c** C S COOKE
LORD'S HILL Local Ecumenical Project *Win 13* **P** *Bp*
V D F CAVEEN
LORTON (St Cuthbert) and Loweswater w Buttermere *Carl 6*
P *Bp and Earl of Lonsdale (alt)* **V** *vacant (01900) 85237*
LOSCOE (St Luke) *Derby 12* **P** *Bp* **V** *vacant (01773) 765631*
LOSTOCK (St Thomas and St John) *Man 11* **P** *Bp and
TR Deane St Mary the Virgin (jt)* **V** W P BREW,
C S M FORREST-REDFERN

LOSTOCK GRALAM (St John the Evangelist) *Ches 6*
P *V Witton* **V** H W STRATTON
LOSTOCK HALL (St James) *Blackb 5* **P** *Bp*
V P D HALLETT, **NSM** D A BAINES, F KENDALL
**LOSTWITHIEL (St Bartholomew), St Winnow w St Nectan's
Chapel, St Veep and Boconnoc** *Truro 10* **P** *D&C and
A D G Fortescue Esq (jt)* **R** F C STEVENS,
Hon C F E STUBBINGS
LOTHERSDALE (Christ Church) *see* Carleton and
Lothersdale *Bradf*
LOTHERTON (St James) *see* Aberford w Micklefield *York*
LOTTISHAM (The Blessed Virgin Mary) *see* Baltonsborough
w Butleigh, W Bradley etc *B & W*
LOUDWATER (St Peter) *Ox 21* **P** *MMCET* **V** T G BUTLIN
LOUGHBOROUGH (All Saints) *see* Thorpe Acre w Dishley
Leic
LOUGHBOROUGH (All Saints) w Holy Trinity *Leic 7* **P** *Bp
and Em Coll Cam (jt)* **R** S A CHERRY, **C** S J RICHARDSON
LOUGHBOROUGH (Emmanuel) (St Mary in Charnwood)
Leic 7 **P** *Patr Bd* **TR** D M F NEWMAN, **TV** S E FIELD,
C C J HODDER
LOUGHBOROUGH (Good Shepherd) *Leic 7* **P** *Bp*
V E K WHITLEY, **NSM** R J WHITLEY
LOUGHBOROUGH (St Peter) *Leic 7* **P** *Bp* **V** D PATERSON
LOUGHTON (All Saints) *see* Watling Valley *Ox*
LOUGHTON (not known) *see* Ditton Priors w Neenton,
Burwarton etc *Heref*
LOUGHTON (St John the Baptist) (St Gabriel) (St Nicholas)
Chelmsf 25 **P** *Patr Bd* **TR** G K WELCH, **TV** S J BREWSTER,
C S L ELMAN, **Hon C** C P COLLINGWOOD
LOUGHTON (St Mary the Virgin) *Chelmsf 25* **P** *Bp*
R A COMFORT
LOUGHTON (St Michael and All Angels) *Chelmsf 25* **P** *Bp*
V P A G RAYNER
LOUND (St Anne) *see* Babworth w Sutton-cum-Lound and
Scofton etc *S'well*
LOUND (St John the Baptist) *see* Somerleyton, Ashby, Fritton,
Herringfleet etc *Nor*
LOUNDSLEY GREEN (Church of the Ascension) *Derby 5*
P *Bp* **P-in-c** F E WILLETT, **NSM** R E SMITH
LOUTH (Holy Trinity) (St James) (St Michael) *Linc 12*
P *Patr Bd* **TR** S D HOLDAWAY, **TV** D R WILLIAMS,
C A P WICKENS, **OLM** R W MANSFIELD
LOVERSALL (St Katherine) *see* Wadworth w Loversall *Sheff*
LOVINGTON (St Thomas à Becket) *see* Six Pilgrims *B & W*
LOW *see also under substantive place name*
LOW FELL (St Helen) *see* Gateshead St Helen *Dur*
LOW HAM (Chapel) *see* Langport Area Chs *B & W*
LOW HILL (Good Shepherd) *see* Bushbury *Lich*
LOW MOOR (Holy Trinity) *Bradf 2* **P** *Bp and V Bradf (jt)*
V F SUDWORTH
LOW VALLEY (St Matthew) *see* Darfield *Sheff*
LOWDHAM (St Mary the Virgin) w Caythorpe, and Gunthorpe
S'well 10 **P** *Bp* **V** E ASHBY, **P-in-c** C A TAINTON,
NSM M A KEENE
LOWER *see also under substantive place name*
LOWER MANOR (St Andrew) *see* Sheff Manor *Sheff*
LOWESBY (All Saints) *see* Whatborough Gp of Par *Leic*
LOWESTOFT (Christ Church) *Nor 9* **P** *CPAS* **V** P R MOON,
C P C W JACKSON
LOWESTOFT (Good Shepherd) *see* Lowestoft St Marg *Nor*
LOWESTOFT (St Andrew) *Nor 9* **P** *Ch Patr Tr*
V M A MCCAGHREY
LOWESTOFT (St Margaret) *Nor 9* **P** *Patr Bd*
TR J B SIMPSON, **NSM** D L ELLSON
LOWESWATER (St Bartholomew) *see* Lorton and Loweswater
w Buttermere *Carl*
LOWFIELD HEATH (St Michael) *see* Crawley *Chich*
LOWGATE (St Mary) *see* Hexham *Newc*
LOWGATE (St Mary the Virgin) *see* Kingston upon Hull
St Mary *York*
LOWICK (St John the Baptist) and Kyloe w Ancroft *Newc 12*
P *D&C Dur (2 turns), Bp (1 turn)* **V** V T DICKINSON
LOWICK (St Luke) *see* Egton-cum-Newland and Lowick w
Colton *Carl*
LOWICK (St Peter) *see* Brigstock w Stanion and Lowick and
Sudborough *Pet*
LOWSONFORD (St Luke) *see* Hatton w Haseley, Rowington w
Lowsonford etc *Cov*
LOWTHER (St Michael) and Askham and Clifton and Brougham
Carl 1 **P** *Earl of Lonsdale* **R** D J RADCLIFFE
LOWTHORPE (St Martin) *see* Burton Agnes w Harpham and
Lowthorpe etc *York*
LOWTON (St Luke) *Liv 16* **P** *Bp* **R** J R MACAULAY
LOWTON (St Mary) *Liv 16* **P** *Bp* **P-in-c** W J STALKER
LOXBEARE (St Michael and All Angels) *see* Washfield,
Stoodleigh, Withleigh etc *Ex*

LOXHORE (St Michael and All Angels) *see* Shirwell, Loxhore, Kentisbury, Arlington, etc *Ex*

LOXLEY (St Nicholas) *see* Hampton Lucy w Charlecote and Loxley *Cov*

LOXTON (St Andrew) *see* Crook Peak *B & W*

LOXWOOD (St John the Baptist) *see* Alfold and Loxwood *Guildf*

LOZELLS (St Paul and St Silas) *Birm 8* **P** Aston Patr Trust **P-in-c** J PRASADAM, **NSM** N P ELY

LUBENHAM (All Saints) *see* Market Harborough and The Transfiguration etc *Leic*

LUCCOMBE (The Blessed Virgin Mary) *see* Selworthy, Timberscombe, Wootton Courtenay etc *B & W*

LUCKER (St Hilda) *see* Belford and Lucker *Newc*

LUCKINGTON (St Mary) *see* Sherston Magna, Easton Grey, Luckington etc *Bris*

LUDBOROUGH (St Mary) *see* Fotherby *Linc*

LUDDENDEN (St Mary) w Luddenden Foot *Wakef 3* **P** *Bp and V Halifax (alt)* **V** vacant (01422) 882127

LUDDESDOWN (St Peter and St Paul) *see* Cobham w Luddesdowne and Dode *Roch*

LUDDINGTON (All Saints) *see* Stratford-upon-Avon, Luddington etc *Cov*

LUDDINGTON (St Margaret) *see* Polebrook and Lutton w Hemington and Luddington *Pet*

LUDDINGTON (St Oswald) *see* Crowle Gp *Linc*

LUDFORD (St Giles) *see* Ludlow, Ludford, Ashford Carbonell etc *Heref*

LUDFORD MAGNA (St Mary) *see* Binbrook Gp *Linc*

LUDGERSHALL (St James) *see* Tidworth, Ludgershall and Faberstown *Sarum*

LUDGERSHALL (St Mary the Virgin) *see* Bernwode *Ox*

LUDGVAN (St Ludgvan and St Paul), Marazion, St Hilary and Perranuthnoe *Truro 5* **P** *D&C, Lord St Levan, and H M Parker Esq (jt)* **R** A J WADE, **NSM** A K WATSON

LUDHAM (St Catherine), Potter Heigham, Hickling and Catfield *Nor 12* **P** *Bp and G M H Mills Esq (jt)* **V** N H KHAMBATTA, **OLM** D M NICHOLSON

LUDLOW (St Laurence) (St John), Ludford, Ashford Carbonell, Ashford Bowdler, Caynham and Richards Castle *Heref 12* **P** *Patr Bd* **TR** B L CURNEW, **TV** J A C SEWELL, **C** N J NIXON, A M BARGE

LUFFENHAM, NORTH (St John the Baptist) *see* Edith Weston w N Luffenham and Lyndon w Manton *Pet*

LUFFENHAM, SOUTH (St Mary the Virgin) *see* Barrowden and Wakerley w S Luffenham etc *Pet*

LUFTON (St Peter and St Paul) *see* Odcombe, Brympton, Lufton and Montacute *B & W*

LUGWARDINE (St Peter) w Bartestree, Weston Beggard and Dormington *Heref 4* **P** *D&C (3 turns), and A T Foley Esq (1 turn)* **V** D J BOWEN

LULLINGSTONE (St Botolph) *see* Eynsford w Farningham and Lullingstone *Roch*

LULLINGTON (All Saints) *see* Beckington w Standerwick, Berkley, Rodden etc *B & W*

LULLINGTON (All Saints) *see* Seale and Lullington w Coton in the Elms *Derby*

LULLINGTON (not known) *see* Alfriston w Lullington, Litlington and W Dean *Chich*

LULWORTHS (St Andrew) (Holy Trinity), Winfrith Newburgh and Chaldon, The *Sarum 8* **P** *Bp (3 turns), Col Sir Joseph Weld (1 turn)* **P-in-c** R J NAYLOR

LUMLEY (Christ Church) *Dur 11* **P** *Bp* **P-in-c** B J ABBOTT

LUND (All Saints) *see* Lockington and Lund and Scorborough w Leconfield *York*

LUND (St John the Evangelist) *Blackb 10* **P** *Ch Ch Ox* **V** G D ALLEN

LUNDWOOD (St Mary Magdalene) *Wakef 7* **P** *Bp* **P-in-c** D NICHOLSON

LUNDY ISLAND (St Helen) Extra-Parochial Place *Ex 15* **P-in-c** P J F GOODEY

LUPPITT (St Mary) *see* Dunkeswell, Luppitt, Sheldon and Upottery *Ex*

LUPSET (St George) *Wakef 12* **P** *Bp* **V** G CLAY, **C** B A J BARRACLOUGH

LUPTON (All Saints) *see* Kirkby Lonsdale *Carl*

LURGASHALL (St Laurence), Lodsworth and Selham *Chich 11* **P** *Rathbone Trust Co and Cowdray Trust, and Lord Egremont (alt)* **R** J A LUSTED

LUSBY (St Peter) *see* Marden Hill Gp *Linc*

LUSTLEIGH (St John the Baptist) *see* Moretonhampstead, Manaton, N Bovey and Lustleigh *Ex*

LUTON (All Saints) (St Peter) *St Alb 14* **P** *Bp* **V** R C H FRANKLIN, **C** C K PERERA, **NSM** T SHACKLADY, J YABSLEY

LUTON (Christ Church) *Roch 5* **P** *R Chatham* **R** C D COLLINS, **C** S J PADFIELD

LUTON Lewsey (St Hugh) *St Alb 14* **P** *Bp* **V** P J LAW, **C** H J CROMPTON, **NSM** C A PULLINGER

LUTON Limbury (St Augustine of Canterbury) *St Alb 14* **P** *Bp* **V** G R CALVERT

LUTON (St Andrew) *St Alb 14* **P** *Bp* **V** G A FINLAYSON

LUTON (St Anne) *St Alb 14* **P** *Peache Trustees, Bp, and V Luton (jt)* **V** P C BUDGELL

LUTON (St Christopher) Round Green *St Alb 14* **P** *Bp* **V** R B ETHERINGTON, **NSM** F M G ETHERINGTON, J M COX

LUTON (St Francis) *St Alb 14* **P** *Peache Trustees, Bp, and V Luton (jt)* **V** M C NEWBON, **C** C J ADAMS

LUTON (St John) *see* Teignmouth, Ideford w Luton, Ashcombe etc *Ex*

LUTON (St Mary) *St Alb 14* **P** *Peache Trustees* **V** N P J BELL, **C** A K E BLYTH, H D THORNTON, K J LOMAX, **NSM** C A MOSS

LUTON (St Matthew) High Town *St Alb 14* **P** *Ch Patr Trust* **V** M J PRITCHARD

LUTON (St Paul) *St Alb 14* **P** *Peache Trustees* **V** A SELLERS, **NSM** P MANUEL

LUTON (St Saviour) *St Alb 14* **P** *Bp* **V** D H GOODBURN, **NSM** D C ANDERSON

LUTTERWORTH (St Mary) w Cotesbach and Bitteswell *Leic 11* **P** *Prime Min (3 turns), Ld Chan (1 turn), and Haberdashers' Co(1 turn)* **R** M H W COUSSENS, **C** M J IRELAND

LUTTON (St Nicholas) w Gedney Drove End, Dawsmere *Linc 16* **P** *The Crown, Ld Chan, and V Long Sutton (by turn)* **P-in-c** M J NOTLEY

LUTTON (St Peter) *see* Polebrook and Lutton w Hemington and Luddington *Pet*

LUTTONS AMBO (St Mary) *see* Weaverthorpe w Helperthorpe, Luttons Ambo etc *York*

LUXBOROUGH (Blessed Virgin Mary) *see* Exton and Winsford and Cutcombe w Luxborough *B & W*

LUXULYAN (St Cyrus and St Julietta) *see* Lanlivery w Luxulyan *Truro*

LYDBROOK (Holy Jesus) *Glouc 4* **P** *Bp* **V** vacant (01594) 860235

LYDBURY NORTH (St Michael and All Angels) *see* Bishop's Castle w Mainstone, Lydbury N etc *Heref*

LYDD (All Saints) *Cant 13* **P** *Abp* **P-in-c** S J A HARDY

LYDDEN (St Mary the Virgin) *see* Temple Ewell w Lydden *Cant*

LYDDINGTON (All Saints) and Wanborough and Bishopstone w Hinton Parva *Bris 7* **P** *Bp and Ld Chan (alt)* **V** J R CARDWELL, **NSM** J J CAMPBELL

LYDDINGTON (St Andrew) w Stoke Dry and Seaton w Caldecott and Glaston and Blisbrooke *Pet 14* **P** *Bp, Burghley Ho Preservation Trust, R E M Elborne Esq, and Peterho Cam (jt)* **P-in-c** J A PORTLOCK

LYDEARD ST LAWRENCE (St Lawrence) w Brompton Ralph, Combe Florey, Ash Priors and Tolland *B & W 19* **P** *Ld Chan (2 turns), W H J Hancock Esq (2 turns), and MMCET (1 turn)* **P-in-c** M B ARMSTRONG

LYDFORD (St Petrock) *see* Peter Tavy, Mary Tavy, Lydford and Brent Tor *Ex*

LYDFORD ON FOSSE (St Peter) *see* Wheathill Priory Gp of Par *B & W*

LYDGATE (St Anne) *see* Saddleworth *Man*

LYDGATE (St Mary) *see* Bansfield *St E*

LYDHAM (Holy Trinity) *see* Wentnor w Ratlinghope, Myndtown, Norbury etc *Heref*

LYDIARD MILLICENT (All Saints) *see* W Swindon and the Lydiards *Bris*

LYDIARD TREGOZE (St Mary) *as above Bris*

LYDIATE and Downholland (St Thomas) *Liv 11* **P** *R Halsall* **V** P L ROBINSON

LYDLINCH (St Thomas à Beckett) *see* Sturminster Newton, Hinton St Mary and Lydlinch *Sarum*

LYDNEY (St Mary the Virgin) *Glouc 4* **P** *Ld Chan* **P-in-c** P C YOUDE, **NSM** M D MILLER, **OLM** A JONES

LYE, THE (Christchurch) and Stambermill *Worc 12* **P** *Bp and CPAS (alt)* **P-in-c** S M FALSHAW, **NSM** C A KENT

LYFORD (St Mary) *see* Cherbury w Gainfield *Ox*

LYME REGIS (St Michael the Archangel) *see* Golden Cap Team *Sarum*

LYMINGE (St Mary and St Ethelburga) w Paddlesworth and Stanford w Postling and Radegund *Cant 5* **P** *Abp* **R** P N ASHMAN

LYMINGTON (St Thomas the Apostle) *Win 11* **P** *Bp* **V** M H WEAVER, **C** J T MCDOWALL

LYMINGTON Woodside (All Saints) *see* Lymington *Win*

LYMINSTER (St Mary Magdalene) *Chich 1* **P** *Eton Coll on nomination of BNC Ox* **V** J E SLEGG

LYMM (St Mary the Virgin) *Ches 4* **P** *Bp* **R** K MAUDSLEY

LYMPNE (St Stephen)   *see* Aldington w Bonnington and Bilsington etc *Cant*

LYMPSHAM (St Christopher)   *see* Brent Knoll, E Brent and Lympsham *B & W*

LYMPSTONE (Nativity of the Blessed Virgin Mary) and Woodbury w Exton   *Ex 1*   **P** *SMF and D&C (jt)*   **R** J CLAPHAM

LYNCH (St Luke) w Iping Marsh and Milland   *Chich 10*   **P** *Rathbone Trust Co, Cowdray Trust and Bp (jt)*   **R** M J SMITH

LYNCHMERE (St Peter) and Camelsdale   *Chich 10*   **P** *Prime Min*   **V** W J MUSSON

LYNCOMBE (St Bartholomew)   *see* Bath St Bart *B & W*

LYNDHURST (St Michael) and Emery Down and Minstead   *Win 11*   **P** *Bp and P J P Green Esq (jt)*   **V** P F MURPHY, **C** C I WALTON,   **NSM** F O BOOT

LYNDON (St Martin)   *see* Edith Weston w N Luffenham and Lyndon w Manton *Pet*

LYNEAL (St John the Evangelist)   *see* Petton w Cockshutt, Welshampton and Lyneal etc *Lich*

LYNEHAM (St Michael) w Bradenstoke   *Sarum 15*   **P** *Ld Chan*   **V** *vacant*

LYNEMOUTH (St Aidan)   *see* Cresswell and Lynemouth *Newc*

LYNESACK (St John the Evangelist)   *Dur 7*   **P** *Bp*   **V** M J SHEARING

LYNG (St Bartholomew)   *see* Stoke St Gregory w Burrowbridge and Lyng *B & W*

LYNG (St Margaret), Sparham, Elsing, Bylaugh, Bawdeswell and Foxley   *Nor 22*   **P** *DBP, Sir Edward Evans-Lombe, and Bp (by turn)*   **R** D N HEAD,   **OLM** T B CANDELAND

LYNGFORD (St Peter)   *see* Taunton Lyngford *B & W*

LYNMOUTH (St John the Baptist)   *see* Combe Martin, Berrynarbor, Lynton, Brendon etc *Ex*

LYNN, NORTH (St Edmund)   *see* King's Lynn St Marg w St Nic *Nor*

LYNN, SOUTH (All Saints)   *Nor 20*   **P** *Bp*   **R** P KINSEY

LYNN, WEST (St Peter)   *see* Clenchwarton and W Lynn *Ely*

LYNSTED (St Peter and St Paul)   *see* Teynham w Lynsted and Kingsdown *Cant*

LYNTON (St Mary the Virgin)   *see* Combe Martin, Berrynarbor, Lynton, Brendon etc *Ex*

LYONS (St Michael and All Angels)   *Dur 14*   **P** *The Crown*   **P-in-c** M L BECK

LYONSDOWN (Holy Trinity)   *St Alb 17*   **P** *Ch Patr Trust*   **V** C W G DOBBIE

LYONSHALL (St Michael and All Angels)   *see* Pembridge w Moor Court, Shobdon, Staunton etc *Heref*

LYSTON (not known)   *see* N Hinckford *Chelmsf*

LYTCHETT MATRAVERS (St Mary the Virgin)   *Sarum 7*   **P** *DBP*   **P-in-c** J A HASTINGS

LYTCHETT MINSTER (not known)   *Sarum 7*   **P** *Bp*   **P-in-c** J H T DE GARIS,   **C** S CROSS,   **OLM** H D PAGE-CLARK

LYTHAM (St Cuthbert)   *Blackb 10*   **P** *DBP*   **V** G I HIRST

LYTHAM (St John the Divine)   *Blackb 10*   **P** J C *Hilton Esq*   **V** *vacant* (01253) 734396

LYTHAM ST ANNE (St Margaret)   *see* St Annes St Marg *Blackb*

LYTHAM ST ANNE (St Thomas)   *see* St Annes *Blackb*

LYTHAM ST ANNES (St Anne)   *see* Heyhouses on Sea *Blackb*

LYTHAM ST ANNES (St Paul)   *see* Fairhaven *Blackb*

LYTHE (St Oswald) w Ugthorpe   *York 22*   **P** *Abp*   **P-in-c** E C R BURGE

MABE (St Laudus)   *Truro 3*   **P** *Bp*   **P-in-c** J SAVAGE

MABLETHORPE (St Mary) w Trusthorpe   *Linc 8*   **P** *Bp Lon (2 turns), Bp Linc (1 turn)*   **P-in-c** L T WHITFIELD

MACCLESFIELD (St John the Evangelist)   *Ches 13*   **P** *Bp*   **V** D TAYLOR,   **NSM** V P SCHOLES

MACCLESFIELD (St Paul)   *Ches 13*   **P** *Bp*   **V** J C TEAR

MACCLESFIELD Team Parish, The (All Saints) (Christ Church) (St Michael and All Angels) (St Peter) (St Barnabas)   *Ches 13*   **P** *Patr Bd*   **TR** J BRIGGS, **TV** R J DOULTON,   D L MOCK,   **C** M W DOUGLAS

MACKWORTH (All Saints)   *Derby 11*   **P** J M *Clark-Maxwell Esq*   **NSM** H M MEYNELL

MACKWORTH (St Francis)   *Derby 9*   **P** *Bp*   **V** S T J MCCAULAY

MADEHURST (St Mary Magdalene)   *see* Slindon, Eartham and Madehurst *Chich*

MADELEY (All Saints)   *Lich 9*   **P** J C *Crewe Esq*   **C** P M JELF, **NSM** M F GELL

MADELEY (St Michael)   *Heref 14*   **P** *Patr Bd*   **TR** H J MORRIS,   **TV** P W H ACHURCH,   S P MANN, **C** R T M J DUCKETT,   **NSM** R FREEMAN

MADINGLEY (St Mary Magdalene)   *Ely 5*   **P** *Bp*   **V** *vacant*

MADLEY (Nativity of the Blessed Virgin Mary) w Tyberton, Peterchurch, Vowchurch and Turnastone   *Heref 1*   **P** *Bp and D&C (jt)*   **R** T R N JONES,   **NSM** F M HANCOCK, B A CHILLINGTON

MADRESFIELD (St Mary)   *see* Powick and Guarlford and Madresfield w Newland *Worc*

MADRON (St Maddern)   *see* Gulval and Madron *Truro*

MAER (St Peter)   *see* Chapel Chorlton, Maer and Whitmore *Lich*

MAESBROOK (St John)   *see* Kinnerley w Melverley and Knockin w Maesbrook *Lich*

MAESBURY (St John the Baptist)   *Lich 19*   **P** *Bp*   **P-in-c** R H MARTIN

MAGDALEN LAVER (St Mary Magdalen)   *see* High Laver w Magdalen Laver and Lt Laver etc *Chelmsf*

MAGHAM DOWN (St Mark)   *see* Hailsham *Chich*

MAGHULL (St Andrew) (St James) (St Peter)   *Liv 11*   **P** *Patr Bd*   **TR** M J DUERDEN,   **TV** P HRYZIUK, S M LEATHLEY,   **C** C DORAN,   **Hon C** W H TULLOCH, **NSM** C R SANDS

MAIDA VALE (St Peter)   *see* Paddington St Pet *Lon*

MAIDA VALE (St Saviour)   *see* Paddington St Sav *Lon*

MAIDEN BRADLEY (All Saints)   *see* Mere w W Knoyle and Maiden Bradley *Sarum*

MAIDEN NEWTON (St Mary)   *see* Melbury *Sarum*

MAIDENHEAD (All Saints)   *see* Boyne Hill *Ox*

MAIDENHEAD (St Andrew and St Mary Magdalene)   *Ox 13*   **P** *Peache Trustees*   **NSM** R E BRAGG

MAIDENHEAD (St Luke)   *Ox 13*   **P** *Bp*   **P-in-c** J R HOLROYD

MAIDENHEAD (St Peter)   *see* Furze Platt *Ox*

MAIDFORD (St Peter and St Paul)   *see* Blakesley w Adstone and Maidford etc *Pet*

MAIDS MORETON (St Edmund)   *see* N Buckingham *Ox*

MAIDSTONE (All Saints) (St Philip) w St Stephen Tovil   *Cant 14*   **P** *Abp*   **V** C J MORGAN-JONES,   **NSM** P S DOE

MAIDSTONE Barming Heath (St Andrew)   *see* Barming Heath *Cant*

MAIDSTONE (St Faith)   *Cant 14*   **P** *Abp*   **V** I H CROFTS

MAIDSTONE (St Luke the Evangelist)   *Cant 14*   **P** *Trustees*   **V** E D DELVE,   **NSM** B H FIELD,   **OLM** R H WILLIAMSON

MAIDSTONE (St Martin)   *Cant 14*   **P** *Abp*   **P-in-c** C A TOMKINS,   **C** S M BIMSON

MAIDSTONE (St Michael and All Angels)   *Cant 14*   **P** *Abp*   **V** P J GIBBONS

MAIDSTONE (St Paul)   *Cant 14*   **P** *Abp*   **P-in-c** K M GORHAM,   **OLM** T R WOOD

MAIDWELL (St Mary) w Draughton and Lamport w Faxton   *Pet 2*   **P** *Bp (3 turns), Sir Ian Isham Bt (1 turn)*   **P-in-c** D J P ISIORHO

MAINSTONE (St John the Baptist)   *see* Bishop's Castle w Mainstone, Lydbury N etc *Heref*

MAISEMORE (St Giles)   *Glouc 6*   **P** *Bp*   **P-in-c** J G EVANS

MAKER (St Mary and St Julian) w Rame   *Truro 11*   **P** *The Crown and Earl of Mount Edgcumbe (jt)*   **R** R A DOYLE

MALBOROUGH (All Saints)   *see* Salcombe and Malborough w S Huish *Ex*

MALDEN (St James)   *S'wark 17*   **P** *Bp*   **V** P E THROWER, **NSM** A HARDY,   **OLM** C PIGGOTT

MALDEN (St John)   *S'wark 17*   **P** *Mert Coll Ox*   **V** K W SCOTT,   **NSM** M D BROOME

MALDEN, NEW (Christ Church) (St John the Divine) and Coombe   *S'wark 17*   **P** *CPAS*   **V** J S DOWNEY, **C** M P WOODCOCK,   S J KUHRT,   **NSM** I R L PRIOR

MALDON (All Saints w St Peter)   *Chelmsf 11*   **P** *Bp*   **V** D J ATKINS,   **NSM** R J R HUMPHRIES

MALDON (St Mary) w Mundon   *Chelmsf 11*   **P** *D&C Westmr*   **R** A M A MCINTOSH,   **NSM** E W CARDEN

MALEW Ballasalla (St Mary the Virgin)   *see* Malew *S & M*

MALEW (St Mark) (St Moluag or St Lupus)   *S & M 1*   **P** *The Crown*   **V** M F ROBERTS

MALIN BRIDGE (St Polycarp)   *Sheff 4*   **P** *Bp*   **V** M G COCKAYNE,   **C** C H STEBBING

MALINS LEE (St Leonard)   *see* Cen Telford *Lich*

MALLERSTANG (St Mary)   *see* Kirkby Stephen w Mallerstang etc *Carl*

MALLING, EAST (St James)   *Roch 7*   **P** *D&C*   **P-in-c** J D BROWN

MALLING, SOUTH (St Michael)   *Chich 18*   **P** *MMCET*   **V** *vacant* (01273) 474387

MALLING, WEST (St Mary) w Offham   *Roch 7*   **P** *Ld Chan and DBP (alt)*   **V** R B STEVENSON

MALMESBURY (St Peter and St Paul) w Westport and Brokenborough   *Bris 6*   **P** *Ch Trust Fund Trust*   **V** *vacant* (01666) 823126

MALPAS (St Andrew)   *see* Truro St Paul and St Clem *Truro*

MALPAS (St Oswald) and Threapwood   *Ches 5*   **P** *DBF*   **R** T ETHERIDGE

MALTBY (St Bartholomew) (Ascension) (Venerable Bede)   *Sheff 5*   **P** *Bp*   **TR** J E CURTIS,   **TV** P F TURNBULL

MALTON, NEW (St Michael)   *York 22*   **P** *Sir Philip Naylor-Leyland Bt*   **V** N N JONES

MALTON, OLD (St Mary the Virgin) *York 6* **P** *Sir Philip Naylor-Leyland Bt* **V** J C MANCHESTER

MALVERN (Holy Trinity) (St James) *Worc 2* **P** *Bp and D&C Westmr (jt)* **V** R J ROSOMAN, **Hon Par Dn** R HERBERT

MALVERN (St Andrew) and Malvern Wells and Wyche *Worc 2* **P** *Bp* **V** P W FINCH

MALVERN, GREAT (Christchurch) *Worc 2* **P** *Bp* **V** P FURBER

MALVERN, GREAT (St Mary and St Michael) *Worc 2* **P** *Bp* **V** M J A BARR, **C** A D PETTIT, **NSM** M E BARR

MALVERN, LITTLE (St Giles) *Worc 2* **P** *Exors T M Berington Esq* **P-in-c** E G KNOWLES

MALVERN, WEST (St James) *see* Malvern H Trin and St Jas *Worc*

MALVERN LINK (Church of the Ascension) (St Matthias) w Cowleigh *Worc 2* **P** *Patr Bd* **TR** G LYALL, **TV** A R N WILLIAMS, **NSM** J M FURBER

MAMBLE (St John the Baptist) w Bayton, Rock w Heightington w Far Forest *Worc 4* **P** *Ld Chan and R Ribbesford w Bewdley etc (alt)* **V** S G F OWENS

MAMHEAD (St Thomas the Apostle) *see* Kenton, Mamhead, Powderham, Cofton and Starcross *Ex*

MANACCAN (St Manaccus and St Dunstan) w St Anthony-in-Meneage and St Martin-in-Meneage *Truro 4* **P** *Ld Chan* **P-in-c** E B L BROWNING

MANATON (St Winifred) *see* Moretonhampstead, Manaton, N Bovey and Lustleigh *Ex*

MANBY (St Mary) *see* Mid Marsh Gp *Linc*

MANCETTER (St Peter) *Cov 5* **P** *Ch Patr Trust* **V** A S MAIRS, **C** D ROPER

MANCHESTER (Apostles) w Miles Platting *Man 1* **P** *DBP* **R** M G CROOK

MANCHESTER (Church of the Resurrection) *see* Manchester Gd Shep and St Barn *Man*

MANCHESTER Clayton (St Cross w St Paul) *Man 1* **P** *Bp* **P-in-c** M THOMPSON, **C** J C BRADING

MANCHESTER Good Shepherd (St Barnabas) (Church of the Resurrection) *Man 1* **P** *Prime Min and Trustees (alt)* **R** T S R CHOW

MANCHESTER (St Ann) *Man 4* **P** *Bp* **R** R A J HILL, **C** G R RAINES

MANCHESTER (St John Chrysostom) Victoria Park *Man 4* **P** *Bp* **P-in-c** I D GOMERSALL, **NSM** E J DISLEY

MANCHESTER (St Werburgh) *see* Chorlton-cum-Hardy St Werburgh *Man*

MANCHESTER Whitworth (not known) *Man 4* **P** *Bp* **TV** I D GOMERSALL

MANEA (St Nicholas) *see* Christchurch and Manea and Welney *Ely*

MANEY (St Peter) *Birm 12* **P** *Bp* **V** P T FISHER

MANFIELD (All Saints) *see* Barton and Manfield and Cleasby w Stapleton *Ripon*

MANGOTSFIELD (St James) *Bris 5* **P** *Peache Trustees* **C** R L FRANCE

MANLEY (St John the Evangelist) *see* Alvanley *Ches*

MANNINGFORD BRUCE (St Peter) *see* Pewsey and Swanborough *Sarum*

MANNINGHAM (St Mary Magdalene and St Michael and All Angels) (St Paul and St Jude) *Bradf 1* **P** *Patr Bd* **TR** G MOFFAT, **TV** D J COOPER, R J HILL

MANNINGS HEATH (Church of the Good Shepherd) *see* Nuthurst *Chich*

MANOR PARK (St Barnabas) *see* Lt Ilford St Barn *Chelmsf*

MANOR PARK (St John the Baptist) *see* W Slough *Ox*

MANOR PARK (St John the Evangelist) *see* Lt Ilford St Mich *Chelmsf*

MANOR PARK (St Mary the Virgin) *as above Chelmsf*

MANOR PARK (St Michael and All Angels) *as above Chelmsf*

MANOR PARK (William Temple) *see* Sheff Manor *Sheff*

MANSEL LACY (St Michael) *see* Credenhill w Brinsop and Wormsley etc *Heref*

MANSERGH (St Peter) *see* Kirkby Lonsdale *Carl*

MANSFIELD Oak Tree Lane *S'well 2* **P** *DBP* **P-in-c** P A CHAPMAN

MANSFIELD (St Augustine) *S'well 2* **P** *Bp* **NSM** P N WOOD

MANSFIELD (St John the Evangelist) *S'well 2* **P** *Bp* **P-in-c** G K KNOTT, **C** R S TAYLOR

MANSFIELD (St Lawrence) *S'well 2* **P** *Bp* **P-in-c** K K BARRON

MANSFIELD (St Mark) *S'well 2* **P** *Bp* **P-in-c** M J DOBBS

MANSFIELD (St Peter and St Paul) *S'well 2* **P** *Bp* **V** *vacant* (01623) 21600

MANSFIELD WOODHOUSE (St Edmund King and Martyr) *S'well 2* **P** *Bp* **C** G E HOLLOWAY

MANSTON (St Catherine) *see* St Laur in Thanet *Cant*

MANSTON (St James) *Ripon 8* **P** *R Barwick in Elmet* **V** G STOTT

MANSTON (St Nicholas) *see* Okeford *Sarum*

MANTHORPE (St John the Evangelist) *see* Grantham, Manthorpe *Linc*

MANTON (St Mary the Virgin) *see* Edith Weston w N Luffenham and Lyndon w Manton *Pet*

MANUDEN (St Mary the Virgin) w Berden *Chelmsf 21* **P** *Patr Bd and Ch Hosp (alt)* **P-in-c** C BISHOP

MAPERTON (St Peter and St Paul) *see* Camelot Par *B & W*

MAPLEBECK (St Radegund) *S'well 14* **P** *Sir Philip Naylor-Leyland Bt* **P-in-c** E F CULLY

MAPLEDURHAM (St Margaret) *see* Caversham and Mapledurham *Ox*

MAPLEDURWELL (St Mary) *see* Newnham w Nately Scures w Mapledurwell etc *Win*

MAPLESTEAD, GREAT (St Giles) *see* Knights and Hospitallers Par *Chelmsf*

MAPLESTEAD, LITTLE (St John) *as above Chelmsf*

MAPPERLEY (Holy Trinity) *see* W Hallam and Mapperley w Stanley *Derby*

MAPPERLEY (St Jude) *see* Nottingham St Jude *S'well*

MAPPLEBOROUGH GREEN (Holy Ascension) *see* Studley *Cov*

MAPPLETON (All Saints) *see* Aldbrough, Mappleton w Goxhill and Withernwick *York*

MAPPLETON (St Mary) *see* Ashbourne w Mapleton *Derby*

MAPPOWDER (St Peter and St Paul) *see* Hazelbury Bryan and the Hillside Par *Sarum*

MARAZION (All Saints) *see* Ludgvan, Marazion, St Hilary and Perranuthnoe *Truro*

MARBURY (St Michael) *Ches 5* **P** *Bp* **P-in-c** M S SEARLE

MARCH (St John) *Ely 16* **P** *Bp* **R** A T SCHOFIELD

MARCH (St Mary) *Ely 16* **P** *Bp* **R** A CHANDLER

MARCH (St Peter) *Ely 16* **P** *Bp* **R** A CHANDLER

MARCH (St Wendreda) *Ely 16* **P** *MMCET* **R** P BAXANDALL

MARCHAM (All Saints) w Garford *Ox 10* **P** *Ch Ch Ox* **P-in-c** E S SHIRRAS

MARCHINGTON (St Peter) *see* Uttoxeter Area *Lich*

MARCHINGTON WOODLANDS (St John) *as above Lich*

MARCHWOOD (St John) *Win 11* **P** *Bp* **R** J D CURTIS

MARCLE, LITTLE (St Michael and All Angels) *see* Ledbury *Heref*

MARDEN (All Saints) *see* Redhorn *Sarum*

MARDEN (St Hilda) *see* Cullercoats St Geo *Newc*

MARDEN (St Mary the Virgin) w Amberley and Wisteston *Heref 4* **P** *D&C* **V** *vacant* (01432) 880256

MARDEN (St Michael and All Angels) *Cant 11* **P** *Abp* **V** J M BOURNE

MARDEN, EAST (St Peter) *see* Compton, the Mardens, Stoughton and Racton *Chich*

MARDEN, NORTH (St Mary) *as above Chich*

MARDEN ASH (St James) *see* High Ongar w Norton Mandeville *Chelmsf*

MARDEN HILL Group, The *Linc 7* **P** *Bp (2 turns), B Eley Esq & DBP, Baroness Willoughby, Duchy of Lanc, J Pain Esq & M Dudley Hewitt Esq, A Lee Esq (1 each)* **R** A M SULLIVAN

MAREHAM-LE-FEN (St Helen) and Revesby *Linc 11* **P** *Bp and Mrs A D Lee (alt)* **OLM** K A BUSH

MAREHAM ON THE HILL (All Saints) *Linc 11* **P** *Bp* **OLM** K A BUSH

MARESFIELD (St Bartholomew) *Chich 21* **P** *Ch Trust Fund Trust* **R** M D S GREIG

MARFLEET (St Giles) (St George) (St Hilda) (St Philip) *York 14* **P** *Patr Bd* **TR** S SHERIFF, **TV** O J LAMBERT

MARGARET MARSH (St Margaret) *see* Shaston *Sarum*

MARGARET RODING (St Margaret) *see* High and Gd Easter w Margaret Roding *Chelmsf*

MARGARET STREET (All Saints) *see* St Marylebone All SS *Lon*

MARGARETTING (St Margaret) *see* Fryerning w Margaretting *Chelmsf*

MARGATE (All Saints) *Cant 9* **P** *Abp* **P-in-c** J W RICHARDSON

MARGATE (Holy Trinity) *Cant 9* **P** *Ch Patr Trust* **V** A J HOUSTON, **C** K M THORPE, J E T STRICKLAND

MARGATE (St John the Baptist in Thanet) *Cant 9* **P** *Abp* **V** B P SHARP, **C** M JACQUES

MARGATE (St Paul) *see* Cliftonville *Cant*

MARGATE (St Philip) Northdown Park *Cant 9* **P** *Ch Patr Trust* **C** P L S ELLISDON

MARHAM (Holy Trinity) *Ely 15* **P** *St Jo Coll Cam* **P-in-c** D J POMERY, **Hon C** A G F VILLER

MARHAMCHURCH (St Marwenne) *see* Bude Haven and Marhamchurch *Truro*

MARHOLM (St Mary the Virgin) *see* Castor w Sutton and Upton w Marholm *Pet*

MARIANSLEIGH (St Mary) *see* Bishopsnympton, Rose Ash,
Mariansleigh etc *Ex*
MARISHES, THE (Chapel) *see* Pickering w Lockton and
Levisham *York*
MARK (Holy Cross) w Allerton *B & W 1* **P** *Bp and D&C (jt)*
P-in-c C NELMES
MARK BEECH (Holy Trinity) *see* Hever, Four Elms and Mark
Beech *Roch*
MARK CROSS (St Mark) *see* Rotherfield w Mark Cross *Chich*
MARKBY (St Peter) *see* Hannah cum Hagnaby w Markby *Linc*
MARKET BOSWORTH (St Peter) *see* Bosworth and Sheepy
Gp *Leic*
MARKET DEEPING (St Guthlac) *Linc 13* **P** *Ld Chan*
R P BRENT
MARKET DRAYTON (St Mary) *see* Drayton in Hales *Lich*
MARKET HARBOROUGH (St Dionysius)
(The Transfiguration) - Little Bowden w Lubenham *Leic 4*
P *Patr Bd* **V** C J E MOODY, **TV** E J SEWELL, **C** P J MESSAM,
NSM J C DUDLEY
MARKET LAVINGTON (St Mary of the Assumption) *see* The
Lavingtons, Cheverells, and Easterton *Sarum*
MARKET OVERTON (St Peter and St Paul) *see* Teigh w
Whissendine and Market Overton *Pet*
MARKET RASEN (St Thomas the Apostle) *Linc 5* **P** *Ld Chan*
V M J CARTWRIGHT, **NSM** D L INKPIN
MARKET STAINTON (St Michael and All Angels)
see Asterby Gp *Linc*
MARKET WEIGHTON (All Saints) *York 5* **P** *Abp*
V P P OCKFORD
MARKET WESTON (St Mary) *see* Hopton, Market Weston,
Barningham etc *St E*
MARKFIELD (St Michael), Thornton, Bagworth and Stanton,
and Copt Oak *Leic 12* **P** MMCET **R** G T WILLETT,
NSM J A DOWNS
MARKHAM, EAST (St John the Baptist) w Askham, Headon w
Upton and Grove *S'well 5* **P** *Grove Settled Estate Trustees and*
SMF (jt) **R** J H LITTLE
MARKHAM CLINTON (All Saints) *see* Tuxford w Weston
and Markham Clinton *S'well*
MARKINGTON (St Michael) w South Stainley and Bishop
Thornton *Ripon 3* **P** *Bp, D&C, Sir Thomas Ingilby Bt and*
N A Hudleston Esq (jt) (by turn) **P-in-c** D W EYLES
MARKS GATE (St Mark) Chadwell Heath *Chelmsf 1* **P** *Bp*
V R K GAYLER
MARKS TEY (St Andrew) and Aldham *Chelmsf 17* **P** CPAS
and MMCET (jt) **R** R T MORGAN
MARKSBURY (St Peter) *see* Farmborough, Marksbury and
Stanton Prior *B & W*
MARKYATE STREET (St John the Baptist) *St Alb 8* **P** *Bp*
P-in-c J F H GREEN
MARLBOROUGH (St Mary the Virgin) *Sarum 18* **P** *Patr Bd*
TR A G STUDDERT-KENNEDY, **NSM** R J OVERTHROW,
OLM D P MAURICE
MARLBROOK (St Luke) *see* Catshill and Dodford *Worc*
MARLBROOK Team Ministry, The *see* Bath Twerton-on-Avon
B & W
MARLDON (St John the Baptist) *see* Totnes w Bridgetown,
Berry Pomeroy etc *Ex*
MARLESFORD (St Andrew) *see* Campsea Ashe w Marlesford,
Parham and Hacheston *St E*
MARLEY HILL (St Cuthbert) *Dur 13* **P** *The Crown*
P-in-c R K HOPPER
MARLINGFORD (Assumption of the Blessed Virgin Mary)
see Easton, Colton, Marlingford and Bawburgh *Nor*
MARLOW, GREAT (All Saints) w Marlow Bottom, Little
Marlow and Bisham *Ox 29* **P** *Patr Bd* **TR** N J MOLONY,
TV S E IRWIN, **NSM** G L C SMITH
MARLOW, LITTLE (St John the Baptist) *see* Gt Marlow w
Marlow Bottom, Lt Marlow and Bisham *Ox*
MARLOW BOTTOM (St Mary the Virgin) *as above Ox*
MARLPIT HILL (St Paulinus) *see* Edenbridge *Roch*
MARLPOOL (All Saints) *Derby 12* **P** *V Heanor* **V** *vacant*
(01773) 712097
MARLSTON (St Mary) *see* Bucklebury w Marlston *Ox*
MARNHULL (St Gregory) *Sarum 5* **P** DBF
P-in-c R D G WEYMAN, **C** M J TREGENZA, **OLM** M J FICKE
MAROWN (Old Parish Church) (St Runius) *S & M 2*
P *The Crown* **V** A M CONVERY
MARPLE (All Saints) *Ches 16* **P** *R Stockport St Mary*
V I R PARKINSON, **C** S M M WALKER, **NSM** B J LOWE
MARPLE, LOW (St Martin) *Ches 16* **P** *Keble Coll Ox*
V J H CAM
MARR (St Helen) *see* Bilham *Sheff*
MARSDEN (St Bartholomew) *Wakef 5* **P** *R Almondbury*
V *vacant* (01484) 847864
MARSDEN, GREAT (St John's Church Centre) w Nelson
St Philip *Blackb 6* **P** *Prime Min and Bp (alt)* **V** *vacant*
(01282) 698161

MARSDEN, LITTLE (St Paul) w Nelson St Mary *Blackb 6*
P *Bp* **V** A H MCMICHAEL, **C** C W HILL
MARSH (St George) *see* Lancaster St Mary w St John and St
Anne *Blackb*
MARSH (St James chapel) *see* Huddersfield H Trin *Wakef*
MARSH BALDON (St Peter) *see* Dorchester *Ox*
MARSH FARM (Holy Cross) *St Alb 14* **P** *Bp*
V J R BELITHER
MARSH GIBBON (St Mary the Virgin) *see* Swan *Ox*
MARSHAM (All Saints) w Burgh-next-Aylsham *Nor 19* **P** *Bp,*
Mercers' Co, and J M Roberts Esq (jt) **R** R J HEWETSON
MARSHCHAPEL (St Mary the Virgin) *see* The North-Chapel
Parishes *Linc*
MARSHFIELD (St Mary the Virgin) w Cold Ashton and
Tormarton w West Littleton *Bris 4* **P** *New Coll Ox and Bp*
(alt) **V** S M DREW
MARSHLAND, The *Sheff 10* **P** *Ld Chan and Bp (alt)*
V J P L WHALLEY
MARSHWOOD (St Mary) *see* Golden Cap Team *Sarum*
MARSKE (St Edmund King and Martyr) *see* Downholme and
Marske *Ripon*
MARSKE, NEW (St Thomas) *York 16* **P** *Abp*
V C M DURNFORD
MARSKE IN CLEVELAND (St Mark) *York 16* **P** *Trustees*
V D H LAMBERT
MARSTON (St Alban) *see* Stafford *Lich*
MARSTON (St Leonard) *as above Lich*
MARSTON (St Mary) *see* Barkston and Hough Gp *Linc*
MARSTON (St Nicholas) w Elsfield *Ox 4* **P** *Bp and D&C (jt)*
V A R PRICE, **NSM** A C HOLMES
MARSTON, NEW (St Michael and All Angels) *Ox 4* **P** *Bp*
V E B BARDWELL, **NSM** R I S RYCRAFT
MARSTON, NORTH (Assumption of the Blessed Virgin Mary)
see Schorne *Ox*
MARSTON, SOUTH (St Mary Magdalene) *see* Stratton
St Margaret w S Marston etc *Bris*
MARSTON BIGOT (St Leonard) *see* Nunney and Witham
Friary, Marston Bigot etc *B & W*
MARSTON GREEN (St Leonard) *Birm 9* **P** *Birm Dioc*
Trustees **V** R V ALLEN
MARSTON MAGNA (Blessed Virgin Mary) *see* Chilton
Cantelo, Ashington, Mudford, Rimpton etc *B & W*
MARSTON MEYSEY (St James) *see* Meysey Hampton w
Marston Meysey and Castle Eaton *Glouc*
MARSTON MONTGOMERY (St Giles) *see* Alkmonton,
Cubley, Marston, Montgomery etc *Derby*
MARSTON MORTEYNE (St Mary the Virgin) w Lidlington
St Alb 13 **P** *Bp and St Jo Coll Cam (alt)* **R** R L HOWLETT
MARSTON ON DOVE (St Mary) *see* Hilton w
Marston-on-Dove *Derby*
MARSTON SICCA (St James the Great) *see* Pebworth,
Dorsington, Honeybourne etc *Glouc*
MARSTON ST LAWRENCE (St Lawrence) *see* Greatworth
and Marston St Lawrence etc *Pet*
MARSTON TRUSSELL (St Nicholas) *see* Welford w
Sibbertoft and Marston Trussell *Pet*
MARSTOW (St Matthew) *see* Walford and St John w
Bishopswood, Goodrich etc *Heref*
MARSWORTH (All Saints) *see* Cheddington w Mentmore and
Marsworth *Ox*
MARTHALL (All Saints) *Ches 12* **P** DBP **P-in-c** S HAWKINS
MARTHAM (St Mary) and Repps with Bastwick, Thurne and
Clippesby *Nor 6* **P** *Bp, D&C, DBP and K Edw VI Gr Sch (jt)*
V P S PAINE
MARTIN (All Saints) *see* W Downland *Sarum*
MARTIN (Holy Trinity) *see* Carr Dyke Gp *Linc*
MARTIN (St Michael) *see* Thornton Gp *Linc*
MARTIN HUSSINGTREE (St Michael) *see* Salwarpe and
Hindlip w Martin Hussingtree *Worc*
MARTINDALE (Old Church) *see* Barton, Pooley Bridge and
Martindale *Carl*
MARTINDALE (St Peter) *as above Carl*
MARTINHOE (St Martin) *see* Combe Martin, Berrynarbor,
Lynton, Brendon etc *Ex*
MARTLESHAM (St Mary the Virgin) w Brightwell *St E 2*
P *Bp* **C** T P B BREENE, **OLM** H L CONOLE, E J CORKER
MARTLEY (St Peter) and Wichenford, Knightwick and
Doddenham, Broadwas and Cotheridge *Worc 3* **P** *D&C*
(2 turns), Bp (1 turn) **P-in-c** D R SHERWIN,
NSM J M WHITTAKER
MARTOCK (All Saints) w Ash *B & W 6* **P** *Bp*
V T J FARMILOE, **C** P R HOGARTH, **Hon Par Dn** H D EVANS
MARTON (Room) *see* Middleton, Newton and Sinnington
York
MARTON (St Esprit) *see* Long Itchington and Marton *Cov*
MARTON (St James) *see* Capesthorne w Siddington and
Marton *Ches*

MARTON (St Margaret of Antioch)   *see* Lea Gp *Linc*
MARTON (St Mark) *Heref 13*   **P** *V Chirbury*   **V** P D HARRATT
MARTON (St Mary)   *see* Sheriff Hutton, Farlington, Stillington etc *York*
MARTON (St Paul) *Blackb 8*   **P** *V Poulton-le-Fylde*
  V C J WREN,   **C** R W BUNDAY, K A WREN
MARTON CUM GRAFTON (Christ Church)   *see* Gt and Lt Ouseburn w Marton cum Grafton etc *Ripon*
MARTON-IN-CHIRBURY (St Mark)   *see* Marton *Heref*
MARTON-IN-CLEVELAND (St Cuthbert) *York 18*   **P** *Abp*
  V M J PROCTOR,   **C** J APPLEBY
MARTON IN CRAVEN (St Peter)   *see* Broughton, Marton and Thornton *Bradf*
MARTON MOSS (St Nicholas) *Blackb 8*   **P** *Bp*
  P-in-c R G RAINFORD
MARTYR WORTHY (St Swithun)   *see* Itchen Valley *Win*
MARWOOD (St Michael and All Angels)   *see* Heanton Punchardon w Marwood *Ex*
MARY TAVY (St Mary)   *see* Peter Tavy, Mary Tavy, Lydford and Brent Tor *Ex*
MARYFIELD (St Philip and St James)   *see* Antony w Sheviock *Truro*
MARYLEBONE ROAD (St Marylebone)   *see* St Marylebone w H Trin *Lon*
MARYPORT (St Mary) (Christ Church) *Carl 7*   **P** *Trustees*
  V D C BICKERSTETH
MARYSTOWE (St Mary the Virgin)   *see* Milton Abbot, Dunterton, Lamerton etc *Ex*
MASBROUGH (St Paul) *Sheff 6*   **P** *Bp and Ld Chan (alt)*
  V P G HARBORD
MASHAM (St Mary the Virgin) and Healey *Ripon 3*
  P *Trin Coll Cam*   **V** D J CLEEVES
MASSINGHAM, GREAT (St Mary) and LITTLE (St Andrew), Harpley, Rougham, Weasenham and Wellingham *Nor 14*
  P *Bp, Earl of Leicester, Mrs P M Brereton, T F North Esq, and DBP (jt)*   **R** J M NOCKELS
MASTIN MOOR (St Paul)   *see* Staveley and Barrow Hill *Derby*
MATCHBOROUGH (Christ Church)   *see* Ipsley *Worc*
MATCHING (St Mary)   *see* High Laver w Magdalen Laver and Lt Laver etc *Chelmsf*
MATCHING GREEN (St Edmund)   *as above Chelmsf*
MATFEN (Holy Trinity)   *see* Stamfordham w Matfen *Newc*
MATFIELD (St Luke)   *see* Lamberhurst and Matfield *Roch*
MATHON (St John the Baptist)   *see* Cradley w Mathon and Storridge *Heref*
MATLASKE (St Peter)   *see* Barningham w Matlaske w Baconsthorpe etc *Nor*
MATLOCK (St Giles) (St John the Baptist) *Derby 7*   **P** *Bp*
  P-in-c B M CROWTHER-ALWYN
MATLOCK BANK (All Saints) *Derby 7*   **P** *Bp*
  P-in-c S I MITCHELL
MATLOCK BATH (Holy Trinity) and Cromford *Derby 7*   **P** *Ch Trust Fund Trust*   **V** J CURRIN,   **NSM** J E STANTON
MATSON (St Katherine) *Glouc 5*   **P** *D&C*   **C** K S ELLIS
MATTERDALE (not known)   *see* Gd Shep TM *Carl*
MATTERSEY (All Saints)   *see* Everton and Mattersey w Clayworth *S'well*
MATTINGLEY (not known)   *see* Heckfield w Mattingley and Rotherwick *Win*
MATTISHALL (All Saints) w Mattishall Burgh, Welborne and Yaxham *Nor 17*   **P** *G&C Coll Cam and Bp (alt)*
  P-in-c G R KEGG
MATTISHALL BURGH (St Peter)   *see* Mattishall w Mattishall Burgh, Welborne etc *Nor*
MAUGHOLD (St Maughold) *S & M 3*   **P** *The Crown*
  V D J GREEN,   **NSM** E C B CORLETT
MAULDEN (St Mary) *St Alb 9*   **P** *Bp*   **R** R C WINSLADE
MAUNBY (St Michael)   *see* Ainderby Steeple w Yafforth and Kirby Wiske etc *Ripon*
MAUTBY (St Peter and St Paul)   *see* S Trin Broads *Nor*
MAVESYN RIDWARE (St Nicholas)   *see* The Ridwares and Kings Bromley *Lich*
MAVIS ENDERBY (St Michael)   *see* Marden Hill Gp *Linc*
MAWDESLEY (St Peter) *Blackb 4*   **P** *R Croston*
  R D J REYNOLDS
MAWGAN (St Mawgan)   *see* Cury and Gunwalloe w Mawgan *Truro*
MAWNAN (St Mawnan) (St Michael) *Truro 3*   **P** *Bp*
  P-in-c G K BENNETT,   **C** C R PINCHBECK
MAXEY (St Peter)   *see* Etton w Helpston and Maxey *Pet*
MAXSTOKE (St Michael and All Angels) *Birm 9*   **P** *Lord Leigh*
  V R G BOLLARD
MAY HILL (All Saints)   *see* Huntley and Longhope, Churcham and Bulley *Glouc*
MAYBRIDGE (St Richard) *Chich 5*   **P** *Bp*   **C** J K GAVIGAN
MAYBUSH Redbridge (All Saints)   *see* Southampton Maybush St Pet *Win*

MAYBUSH (St Peter)   *as above Win*
MAYFAIR (Christ Church) *Lon 3*   **P** *Bp*
  C J P DE COSTOBADIE,   **Hon C** A M ANSELL
MAYFIELD (St Dunstan) *Chich 15*   **P** *Keble Coll Ox*
  V N J PRIOR,   **Hon C** J P CAPERON
MAYFIELD (St John the Baptist) *Lich 15*   **P** *Ch Soc Trust*
  V *vacant* (01335) 342855
MAYFORD (Emmanuel)   *see* Woking St Jo *Guildf*
MAYLAND (St Barnabas) (St Barnabas Family Centre)
  Chelmsf 11   **P** *Bp*   **P-in-c** L BLANEY
MEANWOOD (Holy Trinity) *Ripon 7*   **P** *Bp*   **V** R M WIGGEN
MEARE (Blessed Virgin Mary and All Saints)   *see* Glastonbury w Meare *B & W*
MEARS ASHBY (All Saints) and Hardwick and Sywell w Overstone *Pet 6*   **P** *Duchy of Cornwall (2 turns), Bracegirdle Trustees (1 turn),and Mrs C K Edmiston (1 turn)*   **R** R J LEE
MEASHAM (St Lawrence) *Leic 9*   **P** *CPAS*   **V** J N PEARSON
MEAVY (St Peter)   *see* Yelverton, Meavy, Sheepstor and Walkhampton *Ex*
MEDBOURNE (St Giles)   *see* Six Saints circa Holt *Leic*
MEDMENHAM (St Peter and St Paul)   *see* Hambleden Valley *Ox*
MEDOMSLEY (St Mary Magdalene) *Dur 4*   **P** *Bp*
  V C TODD
MEDSTEAD (St Andrew) cum Wield *Win 2*   **P** *The Crown*
  R *vacant* (01420) 562050
MEERBROOK (St Matthew)   *see* Leek and Meerbrook *Lich*
MEESDEN (St Mary)   *see* Hormead, Wyddial, Anstey, Brent Pelham etc *St Alb*
MEETH (St Michael and All Angels)   *see* Hatherleigh, Meeth, Exbourne and Jacobstowe *Ex*
MEIR (Holy Trinity) *Lich 6*   **P** *Bp*   **P-in-c** J S FOULDS,
  OLM M M ALLBUTT
MEIR HEATH (St Francis of Assisi) *Lich 12*   **P** *Bp*
  V J W PAWSON
MEIR PARK (St Clare)   *see* Meir Heath *Lich*
MELBECKS (Holy Trinity)   *see* Swaledale *Ripon*
MELBOURN (All Saints) *Ely 7*   **P** *D&C*   **V** A D O'BRIEN
MELBOURNE (St Michael) *Derby 15*   **P** *Bp*   **V** J H DAVIES,
  NSM A J FLINTHAM
MELBOURNE (St Monica)   *see* Barmby Moor Gp *York*
MELBURY (St Mary the Virgin) (St Osmund) *Sarum 3*
  P *Patr Bd*   **TV** I BROWN
MELBURY ABBAS (St Thomas)   *see* Shaston *Sarum*
MELBURY BUBB (St Mary the Virgin)   *see* Melbury *Sarum*
MELBURY OSMUND (St Osmund)   *as above Sarum*
MELCHBOURNE (St Mary Magdalene)   *see* The Stodden Churches *St Alb*
MELCOMBE HORSEY (St Andrew)   *see* Milton Abbas, Hilton w Cheselbourne etc *Sarum*
MELDON (St John the Evangelist)   *see* Bolam w Whalton and Hartburn w Meldon *Newc*
MELDRETH (Holy Trinity) *Ely 7*   **P** *D&C*   **V** A D O'BRIEN
MELKSHAM (St Barnabas) (St Michael and All Angels)
  Sarum 14   **P** *DBP*   **TR** D G SMITH,   **TV** M G KUHRT,
  C C M PAINTER
MELKSHAM FOREST (St Andrew)   *see* Melksham *Sarum*
MELLING (St Thomas)   *see* Bickerstaffe and Melling *Liv*
MELLING (St Wilfrid)   *see* E Lonsdale *Blackb*
MELLIS (St Mary the Virgin)   *see* Gislingham and Thorndon *St E*
MELLOR (St Mary) *Blackb 7*   **P** *V Blackb*   **V** J P HUDSON
MELLOR (St Thomas) *Derby 6*   **P** *Bp*   **V** P J JENNER
MELLS (St Andrew) w Buckland Dinham, Elm, Whatley, Vobster and Chantry *B & W 4*   **P** *DBP (2 turns), Bp (1 turns)*
  P-in-c M E WEYMONT
MELMERBY (St John the Baptist)   *see* Skirwith, Ousby and Melmerby w Kirkland *Carl*
MELPLASH (Christ Church)   *see* Beaminster Area *Sarum*
MELSONBY (St James the Great)   *see* Forcett and Aldbrough and Melsonby *Ripon*
MELTHAM Christ the King (St Bartholomew) (St James)
  Wakef 1   **P** *Simeon's Trustees, R Almondbury w Farnley Tyas, and Bp (jt)*   **V** J AUSTIN,   **NSM** P ROLLS, S W DIXON,
  OLM J H HELLIWELL, J F RADCLIFFE
MELTHAM (St Bartholomew)   *see* Meltham *Wakef*
MELTHAM MILLS (St James)   *as above Wakef*
MELTON (St Andrew) and Ufford *St E 7*   **P** *D&C Ely (3 turns), and T R E Blois-Brooke Esq (1 turn)*   **R** P F BLANCH
MELTON, GREAT (All Saints)   *see* Hethersett w Canteloff w Lt and Gt Melton *Nor*
MELTON, HIGH (St James)   *see* Barnburgh w Melton on the Hill etc *Sheff*
MELTON, LITTLE (All Saints)   *see* Hethersett w Canteloff w Lt and Gt Melton *Nor*
MELTON, WEST (St Cuthbert)   *see* Brampton Bierlow *Sheff*

MELTON CONSTABLE (St Peter)   *see* Briston w Burgh Parva and Melton Constable *Nor*
MELTON MOWBRAY (St Mary) *Leic 3*   **P** *Patr Bd*
  TR C A G JENKIN,   **TV** P N GROVES, S A PATERSON,
  C J WHITTAKER
MELTON ROSS (Ascension)   *see* Brocklesby Park *Linc*
MELVERLEY (St Peter)   *see* Kinnerley w Melverley and Knockin w Maesbrook *Lich*
MEMBURY (St John the Baptist)   *see* Axminster, Chardstock, All Saints etc *Ex*
MENDHAM (All Saints)   *see* Fressingfield, Mendham etc *St E*
MENDLESHAM (St Mary) *St E 6*   **P** *SMF*   **V** P T GRAY
MENHENIOT (St Lalluwy and St Antoninus) *Truro 12*
  P *Ex Coll Ox*   **P-in-c** P J CONWAY
MENITH WOOD (Chapel)   *see* Teme Valley N *Worc*
MENSTON (St John the Divine) w Woodhead *Bradf 4*   **P** *Bp*
  V R J YEOMAN
MENTMORE (St Mary the Virgin)   *see* Cheddington w Mentmore and Marsworth *Ox*
MEOLE BRACE (Holy Trinity) *Lich 20*   **P** J K Bather Esq
  V K T ROBERTS,   **C** A S CORNES, C W DEVONISH,
  NSM A M ROBERTS
MEOLS, GREAT (St John the Baptist) *Ches 8*   **P** *Bp*
  V M D HOCKNULL
MEOLS, NORTH (St Cuthbert) *Liv 9*   **P** *Personal Reps R F Hesketh Esq*   **P-in-c** E P TODD,   **C** M J TAYLOR
MEON, EAST (All Saints) *Portsm 4*   **P** *Ld Chan*
  V T E LOUDEN,   **NSM** A M GOTHARD
MEON, WEST (St John the Evangelist) and Warnford *Portsm 4*
  P *Bp and DBP (alt)*   **P-in-c** H G PRIDEAUX
MEONSTOKE (St Andrew) w Corhampton cum Exton *Portsm 1*
  P *Bp*   **P-in-c** J F FOLEY
MEOPHAM (St John the Baptist) w Nurstead *Roch 1*   **P** *D&C and Lt-Col F B Edmeades (jt)*   **R** S H DUNN,
  C P C WOOTTON
MEPAL (St Mary)   *see* Witcham w Mepal *Ely*
MEPPERSHALL (St Mary the Virgin) and Shefford *St Alb 16*
  P *Bp and St Jo Coll Cam (alt)*   **V** *vacant* (01462) 813334
MERE (St Michael the Archangel) w West Knoyle and Maiden Bradley *Sarum 17*   **P** *Bp*   **V** D J J R LINAKER,   **C** J PERRETT,
  NSM S M WOOD
MERESIDE (St Wilfrid)   *see* Blackpool St Wilfrid *Blackb*
MEREVALE (St Mary the Virgin)   *see* Baxterley w Hurley and Wood End and Merevale etc *Birm*
MEREWORTH (St Lawrence) w West Peckham *Roch 7*
  P *Viscount Falmouth and D&C (alt)*   **R** R N MCCONACHIE
MERIDEN (St Laurence) *Cov 4*   **P** *Chapter Cov Cathl*
  R M H DAWKINS
MERRINGTON (St John the Evangelist)   *see* Spennymoor, Whitworth and Merrington *Dur*
MERRIOTT (All Saints) w Hinton, Dinnington and Lopen *B & W 15*   **P** *D&C Bris (2 turns), Bp (1 turn)*   **R** J C KING
MERROW (St John the Evangelist) *Guildf 5*   **P** *Earl of Onslow*
  R A P HODGETTS,   **C** H C ORCHARD,   **OLM** D E C MATTHEWS
MERRY HILL (St Joseph of Arimathea)   *see* Penn Fields *Lich*
MERRYMEET (St Mary)   *see* Menheniot *Truro*
MERSEA, WEST (St Peter and St Paul) w East (St Edmund)
  Chelmsf 16   **P** *Bp and The Crown (alt)*   **R** S C NORTON,
  NSM A R GATES
MERSHAM (St John the Baptist) w Hinxhill and Sellindge
  Cant 12   **P** *Abp*   **P-in-c** J W TIPPING
MERSTHAM (St Katharine) (Epiphany) and Gatton *S'wark 27*
  P *Abp*   **R** J E SMITH,   **C** C E LATHAM
MERSTHAM, SOUTH (All Saints) *S'wark 27*   **P** *Bp*
  P-in-c M S RANDALL
MERSTON (St Giles)   *see* N Mundham w Hunston and Merston *Chich*
MERTON (All Saints)   *see* Shebbear, Buckland Filleigh, Sheepwash etc *Ex*
MERTON (St James) *S'wark 14*   **P** *Bp and V Merton St Mary (jt)*   **V** G N OWEN
MERTON (St John the Divine) *S'wark 14*   **P** *Bp and V Merton St Mary (jt)*   **V** S A ROBERTS
MERTON (St Mary) *S'wark 14*   **P** *Bp*   **V** T G LEARY,
  OLM J F HILLIER
MERTON (St Peter)   *see* Caston, Griston, Merton, Thompson etc *Nor*
MERTON (St Swithun)   *see* Ray Valley *Ox*
MESHAW (St John)   *see* Burrington, Chawleigh, Cheldon, Chulmleigh etc *Ex*
MESSING (All Saints)   *see* Copford w Easthorpe and Messing w Inworth *Chelmsf*
MESSINGHAM (Holy Trinity) *Linc 4*   **P** *Bp*   **V** G D MASSEY
MESTY CROFT (St Luke)   *see* Wednesbury St Paul Wood Green *Lich*
METFIELD (St John the Baptist)   *see* Fressingfield, Mendham etc *St E*

METHERINGHAM (St Wilfred) w Blankney and Dunston
  Linc 18   **P** *Bp (2 turns), Br Field Products Ltd (1 turn)*
  V D C PAYNE
METHLEY (St Oswald) w Mickletown *Ripon 8*   **P** *Bp (3 turns), Duchy of Lanc (1 turn)*   **R** *vacant* (01977) 515278
METHWOLD (St George)   *see* Feltwell and Methwold *Ely*
METTINGHAM (All Saints)   *see* Wainford *St E*
METTON (St Andrew)   *see* Roughton and Felbrigg, Metton, Sustead etc *Nor*
MEVAGISSEY (St Peter) and St Ewe *Truro 1*   **P** *Bp and Penrice Ho (St Austell) Ltd (jt)*   **P-in-c** D G ADAMS
MEXBOROUGH (St John the Baptist) *Sheff 12*   **P** *Adn York*
  V D R WISE
MEYSEY HAMPTON (St Mary) w Marston Meysey and Castle Eaton *Glouc 12*   **P** *Ch Soc Trust*   **R** H BUSK
MICHAEL (St Michael and All Angels) *S & M 3*   **P** *The Crown*
  V *vacant*
MICHAELCHURCH ESCLEY (St Michael)   *see* Clodock and Longtown w Craswall, Llanveynoe etc *Heref*
MICHAELSTOW (St Michael)   *see* St Tudy w St Mabyn and Michaelstow *Truro*
MICHELDEVER (St Mary) and East Stratton, Woodmancote and Popham *Win 7*   **P** *Lord Northbrook (3 turns), Bp (2 turns)*
  V B R G FLENLEY
MICHELMERSH (Our Lady) and Awbridge and Braishfield and Farley Chamberlayne and Timsbury *Win 12*   **P** *Bp*
  R D B KINGTON,   **NSM** S P HEATHER
MICKLEGATE (Holy Trinity) and Bishophill Junior (St Mary)
  York 7   **P** *D&C*   **R** R M C SEED
MICKLEHAM (St Michael)   *see* Leatherhead and Mickleham *Guildf*
MICKLEHURST (All Saints) *Ches 14*   **P** *Bp*
  P-in-c J M MACLEOD
MICKLEOVER (All Saints) *Derby 10*   **P** *MMCET*
  V A W WARD
MICKLEOVER (St John) *Derby 10*   **P** *Bp*   **V** J R HENSON,
  NSM M A PRIDDIN
MICKLETON (St Lawrence), Willersey, Saintbury, Weston-sub-Edge and Aston-sub-Edge *Glouc 10*   **P** *Bp, Lt Col J H Gibbon, Viscount Sandon (1 turn), Ld Chan (1 turn)*
  R D E VINCE
MICKLEY (St George) *Newc 3*   **P** *Bp*   **P-in-c** T EMMETT
MICKLEY (St John the Evangelist)   *see* Fountains Gp *Ripon*
MID MARSH Group, The *Linc 12*   **P** *Rear Admiral G P D Hall, Bp, D&C, and Lord Deramore (by turn)*   **R** B S DIXON,
  OLM L W CARROLL, J R SELFE
MID TRENT *Lich 10*   **P** *Patr Bd*   **TR** J H STERLING,
  TV P H MYERS, J G PEART
MIDDLE   *see also under substantive place name*
MIDDLE RASEN Group, The *Linc 5*   **P** *Bp, Charterhouse, and DBP (jt)*   **R** P C PATRICK
MIDDLEHAM (St Mary and St Alkelda) w Coverdale and East Witton and Thornton Steward *Ripon 4*   **P** *Bp, R Craven-Smith-Milnes Esq, and W R Burdon Esq (jt)*
  R B A GIBLIN
MIDDLESBROUGH (All Saints) *York 18*   **P** *Abp*
  V G HOLLAND,   **C** S L NICHOLSON
MIDDLESBROUGH (Ascension) *York 18*   **P** *Abp*
  V D G HODGSON
MIDDLESBROUGH (Holy Trinity)   *see* N Ormesby *York*
MIDDLESBROUGH (St Agnes) *York 18*   **P** *Abp*
  V P J MOTHERSDALE
MIDDLESBROUGH (St Barnabas)   *see* Linthorpe *York*
MIDDLESBROUGH (St Chad) *York 18*   **P** *Abp*
  V C L BRERETON
MIDDLESBROUGH (St Columba w St Paul) *York 18*   **P** *Abp*
  P-in-c S COOPER
MIDDLESBROUGH (St John the Evangelist) *York 18*   **P** *Abp*
  V G R DREWERY
MIDDLESBROUGH (St Martin of Tours) (St Cuthbert)
  York 18   **P** *Abp*   **V** D JAGO
MIDDLESBROUGH (St Oswald) *York 18*   **P** *Abp*
  V S RICHARDSON,   **NSM** W A DEWING
MIDDLESBROUGH (St Thomas) *York 18*   **P** *Abp*   **V** *vacant*
  (01642) 314504
MIDDLESMOOR (St Chad)   *see* Upper Nidderdale *Ripon*
MIDDLESTOWN (St Luke) *Wakef 12*   **P** *R Thornhill*
  V H C BAKER
MIDDLETON (All Saints)   *see* N Hinckford *Chelmsf*
MIDDLETON (Holy Ghost)   *see* Kirkby Lonsdale *Carl*
MIDDLETON (Holy Trinity)   *see* Bitterley w Middleton, Stoke St Milborough etc *Heref*
MIDDLETON (Holy Trinity) *Heref 13*   **P** *V Chirbury*
  P-in-c P D HARRATT
MIDDLETON (Holy Trinity)   *see* Kelsale-cum-Carlton, Middleton, Theberton etc *St E*
MIDDLETON (St Andrew), Newton and Sinnington *York 20*
  P *Abp (2 turns), Simeon's Trustees (1 turn)*   **R** A M F REED

MIDDLETON (St Cross) *Ripon 6* **P** *DBP* **P-in-c** C BARRETT, NSM J H TURNER

MIDDLETON (St George) (St Laurence) *Dur 8* **P** *Bp* **R** *vacant* (01325) 332557

MIDDLETON (St John the Baptist) *Birm 12* **P** *Bp* **P-in-c** M I RHODES

MIDDLETON (St Leonard) (St Margaret) w Thornham *Man 18* **P** *Bp* **TR** N J FEIST, **TV** C FALLONE, **OLM** F JACKSON, S L SPENCER

MIDDLETON (St Mary) *see* W Winch w Setchey, N Runcton and Middleton *Nor*

MIDDLETON (St Mary the Virgin) *Ripon 6* **P** *V Rothwell* **V** R L A PATERSON, **C** J GOODE

MIDDLETON (St Michael and All Angels) *see* Youlgreave, Middleton, Stanton-in-Peak etc *Derby*

MIDDLETON (St Nicholas) *Chich 1* **P** *D&C* **V** W T MARSTON

MIDDLETON-BY-WIRKSWORTH (Holy Trinity) *see* Wirksworth *Derby*

MIDDLETON CHENEY (All Saints) w Chacombe *Pet 1* **P** *BNC Ox (2 turns), Bp (1 turn)* **R** A VILLAGE

MIDDLETON-IN-CHIRBY (Holy Trinity) *see* Middleton *Heref*

MIDDLETON-IN-TEESDALE (St Mary the Virgin) w Forest and Frith *Dur 7* **P** *Lord Barnard and The Crown (alt)* **R** J E G CLARK

MIDDLETON JUNCTION (St Gabriel) *Man 18* **P** *Bp* **V** I B COOK

MIDDLETON ON LEVEN (St Cuthbert) *see* Rudby in Cleveland w Middleton *York*

MIDDLETON-ON-THE-HILL (St Mary the Virgin) *see* Leominster *Heref*

MIDDLETON-ON-THE-WOLDS (St Andrew) *see* Woldsburn *York*

MIDDLETON SCRIVEN (St John the Baptist) *see* Stottesdon w Farlow, Cleeton St Mary, etc *Heref*

MIDDLETON STONEY (All Saints) *see* Akeman *Ox*

MIDDLETON TYAS (St Michael and All Angels) w Croft and Eryholme *Ripon 2* **P** *Prime Min and V Gilling (alt)* **R** J R WRAIGHT

MIDDLETOWN (St John the Baptist) *see* Gt Wollaston *Heref*

MIDDLEWICH (St Michael and All Angels) w Byley *Ches 6* **P** *Bp* **V** I G BISHOP, **C** L BUTLER, S F HAMILL-STEWART, NSM B W JOBBER

MIDDLEZOY (Holy Cross) and Othery and Moorlinch *B & W 5* **P** *Bp Worc (1 turn), Bp (2 turns)* **P-in-c** M PETERS

MIDGHAM (St Matthew) *see* Woolhampton w Midgham and Beenham Valance *Ox*

MIDHOPE (St James) *see* Penistone and Thurlstone *Wakef*

MIDHURST (St Mary Magdalene and St Denis) *Chich 10* **P** *Rathbone Trust Co and Cowdray Trust (jt)* **V** A T CUNNINGTON

MIDSOMER NORTON (St John the Baptist) w Clandown *B & W 12* **P** *Ch Ch Ox* **V** C G CHIPLIN

MIDVILLE (St Peter) *see* Stickney Gp *Linc*

MILBER (St Luke) *Ex 11* **P** *Bp* **V** J E POTTER

MILBORNE (St Andrew) *see* Puddletown, Tolpuddle and Milborne w Dewlish *Sarum*

MILBORNE PORT (St John the Evangelist) w Goathill *B & W 2* **P** *Mrs J E Smith (2 turns), Trustees (1 turn)* **V** J W B PERRY

MILBORNE WICK (Mission Church) *see* Milborne Port w Goathill *B & W*

MILBOURNE (Holy Saviour) *see* Ponteland *Newc*

MILBURN (St Cuthbert) *see* Long Marton w Dufton and w Milburn *Carl*

MILCOMBE (St Laurence) *see* Bloxham w Milcombe and S Newington *Ox*

MILDEN (St Peter) *see* Monks Eleigh w Chelsworth and Brent Eleigh etc *St E*

MILDENHALL (St John the Baptist) *see* Marlborough *Sarum*

MILDENHALL (St Mary) *St E 11* **P** *Patr Bd (2 turns), Bp (1 turn)* **TR** G C GRIFFITHS, **TV** A W SPENCER, S M HODGES, **C** I COOPER, NSM P W TAMS, **OLM** H B MULLIN, M E RUSTED, B J STEDMAN

MILDMAY GROVE (St Jude and St Paul) *Lon 6* **P** *Islington Ch Trust* **V** D SILVESTER

MILE CROSS (St Catherine) *see* Horsford and Horsham w Newton St Faith *Nor*

MILE CROSS (St Catherine) *Nor 2* **P** *Dr J P English, Canon G F Bridger, Revd K W Habershon, and Revd H Palmer (jt)* **V** P D MACKAY, **C** S J STEWART

MILE END (Holy Trinity) *Lon 7* **P** *Bp and Grocers' Co (jt)* **V** J M PEET

MILE END Old Town (St Paul) *see* Bow Common *Lon*

MILE OAK (The Good Shepherd) *see* Portslade Gd Shep *Chich*

MILEHAM (St John the Baptist) *see* Litcham w Kempston, E and W Lexham, Mileham etc *Nor*

MILES PLATTING (St Cuthbert) *see* Man Apostles w Miles Platting *Man*

MILFORD (Holy Trinity) *see* Hazlewood and Milford *Derby*

MILFORD (St John the Evangelist) *Guildf 4* **P** *V Witley* **V** D J MUSKETT

MILFORD, SOUTH (St Mary the Virgin) *see* Monk Fryston and S Milford *York*

MILFORD-ON-SEA (All Saints) *Win 11* **P** *Bp* **V** A M C DUNN

MILKWALL (St Luke) *see* Coleford w Staunton *Glouc*

MILL END (St Peter) and Heronsgate w West Hyde *St Alb 5* **P** *Bp and V Rickmansworth* **V** M R NICHOLLS, **C** A R LING

MILL HILL (John Keble Church) *Lon 15* **P** *Bp* **V** O R OSMOND, NSM I GODFREY

MILL HILL (St Michael and All Angels) *Lon 15* **P** *Bp* **V** B O WRIGHT

MILL HILL (St Paul) *see* Hendon St Paul Mill Hill *Lon*

MILLAND (St Luke) *see* Lynch w Iping Marsh and Milland *Chich*

MILLBROOK (All Saints) *see* St John w Millbrook *Truro*

MILLBROOK (Christ the King) *see* Kettering Ch the King *Pet*

MILLBROOK (Holy Trinity) *Win 13* **P** *Bp* **P-in-c** W F P PERRY

MILLBROOK Regents Park (St Clement) *see* Millbrook *Win*

MILLBROOK (St James) *Ches 14* **P** *Bp, V Stalybridge St Paul, and Mrs E Bissill (jt)* **P-in-c** P N BROMILEY

MILLBROOK (St Michael and All Angels) *see* Ampthill w Millbrook and Steppingley *St Alb*

MILLERS DALE (St Anne) *see* Tideswell *Derby*

MILLFIELD (St Mark) and Pallion St Luke *Dur 16* **P** *Bp* **V** M R JUDSON, **C** P W JUDSON, NSM S E HOBLEY

MILLFIELD (St Mary) *Dur 16* **P** *The Crown* **V** B SKELTON

MILLHOUSES (Holy Trinity) *Sheff 2* **P** *Bp* **V** E M PERCY, **C** A J ARMITT, **Hon C** M W PERCY, NSM I W DRAFFAN, J LEE

MILLHOUSES (St Oswald) *see* Sheff St Oswald *Sheff*

MILLINGTON (St Margaret) *see* Pocklington and Owsthorpe and Kilnwick Percy etc *York*

MILLOM Holburn Hill (Mission) *see* Millom *Carl*

MILLOM (Holy Trinity) (St George) *Carl 9* **P** *Bp and Trustees (jt)* **P-in-c** R K S BRACEGIRDLE

MILNROW (St James) *Man 20* **P** *TR Rochdale* **V** R R USHER

MILNSHAW (St Mary Magdalen) *see* Accrington Ch the King *Blackb*

MILNTHORPE (St Thomas) *see* Heversham and Milnthorpe *Carl*

MILSON (St George) *see* Cleobury Mortimer w Hopton Wafers etc *Heref*

MILSTED (St Mary and the Holy Cross) *see* Bredgar w Bicknor and Frinsted w Wormshill etc *Cant*

MILSTON (St Mary) *see* Avon Valley *Sarum*

MILTON (All Saints) *Ely 5* **P** *K Coll Cam* **R** I M COWLEY, NSM A L ALDRIDGE

MILTON (St Blaise) *see* Steventon w Milton *Ox*

MILTON (St James) (St Andrew's Church Centre) (St Patrick) *Portsm 6* **P** *V Portsea St Mary* **V** H O ALBY, **C** C W WOOD

MILTON (St John the Evangelist) *see* Adderbury w Milton *Ox*

MILTON (St Mary Magdalene) *Win 9* **P** *V Milford* **R** A H BAILEY, **C** M D SHELDON, **Hon C** G A SMITH

MILTON (St Peter) w St Jude *B & W 11* **P** *Ld Chan* **V** J N O WILLIAMS, NSM G PUTNAM

MILTON (St Philip and St James) *Lich 8* **P** *Bp* **V** D W WATKIN

MILTON (St Simon and St Jude) *see* Gillingham *Sarum*

MILTON, GREAT (St Mary the Virgin) w Little (St James) and Great Haseley *Ox 1* **P** *Bp and D&C Windsor (jt)* **R** V L STORY

MILTON, SOUTH (All Saints) *see* Thurlestone, S Milton, W Alvington etc *Ex*

MILTON ABBAS (St James the Great), Hilton w Cheselbourne and Melcombe Horsey *Sarum 6* **P** *Bp (3 turns) and G A L F Pitt-Rivers Esq (1 turn)* **P-in-c** J M BAILEY, NSM H J P EXON

MILTON ABBOT (St Constantine), Dunterton, Lamerton, Sydenham Damerel, Marystowe and Coryton *Ex 25* **P** *Bp, Bedford Estates, J W Tremayne Esq, Mrs E J Bullock, P T L Newman Esq (jt)* **V** G J STANTON

MILTON BRYAN (St Peter) *see* Woburn w Eversholt, Milton Bryan, Battlesden etc *St Alb*

MILTON CLEVEDON (St James) *see* Evercreech w Chesterblade and Milton Clevedon *B & W*

MILTON COMBE (Holy Spirit) *see* Buckland Monachorum *Ex*

MILTON DAMEREL (Holy Trinity) *see* Holsworthy w Hollacombe and Milton Damerel *Ex*

MILTON ERNEST (All Saints), Pavenham and Thurleigh
St Alb 15   **P** *Bp (2 turns), Lord Luke (1 turn)*
V N A MCINTOSH,   I M MCINTOSH

MILTON KEYNES (Christ the Cornerstone) *Ox 25*   **P** *Bp*
V R M CATTLEY,   **NSM** B J HOLLINS

MILTON KEYNES VILLAGE (All Saints) *see* Walton Milton Keynes *Ox*

MILTON LILBOURNE (St Peter) *see* Pewsey and Swanborough *Sarum*

MILTON MALSOR (Holy Cross) *see* Collingtree w Courteenhall and Milton Malsor *Pet*

MILTON NEXT GRAVESEND (Christ Church) *Roch 4*   **P** *Bp*
V J S KING,   **Hon C** A P WIBROE

MILTON NEXT GRAVESEND (St Peter and St Paul) w Denton
Roch 4   **P** *Bp*   **R** V J LAWRENCE

MILTON NEXT SITTINGBOURNE (Holy Trinity) *Cant 16*
P *D&C*   **V** G H GREEN

MILTON REGIS (Holy Trinity) *see* Milton next Sittingbourne *Cant*

MILTON REGIS (St Mary) *see* Sittingbourne St Mary and St Mich *Cant*

MILTON-UNDER-WYCHWOOD (St Simon and St Jude) *see* Shipton-under-Wychwood w Milton, Fifield etc *Ox*

MILVERTON (St Michael) w Halse and Fitzhead *B & W 19*
P *Adn Taunton (4 turns), Bp and V Wiveliscombe (1 turn)*
R A D NORRIS

MILVERTON, NEW (St Mark) *Cov 11*   **P** *CPAS*   **V** A MORT

MILVERTON, OLD (St James) *see* Leamington Spa H Trin and Old Milverton *Cov*

MILWICH (All Saints) *see* Mid Trent *Lich*

MIMMS *see also* MYMMS

MIMMS, SOUTH (Christ Church) *Lon 14*   **P** *Ch Patr Trust*
V N T W TAYLOR,   **C** K G M HILTON-TURVEY,
NSM P W LIDDELOW, K A P WOODHAMS

MINCHINHAMPTON (Holy Trinity) *Glouc 8*   **P** *Bp*
R M J D IRVING,   **NSM** A GUY, J A JAMES

MINEHEAD (St Andrew) (St Michael) (St Peter) *B & W 16*
P *Lt-Col G W F Luttrell and Bp (jt)*   **V** G J WRAYFORD,
C E D H LEAF

MINETY (St Leonard) *see* Ashton Keynes, Leigh and Minety *Bris*

MININGSBY WITH EAST KIRKBY (St Nicholas) *see* Marden Hill Gp *Linc*

MINLEY (St Andrew) *Guildf 1*   **P** *Bp*   **V** M W NEALE

MINNIS BAY (St Thomas) *see* Birchington w Acol and Minnis Bay *Cant*

MINSKIP (Mission Room) *see* Aldborough w Boroughbridge and Roecliffe *Ripon*

MINSTEAD (All Saints) *see* Lyndhurst and Emery Down and Minstead *Win*

MINSTER (St Mary the Virgin) w Monkton *Cant 9*   **P** *Abp*
P-in-c R R COLES

MINSTER (St Merteriana) *see* Boscastle w Davidstow *Truro*

MINSTER-IN-SHEPPEY (St Mary and St Sexburga) *Cant 16*
P *Ch Patr Trust*   **V** G H SPENCER,   **C** G TOWNSEND,
NSM J G KNELL, S A BIRCH

MINSTER LOVELL (St Kenelm) *Ox 8*   **P** *Eton Coll and Ch Ch Ox (jt)*   **V** A W D GABB-JONES

MINSTERLEY (Holy Trinity) *Heref 13*   **P** *DBP and Bp (alt)*
V A N TOOP

MINSTERWORTH (St Peter) *see* Westbury-on-Severn w Flaxley, Blaisdon etc *Glouc*

MINTERNE MAGNA (St Andrew) *see* Buckland Newton, Cerne Abbas, Godmanstone etc *Sarum*

MINTING (St Andrew) *see* Bardney *Linc*

MIREHOUSE (St Andrew) *Carl 5*   **P** *Bp*   **V** M BARBER

MIRFIELD (St Mary) *Wakef 10*   **P** *Bp*   **V** P J CRAIG-WILD,
C S J BUCHANAN,   **OLM** A POLLARD

MISERDEN (St Andrew) *see* Bisley, Oakridge, Miserden and Edgeworth *Glouc*

MISSENDEN, GREAT (St Peter and St Paul) w Ballinger and Little Hampden *Ox 28*   **P** *Bp*   **P-in-c** R E HARPER

MISSENDEN, LITTLE (St John the Baptist) *Ox 28*
P *Earl Howe*   **P-in-c** B M M O'CONNOR

MISSION (St John the Baptist) *see* Bawtry w Austerfield and Misson *S'well*

MISTERTON (All Saints) and West Stockwith *S'well 1*
P *D&C York and Bp (alt)*   **NSM** J D HENSON

MISTERTON (St Leonard) *see* Haselbury Plucknett, Misterton and N Perrott *B & W*

MISTERTON (St Leonard) *see* Gilmorton, Peatling Parva, Kimcote etc *Leic*

MISTLEY (St Mary and St Michael) w Manningtree and Bradfield *Chelmsf 20*   **P** *DBP and Bp (jt)*   **R** A COLEBROOKE,
NSM J R BRIEN

MITCHAM (Ascension) Pollards Hill *S'wark 14*   **P** *Bp*
V J M THOMAS,   **NSM** J E ROBERTS,   **OLM** P M STEVENSON

MITCHAM (Christ Church) *see* Colliers Wood Ch Ch *S'wark*

MITCHAM (St Barnabas) *S'wark 14*   **P** *Bp*   **V** A J PRICE

MITCHAM (St Mark) *S'wark 14*   **P** *Bp*   **V** S H COULSON,
NSM H NEALE

MITCHAM (St Olave) *S'wark 14*   **P** *The Crown*
V P G ENSOR,   **OLM** R H P BRENCHLEY

MITCHAM (St Peter and St Paul) *S'wark 14*   **P** *Keble Coll Ox*
V J C ANSELL

MITCHELDEAN (St Michael and All Angels) *see* Abenhall w Mitcheldean *Glouc*

MITFORD (St Mary Magdalene) *Newc 11*   **P** *Brig E C Mitford*
V D F MAYHEW

MITHIAN (St Peter) *see* St Agnes and Mithian w Mount Hawke *Truro*

MITTON (All Hallows) *see* Hurst Green and Mitton *Bradf*

MIXBURY (All Saints) *see* Shelswell *Ox*

MIXENDEN (Holy Nativity) *Wakef 4*   **P** *Bp*
C D E FLETCHER,   **NSM** M H NEVILL

MOBBERLEY (St Wilfrid) *Ches 12*   **P** *Bp*   **R** M D GRAY

MOCCAS (St Michael and All Angels) *see* Cusop w Blakemere, Bredwardine w Brobury etc *Heref*

MODBURY (St George), Bigbury, Ringmore w Kingston, Aveton Gifford, Woodleigh, Loddiswell and Allington, East *Ex 14*
P *Patr Bd*   **TV** R C CAMPBELL-SMITH,   **TV** M L JEFFERIES,
C J A ELLIOTT

MODDERSHALL (All Saints) *see* Stone Ch Ch and Oulton *Lich*

MOGGERHANGER (St John the Evangelist) *see* Cople, Moggerhanger and Willington *St Alb*

MOIRA (St Hilda) *see* Donisthorpe and Moira w Stretton-en-le-Field *Leic*

MOLASH (St Peter) *see* Chilham w Challock and Molash *Cant*

MOLDGREEN (Christ Church) and Rawthorpe St James
Wakef 1   **P** *R Kirkheaton and DBP (jt)*   **V** V POLLARD

MOLESCROFT (St Leonard) *see* Beverley Minster *York*

MOLESEY, EAST (St Mary) *Guildf 8*   **P** *Bp*
P-in-c D J ADAMS

MOLESEY, EAST (St Paul) *Guildf 8*   **P** *Bp*
P-in-c A D MILTON,   **OLM** C J C KIRK

MOLESEY, WEST (St Peter) *Guildf 8*   **P** *Canon W K Perry-Gore*   **P-in-c** P A TAILBY

MOLESWORTH (St Peter) *see* Brington w Molesworth and Old Weston *Ely*

MOLLAND (St Mary) *see* Bishopsnympton, Rose Ash, Mariansleigh etc *Ex*

MOLLINGTON (All Saints) *see* Shires' Edge *Ox*

MOLTON, NORTH (All Saints) *see* S Molton w Nymet St George, High Bray etc *Ex*

MOLTON, SOUTH (St Mary Magdalene) w Nymet St George, High Bray, Charles, Filleigh, East Buckland, Warkleigh, Satterleigh, Chittlehamholt, Kingsnympton, Romansleigh, North Molton, Twitchen and Chittlehampton *Ex 18*   **P** *DBP*
TR R D SIMPSON,   **TV** M WARD, D W T RUDMAN,
C P PARKS, C A J DAVIS

MONEWDEN (St Mary) *see* Charsfield w Debach, Monewden, Hoo etc *St E*

MONGEHAM, GREAT (St Martin) w Ripple and Sutton by Dover *Cant 8*   **P** *Abp*   **P-in-c** M CLEEVE,
OLM P J HAMBROOK

MONK BRETTON (St Paul) *Wakef 7*   **P** *V Royston*
V P A BOSTOCK,   **OLM** J CROSSLAND

MONK FRYSTON (St Wilfrid of Ripon) and South Milford
York 4   **P** *Ld Chan and Abp (alt)*   **R** D G RICHARDSON,
C S JUKES

MONK SHERBORNE (All Saints) *see* The Sherbornes w Pamber *Win*

MONK SOHAM (St Peter) *see* Worlingworth, Southolt, Tannington, Bedfield etc *St E*

MONKEN HADLEY (St Mary the Virgin) *Lon 14*
P *N A Dove Esq*   **R** D J NASH,   **NSM** J D LINTHICUM

MONKHOPTON (St Peter) *see* Upton Cressett w Monk Hopton *Heref*

MONKLAND (All Saints) *see* Leominster *Heref*

MONKLEIGH (St George) *see* Bideford, Northam, Westward Ho!, Appledore etc *Ex*

MONKOKEHAMPTON (All Saints) *Ex 19*   **P** *Bp*
P-in-c A S GRAESSER

MONKS COPPENHALL (Christ Church) *see* Crewe Ch Ch and St Pet *Ches*

MONKS ELEIGH (St Peter) w Chelsworth and Brent Eleigh w Milden and Kettlebaston *St E 10*   **P** *Bp, Guild of All So, Ld Chan (2 turns), and M J Hawkins Esq*   **R** *vacant* (01449) 740244

MONKS HORTON (St Peter) *see* Smeeth w Monks Horton and Stowting and Brabourne *Cant*

MONKS KIRBY (St Editha) w Pailton and Stretton-under-Fosse
Cov 6 **P** *Trin Coll Cam* **V** P S RUSSELL
MONKS RISBOROUGH (St Dunstan) *see Risborough Ox*
MONKSEATON (St Mary) *Newc 8* **P** *Bp* **V** C H KNIGHTS,
C B P S VALLIS
MONKSEATON (St Peter) *Newc 8* **P** *Bp* **V** J A ROBERTSON
MONKSILVER (All Saints) *see Quantock Towers B & W*
MONKTON (St Mary Magdalene) *see Minster w Monkton
Cant*
MONKTON (St Mary Magdalene) *see Honiton, Gittisham,
Combe Raleigh, Monkton etc Ex*
MONKTON, WEST (St Augustine) *B & W 18* **P** *Bp*
P-in-c G J BOUCHER
MONKTON COMBE (St Michael) *see Combe Down w
Monkton Combe and S Stoke B & W*
MONKTON FARLEIGH (St Peter), South Wraxall and Winsley
Sarum 14 **P** *D&C Bris (2 turns), Bp (1 turn)* **R** R S GREEN,
NSM M A CLARK
MONKTON WYLD (St Andrew) *see Golden Cap Team Sarum*
MONKWEARMOUTH (All Saints) (St Andrew) (St Peter)
Dur 16 **P** *Bp* **TR** I G STOCKTON, **TV** S G HILL,
E G NDAHANI, **C** J R MCMANNERS
MONKWOOD (Mission Church) *see Bishop's Sutton and
Ropley and W Tisted Win*
MONNINGTON-ON-WYE (St Mary) *see Letton w Staunton,
Byford, Mansel Gamage etc Heref*
MONTACUTE (St Catherine of Alexandria) *see Odcombe,
Brympton, Lufton and Montacute B & W*
MONTFORD (St Chad) *see Bicton, Montford w Shrawardine
and Fitz Lich*
MONTON (St Paul) *see Eccles Man*
MONXTON (St Mary) *see Amport, Grateley, Monxton and
Quarley Win*
MONYASH (St Leonard) *see Taddington, Chelmorton and
Flagg, and Monyash Derby*
MOOR (St Thomas) *see Fladbury w Wyre Piddle and Moor etc
Worc*
MOOR ALLERTON (St John the Evangelist) (St Stephen)
Ripon 5 **P** *Patr Bd* **TR** C P DOBBIN, **TV** N D BEER,
P H AINSWORTH, **NSM** J E SHAW
MOOR COURT (St Mary) *see Pembridge w Moor Court,
Shobdon, Staunton etc Heref*
MOOR GRANGE (St Andrew) *see Hawksworth Wood Ripon*
MOOR MILNER (Church Institute) *see Daresbury Ches*
MOOR MONKTON (All Saints) *see Rufforth w Moor
Monkton and Hessay York*
MOORBRIDGE LANE (St Luke) *see Stapleford S'well*
MOORCOURT (St Mary) *see Pembridge w Moor Court,
Shobdon, Staunton etc Heref*
MOORDOWN (St John the Baptist) *Win 8* **P** *Bp*
V W A SWAIN, **NSM** J L WILLIAMS
MOORENDS (St Wilfrith) *Sheff 10* **P** *Bp* **V** R B PARKER
MOORHOUSE (Chantry Chapel) *see Kneesall w Laxton and
Wellow S'well*
MOORHOUSES (St Lawrence) *see Mareham-le-Fen and
Revesby Linc*
MOORLAND TEAM *see Widecombe-in-the-Moor, Leusdon,
Princetown etc Ex*
MOORLINCH (Blessed Virgin Mary) *see Middlezoy and
Othery and Moorlinch B & W*
MOORSHOLM (St Mary) *see Boosbeck w Moorsholm York*
MOORSIDE (St Thomas) *see Oldham Moorside Man*
MOORSIDE (St Wilfrid) *see Doxford St Wilfrid Dur*
MORBORNE (All Saints) *see Stilton w Denton and Caldecote
etc Ely*
MORCHARD BISHOP (St Mary) *see N Creedy Ex*
MORCOTT (St Mary the Virgin) *see Barrowden and Wakerley
w S Luffenham etc Pet*
**MORDEN (Emmanuel Church Hall) (St George) (St Lawrence)
(St Martin)** *S'wark 14* **P** *Patr Bd* **TR** R F SKINNER,
TV C A WOOD, A L FLOWERDAY, J C BRIGHTWELL,
C L J PROUDLOVE
MORDEN (St Mary) *see Red Post Sarum*
MORDIFORD (Holy Rood) *see Fownhope w Mordiford,
Brockhampton etc Heref*
MORE (St Peter) *see Wentnor w Ratlinghope, Myndtown,
Norbury etc Heref*
MOREBATH (St George) *see Bampton, Morebath, Clayhanger
and Petton Ex*
MORECAMBE (Holy Trinity) *see Poulton-le-Sands w
Morecambe St Laur Blackb*
MORECAMBE (St Andrew) *see Heysham Blackb*
MORECAMBE (St Barnabas) *Blackb 11*
P *R Poulton-le-Sands* **V** G J HUMPHRYES
MORECAMBE (St Christopher) *see Bare Blackb*
MORECAMBE (St James) *see Heysham Blackb*

MORECAMBE (St John) *see Sandylands Blackb*
MORECAMBE (St Peter) *see Heysham Blackb*
MORECAMBE (The Ascension) *see Torrisholme Blackb*
MORELEIGH (All Saints) *see Diptford, N Huish, Harberton,
Harbertonford etc Ex*
MORESBY (St Bridget) *Carl 5* **P** *Earl of Lonsdale*
R A D EDWARDS
MORESBY PARKS (Mission Church) *see Moresby Carl*
MORESTEAD (not known) *see Twyford and Owslebury and
Morestead Win*
MORETON (Christ Church) *Ches 8* **P** *Simeon's Trustees*
R G J COUSINS
MORETON (St Mary) *see Fyfield, Moreton w Bobbingworth
etc Chelmsf*
MORETON (St Mary) *see Bradeley, Church Eaton and
Moreton Lich*
MORETON (St Nicholas) and Woodsford w Tincleton *Sarum 1*
P *Hon Mrs M A Bartenk and Miss M B F Frampton (alt)*
R G F PERRYMAN
**MORETON, SOUTH (St John the Baptist) w North (All Saints),
Aston Tirrold and Aston Upthorpe** *Ox 18* **P** *Adn Berks, Hertf
Coll Ox, and Magd Coll Ox (jt)* **R** C J WALKER
MORETON CORBET (St Bartholomew) *Lich 22*
P C C Corbet Esq **R** D J HUMPHRIES
MORETON HALL (Christ Church) *see Bury St Edmunds Ch
Ch St E*
**MORETON-IN-MARSH (St David) w Batsford, Todenham,
Lower Lemiington and Longborough w Sezincote** *Glouc 14*
P *Bp and Lord Dulverton (1 turn), and Bp, Lord Dulverton, Lord
Leigh, and Mrs S Peake (1 turn)* **R** S M WOOKEY, **C** S P REES
MORETON JEFFRIES (St Peter and St Paul) *see Stoke Lacy,
Moreton Jeffries w Much Cowarne etc Heref*
MORETON MORRELL (Holy Cross) *see Newbold Pacey w
Moreton Morrell Cov*
MORETON-ON-LUGG (St Andrew) *see Wellington w
Pipe-cum-Lyde and Moreton-on-Lugg Heref*
MORETON PINKNEY (St Mary the Virgin) *see Weedon Lois
w Plumpton and Moreton Pinkney etc Pet*
MORETON SAY (St Margaret of Antioch) *see Adderley, Ash,
Calverhall, Ightfield etc Lich*
MORETON VALENCE (St Stephen) *see Eastington, Frocester,
Haresfield etc Glouc*
**MORETONHAMPSTEAD (St Andrew), Manaton, North
Bovey and Lustleigh** *Ex 10* **P** *Bp and DBP (jt)*
R I A HELLYER
MORGAN'S VALE (St Birinus) *see Redlynch and Morgan's
Vale Sarum*
MORLAND (St Lawrence), Thrimby, Gt Strickland and Cliburn
Carl 1 **P** *Lord Hothfield and D&C (jt)* **V** S D RUDKIN
MORLEY (St Botolph) *see High Oak, Hingham and Scoulton
w Wood Rising Nor*
MORLEY (St Matthew) w Smalley and Horsley Woodhouse
Derby 12 **P** *Bp* **R** C HENSON
MORLEY (St Peter) *see High Oak, Hingham and Scoulton w
Wood Rising Nor*
MORLEY (St Peter) (St Paul) *Wakef 8* **P** *Patr Bd*
TR M R EAREY, **TV** M M DYE, A D WOOD
MORNINGTHORPE (St John the Baptist) *see Hempnall Nor*
MORPETH (St Aidan) (St James) (St Mary the Virgin) *Newc 11*
P *Bp* **R** R H MCLEAN, **C** J C PARK, **NSM** M O CHESTER
MORSTON (All Saints) *see Stiffkey and Cockthorpe w
Morston, Langham etc Nor*
MORTEHOE (St Mary Magdalene) *see Ilfracombe, Lee,
Woolacombe, Bittadon etc Ex*
MORTIMER COMMON (St John) *see Stratfield Mortimer and
Mortimer W End etc Ox*
MORTIMER WEST END (St Saviour) *as above Ox*
MORTLAKE (St Mary) w East Sheen *S'wark 18* **P** *Patr Bd*
TR F A JACKSON, **TV** E H LEE, C PALMER, **Hon C** P D KING
MORTOMLEY (St Saviour) High Green *Sheff 3* **P** *Bp*
V E MITCHELL, **C** N J BUNDOCK
MORTON (Holy Cross) and Stonebroom w Shirland *Derby 1*
P *Bp, St Jo Coll Cam, Adn Chesterfield, and trustees (by turn)*
R C A DYER, **C** J C BAINES
MORTON (St Denis) *see Rolleston w Fiskerton, Morton and
Upton S'well*
MORTON (St John the Baptist) *see Ringstone in Aveland Gp
Linc*
MORTON (St Luke) *Bradf 8* **P** *Bp*
NSM A R CULLINGWORTH
MORTON (St Paul) *see Gainsborough and Morton Linc*
MORTON (St Philip and St James) *Lich 19* **P** *Ld Chan*
V *vacant*
MORTON BAGOT (Holy Trinity) *see Spernall, Morton Bagot
and Oldberrow Cov*
MORVAH (St Bridget of Sweden) *see Pendeen w Morvah Truro*

MORVAL (St Wenna)   *see* Duloe, Herodsfoot, Morval and St Pinnock *Truro*

MORVILLE (St Gregory) w Aston Eyre *Heref 9*   **P** *DBP*   **Hon C** H J PATTERSON

MORWENSTOW (St John the Baptist)   *see* Kilkhampton w Morwenstow *Truro*

MOSBROUGH (St Mark) *Sheff 1*   **P** *Bp*   **V** D J HULL

MOSELEY (St Agnes) *Birm 5*   **P** *V Moseley St Mary*   **V** P H ANSELL

MOSELEY (St Anne) *Birm 5*   **P** *V Moseley St Mary*   **NSM** A J JOYCE

MOSELEY (St Mary) *Birm 5*   **P** *Bp*   **V** A BRADBROOK, **C** P A SMITH,   **NSM** J A GRIFFIN, R S F BUCKLEY

MOSLEY COMMON (St John) *Man 13*   **P** *Bp*   **P-in-c** J J HARTLEY

MOSS BANK (Mission Church)   *see* Carr Mill *Liv*

MOSS SIDE (Christ Church) *Man 4*   **P** *Trustees*   **P-in-c** S D A KILLWICK

MOSS SIDE (St James w St Clement) *Man 4*   **P** *Bp*   **P-in-c** S R BULLOCK,   **C** J R GAVIN

MOSSER (St Philip) (Michael's Chapel) *Carl 6*   **P** *Bp*   **P-in-c** K KITCHIN

MOSSLEY (Holy Trinity)   *see* Congleton *Ches*

MOSSLEY (St George) *Man 17*   **P** *R Ashton-under-Lyne St Mich*   **V** R J LINDSAY,   **OLM** P PHILLIPS

MOSSLEY ESTATE (St Thomas Church)   *see* Bloxwich *Lich*

MOSSLEY HILL (St Barnabas) *Liv 4*   **P** *Bp*   **V** *vacant* 0151--733 1432

MOSSLEY HILL (St Matthew and St James) *Liv 4*   **P** *Trustees*   **P-in-c** R A WILKES,   **C** E M STOREY

MOSSWOOD (St Barnabas)   *see* Cannock *Lich*

MOSTERTON (St Mary)   *see* Beaminster Area *Sarum*

MOSTON (St Chad) *Man 5*   **P** *Bp*   **P-in-c** I C J GORTON

MOSTON (St John) Ashley Lane *Man 5*   **P** *Bp*   **R** C S FORD

MOSTON (St Luke)   *see* Lightbowne *Man*

MOSTON (St Mary) *Man 5*   **P** *D&C*   **P-in-c** M R M CALLADINE,   **NSM** J E CALLADINE,   **OLM** G L CORNISH

MOTCOMBE (St Mary)   *see* Shaston *Sarum*

MOTSPUR PARK (Holy Cross) *S'wark 14*   **P** *Bp*   **V** A P ROBBINS-COLE,   **Hon C** S J ROBBINS-COLE

MOTTINGHAM (St Andrew) (St Alban Mission Church) *S'wark 3*   **P** *Bp*   **R** G W DAVIES,   **NSM** D WARREN

MOTTINGHAM (St Edward the Confessor) *S'wark 3*   **P** *Bp*   **V** M J JACKSON

MOTTISFONT (St Andrew)   *see* Broughton, Bossington, Houghton and Mottisfont *Win*

MOTTISTONE (St Peter and St Paul)   *see* Brighstone and Brooke w Mottistone *Portsm*

MOTTRAM IN LONGDENDALE (St Michael) *Ches 14*   **P** *Bp*   **V** P G BURROWS

MOULSECOOMB (St Andrew) *Chich 2*   **P** *Bp*   **TR** J K T ELDRIDGE,   **TV** M A J BUCHAN

MOULSFORD (St John the Baptist)   *see* Streatley w Moulsford *Ox*

MOULSHAM (St John the Evangelist) *Chelmsf 9*   **P** *Dean*   **V** D J NORFIELD,   **NSM** S M SOUTHEE

MOULSHAM (St Luke) *Chelmsf 9*   **P** *Bp*   **V** S M CHAPMAN,   **NSM** S E IVES

MOULSOE (The Assumption of the Blessed Virgin Mary)   *see* Newport Pagnell w Lathbury and Moulsoe *Ox*

MOULTON (All Saints) (St James) (Mission Room) *Linc 17*   **P** *DBP*   **V** *vacant* (01406) 370791

MOULTON (Mission Church)   *see* Middleton Tyas w Croft and Eryholme *Ripon*

MOULTON (St Peter)   *see* Gazeley w Dalham, Moulton and Kentford *St E*

MOULTON (St Peter and St Paul) *Pet 4*   **P** *Ch Soc Trust*   **V** P H BRECKWOLDT,   **C** M S COE

MOULTON (St Stephen the Martyr) *Ches 6*   **P** *R Davenham*   **P-in-c** A Q GREENHOUGH

MOULTON, GREAT (St Michael)   *see* Bunwell, Carleton Rode, Tibenham, Gt Moulton etc *Nor*

MOUNT BURES (St John)   *see* Wormingford, Mt Bures and Lt Horkesley *Chelmsf*

MOUNT HAWKE (St John the Baptist)   *see* St Agnes and Mithian w Mount Hawke *Truro*

MOUNT PELLON (Christ Church) *Wakef 4*   **P** *Bp*   **V** T J E MAYFIELD

MOUNTFIELD (All Saints)   *see* Brightling, Dallington, Mountfield etc *Chich*

MOUNTNESSING (St Giles)   *see* Doddinghurst and Mountnessing *Chelmsf*

MOUNTSORREL (Christ Church) (St Peter) *Leic 7*   **P** *CPAS and Bp*   **C** R A LAMBERT

MOW COP (St Luke's Mission Church)   *see* Odd Rode *Ches*

MOW COP (St Thomas) *Lich 11*   **P** *Prime Min*   **P-in-c** J C WATERS

MOWSLEY (St Nicholas)   *see* Husbands Bosworth w Mowsley and Knaptoft etc *Leic*

MOXLEY (All Saints) *Lich 26*   **P** *Prime Min*   **P-in-c** R E INGLESBY,   **OLM** A J DUCKWORTH

MUCH   *see also under substantive place name*

MUCH BIRCH (St Mary and St Thomas à Becket) w Little Birch, Much Dewchurch, Llanwarne and Llandinabo *Heref 8*   **P** *A W Twiston-Davies Esq (1 turn), Bp (3 turns), and Ld Chan (1 turn)*   **P-in-c** K B GARLICK

MUCH MARCLE (St Bartholomew)   *see* Ledbury *Heref*

MUCHELNEY (St Peter and St Paul)   *see* Langport Area Chs *B & W*

MUCKLESTONE (St Mary) *Lich 7*   **P** *Mrs F F Friend*   **P-in-c** D J WILLIAMS

MUDEFORD (All Saints)   *see* Christchurch *Win*

MUDFORD (Blessed Virgin Mary)   *see* Chilton Cantelo, Ashington, Mudford, Rimpton etc *B & W*

MUGGINTON (All Saints) and Kedleston *Derby 11*   **P** *Major J W Chandos-Pole*   **NSM** H M MEYNELL

MUGGLESWICK (All Saints)   *see* Blanchland w Hunstanworth and Edmundbyers etc *Newc*

MUKER (St Mary)   *see* Swaledale *Ripon*

MULBARTON (St Mary Magdalene) w Bracon Ash, Hethel and Flordon *Nor 7*   **P** *R T Berney Esq (1 turn), Mrs R M Watkinson (2 turns), DBP (1 turn), and Ld Chan (1 turn)*   **R** J W STUBENBORD

MULLION (St Mellanus) *Truro 4*   **P** *Bp*   **V** *vacant* (01326) 240325

MUMBY (St Thomas of Canterbury)   *see* Willoughby *Linc*

MUNCASTER (St Michael)   *see* Eskdale, Irton, Muncaster and Waberthwaite *Carl*

MUNDENS, The (All Saints) w Sacombe *St Alb 22*   **P** *Ch Trust Fund Trust, K Coll Cam, and R M Abel Smith Esq (jt)*   **P-in-c** A E DAVIE

MUNDESLEY (All Saints)   *see* Trunch *Nor*

MUNDFORD (St Leonard) w Lynford *Nor 13*   **P** *Ch Patr Trust*   **P-in-c** P M FARROW,   **OLM** D J HANWELL

MUNDHAM (St Peter)   *see* Brooke, Kirstead, Mundham w Seething and Thwaite *Nor*

MUNDHAM, NORTH (St Stephen) w Hunston and Merston *Chich 3*   **P** *St Jo Coll Cam*   **R** V C DE R MALAN

MUNGRISDALE (St Kentigern)   *see* Gd Shep TM *Carl*

MUNSLEY (St Bartholomew)   *see* Ledbury *Heref*

MUNSLOW (St Michael)   *see* Diddlebury w Munslow, Holdgate and Tugford *Heref*

MUNSTER SQUARE (Christ Church) (St Mary Magdalene) *Lon 17*   **P** *Bp*   **V** S J GRIGG,   **C** P H-S CHO

MUNSTONE (Church Room)   *see* Holmer w Huntington *Heref*

MURCOTT (Mission Room)   *see* Ray Valley *Ox*

MURROW (Corpus Christi)   *see* Southea w Murrow and Parson Drove *Ely*

MURSLEY (St Mary the Virgin)   *see* Newton Longville and Mursley w Swanbourne etc *Ox*

MURSTON (All Saints) w Bapchild and Tonge *Cant 16*   **P** *Abp and St Jo Coll Cam (jt)*   **R** B A SHERSBY,   **Hon C** S A A FAGBEMI

MURTON (St James)   *see* Osbaldwick w Murton *York*

MURTON (St John the Baptist)   *see* Appleby *Carl*

MUSBURY (St Michael)   *see* Colyton, Musbury, Southleigh and Branscombe *Ex*

MUSBURY (St Thomas) *Blackb 1*   **P** *The Crown*   **V** W N PRICE

MUSGRAVE (St Theobald)   *see* Brough w Stainmore, Musgrave and Warcop *Carl*

MUSKHAM, NORTH (St Wilfrid) and SOUTH (St Wilfrid) *S'well 3*   **P** *Ld Chan*   **P-in-c** I A LAMBERT

MUSTON (All Saints)   *see* Hunmanby w Muston *York*

MUSTON (St John the Baptist)   *see* Vale of Belvoir Par *Leic*

MUSWELL HILL (St James) (St Matthew) *Lon 20*   **P** *Bp and CPAS (jt)*   **V** D A ROSS,   **C** P H SUDELL, A R F B GAGE,   **NSM** H C HENDRY, J R LENTON

MUTFORD (St Andrew)   *see* Carlton Colville and Mutford *Nor*

MYDDELTON SQUARE (St Mark)   *see* Clerkenwell St Mark *Lon*

MYDDLE (St Peter) *Lich 22*   **P** *Bp*   **P-in-c** D T W PRICE

MYLAND (St Michael)   *see* Colchester St Mich Myland *Chelmsf*

MYLOR (St Mylor) w Flushing *Truro 3*   **P** *Bp*   **V** J C JAMES

MYLOR BRIDGE (All Saints)   *see* Mylor w Flushing *Truro*

MYMMS, NORTH (St Mary) (St Michael) *St Alb 21*   **P** *Bp*   **V** T W J RANSON

MYMMS, SOUTH (King Charles the Martyr)   *see* Potters Bar K Chas *St Alb*

MYMMS, SOUTH (St Giles) and Ridge *St Alb 17*   **P** *DBP*   **P-in-c** A HARDING

MYNDTOWN (St John the Baptist) *see* Wentnor w Ratlinghope, Myndtown, Norbury etc *Heref*
MYTHOLMROYD (St Michael) *see* Erringden *Wakef*
MYTON ON SWALE (St Mary) *see* Brafferton w Pilmoor, Myton on Swale etc *York*
NABB (Mission Church) *see* Wrockwardine Wood *Lich*
NABURN (St Matthew) *see* Escrick and Stillingfleet w Naburn *York*
NACKINGTON (St Mary) *see* Petham and Waltham w Lower Hardres etc *Cant*
NACTON (St Martin) and Levington w Bucklesham and Foxhall *St E 2* P *DBP* R G L GRANT, NSM J S FOUNTAIN, OLM D E N KING
NADDER VALLEY *Sarum 11* P *Patr Bd (4 turns)*, Ld Chan *(1 turn)* TR H I J SOUTHERN, TV J M STAPLES, C S J PEARCE, NSM R WREN, M A SHALLCROSS, Dss A SYMES
NAFFERTON (All Saints) w Wansford *York 10* P *Abp* V J R BOOTH
NAILSEA (Christ Church) w Tickenham *B & W 13* P *CPAS (3 turns)*, Ld Chan *(1 turn)* R A Q H WHEELER, C C ARGLES
NAILSEA (Holy Trinity) *B & W 13* P *MMCET* R K J BOULLIER, C R J GRAHAM, R BACKHOUSE
NAILSTONE (All Saints) and Carlton w Shackerstone *Leic 13* P *The Crown and DBP (alt)* R W E QUINNEY
NAILSWORTH (St George) w Shortwood, Horsley and Newington Bapath w Kingscote *Glouc 15* P *Bp* V S J EARLEY
NANPANTAN (St Mary in Charnwood) *see* Loughborough Em and St Mary in Charnwood *Leic*
NANPEAN (St George) *see* St Stephen in Brannel *Truro*
NANSTALLION (St Stephen's Mission Room) *see* Bodmin w Lanhydrock and Lanivet *Truro*
NANTWICH (St Mary) *Ches 15* P *Q H Crewe Esq and J C Crewe Esq (jt)* R P T CHANTRY, C D WILSON
NAPTON-ON-THE-HILL (St Lawrence), Lower Shuckburgh and Stockton *Cov 10* P *Ld Chan (2 turns)*, Sir Rupert Shuckburgh Bt *(1 turn)*, and New Coll Ox *(2 turns)* P-in-c M L D GREIG
NARBOROUGH (All Saints) and Huncote *Leic 10* P *SMF* R N J BURTON
NARBOROUGH (All Saints) w Narford and Pentney *Nor 13* P *Bp* R S R NAIRN
NARFORD (St Mary) *see* Narborough w Narford and Pentney *Nor*
NASEBY (All Saints) *see* Clipston w Naseby and Haselbech w Kelmarsh *Pet*
NASH (All Saints) *see* Buckingham *Ox*
NASH (St John the Baptist) *see* Burford I *Heref*
NASSINGTON (St Mary the Virgin and All Saints) w Yarwell and Woodnewton *Pet 12* P *Lord Brassey and Bp (alt)* V R A LOVELESS
NATELY SCURES (St Swithun) *see* Newnham w Nately Scures w Mapledurwell etc *Win*
NATLAND (St Mark) *Carl 10* P *V Kendal H Trin* P-in-c T S EVANS, NSM M P JAYNE
NAUGHTON (St Mary) *see* Bildeston w Wattisham and Lindsey, Whatfield etc *St E*
NAUNTON (St Andrew) *see* The Guitings, Cutsdean, Farmcote etc *Glouc*
NAUNTON BEAUCHAMP (St Bartholomew) *see* Abberton, The Flyfords, Naunton Beauchamp etc *Worc*
NAVENBY (St Peter) *see* Graffoe Gp *Linc*
NAVESTOCK (St Thomas) *see* Bentley Common, Kelvedon Hatch and Navestock *Chelmsf*
NAWTON (St Hilda) *see* Kirkdale w Harome, Nunnington and Pockley *York*
NAYLAND (St James) w Wiston *St E 3* P *Ld Chan (2 turns) and DBP (1 turn)* P-in-c C A GRAY, NSM B WATLING
NAYLAND DRIVE (Church Centre) *see* Clacton St Jas *Chelmsf*
NAZEING (All Saints) (St Giles) *Chelmsf 26* P *Ld Chan* NSM D RICKETTS
NEASDEN (St Catherine w St Paul) *Lon 21* P *Bp and D&C St Paul's (jt)* V E E GAUNT
NEATISHEAD (St Peter) *see* Ashmanhaugh, Barton Turf etc *Nor*
NECHELLS (St Matthew) *Birm 8* P *Bp and V Aston-juxta-Birm (jt)* NSM J M ADAMS
NECTON (All Saints), Holme Hale w Pickenham, North and South *Nor 13* P *Major-Gen R S Broke, Ch Soc Trust, MMCET and S Pickenham Estate Co Ltd (jt)* R P J TAYLOR, NSM D N STEVENS
NEDGING (St Mary) *see* Bildeston w Wattisham and Lindsey, Whatfield etc *St E*
NEEDHAM (St Peter) *see* Redenhall, Harleston, Wortwell and Needham *Nor*

NEEDHAM MARKET (St John the Baptist) w Badley *St E 1* P *PCC* P-in-c P R DALTRY
NEEN SAVAGE (St Mary) *see* Cleobury Mortimer w Hopton Wafers etc *Heref*
NEEN SOLLARS (All Saints) *as above Heref*
NEENTON (All Saints) *see* Ditton Priors w Neenton, Burwarton etc *Heref*
NEITHROP (St Paul) *see* Banbury St Paul *Ox*
NELSON (St Bede) *Blackb 6* P *Bp* V *vacant* (01282) 614197
NELSON (St John the Evangelist) *see* Gt Marsden w Nelson St Phil *Blackb*
NELSON (St Mary) *see* Lt Marsden w Nelson St Mary *Blackb*
NELSON (St Paul) *as above Blackb*
NELSON (St Philip) *see* Gt Marsden w Nelson St Phil *Blackb*
NEMPNETT THRUBWELL (The Blessed Virgin Mary) *see* Chew Stoke w Nempnett Thrubwell *B & W*
NENTHEAD (St John) *see* Alston Moor *Newc*
NESS Group, The *Linc 13* P *Ld Chan (1 turn), Bp and DBP (2 turns)* V J M BEADLE
NESS, GREAT (St Andrew) *see* Ruyton XI Towns w Gt and Lt Ness *Lich*
NESS, LITTLE (St Martin) *as above Lich*
NESTON (St Mary and St Helen) *Ches 9* P *D&C* V R H N ROBB, C G A ROSSITER
NESTON (St Phillip and St James) *see* Gtr Corsham and Lacock *Bris*
NESTON, LITTLE (St Michael and All Angels) *see* Neston *Ches*
NETHER *see also under substantive place name*
NETHER HALL (St Elizabeth) *see* Scraptoft *Leic*
NETHERAVON (All Saints) *see* Avon Valley *Sarum*
NETHERBURY (St Mary) *see* Beaminster Area *Sarum*
NETHEREXE (St John the Baptist) *see* Stoke Canon, Poltimore w Huxham and Rewe etc *Ex*
NETHERFIELD (St George) *S'well 10* P *DBP* R *vacant*
NETHERFIELD (St John the Baptist) *see* Brightling, Dallington, Mountfield etc *Chich*
NETHERHAMPTON (St Katherine) *see* Wilton w Netherhampton and Fugglestone *Sarum*
NETHERLEY (Christ Church) *see* Gateacre *Liv*
NETHERNE (St Luke) *see* Merstham and Gatton *S'wark*
NETHERSEAL (St Peter) *see* Seale and Lullington w Coton in the Elms *Derby*
NETHERTHONG (All Saints) *see* Upper Holme Valley *Wakef*
NETHERTHORPE (St Bartholomew) *see* Sheff St Bart *Sheff*
NETHERTHORPE (St Stephen) *Sheff 4* P *Ch Patr Trust and Sheff Ch Burgesses Trust (jt)* P-in-c N S CRAWLEY, C E P BOSSWARD
NETHERTON (All Souls) *Carl 7* P *Bp* C E E JONES
NETHERTON (St Andrew) *see* Middlestown *Wakef*
NETHERTON (St Andrew) *Worc 9* P *V Dudley* P-in-c W J A BARNES
NETHERTON (St Oswald) *Liv 1* P *Bp* V *vacant* 0151-525 1882
NETHERWITTON (St Giles) *see* Nether Witton *Newc*
NETLEY ABBEY *see* Hound *Win*
NETLEY MARSH (St Matthew) *see* Totton *Win*
NETTLEBED (St Bartholomew) w Bix, Highmoor, Pishill and Rotherfield Greys *Ox 6* P *DBP, Earl of Macclesfield, Ch Patr Trust, and Trin Coll Ox (jt)* R B J BAILEY, OLM E F LAKEY
NETTLECOMBE (Blessed Virgin Mary) *see* Quantock Towers *B & W*
NETTLEDEN (Ashridge Chapel) *see* Potten End w Nettleden *St Alb*
NETTLEDEN (St Lawrence) *as above St Alb*
NETTLEHAM (All Saints) *Linc 3* P *Bp* V G F SLEIGHT, NSM C A ZOTOV
NETTLESTEAD (St Mary) *see* Gt and Lt Blakenham w Baylham and Nettlestead *St E*
NETTLESTEAD (St Mary the Virgin) *see* E Peckham and Nettlestead *Roch*
NETTLETON (St John the Baptist) *see* Swallow *Linc*
NETTLETON (St Mary) *see* By Brook *Bris*
NEVENDON (St Peter) *see* Pitsea w Nevendon *Chelmsf*
NEVILLE'S CROSS (St John) *see* Dur St Marg and Neville's Cross St Jo *Dur*
NEW *see also under substantive place name*
NEW BOROUGH and Leigh (St John the Evangelist) *Sarum 9* P *Ch Soc Trust* V R J A TULLOCH, C R E R DEMERY
NEW BUILDINGS (Beacon Church) *see* Crediton, Shobrooke and Sandford etc *Ex*
NEW FERRY (St Mark) *Ches 8* P *R Bebington* V H A CHARTERIS, NSM A D DRURY
NEW HAW (All Saints) *Guildf 11* P *Bp* V R J GOSTELOW, OLM J J PHILLIPS
NEW MILL (Christ Church) *see* Upper Holme Valley *Wakef*
NEW MILLS (St George) (St James the Less) *Derby 6* P *V Glossop* V D J MURDOCH

NEW SPRINGS (St John the Baptist) and Whelley St Stephen
Liv 14 **P** *Bp* **V** D J ROSCOE
NEW TOWN (St George w St Michael) *see* Edgbaston St Geo
Birm
NEWALL GREEN (St Francis of Assisi) *see* Wythenshawe
Man
**NEWARK-UPON-TRENT (St Mary Magdalene) (St
Augustine's Mission) (Christ Church) (St Leonard)** *S'well 3*
P *The Crown* **TR** V J ENEVER, **TV** D F OLNEY,
P HUTCHINSON, **NSM** D L ROBBINS
NEWBALD (St Nicholas) *York 13* **P** *Abp* **P-in-c** R I JONES
NEWBARNS (St Paul) w Hawcoat *Carl 8* **P** *DBP*
R D H PRICE, **OLM** G T WILSON
NEWBIGGIN (St Edmund) *see* Kirkby Thore w Temple
Sowerby and Newbiggin *Carl*
NEWBIGGIN-BY-THE-SEA (St Bartholomew)
see Woodhorn w Newbiggin *Newc*
NEWBIGGIN HALL (St Wilfrid) *Newc 7* **P** *Bp*
V P D MCLEOD
NEWBOLD (St John the Evangelist) w Dunston *Derby 5*
P *R Chesterfield* **V** N V JOHNSON, **C** S M FRANCE
NEWBOLD (St Peter) *see* S Rochdale *Man*
NEWBOLD DE VERDUN (St James) and Kirkby Mallory
Leic 13 **P** *Bp and Trin Coll Ox (jt)* **R** C E FOX
NEWBOLD ON AVON (St Botolph) *Cov 6*
P *H A F W Boughton Leigh Esq* **V** P M WILKINSON
NEWBOLD ON STOUR (St David) *see* Tredington and
Darlingscott w Newbold on Stour *Cov*
NEWBOLD PACEY (St George) w Moreton Morrell *Cov 8*
P *Qu Coll Ox and Lt-Col J E Little (alt)* **V** G J BURRELL,
C R C FLOATE
NEWBOROUGH (All Saints) *see* Hanbury w Newborough and
Rangemore *Lich*
NEWBOROUGH (St Bartholomew) *Pet 13* **P** *The Crown*
V *vacant* (01733) 810682
NEWBOTTLE (St James) *see* King's Sutton and Newbottle and
Charlton *Pet*
NEWBOTTLE (St Matthew) *Dur 14* **P** *Bp* **V** E WILKINSON
NEWBOURN (St Mary) *see* Waldringfield w Hemley and
Newbourn *St E*
NEWBROUGH (St Peter) *see* Warden w Newbrough *Newc*
NEWBURGH (Christ Church) w Westhead *Liv 11* **P** *Bp and
V Ormskirk (jt)* **V** D G TOWLER, **NSM** D M BURROWS,
OLM J SEPHTON
NEWBURN (St Michael and All Angels) *Newc 7* **P** *MMCET*
V J R SINCLAIR, **NSM** S MCCORMACK
NEWBURY (St John the Evangelist) (St Nicholas and St Mary)
Ox 14 **P** *Bp* **TR** D A STONE, **TV** B DAGNALL, J C WALL,
C A G HOWE, **NSM** J H G LEWIS, R E BALL, V H SMITH,
B J PRITCHARD
NEWBY (St Mark) *York 15* **P** *Abp* **V** M SPENCELEY
NEWCASTLE (Christ Church) (St Ann) *Newc 5* **P** *Bp*
V C M SAVAGE
NEWCASTLE (St Andrew) (St Luke) *Newc 5* **P** *Bp and
V Newcastle (jt)* **P-in-c** G EVANS, **Hon C** J H HARKER
NEWCASTLE (St John the Evangelist) *see* Clun w
Bettws-y-Crwyn and Newcastle *Heref*
**NEWCASTLE (St Philip) and St Augustine and (St Matthew w
St Mary)** *Newc 7* **P** *Bp* **V** R G S DEADMAN
NEWCASTLE UNDER LYME (St George) *Lich 9*
P *R Newcastle w Butterton* **P-in-c** W E J MASH
NEWCASTLE UNDER LYME (St Giles) w Butterton *Lich 9*
P *Simeon's Trustees* **P-in-c** A F CREBER, **OLM** M A TAYLOR,
J WARHAM
NEWCASTLE UNDER LYME (St Paul) *Lich 9* **P** *Trustees*
P-in-c L O FRANKLIN
NEWCASTLE UPON TYNE (Christ Church) *see* Walker *Newc*
NEWCASTLE UPON TYNE (Clayton Memorial Church)
see Jesmond Clayton Memorial *Newc*
NEWCASTLE UPON TYNE (Holy Cross) *Newc 7* **P** *Bp*
V A W MARKS, **C** J E APPLEBY
NEWCASTLE UPON TYNE (Holy Trinity) *see* Jesmond H
Trin *Newc*
NEWCASTLE UPON TYNE (St Anthony) *see* Byker St Ant
Newc
NEWCASTLE UPON TYNE (St Barnabas and St Jude) *Newc 5*
P *V Jesmond Clayton Memorial and CPAS (alt)*
P-in-c R L SIMPSON, **NSM** C SMITH
NEWCASTLE UPON TYNE (St Francis) High Heaton *Newc 6*
P *Bp* **V** C J CLINCH, **C** J P HAGGER
NEWCASTLE UPON TYNE (St Gabriel) Heaton *Newc 6*
P *Bp* **V** M J WEBB, **C** M THRELFALL-HOLMES, H B GILL
NEWCASTLE UPON TYNE (St George) *Newc 5* **P** *Bp*
V F R DEXTER, **C** S A WILSON
NEWCASTLE UPON TYNE (St Hilda) *Newc 5* **P** *Bp*
P-in-c D HOOD

NEWCASTLE UPON TYNE (St James and St Basil)
see Fenham St Jas and St Basil *Newc*
NEWCASTLE UPON TYNE (St John the Baptist) *Newc 5*
P *V Newc* **Hon C** J M CHAMBERLIN
NEWCASTLE UPON TYNE (St Margaret) *see* Scotswood
Newc
NEWCASTLE UPON TYNE (St Martin) *see* Byker St Martin
Newc
NEWCASTLE UPON TYNE (St Michael w St Lawrence)
see Byker St Mich w St Lawr *Newc*
NEWCASTLE UPON TYNE (St Oswald) *see* Byker St Mark
and Walkergate St Oswald *Newc*
NEWCASTLE UPON TYNE (St Paul) *see* High Elswick St
Paul *Newc*
NEWCASTLE UPON TYNE (St Silas) *see* Byker St Silas *Newc*
NEWCASTLE UPON TYNE (St Stephen) *see* Low Elswick
Newc
NEWCASTLE UPON TYNE (St Thomas) Proprietary Chapel
Newc 5 **P** *Trustees of St Thos Chpl Charity*
C-in-c J C WIDDOWS
NEWCASTLE UPON TYNE, WEST Benwell *see* Benwell
Team *Newc*
NEWCHAPEL (St James the Apostle) *Lich 11* **P** *CPAS*
V W E SLATER, **C** M N STEPHENS
NEWCHURCH (All Saints) *Portsm 7* **P** *Bp* **V** P H FORD
NEWCHURCH (not known) w Croft *Liv 16* **P** *Bp*
R C J STAFFORD, **OLM** B SMART
NEWCHURCH (St Nicholas w St John) *see* Rossendale Middle
Valley *Man*
NEWCHURCH (St Peter and St Paul) *see* Dymchurch w
Burmarsh and Newchurch *Cant*
NEWCHURCH-IN-PENDLE (St Mary) *see* Barrowford and
Newchurch-in-Pendle *Blackb*
NEWDIGATE (St Peter) *see* Surrey Weald *Guildf*
NEWENDEN (St Peter) *see* Sandhurst w Newenden *Cant*
NEWENT (St Mary the Virgin) and Gorsley w Cliffords Mesne
Glouc 3 **P** *Bp* **R** R C SIMPSON, **NSM** R G CHIVERS
NEWHALL (St John) *Derby 16* **P** *Bp* **V** R G HOLLINGS
NEWHAVEN (St Michael) *Chich 18* **P** *Ch Patr Trust*
R J F HARPER, **NSM** H E HOWELL
NEWHEY (St Thomas) *Man 20* **P** *Bp* **NSM** G W LINDLEY
NEWICK (St Mary) *Chich 21* **P** *Ch Soc Trust and
J H Cordle Esq (jt)* **R** P P FRANCIS
NEWINGTON (St Christopher) *see* St Laur in Thanet *Cant*
NEWINGTON (St Giles) *see* Dorchester *Ox*
**NEWINGTON (St John the Baptist) w Dairycoates St Mary and
St Peter** *York 14* **P** *Abp* **V** M R B HILLS
NEWINGTON (St Martin) *see* Hull St Martin w
Transfiguration *York*
NEWINGTON (St Mary) *S'wark 10* **P** *Bp* **OLM** J WASH
NEWINGTON (St Mary the Virgin) w Hartlip and Stockbury
Cant 16 **P** *Abp* **V** M A MASCALL, **NSM** B I M DURKAN
NEWINGTON (St Nicholas) *see* Cheriton All So w Newington
Cant
NEWINGTON (St Paul) *S'wark 10* **P** *Bp* **V** G D SHAW,
NSM M BREWSTER
NEWINGTON, SOUTH (St Peter ad Vincula) *see* Bloxham w
Milcombe and S Newington *Ox*
NEWLAND (All Saints) and Redbrook w Clearwell *Glouc 4*
P *Bp* **V** *vacant* (01594) 833777
NEWLAND (St John) *see* Hull Newland St Jo *York*
NEWLAND (St Lawrence) *see* St Lawrence *Chelmsf*
NEWLANDS (not known) *see* Thornthwaite cum Braithwaite,
Newlands etc *Carl*
NEWLAY LANE (St Margaret's Church Hall) *see* Bramley
Ripon
NEWLYN (St Newlyn) *Truro 5* **P** *Bp* **P-in-c** P A ROBSON
NEWLYN (St Peter) *Truro 5* **P** *Bp* **V** R L STRANGE
NEWMARKET (All Saints) *St E 11* **P** *Bp* **V** M E OSBORNE
NEWMARKET (St Mary the Virgin) w Exning St Agnes *St E 11*
P *Bp and DBP (alt)* **R** E J NEWEY
NEWNHAM (St Mark) *see* Cambridge St Mark *Ely*
NEWNHAM (St Michael and All Angels) *see* Badby w
Newnham and Charwelton w Fawsley etc *Pet*
**NEWNHAM (St Nicholas) w Nately Scures w Mapledurwell w
Up Nateley w Greywell** *Win 5* **P** *Bp and Qu Coll Ox (jt)*
C M R M JAGGS
NEWNHAM (St Peter and St Paul) *see* Doddington, Newnham
and Wychling *Cant*
NEWNHAM (St Peter) w Awre and Blakeney *Glouc 3*
P *Haberdashers' Co and Bp (alt)* **V** R J SEAMAN
NEWNHAM (St Vincent) *see* Ashwell w Hinxworth and
Newnham *St Alb*
NEWNTON, NORTH (St James) *see* Pewsey and Swanborough
Sarum
NEWPORT (St John the Baptist) *see* Barnstaple *Ex*

NEWPORT (St John the Baptist) *Portsm 8* **P** *Ch Patr Trust*
V S C PALMER, **NSM** R J WHATLEY
NEWPORT (St Mary the Virgin) *Chelmsf 21* **P** *Bp*
V R J GRIFFITHS
NEWPORT (St Nicholas) w Longford, Chetwynd and Forton
Lich 16 **P** *Bp* **R** R W D BIDDLE
NEWPORT (St Stephen) *see* Howden *York*
NEWPORT (St Thomas) *Portsm 8* **P** *Bp* **V** S C PALMER
NEWPORT PAGNELL (St Luke) w Lathbury and Moulsoe
Ox 27 **P** *Bp, Ch Ch Ox, and Lord Carrington (jt)*
R J H LEWIS, **C** L M CORNWELL, **OLM** G M BELL
NEWQUAY (St Michael) *Truro 7* **P** *Bp* **V** M J ADAMS,
C J C E ANDREW
NEWSHAM (St Bede) *Newc 1* **P** *Bp* **V** J R PRINGLE
NEWSHOLME (St John) *see* Oakworth *Bradf*
NEWSOME (St John the Evangelist) *see* Em TM *Wakef*
NEWSTEAD (St Mary the Virgin) *see* Annesley w Newstead
S'well
NEWTIMBER (St John the Evangelist) *see* Poynings w
Edburton, Newtimber and Pyecombe *Chich*
NEWTON (Church Hall) *see* Blackwell w Tibshelf *Derby*
NEWTON (Good Shepherd) *see* Clifton upon Dunsmore and
Newton *Cov*
NEWTON (Mission Church) *see* Embleton w Rennington and
Rock *Newc*
NEWTON (St Botolph) *see* S Lafford *Linc*
NEWTON (St James) *Ely 6* **P** *Bp* **R** vacant (01945) 870205
NEWTON (St John the Baptist) *see* Clodock and Longtown w
Craswall, Llanveynoe etc *Heref*
NEWTON (St Luke) *see* Bp's Hatfield *St Alb*
NEWTON (St Margaret) *see* Harston w Hauxton and Newton
Ely
NEWTON (St Michael and All Angels) *Ches 8* **P** *R W Kirby*
St Bridget **V** D POTTER
NEWTON (St Oswald) *see* Gt Ayton w Easby and Newton in
Cleveland *York*
NEWTON (St Petrock) *see* Shebbear, Buckland Filleigh,
Sheepwash etc *Ex*
NEWTON, NORTH (St Peter) w St Michaelchurch, Thurloxton
and Durston *B & W 14* **P** *Bp (3 turns), Sir Benjamin Slade Bt*
(1 turn) **C** M H CLEMENTS
NEWTON, OLD (St Mary) *see* Bacton w Wyverstone, Cotton
and Old Newton etc *St E*
NEWTON, SOUTH (St Andrew) *see* Wylye and Till Valley
Sarum
NEWTON, WEST (St Peter and St Paul) *see* Sandringham w W
Newton and Appleton etc *Nor*
NEWTON ABBOT *see* Highweek and Teigngrace *Ex*
NEWTON ABBOT (St Michael) *see* Wolborough and Ogwell
Ex
NEWTON ABBOT (St Paul) *as above Ex*
NEWTON ARLOSH (St John the Evangelist)
see Bowness-on-Solway, Kirkbride and Newton Arlosh *Carl*
NEWTON AYCLIFFE (St Clare) *see* Gt Aycliffe *Dur*
NEWTON BLOSSOMVILLE (St Nicolas) *see* Lavendon w
Cold Brayfield, Clifton Reynes etc *Ox*
NEWTON BROMSWOLD (St Peter) *see* Rushden St Mary w
Newton Bromswold *Pet*
NEWTON-BY-CASTLE-ACRE (All Saints) *see* Castleacre,
Newton, Westacre and Southacre *Nor*
NEWTON BY TOFT (St Michael) *see* Middle Rasen Gp *Linc*
NEWTON CAP (St Paul) *see* Auckland St Andr and St Anne
Dur
NEWTON FERRERS (Holy Cross) w Revelstoke *Ex 20* **P** *Bp*
and Comdr P E Yonge **R** T R DEACON
NEWTON FLOTMAN (St Mary the Virgin), Swainsthorpe,
Tasburgh, Tharston, Saxlingham Nethergate and Shotesham
Nor 5 **P** *Patr Bd* **TR** S A GAZE
NEWTON FLOWERY FIELD (St Stephen) *Ches 14* **P** *Bp*
P-in-c P O BENNISON
NEWTON GREEN (All Saints) *see* Boxford, Edwardstone,
Groton etc *St E*
NEWTON HALL (All Saints) *see* Dur N *Dur*
NEWTON HARCOURT (St Luke) *see* Wistow *Leic*
NEWTON HEATH (All Saints) *Man 5* **P** *Prime Min and*
D&C (alt) **R** vacant 0161-681 3102
NEWTON IN MAKERFIELD (Emmanuel) *Liv 16* **P** *Bp*
P-in-c L MCCLUSKEY
NEWTON IN MAKERFIELD (St Peter) *Liv 16* **P** *Lord*
Newton **V** G B KEEGAN, **NSM** F M A LOVETT
NEWTON IN MOTTRAM (St Mary) *Ches 14* **P** *V Mottram*
P-in-c I C WATTS
NEWTON KYME (St Andrew) *see* Tadcaster w Newton Kyme
York
NEWTON-LE-WILLOWS (All Saints) *Liv 16* **P** *Bp*
V D HALL

NEWTON LINFORD (All Saints) *see* Bradgate Team *Leic*
NEWTON LONGVILLE (St Faith) and Mursley w Swanbourne
and Little Horwood *Ox 26* **P** *Ch Patr Trust, Lord Cottesloe,*
Ch Soc Trust, and New Coll Ox (jt) **R** J M KINCHIN-SMITH,
C L J HOLT
NEWTON ON OUSE (All Saints) *see* Skelton w Shipton and
Newton on Ouse *York*
NEWTON-ON-RAWCLIFFE (St John) *see* Middleton,
Newton and Sinnington *York*
NEWTON-ON-TRENT (St Peter) *see* Saxilby Gp *Linc*
NEWTON POPPLEFORD (St Luke) *see* Ottery St Mary,
Alfington, W Hill, Tipton etc *Ex*
NEWTON PURCELL (St Michael) *see* Shelswell *Ox*
NEWTON REGIS (St Mary) w Seckington and Shuttington
Birm 10 **P** *Birm Dioc Trustees and Mrs E V G*
Inge-Innes-Lillingston (alt) **R** vacant (01827) 830254
NEWTON REIGNY (St John) *see* Penrith w Newton Reigny
and Plumpton Wall *Carl*
NEWTON SOLNEY (St Mary the Virgin) *see* Foremark and
Repton w Newton Solney *Derby*
NEWTON ST CYRES (St Cyr and St Julitta) *see* Thorverton,
Cadbury, Upton Pyne etc *Ex*
NEWTON ST LOE (Holy Trinity) *see* Saltford w Corston and
Newton St Loe *B & W*
NEWTON TONY (St Andrew) *see* Bourne Valley *Sarum*
NEWTON TRACEY (St Thomas à Becket), Horwood,
Alverdiscott, Huntshaw, Yarnscombe, Tawstock, Atherington,
High Bickington, Roborough, St Giles in the Wood and Beaford
Ex 19 **P** *Ld Chan (1 turn), Patr Bd (3 turns)*
TV J C CARVOSSO, S L THORP
NEWTON VALENCE (St Mary) and Selborne and East Tisted w
Colemore *Win 2* **P** *Bp, Earl of Selborne, and Exors Lt Col*
Sir James Scott Bt (jt) **P-in-c** J M PRESTON
NEWTOWN (Holy Spirit) *see* Calbourne w Newtown *Portsm*
NEWTOWN (Holy Trinity) *see* Soberton w Newtown *Portsm*
NEWTOWN (King Charles the Martyr) *see* Loppington w
Newtown *Lich*
NEWTOWN (St Mark) *see* Pemberton St Mark Newtown *Liv*
NEWTOWN (St Mary the Virgin) *see* Hungerford and Denford
Ox
NEWTOWN (St Mary the Virgin and St John the Baptist)
see Burghclere w Newtown and Ecchinswell w Sydmonton *Win*
NEWTOWN (St Paul) *see* Longnor, Quarnford and Sheen *Lich*
NIBLEY, NORTH (St Martin) *see* Wotton-under-Edge w
Ozleworth, N Nibley etc *Glouc*
NICHOLFOREST (St Nicholas) and Kirkandrews on Esk *Carl 2*
P *Bp, Sir Charles Graham Bt, and PCC (jt)*
P-in-c E C ROBINSON
NIDD (St Paul and St Margaret) *Ripon 1* **P** *Viscount*
Mountgarret and R Knaresborough (alt) **V** vacant (01423)
770060
NIDDERDALE, LOWER *Ripon 8* **P** *Trustees K Bell Esq,*
DBP, and C J Dent Esq (jt) **R** M P SPURGEON
NIDDERDALE, UPPER *Ripon 3* **P** *D&C and V Masham and*
Healey (jt) **V** P L DUNBAR, **NSM** T C KEIGHLEY
NINE O'CLOCK COMMUNITY at Hill Top Chapel, The
(extra-parochial place) *Sheff 1* vacant
NINEBANKS (St Mark) *see* Allendale w Whitfield *Newc*
NINEFIELDS (St Lawrence School Worship Centre)
see Waltham H Cross *Chelmsf*
NINFIELD (St Mary the Virgin) *Chich 14* **P** *D&C Cant*
R S R EARL, **NSM** P J DOODES
NITON (St John the Baptist) *Portsm 7* **P** *Qu Coll Ox*
R S E LLOYD
NOAK HILL (St Thomas) *see* Harold Hill St Geo *Chelmsf*
NOCTON (All Saints) *see* Branston w Nocton and
Potterhanworth *Linc*
NOEL PARK (St Mark) *Lon 19* **P** *Bp* **V** R R ROBINSON
NOKE (St Giles) *see* Ray Valley *Ox*
NONINGTON (St Mary the Virgin) w Wymynswold and
Goodnestone w Chillenden and Knowlton *Cant 1* **P** *Abp and*
Lord Fitzwalter (jt) **P-in-c** D J ROPER,
Hon C H D CONNOLL, **NSM** E R G HOPTHROW
NORBITON (St Peter) *S'wark 17* **P** *V Kingston All SS*
V P A HOLMES
NORBURY (All Saints) *see* Wentnor w Ratlinghope,
Myndtown, Norbury etc *Heref*
NORBURY (St Mary and St Barlok) w Snelston *Derby 8*
P *Mrs M F Stanton, L A Clowes Esq, and V Ashbourne*
(by turn) **R** vacant
NORBURY (St Oswald) *S'wark 25* **P** *Bp* **Hon C** M K WATTS
NORBURY (St Peter) *see* Adbaston, High Offley, Knightley,
Norbury etc *Lich*
NORBURY (St Philip) *S'wark 25* **P** *Bp* **V** P L WASHINGTON
NORBURY (St Stephen) and Thornton Heath *S'wark 25* **P** *Bp*
P-in-c A L NICKSON

NORBURY (St Thomas) *Ches 16* **P** *Lord Newton*
  V W F M COLLINS, **C** R H GREEN, H SCARISBRICK
NORDEN (St Paul) w Ashworth *Man 20* **P** *Bp* **V** S C A MAY
NORFOLK PARK (St Leonard) *see* Arbourthorne and
  Norfolk Park *Sheff*
NORHAM (St Cuthbert) and Duddo *Newc 12* **P** *D&C (1 turn),*
  D&C Dur (2 turns), **P-in-c** M J GILLHAM, **C** D F BROOKE
NORK (St Paul) *Guildf 9* **P** *The Crown* **V** P J BROOKS
NORLAND (St Luke) *see* Sowerby Bridge w Norland *Wakef*
NORLANDS (St James) *see* Notting Dale St Clem w St Mark
  and St Jas *Lon*
NORLEY (St John the Evangelist), Crowton and Kingsley *Ches 3*
  P *Bp, V Frodsham, and V Weaverham (jt)* **V** R J GILPIN,
  C J E PEARCE
NORMACOT (Holy Evangelists) *Lich 12* **P** *DBP* **V** *vacant*
  (01782) 319695
NORMANBY (St Andrew) *see* Kirby Misperton w Normanby,
  Edston and Salton *York*
NORMANBY (St George) *see* Eston w Normanby *York*
NORMANBY-LE-WOLD (St Peter) *see* Walesby *Linc*
NORMANTON (All Saints) *Wakef 9* **P** *Trin Coll Cam*
  V D M GILKES
NORMANTON (St Giles) *Derby 10* **P** *CPAS*
  V N A A BARBER, **C** T J HOUGHTON
NORMANTON, SOUTH (St Michael) *Derby 1* **P** *MMCET*
  P-in-c S M POTTER
NORMANTON-LE-HEATH (Holy Trinity) *see* Packington w
  Normanton-le-Heath *Leic*
NORMANTON-ON-SOAR (St James) *see* Sutton Bonington
  w Normanton-on-Soar *S'well*
NORMANTON-ON-TRENT (St Matthew) *see* Sutton w
  Carlton and Normanton upon Trent etc *S'well*
NORRIS BANK (St Martin) *see* Heatons *Man*
NORRIS GREEN (Christ Church) *see* Liv Ch Ch Norris Green
  Liv
NORRIS GREEN (St Christopher) *see* Liv St Chris Norris
  Green *Liv*
NORRISTHORPE (All Souls) *see* Heckmondwike *Wakef*
NORTH *see also under substantive place name*
NORTH BURY Team Ministry *see* Bury St Edmunds All SS w
  St Jo and St Geo *St E*
NORTH CAVE (All Saints) w Cliffe *York 13*
  P P W J Carver Esq **P-in-c** C H GOULDER
NORTH-CHAPEL Parishes, The *Linc 10* **P** *The Revd*
  J M Ashley, Mrs M F Davis, R H C Haigh Esq, and Trustees
  (1 turn), and Duchy of Lanc (1 turn) **R** R K EMM
NORTH CHAPEL (St Michael) w Ebernoe *Chich 11* **P** *Lord*
  Egremont **P-in-c** T P NICHOLSON
NORTH COVE (St Botolph) *see* Worlingham w Barnby and N
  Cove *St E*
NORTH DEVON COAST *see* Combe Martin, Berrynarbor,
  Lynton, Brendon etc *Ex*
NORTH END (Ascension) *see* Portsea Ascension *Portsm*
NORTH END (Chapel of Ease) *see* Burton Dassett *Cov*
NORTH END (St Francis) *see* Portsea N End St Mark *Portsm*
NORTH END (St Mark) *as above Portsm*
NORTH END (St Nicholas) *as above Portsm*
NORTH HILL (St Torney) and Lewannick *Truro 9* **P** *Ld Chan*
  and DBP (alt) **R** *vacant* (01566) 82806
NORTH SHIELDS (Christ Church) *see* N Shields *Newc*
NORTH SHIELDS (St Augustine) (Christ Church) *Newc 5*
  P *Patr Bd* **TR** S H CONNOLLY, **C** P M SCOTT,
  NSM E J CLARK-VINES, T C DUFF
NORTH SHORE (St Paul's Worship Centre) *see* Blackpool
  St Paul *Blackb*
NORTHALLERTON (All Saints) w Kirby Sigston *York 19*
  P *D&C Dur* **C** E KITCHING, **NSM** S C BENFORD
NORTHAM (St Margaret) *see* Bideford, Northam, Westward
  Ho!, Appledore etc *Ex*
NORTHAMPTON (All Saints w St Katharine) (St Peter) *Pet 4*
  P *Bp and R Foundn of St Kath (jt)* **R** S H M GODFREY
NORTHAMPTON (Christ Church) *Pet 4* **P** *Bp*
  V J D V EVANS
NORTHAMPTON (Emmanuel) *Pet 4* **P** *DBP*
  TR M A H JOHNSON, **C** D C BEET
NORTHAMPTON (Holy Sepulchre w St Andrew and
  St Lawrence) *Pet 4* **P** *Bp* **V** *vacant* (01604) 230563
NORTHAMPTON (Holy Trinity) (St Paul) *Pet 4* **P** *Bp*
  V P MOSELING
NORTHAMPTON (St Alban the Martyr) (Glorious Ascension)
  Pet 4 **P** *Bp* **V** I R LOWELL, **NSM** A M MARCH
NORTHAMPTON (St Benedict) *Pet 7* **P** *Bp* **V** E E S JONES,
  C A CUTHBERTSON
NORTHAMPTON (St David) *see* Kingsthorpe w
  Northampton St Dav *Pet*
NORTHAMPTON (St Giles) *Pet 4* **P** *Simeon's Trustees*
  V D R BIRD, **C** L A F ALLWOOD

NORTHAMPTON (St James) *Pet 4* **P** *Bp* **P-in-c** P E NIXON
NORTHAMPTON (St Mary the Virgin) *Pet 4* **P** *Bp*
  P-in-c I S HOLDSWORTH, **NSM** K A I JONGMAN
NORTHAMPTON (St Matthew) *Pet 4* **P** *DBP*
  NSM G C RUMBOLD
NORTHAMPTON (St Michael and All Angels w St Edmund)
  Pet 4 **P** *Bp* **V** M W J HILLS
NORTHAMPTON (St Peter) *see* Northampton All SS w St
  Kath and St Pet *Pet*
NORTHAW (St Thomas of Canterbury) and Cuffley *St Alb 20*
  P *Mrs S Peasley* **V** M T BEER, **NSM** J M BEER
NORTHBOROUGH (St Andrew) *see* Peakirk w Glinton and
  Northborough *Pet*
NORTHBOURNE (St Augustine) *see* Eastry and Northbourne
  w Tilmanstone etc *Cant*
NORTHCHURCH (St Mary) *see* Berkhamsted St Mary *St Alb*
NORTHCOURT (Christ Church) *see* Abingdon *Ox*
NORTHDOWN PARK (St Philip) *see* Margate St Phil *Cant*
NORTHENDEN (St Wilfrid) *Man 8* **P** *Bp* **R** G S FORSTER
NORTHFIELD (St Laurence) *Birm 4* **P** *Keble Coll Ox*
  R R I WARREN
NORTHFLEET (All Saints) *see* Perry Street *Roch*
NORTHFLEET (St Botolph) *Roch 4* **P** *The Crown*
  V A C SMITH
NORTHGATE (St Elizabeth) *see* Crawley *Chich*
NORTHIAM (St Mary) *Chich 20* **P** *MMCET* **R** R H WHITE
NORTHILL (St Mary the Virgin) *see* Caldecote, Northill and
  Old Warden *St Alb*
NORTHINGTON (St John the Evangelist) *see* The Candover
  Valley *Win*
NORTHLEACH (St Peter and St Paul) w Hampnett and
  Farmington, Cold Aston w Notgrove and Turkdean, and
  Compton Abdale w Haselton *Glouc 13* **P** *Bp (2 turns),*
  Ld Chan (1 turn) **R** D C NYE, **Hon C** M G WOODWARD
NORTHLEIGH (St Giles) *see* Offwell, Northleigh, Farway,
  Cotleigh etc *Ex*
NORTHLEW (St Thomas of Canterbury) *see* Okehampton w
  Inwardleigh, Bratton Clovelly etc *Ex*
NORTHMOOR (St Denys) *see* Lower Windrush *Ox*
NORTHMOOR GREEN (St Peter and St John) *see* N
  Petherton w Northmoor Green *B & W*
NORTHOLT (St Joseph) W End *Lon 22* **P** *DBP*
  V S R WINN, **C** E P BLATCHLEY
NORTHOLT (St Mary) (St Hugh) (St Richard) *Lon 22*
  P *BNC Ox* **R** P S WALKER
NORTHOLT PARK (St Barnabas) *Lon 22* **P** *Bp*
  V P B DENTON, **C** P COMPTON, **NSM** G P TUFFIN
NORTHORPE (St John the Baptist) *see* Scotton w Northorpe
  Linc
NORTHOWRAM (St Matthew) *Wakef 2* **P** *Bp*
  V P A HOLMES
NORTHREPPS (St Mary) *see* Overstrand, Northrepps,
  Sidestrand etc *Nor*
NORTHUMBERLAND HEATH (St Paul) *see* Erith St Paul
  Roch
NORTHWICH (St Helen) *see* Witton *Ches*
NORTHWICH (St Luke) (Holy Trinity) *Ches 6* **P** *Bp*
  V S HUGHES
NORTHWOLD (St Andrew) and Wretton w Stoke Ferry and
  Whittington *Ely 14* **P** *Ld Chan (1 turn), Bp and Ch Patr Trust*
  (1 turn) **R** *vacant* (01366) 501075
NORTHWOOD (Emmanuel) *Lon 23* **P** *Ch Trust Fund Trust*
  V D M TALBOT, **C** S G HOWELL, N M COULTHARD,
  NSM P D O GREENE, D F HOYLE
NORTHWOOD (Holy Trinity) *see* Hanley H Ev *Lich*
NORTHWOOD (Holy Trinity) *Lon 23* **P** *Trustees*
  V P M BARON
NORTHWOOD Pinner Road (St Edmund the King)
  see Northwood Hills St Edm *Lon*
NORTHWOOD (St John the Baptist) *Portsm 8* **P** *Bp*
  R G E MORRIS, **NSM** D M NETHERWAY
NORTHWOOD (St Mark) *see* Kirkby *Liv*
NORTHWOOD GREEN (Mission Church)
  see Westbury-on-Severn w Flaxley, Blaisdon etc *Glouc*
NORTHWOOD HILLS (St Edmund the King) *Lon 23* **P** *Bp*
  V B L DRIVER
NORTON (All Saints) *see* Hullavington, Norton and Stanton
  St Quintin *Bris*
NORTON (All Saints) *see* Brington w Whilton and Norton etc
  Pet
NORTON (St Andrew) *see* Pakenham w Norton and Tostock
  St E
NORTON (St Berteline and St Christopher) *Ches 3* **P** *DBP*
  P-in-c S J ARTUS
NORTON (St Egwin) *see* Evesham w Norton and Lenchwick
  Worc

NORTON (St George) (St Nicholas) *St Alb 4* **P** *Bp*
V J N LUSCOMBE, **C** M-A B TISDALE
NORTON (St James) *Sheff 2* **P** *CCC Cam* **R** M N R BOWIE
NORTON (St James) *see* Stoulton w Drake's Broughton and
Pirton etc *Worc*
NORTON (St Mary) *Cant 6* **P** *Ld Chan* **R** *vacant*
NORTON (St Mary) *see* Twigworth, Down Hatherley, Norton,
The Leigh etc *Glouc*
NORTON (St Mary the Virgin) *Dur 10* **P** *Bp* **V** P L WALKER,
C J THORNS
NORTON (St Michael and All Angels) *Dur 10* **P** *V Norton*
St Mary **V** M G T GOBBETT
NORTON (St Michael and All Angels) *see* Stourbridge St Mich
Norton *Worc*
NORTON (St Peter) *see* Norton juxta Malton *York*
NORTON, EAST (All Saints) *see* Hallaton w Horninghold and
Allexton, Tugby etc *Leic*
NORTON, OVER (St James) *see* Chipping Norton *Ox*
NORTON BAVANT (All Saints) *see* Upper Wylye Valley *Sarum*
NORTON BRIDGE (St Luke) *see* Chebsey, Ellenhall and
Seighford-with-Creswell *Lich*
NORTON CANES (St James) *Lich 3* **P** *Bp* **R** N L HIBBINS
NORTON CANON (St Nicholas) *see* Weobley w Sarnesfield
and Norton Canon *Heref*
NORTON CUCKNEY (St Mary) *S'well 6* **P** *Lady Alexandra*
Cavendish Bentinck **V** *vacant* (01623) 842443
NORTON DISNEY (St Peter) *see* Bassingham Gp *Linc*
NORTON FITZWARREN (All Saints) *see* Staplegrove w
Norton Fitzwarren *B & W*
NORTON IN HALES (St Chad) *see* Woore and Norton in
Hales *Lich*
NORTON IN THE MOORS (St Bartholomew) *Lich 8*
P *Walsingham Coll Trust Assn* **R** P S DAVIES
NORTON JUXTA MALTON (St Peter) *York 6* **P** *Abp*
V C W ANKERS
NORTON JUXTA TWYCROSS (Holy Trinity) *see* Appleby Gp
Leic
NORTON LE MOORS *see* Norton in the Moors *Lich*
NORTON LEES (St Paul) *Sheff 2* **P** *R Norton*
V P M BROWN
NORTON LINDSEY (Holy Trinity) *see* Wolverton w Norton
Lindsey and Langley *Cov*
NORTON MALREWARD (Holy Trinity) *see* Chew Magna w
Dundry and Norton Malreward *B & W*
NORTON MANDEVILLE (All Saints) *see* High Ongar w
Norton Mandeville *Chelmsf*
NORTON ST PHILIP (St Philip and St James) *see* Hardington
Vale *B & W*
NORTON SUB HAMDON (Blessed Virgin Mary) w West
Chinnock, Chiselborough and Middle Chinnock *B & W 6*
P *Bp* **R** M P WYNTER
NORTON SUBCOURSE (St Mary) *see* Raveningham Gp *Nor*
NORTON WOODSEATS (St Chad) *see* Woodseats St Chad
Sheff
NORTON WOODSEATS (St Paul) *see* Norton Lees St Paul
Sheff
NORWELL (St Laurence), w Ossington, Cromwell and Caunton
S'well 3 **P** *Bp, SMF, and Mrs P Goedhuis (jt)*
P-in-c A I TUCKER
NORWICH (Christ Church) *see* New Catton Ch Ch *Nor*
NORWICH Heartsease (St Francis) *Nor 1* **P** *Bp*
P-in-c P L HOWARD
NORWICH (Holy Trinity) *see* Heigham H Trin *Nor*
NORWICH Lakenham (St Alban) (St Mark) *Nor 1* **P** *D&C*
V S E WEST-LINDELL
NORWICH (St Andrew) *Nor 1* **P** *PCC* **P-in-c** M H STAGG
NORWICH (St Barnabas) *see* Heigham St Barn w St Bart *Nor*
NORWICH (St George) Colegate *Nor 1* **P** *D&C*
P-in-c M H STAGG
NORWICH (St George) Tombland *Nor 1* **P** *Bp*
NSM J C MINNS
NORWICH (St Giles) *Nor 1* **P** *Ld Chan and Bp (alt)*
P-in-c J A AVES
NORWICH (St Helen) *Nor 1* **P** *Gt Hosp Nor*
P-in-c M M LIGHT
NORWICH (St Julian) *see* Nor St Pet Parmentergate w St Jo
Nor
NORWICH (St Luke) *see* New Catton St Luke w St Aug *Nor*
NORWICH (St Mary in the Marsh) *Nor 1* **P** *D&C* **V** *vacant*
NORWICH (St Mary Magdalene) w St James *Nor 2* **P** *D&C*
V A TYLER, **OLM** J SPENCER
NORWICH (St Michael) Bowthorpe *see* Bowthorpe *Nor*
NORWICH (St Peter Mancroft) (St John Maddermarket) *Nor 1*
P *PCC* **R** P W NOKES, **C** E C KERR, **Hon C** H R G COOKE
NORWICH St Peter Parmentergate w St John de Sepulchre
(St John) (St Julian) *Nor 1* **P** *Patr Bd* **TR** M D SMITH,
Hon C T S P PHELAN

NORWICH (St Stephen) *Nor 1* **P** *D&C* **P-in-c** H R G COOKE
NORWICH (St Thomas) *see* Heigham St Thos *Nor*
NORWICH Timberhill (St John) *see* Nor St Pet Parmentergate
w St Jo *Nor*
NORWICH, Lakenham (St John the Baptist and All Saints) and
Tuckswood St Paul *Nor 1* **P** *Bp and D&C (jt)*
V R M S WOODHAM
NORWOOD (St Mary the Virgin) *Lon 23* **P** *SMF*
P-in-c L LAWRENCE
NORWOOD (St Leonard) *see* Sheff Norwood St Leon *Sheff*
NORWOOD, SOUTH (Holy Innocents) *S'wark 25* **P** *Bp*
V R D NEWMAN
NORWOOD, SOUTH (St Alban the Martyr) *S'wark 25* **P** *Bp*
P-in-c C E BLANKENSHIP, **Hon C** J R HALL
NORWOOD, SOUTH (St Mark) *S'wark 25* **P** *Bp*
P-in-c T W HURCOMBE
NORWOOD, UPPER (All Saints) *S'wark 25* **P** *V Croydon*
P-in-c L S A MARSH
NORWOOD, UPPER (St John) *S'wark 25* **P** *Bp*
V D G MARTIN
NORWOOD, WEST (St Luke) *S'wark 15* **P** *Abp*
V L I WICKINGS
NOTGROVE (St Bartholomew) *see* Northleach w Hampnett
and Farmington etc *Glouc*
NOTTING DALE (St Clement) (St Mark) and Norlands
St James *Lon 12* **P** *Bp* **V** H D J RAYMENT-PICKARD,
C A J HAMPTON
NOTTING HILL (All Saints) (St Columb) *Lon 12* **P** *SMF*
V J K BROWNSELL, **C** J R A SAMPSON, **NSM** R E DUGUID
NOTTING HILL (St John) *Lon 12* **P** *Bp* **V** W H TAYLOR,
NSM R J WRIGHT
NOTTING HILL (St Michael and All Angels) (Christ Church)
(St Francis) *Lon 12* **P** *Trustees* **V** A B ANDREWS
NOTTING HILL (St Peter) *Lon 12* **P** *Bp*
V M K HARGREAVES, **C** A C EDWARDS, **NSM** R J WRIGHT
NOTTINGHAM (St Andrew) *S'well 13* **P** *Peache Trustees*
V R M CLARK
NOTTINGHAM (St Ann w Emmanuel) *S'well 13* **P** *Trustees*
V J P NEILL
NOTTINGHAM (St George w St John the Baptist) *S'well 13*
P *Bp* **V** D C F TUDOR
NOTTINGHAM (St Jude) *S'well 13* **P** *CPAS*
V N R STUART-LEE, **C** M J KIRKHAM
NOTTINGHAM (St Mary the Virgin) and St Catharine
S'well 13 **P** *Bp* **V** J E M NEALE, **C** S F MORRIS
NOTTINGHAM (St Nicholas) *S'well 13* **P** *CPAS*
R T HATTON, **C** S I V MASON
NOTTINGHAM (St Peter w St James) (All Saints) *S'well 13*
P *Bp and trustees (jt)* **R** A G DEUCHAR, **C** D MCCOULOUGH,
NSM F P R J CONNELL
NOTTINGHAM (St Saviour) *S'well 13* **P** *CPAS*
V G E JONES
NOTTINGHAM (St Stephen) *see* Hyson Green and Forest
Fields *S'well*
NOWTON (St Peter) *see* Hawstead and Nowton w
Stanningfield etc *St E*
NUFFIELD (Holy Trinity) *Ox 6* **P** *MMCET* **R** J F SHEARER
NUN MONKTON (St Mary) *see* Lower Nidderdale *Ripon*
NUNBURNHOLME (St James) and Warter and Huggate
York 5 **P** *Abp* **P-in-c** J F HUDGHTON
NUNEATON (St Mary) *Cov 5* **P** *V Nuneaton* **V** G A WELSBY
NUNEATON (St Nicolas) *Cov 5* **P** *The Crown* **V** D JONES,
C S J NICHOLLS, **NSM** D WATERTON
NUNHEAD (St Antony) (St Silas) *S'wark 8* **P** *Bp*
V C A M BRADDICK-SOUTHGATE
NUNNEY (All Saints) and Witham Friary, Marston Bigot,
Wanstrow and Cloford *B & W 4* **P** *Bp, SMF, and*
C N Clarke Esq and Duke of Somerset (jt) **R** J K HODDER
NUNNINGTON (All Saints) *see* Kirkdale w Harome,
Nunnington and Pockley *York*
NUNTHORPE (St Mary the Virgin) (St Mary's Church Hall)
York 21 **P** *Abp* **V** T M THOMPSON, **C** A P WILSON
NUNTON (St Andrew) *see* Chalke Valley *Sarum*
NURSLING (St Boniface) (St John the Evangelist) and
Rownhams *Win 12* **P** *Bp* **R** J T WILLIAMS
NURSTEAD (St Mildred) *see* Meopham w Nurstead *Roch*
NUTBOURNE (St Wilfrid) *see* Chidham *Chich*
NUTFIELD (St Peter and St Paul) *S'wark 27* **P** *Jes Coll Ox*
R G I WILLIAMS
NUTFIELD, LOWER *see* S Nutfield w Outwood *S'wark*
NUTFIELD, SOUTH (Christ Church) w Outwood *S'wark 27*
P *Bp and Ch Patr Trust (jt)* **NSM** M L PUDNEY
NUTHALL (St Patrick) *S'well 7* **P** *Bp* **P-in-c** J HENDERSON,
NSM E B GAMBLE
NUTHURST (St Andrew) *Chich 8* **P** *Bp Lon* **R** D EVANS
NUTHURST (St Thomas) *see* Packwood w Hockley Heath
Birm

NUTLEY (St James the Less) *Chich 21* **P** *R Maresfield*
P-in-c M D S GREIG

NYMET (St George) *see* S Molton w Nymet St George, High
Bray etc *Ex*

NYMET ROWLAND (St Bartholomew) *see* N Creedy *Ex*

NYMET TRACEY (St Bartholomew) *see* Bow w Broad Nymet
Ex

NYMPSFIELD (St Bartholomew) *see* Uley w Owlpen and
Nympsfield *Glouc*

NYNEHEAD (All Saints) *see* Wellington and Distr *B & W*

OADBY (St Paul) (St Peter) *Leic 5* **P** *Bp* **TR** M F RUSK,
C S N MOUSIR-HARRISON, **NSM** H M BENCE

OAK TREE ANGLICAN FELLOWSHIP, The *Lon 22*
Min M L CLARKSON

OAKAMOOR (Holy Trinity) *see* Alton w Bradley-le-Moors
and Oakamoor w Cotton *Lich*

OAKDALE (St George) *Sarum 7* **P** *Bp* **TV** M G OATES,
C A SYER, J E AUDIBERT

OAKE (St Bartholomew) *see* Bradford w Oake, Hillfarrance and
Heathfield *B & W*

OAKENGATES (Holy Trinity) *see* Ketley and Oakengates *Lich*

OAKENROD (St George w St Alban) *see* Rochdale St Geo w St
Alb *Man*

OAKENSHAW (Church of the Good Shepherd) *see* Willington
and Sunnybrow *Dur*

OAKENSHAW (St Andrew) cum Woodlands *Bradf 2* **P** *Bp*
P-in-c G PERCIVAL

OAKFIELD (St John the Baptist) *Portsm 7* **P** *V St Helens*
V H E WRIGHT

OAKFORD (St Peter) *see* Washfield, Stoodleigh, Withleigh etc
Ex

**OAKHAM (All Saints) w Hambleton and Egleton and Braunston
w Brooke** *Pet 14* **P** *Dr E R Hanbury (1 turn), D&C Linc
(2 turns)* **R** M W R COVINGTON, **C** J RIDLEY, R G BROWN

OAKHANGER (St Luke's Mission Church) *see* Alsager Ch Ch
Ches

OAKHANGER (St Mary Magdalene) *see* E and W Worldham,
Hartley Mauditt w Kingsley etc *Win*

OAKHILL (All Saints) *see* Ashwick w Oakhill and Binegar
B & W

OAKHILL Eastwood View (shared church) *see* Clifton St Jas
Sheff

OAKINGTON (St Andrew) *Ely 5* **P** *Qu Coll Cam*
V J C ALEXANDER

OAKLEY (St Leonard) w Wootton St Lawrence *Win 4* **P** *Qu
Coll Ox and D&C (alt)* **R** B W NICHOLSON,
NSM C A VAUGHAN

OAKLEY (St Mary) *see* Worminghall w Ickford, Oakley and
Shabbington *Ox*

OAKLEY (St Mary) *see* Bromham w Oakley and Stagsden
St Alb

OAKLEY (St Nicholas) *see* N Hartismere *St E*

OAKLEY, EAST (St John) *see* Oakley w Wootton St Lawrence
Win

OAKLEY, GREAT (All Saints) w Wix and Wrabness *Chelmsf 20*
P *Ld Chan, Ch Patr Trust, and St Jo Coll Cam (by turn)*
R *vacant* (01255) 880230

OAKLEY, GREAT (St Michael) and LITTLE (St Peter) *Pet 9*
P *H W G de Capell Brooke Esq and Boughton Estates Ltd (alt)*
V *vacant*

OAKLEY SQUARE (St Matthew) *see* Old St Pancras *Lon*

OAKMOOR *see* Bishopsnympton, Rose Ash, Mariansleigh etc
Ex

OAKRIDGE (St Bartholomew) *see* Bisley, Oakridge, Miserden
and Edgeworth *Glouc*

OAKS IN CHARNWOOD (St James the Greater) *see* Shepshed
and Oaks in Charnwood *Leic*

OAKSEY (All Saints) *see* Ashley, Crudwell, Hankerton, Long
Newnton etc *Bris*

OAKWOOD (no dedication) *Derby 9* **P** *Bp and MMCET (jt)*
P-in-c P T WALLER, **C** A D THOMPSON

OAKWOOD (St Thomas) *Lon 18* **P** *Bp* **V** C J P HOBBS,
Hon C J E ROBSON

OAKWORTH (Christ Church) *Bradf 8* **P** *Bp* **V** T G ALLEN

OARE (Blessed Virgin Mary) w Culbone *B & W 16* **P** *Bp*
NSM C D BURKE

OARE (Holy Trinity) *see* Pewsey and Swanborough *Sarum*

OARE (St Bartholomew) *see* Chieveley w Winterbourne and
Oare *Ox*

OARE (St Peter) *see* The Brents and Davington w Oare and
Luddenham *Cant*

OATLANDS (St Mary) *Guildf 8* **P** *Bp* **V** M ANKER,
C M FLETCHER, H WHITEHEAD

OBORNE (St Cuthbert) *see* Queen Thorne *Sarum*

OCCOLD (St Michael) *see* Eye *St E*

OCKBROOK (All Saints) *Derby 13* **P** *Lt-Col T H Pares*
V T M SUMPTER, **C** A C M PETTY, **NSM** J D BISHOP

OCKENDON, NORTH (St Mary Magdalene) *Chelmsf 2* **P** *Bp*
P-in-c M E MILLARD

OCKENDON, SOUTH (St Nicholas) and Belhus Park
Chelmsf 14 **P** *Bp and Guild of All So (jt)*
R B G DUCKWORTH

OCKER HILL (St Mark) *Lich 26* **P** *Bp*
V A R BOYD-WILLIAMS

OCKFORD RIDGE (St Mark) *see* Godalming *Guildf*

OCKHAM (All Saints) *see* E Horsley and Ockham w Hatchford
and Downside *Guildf*

OCKLEY (St Margaret), Okewood and Forest Green *Guildf 7*
P *Bp and J P M H Evelyn Esq (alt)* **R** R R MCALLEN

OCLE PYCHARD (St James the Great) *see* Stoke Lacy,
Moreton Jeffries w Much Cowarne etc *Heref*

**ODCOMBE (St Peter and St Paul), Brympton, Lufton and
Montacute** *B & W 7* **P** *Ch Ch Ox (4 turns),
C E B Clive-Ponsonby-Fane Esq (1 turn)* **R** J F JENKINS

ODD DOWN (St Philip and St James) *see* Bath Odd Down w
Combe Hay *B & W*

ODD RODE (All Saints) *Ches 11* **P** *R Astbury* **R** T R EVANS,
NSM T WARNER

ODDINGLEY (St James) *see* Bowbrook S *Worc*

ODDINGTON (Holy Ascension) *see* Broadwell, Evenlode,
Oddington, Adlestrop etc *Glouc*

ODDINGTON (St Andrew) *see* Ray Valley *Ox*

ODDINGTON (St Nicholas) *see* Broadwell, Evenlode,
Oddington, Adlestrop etc *Glouc*

ODELL (All Saints) *St Alb 15* **P** *Lord Luke*
P-in-c D A STREATER

ODIHAM (All Saints) *Win 5* **P** *Bp* **P-in-c** M C S BEVER

ODSTOCK (St Mary) *see* Chalke Valley *Sarum*

OFFCHURCH (St Gregory) *Cov 10* **P** *Bp*
P-in-c J T H BRITTON, **C** D R PATTERSON

OFFENHAM (St Mary and St Milburgh) *see* Badsey w
Aldington and Offenham and Bretforton *Worc*

OFFERTON (St Alban) (St John) *Ches 18* **P** *Bp* **V** R E READ,
C C A JONES

OFFHAM (Old St Peter) *see* Hamsey *Chich*

OFFHAM (St Michael) *see* W Malling w Offham *Roch*

OFFLEY (St Mary Magdalene) *see* King's Walden and Offley w
Lilley *St Alb*

OFFLEY, HIGH (St Mary the Virgin) *see* Adbaston, High
Offley, Knightley, Norbury etc *Lich*

OFFLEY HAY (Mission Church) *see* Eccleshall *Lich*

OFFORD D'ARCY (All Saints) w Offord Cluny *Ely 13*
P *Ld Chan* **P-in-c** M E SMITH

OFFTON (St Mary) *see* Somersham w Flowton and Offton w
Willisham *St E*

**OFFWELL (St Mary the Virgin), Northleigh, Farway, Cotleigh
and Widworthy** *Ex 5* **P** *Trustees, R T Marker Esq, Cotleigh
PCC, and Bp (jt)* **V** S J H DUNWOODY, **NSM** S J HOUGHTON

OGBOURNE (St Andrew) *see* Ridgeway *Sarum*

OGBOURNE (St George) *as above Sarum*

OGLEY HAY (St James) *Lich 1* **P** *Bp* **V** C N THOMAS,
C D A ACKROYD, R BEVAN

OGWELL (St Bartholomew) *see* Wolborough and Ogwell *Ex*

OKEFORD Benefice, The *Sarum 6* **P** *G A L-F Pitt-Rivers Esq
and DBP (alt)* **R** P J RAHILLY, **NSM** G TURNOCK,
OLM D J MARL

OKEFORD FITZPAINE (St Andrew) *see* Okeford *Sarum*

**OKEHAMPTON (All Saints) (St James) w Inwardleigh; Bratton
Clovelly w Germansweek; Northlew w Ashbury; and Bridestowe
and Sourton** *Ex 12* **P** *Patr Bd* **TR** S W COOK,
TV S A WILSON, **C** J M THOMAS, A PARSONS

OKEWOOD (St John the Baptist) *see* Ockley, Okewood and
Forest Green *Guildf*

OLD *see also under substantive place name*

OLD FORD (St Paul) (St Mark) *Lon 7* **P** *Hyndman Trustees
and CPAS (jt)* **V** P J BOARDMAN, **NSM** J KASOZI NSAMBA,
J E BLACKBURN

OLD HEATH (St Barnabas) *see* Colchester St Barn *Chelmsf*

OLD HILL (Holy Trinity) *Worc 9* **P** *Ch Soc Trust* **V** *vacant*
(01384) 412987

OLD LANE (Mission Church) *see* Bloxwich *Lich*

OLD WIVES LEES (Mission Church) *see* Chilham w Challock
and Molash *Cant*

OLDBERROW (St Mary) *see* Spernall, Morton Bagot and
Oldberrow *Cov*

OLDBROOK (Community Church) *see* Woughton *Ox*

OLDBURY *Sarum 15* **P** *Bp, CPAS, Marquis of Lansdowne, and
C E R Money-Kyrle Esq (jt)* **R** R HURLEY

OLDBURY (Christ Church) *Birm 7* **P** *Bp* **P-in-c** J R BARNETT

OLDBURY (St Nicholas) *see* Bridgnorth, Tasley, Astley
Abbotts, etc *Heref*

OLDBURY-ON-SEVERN (St Arilda) w Shepperdine *Glouc 7*
P *D&C Ch Ch Ox* **V** D E S PRIMROSE, **OLM** G L HILL

OLDCOTES (St Mark's Mission Church)
see Carlton-in-Lindrick and Langold w Oldcotes *S'well*

OLDHAM Moorside (St Thomas) *Man 21* **P** *Trustees*
V J H GRAY
OLDHAM (St Andrew) (St Mary w St Peter) *Man 19*
P *Patr Bd* **TR** J SYKES, **TV** D C MEYER
OLDHAM (St Barnabas) *Man 19* **P** *The Crown*
P-in-c D OATES
OLDHAM (St Chad) *see* Hollinwood and Limeside *Man*
OLDHAM (St James) (St Ambrose) *Man 19* **P** *Bp and*
R Prestwich (jt) **V** P PLUMPTON
OLDHAM (St Paul) *Man 19* **P** *Bp* **Hon C** D J QUARMBY
OLDHAM (St Stephen and All Martyrs) Lower Moor *Man 19*
P *Bp* **V** *vacant* 0161-678 9565
OLDHURST (St Peter) *see* Somersham w Pidley and Oldhurst
Ely
OLDLAND (St Anne) *Bris 5* **P** *Bp* **V** A J M SPEAR
OLDRIDGE (St Thomas) *see* Tedburn St Mary, Whitestone,
Oldridge etc *Ex*
OLDSWINFORD (St Mary) *see* Old Swinford Stourbridge
Worc
OLIVER'S BATTERY (St Mark) *see* Stanmore *Win*
OLLERTON (St Giles) (St Paulinus) w Boughton *S'well 6*
P *Ld Chan and Bp (alt)* **P-in-c** R A KIRTON
OLNEY (St Peter and St Paul) *Ox 27* **P** *Bp* **R** N P H POND,
OLM V M REVELEY
OLTON (St Margaret) *Birm 11* **P** *Bp and V Bickenhill (jt)*
V N I JONES, **C** D G JONES
OLVESTON (St Mary of Malmesbury) *see* Almondsbury and
Olveston *Bris*
OMBERSLEY (St Andrew) w Doverdale *Worc 8* **P** *Bp and Lord*
Sandys (alt) **P-in-c** S P KERR
ONCHAN (St Peter) *S & M 2* **P** *The Crown* **V** N A WELLS,
OLM L N LAWRINSON
ONECOTE (St Luke) *see* Ipstones w Berkhamsytch and
Onecote w Bradnop *Lich*
ONEHOUSE (St John the Baptist) *see* Gt Finborough w
Onehouse, Harleston, Buxhall etc *St E*
ONGAR, HIGH (St Mary the Virgin) w Norton Mandeville
Chelmsf 27 **P** *Ch Soc Trust* **R** R J RENDALL,
NSM A N HITCHING
ONIBURY (St Michael and All Angels) *see* Culmington w
Onibury, Bromfield etc *Heref*
ONSLOW VILLAGE (All Saints) *see* Guildf All SS *Guildf*
OPENSHAW (St Barnabas) *see* Manchester Gd Shep and
St Barn *Man*
OPENSHAW, HIGHER (St Clement) *Man 1* **P** *Trustees*
R W NELSON
OPENWOODGATE (St Mark) *see* Belper *Derby*
ORBY (All Saints) *Linc 8* **P** *Bp* **V** T STEELE
ORCHARD (Community Centre) *see* Egglescliffe *Dur*
ORCHARD PARK (St Michael and All Angels) *see* N Hull
St Mich *York*
ORCHARD PORTMAN (St Michael) *see* Beercrocombe w
Curry Mallet, Hatch Beauchamp etc *B & W*
ORCHARD WAY (St Barnabas) *see* Cheltenham St Mark
Glouc
ORCHARDLEIGH (Blessed Virgin Mary) *see* Beckington w
Standerwick, Berkley, Rodden etc *B & W*
ORCHESTON (St Mary) *see* Wylye and Till Valley *Sarum*
ORCOP (St John the Baptist) *see* St Weonards w Orcop,
Garway, Tretire etc *Heref*
ORDSALL (All Hallows) (St Alban) *S'well 5* **P** *Bp*
P-in-c P S BAGSHAW
ORDSALL (St Clement) *see* Salford Ordsall St Clem *Man*
ORE (Christ Church) *Chich 17* **P** *Simeon's Trustees*
V J G PANGBOURNE
ORE (St Helen) (St Barnabas) *Chich 17* **P** *Simeon's Trustees*
R C H KEY, **C** R J MORTIMER
ORESTON (Church of the Good Shepherd) *see* Plymstock and
Hooe *Ex*
ORFORD (St Andrew) *Liv 12* **P** *Bp* **V** M RAYNOR
ORFORD (St Bartholomew) *see* Wilford Peninsula *St E*
ORFORD (St Margaret) *Liv 12* **P** *Bp* **V** J W REED
ORLESTONE (St Mary) w Snave and Ruckinge w Warehorne
and Kenardington *Cant 13* **P** *Ld Chan and Abp (alt)*
R *vacant* (01233) 732274
ORLETON (St George) *see* Leominster *Heref*
ORLINGBURY (St Mary) *see* Gt w Lt Harrowden and
Orlingbury *Pet*
ORMESBY (St Cuthbert) *York 18* **P** *Abp* **V** R BROWN
ORMESBY, NORTH (Holy Trinity) *York 18* **P** *Abp*
V G B USHER
ORMESBY ST MARGARET (St Margaret) w Scratby,
Ormesby St Michael and Rollesby *Nor 6* **P** *Bp, D&C, DBP*
and R J H Tacon Esq (jt) **V** A SANGSTER
ORMESBY ST MICHAEL (St Michael) *see* Ormesby St Marg
w Scratby, Ormesby St Mich etc *Nor*

ORMSBY Group, The South (St Leonard) *Linc 7*
P *A J Massingberd-Mundy Esq, Sir Thomas Ingilby Bt, Mert*
Coll Ox, Bp, and DBP (jt) **P-in-c** C HILLIAM
ORMSGILL (St Francis) *see* Barrow St Matt *Carl*
ORMSIDE (St James) *Carl 1* **P** *Bp and D&C (jt)*
R P E P NORTON, **NSM** R A COLLINSON
ORMSKIRK (St Peter and St Paul) *Liv 11* **P** *Earl of Derby*
V C H JONES, **C** A A HOUSLEY, **NSM** P A SEWELL, J DUCK
ORPINGTON (All Saints) *Roch 16* **P** *D&C* **V** A A MUSTOE,
NSM Y R MARCUSSEN
ORPINGTON (Christ Church) *Roch 16* **P** *Ch Trust Fund*
Trust, Bp, and V Orpington (jt) **V** J P COLWILL
ORPINGTON (St Andrew) *Roch 16* **P** *Bp*
P-in-c M T SKINNER
ORRELL (St Luke) *Liv 15* **P** *Bp* **Hon C** F S FAIRBAIRN
ORRELL HEY (St John and St James) *Liv 1* **P** *CPAS*
V R J G PANTER, **C** M D COATES
ORSETT (St Giles and All Saints) and Bulphan and Horndon on
the Hill *Chelmsf 14* **P** *Bp and D&C St Paul's (jt)*
R V G CATO, **NSM** S R BLAKE
ORSTON (St Mary) *see* Whatton w Aslockton, Hawksworth,
Scarrington etc *S'well*
ORTON (All Saints) and Tebay w Ravenstonedale and
Newbiggin-on-Lune *Carl 1* **P** *Bp and Ravenstonedale Trustees*
(1 turn), Resident Landowners (1 turn) **R** A I DALTON
ORTON, GREAT (St Giles) *see* Barony of Burgh *Carl*
ORTON GOLDHAY (St John) Conventional District
Ely 13 vacant
ORTON LONGUEVILLE (Holy Trinity) *see* The Ortons,
Alwalton and Chesterton *Ely*
ORTON MALBORNE (not known) *as above Ely*
ORTON-ON-THE-HILL (St Edith of Polesworth)
see Bosworth and Sheepy Gp *Leic*
ORTON WATERVILLE (St Mary) *see* The Ortons, Alwalton
and Chesterton *Ely*
ORTONS, Alwalton and Chesterton, The *Ely 12* **P** *Patr Bd*
TR M SOULSBY, **TV** R A HAMILTON, R A D STURT,
I A PULLINGER
ORWELL Group, The (St Andrew) *Ely 7* **P** *Bp, DBP, and Trin*
Coll Cam (jt) **R** N A BRICE
ORWELL Team Ministry *see* Walton and Trimley *St E*
OSBALDWICK (St Thomas) w Murton *York 2* **P** *Abp*
V A CLEMENTS
OSBOURNBY (St Peter and St Paul) *see* S Lafford *Linc*
OSCOTT, OLD (All Saints) *see* Kingstanding St Mark *Birm*
OSGATHORPE (St Mary the Virgin) *see* Hathern, Long
Whatton and Diseworth w Belton etc *Leic*
OSMASTON (St Martin) *see* Brailsford w Shirley and
Osmaston w Edlaston *Derby*
OSMINGTON (St Osmond) *see* Preston w Sutton Poyntz and
Osmington w Poxwell *Sarum*
OSMONDTHORPE (St Philip) *Ripon 8* **P** *Bp*
P-in-c A M GUBBINS, **C** R J COX
OSMOTHERLEY (St Peter) w Harlsey and Ingleby Arncliffe
York 19 **P** *J B Barnard Esq (1 turn), Ld Chan (2 turns)*
V A H DODD, **NSM** G L MORLEY
OSMOTHERLY (St John) *see* Ulverston St Mary w H Trin *Carl*
OSPRINGE (St Peter and St Paul) *see* Eastling w Ospringe and
Stalisfield w Otterden *Cant*
OSSETT (Holy and Undivided Trinity) and Gawthorpe *Wakef 10*
P *Bp and R Dewsbury (jt)* **V** P D MAYBURY, **C** N W R EVANS
OSSETT, SOUTH (Christ Church) *Wakef 10* **P** *Bp*
P-in-c J HARRIS, **OLM** B R ASQUITH
OSSINGTON (Holy Rood) *see* Norwell w Ossington, Cromwell
and Caunton *S'well*
OSTERLEY ROAD (St Mary) *see* Spring Grove St Mary *Lon*
OSWALDKIRK (St Oswald) *see* Ampleforth w Oswaldkirk,
Gilling E etc *York*
OSWALDTWISTLE (Immanuel) (All Saints) *Blackb 1*
P *Trustees* **V** P W WATSON
OSWALDTWISTLE (St Paul) *Blackb 1* **P** *Trustees*
V M D RATCLIFFE
OSWESTRY (Holy Trinity) *Lich 19* **P** *Bp* **V** A S F BENNETT
OSWESTRY (St Oswald) *Lich 19* **P** *Earl of Powis*
V D B CROWHURST
OTFORD (St Bartholomew) *Roch 10* **P** *D&C Westmr*
V P M HOPKINS
OTFORD LANE (Mission Hall) *see* Knockholt w Halstead
Roch
OTHAM (St Nicholas) w Langley *Cant 15* **P** *Abp and*
CPAS (jt) **R** A W SEWELL, **NSM** D W BOND, C C H COOK
OTHERY (St Michael) *see* Middlezoy and Othery and
Moorlinch *B & W*
OTLEY (All Saints) *Bradf 4* **P** *Bp* **V** G C BUTTANSHAW,
C P MOON
OTLEY (St Mary) *see* Clopton w Otley, Swilland and
Ashbocking *St E*

OTTER VALE   *see* Ottery St Mary, Alfington, W Hill, Tipton etc *Ex*

OTTERBOURNE (St Matthew)   *see* Compton and Otterbourne *Win*

OTTERBURN (St John the Evangelist)   *see* N Tyne and Redesdale Team *Newc*

OTTERFORD (St Leonard)   *see* Blackdown *B & W*

OTTERHAM (St Denis)   *see* Boscastle w Davidstow *Truro*

OTTERINGTON, NORTH (St Michael and All Angels)   *see* The Thorntons and The Otteringtons *York*

OTTERINGTON, SOUTH (St Andrew)   *as above York*

OTTERSHAW (Christ Church)   *Guildf 11*   **P** *Bp*   **V** J W BATT

OTTERTON (St Michael)   *see* E Budleigh w Bicton and Otterton *Ex*

OTTERY ST MARY (St Mary the Virgin), Alfington, West Hill, Tipton St John, Venn Ottery, Newton Poppleford, Harpford and Colaton Raleigh *Ex 7*   **P** *Patr Bd*   **TR** G J FRANKLIN, **TV** W J RIOCH, W G LLOYD,   **C** M J S JACKSON, **NSM** K J BRIMACOMBE

OTTRINGHAM (St Wilfrid)   *see* Keyingham w Ottringham, Halsham and Sunk Is *York*

OUGHTIBRIDGE (Ascension)   *Sheff 3*   **P** *V Wadsley*   **V** J F E MANN

OUGHTRINGTON (St Peter)   *Ches 10*   **P** *Bp*   **R** E M BURGESS

OULTON (St John the Evangelist)   *see* Stone Ch Ch and Oulton *Lich*

OULTON (St John) w Woodlesford   *Ripon 8*   **P** *Bp* **P-in-c** C J TRUMAN

OULTON (St Michael)   *Nor 9*   **P** *Ch Soc Trust* **R** A R PRITCHARD,   **NSM** C S PRITCHARD

OULTON (St Peter and St Paul)   *see* Lt Barningham, Blickling, Edgefield etc *Nor*

OULTON BROAD (St Mark) (St Luke the Evangelist) *Nor 9* **P** *Simeon's Trustees*   **V** B R F ROCHE,   **C** J M THOMSON, W L THOMSON

OUNDLE (St Peter) w Ashton and Benefield w Glapthorn *Pet 12* **P** *Bp and Mrs G S Watts-Russell (jt)*   **R** R J ORMSTON, **C** D L SMITH,   **NSM** T G WILCOCK

OUSBY (St Luke)   *see* Skirwith, Ousby and Melmerby w Kirkland *Carl*

OUSDEN (St Peter)   *see* Bansfield *St E*

OUSEBURN, GREAT (St Mary) and LITTLE (Holy Trinity) w Marton cum Grafton and Whixley w Green Hammerton *Ripon 3*   **P** *Bp, R Knaresborough and DBP (3 turns), St Jo Coll Cam (1 turn)*   **V** D J WHEELER,   **NSM** M SAUNDERS, J NEWHAM

OUT RAWCLIFFE (St John the Evangelist)   *see* Hambleton w Out Rawcliffe *Blackb*

OUTLANE (St Mary Magdalene)   *see* Stainland *Wakef*

OUTWELL (St Clement)   *Ely 17*   **P** *Bp*   **R** A F JESSON

OUTWOOD (St Aidan)   *see* Ringley w Prestolee *Man*

OUTWOOD (St John)   *see* S Nutfield w Outwood *S'wark*

OUTWOOD (St Mary Magdalene)   *Wakef 12*   **P** *V Stanley* **V** J W BUTTERWORTH

OUTWOOD COMMON (St John the Divine)   *see* Billericay and Lt Burstead *Chelmsf*

OVAL WAY (All Saints)   *see* Chalfont St Peter *Ox*

OVENDEN (St George)   *Wakef 4*   **P** *V Halifax* **V** D J ROBERTSON

OVENDEN (St John the Evangelist)   *see* Bradshaw and Holmfield *Wakef*

OVER   *see also under substantive place name*

OVER (St Chad)   *Ches 6*   **P** *Bp*   **V** G BROWN

OVER (St John the Evangelist)   *Ches 6*   **P** *Lord Delamere and W R Cullimore Esq (jt)*   **V** M C GARDNER

OVER (St Mary)   *Ely 5*   **P** *Trin Coll Cam*   **P-in-c** M E RABY, **C** S E WYATT

OVERBURY (St Faith) w Teddington, Alstone and Little Washbourne w Beckford and Ashton under Hill *Worc 4* **P** *D&C and MMCET (jt)*   **V** J M BEVAN

OVERCHURCH (St Mary)   *see* Upton (Overchurch) *Ches*

OVERPOOL (St Francis)   *see* Ellesmere Port *Ches*

OVERSEAL (St Matthew)   *see* Seale and Lullington w Coton in the Elms *Derby*

OVERSTONE (St Nicholas)   *see* Mears Ashby and Hardwick and Sywell etc *Pet*

OVERSTRAND (St Martin), Northrepps, Sidestrand and Trimingham *Nor 21*   **P** *Duchy of Lanc, DBP, and Bp (by turn)* **R** M L LANGAN

OVERTON (St Helen)   *Blackb 11*   **P** *V Lanc* **P-in-c** D E NEWTON

OVERTON (St Mary) w Laverstoke and Freefolk   *Win 6*   **P** *Bp* **R** N P CUMMING,   **C** I K SMALE

OVERTON (St Michael and All Angels)   *see* Upper Kennet *Sarum*

OVING (All Saints)   *see* Schorne *Ox*

OVING (St Andrew)   *see* Tangmere and Oving *Chich*

OVINGDEAN (St Wulfran)   *Chich 2*   **P** *SMF* **P-in-c** A D MAYES,   **C** M WICKENS

OVINGHAM (St Mary the Virgin)   *Newc 3*   **P** *Bp* **P-in-c** M NELSON

OVINGTON (St John the Evangelist)   *see* Watton w Carbrooke and Ovington *Nor*

OVINGTON (St Mary)   *see* N Hinckford *Chelmsf*

OVINGTON (St Peter)   *see* New Alresford w Ovington and Itchen Stoke *Win*

OWERMOIGNE (St Michael)   *see* Watercombe *Sarum*

OWERSBY, NORTH (St Martin)   *see* Kelsey Gp *Linc*

OWLERTON (St John the Baptist)   *Sheff 4*   **P** *Ch Patr Trust* **V** N A DAWSON,   **C** C J TRUMAN

OWLPEN (Holy Cross)   *see* Uley w Owlpen and Nympsfield *Glouc*

OWLSMOOR (St George)   *Ox 16*   **P** *Bp*   **V** R V PARRETT

OWLSWICK (Chapel)   *see* Risborough *Ox*

OWMBY Group, The (St Peter and St Paul)   *Linc 3*   **P** *Duchy of Lanc, Bp and D&C, Mrs S Hutton and Earl of Scarborough, and Mrs B K Cracroft-Eley (by turn)*   **R** P D GODDEN

OWSLEBURY (St Andrew)   *see* Twyford and Owslebury and Morestead *Win*

OWSTON (All Saints)   *Sheff 7*   **P** *DBP*   **V** J Y W RITCHIE

OWSTON (St Andrew)   *see* Whatborough Gp of Par *Leic*

OWSTON (St Martin)   *Linc 1*   **P** *The Crown*   **V** J STAFF

OWTHORNE (St Matthew) and Rimswell w Withernsea *York 12* **P** *Ld Chan and Abp (alt)*   **P-in-c** W J G HEALE

OWTHORPE (St Margaret)   *S'well 8*   **P** *Trustees Sir Rupert Bromley Bt*   **P-in-c** P D S MASSEY

OWTON MANOR (St James)   *Dur 3*   **P** *Bp*   **C** M INESON

OXBOROUGH (St John the Evangelist) w Foulden and Caldecote *Nor 13*   **P** *G&C Coll Cam*   **P-in-c** A D WALKER

OXCLOSE (not known)   *Dur 11*   **P** *R Washington, TR Usworth, and V Fatfield (jt)*   **V** *vacant* 0191-416 2561

OXENDON (St Helen)   *see* Arthingworth, Harrington w Oxendon and E Farndon *Pet*

OXENHALL (St Anne)   *see* Redmarley D'Abitot, Bromesberrow, Pauntley etc *Glouc*

OXENHOPE (St Mary the Virgin)   *Bradf 8*   **P** *Bp* **V** B GRAINGER

OXENTON   *see* Woolstone w Gotherington and Oxenton etc *Glouc*

OXFORD Canning Crescent (St Luke)   *see* Ox St Matt *Ox*

OXFORD (St Aldate)   *Ox 7*   **P** *Simeon's Trustees* **R** C ST G CLEVERLY,   **C** J S W CHORLTON,   S C R PONSONBY, **Hon C** D R KABOLEH

OXFORD (St Andrew)   *Ox 7*   **P** *Trustees* **V** A R WINGFIELD DIGBY,   **C** S D COE,   T M GARRETT, **NSM** R M CUNNINGHAM

OXFORD (St Barnabas and St Paul)   *Ox 7*   **P** *Keble Coll Ox* **V** E M WRIGHT,   **NSM** D W MASON,   A RUSTELL,   L R DENNY

OXFORD (St Clement)   *Ox 4*   **P** *Ox Ch Trust* **R** J B GILLINGHAM,   **C** P A JOYCE,   **NSM** V M SINTON

OXFORD (St Ebbe w Holy Trinity and St Peter-le-Bailey) *Ox 7* **P** *Ox Ch Trust*   **R** V E ROBERTS,   **C** A T JONES, P D L WILKINSON,   J P BIDGOOD

OXFORD (St Giles) (St Philip) (St James) (St Margaret) *Ox 7* **P** *St Jo Coll Ox*   **V** A W H BUNCH,   **C** G SIMPSON, **NSM** M SCREECH

OXFORD (St Mary Magdalene)   *Ox 7*   **P** *Ch Ch Ox* **V** H M WYBREW,   **Hon C** P J GROVES

OXFORD (St Mary the Virgin) (St Cross *or* Holywell) (St Peter in the East) *Ox 7*   **P** *Or Coll Ox and Mert Coll Ox (jt)* **V** B W MOUNTFORD,   **C** H A HARRIS,   **NSM** J A SHAW

OXFORD (St Matthew)   *Ox 7*   **P** *Ox Ch Trust* **P-in-c** S J HELLYER,   **C** P J MCKELLEN,   **NSM** T BRADSHAW, D R KABOLEH

OXFORD (St Michael at the North Gate w St Martin and All Saints) *Ox 7*   **P** *Linc Coll Ox*   **P-in-c** J C H M LEE, **Hon C** R T BECKWITH

OXFORD (St Thomas the Martyr) (St Frideswide) and Binsey *Ox 7*   **P** *Ch Ch Ox*   **V** R M SWEENEY, **NSM** R C DE V MARTIN

OXHEY (All Saints)   *St Alb 7*   **P** *Bp*   **C** S A STARKEY

OXHEY (St Matthew)   *St Alb 7*   **P** *DBP*   **V** D M SHEPHERD

OXHILL (St Lawrence)   *see* Tysoe w Oxhill and Whatcote *Cov*

OXLEY (Epiphany)   *Lich 28*   **P** *Bp*   **V** *vacant* (01902) 783342

OXNEAD (St Michael & all Angels)   *see* Buxton w Oxnead, Lammas and Brampton *Nor*

OXSHOTT (St Andrew)   *Guildf 10*   **P** *Bp*   **V** J P CRESSWELL

OXSPRING (St Aidan)   *see* Penistone and Thurlstone *Wakef*

OXTED (St Mary) and Tandridge   *S'wark 24*   **P** *Bp* **R** A J MAYER,   **NSM** F A HARDING

OXTON (St Peter and St Paul)   *S'well 14*   **P** *Ld Chan, Bp, and C P L Francklin Esq (by turn)*   **V** M J BROCK, **C** J E DRAYCOTT,   **NSM** M N TAYLOR

OXTON (St Saviour)   *Ches 1*   **P** *DBP*   **V** I A DAVENPORT, **C** P M WADDELL,   C B BURGESS

PACKINGTON (Holy Rood) w Normanton-le-Heath *Leic 9*
P *MMCET and The Crown (alt)* **P-in-c** J N PEARSON,
NSM S A B WALTERS
PACKWOOD (St Giles) w Hockley Heath *Birm 6* **P** *Bp and*
M R Parkes Esq (alt) **V** Q D WARBRICK
PADBURY (St Mary the Virgin) *see* Lenborough *Ox*
PADDINGTON (Emmanuel) Harrow Road *Lon 2* **P** *Hyndman*
Trustees **P-in-c** A G THOM, **C** A R SALISBURY, J P TRIFFITT
PADDINGTON (St David's Welsh Church) Extra-Parochial
Place *Lon 2 vacant*
PADDINGTON (St James) *Lon 2* **P** *Bp* **V** W G WILSON,
C D A PETERS, **Hon C** W H BAYNES
PADDINGTON (St John the Evangelist) (St Michael and All
Angels) *Lon 2* **P** *DBP* **V** S D MASON
PADDINGTON (St Luke the Evangelist) *see* W Kilburn
St Luke w St Simon and St Jude *Lon*
PADDINGTON (St Mary) *Lon 2* **P** *Bp* **P-in-c** G S BRADLEY,
C D C CLUES, **NSM** M GIBSON
PADDINGTON (St Mary Magdalene) *Lon 2* **P** *Keble Coll Ox*
P-in-c G S BRADLEY, **C** D C CLUES, **NSM** M GIBSON
PADDINGTON (St Peter) *Lon 2* **P** *Ch Patr Trust*
P-in-c J P WILKES, **NSM** F W WARD
PADDINGTON (St Saviour) *Lon 2* **P** *Bp* **V** G S BRADLEY,
C D C CLUES, **NSM** F E BLACKMORE, M GIBSON, J BROWNING,
A W WAKEHAM-DAWSON
PADDINGTON (St Stephen w St Luke) *Lon 2* **P** *Bp*
P-in-c T A GILLUM
PADDINGTON GREEN (St Mary) *see* Paddington St Mary
Lon
PADDLESWORTH (St Oswald) *see* Lyminge w Paddlesworth,
Stanford w Postling etc *Cant*
PADDOCK WOOD (St Andrew) *Roch 8* **P** *D&C Cant*
V C J DOBSON, **C** C F GILBERT
PADGATE (Christ Church) *Liv 12* **P** *Bp, Adn, and*
R Warrington (jt) **V** S P ATTWATER, **C** D L WILLIAMS
PADIHAM (St Leonard) (St Anne and St Elizabeth) w Hapton
and Padiham Green *Blackb 3* **P** *Bp* **V** M A JONES
PADSTOW (St Petrock) *Truro 7* **P** *C R Prideaux Brune Esq*
V C M MALKINSON
PADWORTH (St John the Baptist) *see* Stratfield Mortimer and
Mortimer W End etc *Ox*
PAGANHILL (Holy Spirit) *see* Whiteshill and Randwick *Glouc*
PAGHAM (St Thomas à Becket) *Chich 1* **P** *Abp* **V** K SMITH
PAGLESHAM (St Peter) *see* Canewdon w Paglesham *Chelmsf*
PAIGNTON (Christ Church) and Preston St Paul *Ex 10* **P** *Bp*
and Peache Trustees (jt) **V** D W WITCHELL, **C** M A BAKER,
NSM E P LEWIS
PAIGNTON (St John the Baptist) (St Andrew) (St Boniface)
Ex 10 **P** *DBP* **V** B R TUBBS, **C** A S PAGETT, M J P CAIN
PAILTON (St Denis) *see* Monks Kirby w Pailton and
Stretton-under-Fosse *Cov*
PAINSWICK (St Mary the Virgin), Sheepscombe, Cranham, The
Edge, Pitchcombe, Harescombe and Brookthorpe *Glouc 1*
P *Bp, D&C, Mrs N Owen (1 turn), and Ld Chan (1 turn)*
V J LONGUET-HIGGINS, **NSM** I C GOBEY, D W NEWELL,
H M SAMMON
PAKEFIELD (All Saints and St Margaret) *Nor 9* **P** *Ch Patr*
Trust **R** R J K BAKER
PAKENHAM (St Mary) w Norton and Tostock *St E 9* **P** *Bp*
and Peterho Cam (jt) **R** I HOOPER
PALFREY (St Mary and All Saints) *see* Caldmore w Palfrey
Lich
PALGRAVE (St Peter) *see* N Hartismere *St E*
PALLION (St Luke) *see* Millfield St Mark and Pallion St Luke
Dur
PALMARSH (Holy Cross) *see* Hythe *Cant*
PALMERS GREEN (St John the Evangelist) *Lon 18*
P *V Southgate Ch Ch* **V** R C KNOWLING, **C** R M FERMER
PALTERTON (St Luke's Mission Room) *see* E Scarsdale *Derby*
PAMBER (St Mary and St John the Baptist) *see* The Sherbornes
w Pamber *Win*
PAMBER HEATH (St Luke) *see* Tadley S and Silchester *Win*
PAMPISFORD (St John the Baptist) *Ely 6*
P *Mrs B A Killander* **V** *vacant*
PANCRASWEEK (St Pancras) *see* Pyworthy, Pancrasweek and
Bridgerule *Ex*
PANFIELD (St Mary the Virgin) and Rayne *Chelmsf 15* **P** *Bp*
and DBP (alt) **R** P J MEADER, **NSM** G B T BAYLISS
PANGBOURNE (St James the Less) w Tidmarsh and Sulham
Ox 12 **P** *Bp, Ch Soc Trust, and Mrs I E Moon (jt)*
R J W STAPLES, **C** K N GRUNEBERG
PANNAL (St Robert of Knaresborough) w Beckwithshaw
Ripon 1 **P** *Bp and Peache Trustees (jt)* **V** N C SINCLAIR
PANSHANGER (United Church) Conventional District *St Alb 7*
TV S Q MOORE
PAPCASTLE (Mission Church) *see* Bridekirk *Carl*

PAPPLEWICK (St James) *see* Linby w Papplewick *S'well*
PAPWORTH (St Peter) *Ely 1* **P** *Patr Bd*
TR J C B PEMBERTON, **TV** A C MCCOLLUM,
C C P HOLLINGSHURST, **NSM** P C M SCOTT
PAR (St Mary the Virgin) (Good Shepherd) *Truro 1*
P *The Crown* **V** *vacant* (01726) 812775
PARHAM (St Mary the Virgin) *see* Campsea Ashe w
Marlesford, Parham and Hacheston *St E*
PARHAM (St Peter) *see* Amberley w N Stoke and Parham,
Wiggonholt etc *Chich*
PARK BARN (St Clare) *see* Westborough *Guildf*
PARKEND (St Paul) and Viney Hill *Glouc 4* **P** *Bp and Univ*
Coll Ox (jt) **V** P A BRUNT
PARKESTON (St Paul) *see* Dovercourt and Parkeston w
Harwich *Chelmsf*
PARKFIELD (Holy Trinity) *see* Langley and Parkfield *Man*
PARKGATE (St Thomas) *see* Neston *Ches*
PARKHAM (St James), Alwington, Buckland Brewer,
Abbotsham, Hartland, Welcombe, Clovelly, Woolfardisworthy
West and Buck Mills *Ex 16* **P** *Patr Bd (4 turns), Crown*
(1 turn) **TR** P J F GOODEY, **TV** A J RICHARDSON,
C R P HANSFORD, C W J HODGETTS, **Hon C** J A WHEELER
PARKSONE (St John) *see* Heatherlands St Jo *Sarum*
PARKSTONE (Good Shepherd) *as above Sarum*
PARKSTONE (St Barnabas) *see* Branksome St Clem *Sarum*
PARKSTONE (St Clement) *as above Sarum*
PARKSTONE (St Luke) *Sarum 7* **P** *Ch Trust Fund Trust*
V C M STRAIN
PARKSTONE (St Peter) and St Osmund w Branksea St Mary
Sarum 7 **P** *Patr Bd* **R** N J C LLOYD, **C** K METZNER,
S P CHAMBERS, **NSM** D J NEWMAN, J P M MARTIN
PARKWOOD (Christ Church) Conventional District *Cant 15*
C-in-c M A MCLAUGHLIN
PARLAUNT ROAD (Christ the Worker) *see* Langley Marish
Ox
PARLEY, WEST (All Saints) (St Mark) *Sarum 9*
P *P E E Prideaux-Brune Esq* **R** E C BOOTH
PARNDON, GREAT (St Mary) *Chelmsf 26* **P** *Patr Bd*
TV J M RAGAN
PARNDON, LITTLE (St Mary) *see* Harlow Town Cen w Lt
Parndon *Chelmsf*
PARR (St Peter) (St Paul) (St Philip) (Holy Trinity) *Liv 10*
P *Patr Bd* **TV** J MARSDEN, J L ROBERTS, C S WOODS,
OLM A KIRKHAM, I A WHITAKER, M E TAYLOR, H MCCANN
PARR MOUNT (Holy Trinity) *see* Parr *Liv*
PARRACOMBE (Christ Church) *see* Combe Martin,
Berrynarbor, Lynton, Brendon etc *Ex*
PARSON CROSS (St Bernard) *see* Southey Green St Bernard
CD *Sheff*
PARSON CROSS (St Cecilia) *see* Sheff Parson Cross St Cecilia
Sheff
PARSON'S GREEN (St Dionis) *see* Fulham St Dionis Parson's
Green *Lon*
PARTINGTON (St Mary) and Carrington *Ches 10* **P** *Bp and*
V Bowdon (alt) **V** P MASON
PARTNEY Group, The (St Nicholas) *Linc 7* **P** *Bp and DBP,*
Baroness Willoughby de Eresby, Mrs E M V Drake, and
Mrs D E P Douglas (by turn) **R** R J BENSON
PARTRIDGE GREEN (St Michael and All Angels) *see* W
Grinstead *Chich*
PARWICH (St Peter) *see* Fenny Bentley, Thorpe, Tissington,
Parwich etc *Derby*
PASSENHAM (St Guthlac) *Pet 5* **P** *MMCET*
R C J MURRAY
PASTON (All Saints) *Pet 13* **P** *Bp* **R** G M JESSOP
PASTON (St Margaret) *see* Trunch *Nor*
PATCHAM (All Saints) *Chich 2* **P** *MMCET*
V N E D MILMINE, **C** J A T RUSSELL, D P CREES
PATCHAM, SOUTH (Christ the King) *Chich 2* **P** *Bp*
V D H HUMPHREY, **NSM** J W M COLLINS
PATCHING (St John the Divine) *see* Findon w Clapham and
Patching *Chich*
PATCHWAY (St Chad) *Bris 5* **P** *Trustees* **V** D R BYRNE
PATELEY BRIDGE (St Cuthbert) *see* Upper Nidderdale *Ripon*
PATRICK (Holy Trinity) *S & M 1* **P** *Bp* **V** G M BREFFITT
PATRICK BROMPTON (St Patrick) and Hunton *Ripon 4*
P *Bp* **V** D J CHRISTIE
PATRICROFT (Christ Church) *see* Eccles *Man*
PATRINGTON (St Patrick) w Hollym, Welwick and Winestead
York 12 **P** *DBP, Ld Chan, and CPAS (by turn)*
P-in-c D R HARRIS
PATRIXBOURNE (St Mary) w Bridge and Bekesbourne *Cant 1*
P *Abp* **P-in-c** P J FILMER
PATTERDALE (St Patrick) *see* Gd Shep TM *Carl*
PATTINGHAM (St Chad) w Patshull *Lich 24* **P** *Bp and Lady*
Kwiatkowska (jt) **P-in-c** J E DAIMOND

PATTISHALL (Holy Cross) w Cold Higham and Gayton w Tiffield *Pet 5*   **P** *Bp, SS Coll Cam, and SMF (jt)*   **R** P J BROADBENT

PAUL (St Pol de Lion) *Truro 5*   **P** *Ld Chan*   **V** G J HANSFORD

PAULERSPURY (St James the Apostle) *see* Silverstone and Abthorpe w Slapton etc *Pet*

PAULL (St Andrew and St Mary) *see* Hedon w Paull *York*

PAULSGROVE (St Michael and All Angels) *Portsm 6*   **P** *Bp*   **V** G R WADDINGTON

PAULTON (Holy Trinity) *B & W 12*   **P** *Bp and R Chewton Mendip (alt)*   **V** J G EDWARDS

PAUNTLEY (St John the Evangelist) *see* Redmarley D'Abitot, Bromesberrow, Pauntley etc *Glouc*

PAVENHAM (St Peter) *see* Milton Ernest, Pavenham and Thurleigh *St Alb*

PAWLETT (St John the Baptist) *see* Puriton and Pawlett *B & W*

PAXFORD (Mission Church) *see* Blockley w Aston Magna and Bourton on the Hill *Glouc*

PAXTON, GREAT (Holy Trinity) *Ely 13*   **P** *D&C Linc*   **P-in-c** N MORGAN

PAXTON, LITTLE (St James) *Ely 13*   **P** *D&C Linc*   **P-in-c** N MORGAN

PAYHEMBURY (St Mary the Virgin) *see* Broadhembury, Payhembury and Plymtree *Ex*

PEACEHAVEN (Ascension) and Telscombe Cliffs *Chich 18*   **P** *Bp*   **V** D A HIDER,   **C** D L N GUTSELL

PEAK DALE (Holy Trinity) *see* Wormhill, Peak Forest w Peak Dale and Dove Holes *Derby*

PEAK FOREST (St Charles the King and Martyr) *as above Derby*

PEAKIRK (St Pega) w Glinton and Northborough *Pet 13*   **P** *D&C*   **R** N E FRY

PEAR TREE (Jesus Chapel) *see* Southampton St Mary Extra *Win*

PEASE POTTAGE (Ascension) *see* Slaugham *Chich*

PEASEDOWN ST JOHN (St John the Baptist) w Wellow *B & W 12*   **P** *Bp and R H Horton-Fawkes Esq (jt)*   **V** H R L BONSEY

PEASEMORE (St Barnabas) *see* Beedon and Peasemore w W Ilsley and Farnborough *Ox*

PEASENHALL (St Michael) *see* Yoxford and Peasenhall w Sibton *St E*

PEASE'S WEST (St George) *see* Crook *Dur*

PEASLAKE (St Mark) *see* Shere, Albury and Chilworth *Guildf*

PEASLEY CROSS (Mission Hall) *see* Parr *Liv*

PEASMARSH (St Michael) *see* Shalford *Guildf*

PEASMARSH (St Peter and St Paul) *see* Beckley and Peasmarsh *Chich*

PEATLING MAGNA (All Saints) *see* Willoughby Waterleys, Peatling Magna etc *Leic*

PEATLING PARVA (St Andrew) *see* Gilmorton, Peatling Parva, Kimcote etc *Leic*

PEBMARSH (St John the Baptist) *see* Knights and Hospitallers Par *Chelmsf*

PEBWORTH (St Peter), Dorsington, Honeybourne and Marston Sicca *Glouc 10*   **P** *Bp*   **R** C G MATTOCK

PECKHAM (St John w St Andrew) *S'wark 8*   **P** *Bp*   **V** M S JOHNSON

PECKHAM (St Mary Magdalene) (St Paul) *S'wark 8*   **P** *Ch Patr Soc*   **V** M F PAYNE,   **C** M E TRASK

PECKHAM (St Saviour) *S'wark 9*   **P** *Bp*   **V** W C HEATLEY,   **NSM** C DAVIES

PECKHAM, EAST (Holy Trinity) and Nettlestead *Roch 8*   **P** *St Pet Coll Ox and D&C Cant (jt)*   **R** A H CARR,   **NSM** S M MORRELL

PECKHAM, WEST (St Dunstan) *see* Mereworth w W Peckham *Roch*

PECKLETON (St Mary Magdalene) *see* Desford and Peckleton w Tooley *Leic*

PEDLINGE (Estate Chapel) *see* Saltwood *Cant*

PEDMORE (St Peter) *Worc 12*   **P** *Oldswinford Hosp*   **R** A L HAZLEWOOD,   **C** T E FFRENCH

PEEL (St Paul) *see* Walkden and Lt Hulton *Man*

PEEL GREEN (St Catherine) *see* Barton w Peel Green *Man*

PEEL GREEN (St Michael and All Angels) *as above Man*

PEGSWOOD (St Margaret) *see* Bothal and Pegswood w Longhirst *Newc*

PELDON (St Mary) w Great and Little Wigborough *Chelmsf 16*   **P** *Ch Soc Trust and T Wheatley-Hubbard Esq*   **P-in-c** S C NORTON,   **NSM** A R GATES

PELSALL (St Michael and All Angels) *Lich 25*   **P** *Bp*   **V** *vacant* (01922) 682098

PELTON (Holy Trinity) *Dur 16*   **P** *R Chester le Street*   **P-in-c** J LINTERN

PELTON, WEST (St Paul) *Dur 11*   **P** *Bp*   **P-in-c** J LINTERN

PELYNT (St Nun) *see* Lanreath, Pelynt and Bradoc *Truro*

PEMBERTON (St Francis of Assisi) Kitt Green *Liv 15*   **P** *R Wigan and Bp (jt)*   **V** N P ANDERSON

PEMBERTON (St John) *Liv 15*   **P** *R Wigan*   **V** C B OXENFORTH

PEMBERTON (St Mark) Newtown *Liv 15*   **P** *Duke of Sutherland, Bp, and R Pemberton St Jo (jt)*   **V** D V ROUCH,   **OLM** E TAULTY, S FULFORD

PEMBRIDGE (St Mary the Virgin) w Moor Court, Shobdon, Staunton-on-Arrow, Byton and Lyonshall *Heref 5*   **P** *Ld Chan (1 turn), Patr Bd (4 turns)*   **R** *vacant* (01544) 388998

PEMBURY (St Peter) *Roch 8*   **P** *Ch Ch Ox*   **V** S SEALY,   **NSM** H A HUGHES

PEN SELWOOD (St Michael) *B & W 2*   **P** *Bp*   **R** S LOW

PENCOMBE (St John) *see* Bredenbury w Grendon Bishop and Wacton etc *Heref*

PENCOYD (St Denys) *see* St Weonards w Orcop, Garway, Tretire etc *Heref*

PENCOYS (St Andrew) *see* Redruth w Lanner and Treleigh *Truro*

PENDEEN (St John the Baptist) w Morvah *Truro 5*   **P** *R A H Aitken Esq and C W M Aitken Esq (jt)*   **V** A ROWELL

PENDEFORD (St Paul) *see* Tettenhall Regis *Lich*

PENDLEBURY (St Augustine) *see* Swinton and Pendlebury *Man*

PENDLEBURY (St John) *Man 6*   **P** *Trustees*   **P-in-c** L S K TIMMINS,   **OLM** V TYLDESLEY

PENDLETON (All Saints) *see* Sabden and Pendleton *Blackb*

PENDLETON (St Ambrose) (St Thomas) *Man 6*   **P** *Patr Bd*   **TR** A I SALMON,   **TV** M K J SMITH, N J ANDREWES,   **C** A W BENNETT, R A ROSS,   **Hon C** D J H KEYTE,   **OLM** J I WHITTINGHAM

PENDOCK CROSS (Holy Redeemer) *see* Berrow w Pendock, Eldersfield, Hollybush etc *Worc*

PENDOMER (St Roch) *see* W Coker w Hardington Mandeville, E Chinnock etc *B & W*

PENGE (Christ Church w Holy Trinity) *see* Anerley *Roch*

PENGE (St John the Evangelist) *Roch 13*   **P** *Simeon's Trustees*   **V** P R M VENABLES

PENGE (St Paul) *see* Anerley St Paul *Roch*

PENGE LANE (Holy Trinity) *Roch 13*   **P** *CPAS*   **V** *vacant* (020) 8778 7258

PENHILL (St Peter) *Bris 7*   **P** *Bp*   **V** S WATERS,   **C** C A WATERS

PENHURST (St Michael the Archangel) *see* Ashburnham w Penhurst *Chich*

PENISTONE (St John the Baptist) and Thurlstone *Wakef 7*   **P** *Bp*   **TR** S W MIDGLEY,   **TV** D J HOPKIN

PENKETH (St Paul) *Liv 13*   **P** *Bp*   **V** P W HOCKLEY

PENKHULL (St Thomas) *Lich 12*   **P** *R Stoke-on-Trent*   **V** I MAITIN

PENKRIDGE Team, The (St Michael and All Angels) *Lich 2*   **P** *Patr Bd*   **TR** G STATON,   **TV** C G HEATH,   **C** L C STARRS,   **NSM** J BISHOP

PENN (Holy Trinity) *Ox 20*   **P** *Earl Howe*   **P-in-c** M D BISSET

PENN (St Bartholomew) (St Anne) *Lich 24*   **P** *Bp*   **V** G M F WILLIAMS,   **C** G WINDON

PENN FIELDS St Philip (St Aidan) *Lich 24*   **P** *Ch Trust Fund Trust*   **V** J S OAKLEY,   **C** P J CANSDALE

PENN STREET (Holy Trinity) *Ox 20*   **P** *Earl Howe*   **P-in-c** M J BOYES

PENNARD, EAST (All Saints) *see* Fosse Trinity *B & W*

PENNARD, WEST (St Nicholas) *see* Baltonsborough w Butleigh, W Bradley etc *B & W*

PENNINGTON (Christ Church) *Man 13*   **P** *Trustees*   **V** P W LEAKEY,   **C** E D COCKSHAW,   **OLM** E J WHITE, J HARNEY

PENNINGTON (St Mark) *Win 11*   **P** *V Milford*   **V** P H RENYARD

PENNINGTON (St Michael and the Holy Angels) and Lindal w Marton and Bardsea *Carl 9*   **P** *Bp and DBP (jt)*   **P-in-c** D E WEBSTER,   **NSM** M WEBSTER

PENNYCROSS (St Pancras) *Ex 21*   **P** *CPAS*   **V** A M M PARKER

PENNYWELL (St Thomas) *see* Sunderland Pennywell St Thos *Dur*

PENPONDS (Holy Trinity) *Truro 2*   **P** *The Crown*   **P-in-c** P DOUGLASS,   **C** M L PASCOE

PENRITH (Christ Church) (St Andrew) w Newton Reigny and Plumpton Wall *Carl 4*   **P** *Bp*   **TR** R W WOODGER,   **TV** A P HUTCHINSON, A M MULLER,   **C** C N CASEY, A M E OSMASTON

PENRUDDOCK (All Saints) *see* Gd Shep TM *Carl*

PENSAX (St James the Great) *see* Teme Valley N *Worc*

PENSBY (St Michael and All Angels) *see* Barnston *Ches*

PENSHAW (All Saints) *Dur 14*   **P** *Bp*   **P-in-c** P M HOOD,   **NSM** M S GOURLEY

PENSHURST (St John the Baptist) and Fordcombe *Roch 12*
  P *Viscount De L'Isle* P-in-c T E HOLME
PENSILVA (St John) *see St Ive and Pensilva w Quethiock Truro*
PENSNETT (St Mark) *Worc 10* P *Bp* V L J WOOLHOUSE,
  C S J MAINWARING
PENTEWAN (All Saints) *see St Austell Truro*
PENTLOW (St George and St Gregory) *see N Hinckford
  Chelmsf*
PENTNEY (St Mary Magdalene) *see Narborough w Narford
  and Pentney Nor*
PENTON MEWSEY (Holy Trinity) *see Hatherden w Tangley,
  Weyhill and Penton Mewsey Win*
PENTONVILLE (St Silas w All Saints) (St James) *Lon 6* P *Bp*
  V S RICHARDS
PENTRICH (St Matthew) *see Swanwick and Pentrich Derby*
PENTRIDGE (St Rumbold) *see Sixpenny Handley w Gussage
  St Andrew etc Sarum*
PENWERRIS (St Michael and All Angels) (Holy Spirit) *Truro 3*
  P *V St Gluvias* V D S SMITH
PENWORTHAM (St Leonard) *Blackb 5* P *Bp*
  V J N MANSFIELD
PENWORTHAM (St Mary) *Blackb 5* P *Miss A M Rawstorne*
  V C J NELSON, C A J LOGAN
PENZANCE (St Mary) (St Paul) (St John the Baptist) *Truro 5*
  P *Bp* TR K R OWEN, TV L C WRIGHT, C C R PERRY,
  NSM N W MARTIN
PEOPLETON (St Nicholas) and White Ladies Aston w Churchill
  and Spetchley and Upton Snodsbury and Broughton Hackett
  Worc 4 P *Bp, Croom Estate Trustees, and Major R J G Berkley
  (1 turn), and Ld Chan (1 turn)* R S M EAST
PEOVER, NETHER (St Oswald) *Ches 12* P *Man Univ*
  V K M BURGHALL
PEOVER, OVER (St Lawrence) *Ches 12* P *DBP*
  P-in-c K M BURGHALL
PEPER HAROW (St Nicholas) *see Compton w Shackleford
  and Peper Harow Guildf*
PEPLOW (The Epiphany) *see Hodnet w Weston under
  Redcastle Lich*
PERIVALE (St Mary w St Nicholas) *Lon 22* P *Trustees*
  P-in-c A R CORSIE, NSM P H F HOBDAY
PERLETHORPE (St John the Evangelist) *S'well 6* P *Earl
  Manvers' Trustees* V *vacant*
PERRANARWORTHAL (St Piran) *see St Stythians w
  Perranarworthal and Gwennap Truro*
PERRANPORTH (St Michael's Mission Church)
  see Perranzabuloe Truro
PERRANUTHNOE (St Michael and St Piran) *see Ludgvan,
  Marazion, St Hilary and Perranuthnoe Truro*
PERRANZABULOE (St Piran) *Truro 6* P *D&C*
  V J B SAUNDERS
PERROTT, NORTH (St Martin) *see Haselbury Plucknett,
  Misterton and N Perrott B & W*
PERROTT, SOUTH (St Mary) *see Beaminster Area Sarum*
PERRY BARR (St John the Evangelist) *Birm 3* P *Bp and
  trustees (jt)* V C S JONES
PERRY BEECHES (St Matthew) *Birm 3* P *St Martin's
  Trustees* V S P M MACKENZIE, C P D JOYCE
PERRY COMMON (St Martin) *Birm 8* P *Bp* V C M FEAK
PERRY GREEN (St Thomas) *see Much Hadham St Alb*
PERRY HILL (St George) *S'wark 5* P *Bp and D&C (alt)*
  P-in-c J R W ACKLAND
PERRY STREET (All Saints) *Roch 4* P *Bp* V P E WAKELIN,
  C J E MOWBRAY
PERSHORE (Holy Cross) w Pinvin, Wick and Birlingham
  Worc 4 P *Patr Bd* NSM D C OWEN
PERTENHALL (St Peter) *see The Stodden Churches St Alb*
PETER TAVY (St Peter), Mary Tavy, Lydford and Brent Tor
  Ex 24 P *Guild of All So and Bp (1 turn), Duchy of Cornwall
  (1 turn)* R I SYKES, Hon C R D ORMSBY, NSM G STILL
PETERBOROUGH (All Saints) *Pet 13* P *Bp* V D J T MILLER
PETERBOROUGH (Christ the Carpenter) *Pet 13* P *Bp*
  V A P HOLFORD, C C R IEVINS, NSM P V IEVINS
PETERBOROUGH (Holy Spirit) Bretton *Pet 13* P *Bp*
  V P M HAWKINS
PETERBOROUGH (St Barnabas) *Pet 13* P *Bp* V *vacant*
PETERBOROUGH (St John the Baptist) (Mission Church)
  Pet 13 P *Bp* V G J STEELE, NSM B J WITHINGTON
PETERBOROUGH (St Jude) *Pet 13* P *Bp* V G J KEATING
PETERBOROUGH (St Mark) *Pet 13* P *Bp* V *vacant* (01733)
  554516
PETERBOROUGH (St Mary) Boongate *Pet 13* P *D&C*
  V D J DUNCANSON, NSM R J BATES, C D MASON
PETERBOROUGH (St Paul) *Pet 13* P *Bp* V P R LARCOMBE
PETERCHURCH (St Peter) *see Madley w Tyberton,
  Peterchurch, Vowchurch etc Heref*
PETERLEE (St Cuthbert) *Dur 2* P *Bp* V P M TEMPLEMAN,
  C D R H MCGOWAN

PETERSFIELD (St Peter) *Portsm 4* P *Bp*
  V W G HARRIS-EVANS, C T C WRIGHT, NSM J C GRACE
PETERSHAM (All Saints) (St Peter) *S'wark 18* P *Bp*
  P-in-c F R BENTLEY
PETERSMARLAND (St Peter) *see Shebbear, Buckland
  Filleigh, Sheepwash etc Ex*
PETERSTOW (St Peter) *see Ross Heref*
PETHAM (All Saints) and Waltham w Lower Hardres and
  Nackington w Upper Hardres and Stelling *Cant 2* P *Abp,
  St Jo Coll Ox, and Trustees Lord Tomlin (jt)*
  P-in-c D W J HOUSTON
PETHERTON, NORTH (St Mary the Virgin) w Northmoor
  Green *B & W 14* P *D&C Windsor* P-in-c S M ROSE,
  C M H CLEMENTS
PETHERTON, SOUTH (St Peter and St Paul) w the
  Seavingtons *B & W 15* P *D&C* R D J M JASPER
PETHERWIN, NORTH (St Paternus) *see Egloskerry,
  N Petherwin, Tremaine and Tresmere Truro*
PETROCKSTOWE (St Petrock) *see Shebbear, Buckland
  Filleigh, Sheepwash etc Ex*
PETT (St Mary and St Peter) *see Fairlight, Guestling and Pett
  Chich*
PETT LEVEL (St Nicholas) *as above Chich*
PETTAUGH (St Catherine) *see Helmingham w Framsden and
  Pettaugh w Winston St E*
PETTISTREE (St Peter and St Paul) *see Wickham Market w
  Pettistree St E*
PETTON (not known) w Cockshutt, Welshampton and Lyneal w
  Colemere *Lich 17* P *Bp and R K Mainwaring Esq (jt)*
  P-in-c T N THOROLD
PETTON (St Petrock) *see Bampton, Morebath, Clayhanger and
  Petton Ex*
PETTS WOOD (St Francis) *Roch 16* P *Bp* V O C G HIGGS
PETWORTH (St Mary) *Chich 11* P *Lord Egremont*
  R D S POLLARD
PEVENSEY (St Nicholas) (St Wilfred) *Chich 16* P *Bp*
  V A C H CHRISTIAN
PEWSEY (St John the Baptist) and Swanborough Team
  Ministry, The *Sarum 19* P *Patr Bd* TV J T M DESROSIERS,
  V S ROWE, OLM G E R OSBORNE
PHEASEY (St Chad) *Lich 25* P *DBP* C S C LUCAS
PHILBEACH GARDENS (St Cuthbert) *see Earl's Court
  St Cuth w St Matthias Lon*
PHILLACK (St Felicitas) *see Godrevy Truro*
PHILLEIGH (St Philleigh) *see Gerrans w St
  Anthony-in-Roseland and Philleigh Truro*
PICCADILLY (St James) *see Westmr St Jas Lon*
PICKENHAM, NORTH (St Andrew) *see Necton, Holme Hale
  w N and S Pickenham Nor*
PICKENHAM, SOUTH (All Saints) *as above Nor*
PICKERING (St Peter and St Paul) w Lockton and Levisham
  York 20 P *Abp* V F J A HEWITT
PICKHILL (All Saints) *see Kirklington w Burneston and Wath
  and Pickhill Ripon*
PICKWELL (All Saints) *see Burrough Hill Pars Leic*
PICKWORTH (All Saints) *see Gt and Lt Casterton w
  Pickworth and Tickencote Pet*
PICKWORTH (St Andrew) *see S Lafford Linc*
PICTON (St Hilary) *see Kirklevington York*
PIDDINGHOE (St John) *Chich 18* P *Bp and Gorham
  Trustees (jt)* V D A HIDER, C D L N GUTSELL
PIDDINGTON (St John the Baptist) *see Hardingstone and
  Horton and Piddington Pet*
PIDDINGTON (St Nicholas) *see Ray Valley Ox*
PIDDLE, NORTH (St Michael) *see Abberton, The Flyfords,
  Naunton Beauchamp etc Worc*
PIDDLEHINTON (St Mary the Virgin) *see Piddletrenthide w
  Plush, Alton Pancras etc Sarum*
PIDDLETRENTHIDE (All Saints) w Plush, Alton Pancras and
  Piddlehinton *Sarum 1* P *Eton Coll, D&C, and D&C Win
  (by turn)* P-in-c J M BAILEY, NSM H J P EXON
PIDLEY CUM FENTON (All Saints) *see Somersham w Pidley
  and Oldhurst Ely*
PIERCEBRIDGE (St Mary) *see Coniscliffe Dur*
PILHAM (All Saints) *see Corringham and Blyton Gp Linc*
PILL (Christ Church) w Easton in Gordano and Portbury
  B & W 13 P *Bp* V R H M LEGG
PILLATON (St Modwen) *see Penkridge Team Lich*
PILLATON (St Odolph) *see St Dominic, Landulph and
  St Mellion w Pillaton Truro*
PILLERTON HERSEY (St Mary) *see Butlers Marston and the
  Pillertons w Ettington Cov*
PILLEY (Mission Church) *see Tankersley, Thurgoland and
  Wortley Sheff*
PILLEY (St Nicholas) *see Boldre w S Baddesley Win*
PILLING (St John the Baptist) *see Stalmine w Pilling Blackb*

PILNING (St Peter) w Compton Greenfield *Bris 2* **P** *Bp*
V B TOPALIAN
PILSLEY (St Mary the Virgin) *see* N Wingfield, Clay Cross and
Pilsley *Derby*
PILTON (All Saints) *see* Aldwincle w Thorpe Achurch, Pilton,
Wadenhoe etc *Pet*
PILTON (St John the Baptist) w Croscombe, North Wootton and
Dinder *B & W 8* **P** *Bp and Peache Trustees (jt)*
R D R OSBORNE, **C** E J THOMSON
PILTON (St Mary the Virgin) *see* Barnstaple *Ex*
PILTON (St Nicholas) *see* Preston and Ridlington w Wing and
Pilton *Pet*
PIMLICO Bourne Street (St Mary) *see* Pimlico St Mary Bourne
Street *Lon*
PIMLICO (St Barnabas) *Lon 3* **P** *Bp* **V** vacant (020) 7730
5054
PIMLICO (St Gabriel) *Lon 3* **P** *Bp* **V** D W SKEOCH,
NSM W D PATTINSON
PIMLICO (St James the Less) *see* Westminster St Jas the Less
Lon
PIMLICO (St Mary) Bourne Street *Lon 3* **P** *Trustees*
C N S MERCER, **Hon C** LORD PILKINGTON OF OXENFORD,
S E YOUNG, **NSM** S N LEAMY
PIMLICO (St Peter) w Westminster Christ Church *Lon 3* **P** *Bp*
V D B TILLYER, **C** L M RODRIGUEZ, **NSM** A R CHIDWICK
PIMLICO (St Saviour) *Lon 3* **P** *Bp* **P-in-c** J P JOBSON
PIMPERNE (St Peter), Stourpaine, Durweston and Bryanston
Sarum 6 **P** *DBP (2 turns), D&C (1 turn)* **R** S P COULTER
PIN GREEN (All Saints) *see* Stevenage All SS Pin Green *St Alb*
PINCHBECK (St Mary) *see* Glen Gp *Linc*
PINCHBECK, WEST (St Bartholomew) *as above Linc*
PINHOE (St Michael and All Angels) (Hall) and Broadclyst
Ex 1 **P** *Patr Bd* **TR** A J MORTIMER, **C** A E WELLS
PINNER (St Anselm) *see* Hatch End St Anselm *Lon*
PINNER (St John the Baptist) *Lon 23* **P** *V Harrow*
V S J POTHEN, **Hon C** M S NATTRASS, **NSM** I W MURRAY
PINNER VIEW (St George) *see* Headstone St Geo *Lon*
PINVIN (St Nicholas) *see* Pershore w Pinvin, Wick and
Birlingham *Worc*
PINXTON (St Helen) (Church Hall) *Derby 1* **P** *Bp* **R** vacant
(01773) 580024
PIPE-CUM-LYDE (St Peter) *see* Wellington w Pipe-cum-Lyde
and Moreton-on-Lugg *Heref*
PIPEWELL (St Mary) *see* Rothwell w Orton, Rushton w
Glendon and Pipewell *Pet*
PIRBRIGHT (St Michael and All Angels) *Guildf 12* **P** *Ld Chan*
P-in-c V K LUCAS, **NSM** J BUSBY
PIRNOUGH (All Hallows) *see* Ditchingham, Hedenham and
Broome *Nor*
PIRTON (St Mary) *St Alb 4* **P** *D&C Ely*
P-in-c J A S PAYNE COOK
PIRTON (St Peter) *see* Stoulton w Drake's Broughton and
Pirton etc *Worc*
PISHILL (not known) *see* Nettlebed w Bix, Highmoor, Pishill
etc *Ox*
PITCHCOMBE (St John the Baptist) *see* Painswick,
Sheepscombe, Cranham, The Edge etc *Glouc*
PITCHFORD (St Michael and All Angels) *see* Condover w
Frodesley, Acton Burnell etc *Heref*
PITCOMBE (St Leonard) *see* Bruton and Distr *B & W*
PITMINSTER (St Mary and St Andrew) *see* Blackdown
B & W
PITNEY (St John the Baptist) *see* Langport Area Chs *B & W*
PITSEA (St Gabriel) w Nevendon *Chelmsf 6* **P** *Bp*
NSM C GOLDSMITH
PITSFORD (All Saints) w Boughton *Pet 2* **P** *Bp* **R** S TROTT
PITSMOOR (Christ Church) *Sheff 3* **P** *Ch Patr Trust*
V M J SNOW
PITTINGTON (St Laurence), Shadforth and Sherburn *Dur 1*
P *D&C* **NSM** E TARREN
PITTON (St Peter) *see* Clarendon *Sarum*
PITTVILLE (All Saints) *see* Prestbury and All SS *Glouc*
PIXHAM (St Mary the Virgin) *see* Dorking w Ranmore *Guildf*
PIXLEY (St Andrew) *see* Ledbury *Heref*
PLAISTOW (Holy Trinity) *see* Kirdford *Chich*
PLAISTOW (St Martin) (St Mary) (St Philip and St James) and
North Canning Town *Chelmsf 3* **P** *Patr Bd* **TR** S D MASON,
TV E O ADOYO, A W M RITCHIE
PLAISTOW (St Mary) *Roch 14* **P** *Bp* **V** S D BURTON-JONES,
Hon C R B HANDFORTH
PLAISTOW The Divine Compassion *see* Plaistow and N
Canning Town *Chelmsf*
PLAITFORD (St Peter) *see* Bramshaw and Landford w
Plaitford *Sarum*
PLAS NEWTON (St Michael) *Ches 2* **P** *Simeon's Trustees*
V R C TOAN, **C** J E JEPSON, **NSM** J A ROBERTS

PLATT (St Mary the Virgin) *Roch 10* **P** *Bp* **P-in-c** J DRAY
PLATT BRIDGE (St Nathaniel) *Liv 14* **P** *Bp* **V** K D CRINKS
PLATT'S HEATH (St Edmund) *see* Len Valley *Cant*
PLAXTOL (not known) *see* Shipbourne w Plaxtol *Roch*
PLAYDEN (St Michael) *see* Rye *Chich*
PLAYFORD (St Mary) *see* Gt and Lt Bealings w Playford and
Culpho *St E*
PLEASLEY (St Michael) *see* E Scarsdale *Derby*
PLEASLEY HILL (St Barnabas) *S'well 2* **P** *Bp*
NSM P N WOOD
PLEASLEY VALE (St Chad) *see* Mansfield Woodhouse *S'well*
PLEMSTALL (St Peter) w Guilden Sutton *Ches 2* **P** *Capt*
P Egerton Warburton **V** M HART
PLESHEY (Holy Trinity) *Chelmsf 8* **P** *Bp*
P-in-c S F COUGHTREY
PLUCKLEY (St Mary) *see* Egerton w Pluckley *Cant*
PLUCKLEY (St Nicholas) *as above Cant*
PLUMBLAND (St Cuthbert) *see* Binsey *Carl*
PLUMPTON (All Saints) (St Michael and All Angels) w East
Chiltington cum Novington *Chich 18* **P** *Ld Chan*
R G D BROSTER
PLUMPTON (St John the Baptist) *see* Weedon Lois w
Plumpton and Moreton Pinkney etc *Pet*
PLUMPTON WALL (St John the Evangelist) *see* Penrith w
Newton Reigny and Plumpton Wall *Carl*
PLUMSTEAD (All Saints) Shooters Hill *S'wark 3* **P** *CPAS*
V H D OWEN
PLUMSTEAD (Ascension) *S'wark 3* **P** *Bp* **V** C R WELHAM
PLUMSTEAD (St John the Baptist) w St James and St Paul
S'wark 3 **P** *Simeon's Trustees and CPAS (alt)* **V** P J ROGERS,
C M S RICHEUX
PLUMSTEAD (St Mark and St Margaret) *S'wark 3* **P** *DBP*
V R W JAMES
PLUMSTEAD (St Michael) *see* Barningham w Matlaske w
Baconsthorpe etc *Nor*
PLUMSTEAD (St Nicholas) *S'wark 3* **P** *V Plumstead St Mark*
w St Marg **V** A G STEVENS
PLUMSTEAD, GREAT (St Mary) and LITTLE (St Gervase
and Protase) w Thorpe End and Witton *Nor 4* **P** *Bp and*
D&C (jt) **R** M M KINGSTON
PLUMTREE (St Mary) *S'well 8* **P** *DBP*
P-in-c M H WAINWRIGHT
PLUNGAR (St Helen) *see* Vale of Belvoir Par *Leic*
PLYMOUTH Crownhill (Ascension) *Ex 22* **P** *Bp*
V P HANCOCK, **C** J A THOMPSON-VEAR
PLYMOUTH Emmanuel, St Paul Efford and St Augustine
Ex 23 **P** *Patr Bd* **TR** K F FREEMAN, **TV** J M BARRETT,
C S M PAYNE
PLYMOUTH (St Andrew) and St Paul Stonehouse *Ex 23*
P *Patr Bd* **TR** N H P MCKINNEL, **TV** M T BAILEY,
C R C H THOMAS, J D G NASH, A J WADSWORTH
PLYMOUTH (St Augustine) *see* Plymouth Em, St Paul Efford
and St Aug *Ex*
PLYMOUTH (St Gabriel) Peverell *Ex 23* **P** *Bp* **V** J J STARK
PLYMOUTH (St James the Less) Ham *Ex 21* **P** *Keble Coll Ox*
V T M S MORLEY
PLYMOUTH (St John the Evangelist) *see* Sutton on Plym *Ex*
PLYMOUTH (St Jude) *Ex 23* **P** *Trustees* **V** S R DINSMORE,
C J A NICKOLS
PLYMOUTH (St Mary the Virgin) *see* Plymouth St Simon and
St Mary *Ex*
PLYMOUTH (St Matthias) *see* Charles w Plymouth St
Matthias *Ex*
PLYMOUTH (St Peter) (All Saints) *Ex 21* **P** *Keble Coll Ox*
V S PHILPOTT
PLYMOUTH (St Simon) and St Mary Laira *Ex 24* **P** *Bp and*
St Simon Trustees (jt) **V** S P PICKERING
PLYMPTON (St Mary the Blessed Virgin) *Ex 22* **P** *Bp*
V M M CAMERON, **C** R W BECK, **NSM** M BRIMICOMBE
PLYMPTON (St Maurice) *Ex 22* **P** *D&C Windsor*
R T E THOMAS
PLYMSTOCK (St Mary and All Saints) and Hooe *Ex 23*
P *Patr Bd* **TR** D J WALLER, **TV** I K PROVOST, J J SPEAR,
NSM M P HINKS
PLYMTREE (St John the Baptist) *see* Broadhembury,
Payhembury and Plymtree *Ex*
POCKLEY (St John the Baptist) *see* Kirkdale w Harome,
Nunnington and Pockley *York*
POCKLINGTON (All Saints) and Owsthorpe and Kilnwick
Percy w Great Givendale and Millington *York 5* **P** *Abp*
R C J SIMMONS, **C** S MITCHELL, **NSM** P H BOWES
PODIMORE (St Peter) *see* Ilchester w Northover, Limington,
Yeovilton etc *B & W*
PODINGTON (St Mary the Virgin) *see* Wymington w
Podington *St Alb*
POINT CLEAR (Mission) *see* St Osyth *Chelmsf*

POINTON (Christ Church) *see* Billingborough Gp *Linc*

POKESDOWN (All Saints) *Win 8* **P** *V Christchurch*
V *vacant* (01202) 423747

POKESDOWN (St James) *Win 8* **P** *Bp* **P-in-c** R L VERNON,
NSM P M SCHOLLAR

POLDENS, WEST *B & W 5* **P** *Bp* **P-in-c** W B GRAHAM,
NSM S L GRAHAM

POLEBROOK (All Saints) and Lutton w Hemington and
Luddington *Pet 12* **P** *Bp, Sir Stephen Hastings, and DBP*
(by turn) **R** I A LOVETT

POLEGATE (St John) *Chich 16* **P** *Bp* **V** M W LUCAS,
NSM R A HERKES

POLEGATE (St Wilfrid) *see* Lower Willingdon St Wilfrid CD
Chich

POLESWORTH (St Editha) *Birm 10* **P** *Ld Chan*
V P A WELLS

POLING (St Nicholas) *Chich 1* **P** *Bp* **V** J E SLEGG

POLLINGTON (St John the Baptist) *see* Gt Snaith *Sheff*

POLPERRO (St John the Baptist) *see* Talland *Truro*

POLRUAN (St Saviour) *see* Lanteglos by Fowey *Truro*

POLSTEAD (St Mary) *see* Stoke by Nayland w Leavenheath
and Polstead *St E*

POLTIMORE (St Mary the Virgin) *see* Stoke Canon, Poltimore
w Huxham and Rewe etc *Ex*

PONDERS END (St Matthew) *Lon 18* **P** *V Enfield*
P-in-c T G CLEMENT, **C** S P J CLARK

PONDERSBRIDGE (St Thomas) *see* Whittlesey,
Pondersbridge and Coates *Ely*

PONSANOOTH (St Michael and All Angels) *see* Mabe *Truro*

PONSBOURNE (St Mary) *see* Lt Berkhamsted and Bayford,
Essendon etc *St Alb*

PONSONBY (not known) *see* Beckermet St Jo and St Bridget w
Ponsonby *Carl*

PONTEFRACT (All Saints) *Wakef 11* **P** *Bp*
P-in-c V IWANUSCHAK

PONTEFRACT (St Giles w St Mary) *Wakef 11* **P** *Bp*
V G HIGGINS

PONTELAND (St Mary the Virgin) *Newc 7* **P** *Mert Coll Ox*
V M J JACKSON, **C** M R SAUNDERS

PONTESBURY First and Second Portions (St George) *Heref 13*
P *St Chad's Coll Dur* **R** D H ROBERTS

PONTON, GREAT (Holy Cross) *see* Colsterworth Gp *Linc*

PONTON, LITTLE (St Guthlac) *as above Linc*

POOL (St Wilfrid) *see* Lower Wharfedale *Ripon*

POOLBROOK (St Andrew) *see* Malvern St Andr and Malvern
Wells and Wyche *Worc*

POOLE (St James w St Paul) *Sarum 7* **P** *Ch Soc Trust and
J H Cordle Esq (jt)* **R** R H G MASON, NSM C E SUGDEN

POOLE KEYNES (St Michael and All Angels) *see* Kemble,
Poole Keynes, Somerford Keynes etc *Glouc*

POOLEY BRIDGE (St Paul) *see* Barton, Pooley Bridge and
Martindale *Carl*

POOLSBROOK (St Alban) *see* Staveley and Barrow Hill *Derby*

POORTON, NORTH (St Mary Magdalene) *see* Askerswell,
Loders and Powerstock *Sarum*

POPLAR (All Saints) *Lon 7* **P** *Patr Bd* **TR** A J WYNNE,
TV A M W WILSON, **C** I E VIBERT, NSM T DUNCAN,
J C SHELDON

POPPLETON, NETHER (St Everilda) w Upper (All Saints)
York 1 **P** *Abp* **V** P W THOMAS, NSM M C S FOSSETT

POPPLETON ROAD (Mission Room) *see* York St Paul *York*

PORCHESTER (St James) *S'well 10* **P** *Bp* **V** P A WILLIAMS,
C J MONEY

PORINGLAND (All Saints) *Nor 8* **P** *Bp, BNC Ox,
J D Alston Esq, and G H Hastings Esq (3 turns) and DBP
(1 turn)* **R** R H PARSONAGE

PORLOCK (St Dubricius) w Stoke Pero *B & W 16* **P** *Ld Chan*
R B E PRIORY, **C** J W MORRISH

PORLOCK WEIR (St Nicholas) *see* Porlock w Stoke Pero
B & W

PORT ERIN (St Catherine) *see* Rushen *S & M*

PORT ISAAC (St Peter) *see* St Endellion w Port Isaac and
St Kew *Truro*

PORT ST MARY (St Mary) *see* Rushen *S & M*

PORTBURY (Blessed Virgin Mary) *see* Pill w Easton in
Gordano and Portbury *B & W*

PORTCHESTER (St Mary) *Portsm 2*
P J R Thistlethwaite Esq **V** M S COOPER, **C** A J MATHESON,
NSM A G BRIDGEN

PORTESHAM (St Peter) *see* Abbotsbury, Portesham and
Langton Herring *Sarum*

PORTHILL (St Andrew) *see* Wolstanton *Lich*

PORTHLEVEN (St Bartholomew) w Sithney *Truro 4* **P** *Bp*
P-in-c H PUGH

PORTHPEAN (St Levan) *see* St Austell *Truro*

PORTINSCALE (Mission) *see* Crosthwaite Keswick *Carl*

PORTISHEAD (St Peter) *B & W 13* **P** *Patr Bd*
TR A C TAYLOR, **TV** C L LAWS

PORTKELLIS (St Christopher) *see* Helston and Wendron
Truro

PORTLAND (All Saints w St Peter) *Sarum 4* **P** *Bp*
P-in-c A D THORNE, **C** P A KEMP, **OLM** M E CADE

PORTLAND (St John) *Sarum 4* **P** *Hyndman Trustees*
P-in-c D D BOTTERILL

PORTLEMOUTH, EAST (St Winwaloe Onocaus)
see Charleton w Buckland Tout Saints etc *Ex*

PORTLOE (All Saints) *see* Veryan w Ruan Lanihorne *Truro*

PORTMAN SQUARE (St Paul) *see* Langham Place All So *Lon*

PORTON (St Nicholas) *see* Bourne Valley *Sarum*

PORTREATH (St Mary) *see* St Illogan *Truro*

PORTSDOWN (Christ Church) *Portsm 5* **P** *Simeon's Trustees*
V P J NORTON

PORTSEA (All Saints) *Portsm 6* **P** *V Portsea St Mary and
Bp (jt)* **P-in-c** L FOX, NSM M E TILLMAN

PORTSEA North End (St Mark) *Portsm 6* **P** *V Portsea
St Mary* **C** J POWELL, NSM P K PAYNE, S K WHITELOCK

PORTSEA (St Alban) *Portsm 6* **P** *Bp* **V** *vacant* (023) 9266
2626

PORTSEA (St Cuthbert) *Portsm 6* **P** *Bp* **V** D M POWER,
NSM J POWER, N J POULTON

PORTSEA (St George) *Portsm 6* **P** *Bp* **P-in-c** K B GREEN,
NSM S MARTIN

PORTSEA (St Luke) *Portsm 6* **P** *Ch Patr Trust*
V M J SMITHSON

PORTSEA (St Mary) (St Faith and St Barnabas) (St Wilfrid)
Portsm 6 **P** *Win Coll* **V** R C WHITE, **C** A P DICKENS,
M J STEADMAN

PORTSEA (St Saviour) *Portsm 6* **P** *Bp* **V** *vacant* (023) 9266
3664

PORTSEA (The Ascension) *Portsm 6* **P** *Bp*
P-in-c R F ROBINSON

PORTSLADE (Good Shepherd) *Chich 4* **P** *Bp* **V** P D CLEGG

PORTSLADE (St Nicolas) (St Andrew) *Chich 4* **P** *Bp*
V R H RUSHFORTH

PORTSWOOD (Christ Church) *Win 13* **P** *Bp*
P-in-c G J ARCHER, **C** M W LEFROY, P HARRIS

PORTSWOOD (St Denys) *Win 13* **P** *Bp* **P-in-c** G J ARCHER,
C K J RANDALL, NSM R A FARRAR

POSBURY (St Francis Proprietary Chapel) *see* Crediton,
Shobrooke and Sandford etc *Ex*

POSLINGFORD (St Mary) *see* Clare w Poslingford, Cavendish
etc *St E*

POSTBRIDGE (St Gabriel) *see* Widecombe-in-the-Moor,
Leusdon, Princetown etc *Ex*

POSTLEBURY *see* Nunney and Witham Friary, Marston Bigot
etc *B & W*

POSTLING (St Mary and St Radegund) *see* Lyminge w
Paddlesworth, Stanford w Postling etc *Cant*

POSTWICK (All Saints) *see* Brundall w Braydeston and
Postwick *Nor*

POTT SHRIGLEY (St Christopher) *Ches 13* **P** *MMCET*
P-in-c J BUCKLEY

POTTEN END (Holy Trinity) w Nettleden *St Alb 2* **P** *Bp*
V J V M KIRKBY

POTTER HEIGHAM (St Nicholas) *see* Ludham, Potter
Heigham, Hickling and Catfield *Nor*

POTTERHANWORTH (St Andrew) *see* Branston w Nocton
and Potterhanworth *Linc*

POTTERNE (St Mary the Virgin) w Worton and Marston
Sarum 16 **P** *Bp* **V** P WILKINSON

POTTERNEWTON (St Martin) *Ripon 5* **P** *Trustees*
V J R W SILLER, **C** C WILLIAMS

POTTERS BAR (King Charles the Martyr) *St Alb 17*
P *Bp Lon* **P-in-c** M J BURNS

POTTERS BAR (St Mary and All Saints) *St Alb 17* **P** *Bp Lon*
V P J BEVAN, **C** R A DESICS, NSM G J RANDALL

POTTERS GREEN (St Philip Deacon) *Cov 1* **P** *Ld Chan*
V M C HATHAWAY

POTTERS MARSTON (St Mary) *see* Barwell w Potters
Marston and Stapleton *Leic*

POTTERSPURY (St Nicholas) w Furtho and Yardley Gobion w
Cosgrove and Wicken *Pet 5* **P** *D&C, Jes Coll Ox, and Soc
Merchant Venturers Bris (jt)* **R** L F STEEL

POTTO (St Mary) *see* Whorlton w Carlton and Faceby *York*

POTTON (St Mary the Virgin) w Sutton and Cockayne Hatley
St Alb 11 **P** *The Crown (3 turns), St Jo Coll Ox (1 turn)*
R V W BEYNON, NSM D L SMITH

POUGHILL (St Michael and All Angels) *see* N Creedy *Ex*

POUGHILL (St Olaf King and Martyr) *Truro 8* **P** *Ch Soc
Trust* **V** P A WHYBROW

POULNER (St John) *see* Ringwood *Win*

POULSHOT (St Peter) *see* Seend, Bulkington and Poulshot
Sarum

POULTON (St Luke) *Ches 7* **P** *Bp* **P-in-c** A J MAUNDER
POULTON (St Michael and All Angels) *see* The Ampneys w
 Driffield and Poulton *Glouc*
POULTON LANCELYN (Holy Trinity) *Ches 8*
 P R Bebington **V** G J MOTE, **NSM** P J GASKELL
POULTON-LE-FYLDE (St Chad) *Blackb 12* **P** DBP
 V M P KEIGHLEY, **C** M F BALL, R NICHOLSON
POULTON-LE-SANDS (Holy Trinity) w Morecambe
 St Laurence *Blackb 11* **P** V Lanc **R** G S INGRAM,
 C D A BUCK
POUND HILL (St Barnabas) *see* Worth *Chich*
POUNDSBRIDGE (Chapel) *see* Penshurst and Fordcombe
 Roch
POUNDSTOCK (St Winwaloe) *see* Week St Mary w
 Poundstock and Whitstone *Truro*
POWDERHAM (St Clement Bishop and Martyr) *see* Kenton,
 Mamhead, Powderham, Cofton and Starcross *Ex*
POWERSTOCK (St Mary the Virgin) *see* Askerswell, Loders
 and Powerstock *Sarum*
POWICK (St Peter) and Guarlford and Madresfield w Newland
 Worc 2 **P** *Bp, Lady Rosalind Morrison, and Croome Estate*
 Trustees (jt) **R** W D NICHOL
POYNINGS (Holy Trinity) w Edburton, Newtimber and
 Pyecombe *Chich 9* **P** Ld Chan (1 turn), Bp and Abp (1 turn)
 P-in-c R G BROWN
POYNTINGTON (All Saints) *see* Queen Thorne *Sarum*
POYNTON (St George) *Ches 17* **P** *Bp* **V** J D THOMPSTONE,
 C P NEWMAN, **NSM** R J BROOKE, F T COOKE
POYNTON, HIGHER (St Martin) *see* Poynton *Ches*
PRADOE (extra-parochial place) *Lich 19* **Min** G C JONES
PRATTS BOTTOM (All Souls) *see* Green Street Green and
 Pratts Bottom *Roch*
PREES (St Chad) *Lich 22* **P** *Bp* **V** vacant (01948) 840243
PREESALL (St Oswald) *Blackb 9* **P** *Bp* **V** E ANGUS,
 Hon C A WHITTAKER
PRENTON (St Stephen) *Ches 1* **P** *Bp* **C** J J STAPLES
PRENTON DELL (St Alban) *see* Prenton *Ches*
PRESCOT (St Mary) (St Paul) *Liv 10* **P** K Coll Cam
 OLM J D ROSE
PRESHUTE (St George) *see* Marlborough *Sarum*
PRESTBURY (St Mary) (St Nicholas) and All Saints *Glouc 9*
 P Patr Bd **TR** S S GREGORY, **TV** M G COZENS,
 C G D BAYLISS, **Hon C** P R ILES, **OLM** P T BROWN
PRESTBURY (St Peter) *Ches 13* **P** Ms C J C B Legh
 V D ASHWORTH
PRESTEIGNE (St Andrew) w Discoed, Kinsham, Lingen and
 Knill *Heref 5* **P** Patr Bd **R** S HOLLINGHURST
PRESTLEIGH (St James Mission Church) *see* Shepton Mallet
 w Doulting *B & W*
PRESTOLEE (Holy Trinity) *see* Ringley w Prestolee *Man*
PRESTON Acregate Lane (Mission) *see* Preston Risen Lord
 Blackb
PRESTON (All Saints) *Blackb 13* **P** *Trustees* **V** J D RUSHTON
PRESTON (All Saints) *see* Siddington w Preston *Glouc*
PRESTON (All Saints) and Sproatley in Holderness *York 12*
 P Abp **R** S ROBINSON
PRESTON (Church of the Ascension) *see* Wembley Park *Lon*
PRESTON (Emmanuel) *Blackb 13* **P** R Preston **V** S HUNT
PRESTON (Good Shepherd) *see* Brighton Gd Shep Preston
 Chich
PRESTON (St Alban) *see* Brighton Resurr *Chich*
PRESTON (St Andrew) w Sutton Poyntz and Osmington w
 Poxwell *Sarum 4* **P** Patr Bd **TR** T R WEST,
 TV A C MACROW-WOOD
PRESTON (St Cuthbert) *Blackb 13* **P** *Bp* **V** C E HALLIWELL
PRESTON (St John) (St George the Martyr) (Christ the King
 Chapel) *Blackb 13* **P** DBP **R** M R GRIFFITHS,
 NSM T H DAVIS
PRESTON (St John the Baptist) *see* Redmarley D'Abitot,
 Bromesberrow, Pauntley etc *Glouc*
PRESTON (St John) w Brighton St Augustine and St Saviour
 Chich 2 **P** *Bp* **V** vacant (01273) 555033
PRESTON St Jude w St Paul *Blackb 13* **P** *Bp and V Preston*
 St John **P-in-c** G W NELSON
PRESTON (St Luke) (St Oswald) *Blackb 13* **P** *Bp and*
 Simeon's Trustees (jt) **P-in-c** G W NELSON
PRESTON (St Mark) *see* Ashton-on-Ribble St Mich w Preston
 St Mark *Blackb*
PRESTON (St Martin) *see* King's Walden and Offley w Lilley
 St Alb
PRESTON (St Mary the Virgin) *see* Lavenham w Preston *St E*
PRESTON (St Matthias) *see* Brighton St Matthias *Chich*
PRESTON (St Mildred) *see* Wingham w Elmstone and Preston
 w Stourmouth *Cant*
PRESTON (St Paul) *see* Paignton Ch Ch and Preston St Paul
 Ex

PRESTON (St Peter and St Paul) and Ridlington w Wing and
 Pilton *Pet 14* **P** *Bp, Baroness Willoughby de Eresby, and*
 DBP (jt) **P-in-c** P A SPENCE
PRESTON (St Stephen) *Blackb 13* **P** *Bp* **V** J N FIELDER
PRESTON The Risen Lord (St Matthew) (St Hilda) (St James's
 church hall) *Blackb 13* **P** Patr Bd **TR** P N TYERS,
 TV P A HARDACRE
PRESTON, EAST (St Mary) w Kingston *Chich 1* **P** D&C
 NSM E J DAVIES
PRESTON, GREAT (St Aidan) *see* Kippax w Allerton Bywater
 Ripon
PRESTON BAGOT (All Saints) *see* Claverdon w Preston Bagot
 Cov
PRESTON BISSET (St John the Baptist) *see* Swan *Ox*
PRESTON BROOK (St Faith) *see* Daresbury *Ches*
PRESTON CAPES (St Peter and St Paul) *see* Badby w Newnham
 and Charwelton w Fawsley etc *Pet*
PRESTON NEXT FAVERSHAM (St Catherine) w Goodnestone
 and Graveney *Cant 6* **P** Abp **V** S C WILSON,
 C W J HORNSBY, A C OEHRING
PRESTON ON STOUR (St Mary) *see* Ilmington w
 Stretton-on-Fosse etc *Cov*
PRESTON ON TEES (All Saints) *Dur 10* **P** *Bp*
 P-in-c A J FARISH, **C** N R SHAVE
PRESTON-ON-WYE (St Lawrence) *see* Cusop w Blakemere,
 Bredwardine w Brobury etc *Heref*
PRESTON PATRICK (St Patrick) *see* Crosscrake and Preston
 Patrick *Carl*
PRESTON PLUCKNETT (St James the Great) (St Peter)
 B & W 7 **P** *Bp (2 turns), Mrs S W Rawlins (1 turn)*
 V A PERRIS
PRESTON UNDER SCARR (St Margaret) *see* Wensley *Ripon*
PRESTON WEALDMOORS (St Lawrence) *see* Edgmond w
 Kynnersley and Preston Wealdmoors *Lich*
PRESTON WYNNE (Holy Trinity) *see* Bodenham w
 Hope-under-Dinmore, Felton etc *Heref*
PRESTONVILLE (St Luke) *Chich 2* **P** CPAS **C** M J T PAYNE
PRESTWICH (St Gabriel) *Man 14* **P** *Bp*
 P-in-c S S WILLIAMS
PRESTWICH (St Hilda) *Man 14* **P** *Trustees*
 Hon C D E BUTLER
PRESTWICH (St Margaret) (St George) *Man 14*
 P R Prestwich St Mary the Virgin **V** M ASHWORTH
PRESTWICH (St Mary the Virgin) *Man 14* **P** *Trustees*
 P-in-c B M HACKETT
PRESTWOLD (St Andrew) *see* Wymeswold and Prestwold w
 Hoton *Leic*
PRESTWOOD (Holy Trinity) and Great Hampden *Ox 28*
 P Bp and Hon I H Hope-Morley (jt) **P-in-c** M MOWFORTH,
 C P A SMITH, **OLM** K WATTERS
PRICKWILLOW (St Peter) *see* Ely *Ely*
PRIDDY (St Lawrence) *B & W 1* **P** *Bp* **V** E A MACPHERSON
PRIESTWOOD (St Andrew) *see* Bracknell *Ox*
PRIMROSE HILL (Holy Trinity) *see* Lydney *Glouc*
PRIMROSE HILL (St Mary the Virgin) w Avenue Road
 (St Paul) *Lon 16* **P** *Trustees* **V** R R ATWELL,
 C P S NICHOLSON, **Hon C** D J H JONES, **NSM** J H ROOSE-EVANS,
 C L VAN DER PUMP
PRINCE ALBERT ROAD (St Mark) *see* Regent's Park St
 Mark *Lon*
PRINCE CONSORT ROAD (Holy Trinity) *see* S Kensington H
 Trin w All SS *Lon*
PRINCE'S PARK (Christ the King) Conventional District *Roch 5*
 Min K G FOOT
PRINCES RISBOROUGH (St Mary) *see* Risborough *Ox*
PRINCETOWN (St Michael and All Angels)
 see Widecombe-in-the-Moor, Leusdon, Princetown etc *Ex*
PRIOR'S DEAN (not known) *see* Greatham w Empshott and
 Hawkley w Prior's Dean *Portsm*
PRIORS HARDWICK (St Mary the Virgin) w Priors Marston
 and Wormleighton *Cov 10* **P** Earl Spencer
 P-in-c G D MORRIS
PRIORS LEE (St Peter) (St Georges) *Lich 21* **P** Bp and
 V Shifnal (jt) **V** P G F LAWLEY
PRIORS MARSTON (St Leonard) *see* Priors Hardwick, Priors
 Marston and Wormleighton *Cov*
PRIORS PARK (Mission Hall) *see* Tewkesbury w Walton
 Cardiff and Twyning *Glouc*
PRISTON (St Luke) *see* Timsbury and Priston *B & W*
PRITTLEWELL (All Saints) *see* Southend *Chelmsf*
PRITTLEWELL (St Luke) *Chelmsf 13* **P** *Bp* **V** M J HALSALL
PRITTLEWELL (St Mary the Virgin) *Chelmsf 13* **P** *Bp*
 V R A MASON, **C** D C STANDEN, **NSM** F M SMITH
PRITTLEWELL (St Peter) w Westcliff St Cedd and the Saints of
 Essex *Chelmsf 13* **P** *Bp* **V** G R STEEL
PRITTLEWELL (St Stephen) *Chelmsf 13* **P** *Bp*
 P-in-c R A MASON, **C** J D PEARSON

PROBUS (St Probus and St Grace), Ladock and Grampound w Creed and St Erme *Truro 6* **P** *DBP* **TR** I H MORRIS, **TV** D H DIXON, **C** M J W WARNER, **Hon C** M E RICHARDS
PRUDHOE (St Mary Magdalene) *Newc 3* **P** *Dioc Soc* **P-in-c** C H HOPE, **OLM** D WEETMAN
PSALTER LANE (St Andrew) *Sheff 2* **P** *Trustees* **V** N P A JOWETT
PUBLOW (All Saints) w Pensford, Compton Dando and Chelwood *B & W 10* **P** *Bp* **P-in-c** G CALWAY, **C** S M E STEVENS
PUCKINGTON (St Andrew) *see* Ilminster and Distr *B & W*
PUCKLECHURCH (St Thomas à Becket) and Abson *Bris 5* **P** *D&C* **V** S K YOUNG
PUDDINGTON (St Thomas à Becket) *see* N Creedy *Ex*
PUDDLETOWN (St Mary the Virgin), Tolpuddle and Milborne w Dewlish *Sarum 1* **P** *Bp, Ch Ch Ox, Viscount Rothermere, and trustees (jt)* **R** J V WALTON
PUDLESTON (St Peter) *see* Leominster *Heref*
PUDSEY (St James the Great) *see* Woodhall *Bradf*
PUDSEY (St Lawrence and St Paul) *Bradf 3* **P** *Bp and V Calverley (jt)* **V** P N AYERS, **C** S R EVANS
PULBOROUGH (St Mary) *Chich 12* **P** *Lord Egremont* **R** P B WELCH
PULFORD (St Mary the Virgin) *see* Eccleston and Pulford *Ches*
PULHAM (St Thomas à Beckett) *see* Dungeon Hill *Sarum*
PULHAM MARKET (St Mary Magdalene) *see* Dickleburgh and The Pulhams *Nor*
PULHAM ST MARY (St Mary the Virgin) *as above Nor*
PULLOXHILL (St James the Apostle) *see* Silsoe, Pulloxhill and Flitton *St Alb*
PULVERBATCH (St Edith) *see* Longden and Annscroft w Pulverbatch *Heref*
PUNCKNOWLE (St Mary the Blessed Virgin) *see* Bride Valley *Sarum*
PUNNETS TOWN (St Peter) *see* Heathfield *Chich*
PURBROOK (St John the Baptist) *Portsm 5* **P** *Bp* **V** R I P COUTTS, **C** R CHAPMAN, **NSM** M M SHERWIN, **B A MOSSE**
PUREWELL (St John) *see* Christchurch *Win*
PURFLEET (St Stephen) *see* Aveley and Purfleet *Chelmsf*
PURITON (St Michael and All Angels) and Pawlett *B & W 14* **P** *Ld Chan (1 turn), D&C Windsor (2 turns)* **V** D J L MACGEOCH
PURLEIGH (All Saints), Cold Norton and Stow Maries *Chelmsf 11* **P** *Charterhouse, Or Coll Ox, and Bp (jt)* **P-in-c** J E BLAND
PURLEY (Christ Church) *S'wark 24* **P** *Bp* **V** C R TREFUSIS, **C** M D FITTER, **OLM** S P BISHOP
PURLEY (St Barnabas) *S'wark 24* **P** *Bp* **P-in-c** R C HAGON
PURLEY (St Mark) Woodcote *S'wark 24* **P** *Bp* **P-in-c** J W S PATON, **Hon C** H RHODES
PURLEY (St Mary the Virgin) *Ox 12* **P** *Ld Chan* **R** R B HOWELL, **NSM** J ROTHERY, **OLM** A MACKIE
PURLEY (St Swithun) *S'wark 24* **P** *Bp* **V** J K GREIG
PURLWELL (St Andrew) *see* Batley All SS and Purlwell *Wakef*
PURSE CAUNDLE (St Peter) *see* The Caundles w Folke and Holwell *Sarum*
PURSTON (St Thomas) cum South Featherstone *Wakef 11* **P** *Bp* **V** A S RAMSDEN
PURTON (St John) *see* Sharpness, Purton, Brookend and Slimbridge *Glouc*
PURTON (St Mary) *Bris 7* **P** *Bp* **V** B A FESSEY
PUSEY (All Saints) *see* Cherbury w Gainfield *Ox*
PUTFORD (St Stephen) *see* Bradworthy, Sutcombe, Putford etc *Ex*
PUTLEY (not known) *see* Ledbury *Heref*
PUTNEY (St Margaret) *S'wark 20* **P** *Bp* **V** W F WARREN, **NSM** P J MILLIGAN
PUTNEY (St Mary) (All Saints) *S'wark 20* **P** *D&C Worc* **V** G A FRASER, **C** D E REES, R M SEWELL, **NSM** T J E MARWOOD
PUTTENHAM (St John the Baptist) *see* Seale, Puttenham and Wanborough *Guildf*
PUTTENHAM (St Mary) *see* Tring *St Alb*
PYE NEST (St James) *see* King Cross *Wakef*
PYECOMBE (Transfiguration) *see* Poynings w Edburton, Newtimber and Pyecombe *Chich*
PYLLE (St Thomas à Becket) *see* Fosse Trinity *B & W*
PYPE HAYES (St Mary the Virgin) *see* Erdington *Birm*
PYRFORD (Church of the Good Shepherd) *see* Wisley w Pyrford *Guildf*
PYRFORD (St Nicolas) *as above Guildf*
PYRTON (St Mary) *see* Icknield *Ox*
PYTCHLEY (All Saints) *see* Isham w Pytchley *Pet*
PYWORTHY (St Swithun), Pancrasweek and Bridgerule *Ex 9* **P** *DBP* **R** *vacant* (01409) 254062

QUADRING (St Margaret) *see* Gosberton, Gosberton Clough and Quadring *Linc*
QUAINTON (Holy Cross and St Mary) *see* Schorne *Ox*
QUANTOCK TOWERS, The *B & W 17* **P** *Bp, D&C Windsor, and D&C Wells (jt)* **R** E B SAUGMAN, **NSM** J C ROBBINS
QUANTOXHEAD (Blessed Virgin Mary) (St Ethelreda) *B & W 17* **P** *Bp, Lady Gass, and Lt-Col W Luttrell (jt)* **R** J D A STEVENS, **NSM** P CUFF, S L CAMPBELL
QUARLEY (St Michael and All Angels) *see* Amport, Grateley, Monxton and Quarley *Win*
QUARNDON (St Paul) *Derby 11* **P** *Exors Viscount Scarsdale* **P-in-c** W F BATES, **NSM** S M BAILEY
QUARNFORD (St Paul) *see* Longnor, Quarnford and Sheen *Lich*
QUARRENDON ESTATE (St Peter) *see* Aylesbury w Bierton and Hulcott *Ox*
QUARRINGTON (St Botolph) w Old Sleaford *Linc 22* **P** *Bp* **P-in-c** P J MANDER
QUARRY BANK (Christ Church) *Worc 10* **P** *Prime Min* **P-in-c** C J WINDLEY, **C** J S MCARTHUR-EDWARDS
QUARRY HILL (St Mary) *see* Leeds City *Ripon*
QUATFORD (St Mary Magdalene) *see* Bridgnorth, Tasley, Astley Abbotts, etc *Heref*
QUATT (St Andrew) *see* Alveley and Quatt *Heref*
QUEDGELEY (St James) *Glouc 5* **P** *Bp* **V** G J B STICKLAND
QUEEN CAMEL (St Barnabas) w West Camel, Corton Denham, Sparkford, Weston Bampfylde and Sutton Montis *B & W 3* **P** *Bp and DBP (2 turns), CPAS, MMCET and Revd G Bennett (1 turn)* **R** M J M PERRY
QUEEN CHARLTON (St Margaret) *see* Keynsham *B & W*
QUEEN THORNE *Sarum 3* **P** *Bp, The Revd J M P Goodden, J K Wingfield Digby Esq, and MMCET (jt)* **R** H G PEARSON, **OLM** A J B MONDS, P M SHERWIN
QUEENBOROUGH (Holy Trinity) *Cant 16* **P** *Abp* **P-in-c** G H SPENCER
QUEENHILL (St Nicholas) *see* Longdon, Castlemorton, Bushley, Queenhill etc *Worc*
QUEEN'S GATE (St Augustine) *see* S Kensington St Aug *Lon*
QUEEN'S PARK (St Barnabas) *see* Holdenhurst and Iford *Win*
QUEENSBURY (All Saints) *Lon 23* **P** *The Crown* **V** R M HILLS, **NSM** P A JONES
QUEENSBURY (Holy Trinity) *Bradf 2* **P** *Bp* **V** P A HEDGE
QUENDON (not known) w Rickling and Wicken Bonhunt and Widdington *Chelmsf 21* **P** *Keble Coll Ox and Bp (alt)* **R** A LINDSAY
QUENIBOROUGH (St Mary) *see* Syston *Leic*
QUENINGTON (St Swithun) *see* Coln St Aldwyns, Hatherop, Quenington etc *Glouc*
QUERNMORE (St Peter) *see* Dolphinholme w Quernmore and Over Wyresdale *Blackb*
QUETHIOCK (St Hugh) *see* St Ive and Pensilva w Quethiock *Truro*
QUIDENHAM Group, The (St Andrew) *Nor 11* **P** *Ld Chan (1 turn), Bp, Sir Thomas Beevor Bt, Major E H C Garnier, Trustees, and New Buckenham PCC (3 turns)* **R** C J DAVIDSON, **C** N P KINSELLA, **OLM** A R WRIGHT, H A MONKHOUSE
QUINTET Group of Parishes *see* Cranborne w Boveridge, Edmondsham etc *Sarum*
QUINTON and PRESTON DEANERY (St John the Baptist) *see* Wootton w Quinton and Preston Deanery *Pet*
QUINTON (St Swithun) *Glouc 9* **P** *D&C Worc and Bp (jt)* **NSM** J Y CARMAN
QUINTON, THE (Christ Church) *Birm 2* **P** *Bp* **C** S C CARTER, R L HUGHES
QUINTON ROAD WEST (St Boniface) *Birm 2* **P** *Bp* **V** W BROWN, **C** J P FFRENCH
QUORN (St Bartholomew) *see* Quorndon *Leic*
QUORNDON (St Bartholomew) *Leic 7* **P** *Bp* **V** D H BOWLER
QUY (St Mary) *see* Anglesey Gp *Ely*
RACKENFORD (All Saints) *see* Washfield, Stoodleigh, Withleigh etc *Ex*
RACKHEATH (Holy Trinity) and Salhouse *Nor 4* **P** *Bp* **P-in-c** G HOWELLS
RACTON (St Peter) *see* Compton, the Mardens, Stoughton and Racton *Chich*
RADBOURNE (St Andrew) *see* Boylestone, Church Broughton, Dalbury, etc *Derby*
RADCLIFFE (St Andrew) Black Lane *Man 14* **P** *R Radcliffe St Mary* **V** P N W GRAYSHON
RADCLIFFE (St Mary) (St Thomas and St John) (St Philip Mission Church) *Man 14* **P** *Patr Bd* **TR** C J C HEWITT
RADCLIFFE-ON-TRENT (St Mary) and Shelford w Holme Pierrepont and Adbolton *S'well 8* **P** *DBP (2 turns), Ld Chan (1 turn)* **P-in-c** N WESTON
RADCLIVE (St John the Evangelist) *see* Buckingham *Ox*

RADDESLEY Group of Parishes, The *Ely 4* **P** *E H Vestey Esq,
Mrs B O Killander, Mrs B A Taylor, F R Egerton Esq, Exors
C L Thomas (5 turns), St Jo Coll Cam (1 turn)*
R D J COCKERELL
RADDINGTON (St Michael) *see* Wiveliscombe w Chipstable,
Huish Champflower etc *B & W*
RADDON *see* Thorverton, Cadbury, Upton Pyne etc *Ex*
RADFORD (All Souls) w Christ Church and St Michael *S'well 13*
P *Bp* **V** D A JONES
RADFORD (St Nicholas) *Cov 2* **P** *Bp* **V** G J MARCER
RADFORD (St Peter) *S'well 13* **P** *Bp*
P-in-c D EDINBOROUGH
RADFORD, NORTH (St Francis of Assisi) *see* Cov St Fran N
Radford *Cov*
RADFORD SEMELE (St Nicholas) *Cov 10* **P** *Bp*
P-in-c R D ALLON-SMITH
**RADIPOLE (Emmanuel) (St Adhelm) (St Ann) and Melcombe
Regis** *Sarum 4* **P** *Patr Bd* **TR** K I HOBBS,
TV I J GREENSLADE, P J SALMON, **C** D P HARKNETT
RADLETT (Christ Church) (St John) *St Alb 1* **P** *V Aldenham*
V G FELLOWS, **NSM** M TAYLOR, V M HARVEY
RADLEY (St James the Great) and Sunningwell *Ox 10*
P *Radley Coll and DBP (by turn)* **R** T P GIBBONS
RADNAGE (St Mary) *see* W Wycombe w Bledlow Ridge,
Bradenham and Radnage *Ox*
RADNOR, OLD (St Stephen) *see* Kington w Huntington, Old
Radnor, Kinnerton etc *Heref*
RADSTOCK (St Nicholas) w Writhlington *B & W 12* **P** *Bp*
R C P J TURNER
RADWAY (St Peter) *see* Warmington w Shotteswell and
Radway w Ratley *Cov*
RADWELL (All Saints) *see* Stotfold and Radwell *St Alb*
RADWINTER (St Mary the Virgin) *see* The Sampfords and
Radwinter w Hempstead *Chelmsf*
RAGDALE (All Saints) *see* Upper Wreake *Leic*
RAINFORD (All Saints) *Liv 11* **P** *V Prescot*
V F R N MICHELL
RAINHAM (St Helen and St Giles) w Wennington *Chelmsf 2*
P *MMCET* **R** A C WARD
RAINHAM (St Margaret) *Roch 3* **P** *Bp* **V** A T VOUSDEN,
C S M PATTLE, **R** OATES, B A MASON
RAINHILL (St Ann) *Liv 13* **P** *Trustees* **C** E COLLISON
RAINOW (Holy Trinity) w Saltersford and Forest *Ches 13*
P *Bp* **P-in-c** S D RATHBONE
RAINTON (not known) *see* Topcliffe, Baldersby w Dishforth,
Dalton etc *York*
RAINTON, EAST (St Cuthbert) *Dur 14* **P** *D&C* **V** D GUEST
RAINTON, WEST (St Mary) *Dur 14* **P** *Bp* **R** D GUEST
RAINWORTH (St Simon and St Jude) *see* Blidworth w
Rainworth *S'well*
RAITHBY (Holy Trinity) *see* Spilsby Gp *Linc*
RAITHBY (St Peter) *see* Legbourne and Wold Marsh *Linc*
RAME (St Germanus) *see* Maker w Rame *Truro*
RAMPISHAM (St Michael and All Angels) *see* Melbury *Sarum*
RAMPSIDE (St Michael) *see* Aldingham, Dendron, Rampside
and Urswick *Carl*
RAMPTON (All Saints) *Ely 5* **P** *Bp* **R** G E TURNER
**RAMPTON (All Saints) w Laneham, Treswell, Cottam and
Stokeham** *S'well 5* **P** *D&C York and The Crown (alt)*
P-in-c M J LEATON
RAMSBOTTOM (St Andrew) *Man 10* **P** *Bp*
V I M ROGERSON
RAMSBOTTOM (St John) (St Paul) *Man 10* **P** *Prime Min
and Bp (alt)* **V** J ARCUS
RAMSBURY (Holy Cross) *see* Whitton *Sarum*
RAMSDALE (Christ Church) *see* Baughurst, Ramsdell,
Wolverton w Ewhurst etc *Win*
RAMSDEN (Church of Unity) *see* Orpington All SS *Roch*
**RAMSDEN (St James), Finstock and Fawler, Leafield w
Wychwood and Wilcote** *Ox 3* **P** *Bp, V Charlbury, and
Sir Mark Norman Bt (jt)* **V** J F KNOWLES, **NSM** B FORD
RAMSDEN BELLHOUSE (St Mary the Virgin) *see* Ramsden
Crays w Ramsden Bellhouse *Chelmsf*
RAMSDEN CRAYS w Ramsden Bellhouse *Chelmsf 6*
P *Reformation Ch Trust* **P-in-c** S HARDIE
RAMSDEN HEATH (St John) *see* Downham w S Hanningfield
Chelmsf
RAMSEY (St Michael) w Little Oakley and Wrabness
Chelmsf 20 **P** *Ld Chan* **C** E G BUCHANAN
RAMSEY, NORTH (St Olave) *see* Lezayre St Olave Ramsey
S & M
RAMSEY, SOUTH (St Paul) *S & M 3* **P** *Bp*
V N D GREENWOOD, **OLM** B EVANS-SMITH
RAMSEY ST MARY'S (St Mary) *see* The Ramseys and
Upwood *Ely*
RAMSEYS (St Thomas à Becket) (St Mary) and Upwood, The
Ely 10 **P** *Patr Bd* **TR** R A DARMODY, **TV** G D WESTHAVER

RAMSGATE (Christ Church) *Cant 9* **P** *Ch Patr Trust*
V P F TIZZARD
RAMSGATE (Holy Trinity) (St George) *Cant 9* **P** *Abp*
R P A ADAMS
RAMSGATE (St Luke) *Cant 9* **P** *CPAS* **V** V G WILKINS
RAMSGATE (St Mark) *Cant 9* **P** *CPAS* **V** *vacant* (01843)
581042
RAMSGILL (St Mary) *see* Upper Nidderdale *Ripon*
RAMSHOLT (All Saints) *see* Wilford Peninsula *St E*
RANBY (St German) *see* Asterby Gp *Linc*
RANBY (St Martin) *see* Babworth w Sutton-cum-Lound and
Scofton etc *S'well*
RAND (St Oswald) *see* Wragby Gp *Linc*
RANDWICK (St John the Baptist) *see* Whiteshill and
Randwick *Glouc*
RANGEMORE (All Saints) *see* Hanbury w Newborough and
Rangemore *Lich*
RANGEWORTHY (Holy Trinity) *see* Wickwar, Rangeworthy
and Hillesley *Glouc*
RANMOOR (St John the Evangelist) *Sheff 4* **P** *Trustees*
V D C KNIGHT, **C** F M ECCLESTON, **Hon C** B C BROOKE
RANMORE (St Barnabas) *see* Dorking w Ranmore *Guildf*
RANSKILL (St Barnabas) *see* Blyth and Scrooby w Ranskill
S'well
RANTON (All Saints) *see* Derrington, Haughton and Ranton
Lich
**RANWORTH (St Helen) w Panxworth, Woodbastwick, South
Walsham and Upton** *Nor 4* **P** *Bp, Qu Coll Cam, and
J Cator Esq (jt)* **R** P MCFADYEN, **C** D M BOND
RASEN, WEST (All Saints) *see* Middle Rasen Gp *Linc*
RASHCLIFFE (St Stephen) *see* Em TM *Wakef*
RASKELF (St Mary) *see* Brafferton w Pilmoor, Myton on
Swale etc *York*
RASTRICK (St John the Divine) *Wakef 2* **P** *Bp*
P-in-c J R BROADHURST
RASTRICK (St Matthew) *Wakef 2* **P** *V Halifax*
V T L SWINHOE
RATBY (St Philip and St James) *see* Bradgate Team *Leic*
RATCLIFFE CULEY (All Saints) *see* Bosworth and Sheepy
Gp *Leic*
RATCLIFFE-ON-SOAR (Holy Trinity) *see* Kingston and
Ratcliffe-on-Soar *S'well*
RATCLIFFE ON THE WREAKE (St Botolph) *see* Syston
Leic
RATHMELL (Holy Trinity) *see* Giggleswick and Rathmell w
Wigglesworth *Bradf*
RATLEY (St Peter ad Vincula) *see* Warmington w Shotteswell
and Radway w Ratley *Cov*
RATLINGHOPE (St Margaret) *see* Wentnor w Ratlinghope,
Myndtown, Norbury etc *Heref*
RATTERY (Blessed Virgin Mary) *see* S Brent and Rattery *Ex*
**RATTLESDEN (St Nicholas) w Thorpe Morieux, Brettenham
and Hitcham** *St E 10* **P** *Bp (3 turns), Ld Chan (1 turn)*
R R S EXCELL
RAUCEBY, NORTH (St Peter) *see* Ancaster Wilsford Gp *Linc*
RAUGHTON HEAD (All Saints) *see* Dalston w Cumdivock,
Raughton Head and Wreay *Carl*
RAUNDS (St Peter) *Pet 10* **P** *Bp* **V** *vacant* (01933) 625637
RAVENDALE, EAST (St Martin) *see* Laceby and Ravendale
Gp *Linc*
RAVENFIELD (St James) *see* Bramley and Ravenfield w
Hooton Roberts etc *Sheff*
RAVENGLASS (Mission Room) *see* Eskdale, Irton, Muncaster
and Waberthwaite *Carl*
RAVENHEAD (St John) *see* Parr *Liv*
RAVENHEAD (St John the Evangelist) *Liv 10* **P** *V St Helens*
V E R DORAN
RAVENINGHAM Group, The (St Andrew) *Nor 8* **P** *Bp, Adn
Nor, Sir Nicholas Bacon Bt, Major C A Boycott, D&C, K Coll
Cam, and DBP (jt)* **R** N J WILL
RAVENSCAR (St Hilda) *see* Cloughton and Burniston w
Ravenscar etc *York*
RAVENSDEN (All Saints) *see* Wilden w Colmworth and
Ravensden *St Alb*
RAVENSHEAD (St Peter) *S'well 4* **P** *Bp* **V** G O SPEDDING,
NSM E S STEINER
RAVENSTHORPE (St Denys) *see* W Haddon w Winwick and
Ravensthorpe *Pet*
**RAVENSTHORPE (St Saviour) and Thornhill Lees w Savile
Town** *Wakef 10* **P** *Bp and V Mirfield (jt)* **V** N L STIMPSON
RAVENSTONE (All Saints) *see* Gayhurst w Ravenstone, Stoke
Goldington etc *Ox*
RAVENSTONE (St Michael and All Angels) and Swannington
Leic 8 **P** *Ld Chan and V Whitwick (alt)* **R** K C EMMETT
RAVENSTONEDALE (St Oswald) *see* Orton and Tebay w
Ravenstonedale etc *Carl*

RAWCLIFFE (St James) *see* Airmyn, Hook and Rawcliffe *Sheff*
RAWCLIFFE (St Mark) *see* Clifton *York*
RAWCLIFFE BRIDGE (St Philip) *see* Airmyn, Hook and Rawcliffe *Sheff*
RAWDON (St Peter) *Bradf 4* **P** Trustees **V** C M MORRIS
RAWMARSH (St Mary the Virgin) w Parkgate *Sheff 6* **P** Ld Chan **R** J T BIRBECK
RAWMARSH (St Nicolas) *see* Ryecroft St Nic *Sheff*
RAWNSLEY (St Michael) *see* Hednesford *Lich*
RAWRETH (St Nicholas) w Rettendon *Chelmsf 12* **P** Ld Chan and Pemb Coll Cam (alt) **P-in-c** L C STEWARD
RAWTENSTALL (St Mary) *Man 15* **P** CPAS **V** G D PARKIN
RAWTHORPE (St James) *see* Moldgreen and Rawthorpe *Wakef*
RAY VALLEY, The *Ox 2* **P** Trustees, Ex Coll Ox, and Piddington PCC (1 turn), D&C Westmr, Qu Coll Ox, and Walsingham Coll Trust Assn Ltd (1 turn) **P-in-c** M P CARNEY, C S D LOCKETT, **Hon C** P M BOND
RAYDON (St Mary) *see* Higham, Holton St Mary, Raydon and Stratford *St E*
RAYLEIGH (Holy Trinity) (St Michael) *Chelmsf 12* **P** Patr Bd **TR** D W PARROTT, **C** A J GOWING-CUMBER
RAYNE (All Saints) *see* Panfield and Rayne *Chelmsf*
RAYNES PARK (St Saviour) *S'wark 14* **P** Bp **P-in-c** M O BLACKMAN
RAYNHAM, EAST (St Mary) *see* E w W Rudham, Helhoughton etc *Nor*
RAYNHAM, SOUTH (St Martin) *as above Nor*
REACH (St Ethelreda) *see* Swaffham Bulbeck and Swaffham Prior w Reach *Ely*
READ IN WHALLEY (St John the Evangelist) *Blackb 7* **P** V Whalley **V** A SOWERBUTTS
READING (All Saints) *Ox 15* **P** Bp **V** R H EVERETT
READING (Christ Church) *Ox 15* **P** Bp **P-in-c** D M WEST
READING Greyfriars (St James) *Ox 15* **P** Ch Trust Fund Trust **V** J A DE B WILMOT, **C** P J ANDREW, J M WESTALL
READING (Holy Trinity) *Ox 15* **P** SMF **V** D A PETERS, **C** C L CARD-REYNOLDS
READING (St Agnes w St Paul) (St Barnabas) *Ox 15* **P** Bp **R** R V ORR
READING (St Giles w St Saviour) *Ox 15* **P** Bp **R** M J G MELROSE, **Hon C** L J C JOY
READING (St John the Evangelist and St Stephen) *Ox 15* **P** Simeon's Trustees **V** A R VIGARS, **NSM** S KNIGHT, A M MARSHALL, N H BENSON
READING (St Luke) (St Bartholomew) *Ox 15* **P** Bp and V Reading St Giles (alt) **V** N J HARDCASTLE, **NSM** B D E BLACKMAN, C F BLACKMAN
READING (St Mark) *Ox 15* **P** Bp **V** D A PETERS, **C** C L CARD-REYNOLDS
READING (St Mary the Virgin) (St Laurence) *Ox 15* **P** Bp **R** B SHENTON, **C** C I RUSSELL
READING (St Matthew) *Ox 15* **P** Bp **P-in-c** J HUDSON, **NSM** P G GROSSE
REAPSMOOR (St John) *see* Longnor, Quarnford and Sheen *Lich*
REARSBY (St Michael and All Angels) *see* Syston *Leic*
RECULVER (St Mary the Virgin) and Herne Bay St Bartholomew *Cant 7* **P** Abp **V** R L HAWKES, **OLM** B R NICHOLSON
RED HOUSE (St Cuthbert) *see* Sunderland Red Ho *Dur*
RED POST *Sarum 6* **P** Mrs V M Chattey, H W Plunkett-Ernle-Erle-Drax Esq, and Bp (by turn) **V** H I M MADDOX
REDBOURN (St Mary) *St Alb 8* **P** Earl of Verulam **V** D J SWAN
REDBROOK (St Saviour) *see* Newland and Redbrook w Clearwell *Glouc*
REDCAR (St Peter) *York 16* **P** Trustees **V** J C WEETMAN, **C** J COWAN, **NSM** J S WATSON
REDCLIFFE BAY (St Nicholas) *see* Portishead *B & W*
REDCLIFFE WAY (St Mary the Virgin) *see* Bris St Mary Redcliffe w Temple etc *Bris*
REDDAL HILL (St Luke) *Worc 9* **P** The Crown **P-in-c** H C HANKE
REDDISH (St Elisabeth) *Man 3* **P** Bp **R** N D HAWLEY, **C** P C S DAVIES, M J APPLEBY, **OLM** R C CRAVEN, H E EVANS
REDDISH (St Mary) *see* Heaton Reddish *Man*
REDDISH, NORTH (St Agnes) *Man 3* **P** The Crown **P-in-c** J M PRESTWOOD
REDDITCH (St Stephen) *Worc 7* **P** Bp **P-in-c** A J SMITH
REDDITCH, The Ridge: Redditch (St George), Headless Cross, Webheath and Crabbs Cross *Worc 7* **P** Bp **TV** A J SMITH, G DEW, M F BARTLETT, **C** M DEW, **NSM** M WOODGATES
REDE (All Saints) *see* Chevington w Hargrave, Chedburgh w Depden etc *St E*

REDENHALL (Assumption of the Blessed Virgin Mary), Harleston, Wortwell and Needham *Nor 10* **P** Bp **R** P MORRIS, **OLM** J E HOLMES
REDFIELD (St Leonard) *see* E Bris St Ambrose and St Leon *Bris*
REDGRAVE cum Botesdale (St Mary) w Rickinghall *St E 16* **P** P J H Wilson Esq **R** C R NORBURN
REDHILL (Christ Church) *see* Wrington w Butcombe *B & W*
REDHILL (Holy Trinity) *S'wark 27* **P** Simeon's Trustees **V** G J JENKINS, **C** M J HOUGH, **NSM** H J COWAN
REDHILL (St John the Evangelist) (Meadvale Hall) *S'wark 27* **P** Bp **V** N J CALVER, **NSM** P H BRADSHAW
REDHILL (St Matthew) *S'wark 27* **P** Bp **V** A N TREDENNICK, **C** J F PERCIVAL
REDHORN *Sarum 16* **P** Patr Bd **TR** M B G PAIN, **TV** G D BAKER
REDISHAM (St Peter) *see* Wainford *St E*
REDLAND (not known) *Bris 3* **P** Ch Trust Fund Trust **P-in-c** R P SYMMONS
REDLINGFIELD (St Andrew) *see* Stradbroke, Horham, Athelington and Redlingfield *St E*
REDLYNCH (St Mary) and Morgan's Vale *Sarum 10* **P** DBF and V Downton (alt) **V** vacant (01725) 510439
REDLYNCH (St Peter) *see* Bruton and Distr *B & W*
REDMARLEY D'ABITOT (St Bartholomew), Bromesberrow, Pauntley, Upleadon, Oxenhall, Dymock, Donnington, Kempley and Preston *Glouc 3* **P** Pemb Coll Ox, Bp, R D Marcon Esq, and Miss C Daniel (jt) **R** P PHILLIPS, **NSM** A W PERRY, **OLM** V G CHESTER
REDMARSHALL (St Cuthbert) *Dur 10* **P** The Crown **R** vacant (01740) 630810
REDMILE (St Peter) *see* Vale of Belvoir Par *Leic*
REDMIRE (St Mary) *see* Aysgarth and Bolton cum Redmire *Ripon*
REDNAL (St Stephen the Martyr) *Birm 4* **P** Bp **V** P W THOMAS, **NSM** F J BERRY
REDRUTH (St Andrew) (St Euny) w Lanner and Treleigh *Truro 2* **P** DBP **TR** R C BUSH, **TV** I M TUCKER
REED (St Mary) *see* Barkway, Reed and Buckland w Barley *St Alb*
REEDHAM (St John the Baptist) *see* Freethorpe, Wickhampton, Halvergate etc *Nor*
REEPHAM (St Mary) and Hackford w Whitwell and Kerdiston, Thurning w Wood Dalling and Salle *Nor 22* **P** Bp, CCC Cam, Pemb Coll Cam, Trin Coll Cam, and Ch Soc Trust (jt) **R** M D W PADDISON
REEPHAM (St Peter and St Paul) *see* S Lawres Gp *Linc*
REGENT'S PARK (Christ Church) *see* Munster Square Ch Ch and St Mary Magd *Lon*
REGENT'S PARK (St Mark) *Lon 16* **P** D&C St Paul's **V** P G BAKER
REGIL (St James Mission Church) *see* Winford w Felton Common Hill *B & W*
REIGATE (St Luke) South Park *S'wark 27* **P** Bp **P-in-c** M J H FOX
REIGATE (St Mark) *S'wark 27* **P** Bp **V** I S BROTHWOOD
REIGATE (St Mary Magdalene) *S'wark 27* **P** Trustees **V** D CONNOLLY, **C** G E MCWATT, P J WARREN, **NSM** D A HAGGAN, D G O ROBINSON
REIGATE (St Peter) Conventional District *S'wark 26 vacant*
REIGATE (St Philip) *S'wark 27* **P** Bp **P-in-c** J P SCOTT, **OLM** E STANGHAN
REIGATE HEATH (not known) *see* Reigate St Mary *S'wark*
REIGHTON (St Peter) *see* Bempton w Flamborough, Reighton w Speeton *York*
REKENDYKE (St Jude) *Dur 15* **P** The Crown and D&C **V** A J BEALING, **C** P R BEALING
REMENHAM (St Nicholas) *see* Henley w Remenham *Ox*
REMPSTONE (All Saints) *see* E and W Leake, Stanford-on-Soar, Rempstone etc *S'well*
RENDCOMB (St Peter) *Glouc 11* **P** Major M T N H Wills **P-in-c** C D JEFFERSON
RENDHAM (St Michael) w Sweffling *St E 19* **P** CPAS **P-in-c** J P T OLANCZUK
RENDLESHAM (St Gregory the Great) *see* Wilford Peninsula *St E*
RENHOLD (All Saints) *St Alb 10* **P** MMCET **P-in-c** C D BRADLEY
RENISHAW (St Matthew) *see* Barlborough and Renishaw *Derby*
RENNINGTON (All Saints) *see* Embleton w Rennington and Rock *Newc*
RENWICK (All Saints) *see* Kirkoswald, Renwick, Gt Salkeld and Lazonby *Carl*
REPPS (St Peter) *see* Martham and Repps with Bastwick, Thurne etc *Nor*

REPTON (St Wystan) *see* Foremark and Repton w Newton Solney *Derby*

RESTON, NORTH (St Edith) *see* Legbourne and Wold Marsh *Linc*

RETFORD (St Michael the Archangel) (St Saviour) (St Swithin) *S'well 5* P *Patr Bd* TR A C ST J WALKER, TV M A STAFFORD, C C BUTLER

RETTENDON (All Saints) *see* Rawreth w Rettendon *Chelmsf*

REVELSTOKE (St Peter) *see* Newton Ferrers w Revelstoke *Ex*

REVESBY (St Lawrence) *see* Mareham-le-Fen and Revesby *Linc*

REWE (St Mary the Virgin) *see* Stoke Canon, Poltimore w Huxham and Rewe etc *Ex*

REYDON (St Margaret) *see* Sole Bay *St E*

REYMERSTON (St Peter) *see* Barnham Broom and Upper Yare *Nor*

RHODES (All Saints) (St Thomas) *Man 18* P *R Middleton* V C A PELL, OLM A BROXTON

RHYDYCROESAU (Christ Church) *Lich 19* P *Bp* R D B CROWHURST

RIBBESFORD (St Leonard) w Bewdley and Dowles *Worc 11* P *E J Winnington-Ingram Esq* Hon C G D MORPHY, NSM L E POCOCK

RIBBLETON (St Mary Magdalene) (St Anne's Church Centre) (Ascension) *Blackb 13* P *Patr Bd* TR D P A FEENEY, C D M OVERTON, D A ARNOLD

RIBBY w Wrea (St Nicholas) *Blackb 10* P *V Kirkham* V J WIXON

RIBCHESTER (St Wilfred) w Stidd *Blackb 13* P *Bp* R J FRANCIS

RIBSTON, LITTLE (St Helen) *see* Spofforth w Kirk Deighton *Ripon*

RIBY (St Edmund) *see* Keelby Gp *Linc*

RICCALL (St Mary) *see* Barlby w Riccall *York*

RICHARDS CASTLE (All Saints) *see* Ludlow, Ludford, Ashford Carbonell etc *Heref*

RICHMOND (Holy Trinity and Christ Church) *S'wark 18* P *CPAS* V T H PATTERSON, C J C WATSON, NSM J F HARTERINK

RICHMOND (St Luke) *see* Kew St Phil and All SS w St Luke *S'wark*

RICHMOND (St Mary Magdalene) (St Matthias) (St John the Divine) *S'wark 18* P *K Coll Cam* TR M C J REINDORP, TV L T FRANCIS-DEHQANI, J D S FRENCH, NSM H R SCOTT, N T SUMMERS

RICHMOND (St Mary w Holy Trinity) w Hudswell *Ripon 2* P *Bp* R R T COOPER

RICHMOND HILL *see* Leeds Richmond Hill *Ripon*

RICKERSCOTE (St Peter) *Lich 10* P *Bp and V Stafford St Paul (jt)* V S J HOTCHEN, NSM G P BOTT

RICKINGHALL (St Mary) *see* Redgrave cum Botesdale w Rickinghall *St E*

RICKLING (All Saints) *see* Quendon w Rickling and Wicken Bonhunt etc *Chelmsf*

RICKMANSWORTH (St Mary the Virgin) *St Alb 5* P *Bp* V S R MEPHAM, NSM A P L SHAW

RIDDINGS (Holy Spirit) *see* Bottesford w Ashby *Linc*

RIDDINGS (St James) and Ironville *Derby 1* P *Wright Trustees and V Alfreton (jt)* V M A YATES

RIDDLESDEN (St Mary the Virgin) *Bradf 8* P *Bp* P-in-c G H COLES

RIDDLESDOWN (St James) *S'wark 24* P *Bp* P-in-c C F SPURWAY, NSM D J ROWLAND

RIDDLESWORTH (St Peter) *see* Guiltcross *Nor*

RIDGE (St Margaret) *see* S Mymms and Ridge *St Alb*

RIDGE, The *see* Redditch, The Ridge *Worc*

RIDGEWAY *Ox 19* P *DBP, CCC Ox, and Qu Coll Ox (jt)* R A WADGE, NSM A P HOPWOOD

RIDGEWAY *Sarum 18* P *Patr Bd* P-in-c R J BULLOCK

RIDGEWAY (St John the Evangelist) *see* Eckington w Ridgeway *Derby*

RIDGEWELL (St Laurence) w Ashen, Birdbrook and Sturmer *Chelmsf 19* P *Duchy of Lanc, Bp, and DBP (by turn)* R M D HEWITT

RIDGMONT (All Saints) *see* Aspley Guise w Husborne Crawley and Ridgmont *St Alb*

RIDING MILL (St James) *Newc 3* P *Viscount Allendale* P-in-c C G LEWIS

RIDLEY (St Peter) *Roch 1* P *J R A B Scott Esq* R J A PEAL

RIDLINGTON (St Mary Magdalene and St Andrew) *see* Preston and Ridlington w Wing and Pilton *Pet*

RIDLINGTON (St Peter) *see* Bacton w Edingthorpe w Witton and Ridlington *Nor*

RIDWARES and Kings Bromley, The *Lich 1* P *Bp, Lord Leigh, and D&C (jt)* P-in-c T J LEYLAND, C J G LISTER

RIEVAULX (St Mary) *see* Helmsley *York*

RIGSBY (St James) *see* Alford w Rigsby *Linc*

RIGTON, NORTH (St John) *see* Lower Wharfedale *Ripon*

RILLINGTON (St Andrew) *see* Buckrose Carrs *York*

RIMPTON (The Blessed Virgin Mary) *see* Chilton Cantelo, Ashington, Mudford, Rimpton etc *B & W*

RIMSWELL (St Mary) *see* Owthorne and Rimswell w Withernsea *York*

RINGLAND (St Peter) *see* Taverham w Ringland *Nor*

RINGLEY (St Saviour) (St Aidan) w Prestolee *Man 14* P *R Prestwich St Mary* P-in-c A ROACHE

RINGMER (St Mary the Virgin) *Chich 18* P *Abp* V W R PRATT, C A W N S CANE

RINGMORE (All Hallows) *see* Modbury, Bigbury, Ringmore w Kingston etc *Ex*

RINGSFIELD (All Saints) *see* Wainford *St E*

RINGSHALL (St Catherine) w Battisford, Barking w Darmsden and Great Bricett *St E 1* P *Bp, Ch Patr Trust, and J C W de la Bere Esq (jt)* P-in-c L E FLETCHER

RINGSTEAD (Nativity of the Blessed Virgin Mary) *see* Denford w Ringstead *Pet*

RINGSTEAD (St Andrew) *see* Hunstanton St Edm w Ringstead *Nor*

RINGSTONE IN AVELAND Group, The *Linc 13* P *Bp (2 turns), Baroness Willoughby de Eresby and Charterhouse (1 turn)* R vacant (01778) 571474

RINGWAY (All Saints) and St Mary *Ches 10* P *Bp* V R M HINTON

RINGWOOD (St Peter and St Paul) *Win 9* P *K Coll Cam* V J R TURPIN, C J R EVANS

RINGWOULD (St Nicholas) w Kingsdown *Cant 8* P *R S C Monins Esq and Ch Patr Trust (jt)* P-in-c S A FALLOWS, OLM A J WINN

RIPE (St John the Baptist) *see* Laughton w Ripe and Chalvington *Chich*

RIPLEY (All Saints) *Derby 12* P *Wright Trustees* V A C EDMUNDS, C J V TAYLOR, NSM C J GRAHAM

RIPLEY (All Saints) *Ripon 3* P *Sir Thomas Ingilby Bt* P-in-c S J BROWN

RIPLEY (St Mary) *Guildf 12* P *Bp* V C J ELSON

RIPON (Holy Trinity) *Ripon 3* P *Simeon's Trustees* V D MANN, C K S BRUCE, NSM J A MONTGOMERY

RIPPINGALE (St Andrew) *see* Ringstone in Aveland Gp *Linc*

RIPPLE (St Mary) *see* Upton-on-Severn, Ripple, Earls Croome etc *Worc*

RIPPLE (St Mary the Virgin) *see* Gt Mongeham w Ripple and Sutton by Dover *Cant*

RIPPONDEN (St Bartholomew) *Wakef 4* P *Bp and V Halifax (jt)* V D F HANDLEY, Hon C N SALT, NSM M JAMES

RISBOROUGH *Ox 21* P *Ld Chan (2 turns), Patr Bd (1 turn)* TR P F B FISKE, TV D E CRITCHELL, A F MEYNELL, C L M TOOZE, Hon C R E PEAKE, P D STEARE, NSM D R DEWICK, M S WITHERS, OLM M J SPENCE

RISBY (St Giles) w Great and Little Saxham *St E 13* P *Ld Chan (1 turn), Mrs E C Gordon-Lennox and Russell-Cooke Trust Co (1 turn)* P-in-c P N MACLEOD-MILLER

RISE (All Saints) *see* Sigglesthorne and Rise w Nunkeeling and Bewholme *York*

RISE PARK *see* Bestwood Park w Rise Park *S'well*

RISEHOLME (St Mary) *see* Nettleham *Linc*

RISELEY (All Saints) w Bletsoe *St Alb 15* P *MMCET* V D J BOURNE

RISHTON (St Peter and St Paul) *Blackb 7* P *Trustees* V P A SMITH

RISHWORTH (St John) *see* Ripponden *Wakef*

RISLEY (All Saints) *see* Stanton-by-Dale w Dale Abbey and Risley *Derby*

RISSINGTONS, The (St John the Baptist) (St Peter) *Glouc 14* P *C T R Wingfield Esq, Ld Chan, and DBP (by turn)* P-in-c S MOTH

RITCHINGS PARK (St Leonard) *see* Iver *Ox*

RIVENHALL (St Mary the Virgin and All Saints) *Chelmsf 24* P *DBP* R N S COOPER

RIVER (St Peter and St Paul) *Cant 4* P *Abp* R S J BOWRING

RIVERHEAD (St Mary) w Dunton Green *Roch 9* P *R Sevenoaks and Bp (jt)* V P E FRANCIS

RIVERSIDE: Colnbrook, Datchet, Dorney, Eton, Eton Wick, Horton, Wraysbury *Ox 23* P *Patr Bd* TR W L KNIGHT, TV P A REYNOLDS, J A HARPER, P W ABRAHAMS, OLM C DEAMER

RIVINGTON (not known) *see* Horwich and Rivington *Man*

ROADE (St Mary the Virgin) and Ashton w Hartwell *Pet 5* P *Ld Chan and Bp (alt)* V M J BURTON

ROADHEAD Kinkry Hill (Mission Room) *see* Bewcastle, Stapleton and Kirklinton etc *Carl*

ROADWATER (St Luke) *see* Old Cleeve, Leighland and Treborough *B & W*

ROBERTSBRIDGE (Mission Room) *see* Salehurst *Chich*

ROBERTTOWN (All Saints) w Hartshead *Wakef 8*
P *V Birstall and TR Dewsbury (jt)* **P-in-c** D E CRAIG-WILD

ROBOROUGH *see* Bickleigh and Shaugh Prior *Ex*

ROBOROUGH (St Peter) *see* Newton Tracey, Horwood, Alverdiscott etc *Ex*

ROBY (St Bartholomew) *Liv 2* **P** *Bp* **V** G S PEARSON, **C** G PINNINGTON

ROCESTER (St Michael) and Croxden w Hollington *Lich 15*
P *Bp and Trustees (jt)* **V** E G WHITTAKER

ROCHDALE (St Chad) (St John the Divine) *Man 20* **P** *Bp*
TR D B FOSS, **TV** D FINNEY, **C** K A C WASEY, **NSM** I G KAY

ROCHDALE (St George w St Alban) *Man 20* **P** *Bp*
P-in-c S B GREY, **NSM** P R ZUCCA

ROCHDALE, SOUTH (St Mary) (St Luke) (St Peter) *Man 20*
P *Patr Bd* **TR** J FARADAY

ROCHE (St Gomonda of the Rock) and Withiel *Truro 1* **P** *Bp and DBP (jt)* **P-in-c** T J B PRITCHARD, **NSM** E C DEELEY

ROCHESTER (St Justus) *Roch 5* **P** *Bp* **V** P T KERR, **NSM** J KERR

ROCHESTER (St Margaret) (St Peter's Parish Centre) *Roch 5*
P *Bp and D&C (jt)* **V** R THOMSON, **C** H DAUBNEY

ROCHESTER ROW (St Stephen) *see* Westmr St Steph w St Jo *Lon*

ROCHFORD (St Andrew) *Chelmsf 12* **P** *Bp*
P-in-c C W COUSINS, **NSM** J M HILL, L SAPWELL

ROCHFORD (St Michael) *see* Teme Valley S *Worc*

ROCK (St Peter and St Paul) *see* Mamble w Bayton, Rock w Heightington etc *Worc*

ROCK (St Philip and St James) *see* Embleton w Rennington and Rock *Newc*

ROCK FERRY (St Peter) *Ches 1* **P** *Bp* **V** P M FROGGATT

ROCKBEARE (St Mary w St Andrew) *see* Aylesbeare, Rockbeare, Farringdon etc *Ex*

ROCKBOURNE (St Andrew) *see* W Downland *Sarum*

ROCKCLIFFE (St Mary the Virgin) and Blackford *Carl 2*
P *D&C* **V** *vacant* (01228) 74209

ROCKHAMPTON (St Oswald) *see* Falfield w Rockhampton *Glouc*

ROCKINGHAM (St Leonard) *see* Gretton w Rockingham and Cottingham w E Carlton *Pet*

ROCKLAND (All Saints) *see* Gt and Lt Ellingham, Rockland and Shropham etc *Nor*

ROCKLAND (All Saints) *as above Nor*

ROCKLAND ST MARY (St Mary) with Hellington, Bramerton, Surlingham, Claxton, Carleton St Peter and Kirby Bedon w Whitlingham *Nor 8* **P** *Bp, Adn Nor, MMCET, and BNC Ox (jt)* **R** C WHEELER, **OLM** G D SAUNDERS

RODBOROUGH (St Mary Magdalene) *Glouc 8* **P** *Bp*
R S J RIGGS

RODBOURNE (Holy Rood) *see* Gt Somerford, Lt Somerford, Seagry, Corston etc *Bris*

RODBOURNE CHENEY (St Mary) *Bris 7* **P** *CPAS*
R N D J LINES, **NSM** A J DEAN

RODDEN (All Saints) *see* Beckington w Standerwick, Berkley, Rodden etc *B & W*

RODE, NORTH (St Michael) *see* Bosley and N Rode w Wincle and Wildboarclough *Ches*

RODE HEATH (Good Shepherd) *see* Odd Rode *Ches*

RODHUISH (St Bartholomew) *see* Dunster, Carhampton and Withycombe w Rodhuish *B & W*

RODING, HIGH (All Saints) *see* Gt Canfield w High Roding and Aythorpe Roding *Chelmsf*

RODING, HIGH (Mission Hall) *as above Chelmsf*

RODINGTON (St George) *see* Wrockwardine Deanery *Lich*

RODLEY (Ecumenical Centre) *see* Bramley *Ripon*

RODLEY (Mission Church) *see* Westbury-on-Severn w Flaxley, Blaisdon etc *Glouc*

RODMARTON (St Peter) *see* Coates, Rodmarton and Sapperton etc *Glouc*

RODMELL (St Peter) *see* Iford w Kingston and Rodmell *Chich*

RODMERSHAM (St Nicholas) *see* Tunstall w Rodmersham *Cant*

RODNEY STOKE (St Leonard) w Draycott *B & W 1* **P** *Bp*
P-in-c S G PRICE

ROEHAMPTON (Holy Trinity) *S'wark 20* **P** *Bp*
V J A MCKINNEY

ROFFEY (All Saints) *see* Roughey *Chich*

ROGATE (St Bartholomew) w Terwick and Trotton w Chithurst *Chich 10* **P** *Ld Chan* **R** E M DOYLE

ROGERS LANE (St Andrew's Chapel) *see* Stoke Poges *Ox*

ROKEBY (St Mary) *see* Startforth and Bowes and Rokeby w Brignall *Ripon*

ROKER (St Aidan) *see* Monkwearmouth *Dur*

ROLLESBY (St George) *see* Ormesby St Marg w Scratby, Ormesby St Mich etc *Nor*

ROLLESBY (St George) w Burgh w Billockby w Ashby w Oby, Thurne and Clippesby *Nor 6* **P** *Bp, R J H Tacon Esq, and DBP (jt)* **R** *vacant* (01493) 740323

ROLLESTON (Holy Trinity) w Fiskerton, Morton and Upton *S'well 14* **P** *Ld Chan* **P-in-c** S SPENCER, **NSM** J E LAMB

ROLLESTON (St John the Baptist) *see* Church Langton cum Tur Langton etc *Leic*

ROLLESTON (St Mary) *Lich 14* **P** *MMCET*
R I R WHITEHEAD

ROLLRIGHT, GREAT (St Andrew) *see* Hook Norton w Gt Rollright, Swerford etc *Ox*

ROLLRIGHT, LITTLE (St Phillip) *see* Chipping Norton *Ox*

ROLVENDEN (St Mary the Virgin) *Cant 17* **P** *Abp*
P-in-c A E WILLIAMS

ROMALDKIRK (St Romald) w Laithkirk *Ripon 2* **P** *Bp and Earl of Strathmore's Trustees (alt)* **R** P S MIDWOOD

ROMANBY (St James) *see* Northallerton w Kirby Sigston *York*

ROMANSLEIGH (St Rumon) *see* S Molton w Nymet St George, High Bray etc *Ex*

ROMFORD (Ascension) Collier Row *Chelmsf 2* **P** *Trustees*
V G P LAUT, **NSM** A BAXTER

ROMFORD (Good Shepherd) Collier Row *Chelmsf 2* **P** *CPAS*
V R C SAMME, **C** P G BLUNDELL

ROMFORD (St Alban) *Chelmsf 2* **P** *Bp* **V** R S P HINGLEY

ROMFORD (St Andrew) (St Agnes) *Chelmsf 2* **P** *New Coll Ox*
R R G FRIENDSHIP

ROMFORD (St Augustine) Rush Green *see* Rush Green *Chelmsf*

ROMFORD (St Edward the Confessor) *Chelmsf 2*
P *New Coll Ox* **V** S J WAINE, **C** M K LAWRENCE, B C DENNIS, **NSM** A D PERRY

ROMFORD (St John the Divine) *Chelmsf 2* **P** *Bp*
P-in-c S J WAINE

ROMILEY (St Chad) *see* Chadkirk *Ches*

ROMNEY, NEW (St Nicholas) w OLD (St Clement) and Midley *Cant 13* **P** *Abp* **V** *vacant* (01797) 362308

ROMSEY (St Mary and St Ethelflaeda) *Win 12* **P** *Bp*
V N C JONES, **C** C F IRVINE, **NSM** D F WILLIAMS, B G TAPHOUSE

ROMSLEY (Mission Room) *see* Halas *Worc*

ROMSLEY (St Kenelm) *as above Worc*

ROOKERY, THE (St Saviour) *see* Mow Cop *Lich*

ROOKHOPE (St John the Evangelist) *see* Eastgate w Rookhope *Dur*

ROOS (All Saints) and Garton in Holderness w Tunstall, Grimston and Hilston *York 12* **P** *Abp (1 turn), SMF (2 turns)*
P-in-c G M SMETHURST

ROOSE (St Perran) *see* Barrow St Geo w St Luke *Carl*

ROPLEY (St Peter) *see* Bishop's Sutton and Ropley and W Tisted *Win*

ROPSLEY (St Peter) *Linc 14* **P** *Bp* **R** M H SABELL

ROSE ASH (St Peter) *see* Bishopsnympton, Rose Ash, Mariansleigh etc *Ex*

ROSEDALE (St Lawrence) *see* Lastingham w Appleton-le-Moors, Rosedale etc *York*

ROSHERVILLE (St Mark) *Roch 4* **P** *DBP*
P-in-c D H HORTON

ROSLEY (Holy Trinity) *see* Westward, Rosley-w-Woodside and Welton *Carl*

ROSLISTON (St Mary) *see* Walton-on-Trent w Croxall, Rosliston etc *Derby*

ROSS Team Ministry, The (St Mary the Virgin) *Heref 8*
P *DBP* **TR** J B HUNNISETT, **TV** A M GRIGOR, S J GEACH, **C** S E SHARP

ROSSENDALE (St Anne) (St Nicholas w St John) Middle Valley *Man 15* **P** *Patr Bd* **TR** C H ELLIS, **C** R C BOWERS

ROSSENDALE (St Peter) *see* Laneside *Blackb*

ROSSENDALE (St Thomas) *see* Musbury *Blackb*

ROSSINGTON (St Michael) *Sheff 9* **P** *Bp* **R** A J LACEY

ROSSINGTON, NEW (St Luke) *Sheff 9* **P** *Bp*
V J P CARLISLE

ROSTHERNE (St Mary) w Bollington *Ches 12*
P *C L S Cornwall-Legh Esq* **V** N D ROGERS

ROTHBURY (All Saints) *Newc 9* **P** *Duchy of Lanc*
P-in-c D R MOORE, **Hon C** A E TREWEEKS

ROTHERBY (All Saints) *see* Upper Wreake *Leic*

ROTHERFIELD (St Denys) w Mark Cross *Chich 19* **P** *Bp, Adn Lewes and Hastings, and Ch Patr Trust (jt)* **R** N F MASON

ROTHERFIELD GREYS (Holy Trinity) *see* Henley H Trin *Ox*

ROTHERFIELD GREYS (St Nicholas) *see* Nettlebed w Bix, Highmoor, Pishill etc *Ox*

ROTHERFIELD PEPPARD (All Saints) and Kidmore End and Sonning Common *Ox 6* **P** *Bp and Jes Coll Ox (jt)*
R G D FOULIS BROWN, **NSM** H J WARWICK

ROTHERHAM (All Saints) *Sheff 6* **P** *Bp* **V** J E M SINCLAIR
ROTHERHAM (St Paul) Ferham Park *see* Masbrough *Sheff*
ROTHERHITHE (Holy Trinity) *S'wark 7* **P** *R Rotherhithe*
St Mary **V** A M DOYLE, **NSM** S R SCOTT
ROTHERHITHE (St Katharine) *see* Bermondsey St Kath w
St Bart *S'wark*
ROTHERHITHE (St Mary) w All Saints *S'wark 7* **P** *Clare*
Coll Cam **R** C E N RICHARDS
ROTHERSTHORPE (St Peter and St Paul) *see* Bugbrooke w
Rothersthorpe *Pet*
ROTHERWICK (not known) *see* Heckfield w Mattingley and
Rotherwick *Win*
ROTHLEY (St Mary the Virgin and St John the Baptist) *Leic 6*
P MMCET **V** R M GLADSTONE
ROTHWELL (Holy Trinity) *Ripon 8* **P** *Bp* **V** P R CRESSALL,
C F M WILSON, **NSM** G W SELLERS
**ROTHWELL (Holy Trinity) w Orton and Rushton w Glendon
and Pipwell** *Pet 11* **P** *Hosp of Jes (1 turn), Bp (2 turns),
J Hipwell Esq (1 turn),and Mert Coll Ox (1 turn)*
R G I BURGON, **NSM** R W SMITH
ROTHWELL (St Mary the Virgin) *see* Swallow *Linc*
ROTTINGDEAN (St Margaret) *Chich 2* **P** *Bp*
V M P MORGAN
ROUGH CLOSE (St Matthew) *see* Meir Heath *Lich*
ROUGH COMMON (St Gabriel) *see* Harbledown *Cant*
ROUGH HAY (St Christopher) *see* Darlaston St Lawr *Lich*
ROUGH HILLS (St Martin) *Lich 28* **P** *Bp* **V** J C OAKES
ROUGHAM (St Mary) *see* Gt w Lt Massingham, Harpley,
Rougham etc *Nor*
ROUGHAM (St Mary), Beyton w Hessett and Rushbrooke
St E 10 **P** *Bp, MMCET (2 turns), and Ld Chan*
R N CUTLER, **OLM** G B RENDLE
ROUGH or Roffey (All Saints) *Chich 8* **P** *Bp*
V K R C AGNEW
ROUGHTON (St Margaret) *see* Thornton Gp *Linc*
**ROUGHTON (St Mary) and Felbrigg, Metton, Sustead,
Bessingham and Gunton w Hanworth** *Nor 21* **P** *Bp and Exors
G Whately Esq (jt)* **P-in-c** E C BAILEY
ROUGHTOWN (St John the Baptist) *Man 17* **P** *Bp*
P-in-c G D ROBINSON
ROUNDHAY (St Edmund King and Martyr) *Ripon 5* **P** *Bp*
V S C COWLING, **C** R A WOOD
ROUNDHAY (St John the Evangelist) *Ripon 5* **P** *DBP*
P-in-c C H CHEESEMAN
ROUNDS GREEN (St James) *Birm 7* **P** *V Langley* **V** *vacant*
0121-552 2822
ROUNDSHAW (St Paul) Conventional District *S'wark 24*
C-in-c J B GOULD
ROUNDSWELL Conventional District *Ex 15*
C-in-c K A ELLIOTT
**ROUNTON, WEST (St Oswald) and East (St Laurence) w
Welbury** *York 19* **P** *Ld Chan* **R** *vacant*
ROUS LENCH (St Peter) *see* Church Lench w Rous Lench and
Abbots Morton etc *Worc*
ROUSHAM (St Leonard and St James) *see* The Heyfords w
Rousham and Somerton *Ox*
ROUTH (All Saints) *York 8* **P** *Ch Soc Trust and Reformation
Ch Trust (jt)* **P-in-c** D C BAILEY
ROWBARTON (St Andrew) *see* Taunton St Andr *B & W*
ROWBERROW (St Michael and All Angels) *see* Axbridge w
Shipham and Rowberrow *B & W*
ROWDE (St Matthew) and Bromham *Sarum 16* **P** *DBP and
S Spicer Esq (jt)* **R** J R J HISCOX
ROWENFIELD (Emmanuel) *see* Cheltenham St Mark *Glouc*
ROWINGTON (St Lawrence) *see* Hatton w Haseley,
Rowington w Lowsonford etc *Cov*
ROWLAND LUBBOCK (Memorial Hall) *see* E Horsley and
Ockham w Hatchford and Downside *Guildf*
ROWLANDS CASTLE (St John the Baptist) *Portsm 5* **P** *Bp*
P-in-c D J LLOYD
ROWLANDS GILL (St Barnabas) *see* High Spen and
Rowlands Gill *Dur*
ROWLEDGE (St James) and Frensham *Guildf 3* **P** *Adn Surrey
and Ld Chan (alt)* **V** C J RICHARDSON, **Hon C** C D SEMPER
ROWLESTONE (St Peter) *see* Ewyas Harold w Dulas,
Kenderchurch etc *Heref*
ROWLEY (St Peter) w Skidby *York 8* **P** *Abp and
N A C Hildyard Esq (jt)* **P-in-c** A BAILEY
ROWLEY REGIS (St Giles) *Birm 7* **P** *Ld Chan*
V J B NIGHTINGALE
ROWNER (St Mary the Virgin) *Portsm 3*
P R J F Prideaux-Brune Esq **R** J W DRAPER, **C** J W FRANKS
ROWNEY GREEN (Mission Chapel) *see* Alvechurch *Worc*
ROWSLEY (St Katherine) *Derby 2* **P** *Duke of Rutland*
V *vacant* (01629) 733296
ROWSTON (St Clement) *see* Digby Gp *Linc*

ROWTON (All Hallows) *see* Wrockwardine Deanery *Lich*
ROXBOURNE (St Andrew) *Lon 23* **P** *Bp* **V** D J COCKBILL
ROXBY (St Mary) *see* Winterton Gp *Linc*
ROXBY (St Nicholas) *see* Hinderwell w Roxby *York*
ROXETH (Christ Church) *Lon 23* **P** *Patr Bd* **TR** M S PHILPS,
TV P S MACKENZIE, **C** S M NEWBOLD, **NSM** F A MEADOWS,
B C COLLINS
ROXHOLME *see* Leasingham *Linc*
ROXTON (St Mary Magdalene) *see* Blunham, Gt Barford,
Roxton and Tempsford etc *St Alb*
ROXWELL (St Michael and All Angels) *Chelmsf 8*
P *New Coll Ox* **P-in-c** B R HOBSON
ROYDON (All Saints) *see* Grimston, Congham and Roydon
Nor
ROYDON (St Peter) *Chelmsf 26* **P** *Earl Cowley*
NSM D RICKETTS
ROYDON (St Remigius) *Nor 10* **P** *DBP*
P-in-c W M C BESTELINK
ROYSTON (St John the Baptist) *St Alb 19* **P** *Bp*
V L D HARMAN, **C** A W A COPPING, **NSM** J H FIDLER
ROYSTON (St John the Baptist) *Wakef 7* **P** *Bp*
V J L HUDSON, **C** J A BOOTH
ROYTON (St Anne) Longsight *Man 22* **P** *Bp*
OLM D J HALFORD
ROYTON (St Paul) *Man 22* **P** *R Prestwich St Mary*
V D BOOTH
RUAN LANIHORNE (St Rumon) *see* Veryan w Ruan
Lanihorne *Truro*
RUAN MINOR (St Rumon) *see* St Ruan w St Grade and
Landewednack *Truro*
RUARDEAN (St John the Baptist) *Glouc 4* **P** *Bp*
R C T DAVIES, **OLM** W J CAMMELL
RUBERY (St Chad) *Birm 4* **P** *The Crown* **V** J J J BARRETT
RUCKINGE (St Mary Magdalene) *see* Orlestone w Snave and
Ruckinge w Warehorne etc *Cant*
RUCKLAND (St Olave) *see* S Ormsby Gp *Linc*
RUDBY IN CLEVELAND (All Saints) w Middleton *York 21*
P *Abp* **V** D F LICKESS
RUDDINGTON (St Peter) *S'well 9* **P** *Simeon's Trustees*
V F G HARRISON
RUDFORD (St Mary the Virgin) *see* Highnam, Lassington,
Rudford, Tibberton etc *Glouc*
RUDGWICK (Holy Trinity) *Chich 8* **P** *Ld Chan*
V R C JACKSON
**RUDHAM, EAST and WEST (St Mary), Helhoughton,
Houghton-next-Harpley, The Raynhams, Tatterford, and
Tattersett** *Nor 15* **P** *Bp, The Most Revd G D Hand, Marquess
of Cholmondeley, and Marquess Townshend (jt)*
R E L BUNDOCK
RUDHEATH (Licensed Room) *see* Witton *Ches*
RUDSTON (All Saints) w Boynton, Carnaby and Kilham *York 9*
P *Ld Chan (1 turn), Abp (3 turns)* **V** H SPARHAM
RUFFORD (St Mary the Virgin) *Blackb 5* **P** *Bp* **R** J D BURNS
RUFFORTH (All Saints) w Moor Monkton and Hessay *York 1*
P *MMCET and Abp (alt)* **R** J A RENDALL, **NSM** B H FRAY
RUGBY (Christ Church) *see* Brownsover *Cov*
RUGBY (St Andrew) (St George) (St John) (St Peter) (St Philip)
Cov 6 **P** *Bp* **TV** T D COCKELL, **C** C C TURNER,
NSM H F COCKELL
RUGBY (St Matthew) *Cov 6* **P** *Ch Trust Fund Trust*
V M P SAXBY
RUGELEY (St Augustine) (Good Shepherd) *Lich 3* **P** *Patr Bd*
TR M J NEWMAN, **TV** C M MASON, **NSM** C BEATSON
RUISHTON (St George) w Thornfalcon *B & W 18* **P** *Bp and
Dr W R Chisholm-Batten (alt)* **V** D F GOODFIELD
RUISLIP (St Martin) *Lon 24* **P** *D&C Windsor* **V** S EVANS,
NSM M A BEDFORD
RUISLIP (St Mary) *Lon 24* **P** *Bp* **V** N G T WHEELER
RUISLIP MANOR (St Paul) *Lon 24* **P** *Bp* **V** A C BALL,
NSM B C ALLEN
RUMBURGH (St Michael and All Angels and St Felix) *see* S
Elmham and Ilketshall *St E*
RUNCORN (All Saints) *Ches 3* **P** *Ch Ch Ox*
P-in-c J H A HAYES
RUNCORN (Holy Trinity) *Ches 3* **P** *Bp*
P-in-c E W LAUTENBACH, **C** N M REDEYOFF
RUNCORN (St John the Evangelist) Weston *Ches 3* **P** *Bp*
V *vacant* (01928) 573798
RUNCORN (St Michael and All Angels) *Ches 3* **P** *Bp*
P-in-c J H A HAYES
RUNCTON, NORTH (All Saints) *see* W Winch w Setchey, N
Runcton and Middleton *Nor*
RUNCTON, SOUTH (St Andrew) *see* Holme Runcton w S
Runcton and Wallington *Ely*
RUNCTON HOLME (St James) *as above Ely*
RUNHALL (All Saints) *see* Barnham Broom and Upper Yare
Nor

RUNHAM (St Peter and St Paul)   *see* S Trin Broads *Nor*
RUNNINGTON (St Peter and St Paul)   *see* Wellington and Distr *B & W*
RUNTON (Holy Trinity)   *see* Aylmerton, Runton, Beeston Regis and Gresham *Nor*
RUNTON, EAST (St Andrew)   *as above Nor*
RUNWELL (St Mary)   *see* Wickford and Runwell *Chelmsf*
RUSCOMBE (St James the Great) and Twyford *Ox 16*   P *Bp*
   V G R HAMBORG,   Hon C T J DAKIN,   NSM D FOOTE
RUSH GREEN (St Augustine) Romford *Chelmsf 2*   P *Bp*
   V M D HOWSE
RUSHALL (Christ the King) (St Michael the Archangel) *Lich 25*
   P *Sir Andrew Buchanan Bt and H C S Buchanan Esq (jt)*
   V D P LINGWOOD,   NSM P F HARRIS
RUSHALL (St Mary)   *see* Dickleburgh and The Pulhams *Nor*
RUSHALL (St Matthew)   *see* Upavon w Rushall and Charlton *Sarum*
RUSHBROOKE (St Nicholas)   *see* Rougham, Beyton w Hessett and Rushbrooke *St E*
RUSHBURY (St Peter) *Heref 11*   P *Bp Birm*   P-in-c J GROVES
RUSHDEN (St Mary)   *see* Sandon, Wallington and Rushden w Clothall *St Alb*
RUSHDEN (St Mary) (St Mark) w Newton Bromswold *Pet 10*
   P *CPAS*   R B J MORRISON,   NSM E J TYE
RUSHDEN (St Peter) *Pet 10*   P *CPAS*   V Q D CHANDLER
RUSHEN Christ Church (Holy Trinity) *S & M 1*   P *The Crown*
   V F H BIRD
RUSHEY MEAD (St Theodore of Canterbury)   *see* Leic St Theodore *Leic*
RUSHFORD (St John the Evangelist)   *see* E w W Harling, Bridgham w Roudham, Larling etc *Nor*
RUSHLAKE GREEN (Little St Mary)   *see* Warbleton and Bodle Street Green *Chich*
RUSHMERE (St Andrew) *St E 4*   P *Bp*   V B WAKELING,
   C M A ADSETTS
RUSHMERE (St Michael)   *see* Kessingland, Gisleham and Rushmere *Nor*
RUSHMOOR (St Francis)   *see* Churt and Hindhead *Guildf*
RUSHOCK (St Michael)   *see* Elmley Lovett w Hampton Lovett and Elmbridge etc *Worc*
RUSHOLME (Holy Trinity) *Man 4*   P *CPAS*   R A PORTER,
   C D A CLARK
RUSHTON (All Saints)   *see* Rothwell w Orton, Rushton w Glendon and Pipewell *Pet*
RUSHTON SPENCER   *see* Horton, Lonsdon and Rushton Spencer *Lich*
RUSKIN PARK (St Saviour)   *see* Herne Hill *S'wark*
RUSKINGTON (All Saints) *Linc 22*   P *DBP*
   R G P WILLIAMS
RUSLAND (St Paul)   *see* Hawkshead and Low Wray w Sawrey and Rusland etc *Carl*
RUSPER (St Mary Magdalene) w Colgate *Chich 8*
   P *Mrs E C Calvert and Bp (alt)*   R N A FLINT
RUSTHALL (St Paul) (St Paul's Mission Church) *Roch 12*
   P R Speldhurst   V R E WHYTE
RUSTINGTON (St Peter and St Paul) *Chich 1*   P *Bp*
   V Z E ALLEN
RUSTON, SOUTH   *see* Tunstead w Sco' Ruston *Nor*
RUSTON PARVA (St Nicholas)   *see* Burton Agnes w Harpham and Lowthorpe etc *York*
RUSWARP (St Bartholomew)   *see* Whitby w Aislaby and Ruswarp *York*
RUYTON XI TOWNS (St John the Baptist) w Great Ness and Little Ness *Lich 17*   P *Bp and Guild of All So (jt) and Ld Chan (alt)*   P-in-c L FOSTER
RYAL (All Saints)   *see* Stamfordham w Matfen *Newc*
RYARSH (St Martin)   *see* Birling, Addington, Ryarsh and Trottiscliffe *Roch*
RYBURGH, GREAT (St Andrew) and LITTLE w Gateley and Testerton *Nor 15*   P *Ch Coll Cam*   R *vacant*
RYDAL (St Mary) *Carl 11*   P *Bp*   V *vacant*
RYDE (All Saints) *Portsm 7*   P *Bp*   V J F REDVERS HARRIS,
   NSM E W BUTCHER, T I CARD
RYDE (Holy Trinity) *Portsm 7*   P *Bp*   V M F JONES
RYDE (St James) Proprietary Chapel *Portsm 7*   P *Ch Soc Trust*
   C-in-c J H A LEGGETT
RYDE (St John the Baptist)   *see* Oakfield St Jo *Portsm*
RYE (St Mary the Virgin) *Chich 20*   P *Patr Bd*
   TR H M MOSELEY,   TV A V BOWMAN,   NSM L E MURDOCH
RYE HARBOUR (Holy Spirit)   *see* Rye *Chich*
RYE PARK (St Cuthbert) *St Alb 20*   P *DBP*
   P-in-c A F BURFORD
RYECROFT (St Nicolas) Rawmarsh *Sheff 6*   P *Bp*
   V T A PARKINSON
RYEDALE, UPPER *York 17*   P *Abp, Adn Cleveland, Sir Richard Beckett Bt, and Sir George Wombwell Bt (jt)*
   P-in-c R A G SHANKS

RYHALL (St John the Evangelist) w Essendine and Carlby *Pet 8*
   P *Burghley Ho Preservation Trust*   V P J MCKEE
RYHILL (St James) *Wakef 9*   P *Bp*   V *vacant* (01226) 722363
RYHOPE (St Paul) *Dur 16*   P *Bp*   V D J MEAKIN
RYLSTONE (St Peter)   *see* Burnsall w Rylstone *Bradf*
RYME INTRINSECA (St Hypolytus)   *see* Wriggle Valley *Sarum*
RYPE (St John the Baptist)   *see* Laughton w Ripe and Chalvington *Chich*
RYSTON (St Michael)   *see* Denver and Ryston w Roxham and W Dereham etc *Ely*
RYTHER (All Saints)   *see* Cawood w Ryther and Wistow *York*
RYTON (Holy Cross) w Hedgefield *Dur 13*   P *Bp*
   R T L JAMIESON
RYTON (Mission Chapel)   *see* Condover w Frodesley, Acton Burnell etc *Heref*
RYTON (St Andrew)   *see* Beckbury, Badger, Kemberton, Ryton, Stockton etc *Lich*
RYTON ON DUNSMORE (St Leonard)   *see* Baginton w Bubbenhall and Ryton-on-Dunsmore *Cov*
SABDEN (St Nicholas) and Pendleton-in-Whalley (All Saints) *Blackb 7*   P *Bp and Trustees (jt)*   P-in-c T VAUGHAN
SACKLETON (St George the Martyr)   *see* Street *York*
SACOMBE (St Catherine)   *see* The Mundens w Sacombe *St Alb*
SACRISTON (St Peter)   *see* Dur N *Dur*
SADBERGE (St Andrew) *Dur 8*   P *Bp*   R *vacant* (01325) 333771
SADDINGTON (St Helen)   *see* Kibworth and Smeeton Westerby and Saddington *Leic*
SADDLEWORTH (St Chad) *Man 21*   P *Patr Bd*
   TR S F BRANDES,   TV J R BROCKLEHURST,   NSM A KERR,
   R WHYBORN,   OLM G B ADAMS, D RHODES
SAFFRON WALDEN (St Mary) w Wendens Ambo, Littlebury, Ashdon and Hadstock *Chelmsf 22*   P *Patr Bd*
   TR D J GREEN,   TV M THOMPSON,   C D A TWINLEY,
   NSM M J B LOVEGROVE, H M DAVEY
SAHAM TONEY (St George)   *see* Ashill w Saham Toney *Nor*
ST AGNES (St Agnes)   *see* Is of Scilly *Truro*
ST AGNES (St Agnes) and Mithian w Mount Hawke *Truro 6*
   P *Bp and D&C (alt)*   V A G BASHFORTH,   C P G WIGNALL,
   NSM H L SAMSON
ST ALBANS (Christ Church) *St Alb 6*   P *Trustees*
   V J M FOLLETT
ST ALBANS (St Luke) *St Alb 6*   P *DBP*   V M A SLATER
ST ALBANS (St Mary) Marshalswick *St Alb 6*   P *Bp*
   V C M DAVEY,   NSM A J T HINKSMAN
ST ALBANS (St Michael) *St Alb 6*   P *Earl of Verulam*
   V T M BEAUMONT,   NSM J A HAYTON
ST ALBANS (St Paul) *St Alb 6*   P *V St Alb St Pet*
   V A R HURLE,   C S Q MOORE,   Hon C G M ABBOTT,
   NSM L M HURLE
ST ALBANS (St Peter) *St Alb 6*   P *The Crown*
   V D J BRENTNALL,   C T HANDLEY MACMATH
ST ALBANS (St Saviour) *St Alb 6*   P *Bp*   NSM M R MUGAN
ST ALBANS (St Stephen) *St Alb 6*   P J N W Dudley Esq
   V D RIDGEWAY,   C R C PYKE,   NSM G I KEIR
ST ALLEN (St Alleyne)   *see* Kenwyn w St Allen *Truro*
ST ANNES-ON-THE-SEA (St Anne)   *see* Heyhouses on Sea *Blackb*
ST ANNES-ON-THE-SEA (St Margaret) *Blackb 10*   P *Bp*
   V A R HODGSON
ST ANNES-ON-THE-SEA (St Thomas) *Blackb 10*
   P J C Hilton Esq   V P D LAW-JONES
ST ANTHONY-IN-MENEAGE (St Anthony)   *see* Manaccan w St Anthony-in-Meneage and St Martin *Truro*
ST AUSTELL (Holy Trinity) *Truro 1*   P *The Crown*
   V D P WHITE,   C P H BAMBER
ST BEES (St Mary and St Bega) *Carl 5*   P *Trustees*
   V P R BRYAN,   NSM A C BAKER
ST BLAZEY (St Blaise) *Truro 1*   P *Bp*   V F M BOWERS,
   C S D MICHAEL
ST BREOKE (St Breoke) and Egloshayle in Wadebridge *Truro 10*   P *Bp and DBP (jt)*   P-in-c T COTTON
ST BREWARD (St Breward)   *see* Blisland w St Breward *Truro*
ST BRIAVELS (St Mary the Virgin) w Hewelsfield *Glouc 4*
   P *D&C Heref*   P-in-c D J LAWRENCE
ST BUDEAUX   *see* Devonport St Budeaux *Ex*
ST BURYAN (St Buriana), St Levan and Sennen *Truro 5*
   P *Duchy of Cornwall*   R A H BURLTON,   NSM H M POOLE,
   OLM C M JAGO
ST CLEER (St Clarus) *Truro 12*   P *Ld Chan*
   P-in-c K LANYON JONES
ST CLEMENT (St Clement)   *see* Truro St Paul and St Clem *Truro*
ST CLEMENT DANES   *see* St Mary le Strand w St Clem Danes *Lon*

ST CLETHER (St Clederus)   *see* Altarnon w Bolventor, Laneast and St Clether *Truro*

ST COLAN (St Colan)   *see* St Columb Minor and St Colan *Truro*

ST COLUMB MAJOR (St Columba) w St Wenn   *Truro 7*   **P** *Bp*   **P-in-c** F T SURRIDGE

ST COLUMB MINOR (St Columba) and St Colan   *Truro 7*   **P** *Bp*   **P-in-c** C C MCQUILLEN-WRIGHT

ST DECUMANS (St Decuman)   *B & W 17*   **P** *Bp*   **V** D C IRESON

ST DENNIS (St Denys)   *Truro 1*   **P** *Bp*   **P-in-c** T J RUSS

ST DEVEREUX (St Dubricius)   *see* Ewyas Harold w Dulas, Kenderchurch etc *Heref*

ST DOMINIC (St Dominica), Landulph and St Mellion w Pillaton   *Truro 11*   **P** *D&C and Trustees Major J Coryton, Duchy of Cornwall, and SMF (by turn)*   **R** P R J LAMB

ST EDMUNDS Anchorage Lane Conventional District   *Sheff 7*   **C-in-c** M J ROWBERRY

ST ENDELLION (St Endelienta) w Port Isaac and St Kew   *Truro 10*   **P** *Bp*   **R** M G BARTLETT,   **NSM** J POLLINGER

ST ENODER (St Enoder)   *Truro 7*   **P** *Bp*   **P-in-c** P A ROBSON,   **OLM** J PRATT

ST ENODOC (St Enodoc)   *see* St Minver *Truro*

ST ERME (St Hermes)   *see* Probus, Ladock and Grampound w Creed and St Erme *Truro*

ST ERNEY (St Erney)   *see* Landrake w St Erney and Botus Fleming *Truro*

ST ERTH (St Erth)   *see* Godrevy *Truro*

ST ERVAN (St Ervan)   *see* St Mawgan w St Ervan and St Eval *Truro*

ST EVAL (St Uvelas)   *as above Truro*

ST EWE (All Saints)   *see* Mevagissey and St Ewe *Truro*

ST GENNYS (St Gennys), Jacobstow w Warbstow and Treneglos   *Truro 8*   **P** *Bp and Earl of St Germans (jt)*   **P-in-c** R C W DICKENSON,   **NSM** J COTTON

ST GEORGE-IN-THE-EAST (St Mary)   *Lon 7*   **P** *Bp*   **V** P MCGEARY

ST GEORGE-IN-THE-EAST w St Paul   *Lon 7*   **P** *Bp*   **P-in-c** J A CULLEN

ST GEORGES (St George)   *see* Priors Lee and St Georges *Lich*

ST GERMANS (St Germans of Auxerre)   *Truro 11*   **P** *D&C Windsor*   **P-in-c** A I JOHNSTON,   **OLM** J M LOBB

ST GILES-IN-THE-FIELDS   *Lon 3*   **P** *Bp*   **R** W M JACOB,   **C** R HAGGIS

ST GILES-IN-THE-HEATH (St Giles)   *see* Boyton, N Tamerton, Werrington etc *Truro*

ST GILES IN THE WOOD (St Giles)   *see* Newton Tracey, Horwood, Alverdiscott etc *Ex*

ST GLUVIAS (St Gluvias)   *Truro 3*   **P** *Bp*   **V** J HARRIS

ST GORAN (St Goranus) w Caerhays   *Truro 1*   **P** *Bp*   **P-in-c** D J ALLAN

ST HELENS (St Helen) (Barton Street Mission) (St Andrew)   *Liv 10*   **P** *Trustees*   **TR** C H B BYWORTH,   **C** C R SMITH,   **V** E HUGHES

ST HELENS (St Helen) (St Catherine by the Green)   *Portsm 7*   **P** *Bp*   **V** M M STRANGE

ST HELENS (St Mark)   *Liv 10*   **P** *Trustees*   **V** A J HASLAM

ST HELENS (St Matthew) Thatto Heath   *Liv 10*   **P** *Bp*   **V** P D RATTIGAN

ST HELIER (St Peter) (Bishop Andrewes Church)   *S'wark 25*   **P** *Bp*   **P-in-c** D M WEBB

ST HILARY (St Hilary)   *see* Ludgvan, Marazion, St Hilary and Perranuthnoe *Truro*

ST ILLOGAN (St Illogan)   *Truro 2*   **P** *Ch Soc Trust*   **R** M J KIPPAX,   **C** Y M BAILEY,   **OLM** P I TREMELLING

ST IPPOLYTS (St Ippolyts)   *St Alb 4*   **P** *Bp*   **P-in-c** I S TATTUM

ST ISSEY (St Issey) w St Petroc Minor   *Truro 7*   **P** *Keble Coll Ox*   **P-in-c** J M WILKINSON

ST IVE (St Ive) and Pensilva w Quethiock   *Truro 12*   **P** *Bp (1 turn), The Crown (2 turns)*   **R** vacant (01579) 82327

ST IVES (All Saints)   *Ely 10*   **P** *Guild of All So*   **V** J S PULLEN

ST IVES (St Ia the Virgin)   *Truro 5*   **P** *V Lelant*   **V** A N COUCH

ST JOHN (St John the Baptist) w Millbrook   *Truro 11*   **P** *Bp and Col Sir John Carew-Pole Bt (alt)*   **R** C D EPPS

ST JOHN-AT-HACKNEY (St John)   *Lon 5*   **P** *Bp, Adn, and Lord Amherst of Hackney (jt)*   **V** J S PRIDMORE,   **NSM** J M KING

ST JOHN IN BEDWARDINE (St John the Baptist)   *Worc 3*   **P** *D&C*   **V** C PULLIN,   **C** D J ARNOLD

ST JOHN IN WEARDALE (St John the Baptist)   *Dur 9*   **P** *Bp*   **P-in-c** P A GREENHALGH

ST JOHN LEE (St John of Beverley)   *Newc 4*   **P** *Viscount Allendale*   **P-in-c** R C CUTLER

ST JOHN ON BETHNAL GREEN   *Lon 7*   **P** *Patr Bd*   **TR** A J E GREEN,   **NSM** R A VAUGHAN

ST JOHN'S-IN-THE-VALE (St John), St Mary's Threlkeld and Wythburn   *Carl 6*   **P** *Bp, Adn, V Crosthwaite, and Earl of Londsale (jt)*   **R** B ROTHWELL

ST JOHN'S WOOD (St John)   *Lon 4*   **P** *Bp*   **V** A K BERGQUIST,   **C** G A D PLATTEN

ST JOHN'S WOOD (St Mark)   *see* St Marylebone St Mark Hamilton Terrace *Lon*

ST JULIOT (St Julitta)   *see* Boscastle w Davidstow *Truro*

ST JUST IN PENWITH (St Just)   *Truro 5*   **P** *Ld Chan*   **V** S W LEACH

ST JUST-IN-ROSELAND (St Just) and St Mawes   *Truro 6*   **P** *A M J Galsworthy Esq*   **P-in-c** J G SLEE

ST KEVERNE (St Keverne)   *Truro 4*   **P** *CPAS*   **P-in-c** T ST J HAWKINS,   **C** L A H COURTNEY

ST KEW (St James the Great)   *see* St Endellion w Port Isaac and St Kew *Truro*

ST KEYNE (St Keyna)   *see* Liskeard and St Keyne *Truro*

ST LAURENCE in the Isle of Thanet (St Laurence)   *Cant 9*   **P** *Patr Bd*   **TV** S IRELAND

ST LAWRENCE (Old Church) (St Lawrence)   *Portsm 7*   **P** *Bp*   **R** S E LLOYD

ST LAWRENCE (St Lawrence)   *Chelmsf 10*   **P** *Bp*   **P-in-c** E H BEAVAN

ST LEONARD (St Leonard)   *see* Hawridge w Cholesbury and St Leonard *Ox*

ST LEONARDS and St Ives (All Saints)   *Win 9*   **P** *Bp*   **C** D L GRACE

ST LEONARDS (Christ Church and St Mary Magdalen)   *Chich 17*   **P** *Bp and Trustees (jt)*   **R** R M HARPER,   **C** A J HOMER,   **NSM** R G RALPH

ST LEONARDS, UPPER (St John the Evangelist)   *Chich 17*   **P** *Trustees*   **P-in-c** A J PERRY

ST LEONARDS-ON-SEA (St Ethelburga)   *Chich 17*   **P** *Hyndman Trustees*   **NSM** V G DOIDGE

ST LEONARDS-ON-SEA (St Leonard)   *Chich 17*   **P** *Hyndman Trustees*   **P-in-c** W D BOULTON

ST LEONARDS-ON-SEA (St Matthew)   *see* Silverhill St Matt *Chich*

ST LEONARDS-ON-SEA (St Peter and St Paul)   *Chich 17*   **P** *Bp*   **V** A P-A BROWN

ST LEVAN (St Levan)   *see* St Buryan, St Levan and Sennen *Truro*

ST MABYN (St Mabena)   *see* St Tudy w St Mabyn and Michaelstow *Truro*

ST MARGARET'S (St Margaret)   *see* Clodock and Longtown w Craswall, Llanveynoe etc *Heref*

ST MARGARETS-AT-CLIFFE (St Margaret of Antioch) w Westcliffe and East Langdon w West Langdon   *Cant 4*   **P** *Abp*   **V** A M DURKIN

ST MARGARET'S-ON-THAMES (All Souls)   *Lon 11*   **P** *Bp*   **P-in-c** H C MACINNES

ST MARTHA-ON-THE-HILL (St Martha)   *see* Guildf Ch Ch w St Martha-on-the-Hill *Guildf*

ST MARTIN (St Martin) w Looe St Nicholas   *Truro 12*   **P** *Bp and Revd W M M Picken (jt)*   **R** B A MCQUILLEN,   **C** L J SMITH,   **OLM** M A TUBBS

ST MARTIN-IN-MENEAGE (St Martin)   *see* Manaccan w St Anthony-in-Meneage and St Martin *Truro*

ST MARTIN-IN-THE-FIELDS   *Lon 3*   **P** *Bp*   **V** N R HOLTAM,   **C** E L GRIFFITHS, R J LAIN-PRIESTLEY, E M V RUSSELL,   **NSM** A HURST

ST MARTIN'S (St Martin)   *Lich 19*   **P** *Lord Trevor*   **V** W J WEBB

ST MARTIN'S (St Martin)   *see* Is of Scilly *Truro*

ST MARY ABBOTS   *see* Kensington St Mary Abbots w St Geo *Lon*

ST MARY-AT-LATTON Harlow   *Chelmsf 26*   **P** *J L H Arkwright Esq*   **V** S CONLON

ST MARY BOURNE (St Peter)   *see* Hurstbourne Priors, Longparish etc *Win*

ST MARY CRAY and St Paul's (St Paulinus) Cray   *Roch 16*   **P** *Bp*   **V** A E COOKE

ST MARY LE STRAND w St Clement Danes   *Lon 3*   **P** *Ld Chan and Burley Ho Preservation Trust (alt)*   **P-in-c** W D F GULLIFORD,   **Hon C** J F A FARRANT

ST MARYCHURCH (St Mary the Virgin)   *Ex 10*   **P** *D&C*   **V** D LASHBROOKE,   **C** R T SILK

ST MARYLEBONE (All Saints)   *Lon 4*   **P** *Bp*   **V** L A MOSES

ST MARYLEBONE (All Souls)   *see* Langham Place All So *Lon*

ST MARYLEBONE (Annunciation) Bryanston Street   *Lon 4*   **P** *Bp*   **V** M W BURGESS

ST MARYLEBONE (St Cyprian)   *Lon 4*   **P** *Bp*   **P-in-c** C R GOWER,   **Hon C** S B CATHIE

ST MARYLEBONE (St Mark) Hamilton Terrace   *Lon 4*   **P** *The Crown*   **V** J A BARRIE

ST MARYLEBONE (St Mark w St Luke)   *see* Bryanston Square St Mary w St Marylebone St Mark *Lon*

ST MARYLEBONE (St Marylebone) (Holy Trinity) *Lon 4*
P *The Crown*   **R** C R GOWER,   **C** J E DAVIES,
Hon C S B CATHIE,   **NSM** R C D MACKENNA
ST MARYLEBONE (St Paul) *Lon 4*   **P** *Prime Min*
R G M BUCKLE,   **C** A R HACK
ST MARYLEBONE (St Peter) *see* Langham Place All So *Lon*
ST MARY'S (St Mary) *see* Is of Scilly *Truro*
ST MARY'S BAY (All Saints) w St Mary-in-the-Marsh (St Mary the Virgin) and Ivychurch *Cant 13*   **P** *Abp*   **V** *vacant* (01303) 874188
ST MAWES (St Mawes) *see* St Just-in-Roseland and St Mawes *Truro*
ST MAWGAN (St Mawgan) w St Ervan and St Eval *Truro 7*
P *D&C and Bp* (*alt*)   **R** *vacant* (01637) 860358
ST MELLION (St Melanus) *see* St Dominic, Landulph and St Mellion w Pillaton *Truro*
ST MERRYN (St Merryn) *Truro 7*   **P** *Bp*
P-in-c J M WILKINSON
ST MEWAN (St Mewan) *Truro 1*   **P** *A J M Galsworthy Esq* (*2 turns*)*, Penrice Ho (St Austell) Ltd (1 turn)*, *and DBP* (*1 turn*)   **P-in-c** D G ADAMS,   **NSM** M P C ROWETT
ST MICHAEL PENKEVIL (St Michael) *Truro 6*   **P** *Viscount Falmouth*   **R** *vacant* (01872) 520431
ST MICHAEL ROCK (St Michael) *see* St Minver *Truro*
ST MICHAELCHURCH (St Michael) *see* N Newton w St Michaelchurch, Thurloxton etc *B & W*
ST MICHAELS-ON-WYRE (St Michael) *see* Garstang St Helen and St Michaels-on-Wyre *Blackb*
ST MINVER (St Menefreda) *Truro 10*   **P** *DBP*
P-in-c R F LAW
ST NECTAN (St Nectan) *see* Lostwithiel, St Winnow w St Nectan's Chpl etc *Truro*
ST NEOT (St Neot) and Warleggan w Cardynham *Truro 12*
P *R G Grylls Esq (2 turns), J Coode Esq (1 turn), and DBP* (*1 turn*)   **R** A C R BALFOUR
ST NEOTS (St Mary) *Ely 13*   **P** *P W Rowley Esq*
V R H W ARGUILE,   **Hon C** T R HENTHORNE
ST NEWLYN EAST (St Newlina) *see* Newlyn St Newlyn *Truro*
ST NICHOLAS (St Nicholas) *see* Shaldon, Stokeinteignhead, Combeinteignhead etc *Ex*
ST NICHOLAS AT WADE (St Nicholas) w Sarre and Chislet w Hoath *Cant 7*   **P** *Abp*   **P-in-c** R R COLES,   **NSM** R D PLANT
ST OSWALD IN LEE w Bingfield (St Mary) *Newc 2*   **P** *Bp*
P-in-c C S PRICE,   **NSM** C F BULL
ST OSYTH (St Peter and St Paul) *Chelmsf 23*   **P** *Bp*
V M J FLOWERDEW
ST PANCRAS (Holy Cross) (St Jude) (St Peter) *Lon 17*   **P** *Bp*
P-in-c P W LEWIS,   **NSM** R W NORWOOD
ST PANCRAS (Holy Trinity) *see* Kentish Town St Silas and H Trin w St Barn *Lon*
ST PANCRAS (Old Church) *Lon 17*   **P** *Patr Bd*
TR N P WHEELER,   **C** R J WICKHAM
ST PANCRAS (St Martin) *see* Kentish Town St Martin w St Andr *Lon*
ST PANCRAS (St Pancras) (St James) (Christ Church) *Lon 17*
P *D&C St Paul's*   **V** P H W HAWKINS,   **Hon C** R I T JARRETT
ST PAUL'S CRAY (St Barnabas) *Roch 16*   **P** *CPAS*
V G C DAY,   **Hon C** J E RAWLING
ST PAUL'S WALDEN (All Saints) *St Alb 4*   **P** *D&C St Paul's*
P-in-c D M DEWEY
ST PETER in the Isle of Thanet (St Peter the Apostle) (St Andrew) *Cant 9*   **P** *Abp*   **V** B P MOORE,
C S D ROWLANDS, J A F TAYLOR
ST PETER-UPON-CORNHILL *see* St Pet Cornhill *Lon*
ST PETROC MINOR (St Petroc) *see* St Issey w St Petroc Minor *Truro*
ST PINNOCK (St Pinnock) *see* Duloe, Herodsfoot, Morval and St Pinnock *Truro*
ST RUAN w St Grade and Landewednack *Truro 4*   **P** *CPAS and A F Vyvyan-Robinson Esq (jt)*   **P-in-c** W COLE
ST SAMPSON (St Sampson) *Truro 1*   **P** *Bp*
P-in-c P DE GREY-WARTER
ST STEPHEN IN BRANNEL (not known) *Truro 1*   **P** *Capt J D G Fortescue*   **P-in-c** E J WESTERMANN-CHILDS
ST STEPHENS (St Stephen) *see* Saltash *Truro*
ST STYTHIANS w Perranarworthal and Gwennap *Truro 2*
P *Viscount Falmouth (2 turns), D&C (1 turn)*   **V** E J M HOGAN,
OLM L BARTER
ST TEATH (St Teatha) *Truro 10*   **P** *Bp*   **P-in-c** S L BRYAN
ST TUDY (St Tudy) w St Mabyn and Michaelstow *Truro 10*
P *Ch Ch Ox, Viscount Falmouth, and Duchy of Cornwall* (*by turn*)   **P-in-c** M L MILLSON
ST VEEP (St Cyricius) *see* Lostwithiel, St Winnow w St Nectan's Chpl etc *Truro*
ST WENN (St Wenna) *see* St Columb Major w St Wenn *Truro*

ST WEONARDS (St Weonard) w Orcop, Garway, Tretire, Michaelchurch, Pencoyd, Welsh Newton and Llanrothal
Heref 8   **P** *Bp, D&C, and MMCET (jt)*   **P-in-c** D S BAILEY,
NSM A CHAPLIN
ST WINNOW (St Winnow) *see* Lostwithiel, St Winnow w St Nectan's Chpl etc *Truro*
SAINTBURY (St Nicholas) *see* Mickleton, Willersey, Saintbury etc *Glouc*
SALCOMBE (Holy Trinity) and Malborough w South Huish
Ex 15   **P** *Keble Coll Ox and D&C Sarum (jt)*   **V** R A OWEN,
C A L HOWMAN
SALCOMBE REGIS (St Mary and St Peter) *see* Sidmouth, Woolbrook, Salcombe Regis, Sidbury etc *Ex*
SALCOT VIRLEY (St Mary the Virgin) *see* Tollesbury w Salcot Virley *Chelmsf*
SALE (St Anne) (St Francis's Church Hall) *Ches 10*   **P** *DBP*
V S A FOSTER,   **C** M B COX
SALE (St Paul) *Ches 10*   **P** *Trustees*   **V** T SHEPHERD
SALEBY (St Margaret) w Beesby and Maltby *Linc 8*   **P** *Bp and DBP (jt)*   **R** R H IRESON
SALEHURST (St Mary) *Chich 15*   **P** *Bp*   **V** J B LAMBOURNE
SALESBURY (St Peter) *Blackb 7*   **P** *V Blackb*
V J W HARTLEY
SALFORD Ordsall (St Clement) *Man 6*   **P** *Bp*
P-in-c R A ROSS
SALFORD (Sacred Trinity) (St Philip) *Man 6*   **P** *D&C Man and Sir Josslyn Gore-Booth Bt (jt)*   **R** P R HOLLEY
SALFORD (St Ambrose) *see* Pendleton *Man*
SALFORD (St Ignatius and Stowell Memorial) *Man 6*   **P** *Bp*
P-in-c R A ROSS
SALFORD (St Mary) *see* Chipping Norton *Ox*
SALFORD (St Mary) *see* Cranfield and Hulcote w Salford *St Alb*
SALFORD (St Paul w Christ Church) *Man 6*   **P** *The Crown and Trustees (alt)*   **R** D S C WYATT
SALFORD PRIORS (St Matthew) *Cov 7*   **P** *Peache Trustees*
P-in-c S R TASH,   **NSM** L E DAVIES
SALFORDS (Christ the King) *S'wark 27*   **P** *Bp*   **V** S M CAPLE,
NSM F PLUMMER
SALHOUSE (All Saints) *see* Rackheath and Salhouse *Nor*
SALING, GREAT (St James) *see* Gt and Lt Bardfield w Gt and Lt Saling *Chelmsf*
SALING, LITTLE (St Peter and St Paul) *as above Chelmsf*
SALISBURY (St Francis) and St Lawrence Stratford sub Castle
Sarum 12   **P** *Bp (3 turns), D&C (1 turn)*   **V** P F D TAYLOR,
Hon C P L RICE
SALISBURY (St Mark) *Sarum 12*   **P** *Bp*
V P J D HAWKSWORTH,   **NSM** T A FISHER
SALISBURY (St Martin) and Laverstock *Sarum 13*   **P** *D&C and Bp (alt)*   **R** K ROBINSON,   **NSM** D E WOODS
SALISBURY (St Paul) *see* Fisherton Anger *Sarum*
SALISBURY (St Thomas and St Edmund) *Sarum 12*   **P** *Bp and D&C (alt)*   **R** J C HATTON,   **NSM** J A TAYLOR
SALKELD, GREAT (St Cuthbert) *see* Kirkoswald, Renwick, Gt Salkeld and Lazonby *Carl*
SALLE (St Peter and St Paul) *see* Reepham, Hackford w Whitwell, Kerdiston etc *Nor*
SALT (St James the Great) *see* Mid Trent *Lich*
SALTASH (St Nicholas and St Faith) *Truro 11*   **P** *Patr Bd*
TR R E B MAYNARD,   **TV** A BUTLER
SALTBURN-BY-THE-SEA (Emmanuel) *York 16*   **P** *Abp, Adn Cleveland, Marquis of Zetland, Mrs M Brignall, and Mrs S L Vernon (jt)*   **V** G W DONEGAN-CROSS
SALTBY (St Peter) *see* High Framland Par *Leic*
SALTDEAN (St Nicholas) *Chich 2*   **P** *Bp*
P-in-c G J BUTTERWORTH
SALTER STREET (St Patrick) and Shirley *Birm 6*   **P** *Patr Bd*
TR M G B C CADDY,   **TV** N LO POLITO, J M KNAPP,
C E M HOWLETT
SALTERHEBBLE (All Saints) *see* Halifax All SS *Wakef*
SALTERSFORD (St John the Baptist) *see* Rainow w Saltersford and Forest *Ches*
SALTFLEETBY (St Peter) *Linc 12*   **P** *Or Coll Ox, Bp, and MMCET (jt)*   **V** *vacant* (01507) 338074
SALTFORD (Blessed Virgin Mary) w Corston and Newton St Loe *B & W 10*   **P** *DBP (2 turns), Duchy of Cornwall* (*1 turn*)   **R** G R W HALL,   **C** T J K BELL,   **NSM** S E WILSON
SALTHOUSE (St Nicholas) *see* Weybourne Gp *Nor*
SALTLEY (St Saviour) and Shaw Hill, Alum Rock *Birm 13*
P *Bp and Trustees (jt)*   **P-in-c** A H TOWNSEND
SALTNEY FERRY (St Matthew) *see* Lache cum Saltney *Ches*
SALTON (St John of Beverley) *see* Kirby Misperton w Normanby, Edston and Salton *York*
SALTWOOD (St Peter and St Paul) *Cant 5*   **P** *Abp*
R R I MARTIN
SALVINGTON (St Peter) *see* Durrington *Chich*

SALWARPE (St Michael) and Hindlip w Martin Hussingtree
Worc 8   **P** *Bp, D&C, and Exors Lady Hindlip (by turn)*
P-in-c I R PETRIE
SALWAY ASH (Holy Trinity)   *see* Beaminster Area *Sarum*
SAMBOURNE (Mission Church)   *see* Coughton *Cov*
SAMBROOK (St Luke)   *see* Cheswardine, Childs Ercall, Hales, Hinstock etc *Lich*
SAMLESBURY (St Leonard the Less)   *see* Walton-le-Dale St Leon w Samlesbury St Leon *Blackb*
SAMPFORD, GREAT (St Michael)   *see* The Sampfords and Radwinter w Hempstead *Chelmsf*
SAMPFORD, LITTLE (St Mary)   *as above Chelmsf*
SAMPFORD ARUNDEL (Holy Cross)   *see* Wellington and Distr *B & W*
SAMPFORD BRETT (St George)   *see* Quantock Towers *B & W*
SAMPFORD COURTENAY (St Andrew)   *see* N Tawton, Bondleigh, Sampford Courtenay etc *Ex*
SAMPFORD PEVERELL (St John the Baptist), Uplowman, Holcombe Rogus, Hockworthy, Burlescombe, Huntsham and Halberton w Ash Thomas *Ex 4*   **P** *Patr Bd*   **TV** K G GALE, **C** R J CLOETE,   **NSM** H M BAYS
SAMPFORD SPINEY (St Mary) w Horrabridge *Ex 24*   **P** *D&C Windsor*   **R** *vacant* (01822) 855198
SAMPFORDS, The (St Michael) (St Mary) and Radwinter with Hempstead *Chelmsf 22*   **P** *Guild of All So, New Coll Ox, and Keble Coll Ox (jt)*   **P-in-c** D MAUDLIN
SANCREED (St Creden) *Truro 5*   **P** *D&C*   **V** S W LEACH
SANCTON (All Saints) *York 5*   **P** *Abp*   **V** P P OCKFORD
SAND HILL (Church of the Good Shepherd)   *see* N Farnborough *Guildf*
SAND HUTTON (St Leonard)   *see* Thirsk *York*
SAND HUTTON (St Mary) *York 6*   **P** *Abp (2 turns), D&C Dur (1 turn)*   **V** J W VALENTINE,   **NSM** R C BENSON
SANDAL (St Catherine) *Wakef 9*   **P** *V Sandal Magna*   **V** M P CROFT,   **C** N LEFROY-OWEN
SANDAL MAGNA (St Helen) *Wakef 9*   **P** *Peache Trustees*   **V** R G MARTIN
SANDBACH (St Mary) *Ches 11*   **P** *DBP*   **P-in-c** D R BUCKLEY,   **NSM** H RUGMAN
SANDBACH HEATH (St John the Evangelist) w Wheelock *Ches 11*   **P** *V Sandbach*   **P-in-c** J A BACON
SANDBANKS (St Nicolas)   *see* Canford Cliffs and Sandbanks *Sarum*
SANDERSTEAD (All Saints) (St Anthony) (St Edmund the King and Martyr) *S'wark 24*   **P** *DBP*   **TR** C J SKILTON, **TV** P EVANS, A M PRINCE,   **C** C J CHILD,   **NSM** M C CAWTE, D M GAMBLE
SANDERSTEAD (St Mary) *S'wark 24*   **P** *Bp* **P-in-c** C J SKILTON,   **C** J J BOWER,   **NSM** M J JOHNSON
SANDFORD (All Saints)   *see* Burrington and Churchill *B & W*
SANDFORD (St Martin)   *see* Westcote Barton w Steeple Barton, Duns Tew etc *Ox*
SANDFORD (St Martin)   *see* Wareham *Sarum*
SANDFORD (St Swithin)   *see* Crediton, Shobrooke and Sandford etc *Ex*
SANDFORD-ON-THAMES (St Andrew) *Ox 4*   **P** *DBP* **P-in-c** R C MORGAN
SANDFORD ORCAS (St Nicholas)   *see* Queen Thorne *Sarum*
SANDGATE (St Paul) w Folkestone (St George) *Cant 5*   **P** *Abp and Ld Chan (alt)*   **P-in-c** J C TAPPER,   **C** S K C RICHARDSON, **OLM** D HADFIELD
SANDHURST (St Lawrence)   *see* Twigworth, Down Hatherley, Norton, The Leigh etc *Glouc*
SANDHURST (St Michael and All Angels) *Ox 16*   **P** *Bp* **R** A T L WILSON,   **NSM** J W WHITE
SANDHURST (St Nicholas) (Mission Church) w Newenden *Cant 17*   **P** *Abp*   **NSM** S M SMALLMAN,   A E WILLIAMS
SANDHURST, LOWER (St Mary)   *see* Sandhurst *Ox*
SANDIACRE (St Giles) *Derby 13*   **P** *Ld Chan* **R** W B COONEY,   **NSM** K W G JOHNSON
SANDIWAY (St John the Evangelist) *Ches 6*   **P** *Bp* **V** G G ROXBY
SANDLEHEATH (St Aldhelm)   *see* Fordingbridge and Breamore and Hale etc *Win*
SANDON (All Saints)   *see* Mid Trent *Lich*
SANDON (All Saints), Wallington and Rushden w Clothall *St Alb 19*   **P** *Duchy of Lanc (1 turn), Marquess of Salisbury (1 turn), and Bp (2 turns)*   **R** D M WILLIAMS, **NSM** L E SUMMERS
SANDON (St Andrew) *Chelmsf 9*   **P** *Qu Coll Cam* **P-in-c** K R PLAISTER
SANDOWN (Christ Church) *Portsm 7*   **P** *Ch Patr Trust* **V** H J CUNNINGTON
SANDOWN, LOWER (St John the Evangelist) *Portsm 7*   **P** *Bp* **V** H J CUNNINGTON
SANDRIDGE (St Leonard) *St Alb 8*   **P** *Earl Spencer*   **V** *vacant* (01727) 866089

SANDRINGHAM (St Mary Magdalene) w West Newton and Appleton, Wolferton w Babingley and Flitcham *Nor 16*   **P** *The Crown*   **R** J B V RIVIERE
SANDS (Church of the Good Shepherd)   *see* Seale, Puttenham and Wanborough *Guildf*
SANDS (St Mary and St George)   *see* High Wycombe *Ox*
SANDSEND (St Mary)   *see* Lythe w Ugthorpe *York*
SANDWELL (St Philip)   *see* W Bromwich St Phil *Lich*
SANDWICH (St Clement) *Cant 8*   **P** *Adn Cant* **R** J M A ROBERTS,   **NSM** J C ROBERTS
SANDY (St Swithun) *St Alb 11*   **P** *Lord Pym* **R** D G WILLIAMS,   **C** S C HILLMAN
SANDY LANE (St Mary and St Nicholas)   *see* Rowde and Bromham *Sarum*
SANDYLANDS (St John) *Blackb 11*   **P** *Bp*   **V** J G REEVES **V** M BUCKLEY
SANTAN (St Sanctain) *S & M 1*   **P** *The Crown*   **V** C A QUINE
SANTON DOWNHAM (St Mary the Virgin)   *see* Brandon and Santon Downham w Elveden *St E*
SAPCOTE (All Saints) and Sharnford w Wigston Parva *Leic 13*   **P** *Ld Chan and DBP (alt)*   **R** M J NORMAN
SAPEY, UPPER (St Michael)   *see* Edvin Loach w Tedstone Delamere etc *Heref*
SAPPERTON (St Kenelm)   *see* Coates, Rodmarton and Sapperton etc *Glouc*
SAPPERTON (St Nicholas) w Braceby *Linc 14*   **P** *Bp (1 turn), Sir Richard Welby Bt (3 turns)*   **R** M H SABELL
SARISBURY (St Paul) *Portsm 2*   **P** *V Titchfield*   **Par Dn** J EVANS
SARK (St Peter) *Win 14*   **P** *Le Seigneur de Sercq* **P-in-c** F M TRICKEY,   **C** G L LEWORTHY
SARN (Holy Trinity)   *see* Churchstoke w Hyssington and Sarn *Heref*
SARNESFIELD (St Mary)   *see* Weobley w Sarnesfield and Norton Canon *Heref*
SARRATT (Holy Cross) *St Alb 5*   **P** *Bp*   **P-in-c** J P HART, **Hon C** M K WILLIAMS
SATLEY (St Cuthbert), Stanley and Tow Law *Dur 9*   **P** *Bp, Ld Chan, and R Brancepeth (by turn)*   **V** P T DAVIS
SATTERTHWAITE (All Saints)   *see* Hawkshead and Low Wray w Sawrey and Rusland etc *Carl*
SAUGHALL, GREAT (All Saints) *Ches 9*   **P** *Bp* **P-in-c** D F HAY
SAUL (St James the Great)   *see* Frampton on Severn, Arlingham, Saul etc *Glouc*
SAUNDERTON (St Mary and St Nicholas)   *see* Risborough *Ox*
SAUNTON (St Anne)   *see* Braunton *Ex*
SAUSTHORPE (St Andrew)   *see* Partney Gp *Linc*
SAVERNAKE (St Katharine) *Sarum 19*   **P** *Patr Bd* **TR** N A LEIGH-HUNT,   **TV** M EDWARDS, R L N HARRISON, **NSM** A J DEBOO
SAW MILLS (St Mary)   *see* Ambergate and Heage *Derby*
SAWBRIDGEWORTH (Great St Mary) *St Alb 18*   **P** *Bp* **V** R F SIBSON
SAWLEY (All Saints) (St Mary) *Derby 13*   **P** *D&C Lich* **R** P HENRY,   **C** L G C E HARRIS
SAWLEY (St Michael)   *see* Fountains Gp *Ripon*
SAWREY (St Peter)   *see* Hawkshead and Low Wray w Sawrey and Rusland etc *Carl*
SAWSTON (St Mary) *Ely 6*   **P** *SMF*   **V** G KENDALL
SAWTRY (All Saints) and Glatton *Ely 12*   **P** *Duke of Devonshire* **R** P M GRIFFITH
SAXBY (St Helen)   *see* Owmby Gp *Linc*
SAXBY (St Peter)   *see* Waltham on the Wolds, Stonesby, Saxby etc *Leic*
SAXBY ALL SAINTS (All Saints) *Linc 6*   **P** *R H H Barton Esq* **R** G A PLUMB
SAXELBYE (St Peter)   *see* Old Dalby, Nether Broughton, Saxelbye etc *Leic*
SAXHAM, GREAT (St Andrew)   *see* Risby w Gt and Lt Saxham *St E*
SAXHAM, LITTLE (St Nicholas)   *as above St E*
SAXILBY Group, The (St Botolph) *Linc 2*   **P** *Bp and DBP (jt)* **R** R PROSSER,   **NSM** S PROSSER
SAXLINGHAM (St Margaret)   *see* Gunthorpe w Bale w Field Dalling, Saxlingham etc *Nor*
SAXLINGHAM NETHERGATE (St Mary)   *see* Newton Flotman, Swainsthorpe, Tasburgh, etc *Nor*
SAXMUNDHAM (St John the Baptist) *St E 19*   **P** *Exors Mrs A H V Aldous*   **P-in-c** R F WEBB
SAXONWELL *Linc 19*   **P** *Duchy of Lanc (2 turns), Ld Chan (1 turn)*   **R** M J HAZELTON,   **OLM** C W B SOWDEN
SAXTEAD (All Saints)   *see* Framlingham w Saxtead *St E*
SAXTHORPE (St Andrew)   *see* Lt Barningham, Blickling, Edgefield etc *Nor*

SAXTON (All Saints)   *see* Sherburn in Elmet w Saxton *York*
SAYERS COMMON (Christ Church)   *see* Albourne w Sayers
  Common and Twineham *Chich*
SCALBY (St Laurence)   *York 15*   P *Abp*   V J W BAKER,
  NSM M J WRIGHT, J J L HAY
SCALDWELL (St Peter and St Paul)   *see* Walgrave w
  Hannington and Wold and Scaldwell *Pet*
SCALEBY (All Saints)   *see* Eden, Gelt and Irthing *Carl*
SCALFORD (St Egelwin) w Goadby Marwood and Wycombe
  and Chadwell, Eastwell and Eaton   *Leic 3*   P *Ld Chan and Bp*
  (alt)   R vacant (01664) 444319
SCAMMONDEN, WEST (St Bartholomew)   *see* Barkisland w
  W Scammonden *Wakef*
SCAMPSTON (St Martin)   *see* Buckrose Carrs *York*
SCAMPTON (St John the Baptist)   *see* Aisthorpe w Scampton w
  Thorpe le Fallows etc *Linc*
SCARBOROUGH (St Columba)   *York 15*   P *Abp*
  P-in-c K D JACKSON,   NSM D B CROUCH
SCARBOROUGH (St James w Holy Trinity)   *York 15*   P *Abp*
  and CPAS *(jt)*   P-in-c P W WHITE
SCARBOROUGH (St Luke)   *York 15*   P *Abp*   V vacant
  (01723) 372831
SCARBOROUGH (St Mark)   *see* Newby *York*
SCARBOROUGH (St Martin)   *York 15*   P *Trustees*
  P-in-c A J MILLS
SCARBOROUGH (St Mary) w Christ Church and (Holy
  Apostles)   *York 15*   P *Abp*   P-in-c M P DUNNING
SCARBOROUGH (St Saviour w All Saints)   *York 15*   P *Abp*
  V A J MILLS,   NSM G G A WARING
SCARCLIFFE (St Leonard)   *see* Ault Hucknall and Scarcliffe
  Derby
SCARISBRICK (St Mark) (Good Shepherd)   *Liv 11*
  P *V Ormskirk*   V vacant (01704) 880317
SCARLE, NORTH (All Saints)   *see* Swinderby *Linc*
SCARLE, SOUTH (St Helena)   *see* Collingham w S Scarle and
  Besthorpe and Girton *S'well*
SCARNING (St Peter and St Paul)   *see* E Dereham and
  Scarning *Nor*
SCARRINGTON (St John of Beverley)   *see* Whatton w
  Aslockton, Hawksworth, Scarrington etc *S'well*
SCARSDALE, EAST   *Derby 3*   P *Patr Bd*
  TR J W HARGREAVES
SCARTHO (St Giles)   *Linc 9*   P *Jes Coll Ox*   R I R S WALKER,
  C L M BUSFIELD
SCAWBY (St Hibald), Redbourne and Hibaldstow   *Linc 6*
  P *Exors Lt Col R Sutton-Nelthorpe (2 turns), Bp (1 turn), and
  Duke of St Alb (1 turn)*   V C H LILLEY,   NSM L Y LUCAS
SCAWTHORPE (St Luke)   *see* Doncaster St Leon and St Jude
  Sheff
SCAWTON (St Mary)   *see* Upper Ryedale *York*
SCAYNES HILL (St Augustine)   *Chich 6*   P *Bp*
  V G B MITCHELL
SCHOLES (St Philip)   *see* Barwick in Elmet *Ripon*
SCHOLES (St Philip and St James)   *Wakef 8*   P *Bp*
  P-in-c M A MCLEAN
SCHORNE   *Ox 24*   P *Patr Bd (2 turns), Ld Chan (1 turn)*
  TV A T BELL,   NSM M D W PARTRIDGE, E A WELTERS,
  OLM S B V DICKINSON
SCILLY   *see* Is of Scilly *Truro*
SCISSETT (St Augustine)   *see* High Hoyland, Scissett and
  Clayton W *Wakef*
SCOFTON (St John the Evangelist)   *see* Babworth w
  Sutton-cum-Lound and Scofton etc *S'well*
SCOLE (St Andrew) w Brockdish, Billingford, Thorpe Abbots and
  Thorpe Parva   *Nor 10*   P *Bp, Ex Coll Ox, MMCET, Adn
  Norfolk, and Exors Lady Mann (jt)*   P-in-c W M C BESTELINK
SCOPWICK (Holy Cross)   *see* Digby Gp *Linc*
SCORBOROUGH (St Leonard)   *see* Lockington and Lund and
  Scorborough w Leconfield *York*
SCORTON (St Peter) and Barnacre All Saints and Calder Vale
  St John the Evangelist   *Blackb 9*   P *Bp, V Lanc St Mary w
  St Jo and St Anne, and Mrs V O Shepherd-Cross (jt)*
  V A FISHWICK,   NSM A BOSS
SCOT WILLOUGHBY (St Andrew)   *see* S Lafford *Linc*
SCOTBY (All Saints) and Cotehill w Cumwhinton   *Carl 2*
  P *Trustees (2 turns), Prime Min (1 turn)*
  P-in-c G M CREGEEN,   C T D HERBERT
SCOTFORTH (St Paul)   *Blackb 11*   P *Rt Revd J Nicholls*
  V M G SMITH,   C K M BUCK, S J WILLIAMS
SCOTHERN (St Germain)   *see* Welton and Dunholme w
  Scothern *Linc*
SCOTSWOOD (St Margaret)   *Newc 7*   P *Bp*   V vacant 0191-
  274 6322
SCOTTER (St Peter) w East Ferry   *Linc 4*   P *Bp*
  R O G FOLKARD
SCOTTON (St Genewys) w Northorpe   *Linc 4*   P *Ld Chan*
  R O G FOLKARD,   OLM W KEAST, D L LANGFORD

SCOTTON (St Thomas)   *see* Walkingham Hill *Ripon*
SCOTTOW (All Saints)   *see* Worstead, Westwick, Sloley,
  Swanton Abbot etc *Nor*
SCOULTON (Holy Trinity)   *see* High Oak, Hingham and
  Scoulton w Wood Rising *Nor*
SCOUTHEAD (St Paul)   *see* Saddleworth *Man*
SCRAMBLESBY (St Martin)   *see* Asterby Gp *Linc*
SCRAPTOFT (All Saints)   *Leic 1*   P *Bp, Dr M J A Sharp, and
  DBP (jt)*   V M J COURT,   NSM A J POOLE
SCRAYINGHAM (St Peter and St Paul)   *see* Stamford Bridge
  Gp of Par *York*
SCREDINGTON (St Andrew)   *see* Helpringham w Hale *Linc*
SCREMBY (St Peter and St Paul)   *see* Partney Gp *Linc*
SCREMERSTON (St Peter)   *Newc 12*   P *Bp*
  P-in-c A S ADAMSON,   NSM S J HARRISON
SCREVETON (St Wilfrid)   *see* Car Colston w Screveton *S'well*
SCRIVELSBY (St Benedict)   *see* Thornton Gp *Linc*
SCROOBY (St Wilfrid)   *see* Blyth and Scrooby w Ranskill *S'well*
SCROPTON (St Paul)   *see* Doveridge, Scropton, Sudbury etc
  Derby
SCRUTON (St Radegund)   *see* Kirkby Fleetham w Langton on
  Swale and Scruton *Ripon*
SCULCOATES (St Mary)   *see* Hull St Mary Sculcoates *York*
SCULCOATES (St Paul) w Christ Church and St Silas   *York 14*
  P *Abp*   Hon C J G LEEMAN
SCULCOATES (St Stephen)   *see* Hull St Steph Sculcoates *York*
SCULTHORPE (St Mary and All Saints)   *see* N and S Creake w
  Waterden, Syderstone etc *Nor*
SCUNTHORPE (All Saints)   *see* Brumby *Linc*
SCUNTHORPE (The Resurrection)   *see* Trentside E *Linc*
SEA MILLS (St Edyth)   *Bris 2*   P *Bp*   V D A IZZARD
SEA PALLING (St Margaret)   *see* Happisburgh, Walcott,
  Hempstead w Eccles etc *Nor*
SEA VIEW (St Peter)   *Portsm 7*   P *Bp*   V M M STRANGE
SEABOROUGH (St John)   *see* Beaminster Area *Sarum*
SEABROOK (Mission Hall)   *see* Cheriton *Cant*
SEACOMBE (St Paul)   *Ches 7*   P *Trustees*   V vacant 0151-638
  3677
SEACROFT (St James) (Church of the Ascension) (St Richard)
  Ripon 8   P *DBF*   TR A F BUNDOCK,   TV M P BENWELL,
  L C PEARSON, C MACLAREN, R H JAMIESON,   C E ROSE
SEAFORD (St Leonard) w Sutton   *Chich 18*   P *Ld Chan*
  V C H ATHERSTONE,   C P J OWEN,   C D OHERTY
SEAFORTH (St Thomas)   *Liv 1*   P *Sir William Gladstone Bt*
  C N FINLAY
SEAGRAVE (All Saints)   *see* Sileby, Cossington and Seagrave
  Leic
SEAGRY (St Mary the Virgin)   *see* Gt Somerford, Lt Somerford,
  Seagry, Corston etc *Bris*
SEAHAM (St Mary the Virgin)   *Dur 2*   P *Bp*   V vacant 0191-
  581 3385
SEAHAM, NEW (Christ Church)   *Dur 2*   P *Bp*
  P-in-c D A ROBERTS
SEAHAM HARBOUR (St John)   *Dur 2*   P *Bp*
  V J C G POLLOCK
SEAL (St Lawrence)   *Roch 9*   P *Bp*   P-in-c M D COOKE
SEAL (St Peter and St Paul)   *Roch 9*   P *DBP*
  V K C BLACKBURN
SEALE (St Lawrence), Puttenham and Wanborough   *Guildf 4*
  P *Adn Surrey, C R I Perkins Esq, and Ld Chan (by turn)*
  R N S MCGREGOR
SEALE (St Peter) (St Matthew) and Lullington w Coton in the
  Elms   *Derby 16*   P *Bp, R D Nielson Esq, and
  C W Worthington Esq (jt)*   R D J ADAMS
SEAMER (St Martin)   *York 15*   P *Abp*   P-in-c H S WATSON,
  NSM T JORDAN
SEAMER IN CLEVELAND (St Martin)   *York 21*   P *Lord
  Egremont*   P-in-c M D A DYKES
SEARBY (St Nicholas)   *see* Caistor Gp *Linc*
SEASALTER (St Alphege)   *see* Whitstable *Cant*
SEASCALE (St Cuthbert) and Drigg   *Carl 5*   P *DBP*
  V W J P GRIME
SEATHWAITE (Holy Trinity)   *see* Broughton and Duddon *Carl*
SEATON (All Hallows)   *see* Lyddington w Stoke Dry and
  Seaton etc *Pet*
SEATON (St Gregory) and Beer   *Ex 5*   P *Lord Clinton and
  D&C (jt)*   V N T SCHOFIELD,   C A THORNE,
  NSM A J COCKRAM
SEATON (St Paul)   *see* Camerton, Seaton and W Seaton *Carl*
SEATON, WEST (Holy Trinity)   *as above Carl*
SEATON CAREW (Holy Trinity)   *Dur 3*   P *Bp*   V W WORLEY
SEATON HIRST (St John) (St Andrew)   *Newc 11*   P *Bp*
  TR D P PALMER,   C D M BEATER
SEATON ROSS (St Edmund)   *see* Holme and Seaton Ross Gp
  York

SEATON SLUICE (St Paul)   *see* Delaval *Newc*
SEAVIEW   *see* Sea View *Portsm*
SEAVINGTON (St Michael and St Mary)   *see* S Petherton w the Seavingtons *B & W*
SEBERGHAM (St Mary)   *see* Caldbeck, Castle Sowerby and Sebergham *Carl*
SECKINGTON (All Saints)   *see* Newton Regis w Seckington and Shuttington *Birm*
SEDBERGH (St Andrew), Cautley and Garsdale   *Bradf 6*   **P** *Trin Coll Cam*   **V** A W FELL
SEDGEBERROW (St Mary the Virgin)   *see* Hampton w Sedgeberrow and Hinton-on-the-Green *Worc*
SEDGEBROOK (St Lawrence)   *see* Saxonwell *Linc*
SEDGEFIELD (St Edmund)   *Dur 5*   **P** *Bp*   **R** M Q KING
SEDGEHILL (St Katherine)   *see* E Knoyle, Semley and Sedgehill *Sarum*
SEDGFORD (St Mary)   *see* Docking, the Birchams, Stanhoe and Sedgeford *Nor*
SEDGLEY (All Saints)   *Worc 10*   **P** *DBP*   **TR** S R BUCKLEY, **C** S K RENSHAW
SEDGLEY (St Mary the Virgin)   *Worc 10*   **P** *Bp and V Sedgley All SS (jt)*   **V** E SMITH,   **NSM** T WESTWOOD
SEDLESCOMBE (St John the Baptist) w Whatlington   *Chich 14*   **P** *Ld Chan and Bp (alt)*   **P-in-c** E F P BRYANT, **NSM** S D HUGGINS
SEEND (Holy Cross), Bulkington and Poulshot   *Sarum 16*   **P** *D&C (2 turns), Bp (1 turn)*   **V** T J ALLEN
SEER GREEN (Holy Trinity) and Jordans   *Ox 20*   **P** *Bp*   **P-in-c** F C CONANT
SEETHING (St Margaret)   *see* Brooke, Kirstead, Mundham w Seething and Thwaite *Nor*
SEFTON (St Helen) and Thornton   *Liv 5*   **P** *Bp*   **R** I C COWELL
SEFTON PARK (Christ Church)   *see* Toxteth Park Ch Ch and St Mich w St Andr *Liv*
SEGHILL (Holy Trinity)   *Newc 1*   **P** *The Crown*   **V** I G FALCONER
SEIGHFORD (St Chad)   *see* Chebsey, Ellenhall and Seighford-with-Creswell *Lich*
SELATTYN (St Mary)   *see* Weston Rhyn and Selattyn *Lich*
SELBORNE (St Mary)   *see* Newton Valence, Selborne and E Tisted w Colemore *Win*
SELBY (St James the Apostle)   *York 4*   **P** *Simeon's Trustees*   **V** D J WOOLLARD
SELBY ABBEY (St Mary and St Germain) (St Richard)   *York 4*   **P** *Abp*   **V** K M JUKES
SELHAM (St James)   *see* Lurgashall, Lodsworth and Selham *Chich*
SELLACK (St Tysilio)   *see* How Caple w Sollarshope, Sellack etc *Heref*
SELLINDGE (St Mary the Virgin)   *see* Mersham w Hinxhill and Sellindge *Cant*
SELLING (St Mary the Virgin) w Throwley and Sheldwich w Badlesmere and Leaveland   *Cant 6*   **P** *Abp and D&C (jt)*   **P-in-c** J M MASON,   **NSM** M JOHNSON, A SKINNER
SELLY OAK (St Mary)   *Birm 2*   **P** *Bp*   **V** M V ROBERTS, **NSM** S A IZZARD
SELLY PARK (St Stephen) (St Wulstan) (St Stephen's Centre)   *Birm 5*   **P** *Trustees*   **V** C B HOBBS,   **C** N A HAND
SELMESTON (St Mary)   *see* Berwick w Selmeston and Alciston *Chich*
SELSDON (St John) (St Francis)   *S'wark 22*   **P** *Bp*   **TR** A C HORTON,   **NSM** K HOLT
SELSEY (St Peter)   *Chich 3*   **P** *Bp*   **R** J C T HARRINGTON
SELSIDE (St Thomas)   *see* Skelsmergh w Selside and Longsleddale *Carl*
SELSLEY (All Saints)   *see* Cainscross w Selsley *Glouc*
SELSTON (St Helen)   *S'well 4*   **P** *Wright Trustees*   **P-in-c** T MITCHELL
SELWORTHY (All Saints), Timberscombe, Wootton Courtenay and Luccombe   *B & W 16*   **P** *Bp*   **R** R MANN, **Hon C** S R B HUMPHREYS
SEMER (All Saints)   *see* Bildeston w Wattisham and Lindsey, Whatfield etc *St E*
SEMINGTON (St George)   *see* Steeple Ashton w Semington and Keevil *Sarum*
SEMLEY (St Leonard)   *see* E Knoyle, Semley and Sedgehill *Sarum*
SEMPRINGHAM (St Andrew)   *see* Billingborough Gp *Linc*
SEND (St Mary the Virgin)   *Guildf 12*   **P** *Bp*   **P-in-c** A J SHUTT, **NSM** G H CLAYTON
SENNEN (St Sennen)   *see* St Buryan, St Levan and Sennen *Truro*
SENNICOTTS (St Mary)   *see* Funtington and Sennicotts *Chich*
SESSAY (St Cuthbert)   *York 19*   **P** *Viscount Downe*   **R** J H DAVIS
SETCHEY (St Mary)   *see* W Winch w Setchey, N Runcton and Middleton *Nor*

SETMURTHY (St Barnabas)   *see* Binsey *Carl*
SETTLE (Holy Ascension)   *Bradf 5*   **P** *Trustees*   **V** S G RIDLEY
SETTRINGTON (All Saints)   *see* W Buckrose *York*
SEVEN KINGS   *see* Gt Ilford St Jo *Chelmsf*
SEVENHAMPTON (St Andrew) w Charlton Abbots, Hawling and Whittington, Dowdeswell and Andoversford w The Shiptons and Cold Salperton, and Withington   *Glouc 13*   **P** *Bp, MMCET, J A Bailey Esq, E M Bailey Esq, and Mrs J A Stringer (1 turn); Bp, MMCET, and Mrs L E Evans (1 turn)*   **R** R A B MORRIS,   **C** A J AXON
SEVENHAMPTON (St James)   *see* Highworth w Sevenhampton and Inglesham etc *Bris*
SEVENOAKS (St John the Baptist)   *Roch 9*   **P** *Guild of All So*   **V** R WARD,   **C** M J R WHITING
SEVENOAKS (St Luke)   *Roch 9*   **P** *Bp*   **V** R CHAVNER
SEVENOAKS (St Nicholas)   *Roch 9*   **P** *Trustees*   **R** A M MACLEAY,   **C** J M DENT, A C N BEWES, **Hon C** N N HENSHAW,   D G MILTON-THOMPSON
SEVENOAKS WEALD (St George)   *Roch 9*   **P** *R Sevenoaks*   **P-in-c** M P P HOWARD
SEVERN BEACH (St Nicholas)   *see* Pilning w Compton Greenfield *Bris*
SEVERN STOKE (St Dennis)   *see* Kempsey and Severn Stoke w Croome d'Abitot *Worc*
SEVERNSIDE Group of Parishes, The   *see* Frampton on Severn, Arlingham, Saul etc *Glouc*
SEVINGTON (St Mary)   *Cant 10*   **P** *Ch Soc Trust*   **P-in-c** J W TIPPING
SEWARDS END (not known)   *see* Saffron Walden w Wendens Ambo, Littlebury etc *Chelmsf*
SEWERBY (St John)   *see* Bridlington H Trin and Sewerby w Marton *York*
SEWSTERN (Holy Trinity)   *see* Wymondham w Edmondthorpe, Buckminster etc *Leic*
SHABBINGTON (St Mary Magdalene)   *see* Worminghall w Ickford, Oakley and Shabbington *Ox*
SHACKERSTONE (St Peter)   *see* Nailstone and Carlton w Shackerstone *Leic*
SHACKLEFORD (St Mary the Virgin)   *see* Compton w Shackleford and Peper Harow *Guildf*
SHADFORTH (St Cuthbert)   *see* Pittington, Shadforth and Sherburn *Dur*
SHADINGFIELD (St John the Baptist)   *see* Hundred River *St E*
SHADOXHURST (St Peter and St Paul)   *see* Kingsnorth and Shadoxhurst *Cant*
SHADWELL (St Paul)   *Ripon 5*   **P** *V Thorner*   **V** H A THOMPSON
SHADWELL (St Paul) w Ratcliffe St James   *Lon 7*   **P** *Bp*   **C** L MCROSTIE
SHAFTESBURY (St James)   *see* Shaston *Sarum*
SHAFTESBURY (St Peter)   *as above Sarum*
SHAFTON (St Hugh)   *see* Felkirk w Brierley *Wakef*
SHALBOURNE (St Michael and All Angels)   *see* Savernake *Sarum*
SHALDEN (St Peter and St Paul)   *see* Bentworth and Shalden and Lasham *Win*
SHALDON (St Nicholas) (St Peter), Stokeinteignhead, Combeinteignhead and Haccombe   *Ex 11*   **P** *SMF and Sir Rivers Carew Bt (jt)*   **R** G S RICHARDSON,   **C** J BUTLER
SHALFLEET (St Michael the Archangel)   *Portsm 8*   **P** *Ld Chan*   **V** D J BEVINGTON,   **NSM** M O'DONNELL
SHALFORD (St Andrew)   *see* Finchingfield and Cornish Hall End etc *Chelmsf*
SHALFORD (St Mary the Virgin)   *Guildf 5*   **P** *Ld Chan*   **V** J J CRUSE
SHALSTONE (St Edward the Confessor)   *see* W Buckingham *Ox*
SHAMLEY GREEN (Christ Church)   *Guildf 2*   **P** *Bp*   **V** M C HUGHES
SHANGTON (St Nicholas)   *see* Church Langton cum Tur Langton etc *Leic*
SHANKLIN (St Blasius)   *Portsm 7*   **P** *Bp*   **P-in-c** A W SWANBOROUGH
SHANKLIN (St Paul)   *see* Gatten St Paul *Portsm*
SHANKLIN (St Saviour on the Cliff)   *Portsm 7*   **P** *Bp*   **V** R M SMITH,   **NSM** B M DOWNER
SHAP (St Michael) w Swindale and Bampton w Mardale   *Carl 1*   **P** *Earl of Lonsdale*   **P-in-c** C MARSDEN
SHAPWICK (Blessed Virgin Mary) w Ashcott and Burtle   *B & W 5*   **P** *Lord Vestey (2 turns), Bp (1 turn)*   **P-in-c** J P ROWE
SHAPWICK (St Bartholomew)   *see* Sturminster Marshall, Kingston Lacy and Shapwick *Sarum*
SHARD END (All Saints)   *Birm 9*   **P** *Keble Coll Ox*   **V** J F WARD

SHARDLOW (St James) *see* Aston on Trent, Elvaston, Weston on Trent etc *Derby*

SHARESHILL (St Luke and St Mary the Virgin) *Lich 2* **P** *Bp* **P-in-c** P H J THORNEYCROFT

SHARLSTON (St Luke) *Wakef 9* **P** *Bp* **V** *vacant* (01924) 862414

SHARNBROOK (St Peter) and Knotting w Souldrop *St Alb 15* **P** *Bp* **P-in-c** I W ARTHUR

SHARNFORD (St Helen) *see* Sapcote and Sharnford w Wigston Parva *Leic*

SHARPNESS (St Andrew), Purton, Brookend and Slimbridge *Glouc 2* **P** *Magd Coll Ox and Bp (alt)* **R** W J BOON

SHARRINGTON (All Saints) *see* Gunthorpe w Bale w Field Dalling, Saxlingham etc *Nor*

SHARROW (St Andrew) *see* Psalter Lane St Andr *Sheff*

SHASTON *Sarum 5* **P** *Patr Bd* **TR** M T P ZAMMIT, **TV** A C HEYWOOD, **C** D R D MASLEN, **NSM** I WITCHER, M E HARDING

SHAUGH PRIOR (St Edward) *see* Bickleigh and Shaugh Prior *Ex*

SHAVINGTON (St Mark) *see* Weston *Ches*

SHAW (Christchurch) *see* Atworth w Shaw and Whitley *Sarum*

SHAW (Holy Trinity) *Man 22* **P** *R Prestwich St Mary* **P-in-c** R R WATSON

SHAW (St Mary) cum Donnington *Ox 14* **P** *DBP* **R** B TAYLOR, **C** E K FORBES STONE

SHAW HILL (St Mary and St John) *see* Saltley and Shaw Hill *Birm*

SHAWBURY (St Mary the Virgin) *Lich 22* **P** *C C Corbet Esq* **V** D J HUMPHRIES

SHAWELL (All Saints) *see* Gilmorton, Peatling Parva, Kimcote etc *Leic*

SHEARSBY (St Mary Magdalene) *see* Arnesby w Shearsby and Bruntingthorpe *Leic*

SHEBBEAR (St Michael), Buckland Filleigh, Sheepwash, Langtree, Newton St Petrock, Petrockstowe, Petersmarland, Merton and Huish *Ex 19* **P** *Ld Chan (1 turn), Patr Bd (2 turns)* **TV** C C R MERIVALE, **P-in-c** M J WARREN, **NSM** R FOALE

SHEDFIELD (St John the Baptist) *Portsm 1* **P** *DBP* **P-in-c** S C HENDERSON, **NSM** B R MCHUGH

SHEEN (St Luke) *see* Longnor, Quarnford and Sheen *Lich*

SHEEN, EAST (All Saints) *see* Mortlake w E Sheen *S'wark*

SHEEN, EAST (Christ Church) *as above S'wark*

SHEEPSCOMBE (St John the Evangelist) *see* Painswick, Sheepscombe, Cranham, The Edge etc *Glouc*

SHEEPSTOR (St Leonard) *see* Yelverton, Meavy, Sheepstor and Walkhampton *Ex*

SHEEPWASH (St Lawrence) *see* Shebbear, Buckland Filleigh, Sheepwash etc *Ex*

SHEEPY (All Saints) *see* Bosworth and Sheepy Gp *Leic*

SHEERING (St Mary the Virgin) *see* Hatfield Heath and Sheering *Chelmsf*

SHEERNESS (Holy Trinity w St Paul) *Cant 16* **P** *V Minster-in-Sheppey* **V** J W STREETING

SHEERWATER (St Michael and All Angels) *see* Woodham *Guildf*

SHEET (St Mary Magdalene) *Portsm 4* **P** *Bp* **V** R M E DEWING, **NSM** J C GRACE

SHEFFIELD Abbeydale St Peter *Sheff 2* **P** *Ch Burgesses* **P-in-c** B R COLEMAN

SHEFFIELD Norwood (St Leonard) *Sheff 3* **P** *Bp* **V** I K DUFFIELD, **C** T E FOUGNER

SHEFFIELD Parson Cross (St Cecilia) *Sheff 3* **P** *Bp* **P-in-c** T H CASWELL

SHEFFIELD (St Aidan w St Luke) *see* Sheff Manor *Sheff*

SHEFFIELD (St Andrew) *see* Psalter Lane St Andr *Sheff*

SHEFFIELD (St Bartholomew) *Sheff 4* **P** *Ch Patr Trust and Sheff Ch Burgesses Trust (jt)* **P-in-c** P W WEST

SHEFFIELD (St Catherine of Siena) Richmond Road *Sheff 1* **P** *The Crown* **V** H LOXLEY

SHEFFIELD (St Cuthbert) *Sheff 3* **P** *Ch Burgesses* **V** I JENNINGS, **C** L RIDLEY

SHEFFIELD (St John the Evangelist) *Sheff 1* **P** *Ch Burgesses* **C** D N MEESE

SHEFFIELD (St Mark) Broomhill *Sheff 4* **P** *Ch Burgesses* **V** A ALKER, **C** S H FAIRWEATHER

SHEFFIELD (St Mary) Bramall Lane *Sheff 2* **P** *Ch Burgesses and Dean (alt)* **V** J C SULLIVAN, **C** P J BATCHFORD, M J BAYLEY, **NSM** G E D DUNCAN

SHEFFIELD (St Matthew) Carver Street *Sheff 2* **P** *Bp and Sheff Ch Burgess Trust (jt)* **V** S M GRIFFITHS

SHEFFIELD (St Oswald) *Sheff 2* **P** *Ch Burgesses* **P-in-c** B R COLEMAN

SHEFFIELD (St Paul) *see* Arbourthorne and Norfolk Park *Sheff*

SHEFFIELD (St Paul) Wordsworth Avenue *Sheff 3* **P** *DBP* **V** *vacant* 0114-246 8137

SHEFFIELD MANOR (St Swithun) *Sheff 1* **P** *Patr Bd* **P-in-c** J C GRENFELL, **C** J W GRENFELL

SHEFFIELD PARK (St John the Evangelist) *see* Sheff St Jo *Sheff*

SHEFFORD (St Michael) *see* Meppershall and Shefford *St Alb*

SHEFFORD, GREAT (St Mary) *see* Welford w Wickham and Gt Shefford, Boxford etc *Ox*

SHEINTON (St Peter and St Paul) *see* Wenlock *Heref*

SHELDON (St Giles) *Birm 9* **P** *J K Wingfield Digby Esq* **R** B A L CAMP

SHELDON (St James the Greater) *see* Dunkeswell, Luppitt, Sheldon and Upottery *Ex*

SHELDON (St Michael and All Angels) *see* Ashford w Sheldon and Longstone *Derby*

SHELDWICH (St James) *see* Selling w Throwley, Sheldwich w Badlesmere etc *Cant*

SHELF St Michael w Buttershaw St Aidan *Bradf 2* **P** *Bp* **TV** M I GASKELL

SHELFANGER (All Saints) *see* Winfarthing w Shelfanger w Burston w Gissing etc *Nor*

SHELFIELD (St Mark) Conventional District *Lich 6 vacant*

SHELFORD (St Peter and St Paul) *see* Radcliffe-on-Trent and Shelford etc *S'well*

SHELFORD, GREAT (St Mary) *Ely 6* **P** *Bp* **P-in-c** M R GOATER

SHELFORD, LITTLE (All Saints) *Ely 6* **P** *Bp* **R** C B G ASH, **C** T M CHAPMAN

SHELLAND (King Charles the Martyr) *see* Gt Finborough w Onehouse, Harleston, Buxhall etc *St E*

SHELLEY (All Saints) *see* Hadleigh, Layham and Shelley *St E*

SHELLEY (Emmanuel) and Shepley *Wakef 6* **P** *V Kirkburton* **P-in-c** J R JONES

SHELLEY (St Peter) *see* Chipping Ongar w Shelley *Chelmsf*

SHELLINGFORD (St Faith) *see* Uffington, Shellingford, Woolstone and Baulking *Ox*

SHELSLEY BEAUCHAMP (All Saints) *see* Clifton-on-Teme, Lower Sapey and the Shelsleys *Worc*

SHELSLEY WALSH (St Andrew) *as above Worc*

SHELSWELL *Ox 2* **P** *Ld Chan (1 turn) and Ch Ch Ox, CCC Ox, Baroness von Maltzahn, and R J Vallings Esq (1 turn)* **R** W J YATES, **NSM** D WENHAM, S L BUSHELL, **OLM** K G WHITE

SHELTHORPE (Good Shepherd) *see* Loughb Gd Shep *Leic*

SHELTON (Christ Church) and Oxon *Lich 20* **P** *V Shrewsbury St Chad w St Mary* **V** J W B TOMLINSON, **OLM** M I FEARNSIDE

SHELTON (St Mark) *see* Hanley H Ev *Lich*

SHELTON (St Mary) *see* Hempnall *Nor*

SHELTON (St Mary) *see* The Stodden Churches *St Alb*

SHELTON (St Mary and All Saints) *S'well 3* **P** *Bp* **R** G A FIRTH

SHELVE (All Saints) *see* Hope w Shelve *Heref*

SHENFIELD (St Mary the Virgin) *Chelmsf 7* **P** *Personal Reps R H Courage* **R** P G BRETT, **NSM** E A LOCKHART

SHENINGTON (Holy Trinity) *see* Ironstone *Ox*

SHENLEY (St Martin) *St Alb 1* **P** *DBP* **P-in-c** V C ORAM

SHENLEY (St Mary) *see* Watling Valley *Ox*

SHENLEY GREEN (St David) *Birm 4* **P** *Bp* **V** N A P EVANS

SHENSTONE (St John the Baptist) *Lich 1* **P** *MMCET* **P-in-c** R W BAILEY, **NSM** J B ASTON

SHENTON (St John the Evangelist) *see* Bosworth and Sheepy Gp *Leic*

SHEPHERD'S BUSH (St Luke) Uxbridge Road *see* Hammersmith St Luke *Lon*

SHEPHERD'S BUSH (St Simon) *see* Hammersmith St Simon *Lon*

SHEPHERD'S BUSH (St Stephen) (St Thomas) *Lon 9* **P** *Bp* **V** D M H REECE, **C** S E ARCHER

SHEPLEY (St Paul) *see* Shelley and Shepley *Wakef*

SHEPPERDINE (Chapel) *see* Oldbury-on-Severn w Shepperdine *Glouc*

SHEPPERTON (St Nicholas) *Lon 13* **P** *Bp* **R** C J SWIFT, **C** E L PENNINGTON

SHEPRETH (All Saints) *see* Fowlmere, Foxton, Shepreth and Thriplow *Ely*

SHEPSHED (St Botolph) and Oaks in Charnwood *Leic 7* **P** *DBP and Lord Crawshaw (jt)* **C** E M REW, **NSM** G MITCHELL

SHEPTON BEAUCHAMP (St Michael) *see* Ilminster and Distr *B & W*

SHEPTON MALLET (St Peter and St Paul) w Doulting *B & W 8* **P** *Duchy of Cornwall and Bp (alt)* **R** E J SMITH

SHEPTON MONTAGUE (St Peter) *see* Bruton and Distr *B & W*

SHEPWELL GREEN (St Matthias)   *see* Willenhall St Giles *Lich*

SHERBORNE (Abbey Church of St Mary) (All Souls) (St Paul) w Castleton and Lillington *Sarum 3*   **P** *J K Wingfield Digby Esq*   **V** E J WOODS,   **C** J P TOOGOOD, J R SWINDELLS, **NSM** D J DUNNING

SHERBORNE (St Mary Magdalene), Windrush, the Barringtons and Aldsworth *Glouc 13*   **P** *C T R Wingfield Esq, Ch Ch Ox, and DBP (by turn)*   **P-in-c** M SELWOOD

SHERBORNES (St Andrew) (Vyne Chapel) w Pamber, The *Win 4*   **P** *Bp and Qu Coll Ox (jt)*   **R** J N HAMILTON

SHERBOURNE (All Saints)   *see* Barford w Wasperton and Sherbourne *Cov*

SHERBURN (St Mary)   *see* Pittington, Shadforth and Sherburn *Dur*

SHERBURN (St Hilda)   *see* Buckrose Carrs *York*

SHERBURN IN ELMET (All Saints) w Saxton *York 4*   **P** *Abp* **V** C I COATES,   **NSM** G A LOWSON, C WILTON

SHERE (St James), Albury and Chilworth *Guildf 2*   **P** *Bp, Mrs H Bray, Duke of Northd, W F P Hugonin Esq, and the Hon M W Ridley (jt)*   **R** H G MEIRION-JONES, **C** C J GRUNDY,   **NSM** K B HOBBS

SHEREFORD (St Nicholas)   *see* Toftrees w Shereford *Nor*

SHERFIELD ENGLISH (St Leonard)   *see* E w Wellow and Sherfield English *Win*

SHERFIELD-ON-LODDON (St Leonard) and Stratfield Saye w Hartley Wespall w Stratfield Turgis *Win 4*   **P** *Bp, Duke of Wellington, and D&C Windsor (jt)*   **R** R W POLITT

SHERFORD (St Martin)   *see* Stokenham w Sherford and Beesands, and Slapton *Ex*

SHERIFF HUTTON (St Helen and the Holy Cross), Farlington, Stillington and Marton w Moxby *York 3*   **P** *Abp (3 turns), DBP (1 turn)*   **V** D W D LEE

SHERIFFHALES (St Mary)   *see* Lilleshall, Muxton and Sheriffhales *Lich*

SHERINGHAM (St Peter) *Nor 21*   **P** *Bp*   **V** A M WINDROSS

SHERINGHAM, UPPER (All Saints)   *see* Weybourne Gp *Nor*

SHERINGTON (St Laud) w Chicheley, North Crawley, Astwood and Hardmead *Ox 27*   **P** *Bp (2 turns), MMCET (1 turn), and Major J G B Chester (1 turn)*   **R** M C STANTON-SARINGER

SHERMANBURY (St Giles)   *see* Henfield w Shermanbury and Woodmancote *Chich*

SHERNBOURNE (St Peter and St Paul)   *see* Dersingham w Anmer and Shernborne *Nor*

SHERRARDS GREEN (St Mary the Virgin)   *see* Gt Malvern Ch Ch *Worc*

SHERRINGTON (St Cosmo and St Damian)   *see* Upper Wylye Valley *Sarum*

SHERSTON MAGNA (Holy Cross), Easton Grey, Luckington, Alderton and Foxley w Bremilham *Bris 6*   **P** *D&C, Bp, Adn Swindon and Lord Lilford (jt)*   **V** M H ROSS

SHERWOOD (St Martin) *S'well 12*   **P** *Bp*   **V** S J GRIFFITHS, **C** M F SHOULER

SHERWOOD PARK (St Philip)   *see* Tunbridge Wells St Jas w St Phil *Roch*

SHEVINGTON (St Anne) *Blackb 4*   **P** *R Standish* **V** J G RILEY,   **Hon C** L A RILEY

SHEVIOCK (Blessed Virgin Mary)   *see* Antony w Sheviock *Truro*

SHIFFORD (St Mary)   *see* Bampton w Clanfield *Ox*

SHIFNAL (St Andrew) *Lich 16*   **P** *R I Legge Esq* **P-in-c** G C FOWELL,   **C** J A MCWHIRTER

SHILBOTEL (St James)   *see* Shilbottle *Newc*

SHILBOTTLE (St James) *Newc 9*   **P** *Dioc Soc* **P-in-c** E M DIXON

SHILDON (St John) *Dur 6*   **P** *Bp*   **V** R CUTHBERTSON

SHILL VALLEY and Broadshire *Ox 8*   **P** *J Heyworth Esq, Mrs P Allen, and Ch Ch Ox (1 turn), Ch Soc Tr, F R Goodenough Esq, and D F Goodenough Esq (1 turn)* **R** R K HARRISON,   **Hon C** J M MOUNT,   **NSM** C D RAWSON, L N USHER-WILSON

SHILLING OKEFORD (Holy Rood)   *see* Okeford *Sarum*

SHILLINGFORD (St George)   *see* Dunchideock and Shillingford St George w Ide *Ex*

SHILLINGSTONE (Holy Rood)   *see* Okeford *Sarum*

SHILLINGTON (All Saints)   *see* Gravenhurst, Shillington and Stondon *St Alb*

SHILTON (Holy Rood)   *see* Shill Valley and Broadshire *Ox*

SHILTON (St Andrew)   *see* Bulkington w Shilton and Ansty *Cov*

SHIMPLINGTHORNE (St George)   *see* Chadbrook *St E*

SHINCLIFFE (St Mary the Virgin) *Dur 1*   **P** *D&C* **P-in-c** S M SANDHAM

SHINEY ROW (St Oswald) *Dur 14*   **P** *The Crown* **P-in-c** P M HOOD,   **NSM** M S GOURLEY

SHINFIELD (St Mary) *Ox 15*   **P** *D&C Heref* **P-in-c** O MURPHY

SHINGAY Group of Parishes, The *Ely 7*   **P** *Bp, Mrs E E Sclater, Ch Patr Trust, Down Coll Cam, New CollOx, and Jes Coll Cam (jt)*   **R** S F C WILLIAMS

SHIPBOURNE (St Giles) w Plaxtol *Roch 10*   **P** *Bp and Sir Edward Cazalet*   **R** S M RAMSARAN

SHIPDHAM (All Saints) w East and West Bradenham *Nor 17* **P** *Bp*   **R** B J WOOD

SHIPHAM (St Leonard)   *see* Axbridge w Shipham and Rowberrow *B & W*

SHIPHAY COLLATON (St John the Baptist) *Ex 10*   **P** *Bp* **V** C E DEACON

SHIPLAKE (St Peter and St Paul) w Dunsden and Harpsden *Ox 6*   **P** *All So Coll Ox, D&C Windsor, and DBP (jt)* **R** M R C PRICE

SHIPLEY (St Mary the Virgin) *Chich 8*   **P** *C R Burrell Esq* **P-in-c** P A SINTON

SHIPLEY (St Paul) *Bradf 1*   **P** *Simeon's Trustees* **V** C R PENFOLD

SHIPLEY (St Peter) *Bradf 1*   **P** *V Shipley St Paul* **V** J C RAINER,   **C** P RUGEN

SHIPPON (St Mary Magdalene) *Ox 10*   **P** *Bp* **V** M A J GOODE,   **Hon C** C R SEAMAN,   **NSM** P E SEAMAN

SHIPSTON-ON-STOUR (St Edmund) w Honington and Idlicote *Cov 9*   **P** *Jes Coll Ox, D&C Worc, Bp (jt)* **P-in-c** D R THURBURN-HUELIN

SHIPTON (Holy Evangelist)   *see* Skelton w Shipton and Newton on Ouse *York*

SHIPTON (St James)   *see* Wenlock *Heref*

SHIPTON BELLINGER (St Peter)   *see* Appleshaw, Kimpton, Thruxton, Fyfield etc *Win*

SHIPTON GORGE (St Martin)   *see* Bride Valley *Sarum*

SHIPTON MOYNE (St John the Baptist) *Glouc 15*   **P** *DBP* **V** A J WRIGHT

SHIPTON OLIFFE (St Oswald)   *see* Sevenhampton w Charlton Abbots, Hawling etc *Glouc*

SHIPTON ON CHERWELL (Holy Cross)   *see* Yarnton w Begbroke and Shipton on Cherwell *Ox*

SHIPTON-UNDER-WYCHWOOD (St Mary) w Milton-under-Wychwood, Fifield and Idbury *Ox 3*   **P** *Bp* **V** W M CALLAN,   **NSM** R V CURTIS

SHIPTONTHORPE (All Saints) and Hayton *York 5*   **P** *Abp* **P-in-c** J F HUDGHTON

SHIREBROOK (Holy Trinity)   *see* E Scarsdale *Derby*

SHIREGREEN (St Hilda) *Sheff 3*   **P** *Bp*   **P-in-c** A H MORGAN

SHIREGREEN (St James and St Christopher) *Sheff 3*   **P** *Dean* **P-in-c** A NASCIMENTO COOK

SHIREHAMPTON (St Mary) *Bris 2*   **P** *Bp* **P-in-c** C A FROUDE

SHIREMOOR (St Mark) *Newc 8*   **P** *Bp*   **V** *vacant* 0191-253 3291

SHIREOAKS (St Luke) *S'well 6*   **P** *Bp*   **P-in-c** T J RENSHAW

SHIRES' EDGE (St Mary)   **OLM** L M ALCOCK

SHIRLAND (St Leonard)   *see* Morton and Stonebroom w Shirland *Derby*

SHIRLEY (Christ the King)   *see* Salter Street and Shirley *Birm*

SHIRLEY (St George) *S'wark 22*   **P** *Bp*   **V** D J FROST

SHIRLEY (St James) (St John) *Win 13*   **P** *Ch Patr Trust* **V** D P HAZLEWOOD,   **C** N R SMART

SHIRLEY (St James the Great)   *see* Salter Street and Shirley *Birm*

SHIRLEY (St John) *S'wark 22*   **P** *Bp*   **V** A H R QUINN, **Hon C** A C COLLIER

SHIRLEY (St John the Divine)   *see* Salter Street and Shirley *Birm*

SHIRLEY (St Luke)   *as above Birm*

SHIRLEY (St Mary Magdalene)   *as above Birm*

SHIRLEY (St Michael)   *see* Brailsford w Shirley and Osmaston w Edlaston *Derby*

SHIRLEY WARREN (St Jude)   *see* Southampton St Jude *Win*

SHIRWELL (St Peter), Loxhore, Kentisbury, Arlington, East Down, Bratton Fleming, Challacombe and Stoke Rivers *Ex 17* **P** *Patr Bd*   **TR** L E AUSTIN,   **TV** C J HUDSPITH

SHOBDON (St John the Evangelist)   *see* Pembridge w Moor Court, Shobdon, Staunton etc *Heref*

SHOBNALL (St Aidan) *Lich 14*   **P** *Bp*   **P-in-c** N A MPUNZI

SHOBROOKE (St Swithin)   *see* Crediton, Shobrooke and Sandford etc *Ex*

SHOCKLACH (St Edith)   *see* Tilston and Shocklach *Ches*

SHOEBURY, NORTH (St Mary the Virgin) *Chelmsf 13* **P** *Ld Chan*   **V** *vacant* (01702) 584053

SHOEBURY, SOUTH (St Andrew) (St Peter) *Chelmsf 13* **P** *Hyndman Trustees*   **R** J R D KEMP

SHOLDEN (St Nicholas)   *see* Deal St Leon and St Rich and Sholden *Cant*

SHOLING (St Francis of Assisi) (St Mary) *Win 13*   **P** *Bp* **V** B J HARTNELL,   **C** K RAPKIN, S M STEVENS

SHOOTERS HILL (All Saints)   *see* Plumstead All SS *S'wark*

SHOOTERS HILL (Christ Church) *S'wark 3* **P** *Bp*
V N C WHITTLE, **NSM** J N PHILPOTT-HOWARD
SHORE (St Barnabas) *Man 20* **P** *D&C* **P-in-c** M S THORP,
OLM B WOODHEAD
SHOREDITCH (All Saints) Haggerston Road *see* Dalston H
Trin w St Phil and Haggerston All SS *Lon*
SHOREDITCH (St Anne) Hoxton Street *see* Hoxton St Anne w
St Columba *Lon*
SHOREDITCH (St Leonard) w St Michael *Lon 5* **P** *Bp and*
Adn (jt) **V** P R TURP
SHOREHAM (St Giles) *see* Kingston Buci *Chich*
SHOREHAM (St Peter and St Paul) *Roch 10* **P** *D&C Westmr*
P-in-c R A FREEMAN
SHOREHAM, NEW (St Mary de Haura) *Chich 4* **P** *Bp*
V V STANDING, **C** R WARHURST
SHOREHAM, OLD (St Nicholas) *Chich 4* **P** *Bp*
V V STANDING, **C** R WARHURST
SHOREHAM BEACH (Good Shepherd) *Chich 4* **P** *Bp*
V Q M RONCHETTI
SHORNE (St Peter and St Paul) *Roch 4* **P** *D&C*
V P E LONGBOTTOM
SHORT HEATH (Holy Trinity) *see* Willenhall H Trin *Lich*
SHORT HEATH (St Margaret) *Birm 8* **P** *Bp*
V T D HILL-BROWN, **C** R M ROGERS, **OLM** S L HOUGH
SHORTHAMPTON (All Saints) *see* Charlbury w
Shorthampton *Ox*
SHORTLANDS (All Saints' Community Church) *see* Bromley
SS Pet and Paul *Roch*
SHORTLANDS (St Mary) *Roch 13* **P** *Bp* **V** P MILLER
SHORTWOOD (All Saints) *see* Nailsworth w Shortwood,
Horsley etc *Glouc*
SHORWELL (St Peter) w Kingston *Portsm 8* **P** *Bp*
V J W RUSSELL, **Hon C** M R HODGE, **NSM** L M HUNTER,
L F HUMPHRYS
SHOSCOMBE (St Julian) *see* Camerton w Dunkerton, Foxcote
and Shoscombe *B & W*
SHOTESHAM (All Saints w St Mary) *see* Newton Flotman,
Swainsthorpe, Tasburgh, etc *Nor*
SHOTLEY (St John) *Newc 3* **P** *Lord Crewe's Trustees*
P-in-c T J ATKINS
SHOTLEY (St Mary) *St E 5* **P** *Bp* **P-in-c** P THORN,
OLM T J CROSBIE
SHOTTERMILL (St Stephen) *Guildf 4* **P** *Adn Surrey*
V A J GREADY, **NSM** H S WILLIAMS
SHOTTERY (St Andrew) *Cov 8* **P** *Bp* **V** J R WARREN
SHOTTESBROOKE (St John the Baptist) *see* White Waltham
w Shottesbrooke *Ox*
SHOTTESWELL (St Lawrence) *see* Warmington w Shotteswell
and Radway w Ratley *Cov*
SHOTTISHAM (St Margaret) *see* Wilford Peninsula *St E*
SHOTTLE (St Lawrence) *see* Hazlewood and Milford *Derby*
SHOTTON (St Saviour) *see* Haswell, Shotton and Thornley *Dur*
SHOTWICK (St Michael) *see* Burton and Shotwick *Ches*
SHOULDHAM (All Saints) *Ely 15* **P** *Bp* **P-in-c** D J POMERY,
Hon C A G F VILLER
SHOULDHAM THORPE (St Mary) *Ely 15* **P** *Bp*
P-in-c D J POMERY, **Hon C** A G F VILLER
SHRAWARDINE (St Mary) *see* Bicton, Montford w
Shrawardine and Fitz *Lich*
SHRAWLEY (St Mary), Witley, Astley and Abberley *Worc 13*
P *Bp and Guild of All So (jt)* **R** A NORKETT
SHRED (Mission Church) *see* Slaithwaite w E Scammonden
Wakef
SHREWSBURY (All Saints and St Michael) *Lich 20* **P** *Bp*
V D F MAWSON
SHREWSBURY (Christ Church) *see* Shelton and Oxon *Lich*
SHREWSBURY (Holy Cross) (St Peter) *Lich 20* **P** *Bp*
P-in-c J A GEAR
SHREWSBURY (Holy Trinity) (St Julian) *Lich 20* **P** *Bp and*
Ch Patr Trust (jt) **P-in-c** R D SPENCER
SHREWSBURY (St Alkmund) *Lich 20* **P** *Bp* **V** *vacant*
SHREWSBURY (St Chad) w St Mary *Lich 20* **P** *Bp*
P-in-c M W THOMAS, **C** R P MCKENZIE
SHREWSBURY (St George of Cappadocia) w Greenfields
United Church *Lich 20* **P** *V Shrewsbury St Chad*
V P F BARNES, **C** P R-M DE G GOWER
SHREWSBURY (St Giles) w Sutton and Atcham *Lich 20* **P** *Bp*
and R L Burton Esq (jt) **R** P J WILLIAMS
SHREWTON (St Mary) *see* Wylye and Till Valley *Sarum*
SHRIVENHAM (St Andrew) and Ashbury *Ox 17* **P** *Ld Chan*
V R M A HANCOCK, **NSM** M R STARR
SHROPHAM (St Peter) *see* Gt and Lt Ellingham, Rockland and
Shropham etc *Nor*
SHROTON (St Mary) *see* Iwerne Valley *Sarum*
SHRUB END (All Saints) (St Cedd) *Chelmsf 16* **P** *Bp*
V C W NEWLANDS, **C** S E A MILES, **NSM** M BROSNAN

SHUCKBURGH, LOWER (St John the Baptist)
see Napton-on-the-Hill, Lower Shuckburgh etc *Cov*
SHUDY CAMPS (St Mary) *see* Linton *Ely*
SHURDINGTON (St Paul) *see* Badgeworth, Shurdington and
Witcombe w Bentham *Glouc*
SHUSTOKE (St Cuthbert) *see* The Whitacres and Shustoke
Birm
SHUTE (St Michael) *see* Kilmington, Stockland, Dalwood,
Yarcombe etc *Ex*
SHUTFORD (St Martin) *see* Wykeham *Ox*
SHUTTINGTON (St Matthew) *see* Newton Regis w
Seckington and Shuttington *Birm*
SHUTTLEWOOD (St Laurence Mission Church) *see* Bolsover
Derby
SHUTTLEWORTH (St John) *see* Ramsbottom St Jo and
St Paul *Man*
SIBBERTOFT (St Helen) *see* Welford w Sibbertoft and Marston
Trussell *Pet*
SIBDON CARWOOD (St Michael) w Halford *Heref 11* **P** *Bp*
and R Holden (alt) **P-in-c** M L COPE
SIBERTSWOLD (St Andrew) *see* Eythorne and Elvington w
Waldershare etc *Cant*
SIBFORD (Holy Trinity) *see* Wykeham *Ox*
SIBLE HEDINGHAM (St Peter) w Castle Hedingham
Chelmsf 19 **P** *Bp, and Hon T R Lindsay (alt)* **R** D N KELLY
SIBSEY (St Margaret) w Frithville *Linc 20* **P** *Ld Chan*
V W G PAGE, **NSM** J M MORTON
SIBSON (St Botolph) *see* Bosworth and Sheepy Gp *Leic*
SIBTHORPE (St Peter) *S'well 3* **P** *Bp* **C** A FIRTH
SIBTON (St Peter) *see* Yoxford and Peasenhall w Sibton *St E*
SICKLINGHALL (St Peter) *see* Lower Wharfedale *Ripon*
SID VALLEY *see* Sidmouth, Woolbrook, Salcombe Regis,
Sidbury etc *Ex*
SIDBURY (Holy Trinity) *see* Stottesdon w Farlow, Cleeton
St Mary, etc *Heref*
SIDBURY (St Giles and St Peter) *see* Sidmouth, Woolbrook,
Salcombe Regis, Sidbury etc *Ex*
SIDCUP (Christ Church) Longland *Roch 17* **P** *Ch Trust Fund*
Trust **V** A K WILSON
SIDCUP (St Andrew) *Roch 17* **P** *Bp* **V** D HILDRED
SIDCUP (St John the Evangelist) *Roch 17* **P** *D&C*
V P WRIGHT, **C** G M BERESFORD JONES
SIDDAL (St Mark) *Wakef 4* **P** *Ch Trust Fund Trust*
P-in-c C SMITH
SIDDINGTON (All Saints) *see* Capesthorne w Siddington and
Marton *Ches*
SIDDINGTON (St Peter) w Preston *Glouc 11* **P** *Ld Chan and*
R T G Chester-Master Esq (alt) **P-in-c** J R CALVERT,
NSM N F LUCKETT
SIDESTRAND (St Michael) *see* Overstrand, Northrepps,
Sidestrand etc *Nor*
SIDFORD (St Peter) *see* Sidmouth, Woolbrook, Salcombe
Regis, Sidbury etc *Ex*
SIDLESHAM (St Mary the Virgin) *Chich 3* **P** *Bp*
P-in-c A K JENKINS
SIDLEY (All Saints) *Chich 14* **P** *R Bexhill*
P-in-c T G BUXTON
SIDLOW BRIDGE (Emmanuel) *S'wark 27* **P** *DBP*
R W G CAMPEN
SIDMOUTH (St Nicholas w St Giles), Woolbrook, Salcombe
Regis, Sidbury w Sidford, and All Saints Sidmouth *Ex 7*
P *Patr Bd* **TR** D H JAMES, **TV** R G PECKHAM, J G STONES,
J S LEE, **C** R J RICHARDSON, **Hon C** S W WILLINK
SIGGLESTHORNE (St Lawrence) and Rise w Nunkeeling and
Bewholme *York 11* **P** *Prime Min and Ld Chan (alt)*
R A MAKEL
SILCHESTER (St Mary) *see* Tadley S and Silchester *Win*
SILCHESTER COMMON (Mission Church) *as above Win*
SILEBY (St Mary), Cossington and Seagrave *Leic 6* **P** *Patr Bd*
TR A S COSTERTON
SILK WILLOUGHBY (St Denis) *Linc 22* **P** *Sir Lyonel*
Tollemache Bt **P-in-c** P J MANDER
SILKSTONE (All Saints) *see* Hoylandswaine and Silkstone w
Stainborough *Wakef*
SILKSTONE COMMON (Mission Room) *as above Wakef*
SILKSWORTH (St Matthew) *Dur 16* **P** *Bp*
P-in-c R G E BRADSHAW
SILLOTH (Christ Church) *see* Solway Plain *Carl*
SILSDEN (St James) *Bradf 8* **P** *Bp, Adn Craven, and*
Trustees (jt) **V** J P GREENWOOD, **C** J MEDHURST
SILSOE (St James), Pulloxhill and Flitton *St Alb 9* **P** *Ball Coll*
Ox and Bp (alt) **V** S C HOLROYD
SILTON (St Nicholas) *Sarum 5* **P** *DBP* **R** *vacant*
SILTON, NETHER (All Saints) *see* Leake w Over and Nether
Silton and Kepwick *York*
SILTON, OVER (St Mary) *as above York*

SILVER END (St Francis) *see* Rivenhall *Chelmsf*
SILVERDALE (St John) *Blackb 14* P *V Warton*
P-in-c P K WARREN
SILVERDALE (St Luke) *Lich 9* P *T H G Howard-Sneyd Esq*
P-in-c S A ANSELL
SILVERHILL (St Matthew) *Chich 17* P *Simeon's Trustees*
R *vacant* (01424) 423790
SILVERSTONE (St Michael) and Abthorpe w Slapton and
Whittlebury and Paulerspury *Pet 5*
P *T L Langton-Lockton Esq, Leeson's Trustees, and New Coll
Ox (3 turns), Prime Min (2 turns)* R B M SMITH, C P A REID
SILVERTON (St Mary), Butterleigh, Bickleigh and Cadeleigh
Ex 8 P *Bp and Sir Rivers Carew Bt* R A H MACDONALD
SILVINGTON (St Michael) *see* Stottesdon w Farlow, Cleeton
St Mary, etc *Heref*
SIMONBURN (St Mungo) *see* Humshaugh w Simonburn and
Wark *Newc*
SIMONSTONE (St Peter) *see* Padiham w Hapton and Padiham
Green *Blackb*
SIMPSON (St Thomas) *see* Woughton *Ox*
SINFIN (St Stephen) *Derby 10* P *CPAS*
P-in-c P R SANDFORD
SINFIN MOOR (not known) *Derby 10* P *Bp* V *vacant*
(01332) 760016
SINGLETON (St Anne) w Weeton (St Michael) *Blackb 12*
P *R Dumbreck and V Kirkham (jt)* V A RENSHAW
SINGLETON (St Mary the Virgin) *Chich 13* P *Bp*
R R T E B WOODS
SINNINGTON (All Saints) *see* Middleton, Newton and
Sinnington *York*
SISLAND (St Mary) *see* Loddon, Sisland, Chedgrave, Hardley
and Langley *Nor*
SISSINGHURST (Holy Trinity) w Frittenden *Cant 11*
P *CPAS* V A E NORRIS
SITHNEY (St Sithney) *see* Porthleven w Sithney *Truro*
SITTINGBOURNE (Holy Trinity) w Bobbing *Cant 16* P *Abp*
P-in-c M J RESCH, NSM E J WILLIAMS
SITTINGBOURNE (St Mary) (St Michael) *Cant 16* P *Abp*
and D&C (jt) V F KENT, C B C LANE
SIX HILLS (Mission) *see* Old Dalby, Nether Broughton,
Saxelbye etc *Leic*
SIX MILE BOTTOM (St George) *see* Lt Wilbraham *Ely*
SIX PILGRIMS, The *B & W 3* P *Ch Soc Trust, D&C, DBF,
and Bp (by turn)* P-in-c P T CRAIG
SIX SAINTS circa Holt: Bringhurst, Great Easton, Medbourne
cum Holt, Stockerston and Blaston *Leic 4* P *D&C Pet and
Adn Leic (2 turns), St Jo Coll Cam (1 turn)* R S J BISHOP
SIXHILLS (All Saints) *see* Barkwith Gp *Linc*
SIXPENNY HANDLEY (St Mary) w Gussage St Andrew and
Pentridge *Sarum 6* P *D&C Windsor and Earl of Shaftesbury
(alt)* R R E WOOD, NSM W M GRIFFITH
SKEEBY (St Agatha's District Church) *see* Easby w Brompton
on Swale and Bolton on Swale *Ripon*
SKEFFINGTON (St Thomas à Beckett) *see* Church Langton
cum Tur Langton etc *Leic*
SKEFFLING (St Helen) *see* Easington w Skeffling, Kilnsea and
Holmpton *York*
SKEGBY (St Andrew) w Teversal *S'well 4* P *DBP and Ld Chan
(alt)* R R KELLETT, C S J TREDWELL
SKEGNESS (St Clement) (St Matthew) and Winthorpe *Linc 8*
P *Bp* P-in-c C M FRANCE
SKELBROOKE (St Michael and All Angels)
see Adwick-le-Street w Skelbrooke *Sheff*
SKELLINGTHORPE (St Lawrence) w Doddington *Linc 18*
P *MMCET* R R G BILLINGHURST
SKELLOW (St Michael and All Angels) *see* Owston *Sheff*
SKELMANTHORPE (St Aidan) *Wakef 6* P *Bp*
P-in-c P D REYNOLDS
SKELMERSDALE (Church at the Centre) *Liv 11* P *Bp*
P-in-c G E GREENWOOD
SKELMERSDALE (St Paul) *Liv 11* P *V Ormskirk*
V G E GREENWOOD, C R HARVEY
SKELSMERGH (St John the Baptist) w Selside and
Longsleddale *Carl 10* P *V Kendal H Trin and DBP (alt)*
V R D J DEW
SKELTON (All Saints) w Upleatham *York 16* P *Abp*
R G J PACEY, C R E HARRISON
SKELTON (St Giles) w Shipton and Newton on Ouse *York 3*
P *Abp* R E W A CRAGG, NSM A P HUGHES
SKELTON (St Michael) and Hutton-in-the-Forest w Ivegill
Carl 4 P *Bp, D&C, and CCC Ox (jt)* P-in-c E M SMITH,
NSM J J H SMITH
SKELTON-CUM-NEWBY (St Helen's Old Church)
see Kirby-on-the-Moor, Cundall w Norton-le-Clay etc *Ripon*
SKENDLEBY (St Peter and St Paul) *see* Partney Gp *Linc*
SKERNE (St Leonard) *see* Hutton Cranswick w Skerne, Watton
and Beswick *York*

SKERTON (St Chad) *Blackb 11* P *Bp* V T A G BILL,
NSM E Y WILSON
SKERTON (St Luke) *Blackb 11* P *Trustees* V G LEWIS
SKEYTON (All Saints) *see* King's Beck *Nor*
SKIDBY (St Michael) *see* Rowley w Skidby *York*
SKILGATE (St John the Baptist) *see* Brompton Regis w Upton
and Skilgate *B & W*
SKILLINGTON (St James) *see* Colsterworth Gp *Linc*
SKIPSEA (All Saints) w Ulrome and Barmston w Fraisthorpe
York 9 P *Abp, The Hon S E Cunliffe-Lister, Trustees A Potter
and D Potter, Mrs R Potter, and P Roworth Esq (jt)*
P-in-c L C MUNT
SKIPTON (Christ Church) *Bradf 7* P *R Skipton H Trin*
V D N WILLIAMS, C A J FERNELEY
SKIPTON (Holy Trinity) *Bradf 7* P *Ch Ch Ox*
R A P BOTWRIGHT, C J L PRITCHARD
SKIPTON ON SWALE (St John) *see* Topcliffe, Baldersby w
Dishforth, Dalton etc *York*
SKIPWITH (St Helen) *see* Bubwith w Skipwith *York*
SKIRBECK (Holy Trinity) *Linc 20* P *Trustees*
C C P BOLAND
SKIRBECK (St Nicholas) *Linc 20* P *DBP* R P V NOBLE
SKIRBECK QUARTER (St Thomas) *Linc 20* P *DBP*
V *vacant* (01205) 367380
SKIRLAUGH (St Augustine) w Long Riston *York 11* P *Abp*
V D W PERRY
SKIRPENBECK (St Mary) *see* Garrowby Hill *York*
SKIRWITH (St John the Evangelist), Ousby and Melmerby w
Kirkland *Carl 4* P *DBP and D&C (jt)* P-in-c R A MOATT,
OLM E M FROGGATT
SLAD (Holy Trinity) *see* Stroud and Uplands w Slad *Glouc*
SLADE GREEN (St Augustine) *Roch 15* P *Bp* V *vacant*
(01322) 333970 *or* 332669
SLAIDBURN (St Andrew) *Bradf 5* P *Ch Soc Trust*
P-in-c M R RUSSELL-SMITH, NSM R E WILSON
SLAITHWAITE (St James) w East Scammonden *Wakef 5*
P *V Huddersfield* V C R TOWNSEND
SLALEY (St Mary the Virgin) *Newc 3* P *Bp*
P-in-c D J IRVINE, NSM J LYNCH
SLAPTON (Holy Cross) *see* Ivinghoe w Pitstone and Slapton
Ox
SLAPTON (St Botolph) *see* Silverstone and Abthorpe w
Slapton etc *Pet*
SLAPTON (St James the Great) *see* Stokenham w Sherford and
Beesands, and Slapton *Ex*
SLAUGHAM (St Mary) *Chich 6* P *Mrs D M Irwin-Clark*
R G D SIMMONS, Hon C K W HABERSHON
SLAUGHTER, LOWER (St Mary) *see* The Guitings,
Cutsdean, Farmcote etc *Glouc*
SLAUGHTER, UPPER (St Peter) *as above Glouc*
SLAUGHTERFORD (St Nicholas) *see* By Brook *Bris*
SLAWSTON (All Saints) *see* Hallaton w Horninghold and
Allexton, Tugby etc *Leic*
SLEAFORD, NEW (St Denys) *Linc 22* P *Bp*
P-in-c J A PATRICK, C A C BUXTON
SLEDMERE (St Mary) *see* Waggoners *York*
SLEEKBURN (St John) *see* Cambois and Sleekburn *Newc*
SLEIGHTS (St John) *see* Eskdaleside w Ugglebarnby and
Sneaton *York*
SLIMBRIDGE (St John the Evangelist) *see* Sharpness, Purton,
Brookend and Slimbridge *Glouc*
SLINDON (St Chad) *see* Eccleshall *Lich*
SLINDON (St Mary), Eartham and Madehurst *Chich 1* P *Bp,
D&C, and Mrs J Izard (jt)* R *vacant* (01243) 814275
SLINFOLD (St Peter) *see* Itchingfield w Slinfold *Chich*
SLINGSBY (All Saints) *see* Street *York*
SLIPTON (St John the Baptist) *Pet 11* P *L G Stopford
Sackville Esq* P-in-c D H P FOOT
SLITTING MILL (St John the Baptist) *see* Rugeley *Lich*
SLOANE STREET (Holy Trinity) *see* Upper Chelsea H Trin w
St Jude *Lon*
SLOLEY (St Bartholomew) *see* Worstead, Westwick, Sloley,
Swanton Abbot etc *Nor*
SLOUGH (St Paul) (Christ Church) *Ox 23* P *Trustees*
V M C COTTERELL, C M HARPER
SLOUGH, WEST *Ox 23* P *Patr Bd* TV J S G COTMAN,
S SMITH, NSM C E COLLINGE, OLM N PLANT
SLYNE (St Luke) w Hest *Blackb 14* P *Bp* V R D SIMPER
SMALL HEATH (All Saints) *Birm 13* P *Patr Bd*
V B A I SMART
SMALLBRIDGE (St John the Baptist) and Wardle *Man 20*
P *Bp* P-in-c A J HOWELL
SMALLBURGH (St Peter) w Dilham w Honing and Crostwight
Nor 12 P *Bp, T R Cubitt Esq, and J C Wickman Esq (jt)*
P-in-c W HILL
SMALLEY (St John the Baptist) *see* Morley w Smalley and
Horsley Woodhouse *Derby*

SMALLFIELD (Church Room)   see Burstow w Horne S'wark
SMALLHYTHE (St John the Baptist)   see Tenterden St Mildred
w Smallhythe Cant
SMALLTHORNE (St Saviour) Lich 11   P R Norton in the
Moors   V R J S GRIGSON
SMALLWOOD (St John the Baptist)   see Astbury and
Smallwood Ches
SMANNELL (Christ Church) w Enham Alamein Win 3   P Bp
P-in-c D F KING
SMARDEN (St Michael)   see Biddenden and Smarden Cant
SMAWTHORPE (St Michael and All Angels) Wakef 11   P Bp
V E I CHETWYND
SMEATON, GREAT (St Eloy) w Appleton Wiske and Birkby and
Danby Wiske w Hutton Bonville Ripon 2   P MMCET
(2 turns), Abp York (1 turn)   R G L BESWICK
SMEETH (St Mary) w Monks Horton and Stowting and
Brabourne Cant 12   P Abp   P-in-c W D COOPER,
NSM R L LE ROSSIGNOL
SMEETON WESTERBY (Christ Church)   see Kibworth and
Smeeton Westerby and Saddington Leic
SMESTOW VALE TEAM Lich 24   P Patr Bd
TR A P BROWN,   TV M INMAN, P J REGAN,
Hon C D J BELCHER
SMETHCOTT (St Michael)   see Dorrington w Leebotwood,
Longnor, Stapleton etc Heref
SMETHWICK (Old Church) Birm 7   P Dorothy Parkes
Trustees   V R M PRYCE
SMETHWICK (Resurrection) (St Stephen and St Michael)
Birm 7   P Bp   V J D R COX
SMETHWICK (St Matthew w St Chad) Birm 7   P Bp and
V Smethwick (alt)   V P E NICHOLSON
SMISBY (St James)   see Ticknall, Smisby and Stanton by Bridge
etc Derby
SMITHILLS HALL (Chapel)   see Halliwell St Pet Man
SMORRALL LANE (St Andrew)   see Bedworth Cov
SNAILBEACH (St Luke)   see Minsterley Heref
SNAILWELL (St Peter) Ely 3   P Mrs A Crawley   R vacant
SNAINTON (St Stephen)   see Brompton by Sawdon w Hutton
Buscel, Snainton etc York
SNAITH (St Laurence Priory)   see Gt Snaith Sheff
SNAITH, GREAT (Holy Trinity) (St John the Baptist) (St Paul)
Sheff 10   P Bp   TR C ROBERTS
SNAPE (St John the Baptist)   see Sternfield w Benhall and Snape
St E
SNAPE CASTLE (Chapel of St Mary)   see W Tanfield and Well
w Snape and N Stainley Ripon
SNARESTONE (St Bartholomew)   see Appleby Gp Leic
SNARGATE (St Dunstan)   see Appledore w Brookland,
Fairfield, Brenzett etc Cant
SNEAD (St Mary the Virgin)   see Wentnor w Ratlinghope,
Myndtown, Norbury etc Heref
SNEATON (St Hilda)   see Eskdaleside w Ugglebarnby and
Sneaton York
SNEINTON (St Christopher) w St Philip S'well 13   P CPAS
and Trustees (alt)   P-in-c A M SMYTHE
SNEINTON (St Cyprian) S'well 13   P Bp   P-in-c K H BALL
SNEINTON (St Matthias) S'well 13   P Bp   V vacant 0115-950
2750
SNEINTON (St Stephen) (St Alban) S'well 13   P SMF and Bp
(alt)   V vacant 0115-958 0508
SNELLAND (All Saints)   see Wragby Gp Linc
SNELSTON (St Peter)   see Norbury w Snelston Derby
SNETTISHAM (St Mary) w Ingoldisthorpe and Fring Nor 16
P Bp, CPAS, and D&C (jt)   R J D GRUNDY,
NSM J M T M GRUNDY
SNEYD (Holy Trinity) Lich 11   P Bp   V B L WILLIAMS
SNEYD GREEN (St Andrew) Lich 11   P Bp   V G R DAVIES
SNIBSTON (St James)   see Hugglescote w Donington, Ellistown
and Snibston Leic
SNITTERBY (St Nicholas)   see Bishop Norton, Wadingham
and Snitterby Linc
SNITTERFIELD (St James the Great) w Bearley Cov 7   P Bp
and V Wootton Wawen   V vacant (01789) 731263
SNODLAND (All Saints) (Christ Church) Roch 1   P Bp and
CPAS (jt)   R J E TIPP,   C E J NORTHERN
SNORING, GREAT (St Mary)   see Barney, Fulmodeston w
Croxton, Hindringham etc Nor
SNORING, LITTLE (St Andrew)   as above Nor
SNOWDEN HILL Chapel Farm (not known)   see Penistone and
Thurlstone Wakef
SNOWSHILL (St Barnabas)   see Childswyckham w Aston
Somerville, Buckland etc Glouc
SOBERTON (St Peter) w Newtown Portsm 1   P Bp
P-in-c S H HOLT
SOCKBURN (All Saints)   see Dinsdale w Sockburn Dur
SODBURY, LITTLE (St Adeline)   see Horton and Lt Sodbury
Glouc

SODBURY, OLD (St John the Baptist)   see Chipping Sodbury
and Old Sodbury Glouc
SOHAM (St Andrew) and Wicken Ely 3   P Pemb Coll Cam
(1 turn), Pemb Coll Cam and Ch Patr Trust (jt) (1 turn)
V T M ALBAN-JONES,   C D B SINGLETON
SOHO (St Anne) (St Thomas) (St Peter) Lon 3
P R Westmr St Jas   R C M HERBERT,   NSM J S FRANCIS
SOLE BAY Team Ministry, The St E 15   P Patr Bd
TR J J WILSON,   TV G W OWEN, L J PAYNE, S W J WARD,
C J B J SAUNDERS,   OLM B R FISHER
SOLIHULL (Catherine de Barnes) (St Alphege) (St Helen)
(St Michael) Birm 11   P Patr Bd   TR T W PILKINGTON,
TV S D LLOYD, M A JONES,   C S A RICHARDS
SOLLARS HOPE (St Michael)   see How Caple w Sollarshope,
Sellack etc Heref
SOLWAY PLAIN Carl 7   P Patr Bd   TR J M S FALKNER,
TV A BYROM,   C P M F STREATFEILD,   Hon C P N HAYWARD,
NSM D TEMBEY, M I STUDHOLME
SOMBORNE w Ashley Win 12   P Bp   V vacant (01794)
388223
SOMERBY (All Saints)   see Burrough Hill Pars Leic
SOMERBY (St Margaret)   see N Wolds Gp Linc
SOMERBY, NEW (St Anne)   see Grantham St Anne New
Somerby and Spitalgate Linc
SOMERBY, OLD (St Mary Magdalene) Linc 14   P Baroness
Willoughby de Eresby   R M H SABELL
SOMERCOTES and Grainthorpe w Conisholme Linc 12
P Duchy of Lanc (2 turns), Magd Coll Cam and Bp (1 turn)
R M K DAVIES
SOMERCOTES (St Thomas) Derby 1   P Bp   V G M KNOX
SOMERCOTES, NORTH (St Mary)   see Somercotes and
Grainthorpe w Conisholme Linc
SOMERFORD (All Saints)   see Astbury and Smallwood Ches
SOMERFORD (St Mary)   see Christchurch Win
SOMERFORD, GREAT (St Peter and St Paul), Little
Somerford, Seagry and Corston w Rodbourne Bris 6   P Bp,
MMCET, and Ex Coll Ox (jt) (3 turns), Ld Chan (2 turns)
R J E G OSWALD
SOMERFORD, LITTLE (St John the Baptist)   see Gt
Somerford, Lt Somerford, Seagry, Corston etc Bris
SOMERFORD KEYNES (All Saints)   see Kemble, Poole
Keynes, Somerford Keynes etc Glouc
SOMERLEYTON (St Mary), Ashby, Fritton, Herringfleet,
Blundeston and Lound Nor 9   P Lord Somerleyton and
SMF (jt)   R J B V RIVIERE,   NSM L HOBBS
SOMERS TOWN (St Mary the Virgin)   see Old St Pancras Lon
SOMERSAL HERBERT (St Peter)   see Doveridge, Scropton,
Sudbury etc Derby
SOMERSBY (St Margaret)   see S Ormsby Gp Linc
SOMERSHAM (St John the Baptist) w Pidley and Oldhurst
Ely 10   P Bp   R C S BARTER
SOMERSHAM (St Mary) w Flowton and Offton w Willisham
St E 1   P Bp and MMCET (jt)   R vacant (01473) 831274
SOMERTON (St James)   see The Heyfords w Rousham and
Somerton Ox
SOMERTON (St Margaret)   see Glem Valley United Benefice
St E
SOMERTON (St Michael and All Angels) w Compton Dundon,
the Charltons and Kingsdon B & W 6   P Bp Lon (1 turn), Bp
(2 turns), and DBP (1 turn)   R C A HADLEY,   C K J HILL
SOMERTON, WEST (St Mary)   see Flegg Coastal Benefice Nor
SOMPTING (St Mary the Virgin) (St Peter) Chich 5   P OStJ
V E K HOWARD
SONNING (St Andrew) (St Patrick) Ox 16   P Bp
V C G CLARKE,   Hon C M D C FORRER
SONNING COMMON (Christ the King)   see Rotherfield
Peppard and Kidmore End etc Ox
SOOKHOLME (St Augustine)   see Warsop S'well
SOOTHILL (St Luke)   see Hanging Heaton Wakef
SOPLEY (St Michael and All Angels)   see Burton and Sopley
Win
SOPWORTH (St Mary the Virgin)   see Boxwell, Leighterton,
Didmarton, Oldbury etc Glouc
SOTHERTON (St Andrew)   see Sole Bay St E
SOTTERLEY (St Margaret)   see Hundred River St E
SOTWELL (St James)   see Wallingford Ox
SOUDLEY (St Michael)   see Cinderford St Jo Glouc
SOULBURY (All Saints)   see Stewkley w Soulbury and Drayton
Parslow Ox
SOULBY (St Luke)   see Kirkby Stephen w Mallerstang etc Carl
SOULDERN (Annunciation of the Blessed Virgin Mary)
see Fritwell w Souldern and Ardley w Fewcott Ox
SOULDROP (All Saints)   see Sharnbrook and Knotting w
Souldrop St Alb
SOUNDWELL (St Stephen) Bris 5   P Bp   V I L WILLS,
NSM C DRURY

SOURTON (St Thomas of Canterbury) *see* Okehampton w
Inwardleigh, Bratton Clovelly etc *Ex*
SOUTH *see also under substantive place name*
SOUTH BANK (St John) *York 18* **P** *Abp* **V** *vacant* (01642)
453679
SOUTH CAVE (All Saints) and Ellerker w Broomfleet *York 13*
P *CPAS and D&C Dur (jt)* **V** P G FAULKNER,
NSM M R BUSHBY
SOUTH COVE (St Lawrence) *see* Sole Bay *St E*
SOUTH HILL (St Sampson) w Callington *Truro 11* **P** *PCC*
R R OAKES, **NSM** B R JENNINGS, **P** A RAYNHAM
SOUTH MOOR (St George) *see* Ch the K *Dur*
SOUTH PARK (St Luke) *see* Reigate St Luke S Park *S'wark*
SOUTH POOL (St Nicholas and St Cyriac) *see* Charleton w
Buckland Tout Saints etc *Ex*
SOUTH SHIELDS (All Saints) *Dur 15* **P** *Patr Bd*
TR J D MILLER, **TV** D BODDY, **C** Y M SMEJKAL
SOUTH SHIELDS St Aidan (St Stephen) The Lawe *Dur 15*
P *Bp and D&C* **R** R SHAW
SOUTH SHIELDS (St Hilda) w St Thomas *Dur 15* **P** *D&C*
V R L BURR
SOUTH SHIELDS (St Lawrence the Martyr) *see* Horsley Hill
St Lawr *Dur*
SOUTH SHIELDS (St Simon) *Dur 15* **P** *The Crown*
V R F TOBIN
SOUTH SHORE (Holy Trinity) *Blackb 8* **P** *J C Hilton Esq*
P-in-c R P W CARTMELL, **NSM** M H WARD
SOUTH SHORE (St Peter) *Blackb 8* **P** *Bp*
P-in-c S EDWARDS
SOUTH TRINITY BROADS Benefice, The: Filby, Thrigby,
Mautby, Stokesby, Runham and Burgh w Billockby *Nor 6*
P *Bp, Adn Nor, DBP, Mrs Z K Cognetti, R T Daniel Esq, and*
1 F M Lucas Esq (jt) **P-in-c** C A LE PREVOST
SOUTHACRE (St George) *see* Castleacre, Newton, Westacre
and Southacre *Nor*
SOUTHALL (Christ the Redeemer) *Lon 22* **P** *Bp*
V N J ORCHARD
SOUTHALL (Emmanuel) Conventional District *Lon 22*
C-in-c A SEN
SOUTHALL (Holy Trinity) *Lon 22* **P** *Ch Patr Trust*
P-in-c M F BOLLEY
SOUTHALL (St George) *Lon 22* **P** *D&C St Paul's*
P-in-c C RAMSAY
SOUTHALL GREEN (St John) *Lon 22* **P** *Ch Patr Trust*
P-in-c M A POULSON, **C** R CHRISTOPHER,
Hon C D J C BOOKLESS
SOUTHAM (Ascension) *see* Bishop's Cleeve *Glouc*
SOUTHAM (St James) *Cov 10* **P** *The Crown* **R** *vacant*
(01926) 812413
SOUTHAMPTON (Christ Church) Portswood *see* Portswood
Ch Ch *Win*
SOUTHAMPTON City Centre (St Mary) (St Michael) *Win 13*
P *Bp* **TR** I L JOHNSON, **TV** S P HALL, B R SEARLE-BARNES,
D T HAOKIP, **C** D L MATTHEWS
SOUTHAMPTON (Holy Trinity) *see* Weston *Win*
SOUTHAMPTON Maybush (St Peter) *Win 13* **P** *Bp*
V N BOAKES, **C** S M PITKIN, K J INGLIS
SOUTHAMPTON (St Alban) *see* Swaythling *Win*
SOUTHAMPTON (St Barnabas) *Win 13* **P** *Bp* **V** B J FRY
SOUTHAMPTON (St Denys) Portswood *see* Portswood
St Denys *Win*
SOUTHAMPTON (St Jude) Warren Road *Win 13* **P** *Bp*
P-in-c G K TAYLOR
SOUTHAMPTON (St Mark) *Win 13* **P** *Ch Patr Trust*
P-in-c G MARCH
SOUTHAMPTON (St Mary Extra) *Win 13* **P** *Bp*
V P G FIRMIN
SOUTHAMPTON Thornhill (St Christopher) *Win 13* **P** *Bp*
V G P ANNAS
SOUTHAMPTON Winkle Street (St Julian) *see* Southampton
(City Cen) *Win*
SOUTHBERGH (St Andrew) *see* Barnham Broom and Upper
Yare *Nor*
SOUTHBOROUGH (St Peter) (Christ Church) (St Matthew)
and Bidborough *Roch 12* **P** *Patr Bd* **TR** G E HOVENDEN,
TV C B WICKS, S A HILLS, **C** N A CHANDRAN
SOUTHBOROUGH (St Thomas) *Roch 12* **P** *Bp*
P-in-c A M HORTON
SOUTHBOURNE (All Saints) *see* Pokesdown All SS *Win*
SOUTHBOURNE (St Christopher) *Win 8* **P** *Bp* **V** *vacant*
(01202) 424886
SOUTHBOURNE (St John the Evangelist) w West Thorney
Chich 13 **P** *Bp* **V** C R JENKINS, **NSM** S BEAVIS
SOUTHBOURNE (St Katharine) (St Nicholas) *Win 8* **P** *Bp*
P-in-c J C WHITE
SOUTHBROOM (St James) *Sarum 16* **P** *D&C*
P-in-c C M TEBBUTT, **NSM** T V F PAPE

SOUTHCHURCH (Christ Church) *Chelmsf 13* **P** *Bp*
V M J HARRIS
SOUTHCHURCH (Holy Trinity) *Chelmsf 13* **P** *Abp Cant*
R M A BALLARD
SOUTHCOATES (St Aidan) *see* Kingston upon Hull St Aid
Southcoates *York*
SOUTHCOURT (Good Shepherd) *see* Walton H Trin *Ox*
SOUTHDENE (St Martin) *see* Kirkby *Liv*
SOUTHEA (Emmanuel) w Murrow and Parson Drove *Ely 17*
P *Bp* **V** S K GARDNER
SOUTHEASE (St Peter) *Chich 18* **P** *Bp and Gorham*
Trustees (jt) **V** D A HIDER, **C** D L N GUTSELL
SOUTHEND (St John the Baptist) (St Mark) (All Saints)
(St Alban) *Chelmsf 13* **P** *Patr Bd* **TR** S M BURDETT,
TV R H CADMAN, P A ROBERTS, **NSM** C R D CHEATLE,
S SAYERS
SOUTHEND (St Peter) *see* Bradfield and Stanford Dingley
Ox
SOUTHEND-ON-SEA (St Saviour) Westcliff *Chelmsf 13*
P *Bp, Adn Southend, and Churchwardens (jt)* **V** R H WILLIAMS,
NSM L M WILLIAMS
SOUTHERY (St Mary) *Ely 15* **P** *Guild of All So*
R D J EVANS
SOUTHEY GREEN (St Bernard) Conventional District *Sheff 3*
C-in-c R GOMERSALL
SOUTHFIELDS (St Barnabas) *S'wark 20* **P** *Bp*
V B M D OLIVIER, **NSM** P A SEABROOK
SOUTHFIELDS (St Michael and All Angels) *see* Wandsworth
St Mich *S'wark*
SOUTHFLEET (St Nicholas) *Roch 4* **P** *CPAS* **R** C D GOBLE,
NSM J C STONE
SOUTHGATE (Christ Church) *Lon 18* **P** *V Edmonton All SS*
V P J E JACKSON, **C** R J WILKINSON
SOUTHGATE Local Ecumenical Project *St E 13*
Min F SCAMMELL
SOUTHGATE (Shared Church) *see* Grange St Andr *Ches*
SOUTHGATE (St Andrew) *Lon 18* **P** *Bp* **V** P M HUNT
SOUTHGATE (St Mary) *Chich 7* **P** *Patr Bd*
TR J M MORTIMER, **TV** R E POOLE, G R HOCKEN,
C S D K TAYLOR
SOUTHGATE, NEW (St Paul) *Lon 14* **P** *V Southgate Ch Ch*
V M C ELLIOTT SMITH
SOUTHILL (All Saints) *see* Clifton and Southill *St Alb*
SOUTHLAKE (St James's Church Centre) *see* Woodley *Ox*
SOUTHLEIGH (St Lawrence) *see* Colyton, Musbury,
Southleigh and Branscombe *Ex*
SOUTHMEAD (St Stephen) *Bris 2* **P** *Bp* **V** J C HALL
SOUTHMINSTER (St Leonard) *Chelmsf 11* **P** *Govs*
Charterhouse **V** G S ANDERSON, **NSM** V J BUTLER
SOUTHOE (St Leonard) *Ely 13* **P** *Mert Coll Ox*
R *vacant*
SOUTHOVER (St John the Baptist) *Chich 18* **P** *CPAS*
R S J DAUGHTERY, **C** M P WOODSFORD
SOUTHOWRAM (St Anne-in-the-Grove) and Claremount
Wakef 4 **P** *V Halifax* **V** *vacant* (01422) 365229
SOUTHPORT (All Saints) (All Souls) *Liv 9* **P** *Trustees*
V T P JARDINE
SOUTHPORT (Christ Church) *Liv 9* **P** *Trustees* **V** S T REID,
C R J GIBBS
SOUTHPORT (Emmanuel) *Liv 9* **P** *PCC* **V** C POPE,
C D J PRESCOTT
SOUTHPORT (Holy Trinity) *Liv 9* **P** *Trustees*
V R G GARNER
SOUTHPORT (St Luke) *Liv 9* **P** *V Southport H Trin*
P-in-c I R SHACKLETON, **NSM** D H MARSTON
SOUTHPORT (St Philip) (St Paul) *Liv 9* **P** *V Southport*
Ch Ch and Trustees (jt) **V** A J EDWARDS
SOUTHPORT (St Simon and St Jude) *Liv 9* **P** *Trustees*
V T P JARDINE
SOUTHREPPS (St James) *see* Trunch *Nor*
SOUTHREY (St John the Divine) *see* Bardney *Linc*
SOUTHROP (St Peter) *see* Coln St Aldwyns, Hatherop,
Quenington etc *Glouc*
SOUTHSEA (Holy Spirit) *Portsm 6* **P** *Bp* **V** M D B LEWIS,
C S P RUNDELL
SOUTHSEA (St Jude) *Portsm 6* **P** *Trustees* **V** J V BYRNE
SOUTHSEA (St Luke) *see* Portsea St Luke *Portsm*
SOUTHSEA (St Peter) *Portsm 6* **P** *Bp* **P-in-c** C D TOWNER,
NSM M R MILLETT
SOUTHSEA (St Simon) *Portsm 6* **P** *Ch Patr Trust*
V M F HOLLAND, **NSM** P A O'GORMAN
SOUTHTOWN (St Mary) *see* Gt Yarmouth *Nor*
SOUTHWARK (Christ Church) *S'wark 10* **P** *Marshall's*
Charity **R** J E PAXTON
SOUTHWARK (Holy Trinity w St Matthew) *S'wark 10* **P** *Bp*
R N A MCKINNON

SOUTHWARK (St George the Martyr) (St Alphege) (St Jude) *S'wark* 10   **P** *Lon Corp (1 turn), Ld Chan (4 turns), Walsingham Coll Trust Assn (1 turn)*   **R** A S LUCAS, **Hon C** M DURRAN,   **OLM** D PAPE

SOUTHWARK (St Hugh)   *see* Bermondsey St Hugh CD *S'wark*

SOUTHWATER (Holy Innocents) *Chich* 8   **P** *V Horsham*   **V** P H JONES

SOUTHWAY (Holy Spirit) *Ex* 22   **P** *Ld Chan*   **C** J W ANDREWS, P IRETON,   **NSM** M J FAIRALL

SOUTHWELL (Holy Trinity) *S'well* 14   **P** *CPAS*   **V** M S TANNER

SOUTHWELL (St Andrew)   *see* Portland All SS w St Pet *Sarum*

SOUTHWICK (Holy Trinity) *Dur* 16   **P** *D&C*   **R** G DRIVER

SOUTHWICK (St Columba) *Dur* 16   **P** *Bp*   **V** vacant 0191--516 0244

SOUTHWICK (St James) w Boarhunt *Portsm* 1   **P** *R Thistlewayte Esq*   **P-in-c** H S GRIFFITHS

SOUTHWICK (St Mary the Virgin)   *see* Warmington, Tansor and Cotterstock etc *Pet*

SOUTHWICK (St Michael and All Angels) *Chich* 4   **P** *Ld Chan*   **R** C L TERRY,   **C** C ALLEN

SOUTHWICK (St Peter) *Chich* 4   **P** *Bp*   **C** D A GUEST

SOUTHWICK (St Thomas)   *see* N Bradley, Southwick and Heywood *Sarum*

SOUTHWOLD (St Edmund King and Martyr)   *see* Sole Bay *St E*

SOUTHWOOD (Mission Church)   *see* Evercreech w Chesterblade and Milton Clevedon *B & W*

SOWERBY (St Mary) (St Peter) *Wakef* 3   **P** *DBP*   **P-in-c** K L S TURNER,   **NSM** C J WARDMAN

SOWERBY (St Oswald) *York* 19   **P** *Abp*   **V** J H DAVIS

SOWERBY BRIDGE (Christ Church) w Norland *Wakef* 4   **P** *V Halifax*   **V** P B STOODLEY,   **NSM** L ENNIS

SOWTON (St Michael and All Angels)   *see* Aylesbeare, Rockbeare, Farringdon etc *Ex*

SPALDING (St John the Baptist) w Deeping St Nicholas *Linc* 17   **P** *Bp*   **V** P S J GARLAND

SPALDING (St Mary and St Nicholas) *Linc* 17   **P** *Feoffees*   **V** T R BARKER,   **C** R J SEAL, A C COX,   **NSM** J C BRUCE

SPALDING (St Paul) *Linc* 17   **P** *Bp and V Spalding (jt)*   **P-in-c** D C MAYLOR

SPALDWICK (St James)   *see* E Leightonstone *Ely*

SPARHAM (St Mary)   *see* Lyng, Sparham, Elsing, Bylaugh, Bawdeswell etc *Nor*

SPARKBROOK (Christ Church) *Birm* 13   **P** *Aston Trustees*   **V** vacant 0121-772 6558

SPARKBROOK (Emmanuel)   *see* Sparkhill w Greet and Sparkbrook *Birm*

SPARKBROOK (St Agatha) w Balsall Heath St Barnabas *Birm* 13   **P** *Bp*   **V** J A HERVE

SPARKFORD (St Mary Magdalene)   *see* Queen Camel w W Camel, Corton Denham etc *B & W*

SPARKHILL (St John the Evangelist) (St Bede and Emmanuel) w Greet St Bede and Sparkbrook *Birm* 13   **P** *Dioc Trustees and Aston Trustees (alt)*   **V** J A SELF,   **C** A A UNDERWOOD

SPARKWELL (All Saints) *Ex* 20   **P** *D&C Windsor*   **V** F G DENMAN

SPARROW HALL (St George)   *see* Fazakerley Em *Liv*

SPARSHOLT (Holy Cross)   *see* Ridgeway *Ox*

SPARSHOLT (St Stephen)   *see* Crawley and Littleton and Sparsholt w Lainston *Win*

SPAXTON (St Margaret) w Charlynch, Goathurst, Enmore and Aisholt *B & W* 14   **P** *Bp, MMCET, and Ch Trust Fund Trust (jt)*   **R** R F PARKER

SPEEN (St Mary the Virgin)   *see* Newbury *Ox*

SPEETON (St Leonard)   *see* Bempton w Flamborough, Reighton w Speeton *York*

SPEKE (St Aidan) (All Saints) *Liv* 4   **P** *Bp*   **TR** M E PLUNKETT,   **TV** C I KIDD

SPELDHURST (St Mary the Virgin) w Groombridge and Ashurst *Roch* 12   **P** *DBP*   **R** D P WREN

SPELSBURY (All Saints)   *see* Chase *Ox*

SPEN, HIGH (St Patrick) and Rowlands Gill *Dur* 13   **P** *Bp*   **P-in-c** S W HEWITT

SPENCER BENEFICE   *see* Brington w Whilton and Norton etc *Pet*

SPENCER PERCIVAL MEMORIAL CHURCH   *see* Ealing All SS *Lon*

SPENCERS WOOD (St Michael and All Angels)   *see* Beech Hill, Grazeley and Spencers Wood *Ox*

SPENNITHORNE (St Michael) w Finghall and Hauxwell *Ripon* 4   **P** *R J Dalton Esq and M C A Wyvill Esq (alt)*   **P-in-c** W J HULSE

SPENNYMOOR (St Paul), Whitworth and Merrington *Dur* 6   **P** *D&C*   **R** L E GOUGH

SPERNALL, Morton Bagot and Oldberrow *Cov* 7   **P** *Mrs J M Pinney and Bp (alt)*   **R** vacant (01527) 892372

SPETISBURY (St John the Baptist) w Charlton Marshall and Blandford St Mary *Sarum* 6   **P** *Worc Coll Ox (1 turn), Bp (2 turns)*   **R** S F TREEBY

SPEXHALL (St Peter)   *see* Blyth Valley *St E*

SPILSBY Group, The (St James) *Linc* 7   **P** *Baroness Willoughby de Eresby (3 turns), Mrs J M Fox-Robinson (1 turn), and Bp (1 turn)*   **P-in-c** P F COATES

SPITAL (St Agnes)   *see* New Windsor *Ox*

SPITAL (St Leonard's Mission Room)   *see* Chesterfield St Mary and All SS *Derby*

SPITALFIELDS (Christ Church w All Saints) *Lon* 7   **P** *MMCET*   **NSM** S M HARTLEY

SPITALGATE (St John the Evangelist)   *see* Grantham St Anne New Somerby and Spitalgate *Linc*

SPITTAL (St John) *Newc* 12   **P** *Bp and Mercers' Co (alt)*   **P-in-c** A S ADAMSON,   **NSM** S J HARRISON

SPIXWORTH (St Peter) w Crostwick and Frettenham *Nor* 2   **P** *Bp, Ch Soc Trust, and DBP (jt)*   **R** A R GOOD

SPOFFORTH (All Saints) w Kirk Deighton *Ripon* 1   **P** *Bp*   **P-in-c** J C TREW

SPONDON (St Werburgh) *Derby* 9   **P** *Mrs L B Palmer*   **V** R J ANDREWS

SPORLE (St Mary)   *see* Gt and Lt Dunham w Gt and Lt Fransham and Sporle *Nor*

SPOTLAND (St Clement) *Man* 20   **P** *Bp*   **V** L CONNOLLY,   **C** E J DAVIES

SPRATTON (St Andrew) *Pet* 2   **P** *Bp*   **V** B LEE

SPREYTON (St Michael)   *see* Chagford, Drewsteignton, Hittisleigh etc *Ex*

SPRIDLINGTON (St Hilary)   *see* Owmby Gp *Linc*

SPRIGG'S ALLEY (Mission Room)   *see* Chinnor w Emmington and Sydenham etc *Ox*

SPRING GROVE (St Mary) *Lon* 11   **P** *Ch Patr Trust*   **V** D G WILSON,   **Hon C** M A WARMAN

SPRING PARK (All Saints) *S'wark* 22   **P** *Bp*   **V** Y V CLARKE

SPRINGFIELD (All Saints) *Chelmsf* 8   **P** *Air Cdre N S Paynter*   **R** R J BROWN,   **NSM** J MANN

SPRINGFIELD (Holy Trinity) *Chelmsf* 8   **P** *Simeon's Trustees*   **V** T W BALL

SPRINGFIELD (St Christopher) *Birm* 5   **P** *Trustees*   **V** S P CORBETT

SPRINGFIELD Wallington   *see* Wallington Springfield Ch *S'wark*

SPRINGFIELD, EAST (Church of Our Saviour) (not known) *Chelmsf* 8   **P** *Bp*   **P-in-c** C NICHOLSON

SPRINGFIELD, NORTH (St Augustine of Canterbury) *Chelmsf* 8   **P** *Bp*   **P-in-c** J V ANDERSON

SPRINGFIELDS (St Stephen)   *see* Wolverhampton St Steph *Lich*

SPRINGTHORPE (St George and St Laurence)   *see* Corringham and Blyton Gp *Linc*

SPRINGWELL (St Mary the Virgin)   *see* Sunderland St Mary and St Pet *Dur*

SPRINGWOOD (All Souls)   *see* Liv All So Springwood *Liv*

SPROATLEY (St Swithin)   *see* Preston and Sproatley in Holderness *York*

SPROTBROUGH (St Mary the Virgin) *Sheff* 7   **P** *Bp*   **R** J M RICHARDS,   **Hon C** C J A HICKLING

SPROUGHTON (All Saints) w Burstall, Copdock w Washbrook and Belstead and Bentley w Tattingstone *St E* 5   **P** *Patr Bd*   **R** C L WINGFIELD,   **OLM** D W MEHEN

SPROWSTON (St Cuthbert) (St Mary and St Margaret) w Beeston *Nor* 2   **P** *D&C*   **R** J D BENNETT,   **C** D WELLS, G M BRIDGES,   **NSM** H M WRIGHT

SPROXTON (St Bartholomew)   *see* High Framland Par *Leic*

SPROXTON (St Chad)   *see* Helmsley *York*

SQUIRRELS HEATH (All Saints) *Chelmsf* 2   **P** *Bp*   **V** P J WILKIN,   **NSM** K F WOOLMER

STADHAMPTON (St John the Baptist)   *see* Dorchester *Ox*

STAFFHURST WOOD (St Silvan)   *see* Limpsfield and Titsey *S'wark*

STAFFORD (Christ Church) (St Chad) (St Mary) *Lich* 10   **P** *Patr Bd*   **TR** P J JEFFERIES,   **TV** M WILLIAMS,   **C** P S HAWKINS,   **NSM** M J FISHER,   **OLM** B BUTTERY

STAFFORD (St John the Baptist) and Tixall w Ingestre *Lich* 10   **P** *Bp and Earl of Shrewsbury and Talbot (jt)*   **V** R M VAUGHAN,   **C** J E EVANS

STAFFORD (St Paul) Forebridge *Lich* 10   **P** *V Castle Ch*   **V** M R METCALF

STAFFORD (St Thomas and St Andrew) Doxey   *see* Castle Town *Lich*

STAFFORD, WEST (St Andrew) w Frome Billet *Sarum* 1   **P** *Bp*   **R** vacant (01305) 264637

STAGSDEN (St Leonard)   *see* Bromham w Oakley and Stagsden *St Alb*

STAGSHAW CHAPEL (St Aidan)   *see* St John Lee *Newc*

STAINBY (St Peter)   *see* Witham Gp *Linc*

STAINCLIFFE (Christ Church) and Carlinghow *Wakef 10*
P *V Brownhill and V Batley (jt)* **V** D J CARPENTER,
C A P ARNOLD
STAINCROSS (St John the Evangelist) *Wakef 7* **P** *Bp*
V J K BUTTERWORTH
STAINDROP (St Mary) *Dur 7* **P** *Lord Barnard* **V** D R JONES
STAINES (Christ Church) *Lon 13* **P** *Bp* **V** L O LINDO
STAINES (St Mary) (St Peter) *Lon 13* **P** *Ld Chan*
P-in-c R J COSH, **C** D J ESHUN
STAINFIELD (St Andrew) *see Bardney Linc*
STAINFORTH (St Mary) *Sheff 10* **P** *Bp* **V** A W ALLINGTON
STAINFORTH (St Peter) *see Langcliffe w Stainforth and*
Horton Bradf
STAINING (St Luke Mission Church) *see Blackpool St Mich*
Blackb
STAINLAND (St Andrew) *Wakef 2* **P** *V Halifax*
V R A CHAPMAN
STAINLEY, NORTH (St Mary the Virgin) *see W Tanfield and*
Well w Snape and N Stainley Ripon
STAINLEY, SOUTH (St Wilfrid) *see Markington w S Stainley*
and Bishop Thornton Ripon
STAINMORE (St Stephen) *see Brough w Stainmore, Musgrave*
and Warcop Carl
STAINTON (St Peter w St Paul) w Hilton *York 21* **P** *Abp*
(2 turns), DBP (1 turn) **P-in-c** W J FORD
STAINTON (St Winifred) *see Tickhill w Stainton Sheff*
STAINTON, GREAT (All Saints) *see Bishopton w Gt Stainton*
Dur
STAINTON BY LANGWORTH (St John the Baptist)
see Barlings Linc
STAINTON DALE (St John the Baptist) *see Cloughton and*
Burniston w Ravenscar etc York
STAINTON LE VALE (St Andrew) *see Walesby Linc*
STAITHES (St Peter) *see Hinderwell w Roxby York*
STAKEFORD (Holy Family) *see Choppington Newc*
STALBRIDGE (St Mary) and Stock *Sarum 5* **P** *CCC Cam*
(4 turns), Col J L Yeatman (1 turn) **R** W T RIDDING
STALHAM (St Mary), East Ruston, Brunstead, Sutton and
Ingham *Nor 12* **P** *Bp, DBP and Mrs S F Baker (jt)*
R D R ANDERSON, **OLM** R H JACKSON
STALISFIELD (St Mary) *see Eastling w Ospringe and*
Stalisfield w Otterden Cant
STALLING BUSK (St Matthew) *see Askrigg w Stallingbusk*
Ripon
STALLINGBOROUGH (St Peter and St Paul) *see Keelby Gp*
Linc
STALMINE (St James) w Pilling St John the Baptist *Blackb 9*
P *Bp, V Lanc St Mary, Mrs C B Mason-Hornby, and*
H D H Elletson Esq (jt) **V** G BILLINGTON, **OLM-**
D A DICKINSON, **C** J PRITCHARD
STALYBRIDGE (Holy Trinity and Christ Church) *Ches 14*
P *Trustees* **V** C A BELL, **Hon C** T N HOWARD
STALYBRIDGE (St George) *Man 17* **P** *Lord Deramore and*
R Ashton-under-Lyne St Mich (jt) **V** I K STUBBS,
NSM R FOX, **OLM** P BRIERLEY
STALYBRIDGE (St Paul) *Ches 14* **P** *Trustees*
P-in-c R H LAWRY
STAMBOURNE (St Peter and St Thomas Becket) *see Upper*
Colne Chelmsf
STAMBRIDGE (St Mary and All Saints) *Chelmsf 12*
P *Ld Chan (1 turn), Charterhouse (3 turns)*
P-in-c C W COUSINS
STAMFORD (All Saints) w St John the Baptist *Linc 13*
P *Ld Chan and Burghley Ho Preservation Trust (alt)*
V N RUSSELL, **C** S M LANGDON-DAVIES, **Hon C** D M BOND
STAMFORD (Christ Church) *Linc 13* **P** *Bp*
P-in-c R J MACKRILL
STAMFORD (St George) (St Paul) *Linc 13* **P** *Burghley Ho*
Preservation Trust **R** M A N TAYLOR
STAMFORD (St Mary) (St Martin) *Linc 13* **P** *Burghley Ho*
Preservation Trust **R** M J THOMPSON
STAMFORD BRIDGE Group of Parishes, The (St John the
Baptist) *York 5* **P** *Lord Egremont (2 turns), Prime Min*
(1 turn) **P-in-c** D R WESTMORELAND
STAMFORD HILL (St Bartholomew) *Lon 19* **P** *The Crown*
V R N S LEECE
STAMFORD HILL (St Thomas) *Lon 19* **P** *R Hackney*
V M J BROWN, **C** S L GREEN
STAMFORDHAM (St Mary the Virgin) w Matfen *Newc 3*
P *Ld Chan* **V** R CAVAGAN
STANBRIDGE (St John the Baptist) *see Totternhoe,*
Stanbridge and Tilsworth St Alb
STANBURY (Mission Church) *see Haworth Bradf*
STAND (All Saints) *Man 14* **P** *Earl of Wilton* **R** R W BAILEY
STANDISH (St Nicholas) *see Eastington, Frocester, Haresfield*
etc Glouc

STANDISH (St Wilfrid) *Blackb 4* **P** *Bp* **R** M J EVERITT,
C B J WARD, S G PRITCHARD
STANDLAKE (St Giles) *see Lower Windrush Ox*
STANDON (All Saints) *see Broughton w Croxton and Cotes*
Heath w Standon Lich
STANDON (St Mary) *St Alb 18* **P** *Ch Fund Trust Fund*
V D L HUMPHREY
STANFIELD (St Margaret) *see Litcham w Kempston, E and W*
Lexham, Mileham etc Nor
STANFORD (All Saints) *see Lyminge w Paddlesworth,*
Stanford w Postling etc Cant
STANFORD (All Saints) *Nor 13* **P** *Bp* **V** *vacant*
STANFORD (St Nicholas) *see Gilmorton, Peatling Parva,*
Kimcote etc Leic
STANFORD BISHOP (St James) *see Acton Beauchamp and*
Evesbatch w Stanford Bishop Heref
STANFORD DINGLEY (St Denys) *see Bradfield and Stanford*
Dingley Ox
STANFORD IN THE VALE (St Denys) w Goosey and Hatford
Ox 17 **P** *D&C Westmr (3 turns), Simeon's Trustees (2 turns)*
V M T WENHAM
STANFORD-LE-HOPE (St Margaret) w Mucking *Chelmsf 14*
P *MMCET* **R** J A K GUEST, **C** J WHITE
STANFORD-ON-SOAR (St John the Baptist) *see E and W*
Leake, Stanford-on-Soar, Rempstone etc S'well
STANFORD-ON-TEME (St Mary) *see Teme Valley N Worc*
STANFORD RIVERS (St Margaret)
see Greensted-juxta-Ongar w Stanford Rivers Chelmsf
STANGROUND (St John the Baptist) (St Michael and All
Angels) *Ely 12* **P** *Em Coll Cam* **V** D E S DE SILVA
STANHOE (All Saints) *see Docking, the Birchams, Stanhoe*
and Sedgeford Nor
STANHOPE (St Thomas) w Frosterley *Dur 9* **P** *Bp and The*
Crown (alt) **P-in-c** P A GREENHALGH, **C** R P C BROWN
STANION (St Peter) *see Brigstock w Stanion and Lowick and*
Sudborough Pet
STANLEY (All Saints) *see W Hallam and Mapperley w Stanley*
Derby
STANLEY (St Agnes) *see Endon w Stanley Lich*
STANLEY (St Andrew) *see W Hallam and Mapperley w*
Stanley Derby
STANLEY (St Anne) *Liv 8* **P** *R W Derby* **V** M C DAVIES,
C M A READ, **Hon C** H PRINCE
STANLEY (St Peter) *Wakef 12* **P** *Dean* **V** W E HENDERSON,
NSM J KILSBY
STANLEY (St Thomas) *see Satley, Stanley and Tow Law Dur*
STANLEY, SOUTH (St Stephen) *see Ch the K Dur*
STANLEY PONTLARGE (Chapel) *see Winchcombe, Gretton,*
Sudeley Manor etc Glouc
STANLEYS, The *Glouc 8* **P** *Mrs L Y K Fisher and Jes Coll*
Cam (jt) **P-in-c** S P PHILLIPSON-MASTERS
STANMER (not known) w Falmer *Chich 2* **P** *Bp*
P-in-c A N ROBINSON
STANMORE (St Luke) *Win 7* **P** *Bp* **V** M R GARDNER,
C R E WISE, **NSM** O N WOODMAN
STANMORE, GREAT (St John the Evangelist) *Lon 23*
P *R O Bernays Esq* **R** A J CHRISTIAN, **C** H A STEWART
STANMORE, LITTLE (St Lawrence) *Lon 23* **P** *Bp*
R P M REECE
STANNEY (St Andrew) *see Ellesmere Port Ches*
STANNINGFIELD (St Nicholas) *see Hawstead and Nowton w*
Stanningfield etc St E
STANNINGLEY (St Thomas) *Ripon 6* **P** *V Leeds St Pet*
R D M GREEN
STANNINGTON (Christ Church) *Sheff 4* **P** *Bp* **V** P W WEST
STANNINGTON (St Mary the Virgin) *Newc 1* **P** *Bp*
P-in-c C R GOUGH
STANSFIELD (All Saints) *see Bansfield St E*
STANSTEAD (St James) *see Glem Valley United Benefice St E*
STANSTEAD ABBOTS (St Andrew) *see Gt Amwell w*
St Margaret's and Stanstead Abbots St Alb
STANSTEAD ST MARGARET (St Mary the Virgin) *as above*
St Alb
STANSTED (St Mary) w Fairseat and Vigo *Roch 10* **P** *Bp*
R C J L NOBLE
STANSTED (St Paul) (Christ Church) *Chich 13* **P** *Stansted*
Park Foundation **P-in-c** A N STAMP, **C** J A L HULBERT
STANSTED MOUNTFITCHET (St John) w Birchanger and
Farnham *Chelmsf 21* **P** *Bp, New Coll Ox, and*
Mrs L A Murphy (jt) **R** A SPURR
STANTON (All Saints) (St John the Baptist) *St E 9*
P *The Crown* **P-in-c** M J HANSEN
STANTON (St Gabriel) *see Golden Cap Team Sarum*
STANTON (St Mary) *see Denstone w Ellastone and Stanton*
Lich
STANTON (St Mary and All Saints) *see Markfield, Thornton,*
Bagworth and Stanton etc Leic

STANTON (St Michael and All Angels)   *see* Toddington, Stanton, Didbrook w Hailes etc *Glouc*

STANTON BY BRIDGE (St Michael)   *see* Ticknall, Smisby and Stanton by Bridge etc *Derby*

STANTON-BY-DALE (St Michael and All Angels) w Dale Abbey and Risley *Derby 13*   **P** *Bp*   **R** I E GOODING

STANTON DREW (Blessed Virgin Mary)   *see* Bishop Sutton and Stanton Drew and Stowey *B & W*

STANTON FITZWARREN (St Leonard)   *see* Stratton St Margaret w S Marston etc *Bris*

STANTON HARCOURT (St Michael)   *see* Lower Windrush *Ox*

STANTON HILL (All Saints)   *see* Skegby w Teversal *S'well*

STANTON-IN-PEAK (Holy Trinity)   *see* Youlgreave, Middleton, Stanton-in-Peak etc *Derby*

STANTON LACY (Hayton Bent Hall)   *see* Culmington w Onibury, Bromfield etc *Heref*

STANTON LACY (St Peter)   *as above Heref*

STANTON ON HINE HEATH (St Andrew) *Lich 22*   **P** *Sir Beville Stanier Bt*   **V** D J HUMPHRIES

STANTON-ON-THE-WOLDS (All Saints)   *see* Keyworth and Stanton-on-the-Wolds and Bunny etc *S'well*

STANTON PRIOR (St Lawrence)   *see* Farmborough, Marksbury and Stanton Prior *B & W*

STANTON ST BERNARD (All Saints)   *see* Pewsey and Swanborough *Sarum*

STANTON ST JOHN (St John the Baptist)   *see* Wheatley *Ox*

STANTON ST QUINTIN (St Quintin)   *see* Hullavington, Norton and Stanton St Quintin *Bris*

STANTONBURY (Christ Church) and Willen *Ox 25*   **P** *Patr Bd*   **TV** A R B JOWITT, P S BALLANTINE, P A SMITH, **OLM** J B ROSE

STANWAY (St Albright) (St Andrew) *Chelmsf 17*   **P** *Magd Coll Ox*   **R** P R MCLAREN-COOK, **NSM** A C BUSHELL

STANWAY (St Peter)   *see* Toddington, Stanton, Didbrook w Hailes etc *Glouc*

STANWELL (St Mary the Virgin) *Lon 13*   **P** *Ld Chan*   **V** W P STAFFORD-WHITTAKER,   **NSM** H S L NICHOLSON

STANWICK (St Laurence) w Hargrave *Pet 10*   **P** *Ld Chan (2 turns), Bp (1 turn)*   **R** vacant (01933) 622317

STANWIX (St Michael) *Carl 3*   **P** *Bp*   **V** R J IRETON

STAPEHILL (All Saints)   *see* Hampreston *Sarum*

STAPENHILL (Immanuel) *Derby 16*   **P** *Ch Soc Trust*   **V** B S P LEATHERS

STAPENHILL (St Peter) w Cauldwell *Derby 16*   **P** *Ch Soc Trust*   **P-in-c** M ANDREYEV,   **C** E Q HOBBS

STAPLE (St James)   *see* Woodnesborough w Worth and Staple *Cant*

STAPLE FITZPAINE (St Peter)   *see* Beercrombe w Curry Mallet, Hatch Beauchamp etc *B & W*

STAPLE TYE (St James)   *see* Gt Parndon *Chelmsf*

STAPLECROSS (St Mark)   *see* Ewhurst *Chich*

STAPLEFIELD COMMON (St Mark) *Chich 6*   **P** *V Cuckfield*   **P-in-c** M S MALKINSON

STAPLEFORD (All Saints)   *see* Bassingham Gp *Linc*

STAPLEFORD (St Andrew) *Ely 13*   **P** *D&C*   **P-in-c** J L R ECHOLS

STAPLEFORD (St Andrew's Mission Church) (St Helen) (St Luke) *S'well 7*   **P** *CPAS*   **V** W N CRAFT, **C** B H BEECROFT, C M BEECROFT

STAPLEFORD (St Mary)   *see* Bramfield, Stapleford, Waterford etc *St Alb*

STAPLEFORD (St Mary)   *see* Wylye and Till Valley *Sarum*

STAPLEFORD ABBOTTS (St Mary)   *see* Lambourne w Abridge and Stapleford Abbotts *Chelmsf*

STAPLEFORD TAWNEY (St Mary the Virgin) w Theydon Mount *Chelmsf 27*   **P** *DBP*   **P-in-c** R WILKINSON

STAPLEGROVE (St John) w Norton Fitzwarren *B & W 18*   **P** *Bp and MMCET (jt)*   **C** C L MARSHALL

STAPLEHURST (All Saints) *Cant 11*   **P** *St Jo Coll Cam*   **R** G M CALVER,   **NSM** P OSLER

STAPLETON (Holy Trinity) *Bris 3*   **P** *Bp*   **P-in-c** M CREGAN, **Hon C** S R EMTAGE

STAPLETON (St John)   *see* Dorrington w Leebotwood, Longnor, Stapleton etc *Heref*

STAPLETON (St Martin)   *see* Barwell w Potters Marston and Stapleton *Leic*

STAPLETON (St Mary)   *see* Bewcastle, Stapleton and Kirklinton etc *Carl*

STARBECK (St Andrew) *Ripon 1*   **P** *V Harrogate Ch Ch*   **V** F S K WAINAINA,   **C** T F P YAP

STARCROSS (St Paul)   *see* Kenton, Mamhead, Powderham, Cofton and Starcross *Ex*

STARSTON (St Margaret)   *see* Dickleburgh and The Pulhams *Nor*

STARTFORTH (Holy Trinity) and Bowes and Rokeby w Brignall *Ripon 2*   **P** *Ld Chan (1 turn), Bp, Earl of Lonsdale and Lords of the Manor of Bowes (2 turns)*   **V** D P RYAN

STATFOLD (St Matthew)   *see* Clifton Campville w Edingale and Harlaston *Lich*

STATHERN (St Guthlac)   *see* Vale of Belvoir Par *Leic*

STAUGHTON, GREAT (St Andrew) *Ely 13*   **P** *St Jo Coll Ox*   **P-in-c** J I CLARKE

STAUGHTON, LITTLE (All Saints)   *see* Keysoe w Bolnhurst and Lt Staughton *St Alb*

STAUNTON (All Saints)   *see* Coleford w Staunton *Glouc*

STAUNTON (St James)   *see* Hartpury w Corse and Staunton *Glouc*

STAUNTON (St Mary) w Flawborough *S'well 3*   **P** E G *Staunton Esq*   **P-in-c** J H BATESON

STAUNTON HAROLD (Holy Trinity)   *see* Breedon cum Isley Walton and Worthington *Leic*

STAUNTON-ON-ARROW (St Peter)   *see* Pembridge w Moor Court, Shobdon, Staunton etc *Heref*

STAUNTON-ON-WYE (St Mary the Virgin)   *see* Letton w Staunton, Byford, Mansel Gamage etc *Heref*

STAVELEY (All Saints)   *see* Walkingham Hill *Ripon*

STAVELEY (St James), Ings and Kentmere *Carl 10*   **P** *V Kendal H Trin*   **V** G WATSON

STAVELEY (St John the Baptist) and Barrow Hill *Derby 3*   **P** *Bp, Adn Chesterfield, and Duke of Devonshire (jt)*   **TR** W A BUTT,   **TV** P W SKINNER

STAVELEY IN CARTMEL (St Mary)   *see* Leven Valley *Carl*

STAVERTON (St Catherine) w Boddington and Tredington w Stoke Orchard and Hardwicke *Glouc 16*   **P** *Bp*   **P-in-c** J C TADMAN, O C BARRACLOUGH

STAVERTON (St Mary the Virgin)   *see* Daventry, Ashby St Ledgers, Braunston etc *Pet*

STAVERTON (St Paul)   *see* Hilperton w Whaddon and Staverton etc *Sarum*

STAVERTON (St Paul de Leon)   *see* Broadhempston, Woodland, Staverton etc *Ex*

STAWELL (St Francis)   *see* Middlezoy and Othery and Moorlinch *B & W*

STAWLEY (St Michael and All Angels)   *see* Wellington and Distr *B & W*

STEANE (St Peter)   *see* Aynho and Croughton w Evenley etc *Pet*

STEART BAY (St Andrew)   *see* Cannington, Otterhampton, Combwich and Stockland *B & W*

STEBBING (St Mary the Virgin) w Lindsell *Chelmsf 18*   **P** *Bp*   **V** B SNELLING,   **NSM** S C BAZLINTON

STECHFORD (All Saints) (St Andrew) *Birm 13*   **P** *St Pet Coll Ox*   **V** vacant 0121-783 2463

STEDHAM (St James) w Iping *Chich 10*   **P** *Bp*   **P-in-c** J W HICKMAN

STEEP (All Saints) and Froxfield w Privett *Portsm 4*   **P** *Ld Chan and Magd Coll Cam (alt)*   **V** P A KENNEDY

STEEPING, GREAT (All Saints)   *see* Spilsby Gp *Linc*

STEEPING, LITTLE (St Andrew)   *as above Linc*

STEEPLE (St Lawrence and All Saints) *Chelmsf 11*   **P** *Bp*   **P-in-c** L BLANEY

STEEPLE (St Michael and All Angels)   *see* Corfe Castle, Church Knowle, Kimmeridge etc *Sarum*

STEEPLE ASHTON (St Mary the Virgin) w Semington and Keevil *Sarum 14*   **P** *D&C Win (1 turn), Magd Coll Cam (3 turns)*   **V** D M HART

STEEPLE ASTON (St Peter and St Paul) w North Aston and Tackley *Ox 9*   **P** *BNC Ox, St Jo Coll Ox, and Exors Lt-Col A D Taylor (jt)*   **R** S A M'CAW

STEEPLE BARTON (St Mary)   *see* Westcote Barton w Steeple Barton, Duns Tew etc *Ox*

STEEPLE BUMPSTEAD (St Mary) and Helions Bumpstead *Chelmsf 19*   **P** *Ld Chan*   **P-in-c** S M GRIFFITHS

STEEPLE CLAYDON (St Michael)   *see* The Claydons *Ox*

STEEPLE LANGFORD (All Saints)   *see* Wylye and Till Valley *Sarum*

STEEPLE MORDEN (St Peter and St Paul)   *see* Shingay Gp of Par *Ely*

STEETLY (All Saints)   *see* Whitwell *Derby*

STEETON (St Stephen) *Bradf 8*   **P** *V Kildwick*   **V** M E PINNOCK

STELLA (St Cuthbert) *Dur 13*   **P** *Bp*   **P-in-c** H DITCHBURN

STELLING (St Mary)   *see* Petham and Waltham w Lower Hardres etc *Cant*

STENIGOT (St Nicholas)   *see* Asterby Gp *Linc*

STEPNEY (St Dunstan and All Saints) *Lon 7*   **P** *Bp*   **R** C M BURKE,   **C** M J HALL, S J PATCH,   **Hon C** G G WHITE, **NSM** M F SCHLEGER

STEPPINGLEY (St Lawrence)   *see* Ampthill w Millbrook and Steppingley *St Alb*

STERNFIELD (St Mary Magdalene) w Benhall and Snape *St E 19*   **P** *Exors Mrs A H V Aldous, Mrs A C V Wentworth, and Mrs M A Bertin (by turn)*   **P-in-c** C E BROOKS

STERT (St James) *see* Redhorn *Sarum*
STETCHWORTH (St Peter) *see* Raddesley Gp *Ely*
STEVENAGE (All Saints) Pin Green *St Alb 23* **P** *Bp*
P-in-c M J LEVERTON
STEVENAGE (Holy Trinity) *St Alb 23* **P** *Bp*
P-in-c G J TICKNER, **C** Y R PENTELOW, **NSM** A MARINER,
J A PAGE
STEVENAGE (St Andrew and St George) *St Alb 23* **P** *Bp*
R M BARNSLEY, **C** J E PAVYER, **NSM** M S HOLFORD,
B M TIPPING
STEVENAGE (St Hugh) (St John) Chells *St Alb 23* **P** *Bp*
V J D CAMPBELL, **C** C M HINA
STEVENAGE (St Mary) Sheppall w Aston *St Alb 23* **P** *Bp*
V G B WHITE, **C** R J RILEY-BRALEY
STEVENAGE (St Nicholas) and Graveley *St Alb 23* **P** *Bp*
V D E DOWLING, **C** N A SOPHIANOU
STEVENAGE (St Peter) Broadwater *St Alb 23* **P** *Bp*
V D H HAGUE, **C** J M B KISSELL, **NSM** J E HATTON
STEVENTON (St Michael and All Angels) w Milton *Ox 10*
P *Ch Ch Ox and D&C Westmr (jt)* **P-in-c** C J PATCHING
STEVENTON (St Nicholas) *see* N Waltham and Steventon,
Ashe and Deane *Win*
STEVINGTON (Church Room) (St Mary the Virgin) *St Alb 15*
P *Bp* **P-in-c** L R MCDONALD
STEWARDS LANE (St Thomas) *see* Ditton St Mich w St Thos
Liv
STEWKLEY (St Michael and All Angels) w Soulbury and
Drayton Parslow *Ox 26* **P** *Bp, Earl of Rosebery, and*
MMCET (jt) **V** N J COTTON, **OLM** P LYMBERY
STEWTON (St Andrew) *see* Louth *Linc*
STEYNING (St Andrew) *Chich 12* **P** *MMCET*
V P M RAMPTON
STIBBARD (All Saints) *see* Twyford, Guist, Bintree,
Themelthorpe etc *Nor*
STIBBINGTON (St John the Baptist) *see* Elton w Stibbington
and Water Newton *Ely*
STICKFORD (St Helen) *see* Stickney Gp *Linc*
STICKLEPATH (St Mary) *see* S Tawton and Belstone *Ex*
STICKLEPATH (St Paul) *see* Barnstaple *Ex*
STICKNEY Group, The (St Luke) *Linc 7* **P** *DBP, Ld Chan, and*
Bp (by turn) **R** C L J CAREY
STIDD (St Saviour) *see* Ribchester w Stidd *Blackb*
STIFFKEY (St John and St Mary) and Cockthorpe w Morston,
Langham and Binham *Nor 18* **P** *Bp, Sir Euan*
Anstruther-Gough-Calthorpe Bt, and DBP (by turn)
P-in-c E J PENNY, **C** M N DALE, **NSM** D E PENNY
STIFFORD (St Cedd) (St Mary) *Chelmsf 14* **P** *Bp*
R A R B HIGGS
STIFFORD, SOUTH (St Mary the Virgin) *see* Grays Thurrock
Chelmsf
STILLINGFLEET (St Helen) *see* Escrick and Stillingfleet w
Naburn *York*
STILLINGTON (St John) *see* Grindon, Stillington and
Wolviston *Dur*
STILLINGTON (St Nicholas) *see* Sheriff Hutton, Farlington,
Stillington etc *York*
STILTON (St Mary Magdalene) w Denton and Caldectoe and
Folkesworth w Morborne and Haddon *Ely 12*
P *Mrs H R Horne and Bp, Ld Chan (alt)* **R** R LONGFOOT
STINCHCOMBE (St Cyr) *see* Cam w Stinchcombe *Glouc*
STINSFORD (St Michael) *see* Charminster and Stinsford
Sarum
STIRCHLEY (All Saints) *see* Cen Telford *Lich*
STIRCHLEY (Ascension) *Birm 4* **P** *R Kings Norton*
V S L HUCKLE
STISTED (All Saints) *see* Cressing w Stisted and Bradwell etc
Chelmsf
STITHIANS (St Stythians) *see* St Stythians w Perranarworthal
and Gwennap *Truro*
STIXWOULD (St Peter) *see* Woodhall Spa Gp *Linc*
STOAK (St Lawrence) *see* Ellesmere Port *Ches*
STOCK (St Barnabas) *see* Stalbridge and Stock *Sarum*
STOCK HARVARD (All Saints) *Chelmsf 9* **P** *Guild of All So*
R N D L DE KEYSER
STOCKBRIDGE (Old St Peter) (St Peter) and Longstock and
Leckford *Win 12* **P** *Bp and St Jo Coll Ox (jt)*
P-in-c G C G TRASLER
STOCKBRIDGE VILLAGE (St Jude) *Liv 2* **P** *Bp and*
R W Derby (jt) **V** E D O'NEILL
STOCKBURY (St Mary Magdalene) *see* Newington w Hartlip
and Stockbury *Cant*
STOCKCROSS (St John) *see* Welford w Wickham and Gt
Shefford, Boxford etc *Ox*
STOCKERSTON (St Peter) *see* Six Saints circa Holt *Leic*
STOCKING FARM (St Luke) *Leic 1* **P** *Bp* **V** P WATSON
STOCKING PELHAM (St Mary) *see* Braughing w Furneux
Pelham and Stocking Pelham *St Alb*

STOCKINGFORD (St Paul) *Cov 5* **P** *V Nuneaton*
V M F VINCENT, **C** S L BENNETT
STOCKLAND (St Mary Magdalene) *see* Cannington,
Otterhampton, Combwich and Stockland *B & W*
STOCKLAND (St Michael and All Angels) *see* Kilmington,
Stockland, Dalwood, Yarcombe etc *Ex*
STOCKLAND GREEN (St Mark) *Birm 8* **P** *The Crown*
V S W POWELL
STOCKLEIGH ENGLISH (St Mary the Virgin) *see* N Creedy
Ex
STOCKLEIGH POMEROY (St Mary the Virgin) *as above Ex*
STOCKLINCH (St Mary Magdalene) *see* Ilminster and Distr
B & W
STOCKPORT South West (St George) (St Mark) (St Gabriel)
Ches 18 **P** *Patr Bd* **TR** A J BELL, **TV** E J H LANE,
D T BREWSTER, **C** R J LAMEY
STOCKPORT (St Augustine) *see* Cheadle Heath *Ches*
STOCKPORT (St Martin) *see* Heatons *Man*
STOCKPORT (St Mary) *Ches 18* **P** *G&C Coll Cam*
R R P SCOONES
STOCKPORT (St Matthew) *Ches 18* **P** *Bp* **V** *vacant* 0161--
480 5515
STOCKPORT (St Saviour) *Ches 18* **P** *Trustees*
V D V COOKSON
STOCKPORT (St Thomas) (St Peter) *Ches 18* **P** *Bp and Soc of*
the Faith (jt) **R** K D N KENRICK, **Hon C** K R BROOKES
STOCKSBRIDGE (St Matthias) *Sheff 3* **P** *Bp*
V S TRICKLEBANK
STOCKSFIELD (St John) *see* Bywell *Newc*
STOCKTON (Holy Trinity) *Dur 10* **P** *Bp* **P-in-c** S J GILES
STOCKTON (St Andrew) *see* Teme Valley N *Worc*
STOCKTON (St Chad) *Dur 10* **P** *Bp* **C** J THORNS,
NSM E WALKER
STOCKTON (St Chad) *see* Beckbury, Badger, Kemberton,
Ryton, Stockton etc *Lich*
STOCKTON (St John the Baptist) *see* Wylye and Till Valley
Sarum
STOCKTON (St Mark) *Dur 10* **P** *Bp* **P-in-c** M M GILLEY
STOCKTON (St Michael and All Angels)
see Napton-on-the-Hill, Lower Shuckburgh etc *Cov*
STOCKTON (St Michael and All Angels) *see* Gillingham w
Geldeston, Stockton, Ellingham etc *Nor*
STOCKTON HEATH (St Thomas) *Ches 4* **P** *P G Greenall Esq*
V J B HARRIS, **C** E A GLOVER
STOCKTON-ON-TEES (St Chad) *see* Stockton St Chad *Dur*
STOCKTON ON TEES (St James) *Dur 10* **P** *Bp*
V D J STEPHENSON
STOCKTON-ON-TEES (St John the Baptist) *Dur 10* **P** *Bp*
V D J STEPHENSON, **C** D J BAGE
STOCKTON-ON-TEES (St Mark) *see* Stockton St Mark *Dur*
STOCKTON-ON-TEES (St Paul) *Dur 10* **P** *The Crown*
V *vacant* (01642) 617869
STOCKTON-ON-TEES (St Peter) *Dur 10* **P** *Bp*
V P D ASHDOWN, **NSM** N G BENZIES
STOCKTON-ON-TEES (St Thomas) *Dur 10* **P** *Bp*
V A FEATHERSTONE
STOCKTON-ON-THE-FOREST (Holy Trinity) w Holtby and
Warthill *York 2* **P** *Abp* **NSM** M E W WILLETTS
STOCKWELL (St Michael) *S'wark 11* **P** *V Kennington*
St Mark **P-in-c** A R GRANT
STOCKWELL GREEN (St Andrew) *S'wark 11* **P** *Abp, Bp, and*
TR N Lambeth (jt) **V** P R SIMMONDS, **OLM** I A BOWMAN
STOCKWITH, EAST (St Peter) *see* Corringham and Blyton
Gp *Linc*
STOCKWITH, WEST (St Mary the Virgin) *see* Misterton and
W Stockwith *S'well*
STOCKWOOD (Christ the Servant) *see* Bris Ch the Servant
Stockwood *Bris*
STODDEN Churches, The *St Alb 15* **P** *MMCET and DBP*
(alt) **P-in-c** J C BROOKSHAW
STODMARSH (St Mary) *see* Littlebourne and Ickham w
Wickhambreaux etc *Cant*
STODY (St Mary) *see* Brinton, Briningham, Hunworth, Stody
etc *Nor*
STOGUMBER (Blessed Virgin Mary) *see* Quantock Towers
B & W
STOGURSEY (St Andrew) w Fiddington *B & W 17* **P** *Eton*
Coll and DBP (alt) **P-in-c** J T TYLER
STOKE (St Mary and St Andrew) *see* Colsterworth Gp *Linc*
STOKE (St Michael) *see* Coventry Caludon *Cov*
STOKE (St Peter and St Paul) *see* Grain w Stoke *Roch*
STOKE, EAST (St Oswald) w Syerston *S'well 3* **P** *Bp*
R G A FIRTH
STOKE, NORTH (St Martin) *see* Bath Weston All SS w N
Stoke and Langridge *B & W*
STOKE, NORTH (St Mary the Virgin) *see* Langtree *Ox*

STOKE, SOUTH (St Andrew)   *see* Goring w S Stoke *Ox*
STOKE, SOUTH (St James the Great)   *see* Combe Down w
Monkton Combe and S Stoke *B & W*
STOKE, SOUTH (St Leonard)   *see* Arundel w Tortington and S
Stoke *Chich*
STOKE, WEST (St Andrew) *Chich 13*   **P** *Bp*   **R** J J HOLLIMAN
STOKE ABBOTT (St Mary)   *see* Beaminster Area *Sarum*
**STOKE ALBANY (St Botolph) w Wilbarston and Ashley w
Weston-by-Welland and Sutton Bassett** *Pet 9*   **P** *Comdr
L M M Saunders-Watson (2 turns), Bp (1 turn), DBP (1 turn)*
R R V STAPLETON
STOKE ALDERMOOR (St Catherine)   *see* Coventry Caludon
Cov
STOKE ASH (All Saints)   *see* Gislingham and Thorndon *St E*
STOKE BARDOLPH (St Luke)   *see* Gedling *S'well*
STOKE BISHOP (St Mary Magdalene) *Bris 2*   **P** *Bp*
V D J R RITCHIE,   **NSM** R C WILSON
STOKE BLISS (St Peter)   *see* Teme Valley S *Worc*
STOKE BRUERNE (St Mary the Virgin)   *see* Blisworth and
Stoke Bruerne w Grafton Regis etc *Pet*
STOKE BY CLARE (St John the Baptist)   *see* Clare w
Poslingford, Cavendish etc *St E*
STOKE BY NAYLAND (St Mary) w Leavenheath and Polstead
St E 3   **P** *Mrs S E F Holden and St Jo Coll Ox (alt)*
R M J A TILLETT,   **NSM** J T FOWLER
**STOKE CANON (St Mary Magdalene), Poltimore w Huxham
and Rewe w Netherexe** *Ex 2*   **P** *D&C, Lady Stucley, and Bp
(by turn)*   **P-in-c** C M SIMPSON,   **C** S A SIMPSON,
NSM S SHEPPARD
STOKE CHARITY (St Mary and St Michael)   *see* Lower Dever
Valley *Win*
STOKE CLIMSLAND (not known) *Truro 9*   **P** *Bp and Duchy of
Cornwall (alt)*   **P-in-c** A R INGLEBY
STOKE D'ABERNON (St Mary the Virgin) *Guildf 10*
P *K Coll Cam*   **R** *vacant* (01932) 862502
STOKE DAMEREL (St Andrew w St Luke) *Ex 21*   **P** *Trustees
Lord St Levan*   **R** *vacant* (01752) 52348
STOKE DOYLE (St Rumbold)   *see* Aldwincle w Thorpe
Achurch, Pilton, Wadenhoe etc *Pet*
STOKE DRY (St Andrew)   *see* Lyddington w Stoke Dry and
Seaton etc *Pet*
STOKE EDITH (St Mary)   *see* Ledbury *Heref*
STOKE FLEMING (St Peter), Blackawton and Strete *Ex 14*
P *Bp and BDP (jt)*   **V** J H BELL
STOKE GABRIEL (St Gabriel) and Collaton *Ex 13*   **P** *Bp*
V D A TREBY
STOKE GIFFORD (St Michael) *Bris 5*   **P** *Bp*
TR D C R WIDDOWS,   **TV** T G E WEBBER,   **C** S L FENBY,
NSM J C BRADLEY
STOKE GOLDING (St Margaret)   *see* Fenn Lanes Gp *Leic*
STOKE GOLDINGTON (St Peter)   *see* Gayhurst w
Ravenstone, Stoke Goldington etc *Ox*
STOKE HAMMOND (St Luke)   *see* Brickhills and Stoke
Hammond *Ox*
STOKE HEATH (St Alban)   *see* Cov E *Cov*
STOKE HILL (St Peter) *Guildf 5*   **P** *Bp*   **V** D J FURNESS,
OLM B J RICH
**STOKE HOLY CROSS (Holy Cross) w Dunston, Arminghall
and Caistor St Edmunds w Markshall** *Nor 8*   **P** *D&C and
Mrs D Pott (jt)*   **R** R J BUNN
**STOKE LACY (St Peter and St Paul) and Moreton Jeffries w
Much Cowarne, Ocle Pychard and Ullingswick** *Heref 2*
P *D&C, Bp Birm, P H G Morgan Esq, and Bp (by turn)*
P-in-c J A DAVIES,   **NSM** C M SYKES
STOKE LYNE (St Peter)   *see* Shelswell *Ox*
STOKE MANDEVILLE (St Mary the Virgin)
see Ellesborough, The Kimbles and Stoke Mandeville *Ox*
STOKE NEWINGTON (St Andrew) *Lon 5*   **P** *Bp*
V R K BALLANTINE
STOKE NEWINGTON St Faith (St Matthias) and All Saints
Lon 5   **P** *City Corp*   **V** C J FULLER
STOKE NEWINGTON (St John the Evangelist)
see Brownswood Park *Lon*
STOKE NEWINGTON (St Mary) (Old Parish Church) *Lon 5*
P *Bp*   **R** J D CLARK,   **C** R P S EASTON
STOKE NEWINGTON (St Olave) *Lon 5*   **P** *Ld Chan*
P-in-c V A ROBERTS
**STOKE NEWINGTON COMMON (St Michael and All
Angels)** *Lon 5*   **P** *Bp*   **V** S J A FARRER
STOKE-NEXT-GUILDFORD (St John the Evangelist) *Guildf 5*
P *Simeon's Trustees*   **R** M R F MACLACHLAN,
NSM R J STEEL, R J PECK
STOKE-ON-TRENT   *see* Stoke-upon-Trent *Lich*
STOKE ORCHARD (St James the Great)   *see* Staverton w
Boddington and Tredington etc *Glouc*
STOKE PARK (St Peter)   *see* Ipswich St Mary at Stoke w St Pet
and St Fran *St E*

STOKE PERO (not known)   *see* Porlock w Stoke Pero *B & W*
STOKE POGES (St Giles) *Ox 23*   **P** *Trustees Duke of Leeds
Trust*   **P-in-c** H N L LATHAM
STOKE PRIOR (St Luke)   *see* Leominster *Heref*
STOKE PRIOR (St Michael), Wychbold and Upton Warren
Worc 8   **P** *Bp and D&C (alt)*   **R** R H ANTELL,
NSM P A BARFORD
STOKE RIVERS (St Bartholomew)   *see* Shirwell, Loxhore,
Kentisbury, Arlington, etc *Ex*
STOKE ROW (St John the Evangelist)   *see* Langtree *Ox*
STOKE ST GREGORY (St Gregory) w Burrowbridge and Lyng
B & W 18   **P** *D&C (2 turns), R O Meade-King Esq (1 turn)*
V C F E ROWLEY,   **NSM** C J WRIGHT
STOKE ST MARY (St Mary)   *see* Beercrocombe w Curry
Mallet, Hatch Beauchamp etc *B & W*
STOKE ST MICHAEL (St Michael)   *see* Leigh upon Mendip w
Stoke St Michael *B & W*
STOKE ST MILBOROUGH (St Milburgha)   *see* Bitterley w
Middleton, Stoke St Milborough etc *Heref*
**STOKE SUB HAMDON (Blessed Virgin Mary) (All Saints
Mission Church)** *B & W 6*   **P** *Ch Patr Trust*
P-in-c P KERTON-JOHNSON
STOKE TALMAGE (St Mary Magdalene)   *see* Thame *Ox*
STOKE TRISTER (St Andrew)   *see* Charlton Musgrove,
Cucklington and Stoke Trister *B & W*
STOKE UPON TERN (St Peter)   *see* Cheswardine, Childs
Ercall, Hales, Hinstock etc *Lich*
STOKE-UPON-TRENT (St Peter-ad-Vincula) (St Paul) *Lich 12*
P *Bp*   **TV** P R SEARLE, P M SHELTON
STOKEHAM (St Peter)   *see* Rampton w Laneham, Treswell,
Cottam and Stokeham *S'well*
STOKEINTEIGNHEAD (St Andrew)   *see* Shaldon,
Stokeinteignhead, Combeinteignhead etc *Ex*
STOKENCHURCH (St Peter and St Paul) and Ibstone *Ox 29*
P *Bp*   **P-in-c** R A FRANCE
**STOKENHAM (St Michael and All Angels) w Sherford and
Beesands, and Slapton** *Ex 14*   **P** *Prime Min*
P-in-c R M HARDING
STOKESAY (St Christopher) (St John the Baptist) *Heref 11*
P *T P D La Touche Esq*   **P-in-c** M L COPE
STOKESBY (St Andrew)   *see* S Trin Broads *Nor*
STOKESLEY (St Peter and St Paul) *York 21*   **P** *Abp*
R M D A DYKES
STOLFORD (St Peter)   *see* Stogursey w Fiddington *B & W*
STON EASTON (Blessed Virgin Mary)   *see* Chewton Mendip w
Ston Easton, Litton etc *B & W*
STONDON (All Saints)   *see* Gravenhurst, Shillington and
Stondon *St Alb*
STONDON MASSEY (St Peter and St Paul)   *see* Blackmore and
Stondon Massey *Chelmsf*
STONE (All Saints)   *see* Berkeley w Wick, Breadstone, Newport,
Stone etc *Glouc*
STONE (Christ Church) and Oulton-with-Moddershall *Lich 13*
P *Simeon's Trustees*   **V** *vacant* (01785) 812669
STONE near Dartford (St Mary) *Roch 2*   **P** *Bp*
P-in-c T M MASON
STONE (St John the Baptist) w Dinton and Hartwell *Ox 21*
P *Bp and Grocers' Co (jt)*   **R** D J COOKE
STONE (St Mary the Virgin)   *see* Chaddesley Corbett and Stone
Worc
STONE (St Michael and St Wulfad) w Aston (St Saviour)
Lich 13   **P** *Bp*   **R** P J WILSON
STONE CROSS (St Luke) w Langney, North *Chich 16*   **P** *Bp*
V J D VINE
STONE-IN-OXNEY (St Mary the Virgin)   *see* Wittersham w
Stone-in-Oxney and Ebony *Cant*
STONE QUARRY (St Luke)   *see* E Grinstead St Swithun *Chich*
STONEBRIDGE (St Michael and All Angels) *Lon 21*   **P** *Bp*
V R L SMITH
STONEBROOM (St Peter)   *see* Morton and Stonebroom w
Shirland *Derby*
STONEGATE (St Peter) *Chich 19*   **P** *E J B Hardcastle Esq and
C J J Reid Esq (jt)*   **V** J R JAMES,   **C** C D LAWRENCE,
NSM R G ALFORD
STONEGRAVE (Holy Trinity)   *see* Ampleforth w Oswaldkirk,
Gilling E etc *York*
STONEHAM, NORTH (St Nicholas) (All Saints) *Win 10*
P R H W Fleming Esq   **R** J E OWEN,   **C** J V LAWRENCE
STONEHAM, SOUTH (St Mary)   *see* Swaythling *Win*
STONEHOUSE (St Cyr) *Glouc 8*   **P** *The Crown*   **V** *vacant*
(01453) 822332
STONEHOUSE (St Paul)   *see* Plymouth St Andr and St Paul
Stonehouse *Ex*
STONELEIGH (St John the Baptist) *Guildf 9*   **P** *Bp*
P-in-c R A KING,   **OLM** I GRACE
STONELEIGH (St Mary the Virgin) w Ashow *Cov 4*   **P** *Lord
Leigh and Bp (jt)*   **P-in-c** V L BALDWIN,   **NSM** D JOHNSON

STONESBY (St Peter) *see* Waltham on the Wolds, Stonesby, Saxby etc *Leic*

STONESFIELD (St James the Great) w Combe Longa *Ox 9*
  P *Duke of Marlborough* **R** G J H B VAN DER WEEGEN

STONEY MIDDLETON (St Martin) *see* Baslow w Curbar and Stoney Middleton *Derby*

STONEY STANTON (St Michael) *see* Broughton Astley and Croft w Stoney Stanton *Leic*

STONEYCROFT (All Saints) *Liv 8* **P** *Bp* **V** *vacant* 0151-228 3581

STONEYCROFT (St Paul) *see* Liv St Paul Stoneycroft *Liv*

STONEYDELPH (St Martin in the Delph) *see* Glascote and Stonydelph *Lich*

STONHAM ASPAL (St Mary and St Lambert) *see* Crowfield w Stonham Aspal and Mickfield *St E*

STONHAM PARVA (St Mary) *see* Creeting St Mary, Creeting St Peter etc *St E*

STONNALL (St Peter) *Lich 1* **P** *V Shenstone*
  P-in-c R W BAILEY, **NSM** J B ASTON, J FORRESTER

STONTON WYVILLE (St Denys) *see* Gt Bowden w Welham, Glooston and Cranoe etc *Leic*

STOODLEIGH (St Margaret) *see* Washfield, Stoodleigh, Withleigh etc *Ex*

STOPHAM (St Mary the Virgin) and Fittleworth *Chich 11*
  P *D&C and Col Sir Brian Barttelot Bt (jt)* **R** A I SMYTH

STOPSLEY (St Thomas) *St Alb 14* **P** *Bp* **V** D G ALEXANDER

STORRIDGE (St John the Baptist) *see* Cradley w Mathon and Storridge *Heref*

STORRINGTON (St Mary) *Chich 12* **P** *Keble Coll Ox*
  R J M ACHESON, **Hon C** S J TURRELL, **NSM** T C HOLLAND

STORTH (All Saints Mission) *see* Arnside *Carl*

STOTFOLD (St Mary the Virgin) and Radwell *St Alb 16* **P** *Bp*
  R P M QUINT

STOTTESDON (St Mary) w Farlow, Cleeton St Mary, Silvington, Sidbury and Middleton Scriven *Heref 9* **P** *Bp*
  R W J BROMLEY

STOUGHTON (Emmanuel) *Guildf 5* **P** *Simeon's Trustees*
  V F SCAMMELL, **C** R P KHAKHRIA, **NSM** T J WEIL

STOUGHTON (St Mary) *see* Compton, the Mardens, Stoughton and Racton *Chich*

STOUGHTON (St Mary and All Saints) *see* Thurnby w Stoughton *Leic*

STOULTON (St Edmund) w Drake's Broughton and Pirton and Norton *Worc 4* **P** *Croome Estate Trustees, D&C, and Bp (jt)*
  R D G SLOGGETT

STOUR, EAST (Christ Church) *see* Gillingham *Sarum*

STOUR, UPPER *Sarum 17* **P** *Exors H P R Hoare (1 turn), Bp (2 turns), and Bourton Chpl Trustees (1 turn)*
  R C A R MOORSOM, **Hon C** P A RUNDLE

STOUR, WEST (St Mary) *see* Gillingham *Sarum*

STOUR PROVOST (St Michael and All Angels) *as above Sarum*

STOUR ROW (All Saints) *as above Sarum*

STOUR VALLEY Group, The *see* Clare w Poslingford, Cavendish etc *St E*

STOURBRIDGE (St John the Evangelist) *see* Old Swinford Stourbridge *Worc*

STOURBRIDGE (St Mary) *as above Worc*

STOURBRIDGE (St Michael and All Angels) Norton *Worc 12*
  P *Bp* **V** E BUTT

STOURBRIDGE (St Thomas) *Worc 12* **P** *Bp* **V** *vacant* (01384) 392401

STOURHEAD *St E 8* **P** *E H Vestey Esq, St Chad's Coll Dur, Ridley Hall Cam, and Walsingham Coll Trust (jt)* **V** J E ELEY,
  NSM S A BAREHAM

STOURPAINE (Holy Trinity) *see* Pimperne, Stourpaine, Durweston and Bryanston *Sarum*

STOURPORT-ON-SEVERN (St Michael and All Angels) and Wilden *Worc 13* **P** *Earl Baldwin of Bewdley and V Kidderminster St Mary and AllSS (jt)* **V** B GILBERT,
  C J E SPECK

STOURTON (St Peter) *see* Kinver and Enville *Lich*

STOURTON (St Peter) *see* Upper Stour *Sarum*

STOURTON CAUNDLE (St Peter) *see* The Caundles w Folke and Holwell *Sarum*

STOVEN (St Margaret) *see* Hundred River *St E*

STOW Group, The (St Mary the Virgin) *Linc 2* **P** *Bp and DBP (jt)* **P-in-c** M A WHITEHEAD

STOW, WEST (St Mary) *see* Lark Valley *St E*

STOW BARDOLPH (Holy Trinity) *see* Wimbotsham w Stow Bardolph and Stow Bridge etc *Ely*

STOW BEDON (St Botolph) *see* Caston, Griston, Merton, Thompson etc *Nor*

STOW BRIDGE Mission (St Peter) *see* Wimbotsham w Stow Bardolph and Stow Bridge etc *Ely*

STOW LONGA (St Botolph) *Ely 9* **P** *Bp* **V** V R A FROST

STOW MARIES (St Mary and St Margaret) *see* Purleigh, Cold Norton and Stow Maries *Chelmsf*

STOW ON THE WOLD (St Edward), Condicote and The Swells
  Glouc 14 **P** *DBP and Ch Ch Ox (jt)* **R** D C FRANCIS

STOWE (Assumption of St Mary the Virgin) *Ox 22*
  P *Stowe Sch* **P-in-c** R M BUNDOCK

STOWE (St Michael and All Angels) *see* Bucknell w Chapel Lawn, Llanfair Waterdine etc *Heref*

STOWE, UPPER (St James) *see* Heyford w Stowe Nine Churches and Flore etc *Pet*

STOWE BY CHARTLEY (St John the Baptist) *see* Mid Trent *Lich*

STOWE NINE CHURCHES (St Michael) *see* Heyford w Stowe Nine Churches and Flore etc *Pet*

STOWELL (St Leonard) *see* Chedworth, Yanworth and Stowell, Coln Rogers etc *Glouc*

STOWELL (St Mary Magdalene) *see* Henstridge and Charlton Horethorne w Stowell *B & W*

STOWEY (St Nicholas and Blessed Virgin Mary) *see* Bishop Sutton and Stanton Drew and Stowey *B & W*

STOWEY, NETHER (Blessed Virgin Mary) w Over Stowey
  B & W 17 **P** *D&C Windsor and MMCET (alt)*
  V P DENISON

STOWEY, OVER (St Peter and St Paul) *see* Nether Stowey w Over Stowey *B & W*

STOWFORD (St John) *see* Lifton, Broadwoodwidger, Stowford etc *Ex*

STOWLANGTOFT (St George) *see* Badwell and Walsham *St E*

STOWMARKET (St Peter and St Mary) *St E 6* **P** *Ch Patr Trust* **P-in-c** M W EDEN, **OLM** R M STRETCH, D WEBB,
  R F GILBERT

STOWTING (St Mary the Virgin) *see* Smeeth w Monks Horton and Stowting and Brabourne *Cant*

STOWUPLAND (Holy Trinity) *see* Haughley w Wetherden and Stowupland *St E*

STRADBROKE (All Saints) w Horham, Athelington and Redlingfield *St E 17* **P** *Bp (3 turns), Lt-Comdr G C Marshall (1 turn), and Dr G I Soden (1 turn)* **R** D J STREETER

STRADISHALL (St Margaret) *see* Bansfield *St E*

STRADSETT (St Mary) *see* Downham Market and Crimplesham w Stradsett *Ely*

STRAGGLETHORPE (St Michael) *see* Brant Broughton and Beckingham *Linc*

STRAITS, THE (St Andrew) *see* Sedgley All SS *Worc*

STRAMSHALL (St Michael and All Angels) *see* Uttoxeter Area *Lich*

STRANTON (All Saints) *Dur 3* **P** *St Jo Coll Dur*
  V M R GILBERTSON, **C** M P DUNSTAN, **NSM** A J CRAIG

STRATFIELD MORTIMER (St Mary) and Mortimer West End w Padworth *Ox 12* **P** *Eton Coll, Ld Chan, and Englefield Estate Trust Corp (by turn)* **V** P CHAPLIN, **C** J KENNEDY,
  NSM C E HETHERINGTON, C G LEA

STRATFIELD SAYE (St Mary) *see* Sherfield-on-Loddon and Stratfield Saye etc *Win*

STRATFORD (St John the Evangelist w Christ Church) and St James *Chelmsf 3* **P** *V W Ham* **V** D A RICHARDS,
  C J T MADDERN, **NSM** J V MEADWAY

STRATFORD NEW TOWN (St Paul) *Chelmsf 3* **P** *Ch Patr Trust* **V** J K OLIVER

STRATFORD ST MARY (St Mary) *see* Higham, Holton St Mary, Raydon and Stratford *St E*

STRATFORD SUB CASTLE (St Lawrence) *see* Salisbury St Fran and Stratford sub Castle *Sarum*

STRATFORD-UPON-AVON (Holy Trinity), Luddington and Clifford Chambers *Cov 8* **P** *Bp* **R** M C W GORICK,
  C J N ROWLAND, L J FARMER, P J M ANGIER

STRATTON (St Andrew) and Launcells *Truro 8* **P** *Duchy of Cornwall and CPAS (alt)* **V** R N STRANACK

STRATTON (St Mary) (St Michael) and Wacton *Nor 5*
  P *G&C Caius Coll Cam, DBP, and New Coll Ox (by turn)*
  R J A NASH

STRATTON (St Mary the Virgin) *see* Bradford Peverell, Stratton, Frampton etc *Sarum*

STRATTON (St Peter), North Cerney, Baunton and Bagendon
  Glouc 11 **P** *Mrs P M Chester Master, Jes Coll Ox, Univ Coll Ox (jt)* **R** P F QUINNELL, **NSM** D H S LEESON, J H MAIS

STRATTON, EAST (All Saints) *see* Micheldever and E Stratton, Woodmancote etc *Win*

STRATTON, UPPER (St Philip) *Bris 7* **P** *Bp* **V** C A STONE

STRATTON AUDLEY (St Mary and St Edburga) *see* Shelswell *Ox*

STRATTON ON THE FOSSE (St Vigor) *see* Chilcompton w Downside and Stratton on the Fosse *B & W*

STRATTON ST MARGARET (St Margaret) w South Marston and Stanton Fitzwarren *Bris 7* **P** *Patr Bd*

TR T D HAWKINGS,   **TV** G K BAKKER,   **C** A L WILLIAMS, **Hon C** R J BURSTON

STRATTON STRAWLESS (St Margaret)   *see* Hevingham w Hainford and Stratton Strawless *Nor*

STREAT (not known) w Westmeston *Chich 9*   **P** *Woodard Schs* **P-in-c** J R TAYLOR

STREATHAM (Christ Church) *S'wark 15*   **P** *R Streatham St Leon*   **V** *vacant* (020) 8674 5723

STREATHAM Furzedown (St Paul)   *see* Streatham St Paul *S'wark*

STREATHAM (Immanuel) (St Andrew) *S'wark 15*   **P** *Bp, Hyndman Trustees, and R Streatham St Leon (jt)*   **V** S BUTLER, **NSM** W E AIRD

STREATHAM (St Leonard) *S'wark 15*   **P** *Bp*   **R** J R WILCOX, **NSM** M E HAWES

STREATHAM (St Paul) (St Andrew's Church Hall) *S'wark 19* **P** *Bp*   **V** A J R DRIVER,   **Hon C** J M DRIVER

STREATHAM (St Peter) *S'wark 15*   **P** *St Steph Ho Ox* **V** P D ANDREWS,   **Hon C** S T MEYER

STREATHAM (St Thomas)   *see* Telford Park St Thos *S'wark*

STREATHAM, WEST (St James) *S'wark 19*   **P** *CPAS* **V** G G HOWARD,   **C** T M MULRYNE,   **OLM** S D WHITE

STREATHAM HILL (St Margaret the Queen) *S'wark 15* **P** *Bp*   **V** G T WILLIAMS

STREATHAM PARK (St Alban) *S'wark 19*   **P** *Ch Soc Trust* **V** *vacant* (020) 8677 4521 or 8769 5415

STREATHAM VALE (Holy Redeemer) *S'wark 15*   **P** *CPAS* **V** I H GILMOUR

STREATLEY (St Margaret) *St Alb 14*   **P** *Bp*   **V** R W WOOD

STREATLEY (St Mary) w Moulsford *Ox 18*   **P** *Bp* **P-in-c** E R M POLOMSKI,   **Hon C** J P MACKNEY

STREET (Holy Trinity) (Mission Church) w Walton *B & W 5* **P** *DBP*   **R** F J GREED,   **Hon C** D N HATREY

STREET Parishes, The *York 6*   **P** *Patr Bd*   **R** *vacant* (01653) 628376

STREETLY (All Saints) *Lich 25*   **P** *Bp*   **V** S A CHAPMAN, **C** C CARSON

STRELLEY (All Saints)   *see* Bilborough w Strelley *S'well*

STRENSALL (St Mary the Virgin) *York 3*   **P** *Abp* **V** M HARRISON

STRETE (St Michael)   *see* Stoke Fleming, Blackawton and Strete *Ex*

STRETFORD (All Saints) *Man 7*   **P** *Bp*   **P-in-c** A DURRANS

STRETFORD (St Bride) *Man 7*   **P** *Trustees*   **R** P J RAWLINGS, **C** G W BRIGGS,   **OLM** V M ECCLES

STRETFORD (St Matthew) *Man 7*   **P** *D&C* **P-in-c** D T THOMAS

STRETFORD (St Peter)   *see* Firswood and Gorse Hill *Man*

STRETHALL (St Mary the Virgin)   *see* Heydon, Gt and Lt Chishill, Chrishall etc *Chelmsf*

STRETHAM (St James)   *see* Ely *Ely*

STRETTON (St John)   *see* Penkridge Team *Lich*

STRETTON (St Mary) w Claymills *Lich 14*   **P** *Baroness Gretton*   **V** P D HOWARD,   **NSM** D V WARNER

STRETTON (St Matthew) and Appleton Thorn *Ches 4* **P** *Mrs P F du Bois Grantham and Dr S P L du Bois Davidson (jt)*   **V** E C HALL,   **C** G H BUCHAN, **NSM** K L WILLIAMSON

STRETTON (St Nicholas)   *see* Greetham and Thistleton w Stretton and Clipsham *Pet*

STRETTON, LITTLE (All Saints)   *see* Church Stretton *Heref*

STRETTON GRANDISON (St Laurence)   *see* Ledbury *Heref*

STRETTON MAGNA (St Giles)   *see* Glen Magna cum Stretton Magna etc *Leic*

STRETTON ON DUNSMORE (All Saints)   *see* Bourton w Frankton and Stretton on Dunsmore etc *Cov*

STRETTON ON DUNSMORE (Mission Church)   *as above Cov*

STRETTON ON FOSSE (St Peter)   *see* Ilmington w Stretton-on-Fosse etc *Cov*

STRETTON PARVA (St John the Baptist)   *see* Gaulby *Leic*

STRETTON SUGWAS (St Mary Magdalene) *Heref 4*   **P** *DBP* **R** J W R MORRISON

STRICKLAND, GREAT (St Barnabas)   *see* Morland, Thrimby, Gt Strickland and Cliburn *Carl*

STRINES (St Paul)   *see* Marple All SS *Ches*

STRINGSTON (not known)   *see* Quantoxhead *B & W*

STRIXTON (St John the Baptist)   *see* Wollaston and Strixton *Pet*

STROOD (St Francis) *Roch 6*   **P** *Bp*   **V** B R INGRAM

STROOD (St Nicholas) w St Mary *Roch 6*   **P** *Bp and D&C (jt)* **V** D W GREEN,   **C** G V HERBERT

STROUD (Holy Trinity) (St Alban Mission Church) *Glouc 1* **P** *Bp*   **V** M J WITHEY

STROUD (Mission Church)   *see* Steep and Froxfield w Privett *Portsm*

STROUD (St Laurence) and Uplands w Slad *Glouc 1*   **P** *Bp* **V** B C E COKER

STROUD GREEN (Holy Trinity) *Lon 20*   **P** *Bp* **P-in-c** N H ASBRIDGE,   **C** P J HENDERSON

STROXTON (All Saints)   *see* Harlaxton Gp *Linc*

STRUBBY (St Oswald)   *see* Legbourne and Wold Marsh *Linc*

STRUMPSHAW (St Peter)   *see* Burlingham St Edmund w Lingwood, Strumpshaw etc *Nor*

STUBBINGS (St James the Less)   *see* Burchetts Green *Ox*

STUBBINS (St Philip)   *see* Edenfield and Stubbins *Man*

STUBBS CROSS (St Francis)   *see* Kingsnorth and Shadoxhurst *Cant*

STUBSHAW CROSS (St Luke)   *see* Ashton-in-Makerfield St Thos *Liv*

STUBTON (St Martin)   *see* Claypole *Linc*

STUDHAM (St Mary the Virgin)   *see* Kensworth, Studham and Whipsnade *St Alb*

STUDLAND (St Nicholas)   *see* Swanage and Studland *Sarum*

STUDLEY (Nativity of the Blessed Virgin Mary) *Cov 7* **P** *DBP*   **V** R W DEIMEL,   **C** P F HARTOPP, **NSM** M M DEIMEL

STUDLEY (St John the Evangelist) *Sarum 14*   **P** *R Trowbridge St Jas*   **P-in-c** P N BARNES

STUKELEY, GREAT (St Bartholomew) w Little (St Martin) *Ely 8*   **P** *SMF and Bp (jt)*   **Hon C** W N C GIRARD

STUKELEY MEADOWS Local Ecumenical Project *Ely 9 vacant*

STUNTNEY (Holy Cross)   *see* Ely *Ely*

STURMER (St Mary)   *see* Ridgewell w Ashen, Birdbrook and Sturmer *Chelmsf*

STURMINSTER MARSHALL (St Mary), Kingston Lacy and Shapwick *Sarum 9*   **P** *Eton Coll and Nat Trust (alt)* **V** A C STEWART-SYKES

STURMINSTER NEWTON (St Mary), Hinton St Mary and Lydlinch *Sarum 5*   **P** *Col J L Yeatman (1 turn), G A L F Pitt-Rivers Esq (3 turns), V Iwerne Valley (1 turn)* **V** D R R SEYMOUR

STURRY (St Nicholas) w Fordwich and Westbere w Hersden *Cant 3*   **P** *Abp, Ld Chan, and St Aug Foundn Cant (by turn)* **R** P A CORNISH

STURTON (St Hugh)   *see* Stow Gp *Linc*

STURTON, GREAT (All Saints)   *see* Hemingby *Linc*

STURTON-LE-STEEPLE (St Peter and St Paul) *see* N Wheatley, W Burton, Bole, Saundby, Sturton etc *S'well*

STUSTON (All Saints)   *see* N Hartismere *St E*

STUTTON (St Aidan)   *see* Tadcaster w Newton Kyme *York*

STUTTON (St Peter)   *see* Holbrook, Stutton, Freston, Woolverstone etc *St E*

STYVECHALE (St James) *Cov 3*   **P** *Col A M H Gregory-Hood* **V** J K MILLS

SUCKLEY (St John the Baptist)   *see* Alfrick, Lulsley, Suckley, Leigh and Bransford *Worc*

SUDBOROUGH (All Saints)   *see* Brigstock w Stanion and Lowick and Sudborough *Pet*

SUDBOURNE (All Saints)   *see* Wilford Peninsula *St E*

SUDBROOKE (St Edward)   *see* Barlings *Linc*

SUDBURY (All Saints)   *see* Doveridge, Scropton, Sudbury etc *Derby*

SUDBURY (All Saints) w Ballingdon and Brundon *St E 12* **P** *Simeon's Trustees*   **V** A M R PLATT

SUDBURY (St Andrew) *Lon 21*   **P** *Bp*   **V** F M-L SCROGGIE, **NSM** L P NORTH

SUDBURY (St Gregory) St Peter and Chilton *St E 12*   **P** *Bp (3 turns), Ch Soc Trust (1 turn)*   **R** L R PIZZEY

SUDDEN (St Aidan) *Man 20*   **P** *Bp*   **V** G C DOBBS, **C** I E BUTTERWORTH

SUDLEY MANOR (St Mary)   *see* Winchcombe, Gretton, Sudeley Manor etc *Glouc*

SUFFIELD (St Margaret)   *see* King's Beck *Nor*

SUFFIELD PARK (St Martin)   *see* Cromer *Nor*

SUGLEY (Holy Saviour) *Newc 7*   **P** *Bp*   **V** S T ROBSON

SULBY (St Stephen's Chapel)   *see* Lezayre *S & M*

SULGRAVE (St James the Less)   *see* Culworth w Sulgrave and Thorpe Mandeville etc *Pet*

SULHAM (St Nicholas)   *see* Pangbourne w Tidmarsh and Sulham *Ox*

SULHAMSTEAD ABBOTS (St Mary) and Bannister w Ufton Nervet *Ox 12*   **P** *Qu Coll Ox and Or Coll Ox (alt)* **P-in-c** P L DEWEY

SULLINGTON (St Mary) and Thakeham w Warminghurst *Chich 12*   **P** *Bp and DBP (alt)*   **R** P MESSENGER

SUMMERFIELD (Christ Church) (Cavendish Road Hall) *Birm 2*   **P** *R Birm St Martin w Bordesley*   **V** J B KNIGHT

SUMMERFIELD (St John's Chapel)   *see* Hartlebury *Worc*

SUMMERSDALE (St Michael)   *see* Chich St Paul and Westhampnett *Chich*

SUMMERSTOWN (St Mary) *S'wark 19*   **P** *Ch Soc Trust* **V** R J RYAN

SUMMERTOWN (St Michael and All Angels) *see* Wolvercote w Summertown *Ox*

SUNBURY, UPPER (St Saviour) *Lon 13* **P** *V Sunbury* **P-in-c** D R MCDOUGALL, **NSM** R L HOLLANDS

SUNBURY-ON-THAMES (St Mary) *Lon 13* **P** *D&C St Paul's* **NSM** H S L NICHOLSON, M WOOD

SUNDERLAND Pennywell (St Thomas) *Dur 16* **P** *Bp* **V** P A BAKER, **C** G W MILLER

SUNDERLAND Red House (St Cuthbert) *Dur 16* **P** *D&C* **V** *vacant* 0191-549 1261

SUNDERLAND (St Chad) *Dur 16* **P** *Bp* **V** J D CHADD, **NSM** P THOMPSON

SUNDERLAND (St Mary the Virgin) (St Peter) *Dur 16* **P** *Bp* **V** K A WALTON, **C** G W MILLER

SUNDERLAND (St Michael) *Dur 16* **P** *Bp* **TR** S R TAYLOR, **TV** D W ROSAMOND, S D HAZLETT, A R M MARSHALL, **NSM** J M M FRANCIS

SUNDERLAND Town End Farm (St Bede) *Dur 16* **P** *Bp* **V** J W POULTER

SUNDERLAND, NORTH (St Paul) *Newc 10* **P** *Lord Crewe's Trustees* **V** D G ROGERSON

SUNDERLAND POINT (Mission Church) *see* Overton *Blackb*

SUNDON (St Mary) *St Alb 14* **P** *Bp* **V** *vacant* (01582) 573236

SUNDRIDGE (St Mary) w Ide Hill *Roch 9* **P** *Abp* **R** D J E ATTWOOD, **NSM** A M BOYLE

SUNNINGDALE (Holy Trinity) *Ox 11* **P** *Bp* **V** H D UFFINDELL, **C** S GAY, **NSM** A M GRIGGS

SUNNINGHILL (St Michael and All Angels) *Ox 11* **P** *St Jo Coll Cam* **V** T W GUNTER

SUNNINGWELL (St Leonard) *see* Radley and Sunningwell *Ox*

SUNNYSIDE (St Barnabas) *see* E Grinstead St Swithun *Chich*

SUNNYSIDE (St Michael and All Angels) w Bourne End *St Alb 2* **P** *CPAS* **V** D J ABBOTT, **C** D M BROOKE, **NSM** R CLARKSON

SURBITON (St Andrew) (St Mark) *S'wark 17* **P** *Bp* **V** J H TIDY, **C** V A CORY, **Hon C** T BRAUN, **NSM** G M AYERST

SURBITON (St Matthew) *S'wark 17* **P** *CPAS* **V** S A HONES, **C** R W J MYERS, **OLM** V CUTHBERT

SURBITON HILL (Christ Church) *S'wark 17* **P** *Ch Soc Trust and Trustees (jt)* **V** G WINTLE, **C** D A BAKER, **NSM** D J BENDELL

SURFLEET (St Lawrence) *see* Glen Gp *Linc*

SURLINGHAM (St Mary) *see* Rockland St Mary w Hellington, Bramerton etc *Nor*

SURREY WEALD *Guildf 7* **P** *Patr Bd (1 turn), Ld Chan (2 turns)* **TR** A D J COE, **TV** P C KNAPPER, **NSM** J R BAXTER

SUSSEX GARDENS (St James) *see* Paddington St Jas *Lon*

SUSTEAD (St Peter and St Paul) *see* Roughton and Felbrigg, Metton, Sustead etc *Nor*

SUTCOMBE (St Andrew) *see* Bradworthy, Sutcombe, Putford etc *Ex*

SUTTERBY (not known) *see* Partney Gp *Linc*

SUTTERTON (St Mary), Fosdyke, Algarkirk and Wigtoft *Linc 21* **P** *Prime Min (1 turn), Bp and DBP (1 turn)* **R** K STEVENTON

SUTTON (All Saints) *see* Potton w Sutton and Cockayne Hatley *St Alb*

SUTTON (All Saints) *see* Wilford Peninsula *St E*

SUTTON (All Saints) w Shopland *Chelmsf 12* **P** *SMF* **P-in-c** C W COUSINS

SUTTON (Christ Church) *S'wark 25* **P** *R Sutton St Nic* **V** C E GALE

SUTTON (Mission Room) *see* Felixkirk w Boltby *York*

SUTTON (St Andrew) *Ely 13* **P** *D&C* **NSM** T M DIXON, M L BRADBURY

SUTTON (St Barnabas' Mission Church) *see* Macclesfield Team Par *Ches*

SUTTON (St Clement), Huttoft and Anderby *Linc 8* **P** *Bp (2 turns), Magd Coll Cam (1 turn)* **R** L ST J R AITKEN

SUTTON (St James) *Ches 13* **P** *Trustees* **V** E W L DAVIES

SUTTON (St James) and Wawne *York 14* **P** *Patr Bd* **TR** A F RABLEN, **TV** C FISHER-BAILEY, H H NESBITT, P COPLEY

SUTTON (St John the Baptist) *see* Barlavington, Burton w Coates, Sutton and Bignor *Chich*

SUTTON (St Mary) *see* Calow and Sutton cum Duckmanton *Derby*

SUTTON (St Michael) *see* Stalham, E Ruston, Brunstead, Sutton and Ingham *Nor*

SUTTON (St Michael and All Angels) *see* Castor w Sutton and Upton w Marholm *Pet*

SUTTON (St Nicholas) *S'wark 25* **P** *Hertf Coll Ox* **R** S J H GOATCHER

SUTTON (St Nicholas) (All Saints) (St Michael and All Angels) *Liv 10* **P** *Patr Bd* **TR** C B SPITTLE, **TV** R A BYWORTH, K D STILL

SUTTON (St Thomas) *Bradf 8* **P** *Ch Ch Ox* **V** M COWGILL

SUTTON w Carlton and Normanton upon Trent and Marnham *S'well 3* **P** *Bp* **P-in-c** S DIXON

SUTTON, EAST (St Peter and St Paul) *see* Sutton Valence w E Sutton and Chart Sutton *Cant*

SUTTON, GREAT (St John the Evangelist) *Ches 9* **P** *V Eastham* **V** C M POTTER, **C** R ORTON

SUTTON, NORTH *see* Plymouth Em, St Paul Efford and St Aug *Ex*

SUTTON AT HONE (St John the Baptist) *Roch 2* **P** *D&C* **V** *vacant* (01322) 862253

SUTTON BASSETT (All Saints) *see* Stoke Albany w Wilbarston and Ashley etc *Pet*

SUTTON BENGER (All Saints) *see* Draycot *Bris*

SUTTON BONINGTON (St Michael) (St Anne) w Normanton-on-Soar *S'well 9* **P** *Bp* **P-in-c** J E PALMER

SUTTON BRIDGE (St Matthew) *Linc 16* **P** *Bp* **P-in-c** D B WOODS

SUTTON BY DOVER (St Peter and St Paul) *see* Gt Mongeham w Ripple and Sutton by Dover *Cant*

SUTTON CHENEY (St James) *see* Bosworth and Sheepy Gp *Leic*

SUTTON COLDFIELD (Holy Trinity) *Birm 12* **P** *Bp* **R** J H LANGSTAFF, **C** B A ROBERTSON

SUTTON COLDFIELD (St Chad) *Birm 12* **P** *Bp* **V** W J ROUTH, **C** A D BARRETT

SUTTON COLDFIELD (St Columba) *Birm 12* **P** *Bp* **V** R P TUCKER

SUTTON COURTENAY (All Saints) w Appleford *Ox 10* **P** *D&C Windsor* **P-in-c** H G KENDRICK, **NSM** K JONES

SUTTON-CUM-LOUND (St Bartholomew) *see* Babworth w Sutton-cum-Lound and Scofton etc *S'well*

SUTTON GREEN (All Souls) *see* Woking St Pet *Guildf*

SUTTON HILL (Pastoral Centre) *see* Madeley *Heref*

SUTTON IN ASHFIELD (St Mary Magdalene) *S'well 4* **P** *Bp* **P-in-c** A N EVANS, **C** S CADDY

SUTTON IN ASHFIELD (St Michael and All Angels) *S'well 4* **P** *Bp* **P-in-c** B HALL

SUTTON IN HOLDERNESS (St Michael) *York 14* **P** *Abp* **V** M BURLEY, **C** C M RABLEN, **NSM** P J NELSON

SUTTON LE MARSH (St Clement) *see* Sutton, Huttoft and Anderby *Linc*

SUTTON MADDOCK (St Mary) *see* Beckbury, Badger, Kemberton, Ryton, Stockton etc *Lich*

SUTTON MANDEVILLE (All Saints) *see* Fovant, Sutton Mandeville and Teffont Evias etc *Sarum*

SUTTON MONTIS (Holy Trinity) *see* Queen Camel w W Camel, Corton Denham etc *B & W*

SUTTON NEW TOWN (St Barnabas) *S'wark 25* **P** *Bp* **V** *vacant* (020) 8661 9619

SUTTON ON DERWENT (St Michael) *see* Elvington w Sutton on Derwent and E Cottingwith *York*

SUTTON ON PLYM (St John the Evangelist) *Ex 23* **P** *Keble Coll Ox* **V** B R LAY

SUTTON-ON-SEA (St Clement) *see* Sutton, Huttoft and Anderby *Linc*

SUTTON ON THE FOREST (All Hallows) *York 3* **P** *Ld Chan* **P-in-c** S K NIGHTINGALE

SUTTON ON THE HILL (St Michael) *see* Boylestone, Church Broughton, Dalbury, etc *Derby*

SUTTON-ON-TRENT (All Saints) *see* Sutton w Carlton and Normanton upon Trent etc *S'well*

SUTTON PARK (St Andrew) *see* Sutton St Jas and Wawne *York*

SUTTON ST EDMUND (St Edmund King and Martyr) *see* The Suttons w Tydd *Linc*

SUTTON ST JAMES (St James) *as above Linc*

SUTTON ST MARY (otherwise known as Long Sutton) (St Mary) *Linc 16* **P** *Lady McGeoch* **P-in-c** J P E SIBLEY

SUTTON ST MICHAEL (St Michael) *see* Sutton St Nicholas w Sutton St Michael *Heref*

SUTTON ST NICHOLAS *see* Lutton w Gedney Drove End, Dawsmere *Linc*

SUTTON ST NICHOLAS (St Nicholas) w Sutton St Michael *Heref 4* **P** *Bp* **P-in-c** N C H VARNON

SUTTON UNDER BRAILES (St Thomas à Becket) *Cov 9* **P** *Bp* **R** N J MORGAN, **NSM** J W ROLFE

SUTTON VALENCE (St Mary the Virgin) w East Sutton and Chart Sutton *Cant 15* **P** *Abp York* **V** D R BARKER

SUTTON VENY (St John the Evangelist) *see* Upper Wylye Valley *Sarum*

SUTTON WALDRON (St Bartholomew) *see* Iwerne Valley *Sarum*

SUTTONS w Tydd, The *Linc 16* **P** *Ld Chan (1 turn), V Long Sutton (2 turns)* **V** I T WHITE

SWABY (St Nicholas) *see* Legbourne and Wold Marsh *Linc*

SWADLINCOTE (Emmanuel) *Derby 16* **P** *V Gresley* **V** D J HORSFALL

SWAFFHAM (St Peter and St Paul) *Nor 13* **P** *Bp* **V** S J SMITH, **NSM** P G BLAMIRE

SWAFFHAM BULBECK (St Mary) and Swaffham Prior w Reach *Ely 3* **P** *Bp and D&C (jt)* **P-in-c** D H LEWIS, **NSM** P M DEBENHAM

SWAFFHAM PRIOR (St Mary) *see* Swaffham Bulbeck and Swaffham Prior w Reach *Ely*

SWAFIELD (St Nicholas) *see* Trunch *Nor*

SWAINSTHORPE (St Peter) *see* Newton Flotman, Swainsthorpe, Tasburgh, etc *Nor*

SWAINSWICK (Blessed Virgin Mary) *see* Bath St Sav w Swainswick and Woolley *B & W*

SWALCLIFFE (St Peter and St Paul) *see* Wykeham *Ox*

SWALECLIFFE (St John the Baptist) *see* Whitstable *Cant*

SWALEDALE *Ripon 2* **P** *Bp* **V** T M TUNLEY

SWALLOW (Holy Trinity) *Linc 5* **P** *The Revd J R H Thorold and J R Thorold Esq (jt), DBP, Bp, and Earl of Yarborough (by turn)* **R** *vacant (01472)* 371560

SWALLOWCLIFFE (St Peter) *see* Nadder Valley *Sarum*

SWALLOWFIELD (All Saints) *Ox 15* **P** *D&C Heref* **P-in-c** P E BANNISTER

SWALWELL (Holy Trinity) *Dur 13* **P** *R Whickham* **P-in-c** H DITCHBURN

SWAN *Ox 24* **P** *Patr Bd* **TV** D A HISCOCK, E A MASON

SWANAGE (All Saints) (St Mary the Virgin) and Studland *Sarum 8* **P** *Patr Bd* **TR** J S WOOD, **TV** W H N WATTS, **OLM** A C HIGGINS

SWANBOURNE (St Swithun) *see* Newton Longville and Mursley w Swanbourne etc *Ox*

SWANLAND (St Barnabas) *York 14* **P** *H Trin Hull and Distr Ch Patr Soc Ltd* **V** R H O HILL

SWANLEY (St Mary) *Roch 2* **P** *Guild of All So* **V** M R BRUNDLE

SWANLEY (St Paul) *Roch 2* **P** *Merchant Taylors' Co* **V** A D PROCTER

SWANMORE (St Barnabas) *Portsm 1* **P** *DBP* **P-in-c** P H KELLY, **NSM** M M MORT

SWANMORE (St Michael and All Angels) *Portsm 7* **P** *SMF* **V** M F JONES

SWANNINGTON (St George) *see* Ravenstone and Swannington *Leic*

SWANNINGTON (St Margaret) *see* Alderford w Attlebridge and Swannington *Nor*

SWANSCOMBE (St Peter and St Paul) *Roch 4* **P** *DBP* **R** D SCOTT

SWANTON ABBOT (St Michael) *see* Worstead, Westwick, Sloley, Swanton Abbot etc *Nor*

SWANTON MORLEY (All Saints) w Beetley w East Bilney and Hoe *Nor 14* **P** *G&C Coll Cam, Ld Chan, and DBP (by turn)* **P-in-c** R AMES-LEWIS

SWANTON NOVERS (St Edmund) *see* Brinton, Briningham, Hunworth, Stody etc *Nor*

SWANWICK (St Andrew) and Pentrich *Derby 1* **P** *Wright Trustees and Duke of Devonshire (alt)* **V** T B JOHNSON

SWANWICK (St Barnabas) *see* Sarisbury *Portsm*

SWARBY (St Mary and All Saints) *see* S Lafford *Linc*

SWARCLIFFE (St Luke) *see* Seacroft *Ripon*

SWARDESTON (St Mary the Virgin) w East Carleton, Intwood, Keswick and Ketteringham *Nor 7* **P** *Bp, DBP, and Miss M B Unthank (jt)* **R** D J CHAMBERLIN

SWARKESTONE (St James) *see* Ticknall, Smisby and Stanton by Bridge etc *Derby*

SWARTHMORE (Mission Church) *see* Pennington and Lindal w Marton and Bardsea *Carl*

SWATON (St Michael) *see* Helpringham w Hale *Linc*

SWAVESEY (St Andrew) *see* Fen Drayton w Conington and Lolworth etc *Ely*

SWAY (St Luke) *Win 11* **P** *Bp* **P-in-c** S L GREEN

SWAYFIELD (St Nicholas) *see* Corby Glen *Linc*

SWAYTHLING (St Mary South Stoneham w St Alban the Martyr) *Win 13* **P** *Bp and TR Southn City Cen (jt)* **P-in-c** G J PHILBRICK, **C** V A MAUNDER

SWEFFLING (St Mary) *see* Rendham w Sweffling *St E*

SWELL (St Catherine) *see* Curry Rivel w Fivehead and Swell *B & W*

SWELL, LOWER (St Mary) *see* Stow on the Wold, Condicote and The Swells *Glouc*

SWELL, UPPER (St Mary) *as above Glouc*

SWEPSTONE (St Peter) *see* Appleby Gp *Leic*

SWERFORD (St Mary) *see* Hook Norton w Gt Rollright, Swerford etc *Ox*

SWETTENHAM (St Peter) *see* Brereton w Swettenham *Ches*

SWILLAND (St Mary) *see* Clopton w Otley, Swilland and Ashbocking *St E*

SWILLINGTON (St Mary) *Ripon 8* **P** *Bp* **P-in-c** J W THEOBALD

SWIMBRIDGE (St James the Apostle) w West Buckland and Landkey *Ex 17* **P** *Bp and Trustees Earl Fortescue (jt)* **R** P BOWERS, **NSM** G F SQUIRE

SWINBROOK (St Mary) *see* Burford w Fulbrook, Taynton, Asthall etc *Ox*

SWINDERBY (All Saints) *Linc 18* **P** *Bp, Ld Chan, E M K Kirk Esq, and D&C (by turn)* **V** G C GOALBY, **NSM** J T ROOKE

SWINDON (All Saints) (St Barnabas) *Bris 7* **P** *Bp* **V** A R STEVENSON

SWINDON (Christ Church) (St Mary) *Bris 7* **P** *Ld Chan* **V** S M STEVENETTE, **C** E V QUIBELL, **Hon C** J A S ASHBY

SWINDON Dorcan *Bris 7* **P** *Bp* **TR** A B KNAPP, **C** E M GARDNER

SWINDON New Town (St Mark) (St Adhelm) (St Luke) (St Saviour) *Bris 7* **P** *Patr Bd* **TR** D B MCCONKEY, **TV** L A PINFIELD

SWINDON (St Andrew) (St John the Baptist) *Bris 7* **P** *Ld Chan* **TR** R J BURLES

SWINDON (St Augustine) *Bris 7* **P** *Bp* **P-in-c** A N ATTWOOD

SWINDON (St John the Evangelist) *see* Smestow Vale *Lich*

SWINDON (St Lawrence) w Uckington and Elmstone Hardwicke *Glouc 10* **P** *Bp* **P-in-c** D R EADY

SWINDON (St Peter) *see* Penhill *Bris*

SWINDON, NORTH (St Andrew) *Bris 7* **P** *Bp* **V** R F I CRAM

SWINDON, WEST and the Lydiards *Bris 7* **P** *Patr Bd* **TR** S J SKINNER, **TV** A MACKENZIE, P M KNIGHT, **Hon C** J M SKINNER

SWINE (St Mary) *York 11* **P** *Abp and Baroness de Stempel (jt)* **V** *vacant (01482)* 815250

SWINEFLEET (St Margaret) *see* The Marshland *Sheff*

SWINESHEAD (St Mary) *Linc 21* **P** *Bp* **V** M A BARSLEY

SWINESHEAD (St Nicholas) *see* The Stodden Churches *St Alb*

SWINFORD (All Saints) *see* Gilmorton, Peatling Parva, Kimcote etc *Leic*

SWINFORD, OLD Stourbridge (St Mary) *Worc 12* **P** *Bp* **R** G S CROSS, **C** C P BRYAN

SWINHOPE (St Helen) *see* Binbrook Gp *Linc*

SWINNOW (Christ the Saviour) *see* Stanningley St Thos *Ripon*

SWINSTEAD (St Mary) *see* Edenham w Witham on the Hill and Swinstead *Linc*

SWINTON (Holy Rood) *Man 2* **P** *TR Swinton and Pendlebury* **P-in-c** C C CLAPHAM

SWINTON (St Margaret) *Sheff 12* **P** *Sir Philip Naylor-Leyland Bt* **V** C J BARLEY

SWINTON (St Peter) and Pendlebury *Man 2* **P** *Patr Bd* **TR** R A FARRELL, **TV** I A HALL, J R SIEMENS, **C** A L WAUDE

SWITHLAND (St Leonard) *see* Woodhouse, Woodhouse Eaves and Swithland *Leic*

SWYNCOMBE (St Botolph) *see* Icknield *Ox*

SWYNNERTON (St Mary) and Tittensor *Lich 13* **P** *Bp and Simeon's Trustees (jt)* **R** B J BREWER

SWYRE (Holy Trinity) *see* Bride Valley *Sarum*

SYDE (St Mary) *see* Brimpsfield w Birdlip, Syde, Daglingworth etc *Glouc*

SYDENHAM (All Saints) *S'wark 5* **P** *V Sydenham St Bart* **V** J O ARDLEY, **NSM** R W POTTIER

SYDENHAM (Holy Trinity) *S'wark 5* **P** *Simeon's Trustees* **P-in-c** S A LASKEY, **C** J F BARRY, **OLM** V J SHIRLEY

SYDENHAM (St Bartholomew) *S'wark 5* **P** *Earl of Dartmouth* **V** M J KINGSTON

SYDENHAM (St Mary) *see* Chinnor w Emmington and Sydenham etc *Ox*

SYDENHAM (St Philip) *S'wark 5* **P** *V Sydenham St Bart* **V** P W TIERNAN

SYDENHAM, LOWER (St Michael and All Angels) Bell Green *S'wark 5* **P** *Bp* **V** S M BURNETT

SYDENHAM DAMEREL (St Mary) *see* Milton Abbot, Dunterton, Lamerton etc *Ex*

SYDERSTONE (St Mary) *see* N and S Creake w Waterden, Syderstone etc *Nor*

SYDLING (St Nicholas) *see* Bradford Peverell, Stratton, Frampton etc *Sarum*

SYERSTON (All Saints) *see* E Stoke w Syerston *S'well*

SYKEHOUSE (Holy Trinity) *see* Fishlake w Sykehouse and Kirk Bramwith etc *Sheff*

SYLEHAM (St Mary) *see* Hoxne w Denham, Syleham and Wingfield *St E*

SYMONDS GREEN (Christ the King) *see* Stevenage H Trin *St Alb*

SYMONDSBURY (St John the Baptist) *Sarum 2* **P** *Bp* **P-in-c** R T SHORTHOUSE

SYRESHAM (St James)   see Helmdon w Stuchbury and
   Radstone etc Pet
SYSTON (St Mary)   see Barkston and Hough Gp Linc
SYSTON Team Ministry, The (St Peter and St Paul) Leic 6
   P Patr Bd   **TR** J F WELLINGTON,   **TV** K F SHEPHERD,
   J F AMBROSE,   **C** S M COOPER
SYSTON (St Anne)   see Warmley, Syston and Bitton Bris
SYSTONBY (not known)   see Melton Mowbray Leic
SYWELL (St Peter and St Paul)   see Mears Ashby and Hardwick
   and Sywell etc Pet
TABLEY, OVER (St Paul) and High Legh Ches 12   **P** Bp and
   Mrs P H Langford-Brooke (1 turn), C L S Cornwall-Legh Esq
   (1 turn)   **P-in-c** M R CAVANAGH
TACKLEY (St Nicholas)   see Steeple Aston w N Aston and
   Tackley Ox
TACOLNESTON (All Saints)   see Ashwellthorpe, Forncett,
   Fundenhall, Hapton etc Nor
TADCASTER (St Mary) w Newton Kyme York 1   **P** Abp
   V R P BURTON,   **C** M D LAYNESMITH
TADDINGTON (St Michael), Chelmorton and Flagg, and
   Monyash Derby 4   **P** V Bakewell   **P-in-c** J O GOLDSMITH,
   NSM M L GOLDSMITH
TADDIPORT (St Mary Magdalene)   see Gt and Lt Torrington
   and Frithelstock Ex
TADLEY, NORTH (St Mary) Win 4   **P** Bp   **V** B J NORRIS,
   NSM S G ARMSTRONG
TADLEY SOUTH (St Peter) (St Paul) and Silchester Win 4
   P Duke of Wellington and Bp (alt)   **R** P D COOPER,
   NSM P V BROWN, A BOWSKILL
TADLOW (St Giles)   see Shingay Gp of Par Ely
TADMARTON (St Nicholas)   see Wykeham Ox
TADWORTH (Good Shepherd) S'wark 27   **P** V Kingswood
   St Andr   **P-in-c** M W ELFRED,   **C** S A C FOUNTAIN,
   OLM A S BLAIN
TAKELEY (Holy Trinity) w Little Canfield Chelmsf 18   **P** Bp
   and Ch Coll Cam   **P-in-c** L BOND,   **NSM** C HAWKES
TALATON (St James the Apostle)   see Whimple, Talaton and
   Clyst St Lawr Ex
TALBOT VILLAGE (St Mark) Sarum 7   **P** Trustees
   V C J F RUTLEDGE,   **C** L S DOBBINS
TALKE O' THE HILL (St Martin) Lich 9   **P** V Audley
   R J T PYE
TALKIN (not known)   see Eden, Gelt and Irthing Carl
TALLAND (St Tallan) Truro 12   **P** DBP and
   W Gundry-Mills Esq (alt)   **P-in-c** C D NEWELL,
   NSM G LONSDALE
TALLINGTON (St Laurence)   see Uffington Gp Linc
TAMERTON, NORTH (St Denis)   see Boyton, N Tamerton,
   Werrington etc Truro
TAMERTON FOLIOT (St Mary) Ex 22   **P** Ld Chan
   V R E AVERY
TAMWORTH (St Editha) Lich 4   **P** Bp   **V** A BARRETT,
   C S J OSBOURNE, V M C VAN DEN BERGH,   **NSM** M J PACEY
TANDRIDGE (St Peter)   see Oxted and Tandridge S'wark
TANFIELD (St Margaret of Antioch)   see Ch the K Dur
**TANFIELD, WEST (St Nicholas) and Well w Snape and North
   Stainley** Ripon 3   **P** Bp and Mrs M E Bourne-Arton (alt)
   R M DE LA P BERESFORD-PEIRSE
TANGLEY (St Thomas of Canterbury)   see Hatherden w
   Tangley, Weyhill and Penton Mewsey Win
TANGMERE (St Andrew) and Oving Chich 3   **P** Bp and Duke
   of Richmond (jt)   **R** C FOWLER
TANKERSLEY (St Peter), Thurgoland and Wortley Sheff 11
   P Dowager Countess of Wharncliffe, Sir Philip
   Naylor-Leyland Bt, and V Silkstone (jt)   **R** K J E HALE
TANNINGTON (St Ethelbert)   see Worlingworth, Southolt,
   Tannington, Bedfield etc St E
TANSLEY (Holy Trinity), Dethick, Lea and Holloway Derby 7
   P Bp, V Crich, and DBF (jt)   **P-in-c** R G LAWRENCE
TANSOR (St Mary)   see Warmington, Tansor and Cotterstock
   etc Pet
TANWORTH (St Mary Magdalene) Birm 6   **P** F D Muntz Esq
   V T J HARMER
TAPLOW (St Nicholas)   see Burnham w Dropmore, Hitcham
   and Taplow Ox
TARDEBIGGE (St Bartholomew) Worc 7   **P** Earl of Plymouth
   P-in-c F R HAZELL
TARLETON (Holy Trinity) Blackb 5   **P** St Pet Coll Ox
   R A J JEYNES,   **Hon C** T TAYLOR
TARLTON (St Osmund)   see Coates, Rodmarton and Sapperton
   etc Glouc
TARPORLEY (St Helen) Ches 5   **P** Bp (4 turns), D&C
   (1 turn), and Sir John Grey Regerton Bt (1 turn)
   R G L COOKSON
TARRANT GUNVILLE (St Mary)   see Chase Sarum
TARRANT HINTON (St Mary)   as above Sarum

TARRANT KEYNSTON (All Saints)   as above Sarum
TARRANT MONKTON (All Saints)   as above Sarum
TARRANT RUSHTON (St Mary)   as above Sarum
TARRING, WEST (St Andrew) Chich 5   **P** Abp   **R** W E JERVIS
TARRING NEVILLE (St Mary)   see Denton w S Heighton and
   Tarring Neville Chich
TARRINGTON (St Philip and St James)   see Ledbury Heref
TARVIN (St Andrew) Ches 2   **P** Bp   **V** D R HERBERT,
   NSM M R MARR
TAS VALLEY   see Newton Flotman, Swainsthorpe, Tasburgh,
   etc Nor
TASBURGH (St Mary)   as above Nor
TASLEY (St Peter and St Paul)   see Bridgnorth, Tasley, Astley
   Abbotts, etc Heref
TATENHILL (St Michael and All Angels)   see Branston w
   Tatenhill Lich
TATHAM (St James the Less)   see E Lonsdale Blackb
TATHAM FELLS (Good Shepherd)   as above Blackb
TATHWELL (St Vedast)   see Legbourne and Wold Marsh Linc
TATSFIELD (St Mary)   S'wark 26   **P** Bp   **P-in-c** C R WOOD
TATTENHALL (St Alban) and Handley Ches 5   **P** Bp and
   D&C (jt)   **R** G G TURNER
TATTENHAM CORNER (St Mark) and Burgh Heath Guildf 9
   P Bp   **V** P J BOULTON-LEA
TATTENHOE (St Giles)   see Watling Valley Ox
TATTERFORD (St Margaret)   see E w W Rudham,
   Helhoughton etc Nor
TATTERSETT (All Saints and St Andrew)   as above Nor
TATTERSHALL (Holy Trinity)   see Coningsby w Tattershall
   Linc
TATTINGSTONE (St Mary)   see Sproughton w Burstall,
   Copdock w Washbrook etc St E
TATWORTH (St John the Evangelist)   see Chard and Distr
   B & W
TAUNTON (All Saints) B & W 18   **P** Bp   **V** D C W FAYLE
TAUNTON (Holy Trinity) B & W 18   **P** Bp
   V J B V LAURENCE,   **Hon C** J J STRATTON
TAUNTON (St Andrew) B & W 18   **P** Bp   **V** J SMITH,
   C J R MORRIS
TAUNTON (St James) B & W 18   **P** Simeon's Trustees
   V A P BANNISTER
TAUNTON (St John the Evangelist) B & W 18   **P** Bp
   P-in-c D ROBERTS
TAUNTON (St Mary Magdalene) B & W 18   **P** Ch Patr Trust
   V N R MADDOCK,   **Hon C** D E CAVAGHAN
TAUNTON (St Peter) Lyngford B & W 18   **P** Bp
   V A L SMITH,   **C** D C SHERWOOD
TAVERHAM (St Edmund) w Ringland Nor 2   **P** Bp and Major
   J M Mills (alt)   **P-in-c** D W JACKSON
TAVISTOCK (St Eustachius) and Gulworthy (St Paul) Ex 24
   P Bp   **V** J E F RAWLINGS,   **C** J M ABECASSIS
TAW VALLEY   see Barnstaple Ex
TAWSTOCK (St Peter)   see Newton Tracey, Horwood,
   Alverdiscott etc Ex
**TAWTON, NORTH (St Peter), Bondleigh, Sampford Courtenay
   and Honeychurch** Ex 12   **P** MMCET, K Coll Cam, and
   D&C (jt)   **R** R W B ARDILL
TAWTON, SOUTH (St Andrew) and Belstone Ex 12   **P** D&C
   Windsor and Bp (jt)   **R** M D THAYER
TAYNTON (St John the Evangelist)   see Burford w Fulbrook,
   Taynton, Asthall etc Ox
TAYNTON (St Laurence)   see Highnam, Lassington, Rudford,
   Tibberton etc Glouc
TEALBY (All Saints)   see Walesby Linc
TEAN, UPPER (Christ Church) Lich 6   **P** R Checkley
   P-in-c M R H TURNER,   **Hon C** E C LAST
TEBAY (St James)   see Orton and Tebay w Ravenstonedale etc
   Carl
**TEDBURN ST MARY (St Mary), Whitestone, Oldridge,
   Holcombe Burnell, Dunsford, Doddiscombsleigh and Cheriton
   Bishop** Ex 6   **P** Patr Bd   **P-in-c** J M S HOLLAND
**TEDDINGTON (St Mark) and Hampton Wick (St John the
   Baptist)** Lon 11   **P** Bp   **V** D P LUND,   **NSM** V F FRAY
TEDDINGTON (St Mary) (St Alban the Martyr) Lon 10   **P** Bp
   V J M CLEAVER
TEDDINGTON (St Nicholas)   see Overbury w Teddington,
   Alstone etc Worc
**TEDDINGTON (St Peter and St Paul) and Fulwell St Michael
   and St George** Lon 10   **P** Bp   **V** S G L WOOD,
   Hon C P R TOPHAM
TEDSTONE DELAMERE (St James)   see Edvin Loach w
   Tedstone Delamere etc Heref
TEDSTONE WAFER (St Mary)   as above Heref
TEFFONT EVIAS (St Michael)   see Fovant, Sutton Mandeville
   and Teffont Evias etc Sarum
TEFFONT MAGNA (St Edward)   as above Sarum

TEIGH (Holy Trinity) Whissendine and Market Overton *Pet 14*
P *Bp and Lady Gretton (alt)* **R** *vacant (01664) 474333*

TEIGNGRACE (St Peter and St Paul) *see Highweek and Teigngrace Ex*

TEIGNMOUTH (St James) (St Michael the Archangel), Ideford w Luton, Ashcombe and Bishopsteignton *Ex 6* P *Patr Bd*
TR P G LUFF, **TV** S P WEST, **C** C M S LUFF, A M HOFBAUER

TELFORD, CENTRAL: Dawley, Lawley, Malinslee, Stirchley, Brookside and Hollinswood *Lich 21* P *Patr Bd (3 turns), The Crown (1 turn)* **TR** S W DEANE, **TV** M A PETERS, E C PHILLIPS

TELFORD PARK (St Thomas) *S'wark 15* P *Trustees*
V S A EVANS

TELLISFORD (All Saints) *see Hardington Vale B & W*

TELSCOMBE VILLAGE (St Laurence) *Chich 18* P *Bp and Gorham Trustees (jt)* **V** D A HIDER

TEME VALLEY, LOWER *see Martley and Wichenford, Knightwick etc Worc*

TEME VALLEY NORTH: Knighton-on-Teme, Lindridge, Pensax, Menith Wood, Stanford-on-Teme and Stockton *Worc 13* P *Bp and D&C (alt)* **R** L S GRACE

TEME VALLEY SOUTH: Eastham, Rochford, Stoke Bliss, Hanley Child, Hanley William and Kyre Wyard *Worc 13*
P *Ld Chan, Bp, and Mrs M M Miles (by turn)* **R** G M REED

TEMPLE (St Catherine) *see Blisland w St Breward Truro*

TEMPLE BALSALL (St Mary) *Birm 11* P *Lady Leveson Hosp*
V J W WOODWARD

TEMPLE BRUER (St John the Baptist) *see Graffoe Gp Linc*

TEMPLE CLOUD (St Barnabas) *see Clutton w Cameley B & W*

TEMPLE EWELL (St Peter and St Paul) w Lydden *Cant 4*
P *Abp* **R** P CHRISTIAN

TEMPLE GRAFTON (St Andrew) w Binton *Cov 7* P *Dioc Trustees* **P-in-c** S R TASH, **NSM** L E DAVIES

TEMPLE GUITING (St Mary) *see The Guitings, Cutsdean, Farmcote etc Glouc*

TEMPLE HIRST (St John the Baptist) *see Haddlesey w Hambleton and Birkin York*

TEMPLE NORMANTON (St James the Apostle) *Derby 5*
P *Bp* **V** M R AINSCOUGH

TEMPLE SOWERBY (St James) *see Kirkby Thore w Temple Sowerby and Newbiggin Carl*

TEMPLECOMBE (Blessed Virgin Mary) *see Abbas and Templecombe w Horsington B & W*

TEMPLETON (St Margaret) *see Washfield, Stoodleigh, Withleigh etc Ex*

TEMPSFORD (St Peter) *see Blunham, Gt Barford, Roxton and Tempsford etc St Alb*

TEN MILE BANK (St Mark) *see Hilgay Ely*

TENBURY (St Mary) *Heref 12* P *The Revd F J Evans*
TR A N JEVONS, **TV** C A LORDING, **NSM** S FOSTER

TENBURY (St Michael and All Angels) *Heref 12* P *St Mich Coll* **V** *vacant (01584) 810702*

TENDRING (St Edmund King and Martyr) and Little Bentley w Beaufort cum Moze *Chelmsf 20* P *Em Coll Cam, DBP, and Ball Coll Ox (by turn)* **R** D W A KING

TENTERDEN (St Michael and All Angels) *Cant 17* P *Abp*
P-in-c J K BUTTERWORTH

TENTERDEN (St Mildred) w Smallhythe *Cant 17* P *D&C*
V D G TRUSTRAM, **NSM** M ROYLANCE

TERLING (All Saints) *see Fairstead w Terling and White Notley etc Chelmsf*

TERRIERS (St Francis) *Ox 29* P *V High Wycombe*
V A W DICKINSON, **NSM** J M WILLIAMS

TERRINGTON (All Saints) *see Howardian Gp York*

TERRINGTON ST CLEMENT (St Clement) *Ely 17*
P *The Crown* **V** R J SLIPPER

TERRINGTON ST JOHN (St John) *see E Marshland Ely*

TERWICK (St Peter) *see Rogate w Terwick and Trotton w Chithurst Chich*

TESTON (St Peter and St Paul) *see Wateringbury and Teston Roch*

TESTWOOD (St Winfrid) *see Totton Win*

TETBURY (St Mary the Virgin) w Beverston *Glouc 15*
P *Lt-Col J J B Pope (5 turns), The Crown (1 turn)*
R A J WRIGHT

TETCOTT (Holy Cross) *see Ashwater, Halwill, Beaworthy, Clawton etc Ex*

TETFORD (St Mary) *see S Ormsby Gp Linc*

TETNEY (St Peter and St Paul) *see The North-Chapel Parishes Linc*

TETSWORTH (St Giles) *see Thame Ox*

TETTENHALL REGIS (St Michael and All Angels) *Lich 24*
P *Patr Bd* **TR** D E NEWSOME, **TV** M R KINDER, P G ASHBY,
C E RATHBONE, **OLM** J LLOYD

TETTENHALL WOOD (Christ Church) and Perton *Lich 24*
P *Patr Bd* **TR** K M ELBOURNE, **OLM** P A P SNAPE,
C A HARLEY

TEVERSAL (St Katherine) *see Skegby w Teversal S'well*

TEVERSHAM (All Saints) *Ely 3* P *Bp* **P-in-c** C D BOULTON,
C J L MEADER

TEW, GREAT (St Michael and All Angels) w Little (St John the Evangelist) *Ox 3* P *Bp and J M Johnston Esq (jt)* **V** *vacant (0160883) 293*

TEWIN (St Peter) *St Alb 21* P *Jes Coll Cam* **V** *vacant*

TEWKESBURY (Holy Trinity) *Glouc 16* P *Ch Soc Trust*
V P L SIBLEY

TEWKESBURY (St Mary the Virgin) w Walton Cardiff and Twyning *Glouc 16* P *Ld Chan (2 turns) and Ch Ch Ox (1 turn)* **V** P R WILLIAMS, **Hon C** A P BISHOP

TEY, GREAT (St Barnabas) and LITTLE (St James the Less) w Wakes Colne and Chappel *Chelmsf 17* P *Bp, DBP, PCC Chappel and Ch Patr Trust (jt)* **R** J RICHARDSON

TEYNHAM (St Mary) (Primary School Worship Centre) w Lynsted and Kingsdown *Cant 6* P *Adn Cant*
P-in-c M A GOOCH

THAKEHAM (St Mary) *see Sullington and Thakeham w Warminghurst Chich*

THAME (All Saints) (St Mary the Virgin) *Ox 1* P *Patr Bd*
TV S F L BRIGNALL, I D MOUNTFORD, **C** I R ADAMS,
Hon C K A A WESTON, J H FIELDSEND, S H BAYNES,
NSM J E M HULETT

THAMES DITTON (St Nicholas) *Guildf 8* P *K Coll Cam*
V J A SILK, **NSM** M J HUSSEY

THAMES VIEW (Christ Church) *see Barking St Marg w St Patr Chelmsf*

THAMESMEAD (Church of the Cross) (St Paul's Ecumenical Centre) (William Temple) *S'wark 3* P *Bp* **TR** B THORLEY,
TV M GODDARD, **Hon C** F J KING, **OLM** L J FRASER

THANET (St Andrew) *see St Peter-in-Thanet Cant*

THANET (St Laurence) *see St Laur in Thanet Cant*

THANET (St Peter the Apostle) *see St Peter-in-Thanet Cant*

THANINGTON (St Nicholas) (St Faith's Mission Church)
Cant 3 P *Abp* **P-in-c** I AVEYARD

THARSTON (St Mary) *see Newton Flotman, Swainsthorpe, Tasburgh, etc Nor*

THATCHAM (St Mary) *Ox 14* P *Patr Bd* **TR** N T MOFFATT,
TV M A E ASTIN, **C** M C ROBBINS, **OLM** M E FONTAINE

THATTO HEATH (St Matthew) *see St Helens St Matt Thatto Heath Liv*

THAXTED (St John the Baptist, Our Lady and St Laurence)
Chelmsf 22 P *Bp* **V** R M TAYLOR

THEALE (Christ Church) *see Wedmore w Theale and Blackford B & W*

THEALE (Holy Trinity) and Englefield *Ox 12* P *Magd Coll Ox and Englefield Est Trust (jt)* **P-in-c** G N BORROWDALE,
Hon C T C EKIN

THEBERTON (St Peter) *see Kelsale-cum-Carlton, Middleton, Theberton etc St E*

THEDDINGWORTH (All Saints) *see Husbands Bosworth w Mowsley and Knaptoft etc Leic*

THEDDLETHORPE (St Helen) *Linc 12* P *Baroness Willoughby de Eresby (2 turns), Bp (1 turn)* **R** *vacant*

THELBRIDGE (St David) *see Burrington, Chawleigh, Cheldon, Chulmleigh etc Ex*

THELNETHAM (St Nicholas) *see Hepworth, Hinderclay, Wattisfield and Thelnetham St E*

THELVETON (St Andrew) *see Dickleburgh and The Pulhams Nor*

THELWALL (All Saints) *Ches 4* P *Keble Coll Ox*
V D J BLACK

THEMELTHORPE (St Andrew) *see Twyford, Guist, Bintree, Themelthorpe etc Nor*

THENFORD (St Mary the Virgin) *see Greatworth and Marston St Lawrence etc Pet*

THERFIELD (St Mary the Virgin) w Kelshall *St Alb 19*
P *Ld Chan and D&C St Paul's (alt)* **R** R M MORGAN

THETFORD (St Cuthbert) (St Peter) *Nor 11* P *Patr Bd*
TR C J HALL, **TV** M W L PICKETT, **C** J FRENCH,
Hon C B R HOGWOOD

THETFORD, LITTLE (St George) *see Ely Ely*

THEYDON BOIS (St Mary) *Chelmsf 25*
P *M G E N Buxton Esq* **V** C J TRAVERS,
NSM A M CANNELL

THEYDON GARNON (All Saints) *see Epping Distr Chelmsf*

THEYDON MOUNT (St Michael) *see Stapleford Tawney w Theydon Mt Chelmsf*

THIMBLEBY (St Margaret) *see Thornton Gp Linc*

THIRKLEBY (All Saints) w Kilburn and Bagby *York 19* P *Abp*
P-in-c R W DAVILL

THIRSK (St Mary) *York 19* P *Abp* **TR** R F ROWLING,
C E M BAXTER, **NSM** S R BAXTER

THISTLETON (St Nicholas) *see* Greetham and Thistleton w Stretton and Clipsham *Pet*

THIXENDALE (St Mary) *see* Waggoners *York*

THOCKRINGTON (St Aidan) *see* Chollerton w Birtley and Thockrington *Newc*

THOMPSON (St Martin) *see* Caston, Griston, Merton, Thompson etc *Nor*

THONGSBRIDGE (St Andrew) *see* Upper Holme Valley *Wakef*

THORESBY, NORTH (St Helen) *see* The North-Chapel Parishes *Linc*

THORESBY, SOUTH (St Andrew) *see* Legbourne and Wold Marsh *Linc*

THORESWAY (St Mary) *see* Swallow *Linc*

THORGANBY (All Saints) *see* Binbrook Gp *Linc*

THORGANBY (St Helen) *see* Wheldrake w Thorganby *York*

THORINGTON (St Peter) *see* Blyth Valley *St E*

THORLEY (St James the Great) *St Alb 18* **P** *Bp* **R** R H V PAYNE

THORLEY (St Swithun) *Portsm 8* **P** *Bp* **V** J A YORKE

THORMANBY (St Mary Magdalene) *see* Brafferton w Pilmoor, Myton on Swale etc *York*

THORNABY, NORTH (St Luke) (St Paul) *York 18* **P** *Abp* **V** H C HOPKINS

THORNABY, SOUTH (St Mark) (St Peter ad Vincula) *York 18* **P** *Abp* **V** vacant (01642) 879584

THORNAGE (All Saints) *see* Brinton, Briningham, Hunworth, Stody etc *Nor*

THORNBOROUGH (St Mary) *see* Buckingham *Ox*

THORNBURY (St Anna) *see* Bredenbury w Grendon Bishop and Wacton etc *Heref*

THORNBURY (St Margaret) *Bradf 3* **P** *Vs Bradf, Calverley, and Laisterdyke (jt)* **V** P C HACKWOOD, **C** J W HINTON

THORNBURY (St Mary) (St Paul) *Glouc 7* **P** *Ch Ch Ox* **V** D E S PRIMROSE, **C** J J PERKINS, **OLM** G L HILL

THORNBURY (St Peter) *see* Black Torrington, Bradf w Cookbury etc *Ex*

THORNBY (St Helen) *see* Cottesbrooke w Gt Creaton and Thornby *Pet*

THORNCOMBE (The Blessed Virgin Mary) *see* Chard and Distr *B & W*

THORNDON (All Saints) *see* Gislingham and Thorndon *St E*

THORNE (St Nicholas) *Sheff 10* **P** *Bp* **NSM** H A F YOUNG

THORNE COFFIN (St Andrew) *see* Tintinhull w Chilthorne Domer, Yeovil Marsh etc *B & W*

THORNE ST MARGARET (St Margaret) *see* Wellington and Distr *B & W*

THORNER (St Peter) *Ripon 8* **P** *Earl of Mexborough* **P-in-c** J D W KING, **NSM** A B HAIGH

THORNES (St James) w Christ Church *Wakef 12* **P** *DBP* **P-in-c** P M MAGUIRE

THORNEY (St Helen) *see* Harby w Thorney and N and S Clifton *S'well*

THORNEY, WEST (St Nicholas) *see* Southbourne w W Thorney *Chich*

THORNEY ABBEY (St Mary and St Botolph) *Ely 17* **P** *Bp* **P-in-c** R P FLINDALL

THORNEY CLOSE (St Peter) *see* Sunderland St Mary and St Pet *Dur*

THORNEY HILL (All Saints) *see* Bransgore *Win*

THORNEYBURN (St Aidan) *see* N Tyne and Redesdale Team *Newc*

THORNFALCON (Holy Cross) *see* Ruishton w Thornfalcon *B & W*

THORNFORD (St Mary Magdalene) *see* Bradford Abbas and Thornford w Beer Hackett *Sarum*

THORNGUMBALD (St Mary) *see* Burstwick w Thorngumbald *York*

THORNHAM (All Saints) *see* Hunstanton St Mary w Ringstead Parva etc *Nor*

THORNHAM (St James) *Man 22* **P** *Bp* **V** P N BARRATT

THORNHAM (St John) *see* Middleton w Thornham *Man*

THORNHAM MAGNA (St Mary Magdalene) *see* Gislingham and Thorndon *St E*

THORNHAM PARVA (St Mary) *as above St E*

THORNHAUGH (St Andrew) and Wansford *Pet 8* **P** *Bp* **P-in-c** T R CHRISTIE

THORNHILL (Mission Church) *see* Beckermet St Jo and St Bridget w Ponsonby *Carl*

THORNHILL (St Christopher) *see* Southampton Thornhill St Chris *Win*

THORNHILL (St Michael and All Angels) and Whitley Lower *Wakef 10* **P** *Lord Savile* **R** L C DEW, **C** G M JOHNSON

THORNHILL LEES (Holy Innocents w St Mary) *see* Ravensthorpe and Thornhill Lees w Savile Town *Wakef*

THORNLEY (St Bartholomew) *see* Haswell, Shotton and Thornley *Dur*

THORNLEY (St Bartholomew) *see* Wolsingham and Thornley *Dur*

THORNTHWAITE (St Mary the Virgin) cum Braithwaite, Newlands and Borrowdale w Grange *Carl 6* **P** *V Keswick St Jo (1 turn), V Crosthwaite (2 turns)* **P-in-c** P H VIVASH, **NSM** C FORD

THORNTHWAITE (St Saviour) *see* Dacre w Hartwith and Darley w Thornthwaite *Ripon*

THORNTON Group, The (St Wilfrid) *Linc 11* **P** *R H Spurrier Esq, Bp, SMF, and Lt Col J L M Dymoke (2 turns), Ld Chan (1 turn)* **R** vacant (01507) 525832

THORNTON (St Frideswyde) *see* Sefton and Thornton *Liv*

THORNTON (St James) *Bradf 1* **P** *V Bradf* **V** w GREEN

THORNTON (St Michael) *see* Barmby Moor Gp *York*

THORNTON (St Peter) *see* Markfield, Thornton, Bagworth and Stanton etc *Leic*

THORNTON, LITTLE (St John) *Blackb 12* **P** *Bp* **V** P R F CLEMENCE

THORNTON CURTIS (St Laurence) *see* Ulceby Gp *Linc*

THORNTON DALE (All Saints) w Allerston, Ebberston, Ellerburn and Wilton *York 20* **P** *Mrs E M Morgan (1 turn), Abp (3 turns)* **R** J D S CLARK

THORNTON HEATH (St Jude w St Aidan) *S'wark 25* **P** *Bp* **P-in-c** N K NTEGE

THORNTON HEATH (St Paul) *S'wark 25* **P** *The Crown* **V** M P N JEWITT

THORNTON HOUGH (All Saints) *Ches 9* **P** *Simeon's Trustees* **P-in-c** D M SEBER

THORNTON IN CRAVEN (St Mary) *see* Broughton, Marton and Thornton *Bradf*

THORNTON IN LONSDALE (St Oswald) w Burton in Lonsdale *Bradf 6* **P** *Bp* **V** vacant (01524) 261579

THORNTON LE FEN (St Peter) *see* Brothertoft Gp *Linc*

THORNTON-LE-FYLDE (Christ Church) *Blackb 12* **P** *Trustees* **A** W FROUD, **C** D J BURY

THORNTON-LE-MOOR (All Saints) *see* Kelsey Gp *Linc*

THORNTON-LE-MOORS (St Mary) w Ince and Elton *Ches 3* **P** *Bp* **P-in-c** K W DAVEY

THORNTON LE STREET (St Leonard) *see* The Thorntons and The Otteringtons *York*

THORNTON RUST (Mission Room) *see* Aysgarth and Bolton cum Redmire *Ripon*

THORNTON STEWARD (St Oswald) *see* Middleham w Coverdale and E Witton etc *Ripon*

THORNTON WATLASS (St Mary the Virgin) *Ripon 4* **P** *Bp and D S Dodsworth Esq (jt)* **P-in-c** A L WOODHOUSE

THORNTONS and The Otteringtons, The *York 19* **P** *Ch Ch Ox, Linc Coll Ox, and Abp (by turn)* **P-in-c** S N FISHER

THOROTON (St Helena) *see* Whatton w Aslockton, Hawksworth, Scarrington etc *S'well*

THORP ARCH (All Saints) w Walton *York 1* **P** *G H H Wheler Esq and G Lane Fox Esq (alt)* **P-in-c** P E BRISTOW

THORPE (St Andrew) (Good Shepherd) *Nor 1* **P** *Trustees W J Birkbeck Esq* **R** A J SNASDELL, **C** J A HAWKINS

Thorpe (St Laurence) *see* Farndon w Thorpe, Hawton and Cotham *S'well*

THORPE (St Leonard) *see* Fenny Bentley, Thorpe, Tissington, Parwich etc *Derby*

THORPE (St Mary) *Guildf 11* **P** *Keble Coll Ox* **V** M J HEREWARD-ROTHWELL

THORPE (St Matthew) *Nor 1* **P** *R Thorpe St Andr* **V** G R DRAKE, **C** A M BEANE

THORPE (St Peter) *see* The Wainfleet Gp *Linc*

THORPE ABBOTS (All Saints) *see* Scole, Brockdish, Billingford, Thorpe Abbots etc *Nor*

THORPE ACHURCH (St John the Baptist) *see* Aldwincle w Thorpe Achurch, Pilton, Wadenhoe etc *Pet*

THORPE ACRE w Dishley (All Saints) *Leic 7* **P** *Bp* **V** A R LEIGHTON, **C** R F FAIR, **NSM** H M NEWMAN

THORPE ARNOLD (St Mary the Virgin) *see* Melton Mowbray *Leic*

THORPE AUDIN (Mission Room) *see* Badsworth *Wakef*

THORPE BASSETT (All Saints) *see* Buckrose Carrs *York*

THORPE BAY (St Augustine) *Chelmsf 13* **P** *Bp* **V** R E FARRELL, **C** R J MAGOR

THORPE CONSTANTINE (St Constantine) *Lich 4* **P** *Mrs E V G Inge-Innes* **P-in-c** A L WHEALE

THORPE EDGE (St John the Divine) *Bradf 3* **P** *Vs Bradf, Calverley, and Idle (jt)* **P-in-c** J D DAGLISH, **NSM** C WATSON

THORPE END (St David) *see* Gt and Lt Plumstead w Thorpe End and Witton *Nor*

THORPE EPISCOPI (St Andrew) *see* Thorpe *Nor*

THORPE HAMLET (St Matthew) *see* Thorpe St Matt *Nor*

THORPE HESLEY (Holy Trinity) *Sheff 6* **P** *Sir Philip Naylor-Leyland Bt* **V** J F HARDY

THORPE LANGTON (St Leonard) *see* Church Langton cum Tur Langton etc *Leic*
THORPE-LE-SOKEN (St Michael) *Chelmsf 23* **P** *Bp*
V P J CARTER
THORPE MALSOR (All Saints) *see* Broughton w Loddington and Cransley etc *Pet*
THORPE MANDEVILLE (St John the Baptist) *see* Culworth w Sulgrave and Thorpe Mandeville etc *Pet*
THORPE MARKET (St Margaret) *see* Trunch *Nor*
THORPE MORIEUX (St Mary the Virgin) *see* Rattlesden w Thorpe Morieux, Brettenham etc *St E*
THORPE-NEXT-HADDISCOE (St Matthias)
see Raveningham Gp *Nor*
THORPE-ON-THE-HILL (St Michael) *see* Swinderby *Linc*
THORPE SALVIN (St Peter) *see* Harthill and Thorpe Salvin *Sheff*
THORPE SATCHVILLE (St Michael and All Angels)
see S Croxton Gp *Leic*
THORPE WILLOUGHBY (St Francis of Assisi) *see* Brayton *York*
THORRINGTON (St Mary Magdalene) *see* Gt Bentley and Frating w Thorrington *Chelmsf*
THORVERTON (St Thomas of Canterbury), Cadbury, Upton Pyne, Brampford Speke and Newton St Cyres *Ex 2*
P *Ld Chan (1 turn), Patr Bd (3 turns)* **P-in-c** D J DETTMER,
C R A POTTER
THRANDESTON (St Margaret) *see* N Hartismere *St E*
THRAPSTON (St James) *Pet 10* **P** *Ld Chan* **R** G D R BELL
THREAPWOOD (St John) *see* Malpas and Threapwood *Ches*
THRECKINGHAM (St Peter) *see* S Lafford *Linc*
THREE LEGGED CROSS (All Saints) *see* Verwood *Sarum*
THREE RIVERS GROUP, The *see* Chippenham *Ely*
THRELKELD (St Mary) *see* St John's-in-the-Vale, Threlkeld and Wythburn *Carl*
THREXTON (All Saints) *see* Gt and Lt Cressingham w Threxton *Nor*
THRIGBY (St Mary) *see* S Trin Broads *Nor*
THRIMBY (St Mary) *see* Morland, Thrimby, Gt Strickland and Cliburn *Carl*
THRINGSTONE (St Andrew) *Leic 8* **P** *Duchy of Lanc*
P-in-c S P MOULT, **NSM** J A BIRD
THRIPLOW (St George) *see* Fowlmere, Foxton, Shepreth and Thriplow *Ely*
THROCKING (Holy Trinity) *see* Cottered w Broadfield and Throcking *St Alb*
THROCKLEY (St Mary the Virgin) *see* Newburn *Newc*
THROCKMORTON (Chapelry) *see* Abberton, The Flyfords, Naunton Beauchamp etc *Worc*
THROOP (St Paul) *Win 8* **P** *Ch Soc Trust* **V** R D PETERS,
C J R CHARLES
THROPTON (St Andrew) *see* Rothbury *Newc*
THROWLEIGH (St Mary the Virgin) *see* Chagford, Drewsteignton, Hittisleigh etc *Ex*
THROWLEY (St Michael and All Angels) *see* Selling w Throwley, Sheldwich w Badlesmere etc *Cant*
THRUMPTON (All Saints) *S'well 9* **P** *Mrs M Gottlieb*
P-in-c S W OSMAN
THRUSCROSS (no dedication) *see* Dacre w Hartwith and Darley w Thornthwaite *Ripon*
THRUSHELTON (St George) *see* Lifton, Broadwoodwidger, Stowford etc *Ex*
THRUSSINGTON (Holy Trinity) *see* Syston *Leic*
THRUXTON (St Bartholomew) *see* Kingstone w Clehonger, Eaton Bishop etc *Heref*
THRUXTON (St Peter and St Paul) *see* Appleshaw, Kimpton, Thruxton, Fyfield etc *Win*
THRYBERGH (St Leonard) *Sheff 6* **P** *Mrs P N Fullerton*
R B E LENG
THUNDERSLEY (St Michael and All Angels) (St Peter)
Chelmsf 10 **P** *Bp* **R** M E STURROCK, **C** S J JERMY,
NSM M A BOYS
THUNDERSLEY, NEW (St George) *Chelmsf 10* **P** *Bp*
V A J ROSE
THUNDRIDGE (St Mary) *St Alb 22* **P** *Bp* **V** H J SHARMAN
THURCASTON (All Saints) w Cropston *Leic 12* **P** *Em Coll Cam* **R** D F BREWIN
THURCROFT (St Simon and St Jude) *Sheff 5* **P** *Bp*
V P HUNTER
THURGARTON (St Peter) w Hoveringham and Bleasby w Halloughton *S'well 14* **P** *Ld Chan and Trin Coll Cam (alt)*
V A P DE BERRY
THURGOLAND (Holy Trinity) *see* Tankersley, Thurgoland and Wortley *Sheff*
THURLASTON (All Saints) *see* Enderby w Lubbesthorpe and Thurlaston *Leic*
THURLASTON (St Edmund) *see* Dunchurch *Cov*

THURLBY (St Firmin) *see* Ness Gp *Linc*
THURLBY (St Germain) *see* Bassingham Gp *Linc*
THURLEIGH (St Peter) *see* Milton Ernest, Pavenham and Thurleigh *St Alb*
THURLESTON (All Saints), South Milton, West Alvington and Churchstow *Ex 15* **P** *Bp Ex and D&C Sarum (jt)*
R A M GIRLING, **C** W J T HAMILTON
THURLOW, GREAT (All Saints) *see* Stourhead *St E*
THURLOW, LITTLE (St Peter) *as above St E*
THURLOXTON (St Giles) *see* N Newton w St Michaelchurch, Thurloxton etc *B & W*
THURLSTONE (St Saviour) *see* Penistone and Thurlstone *Wakef*
THURLTON (All Saints) *see* Raveningham Gp *Nor*
THURMASTON (St Michael and All Angels) *Leic 6* **P** *Bp*
V T R MARTIN, **NSM** I M HILL
THURNBY (St Luke) w Stoughton *Leic 5* **P** *MMCET*
V G W DUNSETH, **C** S J WALTON
THURNBY LODGE (Christ Church) *see* Ascension TM *Leic*
THURNE (St Edmund) *see* Martham and Repps with Bastwick, Thurne etc *Nor*
THURNHAM (St Mary the Virgin) *see* Bearsted w Thurnham *Cant*
THURNING (St Andrew) *see* Reepham, Hackford w Whitwell, Kerdiston etc *Nor*
THURNING (St James the Great) *see* Barnwell w Tichmarsh, Thurning and Clapton *Pet*
THURNSCOE (St Helen) *Sheff 12* **P** *Sir Philip Naylor Leyland Bt* **P-in-c** M P THOMPSON
THURNSCOE (St Hilda) *Sheff 12* **P** *Bp* **V** M P THOMPSON
THURROCK, LITTLE (St John the Evangelist) *see* Grays North *Chelmsf*
THURROCK, LITTLE (St Mary the Virgin) *see* Grays Thurrock *Chelmsf*
THURROCK, WEST (Church Centre) *as above Chelmsf*
THURSBY (St Andrew) *Carl 3* **P** *D&C* **P-in-c** N L ROBINSON
THURSFORD (St Andrew) *see* Barney, Fulmodeston w Croxton, Hindringham etc *Nor*
THURSLEY (St Michael and All Angels) *Guildf 4* **P** *V Witley*
V W D LANG
THURSTASTON (St Bartholomew) *Ches 8* **P** *D&C*
R D E WATSON
THURSTON (St Peter) *St E 9* **P** *Bp* **V** D M B MATHERS
THURSTONLAND (St Thomas) *see* Upper Holme Valley *Wakef*
THURTON (St Ethelbert) w Ashby Saint Mary, Bergh Apton w Yelverton and Framingham Pigot *Nor 8* **P** *Bp and Major J H Thursby, Bp and MMCET, and Ld Chan (by turn)*
R P M KNIGHT, **NSM** R J M COLLIER
THUXTON (St Paul) *see* Barnham Broom and Upper Yare *Nor*
THWAITE (All Saints) *see* Erpingham w Calthorpe, Ingworth, Aldborough etc *Nor*
THWAITE (St George) *see* Gislingham and Thorndon *St E*
THWAITE (St Mary) *see* Brooke, Kirstead, Mundham w Seething and Thwaite *Nor*
THWAITE (St Anne) *see* Millom *Carl*
THWAITES BROW (St Barnabas) *Bradf 8* **P** *DBP* **V** *vacant* (01535) 602830
THWING (All Saints) *see* Langtoft w Foxholes, Butterwick, Cottam etc *York*
TIBBERTON (All Saints) w Bolas Magna and Waters Upton *Lich 16* **P** *R Edgmond w Kynnersley etc, MMCET, and A B Davies Esq (jt)* **P-in-c** W E WARD
TIBBERTON (Holy Trinity) *see* Highnam, Lassington, Rudford, Tibberton etc *Glouc*
TIBBERTON (St Peter ad Vincula) *see* Bowbrook S *Worc*
TIBENHAM (All Saints) *see* Bunwell, Carleton Rode, Tibenham, Gt Moulton etc *Nor*
TIBSHELF (St John the Baptist) *see* Blackwell w Tibshelf *Derby*
TICEHURST (St Mary) and Flimwell *Chich 19* **P** *Bp, E J B Harcastle Esq, and K M H Millar Esq (jt)*
V W M SIMPSON
TICHBORNE (St Andrew) *see* Upper Itchen *Win*
TICHMARSH (St Mary the Virgin) *see* Barnwell w Tichmarsh, Thurning and Clapton *Pet*
TICKENCOTE (St Peter) *see* Gt and Lt Casterton w Pickworth and Tickencote *Pet*
TICKENHAM (St Quiricus and St Julietta) *see* Nailsea Ch Ch w Tickenham *B & W*
TICKHILL (St Mary) w Stainton *Sheff 9* **P** *Bp* **V** G TAYLOR
TICKNALL (St George), Smisby and Stanton by Bridge, Barrow on Trent w Twyford and Swarkestone *Derby 15* **P** *Bp, Exors Miss A I M Harpur-Crewe, and Repton Sch (jt)*
V M G ALEXANDER
TICKTON (St Paul) *see* Beverley Minster *York*
TIDCOMBE (St Michael) *see* Savernake *Sarum*

TIDDINGTON   *see* Wheatley *Ox*
TIDDINGTON (St Peter)   *see* Alveston *Cov*
TIDEBROOK (St John the Baptist) *Chich 19*   **P** *V Wadhurst and V Mayfield (alt)*   **V** J R JAMES,   **C** C D LAWRENCE
TIDEFORD (St Luke)   *see* St Germans *Truro*
TIDENHAM (St Mary) w Beachley and Lancaut *Glouc 4*   **P** *Bp*   **V** R J M GROSVENOR,   **NSM** N R BROMFIELD
TIDENHAM CHASE (St Michael and All Angels)   *see* Tidenham w Beachley and Lancaut *Glouc*
TIDESWELL (St John the Baptist) *Derby 4*   **P** *D&C Lich*   **P-in-c** F E YATES
TIDMARSH (St Laurence)   *see* Pangbourne w Tidmarsh and Sulham *Ox*
TIDMINGTON (not known)   *see* Shipston-on-Stour w Honington and Idlicote *Cov*
TIDWORTH (Holy Trinity), Ludgershall and Faberstown *Sarum 13*   **P** *Ld Chan and DBP (alt)*   **R** M R FREEMAN
TIFFIELD (St John the Baptist)   *see* Pattishall w Cold Higham and Gayton w Tiffield *Pet*
TILBROOK (All Saints) *Ely 9*   **P** *SMF*   **P-in-c** S P MEWS,   **NSM** J RAWLINSON
TILBURY, EAST (St Katherine) and West Tilbury and Linford *Chelmsf 14*   **P** *Ld Chan*   **P-in-c** W L WHITFORD
TILBURY DOCKS (St John the Baptist) *Chelmsf 14*   **P** *Bp*   **V** T M CODLING
TILBURY-JUXTA-CLARE (St Margaret)   *see* Upper Colne *Chelmsf*
TILE CROSS (St Peter) *Birm 9*   **P** *Bp*   **V** B S CASTLE,   **NSM** M MACLACHLAN
TILE HILL (St Oswald) *Cov 3*   **P** *Bp*   **V** B REGAN
TILEHURST (St Catherine of Siena) *Ox 15*   **P** *Magd Coll Ox*   **P-in-c** D R SMITH
TILEHURST (St George) *Ox 15*   **P** *Bp*   **V** A J CARLILL,   **NSM** M J OKE
TILEHURST (St Mary Magdalen) *Ox 15*   **P** *Bp*   **P-in-c** A J CARLILL,   **NSM** M J OKE
TILEHURST (St Michael) *Ox 15*   **P** *Magd Coll Ox*   **R** F W DAWSON
TILFORD (All Saints)   *see* The Bourne and Tilford *Guildf*
TILGATE (Holy Trinity)   *see* Southgate *Chich*
TILLINGHAM (St Nicholas) *Chelmsf 11*   **P** *D&C St Paul's*   **P-in-c** C F WELLS,   **NSM** B M H MAIN
TILLINGTON (All Hallows) *Chich 11*   **P** *Lord Egremont*   **P-in-c** R A STAVELEY-WADHAM
TILMANSTONE (St Andrew)   *see* Eastry and Northbourne w Tilmanstone etc *Cant*
TILNEY ALL SAINTS (All Saints)   *see* E Marshland *Ely*
TILNEY ST LAWRENCE (St Lawrence)   *as above Ely*
TILSHEAD (St Thomas à Becket)   *see* Wylye and Till Valley *Sarum*
TILSTOCK (Christ Church), Edstaston and Whixall *Lich 22*   **P** *V Prees, R Wem, and R Whitchurch (jt)*   **V** D F B BALDWIN
TILSTON (St Mary) and Shocklach *Ches 5*   **P** *Bp*   **R** *vacant* (01829) 250628
TILSTONE FEARNALL (St Jude)   *see* Bunbury and Tilstone Fearnall *Ches*
TILSWORTH (All Saints)   *see* Totternhoe, Stanbridge and Tilsworth *St Alb*
TILTON ON THE HILL (St Peter)   *see* Whatborough Gp of Par *Leic*
TILTY (St Mary the Virgin)   *see* Broxted w Chickney and Tilty etc *Chelmsf*
TIMBERLAND (St Andrew)   *see* Carr Dyke Gp *Linc*
TIMBERSCOMBE (St Petroc)   *see* Selworthy, Timberscombe, Wootton Courtenay etc *B & W*
TIMPERLEY (Christ Church) (St Andrew) (St Catherine) *Ches 10*   **P** *Trustees*   **V** J SUTTON,   **C** B E SHARP,   **Hon C** V W HYDON
TIMSBURY (Blessed Virgin Mary) and Priston *B & W 12*   **P** *Ball Coll Ox (3 turns), R W Lovegrove Esq (1 turn)*   **P-in-c** C S HARE
TIMSBURY (St Andrew)   *see* Michelmersh and Awbridge and Braishfield etc *Win*
TIMWORTH (St Andrew)   *see* Lark Valley *St E*
TINCLETON (St John the Evangelist)   *see* Moreton and Woodsford w Tincleton *Sarum*
TINDALE (Mission Church)   *see* Lanercost, Walton, Gilsland and Nether Denton *Carl*
TINGEWICK (St Mary Magdalene)   *see* W Buckingham *Ox*
TINGRITH (St Nicholas)   *see* Westoning w Tingrith *St Alb*
TINSLEY (St Lawrence)   *see* Attercliffe, Darnall and Tinsley *Sheff*
TINTAGEL (St Materiana) *Truro 10*   **P** *D&C Windsor*   **P-in-c** D J RAKE
TINTINHULL (St Margaret) w Chilthorne Domer, Yeovil Marsh and Thorne Coffin *B & W 7*   **P** *Guild of All So*   **NSM** A J YOUNG

TINTWISTLE (Christ Church)   *see* Hollingworth w Tintwistle *Ches*
TINWELL (All Saints)   *see* Ketton, Collyweston, Easton-on-the-Hill etc *Pet*
TIPTOE (St Andrew)   *see* Hordle *Win*
TIPTON Great Bridge (St Luke)   *see* Tipton St Martin and St Paul *Lich*
TIPTON (St John)   *see* Ottery St Mary, Alfington, W Hill, Tipton etc *Ex*
TIPTON (St John the Evangelist) *Lich 26*   **P** *V W Bromwich St Jas*   **V** B W PIERCE
TIPTON (St Mark)   *see* Ocker Hill *Lich*
TIPTON (St Martin) (St Paul) *Lich 26*   **P** *MMCET*   **V** J F DUNN
TIPTON (St Matthew) *Lich 26*   **P** *Simeon's Trustees*   **V** C E HOWARD
TIPTREE (St Luke)   *see* Tolleshunt Knights w Tiptree and Gt Braxted *Chelmsf*
TIRLEY (St Michael)   *see* Hasfield w Tirley and Ashleworth *Glouc*
TISBURY (St John the Baptist)   *see* Nadder Valley *Sarum*
TISMANS COMMON (St John the Baptist)   *see* Rudgwick *Chich*
TISSINGTON (St Mary)   *see* Fenny Bentley, Thorpe, Tissington, Parwich etc *Derby*
TISTED, EAST w Colemore (St James)   *see* Newton Valence, Selborne and E Tisted w Colemore *Win*
TISTED, WEST (St Mary Magdalene)   *see* Bishop's Sutton and Ropley and W Tisted *Win*
TITCHFIELD (St Peter) *Portsm 2*   **P** *D&C Win*   **V** W C DAY,   **NSM** L E SNAPE
TITCHWELL (St Mary)   *see* Hunstanton St Mary w Ringstead Parva etc *Nor*
TITLEY (St Peter)   *see* Kington w Huntington, Old Radnor, Kinnerton etc *Heref*
TITTENSOR (St Luke)   *see* Swynnerton and Tittensor *Lich*
TITTLESHALL (St Mary)   *see* Litcham w Kempston, E and W Lexham, Mileham etc *Nor*
TIVERTON (St Andrew) *Ex 8*   **P** *Bp*   **P-in-c** D M FLETCHER
TIVERTON (St George) (St Paul) *Ex 8*   **P** *MMCET and Peache Trustees (jt)*   **V** M J PARTRIDGE,   **C** M J CLARK,   **NSM** D A LYDDON
TIVERTON (St Peter) and Chevithorne w Cove *Ex 8*   **P** *Peache Trustees (3 turns), Ld Chan (1 turn)*   **P-in-c** A R GIBSON
TIVETSHALL (St Mary and St Margaret)   *see* Winfarthing w Shelfanger w Burston w Gissing etc *Nor*
TIVIDALE (St Michael the Archangel) (Holy Cross) (St Augustine) *Lich 26*   **P** *Bp*   **V** C R MARSHALL,   **C** C W FULLARD
TIVINGTON (St Leonard)   *see* Selworthy, Timberscombe, Wootton Courtenay etc *B & W*
TIXALL (St John the Baptist)   *see* Stafford St Jo and Tixall w Ingestre *Lich*
TIXOVER (St Luke)   *see* Barrowden and Wakerley w S Luffenham etc *Pet*
TOCKENHAM (St Giles)   *see* Broad Town, Clyffe Pypard, Hilmarton etc *Sarum*
TOCKHOLES (St Stephen)   *see* Darwen St Cuth w Tockholes St Steph *Blackb*
TOCKWITH (Epiphany) and Bilton w Bickerton *York 1*   **P** *Abp and D&C (jt)*   **P-in-c** J A RENDALL,   **NSM** B H FRAY
TODBER (St Andrew)   *see* Gillingham *Sarum*
TODDINGTON (St Andrew), Stanton, Didbrook w Hailes and Stanway *Glouc 16*   **P** *DBP, Lord Neidpath, and Bp (by turn)*   **R** *vacant* (01242) 620126
TODDINGTON (St George of England) *St Alb 12*   **P** *Bp*   **R** *vacant* (01525) 872298
TODENHAM (St Thomas of Canterbury)   *see* Moreton-in-Marsh w Batsford, Todenham etc *Glouc*
TODMORDEN (St Mary) (Christ Church) *Wakef 3*   **P** *Bp*   **V** P N CALVERT,   **C** T A IBBOTSON
TODWICK (St Peter and St Paul) *Sheff 5*   **P** *Bp*   **V** D C BLISS
TOFT (St Andrew) w Caldecote and Childerley *Ely 1*   **P** *Ch Coll Cam*   **R** *vacant*
TOFT (St John the Evangelist)   *see* Knutsford St Jo and Toft *Ches*
TOFT MONKS (St Margaret)   *see* Raveningham Gp *Nor*
TOFTREES (All Saints) w Shereford *Nor 15*   **P** *Marquess Townshend*   **V** *vacant*
TOFTS, WEST and Buckenham Parva *Nor 13*   **P** *Guild of All So*   **R** *vacant*
TOKYNGTON (St Michael) *Lon 21*   **P** *Bp*   **V** P J HARNDEN
TOLLADINE (Christ Church)   *see* Worc St Barn w Ch Ch *Worc*
TOLLAND (St John the Baptist)   *see* Lydeard St Lawrence w Brompton Ralph etc *B & W*
TOLLARD ROYAL (St Peter ad Vincula)   *see* Chase *Sarum*

TOLLER FRATRUM (St Basil)   *see* Melbury *Sarum*
TOLLER LANE St Chad *Bradf 1*   **P** *Keble Coll Ox*
V S R CROWE
TOLLER PORCORUM (St Andrew)   *see* Beaminster Area
Sarum
TOLLER WHELME (St John)   *see* Melbury *Sarum*
TOLLERTON (St Michael)   *see* Alne *York*
TOLLERTON (St Peter) *S'well 8*   **P** *Ld Chan*
P-in-c M H WAINWRIGHT
TOLLESBURY (St Mary) w Salcot Virley *Chelmsf 24*   **P** *Bp*
(1 turn), Ex Coll Ox (3 turns)   **V** K M B LOVELL
TOLLESHUNT D'ARCY (St Nicholas) and Tolleshunt Major
Chelmsf 24   **P** *Mrs E A Comerford and MMCET (jt)*
V P R SOUTHERN
TOLLESHUNT KNIGHTS w Tiptree and Great Braxted
Chelmsf 24   **P** *Bp (2 turns), Ld Chan (2 turns), and CCC Cam*
(1 turn)   **R** vacant (01621) 815260
TOLLESHUNT MAJOR (St Nicholas)   *see* Tolleshunt D'Arcy
and Tolleshunt Major *Chelmsf*
TOLLINGTON (St Mark) *Lon 6*   **P** *Patr Bd*
TV T L WAMBUNYA,   **NSM** E MCCARTNEY
TOLPUDDLE (St John the Evangelist)   *see* Puddletown,
Tolpuddle and Milborne w Dewlish *Sarum*
TOLWORTH (Emmanuel)   *see* Surbiton Hill Ch Ch *S'wark*
TOLWORTH (St George)   *see* Surbiton St Matt *S'wark*
TONBRIDGE (St Peter and St Paul) (St Saviour) *Roch 11*
P *Mabledon Trust*   **V** S J G SEAMER,   **C** G CLARKE
TONBRIDGE (St Stephen) (St Eanswythe Mission Church)
Roch 11   **P** *CPAS*   **V** W D MACDOUGALL
TONG (St Bartholomew) *Lich 16*   **P** *Bp*   **V** J B HALL
TONG (St James) *Bradf 3*   **P** *CR*   **TR** C G N DEY,
C C S HOWSON
TONGE (St Giles)   *see* Murston w Bapchild and Tonge *Cant*
TONGE (St Michael) w Alkrington *Man 18*   **P** *R Middleton*
St Leon   **V** G F JOYCE
TONGE FOLD (St Chad) *Man 9*   **P** *Bp and Wm Hulme*
Trustees (alt)   **V** A J BUTTERWORTH,   **OLM** S P MCGREGOR
TONGE MOOR (St Augustine) (St Aidan) *Man 16*   **P** *Keble*
Coll Ox   **V** D A DAVIES,   **Hon C** J M DRUMMOND
TONGHAM (St Paul) *Guildf 1*   **P** *Adn Surrey*
P-in-c E GIBBONS
TONWELL (St Mary the Virgin)   *see* Bengeo *St Alb*
TOOT BALDON (St Lawrence)   *see* Dorchester *Ox*
TOOTING (All Saints) *S'wark 19*   **P** *Bp*   **V** P D MAURICE,
NSM R J S ALLEN,   **OLM** J ANNON
TOOTING (St Augustine) *S'wark 19*   **P** *Bp*   **V** vacant (020)
8672 4712
TOOTING, UPPER (Holy Trinity) *S'wark 19*   **P** *R Streatham*
St Leon   **NSM** B E NICHOLS
TOOTING GRAVENEY (St Nicholas) *S'wark 19*   **P** *MMCET*
R J B HALL,   **NSM** R A S THOMSON
TOP VALLEY (St Philip)   *see* Bestwood St Matt w St Phil *S'well*
TOPCLIFFE (St Columba), Baldersby w Dishforth, Dalton and
Skipton on Swale *York 19*   **P** *Abp, Viscount Downe, and*
D&C (jt)   **V** C M HADDON-REECE
TOPCROFT (St Margaret)   *see* Hempnall *Nor*
TOPPESFIELD (St Margaret)   *see* Upper Colne *Chelmsf*
TOPSHAM (St Margaret) *Ex 1*   **P** *D&C*   **V** R W C JEFFERY
TORBRYAN (Holy Trinity)   *see* Ipplepen, Torbryan and
Denbury *Ex*
TORKSEY (St Peter)   *see* Stow Gp *Linc*
TORMARTON (St Mary Magdalene)   *see* Marshfield w Cold
Ashton and Tormarton etc *Bris*
TORPENHOW (St Michael and all Angels)   *see* Binsey *Carl*
TORPOINT (St James) *Truro 11*   **P** *R Antony*
P-in-c B A ANDERSON,   **C** J JOHNSON
TORQUAY (St John) and Ellacombe *Ex 10*   **P** *Ch Patr Trust*
and Bp (jt)   **V** vacant (01803) 293441
TORQUAY (St Luke) *Ex 10*   **P** *D&C*   **P-in-c** C J BAKER
TORQUAY (St Martin) Barton *Ex 10*   **P** *V St Marychurch*
V G CHAPMAN
TORQUAY (St Mary Magdalene)   *see* Upton *Ex*
TORQUAY (St Matthias) (St Mark) (Holy Trinity) *Ex 10*
P *Ch Patr Trust, Bp and Torwood Trustees (jt)*   **R** G R PERCY
TORRE (All Saints) *Ex 10*   **P** *Bp*   **P-in-c** R W SHAMBROOK
TORRIDGE ESTUARY   *see* Bideford, Northam, Westward
Ho!, Appledore etc *Ex*
TORRINGTON, EAST (St Michael)   *see* Barkwith Gp *Linc*
TORRINGTON, GREAT (St Michael), Little Torrington and
Frithelstock *Ex 19*   **P** *Ch Ch Ox (8 turns), Lord Clinton*
(1 turn), J de C Stevens-Guille Esq (1 turn)
V J D HUMMERSTONE,   **C** G M YOULD,   **Hon C** J C ALLEN
TORRINGTON, LITTLE (St Giles)   *see* Gt and Lt Torrington
and Frithelstock *Ex*
TORRINGTON, WEST (St Michael)   *see* Barkwith Gp *Linc*
TORRISHOLME (Ascension) *Blackb 11*   **P** *Bp*   **C** G HALSALL

TORTWORTH (St Leonard)   *see* Cromhall w Tortworth and
Tytherington *Glouc*
TORVER (St Luke) *Carl 9*   **P** *Peache Trustees*
P-in-c M R EAST
TOSELAND (St Michael)   *see* Papworth *Ely*
TOSSIDE (St Bartholomew)   *see* Long Preston w Tosside *Bradf*
TOSTOCK (St Andrew)   *see* Pakenham w Norton and Tostock
St E
TOTHAM, GREAT (St Peter) and LITTLE (All Saints) w
Goldhanger *Chelmsf 24*   **P** *Bp and Ld Chan (alt)*
R M J HATCHETT
TOTLAND BAY (Christ Church) *Portsm 8*   **P** *Ch Patr Trust*
V J A YORKE
TOTLEY (All Saints) *Sheff 2*   **P** *Bp*   **V** D G RHODES
TOTNES (St Mary) w Bridgetown, Berry Pomeroy, Dartington
and Marldon *Ex 14*   **P** *Patr Bd*   **TR** N R MARTIN,
TV N G BATCOCK,   P C BELLENES,   C N J C PIGOTT,
M A JEAVONS
TOTON (St Peter) *S'well 7*   **P** *CPAS*   **V** P W GIBBS
TOTTENHAM (All Hallows) *Lon 19*   **P** *D&C St Paul's*
V R B PEARSON
TOTTENHAM (Holy Trinity) *Lon 19*   **P** *Bp*   **V** O A FAGBEMI
TOTTENHAM (St Bartholomew)   *see* Stamford Hill St Bart
Lon
TOTTENHAM (St Benet Fink) *Lon 19*   **P** *D&C St Paul's*
V M A DAVENPORT
TOTTENHAM (St Cuthbert)   *see* Chitts Hill St Cuth *Lon*
TOTTENHAM (St Mary) *Lon 19*   **P** *Bp*   **V** L J MILLER
TOTTENHAM (St Paul) *Lon 19*   **P** *V Tottenham All Hallows*
V A K DANGERFIELD,   **C** J R FOX,   C J DICKSON,
NSM M A R HAYNES
TOTTENHAM (St Philip the Apostle) *Lon 19*   **P** *Bp*
P-in-c K EVANS
TOTTENHAM, SOUTH (St Ann) *Lon 19*   **P** *D&C St Paul's*
V J M WOOD
TOTTENHILL (St Botolph) w Wormegay *Ely 15*   **P** *Bp*
V J C W NOLAN
TOTTERIDGE (St Andrew) *St Alb 17*   **P** *R Hatfield*
V C P HUITSON
TOTTERNHOE (St Giles), Stanbridge and Tilsworth *St Alb 12*
P *Bp*   **V** D J R SPICER
TOTTINGTON (St Anne) *Man 10*   **P** *R Bury St Mary*
V H W BEARN,   **Hon C** S G MARTIN,   **NSM** A W INGHAM
TOTTON *Win 11*   **P** *Bp*   **TR** P BAYES,   **TV** E J WETHERELL,
C M ROWBERRY,   J R REEVE,   **NSM** M B WHITE
TOW LAW (St Philip and St James)   *see* Satley, Stanley and Tow
Law *Dur*
TOWCESTER (St Lawrence) w Easton Neston *Pet 5*   **P** *Bp and*
Lord Hesketh (alt)   **V** M R H BAKER
TOWEDNACK (St Tewinock) *Truro 5*   **P** *Bp*
P-in-c J M PILGRIM
TOWER CHAPEL (St Nicholas)   *see* Whitehaven *Carl*
TOWERSEY (St Catherine)   *see* Thame *Ox*
TOWN END FARM (St Bede)   *see* Sunderland Town End Farm
Dur
TOWNEND (St Paul)   *see* Morley *Wakef*
TOWNSTAL (St Clement)   *see* Dartmouth *Ex*
TOXTETH (St Bede) (St Clement) *Liv 6*   **P** *Simeon's Trustees*
and Trustees (jt)   **V** F R CAIN
TOXTETH (St Cyprian w Christ Church)   *see* Edge Hill St Cypr
w St Mary *Liv*
TOXTETH (St Margaret) *Liv 6*   **P** *St Chad's Coll Dur*
V R GALLAGHER
TOXTETH (St Philemon) (St Gabriel) St Cleopas *Liv 6*
P *Patr Bd*   **TV** R V STOCK,   M R STANFORD,
P-in-c D G GAVIN,   **C** P HANOVA
TOXTETH PARK (Christ Church) (St Michael-in-the-Hamlet)
(St Andrew) *Liv 6*   **P** *Simeon's Trustees and Trustees (jt)*
V D H HARRISON
TOXTETH PARK (St Agnes and St Pancras) *Liv 6*
P *St Chad's Coll Dur*   **P-in-c** J S WEBB,   **C** L M DANIELS
TOXTETH PARK St Paul   *see* Prince's Park St Paul *Liv*
TOYNTON, HIGH (St John the Baptist) *Linc 11*   **P** *Bp*
V M E BURSON-THOMAS,   **C** A C V HARVEY,
NSM J F PARKIN,   A C FORD
TOYNTON ALL SAINTS (All Saints)   *see* Marden Hill Gp
Linc
TOYNTON ST PETER (St Peter)   *as above Linc*
TOYS HILL (Hall)   *see* Hever, Four Elms and Mark Beech *Roch*
TRAFALGAR SQUARE (St Martin-in-the-Fields)   *see* St
Martin-in-the-Fields *Lon*
TRAFFORD, OLD (St Bride)   *see* Stretford St Bride *Man*
TRAFFORD, OLD (St Hilda)   *see* Firswood and Gorse Hill
Man
TRAFFORD, OLD (St John the Evangelist) *Man 7*
P *The Crown*   **R** D I WHEELER,   **C** K S NJENGA

TRANMERE (St Catherine) *Ches 1* **P** *R Bebington* **V** *vacant* 0151-645 4533

TRANMERE (St Paul w St Luke) *Ches 1* **P** *Bp* **P-in-c** P ENNION

TRANMERE PARK (St Peter's Hall) *see* Guiseley w Esholt *Bradf*

TRAWDEN (St Mary the Virgin) *see* Colne and Villages *Blackb*

TREALES (Christ Church) *see* Wesham and Treales *Blackb*

TREBOROUGH (St Peter) *see* Old Cleeve, Leighland and Treborough *B & W*

TREDINGTON (St Gregory) and Darlingscott w Newbold on Stour *Cov 9* **P** *Jes Coll Ox* **R** *vacant* (01608) 661264

TREDINGTON (St John the Baptist) *see* Staverton w Boddington and Tredington etc *Glouc*

TREETON (St Helen) *see* Brinsworth w Catcliffe and Treeton *Sheff*

TREFONEN (All Saints) *see* Llanyblodwel and Trefonen *Lich*

TREGADILLET (St Mary's Mission) *see* Launceston *Truro*

TREGONY (not known) w St Cuby and Cornelly *Truro 6* **P** *Bp* **P-in-c** M J W WARNER

TREKNOW (Holy Family) *see* Tintagel *Truro*

TRELEIGH (St Stephen) *see* Redruth w Lanner and Treleigh *Truro*

TRELYSTAN (St Mary the Virgin) *Heref 13* **P** *Bp* **V** P D HARRATT

TREMAINE (St Winwalo) *see* Egloskerry, N Petherwin, Tremaine and Tresmere *Truro*

TRENDLEWOOD *see* Nailsea H Trin *B & W*

TRENEGLOS (St Gregory) *see* St Gennys, Jacobstow w Warbstow and Treneglos *Truro*

TRENT (St Andrew) *see* Queen Thorne *Sarum*

TRENT PARK (Christ Church) *see* Enfield Ch Ch Trent Park *Lon*

TRENT VALE (St John the Evangelist) *Lich 12* **P** *R* Stoke-on-Trent **V** M D ALLABY

TRENTHAM (St Mary and All Saints) *Lich 13* **P** *CPAS* **V** N A DI CASTIGLIONE, **C** R M D ORAM, G R ETHERTON

TRENTISHOE (St Peter) *see* Combe Martin, Berrynarbor, Lynton, Brendon etc *Ex*

TRENTSIDE EAST *Linc 4* **P** *Bp Linc (2 turns), Bp Lon (1 turn)* **R** D J BEVERLEY

TRESCO (St Nicholas) *see* Is of Scilly *Truro*

TRESHAM (not known) *see* Wotton-under-Edge w Ozleworth, N Nibley etc *Glouc*

TRESILLIAN (no dedication) *see* Lamorran and Merther *Truro*

TRESLOTHAN (St John the Evangelist) *see* Crowan and Treslothan *Truro*

TRESMERE (St Nicholas) *see* Egloskerry, N Petherwin, Tremaine and Tresmere *Truro*

TRESWELL (St John the Baptist) *see* Rampton w Laneham, Treswell, Cottam and Stokeham *S'well*

TRETHEVY (St Piran) *see* Tintagel *Truro*

TRETIRE (St Mary) *see* St Weonards w Orcop, Garway, Tretire etc *Heref*

TREVALGA (St Petroc) *see* Boscastle w Davidstow *Truro*

TREVENSON (St Illogan) *see* St Illogan *Truro*

TREVERBYN (St Peter) *Truro 1* **P** *The Crown* **P-in-c** K P ARTHUR, **OLM** L N P HORE

TREVONE (St Saviour) *see* Padstow *Truro*

TREWEN (St Michael) *see* Lezant w Lawhitton and S Petherwin w Trewen *Truro*

TREYFORD CUM DIDLING (St Andrew) *see* Harting w Elsted and Treyford cum Didling *Chich*

TRIMDON GRANGE (St Alban) *see* The Trimdons *Dur*

TRIMDON STATION (St Paul) *as above Dur*

TRIMDONS, The (St Mary Magdalene) (St Alban) (St Paul) *Dur 5* **P** *Bp* **NSM** J A ROGERS

TRIMINGHAM (St John the Baptist) *see* Overstrand, Northrepps, Sidestrand etc *Nor*

TRIMLEY (St Martin) *see* Walton and Trimley *St E*

TRIMLEY (St Mary the Virgin) *as above St E*

TRIMPLEY (Holy Trinity) *see* Kidderminster St Mary and All SS w Trimpley etc *Worc*

TRING (St Martha) (St Peter and St Paul) (St Mary) *St Alb 2* **P** *Bp* **TR** F J C MERCURIO, **TV** H BELLIS, P L SEGRAVE-PRIDE, **Hon C** J E K RIDGWAY, **NSM** M S H MACDONALD

TROSTON (St Mary the Virgin) *see* Blackbourne *St E*

TROTTISCLIFFE (St Peter and St Paul) *see* Birling, Addington, Ryarsh and Trottiscliffe *Roch*

TROTTON (St George) *see* Rogate w Terwick and Trotton w Chithurst *Chich*

TROUTBECK (Jesus Church) *see* Windermere St Mary and Troutbeck *Carl*

TROWBRIDGE (Holy Trinity) *Sarum 14* **P** *Patr Bd* **TR** B C ATKINSON, **C** S E HUTTON, A J OTTO

TROWBRIDGE (St James) *Sarum 14* **P** *Ch Patr Trust* **R** C F BROWN

TROWBRIDGE (St Thomas) and West Ashton *Sarum 14* **P** *CPAS* **P-in-c** J A COUTTS

TROWELL (St Helen) *see* Trowell, Awsworth and Cossall *S'well*

TROWELL (St Helen), Awsworth and Cossall *S'well 7* **P** *Bp and Lord Middleton (jt)* **R** G R BOOTH, **NSM** J WHYSALL, D C LESTER

TROWSE (St Andrew) *Nor 1* **P** *D&C* **P-in-c** M D B LONG

TRULL (All Saints) w Angersleigh *B & W 18* **P** *DBP and M V Spurway Esq (jt)* **Hon C** G C BOWYER

TRUMPINGTON (St Mary and St Michael) *Ely 2* **P** *Trin Coll Cam* **V** T AMBROSE

TRUNCH (St Botolph) *Nor 21* **P** *Duchy of Lanc (3 turns), Patr Bd (1 turn)* **TR** P B ALLAN, **TV** D W BARTLETT, **NSM** R H MACPHEE

TRURO (St George the Martyr) (St John the Evangelist) *Truro 6* **P** *Prime Min and V Kenwyn St Cuby (alt)* **V** *vacant* (01872) 272630

TRURO (St Mary's Cathedral and Parish Church) *Truro 6* **P** *The Crown* **R** M A MOXON

TRURO (St Paul) (St Clement) *Truro 6* **P** *Bp* **V** *vacant* (01872) 272576

TRUSHAM (St Michael and All Angels) *see* Chudleigh w Chudleigh Knighton and Trusham *Ex*

TRUSLEY (All Saints) *see* Boylestone, Church Broughton, Dalbury, etc *Derby*

TRUSTHORPE (St Peter) *see* Mablethorpe w Trusthorpe *Linc*

TRYSULL (All Saints) *see* Smestow Vale *Lich*

TRYTHALL (Mission Church) *see* Gulval and Madron *Truro*

TUBNEY (St Lawrence) *see* Fyfield w Tubney and Kingston Bagpuize *Ox*

TUCKHILL (Holy Innocents) *see* Claverley w Tuckhill *Heref*

TUCKINGMILL (All Saints) *Truro 2* **P** *Bp* **P-in-c** E C WOON

TUCKSWOOD (St Paul) *see* Nor Lakenham St Jo and All SS and Tuckswood *Nor*

TUDDENHAM (St Martin) *see* Westerfield and Tuddenham w Witnesham *St E*

TUDDENHAM (St Mary) *see* Mildenhall *St E*

TUDDENHAM, EAST (All Saints) *see* Hockering, Honingham, E and N Tuddenham *Nor*

TUDDENHAM, NORTH (St Mary the Virgin) *as above Nor*

TUDELEY (All Saints) cum Capel w Five Oak Green *Roch 11* **P** *Bp* **P-in-c** J G A IVE, **C** P F IVE

TUDHOE (St David) *see* Croxdale and Tudhoe *Dur*

TUDHOE GRANGE (St Andrew) *Dur 6* **P** *Bp* **V** N D BAKER

TUEBROOK (St John) *see* W Derby St Jo *Liv*

TUFFLEY (St Barnabas) *Glouc 5* **P** *Bp* **V** M SHARLAND, **NSM** A W GAGE

TUFNELL PARK (St George and All Saints) *Lon 6* **P** *Trustees and CPAS (jt)* **V** S F F PARKE, **C** J S B TODD, J V MOWBRAY

TUFTON (St Mary) *see* Whitchurch w Tufton and Litchfield *Win*

TUGBY (St Thomas à Becket) *see* Hallaton w Horninghold and Allexton, Tugby etc *Leic*

TUGFORD (St Catherine) *see* Diddlebury w Munslow, Holdgate and Tugford *Heref*

TULSE HILL (Holy Trinity and St Matthias) *S'wark 12* **P** *Simeon's Trustees and Peache Trustees (jt)* **V** B A MUSK, **C** M N PRENTICE, **NSM** D J LUBBOCK

TUNBRIDGE WELLS (Holy Trinity w Christ Church) *Roch 12* **P** *Mabledon Trust and CPAS (jt)* **V** J W BANNER

TUNBRIDGE WELLS (King Charles the Martyr) *Roch 12* **P** *Trustees* **V** *vacant* (01892) 525455

TUNBRIDGE WELLS (St Barnabas) *Roch 12* **P** *Guild of All So* **V** K E MACNAB

TUNBRIDGE WELLS (St James) w (St Philip) *Roch 12* **P** *Patr Bd* **TR** J P STEWART, **TV** B S SENIOR, **C** S R BIGGS

TUNBRIDGE WELLS (St John) *Roch 12* **P** *CPAS and V Tunbridge Wells H Trin (jt)* **V** G R WALTER, **C** S J GOODBODY

TUNBRIDGE WELLS (St Luke) *Roch 12* **P** *Five Trustees* **V** J A WHEELER

TUNBRIDGE WELLS (St Mark) Broadwater Down *Roch 12* **P** *Bp Chich* **V** B C H FORTNUM

TUNBRIDGE WELLS (St Peter) Windmill Fields *Roch 12* **P** *Trustees and CPAS (jt)* **V** P R PAYN

TUNSTALL (All Saints) *see* Roos and Garton in Holderness w Tunstall etc *York*

TUNSTALL (Christ Church) *Lich 11* **P** *Bp* **V** A D BUIK, **C** K A PALMER

TUNSTALL (Holy Trinity) *see* Catterick *Ripon*

TUNSTALL (St John the Baptist) *see* E Lonsdale *Blackb*

TUNSTALL (St John the Baptist) w Rodmersham *Cant 16* **P** *D&C and G L Doubleday Esq (jt)* **R** D MATTHIAE

TUNSTALL (St Michael and All Angels)   *see* Wilford Peninsula *St E*

TUNSTEAD (Holy Trinity) *Man 15*   **P** *Bp and Dioc Chan (jt)* **P-in-c** S E BROOK

TUNSTEAD (St Mary) w Sco' Ruston *Nor 12*   **P** *Bp* **P-in-c** A R LONG

TUNWORTH (All Saints)   *see* Herriard w Winslade and Long Sutton etc *Win*

TUPSLEY (St Paul) w Hampton Bishop *Heref 3*   **P** *Bp* **V** J D REESE,   **C** M J MORRIS

TUPTON (St John)   *see* N Wingfield, Clay Cross and Pilsley *Derby*

TUR LANGTON (St Andrew)   *see* Church Langton cum Tur Langton etc *Leic*

TURKDEAN (All Saints)   *see* Northleach w Hampnett and Farmington etc *Glouc*

TURNASTONE (St Mary Magdalene)   *see* Madley w Tyberton, Peterchurch, Vowchurch etc *Heref*

TURNDITCH (All Saints)   *see* Belper Ch Ch w Turnditch *Derby*

TURNERS HILL (St Leonard) *Chich 7*   **P** *Bp* **P-in-c** D M JARMY

TURNFORD (St Clement) Conventional District *St Alb 6*   **Min** C J SELBY

TURNHAM GREEN (Christ Church) *Lon 11*   **P** *Bp* **V** J E DAINTY,   **C** A J DENNISS

TURNWORTH (St Mary)   *see* Winterbourne Stickland and Turnworth etc *Sarum*

TURTON MOORLAND MINISTRY (St Anne) (St James) *Man 16*   **P** *Patr Bd* **TR** D M DUNN,   **TV** M R SHORT, J MCGRATH,   **NSM** R E IDDON, D R JONES,   **OLM** S HAWORTH, L TAYLOR, A J HESLOP

TURVEY (All Saints) *St Alb 15*   **P** *Mrs P K C Hanbury* **P-in-c** J A SPRAY

TURVILLE (St Mary)   *see* Hambleden Valley *Ox*

TURWESTON (Assumption of the Blessed Virgin Mary)   *see* W Buckingham *Ox*

TUSHINGHAM (St Chad) and Whitewell (St Mary) *Ches 5*   **P** *MMCET* **P-in-c** M S SEARLE

TUTBURY (St Mary the Virgin) *Lich 14*   **P** *Duchy of Lancaster* **V** T J GANZ

TUTSHILL (St Luke)   *see* Tidenham w Beachley and Lancaut *Glouc*

TUTTINGTON (St Peter and St Paul)   *see* King's Beck *Nor*

TUXFORD (St Nicholas) w Weston and Markham Clinton *S'well 3*   **P** *Ld Chan and Bp (alt)* **P-in-c** E A THOMAS

TWEEDMOUTH (St Bartholomew) *Newc 12*   **P** *D&C Dur* **V** A S ADAMSON,   **OLM** K R COULTER

TWERTON-ON-AVON   *see* Bath Twerton-on-Avon *B & W*

TWICKENHAM (All Hallows) *Lon 10*   **P** *D&C St Paul's* **V** N R EVANS

TWICKENHAM (All Saints) *Lon 10*   **P** *Bp* **V** P L BUSTIN

TWICKENHAM (St Mary the Virgin) *Lon 10*   **P** *D&C Windsor* **V** R J H WILLIAMS,   **Hon C** A F B ROGERS, D J ELLIOTT, G A BYRNE,   **NSM** J T MARTIN

TWICKENHAM, EAST (St Stephen) (St Paul) *Lon 10*   **P** *CPAS* **V** A J WATSON,   **C** R L PENISTAN, A N BEAVIS

TWICKENHAM COMMON (Holy Trinity) *Lon 10*   **P** *Bp* **V** M S STARKEY,   **C** L HELLMUTH

TWIGWORTH (St Matthew), Down Hatherley, Norton, The Leigh, Evington and Sandhurst *Glouc 6*   **P** *Bp (1 turn), Ld Chan (2 turns), and D&C Bris (1 turn)*   **V** *vacant* (01452) 731483

TWINEHAM (St Peter)   *see* Albourne w Sayers Common and Twineham *Chich*

TWINSTEAD (St John the Evangelist)   *see* N Hinckford *Chelmsf*

TWITCHEN (St Peter)   *see* S Molton w Nymet St George, High Bray etc *Ex*

TWO GATES (St Peter)   *see* Wilnecote *Lich*

TWO MILE ASH (not known)   *see* Watling Valley *Ox*

TWO MILE HILL (St Michael) *Bris 3*   **P** *Prime Min* **V** S ALLMAN

TWO RIVERS   *see* Newton Tracey, Horwood, Alverdiscott etc *Ex*

TWYCROSS (St James)   *see* Bosworth and Sheepy Gp *Leic*

TWYFORD (Assumption of the Blessed Virgin Mary)   *see* Swan *Ox*

TWYFORD (St Andrew)   *see* Ticknall, Smisby and Stanton by Bridge etc *Derby*

TWYFORD (St Andrew)   *see* S Croxton Gp *Leic*

TWYFORD (St Mary) and Owslebury and Morestead *Win 7*   **P** *Em Coll Cam and Bp (alt)* **P-in-c** M D BAILEY,   **NSM** M I JACKSON

TWYFORD (St Mary the Virgin)   *see* Ruscombe and Twyford *Ox*

TWYFORD (St Nicholas), Guist, Bintree, Themelthorpe, Wood Norton and Stibbard *Nor 22*   **P** *Bp and Mrs H M Cook (2 turns), DBP (1 turn)* **R** A K GREENHOUGH

TWYNING (St Mary Magdalene)   *see* Tewkesbury w Walton Cardiff and Twyning *Glouc*

TWYWELL (St Nicholas)   *see* Cranford w Grafton Underwood and Twywell *Pet*

TYBERTON (St Mary)   *see* Madley w Tyberton, Peterchurch, Vowchurch etc *Heref*

TYDD (St Mary)   *see* The Suttons w Tydd *Linc*

TYDD ST GILES (St Giles) *Ely 17*   **P** *Bp* **R** *vacant*

TYE GREEN (St Barnabas)   *see* Fairstead w Terling and White Notley etc *Chelmsf*

TYE GREEN (St Stephen) w St Andrew Netteswell *Chelmsf 26*   **P** *J L H Arkwright Esq* **R** A V WATSON

TYLDESLEY (St George) w Shakerley *Man 13*   **P** *Bp* **P-in-c** C J STRATON

TYLER HILL (St Francis)   *see* Hackington *Cant*

TYLERS GREEN (St Margaret) *Ox 29*   **P** *Earl Howe* **P-in-c** M D BISSET

TYLER'S HILL (St George)   *see* Gt Chesham *Ox*

TYNE, NORTH and Redesdale Team *Newc 2*   **P** *Patr Bd* **TR** W R LARGE,   **Hon C** B M JONES

TYNEMOUTH Balkwell (St Peter)   *see* Balkwell *Newc*

TYNEMOUTH Cullercoats (St Paul) *Newc 8*   **P** *Dioc Soc* **V** G F GILCHRIST,   **C** D W CARBERRY

TYNEMOUTH Shiremoor (St Mark)   *see* Shiremoor *Newc*

TYNEMOUTH (St John Percy) *Newc 8*   **P** *Dioc Soc* **V** *vacant* 0191-257 1819

TYNEMOUTH PRIORY (Holy Saviour) *Newc 8*   **P** *Dioc Soc* **V** R G FORD

TYNINGS LANE (St Mary's Mission Church)   *see* Aldridge *Lich*

TYRINGHAM (St Peter)   *see* Lamp *Ox*

TYRLEY (Mission Room)   *see* Drayton in Hales *Lich*

TYSELEY (St Edmund) *Birm 13*   **P** *The Crown* **V** J A BRADSHAW

TYSOE (Assumption of the Blessed Virgin Mary) w Oxhill and Whatcote *Cov 9*   **P** *Marquess of Northampton and DBP (jt)* **V** D A KNIGHT

TYTHBY (Holy Trinity)   *see* Cropwell Bishop w Colston Bassett, Granby etc *S'well*

TYTHERINGTON (St James)   *see* Cromhall w Tortworth and Tytherington *Glouc*

TYTHERINGTON (St James)   *see* Upper Wylye Valley *Sarum*

TYTHERLEY, EAST (St Peter)   *see* Lockerley and E Dean w E and W Tytherley *Win*

TYTHERLEY, WEST (St Peter)   *as above Win*

TYTHERTON KELLAWAYS (St Giles)   *see* Draycot *Bris*

TYTHERTON LUCAS (St Nicholas)   *see* Chippenham St Andr w Tytherton Lucas *Bris*

TYWARDREATH (St Andrew) w Tregaminion *Truro 1*   **P** *DBP* **P-in-c** F M BOWERS

UBLEY (St Bartholomew)   *see* Blagdon w Compton Martin and Ubley *B & W*

UCKFIELD (Holy Cross) (St Saviour) *Chich 21*   **P** *Abp* **R** B H WILCOX,   **C** P K H LO,   **NSM** C HOWARTH

UDIMORE (St Mary)   *see* Brede w Udimore *Chich*

UFFCULME (St Mary the Virgin)   *see* Cullompton, Willand, Uffculme, Kentisbeare etc *Ex*

UFFINGTON Group, The (St Michael and All Angels) *Linc 13*   **P** *Ld Chan (2 turns), Bp (2 turns), D&C (1 turn)* **R** C R KENNEDY

UFFINGTON (Holy Trinity)   *see* Wrockwardine Deanery *Lich*

UFFINGTON (St Mary), Shellingford, Woolstone and Baulking *Ox 17*   **P** *Bp (2 turns), J J Twynam Esq (1 turn)* **R** J GAWNE-CAIN,   **Hon C** J J H PAYNE

UFFORD (Assumption of the Blessed Virgin Mary)   *see* Melton and Ufford *St E*

UFFORD (St Andrew)   *see* Barnack w Ufford and Bainton *Pet*

UFTON (St Michael and All Angels) *Cov 10*   **P** *Bp* **V** *vacant*

UGBOROUGH (St Peter)   *see* Ermington and Ugborough *Ex*

UGGESHALL (St Mary)   *see* Sole Bay *St E*

UGGLEBARNBY (All Saints)   *see* Eskdaleside w Ugglebarnby and Sneaton *York*

UGLEY (St Peter)   *see* Henham and Elsenham w Ugley *Chelmsf*

UGTHORPE (Christ Church)   *see* Lythe w Ugthorpe *York*

ULCEBY (All Saints)   *see* Willoughby *Linc*

ULCEBY Group, The (St Nicholas) *Linc 6*   **P** *Ld Chan* **V** *vacant* (01469) 588239

ULCOMBE (All Saints)   *see* Len Valley *Cant*

ULDALE (St James)   *see* Binsey *Carl*

ULEY (St Giles) w Owlpen and Nympsfield *Glouc 2*   **P** *Ld Chan* **P-in-c** N H TUCKER

ULGHAM (St John the Baptist) *Newc 11*   **P** *Bp* **P-in-c** A E HARRISON

ULLENHALL (St Mary the Virgin)   *see* Beaudesert and Henley-in-Arden w Ullenhall *Cov*

ULLESKELFE (St Saviour)   *see* Kirk Fenton w Kirkby Wharfe and Ulleskelfe *York*

ULLEY (Holy Trinity)   *see* Aston cum Aughton w Swallownest and Ulley *Sheff*

ULLINGSWICK (St Luke)   *see* Stoke Lacy, Moreton Jeffries w Much Cowarne etc *Heref*

ULPHA (St John)   *see* Broughton and Duddon *Carl*

ULROME (St Andrew)   *see* Skipsea w Ulrome and Barmston w Fraisthorpe *York*

ULTING (All Saints)   *see* Hatfield Peverel w Ulting *Chelmsf*

ULVERSTON (St Mary w Holy Trinity) (St Jude) *Carl 9*   **P** *Peache Trustees*   **P-in-c** A C BING,   **C** P J M TOLLERSON

UMBERLEIGH (Church of the Good Shepherd)   *see* S Molton w Nymet St George, High Bray etc *Ex*

UNDERBARROW (All Saints) *Carl 10*   **P** *V Kendal H Trin*   **V** *vacant*

UNDERRIVER (St Margaret) *Roch 9*   **P** *Bp*   **P-in-c** M D COOKE

UNDERSKIDDAW (Parish Room)   *see* Crosthwaite Keswick *Carl*

UNDERWOOD (St Michael and All Angels)   *see* Brinsley w Underwood *S'well*

UNSTONE (St Mary)   *see* Dronfield w Holmesfield *Derby*

UNSWORTH (St George) *Man 14*   **P** *R Prestwich St Mary*   **V** R E MALLINSON

UP HATHERLEY (St Philip and St James) *Glouc 10*   **P** *Soc of the Faith*   **V** K M WRAY,   **C** D G HUMPHRIES

UP MARDEN (St Michael)   *see* Compton, the Mardens, Stoughton and Racton *Chich*

UP NATELY (St Stephen)   *see* Newnham w Nately Scures w Mapledurwell etc *Win*

UP WALTHAM (St Mary the Virgin) *Chich 11*   **P** *Lord Egremont*   **P-in-c** R A STAVELEY-WADHAM

UPAVON (St Mary the Virgin) w Rushall and Charlton *Sarum 19*   **P** *Mert Coll Ox, Ld Chan, and Ch Ch Ox (by turn)*   **P-in-c** H L GIBBONS

UPCHURCH (St Mary the Virgin) w Lower Halstow *Cant 16*   **P** *D&C*   **V** J P LEFROY,   **NSM** R W PARTRIDGE

UPHAM (All Saints) (Blessed Mary of Upham) *Portsm 1*   **P** *Ld Chan*   **R** A G DAVIS,   **C** J M HEMMINGS

UPHILL (St Nicholas) (St Barnabas Mission Church) *B & W 11*   **P** *Patr Bd*   **TR** E W MCLEOD,   **TV** A W G CHALKLEY

UPHOLLAND (St Thomas the Martyr) *Liv 11*   **P** *Patr Bd*   **TR** P D D BRADLEY,   **TV** A DILWORTH,   **C** J A BALL

UPLANDS (All Saints)   *see* Stroud and Uplands w Slad *Glouc*

UPLEADON (St Mary the Virgin)   *see* Redmarley D'Abitot, Bromesberrow, Pauntley etc *Glouc*

UPLOWMAN (St Peter)   *see* Sampford Peverell, Uplowman, Holcombe Rogus etc *Ex*

UPLYME (St Peter and St Paul) w Axmouth *Ex 5*   **P** *CPAS and Hyndman Trustees (jt)*   **R** J S WHITE

UPMINSTER (St Laurence) *Chelmsf 2*   **P** *Revd W R Holden*   **R** C J MANN,   **C** T J HIDE

UPNOR (St Philip and St James)   *see* Frindsbury w Upnor *Roch*

UPOTTERY (St Mary the Virgin)   *see* Dunkeswell, Luppitt, Sheldon and Upottery *Ex*

UPPER   *see also* under substantive place name

UPPER ITCHEN *Win 1*   **P** *Prime Min (2 turns), D&C (1 turn)*   **R** G A HENDY,   **Hon C** R J GUYMER

UPPERBY (St John the Baptist)   *see* S Carl TM *Carl*

UPPERTHONG (St John the Evangelist)   *see* Upper Holme Valley *Wakef*

UPPINGHAM (St Peter and St Paul) w Ayston and Wardley w Belton *Pet 14*   **P** *Bp*   **R** S J EVANS,   **C** K M O'BRIEN

UPPINGTON (Holy Trinity)   *see* Wrockwardine Deanery *Lich*

UPSHIRE (St Thomas)   *see* Waltham H Cross *Chelmsf*

UPTON (All Saints)   *see* Lea Gp *Linc*

UPTON (Holy Ascension) *Ches 2*   **P** *Duke of Westmr*   **V** G H CONWAY

UPTON (St Dunstan)   *see* Lytchett Minster *Sarum*

UPTON (St James)   *see* Brompton Regis w Upton and Skilgate *B & W*

UPTON (St John the Baptist)   *see* Castor w Sutton and Upton w Marholm *Pet*

UPTON (St Laurence)   *see* Upton cum Chalvey *Ox*

UPTON (St Margaret)   *see* Ranworth w Panxworth, Woodbastwick etc *Nor*

UPTON (St Margaret) and Copmanford *Ely 9*   **P** *Bp*   **V** *vacant*

UPTON (St Mary) *Ches 8*   **P** *Simeon's Trustees*   **V** R J SHIMWELL,   **C** M C BAKER,   D M MUIR

UPTON (St Mary Magdalene) *Ex 10*   **P** *Simeon's Trustees and Ch Patr Trust (alt)*   **R** B J R GERRY,   **NSM** J H GARNER

UPTON (St Mary the Virgin)   *see* Blewbury, Hagbourne and Upton *Ox*

UPTON (St Peter and St Paul)   *see* Rolleston w Fiskerton, Morton and Upton *S'well*

UPTON BISHOP (St John the Baptist)   *see* Ross *Heref*

UPTON CRESSETT w Monk Hopton *Heref 9*   **P** *DBP and Miss E A Bird (alt)*   **Hon C** H J PATTERSON

UPTON CROSS (St Paul)   *see* Linkinhorne *Truro*

UPTON CUM CHALVEY (St Mary) *Ox 23*   **P** *Bp*   **TR** D K MIELL,   **TV** D E WEST,   **C** J A LOEWE

UPTON GREY (St Mary)   *see* Herriard w Winslade and Long Sutton etc *Win*

UPTON HELLIONS (St Mary the Virgin)   *see* Crediton, Shobrooke and Sandford etc *Ex*

UPTON LOVELL (St Augustine of Canterbury)   *see* Upper Wylye Valley *Sarum*

UPTON MAGNA (St Lucia)   *see* Wrockwardine Deanery *Lich*

UPTON NOBLE (St Mary Magdalene)   *see* Bruton and Distr *B & W*

UPTON-ON-SEVERN (St Peter and St Paul), Ripple, Earls Croome w Hill Croome and Strensham *Worc 5*   **P** *Bp (2 turns), Mrs A J Hyde-Smith and Mrs A L Wynne (1 turn)*   **R** C G HARDWICK,   **C** P A ALLSOPP,   **NSM** J A FRASER

UPTON PARK (St Alban)   *see* E Ham w Upton Park St Alb *Chelmsf*

UPTON PRIORY (Church of the Resurrection) *Ches 13*   **P** *Bp*   **V** J H FIFE

UPTON PYNE (Our Lady)   *see* Thorverton, Cadbury, Upton Pyne etc *Ex*

UPTON SCUDAMORE (St Mary the Virgin)   *see* Cley Hill Warminster *Sarum*

UPTON SNODSBURY (St Kenelm)   *see* Peopleton and White Ladies Aston w Churchill etc *Worc*

UPTON ST LEONARDS (St Leonard) *Glouc 5*   **P** *Bp*   **P-in-c** P R LECKEY

UPTON WARREN (St Michael)   *see* Stoke Prior, Wychbold and Upton Warren *Worc*

UPWELL (St Peter) *Ely 17*   **P** R T Townley Esq   **R** A F JESSON

UPWELL CHRISTCHURCH (Christ Church)   *see* Christchurch and Manea and Welney *Ely*

UPWEY (St Laurence)   *see* Bincombe w Broadwey, Upwey and Buckland Ripers *Sarum*

UPWOOD (St Peter)   *see* The Ramseys and Upwood *Ely*

URCHFONT (St Michael and All Angels)   *see* Redhorn *Sarum*

URMSTON (St Clement) *Man 7*   **P** *Bp*   **P-in-c** C C BROWN,   **OLM** C E FAULKNER

URSWICK (St Mary the Virgin and St Michael)   *see* Aldingham, Dendron, Rampside and Urswick *Carl*

USHAW MOOR (St Luke)   *see* Bearpark and Ushaw Moor *Dur*

USSELBY (St Margaret)   *see* Kelsey Gp *Linc*

USWORTH (Holy Trinity) (St Michael and All Angels) *Dur 11*   **P** *Patr Bd*   **TR** A MELTON,   **TV** P T HARRISON

UTKINTON (St Paul)   *see* Tarporley *Ches*

UTLEY (St Mark) *Bradf 8*   **P** *Bp and R Keighley St Andr (jt)*   **V** D WALMSLEY

UTTERBY (St Andrew)   *see* Fotherby *Linc*

UTTOXETER AREA (St Mary the Virgin) *Lich 15*   **P** *Patr Bd*   **TR** D V EVANS,   **TV** D C STONE,   E C GARRETT,   **C** A S E PENNY,   **OLM** I M SMITH,   C M MILNER,   I L SMITH,   C H BROWN

UXBRIDGE (St Andrew) (St Margaret) (St Peter) *Lon 24*   **P** *Bp*   **TR** A F SHEARD,   **TV** S W COOPER,   **C** J A HUGHMAN,   E J MOODY

VALE OF BELVOIR Parishes *Leic 3*   **P** *Patr Bd (2 turns), Ld Chan (1 turn)*   **TR** C A BRADSHAW,   **TV** R D STAPLEFORD,   **C** S P J BURNHAM

VALLEY END (St Saviour)   *see* Chobham w Valley End *Guildf*

VALLEY PARK (St Francis) *Win 10*   **P** *Bp*   **V** P F HUTCHINSON

VANGE (St Chad) *Chelmsf 6*   **P** *MMCET*   **P-in-c** D A EATON

VAUXHALL (St Peter)   *see* N Lambeth *S'wark*

VENN OTTERY (St Gregory)   *see* Ottery St Mary, Alfington, W Hill, Tipton etc *Ex*

VENTA Group, The   *see* Stoke H Cross w Dunston, Arminghall etc *Nor*

VENTNOR (Holy Trinity) *Portsm 7*   **P** *Bp*   **V** D H LAURIE,   **NSM** C A DAVIES

VENTNOR (St Alban)   *see* Godshill *Portsm*

VENTNOR (St Catherine) *Portsm 7*   **P** *Ch Patr Trust*   **V** D H LAURIE,   **NSM** C A DAVIES

VERNHAM DEAN (St Mary the Virgin)   *see* Hurstbourne Tarrant, Faccombe, Vernham Dean etc *Win*

VERWOOD (St Michael and All Angels) *Sarum 9*   **P** *Bp*   **V** A J M SINCLAIR,   **C** A J W ROWLAND,   **NSM** P MILES,   **OLM** N F MOULAND,   P M BASAVARAJ

VERYAN (St Symphorian) w Ruan Lanihorne *Truro 6*   **P** *D&C and DBP (jt)*   **P-in-c** C J BUDDEN

VICTORIA DOCKS (Ascension) *Chelmsf 3*   **P** *Bp*   **V** J A W BRICE

VICTORIA DOCKS St Luke *Chelmsf 3* **P** *Ld Chan*
V D P WADE, **NSM** G ANAN
VICTORIA PARK (St John Chrysostom) *see* Man Victoria
Park *Man*
VICTORIA PARK (St Mark) *see* Old Ford St Paul and St Mark
Lon
VIGO (Village Hall) *see* Stansted w Fairseat and Vigo *Roch*
VINEY HILL (All Saints) *see* Parkend and Viney Hill *Glouc*
VIRGINIA WATER (Christ Church) *Guildf 11* **P** *Simeon's
Trustees* **V** S R SIZER, **C** J T HUGHES
VIRGINSTOW (St Bridget) *see* Boyton, N Tamerton,
Werrington etc *Truro*
VOWCHURCH (St Bartholomew) *see* Madley w Tyberton,
Peterchurch, Vowchurch etc *Heref*
WABERTHWAITE (St John) *see* Eskdale, Irton, Muncaster
and Waberthwaite *Carl*
WACTON (All Saints) *see* Stratton St Mary w Stratton
St Michael etc *Nor*
WADDESDON (St Michael and All Angels) *see* Schorne *Ox*
WADDINGHAM (St Mary and St Peter) *see* Bishop Norton,
Wadingham and Snitterby *Linc*
WADDINGTON (St Helen) *Bradf 5* **P** E C Parker Esq
V A G BAILEY
WADDINGTON (St Michael) *Linc 18* **P** *Linc Coll Ox*
R R J G PARKER
WADDON (St George) *see* Croydon St Jo *S'wark*
WADEBRIDGE *see* St Breoke and Egloshayle *Truro*
WADENHOE (St Michael and All Angels) *see* Aldwincle w
Thorpe Achurch, Pilton, Wadenhoe etc *Pet*
WADHURST (St Peter and St Paul) *Chich 19*
P J M Hardcastle Esq and M R Toynbee Esq (jt) **V** J R JAMES,
C C D LAWRENCE, **NSM** R G ALFORD
WADINGHAM (St Mary and St Peter) *see* Bishop Norton,
Wadingham and Snitterby *Linc*
WADSHELF (Mission Room) *see* Old Brampton *Derby*
WADSLEY (no dedication) *Sheff 4* **P** *Ch Patr Trust*
V G J HUTCHISON
WADWORTH (St John the Baptist) w Loversall *Sheff 9*
P *V Doncaster and DBP (alt)* **V** R W IVELL
WAGGONERS *York 10* **P** *Abp and Sir Tatton Sykes Bt, and
Ld Chan (alt)* **V** M TEARE
WAINCLIFFE (St David) *see* Beeston *Ripon*
WAINFLEET (All Saints) *see* The Wainfleet Gp *Linc*
WAINFLEET Group, The (All Saints) (St Mary) (St Michael)
Linc 8 **P** *Ld Chan, Bp and T E Pitts Esq (alt)* **R** *vacant*
(01754) 880401
WAINFLEET (St Mary) *see* The Wainfleet Gp *Linc*
WAINFLEET (St Michael) *as above Linc*
WAINFORD *St E 14* **P** *Bp, Mrs B I T Suckling, CPAS, Magd
Coll Cam, and Ch Soc Trust (jt)* **R** A T HINDLEY,
OLM J F W BUCHANAN, N H SIMISTER
WAITHE (St Martin) *see* The North-Chapel Parishes *Linc*
WAKEFIELD (St Andrew and St Mary) (St Swithun) *Wakef 12*
P *Peache Trustees* **P-in-c** K S BURKE
WAKEFIELD (St John the Baptist) *Wakef 12* **P** *Dean*
V P M DOWLING, **Hon C** R B GRAINGER, **NSM** M WALKER
WAKEFIELD (St Mary) Chantry Bridge *see* Wakef Cathl
Wakef
WAKEFIELD (St Michael the Archangel) *see* Westgate
Common *Wakef*
WAKERING, GREAT (St Nicholas) w Foulness *Chelmsf 13*
P *Bp* **P-in-c** W C FREWIN
WAKERING, LITTLE (St Mary the Virgin) *see* Barling w Lt
Wakering *Chelmsf*
WAKERLEY (St John the Baptist) *see* Barrowden and
Wakerley w S Luffenham etc *Pet*
WAKES COLNE (All Saints) *see* Gt and Lt Tey w Wakes Colne
and Chappel *Chelmsf*
WALBERSWICK (St Andrew) *see* Sole Bay *St E*
WALBERTON (St Mary) w Binsted *Chich 21* **P** *Bp*
V T J C WARD
WALBROOK Epiphany *Derby 10* **P** *Patr Bd* **TR** A J FITCH,
TV D N GOUGH, A J WARD, **C** D J J EADES,
NSM A J CLARK
WALCOT *see* Bath Walcot *B & W*
WALCOT (All Saints) *see* Happisburgh, Walcott, Hempstead w
Eccles etc *Nor*
WALCOT (St Nicholas) *see* S Lafford *Linc*
WALCOT (St Oswald) *see* Carr Dyke Gp *Linc*
WALDEN, LITTLE (St John) *see* Saffron Walden w Wendens
Ambo, Littlebury etc *Chelmsf*
WALDERSLADE (St William) *see* S Chatham H Trin *Roch*
WALDINGFIELD, GREAT (St Lawrence) *see* Acton w Gt
Waldingfield *St E*
WALDINGFIELD, LITTLE (St Lawrence) *see* Boxford,
Edwardstone, Groton etc *St E*
WALDITCH (St Mary) *see* Bridport *Sarum*

WALDRINGFIELD (All Saints) w Hemley and Newbourn
St E 2 **P** *Canon T Waller and Revd A H N Waller, Ld Chan,
and Mrs S E F Holden (by turn)* **R** J P WALLER
WALDRON (All Saints) *Chich 15* **P** *Ex Coll Ox*
P-in-c J SHERWIN
WALES (St John the Baptist) *Sheff 5* **P** *Bp* **V** G SCHOFIELD
WALESBY (St Edmund) *S'well 3* **P** *DBP* **V** C C LEVY
WALESBY (St Mary and All Saints) *Linc 5* **P** *Bp, DBP, and
C Drakes Esq (jt)* **R** J H F CARR
**WALFORD (St Michael and All Angels) and St John, w
Bishopswood, Goodrich, Marstow and Welsh Bicknor** *Heref 8*
P *Bp and Ld Chan (alt)* **P-in-c** O D WILLIAMS
WALGRAVE (St Peter) w Hannington and Wold and Scaldwell
Pet 2 **P** *Bp (2 turns), BNC Ox (1 turn)* **R** *vacant* (01604)
781974
WALHAM GREEN (St John) (St James) *Lon 9* **P** *Bp*
P-in-c M W OSBORNE, **NSM** J C HUNTER
WALKDEN (St Paul) (St Barnabas' Mission) and Little Hulton
Man 12 **P** *Patr Bd* **TR** C A BRACEGIRDLE,
TV C H PHARAOH, K R GOVAN, **OLM** K HOPWOOD OWEN
WALKER (Christ Church) *Newc 6* **P** *Bp* **V** K HUNT,
NSM J LANCASTER
WALKERGATE (St Oswald) *see* Byker St Mark and
Walkergate St Oswald *Newc*
WALKERINGHAM (St Mary Magdalene) *see* Beckingham w
Walkeringham and Gringley *S'well*
WALKERN (St Mary the Virgin) *see* Benington w Walkern
St Alb
WALKHAMPTON (St Mary the Virgin) *see* Yelverton, Meavy,
Sheepstor and Walkhampton *Ex*
WALKINGHAM HILL *Ripon 1* **P** *Bp, DBP, R Knaresborough,
MMCET, and Major Sir Arthur Collins (jt)* **R** C WRAY
WALKINGTON (All Hallows) *see* Bishop Burton w
Walkington *York*
WALKLEY (St Mary) *Sheff 4* **P** *Bp* **P-in-c** M A FITZGERALD
WALL (St George) *see* St Oswald in Lee w Bingfield *Newc*
WALL (St John the Baptist) *see* Lich St Mich w St Mary and
Wall *Lich*
WALL HEATH (Ascension) *see* Kingswinford St Mary *Worc*
WALLASEY (St Hilary) *Ches 7* **P** *Bp* **P-in-c** P L ROBINSON,
C K J HODGSON
WALLASEY (St Nicholas) *Ches 7* **P** *Bp* **V** *vacant* 0151-639
3589
WALLINGFORD (St Mary le More w All Hallows) (St Leonard)
Ox 18 **P** *Bp* **TR** D RICE, **TV** J M RUSSELL,
C M E RUDALL, **Hon C** J K SPENCE
WALLINGTON (Holy Trinity) (St Patrick) *S'wark 25*
P *Ch Soc Trust* **C** P J BATEMAN, M C BREADMORE
WALLINGTON (Springfield Church) Extra-Parochial Place
S'wark 25 **Min** W COOKSON
WALLINGTON (St Mary) *see* Sandon, Wallington and
Rushden w Clothall *St Alb*
WALLINGTON (St Michael and All Angels) *see* S Beddington
St Mich *S'wark*
WALLINGTON (St Paul) *see* Roundshaw St Paul CD *S'wark*
WALLISDOWN (St Saviour) *see* Talbot Village *Sarum*
WALLOP, NETHER (St Andrew) *see* Over Wallop w Nether
Wallop *Win*
WALLOP, OVER (St Peter) w Nether Wallop *Win 3* **P** *D&C
York and Earl of Portsm (alt)* **P-in-c** F P MATTHEWS
WALLSEND (St John the Evangelist) *Newc 8* **P** *Bp*
P-in-c C R BATES
WALLSEND (St Peter) (St Luke) *Newc 8* **P** *Bp* **R** M C VINE,
NSM A J ELDER
WALMER (St Mary) (St Saviour) (Blessed Virgin Mary) *Cant 8*
P *Abp* **V** B A HAWKINS, **C** L A HARDING, **NSM** S M LEE,
A K GALLON
WALMERSLEY (Christ Church) *Man 10* **P** *Trustees*
V *vacant* 0161-797 9273
WALMGATE (St Denys) *see* York St Denys *York*
WALMLEY (St John the Evangelist) *Birm 12* **P** *Trustess*
C O HARRISON
WALMSLEY (Christ Church) *see* Turton Moorland Min *Man*
WALNEY ISLAND (St Mary the Virgin) *Carl 8*
P *V Dalton-in-Furness* **V** J D HODGKINSON, **C** M PEAT
WALPOLE (St Mary the Virgin) *see* Blyth Valley *St E*
**WALPOLE ST PETER (St Peter and St Paul) w Walpole
St Andrew** *Ely 17* **P** *The Crown and DBP (alt)* **R** *vacant*
(01945) 780252
WALSALL (Annunciation of Our Lady) *see* Walsall St Gabr
Fulbrook *Lich*
WALSALL (St Andrew) *Lich 25* **P** *Bp* **P-in-c** M LIDDELL
WALSALL (St Gabriel) Fulbrook *Lich 25* **P** *Bp*
V T R H COYNE, **NSM** W H POULTNEY
WALSALL (St Matthew) (St Luke) (St Martin) *Lich 25*
P *Patr Bd* **TR** C T GIBSON, **TV** A P L SMITH, M C IRELAND,
P O HART, **C** D N ASH, **NSM** D N H STOKES-HARRISON

WALSALL (St Michael and All Angels)   *see* Caldmore w Palfrey *Lich*

WALSALL St Paul *Lich 25*   **P** *R Walsall*   **P-in-c** P J WILCOX,
C S J HARVEY,   **NSM** R W JORDAN

WALSALL (St Peter) *Lich 25*   **P** *R Walsall*   **V** S R KIRBY

WALSALL THE PLECK (St John) and Bescot *Lich 25*
P *V Walsall*   **V** B N WHITMORE,   **C** P SHEPHERD

WALSALL WOOD (St John) *Lich 25*   **P** *R Walsall*
C J C HILL

WALSDEN (St Peter)   *see* Cornholme and Walsden *Wakef*

WALSGRAVE ON SOWE (St Mary) *Cov 1*   **P** *Ld Chan*
V M TYLER,   **NSM** F E TYLER

WALSHAM, NORTH (St Nicholas) w Antingham *Nor 12*
P *Bp*,   **V** S D EARIS,   **NSM** V A WATTS,
OLM N J M PATERSON

WALSHAM, SOUTH (St Mary)   *see* Ranworth w Panxworth,
Woodbastwick etc *Nor*

WALSHAM LE WILLOWS (St Mary)   *see* Badwell and
Walsham *St E*

WALSHAW (Christ Church) *Man 10*   **P** *Simeon's Trustees*
V S FOSTER,   **OLM** I J HALSALL

**WALSINGHAM (St Mary and All Saints) (St Peter), Houghton
and Barsham** *Nor 15*   **P** *J Gurney Esq and Capt
J D A Keith (jt)*   **V** N BANKS,   **NSM** J H DAVIES

WALSOKEN (All Saints) *Ely 17*   **P** *DBP*   **R** A R LANDALL

WALTERSTONE (St Mary)   *see* Ewyas Harold w Dulas,
Kenderchurch etc *Heref*

WALTHAM (All Saints) *Linc 10*   **P** *The Crown*
R I R SHELTON

WALTHAM (Holy Cross) *Chelmsf 25*   **P** *Patr Bd*
TR M D WEBSTER,   **TV** J PEARCE,   **C** L C VINCER, J M SMITH,
NSM T I SCOTT,   D E CROOK

WALTHAM (St Bartholomew)   *see* Petham and Waltham w
Lower Hardres etc *Cant*

WALTHAM, GREAT (St Mary and St Lawrence) w Ford End
Chelmsf 8   **P** *Trin Coll Ox*   **P-in-c** K L HACKER HUGHES

WALTHAM, LITTLE (St Martin) *Chelmsf 8*   **P** *Ex Coll Ox*
P-in-c C J ELLIOTT,   **C** D P RITCHIE

WALTHAM, NEW (St Matthew) *Linc 10*   **P** *The Crown*
V M E THORNE

**WALTHAM, NORTH (St Michael) and Steventon, Ashe and
Deane** *Win 6*   **P** *DBP*   **R** M S KENNING

WALTHAM ABBEY (Holy Cross)   *see* Waltham H Cross
Chelmsf

WALTHAM CROSS (Christ Church) *St Alb 20*   **P** *V Cheshunt*
V M J BANISTER,   **C** E R BELL

**WALTHAM ON THE WOLDS (St Mary Magdalene),
Stonesby, Saxby w Stapleford and Wyfordby** *Leic 3*   **P** *Duke
of Rutland, Lady Gretton, and Sir Lyonel Tollemache Bt (jt)*
R vacant (01664) 464774

WALTHAM ST LAWRENCE (St Lawrence) *Ox 13*   **P** *Lord
Braybrooke*   **NSM** R E NUNN

WALTHAMSTOW (St Andrew) *Chelmsf 5*   **P** *Bp*
V M R J LAND

WALTHAMSTOW (St Barnabas and St James the Great)
Chelmsf 5   **P** *Bp*   **V** A D COUCHMAN

**WALTHAMSTOW (St Gabriel) (St Luke) (St Mary)
(St Stephen)** *Chelmsf 5*   **P** *Patr Bd*   **TR** P R BUTLER,
TV N J ANSTEY,   A M KENNEDY,   **C** D J WELCH

WALTHAMSTOW (St John) *Chelmsf 5*   **P** *TR Walthamstow*
V A J BISHOP

WALTHAMSTOW (St Michael and All Angels) *Chelmsf 5*
P *Bp*   **V** J C RAVENSDALE

WALTHAMSTOW (St Peter-in-the-Forest) *Chelmsf 5*   **P** *Bp*
V S M P SAXBY,   **NSM** W S ROBINS

WALTHAMSTOW (St Saviour) *Chelmsf 5*   **P** *Bp*
V D A WALLER

WALTON (Holy Trinity)   *see* Street w Walton *B & W*

WALTON (Holy Trinity) *Ox 21*   **P** *Patr Bd and DBP (jt)*
TV L P R MEERING,   S C WILLIAMS

WALTON Milton Keynes *Ox 25*   **P** *Patr Bd*   **TR** D LUNN,
TV S JACKSON

WALTON (not known)   *see* Gilmorton, Peatling Parva, Kimcote
etc *Leic*

WALTON (St John)   *see* Brampton St Thos *Derby*

WALTON (St John) *Derby 5*   **P** *Bp*   **V** A C BROOM

WALTON (St John the Evangelist) *Ches 4*   **P** *P G Greenall Esq*
P-in-c J E HARRIES

WALTON (St Mary)   *see* Lanercost, Walton, Gilsland and
Nether Denton *Carl*

WALTON (St Mary) (St Philip) and Trimley *St E 2*   **P** *Patr Bd
(2 turns), Ld Chan (1 turn)*   **TR** R G CORKE,
TV T R J WELLS,   P R GARBETT,   **C** K O DUNNETT,
OLM I W BARLEY,   A C BARLEY,   B PERCY

WALTON (St Paul)   *see* Sandal St Helen *Wakef*

WALTON (St Peter)   *see* Thorp Arch w Walton *York*

WALTON (St Thomas)   *see* Baswich *Lich*

WALTON, EAST (St Mary)   *see* Gayton, Gayton Thorpe, E
Walton, E Winch etc *Nor*

WALTON, HIGHER (All Saints) *Blackb 5*   **P** *V Blackb*
V S J HUNT

WALTON, WEST (St Mary) *Ely 17*   **P** *Ld Chan*   **R** vacant
(01945) 61873

WALTON BRECK (Christ Church) *Liv 7*   **P** *Simeon's Trustees*
P-in-c E J FLEMING

WALTON BRECK (Holy Trinity) *Liv 7*   **P** *Simeon's Trustees*
V vacant 0151-263 1538

WALTON CLEVEDON (St Mary)   *see* E Clevedon w Clapton
in Gordano etc *B & W*

WALTON D'EIVILLE (St James) *Cov 8*   **P** *Sir Richard
Hamilton Bt*   **R** vacant

WALTON IN GORDANO (St Paul)   *see* E Clevedon w Clapton
in Gordano etc *B & W*

**WALTON-LE-DALE (St Leonard) w Samlesbury St Leonard the
Less** *Blackb 5*   **P** *V Blackb St Mary and St Paul*
V R MCCULLOUGH

WALTON LE SOKEN (All Saints) (St George) *Chelmsf 23*
P *Bp*   **V** S SANDERSON

WALTON LE WOLDS (St Mary)   *see* Barrow upon Soar w
Walton le Wolds *Leic*

WALTON-ON-THAMES (St Mary) *Guildf 8*   **P** *Bp*
V T J SEDGLEY,   **C** M P STOKES,   **NSM** G M HOLDAWAY,
OLM G L HORREX

WALTON ON THE HILL (St John) *Liv 7*   **P** *Bp, Adn, and
R Walton (jt)*   **V** S L WILLIAMS

WALTON ON THE HILL (St Luke) *Liv 7*   **P** *Bp*   **V** H E ROSS

WALTON-ON-THE-HILL (St Mary) (St Aidan) *Liv 5*   **P** *Bp*
TR T M LATHAM,   **TV** T H ALLEN,   **C** S W BOYD

WALTON-ON-THE-HILL (St Peter) *Guildf 9*   **P** *Bp*
P-in-c R J WHITTLE

**WALTON-ON-TRENT (St Lawrence) w Croxall, Rosliston w
Linton and Castle Gresley** *Derby 16*   **P** *Bp and
R D Nielson Esq (jt)*   **R** L A de POMERAI,
NSM D I M de POMERAI

WALTON STREET (St Saviour)   *see* Upper Chelsea *Lon*

WALWORTH (St Christopher) *S'wark 10*   **P** *Bp and Pemb Coll
Miss*   **V** M WILLIAMS

WALWORTH (St John w the Lady Margaret) *S'wark 10*   **P** *Bp*
V J F WALKER

WALWORTH (St Peter) *S'wark 10*   **P** *Bp*   **TR** G W GODDARD,
NSM I G THOMPSON,   **OLM** A J WILD

WAMBROOK (Blessed Virgin Mary)   *see* Combe St Nicholas w
Wambrook *B & W*

WANBOROUGH (St Andrew)   *see* Lyddington and
Wanborough and Bishopstone etc *Bris*

WANBOROUGH (St Bartholomew)   *see* Seale, Puttenham and
Wanborough *Guildf*

WANDSWORTH (All Saints) (Holy Trinity) *S'wark 20*
P *Ch Soc Trust*   **V** G L WINCHESTER

WANDSWORTH (St Anne) *S'wark 20*   **P** *Bp*   **V** G P JEANES,
NSM P M LEAR

WANDSWORTH (St Faith) *S'wark 20*   **P** *Bp*   **V** vacant

WANDSWORTH (St Michael and All Angels) Southfields
S'wark 20   **P** *Ch Soc Trust*   **P-in-c** S MELLUISH,
C R G WILSON,   **NSM** R J COLLINS

WANDSWORTH (St Paul) Wimbledon Park *S'wark 20*   **P** *Bp*
V H D TOLLER,   **Hon C** E M TOLLER,
NSM G E D BONHAM-CARTER,   A J TOWNSEND

WANDSWORTH (St Stephen) *S'wark 20*   **P** *CPAS*
V S MELLUISH,   **NSM** R J COLLINS

WANDSWORTH COMMON (St Mary Magdalene) *S'wark 19*
P *Bp*   **V** K PARKES

WANDSWORTH COMMON (St Michael)   *see* Battersea
St Mich *S'wark*

WANGFORD (St Peter)   *see* Sole Bay *St E*

WANLIP (Our Lady and St Nicholas)   *see* Birstall and Wanlip
Leic

WANSFORD (St Mary)   *see* Nafferton w Wansford *York*

WANSFORD (St Mary the Virgin)   *see* Thornhaugh and
Wansford *Pet*

WANSTEAD (Holy Trinity) Hermon Hill *Chelmsf 4*   **P** *Bp*
V R E HAMPSON

WANSTEAD (St Mary) (Christ Church) *Chelmsf 4*   **P** *Bp*
R R W SPRINGETT,   **C** P R THOMAS

WANSTROW (Blessed Virgin Mary)   *see* Nunney and Witham
Friary, Marston Bigot etc *B & W*

WANTAGE (St Peter and St Paul) *Ox 19*   **P** *D&C Windsor*
V J L SALTER,   **C** N J CHEESEMAN

WANTAGE DOWNS *Ox 19*   **P** *Bp, CCC Ox, and
C L Loyd Esq (jt)*   **R** E G ADLEY,   **NSM** D J PAGE

WANTISDEN (St John the Baptist)   *see* Wilford Peninsula *St E*

WAPLEY (St Peter)   *see* Yate New Town *Bris*

WAPPENBURY (St John the Baptist) w Weston under Wetherley *Cov 10* **P** *Bp* **P-in-c** J T H BRITTON, **C** D R PATTERSON

WAPPENHAM (St Mary the Virgin) *see* Weedon Lois w Plumpton and Moreton Pinkney etc *Pet*

WARBLETON (St Mary) and Bodle Street Green *Chich 15* **P** *Revd E S Haviland* **R** *vacant* (01435) 830421

WARBLINGTON (St Thomas à Becket) w Emsworth *Portsm 5* **P** *Bp and J H Norris Esq (alt)* **R** S P SAYERS

WARBOROUGH (St Lawrence) *Ox 1* **P** *CCC Ox* **V** *vacant* (01867) 328381

WARBOYS (St Mary Magdelene) w Broughton and Bury w Wistow *Ely 10* **P** *Bp and Ch Soc Trust (jt)* **R** P R DOWMAN

WARBSTOW (St Werburgh) *see* St Gennys, Jacobstow w Warbstow and Treneglos *Truro*

WARBURTON (St Werburgh) *Ches 10* **P** *Hon M L W Flower* **P-in-c** E M BURGESS

WARCOP (St Columba) *see* Brough w Stainmore, Musgrave and Warcop *Carl*

WARD END (Christ Church) *see* Burney Lane *Birm*

WARD END (St Margaret) *Birm 13* **P** *Aston Trustees* **V** *vacant* 0121-327 0555

WARDEN (St Michael and All Angels) w Newbrough *Newc 4* **P** *Bp* **P-in-c** R C CUTLER

WARDEN, OLD (St Leonard) *see* Caldecote, Northill and Old Warden *St Alb*

WARDINGTON (St Mary Magdalene) *see* Shires' Edge *Ox*

WARDLEWORTH (St Mary w St James) *see* Rochdale *Man*

WARDLEY (All Saints) *see* Swinton and Pendlebury *Man*

WARDLEY (St Botolph) *see* Uppingham w Ayston and Wardley w Belton *Pet*

WARDLOW (Good Shepherd) *see* Ashford w Sheldon and Longstone *Derby*

WARE (Christ Church) *St Alb 22* **P** *CPAS* **V** D J PROUD, **C** N PLEDGER

WARE (St Mary the Virgin) *St Alb 22* **P** *Trin Coll Cam* **V** H E WILCOX, **NSM** M S E M BEAZLEY, P A VOSS

WAREHAM (Lady St Mary) (St Martin) *Sarum 8* **P** *Patr Bd* **TR** W G BLAKEY, **TV** P S SIMESTER, **C** H K JAMESON, **NSM** J CLEATON

WAREHORNE (St Matthew) *see* Orlestone w Snave and Ruckinge w Warehorne etc *Cant*

WARESIDE (Holy Trinity) *see* Hunsdon w Widford and Wareside *St Alb*

WARESLEY (St James) *see* Gt Gransden and Abbotsley and Lt Gransden etc *Ely*

WARFIELD (St Michael the Archangel) *Ox 11* **P** *DBP* **V** B H MEARDON, **Hon C** B J WEAVER

WARGRAVE (St Mary the Virgin) w Knowl Hill *Ox 16* **P** *Lord Remnant* **V** J W RATINGS, **NSM** P A GORDON, D J THOMAS

WARHAM (All Saints) *see* Holkham w Egmere w Warham, Wells and Wighton *Nor*

WARK (St Michael) *see* Humshaugh w Simonburn and Wark *Newc*

WARKLEIGH (St John) *see* S Molton w Nymet St George, High Bray etc *Ex*

WARKTON (St Edmund King and Martyr) *see* Barton Seagrave w Warkton *Pet*

WARKWORTH (St Lawrence) and Acklington *Newc 9* **P** *Bp and Duke of Northd (alt)* **V** J M BREARLEY, **NSM** J A RICHARDSON

WARKWORTH (St Mary the Virgin) *see* Greatworth and Marston St Lawrence etc *Pet*

WARLEGGAN (St Bartholomew) *see* St Neot and Warleggan w Cardynham *Truro*

WARLEY (Christ Church) and Gt Warley St Mary *Chelmsf 7* **P** *Bp and Hon G C D Jeffreys (jt)* **V** A J PUGSLEY, **C** C W WRAGG

WARLEY (St John the Evangelist) *Wakef 4* **P** *V Halifax* **V** A J STREET, **NSM** J S BRADBERRY

WARLEY, GREAT (St Mary the Virgin) *see* Warley Ch Ch and Gt Warley St Mary *Chelmsf*

WARLEY, LITTLE (St Peter) *see* E and W Horndon w Lt Warley and Childerditch *Chelmsf*

WARLEY WOODS (St Hilda) *Birm 7* **P** *Bp* **V** M R DUNK

WARLINGHAM (All Saints) w Chelsham and Farleigh *S'wark 25* **P** *Patr Bd* **TR** A D MIDDLETON, **TV** A E HEFFERNAN, **C** H M GREAR, **NSM** J H STEVENS

WARMFIELD (St Peter) *Wakef 9* **P** *Oley Trustees Clare Coll Cam* **V** *vacant* (01924) 893089

WARMINGHAM (St Leonard) *see* Elworth and Warmingham *Ches*

WARMINGTON (St Mary the Blessed Virgin), Tansor and Cotterstock and Fotheringhay and Southwick *Pet 12* **P** *Bp and D&C Linc (alt)* **B** V ROGERS

WARMINGTON (St Michael) w Shotteswell and Radway w Ratley *Cov 8* **P** *Bp* **R** C A LAMB

WARMINSTER (Christ Church) *Sarum 17* **P** *R Warminster St Denys etc* **P-in-c** P W HUNTER, **C** T SMITH

WARMINSTER (St Denys) *see* Cley Hill Warminster *Sarum*

WARMLEY (St Barnabas), Syston and Bitton *Bris 5* **P** *Bp* **R** P H DENYER, **C** S A WILLIAMS, S R WILLIAMS, **Hon C** J E NORMAN

WARMSWORTH (St Peter) *Sheff 9* **P** *Bp* **R** S F BOND

WARMWELL (Holy Trinity) *see* Watercombe *Sarum*

WARNBOROUGH, SOUTH (St Andrew) *see* Herriard w Winslade and Long Sutton etc *Win*

WARNDON (St Nicholas) *Worc 6* **P** *Bp* **P-in-c** K I CRAWFORD

WARNDON (St Wulstan) *see* Worc St Wulstan *Worc*

WARNERS END (St Alban) *see* Hemel Hempstead *St Alb*

WARNFORD (Our Lady) *see* W Meon and Warnford *Portsm*

WARNHAM (St Margaret) *Chich 8* **P** *J C Lucas Esq* **V** C H LOVELESS

WARNINGLID (St Andrew) *see* Slaugham *Chich*

WARREN PARK (St Clare) *Portsm 5* **P** *Bp* **V** J G P JEFFERY, **C** S HEWITT, J M B HONNOR, **NSM** M S HARPER, **W** P KENNEDY

WARREN ROW (St Paul) *see* Wargrave w Knowl Hill *Ox*

WARRINGTON (Holy Trinity) *Liv 12* **P** *R Warrington* **V** I D ELLIOTT, **NSM** R E LICHTENBERGER

WARRINGTON St Ann *Liv 12* **P** *Simeon's Trustees* **V** S R PARISH, **OLM** P LOVATT, M M MCDONNELL, J M WEAVER

WARRINGTON (St Barnabas) Bank Quay *Liv 12* **P** *R Warrington and Bp (jt)* **V** K L F TIMMIS

WARRINGTON (St Elphin) (St John) *Liv 12* **P** *Lord Lilford* **R** M S FINLAY, **C** C N PERRINS

WARSLOW (St Lawrence) *see* Alstonfield, Butterton, Ilam etc *Lich*

WARSOP (St Peter and St Paul) *S'well 2* **P** *Trustees* **R** K HERROD, **C** M J CANTRILL, **NSM** M-J PORTER

WARTER (St James) *see* Nunburnholme and Warter and Huggate *York*

WARTHILL (St Mary) *see* Stockton-on-the-Forest w Holtby and Warthill *York*

WARTLING (St Mary Magdalene) *see* Herstmonceux and Wartling *Chich*

WARTNABY (St Michael) *see* Old Dalby, Nether Broughton, Saxelbye etc *Leic*

WARTON (Holy Trinity) *see* Austrey and Warton *Birm*

WARTON (St Oswald or Holy Trinity) w Yealand Conyers *Blackb 14* **P** *Bp* **V** J M HALL

WARTON (St Paul) *Blackb 10* **P** *Ch Ch Ox* **V** P FORD

WARWICK (St Leonard) *see* Wetheral w Warwick *Carl*

WARWICK Team, The New (St Mary) (St Nicholas) (St Paul) *Cov 11* **P** *Ld Chan and Patr Bd (alt)* **TV** R C GARRATT, A W J FITZMAURICE, J HEARN

WARWICK SQUARE (St Gabriel) *see* Pimlico St Gabr *Lon*

WASDALE, NETHER (St Michael) *see* Gosforth w Nether Wasdale and Wasdale Head *Carl*

WASDALE HEAD (not known) *as above Carl*

WASH COMMON (St George) *see* Newbury *Ox*

WASHBOURNE, GREAT (St Mary) *see* Alderton, Gt Washbourne, Dumbleton etc *Glouc*

WASHFIELD (St Mary the Virgin), Stoodleigh, Withleigh, Calverleigh, Oakford, Templeton, Loxbeare, Rackenford, and Cruwys Morchard *Ex 8* **P** *Patr Bd* **TV** G B BELL, **C** D C CHEDZEY, **NSM** J C W ROBERTS

WASHFORD (St Mary) *see* Old Cleeve, Leighland and Treborough *B & W*

WASHFORD PYNE (St Peter) *see* N Creedy *Ex*

WASHINGBOROUGH (St John) w Heighington and Canwick *Linc 18* **P** *DBP and Mercers' Co (jt)* **R** S JONES-CRABTREE, **NSM** J FRESHNEY

WASHINGTON (Holy Trinity) *Dur 11* **P** *Bp* **P-in-c** J E HOWES, **C** D J BELL

WASHINGTON (St Mary) *see* Ashington, Washington and Wiston w Buncton *Chich*

WASHWOOD HEATH (St Mark) *Birm 13* **P** *V Saltley* **P-in-c** A H TOWNSEND

WASING (St Nicholas) *see* Aldermaston w Wasing and Brimpton *Ox*

WASKERLEY (St Andrew) *see* Blanchland w Hunstanworth and Edmundbyers etc *Newc*

WASPERTON (St John the Baptist) *see* Barford w Wasperton and Sherbourne *Cov*

WASS (St Thomas) *see* Coxwold and Husthwaite *York*

WATCHET (Holy Cross Chapel) *see* St Decumans *B & W*

WATCHET (St Decuman) *as above B & W*

WATCHFIELD (St Thomas's Chapel) *see* Shrivenham and Ashbury *Ox*

WATER EATON (St Frideswide) *Ox 25* **P** *Bp* **P-in-c** A J MARRIOTT

WATER NEWTON (St Remigius) *see* Elton w Stibbington and Water Newton *Ely*
WATER ORTON (St Peter and St Paul) *Birm 9* **P** *Patr Bd* **V** S T MAYES
WATER STRATFORD (St Giles) *see* W Buckingham *Ox*
WATERBEACH (St John) *Ely 5* **P** *Bp* **V** N I MOIR
WATERCOMBE *Sarum 1* **P** *M Cree Esq (1 turn), MMCET (2 turns), and Sir Robert Williams Bt (1 turn)* **R** J M COATES, **C** M R B DURRANT
WATERDEN (All Saints) *see* N and S Creake w Waterden, Syderstone etc *Nor*
WATERFALL (St James and St Bartholomew) *see* Calton, Cauldon, Grindon, Waterfall etc *Lich*
WATERFOOT (St James the Great) *Man 15* **P** *Trustees* **V** *vacant*
WATERFORD (St Michael and All Angels) *see* Bramfield, Stapleford, Waterford etc *St Alb*
WATERHEAD (Holy Trinity) *Man 21* **P** *The Crown* **P-in-c** G WHITTAKER, **C** D R PENNY
WATERHOUSES (St Paul) *Dur 1* **P** *R Brancepeth Esq* **V** M J PEERS, **C** T E HUBBLE
WATERINGBURY (St John the Baptist) and Teston *Roch 7* **P** *D&C and Peache Trustees (jt)* **P-in-c** J D BROWN
WATERLOO (Christ Church) (St John) *Liv 1* **P** *Trustees and Simeon's Trustees (jt)* **V** G J CUFF, **NSM** D A MCDOUGALL, **OLM** A L BROOKS
WATERLOO (St John the Evangelist) (St Andrew) *S'wark 13* **P** *Abp and CPAS (jt)* **V** C R TRUSS, **C** J FREEMAN, **OLM** D PAPE, G S N KAZIRO
WATERLOO PARK (St Mary the Virgin) *see* Gt Crosby St Faith and Waterloo Park St Mary *Liv*
WATERLOOVILLE (St George the Martyr) *Portsm 5* **P** *Bp* **V** M FERRIER
WATERMILLOCK (All Saints) *see* Gd Shep TM *Carl*
WATERMOOR (Holy Trinity) *see* Cirencester *Glouc*
WATERPERRY (St Mary the Virgin) *see* Wheatley *Ox*
WATERS UPTON (St Michael) *see* Tibberton w Bolas Magna and Waters Upton *Lich*
WATERSTOCK (St Leonard) *see* Wheatley *Ox*
WATERTHORPE (Emmanuel) *see* Mosbrough *Sheff*
WATFORD (Christ Church) (St Mark) *St Alb 7* **P** *Bp, V Watford, and Churchwardens (jt)* **V** R C LEWIS, **C** A J HARTROPP
WATFORD (St Andrew) *St Alb 7* **P** *Bp and Churchwardens (jt)* **V** G R WARREN, **C** S M TALBOTT
WATFORD (St John) *St Alb 7* **P** *Bp* **V** J B A COPE
WATFORD (St Luke) *St Alb 7* **P** *Bp, Adn St Alb, V Watford, and Ch Trust Fund Trust (jt)* **V** J KIDDLE, **C** P J STEVENSON
WATFORD (St Mary) *St Alb 7* **P** *Ch Trust Fund Trust* **V** J A ALDIS, **C** W D HUNTER SMART
WATFORD (St Michael and All Angels) *St Alb 7* **P** *Bp* **V** J B BROWN, **C** E C MACFARLANE
WATFORD (St Peter) *St Alb 7* **P** *Bp* **V** C P COTTEE, **C** R W YULE, **NSM** A D T GORTON
WATFORD (St Peter and St Paul) *see* Long Buckby w Watford *Pet*
WATH (St Mary) *see* Kirklington w Burneston and Wath and Pickhill *Ripon*
WATH BROW (Mission Church) *see* Crosslacon *Carl*
WATH-UPON-DEARNE (All Saints) *Sheff 12* **P** *Ch Ch Ox* **V** T E LEACH, **C** D AKRILL
WATLING VALLEY, Milton Keynes (not known) *Ox 25* **P** *Patr Bd* **TV** T NORWOOD
WATLINGTON (St Leonard) *see* Icknield *Ox*
WATLINGTON (St Peter and St Paul) *Ely 15* **P** *Bp* **R** J C W NOLAN
WATTISFIELD (St Margaret) *see* Hepworth, Hinderclay, Wattisfield and Thelnetham *St E*
WATTLESBOROUGH (St Margaret) *see* Alberbury w Cardeston *Heref*
WATTON (St Mary) *see* Hutton Cranswick w Skerne, Watton and Beswick *York*
WATTON (St Mary) w Carbrooke and Ovington *Nor 13* **P** *Ld Chan (3 turns), Cam Univ (1 turn), and SMF (2 turns)* **P-in-c** M J TALBOT, **C** A J PEARS, M J DOWN, **OLM** S D H MAWDITT
WATTON AT STONE (St Mary and St Andrew) *see* Bramfield, Stapleford, Waterford etc *St Alb*
WAVENDON (Assumption of the Blessed Virgin Mary) *see* Walton Milton Keynes *Ox*
WAVERTON (Christ Church) *see* Solway Plain *Carl*
WAVERTON (St Peter) *Ches 5* **P** *Bp* **R** *vacant* (01244) 335581
WAVERTREE (Holy Trinity) *Liv 6* **P** *Bp* **R** J EASTWOOD, **C** J DAVIES, **Hon C** L B BRUCE
WAVERTREE (St Bridget) (St Thomas) *Liv 6* **P** *Simeon's Trustees and R Wavertree H Trin (jt)* **V** W J SANDERS

WAVERTREE (St Mary) *Liv 6* **P** *Bp* **R** J M MATTHEWS
WAWNE (St Peter) *see* Sutton St Jas and Wawne *York*
WAXHAM, GREAT (St John) *see* Happisburgh, Walcott, Hempstead w Eccles etc *Nor*
WAYFORD (St Michael and All Angels) *see* Crewkerne w Wayford *B & W*
WEALD (St George) *see* Sevenoaks Weald *Roch*
WEALD, NORTH Bassett (St Andrew) *Chelmsf 27* **P** *Bp* **V** T C THORPE
WEALD, SOUTH (St Peter) *Chelmsf 7* **P** *Bp* **V** I H JORYSZ
WEAR (St Luke) *see* Countess Wear *Ex*
WEARE (St Gregory) *see* Crook Peak *B & W*
WEARE GIFFARD (Holy Trinity) *see* Bideford, Northam, Westward Ho!, Appledore etc *Ex*
WEASENHAM (All Saints) *see* Gt w Lt Massingham, Harpley, Rougham etc *Nor*
WEASENHAM (St Peter) *as above Nor*
WEASTE (St Luke w All Saints) *Man 6* **P** *Bp and V Eccles (jt)* **V** K M ARCHER
WEAVERHAM (St Mary the Virgin) *Ches 6* **P** *Bp* **V** M L RIDLEY
WEAVERTHORPE (St Andrew) w Helperthorpe, Luttons Ambo and Kirby Grindalythe w Wharram *York 6* **P** *Abp and D&C (jt)* **P-in-c** C J HAYES
WEBHEATH (St Philip) *see* Redditch, The Ridge *Worc*
WEDDINGTON (St James) and Caldecote *Cov 5* **P** *Bp* **R** *vacant* (024) 7635 3400 *or* 7638 2615
WEDMORE (St Mary) w Theale and Blackford *B & W 1* **P** *Bp* **V** E M CROSS, **NSM** G E C FENTON
WEDNESBURY (St Bartholomew) *Lich 26* **P** *Bp* **V** M S BRIDGEN, **NSM** D MARSH
WEDNESBURY (St James and St John) *Lich 26* **P** *Trustees* **R** I B COOK, **NSM** R C GILBERT
WEDNESBURY (St Paul) Wood Green *Lich 26* **P** *Bp* **V** G WARREN
WEDNESFIELD (St Gregory) *Lich 28* **P** *Bp* **P-in-c** C R SUCH
WEDNESFIELD (St Thomas) (St Augustine and St Chad) (St Alban) *Lich 28* **P** *Patr Bd* **TR** J D POINTS, **TV** H L DUCKETT, **C** S D GULLIFORD, G W WARD
WEDNESFIELD HEATH (Holy Trinity) *Lich 28* **P** *CPAS* **V** D A VESTERGAARD
WEEDON (School Chapel) *see* Schorne *Ox*
WEEDON BEC (St Peter and St Paul) w Everdon and Dodford *Pet 3* **P** *Bp* **P-in-c** H E RAYMENT
WEEDON LOIS (St Mary and St Peter) w Plumpton and Moreton Pinkney and Wappenham *Pet 1* **P** *Bp, Jes Coll Ox, and Or Coll Ox (by turn)* **P-in-c** J H ROBERTS, **NSM** P J ALLEN
WEEFORD (St Mary the Virgin) *see* Whittington w Weeford *Lich*
WEEK ST MARY (St Mary the Virgin) w Poundstock and Whitstone *Truro 8* **P** *SS Coll Cam, Walsingham Coll, and Guild of All So (jt)* **P-in-c** R C W DICKENSON
WEEKE *see* Win St Matt *Win*
WEEKLEY (St Mary the Virgin) *see* Geddington w Weekley *Pet*
WEELEY (St Andrew) and Little Clacton *Chelmsf 23* **P** *Bp and BNC Ox (alt)* **R** D M NEWMAN
WEETHLEY (St James) *see* Alcester and Arrow w Oversley and Weethley *Cov*
WEETING (St Mary) *Ely 14* **P** *G&C Coll Cam* **R** S BETSON
WEETON (St Barnabas) *see* Lower Wharfedale *Ripon*
WEETON (St Michael) *see* Singleton w Weeton *Blackb*
WEETSLADE (St Paul) *Newc 1* **P** *Bp* **V** A MAUGHAN
WELBORNE (All Saints) *see* Mattishall w Mattishall Burgh, Welborne etc *Nor*
WELBOURN (St Chad) *Linc 23* **P** *Hyndman Trustees* **R** A J MEGAHEY
WELBURN (St John the Evangelist) *see* Howardian Gp *York*
WELBURY (St Leonard) *see* Rounton w Welbury *York*
WELBY (not known) *see* Melton Mowbray *Leic*
WELBY (St Bartholemew) *see* Ancaster Wilsford Gp *Linc*
WELCOMBE (St Nectan) *see* Parkham, Alwington, Buckland Brewer etc *Ex*
WELDON (St Mary the Virgin) w Deene *Pet 9* **P** *DBP and E Brudenell Esq (jt)* **P-in-c** J M COLLINS
WELFORD (St Gregory) w Wickham and Great Shefford, Boxford and Stockcross *Ox 14* **P** *Bp and BNC Ox (jt)* **R** N C SANDS
WELFORD (St Mary the Virgin) w Sibbertoft and Marston Trussell *Pet 2* **P** *Bp* **P-in-c** C M LOOKER
WELFORD (St Peter) w Weston *Glouc 10* **P** *DBP* **R** R D WYATT
WELHAM (St Andrew) *see* Gt Bowden w Welham, Glooston and Cranoe etc *Leic*
WELL (St Margaret) *Linc 8* **P** *Bp* **R** R H IRESON

WELL (St Michael)   *see* W Tanfield and Well w Snape and N
Stainley *Ripon*
WELL HILL (Mission)   *see* Chelsfield *Roch*
WELLAND (St James)   *see* Hanley Castle, Hanley Swan and
Welland *Worc*
WELLESBOURNE (St Peter)   *Cov 8*   **P** *Ld Chan*   **V** *vacant*
(01789) 840262
WELLING (St John the Evangelist)   *Roch 15*   **P** *Bp*
V A J D FOOT
WELLING (St Mary the Virgin)   *S'wark 3*   **P** *Bp*   **V** L C GALE
WELLINGBOROUGH (All Hallows)   *Pet 6*   **P** *Exors Major
E C S Byng-Maddick*   **V** A READER-MOORE,   **C** J D NAUDE
WELLINGBOROUGH (All Saints)   *Pet 6*   **P** *V Wellingborough*
V A M LYNETT
WELLINGBOROUGH (St Andrew)   *Pet 6*   **P** *Bp*
V C M UPTON
WELLINGBOROUGH (St Barnabas)   *Pet 6*   **P** *Bp*
V J P LEADER
WELLINGBOROUGH (St Mark)   *Pet 6*   **P** *Bp*   **V** *vacant*
(01933) 673893
WELLINGBOROUGH (St Mary the Virgin)   *Pet 6*   **P** *Guild of
All So*   **V** R J T FARMER
WELLINGHAM (St Andrew)   *see* Gt w Lt Massingham,
Harpley, Rougham etc *Nor*
WELLINGORE (All Saints)   *see* Graffoe Gp *Linc*
WELLINGTON (All Saints w (St John the Baptist) and District
B & W 19   **P** *Patr Bd*   **TR** C M S RANDALL,
TV D P RANDELL,   **C** M R WILLIAMS, C I BRIERLEY,
NSM J M HARRISON
WELLINGTON (All Saints) w Eyton (St Catherine)   *Lich 21*
P *Ch Trust Fund Trust*   **V** M E POTTER,   **C** J J FROST
WELLINGTON (Christ Church)   *Lich 21*   **P** *V Wellington w
Eyton*   **C** M A HALL
WELLINGTON (St Margaret of Antioch) w Pipe-cum-Lyde and
Moreton-on-Lugg   *Heref 4*   **P** *Bp, Soc of the Faith, and D&C
(by turn)*   **P-in-c** J W R MORRISON
WELLINGTON HEATH (Christ Church)   *see* Ledbury *Heref*
WELLOW (St Julian the Hospitaller)   *see* Peasedown St John w
Wellow *B & W*
WELLOW (St Swithun)   *see* Kneesall w Laxton and Wellow
S'well
WELLOW, EAST w WEST (St Margaret) and Sherfield English
Win 12   **P** *Bp and CPAS (jt)*   **V** G R BIGGS
WELLS (St Cuthbert) w Wookey Hole   *B & W 8*   **P** *D&C*
V P G P FARRELL,   **C** M R WOOD
WELLS (St Thomas) w Horrington   *B & W 8*   **P** *D&C*
V C T TOOKEY
WELLS-NEXT-THE-SEA (St Nicholas)   *see* Holkham w
Egmere w Warham, Wells and Wighton *Nor*
WELNEY (St Mary)   *see* Christchurch and Manea and Welney
Ely
WELSH BICKNOR (St Margaret)   *see* Walford and St John w
Bishopswood, Goodrich etc *Heref*
WELSH FRANKTON (St Andrew)   *see* Criftins w Dudleston
and Welsh Frankton *Lich*
WELSH NEWTON (St Mary the Virgin)   *see* St Weonards w
Orcop, Garway, Tretire etc *Heref*
WELSH NEWTON COMMON (St Faith)   *as above Heref*
WELSHAMPTON (St Michael)   *see* Petton w Cockshutt,
Welshampton and Lyneal etc *Lich*
WELTON (St Helen) w Melton   *York 14*   **P** *DBP*
P-in-c E E BIELBY
WELTON (St James)   *see* Westward, Rosley-w-Woodside and
Welton *Carl*
WELTON (St Martin)   *see* Daventry, Ashby St Ledgers,
Braunston etc *Pet*
WELTON (St Mary) and Dunholme w Scothern   *Linc 3*   **P** *Bp
and DBP (jt)*   **V** G S DARLISON,   **OLM** J M JOHNSON
WELTON-LE-MARSH (St Martin) w Gunby   *Linc 8*
P *J M Montgomery-Massingberd Esq*   **R** T STEELE
WELTON-LE-WOLD (St Martin)   *see* Louth *Linc*
WELWICK (St Mary)   *see* Patrington w Hollym, Welwick and
Winestead *York*
WELWYN (St Mary the Virgin) (St Michael) w Ayot (St Peter)
St Alb 21   **P** *All So Coll Ox*   **R** A P WINTON,
C C C MCCLUSKEY
WELWYN GARDEN CITY (St Francis of Assisi)   *St Alb 21*
P *Bp*   **V** P A LOUIS,   **NSM** J K TEGALLY, J GRAY
WEM (St Peter and St Paul)   *Lich 22*   **P** *Lord Barnard*
P-in-c C S COOKE
WEMBDON (St George)   *B & W 14*   **P** *Ch Soc Trust*
V J S BARKS
WEMBLEY (St Augustine)   *see* Wembley Park *Lon*
WEMBLEY (St John the Evangelist)   *Lon 21*   **P** *Ch Patr Trust*
V F ADU-BOACHIE,   **NSM** M E REYNOLDS
WEMBLEY, NORTH (St Cuthbert)   *Lon 21*   **P** *Bp*
V F G MCDERMOTT

WEMBLEY PARK (Church of the Ascension) (St Augustine)
(Annunciation)   *Lon 21*   **P** *Bp*   **TR** R W BUCKLEY,
TV F C PAPANTONIOU, H L YOUNG,   **Hon C** J M WARNER
WEMBURY (St Werburgh)   *Ex 20*   **P** *D&C Windsor*
V T FREEMAN
WEMBWORTHY (St Michael)   *see* Burrington, Chawleigh,
Cheldon, Chulmleigh etc *Ex*
WENDENS AMBO (St Mary the Virgin)   *see* Saffron Walden w
Wendens Ambo, Littlebury etc *Chelmsf*
WENDLEBURY (St Giles)   *see* Akeman *Ox*
WENDLING (St Peter and St Paul)   *see* Gressenhall w
Longham w Wendling etc *Nor*
WENDOVER (St Agnes's Chapel)   *see* Wendover and Halton
Ox
WENDOVER (St Mary)   *as above Ox*
WENDOVER (St Mary) (St Agnes's Chapel) and Halton   *Ox 28*
P *Ld Chan*   **R** M C DEARNLEY
WENDRON(St Wendron)   *see* Helston and Wendron *Truro*
WENDY (All Saints)   *see* Shingay Gp of Par *Ely*
WENHAM, GREAT (St John)   *see* Capel St Mary w Lt and Gt
Wenham *St E*
WENHASTON (St Peter)   *see* Blyth Valley *St E*
WENLOCK   *Heref 11*   **P** *Patr Bd*   **TR** S A LOWE,
TV M J SMALL,   **NSM** W K ROWELL
WENLOCK, LITTLE (St Lawrence)   *see* Coalbrookdale,
Iron-Bridge and Lt Wenlock *Heref*
WENLOCK, MUCH (Holy Trinity)   *see* Wenlock *Heref*
WENNINGTON (St Mary and St Peter)   *see* Rainham w
Wennington *Chelmsf*
WENSLEY (Holy Trinity)   *Ripon 4*   **P** *Lord Bolton*
P-in-c M R MILES
WENT VALLEY   *Wakef 11*   **P** *Bp, Earl of Rosse, and Sir Philip
Naylor-Leyland Bt (jt)*   **V** A T JUDD
WENTBRIDGE (St John)   *see* Went Valley *Wakef*
WENTNOR (St Michael and All Angels) w Ratlinghope,
Myndtown, Norbury, More, Lydham and Snead   *Heref 10*
P *Ch Ch Ox (4 turns) and J J C Coldwell Esq (1 turn)*
R N F M MORRIS
WENTWORTH (Harley Mission Church) (Holy Trinity)
Sheff 12   **P** *Sir Philip Naylor-Leyland Bt*   **V** R IMPEY
WENTWORTH (St Peter)   *see* Witchford w Wentworth *Ely*
WEOBLEY (St Peter and St Paul) w Sarnesfield and Norton
Canon   *Heref 5*   **P** *Bp (2 turns), R A Marshall Esq (1 turn)*
V R D KING,   **C** N R SPENCER
WEOLEY CASTLE (St Gabriel)   *Birm 2*   **P** *Bp*
V M D CASTLE,   **NSM** H A G HOUGHTON
WEREHAM (St Margaret)   *Ely 15*   **P** *Bp*   **V** *vacant*
WERNETH (St Paul)   *Ches 16*   **P** *Trustees*
P-in-c B S PERCIVAL,   **NSM** W S ATKINSON
WERNETH (St Thomas)   *Man 19*   **P** *Bp*   **V** *vacant* 0161-678
8926
WERRINGTON (St John the Baptist w Emmanuel)   *Pet 13*
P *Bp*   **V** G H ROGERS,   **C** S P DOWSON
WERRINGTON (St Martin of Tours)   *see* Boyton,
N Tamerton, Werrington etc *Truro*
WERRINGTON (St Philip)   *Lich 6*   **P** *V Caverswall*
V J L HUMPHREYS,   **NSM** I T COPELAND
WESHAM (Christ Church) and Treales   *Blackb 10*
P *V Kirkham*   **V** P W BENNETT
WESSINGTON (Christ Church)   *see* Ashover and Brackenfield
w Wessington *Derby*
WEST   *see also under substantive place name*
WEST BAY (St John)   *see* Bridport *Sarum*
WEST DEAN (St Andrew)   *Chich 13*   **P** *D&C*
V R T E B WOODS
WEST DOWN (St Calixtus)   *see* Ilfracombe SS Phil and Jas w W
Down *Ex*
WEST END (Holy Trinity)   *see* Bisley and W End *Guildf*
WEST END (St George)   *see* Esher *Guildf*
WEST END (St James)   *Win 10*   **P** *Bp*   **P-in-c** B L PICKETT,
C A J TARPER,   **NSM** J E PICKETT
WEST END (St John the Evangelist)   *see* High Wycombe *Ox*
WEST GREEN (Christ Church w St Peter)   *Lon 19*   **P** *Bp*
V M O BRACKLEY
WEST GREEN (St Peter)   *see* Crawley *Chich*
WEST HAM (All Saints)   *Chelmsf 3*   **P** *The Crown*
V U E E J SCHARF,   **C** V N ARNOLD
WEST HAM (St Matthew)   *see* Forest Gate St Sav w W Ham
St Matt *Chelmsf*
WEST HEATH (St Anne)   *Birm 4*   **P** *Bp*   **V** S P MAYOSS-HURD
WEST HILL (St Michael the Archangel)   *see* Ottery St Mary,
Alfington, W Hill, Tipton etc *Ex*
WEST MOORS (St Mary the Virgin) (St John the Evangelist)
Sarum 9   **P** *Bp*   **V** S W MILLER
WEST NEWTON (St Matthew)   *see* Solway Plain *Carl*
WEST ORCHARD (St Luke)   *see* Shaston *Sarum*

WEST ROW (St Peter)   *see* Mildenhall *St E*
WEST WINCH (St Mary) w Setchey, North Runcton and
   Middleton *Nor 20*   **P** *H N D Gurney Esq (1 turn) and Ld Chan*
   (2 turns)   **R** J F RYAN
WESTACRE (All Saints)   *see* Castleacre, Newton, Westacre and
   Southacre *Nor*
WESTBERE (All Saints)   *see* Sturry w Fordwich and Westbere w
   Hersden *Cant*
WESTBOROUGH (All Saints)   *see* Claypole *Linc*
WESTBOROUGH (St Clare) (St Francis) *Guildf 5*   **P** *Bp*
   TR C G POTTER,   **TV** J BOULTON-REYNOLDS,
   NSM S A BRASSIL
WESTBOURNE (Christ Church) Conventional District
   Win 8 vacant
WESTBOURNE (St John the Baptist) *Chich 13*   **P** *Bp*
   R R J WELLS
WESTBROOK (All Saints)   *see* Margate All SS *Cant*
WESTBROOK (St James) Hood Manor *Liv 12*   **P** *Bp,*
   R Warrington, and V Gt Sankey (jt)   **V** vacant (01925) 633873
WESTBROOK (St Philip) Old Hall and Callands *Liv 12*   **P** *Bp*
   and R Warrington (jt)   **V** M X THORPE,   **C** A KENNEDY
WESTBURY (All Saints)   *see* White Horse *Sarum*
WESTBURY (St Augustine)   *see* W Buckingham *Ox*
WESTBURY (St Mary) *Heref 13*   **P** *Bp*   **R** C B BULL
WESTBURY-ON-SEVERN (St Peter and St Paul) w Flaxley,
   Blaisdon and Minsterworth *Glouc 3*   **P** *Bp, D&C Heref, and*
   Sir Thomas Crawley-Boevey Bt (jt)   **V** C A EDMONDS
WESTBURY-ON-TRYM (Holy Trinity) *Bris 2*   **P** *SMF*
   V A H HART,   **C** T R CRANSHAW
WESTBURY-ON-TRYM (St Alban) *Bris 2*   **P** *Bp*
   V J A H BOWES,   **NSM** R Q GREATREX
WESTBURY PARK (St Alban)   *see* Westbury-on-Trym St Alb
   Bris
WESTBURY SUB MENDIP (St Lawrence) w Easton *B & W 1*
   P *Bp*   **V** E A MACPHERSON
WESTCLIFF (Church of Reconciliation)   *see* Brumby *Linc*
WESTCLIFF (St Alban)   *see* Southend *Chelmsf*
WESTCLIFF (St Andrew) *Chelmsf 13*   **P** *Bp*   **V** S F KIMBER
WESTCLIFF (St Cedd and the Saints of Essex)   *see* Prittlewell w
   Westcliff *Chelmsf*
WESTCLIFF (St Michael and All Angels) *Chelmsf 13*   **P** *Bp*
   V P C NICHOLSON
WESTCLIFF (St Paul)   *see* Prittlewell *Chelmsf*
WESTCLIFF (St Saviour)   *see* Southend St Sav Westcliff
   Chelmsf
WESTCLIFFE (St Peter)   *see* St Margarets-at-Cliffe w Westcliffe
   etc *Cant*
WESTCOMBE PARK (St George)   *see* E Greenwich *S'wark*
WESTCOTE (St Mary the Virgin)   *see* Broadwell, Evenlode,
   Oddington, Adlestrop etc *Glouc*
WESTCOTE BARTON (St Edward the Confessor) w Steeple
   Barton, Duns Tew and Sandford St Martin *Ox 9*   **P** *Duke of*
   Marlborough, Exors Mrs Rittson-Thomas, and Bp (jt)
   D C D Webb Esq, and Bp (jt)   **R** G R ARTHUR
WESTCOTT (Holy Trinity) *Guildf 7*   **P** *Bp*   **P-in-c** A C JONAS
WESTCOTT (St Mary)   *see* Schorne *Ox*
WESTDENE (The Ascension)   *see* Patcham *Chich*
WESTERDALE (Christ Church)   *see* Ingleby Greenhow w
   Bilsdale Priory, Kildale etc *York*
WESTERFIELD (St Mary Magdalene) and Tuddenham w
   Witnesham *St E 4*   **P** *Bp, Peterho Cam, and DBP (alt)*
   P-in-c S H COWLEY
WESTERHAM (St Mary the Virgin) *Roch 9*
   P *J St A Warde Esq*   **V** P S MCVEAGH
WESTERLEIGH (St James the Great)   *see* Yate New Town *Bris*
WESTERN DOWNLAND *Sarum 11*   **P** *Hyndman Trustees,*
   A N Hanbury Esq, and W J Purvis Esq (jt)   **R** L M PLAYER
WESTFIELD (St Andrew)   *see* Barnham Broom and Upper
   Yare *Nor*
WESTFIELD (St John the Baptist) *Chich 20*   **P** *Bp*
   V E N L FRANCE
WESTFIELD (St Mark)   *see* Woking St Pet *Guildf*
WESTFIELD (St Mary) *Carl 7*   **P** *Bp*   **V** A M ARMSTRONG,
   C C R SHAW,   **NSM** M T STILWELL
WESTFIELD (St Peter) *B & W 12*   **P** *Bp*   **V** J B THICKE,
   Hon C P M DOWN
WESTGATE (St Andrew) *Dur 9*   **P** *Bp*
   P-in-c P A GREENHALGH
WESTGATE (St James) *Cant 9*   **P** *Abp*   **P-in-c** R T BASHFORD
WESTGATE (St Martin of Tours)   *see* Torrisholme *Blackb*
WESTGATE COMMON (St Michael the Archangel) *Wakef 12*
   P *V Alverthorpe*   **V** A S MACPHERSON,   **C** S E KENT,
   NSM C M FOGG
WESTGATE-ON-SEA (St Saviour) *Cant 9*   **P** *Abp*
   P-in-c J W RICHARDSON
WESTHALL (St Andrew)   *see* Hundred River *St E*

WESTHAM (St Mary) *Chich 16*   **P** *Duke of Devonshire*
   V G J BARRETT
WESTHAMPNETT (St Peter)   *see* Chich St Paul and
   Westhampnett *Chich*
WESTHEAD (St James)   *see* Newburgh w Westhead *Liv*
WESTHIDE (St Bartholomew)   *see* Withington w Westhide
   Heref
WESTHOPE (Mission Room)   *see* Canon Pyon w Kings Pyon
   and Birley *Heref*
WESTHORPE (St Margaret)   *see* Badwell and Walsham *St E*
WESTHOUGHTON (St Bartholomew) and Wingates *Man 11*
   P *Patr Bd*   **TR** G A LAWSON,   **TV** B STANNARD,
   NSM G J SMETHURST
WESTHOUGHTON (St James)   *see* Daisy Hill *Man*
WESTHOUSES (St Saviour)   *see* Blackwell w Tibshelf *Derby*
WESTLANDS (St Andrew) *Lich 9*   **P** *Simeon's Trustees*
   V W G H GARDINER
WESTLEIGH (St Paul) *Man 13*   **P** *V Leigh St Mary*
   V T D HARGREAVES-STEAD
WESTLEIGH (St Peter) *Ex 16*   **P** *D&C*   **P-in-c** C A C COOPER
WESTLEIGH (St Peter) *Man 13*   **P** *Bp, Dioc Chan, and*
   V Leigh St Mary (jt)   **P-in-c** S POLLARD
WESTLETON (St Peter) w Dunwich *St E 19*   **P** *Ch Patr Trust*
   (2 turns), Shadingfield Properties Ltd (1 turn)   **V** R J GINN,
   C R S SMITH,   **OLM** E A MORRIS
WESTLEY (St Mary)   *see* Horringer *St E*
WESTLEY WATERLESS (St Mary the less)   *see* Raddesley Gp
   Ely
WESTMEADS (St Michael and All Angels)   *see* Aldwick *Chich*
WESTMESTON (St Martin)   *see* Streat w Westmeston *Chich*
WESTMILL (St Mary the Virgin)   *see* Aspenden, Buntingford
   and Westmill *St Alb*
WESTMINSTER Hanover Square (St George)   *see* Hanover
   Square St Geo w St Mark *Lon*
WESTMINSTER (St James) Piccadilly *Lon 3*   **P** *Bp (2 turns),*
   Ld Chan (1 turn)   **R** C J W HEDLEY,   **C** G K HENWOOD,
   Hon C M K ROBINS,   **NSM** H W J VALENTINE
WESTMINSTER (St James the Less) *Lon 3*   **P** *D&C Westmr*
   V R P DORMANDY,   **NSM** A KEIGHLEY,   **W M CHOW**
WESTMINSTER (St Mary le Strand)   *see* St Mary le Strand w
   St Clem Danes *Lon*
WESTMINSTER (St Matthew) *Lon 3*   **P** *D&C Westmr*
   V P A E CHESTER,   **Hon C** R CRAWFORD,   J M GOODALL,
   NSM P L HANAWAY
WESTMINSTER (St Michael)   *see* Ches Square St Mich w
   St Phil *Lon*
WESTMINSTER (St Saviour)   *see* Pimlico St Sav *Lon*
WESTMINSTER (St Stephen) w St John *Lon 3*   **P** *The Crown*
   V P P WELSH
WESTOE, SOUTH (St Michael and All Angels) *Dur 15*   **P** *Bp*
   V J M HANCOCK
WESTON (All Saints)   *see* Bath Weston All SS w N Stoke and
   Langridge *B & W*
WESTON (All Saints) *Ches 15*   **P** *Bp*   **V** S R MITCHELL
WESTON (All Saints)   *see* Welford w Weston *Glouc*
WESTON (All Saints) *Guildf 8*   **P** *Bp*   **V** J V PERCIVAL
WESTON (All Saints)   *see* Tuxford w Weston and Markham
   Clinton *S'well*
WESTON (All Saints) w Denton *Bradf 4*   **P** *Lt-Col H V Dawson*
   and C Wyvill Esq (jt)   **V** vacant (01943) 461139
WESTON (Emmanuel)   *see* Bath Weston St Jo w Kelston *B & W*
WESTON (Holy Trinity) *St Alb 23*   **P** *Mrs A M Pryor*
   P-in-c L KLIMAS
WESTON (Holy Trinity) *Win 13*   **P** *Bp*   **V** R A BURNINGHAM
WESTON (St John the Evangelist)   *see* Bath Weston St Jo w
   Kelston *B & W*
WESTON (St John the Evangelist)   *see* Runcorn St Jo Weston
   Ches
WESTON (St Mary)   *see* Cowbit *Linc*
WESTON (St Peter)   *see* Hundred River *St E*
WESTON, OLD (St Swithun)   *see* Brington w Molesworth and
   Old Weston *Ely*
WESTON, SOUTH (St Lawrence)   *see* Thame *Ox*
WESTON BAMPFLYDE (Holy Cross)   *see* Queen Camel w
   W Camel, Corton Denham etc *B & W*
WESTON BEGGARD (St John the Baptist)   *see* Lugwardine w
   Bartestree, Weston Beggard etc *Heref*
WESTON BY WELLAND (St Mary)   *see* Stoke Albany w
   Wilbarston and Ashley etc *Pet*
WESTON COLVILLE (St Mary)   *see* Balsham, Weston Colville,
   W Wickham etc *Ely*
WESTON COYNEY (St Andrew)   *see* Caverswall and Weston
   Coyney w Dilhorne *Lich*
WESTON ESTATE CHURCH (not known)   *see* Otley *Bradf*
WESTON FAVELL (St Peter) *Pet 4*   **P** *DBP*   **R** C W WAKE,
   C J R KIMBER

WESTON HILLS (St John the Evangelist) *see* Cowbit *Linc*
WESTON IN GORDANO (St Peter and St Paul) *see* E
   Clevedon w Clapton in Gordano etc *B & W*
WESTON LONGVILLE (All Saints) **w Morton on the Hill w**
   Great w Little Witchingham *Nor 22* **P** *J V Berney Esq*
   (1 turn), New Coll Ox (3 turns) **R** J P P ILLINGWORTH
WESTON LULLINGFIELD (Holy Trinity) *see* Baschurch and
   Weston Lullingfield w Hordley *Lich*
WESTON MILL (St Philip) *see* Devonport St Boniface and
   St Phil *Ex*
WESTON-ON-THE-GREEN (St Mary) *see* Akeman *Ox*
WESTON ON TRENT (St Mary the Virgin) *see* Aston on
   Trent, Elvaston, Weston on Trent etc *Derby*
WESTON PATRICK (St Lawrence) *see* Herriard w Winslade
   and Long Sutton etc *Win*
WESTON POINT (Christ Church) *see* Runcorn St Jo Weston
   Ches
WESTON RHYN (St John) and Selattyn *Lich 19* **P** *Bp and*
   Mrs A F Hamilton-Hill (jt) **R** N G COATSWORTH
WESTON-SUB-EDGE (St Lawrence) *see* Mickleton, Willersey,
   Saintbury etc *Glouc*
WESTON SUPER MARE (All Saints) and St Saviour *B & W 11*
   P *Bp* **V** P G CLARKE
WESTON-SUPER-MARE (Christ Church) *B & W 11*
   P *Trustees* **V** G W HOBDEN
WESTON SUPER MARE (Emmanuel) *B & W 11* **P** *Trustees*
   C G P EALES
WESTON-SUPER-MARE (St Andrew) Bournville *B & W 11*
   P *Bp* **V** H M WILLIAMS, **C** F M B GUTTRIDGE
WESTON SUPER MARE (St John the Baptist) *B & W 11*
   P *Bp and Trustees (jt)* **R** B IRONS
WESTON-SUPER-MARE (St Paul) *B & W 11* **P** *Bp*
   V P H DAVIES, **C** A M ALDEN
WESTON TURVILLE (St Mary the Virgin) *Ox 28*
   P *All So Coll Ox* **P-in-c** D N WALES, **NSM** S E FELLOWS
WESTON-UNDER-LIZARD (St Andrew) *see* Blymhill w
   Weston-under-Lizard *Lich*
WESTON-UNDER-PENYARD (St Lawrence) *see* Ross *Heref*
WESTON UNDER REDCASTLE (St Luke) *see* Hodnet w
   Weston under Redcastle *Lich*
WESTON UNDER WETHERLEY (St Michael)
   see Wappenbury w Weston under Wetherley *Cov*
WESTON UNDERWOOD (St Laurence) *see* Gayhurst w
   Ravenstone, Stoke Goldington etc *Ox*
WESTON UPON TRENT (St Andrew) *see* Mid Trent *Lich*
WESTON ZOYLAND (Blessed Virgin Mary) w Chedzoy
   B & W 14 **P** *Bp* **P-in-c** P J RICHMOND
WESTONBIRT and Lasborough *Glouc 15* **P** *Westonbirt Sch*
   V *vacant*
WESTONING (St Mary Magdalene) w Tingrith *St Alb 9*
   P *Ld Chan* **V** M J BETTIS, **NSM** N L WASHINGTON
WESTOW (St Mary) *see* W Buckrose *York*
WESTWARD (St Hilda), Rosley-with-Woodside and Welton
   Carl 3 **P** *D&C* **P-in-c** N L ROBINSON
WESTWARD HO! (Holy Trinity) *see* Bideford, Northam,
   Westward Ho!, Appledore etc *Ex*
WESTWAY (St Katherine) *see* N Hammersmith St Kath *Lon*
WESTWELL (St Mary) *see* Shill Valley and Broadshire *Ox*
WESTWELL (St Mary) w Hothfield and Eastwell w Boughton
   Aluph *Cant 10* **P** *Abp and Lord Hothfield (jt)* **V** *vacant*
   (01233) 712576
WESTWICK (St Botolph) *see* Worstead, Westwick, Sloley,
   Swanton Abbot etc *Nor*
WESTWOOD (Mission Church) *see* Golcar *Wakef*
WESTWOOD (St John the Baptist) *Cov 3* **P** *Bp*
   V P FINDLEY
WESTWOOD (St Mary) Jacksdale *see* Selston *S'well*
WESTWOOD (St Mary the Virgin) and Wingfield *Sarum 14*
   P *D&C Bris, CPAS, and Bp (jt)* **R** R M LOWRIE
WESTWOOD, LOW (Christ Church) *see* Ebchester *Dur*
WETHERAL (Holy Trinity and St Constantine) w Warwick
   Carl 2 **P** *D&C* **P-in-c** C A RANDALL,
   C K S CAPELIN-JONES, **NSM** J TIPLADY
WETHERBY (St James) *Ripon 1* **P** *Bp* **V** P R EVANS,
   C C E BREWSTER
WETHERDEN (St Mary the Virgin) *see* Haughley w
   Wetherden and Stowupland *St E*
WETHERINGSETT (All Saints) *see* Gislingham and
   Thorndon *St E*
WETHERSFIELD (St Mary Magdalene) *see* Finchingfield and
   Cornish Hall End etc *Chelmsf*
WETLEY ROCKS (St John the Baptist) *Lich 8* **P** *Bp*
   P-in-c S E GOODWIN
WETTENHALL (St David) *see* Acton and Worleston, Church
   Minshull etc *Ches*
WETTON (St Margaret) *see* Alstonfield, Butterton, Ilam etc
   Lich

WETWANG (St Nicholas) *see* Waggoners *York*
WEXHAM (St Mary) *Ox 26* **P** *Ld Chan*
   P-in-c R M DONOVAN
WEYBOURNE (All Saints), Upper Sheringham, Kelling,
   Salthouse, Bodham and East and West Beckham (The
   Weybourne Group) *Nor 18* **P** *Bp (2 turns), Sir Charles*
   Mott-Radclyffe (1 turn), D&C (1 turn), and Lord Walpole
   (1 turn) **R** *vacant* (01263) 588268
WEYBREAD (St Andrew) *see* Fressingfield, Mendham etc
   St E
WEYBRIDGE (St James) *Guildf 8* **P** *Ld Chan*
   C E R JENKINS, **NSM** A J WOODWARD,
   OLM H E KEMPSTER
WEYHILL (St Michael and All Angels) *see* Hatherden w
   Tangley, Weyhill and Penton Mewsey *Win*
WEYMOUTH (Holy Trinity) (St Nicholas) *Sarum 4* **P** *Bp*
   V R H FRANKLIN, **C** D B EVANS, **NSM** A J WHITTOCK
WEYMOUTH (St Edmund) *Sarum 4* **P** *R Wyke Regis*
   P-in-c P S THOMAS
WEYMOUTH (St John) *see* Radipole and Melcombe Regis
   Sarum
WEYMOUTH (St Mary) *as above Sarum*
WEYMOUTH (St Paul) *Sarum 4* **P** *Bp* **V** R M HARPER
WHADDON (St Margaret) *see* Glouc St Geo w Whaddon
   Glouc
WHADDON (St Mary) *Ely 7* **P** *D&C Windsor*
   V J E ARMSTRONG
WHADDON (St Mary) *see* Buckingham *Ox*
WHADDON (St Mary) *see* Clarendon *Sarum*
WHADDON (St Mary the Virgin) *see* Hilperton w Whaddon
   and Staverton etc *Sarum*
WHALEY BRIDGE (St James) *Ches 16* **P** *Bp and Bp Derby*
   (alt) **R** A M BRINDLEY
WHALEY THORNS (St Luke) *see* E Scarsdale *Derby*
WHALLEY (St Mary and All Saints) *Blackb 7* **P** *Hulme*
   Trustees **V** C STERRY
WHALLEY RANGE St Edmund *Man 4* **P** *Simeon's Trustees*
   P-in-c S R BULLOCK, **C** J R GAVIN
WHALLEY RANGE (St Margaret) *Man 4* **P** *Trustees*
   P-in-c R G BOULTER
WHALTON (St Mary Magdalene) *see* Bolam w Whalton and
   Hartburn w Meldon *Newc*
WHAPLODE (St Mary) *Linc 16* **P** *Ld Chan* **V** *vacant*
   (01406) 370318
WHAPLODE DROVE (St John the Baptist) *Linc 16*
   P *Feoffees* **V** R J MORRISON
WHARFEDALE, LOWER *Ripon 1* **P** *Bp, V Otley, and*
   W G C Sheepshanks Esq (jt) **R** S W LEWIS,
   Hon C J E BASSETT
WHARNCLIFFE SIDE (not known) *see* Oughtibridge
   Sheff
WHARRAM (St Mary) *see* Weaverthorpe w Helperthorpe,
   Luttons Ambo etc *York*
WHARTON (Christ Church) *Ches 6* **P** *R Davenham*
   V T D HANSON
WHATBOROUGH Group of Parishes, The *Leic 4* **P** *Bp*
   V H R BROAD
WHATCOTE (St Peter) *see* Tysoe w Oxhill and Whatcote *Cov*
WHATFIELD (St Margaret) *see* Bildeston w Wattisham and
   Lindsey, Whatfield etc *St E*
WHATLEY (St George) *see* Mells w Buckland Dinham, Elm,
   Whatley etc *B & W*
WHATLINGTON (St Mary Magdalene) *see* Sedlescombe w
   Whatlington *Chich*
WHATSTANDWELL (Mission Room) *see* Crich and S
   Wingfield *Derby*
WHATTON (St John of Beverley) w Aslockton, Hawksworth,
   Scarrington, Orston and Thoroton *S'well 8* **P** *Trustees*
   P-in-c R A WALTON, **NSM** P C CONNELL
WHEATACRE (All Saints) *see* Raveningham Gp *Nor*
WHEATCROFT (St Michael and All Angels) *see* Scarborough
   St Martin *York*
WHEATFIELD (St Andrew) *see* Thame *Ox*
WHEATHAMPSTEAD (St Helen) *St Alb 8* **P** *Bp*
   R A P C DOYE, **NSM** J HAZELWOOD
WHEATHILL (Holy Trinity) *see* Ditton Priors w Neenton,
   Burwarton etc *Heref*
WHEATHILL PRIORY Group of Parishes, The *B & W 3*
   P *Ch Soc Trust and J H Cordle Esq (1 turn), A J Whitehead Esq*
   (2 turns), Bp (1 turn), and Mrs E J Burden (1 turn)
   R P N LITTLEWOOD
WHEATLEY (St Mary) *see* Doncaster St Mary *Sheff*
WHEATLEY (St Mary the Virgin) *Ox 1* **P** *Patr Bd*
   TR J J FULLER, **TV** W D BRIERLEY, R M COWLES,
   C C N KING, **NSM** J EDMONDS-SEAL, M D CHAPMAN,
   OLM B E KNIGHT

WHEATLEY, NORTH (St Peter and St Paul) and West Burton w Bole and Saundby and Sturton w Littleborough *S'well 5* **P** *Lord Middleton and G M T Foljambe Esq (alt)* **R** M W BRIGGS

WHEATLEY HILL (All Saints) and Wingate w Hutton Henry *Dur 2* **P** *Bp* **V** M J VAIZEY

WHEATLEY HILLS (St Aidan) *Sheff 8* **P** *Bp* **V** D J GOSS

WHEATLEY PARK (St Paul) *Sheff 8* **P** *Bp* **V** *vacant* (01302) 326041

WHEATON ASTON (St Mary) *see* Lapley w Wheaton Aston *Lich*

WHEELOCK (Christ Church) *see* Sandbach Heath w Wheelock *Ches*

WHELDRAKE (St Helen) w Thorganby *York 2* **P** *Abp and Sir Mervyn Dunnington-Jefferson Bt (jt)* **R** D C W POST, **NSM** P A BURGESS

WHELFORD (St Anne) *see* Fairford and Kempsford w Whelford *Glouc*

WHELLEY (St Stephen) *see* New Springs and Whelley *Liv*

WHELNETHAM, GREAT (St Thomas à Becket) and Little (St Mary) w Bradfield St George *St E 10* **P** *Bp* **R** *vacant* (01284) 386332

WHELPLEY HILL (St Michael and All Angels) *see* Gt Chesham *Ox*

WHENBY (St Martin) *see* Howardian Gp *York*

WHEPSTEAD (St Petronilla) *see* Horringer *St E*

WHERSTEAD (St Mary) *see* Holbrook, Stutton, Freston, Woolverstone etc *St E*

WHERWELL (St Peter and Holy Cross) *see* Chilbolton cum Wherwell *Win*

WHETSTONE (St John the Apostle) *Lon 14* **P** *Bp* **V** K MITCHELL

WHETSTONE (St Peter) *Leic 10* **P** *Bp* **V** *vacant* 0116-284 8713

WHICHAM (St Mary) *see* Bootle, Corney, Whicham and Whitbeck *Carl*

WHICHFORD (St Michael) *see* Long Compton, Whichford and Barton-on-the-Heath *Cov*

WHICKHAM (St Mary the Virgin) *Dur 13* **P** *Ld Chan* **C** D E CHADWICK

WHILTON (St Andrew) *see* Brington w Whilton and Norton etc *Pet*

WHIMPLE (St Mary), Talaton and Clyst St Lawrence *Ex 7* **P** *DBP, D&C and MMCET (jt)* **P-in-c** R S WILKINSON

WHINBURGH (St Mary) *see* Barnham Broom and Upper Yare *Nor*

WHINMOOR (St Paul) *see* Seacroft *Ripon*

WHINNEY HILL (St Peter) *see* Thrybergh *Sheff*

WHIPPINGHAM (St Mildred) w East Cowes *Portsm 8* **P** *Ld Chan* **R** J HALL

WHIPSNADE (St Mary Magdalene) *see* Kensworth, Studham and Whipsnade *St Alb*

WHIPTON (St Boniface) *Ex 3* **P** *Bp* **P-in-c** P K FITZPATRICK

WHISSENDINE (St Andrew) *see* Teigh w Whissendine and Market Overton *Pet*

WHISSONSETT (St Mary) *see* Colkirk w Oxwick w Pattesley, Whissonsett etc *Nor*

WHISTON (St Mary Magdalene) *Sheff 6* **P** *Bp* **R** A R WOOD, **C** G J OWEN

WHISTON (St Mary the Virgin) *see* Yardley Hastings, Denton and Grendon etc *Pet*

WHISTON (St Mildred) *see* Kingsley and Foxt-w-Whiston *Lich*

WHISTON (St Nicholas) *Liv 2* **P** *V Prescot* **V** A J TELFER

WHITACRE, NETHER (St Giles) *see* The Whitacres and Shustoke *Birm*

WHITACRE, OVER (St Leonard) *as above Birm*

WHITACRES and Shustoke, The *Birm 9* **P** *J K Wingfield Digby Esq (1 turn), Bp (2 turns), and Ld Chan (1 turn)* **R** D MAWBEY, **NSM** M S WALTON

WHITBECK (St Mary) *see* Bootle, Corney, Whicham and Whitbeck *Carl*

WHITBOURNE (Bringsty Iron Church) *see* Edvin Loach w Tedstone Delamere etc *Heref*

WHITBOURNE (St John the Baptist) *as above Heref*

WHITBURN (no dedication) *Dur 16* **P** *Bp* **R** K R SMITH

WHITBY (St Hilda) (St John) (St Mary) w Aislaby and Ruswarp *York 22* **P** *Abp* **TR** D W SMITH, **TV** M LOCKEY, **C** T M LEATHLEY, **NSM** G E C RIDGEWELL

WHITBY (St Thomas) *see* Ellesmere Port *Ches*

WHITBY ROAD (St Michael) *see* W Slough *Ox*

WHITCHURCH (All Hallows) w Tufton and Litchfield *Win 6* **P** *Bp* **V** M J GRYLLS

WHITCHURCH (St Alkmund) *Lich 22* **P** *Bp* **R** A R RIDLEY

WHITCHURCH (St Andrew) *Ex 24* **P** *Bp* **V** S G MAY, **C** A T WILLIAMS

WHITCHURCH (St Augustine) (St Nicholas) *Bris 1* **P** *Bp* **V** R A D'V THORN, **C** J WILSON

WHITCHURCH (St Dubricius) *see* Llangarron w Llangrove, Whitchurch and Ganarew *Heref*

WHITCHURCH (St John the Evangelist) *see* Schorne *Ox*

WHITCHURCH (St Lawrence) *see* Lt Stanmore St Lawr *Lon*

WHITCHURCH (St Mary the Virgin) *see* Ilmington w Stretton-on-Fosse etc *Cov*

WHITCHURCH (St Mary the Virgin) *Ox 6* **P** *Bp* **P-in-c** K G DAVIES, **NSM** P J R STEDDON

WHITCHURCH CANONICORUM (St Candida and Holy Cross) *see* Golden Cap Team *Sarum*

WHITCHURCH HILL (St John the Baptist) *see* Whitchurch St Mary *Ox*

WHITE COLNE (St Andrew) *see* Earls Colne w White Colne and Colne Engaine *Chelmsf*

WHITE HORSE, The *Sarum 17* **P** *Bp* **TR** P RICHARDSON, **TV** G F HUGHES, **C** S F DEACON, **NSM** M A DAVIES

WHITE LADIES ASTON (St John) *see* Peopleton and White Ladies Aston w Churchill etc *Worc*

WHITE NOTLEY (St Etheldreda) *see* Fairstead w Terling and White Notley etc *Chelmsf*

WHITE RODING (St Martin) *see* Leaden Roding and Abbess Roding etc *Chelmsf*

WHITE WALTHAM (St Mary the Virgin) w Shottesbrooke *Ox 13* **P** *Sir John Smith* **P-in-c** D N ANDREW

WHITE WELL (St Mary) *see* St Paul's Walden *St Alb*

WHITECHAPEL (St James) *see* Fellside Team *Blackb*

WHITEFIELD (St Andrew) *see* Hillock *Man*

WHITEGATE (St Mary) w Little Budworth *Ches 6* **P** *Bp, Lord Delamere and W R Cullimore Esq (alt)* **V** L P EDEN

WHITEHALL (St Ambrose) *see* E Bris St Ambrose and St Leon *Bris*

WHITEHALL PARK (St Andrew) *see* Upper Holloway *Lon*

WHITEHAVEN (St James) *Carl 5* **P** *Patr Bd* **TR** J H BAKER, **TV** J L BANNISTER

WHITEHAWK (St Cuthman) *Chich 2* **P** *Bp* **P-in-c** J D WRIGHT, **NSM** D R S PORTER

WHITEHILLS (St Mark) *see* Kingsthorpe w Northampton St Dav *Pet*

WHITELACKINGTON (The Blessed Virgin Mary) *see* Ilminster and Distr *B & W*

WHITELEAS (St Mary and St Martin) *see* S Shields All SS *Dur*

WHITELEY Conventional District *Portsm 2* **C-in-c** J HENNING

WHITEPARISH (All Saints) *see* Clarendon *Sarum*

WHITESHILL (St Paul) and Randwick *Glouc 1* **P** *Bp* **OLM** D H COLE

WHITESTAUNTON (St Andrew) *B & W 15* **P** *Personal Reps Gp Capt N W D Marwood-Elton* **R** P REGAN

WHITESTONE (St Catherine) *see* Tedburn St Mary, Whitestone, Oldridge etc *Ex*

WHITESTONE PATHFINDER (St John the Evangelist) *as above Ex*

WHITEWELL (St Mary) *see* Tushingham and Whitewell *Ches*

WHITEWELL (St Michael) *see* Chipping and Whitewell *Blackb*

WHITFIELD (Holy Trinity) *see* Allendale w Whitfield *Newc*

WHITFIELD (St James) (St Luke) *Derby 6* **P** *Bp* **V** C COOPER, **C** T P CLARK

WHITFIELD (St John) *see* Allendale w Whitfield *Newc*

WHITFIELD (St John the Evangelist) *see* Helmdon w Stuchbury and Radstone etc *Pet*

WHITFIELD (St Peter) w Guston *Cant 4* **P** *Abp and D&C (alt)* **P-in-c** B E WAY

WHITFORD (St Mary at the Cross) *see* Kilmington, Stockland, Dalwood, Yarcombe etc *Ex*

WHITGIFT (St Mary Magdalene) *see* The Marshland *Sheff*

WHITGREAVE (St John the Evangelist) *see* Stafford *Lich*

WHITKIRK (St Mary) *Ripon 8* **P** *Meynell Trustees* **V** I C BLACK

WHITLEIGH (St Chad) *Ex 22* **P** *Bp* **P-in-c** J C DOWDING

WHITLEY (Christ Church) *see* Reading Ch Ch *Ox*

WHITLEY (St Helen) *Newc 4* **P** *Bp* **V** A J PATTERSON

WHITLEY (St James) *Cov 1* **P** *Bp* **NSM** P A STOTE

WHITLEY, LOWER or NETHER (St Luke) *see* Antrobus, Aston by Sutton, Lt Leigh etc *Ches*

WHITLEY BRIDGE (All Saints) *see* Knottingley and Kellington w Whitley *Wakef*

WHITLEY LOWER (St Mary and St Michael) *see* Thornhill and Whitley Lower *Wakef*

WHITMINSTER (St Andrew) *see* Eastington, Frocester, Haresfield etc *Glouc*

WHITMORE (St Mary and All Saints) *see* Chapel Chorlton, Maer and Whitmore *Lich*

WHITNASH (St Margaret) *Cov 11* **P** *Lord Leigh* **R** R W S SUFFERN, **C** C GALE

WHITNEY (St Peter and St Paul) *see* Eardisley w Bollingham, Willersley, Brilley etc *Heref*

WHITSBURY (St Leonard) *see* W Downland *Sarum*

WHITSTABLE (All Saints) (St Alphage) (St Andrew) (St Peter)
Cant 7 **P** *DBP* **TR** S J CONEYS, **TV** P D SALES, A J EVANS,
A BIENFAIT, **Hon C** J M J OUTEN, **OLM** A L MORETON
WHITSTONE (St Anne) *see* Week St Mary w Poundstock and
Whitstone *Truro*
**WHITTINGHAM (St Bartholomew) and Edlingham w Bolton
Chapel** *Newc 9* **P** *D&C Carl and D&C Dur (alt)*
V M D CATLING
WHITTINGTON (Christ Church) *see* Northwold and Wretton
w Stoke Ferry etc *Ely*
WHITTINGTON (St Bartholomew) *Derby 5* **P** *Bp*
P-in-c J V LEWIS
WHITTINGTON (St Bartholomew) *see* Sevenhampton w
Charlton Abbots, Hawling etc *Glouc*
WHITTINGTON (St Giles) w Weeford *Lich 1* **P** *Bp*
V J H MARTIN, **Hon C** C M J IBALL
WHITTINGTON (St John the Baptist) *Lich 19*
P *Mrs P Hamilton Hill* **R** D R NORTH
WHITTINGTON (St Michael the Archangel) *see* Hornby w
Claughton and Whittington etc *Blackb*
WHITTINGTON (St Philip and St James) *see* Worc SE *Worc*
WHITTINGTON, NEW (St Barnabas) *Derby 5* **P** *Bp*
V J PINDER-PACKARD
WHITTLE-LE-WOODS (St John the Evangelist) *Blackb 4*
P *V Leyland* **V** vacant (01257) 263306
WHITTLEBURY (St Mary) *see* Silverstone and Abthorpe w
Slapton etc *Pet*
**WHITTLESEY (St Andrew) (St Mary), Pondersbridge and
Coates** *Ely 16* **P** *Ld Chan (2 turns), Patr Bd (1 turn)*
TR N A WHITEHOUSE, **TV** B J HYDER-SMITH, **C** G STEVENS
WHITTLESFORD Local Ecumenical Project *Ely 7* vacant
WHITTLESFORD (St Mary and St Andrew) *Ely 6* **P** *Jes Coll
Cam* **V** vacant (01223) 833382
WHITTON *Sarum 18* **P** *Patr Bd* **TR** J R H RAILTON,
TV S RAILTON, **OLM** J PROUT
WHITTON (St Augustine of Canterbury) *Lon 10* **P** *Bp*
V I L PHILLIPS, **C** R R R O'CALLAGHAN
WHITTON (St John the Baptist) *see* Alkborough *Linc*
WHITTON (St Mary) *see* Burford II w Greete and Hope Bagot
Heref
WHITTON (St Mary) (Ascension) and Thurleston w Akenham
St E 4 **P** *Bp (2 turns), Exors G K Drury Esq (1 turn)*
R G G BAULCOMB
WHITTON (St Philip and St James) *Lon 10* **P** *V Twickenham
St Mary* **V** L J VINCENT, **NSM** M E GREENWOOD
WHITTONSTALL (St Philip and St James) *Newc 3* **P** *D&C*
P-in-c D J IRVINE, **NSM** J LYNCH
**WHITWELL (St John the Evangelist) w Crambe, Flaxton and
Foston** *York 6* **P** *Abp and D&C Dur (jt)* **NSM** R C BENSON
WHITWELL (St Lawrence) *Derby 3* **P** *Bp* **R** G REES
WHITWELL (St Mary) *see* St Paul's Walden *St Alb*
WHITWELL (St Mary and St Rhadegunde) *Portsm 7* **P** *Bp*
V S E LLOYD
WHITWELL (St Michael and All Angels) *see* Reepham,
Hackford w Whitwell, Kerdiston etc *Nor*
WHITWELL (St Michael and All Angels) *see* Empingham and
Exton w Horn w Whitwell *Pet*
WHITWICK (St John the Baptist) *Leic 8* **P** *Duchy of Lanc*
V D I CHARNOCK, **NSM** E T SKINNER
WHITWOOD (All Saints) *see* Castleford *Wakef*
WHITWORTH (not known) *see* Spennymoor, Whitworth and
Merrington *Dur*
WHITWORTH (not known) *see* Man Whitworth *Man*
WHITWORTH (St Bartholomew) w Facit *Man 20* **P** *Bp and
Keble Coll Ox (jt)* **V** J A READ
WHIXALL (St Mary) *see* Tilstock, Edstaston and Whixall *Lich*
WHIXLEY (Ascension) *see* Gt and Lt Ouseburn w Marton cum
Grafton etc *Ripon*
WHORLTON (Holy Cross Old Church) w Carlton and Faceby
York 21 **P** *Mrs A P F Kynge* **P-in-c** D J BOASE
WHORLTON (St John the Evangelist) *Newc 7* **P** *Bp*
V A D BOWDEN, **C** L B VASEY-SAUNDERS
WHORLTON (St Mary) *see* Barnard Castle w Whorlton *Dur*
**WHYKE (St George) w Rumboldswhyke St Mary and Portfield
All Saints** *Chich 3* **P** *Bp* **R** P R SEAMAN,
Hon C J RHODES-WRIGLEY, **NSM** B M WATERS
WHYTELEAFE (St Luke) *see* Caterham *S'wark*
WIBTOFT (Assumption of Our Lady) *see* Claybrooke cum
Wibtoft and Frolesworth *Leic*
WICHENFORD (St Lawrence) *see* Martley and Wichenford,
Knightwick etc *Worc*
WICK (All Saints) *see* Littlehampton and Wick *Chich*
WICK (St Bartholomew) w Doynton and Dyrham *Bris 5*
P *Simeon's Trustees, Ld Chan, and M H W Blaythwayt Esq
(by turn)* **V** V J HOWLETT

WICK (St Mary) *see* Pershore w Pinvin, Wick and Birlingham
Worc
WICK ST LAWRENCE (St Lawrence) *see* Kewstoke w Wick
St Lawrence *B & W*
WICKEN (St John the Evangelist) *see* Potterspury w Furtho
and Yardley Gobion etc *Pet*
WICKEN (St Laurence) *see* Soham and Wicken *Ely*
WICKEN BONHUNT (St Margaret) *see* Quendon w Rickling
and Wicken Bonhunt etc *Chelmsf*
WICKENBY (St Peter and St Laurence) *see* Wragby Gp *Linc*
WICKERSLEY (St Alban) *Sheff 6* **P** *DBP* **P-in-c** J M WRAW
WICKFORD (St Andrew) (St Catherine) and Runwell *Chelmsf 6*
P *Patr Bd* **TR** P G KEARNS, **TV** J H DELFGOU,
A T FRANKLAND, **C** P K TRATHEN
WICKHAM (St Nicholas) *Portsm 1* **P** *Sir Richard Rashleigh Bt*
R R A A HIRST
WICKHAM (St Swithun) *see* Welford w Wickham and Gt
Shefford, Boxford etc *Ox*
WICKHAM, EAST (St Michael) *S'wark 3* **P** *D&C*
C P ORGAN, **Hon C** C HEARD, **NSM** J A CONALTY
WICKHAM, WEST (St Francis) (St Mary of Nazareth)
S'wark 21 **P** *Bp* **V** M R MCKINNEY, **C** P C GULVIN
WICKHAM, WEST (St John) *S'wark 22* **P** *Bp* **V** T D GILES,
NSM J C HAWKINS, **OLM** K J D GAVED
WICKHAM, WEST (St Mary) *see* Balsham, Weston Colville,
W Wickham etc *Ely*
WICKHAM BISHOPS (St Bartholomew) w Little Braxted
Chelmsf 24 **P** *Bp (3 turns), CCC Cam (1 turn)*
R J T HOWDEN, **NSM** E A LAW
WICKHAM MARKET (All Saints) w Pettistree *St E 18*
P *Ch Trust Fund Trust and Ld Chan (alt)* **P-in-c** J F ELDRIDGE
WICKHAM ST PAUL (St Paul and All Saints) *see* N Hinckford
Chelmsf
WICKHAM SKEITH (St Andrew) *see* Bacton w Wyverstone,
Cotton and Old Newton etc *St E*
WICKHAMBREAUX (St Andrew) *see* Littlebourne and
Ickham w Wickhambreaux etc *Cant*
WICKHAMBROOK (All Saints) *see* Bansfield *St E*
WICKHAMFORD (St John the Baptist) *see* Broadway w
Wickhamford *Worc*
WICKHAMPTON (St Andrew) *see* Freethorpe, Wickhampton,
Halvergate etc *Nor*
WICKLEWOOD (All Saints) *see* High Oak, Hingham and
Scoulton w Wood Rising *Nor*
WICKMERE (St Andrew) *see* Lt Barningham, Blickling,
Edgefield etc *Nor*
WICKWAR (Holy Trinity), Rangeworthy and Hillesley *Glouc 7*
P *Bp and Earl of Ducie (jt)* **R** D J RUSSELL
WIDCOMBE *see* Bath Widcombe *B & W*
WIDDINGTON (St Mary) *see* Quendon w Rickling and
Wicken Bonhunt etc *Chelmsf*
WIDDRINGTON (Holy Trinity) *Newc 11* **P** *Bp*
P-in-c A E HARRISON
WIDDRINGTON STATION (St Mary) *see* Ulgham *Newc*
**WIDECOMBE-IN-THE-MOOR (St Pancras), Leusdon,
Princetown, Postbridge, Huccaby and Holne** *Ex 10* **P** *Duchy
of Cornwall (1 turn), Patr Bd (2 turns)* **TR** D J NEWPORT,
C C E COOPER
WIDEMOUTH BAY (Our Lady and St Anne) *see* Week
St Mary w Poundstock and Whitstone *Truro*
WIDFORD (St John the Baptist) *see* Hunsdon w Widford and
Wareside *St Alb*
WIDFORD (St Mary) (Holy Spirit) *Chelmsf 9* **P** *CPAS*
R D R W ROBBINS, **C** C A KOSLA
WIDFORD (St Oswald) *see* Burford w Fulbrook, Taynton,
Asthall etc *Ox*
WIDLEY w Wymering *Portsm 6* **P** *E G Nugee Esq*
V M L HILL-TOUT, **NSM** L C DENNESS
WIDMER END (Good Shepherd) *see* Hazlemere *Ox*
WIDMERPOOL (St Peter) *see* Willoughby-on-the-Wolds w
Wysall and Widmerpool *S'well*
WIDNES (St Ambrose) *Liv 13* **P** *Trustees* **P-in-c** J P LEFFLER
WIDNES (St John) *Liv 13* **P** *Bp and V Farnworth (jt)*
V D J GAIT
WIDNES (St Mary) *Liv 13* **P** *Bp* **P-in-c** G C ELSMORE,
C S J COKE-WOODS, **NSM** R JONES
WIDNES (St Paul) *Liv 13* **P** *Bp* **P-in-c** G C ELSMORE,
NSM R JONES
WIDWORTHY (St Cuthbert) *see* Offwell, Northleigh, Farway,
Cotleigh etc *Ex*
WIELD (St James) *see* Medstead cum Wield *Win*
WIGAN (All Saints) *Liv 14* **P** *Bp* **R** K M FORREST
WIGAN (St Andrew) *Liv 15* **P** *R Wigan* **V** C HURST
WIGAN (St Anne) *Liv 15* **P** *Bp* **V** P A LOCK
WIGAN (St Barnabas) Marsh Green *Liv 15* **P** *V Pemberton
St Mark Newtown and Bp (jt)* **P-in-c** D V ROUCH

WIGAN (St Catherine) *Liv 14* **P** *R Wigan* **P-in-c** G J BIRCH
WIGAN (St George) *Liv 14* **P** *R Wigan* **V** *vacant (01942) 244500*
WIGAN (St James) (St Thomas) *Liv 15* **P** *R Wigan and Bp (jt)* **V** J A TAYLOR
WIGAN (St John the Baptist) New Springs *see* New Springs and Whelley *Liv*
WIGAN (St Michael and All Angels) *Liv 15* **P** *R Wigan* **V** R GIBBARD
WIGAN (St Stephen) Whelley *see* New Springs and Whelley *Liv*
WIGBOROUGH, GREAT (St Stephen) *see* Peldon w Gt and Lt Wigborough *Chelmsf*
WIGBOROUGH, LITTLE (St Nicholas) *as above Chelmsf*
WIGGATON (St Edward the Confessor) *see* Ottery St Mary, Alfington, W Hill, Tipton etc *Ex*
WIGGENHALL ST GERMANS (St Mary the Virgin) *see* E Marshland *Ely*
WIGGENHALL ST MARY (St Mary Magdalene) *as above Ely*
WIGGINTON (St Bartholomew) *St Alb 2* **P** *Bp* **P-in-c** W B CARPENTER
WIGGINTON (St Giles) *see* Hook Norton w Gt Rollright, Swerford etc *Ox*
WIGGINTON (St Leonard) (St James) *Lich 4* **P** *V Tamworth* **P-in-c** I R CARDINAL, **NSM** R DAVIES
WIGGINTON (St Mary and St Nicholas) *see* Haxby w Wigginton *York*
WIGGLESWORTH (School) *see* Giggleswick and Rathmell w Wigglesworth *Bradf*
WIGGONHOLT (not known) *see* Amberley w N Stoke and Parham, Wiggonholt etc *Chich*
WIGHILL (All Saints) *see* Healaugh w Wighill, Bilbrough and Askham Richard *York*
WIGHTON (All Saints) *see* Holkham w Egmere w Warham, Wells and Wighton *Nor*
WIGMORE (St James the Apostle) *see* Wigmore Abbey *Heref*
WIGMORE ABBEY *Heref 7* **P** *Trustees* **R** S J TURNER, **Hon C** M P THOMPSON-MCCAUSLAND, **NSM** D W G VICKERS
WIGSLEY *see* Harby w Thorney and N and S Clifton *S'well*
WIGSTON, SOUTH (St Thomas) *see* Glen Parva and S Wigston *Leic*
WIGSTON MAGNA (All Saints) (St Wistan) *Leic 5* **P** *Haberdashers' Co* **P-in-c** L R CURTIS, **C** P E GIBSON
WIGSTON PARVA (St Mary the Virgin) *see* Sapcote and Sharnford w Wigston Parva *Leic*
WIGTOFT (St Peter and St Paul) *see* Sutterton, Fosdyke, Algarkirk and Wigtoft *Linc*
WIGTON (St Mary) *Carl 3* **P** *Bp* **V** G P RAVALDE, **C** S P RACE
WIKE (School Room) *see* Bardsey *Ripon*
WILBARSTON (All Saints) *see* Stoke Albany w Wilbarston and Ashley etc *Pet*
WILBERFOSS (St John the Baptist) *see* Kexby w Wilberfoss *York*
WILBRAHAM, GREAT (St Nicholas) *Ely 3* **P** *DBP* **C** R M NANCARROW
WILBRAHAM, LITTLE (St John) *Ely 3* **P** *CCC Cam* **C** R M NANCARROW
WILBURTON (St Peter) *Ely 13* **P** *Adn Ely* **V** F E G BRAMPTON, **NSM** P M DUFFETT-SMITH
WILBURY (St Thomas) *St Alb 4* **P** *Bp* **V** B E C PATE
WILBY (All Saints) *see* Quidenham Gp *Nor*
WILBY (St Mary the Virgin) *see* Gt Doddington and Wilby *Pet*
WILBY (St Mary) w Brundish *St E 17* **P** *Dr F H C Marriott and Miss A W G Marriott (3 turns), Bp (1 turn)* **P-in-c** F O NEWTON
WILCOT (Holy Cross) *see* Pewsey and Swanborough *Sarum*
WILCOTE (St Peter) *see* Ramsden, Finstock and Fawler, Leafield etc *Ox*
WILDBOARCLOUGH (St Saviour) *see* Bosley and N Rode w Wincle and Wildboarclough *Ches*
WILDEN (All Saints) *see* Stourport and Wilden *Worc*
WILDEN (St Nicholas) w Colmworth and Ravensden *St Alb 15* **P** *Ld Chan, Bp, and DBP (by turn)* **R** S MORTON
WILFORD (St Wilfrid) *S'well 9* **P** *Lt Col Peter Clifton* **P-in-c** D B ROWE, **C** R J WITCOMBE
WILFORD HILL (St Paul) *S'well 9* **P** *DBP* **V** G J PIGOTT, **NSM** B M GRIFFITHS, S D HIPPISLEY-COX
WILFORD PENINSULA, The *St E 7* **P** *Patr Bd* **TR** R W CLIFTON, **TV** C MACDONALD, G P CLEMENT, P T S KERLEY, **OLM** J M ANDREWS
WILKSBY (All Saints) *see* Mareham-le-Fen and Revesby *Linc*
WILLAND (St Mary the Virgin) *see* Cullompton, Willand, Uffculme, Kentisbeare etc *Ex*
WILLASTON (Christ Church) *Ches 9* **P** *DBF* **V** R W DENT
WILLASTON (St Luke) *see* Wistaston *Ches*
WILLEN (St Mary Magdalene) *see* Stantonbury and Willen *Ox*

WILLENHALL (Holy Trinity) *Lich 28* **P** *Patr Bd* **TR** B PRENTICE, **TV** M S HATHORNE, **C** I R M POOLE
WILLENHALL (St Anne) *Lich 28* **P** *Mrs L Grant-Wilson* **V** C A ST A RAMSAY
WILLENHALL (St Giles) *Lich 28* **P** *Trustees* **P-in-c** K H JOHNSON
WILLENHALL (St John the Divine) *Cov 1* **P** *V Cov H Trin* **C** D R TILLEY
WILLENHALL (St Stephen) *Lich 28* **P** *Bp* **P-in-c** G E T BENNETT
WILLERBY (St Luke) *see* Kirk Ella *York*
WILLERBY (St Peter) w Ganton and Folkton *York 15* **P** *M H Wrigley Esq, MMCET, and the Revd C G Day (by turn)* **R** *vacant (01944) 710364*
WILLERSEY (St Peter) *see* Mickleton, Willersey, Saintbury etc *Glouc*
WILLESBOROUGH (St Mary the Virgin) *Cant 10* **P** *D&C* **P-in-c** A K MCNICOL, **NSM** L J SCHRYVER
WILLESDEN (St Mark) *see* Kensal Rise St Mark and St Martin *Lon*
WILLESDEN (St Martin) *as above Lon*
WILLESDEN (St Mary) *Lon 21* **P** *D&C St Paul's* **V** D C CLUES
WILLESDEN (St Matthew) *Lon 21* **P** *Bp* **V** A F HILL, **NSM** D NEW
WILLESDEN (St Michael and All Angels) *see* Stonebridge St Mich *Lon*
WILLESDEN GREEN (St Andrew) (St Francis of Assisi) *Lon 21* **P** *Bp* **V** P S ANDERSON, **C** R A WAKELING
WILLEY (St Leonard) *see* Churchover w Willey *Cov*
WILLIAN (All Saints) *see* Letchworth St Paul w Willian *St Alb*
WILLINGALE (St Christopher) *see* Fyfield, Moreton w Bobbingworth etc *Chelmsf*
WILLINGDON (St Mary the Virgin) *Chich 16* **P** *D&C* **V** M G ONIONS, **C** D S MILES
WILLINGDON, LOWER (St Wilfrid) Conventional District *Chich 16* **C-in-c** A M TUCKER
WILLINGHAM (St Mary and All Saints) *Ely 5* **P** *Bp* **R** G E TURNER
WILLINGHAM, NORTH (St Thomas) *see* Walesby *Linc*
WILLINGHAM, SOUTH (St Martin) *see* Barkwith Gp *Linc*
WILLINGHAM BY STOW (St Helen) *see* Stow Gp *Linc*
WILLINGTON (St Lawrence) *see* Cople, Moggerhanger and Willington *St Alb*
WILLINGTON (St Michael) *Derby 16* **P** *CPAS* **V** *vacant (01283) 702203*
WILLINGTON (St Stephen) and Sunnybrow *Dur 9* **P** *R Brancepeth* **R** P GRUNDY
WILLINGTON Team, The (Good Shepherd) (St Mary the Virgin) (St Paul) *Newc 8* **P** *Prime Min* **TR** J M DOTCHIN, **TV** R A STONE, **C** D MACNAUGHTON, **NSM** S HAMIL
WILLINGTON QUAY (St Paul) *see* Willington Team *Newc*
WILLISHAM (St Mary) *see* Somersham w Flowton and Offton w Willisham *St E*
WILLITON (St Peter) *B & W 17* **P** *V Watchet* **V** R J ALLEN
WILLOUGHBY (St Helen) *Linc 8* **P** *Baroness Willoughby de Eresby, Ball Coll Ox, and Bp (jt)* **R** D C ROBINSON
WILLOUGHBY (St Nicholas) *see* Leam Valley *Cov*
WILLOUGHBY-ON-THE-WOLDS (St Mary and All Saints) w Wysall and Widerpool *S'well 8* **P** *MMCET* **P-in-c** C TURNER
WILLOUGHBY WATERLEYS (St Mary), Peatling Magna and Ashby Magna *Leic 10* **P** *Bp* **P-in-c** C W DOIDGE
WILLOUGHTON (St Andrew) *see* Glentworth Gp *Linc*
WILMCOTE (St Andrew) *see* Aston Cantlow and Wilmcote w Billesley *Cov*
WILMINGTON (St Mary and St Peter) _see_ Arlington, Folkington and Wilmington *Chich*
WILMINGTON (St Michael) *Roch 2* **P** *D&C* **V** R ARDING, **Hon C** P J IVESON, **NSM** T WYATT
WILMSLOW (St Bartholomew) *Ches 12* **P** *Bp* **R** A G SPARHAM, **C** S A STUTZ, P J PARRY, **NSM** R A YATES, N J WALTHEW
WILNE (St Chad) and Draycott w Breaston *Derby 13* **P** *Bp* **R** C J SMEDLEY
WILNECOTE (Holy Trinity) *Lich 4* **P** *V Tamworth* **V** M J G BINNEY, **C** S M ROSSETER, S K WELLER, **OLM** C J ROBINSON
WILSDEN (St Matthew) *see* Harden and Wilsden *Bradf*
WILSFORD (St Mary) *see* Ancaster Wilsford Gp *Linc*
WILSFORD (St Michael) *see* Woodford Valley *Sarum*
WILSFORD (St Nicholas) *see* Redhorn *Sarum*
WILSHAMSTEAD (All Saints) and Houghton Conquest *St Alb 13* **P** *St Jo Coll Cam and Bp (alt)* **V** S J TOZE, **NSM** R C WHITE

WILSHAW (St Mary) *see* Meltham *Wakef*
WILSILL (St Michael and All Angels) *see* Upper Nidderdale *Ripon*
WILSTHORPE (St Faith) *see* Uffington Gp *Linc*
WILSTONE (St Cross) *see* Tring *St Alb*
WILTON (St Cuthbert) *York 16* **P** *Abp* **V** C M DURNFORD
WILTON (St George) *B & W 18* **P** *Mrs E C Cutbush*
TR N J TAYLOR, TV C SNELL, NSM C F CRAGGS,
J A JEFFERY
WILTON (St George) *see* Thornton Dale w Allerston, Ebberston etc *York*
WILTON (St Mary and St Nicholas) w Netherhampton and **Fugglestone** *Sarum 12* **P** *Earl of Pembroke* **R** B R COOPER,
NSM J MALINS, S PORTER, G SPENCER
WILTON PLACE (St Paul) *Lon 3* **P** *Bp* **P-in-c** A G GYLE,
NSM N DAWSON
WIMBISH (All Saints) *see* Debden and Wimbish w Thunderley *Chelmsf*
WIMBLEDON (Emmanuel) Ridgway Proprietary Chapel
S'wark 12 **Min** J J M FLETCHER, C R A R WEEKES, C J DAVIS,
P R DAWSON, **Hon C** D L JOHNSON, NSM R J COEKIN
WIMBLEDON (St Mary) (St Matthew) (St Mark) (St John the Baptist) *S'wark 14* **P** *Patr Bd* TR C J DAVIES,
TV C D EYDEN, C R S TAYLOR, G M PAWSON,
NSM H A JOHNSON, C JACKSON, R G STEVENS
WIMBLEDON, SOUTH (All Saints) *S'wark 14* **P** *Bp*
P-in-c M O BLACKMAN
WIMBLEDON, SOUTH (Holy Trinity and St Peter) *S'wark 14*
P *Bp and TR Wimbledon (jt)* **P-in-c** D R M MONTEITH
WIMBLEDON, SOUTH (St Andrew) *S'wark 14* **P** *Bp*
V A D WAKEFIELD
WIMBLEDON, WEST (Christ Church) *S'wark 14*
P *TR Wimbledon* **V** vacant (020) 8946 4491
WIMBLEDON PARK (St Luke) *S'wark 14* **P** *Simeon's Trustees* **V** S D N VIBERT, C J C POOLE
WIMBLEDON PARK (St Paul) *see* Wandsworth St Paul *S'wark*
WIMBLINGTON (St Peter) *see* Doddington w Benwick and Wimblington *Ely*
WIMBORNE (St John the Evangelist) *see* New Borough and Leigh *Sarum*
WIMBORNE MINSTER (St Cuthberga) *Sarum 9* **P** *Qu Eliz Free Gr Sch* **R** J E HOLBROOK, C P SEABROOK
WIMBORNE ST GILES (St Giles) *see* Cranborne w Boveridge, Edmondsham etc *Sarum*
WIMBOTSHAM (St Mary) w Stow Bardolph and Stow Bridge w Nordelph *Ely 15* **P** *Bp* **R** S J W NORMAND
WIMPOLE (St Andrew) *see* Orwell Gp *Ely*
WINCANTON (St Peter and St Paul) *B & W 2* **P** *D&C*
R S LOW
WINCHAM (St Andrew) *see* Lostock Gralam *Ches*
WINCHCOMBE (St Peter), Gretton, Sudeley Manor and Stanley Pontlarge *Glouc 16* **P** *Lady Ashcombe*
C M M LUDLOW
WINCHELSEA (St Thomas) (St Richard) and Icklesham
Chich 20 **P** *Bp and Guild of All So (jt)* **R** G W SILLIS
WINCHENDON, NETHER (St Nicholas) *see* Long Crendon w Chearsley and Nether Winchendon *Ox*
WINCHENDON, OVER (St Mary Magdalene) *see* Schorne *Ox*
WINCHESTER (All Saints), Chilcomb St Andrew and Chesil St Peter *Win 7* **P** *Bp and Ld Chan (alt)* **R** C BASTON,
NSM T E HEMMING
WINCHESTER (Christ Church) *Win 7* **P** *Simeon's Trustees*
V D G WILLIAMS, C H C SCAMMAN, J L SCAMMAN,
NSM B R WAKELIN
WINCHESTER (Holy Trinity) *see* Winnall *Win*
WINCHESTER (St Barnabas) *Win 7* **P** *Bp*
P-in-c T H ROBERTS, NSM A M DAVIES
WINCHESTER (St Cross Hospital w St Faith) *Win 7* **P** *Bp*
V S A OUTHWAITE, R C SWEET
WINCHESTER (St John the Baptist w St Martin Winnall) *see* Winnall *Win*
WINCHESTER (St Lawrence and St Maurice) (St Swithun-upon-Kingsgate) *Win 7* **P** *Ld Chan*
R D V SCOTT, NSM N H de la MOUETTE
WINCHESTER (St Luke) *see* Stanmore *Win*
WINCHESTER St Matthew (St Paul's Mission Church) *Win 7*
P *Bp* **P-in-c** N P SEAL, NSM N W BIRKETT
WINCHESTER HYDE (St Bartholomew) *Win 7* **P** *Ld Chan*
P-in-c M R STARR
WINCHFIELD (St Mary the Virgin) *see* Hartley Wintney, Elvetham, Winchfield etc *Win*
WINCHMORE HILL (Holy Trinity) *Lon 18* **P** *V Winchmore Hill St Paul* **V** C M GRAY
WINCHMORE HILL (St Andrew) *see* Amersham *Ox*

WINCHMORE HILL (St Paul) *Lon 18* **P** *V Edmonton*
V J M PAUL, C J M AMEY, NSM C M MORTON
WINCLE (St Michael) *see* Bosley and N Rode w Wincle and Wildboarclough *Ches*
WINCOBANK (St Thomas) *see* Brightside w Wincobank *Sheff*
WINDERMERE (St Martin) *Carl 11* **P** *Bp and Trustees (jt)*
R J J RICHARDS, C S C BICKERSTETH
WINDERMERE (St Mary) Applethwaite and Troutbeck *Carl 11*
P *Bp* **V** D M B WILMOT, NSM J M WARE
WINDHILL (Christ Church) *Bradf 1* **P** *Bp* **V** vacant (01274) 581502
WINDLESHAM (St John the Baptist) *Guildf 6* **P** *Ld Chan*
R P W MICKLETHWAITE
WINDRUSH (St Peter) *see* Sherborne, Windrush, the Barringtons etc *Glouc*
WINDRUSH, LOWER *Ox 8* **P** *Bp, DBP, St Jo Coll Ox, D&C Ex, and B Babington-Smith Esq (jt)* **R** S E SHARP
WINDSOR, NEW (Holy Trinity) (St John the Baptist w All Saints) *Ox 13* **P** *Ld Chan* TV M J BARNES,
P-in-c A L SWIFT, OLM J M QUICK
WINDSOR, OLD (St Luke's Mission Room) (St Peter and St Andrew) *Ox 13* **P** *Ld Chan* **V** N J POCOCK
WINESTEAD (St German) *see* Patrington w Hollym, Welwick and Winestead *York*
WINFARTHING (St Mary) w Shelfanger w Burston w Gissing and Tivetshall *Nor 10* **P** *Ld Chan, Bp, and DBP (jt), Hertf Coll Ox (alt)* **R** D F MILLS
WINFORD (Blessed Virgin Mary and St Peter) w Felton Common Hill *B & W 10* **P** *Worc Coll Ox and Mrs H D Pullman (jt)* **R** P M HAND
WINFORTON (St Michael and All Angels) *see* Eardisley w Bollingham, Willersley, Brilley etc *Heref*
WINFRITH NEWBURGH (St Christopher) *see* The Lulworths, Winfrith Newburgh and Chaldon *Sarum*
WING (St Peter and St Paul) *see* Preston and Ridlington w Wing and Pilton *Pet*
WING w Grove (All Saints) *Ox 26* **P** *Bp* **V** vacant (01296) 688496
WINGATE GRANGE (Holy Trinity) *see* Wheatley Hill and Wingate w Hutton Henry *Dur*
WINGATES (St John the Evangelist) *see* Westhoughton and Wingates *Man*
WINGERWORTH (All Saints) *Derby 5* **P** *Bp* **R** R M WATTS,
C M P SMITH
WINGFIELD (St Andrew) *see* Fressingfield, Mendham etc *St E*
WINGFIELD (St Mary) *see* Westwood and Wingfield *Sarum*
WINGFIELD, NORTH (St Lawrence), Clay Cross and Pilsley
Derby 5 **P** *Bp* TR C E BERESFORD, TV L S LIVERSIDGE,
M J BARNES, C J HILLMAN
WINGFIELD, SOUTH (All Saints) *see* Crich and S Wingfield *Derby*
WINGHAM (St Mary the Virgin) w Elmstone and Preston w Stourmouth *Cant 1* **P** *Lord Fitzwalter and D&C (alt)*
V M R GRIFFIN
WINGRAVE (St Peter and St Paul) w Rowsham, Aston Abbotts and Cublington *Ox 26* **P** *Bp and Linc Coll Ox (jt)*
R R O N WILLMOTT, OLM S TUNNICLIFFE
WINKBURN (St John of Jerusalem) *S'well 14* **P** *Bp*
P-in-c E F CULLY
WINKFIELD (St Mary the Virgin) and Cranbourne *Ox 11*
P *Bp* **V** R W NEILL
WINKLEBURY (Good Shepherd) *Win 4* **P** *MMCET*
V D T PERRETT, NSM R P BOWSKILL
WINKLEIGH (All Saints) *Ex 19* **P** *D&C* **V** P J NORMAN
WINKSLEY (St Cuthbert and St Oswald) *see* Fountains Gp *Ripon*
WINLATON (St Paul) *Dur 13* **P** *Bp* **P-in-c** G W R HARPER
WINMARLEIGH (St Luke) *see* Cockerham w Winmarleigh and Glasson *Blackb*
WINNALL (Holy Trinity) (St John the Baptist w St Martin)
Win 7 **P** *Bp* **R** R J H TEARE
WINNERSH (St Mary the Virgin) *see* Hurst *Ox*
WINSCOMBE (St James) *B & W 11* **P** *D&C* **V** M J SLADE
WINSFORD (St Mary Magdalene) *see* Exton and Winsford and Cutcombe w Luxborough *B & W*
WINSHAM (St Stephen) *see* Chard and Distr *B & W*
WINSHILL (St Mark) *Derby 16* **P** *Lady H M Gretton and Baroness Gretton (jt)* **V** M M MOOKERJI
WINSLEY (St Nicholas) *see* Monkton Farleigh, S Wraxall and Winsley *Sarum*
WINSLOW (St Laurence) w Great Horwood and Addington
Ox 24 **P** *Ld Chan (3 turns), New Coll Ox (2 turns), and DBP (1 turn)* **R** A A WHALLEY, C T E DOYLE
WINSON (St Michael) *see* Bibury w Winson and Barnsley *Glouc*

WINSTER (Holy Trinity) *Carl 10* **P** *V Kendal H Trin*
P-in-c W F GREETHAM
WINSTER (St John the Baptist) *see* S Darley, Elton and Winster *Derby*
WINSTON (St Andrew) *Dur 7* **P** *Bp* **P-in-c** M ALDERSON
WINSTON (St Andrew) *see* Helmingham w Framsden and Pettaugh w Winston *St E*
WINSTONE (St Bartholomew) *see* Brimpsfield w Birdlip, Syde, Daglingworth etc *Glouc*
WINTERBOURNE (St James) *see* Chieveley w Winterbourne and Oare *Ox*
WINTERBOURNE (St Michael the Archangel) *Bris 5*
P *St Jo Coll Ox* **R** E I BAILEY, **Hon C** W J DEIGHTON
WINTERBOURNE ABBAS (St Mary) *see* The Winterbournes and Compton Valence *Sarum*
WINTERBOURNE BASSETT (St Katharine) *see* Upper Kennet *Sarum*
WINTERBOURNE CLENSTON (St Nicholas)
see Winterbourne Stickland and Turnworth etc *Sarum*
WINTERBOURNE DOWN (All Saints) *see* Frenchay and Winterbourne Down *Bris*
WINTERBOURNE EARLS (St Michael and All Angels)
see Bourne Valley *Sarum*
WINTERBOURNE GUNNER (St Mary) *as above Sarum*
WINTERBOURNE HOUGHTON (St Andrew)
see Winterbourne Stickland and Turnworth etc *Sarum*
WINTERBOURNE KINGSTON (St Nicholas) *see* Red Post *Sarum*
WINTERBOURNE MONKTON (St Mary Magdalene)
see Upper Kennet *Sarum*
WINTERBOURNE MONKTON (St Simon and St Jude)
see Dorchester *Sarum*
WINTERBOURNE ST MARTIN (St Martin) *see* The Winterbournes and Compton Valence *Sarum*
WINTERBOURNE STEEPLETON (St Michael) *as above Sarum*
WINTERBOURNE STICKLAND (St Mary) and Turnworth, Winterbourne Houghton, Winterbourne Whitechurch and Winterbourne Clenston *Sarum 6* **P** *Bp (3 turns), P D H Chichester Esq and Exors Mrs V P Railston (1 turn)*
P-in-c R N HUNGERFORD
WINTERBOURNE STOKE (St Peter) *see* Wylye and Till Valley *Sarum*
WINTERBOURNE WHITECHURCH (St Mary)
see Winterbourne Stickland and Turnworth etc *Sarum*
WINTERBOURNE ZELSTONE (St Mary) *see* Red Post *Sarum*
WINTERBOURNES and Compton Valence, The *Sarum 1*
P *Adn Sherborne, Linc Coll Ox, and Sir Robert Williams Bt (by turn)* **P-in-c** J R ADAMS, **NSM** R L BASSETT, M C MILES
WINTERBURN (Chapel of Ease) *see* Gargrave *Bradf*
WINTERINGHAM (All Saints) *see* Alkborough *Linc*
WINTERSLOW (All Saints) *see* Clarendon *Sarum*
WINTERSLOW (St John) *as above Sarum*
WINTERTON Group, The (All Saints) *Linc 4* **P** *Lord St Oswald, Bp, and Exors Capt J G G P Elwes (jt)*
V A C NUNN, **OLM** J D AIZLEWOOD, J J WHITEHEAD
WINTERTON (Holy Trinity and All Saints) *see* Flegg Coastal Benefice *Nor*
WINTHORPE (All Saints) *see* Coddington and Winthorpe and Langford w Holme *S'well*
WINTHORPE (St Mary) *see* Skegness and Winthorpe *Linc*
WINTON (St Mary Magdalene) *Man 2* **P** *Trustees*
V D R SUTTON
WINTRINGHAM (St Peter) *see* Buckrose Carrs *York*
WINWICK (All Saints) *Ely 9* **P** *Bp* **P-in-c** C M FURLONG
WINWICK (St Michael and All Angels) *see* W Haddon w Winwick and Ravensthorpe *Pet*
WINWICK (St Oswald) *Liv 16* **P** *Bp* **R** R G LEWIS
WIRKSWORTH (St Mary) *Derby 7* **P** *Bp* **TV** J D HAYWARD, **C** S J LUMBY, **NSM** K J ORFORD, G M MANN
WISBECH (St Augustine) *Ely 17* **P** *Bp* **P-in-c** W A L ZWALF, **C** N K GARDNER
WISBECH (St Peter and St Paul) *Ely 17* **P** *Bp*
V W A L ZWALF, **C** N K GARDNER
WISBECH ST MARY (St Mary) *Ely 17* **P** *Bp*
P-in-c C HURST
WISBOROUGH GREEN (St Peter ad Vincula) *Chich 11*
P *Bp Lon* **V** D F PIKE
WISHAW (St Chad) *Birm 12* **P** *Bp* **P-in-c** M I RHODES
WISHFORD, GREAT (St Giles) *see* Wylye and Till Valley *Sarum*
WISLEY (not known) w Pyrford *Guildf 12* **P** *Bp* **R** N J AIKEN, **C** H M MACDONALD, **NSM** K R CROOKS, B A STEELE-PERKINS, **OLM** C D GIBSON
WISSETT (St Andrew) *see* Blyth Valley *St E*

WISSINGTON (St Mary the Virgin) *see* Nayland w Wiston *St E*
WISTANSTOW (Holy Trinity) *Heref 11* **P** *Bp*
P-in-c P C ROBSON
WISTASTON (St Mary) *Ches 15* **P** *Trustees* **R** W J WHITE
WISTON (St Mary) *see* Ashington, Washington and Wiston w Buncton *Chich*
WISTOW (All Saints) *see* Cawood w Ryther and Wistow *York*
WISTOW (St John the Baptist) *see* Warboys w Broughton and Bury w Wistow *Ely*
WISTOW (St Wistan) *Leic 5* **P** *Bp and The Hon Ann Brooks (jt)* **V** P J O'REILLY
WITCHAM (St Martin) w Mepal *Ely 13* **P** *D&C*
NSM T M DIXON, M L BRADBURY
WITCHAMPTON (St Mary and St Cuthberga and All Saints), Stanbridge and Long Crichel w More Crichel *Sarum 9* **P** *Hon Mrs M A S E Marten* **P-in-c** J E HOLBROOK,
Hon C P H ELSTON
WITCHFORD (St Andrew) w Wentworth *Ely 13* **P** *D&C*
P-in-c A E H HULT
WITCHINGHAM GREAT (St Mary) *see* Weston Longville w Morton and the Witchinghams *Nor*
WITCOMBE, GREAT (St Mary) *see* Badgeworth, Shurdington and Witcombe w Bentham *Glouc*
WITHAM Group, The *Linc 14* **P** *Sir Lyonel Tollemache Bt, The Revd J R H Thorold, J R Thorold Esq, and Bp (jt)*
R N S F ALLDRIT
WITHAM (St Nicholas) *Chelmsf 24* **P** *Patr Bd*
TR J M SUDDARDS, **C** P A JOHNSON
WITHAM, NORTH (St Mary) *see* Witham Gp *Linc*
WITHAM, SOUTH (St John the Baptist) *as above Linc*
WITHAM FRIARY (Blessed Virgin Mary and St John the Baptist and All Saints) *see* Nunney and Witham Friary, Marston Bigot etc *B*
WITHAM-ON-THE-HILL (St Andrew) *see* Edenham w Witham on the Hill and Swinstead *Linc*
WITHCALL (St Martin) *see* Legbourne and Wold Marsh *Linc*
WITHERIDGE (St John the Baptist) *see* Burrington, Chawleigh, Cheldon, Chulmleigh etc *Ex*
WITHERLEY (St Peter) *see* Fenn Lanes Gp *Leic*
WITHERNSEA (St Nicholas) *see* Owthorne and Rimswell w Withernsea *York*
WITHERNWICK (St Alban) *see* Aldbrough, Mappleton w Goxhill and Withernwick *York*
WITHERSDALE (St Mary Magdalene) *see* Fressingfield, Mendham etc *St E*
WITHERSFIELD (St Mary the Virgin) *see* Haverhill w Withersfield *St E*
WITHERSLACK (St Paul) *Carl 10* **P** *DBP*
P-in-c W F GREETHAM
WITHIEL (St Clement) *see* Roche and Withiel *Truro*
WITHIEL FLOREY (St Mary Magdalene) *see* Brompton Regis w Upton and Skilgate *B & W*
WITHINGTON (St Christopher) *Man 8* **P** *The Crown*
P-in-c R M GOVENDER
WITHINGTON (St Crispin) *Man 4* **P** *Bp*
P-in-c M A NARUSAWA
WITHINGTON (St John the Baptist) *see* Wrockwardine Deanery *Lich*
WITHINGTON (St Michael and All Angels) *see* Northleach w Hampnett and Farmington etc *Glouc*
WITHINGTON (St Paul) *Man 8* **P** *Trustees*
R S B WOODHEAD, **C** K J STANTON
WITHINGTON (St Peter) w Westhide *Heref 4* **P** *Bp*
P-in-c N C H VARNON
WITHINGTON, LOWER (St Peter) *see* Chelford w Lower Withington *Ches*
WITHLEIGH (St Catherine) *see* Washfield, Stoodleigh, Withleigh etc *Ex*
WITHNELL (St Paul) *see* Heapey St Barnabas and Withnell St Paul *Blackb*
WITHYBROOK (All Saints) *see* Wolvey w Burton Hastings, Copston Magna etc *Cov*
WITHYCOMBE (St Nicholas) *see* Dunster, Carhampton and Withycombe w Rodhuish *B & W*
WITHYCOMBE RALEIGH (St John the Evangelist) (St John in the Wilderness) (All Saints) *Ex 1* **P** *Patr Bd* **TR** F A OSWIN, **TV** S J HOYLE, T C SMYTH
WITHYHAM (St John the Evangelist) *see* Crowborough St Jo *Chich*
WITHYHAM (St Michael and All Angels) *Chich 19* **P** *Earl De la Warr* **P-in-c** G R PARISH
WITHYPOOL (St Andrew) *see* Exford, Exmoor, Hawkridge and Withypool *B & W*
WITHYWOOD (shared church) *Bris 1* **P** *Bp*
V J M CARPENTER

WITLEY (All Saints) *Guildf 4*   **P** *Bp*   **V** B M SHAND
WITLEY, GREAT (St Michael) *see* Shrawley, Witley, Astley and Abberley *Worc*
WITLEY, LITTLE (St Michael) *as above Worc*
WITNESHAM (St Mary) *see* Westerfield and Tuddenham w Witnesham *St E*
WITNEY (St Mary the Virgin) (Holy Trinity) *Ox 8*   **P** *Patr Bd* **TR** C J BUTLAND,   **TV** D R CHILDS,   **Hon C** J H COOK,   **OLM** C TITCOMB
WITTENHAM, LITTLE (St Peter) *see* Dorchester *Ox*
WITTERING (All Saints) *see* Ketton, Collyweston, Easton-on-the-Hill etc *Pet*
WITTERING, EAST (St Anne) *see* Earnley and E Wittering *Chich*
WITTERING, WEST (St Peter and St Paul) and Birdham w Itchenor *Chich 3*   **P** *Bp*   **R** J B WILLIAMS, **Hon C** C J HANKINS,   **NSM** B F HOLBEN
WITTERSHAM (St John the Baptist) w Stone-in-Oxney and Ebony *Cant 13*   **P** *Abp*   **P-in-c** S M HALMSHAW
WITTON (St Helen) *Ches 6*   **P** *Bp*   **V** P C O DAWSON, **C** A L D FRIEND
WITTON (St Margaret) *see* Bacton w Edingthorpe w Witton and Ridlington *Nor*
WITTON (St Margaret) *see* Gt and Lt Plumstead w Thorpe End and Witton *Nor*
WITTON (St Mark) *Blackb 2*   **P** *V Blackb*   **V** vacant (01254) 676615
WITTON, EAST (St John the Evangelist) *see* Middleham w Coverdale and E Witton etc *Ripon*
WITTON, NETHER (St Giles) *Newc 11*   **P** *Ld Chan* **V** G F REVETT
WITTON, WEST (St Bartholomew) *Ripon 4*   **P** *Lord Bolton* **P-in-c** M R MILES
WITTON GILBERT (St Michael and All Angels) *see* Dur N *Dur*
WITTON LE WEAR (St Philip and St James) *see* Hamsterley and Witton-le-Wear *Dur*
WITTON PARK (St Paul) *Dur 6*   **P** *Bp*   **V** M L DENT
WIVELISCOMBE (St Andrew) w Chipstable, Huish Champflower and Clatworthy *B & W 19*   **P** *Bp and A H Trollope-Bellew Esq (jt)*   **R** G A OWEN, **Hon C** A C ARMSTRONG,   **NSM** S M GREEN
WIVELSFIELD (St Peter and St John the Baptist) *Chich 6* **P** *DBP*   **V** C R BREEDS
WIVENHOE (St Mary) *Chelmsf 16*   **P** *Bp*   **R** D G THOMAS, **NSM** B HADFIELD
WIVERTON GROUP *see* Cropwell Bishop w Colston Bassett, Granby etc *S'well*
WIVETON (St Mary) *see* Blakeney w Cley, Wiveton, Glandford etc *Nor*
WIX (St Mary the Virgin) *see* Gt Oakley w Wix and Wrabness *Chelmsf*
WIXFORD (St Milburga) *see* Exhall w Wixford *Cov*
WIXOE (St Leonard) *see* Clare w Poslingford, Cavendish etc *St E*
WOBURN (St Mary) w Eversholt, Milton Bryan, Battlesden and Pottesgrove *St Alb 9*   **P** *Bedf Estates Trustees* **P-in-c** J A HESLOP
WOBURN SANDS (St Michael) *St Alb 9*   **P** *Bp*   **V** N JEFFERY, **NSM** N J PARKINSON
WOBURN SQUARE (Christ Church) *see* Bloomsbury St Geo w Woburn Square Ch Ch *Lon*
WOKING (Christ Church) *Guildf 12*   **P** *Ridley Hall Cam* **V** P J HARWOOD,   **C** C SIMONS,   **NSM** M S SMITH, **OLM** J A M VICKERS
WOKING (St John the Baptist) *Guildf 12*   **P** *V Woking St Pet* **V** G P WILLIAMS,   **C** A C PARTRIDGE
WOKING (St Mary of Bethany) *Guildf 12*   **P** *V Woking Ch Ch* **V** R DERBRIDGE,   **NSM** S R BEAK
WOKING (St Paul) *Guildf 12*   **P** *Ridley Hall Cam* **V** J HUNTER
WOKING (St Peter) *Guildf 12*   **P** *Patr Bd*   **TR** B J GRIMSTER, **TV** I D TWEEDIE-SMITH,   **OLM** M W MOORSE
WOKING, SOUTH Team Ministry *see* Woking St Pet *Guildf*
WOKINGHAM (All Saints) *Ox 16*   **P** *Bp*   **R** D P HODGSON, **C** P H COWAN,   **NSM** C R JAMES, A E KEMP
WOKINGHAM (St Paul) *Ox 16*   **P** *DBP*   **R** R J STILLMAN, **C** R G BURGESS,   **NSM** R G HOLMES
WOKINGHAM (St Sebastian) *Ox 16*   **P** *Bp*   **V** A P MARSDEN, **NSM** A E CLEGG,   **OLM** M V KINGDON, M BRAIN
WOLBOROUGH (St Mary) and Ogwell *Ex 11*   **P** *Earl of Devon and Bp (jt)*   **R** R C CHAMBERLAIN,   **C** G A MILFORD, **NSM** A K CLARKE,   M J FLETCHER
WOLD (St Andrew) *see* Walgrave w Hannington and Wold and Scaldwell *Pet*
WOLD NEWTON (All Saints) *see* Binbrook Gp *Linc*

WOLD NEWTON (All Saints) *see* Burton Fleming w Fordon, Grindale etc *York*
WOLDINGHAM (St Agatha) *see* Caterham *S'wark*
WOLDINGHAM (St Paul) *as above S'wark*
WOLDS, NORTH Group *Linc 6*   **P** *Bp, DBP, and D&C (jt)* **V** M A BATTY
WOLDSBURN *York 10*   **P** *Abp, St Jo Coll Ox, and A J Page Esq (1 turn), and Ld Chan (1 turn)*   **R** J TALLANT, **NSM** C CONNER
WOLFERLOW (St Andrew) *see* Edvin Loach w Tedstone Delamere etc *Heref*
WOLFERTON (St Peter) *see* Sandringham w W Newton and Appleton etc *Nor*
WOLFORD (St Michael and All Angels) w Burmington *Cov 9* **P** *Mert Coll Ox*   **P-in-c** R K SMITH,   **C** H C W PARBURY
WOLLASTON (St James) *Worc 12*   **P** *Bp*   **V** M J WILLOWS
WOLLASTON (St Mary) and Strixton *Pet 6*   **P** *Bp* **V** A SMITH
WOLLASTON, GREAT (All Saints) (St John the Baptist) *Heref 13*   **P** *Bp*   **V** C B BULL
WOLLATON (St Leonard) *S'well 13*   **P** *Lord Middleton* **R** J J LEPINE,   **C** A J MADDOCKS,   **NSM** P D C BROWN
WOLLATON PARK (St Mary) *S'well 13*   **P** *CPAS* **V** A R HOWE,   **NSM** P W WOMAIN
WOLLESCOTE (St Andrew) *Worc 12*   **P** *Bp* **V** R A BROADBENT
WOLSINGHAM (St Mary and St Stephen) and Thornley *Dur 9* **P** *Bp*   **R** M GOODALL
WOLSTANTON (St Margaret) *Lich 9*   **P** *Bp*   **TR** J P EADES, **TV** R M MCINTYRE
WOLSTON (St Margaret) and Church Lawford *Cov 6*   **P** *DBP (2 turns), Bp (1 turn)*   **V** T J PULLEN
WOLVERCOTE (St Peter) w Summertown *Ox 7*   **P** *Patr Bd* **TV** D A E MICHAELS,   **P-in-c** J M RUSHTON, **NSM** W L A PRYOR
WOLVERHAMPTON Pond Lane (Mission Hall) *see* Wolverhampton St Luke *Lich*
WOLVERHAMPTON (St Andrew) *Lich 28*   **P** *Bp* **V** J L SMITH,   **NSM** T B FYFFE
WOLVERHAMPTON (St Jude) *Lich 28*   **P** *CPAS* **V** R E CARTER
WOLVERHAMPTON (St Luke) Blakenhall *Lich 28* **P** *Trustees*   **V** R J ESPIN-BRADLEY,   **C** R K MODY
WOLVERHAMPTON (St Martin) *see* Rough Hills *Lich*
WOLVERHAMPTON (St Matthew) *Lich 28*   **P** *Baldwin Pugh Trustees*   **V** D GHOSH
WOLVERHAMPTON (St Stephen) *Lich 28*   **P** *Bp* **P-in-c** J C OAKES,   **Hon C** M JEAVONS
WOLVERHAMPTON, CENTRAL (St Chad) (St John's in the Square) (St Mark's Centre) (St Peter) *Lich 28*   **P** *Patr Bd* **TR** D W FRITH,   **TV** M Y CLAYTON, D P COOPER, O SMITH, H HINGLEY,   **OLM** E W BROOKES
WOLVERLEY (St John the Baptist) and Cookley *Worc 11* **P** *D&C and Bp (jt)*   **V** G SHILVOCK
WOLVERTON (Holy Trinity) (St George the Martyr) *Ox 25* **P** *Bp*   **R** J M TRIGG
WOLVERTON (St Katherine) *see* Baughurst, Ramsdell, Wolverton w Ewhurst etc *Win*
WOLVERTON (St Mary the Virgin) w Norton Lindsey and Langley *Cov 7*   **P** *Bp*   **P-in-c** R LIVINGSTON
WOLVEY (St John the Baptist) w Burton Hastings, Copston Magna and Withybrook *Cov 5*   **P** *Bp*   **V** T J COLLING
WOLVISTON (St Peter) *see* Grindon, Stillington and Wolviston *Dur*
WOMBOURNE (St Benedict) *see* Smestow Vale *Lich*
WOMBRIDGE (St Mary and St Leonard) *Lich 21* **P** *W J Charlton Meyrick Esq*   **P-in-c** K S EVANS
WOMBWELL (St Mary) (St George) *Sheff 12*   **P** *Trin Coll Cam*   **R** A MAUCHAN,   **C** T C KEIGHTLEY
WOMERSLEY (St Martin) *see* Went Valley *Wakef*
WONERSH (St John the Baptist) w Blackheath *Guildf 2* **P** *Selw Coll Cam*   **V** J R WATTLEY,   **NSM** M P W SPENCER, C V SOWTER,   **OLM** K N BATESON
WONSTON (Holy Trinity) *see* Lower Dever Valley *Win*
WONSTON, SOUTH (St Margaret) Conventional District *Win 7*   **Min** S A FOSTER
WOOBURN (St Paul) *Ox 29*   **P** *Bp*   **P-in-c** M J WALLINGTON, **NSM** R A PAYNE
WOOD DALLING (St Andrew) *see* Reepham, Hackford w Whitwell, Kerdiston etc *Nor*
WOOD DITTON (St Mary) w Saxon Street *Ely 4*   **P** *Duke of Sutherland*   **V** C A SMITH,   **Hon C** L M RUTHERFORD
WOOD END (St Chad) *Cov 1*   **P** *Ld Chan*   **V** V I WOODS
WOOD END (St Michael and All Angels) *see* Baxterley w Hurley and Wood End and Merevale etc *Birm*

WOOD GREEN (St Michael) w Bounds Green (St Gabriel) (St Michael-at-Bowes) *Lon 19* **P** *Patr Bd* **TR** C W COPPEN, **C** J C NEAL
WOOD GREEN (St Paul) *see* Wednesbury St Paul Wood Green *Lich*
WOOD NORTON (All Saints) *see* Twyford, Guist, Bintree, Themelthorpe etc *Nor*
WOOD STREET (St Alban) *see* Worplesdon *Guildf*
WOODBASTWICK (St Fabian and St Sebastian) *see* Ranworth w Panxworth, Woodbastwick etc *Nor*
WOODBERRY DOWN (St Olave) *see* Stoke Newington St Olave *Lon*
WOODBOROUGH (St Mary Magdalene) *see* Pewsey and Swanborough *Sarum*
WOODBOROUGH (St Swithun) *S'well 14* **P** *Bp* P-in-c M J BROCK, **NSM** M N TAYLOR
WOODBRIDGE (St John the Evangelist) and Bredfield *St E 7* **P** *Ch Patr Trust (3 turns), and Ld Chan (1 turn)* **V** D GARDNER
WOODBRIDGE (St Mary the Virgin) *St E 7* **P** *Bp* **R** K S MCCORMACK, **C** A S G PLATTEN
WOODBURY (Holy Cross) *see* Axminster, Chardstock, All Saints etc *Ex*
WOODBURY (St Swithun) *see* Lympstone and Woodbury w Exton *Ex*
WOODBURY SALTERTON (Holy Trinity) *see* Clyst St Mary, Clyst St George etc *Ex*
WOODCHESTER (St Mary) and Brimscombe *Glouc 8* **P** *Simeon's Trustees* **R** S A BOWEN, **NSM** D E STODDART
WOODCHURCH (All Saints) *Cant 10* **P** *Abp* P-in-c D M MADZIMURE
WOODCHURCH (Holy Cross) *Ches 1* **P** *DBP* **R** M A DAVIS, **NSM** P J MILLS
WOODCOTE (St Leonard) *see* Langtree *Ox*
WOODCOTE (St Mark) *see* Purley St Mark *S'wark*
WOODCOTE (St Peter) *see* Lilleshall, Muxton and Sheriffhales *Lich*
WOODCOTT (St James) *see* Hurstbourne Priors, Longparish etc *Win*
WOODDITTON (St Mary) *see* Wood Ditton w Saxon Street *Ely*
WOODEATON (Holy Rood) *see* Ray Valley *Ox*
WOODFORD (Christ Church) *Ches 12* **P** *W A B Davenport Esq* P-in-c F H BARKER
WOODFORD (St Barnabas) *Chelmsf 4* **P** *Bp* **V** A CROSS
WOODFORD (St Mary the Virgin) *see* Gt w Lt Addington and Woodford *Pet*
WOODFORD (St Mary w St Philip and St James) *Chelmsf 4* **P** *Bp* **R** G R SMITH, **C** C A HAWKINS
WOODFORD, SOUTH (Holy Trinity) Hermon Hill *see* Wanstead H Trin Hermon Hill *Chelmsf*
WOODFORD BRIDGE (St Paul) *Chelmsf 4* **P** *R Woodford* **V** J H SPRINGBETT, **NSM** I K MONKS
WOODFORD HALSE (St Mary the Virgin) w Eydon *Pet 1* **P** *Ld Chan (2 turns), Bp (1 turn)* **V** T C OAKLEY
WOODFORD VALLEY (All Saints) *Sarum 13* **P** *Bp* P-in-c A C PHILP, **NSM** P POWELL
WOODFORD WELLS (All Saints) (St Andrew) *Chelmsf 4* **P** *Trustees* **V** P G HARCOURT, **C** S MARSHALL, S P CLARKE, **NSM** D J BLACKLEDGE
WOODGATE VALLEY Conventional District *Birm 2 vacant*
WOODGATE VALLEY (St Francis) *see* Bartley Green *Birm*
WOODGREEN (St Boniface) *see* Fordingbridge and Breamore and Hale etc *Win*
WOODHALL (St James the Great) *Bradf 3* **P** *Bp* **C** G S JAMIESON
WOODHALL, OLD *see* Woodhall Spa Gp *Linc*
WOODHALL SPA Group *Linc 11* **P** *Bp and DBP (jt)* **R** S C WITCOMBE
WOODHAM (All Saints) *Guildf 12* **P** *Bp* **V** I W FORBES, **C** P P LEONARD, **OLM** S V TASSELL
WOODHAM (St Elizabeth of Hungary) *see* Gt Aycliffe *Dur*
WOODHAM FERRERS (St Mary) and Bicknacre *Chelmsf 9* **P** *Lord Fitzwalter* P-in-c M J COTTEE
WOODHAM FERRERS, SOUTH (Holy Trinity) (St Mary) *Chelmsf 9* **P** *Bp* P-in-c P HAWORTH, **C** K R MAGEE
WOODHAM MORTIMER (St Margaret) w Hazeleigh *Chelmsf 11* **P** *Bp* P-in-c M D MOORE
WOODHAM WALTER (St Michael) *Chelmsf 11* **P** *Ch Soc Trust* P-in-c M D MOORE
WOODHAY, EAST (St Martin) and Woolton Hill *Win 6* **P** *Bp* **R** C DALE
WOODHAY, WEST (St Laurence) w Enborne, Hampstead Marshall, Inkpen and Combe *Ox 14* **P** *Bp, D&C Windsor, and J R Henderson Esq (jt)* **R** J F RAMSBOTTOM, **NSM** I J BLYTH
WOODHORN w Newbiggin *Newc 11* **P** *Bp* P-in-c J M GRIEVE

WOODHOUSE (Christ Church) *Wakef 5* **P** *Bp* **V** M GARSIDE
WOODHOUSE (St James) *Sheff 1* **P** *Bp* **V** S BARBER
WOODHOUSE (St Mark) and Wrangthorn *Ripon 7* **P** *DBP* **V** D A CALDER
WOODHOUSE (St Mary in the Elms), Woodhouse Eaves and Swithland *Leic 7* **P** *Ld Chan and DBP (alt)* **R** R A HORTON, **NSM** P SHERIDAN
WOODHOUSE CLOSE (not known) *see* Bishop Auckland Woodhouse Close CD *Dur*
WOODHOUSE EAVES (St Paul) *see* Woodhouse, Woodhouse Eaves and Swithland *Leic*
WOODHOUSE MILL (St James) *see* Woodhouse St Jas *Sheff*
WOODHOUSE PARK (Wm Temple Church) *see* Wythenshawe *Man*
WOODHOUSES (not known) *see* Bardsley *Man*
WOODHOUSES (St John the Divine) *see* Dunham Massey St Marg and St Mark *Ches*
WOODHURST (St John the Baptist) *see* Bluntisham cum Earith w Colne and Woodhurst *Ely*
WOODINGDEAN (Holy Cross) *Chich 2* **P** *Bp* **V** R A BROMFIELD
WOODKIRK (St Mary) *see* W Ardsley *Wakef*
WOODLAND (St John the Baptist) *see* Broadhempston, Woodland, Staverton etc *Ex*
WOODLAND (St John the Evangelist) *see* Broughton and Duddon *Carl*
WOODLAND (St Mary) *see* Lynesack *Dur*
WOODLANDS (All Saints) *Sheff 7* **P** *Bp* **V** M J GODFREY
WOODLANDS (Ascension) *see* Cranborne w Boveridge, Edmondsham etc *Sarum*
WOODLANDS (Mission Chapel) *see* W Meon and Warnford *Portsm*
WOODLANDS (St Katherine) *B & W 4* **P** *DBP* **V** C ALSBURY
WOODLANDS (St Mary) *see* Kemsing w Woodlands *Roch*
WOODLANDS (St Stephen) *see* Welford w Wickham and Gt Shefford, Boxford etc *Ox*
WOODLEIGH (St Mary the Virgin) *see* Modbury, Bigbury, Ringmore w Kingston etc *Ex*
WOODLEY (St John the Evangelist) *Ox 15* **P** *DBP* **TR** A P DOUGLAS, **TV** P C ROBERTS, J P HONOUR, **C** C J REID, **OLM** S L COMERFORD
WOODMANCOTE (Mission Church) *see* Westbourne *Chich*
WOODMANCOTE (St James) *see* Micheldever and E Stratton, Woodmancote etc *Win*
WOODMANCOTE (St Mark) *see* Dursley *Glouc*
WOODMANCOTE (St Peter) *see* Henfield w Shermanbury and Woodmancote *Chich*
WOODMANSEY (St Peter) *see* Beverley Minster *York*
WOODMANSTERNE (St Peter) *S'wark 28* **P** *Ld Chan* **R** N A BARKER
WOODNESBOROUGH (St Mary the Blessed Virgin) w Worth and Staple *Cant 8* **P** *Abp* **V** vacant (01304) 613056
WOODNEWTON (St Mary) *see* Nassington w Yarwell and Woodnewton *Pet*
WOODPLUMPTON (St Anne) *Blackb 9* **P** *V St Michael's-on-Wyre* **V** J V J G WATSON
WOODRISING (St Nicholas) *see* High Oak, Hingham and Scoulton w Wood Rising *Nor*
WOODSEATS (St Chad) *Sheff 2* **P** *Bp* **V** M J PORTER, **C** T P PHENNA
WOODSETTS (St George) *Sheff 5* **P** *Bp* **V** A P FEREDAY
WOODSFORD (St John the Baptist) *see* Moreton and Woodsford w Tincleton *Sarum*
WOODSIDE (St Andrew) w East Hyde *St Alb 14* **P** *D&C* **P-in-c** J DANIEL
WOODSIDE (St James) *Ripon 7* **P** *Bp* **V** C PUCKRIN
WOODSIDE (St Luke) *see* Croydon Woodside *S'wark*
WOODSIDE GREEN (St Andrew) *see* Gt Hallingbury and Lt Hallingbury *Chelmsf*
WOODSIDE PARK (St Barnabas) *Lon 14* **P** *Ch Patr Trust* **V** J S H COLES, **C** H D KENDAL, R G MORTON, S T KIRBY
WOODSTOCK (St Mary Magdalene) *see* Bladon w Woodstock *Ox*
WOODSTON (St Augustine of Canterbury) (Mission Church) *Ely 12* **P** *Bp* **R** W P L GAMMON
WOODTHORPE (St Mark) *S'well 10* **P** *Bp* **V** P J THOMAS
WOODTHORPE (St Peter) *see* Staveley and Barrow Hill *Derby*
WOODTON (All Saints) *see* Hempnall *Nor*
WOODVILLE (St Stephen) *see* Blackfordby and Woodville *Leic*
WOOKEY (St Matthew) *see* Coxley w Godney, Henton and Wookey *B & W*
WOOKEY HOLE (St Mary Magdalene) *see* Wells St Cuth w Wookey Hole *B & W*
WOOL (Holy Rood) and East Stoke *Sarum 8* **P** *Bp (3 turns), Keble Coll Ox (1 turn)* P-in-c G J BUTLER

WOOLACOMBE (St Sabinus)   *see* Ilfracombe, Lee, Woolacombe, Bittadon etc *Ex*
WOOLASTON (St Andrew) w Alvington and Aylburton *Glouc 4*   **P** *DBP and Ld Chan (by turn)*   **R** J E TAYLOR
WOOLAVINGTON (Blessed Virgin Mary) w Cossington and Bawdrip *B & W 14*   **P** *D&C Windsor and J A Church Esq (alt)*   **V** S J BROWN
WOOLBEDING (All Hallows) *Chich 10*   **P** *Rathbone Trust Co and Cowdray Trust (jt)*   **R** A T CUNNINGTON
WOOLBROOK (St Francis of Assisi)   *see* Sidmouth, Woolbrook, Salcombe Regis, Sidbury etc *Ex*
WOOLER (St Mary)   *see* Glendale Gp *Newc*
WOOLFARDISWORTHY (Holy Trinity)   *see* Parkham, Alwington, Buckland Brewer etc *Ex*
WOOLFARDISWORTHY EAST (St Mary)   *see* N Creedy *Ex*
WOOLFOLD (St James) *Man 10*   **P** *R Bury St Mary*   **P-in-c** S EDWARDS
WOOLHAMPTON (St Peter) w Midgham and Beenham Valance *Ox 12*   **P** *Bp, Keble Coll Ox, and CPAS (jt)*   **P-in-c** C H REDGRAVE,   **NSM** E M OKE
WOOLHOPE (St George)   *see* Fownhope w Mordiford, Brockhampton etc *Heref*
WOOLLAND (not known)   *see* Hazelbury Bryan and the Hillside Par *Sarum*
WOOLLEY (All Saints)   *see* Bath St Sav w Swainswick and Woolley *B & W*
WOOLLEY (St Mary)   *see* E Leightonstone *Ely*
WOOLLEY (St Peter) *Wakef 9*   **P** *Bp*   **P-in-c** S P KELLY
WOOLMER GREEN (St Michael)   *see* Welwyn w Ayot St Peter *St Alb*
WOOLPIT (Blessed Virgin Mary) w Drinkstone *St E 10*   **P** *Bp and A Harvie-Clark Esq (alt)*   **P-in-c** P F HOCKING
WOOLSTASTON (St Michael and All Angels)   *see* Dorrington w Leebotwood, Longnor, Stapleton etc *Heref*
WOOLSTHORPE (St James)   *see* Harlaxton Gp *Linc*
WOOLSTON (Ascension) *Liv 12*   **P** *Bp, Adn, and R Warrington (jt)*   **V** B F DRYDEN
WOOLSTON (St Mark) *Win 13*   **P** *Bp*   **V** M J A NEWTON,   **NSM** A R BEVIS
WOOLSTONE (All Saints)   *see* Uffington, Shellingford, Woolstone and Baulking *Ox*
WOOLSTONE (not known)   *see* Woughton *Ox*
WOOLSTONE (St Martin) w Gotherington and Oxenton, and Kemerton *Glouc 16*   **P** *DBP and Croome Estate*   **P-in-c** J WILBY
WOOLTON, MUCH (St Peter) *Liv 4*   **P** *Bp*   **R** C J CROOKS
WOOLTON HILL (St Thomas)   *see* E Woodhay and Woolton Hill *Win*
WOOLVERSTONE (St Michael)   *see* Holbrook, Stutton, Freston, Woolverstone etc *St E*
WOOLVERTON (St Lawrence)   *see* Hardington Vale *B & W*
WOOLWICH (St Mary Magdelene and St Andrew) (St Michael and All Angels) *S'wark 3*   **P** *Bp and Keble Coll Ox (jt)*   **R** J VAN DER VALK,   **OLM** G F H STEPHENS
WOOLWICH (St Thomas)   *see* Charlton *S'wark*
WOOLWICH, NORTH (St John) w Silvertown *Chelmsf 3*   **P** *Bp and Lon Corp (alt)*   **V** vacant (020) 7476 2388
WOONTON (Mission Room)   *see* Eardisley w Bollingham, Willersley, Brilley etc *Heref*
WOORE (St Leonard) and Norton in Hales *Lich 18*   **P** *Bp and CPAS (jt)*   **P-in-c** A B LEIGHTON
WOOSEHILL (Community Church)   *see* Bearwood *Ox*
WOOTTON (St Andrew)   *see* Ulceby Gp *Linc*
WOOTTON (St Edmund) *Portsm 8*   **P** *DBP*   **P-in-c** K F ABBOTT
WOOTTON (St George the Martyr) w Quinton and Preston Deanery *Pet 7*   **P** *Ex Coll Ox and Bp (alt)*   **R** D SCHOLEY
WOOTTON (St Martin)   *see* Elham w Denton and Wootton *Cant*
WOOTTON (St Mary the Virgin) *St Alb 13*   **P** *MMCET*   **V** P M ACKROYD
WOOTTON (St Mary) w Glympton and Kiddington *Ox 9*   **P** *New Coll Ox (2 turns), Bp (1 turn), and Exors E W Towler Esq (1 turn)*   **P-in-c** A P ADAMS
WOOTTON (St Peter) and Dry Sandford *Ox 10*   **P** *Bp and Ox Churches Trust (jt)*   **V** J N COOPER
WOOTTON, NORTH (All Saints) w SOUTH (St Mary) *Nor 20*   **P** *Ld Chan and G Howard Esq (alt)*   **R** B R OAKE,   **C** C A GARROD
WOOTTON, NORTH (St Peter)   *see* Pilton w Croscombe, N Wootton and Dinder *B & W*
WOOTTON BASSETT (St Bartholomew and All Saints) *Sarum 15*   **P** *DBP*   **V** B J GARRATT,   **Hon C** B W HORLOCK
WOOTTON BRIDGE (St Mark)   *see* Wootton *Portsm*
WOOTTON COURTENAY (All Saints)   *see* Selworthy, Timberscombe, Wootton Courtenay etc *B & W*

WOOTTON FITZPAINE (not known)   *see* Golden Cap Team *Sarum*
WOOTTON RIVERS (St Andrew)   *see* Pewsey and Swanborough *Sarum*
WOOTTON ST LAWRENCE (St Lawrence)   *see* Oakley w Wootton St Lawrence *Win*
WOOTTON WAWEN (St Peter) *Cov 7*   **P** *K Coll Cam*   **P-in-c** L G MORTIMER
WORCESTER (St Andrew and All Saints w St Helen)   *see* Worc City St Paul and Old St Martin etc *Worc*
WORCESTER (St Barnabas) (Christ Church) *Worc 6*   **P** *Bp*   **TR** R G JONES,   **TV** J A PARSONS,   **C** D C J BALLARD
WORCESTER (St Clement) (St David) *Worc 3*   **P** *D&C*   **R** vacant (01905) 422675
WORCESTER (St George w St Mary Magdalene) *Worc 6*   **P** *Bp and V Claines (alt)*   **P-in-c** M BADGER
WORCESTER (St John in Bedwardine)   *see* St Jo in Bedwardine *Worc*
WORCESTER (St Martin in the Cornmarket)   *see* Worc City St Paul and Old St Martin etc *Worc*
WORCESTER (St Michael) *Worc 3*   **P** *Bp*   **P-in-c** A J SMITH
WORCESTER (St Stephen)   *see* Barbourne *Worc*
WORCESTER (St Wulstan) *Worc 6*   **P** *Bp*   **V** D MELVILLE,   **NSM** S NALL
WORCESTER CITY (St Paul) (Old St Martin w St Swithun) (St Nicholas and All Saints) *Worc 6*   **P** *Bp and D&C (jt)*   **R** P D A COLLINS,   **C** P D J SWANN
WORCESTER PARK (Christ Church w St Philip) *S'wark 25*   **P** *R Cheam*   **P-in-c** C E ELVEY
WORCESTER SOUTH EAST (St Martin w St Peter) (St Mark in the Cherry Orchard) (Holy Trinity w St Matthew) *Worc 6*   **P** *Patr Bd*   **TR** K A BOYCE,   **TV** J HOUSE, J E FOX, P E JONES, C K SALTWELL,   **NSM** A M WHERRY
WORDSLEY (Holy Trinity) *Worc 10*   **P** *Patr Bd*   **TR** D A PICKEN,   **TV** C T ROGERSON, C WATKINS, C G A WADE,   **NSM** G HODGSON
WORFIELD (St Peter) *Heref 9*   **P** *Trustees of the late J R S Greenshields Esq*   **V** G FLEMING,   **OLM** S C MONDON
WORKINGTON (St John) *Carl 7*   **P** *R Workington*   **V** J M COOK
WORKINGTON (St Michael) *Carl 7*   **P** *Mrs E H S Thornely*   **R** B ROWE
WORKSOP (St Anne) *S'well 6*   **P** *Bp*   **V** F T BEECH
WORKSOP (St John the Evangelist) (Christchurch Centre) *S'well 6*   **P** *CPAS*   **V** N R HOGG,   **C** M C ALVEY
WORKSOP (St Paul) *S'well 6*   **P** *Bp*   **V** B C B BROWN
WORKSOP PRIORY (St Mary and St Cuthbert) *S'well 6*   **P** *St Steph Ho Ox*   **V** A R WAGSTAFF,   **C** S F JONES, S LUMBY
WORLABY (St Clement) *Linc 6*   **P** *DBP*   **V** G A PLUMB
WORLDHAM, EAST (St Mary the Virgin) and WEST (St Nicholas), Hartley Mauditt w Kingsley and Oakhanger *Win 2*   **P** *D&C and Bp (alt)*   **V** P BRADFORD
WORLE (St Martin) (St Mark's Church Centre) *B & W 11*   **P** *Ld Chan*   **TR** N KENT,   **TV** C D BLAKE, M D H FRANKUM
WORLESTON (St Oswald)   *see* Acton and Worleston, Church Minshull etc *Ches*
WORLINGHAM (All Saints) w Barnby and North Cove *St E 14*   **P** *Ld Chan*   **R** S M ELLIS
WORLINGTON (All Saints)   *see* Mildenhall *St E*
WORLINGTON, EAST (St Mary)   *see* Burrington, Chawleigh, Cheldon, Chulmleigh etc *Ex*
WORLINGTON, WEST (St Mary)   *as above* *Ex*
WORLINGWORTH (St Mary) w Southolt, Tannington, Bedfield and Monk Soham *St E 17*   **P** *Lord Henniker, R C Rous Esq and Bp, and DBP (by turn)*   **P-in-c** N D G DEAR
WORMBRIDGE (St Peter)   *see* Ewyas Harold w Dulas, Kenderchurch etc *Heref*
WORMEGAY (St Michael and All Angels and Holy Cross)   *see* Tottenhill w Wormegay *Ely*
WORMHILL (St Margaret) and Peak Forest w Peak Dale and Dove Holes *Derby 4*   **P** *Bp and Duke of Devonshire (jt)*   **P-in-c** D J PHYPERS
WORMINGFORD (St Andrew), Mount Bures and Little Horkesley *Chelmsf 17*   **P** *J J Tufnell Esq, Mrs F Reynolds, and Keble Coll Ox (jt)*   **V** A M WHAWELL
WORMINGHALL (St Peter and St Paul) w Ickford, Oakley and Shabbington *Ox 21*   **P** *Bp and Guild of All So (jt)*   **P-in-c** L M WILFORD,   **NSM** D A R WALLACE, N J WALLACE
WORMINGTON (St Katharine)   *see* Alderton, Gt Washbourne, Dumbleton etc *Glouc*
WORMLEIGHTON (St Peter)   *see* Priors Hardwick, Priors Marston and Wormleighton *Cov*
WORMLEY (Church Room)   *see* Broxbourne w Wormley *St Alb*
WORMLEY (St Laurence)   *as above* *St Alb*

WORMSHILL (St Giles)   *see* Bredgar w Bicknor and Frinsted w Wormshill etc *Cant*

WORPLESDON (St Mary the Virgin) *Guildf 5*   **P** *Eton Coll*   **R** A W BRYANT,   **Hon C** A S LEAK,   **NSM** J A ROBINSON

WORSALL, HIGH AND LOW (All Saints) *York 21*   **P** *Abp* (3 turns), V Northallerton (1 turn)   **V** vacant

WORSBROUGH (St Mary) *Sheff 11*   **P** *DBP*   **P-in-c** R M JARRATT,   **NSM** C KELLEHER

WORSBROUGH (St Thomas) (St James) *Sheff 11*   **P** *Bp and The Crown (alt)*   **V** G R HOLMES

WORSBROUGH COMMON (St Luke) *Sheff 11*   **P** *Bp*   **V** vacant (01226) 282619

WORSLEY (St Mark) *Man 2*   **P** *Bp*   **TR** M R AINSWORTH,   **TV** P BRODY

WORSLEY MESNES (not known)   *see* Wigan St Jas w St Thos *Liv*

WORSTEAD (St Mary), Westwick, Sloley, Swanton Abbot and Scottow *Nor 12*   **P** *DBP, J T D Shaw Esq, D&C, and Bp (by turn)*   **R** A R LONG

WORSTHORNE (St John the Evangelist) *see* Holme-in-Cliviger w Worsthorne *Blackb*

WORTH (St Nicholas) *Chich 7*   **P** *DBP*   **TV** J R BROWN,   V T LEONARD,   **NSM** A F STICKLEY

WORTH (St Peter and St Paul)   *see* Woodnesborough w Worth and Staple *Cant*

WORTH MATRAVERS (St Aldhelm)   *see* Kingston, Langton Matravers and Worth Matravers *Sarum*

WORTH MATRAVERS (St Nicholas)   *as above Sarum*

WORTHAM (St Mary the Virgin)   *see* N Hartismere *St E*

WORTHEN (All Saints) *Heref 13*   **P** *New Coll Ox (8 turns), J J C Coldwell Esq (1 turn), I Chirbury (1 turn)*   **P-in-c** A KNIGHT

WORTHING Christ the King (Christ Church) (Holy Trinity) (St Matthew) *Chich 5*   **P** *Patr Bd*   **TR** G G GUINNESS,   **TV** E J CHITHAM,   **NSM** M E PARGETER, M E PARISH

WORTHING (St Andrew) *Chich 5*   **P** *Keble Coll Ox*   **P-in-c** M J GUDGEON

WORTHING (St George) (Emmanuel) *Chich 5*   **P** *Ch Soc Trust*   **V** D E A MARROW

WORTHING (St Margaret)   *see* N Elmham w Billingford and Worthing *Nor*

WORTHING, WEST (St John the Divine) *Chich 5*   **P** *Bp*   **V** A M MITCHAM

WORTHINGTON (St Matthew)   *see* Breedon cum Isley Walton and Worthington *Leic*

WORTING (St Thomas of Canterbury) *Win 4*   **P** *MMCET*   **R** C J M VAUGHAN

WORTLEY (St Leonard)   *see* Tankersley, Thurgoland and Wortley *Sheff*

WORTLEY, NEW (St Mary's Parish Centre)   *see* Armley w New Wortley *Ripon*

WORTLEY DE LEEDS (St John the Evangelist) *Ripon 6*   **P** *Trustees*   **V** K A P DOWLING

WORTON (Christ Church)   *see* Potterne w Worton and Marston *Sarum*

WORTON, NETHER (St James)   *see* Over w Nether Worton *Ox*

WORTON, OVER (Holy Trinity) w Nether Worton *Ox 5*   **P** *Exors J B Schuster Esq*   **R** vacant

WOTTON (St John the Evangelist) and Holmbury St Mary *Guildf 7*   **P** *Bp and J P M H Evelyn Esq (jt)*   **NSM** P J ROBSON

WOTTON ST MARY WITHOUT (Holy Trinity) *Glouc 5*   **P** *Bp*   **C** A E BRADLEY

WOTTON-UNDER-EDGE (St Mary the Virgin) w Ozleworth, N Nibley and Alderley *Glouc 2*   **P** *Ch Ch Ox and Bp (jt)*   **V** J A C MAY,   **C** A J MARKEY

WOTTON UNDERWOOD (All Saints)   *see* Bernwode *Ox*

WOUGHTON *Ox 25*   **P** *Patr Bd*   **TV** K F MCGARAHAN,   D C BARNES,   **NSM** D J RUDIGER

WOUGHTON-ON-THE-GREEN (St Mary)   *see* Woughton *Ox*

WOULDHAM (All Saints)   *see* Burham and Wouldham *Roch*

WRABNESS (All Saints)   *see* Gt Oakley w Wix and Wrabness *Chelmsf*

WRAGBY Group, The (All Saints) *Linc 11*   **P** *Bp, MMCET, and DBP (jt)*   **R** M N HOLDEN

WRAGBY (St Michael and Our Lady)   *see* Kinsley w Wragby *Wakef*

WRAMPLINGHAM (St Peter and St Paul)   *see* Barnham Broom and Upper Yare *Nor*

WRANGBROOK (St Michael)   *see* Badsworth *Wakef*

WRANGLE (St Mary and St Nicholas)   *see* Old Leake w Wrangle *Linc*

WRANGTHORN (St Augustine of Hippo)   *see* Woodhouse and Wrangthorn *Ripon*

WRATTING, GREAT (St Mary)   *see* Stourhead *St E*

WRATTING, LITTLE (St Mary)   *as above St E*

WRATTING, WEST (St Andrew)   *see* Balsham, Weston Colville, W Wickham etc *Ely*

WRAWBY (St Mary the Virgin)   *see* Brigg, Wrawby and Cadney cum Howsham *Linc*

WRAXALL (All Saints) *B & W 13*   **P** *Trustees*   **R** vacant (01275) 857086

WRAXALL (St Mary)   *see* Melbury *Sarum*

WRAXALL, NORTH (St James)   *see* Colerne w N Wraxall *Bris*

WRAXALL, SOUTH (St James)   *see* Monkton Farleigh, S Wraxall and Winsley *Sarum*

WRAY (Holy Trinity)   *see* E Lonsdale *Blackb*

WRAY, LOW (St Margaret)   *see* Hawkshead and Low Wray w Sawrey and Rusland etc *Carl*

WRAYSBURY (St Andrew)   *see* Riverside *Ox*

WREAKE, UPPER *Leic 3*   **P** *Bp and DBP (jt)*   **V** H M FLINT

WREAY (St Mary)   *see* Dalston w Cumdivock, Raughton Head and Wreay *Carl*

WRECCLESHAM (St Peter) *Guildf 3*   **P** *Bp*   **V** S E FORD

WRENBURY (St Margaret)   *see* Baddiley and Wrenbury w Burleydam *Ches*

WRENINGHAM (All Saints)   *see* Ashwellthorpe, Forncett, Fundenhall, Hapton etc *Nor*

WRENTHAM (St Nicholas)   *see* Sole Bay *St E*

WRENTHORPE (St Anne) *Wakef 12*   **P** *Bp*   **V** P WHITTINGHAM,   **C** E M WOODCOCK

WRESSLE (St John of Beverly)   *see* Howden *York*

WRESTLINGWORTH (St Peter)   *see* Dunton w Wrestlingworth and Eyeworth *St Alb*

WRETHAM (St Ethelbert)   *see* Thetford *Nor*

WRETTON (All Saints)   *see* Northwold and Wretton w Stoke Ferry etc *Ely*

WRIBBENHALL (All Saints) *Worc 11*   **P** *V Kidderminster*   **P-in-c** H HUGHES

WRIGGLE VALLEY, The *Sarum 3*   **P** *Duchy of Cornwall (1 turn), Bp (3 turns)*   **R** P J RINGER,   **OLM** D F BAYLEY

WRIGHTINGTON (St James the Great) *Blackb 4*   **P** *Bp*   **V** R TOWNLEY

WRINGTON (All Saints) w Butcombe *B & W 11*   **P** *SMF*   **R** vacant (01934) 862201

WRITTLE (All Saints) w Highwood *Chelmsf 8*   **P** *New Coll Ox*   **V** D M JONES,   **NSM** M J ASTON

WROCKWARDINE, The Deanery of (St Peter) *Lich 23*   **P** *Patr Bd*   **TR** G HORNER,   **TV** P H CAWTHORNE,   G S GOODWIN,   **C** C W PENN

WROCKWARDINE WOOD (Holy Trinity) *Lich 21*   **P** *Bp*   **P-in-c** M C STAFFORD

WROOT (St Pancras)   *see* Epworth Gp *Linc*

WROSE (St Cuthbert) *Bradf 3*   **P** *The Crown*   **V** P G WALKER,   **C** S IRVINE

WROTHAM (St George) *Roch 10*   **P** *D&C*   **P-in-c** B E HURD

WROUGHTON (St John the Baptist) *Bris 7*   **P** *Bp*   **V** M A JOHNSON,   **C** R M BENNETTS

WROXALL (St John the Evangelist) *Portsm 7*   **P** *Bp*   **V** vacant (01983) 852744

WROXALL (St Leonard)   *see* Hatton w Haseley, Rowington w Lowsonford etc *Cov*

WROXETER (St Mary)   *see* Wrockwardine Deanery *Lich*

WROXHAM (St Mary) w Hoveton St John w Hoveton St Peter and Belaugh *Nor 12*   **P** *Bp*   **R** A D PARSONS,   **OLM** J DODD

WROXTON (All Saints)   *see* Ironstone *Ox*

WYBERTON (St Leodegar) *Linc 21*   **P** *DBP*   **R** A M HUGHES

WYBUNBURY (St Chad) w Doddington (St John) *Ches 15*   **P** *Bp and Sir Evelyn Broughton Bt (jt)*   **V** A A LONG

WYCH, HIGH (St James) and Gilston w Eastwick *St Alb 18*   **P** *V Sawbridgeworth (2 turns), P T S Bowlby Esq (1 turn)*   **P-in-c** R B REYNOLDS

WYCHBOLD (St Mary de Wyche)   *see* Stoke Prior, Wychbold and Upton Warren *Worc*

WYCHE (All Saints)   *see* Malvern St Andr and Malvern Wells and Wyche *Worc*

WYCHLING (St Margaret)   *see* Doddington, Newnham and Wychling *Cant*

WYCHNOR (St Leonard) *Lich 1*   **P** *Personal Reps W H Harrison Esq*   **V** J W ALLAN,   **NSM** P A L MADDOCK

WYCK RISSINGTON (St Laurence)   *see* The Rissingtons *Glouc*

WYCLIFFE (St Mary)   *see* Barningham w Hutton Magna and Wycliffe *Ripon*

WYCOMBE, HIGH (All Saints) (St Peter) *Ox 29*   **P** *Patr Bd*   **TV** M S GURR,   S A WHITMORE,   S A SIMPSON,   D B FOSTER,   P E BRADLEY,   **NSM** P VINEY,   V J BEAUMONT,   J D ARTHUR,   E S CARR,   **OLM** D GOSLING,   M A JACKSON,   R M WOOSTER,   R R HEWSON

WYCOMBE, WEST (St Laurence) (St Paul) w Bledlow Ridge, Bradenham and Radnage *Ox 29* **P** *Bp, DBP, Peache Trustees, and Sir Francis Dashwood Bt (jt)* **P-in-c** N J LACEY, **OLM** E NICHOLSON

WYCOMBE AND CHADWELL (St Mary) *see* Scalford w Goadby Marwood and Wycombe etc *Leic*

WYCOMBE LANE (St Mary) *see* Wooburn *Ox*

WYCOMBE MARSH (St Anne) *see* High Wycombe *Ox*

WYDDIAL (St Giles) *see* Hormead, Wyddial, Anstey, Brent Pelham etc *St Alb*

WYE (St Gregory and St Martin) w Brook *Cant 2* **P** *Abp*
V J S RICHARDSON, **C** S H LILLICRAP, **NSM** L C CLEVELAND

WYE, SOUTH Team Ministry *see* Heref S Wye *Heref*

WYESHAM (St James) *see* Dixton *Heref*

WYFORDBY (St Mary) *see* Waltham on the Wolds, Stonesby, Saxby etc *Leic*

WYKE *see* Win St Matt *Win*

WYKE (Holy Trinity) *see* Bruton and Distr *B & W*

WYKE (St Mark) *Guildf 5* **P** *Bp* **V** P A GODFREY

WYKE (St Mary the Virgin) *Bradf 2* **P** *Bp* **V** *vacant* (01274) 678216

WYKE REGIS (All Saints) *Sarum 4* **P** *D&C* **R** K A HUGO

WYKEHAM (All Saints) *see* Brompton by Sawdon w Hutton Buscel, Snainton etc *York*

WYKEHAM (St Nicholas) *see* Wickham *Portsm*

WYKEHAM: Broughton w North Newington, Epwell w Sibford, Shutford, Swalcliffe, and Tadmarton *Ox 5* **P** *New Coll, Worc Coll, and Lord Saye and Sele (jt)* **R** T WIMBUSH, **NSM** K WALKLATE

WYKEN (Church of Risen Christ) *see* Coventry Caludon *Cov*

WYKEN (Holy Cross) *as above Cov*

WYKEN (St Mary Magdalene) *as above Cov*

WYLAM (St Oswin) *Newc 3* **P** *Bp* **P-in-c** D E CANT

WYLDE GREEN (Emmanuel) *Birm 12* **P** *Bp* **V** R E CRANE

WYLYE (St Mary the Virgin) *see* Wylye and Till Valley *Sarum*

WYLYE AND TILL VALLEY *Sarum 13* **P** *Patr Bd (2 turns), Ld Chan (1 turn)* **TR** D M K DURSTON, **TV** P F SMITH, M W FEARN, **NSM** L E HALLIDAY

WYLYE VALLEY TEAM, UPPER *Sarum 17* **P** *Patr Bd (5 turns), Ld Chan (1 turn)* **TR** H G HOSKINS, **C** H BEGLEY, **NSM** G I DUFF

WYMERING (St Peter and St Paul) *see* Widley w Wymering *Portsm*

WYMESWOLD (St Mary) and Prestwold w Hoton *Leic 7* **P** *S J Packe-Drury-Lowe Esq and Bp (by turn)* **P-in-c** J S HOPEWELL

WYMINGTON (St Lawrence) w Podington *St Alb 15* **P** *R M Orlebar Esq (1 turn), DBP (3 turns)* **P-in-c** R A EVENS

WYMONDHAM (St Mary and St Thomas) *Nor 7* **P** *Bp* **V** M W SMITH, **C** R W NICHOLS, **R** M EASTWOOD

WYMONDHAM (St Peter) w Edmondthorpe, Buckminster w Sewstern, Coston and Garthorpe *Leic 3* **P** *Ld Chan and Sir Lyonel Tollemache Bt (alt)* **P-in-c** R M SAMUEL

WYMONDLEY, GREAT (St Mary the Virgin) and LITTLE (St Mary the Virgin) *St Alb 4* **P** *Bp and MMCET (jt)* **P-in-c** I S TATTUM

WYMYNSWOLD (St Margaret) *see* Nonington w Wymynswold and Goodnestone etc *Cant*

WYNYARD PARK (Chapel) *see* Grindon, Stillington and Wolviston *Dur*

WYRE PIDDLE (not known) *see* Fladbury w Wyre Piddle and Moor etc *Worc*

WYRESDALE, OVER (Christ Church) *see* Dolphinholme w Quernmore and Over Wyresdale *Blackb*

WYRLEY, GREAT (St Mark) *Lich 3* **P** *R Cannock*
V R P OAKLEY, **C** A M JONES, J TRANTER, **OLM** M J PRICE

WYSALL (Holy Trinity) *see* Willoughby-on-the-Wolds w Wysall and Widmerpool *S'well*

WYTHALL (no church) *Birm 6* **P** *R Kings Norton* **V** *vacant* (01564) 823381

WYTHAM (All Saints) *see* N Hinksey and Wytham *Ox*

WYTHBURN (not known) *see* St John's-in-the-Vale, Threlkeld and Wythburn *Carl*

WYTHENSHAWE Lawton Moor (St Michael and All Angels) *see* Lawton Moor *Man*

WYTHENSHAWE (St Francis of Assisi) (St Luke) (St Martin) (St Richard of Chichester) (William Temple Church) *Man 8* **P** *Patr Bd* **TR** G BABB, **TV** A J HODGSON, A PILKINGTON, S E HERBERT, **C** J D HUGHES, S L MILLER, J S A LAW, **NSM** O E MARLOW

WYTHER (Venerable Bede) *Ripon 6* **P** *Bp* **V** G W COOPER

WYTHOP (St Margaret) *see* Cockermouth w Embleton and Wythop *Carl*

WYVERSTONE (St George) *see* Bacton w Wyverstone, Cotton and Old Newton etc *St E*

WYVILL (St Catherine) *see* Harlaxton Gp *Linc*

YAFFORTH (All Saints) *see* Ainderby Steeple w Yafforth and Kirby Wiske etc *Ripon*

YALDING (St Peter and St Paul) w Collier Street *Roch 8* **P** *Ld Chan* **V** C J REED

YANWORTH (St Michael) *see* Chedworth, Yanworth and Stowell, Coln Rogers etc *Glouc*

YAPHAM (St Martin) *see* Barmby Moor Gp *York*

YAPTON (St Mary) *see* Clymping and Yapton w Ford *Chich*

YARCOMBE (St John the Baptist) *see* Kilmington, Stockland, Dalwood, Yarcombe etc *Ex*

YARDLEY (St Cyprian) Hay Mill *Birm 13* **P** *Bp* **V** *vacant* 0121-773 1278

YARDLEY (St Edburgha) *Birm 13* **P** *St Pet Coll Ox* **P-in-c** J A OMOYAJOWO

YARDLEY (St Lawrence) *see* Ardeley *St Alb*

YARDLEY, SOUTH (St Michael and All Angels) *Birm 13* **P** *Bp* **V** C G GRAHAM, **NSM** G R PIKE

YARDLEY GOBION (St Leonard) *see* Potterspury w Furtho and Yardley Gobion etc *Pet*

YARDLEY HASTINGS (St Andrew), Denton and Grendon w Castle Ashby and Whiston *Pet 7* **P** *Marquess of Northampton and Bp (alt)* **R** D L SPOKES

YARDLEY WOOD (Christ Church) *Birm 5* **P** *Bp* **V** J G RICHARDS

YARKHILL (St John the Baptist) *see* Ledbury *Heref*

YARLINGTON (Blessed Virgin Mary) *see* Camelot Par *B & W*

YARM (St Mary Magdalene) *York 21* **P** *Abp* **R** B C GURD, **C** J C ROUNDTREE

YARMOUTH (St James) *Portsm 8* **P** *Keble Coll Ox* **R** M E C WHATSON, **Hon C** D L GAMBLE, **NSM** D K BELLAMY, G M HURT

YARMOUTH, GREAT (St John) (St Nicholas) (St Paul) (St Luke) (St Mary) *Nor 6* **P** *Patr Bd* **TR** M S WOODS, **TV** M I KNOWLES, **OLM** A W BOWLES, J M GREENWAY

YARNFIELD (Mission Room St Barnabas) *see* Swynnerton and Tittensor *Lich*

YARNSCOMBE (St Andrew) *see* Newton Tracey, Horwood, Alverdiscott etc *Ex*

YARNTON (St Bartholomew) w Begbroke and Shipton on Cherwell *Ox 9* **P** *BNC Ox, Duke of Marlborough, and C Wolfson Trust (jt)* **R** E CRAIG, **NSM** G G WRIGHT

YARPOLE (St Leonard) *see* Leominster *Heref*

YARWELL (St Mary Magdalene) *see* Nassington w Yarwell and Woodnewton *Pet*

YATE New Town (St Mary) *Bris 5* **P** *Bp* **TR** D B HARREX, **TV** I P MACFARLANE, T ASHWORTH, **Hon C** D T R WILCOX, V ASHWORTH, **NSM** C A COSTER

YATELEY (St Peter) and Eversley *Win 5* **P** *Bp* **R** N D BEAMER, **C** I S WHITHAM, M W SAUNDERS

YATESBURY (All Saints) *see* Oldbury *Sarum*

YATTENDON (St Peter and St Paul) *see* Hermitage *Ox*

YATTON (All Saints) *see* Ledbury *Heref*

YATTON KEYNELL (St Margaret) *see* By Brook *Bris*

YATTON MOOR (Blessed Virgin Mary) *B & W 13* **P** *DBF* **TR** I M HUBBARD, **TV** C J HORDER, J C ANDREWS, **C** W M MITCHELL, **NSM** C M HORSEMAN, C R LLEWELYN-EVANS

YAVERLAND (St John the Baptist) *see* Brading w Yaverland *Portsm*

YAXHAM (St Peter) *see* Mattishall w Mattishall Burgh, Welborne etc *Nor*

YAXLEY (St Mary the Virgin) *see* Gislingham and Thorndon *St E*

YAXLEY (St Peter) and Holme w Conington *Ely 12* **P** *Ld Chan (2 turns), J H B Heathcote Esq (1 turn)* **Hon C** G LIMBRICK

YEADON (St Andrew) *Bradf 4* **P** *Bp* **P-in-c** P J SUTCLIFFE

YEADON (St John the Evangelist) *Bradf 4* **P** *R Guiseley w Esholt* **V** H M WIGLEY, **NSM** J L SMITH

YEALAND CONYERS (St John the Evangelist) *see* Warton St Oswald w Yealand Conyers *Blackb*

YEALMPTON (St Bartholomew) and Brixton *Ex 20* **P** *D&C Windsor and Bp (jt)* **V** D ARNOTT

YEARSLEY (Holy Trinity) *see* Crayke w Brandsby and Yearsley *York*

YEAVELEY (Holy Trinity) *see* Alkmonton, Cubley, Marston, Montgomery etc *Derby*

YEDINGHAM (St John the Baptist) *see* Buckrose Carrs *York*

YELDEN (St Mary) *see* The Stodden Churches *St Alb*

YELDHAM, GREAT (St Andrew) *see* Upper Colne *Chelmsf*

YELDHAM, LITTLE (St John the Baptist) *as above Chelmsf*

YELFORD (St Nicholas and St Swithin) *see* Lower Windrush *Ox*

YELLING (Holy Cross) *see* Papworth *Ely*

YELVERTOFT (All Saints) *see* Crick and Yelvertoft w Clay Coton and Lilbourne *Pet*

YELVERTON (St Mary) *see* Thurton *Nor*

YELVERTON (St Paul), Meavy, Sheepstor and Walkhampton
 Ex 24 **P** *Patr Bd* **TR** R H TEBBS, **NSM** J W M WEIR,
 M SALMON, N S SHUTT
YEOFORD CHAPEL (Holy Trinity) *see* Crediton, Shobrooke
 and Sandford etc *Ex*
YEOVIL (Holy Trinity) w Barwick *B & W 7* **P** *Ms Y L Bennett*
 and Ms R S Mullen (1 turn), The Crown (3 turns)
 R T J COOK, **C** D R GENT
YEOVIL (St Andrew) (St John the Baptist) w Kingston Pitney
 B & W 7 **P** *Mrs S W Rawlins (3 turns), DBP (1 turn)*
 R I G HUGHES, **C** M R CAMPBELL, **NSM** E N BANGAY
YEOVIL (St Michael and All Angels) *B & W 7* **P** *Bp*
 V M D ELLIS, **C** N A F MCKINTY, **NSM** C Y JONES
YEOVIL (St Peter) *see* Preston Plucknett *B & W*
YEOVIL MARSH (All Saints) *see* Tintinhull w Chilthorne
 Domer, Yeovil Marsh etc *B & W*
YETMINSTER (St Andrew) *see* Wriggle Valley *Sarum*
YIEWSLEY (St Matthew) *Lon 24* **P** *V Hillingdon*
 V S A GROOM
YOCKLETON (Holy Trinity) *Heref 13* **P** *Bp* **R** C B BULL
YORK Acomb (St Aidan) *see* Acomb St Steph *York*
YORK (All Saints) *see* Huntington *York*
YORK (All Saints) North Street *York 7* **P** *D&C*
 P-in-c B L GANT
YORK (All Saints) Pavement w St Crux and St Michael
 Spurriergate *York 7* **P** *Abp* **R** *vacant* (01904) 631116
YORK (Christ Church) *see* Heworth Ch Ch *York*
YORK (Holy Redeemer) *see* Acomb H Redeemer *York*
YORK (Holy Trinity) *see* Heworth H Trin *York*
YORK (Holy Trinity) Micklegate *see* Micklegate H Trin and
 Bishophill Junior St Mary *York*
YORK (James the Deacon) *see* Acomb Moor *York*
YORK (St Barnabas) *York 7* **P** *CPAS*
 P-in-c K BURNETT-HALL
YORK (St Chad) *York 7* **P** *Abp* **P-in-c** S R STANLEY
YORK (St Clement w St Mary) Bishophill Senior *York 7* **P** *Abp*
 R *vacant*
YORK (St Denys) *York 7* **P** *Abp* **P-in-c** D J GOODHEW

YORK (St Edward the Confessor) *see* Dringhouses *York*
YORK (St Helen) Stonegate w (St Martin) Coney Street *York 7*
 P *Abp* **V** A C HODGE
YORK (St Hilda) *York 7* **P** *Abp* **V** A P G MORGAN
YORK (St Lawrence w St Nicholas) *York 7* **P** *D&C* **V** *vacant*
 (01904) 411916
YORK (St Luke) *York 7* **P** *Abp* **V** *vacant* (01904) 630354
YORK (St Martin-cum-Gregory) *see* Micklegate H Trin and
 Bishophill Junior St Mary *York*
YORK (St Mary) Bishophill Junior *as above York*
YORK (St Michael-le-Belfrey) (St Cuthbert) *York 7* **P** *Abp*
 V R W SIMPSON, **C** I G BIRKINSHAW, R V JACKSON,
 NSM W J ROBERTS
YORK (St Olave w St Giles) *York 7* **P** *Abp* **V** A C HODGE,
 NSM S A WHITTINGTON
YORK (St Oswald) *see* Fulford *York*
YORK (St Paul) Holgate Road *York 7* **P** *CPAS* **R** J M A LEE
YORK (St Philip and St James) *see* Clifton *York*
YORK (St Stephen) *see* Acomb St Steph *York*
YORK (St Thomas w St Maurice) *York 7* **P** *Abp*
 P-in-c S A WHITTINGTON
YORK (St Wulstan) *see* Heworth H Trin *York*
YORKLEY, LOWER (St Luke's Church Centre) *see* Parkend
 and Viney Hill *Glouc*
YORKTOWN (St Michael) *see* Camberley St Mich Yorktown
 Guildf
YOULGREAVE (All Saints), Middleton, Stanton-in-Peak and
 Birchover *Derby 2* **P** *Duke of Devonshire and N B B*
 Davie-Thornhill Esq (jt) **P-in-c** O J POST
YOXALL (St Peter) *Lich 1* **P** *Bp* **P-in-c** J G LISTER
YOXFORD (St Peter) and Peasenhall w Sibton *St E 19* **P** *Bp*
 (1 turn), Exors Lt-Col J A Brooke and CPAS (1 turn)
 P-in-c R J GINN, **C** R S SMITH
ZEAL, SOUTH (St Mary) *see* S Tawton and Belstone *Ex*
ZEAL MONACHORUM (St Peter) *Ex 2* **P** *DBP*
 R J C HALL
ZEALS (St Martin) *see* Upper Stour *Sarum*
ZENNOR (St Senera) *Truro 5* **P** *Bp* **P-in-c** J M PILGRIM

WELSH BENEFICES AND CHURCHES

An index of benefices of the Church in Wales (shown in bold type), together with entries for churches and other licensed places of worship. Where the church name is the same as the benefice (or the first place name in the benefice), the church entry is omitted. Church dedications are indicated in brackets.

The benefice entry gives the full legal name, followed by the diocese, its deanery number (p. 952), and the name(s) and appointment(s) of the clergy serving there (if there are none, the telephone number of the parsonage house is given). The following are the main abbreviations used; for others see the full list of abbreviations.

C	Curate	P-in-c	Priest-in-charge
C-in-c	Curate-in-charge	Par Dn	Parish Deacon
Dn-in-c	Deacon-in-charge	R	Rector
Dss	Deaconess	TM	Team Minister
Hon C	Honorary Curate	TR	Team Rector
Hon Par Dn	Honorary Parish Deacon	TV	Team Vicar
NSM	Non-stipendiary Minister	V	Vicar

ABBEY CWMHIR (St Mary the Virgin)   see Llanbadarn Fawr, Llandegley and Llanfihangel etc S & B
ABER (St Bodfan)   see Llanfairfechan w Aber Ban
ABERAERON (Holy Trinity)   see Henfynyw w Aberaeron and Llanddewi Aberarth St D
ABERAMAN (St Margaret) and Abercwmboi w Cwmaman Llan 9   **V** D C WAY
ABERAVON (St Mary) (St Paul) (Holy Trinity) Llan 7   **TR** S P KIRK,   **TV** M D GABLE, J J JENKINS,   **C** M R D THOMAS
ABERBARGOED (St Peter)   see Bedwellty Mon
ABERCANAID (St Peter) Llan 10   **P-in-c** G G FOSTER
ABERCARN and Cwmcarn Mon 7   **V** J J WILKINS,   **NSM** M REDWOOD
ABERCRAF (St David)   see Cwmtawe Uchaf S & B
ABERCWMBOI   see Aberaman and Abercwmboi w Cwmaman Llan
ABERCYNON (St Donat) (St Gwynno) Llan 9   **V** P S WEEDING
ABERDARE (St Fagan) Llan 9   **V** P J BENNETT
ABERDARE (St John the Baptist) (St Elvan) (St Matthew) (St John the Evangelist) Llan 9   **V** R E DAVIES
ABERDARON (St Hywyn) w Rhiw and Llanfaelrhys w Llangwnnadl and Penllech Ban 11   **R** P D JAMES,   **P-in-c** E D DAVIES
ABERDYFI (St Peter)   see Llanegryn w Aberdyfi w Tywyn Ban
ABEREDW (St Cewydd) w Llandeilo Graban and Llanbadarn-y-Garreg w Crickadarn and Gwenddwr S & B 2   **V** T J WILLIAMS,   **NSM** M C M LEWIS
ABERERCH (St Cawrdaf)   see Denio w Abererch Ban
ABERFFRAW (St Beuno)   see Trefdraeth w Aberffraw, Llangadwaladr etc Ban
ABERGAVENNY (Holy Trinity) (Christ Church) Mon 1   **V** R P MATTHEWS,   **OLM** C R WALTERS
ABERGAVENNY (St Mary) (Christchurch) w Llanwenarth Citra Mon 1   **V** J H WINSTON,   **Par Dn** M C G LANE
ABERGELE (St Michael) (St David) St As 6   **V** S T GRIFFITHS
ABERGORLECH (St David)   see Brechfa w Abergorlech etc St D
ABERGWILI (St David) w Llanfihangel-uwch-Gwili and Capel-y-Groes St D 11   **V** L L RICHARDSON
ABERGWYNFI (St Thomas)   see Glyncorrwg and Upper Afan Valley Llan
ABERGWYNGREGYN (St Bodfan)   see Llanfairfechan w Aber Ban
ABERGYNOLWYN   see Llanegryn w Aberdyfi w Tywyn Ban
ABERHAFESP (St Gwynog)   see Newtown w Llanllwchaiarn w Aberhafesp St As
ABERKENFIG (St John)   see St Brides Minor w Bettws w Aberkenfig Llan
ABERNANT (St Lucia)   see Tre-lech a'r Betws w Abernant and Llanwinio St D
ABERNANT (St Matthew)   see Aberdare Llan
ABERPERGWM (St Cadoc) and Blaengwrach Llan 8   **V** P A LEWIS
ABERPORTH (St Cynwyl) w Tremain w Blaenporth and Betws Ifan St D 6   **R** J O ESAU
ABERSYCHAN and Garndiffaith Mon 10   **P-in-c** J A V FLORANCE
ABERTILLERY (St Michael) w Cwmtillery w Six Bells Mon 8   **V** M J BEASLEY,   **C** P W S KING
ABERTYSSWG (St Paul)   see New Tredegar Mon
ABERYSKIR (St Mary and St Cynidr)   see Trallwng w Bettws Penpont w Aberyskir etc S & B
ABERYSTWYTH (St Michael) (Holy Trinity) (St Mary) (St Anne) St D 10   **R** S R BELL,   **TV** C HUGHES, I H AVESON, A F HERRICK
AFAN VALE   see Glyncorrwg and Upper Afan Valley Llan

ALLTMAWR (St Mauritius)   see Builth and Llanddewi'r Cwm w Llangynog etc S & B
ALLTWEN (St John the Baptist)   see Cilybebyll Llan
AMBLESTON (St Mary)   see Spittal w Trefgarn and Ambleston w St Dogwells St D
AMLWCH (St Eleth) (St Peter) (St Gwenllwyfo) (St Eilian) Ban 7   **P-in-c** D J WILLIAMS
AMMANFORD (All Saints)   see Betws w Ammanford St D
AMMANFORD (St Michael)   as above St D
AMROTH (St Elidyr)   see St Issell's and Amroth St D
ANGLE (St Mary)   see Castlemartin w Warren and Angle etc St D
ARTHOG (St Catherine) w Fairbourne w Llangelynnin w Rhoslefain Ban 12   **R** N FAIRLAMB
BAGILLT (St Mary) (St Peter) St As 4   **V** B TAYLOR
BAGLAN (St Catherine) (St Baglan) Llan 7   **V** D W LEWIS
BALA (Christ Church)   see Llanycil w Bala and Frongoch and Llangower etc St As
BANGOR (Cathedral of St Deiniol) (St Mary) (Eglwys y Groes) (St James) (St David) (St Peter) Ban 5   **R** A J HAWKINS,   **TV** L J PERRY, S H JONES, A W COLEMAN
BANGOR MONACHORUM (St Dunawd) and Worthenbury St As 11   **R** vacant (01978) 780608
BANGOR TEIFI (St David)   see Llandysul w Bangor Teifi w Henllan etc St D
BARGOED (St Gwladys) and Deri w Brithdir Llan 1   **V** A P BOOKLESS,   **C** S F ATKINSON-JONES
BARMOUTH   see Llanaber w Caerdeon Ban
BARRY (All Saints) (St John w St Baruc) Llan 5   **R** J G D OEPPEN,   **C** I K REES
BARRY (St Paul)   see Merthyr Dyfan Llan
BASSALEG (St Basil) Mon 6   **TR** J S WILLIAMS,   **TV** P D CROCKER,   **C** N R TOTTLE,   **OLM** G M JAMES
BATTLE (St Cynog)   see Trallwng w Bettws Penpont w Aberyskir etc S & B
BEAUFORT (St Andrew)   see Ebbw Vale Mon
BEAUFORT (St David)   as above Mon
BEAUMARIS (St Mary and St Nicholas) (St Catherine) (St Seiriol) (St Cawrdaf) (St Michael) Ban 6   **R** vacant (01248) 810146
BEDDGELERT (St Mary)   see Penrhyndeudraeth w Llanfrothen w Beddgelert Ban
BEDLINOG (St Cadoc)   see Treharris w Bedlinog Llan
BEDLINOG (St Mary)   as above Llan
BEDWAS (St Barrwg) and Rudry Mon 6   **R** P M WINCHESTER
BEDWELLTY (St Sannan) Mon 7   **V** J M T CARLYON,   **Par Dn** K HEMMINGS
BEGELLY (St Mary) w Ludchurch and Crunwere St D 4   **R** D G BATE
BEGUILDY (St Michael and All Angels)   see Beguildy and Heyope and Llangynllo and Bleddfa S & B
BEGUILDY (St Michael and All Angels) (St Peter) and Heyope and Llangynllo and Bleddfa S & B 5   **P-in-c** R HART
BENLLECH (St Andrew)   see Llanfair Mathafarn Eithaf w Llanbedrgoch Ban
BERRIEW (St Beuno) St As 10   **V** J B THELWELL
BERSE (Parish Church)   see Bwlchgwyn w Berse w Southsea St As
BETTISFIELD (St John the Baptist)   see Hanmer, Bronington, Bettisfield, Tallarn Green St As
BETTWS   see Trallwng w Bettws Penpont w Aberyskir etc S & B
BETTWS (St David)   see St Brides Minor w Bettws w Aberkenfig Llan
BETTWS (St David) Mon 9   **R** vacant (01633) 855193
BETTWS CHAPEL   see Llantilio Pertholey w Bettws Chpl etc Mon
BETTWS DISSERTH (St Mary)   see Llanelwedd w Llanfaredd w Llansantffraed etc S & B

BETTWS NEWYDD (not known) w Trostrey and Kemeys Commander and Llanfihangel Gobion w Llanfair Kilgeddin *Mon 5*   R T G CLEMENT

BETWS (Holy Trinity)   *see* Glasbury and Llowes w Clyro and Betws *S & B*

BETWS (St David) w Ammanford *St D 13*   V A TEALE, D BOWEN,   C P H DAVIES

BETWS BLEDRWS (St Bledrws or St Michael) *St D 9*   R *vacant*

BETWS CEDEWAIN (St Beuno) and Tregynon and Llanwyddelan *St As 7*   V G K MARSHALL

BETWS GARMON (St Garmon)   *see* Llanbeblig w Caernarfon and Betws Garmon etc *Ban*

BETWS GWERFUL GOCH (St Mary) w Llangwm, Gwyddelwern and Llawrybetws *St As 12*   NSM D EVANS

BETWS LEUCU (St Lucia)   *see* Llangeitho and Blaenpennal w Betws Leucu etc *St D*

BETWS-Y-COED (St Mary) and Capel Curig w Penmachno w Dolwyddelan *Ban 2*   P-in-c K L JONES

BETWS-YN-RHOS (St Michael) w Petryal *St As 6*   R J R MATTHIAS

BEULAH   *see* Llanwrtyd w Llanddulas in Tir Abad etc *S & B*

BIRCHGROVE (St John)   *see* Llansamlet *S & B*

BISHOPSTON (St Teilo) *S & B 8*   R C G LEE

BISHTON (St Cadwaladr) *Mon 4*   V B M W STARES, NSM D E COLLINGBOURNE

BISTRE (Emmanuel) (All Saints) (St Cecilia) *St As 16*   V M W HILL,   C A ANTHAPURUSHA, P A WALKER

BLACKWOOD (St Margaret) *Mon 7*   V D JONES

BLAENAU FFESTINIOG (St David)   *see* Ffestiniog w Blaenau Ffestiniog *Ban*

BLAENAVON (St Peter) w Capel Newydd *Mon 10*   V J S BRAY

BLAENCELYN (St David)   *see* Llangrannog w Llandysiliogogo w Penbryn *St D*

BLAENGARW (St James)   *see* Pontycymer and Blaengarw *Llan*

BLAENGWRACH (St Mary)   *see* Aberpergwm and Blaengwrach *Llan*

BLAENLLECHAU (St Thomas)   *see* Ferndale w Maerdy *Llan*

BLAENPENNAL (St David)   *see* Llangeitho and Blaenpennal w Betws Leucu etc *St D*

BLAENPORTH (St David)   *see* Aberporth w Tremain w Blaenporth and Betws Ifan *St D*

BLAINA (St Peter) and Nantyglo *Mon 8*   R R L HEWETT, Par Dn C MORGAN

BLEDDFA (St Mary Magdalene)   *see* Beguildy and Heyope and Llangynllo and Bleddfa *S & B*

BLETHERSTON (St Mary)   *see* Llawhaden w Bletherston and Llanycefn *St D*

BODEDERN (St Edern) w Llanfaethlu *Ban 3*   P-in-c P MCLEAN

BODELWYDDAN (St Margaret) *St As 1*   V G B HUGHES,   C P A RIMMER

BODEWRYD (St Mary)   *see* Llanfechell w Bodewryd w Rhosbeirio etc *Ban*

BODFARI (St Stephen)   *see* Caerwys and Bodfari *St As*

BODWROG (St Twrog)   *see* Llandrygarn w Bodwrog and Heneglwys etc *Ban*

BONTDDU   *see* Llanaber w Caerdeon *Ban*

BONVILSTON (St Mary)   *see* St Nicholas w Bonvilston and St George-super-Ely *Llan*

BONYMAEN (St Margaret)   *see* Glantawe *S & B*

BORTH (St Matthew) and Eglwys-fach w Llangynfelyn *St D 10*   V G A DAVIES

BOSHERSTON (St Michael)   *see* Pembroke Gp *St D*

BOTWNNOG (St Beuno) w Bryncroes (St Mary) *Ban 11*   R P D JAMES,   NSM S M M WILLIAMS

BOUGHROOD (St Cynog)   *see* Llandefalle and Llyswen w Boughrood etc *S & B*

BOULSTON   *see* Slebech and Uzmaston w Boulston *St D*

BRAWDY (St David)   *see* Dewisland *St D*

BRECHFA (St Teilo) w Abergorlech and Llanfihangel Rhos-y-corn *St D 14*   P-in-c G A SYKES

BRECON (Cathedral of St John the Evangelist) (St Mary) w Llanddew *S & B 1*   V J D E DAVIES

BRECON (St David) w Llanspyddid and Llanilltyd *S & B 1*   V D E THOMAS

BRIDELL (St David)   *see* Cilgerran w Bridell and Llantwyd *St D*

BRIDGEND (St Illtud)   *see* Newcastle *Llan*

BRIDGEND (St Mary)   *see* Coity w Nolton *Llan*

BRIGHTON, NEW (St James)   *see* Mold *St As*

BRITHDIR (St David)   *see* Bargoed and Deri w Brithdir *Llan*

BRITHDIR (St Mark)   *see* Dolgellau w Llanfachreth and Brithdir etc *Ban*

BRITHDIR (St Mary)   *see* Llanrhaeadr-ym-Mochnant etc *St As*

BRITON FERRY (St Clement)   *see* Llansawel, Briton Ferry *Llan*

BRONGWYN (St Mary)   *see* Newcastle Emlyn w Llandyfriog etc *St D*

BRONINGTON (Holy Trinity)   *see* Hanmer, Bronington, Bettisfield, Tallarn Green *St As*

BRONLLYS (St Mary) w Llanfilo *S & B 4*   V A J R THOMAS

BRONWYDD (St Celynnin)   *see* Llanpumsaint w Llanllawddog *St D*

BROUGHTON (St Mary)   *see* Hawarden *St As*

BROUGHTON (St Paul) (St Peter) *St As 15*   V J G AYLWARD

BRYMBO (St Mary) *St As 15*   V R P BILLINGSLEY

BRYN (St Tydfil)   *see* Llangynwyd w Maesteg *Llan*

BRYNAMAN (St Catherine) w Cwmllynfell *St D 13*   V *vacant* (01269) 822275

BRYNCETHIN   *see* St Brides Minor w Bettws w Aberkenfig *Llan*

BRYNCOEDIFOR (St Paul)   *see* Dolgellau w Llanfachreth and Brithdir etc *Ban*

BRYNCROES (St Mary)   *see* Botwnnog w Bryncroes *Ban*

BRYNEGLWYS (St Tysilio) *St As 12*   V *vacant*

BRYNFORD (St Michael)   *see* Gorsedd w Brynford, Ysgeifiog and Whitford *St As*

BRYNGWRAN   *see* Valley w Llechylched and Caergeiliog *Ban*

BRYNGWYN (St Mary)   *see* Newcastle Emlyn w Llandyfriog etc *St D*

BRYNGWYN (St Michael) and Newchurch and Llanbedr Painscastle and Llanddewi Fach *S & B 2*   NSM H J FISHER

BRYNGWYN (St Peter)   *see* Raglan w Llandenny and Bryngwyn *Mon*

BRYNMAWR (St Mary the Virgin) *S & B 3*   V R T GREY

BRYNNA   *see* Llanharan w Peterston-super-Montem *Llan*

BRYNYMAEN (Christ Church)   *see* Colwyn *St As*

BUCKHOLT   *see* Penallt and Trellech *Mon*

BUCKHOLT (St John the Baptist)   *see* Monmouth w Overmonnow etc *Mon*

BUCKLEY (St Matthew) (Good Shepherd) *St As 16*   V J T HUGHES

BUILTH (St Mary) and Llanddewi'r Cwm w Llangynog and Maesmynis and Llanynys and Alltmawr *S & B 2*   V N D HALL, NSM P J MORRIS

BULWARK (St Christopher)   *see* Chepstow *Mon*

BURRY PORT (St Mary) and Pwll *St D 12*   V G D HARRIES

BURTON (St Mary) and Rosemarket *St D 5*   R *vacant* (01646) 600275

BUTE TOWN (St Aidan)   *see* Pontlottyn w Fochriw *Llan*

BUTTINGTON (All Saints)   *see* Guilsfield w Buttington *St As*

BWLCH (All Saints)   *see* Llyn Safaddan *S & B*

BWLCHGWYN (Christ Church)   *see* Bwlchgwyn w Berse w Southsea *St As*

BWLCHGWYN (Christ Church) w Berse w Southsea *St As 15*   V D T B LEWIS

BWLCHYCIBAU (Christ Church)   *see* Llanfyllin and Bwlchycibau *St As*

BYLCHAU (St Thomas)   *see* Henllan and Llannefydd and Bylchau *St As*

CADOXTON-JUXTA-BARRY (St Cadoc) (St Mary) *Llan 5*   R J M HUGHES

CADOXTON-JUXTA-NEATH (St Catwg) *Llan 8*   V N LEA

CAERAU (St Cynfelin) (St Peter) *Llan 7*   V K ANDREWS

CAERAU w Ely (St David) (St Timothy) *Llan 3*   V N CAHILL,   C M GIBBON

CAERDEON (St Philip)   *see* Llanaber w Caerdeon *Ban*

CAEREITHIN (St Teilo) *S & B 12*   P-in-c J W WEDGBURY

CAERFALLWCH (St Paul)   *see* Halkyn w Caerfallwch w Rhesycae *St As*

CAERGEILIOG   *see* Valley w Llechylched and Caergeiliog *Ban*

CAERGYBI   *see* Holyhead *Ban*

CAERHUN (St Mary) w Llangelynin w Llanbedr-y-Cennin *Ban 2*   V W BYNON

CAERLEON (St Cadoc) w Llanhennock *Mon 9*   V A J EDWARDS,   C C GRIFFITHS

CAERLEON-ULTRA-PONTEM (Holy Spirit)   *see* Newport Ch Ch *Mon*

CAERNARFON (St Mary)   *see* Llanbeblig w Caernarfon and Betws Garmon etc *Ban*

CAERPHILLY (St Martin) (St Catherine) (St Andrew) *Llan 1*   R M J SHORT,   C D M PRICHARD, A J DAVIES

CAERSWS (St Mary)   *see* Llanwnnog and Caersws w Carno *Ban*

CAERWENT (St Stephen and St Tathan) w Dinham and Llanfair Discoed and Shirenewton w Newchurch *Mon 2*   V H TRENCHARD,   NSM E N M DAVIES

CAERWYS (St Michael) and Bodfari *St As 2*   R J T EVANS, NSM G L HUGHES

CALDICOT (St Mary) *Mon 4*   TR D J JONES,   TV L HARRISON,   C D C BOUTFLOWER

CALLWEN (St John the Baptist)   *see* Cwmtawe Uchaf *S & B*

CAMROSE (St Ishmael) and St Lawrence w Ford and Haycastle *St D 5* **V** B JONES
CANTON Cardiff (St Luke) *Llan 2* **TR** M R PREECE, **TV** R N PARRY, **C** C W COLES, **NSM** H J DAVIES
CANTON (St Catherine) *Llan 2* **V** *vacant* (029) 2038 2796
CANTON (St John) *Llan 2* **Hon C** R P GREENWOOD
CANTREF (St Mary) *see* Llanfrynach and Cantref w Llanhamlach *S & B*
CAPEL (Dewi Sant) *see* Llansadwrn w Llanwrda and Manordeilo *St D*
CAPEL BANGOR (Church) *see* Elerch w Penrhyncoch w Capel Bangor and Goginan *St D*
CAPEL COELBREN (Capel Coelbren) *see* Cwmtawe Uchaf *S & B*
CAPEL COLMAN (St Colman) *see* Maenordeifi and Capel Colman w Llanfihangel etc *St D*
CAPEL CYNON (St Cynon) *see* Llanarth and Capel Cynon w Talgarreg etc *St D*
CAPEL DEWI (St David) *see* Llanfihangel-ar-arth w Capel Dewi *St D*
CAPEL GARMON *see* Llanrwst and Llanddoget and Capel Garmon *St As*
CAPEL IFAN (St John the Baptist) *see* Cwm Gwendraeth *St D*
CAPEL LLANILLTERNE (St Ellteyrn) *see* Pentyrch w Capel Llanillterne *Llan*
CAPEL MAIR *see* Llangeler w Pen-Boyr *St D*
CAPEL NEWYDD (St Paul) *see* Blaenavon w Capel Newydd *Mon*
CAPEL TYGWYDD *see* Llandygwydd and Cenarth w Cilrhedyn etc *St D*
CAPEL-Y-FFIN (St Mary) *see* Hay w Llanigon and Capel-y-Ffin *S & B*
CAPEL-Y-GROES *see* Abergwili w Llanfihangel-uwch-Gwili etc *St D*
CARDIFF (Christ Church) Roath Park *Llan 2* **V** E E DAVIES
CARDIFF (Dewi Sant) *Llan 2* **V** M L WILLIAMS
CARDIFF (St Luke) *see* Canton Cardiff *Llan*
CARDIFF (St Mary) (St Stephen) w Cardiff (St Dyfrig and St Samson) *Llan 2* **V** G J FRANCIS
CARDIFF, CENTRAL (St Andrew and St Teilo) (St John the Baptist) (St James the Great) (St Michael) *Llan 2* **TR** J K KIMBER, **TV** J WIGLEY, **C** P BOYLE
CARDIGAN (St Mary) w Mwnt and Y Ferwig w Llangoedmor *St D 6* **V** J POWELL, **C** J R THOMAS
CAREW (St Mary) *see* Lamphey w Hodgeston and Carew *St D*
CARMARTHEN (St David) (Christ Church) *St D 11* **V** P H B THOMAS, **C** J E GOUPILLON
CARMARTHEN (St Peter) (St John the Evangelist) *St D 11* **C** R B MORGAN, **NSM** M K THORLEY
CARMEL (Eglwys Fair) *see* Gors-las *St D*
CARNHEDRYN *see* Dewisland *St D*
CARNO (St John) *see* Llanwnnog and Caersws w Carno *Ban*
CARROG (St Ffraid) *see* Corwen w Llangar, Glyndyfrdwy etc *St As*
CASCOB (St Michael) *see* Knighton, Norton, Whitton, Pilleth and Cascob *S & B*
CASTELL DWYRAN *see* Llanfallteg w Clunderwen and Castell Dwyran *St D*
CASTELLAN *see* Maenordeifi and Capel Colman w Llanfihangel etc *St D*
CASTLE BYTHE *see* Letterston w Llanfair Nant-y-Gof etc *St D*
CASTLE CAEREINION (St Garmon) *see* Welshpool w Castle Caereinion *St As*
CASTLEMARTIN (St Michael and All Angels) w Warren and Angle and Rhoscrowther and Pwllcrochan *St D 1* **R** A J TURNER
CATBROOK (St John the Baptist) *see* Penallt and Trellech *Mon*
CATHEDINE (St Michael) *see* Llyn Safaddan *S & B*
CEFN (St Mary) (All Saints) w Trefnant w Tremeirchion *St As 2* **R** S D GREEN, **NSM** P WYKES
CEFN CRIBWR (St Colman) *see* Kenfig Hill *Llan*
CEFN FOREST (St Thomas) *see* Fleur-de-Lis *Mon*
CEFN HENGOED (St Anne) *see* Gelligaer *Llan*
CEFN PENNAR (St Illtyd) *see* Mountain Ash and Miskin *Llan*
CEFNLLYS (St Michael) *see* Llandrindod w Cefnllys and Disserth *S & B*
CEIRCHIOG (St David) *see* Valley w Llechylched and Caergeiliog *Ban*
CELLAN (All Saints) *see* Lampeter and Llanddewibrefi Gp *St D*
CEMAES *see* Llanfechell w Bodewryd w Rhosbeirio etc *Ban*
CEMAIS (St Tydecho) *see* Mallwyd w Cemais, Llanymawddwy, Darowen etc *Ban*

CENARTH (St Llawddog) *see* Maenordeifi and Capel Colman w Llanfihangel etc *St D*
CERRIGCEINWEN (St Ceinwen) *see* Trefdraeth w Aberffraw Llangadwaladr etc *Ban*
CERRIGYDRUDION (St Mary Magdalene) w Llanfihangel Glyn Myfyr, Pentrefoelas and Ysbyty Ifan *St As 12* **V** S BRUSH
CHEPSTOW (St Mary) *Mon 2* **V** C J BLANCHARD, **C** D R MILTON
CHERITON *see* Pembroke Gp *St D*
CHERITON (St Cadoc) *see* Llanrhidian w Llanmadoc and Cheriton *S & B*
CHIRK (St Mary) *St As 14* **V** A J REES
CIL-Y-CWM (St Michael) and Ystrad-ffin w Rhandirmwyn Llanfair-ar-y-Bryn *St D 14* **V** *vacant* (01550) 21011
CILCAIN (St Mary) and Nannerch and Rhyd-y-mwyn *St As 16* **R** S L BLOOMER
CILCENNIN (Holy Trinity) *see* Llanfihangel Ystrad and Cilcennin w Trefilan etc *St D*
CILFYNYDD (St Luke) *see* Pontypridd St Matt and Cilfynydd *Llan*
CILGERRAN (St Llawddog) w Bridell and Llantwyd *St D 6* **R** E L THOMAS
CILGWYN (St Mary) *see* Newport w Cilgwyn and Dinas w Llanllawer *St D*
CILIAU AERON (St Michael) *see* Llanerch Aeron w Ciliau Aeron and Dihewyd etc *St D*
CILYBEBYLL (St John the Evangelist) *Llan 8* **R** M PERRY
CILYMAENLLWYD (St Philip and St James) *see* Llandysilio w Egremont and Llanglydwen etc *St D*
CLARBESTON (St Martin of Tours) *see* Wiston w Walton E and Clarbeston *St D*
CLOCAENOG (St Foddhyd) *see* Llanfwrog and Clocaenog and Gyffylliog *St As*
CLUNDERWEN (St David) *see* Llanfallteg w Clunderwen and Castell Dwyran *St D*
CLYDACH (St John the Evangelist) (St Mary) (St Michael) *S & B 7* **V** T J HEWITT, **C** S M KNIGHT
CLYDACH VALE (St Thomas) *see* Tonypandy w Clydach Vale *Llan*
CLYDAU (St Clydai) *St D 6* **P-in-c** E L THOMAS
CLYNNOG FAWR (St Beuno) *see* Llanaelhaearn w Clynnog Fawr *Ban*
CLYRO (St Michael and All Angels) *see* Glasbury and Llowes w Clyro and Betws *S & B*
CLYTHA *see* Llanddewi Rhydderch w Llangattock-juxta-Usk etc *Mon*
COCKETT (St Peter) *see* Swansea St Pet *S & B*
COEDKERNEW *see* Marshfield and Peterstone Wentloog etc *Mon*
COEDYPAEN (Christchurch) *see* Llangybi and Coedypaen w Llanbadoc *Mon*
COETMOR *see* Glanogwen w St Ann's w Llanllechid *Ban*
COITY (St Mary) w Nolton *Llan 6* **R** D YEOMAN, **C** P M WILLIAMS, R T PITMAN
COLVA (St David) *see* New Radnor and Llanfihangel Nantmelan etc *S & B*
COLWINSTON (St Michael) w Llandow and Llysworney *Llan 4* **R** P M LEONARD
COLWYN (St Catherine) (St John the Baptist) (St Paul) (St Andrew) (St David) *St As 6* **TV** M JONES
COMINS COCH *see* Llanbadarn Fawr *St D*
CONNAH'S QUAY (St Mark) (St David's Mission Church) *St As 16* **V** P H VARAH, **C** C P BEECH
CONWY (St Mary and All Saints) w Gyffin *Ban 2* **V** P R JONE
CORRIS (Holy Trinity) *see* Pennal w Corris and Esgairgeiliog *Ban*
CORWEN (St Mael and St Sulien) w Llangar, Glyndyfrdwy and Llansantffraid Glyn Dyfrdwy *St As 12* **V** *vacant*
COSHESTON (St Michael) w Nash and Upton *St D 1* **R** R A GORDON
COWBRIDGE (Holy Cross) *Llan 4* **TR** D G BELCHER, **TV** D Y L HELLARD, R H SPENCER, **C** L L WILLIAMS
COYCHURCH (St Crallo) w Llangan and St Mary Hill *Llan 6* **R** *vacant* (01656) 860785
COYTREAHEN (St Thomas) *see* St Brides Minor w Bettws w Aberkenfig *Llan*
CRAI (St Ilid) *see* Defynnog, Llandilo'r Fan, Llanulid, Llywel etc *S & B*
CREGRINA (St David) *see* Llanelwedd w Llanfaredd w Llansantffraed etc *S & B*
CRIBYN (St Silin) *see* Llanfihangel Ystrad and Cilcennin w Trefilan etc *St D*
CRICCIETH (St Catherine) and Treflys w Llanystumdwy w Llangybi and Llanarmon *Ban 11* **R** S WILLIAMS
CRICKADARN (St Mary) *see* Aberedw w Llandeilo Graban and Llanbadarn etc *S & B*

CRICKHOWELL (St Edmund) w Cwmdu and Tretower *S & B 3*
V B LETSON
CRIGGION (St Michael) *see* Llandysilio and Penrhos and
Llandrinio etc *St As*
CRINDAU (All Saints) *see* Newport All SS *Mon*
CRINOW (St Teilo) *see* Narberth w Mounton w Robeston
Wathen and Crinow *St D*
CROESCEILIOG (St Mary) *see* Cwmbran *Mon*
CROESERW (St Clare) *see* Glyncorrwg and Upper Afan Valley
Llan
CROSS HANDS (St Anne) *see* Gors-las *St D*
CROSS INN (Holy Trinity) *see* Llanllwchaearn and Llanina
St D
CROSS KEYS (St Catherine) *see* Risca *Mon*
CROSSGATES *see* Llanbadarn Fawr, Llandegley and
Llanfihangel etc *S & B*
CRUGYBYDDAR (St Peter) *see* Beguildy and Heyope and
Llangynllo and Bleddfa *S & B*
CRUMLIN (St Mary) *see* Newbridge w Crumlin *Mon*
CRUNWERE (St Elidyr) *see* Begelly w Ludchurch and
Crunwere *St D*
CRYNANT (Chapel of Ease) *see* Dulais Valley *Llan*
CRYNANT (St Margaret) *as above Llan*
CWM (St Mael and St Sulien) *see* Dyserth and Trelawnyd and
Cwm *St As*
CWM (St Paul) *see* Ebbw Vale *Mon*
CWM-COCH (St Mark) *see* Llandybie *St D*
CWM GWENDRAETH *St D 12* **TR** S R THOMAS,
TV A C WILLIAMS-POTTER, B MCNIVEN
CWMAMAN (Christ Church) *St D 13* **V** W P NASH
CWMAMAN (St Joseph) *see* Aberaman and Abercwmboi w
Cwmaman *Llan*
CWMANN (St James) *see* Pencarreg and Llanycrwys *St D*
CWMAVON (St Michael) *Llan 7* **P-in-c** H M O'SHEA
CWMBACH (St Mary Magdalene) *Llan 9* **V** B H SHARP
CWMBACH LLECHRYD (St John the Divine) *see* Upper Wye
S & B
CWMBRAN (St Gabriel) *Mon 10* **TR** M J PHILLIPS,
TV D RICHARDS, G R EVANS, L C HALL, **OLM** G M PROSSER
CWMBWRLA (St Luke) *see* Swansea St Luke *S & B*
CWMCARN (St John the Evangelist) *see* Abercarn and
Cwmcarn *Mon*
CWMCARVAN (St Clement) *see* Dingestow and Llangovan w
Penyclawdd etc *Mon*
CWMDARE (St Luke) *see* Aberdare St Fagan *Llan*
CWMDDAUDDWR (St Winifred) (St Bride) w St Harmon's and
Llanwrthwl *S & B 5* **P-in-c** P BROOKS
CWMDU (St Michael the Archangel) *see* Crickhowell w
Cwmdu and Tretower *S & B*
CWMDUAD (St Alban) *see* Cynwil Elfed and Newchurch *St D*
CWMFFRWD (St Anne) *see* Llangunnor w Cwmffrwd *St D*
CWMFFRWDOER (All Saints) *see* Pontypool *Mon*
CWMLLYNFELL (St Margaret) *see* Brynaman w Cwmllynfell
St D
CWMOGWR (St John the Baptist) *Llan 6* **V** P J ABBOTT
CWMPARC (St George) *Llan 12* **V** B TAYLOR
CWMTAWE UCHAF *S & B 7* **P-in-c** A J BROOKFIELD
CWMTILLERY (St Paul) *see* Abertillery w Cwmtillery w Six
Bells *Mon*
CWMYOY (St Martin) *see* Llanfihangel Crucorney w Oldcastle
etc *Mon*
CWRT-HENRI (St Mary) *see* Llangathen w Llanfihangel
Cilfargen etc *St D*
CYDWELI (St Mary) (St Teilo) and Llandyfaelog *St D 12*
V vacant (01554) 890295
CYFFIG (St Cyffig) *see* Whitland w Cyffig and Henllan
Amgoed etc *St D*
CYMAU (All Saints) *see* Llanfynydd *St As*
CYMMER (St John the Evangelist) and Porth *Llan 12*
V R G LLOYD
CYMMER AFAN (St John the Evangelist) *see* Glyncorrwg and
Upper Afan Valley *Llan*
CYNCOED (All Saints) (St Edeyrn) *Mon 6* **TR** S G WILLSON,
TV S G CARBY, C M LAWSON-JONES, E PAYNE
CYNWIL ELFED (St Cynwyl) and Newchurch *St D 11*
V P A CROCKETT
CYNWYL GAEO (St Cynwyl) w Llansawel and Talley *St D 14*
V J S PENBERTHY
DAFEN (St Michael and All Angels) *St D 12* **V** D M C DAVIES
DALE (St James) and St Brides w Marloes *St D 5*
V D M WIGHT, **NSM** S H WIGHT
DAROWEN (St Tudur) *see* Mallwyd w Cemais,
Llanymawddwy, Darowen etc *Ban*
DEFYNNOG (St Cynog) and Llandilo'r Fan and Llanulid and
Llywel and Traean-glas *S & B 1* **V** M P WILDING
DEGANWY (All Saints) *see* Llanrhos *St As*

DENBIGH (St Mary) (St Marcella) (St David) *St As 2*
R J P SMITH, **C** J M BAKER
DENIO (St Peter) w Abererch *Ban 11* **V** J M A GRIFFITHS
DERI (St Peter) *see* Bargoed and Deri w Brithdir *Llan*
DERWEN (St Mary) *see* Llanfair DC, Derwen, Llanelidan and
Efenechtyd *St As*
DEVAUDEN (St James) *see* Itton and St Arvans w Penterry and
Kilgwrrwg etc *Mon*
DEWISLAND (Cathedral of St David and St Andrew) *St D 3*
TR J W EVANS, **TV** R P DAVIES, D J R LEAN, J S BENNETT,
NSM M I PLANT
DIHEWYD (St Vitalis) *see* Llanerch Aeron w Ciliau Aeron and
Dihewyd etc *St D*
DINAS (Mission) and Penygraig w Williamstown *Llan 12*
V C R LEWIS-JENKINS
DINAS (St Brynach) *see* Newport w Cilgwyn and Dinas w
Llanllawer *St D*
DINGESTOW (St Dingad) and Llangovan w Penyclawdd and
Tregaer and Cwmcarvan *Mon 3* **V** vacant (01600) 740206
DINHAM *see* Caerwent w Dinham and Llanfair Discoed etc
Mon
DINMAEL (St Catherine) *see* Betws Gwerful Goch w
Llangwm, Gwyddelwern etc *St As*
DISSERTH (St Cewydd) *see* Llandrindod w Cefnllys and
Disserth *S & B*
DOLBENMAEN (St Mary) *see* Porthmadoc and
Ynyscynhaearn and Dolbenmaen *Ban*
DOLFOR (St Paul) *see* Kerry and Llanmerewig and Dolfor
St As
DOLGARROG (St Mary) *see* Caerhun w Llangelynin w
Llanbedr-y-Cennin *Ban*
DOLGELLAU (St Mary) w Llanfachreth and Brithdir and
Bryncoedifor and Llanelltud *Ban 12* **R** A WILLIAMS,
TV P J CROOKS
DOLWYDDELAN (St Gwyddelan) *see* Betws-y-Coed and
Capel Curig w Penmachno etc *Ban*
DOWLAIS (St John the Baptist) (Christ Church) *Llan 10*
R M L WISHART
DULAIS VALLEY *Llan 8* **V** S BARNES
DWYGYFYLCHI or Penmaenmawr (St Gwynin) (St Seiriol)
(St David) *Ban 2* **V** vacant (01492) 623300
DYFFRYN *see* Llanenddwyn w Llanddwywe, Llanbedr w
Llandanwg *Ban*
DYFFRYN (St Matthew) *Llan 8* **V** S J BODYCOMBE,
NSM E HARRIS
DYFFRYN HONDDU (St Cynog) *see* Merthyr Cynog and
Dyffryn Honddu etc *S & B*
DYSERTH (St Bridget) (St Michael) (St Mael and St Sulien) and
Trelawnyd and Cwm *St As 1* **V** R W ROWLAND
EBBW VALE (Christchurch) (St John the Baptist) *Mon 8*
TR G J WAGGETT, **C** J A CARTER
EDERN (St Edern) *see* Nefyn w Tudweiliog w Llandudwen w
Edern *Ban*
EFENECHTYD (St Michael) *see* Llanfair DC, Derwen,
Llanelidan and Efenechtyd *St As*
EGLWYS-FACH (St Michael) *see* Borth and Eglwys-fach w
Llangynfelyn *St D*
EGLWYS FAIR GLYN-TAF *see* Whitland w Cyffig and
Henllan Amgoed etc *St D*
EGLWYS GYMYN (St Margaret) *see* Pendine w Llanmiloe
and Eglwys Gymyn w Marros *St D*
EGLWYS NEWYDD *see* Ysbyty Cynfyn w Llantrisant and
Eglwys Newydd *St D*
EGLWYS OEN DUW *see* Llanwrtyd w Llanddulas in Tir Abad
etc *S & B*
EGLWYSBREWIS (St Brewis) w St Athan w Gileston *Llan 4*
R vacant (01446) 750540
EGLWYSFACH *see* Llansantffraid Glan Conwy and
Eglwysbach *St As*
EGLWYSILAN (St Ilan) *Llan 1* **R** A H STEVENS
EGLWYSRHOS (St Eleri and St Mary) *see* Llanrhos *St As*
EGLWYSWEN (St Michael) *see* Nevern and Y Beifil w
Eglwyswrw and Meline etc *St D*
EGLWYSWRW (St Cristiolus) *as above St D*
EGREMONT *see* Llandysilio w Egremont and Llanglydwen etc
St D
ELERCH (St Peter) w Penrhyncoch w Capel Bangor and Goginan
St D 10 **V** J P LIVINGSTONE
ELY (St David) *see* Caerau w Ely *Llan*
ELY (St Timothy) *as above Llan*
ERBISTOCK (St Hilary) *see* Overton and Erbistock and Penley
St As
ESCLUSHAM (Holy Trinity) *St As 15* **V** P T ALLSWORTH
ESGAIRGEILIOG *see* Pennal w Corris and Esgairgeiliog *Ban*
EVANCOYD (St Peter) *see* New Radnor and Llanfihangel
Nantmelan etc *S & B*

EWENNY (St Michael) w St Brides Major *Llan 6*   **V**   M KOMOR, **NSM**   D C TILT
EYTON (St Deiniol)   *see* Bangor Monachorum and Worthenbury *St As*
FAIRBOURNE (St Cynon)   *see* Arthog w Fairbourne w Llangelynnin w Rhoslefain *Ban*
FAIRHILL   *see* Cwmbran *Mon*
FAIRWATER (St Peter) *Llan 3*   **V** vacant (029) 2056 2551
FAIRWATER (St Peter)   *see* Cwmbran *Mon*
FAWR   *see* Llandeilo Fawr and Taliaris *St D*
FELIN-FOEL (Holy Trinity)   *see* Llanelli *St D*
FELIN-GWM (St John)   *see* Llanegwad w Llanfynydd *St D*
FELINDRE (St Barnabas)   *see* Llangeler w Pen-Boyr *St D*
FERNDALE (St Dunstan) (St Thomas) w Maerdy *Llan 12*   **V** N PARFITT
FERRYSIDE (St Thomas)   *see* St Ishmael's w Llan-saint and Ferryside *St D*
FFESTINIOG (St Michael) w Blaenau Ffestiniog *Ban 8*   **P-in-c** P A JONES
FFYNNONGROYW (All Saints)   *see* Mostyn w Ffynnongroyw *St As*
FISHGUARD (St Mary) w Llanychar and Pontfaen w Morfil and Llanychlwydog *St D 3*   **V** vacant
FLEMINGSTON (St Michael)   *see* Cowbridge *Llan*
FLEUR-DE-LIS (St David) *Mon 7*   **V** P K MCMULLEN, **OLM** T MORGAN
FLINT (St Mary) (St Thomas) (St David) *St As 4*   **NSM** M M GRAHAM
FOCHRIW (St Mary and St Andrew)   *see* Pontlottyn w Fochriw *Llan*
FORD (Church)   *see* Camrose and St Lawrence w Ford and Haycastle *St D*
FORDEN (St Michael)   *see* Montgomery and Forden and Llandyssil *St As*
FREYSTROP (St Justinian)   *see* Llangwm w Freystrop and Johnston *St D*
FRON (Mission Church)   *see* Berriew *St As*
FRONCYSYLLTE (St David)   *see* Chirk *St As*
FRONGOCH   *see* Llancil w Bala and Frongoch and Llangower etc *St As*
FURNACE (Mission Church)   *see* Llanelli *St D*
GABALFA (St Mark) (Highfields Centre and Mynachdy Institute) *Llan 2*   **V** R M CAPPER,   **C** M A PRINCE
GAERWEN   *see* Llanfihangel Ysgeifiog w Llangristiolus etc *Ban*
GARNDIFFAITH (St John the Evangelist)   *see* Abersychan and Garndiffaith *Mon*
GARTHBEIBIO (St Tydecho) w Llanerfyl w Llangadfan *St As 8*   **V** D E B FRANCIS
GARTHBRENGY (St David)   *see* Merthyr Cynog and Dyffryn Honddu etc *S & B*
GARTHELI (St Gartheli)   *see* Llangeitho and Blaenpennal w Betws Leucu etc *St D*
GAUFRON (St David)   *see* Rhayader and Nantmel *S & B*
GELLIGAER (St Catwg) (St Margaret) (St Anne) *Llan 1*   **R** D K WATERS,   **NSM** S G BROWN
GILESTON (St Giles)   *see* Eglwysbrewis w St Athan w Gileston *Llan*
GILFACH GOCH (St Barnabas)   *see* Tonyrefail w Gilfach Goch and Llandyfodwg *Llan*
GILVACH (St Margaret)   *see* Gelligaer *Llan*
GLADWESTRY (St Mary)   *see* New Radnor and Llanfihangel Nantmelan etc *S & B*
GLAIS (St Paul)   *see* Llansamlet *S & B*
GLAN ELY (Resurrection) *Llan 3*   **V** S LISK,   **C** B A WOOD
GLANAMAN (St Margaret)   *see* Cwmaman *St D*
GLANGWRYNE (Mission Church)   *see* Llangenni and Llanbedr Ystrad Yw w Patricio *S & B*
GLANOGWEN (Christ Church) w St Ann's w Llanllechid *Ban 5*   **V** M C PARRY,   **C** R J K ELLIS
GLANTAWE (St Margaret) (St Peter) *S & B 11*   **V** C P G DICKSON
GLASBURY (St Peter) (All Saints) and Llowes w Clyro and Betws *S & B 4*   **P-in-c** H E BAKER
GLASCOED (St Michael)   *see* Usk and Monkswood w Glascoed Chpl and Gwehelog *Mon*
GLASCOMBE (St David)   *see* Llanelwedd w Llanfaredd w Llansantffraed etc *S & B*
GLYN   *see* Brecon St David w Llanspyddid and Llanilltyd *S & B*
GLYNCOCH (All Saints' Church Centre)   *see* Pontypridd St Matt and Cilfynydd *Llan*
GLYNCORRWG (St John the Baptist) (St Clare) (St Thomas) and Upper Afan Valley *Llan 7*   **P-in-c** C E LASKEY
GLYNDYFRDWY (St Thomas)   *see* Corwen w Llangar, Glyndyfrdwy etc *St As*
GLYNTAFF (St Mary) *Llan 11*   **V** K D LERRY
GOETRE (St Peter) w Llanover *Mon 5*   **R** P F COLEMAN

GOGINAN (Church)   *see* Elerch w Penrhyncoch w Capel Bangor and Goginan *St D*
GOLDCLIFFE (St Mary Magdalen)   *see* Magor *Mon*
GOODWICK (St Peter)   *see* Llanwnda, Goodwick w Manorowen and Llanstinan *St D*
GORS-LAS (St Lleian) *St D 13*   **V** M L REES
GORSEDD (St Paul) w Brynford, Ysgeifiog and Whitford *St As 4*   **V** S CAWLEY,   **Par Dn** S M MORIARTY
GORSEINON (St Catherine) *S & B 9*   **V** D H E MOSFORD, **NSM** W G G JAMES
GOVILON (Christchurch) w Llanfoist w Llanelen *Mon 1*   **R** A F PYE,   **NSM** D W F ROSSITER
GOWERTON (St John the Evangelist) *S & B 9*   **P-in-c** T J WHETTLETON
GRAIG (St John) *Llan 11*   **V** vacant (01443) 651810
GRANDSTON (St Catherine)   *see* Mathry w St Edren's and Grandston etc *St D*
GRANGETOWN (St Paul) *Llan 2*   **V** vacant (029) 2022 8707
GREENWAY (St Hilary)   *see* Trowbridge Mawr *Mon*
GREENWAY (St Hilary)   *as above Mon*
GRESFORD (All Saints) *St As 13*   **V** D GRIFFITHS
GRIFFITHSTOWN (St Hilda) *Mon 10*   **V** C J WILCOX
GROESWEN (St David)   *see* Pentyrch w Capel Llanilterne *Llan*
GRONANT (St Winifred)   *see* Llanasa *St As*
GROSMONT (St Nicholas) and Skenfrith and Llangattock Lingoed and Llanfair Chapel *Mon 1*   **OLM** J PROSSER
GUILSFIELD (St Aelhaiarn) w Buttington *St As 10*   **V** R A BIRD
GUMFRESTON (St Lawrence)   *see* Tenby *St D*
GWAENYSGOR   *see* Meliden and Gwaenysgor *St As*
GWAUN-CAE-GURWEN *St D 13*   **V** J G M LADD
GWEHELOG   *see* Usk and Monkswood w Glascoed Chpl and Gwehelog *Mon*
GWENDDWR (St Dubricius)   *see* Aberedw w Llandeilo Graban and Llanbadarn etc *S & B*
GWENLLI (St Mark)   *see* Llanarth and Capel Cynon w Talgarreg etc *St D*
GWERNAFFIELD (Holy Trinity) and Llanferres *St As 16*   **V** vacant (01352) 740205
GWERNAMYNYDD (St Mark)   *see* Mold *St As*
GWERNESNEY (St Michael)   *see* Llangwm Uchaf and Llangwm Isaf w Gwernesney etc *Mon*
GWERNFFRWD (St David)   *see* Llanyrnewydd *S & B*
GWERSYLLT (Holy Trinity) *St As 13*   **V** S M HUYTON
GWYDDELWERN (St Beuno)   *see* Betws Gwerful Goch w Llangwm, Gwyddelwern etc *St As*
GWYNFE (All Saints)   *see* Llangadog and Gwynfe w Llanddeusant *St D*
GWYTHERIN (St Winifred)   *see* Betws-yn-Rhos w Petryal *St As*
GYFFIN (St Benedict)   *see* Conwy w Gyffin *Ban*
GYFFYLLIOG (St Mary)   *see* Llanfwrog and Clocaenog and Gyffylliog *St As*
HAFOD (St John)   *see* Cen Swansea *S & B*
HAKIN (St Mary)   *see* Hubberston *St D*
HALKYN (St Mary the Virgin) w Caerfallwch w Rhesycae *St As 4*   **R** K R SOUTHERTON
HANMER (St Chad) and Bronington and Bettisfield and Tallarn Green *St As 11*   **V** D F BUTTERWORTH
HARLECH (St Tanwg) and Llanfair-juxta-Harlech w Llanfihangel-y-Traethau and Llandecwyn *Ban 8*   **V** R A BEACON
HAROLDSTON ST ISSELLS (St Issell)   *see* Haverfordwest St Mary and St Thos w Haroldston *St D*
HAROLDSTON WEST (St Madog)   *see* Walton W w Talbenny and Haroldston W *St D*
HAVERFORDWEST (St Martin) w Lambston *St D 5*   **V** C W BOWEN
HAVERFORDWEST (St Mary) and St Thomas w Haroldston St Issells *St D 5*   **R** D EVANS
HAWARDEN (St Deiniol) (Holy Spirit) *St As 16*   **TR** T F L GRIFFITHS,   **TV** M J BATCHELOR,   C A HILL, **C** G BECKETT,   **NSM** M QUINN,   J STEPHENS
HAY (St Mary) (St John) w Llanigon and Capel-y-Ffin *S & B 4*   **V** R D WILLIAMS
HAYCASTLE (St Mary)   *see* Camrose and St Lawrence w Ford and Haycastle *St D*
HENDY (St David)   *see* Llangennech and Hendy *St D*
HENEGLWYS (St Llwydian)   *see* Llandrygarn w Bodwrog and Heneglwys etc *Ban*
HENFYNYW (St David) w Aberaeron and Llanddewi Aberarth *St D 8*   **V** A T G JOHN,   **C** D L R BROWNRIDGE, **NSM** H G LEWIS
HENLLAN (St David)   *see* Llandysul w Bangor Teifi w Henllan etc *St D*

HENLLAN (St Sadwrn) and Llannefydd and Bylchau *St As 2*
R J P P WILLIAMS
HENLLAN AMGOED (St David) *see* Whitland w Cyffig and Henllan Amgoed etc *St D*
HENLLYS (St Peter) *see* Cwmbran *Mon*
HENRY'S MOAT (St Bernard) *see* Maenclochog and New Moat etc *St D*
HEOL-Y-CYW (St Paul) *see* Llanilid w Pencoed *Llan*
HERBRANDSTON (St Mary) and Hasguard w St Ishmael's *St D 5*　　**R** L A F C WATKINS
HEYOPE (St David) *see* Beguildy and Heyope and Llangynllo and Bleddfa *S & B*
HIGH CROSS (St Anne) *see* Bassaleg *Mon*
HIRWAUN (St Lleurwg) (St Winifred) *Llan 9*　**V** B L JONES
HODGESTON (Church) *see* Lamphey w Hodgeston and Carew *St D*
HOLT (St Chad) *St As 13*　**V** D GRIFFITHS
HOLYHEAD (St Cybi) (Morawelon) (St Ffraid) (St Gwenfaen) *Ban 3*　**R** J E NICE,　**TV** C A LLEWELLYN,　**C** N A RIDINGS
HOLYWELL (St James) (Holy Trinity) *St As 4*　**V** J D P LOMAS
HOPE (Parish Church) *St As 16*　**R** M K SNELLGROVE
HOWEY (St David) *see* Llandrindod w Cefnllys and Disserth *S & B*
HUBBERSTON (St David) (Holy Spirit) *St D 5*
R A M CHADWICK,　**C** P E MARSH
HUNDLETON (St David) *see* Monkton *St D*
ILSTON (St Illtyd) w Pennard *S & B 8*　**V** D J WILKINSON
IRFON VALLEY *S & B 2*　**P-in-c** C M HAYNES
ISYCOED (St Paul) *see* Marchwiel and Isycoed *St As*
ITTON (St Deiniol) and St Arvans w Penterry and Kilgwrrwg w Devauden *Mon 2*　**V** M J GOLLOP,　**NSM** M E ZORAB
JAMESTON *see* Manobier and St Florence w Redberth *St D*
JEFFREYSTON (St Jeffrey) w Reynoldston and East Williamston and Loveston *St D 4*　**R** N P DAVIES
JOHNSTON (St Peter) *see* Llangwm w Freystrop and Johnston *St D*
JORDANSTON (St Cawrda) *see* Mathry w St Edren's and Grandston etc *St D*
KEMEYS COMMANDER (All Saints) *see* Bettws Newydd w Trostrey etc *Mon*
KENFIG *see* Pyle w Kenfig *Llan*
KENFIG HILL (St Theodore) (St Colman) *Llan 7*
P-in-c P G MORRIS
KERRY (St Michael) and Llanmerewig and Dolfor *St As 7*
V A T W REYNOLDS
KILGETTY *see* Begelly w Ludchurch and Crunwere *St D*
KILGWRRWG (Holy Cross) *see* Itton and St Arvans w Penterry and Kilgwrrwg etc *Mon*
KILLAY (St Hilary) (St Martin) *S & B 6*　**V** T J WILLIAMS
KILVEY (All Saints) *see* Swansea St Thos and Kilvey *S & B*
KNELSTON *see* Port Eynon w Rhosili and Llanddewi and Knelston *S & B*
KNIGHTON (St Edward) and Norton and Whitton and Pilleth and Cascob *S & B 5*　**V** A J PEARCE
LALESTON (St David) w Tythegston and Merthyr Mawr *Llan 6*
V E J EVANS,　**NSM** J M LEWIS
LAMBSTON (St Ishmael) *see* Haverfordwest St Martin w Lambston *St D*
LAMPETER and Llanddewibrefi Group, The *St D 9*
V A W WILLIAMS,　**C** M H JOHN, J G MATTHEWS
LAMPETER PONT STEFFAN (St Peter) *see* Lampeter and Llanddewibrefi Gp *St D*
LAMPETER VELFREY (St Peter) and Llanddewi Velfrey *St D 15*　**R** M G R MORRIS
LAMPHEY (St Faith and St Tyfei) w Hodgeston and Carew *St D 1*　**V** vacant
LANDORE (St Paul) *S & B 10*　**P-in-c** R G JONES,
NSM N P DOYLE
LANGSTONE (not known) *see* Bishton *Mon*
LANKNANSH (St Mary) *see* Llantwit Major *Llan*
LAUGHARNE (St Martin) w Llansadwrnen and Llandawke *St D 15*　**V** vacant (0199421) 218
LAVERNOCK (St Lawrence) *see* Penarth w Lavernock *Llan*
LAWRENNY (St Caradog) *see* Martletwy w Lawrenny and Minwear etc *St D*
LECKWITH *see* Llandough w Leckwith *Llan*
LETTERSTON (St Giles) w Llanfair Nant-y-Gof and Puncheston w Little Newcastle and Castle Bythe *St D 3*
R R GRIFFITHS,　**NSM** M C CHARLES
LISVANE (St Denys) *Llan 2*　**V** P N THOMPSON
LISWERRY *see* Newport St Andr *Mon*
LITTLE NEWCASTLE (St Peter) *see* Letterston w Llanfair Nant-y-Gof etc *St D*
LLAN-GAN *see* Whitland w Cyffig and Henllan Amgoed etc *St D*
LLAN-LLWCH (St Mary) w Llangain and Llangynog *St D 11*
V R I PROTHEROE

LLAN-NON (St Non) *see* Cwm Gwendraeth *St D*
LLAN-SAINT (All Saints) *see* St Ishmael's w Llan-saint and Ferryside *St D*
LLAN-Y-BRI (Holy Trinity) *see* Llansteffan and Llan-y-bri etc *St D*
LLANABER (St Mary) (St John) (St David) w Caerdeon *Ban 8*
R K G HORSWELL
LLANAELHAEARN (St Aelhaiarn) w Clynnog Fawr *Ban 1*
R I THOMAS
LLANAFAN FAWR (St Afan) *see* Upper Wye *S & B*
LLANAFAN-Y-TRAWSCOED (St Afan) *see* Llanfihangel w Llanafan and Llanwnnws etc *St D*
LLANALLGO (St Gallo) *see* Llaneugrad w Llanallgo and Penrhosllugwy etc *Ban*
LLANANNO (St Anno) *see* Llanbister w Llanbadarn Fynydd w Llananno etc *S & B*
LLANARMON (St Garmon) *see* Criccieth and Treflys w Llanystumdwy etc *Ban*
LLANARMON DYFFRYN CEIRIOG (St Garmon)
see Llansantffraid Glyn Ceirog and Llanarmon etc *St As*
LLANARMON MYNYD (St Garmon)
see Llanrhaeadr-ym-Mochnant etc *St As*
LLANARMON YN IAL (St Garmon) *see* Llanbedr DC w Llangynhafal, Llanychan etc *St As*
LLANARTH (St David) (St Teilo) and Capel Cynon w Talgarreg and (St Mark) *St D 8*　**V** C L BOLTON
LLANARTH (St Teilo) *see* Llanddewi Rhydderch w Llangattock-juxta-Usk etc *Mon*
LLANARTHNE (St David) and Llanddarog *St D 11*　**V** vacant (0126786) 268
LLANASA (St Asaph and St Cyndeyrn) (St Winifred) *St As 4*
V G H TRIMBY
LLANBABO (St Pabo) *see* Valley w Llechylched and Caergeiliog *Ban*
LLANBADARN FAWR (St Padarn) *St D 10*　**V** W S T MORGAN
LLANBADARN FAWR (St Padarn) and Llandegley and Llanfihangel Rhydithon w Abbey Cwmhir *S & B 5*
P-in-c A C BALLARD
LLANBADARN FYNYDD (St Padarn) *see* Llanbister w Llanbadarn Fynydd w Llananno etc *S & B*
LLANBADARN ODWYN (St Padarn) *see* Lampeter and Llanddewibrefi Gp *St D*
LLANBADARN TREFEGLWYS (St Padarn)
see Llansantffraed and Llanbadarn Trefeglwys etc *St D*
LLANBADARN-Y-GARREG (St Padarn) *see* Aberedw w Llandeilo Graban and Llanbadarn etc *S & B*
LLANBADOC (St Madog) *see* Llangybi and Coedypaen w Llanbadoc *Mon*
LLANBADRIG (St Padrig) *see* Llanfechell w Bodewryd w Rhosbeirio etc *Ban*
LLANBEBLIG (St Peblig) w Caernarfon and Betws Garmon w Waunfawr *Ban 1*　**R** R F DONALDSON, R J HUGHES
LLANBEDR (St Peter) *see* Llanenddwyn w Llanddwywe, Llanbedr w Llandanwg *Ban*
LLANBEDR DYFFRYN CLWYD (St Peter) w Llangynhafal, Llanychan, and Llanarmon yn Ial *St As 3*　**R** H BUTLER,
NSM V C ROWLANDS
LLANBEDR PAINSCASTLE (St Peter) *see* Bryngwyn and Newchurch and Llanbedr etc *S & B*
LLANBEDR-Y-CENNIN (St Peter) *see* Caerhun w Llangelynin w Llanbedr-y-Cennin *Ban*
LLANBEDR YSTRAD YW (St Peter) *see* Llangenni and Llanbedr Ystrad Yw w Patricio *S & B*
LLANBEDRGOCH (St Peter) *see* Llanfair Mathafarn Eithaf w Llanbedrgoch *Ban*
LLANBEDROG (St Pedrog) w Llannor and Llangian *Ban 11*
R A JONES
LLANBERIS (St Peris) (St Padarn) w Llanrug *Ban 1*
C V R HANCOCK
LLANBISTER (St Cynllo) w Llanbadarn Fynydd w Llananno and Llanddewi Ystradenni *S & B 5*　**P-in-c** L A MARSHALL
LLANBLETHIAN (St Blethian) *see* Cowbridge *Llan*
LLANBOIDY (St Brynach) *see* Meidrim and Llanboidy and Merthyr *St D*
LLANBRADACH (All Saints) *see* Ystrad Mynach w Llanbradach *Llan*
LLANBRYN-MAIR (St Mary) *see* Mallwyd w Cemais, Llanymawddwy, Darowen etc *Ban*
LLANCARFAN (St Cadoc) w Llantrithyd *Llan 4*　**V** vacant (01446) 750241
LLANDAFF (Cathedral of St Peter and St Paul w St Dyfrig, St Teilo and St Euddogwy) *Llan 3*　**V** J T LEWIS
LLANDAFF North (All Saints) *Llan 3*　**V** T J G S COOPER
LLANDANWG *see* Llanenddwyn w Llanddwywe, Llanbedr w Llandanwg *Ban*
LLANDAVENNY *see* Penhow, St Brides Netherwent w Llandavenny etc *Mon*

LLANDAWKE (St Odoceus)   *see* Laugharne w Llansadwrnen and Llandawke *St D*
LLANDDANIEL-FAB (St Deiniolfab)   *see* Llanfair-pwll and Llanddaniel-fab etc *Ban*
LLANDDAROG (St Twrog)   *see* Llanarthne and Llanddarog *St D*
LLANDDEINIOL (St Deiniol)   *see* Llanychaearn w Llanddeiniol *St D*
LLANDDEINIOLEN (St Deiniol) w Llanfair-is-gaer w Penisa'r-waun *Ban 1*   **V** E A SMITHAM
LLANDDERFEL (St Derfel)   *see* Llandrillo and Llandderfel *St As*
LLANDDEW (St David)   *see* Brecon St Mary w Llanddew *S & B*
LLANDDEWI   *see* Llanwrtyd w Llanddulas in Tir Abad etc *S & B*
LLANDDEWI (St David)   *see* Port Eynon w Rhosili and Llanddewi and Knelston *S & B*
LLANDDEWI ABERARTH (St David)   *see* Henfynyw w Aberaeron and Llanddewi Aberarth *St D*
LLANDDEWI FACH (St David)   *see* Bryngwyn and Newchurch and Llanbedr etc *S & B*
LLANDDEWI RHONDDA (St Barnabas)   *see* Pwllgwaun w Llanddewi Rhondda *Llan*
LLANDDEWI RHONDDA (St David)   *as above Llan*
LLANDDEWI RHYDDERCH (St David) w Llangattock-juxta-Usk and Llanarth w Clytha and Llansantffraed *Mon 1*   **V** M S SADLER
LLANDDEWI YSTRADENNI (St David)   *see* Llanbister w Llanbadarn Fynydd w Llananno etc *S & B*
LLANDDEWIBREFI (St David)   *see* Lampeter and Llanddewibrefi Gp *St D*
LLANDDEWI'R CWM (St David)   *see* Builth and Llanddewi'r Cwm w Llangynog etc *S & B*
LLANDDOGET (St Doged)   *see* Llanrwst and Llanddoget and Capel Garmon *St As*
LLANDDONA (St Dona)   *see* Llansadwrn w Llanddona and Llaniestyn etc *Ban*
LLANDDOWROR (St Teilo)   *see* St Clears w Llangynin and Llanddowror etc *St D*
LLANDDULAS (St Cynfryd)   *see* Colwyn *St As*
LLANDDWYWE (St Ddwywe)   *see* Llanenddwyn w Llanddwywe, Llanbedr w Llandanwg *Ban*
LLANDDYFNAN (St Ddyfnan)   *see* Llansadwrn w Llanddona and Llaniestyn etc *Ban*
LLANDDYFNAN (St Deiniol)   *as above Ban*
LLANDECWYN (St Tecwyn)   *see* Harlech and Llanfair-juxta-Harlech etc *Ban*
LLANDEFAELOG-FACH (St Maelog)   *see* Merthyr Cynog and Dyffryn Honddu etc *S & B*
LLANDEFALLE (St Matthew) and Llyswen w Boughrood and Llanstephen w Talachddu *S & B 4*   **R** I P CHARLESWORTH
LLANDEGFAN (St Tegfan) w Llandysilio *Ban 6*   **V** R G R SMITH
LLANDEGLA (St Tecla) *St As 3*   **R** M SQUIRES
LLANDEGLEY (St Tecla)   *see* Llanbadarn Fawr, Llandegley and Llanfihangel etc *S & B*
LLANDEGVETH (St Tegfeth)   *see* Llanfrechfa and Llanddewi Fach w Llandegveth *Mon*
LLANDEILO   *see* Maenclochog and New Moat etc *St D*
LLANDEILO ABERCYWYN   *see* Llansteffan and Llan-y-bri etc *St D*
LLANDEILO FAWR (St Teilo) and Taliaris *St D 14*   **V** P J BEMENT,   **C** R J DAVIES
LLANDEILO GRABAN (St Teilo)   *see* Aberedw w Llandeilo Graban and Llanbadarn etc *S & B*
LLANDEILO TAL-Y-BONT (St Teilo) (St Michael) *S & B 9*   **V** J P H WALTERS
LLANDELOY (St Teilo)   *see* Dewisland *St D*
LLANDENNY (St John the Apostle)   *see* Raglan w Llandenny and Bryngwyn *Mon*
LLANDEUSSANT (St Simon and St Jude)   *see* Llangadog and Gwynfe w Llanddeusant *St D*
LLANDEVAUD (St Peter)   *see* Penhow, St Brides Netherwent w Llandavenny etc *Mon*
LLANDEWI FACH   *see* Llanfrechfa and Llanddewi Fach w Llandegveth *Mon*
LLANDEWI SKIRRID (St David)   *see* Llantilio Pertholey w Bettws Chpl etc *Mon*
LLANDEWI VELFREY (St David)   *see* Lamp Velfrey and Llanddewi Velfrey *St D*
LLANDILO'R FAN (St Teilo)   *see* Defynnog, Llandilo'r Fan, Llanulid, Llywel etc *S & B*
LLANDINAM (St Llonio) w Trefeglwys w Penstrowed *Ban 9*   **V** K FERGUSON
LLANDINGAT (St Dingad) w Myddfai *St D 14*   **V** B T RICE

LLANDINORWIG (Christ Church) (St Mary) *Ban 1*   **V** *vacant*
LLANDOGO (St Oudoceus) w Whitebrook Chapel and Tintern Parva *Mon 2*   **R** J P W REES,   **NSM** J W DEARNLEY,   **N** HILL
LLANDOUGH (St Dochdwy) w Leckwith *Llan 5*   **R** B M LODWICK
LLANDOUGH (St Dochwy)   *see* Cowbridge *Llan*
LLANDOVERY   *see* Llandingat w Myddfai *St D*
LLANDOW (Holy Trinity)   *see* Colwinston w Llandow and Llysworney *Llan*
LLANDRILLO (St Trilio) (St Derfel) and Llandderfel *St As 17*   **V** S J ROBERTS
LLANDRILLO-YN-RHOS (St Trillo) (St George) *St As 6*   **V** D JACKS
LLANDRINDOD (Holy Trinity) (Old Parish Church) w Cefnllys and Disserth *S & B 5*   **R** A G LOAT,   **NSM** A TWEED
LLANDRINIO (St Trinio, St Peter and St Paul)   *see* Llandysilio and Penrhos and Llandrinio etc *St As*
LLANDRYGARN (St Trygarn) w Bodwrog, Heneglwys, Trewalchmai and Llanerch-y-medd *Ban 4*   **NSM** E D JERMAN
LLANDUDNO (St George) (St Tudno) (Holy Trinity) (Our Saviour) *Ban 2*   **R** P J COUSINS,   **C** J R ALLEN
LLANDUDWEN (St Tudwen)   *see* Nefyn w Tudweiliog w Llandudwen w Edern *Ban*
LLANDULAIS IN TIR ABAD (St David)   *see* Llanwrtyd w Llanddulas in Tir Abad etc *S & B*
LLANDWROG (St Twrog) and Llanwnda *Ban 1*   **V** D C BRYANT
LLANDYBIE (St Tybie) *St D 13*   **V** J H GRAVELL
LLANDYFAELOG (St Maelog)   *see* Cydweli and Llandyfaelog *St D*
LLANDYFAN (Church)   *see* Llandybie *St D*
LLANDYFODWG (St Tyfodwg)   *see* Tonyrefail w Gilfach Goch and Llandyfodwg *Llan*
LLANDYFRIOG (St Tyfriog)   *see* Newcastle Emlyn w Llandyfriog etc *St D*
LLANDYFRYDOG (St Tyfrydog)   *see* Llandrygarn w Bodwrog and Heneglwys etc *Ban*
LLANDYGAI (St Tegai) and Maes y Groes *Ban 5*   **P-in-c** A W COLEMAN
LLANDYGWYDD (St Tygwydd)   *see* Maenordeifi and Capel Colman w Llanfihangel etc *St D*
LLANDYRNOG (St Tyrnog) (St Cwyfan) and Llangwyfan *St As 2*   **R** E B THOMAS
LLANDYRY (Church)   *see* Pen-bre *St D*
LLANDYSILIO (St Tysilio)   *see* Llandegfan w Llandysilio *Ban*
LLANDYSILIO (St Tysilio) (St Mary) and Penrhos and Llandrinio w Criggion *St As 10*   **R** *vacant* (01691) 830533
LLANDYSILIO (St Tysilio) w Egremont and Llanglydwen w Cilymaenllwyd and Llanfyrnach *St D 15*   **V** *vacant* (01437) 563203
LLANDYSILIOGOGO (St Tysilio)   *see* Llangrannog w Llandysiliogogo w Penbryn *St D*
LLANDYSSIL (St Tyssil)   *see* Montgomery and Forden and Llandyssil *St As*
LLANDYSUL (St Tysul) w Bangor Teifi w Henllan and Llanfairorllwyn w Llangynllo *St D 7*   **V** E ROBERTS,   **C** I D FORSTER
LLANEDEYRN (All Saints)   *see* Cyncoed *Mon*
LLANEDI (St Edith) w Tycroes and Saron *St D 13*   **V** D G DAVIES
LLANEDWEN (St Edwen)   *see* Llanfair-pwll and Llanddaniel-fab etc *Ban*
LLANEGRYN (St Mary and St Egryn) w Aberdyfi w Tywyn *Ban 12*   **V** J M RILEY,   **NSM** C C TEN WOLDE
LLANEGWAD (St Egwad) w Llanfynydd *St D 14*   **V** P S JOHNES
LLANEILIAN (St Eilian)   *see* Amlwch *Ban*
LLANELEN (St Helen)   *see* Govilon w Llanfoist w Llanelen *Mon*
LLANELIAN (St Elian)   *see* Colwyn *St As*
LLANELIDAN (St Elidan)   *see* Llanfair DC, Derwen, Llanelidan and Efenechtyd *St As*
LLANELLI (St Elli) *S & B 3*   **V** A FRANCIS
LLANELLI (St Elli) (All Saints) (St Alban) (Christ Church) (St David) (St John) (St Peter) *St D 12*   **TR** I M THOMAS,   **TV** D R PAYNE, C J DAVIES,   **C** P R MACKNESS
LLANELLTUD (St Illtyd)   *see* Dolgellau w Llanfachreth and Brithdir etc *Ban*
LLANELWEDD (St Matthew) w Llanfaredd w Llansantffraed-in-Elwell w Bettws Disserth and Cregrina w Glascombe and Rhulen *S & B 2*   **V** *vacant*
LLANENDDWYN (St Enddwyn) w Llanddwywe and Llanbedr w Llandanwg *Ban 8*   **R** S K N BEACON
LLANENGAN (St Engan)   *see* Llanbedrog w Llannor and Llangian *Ban*
LLANERCH AERON (St Non) w Ciliau Aeron and Dihewyd and Mydroilyn *St D 8*   **R** D B DAVIES

LLANERCH-Y-MEDD (Eglwys Crist) *see* Llandyrgarn w Bodwrog and Heneglwys etc *Ban*

LLANERCH-Y-MEDD (St Mair) *as above Ban*

LLANERFYL (St Erfyl) *see* Garthbeibio w Llanerfyl w Llangadfan *St As*

LLANEUGRAD (St Eugrad) w Llanallgo and Penrhosllugwy w Llanfihangel Tre'r Beirdd *Ban 7* **R** G D LOVELUCK

LLANFABON (St Mabon) (St John the Baptist) *Llan 1* **R** C T REANEY

LLANFACHRAETH (St Machraeth) *see* Bodedern w Llanfaethlu *Ban*

LLANFACHRETH (St Machreth) *see* Dolgellau w Llanfachreth and Brithdir etc *Ban*

LLANFAELOG (St Maelog) and Llangwyfan *Ban 3* **R** M M BRADY

LLANFAELRHYS (St Maelrhys) *see* Aberdaron w Rhiw and Llanfaelrhys etc *Ban*

LLANFAES *see* Brecon St David w Llanspyddid and Llanilltyd *S & B*

LLANFAETHLU (St Maethlu) *see* Bodedern w Llanfaethlu *Ban*

LLANFAGLAN (St Mary) *see* Llandwrog and Llanwnda *Ban*

LLANFAIR (Church) *see* Gwaun-cae-Gurwen *St D*

LLANFAIR (Church) *see* Llandingat w Myddfai *St D*

LLANFAIR (St Mary) *see* Grosmont and Skenfrith and Llangattock etc *Mon*

LLANFAIR-AR-Y-BRYN (St Mary) *see* Cil-y-Cwm and Ystrad-ffin w Rhandir-mwyn etc *St D*

LLANFAIR CAEREINION (St Mary) w Llanllugan *St As 8* **V** P K D EVANS

LLANFAIR CLYDOGAU (St Mary) *see* Lampeter and Llanddewibrefi Gp *St D*

LLANFAIR DISCOED (St Mary) *see* Caerwent w Dinham and Llanfair Discoed etc *Mon*

LLANFAIR DYFFRYN CLWYD (St Cynfarch and St Mary) (Jesus Chapel) and Derwen and Llanelidan and Efenechtyd *St As 3* **V** T E MART

LLANFAIR-IS-GAER (Old Parish Church) *see* Llanddeiniolen w Llanfair-is-gaer etc *Ban*

LLANFAIR-IS-GAER (St Mary) *as above Ban*

LLANFAIR-JUXTA-HARLECH (St Mary) *see* Harlech and Llanfair-juxta-Harlech etc *Ban*

LLANFAIR KILGEDDIN *see* Bettws Newydd w Trostrey etc *Mon*

LLANFAIR MATHAFARN EITHAF (St Mary) w Llanbedrgoch *Ban 6* **R** P H PRITCHARD

LLANFAIR NANT-GWYN (St Mary) *see* Nevern and Y Beifil w Eglwyswrw and Meline etc *St D*

LLANFAIR NANT-Y-GOF (St Mary) *see* Letterston w Llanfair Nant-y-Gof etc *St D*

LLANFAIR-PWLL (St Mary) and Llanddaniel-fab w Penmynydd w Llanedwen *Ban 6* **R** P HUGHES, **NSM** L M EDWARDS

LLANFAIR TALHAEARN (St Mary) *see* Betws-yn-Rhos w Petryal *St As*

LLANFAIR-YN-NEUBWLL *see* Valley w Llechylched and Caergeiliog *Ban*

LLANFAIR-YN-Y-CWMWD (St Mary) *see* Newborough w Llanidan and Llangeinwen etc *Ban*

LLANFAIR-YNG-NGHORNWY (St Mary) *see* Bodedern w Llanfaethlu *Ban*

LLANFAIRFECHAN (St Mary) (Christ Church) w Aber *Ban 2* **R** C M EVANS

LLANFAIRORLLWYN (St Mary) *see* Llandysul w Bangor Teifi w Henllan etc *St D*

LLANFAIRPWLL (St Mary) *see* Llanfair-pwll and Llanddaniel-fab etc *Ban*

LLANFALLTEG (St Mallteg) w Clunderwen and Castell Dwyran *St D 15* **R** *vacant*

LLANFAREDD (St Mary) *see* Llanelwedd w Llanfaredd w Llansantffraed etc *S & B*

LLANFECHAIN (St Garmon) *see* Llansantffraid-ym-Mechain and Llanfechain *St As*

LLANFECHAN (St Afan) *see* Irfon Valley *S & B*

LLANFECHELL (St Mechell) w Bodewryd w Rhosbeirio w Llanfflewin and Llanbadrig *Ban 7* **R** G W EDWARDS

LLANFERRES (St Berres) *see* Gwernaffield and Llanferres *St As*

LLANFEUGAN (St Meugan) w Llanthetty w Llansantffraed-juxta-Usk *S & B 3* **R** W S P JACKSON

LLANFFINAN (St Ffinan) *see* Llanfihangel Ysgeifiog w Llangristiolus etc *Ban*

LLANFFLEWIN (St Fflewin) *see* Llanfechell w Bodewryd w Rhosbeirio etc *Ban*

LLANFIHANGEL (St Michael) *see* Llantwit Major *Llan*

LLANFIHANGEL ABERCYWYN (St Michael) *see* St Clears w Llangynin and Llanddowror etc *St D*

LLANFIHANGEL ABERGWESSIN *see* Llanwrtyd w Llanddulas in Tir Abad etc *S & B*

LLANFIHANGEL ABERYTHYCH (St Michael) *see* Llangathen w Llanfihangel Cilfargen etc *St D*

LLANFIHANGEL-AR-ARTH (St Michael) w Capel Dewi *St D 7* **V** J H A JAMES

LLANFIHANGEL BRYNPABUAN (St Michael and All Angels) *see* Upper Wye *S & B*

LLANFIHANGEL CILFARGEN *see* Llangathen w Llanfihangel Cilfargen etc *St D*

LLANFIHANGEL CRUCORNEY (St Michael) w Oldcastle and Cwmyoy and Llanthony *Mon 1* **V** D J YOUNG

LLANFIHANGEL FECHAN (St Michael) *see* Merthyr Cynog and Dyffryn Honddu etc *S & B*

LLANFIHANGEL GENAU'R-GLYN (St Michael) and Llangorwen *St D 10* **V** D B THOMAS

LLANFIHANGEL GLYN MYFYR (St Michael) *see* Cerrigydrudion w Llanfihangel Glyn Myfyr etc *St As*

LLANFIHANGEL GOBION (St Michael) *see* Bettws Newydd w Trostrey etc *Mon*

LLANFIHANGEL HELYGEN (St Michael) *see* Upper Wye *S & B*

LLANFIHANGEL LLEDROD (St Michael) *see* Llanilar w Rhostie and Llangwyryfon etc *St D*

LLANFIHANGEL NANTBRAN (St Michael) *see* Trallwng w Bettws Penpont w Aberyskir etc *S & B*

LLANFIHANGEL NANTMELAN (St Michael) *see* New Radnor and Llanfihangel Nantmelan etc *S & B*

LLANFIHANGEL PENBEDW *see* Maenordeifi and Capel Colman w Llanfihangel etc *St D*

LLANFIHANGEL PONTYMOILE (St Michael) *see* Mamhilad and Llanfihangel Pontymoile *Mon*

LLANFIHANGEL RHOS-Y-CORN (St Michael) *see* Brechfa w Abergorlech etc *St D*

LLANFIHANGEL RHYDITHON (St Michael) *see* Llanbadarn Fawr, Llandegley and Llanfihangel etc *S & B*

LLANFIHANGEL ROGIET *see* Caldicot *Mon*

LLANFIHANGEL TALYLLYN (St Michael) *see* Llyn Safaddan *S & B*

LLANFIHANGEL-TOR-Y-MYNYDD (St Michael) *see* Llanishen w Trellech Grange and Llanfihangel etc *Mon*

LLANFIHANGEL TRE'R BEIRDD (St Mihangel) *see* Llaneugrad w Llanallgo and Penrhosllugwy etc *Ban*

LLANFIHANGEL-UWCH-GWILI (St Michael) *see* Abergwili w Llanfihangel-uwch-Gwili etc *St D*

LLANFIHANGEL-Y-CREUDDYN (St Michael) w Llanafan-y-Trawscoed and Llanwnnws and Ysbyty Ystwyth *St D 10* **V** H A CHIPLIN

LLANFIHANGEL-Y-PENNANT (St Michael) *see* Llanegryn w Aberdyfi w Tywyn *Ban*

LLANFIHANGEL-Y-TRAETHAU (St Michael) *see* Harlech and Llanfair-juxta-Harlech etc *Ban*

LLANFIHANGEL-YN-NHYWYN *see* Valley w Llechylched and Caergeiliog *Ban*

LLANFIHANGEL-YNG-NGHWYNFA (St Michael) *see* Llanwddyn and Llanfihangel-yng-Nghwynfa etc *St As*

LLANFIHANGEL YSGEIFIOG (St Michael) w Llangristiolus w Llanffinan *Ban 4* **R** *vacant*

LLANFIHANGEL-YSTERN-LLEWERN (St Michael) *see* Rockfield and St Maughen's w Llangattock etc *Mon*

LLANFIHANGEL YSTRAD (St Michael) and Cilcennin w Trefilan and Nantcwnlle *St D 8* **V** B W THOMAS

LLANFILO (St Bilo) *see* Bronllys w Llanfilo *S & B*

LLANFOIST (St Ffwyst) *see* Govilon w Llanfoist w Llanelen *Mon*

LLANFOR (St Mor and St Deiniol) w Rhosygwaliau *St As 17* **R** *vacant*

LLANFRECHFA (All Saints) and Llanddewi Fach w Llandegveth *Mon 10* **V** A SILVERTHORN

LLANFROTHEN (St Brothen) *see* Penrhyndeudraeth w Llanfrothen w Beddgelert *Ban*

LLANFRYNACH (St Brynach) *see* Cowbridge *Llan*

LLANFRYNACH (St Brynach) and Cantref w Llanhamlach *S & B 3* **V** P G R SIMS

LLANFUGAIL (St Migail) *see* Valley w Llechylched and Caergeiliog *Ban*

LLANFWROG (St Mwrog and St Mary) and Clocaenog and Gyffylliog *St As 3* **R** J B DAVIES

LLANFYLLIN (St Myllin) and Bwlchycibau *St As 9* **R** M R BALKWILL

LLANFYNYDD (St Egwad) *see* Llanegwad w Llanfynydd *St D*

LLANFYNYDD (St Michael) (St Egwad) *St As 16* **R** A J POOLMAN

LLANFYRNACH (St Brynach) *see* Llandysilio w Egremont and Llanglydwen etc *St D*

LLANGADFAN (St Cadfan) *see* Garthbeibio w Llanerfyl w Llangadfan *St As*

LLANGADOG (St Cadog) and Gwynfe w Llanddeusant *St D 14* **V** K M D COTTAM

LLANGADWALADR (St Cadwaladr) *see* Llansilin w Llangadwaladr and Llangedwyn *St As*

LLANGADWALADR (St Cadwaladr) *see* Trefdraeth w Aberffraw, Llangadwaladr etc *Ban*

LLANGAFFO (St Caffo) *see* Newborough w Llanidan and Llangeinwen etc *Ban*

LLANGAIN (St Cain) *see* Llan-llwch w Llangain and Llangynog *St D*

LLANGAMMARCH (St Cadmarch) *see* Irfon Valley *S & B*

LLANGAN (St Canna) *see* Coychurch w Llangan and St Mary Hill *Llan*

LLANGANTEN (St Cannen) *see* Irfon Valley *S & B*

LLANGAR (St John the Evangelist) *see* Corwen w Llangar, Glyndyfrdwy etc *St As*

LLANGASTY TALYLLYN (St Gastyn) *see* Llyn Safaddan *S & B*

LLANGATHEN (St Cathen) w Llanfihangel Cilfargen and Llanfihangel Aberythych *St D 14* **V** W R HUGHES

LLANGATTOCK (St Cattwg) and Llangynidr *S & B 3* **R** K RICHARDS, **NSM** A S ROBINSON

LLANGATTOCK-JUXTA-USK (St Cadoc) *see* Llanddewi Rhydderch w Llangattock-juxta-Usk etc *Mon*

LLANGATTOCK LINGOED (St Cadoc) *see* Grosmont and Skenfrith and Llangattock etc *Mon*

LLANGATTOCK-VIBON-AVEL (St Cadoc) *see* Rockfield and St Maughen's w Llangattock etc *Mon*

LLANGEDWYN (St Cedwyn) *see* Llansilin w Llangadwaladr and Llangedwyn *St As*

LLANGEFNI (St Cyngar) w Tregaean *Ban 4* **P-in-c** T L JENKINS

LLANGEINOR (St Ceinor) *Llan 6* **P-in-c** D J MORTIMORE

LLANGEINWEN (St Ceinwen) *see* Newborough w Llanidan and Llangeinwen etc *Ban*

LLANGEITHO (St Ceitho) and Blaenpennal w Betws Leucu and Gartheli *St D 9* **P-in-c** J D E JONES

LLANGELER (St Celer) w Pen-Boyr *St D 7* **V** E HOWELLS

LLANGELYNIN (St Celynnin) *see* Caerhun w Llangelynin w Llanbedr-y-Cennin *Ban*

LLANGELYNNIN (St Celynin) *see* Arthog w Fairbourne w Llangelynnin w Rhoslefain *Ban*

LLANGENNECH (St Gwynog) and Hendy *St D 12* **V** B D WITT

LLANGENNI (St Cenau) and Llanbedr Ystrad Yw w Patricio *S & B 3* **R** K J M EWEN, **NSM** R O MULLIS

LLANGENNITH (St Cenydd) *see* Reynoldston w Penrice and Llangennith *S & B*

LLANGERNYW (St Digain) *see* Betws-yn-Rhos w Petryal *St As*

LLANGEVIEW (St David) *see* Llangwm Uchaf and Llangwm Isaf w Gwernesney etc *Mon*

LLANGIAN (St Gian) *see* Llanbedrog w Llannor and Llangian *Ban*

LLANGIWG (St Ciwg) *S & B 7* **V** G H GREEN

LLANGLYDWEN (St Cledwyn) *see* Llandysilio w Egremont and Llanglydwen etc *St D*

LLANGOEDMOR (St Cynllo) *see* Cardigan w Mwnt and Y Ferwig w Llangoedmor *St D*

LLANGOLLEN (St Collen) (St John) w Trevor and Llantysilio *St As 14* **V** W L JONES, **C** O B PARRY

LLANGOLMAN (St Colman) *see* Maenclochog and New Moat etc *St D*

LLANGORSE (St Paulinus) *see* Llyn Safaddan *S & B*

LLANGORWEN (All Saints) *see* Llanfihangel Genau'r-glyn and Llangorwen *St D*

LLANGOWER (St Cywair) *see* Llanycil w Bala and Frongoch and Llangower etc *St As*

LLANGRANNOG (St Carannog) w Llandysiliogogo w Penbryn *St D 8* **V** *vacant* (01239) 654003

LLANGRISTIOLUS (St Cristiolus) *see* Llanfihangel Ysgeifiog w Llangristiolus etc *Ban*

LLANGUNNOG *see* Llanishen w Trellech Grange and Llanfihangel etc *Mon*

LLANGUNNOR (St Ceinwr) w Cwmffrwd *St D 11* **V** W D A GRIFFITHS, **NSM** C M STEEL

LLANGURIG (St Curig) *see* Llanidloes w Llangurig *Ban*

LLANGWLLOG (St Cwyllog) *see* Llandrygarn w Bodwrog and Heneglwys etc *Ban*

LLANGWLLONG (St Anau) *as above Ban*

LLANGWM (St Catherine) *see* Betws Gwerful Goch w Llangwm, Gwyddelwern etc *St As*

LLANGWM (St Jerome) w Freystrop and Johnston *St D 5* **R** W G HOOPER

LLANGWM ISAF (St John) *see* Llangwm Uchaf and Llangwm Isaf w Gwernesney etc *Mon*

LLANGWM UCHAF (St Jerome) and Llangwm Isaf w Gwernesney and Llangeview w Wolvesnewton *Mon 5* **P-in-c** D WOOD

LLANGWNNADL (St Gwynhoedl) *see* Aberdaron w Rhiw and Llanfaelrhys etc *Ban*

LLANGWYFAN *see* Llandyrnog and Llangwyfan *St As*

LLANGWYFAN (St Cwyfan) *see* Llanfaelog and Llangwyfan *Ban*

LLANGWYFAN (St Cwyfan Old Church) *as above Ban*

LLANGWYRYFON (St Ursula) *see* Llanilar w Rhostie and Llangwyryfon etc *St D*

LLANGYBI (St Cybi) *see* Criccieth and Treflys w Llanystumdwy etc *Ban*

LLANGYBI (St Cybi) *see* Lampeter and Llanddewibrefi Gp *St D*

LLANGYBI (St Cybi) and Coedypaen w Llanbadoc *Mon 5* **R** A E MORTON, **NSM** A T BOYLAND

LLANGYFELACH (St David and St Cyfelach) (St Teilo-on-the-Clase) *S & B 7* **V** R J DAVIES-HANNEN

LLANGYNDEYRN (St Cyndeyrn) *see* Cwm Gwendraeth *St D*

LLANGYNDIR (St Cynidr and St Mary) *see* Llangattock and Llangynidr *S & B*

LLANGYNFELYN (St Cynfelyn) *see* Borth and Eglwys-fach w Llangynfelyn *St D*

LLANGYNHAFAL (St Cynhafal) *see* Llanbedr DC w Llangynhafal, Llanychan etc *St As*

LLANGYNIN (St Cynin) *see* St Clears w Llangynin and Llanddowror etc *St D*

LLANGYNLLO (St Cynllo) *see* Llandysul w Bangor Teifi w Henllan etc *St D*

LLANGYNLLO (St Cynllo) *see* Beguildy and Heyope and Llangynllo and Bleddfa *S & B*

LLANGYNOG *see* Builth and Llanddewi'r Cwm w Llangynog etc *S & B*

LLANGYNOG (St Cynog) *see* Llan-llwch w Llangain and Llangynog *St D*

LLANGYNOG (St Cynog) (St Melangel) *St As 9* **R** *vacant*

LLANGYNWYD (St Cynwyd) (St Stephen) (St Tydfil) w Maesteg *Llan 6* **V** E M R MORGAN, **C** A M LATIFA, J HARMAN

LLANGYNYW (St Cynyw) *see* Meifod w Llangynyw w Pont Robert w Pont Dolanog *St As*

LLANGYSTENNIN (St Cystenin) (St Michael) (St Katherine) (St Mary) *St As 5* **P-in-c** J C HARVEY, **NSM** D KAY

LLANHAMLACH (St Peter and St Illtyd) *see* Llanfrynach and Cantref w Llanhamlach *S & B*

LLANHARAN (St Julius and St Aaron) w Peterston-super-Montem *Llan 6* **V** R E MOVERLEY

LLANHARRY (St Illtud) *Llan 4* **P-in-c** G A BLYTH, **NSM** B J REANEY

LLANHENNOCK (St John) *see* Caerleon w Llanhennock *Mon*

LLANHILLETH (Christchurch) (St Mark) *Mon 8* **P-in-c** M T MESLEY

LLANHYWEL (St Hywel) *see* Dewisland *St D*

LLANIDAN (St Nidan) *see* Newborough w Llanidan and Llangeinwen etc *Ban*

LLANIDLOES (St Idloes) w Llangurig *Ban 9* **V** R P PITCHER, **NSM** A N FIRTH

LLANIESTYN (St Iestyn) *see* Llansadwrn w Llanddona and Llaniestyn etc *Ban*

LLANIESTYN (St Iestyn) *see* Botwnnog w Bryncroes *Ban*

LLANIGON (St Eigon) *see* Hay w Llanigon and Capel-y-Ffin *S & B*

LLANILAR (St Hilary) w Rhostie and Llangwyryfon w Llanfihangel Lledrod *St D 10* **P-in-c** R W TOWNSEND

LLANILID (St Illid and St Curig) w Pencoed *Llan 6* **R** N P JONES

LLANILLTYD (St John) *see* Brecon St David w Llanspyddid and Llanilltyd *S & B*

LLANINA (St Ina) *see* Llanllwchaearn and Llanina *St D*

LLANISHEN (Christ Church) *see* Cardiff Ch Ch Roath Park *Llan*

LLANISHEN (St Dennis) w Trellech Grange and Llanfihangel Tor-y-Mynydd w Llangunnog and Llansoy *Mon 3* **P-in-c** D M OWEN

LLANISHEN (St Isan) (St Faith) *Llan 2* **V** M D WITCOMBE, **C** G J R GEORGE-ROGERS

LLANLLAWDDOG (St Llawddog) *see* Llanpumsaint w Llanllawddog *St D*

LLANLLAWER *see* Newport w Cilgwyn and Dinas w Llanllawer *St D*

LLANLLECHID (St Cross) *see* Llandygai and Maes y Groes *Ban*

LLANLLECHID (St Llechid)   *see* Glanogwen w St Ann's w Llanllechid *Ban*
LLANLLEONFEL (Parish Church)   *see* Irfon Valley *S & B*
LLANLLOWELL (St Llywel) *Mon 9*   **V** *vacant*
LLANLLUGAN (St Mary)   *see* Llanfair Caereinion w Llanllugan *St As*
LLANLLWCHAEARN (St Llwchaiarn) and Llanina *St D 8*   **R** M J NEEDS
LLANLLWCHAIARN (All Saints)   *see* Newtown w Llanllwchaiarn w Aberhafesp *St As*
LLANLLWCHAIARN (St Llwchaiarn)   *as above St As*
LLANLLWNI (St Luke or St Llonio)   *see* Llanybydder and Llanwenog w Llanllwni *St D*
LLANLLYFNI (St Rhedyw) (St John) (Christ Church) *Ban 1*   P-in-c R B D REES
LLANLLYR-YN-RHOS (St Llyr)   *see* Upper Wye *S & B*
LLANMADOC (St Madoc)   *see* Llanrhidian w Llanmadoc and Cheriton *S & B*
LLANMAES (St Catwg)   *see* Llantwit Major *Llan*
LLANMARTIN (St Martin)   *see* Bishton *Mon*
LLANMEREWIG (St Llwchaiarn)   *see* Kerry and Llanmerewig and Dolfor *St As*
LLANMILOE (St Barbara)   *see* Pendine w Llanmiloe and Eglwys Gymyn w Marros *St D*
LLANNEFYDD (St Nefydd and St Mary)   *see* Henllan and Llannefydd and Bylchau *St As*
LLANNOR (Holy Cross)   *see* Llanbedrog w Llannor and Llangian *Ban*
LLANOVER (St Bartholomew)   *see* Goetre w Llanover *Mon*
LLANPUMSAINT (Five Saints) w Llanllawddog *St D 11*   P-in-c M A ROWLANDS
LLANRHAEADR-YM-MOCHNANT (St Dogfan), Llanarmon Mynydd Mawr and Penybontfawr *St As 9*   **V** J H C DAVIES
LLANRHAEADR-YNG-NGHINMEIRCH (St Dyfnog) w Prion and Nantglyn *St As 2*   **V** J M WILLIAMS
LLANRHEITHAN (St Rheithan)   *see* Dewisland *St D*
LLANRHIAN (St Rhian)   *as above St D*
LLANRHIDIAN (St Rhidian and St Illtyd) w Llanmadoc and Cheriton *S & B 8*   P-in-c J E PHILLIPS
LLANRHOS (St Paul) *St As 5*   **V** R H GRIFFITHS, C S S M DAVIES, V A BURTON, **NSM** P A WRIGHT
LLANRHUDDLAD (St Rhuddlad)   *see* Bodedern w Llanfaethlu *Ban*
LLANRHYWDRUS   *as above Ban*
LLANRHYCHWYN (St Rhychwyn)   *see* Caerhun w Llangelynin w Llanbedr-y-Cennin *Ban*
LLANRHYDD (St Meugan)   *see* Ruthin w Llanrhydd *St As*
LLANRHYSTUD (St Restitutis)   *see* Llansantffraed and Llanbadarn Trefeglwys etc *St D*
LLANRUG (St Gabriel)   *see* Llanberis w Llanrug *Ban*
LLANRUG (St Michael)   *as above Ban*
LLANRUMNEY (St Dyfrig) *Mon 6*   **V** *vacant* (029) 2079 2761
LLANRWST (St Grwst) and Llanddoget and Capel Garmon *St As 5*   **R** N H WILLIAMS, **C** N C WILLIAMS
LLANSADWRN (St Sadwrn) w Llanddona and Llaniestyn w Pentraeth w Llanddyfnan *Ban 6*   **R** D PRYS
LLANSADWRN (St Sadwrn) w Llanwrda and Manordeilo *St D 14*   **V** A J LEGG
LLANSADWRNEN (St Sadwrnen)   *see* Laugharne w Llansadwrnen and Llandawke *St D*
LLANSAMLET (St Samlet) (St John) (St Paul) *S & B 7*   **V** C M DARVILL, **C** P KEOWN
LLANSANNAN (St Sannan)   *see* Betws-yn-Rhos w Petryal *St As*
LLANSANNOR (St Senwyr)   *see* Cowbridge *Llan*
LLANSANTFFRAED (St Bridget)   *see* Llanddewi Rhydderch w Llangattock-juxta-Usk etc *Mon*
LLANSANTFFRAED (St Bridget) and Llanbadarn Trefeglwys w Llanrhystud *St D 8*   **V** J W SMITH
LLANSANTFFRAED-IN-ELWELL (St Bridget)   *see* Llanelwedd w Llanfaredd w Llansantffraed etc *S & B*
LLANSANTFFRAED-JUXTA-USK (St Bride)   *see* Llanfeugan w Llanthetty etc *S & B*
LLANSANTFFRAID GLAN CONWY (St Ffraid) (St Martin) and Eglwysbach *St As 5*   **R** C R OWEN
LLANSANTFFRAID GLYN CEIRIOG (St Ffraid) and Llanarmon Dyffryn Ceiriog and Pontfadog *St As 14*   **V** P J CLARKE
LLANSANTFFRAID-YM-MECHAIN (St Ffraid) and Llanfechain *St As 9*   **V** M J BENNETT
LLANSANTFFRAID GLYN DYFRDWY (St Ffraid)   *see* Corwen w Llangar, Glyndyfrdwy etc *St As*
LLANSAWEL (St Mary), Briton Ferry *Llan 8*   **V** G C POWELL
LLANSAWEL (St Sawyl)   *see* Cynwyl Gaeo w Llansawel and Talley *St D*
LLANSILIN (St Silin) w Llangadwaladr and Llangedwyn *St As 9*   **V** C F CARTER

LLANSOY (St Tysoi)   *see* Llanishen w Trellech Grange and Llanfihangel etc *Mon*
LLANSPYDDID (St Cattwg)   *see* Brecon St David w Llanspyddid and Llanilltyd *S & B*
LLANSTADWEL (St Tudwal) *St D 5*   **V** P W D FLAVELL
LLANSTEFFAN (St Ystyffan) and Llan-y-bri and Llandeilo Abercywyn *St D 11*   **V** S E JONES
LLANSTEPHEN (St Steffan)   *see* Llandefalle and Llyswen w Boughrood etc *S & B*
LLANSTINAN (St Justinian)   *see* Llanwnda, Goodwick w Manorowen and Llanstinan *St D*
LLANTARNAM (St Michael)   *see* Cwmbran *Mon*
LLANTHETTY (St Tetti)   *see* Llanfeugan w Llanthetty etc *S & B*
LLANTHONY (St David)   *see* Llanfihangel Crucorney w Oldcastle etc *Mon*
LLANTILIO CROSSENNY (St Teilo) and Penrhos w Llanvetherine and Llanvapley *Mon 1*   **V** C H A PRINCE
LLANTILIO PERTHOLEY (St Teilo) w Bettws Chapel and Llanddewi Skirrid *Mon 1*   **V** J R CONNELL, **OLM** D A LEE
LLANTOOD   *see* Cilgerran w Bridell and Llantwyd *St D*
LLANTOOD (St Illtud)   *as above St D*
LLANTRISANT (Church)   *see* Ysbyty Cynfyn w Llantrisant and Eglwys Newydd *St D*
LLANTRISANT (St Afran, St Ieuan and St Sanan)   *see* Valley w Llechylched and Caergeiliog *Ban*
LLANTRISANT (St Illtyd, St Gwynno and St Dyfodwg) (St Michael) (St David) *Llan 11*   **V** V L PARKINSON, **C** C E BURR, **NSM** R M GRIFFITHS
LLANTRISANT (St Peter, St Paul and St John) *Mon 9*   **V** *vacant*
LLANTRITHYD (St Illtyd)   *see* Llancarfan w Llantrithyd *Llan*
LLANTWIT (St Illtyd)   *see* Neath *Llan*
LLANTWIT FARDRE (St Illtyd) (St Andrew) *Llan 11*   **V** M K JONES, **NSM** K G SIMPSON
LLANTWIT MAJOR (St Illtud) (St Donat) *Llan 4*   **TV** J L JONES, **C** E EVANS
LLANTWYD (St Illtud)   *see* Cilgerran w Bridell and Llantwyd *St D*
LLANTYSILIO (St Tysilio)   *see* Llangollen w Trevor and Llantysilio *St As*
LLANULID (St Ilid)   *see* Defynnog, Llandilo'r Fan, Llanulid, Llywel etc *S & B*
LLANUWCHLLYN (St Deiniol)   *see* Llanycil w Bala and Frongoch and Llangower etc *St As*
LLANVACHES (St Dyfrig)   *see* Penhow, St Brides Netherwent w Llandavenny etc *Mon*
LLANVAPLEY (St Mable)   *see* Llantilio Crossenny w Penrhos, Llanvetherine etc *Mon*
LLANVETHERINE (St James the Elder)   *as above Mon*
LLANWDDYN (St Wyddyn) and Llanfihangel-yng-Nghwynfa and Llwydiarth *St As 9*   **V** J E T YENDALL
LLANWELLWYFO (St Gwenllwyfo)   *see* Amlwch *Ban*
LLANWENARTH CITRA (St Peter)   *see* Abergavenny St Mary w Llanwenarth Citra *Mon*
LLANWENOG (St Gwenog)   *see* Llanybydder and Llanwenog w Llanllwni *St D*
LLANWERN (St Mary)   *see* Bishton *Mon*
LLANWINIO (St Gwynio)   *see* Tre-lech a'r Betws w Abernant and Llanwinio *St D*
LLANWNDA (St Baglan Old Church)   *see* Llandwrog and Llanwnda *Ban*
LLANWNDA (St Gwyndaf)   *as above Ban*
LLANWNDA (St Gwyndaf) and Goodwick (St Peter) w Manorowen and Llanstinan *St D 3*   **V** B BARNES
LLANWNNEN (St Lucia)   *see* Lampeter and Llanddewibrefi Gp *St D*
LLANWNNOG (St Gwynog) and Caersws w Carno *Ban 9*   **V** D J CHAPMAN
LLANWNNWS (St Gwnnws)   *see* Llanfihangel w Llanafan and Llanwnnws etc *St D*
LLANWRDA (St Cwrdaf)   *see* Llansadwrn w Llanwrda and Manordeilo *St D*
LLANWRIN (St Ust and St Dyfrig)   *see* Machynlleth w Llanwrin and Penegoes *Ban*
LLANWRTHWL (St Gwrthwl)   *see* Cwmdduadwr w St Harmon's and Llanwrthwl *S & B*
LLANWRTYD (St James) (St David) w Llanddulas in Tir Abad and Eglwys Oen Duw and Llanfihangel Abergwessin and Llanddewi *S & B 2*   **V** I B BESSANT
LLANWYDDELAN (St Gwyddelan)   *see* Betws Cedewain and Tregynon and Llanwyddelan *St D*
LLANWYNNO (St Gwynno) (Christ Church) *Llan 11*   **V** D GIBBS
LLANYBYDDER (St Peter) and Llanwenog w Llanllwni *St D 9*   **V** W R FILLERY

LLANYCEFN (Church)   *see* Llawhaden w Bletherston and
Llanycefn *St D*
LLANYCHAEARN (St Llwchaiarn) w Llanddeiniol *St D 10*
V B J H JONES
LLANYCHAN (St Hychan)   *see* Llanbedr DC w Llangynhafal,
Llanychan etc *St As*
LLANYCHAR (Church)   *see* Fishguard w Llanychar and
Pontfaen w Morfil etc *St D*
LLANYCHLWYDOG   *as above St D*
LLANYCIL (St Beuno) w Bala and Frongoch and Llangower w
Llanuwchllyn *St As 17*   R vacant
LLANYCRWYS (St David)   *see* Pencarreg and Llanycrwys *St D*
LLANYMAWDDWY (St Tydecho)   *see* Mallwyd w Cemais,
Llanymawddwy, Darowen etc *Ban*
LLANYNGHENEDL VALLEY (St Michael)   *see* Valley w
Llechylched and Caergeiliog *Ban*
LLANYNYS   *see* Builth and Llanddewi'r Cwm w Llangynog etc
S & B
LLANYNYS (St Saeran) *St As 3*   V vacant
LLANYRE   *see* Upper Wye *S & B*
LLANYRNEWYDD (St Gwynnor) *S & B 8*
P-in-c D M T WALTERS
LLANYSTYMDWY (St John the Baptist)   *see* Criccieth and
Treflys w Llanystumdwy etc *Ban*
LLANYWERN (St Mary the Virgin)   *see* Llyn Safaddan *S & B*
LLAWHADEN (St Aidan) w Bletherston and Llanycefn *St D 2*
V D E FAULKNER
LLAWRYBETWS (St James)   *see* Betws Gwerful Goch w
Llangwm, Gwyddelwern etc *St As*
LLAY (St Martin) *St As 13*   V D Q BELLAMY
LLECHGYNFARWY (St Cynfarwy)   *see* Bodedern w
Llanfaethlu *Ban*
LLECHRYD (St Tydfil)   *see* Maenordeifi and Capel Colman w
Llanfihangel etc *St D*
LLECHYLCHED (Holy Trinity)   *see* Valley w Llechylched and
Caergeiliog *Ban*
LLISWERRY   *see* Newport St Andr *Mon*
LLOWES (St Meilig)   *see* Glasbury and Llowes w Clyro and
Betws *S & B*
LLWYDCOED (St James)   *see* Aberdare St Fagan *Llan*
LLWYDIARTH (St Mary)   *see* Llanwddyn and
Llanfihangel-yng-Nghwynfa etc *St As*
LLWYNCELLYN (St Luke)   *see* Cymmer and Porth *Llan*
LLWYNDERW (Holy Cross) (Clyne Chapel) *S & B 6*
V G E BENNETT
LLWYNGWRIL   *see* Arthog w Fairbourne w Llangelynnin w
Rhoslefain *Ban*
LLWYNHENDY (St David) *St D 12*   V A M GRAY
LLWYNYPIA   *see* Ystrad Rhondda w Ynyscynon *Llan*
LLYN SAFADDAN *S & B 4*   V R T EDWARDS
LLYS-Y-FRAN (St Meilyr)   *see* Maenclochog and New Moat
etc *St D*
LLYSFAEN (St Cynfran)   *see* Colwyn *St As*
LLYSWEN (St Gwendoline)   *see* Llandefalle and Llyswen w
Boughrood etc *S & B*
LLYSWORNEY (St Tydfil)   *see* Colwinston w Llandow and
Llysworney *Llan*
LLYWEL (St David)   *see* Defynnog, Llandilo'r Fan, Llanulid,
Llywel etc *S & B*
LOUGHOR (St Michael) (St David) (St Paul) *S & B 9*
V D ROBERTS,   NSM K MORGAN
LOVESTON (St Leonard)   *see* Jeffreyston w Reynoldston and E
Williamston etc *St D*
LUDCHURCH (St Elidyr)   *see* Begelly w Ludchurch and
Crunwere *St D*
MACHEN (St Michael) (St John the Baptist) *Mon 6*
R P VANN,   Par Dn D A WRIGHT
MACHYNLLETH (St Peter) w Llanwrin and Penegoes *Ban 10*
R E W ROWLANDS,   C T R WEBB
MAENCLOCHOG (St Mary) and Llandeilo w Henry's Moat w
Mynachlogddu w Llangolman w New Moat w Llys y Fran
St D 2   V M N H GRAINGER
MAENORDEIFI (St Mary) (Old Parish Church) and Capel
Colman w Llanfihangel Penbedw w Penrhydd and Castellan w
Llandygwydd w Cenarth w Cilrhedyn and Llechryd *St D 6*
R G H J BALL
MAENTWROG (St Twrog) w Trawsfynydd *Ban 8*   R vacant
(0176687) 472
MAERDY (All Saints)   *see* Ferndale w Maerdy *Llan*
MAESGLAS and Duffryn *Mon 9*   V J V MOLE,   C D J SUTTON
MAESMYNIS AND LLANYNYS (St David)   *see* Builth and
Llanddewi'r Cwm w Llangynog etc *S & B*
MAESTEG (St David)   *see* Llangynwyd w Maesteg *Llan*
MAESTEG (St Michael)   *as above Llan*
MAESTEILO (St John)   *see* Llandeilo Fawr and Taliaris *St D*
MAESTIR (St Mary)   *see* Lampeter and Llanddewibrefi Gp
St D

MAGOR (St Mary) *Mon 4*   TR B J PARFITT,   Par
Dn A M PRICE,   NSM N D HOWARD
MAINDEE (St John the Evangelist) (St Mary) *Mon 9*
V D NEALE,   C H PORTER,   NSM J K BEARDMORE
MALLWYD (St Tydecho) w Cemais, Llanymawddwy, Darowen
and Llanbryn-Mair *Ban 10*   R vacant (01650) 531217
MALPAS (St Mary) *Mon 9*   V D G PARFITT,   C C M MORRIS,
C MORRIS,   OLM F M A EVANS
MAMHILAD (St Illtud) and Llanfihangel Pontymoile *Mon 5*
R R G HACKETT
MANAFON (St Michael) *St As 10*   R vacant
MANCOT (St Michael)   *see* Hawarden *St As*
MANOBIER (St James) and St Florence w Redberth *St D 1*
V V F MILLGATE
MANORDEILO (St Paul)   *see* Llansadwrn w Llanwrda and
Manordeilo *St D*
MANOROWEN (St Mary)   *see* Llanwnda, Goodwick w
Manorowen and Llanstinan *St D*
MANSELTON (St Michael and All Angels) *S & B 10*
V T H JONES
MARCHWIEL (St Marcella) and Isycoed *St As 11*   R D A SLIM
MARCROSS (Holy Trinity)   *see* Llantwit Major *Llan*
MARGAM (St Mary) (St David) *Llan 7*   V T A DOHERTY
MARLOES (St Peter)   *see* Dale and St Brides w Marloes *St D*
MARROS (St Lawrence)   *see* Pendine w Llanmiloe and Eglwys
Gymyn w Marros *St D*
MARSHFIELD (St Mary) and Peterstone Wentloog and
Coedkernew w St Bride's Wentloog *Mon 6*   V D C MATTHEWS,
Par Dn A J JENKINS
MARTLETWY (St Marcellus) w Lawrenny and Minwear and
Yerbeston w Templeton *St D 4*   V S M TEMPLE
MATHERN (St Tewdric) and Mounton w St Pierre *Mon 2*
V J E L WHITE
MATHRY (Holy Martyrs) w St Edren's and Grandston w
St Nicholas and Jordanston *St D 3*   V P L DAVIES
MATTHEWSTOWN (All Saints)   *see* Penrhiwceiber w
Matthewstown and Ynysboeth *Llan*
MAUDLAM (St Mary Magdalene)   *see* Pyle w Kenfig *Llan*
MEIDRIM (St David) and Llanboidy and Merthyr *St D 15*
V J GAINER
MEIFOD (St Tysilio and St Mary) w Llangynyw w Pont Robert w
Pont Dolanog *St As 8*   V J L W WILLIAMS
MELIDEN (St Melyd) (St Mary Magdalene) and Gwaenysgor
St As 1   V D P D H REES
MELINE (St Dogmael)   *see* Nevern and Y Beifil w Eglwyswrw
and Meline etc *St D*
MENAI BRIDGE (St Mary)   *see* Llandegfan w Llandysilio *Ban*
MERLIN'S BRIDGE (St Mark)   *see* Haverfordwest St Mary
and St Thos w Haroldston *St D*
MERTHYR (St Martin)   *see* Meidrim and Llanboidy and
Merthyr *St D*
MERTHYR CYNOG (St Cynog) and Dyffryn Honddu w
Garthbrengy w Llandefaelog-Fach and Llanfihangel Fechan
S & B 1   P-in-c J A I BROWN
MERTHYR DYFAN (St Dyfan and St Teilo) *Llan 5*
R R C PARRISH,   NSM B BUTLER
MERTHYR MAWR (St Teilo)   *see* Laleston w Tythegston and
Merthyr Mawr *Llan*
MERTHYR TYDFIL (Christ Church) (St Luke) *Llan 10*
V S S MORGAN,   C J E PARKIN,   C M L STONE,   W M TSANG
MERTHYR TYDFIL (St Tydfil) (St Tydfil's Well) *Llan 10*
R M J DAVIES,   C J A HAMMOND
MERTHYR VALE (St Mary and Holy Innocents)
see Troedyrhiw w Merthyr Vale *Llan*
MICHAELSTON-LE-PIT (St Michael and All Angels)   *see* St
Andrews Major w Michaelston-le-Pit *Llan*
MICHAELSTON-SUPER-AVON   *see* Cwmavon *Llan*
MICHAELSTON-SUPER-ELY (St Michael)   *see* St Fagans w
Michaelston-super-Ely *Llan*
MICHAELSTON-Y-FEDW (St Michael) *Mon 6*
P-in-c J A DALE
MICHEL TROY (St Michael)   *see* Monmouth w Overmonnow
etc *Mon*
MILFORD HAVEN (St Katherine) (St Peter) (St Thomas à
Becket) *St D 5*   V J H M DAVIES,   C E L MATHIAS-JONES
MINERA (St Mary) (St Tudfil) (St Andrew) (St David) *St As 15*
V J G CANHAM
MINWEAR (St Womar)   *see* Martletwy w Lawrenny and
Minwear etc *St D*
MISKIN (St John the Baptist)   *see* Mountain Ash and Miskin
Llan
MOCHDRE (All Saints) *St As 7*   P-in-c A R MARSHALL
MOLD (St Mary) *St As 16*   V C I DAY
MONINGTON (St Nicholas)   *see* St Dogmael's w Moylgrove
and Monington *St D*
MONKSWOOD (St Matthew)   *see* Usk and Monkswood w
Glascoed Chpl and Gwehelog *Mon*

MONKTON (St Nicholas and St John) *St D 1* **V** M L COX
MONMOUTH (St Mary the Virgin) w Overmonnow w Wonastow w Michel Troy *Mon 3* **V** R E PAIN, **NSM** S A DAVIES
MONTGOMERY (St Nicholas) and Forden and Llandyssil *St As 10* **R** A M HIRST, **C** S M CONSTABLE, **NSM** R BRIGNELL
MORFIL *see* Fishguard w Llanychar and Pontfaen w Morfil etc *St D*
MORRISTON (St David) (St John) *S & B 7* **V** H M LERVY, **NSM** E G PHILLIPS
MOSTYN (Christ Church) w Ffynnongroyw *St As 4* **P-in-c** J P ATACK
MOUNTAIN ASH (St Margaret) (St Illtyd) and Miskin *Llan 9* **C** M J CHILDS
MOUNTON *see* Narberth w Mounton w Robeston Wathen and Crinow *St D*
MOUNTON (St Andoenus) *see* Mathern and Mounton w St Pierre *Mon*
MOYLGROVE (St Mynno, St David and St Andrew) *see* St Dogmael's w Moylgrove and Monington *St D*
MWNT (Holy Cross) *see* Cardigan w Mwnt and Y Ferwig w Llangoedmor *St D*
MYDDFAI (St Michael) *see* Llandingat w Myddfai *St D*
MYDROILYN (Holy Trinity) *see* Llanerch Aeron w Ciliau Aeron and Dihewyd etc *St D*
MYNACHLOGDDU (St Dogmael) *see* Maenclochog and New Moat etc *St D*
MYNYDD ISA *see* Bistre *St As*
MYNYDDISLWYN (St Tudor) *Mon 7* **TR** R J SUMMERS, **TV** A S HUNT, R JEFFORD, **OLM** M BARGE
NANNERCH (St Michael) *see* Cilcain and Nannerch and Rhyd-y-mwyn *St As*
NANTCWNLLE (St Cynllo) *see* Llanfihangel Ystrad and Cilcennin w Trefilan etc *St D*
NANTGLYN (St James) *see* Llanrhaeadr-yng-Nghinmeirch w Prion and Nantglyn *St As*
NANTMEL (St Cynllo) *see* Rhayader and Nantmel *S & B*
NANTYGLO (Holy Trinity and St Anne) *see* Blaina and Nantyglo *Mon*
NARBERTH (St Andrew) w Mounton w Robeston Wathen and Crinow *St D 4* **R** T P LEWIS
NASH (St Mary) *see* Cosheston w Nash and Upton *St D*
NASH (St Mary) *see* Magor *Mon*
NEATH (St Thomas) (St David) (St Catherine) (St Peter and St Paul) *Llan 8* **TR** S J RYAN, **TV** A PIERCE JONES, **C** W M T V COUGHLIN, **NSM** C A MULLIGAN
NEBO (Dewi Sant) *see* Llansantffraed and Llanbadarn Trefeglwys etc *St D*
NEFYN (St David) (St Mary) w Tudweiliog w Llandudwen w Edern *Ban 11* **V** E OWEN, **NSM** N M HAWKINS
NELSON (St John the Baptist) *see* Llanfabon *Llan*
NERCWYS (St Mary) *see* Treuddyn w Nercwys *St As*
NEVERN (St Brynach) and Y Beifil w Eglwyswrw and Meline and Eglwyswen and Llanfair Nant-gwyn *St D 6* **V** J P LEWIS
NEW HEDGES (St Anne) *see* Tenby *St D*
NEW MOAT (St Nicholas) *see* Maenclochog and New Moat etc *St D*
NEW RADNOR (St Mary) and Llanfihangel Nantmelan and Evancoyd w Gladwestry and Colva *S & B 5* **NSM** P C F GERRARD
NEW TREDEGAR (St Dingat) *Mon 7* **Par Dn** J EVANS
NEWBOROUGH (St Peter) w Llanidan, Llangeinwen, Llanfair-yn-y-Cwmwd and Llangaffo *Ban 4* **R** R L NEWALL
NEWBRIDGE (St Paul) (St Peter) w Crumlin *Mon 7* **V** M J JEFFORD
NEWBRIDGE-ON-WYE (All Saints) *see* Upper Wye *S & B*
NEWCASTLE (St Illtud) *Llan 6* **V** D E C LLOYD, **NSM** O M PARRY
NEWCASTLE EMLYN (Holy Trinity) w Llandyfriog and Troed-yr-aur w Brongwyn *St D 7* **V** D J L ROBERTS
NEWCHURCH (St Mary) *see* Cynwil Elfed and Newchurch *St D*
NEWCHURCH (St Mary) *see* Bryngwyn and Newchurch and Llanbedr etc *S & B*
NEWCHURCH (St Michael) *see* Cynwil Elfed and Newchurch *St D*
NEWCHURCH (St Peter) *as above St D*
NEWCHURCH (St Peter) *see* Caerwent w Dinham and Llanfair Discoed etc *Mon*
NEWMARKET *see* Dyserth and Trelawnyd and Cwm *St As*
NEWPORT (All Saints) *Mon 9* **V** G HOLLOWOOD
NEWPORT (Cathedral of St Woolos) (St Martin) *Mon 9* **V** R D FENWICK, **C** G P HOWELL
NEWPORT (Christ Church) *Mon 9* **V** I S DOULL
NEWPORT (St Andrew) (St Philip) *Mon 9* **C** V I D F POWELL

NEWPORT (St John Baptist) *Mon 9* **V** C D WESTBROOK
NEWPORT (St John the Evangelist) *see* Maindee *Mon*
NEWPORT St Julian (St Julius and St Aaron) *Mon 9* **V** D R WILLIAMS
NEWPORT (St Mark) *Mon 9* **V** A R WILLIE
NEWPORT (St Mary) *see* Maindee *Mon*
NEWPORT (St Mary) w Cilgwyn and Dinas w Llanllawer *St D 6* **R** N A BRYAN
NEWPORT (St Matthew) *Mon 9* **P-in-c** P MUSINDI
NEWPORT St Paul *Mon 9* **P-in-c** S P TOMS
NEWPORT (St Stephen) and Holy Trinity *Mon 9* **V** *vacant* (01633) 65192
NEWPORT (St Teilo) *Mon 9* **P-in-c** T H J PALMER
NEWQUAY (St Llwchaiarn) *see* Llanllwchaearn and Llanina *St D*
NEWTON (St Peter) *S & B 6* **V** C M P JONES
NEWTON NORTH *see* Slebech and Uzmaston w Boulston *St D*
NEWTON NOTTAGE (St John the Baptist) (All Saints) (St David) *Llan 7* **R** P R MASSON, **C** B ANDREWS, P A LEYSHON
NEWTOWN (St David) w Llanllwchaiarn w Aberhafesp *St As 7* **R** *vacant* (01686) 625795
NEYLAND (St Clement) *see* Llanstadwel *St D*
NICHOLASTON (St Nicholas) *see* Oxwich w Penmaen and Nicholaston *S & B*
NOLTON (St Madog) w Roch *St D 5* **P-in-c** M H ROWLANDS
NOLTON (St Mary) *see* Coity w Nolton *Llan*
NORTHOP (St Eurgain and St Peter) (St Mary) *St As 16* **V** R J PEARCE
NORTON (Mission Church) *see* Oystermouth *S & B*
NORTON (St Andrew) *see* Knighton, Norton, Whitton, Pilleth and Cascob *S & B*
NOTTAGE (St David) *see* Newton Nottage *Llan*
OAKWOOD (St John) (St Teilo) *Llan 7* **V** *vacant*
OGMORE VALE (St John the Baptist) *see* Cwmogwr *Llan*
OVERMONNOW (St Thomas) *see* Monmouth w Overmonnow etc *Mon*
OVERTON (St Mary the Virgin) and Erbistock and Penley *St As 11* **R** M V JONES
OXWICH (St Illtyd) w Penmaen and Nicholaston *S & B 8* **V** R H MORGAN
OYSTERMOUTH (All Saints) *S & B 6* **V** K EVANS, **C** J ANDREW, **NSM** D J H WATKINS
PANTEG (St Mary) *Mon 10* **R** P K WALKER, **OLM** P EVANS
PANTYFFRID (Mission Church) *see* Manafon *St As*
PATRICIO (St Issui the Martyr) *see* Llangenni and Llanbedr Ystrad Yw w Patricio *S & B*
PEMBROKE Group, The (St Mary) (St Michael) (St Daniel) *St D 1* **V** R JONES, **C** H Q GREGORY-SMITH
PEMBROKE DOCK (St John) (St Patrick) (St Teilo) *St D 1* **V** A J DAVIES, **C** D E HAMMON
PEN-BOYR (St Llawddog) *see* Llangeler w Pen-Boyr *St D*
PEN-BRE (St Illtud) *St D 12* **V** A J MEATS
PENALLT (Old Church) and Trellech *Mon 3* **V** S J HOWELLS
PENALLY (St Nicholas) *see* Tenby *St D*
PENARTH (All Saints) (St Peter) (St Luke) *Llan 5* **V** P A COX, **C** S M REES
PENARTH (St Augustine) (Holy Nativity) w Lavernock *Llan 5* **R** R DONKIN, **C** S JENKYNS
PENBRYN (St Michael) *see* Llangrannog w Llandysiliogogo w Penbryn *St D*
PENCADER (St Mary) *see* Llanfihangel-ar-arth w Capel Dewi *St D*
PENCARREG (St Patrick) and Llanycrwys *St D 9* **V** B E MORRIS
PENCLAWDD *see* Llanyrnewydd *S & B*
PENCOED (St David) *see* Llanilid w Pencoed *Llan*
PENCOED (St Paul) *as above Llan*
PENCOEDCAE (Mission) *see* Graig *Llan*
PENDERYN (St Cynog) w Ystradfellte and Pontneathvaughan *S & B 1* **R** J H SCOTT
PENDINE (St Margaret) w Llanmiloe and Eglwys Gymyn w Marros *St D 15* **R** K T LITTLER
PENDOYLAN (St Cadoc) w Welsh St Donats *Llan 3* **V** E C R COUNSELL
PENEGOES (St Cadfarch) *see* Machynlleth w Llanwrin and Penegoes *Ban*
PENHOW (St John the Baptist) and St Brides Netherwent w Llandavenny and Llanvaches and Llandevaud *Mon 4* **V** J HEALES
PENISARWAEN (St Helen) *see* Llanddeiniolen w Llanfair-is-gaer etc *Ban*
PENLEY (St Mary Magdalene) *see* Overton and Erbistock and Penley *St As*
PENLLECH *see* Aberdaron w Rhiw and Llanfaelrhys etc *Ban*

REDWICK (St Thomas)   see Magor Mon
RESOLVEN (St David) w Tonna   Llan 8   V   N HADFIELD,
NSM   C GALSWORTHY
REYNOLDSTON (Church)   see Jeffreyston w Reynoldston and
E Williamston etc St D
REYNOLDSTON (St George) w Penrice and Llangennith
S & B 8   R   P J WILLIAMS
RHANDIRMWYN (St Barnabas)   see Cil-y-Cwm and
Ystrad-ffin w Rhandir-mwyn etc St D
RHAYADER (St Clement) and Nantmel   S & B 5   V vacant
(01597) 810223
RHESYCAE (Christ Church)   see Halkyn w Caerfallwch w
Rhesycae St As
RHEWL (Church)   see Llanbedr DC w Llangynhafal,
Llanychan etc St As
RHIWLAS (Mission Church)   see Llansilin w Llangadwaladr
and Llangedwyn St As
RHOS (St James)   see Llangeler w Pen-Boyr St D
RHOSBEIRIO   see Llanfechell w Bodewryd w Rhosbeirio etc
Ban
RHOSCOLYN   see Holyhead Ban
RHOSCROWTHER (St Decumanus)   see Castlemartin w
Warren and Angle etc St D
RHOSDDU   see Wrexham St As
RHOSESEMOR   see Halkyn w Caerfallwch w Rhesycae St As
RHOSILI (St Mary the Virgin)   see Port Eynon w Rhosili and
Llanddewi and Knelston S & B
RHOSLEFAIN (St Mary)   see Arthog w Fairbourne w
Llangelynnin w Rhoslefain Ban
RHOSLLANNERCHRUGOG (St John the Evangelist)
(St David) (St Mary)   St As 14   V   J S EVANS
RHOSTIE   see Llanilar w Rhostie and Llangwyryfon etc St D
RHOSYGWALIAU (Holy Trinity)   see Llanfor w Rhosygwaliau
St As
RHOSYMEDRE (St John the Evangelist) w Penycae   St As 14
V   R EVANS,   NSM   E C H OWEN
RHUDDLAN (St Mary)   St As 1   V   J G GRIFFITHS
RHULEN (St David)   see Llanelwedd w Llanfaredd w
Llansantffraed etc S & B
RHYD-Y-MWYN (St John the Evangelist)   see Cilcain and
Nannerch and Rhyd-y-mwyn St As
RHYDYBRIW (Capel Rhydybriw)   see Defynnog, Llandilo'r
Fan, Llanulid, Llywel etc S & B
RHYDYFELIN (St Luke)   Llan 11   V   C P SUTTON
RHYL (Holy Trinity) (St Thomas) (St John) (St Ann)   St As 1
V   J GLOVER,   P-in-c   A S GRIMWOOD,   C   N W ROBERTS
RHYMNEY (St David)   Mon 7   V   M A ADSETTS
RISCA (St Mary)   Mon 6   NSM   J A WELSH
ROATH (St German)   Llan 2   V   R D DOXSEY,   C   D J ATKINS
ROATH (St Margaret) (St Anne) (St Edward) (St Teilo's School)
Llan 2   V   R S EVANS,   C   C R DOWNS,   NSM   M J PRICE
ROATH (St Martin)   Llan 2   V   I D HAMER,   NSM   T G WATKIN
ROATH (St Philip)   see Tremorfa St Phil CD Llan
ROATH (St Saviour)   Llan 2   V   A RABJOHNS
ROATH PARK (Christ Church)   see Cardiff Ch Ch Roath Park
Llan
ROBERTSTOWN (St John the Evangelist)   see Aberdare Llan
ROBESTON WATHEN (Church)   see Narberth w Mounton w
Robeston Wathen and Crinow St D
ROBESTON WEST (St Andrew)   see Walwyn's Castle w
Robeston W St D
ROCH (St Mary)   see Nolton w Roch St D
ROCKFIELD (St Cenedlon) and St Maughen's w
Llangattock-vibon-Avel and Llanfihangel-ystern-Llewern
Mon 3   P-in-c   J R ELLIS,   NSM   J M ELLIS
ROGERSTONE (St John the Baptist)   see Bassaleg Mon
ROGIET (St Mary)   see Caldicot Mon
ROSEMARKET (St Ishmael)   see Burton and Rosemarket St D
ROSSETT (Christ Church)   St As 13   V   R A SUTER
RUABON (St Mary) (All Saints)   St As 14   V vacant (01978)
822176
RUDBAXTON (St Michael)   see Prendergast w Rudbaxton
St D
RUDRY (St James)   see Bedwas and Rudry Mon
RUMNEY (St Augustine)   Mon 6   V   D A G HATHAWAY
RUTHIN (St Peter) w Llanrhydd   St As 3   R   R BAYLEY
ST ANDREWS MAJOR (St Andrew) (St Peter) w
Michaelston-le-Pit   Llan 5   R   D H RHYDDERCH
ST ARVANS (St Arvan)   see Itton and St Arvans w Penterry and
Kilgwrrwg etc Mon
ST ASAPH (Cathedral of St Asaph and St Cyndeyrn)   St As 1
TR   C N L POTTER,   TV   A C SULLY
ST ATHAN (St Tathan)   see Eglwysbrewis w St Athan w
Gileston Llan
ST BRIDES (St Bridget)   see Dale and St Brides w Marloes St D
ST BRIDES MAJOR (St Bridget)   see Ewenny w St Brides
Major Llan

ST BRIDES MINOR (St Bride) w Bettws w Aberkenfig   Llan 6
C   G E DANIEL
ST BRIDES NETHERWENT (St Bridget)   see Penhow, St
Brides Netherwent w Llandavenny etc Mon
ST BRIDES-SUPER-ELY (St Bride)   see Peterston-super-Ely w
St Brides-super-Ely Llan
ST BRIDE'S WENTLOOG   see Marshfield and Peterstone
Wentloog etc Mon
ST CLEARS (St Mary Magdalene) w Llangynin and
Llanddowror and Llanfihangel Abercywyn   St D 15
V   R THOMAS
ST DAVIDS (Cathedral of St David and St Andrew)
see Dewisland St D
ST DOGMAEL'S (St Thomas) w Moylgrove and Monington
St D 6   V   D P DAVIES
ST DOGWELLS (St Dogfael)   see Spittal w Trefgarn and
Ambleston w St Dogwells St D
ST EDREN'S   see Mathry w St Edren's and Grandston etc St D
ST ELVIS   see Dewisland St D
ST FAGANS (St Mary) w Michaelston-super-Ely   Llan 3
R   A R WINTLE
ST FLORENCE (St Florentius)   see Manobier and St Florence
w Redberth St D
ST GEORGE (St George)   see Towyn and St George St As
ST GEORGE-SUPER-ELY (St George)   see St Nicholas w
Bonvilston and St George-super-Ely Llan
ST HARMON'S (St Garmon)   see Cwmddauddwr w St
Harmon's and Llanwrthwl S & B
ST HILARY Greenway (St Hilary)   see Trowbridge Mawr Mon
ST HILARY (St Hilary)   see Cowbridge Llan
ST ISHMAEL'S (St Ishmael)   see Herbrandston and Hasguard
w St Ishmael's St D
ST ISHMAEL'S (St Ishmael) w Llan-saint and Ferryside   St D 12
V   R M JENKINS
ST ISSELL'S (St Issell) and Amroth   St D 4   V   M BUTLER
ST LAWRENCE (St Lawrence)   see Camrose and St Lawrence w
Ford and Haycastle St D
ST LYTHANS (St Bleiddian)   see Wenvoe and St Lythans Llan
ST MARY CHURCH (St Mary)   see Cowbridge Llan
ST MARY HILL (St Mary)   see Coychurch w Llangan and
St Mary Hill Llan
ST MAUGHEN'S (St Meugan)   see Rockfield and St Maughen's
w Llangattock etc Mon
ST MELLONS (St Mellon)   Mon 6   V   D KELLEN,
C   M I R DOWSETT,   NSM   G R DAVIES
ST NICHOLAS (St Nicholas)   see Mathry w St Edren's and
Grandston etc St D
ST NICHOLAS (St Nicholas) w Bonvilston and
St George-super-Ely   Llan 5   R   E T WILSON
ST PETROX (St Pedrog)   see Pembroke Gp St D
ST PIERRE (St Peter)   see Mathern and Mounton w St Pierre
Mon
ST THOMAS   see Haverfordwest St Mary and St Thos w
Haroldston St D
ST TWYNNELLS (St Gwynog)   see Pembroke Gp St D
SANDFIELDS   see Aberavon Llan
SANDYCROFT (Holy Spirit)   see Hawarden St As
SANDYCROFT (St Francis)   as above St As
SARON (St David)   see Llanedi w Tycroes and Saron St D
SAUNDERSFOOT   see St Issell's and Amroth St D
SEALAND (St Barth)   see Hawarden St As
SEBASTOPOL (St Oswald)   see Griffithstown Mon
SENGHENYDD (St Peter)   see Eglwysilan Llan
SEVEN SISTERS (St David)   see Dulais Valley Llan
SEVEN SISTERS (St Mary)   as above Llan
SHIRENEWTON (St Thomas à Becket)   see Caerwent w
Dinham and Llanfair Discoed etc Mon
SHOTTON (St Ethelwold)   St As 16   V   D P MORRIS,
NSM   M F WILKINSON
SILIAN (St Sulien)   see Lampeter and Llanddewibrefi Gp St D
SINAN (All Saints)   see Cefn w Trefnant w Tremeirchion St As
SIX BELLS (St John)   see Abertillery w Cwmtillery w Six Bells
Mon
SKENFRITH (St Bride)   see Grosmont and Skenfrith and
Llangattock etc Mon
SKETTY (St Paul) (Holy Trinity)   S & B 6   V   A J KNIGHT,
C   S SARAPUK
SKEWEN (St John) (All Saints) (St Mary)   Llan 8
V   M WILLIAMS,   C   D O JONES
SLEBECH (St John the Baptist Parish Centre) and Uzmaston w
Boulston   St D 2   V   D M GRIFFITHS
SOLVA (St Aidan)   see Dewisland St D
SOUTHERNDOWN (All Saints)   see Ewenny w St Brides
Major Llan
SOUTHSEA (All Saints)   see Bwlchgwyn w Berse w Southsea
St As

SOUTHSEA (St Alban) *as above St As*
SPITTAL (St Mary) w Trefgarn and Ambleston w St Dogwells
St D 2   **V** D R REES
STACKPOLE ELIDOR (St James and St Elidyr) *see Pembroke Gp St D*
STEYNTON (St Cewydd and St Peter) *St D 5*
V J I HOLDSWORTH
STRATA FLORIDA (St Mary) *see Tregaron w Ystrad Meurig and Strata Florida St D*
SULLY (St John the Baptist) *Llan 5*   **R** E B DOWDING
SWANSEA (St Barnabas) *S & B 11*   **V** P C FRENCH
SWANSEA (St Gabriel) *S & B 6*   **V** D M GRIFFITHS
SWANSEA (St James) *S & B 11*   **V** D A WALKER
SWANSEA (St Jude) *S & B 11*   **P-in-c** H V PARSELL
SWANSEA (St Luke) *S & B 10*   **V** *vacant* (01792) 586300
SWANSEA (St Nicholas-on-the-Hill) *S & B 11*   **V** J W GRIFFIN, **NSM** I JONES
SWANSEA (St Peter) *S & B 10*   **V** H M WILLIAMS
SWANSEA (St Thomas) (St Stephen) and Kilvey *S & B 11*
V A J M MEREDITH,   **C** R M HAWKEN
SWANSEA, CENTRAL (St Mary) (Holy Trinity) (Christ Church) (St Matthew) (St Mark) (St John) *S & B 11*
TR A W EVANS,   **C** C L WILLIAMS
TAI'RGWAITH (St David) *see Gwaun-cae-Gurwen St D*
TAL-Y-LLYN (St David) *see Llanegryn w Aberdyfi w Tywyn Ban*
TALACHDDU (St Mary) *see Llandefalle and Llyswen w Boughrood etc S & B*
TALBENNY (St Mary) *see Walton W w Talbenny and Haroldston W St D*
TALGARREG (St David) *see Llanarth and Capel Cynon w Talgarreg etc St D*
TALGARTH (St Gwendoline) and Llanelieu *S & B 4*
V D T WALTERS
TALIARIS (Holy Trinity) *see Llandeilo Fawr and Taliaris St D*
TALLARN GREEN (St Mary Magdalene) *see Hanmer, Bronington, Bettisfield, Tallarn Green St As*
TALLEY (St Michael) *see Cynwyl Gaeo w Llansawel and Talley St D*
TALYBONT (St Cross) *see Llandygai and Maes y Groes Ban*
TALYBONT (St David) *see Llanfihangel Genau'r-glyn and Llangorwen St D*
TALYGARN (St Anne) *see Pontyclun w Talygarn Llan*
TALYLLYN *see Pennal w Corris and Esgairgeiliog Ban*
TALYLLYN (St Mary) *see Llanegryn w Aberdyfi w Tywyn Ban*
TEMPLETON (St John) *see Martletwy w Lawrenny and Minwear etc St D*
TENBY (St Mary) (St Julian's Chapel) *St D 4*
TR W D JENKINS,   **TV** M SOADY,   **C** B D TIMOTHY
TINTERN (St Michael) *see Llandogo w Whitebrook Chpl and Tintern Parva Mon*
TIRABAD (St David) *see Llanwrtyd w Llanddulas in Tir Abad etc S & B*
TIRTHIL (St Michael) *see Pontlottyn w Fochriw Llan*
TON-YR-YWEN (School) *see Llanishen Llan*
TONDU (St John) *see St Brides Minor w Bettws w Aberkenfig Llan*
TONDU (St Thomas) *as above Llan*
TONGWYNLAIS (St Michael) (St James) *Llan 3*   **V** V J PAYNE
TONMAWR (St Teilo) *see Oakwood Llan*
TONNA (St Anne) *see Resolven w Tonna Llan*
TONPENTRE *see Ystradyfodwg Llan*
TONYPANDY (St Andrew) w Clydach Vale *Llan 12*
V M J GILL
TONYREFAIL (St Alban) *see Tonyrefail w Gilfach Goch and Llandyfodwg Llan*
TONYREFAIL (St David) *as above Llan*
TONYREFAIL (St David) (St Alban) w Gilfach Goch and Llandyfodwg *Llan 12*   **V** S F AMBANI
TOWNHILL *see Swansea St Nic S & B*
TOWYN (St Mary) and St George *St As 1*   **V** H G A JALLAND
TRAEAN-GLAS (St Mary) *see Defynnog, Llandilo'r Fan, Llanulid, Llywel etc S & B*
TRALLWNG (St David) w Bettws Penpont w Aberyskir w Llanfihangel Nantbran w Battle *S & B 1*
V G L J WARRINGTON,   **NSM** K I WARRINGTON
TRAWSFYNYDD (St Madryn) *see Maentwrog w Trawsfynydd Ban*
TRE-GROES (St Ffraid) *see Llandysul w Bangor Teifi w Henllan etc St D*
TRE-LECH A'R BETWS (St Teilo) w Abernant and Llanwinio *St D 11*   **V** *vacant* (019948) 335
TREALAW (All Saints) *see Porth w Trealaw Llan*
TREBANOS (St Michael) *see Clydach S & B*
TREBOETH (St Alban) (Penlan Church) *S & B 10*
P-in-c R G JONES,   **NSM** N P DOYLE

TREDEGAR (St George) *Mon 7*   **V** J G DAVIS
TREDEGAR (St James) *Mon 7*   **V** D S TURNER
TREDUNNOC (St Andrew) *Mon 5*   **V** *vacant*
TREFDRAETH (St Beuno) (Eglwys Crist y Brenin) w Aberffraw w Llangadwaladr w Cerrigceinwen *Ban 4*   **P-in-c** A R M van den HOF
TREFEGLWYS (St Michael) *see Llandinam w Trefeglwys w Penstrowed Ban*
TREFGARN (St Michael) *see Spittal w Trefgarn and Ambleston w St Dogwells St D*
TREFILAN (St Hilary) *see Llanfihangel Ystrad and Cilcennin w Trefilan etc St D*
TREFLYS (St Michael) *see Criccieth and Treflys w Llanystumdwy etc Ban*
TREFNANT (Holy Trinity) *see Cefn w Trefnant w Tremeirchion St As*
TREFOR (St George) *see Llanaelhaearn w Clynnog Fawr Ban*
TREFRIW (St Mary) *see Caerhun w Llangelynin w Llanbedr-y-Cennin Ban*
TREGAEAN (St Caian) *see Llangefni w Tregaean Ban*
TREGAER (St Mary) *see Dingestow and Llangovan w Penyclawdd etc Mon*
TREGARON (St Caron) w Ystrad Meurig and Strata Florida *St D 9*   **V** P W DAVIES
TREGARTH (St Mair) *Ban 5*   **NSM** E PARRI
TREGYNON (St Cynon) *see Betws Cedewain and Tregynon and Llanwyddelan St As*
TREHARRIS (St Matthias) w Bedlinog *Llan 10*
V P M N GULLIDGE
TREHERBERT (St Alban) *see Treorchy and Treherbert Llan*
TREHERBERT (St Mary Communion Centre) *as above Llan*
TRELAWNYD (St Michael) *see Dyserth and Trelawnyd and Cwm St As*
TRELEWIS *see Treharris w Bedlinog Llan*
TRELLECH (St Nicholas) *see Penallt and Trellech Mon*
TRELLECH GRANGE (not known) *see Llanishen w Trellech Grange and Llanfihangel etc Mon*
TREMAIN (St Michael) *see Aberporth w Tremain w Blaenporth and Betws Ifan St D*
TREMEIRCHION (Corpus Christi) *see Cefn w Trefnant w Tremeirchion St As*
TREMORFA (St Philip) Conventional District *Llan 5*
NSM M K JONES
TREORCHY (St Matthew) and Treherbert *Llan 12*
C N V J ROPER
TRETHOMAS (St Thomas) *see Bedwas and Rudry Mon*
TRETOWER (St John the Evangelist) *see Crickhowell w Cwmdu and Tretower S & B*
TREUDDYN (St Mary) w Nercwys *St As 16*   **V** J B JONES
TREVETHIN (St Cadoc) *see Pontypool Mon*
TREVETHIN (St John the Divine) *as above Mon*
TREVOR (Church) *see Llangollen w Trevor and Llantysilio St As*
TREWALCHMAI (St Morhaiarn) *see Llandrygarn w Bodwrog and Heneglwys etc Ban*
TROED-YR-AUR (St Michael) *see Newcastle Emlyn w Llandyfriog etc St D*
TROEDRHIWGARTH (St Mary the Virgin) *Llan 7*
V D G MORRIS
TROEDYRHIW (St John) w Merthyr Vale *Llan 10*
V S J BARNES
TROFARTH (St John) *see Colwyn St As*
TROSTEY (St David) *see Bettws Newydd w Trostrey etc Mon*
TROWBRIDGE MAWR (St Hilary) *Mon 6*   **V** A C N BUCKLEY
TUDWEILIOG (St Cwyfan) *see Nefyn w Tudweiliog w Llandudwen w Edern Ban*
TUMBLE (Dewi Sant) *see Cwm Gwendraeth St D*
TY SIGN (St John) *see Risca Mon*
TYCOCH (All Souls) *S & B 6*   **V** P J GWYNN
TYCROES (St Edmund) *see Llanedi w Tycroes and Saron St D*
TYLORSTOWN (Holy Trinity) (St Mary Magdalene) w Ynyshir
Llan 12   **V** G P BIGMORE
TYNANT (Mission Church) *see Maentwrog w Trawsfynydd Ban*
TYTHEGSTON (St Tydwg) *see Laleston w Tythegston and Merthyr Mawr Llan*
TYWYN (St Cadfan) *see Llanegryn w Aberdyfi w Tywyn Ban*
TYWYN (St Matthew) *as above Ban*
UNDY (St Mary) *see Magor Mon*
UPPER WYE, The *S & B 2*   **V** N HOOK
UPTON *see Cosheston w Nash and Upton St D*
USK (St Mary) and Monkswood w Glascoed Chapel and Gwehelog *Mon 5*   **V** J F GRAY
UZMASTON (St Ismael) *see Slebech and Uzmaston w Boulston St D*

VALLEY (St Michael) w Llechylched and Caergeiliog *Ban 3*
R T BONNET
VAYNOR (St Gwynno) *see* Cefn Coed w Vaynor *S & B*
WALTON EAST (St Mary) *see* Wiston w Walton E and
Clarbeston *St D*
WALTON WEST (All Saints) w Talbenny and Haroldston West
St D 5 **R** A P JOHNSON, **NSM** R M M JOHNSON
WALWYN'S CASTLE (St James the Great) w Robeston West
St D 5 **R** D J LOWEN
WARREN *see* Castlemartin w Warren and Angle etc *St D*
WATERSTON *see* Llanstadwel *St D*
WATTSTOWN (St Thomas) *see* Tylorstown w Ynyshir *Llan*
WAUNARLLWYDD (St Barnabas) *S & B 9* **V** L J TAYLOR
WAUNFAWR (St John the Evangelist) *see* Llanbeblig w
Caernarfon and Betws Garmon etc *Ban*
WAUNFELIN (St John the Divine) *see* Pontypool *Mon*
WAUNWEN (St Mark) *see* Cen Swansea *S & B*
WELSH ST DONATS (St Donat) *see* Pendoylan w Welsh
St Donats *Llan*
WELSHPOOL (St Mary) (Christ Church) w Castle Caereinion
St As 10 **R** R L BROWN, **C** L D NORMAN
WENVOE (St Mary) and St Lythans *Llan 5* **P-in-c** A C BERRY
WHISTON (not known) *see* Magor *Mon*
WHITCHURCH (St David) *see* Dewisland *St D*
WHITCHURCH (St Mary) (St Thomas) (All Saints) *Llan 3*
TR J H L ROWLANDS, **TV** M GREENAWAY-ROBBINS,
C C E P EVANS, M P COLTON, **Hon C** H G LEWIS
WHITEBROOK (Holy Trinity) *see* Llandogo w Whitebrook
Chpl and Tintern Parva *Mon*
WHITECHURCH IN KEMES *see* Nevern and Y Beifil w
Eglwyswrw and Meline etc *St D*
WHITFORD (St Mary and St Beuno) *see* Gorsedd w Brynford,
Ysgeifiog and Whitford *St As*
WHITLAND (St Mary) w Cyffig and Henllan Amgoed and
Llan-gan *St D 15* **V** K G TAYLOR
WHITTON (St David) *see* Knighton, Norton, Whitton, Pilleth
and Cascob *S & B*
WICK (St James) *see* Llantwit Major *Llan*
WILCRICK (St Mary) *see* Bishton *Mon*
WILLIAMSTON, EAST (Church) *see* Jeffreyston w
Reynoldston and E Williamston etc *St D*
WILLIAMSTOWN (St Illtud) *see* Dinas and Penygraig w
Williamstown *Llan*
WISTON (St Mary Magdalene) w Walton East and Clarbeston
St D 2 **V** N CALE
WOLVESNEWTON (St Thomas à Becket) *see* Llangwm Uchaf
and Llangwm Isaf w Gwernesney etc *Mon*
WONASTOW (St Wonnow) *see* Monmouth w Overmonnow etc
Mon

WORTHENBURY (St Deiniol) *see* Bangor Monachorum and
Worthenbury *St As*
WREXHAM (St Giles's Parish Church) (St David) (St Mark)
(St Mary) (All Saints) (St Margaret) (St James) (St John)
St As 18 **R** G O MARSHALL, **TV** M A HARRISON, G J OWEN,
K B COLLINS, **C** M R J G WALKER, K A JOHNSON, P POWELL
WYNDHAM (St David) *see* Cwmogwr *Llan*
Y BEIFIL (St Andrew) *see* Nevern and Y Beifil w Eglwyswrw
and Meline etc *St D*
Y FERWIG (St Pedrog) *see* Cardigan w Mwnt and Y Ferwig w
Llangoedmor *St D*
YERBESTON *see* Martletwy w Lawrenny and Minwear etc
St D
YNYSBOETH *see* Penrhiwceiber w Matthewstown and
Ynysboeth *Llan*
YNYSCYHAEARN (Mission Church) *see* Porthmadoc and
Ynyscynhaearn and Dolbenmaen *Ban*
YNYSCYHAEARN (St Cynhaearn) *as above Ban*
YNYSCYNON (St Cynon) *see* Ystrad Rhondda w Ynyscynon
Llan
YNYSDDU (St Theodore) *see* Mynyddislwyn *Mon*
YNYSHIR (St Anne) *see* Tylorstown w Ynyshir *Llan*
YNYSHIR (St Thomas) *as above Llan*
YNYSMEUDW (St Mary) *see* Llangiwg *S & B*
YSBYTY CYNFYN (St John the Baptist) w Llantrisant and
Eglwys Newydd *St D 10* **V** *vacant* (01970) 890663
YSBYTY IFAN (St John the Baptist) *see* Cerrigydrudion w
Llanfihangel Glyn Myfyr etc *St As*
YSBYTY YSTWYTH (St John the Baptist) *see* Llanfihangel w
Llanafan and Llanwnnws etc *St D*
YSFA (St Mark) *see* Rhayader and Nantmel *S & B*
YSGEIFIOG (St Mary) *see* Gorsedd w Brynford, Ysgeifiog and
Whitford *St As*
YSTALYFERA (St David) *S & B 7* **V** G TURNER
YSTRAD-FFIN (St Paulinus) *see* Cil-y-Cwm and Ystrad-ffin w
Rhandir-mwyn etc *St D*
YSTRAD MEURIG (St John the Baptist) *see* Tregaron w
Ystrad Meurig and Strata Florida *St D*
YSTRAD MYNACH (Holy Trinity) w Llanbradach *Llan 1*
V M D BROOKS
YSTRAD RHONDDA (St Stephen) w Ynyscynon *Llan 12*
V P S GALE
YSTRAD ROAD (St Illtyd) *see* Swansea St Pet *S & B*
YSTRADFELLTE (St Mary) *see* Penderyn w Ystradfellte and
Pontneathvaughan *S & B*
YSTRADGYNLAIS (St Cynog) *S & B 7* **R** D I DAVIES
YSTRADOWEN (St Owain) *see* Cowbridge *Llan*
YSTRADYFODWG (St John the Baptist) *Llan 12*
R P N COLEMAN, **NSM** E M JONES

SCOTTISH INCUMBENCIES

An index of incumbencies of the Scottish Episcopal Church. The incumbency entry gives the full legal name, followed by the diocese name(s) and appointment(s) of the clergy serving there (if there are none, the telephone number of the parsonage house is given). Church dedications are indicated in brackets. The following are the main abbreviations used; for others see the full list of abbreviations.

C	Curate	NSM	Non-stipendiary Minister
C-in-c	Curate-in-charge	P-in-c	Priest-in-charge
Dn-in-c	Deacon-in-charge	Par Dn	Parish Deacon
Dss	Deaconess	R	Rector
Hon C	Honorary Curate	TM	Team Minister

ABERCHIRDER (St Marnan) *Mor*   **R** A J SIMPSON
ABERDEEN (Cathedral of St Andrew) *Ab*   **R** R E KILGOUR,
   NSM R FINNIE
ABERDEEN (St Clement) *Ab*   **R** *vacant* (01224) 662247
ABERDEEN (St James) *Ab*   **P-in-c** T P BENNISON,
   NSM R B EDWARDS
ABERDEEN (St John the Evangelist) *Ab*   **R** I M POOBALAN
ABERDEEN (St Margaret of Scotland) *Ab*   **R** A E NIMMO
ABERDEEN (St Mary) *Ab*   **R** C H CLAPSON
ABERDEEN (St Ninian) *Ab*   **P-in-c** R E KILGOUR
ABERDEEN (St Peter) *Ab*   **R** *vacant*
ABERDOUR (St Columba) - West Fife Team Ministry *St And*
   C N BARR
ABERFOYLE (St Mary) *St And*   **R** A BUNNELL
ABERLOUR (St Margaret of Scotland) *Mor*   **NSM** R E TAIT
ABOYNE (St Peter) *Ab*   **R** C C HUGHES
AIRDRIE (St Paul) *Glas*   **R** G B FYFE
ALEXANDRIA (St Mungo) *Glas*   **R** *vacant* (01389) 752633
ALFORD (St Andrew) *Ab*   **I** J WALKER, **P-in-c** A L JAMES,
   NSM J BURCHILL
ALLOA (St John the Evangelist) *St And*   **C** S B F LOBLEY,
   NSM E FORGAN
ALYTH (St Ninian) *St And*   **R** K W RATHBAND,
   NSM P S FERNANDO, D A CAMERON
ANNAN (St John the Evangelist) *Glas*
   P-in-c M P CALLAGHAN, **Hon C** J L HIGGINS
APPIN   *see* Portnacrois *Arg*
ARBROATH (St Mary) *Bre*   **R** *vacant* (01241) 73392
ARDBRECKNISH (St James) *Arg*   **R** A M MACLEAN
ARDCHATTAN (Holy Spirit) *Arg*   **R** A M MACLEAN
ARDROSSAN (St Andrew) *Glas*   **P-in-c** S ROBERTSON,
   NSM A MONTGOMERIE
ARPAFEELIE (St John the Evangelist) *Mor*   **R** R F BURKITT
ARRAN, ISLE OF *Arg*   **R** *vacant*
AUCHENBLAE   *see* Drumtochty *Bre*
AUCHINDOIR (St Mary) *Ab*   **R** J WALKER,
   NSM J BURCHILL
AUCHMITHIE (St Peter) *Bre*   **P-in-c** S FOX
AUCHTERARDER (St Kessog) *St And*   **R** R G L MACALISTER
AYR (Holy Trinity) *Glas*   **R** D G JONES,   **C** A L NAYLOR,
   NSM J A MASON
BAILLIESTON (St John)   *see* Glas E End *Glas*
BALERNO (St Mungo) *Edin*   **R** M J H ROUND,
   NSM N F HALLAM
BALLACHULISH (St John) *Arg*   **R** J R BETTELEY
BALLATER (St Kentigern) *Ab*   **R** C C HUGHES
BANCHORY (St Ternan) *Ab*   **R** W A D BERRYMAN
BANFF (St Andrew) *Ab*   **P-in-c** J M PAISEY
BARROWFIELD (St John the Baptist) *Glas*   **R** *vacant*
BATHGATE (St Columba) *Edin*   **NSM** P F KIRK
BEARSDEN (All Saints) *Glas*   **TR** K T ROACH,
   TV E M FARROW
BELLS WYND   *see* Douglas *Glas*
BIELDSIDE (St Devenick) *Ab*   **R** E MARQUIS-FAULKES,
   NSM P W BRUNT,   **Dss** J E MACCORMACK
BIRNAM   *see* Dunkeld *St And*
BISHOPBRIGGS (St James-the-Less) *Glas*   **P-in-c** S R PAISLEY,
   Hon C G E W SCOBIE
BLAIR ATHOLL   *see* Kilmaveonaig *St And*
BLAIRGOWRIE (St Catherine) *St And*   **R** K W RATHBAND,
   NSM P S FERNANDO, D A CAMERON
BO'NESS (St Catharine) *Edin*   **P-in-c** N D MACCALLUM,
   D R BUNYAN,   **Hon C** T J LENNARD, E J M P LENNARD
BRAEMAR (St Margaret) *Ab*   **R** *vacant*
BRECHIN (St Andrew) *Bre*   **R** S FOX, **NSM** J G C BARR
BRIDGE OF ALLAN (St Saviour) *St And*   **R** K HOLDSWORTH
BRIDGE OF WEIR (St Mary) *Glas*
   P-in-c P J C MCGRANAGHAN
BRIDGEND   *see* Islay *Arg*
BRORA (St Columba) *Mor*   **R** *vacant*
BROUGHTY FERRY (St Mary) *Bre*   **R** R W BREADEN
BUCKIE (All Saints) *Ab*   **P-in-c** J M PAISEY

BUCKSBURN (St Machar) *Ab*   **P-in-c** D HEDDLE
BUCKSTONE (St Fillan)   *see* Edin St Fillan *Edin*
BURNSIDE   *see* Moffat *Glas*
BURNTISLAND (St Serf) - West Fife Team Ministry *St And*
   R *vacant*
BURRAVOE (St Colman) *Ab*   **P-in-c** M N OXLEY,
   NSM E H MCNAB
CALLANDER (St Andrew) *St And*   **R** A BUNNELL
CAMBUSLANG (St Cuthbert) *Glas*   **P-in-c** D M IND,
   NSM M A DANSON
CAMPBELTOWN (St Kiaran) *Arg*   **NSM** A J WILLIAMSON
CARNOUSTIE (Holy Rood) *Bre*   **R** K G G GIBSON,
   C E M LAMONT,   **Hon C** J B HARDIE
CASTLE DOUGLAS (St Ninian) *Glas*   **P-in-c** D W BAYNE
CATTERLINE (St Philip) *Bre*   **R** *vacant* (01569) 62694
CHALLOCH (All Saints) *Glas*   **P-in-c** N E H NEWTON,
   NSM A WYLIE
CHAPELHILL   *see* Cruden Bay *Ab*
CLARKSTON (St Aidan) *Glas*   **R** P G M FLETCHER,
   Hon C C CURTIS
CLERMISTON   *see* Edin Clermiston Em *Edin*
CLYDEBANK (St Columba) *Glas*   **R** *vacant*
COATBRIDGE (St John the Evangelist) *Glas*   **R** G B FYFE
COLDSTREAM (St Mary and All Souls) *Edin*   **R** *vacant*
COLINTON   *see* Edin St Cuth *Edin*
COMRIE (St Serf) *St And*   **P-in-c** C P SHERLOCK
COUPAR ANGUS (St Anne) *St And*   **R** K W RATHBAND,
   NSM P S FERNANDO, D A CAMERON
COURTHILL Chapel   *see* Kishorn *Mor*
COVE BAY (St Mary) *Ab*   **R** *vacant* (01224) 895033
CRAIGHALL   *see* Ellon *Ab*
CRIEFF (St Columba) *St And*   **P-in-c** C P SHERLOCK
CROACHY   *see* Strathnairn St Paul *Mor*
CROMARTY (St Regulus) *Mor*   **R** R F BURKITT
CRUDEN BAY (St James the Less) *Ab*
   R G H STRANRAER-MULL,   **NSM** J F F SHEPHERD,
   G P WHALLEY, R SPENCER
CULLODEN (St Mary-in-the-Fields) *Mor*
   P-in-c A A SINCLAIR
CUMBERNAULD (Holy Name) *Glas*   **P-in-c** D A COOK
CUMBRAE (Cathedral of The Isles and Collegiate Church of the
   Holy Spirit) *Arg*   **P-in-c** A J BURDON, **NSM** P M BURDON
CUMINESTOWN (St Luke) *Ab*   **P-in-c** G G MACINTOSH,
   C J F F STENHOUSE
CUPAR (St James the Great) *St And*   **R** M C ALDCROFT
DALBEATTIE (Christ Church) *Glas*   **R** D J NORWOOD
DALKEITH (St Mary) *Edin*   **R** M A S GOODMAN,
   C J O GODFREY
DALMAHOY (St Mary) *Edin*   **NSM** B M JOHNSON
DALRY (St Peter) *Glas*   **P-in-c** I BOFFEY, S ROBERTSON
DENNISTOUN (St Kentigern)   *see* Glas E End *Glas*
DINGWALL (St James the Great) *Mor*   **P-in-c** M F HICKFORD,
   NSM R FLOCKHART
DOLLAR (St James the Great) *St And*   **R** G J GRÜNEWALD,
   C R E CARMAN,   **NSM** F A M LAWRY, H I SOGA
DORNOCH (St Finnbarr) *Mor*   **R** *vacant*
DOUGLAS (Sancta Sophia) *Glas*   **R** B H C GORDON
DOUNE (St Modoc) *St And*   **NSM** S M COATES
DRUMLITHIE (St John the Baptist) *Bre*   **R** M J R TURNER
DRUMTOCHTY (St Palladius) *Bre*   **R** M J R TURNER
DUFFTOWN (St Michael and All Angels) *Ab*   **NSM** R E TAIT
DUMBARTON (St Augustine) *Glas*   **P-in-c** K L MACAULAY
DUMFRIES (St John the Evangelist) *Glas*   **R** L S SMITH,
   NSM I MEREDITH
DUNBAR (St Anne) *Edin*   **P-in-c** P LEWER ALLEN,
   NSM J WOOD, R B COPLETON
DUNBLANE (St Mary) *St And*   **R** J I CAMERON
DUNDEE (Cathedral of St Paul) *Bre*   **R** M A F BYRNE
DUNDEE (St John the Baptist) *Bre*   **P-in-c** J J MORROW,
   Hon C J P FORBES
DUNDEE (St Luke) *Bre*   **R** K J CAVANAGH
DUNDEE (St Margaret) *Bre*   **R** J H MILNE,   **C** P M BALFOUR

DUNDEE (St Martin) *Bre* **P-in-c** D ELDER
DUNDEE (St Mary Magdalene) *Bre* **R** D SHEPHERD
DUNDEE (St Ninian) *Bre* **P-in-c** J J MORROW
DUNDEE (St Salvador) *Bre* **R** T STEVENS
DUNFERMLINE (Holy Trinity) - West Fife Team Ministry
St And **R** D CAMPBELL
DUNKELD (St Mary) w Birnam *St And* **R** P S CAMERON
DUNOON (Holy Trinity) *Arg* **R** H G C LEE
DUNS (Christ Church) *Edin* **P-in-c** K G WEBB,
NSM M E JONES, E S JONES
DUROR (St Adamnan) *Arg* **R** D W DAY
EAST END *see* Glas E End *Glas*
EAST KILBRIDE (St Mark) *Glas* **P-in-c** K H MARSHALL
EASTGATE (St Peter) *see* Peebles *Edin*
EASTRIGGS (St John the Evangelist) *Glas*
P-in-c M P CALLAGHAN
EDINBURGH (Cathedral of St Mary) *Edin* **R** G J T FORBES,
TV D J B FOSTEKEW, C P V P BLACKLEDGE,
NSM J M MILLARD
EDINBURGH (Christ Church) *Edin* **R** J A MEIN,
TV D L COLLINGWOOD, C M F CHATTERLEY,
NSM R H PROCTER, J P MITCHELL
EDINBURGH (Emmanuel) *Edin* **P-in-c** R K WILES
EDINBURGH (Good Shepherd) *Edin* **R** T D MORRIS,
C G J M SAUNDERS
EDINBURGH (Holy Cross) *Edin* **R** W D KORNAHRENS,
NSM M F HARRISON
EDINBURGH (Old St Paul) *Edin* **R** I J PATON,
C M I HOUSTON, **Hon C** C S DAVIES-COLE
EDINBURGH (St Andrew and St Aidan) *Edin* **R** *vacant*
EDINBURGH (St Barnabas) *Edin* **P-in-c** P D DIXON,
NSM A C ANDERSON
EDINBURGH (St Columba) *Edin* **R** A J FULLER,
TV R O GOULD, J S RICHARDSON
EDINBURGH (St Cuthbert) *Edin* **R** S C PARSONS,
C A WAGSTAFF, **NSM** D YEOMAN, J W SEARL
EDINBURGH (St David of Scotland) *Edin* **R** *vacant*
EDINBURGH (St Fillan) *Edin* **NSM** D L COLLINGWOOD
EDINBURGH (St Hilda) *Edin* **NSM** D L COLLINGWOOD
EDINBURGH (St James the Less) *Edin* **R** S I BUTLER,
NSM M S NORTHCOTT
EDINBURGH (St John the Evangelist) *Edin* **R** J A ARMES,
C J M MCLUCKIE, **NSM** P J BRAND, C A HUME
EDINBURGH (St Luke) *see* Wester Hailes St Luke *Edin*
EDINBURGH (St Margaret of Scotland) *Edin*
P-in-c H L WILLIAMSON
EDINBURGH (St Mark) *Edin* **R** E MORSON
EDINBURGH (St Martin of Tours) *Edin* **R** J A CONWAY,
NSM S KILBEY
EDINBURGH (St Michael and All Saints) *Edin* **R** K PEARSON
EDINBURGH (St Ninian) *Edin* **P-in-c** P J D ALLEN,
C A B SHEWAN, **NSM** R T PERCIVAL
EDINBURGH (St Paul and St George) *Edin* **R** D G RICHARDS,
C M P MAUDSLEY
EDINBURGH (St Peter) *Edin* **R** F W TOMLINSON,
C K R MACAULAY, B A MACAULAY
EDINBURGH (St Philip and St James) *Edin* **R** K F SCOTT
EDINBURGH (St Salvador) *Edin* **C** C NAISMITH,
G J M SAUNDERS
EDINBURGH (St Thomas) Private Chapel *Edin*
R M J PARKER, **C** I R HOPKINS, A R MACDONALD
EDINBURGH (St Vincent) Private Chapel *Edin*
P-in-c R A GRANT
ELGIN (Holy Trinity) w Lossiemouth (St Margaret) *Mor*
R M J STRANGE, **Par Dn** J SCLATER
ELIE AND EARLSFERRY (St Michael and All Angels) *St And*
P-in-c J A RANDALL
ELLON (St Mary on the Rock) *Ab* **R** G H STRANRAER-MULL,
NSM J F F SHEPHERD, G P WHALLEY, R SPENCER, C A FOX
EORROPAIDH (St Moluag) *Arg* **NSM** B A MORRISON,
C P A LOCKHART
ERSKINE *see* Renfrew *Glas*
EYEMOUTH (St Ebba) *Edin* **NSM** S S COX
FALKIRK (Christ Church) *Edin* **R** M V SMITH
FASQUE (St Andrew) *Bre* **R** M J R TURNER
FETTERCAIRN *see* Fasque *Bre*
FOCHABERS Gordon Chapel *Mor* **R** *vacant* (01343) 820337
FORFAR (St John the Evangelist) *St And* **R** J M RICHARDSON,
NSM J M PRIOR
FORRES (St John the Evangelist) *Mor* **R** J CUTHBERT
FORT WILLIAM (St Andrew) *Arg* **R** G A GUINNESS
FORTROSE (St Andrew) *Mor* **R** F BURKITT
FRASERBURGH (St Peter) *Ab* **P-in-c** P J LEES,
NSM A J MURPHY
FYVIE (All Saints) *Ab* **R** A B MACGILLIVRAY
GALASHIELS (St Peter) *Edin* **R** D I MCCOSH
GALLOWGATE *see* Aberdeen St Marg *Ab*
GARTCOSH (St Andrew) *Glas* **R** *vacant*

GATEHOUSE OF FLEET (St Mary) *Glas* **R** P J TAYLOR
GIRVAN (St John) *Glas* **R** D G JONES, **C** A L NAYLOR,
NSM B H G COLLIE, J A MASON
GLASGOW (All Saints) *Glas* **P-in-c** V J PERRICONE
GLASGOW (Cathedral of St Mary the Virgin) *Glas*
R P J DINES, **C** A R SHERIDAN, **Hon C** K J SHAW
GLASGOW East End (St John) (St Kentigern) (St Serf) *Glas*
TV C G WYLIE
GLASGOW (Good Shepherd and Ascension) *Glas*
P-in-c J F LYON
GLASGOW (Holy Cross) *Glas* **NSM** D D KEEBLE
GLASGOW (St Bride) *Glas* **R** R F JONES, **NSM** I T DRAPER
GLASGOW (St Gabriel) *Glas* **R** *vacant*
GLASGOW (St George) *Glas* **Hon C** S M P MAITLAND
GLASGOW (St Margaret) *Glas* **R** T C O MONTGOMERY
GLASGOW (St Matthew) *Glas* **R** P J SWIFT,
NSM C A MCKILLOP
GLASGOW (St Ninian) *Glas* **R** G D DUNCAN,
C P R WATSON
GLASGOW (St Oswald) *Glas* **P-in-c** R N O'SULLIVAN
GLASGOW (St Silas) Private Chapel *Glas* **R** D W MCCARTHY
GLENCARSE (All Saints) *Bre* **R** G F W NEWELL OF STAFFA
GLENCOE (St Mary) *Arg* **R** J R BETTELEY
GLENROTHES (St Luke the Evangelist) - Central Fife Team
Ministry *St And* **R** J W ALLAN, TV J D MARTIN,
D N CALVIN-THOMAS, **NSM** M LAWRENSON
GLENURQUHART (St Ninian) *Mor* **P-in-c** D P HINDER
GOUROCK (St Bartholomew) *Glas* **R** G F HOLLEY
GOVAN *see* Glas St Gabr *Glas*
GRANGEMOUTH (St Mary) *Edin* **R** N D MACCALLUM,
D R BUNYAN, **Hon C** T J LENNARD, E J M P LENNARD
GRANTOWN-ON-SPEY (St Columba) *Mor*
P-in-c D H BENNETT, **NSM** A WHEATLEY
GREENOCK (St John the Evangelist) *Glas* **R** *vacant* (01475)
720750
GRETNA (All Saints) *Glas* **P-in-c** M P CALLAGHAN
GREYFRIARS *see* Kirkcudbright *Glas*
GRULINE (St Columba) *Arg* **P-in-c** D W DAY
GULLANE (St Adrian) *Edin* **R** J C LINDSAY, **C** L A MORTIS
HADDINGTON (Holy Trinity) *Edin* **R** A J BAIN,
NSM J WOOD, R B COPLETON
HAMILTON (St Mary the Virgin) *Glas* **R** I D BARCROFT
HARRIS, ISLE OF *see* Leverburgh *Arg*
HAWICK (St Cuthbert) *Edin* **R** I E WALTER,
Hon C G P WEDGWOOD
HAY DRIVE *see* Edin St Andr and St Aid *Edin*
HELENSBURGH (St Michael and All Angels) *Glas*
R A B LAING, **NSM** A J MANN, B M THATCHER
HUNTLY (Christ Church) *Mor* **R** A J SIMPSON
HYNDLAND (St Bride) *see* Glas St Bride *Glas*
INNERLEITHEN (St Andrew) *Edin* **P-in-c** R D LEE,
NSM C B AITCHISON
INSCH (St Drostan) *Ab* **R** A B MACGILLIVRAY
INVERARAY (All Saints) *Arg* **R** F F FLATT
INVERBERVIE (St David) *Bre* **P-in-c** I G STEWART
INVERGORDON (St Ninian) *Mor* **R** *vacant* (01349) 852392
INVERGOWRIE (All Souls) *Bre* **P-in-c** A W CUMMINS
INVERKEITHING (St Peter) - West Fife Team Ministry *St And*
R *vacant*
INVERNESS (Cathedral of St Andrew) *Mor* **R** *vacant*
INVERNESS (St John the Evangelist) *Mor*
P-in-c A A SINCLAIR
INVERNESS (St Michael and All Angels) *Mor* **R** L A BLACK
INVERURIE (St Mary) *Ab* **R** J WALKER, **NSM** J BURCHILL
IONA (St Columba) *Arg* **R** *vacant*
IRVINE (St Andrew) Local Ecumenical Project *Glas*
P-in-c S ROBERTSON, **NSM** A MONTGOMERIE
ISLAY (St Columba) *Arg* **R** *vacant*
JEDBURGH (St John the Evangelist) *Edin* **R** D B H HERBERT,
Hon C W J GROVER
JOHNSTONE (St John) *Glas* **P-in-c** S A MARSH
KEITH (Holy Trinity) *Mor* **R** A J SIMPSON
KELSO (St Andrew) *Edin* **R** C R DORMER,
Hon C I D L CLARK, D C MYLNE, R JONES
KEMNAY (St Anne) *Ab* **P-in-c** J WALKER,
NSM J BURCHILL
KENTALLEN (St Moluag) *Arg* **P-in-c** D W DAY
KESSOCK-TORE *see* Arpafeelie *Mor*
KILLIN (St Fillan) *St And* **R** *vacant*
KILMACOLM (St Fillan) *Glas* **P-in-c** P J C MCGRANAGHAN
KILMARNOCK (Holy Trinity) *Glas* **R** K G STEPHEN
KILMARTIN (St Columba) *Arg* **R** F F FLATT
KILMAVEONAIG (St Adamnan) *St And* **R** R G DEVONSHIRE
KINCARDINE O'NEIL (Christ Church) *Ab*
P-in-c W A D BERRYMAN
KINGHORN (St Mary and St Leonard) *St And*
NSM G N BENSON
KINLOCH RANNOCH (All Saints) *St And* **R** *vacant*

KINLOCHLEVEN (St Paul) *Arg*   **P-in-c** D W DAY
KINLOCHMOIDART (St Finian) *Arg*   **R** vacant
KINROSS (St Paul) *St And*   **R** K S NICHOLSON
KIRKCALDY (St Peter) *St And*   **P-in-c** J B PENMAN,
   NSM G N BENSON
KIRKCUDBRIGHT (St Francis of Assisi) *Glas*   **R** P J TAYLOR
KIRKWALL (St Olaf) *Ab*   **R** A FINCH,   **NSM** D DAWSON
KIRRIEMUIR (St Mary) *St And*   **P-in-c** R P HARLEY,
   NSM J M PRIOR
KISHORN Chapel *Mor*   **NSM** H S WIDDOWS
LADYBANK (St Mary) *St And*   **R** M C ALDCROFT
LADYCROFT   *see Balerno Edin*
LANARK (Christ Church) *Glas*   **R** B H C GORDON
LANGHOLM (All Saints) *Glas*   **R** vacant (01461) 38268
LARGS (St Columba) *Glas*   **R** P M POTTER,   **Hon C** J POW
LASSWADE (St Leonard) *Edin*   **R** M A S GOODMAN,
   C J O GODFREY
LAURENCEKIRK (St Laurence) *Bre*   **R** M J R TURNER
LEITH (St James the Less)   *see Edin St Jas Edin*
LENZIE (St Cyprian) *Glas*   **R** J E MARSBURG,
   Hon C B A OGUGUO,   **NSM** S H B GORTON
LERWICK (St Magnus) *Ab*   **P-in-c** M N OXLEY,
   NSM E H MCNAB
LEVEN (St Margaret) - Central Fife Team Ministry *St And*
   TV J D MARTIN,   **NSM** M LAWRENSON
LEVERBURGH *Arg*   **P-in-c** J H DOWNIE
LEWIS, ISLE OF   *see Stornoway Arg*
LINLITHGOW (St Peter) *Edin*   **R** vacant
LIVINGSTON Local Ecumenical Project *Edin*   **C** J DYER,
   NSM M KESTON
LOCHALSH (St Donnan) *Mor*   **R** vacant
LOCHBUIE (St Kilda) *Arg*   **R** vacant
LOCHEARNHEAD (St Angus) *St And*   **P-in-c** C P SHERLOCK
LOCHGELLY (St Finnian) - Central Fife Team Ministry *St And*
   TV J D MARTIN,   **NSM** M LAWRENSON
LOCHGILPHEAD (Christ Church) *Arg*   **R** R F F FLATT,
   P-in-c J D L DAVIES
LOCKERBIE (All Saints) *Glas*   **P-in-c** M D ROBSON,
   M P CALLAGHAN
LONGSIDE (St John) *Ab*   **P-in-c** D V OVERINGTON
LOSSIEMOUTH (St Margaret)   *see Elgin w Lossiemouth Mor*
LUNAN HEAD (St Margaret) *St And*   **R** vacant
MARYGATE   *see Pittenweem St And*
MAYBOLE (St Oswald) *Glas*   **R** D G JONES,   **C** A L NAYLOR,
   NSM B H G COLLIE, J A MASON
MELROSE (Holy Trinity) *Edin*   **R** K L JUSTICE,
   NSM D W WOOD
MILLPORT   *see Cumbrae (or Millport) Arg*
MILNGAVIE (St Andrew) *Glas*   **R** vacant
MOFFAT (St John the Evangelist) *Glas*   **P-in-c** M D ROBSON,
   M P CALLAGHAN,   **Hon C** R J AMES
MONIFIETH (Holy Trinity) *Bre*   **C** E M LAMONT
MONKLANDS   *see Airdrie Glas*
MONKSTOWN   *see Ladybank St And*
MONTROSE (St Mary and St Peter) *Bre*   **R** I G STEWART,
   NSM M H KING
MOTHERWELL (Holy Trinity) *Glas*   **NSM** M COLEMAN
MUCHALLS (St Ternan) *Bre*   **C** J NELSON
MULL, ISLE OF   *see Gruline Arg*
MULL, ISLE OF   *see Lochbuie Arg*
MURRAYFIELD (Good Shepherd)   *see Edin Gd Shep Edin*
MUSSELBURGH (St Peter) *Edin*   **C** R COOKE,   R COOKE
MUTHILL (St James) *St And*   **R** G L MACALISTER
NAIRN (St Columba) *Mor*   **P-in-c** D MCALISTER
NETHER LOCHABER (St Bride) *Arg*   **R** vacant
NEW GALLOWAY (St Margaret of Scotland) *Glas*
   P-in-c J R REPATH
NEW PITSLIGO (St John the Evangelist) *Ab*   **R** vacant
NEWBURGH (St Katherine) *St And*   **R** vacant
NEWPORT-ON-TAY (St Mary) *St And*   **R** N POUNDE,
   P-in-c D CAMPBELL
NEWTON STEWART   *see Challoch Glas*
NORTH BALLACHULISH   *see Onich Arg*
NORTH BERWICK (St Baldred) *Edin*   **R** J C LINDSAY,
   C L A MORTIS
OBAN (Cathedral of St John) *Arg*   **R** A M MACLEAN
OLD DEER (St Drostan) *Ab*   **P-in-c** D V OVERINGTON
OLDMELDRUM (St Matthew) *Ab*   **R** A B MACGILLIVRAY,
   Hon C D W MCHARDY
ONICH (St Bride) *Arg*   **R** J R BETTELEY
OXGANGS (St Hilda)   *see Edin St Hilda Edin*
PAISLEY (Holy Trinity) *Glas*   **R** D W MCFARLAND,
   NSM A G BOYD
PAISLEY (St Barnabas) *Glas*   **R** D W MCFARLAND,
   NSM A G BOYD
PEEBLES (St Peter) *Edin*   **R** R D LEE,   **NSM** C B AITCHISON
PENICUIK (St James the Less) *Edin*   **R** J H BRUCE,
   NSM N F SUTTLE, F E MCLEAN, T A BRAMLEY

PERTH (Cathedral of St Ninian) *St And*   **C** K HOLDSWORTH,
   NSM R F SAUNDERS
PERTH (St John the Baptist) *St And*   **R** R C FYFFE,
   Hon C H L YOUNG, R H DARROCH, W F HARRIS,
   W L GLAZEBROOK,   **NSM** F FORSHAW
PETERHEAD (St Peter) *Ab*   **P-in-c** G H STRANRAER-MULL
PINMORE *Glas*   **NSM** B H G COLLIE
PITLOCHRY (Holy Trinity) *St And*   **R** R G DEVONSHIRE
PITTENWEEM (St John the Evangelist) *St And*
   P-in-c J A RANDALL
POLTALLOCH   *see Kilmartin Arg*
POOLEWE (St Maelrubha) *Mor*   **R** vacant
PORT GLASGOW (St Mary the Virgin) *Glas*
   R S D N BARRETT
PORTNACROIS (Holy Cross) *Arg*   **P-in-c** D W DAY
PORTPATRICK (St Ninian) *Glas*   **P-in-c** R UNDERHILL
PORTREE (St Columba) *Arg*   **P-in-c** J M PORTEUS,
   NSM J O LEAWORTHY
PORTSOY (St John the Baptist) *Ab*   **P-in-c** J M PAISEY
PRESTONPANS (St Andrew) *Edin*   **C** R COOKE,   R COOKE
PRESTWICK (St Ninian) *Glas*   **R** P D NOBLE
RENFREW (St Margaret) w Erskine *Glas*   **P-in-c** S A MARSH
ROSLIN (Collegiate Church of St Matthew) *Edin*
   NSM M J FASS
ROTHESAY (St Paul) *Arg*   **R** vacant
ROTHIEMURCHUS (St John the Baptist) *Mor*
   C H K M COOK,   **Hon C** R K SHAW
ST ANDREWS (All Saints) *St And*   **R** J P MASON,
   C M-L MOFFETT,   **Hon C** G D WHITE
ST ANDREWS (St Andrew) - Central Fife Team Ministry
   St And   **R** R A GILLIES,   **C** P B ROBERTSON, J H AITON,
   Hon C E W EYDEN,   **NSM** D A BEADLE, M LAWRENSON,
   R T EVANS, T A HART, W R BLACKBURN
ST FILLANS (Church of the Holy Spirit) *St And*   **R** vacant
SANDYLOAN   *see Gullane Edin*
SELKIRK (St John the Evangelist) *Edin*   **R** W B ELLIOT
SHETTLESTON (St Serf)   *see Glas E End Glas*
SKYE, ISLE OF   *see Portree Arg*
SOUTH QUEENSFERRY (Priory Church St Mary of Mount
   Carmel) *Edin*   **P-in-c** T J HARKIN,   **NSM** I MACROBERT
STANLEY (St Columba) *St And*   **NSM** R F SAUNDERS
STIRLING (Holy Trinity) *St And*   **R** C JARMAN,
   NSM G J WILLEY
STONEHAVEN (St James) *Bre*   **R** vacant (01569) 62694
STORNOWAY (St Peter) *Arg*   **R** S J G BENNIE
STRANRAER (St John the Evangelist) *Glas*
   P-in-c R UNDERHILL
STRATHNAIRN (St Paul) *Mor*   **P-in-c** E P MOSLEY
STRATHPEFFER (St Anne) *Mor*   **P-in-c** M F HICKFORD,
   NSM R FLOCKHART
STRATHTAY (St Andrew) *St And*   **R** P S CAMERON
STRICHEN (All Saints) *Ab*   **P-in-c** D V OVERINGTON,
   C G G KELMAN
STROMNESS (St Mary) *Ab*   **P-in-c** A FINCH,
   NSM I ST C COSBY
STRONTIAN *Arg*   **R** vacant
TAIN (St Andrew) *Mor*   **P-in-c** C J PIPER
TARFSIDE (St Drostan) *Bre*   **R** S FOX
TAYPORT (St Margaret of Scotland) *St And*
   P-in-c R G SOMMERVILLE
TEINDHILLGREEN   *see Duns Edin*
THURSO (St Peter and Holy Rood) *Mor*   **P-in-c** J STEVENSON,
   Hon C F E DAVIES, G R TYLER
TIGHNABRUAICH *Arg*   **R** vacant
TOFTS   *see Dalry Glas*
TORRY   *see Aberdeen St Pet Ab*
TROON (St Ninian) *Glas*   **R** D S MUNGAVIN
TURRIFF (St Congan) *Ab*   **P-in-c** G G MACINTOSH,
   NSM S M DYER, R M HAINES
UDDINGSTON (St Andrew) *Glas*   **P-in-c** D M IND,
   NSM M A DANSON
ULLAPOOL (St Mary the Virgin) *Mor*   **R** vacant (01854)
   612143
WEST FIFE Team Ministry - *see* ABERDOUR;
   BURNTISLAND; DUNFERMLINE; INVERKEITHING
   and LOCHGELLY *St And*   **NSM** V A NELLIST
WEST LINTON (St Mungo) *Edin*   **R** J H BRUCE,
   NSM F E MCLEAN, T A BRAMLEY
WESTER HAILES (St Luke) *Edin*   **C** K R WHITEFIELD
WESTGATE   *see Dunbar Edin*
WESTHILL (Trinity) *Ab*   **R** I J FERGUSON
WHITERASHES (All Saints) *Ab*   **R** A B MACGILLIVRAY
WHITING BAY   *see Is of Arran Arg*
WICK (St John the Evangelist) *Mor*   **P-in-c** J STEVENSON,
   Hon C F E DAVIES, G R TYLER
WISHAW (St Andrew) *Glas*   **NSM** M COLEMAN
WOODHEAD OF FETTERLETTER   *see Fyvie Ab*
YELL   *see Burravoe Ab*

IRISH BENEFICES AND CHURCHES

An index of benefices of the Church of Ireland (shown in bold type), together with entries for churches and other licensed places of worship. Where the church name is the same as that of the benefice (or the first place name in the benefice), the church entry is omitted. Church dedications are indicated in brackets.

The benefice entry gives the full legal name, together with the diocese and the name(s) and appointment(s) of clergy serving there (if there are none, the telephone number of the parsonage house is given). The following are the main abbreviations used; for others see the full list of abbreviations.

Bp's C	Bishop's Curate	**Hon C**	Honorary Curate
C	Curate	**I**	Incumbent (includes Rector or Vicar)
C-in-c	Curate-in-charge	**NSM**	Non-stipendiary Minister

AASLEAGH (St John the Baptist)   *see* Tuam w Cong and Aasleagh *T, K & A*
ABBEYLEIX (no dedication) w The Old Church, Ballyroan, Ballinakill, Killermogh, Aughmacart, Durrow and Attanagh *C & O*   **I** P A HARVEY,   **NSM** A WALLACE
ABBEYSTREWRY (no dedication) w Creagh, Tullagh, Castlehaven and Caheragh *C, C & R*   **I** vacant
ABINGDON (no dedication)   *see* Killaloe w Stradbally *L & K*
ACHILL (Holy Trinity)   *see* Aughaval w Achill, Knappagh, Dugort etc *T, K & A*
ACHONRY (Cathedral of St Crumnathy) w Tubbercurry and Killoran *T, K & A*   **I** S F GILLMOR
ACTON (no dedication) and Drumbanagher *Arm* **Bp's C** J M BARTON
ADARE (St Nicholas)   *see* Adare and Kilmallock w Kilpeacon, Croom etc *L & K*
ADARE (St Nicholas) and Kilmallock w Kilpeacon, Croom, Kilflynn, Kilfinane, Knockaney, Bruff and Caherconlish *L & K* **I** R V C LEWIS
AGHABOG (no dedication)   *see* Ematris w Rockcorry, Aghabog and Aughnamullan *Clogh*
AGHADE (All Saints)   *see* Fenagh w Myshall, Aghade and Ardoyne *C & O*
AGHADERG (St Mellan) w Donaghmore and Scarva *D & D* **I** G N LITTLE
AGHADOE   *see* Killarney w Aghadoe and Muckross *L & K*
AGHADOWEY (St Guaire) w Kilrea *D & R*   **I** J R D SLATER
AGHADOWN (Church Cross)   *see* Ballydehob w Aghadown *C, C & R*
AGHADOWN (St Matthew)   *as above C, C & R*
AGHADRUMSEE (no dedication) w Clogh and Drumsnatt *Clogh*   **I** V E KILLE
AGHALEE (Holy Trinity)   *D & D*   **I** vacant
AGHALURCHER (no dedication) w Tattykeeran, Cooneen and Mullaghfad *Clogh*   **I** R T GILLIAN
AGHANAGH (no dedication)   *see* Boyle and Elphin w Aghanagh, Kilbryan etc *K, E & A*
AGHANCON (no dedication)   *see* Shinrone w Aghancon etc *L & K*
AGHANLOO (St Lugha)   *see* Tamlaghtard w Aghanloo *D & R*
AGHAVEA (no dedication) *Clogh*   **I** D W ROBINSON
AGHAVILLY (St Mary)   *see* Tynan w Middletown and Aghavilly *Arm*
AGHAVOE (no dedication)   *see* Rathdowney w Castlefleming, Donaghmore etc *C & O*
AGHER (no dedication)   *see* Rathmolyon w Castlerickard, Rathcore and Agher *M & K*
AGHERTON (St John the Baptist) *Conn*   **I** P W ROOKE,   **C** D I GILLESPIE
AGHOLD (no dedication)   *see* Tullow w Shillelagh, Aghold and Mullinacuff *C & O*
AGHOUR (St Lachtan)   *see* Kilkenny w Aghour and Kilmanagh *C & O*
AHASCRAGH   *see* Aughrim w Ballinasloe etc *L & K*
AHERLA   *see* Moviddy Union *C, C & R*
AHOGHILL (St Colmanell) w Portglenone *Conn* **I** W K M BREW
ALDERGROVE   *see* Killead w Gartree *Conn*
ALMORITIA (St Nicholas)   *see* Mullingar, Portnashangan, Moyliscar, Kilbixy etc *M & K*
ALTEDESERT (no dedication)   *see* Kildress w Altedesert *Arm*
ANNACLONE (Christ Church)   *see* Magherally w Annaclone *D & D*
ANNADUFF (St Ann)   *see* Kiltoghart w Drumshambo, Annaduff and Kilronan *K, E & A*
ANNAGH (St Andrew) w Drumaloor, Cloverhill, Drumgoon, Dernakesh, Ashfield and Killesherdoney *K, E & A* **I** E R G WEST,   **NSM** R W STAFFORD
ANNAGHMORE (St Francis) *Arm*   **I** K P WHITTAKER
ANNAHILT (Ascension) w Magherahamlet *D & D* **I** J R HOWARD

ANNALONG (no dedication) *D & D*   **I** vacant (028) 4376 8246
Mobile 07715-773979
ANNESTOWN   *see* Waterford w Killea, Drumcannon and Dunhill *C & O*
ANTRIM (All Saints) *Conn*   **I** S R MCBRIDE,   **C** E R MURRAY
ANTRIM (St Patrick)   *see* Connor w Antrim St Patr *Conn*
ARBOE (no dedication)   *see* Ballinderry, Tamlaght and Arboe *Arm*
ARDAGH (St Patrick) w Tashinny, Shrule and Kilcommick *K, E & A*   **Bp's C** A W KINGSTON
ARDAMINE (St John the Evangelist) w Kiltennel, Glascarrig, Kilnamanagh, Kilmuckridge and Monamolin *C & O* **I** R J GRAY
ARDARA (St Connall) w Glencolumbkille, Inniskeel, Glenties and Lettermacaward *D & R*   **I** G B FREEMAN,
NSM M C CLASSON
ARDCARNE (no dedication)   *see* Boyle and Elphin w Aghanagh, Kilbryan etc *K, E & A*
ARDCLINIS (St Mary) and Tickmacrevan w Layde and Cushendun *Conn*   **P-in-c** J C WILSON
ARDCOLM (no dedication)   *see* Wexford w Ardcolm and Killurin *C & O*
ARDEE (St Mary)   *see* Drogheda w Ardee, Collon and Termonfeckin *Arm*
ARDGLASS (St Nicholas)   *see* Lecale Gp *D & D*
ARDKEEN (Christ Church)   *see* Ballyhalbert w Ardkeen *D & D*
ARDMORE (no dedication) w Craigavon *D & D*   **I** vacant (028) 3834 0357
ARDMORE (St Paul)   *see* Youghal Union *C, C & R*
ARDNAGEEHY (no dedication)   *see* Fermoy Union *C, C & R*
ARDOYNE (Holy Trinity)   *see* Fenagh w Myshall, Aghade and Ardoyne *C & O*
ARDOYNE (Immanuel)   *see* Belfast H Trin and St Silas *Conn*
ARDQUIN (no dedication)   *see* Ballyphilip w Ardquin *D & D*
ARDRAHAN   *see* Aughrim w Ballinasloe etc *L & K*
ARDSTRAW (St Eugene) w Baronscourt, Badoney Lower and Badoney Upper and Greenan *D & R*   **I** W C MCNEE
ARDTREA (St Andrew) w Desertcreat *Arm*   **I** D J BELL
ARKLOW (St Saviour) w Inch and Kilbride *D & G* **I** N J W SHERWOOD
ARMAGH (Cathedral of St Patrick) *Arm*   **I** H CASSIDY
ARMAGH (St Mark) *Arm*   **I** J W MCKEGNEY
ARMAGHBREAGUE (no dedication)   *see* Keady w Armaghbreague and Derrynoose *Arm*
ARMOY (St Patrick) w Loughguile and Drumtullagh *Conn* **I** F M BEACH
ARVAGH (no dedication) w Carrigallen, Gowna and Columbkille *K, E & A*   **I** vacant
ASHFIELD (no dedication)   *see* Annagh w Drumgoon, Ashfield etc *K, E & A*
ASKEATON (St Mary)   *see* Rathkeale w Askeaton, Kilcornan and Kilnaughtin *L & K*
ATHBOY (St James)   *see* Trim and Athboy Gp *M & K*
ATHLONE (St Mary) w Benown, Kiltoom and Forgney *M & K* **I** vacant
ATHY (St Michael) w Kilberry, Fontstown and Kilkea *D & G* **I** F X MURENZI
ATTANAGH   *see* Abbeyleix w Old Church, Ballyroan etc *C & O*
AUGHANUNSHIN   *see* Conwal Union w Gartan *D & R*
AUGHAVAL (no dedication) w Achill, Knappagh, Dugort, Castlebar and Turlough *T, K & A*   **I** G L HASTINGS
AUGHAVAS (no dedication)   *see* Mohill w Farnaught, Aughavas, Oughteragh etc *K, E & A*
AUGHER (no dedication) w Newtownsaville and Eskrahoole *Clogh*   **I** B M BOWER
AUGHMACART (St Tighernagh)   *see* Abbeyleix w Old Church, Ballyroan etc *C & O*
AUGHNACLIFFE   *see* Arvagh w Carrigallen, Gowna and Columbkille *K, E & A*
AUGHNACLOY   *see* Carnteel and Crilly *Arm*

AUGHNAMULLAN (Christ Church) *see* Ematris w Rockcorry, Aghabog and Aughnamullan *Clogh*

AUGHRIM (Holy Trinity) w Ballinasloe, Clontuskert, Ahascragh, Woodlawn, Kilmacduagh and Ardrahan *L & K*
I T A SULLIVAN

AUGHRIM (St John the Evangelist) *see* Castlemacadam w Ballinaclash, Aughrim etc *D & G*

BADONEY LOWER (St Patrick) *see* Ardstraw w Baronscourt, Badoney Lower etc *D & R*

BADONEY UPPER (St Aichen) *as above D & R*

BAGENALSTOWN *see* Dunleckney w Nurney, Lorum and Kiltennel *C & O*

BAILIEBOROUGH (no dedication) w Knockbride, Shercock and Mullagh *K, E & A* I *vacant* (00353) (42) 966 5436

BALBRIGGAN (St George) *see* Holmpatrick w Balbriggan and Kenure *D & G*

BALGRIFFIN (St Doulagh) *see* Malahide w Balgriffin *D & G*

BALLAGHTOBIN (no dedication) *see* Kells Gp *C & O*

BALLEE (no dedication) *see* Bright w Ballee and Killough *D & D*

BALLIGAN *see* Ballywalter w Inishargie *D & D*

BALLINACLASH (no dedication) *see* Castlemacadam w Ballinaclash, Aughrim etc *D & G*

BALLINADEE (no dedication) *see* Bandon Union *C, C & R*

BALLINAFAD *see* Boyle and Elphin w Aghanagh, Kilbryan etc *K, E & A*

BALLINALEA *see* Mostrim w Granard, Clonbroney, Killoe etc *K, E & A*

BALLINALECK *see* Cleenish w Mullaghdun *Clogh*

BALLINAMALLARD *see* Magheracross *Clogh*

BALLINAMORE *see* Mohill w Farnaught, Aughavas, Oughteragh etc *K, E & A*

BALLINASLOE (St John the Evangelist) *see* Aughrim w Ballinasloe etc *L & K*

BALLINATONE *see* Castlemacadam w Ballinaclash, Aughrim etc *D & G*

BALLINDERRY (no dedication) *Conn* I E J HARRIS

BALLINDERRY (St John), Tamlaght and Arboe *Arm*
I H J W MOORE

BALLINEEN *see* Kinneigh Union *C, C & R*

BALLINGARRY (no dedication) *see* Cloughjordan w Borrisokane etc *L & K*

BALLINLOUGH *see* Roscommon w Donamon, Rathcline, Kilkeevin etc *K, E & A*

BALLINROBE (St Mary) *see* Tuam w Cong and Aasleagh *T, K & A*

BALLINTEMPLE (no dedication) *see* Kilmore w Ballintemple, Kildallon etc *K, E & A*

BALLINTEMPLE (St Mary) *see* Cashel w Magorban, Tipperary, Clonbeg etc *C & O*

BALLINTOGHER *see* Taunagh w Kilmactranny, Ballysumaghan etc *K, E & A*

BALLINTOY (no dedication) w Rathlin and Dunseverick *Conn*
I J N PATTERSON

BALLINTUBBERT (St Brigid) *see* Stradbally w Ballintubbert, Coraclone etc *C & O*

BALLISODARE (Holy Trinity) w Collooney and Emlaghfad
T, K & A I R E DADSWELL

BALLIVOR *see* Trim and Athboy Gp *M & K*

BALLNACARGY *see* Mullingar, Portnashangan, Moyliscar, Kilbixy etc *M & K*

BALLYBAY (Christ Church) w Mucknoe and Clontibret *Clogh*
I J P HEYHOE

BALLYBEEN (St Mary) *D & D* I J MCK WHITE,
NSM J HARRIS

BALLYBRACK (St Matthias) *see* Killiney Ballybrack *D & G*

BALLYBUNNION *see* Tralee w Kilmoyley, Ballymacelligott etc *L & K*

BALLYCANEW (no dedication) *see* Gorey w Kilnahue, Leskinfere and Ballycanew *C & O*

BALLYCARNEY (no dedication) *see* Ferns w Kilbride, Toombe, Kilcormack etc *C & O*

BALLYCARRY *see* Kilroot and Templecorran *Conn*

BALLYCASTLE (Holy Trinity) *see* Ramoan w Ballycastle and Culfeightrin *Conn*

BALLYCLARE *see* Ballynure and Ballyeaston *Conn*

BALLYCLOG (St Patrick) *see* Brackaville w Donaghendry and Ballyclog *Arm*

BALLYCLUG (St Patrick) *see* Ballymena w Ballyclug *Conn*

BALLYCOMMON *see* Geashill w Killeigh and Ballycommon *M & K*

BALLYCONNELL *see* Swanlinbar w Tomregan, Kinawley, Drumlane etc *K, E & A*

BALLYCOTTON *see* Youghal Union *C, C & R*

BALLYCULTER (Christ Church) *see* Lecale Gp *D & D*

BALLYDEHOB (St Matthias) w Aghadown *C, C & R*
I P R DRAPER

BALLYEASTON (St John the Evangelist) *see* Ballynure and Ballyeaston *Conn*

BALLYEGLISH (St Matthias) *see* Desertlyn w Ballyeglish *Arm*

BALLYFIN (no dedication) *see* Maryborough w Dysart Enos and Ballyfin *C & O*

BALLYGAWLEY (no dedication) *see* Errigle Keerogue w Ballygawley and Killeshil *Arm*

BALLYHAISE *see* Drung w Castleterra, Larah and Lavey etc *K, E & A*

BALLYHALBERT (St Andrew) w Ardkeen *D & D*
I J J HEMPHILL

BALLYHOLME (St Columbanus) *D & D* I A F ABERNETHY,
C N J DARK

BALLYHOOLEY (no dedication) *see* Fermoy Union *C, C & R*

BALLYJAMESDUFF (no dedication) *see* Kildrumferton w Ballymachugh and Ballyjamesduff *K, E & A*

BALLYKELLY *see* Tamlaghtfinlagan w Myroe *D & R*

BALLYLESSON *see* Drumbo *D & D*

BALLYMACARRETT (St Patrick) (St Christopher) (St Martin)
D & D I C L HALL-THOMPSON, NSM S P HOOPER

BALLYMACASH (St Mark) *Conn* I W G IRWIN,
C E HENDERSON

BALLYMACELLIGOTT (no dedication) *see* Tralee w Kilmoyley, Ballymacelligott etc *L & K*

BALLYMACHUGH (St Paul) *see* Kildrumferton w Ballymachugh and Ballyjamesduff *K, E & A*

BALLYMACKEY (St Michael) *see* Nenagh *L & K*

BALLYMACORMACK (no dedication) *see* Templemichael w Clongish, Clooncumber etc *K, E & A*

BALLYMAGLASSON *see* Dunboyne Union *M & K*

BALLYMAHON *see* Ardagh w Tashinny, Shrule and Kilcommick *K, E & A*

BALLYMARTLE (no dedication) *see* Kinsale Union *C, C & R*

BALLYMASCANLAN (St Mary) w Creggan and Rathcor *Arm*
I G M KINGSTON

BALLYMENA (St Patrick) w Ballyclug *Conn* I S G E LLOYD,
C N D S PHAIR, J R ANDERSON

BALLYMONEY *see* Kinneigh Union *C, C & R*

BALLYMONEY (St Patrick) w Finvoy and Rasharkin *Conn*
I E R LAVERY, NSM W J HOLMES, R J SIMPSON

BALLYMORE *see* Clondehorkey w Cashel *D & R*

BALLYMORE (St Mark) *Arm* I S J BLACK

BALLYMORE EUSTACE (St John) *see* Blessington w Kilbride, Ballymore Eustace etc *D & G*

BALLYMOTE *see* Ballisodare w Collooney and Emlaghfad *T, K & A*

BALLYMOYER (St Luke) *see* Newtownhamilton w Ballymoyer and Belleck *Arm*

BALLYNAFEIGH (St Jude) *D & D* I *vacant*

BALLYNAHINCH *see* Magheradroll *D & D*

BALLYNAKILL (All Saints) *see* Abbeyleix w Old Church, Ballyroan etc *C & O*

BALLYNAKILL (St Thomas) *see* Omey w Ballynakill, Errislannan and Roundstone *T, K & A*

BALLYNASCREEN *see* Kilcronaghan w Draperstown and Sixtowns *D & R*

BALLYNURE (Ascension) *see* Baltinglass w Ballynure etc *C & O*

BALLYNURE (Christ Church) and Ballyeaston *Conn*
I R M MCCONNELL

BALLYPHILIP (no dedication) w Ardquin *D & D*
P-in-c M J HOUSTON

BALLYRASHANE (St John the Baptist) w Kildollagh *Conn*
I S S HEANEY

BALLYROAN (no dedication) *see* Abbeyleix w Old Church, Ballyroan etc *C & O*

BALLYSALLY (St Andrew) *see* Coleraine *Conn*

BALLYSCULLION (no dedication) *see* Drummaul w Duneane and Ballyscullion *Conn*

BALLYSCULLION (St Tida) *D & R* I F J REILLY

BALLYSEEDY (no dedication) *see* Tralee w Kilmoyley, Ballymacelligott etc *L & K*

BALLYSHANNON *see* Kilbarron w Rossnowlagh and Drumholm *D & R*

BALLYSILLAN *see* Belfast St Mark *Conn*

BALLYSUMAGHAN (no dedication) *see* Taunagh w Kilmactranny, Ballysumaghan etc *K, E & A*

BALLYWALTER (Holy Trinity) w Inishargie *D & D*
I J R L BOWLEY

BALLYWARD *see* Drumgath w Drumgooland and Clonduff *D & D*

BALLYWILLAN (Holy Trinity) *Conn* I G E GRAHAM,
NSM D J STEELE

BALRATHBOYNE *see* Kells Union *M & K*

BALTEAGH (St Canice) w Carrick *D & R*   I *vacant*
BALTIMORE   *see* Abbeystrewry Union *C, C & R*
BALTINGLASS (St Mary) w Ballynure, Stratford-on-Slaney and
Rathvilly *C & O*   I M A MCCULLAGH
BANAGHER (St Moresuis) *see* Cumber Lower w Banagher
D & R
BANAGHER (St Paul) *see* Clonfert Gp of Par *L & K*
BANBRIDGE *see* Seapatrick *D & D*
BANDON (St Peter) w Rathclaren, Innishannon, Ballinadee and
Brinny *C, C & R*   I N K DUNNE,   C S F MIKHAIL
BANGOR Primacy (Christ Church) *D & D*
Bp's C J E C RUTTER
BANGOR (St Comgall) *D & D*   I W R D MCCREERY,
C G WITHERS
BANGOR ABBEY (Bangor Abbey) *D & D*   I R NESBITT,
C E HANNA,   NSM D W R DUNN
BANNOW (no dedication) *see* Taghmon w Horetown and
Bannow *C & O*
BANTRY *see* Kilmocomogue Union *C, C & R*
BARONSCOURT (no dedication) *see* Ardstraw w Baronscourt,
Badoney Lower etc *D & R*
BARR (no dedication) *see* Donacavey w Barr *Clogh*
BEARA (St Peter) *C, C & R*   I *vacant* (00353) (21) 63036
BECTIVE   *see* Trim w Bective and Galtrim *M & K*
BELFAST (All Saints) *Conn*   I B A FOLLIS
BELFAST (Cathedral of St Anne) *Conn*   I *vacant*
BELFAST (Christ Church) *Conn*   I *vacant*
BELFAST (Holy Trinity) (St Silas) *Conn*   I T R WILLIAMS
BELFAST Malone (St John) *Conn*   I J O MANN,
C A L STEWART
BELFAST (St Aidan) *Conn*   I E P DUNDAS
BELFAST (St Andrew) *Conn*   NSM S K HOUSTON
BELFAST (St Bartholomew) *Conn*   I R ELSDON
BELFAST (St Brendan) *D & D*   I F MCCREA
BELFAST (St Christopher) *see* Ballymacarrett *D & D*
BELFAST (St Clement) *D & D*   I S D LOGAN
BELFAST (St Donard) *D & D*   I *vacant*
BELFAST (St George) *Conn*   I B STEWART
BELFAST (St Jude) *see* Ballynafeigh St Jude *D & D*
BELFAST (St Katharine) *Conn*   I W J TAGGART
BELFAST (St Mark) *Conn*   I *vacant*
BELFAST (St Martin) *see* Ballymacarrett *D & D*
BELFAST (St Mary) (Holy Redeemer) *Conn*   I J P WALKER
BELFAST (St Mary Magdalene) *Conn*   Bp's C R H MOORE
BELFAST (St Matthew) *Conn*   I G J O DUNSTAN
BELFAST (St Michael) *Conn*   I N B DODDS,   C E QUIREY
BELFAST (St Nicholas) *Conn*   I G CLUNIE
BELFAST (St Ninian) *Conn*   I *vacant*
BELFAST (St Patrick) *see* Ballymacarrett *D & D*
BELFAST (St Paul) (St Barnabas) *Conn*   I K M BROWN
BELFAST (St Peter) (St James) *Conn*   I C J MCCOLLUM
BELFAST (St Simon) (St Philip) *Conn*   I W T LONG
BELFAST (St Stephen) (St Luke) *Conn*   I *vacant*
BELFAST (St Thomas) *Conn*   I W A LEWIS,
NSM J M ELSDON
BELFAST Upper Falls (St John the Baptist) *Conn*
I T CLELAND
BELFAST Upper Malone (Epiphany) *Conn*   I P K MCDOWELL
BELFAST Whiterock (St Columba) *Conn*
Bp's C J T P TWOMEY
BELLAGHY *see* Ballyscullion *D & R*
BELLEEK (no dedication) *see* Garrison w Slavin and Belleek
Clogh
BELLEEK (St Luke) *see* Newtownhamilton w Ballymoyer and
Belleck *Arm*
BELLERENA *see* Tamlaghtard w Aghanloo *D & R*
BELMONT (St Peter) *see* Culmore w Muff and Belmont *D & R*
BELTURBET *see* Annagh w Drumgoon, Ashfield etc *K, E & A*
BELVOIR (Transfiguration) *D & D*   I T KEIGHTLEY,
C A A MCCARTNEY
BENOWN (no dedication) *see* Athlone w Benown, Kiltoom and
Forgney *M & K*
BILBO (no dedication) *see* Castlecomer w Colliery Ch, Mothel
and Bilbo *C & O*
BILLIS (no dedication) *see* Lurgan w Billis, Killinkere and
Munterconnaught *K, E & A*
BILLY (no dedication) w Derrykeighan *Conn*   I *vacant*
BIRR (St Brendan) w Eglish, Lorrha, Dorrha and Lockeen
L & K   I *vacant*
BLACKLION *see* Killinagh w Kiltyclogher and Innismagrath
K, E & A
BLACKROCK (All Saints) *see* Stillorgan w Blackrock *D & G*
BLACKROCK (St Michael) *see* Douglas Union w Frankfield
C, C & R
BLARNEY *see* Carrigrohane Union *C, C & R*

BLESSINGTON (St Mary) w Kilbride, Ballymore Eustace and
Holywood *D & G*   I *vacant*
BOHO (no dedication) *see* Devenish w Boho *Clogh*
BOOTERSTOWN *see* Dublin Booterstown *D & G*
BORNACOOLA *see* Templemichael w Clongish, Clooncumber
etc *K, E & A*
BORRIS Clonagoose *see* Leighlin w Grange Sylvae, Shankill etc
C & O
BORRIS Littleton *see* Kilcooley w Littleon, Crohane and
Fertagh *C & O*
BORRIS-IN-OSSORY (no dedication) *see* Clonenagh w
Offerlane, Borris-in-Ossory etc *C & O*
BORRISNAFARNEY (no dedication) *see* Cloughjordan w
Borrisokane etc *L & K*
BORRISOKANE (no dedication) *as above L & K*
BOURNEY (St Burchin) *see* Roscrea w Kyle, Bourney and
Corbally *L & K*
BOVEVAGH (St Eugenius) *see* Dungiven w Bovevagh *D & R*
BOYLE (no dedication) and Elphin w Aghanagh, Kilbryan,
Ardcarne and Croghan *K, E & A*   I *vacant*
BRACKAVILLE (Holy Trinity) w Donaghendry and Ballyclog
Arm   I G M S WATSON, K R J HALL
BRANTRY (Holy Trinity) *see* Caledon w Brantry *Arm*
BRAY (Christ Church) *D & G*   I B T STANLEY, H E A LEW,
NSM S A KINGSTON
BRIGHT (no dedication) w Ballee and Killough *D & D*
I G J WHITEHEAD
BRIGOWN (St George) *see* Fermoy Union *C, C & R*
BRINNY (no dedication) *see* Bandon Union *C, C & R*
BROOKEBOROUGH *see* Aghavea *Clogh*
BROOMHEDGE (St Matthew) *Conn*   I P J GALBRAITH
BROUGHSHANE *see* Skerry w Rathcavan and
Newtowncrommelin *Conn*
BRYANSFORD *see* Castlewellan w Kilcoo *D & D*
BUNBEG *see* Gweedore, Carrickfin and Templecrone *D & R*
BUNCLODY (St Mary) w Kildavin, Clonegal and Kilrush
C & O   I A J NEVIN
BUNCRANA *see* Fahan Lower and Upper *D & R*
BUNDORAN *see* Cloonclare w Killasnett, Lurganboy and
Drumlease *K, E & A*
BUSH *see* Ballymascanlan w Creggan and Rathcor *Arm*
BUSHMILLS *see* Dunluce *Conn*
CAHERAGH (St Mary) *see* Abbeystrewry Union *C, C & R*
CAHERCONLISH (St Ailbe) *see* Adare and Kilmallock w
Kilpeacon, Croom etc *L & K*
CAHIR (St Paul) *see* Clonmel w Innislounagh, Tullaghmelan etc
C & O
CAIRNCASTLE (St Patrick) *see* Kilwaughter w Cairncastle
and Craigy Hill *Conn*
CALARY (no dedication) *see* Newcastle w
Newtownmountkennedy and Calary *D & G*
CALEDON (St John) w Brantry *Arm*   I D B WILSON
CALRY (no dedication) *K, E & A*   I M E E MCELHINNEY
CAMLOUGH (Christ the Redeemer) w Mullaglass *Arm*
I R G HOEY,   NSM J MOORE
CAMP *see* Dingle w Killiney and Kilgobbin *L & K*
CAMUS-JUXTA-BANN (St Mary) *D & R*
I J J CUNNINGHAM
CAMUS-JUXTA-MOURNE (Christ Church) *D & R*
I G S A WILSON
CAPPAGH (St Eugene) w Lislimnaghan *D & R*   I D J QUINN
CAPPOQUIN (St Anne) *see* Lismore w Cappoquin,
Kilwatermoy, Dungarvan etc *C & O*
CARBURY (no dedication) *see* Clonsast w Rathangan,
Thomastown etc *M & K*
CARLOW (St Mary) w Urglin and Staplestown *C & O*
I G G DOWD
CARNALEA (St Gall) *D & D*   I M A PARKER
CARNALWAY (St Patrick) *see* Newbridge w Carnalway and
Kilcullen *M & K*
CARNDONAGH *see* Moville w Greencastle, Donagh, Cloncha
etc *D & R*
CARNEW (All Saints) *see* Crosspatrick Gp *C & O*
CARNLOUGH *see* Ardclinis and Tickmacrevan w Layde and
Cushendun *Conn*
CARNMONEY (Holy Evangelists) *Conn*   I M A MALCOLM
CARNTEEL (St James) and Crilly *Arm*   I W R FERGUSON
CARRICK (no dedication) *see* Balteagh w Carrick *D & R*
CARRICK-ON-SHANNON *see* Kiltoghart w Drumshambo,
Annaduff and Kilronan *K, E & A*
CARRICKFERGUS (St Nicholas) *Conn*   I J A MCMASTER,
C T S JOHNSTON
CARRICKFIN (St Andrew) *see* Gweedore, Carrickfin and
Templecrone *D & R*
CARRICKMACROSS (St Fin Barre) w Magheracloone *Clogh*
I D COLE

CARRIGALINE (St Mary) w Killanully and Monkstown
C, C & R   **I** S D ARMSTRONG
CARRIGALLEN (no dedication)   *see* Arvagh w Carrigallen,
Gowna and Columbkille *K, E & A*
CARRIGANS   *see* Taughboyne, Craigadooish,
Newtowncunningham etc *D & R*
CARRIGART   *see* Mevagh w Glenalla *D & R*
**CARRIGROHANE (St Peter) w Garrycloyne, Inniscarra and
Magourney** *C, C & R*   **I** F G RUTLEDGE, **C** W P MASSEY
CARRIGTWOHILL (St David)   *see* Rathcooney Union
C, C & R
CARROWDORE (Christ Church) w Millisle *D & D*
I D I BLAKELY
CARRYDUFF (St Ignatius)   *see* Killaney w Carryduff *D & D*
**CASHEL (Cathedral of St John the Baptist) w Magorban,
Tipperary, Clonbeg and Ballintemple** *C & O*   **I** P J KNOWLES
CASHEL (no dedication)   *see* Clondehorkey w Cashel *D & R*
CASTLEARCHDALE (St Patrick)   *see* Derryvullen N w
Castlearchdale *Clogh*
CASTLEBAR (Christ Church)   *see* Aughaval w Achill,
Knappagh, Dugort etc *T, K & A*
CASTLEBLAYNEY   *see* Ballybay w Mucknoe and Clontibret
Clogh
**CASTLECOMER (St Mary) w the Colliery Church, Mothel and
Bilbo** *C & O*   **I** T A SHERLOCK
CASTLECONNELL   *see* Killaloe w Stradbally *L & K*
CASTLECONNOR (no dedication)   *see* Killala w Dunfeeny,
Crossmolina, Kilmoremoy etc *T, K & A*
CASTLEDAWSON (Christ Church) *D & R*   **I** vacant
CASTLEDERG   *see* Derg w Termonamongan *D & R*
CASTLEDERMOT (St James)   *see* Narraghmore and Timolin
w Castledermot etc *D & G*
CASTLEFLEMING (no dedication)   *see* Rathdowney w
Castlefleming, Donaghmore etc *C & O*
CASTLEGREGORY   *see* Dingle w Killiney and Kilgobbin
L & K
CASTLEHAVEN (no dedication)   *see* Abbeystrewry Union
C, C & R
CASTLEKNOCK (St Brigid) and Mulhuddart, w Clonsilla
D & G   **I** A D H ORR, **C** S A PRAGNELL
CASTLELOST   *see* Mullingar, Portnashangan, Moyliscar,
Kilbixy etc *M & K*
**CASTLEMACADAM (Holy Trinity) w Ballinaclash, Aughrim
and Macreddin** *D & G*   **I** G W BUTLER
CASTLEMAINE   *see* Kilcolman w Kiltallagh, Killorglin,
Knockane etc *L & K*
CASTLEMARTYR (St Anne)   *see* Youghal Union *C, C & R*
**CASTLEPOLLARD (St Michael) and Oldcastle w Loughcrew,
Mount Nugent, Mayne and Drumcree** *M & K*   **I** G A R MILNE
CASTLEREA   *see* Roscommon w Donamon, Rathcline,
Kilkeevin etc *K, E & A*
CASTLERICKARD   *see* Rathmolyon w Castlerickard,
Rathcore and Agher *M & K*
CASTLEROCK (Christ Church) w Dunboe and Fermoyle *D & R*
I M R K FERRY, **NSM** A QUIGLEY
CASTLETERRA (no dedication)   *see* Drung w Castleterra,
Larah and Lavey etc *K, E & A*
CASTLETOWN   *see* Killeshin w Cloydagh and Killabban
C & O
CASTLETOWN   *see* Rathkeale w Askeaton, Kilcornan and
Kilnaughtin *L & K*
CASTLETOWN   *see* Kells Union *M & K*
CASTLETOWNBERE   *see* Beara *C, C & R*
CASTLETOWNROCHE (no dedication)   *see* Mallow Union
C, C & R
CASTLETOWNSEND   *see* Abbeystrewry Union *C, C & R*
CASTLEVENTRY (no dedication)   *see* Ross Union *C, C & R*
CASTLEWELLAN (St Paul) w Kilcoo *D & D*
NSM G G GRAHAM
CAVAN   *see* Urney w Denn and Derryheen *K, E & A*
CELBRIDGE (Christ Church) w Straffan and Newcastle-Lyons
D & G   **I** M A WOODERSON
CHAPELIZOD (St Laurence)   *see* Dublin Crumlin w
Chapelizod *D & G*
CHARLEMONT (no dedication)   *see* Moy w Charlemont *Arm*
CLABBY (St Margaret)   *see* Tempo and Clabby *Clogh*
CLANABOGAN (no dedication)   *see* Edenderry w Clanabogan
D & R
**CLANE (St Michael and All Angels) w Donadea and
Coolcarrigan** *M & K*   **I** D FRAZER, **C** A V STEWART
CLARA (St Brigid) w Liss, Moate and Clonmacnoise *M & K*
I vacant (00353) (506) 31406
CLARE (no dedication)   *see* Loughgilly w Clare *Arm*
CLAUDY   *see* Cumber Upper w Learmount *D & R*
CLEENISH (no dedication) w Mullaghdun *Clogh*
I G P BRIDLE

CLIFDEN   *see* Omey w Ballynakill, Errislannan and
Roundstone *T, K & A*
CLOGH (Holy Trinity)   *see* Aghadrumsee w Clogh and
Drumsnatt *Clogh*
CLOGHER (Cathedral of St Macartan) w Errigal Portclare
Clogh   **I** T R MOORE
CLOGHERNY (St Patrick) w Seskinore and Drumnakilly *Arm*
R vacant (028) 8075 8219
CLONAGOOSE (St Moling)   *see* Leighlin w Grange Sylvae,
Shankill etc *C & O*
CLONAKILTY   *see* Kilgariffe Union *C, C & R*
CLONALLON (no dedication) w Warrenpoint *D & D*
C J H SIMS
CLONARD   *see* Mullingar, Portnashangan, Moyliscar, Kilbixy
etc *M & K*
CLONASLEE   *see* Mountmellick w Coolbanagher, Rosenallis
etc *M & K*
CLONBEG (St Sedna)   *see* Cashel w Magorban, Tipperary,
Clonbeg etc *C & O*
CLONBRONEY (St John)   *see* Mostrim w Granard,
Clonbroney, Killoe etc *K, E & A*
CLONBULLOGUE   *see* Clonsast w Rathangan, Thomastown
etc *M & K*
CLONCHA (no dedication)   *see* Moville w Greencastle,
Donagh, Cloncha etc *D & R*
CLONDALKIN (St John) w Rathcoole *D & G*
I W P HOUSTON, **NSM** O BOOTHMAN
CLONDEHORKEY (St John) w Cashel *D & R*   **I** S JOHNSON
**CLONDEVADDOCK (Christ the Redeemer) w Portsalon and
Leatbeg** *D & R*   **NSM** S JOHNSON
CLONDUFF (St John)   *see* Drumgath w Drumgooland and
Clonduff *D & D*
CLONE (St Paul)   *see* Enniscorthy w Clone, Clonmore, Monart
etc *C & O*
CLONEGAL (no dedication)   *see* Bunclody w Kildavin,
Clonegal and Kilrush *C & O*
CLONEGAM (Holy Trinity)   *see* Fiddown w Clonegam,
Guilcagh and Kilmeaden *C & O*
**CLONENAGH (no dedication) w Offerlane, Borris-in-Ossory,
Seirkieran and Roskelton** *C & O*   **I** C P JEFFERS
CLONES (St Tighernach) w Killeevan *Clogh*
P-in-c A P R WAKELY
CLONEYHURKE (no dedication)   *see* Portarlington w
Cloneyhurke and Lea *M & K*
CLONFADFORAN   *see* Tullamore w Durrow,
Newtownfertullagh, Rahan etc *M & K*
CLONFEACLE (St Patrick) w Derrygortreavy *Arm*
I A J PARKHILL
**CLONFERT (Cathedral of St Brendan) w Donanaughta,
Banagher and Lickmolassy** *L & K*   **I** R W CARNEY,
NSM E C L ROBINSON
CLONGISH (St Paul)   *see* Templemichael w Clongish,
Clooncumber etc *K, E & A*
CLONLARA   *see* Killaloe w Stradbally *L & K*
CLONLEIGH (St Lugadius)   *see* Raphoe w Raymochy and
Clonleigh *D & R*
CLONMACNOISE (St Kieran)   *see* Clara w Liss, Moate and
Clonmacnoise *M & K*
**CLONMEL (St Mary) w Innislounagh, Tullaghmelan, Fethard,
Kilvemnon and Cahir** *C & O*   **I** G A KNOWD, **C** A CARTER
CLONMEL UNION (Christ Church) *C, C & R*   **I** vacant
(00353) (21) 811790
CLONMELLON   *see* Trim and Athboy Gp *M & K*
CLONMORE (St John)   *see* Enniscorthy w Clone, Clonmore,
Monart etc *C & O*
CLONMORE (St John)   *see* Kiltegan w Hacketstown, Clonmore
and Moyne *C & O*
CLONOE (St Michael)   *see* Tullaniskin w Clonoe *Arm*
**CLONSAST (no dedication) w Rathangan, Thomastown,
Monasterois, Carbury and Rahan** *M & K*   **I** L E A PEILOW
CLONSILLA (St Mary)   *see* Castleknock and Mulhuddart, w
Clonsilla *D & G*
CLONTARF   *see* Dublin Clontarf *D & G*
CLONTIBRET (St Colman)   *see* Ballybay w Mucknoe and
Clontibret *Clogh*
CLONTUSKERT (St Matthew)   *see* Aughrim w Ballinasloe etc
L & K
**CLOONCLARE (no dedication) w Killasnett, Lurganboy and
Drumlease** *K, E & A*   **Bp's C** C J STEVENSON
CLOONCUMBER (no dedication)   *see* Templemichael w
Clongish, Clooncumber etc *K, E & A*
CLOONEY (All Saints) w Strathfoyle *D & R*   **I** J C D MAYES,
C P THOMPSON
CLOUGH   *see* Craigs w Dunaghy and Killagan *Conn*
CLOUGHFERN (Ascension) *Conn*   **I** D LOCKHART,
C A E STEWART

CLOUGHJORDAN (St Kieran) w Borrisokane, Ballingary, Borrisnafarney and Templeharry *L & K* **I** S M NEILL
CLOUGHMILLS *see* Craigs w Dunaghy and Killagan *Conn*
CLOVERHILL (St John) *see* Annagh w Drumgoon, Ashfield etc *K, E & A*
CLOYDAGH (no dedication) *see* Killeshin w Cloydagh and Killabban *C & O*
CLOYNE (Cathedral of St Colman) w Inch, Corkbeg, Midleton and Gurranekennefeake *C, C & R* **I** A G MARLEY
COACHFORD *see* Carrigrohane Union *C, C & R*
COALISLAND *see* Brackaville w Donaghendry and Ballyclog *Arm*
COBH *see* Clonmel Union *C, C & R*
COLAGHTY *see* Lack *Clogh*
COLEBROOK *see* Aghalurcher w Tattykeeran, Cooneen etc *Clogh*
COLERAINE *see* Killowen *D & R*
COLERAINE (St Patrick) *Conn* **I** C R A EASTON, **C** J HALES, D RICHARDSON
COLIN (St Andrew) *see* Derriaghy w Colin *Conn*
COLLIERY CHURCH, THE *see* Castlecomer w Colliery Ch, Mothel and Bilbo *C & O*
COLLON (no dedication) *see* Drogheda w Ardee, Collon and Termonfeckin *Arm*
COLLOONEY (St Paul) *see* Ballisodare w Collooney and Emlaghfad *T, K & A*
COLPE (St Columba) *see* Julianstown and Colpe w Drogheda and Duleek *M & K*
COLUMBKILLE (St Thomas) *see* Arvagh w Carrigallen, Gowna and Columbkille *K, E & A*
COMBER (St Mary) *D & D* **I** J P O BARRY, **NSM** R A B MOLLAN
COMERAGH *see* Lismore w Cappoquin, Kilwatermoy, Dungarvan etc *C & O*
CONARY (St Bartholomew) *see* Dunganstown w Redcross and Conary *D & G*
CONG (St Mary) *see* Tuam w Cong and Aasleagh *T, K & A*
CONNOR (St Saviour) w Antrim St Patrick *Conn* **I** S GILCHRIST
CONVOY (St Ninian) w Monellan and Donaghmore *D & R* **I** K L J HOMFRAY
CONWAL (no dedication) w Aughanunshin and Gartan *D & R* **I** W C S WRIGHT
COOKSTOWN *see* Derryloran *Arm*
COOLBANAGHER (St John) *see* Mountmellick w Coolbanagher, Rosenallis etc *M & K*
COOLCARRIGAN (no dedication) *see* Clane w Donadea and Coolcarrigan *M & K*
COOLKELLURE (St Edmund) *see* Fanlobbus Union *C, C & R*
COOLOCK (St John) *see* Raheny w Coolock *D & G*
COONEEN (no dedication) *see* Aghalurcher w Tattykeeran, Cooneen etc *Clogh*
COOTEHILL *see* Annagh w Drumgoon, Ashfield etc *K, E & A*
CORACLONE (St Peter) *see* Stradbally w Ballintubbert, Coraclone etc *C & O*
CORBALLY (Christ Church) *see* Roscrea w Kyle, Bourney and Corbally *L & K*
CORK (Cathedral of St Fin Barre) (St Nicholas) *C, C & R* **I** M A J BURROWS, **NSM** E W HUNTER
CORK (St Luke) w Shandon (St Ann) w St Mary *C, C & R* **I** B J G O'ROURKE, **NSM** P T HANNA
CORKBEG (St Michael and All Angels) *see* Cloyne Union *C, C & R*
CORRAWALLEN (no dedication) *see* Kilmore w Ballintemple, Kildallon etc *K, E & A*
COURTMACSHERRY (St John the Evangelist) *see* Kilgariffe Union *C, C & R*
CRAIGADOOISH (no dedication) *see* Taughboyne, Craigadooish, Newtowncunningham etc *D & R*
CRAIGAVAD *see* Glencraig *D & D*
CRAIGAVON (St Saviour) *see* Ardmore w Craigavon *D & D*
CRAIGS (no dedication) w Dunaghy and Killagan *Conn* **I** W R G WILLANS
CRAIGY HILL (All Saints) *see* Kilwaughter w Cairncastle and Craigy Hill *Conn*
CREAGH *see* Abbeystrewry Union *C, C & R*
CREAGH *see* Aughrim w Ballinasloe etc *L & K*
CRECORA *see* Adare and Kilmallock w Kilpeacon, Croom etc *L & K*
CREGAGH (St Finnian) *D & D* **I** J N BATTYE, **C** B J HAYES
CREGGAN (no dedication) *see* Ballymascanlan w Creggan and Rathcor *Arm*
CRILLY (St George) *see* Carnteel and Crilly *Arm*
CRINKEN (St James) *D & G* **I** G FYLES
CROGHAN (Holy Trinity) *see* Boyle and Elphin w Aghanagh, Kilbryan etc *K, E & A*

CROHANE (no dedication) *see* Kilcooley w Littleon, Crohane and Fertagh *C & O*
CROM (Holy Trinity) *see* Kinawley w H Trin *K, E & A*
CROOKHAVEN (St Brendan) *see* Kilmoe Union *C, C & R*
CROOM (no dedication) *see* Adare and Kilmallock w Kilpeacon, Croom etc *L & K*
CROSSGAR *see* Kilmore and Inch *D & D*
CROSSHAVEN *see* Templebreedy w Tracton and Nohoval *C, C & R*
CROSSMOLINA (no dedication) *see* Killala w Dunfeeny, Crossmolina, Kilmoremoy etc *T, K & A*
CROSSPATRICK Group (no dedication) w Kilcommon, Kilpipe, Preban and Carnew, The *C & O* **I** D P M DUNNE
CRUMLIN *see* Dublin Crumlin w Chapelizod *D & G*
CRUMLIN (St John) *see* Glenavy w Tunny and Crumlin *Conn*
CRUMLIN ROAD *see* Belfast St Mary w H Redeemer *Conn*
CULDAFF (no dedication) *see* Moville w Greencastle, Donagh, Cloncha etc *D & R*
CULFEIGHTRIN (no dedication) *see* Ramoan w Ballycastle and Culfeightrin *Conn*
CULLYBACKEY *see* Craigs w Dunaghy and Killagan *Conn*
CULMORE (Holy Trinity) w Muff and Belmont *D & R* **I** M E G MOORE
CUMBER LOWER (Holy Trinity) w Banagher *D & R* **I** J A MARTIN
CUMBER UPPER (no dedication) w Learmount *D & R* **I** J A MARTIN
CURRAGH (Garrison Church of St Paul) *see* Kildare w Kilmeague and Curragh *M & K*
CURRIN (St Andrew) w Drum and Newbliss *Clogh* **I** *vacant* (00353) (47) 56103
CUSHENDALL *see* Ardclinis and Tickmacrevan w Layde and Cushendun *Conn*
CUSHENDUN (no dedication) *as above Conn*
DALKEY (St Patrick) *D & G* **I** W B A NEILL
DARTREY *see* Ematris w Rockcorry, Aghabog and Aughnamullan *Clogh*
DELGANY (Christ Church) *D & G* **I** N J W WAUGH
DENN (no dedication) *see* Urney w Denn and Derryheen *K, E & A*
DERG (no dedication) w Termonamongan *D & R* **I** W P QUILL
DERNAKESH (Chapel of Ease) *see* Annagh w Drumgoon, Ashfield etc *K, E & A*
DERRALOSSARY *see* Rathdrum w Glenealy, Derralossary and Laragh *D & G*
DERRIAGHY (Christ Church) w Colin *Conn* **I** J C BUDD
DERRYBRUSK (St Michael) *see* Maguiresbridge w Derrybrusk *Clogh*
DERRYGONNELLY *see* Inishmacsaint *Clogh*
DERRYGORTREAVY (St Columba) *see* Clonfeacle w Derrygortreavy *Arm*
DERRYHEEN (no dedication) *see* Urney w Denn and Derryheen *K, E & A*
DERRYKIGHAN (St Colman) *see* Billy w Derrykeighan *Conn*
DERRYLANE (no dedication) *see* Killeshandra w Killegar and Derrylane *K, E & A*
DERRYLIN *see* Kinawley w H Trin *K, E & A*
DERRYLORAN (St Luran) *Arm* **I** R J N PORTEUS, **C** J EWART
DERRYNOOSE (St John) *see* Keady w Armaghbreague and Derrynoose *Arm*
DERRYVOLGIE (St Columba) *Conn* **I** C J POLLOCK
DERRYVULLEN NORTH (St Tighernach) w Castlearchdale *Clogh* **I** R C THOMPSON
DERRYVULLEN SOUTH (St Tighernach) w Garvary *Clogh* **I** J W STEWART
DERVOCK *see* Billy w Derrykeighan *Conn*
DESERTCREAT (no dedication) *see* Ardtrea w Desertcreat *Arm*
DESERTLYN (St John) w Ballyeglish *Arm* **I** A N STRINGER
DESERTMARTIN (St Conghall) w Termoneeny *D & R* **I** K R KINGSTON
DESERTOGHILL (no dedication) *see* Errigal w Garvagh *D & R*
DESERTSERGES (no dedication) *see* Kinneigh Union *C, C & R*
DEVENISH (St Molaise) w Boho *Clogh* **I** D P KERR
DIAMOND (St Paul) *see* Tartaraghan w Diamond *Arm*
DINGLE (St James) w Killiney and Kilgobbin *L & K* **I** *vacant*
DOAGH *see* Kilbride *Conn*
DOLLINGSTOWN (St Saviour) *see* Magheralin w Dollingstown *D & D*
DONABATE (St Patrick) *see* Swords w Donabate and Kilsallaghan *D & G*
DONACAVEY (no dedication) w Barr *Clogh* **I** *vacant*
DONADEA (St Peter) *see* Clane w Donadea and Coolcarrigan *M & K*

DONAGH (no dedication)   *see* Moville w Greencastle, Donagh, Cloncha etc *D & R*
DONAGH (St Salvator) w Tyholland and Errigal Truagh   *Clogh*   I *vacant* (00353) (47) 88277
DONAGHADEE (no dedication)   *D & D*   R I R GAMBLE, C A YOUNG
DONAGHCLONEY (St Patrick) w Waringstown   *D & D*   I T D ALLEN
DONAGHEADY (St James)   *D & R*   I D H J FERRY
DONAGHENDRY (St Patrick)   *see* Brackaville w Donaghendry and Ballyclog *Arm*
DONAGHMORE (no dedication)   *see* Rathdowney w Castlefleming, Donaghmore etc *C & O*
DONAGHMORE (St Bartholomew)   *see* Aghaderg w Donaghmore and Scarva *D & D*
DONAGHMORE (St Michael) w Upper Donaghmore   *Arm*   I T S FORSTER
DONAGHMORE (St Patrick)   *see* Convoy w Monellan and Donaghmore *D & R*
DONAGHMORE, UPPER (St Patrick)   *see* Donaghmore w Upper Donaghmore *Arm*
DONAGHPATRICK (St Patrick)   *see* Kells Union *M & K*
DONAMON (no dedication)   *see* Roscommon w Donamon, Rathcline, Kilkeevin etc *K, E & A*
DONANAUGHTA (St John the Baptist)   *see* Clonfert Gp of Par *L & K*
DONARD (no dedication)   *see* Donoughmore and Donard w Dunlavin *D & G*
DONEGAL (no dedication) w Killymard, Lough Eske and Laghey   *D & R*   I R FOX
DONEGORE (St John)   *see* Templepatrick w Donegore *Conn*
DONEMANA   *see* Donagheady *D & R*
DONERAILE (St Mary)   *see* Mallow Union *C, C & R*
DONNYBROOK (St Mary)   *see* Dublin Irishtown w Donnybrook *D & G*
DONOUGHMORE (no dedication) and Donard w Dunlavin   *D & G*   I G D B SMITH
DORRHA (no dedication)   *see* Birr w Lorrha, Dorrha and Lockeen *L & K*
DOUGLAS (St Luke) w Blackrock, Frankfield and Marmullane   *C, C & R*   I R E B WHITE, A M WILKINSON,   C E V CREMIN, NSM A D KINGSTON
DOWN (Cathedral of the Holy and Undivided Trinity)   *D & D*   I *vacant*
DOWN (St Margaret) w Hollymount   *D & D*   I S M J DICKSON, Hon C M S WALSHE
DOWNPATRICK   *see* Down H Trin w Hollymount *D & D*
DOWNPATRICK   *see* Down Cathl *D & D*
DRAPERSTOWN (St Columb)   *see* Kilcronaghan w Draperstown and Sixtowns *D & R*
DREW MEMORIAL   *see* Belfast St Simon w St Phil *Conn*
DRIMOLEAGUE (St Matthew)   *see* Fanlobbus Union *C, C & R*
DRINAGH (Christ Church)   *as above C, C & R*
DROGHEDA (St Mary)   *see* Julianstown and Colpe w Drogheda and Duleek *M & K*
DROGHEDA (St Peter) w Ardee, Collon and Termonfeckin   *Arm*   I M GRAHAM,   NSM R W MOORE
DROMAHAIR   *see* Cloonclare w Killasnett, Lurganboy and Drumlease *K, E & A*
DROMARA (St John) w Garvaghy   *D & D*   I *vacant*
DROMARD (Christ Church)   *see* Skreen w Kilmacshalgan and Dromard *T, K & A*
DROMOD (St Michael and All Angels)   *see* Kenmare w Sneem, Waterville etc *L & K*
DROMORE (Cathedral of Christ the Redeemer)   *D & D*   I S H LOWRY
DROMORE (Holy Trinity)   *Clogh*   I T K HANLON
DRUM (no dedication)   *see* Currin w Drum and Newbliss *Clogh*
DRUMACHOSE (Christ Church)   *D & R*   I S MCVEIGH, NSM N I LYTTLE
DRUMALOOR (St Andrew)   *see* Annagh w Drumgoon, Ashfield etc *K, E & A*
DRUMANY (Christ Church)   *see* Kinawley w H Trin *K, E & A*
DRUMBANAGHER (St Mary)   *see* Acton and Drumbanagher *Arm*
DRUMBEG (St Patrick)   *D & D*   I R R W DEVENNEY
DRUMBO (Holy Trinity)   *D & D*   I R C NEILL
DRUMCANNON (Christ Church)   *see* Waterford w Killea, Drumcannon and Dunhill *C & O*
DRUMCAR   *see* Kilsaran w Drumcar, Dunleer and Dunany *Arm*
DRUMCLAMPH (no dedication) w Lower Langfield and Upper Langfield   *D & R*   I R G KEOGH
DRUMCLIFFE (St Columba) w Kilrush, Kilfenora, Kilfarboy, Kilnasoolagh, Shannon and Kilferagh   *L & K*   I R C HANNA, NSM P E HANNA

DRUMCLIFFE (St Columba) w Lissadell and Munninane   *K, E & A*   I A J FORSTER
DRUMCONDRA   *see* Dublin Drumcondra w N Strand *D & G*
DRUMCONRATH (St Peter)   *see* Kingscourt w Drumconrath, Syddan and Moybologue *M & K*
DRUMCREE (Ascension)   *Arm*   I J A PICKERING
DRUMCREE (St John)   *see* Castlepollard and Oldcastle w Loughcrew etc *M & K*
DRUMGATH (St John) w Drumgooland and Clonduff   *D & D*   I D SOMERVILLE
DRUMGLASS (St Anne) w Moygashel   *Arm*   I F D SWANN, C A W MILLAR, G W MACARTNEY
DRUMGOOLAND (no dedication)   *see* Drumgath w Drumgooland and Clonduff *D & D*
DRUMGOON (All Saints)   *see* Annagh w Drumgoon, Ashfield etc *K, E & A*
DRUMHOLM (no dedication)   *see* Kilbarron w Rossnowlagh and Drumholm *D & R*
DRUMINISKILL (Chapel of Ease)   *see* Killesher *K, E & A*
DRUMKEERAN   *see* Killinagh w Kiltyclogher and Innismagrath *K, E & A*
DRUMKEERAN (no dedication) w Templecarne and Muckross   *Clogh*   I *vacant* (028) 6863 1210
DRUMLANE (no dedication)   *see* Annagh w Drumgoon, Ashfield etc *K, E & A*
DRUMLEASE (no dedication)   *see* Cloonclare w Killasnett, Lurganboy and Drumlease *K, E & A*
DRUMMAUL (St Brigid) w Duneane and Ballyscullion   *Conn*   I T P KERR
DRUMMULLY (no dedication)   *see* Galloon w Drummully *Clogh*
DRUMNAKILLY (Holy Trinity)   *see* Clogherny w Seskinore and Drumnakilly *Arm*
DRUMQUIN   *see* Drumclamph w Lower and Upper Langfield *D & R*
DRUMRAGH (St Columba) w Mountfield   *D & R*   I W A SEALE,   C L D A CRAWFORD
DRUMREILLY (no dedication)   *see* Mohill w Farnaught, Aughavas, Oughteragh etc *K, E & A*
DRUMSHAMBO (St John)   *see* Kiltoghart w Drumshambo, Annaduff and Kilronan *K, E & A*
DRUMSNATT (St Molua)   *see* Aghadrumsee w Clogh and Drumsnatt *Clogh*
DRUMTALLAGH (no dedication)   *see* Armoy w Loughguile and Drumtullagh *Conn*
DRUNG (no dedication) w Castleterra, Larah and Lavey and Killoughter   *K, E & A*   I *vacant* Cavan (49) 38204
DUBLIN Booterstown (St Philip and St James)   *D & G*   I K A L BARRETT
DUBLIN (Christ Church Cathedral) Group: (St Andrew) (St Werburgh) (St Michan) St Paul and Grangegorman   *D & G*   I J T F PATERSON, D A PIERPOINT,   Min W J STEWART, C T IRVINE
DUBLIN Clontarf (St John the Baptist)   *D & G*   I D C SARGENT
DUBLIN Crumlin (St Mary) w Chapelizod   *D & G*   I I J POWER,   C A E J BENNETT
DUBLIN Drumcondra (no dedication) w North Strand   *D & G*   I W H BLACK,   NSM A A SHINE
DUBLIN (Irish Church Missions) and St Thomas   *D & G*,   E J COULTER
DUBLIN Irishtown (St Matthew) w Donnybrook   *D & G*   I E G ARDIS,   NSM J M GORDON
DUBLIN Mount Merrion (St Thomas)   *D & G*   I K A L BARRETT
DUBLIN Rathfarnham (no dedication)   *D & G*   I E C J WOODS
DUBLIN Rathmines (Holy Trinity) w Harold's Cross   *D & G*   I N G MCENDOO
DUBLIN Sandford (no dedication) w Milltown   *D & G*   I R D HARMAN
DUBLIN Sandymount (St John the Evangelist)   *D & G*   P-in-c K J MORONEY
DUBLIN Santry (St Pappan) w Glasnevin and Finglas   *D & G*   I D W OXLEY,   NSM M A GILBERT
DUBLIN (St Ann) (St Stephen)   *D & G*   I T HASKINS
DUBLIN (St Bartholomew) w Leeson Park   *D & G*   I W J RITCHIE
DUBLIN (St George and St Thomas)   *D & G*   Bp's C K M POULTON
DUBLIN (St Patrick's Cathedral) Group: (St Catherine and St James) (St Audoen)   *D & G*   TV J W R CRAWFORD,   NSM C E BAKER
DUBLIN Whitechurch (no dedication)   *D & G*   I A H N MCKINLEY,   NSM P COMERFORD
DUBLIN (Zion Church)   *D & G*   I W R J GOURLEY
DUGORT (St Thomas)   *see* Aughaval w Achill, Knappagh, Dugort etc *T, K & A*

GLASLOUGH   *see* Donagh w Tyholland and Errigal Truagh *Clogh*
GLASNEVIN (St Mobhi)   *see* Dublin Santry w Glasnevin and Finglas *D & G*
GLENAGEARY (St Paul)   *D & G*   I G C S LINNEY
GLENALLA (St Columbkille)   *see* Mevagh w Glenalla *D & R*
GLENARM   *see* Ardclinis and Tickmacrevan w Layde and Cushendun *Conn*
GLENAVY (St Aidan) w Tunny and Crumlin   *Conn*
I W E C STOREY,   C P L STOREY
GLENBEIGH (St John)   *see* Kilcolman w Kiltallagh, Killorglin, Knockane etc *L & K*
GLENCAIRN   *see* Belfast St Andr *Conn*
GLENCAR   *see* Cloonclare w Killasnett, Lurganboy and Drumlease *K, E & A*
GLENCOLUMBKILLE (St Columba)   *see* Ardara w Glencolumbkille, Inniskeel etc *D & R*
GLENCRAIG (Holy Trinity)   *D & D*   I P S P HEWITT,
NSM B W PARKER
GLENDERMOTT (no dedication)   *D & R*   I F D CREIGHTON,
C I DINSMORE
GLENEALY (no dedication)   *see* Rathdrum w Glenealy, Derralossary and Laragh *D & G*
GLENOE   *see* Glynn w Raloo *Conn*
GLENTIES (no dedication)   *see* Ardara w Glencolumbkille, Inniskeel etc *D & R*
GLENVILLE   *see* Fermoy Union *C, C & R*
GLYNN (St John) w Raloo   *Conn*   I S B FORDE
GORESBRIDGE   *see* Leighlin w Grange Sylvae, Shankill etc *C & O*
GOREY (Christ Church) w Kilnahue, Leskinfere and Ballycanew
C & O   I M J J HAYDEN,   NSM J F FORBES
GORTIN   *see* Ardstraw w Baronscourt, Badoney Lower etc *D & R*
GOWNA (no dedication)   *see* Arvagh w Carrigallen, Gowna and Columbkille *K, E & A*
GRACEFIELD (no dedication)   *see* Woodschapel w Gracefield *Arm*
GRANARD (St Patrick)   *see* Mostrim w Granard, Clonbroney, Killoe etc *K, E & A*
GRANGE (St Aidan)   *see* Loughgall w Grange *Arm*
GRANGE SYLVAE (St George)   *see* Leighlin w Grange Sylvae, Shankill etc *C & O*
GRANGEGORMAN (All Saints)   *see* Dublin Ch Ch Cathl Gp *D & G*
GREENAN (no dedication)   *see* Ardstraw w Baronscourt, Badoney Lower etc *D & R*
GREENCASTLE (St Finian)   *see* Moville w Greencastle, Donagh, Cloncha etc *D & R*
GREENISLAND (Holy Name)   *Conn*   I P LYONS
GREY ABBEY (St Saviour) w Kircubbin   *D & D*
I R D SEYMOUR-WHITELEY
GREYSTONES (St Patrick)   *D & G*   I E J SWANN,
C O H WILLIAMS
GROOMSPORT (no dedication)   *D & D*   I D J M POLLOCK
GUILCAGH (St John the Evangelist)   *see* Fiddown w Clonegam, Guilcagh and Kilmeaden *C & O*
GURRANEKENNEFEAKE (no dedication)   *see* Cloyne Union *C, C & R*
GWEEDORE (St Patrick), Carrickfin and Templecrone   *D & R*
Bp's C W B JOHNSTON
HACKETSTOWN (St John the Baptist)   *see* Kiltegan w Hacketstown, Clonmore and Moyne *C & O*
HAROLD'S CROSS (no dedication)   *see* Dublin Rathmines w Harold's Cross *D & G*
HELEN'S BAY (St John the Baptist)   *D & D*   I L J MEDHURST
HEYNESTOWN (St Paul)   *see* Dundalk w Heynestown *Arm*
HIGHFIELD   *see* Belfast Whiterock *Conn*
HILLSBOROUGH (St Malachi)   *D & D*   I J F DINNEN,
C W S NIXON
HILLTOWN   *see* Drumgath w Drumgooland and Clonduff *D & D*
HOLLYFORT   *see* Gorey w Kilnahue, Leskinfere and Ballycanew *C & O*
HOLLYMOUNT (no dedication)   *see* Down H Trin w Hollymount *D & D*
HOLMPATRICK (St Patrick) w Balbriggan and Kenure   *D & G*
I A J RUFLI,   NSM K E LONG
HOLYCROSS   *see* Templemore w Thurles and Kilfithmone *C & O*
HOLYWOOD (St Kevin)   *see* Blessington w Kilbride, Ballymore Eustace etc *D & G*
HOLYWOOD (St Philip and St James)   *D & D*   I R M ELKS,
C C J MATCHETT, C I BENNETT
HORETOWN (St James)   *see* Taghmon w Horetown and Bannow *C & O*

HORSELEAP   *see* Clara w Liss, Moate and Clonmacnoise *M & K*
HOWTH (St Mary)   *D & G*   I C G HYLAND
INCH   *see* Cloyne Union *C, C & R*
INCH (no dedication)   *see* Kilmore and Inch *D & D*
INCH (no dedication)   *see* Arklow w Inch and Kilbride *D & G*
INISHARGIE (St Andrew)   *see* Ballywalter w Inishargie *D & D*
INISHMACSAINT (St Ninnidh)   *Clogh*   I S G BOURKE
INISTIOGE (St Mary)   *see* Kells Gp *C & O*
INNISCALTRA (St Caimin)   *see* Killaloe w Stradbally *L & K*
INNISCARRA (no dedication)   *see* Carrigrohane Union *C, C & R*
INNISHANNON (Christ Church)   *see* Bandon Union *C, C & R*
INNISKEEL (no dedication)   *see* Ardara w Glencolumbkille, Inniskeel etc *D & R*
INNISLOUNAGH (St Patrick)   *see* Clonmel w Innislounagh, Tullaghmelan etc *C & O*
INNISMAGRATH (no dedication)   *see* Killinagh w Kiltyclogher and Innismagrath *K, E & A*
INVER   *see* Larne and Inver *Conn*
INVER (St John the Evangelist) w Mountcharles, Killaghtee and Killybegs   *D & R*   I *vacant* Donegal (73) 36013
INVER, Mountcharles and Killaghtee   *D & R*
P-in-c H J K MCLAUGHLIN
IRISHTOWN   *see* Dublin Irishtown w Donnybrook *D & G*
IRVINESTOWN   *see* Derryvullen N w Castlearchdale *Clogh*
ISLANDMAGEE (St John)   *see* Whitehead and Islandmagee *Conn*
JOANMOUNT   *see* Belfast H Trin and St Silas *Conn*
JOHNSTOWN   *see* Kilcooley w Littleon, Crohane and Fertagh *C & O*
JORDANSTOWN (St Patrick)   *Conn*   I N P BAYLOR
JULIANSTOWN (St Mary) and Colpe w Drogheda and Duleek
M & K   I P H A LAWRENCE
KEADY (St Matthew) w Armaghbreague and Derrynoose   *Arm*
I W G NEELY
KELLS (St Columba) w Balrathboyne, Moynalty, Donaghpatrick and Castletown   *M & K*   I *vacant*
KELLS (St Mary) w Ballaghtobin, Kilmoganny, Ennisnag, Inistioge and Kilfane   *C & O*   I D L SANDES
KENAGH   *see* Ardagh w Tashinny, Shrule and Kilcommick *K, E & A*
KENMARE (St Patrick) w Sneem, Dromod and Valentia   *L & K*
NSM A W SHAW
KENTSTOWN (St Mary)   *see* Navan w Kentstown, Tara, Slane, Painestown etc *M & K*
KENURE (no dedication)   *see* Holmpatrick w Balbriggan and Kenure *D & G*
KESH   *see* Magheraculmoney *Clogh*
KILBARRON (St Anne) w Rossnowlagh and Drumholm   *D & R*
I B R RUSSELL
KILBERRY (no dedication)   *see* Athy w Kilberry, Fontstown and Kilkea *D & G*
KILBIXY (St Bigseach)   *see* Mullingar, Portnashangan, Moyliscar, Kilbixy etc *M & K*
KILBONANE (St Mark)   *see* Moviddy Union *C, C & R*
KILBRIDE (Holy Trinity)   *see* Ferns w Kilbride, Toombe, Kilcormack etc *C & O*
KILBRIDE (no dedication)   *see* Blessington w Kilbride, Ballymore Eustace etc *D & G*
KILBRIDE (St Bride)   *Conn*   I P REDFERN
KILBRIDE (St Brigid)   *see* Arklow w Inch and Kilbride *D & G*
KILBRIDE BRAY (no dedication)   *see* Powerscourt w Kilbride *D & G*
KILBRONEY (no dedication)   *D & D*   Bp's C S JONES
KILBRYAN (no dedication)   *see* Boyle and Elphin w Aghanagh, Kilbryan etc *K, E & A*
KILCLEAGH   *see* Clara w Liss, Moate and Clonmacnoise *M & K*
KILCLIEF (no dedication)   *see* Lecale Gp *D & D*
KILCLUNEY (St John)   *see* Mullabrack w Markethill and Kilcluney *Arm*
KILCOCK   *see* Dunboyne Union *M & K*
KILCOLMAN (no dedication) w Kiltallagh, Killorglin, Knockane and Glenbeigh   *L & K*   I M J D SHANNON,   C J C STEPHENS
KILCOMMICK (no dedication)   *see* Ardagh w Tashinny, Shrule and Kilcommick *K, E & A*
KILCOMMON (no dedication)   *see* Crosspatrick Gp *C & O*
KILCOO (no dedication)   *see* Castlewellan w Kilcoo *D & D*
KILCOOLEY (no dedication) w Littleton, Crohane and Fertagh
C & O   I B Y FRYDAY
KILCOOLEY (St Columba)   *see* Bangor Abbey *D & D*
KILCORMACK (St Cormac)   *see* Ferns w Kilbride, Toombe, Kilcormack etc *C & O*
KILCORNAN (no dedication)   *see* Rathkeale w Askeaton, Kilcornan and Kilnaughtin *L & K*

KILCROHANE *see* Kenmare w Sneem, Waterville etc *L & K*
KILCRONAGHAN (no dedication) w Draperstown and Sixtowns
D & R **I** D MORROW
KILCULLEN (St John) *see* Newbridge w Carnalway and
Kilcullen *M & K*
KILCUMMIN (no dedication) *see* Galway w Kilcummin
T, K & A
KILDALLON (no dedication) *see* Kilmore w Ballintemple,
Kildallon etc *K, E & A*
KILDARE (Cathedral of St Brigid) w Kilmeague and Curragh
Garrison Church *M & K* **I** R K TOWNLEY
KILDARTON (no dedication) *see* Lisnadill w Kildarton *Arm*
KILDAVIN (St Paul) *see* Bunclody w Kildavin, Clonegal and
Kilrush *C & O*
KILDOLLAGH (St Paul) *see* Ballyrashane w Kildollagh *Conn*
KILDRESS (St Patrick) w Altedesert *Arm* **I** B J A CRUISE
KILDRUMFERTON (St Patrick) w Ballymachugh and
Ballyjamesduff *K, E & A* **I** J R SIDES
KILFANE (no dedication) *see* Kells Gp *C & O*
KILFARBOY (Christ Church) *see* Drumcliffe w Kilnasoolagh
L & K
KILFAUGHNABEG (Christ Church) *see* Ross Union *C, C & R*
KILFENORA (Cathedral of St Fachan) *see* Drumcliffe w
Kilnasoolagh *L & K*
KILFERAGH (no dedication) *as above L & K*
KILFINANE (St Andrew) *see* Adare and Kilmallock w
Kilpeacon, Croom etc *L & K*
KILFITHMONE (no dedication) *see* Templemore w Thurles
and Kilfithmone *C & O*
KILFLYNN (no dedication) *see* Adare and Kilmallock w
Kilpeacon, Croom etc *L & K*
KILGARIFFE (no dedication) w Kilmalooda, Kilnagross,
Timoleague and Courtmacsherry *C, C & R* **I** I R JONAS
KILGLASS (no dedication) *see* Killala w Dunfeeny,
Crossmolina, Kilmoremoy etc *T, K & A*
KILGLASS (St Anne) *see* Mostrim w Granard, Clonbroney,
Killoe etc *K, E & A*
KILGOBBIN (no dedication) *see* Dingle w Killiney and
Kilgobbin *L & K*
KILHORNE *see* Annalong *D & G*
KILKEA (no dedication) *see* Athy w Kilberry, Fontstown and
Kilkea *D & G*
KILKEE *see* Drumcliffe w Kilnasoolagh *L & K*
KILKEEL (Christ Church) *D & D* **I** G MILLAR,
NSM S J K TEGGARTY
KILKEEVIN (Holy Trinity) *see* Roscommon w Donamon,
Rathcline, Kilkeevin etc *K, E & A*
KILKENNY (Cathedral of St Canice) (St John), Aghour and
Kilmanagh *C & O* **I** N N LYNAS, **C** M E JOHNSTON
KILKENNY WEST *see* Athlone w Benown, Kiltoom and
Forgney *M & K*
KILL (no dedication) *D & G* **I** S F GLENFIELD,
C C W L MCCAULEY
KILL (St John) *see* Naas w Kill and Rathmore *M & K*
KILL O' THE GRANGE *see* Kill *D & G*
KILLABBAN (no dedication) *see* Killeshin w Cloydagh and
Killabban *C & O*
KILLADEAS (Priory Church) *see* Trory w Killadeas *Clogh*
KILLAGAN (no dedication) *see* Craigs w Dunaghy and
Killagan *Conn*
KILLAGHTEE (St Peter) *see* Inver w Mountcharles, Killaghtee
and Killybegs *D & R*
KILLALA (Cathedral of St Patrick) w Dunfeeny, Crossmolina,
Kilmoremoy, Castleconnor, Easkey and Kilglass *T, K & A*
C N J O'RAW, **NSM** D T S CLEMENTS
KILLALLON (St John) *see* Trim and Athboy Gp *M & K*
KILLALOE (Cathedral of St Flannan) w Stradbally, Clonlara,
Mountshannon, Abingdon and Tuomgraney *L & K*
NSM S G EVANS
KILLANEY (St Andrew) w Carryduff *D & D*
I J R AUCHMUTY, **NSM** R L RENNIX
KILLANNE (St Anne) w Killegney, Rossdroit and Templeshanbo
C & O **I** R J HARMSWORTH
KILLANULLY *see* Carrigaline Union *C, C & R*
KILLARGUE (no dedication) *see* Killinagh w Kiltyclogher and
Innismagrath *K, E & A*
KILLARNEY (St Mary) w Aghadoe and Muckross *L & K*
I B F B LOUGHEED
KILLASHEE (St Paul) *see* Templemichael w Clongish,
Clooncumber etc *K, E & A*
KILLASNETT (no dedication) *see* Cloonclare w Killasnett,
Lurganboy and Drumlease *K, E & A*
KILLCONNELL *see* Aughrim w Ballinasloe etc *L & K*
KILLEA (St Andrew) *see* Waterford w Killea, Drumcannon and
Dunhill *C & O*
KILLEA (St Fiach) *see* Taughboyne, Craigadooish,
Newtowncunningham etc *D & R*

KILLEAD (St Catherine) w Gartree *Conn* **Bp's C** J C IRVINE
KILLEDMOND *see* Dunleckney w Nurney, Lorum and
Kiltennel *C & O*
KILLEEVAN (no dedication) *see* Clones w Killeevan *Clogh*
KILLEGAR (no dedication) *see* Killeshandra w Killegar and
Derrylane *K, E & A*
KILLEGNEY (no dedication) *see* Killanne w Killegney,
Rossdroit and Templeshanbo *C & O*
KILLEIGH (no dedication) *see* Geashill w Killeigh and
Ballycommon *M & K*
KILLELAGH (no dedication) *see* Maghera w Killelagh *D & R*
KILLENAULE (no dedication) *see* Kilcooley w Littleon,
Crohane and Fertagh *C & O*
KILLERMOGH (no dedication) *see* Abbeyleix w Old Church,
Ballyroan etc *C & O*
KILLERY *see* Taunagh w Kilmactranny, Ballysumaghan etc
K, E & A
KILLESHANDRA (no dedication) w Killegar and Derrylane
K, E & A **I** G T DOYLE
KILLESHER (St John) *K, E & A* **NSM** T J WOODS
KILLESHERDONEY (St Mark) *see* Annagh w Drumgoon,
Ashfield etc *K, E & A*
KILLESHIL (St Paul) *see* Errigle Keerogue w Ballygawley and
Killeshil *Arm*
KILLESHIN (no dedication) w Cloydagh and Killabban *C & O*
I R H BYRNE
KILLESK (All Saints) *see* New w Old Ross, Whitechurch,
Fethard etc *C & O*
KILLETER *see* Derg w Termonamongan *D & R*
KILLINAGH (no dedication) w Kiltyclogher and Innismagrath
K, E & A **I** vacant
KILLINCHY (no dedication) w Kilmood and Tullynakill *D & D*
I N D J KIRKPATRICK
KILLINEY Ballybrack (St Matthias) *D & G* **I** I P POULTON
KILLINEY (Holy Trinity) *D & G* **I** H C MILLS
KILLINEY (St Brendan) *see* Dingle w Killiney and Kilgobbin
L & K
KILLINICK (no dedication) *see* Kilscoran w Killinick and
Mulrankin *C & O*
KILLINKERE (no dedication) *see* Lurgan w Billis, Killinkere
and Munterconnaught *K, E & A*
KILLISKEY (no dedication) *see* Wicklow w Killiskey *D & G*
KILLODIERNAN (no dedication) *see* Nenagh *L & K*
KILLOE (St Catherine) *see* Mostrim w Granard, Clonbroney,
Killoe etc *K, E & A*
KILLORAN (no dedication) *see* Achonry w Tubbercurry and
Killoran *T, K & A*
KILLORGLIN (no dedication) *see* Kilcolman w Kiltallagh,
Killorglin, Knockane etc *L & K*
KILLOUGH (St Anne) *see* Bright w Ballee and Killough *D & D*
KILLOUGHTER (no dedication) *see* Drung w Castleterra,
Larah and Lavey etc *K, E & A*
KILLOUGHY (no dedication) *see* Tullamore w Durrow, Newtownfertullagh,
Rahan etc *M & K*
KILLOWEN *see* Kinneigh Union *C, C & R*
KILLOWEN (St John) *D & R* **I** D M COLLINS
KILLSALLAGHAN (St David) *see* Swords w Donabate and
Kilsallaghan *D & G*
KILLUCAN (St Etchen) *see* Mullingar, Portnashangan,
Moyliscar, Kilbixy etc *M & K*
KILLURIN (no dedication) *see* Wexford w Ardcolm and
Killurin *C & O*
KILLYBEGS (no dedication) *see* Inver w Mountcharles,
Killaghtee and Killybegs *D & R*
KILLYGARVAN (St Columb) *see* Tullyaughnish w
Kilmacrennan and Killygarvan *D & R*
KILLYLEA (St Mark) *see* Eglish w Killylea *Arm*
KILLYLEAGH (St John the Evangelist) *D & D*
I J C MUNYANGAJU
KILLYMAN (St Andrew) *Arm* **I** A S J WARKE
KILLYMARD (no dedication) *see* Donegal w Killymard,
Lough Eske and Laghey *D & R*
KILMACABEA (no dedication) *see* Ross Union *C, C & R*
KILMACDUAGH (no dedication) *see* Aughrim w Ballinasloe
etc *L & K*
KILMACRENNAN (St Finnian and St Mark)
see Tullyaughnish w Kilmacrennan and Killygarvan *D & R*
KILMACSHALGAN (St Mary) *see* Skreen w Kilmacshalgan
and Dromard *T, K & A*
KILMACTHOMAS (no dedication) *see* Lismore w Cappoquin,
Kilwatermoy, Dungarvan etc *C & O*
KILMACTRANNY (no dedication) *see* Taunagh w
Kilmactranny, Ballysumaghan etc *K, E & A*
KILMAKEE (St Hilda) *Conn* **I** D H BOYLAND,
NSM R MOORE
KILMALLOCK (St Peter and St Paul) *see* Adare and
Kilmallock w Kilpeacon, Croom etc *L & K*

KILMALOODA (All Saints)   *see* Kilgariffe Union *C, C & R*
KILMANAGH (no dedication)   *see* Kilkenny w Aghour and
Kilmanagh *C & O*
KILMEADEN (St Mary)   *see* Fiddown w Clonegam, Guilcagh
and Kilmeaden *C & O*
KILMEAGUE (no dedication)   *see* Kildare w Kilmeague and
Curragh *M & K*
KILMEEN (Christ Church)   *see* Kinneigh Union *C, C & R*
KILMEGAN (no dedication) w Maghera *D & D*   **I** C J CARSON
KILMOCOMOGUE Union (no dedication) *C, C & R*
I P M WILLOUGHBY
**KILMOE (no dedication) w Teampol-na-mbocht, Schull and
Crookhaven** *C, C & R*   **I** E E M LYNCH
KILMOGANNY (St Matthew)   *see* Kells Gp *C & O*
KILMOOD (St Mary)   *see* Killinchy w Kilmood and Tullynakill
D & D
**KILMORE (Cathedral of St Fethlimidh) w Ballintemple,
Kildallon, Newtowngore and Corrawallen** *K, E & A*
I D S G GODFREY,   **C** S M PATTERSON,   **NSM** A J LINDSAY,
G W BROWNE
KILMORE (Christ Church) and Inch *D & D*   **I** *vacant*
KILMORE (no dedication)   *see* Monaghan w Tydavnet and
Kilmore *Clogh*
KILMORE (no dedication)   *see* Kiltoghart w Drumshambo,
Annaduff and Kilronan *K, E & A*
KILMORE (St Aidan) (St Saviour) *Arm*   **I** E T DUNDAS
KILMOREROY (St Michael)   *see* Killala w Dunfeeny,
Crossmolina, Kilmoremoy etc *T, K & A*
KILMOYLEY   *see* Tralee w Kilmoyley, Ballymacelligott etc
L & K
KILMUCKRIDGE (no dedication)   *see* Ardamine w Kiltennel,
Glascarrig etc *C & O*
KILMURRY (St Andrew)   *see* Moviddy Union *C, C & R*
KILNAGROSS (no dedication)   *see* Kilgariffe Union *C, C & R*
KILNAHUE (St John the Evangelist)   *see* Gorey w Kilnahue,
Leskinfere and Ballycanew *C & O*
KILNALECK   *see* Kildrumferton w Ballymachugh and
Ballyjamesduff *K, E & A*
KILNAMANAGH (St John)   *see* Ardamine w Kiltennel,
Glascarrig etc *C & O*
KILNASOOLAGH (no dedication)   *see* Drumcliffe w
Kilnasoolagh *L & K*
KILNAUGHTIN (St Brendan)   *see* Rathkeale w Askeaton,
Kilcornan and Kilnaughtin *L & K*
KILPEACON (St Beacon)   *see* Adare and Kilmallock w
Kilpeacon, Croom etc *L & K*
KILPIPE (no dedication)   *see* Crosspatrick Gp *C & O*
KILREA (St Patrick)   *see* Aghadowey w Kilrea *D & R*
KILRONAN (St Thomas)   *see* Kiltoghart w Drumshambo,
Annaduff and Kilronan *K, E & A*
KILROOT (St Colman) and Templecorran *Conn*
I M J MCCANN,   **NSM** W STEWART
KILROSSANTY (no dedication)   *see* Lismore w Cappoquin,
Kilwatermoy, Dungarvan etc *C & O*
KILRUSH   *see* Drumcliffe w Kilnasoolagh *L & K*
KILRUSH (St Brigid)   *see* Bunclody w Kildavin, Clonegal and
Kilrush *C & O*
KILSARAN (St Mary) w Drumcar, Dunleer and Dunany *Arm*
Bp's C P D THORNBURY
KILSCORAN (no dedication) w Killinick and Mulrankin *C & O*
P-in-c N T RUDDOCK,   **C** M P JANSSON
KILSKEERY (no dedication) w Trillick *Clogh*   **I** *vacant*
KILTALLAGH (St Carthage)   *see* Kilcolman w Kiltallagh,
Killorglin, Knockane etc *L & K*
KILTEEVOGUE (St John)   *see* Stranorlar w Meenglas and
Kilteevogue *D & R*
KILTEGAN (St Peter) w Hacketstown, Clonmore and Moyne
C & O   **P-in-c** M A MCCULLAGH,   **C** S E B DURAND
KILTENNEL (no dedication)   *see* Ardamine w Kiltennel,
Glascarrig etc *C & O*
KILTENNEL (St Peter)   *see* Dunleckney w Nurney, Lorum and
Kiltennel *C & O*
KILTERNAN (St Kiernan) *D & G*   **I** D G MOYNAN
KILTINANLEA (no dedication)   *see* Killaloe w Stradbally
L & K
**KILTOGHART (St George) w Drumshambo, Anaduff and
Kilronan** *K, E & A*   **I** *vacant* (00353) (61) 20053
KILTOOM   *see* Athlone w Benown, Kiltoom and Forgney
M & K
KILTUBRIDE (St Brigid)   *see* Mohill w Farnaught, Aughavas,
Oughteragh etc *K, E & A*
KILTULLAGH (no dedication)   *see* Roscommon w Donamon,
Rathcline, Kilkeevin etc *K, E & A*
KILTYCLOGHER (no dedication)   *see* Killinagh w
Kiltyclogher and Innismagrath *K, E & A*
KILVEMNON (St Hugh)   *see* Clonmel w Innislounagh,
Tullaghmelan etc *C & O*

KILWARLIN UPPER (St John) w LOWER (St James) *D & D*
I T D B PIERCE
KILWATERMOY (St Mary)   *see* Lismore w Cappoquin,
Kilwatermoy, Dungarvan etc *C & O*
KILWAUGHTER (no dedication) w Cairncastle and Craigy Hill
Conn   **I** *vacant*
KINAWLEY (no dedication) w Holy Trinity *K, E & A*
I G T W DAVISON
KINAWLEY (St Paul)   *see* Swanlinbar w Tomregan, Kinawley,
Drumlane etc *K, E & A*
**KINGSCOURT (St Ernan) w Drumconrath, Syddan and
Moybologue** *M & K*   **I** R S J BOURKE
KINLOUGH   *see* Killinagh w Kiltyclogher and Innismagrath
K, E & A
KINNEAGH (no dedication)   *see* Narraghmore and Timolin w
Castledermot etc *D & G*
**KINNEIGH (St Bartholomew) w Ballymoney, Kilmeen,
Desertserges, Killowen and Murragh** *C, C & R*
I J F HUBBARD-JONES
KINNITTY (St Trinnian)   *see* Shinrone w Aghancon etc *L & K*
**KINSALE (St Multose) w Runcurran, Ballymartle and
Templetrine** *C, C & R*   **I** D WILLIAMS,   **C** W P MASSEY,
NSM P T HANNA
KIRCONRIOLA   *see* Ballymena w Ballyclug *Conn*
KIRCUBBIN (Holy Trinity)   *see* Grey Abbey w Kircubbin
D & D
KNAPPAGH (St Thomas)   *see* Aughaval w Achill, Knappagh,
Dugort etc *T, K & A*
KNOCK (St Columba) *D & D*   **I** G A MCCAMLEY,
C T K D GRAHAM,   **NSM** J F GOWEN
KNOCKANE (no dedication)   *see* Kilcolman w Kiltallagh,
Killorglin, Knockane etc *L & K*
KNOCKANEY (St John)   *see* Adare and Kilmallock w
Kilpeacon, Croom etc *L & K*
KNOCKBREDA (no dedication) *D & D*   **I** P F PATTERSON
KNOCKBRIDE (no dedication)   *see* Bailieborough w
Knockbride, Shercock and Mullagh *K, E & A*
KNOCKLOUGHRIM   *see* Desertmartin w Termoneeny *D & R*
KNOCKMOURNE (no dedication)   *see* Fermoy Union
C, C & R
KNOCKNAGONEY (Annunciation) *D & D*
Bp's C D L BROWN
KNOCKNAMUCKLEY (St Matthias) *D & D*   **I** B T BLACOE
KNOCKNAREA (St Anne)   *see* Sligo w Knocknarea and
Rosses Pt *K, E & A*
KYLE (no dedication)   *see* Roscrea w Kyle, Bourney and
Corbally *L & K*
LACK (no dedication) *Clogh*   **I** W A CAPPER
LAGHEY (no dedication)   *see* Donegal w Killymard, Lough
Eske and Laghey *D & R*
LAMBEG (no dedication) *Conn*   **I** K A MCREYNOLDS
LANESBOROUGH   *see* Roscommon w Donamon, Rathcline,
Kilkeevin etc *K, E & A*
LANGFIELD, LOWER (no dedication)   *see* Drumclamph w
Lower and Upper Langfield *D & R*
LANGFIELD, UPPER (no dedication)   *as above D & R*
LARAGH (St John)   *see* Rathdrum w Glenealy, Derralossary
and Laragh *D & G*
LARAH AND LAVEY (no dedication)   *see* Drung w
Castleterra, Larah and Lavey etc *K, E & A*
LARNE AND INVER (St Cedma) *Conn*   **I** S B FORDE,
C M W J LONEY,   **NSM** M A HUTCHINSON
LAVEY   *see* Drung w Castleterra, Larah and Lavey etc *K, E & A*
LAYDE (no dedication)   *see* Ardclinis and Tickmacrevan w
Layde and Cushendun *Conn*
LEA (no dedication)   *see* Portarlington w Cloneyhurke and Lea
M & K
LEAP   *see* Ross Union *C, C & R*
LEARMOUNT (no dedication)   *see* Cumber Upper w
Learmount *D & R*
LEATBEG (no dedication)   *see* Clondevaddock w Portsalon and
Leatbeg *D & R*
LECALE Group   *see* Down Cathl *D & D*
**LECALE Group: Saul, Ardglass, Dunsford, Ballyculter and
Kilclief** *D & D*   **I** T H HULL,   **Bp's C** S M J DICKSON,
NSM G J SAVAGE,   P A F MOLLAN
LECKPATRICK (St Patrick) w Dunnalong *D & R*
I E G BUNTING
LEESON PARK (Christ Church)   *see* Dublin St Bart w Leeson
Park *D & G*
**LEIGHLIN (Cathedral of St Laserian) w Grange Sylvae,
Shankill, Clonagoose and Gowran** *C & O*   **P-in-c** C A FAULL,
NSM K H SHERWOOD
LEIXLIP (St Mary)   *see* Lucan w Leixlip *D & G*
LESKINFERE (no dedication)   *see* Gorey w Kilnahue,
Leskinfere and Ballycanew *C & O*
LETTERKENNY   *see* Conwal Union w Gartan *D & R*

LETTERMACAWARD (no dedication)　see Ardara w Glencolumbkille, Inniskeel etc *D & R*
LICKMOLASSY　see Clonfert Gp of Par *L & K*
LIFFORD　see Raphoe w Raymochy and Clonleigh *D & R*
LIMAVADY　see Drumachose *D & R*
LIMAVADY　see Tamlaghtfinlagan w Myroe *D & R*
LIMERICK CITY (Cathedral of St Mary) (St Michael) *L & K*
　I J M G SIRR
LISBELLAW (no dedication) *Clogh*　I M A G BRYCE
LISBURN (Christ Church) *Conn*　I S MCCOMB
LISBURN (Christ Church Cathedral) *Conn*　I W S WRIGHT, **C** R Q THOMPSON, K D MCGRATH
LISBURN (St Paul) *Conn*　I J J CARSON
LISLIMNAGHAN (Holy Trinity)　see Cappagh w Lislimnaghan *D & R*
LISMORE (Cathedral of St Carthage) w Cappoquin, Kilwatermoy, Dungarvan, Kilrossanty, Stradbally and Kilmacthomas *C & O*　I W BEARE
LISNADILL (St John) w Kildarton *Arm*　I M C KENNEDY
LISNASKEA (Holy Trinity) *Clogh*　I S A CROWTHER
LISS (no dedication)　see Clara w Liss, Moate and Clonmacnoise *M & K*
LISSADELL (no dedication)　see Drumcliffe w Lissadell and Munninane *K, E & A*
LISSAN (no dedication) *Arm*　I R H BOYD
LISTOWEL　see Tralee w Kilmoyley, Ballymacelligott etc *L & K*
LITTLE ISLAND (St Lappan)　see Rathcooney Union *C, C & R*
LITTLETON (no dedication)　see Kilcooley w Littleon, Crohane and Fertagh *C & O*
LOCKEEN (no dedication)　see Birr w Lorrha, Dorrha and Lockeen *L & K*
LONDONDERRY　see Templemore *D & R*
LONDONDERRY (Christ Church) *D & R*　I D S MCLEAN
LONDONDERRY (St Augustine) *D & R*　I vacant
LONGFORD　see Templemichael w Clongish, Clooncumber etc *K, E & A*
LORRHA (St Ruadhan)　see Birr w Lorrha, Dorrha and Lockeen *L & K*
LORUM (no dedication)　see Dunleckney w Nurney, Lorum and Kiltennel *C & O*
LOUGH ESKE (Christ Church)　see Donegal w Killymard, Lough Eske and Laghey *D & R*
LOUGHBRICKLAND　see Aghaderg w Donaghmore and Scarva *D & D*
LOUGHCREW　see Castlepollard and Oldcastle w Loughcrew etc *M & K*
LOUGHGALL (St Luke) w Grange *Arm*　I G P MCADAM
LOUGHGILLY (St Patrick) w Clare *Arm*　I J L WILSON
LOUGHGUILE (All Saints)　see Armoy w Loughguile and Drumtullagh *Conn*
LOUGHINISLAND (no dedication) *D & D*　**Bp's C** S M J DICKSON
LUCAN (St Andrew) w Leixlip *D & G*　I J S PEOPLES, **C** S L HALES
LUGGACURREN (Resurrection)　see Stradbally w Ballintubbert, Coraclone etc *C & O*
LURGAN (Christ the Redeemer) (St Andrew) *D & D*　I M J ELLIOTT, **C** D S MCVEIGH, W J C JORR
LURGAN (no dedication) w Billis, Killinkere and Munterconnaught *K, E & A*　I vacant
LURGAN (St John the Evangelist) *D & D*　I vacant
LURGANBOY (Chapel of Ease)　see Cloonclare w Killasnett, Lurganboy and Drumlease *K, E & A*
MACOSQUIN　see Camus-juxta-Bann *D & R*
MACREDDIN　see Castlemacadam w Ballinaclash, Aughrim etc *D & G*
MACROOM　see Moviddy Union *C, C & R*
MAGHERA (no dedication)　see Kilmegan w Maghera *D & D*
MAGHERA (St Lurach) w Killelagh *D & R*　I vacant
MAGHERACLOONE (St Molua)　see Carrickmacross w Magheracloone *Clogh*
MAGHERACROSS (no dedication) *Clogh*　I D P HOEY
MAGHERACULMONEY (St Mary) *Clogh*　I W E MCGIRR
MAGHERADROLL (no dedication) *D & D*　I W W RUSSELL
MAGHERAFELT (St Swithin) *Arm*　I T SCOTT
MAGHERAGALL (no dedication) *Conn*　I G A CHEEVERS
MAGHERAHAMLET (no dedication)　see Annahilt w Magherahamlet *D & D*
MAGHERALIN (Holy and Undivided Trinity) w Dollingstown *D & D*　I G A HARRON, **C** B R MARTIN
MAGHERALLY (St John the Evangelist) w Annaclone *D & D*　I vacant
MAGORBAN (no dedication)　see Cashel w Magorban, Tipperary, Clonbeg etc *C & O*
MAGOURNEY　see Carrigrohane Union *C, C & R*

MAGUIRESBRIDGE (Christ Church) w Derrybrusk *Clogh*　I P S WILSON
MALAHIDE (St Andrew) w Balgriffin *D & G*　I N E C GAMBLE
MALIN　see Moville w Greencastle, Donagh, Cloncha etc *D & R*
MALLOW (St James) w Doneraile and Castletownroche *C, C & R*　I R G KINGSTON
MALLUSK (St Brigid) *Conn*　I I C BALLENTINE
MALONE　see Belfast Malone St Jo *Conn*
MALONE, UPPER　see Belfast Upper Malone (Epiphany) *Conn*
MANORCUNNINGHAM　see Raphoe w Raymochy and Clonleigh *D & R*
MANORHAMILTON　see Cloonclare w Killasnett, Lurganboy and Drumlease *K, E & A*
MARKETHILL (no dedication)　see Mullabrack w Markethill and Kilcluney *Arm*
MARMULLANE (St Mary)　see Douglas Union w Frankfield *C, C & R*
MARYBOROUGH (St Peter) w Dysart Enos and Ballyfin *C & O*　I H A DUNGAN, **P-in-c** N G GILLESPIE
MAYNE　see Castlepollard and Oldcastle w Loughcrew etc *M & K*
MAYNOOTH (St Mary)　see Dunboyne Union *M & K*
MAYO (no dedication)　see Killeshin w Cloydagh and Killabban *C & O*
MEALIFFE　see Templemore w Thurles and Kilfithmone *C & O*
MEENGLASS (Ascension)　see Stranorlar w Meenglas and Kilteevogue *D & R*
MEVAGH (Holy Trinity) w Glenalla *D & R*　I vacant
MIDDLE CHURCH (no dedication)　see Ballinderry *Conn*
MIDDLETOWN (St John)　see Tynan w Middletown and Aghavilly *Arm*
MIDLETON (St John the Baptist)　see Cloyne Union *C, C & R*
MILLISLE (St Patrick)　see Carrowdore w Millisle *D & D*
MILLTOWN　see Kilcolman w Kiltallagh, Killorglin, Knockane etc *L & K*
MILLTOWN (St Andrew) *Arm*　I vacant
MILLTOWN (St Philip)　see Dublin Sandford w Milltown *D & G*
MILLTOWN MALBAY　see Drumcliffe w Kilnasoolagh *L & K*
MITCHELSTOWN　see Fermoy Union *C, C & R*
MOATE (St Mary)　see Clara w Liss, Moate and Clonmacnoise *M & K*
MOHILL (St Mary) w Farnaught, Aughavas, Oughteragh, Kiltubride and Drumreilly *K, E & A*　I F W ATKINS, **NSM** C LINDSAY
MOIRA (St John) *D & D*　I T R WEST, **C** M J MEGARRELL
MONAGHAN (St Patrick) w Tydavnet and Kilmore *Clogh*　I I T H BERRY
MONAMOLIN (St Molig)　see Ardamine w Kiltennel, Glascarrig etc *C & O*
MONART (St Peter)　see Enniscorthy w Clone, Clonmore, Monart etc *C & O*
MONASTEREVAN (St John the Evangelist) w Nurney and Rathdaire *M & K*　I vacant Monasterevan (45) 25411
MONASTERORIS (no dedication)　see Clonsast w Rathangan, Thomastown etc *M & K*
MONELLAN (St Anne)　see Convoy w Monellan and Donaghmore *D & R*
MONEYMORE　see Desertlyn w Ballyeglish *Arm*
MONEYREAGH (no dedication)　see Orangefield w Moneyreagh *D & D*
MONKSTOWN (Good Shepherd) *Conn*　I A P S SYNNOTT
MONKSTOWN (no dedication) *D & G*　I K DALTON
MONKSTOWN (St John)　see Carrigaline Union *C, C & R*
MOSSLEY (Holy Spirit) *Conn*　I N R CUTCLIFFE
MOSTRIM (St John) w Granard, Clonbroney, Killoe, Rathaspeck and Streete *K, E & A*　**P-in-c** J M CATTERALL
MOTHEL (no dedication)　see Castlecomer w Colliery Ch, Mothel and Bilbo *C & O*
MOUNT MERRION　see Dublin Mt Merrion *D & G*
MOUNT MERRION (Pentecost) *D & D*　**Bp's C** B E BIRD
MOUNT NUGENT (St Bride)　see Castlepollard and Oldcastle w Loughcrew etc *M & K*
MOUNTCHARLES (Christ Church)　see Inver w Mountcharles, Killaghtee and Killybegs *D & R*
MOUNTFIELD (no dedication)　see Drumragh w Mountfield *D & R*
MOUNTMELLICK (St Paul) w Coolbanagher, Rosenallis and Clonaslee *M & K*　I J O M DONOHOE
MOUNTRATH　see Clonenagh w Offerlane, Borris-in-Ossory etc *C & O*
MOUNTSHANNON　see Killaloe w Stradbally *L & K*
MOVIDDY (no dedication), Kilbonane, Kilmurry, Templemartin and Macroom *C, C & R*　I vacant (00353) (21) 733 1511
MOVILLA (no dedication) *D & D*　I K HIGGINS

MOVILLE (St Columb) w Greencastle, Donagh, Cloncha and Culdaff *D & R* I H GILMORE

MOY (St James) w Charlemont *Arm* I J STEWART

MOYBOLOGUE *see* Kingscourt w Drumconrath, Syddan and Moybologue *M & K*

MOYDOW (no dedication) *see* Ardagh w Tashinny, Shrule and Kilcommick *K, E & A*

MOYGASHEL (no dedication) *see* Drumglass w Moygashel *Arm*

MOYGLARE (All Saints) *see* Dunboyne Union *M & K*

MOYLISCAR *see* Mullingar, Portnashangan, Moyliscar, Kilbixy etc *M & K*

MOYNALTY (St Mary) *see* Kells Union *M & K*

MOYNE (St John) *see* Kiltegan w Hacketstown, Clonmore and Moyne *C & O*

MOYNTAGHS *see* Ardmore w Craigavon *D & D*

MOYRUS *see* Omey w Ballynakill, Errislannan and Roundstone *T, K & A*

MUCKAMORE (St Jude) (St Matthias) *Conn* I B S CADDEN

MUCKNOE (St Maeldoid) *see* Ballybay w Mucknoe and Clontibret *Clogh*

MUCKROSS (Holy Trinity) *see* Killarney w Aghadoe and Muckross *L & K*

MUCKROSS (St John) *see* Drumkeeran w Templecarne and Muckross *Clogh*

MUFF (no dedication) *see* Culmore w Muff and Belmont *D & R*

MULHUDDART (St Thomas) *see* Castleknock and Mulhuddart, w Clonsilla *D & G*

MULLABRACK (no dedication) w Markethill and Kilcluney *Arm* I N J HUGHES

MULLAGH (no dedication) *see* Bailieborough w Knockbride, Shercock and Mullagh *K, E & A*

MULLAGHDUN (no dedication) *see* Cleenish w Mullaghdun *Clogh*

MULLAGHFAD (All Saints) *see* Aghalurcher w Tattykeeran, Cooneen etc *Clogh*

MULLAGLASS (St Luke) *see* Camlough w Mullaglass *Arm*

MULLAVILLY (no dedication) *Arm* I B J HARPER

MULLINACUFF (no dedication) *see* Tullow w Shillelagh, Aghold and Mullinacuff *C & O*

MULLINGAR (All Saints) w Portnashangan, Moyliscar, Kilbixy, Almoritia, Killucan, Clonard and Castlelost *M & K* I D P R CARMODY, NSM D HUTTON-BURY

MULRANKIN (St David) *see* Kilscoran w Killinick and Mulrankin *C & O*

MUNNINANE (St Kevin) *see* Drumcliffe w Lissadell and Munninane *K, E & A*

MUNTERCONNAUGHT (no dedication) *see* Lurgan w Billis, Killinkere and Munterconnaught *K, E & A*

MURRAGH (no dedication) *see* Kinneigh Union *C, C & R*

MYROE (St John) *see* Tamlaghtfinlagan w Myroe *D & R*

MYROSS *see* Ross Union *C, C & R*

MYSHALL (Christ the Redeemer) *see* Fenagh w Myshall, Aghade and Ardoyne *C & O*

NAAS (St David) w Kill and Rathmore *M & K* I M G WOODERSON

NARRAGHMORE (Holy Saviour) and Timolin w Castledermot and Kinneagh *D & G* I K V KENNERLEY

NAVAN (St Mary) w Kentstown, Tara, Slane, Painestown and Stackallen *M & K* I J D M CLARKE

NENAGH (St Mary) w Ballymackey, Templederry and Killodiernan *L & K* I S E MOURANT, NSM P E HANNA

NEWBLISS (no dedication) *see* Currin w Drum and Newbliss *Clogh*

NEWBRIDGE (St Patrick) w Carnalway and Kilcullen *M & K* I J J MARSDEN

NEWCASTLE (no dedication) w Newtownmountkennedy and Calary *D & G* I W L BENNETT

NEWCASTLE (St John) *D & D* I I M ELLIS

NEWCASTLE-LYONS (no dedication) *see* Celbridge w Straffan and Newcastle-Lyons *D & G*

NEWCESTOWN *see* Kinneigh Union *C, C & R*

NEWMARKET-ON-FERGUS *see* Drumcliffe w Kilnasoolagh *L & K*

NEWRY (St Mary) (St Patrick) *D & D* I K E SUTTON

NEWTOWNARDS (St Mark) *D & D* I K J SMYTH, C I G DELAMERE, Hon C N L WHITE

NEWTOWNBARRY *see* Bunclody w Kildavin, Clonegal and Kilrush *C & O*

NEWTOWNBUTLER *see* Galloon w Drummully *Clogh*

NEWTOWNCROMMELIN (no dedication) *see* Skerry w Rathcavan and Newtowncrommelin *Conn*

NEWTOWNCUNNINGHAM (All Saints) *see* Taughboyne, Craigadooish, Newtowncunningham etc *D & R*

NEWTOWNFERTULLAGH *see* Tullamore w Durrow, Newtownfertullagh, Rahan etc *M & K*

NEWTOWNFORBES *see* Templemichael w Clongish, Clooncumber etc *K, E & A*

NEWTOWNGORE (no dedication) *see* Kilmore w Ballintemple, Kildallon etc *K, E & A*

NEWTOWNHAMILTON (St John) w Ballymoyer and Belleck *Arm* I vacant

NEWTOWNMOUNTKENNEDY (St Matthew) *see* Newcastle w Newtownmountkennedy and Calary *D & G*

NEWTOWNSAVILLE (no dedication) *see* Augher w Newtownsaville and Eskrahoole *Clogh*

NEWTOWNSTEWART *see* Ardstraw w Baronscourt, Badoney Lower etc *D & R*

NOHOVAL (no dedication) *see* Templebreedy w Tracton and Nohoval *C, C & R*

NURNEY (no dedication) *see* Monasterevan w Nurney and Rathdaire *M & K*

NURNEY (St John) *see* Dunleckney w Nurney, Lorum and Kiltennel *C & O*

OFFERLANE (no dedication) *see* Clonenagh w Offerlane, Borris-in-Ossory etc *C & O*

OLD CHURCH, THE *see* Abbeyleix w Old Church, Ballyroan etc *C & O*

OLD LEIGHLIN *see* Leighlin w Grange Sylvae, Shankill etc *C & O*

OLDCASTLE (St Bride) *see* Castlepollard and Oldcastle w Loughcrew etc *M & K*

OMAGH *see* Drumragh w Mountfield *D & R*

OMEY (Christ Church) w Ballynakill, Errislannan and Roundstone *T, K & A* I A M A PREVITE

ORANGEFIELD (St John the Evangelist) w Moneyreagh *D & D* I W J R LAVERTY, NSM I M FRAZER

OSSORY *see* Kilcooley w Littleon, Crohane and Fertagh *C & O*

OUGHTERAGH (no dedication) *see* Mohill w Farnaught, Aughavas, Oughteragh etc *K, E & A*

OUGHTERARD *see* Galway w Kilcummin *T, K & A*

PACKANE *see* Nenagh *L & K*

PAINESTOWN *see* Navan w Kentstown, Tara, Slane, Painestown etc *M & K*

PALLASKENRY *see* Rathkeale w Askeaton, Kilcornan and Kilnaughtin *L & K*

PASSAGE WEST *see* Douglas Union w Frankfield *C, C & R*

PAULSTOWN *see* Leighlin w Grange Sylvae, Shankill etc *C & O*

PETTIGO *see* Drumkeeran w Templecarne and Muckross *Clogh*

PILTOWN *see* Fiddown w Clonegam, Guilcagh and Kilmeaden *C & O*

POMEROY (no dedication) *Arm* NSM W J A DAWSON

PORT LAOIS *see* Maryborough w Dysart Enos and Ballyfin *C & O*

PORTADOWN (St Columba) *Arm* I W M ADAIR, C D M QUIGLEY

PORTADOWN (St Mark) *Arm* I J N T CAMPBELL, C R E JACKSON

PORTAFERRY *see* Ballyphilip w Ardquin *D & D*

PORTARLINGTON (St Paul) w Cloneyhurke and Lea *M & K* I L T C STEVENSON

PORTGLENONE (no dedication) *see* Ahoghill w Portglenone *Conn*

PORTLAOISE *see* Maryborough w Dysart Enos and Ballyfin *C & O*

PORTLAW *see* Fiddown w Clonegam, Guilcagh and Kilmeaden *C & O*

PORTNASHANGAN *see* Mullingar, Portnashangan, Moyliscar, Kilbixy etc *M & K*

PORTRUSH *see* Ballywillan *Conn*

PORTSALON (All Saints) *see* Clondevaddock w Portsalon and Leatbeg *D & R*

PORTSTEWART *see* Agherton *Conn*

PORTUMNA (Christ Church) *see* Clonfert Gp of Par *L & K*

POWERSCOURT (St Patrick) w Kilbride *D & G* I R B ROUNTREE

PREBAN (St John) *see* Crosspatrick Gp *C & O*

RAHAN *see* Clonsast w Rathangan, Thomastown etc *M & K*

RAHAN (St Carthach) *see* Tullamore w Durrow, Newtownfertullagh, Rahan etc *M & K*

RAHENY (All Saints) w Coolock *D & G* I J T CARROLL

RALOO (no dedication) *see* Glynn w Raloo *Conn*

RAMELTON *see* Tullyaughnish w Kilmacrennan and Killygarvan *D & R*

RAMOAN (St James) w Ballycastle and Culfeightrin *Conn* I D M PALMER

RANDALSTOWN *see* Drummaul w Duneane and Ballyscullion *Conn*

RAPHOE (Cathedral of St Eunan) w Raymochy and Clonleigh *D & R* **I** J HAY
RASHARKIN (St Andrew) *see* Ballymoney w Finvoy and Rasharkin *Conn*
RATHANGAN (no dedication) *see* Clonsast w Rathangan, Thomastown etc *M & K*
RATHASPECK (St Thomas) *see* Mostrim w Granard, Clonbroney, Killoe etc *K, E & A*
RATHBARRON *see* Achonry w Tubbercurry and Killoran *T, K & A*
RATHCAVAN (no dedication) *see* Skerry w Rathcavan and Newtowncrommelin *Conn*
RATHCLAREN (Holy Trinity) *see* Bandon Union *C, C & R*
RATHCLINE (no dedication) *see* Roscommon w Donamon, Rathcline, Kilkeevin etc *K, E & A*
RATHCOOLE (no dedication) *see* Clondalkin w Rathcoole *D & G*
RATHCOOLE (St Comgall) *Conn* **I** C D BELL
RATHCOONEY (St Mary and All Saints) w Little Island and Carrigtwohill *C, C & R* **I** D J OWEN
RATHCOR (no dedication) *see* Ballymascanlan w Creggan and Rathcor *Arm*
RATHCORE (St Ultan) *see* Rathmolyon w Castlerickard, Rathcore and Agher *M & K*
RATHDAIRE (Ascension) *see* Monasterevan w Nurney and Rathdaire *M & K*
RATHDOWNEY (no dedication) w Castlefleming, Donaghmore, Rathsaran and Aghavoe *C & O* **I** J G MURRAY
RATHDRUM (St Saviour) w Glenealy, Derralossary and Laragh *D & G* **P-in-c** O E HENDERSON
RATHFARNHAM *see* Dublin Rathfarnham *D & G*
RATHFRILAND *see* Drumgath w Drumgooland and Clonduff *D & D*
RATHGAR *see* Dublin Zion Ch *D & G*
RATHKEALE (Holy Trinity) w Askeaton, Foynes, Kilcornan and Kilnaughtin *L & K* **I** W M ROMER
RATHLIN (St Thomas) *see* Ballintoy w Rathlin and Dunseverick *Conn*
RATHMICHAEL (no dedication) *D & G* **I** F C APPELBE
RATHMINES *see* Dublin Rathmines w Harold's Cross *D & G*
RATHMOLYON (St Michael and All Angels) w Castlerickard, Rathcore and Agher *M & K* **P-in-c** D P R CARMODY
RATHMORE (St Columbkille) *see* Naas w Kill and Rathmore *M & K*
RATHMULLAN *see* Tullyaughnish w Kilmacrennan and Killygarvan *D & R*
RATHMULLAN (no dedication) w Tyrella *D & D* **Bp's** S M J DICKSON, **Hon C** M S WALSHE
RATHOWEN *see* Mostrim w Granard, Clonbroney, Killoe etc *K, E & A*
RATHSARAN (no dedication) *see* Rathdowney w Castlefleming, Donaghmore etc *C & O*
RATHVILLY (St Mary) *see* Baltinglass w Ballynure etc *C & O*
RAYMOCHY (no dedication) *see* Raphoe w Raymochy and Clonleigh *D & R*
RAYMUNTERDONEY (St Paul) *see* Dunfanaghy, Raymunterdoney and Tullaghbegley *D & R*
REDCROSS (Holy Trinity) *see* Dunganstown w Redcross and Conary *D & G*
REDHILLS *see* Drung w Castleterra, Larah and Lavey etc *K, E & A*
RICHHILL (St Matthew) *Arm* **I** D COE
RIVERSTOWN *see* Taunagh w Kilmactranny, Ballysumaghan etc *K, E & A*
ROCHFORT BRIDGE *see* Mullingar, Portnashangan, Moyliscar, Kilbixy etc *M & K*
ROCKCORRY (no dedication) *see* Ematris w Rockcorry, Aghabog and Aughnamullan *Clogh*
ROSCOMMON (St Colman) w Donamon, Rathcline, Kilkeevin, Kiltullagh and Tybohine *K, E & A* **I** *vacant* Roscommon (903) 26230
ROSCREA (St Cronan) w Kyle, Bourney and Corbally *L & K* **I** J A A CONDELL, **NSM** L W RUDDOCK
ROSENALLIS (St Brigid) *see* Mountmellick w Coolbanagher, Rosenallis etc *M & K*
ROSKELTON (no dedication) *see* Clonenagh w Offerlane, Borris-in-Ossory etc *C & O*
ROSS (Cathedral of St Fachtna) w Kilmacabea, Myross, Kilfaughnabeg and Castleventry *C, C & R* **I** *vacant*
ROSS, NEW (St Mary) w OLD (St Mary), Whitechurch, Fethard, Killesk and Tintern *C & O* **I** P G MOONEY
ROSSCARBERY *see* Ross Union *C, C & R*
ROSSDROIT (St Peter) *see* Killanne w Killegney, Rossdroit and Templeshanbo *C & O*
ROSSES POINT (no dedication) *see* Sligo w Knocknarea and Rosses Pt *K, E & A*

ROSSINVER (no dedication) *see* Killinagh w Kiltyclogher and Innismagrath *K, E & A*
ROSSMIRE *see* Lismore w Cappoquin, Kilwatermoy, Dungarvan etc *C & O*
ROSSNAKILL *see* Clondevaddock w Portsalon and Leatbeg *D & R*
ROSSNOWLAGH (St John) *see* Kilbarron w Rossnowlagh and Drumholm *D & R*
ROSSORY (no dedication) *Clogh* **I** C T PRINGLE, **NSM** F I NIXON
ROSTREVOR *see* Kilbroney *D & D*
ROUNDSTONE (no dedication) *see* Omey w Ballynakill, Errislannan and Roundstone *T, K & A*
RUNCURRAN *see* Kinsale Union *C, C & R*
RUSHBROOKE *see* Clonmel Union *C, C & R*
RUTLAND *see* Carlow w Urglin and Staplestown *C & O*
RYNAGH *see* Clonfert Gp of Par *L & K*
SAINTFIELD (no dedication) *D & D* **I** *vacant*
SALLAGHY (no dedication) *Clogh* **I** *vacant*
SANDFORD *see* Dublin Sandford w Milltown *D & G*
SANDHILL *see* Sligo w Knocknarea and Rosses Pt *K, E & A*
SANDYMOUNT *see* Dublin Sandymount *D & G*
SANTRY *see* Dublin Santry w Glasnevin and Finglas *D & G*
SAUL (St Patrick) *see* Lecale Gp *D & D*
SCARVA (St Matthew) *see* Aghaderg w Donaghmore and Scarva *D & D*
SCHULL (Holy Trinity) *see* Kilmoe Union *C, C & R*
SCOTSHOUSE *see* Currin w Drum and Newbliss *Clogh*
SEAFORDE *see* Lecale Gp *D & D*
SEAGOE (St Gobhan) *D & D* **I** D R CHILLINGWORTH, **C** P JACK
SEAPATRICK (Holy Trinity) (St Patrick) *D & D* **I** W J SCOTT, **C** A GALLIGAN, **NSM** R M MCCLEAN
SEIRKIERAN (St Kieran) *see* Clonenagh w Offerlane, Borris-in-Ossory etc *C & O*
SESKINORE (no dedication) *see* Clogherny w Seskinore and Drumnakilly *Arm*
SEYMOUR HILL *see* Kilmakee *Conn*
SHANDON (St Ann) *see* Cork St Luke Union *C, C & R*
SHANKILL *see* Belfast St Matt *Conn*
SHANKILL *see* Lurgan Ch the Redeemer *D & D*
SHANKILL (St John) *see* Leighlin w Grange Sylvae, Shankill etc *C & O*
SHANNON (Christ Church) *see* Drumcliffe w Kilnasoolagh *L & K*
SHERCOCK (no dedication) *see* Bailieborough w Knockbride, Shercock and Mullagh *K, E & A*
SHILLELAGH (no dedication) *see* Tullow w Shillelagh, Aghold and Mullinacuff *C & O*
SHINRONE (St Mary) w Aghancon, Dunkerrin and Kinnitty *L & K* **I** A MINION, **NSM** J J WHITE SPUNNER
SHRULE (no dedication) *see* Ardagh w Tashinny, Shrule and Kilcommick *K, E & A*
SION MILLS (Good Shepherd) *see* Urney w Sion Mills *D & R*
SIXMILECROSS (St Michael) w Termonmaguirke *Arm* **I** *vacant*
SIXTOWNS (St Anne) *see* Kilcronaghan w Draperstown and Sixtowns *D & R*
SKERRIES *see* Holmpatrick w Balbriggan and Kenure *D & G*
SKERRY (St Patrick) w Rathcavan and Newtowncrommelin *Conn* **I** J F A BOND
SKIBBEREEN *see* Abbeystrewry Union *C, C & R*
SKREEN (no dedication) w Kilmacshalgan and Dromard *T, K & A* **I** A M O'S FERGUSON
SLANE (St Patrick) *see* Navan w Kentstown, Tara, Slane, Painestown etc *M & K*
SLAVIN (no dedication) *see* Garrison w Slavin and Belleek *Clogh*
SLIGO (Cathedral of St Mary and St John the Baptist) w Knocknarea and Rosses Point *K, E & A* **I** D GRISCOME
SNEEM (Transfiguration) *see* Kenmare w Sneem, Waterville etc *L & K*
SPANISH POINT *see* Drumcliffe w Kilnasoolagh *L & K*
STACKALLEN *see* Navan w Kentstown, Tara, Slane, Painestown etc *M & K*
STAPLESTOWN (no dedication) *see* Carlow w Urglin and Staplestown *C & O*
STEWARTSTOWN *see* Brackaville w Donaghendry and Ballyclog *Arm*
STILLORGAN (St Brigid) w Blackrock *D & G* **I** I GALLAGHER, **C** A W MATCHETT, **NSM** R D MARSHALL
STONEYFORD (St John) *Conn* **Bp's C** A MALLON
STORMONT (St Molua) *D & D* **I** W D HUMPHRIES
STRABANE *see* Camus-juxta-Mourne *D & R*
STRADBALLY (All Saints) *see* Killaloe w Stradbally *L & K*
STRADBALLY (St James) *see* Lismore w Cappoquin, Kilwatermoy, Dungarvan etc *C & O*

STRADBALLY (St Patrick) w Ballintubbert, Coraclone, Timogue and Luggacurren *C & O*　**I** N G GILLESPIE

STRAFFAN (no dedication)　*see* Celbridge w Straffan and Newcastle-Lyons *D & G*

STRAID (no dedication) *T, K & A*　**I** *vacant*

STRAND, NORTH (no dedication)　*see* Dublin Drumcondra w N Strand *D & G*

STRANGFORD　*see* Lecale Gp *D & D*

STRANORLAR (no dedication) w Meenglas and Kilteevogue *D & R*　**I** S IRVINE

STRATFORD-ON-SLANEY (St John the Baptist) *see* Baltinglass w Ballynure etc *C & O*

STRATHFOYLE (no dedication)　*see* Clooney w Strathfoyle *D & R*

STREETE (no dedication)　*see* Mostrim w Granard, Clonbroney, Killoe etc *K, E & A*

SUMMER COVE　*see* Kinsale Union *C, C & R*

SWANLINBAR (St Augustine) w Tomregan, Kinawley, Drumlane and Templeport *K, E & A*　**I** *vacant*

SWATRAGH　*see* Maghera w Killelagh *D & R*

SWORDS (St Columba) w Donabate and Kilsallaghan *D & G*　**I** R W DEANE

SYDDAN (St David)　*see* Kingscourt w Drumconrath, Syddan and Moybologue *M & K*

SYDENHAM　*see* Belfast St Brendan *D & D*

TAGHMON (St Munn) w Horetown and Bannow *C & O*　**I** N T RUDDOCK

TALLAGHT (St Maelruain) *D & G*　**I** W R H DEVERELL

TAMLAGHT　*see* Derryvullen S w Garvary *Clogh*

TAMLAGHT (St Luke)　*see* Ballinderry, Tamlaght and Arboe *Arm*

TAMLAGHT O'CRILLY UPPER (no dedication) w LOWER (no dedication) *D & R*　**I** R J STEWART

TAMLAGHTARD (St Gedanus) w Aghanloo *D & R*　**I** *vacant* (015047) 239

TAMLAGHTFINLAGAN (St Findlunganus) w Myroe *D & R*　**I** H R GIVEN

TANEY (Christ Church) (St Nahi) *D & G*　**I** W D SINNAMON, **C** J D M PIERCE, R H WATTS, S GYLES, J TANNER

TARA　*see* Navan w Kentstown, Tara, Slane, Painestown etc *M & K*

TARBERT　*see* Tralee w Kilmoyley, Ballymacelligott etc *L & K*

TARTARAGHAN (St Paul) w Diamond *Arm*　**I** D HILLIARD

TASHINNY (no dedication)　*see* Ardagh w Tashinny, Shrule and Kilcommick *K, E & A*

TATTYKEERAN (no dedication)　*see* Aghalurcher w Tattykeeran, Cooneen etc *Clogh*

TAUGHBOYNE (St Baithan) w Craigadooish, Newtowncunningham and Killea *D & R*　**I** D W T CROOKS

TAUNAGH (no dedication) w Kilmactranny, Ballysumaghan and Killery *K, E & A*　**C** N H L REGAN

TEAMPOL-NA-MBOCHT (Altar)　*see* Kilmoe Union *C, C & R*

TEMPLEBREEDY (Holy Trinity) w Tracton and Nohoval *C, C & R*　**I** D R NUZUM,　**NSM** H E A MINION

TEMPLECARNE (no dedication)　*see* Drumkeeran w Templecarne and Muckross *Clogh*

TEMPLECORRAN (St John)　*see* Kilroot and Templecorran *Conn*

TEMPLECRONE (St Crone)　*see* Gweedore, Carrickfin and Templecrone *D & R*

TEMPLEDERRY (no dedication)　*see* Nenagh *L & K*

TEMPLEHARRY (no dedication)　*see* Cloughjordan w Borrisokane etc *L & K*

TEMPLEMARTIN (St Martin)　*see* Moviddy Union *C, C & R*

TEMPLEMICHAEL (St John) w Clongish, Clooncumber, Killashee and Ballymacormack *K, E & A*　**I** D A CATTERALL

TEMPLEMORE Londonderry (Cathedral of St Columb) *D & R*　**I** W W MORTON

TEMPLEMORE (St Mary) w Thurles and Kilfithmone *C & O*　**I** P M COLE-BAKER

TEMPLEPATRICK (St Patrick) w Donegore *Conn*　**I** S A FIELDING

TEMPLEPORT (St Peter)　*see* Swanlinbar w Tomregan, Kinawley, Drumlane etc *K, E & A*

TEMPLESCOBIN (St Paul)　*see* Enniscorthy w Clone, Clonmore, Monart etc *C & O*

TEMPLESHANBO (St Colman)　*see* Killanne w Killegney, Rossdroit and Templeshanbo *C & O*

TEMPLETRINE (no dedication)　*see* Kinsale Union *C, C & R*

TEMPO (no dedication) and Clabby *Clogh*　**I** M A ARMSTRONG

TERMONAMONGAN (St Bestius)　*see* Derg w Termonamongan *D & R*

TERMONEENY (no dedication)　*see* Desertmartin w Termoneeny *D & R*

TERMONFECKIN (St Feckin)　*see* Drogheda w Ardee, Collon and Termonfeckin *Arm*

TERMONMAGUIRKE (St Columbkille)　*see* Sixmilecross w Termonmaguirke *Arm*

THOMASTOWN (no dedication)　*see* Clonsast w Rathangan, Thomastown etc *M & K*

THURLES (no dedication)　*see* Templemore w Thurles and Kilfithmone *C & O*

TICKMACREVAN (St Patrick)　*see* Ardclinis and Tickmacrevan w Layde and Cushendun *Conn*

TIMOGUE (St Mogue)　*see* Stradbally w Ballintubbert, Coraclone etc *C & O*

TIMOLEAGUE (Ascension)　*see* Kilgariffe Union *C, C & R*

TIMOLIN (St Mullin)　*see* Narraghmore and Timolin w Castledermot etc *D & G*

TINTERN (St Mary)　*see* New w Old Ross, Whitechurch, Fethard etc *C & O*

TIPPERARY (St Mary)　*see* Cashel w Magorban, Tipperary, Clonbeg etc *C & O*

TOBERMORE　*see* Kilcronaghan w Draperstown and Sixtowns *D & R*

TOMREGAN (no dedication)　*see* Swanlinbar w Tomregan, Kinawley, Drumlane etc *K, E & A*

TOOMBE (St Catherine)　*see* Ferns w Kilbride, Toombe, Kilcormack etc *C & O*

TOOMNA (no dedication)　*see* Kiltoghart w Drumshambo, Annaduff and Kilronan *K, E & A*

TOORMORE　*see* Kilmoe Union *C, C & R*

TRACTON　*see* Templebreedy w Tracton and Nohoval *C, C & R*

TRALEE (St John the Evangelist) w Kilmoyley, Ballymacelligott, Ballyseedy, Listowel and Ballybunnion *L & K*　**I** R WARREN, **NSM** M HANLEY

TRAMORE　*see* Waterford w Killea, Drumcannon and Dunhill *C & O*

TRILLICK (Christ Church)　*see* Kilskeery w Trillick *Clogh*

TRIM (Cathedral of St Patrick) and Athboy Group, The *M & K*　**I** R W JONES

TRORY (St Michael) w Killadeas *Clogh*　**I** V E S MCKEON

TUAM (Cathedral of St Mary) w Cong and Aasleagh *T, K & A*　**I** A J GRIMASON,　**C** M RYAN

TUAMGRANEY (St Cronan)　*see* Killaloe w Stradbally *L & K*

TUBBERCURRY (St George)　*see* Achonry w Tubbercurry and Killoran *T, K & A*

TUBRID　*see* Drumkeeran w Templecarne and Muckross *Clogh*

TULLAGH (no dedication)　*see* Abbeystrewry Union *C, C & R*

TULLAGHBEGLEY (St Ann)　*see* Dunfanaghy, Raymunterdoney and Tullaghbegley *D & R*

TULLAGHMELAN (no dedication)　*see* Clonmel w Innislounagh, Tullaghmelan etc *C & O*

TULLAMORE (St Catherine) w Durrow, Newtownfertullagh, Rahan, Tyrellspass and Killoughy *M & K*　**I** G G FIELD

TULLANISKIN (Holy Trinity) w Clonoe *Arm*　**I** E M CULBERTSON

TULLOW (no dedication) *D & G*　**I** C W BRYAN

TULLOW (St Columba) w Shillelagh, Aghold and Mullinacuff *C & O*　**I** *vacant*

TULLYAUGHNISH (St Paul) w Kilmacrennan and Killygarvan *D & R*　**I** R C LOGUE

TULLYLISH (All Saints) *D & D*　**I** R S MILLER

TULLYNAKILL (no dedication)　*see* Killinchy w Kilmood and Tullynakill *D & D*

TUNNY (St Andrew)　*see* Glenavy w Tunny and Crumlin *Conn*

TURLOUGH (no dedication)　*see* Aughaval w Achill, Knappagh, Dugort etc *T, K & A*

TYBOHINE (no dedication)　*see* Roscommon w Donamon, Rathcline, Kilkeevin etc *K, E & A*

TYDAVNET (St Davnet)　*see* Monaghan w Tydavnet and Kilmore *Clogh*

TYHOLLAND (St Sillian)　*see* Donagh w Tyholland and Errigal Truagh *Clogh*

TYNAN (St Vindic) w Middletown and Aghavilly *Arm*　**I** W B PAINE

TYRELLA (St John)　*see* Rathmullan w Tyrella *D & D*

TYRELLSPASS (St Sinian)　*see* Tullamore w Durrow, Newtownfertullagh, Rahan etc *M & K*

UPPER DONAGHMORE (St Patrick)　*see* Donaghmore w Upper Donaghmore *Arm*

URGLIN (no dedication)　*see* Carlow w Urglin and Staplestown *C & O*

URNEY (Christ Church) w Sion Mills *D & R*　**I** D SKUCE

URNEY (no dedication) w Denn and Derryheen *K, E & A*　**I** M R LIDWILL,　**NSM** R W STAFFORD

VALENTIA (St John the Baptist)　*see* Kenmare w Sneem, Waterville etc *L & K*

VIRGINIA   *see* Lurgan w Billis, Killinkere and
Munterconnaught *K, E & A*
WARINGSTOWN (Holy Trinity)   *see* Donaghcloney w
Waringstown *D & D*
WARRENPOINT (no dedication)   *see* Clonallon w Warrenpoint
D & D
**WATERFORD (Christ Church Cathedral) w Killea, Drumcannon
and Dunhill** *C & O*   **I** T R LESTER,   **C** J E CROWLEY
WATERVILLE   *see* Kenmare w Sneem, Waterville etc *L & K*
WESTPORT   *see* Aughaval w Achill, Knappagh, Dugort etc
T, K & A
WEXFORD (St Iberius) w Ardcolm and Killurin *C & O*
I N T RUDDOCK,   **C** M P JANSSON,   **NSM** R G GRAHAM
WHITECHURCH   *see* Dublin Whitechurch *D & G*
WHITECHURCH (no dedication)   *see* New w Old Ross,
Whitechurch, Fethard etc *C & O*

WHITEGATE   *see* Cloyne Union *C, C & R*
WHITEHEAD (St Patrick) and Islandmagee *Conn*
I M F TAYLOR
WHITEHOUSE (St John) *Conn*   **I** *vacant*
WHITEROCK   *see* Belfast Whiterock *Conn*
WICKLOW (no dedication) w Killiskey *D & G*   **I** J P CLARKE
WILLOWFIELD (no dedication) *D & D*   **I** D A MCCLAY,
C W A BOYCE
WOODBURN (Holy Trinity) *Conn*   **I** T A G MCCANN
WOODLAWN (no dedication)   *see* Aughrim w Ballinasloe etc
L & K
WOODSCHAPEL (St John) w Gracefield *Arm*
I S R T BOYD
**YOUGHAL (St Mary's Collegiate) w Ardmore, Castlemartyr
and Ballycotton** *C, C & R*   **I** S M WATTERSON
ZION   *see* Dublin Zion Ch *D & G*

THE DIOCESE IN EUROPE

Diocesan Office, 14 Tufton Street, London SW1P 3QZ
Tel (020) 7898 1155   Fax 7898 1166
E-mail diocesan.office@europe.c-of-e.org.uk
Web site www.europe.anglican.org

ARCHDEACONS
1. Eastern P M S CURRAN
2. France A M G WELLS
3. Gibraltar H C SASSER
4. Italy and Malta W G REID
5. North West Europe G G ALLEN
6. Scandinavia and Germany D W RATCLIFF
7. Switzerland P J HAWKER

Further information may be obtained from the appropriate archdeacon (the archdeaconry number is given after the name of each country), and a detailed leaflet is obtainable from the diocesan office. Mission to Seafarers chaplaincies are listed separately at the end of the section.

Albania 1
Served from Naples (Italy)

Andorra 3
Served from Barcelona (Spain)

Armenia 1
YEREVAN   **P-in-c** W S GRIFFITH

Austria 1
VIENNA (Christ Church)   **Chapl** P M S CURRAN,
Asst Chapl A P HACKL

Azerbaijan 1
BAKU   **P-in-c** W S GRIFFITH

Belgium 5
ANTWERP (St Boniface)   **Chapl** D W VAN LEEUWEN,
Asst Chapl E B E LAMMENS,   **C** J M DAY
BRUSSELS (Pro-Cathedral of the Holy Trinity)
Chapl N M WALKER (Chan), **Asst Chapl** P F WALLEY,
I K MENSAH, J-P HERMAN
CHARLEROI w Liège   **P-in-c** P M YIEND
GHENT (St John)   **P-in-c** P R TILLEY
LEUVEN   **Chapl** N M WALKER
OSTEND w Knokke (St George) and Bruges (St Peter)
P-in-c D W VAN LEEUWEN,   **C** J M DAY
TERVUREN   **Chapl** H T COX, **Asst Chapl** S C RIORDAN
YPRES (St George)   **P-in-c** R T JONES

Bosnia and Herzegovina 1
Served from Vienna (Austria)

Bulgaria 1
Served from Bucharest (Romania)

Croatia 1
Served from Vienna (Austria)

Czech Republic 1
PRAGUE   **P-in-c** J D PHILPOTT

Denmark 6
COPENHAGEN (St Alban) w Aarhus
Chapl T O MENDEL

Estonia 6
TALLINN   **P-in-c** G PIIR

Finland 6
HELSINKI w Tampere   **Chapl** R R J MORETON,
C M K T PAJUNEN

France 2
AIX-EN-PROVENCE   *see* Marseille w Aix-en-Provence
AQUITAINE (Bordeaux, Limeuil, Monteton, Périgueux-Chancelade, Petites Côtes and Ribérac)   **Chapl** M R SELMAN
ARRAS   *see* Pas de Calais
BEAULIEU-SUR-MER (St Michael)
P-in-c R T GREENACRE
BEAULIEU-SUR-SONNETTE   *see* Poitou-Charentes
BIARRITZ   **Chapl** J M LIVINGSTONE
BORDEAUX   *see* Aquitaine
BOULOGNE-SUR-MER   *see* Pas de Calais
BRILLAC   *see* Poitou-Charentes
BRITTANY   **P-in-c** R W FRAY
CAEN   *see* Paris St George
CAHORS   *see* Toulouse
CALAIS   *see* Pas de Calais
CANNES (Holy Trinity)   **Chapl** P J ANDERSON
CHANTILLY (St Peter)   **Chapl** J A WILKINSON
CHEVRY   *see* Versailles w Chevry
COGNAC (Charente)   *see* Poitou-Charentes
DINARD (St Bartholomew)   **P-in-c** A C CHARTERS
FONTAINEBLEAU   **Asst Chapl** D G NEWSTEAD
GIF SUR YVETTE   *see* Versailles
GRAND MADIEU   *see* Poitou-Charentes
GRASSE   *see* Cannes
GRENOBLE   **Chapl** S COFFIN
LILLE (Christ Church)   *see* Nord
LIMEUIL   *see* Aquitaine
LYON   **Chapl** C J MARTIN
MAISONS-LAFFITTE (Holy Trinity)
Chapl T WHITFIELD,   **C** D M R FLACH
MARSEILLE (All Saints) w Aix-en-Provence
Chapl P N CASSIDY
MENTON (St John)   **P-in-c** B E WARRILLOW
MONTETON   *see* Aquitaine
MORBIHAN   *see* Brittany
NICE (Holy Trinity) w Vence   **Chapl** K J LETTS
NORD   **Chapl** W R KILFORD
PARIS (St George)   **Chapl** D J HOUGHTON,   **C** B SIXTUS
PARIS (St Michael)   **Chapl** A M G WELLS,   **C** A T GRIFFITHS
PAS-DE-CALAIS (Arras, Boulogne-sur-Mer, Calais)
Chapl W R KILFORD
PAU (St Andrew)   **P-in-c** R J HALLIBURTON
PÉRIGUEUX-CHANCELADE   *see* Aquitaine
PETITES CÔTES   *see* Aquitaine
POITOU-CHARENTES (Beaulieu-sur-Sonnette, Brillac, Cognac (Charente), Grand Madieu Salles de Villefagnan, St Léger de la Martinière, and St Médard de Magné)
P-in-c C M A HEPPER,   **NSM** C GORDON-WALKER
ROUEN (All Saints)   *vacant*
ST LÉGER DE LA MARTINIÈRE   *see* Poitou-Charentes
ST MÉDARD DE MAGNÉ   *see* Poitou-Charentes
ST RAPHAËL (St John the Evangelist)   **P-in-c** O B EATON
SALLES DE VILLEFAGNAN   *see* Poitou-Charentes
STRASBOURG   **Chapl** A R GORDON,
Asst Chapl J L MURRAY
TOULOUSE   **Chapl** I L MORT
VENCE (St Hugh)   *see* Nice w Vence
VERSAILLES (St Mark) w Chevry   **Chapl** D C MARSHALL,
Asst Chapl A MARSHALL, J K BROWN

Georgia 1
TBILISI   **P-in-c** W S GRIFFITH

Germany 6

BERLIN (St George) Chapl C W JAGE-BOWLER,
Asst Chapl I K E AHRENS
BONN w Cologne Chapl I WRIGHT,
Asst Chapl C METHUEN
DÜSSELDORF (Christ Church) Chapl R D BUCKMAN
FREIBURG-IM-BREISAU P-in-c R P STOCKITT
HAMBURG (St Thomas à Becket) Chapl R I S WHITE,
NSM E G ANDERS
HEIDELBERG *vacant*
LEIPZIG Chapl G M REAKES-WILLIAMS
STUTTGART *vacant*
WIESBADEN (St Augustine of Canterbury)
Chapl K E BELL

Gibraltar 3

GIBRALTAR (Cathedral of the Holy Trinity)
Chapl A G WOODS (Dean)

Greece 1

ATHENS, GREATER Sen Chapl M M BRADSHAW,
Asst Chapl V AGGETT, Hon Asst Chapl D W HEWITT,
W J BURKE
CORFU (Holy Trinity) P-in-c P C OWEN

Hungary 1

BUDAPEST Chapl D MOSS

Italy 4

FLORENCE (St Mark) w Siena (St Peter)
Chapl L A C MACLEAN
LIGURIA w Genoa (The Holy Ghost) and Bordighera
Chapl W G REID
MILAN (All Saints) and Varese Chapl W G REID,
Asst Chapl P M RUTHERFORD
NAPLES (Christ Church) w Sorrento, Capri and Bari
Chapl M W GRANT
PALERMO (Holy Cross) *see* Sicily
ROME (All Saints) Chapl J BOARDMAN
SICILY P-in-c R J ROGERS
TAORMINA (St George) *see* Sicily
VENICE (St George) w Trieste Chapl J LANCASTER

Latvia 6

RIGA (St Saviour) Chapl J CALITIS

Lithuania 6

KLAIPEDA P-in-c J R BALL

Luxembourg 5

LUXEMBOURG Chapl C LYON

Malta and Gozo 4

VALLETTA (Pro-Cathedral of St Paul) w Sliema
(Holy Trinity) Chapl P G WOLFENDEN

Monaco 2

MONTE CARLO (St Paul) *vacant*

Montenegro *see Yugoslavia*

Morocco 3

CASABLANCA (St John the Evangelist) Chapl J E GOOCH
TANGIER (St Andrew) *vacant*

The Netherlands 5

AMSTERDAM (Christ Church) w Den Helder and Heiloo
Chapl M P C COLLINSON, **C** H K ADAN, J R ALBERS
ARNHEM *see* East Netherlands
EAST NETHERLANDS Chapl G G ALLEN
EINDHOVEN Chapl F P NOORDANUS
HAARLEM P-in-c B RICHARDS
HAGUE, THE (St John and St Philip) Chapl M B SANDERS,
Asst Chapl R K PRICE, **C** R DYMOND

NIJMEGEN *see* East Netherlands
ROTTERDAM (St Mary) *vacant*
TWENTE (St Mary) *see* East Netherlands
UTRECHT (Holy Trinity) w Amersfoort, Harderwijk and
Zwolle Asst Chapl P STAPLES
VOORSCHOTEN Chapl P J BOURNE

Norway 6

OSLO (St Edmund) w Bergen, Trondheim and Stavanger
Chapl T PARK, Asst Chapl D T LEWIS, NSM M STRØMMEN

Poland 1

WARSAW w Gdansk Chapl S L ROBERTSON

Portugal 3

ALGARVE (St Vincent) Chapl E S BRITT,
Asst Chapl D A KIRBY
LISBON (St George) w Estoril (St Paul)
Chapl M BULLOCK
MADEIRA (Holy Trinity) P-in-c H C SMART
PORTO (*or* OPORTO) (St James) Chapl H C SASSER

Romania 1

BUCHAREST (The Resurrection) Chapl J A RAMSAY

Russian Federation 1

MOSCOW (St Andrew) Chapl S E STEPHENS
ST PETERSBURG *vacant*

Serbia *see Yugoslavia*

Slovakia

Served from Vienna (Austria)

Slovenia

Served from Vienna (Austria)

Spain 3

BARCELONA (St George) Chapl P H JORDAN
COSTA BLANCA Chapl E LEWIS,
Asst Chapl C MCCORMACK
COSTA DEL SOL EAST *see* Fuengirola
COSTA DEL SOL WEST Chapl P S C WALKER
FUENGIROLA (St Andrew) P-in-c D E C WRIGHT
IBIZA *vacant*
LANZAROTE P-in-c W D S LARK
LAS PALMAS (Holy Trinity) *vacant*
MADRID (St George) Chapl R L HODSON
MALAGA (St George) Chapl R J A HASLAM,
NSM R J TAYLER
MENORCA Chapl M J BUNCE
MOJACAR P-in-c H D BROAD
NERJA and Almuñécar P-in-c K W REEVES
PALMA DE MALLORCA (St Philip and St James)
Chapl R A ELLIS, Asst Chapl J A D ROBERTS
PLAYA DE LAS AMERICAS Tenerife *see* Tenerife Sur
PUERTO DE LA CRUZ Tenerife (All Saints)
Chapl D T JENKINS
PUERTO POLLENSA Mallorca Chapl R A ELLIS,
Asst Chapl J A D ROBERTS
TENERIFE SUR (St Eugenio) P-in-c K A GORDON
TORREVIEJA Chapl R E H JOHNSON

Sweden 6

GOTHENBURG (St Andrew) w Halmstad, Jönköping and
Uddevalla Chapl J S ASKEY
STOCKHOLM (St Peter and St Sigfrid) w Gävle and Västerås
Chapl B J EVENSON

Switzerland 7

BASLE Chapl G P READ, Asst Chapl R STOCKITT
BERNE (St Ursula) w Neuchâtel Chapl R L PAMPLIN,
Asst Chapl L D BISIG, **C** S W VAN LEER
GENEVA (Holy Trinity) Chapl M A FRENCH
LA CÔTE P-in-c P R HOLLEY

LAUSANNE (Christ Church)   Chapl S J HABIBY
LUGANO (St Edward the Confessor)   Chapl A L THOMAS
MONTREUX (St John) w Gstaad   Chapl J R WILLIAMS,
  Asst Chapl C DIZERENS, NSM P J PARRY
VEVEY (All Saints) w Château d'Oex and Villars
  Chapl C J ATKINSON
ZÜRICH (St Andrew) w Lucerne and St Moritz
  Chapl J K NEWSOME, Asst Chapl G J AMAT-TORREGROSA,
  C R HILLIARD

Turkey 1
ANKARA (St Nicholas)   P-in-c G B EVANS

ISTANBUL (Christ Church) (Chapel of St Helena) w Moda
  (All Saints)   Chapl I W L SHERWOOD
IZMIR (SMYRNA) (St John the Evangelist) w Bornova
  (St Mary Magdalene)   P-in-c R W EVANS

Ukraine 1
KIEV (Christ Church)   Chapl J J FRAIS

Yugoslavia, Federal Republic of 1
BELGRADE   Chapl J P WARNER

MISSION TO SEAFARERS CHAPLAINCIES

Belgium 5
ANTWERP *Lay Chapl*
GHENT   Chapl P R TILLEY

France 2
DUNKERQUE   Chapl P G HISCOCK
ROUEN   *vacant*

The Netherlands 5
ROTTERDAM and Schiedam   Chapl M K SPARROW
VLISSINGEN   *vacant*

CHAPLAINS TO HER MAJESTY'S SERVICES

ROYAL NAVY

Chaplain of the Fleet and Archdeacon for the Royal Navy
Director General Naval Chaplaincy Service
The Ven B K HAMMETT QHC
Royal Navy Chaplaincy Service, Room 205, Victory Buildings, HM Naval Base, Portsmouth PO1 3LS
Tel (023) 9272 7900   Fax 9272 7111

Chaplains RN

J P AMES	M J GOUGH	N J KELLY
D BARLOW	S J N GRAY	S I LAMB
S A R BEVERIDGE	J GREEN	C J LUCKRAFT
K C BROMAGE	S P HALLAM	J O MORRIS
M BROTHERTON	M J HARMAN	I F NAYLOR
A M CALLON	C J HEYCOCKS	A G PHILLIPS
M L CATHERALL	J HILL	M G POLL
B R CLARKE	R G HILLIARD	R L PYNE
D P CONNING	M J HILLS	P J D S SCOTT
G M ELMORE	G E D HITCHINS	S P SPRINGETT
M L EVANS	C W W HOWARD	D W W THOMAS
B D S FAIRBANK	B J HUGHES	I J WHEATLEY
W H FRANKLIN	M H JACKSON	D V WYLIE

ARMY

Chaplain-General to the Forces and Archdeacon for the Army
The Ven J BLACKBURN QHC
Tel (01980) 615801

Deputy Chaplain-General
The Revd D E WILKES OBE QHC
(The present Deputy Chaplain-General is a minister of the Methodist Church)
Ministry of Defence, Chaplains (Army), Trenchard Lines, Upavon, Pewsey SN9 6BE
Tel (01980) 615802   Fax 615800

Chaplains to the Forces

W G ASHTON	C J GROOCOCK	B D MILLSON
D G BAILEY	G F HADFIELD	R M MITCHELL
J BALL	R A B HALL	J S MOESEL
K G BARRY	R J HALL	M P MORTON
K D BELL	R W HAYTER	F E MYATT
P R BOSHER	R A HEMMINGS	R OLLIFF
K M BRETEL	L T J HILLARY	S P PARSELLE
C S T BRODDLE	J M HULME	G S PETZER
C S BUTLER	P A IRWIN	K J PILLAR
P J CABLE	R C M JARVIS	T R PLACE
M R CHRISTIAN	M V JONES	R PLUCK
T A R COLE	K R JOYCE	J A H POLLARD
J C D COOK	N A KNIGHTS JOHNSON	R M PRIEST
N L COOK	C M LANGSTON	S ROBBINS
A J COOPER	W B LISTER	M P ROEMMELE
C P CRAVEN	N A LLEWELLYN	P F A SPRINGFORD
A M CROSBIE	S H LODWICK	A C STEELE
N N CROSSEY	J M LOVEDAY	M R N STEVENSON
A W CUMBERLIDGE	W A MCCAFFERTY	M P M STEWART
D W DAVIES	R C MCCARTNEY	S B THATCHER
R J DOWNES	C MACDONALD	A H THOMAS
A J DUFF	R A MCDOWALL	A J TOTTEN
W J N DURANT	T R MCKNIGHT	P VICKERS
P A EAGLES	K MADDY	B WALTON
B ELLIOTT	A C MARTLEW	H WANLISS
S A FRANKLIN	N A MAXTED	D C WEAVER
L F GANDIYA	K D MENTZEL	R E WILLIAMS
R L GREEN	D J MERCERON	B WOOLLASTON
S E GRIFFITH	P J MILLS	P S WRIGHT

ROYAL AIR FORCE

Chaplain-in-Chief
The Ven **R D HESKETH** QHC

Command Chaplains
E CORE, J E COYNE
Chaplaincy Service (RAF), HQ, Personnel and Training Command, RAF Innsworth, Gloucester GL3 1EZ
Tel (01452) 712 ext 5164   Fax 510828

Chaplains RAF

N B P BARRY	A D HEWETT	S J RADLEY
J M BEACH	C E HEWITT	E J RANCE
C W K BERRY-DAVIES	S P IREDALE	P A RENNIE
G S BROWN	I A JONES	J R RUSSELL
J P M CHAFFEY	D E KENDRICK	L E SPICER
A T COATES	M P D KENNARD	J W K TAYLOR
G L COLLINGWOOD	S P LAMOND	A J TURNER
A J DAVIES	T R LEE	I S WARD
V R DUNSTAN-MEADOWS	C W LONG	S J WARE
M J ELLIOTT	A B MCMULLON	G WILLIAMS
A C GATRILL	C A MITCHELL	J K WILSON
A J D GILBERT	W L F MOUNSEY	G E WITHERS
I F GREENHALGH	D T OSBORN	T WRIGHT
N P HERON	R J PENTLAND	D WYNNE-JONES
J C HETHERINGTON	N P A PNEMATICATOS	

PRISON CHAPLAINS
HM PRISON SERVICE
(England and Wales)

Chaplain General to HM Prisons
The Ven W A NOBLETT

Church of England members of Chaplaincy HQ staff:

P J TAYLOR (Assistant Chaplain General)
R M WILTSHIRE (Assistant Chaplain General)
W M CAREY (Training Officer)

HM Prison Service Chaplaincy, 6th Floor Horseferry House, Dean Ryle Street, London SW1P 2AW

Tel (020) 7217 8960 *or* 7217 8678   Fax (020) 7217 8980
E-mail chaplaincy@prisons-chap-hq.demon.co.uk

Prisons

Acklington B K COOPER, M D TETLEY
Altcourse M T RANDALL
Ashfield N J HAY
Ashwell R J LUBKOWSKI
Askham Grange R A CLEGG
Bedford R M M CREIGHTON
Belmarsh D J H POWE
Birmingham B J GRACIE
Blakenhurst J W GEEN
Blantyre House R T GREEN
Blundeston W J SALMON, M R RENNARD
Bristol P M L PHILLIPS, E M DESMOND
Brixton S W P ROSHEUVEL, J R GRIFFITHS
Brockhill I E MCINTYRE DE ROMERO, F M BATTIN (NÉE WEBB)
Buckley Hall B A EATON
Bullingdon P D DERBYSHIRE, T P EDGE
Bullwood Hall S SAYERS
Camp Hill T J MANN
Canterbury C I GREEN, P B D CRICK
Cardiff M C JOHN, L T IRVINE-CAPEL
Channings Wood J B SMITH
Chelmsford G C PEARSON
Coldingley E L GUTSELL, J HUNTER
Cookham Wood J E G DASH
Dartmoor W H BIRDWOOD
Doncaster P IRESON
Dorchester T A M SANKEY
Downview R A DEEDES
Drake Hall D J HOWARD
Durham F A ELTRINGHAM
East Sutton Park N FRY
Eastwood Park J M PHILLIPS
Elmley T G JACQUET
Everthorpe P MOORHOUSE
Exeter C V CURD, J G WITHERS
Featherstone J BARNES
Ford D E TWISS
Forest Bank S A JONES
Frankland E CUMMINGS
Full Sutton P J WALKER
Garth A J B KEITH
Gartree S M JOHN, I L JOHNSON
Gloucester D B SMALL
Guys Marsh M J RIDGEWELL
Haslar N G STARTIN
Haverigg D J E CLARKE
Hewell Grange P HAMMERSLEY
High Down M D ENGLER
Highpoint J M N HUNT
Hollesley Bay R B THOMPSON
Holloway K WILKIN
Holme House T A MCCARTHY, J N GREENWOOD,
S L NICHOLSON
Hull N J WHETTON, R P YATES
Kingston (Portsmouth) S R NUNN

Kirkham S E MASKREY
Lancaster Castle C WOODCOCK
Latchmere House F R BENTLEY
Leeds P TARLETON, R H BAILEY
Leicester A V HEDGES
Lewes E J POOLE
Leyhill S BRACE
Lincoln J D BIRD
Lindholme M D J MCCREADY
Littlehey R C BUNYAN
Liverpool E SUTHERLAND, I R SHACKLETON
Long Lartin P J KNIGHT, F L MIDDLEMISS
Low Newton C M PROUSE
Lowdham Grange C KNIGHT
Maidstone G L LONG
Manchester L H COOPER, R A H MARSHALL
Moorland T M BAYFORD
Morton Hall C C MUNN
Mount, The H K DODHIA, P J ABREY
New Hall E J CLAY, J T PERRY
North Sea Camp J F GLEADALL
Norwich J A WILSON
Nottingham M T PHILLIPS
Parc (Bridgend) N R SANDFORD
Parkhurst T LANE
Pentonville R J S PEARSON
Preston P C BROWNE
Ranby A HIRST
Reading D J LITTLE
Risley R TAGUE, J SEPHTON
Rochester Y R MARCUSSEN
Rye Hill P D STELL, G D MORRIS
Send A J FORAN
Shrewsbury D S FARLEY, J J WADDINGTON-FEATHER
Stafford J M DIXON, R C PAYNE
Standford Hill C E N DAVIS, B I M DURKAN
Stocken E GHINN
Styal G D MANCO
Sudbury P A GOWER
Swaleside J H WAITE
Swansea L HOPKINS
Verne, The A M BALL
Wakefield J K HAYWARD
Wandsworth S EDWARDS, J A F GALBRAITH
Wayland N TIVEY, S G STEPHENSON
Wealstun F FLETCHER
Wellingborough S J MAYES
Whatton D G WAKEFIELD, J D HENSON
Whitemoor D J BURTON
Winchester P A NEWMAN
Wolds, The S FOSTER
Woodhill S C LISTON
Wormwood Scrubs A R TYLER, M P STRANGE
Wymott R A LANE

Young Offender Institutions

Aylesbury   J M WILLIAMS
Brinsford   G BIRD
Castington   C R MURRIE, F V G BALLENTYNE
Deerbolt   D G HARTLEY, G KIRTLEY
Dover   R HIGGINBOTTOM
Feltham   P FOSTER
Foston Hall   J C HONOUR, S BAXTER
Glen Parva   J E FITZGERALD
Hatfield   C D LETHBRIDGE

Huntercombe and Finnamore Wood   I D THACKER
Lancaster Farms   B J MAYNE
Northallerton   A F WAKEFIELD
Onley   P R GOULD
Portland   P THOMPSON
Stoke Heath   M J NEWSOME, R C PAYNE
Thorn Cross   D W GOODWIN, N G SHAW
Wetherby   G JONES

SCOTTISH PRISON SERVICE

Scottish Prison Service, Calton House, 5 Redheughs Rigg, Edinburgh E12 9HW
Tel (0131) 556 8400   Fax 244 8774

Aberdeen   J D ALEXANDER
Edinburgh   M C REED
Glenochil   F A M LAWRY

Inverness   A WHEATLEY
Perth   M LAWRENSON

NORTHERN IRELAND PRISON SERVICE

Northern Ireland Office, Dundonald House, Upper Newtownards Road, Belfast BT4 3SU
Tel (028) 9052 0700   Fax 9052 5327

Belfast   N B DODDS
Maghaberry   J R HOWARD

Maze, The   W A MURPHY

IRISH PRISON SERVICE

Department of Justice, 72–76 St Stephen's Green, Dublin 2, Irish Republic
Tel (00353) (1) 678 9711   Fax 676 4718

Limerick   J M G SIRR

HOSPITAL CHAPLAINS

An index of whole-time and part-time hospital chaplains

Secretary to the Hospital Chaplaincies Council
The Revd E J LEWIS
Church House, Great Smith Street, London SW1P 3NZ
Tel (020) 7898 1894   Fax 7898 1891

At institutions with more than one chaplain the names are listed in order of senority.

ABERDEEN ROYAL INFIRMARY   *see* Grampian Univ Hosp NHS Trust
ABRAHAM COWLEY UNIT Chertsey   *see* NW Surrey Mental Health NHS Trust
ADDENBROOKE'S NHS TRUST   J M LAW, I J P MORRIS, V F D NAYLOR, B M WOOLLARD
ADELAIDE AND MEATH Dublin   S D GREEN, R H WATTS
AINTREE HOSPITALS NHS TRUST Liverpool   I J LOVETT
AIREDALE GENERAL   *see* Airedale NHS Trust
AIREDALE NHS TRUST   G L HALL, B M WILKINSON, J P SMITH
ALDER HEY CHILDREN'S Liverpool   *see* Royal Liverpool Children's NHS Trust
ALEXANDRA Redditch   *see* Worcs Acute Hosps NHS Trust
ALL SAINTS' Birmingham   *see* N Birm Mental Health Trust
ALLINGTON NHS TRUST   M R RENNARD
ALLNUTT'S Goring Heath, I C HUNT
ALNWICK INFIRMARY   *see* Northumbria Healthcare NHS Trust
ALTON COMMUNITY   *see* N Hants Loddon Community NHS Trust
AMBERSTONE Hailsham   *see* Eastbourne and Co Healthcare NHS Trust
AMERSHAM   *see* S Bucks NHS Trust
ANDOVER DISTRICT COMMUNITY HEALTH CARE NHS TRUST   D F KING
ANDOVER WAR MEMORIAL COMMUNITY HOSPITAL   *see* Andover District Community Health Care NHS Trust
ARMAGH AND DUNGANNON HEALTH AND SOCIAL SERVICES TRUST   C W M ROLSTON
ARNOLD LODGE Leicester   *see* Leics and Rutland Healthcare NHS Trust
ASHFORD   *see* E Kent Hosps NHS Trust
ASHINGTON   *see* Northumbria Healthcare NHS Trust
ASHWORTH Magull   G A PERERA
ASTON HALL   *see* S Derbyshire Community and Mental Health Trust
ATKINSON MORLEY London   *see* SW Lon and St George's Mental Health Trust
AYLESBURY VALE COMMUNITY HEALTHCARE NHS TRUST   S L BUSHELL
BARNET   *see* Barnet and Chase Farm Hosps NHS Trust
BARNET, ENFIELD AND HARINGEY MENTAL HEALTH TRUST   T M BARON
BARNET AND CHASE FARM HOSPITALS NHS TRUST   T M BARON, J D LINTHICUM, H D MOORE, J D A WALKER
BARNSLEY COMMUNITY AND PRIORITY SERVICES NHS TRUST   J G FAIRHURST
BARNSLEY DISTRICT GENERAL HOSPITAL NHS TRUST   M P YATES
BARNSLEY DISTRICT GENERAL PSYCHIATRIC UNIT   *see* Barnsley Community & Priority Services NHS Trust
BARROW Bristol   *see* United Bris Healthcare NHS Trust
BART'S AND THE LONDON NHS TRUST   P J COWELL
BASILDON   *see* S Essex Mental Health & Community Care NHS Trust
BASILDON AND THURROCK GENERAL HOSPITALS NHS TRUST   V G CATO, J M BARHAM
BASSETLAW DISTRICT GENERAL Worksop   *see* Doncaster and Bassetlaw Hosps NHS Trust
BATH AND WEST COMMUNITY NHS TRUST   H ANDREWES UTHWATT, M JOYCE, C T TOOKEY
BATTLE Reading   *see* R Berks and Battle Hosps NHS Trust
BAY COMMUNITY TRUST   D V A BROWN
BEBINGTON   M B KELLY
BECKENHAM   *see* Bromley Hosps NHS Trust
BEDFORD HOSPITAL NHS TRUST   P N S GIBSON
BEIGHTON CENTRE Sheffield   *see* Community Health Sheff NHS Trust
BENENDEN Kent   C F SMITH
BENNION CENTRE Leicester   *see* Leics and Rutland Healthcare NHS Trust
BENSHAM Gateshead   *see* Gateshead Health NHS Trust
BERWICK INFIRMARY   *see* Northumbria Healthcare NHS Trust

BETHLEM ROYAL Beckenham   *see* S Lon and Maudsley NHS Trust
BIDEFORD   *see* N Devon Healthcare NHS Trust
BILLINGE   *see* Wrightington Wigan and Leigh NHS Trust
BIRCH HILL   *see* Rochdale Healthcare NHS Trust
BIRMINGHAM Monyhull Learning Disabilities Service   *see* S Birm Mental Health NHS Trust
BIRMINGHAM AND MIDLAND EYE   *see* City Hosp NHS Trust Birm
BIRMINGHAM CHILDREN'S HOSPITAL NHS TRUST   C M ROBERTS, P NASH
BIRMINGHAM CITY   *see* City Hosp NHS Trust Birm
BIRMINGHAM HEARTLANDS AND SOLIHULL NHS TRUST   A M BOYD, W E HASSALL, E C LOUIS
BIRMINGHAM SKIN   *see* City Hosp NHS Trust Birm
BIRMINGHAM SPECIALIST COMMUNITY HEALTH NHS TRUST   H A N PLATTS, L M MORRIS
BIRMINGHAM WOMEN'S HEALTHCARE NHS TRUST   S W BARTON
BISHOP AUCKLAND GENERAL   *see* S Durham Healthcare NHS Trust
BLACKBERRY HILL Bristol   *see* N Bris NHS Trust
BLACKBURN, HYNDBURN AND RIBBLE VALLEY HEALTHCARE NHS TRUST   J R L CLARK
BLACKBURN ROYAL INFIRMARY   *see* Blackb, Hyndburn and Ribble Valley NHS Trust
BLACKPOOL, WYRE AND FYLDE COMMUNITY HEALTH SERVICES NHS TRUST   P D LAW-JONES
BLACKPOOL VICTORIA HOSPITAL NHS TRUST   J M TURNER
BLYTH COMMUNITY   *see* Northumbria Healthcare NHS Trust
BOGNOR REGIS WAR MEMORIAL   *see* Sussex Weald and Downs NHS Trust
BOLTON GENERAL   *see* Bolton Hosps NHS Trust
BOLTON HOSPITALS NHS TRUST   N K GRAY, G F WEIR, A J EDWARDS
BOOKER   *see* S Bucks NHS Trust
BOOTH HALL CHILDREN'S Manchester   *see* Cen Man/Man Children's Univ Hosp NHS Trust
BOOTHAM PARK   *see* York Health Services NHS Trust
BORDERS GENERAL NHS TRUST   D L MAYBURY
BOURNE Lincs   *see* NW Anglia Healthcare NHS Trust
BOURNEMOUTH, ROYAL GENERAL   *see* R Bournemouth and Christchurch Hosps NHS Trust
BRADFORD CITY PRIMARY CARE TRUST, A M E BROWN
BRADFORD HOSPITALS NHS TRUST   C P JOHNSON, J JACKSON
BRADGATE MENTAL HEALTH UNIT Leicester   *see* Leics and Rutland Healthcare NHS Trust
BRETBY HALL ORTHOPAEDIC   *see* S Derbyshire Acute Hosps NHS Trust
BRIDLINGTON AND DISTRICT   *see* Scarborough and NE Yorks Healthcare NHS Trust
BRIDPORT COMMUNITY   *see* SW Dorset Primary Care Trust
BRIGHTON GENERAL   *see* Brighton Health Care NHS Trust
BRIGHTON HEALTH CARE NHS TRUST   C J MIDLANE, R E ADFIELD
BRISTOL GENERAL   *see* United Bris Healthcare NHS Trust
BRISTOL ROYAL FOR SICK CHILDREN   *as above*
BRISTOL ROYAL INFIRMARY   *as above*
BROADMOOR Crowthorne   T W WALT
BROMLEY HOSPITALS NHS TRUST   T J MERCER
BROOMFIELD Chelmsford   *see* Mid-Essex Hosp Services NHS Trust
BUCKLAND Dover   *see* E Kent Hosps NHS Trust
BURNLEY HEALTH CARE NHS TRUST   R L ALLEN, D ALTHAM
BURTON HOSPITALS NHS TRUST   B WILLIAMS
CAERPHILLY DISTRICT MINERS'   *see* Gwent Healthcare NHS Trust
CALDERDALE AND HUDDERSFIELD NHS TRUST   S V BROOKS, M W PARROTT, M D ELLERTON
CANNOCK CHASE   *see* Mid Staffs Gen Hosps NHS Trust

CANTERBURY St Martin's   *see* E Kent Community NHS
Trust
CARDIFF COMMUNITY HEALTHCARE NHS TRUST
J H L ROWLANDS
CARDIFF ROYAL INFIRMARY   *see* Univ Hosp of Wales
and Llandough NHS Trust
CARLETON CLINIC Carlisle   *see* N Cumbria Mental Health
NHS Trust
CARLISLE HOSPITALS NHS TRUST   N N STEADMAN
CARLTON HAYES Narborough   *see* Leics and Rutland
Healthcare NHS Trust
CASTEL   *see* States of Guernsey Bd of Health
CASTLE Okehampton   *see* Mid Devon Primary Care Trust
CASTLE HILL Cottingham   *see* Hull and E Yorks Hosps NHS
Trust
CASTLEFORD NORMANTON AND DISTRICT   *see* Mid
Yorks Hosps NHS Trust
CATERHAM   *see* Surrey and Sussex Healthcare NHS Trust
CEFN COED Swansea   *see* Swansea NHS Trust
CENTRAL MANCHESTER/MANCHESTER CHILDREN'S
UNIVERSITY HOSPITAL NHS TRUST   M W FOLLAND,
S TURNER, A-M HUMPHREYS
CENTRAL MIDDLESEX NHS TRUST   K N HALL,
M D MOORHEAD
CENTRAL SHEFFIELD UNIVERSITY HOSPITALS NHS
TRUST   M R COBB, H C BLACKBURN
CHADWELL HEATH Romford   *see* Redbridge Health Care
NHS Trust
CHAILEY HERITAGE Lewes   G A LAY
CHALFONTS AND GERRARDS CROSS, THE   *see* S Bucks
NHS Trust
CHAPEL ALLERTON Leeds   *see* Leeds Teaching Hosps NHS
Trust
CHARING CROSS   *see* Hammersmith Hosps NHS Trust
CHARLTON LANE CENTRE Leckhampton   *see* Glos Hosps
NHS Trust
CHASE, THE Bordon   *see* N Hants Loddon Community NHS
Trust
CHASE FARM Enfield   *see* Barnet and Chase Farm Hosps
NHS Trust
CHEDDON ROAD   *see* Taunton and Somerset NHS Trust
CHELMSFORD Broomfield   *see* Mid-Essex Hosp Services
NHS Trust
CHELSEA AND WESTMINSTER HEALTHCARE NHS
TRUST   S B SMITH, C BEARDSLEY
CHELTENHAM GENERAL   *see* Glos Hosps NHS Trust
CHEPSTOW COMMUNITY   *see* Gwent Healthcare NHS
Trust
CHERRY KNOWLE Sunderland   *see* Priority Healthcare
Wearside NHS Trust
CHERRY TREE Stockport   *see* Stockport NHS Trust
CHESHAM   *see* S Bucks NHS Trust
CHESHIRE AND WIRRAL PARTNERSHIP NHS TRUST
G R ROWLANDS, R T NELSON, H J ALDRIDGE, D R NUGENT
CHESTERFIELD AND NORTH DERBYSHIRE NHS
TRUST   J K BUTTERFIELD
CHESTERTON Cambridge   *see* Addenbrooke's NHS Trust
CHICHESTER St Richard's   *see* R W Sussex Trust
CHIPPENHAM COMMUNITY   *see* Wilts and Swindon
Healthcare NHS Trust
CHORLEY AND SOUTH RIBBLE DISTRICT GENERAL
see Lanc Teaching Hosps NHS Trust
CHRISTCHURCH   *see* R Bournemouth and Christchurch
Hosps NHS Trust
CHRISTIE HOSPITAL NHS TRUST Manchester   D K PRYCE,
J A HORROCKS
CHURCHILL, THE Oxford   *see* Ox Radcliffe Hosps NHS Trust
CIRENCESTER   *see* Cotswold and Vale Primary Care Trust
CIRENCESTER   *see* Glos Hosps NHS Trust
CITY AND HACKNEY COMMUNITY SERVICES NHS
TRUST   A J MARCETTI
CITY GENERAL Carlisle   *see* Carl Hosps NHS Trust
CITY HOSPITAL York   *see* York Health Services NHS Trust
CITY HOSPITAL NHS TRUST Birmingham   G DOWNS
CITY HOSPITALS SUNDERLAND NHS TRUST   P H WEBB,
M A MILLWARD
CLACTON GENERAL   *see* Essex Rivers Healthcare NHS
Trust
CLATTERBRIDGE Wirral   *see* Cheshire and Wirral
Partnership NHS Trust
CLAYBURY Woodford Bridge   *see* Forest Healthcare NHS
Trust Lon
CLAYTON Wakefield   *see* Mid Yorks Hosps NHS Trust
CLEVELAND, SOUTH Middlesbrough   *see* S Tees Hosps NHS
Trust
COALVILLE COMMUNITY   *see* Leics and Rutland
Healthcare NHS Trust

COLCHESTER GENERAL   *see* Essex Rivers Healthcare NHS
Trust
COLCHESTER MATERNITY   *as above*
COLINDALE   *see* Enfield Primary Care Trust
COMMUNITY HEALTH SHEFFIELD NHS TRUST
H G SMART, C P ARNESEN
CONQUEST, THE Bexhill   *see* Hastings and Rother NHS Trust
COOKRIDGE Leeds   *see* Leeds Teaching Hosps NHS Trust
CORNWALL AND ISLES OF SCILLY MENTAL HEALTH
UNIT   M G SELLIX
CORNWALL HEALTHCARE TRUST   R E B MAYNARD,
T J G NEWCOMBE, R N STRANACK, J C GREATBATCH,
G G C MINORS, J T MCCABE
COTSWOLD AND VALE PRIMARY CARE TRUST
M J WITHEY
COUNTESS MOUNTBATTEN HOSPICE Southampton
see Southn Univ Hosps NHS Trust
COUNTESS OF CHESTER   *see* Cheshire and Wirral
Partnership NHS Trust
COUNTY DURHAM AND DARLINGTON PRIORITY
SERVICES NHS TRUST   C JAY, M Q KING
COVENTRY AND WARWICKSHIRE   *see* Walsgrave Hosps
NHS Trust Cov
CRAIGAVON AREA HOSPITAL GROUP TRUST
C W M ROLSTON
CROMER   *see* Norfolk and Nor Univ Hosp NHS Trust
CROSSLANE Newby   *see* Tees and NE Yorks NHS Trust
CROYDON MENTAL HEALTH SERVICES Warlingham
see S Lon and Maudsley NHS Trust
CUMBERLAND INFIRMARY   *see* Carl Hosps NHS Trust
CYNTHIA SPENCER HOUSE Northampton   *see* Northants
Healthcare NHS Trust
DARLINGTON MEMORIAL   *see* S Durham Healthcare NHS
Trust
DARTFORD AND GRAVESHAM NHS TRUST   P J IVESON,
K E W MATHERS
DELANCEY Leckhampton   *see* Glos Hosps NHS Trust
DELLWOOD Reading   *see* R Berks and Battle Hosps NHS
Trust
DERBY CITY GENERAL   *see* S Derbyshire Acute Hosps
NHS Trust
DERBYSHIRE CHILDREN'S   *as above*
DERBYSHIRE ROYAL INFIRMARY   *as above*
DEREHAM   *see* Norwich Primary Care Trust
DERRIFORD   *see* Plymouth Hosps NHS Trust
DEVIZES COMMUNITY   *see* Wilts and Swindon Healthcare
NHS Trust
DEWI SANT Pontypridd   *see* Pontypridd and Rhondda NHS
Trust
DEWSBURY AND DISTRICT   *see* Mid Yorks Hosps NHS
Trust
DIANA, PRINCESS OF WALES Grimsby   *see* N Lincs and
Goole Hosps NHS Trust
DODDINGTON COUNTY March   *see* NW Anglia Healthcare
NHS Trust
DONCASTER AND BASSETLAW HOSPITALS NHS TRUST
M C WRIGHT, R D BENNETT, C L SMITH, J E ASHTON
DONCASTER AND SOUTH HUMBER HEALTHCARE
NHS TRUST   J E PALIN
DONCASTER ROYAL INFIRMARY   *see* Doncaster and
Bassetlaw Hosps NHS Trust
DONCASTER ROYAL INFIRMARY PSYCHIATRIC UNIT
see Doncaster and S Humber Healthcare NHS Trust
DORKING   *see* Surrey and Sussex Healthcare NHS Trust
DORSET HEALTH CARE NHS TRUST   K S TIMBRELL
DRYBURN Durham   *see* N Dur Healthcare NHS Trust
DUCHESS OF KENT HOUSE St Andrews   *see* States of
Guernsey Bd of Health
DUDLEY GROUP OF HOSPITALS NHS TRUST   P TONGUE,
A E COLES
DUNSTON HILL Gateshead   *see* Gateshead Health NHS Trust
DURHAM AND DARLINGTON PRIORITY SERVICES
NHS TRUST   *see* Co Dur & Darlington Priority Services NHS
Trust
EALING HOSPITAL NHS TRUST   C P GUINNESS, J L OSBORNE
EARLS HOUSE Durham   *see* Co Dur & Darlington Priority
Services NHS Trust
EAST AND NORTH HERTFORDSHIRE NHS TRUST
G N BUSTARD, S J MANLEY-COOPER, D J PROUD, K A BUCKLER,
F S E GIBBS
EAST BERKSHIRE NHS TRUST FOR PEOPLE WITH
LEARNING DISABILITIES   G F THEOBALD
EAST CHESHIRE NHS TRUST   D W MOIR
EAST KENT COMMUNITY NHS TRUST   A E WILLIAMS,
D J VENABLES, G D KENDREW, R P C PODGER, J A F TAYLOR
EAST KENT HOSPITALS NHS TRUST   P M KIRBY, B E WAY,
P F HILL, K FAZZANI

EAST RIDING COMMUNITY HEALTH TRUST   A BAILEY
EAST SOMERSET NHS TRUST   E N BANGAY, E J ROTHWELL
EAST SURREY LEARNING DISABILITY AND MENTAL
  HEALTH SERVICES NHS TRUST   C E LATHAM
EAST SURREY PRIORITY CARE NHS TRUST   N J COPSEY
EASTBOURNE AND COUNTY HEALTHCARE NHS
  TRUST   M J ELWIS, A C J CORNES
EASTBOURNE HOSPITALS NHS TRUST   J H KIMBERLEY,
  N P CHATFIELD
EASTRY   see E Kent Community NHS Trust
EDGWARE COMMUNITY   see Barnet and Chase Farm
  Hosps NHS Trust
EDINBURGH HEALTHCARE NHS TRUST   D YEOMAN
EDITH CAVELL Peterborough   see Pet Hosps NHS Trust
EDWARDS UNIT   see Rochdale Healthcare NHS Trust
ELLESMERE PORT   see Cheshire and Wirral Partnership NHS
  Trust
ELY Cardiff   see Cardiff Community Healthcare NHS Trust
ENFIELD PRIMARY CARE TRUST   T M BARON, T D ATKINS
EPPING FOREST PRIMARY CARE TRUST   B C MORRISON
EPSOM St Ebba's   see Surrey Oaklands NHS Trust
EPSOM AND ST HELIER NHS TRUST   C VALLINS,
  A WALFORD, D WALFORD, I G WOODROFFE
EPSOM GENERAL   see Epsom and St Helier NHS Trust
ERITH AND DISTRICT   see Qu Mary's Sidcup NHS Trust
ESSEX COUNTY   see Essex Rivers Healthcare NHS Trust
ESSEX RIVERS HEALTHCARE NHS TRUST   R SMITH,
  M W THOMPSON, J I SEARS
EVESHAM COMMUNITY   see Worcs Community and
  Mental Health Trust
EXETER HEALTH AUTHORITY (Mental Health/Handicap),
  D J WALFORD
FAIRMILE Wallingford   see W Berks Priority Care Services
  NHS Trust
FALMOUTH   see R Cornwall Hosps Trust
FARNHAM ROAD Guildford   see Surrey Hants Borders NHS
  Trust
FAZAKERLEY Liverpool   see Aintree Hosps NHS Trust Liv
FIELDHEAD Wakefield   see Wakef and Pontefract Community
  NHS Trust
FINCHLEY MEMORIAL   see Enfield Primary Care Trust
FOREST HEALTHCARE NHS TRUST London
  M O PRITCHARD, D J DALAIS
FRENCHAY Bristol   see N Bris NHS Trust
FRIARAGE Northallerton   see Northallerton Health Services
  NHS Trust
FRIMLEY PARK HOSPITAL NHS TRUST   A W WARNER
FULBOURN Cambridge   see Addenbrooke's NHS Trust
GARLANDS Carlisle   see North Lakeland Healthcare NHS
  Trust
GATESHEAD HEALTH NHS TRUST   J R PERRY,
  R L FERGUSON
GEORGE ELIOT HOSPITAL NHS TRUST Nuneaton
  E C POGMORE, D R L WHITE, P DODDS
GLENFIELD Leicester   see Univ Hosps Leic NHS Trust
GLENFIELD GENERAL Bennion Centre   see Leics and
  Rutland Healthcare NHS Trust
GLENFIELD GENERAL Bradgate Mental Health Unit
  as above
GLENSIDE Bristol   R MEREDITH-JONES
GLOUCESTERSHIRE HOSPITALS NHS TRUST
  W B IRVINE, D H GODWIN, R T SWAIN
GLOUCESTERSHIRE PARTNERSHIP TRUST   M J WITHEY
GLOUCESTERSHIRE ROYAL   see Glos Hosps NHS Trust
GOGARBURN Edinburgh   see Edinburgh Healthcare NHS
  Trust
GOOD HOPE HOSPITAL NHS TRUST Sutton Coldfield
  A T BALL
GOOLE AND DISTRICT   see N Lincs and Goole Hosps NHS
  Trust
GORSE HILL Leicester   see Leics and Rutland Healthcare NHS
  Trust
GOSPORT WAR MEMORIAL   see Portsm Healthcare NHS
  Trust
GRAMPIAN UNIVERSITY HOSPITAL NHS TRUST
  S SPENCER
GRAYLINGWELL Chichester   see Sussex Weald and Downs
  NHS Trust
GREAT ORMOND STREET HOSPITAL FOR CHILDREN
  NHS TRUST   N WALTER, D A MOORE BROOKS, J W CROSSLEY
GRIMSBY   see N Lincs and Goole Hosps NHS Trust
GUILDFORD St Luke's   see R Surrey Co Hosp NHS Trust
GUY'S AND ST THOMAS' HOSPITALS NHS TRUST
  London   M A K HILBORN, R A SHAW
GWENT COUNTY Griffithstown   see Gwent Healthcare NHS
  Trust

GWENT HEALTHCARE NHS TRUST   A W TYLER,
  M J MARSDEN, M C G LANE
GWYNEDD Bangor   W ROBERTS
GWYNEDD HOSPITALS NHS TRUST   R H GRIFFITHS
HAINE Ramsgate   see E Kent Community NHS Trust
HALSTEAD COMMUNITY   see Essex Rivers Healthcare
  NHS Trust
HALTON GENERAL   see N Cheshire Hosps NHS Trust
HAM GREEN Bristol   see N Bris NHS Trust
HAMMERSMITH HOSPITALS NHS TRUST   E MORRIS
HAROLD WOOD   see Havering Hosps NHS Trust
HARROGATE HEALTH CARE NHS TRUST   P GREENWELL
HARROW   see NW Lon Hosp NHS Trust
HARROW AND HILLINGDON HEALTHCARE NHS
  TRUST   D P BYRNE
HARTLEPOOL GENERAL   see N Tees and Hartlepool NHS
  Trust
HARTLEPOOL GENERAL   see also Tees and NE Yorks NHS
  Trust
HARTSHILL ORTHOPAEDIC   see N Staffs Hosp NHS Trust
HARWICH COMMUNITY   see Essex Rivers Healthcare NHS
  Trust
HASTINGS AND ROTHER NHS TRUST   D J JEFFREYS
HAVERING HOSPITALS NHS TRUST   M R JUDGE
HEATHERWOOD AND WEXHAM PARK HOSPITAL NHS
  TRUST   P L DEEMING, D S JONES, R A CHEEK
HELLESDON Norfolk   see Norfolk Mental Health Care NHS
  Trust
HEMEL HEMPSTEAD GENERAL   see W Herts Hosps NHS
  Trust
HEREFORD HOSPITALS NHS TRUST   P A ROBERTS,
  L C RHODES
HEXHAM   see Northumbria Healthcare NHS Trust
HIGHBURY Bulwell   see Notts Healthcare NHS Trust
HILL HOUSE Swansea   see Swansea NHS Trust
HILLINGDON HOSPITAL NHS TRUST   W F WHITE
HINCHINGBROOKE HEALTH CARE NHS TRUST
  A-L K GARVIE, P M DUFFETT-SMITH
HITCHIN   see E and N Herts NHS Trust
HITHER GREEN London   see Lewisham Hosp NHS Trust
HOMERTON UNIVERSITY HOSPITAL NHS TRUST
  London   A J MARCETTI, R J OGSTON
HOPE Salford   see Salford R Hosps NHS Trust
HOUNSLOW AND SPELTHORNE COMMUNITY AND
  MENTAL HEALTH NHS TRUST   M A WARMAN
HUDDERSFIELD ROYAL INFIRMARY   see Calderdale and
  Huddersfield NHS Trust
HULL AND EAST YORKSHIRE HOSPITALS NHS TRUST
  S SMITH, S E CEELY, P J NELSON, J A SHARP
HULL MATERNITY   see Hull and E Yorks Hosps NHS Trust
HULL ROYAL INFIRMARY   as above
HURSTWOOD PARK Haywards Heath   see Mid Sussex NHS
  Trust
IDA DARWIN Cambridge   see Addenbrooke's NHS Trust
INVICTA COMMUNITY CARE NHS TRUST
  S A J MITCHELL, R J CASTLE, R WARD
IPSWICH HOSPITAL NHS TRUST   G T MELVIN, S CARLSSON,
  M GREEN, R A FINCH
ISEBROOK Wellingborough   see Northants Healthcare NHS
  Trust
ISLE OF MAN DEPARTMENT OF HEALTH AND SOCIAL
  SECURITY   P S FREAR
ISLE OF WIGHT HEALTHCARE NHS TRUST
  G J CLIFTON-SMITH, M D H JOHNSTON, G M HURT
JAMES PAGET HEALTHCARE NHS TRUST   V M STEADY,
  J A FAIRBAIRN
JERSEY GROUP   H M A CERMAKOVA
JESSOP WOMEN'S Sheffield   see Cen Sheff Univ Hosps NHS
  Trust
JOHN RADCLIFFE Oxford   see Ox Radcliffe Hosps NHS
  Trust
KELLING   see Norwich Primary Care Trust
KENDRAY Barnsley   see Barnsley Community & Priority
  Services NHS Trust
KENT AND CANTERBURY   see E Kent Hosps NHS Trust
KENT AND SUSSEX Tunbridge Wells   see Maidstone and
  Tunbridge Wells NHS Trust
KERESFORTH CENTRE Barnsley   see Barnsley Community
  & Priority Services NHS Trust
KETTERING GENERAL HOSPITAL NHS TRUST
  L S MCCORMACK
KEYCOL Kent   see Thames Gateway NHS Trust
KIDDERMINSTER   see Worcs Acute Hosps NHS Trust
KIDDERMINSTER GENERAL   see Worcs Community and
  Mental Health Trust
KING EDWARD VII Castel   see States of Guernsey Bd of
  Health

KING EDWARD VII Midhurst   D B WELSMAN
KING GEORGE Redbridge   see Redbridge Health Care NHS
Trust
KING'S HEALTHCARE NHS TRUST   S T MEYER,
A J MCCULLOCH, D W RUSHTON
KING'S LYNN AND WISBECH HOSPITALS NHS TRUST
A L HAIG
KINGS MILL CENTRE FOR HEALTH CARE SERVICES
NHS TRUST   J A S WOOD
KING'S WOOD CENTRE Colchester   see N Essex Mental
Health Partnership NHS Trust
KINGSBURY COMMUNITY London   see Parkside
Community NHS Trust Lon
KINGSWAY Derby   see S Derbyshire Community and Mental
Health Trust
KNEESWORTH HOUSE Royston   N TAYLOR
LANCASHIRE TEACHING HOSPITALS NHS TRUST
R J FISHER, J G PRYSOR-JONES
LANCASTER MOOR Lancaster   see Bay Community Trust
LANGBAURGH PRIMARY CARE TRUST   P L BISHOP
LEEDS St Mary's   see Leeds Mental Health Teaching NHS
Trust
LEEDS GENERAL INFIRMARY   see Leeds Teaching Hosps
NHS Trust
LEEDS MENTAL HEALTH TEACHING NHS TRUST
M I KIMBALL
LEEDS TEACHING HOSPITALS NHS TRUST, The
D J RIVERS, C J SWIFT, G HANCOCKS, R S CAMPBELL,
B J TURNER, T P LUSTY
LEICESTER GENERAL   see Univ Hosps Leic NHS Trust
LEICESTER GENERAL Brandon Unit   see Leics and Rutland
Healthcare NHS Trust
LEICESTER ROYAL INFIRMARY   see Univ Hosps Leic
NHS Trust
LEICESTERSHIRE AND RUTLAND HEALTHCARE NHS
TRUST   J E K MOULT, R G BROWN
LEIGH INFIRMARY   see Wrightington Wigan and Leigh
NHS Trust
LEIGHTON Crewe   see Mid Cheshire Hosps Trust
LEWISHAM HOSPITAL NHS TRUST   A L SHAW,
G W HOLMES, B RHODES
LIBERTON Edinburgh   see Lothian Univ Hosps NHS Trust
LIFECARE Caterham   see Surrey Oaklands NHS Trust
LINCOLN Witham Court ESMI Unit   see Linc Distr
Healthcare NHS Trust
LINCOLN COUNTY   see United Lincs Hosps NHS Trust
LINCOLN DISTRICT HEALTHCARE NHS TRUST
R G WILKINSON, G P POND, D YOUNG
LINDEN CENTRE Broomfield   see N Essex Mental Health
Partnership NHS Trust
LISTER Stevenage   see E and N Herts NHS Trust
LITTLE PLUMSTEAD   see Norwich Primary Care Trust
LITTLEMORE Oxford   see Oxon Mental Healthcare NHS
Trust
LIVERPOOL St Helen's   see St Helen's and Knowsley Hosps
Trust
LIVERPOOL WOMEN'S HOSPITAL NHS TRUST   N BLACK
LLANDOUGH   see Univ Hosp of Wales and Llandough NHS
Trust
LLANDUDNO GENERAL   see Gwynedd Hosp NHS Trust
LLANFRECHFA GRANGE Cwmbran   see Gwent Healthcare
NHS Trust
LLANTRISANT Royal Glamorgan   see Pontypridd and
Rhondda NHS Trust
LLWYNYPIA   as above
LONDON AND SURREY   see R Marsden NHS Trust Lon
and Surrey
LONDON CHEST   see Bart's and the Lon NHS Trust
LOTHIAN PRIMARY HEALTHCARE NHS TRUST
J D R WHITLEY
LOTHIAN UNIVERSITY HOSPITALS NHS TRUST
C T UPTON, P D SKELTON
LOUGHBOROUGH   see Leics and Rutland Healthcare NHS
Trust
LOUTH COUNTY   see United Lincs Hosps NHS Trust
LOVERSALL Doncaster   see Doncaster and S Humber
Healthcare NHS Trust
LOWESTOFT AND NORTH SUFFOLK   see Jas Paget
Healthcare NHS Trust
LUDLOW   see Shropshire's Community NHS Trust
LUTON AND DUNSTABLE HOSPITAL NHS TRUST
E A BRADLEY
LYMINGTON HOSPITAL   see Southampton Community
Services NHS Trust
MACCLESFIELD DISTRICT GENERAL   see E Cheshire
NHS Trust

MAIDSTONE AND TUNBRIDGE WELLS NHS TRUST
P J PLUMLEY, D F L PETZSCH, S J BLADE
MAINDIFF COURT Abergavenny   see Gwent Healthcare NHS
Trust
MANCHESTER AND SALFORD SKIN   see Salford R Hosps
NHS Trust
MANCHESTER ROYAL EYE   see Cen Man/Man Children's
Univ Hosp NHS Trust
MANCHESTER ROYAL INFIRMARY   as above
MANSFIELD DISTRICT PRIMARY CARE TRUST
P BENTLEY
MANYGATES MATERNITY Wakefield   M P CROFT
MARIE CURIE CENTRE Newcastle upon Tyne   R FINDLAYSON
MARLOW COMMUNITY   see S Bucks NHS Trust
MAUDSLEY Denmark Hill   see S Lon and Maudsley NHS
Trust
MAYDAY HEALTHCARE NHS TRUST Thornton Heath
H A FIFE, P L GIBBS
MAYDAY UNIVERSITY   see Mayday Healthcare NHS Trust
Thornton Heath
MEANWOOD PARK Leeds   see Leeds Mental Health Teaching
NHS Trust
MEDWAY Gillingham   see also Thames Gateway NHS Trust
MEDWAY NHS TRUST   A J AMOS, R THOMSON, P A MCKENZIE
MELKSHAM COMMUNITY   see Wilts and Swindon
Healthcare NHS Trust
MEMORIAL Darlington   see Co Dur & Darlington Priority
Services NHS Trust
MENDIP PRIMARY CARE TRUST   E J SMITH
MID CHESHIRE HOSPITALS TRUST   G D GEDDES,
S HUGHES
MID DEVON PRIMARY CARE TRUST   D J WALFORD,
D M FLETCHER
MID-ESSEX HOSPITAL SERVICES NHS TRUST
C I HAMPTON, R J R HUMPHRIES
MID STAFFORDSHIRE GENERAL HOSPITALS NHS
TRUST   I S VAUGHAN, P J GRAYSMITH
MID SUSSEX NHS TRUST   R J ST C HARLOW-TRIGG
MID YORKSHIRE HOSPITALS NHS TRUST   M GASKELL,
M J WINBOLT LEWIS, J P TAYLOR
MIDDLESBROUGH GENERAL   see S Tees Hosps NHS
Trust
MIDDLESEX   see Univ Coll Lon Hosps NHS Trust
MILDMAY MISSION   M F SCHLEGER
MILL HILL Huddersfield   W L HALLING
MILLBROOK MENTAL HEALTH UNIT Sutton-in-Ashfield
see Notts Healthcare NHS Trust
MILTON KEYNES COMMUNITY NHS TRUST   C E HOUGH
MILTON KEYNES GENERAL NHS TRUST   C E HOUGH,
T CLAPTON
MONTAGU Mexborough   see Doncaster and Bassetlaw Hosps
NHS Trust
MONYHULL LEARNING DISABILITIES SERVICE
Birmingham   see S Birm Mental Health NHS Trust
MOORFIELDS EYE HOSPITAL NHS TRUST   I C YOUNG
MOORGREEN West End Southampton   see Southampton
Community Services NHS Trust
MORECAMBE BAY HOSPITALS NHS TRUST   J L TYRER,
D V A BROWN, G GARBUTT
MORPETH COTTAGE   see Northumbria Healthcare NHS
Trust
MORRISTON Swansea   see Swansea NHS Trust
MOSELEY HALL Birmingham   see Birm Specialist
Community Health NHS Trust
MOUNT, THE Bishopstoke   see Win and Eastleigh Healthcare
NHS Trust
MOUNT VERNON Barnsley   see Barnsley Community &
Priority Services NHS Trust
MUSGROVE PARK Taunton   see Taunton and Somerset NHS
Trust
NAPSBURY St Albans   see Enfield Primary Care Trust
NEVILL HALL Abergavenny   see Gwent Healthcare NHS
Trust
NEW CROSS Wolverhampton   see R Wolv Hosps NHS Trust
NEWARK NHS TRUST   P HUTCHINSON
NEWBURY AND COMMUNITY PRIMARY CARE TRUST
B DAGNALL
NEWBURY DISTRICT   see W Berks Priority Care Services
NHS Trust
NEWCASTLE Royal Victoria Infirmary   see Newcastle upon
Tyne Hosps NHS Trust
NEWCASTLE St Nicholas   see Newc City Health NHS Trust
NEWCASTLE CITY HEALTH NHS TRUST   F B ALLEN,
A E MARR
NEWCASTLE GENERAL   see Newcastle upon Tyne Hosps
NHS Trust

NEWCASTLE UPON TYNE HOSPITALS NHS TRUST
M J SHIPTON, A MAUDE, R FINDLAYSON
NEWHAM GENERAL   see Newham Healthcare NHS Trust
Lon
NEWHAM HEALTHCARE NHS TRUST London
I MCDOWELL
NEWHAM PRIMARY CARE TRUST   N J COPSEY
NEWTON ABBOT   see S Devon Healthcare NHS Trust
NEWTOWN Worcester   see Worcs Community and Mental
Health Trust
NORFOLK AND NORWICH UNIVERSITY HOSPITAL
NHS TRUST   E S LANGAN, C B REED, P A ATKINSON,
T W HARRIS, J M STEWART
NORFOLK MENTAL HEALTH CARE NHS TRUST
W F BAZELY, M I KNOWLES
NORTH BIRMINGHAM MENTAL HEALTH TRUST
D L HART
NORTH BRISTOL NHS TRUST   D C DAVIES, N A HECTOR,
A J PARKER, C A G LEGGATE, A M BUCKNALL, A J GAUNT,
A R GOOD
NORTH CAMBRIDGESHIRE Wisbech   see King's Lynn and
Wisbech Hosps NHS Trust
NORTH CHESHIRE HOSPITALS NHS TRUST   J E DUFFIELD
NORTH CUMBRIA MENTAL HEALTH AND LEARNING
DISABILITIES NHS TRUST   A M MULLER
NORTH DEVON DISTRICT Barnstaple   see N Devon
Healthcare NHS Trust
NORTH DURHAM HEALTHCARE NHS TRUST
M MASTERMAN, D J WILSON
NORTH EAST LONDON MENTAL HEALTH TRUST
R B WHITE
NORTH EAST WALES NHS TRUST   K B COLLINS
NORTH ESSEX MENTAL HEALTH PARTNERSHIP NHS
TRUST   R SMITH
NORTH HAMPSHIRE HOSPITALS NHS TRUST
P J GOOLD, A J ASKEW
NORTH HAMPSHIRE LODDON COMMUNITY NHS
TRUST   P J GOOLD
NORTH LAKELAND HEALTHCARE NHS TRUST
N N STEADMAN
NORTH MANCHESTER GENERAL   see N Man Health
Care NHS Trust
NORTH MANCHESTER HEALTH CARE NHS TRUST
M R MORGAN
NORTH MERSEY COMMUNITY NHS TRUST   M C DAVIES,
F R CAIN
NORTH MIDDLESEX HOSPITAL NHS TRUST
B D FENTON, P C ATHERTON
NORTH STAFFORDSHIRE HOSPITAL NHS TRUST
J M AUSTERBERRY
NORTH TEES AND HARTLEPOOL NHS TRUST
M WARNER, J E LUND, L PURVIS
NORTH TEES GENERAL   see Tees and NE Yorks NHS
Trust
NORTH TYNESIDE GENERAL North Shields
see Northumbria Healthcare NHS Trust
NORTH WEST ANGLIA HEALTHCARE NHS TRUST
K G PRATT, S J SMITH
NORTH WEST LONDON HOSPITALS NHS TRUST
D P BYRNE
NORTH WEST SURREY MENTAL HEALTH NHS TRUST
A B OLSEN
NORTHALLERTON HEALTH SERVICES NHS TRUST
A H DODD
NORTHAMPTON GENERAL HOSPITAL NHS TRUST
G A SARMEZEY
NORTHAMPTONSHIRE HEALTHCARE NHS TRUST
R J T FARMER, C R GOODLEY, J A PARKIN, G C RUMBOLD,
M WRAY
NORTHERN DEVON HEALTHCARE NHS TRUST
J R ILSON, R M REYNOLDS, P D PILDITCH
NORTHERN GENERAL HOSPITAL NHS TRUST Sheffield
D E R EQUEALL, J A FRYER
NORTHERN LINCOLNSHIRE AND GOOLE HOSPITALS
NHS TRUST   J R SIMPSON
NORTHGATE Great Yarmouth   see Jas Paget Healthcare NHS
Trust
NORTHGATE Morpeth   see Northgate and Prudhoe NHS
Trust
NORTHGATE AND PRUDHOE NHS TRUST   D F MAYHEW
NORTHUMBERLAND MENTAL HEALTH NHS TRUST
R H MCLEAN
NORTHUMBRIA HEALTHCARE NHS TRUST
F V G BALLENTYNE, C F MEEHAN, J WAIYAKI, B BENISON,
R H MCLEAN
NORWICH, WEST   see Norfolk and Nor Univ Hosp NHS
Trust

NORWICH PRIMARY CARE TRUST   P A ATKINSON,
R D BRANSON, S F NUNNEY, M M KINGSTON
NOTTINGHAM CITY HOSPITAL NHS TRUST   M J KERRY,
Y E GLASS, C BROWN
NOTTINGHAMSHIRE HEALTHCARE NHS TRUST
C M J THODY, M EVANS, K D WILLIAMS, K R EVANS
NUFFIELD ORTHOPAEDIC CENTRE NHS TRUST
J E COCKE
NUNNERY FIELDS Canterbury   see E Kent Hosps NHS Trust
ODIHAM COTTAGE   see N Hants Loddon Community NHS
Trust
OKEHAMPTON AND DISTRICT   see Mid Devon Primary
Care Trust
OLDCHURCH Romford   see Havering Hosps NHS Trust
OLDHAM NHS TRUST   I S CARTER, R R WATSON
ORMSKIRK AND DISTRICT GENERAL   see W Lancashire
NHS Trust
ORSETT   see Basildon and Thurrock Gen Hosps NHS Trust
OVERDALE St Helier   see Jersey Gp of Hosps
OXFORD RADCLIFFE HOSPITALS NHS TRUST
A C MCGOWAN, G A BARKER, C A SMITH, N P FENNEMORE,
D E MICKLETHWAITE
OXFORDSHIRE MENTAL HEALTHCARE NHS TRUST
F B STEVENSON, E J JOHNSON
OXLEAS NHS TRUST   N J BUNKER
OXTED   see Surrey and Sussex Healthcare NHS Trust
PADDINGTON COMMUNITY London   see Parkside
Community NHS Trust Lon
PAIGNTON   see S Devon Healthcare NHS Trust
PAPWORTH HOSPITAL NHS TRUST   J A COOMBS
PARK LEE Blackburn   see Blackb, Hyndburn and Ribble Valley
NHS Trust
PARK PREWETT   see N Hants Loddon Community NHS
Trust
PARKSIDE COMMUNITY NHS TRUST London
R G THOMPSON
PATRICK STEAD Halesworth   see Allington NHS Trust
PEMBURY Tunbridge Wells   see Maidstone and Tunbridge
Wells NHS Trust
PENRITH   see N Cumbria Mental Health NHS Trust
PETER HODGKINSON CENTRE Lincoln   see Linc Distr
Healthcare NHS Trust
PETERBOROUGH HOSPITALS NHS TRUST   R E HIGGINS
PIERREMONT UNIT Darlington   see Co Dur & Darlington
Priority Services NHS Trust
PILGRIM Boston   see United Lincs Hosps NHS Trust
PINDERFIELDS GENERAL Wakefield   see Mid Yorks Hosps
NHS Trust
PLAISTOW   see Newham Primary Care Trust
PLUMSTEAD, LITTLE   see Norwich Primary Care Trust
PLYMOUTH HOSPITALS NHS TRUST
A P R KYRIAKIDES-YELDHAM, M CHURCHER
PONTEFRACT GENERAL INFIRMARY   see Mid Yorks
Hosps NHS Trust
PONTYPRIDD AND RHONDDA NHS TRUST   G A BLYTH
POOLE St Ann's   see Dorset Health Care NHS Trust
POOLE HOSPITAL NHS TRUST   E J LLOYD, S C PARRETT,
I R PEARCE
PORTSMOUTH HEALTHCARE NHS TRUST   J E HAIR,
J C GRACE
PORTSMOUTH HOSPITALS NHS TRUST   F D HILLEBRAND,
A P BURR, B A MOSSE, J POWER, P A W JONES, B R SMITH
PRINCESS ALEXANDRA Harlow   see N Essex Mental
Health Partnership NHS Trust
PRINCESS ALEXANDRA HOSPITAL NHS TRUST Harlow
T COLEMAN
PRINCESS ALICE Eastbourne   see Eastbourne Hosps NHS
Trust
PRINCESS ANNE Southampton   see Southn Univ Hosps NHS
Trust
PRINCESS ELIZABETH St Martin   see States of Guernsey Bd
of Health
PRINCESS LOUISE London   see Parkside Community NHS
Trust Lon
PRINCESS MARGARET ROSE ORTHOPAEDIC Edinburgh
see Lothian Univ Hosps NHS Trust
PRINCESS MARINA Northampton   see Northants Healthcare
NHS Trust
PRINCESS OF WALES COMMUNITY Bromsgrove
see Worcs Community and Mental Health Trust
PRINCESS ROYAL Haywards Heath   see Mid Sussex NHS
Trust
PRINCESS ROYAL Hull   see Hull and E Yorks Hosps NHS
Trust
PRIORITY HEALTHCARE WEARSIDE NHS TRUST
C J WORSFOLD
PUREY CUST NUFFIELD York   J A RENDALL

QUEEN ALEXANDRA Cosham *see* Portsm Healthcare NHS Trust
QUEEN ALEXANDRA Portsmouth *see* Portsm Hosps NHS Trust
QUEEN ALEXANDRA HOSPITAL HOME Worthing D S FARRANT
QUEEN CHARLOTTE Hammersmith *see* Hammersmith Hosps NHS Trust
QUEEN ELIZABETH Birmingham *see* Univ Hosp Birm NHS Trust
QUEEN ELIZABETH King's Lynn *see* King's Lynn and Wisbech Hosps NHS Trust
QUEEN ELIZABETH Woolwich *see* Qu Eliz Hosp NHS Trust
QUEEN ELIZABETH HOSPITAL NHS TRUST D M FLAGG, G M HESKINS
QUEEN ELIZABETH HOUSE Gateshead *see* Gateshead Health NHS Trust
QUEEN ELIZABETH II Welwyn Garden City *see* E and N Herts NHS Trust
QUEEN ELIZABETH PSYCHIATRIC Birmingham *see* S Birm Mental Health NHS Trust
QUEEN ELIZABETH THE QUEEN MOTHER Margate *see* E Kent Hosps NHS Trust
QUEEN MARY'S SIDCUP NHS TRUST L A GREEN, J A PEAL
QUEEN VICTORIA HOSPITAL NHS TRUST East Grinstead C EVERETT-ALLEN
QUEEN VICTORIA MEMORIAL Welwyn *see* E and N Herts NHS Trust
QUEEN'S Burton-on-Trent *see* Burton Hosps NHS Trust
QUEEN'S MEDICAL CENTRE NOTTINGHAM UNIVERSITY HOSPITAL NHS TRUST W P WATERS, S M CUMMING, J HEMSTOCK, A M BROOKS, B M S CHAMBERS
QUEEN'S MEDICAL CENTRE UNIVERSITY HOSPITAL Nottingham, Department of Psychiatry and Psychiatric Medicine *see* Notts Healthcare NHS Trust
QUEEN'S PARK Blackburn *see* Blackb, Hyndburn and Ribble Valley NHS Trust
RADCLIFFE INFIRMARY Oxford *see* Ox Radcliffe Hosps NHS Trust
RAIGMORE HOSPITAL NHS TRUST Inverness A A SINCLAIR
RAMPTON Retford *see* Notts Healthcare NHS Trust
RAMSGATE GENERAL *see* E Kent Hosps NHS Trust
RATHBONE Liverpool *see* N Mersey Community NHS Trust
REDBRIDGE HEALTH CARE NHS TRUST P MARTIN
RICHARDSON Barnard Castle *see* S Durham Healthcare NHS Trust
ROBERT JONES/AGNES HUNT ORTHOPAEDIC HOSPITAL NHS TRUST Oswestry A M ROBERTS, A R BAILEY
ROCHDALE HEALTHCARE NHS TRUST K L DUNN, B A HARRISON
ROCHFORD *see* S Essex Mental Health & Community Care NHS Trust
ROSSENDALE GEN Rawtenstall *see* Burnley Health Care NHS Trust
ROTHERHAM GENERAL HOSPITALS NHS TRUST A J ATKINS
ROTHERHAM PRIORITY HEALTH SERVICES NHS TRUST A J ATKINS
ROUNDWAY Devizes P WILKINSON
ROYAL ALBERT EDWARD INFIRMARY *see* Wrightington Wigan and Leigh NHS Trust
ROYAL ALEXANDRA CHILDREN'S Brighton *see* Brighton Health Care NHS Trust
ROYAL BERKSHIRE AND BATTLE HOSPITALS NHS TRUST M W SSERUNKUMA, D H LOVERIDGE
ROYAL BOURNEMOUTH AND CHRISTCHURCH HOSPITALS NHS TRUST A SESSFORD, J R EVANS
ROYAL BROMPTON AND HAREFIELD NHS TRUST A J R GANDON
ROYAL CHELSEA T B F HINEY, R H WHITTINGTON
ROYAL CORNWALL HOSPITALS TRUST M A TREMBATH, M L BARRETT, D G MILLER, D POWELL
ROYAL DEVON AND EXETER HEALTHCARE NHS TRUST D J WALFORD
ROYAL EARLSWOOD Redhill *see* E Surrey Learning Disability NHS Trust
ROYAL EDINBURGH *see* Edinburgh Healthcare NHS Trust
ROYAL FREE HAMPSTEAD NHS TRUST R H MITCHELL, R M C LEIGH, P D CONRAD
ROYAL GLAMORGAN Llantrisant *see* Pontypridd and Rhondda NHS Trust
ROYAL GROUP OF HOSPITALS AND DENTAL HOSPITALS HEALTH AND SOCIAL SERVICES TRUST Belfast A MALLON, E HENDERSON
ROYAL GWENT Newport *see* Gwent Healthcare NHS Trust

ROYAL HALLAMSHIRE Sheffield *see* Cen Sheff Univ Hosps NHS Trust
ROYAL HAMPSHIRE COUNTY Winchester *see* Win and Eastleigh Healthcare NHS Trust
ROYAL HOSPITAL FOR NEURO-DISABILITY G E D BONHAM-CARTER
ROYAL HOSPITAL FOR SICK CHILDREN Edinburgh *see* Lothian Univ Hosps NHS Trust
ROYAL INFIRMARY OF EDINBURGH *as above*
ROYAL LIVERPOOL CHILDREN'S NHS TRUST D J WILLIAMS
ROYAL LONDON *see* Bart's and the Lon NHS Trust
ROYAL MANCHESTER CHILDREN'S *see* Cen Man/Man Children's Univ Hosp NHS Trust
ROYAL MARSDEN NHS TRUST London and Surrey D F BROWN, A R MIR, S F SEWELL
ROYAL NATIONAL ORTHOPAEDIC HOSPITAL NHS TRUST W A BROOKER, P M REECE
ROYAL OLDHAM *see* Oldham NHS Trust
ROYAL PRESTON *see* Lanc Teaching Hosps NHS Trust
ROYAL SHREWSBURY HOSPITALS NHS TRUST D W JOHNSON, M I FEARNSIDE
ROYAL SOUTH HAMPSHIRE *see* Southn Univ Hosps NHS Trust
ROYAL SURREY COUNTY HOSPITAL NHS TRUST D N HOBDEN
ROYAL SUSSEX COUNTY Brighton *see* Brighton Health Care NHS Trust
ROYAL UNITED HOSPITAL BATH NHS TRUST P F SUTTON, S A MUNDAY, G OAKES
ROYAL VICTORIA Belfast *see* R Group of Hosps Health and Soc Services Trust
ROYAL VICTORIA Edinburgh *see* Lothian Univ Hosps NHS Trust
ROYAL VICTORIA Folkestone *see* E Kent Hosps NHS Trust
ROYAL WEST SUSSEX TRUST J P COOPER
ROYAL WOLVERHAMPTON HOSPITALS NHS TRUST S PETTY
RUNWELL *see* S Essex Mental Health & Community Care NHS Trust
RUSH GREEN Romford *see* Havering Hosps NHS Trust
RUSSELLS HALL Dudley *see* Dudley Gp of Hosps NHS Trust
ST ANDREW'S Billericay *see* Thameside Community Healthcare NHS Trust
ST ALBANS Napsbury *see* Enfield Primary Care Trust
ST ALBANS CITY *see* W Herts Hosps NHS Trust
ST ANDREW'S London *see* Newham Healthcare NHS Trust Lon
ST ANDREW'S Northampton J Z RAY
ST ANN'S Poole *see* Dorset Health Care NHS Trust
ST ANN'S Tottenham *see* Barnet, Enfield and Haringey Mental Health Trust
ST BARHOLOMEW'S London *see* Bart's and the Lon NHS Trust
ST BARNABAS Saltash *see* Cornwall Healthcare Trust
ST BARTHOLOMEW'S Rochester *see* Medway NHS Trust
ST CADOC'S Caerleon *see* Gwent Healthcare NHS Trust
ST CATHERINE'S Doncaster *see* Doncaster and S Humber Healthcare NHS Trust
ST CATHERINE'S COMMUNITY Birkenhead *see* Cheshire and Wirral Partnership NHS Trust
ST CHARLES COMMUNITY London *see* Parkside Community NHS Trust Lon
ST CHRISTOPHER'S Fareham *see* Portsm Healthcare NHS Trust
ST EBBA'S Epsom *see* Surrey Oaklands NHS Trust
ST EDMUND'S Northampton *see* Northn Gen Hosp NHS Trust
ST GEORGE'S Morpeth *see* Northd Mental Health NHS Trust
ST GEORGE'S Stafford *see* S Staffs Healthcare NHS Trust
ST GEORGE'S HEALTHCARE NHS TRUST London H A JOHNSON, I M AINSWORTH-SMITH, J DEVERILL, J M FARMAN, C J CARTER
ST HELEN'S AND KNOWSLEY HOSPITALS TRUST J E SHEPHERD, L MCCLUSKEY
ST HELIER Carshalton *see* Epsom and St Helier NHS Trust
ST HELIER GENERAL *see* Jersey Gp of Hosps
ST JAMES' Portsmouth *see* Portsm Healthcare NHS Trust
ST JAMES' UNIVERSITY Leeds *see* Leeds Mental Health Teaching NHS Trust
ST JAMES'S UNIVERSITY Leeds *see* Leeds Teaching Hosps NHS Trust
ST JOHN'S Axbridge J SMITH
ST JOHN'S Canterbury A A W DAWKINS
ST LUKE'S Armagh *see* Armagh and Dungannon Health and Soc Services

TAUNTON AND SOMERSET NHS TRUST　C F CRAGGS, G J WRAYFORD, R J ALLEN, M M MASLEN, G M KIRK, P CUFF, P A SELF
TAYSIDE UNIVERSITY HOSPITALS NHS TRUST　D J GORDON
TEES AND NORTH EAST YORKSHIRE NHS TRUST　P L BISHOP
TEIGNMOUTH　see S Devon Healthcare NHS Trust
TEWKESBURY　see Glos Hosps NHS Trust
THAMES GATEWAY NHS TRUST　P R BECKINSALE, C D COLLINS, G H SPENCER, J PEAL
THAMESIDE COMMUNITY HEALTHCARE NHS TRUST　J E EATON
THETFORD COTTAGE DAY　see W Suffolk Hosps NHS Trust
THURROCK COMMUNITY　see S Essex Mental Health & Community Care NHS Trust
TICKHILL ROAD Doncaster　see Doncaster and S Humber Healthcare NHS Trust
TINDAL CENTRE Aylesbury　see Aylesbury Vale Community Healthcare NHS Trust
TINDALE CRESCENT Bishop Auckland　see S Durham Healthcare NHS Trust
TIVERTON AND DISTRICT　see Mid Devon Primary Care Trust
TONE VALE　see Taunton and Somerset NHS Trust
TORBAY DISTRICT GENERAL　see S Devon Healthcare NHS Trust
TOWERS Humberstone　see Leics and Rutland Healthcare NHS Trust
TRANWELL UNIT Gateshead　see Gateshead Health NHS Trust
TREDEGAR GENERAL　see Gwent Healthcare NHS Trust
TREORCHY Ysbyty George Thomas　see Pontypridd and Rhondda NHS Trust
TRINITY Retford　P W WIGGINTON
TRINITY Somerset　see Taunton and Somerset NHS Trust
TROWBRIDGE COMMUNITY　see Wilts and Swindon Healthcare NHS Trust
UNITED BRISTOL HEALTHCARE NHS TRUST　P R ELLMORE, E A POWELL, J E NORMAN
UNITED LINCOLNSHIRE HOSPITALS NHS TRUST　D X LOMAS, C M BONNEYWELL, D R WILLIAMS, M R SAUNDERS
UNIVERSITY Hartlepool　see N Tees and Hartlepool NHS Trust
UNIVERSITY Stockton-on-Tees　as above
UNIVERSITY COLLEGE LONDON HOSPITALS NHS TRUST　P ROWNTREE, S J FLATT, G J A COOK
UNIVERSITY HOSPITAL BIRMINGHAM NHS TRUST　R FARMAN
UNIVERSITY HOSPITAL BIRMINGHAM NHS TRUST　E F BUXTON
UNIVERSITY HOSPITAL OF WALES AND LLANDOUGH NHS TRUST　D R LLOYD-RICHARDS, B M LODWICK, E J BURKE
UNIVERSITY HOSPITALS OF LEICESTER NHS TRUST　M T SHARPE, T H GIRLING, M TURNER, S C POLASHEK, R SEMEONOFF, M J MORRIS
VERRINGTON Wincanton　see E Somerset NHS Trust
WAKEFIELD AND PONTEFRACT COMMUNITY NHS TRUST　C M GARTLAND
WALSGRAVE HOSPITALS NHS TRUST Coventry　A BEECH, H PRIESTNER
WALTON Liverpool　see Aintree Hosps NHS Trust Liv
WANSBECK GENERAL Ashington　see Northumbria Healthcare NHS Trust
WAREHAM　see S and E Dorset Primary Care Trust
WARMINSTER COMMUNITY　see Wilts and Swindon Healthcare NHS Trust
WARNEFORD Leamington Spa　see S Warks Health Care NHS Trust
WARNEFORD PARK Oxford　see Oxon Mental Healthcare NHS Trust
WARRINGTON　see N Cheshire Hosps NHS Trust
WARRINGTON COMMUNITY HEALTH CARE NHS TRUST　P LOVATT
WARWICKSHIRE, SOUTH　see S Warks Health Care NHS Trust
WATFORD GENERAL　see W Herts Hosps NHS Trust
WAYLAND Attleborough　see Norwich Primary Care Trust
WELLS ROAD CENTRE, THE Mapperley　see Notts Healthcare NHS Trust
WELWYN Queen Victoria Memorial　see E and N Herts NHS Trust
WELWYN GARDEN CITY Queen Elizabeth II　as above

WESHAM PARK Preston　see Blackpool, Wyre and Fylde Community NHS Trust
WEST BERKSHIRE PRIORITY CARE SERVICES NHS TRUST　R J STILLMAN
WEST CHESHIRE　see Cheshire and Wirral Partnership NHS Trust
WEST CORNWALL　see R Cornwall Hosps Trust
WEST CUMBERLAND　see W Cumbria Health Care NHS Trust
WEST CUMBRIA HEALTH CARE NHS TRUST　C K WRIGHT
WEST DORSET GENERAL HOSPITALS NHS TRUST　N D TOOTH
WEST HAMPSHIRE NHS TRUST　A D MACDONALD
WEST HEATH Birmingham　see Birm Specialist Community Health NHS Trust
WEST HERTFORDSHIRE HOSPITALS NHS TRUST　G R COBB, P S HOLLINS
WEST HILL Dartford　see Dartford and Gravesham NHS Trust
WEST LANCASHIRE NHS TRUST　R MOUGHTIN, C H JONES
WEST LONDON MENTAL HEALTH NHS TRUST　D I BARNES
WEST MIDDLESEX UNIVERSITY HOSPITAL NHS TRUST　J L OSBORNE
WEST PARK Macclesfield　R J DOULTON
WEST SUFFOLK HOSPITALS NHS TRUST　D CRAWLEY
WESTERN COMMUNITY Southampton　see Southampton Community Services NHS Trust
WESTERN GENERAL Edinburgh　see Lothian Univ Hosps NHS Trust
WESTHAVEN Weymouth　P S THOMAS
WESTON AREA HEALTH TRUST　G P EALES
WESTON GENERAL Weston-super-Mare　see Weston Area Health Trust
WESTON PARK Sheffield　see Cen Sheff Univ Hosps NHS Trust
WEXHAM PARK Slough　see Heatherwood and Wexham Park Hosp NHS Trust
WHARFEDALE GENERAL Otley　see Leeds Teaching Hosps NHS Trust
WHELLEY　see Wrightington Wigan and Leigh NHS Trust
WHIPPS CROSS　see Forest Healthcare NHS Trust Lon
WHISTON Prescot　see St Helen's and Knowsley Hosps Trust
WHITBY　see Scarborough and NE Yorks Healthcare NHS Trust
WHITCHURCH　see Shropshire's Community NHS Trust
WHITCHURCH Cardiff　see Cardiff Community Healthcare NHS Trust
WHITTINGTON HALL　J PINDER-PACKARD
WILLIAM HARVEY Ashford　see E Kent Hosps NHS Trust
WILTSHIRE AND SWINDON HEALTHCARE NHS TRUST　P F YACOMENI, S E TEBBUTT, R M LOWRIE, J A COUTTS
WIMBORNE　see S and E Dorset Primary Care Trust
WINCHESTER AND EASTLEIGH HEALTHCARE NHS TRUST　N R FLOOD, D J COTTRILL, R C STONE
WINWICK Warrington　see Warrington Community Health Care NHS Trust
WISBECH　see King's Lynn and Wisbech Hosps NHS Trust
WITHAM COURT ESMI UNIT Lincoln　see Linc Distr Healthcare NHS Trust
WITHINGTON Manchester　see S Man Univ Hosps NHS Trust
WOKING COMMUNITY　see NW Surrey Mental Health NHS Trust
WOKINGHAM　see W Berks Priority Care Services NHS Trust
WORCESTER ROYAL INFIRMARY　see Worcs Acute Hosps NHS Trust
WORCESTERSHIRE ACUTE HOSPITALS NHS TRUST　B M JONES, L R D RYDER, I SCOTT, L A W SWABY
WORCESTERSHIRE COMMUNITY AND MENTAL HEALTH TRUST, The　L L BURN, M E BARR
WORDSLEY　see Dudley Gp of Hosps NHS Trust
WORTHING AND SOUTHLANDS HOSPITALS NHS TRUST　A G SAGE
WORTHING PRIORITY CARE NHS TRUST　R J CASWELL
WREXHAM MAELOR　see NE Wales NHS Trust
WRIGHTINGTON WIGAN AND LEIGH NHS TRUST　R J HUTCHINSON, T D HARGREAVES-STEAD, R TOWNLEY
WYCOMBE GENERAL　see S Bucks NHS Trust
WYTHENSHAWE Manchester　see S Man Univ Hosps NHS Trust
YEOVIL DISTRICT　see E Somerset NHS Trust
YORK HEALTH SERVICES NHS TRUST　R ROGERS, E W A CRAGG
YSBYTY GEORGE THOMAS Treorchy　see Pontypridd and Rhondda NHS Trust
YSTRAD MYNACH Hengoed　see Gwent Healthcare NHS Trust

HOSPICE CHAPLAINS

AYRSHIRE   J JENKINS
BARNSLEY   A PRITCHETT
BOLTON   S C NEAL
CHILDREN'S SOUTH WEST Fremington   P H HOCKEY
COMPTON Wolverhampton   H J SMART
DOUGLAS MACMILLAN Stoke-on-Trent   D A HEWITSON
EARL MOUNTBATTEN Newport   G M HURT
EAST ANGLIA'S CHILDREN'S   D M OSBORN
EAST HERTFORDSHIRE HOSPICE CARE   G G BROWN
EAST LANCASHIRE Blackburn   J R L CLARK
EDEN HALL MARIE CURIE Hampstead   T J BELL
EXETER HOSPISCARE   R J YEOMANS
GARDEN HOUSE Letchworth   A DE C LADD
JERSEY   G J HOUGHTON
KATHARINE HOUSE Banbury   P C SMITH
KATHARINE HOUSE Stafford   P J GRAYSMITH
KEMP Kidderminster   R S MURRIN
KIRKWOOD Huddersfield   M E WOOD
MARIE CURIE Warren Pearl   C A HIBBERD
MARTLETS Hove   C G SPINKS
MARY ANN EVANS Nuneaton   D R L WHITE
MOUNT EDGCUMBE   A D WEST
MYTON HAMLET Warwick   W S GRAHAM
PHYLLIS TUCKWELL Farnham   M J FARRANT
PILGRIM'S Canterbury   E R G HOPTHROW
RUSHDEN SANATORIUM   A SMITH
ST ANDREW'S Grimsby   A R MARSDEN

ST BARNABAS' Worthing   J H MCCORMACK
ST CATHERINE'S Crawley   J BROWN
ST CATHERINE'S Scarborough   K D JACKSON
ST ELIZABETH Ipswich   M CARTER
ST FRANCIS Berkhamsted   E J HUGHES
ST GILES Lichfield   D J SHERIDAN,   P L HOLLIDAY
ST JOHN'S Wirral   P B PRITCHARD
ST LEONARD'S York   A G PEARSE
ST LUKE'S Plymouth   T A SMITH
ST LUKE'S Sheffield   J SANKEY
ST MARGARET'S Taunton   S TUCKER
ST MICHAEL'S Basingstoke   A EDMEADS
ST MICHAEL'S Hereford   J M NEVILL
ST MICHAEL'S St Leonards-on-Sea   H E PATTEN
ST OSWALD'S Newcastle upon Tyne   J L JACKSON
ST PETER AND ST JAMES North Chailey   R A MOORE,
   R J ST C HARLOW-TRIGG
ST PETER'S Bristol   W B M DOWIE
ST WILFRID'S Eastbourne   C R BEARD
SHROPSHIRE AND MID-WALES   H J EDWARDS
STRATHCARRON Denny   S M COATES
SUSSEX BEACON Brighton   J K T ELDRIDGE
TRINITY London   P R WELLS
TRINITY IN THE FYLDE Blackpool   J E DENNETT
WESTON   C J S TURNER
WILLEN Milton Keynes   S W BARNES

EDUCATIONAL CHAPLAINS

This index only lists deans and chaplains, and does not aim to provide a comprehensive list of clergy serving at educational institutions. Those institutions which do not currently have Anglican chaplains are not recorded.

General Synod Board of Education: Secretary The Reverend Canon J Hall
Church House, Great Smith Street, London SW1P 3NZ
Tel (020) 8987 1501   Fax 8987 1520

UNIVERSITIES

ABERDEEN   D HEDDLE
ABERTAY   P M BALFOUR
ANGLIA POLYTECHNIC   I R MOODY
BATH   B F CHAPMAN, J W LLOYD
BATH SPA UNIVERSITY COLLEGE   J P KNOTT
BIRMINGHAM   E D COOMBES, A D LITTLEWOOD
BRADFORD   A P BOWSHER
BRIGHTON   C R LAWLOR
   Eastbourne Campus   G T RIDEOUT
BRISTOL   J MUELLER-SCHNURR, M SCHNURR, A F STUART
BRUNEL   *Uxbridge Campus*   S B ROBERTS
BUCKINGHAMSHIRE CHILTERNS
   UNIVERSITY COLLEGE   T A STACEY
CAMBRIDGE
   Christ's   P C A HARBRIDGE
   Churchill   J RAWLINSON
   Clare   R D GREEVES
   Corpus Christi   J B LAWSON
   Downing   K J EYEONS
   Emmanuel   J L CADDICK
   Fitzwilliam   L M CAVANAGH
   Girton   A M GUITE
   Gonville and Caius   J D McDONALD
   Jesus   J COLLIS
   King's   C J RYAN
   Magdalene   S BARRINGTON-WARD
   Newnham   I M THOMPSON
   Pembroke   L A ADAM, B WATCHORN
   Peterhouse   J B QUASH, G J WARD
   Queens'   J M HOLMES
   Robinson   M E DAWN
   Selwyn   I M THOMPSON
   St Catharine's   P H RICHMOND
   St John's   D J DORMOR, C R HILLMAN
   Trinity   R H ADAMS, A S BROWNE, A J CHRICH
   Trinity Hall   W F CLOCKSIN
   Trinity Hall (Dean)   C M ELLIOTT, J N MORRIS
CENTRAL ENGLAND IN BIRMINGHAM   N R M ELLIOT
CENTRAL LANCASHIRE   W E TURNER
CORK   *University College*   G P St J HILLIARD
COVENTRY   M A J WARD
DE MONTFORD   M RAILTON-CROWDER
DE MONTFORT   J D CURTIS, P J LITTLEFORD
DERBY   A E HOLLINGHURST
DUBLIN   *Trinity College*   A W McCORMACK
DUNDEE   A W CUMMINS
DURHAM
   Collingwood   B J H de la MARE
   Grey   D J KENNEDY
   Hatfield   R W LAWRANCE
   St Hild and St Bede   F A BAYES
   Trevelyan   K ANDERSON
   University   B N GORDON-TAYLOR
   Van Mildert   K ANDERSON
EAST ANGLIA   T M GOULDSTONE
EDINBURGH   A J FULLER, D P WILLIAMS
ESSEX   P J MOSSOP
EXETER   J T LAW, D J NIXON
GLAMORGAN   J P HARRIS
GLOUCESTERSHIRE   K J HITCHMAN
GREENWICH   D W CHERRY, J E DICKER
HUDDERSFIELD   M R POLLARD
HULL   J C BRYAN
KEELE   C M LACK
KENT   S C E LAIRD
KINGSTON   D BUCKLEY
LANCASTER   K J HUGGETT
LEEDS   S J ROBINSON
LEEDS METROPOLITAN   D A CALDER

LEICESTER   A S KASIBANTE
LINCOLN   L C ACKLAM
LIVERPOOL   M L CHAMBERLAIN
LIVERPOOL JOHN MOORES   R E DICKINSON
LONDON
   Central Chaplaincies   S G WILLIAMS
   Goldsmiths' College   P E COLLIER
   Imperial College of Science, Technology and Medicine
      C E SARGENT, A W WILLSON
   King's (Dean)   R A BURRIDGE
   King's   T F DITCHFIELD, H J MARSHALL
   London School of Economics and Political Science   D T PEEBLES
   Queen Mary and Westfield   J E PETERSEN
   Royal Free Hospital School of Medicine   G L LEGOOD
   Royal Holloway and Bedford New   A D TAYLOR
   Royal Veterinary College   G L LEGOOD
   University College Medical School   G L LEGOOD
   Wye   J S RICHARDSON
LONDON METROPOLITAN   W G CAMPBELL-TAYLOR,
   F M WEAVER
LOUGHBOROUGH   D A T MACGREGOR, S J RICHARDSON
LUTON   H D THORNTON
MANCHESTER   T E BIDDINGTON, I D GOMERSALL
MANCHESTER METROPOLITAN   T E BIDDINGTON,
   I D GOMERSALL
MIDDLESEX   J M BEER
NAPIER   D L COLLINGWOOD
NEWCASTLE   M H HASLAM
NORTHUMBRIA AT NEWCASTLE   A J SHIPTON
NOTTINGHAM   J W BENTHAM, I D TARRANT
NOTTINGHAM TRENT   L A JEFFREYS
OXFORD
   All Souls   M SCREECH
   Balliol   H D DUPREE
   Brasenose   P J GROVES
   Christ Church   J A SHAW, R J WILLIAMSON
   Christ Church (Dean)   J H DRURY
   Corpus Christi   J D MALTBY
   Exeter   M R BIRCH
   Hertford   R M CHANTRY, S A OLIVER
   Jesus   E A GODDARD
   Keble   M A BUTCHERS
   Lady Margaret Hall   A G DOIG
   Lincoln   A F GREGORY
   Magdalen   M J PIRET
   Mansfield   J B MUDDIMAN
   Merton   S M JONES
   New   J A SHAW
   Oriel   T H C MEYRICK
   Queen's   P J M SOUTHWELL
   St Edmund Hall   D A S MacLAREN
   St Hilda's   B W MOUNTFORD
   St Hugh's   J D GILPIN
   St John's   E D H CARMICHAEL
   St Peter's   C M JONES
   Somerville   R M CHANTRY
   Trinity   T S M WILLIAMS
   University   W G D SYKES
   Wadham   H A HARRIS
   Wycliffe Hall   G N MAUGHAN
OXFORD BROOKES   J L MacLAREN
PLYMOUTH   R S WILLIAMS
PORTSMOUTH   F L STEWART-DARLING
QUEEN'S   *Belfast (Dean of Residence)*   P G McGLINCHEY
READING   G N RAINEY
ROEHAMPTON INSTITUTE   L HARKNETT, R P LANE
ROYAL COLLEGE OF ART   A W WILLSON
ST ANDREWS   J P MASON
SALFORD   D J PALMER

1180

SHEFFIELD   W R S LAMB
SOUTH BANK   F Y-C HUNG
SOUTHAMPTON   D J SIMPSON
STAFFORDSHIRE   W G McNAMEE
STIRLING   K HOLDSWORTH
SUNDERLAND   A R M MARSHALL
SURREY   J H FROST
SUSSEX   G R P ASHENDEN, A N ROBINSON
TEESSIDE   D M LEPPINGTON
THAMES VALLEY *Ealing Campus*   P J NOTT
ULSTER   J E G BACH

WALES
Aberystwyth   S R BELL
Bangor   J P BUTLER
Cardiff   P OVEREND
Lampeter   B D B O'MALLEY
Swansea   N JOHN
WARWICK   M Q BRATTON
WEST OF ENGLAND   D GRASBY
WOLVERHAMPTON   G WYNNE
YORK   D G CANTRELL

COLLEGES OF HIGHER EDUCATION

This index only includes those establishments known to have Anglican chaplains. It is not intended to be comprehensive.

ASHRIDGE MANAGEMENT   J V M KIRKBY
ASKHAM BRYAN   D S COOK
BISHOP GROSSETESTE *Lincoln*   M F BAYNHAM
BOLTON INSTITUTE   P G EDWARDS
CANTERBURY *Christ Church University College*   B E KELLY
CENTRAL LANCASHIRE   A P HUTCHINSON
CHESTER   L DIXON
GUILDHALL SCHOOL OF MUSIC AND DRAMA   J BRUECK
HARPER ADAMS   W E WARD
KENT INSTITUTE OF ART AND DESIGN   J E DICKER
KING ALFRED'S *Winchester*   J WATKINS
LIVERPOOL HOPE   I C STUART
LONDON INSTITUTE *Chelsea College of Art and Design*   A D NORWOOD
NEWCASTLE   W E J MASH
NORTH EAST SURREY COLLEGE OF
   TECHNOLOGY *Ewell*   A J HURD

NORTH EAST WALES INSTITUTE   M R J G WALKER
NORTHAMPTON   P MOSELING
NORWICH CITY   C J BLACKMAN, B A HOPKINS
NORWICH SCHOOL OF ART AND DESIGN   J C MINNS
PETERBOROUGH REGIONAL   D J DUNCANSON
RICHMOND-UPON-THAMES   J F HARTERINK
RIPON AND YORK ST JOHN   J M S CLINES
ROYAL NAVAL *Greenwich*   S J DAVIES, G HARCOURT
ST MARTIN'S *Lancaster*   M R PEATMAN
SOUTHAMPTON INSTITUTE   J A GORDON
SPURGEON'S   S J OSGOOD
SUFFOLK *Ipswich*   A L FOWLER
TRINITY *Carmarthen*   P C JONES
UNIVERSITY COLLEGE *Chichester*   P J SIEJKOWSKI
W ANGLIA   S C STOKES
WESTMINSTER *Oxford*   P J BUDD
WORCESTER   P K HUGHES

COLLEGES OF FURTHER EDUCATION

This index only includes those establishments known to have Anglican chaplains. It is not intended to be comprehensive.

BISHOP BURTON COLLEGE OF AGRICULTURE *York*
   M J WESTBY
BOURNEMOUTH AND POOLE   D A HART, S A WOAN
BRADFORD   A P BOWSHER
CANNINGTON   P MARTIN
CENTRAL LIVERPOOL   J S WILLIAMS
CITY COLLEGE *Liverpool*   J S WILLIAMS
CITY OF BATH   A R HAWKINS
DUDLEY COLLEGE OF TECHNOLOGY   M C BRAIN
EVESHAM   J R N J BOMYER
HIGHBURY *Portsmouth*   G J SMITH
LEICESTER   J S PARKIN
MERRIST WOOD COLLEGE OF AGRICULTURE
   AND HORTICULTURE   A W BRYANT
NEW COLLEGE *Swindon*   D ORMSTON
NORTH LINDSEY *Scunthorpe*   S J WALKER

NORTH WEST LONDON   F B CAPIE
NORTHD *Coll*   D P PALMER
NORTON RADSTOCK   J B THICKE
OAKLANDS   P A LOUIS
ROYAL ACADEMY OF MUSIC   G E FRANCIS-DEHQANI
ST MARK AND ST JOHN *Plymouth*   C E EDMONDS
SOMERSET COLLEGE OF ARTS AND
   TECHNOLOGY   D ROBERTS
SOUTH TYNESIDE   A RAINE
ST MARTIN'S *Carlisle*   A V WEST
TAMESIDE   D J WISEMAN
WEALD   F D JAKEMAN
WEYMOUTH   G J MUGRIDGE
WORCESTER COLLEGE OF TECHNOLOGY
   P D J SWANN
YEOVIL COLLEGE   D R GENT

SIXTH-FORM COLLEGES

This index only includes those colleges known to have Anglican chaplains. It is not intended to be comprehensive.

FARNBOROUGH   N L SHARP

SCHOOLS

This index only includes those schools known to have Anglican chaplains. It is not intended to be comprehensive.

ALDENHAM *Hertfordshire* S P SEATON, A M STEAD
ALLEYN'S *Dulwich* J H JONES
AMESBURY CHURCH OF ENGLAND JUNIOR A J GREADY
ARCHBISHOP TENISON'S *Kennington* A J REID
ARDINGLY COLLEGE *Haywards Heath* I R COLSON
BANCROFT'S *Woodford Green* I MOORE
BARNARD CASTLE S J RIDLEY
BEDFORD D L LAWRENCE-MARCH
BEDGEBURY *Kent* N R GALLAGHER
BENNETT MEMORIAL *Tunbridge Wells* J P CAPERON,
C J S GILL
BERKHAMSTED COLLEGIATE *Hertfordshire* S GOLDING
BETHANY *Goudhurst* S C BATTERSBY
BIRKENHEAD *Merseyside* H L KIRK
BISHOP BELL *Eastbourne* R J R PAICE
BISHOP RAMSEY A V COLEMAN, L C F HILLEL
BISHOP RAWSTORNE *Preston* R J BRUNSWICK
BISHOP WORDSWORTH *Salisbury* J A BERSWEDEN
BISHOP'S BLUE COAT CHURCH OF ENGLAND
HIGH *Chester* I J HUTCHINGS
BLOXHAM M G PRICE
BLUE COAT *Birmingham* J H D JENKINS
BLUE COAT *Reading* N J BENNETT
BLUECOAT *Nottingham* S KRZEMINSKI
BLUNDELL'S *Tiverton* T C HUNT
BOX HILL B STEADMAN-ALLEN
BRADFIELD *Berkshire* C PYNN
BRAMCOTE *Nottinghamshire* C F ANDREWS
BRENTWOOD *Essex* D J GILCHRIST
BRISTOL CATHEDRAL S B TAYLOR
BROMSGROVE E C REED
BRYANSTON *Dorset* A J DAYNES
CANFORD *Wimborne* C JERVIS, K K SUGDEN
CASTERTON *Lancashire* P S ATKINSON
CHARTERHOUSE *Godalming* S J HARKER
CHELTENHAM COLLEGE R de la BAT SMIT
CHELTENHAM LADIES' COLLEGE D T MERRY, H R WOOD
CHIGWELL *Essex* C P COLLINGWOOD
CHRIST'S COLLEGE *Brecon* R M LLEWELLYN
CHRIST'S HOSPITAL *Horsham* A MITRA, N J MITRA
CITY OF LONDON FREEMEN'S *Ashtead Park*
D F P RUTHERFORD
CLAYESMORE *Blandford* A J H EDWARDS
CLIFTON COLLEGE *Bristol* K TAPLIN
COKETHORPE *Witney* A R TURNER
COLFE'S *London* A C COLLIER
COLSTON'S *Bristol* M CREGAN
CRANBROOK *Kent* D COOK
CRANFORD HOUSE *Oxford* L M S COOK
CRANLEIGH *Surrey* J P FRITH
DAUNTSEY'S *Devizes* D R JOHNSON
DEAN CLOSE *Cheltenham* L J BROWNE, D G H YOUNG
DENSTONE COLLEGE *Uttoxeter* M A SMITH
DERBY GRAMMAR P R JONES
DERBY HIGH A K MATTHEWS
DOVER COLLEGE J A ROBERTSON
DUKE OF YORK'S ROYAL MILITARY *Dover*
J R BROUGHTON
DULWICH COLLEGE S E YOUNG
DULWICH PREPARATORY *Cranbrook* I M BUTLER
EASTBOURNE COLLEGE C K MACDONALD
ELIZABETH COLLEGE *Guernsey* R G HARNISH
ELMHURST BALLET *Camberley* P J DYKES
EMMANUEL *Wandsworth* E M HILL
EPSOM COLLEGE C D BROWN, P THOMPSON
ETON COLLEGE *Berkshire* D COOPER, D S COULTON,
C M JONES, C W MITCHELL-INNES, T D MULLINS
FELSTED *Essex* J HART
FETTES COLLEGE *Edinburgh* P J D ALLEN
FOREMARK PREPARATORY *Derby* N A BAILEY
GIGGLESWICK J J N SYKES
GLENALMOND COLLEGE P M KONIG
GODOLPHIN *Salisbury* P D SLATER
GORDON'S *Woking* D H ROBINSON
GOSDEN HOUSE J N E BUNDOCK
GRENVILLE COLLEGE *Bideford* J M GRAVES
GRESHAM'S *Holt* R N MYERSCOUGH, B R ROBERTS
HABERDASHERS' ASKE'S *Elstree* D M LINDSAY
HAILEYBURY COLLEGE *Hertfordshire* C R BRIGGS
HARROGATE LADIES' COLLEGE J CHEESEMAN

HARROW V L BARON, J E POWER
HEADINGTON *Oxford* A C HOLMES
HEATHFIELD *Ascot* F J R OTTO
HEREFORD CATHEDRAL P A ROW
HIGHGATE *London* P J J KNIGHT
HOLMEWOOD HOUSE *Tunbridge Wells* R NOBLE
HURSTPIERPOINT COLLEGE *Hassocks* P A HESS
IAN RAMSEY *Stockton* S J GILES
JOHN NIGHTINGALE *West Molesley* D GODDARD
KENT COLLEGE *Pembury* S M MORRELL
KIMBOLTON *Cambridgeshire* A P GOODCHILD
KING EDWARD VI *Southampton* J G POPPLETON
KING EDWARD'S *Birmingham* D H RAYNOR
KING EDWARD'S *Witley* R W E MILLINGTON
KING'S *Bruton* N H WILSON-BROWN
KING'S COLLEGE SCHOOL *Wimbledon* S J ROBBINS-COLE,
R G STEVENS
KING'S COLLEGE *Taunton* M F LOVELESS
KING'S *Gloucester* J B P J HADFIELD
KING'S HOSPITAL *Dublin* R H WHITESIDE
KING'S *Rochester* S R ALLSOPP, J A THACKRAY
KING'S *Tynemouth* W D MILLER
KING'S *Worcester* M R DORSETT
KING'S, THE *Canterbury* C F ARVIDSSON
LANCING COLLEGE R P MARSH
LIVERPOOL COLLEGE E M STOREY
LORD MAYOR TRELOAR COLLEGE *Alton* E B PRUEN
LORD WANDSWORTH COLLEGE *Basingstoke* B KEMP,
S LEYSHON
LORETTO *Musselburgh* A F C KEULEMANS
LOUGHBOROUGH GRAMMAR A J S COX
LUCKLEY-OAKFIELD *Wokingham* J WAKELING
MAGDALEN COLLEGE SCHOOL *Oxford* R C de V MARTIN,
N SEWARD
MALVERN COLLEGE A P LAW, N A T MENON
MALVERN GIRLS COLLEGE F L MIDDLEMISS
MANOR HOUSE C A E LAWRENCE
MANOR *York* M A HAND
MARLBOROUGH COLLEGE D J DALES, J G W DICKIE
MERCHANT TAYLORS' *Crosby* D A SMITH
MERCHANT TAYLORS' *Northwood* R D E BOLTON
MILLFIELD *Somerset* S F BLOXAM-ROSE
MILTON ABBEY *Dorset* R W B THOMSON
MOIRA HOUSE *East Sussex* G T RIDEOUT
MONKTON COMBE *Bath* P STEPHENS
MONMOUTH J B HENCHER
MORETON HALL A B STRATFORD
NATIONAL *Hucknall* A TURNER-LOISEL
NORTH FORELAND LODGE *Basingstoke* A F J CHAMBERS
NORWICH A M R HOUSMAN
OAKHAM A C V ALDOUS
ORMSKIRK A J M WATKINSON
OUNDLE *Peterborough* I C BROWNE, D R H EDWARDSON
PANGBOURNE COLLEGE *Berkshire* B J CUNNINGHAM
PETER SYMONDS COLLEGE *Winchester* N P SEAL
PETERBOROUGH HIGH P A W COTTON
POCKLINGTON *York* M A SMITH
PORT REGIS PREPARATORY *Shaftesbury* M T P ZAMMIT
PORTORA ROYAL *Enniskillen* J D G KINGSTON
PORTSMOUTH GRAMMAR A K BURTT
PREBENDAL *Chichester* D NASON
PRIOR'S FIELD J M FELLOWS
PRIORY, THE A C JONAS
QUEEN ANNE'S *Caversham* H C BENSON
QUEEN ETHELBURGA'S COLLEGE *York* B A ARMITAGE
QUEEN MARGARET'S *York* R L OWEN
RADLEY COLLEGE *Oxfordshire* T J E FERNYHOUGH,
R A STIDOLPH
RAINES FOUNDATION *Tower Hamlets*
I C CZERNIAWSKA EDGCUMBE
RANBY HOUSE *Retford* R A WHITTAKER
RATHDOWN *Dublin* G V WHARTON
RAVENSCLIFFE HIGH *Halifax* A MAUDE
REED'S *Cobham* A J CLARKE
REIGATE GRAMMAR M J H FOX
RENDCOMB COLLEGE *Cirencester* C D JEFFERSON
REPTON *Derby* H L SHORT
ROSSALL *Fleetwood* S P C COOPER
ROYAL RUSSELL *Croydon* P L TAIT
ROYAL WOLVERHAMPTON P C ATKINSON

RUGBY   R M HORNER
ST AIDAN'S *Harrogate*   S W LEWIS
ST ALBANS   C D PINES
ST ALBANS HIGH SCHOOL FOR GIRLS
   D C FITZGERALD CLARK
ST BEDE'S ECUMENICAL *Reigate*   J P SCOTT
ST BEDE'S *Upper Dicker*   S J MORGAN
ST BEES *Cumbria*   P R BRYAN
ST CATHERINE'S *Bramley*   C DE F TICKNER
ST CATHERINE'S *Ventnor*   D H LAURIE
ST COLUMBA'S *Dublin*   M R HEANEY
ST DAVID'S COLLEGE *Llandudno*   T R HALL
ST DUNSTAN'S ABBEY *Plymouth*   M T BAILEY
ST EDMUND'S *Canterbury*   M J HORTON
ST EDWARD'S *Oxford*   D S WIPPELL
ST ELPHIN'S *Matlock*   A J WILLIAMS
ST GEORGE'S *Edgbaston*   S G THORBURN
ST GEORGE'S *Harpenden*   A P MANNING
ST HELEN'S AND ST KATHARINE'S *Abingdon*   P E SEAMAN
ST JAMES AND THE ABBEY *Malvern*   C N H ATTWOOD
ST JOHN'S *Leatherhead*   M J LAWSON
ST LAWRENCE COLLEGE *Ramsgate*   D J PEAT
ST MARGARET'S *Exeter*   R J A BARRETT
ST MARY AND ST ANNE *Abbots Bromley*   B F WILSON
ST MARY'S *Calne*   P M O GILES
ST MARY'S HALL *Brighton*   A H MANSON-BRAILSFORD
ST MARY'S *Wantage*   R F CLAYTON-JONES
ST MARY'S *Westbrook*   B D R WOOD
ST MARYLEBONE CHURCH OF ENGLAND
   G E FRANCIS-DEHQANI
ST OLAVE'S GRAMMAR *Orpington*   H P C BROADBENT
ST OLAVE'S *York*   A P HUGHES
ST PAUL'S *Barnes*   P L F ALLSOP
ST PAUL'S GIRLS' *Hammersmith*   L R F COLLINS
ST PETER'S *York*   J DALY
ST SWITHUN'S *Winchester*   T E HEMMING
SEAFORD COLLEGE *Petworth*   P M GILBERT
SEDBERGH   C D GRIFFIN
SEVENOAKS   N N HENSHAW

SHERBORNE   C W M AITKEN
SHIPLAKE *Henley-on-Thames*   R P PRANCE
SHREWSBURY   G W DOBBIE
SIR THOMAS BOTELER HIGH *Warrington*   J E HARRIES
SMALLWOOD MANOR
   PREPARATORY *Uttoxeter*   C J CANN
SOLIHULL   A C HUTCHINSON
STAMFORD   M R RUFF
STOCKPORT GRAMMAR   L E J LEAVER
STOWE *Buckingham*   R B JACKSON
SUMMER FIELDS *Oxford*   B S A GADD
SUTTON VALENCE *Kent*   P A KISH
TAUNTON   G D EVANS
TETTENHALL COLLEGE *Wolverhampton*   J G PARRY
TONBRIDGE   S M BEAUMONT, T D PAGE
TRENT COLLEGE *Nottingham*   T R HAGGIS
TRINITY *Belvedere*   C W JONES
TRINITY *Teignmouth*   C M S LUFF
UPPER CHINE *Shanklin*   A W SWANBOROUGH
UPPINGHAM *Leicestershire*   B E CLOSE
WAKEFIELD CATHEDRAL   P M MAGUIRE
WARWICK   A W GOUGH
WELLINGBOROUGH   M J WALKER
WELLINGTON COLLEGE *Berkshire*   A D T RICHARDS,
   R J WARDEN
WELLINGTON *Somerset*   J P HELLIER
WELLS CATHEDRAL   A J KEEP
WEST BUCKLAND *Barnstaple*   A M KETTLE
WEST OF ENGLAND *School for those with little or no sight*
   P J S CROCKETT
WESTMINSTER   G J WILLIAMS
WESTONBIRT   P DIXON
WINCHESTER COLLEGE   R G A FERGUSON, J D SMITH,
   N C A VON MALAISE
WISPERS *Haslemere*   N JONES
WOODBRIDGE   I A WILSON
WORKSOP COLLEGE *Nottinghamshire*   P FINLINSON
WORTH   D M JARMY
WYCOMBE ABBEY *High Wycombe*   T J WRIGHT

THEOLOGICAL COLLEGES AND COURSES

This index includes the name of the principal or warden and the names of staff members who are Anglican clergy and whose appointments are at least half-time.

Theological Colleges

Church of Ireland Theological College
Braemor Park, Dublin 14, Irish Republic
Tel (00353) (1) 492 3506   Fax 492 3082
E-mail admin@citc.ie
PRIN C A EMPEY   TUTORS/LECTS A S JENSEN, K J MORONEY, B T DALY,
T W GORDON

College of the Resurrection
Stocks Bank Road, Mirfield WF14 0BW
Tel (01924) 490441   Fax 492738
E-mail cirvine@mirfield.org.uk
PRIN C P IRVINE   DIR STUDIES P G ALLAN CR
TUTOR/LECT J GRIBBEN CR

Cranmer Hall
St John's College, 3 South Bailey, Durham DH1 3RJ
Tel 0191–334 3500   Fax 334 3501
E-mail sj-cranmer-hall@durham.ac.uk
PRIN S W SYKES   WARDEN S J L CROFT
DIR MISS AND PAST STUDIES G T WAKEFIELD
DIR MIN FORMATION J HIRST
TUTORS/LECTS A B BARTLETT, M J WHIPP, C W READ

Oak Hill Theological College
Chase Side, London N14 4PS
Tel (020) 8449 0467   Fax 8441 5996
E-mail mailbox@oakhill.ac.uk
PRIN D G PETERSON   VICE-PRIN C M GREEN
TUTORS/LECTS H C HENDRY, M J OVEY, J E ROBSON

The Queen's College
Somerset Road, Edgbaston, Birmingham B15 2QH
Tel 0121–454 1527   Fax 454 8171
E-mail enquire@queens.ac.uk
PRIN D J P HEWLETT
TUTORS/LECTS J L HUGHES, S BURNS

Ridley Hall
Ridley Hall Road, Cambridge CB3 9HG
Tel (01223) 741080   Fax 741081
E-mail ridley-pa@lists.cam.ac.uk
PRIN C J COCKSWORTH   ASSOC PRIN J S BEGBIE
VICE-PRIN M B THOMPSON   DIR PAST STUDIES M P M BOOKER
TUTORS/LECTS S M BARCLAY, R W MAYO, P S HESLAM, J B WELLS,
S M GRIFFITHS, P D A WESTON

Ripon College
Cuddesdon, Oxford OX44 9EX
Tel (01865) 874404   Fax 875431
E-mail admin@ripon-cuddesdon.ac.uk
PRIN J M CLARKE   VICE-PRIN AND DIR STUDIES B C CASTLE
TUTORS/LECTS M D CHAPMAN, R A FAIRHURST

St John's College
Chilwell Lane, Bramcote, Beeston, Nottingham NG9 3DS
Tel 0115–925 1114   Fax 943 6438
E-mail principal@stjohns-nottm.ac.uk
PRIN C BAXTER[1]   DEAN J J WITCOMBE   DIR STUDIES H J WORSLEY
TUTORS/LECTS J H DARCH, M D MOYNAGH, S D DYAS, J G KELLY,
P NASH

St Michael and All Angels' College
54 Cardiff Road, Llandaff, Cardiff CF5 2YJ
Tel (029) 2056 3379 or 2057 6377
E-mail stmichaels@nildram.co.uk
PRIN vacant   VICE-PRIN G W WILLIAMS
TUTORS/LECTS J C CUTTELL, R G AUSTIN, J V THOMPSON,
R K A THOMPSON

St Stephen's House
16 Marston Street, Oxford OX4 1JX
Tel (01865) 247874   Fax 794338
E-mail dgmoss@ermine.ox.ac.uk or
jeremy.sheehy@theology.oxford.ac.uk
PRIN J P SHEEHY   VICE-PRIN R E M DOWLER
TUTOR M F LLOYD

Theological Institute of the Scottish Episcopal Church
Old Coates House, 32 Manor Place, Edinburgh EH3 7EB
Tel 0131–220 2272   Fax 220 2294
E-mail tisec@scotland.anglican.org
PRIN M J FULLER   DIR PAST STUDIES A L TOMLINSON
DIR LITURG STUDIES I J PATON   COURSE DIR M KESTON
TUTOR R K ACARNLEY

Trinity College
Stoke Hill, Bristol BS9 1JP
Tel 0117–968 2803   Fax 968 7470
E-mail principal@trinity-bris.ac.uk
PRIN F W BRIDGER   VICE-PRIN R H PESKETT
TUTORS/LECTS P P JENSON, J L NOLLAND, R P SYMMONS,
J H S STEVEN, J M GOSNEY

Westcott House
Jesus Lane, Cambridge CB5 8BP
Tel (01223) 741000   Fax 741002
E-mail westcott-house@lists.cam.ac.uk
PRIN M G V ROBERTS   VICE-PRIN A C W TILBY
DIR STUDIES V E RAYMER   TUTOR S SCHOFIELD

Wycliffe Hall
54 Banbury Road, Oxford OX2 6PW
Tel (01865) 274200   Fax 274215
E-mail enquiries@wycliffe.ox.ac.uk
PRIN A E MCGRATH   VICE-PRIN G S TOMLIN
DIR MIN G N MAUGHAN   SEN TUTOR P J M SOUTHWELL
TUTORS A J GODDARD, C J HEADLEY, P W L WALKER, D WENHAM

Regional Courses

Carlisle and Blackburn Diocesan Training Institute
Church House, West Walls, Carlisle CA3 8UE
Tel (01228) 522573   Fax 562366
E-mail therbert@globalnet.co.uk
PRIN T D HERBERT   DEP PRIN T S EVANS
TUTOR G E MARRISON

East Anglian Ministerial Training Course
EAMTC Office, 5 Pound Hill, Cambridge CB3 0AE
Tel (01223) 741026   Fax 741027
E-mail admin@eamtc.org.uk
PRIN M A BROWN   DIR PAST STUDIES H J STANTON[2]
TUTORS R M MORGAN, E SHREEVE[3]

East Midlands Ministry Training Course
Room C90, School of Continuing Education,
University of Nottingham,
Jubilee Campus, Wollaton Road, Nottingham NG8 1BB
Tel 0115–951 4854   Fax 951 4817
E-mail emmtc@nottingham.ac.uk
PRIN M J TAYLOR

North East Oecumenical Course
Ushaw College, Durham DH7 9RH
Tel 0191–373 7600   Fax 373 7601
E-mail neocoffice@aol.com
PRIN T PITT   DIR STUDIES G L MORLEY   TUTOR P K LEE

Northern Ordination Course
Luther King House, Brighton Grove, Rusholme,
Manchester M14 5JP
Tel 0161–249 2511   Fax 248 9201
E-mail office@thenoc.org.uk
PRIN C J BURDON   TUTOR M E LEIGH, S C SPENCER,
K CARVELEY[4], C MCMULLEN[5]

North Thames Ministerial Training Course
Chase Side, London N14 4PS
Tel (020) 8364 9442   Fax 8364 8889
E-mail davids@ntmtc.org.uk
PRIN D D SCEATS   TUTORS A V COLEMAN, A OSBORN, D E P PALK

---

[1] Dr Baxter is a lay person.   [2] Ms Stanton is a lay person.   [3] Dr Shreeve is a Methodist.   [4] Dr Carveley is a Methodist minister.
[5] Mrs McMullen is a lay person.

St Albans and Oxford Ministry Course
Diocesan Church House,
North Hinksey Lane, Botley, Oxford OX2 0NB
Tel (01865) 208260   Fax 790470
PRIN G M BUTTERWORTH VICE-PRIN G HEGARTY
DIR STUDIES S MOYISE[1]   TUTORS A J P GARROW, E C CARDALE

The South East Institute for Theological Education
Ground Floor, Sun Pier House, Medway Street,
Chatham ME4 4HF
Tel (01634) 832299
E-mail principal@seite.fsnet.co.uk
PRIN A LE GRYS   TUTOR J F WORTHEN

Southern Theological Education and Training Scheme
19 The Close, Salisbury SP1 2EE
Tel (01722) 424820   Fax 424811
E-mail principal@sarum.ac.uk
DIR V P WHITE   DEP DIR D A HOLGATE
MINL DEVELOPMENT OFFICER R G A RIEM   TUTOR R BROWN

South West Ministry Training Course
SWMTC Office, Petherwin Gate,
North Petherwin, Launceston PL15 8LW
Tel (01566) 785545   Fax 785749
E-mail principal@swmtc.org.uk
PRIN vacant   TUTOR H M ISON

West Midlands Ministerial Training Course
The Queen's Foundation for Ecumenical Theological
Education,
Somerset Road, Edgbaston, Birmingham B15 2QH
Tel 0121–454 1527
E-mail enquire@queens.ac.uk
PRIN D J P HEWLETT   TUTOR C A WORSLEY

West of England Ministerial Training Course
7C College Green, Gloucester GL1 2LX
Tel (01452) 300494   Fax as telephone
E-mail office@wemtc.freeserve.co.uk
PRIN R CLUTTERBUCK[2]   VICE-PRIN K M CROUCH
DIR STUDIES M DAVIES[3]

Ordained Local Ministry Schemes

Blackburn OLM Scheme
Dean House, 449 Padiham Road, Burnley BB12 6TE
Tel (01282) 412291   Fax 470361
E-mail vgoddard@clara.co.uk
DIR V GODDARD

Canterbury OLM Scheme
Diocesan House, Lady Wootton's Green, Canterbury CT1 1NQ
Tel (01227) 459401   Fax 450964
E-mail gwalker@diocant.org
PRIN P G WALKER   VICE-PRIN L A WALKER

Carlisle OLM Scheme
Church House, West Walls, Carlisle CA3 8UE
Tel (01228) 22573   Fax 562366
E-mail admin@cbdti.org.uk
DIR T D HERBERT

Coventry OLM Scheme
The Vicarage, 4 Hill Wootton Road, Leek Wootton,
Warwick CV35 7QL
Tel (01926) 854832   Fax 859117
E-mail brian@bwpvic.fslife.co.uk
DIR B W PEARSON

Gloucester OLM
4 College Green, Gloucester GL1 2LR
Tel (01452) 410022 ext 231   Fax 382905
E-mail dhoyle@glosdioc.org.uk
DIR D M HOYLE

Guildford Diocesan Ministry Course
The Vicarage, 5 Burwood Road, Hersham, Walton-on-Thames
KT12 4AA
Tel (01932) 269343   Fax 230274
E-mail hazel@gdmc.screaming.net
DIR H WHITEHEAD

Hereford Local Ministry Scheme
The Cottage, Bishop Mascall Centre, Lower Galdeford,
Ludlow SY8 1RZ
Tel (01584) 872822   Fax 877945
E-mail localmin@lineone.net
DIR G H EARNEY

Lichfield OLM Scheme
Backcester Lane, Lichfield WS13 6JH
Tel (01543) 306222   Fax 306229
E-mail rob.daborn@lichfield.anglican.org
DIR R F DABORN

Lincoln OLM Scheme
The Forum, Church House, Lincoln LN2 1PU
Tel (01522) 528886   Fax 512717
E-mail matthew.naylor@lincoln.anglican.org
DIR vacant

Liverpool OLM Scheme
The Rectory, 10 Church Lane, Ormskirk L39 6SB
Tel (01695) 423204   Fax as telephone
E-mail mpadams@cix.co.uk
DIR M P ADAMS

Manchester OLM Scheme
Church House, 90 Deansgate, Manchester M3 2GJ
Tel 0161–8281409 or 828 1410
E-mail annedawtry@manchester.anglican.org
DIR A F DAWTRY

Newcastle OLM Scheme
Church House, St John's Terrace, North Shields NE29 6HS
Tel 0191–270 4150   Fax 270 4101
E-mail r.bryant@lineone.net or
r.bryant@newcastle.anglican.org
DIR R K BRYANT

Norwich OLM Scheme
Emmaus House, 65 The Close, Norwich NR1 4DH
Tel (01603) 611196   Fax 766476
E-mail johngoodchild@norwich-anglican.org
DIR J M GOODCHILD

Oxford OLM Scheme
St Albans and Oxford Ministry Course,
Diocesan Church House,
North Hinksey Lane, Botley, Oxford OX2 0NB
Tel (01865) 208200
E-mail beren.hartless@oxford.anglican.org
PRIN B I de la T HARTLESS

St Edmundsbury and Ipswich Diocesan Ministry Course
Churchgates House, Cutler Street, Ipswich IP1 1UQ
Tel (01473) 298552   Fax 298501 or 298502
E-mail sheila@stedmundsbury.anglican.org
PRIN M F WEST

Salisbury OLM Scheme
Board of Ministry, Church House, Crane Street,
Salisbury SP1 2QB
Tel (01722) 411944
E-mail david.heslop@salisbury.anglican.org
PRIN D A HESLOP VICE-PRIN R BROWN

Southwark OLM Scheme
Diocese of Southwark, Trinity House, 4 Chapel Court, Borough
High Street, London SE1 1HW
Tel (020) 7939 9472   Fax 7939 9466
E-mail nigel.godfrey@dswark.org.uk
PRIN N P GODFREY

Wakefield Ministry Scheme
Church House, 1 South Parade, Wakefield WF1 1LP
Tel (01422) 321740   Fax (01924) 364834
E-mail ministry@wakefield.anglican.org
PRIN E M BRADNUM

[1] Dr Moyise is a lay person.
[2] Dr Clutterbuck is a Methodist.
[3] Dr Davies is a Roman Catholic lay person.

BISHOPS OF ANGLICAN DIOCESES OVERSEAS

AUSTRALIA

PROVINCE OF NEW SOUTH WALES

Armidale	Peter Robert Brain Anglican Diocesan Registry, PO Box 198, Armidale, NSW 2350, Australia Tel (0061) (2) 6772 4491 Fax (0061) (2) 6772 9261 E-mail diocarm@northnet.com.au
Bathurst	Richard Warwick Hurford PO Box 23, Bathurst, NSW 2795, Australia Tel (0061) (2) 6331 1976 Fax (0061) (2) 6332 2772 E-mail bxbishop@ix.net.au
Canberra and Goulburn	George Victor Browning GPO Box 1981, Canberra, ACT 2601, Australia Tel (0061) (2) 6248 0811 Fax (0061) (2) 6247 6829 E-mail george.browning@anglican.org.au
(Assistant)	Godfrey Charles Fryar St John's Rectory, 1 Church Street, Wagga Wagga, NSW 2650, Australia Tel (0061) (2) 6921 2323 Fax (0061) (2) 6921 6259 E-mail stjohns@wagga.net.au
Grafton	Keith Slater Bishopsholme, PO Box 4, Grafton, NSW 2460, Australia Tel (0061) (2) 6643 4122 Fax (0061) (2) 6643 1814 E-mail angdiog@nor.com.au
Newcastle	Roger Adrian Herft The Bishop's Registry, PO Box 817, Newcastle, NSW 2300, Australia Tel (0061) (2) 4926 3733 Fax (0061) (2) 4936 1968 or 4925 2526 E-mail bishop@angdon.com
(Assistant)	Graeme Stanley Rutherford PO Box 9095, Wyoming, NSW 2250, Australia Tel (0061) (2) 4329 2902 Fax (0061) (2) 4329 5501 E-mail bishopgraeme@bigpond.com
Riverina	Bruce Quinton Clark PO Box 10, Narrandera, NSW 2700, Australia Tel (0061) (2) 6959 1648 Fax (0061) (2) 6959 2903 E-mail rivdio@dragnet.net.au
Sydney (Archbishop and Metropolitan)	Peter Frederick Jensen PO Box Q190, Queen Victoria Buildings, Sydney, NSW 1230, Australia Tel (0061) (2) 9265 1521 Fax (0061) (2) 9265 1504 E-mail res@sydney.anglican.asn.au
(Liverpool)	Peter Tasker *address as above* Tel (0061) (2) 9265 1530 Fax (0061) (2) 9265 1543 E-mail ptasker@sydney.anglican.asn.au
(North Sydney)	Glenn Naunton Davies *address as above* Tel (0061) (2) 9265 1527 Fax (0061) (2) 9265 1543 E-mail sdc@sydney.anglican.asn.au
(South Sydney)	Robert Charles Forsyth PO Box Q190, Queen Victoria Buildings, Sydney, NSW 1230, Australia Tel (0061) (2) 9265 1501 Fax (0061) (2) 9265 1543 E-mail robforsyth@sydney.anglican.asn.au
(Western Sydney)	Ivan Yin Lee PO Box 1443, Parramatta, NSW 2124, Australia Tel (0061) (2) 9635 3186 Fax (0061) (2) 9633 3636 E-mail ilee@westernsydney.anglican.asn.au
(Wollongong)	Reginald John Piper 74 Church Street, Wollongong, NSW 2500, Australia Tel (0061) (2) 4225 2800 Fax (0061) (2) 4228 4296 E-mail rpiper@wollongong.anglican.asn.au

PROVINCE OF QUEENSLAND

Brisbane (Archbishop)	Phillip John Aspinall PO Box 421, Brisbane, QLD 4001, Australia Tel (0061) (7) 3835 2222 Fax (0061) (7) 3832 5030 E-mail archbishop@anglicanbrisbane.org.au
(Northern Region)	Richard Franklin Appleby *address as above* Tel (0061) (7) 3835 2213 or 3352 5053 Fax (0061) (7) 3832 5030 or 3352 4907 E-mail rappleby@anglicanbrisbane.org.au
(Southern Region)	Ronald John Chantler Williams *address and fax as above* Tel (0061) (7) 3835 2213 E-mail rwilliams@anglicanbrisbane.org.au or rkwill@gil.com.au
(Western Region)	Robert William Nolan PO Box 2600, Toowomba, QLD 4350, Australia Tel (0061) (7) 4639 1875 Fax (0061) (7) 4632 6882 E-mail rwnolan@bigpond.com
North Queensland	John Ashley Noble PO Box 1244, Townsville, QLD 4810, Australia Tel (0061) (7) 4771 4175 Fax (0061) (7) 4721 1756 E-mail bishopnq@anglicannq.org
(National Aboriginal Bishop)	James Randolph Leftwich 129A Lake Street, Cairns, QLD 4878, Australia Tel: (0061) (7) 4051 1055 Fax (0061) (7) 4051 1033 E-mail bishopab@bigpond.com
(Torres Strait Islands)	Saibo Mabo PO Box 714, Thursday Island, QLD 4875, Australia Tel (0061) (7) 4069 1960
Northern Territory, The	Philip Leslie Freier GPO Box 2950, Darwin, NT 0801, Australia Tel (0061) (8) 8941 7440 Fax (0061) (8) 8941 7446 or 8941 7227 E-mail philipfreier@optuset.com.au
Rockhampton	*vacant* PO Box 6158, Central Queensland Mail Centre, Rockhampton, QLD 4702, Australia Tel (0061) (7) 4927 3188 Fax (0061) (7) 4922 4562 E-mail bishop@anglicanrock.org.au

PROVINCE OF SOUTH AUSTRALIA

Adelaide (Archbishop)	Ian Gordon Combe George 26 King William Road, North Adelaide, SA 5006, Australia Tel (0061) (8) 8305 9353 Fax (0061) (8) 8305 9399 E-mail igeorge.churchoffice@anglicare- sa.org.au or ian.george@accnet.net.au
The Murray	Graham Howard Walden PO Box 269, Murray Bridge, SA 5253, Australia Tel (0061) (8) 8532 2270 Fax (0061) (8) 8532 5760 E-mail registry@murray.anglican.org
Willochra	Garry John Weatherill Bishop's House, Gladstone, SA 5473, Australia Tel (0061) (8) 8662 2249 Fax (0061) (8) 8662 2027 E-mail garth@tell.net.au

PROVINCE OF VICTORIA

Ballarat	*vacant* PO Box 89, Ballarat, VIC 3350, Australia Tel (0061) (3) 5331 1183 Fax (0061) (3) 5332 2982 E-mail bpsec@ballaratanglican.org.au
(Assistant)	Michael George Hough PO Box 241, Creswick,VIC 3363, Australia Tel (0061) (3) 5345 2060 *fax as telephone* E-mail benmike@gatewaybbs.com.au
Bendigo	Andrew William Curnow PO Box 2, Bendigo, VIC 3552, Australia Tel (0061) (3) 5443 4668 Fax (0061) (3) 5441 2173 E-mail bishop@bendigoanglican.org.au
Gippsland	Jeffrey William Driver PO Box 928, Sale, VIC 3850, Australia Tel (0061) (3) 5144 2044 *or* 2248 Fax (0061) (3) 5144 7183
Melbourne (Archbishop)	Peter Robert Watson The Anglican Centre, 209 Flinders Lane, Melbourne, VIC 3000, Australia Tel (0061) (3) 9653 4220 Fax (0061) (3) 9650 2184 E-mail archbishop@melbourne.anglican.com.au
(Eastern Region)	Stephen John Hale *address etc as above* E-mail shale@melbourne.anglican.com.au
(Northern Region)	*vacant* *address etc as above* E-mail nthregbishop@melbourne.anglican.com.au
(Southern Region)	John Warwick Wilson *address as above* Tel (0061) (3) 9653 4220 Fax (0061) (3) 9653 4268 E-mail sthregbishop@melbourne.anglican.com.au
(Western Region)	Paul Raymond White *address etc as above* E-mail pwhite@melbourne.anglican.com.au
Wangaratta	Ralph David Farrer Bishop's Lodge, PO Box 457, Wangaratta, VIC 3676, Australia Tel (0061) (3) 5721 3643 *or* 5722 3478 Fax (0061) (3) 5721 3484 *or* 5722 1427 E-mail diowang@w140.aone.net.au

PROVINCE OF WESTERN AUSTRALIA

Bunbury	William David Hair McCall Bishopscourt, PO Box 15, Bunbury, WA 6231, Australia Tel (0061) (8) 9721 2100 Fax (0061) (8) 9791 2300 E-mail bishop@diocese.geo.net.au *or* office@diocese.geo.net.au
North West Australia	David Mulready PO Box 171, Geraldton, WA 6530, Australia Tel (0061) (8) 9921 7277 Fax (0061) (8) 9964 2220 E-mail bishop@anglicandnwa.org
Perth (Archbishop and Primate)	Peter Frederick Carnley GPO Box W2067, Perth, WA 6846, Australia Tel (0061) (8) 9325 7455 Fax (0061) (8) 9325 6741 E-mail abcsuite@perth.anglican.org
(Fremantle)	David Owen Murray 3rd Level, 26 Queen Street, Fremantle, WA 6160, Australia Tel (0061) (8) 9430 7224 Fax (0061) (8) 9336 3374 E-mail srbishop@iinet.net.au *or* plusdave@iinet.net.au

(Goldfields Region)	Gerald Edward Beaumont PO Box 439, Kalgoorlie, WA 6430, Australia Tel (0061) (8) 9022 7382 Fax (0061) (8) 9022 8358 E-mail kalang@emerge.net.au
(Northern Region)	Brian George Farran PO Box 42, Joondalup, WA 6919, Australia Tel (0061) (8) 9300 0833 Fax (0061) (8) 9300 0893 E-mail nrbishop@nw.com.au
Defence Force (Honorary Assistant Bishop of Perth and Episcopal Assistant to the Primate)	Thomas Robert Frame 12 Coghill Close, Kambah, ACT 2902, Australia Tel (0061) (2) 6296 4465 Fax (0061) (2) 6296 4431 E-mail dfc@anglican.org.au

DIOCESE OF TASMANIA

Tasmania	John Douglas Harrower GPO Box 748H, Hobart, Tas, Australia 7001 Tel (0061) (3) 6223 8811 Fax (0061) (3) 6223 8968 E-mail bishop@anglicantas.org.au

BRAZIL

Brasilia	Mauricio José Arurjo de Andrade Caixa Postal 00515 Brasilia, DF, 70.359–970, Brazil Tel (0055) (61) 443 4305 Fax (0055) (61) 443 8074 E-mail mandrade@ieab.org.br
Curitiba	Naudal Alves Gomes Av Sete de Setembro, 3927 sl. 8-Centro, 802–010 Curitiba, PR, Brazil Tel (0055) (41) 366 0007 E-mail ngomes@ieab.org.br
Pelotas	Sebastiao Armando Gameleira Soares Caixa Postal 791-Centro, 96001–970 Pelotas, RS, Brazil Tel (0055) (532) 277120 Fax (0055) (532) 2316532 E-mail sgameleira@hotmail.
Recife	Edward Robinson de Barros Cavalcanti Caixa Postal 4704, Boa Viagem, 51012–970, Recife, PE, Brazil Tel (0055) (81) 3325 5586 *fax as telephone* E-mail cavalcanti@ieab.org.br
(Suffragan)	Filadelfo Oliveira Neto *address etc as above* E-mail foliveira@ieab.org.br
Rio de Janeiro	Celso Franco de Oliveira Av Rio Branco 277/907, Cinelândia, 20047–900, RJ, Brazil Tel (0055) (21) 2220 2148 Fax (0055) (21) 2220 2705 E-mail coliveira@ieab.org.br
São Paulo	Hiroshi Ito Rua Borges Lagoa, 172, Vila Clementino, 04038–030 São Paulo, SP, Brazil Tel (0055) (11) 5549 9086 Fax (0055) (11) 5083 2619 E-mail hito@ieab.org.br
South Western Brazil	Jubal Pereira Neves Caixa Postal 116, 97010–970, Santa Maria, RS, Brazil Tel (0055) (55) 223 1196 *fax as telephone* E-mail jneves@ieab.org.br

Southern Brazil (Primate)	Orlando Santos de Oliveira Caixa Postal 11.510, Teresópolis, Porto Alegre, RS, Brazil Tel (0055) (51) 318 6199 *fax as telephone* E-mail soliveira@ieab.org.br

BURMA (MYANMAR)

Hpa-an	Daniel Hoi Kyin c/o Church of the Province of Myanmar, 140 Pyidaungsu Yeiktha Road, Dagon PO (11191), Yangon, Myanmar Tel (0095) (1) 72668 Fax (0095) (1) 77512
Mandalay	Andrew Hla Aung Bishopscourt, 22nd Street, 'C' Road (between 85–86 Road), Mandalay, Myanmar Tel (0095) (2) 22175
Mytikyina	David Than Lwin Diocesan Office, 147 Tha Kin Nat Pe Road, Thida Ya, Myitkyina, Kachin State, Myanmar Tel (0095) (74) 23104
Sittwe	Barnabas Theaung Hawi St John's Church, Paletwa, Southern Chin State, via Sittwe, Myanmar
(Assistant)	Aung Tha Tun *address as above*
Toungoo	Saw John Wilme Diocesan Office, Nat-shin-Naung Road, Toungoo, Myanmar Tel (0095) (54) 21519
Yangon (Archbishop)	Samuel San Si Htay 140 Pyidaungsu-Yeiktha Road Dagon PO, Yangon 11191, Myanmar Tel (0095) (1) 246 813 Fax (0095) (1) 251 405 E-mail cpm.140@mptmail.net.mm
(Assistant)	Joseph Than Pe 44 Pay Road, Dagon PO, Yangon 11191, Myanmar Tel (0095) (1) 72668 *or* 72300 Fax (001) 77512

BURUNDI

Bujumbura	Pie Ntukamazina BP 1300, Bujumbura, Burundi Tel (00257) (2) 22641 *or* 35374 Fax (00257) (2) 27496 E-mail mgrpie@eebbuja.org
Buye (Archbishop)	Samuel Ndayisenga BP 94, Ngozi, Burundi Tel (00257) (30) 2210 Fax (00257) (30) 2317
Gitega	Jean W Nduwayo BP 23, Gitega, Burundi Tel (00257) (40) 2247 E-mail eebgitega@cbinf.com
Makamba	Martin Blaise Nyaboho BP 96, Makamba, Burundi Mobile (00257) (92) 6491 Fax (00257) (22) 9129 E-mail eebprov@cbinet.
Matana	Bernard Ntahoturi BP 447, Bujumbura, Burundi Tel (00257) (27) 0361 Fax (00257) (9) 9129 E-mail ntahober@cbinf.com

CANADA

Primate of Canada	*vacant* Anglican Church of Canada 80 Hayden Street, Toronto ON M4Y 3G2, Canada Tel (001) (416) 924 9192 Fax (001) (416) 924 0211 E-mail primate@national.anglican.ca

PROVINCE OF BRITISH COLUMBIA

British Columbia	*vacant* 900 Vancouver Street, Victoria BC V8V 3V7, Canada Tel (001) (250) 386 7781 Fax (001) (250) 386 4013 E-mail bishop@acts.bc.ca
Caledonia	William J Anderson PO Box 278, Prince Rupert BC V8J 3P6, Canada Tel (001) (250) 624 6013 Fax (001) (250) 624 4299 E-mail synodofc@citytel.net
Kootenay (Archbishop and Metropolitan)	David P Crawley 1876 Richter Street, Kelowna BC V1Y 2M9, Canada Tel (001) (250) 762 3306 Fax (001) (250) 762 4150 *or* 862 5895 E-mail diocese_of_kootenay@telus.net
New Westminster	Michael C Ingham 580–401 W Georgia Street, Vancouver BC V6B 5A1, Canada Tel (001) (604) 684 6306 Fax (001) (604) 684 7017 E-mail bishop@vancouver.anglican.ca
Yukon	Terrence O Buckle PO Box 31136, Whitehorse YT Y1A 5P7, Canada Tel (001) (867) 667 7746 Fax (001) (867) 667 6125 E-mail synof@dioyukon.org

PROVINCE OF CANADA

Central Newfoundland	Donald Young 34 Fraser Road, Gander NF A1V 2E8, Canada Tel (001) (709) 256 2372 Fax (001) (709) 256 2396 E-mail bishopcentral@nfld.net
Eastern Newfoundland and Labrador	Donald F Harvey 19 King's Bridge Road, St John's NF A1C 3K4, Canada Tel (001) (709) 576 6697 Fax (001) (709) 576 7122 E-mail dharvey@anglicanenl.nf.net
Fredericton	Claude E W Miller 115 Church Street, Fredericton NB E3B 4C8, Canada Tel (001) (506) 459 1801 Fax (001) (506) 460 0520 E-mail bishfton@nbnet.nb.ca
Montreal (Archbishop and Metropolitan)	Andrew S Hutchison 1444 Union Avenue, Montreal QC H3A 2B8, Canada Tel (001) (514) 843 6577 Fax (001) (514) 843 3221 *or* 843 6344 E-mail bishops.office@montreal.anglican.org
(Assistant Bishop)	G Russell Hatton 54 rue Principale South, Sutton QC J0E 2K0, Canada Tel (001) (450) 538 0287 Fax (001) (450) 538 0511 E-mail hatton@estrie.qc.ca
Nova Scotia and Prince Edward Island	Frederick J Hiltz 5732 College Street, Halifax NS B3H 1X3, Canada Tel (001) (902) 420 0717 Fax (001) (902) 425 0717 E-mail office@nspeidiocese.ca
Quebec	A Bruce Stavert 31 rue des Jardins, Quebec QC G1R 4L6, Canada Tel (001) (418) 692 3858 Fax (001) (418) 692 3876 E-mail synodoffice@quebec.anglican.ca

Western   Percy D Coffin
Newfoundland 25 Main Street, Corner Brook
                   NF A2H 1C2, Canada
                   Tel (001) (709) 639 8712
                   Fax (001) (709) 639 1636
                   E-mail dsown@nf.aibn.ca

PROVINCE OF ONTARIO

Algoma   Ronald C Ferris
                   PO Box 1168, Sault Ste Marie
                   ON P6A 5N7, Canada
                   Tel (001) (705) 256 5061 *or* 256 2791
                   Fax (001) (705) 946 1860
                   E-mail dioceseofalgoma@on.aibn.

Huron   Bruce H W Howe
                   190 Queens Avenue, London
                   ON N6A 5R8, Canada
                   Tel (001) (519) 434 6893
                   Fax (001) (519) 673 4151
                   E-mail bishops@huron.anglican.org

(Suffragan)   Robert F Bennett
                   address etc as above

Moosonee   Caleb J Lawrence
                   Box 841, Schumacher
                   ON P0N 1G0, Canada
                   Tel (001) (705) 360 1129
                   Fax (001) (705) 360 1120
                   E-mail moosonee@ntl.sympatico.ca *or*
                   lawrence@ntl.sympatico.ca

Niagara   David Ralph Spence
                   Cathedral Place, 252 James Street N,
                   Hamilton ON L8R 2L3, Canada,
                   Tel (001) (905) 527 1316 *or* 527 1317
                   Fax (001) (905) 527 1281
                   E-mail bishop@niagara.anglican.ca

Ontario   George L R Bruce
                   90 Johnson Street, Kingston
                   ON K7L 1X7, Canada
                   Tel (001) (613) 544 4774
                   Fax (001) (613) 547 3745
                   E-mail gbruce@ontario.anglican.ca

Ottawa   Peter Robert Coffin
                   71 Bronson Avenue, Ottawa
                   ON K1R 6G6, Canada
                   Tel (001) (613) 232 7124 *or* 233 7741 ext 223
                   Fax (001) (613) 232 3955
                   E-mail ann-day@ottawa.anglican.ca

Toronto   Terence E Finlay
(Archbishop   135 Adelaide Street East, Toronto
and   ON M5C 1L8, Canada
Metropolitan) Tel (001) (416) 363 6021
                   Fax (001) (416) 363 3683 *or* 363 7678
                   E-mail tfinlay@toronto.anglican.ca

(York-Simcoe) George Elliott
                   2174 King Road, Suite 2, King City
                   ON L7B 1L6, Canada
                   Tel (001) (905) 833 8327
                   E-mail ysimcoe@neptune.on.ca

(Credit Valley) Ann Elizabeth Tottenham
                   256 Sheldon Avenue,
                   Etobicoke
                   ON M8W 4X8, Canada
                   Tel (001) (416) 503 9903
                   Fax (001) (416) 503 8299
                   E-mail cvalley@tap.net *or* atottenham@tap.net

(Trent-Durham) Colin R Johnson
                   135 Adelaide Street East,Toronto
                   ON M5C 1L8, Canada
                   Tel (001) (416) 363 6021
                   Fax (001) (416) 363 3683
                   E-mail cjohnon@toronto.anglican.ca

(York-   Michael Hugh Harold Bedford-Jones
Scarborough)   St Paul's L'Amoreaux,
                   3333 Finch Avenue East,
                   Scarborough ON M1W 2R9, Canada
                   Tel (001) (416) 497 7750
                   Fax (001) (416) 497 4103
                   E-mail mbj@total.net

PROVINCE OF RUPERT'S LAND

The Arctic   Andrew P Atagotaaluk
                   PO Box 190, Yellowknife
                   NT X1A 2N2, Canada
                   Tel (001) (867) 873 5432
                   Fax (001) (867) 837 8478
                   E-mail diocese@theedge.ca

(Baffin and   Paul O Idlout
Keewatin   PO Box 2219, Iqaluit
Region)   NT X0A 0H0, Canada
                   Tel (001) (867) 979 6307
                   Fax (001) (867) 979 7814
                   E-mail pidlout@nunanet.com

(Mackenzie   Larry D Robertson
and   PO Box 1040, Inuvik
Kitikmeot   NT X0E 0T0, Canada
Region)   Tel (001) (867) 777 2229
                   Fax (001) (867) 777 4960
                   E-mail larryr@permafrost.com

(Nunavik   Benjamin T Arreak
Region)   PO Box 154, Kuujjuaqq
                   QC J0M 1C0, Canada
                   Tel (001) (819) 964 2324
                   Fax (001) (819) 964 2113
                   E-mail btarreak@sympatico.ca

Athabasca   John R Clarke
(Archbishop   Box 6868, Peace River
and   AB T8S 1S6, Canada
Metropolitan) Tel (001) (780) 624 2767
                   Fax (001) (780) 624 2365
                   E-mail dioath@telusplanet.net

Brandon   James D. Njegovan
                   PO Box 21009, WE PO, Brandon
                   MB R7B 3W8, Canada
                   Tel (001) (204) 727 7550
                   Fax (001) (204) 727 4135
                   E-mail bishopbdn@mts.net

Calgary   Barry Craig Bates Hollowell
                   #560 – 1207 11th Avenue SW
                   Calgary AB T3C 0M5, Canada
                   Tel (001) (403) 243 3673
                   Fax (001) (403) 243 2182
                   E-mail synod@calgary.anglican.ca

Edmonton   Victoria Matthews
                   10035–103 Street, Edmonton
                   AB T5J 0X5, Canada
                   Tel (001) (780) 439 7344
                   Fax (001) (780) 439 6549
                   E-mail bishopv@telusplanet.net

Keewatin   David N Ashdown
                   915 Ottawa Street, Keewatin
                   ON P0X 1C0, Canada
                   Tel (001) (807) 547 3353
                   Fax (001) (807) 547 3356
                   E-mail keewatinbishop@gokenora.com

Qu'Appelle   Duncan Douglas Wallace
                   1501 College Avenue, Regina
                   SK S4P 1B8, Canada
                   Tel (001) (306) 522 1608
                   Fax (001) (306) 352 6808
                   E-mail quappelle@sasktel.net

Rupert's Land Donald D Phillips
                   935 Nesbitt Bay, Winnipeg
                   MB R3T 1W6, Canada
                   Tel (001) (204) 453 6130 *or* 453 6248
                   Fax (001) (204) 452 3915
                   E-mail general@rupertsland.ca

Saskatchewan Anthony John Burton
                   1308 Fifth Avenue East, Prince Albert
                   SK S6V 2H7, Canada
                   Tel (001) (306) 763 2455
                   Fax (001) (306) 764 5172
                   E-mail burton@sasktel.net *or*
                   diosask@hotmail.com

(Suffragan)   Charles J Arthurson
                   Box 96, La Ronge
                   SK S0J 1L0, Canada
                   Tel (001) (306) 425 2492

Saskatoon *vacant*
PO Box 1965, Saskatoon
SK S7K 3S5, Canada
Tel (001) (306) 244 5651 *or* 242 0837
Fax (001) (306) 933 4606
E-mail anglicanbishop@sasktel.net

CENTRAL AFRICA

Botswana Theophilus Tswere Naledi
PO Box 769, Gaborone, Botswana
Tel (00267) 395 3779
Fax (00267) 391 3015
E-mail anglidiocese@info.bw

Central Zambia Derek Kamukwanba
PO Box 70172, Ndola, Zambia
Tel (00260) (2) 612 431
Fax (00260) (2) 615 954
E-mail adcznla@zamnet.zm

Central Ishmael Mukuwanda
Zimbabwe PO Box 25, Gweru, Zimbabwe
Tel (00263) (54) 21030
Fax (00263) (54) 21097
E-mail diocent@telconet.co.zw

Eastern Zambia William Muchombo
PO Box 510154, Chipata, Zambia
Tel (00260) (62) 21294
fax as telephone
E-mail dioeastzm@zamtel.zm

Harare Nolbert Kunonga
Bishopsmount Close,
PO Box UA7, Harare, Zimbabwe
Tel (00263) (4) 702253 *or* 702254
Fax (00263) (4) 700419
E-mail angbishophre@mango.zw

Lake Malawi Peter Nathaniel Nyanja
PO Box 30349, Lilongwe 3, Malawi
Tel (00265) 797 858
Fax (00265) 797 548
E-mail nyanja@comw.net

Lusaka Leonard Jameson Mwenda
Bishop's Lodge, PO Box 30183
Lusaka, Zambia
Tel (00260) (1) 264515
Fax (00260) (1) 262379
E-mail angdiolu@zamnet.zm

Manicaland Sebastian Bakare
115 Herbert Chitepo Street
Mutare, Zimbabwe
Tel (00263) (20) 64194
Fax (00262) (20) 63076
E-mail diomani@syscom.co.zw

Masvingo Godfrey Taonezvi
PO Box 1421, Masvingo, Zimbabwe
Tel (00263) (39) 362 536
E-mail anglicandiopmsv@comone.co.zw

Matabeleland Wilson Sitshebo
PO Box 2422, Bulawayo, Zimbabwe
Tel (00263) (9) 61370
Fax (00263) (9) 68353
E-mail angdiomat@telconet.co.zw

Northern Christopher John Boyle
Malawi PO Box 120, Mzuzu, Malawi
Tel (00265) 331486
Fax (00265) 333805
E-mail bishopboyle@sdnp.org.mw

Northern Albert Chama
Zambia PO Box 20798, Kitwe, Zambia
Tel (00260) (2) 223264
Fax (00260) (2) 224778
E-mail dionorth@zamnet.zm

Southern James Tengatenga
Malawi PO Box 30220, Chichiri, Blantyre 3, Malawi
Tel (00265) (1) 641 218
Fax (00265) (1) 641 235
E-mail angsoma@clcom.net

Southern Bernard Amos Malango
Malawi – Private Bag 1, Chilema, Zomba, Malawi
Upper Shire Tel (00265) (1) 539 203
(Archbishop) E-mail dionorth@zamnet.zm

CENTRAL AMERICA

Costa Rica Hector Monterroso
Iglesia Episcopal Costarricense, Apt 2773,
1000 San Jose, Costa Rica
Tel (00506) 225 0209 *or* 253 0790
Fax (00506) 253 8331
E-mail anglicancr@sol.rasca.co.cr

El Salvador Martin de Jesus Barhona
(Primate) 47 Avenida Sur, 723 Col Flor Blanca,
Apt Postal (01), 274 San Salvador,
El Salvador
Tel (00503) 223 2252
Fax (00503) 223 7952
E-mail anglican@saltel.net

Guatemala Armando Roman Guerra-Soria
Apartado 58A, Avenida La Castellana 40–06,
Guatemala City, Guatemala
Tel (00502) 472 0852
Fax (00502) 472 0764
E-mail diocesis@terra.com.gt

Nicaragua Sturdie Downs
Apartado 1207, Managua, Nicaragua
Tel (00505) 222 5174
Fax (00505) 222 6701
E-mail episcnic@cablenet.com.ni

Panama Julio Murray
Box R, Balboa, Republic of Panama
Tel (00507) 212 0062
Fax (00507) 262 2097

CEYLON (SRI LANKA)

Colombo Duleep Kamil de Chickera
368/3A Bauddhaloka Mawatha,
Colombo 7, Sri Lanka
Tel (0094) (1) 684810
Fax (0094) (1) 684811
E-mail bishop@eureka.lk

Kurunegala Kumara Bandara Samuel Illangasinghe
Bishop's Office, Cathedral Close,
Kurunegala, Sri Lanka
Tel (0094) (37) 22191
Fax (0094) (37) 26806

CONGO (formerly ZAÏRE)

Boga Patrice Byankya Njojo
PO Box 25586, Kampala, Uganda
Tel (00256) (41) 273817
Mobile (00256) 77–647495
E-mail eac-mags@infocom.co.ug

Bukavu Fidèle Dirokpa Balufuga
(Archbishop) BP 134, Cyangugu, Rwanda
Mobile (00250) 841 7697
E-mail anglicadiobkv@yahoo.co.uk *or*
dirokpa1@hotmail.com

Katanga Henri Isingoma Kahwa
PO Box 22037, Kitwe, Zambia
Tel (00243) 998 9288
E-mail peac_isingoma@yahoo.fr

Kindu Zacharie Masimango Katanda
BP 458, Gisenyi, Rwanda
E-mail angkindu@yahoo.fr

Kisangani Lambert Funga Botolome
PO Box 25586, Kampala, Uganda
E-mail lambertfunga@hotmail.com

Nord Kivu Munzenda Methusela Musababo
PO Box 506, Bwera-Kasese, Uganda
E-mail munzenda_eac@yahoo.fr

HONG KONG

Eastern Louis Tsui
Kowloon Diocesan Office,
4/F Holy Trinity Bradbury Centre,
139 Ma Tau Chung Road,
Kowloon, Hong Kong, China
Tel (00852) 2713 9983
Fax (00852) 2711 1609
E-mail ekoffice@ekhkskh.org.hk

Hong Kong Island (Archbishop)	Peter Kwong Kong Kit Bishop's House, 1 Lower Albert Road, Hong Kong, China Tel (00852) 2526 5355 Fax (00852) 2525 2537 E-mail office1@hkskh.org
Western Kowloon	Thomas Yee-po Soo 15/F Ultragrace Commercial Building, 5 Jordan Road, Kowloon, Hong Kong, China Tel (00852) 2783 0811 Fax (00852) 2783 0799 E-mail hkskhdwk@netvigator.com

INDIAN OCEAN

Antananarivo (Archbishop)	Remi Joseph Rabenirina Evêché Anglican, Lot VK57 ter, Ambohimanoro, 101 Antananarivo, Madagascar Tel (00261) (20) 222 0827 Fax (00261) (20) 226 1331 E-mail eemdanta@dts.mg
Antsiranana	Roger Chung Po Chuen Evêché Anglican, BP 278, 201 Antsiranana, Madagascar Tel (00261) 822650 *fax as telephone*
Fianarantsoa	Gilbert Rateloson Rakotondravelo Évêché Anglican Mananjary 317, Madagascar
Mahajanga	Jean-Claude Andrianjafimanana BP 169, Mahajanga 401, Madagascar E-mail eemdmaha@dts.mg *or* revmctod@dts.mg
Mauritius	Gerald James Ernest Bishop's House, Nallelamby Road, Phoenix, Mauritius Tel (00230) 686 5158 Fax (00230) 697 1096 E-mail dioang@intnet.mu
Seychelles	*vacant* Bishop's House, PO Box 44, Victoria, Seychelles Tel (00248) 224242 Fax (00248) 224296 E-mail angdio@seychelles.net
Toamasina	Jean Paul Solo Evêché Anglican, Rue James Seth, BP 531, Toamasina 501, Madagascar Tel (00261) (2) 0533 1663 Fax (00261) (2) 0533 1689

JAPAN

Chubu	Francis Toshiaki Mori 1–47 Yamawaki-cho 1-chome, Showa-ku, Nagoya 466–0063, Japan Tel (0081) (52) 731 6008 Fax (0081) (52) 731 6222 E-mail: office.chubu@nskk.org
Hokkaido	Nathaniel Makoto Uematsu Kita 15 jo, Nishi 5–20, Kita-ku, Sapporo 001–0015, Japan Tel (0081) (11) 717 8181 Fax (0081) (11) 736 8377 E-mail bishop.hok@nskk.org
Kita Kanto (Acting)	James Satoru Endo 2–172 Sakuragi-cho, Omiya-shi, Saitama 331–0852, Japan Tel (0081) (48) 642 2680 Fax (0081) (48) 648 0358 E-mail n.kantou@vega.ocn.ne.jp
Kobe	John Jun'ichiro Furumoto 5–11–1 Yamatedori, Chuo-ku, Kobe-shi 650–0011, Japan Tel (0081) (3) 5228 3171 *or* (78) 351 5469 Fax (0081) (3) 5228 3175 *or* (78) 382 1095 E-mail aao52850@syn.odn.ne.jp

Kyoto	Stephen Takashi Kochi 380 Okakuen, Shimotachiuri-agaru, Karasumadori, Kamikyo-ku, Kyoto 602–8011, Japan Tel (0081) (75) 431 7204 Fax (0081) (75) 441 4238 *or* 432 6723 E-mail stmaria.kyoto@nskk.org
Kyushu	Gabriel Shoji Igarashi 2–9–22 Kusakae, Chuo-ku, Fukuoka 810–0045, Japan Tel (0081) (92) 771 2050 Fax (0081) (92) 771 9857 E-mail d-kyushu@try-net.or.jp
Okinawa (Acting Primate)	David Shoji Tani 101 Azayoshihara, Chatan-cho, Okinawa 904–0105, Japan Tel (0081) (98) 936 3019 Fax (0081) (98) 936 0606 E-mail office.okinawa@nskk.org
Osaka	James Toro Uno 2–1–8 Matsuzaki-cho, Abeno-ku, Osaka 545–0053, Japan Tel (0081) (6) 621 2179 Fax (0081) (6) 621 3097 E-mail osaka@nskk.org
Tohoku	John Hiromichi Kato 2–13–15 Kokobun-cho, Aoba-ku, Sendai 980–0803, Japan Tel (0081) (22) 223 2349 Fax (0081) (22) 223 2387 E-mail fujishima.tohoku@nskk.org
Tokyo	Peter Jintaro Ueda 3–6–18 Shiba Koen, Minato-ku, Tokyo 105–0011, Japan Tel (0081) (3) 3433 0987 *or* 3433 2417 Fax (0081) (3) 3433 8678 E-mail general-sec.tko@nskk.org
Yokohama	James Satoru Endo 14–57 Mitsuzawa Shimo-cho, Kanagawa-ku, Yokohama 221–0852, Japan Tel (0081) (45) 321 4988 Fax (0081) (45) 323 2763 E-mail yokohama@nskk.org

JERUSALEM AND THE MIDDLE EAST

Cyprus and the Gulf (Bishop *in*) (President)	George Clive Handford PO Box 22075, CY 1517 – Nicosia, Cyprus Tel (00357) (2) 671220 Fax (00357) (2) 674553 E-mail bishop@spidernet.com.cy *or* georgia@spidernet.com.cy
Egypt (Bishop *in*)	Mouneer Hanna Anis Diocesan Office, PO Box 87, Zamalek Distribution, 11211, Cairo, Egypt Tel (0020) (2) 332 0313 *or* 332 0823 Fax (0020) (2) 340 8941 E-mail diocese@intouch.com *or* bishop@intouch.
Iran (Bishop *in*)	*vacant* PO Box 135, Postal Code 81465, Isfahan, Iran Tel (0098) (31) 231435 Fax (0098) (31) 234675
Jerusalem (Bishop *in*)	Riah Hanna Abu El-Assal St George's Close, PO Box 19122, Jerusalem, Israel Tel (00972) (2) 627 1670 *or* 627 2932 Fax (00972) (2) 627 3847 *or* 565 3649 E-mail riahasal@netvision.net.il *or* edioces@netvision.net.il

KENYA

All Saints Cathedral (Archbishop)	Benjamin M Nzimbi PO Box 40502, 00100 Nairobi, Kenya Tel (00254) (20) 714 755 Fax (00254) (20) 718 442 *or* 714 750 E-mail archoffice@swiftkenya.com

Bondo
Johannes Otieno Angela
PO Box 240, 40601 Bondo, Kenya
Tel (00254) (335) 20415
E-mail ackbondo@swiftkenya.com

Bungoma
Eliud Wabukala
PO Box 2392, 50200 Bungoma, Kenya
Tel (00254) (337) 30481
fax as telephone
E-mail wabukala@africaonline.com.ke *or*
ackbungoma@swiftkenya.com

Butere
Horace Etemesi
PO Box 54, 50101 Butere, Kenya
Tel (00254) (333) 20038
E-mail ackbutere@swiftkenya.com

Eldoret
Thomas Kogo
PO Box 3404, 30100 Eldoret, Kenya
Tel (00254) (321) 62785
E-mail ackeldoret@africaonline.co.ke

Embu
Moses Njeru Njue
PO Box 189, 60100 Embu, Kenya
Tel (00254) (161) 20618 *or* 20264
Fax (00254) (161) 30468
E-mail ackembu@maf.org.ke *or*
ackembu@swiftkenya.com

Kajiado
Jeremiah John Mutua Taama
PO Box 203, 01100 Kajiado, Kenya
Tel (00254) (301) 21105 *or* 21201
Fax (00254) (301) 21106
E-mail ackajiado@swiftkenya.com

Katakwa
Eliud Odera Okiring
PO Box 68, 50244 Amagoro, Kenya
Tel (00254) (337) 54079
E-mail ackatakwa@swiftkenya.com

Kirinyaga
Daniel Munene Ngoru
PO Box 95, 10304 Kutus, Kenya
Tel (00254) (163) 44221 *or* 44028
Fax (00254) (163) 44020
E-mail kirinyagaACK@maf.org

Kitale
Stephen Kewasis
PO Box 4176, 30200 Kitale, Kenya
Tel (00254) (325) 31631
Fax (00254) (325) 31387
E-mail ack.ktl@africaonline.co.ke

Kitui
Josephat Vundi Mule
PO Box 1054, 90200 Kitui, Kenya
Tel (00254) (141) 22682
Fax (00254) (141) 22119
E-mail ackitui@swiftkenya.com

Machakos
Joseph Mutie Kanuku
PO Box 282, 90100 Machakos, Kenya
Tel (00254) (145) 21379
Fax (00254) (145) 20178
E-mail ackmachakos@swiftkenya.com

Maseno
North
Simon Mutingole Oketch
PO Box 416, Kakemega, Kenya
Tel (00254) (331) 20412
Fax (00254) (331) 30729
E-mail ackmnorth@swiftkenya.com

Maseno
South
Francis Mwayi Abiero
PO Box 114, 40100 Kisumu, Kenya
Tel (00254) (57) 43116 *or* 43511 *or* 45147
Fax (00254) (57) 21009
E-mail ackmsouth@swiftkenya.com

Maseno
West
Joseph Otieno Wasonga
PO Box 793, 40600 Siaya, Kenya
Tel (00254) (334) 21305
Fax (00254) (334) 21483

Mbeere
Gideon Grishon Ireri
PO Box 122, 60104 Siakago, Kenya
Tel (00254) (162) 21261
Fax (00254) (162) 21083
E-mail ackmbeere@swiftkenya.com

Meru
Charles Ndiga Mwendwa
PO Box 427, 60200 Meru, Kenya
Tel (00254) (164) 30719
E-mail ackmeru@swiftkenya.com

Mombasa
Julius Robert Kalu Katoi
PO Box 80072, 80100 Mombasa, Kenya
Tel (00254) (11) 311 105 *or* 316 361
Fax (00254) (11) 227 837
E-mail ackmsa@swiftmombasa.com

Mt Kenya
Central
Julius Gatambo Gachuche
PO Box 121, 10200 Murang'a, Kenya
Tel (00254) (156) 30560 *or* 30559
Fax (00254) (156) 22642
E-mail ackmkcentral@wananchi.com

(Assistant
Bishop)
Allan Waithaka
address etc as above

Mt Kenya
South
Peter Njenga
PO Box 886, 00900 Kiambu, Kenya
Tel (00254) (154) 22997 *or* 22521
Fax (00254) (154) 22408
E-mail ackmtksouth@swiftkenya.com

Mt Kenya
West
Alfred Charles Chipman
PO Box 229, 10100 Nyeri, Kenya
Tel (00254) (61) 2281 *or* 2191
Fax (00254) (61) 30214
E-mail ackmtkwest@africaonline.co.ke

Mumias
Beneah Justin Salala Okumu
PO Box 213, 50102 Mumias, Kenya
Tel (00254) (333) 41021
Fax (00254) (333) 41232
E-mail ackmumias@swiftkenya.com

Nairobi
Peter Njagi Njoka
PO Box 72846, 00200 Nairobi, Kenya
Tel (00254) (20) 228 146 *or* 226 337 *or* 229 189
Fax (00254) (20) 226 259
E-mail acknairobi@swiftkenya.com

Nakuru
Stephen Njihia Mwangi
PO Box 56, 20100 Nakuru, Kenya
Tel (00254) (37) 212 155 *or* 212 151
Fax (00254) (37) 44379
E-mail acknkudioc@net2000ke.com

Nambale
Josiah Makhandia Were
PO Box 4, 50409 Nambale, Kenya
Tel (00254) (336) 24040
Fax(00254) (336) 24071
E-mail acknambale@swiftkenya.com

Nyahururu
Charles Gaikia Gaita
PO Box 926, 20300 Nyahururu, Kenya
Tel (00254) (365) 32179
E-mail nyahu-dc@africaonline.co.ke

Southern
Nyanza
James Kenneth Okiel
PO Box 65, 40300 Homa Bay, Kenya
Tel (00254) (385) 22127
Fax (00254) (385) 22056
E-mail acksnyanza@swiftkenya.comcom *or*
acksnyanza@africaonline.co.ke

Taita Taveta
Samson Mwakitawa Mwaluda
PO Box 75, 80300 Voi, Kenya
Tel (00254) (147) 30096
Fax (00254) (147) 30364 *or* 31387
E-mail acktaita@swiftmombasa.com

Thika
Gideon Gichuhi Githiga
PO Box 214, Thika, Kenya
Tel (00254) (151) 21735 *or* 21561
Fax (00254) (151) 31544
E-mail ackthika@swiftkenya.com

KOREA

Pusan
Joseph Dae-yong Lee
455–2 Onchen-1-dong, Dongrea-Ku,
Pusan 607–600,
Republic of Korea
Tel (0082) (51) 554 5742
Fax (0082) (51) 553 9643
E-mail bpjoseph@hanmail.net

Seoul
(Primate)
Matthew Chul Bum Chung
3 Chong Dong, Chung Ku,
Seoul 100–120, Republic of Korea
Tel (0082) (2) 735 6157
Fax (0082) (2) 723 2640
E-mail mcbchung@hotmail.com

Taejon
Andrew Hyun Sam Sin
Anglican Church, PO Box 22,
Taejon 300–600, Republic of Korea
Tel (0082) (42) 256 9987
Fax (0082) (42) 255 8918
E-mail TDIO@unitel.co.kr

MELANESIA

Banks and Torres (formerly North Vanuatu)	Charles Tome c/o PO Box 19, Sola, Vanualava, Torba Province, Vanuatu Tel (00678) 38520 fax as telephone
Central Melanesia (Archbishop)	Sir Ellison Leslie Pogo Church of Melanesia, PO Box 19, Honiara, Solomon Islands Tel (00677) 21892 or 26601 Fax (00677) 21098 or 22072
Central Solomons	Charles Koete Church of Melanesia, PO Box 52, Tulagi, CIP, Solomon Islands Tel (00677) 32006 Fax (00677) 32199
Hanuato'o	James Philip Mason PO Box 20, Kira Kira, Makira/Ulawa Province, Solomon Islands Tel (00677) 50012 Fax (00677) 50155 or 50128
Malaita	Terry Michael Brown Bishop's House, PO Box 7, Auki Malaita, Solomon Islands Tel (00677) 40144 Fax (00677) 40027 E-mail terrymalaita@yahoo.com
Temotu	David Vunagi Bishop's House, Luesalo, Lata, Santa Cruz, Temotu Province, Solomon Islands Tel (00677) 53080 Fax (00677) 53092
Vanuatu	Hugh Blessing Boe Bishop's House, PO Box 238, Luganville, Santo, Vanuatu Tel (00678) 36026 or 36631 Fax (00678) 36631
Ysabel	vacant PO Box 6, Buala, Jejevo, Ysabel Province, Solomon Islands Tel (00677) 35034 Fax (00677) 35071

MEXICO

Cuernavaca	Ramiro Delgado-Vera Minerva No 1 Fracc. Delicias, Cuernavaca, Morelos, Mexico 62330 Tel (0052) (1777) 315 2870 or 322 2559 E-mail diovca@edsa.net.mx
Mexico	Carlos Touché Porter Ave San Jeronimo 117, Col S Angel, Deleg A Obregon, 01000, Mexico Tel (0052) (5) 616 3193 Fax (0052) (5) 616 2205 E-mail diomex@avantel.net
Northern Mexico	Marcelino Rivera Delgado Simón Bolivar 2005 Norte, Mitras Centro CP 64460, Monterrey NL, Mexico Tel (0052) (181) 8333 0392 Fax (0052) (181) 8348 7362 E-mail diocesisdelnorte@att.net.mx
Southeastern Mexico	Benito Juárez-Martinez Avenida de Las Americas #73, Col Aguacatal 91130 Xalapa, Vera Cruz, Mexico Tel (0052) (1228) 814 6951 Fax (0052) (1228) 814 4387 E-mail dioste99@aol.com
Western Mexico	Lino Rodriguez Amaro Fco. Javier Gamboa #255, Col Sector Juarez, 44100 Guadalajara, Jalisco, Mexico Tel (0052) (133) 3615 5070 Fax (0052) (133) 6616 4413 E-mail iamoccidente@prodigy.net

MYANMAR see **BURMA**

NEW ZEALAND
(AOTEAROA, NEW ZEALAND AND POLYNESIA)

Aotearoa	Whakahuihui Vercoe PO Box 146, Rotorua, New Zealand Tel (0064) (7) 348 6093 Fax (0064) (7) 348 6091 E-mail wvercoe@tpoa.org.nz
(East Coast Region)	William Brown Turei PO Box 1128, Napier, New Zealand Tel (0064) (6) 835 7467 Fax (0064) (6) 835 7465 E-mail browntmihi@xtra.co.nz
(Northern Region)	Te Kitohi Wiremu Pikaahu PO Box 43160, Mangere, Auckland, New Zealand Tel (0064) (9) 275 5335 Fax (0064) (9) 275 5341 E-mail tkwp@tokerau.ang.org.nz
(South Island)	John Robert Kuru Gray PO Box 10 086, Christchurch, New Zealand Tel (0064) (3) 389 1683 Fax (0064) (3) 389 0912 E-mail hawaipounamu@xtra.co.nz
(Southern Region)	Muru Walters 6 Rajaputana Way, Khandallah, Wellington, New Zealand Tel (0064) (4) 479 8549 Fax (0064) (4) 479 8513 E-mail muruwalters@compuserve.com
Auckland (Presiding Bishop and Primate)	John Campbell Paterson PO Box 37 242, Parnell, Auckland 1033, New Zealand Tel (0064) (9) 302 7202 Fax (0064) (9) 303 3321 E-mail bishop.auckland@xtra.co.nz or jampaterson68@hotmail.com
Christchurch	David John Coles PO Box 4438, Christchurch 8001, New Zealand Tel (0064) (3) 379 5950 Fax (0064) (3) 372 3357 or 384 8485 E-mail bishop@chch.ang.org.nz
Dunedin	Penelope Ann Bansall Jamieson PO Box 5445, Dunedin, New Zealand Tel (0064) (3) 477 4931 Fax (0064) (3) 477 4932 or 351 7917 E-mail pennydn@dn.ang.org.nz
Nelson	Derek Lionel Eaton PO Box 100, Nelson, New Zealand Tel (0064) (3) 548 3124 Fax (0064) (3) 548 2125 or 548 8991 E-mail +derek@nn.ang.org.nz
Polynesia (Co-Presiding Bishop)	Jabez Leslie Bryce Bishop's House, Box 35, Suva, Fiji Tel (00697) 330 4716 Fax (00697) 330 2687 E-mail episcopus@is.com.fj or diopolynesia@is.com.fj
Waiapu	John William Bluck PO Box 227, Napier, New Zealand Tel (0064) (6) 835 8230 Fax (0064) (6) 835 0680 E-mail john.waiapu@hb.ang.org.nz
(The Bay of Plenty)	George Howard Douglas Connor Bishop's House, 60 Judea Road, Tauranga, New Zealand Tel (0064) (7) 578 8619 Fax (0064) (7) 577 0684 E-mail georgebop@ang.org.nz or seoirse@clear.net.nz
Waikato	David John Moxon PO Box 21, Hamilton, New Zealand Tel (0064) (7) 838 2309 Fax (0064) (7) 838 0052 E-mail bishop@hn-ang.org.nz
(Taranaki)	Philip Richardson Te Awhina-Bishop's House, 566 Mangorei Road, New Plymouth, RD1, New Zealand Tel (0064) (6) 759 1178 Fax (0064) (6) 759 1180 E-mail philip.richardson@xtra.co.nz

Wellington	Thomas John Brown PO Box 12–046, Wellington, New Zealand Tel (0064) (4) 472 1057 Fax (0064) (4) 499 1360 E-mail bishoptom@paradise.net.nz

NIGERIA

PROVINCE OF ABUJA

Abuja (Primate and Archbishop)	Peter Jasper Akinola Archbishop's Palace, PO Box 212, ADCP, Abuja, Nigeria Tel (00234) (9) 523 6950 Fax (00234) (9) 523 0986 E-mail abuja@anglican.skannet.com.ng
(Suffragan)	Emmanuel Sokowamju Egbunu *address etc as above*
Bida	Jonah Kolo Bishop's House, St John's Mission Compound, PO Box 14, Bida, Nigeria Tel (00234) (66) 461 694
Gwagwalada	Tanimu Samari Aduda Diocesan Headquarters, Secretariat Road, PO Box 287, Gwagwalada, Abuja, Nigeria Tel (00234) (9) 882 2083 E-mail anggwag@skannet.com.ng
Kafanchan	William Weh Diya Bishopscourt, 5B Jemma'a Street, PO Box 29, Kafanchan, Kaduna State, Nigeria Tel (00234) (61) 20 634
Lafia	Miller Kangdim Maza PO Box 560, Lafia, Nasarawa State, Nigeria Tel (00234) (47) 20 700
Lokoja	George Bako PO Box 11, Lokoja, Kogi State, Nigeria Tel (00234) (58) 220 588 Fax (00234) (58) 220 788 E-mail lok-anglican@beta.linkserve.com
Makurdi	Nathaniel Nyitar Inyom Bishopscourt, PO Box 1, Makurdi, Benue State, Nigeria Tel (00234) (44) 533 349 *fax as telephone* E-mail makurdi@anglican.skannet.com.ng
Minna	Nathaniel Yisa Bishopscourt, Dutsen Kura, PO Box 2469, Minna, Nigeria Tel (00234) (66) 220 035
Oturkpo	Ityobe Ugede St John's Cathedral, Sgt Ugbade Ave, PO Box 360, Oturkpo, Benue State, Nigeria

PROVINCE OF BENDEL

Asaba	Nicholas D Okoh Bishopscourt, Cable Point, PO Box 216, Asaba, Delta State, Nigeria Tel (00234) (56) 280 682
Benin	Abednego A Edionwe Bishopscourt, PO Box 82, Benin City, Edo State, Nigeria Tel (00234) (52) 250 552
Esan	Friday John Imaekhai Bishopscourt, Ujoelen, PO Box 921, Ekpoma, Edo State, Nigeria Tel (00234) (55) 981 079
Ikka	Peter Onekpe Bishopscourt, c/o PO Box 5, Agbor, Delta State, Nigeria Tel (00234) (55) 25 014
Oleh	Jonathan Francis Ekokotu Edewor, JP PO Box 8, Oleh, Delta State, Nigeria Tel (00234) (53) 701 062
Sabongidda-Ora (Archbishop)	Albert A Agbaje Bishopscourt, PO Box 13, Sabongidda-Ora, Edo State, Nigeria Tel (00234) (57) 54 132

Ughelli	Vincent O Muoghereh Bishopscourt, Ovurodawanre, PO Box 760, Ughelli, Delta State, Nigeria Tel (00234) (53) 600 403 Fax (00234) (53) 250 091
Warri	Nathaniel A Enuku Bishopscourt, 17 Mabiaku Road, GRA, PO Box 4571, Warri, Nigeria Tel (00234) (53) 255 857 E-mail angwar@skannet.com

PROVINCE OF IBADAN

Ibadan (Archbishop)	Joseph Akinfenwa Bishopscourt, PO Box 3075, Mapo, Ibadan, Nigeria Tel (00234) (2) 810 1400 Fax (00234) (2) 810 1413 E-mail ibadan@anglican.skannet.com.ng *or* bishop@ibadan.skannet.com.ng
Ibadan North	'Segun Okubadejo Bishopscourt, Moyede, PO Box 182, Dugbe, Ibadan, Nigeria Tel (00234) (2) 8107 482 E-mail angibn@skannet.com
Ibadan South	Jacob Ademola Ajetunmobi Bishopscourt, PO Box 166, St David's Compound, Kudeti, Ibadan, Nigeria Tel (00234) (2) 231 9141 *or* 241 4409 Fax (00234) (22) 231 9141 E-mail jacajet@skannet.com.ng
Ife	Gabriel B Oloniyo Bishopscourt, PO Box 312, Ile-Ife, Osun State, Nigeria Tel (00234) (36) 230 046
Igbomina	Michael Oluwakayode Akinyemi Bishopscourt, Esie, PO Box 102, Oro PA , Kwara State, Nigeria
Ilesa	Olubayu Samuel Sowale Diocesan Headquarters, Muroko Road, PO Box 237, Ilesa, Nigeria Tel (00234) (36) 460138 *or* 460592
Kwara	Jeremiah Olagbamigbe A Fabuluje Bishopscourt, Fate Road, PO Box 1884, Ilorin, Kwara State, Nigeria Tel (00234) (31) 220 879 E-mail kwara@anglican.skannet.com.ng
Offa	Gabriel Akinbolarin Akinbiyi PO Box 21, Offa, Kwarra State, Nigeria Tel (00234) (31) 801 011 E-mail offa@anglican.skannet.com.ng
Oke-Osun	Nathaniel Fasogbon Bishopscourt, PO Box 251, Gbongan, Osun State, Nigeria
Osun	James Afolabi Popoola Bishopscourt, Isale-Aro, PO Box 285, Osogbo, Nigeria Tel (00234) (35) 240 325

PROVINCE OF JOS

Bauchi	Laudamus Ereaku Bishop's House, 2 Hospital Road, PO Box 2450, Bauchi, Nigeria Tel (00234) (77) 543460 E-mail bauchi@anglican.skannet.com.ng
Damaturu	Daniel Abu Yisa PO Box 312, Damaturu, Yobe State, Nigeria Tel (00234) (76) 522142
Gombe	Henry Chukwudum Ndukuba St Peter's Cathedral, PO Box 39, Gombe, Nigeria Tel (00234) (72) 220 489 *or* 221212 Fax (00234) (72) 221 141 E-mail hcndukuba@yahoo.com
Jalingo	Simon Peters Mutum PO Box 4, Jalingo, Taraba State, Nigeria Tel (00234) (79) 23312 *fax as telephone* E-mail jalingo@anglican.skannet.com.ng *or* bishop@cyberspace.net.ng

Jos
Benjamin Argak Kwashi
Bishopscourt, PO Box 6283,
Jos, Plateau State, Nigeria
Tel (00234) (73) 612 221
fax as telephone
E-mail jos@anglican.skannet.com.ng *or*
hillcrest@maf.org

Maiduguri
(Archbishop)
Emmanuel K Mani
Bishopscourt, Off Lagos Street,
GRA PO Box 1693, Maiduguri,
Borno State, Nigeria
Tel (00234) (76) 234 010
fax as telephone
E-mail maiduguri@anglican.skannet.com.ng

Yola
Christian Ogochukwu Efobi
PO Box 601, Yola, Adamawa State, Nigeria
Tel (00234) (75) 624 303

PROVINCE OF KADUNA

Dutse
Yesufu Ibrahim Lumu
PO Box 67, Yadi, Dutse, Jigawa State, Nigeria
Tel (00234) (64) 721 379

Gusau
Simon Bala
PO Box 64, Gusau, Zamfara State, Nigeria
Tel (00234) (63) 200 957
E-mail gusau@anglican.skannet.com.ng

Kaduna
(Archbishop)
Josiah Idowu-Fearon
PO Box 72, Kaduna, Nigeria
Tel (00234) (62) 240 085
Fax (00234) (62) 244 408
E-mail manasoko@infoweb.abs.net

Kano
Zakka Lalle Nyam
Bishopscourt, PO Box 362, Kano, Nigeria
Tel (00234) (64) 647 816
fax as telephone
E-mail kano@anglican.skannet.com.ng

Katsina
James Sekari Kwasu
Bishop's Lodge, PO Box 904, Katsina, Nigeria
Tel (00234) (65) 32 718

Kebbi
Edmund Efoyikeye Akanya
PO Box 701, Birnin Kebbi, Kebbi State, Nigeria
Tel (00234) (68) 321 179
fax as telephone
E-mail kebbi@anglican.skannet.com

Sokoto
Augustine Omole
Bishop's Lodge, 68 Shuni Road,
PO Box 3489, Sokoto, Nigeria
Tel (00234) (60) 234 639
E-mail sokoto@anglican.skannet.com.ng

Wusasa
Ali Buba Lamido
Box 28, Wusasa Zaria, Kaduna State, Nigeria
Tel (00234) (69) 334 594
E-mail wusasa@anglican.skannet.com.ng

PROVINCE OF LAGOS

Egba
Matthew Oluremi Owadayo
Bishopscourt, Onikolobo, PO Box 267,
Ibara, Abeokuta, Nigeria
Tel (00234) (39) 241 235
Fax (00234) (39) 240 933
E-mail angega-egba@anglican.scannet.com.ng

Ijebu
Joseph Akinyele Omoyajowo
Bishopscourt, Ejirin Road,
PO Box 112, Ijebu-Ode, Nigeria
Tel (00234) (37) 431 801

Ikale-Ilaje
Joshua Ogunele
Bishopscourt, Ikoya Road, PMB 3,
Ilutitun-Osooro, Ondo State, Nigeria

Lagos
(Archbishop)
Ephraim Adebola Ademowo
Archbishop's Palace, 29 Marina,
PO Box 13, Lagos, Nigeria
Tel (00234) (1) 263 6026
Fax (00234) (1) 263 6536
E-mail bishop@rcl.nig.com

Lagos West
Peter A Adebiyi
Vining House (2nd Floor),
Archbishop Vining Memorial Cathedral,
Oba Akinjobi Road, GRA Ikeja, Nigeria
Tel (00234) (51) 493 7333

Remo
Elijah Oluremi Ige Ogundana
Bishopscourt, Ewusi Street, PO Box 522,
Sagamu, Ogun State, Nigeria
Tel (00234) (37) 640 598

Yewa
Simeon O M Adebola
Bishopscourt, PO Box 484,
Ilaro, Ogun State, Nigeria
Tel (00234) (39) 440 695

PROVINCE OF THE NIGER

Abakaliki
Benson C B Onyeibor
All Saints' Cathedral, PO Box 112,
Abakaliki, Ebonyi State, Nigeria
Tel (00234) (43) 20 762

Awka
(Archbishop)
Maxwell Samuel Chike Anikwenwa
Bishopscourt, Ifite Road, PO Box 130,
Awka, Anambra State, Nigeria
Tel (00234) (48) 550 058
Fax (00234) (48) 550 052
E-mail angawka@infoweb.abs.net

Enugu
Emmanuel O Chukwuma
Bishop's House, PO Box 418, Enugu, Nigeria
Tel (00234) (42) 339 808
Fax (00234) (42) 259 808

The Niger
(Bishop *on*)
Ken Okeke
PO Box 42, Onitsha, Nigeria
Tel (00234) (46) 210 337

Nnewi
Godwin Izundu Nmezinwa Okpala
c/o Bishopscourt
(opposite Total Filling station),
PO Box 2630, Uruagu-Nnewi,
Anambra State, Nigeria
Tel (00234) (46) 460 226
Fax (00234) (46) 462 676
E-mail nnewi@anglican.skannet.com.ng

Nsukka
Jonah C Iloñuba
PO Box 516, Nsukka, Enugu State, Nigeria
Tel (00234) (42) 771 229

Oji River
Amos Amankechinelo Madu
PO Box 213, Oji River,
Enuga, Nigeria

PROVINCE OF NIGER DELTA

Aba
Ugochuckwu Uwaoma Ezuoke
Bishopscourt, 70/72 St Michael's Road,
PO Box 212, Aba, Nigeria
Tel (00234) (82) 220 231

Calabar
Tunde Adeleye
Bishopscourt, PO Box 74, Calabar,
Cross River State, Nigeria
Tel (00234) (87) 232 812
Fax (00234) (88) 220 835

The Niger
Delta
Gabriel H Pepple
Bishopcourt, PO Box 115,
Port Harcourt, Rivers State, Nigeria
Tel (00234) (84) 233 308

Niger Delta
North
Ignatius Kattey
PO Box 53, Port Harcourt,
Rivers State, Nigeria
Tel (00234) (84) 231 338
E-mail niger-delta-
north@anglican.skannet.com.ng

Niger Delta
West
Adoluphus Amabebe
Bishopscourt, PO Box 10,
Yenagoa, Bayelsa, Nigeria
Tel (00234) (84) 490 010

Ukwa
Uju Otuokwesiri Wachukwu Obinya
PO Box 20468, Aba, Nigeria

Uyo
(Archbishop)
Emmanuel E Nglass
Bishopscourt, PO Box 70, Uyo,
Akwa Ibom State, Nigeria
Tel (00234) (85) 204 142
Fax (00234) (85) 200 451

PROVINCE OF ONDO

Akoko
O O Obijole
PO Box 572, Ikare-Akoko,
Ondo State, Nigeria
Tel (00234) (50) 670 668
E-mail
akoko@anglican.skannet.com.ng

Akure	Michael Ipinmoye Bishopscourt, PO Box 1622, Akure, Nigeria Tel (00234) (34) 241 572 *fax as telephone* E-mail akdangc@akure.rcl.nig.com	New Guinea Islands, The	Allan Migi Bishop's House, PO Box 806, Kimbe, Papua New Guinea Tel (00675) 9 835 120 *fax as telephone*
Ekiti (Archbishop)	Samuel Adedaye Abe Bishopscourt, PO Box 12, Okesa Street, Ado-Ekiti, Ekiti State, Nigeria Tel (00234) (30) 250 305 E-mail ekiti@anglican.skannet.com.ng	Popondota	Roger Jupp Anglican Diocese of Popondota, PO Box 26, Popondetta, Oro Province, Papua New Guinea Tel (00675) 329 7194
Ekiti West	Samuel Oludare Oke Bishop's Residence, 6 Ifaki Street, PO Box 477, Ijero-Ekiti, Nigeria Tel (00234) (30) 850 314		Fax (00675) 329 7476 E-mail acpngpop@global.net.pg
		Port Moresby	Peter John Fox PO Box 6491, Boroko, NCD
Kabba	Solomon Olaife Oyelade Bishopscourt, Obaro Way, PO Box 62, Kabba, Kogi State, Nigeria Tel (00234) (58) 300 633		Port Moresby, Papua New Guinea Tel (00675) 323 2489 Fax (00675) 326 2493 E-mail acpngpom@global.net.pg *or*
Ondo	George L Lasebikan Bishopscourt, College Road, PO Box 265, Ondo, Nigeria Tel (00234) (34) 610 718		foxfamily@daltron.com.pg

THE PHILIPPINES

Owo	James Adedayo Oladunjoye Bishopscourt, PO Box 472, Owo, Ondo State, Nigeria Tel (00234) (51) 241 463 E-mail owo@anglican.skannet.com.ng	Prime Bishop	Ignacio Capuyan Soliba PO Box 10321, Broadway Centrum 1112 Quezon City, Philippines *or* 275 E Rodriguez Sr Avenue 1102 Quezon City, Philippines Tel (0063) (2) 722 8478, 722 8481 *or* 722 9459 Fax (0063) (2) 721 1923

PROVINCE OF OWERRI

Egbu	Emmanuel Uchechukwu Iheagwam All Saints' Cathedral, PO Box 1967, Owerri, Imo State, Nigeria Tel (00234) (83) 231 797		E-mail soliba@edsamail.com.ph, ECT@phil.gn.apc.org *or* soliba@ail.com.ph
		Central Philippines	Benjamin Gayno Botengan *address as above* Tel (0063) (2) 412 8561 *or* 412 8558 Fax (0063) (2) 724 2143
Ideato	Godson Chinyere Echefu Bishopscourt, PO Box 2, Ndizuogu, Imo State, Nigeria	North Central Philippines	Joel A Pachao 358 Magsaysay Avenue,
Mbaise	Bright Joseph Egemasi Ogu Bishopscourt, PO Box 10, Ife, Ezinihitte Mbaise, Imo State, Nigeria Tel (00234) (83) 233 438 Fax (00234) (83) 233 575		Baguio City 2600, Philippines Tel (0063) (74) 443 7705 Fax (0063) (74) 442 2432 E-mail edncp@bgo.csi.com.ph
	E-mail bon@infoweb.abs.net	Northern Luzon	Renato M Abibico Bulanao, 3800 Tabuk,
Okigwe North	Alfred Iheanyichukwu Sunday Nwaizuzu PO Box 156, Okigwe, Imo State, Nigeria Tel (00234) (88) 420 800		Kalinga, Philippines Tel (0063) (74) 872 2295 Fax (0063) (74) 872 2013
Okigwe South	Caleb Anny Maduoma Bishopscourt, Ezeoke Nsu, PO Box 235, Nsu, Ehime Mbano LGA, Imo State, Nigeria	Northern Philippines	Edward Pacyaya Malecdan Diocesan Center, Bontoc 2616, Mountain Province, Philippines Tel (0063) (74) 602 1026 *fax as telephone*
Orlu (Archbishop)	Bennett C I Okoro Bishopscourt, PO Box 260, Nkwerre, Imo State, Nigeria Tel (00234) (82) 440 538	(Suffragan)	Miguel Paredes Yamoyam *address etc as above* E-mail brentednp@hotmail.com
Owerri	Cyril Chukwunonyerem Okorocha Bishop's Bourne, PO Box 31, Owerri, Imo State, Nigeria Tel (00234) (83) 230 417	Santiago	Alexander A Wandag Sr Episcopal Diocese of Santiago, Divisoria, 3311 Santiago City, Isabela, Philippines
	Fax (00234) (82) 440 183 E-mail owerri@anglican.skannet.com.ng	Southern Philippines	James Buanda Manguramas 186 Sinsuat Avenue, Rosario Heights,
Umuahia	Ikechi Nwachukwa Nwosu St Stephen's Cathedral Church Compound, PO Box 96, Umuahia, Nigeria Tel (00234) (88) 220 037 *fax as telephone* E-mail umuahia@ang-nig.org		Cotabato City 9600, Philippines Tel (0063) (64) 421 2960 Fax (0063) (64) 421 1703 E-mail edsp@ndu.fapenet.org

PAPUA NEW GUINEA

RWANDA

		Butare	Venuste Mutiganda BP 255, Butare, Rwanda
Aipo Rongo (Archbishop)	James Simon Ayong PO Box 893, Mount Hagen, Western Highlands Province, Papua New Guinea Tel (00675) 542 1131 Fax (00675) 542 1181 E-mail acpnghgn@global.net.pg		Tel (00250) 30710 Fax (00250) 30504
		Byumba	Onesphore Rwaje BP 17, Byumba, Rwanda Tel (00250) 64242 *fax as telephone* E-mail mangab@rwandatel1.rwanda1.com
Dogura	Tevita Talanoa PO Box 19, Dogura, MBP, Papua New Guinea Tel (00675) 641 1530 Fax (00675) 641 1129	Cyangugu	Geoffrey Rwubusisi PO Box 52, Cyangugu, Rwanda Tel (00250) 537877 *or* 537878 Fax (00250) 537877

Gahini   Alexis Bilindabagabo
BP 22, Kigali, Rwanda
Tel (00250) 67422
Fax (00250) 67831

Kibungo   Josias Sendegaya
EER Kibungo Diocese,
BP 719, Kibungo, Rwanda
Tel (00250) 566194
E-mail peer@rwanda.com

Kigali   Emmanuel Musaba Kolini
(Archbishop)   EER/DK, BP 61, Kigali, Rwanda
Tel (00250) 573213
fax as telephone
E-mail sonja914@compuserve.com

Kigeme   Augustin Mvunabandi
BP 67, Gikongoro, Rwanda
Tel (00250) 535086 *or* 535088
E-mail dkigeme@mail.rw

Shyira   John Rucyahana Kabango
EER – Shyira Diocese, BP 26, Kigali, Rwanda
Tel (00250) 546449
fax as telephone
E-mail bpjohnr@rwanda1.com

Shyogwe   Jéred Kalimba
BP 27, Gitarama, Rwanda
Tel (00250) 62460 *or* 62469
Fax (00254) 62469
E-mail rds@rwandatel1.rwanda1.com

SOUTH EAST ASIA

Kuching   Made Katib
Bishop's House, PO Box 347,
93704 Kuching, Sarawak, Malaysia
Tel (0060) (82) 240 187 *or* 240 188
Fax (0060) (82) 426 488
E-mail bkg@pc.jaring.my

(Assistant)   Bolly Anak Lapok
address and fax as above
Tel (0060) (82) 429 755
E-mail blapok@tm.net.my

Sabah   Datuk Ping Chung Yong
(Archbishop)   PO Box 10811, 88809 Kota Kinabalu,
Sabah, Malaysia
Tel (0060) (88) 245 846 *or* 249 296
Fax (0060) (88) 245 942
E-mail pcyong@pc.jaring.my

(Assistant)   Chen Fah Yong
Church of the Good
Samaritan, PO Box 12320,
88826 Kota Kinabalu, Sabah, Malaysia
Tel (0060) (88) 212 686
Fax (0060) (88) 211 807
E-mail goodsam@pd.jaring.my

Singapore   John Chew
4 Bishopsgate, Singapore 249970
Tel (0065) 6474 1661
Fax (0065) 6479 1054
E-mail johnchew@anglican.org.sg

West Malaysia   Tan Sri Datuk Dr Lim Cheng Ean
14 Pesiaran Stonor,
50450 Kuala Lumpur, Malaysia
Tel (0060) (3) 2031 2728
Fax (0060) (3) 2031 3225
E-mail diocese@tm.net.my

(Assistant)   Moses Elisha Ponniah
St Barnabas Church,
4 Jalan Dato Hamzah, 41000 Kelang
Selangor, Malaysia
Tel (0060) (3) 3372 8191
Fax (0060) (3) 3373 7223
E-mail stbarnak@tm.net.my

SOUTHERN AFRICA

Angola   Andre Soares
(missionary   Av Lenini, Travessa D Antonia,
diocese)   Saldanha N 134, CP 10 1498, Angola
Tel (00224) (2) 395 792
Fax (00224) (2) 393 746

Bloemfontein   Elistan Patrick Glover
PO Box 411, Bloemfontein
9300, South Africa
Tel (0027) (51) 447 6053
Fax (0027) (51) 447 5874
E-mail pglover@yebo.co.za

Cape Town   Njongonkulu Winston Hugh Ndungane
(Archbishop)   20 Bishopscourt, Claremont,
Cape Town 7708, South Africa
Tel (0027) (21) 761 2531
Fax (0027) (21) 797 1298 *or* 761 4193
E-mail archbish@iafrica.com

(False Bay)   Mervyn Edwin Castle
PO Box 2804, Somerset West
7129, South Africa
Tel (0027) (21) 852 9544
Fax (0027) (21) 852 9430
E-mail mcastle@cpsa.org.za

(Table Bay)   *vacant*
Diocesan Office, PO Box 1932,
Cape Town 8000, South Africa
Tel (0027) (21) 465 1557
Fax (0027) (21) 465 7686
E-mail tablebay@ctdiocese.org.za

(Saldanha Bay)   Justus Mauritius Marcus,
PO Box 420, Malmesbury 7299, South Africa
Tel (0027) (22) 487 3885
Fax (0027) (22) 487 3886
E-mail justus@xsinet.co.za

Christ the King   Peter John Lee
Diocese of Christ the King, PO Box 1653,
Rosettenville 2130, South Africa
Tel (0027) (11) 435 0097
Fax (0027) (11) 435 2868
E-mail dckpeter@corpdial.co.za

George   Donald Frederick Harker
PO Box 227, George 6530, South Africa
Tel (0027) (44) 873 5646
Fax (0027) (44) 873 2267 *or* 873 5680
E-mail dharker@intekom.co.za *or*
diocese.g@pixie.co.za

Grahamstown   David Patrick Hamilton Russell
Bishopsbourne, PO Box 162,
Grahamstown 6140, South Africa
Tel (0027) (46) 636 1995 *or* 636 1996
Fax (0027) (46) 622 5231
E-mail bpgtn@intekom.co.za

(Suffragan)   Thabo Cecil Makgoba
PO Box 1772, Queenstown 5320, South Africa
Tel (0027) (45) 838 2874
fax as telephone
E-mail thabom@pixie.co.za

The Highveld   David Albert Beetge
(formerly   PO Box 563, Brakpan 1540, South Africa
South Eastern   Tel (0027) (11) 740 1154 *or* 740 1447
Transvaal)   Fax (0027) (11) 740 9156
E-mail dbeetge@iafrica.com

Johannesburg   Brian Charles Germond
PO Box 1131, Johannesburg 2000, South Africa
Tel (0027) (11) 336 8724
Fax (0027) (11) 333 3053 *or* 486 1015
E-mail jhbishop@cpsa.org.za

Kimberley and   Itumeleng Baldwin Moseki
Kuruman   PO Box 45, Kimberley 8300, South Africa
Tel (0027) (53) 833 2433
Fax (0027) (53) 831 2730
E-mail ibmoseki@cpsa.org.za

Lebombo   Dinis Salomão Sengulane
CP 120, Maputo, Mozambique
Tel (00258) (1) 405364 *or* 404885
Fax (00258) (1) 401093
E-mail libombos@zebra.uem.mz

Lesotho   Joseph Mahapu Tsubella
PO Box 87, Maseru 100, Lesotho
Tel (00266) 311974 *or* 314185
Fax (00266) 310161
E-mail diocese@ilesotho.com

Matlosane	David Cecil Tapi Nkwe PO Box 11417, Klerksdorp 2570, South Africa Tel (0027) (18) 462 5530 *or* 464 2260 Fax (0027) (18) 462 4939 E-mail dnkwe@wn.apc.org
Namibia	Nehemiah Shihala Hamupembe PO Box 57, Windhoek 9000, Namibia Tel (00264) (61) 238920 *fax as telephone* E-mail anglican@iafrica.com.na
(Suffragan)	Petrus Hidulika Hilukiluah PO Box 65, Windhoek, Namibia Tel (00264) (61) 236 009 Mobile (00264) 81 127 7089 Fax (00264) (61) 203 5057
Natal	Rubin Phillip PO Box 47439, Greyville 4023, South Africa Tel (0027) (31) 309 2066 Fax (0027) (31) 308 9316 E-mail rphillip@cpsa.org.za
(Central)	Funginkosi Mbhele Private Bag 899, Pietermaritzburg 3200, South Africa Tel (0027) (33) 394 1560 Fax (0027) (33) 394 8785 E-mail bisnatal@mweb.co.za
(Coast)	Elijah Thwala PO Box 47439, Greyville 4023, South Africa Tel (0027) (31) 308 9314 Fax (0027) (31) 308 9316 E-mail bishsuff@mweb.co.za
Niassa	Mark van Koevering Diocese do Niassa, CP 264, Lichinga, Niassa, Mozambique Tel (00258) 712 0735 *fax as telephone* E-mail diocese.niassa@teledata.mz *or* mark@koev.freeserve.co.uk
Order of Ethiopia (Bishop of the)	Sigzibo Dwane PO Box 46803, Glosderry 7702, South Africa Tel (0027) (21) 683 0006 Fax (0027) (21) 683 0008 E-mail sdwane@yebo.co.za
Port Elizabeth	Nceba Bethlehem Nopece PO Box 7109, Newton Park 6055, South Africa Tel (0027) (41) 365 1387 Fax (0027) (41) 365 2049 E-mail pebishop@iafrica.com
Pretoria	Johannes T Seoka PO Box 1032, Pretoria 0001, South Africa Tel (0027) (12) 322 2218 Fax (0027) (12) 322 9411 E-mail ptabish@cpsa.org.za
(Suffragan)	Mazwi Ernst Tisani PO Box 688, White River 1240, South Africa Tel (0027) (13) 750 3093 *fax as telephone* E-mail mazwi@inx.co.za
St Helena	John William Salt Bishopsholme, PO Box 62, St Helena Island, South Atlantic Ocean Tel (00290) 4471 Fax (00290) 4728 E-mail bishop@helanta.sh
St John's	Sitembele Tobela Mzamane PO Box 25, Umtata 5100, South Africa Tel (0027) (47) 432 4450 Fax (0027) (47) 532 4191 E-mail diocese@intekom.co.za
St Mark the Evangelist	Martin Andre Breytenbach PO Box 643, Pietersburg 0700, South Africa Tel (0027) (15) 297 3297 Fax (0027) (15) 297 0408 E-mail stmarks@pixie.co.za *or* breytie@cpsa.org.za

Swaziland	Meshack Boy Mabuza Bishop's House, Muir Street, Mbabane, Swaziland Tel (00268) 404 3624 Fax (00268) 404 6571 E-mail anglicanchurch@africaonline.co.sz *or* bishopmabuza@africaonline.co.sz
Umzimvubu	Geoffrey Francis Davies PO Box 644, Kokstad 4700, South Africa Tel (0027) (39) 727 6351 Fax (0027) (39) 727 4117 E-mail umzimvubu@futurenet.co.za
Zululand	Anthony Thembinkosi Mdletshe PO Box 147, Eshowe, Zululand 3815, South Africa Tel (0027) (354) 742047 *fax as telephone* E-mail zlddio@netactive.co.za

SOUTHERN CONE OF AMERICA

Argentina	Gregory James Venables Conesa 1925 1B, (1428) Belgrano, Capital Federal, Buenos Aires, Argentina Tel (0054) (11) 4342 4618 Fax (0054) (11) 4784 1277 E-mail bpgreg@ciudad.com.ar
Bolivia	Franciso Lyons Iglesia Anglicana Episcopal de Bolivia, Casilla 848, Cochabamba, Bolivia Tel (00591) (2) 371414 *fax as telephone* E-mail anglicanabolivia@mail.megalink.com
Chile	Hector Zavala Casilla 50675, Correo Central, Santiago, Chile Tel (0056) (2) 638 3009 *or* 639 1509 Fax (0056) (2) 639 4581 E-mail tzavala@evangel.cl *or* episcopado.iach@evangel.cl
(Assistant)	Abelino Manuel Apeleo Casilla de Correo 26-D, Temuco, Chile Tel (0056) (45) 211 1130 *fax as telephone* E-mail apeleo@entelchile.net
Northern Argentina	Maurice Sinclair Iglesia Anglicana, Casilla de Correo 187, 4400 Salta, Argentina Tel (0054) (387) 431 1718 Fax (0054) (387) 431 2622 E-mail sinclair@salnet.com.ar
(Assistants)	Mario Lorenzo Mariño Casilla 19, CP 3636 Ingeniero Juárez, FCNGB Formosa, Argentina Tel (0054) (387) 431 1718 Fax (0054) (387) 431 2622
	Humberto Edmundo Axt Casilla de Correo 187, 4400 Salta, Argentina Tel (0054) (387) 431 1718 *or* 439 1033 Fax (0054) (387) 431 2622 E-mail diamd.epi@salnet.com.ar *or* flnaxt@salnet.com.ar
Paraguay	John Alexander Ellison Iglesia Anglicana Paraguya, Casilla de Correo 1124, Asunción, Paraguay Tel (00595) (21) 200 933 *or* 214 795 Fax (00595) (21) 214 328 E-mail jellison@pla.net.py *or* lapar@sce.cnc.una.py
Peru	Harold William Godfrey Calle Alcalá 336, Urb la Castellana, Santiago de Surco, Lima 33, Peru Tel (0051) (1) 444 9622 Fax (0051) (1) 445 3044 E-mail wgodfrey@amauta.rcp.net.pe
Uruguay	Miguel Tamayo Casilla de Correos 6108, 11000 Montevideo, Uruguay Tel (00598) (2) 915 9627 Fax (00598) (2) 916 2519 E-mail mtamayo@netgate.com.uy *or* anglican@netgate.com.uy

SUDAN

Bor
Nathaniel Garang Anyieth
c/o NSCC, PO Box 66168, Nairobi, Kenya
Tel (00254) (733) 855 521
E-mail nscc@iconnect.c.ke

Cueibet
Reuben Macier Makoi
c/o CEAS, PO Box 40870, Nairobi, Kenya
Fax (00254) (2) 570 807

El-Obeid
Ismail Gibreil Abudigan
PO Box 211, El-Obeid, Sudan
E-mail ecsprovince@hotmail.com

Ezo
Benjamin John Ruati
c/o ECS, PO Box 7576, Kampala, Uganda
Tel (00256) (41) 343 497
E-mail ecs-kpa@africaonline.co.ug

Ibba
Levi Hassan Nzakora
c/o ECS, PO Box 7576, Kampala, Uganda
Tel (00256) (41) 343 497
E-mail ecs-kpa@africaonline.co.ug

Juba
(Archbishop)
Joseph Biringi Hassan Marona
PO Box 110, Juba, Sudan
Tel (00249) (811) 20065
E-mail ecsprovince@hotmail.com

Kadugli and
Nuba
Mountains
Andudu Adam Elnail
PO Box 35, Kadugli, Sudan
Tel (00249) (631) 22898
E-mail kadudiocese@hotmail.com

Kajo-Keji
Manasseh Benyi Dawidi
PO Box 26833, Kampala, Uganda
Tel (00256) (41) 343 497
E-mail ecs-kpa@africaonline.co.ug

Khartoum
Bulus T Idris Tia
PO Box 65, Omdurman, 35 Khartoum, Sudan
Fax (00249) (11) 556 931
E-mail ecsprovince@hotmail.com

Lainya
Peter Amidi
c/o ECS, PO Box 7576, Kampala, Uganda
Tel (00256) (77) 658 753
E-mail petamidi@yahoo.com

Lui
Bullen A Dolli
PO Box 60837, Nairobi, Kenya
Tel (00452) (2) 720 037
Fax (00254) (2) 714 420
E-mail luidiocese@wananchi.com

Malakal
(Vicar General)
Daniel Deng Anyaiany
c/o PO Box 604, Khartoum, Sudan
E-mail ecsprovince@hotmail.com

Maridi
Justin Badi Arama
c/o ECS, PO Box 7576, Kampala, Uganda
Tel (00256) (41) 343 497
E-mail ecs-kpa@africaonline.co.ug

Mundri
(Dean of the
Province)
Eluzai Gima Munda
c/o ECS, PO Box 7576, Kampala, Uganda
Tel (00256) (41) 343 497
E-mail ecs-kpa@africaonline.co.ug

Port Sudan
Yousif Abdalla Kuku
PO Box 278, Port Sudan, Sudan
Tel (00249) (311) 21224
E-mail ecsprovince@hotmail.com

Rejaf
Michael Sokiri Lugör
PO Box 110, Juba, Sudan
Tel (00249) (811) 20065
E-mail ecsprovince@hotmail.com

Renk
Daniel Deng Bul
PO Box 1532, Khartoum North, Sudan
Tel (00249) (11) 775 742
Mobile (00249) 122 99275
E-mail ecs_renk@hotmail.com

Rokon
Francis Loyo
PO Box 6702, Nairobi 00100 APO, Kenya
or PO Box 734 Arua, Uganda
Tel (00254) (2) 568 541 or 539
Fax (00254) (2) 560 864

Reumbek
(Vicar General)
Abraham Mayom Athian
c/o ECS, PO Box 7576, Kampala, Uganda
Tel (00256) (41) 343 497
E-mail ecs-kpa@africaonline.co.ug

Torit
Wilson Arop
PO Box 26157, Kampala, Uganda
Tel (00256) (41) 230 015
E-mail ecstorit@africaonline.co.ug

Wau
Henry Cuir Riak
c/o CMS Nairobi, Po Box 56 Nakuru, Kenya
Tel (00254) (37) 43186
E-mail riakcuir@yahoo.com

Yambio
Peter Munde Yacoub
c/o ECS, PO Box 7576, Kampala, Uganda
Tel (00256) (41) 343 497
Mobile (00256) 77 622 367
fax as telephone
E-mail ecs-kpa@africaonline.co.ug *or*
esc-kpa@africaonline.org

Yei
Seme Luate Solomona
c/o PO Box 370, Arua, Uganda
Tel (00256) (41) 343 497
E-mail ecs-kpa@africaonline.co.ug

(Assistant)
Hilary Luate Adeba
PO Box 588, Arua, Uganda
Tel (00256) (756) 56175
E-mail ecs-kpa@africaonline.co.ug

Yirol
Benjamin Mangar Mamur
c/o St Matthew's Church, PO Box 39,
Eldoret, Kenya
Tel (00254) (2) 720037 *or* 720056
Fax (00254) (2) 714420
E-mail cms-nbi@maf.org

TANZANIA

Central
Tanganyika
Godfrey Mdimi Mhogolo
Makay House, PO Box 15,
Dodoma, Tanzania
Tel (00255) (26) 232 4050 *or* 221509
Fax (00255) (26) 232 0004
E-mail mhogolo@twiga.com

(Assistant)
Ainea Kusenha
address etc as above

Dar-es-Salaam
Valentino Mokiwa
PO Box 25016, Ilala,
Dar-es-Salaam, Tanzania
Tel (00255) (22) 286 5839
Fax (00255) (22) 286 5840
E-mail mokiwa_valentine@hotmail.com

Kagera
Aaron Kijanjali
PO Box 18, Ngara, Tanzania
Tel (00255) (28) 222 3624
Fax (00255) (871) 176 0266
E-mail act-kagera@maf.or.tz

Kondoa
Yohana Zakaria Mkavu
PO Box 7, Kondoa, Tanzania
Tel (00255) (26) 2321 543

Mara
Hilkiah Deya Omindo
PO Box 131, Musoma, Tanzania
Tel (00255) (28) 262 2376
Fax (00255) (28) 262 2414
E-mail maracpt@maf.org

Masasi
Patrick Mwachiko
Private Bag, PO Masasi, Mtwara Region,
Tanzania
Tel (00255) (23) 251 0016
Fax (00255) (23) 251 0351
E-mail actmasisi@intafrica.com

Morogoro
Dudley Mageni
PO Box 320, Morogoro, Tanzania
Tel (00255) (23) 24602 *or* 24601
Fax (00255) (23) 24602
E-mail phunter@maf.org

Mount
Kilimanjaro
Simon Elilekia Makundi
PO Box 1057, Arusha, Tanzania
Tel (00255) (27) 254 8396
E-mail dmk@khabari.co.tz

Mpwapwa
Simon E Chiwanga
PO Box 2, Mpwapwa, Tanzania
Tel (00255) (26) 232 4123
E-mail dmp@maf.or.tz

Rift Valley — Alpha Francis Mohamed
PO Box 16, Manyoni, Tanzania
Fax (00255) (26) 232 4565
E-mail act-drv@maf.or.tz

Ruaha
(Archbishop) — Donald Leo Mtetemela
Box 1028, Iringa, Tanzania
Tel (00255) (26) 270 2667
Mobile (00255) 7 443 64393
Fax (00225) (26) 270 2479
E-mail ruaha@maf.or.tz

Ruvuma — Maternus K Kapinga
PO Box 1357, Songea, Ruvuma, Tanzania
Tel (00255) (25) 260 0090
Fax (00255) (25) 260 2987

South West
Tanganyika — Michael Robert Westall
Bishop's House, PO Box 32,
Njombe, Tanzania
Tel (00255) (26) 278 2010
Fax (00255) (26) 278 2403
E-mail punitha@africaonline.co.tz

Southern
Highlands — John Mwela
PO Box 198, Mbeya, Tanzania
Tel (00255) (25) 250 0216
E-mail bishop-dsh@twiga.com

Tabora — Francis Nzaganya Ntiruka,
PO Box 1408, Tabora, Tanzania
Tel (00255) (26) 260 4124
Fax (00255) (26) 260 4899
E-mail gilesannic@taboraonline.com

Tanga — Philip D Baji
PO Box 35, Korogwe, Tanga, Tanzania
Tel (00255) (27) 264 0631
E-mail baji@kaributanga.com

Victoria
Nyanza — John Paul Changae
PO Box 278, Mwanza, Tanzania
Tel (00255) (28) 250 0627
E-mail mfuko@africaonline.co.tz

Western
Tanganyika — Gerard E Mpango
PO Box 13, Kasulu, Tanzania
Tel (00255) (28) 281 0321
fax as telephone
E-mail bpmpango@maf.or.tz

(Northern Zone
of Kibondo
District) — Sadock Makaya
PO Box 15, Kibondo, Tanzania
Tel (00255) (28) 282 0054
E-mail smakaya@hotmail.com

(Lake Zone of — Naftali Bikaka
Kigoma District) PO Box 175, Kigoma, Tanzania
Tel (00255) (28) 280 2053

(Southern Zone — Mark Badeleya
of Rukwa Region PO Box 226, Sumbawanga
in Sumbawanga) Tel (00255) (25) 280 2392

Zanzibar — Douglas Toto
PO Box 5, Mkunazini, Zanzibar, Tanzania
Tel (00255) (24) 223 2484
Fax (00255) (24) 223 6772
E-mail actzanzibar@zanzinet.com

UGANDA

Ankole — Elisha Kyamugambi
PO Box 14, Mbarara, Ankole, Uganda
Tel (00256) (485) 20290
Mobile (00256) 77 525 847

Bukedi — Nicodemus Engwalas-Okille
PO Box 170, Tororo, Uganda
Mobile (00256) 77 542 164

Bunyoro-Kitara — Nathan Kyamanywa
PO Box 20, Hoima, Uganda
Tel (00256) (465) 40128
Mobile (00256) 77 648 232
E-mail bkdioces@infocom.co.ug

Busoga — Michael Kyomya
PO Box 1658, Jinja, Uganda
Mobile (00256) 75 649 102

Central Buganda — Jackson Matovu
PO Box 1200, Karoni-Gomba,
Mpigi, Uganda
Mobile (00256) (77) 475 640
E-mail veldhuis@africaonline.co.ug

Kampala
(Archbishop) — Henry Luke Orombi
PO Box 14123, Kampala, Uganda
Tel (00256) (41) 270 218
Mobile (00256) 77 476 476
Fax (00256) (41) 251925
E-mail coups@uol.co.ug

(Assistant) — Eliphaz K Maari
PO Box 335, Kampala, Uganda
Tel (00256) (41) 290 231 *or* 290 139
Mobile (00256) 77 435 978
Fax (00256) (41) 342 601

Karamoja — Peter Lomongin
PO Box 1, Kampala, Uganda
Mobile (00256) 77 961 353

Kigezi — George Katwesigye
PO Box 3, Kabale, Uganda
Tel (00256) (486) 22 003
Mobile (00256) 77 446 954
Fax (00256) (486) 22 802

Kinkizi — John Ntegyereize
PO Box 77, Karuhinda, Rukungiri, Uganda
Tel (00873) (761) 604794 *or* 604795
Mobile (00256) 77 507 163
Fax (00873) (761) 604796 *or* 604797

Kitgum — Benjamin Ojwang
PO Box 187, Kitgum, Uganda
Mobile (00256) 77 361 201

Kumi — Thomas Edison Irigei
PO Box 18, Kumi, Uganda
Tel (00256) (45) 617 95
Mobile (00256) 77 659 460
Fax (00256) (45) 613 25

Lango — John Charles Odrukami
PO Box 6, Lira, Uganda
Mobile (00256) 77 614 000

Luweero — Evans Mukasa Kisekka
PO Box 125, Luweero, Uganda
Tel (00256) (41) 610048 *or* 610070
Mobile (00256) 77 421 220
Fax (00256) (41) 610132 *or* 610070

Madi/
West Nile — Enock Lee Drati
PO Box 370, Arua, Uganda
Mobile (00256) 77 473 733

Mbale — Samwiri Namakhetsa Khaemba Wabulakha
Bishop's House, PO Box 473,
Mbale, Uganda
Tel (00256) (45) 33 533
Mobile (00256) 77 512 051

Mityana — Dunstan Bukenya
PO Box 102, Mityana, Uganda
Tel (00256) (46) 2017
Mobile (00256) 77 615 789

Muhabura — *vacant*
PO Box 22, Kisoro, Uganda
Tel (00256) (486) 30014 *or* 30058
Fax (00256) (486) 30059

Mukono — Elia Paulo Luzinda Kizito
PO Box 39, Mukono, Uganda
Tel (00256) (41) 290 229
Mobile (00256) 77 603 348

Namirembe — Samuel Balagadde Ssekkadde
PO Box 14297, Kampala, Uganda
Tel (00256) (41) 271 682
Mobile (00256) 77 500 494
E-mail namid@infocom.co.ug

Nebbi — *vacant*
PO Box 27, Nebbi, Uganda

North Ankole — John Muhanguzi
c/o PO Box 14. Mbarara,
Ankole, Uganda

North Kigezi — Edward Muhima
PO Box 23, Rukungiri, Uganda
Tel (00256) (486) 42 028

North Mbale — *vacant*
PO Box 1837, Mbale, Uganda
Fax (00256) (41) 254576

Northern
Uganda — Nelson Onono-Onweng
PO Box 232, Gulu, Uganda
Mobile (00256) 77 587 840
Fax : (00256) (250) 828

Ruwenzori	Benezeri Kisembo Bishop's House, PO Box 37, Fort Portal, Uganda Tel (00256) (493) 22 271 Mobile (00256) 77 470 671 Fax (00256) (493) 22 636
Sebei	Augustine Joe Arapyona Salimo PO Box 23, Kapchorwa, Uganda Tel (00256) (45) 51 072 Mobile (00256) 77 550 520
Soroti	Charles Bernard Obaikol-Ebitu PO Box 107, Soroti, Uganda Tel (00256) (45) 61 795 Mobile (00256) 77 557 909
South Ruwenzori	Jackson T Nzerebende PO Box 142, Kasese, Uganda Tel (00256) (483) 44 132 Fax (00256) (483) 44 450
West Ankole	William Magambo PO Box 140, Bushenyi, Uganda Tel (00256) (485) 42 080 Mobile (00256) 77 465 488 Fax (00256) (485) 21 304
West Buganda	Samuel Cephas Kamya PO Box 242, Masaka, Uganda Mobile (00256) 77 413 400

UNITED STATES OF AMERICA

The roman numerals indicate to which of the nine provinces of ECUSA the diocese belongs

Presiding Bishop and Primate	Frank Tracy Griswold Episcopal Church Center, 815 Second Avenue, New York, NY 10017, USA Tel (001) (212) 716 6276 Fax (001) (212) 490 3298 E-mail stolley@episcopalchurch.org
(Office of Pastoral Development)	Frank Clayton Matthews 8100 Three Chopt Road, Suite 102, Richmond, VA 23229, USA Tel (001) (804) 282 6007 Fax (001) (804) 282 6008 E-mail f_clayton_matthews@ecunet.org
(Armed Forces and Micronesia)	George Elden Packard Episcopal Church Center, 815 Second Avenue, New York, NY 10017, USA Tel (001) (800) 334 7626 ext 6065 Fax (001) (212) 867 1654 E-mail obaf@aol.com or gpackard@dfms.org
Alabama (IV)	Henry Nutt Parsley 521 North 20th Street, Birmingham, AL 352032611, USA Tel (001) (205) 715 2060 Fax (001) (205) 715 2066 E-mail hparsley@dioala.org
(Suffragan)	Mark H. Andrus address etc as above E-mail mandrus@dioala.org
Alaska (VIII)	Mark Lawrence MacDonald 1205 Denali Way, Fairbanks, AK 99701–4137, USA Tel (001) (907) 452 3040 Fax (001) (907) 456 6552 E-mail mmacdonald@gci.net
Albany (II)	Daniel William Herzog 68 South Swan Street, Albany, NY 12210, USA Tel (001) (518) 465 4737 Fax (001) (518) 436 1182 E-mail bishopherzog@albanydiocese.org
(Suffragan)	David John Bena address etc as above E-mail bishopbena@albanydiocese.org

Arizona (VIII)	Robert Reed Shahan 114 West Roosevelt Street, Phoenix, AZ 85003–1406, USA Tel (001) (602) 254 0976 Fax (001) (602) 495 6603 Email ofcmgraz@qwest.net or robrshahan@aol.com
Arkansas (VII)	Larry Earl Maze Cathedral House, PO Box 164668, Little Rock, AR 72216, USA Tel (001) (501) 372 2168 Fax (001) (501) 372 2147 E-mail diocese@arkansas.anglican.org
Atlanta (IV)	John Neil Alexander 2744 Peachtree Road NW, Atlanta, GA 30363–0701, USA Tel (001) (404) 365 1016 Fax (001) (404) 261 2515 E-mail bishop@episcopalatlanta.org
Bethlehem (III)	Paul Victor Marshall 333 Wyandotte Street, Bethlehem, PA 18015–1527, USA Tel (001) (610) 691 5655 Fax (001) (610) 691 1682 E-mail bishop@diobeth.org
California (VIII)	William Edwin Swing 1055 Taylor Street, San Francisco, CA 94108, USA Tel (001) (415) 673 9268 Fax (001) (415) 673 1510 E-mail bishopsoffice@diocal.org
(Assistants)	George Richard Millard address etc as above John Raymond Wyatt address etc as above
Central Ecuador (IX)	Jose Neptali Larrea Avenue Amazonas 4430 Y Villalengua, Piso 7 Oficina 708, Edificio Banco Amazonas, Quito, Ecuador Tel (00593) (2) 252225 Fax (00593) (2) 296083 or 252226 E-mail nelar@uio.satnet.net or ecuacen@uio.satnet.net
Central Florida (IV)	John Wadsworth Howe Diocesan Office, 1017 E Robinson Street, Orlando, FL 32801–2023, USA Tel (001) (407) 423 3567 Fax (001) (407) 872 0006 E-mail bcf3@aol.com
(Assistant)	Hugo Luis Pina-Lopez address etc as above E-mail hisporlfl@aol.com
Central Gulf Coast (IV)	Philip Menzie Duncan PO Box 13330, Pensacola, FL 32591–3330, USA Tel (001) (850) 434 7337 Fax (001) (850) 434 8577 E-mail bishopduncan@diocgc.org
Central New York (II)	Gladstone Skip Adams 310 Montgomery Street, Suite 200, Syracuse, NY 13202–2093, USA Tel (001) (315) 474 6596 Fax (001) (315) 478 1632 E-mail office@cny.anglican.org
Central Pennsylvania (III)	Michael Whittington Creighton Box 11937, Harrisburg, PA 17108–1937, USA Tel (001) (717) 236 5959 Fax (001) (717) 236 6448 E-mail bishopcpa@aol.com
Chicago (V)	William Dailey Persell 65 East Huron Street, Chicago, IL 60611, USA Tel (001) (312) 751 4217 Fax (001) (312) 787 5872 E-mail bishop@epischicago.org
(Assistant)	Victor Alfonso Scantlebury address as above Tel (001) (312) 751 4216 E-mail bpvictor864@aol.com

Colombia (IX)   Francisco J Duque-Gomez
Carrera 6 # 49–85,
Apartado Aereo 52964,
Bogota 2, Colombia
Tel (0057) (1) 288 3187 or 288 3167
Fax (0057) (1) 288 3248
E-mail iec@iglesiaepiscopal.org.co or
obispoduque@iglesiaepiscopal.org.co

Colorado (VI)   Robert J. O'Neill
1300 Washington Street,
Denver, CO 80203–2008, USA
Tel (001) (303) 837 1173
Fax (001) (303) 837 1311
E-mail bishop@coloradodiocese.org

Connecticut (I)   Andrew Donnan Smith
1335 Asylum Avenue, Hartford,
CT 06105–2295, USA
Tel (001) (860) 233 4481
Fax (001) (860) 523 1410
E-mail jburnep@ctdiocese.org

(Suffragans)   James Elliott Curry
address etc as above
E-mail jcurry@ctdiocese.org

Wilfrido Ramos-Orench
address etc as above
E-mail wramos@ctdiocese.org

Dallas (VII)   James Monte Stanton
1630 North Garrett Ave, Dallas,
TX 75206, USA
Tel (001) (214) 826 8310
Fax (001) (214) 826 5968
E-mail jstanton@episcopal-dallas.org or
jmsdallas@aol.com

(Suffragan)   David Bruce MacPherson
address etc as above
E-mail bmacpher@episcopal-dallas.org

Delaware (III)   Wayne Parker Wright
2020 Tatnall Street,
Wilmington, DE 19802, USA
Tel (001) (302) 656 5441
Fax (001) (302) 656 7342
E-mail bishop@dioceseofdelaware.net

Dominican   Julio Cesar Holguin Khoury
Republic (IX)   Apartado 764, Calle Santiago No 114,
Santo Domingo, Dominican Republic
Tel (001) (809) 686 7493 or 686 6465
Fax (001) (809) 686 6364
E-mail iglepidom@codetel.net.do

East Carolina   Clifton Daniel
(IV)   Box 1336, Kinston, NC 28503, USA
Tel (001) (252) 522 0885
Fax (001) (252) 523 5272
E-mail diocese@diocese-eastcarolina.org

East Tennessee   Charles Glen von Rosenberg
(IV)   814 Episcopal School Way,
Knoxville, TN 37932, USA
Tel (001) (865) 966 2110
Fax (001) (865) 966 2536
E-mail cgvonr@etdiocese.net

Eastern   Edwin Max Leidel
Michigan (V)   Diocesan Office, 924 N Niagara Street
Saginaw, MI 48602, USA
Tel (001) (989) 752 6020
Fax (001) (989) 752 6120 or (517) 797 8148
E-mail bishopml@eastmich.org

Eastern   William Otis Gregg
Oregon (VIII)   PO Box 1548, The Dalles, OR 97058, USA
Tel (001) (541) 298 4477
Fax (001) (541) 296 0939
E-mail edeo@gorge.net

Easton (III)   James J. Shand
314 North, Easton, MD 21601–3684, USA
Tel (001) (410) 822 1919
Fax (001) (410) 763 8259
E-mail reese@dioceseofeaston.org

Eau Claire (V)   Keith Bernard Whitmore
510 South Farwell Street,
Eau Claire, WI 54701, USA
Tel (001) (715) 835 3331
Fax (001) (715) 835 9212
E-mail bishopkeith@dioceseofeauclaire.org

El Camino   Richard L Shimpfky
Real (VIII)   PO Box 1903, Monterey, CA 93942, USA
Tel (001) (831) 394 4465
Fax (001) (408) 394 7133
E-mail saltig@redshift.com

Europe,   Pierre Welté Whalon
Convocation of   American Cathedral of the Holy Trinity,
American   23 Avenue George V, 75008 Paris, France
Churches in   Tel (0033) (1) 47 20 02 23
(VII)   fax as telephone
E-mail ecusa.eu@american-cath.asso.fr or
bppwhalon@aol.com

Florida (IV)   Stephen Hays Jecko
325 Market Street, Jacksonville,
FL 32202, USA
Tel (001) (904) 356 1328
Fax (001) (904) 355 1934
E-mail bfl7@diocesefl.org or bfl7@crci.net

Fond du Lac   Russell Edward Jacobus
(V)   PO Box 149, Fond du Lac, WI 54936–0149,
USA
Tel (001) (920) 921 8866
Fax (001) (920) 921 8761
E-mail bishop@episcopalfonddulac.org

Fort Worth   Jack Leo Iker
(VII)   2900 Alemeda Street, Fort Worth, TX 76116,
USA
Tel (001) (817) 244 2885
Fax (001) (817) 244 3363
E-mail jliker@fwepiscopal.org or
diocese@fwepiscopal.org

Georgia (IV)   Henry Irving Louttit
611 East Bay Street, Savannah,
GA 31401–1296, USA
Tel (001) (912) 236 4279
Fax (001) (912) 236 2007
E-mail diocesega@att.net

Haiti (II)   Jean-Zaché Duracin
Eglise Episcopale d'Haiti,
BP 1309, Port-au-Prince, Haiti
Tel (00509) 257 1624
Fax (00509) 257 2637
E-mail epihaiti@hotmail.com

Hawaii (VIII)   Richard Sui On Chang
Diocesan Office, 229 Queen Emma Square,
Honolulu, HI 96813–2304, USA
Tel (001) (808) 536 7776
Fax (001) (808) 538 7194
E-mail RSOChang@lanakila.org

Honduras (IX)   Lloyd Emmanuel Allen
13th Calle Bloque w#3316, Tegucigalpa,
Honduras, Central America
Tel (00504) 566 6155 or 556 6268
Fax (00504) 556 6467
E-mail episcopal@mayanet.hn

Idaho (VIII)   Harry Bainbridge
PO Box 936, Boise, ID 83701, USA
Tel (001) (208) 345 4440
Fax (001) (208) 345 9735
E-mail carrolk@idahodiocese.org

Indianapolis (V)   Catherine Elizabeth Maples Waynick
1100 West 42nd Street,
Indianapolis, IN 46208, USA
Tel (001) (317) 926 5454
Fax (001) (317) 926 5456
E-mail bishop@indianapolis.anglican.org

Iowa (VI)   Alan Scarfe
225 37th Street, Des Moines,
IA 50312–4399, USA
Tel (001) (515) 277 6165
Fax (001) (515) 277 0273
E-mail diocese@iowaepiscopal.org

Kansas (VII)   William Edward Smalley
Bethany Place, 833–35 Polk Street,
Topeka, KS 66612, USA
Tel (001) (785) 235 9255
Fax (001) (785) 235 2449
E-mail wsmalley@episcopal-ks.org or
diocese@episcopal-ks.org

Kentucky (IV)   Edwin Funsten Gulick
                  425 South Second Street,
                  Louisville, KY 40202–1417, USA
                  Tel (001) (502) 584 7148
                  Fax (001) (502) 587 8123
                  E-mail tedg@episcopalky.org

Lexington (IV)   Stacy Fred Sauls
                  PO Box 610, Lexington, KY, 40586, USA
                  Tel (001) (859) 252 6527
                  Fax (001) (859) 231 9077
                  E-mail sfsauls@ure.net

Litoral   Alfredo Ulloa Morante
Diocese of   Box 0901–5250,
Ecuador (IX)   Guayaquil, Ecuador
                  Tel (00593) (4) 2 443 050 or 446 699
                  Fax (00593) (4) 2 443 088
                  E-mail iedlgye@satnet.net or
                  bishopmorante@hotmail.com

Long Island   Orris George Walker
(II)   36 Cathedral Avenue,
                  Garden City, NY 11530, USA
                  Tel (001) (516) 248 4800
                  Fax (001) (516) 877 1349 or 248 1616
                  E-mail owalker@dioceseli.org

(Suffragan)   Rodney Rae Michel
                  address and tel as above
                  Fax (001) (516) 742 6073
                  E-mail rmichel@dioceseli.org or
                  rodmitre@aol.com

Los Angeles   Joseph Jon Bruno
(VIII)   Box 512164, Los Angeles,
                  CA 90051–0164, USA
                  Tel (001) (213) 482 2040 ext 236
                  Fax (001) (213) 482 0844
                  E-mail bishop@ladiocese.org

(Suffragan)   Chester Lovelle Talton
                  address and fax as above
                  Tel (001) (213) 482 2040 x 243
                  E-mail suffragan@ladiocese.org

Louisiana (IV)   Charles Edward Jenkins
                  1623 Seventh Street,
                  New Orleans,
                  LA 70115–4411, USA
                  Tel (001) (504) 895 6634
                  Fax (001) (504) 895 6637
                  E-mail vhendrickson@edola.org

Maine (I)   Chilton Abbie Richardson Knudsen
                  Loring House, 143 State Street,
                  Portland, ME 04101, USA
                  Tel (001) (207) 772 1953
                  Fax (001) (207) 773 0095
                  E-mail revcrk@aol.com or
                  chilton_knudsen@ecunet.org

Maryland (III)   Robert Wilkes Ihloff
                  4 East University Parkway,
                  Baltimore, MD 21218–2437, USA
                  Tel (001) (800) 443 1399 or (410) 467 1399
                  Fax (001) (410) 554 6387
                  E-mail rihloff@ang-md.org

(Suffragan)   John Leslie Rabb
                  address etc as above
                  E-mail jrabb@ang-md.org

Massachusetts   M Thomas Shaw
(I)   Society of St John the Evangelist,
                  138 Tremont Street, Boston, MA 02111, USA
                  Tel (001) (617) 482 4826 ext 407
                  Fax (001) (617) 451 6446
                  E-mail chigbe@diomass.org

(Suffragans)   Roy F (Bud) Cederholm
                  address etc as above
                  E-mail budc@diomass.org

                  Gayle E Harris
                  address etc as above
                  E-mail SHP@diomass.org

Michigan (V)   Wendell Nathaniel Gibbs
                  4800 Woodward Avenue,
                  Detroit, MI 48201, USA
                  Tel (001) (313) 832 4400
                  Fax (001) (313) 831 0259
                  E-mail info@edomi.org or wgibbs@edomi.org

Milwaukee (V)   Roger John White
                  804 East Juneau Street,
                  Milwaukee, WI 53202, USA
                  Tel (001) (414) 291 2883
                  Fax (001) (414) 272 7790
                  E-mail bishop@episcopalmilwaukee.org

Minnesota   James Louis Jelinek
(VI)   1730 Clifton Place, Suite 201,
                  Minneapolis, MN 55403, USA
                  Tel (001) (612) 871 5311
                  Fax (001) (612) 871 0552
                  E-mail episcopal.center@episcopalmn.org

Mississippi   Duncan Montgomery Gray III
(IV)   PO Box 23107,
                  Jackson, MS 39225–3107, USA
                  Tel (001) (601) 948 5954
                  Fax (001) (601) 354 3401
                  E-mail kathryn.weathersby@ecunet.org

Missouri (V)   Hays Rockwell
                  1210 Locust Street,
                  St Louis, MO 63103, USA
                  Tel (001) (314) 231 1220
                  Fax (001) (314) 231 3373
                  E-mail bishop@missouri.anglican.org

Montana (VI)   Charles Irving Jones
                  515 North Park Avenue,
                  Helena, MT 59601, USA
                  Tel (001) (406) 422 2230
                  Fax (001) (406) 442 2238
                  E-mail bpci@aol.com

Navajoland   Steven Tsosie Plummer
Area Mission   PO Box 720,
(VIII)   Harmington,
                  NM 87499–0720, USA
                  Tel (001) (505) 327 7549
                  Fax (001) (505) 327 6904

Nebraska   Joe Goodwin Burnett
(VIII)   109 North 18th Street,
                  Omaha, NE 68102–4903, USA
                  Tel (001) (402) 341 5373
                  Fax (001) (402) 341 8683
                  E-mail diocese@episcopal-ne.org or
                  jburnett@episcopal-ne.org

Nevada (VIII)   Katharine Jefferts Schori
                  6135 Harrison Drive, Suite 1,
                  Las Vegas,
                  NV 89120–4076, USA
                  Tel (001) (702) 737 9190
                  Fax (001) (702) 737 6488
                  E-mail episcopaldionv@earthlink.net

New   Douglas Edwin Theuner
Hampshire (I)   63 Green Street,
                  Concord, NH 03301, USA
                  Tel (001) (603) 224 1914
                  Fax (001) (603) 225 7884
                  E-mail douglas.theuner@ecunet.org

(Coadjutor)   Gene Robinson
                  address etc as above
                  E-mail grinnh@aol.com

New Jersey   David Bruce Joslin
(II)   808 West State Street,
                  Trenton, NJ 08618, USA
                  Tel (001) (609) 394 5281
                  Fax (001) (609) 394 8015
                  E-mail djoslin@newjersey.anglican.org

New York (II)   Mark Sean Sisk
                  Synod House, 1047 Amsterdam Avenue,
                  Cathedral Heights, New York, NY 10025,
                  USA
                  Tel (001) (212) 316 7400
                  Fax (001) (212) 316 7405
                  E-mail diocese@diocesenv.org

(Suffragan)   Catherine Scimeca Roskam
                  Region Two Office, 55 Cedar Street,
                  Dobbs Ferry, NY 10522, USA
                  Tel (001) (914) 693 3848
                  Fax (001) (914) 693 0407
                  E-mail CSR125@aol.com

(Assistant)   Egbert Don Taylor
Synod Office, 1047 Amsterdam Avenue,
Cathedral Heights,
New York, NY 10025, USA
Tel (001) (212) 932 7349
Fax (001) (212) 932 7345
E-mail bishopdontaylor@mindspring.com

Newark (II)   John Palmer Croneberger
31 Mulberry Street, Newark, NJ 07102,
USA
Tel (001) (973) 622 4306
Fax (001) (973) 622 3503
E-mail thebishop@dioceseofnewark.org

North   Michael Bruce Curry
Carolina (IV)   PO Box 17025, 201 St Alban's Drive,
Raleigh, NC 27619–7025, USA
Tel (001) (919) 787 6313
Fax (001) (919) 787 0156
E-mail smanning@episdionc.org

(Suffragan)   James Gary Gloster
address etc as above
E-mail ggloster@episdionc.org

North Dakota   Andrew Hedtler Fairfield
(VI)   Box 10337, Fargo, ND 58106–0337, USA
Tel (001) (701) 235 6688
Fax (001) (701) 232 3077
E-mail RobinsNest72176@aol.com

Northern   Jerry Alban Lamb
California   Box 161268, Sacramento, CA 95816–5902,
(VIII)   USA
Tel (001) (916) 442 6918
Fax (001) (916) 442 6927
E-mail bishopjal@dncweb.org

Northern   Edward Stuart Little
Indiana (V)   117 North Lafayette Boulevard,
South Bend, IN 46601, USA
Tel (001) (219) 233 6489
Fax (001) (219) 287 7914
E-mail eslittle@juno.com

Northern   James Arthur Kelsey
Michigan (V)   131 East Ridge Street,
Marquette, MI 49855, USA
Tel (001) (906) 228 7160
Fax (001) (906) 228 7171
E-mail jimkelsey@dionomi.org

Northwest   Charles Wallis Ohl
Texas (VII)   The Episcopal Church Center,
1802 Broadway, Lubbock, TX 79401, USA
Tel (001) (806) 763 1370
Fax (001) (804) 472 0641
E-mail wallisohl@hub.of the.net

Northwestern   Robert Deane Rowley
Pennsylvania   145 West 6th Street, Erie, PA 16501, USA
(III)   Tel (001) (814) 456 4203 or (800) 643 2351
Fax (001) (814) 454 8703
E-mail rdrowleyjr@aol.com or
dionwpa@aol.com

Ohio (V)   Joseph Clark Grew
2230 Euclid Avenue,
Cleveland, OH 44115–2499, USA
Tel (001) (216) 771 4815
Fax (001) (216) 623 0735
E-mail bishop@dohio.org

(Suffragan)   Arthur Benjamin Williams
address etc as above
E-mail bishsuff@diohio.org

Oklahoma   Robert Manning Moody
(VII)   924 North Robinson,
Oklahoma City, OK 73102, USA
Tel (001) (405) 232 4820
Fax (001) (405) 232 4912

Olympia (VIII)   Vincent Waydell Warner
PO Box 12126, Seattle, WA 98102, USA
Tel (001) (206) 325 4200
Fax (001) (206) 325 4631
E-mail info@ecww.org

(Assistant)   Sanford Zangwill Kaye Hampton
address etc as above

Oregon (VIII)   Johncy Itty
11800 S.W. Military Lane, Portland,
OR 97219, USA
Tel (001) (503) 636 5613
Fax (001) (503) 636 5616
E-mail johncyi@diocese-oregon.org

Pennsylvania   Charles Ellesworth Bennison
(III)   240 South Fourth Street,
Philadelphia, PA 19106, USA
Tel (001) (215) 627 6434 ext 112 or 131
Fax (001) (215) 627 7750
E-mail charlesb@diopa.org

(Assisting   Clarence Coleridge
Bishop)   240 South Fourth Street,
address etc as above
E-mail clarencec@diopa.org

Pittsburgh   Robert William Duncan
(III)   900 Oliver Building, 535 Smithfield Street,
Pittsburgh, PA 15222, USA
Tel (001) (412) 281 6131
Fax (001) (412) 471 5591
E-mail duncan@pgh.anglican.org

(Assistant)   Henry William Scriven
1437 Greystone Drive,
Pittsburgh, PA 15206, USA
E-mail scriven@pgh.anglican.org

Puerto Rico   David Andres Alvarez-Velazquez
(IX)   PO Box 902, Saint Just Station,
Saint Just, 00978, Puerto Rico
Tel (001) (787) 761 9800
Fax (001) (787) 761 0320
E-mail iep@centennialpr.net

Quincy (V)   Keith Lynn Ackerman
3601 N North Street,
Peoria, IL 61604–1599, USA
Tel (001) (309) 688 8221
Fax (001) (309) 688 8229 or 692 2421
E-mail doq@ocslink.com or
quincy8@ocslink.com

Rhode Island   Geralyn Wolf
(I)   275 North Main Street,
Providence, RI 02903–1298, USA
Tel (001) (401) 274 4500
Fax (001) (401) 331 9430
E-mail bishop@episcopalri.org

Rio Grande   Terence Kelshaw
(VII)   4304 Carlisle Boulevard N.E.,
Albuquerque, NM 87107–4811, USA
Tel (001) (505) 881 0636
Fax (001) (505) 883 9048
E-mail tkelshaw@aol.com

Rochester (II)   Jack Marston McKelvey
935 East Avenue, Rochester, NY 14607, USA
Tel (001) (716) 473 2977
Fax (001) (716) 473 3195
E-mail BpJackM@aol.com

San Diego   Gethin Benwil Hughes
(VIII)   2728 Sixth Avenue,
San Diego, CA 92103–6397, USA
Tel (001) (619) 291 5947
Fax (001) (619) 291 8362
E-mail diocsd@edsd.org

San Joaquin   John-David Mercer Schofield
(VIII)   4159 East Dakota Avenue,
Fresno, CA 93726, USA
Tel (001) (559) 244 4828
Fax (001) (209) 244 4832
E-mail sjoaquin@sjoaquin.net

South Carolina   Edward Lloyd Salmon
(IV)   Box 20127, Charleston,
SC 29413–0127, USA
Tel (001) (843) 722 4075
Fax (001) (843) 723 7628
E-mail elsalmon@dioceseofsc.org

(Suffragan)   William Jones Skilton
address etc as above
E-mail bskilton@dioceseofsc.org

South   Creighton Leland Robertson
Dakota (VI)   500 South Main Street,
Sioux Falls, SD 57104–6814, USA
Tel (001) (605) 338 9751
Fax (001) (605) 336 6243
E-mail crobertson@qwest.net

Southeast Florida (IV)	Leopold Frade 525 North East 15th Street, Miami, FL 33132, USA Tel (001) (305) 373 0881 Fax (001) (305) 375 8054 E-mail info@diosef.org
(Assistant Bishop)	James H. Ottley *address etc as above*
Southern Ohio (V)	Herbert Thompson 412 Sycamore Street, Cincinnati, OH 45202–4179, USA Tel (001) (513) 421 0311 Fax (001) (513) 421 0315 E-mail bishop_thompson@episcopal-dso.org
(Suffragan)	Kenneth Lester Price 125 East Broad Street, Columbus, OH 43215, USA Tel (001) (614) 461 8429 Fax (001) (614) 461 1015 E-mail bishop_price@episcopal-dso.org
Southern Virginia (III)	David Conner Bane 600 Talbot Hall Road, Norfolk, VA 23505, USA Tel (001) (757) 423 8287 Fax (001) (757) 440 5354 E-mail dcbane@southernvirginia.anglican.org
(Suffragan)	Carol J Gallagher 112 North Union Street, Petersburgh, VA 23803, USA Tel (001) (804) 863 2095 Fax (001) (804) 863 2096 E-mail dsvwo@verizon.net
Southwest Florida (IV)	John Bailey Lipscomb 7313 Merchant Court, Sarasota, FL 34240–8437, USA Tel (001) (941) 776 1018 *or* (800) 992 7699 Fax (001) (941) 776 9811 E-mail jlipscomb@dioceseswfla.org
(Assistant)	Telesforo Alexander Isaac *address as above* Tel (001) (813) 823 2737 Fax (001) (813) 821 9254
Southwestern Virginia (III)	Frank Neff Powell PO Box 2279, Roanoke, VA 24009–2279, USA Tel (001) (540) 342 6797 Fax (001) (540) 343 9114 E-mail npowell@dioswva.org
Spokane (VIII)	James Edward Waggoner 245 East 13th Avenue, Spokane, WA 99202–1114, USA Tel (001) (509) 624 3191 Fax (001) (509) 747 0049 E-mail jimw@spokanediocese.org
Springfield (V)	Peter Hess Beckwith 821 South 2nd Street, Springfield, IL 62704–2694, USA Tel (001) (217) 525 1876 Fax (001) (217) 525 1877 E-mail episspi@midwest.net
Taiwan (VIII)	David J H Lai #7 Lane 105, Hangchow South Road, Sec. 1, Taipei, Taiwan 100, Republic of China Tel (00886) (2) 2341 1265 Fax (00886) (2) 2396 2014 E-mail skhtpe@ms12.hinet.net
Tennessee (IV)	Bertram Nelson Herlong The Diocese of Tennessee, 50 Vantage Way, Suite 107, Nashville, TN 37228, USA Tel (001) (615) 251 3322 Fax (001) (615) 251 8010 E-mail info@episcopaldiocese-tn.org
Texas (VII)	Don Adger Wimberly 3203 West Alabama Street, Houston, TX 77098, USA Tel (001) (713) 520 6444 *or* (800) 318 4452 Fax (001) (713) 520 5723 *or* 782 2933 E-mail dwimberly@epicenter.org
(Assistant)	Theodore Athelbert Daniels *address etc as above* E-mail tdaniels@epicenter.org

(Suffragan)	Rayford High *address etc as above* E-mail rhigh@epicenter.org
Upper South Carolina (IV)	Dorsey Felix Henderson 1115 Marion Street, Columbia, SC 29201, USA Tel (001) (803) 771 7800 Fax (001) (803) 799 5119 E-mail diocese@edusc.org
Utah (VIII)	Carolyn Tanner Irish 80 South 300 East Street, PO Box 3090, Salt Lake City, UT 84110–3090, USA Tel (001) (801) 322 4131 Fax (001) (801) 322 5096 E-mail cirish@episcopal-ut.org
Venezuela (IX)	Orlando Guerrero Apartado 49–143, Avenida Caroní 100, Colinas de Bello Monte, Caracas 1042-A, Venezuela Tel (0058) (212) 753 0723 Fax (0058) (212) 751 3180
Vermont (I)	Thomas Clark Ely Diocesan House, 5 Rock Point Road, Burlington, VT 05401–2735, USA Tel (001) (802) 863 3431 Fax (001) (802) 860 1562 E-mail tely@dioceseofvermont.org
Virgin Islands (II)	*vacant* Box 10437, St Thomas, VI 00801, USA Tel (001) (340) 776 1797 *or* 776 3108 Fax (001) (809) 777 8485
Virginia (III)	Peter James Lee 110 West Franklin Street, Richmond, VA 23220, USA Tel (001) (804) 643 8451 Fax (001) (804) 644 6928 E-mail pjlee@thediocese.net
(Assistant)	Francis Campbell Gray *address etc as above* E-mail fcgray@thediocese.net
(Suffragan)	David Colin Jones 6043 Burnside Landing Drive, Burke, VA 22015, USA Tel (001) (703) 461 1776 Fax (001) (703) 823 9524 E-mail djones@thediocese.net
Washington (III)	John Bryson Chane Episcopal Church House, Mount St Alban, Washington, DC 20016, USA Tel (001) (202) 537 6555 Tel (001) (202) 364 6605 E-mail jchane@edow.org
(Assistant)	Allen Lyman Bartlett 316 South Tenth Street, Philadelphia, PA 19107, USA Tel (001) (202) 537 6525 *or* (215) 928 0506 E-mail abartlett@edow.org
West Missouri (VII)	Barry Robert Howe PO Box 413227, Kansas City, MO 64141–3227, USA Tel (001) (816) 471 6161 *or* (800) 471 6160 Fax (001) (816) 471 0379 E-mail diooffice@diowestmo.org *or* barryroberthowe@cs.com
West Tennessee (IV)	Don Edward Johnson 692 Poplar Avenue, Memphis, TN 38105, USA Tel (001) (901) 526 0023 Fax (001) (901) 526 1555 E-mail jdenman@episwtn.org
West Texas (VII)	James Edward Folts PO Box 6885, San Antonio, TX 78209, USA Tel (001) (210) 824 5387 Fax (001) (210) 822 8779 E-mail marjorie.george@dwtx.org
(Suffragan)	Robert Boyd Hibbs *address etc as above* E-mail bphibbs@aol.com

West Virginia (III)	William Michie Klusmeyer PO Box 5400, Charleston, WV 25361–5400, USA Tel (001) (304) 344 3597 Fax (001) (304) 343 3295 E-mail mklusmeyer@wvdiocese.org	The Gambia	Solomon Tilewa E W Johnson Bishopscourt, PO Box 51, Banjul, The Gambia Tel (00220) 227 405 or 497 349 Mobile (00220) 905 227 Fax (00220) 229 495 E-mail anglican@qanet.net
Western Kansas (VII)	James Marshall Adams Jr Box 2507, Salina, KS 67402–2507, USA Tel (001) (785) 825 1626 Fax (001) (785) 825 0974 E-mail bishopadams@diowks.org	Guinea	Albert D Gomez BP 1187, Conakry, Guinea Tel (00224) (451) 323 E-mail ymcarthy@yahoo.com
Western Louisiana (VII)	Robert Jefferson Hargrove PO Box 2031, Alexandria, LA 71309, USA Tel (001) (318) 442 1304 Fax (001) (318) 442 8712 E-mail bphargrove@aol.com	Ho	Matthias K Mededues-Badohu Bishopslodge, PO Box MA 300 Ho, Volta Region, Ghana Tel (00233) (91) 26644 or 26806 E-mail matthoda@ucomgh.com
Western Massachusetts (I)	Gordon Scruton 37 Chestnut Street, Springfield, MA 01103, USA Tel (001) (413) 737 4786 Fax (001) (413) 746 9873 E-mail JLewis@diocesewma.org	Koforidua	Francis B. Quashie PO Box 980, Koforidua, Ghana Tel (00233) (81) 22329 Fax (00233) (81) 22060 E-mail cpwa@ghana.com or cpwa_gh@yahoo.com
Western Michigan (V)	Edward Lewis Lee 2600 Vincent Avenue, Portage, MI 49024–5653, USA Tel (001) (616) 381 2710 or 381 2711 Fax (001) (616) 381 7067 E-mail diowestmi@aol.com	Kumasi	Daniel Yinkah Safo St Cyprian's Avenue, PO Box 144, Kumasi, Ghana Tel (00233) (51) 24117 fax as telephone E-mail kumangli@africaonline.com.gh
Western New York (II)	J Michael Garrison 1114 Delaware Avenue, Buffalo, NY 14209, USA Tel (001) (716) 881 0660 or 839 2116 Fax (001) (716) 881 1724 E-mail jmgarrison@EpiscopalWNY.org	Liberia	Edward W Neufville PO Box 10–0277, 1000 Monrovia 10, Liberia Tel (00231) 224760 Mobile (00377) (47) 516440 Fax (00231) 224 760 E-mail bishop@liberia.net
Western North Carolina (IV)	Robert Hodges Johnson 900B Center Park Drive, Asheville, NC 28805, USA Tel (001) (828) 225 6656 Fax (001) (828) 225 6657 E-mail bishop@diocesewnc.org	Sekondi	vacant PO Box 85, Sekondi, Ghana Tel (00233) (31) 46048 E-mail angdiosek@yahoo.com
Wyoming (VI)	Bruce Edward Caldwell 104 South Fourth Street, Laramie, WY 82070, USA Tel (001) (307) 742 6606 Fax (001) (307) 742 6782 E-mail bruce@wydiocese.org	Sunyani	Thomas Ampah Brient PO Box 23, Sunyani, Ghana Tel (00233) (61) 213 Fax (00233) (61) 7203 E-mail anglicandiocese@hotmail.com
		Tamale	Emmanuel Anyindana Arongo PO Box 110, Tamale NR, Ghana Tel (00233) (71) 22906 Fax (00233) (71) 22906

WEST AFRICA

WEST INDIES

Accra (Archbishop)	Justice Ofei Akrofi Bishopscourt, PO Box 8, Accra, Ghana Tel (00233) (21) 662 292 Fax (00233) (21) 669 125 E-mail adaccra@ghana.com	Barbados	John Walter Dunlop Holder Mandeville House, Collymore Rock, St Michael, Barbados, West Indies Tel (001246) 426 2761 Fax (001246) 426 0871 E-mail jwdh@sunbeach.net
Bo	Samuel Sao Gbonda 1 A MacRobert Street, PO Box 21, Bo, Southern Province, Sierra Leone Tel (00232) (32) 648 Fax (00232) (32) 605 E-mail bomission@justice.com	Belize	Sylvestre Donato Romero-Palma Bishopsthorpe, Southern Foreshore, PO Box 535, Belize City, Belize Tel (00501) (2) 73 029 Fax (00501) (2) 76 898 E-mail bzediocese@btl.net
Cameroon (missionary area)	Jonathan Ruhumuliza BP 15705, New Bell, Duala, Cameroon Tel (00237) 408 552 fax as telephone E-mail camanglica-church@camnet.cm	Guyana	Randolph Oswald George The Diocesan Office, PO Box 10949, 49 Barrack Street, Kingston, Georgetown 1, Guyana Tel (00592) (22) 64 775 Fax (00592) (22) 76 091
Cape Coast	Daniel S A Allotey Bishopscourt, PO Box A233, Adisadel Estates, Cape Coast, Ghana Tel (00233) (42) 32 502 Fax (00233) (42) 32 637 E-mail anglidioc@yahoo.com	Jamaica and the Cayman Islands	Alfred Charles Reid 2 Caledonia Avenue, Kingston 5 JA, Jamaica, West Indies Tel (001876) 920 2712 Fax (001876) 960 1774 E-mail bishop@anglicandiocese.com
Freetown	Julius Olotu Prince Lynch Bishop's Court, PO Box 537, Freetown, Sierra Leone Tel (00232) (22) 251 307 Mobile (00232) 76 620 690 Fax (00233) (22) 251 306 (via Ghana) E-mail bishop@sierratel.sl	(Kingston)	Herman Spence address as above Tel (001876) 926 2498 or 960 0905 Fax (001876) 960 1774 E-mail sspence@toj.com

(Mandeville)	Harold Benjamin Daniel Bishop's Residence, 3 Cotton Tree Road, PO Box 84, Mandeville, Jamaica Tel (001876) 625 6817 Fax (001876) 625 6819 E-mail hbdaniel@cwjamaica.com	Windward Islands	Sehon S Goodridge Bishop's Court, Montrose, PO Box 502, St Vincent, West Indies Tel (001784) 456 1895 Fax (001784) 456 2591 E-mail diocesewi@vincysurf.com

(Montego Bay)	Howard Gregory PO Box 346, Montego Bay, Jamaica, West Indies Tel (001876) 952 4963 Fax (001876) 971 8838 E-mail hkagregory@hotmail.com

EXTRA-PROVINCIAL DIOCESES

Bermuda (Canterbury)	Alexander Ewen Ratteray Diocesan Office, PO Box HM 769, Hamilton HM CX, Bermuda Tel (001441) 292 2967 *or* 292 6987 Fax (001441) 292 5421 *or* 296 0592 E-mail bishopratteray@ibl.bm *or* diocoff@ibl.bm

Nassau and The Bahamas (Archbishop)	Drexel Wellington Gomez Church House, PO Box N-7107, Nassau, Bahamas Tel (001242) 322 3015 Fax (001242) 322 7943 E-mail primate@batelnet.bs
(New Providence)	Gilbert Arthur Thompson *address etc as above*
North Eastern Caribbean and Aruba	Leroy Errol Brooks St Mary's Rectory, PO Box 180, The Valley, Anguilla, West Indies Tel (001264) 497 2235 Fax (001264) 497 8555 E-mail brookr@anguilla.net.com
Trinidad and Tobago	Calvin Wendell Bess Hayes Court, 21 Maraval Road, Port of Spain, Trinidad, West Indies Tel (001868) 622 7387 Fax (001868) 628 1319 E-mail bessc@tstt.net.tt

§Cuba	Jorge Perera Hurtado Calle 6 No 273, Vedado, Ciudad de la Habana 4, C.P. 10400, Cuba Tel (0053) (7) 321120 Fax (0053) (7) 333293
Lusitanian Church (Canterbury)	Fernando da Luz Soares Secretaria Diocesana, Apartado 392, P-4431–905 Vila Nova de Gaia, Portugal Tel (00351) (22) 375 4018 Fax (00351) (22) 375 2016 E-mail ilcae@mail.telepac.pt
Spanish Episcopal Reformed Church (Canterbury)	Carlos López Lozano Calle Beneficencia 18, 28004 Madrid, Spain Tel (0034) (91) 445 2560 Fax (0034) (91) 594 4572 E-mail eclesiae@arrakis.es

§ Under a Metropolitan Council of the Primate of Canada, the Archbishop of the West Indies and the President-Bishop of the Episcopal Church's Province IX.

BISHOPS OF CHURCHES WHERE ANGLICANS HAVE UNITED WITH CHRISTIANS OF OTHER TRADITIONS

NORTH INDIA

Agra	Samuel R Cutting Bishop's House, St Paul's Church Compound, 4/116-B Church Road, Civil Lines, Agra 282 002, UP, India Tel (0091) (562) 354845 Fax (0091) (562) 220074 E-mail doacni@nde.vsnl.net.in
Amritsar	Pradeep Kumar Samantaroy 26 R B Prakash Chand Road, opp Police Ground, Amritsar 143 001, Punjab, India Tel (0091) (183) 222910 *fax as telephone* E-mail bunul3@rediffmail.com
Andaman and Car Nicobar Islands	Christopher Paul Cathedral Church Compound, House No 1, Staging Post, Car Nicobar 744 301, Andaman and Nicobar Islands Tel (0091) (3192) 021102 Fax (0091) (3192) 31362
Barrackpore	Brojen Malakar Bishop's Lodge, 86 Middle Road, Barrackpore 743 101, North 24 Parganas, India Tel (0091) (33) 560 0147 Fax (0091) (33) 561 1852
Bhopal	Laxman L Maida Mission Compound, Ratlam 457 001, MP, India Tel (0091) (7412) 3371 Fax (0091) (7412) 33771

Calcutta	P S P Raju Bishop's House, 51 Chowringhee Road, Calcutta 700 071, WB, India Tel (0091) (33) 282 2426 Fax (0091) (33) 282 6340
Chandigarh (Deputy Moderator)	Joel Vidyasagar Mal Bishop's House, Mission Compound, Brown Road, Ludhiana 141 008, Punjab, India Tel (0091) (161) 665 706 *or* 609 431 *fax as telephone*
Chotanagpur (Moderator)	Zechariah James Terom Bishop's Lodge, PO Box 1, Hazari Bagh Road, Ranchi 834 001, Jharkhand, India Tel (0091) (651) 235 1181 Fax (0091) (651) 235 1184
Cuttack	Reuben Senapati Bishop's House, Mission Road, Cuttack 753 001, Orissa, India Tel (0091) (671) 301 448 *fax as telephone* E-mail diocese@vsnl.net
Delhi	Karam Masih Bishop's House, 1 Church Lane, off North Avenue, New Delhi 110 001, India Tel (0091) (11) 2371 7471 Fax (0091) (11) 2335 8264 E-mail stmartin@dels.vsnl.net.in

Durgapur	*vacant* Bishop's House, PO Box 20, South East Railway, Bankura 722 101, West Bengal, India Tel (0091) (343) 50726
Eastern Himalayas	Dhirendra Kumar Sahu Bishop's Lodge, PO Box 4, Darjeeling 734 101, West Bengal, India Tel (0091) (354) 53882 *fax as telephone* E-mail bpsahuehd@sify.com
Gujarat	Vinodkumar Mathushellah Malaviya Bishop's House, Ellis Bridge, Ahmedabad 380 006, Gujarat State, India Tel (0091) (79) 6561 950 *fax as telephone* E-mail gujdio@wilnetonline.net
Jabalpur	Sunil Cak Bishop's House, 2131 Napier Town, Jabalpur 482 001, MP, India Tel (0091) (761) 622 109 E-mail cnijbdio@sancharnet.in
Kolhapur	Bathuel Ramchandra Tiwade Bishop's House, EP School Compound, Kolhapur 416 003, Maharashtra, India Tel (0091) (231) 654 832 *fax as telephone* E-mail kdccni@vsnl.
Lucknow	Anil R Stephen Bishop's House, 25 Mahatma Gandhi Marg, Allahabad 211 001, UP, India Tel (0091) (532) 623 324 *fax as telephone*
Marathwada	A K Pradhan Bishop's House, Mission Compound, Jalna 431 203, MS, India Tel (0091) (240) 373 310
Mumbai	Baiju F Gavit St John's House, Duxbury Lane, Colaba, Mumbai 400 005, India Tel (0091) (22) 215 4126 *or* 1439 *fax as telephone*
Nagpur	*vacant* Cathedral House, Opp. Indian Coffee House, Sadar, Nagpur 440 001, MS, India Tel (0091) (712) 523 089 Fax (0091) (712) 556 740 E-mail bishop@nagpur.dot.net.in
Nasik	Kamble Lemuel Pradip Bishop's House, Tarakpur, 1 Outram Road, Ahmednagar 414 001, MS, India Tel (0091) (241) 428 746 Fax (0091) (241) 328 682 E-mail ndshd@pn3.vsnl.net.in
North East India	Purely Lyngdoh Bishop's Kuti, Shillong, Meghalaya 793 001, India Tel (0091) (364) 501 178 *or* 223 155 Fax(0091) (364) 223 155 E-mail bishopnei15@hotmail.com
Patna	Philip Phembuar Marandih Bishop's House, Christ Church Compound, Bhagalpur 812 001, Bihar, India Tel (0091) (641) 400 033 *or* 400 314 Fax (0091) (641) 400 314
Phulbani	Banchha Nidhi Nayak Bishop's House, G Udaigiri, Phulbani 762 100, Kandhamal, Orissa, India Tel (0091) (684) 760 185
Pune	Vijay Bapurao Sathe Pune Diocesan Council, 1 General Bhagat Marg, Pune 411 001, MS, India Tel (0091) (20) 633 4371
Rajasthan	Collin Theodore 2/10 CNI Social Centre, Civil Lines, Opp. Bus Stand, Jaipur Road, Ajmer 305 001, Rajasthan, India Tel (0091) (145) 420 633

Sambalpur	Christ Kiron Das Bishop's House, Mission Compound, Bolangir 767 001, Orissa, India Tel (0091) (6652) 32891 *fax as telephone*

SOUTH INDIA

Chennai	V Devasahayam Diocesan Office, PO Box 4914, Chennai 600 086, TN, India Tel (0091) (44) 2811 3933 Fax (0091) (44) 2811 0608
Coimbatore	M. Dorai Bishop's House, 204 Race Course Road, Coimbatore 641 018, TN1, India Tel (0091) (422) 213605 Fax (0091) (442) 213369
Dornakal	Allu Rajarathnam Bishop's House, Cathedral Compound, Dornakal 506 381, Andhra Pradesh, India Tel (0091) (8719) 25747 *or* 27747 *or* 27376 E-mail bishoprajarathnam@usa.net
East Kerala (Moderator)	Kunnumpurathu Joseph Samuel Bishop's House, Melukavumattom, Kottayam 686 652, Kerala State, India Tel (0091) (482) 291026 Fax (0091) (482) 291044
Jaffna	Subramaniam Jebanesan 17 Francis Lane, Colombo 6, Sri Lanka Tel (0094) (75) 511 233 Fax (0094) (1) 584 836
Kanyakumari	G Devakadasham CSI Diocesan Office, 71A Dennis Street, Nagercoil 629 001, India Tel (0091) (4652) 31539 Fax (0091) (4652) 31295
Karimnagar	Sanki John Theodore Bishop's House, PO Box 40, Mukarampura Post, Karimnagar 505 001, Andhra Pradesh, India Tel (0091) (8722) 42229
Karnataka Central	Vasanthkumar Suputhrappa Diocesan Office, 20 Third Cross, CSI Compound, Bangalore 560 027, Karnataka, India Tel (0091) (80) 222 3766
Karnataka North	Paul Sadananda John Kattennur Balmi Bishop's House, Haliyal Road, Dharwad 580 008, Karnataka State, India Tel (0091) (836) 745 593 *or* 447733 Fax (0091) (836) 745461 E-mail pjkbalmi@email.com
Karnataka South	Christopher Lazarus Furtado Bishop's House, Balmatta, Mangalore 575 001, Karnataka, India Tel (0091) (824) 429 657 Fax (0091) (824) 425 042 *or* 422363
Krishna- Godavari	G Dyvasirvadam CSI St Andrew's Cathedral Campus, Main Road, Machilipatnam 521 002, Andhra Pradesh, India Tel (0091) (8672) 220 623
Madhya Kerala	Thomas Samuel Bishop's House, Cathedral Road, Kottayam 686 001, Kerala State, India Tel (0091) (481) 566 536 Fax (0091) (481) 566 531
Madurai- Ramnad (Deputy Moderator)	Thavaraj David Eames CSI New Mission Compound, Thirumangalam 625 706, Madurai District, Tamil Nadu, India Tel (0091) (452) 732 541 *fax as telephone*
Medak	Badda Peter Sugandhar Bishop's Annexe, 145 MacIntyre Road, Secunderabad 500 003, Andhra Pradesh, India Tel (0091) (40) 783 3151 Fax (0091) (40) 782 084

Nandyal	Gondi Theodore Abraham Bishop's House, Nandyal RS 518 502, Kurnool District, Andhra Pradesh, India Tel (0091) (8514) 45731 Fax (0091) (8514) 42255	

North Kerala	George Isaac Bishop's House, Shoranur 679 121, Kerala State, India Tel (0091) (4921) 622 545 Fax (0091) (4921) 622 798
Rayalaseema	Chowtipalle Bellam Moses Frederick Bishop's House, CSI Compound, Gooty 515 401, Ananthapur District, Andhra Pradesh, India Tel (0091) (855) 242 375 Fax (0091) (855) 242 668
South Kerala	John Wilson Gladstone Bishop's House, LMS Compound, Trivandrum 695 033, Kerala State, India Tel (0091) (471) 318 662 Fax (0091) (471) 316 439 E-mail bishopgladstone@yahoo.com
Tirunelveli	Jeyapaul David Bishopstowe, PO Box 18, Tirunelveli 627 002, Tamil Nadu, India Tel (0091) (462) 572 744 *or* 579 499 E-mail bpcsitvl@pronet.in
Trichy-Tanjore	Daniel James Srinivasan PO Box 31, 8 Racquet Court Lane, Tiruchirapalli 620 001, Tamil Nadu, India Tel (0091) (431) 771 254 Fax (0091) (431) 418 486 E-mail csittd@tr.net.in
Vellore	Mahamai Rufus CSI Diocesan Office, 1/A Officer's Lane, Vellore 632 001, North Arcot District, India Tel (0091) (416) 232 160 Fax (0091) (416) 223 835

BANGLADESH

Dhaka (Moderator)	Michael S. Baroi St Thomas's Church, 54 Johnson Road, Dhaka-1100, Bangladesh Tel (00880) (2) 711 6546 Fax (00880) (2) 711 8218 E-mail cbdacdio@bangla.net
Kushtia	Paul S. Sarkar 94 NS Road, Thanapara, Kushtia, Bangladesh Tel (00880) (71) 61892 *fax as telephone* E-mail cob@citechco.net

PAKISTAN

The Arabian Gulf (Bishop *for*) (Area Bishop in Diocese of Cyprus)	Azad Marshall PO Box 3192, Gulberg-1, Lahore, Punjab, 54660, Pakistan Tel (0092) (42) 5220 286 Fax (0092) (42) 5220 591
Faisalabad	John Samuel Bishop's House, PO Box 27, Mission Road, Gojra District, Toba Tek Sing, Faisalabad, Pakistan Tel (0092) (4651) 511290 *fax as telephone* E-mail jsamuel@brain.net.pk
Hyderabad	Raffique Masih 27 Liaquat Road, Civil Lines, Hyderabad, Sind, 71000, Pakistan Tel (0092) (221) 780221 Fax (0092) (221) 28772 E-mail hays@hyd.infolink.net.pk
Karachi (Deputy Moderator)	Sadiq Daniel Bishop's House, Trinity Close, Karachi, 0405, Pakistan Tel (0092) (21) 521 8112 Fax (0092) (21) 565 3175 E-mail sadiqdaniel@hotmail.com
Lahore (Moderator)	Alexander John Malik Bishopsbourne, Cathedral Close, The Mall, Lahore, 54000, Pakistan Tel (0092) (42) 723 3560 Fax (0092) (42) 722 1270 E-mail bishop_Lahore@hotmail.com
Multan	John Victor Mall 113 Qasim Road, PO Box 204, Multan Cantt, Pakistan Tel (0092) (61) 588799 *fax as telephone* E-mail bishop@mul.paknet.com.pk
Peshawar	*vacant* St John's Cathedral, 1 Sir-Syed Road, Peshawar, NWFP, 25000, Pakistan Tel (0092) (91) 276519 Fax (0092) (91) 277499
Rawind	Samuel Azariah 17 Warris Road, PO Box 2319, Lahore 3, Pakistan Tel (0092) (42) 758 8950 Fax (0092) (42) 757 7255 E-mail azariahs@lhr.comsats.net.pk *or* bishop@nexlinx.net.pk
Sialkot	Samuel Pervez Sant Masih Lal Kothi, Barah Patthar, Sialkot 2, Punjab, Pakistan Tel (0092) (432) 264895 Fax (0092) (432) 264828

PROVINCIAL OFFICES

From which further information may be sought

Anglican Communion Office   Partnership House, 157 Waterloo Road, London SE1 8UT, UK
Tel (020) 7620 1110   Fax (020) 7620 1070   E-mail aco@anglicancommunion.org

Australia   PO Box Q190, Queen Victoria PO, Sydney, NSW, Australia 1230
Tel (0061) (2) 9265 1525   Fax (0061) (2) 9264 6552   E-mail gensec@anglican.org.au

Bangladesh   St Thomas's Church, 54 Johnson Road, Dhaka 1100, Bangladesh
Fax (00880) (2) 238218

Brazil   Caixa Postal 11510, Cep 90841-970, Porto Alegre, RS, Brazil   Fax (0055) (51) 336 5087
E-mail m_andrade@conex.com.br

Burundi   BP 2098, Bujumbura, Burundi

Canada   600 Jarvis Street, Toronto, ON, Canada, M4Y 2J6
Tel (001) (416) 924 9192   Fax (001) (416) 968 7983) 968 7983

Central Africa   PO Box 769, Gaborone, Botswana   Fax (00267) 352075

Central America   Iglesia Episcopal Costarricense, Apartado 2773, 1000 San Jose, Costa Rica
Fax (00506) 253 8331   E-mail amiecr@sol.racsa.co.cr

Ceylon   Bishop's House, 358/2 Bauddhaloka Mawatha, Colombo 7, Sri Lanka   Fax (0094) (1) 684811

Congo (formerly Zaïre)   CAC – Bunia, PO Box 21285, Nairobi, Kenya

England   Church House, Great Smith Street, London SW1P 3NZ, UK
Tel (020) 7898 1000   Fax (020) 7898 1001   E-mail feedback@c-of-e.org.uk

Hong Kong   1 Lower Albert Road, Hong Kong

Indian Ocean   Evêché Anglican, Ambohimanoro, 101-Antananarivo, Madagascar

Ireland   Church of Ireland House, Church Avenue, Rathmines, Dublin 6, Irish Republic
Tel (00353) (1) 497 8422   Fax (00353) (1) 497 8821

Japan   65 Yarai-cho, Shinjuku-ku,Tokyo 162-0805, Japan   Fax (0081) (52) 283175

Jerusalem and the Middle East   Christ Church, PO Box 75, Nazareth, Israel
Fax (00972) (66) 563649

Kenya   PO Box 40502, Nairobi, Kenya   Fax (00254) 714750   E-mail ackenya@insightkenya.com

Korea   3 Chong-dong, Chung-ku, Seoul 100-120, Korea   Fax (0082) (2) 737 4210   E-mail anck@peacenet.or.kr

Melanesia   Provincial Headquarters, PO Box 19, Honiara, Solomon Islands   Fax (0067) 21098

Mexico   Calle La Otra Banda 40, Col. San Angel, Delegacion Alvaro Obregon, 01000 Mexico, DF,
Mexico   Fax (0052) 616 4063   E-mail ofipam@planet.com.mx

Myanmar (formerly Burma)   140 Pyidaungsu-Yeiktha Road, Dagon PO (11191), Yangon, Myanmar
Fax (0095) (1) 251405

New Zealand (Aotearoa, New Zealand and Polynesia)   PO Box 885, Hastings, New Zealand
Tel (0064) (6) 878 7902   Fax (0064) (6) 878 7905   E-mail gensec@hb.ang.org.nz

Nigeria   Church House, 29 Marina, PO Box 78, Lagos, Nigeria

North India   CNI, 16 Pandit Pant Marg, New Delhi 110001, India

Pakistan   Cathedral Close, The Mall, Lahore 54000, Pakistan   Fax (0092) (42) 722 1270

Papua New Guinea   Box 673, Lae, MP, Papua New Guinea   Fax (00675) 472 1852   E-mail acpng@global.net.pg

Philippines   PO Box 10321, Broadway Centrum, 1112 Quezon City, Philippines
Fax (0063) (2) 721 1923   E-mail ecp@phil.gn.apc.org

Rwanda   BP 2487, Kigali, Rwanda   Tel and fax (00250) 514160   E-mail peer@rwandatel1.rwanda1.com

Scotland   21 Grosvenor Crescent, Edinburgh EH12 5EE, UK   Tel 0131-255 6357
Fax 0131-346 7247   E-mail office@scotland.anglican.org

South East Asia   PO Box 347, Kuching, 93704 Sarawak, Malaysia   Fax (0060) (82) 426488

South India   CSI Centre, 5 Whites Road, Royapettah, Madras 600041, India

Southern Africa   Provincial Office, 4th Floor Khotso House, 62 Marshall Street, Johannesburg, 2001 South
Africa   Tel (0027) (11) 836 5825   Fax (0027) (11) 836 578   E-mail peocpsa@cpsa.org.za

South America   Casilla 1123, Asunción, Paraguay

Sudan   PO Box 110, Juba, Sudan

Tanzania   PO Box 899, Dodoma, Tanzania   Tel (00255) (61) 21437   E-mail cpt@maf.org

Uganda   PO Box 14123, Kampala, Uganda

USA   Episcopal Church Center, 815 Second Avenue, New York, NY 10017, USA

Wales   39 Cathedral Road, Cardiff CF1 9XF, UK   Tel (029) 2023 1638   Fax (029) 2038 7835

West Africa   PO Box 8, Accra, Ghana

West Indies   PO Box N-7107, Nassau, Bahamas   Fax (001) (242) 322 7943

DIRECTORIES OF THE ANGLICAN PROVINCES

The following provinces of the Anglican Communion are known to publish directories of their clergy.

Australia   *The Australian Anglican Directory*   Published annually
   Angela Grutzner & Associates Pty Ltd, PO Box 306, Malvern, Vic, Australia 3144
   Fax (0061) (3) 9822 5927

Canada   *The Anglican Year Book*   Published annually
   Anglican Book Centre, 600 Jarvis Street, Toronto ON, Canada, M4Y 2J6
   Tel (001) (416) 924 9192   Fax (001) (416) 924 270

Ireland   *Church of Ireland Directory*   Published annually
   Styletype Publishing Co (Ireland) Ltd, Sheldon House, 60 Pembroke Road, Dublin 4, Irish Republic

Japan (in Japanese)   *Seikokai Yearbook*   Published annually
   Nippon Sei Ko Kai Provincial Office, 65 Yarai-cho, Shinijuku, Tokyo 162-0805, Japan

Jerusalem and the Middle East   *A Provincial Directory*
   Provincial Office, Box 1248, 20 Nablus Road, Jerusalem

New Zealand   *Clerical Directory*   Published annually
   General Synod Office, PO Box 885, Hastings, New Zealand
   Tel (0064) (6) 878 7902   Fax (0064) (6) 878 7905

Nigeria   *Nigeria Churchman's Year Book*
   Church House, 29 Marina, PO Box 78, Lagos, Nigeria

Scotland   *Scottish Episcopal Church Directory*   Published annually
   Secretary General and Treasurer, 21 Grosvenor Crescent, Edinburgh EH12 5EE

Southern Africa   *Clerical Directory*   Published annually
   Provincial Office, 4th Floor Khotso House, 62 Marshall Street, Johannesburg, 2001 South Africa
   Tel (0027) (11) 836 5825   Fax (0027) (11) 836 5782

Southern Cone of America   *Directorio Provincial*   Published every three years
   Casilla 50675, Correo Central, Santiago, Chile

United States of America   *Episcopal Clerical Directory*   Published annually
   Church Publishing Incorporated, 445 Fifth Avenue, New York, NY 100016-0109, USA
   Tel (001) (800) 242 1918   Fax (001) (212) 779 3392   E-mail churchpublishing@cpg.org

Diocesan lists are the source of information for the Churches of Brazil, Central Africa and Ceylon. In the West Indies, the Diocese of Jamaica (fax (001) (876) 968 0618) publishes a *Clerical Directory*. For the provinces not listed above, information should be sought from the provincial secretary or from dioceses.

Close links with many overseas provinces are maintained by the following missionary organizations:

Church Mission Society
   Partnership House, 157 Waterloo Road, London SE1 8UU
   Tel (020) 7928 8681   Fax (020) 7401 3215   E-mail info@cms-uk.org

Crosslinks   (formerly the Bible Churchmen's Missionary Society)
   251 Lewisham Way, London SE4 1XF
   Tel (020) 8691 6111   Fax (020) 8694 8023   E-mail crosslinks@pro-net.co.uk)

Mid-Africa Ministry   (formerly Ruanda Mission)
   Partnership House, 157 Waterloo Road, London SE1 8UU
   Tel (020) 7261 1370   Fax (020) 7401 2910   E-mail mid_africa_ministry@compuserve.com

Mission to Seafarers   (formerly The Missions to Seamen)
   St Michael Paternoster Royal, College Hill, London EC4R 2RL
   Tel (020) 7248 5202   Fax (020) 7248 4761   E-mail general@missiontoseafarers.org

Mothers' Union
   Mary Sumner House, 24 Tufton Street, London SW1P 3RB
   Tel (020) 7222 5533   Fax (020) 7222 1591   E-mail mu@themothersunion.org

Society for Promoting Christian Knowledge
   Holy Trinity Church, Marylebone Road, London NW1 4DU
   Tel (020) 7387 5282   Fax (020) 7388 2352   E-mail spck@spck.org.uk

South American Mission Society
   Allen Gardiner House, 12 Fox Hill, Birmingham B29 4AG
   Tel 0121-472 2616   Fax 0121-472 7977   E-mail gensec@samsgb.org

United Society for the Propagation of the Gospel
   Partnership House, 157 Waterloo Road, London SE1 8XA
   Tel (020) 7928 8681   Fax (020) 7928 2371   E-mail enquiries@uspg.org.uk

ADDRESSES UNKNOWN

The following are clergy whose addresses are currently unknown. Fuller details are contained in the biographical section. We should be grateful for any information to help us complete our records in respect of these clergy.

ARNDT, Miss Sarah. b 76. **d** 00. C Flint *St As* 00-02
ATHERLEY, Keith Philip. b 56. **d** 80. CF 89-03
ATHERTON, Philip Andrew. b 51. **d** 84. Perm to Offic *Man* from 00
AVERY, Russel Harrold. b 46. **d** 77. Australia 77-78, 88-98 and from 02; rtd 02
BAKER, Stephen Anthony. b 55. **d** 91. Chapl Eliz Coll Guernsey 97-01
BAMBER, David Beverley. b 51. **d** 77. C E Retford *S'well* 91-92
BARKER, Prof Charles Philip Geoffrey. b 50. **d** 98. NSM Alverstoke *Portsm* 98-02
BARRETT, Graham Crichton. b 51. **d** 90. P-in-c St Issey w St Petroc Minor *Truro* 95-00; Dioc Children's Adv 95-00
BARTLE, Alan. b 45. **d** 84. P-in-c Thorney Abbey *Ely* 93-95
BENFORD, Brian. b 47. **d** 85. NSM Gawber *Wakef* from 90
BENNETT, Paul Jonathan. b 61. **d** 87. V Patrick *S & M* 96-00; V Foxdale 96-00; V German St Jo 96-00
BESTLEY, Peter Mark. b 60. **d** 92. Chapl W Middx Univ Hosp NHS Trust 95-99
BISHOP, Huw Daniel. b 49. **d** 73. CF (TA) from 85
BLENCOE, Charles Dennis. b 17. **d** 41. Canada from 61
BOOKER, James Howard. b 57. **d** 90. R Peterhead *Ab* 93-00
BOSSOM, Peter Emery. b 28. **d** 82. rtd 86
BOULT, Geoffrey Michael. b 56. **d** 80. Perm to Offic *Sarum* 95-98
BOWLES, David Anthony. b 44. **d** 68. Perm to Offic *Derby* 93-95 and *Roch* 95-98
BRYAN, Leslie Harold. b 48. **d** 73. CF 79-03
BURGESS, Paul Christopher James. b 41. **d** 68. TV Livingston LEP *Edin* 88-92
BURN, Ms Kathleen Doreen. b 48. **d** 82. USA from 95
CARTER, Noel William. b 53. **d** 83. R Jersey St Brelade *Win* 98-01; Vice-Dean Jersey 00-01
CARTER, Paul Mark. b 56. **d** 81. Canada 00-03
CHAFFEY, Jane Frances. b 59. **d** 88. Perm to Offic RAF from 98
CHRICH-SMITH, Joanne Elizabeth. b 71. **d** 97. Chapl Girton Coll Cam 00-02
CLARK, Lance Edgar Dennis. b 52. **d** 77. Chapl RAF 87-02
COOPER, Ms Gillian Anne. b 55. **d** 87. New Zealand from 01
COSLETT, Anthony Allan. b 49. **d** 84. CF 92-02
COUSLAND, Andrew Oliver. b 41. **d** 65. rtd 03
COWIE, John William Stephen. b 64. **d** 97. C Shoreditch St Leon and Hoxton St Jo *Lon* 97-00
CROWE, Brian David. **d** 98. I Galloon w Drummully *Clogh* 01-02
CRUTTENDEN, Leslie Roy. b 39. **d** 84. NSM River *Cant* 90-01
CUMBERLAND, The Very Revd Barry John. b 44. **d** 88. P-in-c Las Palmas *Eur* 01-03
DAVIES, Benjamin John. b 27. **d** 88. Perm to Offic *Glouc* 98-00
DAVIES, Ian Elliott. b 64. **d** 88. C St Marylebone All SS *Lon* 96-01
DAVIES, Jonathan Byron. b 69. **d** 96. C Betws w Ammanford *St D* 96-00
DAVIES, Richard James. b 42. **d** 69. Zimbabwe from 80
DAVIES, Roger Charles. b 46. **d** 73. CF (TAVR) 75-94; R Lavant *Chich* 91-94; Chapl Lavant Ho Sch W Sussex 91-94
DAY, Prof James Meredith. b 55. **d** 03. C Antwerp St Boniface *Eur* from 03; C Ostend from 03
DAY, Paul Geoffrey. b 56. **d** 89. Lic to Adn Loughb *Leic* 98
DAY, Robert Murray. b 63. **d** 97. Chapl Sexey's Sch Bruton 02-03
DE VERNY, David Dietrich. b 55. **d** 83. Gen Sec Fellowship of St Alb and St Sergius 90-92
DELAMERE, Allen Stephen. **d** 90. I Saintfield *D & D* 93-03
DOLAN, Miss Louise. b 68. **d** 96. C N Stoneham *Win* 96-99
DOUGLAS, Peter Melvyn. b 47. **d** 96. Chapl HM Pris Dovegate 01-03
DURIE, David James. b 63. **d** 99. C Briercliffe *Blackb* 99-01
DYMOND, Rosie. **d** 03. C The Hague *Eur* from 03
FARAH, The Ven Rafiq Amin. b 21. **d** 46. Canada 92-95
FLETCHER, Steven John Carylon. b 60. **d** 92. C Newquay *Truro* 92-93
FORDHAM, Richard George. b 34. **d** 91. Perm to Offic *Ox* from 01
FOX, Jonathan Alexander. b 56. **d** 81. TV Madeley *Heref* 97-02
FOX, Mrs Lynn. b 51. **d** 92. TM Clifton *S'well* 96-98
FRANK, Derek John. b 49. **d** 85. Vevey w Château d'Oex and Villars *Eur* 93-02
FULFORD, Susan. **d** 03. NSM Pemberton St Mark Newtown *Liv* from 03
GARNER, John. **d** 03. NSM Kirkdale St Lawr *Liv* from 03
GARRUD, Christopher Charles. b 54. **d** 85. R Farnley *Ripon* 95-02
GASKELL, Peter John. b 70. **d** 03. NSM Poulton Lancelyn H Trin *Ches* from 03

GILBERT, Caroline Margaret. b 62. **d** 90. Hon C Aston SS Pet and Paul *Birm* 90-93
GILBERT, Christopher Anthony. b 60. **d** 89. TV Cannock *Lich* 97-01
GRAHAM, George Gordon. b 34. **d** 96. NSM Castlewellan w Kilcoo *D & D* from 03
GRAHAM, Michael Alistair. b 47. **d** 70. Soc Worker E Health Bd Dub from 00
GREEN, Gareth David. b 60. **d** 97. V W Ardsley *Wakef* 00-03
GRIFFITHS, Roger Michael. b 47. **d** 86. V Fishguard w Llanychar and Pontfaen w Morfil etc *St D* 94-03
GRIMSDALE, Mrs Margaret. b 24. **d** 87. rtd 90
GUILLAN, Miss Barbara Doris. b 19. **d** 87. rtd 89
GUTTERIDGE, John Philip. b 52. **d** 78. P-in-c Beeston Hill H Spirit *Ripon* 85-00
GWILLIAM, Christopher. b 44. **d** 67. Relig Progr Producer BBC Radio 4 (Man) 93-94
HAMMOND, Frank. b 49. **d** 77. C Blundellsands St Nic *Liv* 80-83
HAMPTON, Stephen William Peter. b 72. **d** 96. Chapl Ex Coll Ox 98-03
HANDLEY, Terence Anthony. b 55. **d** 87. V Stafford St Paul Forebridge *Lich* 91-94
HARRISON, Ernest Wilfrid. b 17. **d** 40. Canada from 52
HART, David Alan. b 54. **d** 83. Past Services Development Co-ord Derby Univ 98-02
HART, David John. b 58. **d** 85. V Rhosllannerchrugog *St As* 91-01
HARVEY, Anthony Peter. b 42. **d** 81. Chapl HM Pris Kirkham 95-01
HAVARD, David William. b 56. **d** 85. Canada from 88
HAYNES, Cyril Michael. b 26. **d** 84. Perm to Offic *Heref* 96-99
HEMPENSTALL, John Albert. b 43. **d** 67. Chapl RN 70-99
HENSON, Richard Clive. b 41. **d** 88. rtd 99
HERBERT, Graham Paul. b 54. **d** 81. C Claygate *Guildf* 99-01
HILLIARD, Russell. **d** 03. C Zürich *Eur* from 03
HOGG, William Ritson. b 47. **d** 72. V Catterick *Ripon* 88-97
HOLDSWORTH, Michael Andrew. b 65. **d** 93. TV Sheff Manor *Sheff* 97-99; Tutor Ripon Coll Cuddesdon 97-99
HOPKIN, Neil Richard. b 67. **d** 95. C Easton H Trin w St Gabr and St Lawr and St Jude *Bris* 95
HOWE, Harry Norman. b 10. **d** 73. rtd 92
HUGHES, John William George. b 48. **d** 72. Chapl RAF 86-02
HUNT, Andrew Collins. b 54. **d** 00. NSM Cainscross w Selsley *Glouc* 00-02
HUNT, Paul Firth. b 62. **d** 89. V Leeds Richmond Hill *Ripon* 95-01
HURLEY, Mark Tristan. b 57. **d** 91. V Bicker *Linc* 00-02
HYSON, Peter Raymond. b 51. **d** 87. TV Whitton *Sarum* 92-99
INGHAM, Russell Edward. b 39. **d** 64. Ankara *Eur* 96-00
JAUNDRILL, John Warwick. b 47. **d** 88. V Towyn and St George *St As* 92-02
JEFFRIES, Keith. b 48. **d** 93. Tenerife Sur *Eur* 02-03
JONES, Helen Alison. b 59. **d** 96. C Brocklesby Park *Linc* 97-98
JONES, Jennifer Margaret. b 49. **d** 89. R Musselburgh *Edin* 95-02; R Prestonpans 95-02
JONES, Trevor Charles. b 50. **d** 91. V Stowmarket *St E* 96-01
KING, Charles John. b 14. **d** 76. NSM Wantage Downs *Ox* 78-99
KNIGHT, Jonathan Morshead. b 59. **d** 88. OCF from 99; C (TAVR) from 00; Hon Lect Th Kent Univ from 00
LA TOUCHE, Francis William Reginald. b 51. **d** 76. V Burstwick w Thorngumbald *York* 91-02
LANGRIDGE, Molly Deirdre. b 48. **d** 98. NSM King's Lynn St Marg w St Nic *Nor* 98-03
LEFEVER, Henry Charles. b 06. **d** 65. rtd 75
LENNOX, Joan Baxter. b 50. **d** 96. C Baillieston *Glas* 96-97
LEWIS, Timothy John. b 56. **d** 86. Chapl RN 89-02
LISTER (née AISBITT), Mrs Joanne. b 69. **d** 93. NSM Mill End and Heronsgate w W Hyde *St Alb* 93-96
LOCOCK (née MILES), Mrs Jillian Maud. b 33. **d** 87. NSM Dumbarton *Glas* 93-96
LYNAS, Mrs Judith. b 53. **d** 92. Hon C Longfleet *Sarum* 97-99
McCANN, Hilda. **d** 03. NSM Parr *Liv* from 03
McGRATH, Kenneth. **d** 03. C Lisburn Ch Ch Cathl *Conn* from 03
McKERRELL, Euan Harvey. b 45. **d** 01. C Ness Gp *Linc* 01-03
MALDOOM, Ms Julie Marilyn. b 65. **d** 96. C Chinnor w Emmington and Sydenham etc *Ox* 96-99
MATCHETT, Alan William. b 70. **d** 01. C Stillorgan w Blackrock *D & G* from 03
MERRETT, Jonathan Charles. b 55. **d** 81. Asst Dioc Educn Officer *Cov* 87-94

MITCHELL, Christopher Derek. b 61. **d** 89. C Brookfield St Mary *Lon* 92-96

MNGOMEZULU, Sipho Percy. **d** 78. Swaziland from 03

✠MONDAL, The Rt Revd Barnabas Dwijen. b 37. **d** 64. rtd 03

MOORE, William Morris. b 33. **d** 61. rtd 03

MOULD, James Michael. b 46. **d** 98. NSM Wallington H Trin *S'wark* 98-03

MOY, Mrs Joy Patricia. b 35. **d** 90. Perm to Offic *Win* 96-02

MURRAY, Elizabeth Ruth. **d** 03. C Antrim All SS *Conn* from 03

NASORO, Howard Chimvano. b 64. **d** 88. R Zomba St Geo and Teacher Zomba Th Coll from 98

PARKER, Robert William. b 18. **d** 81. rtd 90

PARKER, Stephen George. b 65. **d** 98. Harborne St Pet *Birm* 98

PARRY, Richard Nigel. b 56. **d** 86. V Holywell *St As* 96-00

PATTERSON, William Alfred. b 54. **d** 79. Canada from 81

PEARMAIN, Andrew Neil. b 55. **d** 81. Chapl Frimley Park Hosp 87

PEEK, John Richard. b 51. **d** 76. Chapl Bearwood Coll Wokingham 96-98

PERRY, Timothy Richard. b 64. **d** 93. New Life Outreach from 97

PIERCE, Bruce Andrew. b 58. **d** 89. Canada 02-03

PITYANA, Nyameko Barney. b 45. **d** 82. Perm to Offic *Ox* 92-98

POWELL, Kelvin. b 49. **d** 74. R Hesketh w Becconsall *Blackb* 85-99

PRICE, Alun Huw. b 47. **d** 70. CF 77-03

QUILL, John Stephen. b 51. **d** 79. Adv to Bd of Soc Resp *Worc* 90-95

RADFORD, Leslie. b 24. **d** 85. NSM Scotter w E Ferry *Linc* 85-94

RADLEY, Stephen Gavin. b 62. **d** 89. P-in-c Marley Hill *Dur* 96-01

RAINSBURY, Mark James. b 56. **d** 88. TV Hampreston *Sarum* 97-99

RAMSAY, Eric Nicolson. b 29. **d** 94. Asst Chapl Gtr Athens *Eur* 99-00

RAYNER, David. b 49. **d** 78. Perm to Offic *Lon* from 99

REEVE, Kenneth John. b 42. **d** 93. P-in-c S Lynn *Nor* 96-99

ROBERTS, John Anthony Duckworth. b 43. **d** 66. Asst Chapl Palma de Mallorca *Eur* from 03

ROSKELLY, James Hereward Emmanuel. b 57. **d** 86. CF 95-03

SCOTT, John. b 54. **d** 81. I Bright w Ballee and Killough *D & D* 96-01

SEARS, Jeanette. b 59. **d** 92. NSM Ox St Aldate *Ox* 95-96

SHARPLES, Ms Susan Margaret. b 58. **d** 94. USA from 01

SHENTON, David. b 57. **d** 95. TV Melton Mowbray *Leic* 99-01

SIXTUS, Bernd. **d** 03. C Paris St Geo *Eur* from 03

SMITH, Miss Audrey. b 47. **d** 92. P-in-c Redmarley D'Abitot, Bromesberrow w Pauntley etc *Glouc* 98-00

SMITH, Gary Russell. b 56. **d** 96. C Southampton Maybush St Pet *Win* 96-00

SMITH, Graeme Richard. b 65. **d** 89. Tutor Westmr Coll Ox 97-02; Co Ecum Officer *Ox* 97-02

SMYTH, Peter Charles Gordon. b 72. **d** 98. Canada from 02

STACKPOLE, Robert Aaron. b 59. **d** 90. Canada from 93

STARTIN, Geoffrey Neil. b 56. **d** 88. C Rowner *Portsm* 00-02

STEVENS, Alan Robert. b 55. **d** 89. P-in-c N w S Kilworth and Misterton *Leic* 97-00

STRANGE, William Anthony. b 53. **d** 82. Trin Coll Carmarthen 96-01

STRINGER, Adrian Nigel. b 60. **d** 88. I Desertlyn w Ballyeglish *Arm* from 03

TARRANT, Paul John. b 57. **d** 82. R Edin Old St Paul *Edin* 96-97

TAYLOR, John Charles Browne. b 23. **d** 82. rtd 89; Lic to Offic *Chelmsf* from 89

TEE, John. b 59. **d** 82. CF 89-03

THOMPSON, Kevin. b 55. **d** 89. Perm to Offic *Sheff* from 98

TOWNSEND, Derek William (Bill). b 52. **d** 91. V Banbury St Paul *Ox* 98-01

TULLETT, Peter Watts. b 46. **d** 94. Chapl HM YOI Portland 96-01

WALKER, Richard David. b 45. **d** 95. Chapl HM Pris Leic 00-03

WALLS, Simon Conor. b 67. **d** 91. Chapl Brighton Health Care NHS Trust 95-96

WELLS, Jeremy Stephen. b 47. **d** 73. R Brent Knoll, E Brent and Lympsham *B & W* 84-99

WELTON, Peter Abercrombie. b 62. **d** 86. Community Priest *Chelmsf* 89-93

WHEELER, David Robert. b 62. **d** 95. C Lancaster St Thos *Blackb* 95-96

WILLIS, Andrew Lyn. b 48. **d** 74. Chapl RAF 83-02

WOODSIDE, David. b 60. **d** 90. C Stoke Newington St Mary *Lon* 90-92

WYLIE, Nigel Bruce. b 62. **d** 91. C Selly Park St Steph and St Wulstan *Birm* 91-94

YOUNG, Simon Robert. b 72. **d** 99. C Plaistow St Mary *Roch* 99-00

ZANDSTRA-HOUGH, Wendy Lorraine. **d** 00. C The Hague *Eur* 00-03

CLERGY WHO HAVE DIED SINCE THE LAST EDITION

A list of clergy who have died since 31 July 2001, when the compilation of the 2002/03 edition was completed. The month and year of death (if known) are recorded with each entry.

ADAMS, Raymond Michael 08/02
ADDINGTON HALL, Gerald Richard 07/02
ADLER, Thomas Payne 04/02
AINSWORTH, David Lawrence 07/02
AKERMAN, Roy 08/02
AKIN-FLENLEY, Kenneth Bernard 08/02
ALLARD, Victor James 11/02
ALLEN, Donovan Bawden 11/01
ANDERSON, Gordon Roy 03/03
ANDREWS, Alan Robert Williams 10/01
ANDREWS, Paul Rodney Gwyther 08/01
ANNET, John Thomas 03/02
ANSDELL-EVANS, Peter 12/02
APPLEYARD, Edward 09/01
ARCHER, Frederick John 12/02
ARMSTRONG, George 07/02
ARMSTRONG, Guy Lionel Walter 12/02
ARMSTRONG, Ronald 02/03
ARNOLD, Arthur Philip 12/01
ASHBY, John Robert Patrick 06/03
ASHTON, Thomas Eyre Maunsell 11/02
ATKINS, William Maynard 02/03
AUCKLAND, Allan Frank 12/01
AYLING, John Charles 01/03
BAGGOTT, Michael 03/02
BAINBRIDGE, Jean Waite 08/03
BAISLEY, Barbara Pauline 09/01
BAKER, Elsie Florence 06/03
BALE, James Henry 10/01
BALL, Graham 04/03
BANKS, Ernest Leslie 10/01
BANNISTER, John 07/02
BARKER, Leonard Ralph 05/02
BARNES, James Barrie 11/02
BARNES-CEENEY, Brian 04/02
BARNETT, Peter John 08/03
BARR, David James Osborne 07/02
✠BARTLEET, David Henry 11/02
BARTLETT, Basil Gordon 11/01
BARTLETT, Clifford William Tudor 06/02
BATEMAN, Alfred Neville 05/02
BATH, Edward Nelson 09/02
BAYLEY, Albert William David 08/03
BAYLEY, Audrey 05/03
BAYNHAM, George Thorp 10/02
BEAKE, Kenneth George 07/03
BEARD, Peter Harley 08/03
BEARMAN, Leslie Raymond Livingstone 09/02
BEAVER, Christopher Martin 03/03
BEDLOE, Horace Walter 12/02
BEESLEY, Symon Richard 10/02
BELBEN, Kenneth Frank 03/02
BENSON, Douglas Arthur Terrell 04/03
BENSON, James Christopher Reginald 09/02
BENSON, Riou George 02/02
BENSON, Roy William 01/02
BENSON, William George 04/03
✠BENZIES, Keith John 05/02
BERNERS-WILSON, Daniel Downing 01/03
BERRY, Michael 12/02
✠BETTS, Stanley Woodley 06/03

BEVAN, Dennis Butler 12/01
BEXON, Mavis Adelaide 11/01
BIGGS, Ivan Richard 11/01
BINDON, David Charles 09/01
BIRCHNALL, Simeon Robert 06/02
BIRT, William Raymond 03/02
BLAKE, William Cornford 11/01
BLAKISTON, Patrick 04/03
BLANCHARD, Ernest Desmond 06/02
BLATHWAYT, Linley Dennys 12/02
BLIGH, Peter Alan 03/03
BLYTH, John Stuart 03/03
BOADEN, John Edward 10/02
BOURKE, Francis Robert 09/01
BOWDLER, Ernest Roy 12/01
BOWEN, Daniel Austin 01/02
BOWKER, Archibald Edward 01/03
BOWLZER, Ronald 04/03
BRADLEY, Hazel 07/03
BRADY, Ernest William 05/03
BRAMMER, Charles Harold 07/02
BRAY, David Charles 11/02
BRECHIN, Valerie Becky Allan 01/02
BREWSTER, William Taylor 05/03
BRIDGE-COLLYNS, Douglas Herbert 03/03
BRIDGER, Malcolm John 12/02
BRIDGER, Renee Winifred 03/03
BRIERLEY, William Peter 03/02
BROOKE, Michael Zachery 04/03
BROOKS, John Cowell 10/01
BROOM, Bernard William 01/03
BROOM, Donald Rees 05/02
BROOME, William Harold 06/02
BROTHERTON, Leslie Charles 04/03
BROWN, Gerald Arthur Charles 01/02
BROWN, Walter Bertram John 07/02
BROWNE, Arthur Donal 03/02
BROWNE, John Burnell 05/02
BROWNE, Norman Desmond 08/03
BROWNING, Robert Frank 07/03
BRUNING, Arthur Frederick 10/02
BRUNNING, Sidney John George 11/02
BUBBINGS, Charles Gardam 12/01
BUCKLER, Peter 06/02
BUCKMASTER, Charles 10/02
BURNHAM, Cecil Champneys 07/02
BURR, Geoffrey Charles 07/03
✠BURROUGH, John Paul 01/03
BURTON, Frank Victor 02/02
BURTON, John Richard 09/02
BUSH, Alfred Edward Leonard 01/02
BUTLER, Frederick Walter 10/01
BUXTON, Edmund Digby 11/01
CAIGER, Douglas George Colley 06/03
CALTHROP-OWEN, William Gordon 11/01
CAMENISCH, Richard Frank 01/02
CAMPBELL, John Frederick Stuart 07/03
CAPPER, John Raymond 03/02
CARPENTER, Frederick Charles 02/03
CARR, James Arthur 05/02
CARTWRIGHT, Cyril Hicks 09/02
CARTWRIGHT, Hugh Bent 01/02
CATES, Geoffrey Charles 05/03
CHADWICK, George Bancroft 09/02

CHAPMAN, William Henry Stanley (Peter) 08/02
CHARNOCK, Ernest Burrell 02/03
CHESTERS, Peter Durrant 06/03
CHETWOOD, Noah 04/02
CHEVALIER, Harry Ensor Estienne 05/02
CHITTLEBOROUGH, Gordon Arthur 07/02
CHIVERS, Ronald 05/02
CHRISTIE, Graham 01/02
CLARK, Alexander Rees 08/03
CLARK, Arthur Towers 05/03
CLARK, Malcolm Aiken 12/02
CLARK, Michael Wilford 03/03
CLARK, Roy 08/02
CLARKE, Benjamin Blanchard 06/03
CLARKE, Colin David Emrys 10/02
CLARKE, Herbert Lewis 04/03
CLARKE, Joyce Willoughby Price 05/02
CLARKE, Malcolm Methuen 06/03
CLAXTON, Leslie Edward Mitchell 01/03
CLAYTON, Giles 06/02
CLIFT, Norman Charles 08/02
CLULEE, Elsie Ethel 03/02
COGGINS, Edwin Stanley Claude 03/03
COLE, Robert Alan 08/03
COLEMAN, John Wycliffe 08/03
COLEMAN, Mary Eileen 02/02
✠COLEMAN, Peter Everard 12/01
COLEY, Frederick Albert 06/03
COLLARD, Fred 08/03
COLLIN, David John 04/03
COLLINS, Maurice Arthur Reily 09/02
COLLINSON, Joan Irene 12/01
COLTON, Leonard Henry 01/02
COLWILL, Raymond William 02/02
CONEY, Mary Margaret 03/02
COOKE, Arthur Lewis 07/02
COOKMAN, Alan George 07/02
COOPER, Dennis Bradley 03/03
COOPER, Donald Martin 07/03
COOPER-SMITH, Alfred Riddington 06/03
COPESTAKE, Leslie 07/02
COPINGER, Stephen Hubert Augustine (Brother Hubert) 02/03
COPSEY, Harry Charles Frederick 03/02
CORBETT, Charles Eric 04/02
CORNWALL-JONES, Guy Rupert 06/02
COTGROVE, Alan Edward 05/02
COTTRELL, Bertram Lionel 01/02
COURAGE, Roy Kenneth 12/01
COUSINS, Stanley Frank 05/03
COWDRY, Gilbert 06/03
COWLEY, Geoffrey Willis 06/02
COX, Bryan Leslie 11/02
CRAWFORD, Philip Hugh Southern 08/03
CROFT, William Alan 05/03
CROOK, Frederick Herbert 03/02
CROOKSHANK, Stephen Graham 02/03
CUNLIFFE, Gerald Thomas 07/02
CURGENVEN, Peter 03/02
CURRIE, Ian Andrew 06/03

1214

CUTHBERT, Frederick Norton 06/03
DACRE, Roy Aubrey 10/02
✠DAIN, Arthur John 03/03
DAKERS, Fergus Logie 04/02
DALBY, John 04/03
DANA, Edmund Francis
  Kinnaird 10/01
DANIEL, Michael George 09/02
DAVENPORT, George Parry 03/02
DAVEY, Clive Herbert George 02/03
DAVIDSON, Sinclair Melville 01/03
DAVIES, Alcwyn Ivor 04/03
DAVIES, Alun Radcliffe 06/03
DAVIES, David Hywel 02/02
DAVIES, Evan Wallis 02/03
DAVIES, Hedleigh Llewelyn 10/02
DAVIES, Hugh Middlecott 04/02
DAVIES, John Conway de la
  Tour 02/03
DAVIES, John Neville Milwyn 03/02
DAVIES, John Vernon 08/02
DAVIES, Lawrence 07/03
DAVISON, Ralph Guild 01/03
DAWKINS, Roy Collin 03/02
DAWSON, Clifford Mildmay
  Asquith 08/02
DAWSON, Peter 06/02
DAY, Hilary Paul Wilfrid 06/02
DE GRUYTHER, Albert Alfred 12/02
DE MEL, Basil William 05/03
DEACON, Peter Olford 09/01
DEFTY, Henry Gordon 01/03
DEGG, Ralph William 04/03
DENNIS, John William 02/02
DERMOTT, David John 04/02
DEUCHAR, John 03/03
DIXON, Anne Nicholson 12/02
DIXON, Edward Ashby 09/01
D'MORIAS, Sydney James 04/03
DODD, Cyril 06/03
DODD, Ian Neville 07/02
DONCASTER, Reginald Arthur 11/01
DOUGLAS, George Gawain 08/01
DOVER, Oswald Leslie Simpson 08/02
DRAPER, Jack William 05/02
DRINKWATER, Frank 08/02
DRIVER, Anthony 04/02
DRURY, Esmond Peter 09/01
DUNCAN, Anthony Douglas 05/03
DUNCAN, Virginia Elinor 06/03
DYKE, Kenneth Aubrey 05/02
DYSON, Thomas 12/01
EAGLE, John Frederick
  Laurence 01/03
EARDLEY, Paul Wycliffe 08/01
EDE, Oswald George 12/02
EDMONDS, Bernard Bruce 06/03
EDWARDS, Emrys Llewelyn 01/02
EDWARDS, Kenneth Barnsley 09/01
EDWARDS, Leigh Cameron 04/03
EDWARDS, Rhys Meurig 02/02
EGERTON, Ronald 11/01
ELLA, David John 03/03
ELLEL, Thomas Fielding 07/02
ELLIS, John 01/03
ELLIS, John Frederick
  Alexander 09/03
ELLIS, Joseph Walter 05/02
ELTON, Clarence Edward 04/02
ENGH, Timm Gray 02/03
ENOCH, David John 04/03
ENSOR, David Alec 06/02
ENSOR, Keith Victor 06/03
ENSOR, Stephen Herbert Paulett 11/02
ENTWISTLE, Alan 11/02
ETHERINGTON, Ernest Hugh 09/01
EVANS, Alan David Carter 08/03
EVANS, Benjamin John 03/03
EVANS, David Conrad 08/01
EVANS, Emrys 07/02

EVANS, Guy Maxwell Lyon 07/02
EVANS, John Morgan 06/02
EVANS, Thomas Howell 08/01
EVANS, William Brewster 01/03
EYDEN, Eric Westley 08/03
FALL, John David McPherson 08/02
FARLIE, Hugh 05/02
FAULKNER, Robert Henry 03/02
FEARN, Robert Benjamin 02/03
FELL, Willis Marshall 02/02
FELLINGHAM, John 05/03
FIELD, Donald Charles 04/03
FINCH, Frederick 07/02
FLAHERTY, Alan Thomas 01/02
FLEETWOOD, John Arnold 07/02
FORBES, James Paterson 08/03
FOSTER, John Francis 03/03
FOSTER, Robin 03/03
FRANCIS, Hilton Barrington 12/01
FRANKLIN, Eric Edward
  Joseph 03/02
FRASER, Ernest William
  Emerson 05/03
FRAZER, Milburn Ronald 08/03
FRIZELLE, Thomas Herbert 01/02
GARDINER, John 08/03
GARDNER, David Edward 04/02
GAZE, George Henry 07/03
GENT, Anthony Leonard 07/02
GIBBON, Edward Herbert
  Morgan 05/02
GIBBS, Robert John 05/03
GILBERT, John Michael 07/03
GILES, Frank Edwin 02/03
GILES, Maurice Alfred Douglas 11/02
GILL, William 06/03
GILLIAT, Patrick Neville 05/02
GILLION, Frederick Arthur 07/02
GINEVER, John Haynes 05/03
GLOVER, Brian Reginald 07/02
GODDARD, William Edwin
  George 09/01
GODFREY, Robert John 04/03
GODSELL, Arthur Norman 10/01
GOLDIE, David 04/02
GOODERSON, William Dennis 12/01
GOODMAN, Ernest Edwin 04/03
GOWDEY, Alan Lawrence 07/02
GRAHAM, John 11/01
GRAHAM, Malcolm Frederick 08/03
GRANT, Douglas Wyndham
  Maling 08/02
GREEN, Ernest Swinfen 09/02
GREEN, Frederick George 03/02
GREEN, James Hardman 06/02
GREENLAND, Clifford James
  Gomm 06/02
GREENWOOD, Robert John
  Teale 01/03
GREGORY, Pauline Beatrice
  Joan 08/03
GRIBBLE, Arthur Stanley 03/02
GRIFFITH, Dermot George
  Wallace 05/03
GRIGGS, Kenneth Courtenay 01/03
GUEST, Leslie Leonard 04/02
GUNN, Frederick George 11/01
GUNN, Geoffrey Charles 08/02
HAGGARD, Amyand Richard 01/03
HAILSTONE, Kitty 10/02
HAKE, Andrew Augustus
  Gordon 08/03
HALDANE-STEVENSON, James
  Patrick 09/02
HALL, John Bellamy 10/01
HALL, Joseph Hayes 04/03
HAMEL COOKE, Christopher
  Kingston 06/02
HAMER, Roderick John
  Andrew 06/02

HAMER, Thomas 10/02
✠HAMILTON, Alexander
  Kenneth 12/01
HAMMERTON, Howard
  Jaggar 05/02
HAMMOND, Betty Marian 08/02
HANCOCK, Michael John 06/03
HANNAH, John Douglas 02/03
HANSEN, Harold Percy 08/02
HARDY, Bertram Frank 03/03
HARE, Stanley Thomas 12/01
HARLAND, Albert Henry 05/02
HARMAN, John Gordon
  Kitchener 12/02
HARRE, Kenneth Michael 02/02
HARRIES, Lewis John 04/02
HARRINGTON, Peter Anthony
  Saunders 07/02
HARRIS, Claude Anthony 07/02
HARRIS, Gerald Alfred 03/02
HARRIS-EVANS, Francis Douglas
  Harris 01/03
HARRISON, Jack 10/02
HART, John Richard 03/03
HARVEY, Victor Llewellyn
  Tucker 01/02
HATCLIFFE, Charles John William
  Coombes 08/03
HATHWAY, Richard Peter 04/02
✠HAWKER, Dennis Gascoyne 01/03
HAWKINS, Alfred Pryse 09/01
HAYWARD, Edwin Calland 03/02
HAYWARD, John David 11/01
HAZLEWOOD, George Ian 08/03
HEDLEY, Henry 08/01
HEGGS, Thomas James 08/02
HENRY, Bryan George 05/03
HILL, Harry Baxter 10/02
HILL, Norman 11/02
HILL, Raymond John Walter 08/03
HINDLEY, John 07/02
HINTON, John Dorsett Owen 10/02
HINTON, Roger Amos 02/02
HOBDAY, Walter William
  Henry 04/03
HOBSON, Anthony John 12/02
HODGE, John Shaw 03/03
HODGINS, George Eric 09/01
HODGINS, John Henry 03/03
HOGGETT, Robert William
  John 02/03
HOLLIS, Peter 02/02
HOLROYD, Gordon Eric 11/02
HOLT, Alan Leonard 03/02
HOLTBY, Robert Tinsley 03/03
HOOLEY, John Philip 04/03
HOPKINS, John Alun 06/02
HORN, Michael Leonard 04/03
HORNER, Robert William 03/03
HORSFIELD, Robert Alan 04/03
HOUGHTBY, Frank 09/02
HOWARD, Ronald Trevor 11/02
HOWARTH, Leslie John 05/02
✠HOWES, Peter Henry Herbert 04/03
HUCKLE, Sydney George 02/03
HUETT, Basil George Pringle 09/01
HUGHES, Henry 04/03
HUGHES, John Stunt Dickson 12/01
HUGHES, Owen 11/02
HUME, Leslie Paul 08/02
HUMPHREYS, Neil Edgar 09/01
HUNT, Bruce Allan 05/02
HUNT, Charles Evans 06/02
HUNT, Edward Trebble 06/03
HUNT, Michael Francis 09/02
✠HUNTER, Anthony George
  Weaver 06/02
HUNTER, Harold Hamilton 01/02
HURDMAN, William Richard 05/02
HURST, JOHN Cecil 08/03

HURST-BANNISTER, Michael Barnabas St Leger 01/02
HUSBANDS, Norman 12/01
HUTCHINSON, Raymond 07/02
HUTCHISON, Henry Peter 06/02
HUTTON, David James 02/02
HUXLEY, Keith 04/02
INCE, Edgar Kenelm Peter 09/01
IRESON, Brian Walter 08/02
ISAAC, Arthur Kenneth 03/02
ISDELL-CARPENTER, Philip Wynn Howard 03/03
IVEY, (née HODGE), Marilyn Elizabeth 01/02
JACKSON, Lawrence 11/02
JACKSON, Stephen Alexander 03/02
JACOBSON, William Walter 05/02
JAMES, Brian Percival Harold 02/02
JAMESON, John Edward 10/01
JENNINGS, Ronald Osmund 02/03
JERMAN, Cecil Maldwyn 05/02
JOHN, David Llewelyn 05/03
JOHNSON, Charles Edmund 04/02
JOHNSON, Gordon 11/01
JOHNSON, Harold Barnett 08/01
JOHNSON, John Alan 03/02
JOHNSTONE, Ian Douglas 03/03
JOHNSTONE, Leslie William 10/02
JONES, Andrew Theodore Hugh 05/03
JONES, David John 01/03
JONES, Edward Gareth 05/02
JONES, Elidyr Price 02/03
JONES, Evan Trevor 02/02
JONES, Fred Leslie 03/02
✠JONES, Haydon Harold 06/02
JONES, Howell Arfon 05/03
JONES, Idwal 05/02
JONES, Joseph Howell 12/02
JONES, Maurice Hughes Rowlestone 02/03
JONES, Paul Harwood 11/01
JONES, Robin Lang Wilson 01/02
JUDGE, Michael Charles 09/01
KANE, Margaret 05/03
KEATING, William Edward 04/02
KELLAM, Margaret June 09/01
KELLY, John Henry 09/02
KELLY, Norman James 03/03
KENNY, Thomas Patrick Francis 04/02
KEYES, William Pascall 03/02
KING, John David 06/02
KING, Terence Reginald 10/02
KITCHEN, Alan 01/02
✠KNAPP-FISHER, Edward George 02/03
LACK, Leonard James Westbrook 11/02
LAISTER, Peter 10/02
LAMBERT, Norman 02/03
LANCASTER, Frederick Charles Thomas 05/02
LANDRETH, Derek 01/03
LANE, Stephen Toller 03/02
LANGFORD, James Michael 02/03
LANGHAM, John Godfrey 01/02
LARGE, Denis Henry 01/03
LARTER, John William 08/02
LAWSON, Clifford John 10/01
LEE, Arnold John 11/01
LEE, Frederick William Maxwell 03/03
LEE, Hector 08/03
LEGG, Reginald John 06/03
LENNARD, Edward Stuart Churchill 09/02
LENYGON, Herbert Edward 12/01
LEVER, Edmund Arthur (Ted) 10/01
LEVEY, Colin Russell 04/02
LEWIS, Benjamin Alec 01/03

LEWTHWAITE, David 07/02
LISEMORE, Frederick John Henry 03/03
LISTER, Edmund 01/02
LITTLE, Harold Clifford 08/02
LONG, Harry 03/03
LONGWORTH-DAMES, Francis Robert 08/02
LOVEGROVE, Walter John 09/02
LOWE, Raymond John 03/02
LOWRIE, Robert Colledge 02/02
LUCAS, Janet Rosemary 04/03
LUDLOW, Arthur Percival 05/02
LUSTY, Ronald Henry 11/02
McALEESE, William Henry 05/02
McATEER, John Alexander 08/03
McCULLOUGH, Sidney 03/02
MACDONALD, Ranald Alexander (Alec) 10/01
✠MACGREGOR, Gregor 06/03
McINTOSH, Hugh 03/02
McKEE, William Thomas 09/01
MacKENZIE, Iain MacGregor 06/03
McLEOD, Kenneth 09/02
MACNAUGHTON, Alexander 02/03
McNEIGHT, Herbert Frank 01/02
MacQUAIDE, Arthur John Allan 03/03
MADDOX, Edwin Joseph Crusha 10/02
MAIR, James Fraser 11/01
MANCHESTER, Charles 09/02
MANDER, Dennis Stanley 08/03
MANNING, Brian Hawthorne 10/02
MAPLES, Jeffrey Stanley 09/01
MARKHAM, John Gabriel 03/03
MARSDEN, Geoffrey 10/01
MARSHALL, Bernard Godfrey Graham 01/03
MARTIN, Anthony George 10/02
MARTIN, Roy Ernest 10/01
MASON, Frederick Michael Stewart 03/02
MASTERTON, Paul Robert 10/02
MATTHEWS, Percival Charles Halls 06/03
MAY, Arthur John 09/02
MAYHEW, Peter 09/01
MEEK, John Conway 05/02
MERCHANT, David Clifford 07/02
MIDDLETON, Leonard James 01/02
MILES, Charles Reginald (Reg) 06/03
MILLAR, Frank 02/03
MILLER, David Reginald 02/03
MILLER, Edward Jeffery 09/01
MILLS, Walter Charles 08/02
MITCHELL, Frank Leonard 11/01
MITCHELL, Henry Gordon 08/02
MOBLEY, Ronald John 03/03
MONROE, James Allen 06/03
MOORSOM, Robert Coverdale 07/02
MORAN, John Philip 10/02
MORRIS, Thomas Gordon 11/01
MORROW, Canon Edward Sydney 08/03
MORSE, Harry Arthur Carminowe 01/03
MORTON, John Ivan 12/02
MOSS, Ivan Douglas Francis 04/03
MOSSMAN, Donald Wyndham Cremer 02/03
MULLINEAUX, John 12/02
MUNT, Neil 04/03
MYHILL, Christopher John 09/02
NAPLEY, David John 01/02
NASH, William Warren 11/02
NAYLOR, Stanley 07/03
NDUMBU, Joel Mbithi Gideon 03/02
✠NESTOR, Donald Patrick 01/03
NICHOLL, Joseph Edward Chancellor 07/03

NICHOLSON, Donald 10/02
NICHOLSON, William Surtees 11/02
NOBLE, Francis Alick 09/01
NORMAN, William John 02/02
NORTHCOTT, Geoffrey Stephen 10/02
NUNN, Sheila Jean 07/03
NYE, Nathaniel Kemp (Niel) 01/03
OLDHAM, Charles Harry 01/02
OLIVER, Roland John 05/03
ORME, Stewart 01/03
OSBORNE, Arthur Frederick 11/01
OTTOSSON, Krister Alexander 03/03
OWEN, Cledwyn 03/02
OWEN, Noah 03/02
OWEN, Robert David Glyn 12/01
PAISH, Muriel Dorothy 04/03
PALMER, Bernard Joseph 12/02
PALMER, Derek George 03/02
PALMER, William Frederick 02/02
PANTER, Noel 08/02
PARKER, Arthur Townley 12/02
PARKER, Ian Saunders 11/01
PARKINSON, Arthur Norman 11/01
PARKINSON, Joseph Greenwood 05/03
PARLETT, Gordon Alec 08/03
PARR, James Edwin Cecil 11/01
PARRY, John Seth 01/03
PATTENDEN, Henry Albert 08/02
PATTERSON, William James 04/02
PAUL, John Wilfred 01/03
PAYNE, Charles Thomas Leonard 08/01
PAYNE, John Charles 10/01
PEACOCK, William John 03/03
PEAKE, Charles Clifford 09/01
PEARCEY, Paul Alan Cyril 12/02
PEARE, Oliver Arthur Patrick 12/02
PENNANT, Philip Vivian Rogers 01/02
PERRENS, Eric George 05/03
PHILIPSON, John Wharton 07/02
PHILLIPS, Raymond Arthur 02/02
PIERSSENE, Jeremy Anthony Rupert 10/02
PITMAN, Clifford George 07/03
POOLE, John Denys Barlow 07/02
POPE, Robert William 09/02
PORTEUS, Alan Cruddas 08/01
POTTER, Frank Higton 05/02
POTTS, Hugh Cuthbert Miller 04/02
PRESTON, Ronald Haydn 12/01
PRESTON, Rosemary Muriel 01/03
PRESTON, Thomas Leonard 03/02
PRICE, Eric 07/03
PRIESTNER, James Arthur 01/03
PRINT, Norman George 01/02
PROUD, Clyde Douglas 02/02
PROUT, David William 07/02
PRYER, Frances Margaret 01/02
RADCLIFF, Henry Robert Moshe 09/02
RADCLIFFE, James Warner 02/02
RAMM, Norwyn MacDonald 01/02
RANDLE, Howard Stanley 02/02
RANKEN, Michael David 05/03
RATHBONE, Royston George 02/03
REANEY, Joseph Silvester 09/01
REES, Peter Frederick Ransom 06/02
REES, Sidney 02/02
REES, Simon Jonathan 01/02
REEVES, James Lacey 08/02
REEVES, Kenneth Gordon 03/03
RENOWDEN, Glyndwr Rhys 08/02
REYNOLDS, Derrick Wilfrid 05/03
RIDGWAY, Maurice Hill 12/02
RIDLEY, Laurence Roy 07/02
RIGBY, John Basil 12/01
RILEY, Reuben Cecil 11/02

ROACH, Charles Alan 05/03
ROBERTS, Frederick Henry 06/02
ROBERTS, John Edward
   Meyrick 06/02
ROBERTS, John William 12/01
ROBERTSON-GLASGOW, John
   Nigel 06/03
ROBINSON, Brian 05/03
ROBINSON, James 10/01
ROBINSON, William David 06/03
✠RODGER, Patrick Campbell 07/02
ROGERS, Alan Chad John 10/01
ROLLINSON, Frederick Mark 09/02
ROM, Hugh 01/03
ROONEY, James 05/03
ROSE, Glyn Clee 02/02
ROWE, John Nigel 03/03
ROWE, Samuel Ernest Allen 03/02
ROWE, William Alfred 02/02
ROWLANDS, Mark 06/02
RUDLAND, Patrick Ivor 10/01
RUFFLE, Leslie Norman 09/01
RUMSEY, Thomas Philip 12/01
RUSSELL-SMITH, Joy
   Dorothea 04/03
RYCROFT, Stanley 04/02
RYECART, John Reginald 08/02
SAKER, Sidney William 10/02
SAMS, David Stevenson 11/02
SANDERS, Allan Cameron
   Ebblewhite 12/01
SARGAN, Phyllis Elsie 03/02
SAUNDERS, Guy 05/02
SAXBY, Harold 07/02
SAXON, Doreen Harold
   Graham 02/03
SAXON, Eric 10/02
SAYER, Harold John 11/02
SAYERS, Guy Anthony 02/02
SCHIFF, Leonard Maro 07/02
SCHOLER, Douglas William 01/02
SCHWABACHER, Kurt
   Frederick 09/01
SCOTT, Michael Bernard
   Campion 05/03
SEAL, William George 11/01
SEARS, Frank 10/01
SELLARS, Charles Harold 01/03
SHAKESPEARE, Daniel 05/02
SHARMAN, Herbert Leslie
   John 03/03
SHARPUS-JONES, Trevor 09/01
SHAW, Denis 09/01
SHAW, Jack Firth 12/01
SHAW, Ronald Forbes 02/03
SHEARD, Neil Jeremy 09/01
SHELDON, John Gordon 06/03
SHELLEY, George 07/02
SHEPHERD, John William 04/03
SHERWOOD, Denys Charles 11/01
SHOLL, Ernest Redfern 02/03
SILLITOE, Pauline Ann 02/02
SIMMONS, Norman 10/01
SIMMS, Ernest Desmond Ross 10/02
SIMPSON, Athol 03/02
SIMPSON, Patrick Verrent 01/02
SIMPSON, Peter 03/03
SKEET, Edward Kenneth Walter 05/03
SKELTON, Frank Seymour 05/03
✠SKELTON, Kenneth John
   Fraser 07/03
SLADER, William Basil 08/01
SMITH, Colin Ian
   McNaughton 02/02
SMITH, David Graham 08/01
SMITH, Ian Charles 01/03
SMITH, Patricia Ann 09/02
SMITH, Peter Anson Stewart 04/03
SMITH, Roger Douglas St John 01/02
SMITH, Ronald William 12/01

SMITH, Sydney John 02/02
SOLOMON, Gerald Tankerville
   Norris 05/02
SOUTHGATE, Geoffrey Trevor
   Stanley 09/01
SOUTTAR, Edward Herbert 05/02
SPENCER, John Leslie 05/02
STALLARD, Frederick Hugh 03/03
STANTON, Ronald Geoffrey 05/03
STAPLES, Edward Eric 09/02
STEPHENS, Francis William 03/02
STEPHENS, Geoffrey Elford 08/01
STEPHENSON, Robert
   Ommanney 02/02
STEPPAT, Ida Margaret Agnes (Sister
   Stephanie) 04/03
STEWART, John Vernon 02/02
STEWART, Robert Stevenson 11/01
STOCKS, John Cedric
   Hawkesworth 06/02
STOCKTON, Wilfred 03/03
STOKES, Peter 12/02
STOPPARD, Henry 01/02
STRATTON, Geoffrey
   Frederick 10/02
STRATTON, Leslie Verdun 01/03
STRICKLAND, Derek 08/03
SURTEES, Geoffrey 11/01
SUTTERS, Herbert John 02/03
SWENARTON, John Creighton 06/03
SWIDENBANK, Stephen 08/03
TALENT, Jack 01/02
TANNER, Laurence Ernest 02/03
TAYLOR, James McMurray 08/01
TAYLOR, John Alfred 05/03
TAYLOR, Kenneth Gordon 09/01
TAYLOR, Marcus Beresford 11/01
TELFORD, John Edward 08/01
TEMPLE, George Frederick 01/03
TENNANT, Charles Roger 06/03
THACKRAY, Peter Michael 01/02
✠THOMAS, Eryl Stephen 12/01
THOMAS, Hugh 12/02
THOMAS, James Morris 11/01
THOMAS, John Elwern 10/02
THOMAS, Roger James 02/03
THOMAS, Tristan Emmanuel
   Douglas 06/03
THOMAS, William Alwyn 06/02
THOMPSON, Barry (Brother
   Aidan) 09/01
THOMPSON, John Miller 03/03
THOMPSON, Thomas 03/02
THOMSON, George Miller
   McMillan 11/02
THORNE, Ralph Frederick 04/03
THORNTON, Kenneth 06/03
THORP, Thomas Malcolm 03/03
THORPE, Harry Fletcher
   Cyprian 05/02
THURSTON, Colin Benedict 05/03
TINKER, Michael Jonathan
   Russell 01/03
TIPPING, John Henry 04/03
TOMLINSON, Geoffrey 07/03
TOMLINSON, Thelma
   Marcelle 01/02
TOTTY, Lawrence Harold 11/01
TOWNSON, Eric James 09/01
TOWSE, Anthony Norman
   Beresford 03/02
TREEN, Anthony Robert 04/02
TRNKA, Oldrich Joseph 01/03
TROSS, Julian Chamings 07/02
TRUNDLE, Herbert Edward 05/03
TUCKEY, John William
   Townsend 10/02
TURNBULL, John Smith
   Gardiner 02/03
TURNER, Douglas John 09/01

TURNER, Walter 07/03
TYE, Leslie Bernard 04/02
TYTE, Keith Arthur Edwin 02/02
TYZACK, Leonard George 02/02
UNDERWOOD, Luke William 05/03
VANE, Walter Brian 08/03
VAUGHAN, Benjamin Noel
   Young 08/03
VAUGHAN-JONES, Geraint
   James 12/02
VEVERS, Eric 01/03
VYSE, Jack Walter Miller 12/01
WAIN, Frank 11/02
WALKER, Kingsley 01/02
WALKER, Michael John
   Maynard 12/02
WALKER, Robert Edward Lea 05/03
WALLS, Raymond William 11/02
WALMSLEY, George Bernard 06/03
WALTERS, Thomas 04/03
WALTON, Wilfred James 01/02
WARBURTON, Robert Tinsley 06/02
WARD, David Towle Greenfield 05/02
WARREN, Christopher Bruce 10/02
WATERS, Charles Eric 03/03
WATKINS, Walter 06/03
WATSON, Douglas John
   Muirhead 03/03
WATTERSON, William
   Howard 11/02
WEARMOUTH, Paul
   Frederick 09/01
WELLS, Ronald Charles 09/01
WELSBY, Paul Antony 03/02
WESSON, Basil 09/02
WEST, Ronald Cameron 08/03
WESTCOTT, Donald Ralph 12/02
WESTMACOTT, Ian Field 01/03
✠WESTON, Frank Valentine 04/03
WESTON, Harold John 05/02
WHATLEY, Henry Lawson 01/02
WHEATLEY, James 08/02
WHITE, Joseph George 08/01
WIDDICOMBE, Alexander Charles
   Ernest 04/02
WILCOX, Joe 03/02
WILCOX, Raymond Trevor 08/01
WILD, William Stanley 09/01
WILKES, Keith Reid 09/03
WILLIAMS, Alfred George 08/02
WILLIAMS, Allen Philpin 10/01
WILLIAMS, Arthur James
   Daniel 09/01
WILLIAMS, Derek Howard 04/02
WILLIAMS, Geoffrey
   Ainsworth 09/02
WILLIAMS, Gwilym Kenneth 05/02
WILLIAMS, Hugh 03/03
WILLIAMS, John Charles 08/02
WILLIAMS, John Glyn 03/03
WILLIAMS, Maxwell Holman
   Bentley 12/01
WILLIAMS, Peter David 11/02
WILLIAMS, Sidney Austen 12/01
WILLIAMS, Thomas Gerald 09/01
WILSON, John Stafford 06/03
WILSON, Robert Michael 10/01
✠WILSON, Roger Plumpton 03/02
WISKER, George Richard 05/03
WOMERSLEY, Walter John 04/02
WOOD, Gordon Edward 02/03
WOODHOUSE, David 12/02
WOODHOUSE, William Henry 01/03
WOOLFENDEN, Dennis
   George 03/03
WORTHEN, Peter Frederick 10/02
WORWOOD, Frank Edward 01/02
WRAGG, John Gordon 09/01
WRIGHT, Frank Sidney 12/02
YOUNG, Michael James Frank 02/02

ENGLAND AND WALES

Provincial Boundary
Diocesan Boundary
Cathedral City

50miles 80km
0 10 20 30 40 50
0 20 40 60 80

SCOTLAND

IRELAND

NEWCASTLE

DURHAM

CARLISLE

YORK

RIPON
AND
LEEDS

BRADFORD

BLACKBURN

WAKEFIELD

MANCHESTER

LIVERPOOL

SHEFFIELD

CHESTER

DERBY

SOUTHWELL

LINCOLN

ST ASAPH

SODOR
AND MAN

1218

The Channel Islands are annexed to the Diocese of Winchester

The Isles of Scilly are included in the Diocese of Truro

NORWICH

ST EDMUNDSBURY AND IPSWICH

CHELMSFORD

CANTERBURY

ELY

ST ALBANS

ROCHESTER

SOUTHWARK

LONDON

CHICHESTER

PETERBOROUGH

LEICESTER

GUILDFORD

COVENTRY

OXFORD

WINCHESTER

BIRMINGHAM

PORTSMOUTH

WORCESTER

GLOUCESTER

BRISTOL

SALISBURY

HEREFORD

MONMOUTH

BATH AND WELLS

SWANSEA AND BRECON

LLANDAFF

BANGOR

EXETER

ST DAVIDS

TRURO

SCOTLAND

0	10	20	30	40	50miles

0	20	40	60	80km

～ Provincial Boundary

～ Diocesan Boundary

• Location of Cathedral

ABERDE
AND
ORKNE

ABERDEEN
AND
ORKNEY

MORAY,

ROSS

AND

CAITHNESS

SHETL
ISLAND

Inverness

ARGYLL

ABERDEEN

AND

ORKNEY

Aberdeen •

AND

ST ANDREWS,

BRECHIN

Oban •

DUNKELD

THE ISLES

AND

Dundee

DUNBLANE

Perth

Edinburgh •

Glasgow •

GLASGOW

AND

EDINBURGH

GALLOWAY

IRELAND

ENGLAND

IRELAND

0	10	20	30	40	50miles
0	20	40	60		80km

▬ Provincial Boundary

— Diocesan Boundary

⌒ National Boundary

● Location of Cathedral

CONNOR

● Londonderry

Raphoe

DERRY AND RAPHOE

Belfast ●
Lisburn

ARMAGH

Dromore ●

Clogher ● Downpatrick ●

DOWN
AND
DROMORE

Enniskillen ● ● Armagh

CLOGHER

● Sligo

Killala ●

Kilmore ●

KILMORE, ELPHIN
AND ARDAGH

Trim ●

TUAM, KILLALA
AND ACHONRY

MEATH AND KILDARE

Dublin ●

● Tuam

Clonfert ●

Kildare ●

DUBLIN AND
GLENDALOUGH

LIMERICK, ARDFERT, AGHADOE,
KILLALOE, KILFENORA, CLONFERT,
KILMACDUAGH AND EMLY

Leighlin ●

Kilkenny ●

Ferns ●

● Killaloe

CASHEL, WATERFORD, LISMORE,
OSSORY, FERNS AND LEIGHLIN

● Limerick

Cashel ●

Waterford ●

Lismore ●

CORK, CLOYNE
AND ROSS

Cork ● ● Cloyne

Ross ●

1221

Our work is caring ...

The Church of England Pensions Board offers support to retired clergy and their spouses, the widows or widowers of clergy, and church workers retired from full time ministry.

Our greatest concern is for the welfare of our older pensioners who, because of age or infirmity may need supported housing or nursing care. In accommodation specifically designed for the needs of the elderly the Pensions Board can offer such assistance, providing security and peace of mind to those who have given their lives towards helping others in the name of Christ.

Many of our pensioners may need help to pay for this care.

**Your donation or legacy will help us
to continue this much needed work.**

Please help us in any way you can.

For further information about ways to help, including Gift Aid giving, a form of words for inclusion in a Will, or more details about our work, please write to:

1229

The Church Union

Founded in 1859, at the time of the "Oxford Movement", to promote catholic faith and order. Today, the Church Union works to evangelise and proclaim the Gospel to all whom will hear; to build up the body of Christ by effective means of formation and education; to support clergy and encourage all the baptised in joyful service of our Lord. It publishes books, tracts, and produces a house magazine "The Church Observer". The Church Union is a registered Charity and a membership organisation, full details can be obtained from Faith House, 7 Tufton Street, London SW1P 3QN.

Tel: 020 7222 6952   Fax: 020 7976 7180
E-mail: churchunion@care4free.net

Charity No. 243535

**The Guild of
Church Musicians**

Founded in 1888

The Guild is
Interdenominational
And exists to encourage
All church musicians
to foster the highest
Standards in music
And the liturgy.

The Guild is
International and especially
strong in Australia.

The Archbishops' Award
and Certificate in Church
Music, as well as the Fellowship.
Archbishop's Certificate in Public Worship
Examinations are taken annually
and presented by one of the Patrons.

President: Dr Mary Archer

AGM and One
Day Conference
on Saturday
Before first May
Bank Holiday,
Usually at a
Cathedral

**Warden: The Very Revd. Dr. Richard Fenwick
New — The Archbishops' Cert. in Public Worship**

All enquiries: John Ewington, OBE,
General Secretary, Hillbrow,
Godstone Road, Blechingley,
Surrey RH1 4PJ.
Phone: 01883 743168

Patrons: Archbishops of Canterbury and Westminster

Broaden your horizons...

...read The Tablet.

The Tablet embodies the essence of Christian Humanism. It offers superb analysis of politics, religion and social issues and current world affairs, as well as international Church news and quality book, film, art, music and theatre reviews.

It tackles the most controversial issues of our time, in a way that is both balanced and uncompromising. Our writers are experts in their fields and are drawn from different denominations and faiths.

Find out why subscribers in over 120 countries consider *The Tablet*, the international Catholic weekly, to be the best Christian publication in the English-speaking world.

....

'Weekly, Tablet, for best religious journalism.'
Rowan Williams

TABLET